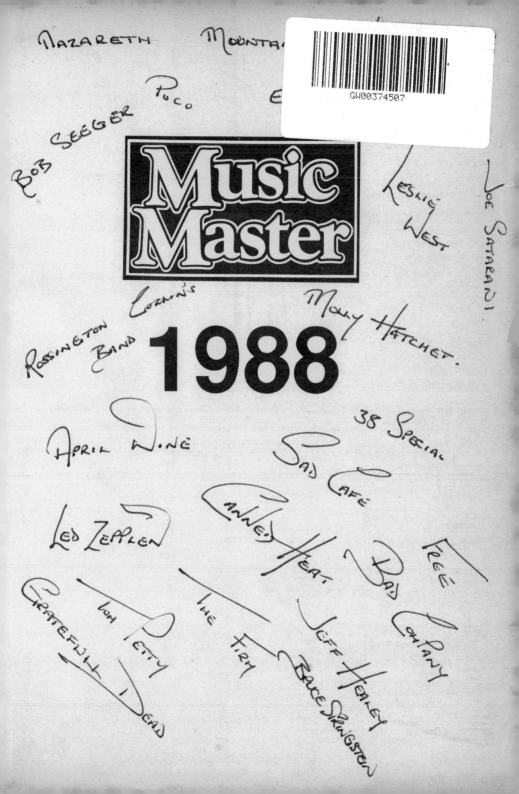

Music Master

1988

The world's greatest record catalogue

First published by John Humphries 1974 (reprinted 1975); second edition 1976, third edition 1977, fourth edition 1978, fifth edition 1979, sixth edition 1980, seventh edition 1981, eighth edition 1982, ninth edition 1983, tenth edition 1984, eleventh edition 1985, twelfth edition 1986, thirteenth edition (Hardback) 1987, thirteenth edition (Paperback) 1988.

ISBN 0 904520 30 7

John Humphries (Publishing) Ltd
Music House, 1 De Cham Avenue, Hastings,
Sussex, England TN37 6HE

Telephone: 0424 (Hastings) 715181
Telex: 957485 ROBINC G
FAX: 0424 422805.

The world's greatest record catalogue

This paperback thirteenth edition of Music Master lists all popular records and tapes known by us to be generally available from British record companies at 1st September 1987.

Contents

General editor   John Humphries

John Humphries (Publishing) Ltd.
Music House, 1 De Cham Avenue, Hastings, Sussex,
England TN37 6HE.
Telephone: 0424 (Hastings) 715181
Telex: 957485 ROBINC G
Fax: 0424 422805

INTRODUCTION

Welcome to the thirteenth edition of Music Master. This 1988 publication is the very first to be produced entirely by computer technology. The computer system was installed during the early part of 1987 and it has taken the best part of six months to transfer the bulk of the original data held on approximately two hundred and fifty thousand cards onto the computer database. The layout of the catalogue, which has changed little during it's thirteen year history, has been revised to make entry reconciliation a lot easier.

Indexed A to Z each entry is headed with a prominent black strip to signify the artist's name (or the title if the work is a 'various artists' compilation) followed by the artist's available repertoire with track details (if known) and media details which include label information such as label name, company and distributor. Albums, cassettes, compact discs, singles and videos are included with a date of release and a note of any deletions which may have been notified. Prices of items given in this catalogue are there purely as a guide to approximate prices of actual items. Music Master advises readers to always check with a record retailer for up-to-date prices. Many deleted records and tapes have been omitted altogether for reasons of space and quality. Readers can, however, readily purchase back-copies of Music Master which include all the old deletions; for details see under 'Previous

Editions' on page . The same factors of space and quality forced a reluctant decision to omit track listings for recordings released prior to December 1985, details of which are in the 1986 catalogue.

Every effort is made to ensure the accuracy of Music Master, but the comprehensiveness of the catalogue is dependent on the publisher receiving up to date information of records and tapes from the companies concerned. Occasionally some companies fail to supply us with adequate information of their new releases, and while we constantly seek to obtain this information, the result is that sometimes omissions are inevitable. Readers are encouraged to write to the editor with details of any omissions or discrepancies they may find.

This thirteenth edition of the Music Master catalogue contains details of albums, cassettes, compact discs, seven-and-twelve-inch singles and music videos. This catalogue contains approximately eighty thousand entries and includes releases up to September 1987.

John Humphries

March 1988

PREVIOUS EDITIONS

1974

The very first edition; 370 pages; albums only listed, no cassettes or singles; reprinted 1975; yellow cover, paperback; now out of print and a collector's item.

1976

Second edition: 476 pages, albums only listed; yellow hardback cover; now out of print.

1977

Third edition: 976 pages, the only edition so far published with smaller A5-size pages; cassettes, cartridges and singles included for the first time; still available from Music Master at £9.95 post free.

1978

Fourth edition: 660 pages, black cover; now out of print.

1979

Fifth edition: 736 pages; lists albums, cassettes, cartridges and singles; still available at £9.95 post free.

1980

Sixth edition: 696 pages; again singles, albums, cassettes and cartridges listed; black cover; available from MM at £9.95 post free.

1981

Seventh edition: 988 pages; track listings included for many albums for the first time; red hardback cover. This edition still available at £9.95 post free.

1982

Eighth edition: 1004 pages; separate sections integrated into one listing; cartridges and quadraphonic sections dropped from the catalogue. Red hardback cover. This edition still available at £9.95 post free.

1983

Ninth edition: 800 pages; integration of all sections into one alphabetical sequence continued; red hardback cover; this edition now out of print.

1984

Tenth edition: red covered **hardback** edition; 1216 pages; all sections now integrated into one alphabetical list; compact discs listed for the first time; singles titles listed as separate section. **Paperback** edition with 'Genesis' on cover, 864 pages; as hardback but without singles titles or deletions 1980-1983 sections. Both editions carry photographs for the first time. Both editions now out of print.

1985

Eleventh edition: 1300 pages; albums, singles and casettes listed in one alphabetical sequence; about 300 photos of artists included; about 600 biographies included; total current items listed: 52,000, plus 18,000 deletions; grand total 70,000 items; red covered hardback edition available at £19.95 post free; paperback edition (pink design cover) £9.95 post free.

1986

Twelfth edition: 1840 pages listing all singles, albums and compact discs in one alphabetical sequence. Contains full track-listing and biographical details. Red covered hardback edition only published. Still available at £29.95. Post free

Please send orders with remittances or enquiries about the above, and other publications to: MUSIC MASTER SALES, JOHN HUMPHRIES PUBLISHING LTD,
MUSIC HOUSE, 1 DE CHAM AVENUE, HASTINGS, SUSSEX TN37 6HE. Telephone: Hastings (0424) 715181 Telex:957485
ROBINC G.

HOW TO USE THE CATALOGUE

Boxcar Willie ────────────────────── **BLACK STRIP**

Biographical Details: This American singer
has spent his career in the second division of ──── **BIOGRAPHICAL DETAILS**
country music, without ever breaking into the
big league. His brand of humorous country enjoys more popularity in Britain than at home. His
TV advertised "King of the road" compilation
gave him a one-off chart album, reaching No.5
on the UK list. B.M 84

BOXCAR WILLIE. ────────────────── **TITLES**
Tracks: / Songs of songs / Dreary days / Gypsy
lady & the hobo / Honey I love you / Cheating
wife / Boxcar's my home / My hearts deep in the ──── **TRACK LISTING**
heart of Texas / Hooo heaven / Big freight train
carry me home / Ain't gonna be your day.
Notes: The album is produced by Boxcar Willie ──── **NOTES**
& features two tracks with Willie Nelson ,'Songs
of Songs' & 'Boxcar's My Home'. Since his
memorable Wembley appearance,Boxcar has
become a firm favourite with British audiences.
Album: released on MCA in Mar'86 by MCA ──── **RELEASE DATE**
Records. Distributed by: Polygram. MCA

Cassette: released on MCA in Mar'86 by MCA
Records. Distributed by: Polygram, MCA

Album: released on Big R in Nov'80 by Big R
Records. Distributed by: Pinnacle, Wynd-Up
Distribution, Solomon & Peres Distribution, I & ──── **FURTHER INFO**
B, JSU, Swift, Record Merchandisers Distribu-
tion. Spartan

Black strip: all the recordings by a particular artist or group are filed under one black strip which
is sometimes abbreviated. The black strips are in
strict alphabetical order, regardless of surname
or forename eg. "Smithers, Charlie" is found after
"Smith, Ernie" but before "Smith, Fenton":

> Smith, Arthur
> Smith, Bessie
> Smith, Connie
> Smith, Derek
> Smith, Ernie
> Smithers, Charlie
> Smith, Fenton
> Smith, George
> Smith, Huey

Numerical black strips such as "20 Golden Greats"
or "10cc" will be found under the spelled versions
of the names: "Twenty Golden Greats" or "Ten
cc".

Not all headings are artists or groups, many are
the **titles** of records by **various artists** or of **film
soundtracks** or **show titles** or even of types of
music by various artists, (eg. **'Greece'**) or of
special categories such as **'Bird Songs'** or **'Football Records'.** They are all, however, fully integrated with the artists and groups into a single
alphabetical sequence.

Prices: any prices quoted in Music Master are
usually estimated retail prices including VAT or
occasionally recommended retail prices including

VAT. In both cases the date at which the price information was known to be correct is stated.
Readers are advised to check with their record
dealers for current prices.

Titles: the recordings listed under a black strip
are arranged in alphabetical order irrespective of
whether they are albums, tapes, CDs, or singles.

Track listings: where the information has been
supplied, full track listings are given for all recordings released since the last main catalogue (1986)
went to press. For track details of items released
prior to December 1985 please refer to the 1986
main catalogue.

Technical information: of relevance mainly to
our trade users: it gives the record label, the
record company, trade distributor(s) and release
date. Please note that some of this information
may have changed since going to press.

Notes: these are often supplied to us by the
record companies.

Release date: date of release of a record or tape
as scheduled and notified to us by the record companies.

Deletion date: this is the date given to us by a
record company on which the record or tape is
considered to be deleted, that is, no longer stock-
ed or supplied by the record company.

A11Z

Witch of Berkeley, The.
Musiccassette: released on Polydor in Oct'80 by Polydor Records. Distributed by: Polygram, Polydor

Aaberg, Philip

High plains.
Album: released on A&M in Aug'87 by A&M Records. Distributed by: Polygram

Musiccassette: released on A&M in Aug'87 by A&M Records. Distributed by: Polygram

Compact disc: released on Windham Hill in Aug'87. Distributed by: AM

Aardvark

Put that in your pipe and smoke it.
Tracks: / Copper sunset / Very nice of you to call / Many things to do / Greencap, The / I can't stop / Outing- yes, The / Once upon a hill / Put that in your pipe and smoke it.
Album: released on See For Miles in Jan'85 by See For Miles Records. Distributed by: Pinnacle

Aaron, Lee

Barely holding on.
Single (7"): released on Attic-Roadrunner in Jul'85

Single (12"): released on Attic-Roadrunner in Jul'85

Single (12"): released on Attic-Roadrunner in Aug'85

Call of the wild Call of the wild.
Tracks: / Rock me all over / Running from the fire / Champion / Barely holding on / Burning love / Beat 'em up / Paradise / Evil game / Danger zone / Hot to be rocked.
Album: released on Ten in Aug'86

Musiccassette: released on 10 in Aug'86 by 10 Records. Distributed by: Virgin, EMI

Album: released on Road Runner in Oct'85

Lee Aaron Project, The.
Album: released on Music For Nations in Jul'84 by Music For Nations Records. Distributed by: Pinnacle

Metal Queen.
Tracks: / Metal Queen / Lady of the darkest night / Head above water / Got to be the one / Got to be the one / Shake it up / Deciever / Steal away your love / Hold out / Breakdown / We will be rockin'.
Album: released on 10 in Aug'86 by 10 Records. Distributed by: Virgin, EMI

Musiccassette: released on Music For Nations in Jul'84 by Music For Nations Records. Distributed by: Pinnacle

Single (12"): released on Music For Nations in Sep'84 by Music For Nations Records. Distributed by: Pinnacle

Only human.
Tracks: / Only human / Empty heart / Call of the wild.
Single (7"): released on 10 in '87 by 10 Records. Distributed by: Virgin, EMI

Single (12"): released on 10 in '87 by 10 Records. Distributed by: Virgin, EMI

Rock me all over.
Single (12"): released on Attic in Jun'85. Distributed by: Pinnacle

Aaron, Paul

Streets of heaven.
Single (7"): released on Music UK in Jan'87.

Distributed by: PRT Distribution

Aaronson

Through the fire (Aaronson, Hager, Schon, Shrieve).

Abacush

Stand firm.
Tracks: / Sand firm / Africa.
Single (12"): released on Abacush in May'86 by Abacush. Distributed by: Abacush, Jetstar

Sunshine Island.
Tracks: / Sunshine Island / Sunshine Island (version).
Single (7"): released on Abacush in Jun'86 by Abacush. Distributed by: Abacush, Jetstar

Single (12"): released on Abacush in Jun'86 by Abacush. Distributed by: Abacush, Jetstar

Train is coming, The.
Single (12"): released on Abacush in Jun'84 by Abacush. Distributed by: Abacush, Jetstar

Abba

Abba.
Musiccassette: released on Epic in Aug'82 by CBS Records. Distributed by: CBS

Album, The.
Tracks: / Eagle / Take a chance on me / One man one woman / Name of the game, The / Move on / Hole in your soul / Girl with the golden hair, The / 3 scenes from a mini musical*
Album: released on Epic in Mar'84 by CBS Records. Distributed by: CBS

Musiccassette: released on Epic in Mar'84 by CBS Records. Distributed by: CBS

Arrival.
Tracks: / Dancing Queen / My love my life / When I kissed the teacher / Dancing Queen / My love my life / Dum dum diddle / Knowing me, knowing you / Money money money / That's me / Why did it have to be me / Tiger / Arrival.
Album: released on Epic in Jul'83 by CBS Records. Distributed by: CBS

Musiccassette: released on Epic in Jul'83 by CBS Records. Distributed by: CBS

Boxed set.
Notes: Boxed set of 26 singles
Boxed set: released on Epic in Apr'84 by CBS Records. Distributed by: CBS

Chiquitita.
Single (7"): released on Epic in May'82 by CBS Records. Distributed by: CBS

Day before you came.
Single (7"): released on Epic in Oct'82 by CBS Records. Distributed by: CBS

Does your Mother know.
Single (7"): released on Epic in May'82 by CBS Records. Distributed by: CBS

Fernando.
Single (7"): released on Epic in May'82 by CBS Records. Distributed by: CBS

Greatest hits: Abba Vol.1.
Tracks: / Fernando / SOS / He is your brother / Hasta manana / Dance (while the music still goes on) / Another town, another train / Mamma mia / Waterloo / I do, I do, I do / Honey honey / People need love / Ring ring / Hang-a-boomerang / Nina pretty ballerina / So long.
Album: released on Epic in Apr'85 by CBS Records. Distributed by: CBS

Musiccassette: released on Epic in Apr'85 by CBS Records. Distributed by: CBS

Greatest hits: Abba.
Tracks: / Take a chance on me / Gimme gimme gimme / Money money money / Rock me / Eagle / Angel eyes / Dancing queen / Does your mother know / Chiquitita / Summer night city / I wonder / Name of the game, The / Thank you for the music / Knowing me, knowing you.
Album: released on Epic in Oct'79 by CBS Records. Distributed by: CBS

Musiccassette: released on Epic in Oct'79 by CBS Records. Distributed by: CBS

Compact disc: released on Epic in Oct'79 by CBS Records. Distributed by: CBS

Album: released on Epic in May'87 by CBS Records. Distributed by: CBS

Musiccassette: released on Epic in May'87 by CBS Records. Distributed by: CBS

Greatest original hits.
Extended-play record: released on Epic in Mar'83 by CBS Records. Distributed by: CBS

Hits, The.
Compact disc: by Pickwick Records. Distributed by: Pickwick Distribution, Prism Leisure Distribution, Lugtons

Album: released on Hallmark in Oct'87 by Pickwick Records. Distributed by: Pickwick Distribution, PRT, Taylors

Musiccassette: released on Hallmark in Oct'87 by Pickwick Records. Distributed by: Pickwick Distribution, PRT, Taylors

Knowing me knowing you.
Single (7"): released on Epic in May'82 by CBS Records. Distributed by: CBS

Mama mia.
Single (7"): released on Epic in May'82 by CBS Records. Distributed by: CBS

Money money money.
Single (7"): released on Epic in May'82 by CBS Records. Distributed by: CBS

Most of Abba, The.
Album: released on Epic (EEC import) in Nov'82 by CBS Records. Distributed by: CBS

Movie (The).
Video-cassette (VHS): released on MGM/UA in Jan'84. Distributed by: Pickwick Distribution

Name of the game.
Single (7"): released on Epic in May'82 by CBS Records. Distributed by: CBS

One of us.
Single (7"): released on Epic in Dec'81 by CBS Records. Distributed by: CBS

Singles, The (the first ten years).
Tracks: / Ring ring / Waterloo / So long / I do I do I do / SOS / Mamma Mia / Dancing Queen / Money money money / Knowing me knowing you / Name of the game, The / Take a chance on me / Summer night city / Chiquitita / Does you Mother know / Voulez vous / Gimme gimme gimme / Super trouper / One of us / Day before you came, The / Under attack.
Album: released on Epic in Nov'82 by CBS Records. Distributed by: CBS

Musiccassette: released on Epic in Nov'82 by CBS Records. Distributed by: CBS

Singles-The First 10 Years, The.
Tracks: / Ring ring / Waterloo / So long / I do I do I do / SOS / Mama Mia / Fernando / Danc-

ing Queen / Money money money / Knowing me knowing you / Name of the game, The / Take a chance on me / Summer night city / Chiquitita / Does your mother know / Voulez vous / Gimme gimme gimme (A man after midnight) / I have a dream / Winner takes all, The / Super trouper / One of us / Day before you came, The / Under attack.
Compact disc: by CBS Records. Distributed by: CBS

Story of Abba.
Notes: A compilation of 25 tracks with a total playing time of 54 mins.
Video-cassette (VHS): released on MGM in May'86. Distributed by: Polygram Distribution, Swift Distribution

Summer night city.
Single (7"): released on Epic in May'82 by CBS Records. Distributed by: CBS

Super Trouper.
Tracks: / Winner takes it all / On and on and / Andante andante / Me and I / Super trouper / Happier New Year / Our last summer / Piper / Lay all your love on me / Way old friends do / Super Trouper / Winner takes it all, The / On and on and on / Andante Andante / Me and I / Happy New Year / Our last summer / Piper, The / Lay all your love on me / Lay all your love on me / Way old friends do, The.
Album: released on Epic in Nov'80 by CBS Records. Distributed by: CBS

Musiccassette: released on Epic in Nov'80 by CBS Records. Distributed by: CBS

Compact disc: released on Epic in '82 by CBS Records. Distributed by: CBS

Take a chance on me.
Single (7"): released on Epic in May'82 by CBS Records. Distributed by: CBS

Thank you for the music.
Tracks: / My love, my life / I wonder / Happy new year / Slipping through my fingers / Fernando / One man, one woman / Eagle / I have a dream / Our last summer / Day before you came, The / Chiquitita / Should I laugh or cry / Old way friends do, The / Thank-you for the music.
Album: released on Epic in Nov'83 by CBS Records. Distributed by: CBS Deleted '87.

Musiccassette: released on Epic in Nov'83 by CBS Records. Distributed by: CBS

Visitors, The.
Tracks: / Visitors, The / Head over heels / When all is said and done / Soldiers / I let the music speak / One of us / Two for the price of one / Slipping through my fingers / Like an angel / Passing through my room / Eagle.
Album: released on Epic in Dec'81 by CBS Records. Distributed by: CBS

Musiccassette: released on Epic in Dec'81 by CBS Records. Distributed by: CBS

Compact disc: released on Epic in Dec'81 by CBS Records. Distributed by: CBS

Voulez vous.
Tracks: / As good as new / Voulez vous / I have a dream / Angel eyes / Kings has lost his crown, / Does your mother know / If it wasn't for the night / Chiquitita / Lovers (Like a little longer) / Kisses of fire.
Album: released on Epic in Jul'86 by CBS Records. Distributed by: CBS

Musiccassette: released on Epic in Jul'86 by CBS Records. Distributed by: CBS

Musiccassette: released on Epic in May'79 by CBS Records. Distributed by: CBS

Waterloo.
Tracks: / Waterloo / Watch out / Sitting in the palm tree / King Kong song / Hasta manana / My mama said / Dance (while the music still goes on) / Honey honey / Watch out / What about Livingstone / Gonna sing you my love

song / Suzy hang around / Ring ring.
Single (7"): released on Epic in Nov'86 by CBS Records. Distributed by: CBS

Musicassette: released on Epic in Mar'81 by CBS Records. Distributed by: CBS

Winner takes it all.
Single (7"): released on Epic in May'82 by CBS Records. Distributed by: CBS

Abbatoir

Vicious attack.
Album: released on Roadrunner (Dutch) in Jul'85. Distributed by: Pinnacle

Abbey Radar

Thing, The.
Album: released on Atmosphere in Sep'79 by E.S.S.P.

Abbot, Russ

Biographical Details: ITV's Saturday night musical satirist scored a minor hit sngle n 1982 with "A Day In The Life Of Vince Prince". In 1983 he found himself in commercial breaks as well as programmes, to promote Ronco's compilation.

All night holiday.
Single (7"): released on Spirit in Jun'87 by Spirit Records. Distributed by: WEA

Single (12"): released on Spirit in Jun'85 by Spirit Records. Distributed by: WEA

Atmosphere.
Single (7"): released on Spirit in Dec'86 by Spirit Records. Distributed by: WEA

Single (12"): released on Spirit in Dec'86 by Spirit Records. Distributed by: WEA

I love a party.
Album: released on K-Tel in Nov'85 by K-Tel Records. Distributed by: Record Merchandisers Distribution, Taylors, Terry Blood Distribution, Wynd-Up Distribution, Relay Distribution, Pickwick Distribution, Solomon & Peres Distribution, Polygram

Musicassette: released on K-Tel in Nov'85 by K-Tel Records. Distributed by: Record Merchandisers Distribution, Taylors, Terry Blood Distribution, Wynd-Up Distribution, Relay Distribution, Pickwick Distribution, Solomon & Peres Distribution, Polygram

Let's go to the disco.
Tracks: / Let's go to the disco / Atmosphere.
Single (7"): released on Spirit in Dec'85 by Spirit Records. Distributed by: WEA

Single (12"): released on Spirit in Nov'85 by Spirit Records. Distributed by: WEA

Russ Abbot's Madhouse.
Album: released on Ronco in Nov'83

Abbott, Gregory

I got the feeling.
Tracks: / Rhyme and Reason.
Single (7"): released on CBS in Feb'87 by CBS Records. Distributed by: CBS

Single (12"): released on CBS in Feb'87 by CBS Records. Distributed by: CBS

Shake you down.
Tracks: / Shake you down / Shake you down (ext. version) / Wait until tomorrow.
Single (7"): released on CBS in Sep'86 by CBS Records. Distributed by: CBS

Single (12"): released on CBS in Sep'86 by CBS Records. Distributed by: CBS

Compact disc: by CBS Records. Distributed by: CBS

You're my angel.
Single (7"): released on CBS in May'87 by CBS Records. Distributed by: CBS

Single (12"): released on CBS in May'87 by CBS Records. Distributed by: CBS

Abbreviated Calling

D.W.I..
Single (12"): released on Homestead in Apr'85. Distributed by: Rough Trade, Cartel, Shigaku

ABC

Biographical Details: ABC were formed at the end of 1980 by singer Martin Fry. The orignal line-up included fifth member, bassist Mark Lickley, who came to be regarded as a guest musician rather than a permanent fixture. The group enjoyed rapid success, their first single climbing to No.19 in the autumn of '81 ("Tears Are Not Enough"). Fry then hired ex-Buggles/Yes member Trevor Horn, who had recently scored a Top 20 single with his lush, multi-textured production of Dollar's "Hand Held In Black And White". The combination was a winner. The Sheffield-based band wrote strong, commercial love songs, Fry sung them powerfully, and Horn's majestic, orchestrated production gave them a sleek commercial appeal. In addition the group's hi-gloss, dapper image made them magazine pin-up favourites. The result was three consecutive Top 10 singles, all included on the band's debut LP "The Lexicon Of Love", which entered the album chart at No.1 in July '82 and stayed there for four weeks. ABC also achieved Top 30 single and album success in the States. However the follow-up album "Beauty Stab", released in November '83, was a major disappointment. The LP could only manage a meagre chart run, with its first single "That Was Then But This Is Now" quickly dropping down after peaking at No.18. The second 45, appropriately titled "SOS", reached only No.39. The absence of Trevor Horn was the clear reason. Also on his way out was drummer David Palmer, leaving ABC as a three-piece. The depleted outfit returned in October 1984 optimistically titled "Millionaire".

Beauty Stab.
Tracks: / That was then but this is now / Love's a dangerous language / If I ever thought you'd be lonely / Power of persuassion / Beauty stab / By default by design / Hey citizen / King money / Bite the hand / Unzip / SOS / United kingdom.
Compact disc: released on Neutron in Nov'83 by Neutron Records. Distributed by: Polygram

Be near me.
Tracks: / Be near me / Be near me.
Notes: This is an extra track which is only on the 12" single.

How to be a zillionaire.
Tracks: / A to Z / How to be a zillionaire / Tower of London / So hip it hurts / Between you and me / Fear of the world / Be near me / Vanity kills / Ocean blue / 15 story halo.
Compact disc: released on Neutron in Oct'85 by Neutron Records. Distributed by: Polygram

Lexicon of love, The.
Tracks: / Show me / Poison arrow / Many happy returns / Tears are not enough / Valentin's day / Look of love, The (part 1) / Date stamp / All of my heart / 4 Ever 2 gether / Look of love.
Album: released on Neutron in Jun'82 by Neutron Records. Distributed by: Polygram

Musicassette: released on Neutron in Jun'82 by Neutron Records. Distributed by: Polygram

Compact disc: released on Neutron in Jun'82 by Neutron Records. Distributed by: Polygram

Look of love, The.
Single (7"): released on Neutron in Oct'84 by Neutron Records. Distributed by: Polygram

Single (12"): released on Neutron in Oct'84 by Neutron Records. Distributed by: Polygram

Night you murdered love.
Single (7"): released on Neutron in Aug'87 by Neutron Records. Distributed by: Polygram

Single (12"): released on Neutron in Aug'87 by Neutron Records. Distributed by: Polygram

Ocean blue.
Tracks: / Ocean blue / Tower of London / Be near me.
Single (7"): released on Phonogram in Dec'85 by Phonogram Records. Distributed by: Polygram

Single (12"): released on Neutron in Dec'85 by Neutron Records. Distributed by: Polygram

Rhythm on the radio.
Single (7"): released on Oval in May'82. Distributed by: Projection

Tower of London.
Tracks: / Tower of London.

Vanity kills.
Single (12"): released on Neutron in Jun'85 by Neutron Records. Distributed by: Polygram

When Smokey sings.
Tracks: / When Smokey sings / Chicago pt.1.

Single (7"): released on Neutron in 23 May'87 by Neutron Records. Distributed by: Polygram

Single (12"): released on Neutron in 23 May'87 by Neutron Records. Distributed by: Polygram

Abdel Aziz El Mubarek

Songs from the city.
Album: released on World Circuit in Jun'87 by Taurus Records. Distributed by: Sterns/Triple Earth Distribution

Abecedarians

Benway's carnival.
Single (12"): released on Factory in Aug'85 by Factory Records. Distributed by: Cartel, Pinnacle

Smiling monarchs.
Single (12"): released on Factory in May'85 by Factory Records. Distributed by: Cartel, Pinnacle

Abercrombie, John

Current Events.
Tracks: / Clint / Alice In Wonderland / Ralph's Piano Waltz / Lisa / Hippityville / Killing Time / Still.
Album: released on ECM (Germany) in Jun'86 by ECM Records. Distributed by: IMS, Polygram, Virgin through EMI

Compact disc: released on ECM (Germany) in Aug'86 by ECM Records. Distributed by: IMS, Polygram, Virgin through EMI

Five years later (Abercrombie, John & Ralph Towner).

Gateway.
Compact disc: by ECM Records. Distributed by: IMS, Polygram, Virgin through EMI

Night.
Tracks: / Etherreggae / Night / 3 East / Look around / Believe you me / Four on one.
Notes: American guitarist john Abercrombie has come up with a real winner on this LP. the opening track, an infectious reggae influenced piece is ideal for mainstreamradio plays. Excellent support from Jan Hammer on keyboards, Jack DeJohnette drums, and Mike Brecker tenor saxophone. Digital Stereo
Compact disc: by ECM Records. Distributed by: IMS, Polygram, Virgin through EMI
Cat.no °232122
Album: released on ECM (Germany) in Nov'84 by ECM Records. Distributed by: IMS, Polygram, Virgin through EMI

Sargasso Sea (see Towner, Ralph) (Abercrombie, John & Ralph Towner).
Album: released on ECM (Germany) in Oct'76 by ECM Records. Distributed by: IMS, Polygram, Virgin through EMI

Solar (Abercrombie, John & John Scofield).

Timeless.
Tracks: / Lungs / Love song / Ralph's piano waltz / Red and orange / Remembering / Timeless.
Compact disc: by ECM Records. Distributed by: IMS, Polygram, Virgin through EMI

Abercrombie Quartet

M.
Album: released on ECM (France) in Jun'81 by ECM Records. Distributed by: IMS, Polygram, Virgin through EMI

Aberdeen, Angus

10 Solo.
Tracks: / Jet Plane / Cracklin' Rosie / For the good times.
Notes: Angus Aberdeen: Vocalist and multi-instrumentalist. Popular songs plus some Italian and Greek songs and classics set to bossanova rhythms. Eron Songs, 27, Balmoral Road, Kingsdown, Deal, Kent CT14 8BX
Album: released on Eron in Sep'85 by Eron Records. Distributed by: Eron Records

Musicassette: released on Eron in Sep'85 by Eron Records. Distributed by: Eron Records

Aberdeen Football Club

European song.
Single (7"): released on AFC in Mar'83 by AFC Records. Distributed by: Spartan

Abide With Us

Abide with us (Falklands Task Force Collection Of Hymns).
Notes: At one minute to midnight GMT on Monday June 14 1982, General Menendez surrendered all Argentine troops on the Falklands to general Moore. At the request of theBritish ships companies and families involved in the campaign, and with the active support of rear admiral Sir John Woodward KVBASV are releasing an album of hymns selected by the ships that took part, to commenerate this anniversary, now and for the future. Rear admiral John Woodward KCB and the ministry of defence (Navy) have co-operated fully with this recording. The Falklands task force and their families has choosen this collection of favourite hymns which in times of danger, tradgedy and triumph gave strenght, comfort and hope.
Sung by the choir of Seaford college chapel and members of the Falklands task force. Directed by Phillip Hill.
Album: released on ASV in Jun'83 by Academy Sound & Vision Records. Distributed by: Pinnacle

Musicassette: released on ASV in Jun'83 by Academy Sound & Vision Records. Distributed by: Pinnacle

Abie

Mona Lisa's lost her smile.
Single (7"): released on Klub in May'85

While the feelings good.
Tracks: / While the feelings good / My mother's eyes / From a Jack to a King / Funny familiar forgotten feelings / Vincent / Unchanged melody / 500 miles away from home / If I had my life to live over / Blueberry hill / Funny how time slips away / This a story of a starry night / Somewhere.
Notes: Abie fast established himself as a popular mor singer in Scotland,We are sure this album will bring much pleasure to his growing number of fans and find him many new admirers.
Album: released on Klub in Jun'84

Musicassette: released on Klub in Jun'84

Abiodun, Dele

Confrontation.
Album: released on Earthworks in Apr'85 by Earthworks Records. Distributed by: Earthworks Distributors, Rough Trade, Cartel, Projection

It's time for juju music.
Album: released on Leader (Nigeria) in Apr'84 by Earthworks Records. Distributed by: Rough Trade

Abi-Ola

Yours until tomorrow.
Tracks: / Yours until tomorrow / Play me all night.
Single (12"): released on MGR in Apr'86. Distributed by: Jetstar Records

Abnormals

Skins'n'Punks volume 4 (Abnormals & Barbed Wire).
Album:

A Bones

Tempo Tantrum EP.
Single 10": released on Exile in May'86 by Exile Records. Distributed by: Pinnacle

Aborted

No rules.
Single (7"): released on Chaos in Nov'83 by Backs Records. Distributed by: Nine Mile, Cartel

About Last Night

About last night Original motion picture soundtrack (Various Artists).
Tracks: / So far so good / Shape of things to come (She's the) / Natural love / Words into action / Step by step / Living inside my heart / Trials of the heart / 'Til you love somebody / If we can get through the night / True love / If anybody had a heart.
Notes: Tracks 1-5 John Oates/Jermaine Jackson appear courtesy of Arista Records Tracks 6-11 Bob Seger appears cuortesy of Capitol Records Inc. a subsidairy of Capitol Industriers-EMI Inc.
Album: released on EMI America in Oct'86 by EMI Records. Distributed by: EMI

Musicassette: released on EMI America in Oct'86 by EMI Records. Distributed by: EMI

About Love

About love (Various Artists).
Album: released on Hallmark in Feb'82 by Pickwick Records. Distributed by: Pickwick Distribution, PRT, Taylors

Musicassette: released on Hallmark in Feb'82 by Pickwick Records. Distributed by: Pickwick Distribution, PRT, Taylors

Abrahams, Chris

Piano.
Album: released on Hot in Aug'85 by Hot Records. Distributed by: Rough Trade Cartel

Abrahams, Mike

Have fun learning the guitar.

Album: released on SRT in Nov'79 by SRT Records. Distributed by: Pinnacle, Solomon & Peres Distribution, SRT Distribution, H.R. Taylor Distribution, PRT Distribution

Abrams, Colonel

How soon we forget.
Tracks: / How soon we forget / How soon we forget (dub).
Single (7"): released on MCA in Jul'87 by MCA Records. Distributed by: Polygram, MCA

Single (12"): released on MCA in Jul'87 by MCA Records. Distributed by: Polygram, MCA

I'm not gonna let you.
Tracks: / I'm not gonna let you / I'm not gonna let you (percapella mix) / I'm not gonna let you (ext) / I'm not gonna let you (ext dub).
Single (7"): released on MCA in Mar'86 by MCA Records. Distributed by: Polygram MCA

Single (12"): released on MCA in Mar'86 by MCA Records. Distributed by: Polygram, MCA

Single (12"): released on MCA in Mar'86 by MCA Records. Distributed by: Polygram MCA

Abrams, Muhal Richard

1-0 QA + 19.
Album: released on Black Saint in Jul'78. Distributed by: Projection, IMS, Polygram, Chris Wellard, Harmonia Mundi, Swift

Duet with Amina Claudine Myers.
Album: released on Black Saint in Jul'82. Distributed by: Projection, IMS, Polygram, Chris Wellard, Harmonia Mundi, Swift

Sight song.
Album: released on Black Saint in Jul'78. Distributed by: Projection, IMS, Polygram, Chris Wellard, Harmonia Mundi, Swift

Abrams, Richard

Bevels & degrees of light.
Album: . Distributed by: Projection, Swift, Cadillac

Young at heart.
Album: . Distributed by: Projection, Swift, Cadillac

Abrasive Wheels

Army song (EP).
Single (7"): released on Riot City in Mar'82 by Riot City Records. Distributed by: Revolver

Banner of hope.
Single (7"): released on Clay in Nov'83 by Clay Records. Distributed by: Pinnacle

Black leather girl.
Album: released on Clay in Mar'84 by Clay Records. Distributed by: Pinnacle

Burn the schools.
Single (7"): released on Riot City in Oct'82 by Riot City Records. Distributed by: Revolver

Jailhouse rock.
Single (7"): released on Clay in May'83 by Clay Records. Distributed by: Pinnacle

Prisoner, The.
Single (7"): released on Clay in May'84 by Clay Records. Distributed by: Pinnacle

Single (12"): released on Clay in May'84 by Clay Records. Distributed by: Pinnacle

Vicious circle (EP).
Single (12"): released on Riot City in Feb'82 by Riot City Records. Distributed by: Revolver

When the punks go in.
Album: released on Riot City in Nov'82 by Riot City Records. Distributed by: Revolver

Abs

Grease your Ralph.
Single (7"): released on Winking Ring in Aug'87 by Winking Ring Records. Distributed by: Revolver, Cartel

Abshire, Nathan

Best of....
Album: released on Swallow (USA) in Oct'86. Distributed by: Swift Distribution

Cajun legend, A The best of Nathan Abshire.
Album:

Cajuns Vol.2, The.
Album: released on Sonet in '73 by Sonet Records. Distributed by: PRT

Good times are killing me (Abshire, Nathan & Belfa Brothers).
Album: released on Swallow in Feb'79

Good times are killing me.
Album:

Nathan Abshire and The Pinegrove Boys (Abshire, Nathan And The Pinegrove Boys).
Notes: MONO Best European cajun LP
Album: released on Flyright in Jun'86 by Flyright Records. Distributed by: Krazy Kat, Swift, Jazz Music

Nathan Abshire & Other Cajun Gems.
Album: released on Arhoolie in May'81 by Arhoolie Records. Distributed by: Projection, Topic, Jazz Music, Swift, Roots

Pine grove blues.
Album: released on Swallow in Feb'79

Absolute

Can't you see.
Tracks: / Can't you see / Love in my heart.
Single (7"): released on Absolute in May'87 by Absolute. Distributed by: Spartan

TV glare.
Single (7"): released on Reset in Apr'85 by Vince Clarke/Eric Radcliffe. Distributed by: Spartan

Absolute, Albert

Noises.
Single (7"): released on Completely Different in Apr'82

Absolute Beginners

Absolute Beginners Original Soundtrack (Various Artists).
Album: released on Virgin in Apr'86 by Virgin Records. Distributed by: EMI, Virgin Distribution

Musicassette: released on Virgin in Apr'86 by Virgin Records. Distributed by: EMI, Virgin Distribution

Compact disc: released on Virgin in Jul'87 by Virgin Records. Distributed by: EMI, Virgin Distribution

Dream in a haze.
Single (7"): released on Roundabout in Sep'84 by Roundabout Records. Distributed by: ILA Distribution

Absolute Rock'n'Roll

Absolute Rock'n'Roll (Various Artists).
Album: released on Starblend in Aug'86 by Starblend Records. Distributed by: PRT Distribution

Musicassette: released on Starblend in Aug'86 by Starblend Records. Distributed by: PRT Distribution

Absurd Take Away

Absurd take away (Various Artists).
Album: released on Absurd in Jul'80 by Absurd. Distributed by: Pinnacle, Rough Trade

Abuse

Abuse (Various Artists).
Album: released on Artists For Animals in Sep'86. Distributed by: Revolver, Cartel

Abuser

Songs of sex and not of war.
Album: released on Flux in Oct'84 by Flux Records. Distributed by: Cartel

Abwarts

Der western ist einsam.
Album: released on Philips (Germany) in Jul'72

Out of order Original soundtrack.
Album: released on RG (West Germany) in Mar'86. Distributed by: Silva Screen Distribution

Academy

Keep on pushing.
Tracks: / Kep on pushing / Turn it up.
Single (7"): released on RCA in Apr'86 by RCA Records. Distributed by: RCA, Roots, Swift Wellard, Chris, I & B, Solomon & Peres Distribution

On the beach.
Single (7"): by RCA Records. Distributed by: RCA, Roots, Swift, Wellard, Chris, I & B Solomon & Peres Distribution

Single (12"): released on RCA in Mar'84 by RCA Records. Distributed by: RCA, Roots, Swift, Wellard, Chris, I & B, Solomon & Peres Distribution

Stand up.
Single (7"): released on RCA in Aug'85 by RCA Records. Distributed by: RCA, Roots, Swift, Wellard, Chris, I & B, Solomon & Peres Distribution

Single (12"): released on RCA in Aug'85 by RCA Records. Distributed by: RCA, Roots, Swift, Wellard, Chris, I & B, Solomon & Peres Distribution

Tonight (the world keeps swinging).
Single (7"): released on RCA in May'85 by RCA Records. Distributed by: RCA, Roots, Swift, Wellard, Chris, I & B, Solomon & Peres Distribution

Single (12"): released on RCA in May'85 by RCA Records. Distributed by: RCA, Roots, Swift, Wellard, Chris, I & B, Solomon & Peres Distribution

You're in my system.
Tracks: / You're in my system / You're in my system (extra inch remix) / Heaven waits / System (Bernard remix).
Single (7"): released on RCA in Jan'86 by RCA Records. Distributed by: RCA, Roots, Swift, Wellard, Chris, I & B, Solomon & Peres Distribution

Single (12"): released on RCA in Jan'86 by RCA Records. Distributed by: RCA, Roots, Swift, Wellard, Chris, I & B, Solomon & Peres Distribution

Academy Award Winners

Academy Award Winners (Various Artists).
Album: released on Meteor in Jun'87 by Magnum Music Group Ltd. Distributed by: Magnum Music Group Ltd, PRT Distribution, Spartan Distribution

Academy Of Unrest

Sheol hex.
Single (7"): released on Dead Fly in Jun'85. Distributed by: Cartel

Academy One

Forever and ever.
Single (7"): released on Armageddon in Apr'82 by Armageddon Records. Distributed by: Revolver, Cartel, Pinnacle

Acapella Gospel Singing

Acapella Gospel Singing (Various Artists).
Album: released on Folklyric (USA) in Jan'87 by Arhoolie Records. Distributed by: Topic, Projection

Accelerators

Reason for treason (EP).
Single (12"): released on Spiv in Feb'80 by Spiv Records

Accent

We are lost.
Single (7"): released on Motion in Dec'84 by Motion Records. Distributed by: ILA Distribution

Accept

Biographical Details: German five-piece heavy rock group formed 1977. First signed to the German Metronome label. In 1978 released first album 'Accept'. Second album 'Breaker' appeared 79/80. First appeared in UK as back-up group to Judas Priest, in 1981. Third album was 'Restless & Wild'. They made a UK tour in 82/83. Fourth album 'Balls To The Walls' was released in Jan 1984 by Epic.

Accept.
Tracks: / Lady Lou / Tire of me / Seawinds / Take him in my heart / Sounds of war / Free me now / Glad to be alone / That's rock 'n' roll / Hell driver / Street fighter.
Album: released on Brain (Germany) in Jul'83

Picture disc album: released on Razor in Mar'85 by Razor. Distributed by: Pinnacle

Balls to the wall.
Album: released on Portrait in Jan'84 by CBS Records. Distributed by: CBS

Musicassette: released on Portrait in Jan'84 by CBS Records. Distributed by: CBS Deleted '86.

Balls to the wall/ Metal heart.
Album: released on Portrait in Aug'87 by CBS Records. Distributed by: CBS

Best of Accept.
Tracks: / Burning / Restless and wild / Son of a bitch / Breaker / Do it / I'm rebel / China lady / No time to lose / Princess of the Dawn / Lady Lou.
Album: released on Metronome (Germany) in Dec'83. Distributed by: Jazz Music Distribution

Breaker.
Album: released on Polydor (Germany) in Dec'81. Distributed by: IMS-Polygram

I'm a rebel.
Tracks: / I'm a rebel / Save us / No time to lose / Thunder & lightning / China lady / I wanna be no hero / The king / Do it.
Album: released on Brain (Germany) in Jul'83

Kaisoku-ban.
Tracks: / Metal heart / Screaming for a love bite / Up to the limit / Head over heels / Love child / Living for tonite.
Album: released on Portrait in Feb'86 by CBS Records. Distributed by: CBS

Musicassette: released on Portrait in Feb'86 by CBS Records. Distributed by: CBS

Metal heart.
Tracks: / Metal heart / Midnight mover / Up to the limit / Wrong is right / Screaming for a love bite / Too high to get it right / Dogs on leads / Teach us to survive / Living for tonight / Bound to fail.
Album: released on Portrait in Mar'85 by CBS Records. Distributed by: CBS

Musicassette: released on Portrait in Mar'85 by CBS Records. Distributed by: CBS

Metal masters.
Album: released on Razor in Jun'84 by Razor. Distributed by: Pinnacle

Musicassette: released on Razor in Jun'84 by Razor. Distributed by: Pinnacle

Restless and wild.
Tracks: / Fast as a shark / Restless and wild / Ahead of the pack / Shake your hands / Neon nights / Get ready / Demons night / Flash rockin' man / Don't go stealing my soul away / Princess of the dawn / Fat as a shark / Restless and wild / Ahead of the pack / Shake your hands / Neon nights / Get ready / Flash rockin' man / Don't go stealing my soul away / Princess of the dawn.
Notes: All tracks composed and produced by Accept, recorded in 1982 at Dierks Studios in Cologne, Germany. Recorded and mixed by Michael Wagener. Accept are: Hermann Frank Jnr., Stefan Kaufmann, Udo Dirkschneider, Wolf Hoffmanand Peter Baltes.
Album: released on Portrait in Aug'86 by CBS Records. Distributed by: CBS

Musicassette: released on Portrait in Aug'86 by CBS Records. Distributed by: CBS

Album: released on Heavy Metal Worldwide in Apr'87 by FM-Revolver Records. Distributed by: EMI

Musicassette: released on Heavy Metal Worldwide in Apr'87 by FM-Revolver Records. Distributed by: EMI

Compact disc: released on Heavy Metal Worldwide in Apr'87 by FM-Revolver Records. Distributed by: EMI

Picture disc album: released on Heavy Metal in Mar'83 by FM-Revolver Records. Distributed by: EMI

Single (12"): released on Heavy Metal in Feb'84 by FM-Revolver Records. Distributed by: EMI

Russian Roulette.
Tracks: / T.V. war / Monsterman / Russian roulette / It's hard to find a way / Aiming high / Heaven is hell / Another second to be / Wiking in the shadow / Man enough to cry / Stand tight.
Album: released on Portrait in Apr'86 by CBS Records. Distributed by: CBS

Musicassette: released on Portrait in Apr'86 by CBS Records. Distributed by: CBS

Accident

Clockwork legion, A.
Album: released on Flicknife in Jul'84 by Flicknife Records. Distributed by: Spartan

Crazy!.
Tracks: / Crazy / Get ready / Valerie / Camouflage / Band played on / Get ready dub / Sherwood rangers / Bad co. / Leaders / Sorry / Man on the wall, The / Respectable / Twisted mind / Cue the dead.
Notes: Produced by Brian Collinson & Accident. Engineered by Neil Ferguson.
Album: released on Link in Jul'87. Distributed by: DMS, RCA

Accordian...

Accordeon de camera (Various Artists).
Tracks: / Bewegungen fur akkordeon und streichquartett... / Duell fur akkordeon und schlagzeug, sechs zweistimmage....
Album: released on ARC (Accordion Records) in '84. Distributed by: Accordion Record Club

Accordian a la carte Various artists (Various Artists).
Musicassette: released on Aim in Feb'83. Distributed by: H.R. Taylor

Accordion Album Vol.1 (Various Artists).
Musicassette: released on Ross in Jun'86 by Ross Records. Distributed by: Ross Distribution, Roots Distribution

Accordion Bonanza no.3 (Various Artists).
Notes: Introduced by Bill Torrance. Artists include: Jim Johnstone and His Band/Robert & Duncan Black/Graham Geddes/Graham & Jeffrey/John Douglas/Jimmy Lindsay/Una Bryson/Bill Black/Tommy Walker/Iain MacPhail & Brian Griffen/Melrose Accordion Orchestra. Other details as for no.1
Album: released on Accordion Record Club in Jul'86 by Accordion Record Club Records. Distributed by: Accordion Record Club

Accordion Bonanza no.1 (Various Artists).
Notes: Introduced by Bill Torrance. Artists include: Jim Johnston & His Band/Jim Halcrow/Eric Goodfellow/Iain MacPhail & Brian Griffin/John Leslie/Dave Stewart & The Merger/Raymond Chuckuck & Brian Forrest/Andrew Rankine/The Donaldson Bros./Ray Laidlaw/Jim Sharp/Paddy Neary. Price details and address as for "Accordion Album vol.1"

Accordion Bonanza no.2 (Various Artists).
Notes: Introduced by Bill Torrance. Artists include: Iain MacPhail and His Band/Alex MacArthur/Ian Wilkie/Robert Whitehead/Paddy Neary/Addie Harper Jnr./The Jimmy Blair Quartet/MacLeod & Johnstone/Max Houliston etc. Other details as for vol.1
Album: released on Accordion Record Club in Jul'86 by Accordion Record Club Records. Distributed by: Accordion Record Club

Accordion Revue Various Artists (Various Artists).
Compact disc: by Delta Records. Distributed by: Target

Accordion round the Antipodes (The) (Various Artists).
Tracks: / Jeepers creepers / Sweet Georgia Brown / Dark island / James D Law's reel / A banda / Una Paloma Blanca / Y viva Espana / Spanish eyes / yours / September in the rain / Guantanamera / Maria Elena / Schnee Waltzer / Wer soll da bezahlen? (Who'll pay for the next round?) / Samo nemoj ti / Lipa moja mala / Zasto da te me uzmen.
Notes: No price given. Other details as for "Accordion Bonanza"
Album: released on Accordion Record Club in Jul'86 by Accordion Record Club Records. Distributed by: Accordion Record Club

Accordions of Scotland vol.2 (Various Artists).
Tracks: / Scotch on the rocks / Cambeltown Loch / Tom Burns polka / Scalloway Voe / Bonnie wells of Wearie / Ballochmyle / Masons apron / Bluebells of Scotland / Star o' Rabbie Burns / Scots wha hae / Annie Laurie / Bonnie Charlie / Rothesay bay / Come by the stream.
Notes: A collection of 34 great tunes by Jim MacLeod/Dick Black/Bert Shorthouse/Star Accordion Band/Gordon Young/Rigadoon/Tommy Darky.
Album: released on Lochshore in Ap.'86 by Klub Records. Distributed by: PRT

Musicassette: released on Lochshore in Apr'86 by Klub Records. Distributed by: PRT

Accordions of Scotland Various artists (Various Artists).
Tracks: / My love is like a red red rose / Flowers of Edinburgh / Lucky Scaup / Wee dug Tim, The / Jessie the flower of Dunblane / Ye banks & braes / Will ye gang to Kelvinside / Jacqueline waltz / My heart is sair / Auld Scotch sangs / Nameless lassie, The / Annie Laurie / Laird of Dunblair, The / Masons apron, The / Miss Delicia Chisholm / Gay Gordons / Dark lochnager / My ain folk / Corn rigs / My love she's but a lassie yet / High laddie / There was a lad / Eriogal cree / Jessie's hornpipe / Kirk's hornpipe / Drumlees / Cuckoo, The / Tocherless lass, The / Leaving stornoway.
Notes: A collection of Scotlan's finest tunes played by Top Accordion Bands and Soloists. Bands: Jim MacLeod/John Carmichael/Bert Shorthouse/Angus Fitchet/Ian Holmes. Soloists: Gordon Patullo/Gordon Young.
Album: released on Lochshore in Ap.'85 by Klub Records. Distributed by: PRT

Musicassette: released on Lochshore in Apr'85 by Klub Records. Distributed by: PRT

Bach to Bernstein Fred Hecto, Hamburg (Accordion Orchestra).
Tracks: / Praefugium nr1 / Marsch in B / Black bolero / Nina / Danza Siziliana / West Side Story / Tango Della Marquesa / Western swing / Praefugium no.3 "In nomine J.S. Bach" (ehme).
Notes: Retail price given by ARC is 7.35 (exc. P&P) Other details as for "Accordion Bonanza"
Album: released on Accordion Record Club in Jul'86 by Accordion Record Club Records. Distributed by: Accordion Record Club

Accursed

Aggressive punk.
Album: released on Wreck 'Em in May'86 by Wreck 'Em Records. Distributed by: Cartel

Going down.
Single (7"): released on Wreck 'Em in Mar'84 by Wreck 'Em Records. Distributed by: Cartel

Laughing at breakage.
Album: released on Wreck 'Em in Oct'84 by Wreck 'Em Records. Distributed by: Cartel

Up with the punks.
Album: released on Wreck 'Em in Dec'83 by Wreck 'Em Records. Distributed by: Cartel

AC/DC

Biographical Details: AC/DC were formed in Australia by the Young brothers in 1974. After building a following in their home country, they toured Britain in 1976 and released two albums, "Dirty Deeds Done Dirt Cheap" and " Dirty Deeds Done Dirt Cheap". They arrived in the UK at the worst possible time for a heavy metal band-right at the start of the punk era. Atlantic Records overcame this disadvantage by opportunistically presenting them as a punk band with a schoolboy image. This pretence could not be kept up for long, though, and AC/DC were soon given deserved credit for being one of the few HM act to break through during the Punk/New Wave period. "Let There Be Rock" was their first UK chart album, reaching the Top 20 in 1977, the same year that original basssist Mark Evans was replaced by C.Williams. The group's sixth album "Highway To Hell", issued in 1979 was one of the forerunners of a major heavy metal resurgence in the charts. But just as the band wereentering the top league tragedy struck. Vital vocalist Bon Scott, whose supersonic singing was one of AC/DC's main trademarks, died from alcohol abuse in early 1980. The remaining members quickly overcame this bombshell by finding an equally energetic replacement in British singer Brian Johnson, formerly of early Seventies singles band Geordie. Public acceptance of the new recruit was immediate. "Back In Black" (title being a tasteful tribute to Scott) entered the album chart at No.1 and yielded the band's first Top 20 single, "Rock 'n' Roll Aint't Noise Pollution". "Rock 'n' Roll Damnation" had been their first hit single in 1978, peaking at No.24, but most of their 45's had tended to be only minor hits. AC/DC's biggest single came in 1982 when "Let's Get It Up" reached No.13, and both albums and singles have continued to sell well. In August 1984 they reiterated their status as one of the world's leading heavy bands by headlining the "Monsters Of Rock" festival at Castle Donnington. Their biggest Stateside triumph csme at the end of '81, when "For Those About To Rock" topped the Billboard album chart.

AC/DC blues gay jazz reissues Various Artists (AC/DC Blues Gay Jazz Reissues).
Album: . Distributed by: Swift Distribution, Jazz Music Distribution, Jazz Horizons Distribution, Celtic Music Distribution, Cadillac, JSU Distribution, Zodiac Distribution

Back in black.
Tracks: / Hell's bells / Shoot to thrill / What do you do for money honey? / Give the dog a bone / Let me put my love into you / Back in black / You shook me all night long / Have a drink on me / Shake a leg / Rock and roll ain't noise pollution / Back in black / Hell's bells / Shoot to thrill / Give the dog a bone / What do you do for money honey? / Rock 'n' roll ain't no noise pollution / Let me put my love into you / You shook me all night long / Shake a leg / Have a drink on me.

Back in black.
Compact disc: released on Atlantic in Feb'87 by WEA Records. Distributed by: WEA

Album: by WEA Records. Distributed by: WEA

Dirty deeds done dirt cheap.
Tracks: / Dirty deeds done dirt cheap / Love at first feel / Big balls / Rocker / Problem child / There's gonna be some rockin' / Ain't no fun waiting round to be a millionaire / Ride on / Squealer.
Album: by WEA Records. Distributed by: WEA

Musicassette: by WEA Records. Distributed by: WEA

Compact disc: released on Atlantic in Aug'87 by WEA Records. Distributed by: WEA

Flick of the switch.
Tracks: / Rising power / Badlands / Brain shake / Flick of the switch / Deep in the hole / Landslide / Guns for hire / Bedlam in Belgium.
Album: by WEA Records. Distributed by: WEA

Musicassette: by WEA Records. Distributed by: WEA

Fly on the wall.
Tracks: / Fly on the wall / Shake your foundations / First blood / Danger / Sink in pink / Playing with the girls / Stand up / Stand up / Hell or high water / Back in business / Send for the man.
Video-cassette (VHS): released on Atlantic in Jun'86 by WEA Records. Distributed by: WEA

Video-cassette [Betamax]: released on Atlantic in Jun'86 by WEA Records. Distributed by: WEA

Compact disc: released on Atlantic in Jul'85 by WEA Records. Distributed by: WEA

Fly on the wall.
Tracks: / Fly on the wall / Fly on the wall / Shake your foundations / First blood / Danger / Sink in the pink / Playing with the girls / Stand up / Hell or high water / Back in business / Send for the man.
Album: released on Atlantic in Jul'85 by WEA Records. Distributed by: WEA

Musicassette: released on Atlantic in Jul'85 by WEA Records. Distributed by: WEA

For those about to rock (we salute you).
Album: by WEA Records. Distributed by: WEA

Musicassette: by WEA Records. Distributed by: WEA

Compact disc: released on Atlantic in Jul'87 by WEA Records. Distributed by: WEA

High voltage.
Tracks: / It's a long way to the top / Rock 'n' roll singer / She's got the jack / Live wire / TNT / Can I sit next to you girl / Little lover / She's go balls / High voltage.
Album: by WEA Records. Distributed by: WEA

High voltage/live wire.
Single (7"): released on Atlantic in Jun'80 by WEA Records. Distributed by: WEA

Highway to Hell.
Tracks: / Highway to Hell / Girl got rhythm / Touch too much / Beating around the bush / Shot down / In flames / Get it hot / If you want blood (you've got it) / Love hungry / Night prowler.
Album: released on Atlantic in Aug'79 by WEA Records. Distributed by: WEA

Musicassette: released on Atlantic in Aug'79 by WEA Records. Distributed by: WEA

Compact disc: released on Atlantic in Jul'87 by WEA Records. Distributed by: WEA

Highway to Hell/If you want blood.
Single (7"): by WEA Records. Distributed by: WEA

If you want blood you've got it.
Tracks: / Riff raff / Hell ain't a bad place to be / Bad boy boogie / The Jack / Problem child / Whole lotta Rosie / Rock 'n' roll damnation / High voltage / Let there be rock / Rocker.
Album: released on Atlantic in '78 by WEA Records. Distributed by: WEA

Musicassette: released on Atlantic in '78 by WEA Records. Distributed by: WEA

It's a long way to the top if you wanna ....
Single (7"): by WEA Records. Distributed by: WEA

Let there be rock.
Tracks: / Go down / Dog eat dog / Let there be rock / Bad boy boogie / Overdose / Crapsody in blue / Hell ain't a bad place to be / Whole lotta Rosie.
Notes: 13 track live recording. Playing time 94 mins.
Video-cassette (VHS): released on WHV in Jan'86

Album: released on Atlantic in Sep'77 by WEA Records. Distributed by: WEA

Musicassette: released on Atlantic in Sep'77 by WEA Records. Distributed by: WEA

Nervous shakedown.
Single (12"): released on Atlantic in Jul'84 by WEA Records. Distributed by: WEA

Powerage.
Tracks: / Gimme a bullet / Down payment blues / Gone shootin' / Riff raff / Sin city / Up to my neck in you / What's next to the moon / Cold hearted man / Kicked in the teeth.
Album: released on Atlantic in May'78 by WEA Records. Distributed by: WEA

Musicassette: released on Atlantic in May'78 by WEA Records. Distributed by: WEA

Shake your foundations.
Tracks: / Shake your foundations / Stand up / Jailbreak.
Single (7"): released on Atlantic in Jan'86 by WEA Records. Distributed by: WEA

Single (12"): released on Atlantic in Jan'86 by WEA Records. Distributed by: WEA

Touch too much/Live wire.
Single (7"): released on Atlantic in Jan'80 by WEA Records. Distributed by: WEA

Whole lotta Rosie/Hell ain't a bad ....
Single (7"): released on Atlantic in Jun'80 by WEA Records. Distributed by: WEA

Who made who.
Tracks: / Who made who / You shook me all night / D.T. / Sink the pink / Ride on / Hells bells / Shake your foundations / Chase the ace / For those about to rock (we salute you).
Album: released on Atlantic in May'86 by WEA Records. Distributed by: WEA

Musicassette: released on Atlantic in May'86 by WEA Records. Distributed by: WEA

Compact disc: by WEA Records. Distributed by: WEA

Who made who (single).
Tracks: / Who made who / Guns for hire (live).
Single (12"): released on Atlantic in May'85 by WEA Records. Distributed by: WEA

You shook me all night long.
Tracks: / You shook me all night long / She's got balls (version).
Single (7"): released on Atlantic in Sep'86 by WEA Records. Distributed by: WEA

Single (12"): released on Atlantic in Sep'86 by WEA Records. Distributed by: WEA

Ace

Biographical Details: Ace were formed as a pub band in 1972 by Comer, Harris and King. Vocalist Carrick joined in '73 and Byrne in '74. "How Long", a pre-Hall & Oates style soft rock/soul single, reached No.3 in the US in '75. However the group failed to live up to its early promise and quickly faded. Paul Carrack later enjoyed record success with Squeeze, toured with Nick Lowe and then pursued a solo career.

How long.
Single (7"): released on Old Gold in Jun'84 by Old Gold Records. Distributed by: Lightning, Jazz Music, Spartan, Counterpoint

Ace, Johnny

Memorial album for Johnny Ace.
Tracks: / Pledging my love / Ace's wild / Anymore / Yes baby / My song / Never let me go / The clock / No money / Angel / Follow the rule / Burley cutie / Please forgive me / You've been gone so long.
Notes: All tracks Johnny Ace with the Johnny Board Orchestra except tracks 1 & 3 with the Beale Streeters, and track 6 with the Johnny Otis Orchestra.
Album: released on Ace in Oct'81 by Ace Records. Distributed by: Pinnacle, Swift, Hotshot, Cadillac

Ace Of Clubs

Ace of clubs Various Artists (Various Artists).
Tracks: / You'll never know / Very last drop / You can handle it / Give it to me / A little bit of Jazz / Hot summer night / Searvhing to find the one / Dyin' to be dancin' / Who's been kissing you / Inch by inch.

Notes: This is a British compilation of ten of this year's most successful floor fillers from the New York based prelude label. Included are classics like 'You'll never know,' from Hi-gloss and the re-mixed version of Sharon Redd's 'Can you feel it' which has never previously been released in Britain.

Album: released on Epic in Dec'81 by CBS Records. Distributed by: CBS

Musicassette: released on Epic in Dec'81 by CBS Records. Distributed by: CBS

Aces

Got to get some money.
Single (12"): released on Clair in Aug'84 by Clair Records. Distributed by: Jetstar

One way street/Why it should be.
Single (7"): released on ETC in Oct'82 by ETC Records. Distributed by: Menace Breaker Distributors

Aces International

Aces International Various Artists (Various Artists).
Album: released on Greensleeves in Jan'83 by Greensleeves Records. Distributed by: BMG, Jetstar, Spartan

Ace Story

Ace story vol 1, The Various Artists (Various Artists).
Album: released on Chiswick-Ace in Mar'79 by Ace Records. Distributed by: Pinnacle

Ace story vol 2, The Various Artists (Various Artists).
Album: released on Chiswick-Ace in Mar'79 by Ace Records. Distributed by: Pinnacle

Ace story vol 3, The Various Artists (Various Artists).
Album: released on Ace in Sep'82 by Ace Records. Distributed by: Pinnacle, Swift, Hotshot, Cadillac

Ace story vol 4, The Various Artists (Various Artists).
Tracks: / Teenage wedding / Tee-na-na / Walk on / I wanna know why / Wherever you may be / Free single and disengaged / Charlie Broewn got expelled / Scald dog / Can I have a word / Can't let you go I love you so / Yum yum yum / Mothers advice / I'll keep on trying / Walking with Frankie.
Notes: Side One: All tracks EMI Music Publishing Co Ltd. except track 4 Copright Control. Side Two: All tracks Emi Music Publishing Co Ltd except track 3 Copyright Control
Album: released on Ace in Apr'84 by Ace Records. Distributed by: Pinnacle, Swift, Hotshot, Cadillac

Ace story vol 5, The Various Artists (Various Artists).
Tracks: / Well I never get tired / Educated fool / Let's get it / Hey hey baby come home / Baby say you will / Somebody else is taking my place / Roll on train / Well goodbye baby / Doin' the rock 'n' roll / Classy lassie / Love is my business / Packing up / (Something) keeps dragging me on / Loves like a river / Who can I turn to / Roll 'em back.
Notes: MONO (P) Ace Records Inc.
Album: released on Ace in Nov'84 by Ace Records. Distributed by: Pinnacle, Swift, Hotshot, Cadillac

Acetate Sessions, The

Acetate Sessions, The (Various Artists).
Album: released on White in Feb'87

Acid

Hell on wheels/Hooked on metal.
Single (7"): released on Roadrunner (Dutch) in Jul'82. Distributed by: Pinnacle

Maniac.
Album: released on Megaton in Jan'84 by Megaton Records. Distributed by: Rough Trade Distribution, Cartel Distribution

Ackah, Jewel

Supa pawa.
Album: released on Koaky International in Apr'84. Distributed by: Earthworks Distributors, Rough Trade

Ackerman, Bob

Heart song (Ackerman, Bob & Pam Purvis).
Notes: See under Purvis, Pam...

Ackerman, Tracy

Don't want it.
Tracks: / Don't want it (don't need it) / With regrets.
Single (7"): released on Polydor in Mar'86 by Polydor Records. Distributed by: Polygram, Polydor

Single (12"): released on Polydor in Mar'86 by Polydor Records. Distributed by: Polygram, Polydor

Love hangover.
Tracks: / Love hangover / Head over heels.
Single (7"): released on Debut in Nov'86 by Skratch Music. Distributed by: PRT

Single (12"): released on Debut in Nov'86 by Skratch Music. Distributed by: PRT

Ackerman, Will

Conferring With The Moon.
Album: released on A&M in Jun'86 by A&M Records. Distributed by: Polygram

Musicassette: released on A&M in Jun'86 by A&M Records. Distributed by: Polygram

Compact disc: by A&M Records. Distributed by: Polygram

Passage.
Tracks: / Remedios / Processional / Independing death of the virgin spirit / Pacific I / Bricklayer's beautiful daughter, The / Hawk circle / Annie's song / Passage.
Notes: Four pieces of solo guitar from the label's founder,together with four duets featuring Cello,English Horn,Piano and Violin
Album: released on A&M in Nov'85 by A&M Records. Distributed by: Polygram

Musicassette: released on A&M in Nov'85 by A&M Records. Distributed by: Polygram

Compact disc: released on Windham Hill in Feb'85. Distributed by: AM

Past Light.
Album: released on A&M in Nov'85 by A&M Records. Distributed by: Polygram

Musicassette: released on A&M in Nov'85 by A&M Records. Distributed by: Polygram
Cat.no .... **WHC 1028**
Compact disc: . Distributed by: AM

Past light.
Album: released on Windham Hill (Germany) in Sep'84

Acklin, Barbara

Am I the same.
Tracks: / Am I the same / Love makes a woman.
Single (7"): released on Debut in 20 Jun'87 by Skratch Music. Distributed by: PRT

Am I the same girl.
Tracks: / Am I the same girl / Love makes a woman.
Single (12"): released on Debut in May'87 by Skratch Music. Distributed by: PRT

Groovy ideas.
Album: released on Kent in 7 Sep'87 by Ace Records. Distributed by: Pinnacle

Acoustic Alchemy

Casino/Sarah Victoria.
Single (7"): released on Moonstone in Sep'83 by Ampersand Music Ltd. Distributed by: Belwin Mills Music Ltd., ILA Distribution

Red dust & Spanish lace.
Tracks: / Mr.Chow / Ricochet / Stone Circle / Rideout, The / Girl with a red carnation / Colonel and the ashes, The / One for the road / Sarah Victoria / Red dust and Spanish lace.
Album: released on MCA in Jul'87 by MCA Records. Distributed by: Polygram, MCA

Musicassette: released on MCA in Jul'87 by MCA Records. Distributed by: Polygram, MCA

Compact disc: released on MCA in Jul'87 by MCA Records. Distributed by: Polygram, MCA

Across The Border

Can't get through.
Single (7"): released on President in Sep'85 by President Records. Distributed by: Taylors, Spartan

Act

Highlights from snobbery and decay.
Tracks: / Highlights from snobbery and decay / I'd be surprisingly good for you.
Compact disc single: released on ZTT in May'87 by Island Records. Distributed by: Polygram

Naked civil snobbery & decay, The.
Tracks: / Naked civil... / Strong poison / Snobbery & decay (theme from).
Single (12"): released on ZTT in 30 May'87 by Island Records. Distributed by: Polygram

Snobbery and Decay.
Tracks: / Snobbery and Decay / Poison / I'd be surprisingly good for you.
Single (7"): released on ZTT in Apr'87 by Island Records. Distributed by: Polygram

Single (12"): released on ZTT in Apr'87 by Island Records. Distributed by: Polygram

Single (12"): released on ZTT in Apr'87 by Island Records. Distributed by: Polygram

Musicassette: released on ZTT in May'87 by Island Records. Distributed by: Polygram

Too late at 20.
Single (7"): released on Hannibal in Sep'81 by Hannibal Records. Distributed by: Charly, Harmonia Mundi, Projection, Celtic Music, Roots

Who let the flowers fall?.
Single (7"): released on Act in Oct'81. Distributed by: Rough Trade

Act Fusell

Beg beg richer.
Single (7"): released on Trinity Disques in Dec'85

Single (12"): released on Trinity Disques in Dec'85

Solange.
Tracks: / Solange / White silence / Benjamin boy / Solange pavana.
Single (7"): released on WEA in Jun'86 by WEA Records. Distributed by: WEA

Single (12"): released on WEA in Jun'86 by WEA Records. Distributed by: WEA

Actified

Crucifixion.
Single (12"): released on Jungle in Jun'84 by Jungle Records. Distributed by: Jungle, Cartel

Dawn of a legion.
Extended-play record: released on Jungle in Aug'83 by Jungle Records. Distributed by: Jungle, Cartel

Action

Action (Various Artists).
Tracks: / Orchestral dub / Gemini dream / What do boys dream / World at large, The / On a storytellers night / Green glass windows / Love and peace / Red letter day / Action / Still on my mind / Action instrumental.
Notes: Licensed from the West Midlands Childrens Hospice. 1986 An FM release. FM is a division of FM/Revolver Records Ltd.
Album: released on FM in May'86 by FM-Revolver Records. Distributed by: EMI

Musicassette: released on FM in May'86 by FM-Revolver Records. Distributed by: EMI

Single (7"): released on Trapper in Sep'84. Distributed by: Pinnacle, Rough Trade

Actions speak louder than.
Tracks: / Only dreaming / Dustbin full of rubbish / An understanding love / My favourite day / Saying for today, A.
Album: released on Dojo in Apr'86 by Castle Communications Records. Distributed by: Cartel

Hey Sha-lo-ney.
Single (7"): released on Edsel in May'84 by Demon Records. Distributed by: Pinnacle, Jazz Music, Projection

I'll keep holding on.
Single (7"): released on Edsel in Jul'81 by Demon Records. Distributed by: Pinnacle, Jazz Music, Projection

Shadows and reflections.
Single (7"): released on Edsel in Jun'82 by Demon Records. Distributed by: Pinnacle, Jazz Music, Projection

Since I lost my baby.
Single (7"): released on Edsel in Sep'81 by Demon Records. Distributed by: Pinnacle, Jazz Music, Projection

Ultimate action, (The).
Tracks: / I'll keep holding on / Harlem shuffle / Never ever / Twenty fourth hour / Since I lost my baby / My lonely room / Hey sah-lo-ney / Sadows and reflections / Something has hit me / The place / The cissy / Baby you got it / I love you (yeah) / Land of a thousand dances.
Notes: One of the great London groups finally available in album form. All five of their singles and four previously unissued tracks. Produced by Geoerge Martin between 1965 and 1967. reg King was one of the finest British singers and the group had a large mod following. Sleeve notes by Paul Weller
Album: released on Edsel in May'81 by Demon Records. Distributed by: Pinnacle, Jazz Music, Projection

Action Movie Themes

Action movie themes (Various Artists).
Compact disc: released on Delta in Apr'87 by Delta Records. Distributed by: Target

Action Pact

Cocktail credibility.
Single (7"): released on Fall Out in Oct'84. Distributed by: Swift, Red Rhino, Cartel

London bouncers.
Single (7"): released on Fall Out in Jul'83. Distributed by: Swift, Red Rhino, Cartel
Cat.no .... **FALL 016**
Single (12"): released on Fall Out in Jul'83. Distributed by: Swift, Red Rhino, Cartel

People/Times must change.
Single (7"): released on Fall Out in Mar'83. Distributed by: Swift, Red Rhino, Cartel

Question of choice/Hook, line and sinker/Suss of the Swiss.
Single (7"): released on Fall Out in Nov'83. Distributed by: Swift, Red Rhino, Cartel

Suicide bag.
Single (7"): released on Fall Out in Aug'82. Distributed by: Swift, Red Rhino, Cartel

Survival of the fattest.
Album: released on Fall Out in Nov'84. Distributed by: Swift, Red Rhino, Cartel

Yet another dole queue song.
Single (7"): released on Fall Out in Aug'84. Distributed by: Swift, Red Rhino, Cartel

Single (12"): released on Fall Out in Aug'84. Distributed by: Swift, Red Rhino, Cartel

Action Tracks

Action tracks Various artists (Various Artists).
Album: released on K-Tel in Feb'82 by K-Tel Records. Distributed by: Record Merchandisers Distribution, Taylors, Terry Blood Distribution, Wynd-Up Distribution, Relay Distribution, Pickwick Distribution, Solomon & Peres Distribution, Polygram

Musicassette: released on K-Tel in Feb'82 by K-Tel Records. Distributed by: Record Merchandisers Distribution, Taylors, Terry Blood Distribution, Wynd-Up Distribution, Relay Distribution, Pickwick Distribution, Solomon & Peres Distribution, Polygram

Action Transfers

If I lose it.
Single (7"): released on Rewind in Oct'84 by Rewind Records. Distributed by: Spartan

Light oh baby , The.
Single (7"): released on Rewind in Apr'84 by Rewind Records. Distributed by: Spartan

Light (oh baby), The.
Single (12"): released on Rewind in Aug'84 by Rewind Records. Distributed by: Spartan

Active Force

Gimme your love.
Tracks: / Gimme your love / My sunshine.
Single (7"): released on A&M in Aug'86 by A&M Records. Distributed by: Polygram

Single (12"): released on A&M in Aug'86 by A&M Records. Distributed by: Polygram

Active Minds

Murder in the laboratory.
Single (7"): released on Looney Tune in Jul'87 by Looney Tune Records. Distributed by: Red Rhino, Cartel

Actives

Riot (EP).
Single (7"): released on Quiet in Jun'83 by Quiet Records. Distributed by: Nine Mile, Cartel

Wait and see.
Single (12"): released on Quiet in Jun'84 by Quiet Records. Distributed by: Nine Mile, Cartel

Actors & Famous People

It don't matter (EP).
Single (12"): released on Actor in Sep'84 by Actor Records. Distributed by: Backs, Cartel

Acuff, Roy

Fireball mail/ Stage (Acuff, Roy & Boxcar Willie).
Single (7"): released on Everest (Premier) in Jun'83 by Everest Records. Distributed by: Pinnacle

Greatest hits: Roy Acuff Vol.1.
Double Album: released on Elektra (USA) in Feb'79 by Elektra/Asylum/Nonesuch Records. Distributed by: WEA

Songs of the smoky mountain (Acuff, Roy & His Smokey Mountain Boys).
Album: released on Stetson in Jul'87 by Hasmick Promotions Ltd.. Distributed by: Counterpoint Distribution, H.R. Taylor Distribution, Swift Distribution, Chris Wellard Distribution

Musicassette: released on Stetson in Jul'87 by Hasmick Promotions Ltd.. Distributed by: Counterpoint Distribution, H.R. Taylor Distribution, Swift Distribution, Chris Wellard Distribution

Steamboat whistle blues.
Album: released on Rounder (USA) in Dec'85. Distributed by: Mike's Country Music Room Distribution, Jazz Music Distribution, Swift Distribution, Roots Records Distribution, Projection Distribution, Topic Distribution

Two different worlds.
Album: released on Sundown in Oct'86 by Magnum Music Group Ltd. Distributed by: Magnum Music Group Ltd, PRT Distribution, Spartan Distribution

AD

Art of the state.
Album: released on Kerygma in Sep'85

Musicassette: released on Kerygma in Sep'85

Reconstructions.
Notes: Kery Livgren, Michael Gleason, Dennis Holt and Dave Hope make up the group. Together they have an incredible number of years experience from the legendary Kansas (total 14 million sales) through to jingle and session work. The music is typical American rock in the style of Journey and Foreigner and will certainly win AD a new set of fans. Once again the album has been digitally recorded resulting in production which stands alongside any contemporary album.
Album: released on Kerygma in Feb'87

Musicassette: released on Kerygma in Feb'87

AD 1984

1984/ Mushroom music.
Single (7"): released on Grand Prix in Dec'83 by Grand Prix Records. Distributed by: Cartel

AD 2000

Hang on snoopy/ Doggy dub.
Single (7"): released on Excaliber in Jul'83 by Red Bus Records. Distributed by: PRT

Single (12"): released on Excaliber in Jul'83 by Red Bus Records. Distributed by: PRT

Papa was a rolling stone.
Single (7"): released on Excaliber in Mar'83 by Red Bus Records. Distributed by: PRT

Single (12"): released on Excaliber in Mar'83 by Red Bus Records. Distributed by: PRT

Rhythm and chips.
Single (7"): released on Ash in Apr'82 by Ash Records. Distributed by: Ash

Adagio

Adagio (Various Artists).
Album: released on Celestial Harmonies in Feb'87 by TM Records. Distributed by: PRT

Musicassette: released on Celestial Harmonies in Feb'87 by TM Records. Distributed by: PRT

Adama Dream

African percussion.
Tracks: / B mondet / Dougouba dya / Barra / Abounaye / Solo sandia / Sabouyouma / Badina / Elodia / Layana.
Album: released on Sunset in Jan'85. Distributed by: EMI

Album: released on Sunset (France) in Sep'84. Distributed by: IMS-Polygram Distribution

Adams, Bryan

Christmas time.
Single (7"): released on A&M in Dec'85 by A&M Records. Distributed by: Polygram

Single (12"): released on A&M in Dec'85 by A&M Records. Distributed by: Polygram

Cuts Like A Knife.
Tracks: / Only one (The) / Take me back / This time / Straight from the heart / Cut's like a knife / I'm ready / What's it gonna be / Don't leave me lonely / Best was yet to come (The).
Compact disc: by A&M Records. Distributed by: Polygram

Album: released on A&M in Mar'86 by A&M Records. Distributed by: Polygram

Musicassette: released on A&M in Mar'86 by A&M Records. Distributed by: Polygram

Hearts on fire.
Tracks: / Hearts on fire / Run to you / Native sun*.
Single (7"): released on A&M in 23 May'87 by A&M Records. Distributed by: Polygram

Single (12"): released on A&M in 23 May'87 by A&M Records. Distributed by: Polygram

Single (cassette): released on A&M in 23 May'87 by A&M Records. Distributed by: Polygram

Heat of the night.
Tracks: / Heat of the night / Another day.
Single (7"): released on A&M in Mar'87 by A&M Records. Distributed by: Polygram

Single (12"): released on A&M in Mar'87 by A&M Records. Distributed by: Polygram

Into the fire.
Tracks: / Heat of the night / Into the fire / Victim of love / Another day / Native son / Only the strong survive / Rebel / Rebel / Remembrance day / Hearts on fire / Home again.
Notes: His finest album to date, ranging in mood from the reflective 'Native Son' through the hit 'Heat of the Night' to the all out rocker 'Only the Strong Survive'.
Album: released on A&M in Apr'87 by A&M Records. Distributed by: Polygram

Musicassette: released on A&M in Apr'87 by A&M Records. Distributed by: Polygram

Compact disc: released on A&M in Apr'87 by A&M Records. Distributed by: Polygram

One good reason.
Single (7"): released on A&M in Jan'84 by A&M Records. Distributed by: Polygram

Album: released on A&M in Feb'85 by A&M Records. Distributed by: Polygram

Musicassette: released on A&M in Feb'85 by A&M Records. Distributed by: Polygram

Compact disc: released on A&M in Feb'85 by A&M Records. Distributed by: Polygram

Reckless.
Tracks: / One night love affair / She's only happy when she's dancin' / Run to you / Heaven / Somebody / Summer of '69 / Kids wanna rock / It's only love / Long gone / Ain't gonna cry.
Compact disc: by A&M Records. Distributed by: Polygram

Somebody.
Picture disc single: released on A&M in Mar'85 by A&M Records. Distributed by: Polygram

Straight from the heart.
Tracks: / Straight from the heart / Fits you good / Straight from the heart (live) / Run to close / Somebody.
Single (7"): released on A&M in Jun'86 by A&M Records. Distributed by: Polygram

Single (12"): released on A&M in Jun'86 by A&M Records. Distributed by: Polygram

Double-pack single: released on A&M in Jun'86 by A&M Records. Distributed by: Polygram

This time.
Tracks: / This time / I'm ready / Lonely nights.
Single (7"): released on A&M in Feb'86 by A&M Records. Distributed by: Polygram

Single (12"): released on A&M in Feb'86 by A&M Records. Distributed by: Polygram

You Want It, You Got It.
Compact disc: by A&M Records. Distributed by: Polygram

Adams, Cliff Singers

Sing something Disney.

Sing something silver.
Album: released on BBC in Nov'84 by BBC Records & Tapes. Distributed by: EMI, PRT, Pye

Musicassette: released on BBC in Nov'84 by BBC Records & Tapes. Distributed by: EMI, PRT, Pye

Sing something simple (100 golden greats).
Album: released on Ronco in Nov'83

Musicassette: released on Ronco in Nov'83

Songs to remember (50 old time favourites).
Album: released on Ronco in Nov'83

Musicassette: released on Ronco in Nov'83

Adams, Danny

I will never let you go out of my life.
Single (12"): released on Tree Roots in Feb'83 by Tree Roots Records. Distributed by: Jetstar

Adams, Dave

Dancing in my sleep.
Tracks: / Tars / Dancing in my sleep / Love love / Something's happening / What do you say say / Fighting / Tea & symphony / Where do we go from here / Shattering.
Album: released on Elektra (USA) in Sep'86 by Elektra/Asylum/Nonesuch Records. Distributed by: WEA

Musicassette: released on Elektra (USA) in Sep'86 by Elektra/Asylum/Nonesuch Records. Distributed by: WEA

Adams, Douglas

Life, the universe & everything.
Musicassette: released on Listen For Pleasure in Oct'84 by MFP Records. Distributed by: EMI

Adams Family

Wartown.
Single (12"): released on Adams Family in May'84 by Revolver Records. Distributed by: Cartel

Adams, Gayle

I'm warning you.
Single (7"): released on Fourth & Broadway in Oct'84 by Island Records. Distributed by: Polygram, EMI

Single (12"): released on Fourth & Broadway in Oct'84 by Island Records. Distributed by: Polygram, EMI Deleted '87.

Adams, George

All that funk (Adams, George & Don Pullen).
Tracks: / Alfie / Intentions / Big Alice.
Notes: Cameron Brown, Danny Richmond (Recorded live at Ciak, Milano, Italy, 2nd November, 1979.
Album: released on Palcoscenico (Italy) in Nov'79. Distributed by: Jazz Music

City gates (Adams, George & Don Pullen Quartet).
Album: released on Timeless (Holland) in Feb'84. Distributed by: JSU Distribution, Jazz Music Distribution, Jazz Horizons Distribution, Cadillac, Celtic Music Distribution

Don't Lose Control (Adams, George & Don Pullen Quartet).
Compact disc: released on Soul Note (Italy) in Jan'87. Distributed by: Harmonia Mundi Distributors

Earth beams.
Tracks: / Earth beams.
Musicassette: released on Timeless in Oct'86

Earth beams (Adams, George & Don Pullen Quartet).
Tracks: / Magnetic love / Dionysus / Saturday nite in the cosmos / More flowers / Sophisticated Alice.
Notes: Adams ten; flute; Pullen pn; Cameron Brown bs; Dennis Richmond d.
Album: released on Timeless in Apr'81

Hand to hand (Adams, George & Danny Richmond Quartet).
Compact disc: released on Soul Note (Italy) in Jun'86. Distributed by: Harmonia Mundi Distributors

Live at Village Vanguard (Adams, George & Don Pullen Quartet).
Tracks: / Necessary blues, The / Solitude / Intentions / Diane.
Album: released on Soul Note in May'85. Distributed by: Projection, Celtic Music, Chris Wellard

Compact disc: released on Soul Note in May'85. Distributed by: Harmonia Mundi Distributors

Live at Village Vanguard.
Tracks: / Necessary blues (The) / Solitude / Intentions / Diane.
Notes: Recorded 19th August 1983.
Compact disc: . Distributed by: Harmonia Mundi Distributors

Melodic excursions.
Tracks: / Calling, The / God has smiled on me / Kahji / Playground Uptown and Downtown / Decisions / Reflexions inward / Resolution of conflicts.
Album: released on Timeless in Jun'82

More funk (Adams, George & Don Pullen).
Tracks: / Metamorphosis for Charles Mingus.
Notes: Recorded live at Ciak, Milano, Italy, 3rd November, 1979.
Album: released on Palcoscenico (Italy) in Nov'79. Distributed by: Jazz Music

More sightings (Adams, George, Hannibal & friends).
Album: released on Enja (Germany) in Feb'85 by Enja Records (W.Germany). Distributed by: Cadillac Music

Paradise space shuttle (Adams, George Quintet).
Tracks: / Paradise space shuttle / Intentions / Send in the clowns / Metamorthesis for Mingus / City of peace / Funk-roonie-peacock.
Album: released on Timeless in Jan'85

Adams, Glen Affair

Just a groove/We've got to make it.
Single (7"): released on Excaliber in Nov'80 by Red Bus Records. Distributed by: PRT

Single (12"): released on Excaliber in Nov'80 by Red Bus Records. Distributed by: PRT

Saturday night.
Single (12"): released on Nunk in Nov'84 by Nunk. Distributed by: Lightning

Adams, John

Harmonie lehre.
Album: released on Nonesuch in Mar'86

Harmonium.
Tracks: / Part1 - Negative love / Part2 - Because I could not stop for death - Wild nights / Negative love / Because I could not stop for death / Wild nights / Why do I ? / Laughin' and clownin' / If I ever had a good time / Scarred knees / Scarred knees / Your love is doggone' good / We don't see eye to eye / Road block / Teach me to forget.
Notes: San Francisco Symphony Orchestra Chorus/Edo de Waart Vance George-chorus director, John Adams is currently the Composer-in-residence with the San Fransisco Symphony and has played a large role in the creation of its New and Unusual Music series. Mr. Adams continues to serve the New Music Adviser to Director Edo de Waart.
Compact disc: by ECM Records. Distributed by: IMS, Polygram, Virgin through EMI

Album: released on ECM (Germany) in Nov'84 by ECM Records. Distributed by: IMS, Polygram, Virgin through EMI

Compact disc: released on ECM (Germany) in Nov'84 by ECM Records. Distributed by: IMS, Polygram, Virgin through EMI

Strip this heart.
Tracks: / Strip this heart / Precious one.
Notes: Available on 7" and 4-track 12" re-mixed by D.J. mixer Bruce Forest.
Single (7"): released on A&M in Jul'87 by A&M Records. Distributed by: Polygram

Single (12"): released on A&M in Jul'87 by A&M Records. Distributed by: Polygram

Through the eyes of love.
Single (12"): released on Parlophone in Sep'85 by EMI Records. Distributed by: EMI

Adams, Johnny

After dark.
Compact disc: released on Rounder (USA) in Dec'86. Distributed by: Mike's Country Music Room Distribution, Jazz Music Distribution,

Swift Distribution, Roots Records Distribution, Projection Distribution, Topic Distribution

Album: released on Rounder Europa in Feb'87

From the heart.
Tracks: / I feel like breaking up / Somebody's home.
Album: released on Demon in Sep'84 by Demon Records. Distributed by: Pinnacle

Reconsider me.
Tracks: / I won't cry / Losing battle, A / Release me / You made a new man out of me / Reconsider me / If I could just see you one more time / I can't be all bad / In a moment of weakness / Proud woman / Real live living hurting man / Georgia morning dew / Living on your love / Lonely man / Too much pride / I want to walk through this life with you / Down by the river / I don't worry myself / I have no-one / South side of soul street / Something worth leaving for / You can depend on me / Let me be myself.
Notes: (*) Original RIC recordings via SSS International. All other tracks original SSS International recordings licensed from Charly Records International APS. This CD P 1987 Charly Holdings Inc. C Charly Records Ltd.
Compact disc: released on Charly in Apr'87 by Charly Records. Distributed by: Charly, Cadillac

Tan nightingale, The.
Tracks: / Release me / You made a new man out of me / How can I prove I love you / You depend on me / Real live living hurtin' man / I won't cry / A losing battle / I have no one / Love me now / Proud woman / Reconsider me / Something worth leaving for / Let me be myself / It's got to be something / Hell yes, I cheated.
Album: released on Charly(R&B) in '84 by Charly Records. Distributed by: Charly, Cadillac

When I need you / Cry cry darling.
Single (7"): released on Hep Me in Oct'83. Distributed by: Swift

Adams, Linda & Paul

Among the old familiar mountains.
Tracks: / The witch of the Westmorlands / The fall of the leaf / Fine hunting day / The banks of red roses / Copshawholme fair / Keswick bonnie lassies / Rosie Nell / Long Meg and her daughters / The horn of the hunter / The female drummer / The dowie dens of Yarrow / Caroline and her young sailor bold / Swarthfell rocks / My miner lad / Farewell to the fells.
Notes: Artists include: Linda Adams-vocals, guitar, concertina; Paul Adams-vocals, flageolet percussion; Terry Docherty-guitar, appalachian dulcimer, chorus; John Reay-bouzouki, mandolin, chorus; Geoff Purvis-fiddle; Tony Renney-bass.
Album: by Fellside Records. Distributed by: Roots, Jazz Music, Celtic Music, Projection

Country hirings.
Tracks: / Songs of Cumbria and the Border / Country hirings / Wellington disaster / Shepherds life / Lark in the morning / Bonnie Maisry / Tups / John Peels lament / Blackthorn stick / Widow of the Westmorlands daughter / Saddle the pony / Parton Colliers lament / Beagle Inn / Philipsons curse / Walney Cockfighting song / Eskdale and Ennerdale hunt song / North Country lass.
Album: by Sweet Folk All Records. Distributed by: Sweet Folk All, Roots, Celtic Music, Dragon, Impetus, Projection, Chris Wellard, Festival Records

Far over the fell.
Tracks: / Keswick driver, The / German clockwinder, The / Jimmy's enlisted / Brisk young sailor, A / Jolly boys song, The / King Dunmail / Lament of the border widow, The / Tarry Woo / Sun shines fair on Carlisle wall, The / Paul Jones / Farewell to the miner / Witch of the Westmoorlands, The.
Album: by Sweet Folk All Records. Distributed by: Sweet Folk All, Roots, Celtic Music, Dragon, Impetus, Projection, Chris Wellard, Festival Records

Adamson, Joy

Born free.
Notes: Read by Virginia McKenna. Running time approx 2hrs. Double cassette. 'Born free' was written by Joy Adamson, whose husband George was senior game warden of a huge territory in Kenya. It tells the story of the extraordinary up-bringing of Elsa the lioness and her subsequent return to freedom. Read by Virginia McKenna, who played the part of Joy in the enormously successful film, it is one of the most enchanting of true life animal stories.
Musicassette: released on Listen For Pleasure in Sep'86 by MFP Records. Distributed by: EMI

Adam's People

Don't want to lose you.
Single (7"): released on Kent Town in Apr'85

Adams, Pepper

10 to 4 at The 5-Spot (Adams, Pepper Quintet).
Album: released on Original Jazz Classics (USA) in Jun'86. Distributed by: Fantasy (USA) Distribution, Chris Wellard Distribution, IMS-Polygram Distribution

Ephemera.
Tracks: / Ephemera / Bouncing with Bud / Civilization and its discontents / Jitterbug waltz / Quiet lady / Patrice / Hellure (How are you're).
Notes: With Roland Hanna, George Mraz and Mel Lewis.
Album: by Spotlite Records. Distributed by: Cadillac, Jazz Music, Spotlite

Julian.
Album: released on Enja (Germany) in Jan'82 by Enja Records (W.Germany). Distributed by: Cadillac Music

Master, (The).
Tracks: / Enchilada / Chelsea Bridge / Bossallegro / Rue Serpente / Lovers of their time / My shining hour.
Notes: Adams on bassoon; Tommy Flanagan on piano; George Mraz on bass; Leroy Williams on drums. Recorded March 11, 1980.
Album: released on Muse in Apr'81 by Peerless Records. Distributed by: Lugtons Distributors

Pure Pepper.
Album: released on Savoy (France) in Feb'85

Reflectory.
Tracks: / Reflectory / Sophisticated lady / Etude Diabolique / Claudette's way / I carry your heart / That's all.
Notes: Roland Hanna on piano; George Mraz on bass; Billy Hart on drums; Adams on bassoon. Recorded on June 14, 1978.
Album: released on Muse in Apr'81 by Peerless Records. Distributed by: Lugtons Distributors

Twelfth and pingree.
Album: released on Enja (Germany) in Jan'82 by Enja Records (W.Germany). Distributed by: Cadillac Music

Urban dreams.
Album: released on Palo Alto (Italy) in Jul'86

Musicassette: released on Palo Alto (Italy) in Jul'86

Album: released on Palo Alto (Italy) in Jan'84

Musicassette: released on Palo Alto (Italy) in Jan'84

Adams, Richard

Watership Down.
Notes: Read by Roy Dotrice. Music by George Butterworth. The Academy of St. Martin in the Fields. Directed by Neville Marriner. A Demetriou Production recorded in association with Watership Productions Ltd. Produced by Evdoros Demetriou. Directed and edited by Harley Usill. Adapted by Lissa Demetriou.
Musicassette: released on Conifer in Sep'86 by Conifer Records. Distributed by: Conifer

Adams, Rusty (Ko Ko)

Beyond the Sunset.
Musicassette: released on Big R Adams in Jan'87. Distributed by: Ross

Adams Singers

Sing something simple.
Musicassette: released on BBC in Oct'79 by BBC Records & Tapes. Distributed by: EMI, PRT, Pye

Adams, Suzie

Songbird (Adams, Suzie & Helen Watson).
Album: by Dingles Records. Distributed by: Projection

Adams, Trevor

Country classics.
Album: released on Tank in Jun'79 by Tank Records

I believe in country music.
Album: released on Tank in Jun'79 by Tank Records

Adam & The Ants

Biographical Details: Londoner Adam Ant (real name Stuart Goddard), began his career in the punk era, when he became associated with Sex Pistols' manager Malcolm McLaren. The young Ant was fascinated by fashion aspects of punk, an interest which he was able to fully indulge in McLaren's "Sex" clothing store. The Ants cut a number of singles in the late Seventies and won support from John Peel. McLaren (who always claims to have suggested Adam's pirate image), became their manager but then persuaded some of the band's key members to leave to form Bow Wow Wow. At the beginning of 1980 Adam formed a new line-up comprising 'Marco, Merrrick, Terry Lee, Gary Tibbs and yours truly' (as shouted repeatedly in "Antrap"), and rapidly prefected his primeval rhythms and swashbuckling lyrics. The act's singles chart debut came in August of that year, when "Kings Of TheFrontier", achieved a minor placing. This was the vital toehold they needed. The next record "Dog Eat Dog" reached No.4, followed by the "Antmusic" anthem at No.2. In 1981 they were the biggest act in Britain, scoring as string of Top 3 singles including two No. 1s ("Stand And Deliver" and "Prince Charming"), plus simultaneous success with much of Adam's old material. 'Kings Of The Wild Frontier" was the biggest selling album of the year. Each single was backed with a stunning promotional video, an important ingredient in the Ants' success. The following year saw Adam disband his Ants and opt for a solo career, although his writing partnership with Marco continued. In the preceding five years Goddard had gradually progressed from rebellious punk to teenybop idol. The more successful he had grown, the younger his audience had become.

Car trouble/ kick.
Single (7"): released on Do-It in Feb'81 by Do-It Records. Distributed by: Virgin, EMI

Deutsher girls/ plastic surgery (Adam & The Ants (original)).
Single (7"): released on E.G. in Feb'82 by Virgin Records. Distributed by: Virgin, EMI

Friends/ Kicks/ Physical.
Single (7"): released on Do-It in Feb'82 by Do-It Records. Distributed by: Virgin, EMI

Young Parisians.
Single (7"): released on Decca in Nov'80 by Decca Records. Distributed by: Polygram

Zerox/ Whip.
Single (7"): released on Do-It in Feb'81 by Do-It Records. Distributed by: Virgin, EMI

A Data-Bank

Continental drift.
Album: released on New Rose in Sep'87. Distributed by: Rough Trade, Cartel. Estim retail price in Sep'87 was £6.29.

ADC Band

Brother Luck.
Tracks: / Brother luck / Celebrate / Waiting for you / Nothing you can do / Superfreak / Hot box / Nuclear funk out / Our thought(lovers and friends).
Album: released on Atlantic in '81 by WEA Records. Distributed by: WEA

Roll with the punches.
Album: released on Cotillion (Import) in Apr'82 by Atlantic Records. Distributed by: WEA

Adderley, Cannonball

Accent on Africa.
Tracks: / Ndo Lima / Hamba Nami / Dikhutsana (Khutsana) / Up and at it / Gumba Gumba / Marabi / Gun-Jah / Lehadima.
Notes: Licensed from EMI Records Ltd. This compilation P 1986 C 1976 Charly Records Ltd.
Album: released on Affinity in Apr'86 by Charly Records. Distributed by: Charly, Cadillac

Musicassette: released on Affinity in Apr'86 by Charly Records. Distributed by: Charly, Cadillac

Alabama/Africa.
Tracks: / African waltz / Kelly blue / Smoke gets in your eyes / West coast blues / Letter from home / Somethin' different / Blue brass groove / I'll close my eyes / Stockholm sweetin' / The uptown / This here / John Benson Brooks / Alabama concerto (in four movements).
Double Album: released on Milestone in Dec'81 by Ace Records. Distributed by: PRT

Alto giant.
Tracks: / Scavenger / Sweet Emma / Ballads Medley / This here / Manha De Carnival / Walk tall.
Notes: Nat Adderley on cornet; Joe Zawinul on piano; Victor Gaskin on bass; Louis Hayes on drums. Recorded live in Milan Italy in 1969, and previously unissued.
Album: . Distributed by: Counterpoint

Cannonball & 8 giants.
Double Album: released on Milestone in '74 by Ace Records. Distributed by: PRT

Cannonball Adderley.
Album: released on Milestone in Dec'75 by Ace Records. Distributed by: PRT

Cannonball's Bosa Nova vol.2.
Tracks: / Clouds (take 7) / Groovy samba / Joyce's samba / Corcovado / Sambop / Batida diferente / Once I loved / Minha Suadade / Clouds.
Notes: Personnel: Julian Adderley - alto sax Bossa Rios Sextet: Sregio Mendes - poano/Durval Ferreira - guitar/Octavio Bailly, Jnr. - bass/Dom Um Romao - drums/Pedro Paulo - trumpet/Paulo Moura - alto sax. Recorded in New York in 1962 Recommended tracks: *Once I loved, Clouds, Groovy Samba*
Album: released on Fantasy (USA) in Jun'86 by Fantasy Inc USA Records. Distributed by: IMS, Polygram

Musicassette: released on Fantasy (USA) in Jun'86 by Fantasy Inc USA Records. Distributed by: IMS, Polygram

Coast to coast.
Tracks: / This hare / Spontaneous combustion / High fly / Straight no chaser / You got it / Gemini / Planet earth / Dizzy's business / Syn anthesia / Scotch and water / Cannon's theme.
Double Album: released on Milestone in Mar'81 by Ace Records. Distributed by: PRT

Ease It

In San Francisco.
Compact disc: released on JVC Fantasy (Japan) in Apr'86

Jazz workshop revisited vol.3.
Tracks: / An opening comment by Cannonball / Pimitiva / Jessica's day / Unit 7 / Another few words / Jive samba (The) / Marney / Mellow buno / Time to go now - really.
Notes: Personnel: Nat Adderley - cornet/Julian Adderley - alto sax/Yusef Lateef - flute, oboe, tenor sax/Joe Zawinful - piano/Sam Jones - bass/Louis Hayes - drums. Recorded live in San Francisco in 1962. Recommended track: *The Jive Samba*
Album: released on Fantasy (USA) in Jun'86 by Fantasy Inc USA Records. Distributed by: IMS, Polygram

Just Friends.
Compact disc: released on Charly in Jan'87 by Charly Records. Distributed by: Charly, Cadillac

Know What I Mean?.
Compact disc: released on JVC Fantasy (Japan) in Apr'86

Know what I mean.
Album: released on Riverside (USA) in Aug'84. Distributed by: Fantasy (USA) Distribution

Mercy, mercy, mercy.
Album: released on EMI (Germany) in Aug'83 by EMI Records. Distributed by: Conifer

Somethin' else.
Tracks: / Autumn leaves / Love for sale / Somethin' else / One for Daddy O / Dancing in the dark / Alison's uncle.
Album: released on Blue Note in May'85 by EMI Records. Distributed by: EMI

Musicassette: released on Blue Note in May'85 by EMI Records. Distributed by: EMI

Compact disc: released on Manhattan-Blue Note in Jul'87 by EMI America Records (USA). Distributed by: EMI

Compact disc: released on Blue Note in Sep'87 by EMI Records. Distributed by: EMI. Estim retail price in Sep'87 was £11.99.

Spontaneous combustion, the Savoy session.
Album: released on Savoy (USA) in Mar'85 by Arista Records. Distributed by: Polygram, Swift

Spontaneous combustion.
Tracks: / Still talkin' to ya / Little taste, A / Caribbean cutie / Bohemia after dark / Chasm / Willow weep for me / Late entry / Spontaneous combustion / Flamingo / Hear me talkin' to ya / With apologies to Oscar / We'll be together again.
Compact disc: released on RCA in Nov'86 by RCA Records. Distributed by: RCA, Roots, Swift, Wellard, Chris, I & B, Solomon & Peres Distribution

Double Album: released on Savoy in Jun'86

Musicassette: released on Savoy in Jun'86

Double Album: released on Savoy (France) in Oct'85

Sticks and Soul.
Tracks: / Sticks / Games / I'm on my way / Mercy mercy mercy / Mini man / Why am I treated so bad / Walk tall (Baby that's what I need) / Country Preacher.
Album: released on Affinity in Nov'86 by Char-

ly Records. Distributed by: Charly, Cadillac

Them dirty blues.
Tracks: / Dat dere (take 5) / Dat dere (3) / Del sasser / Soon / Work song / Work song (take 4) / Jeannine / Easy living / Them dirty blues.
Notes: Personnel: J. Adderley - alto sax/Nat Adderley - cornet/Bobby Timmoms - piano/Barry Harris - piano (side 2)/Sam Jones - bass/Louis Hayes - drums. Recorded in Chicago in 1960. Recommended tracks *Dat dere, Work song*
Album: released on Fantasy (USA) in Jun'86 by Fantasy Inc USA Records. Distributed by: IMS, Polygram

Musicassette: released on Fantasy (USA) in Jun'86 by Fantasy Inc USA Records. Distributed by: IMS, Polygram

What is this thing called soul?.
Tracks: / Azule serape / Big 'p' / One for daddy-o / Chant, The / What is this thing called love? / Cannonball's theme.
Notes: Personnel: Nat Adderley/Vic Feldman/Sam Jones and Louis Hayes. Recorded live in Europe 1960.
Album: released on Pablo (USA) in May'84 by Pablo Records (USA). Distributed by: Wellard, Chris, IMS-Polygram, BMG

Musicassette: released on Pablo (USA) in May'84 by Pablo Records (USA). Distributed by: Wellard, Chris, IMS-Polygram, BMG

Adderley, Nat

Benny Carters All Stars (Adderley, Nat & Red Norvo).
Album: released on Sonet in May'86 by Sonet Records. Distributed by: PRT

Don't look back.
Album: released on Steeplechase in Mar'77

Nat & Julian Cannonball Adderley (Adderley, Nat & Julian Cannonball Adderley).
Tracks: / Stay on it / Autumn leaves / This here / Prelude / Gemii.
Notes: Recorded New York City 13th August, 1960.
Album: released on Kings Of Jazz in '81. Distributed by: Jazz Horizons, Jazz Music, Celtic Music

That's Nat.
Notes: Artists include: Nat Adderley - cornet/Jerome Richardson - flute, tenor sax/Hank Jones - piano/Wendell Marshall - bass/Kenny Clarke - drums. Nat, brother of Cannonball, says now of this album:- "For 1955, I think it was a reasonably good album.Playing with that rhythm section was a major thrill for me at the time" Since he made this, Nat has experimented with funk, electronics and 'out' music, but recently he's returned to a style of playing not dissimilar to this straight-ahead hard-bop album. Recorded in New Jersey in 1955.
Album: released on Savoy Jazz in Dec'85 by RCA Records (Germany). Distributed by: Conifer

Work song (Adderley, Nat & Wes Montgomery).
Compact disc: released on JVC Fantasy (Japan) in May'87

Yokohama concert, (The) (Adderley, Nat & J.J. Johnson).
Double Album: by Pablo Records (USA). Distributed by: Wellard, Chris, IMS-Polygram, BMG

Double musicassette: by Pablo Records (USA). Distributed by: Wellard, Chris, IMS-Polygram, BMG

Addis Rockers

Addis Rockers.
Album: released on Warriors in Dec'84

Addotta, Kip

Life in the slow lane.
Album: released on Rhino (USA) in May'86 by Rhino Records (USA)

Addy, Mustapha Tettey

Master drummer from Ghana.
Album: . Distributed by: Roots Distribution, Lugtons Distributors, Taylors, JSU Distribution, Spartan Distribution

Volume two.
Album: released on Tangent in Jan'82. Distributed by: Roots Distribution, Lugtons Distributors, Taylors, JSU Distribution, Spartan Distribution

Adebambo, Jean

I like it.
Single (12"): released on Ade J. in Jun'84 by Ade J., Records. Distributed by: Jetstar, Rough Trade, Jungle

Off key loving.
Album: released on Ade J. in Sep'85 by Ade J., Records. Distributed by: Jetstar, Rough Trade, Jungle

Pain.
Tracks: / Pain / Aches and pains.
Single (12"): released on Now Generation in Mar'86. Distributed by: Jetstar Distribution

Pipedrums/Dub.
Single (12"): released on Ade J. in Jul'82 by Ade J., Records. Distributed by: Jetstar, Rough Trade, Jungle

Re-united/United dub.
Single (12"): released on Ital in Jul'83. Distributed by: Pinnacle

Say that you love me.
Single (12"): released on Ade J. in Aug'81 by Ade J., Records. Distributed by: Jetstar, Rough Trade, Jungle

Tell me/Version.
Single (12"): released on Ade J. in Sep'83 by Ade J., Records. Distributed by: Jetstar, Rough Trade, Jungle

Wake up/Hardships of life.
Single (12"): released on Ade J. in Sep'82 by Ade J., Records. Distributed by: Jetstar, Rough Trade, Jungle

Adekile, Toyin

Smile (Adekile, Toyin & George Posse).
Single (12"): released on Sir George in Mar'85 by Sir George Records. Distributed by: Jetstar, Pinnacle

Ade, King Sunny

Aura.
Album: released on Island in Apr'87 by Island Records. Distributed by: Polygram

Musicassette: released on Island in Apr'87 by Island Records. Distributed by: Polygram

Explosion.
Album: released on Sar (Nigeria) in Feb'85

Gratitude (Ade, King Sunny & Mo Dupe).
Album: released on Sar (Nigeria) in Aug'85

Synchro system (Ade, King Sunny & His African Beats).
Album: released on Island in Jun'83 by Island Records. Distributed by: Polygram

Musicassette: released on Island in Jun'83 by Island Records. Distributed by: Polygram

Togetherness.
Album: released on Sar (Nigeria) in Aug'85

Truth, The (Ade, King Sunny & Otito).
Album: released on Sar (Nigeria) in Aug'85

Vintage King Sunny Ade.
Album: released on Nigeria (Import) in Mar'84, Pinnacle

Adewale, Segun

Ojo je.
Album: released on Sterns in Aug'85 by Sterns Records. Distributed by: Sterns/Triple Earth Distribution

Ojo Je (Nigeria).
Tracks: / Ojo Je / Bobo / Gbe mi leke / Atewo / Lara / Ka tepa mo se / E ma fi lle iwe sere.
Notes: More progressive juju with a stamp of Afro-beat from a Nigerian favourite making good in Britain and Europe. "...this one could catch-a-fire!" Blues & Soul
Album: released on Sterns in Sep'86 by Sterns Records. Distributed by: Sterns/Triple Earth Distribution

Play for me (Adewale, Segun & His Superstars International).
Tracks: / Yo-pop music / Oshogbo oroki / Odaran kan to sa / Adewale play for me / Kole sori apata / Sisi alafe (omoge) / Peko o gbodo gbin.
Notes: Recorded at Decca Recording Studios, Lagon Nigeria. Engineer:Lak Adeniran Captain: Kabiru Ayalsola

Album: released on Sterns African in Dec'83 by Sterns African Records. Distributed by: Stern's Distribution, Rough Trade Distribution

Play for me (Nigeria).
Tracks: / Yo-pop music / Oshogbo oroki / Odaran kan to sa / Adewale play for me / Kole sori apata / Sisi alafe / Peke o gbodo / Gbin.
Notes: Introducing 'Yopop' music, a fusion of juju with pop, jazz and funk from Nigeria's dynamic young 'Crown Prince' 'African record of the year' - Time Out 1984
Album: released on Sterns in Sep'86 by Sterns Records. Distributed by: Sterns/Triple Earth Distribution

Adicts

Biographical Details: This pleasant bunch of lads, who fail to even spell their own name correctly, secured their only piece of chart immortality in late '82. Their "Sound Of Music" album spent one week on the LP charts, just 380 less than the Julie Andrews version.

Bad boy/Shake, rattle, bang your head.
Single (7"): released on Razor in Jun'83 by Razor. Distributed by: Pinnacle

Picture disc single: released on Razor in Jun'83 by Razor. Distributed by: Pinnacle

Bar room bop - Champs Elysees.
Single (12"): released on Fall Out in Nov'85. Distributed by: Swift, Red Rhino, Cartel

Chinese takeaway/You'll never walk ....
Single (7"): released on Razor in Nov'82 by Razor. Distributed by: Pinnacle

Live and loud!! Official bootleg.
Tracks: / Sensitive / Easy way out / Joker in the pack / Chinese take away / How sad / Hurt / Tango / Viva la revolution / Just like me / Numbers / Steamroller / Too young / Straight jacket / Let's go.
Album: released on Link in Jul'87. Distributed by: DMS, RCA

Lunch with the Adicts.
Single (7"): released on Dining Out in Jun'81 by Dining Out Records. Distributed by: IKF, Independent

Songs of praise.
Tracks: / England / Hurt / Just like me / Tango / Telepathic people / Mary Whitehouse / Distortion / Get addicted / Viva la revolution / Calling calling / In the background / Dynasty / Peculiar music numbers / Sensitive / Songs of praise.
Notes: Limited edition of 2,000 in yellow vinyl.
Album: released on Fall Out in Apr'86. Distributed by: Swift, Red Rhino, Cartel

Sound of music.
Album: released on Razor in Nov'82 by Razor. Distributed by: Pinnacle

This is your life (1978 -1980).
Album: released on Fall Out in Jan'85. Distributed by: Swift, Red Rhino, Cartel

Viva la revolution/Steanroller.
Single (7"): released on Fall Out in Jul'82. Distributed by: Swift, Red Rhino, Cartel

Ad Infinitum

Telstar.
Single (7"): released on Factory in Mar'84 by Factory Records. Distributed by: Cartel, Pinnacle

Adkins, Hasil

Chicken rock.
Album: released on Dee Jay Schallplatten (Germany) in Jun'85 by Dee Jay Schallplatten

He said.
Tracks: / She said / My baby loves me / D.P.A. on the moon / Baby rock / Let's make it up / Louise wait for me / I'm in misery / Comin' home to you / We got a date / Reagun blues / Chicken twist / W.P.A / Fast run / You're my baby / Turn my coat tails loose.
Album: released on Big Beat in May'85 by Ace Records. Distributed by: Projection, Pinnacle

Rock & roll tonight (Adkins, Hasil (Haze)).
Album: released on Dee Jay Schallplatten (Germany) in Jun'85 by Dee Jay Schallplatten

She said (Adkins, Hasil (Haze)).
Single (7"): released on Bison Bop in Jan'85. Distributed by: Swift

Adkins, Wendell

If that ain't country.
Album: released on Sundown in Aug'86 by Magnum Music Group Ltd. Distributed by: Magnum Music Group Ltd, PRT Distribution, Spartan Distribution

Adler, Danny

Danny Adler story, (The).
Album: released on Do-It in Aug'79 by Do-It Records. Distributed by: Virgin, EMI

Gusha gusha music.
Album: released on Armageddon in Mar'82 by Armageddon Records. Distributed by: Revolver, Cartel, Pinnacle

Roogalator Years, The.
Tracks: / Zero hero / Tasty too / Cincinnati fatback / Water / Sweet mama Kundalini / Sock it to my pocket / All abroad / Humanitation / Change.
Notes: Licensed from Charly Records International APS This compilation: P 1986 Charly Holdings Inc C 1986 Charly Records Ltd
Album: released on Charly in Jul'87 by Charly Records. Distributed by: Charly, Cadillac

Musicassette: released on Charly in Jul'87 by Charly Records. Distributed by: Charly, Cadillac

Adler, Larry

Golden Age of Larry Adler.
Album: released on Golden Age in Mar'86 by Music For Pleasure Records. Distributed by: EMI

Musicassette: released on Golden Age in Mar'86 by Music For Pleasure Records. Distributed by: EMI

Larry Adler works for harmonica and orchestra (Adler, Larry & Royal Philharmonic).
Tracks: / Blues / Lullaby time / Merry Andrew (Gershwin) / Harmonica concerto (Benjamin) / Morton Gould Orchestra, The / Romance / Harmonica Concerto (Arnold) / Suite for harmonica & Orchestra.
Notes: Mail order distribution: Accordion Record Club, 146 Birmingham Road, Kidderminster, Worcs. DY10 2SL. Tel: 0562-746105.
Album: . Distributed by: Accordion Record Club

Ad Libs

New York in the dark/ Boy from New York.
Single (7"): released on Inferno in May'79 by Inferno Records. Distributed by: Inferno, Cartel, Pinnacle

Administrators

This is reggae music.
Tracks: / This is reggae music / Ufinished symphony.
Single (12"): released on Groove & A Quarter in Sep'86. Distributed by: Jetstar

Admiral

General govenor.
Single (12"): released on Jah Tubbys in Jul'85 by Jah Tubbys Records. Distributed by: Jetstar

Admiral Tibet

Leave people business alone.
Tracks: / Leave people business alone / Gone man lyric.
Single (12"): released on Technique in May'86 by Technique. Distributed by: CBS

Terrorist.
Tracks: / Terrorist / Terrorist (version).
Single (12"): released on Technics in Jun'87 by Technics Records. Distributed by: Jetstar Distribution

Admit Your S

Expect no mercy.
Single (7"): released on Mortarhate in Sep'85 by Dorane Ltd

Ad Nauseum

Brainstorm (4 track EP).
Single (7"): released on Flicknife in Jan'83 by Flicknife Records. Distributed by: Spartan

Adonis

No way back.
Tracks: / No way back / No way (do it properly).
Single (7"): released on London in 30 May'87 by London Records. Distributed by: Polygram

Single (12"): released on London in 30 May'87 by London Records. Distributed by: Polygram

Adrenalin O.D

Humongousfungusamongus.
Album: released on Rough Justice in Jan'87 by MFN Records. Distributed by: Pinnacle

Adrian Mole

Secret diary of Adrian Mole (part 1) By Sue Townsend (Lowe, Alex).
Musicassette: released on Talking Tape Company in '84 by Talking Tape Company Records

Secret diary of Adrian Mole (part 2) By Sue Townsend (Lowe, Alex).
Musicassette: released on Talking Tape Company in '84 by Talking Tape Company Records

Adu

Echoes from teletania.
Single (7"): released on Arro in Sep'83 by Arro. Distributed by: Pinnacle

Working for the government.
Single (7"): released on Modtone in Aug'85. Distributed by: EMI, Priority Distribution

Single (12"): released on Modtone in Aug'85. Distributed by: EMI, Priority Distribution

Adult Net

Edie.
Tracks: / Edie / Get around / Phantom power.
Single (7"): released on Beggars Banquet in Dec'85 by Beggars Banquet Records. Distributed by: WEA

Single (12"): released on Beggars Banquet in Dec'85 by Beggars Banquet Records. Distributed by: WEA

Incense and peppermints.
Single (7"): released on Beggars Banquet in Apr'85 by Beggars Banquet Records. Distributed by: WEA

Single (12"): released on Beggars Banquet in Apr'85 by Beggars Banquet Records. Distributed by: WEA

Stars say go (White nights).
Tracks: / Stars say go / Walking in the sand.
Single (7"): released on Beggars Banquet in Jun'86 by Beggars Banquet Records. Distributed by: WEA

Waking up in the sun.
Tracks: / Waking up in the sun / Walking in the sand (Remember).
Single (7"): released on Beggars Banquet in Sep'86 by Beggars Banquet Records. Distributed by: WEA

Single (12"): released on Beggars Banquet in Sep'86 by Beggars Banquet Records. Distributed by: WEA

Adults

Where did our love go.
Single (7"): released on Loose in Oct'84 by Loose Records. Distributed by: Nine Mile, Cartel

Single (12"): released on Loose in Oct'84 by Loose Records. Distributed by: Nine Mile, Cartel

Advanced Fingerpicking...

Advanced fingerpicking guitar techniques Various artists (Various Artists).
Album: released on Kicking Mule in Jan'78 by Sonet. Distributed by: Roots, PRT-Pye Distribution

Adventures

Another silent day.
Single (7"): released on Chrysalis in Jul'84 by Chrysalis Records. Distributed by: CBS

Single (12"): released on Chrysalis in Jul'84 by Chrysalis Records. Distributed by: CBS

Theodore and friends.
Tracks: / Always / Feel the raindrops / Send my heart / Two rivers / Don't tell me / Another silent day / When the world turns upside down / Love in chains / Hollywood / These children.
Notes: Produced by;Gary Bell/Bob Sargeant/Steve Harvey.
Album: released on Chrysalis in May'85 by Chrysalis Records. Distributed by: CBS

Musicassette: released on Chrysalis in May'85 by Chrysalis Records. Distributed by: CBS

Adventures In The Mist

Adventures in the mist (Various Artists).
Album: released on Bam Caruso in Jan'87 by Bam Caruso Records. Distributed by: Rough Trade, Revolver, Cartel

Adventures Of...

Adventures of Creamcake and company Zabel,Jennifer (Stubbs,Una).
Notes: The ever-popular Una Stubbs,star of televisions "Give Us A Clue" and "Aunt sallyof Sothern Television's "Worzel Gummidge" T.V series,reads six delightful new stories,written by Jennifer Zabel,featuring Creamcake,a naughty but lovable fluffykitten.Una,in her inimitable way,shares the adventures of Creamcake and his friends in the magical palace of Plumbstone.This is the home of King Pickle,Queen Peardrop and Princess Peppermint and Creamcake enjoy adventures with his friends-Fisher,Ginger George,Whisk and Spangle.
Musicassette: released on Tempo Storytime in May'84

Adventures of Doctor Snuggles (Craven, John).
Musicassette: released on Tempo Storytime in May'84

Adventures of Dusty & the dinosaurs (Newman,Nannette).
Musicassette: released on Tempo Storytime in May'84

Adventures of Heggarty Haggerty (Cole, George).
Album: released on Super Tempo in Aug'84 by Multiple Sounds Records. Distributed by: Multiple Sound Distributors

Musicassette: released on Super Tempo in Aug'84 by Multiple Sounds Records. Distributed by: Multiple Sound Distributors

Adventures of Mary mouse Blyton,Enid (Kent, Cindy).
Album: released on Super Tempo in May'84 by Multiple Sounds Records. Distributed by: Multiple Sound Distributors

Musicassette: released on Super Tempo in May'84 by Multiple Sounds Records. Distributed by: Multiple Sound Distributors

Adventures of Milly-Molly-Mandy (Rayne, Janie).
Album: released on Super Tempo in May'84 by Multiple Sounds Records. Distributed by: Multiple Sound Distributors

Musicassette: released on Super Tempo in May'84 by Multiple Sounds Records. Distributed by: Multiple Sound Distributors

Adventures of Mr Men:Mr Small (Percival, Lance).
Notes: Cassette with 32 page book.
Musicassette: released on Tempo in Aug'84 by Warwick Records. Distributed by: Multiple Sound Distributors

Adventures of Mr Men:Mr Chatterbox (Percival, Lance).
Musicassette: released on Tempo in Aug'84 by Warwick Records. Distributed by: Multiple Sound Distributors

Adventures of Mr Men:Mr Greedy (Percival, Lance).
Musicassette: released on Tempo in Aug'84 by Warwick Records. Distributed by: Multiple Sound Distributors

Adventures of Mr Men:Mr Messy (Percival, Lance).
Musicassette: released on Tempo in Aug'84 by Warwick Records. Distributed by: Multiple Sound Distributors

Adventures of Mr Men:Mr Noisy (Percival, Lance).
Musicassette: released on Tempo in Aug'84 by Warwick Records. Distributed by: Multiple Sound Distributors

Adventures of Mr Men:Mr Silly (Percival, Lance).
Musicassette: released on Tempo in Aug'84 by Warwick Records. Distributed by: Multiple Sound Distributors

Adventures of Mr Men: Mr Tickle (Percival, Lance).
Musicassette: released on Tempo in Aug'84 by Warwick Records. Distributed by: Multiple Sound Distributors

Adventures of Mr Men:Mr Sneeze (Percival, Lance).
Musicassette: released on Tempo in Aug'84 by Warwick Records. Distributed by: Multiple Sound Distributors

Adventures of Mr Pinkwhistle (Bennett, Clive).
Album: released on Super Tempo in May'84 by Multiple Sounds Records. Distributed by: Multiple Sound Distributors

Musicassette: released on Super Tempo in May'84 by Multiple Sounds Records. Distributed by: Multiple Sound Distributors

Adventures of naughty Amelia Jane (Pollard,Sue).
Album: released on Super Tempo in May'84 by Multiple Sounds Records. Distributed by: Multiple Sound Distributors

Musicassette: released on Super Tempo in May'84 by Multiple Sounds Records. Distributed by: Multiple Sound Distributors

Adventures of Orlando (The Marmalade Cat) (Various Artists).
Tracks: / Orlando buys a farm / Orlando & the water cats.
Musicassette: released on Tellastory in Dec'86 by Bartlett Bliss Productions. Distributed by: PRT Distribution, Hayward Promotions Distribution, H.R. Taylor Distribution

Musicassette: released on Tellastory in Oct'79 by Bartlett Bliss Productions. Distributed by: PRT Distribution, Hayward Promotions Distribution, H.R. Taylor Distribution

Adventures of Portland Bill (Rossington,Norman).
Album: released on Super Tempo in Aug'84 by Multiple Sounds Records. Distributed by: Multiple Sound Distributors

Musicassette: released on Super Tempo in Aug'84 by Multiple Sounds Records. Distributed by: Multiple Sound Distributors

Adventures of Robin Hood Original film score (Various Artists).
Compact disc: released on That's Entertainment in Jul'84 by That's Entertainment Records. Distributed by: Pinnacle, PRT

Adventures of Robin Hood By Patricia Leitch (Barron, Keith).
Notes: There are few adventure stories greater than that of Robin Hood and His Merry Men of Sherwood Forest. In this 2 hour abridgement read by Keith Barron we follow Robin from his ejection from Loxley Hall, his ancestral home, by the wicked Abbot of St. Marie, through his adventures in the forest, to his service with King Richard, and his death and burial where his last arrow fell. To quote the last words of the story - "Allan A'Dale went on down the long roads of England, playing his harp and singing the ballads of Robin Hood, which he had sung so often round the outlaw's camp fire. The wind caught the words and sent them blowing through time and space - Little John, Maid Marion, Friar Tuck - the magic names which echo in our dreams - Robin Hood and Sherwood"
Musicassette: released on Listen For Pleasure in Jun'86 by MFP Records. Distributed by: EMI

Adventures of Robin Hood Sound book (Various Artists).
Musicassette: released on Caedmon(USA) in '81 by Caedmon (USA) Records. Distributed by: Gower, Taylors, Discovery

Adventures of Robin Hood Original Film Score (Adventures Of Robin Hood).
Album: released on TER in Dec'83. Distributed by: Pinnacle

Adventures of Sherlock Holmes, The Doyle, Sir Arthur Conan (Pickering, Donald).
Musicassette: released on Pickwick Talking Books in Jan'83

Adventures of Sinbad the sailor (Various Artists).
Musicassette: released on Tellastory in Oct'79 by Bartlett Bliss Productions. Distributed by: PRT Distribution, Hayward Promotions Distribution, H.R. Taylor Distribution

Adventures of Teddy Robinson (Aitken, Tony).
Album: released on Super Tempo in May'84 by Multiple Sounds Records. Distributed by: Multiple Sound Distributors

Musicassette: released on Super Tempo in May'84 by Multiple Sounds Records. Distributed by: Multiple Sound Distributors

Adventures of the secret seven Blyton, Enid (Castle, Roy).
Musicassette: released on Pickwick Talking Books in Oct'81

Adventures of Tom Sawyer Twain, Mark (Crosby, Bing).
Musicassette: released on Argo (Spokenword) in Jul'82 by Decca Records. Distributed by: Polygram

Adventures of Victoria Plum Rippon, Angela (Rippon, Angela).
Album: released on Super Tempo in May'84 by Multiple Sounds Records. Distributed by: Multiple Sound Distributors

Musicassette: released on Super Tempo in May'84 by Multiple Sounds Records. Distributed by: Multiple Sound Distributors

Adventures of Worzel Gummidge, (The) (Pertwee, Jon).
Musicassette: released on Pickwick Talking Books in Jan'83

More adventures of Milly - Molly - Mandy (Harris, Anita).
Musicassette: released on Tempo Storytime in May'84

More adventures of Teddy Robinson (More adventures of Teddy Robinson).
Musicassette: released on Tempo Storytime in May'84

Adverse, Anthony

Our fairy tale.
Tracks: / Our fairy tale / Eine symphonie des grauens.
Single (7"): released on EL in Jul'86 by El Records. Distributed by: Rough Trade, Cartel, Pinnacle

Ruling class.
Tracks: / Ruling class / T-R-O-U-B-L-E / Straits of Malacs / How to get on in society.
Single (7"): released on EL in Jun'86 by El Records. Distributed by: Rough Trade, Cartel, Pinnacle

Single (12"): released on EL in Jun'86 by El Records. Distributed by: Rough Trade, Cartel, Pinnacle

Adverts

Biographical Details: In 1977 the Adverts hit the Top 20 with one of the most acclaimed singles of the punk era, "Gary Gimore's Eyes". Early promise was not fulfilled, however, and the band could only manage one lesser hit "No Time To Be 21" and a one-week chart album "Crossing The Red Sea With The Adverts". Gaye Advert and TV Smith have continued to attract spasmodic attention from the music press in their subsequent ventures. All members of the Adverts were British.

Crossing the red sea.
Album: released on Butt in Mar'82 by Butt Records. Distributed by: Counterpoint

Gary Gilmore's eyes/ New day dawning.
Single (7"): released on Bright in Jun'83

Aengus

Aengus.
Album: released on Tara (Ireland) in Jan'82 by Tara Records. Distributed by: I & B Records Distribution, Record Services Distribution (Ireland), Roots Distribution

Musicassette: released on Tara (Ireland) in Jan'82 by Tara Records. Distributed by: I & B Records Distribution, Record Services Distribution (Ireland), Roots Distribution

Aerial FX

Instant feelings.
Single (7"): released on Kamera in Oct'82

So hard / It's about time.
Single (7"): released on Square in Feb'81

Aerial Shots

Aerial shots Various artists (Various Artists).
Musicassette: released on Cockpit in Apr'84. Distributed by: Vibes

Aero

California gold/ summer girls.
Single (7"): released on Polo in Jun'80 by Polo Records. Distributed by: PRT

Single (12"): released on Polo in Jun'80 by Polo Records. Distributed by: PRT

Aerobicise...

The Californian Excercise Craze

Aerobicise- the California exercise craze Various artists (Various Artists).
Album: released on Ronco in May'83

Musicassette: released on Ronco in May'83

Aerosmith

Classics live.
Album: released on CBS in Sep'86 by CBS Records. Distributed by: CBS

Musicassette: released on CBS in Sep'86 by CBS Records. Distributed by: CBS

Classics live 2.
Notes: Volume two of the USA-only live albums, featuring: 'Back in the saddle', 'Walk this way', 'Movin' out', 'Draw the line', 'Same old song and dance', 'Last child', 'Let the music do the talking' & 'Toys in the attic'.
Album: released on Columbia (USA) in Aug'87

Done with mirrors.
Tracks: / Let the music do the talking / My fist your face / Shame on you / Reason a dog, The / Shela / Gypsy boots / She's on fire / Hop, The / Darkness".
Album: released on Geffen in Dec'85 by Geffen Records. Distributed by: WEA, CBS

Musicassette: released on Geffen in Dec'85 by Geffen Records. Distributed by: WEA, CBS

Live bootleg.
Tracks: / Back in the sadle / Sweet emotion / Lord of the thighs / Toys in the attach / Last child / Come together / Walk this way / Sick as a dog / Dream on / Mama kin / S.O.S / Train kept a rollin' / Sight for sore eyes / Chip away the stone / A ain't got you / Mother popcorn.
Double Album: released on CBS in Jan'79 by CBS Records. Distributed by: CBS

Permanent vacation.
Tracks: / Hearts done time / Dude / Magic touch / Rag doll / Simoriah / St John / Hangman jury / Girl keeps comin' apart / Angel / Permanent vacation / I'm down / Movie, The.
Album: released on Geffen in Aug'87 by Geffen Records. Distributed by: WEA, CBS

Musicassette: released on Geffen in Aug'87 by Geffen Records. Distributed by: WEA, CBS

Permanent vocation.
Album: released on Geffen in Aug'87 by Geffen Records. Distributed by: WEA, CBS

Musicassette: released on Geffen in Aug'87 by Geffen Records. Distributed by: WEA, CBS

Compact disc: released on Geffen in Aug'87 by Geffen Records. Distributed by: WEA, CBS

Aesop...

Aesop Simak, Clifford (Simak, Clifford).
Musicassette: released on Caedmon(USA) in Jan'81 by Caedmon (USA) Records. Distributed by: Gower, Taylors, Discovery

Aesop in fableland (Lowe, Arthur with the London Symphony Orchestra).
Album: released on Music For Pleasure in Nov'81 by EMI Records. Distributed by: EMI

Musicassette: released on Music For Pleasure in Nov'81 by EMI Records. Distributed by: EMI

Aesop's fables book 2 Various artists (Various Artists).
Musicassette: released on Tell-A-Tale in Oct'84 by Pickwick Records. Distributed by: Spartan-Taylors Distribution

Affair

If we're not in love.
Single (7"): released on Bronze in May'84 by Polygram Records. Distributed by: Polydor

Affairs of The Heart

Waterloo sunset.
Single (7"): released on Riot City in Jun'84 by Riot City Records. Distributed by: Revolver

Single (12"): released on Riot City in Jun'84 by Riot City Records. Distributed by: Revolver

Afflicted Man's...

Afflicted man's musical box Various artists (Various Artists).
Album: released on United Dairies in Jul'85. Distributed by: Rough Trade, Indies

Afghanistan

Folk music of Afghanistan.
Album: released on Lyrichord (USA) in Oct'81 by Lyrichord Records (USA). Distributed by: Flexitron Distributors Ltd

Album: released on Lyrichord (USA) in Oct'81 by Lyrichord Records (USA). Distributed by: Flexitron Distributors Ltd

Music from Kabul.
Album: released on Lyrichord (USA) in Oct'81 by Lyrichord Records (USA). Distributed by: Flexitron Distributors Ltd

A For Action

'A' for action (Various Artists).
Album: released on MFP in Jul'85 by EMI Records. Distributed by: EMI

Musicassette: released on MFP in Jul'85 by EMI Records. Distributed by: EMI

Afraid Of Mice

Afraid of mice.
Album: released on Charisma in Sep'83 by Virgin Records. Distributed by: EMI

Africa

Africa, New York.
Album: released on Lyrichord (USA) in Oct'81 by Lyrichord Records (USA). Distributed by: Flexitron Distributors Ltd

African rhythms and instrumentals vol2.
Album: released on Lyrichord (USA) in Oct'81 by Lyrichord Records (USA). Distributed by: Flexitron Distributors Ltd

African rhythms & instruments.
Album: released on Lyrichord (USA) in Oct'81 by Lyrichord Records (USA). Distributed by: Flexitron Distributors Ltd

Musicassette: released on Lyrichord (USA) in Aug'82 by Lyrichord Records (USA). Distributed by: Flexitron Distributors Ltd

African rhythms & instruments vol3.
Album: released on Lyrichord (USA) in Oct'81 by Lyrichord Records (USA). Distributed by: Flexitron Distributors Ltd

Drums of West Africa.
Album: released on Lyrichord (USA) in Oct'81 by Lyrichord Records (USA). Distributed by: Flexitron Distributors Ltd

From slavery to freedom.
Album: released on Lyrichord (USA) in Jan'82 by Lyrichord Records (USA). Distributed by: Flexitron Distributors Ltd

Ghana- music of the northern tribes.
Album: released on Lyrichord (USA) in Oct'81 by Lyrichord Records (USA). Distributed by: Flexitron Distributors Ltd

Mali - epic historical political and propaganda song.
Album: released on Lyrichord (USA) in Oct'81 by Lyrichord Records (USA). Distributed by: Flexitron Distributors Ltd

Music & musicians of the tshokwe people of Angola.
Album: released on Lyrichord (USA) in Oct'81 by Lyrichord Records (USA). Distributed by: Flexitron Distributors Ltd

Music of the Nile valley.
Album: released on Lyrichord (USA) in Jan'82 by Lyrichord Records (USA). Distributed by: Flexitron Distributors Ltd

Music of the rain forest pygmies.
Album: released on Lyrichord (USA) in Oct'81 by Lyrichord Records (USA). Distributed by: Flexitron Distributors Ltd

Musicassette: released on Lyrichord (USA) in Aug'82 by Lyrichord Records (USA). Distributed by: Flexitron Distributors Ltd

Percussion of Senegal.
Album: released on Sunset (France) in Mar'85. Distributed by: IMS-Polygram Distribution

Sanza & guitar.
Album: released on Lyrichord (USA) in Oct'81 by Lyrichord Records (USA). Distributed by: Flexitron Distributors Ltd

Sounds of West Africa.
Album: released on Lyrichord (USA) in Oct'81 by Lyrichord Records (USA). Distributed by: Flexitron Distributors Ltd

African...

African journey vol 1 (African Journey).
Tracks: / Kelefa ba / Alfayaya / Jola dance / Kedo / Mandingo street drumming / Bowdi / Fula procession, A / Almami Samari Touray.
Album: released on Sonet in Mar'75 by Sonet Records. Distributed by: PRT

African journey vol 2 (African Journey).
Album: released on Sonet in Mar'75 by Sonet Records. Distributed by: PRT

African magic Various artists (Various Artists).
Album: released on Circle in Jan'80. Distributed by: Jazz Music

African museum selection Carious artists (Various Artists).
Album: released on Heartbeat in Jul'85. Distributed by: Revolver, Pinnacle

African reggae various artists (Various Artists).
Tracks: / Le telephone sonne / Sir Victor Uwaifo & his melody / Ekassa / Ready, aim, fire / Ndito isong emana nyin / Onu kwulunjo / Mo fe mu yan / In the future / Let them say / Igede / What is it? / Obiako Nnwam / Odindu Nyuliba / Who?.
Notes: Continuing on from the successful African music/ High Life album(8144801) this excellent compilation contains 14 great dance tracks
Musicassette: released on Mercury (France) in Nov'84

African Blood

Angel (The).
Single (12"): released on Three Kings in Sep'85 by Three Kings Records. Distributed by: Jetstar Distribution

African Brothers

Madam Fo Pa Wuo (African Brothers Band International).
Album: released on African Brothers in Dec'84. Distributed by: IKF, Cartel

Me maane.
Album: released on African Brothers in May'84. Distributed by: IKF, Cartel

Me Poma Ghana (African Brothers Band).
Tracks: / Me poma / Getty / Yemo breoo / Gye mani / Me bisa.
Notes: Vintage guitar band highlife from Ghana's most popular band. Another milestone in Ampadu's distinguished career, "...cross breeding cannon-shot rhythms" - Sounds
Album: released on Sterns in Sep'86 by Sterns Records. Distributed by: Sterns/Triple Earth Distribution

African Connexion

C'est la dase.
Single (12"): released on Oval in Feb'84. Distributed by: Projection

Dancing on the sidewalk.
Single (12"): released on Oval in Dec'84. Distributed by: Projection

Tell Mandela (things are going to change).
Single (7"): released on Tout Ensemble in Aug'86. Distributed by: Pinnacle

Single (12"): released on Tout Ensemble in Aug'86. Distributed by: Pinnacle

African Disciples

Place called Earth, A.
Album: released on Ziongate (Import) in Jul'84. Distributed by: Jetstar

African Music

Highlife.
Album:

African Pearl

Bandwagon.
Single (12"): released on Ariwa in Apr'84 by Ariwa Records. Distributed by: Revolver, Cartel, Jetstar, Rough Trade

African Pioneers

Crazy Zulu (London mix) (African Pioneers & Robin Scott).
Single (7"): released on Ten in Aug'84

Single (12"): released on Ten in Aug'84

African Queen

English Girl/Audrey.
Single (12"): released on Jah Shaka in Oct'82 by Jah Shaka Records. Distributed by: Jetstar

African Roots

Act V.
Album: released on Wackies in Jul'85 by Wackies Records. Distributed by: Jetstar

African Star

Too rude/Let the muisc play Marshall, Larry.
Single (12"): released on Mobiliser in Nov'83 by Jetstar Records. Distributed by: Jetstar Distribution

Africka Korps

God, it's them again.
Album: released on New Rose in Aug'87. Distributed by: Rough Trade, Cartel

Afro-Cuba

Early Afro Cuban Songs Various artists.
Album: released on Albatross(Italy) in Jul'84

Musicassette: released on Albatross(Italy) in Jul'84

Afro International

Effacer le tableau.
Album: released on Vercky's (Zaire) in Jul'84. Distributed by: Earthworks Distributors, Rough Trade

Afro Latino

Live From The Bass Clef, London

Afro Latino - live from the Bass Clef, London Various Artists (Various Artists).
Notes: Artists include Cayenne, Somo Somo.
Album: released on Wave in Sep'85 by Charly Records. Distributed by: Charly

After Dark

After dark The party album (Various Artists).
Tracks: / Flowers in the rain / Alright now / Ride a white swan / Down the dustpipe / Black night / Lola / When I'm dead and gone / Resurrection shuffle / Silver machine / Whisky in the jar / See my baby jive / Roll over Beethoven / Walk on the wild side / Fox on the run / Make me smile (come up and see me) / This town ain't big enough for two of us / You to me are everything / Shotgun wedding / Nutbush city limits / Israelites, The / Everything I own / How long / Sad sweet dreamer / Rock me gently / Baby love / Reach out (I'll be there) / What becomes of the broken hearted / Yester me yester you yesterday / Tears of a clown / This old heart of mine / Don't leave me this way.
Double Album: released on Impression in Nov'84. Distributed by: CBS

Musicassette: released on Impression in Nov'84. Distributed by: CBS

Deathbringer.
Picture disc single: released on Lazer in Oct'83 by Lazer Records. Distributed by: Neon Distribution

After Eight

After eight Various Artists (Various Artists).
Tracks: / Fantasia on greensleeves / Cavatina / Gymnopedie No.3 / Belladonna / Fool on the hill / Rachmaninov 18th variation from rhapsody / Tonight / Send in the clowns / Morning from "Peer Gynt" / Barcarolle / Clair de lune / Fur elsie / Swan, The / Mack the knife / Bess, you is my woman now / Man in love, The.
Album: released on CBS in Nov'84 by CBS Records. Distributed by: CBS

Musicassette: released on CBS in Nov'84 by CBS Records. Distributed by: CBS

After The Fire

After the fire.
Album: released on Rapid in Apr'78

Batteries not included.
Tracks: / Short change / Frozen rivers / Sometimes / Sailing ship / I don't understand your love / Stranger, The / Carry me home / Dancing in the shadows / Space walking / Gina / Stuck in Paris (nowhere to go) / Bright lights.
Album: released on CBS in Feb'84 by CBS Records. Distributed by: CBS

Musicassette: released on CBS in Feb'84 by CBS Records. Distributed by: CBS

Der Kommissar.
Tracks: / Der Kommissar / Who's gonna love you (when you're old and fat and ugly) / Frozen rivers / Joy / Dancing in the shadows / Billy / 1980-F / Rich boys / Starlight / Laser love / Love wll always make you cry / One rule for you / Sailing ship / Rich boys.

Eight ball in the top pocket.
Single (7"): released on CBS in Oct'83 by CBS Records. Distributed by: CBS

Kommissar, (Der).
Musicassette: released on CBS in Dec'82 by CBS Records. Distributed by: CBS

After The Hop

After the hop Various artists (Various Artists).
Tracks: / There'll be no teardrops tonight / Ootchie Kootchie / Sally's got a sister / You're just my kind / High school rock / After the hop / Cattywampus / Bo Diddley / Willie Brown / Crazy baby / Ooh wee / Hey good lookin' / College man / Stagger Lee / No teardrops tonight.
Album: released on Sun in Apr'87 by Charly Records. Distributed by: Charly Distribution

After The Session

After the session (Various Artists).
Album: released on Soul Supply in May'86 by High Energy Records. Distributed by: Charly

After This

Fields.
Single (7"): released on Himalaya in Feb'86 by Himalaya Records. Distributed by: Rough Trade, Cartel

Single (12"): released on Himalaya in Feb'86 by Himalaya Records. Distributed by: Rough Trade, Cartel

After Tonite

Time for a change.
Single (12"): released on IDK in Nov'86. Distributed by: Rough Trade

Against All Odds

Against all odds Various Artists (Various Artists).
Notes: Soundtracks songs. Artists on this album include Phil Collins, Peter Gabriel, Stevie Nicks, Mike Rutherford, Larry Carlton, Kid Creole & Coconuts and Michel Colombier.
Album: released on Virgin in Apr'84 by Virgin Records. Distributed by: EMI, Virgin Distribution

Musicassette: released on Virgin in Apr'84 by Virgin Records. Distributed by: EMI, Virgin Distribution

Agajanian, Dennis

Where are the heroes.
Album: released on Sparrow in Jun'84 by Word Records. Distributed by: Spartan

Musicassette: released on Sparrow in Jun'84 by Word Records. Distributed by: Spartan

Agapeland

Music machine medley.
Tracks: / Land called love, (A) / Music machine, (The) / Whistle song, (The) / Smile / String song, (The) / Patience / Gentleness / Joy / Peace / Self control / Goodness / Music machine, (The) Reprise / Nathaniel the Grublet medley (consists of next 3 tracks) / Diddle daddle day / Nathaniel's song / Sunshine / Sir Oliver's Song medley (consists of next tracks) / Sir Oliver's Song / Je t'aime King of Kings / Yodel song / Handle with care / Always be true / Be thankful / His love / Bullfrogs & Butterflies medley (consists of next 5 tracks) / This is the day / Good morning / I like knowing God best / My hands belong to you / Bullfrogs & butterflies.
Album: released on Birdwing in May'82 by Word Records. Distributed by: Word Distribution

Musicassette: released on Birdwing in May'82 by Word Records. Distributed by: Word Distribution

Agee, Ray

Black night is gone.
Album: released on Mr. R&B (Sweden) in Mar'84

I'm not looking back.
Album: released on Mr. R&B (Sweden) in Aug'85

Tin pan alley.
Album: released on Diving Duck in Oct'82

Agency Music

Painter pains.
Single (7"): released on Out Of Town in Jun'82

Agent Steel

Mad locust rising.
Tracks: / Swarm is on us / Mad locust rising / Ripper (The) / Let it be done / Day at Guyana (The).
Single (12"): released on Music For Nations in Aug'86 by Music For Nations Records. Distributed by: Pinnacle

Skeptics apocalypse.
Album: released on Roadrunner (Dutch) in Sep'85. Distributed by: Pinnacle

Age Of Chance

Bible of the beat.
Single (7"): released on Riot Bible in Jan'86. Distributed by: Red Rhino, Cartel

Kiss.
Single (7"): released on Fon in Nov'86 by Fon Records. Distributed by: Rough Trade, Red Rhino, Cartel

Single (12"): released on Fon in Nov'86 by Fon Records. Distributed by: Rough Trade, Red Rhino, Cartel

Motor city.
Single (7"): released on Riot Bible in Apr'85. Distributed by: Red Rhino, Cartel

Twilight world of Sonic Disco (The).
Single (7"): released on Riot Bible in May'86. Distributed by: Red Rhino, Cartel

Who's afraid of the big bad noise.
Tracks: / Who's afraid of the big bad noise / Big bad rap.
Single (7"): released on Virgin in May'87 by Virgin Records. Distributed by: EMI, Virgin Distribution

Single (12"): released on Virgin in May'87 by Virgin Records. Distributed by: EMI, Virgin Distribution

Age Of Reggae

Age of reggae Various Artists (Various Artists).
Album: released on Twinkle in Sep'84 by Twinkle Records. Distributed by: Jetstar

Age of reggae volume 2 (Various Artists).
Album: released on Twinkle in Feb'87 by Twinkle Records. Distributed by: Jetstar

Age Of Rock & Roll

Age of rock & roll Various Artists (Various Artists).
Musicassette: released on K-Tel Goldmasters in Aug'84 by K-Tel Records. Distributed by: K-Tel

Ages Of Man

Ages of man (Gielgud, Sir John).
Double Album: released on Caedmon(USA) in Sep'79 by Caedmon (USA) Records. Distributed by: Gower, Taylors, Discovery

Aggrovators

Jammies in the lion dub style.
Album: released on Love & Live in Jul'78

Kaya dub.
Album: released on Third World in Jul'78. Distributed by: Jetstar Distribution

Agnes Of God

Agnes of God Film soundtrack (Various Artists).
Notes: Agnes of God, starring Ann Bancroft and Jane Fonda, is a murder mystery set in a convent. The music is by Georges Delerue ('Borgias','Silkwood') and has a strong religious feel to it, being performed by a symphony orchestra and choir.
Album: released on TER in Feb'86. Distributed by: Pinnacle

Agnetha

Heat is on.
Single (7"): released on Epic in May'83 by CBS Records. Distributed by: CBS

Picture disc single: released on Epic in May'83 by CBS Records. Distributed by: CBS

Agnostic Front

Cause for alarm.
Album: released on Music For Nations in May'86 by Music For Nations Records. Distributed by: Pinnacle

Compact disc: released on Rough Justice in Aug'87 by Rough Justice Records. Distributed by: Jetstar Distribution

Victim in pain.
Album: released on Combat Core (USA) in Aug'87

Agony Column

Love is a blanket expression.
Single (7"): released on Lightbeat in Jul'82 by Lightbeat Records. Distributed by: Pinnacle

Agra

Gandhi's prayer (Agra Featuring Deepack).
Single (7"): released on Sticky in Nov'83

Agrumh

Rebearth.
Album: released on Play It Again Sam in Jan'86. Distributed by: Red Rhino, Cartel

Underground.
Single (12"): released on Play It Again Sam in Aug'86. Distributed by: Red Rhino, Cartel

Agyeman, Eric

Wonko menko.
Album: released on Sterns African in Jan'84 by Sterns African Records. Distributed by: Stern's Distribution, Rough Trade Distribution

A-ha

Hunting high and low.
Tracks: / Hunting high and low / Hunting high and low (remix) / Blue sky (demon version) / Take on me / Train of thought / Hunting high and low / Blue sky, The / Living a boy's adventures tale / Sun always shines on T.V., The / And you tell me / Love is reason / Dream myself alive / Here I stand and face the rain.
Single (7"): released on Warner Brothers in May'86 by Warner Bros Records. Distributed by: WEA

Single (12"): released on Warner Brothers in May'86 by Warner Bros Records. Distributed by: WEA

Hunting high and low.
Album: released on Warner Bros. in Nov'85 by Warner Bros Records. Distributed by: WEA

Musicassette: released on Warner Bros. in Nov'85 by Warner Bros Records. Distributed by: WEA

Compact disc: released on Warner Bros. in Nov'85 by Warner Bros Records. Distributed by: WEA

I've been losing you.
Tracks: / I've been losing you / This alone is love.
Single (7"): released on Warner Brothers in Sep'86 by Warner Bros Records. Distributed by: WEA

Single (12"): released on Warner Brothers in Sep'86 by Warner Bros Records. Distributed by: WEA

Living daylights,The.
Tracks: / Living daylights,The / Living daylights,The (inst.).
Single (7"): released on Warner Bros. in 20 Jun'87 by Warner Bros Records. Distributed by: WEA

Single (12"): released on Warner Bros. in 20 Jun'87 by Warner Bros Records. Distributed by: WEA

Single (7"): released on Uptown (USA) in 20 Jun'87 by Uptown Records. Distributed by: Jazz Music

Single (12"): released on Uptown (USA) in 20 Jun'87 by Uptown Records. Distributed by: Jazz Music

Manhatten Skyline.
Tracks: / We're looking for the whales (live version).
Single (7"): released on Warner Bros. in Feb'87 by Warner Bros Records. Distributed by: WEA

Single (12"): released on Warner Bros. in Feb'87 by Warner Bros Records. Distributed by: WEA

Scoundrel Days.
Tracks: / Scoundrel days / Swing of things (The) / I've been losing you / October / Manhattan skyline / Cry wolf / Looking for the whales / Weight of the wind (The) / Maybe maybe / Soft rains of April.
Compact disc: by Warner Bros Records. Distributed by: WEA

Album: released on Warner Brothers in Oct'86 by Warner Bros Records. Distributed by: WEA

Musicassette: released on Warner Brothers in Oct'86 by Warner Bros Records. Distributed by: WEA

Sun always shines on TV.
Tracks: / Sun always shines on TV (The) / Driftwood.
Single (7"): released on Warner Brothers in Dec'85 by Warner Bros Records. Distributed by: WEA

Single (12"): released on Warner Brothers in Dec'85 by Warner Bros Records. Distributed by: WEA

Take on me.
Single (7"): released on Warner Bros. in Sep'85 by Warner Bros Records. Distributed by: WEA

Single (12"): released on Warner Bros. in Sep'85 by Warner Bros Records. Distributed by: WEA

Train of thought.
Tracks: / Train of thought / And you tell me.
Single (7"): released on Warner Brothers in Mar'86 by Warner Bros Records. Distributed by: WEA

Single (12"): released on Warner Brothers in Mar'86 by Warner Bros Records. Distributed by: WEA

Ahab

Party girl.
Single (7"): released on Chicken Jazz in Sep'82 by Chicken Jazz Records. Distributed by: Rough Trade

A Head Of His Time

Head of his time, A various artists (Various Artists).
Tracks: / We're the crackers / William Tell overture / All I need / Ballad of Job Cain / Country fever / Lonely rider, The / Camino/used horse salesman / Camino / Gravedigger / Shy Ann / Matthew / Zachariah (end title) / Zachariah (main title) / Lagune salada.
Notes: All tracks produced by Bill Szymczyk Original sound recordings made by ABC Blues-way/MCA Records Inc Published 1971 by ABC Paramount/MCA Records Inc. Copyright 1987 See For Miles Records Ltd.
Album: released on See For Miles in May'87 by See For Miles Records. Distributed by: Pinnacle

A-Heads

Dying man.
Single (7"): released on T.W. in Mar'83 by T.W. Records. Distributed by: Cartel

Ahlberg, Alan

Happy family stories, The.
Notes: For full information see under: AHLBERG, Allen.

Ahlberg, Janet

Jeremiah in the dark woods (Ahlberg, Janet & Allan).
Notes: For full information see under: Ahlberg, Janet & Allan - "Jeremiah in the dark woods"

A House

Kick me again Jesus.
Tracks: / Kick me again Jesus.
Single (7"): released on Rip in '87 by Rip Records. Distributed by: Red Rhino, Cartel

Single (12"): released on Rip in '87 by Rip Records. Distributed by: Red Rhino, Cartel

Snowball down.
Tracks: / Snowball down / Y.O.U..
Single (7"): released on Rip in 6 Jun'87 by Rip Records. Distributed by: Red Rhino, Cartel

Ahvenainen, Veikko

Accordion variety concert.

Tracks: / Granada / Preludio and fugue / Ritual fire dance / Idyll finlandia / La mariposita / Dizzy fingers / Gershwin melodies / Cuckoo, The / Midsummer night waltz / Sakkjarven polkka.
Album: released on ARC (Accordion Records) in '84. Distributed by: Accordion Record Club

Bach, Handel.
Tracks: / Organ concerto no. 14-A major / Largo / Allegro / Adante / Grave / Bach prelude and fugue E minor / Toccata and fugue D minor.
Album: released on ARC (Accordion Records) in '84. Distributed by: Accordion Record Club

Celebration Concert.
Tracks: / Preludi ja fugga / Sontaine / Sonsati d-duuri / La campanella idyll op 27 no.1 / Polkka balettisarjasta no.1 / Kesaillan valssi / Al, al / Sorja sinisilmapoika / Sorja sinisilmapoika / Valssi fantasia / La mariposita / Dizzy fingers.
Album: released on ARC (Accordion Records) in '84. Distributed by: Accordion Record Club

Old dance music of Finland.
Album: released on ARC (Accordion Records) in '84. Distributed by: Accordion Record Club

Old Finnish dance music.
Tracks: / Taikayo / Nikkelimarkka / Kenosen polkka / Mandshurian kukkuloilla / Talikkalan markkinoila / Raatikkoon / Rantakoivun alla / Kyllikki valssi / Amalia armas / Kulkurin kaiho / Karjalan polkka / Amalia armas / Kulkurin masurkka / Hulivili polkka / Soita humupekka / Kulkurin kaiho / Karjalan polkka.
Album: released on ARC (Accordion Records) in '84. Distributed by: Accordion Record Club

Aida

Cupid.
Single (12"): released on Carrere in Oct'85 by Carrere Records. Distributed by: PRT, Spartan

Aide Memoire.....

Aide memoire, folkmusic & sonaty slavicklove (Various Artists).
Album: released on Recommended in Mar'86 by Recommended Records. Distributed by: Recommended, Impetus, Rough Trade

Aiken, Joan

Wolves of Willoughby Chase, (The).
Musicassette: released on Caedmon(USA) in '78 by Caedmon (USA) Records. Distributed by: Gower, Taylors, Discovery

Ailana

New Orchestra, The.

Ainsworth, Alyn

Themes & Dreams (Ainsworth, Alyn Orchestra).
Tracks: / Theme from 'The deerhunter' (Cavatina) / Fantasy / Bright eyes / North star / Xanadu magic / Angel of the morning / Give us shelter / Chariots of fire / Theme from 'MASH' / Chi mai / Waterfalls / Bermuda triangle / Made it through the rain / Imagine / To love the Lord / Riders in the sky / For your eyes only / Sukiyaki / Sailing.
Album: released on Hallmark in Feb'82 by Pickwick Records. Distributed by: Pickwick Distribution, PRT, Taylors

Musicassette: released on Hallmark in Feb'82 by Pickwick Records. Distributed by: Pickwick Distribution, PRT, Taylors

True love (Ainsworth, Alyn Orchestra).
Tracks: / Never knew love like this before / Little in love, A / Do that to me one more time / Woman / One day in your life / Woman in love / Suddenly / Lately / One day I'll fly away / Take me as I am / With you I'm born again / Keep on loving you / When he shines / More than I can say / Crying / All out of love / More than a lover / Winner takes it all, The / After the love has gone / You've lost that lovin' feeling / Just as I am / Power of love, The / I can't let go / After all / I wanna hold you tonight / When the time is right / Sandy / Great Pioneer / Black and blue / Sunset / Never fade away.
Album: released on Hallmark in Feb'82 by Pickwick Records. Distributed by: Pickwick Distribution, PRT, Taylors

Album: released on Hallmark in Feb'82 by Pickwick Records. Distributed by: Pickwick Distribution, PRT, Taylors

Musicassette: released on Hallmark in Feb'82 by Pickwick Records. Distributed by: Pickwick Distribution, PRT, Taylors

Air

Air song.
Album: released on Whynot in Aug'77

Airborne

Burn in Hell.
Album: released on Clubland in Nov'83 by Clubland Records. Distributed by: EMI, Pinnacle

Airbridge

Paradise moves.
Tracks: / Round dance / Paradise moves / With the turning of the centuries / Better times / To absent friends / Wave length / Night and silence / More than just to win / Visitation.
Album: released on Carve Up in Feb'83. Distributed by: Jazz Music, Red Lightnin' Distribution, Rough Trade, Pinnacle

Aircraft Sounds

Great British aircraft various (British aircraft).
Musicassette: released on Audiocord Cassettes in May'83

Aire, Jane

I close my eyes and count to ten.
Single (7"): released on Stiff in May'82 by Stiff Records. Distributed by: EMI, Record Services Distribution (Ireland)

Jane Aire & Belverderes (Aire, Jane / Belverderes).
Musicassette: released on Virgin in Oct'79 by Virgin Records. Distributed by: EMI, Virgin Distribution

Airplay

Airplay Various artists (Various Artists).
Album: released on White Dove in Dec'81 by White Dove Records. Distributed by: Pinnacle

Deja vu/Miss you baby.
Single (7"): released on Out Of Town in Jun'82

Airrace

I don't care.
Single (7"): released on Atco in Dec'84 by Atlantic Records. Distributed by: WEA

Airstrip 1

Longer to live / English guns / Crime.
Single (12"): released on Oval in Jun'82. Distributed by: Projection

Air Supply

Air Supply.
Tracks: / Just as I am / Power of love (The) / I can't let go / After all / Wanna hold you tonight / Make it right / When the time is right / Sandy / Great pioneer / Black and blue / Sunset / Never fade away.
Compact disc: by Arista Records. Distributed by: RCA

Air supply.
Album: released on Arista in Aug'85 by Arista Records. Distributed by: RCA

Musicassette: released on Arista in Aug'85 by Arista Records. Distributed by: RCA

All out of love.
Single (7"): released on Old Gold in Jul'84 by Old Gold Records. Distributed by: Lightning, Jazz Music, Spartan, Counterpoint

Just as I am.
Tracks: / Just as I am / Crazy love / All out of love / Lost in love / Even the nights are better.
Single (7"): released on Arista in Jul'85 by Arista Records. Distributed by: RCA

Single (12"): released on Arista in Jul'85 by Arista Records. Distributed by: RCA

Lonely is the night.
Tracks: / Every woman in the world / Lonely is the night / I'd die for you / I'm all out of love / It's not too late / Lonely is the night / Put love in your life / One more chance / Stars in your eyes / My heart's with you / I'd die for you / You're only in love / Time for love / Heart and soul / Hope springs eternal.
Single (7"): released on Arista in Sep'86 by Arista Records. Distributed by: RCA

Single (12"): released on Arista in Sep'86 by Arista Records. Distributed by: RCA

Compact disc: released on Arista in Jan'87 by Arista Records. Distributed by: RCA

Album: released on Arista in Sep'86 by Arista Records. Distributed by: RCA

Musicassette: released on Arista in Sep'86 by Arista Records. Distributed by: RCA

Lost in love.
Tracks: / Lost in love / All out of love / Every woman in the world / Just another woman / Having you near me / American hearts / Chances / Old habits die hard / I can't get excited / My best friend.
Album: released on Arista in Oct'80 by Arista Records. Distributed by: RCA

Musicassette: released on Arista in Oct'80 by Arista Records. Distributed by: RCA

Making love.....the best of air supply.
Tracks: / Lost in love / Even the nights are better / One that you love, The / Every woman in the world / Two less lonely people on the world / Chances / Making love out of nothing at all / All out of love / Here I am / Sweet dreams / Keeping the love alive / Now and forever.
Album: released on Arista in Oct'83 by Arista Records. Distributed by: RCA

Musicassette: released on Arista in Oct'83 by Arista Records. Distributed by: RCA

Now and forever.
Album: released on Arista in Sep'82 by Arista Records. Distributed by: RCA

Musicassette: released on Arista in Sep'82 by Arista Records. Distributed by: RCA

One that you love, (The).
Tracks: / Don't turn me away / Here I am / Keeping the love alive / One that you love, The / This heart belongs to me / Sweet dreams / I want to give it all / I'll never get enough of you / Tonite / I've got your love.
Album: released on Arista in May'81 by Arista Records. Distributed by: RCA

Musicassette: released on Arista in May'81 by Arista Records. Distributed by: RCA

Aisha

High priestess.
Album: released on Ariwa in Jul'87 by Ariwa Records. Distributed by: Revolver, Cartel, Jetstar, Rough Trade

High Priestess of Hi-Tec.
Album: released on Ariwa in Aug'86 by Ariwa Records. Distributed by: Revolver, Cartel, Jetstar, Rough Trade

Prophecy.
Single (12"): released on Ariwa in May'87 by Ariwa Records. Distributed by: Revolver, Cartel, Jetstar, Rough Trade

That's how heartaches are made.
Tracks: / That's how heartaches are made / Prophesy.
Single (12"): released on Ariwa in Aug'86 by Ariwa Records. Distributed by: Revolver, Cartel, Jetstar, Rough Trade

Aitch Brothers

Won't change my mind.
Single (7"): released on Ashland in Nov'85. Distributed by: M.I.S.

Aitken, Laurel

Come down to the party.
Tracks: / Come down to the party / Let me love you little darling.
Single (12"): released on Fantasy in May'86 by RCA Records. Distributed by: RCA, Jetstar

Fire in your wire.
Notes: This Jamaican reggae singer charted briefly, with backing group the Unitone, in 1980 with "Rudi Got Married". This was due to the fact that ot was embraced by the then prevalent 2 Tone/ska community, a sort of answer to the Specials' "A Message To You Rudy". (Bob McDonald)
Single (12"): released on Black Fantasy in Sep'84 by Black Fantasy Records. Distributed by: Jetstar

Long time (Aitken, Laurel & The Potato 5).

My confession (to the one I love).
Tracks: / My confession / Million years, A.
Single (12"): released on BB in Dec'85. Distributed by: Jetstar

No more sorrows (2 parts).
Single (12"): released on Salamo in Oct'82 by Aitken, Laurel Records. Distributed by: Pinnacle

Sahara (Aitken, Laurel & The Potato 5).
Single (7"): released on Gaz's in Jan'87 by Gaz's Records. Distributed by: Backs, Cartel

Akabu

Watch yourself.
Single (12"): released on Body Rock in Jun'84. Distributed by: Cartel

AK Band

Manhole kids.
Album: released on RCA in May'81 by RCA Records. Distributed by: RCA, Roots, Swift, Wellard, Chris, I & B, Solomon & Peres Distribution

Musicassette: released on RCA in May'81 by RCA Records. Distributed by: RCA, Roots, Swift, Wellard, Chris, I & B, Solomon & Peres Distribution

Akela & The Cubs

Modern girl.
Single (7"): released on Hot Shot in Jul'83 by Hotshot Records. Distributed by: Rough Trade

Akendengue

Mando.
Tracks: / Epuguzu / Okuwa / Mando / Evogamanga / Ewaka / Ekuru / Okongo / Ilumbu / Imbunga / Vigego.
Notes: The first British album from France's leading exponenet of African music. Very much in the style of King Sunny Ade and Fela Kuti.
Album: released on CBS in Aug'83 by CBS Records. Distributed by: CBS

Musicassette: released on CBS in Aug'83 by CBS Records. Distributed by: CBS

Akimbo

So long trouble.
Tracks: / So long trouble / Machine (The).
Single (7"): released on Forward Sounds in Jan'86 by Forward Sounds Records. Distributed by: Rough Trade, Cartel

Single (12"): released on Forward Sounds in Oct'85 by Forward Sounds Records. Distributed by: Rough Trade, Cartel

Akimbo Akimbo

Forward sounds.
Album: released on Forward Sounds in May'86 by Forward Sounds Records. Distributed by: Rough Trade, Cartel

Akiyoshi, Toshiko

Insights (Akiyoshi, Toshiko and Lew Tabackin).
Album: released on RCA (France) in '83 by RCA Records. Distributed by: Discovery

Live at Newport '77.
Album: released on RCA (France) in Feb'85 by RCA Records. Distributed by: Discovery

Sumi-e (Akiyoshi, Toshiko and Lew Tabackin).
Album: released on RCA (France) in '83 by RCA Records. Distributed by: Discovery

Toshiko At The Top Of The Gate.
Compact disc: by Denon Records. Distributed by: Harmonia Mundi

Toshoko at the top of the gate (Akiyoshi, Toshiko Quintet).
Compact disc: released on Denon in May'86 by Denon Records. Distributed by: Harmonia Mundi

Akkerman, Jan

Can't stand noise.
Tracks: / Pietons / Everything must change / Back to the factory / Journey (A real elegant gypsy) / Heavy treasure / Just because / Who knows.
Album: released on Charly in May'86 by Charly Records. Distributed by: Charly, Cadillac

Complete guitarist, The.
Tracks: / Old tennis shoes / Come closer / Funkology / It could happen to you / Pietons / Journey (a real elegant gipsy).
Compact disc: released on Charly in Jun'86 by Charly Records. Distributed by: Charly, Cadillac

It could happen to you.
Tracks: / Old tennis shoes / Come closer / Funkology / It could happen to you.
Album: released on Charly in Dec'85 by Charly Records. Distributed by: Charly, Cadillac

Jan Akkerman 3.
Album: released on Atlantic in Jan'80 by WEA Records. Distributed by: WEA

Pleasure point.
Tracks: / Valdez / Heavy pleasure / Cool in the shadow / Visions of blue / C.S. / Bird island / Valdez / Heavy Pleasure / Cool in the shadow / Visions of blue / C.S. / Bird Island.
Notes: Licensed from Joe Sweetinburgh. (P)1987 Charly Records Ltd. (C)1987 Charly Records Ltd.
Album: released on Decal in Jul'87 by Charly Records. Distributed by: Charly

Musicassette: released on Decal in Jul'87 by Charly Records. Distributed by: Charly

Compact disc: released on Charly in Jul'87 by Charly Records. Distributed by: Charly, Cadillac

Album: released on Decal in Aug'87 by Charly Records. Distributed by: Charly

Musicassette: released on Decal in Aug'87 by Charly Records. Distributed by: Charly

Profile.
Album: released on EMI (Holland) in Aug'84 by EMI Records. Distributed by: Conifer

Akkerman & Ogerman

Golden highlights of....
Album: released on CBS(Import) in Jun'86 by CBS Records. Distributed by: Conifer, Discovery, Swift

Musicassette: released on CBS(Import) in Jun'86 by CBS Records. Distributed by: Conifer, Discovery, Swift

Akron Compilation

Akron compilation Various artists (Various Artists).
Album: released on Stiff in Jun'78 by Stiff Records. Distributed by: EMI, Record Services Distribution (Ireland)

Alabama

40 hour week.
Compact disc: by RCA Records. Distributed by: RCA, Roots, Swift, Wellard, Chris, I & B, Solomon & Peres Distribution

Album: released on RCA in Mar'85 by RCA Records. Distributed by: RCA, Roots, Swift, Wellard, Chris, I & B, Solomon & Peres Distribution

Musicassette: released on RCA in Mar'85 by RCA Records. Distributed by: RCA, Roots, Swift, Wellard, Chris, I & B, Solomon & Peres Distribution

Alabama.
Tracks: / My homes in Alabama / Feels so right / Love in the first degree / Why lady why / Getting over you / I wanna come over / Fantasy / Old flame / Tennessee River / Some other place, some other time / Can't forget about you / Get it while it' hot / Woman back home / See the embers, feel the flame / I'm stoned.
Album: released on RCA in Mar'84 by RCA Records. Distributed by: RCA, Roots, Swift, Wellard, Chris, I & B, Solomon & Peres Distribution

Musicassette: released on RCA in Mar'84 by RCA Records. Distributed by: RCA, Roots, Swift, Wellard, Chris, I & B, Solomon & Peres Distribution

Alabama's Greatest Hits.
Compact disc: by RCA Records. Distributed by: RCA, Roots, Swift, Wellard, Chris, I & B, Solomon & Peres Distribution

Closer You Get.
Compact disc: released on RCA in Sep'85 by RCA Records. Distributed by: RCA, Roots, Swift, Wellard, Chris, I & B, Solomon & Peres Distribution

Closer you get.
Tracks: / Closer you get / Lady down on love / She put the sad in all his songs / Red river / What in the name of love / Dixieland delight / Alabams sky / Very special love / Dixie boy / Lovin' man.
Compact disc: released on RCA in Sep'85 by RCA Records. Distributed by: RCA, Roots, Swift, Wellard, Chris, I & B, Solomon & Peres Distribution

Closer you get/Dixieland delight.
Single (7"): released on RCA in Jun'83 by RCA Records. Distributed by: RCA, Roots, Swift, Wellard, Chris, I & B, Solomon & Peres Distribution

Fantasy.
Single (7"): released on RCA in May'84 by RCA Records. Distributed by: RCA, Roots, Swift, Wellard, Chris, I & B, Solomon & Peres Distribution

Feels so right/See the embers feel the flame.
Single (7"): released on RCA in Feb'84 by RCA Records. Distributed by: RCA, Roots, Swift, Wellard, Chris, I & B, Solomon & Peres Distribution

Single (7"): released on RCA in Feb'84 by RCA Records. Distributed by: RCA, Roots, Swift, Wellard, Chris, I & B, Solomon & Peres Distribution

Greatest hits:Alabama.
Tracks: / She and I / Mountain music / Feels so right / Old flame / Tennessee river / Love in the first degree / Forty hour week (for a livin') / Why lady why / Fans, The / My home's in Alabama.
Album: released on RCA in Mar'86 by RCA Records. Distributed by: RCA, Roots, Swift, Wellard, Chris, I & B, Solomon & Peres Distribution

Musicassette: by RCA Records. Distributed by: RCA, Roots, Swift, Wellard, Chris, I & B, Solomon & Peres Distribution

Compact disc: by RCA Records. Distributed by: RCA, Roots, Swift, Wellard, Chris, I & B, Solomon & Peres Distribution

Mountain music.
Tracks: / Mountain music / Close enough to perfect / Words at twenty paces / Changes comin' on / Green river / Take me down / You turn me on / Never be one / Loving you is killing me / Gonna have a party.
Album: released on RCA in '84 by RCA Records. Distributed by: RCA, Roots, Swift, Wellard, Chris, I & B, Solomon & Peres Distribution

Musicassette: released on RCA in '84 by RCA Records. Distributed by: RCA, Roots, Swift, Wellard, Chris, I & B, Solomon & Peres Distribution

Compact disc: released on RCA in '84 by RCA Records. Distributed by: RCA, Roots, Swift, Wellard, Chris, I & B, Solomon & Peres Distribution

My home's in Alabama.
Tracks: / My home's in Alabama / Hanging up my travelling shoes / Why lady why / I wanna come over / Getting over you / I wanna come over / Tennessee river / Some other place / Can't forget about you / Get it while it's hot / Keep on dreamin'.
Musicassette: released on RCA in Oct'86 by RCA Records. Distributed by: RCA, Roots, Swift, Wellard, Chris, I & B, Solomon & Peres Distribution

Album: released on RCA in Oct'86 by RCA Records. Distributed by: RCA, Roots, Swift, Wellard, Chris, I & B, Solomon & Peres Distribution

Roll on.
Tracks: / Roll on (18 wheeler) / Carolina mountain dew / End of the lyin', The / I'm not the way anymore / If your gonna play in Texas (you gotta have a fiddler...) / There's a fire in the night / When we make love / Country side of life / Boy, The / Food on the table.
Compact disc: released on RCA in Dec'84 by RCA Records. Distributed by: RCA, Roots, Swift, Wellard, Chris, I & B, Solomon & Peres Distribution

Roll On.
Tracks: / Roll on (18 wheeler) / Carolina mountain dew / End of lyin', The / I'm not that way anymore / If you're gonna play in Texas(you gotta have a fiddler in th / When we make love / Country side of life / Boy, The / Food on the table.

Take me down/Love in the first.
Single (7"): released on RCA in Jul'82 by RCA Records. Distributed by: RCA, Roots, Swift, Wellard, Chris, I & B, Solomon & Peres Distribution

There's no way.
Single (7"): released on RCA in Apr'85 by RCA Records. Distributed by: RCA, Roots, Swift, Wellard, Chris, I & B, Solomon & Peres Distribution

Touch, The.
Tracks: / Cruisin' / Touch me when we're dancing / Let's hear it for the girl / It's all coming back to me now / I taught her everything she knows / Pony express / You've got the touch / Vacation / True true housewife / Is this how love begins? / You've got the touch / Vacation / True true housewife / Is this how love begins.
Album: released on RCA in Nov'86 by RCA Records. Distributed by: RCA, Roots, Swift, Wellard, Chris, I & B, Solomon & Peres Distribution

Musicassette: released on RCA in Nov'86 by RCA Records. Distributed by: RCA, Roots, Swift, Wellard, Chris, I & B, Solomon & Peres Distribution

Alabama Rocks

Alabama rocks Various artists (Various Artists).
Album: released on Collector (White Label Holland) in Jan'85. Distributed by: Swift

Alabama Singers

Negro spiritual music.
Album: released on Joker in '79. Distributed by: Counterpoint, Mainline, Record Services Distribution (Ireland)

Alabama Soul

Alabama soul (Various Artists).
Notes: Includes the Frankie Saunders single "Blues Time In Birmingham" and also features True Image, The Controllers and Anita Ward.
Album: released on Timeless in Aug'87

A La Carte

Have you forgotten (volga song).
Single (7"): released on PRT in Oct'82 by PRT Records. Distributed by: PRT

Aladdin...

Aladdin Original cast.
Tracks: / Spell, (The) / Aladdin / Hang chow / Proclamation, (The) / Tuang Kee Po / It is written in the sands / There & then / Love's a luxury / Dream about me / Song of the genie of the ring / Song of the genie of the lamp / Chopsticks / All I did / Wicked / Dirge, (The) / Life in the laundry / Give him the old kung fu / Reprise - Aladdin.
Notes: Book and cassette with exciting dramatised cassette recordings colourfully illustrated pages and delightful incidental music.
Album: released on President in Apr'80 by President Records. Distributed by: Taylors, Spartan

Musicassette: released on Tell-A-Tale in Oct'84 by Pickwick Records. Distributed by: Spartan-Taylors Distribution

Aladdin 14 magic lamps Various artists (Various Artists).
Notes: A rockin' and stompin' of R' n B gems featuring artists like Haflod Burrage, Jimmy Liggins, Velma Nelson, Chuck Higgins and many more. An exciting follow up to the 'Rock 'n' Roll Sock Hop' album.
Album: released on Pathe MarconiFrance) in Jun'86

Musicassette: released on Pathe MarconiFrance) in Jun'86

Aladdin and his magic lamp and other favourite stories for children aged 5-9 (Various Artists).
Musicassette: released on VFM in Jul'85 by VFM Records. Distributed by: Taylors, Wynd-Up Distribution

Aladdin and the wonderful lamp (Jones, Terry).
Musicassette: released on Listen Productions in Nov'84. Distributed by: H.R. Taylor, Hayward Promotions Distribution

Aladdin rocks and rolls Various artists (Various Artists).
Album: released on Pathe MarconiFrance) in Apr'85

Aladdin's rock 'n' roll "Sock hop" Various artists (Various Artists).
Notes: Rock 'n' roll Sock Hop is a compilation of the famous label of the forties, titles. Aladdin founded by the Mesner brothers in 1946. Aladdin was composed of several different styles. Jazz blues R & B gospel and rock 'n' roll. In this 'swinging' album we rediscover rock 'n' roll R & B that have not aged in the slightest.
Album: released on Pathe Marconi in Sep'84. Distributed by: Swift

Alair, John

Larkspur.
Tracks: / Rockin' the joint / My back went out / Ravel / Since I fell for you / Mess around / Sugar mama / Evil woman / Go to the high place in your mind / Doin' watcha want me / Long legs / Stagger Lee / Mendekshon / Rockin' the joint / My back went out / Ravel / Since I fell for you / Mess around / Sugar Mama / Evil woman / Go to the high place in your mind / Doin' watcha want me / Ives / Long legs / Stagga Lee / Mendekshon.
Compact disc: by MMC Records. Distributed by: PRT Distribution, Pinnacle

Album: released on MMC in Nov'83 by MMC Records. Distributed by: PRT Distribution, Pinnacle

Album: released on MMC in Mar'85 by MMC Records. Distributed by: PRT Distribution, Pinnacle

Alamo Bay

Alamo Bay (Various Artists).
Notes: Includes: Ry Cooder/John Haitt/Caeser Rosas.
Album: released on Slash in Feb'86 by London Records. Distributed by: Polygram

Musicassette: released on Slash in Feb'86 by London Records. Distributed by: Polygram

Alarm

68 Guns.
Single (7"): released on IRS in Sep'83. Distributed by: Polygram

Absolute reality.
Single (7"): released on Priority in Feb'85 by Priority Records. Distributed by: RCA

Single (12"): released on Priority in Feb'85 by Priority Records. Distributed by: RCA

Chant has just begun.
Single (7"): released on IRS in Oct'84. Distributed by: Polygram

Single (12"): released on IRS in Oct'84. Distributed by: Polygram

Album: released on I.R.S.(Independent Record Syndicate) in Feb'84 by I.R.S.. Distributed by: MCA

Musicassette: released on I.R.S.(Independent Record Syndicate) in Feb'84 by I.R.S.. Distributed by: MCA

Deceiver (The).
Single (7"): released on I.R.S.(Independent Record Syndicate) in Mar'84 by I.R.S.. Distributed by: MCA

Single (12"): released on I.R.S.(Independent Record Syndicate) in Mar'84 by I.R.S.. Distributed by: MCA

Declaration.
Tracks: / Declaration / Marching on / Where were you when the storm broke? / Third light / Sixty eight guns / We are the light / Shout to the devil / Blaze of glory / Tell me / Deceiver (The) / Stand (The) / Howling wind.
Album: released on I.R.S.(Independent Record Syndicate) in Apr'86 by I.R.S.. Distributed by: MCA

Musicassette: released on I.R.S.(Independent Record Syndicate) in Apr'86 by I.R.S.. Distributed by: MCA

Knife edge.
Tracks: / Knife edge / Caroline Isenberg / Howling wind / Promise (The).
Single (7"): released on I.R.S.(Independent Record Syndicate) in Apr'86 by I.R.S.. Distributed by: MCA

Single (12"): released on I.R.S.(Independent Record Syndicate) in Apr'86 by I.R.S.. Distributed by: MCA

Marching on Across the border.
Extended-play record: released on Illegal in Oct'82 by Faulty Products Records. Distributed by: Pinnacle, Lightning, Cartel

Spirit of '76.
Tracks: / Spirit of '76 / Where were you hiding when the storm broke? / Deeside / Knocking on heaven's door / 68 guns.
Single (7"): released on I.R.S.(Independent Record Syndicate) in Jan'86 by I.R.S.. Distributed by: MCA

Single (12"): released on I.R.S.(Independent Record Syndicate) in Jan'86 by I.R.S.. Distributed by: MCA

Double-pack single: released on I.R.S.(Independent Record Syndicate) in Jan'86 by I.R.S.. Distributed by: MCA

Spirit of '86.
Video-cassette (VHS): released on Hendring Video in Sep'86 by Charly Records. Distributed by: Charly, PVG

Strength.
Tracks: / Knife edge / Strength / Dawn chorus / Spirit of '76 / Day the ravens left the tower / Deeside / Father to son / Only the thunder / Walk forever by my side.
Compact disc: by I.R.S.. Distributed by: MCA

Album: released on I.R.S.(Independent Record Syndicate) in Dec'85 by I.R.S.. Distributed by: MCA

Musicassette: released on I.R.S.(Independent Record Syndicate) in Dec'85 by I.R.S.. Distributed by: MCA

Single (7"): released on IRS in Sep'85. Distributed by: Polygram

Single (12"): released on IRS in Sep'85. Distributed by: Polygram

Where were you hiding when the storm broke Pavillion steps/What kind of hell.
Single (7"): released on IRS in Jan'84. Distributed by: Polygram

Single (12"): released on IRS in Jan'84. Distributed by: Polygram

Alaska

Bailando Red Rum (Alaska / The Pegamoides).
Single (7"): released on Kingdom Records in Oct'82 by Kingdom Records. Distributed by:

Kingdom Records

Single (12"): released on Kingdom Records in Oct'82 by Kingdom Records. Distributed by: Kingd·

Heart of the storm.
Album: released on Music For Nations in May'84 by Music For Nations Records. Distributed by: Pinnacle

Miss you tonight.
Single (7"): released on Music For Nations in May'85 by Music For Nations Records. Distributed by: Pinnacle

Single (12"): released on Music For Nations in May'85 by Music For Nations Records. Distributed by: Pinnacle

Pack (The).
Album: released on Music For Nations in Mar'85 by Music For Nations Records. Distributed by: Pinnacle

Susie blue.
Single (7"): released on Music For Nations in Apr'84 by Music For Nations Records. Distributed by: Pinnacle

Single (12"): released on Music For Nations in Apr'84 by Music For Nations Records. Distributed by: Pinnacle

Alas Smith and Jones

Alas Smith and Jones (Various Artists).
Album: released on BBC in Nov'85 by BBC Records & Tapes. Distributed by: EMI, PRT, Pye

Musicassette: released on BBC in Nov'85 by BBC Records & Tapes. Distributed by: EMI, PRT, Pye

Alba

Alba.
Tracks: / Glen Rinnes / Jig of slurs, (The) / Overgate, (The) / King's favourites / Van Diemen's land / Mermaid's song, (The) / John Murray of Lochlee / Pipe Major George Allen / Blacksmith's reel, (The) / Star of Munster, (The) / Fear ah bhata / Drummond Castle / Paddy's leather breeches / Captain Ward / Garten mother's lullaby, (The) / Geese in the bog, (The) / Dr. McInnes' fancy.
Album: released on Rubber in Jun'82 by Rubber Records. Distributed by: Roots Distribution, Projection Distribution, Jazz Music Distribution, Celtic Music Distribution, JSU Distribution, Spartan Distribution

Albam, Manny

Jazz workshop, (The).
Tracks: / Anything goes / Headstrong / Black bottom / Changing scene, (The) / Turning point, (The) / Charmaine / Diga diga doo / Royal garden blues / Swingin' on a star / Intermezzo / Ferris wheel urbanity.
Album: released on RCA (France) in '83 by RCA Records. Distributed by: Discovery

Manny Albam and the greats of our time vol 1.
Tracks: / Blues for neither coast / Latined fracture / Poor Dr. Millmoss / Minor matters / My sweetie went away / All too soon / See here Miss Bromley.
Album: released on Jasmine in Feb'83 by Jasmine Records. Distributed by: Counterpoint, Lugtons, Taylor, H.R., Wellard, Chris, Swift, Cadillac

West Side story (Albam, Manny/his Jazz Greats).
Tracks: / Prologue & Jet song / Something's coming (could be) / Cool / Maria / Tonight / I feel pretty / Somewhere / Finale.
Album: released on Jasmine in Feb'83 by Jasmine Records. Distributed by: Counterpoint, Lugtons, Taylor, H.R., Wellard, Chris, Swift, Cadillac

Albania

Albanian summer Various artists (Various Artists).
Notes: 'Albanian Summer' features the compositions of Dave Smith and features the Alto Saxophone of Jan Steele and the piano of Jane Sherbourne (known collectively as ZIZ).
Album: released on Practical Music in Jul'85

Could this be love Little baby.
Single (7"): released on Stiff in Sep'82 by Stiff Records. Distributed by: EMI, Record Services Distribution (Ireland)

Single (12"): released on Stiff in Sep'82 by Stiff Records. Distributed by: EMI, Record Services Distribution (Ireland)

Folk music of Albania.

Album: released on Topic in '81. Distributed by: Roots Distribution

Albany, Joe

At home.
Tracks: / What's new / You're blase / Why was I born / Jitterbug waltz / Night and day / What are you doing the rest of your life / Barbados / Can't we be friends / Everything happens to me / You've changed / Birdtown birds / Isn't it romantic.
Notes: Solo piano recorded in Hollywood
Album: released on Spotlite in '83 by Spotlite Records. Distributed by: Cadillac, Jazz Music, Spotlite

Proto-bopper.
Tracks: / When lights are low / Our love affair is over / You don't know what love is / For heaven's sake / Getting sentimental over you / Yardbird suite / Imagination / Like someone in love / C.C rider / You're balse / Suddenly it's spring.
Notes: Solo and trio performances by the legendary Albany
Album: released on Spotlite in '83 by Spotlite Records. Distributed by: Cadillac, Jazz Music, Spotlite

Albert, Dale

I've been hurt by love.
Single (12"): released on Mass Media Music in Jul'82

Albert, Edward

Flight into danger.
Notes: This exciting and plausible story is read by Edward Albert and was first published in 1958. It was also known by the title Runaway Zero Eight. Flight into danger is the story of a major airline disaster. When the entire crew and half the passengers collapse with food poisoning in mid-flight it is left to one passenger with war-time flying experience to take over the controls and try to manoeuvre the plane to safety. Written by Arthur Hailey and John Castle
Musicassette: released on Listen For Pleasure in Apr'87 by MFP Records. Distributed by: EMI

Albert, Morris

Lark rise to candleford.
Album: released on Charisma in Sep'83 by Virgin Records. Distributed by: EMI

Album: released on Albino in Sep'84 by Albino Records. Distributed by: Projection, Celtic Music, Roots

Feelings Natural high (Bloodstone).
Single (7"): released on Old Gold in Oct'83 by Old Gold Records. Distributed by: Lightning, Jazz Music, Spartan, Counterpoint

Alberto

Cruising with santa (Alberto Y Los Trios Paranoias).
Single (7"): released on New Hormones in Dec'82 by New Hormones Records

Albion Band

Light shining.
Album: released on Albino in Sep'84 by Albino Records. Distributed by: Projection, Celtic Music, Roots

Rise up like the sun.
Album: released on Harvest in Mar'78 by EMI Records. Distributed by: Roots, EMI

Shuffle off.
Album: released on Spindrift in Sep'84. Distributed by: Roots

Under the rose.
Album: released on Spindrift in Nov'84. Distributed by: Roots

Alcapone, Dennis

Greatest lover.
Single (12"): released on Stop 'N' Rock in Nov'86

Three wise men Wise men dub.
Single (12"): released on Empire (reggae) in Nov'82. Distributed by: Jetstar

World cup football Football dub.
Single (7"): released on Empire in Jul'82 by Empire Records. Distributed by: Backs, Cartel, Jetstar

Single (12"): released on Empire in Jul'82 by Empire Records. Distributed by: Backs, Cartel, Jetstar

Alcatrazz

Disturbing the peace.
Tracks: / God bless video / Mercy / Will you be home tonight / Wire and wood / Desert diamond / Stripper / Painted lover / Ligher shade of green / Sons and lovers / Sky fire / Breaking the heart of the city.
Notes: Fronted by Ex rainbow lead singer Graham bonnet, Disturbing the peace is the debut album from this impressive rock outfit. The album is produced by Eddie Kramer, whose years of musical experience include work with Jimi Hendrix, Led Zeppelin and Kiss.
Album: released on Capitol in Aug'85 by Capitol Records. Distributed by: EMI

Musicassette: released on Capitol in Aug'85 by Capitol Records. Distributed by: EMI

Island in the sun.
Single (7"): released on Rocshire in Aug'84

Single (12"): released on Rocshire in Aug'84

Parole from rock 'n' roll.
Album: released on RCA in Aug'84 by RCA Records. Distributed by: RCA, Roots, Swift, Wellard, Chris, I & B, Solomon & Peres Distribution

Musicassette: released on RCA in Aug'84 by RCA Records. Distributed by: RCA, Roots, Swift, Wellard, Chris, I & B, Solomon & Peres Distribution

Alcock, Gary

Gary Alcock and Midland All Stars Big Band.
Album: released on Regis in Mar'77 by Wellard, Chris. Distributed by: Wellard, Chris

Alcool d'Apres

Beginning (EP).
Tracks: / On Broadway / One little girl / Wasting your time / Night fright.
Single (12"): released on JJ in Feb'87. Distributed by: Stage One

Alcorn, Alvin

Alvin Alcorn & His New Orleans Jazz Band (Alcorn, Alvin & His New Orleans Jazz Band).
Album: released on New Orleans in Sep'86. Distributed by: Swift, Zodiac Distribution, Jazz Music, JSU

Alcott, Louisa May

Little women.
Musicassette: released on Argo in Apr'84 by Decca Records. Distributed by: Polygram

Aldbrickham Band

Aldbrickham Band.
Musicassette: released on Acoustics in Jul'87 by Acoustics Records. Distributed by: Cartel

Aldeberts

Los Angeles.
Tracks: / Toi et moi samba / Life's mockinbird / In the middle of the night / Manarin man / La fiesta / Los Angeles / Without a friend / When you know / It happens everyday / When we go to San Francisco.
Album: released on Trend (USA) in Jan'84 by Discovery Records. Distributed by: Flexitron Distributors Ltd, Swift

Aldiss, Brian

Best science fiction of Brian Aldiss.
Musicassette: released on Listen Productions in Nov'84. Distributed by: H.R. Taylor, Hayward Promotions Distribution

Musicassette: released on Listen For Pleasure in '84 by MFP Records. Distributed by: EMI

Aldrich, Ronnie

28 great piano classics (Aldrich, Ronnie & His Orchestra).
Tracks: / As time goes by / Stardust / Barefoot in the park / Old-fashioned way / People / You are the sunshine of my life / Hey Jude / Bewitched / My cherie amour / Shadow of your smile / Unforgettable / Ode to Billy Joe / Tie a yellow ribbon / You made me feel brand new / Macarthur Park / Wave / Man & a woman, (A) / Something / Candy man / Autumn leaves / Somewhere my love / Onedin line / Way we were, (The) / Love is blue / Michelle / Summer of 42 / Bridge over troubled water / Sound of silence, (The).
Double Album: released on Horatio Nelson in Nov'85. Distributed by: PRT

Musicassette: released on Horatio Nelson in Nov'85. Distributed by: PRT

Aldrich feeling, The (Aldrich, Ronnie & His Two Pianos).
Tracks: / My favourite things / Theme from 'Picnic' / Melodie d'amour / Mona Lisa / Magic moments / When I fall in love / Memories are made of this / Spanish Harlem / Sweetest sounds (The) / Come closer to me / If the rain's got to fall / If ever I would leave you.
Compact disc: by Decca Records. Distributed by: Polygram

All-time piano hits.
Tracks: / Mosirlou / Bewitched / Nola / Stardust / Near you / Dancing in the dark / Autumn leaves / Voodoo moon / As time goes by / Inka dinka doo / Canadian sunset / Exodus.
Compact disc: released on Decca in Jan'86 by Decca Records. Distributed by: Polygram

An hour of Ronnie Aldrich (Aldrich, Ronnie His Piano and Orchestra).
Tracks: / La Mer / Hello / Bermuda triangle / Sound of the sea, The / Last farewell, The / Calypso / Stranger on the shore / Sailing / Trade winds / Begin the beguine / Arthur's theme / Memory / Hill street blues / Chariots of fire / Nights birds / Albareda / Stay / For Lisa.
Musicassette: released on Hour Of Pleasure in Sep'87 by Music For Pleasure Records. Distributed by: EMI. Estim retail price in Sep'87 was £1.99.

Focus on Ronnie Aldrich.
Tracks: / Tha way we were / By the time I get to Phoenix / What are you doing the rest of your life / The old fashioned way / Chim chim cheree / MacArthur's park / Autumn leaves / Scarborough fair / More / Concierto de Aran juez / The entertainer / It's impossible / The summer of 42 / Sun dance / Felicdade / She / Wave / Amazing grace / In the gentle hours / Man and a woman, A / Whiter shade of pale, A / Tie a yellow ribbon round the old oak tree / This guy's in love with you / Love story / With the London festival orchestra anc chorus.
Album: released on Decca in Jul'86 by Decca Records. Distributed by: Polygram

Musicassette: released on Decca in Jul'86 by Decca Records. Distributed by: Polygram

For the one you love (Aldrich, Ronnie & His Orchestra).
Tracks: / You needed me / Main event, The / Fight / She believes in me / Just when I needed you most / Can't smile without you / I know I'll never love this way again / Gypsomania / Reunited / Just the way you are / You take my breath away / You're the only one / After the love has gone.
Album: released on Decca in Mar'80 by Decca Records. Distributed by: Polygram

Musicassette: released on Decca in Mar'80 by Decca Records. Distributed by: Polygram

Night birds (Aldrich, Ronnie & His Two Pianos).
Tracks: / Begin the beguine / Arthur's theme / Memory / Santa Catalina / Hill street blues / Chariots of fire / Night birds / Have you ever been in love / Little peace, A / Albareda / Stay / For Liza.
Album: released on MFP in Nov'82 by EMI Records. Distributed by: EMI

Musicassette: released on MFP in Nov'82 by EMI Records. Distributed by: EMI

One fine day.
Tracks: / Woman in love / One fine day / Shadow waltz / Fame / On broadway / Stand by me / Reminiscing / Autumn tears / Magic / Romeos tune.
Notes: Woman in love/One fine day/ Shadow waltz/ Fame/On Broadway/Stand by me/ Reminiscing/Autumn tears/Magic/Romeo's tune
Album: released on Decca in Aug'81 by Decca Records. Distributed by: Polygram

Musicassette: released on Decca in Aug'81 by Decca Records. Distributed by: Polygram

Ronnie Aldrich - for all seasons (Aldrich, Ronnie, His Piano & The Festival Orchestra).
Tracks: / April in Paris / Spring song / It might as well be spring / Summertime / Solway in summer / Summer wind / Early autumn / September song / Forever autumn / When winter comes / Winter world of love / June in January.
Compact disc: released on MFP in Sep'87 by EMI Records. Distributed by: EMI

Musicassette: released on MFP in Sep'87 by EMI Records. Distributed by: EMI

Musicassette: released on MFP in Sep'87 by EMI Records. Distributed by: EMI

Sea dreams (Aldrich, Ronnie & His Two Pianos).
Tracks: / La mer / Hello / Sailing by / Bermuda triangle / The sound of the sea / Last farewell / Calypso / Stranger on the shore / Sailing / Trading winds / To all the girls I've loved before / How deep is the ocean.
Notes: The second album from Ronnie Aldrich-master musician. Following the sucess of Night Birds, 12 superb tracks which all have a link with the sea, which is reflected in the evocative sleeve design. Featured tracks include La Mer, Bermuda triangle, Calypso and a beautiful version of Lionel Richie's Hello
Album: released on Music For Pleasure in

Oct'84 by EMI Records. Distributed by: EMI

Musicassette: released on Music For Pleasure in Oct'84 by EMI Records. Distributed by: EMI

Silver bells.
Album: released on Audio Fidelity in Oct'84 Distributed by: PRT

Musicassette: released on Audio Fidelity in Oct'84. Distributed by: PRT

Soft and wicked (Aldrich, Ronnie & His Two Pianos).
Tracks: / Last tango in Paris / You're so vain / Tie a yellow ribbon round the old oak tree / Call me (come back home) / Good time charlies got the blues / Oh babe what would you say / Last song / Love theme / It never rains in southern California.
Notes: Side One Track 1 United Partnership. Track 2 Warner Bros Ltd. Track 3: -4 EMI Pub Co Ltd. Track 5 O'Sullivan Songs Ltd. Track 6 Burlington Music Co Ltd. Side Two Track 1 Burlington Music Co Ltd. Track 2 Chappell Music Ltd. Track 3 Westminster M Ltd. Track 4 Page One Music. Track 5 Cyril Shane M 50%-S.I.A.E 50% Track 6 Rondor M (Lon) Ltd.
Album: released on Jasmine in Mar'85 by Jasmine Records. Distributed by: Counterpoint, Lugtons, Taylor, H.R., Wellard, Chris, Swift, Cadillac

Musicassette: released on Jasmine in Mar'85 by Jasmine Records. Distributed by: Counterpoint, Lugtons, Taylor, H.R., Wellard, Chris, Swift, Cadillac

Tender love...tender moments (Aldrich, Ronnie & His Orchestra).
Tracks: / Cavatina / Light my fire / My one and only love / United we stand / Ruby / What are you doing the rest of my love / For once in my life / Don't cry for me Argentina / Clair / Save your kisses for me / Amazing grace / I left my heart in San Francisco / Theme from 'Summer of 42' / Summer knows, The / Can't smile without you / I wish you love.
Album: released on Contour in Feb'82 by Pickwick Records. Distributed by: Pickwick Distribution, PRT

Musicassette: released on Contour in Feb'82 by Pickwick Records. Distributed by: Pickwick Distribution, PRT

Unforgettable sound of Ronnie Aldrich and his two pianos.
Tracks: / Bewitched / Stardust / The look of love / The windmills of your mind / The sound of silence / How deep is the ocean / I didn't know what time it was / Mas que nada / The entertainer / Amazing grace / Imagine / The long and winding road / Adaigo / The way we were / Embraceable you / The things you are / Bridge over troubled water / Both sides now / The impossible dream / Love is blue / Where or when / Spanish harlem / When I fall in love / If you leave me now / Love me tonight / How deep is your love / Memories are made of this.
Notes: Full title of recording: The unforgettable sound of Ronnie Aldrich and His Two Pianos.
Double Album: released on Decca in Apr'84 by Decca Records. Distributed by: Polygram

Winter wonderland.
Album: released on Audio Fidelity in Dec'81. Distributed by: PRT

With love and understanding.
Album: released on Decca in Jun'77 by Decca Records. Distributed by: Polygram

Musicassette: released on Decca in Jun'77 by Decca Records. Distributed by: Polygram

Aleem

Casually formal.
Tracks: / Love's on fire / Two faces / Confusion / Stay / More than a million / Think / Fine young tender / Dance to the groove.
Album: released on Atlantic in Apr'86 by WEA Records. Distributed by: WEA

Musicassette: released on Atlantic in Apr'86 by WEA Records. Distributed by: WEA

Fine young tender (Aleem & Leroy Burgess).
Tracks: / Fine young tender / Two faces.
Single (7"): released on Atlantic in Jul'86 by WEA Records. Distributed by: WEA

Single (12"): released on Atlantic in Jun'86 by WEA Records. Distributed by: WEA

Get loose.
Single (12"): released on Streetwave in Dec'85 by Streetwave Records. Distributed by: PRT Distribution

Alex

Reliable/Sugar me.
Single (12"): released on Roots Radics in Mar'82

Alexander...

Alexander and the terrible, horrible, ...day (Alexander and the Terrible...).
Notes: Full title "Alexander and the terrible, horrible, no good, very bad day".
Musicassette: released on Caedmon(USA) in Sep'84 by Caedmon (USA) Records. Distributed by: Gower, Taylors, Discovery

Alexander, Arthur

Shot of rhythm & soul, A.
Tracks: / Anna / Sally Sue Brown / You're the reason / Dream girl / Go home girl / Shot of rhythm & blues, (A) / Pretty girls everywhere / I wonder where you are tonight / You better move on / Girl that radiates that charm, (The) / Black night / Soldiers of love / I hang my head & cry / Where have you been / You don't care / Old John Amos.
Album: released on Ace in Jan'85 by Ace Records. Distributed by: Pinnacle, Swift, Hotshot, Cadillac

Musicassette: released on Ace in Jan'85 by Ace Records. Distributed by: Pinnacle, Swift, Hotshot, Cadillac

Soldier of love.
Album: released on Ace in Apr'87 by Ace Records. Distributed by: Pinnacle, Swift, Hotshot, Cadillac

Alexander, Ashley

Plays Frank Mantooth (Alexander, Ashley Big Band).
Tracks: / Secret love / Prelude to a kiss / Stone lizard / Outside St. Louis / Spring can really hang you up the most / Mixolydiasn soul frog / Latin schizophrenia.
Album: released on AM-PM USA in Aug'84. Distributed by: Swift

Alexander Brothers

Alexander Brothers collection.
Tracks: / Boys of killybegs, The / Rose of Allandale, The / Typewriter, The / Marriage / Carnival is over, The / Auld meal mill, The / Old rustic bridge / I have a dream / Happy hours / Village where I went to school, The / Village where I went to school, The / All my life / Alpine Express / Through the eyes of a child / Teuchter music.
Album: released on Lismor in '84 by Lismor Records. Distributed by: Lismor, Roots, Celtic Music

Musicassette: released on Lismor in '84 by Lismor Records. Distributed by: Lismor, Roots, Celtic Music

Farewell my love.
Single (7"): released on Lismor in Nov'86 by Lismor Records. Distributed by: Lismor, Roots, Celtic Music

Gentle annie.
Single (7"): released on Lismor in Nov'86 by Lismor Records. Distributed by: Lismor, Roots, Celtic Music

Glorious north, The.
Notes: Specially selected tracks by the Alexander Brothers of their most popular material they perform in the Aberdeen and Northern area of Scotland. Should prove an attractive package for the tourist as the sleeve features photographs of Aberdeen, Inverness, Braemar, Balmoral and other beauty spots.
Album: released on PRT in Jan'84 by PRT Records. Distributed by: PRT

Musicassette: released on PRT in Jan'84 by PRT Records. Distributed by: PRT

Legends of Scotland.
Tracks: / Lass O'Bon-Accord (The) / Road to Dundee (The) / Flying Scotsman, The / Wild side of life / All along Loch Long / Nobody's child / Flowe of Scotland, The / Northern lights of Aberdeen / Dark island / These are my mountains / Blackboard of my heart / My big Kilmarnock bunnet / Soor mulk cairt, The / Johnnie lad.
Musicassette: released on Lochshore in Jun'86 by Klub Records. Distributed by: PRT

Sincerely yours.
Album: released on Lismor in Dec'86 by Lismor Records. Distributed by: Lismor, Roots, Celtic Music

Tom and Jack.
Musicassette: released on PRT in May'79 by PRT Records. Distributed by: PRT

Tribute to Sir Harry Lauder.
Tracks: / Weddin' of Lauchie M'Graw, The / End of the road, The / Killiekrankie / There is somebody waiting for me / I love you / It's nice to get up in the morning (but it's nicer to ...) / Wee hoose among the heather / Medley / Waggle o' the kilt, The.

Musicassette: released on Highlander in Jun'86. Distributed by: PRT

Very best of Alexander Brothers, The.
Musicassette: released on PRT in May'77 by PRT Records. Distributed by: PRT

Way old friends do.
Single (7"): released on Lismor in Nov'81 by Lismor Records. Distributed by: Lismor, Roots, Celtic Music

Single (7"): released on Mervyn Conn Presents in Dec'82. Distributed by: MSD Distribution

Way old friends do, The.
Tracks: / Catch me if you can / Caledonia / Le manege / Kingdom I call home, The / Music box dancer / Mary Milne / Golden days / Way old friends do, The / Kilt song, The / Theme from Bilitis / Do you want your old lobby washed down / On the rebound / La di da di da / Scotland forever.
Album: released on Lismor in Nov'81 by Lismor Records. Distributed by: Lismor, Roots, Celtic Music

Musicassette: released on Lismor in Nov'81 by Lismor Records. Distributed by: Lismor, Roots, Celtic Music

Welcome the Alexander Brothers.
Tracks: / Alud Scots sangs medley, The / Hundred thousand welcomes / Lass o'leven vale, The / Jacqueline waltz / Dancing in Kyle, The / Dark lochs of Scotland, The / Ballad of Glen Coe, The / Let's have a ceilidh / Two highland lads / Flying Scotsman / Nobody's child / Rose of Allendale / When you and I were young Maggie / Lily McNally McNair / Rowen tree, The / Reine du musette / Flower of Scotland, The / Calin mo ruin sa / Waters of Kylesku / These are my mountains / All along Loch Long / High level hornpipe, The / Tillietudlem castle / Old Scots mother o mine / Haste ye back.
Double Album: released on PRT in Dec'81 by PRT Records. Distributed by: PRT

Double musicassette: released on PRT in Dec'81 by PRT Records. Distributed by: PRT

Welcome the Alexander Brothers - Vol.2.
Tracks: / Caledonia (Wild rose of the mountain) / Lass O'Bon-Accord, The / Jolly Caballero, The / He bought my soul at Calvary / Friendly folk O' the border / Auld Scots sangs, The / Rowan tree, The / Auld hoose, The / Forty shades of green / Whistlin' Rufus / Scotland Scotland / Road to Dundee, The / Let's have one more / One day at a time / Amazing Grace / Reels medley / Jim Johnstone / Colonel, The / Kilwaughter house / Poor little rich boy / Tartan, The / Star O' Robbie Burns / Mull of Kintyre / Whisky on a sunday / Dance of the comedians, The / Old Shep / Here's to the Gordons / My big Kilmarnock Bunnet / Soor Mulk Cairt / Johnnie lad / Scotland the brave / Auld Scots sangs, The (medley).
Double Album: released on PRT in Jun'83 by PRT Records. Distributed by: PRT

Musicassette: released on PRT in Jun'83 by PRT Records. Distributed by: PRT

Welcome to the Alexander brothers- Vol2.
Album: released on PRT in Jun'83 by PRT Records. Distributed by: PRT

Musicassette: released on PRT in Jun'83 by PRT Records. Distributed by: PRT

Words and music, The.
Musicassette: released on PRT in Oct'79 by PRT Records. Distributed by: PRT

Alexander, Dave

Dirt on the ground.
Album: released on Arhoolie in May'81 by Arhoolie Records. Distributed by: Projection, Topic, Jazz Music, Swift, Roots

Rattler, The.
Album: released on Arhoolie in May'81 by Arhoolie Records. Distributed by: Projection, Topic, Jazz Music, Swift, Roots

Alexander, Goldie

Knocking down your love (2 parts).
Single (12"): released on Proto in Mar'83 by Proto Records. Distributed by: WEA

Alexander, Gorden

Save your kisses for me.
Single (7"): released on Starward in '81. Distributed by: Roots Distribution, Red Sky Distribution, Celtic Music Distribution, Projection Distribution

Alexander, Mel

My baby drives a Ford Cortina.
Single (7"): released on Big Boy in '85 by Big Boy Records. Distributed by: Pinnacle

Alexander, Monty

Cobilimbo.
Album: released on MPS Jazz in '81

Duke Ellington song book.
Tracks: / I let a song go out of my heart / Sophisticated lady / Things ain't what they used to be / Love you madly / Eastside Westside / In a mellow tone / In a sentimental mood / C jam blues.
Notes: This new album with bass player John Clayton features ten of the most popular compositions by the late-great Duke Ellington.
Album: released on MPS (Germany) in '84. Distributed by: IMS-Polygram Distribution, Parnote Distribution (Formerly MDC)

Compact disc: released on MPS (Germany) in '84. Distributed by: IMS-Polygram Distribution, Parnote Distribution (Formerly MDC)

Ellington songbook.
Tracks: / I let a song go out of my heart / Sophisticated lady / Things ain't what they used to be / Love you madly / East side west one / In a mellow tone / Caravan / Just squeeze me / In a sentimental mood / C jam blues.

Full steam ahead.
Tracks: / Freddie freeloader / Once I love / Ray's idea / Because you're mine / Satisfaction / Happy talk / Estate / Hi-fly / Just friends.
Album: released on Concord Jazz (USA) in Dec'85 by Concord Jazz Records (USA). Distributed by: IMS, Polygram

Musicassette: released on Concord Jazz (USA) in Dec'85 by Concord Jazz Records (USA). Distributed by: IMS, Polygram

Compact disc: released on Concord Jazz (USA) in Nov'86 by Concord Jazz Records (USA). Distributed by: IMS, Polygram

Jamento (Alexander, Monty Seven).
Tracks: / Accompong / Slippery / Sugar loaf at twilight / Weekend in L.A. / Jamento / Mango rengue.
Album: released on Pablo (USA) in '82 by Pablo Records (USA). Distributed by: Wellard, Chris, IMS-Polygram, BMG

Musicassette: released on Pablo (USA) in '82 by Pablo Records (USA). Distributed by: Wellard, Chris, IMS-Polygram, BMG

Love and Sunshine.
Album: released on MPS Jazz in '81

Compact disc: released on Pablo in '84 by Pablo Records. Distributed by: Wellard, Chris, IMS-Polygram, BMG

Montreaux Alexander.
Album: released on MPS Jazz in '81

Montreux Alex.
Tracks: / Nite mist blues / Feelings / Satin doll / Work song / Drown in my own tears / Battle hymn of the Republic.
Compact disc: released on Pablo in Apr'84 by Pablo Records. Distributed by: Wellard, Chris, IMS-Polygram, BMG

Monty Alexander in Tokyo.
Tracks: / Broadway / Just in time / Sweet lady / Tricrotism / Never let me go / Montevideo / Pawnbroker / See see rider.
Album: released on Pablo (USA) in '82 by Pablo Records (USA). Distributed by: Wellard, Chris, IMS-Polygram, BMG

Musicassette: released on Pablo (USA) in '82 by Pablo Records (USA). Distributed by: Wellard. Chris, IMS-Polygram, BMG

Monty strikes again.
Album: released on MPS Jazz in '81

Overseas special.
Tracks: / But not for me / Time for love, A / Orange in pain / F S R / For all we know / C C rider.
Notes: "Overseas Special" marks Monty Alexander, Ray Brown and Herb Ellis third collaboration for Concord Records. This superb trio exites the live audience while pushing itself to its swinging best with a concert of great standards and finely tailored original compostions. Personnel: Monty Alexander - piano/ Ray Brown - bass/ Herb Ellis - guitar.
Compact disc: released on Concord Jazz (USA) in '84 by Concord Jazz Records (USA). Distributed by: IMS, Polygram

Perception.
Album: released on MPS Jazz in '81

Trio (Alexander / Brown / Ellis).
Album: released on Concord Jazz (USA) in Mar'81 by Concord Jazz Records (USA). Distributed by: IMS, Polygram

Triple treat (Alexander, Monty, Ray Brown, Herb Ellis).
Tracks: / Flintstones,The / Body and soul / Small fry / When lights are low / Triple treat blues / Fungi mama / Sweet lady / But not for me.
Album: released on Concord Jazz (USA) in '82 by Concord Jazz Records (USA). Distributed by: IMS, Polygram

Way it is,The.
Album: released on MPS Jazz in '81

Alexander, Peter

Rocky Tocky baby.
Tracks: / Rocky tocky baby / O Josefin, die nacht in Napoli / Hol Den Peter / Titino tinn / Immer zieht es mich zu ihr (& Bill Ramsey) / Der Himmel uber der prarie / Missouri cowboy (& Bill Ramsey) / Ich Zahle taglich meine sorgen / Wunderbares madchen / Mandolinen und mondschein / Bimbombee / Der gitarrentramp / Das schone spiel / Komm bald wieder / Bist du einsam heut'nacht / Und... Wilma Lucini / Ja,Ich einsam heut'nacht.
Album: released on Bear Family in '84 by Bear Family Records. Distributed by: Rollercoaster Distribution, Swift

Alexander, Texas

Texas Alexander.Vol 1 (1927-28).
Tracks: / Range in my kitchen blues / Long lonesome day blues / Corn bread blues / Section gang blues / Levee camp moan blues / Mama I heard you brought it right back home / Farm hand blues / Evil woman blues / Sabine River blues / Death bed blues / Yellow girl blues / West Texas blues / Bantam rooster blues / Deep blue sea blues / No more woman blues / Don't you wish your baby was built up like mine / Bell cow blues.
Album: released on Matchbox (Bluesmaster) in '82

Texas Alexander Vol.2.
Tracks: / Sittin' on a log / Mam's bad luck child / Bo hog blues / Work ox blues / Risin' sun,The / Penitentiary moan blues / Blue devil blues / Tell me woman blues / Frisco train blues / St.Louis fair blues / I am calling blues / Double crossing blues / Ninety-eight degree blues / Someday baby your troubles is gonna be like mine / Water bound blues / Awful moaning blues part 1&2.
Album: released on Matchbox in '83 by Saydisc Records. Distributed by: Roots, Projection, Jazz Music, JSU, Celtic Music

Vol.3 1929-30.
Tracks: / Gold tooth blues / Johnny Behren's blues / Rolling mill blues / Broken yo yo / Texas special / When you get to thinking / Thirty day blues / Peaceful blues / Days is lonesome / Last stage blues / See better days / Stealing to her man / She's so fair / Rolling and stumbling blues / Frost Texas tornado blues / Texas troublesome blues.
Notes: The complete recorded output of one of the most influentual and enigmatic country blues singers will run to 4 vols. This 3rd vol. shows again the variety of accompanists that he attracted. He was unusual amongst blues singers in that he didn't play an instrument and his individual style was a challenge to some of the great blues and jazz instrumentalists. MONO
Album: released on Matchbox in Aug'86 by Saydisc Records. Distributed by: Roots, Projection, Jazz Music, JSU, Celtic Music

Alexander The Great

Alexander the Great Various artists (Various Artists).
Musicassette: released on Anvil in '81. Distributed by: Anvil

Tell-a-tale.
Musicassette: released on Pickwick (Tell-a-tale) in '84 by Pickwick Records. Distributed by: Pickwick Distribution

Alexander, Van

Savoy stomp.
Tracks: / Let's get together / Chant of the weed / Until the real thing comes along / Uptown Rhapsody / Stompin' at the Savoy / Undecided / I would do anything for you / A-tisket a-tasket / East St.Louis toodle-o / Organ grinder's swing / Christopher Columbus / Ride, red, ride.
Album: released on Capitol(USA) in '84 by Capitol (USA) Records. Distributed by: EMI

Swing goes on.Vol 2,The.
Tracks: / Get me to the church on time / Way down yonder in New Orleans / In a mellow tone / Ol' man river / Say it isn't so / Blues in twos / Uptown rhapsody / Let's get together / Chant of the weed / Lulu's back in town / Until the real thing comes along / A-tisket, a-tisket / Christopher Columbus / Ride, red, ride.
Album: released on EMI (Germany) in '83 by EMI Records. Distributed by: Conifer

Alexander, Willie 'Loco'

Greatest Hits:Willie Loco Alexander.
Album: released on Decca in Nov'85 by Decca Records. Distributed by: Polygram

Taxi-stand Diane.
Tracks: / Taxi-stand Diane / Telephone sex / Walkman woman / Just another fool.
Album: released on New Rose in '84. Distributed by: Rough Trade, Cartel

Alexandre

My Lancashire (Alexandre, Kipling & Alani).
Tracks: / My Lancashire / It's Xmas.
Single (7"): released on Rockin' Ronnie in Feb'86. Distributed by: M.I.S. Distribution

Alexandria, Lorez

Sings songs of Johnny Mercer Vol.II Harlem Butterfly (Alexandria, Lorez & The Gildo Mahones Quartet).
Tracks: / Lazy mood (Love's got me in a) / This time the dream's on me / Mandy is two / Come rain or shine / Harlem butterfly / Mandy is two / Skylark / P.S. I love you / Too marvelous for words.
Notes: Lorez Alexandria - vocals/Gildo Mahones - piano/Andy Simpkins - bass/Herman Riley - sax/Carl Burnett - drums
Compact disc: released on Discovery (USA) in Sep'86 by Discovery Records (USA). Distributed by: Swift, Flexitron-Audio, Jazz Music

Sings the songs of Johnny Mercer Vol.2 Harlem Butterfly (Alexandria, Lorez & The Gildo Mahones Quartet).
Tracks: / (Love's got me in a) lazy mood / This time the dream's on me / Mandy is two / Come rain or shine / Harlem Butterfly / Skylark / P.S. I love you / Too marvelous for words.
Album: released on Discovery (USA) in '84 by Discovery Records (USA). Distributed by: Swift, Flexitron-Audio, Jazz Music

Musicassette: released on Discovery (USA) in '84 by Discovery Records (USA). Distributed by: Swift, Flexitron-Audio, Jazz Music

Tangerine.
Tracks: / Bittersweet / I'm old fashioned / When the world was young / Any place I hang my hat / That old black magic / Namely you / Midnight sun / I'm building up to an awful let-down / Day in, day out / Days of wine & roses / Travellin' light / When a woman loves a man / I remember you / My shining hour.
Compact disc: by Discovery Records. Distributed by: Flexitron Distributors Ltd, Swift

Alexiades, Minas

Integra.
Album: released on Praxis (Greece) in '84. Distributed by: Mole Jazz

Alf

Alf on faulty five.
Single (7"): released on Singing Dog in '81

Alfie

Star.
Single (7"): released on Motown in '85 by Motown Records. Distributed by: BMG Distribution

Single (12"): released on Motown in '85 by Motown Records. Distributed by: BMG Distribution

Alf & Tel

Caribbean blues.
Tracks: / Sally.
Single (7"): released on Sahara in Aug'87

Ali Baba

Ali Baba Various artists (Various Artists).
Musicassette: released on Tell-A-Tale in '84 by Pickwick Records. Distributed by: Spartan-Taylors Distribution

& other favourite stories for... (Ali Baba & The Forty Thieves).
Notes: Full title: & other favourite stories for children aged 5 - 9
Musicassette: released on VFM in '85 by VFM Records. Distributed by: Taylors, Wynd-Up Distribution

Ali Baba 85

Kai Haba.
Album: released on Safari sound (African) in '85

Alice In Wonderland

Alice in wonderland Various artists.
Album: released on MFP in '81 by EMI Records. Distributed by: EMI. Estim retail price in Jul'87 was £2.25.

Musicassette: released on MFP in '81 by EMI Records. Distributed by: EMI

Album: released on Disneyland in '82 by Disneyland-Vista Records (USA). Distributed by: BBC Records & Tapes, Rainbow Communications Ltd(Distribution)

Musicassette: released on Disneyland in '82 by Disneyland-Vista Records (USA). Distributed by: BBC Records & Tapes, Rainbow Communications Ltd(Distribution)

Alice, Lynn

You keep me hangin' on/Pretty girl.
Single (12"): released on RST in '82

Alien

Alien Original Soundtrack.
Album: released on Silva Screen in Jun'87 by Silva Screen Records. Distributed by: Silva Screen

Musicassette: released on Silva Screen in Jun'87 by Silva Screen Records. Distributed by: Silva Screen

Space Fantasy.
Album:

Aliens

Aliens Original soundtrack (Various Artists).
Album: released on TER in Aug'86. Distributed by: Pinnacle

Single (12"): released on TER in Aug'86. Distributed by: Pinnacle

Album: released on Silva Screen in Jun'87 by Silva Screen Records. Distributed by: Silva Screen

Musicassette: released on Silva Screen in Jun'87 by Silva Screen Records. Distributed by: Silva Screen

Alien Sex Fiend

Acid bath.
Tracks: / In God we trust / Dead & reburied / She's a killer / Hee-haw (here come the bone people) / Smoke my bones / Breakdown & cry (lay down & die goodbye) / E.S.T. (trip to the moon) / Attack + 2.
Album: released on Anagram in '84 by Cherry Red Records. Distributed by: Pinnacle

Musicassette: released on Anagram in '84 by Cherry Red Records. Distributed by: Pinnacle

Dead and buried.
Single (7"): released on Anagram in '84 by Cherry Red Records. Distributed by: Pinnacle

Single (12"): released on Anagram in '84 by Cherry Red Records. Distributed by: Pinnacle

Picture disc single: released on Anagram in '84 by Cherry Red Records. Distributed by: Pinnacle

E.S.T (Trip to the moon).
Single (7"): released on Anagram in '84 by Cherry Red Records. Distributed by: Pinnacle

Single (12"): released on Anagram in '84 by Cherry Red Records. Distributed by: Pinnacle

First Alien Sex Fiend CD.
Tracks: / I'm doing time in a maximum security twilight home / Mine's full of maggots / Do you sleep / In and out of my mind / Spies / Fly in the ointment / Seconds to nowhere / Beaver destroys forests, The / Do you sleep / Depravity lane / E.S.T. (Trip to the moon) / Boneshaker baby / Ignore the machine / Attack.
Compact disc: by Cherry Red Records. Distributed by: Pinnacle

Here cum germs.
Single (7"): released on Anagram in Aug'87 by Cherry Red Records. Distributed by: Pinnacle

Single (12"): released on Anagram in Aug'87 by Cherry Red Records. Distributed by: Pinnacle

Hurricane fighter plane.
Tracks: / It lives again.
Single (7"): released on Anagram in Feb'87 by Cherry Red Records. Distributed by: Pinnacle

Single (12"): released on Anagram in Feb'87 by Cherry Red Records. Distributed by: Pinnacle

Ignore the machine.
Single (7"): released on Anagram in '85 by Cherry Red Records. Distributed by: Pinnacle

Single (12"): released on Anagram in '85 by Cherry Red Records. Distributed by: Pinnacle

Picture disc single: released on Anagram in '85 by Cherry Red Records. Distributed by: Pinnacle

I'm doing time in a maximum security twilight.
Single (12"): released on Anagram in '85 by Cherry Red Records. Distributed by: Pinnacle

Impossible mission, The.
Tracks: / Impossible mission / My brain is in the cupboard above the kitchen sink / Impossible mission 2.
Single (7"): released on Anagram in 13 Jun'87 by Cherry Red Records. Distributed by: Pinnacle

Single (12"): released on Anagram in 13 Jun'87 by Cherry Red Records. Distributed by: Pinnacle

It B/W maximum security.
Tracks: / Smells like sh.. / Manic depression / Believe it or not / April showers / Wop-bop / Get into it / Lesson one / Do it right / To be continued / I'm doing time... / Mine's full of maggots / Do you sleep / In out of my mind / Spies / Fly in the ointment / Seconds to nowhere / Beaver destroys forests / Do you sleep (version) / Depravity lane.
Musicassette: released on Anagram in Oct'86 by Cherry Red Records. Distributed by: Pinnacle

I walk the line.
Tracks: / I walk the line / School's out / Here she comes / Can't stop smoking.
Single (7"): released on Flicknife in Apr'86 by Flicknife Records. Distributed by: Spartan

Single (12"): released on Flicknife in Apr'86 by Flicknife Records. Distributed by: Spartan

Lips can't go/Drive my rocket.
Single (7"): released on Anagram in '83 by Cherry Red Records. Distributed by: Pinnacle

Single (12"): released on Anagram in '83 by Cherry Red Records. Distributed by: Pinnacle

Liquid head in Tokyo.
Tracks: / R.I.P. / E.S.T. / Dead & buried / In God we trust / Back to the egg / Attack / Lips can't go / Wild women.
Album: released on Anagram in '85 by Cherry Red Records. Distributed by: Pinnacle

Maximum security.
Tracks: / I'm doing time in a maximum security / Twilight home / Mine's full of maggots / Do you sleep / In & out of my mind / Spies / Fly in the ointment / Seconds to nowhere / Beaver destroys forset, (The) / Do you sleep (not of one mind) / Depravity Lane.
Album: released on Anagram in '85 by Cherry Red Records. Distributed by: Pinnacle

R.I.P..
Single (7"): released on Anagram in '84 by Cherry Red Records. Distributed by: Pinnacle

Single 10": released on Anagram in '84 by Cherry Red Records. Distributed by: Pinnacle

Single (12"): released on Anagram in '84 by Cherry Red Records. Distributed by: Pinnacle

Smells like sh...
Tracks: / Smells like shit / Biggin' me.
Single (7"): released on Anagram in Oct'86 by Cherry Red Records. Distributed by: Pinnacle

Single (12"): released on Anagram in Oct'86 by Cherry Red Records. Distributed by: Pinnacle

Who's been sleeping in my brian.
Album: released on Anagram in '83 by Cherry Red Records. Distributed by: Pinnacle

Who's been sleepng in my brain (USA version).
Album: released on Anagram in '84 by Cherry Red Records. Distributed by: Pinnacle

Alien, The

Alien,The Original soundtrack.
: released on 20th Century in '79. Distributed by: RCA, IMS-Polygram

Alligator Shoes

Alligator shoes Various artists (Various Artists).
Album: released on Sonet in Oct'83 by Sonet Records. Distributed by: PRT

Aliki

Dancing through the night.

Single (7"): released on Ecstasy in '84 by Creole Records. Distributed by: CBS

Single (12"): released on Ecstasy in '84 by Creole Records. Distributed by: CBS

Don't you want to know about the.
Single (7"): released on President in '82 by President Records. Distributed by: Taylors, Spartan

Alimantado, Doctor

In the mix - part 3.
Album: released on Keyman in Nov'86 by Keyman Records. Distributed by: Keyman, Revolver

Alisha

All night passion.
Single (12"): released on Fourth & Broadway in Mar'84 by Island Records. Distributed by: Polygram, EMI

Baby talk.
Tracks: / Baby talk / Baby talk (dub vocals).
Single (7"): released on Total Control in Jan'86

Single (12"): released on Total Control in Jan'86

Alison's Secret

Frankie's Room.
Single (7"): released on Surprise in Feb'85 by Surprise Records. Distributed by: ILA Distribution

Alive At The...

Alive at the living room Various artists (Various Artists).
Album: released on Creation Artefact in Jun'84. Distributed by: Rough Trade, Cartel

Alive Down Your Prong

Alive down your prong.
Musicassette: by Folktracks Cassettes. Distributed by: Folktracks

Al Jolson

20 golden greats.
Album: released on MCA in Feb'81 by MCA Records. Distributed by: Polygram, MCA

Musicassette: released on MCA in Feb'81 by MCA Records. Distributed by: Polygram, MCA

20 more golden greats.
Album: released on MCA in Sep'81 by MCA Records. Distributed by: Polygram, MCA

Musicassette: released on MCA in Sep'81 by MCA Records. Distributed by: Polygram, MCA

Al Jolson Collection,The.
Album: released on Deja Vu in Aug'85 by Deja Vu Records. Distributed by: Counterpoint Distribution, Record Services Distribution (Ireland)

Musicassette: released on Deja Vu in Aug'85 by Deja Vu Records. Distributed by: Counterpoint Distribution, Record Services Distribution (Ireland)

Al Jolson collection (Vol 1&2).
Album: released on Ronco in Nov'83

Musicassette: released on Ronco in Nov'83

Jolie live in '35.
Album: released on Sandy Hook (USA) in May'84. Distributed by: Swift, Jazz Music, IMS-Polygram

Man and the legend,The (2).
Album: released on Rhapsody in Sep'82 by President Records. Distributed by: Taylors, Swift, Jazz Music, Wellard, Chris

Man and the legend,The (1).
Album: released on Rhapsody in Sep'82 by President Records. Distributed by: Taylors, Swift, Jazz Music, Wellard, Chris

Man and the legend,The (3).
Album: released on Rhapsody in Sep'83 by President Records. Distributed by: Taylors, Swift, Jazz Music, Wellard, Chris

On the air 1 Vol 1.
Album: released on Totem in Jun'79. Distributed by: Jazz Music, Projection, Swift

On the air 1943 Plus sections from 34,39,44 & 48.
Album: released on Sandy Hook (USA) in Apr'79. Distributed by: Swift, Jazz Music, IMS-Polygram

On the air 2 Vol 2.
Album: released on Totem in Jun'79. Distributed by: Jazz Music, Projection, Swift

On the air 3 Vol 3.
Album: released on Totem in Jul'79. Distributed by: Jazz Music, Projection, Swift

On the air 4 Vol 4.
Album: released on Totem in May'79. Distributed by: Jazz Music, Projection, Swift

Swanee river (1945 broadcast) (Al Jolson and Dennis Morgan).
Album: released on Totem in May'79. Distributed by: Jazz Music, Projection, Swift

World's greatest entertainer,The.
Album: released on MCA in Jan'83 by MCA Records. Distributed by: Polygram, MCA

Musicassette: released on MCA in Jan'83 by MCA Records. Distributed by: Polygram, MCA

You ain't heard nothing yet.
Album: released on MCA in Dec'84 by MCA Records. Distributed by: Polygram, MCA

Musicassette: released on MCA in Dec'84 by MCA Records. Distributed by: Polygram, MCA

Alkatrazz

Radio 5.
Tracks: / Blinded / Blame it on the night / Long time no love / Half way there / Long time no love / Half way there / Short change / Think it over / Communication / Save my heart / So hard / Miles away.
Album: released on RCA in May'82 by RCA Records. Distributed by: RCA, Roots, Swift, Wellard, Chris, I & B, Solomon & Peres Distribution

Musicassette: released on RCA in May'82 by RCA Records. Distributed by: RCA, Roots, Swift, Wellard, Chris, I & B, Solomon & Peres Distribution

Young Blood.
Tracks: / Rockin' high / Young blood / Maybe tomorrow / Late news / Deadline / Crazy dancer / Give it all away / Live fast, die hard / You and the night / Run wild.
Album: released on RCA in May'81 by RCA Records. Distributed by: RCA, Roots, Swift, Wellard, Chris, I & B, Solomon & Peres Distribution

Musicassette: released on RCA in May'81 by RCA Records. Distributed by: RCA, Roots, Swift, Wellard, Chris, I & B, Solomon & Peres Distribution

All...

All around bluegrass Various artists (Various Artists).
Tracks: / On the southbound / Chalk up another one / Blue moon of Kentucky / You can't go in the red playing bluegrass / Carolina breakdown / Have you come to say goodbye / It's only a phonograph record / I'll go steppin' too / Windy mountain / Save it save it / Cuttin the grass / Corn cob blues / Kentucky ridgerunner / Bringin in the Georgia mail / I won't be hanging around / Nashville grass breakdown / Kentucky / Special / When it's peach pickin time in Georgia / Williams lake stampede.
Album: released on RCA International (USA) in May'84 by RCA Records. Distributed by: RCA

Musicassette: released on RCA International (USA) in May'84 by RCA Records. Distributed by: RCA

All for art and art for all Various artists (Various Artists).
Album: released on Whaam in Jun'84. Distributed by: Pinnacle

Musicassette: released on Whaam in Jun'84. Distributed by: Pinnacle

All night dancing Various artists (Various

Tracks: / Feelings / Crying game, The / Alone again / Little love, A / All by myself / I will wait for you / Good life, The / One less bell to answer / Don't throw it all away / As tears go by / Last night I did'nt get to sleep at all / I'm not in love.
Album: released on Hallmark in Oct'82 by Pickwick Records. Distributed by: Pickwick Distribution, PRT, Taylors

Musicassette: released on Hallmark in Oct'82 by Pickwick Records. Distributed by: Pickwick Distribution, PRT, Taylors

Album: released on K-Tel in Sep'84 by K-Tel Records. Distributed by: Record Merchandisers Distribution, Taylors, Terry Blood Distribution, Wynd-Up Distribution, Relay Distribution, Pickwick Distribution, Solomon & Peres Distribution, Polygram

Musicassette: released on K-Tel in Sep'84 by K-Tel Records. Distributed by: Record Merchandisers Distribution, Taylors, Terry Blood Distribution, Wynd-Up Distribution, Relay Distribution, Pickwick Distribution, Solomon & Peres Distribution, Polygram

Artists).
Album: released on RCA in Nov'84 by RCA Records. Distributed by: RCA, Roots, Swift, Wellard, Chris, I & B, Solomon & Peres Distribution

Musicassette: released on RCA in Nov'84 by RCA Records. Distributed by: RCA, Roots, Swift, Wellard, Chris, I & B, Solomon & Peres Distribution

All our own work Various artists (Various Artists).
Album: released on World Records in Jun'78. Distributed by: Polygram

All our tomorrows Allbeury,Ted (Davenport, Nigel).
Musicassette: released on LFP in May'85

All platinum Various artists (Various Artists).
Album: released on Chess in Apr'81 by Charly Records. Distributed by: Charly, Swift, PRT, Discovery, IMS, Polygram

All round cowboys Various artists (Various Artists).
Tracks: / Lorne Green / Cool water / Reno / Jesse James / Old Doc Brown / My adobe hacienda / That palomino pal of mine / Gunslinger's Prayer / Rancho Grande, (El) / Fools Paradise, (The) / Cattle call / Last gunfighter ballad, (The) / Hang the key on the bunkhouse door / Marshal of Silver City, (The) / When the work's all done this fall / She's in love with a rodeo man / Pinto pal, (A) / Strawberry roan, (The) / Streets of Laredo / Bandit, (The).
Album: released on RCA International in Oct'84

Musicassette: released on RCA International in Oct'84

All round England & back again (English customs & tradition) Various artists (Various Artists).
Tracks: / Furry Dance & Hal-an-Tow, (The), (Helston, Cornwall) / Hobby Horse Day (Padstow, Cornwall) / Oak Apple-Garland Day (Castleton, Derbyshire) / Whit Monday Morris, (The), (Bampton-in-the-Bush, Oxfordshire / Horn Dance, (The), (Abbots Bromley, Staffordshire) / Soul Cakers, (The), (Antrobus, Cheshire) / Plough Jags, (The), (Barrow-on-Humber, Lincolnshire) / Easter Jolly Boys, (The), (Far & Near Sawrey, Cumberland) / Wassailers (Cornwall & Somerset).
Album: released on Saydisc in Nov'82 by Saydisc Records. Distributed by: Essex, Harmonia Mundi, Roots, H.R. Taylor, Jazz Music, Swift, Projection, Gamut

Musicassette: released on Saydisc in Nov'82 by Saydisc Records. Distributed by: Essex, Harmonia Mundi, Roots, H.R. Taylor, Jazz Music, Swift, Projection, Gamut

All that jazz Original Soundtrack (All That Jazz).
Tracks: / On Broadway / Michelle / Take off with us / Ponte vecchio / Everything old is new again / South mt Sinai parade / After you've gone / There'll be some changes made / Who's sorry now / Some of these days / Going home now / Bye bye love.
Album: released on Casablanca(Holland) in Sep'84. Distributed by: IMS, Polygram

All that's jazz/Jubilee jazz (Various Artists).
Musicassette:

All that trad Various trad bands (Various Artists).
Double musicassette: released on Pickwick in Mar'83 by Pickwick Records. Distributed by: Pickwick Distribution, Prism Leisure Distribution, Lugtons

All the best from scotland Various artists (Various Artists).
Album: released on Lismor in Jul'80 by Lismor Records. Distributed by: Lismor, Roots, Celtic Music

Musicassette: released on Lismor in Jul'80 by Lismor Records. Distributed by: Lismor, Roots, Celtic Music

All the best from Scotland - Vol.2 Various artists (Various Artists).
Tracks: / Bonnie Aberdeen / Highland bridge depot / Major J. McGillivary / My ain folk / Lock Lomond / Dark island / Sweet afton / Bonnie lass of Fyvie / Jessies hornpipe / Kirks hornpipes / Drumlees / Island spinning song / Banjo breakdown / Fiddlers choice / Scotland your a lady / Flowers of Edinburgh / Wee dug Tim, The / Lucky scaup / Rose of Allandale / Skye boat song / Morag of Dunvegan / When you and I were young Maggie / Twa recruiting sergants.
Album: released on Lochshore in May'81 by Klub Records. Distributed by: PRT

Musicassette: released on Lochshore in May'81 by Klub Records. Distributed by: PRT

All the folk that fits Various artists (Various Artists).
Double Album: released on Polydor in Jul'81 by Polydor Records. Distributed by: Polygram, Polydor

Double musicassette: released on Polydor in Jul'81 by Polydor Records. Distributed by: Polygram, Polvdor

All the great motown Various artists (Various Artists).
Album: released on Motown in Mar'85 by Motown Records. Distributed by: BMG Distribution

Musicassette: released on Motown in Mar'85 by Motown Records. Distributed by: BMG Distribution

All things wise and wonderful (Herriot, James).
Notes: See under "Herriot, James"
Musicassette: released on Listen For Pleasure in Aug'86 by MFP Records. Distributed by: EMI

All time hits from the sixties Original artists (Various Artists).
Tracks: / Young girl / Hippy hippy shake / Charlie Brown / Let's twist again / Wild thing / Silence is golden / Whem a man loves a woman / Those were the days / Da doo ron ron / My old man's a dustman / You'll never walk alone / Run to him / You've got your troubles / Hold me / Crying game, The / I think of you / That same old feeling / Everlasting love.
Album: released on Showcase in '86. Distributed by: Counterpoint

Musicassette: released on Showcase in '86. Distributed by: Counterpoint

All together like the foaks o'shields Various artists (Various Artists).
Album: released on Greenwich Village in Jan'82 by Sweet Folk All Records. Distributed by: Roots, Projection, Lightning, Celtic Music, Wellard, Chris

All you need is love Various artists (Various Artists).
Album: released on Philips in Feb'78. Distributed by: IMS-Polygram

All your favourite TV themes Various artists (Various Artists).
Musicassette: released on Aim in Jan'25. Distributed by: H.R. Taylor

Alla Blues

Alla Blues(California 1947-54) Various artists (Various Artists).
Album: released on Muskadine in Apr'35. Distributed by: Swift Distribution

All Aboard

20 All Time Children's Favourites

All aboard Various Artists (Various Artists).
Album: released on EMI in Sep'79 by EMI Records. Distributed by: EMI

All aboard-20 all time children's favourites Various artists (Various Artists).
Album: released on EMI in Sep'79 by EMI Records. Distributed by: EMI

All aboard-24 original all time children's favourites Various artists (Various Artists).
Musicassette: released on EMI in Sep'79 by EMI Records. Distributed by: EMI

All About...

All about my naughty little sister (Kendall, Felicity).
Musicassette: released on Listen For Pleasure in Nov'77 by MFP Records. Distributed by: EMI

All About Eve

D for Desire.
Single (7"): released on Eden in Jun'85 by Eden Records. Distributed by: Pinnacle

Flowers in our hair.
Tracks: / Flowers in our hair / Paradise devil woman.

Single (7"): released on Eden in Jul'87 by Eden Records. Distributed by: Pinnacle

Single (12"): released on Eden in Jul'87 by Eden Records. Distributed by: Pinnacle

In the clouds.

Our summer.
Tracks: / Our summer / Lady Moonlight / Shelter from the rain*.
Notes: * = Extra track on 12" only.
Single (7"): released on Eden in Apr'87 by Eden Records. Distributed by: Pinnacle

Single (12"): released on Eden in Apr'87 by Eden Records. Distributed by: Pinnacle

Allah, Ras

Showcase.
Album: released on Vista Sounds in Dec'84 by Vista Sounds Records. Distributed by: Jetstar

Allair, John

Larkspur.
Notes: John Allaff is presently living in Larkspur, California where he tunes pianos between his involvement with Van Morrison. This is his debut album and shows on the great R & B voices as well as his unique piano style which moves freely between classical and R & B improvisation.

All American...

All American rock vol. 4 (Various Artists).
Album: released on Starclub in Jun'87

All American swing groups-vol.5 Various artists (Various Artists).
Album: released on Rarities in Sep'79

Allan, Denis

Limerick you're a lady.
Single (7"): released on Release in Oct'79 by Release Records. Distributed by: I & B, Wynd-Up Distribution, Taylors, Solomon & Peres Distribution

Allan, Johnnie

1959-1960's (Allen, Johnnie & The Crazy Cats).
Tracks: / I'll be waiting / My baby is gone / Tell me do you love me so / Lonely days lonely nights / Rubber dolly / Letter of love / Family rules / Prisoner's song / One more chance / Give me more of your kisses / Crying over you / Please accept my love / You got me whistling / Nobody's darling but mine.
Album: released on Krazy Kat in Jan'85. Distributed by: Projection

Another man's woman.
Album: released on Jin in Feb'79. Distributed by: Swift

Cajun country.
Album: . Distributed by: Swift

Dedicated to you.
Album: released on Jin in Feb'79 by Priority Records. Distributed by: EMI

Good timin' man.
Album: released on Flyright in Feb'87 by Flyright Records. Distributed by: Krazy Kat, Swift, Jazz Music

Johnnie Allan Sings.
Album: released on Jin in Feb'79 by Priority Records. Distributed by: EMI

Johnnie's Allen's greatest hits.
Album: released on Jin in Feb'79. Distributed by: Swift

Portrait of Johnnie Allan.
Album: released on Jin in Feb'79. Distributed by: Swift

Promised Land.
Single (7"): released on Oval in Mar'82. Distributed by: Projection

South to Louisiana.
Album: released on Jin in Feb'79. Distributed by: Swift

Album: released on Ace in Sep'85 by Ace Records. Distributed by: Pinnacle, Swift, Hotshot, Cadillac

Thanks for the memories.

Album: . Distributed by: Swift

Allanson, Susie

Susie.
Album: released on Liberty in May'81 by Liberty-United. Distributed by: EMI

Allcorn, Alvin

Alvin Allcorn & His New Orleans Jazz Band.
Album: released on New Orleans in Apr'79. Distributed by: Swift, Zodiac Distribution, Jazz Music, JSU

Alleluja

Alleluja Various artists (Various Artists).
Album: released on Dove in May'79 by Dove Records. Distributed by: Jetstar

Allen, Alan

French girls/City (Allen, Alan & Garfield Sober).
Single (12"): released on Cynic in Feb'83 by Cynic Records. Distributed by: Stage One

Allen, Chris

We're having a party (Allen, Chris Orchestra).
Tracks: / Having a party / Sweeney,The / Love me / Save your kisses for me / Honey pie / Una Paloma Blanca / United we stand / Don't give up on us baby / Get ready / Beautiful noise / Highway affair / Hawaii Five-O / Little bit more,A / Y viva Espana.
Album: released on Grosvenor in '77 by Grosvenor Records. Distributed by: Taylors

Allen, Clinton

Loaf ina de dance.
Single (12"): released on Gorgon in Oct'84 by Gorgon Records. Distributed by: Jetstar

Allen, Daevid

Allen in New York.
Single (12"): released on Charly in May'83 by Charly Records. Distributed by: Charly, Cadillac

Banana moon.
Album: released on Charly in May'79 by Charly Records. Distributed by: Charly, Cadillac

Death of rock and other entrances, The.
Album: released on Shanghai in Nov'82

Divided Allen playbax 80.
Album: released on Charly in '82 by Charly Records. Distributed by: Charly, Cadillac

Ex.
Album: released on Shanghai in Aug'86

Good morning.
Tracks: / Children of the New World / Good morning / Spirit / Song of satisfaction / Have you seen my friend / French garden / Wise man in your heart / She doesn't she....
Album: released on Virgin in May'76 by Virgin Records. Distributed by: EMI, Virgin Distribution

Jungle Window (Allen, Daevid & New York Gang).
Single (7"): released on Charly in Jan'82 by Charly Records. Distributed by: Charly, Cadillac

N'existe pas.
Album: released on Charly in May'79 by Charly Records. Distributed by: Charly, Cadillac

Now is the happiest time.
Tracks: / Flamenco zero / Why do we treat ourselves like we do / Tally & Orlando / Meet the cockpot Pixie / See you on the moontower / Poet for sale / Only make love if you want to / I am / Deya Goddess.
Album: released on Affinity in Nov'77 by Charly Records. Distributed by: Charly, Cadillac

Obsolete (Allen, Daevid & Dashiel Heydayat).

Stop/Don't (Allen, Daevid & David Tolley).
Album: released on Shanghai in Sep'84

Allen, Dennis

Limerick, you're a lady & other favourites.
Album: released on Stoic (Ireland) in Jul'84

Musicassette: released on Stoic (Ireland) in Jul'84

Allen, Dolly

Dolly Allen solo album.
Album: released on Broadside in Jun'81 by Broadside Records. Distributed by: Celtic Distributions, H.R. Taylor, Jazz Music, Projection, Jazz Services Unlimited Dist. (JSU)

Musicassette: released on Broadside in Jun'81 by Broadside Records. Distributed by: Celtic Distributions, H.R. Taylor, Jazz Music, Projection, Jazz Services Unlimited Dist. (JSU)

Allen, Donna

Perfect timing.
Tracks: / Serious / Sweet somebody / Satisfied / Daydreams / Wild nights / Perfect timing / Bit by bit / Another affair / Bad love.
Album: released on Portrait in May'87 by CBS Records. Distributed by: CBS

Musicassette: released on Portrait in May'87 by CBS Records. Distributed by: CBS

Compact disc: released on Portrait in Jul'87 by CBS Records. Distributed by: CBS

Satisfied.
Tracks: / Satisfied / Another affair.
Single (7"): released on Portrait in Jun'87 by CBS Records. Distributed by: CBS

Single (12"): released on Portrait in Jun'87 by CBS Records. Distributed by: CBS

Single (7"): released on Epic in Jun'87 by CBS Records. Distributed by: CBS

Satisfied (blue mix).
Tracks: / Satisfied (blue mix) / Satisfied (acappella version) / Another affair / Serious.
Single (7"): released on Portrait in Jul'87 by CBS Records. Distributed by: CBS

Serious.
Single (7"): released on Portrait in Mar'87 by CBS Records. Distributed by: CBS

Single (12"): released on Portrait in Mar'87 by CBS Records. Distributed by: CBS

Allen, Doris

Them changes (Allen, Doris & John Hamilton).

Allen, Fred

Linit bath club revue.
Album: released on Radio Archives in Aug'77. Distributed by: Jazz Music, Swift

Two complete linit bath club revues.
Album: released on Radio Archives in Jun'79. Distributed by: Jazz Music, Swift

Allen, Henry 'Red'

At Newport festival 1957 (Allen, Henry Red / Kid Ory & Jack Teagarden).
Tracks: / Struttin' with some barbecue / St.James infirmary / China boy / Basin street blues / Muskrat ramble / High society.
Notes: All-star jam session in celebration of Louis Armstrong's 57th Birthday.
Album: released on Verve (France) in Apr'84

Henry Red Allen.
Album: released on Jazz Reactivation in Jul'82. Distributed by: PRT

Henry 'Red' Allen 1939/41.
Album: released on Everybody's in Jul'82 by Everybody's Records. Distributed by: Jazz Music, Swift

Nice.
Tracks: / Theme, The / Red jump / Ride red, ride / Dark eyes / Dear old southland / Get the mop / Just a feeling / Wild man blues / Rosetta / Memphis blues / Yellow dog blues / Cherry / Fidgety feet.
Notes: Allen tpt.vcl./ J.C. Higginbotham tbn./ Don Stovall alt./ Al Williams pn./ Clarence Moten bs./ Alvin Burroughs d./ Rex Stewart cor./ Vic Dickerson tbn./ Pee Wee Russel clnt./ Coleman Hawkins ten./ Nat Pierce pn./ Danny Parker gt./ Milt Hinton bs./ Jo Jones d./ TV show July 12th 1957: Cutty Cutshall tbn./ Tony Parent clnt./ Ralph Sutton pn./ Clarence Moten bs./ Mickey Sheen d./ February 1963:
Album: released on Phoenix in Apr'81 by Audio Fidelity Enterprises. Distributed by: Stage One, Lugtons

Very great Henry 'Red' Allen with 'Kid' Ory's Creole, The.
Tracks: / Peoria / Basin street blues / St.James infirmary blues / Wolverine blues / Savoy blues / Tin roof blues / That's a plenty / Aunt Hagar's blues / Panama rag / At the Jazz Band Ball.
Notes: Personnel: Henry 'Red' Allen, tpt.,vcls., Edward 'Kid' Ory, tmbn., Bob McCracken, cl., Cedric Haywood, pno., Alton Redd, dms., Squire Gersh, Bass. Recorded: 9th November, 1959, Basle, Switzerland.
Album: released on Rarities in Apr'81

Very great Henry 'Red' Allen-vol.1.
Tracks: / Sometimes I'm happy / Ol' man River / Siesta at the Fiesta / Jack the Bellboy / Ride, red ride / Dark eyes / Dear old Southland / Red jump / Crawl,The / Buzz me / Drink hearty / Get the mop / Count me out / Check up / If it's love you want / Let me miss you.
Notes: Personnel: Features Red Allen, J.C. Higginbotham, Don Stovall, Benny Moten, Bill Thompson, Ed Hall. Recorded: (A) 1/2-17/4/41, 3/4-22/7/41, (B) 1/2/3/4-1944, (C) 1/2/3/4-14/1/46, (D) 1/2/3/4-16/7/46.
Album: released on Rarities in Apr'81

Allen, Jerry

Hands of Jerry Allen.
Album: released on Alamo in May'78. Distributed by: Jazz Music

Party time.
Album: released on Alamo in May'78. Distributed by: Jazz Music

Allen, Lee

Lee Allen's Rhythm & Blues Band.
Musicassette: released on Nola in May'87. Distributed by: JSU, Jazz Music, Cadillac, Chris Wellard

Allen, Les

Down on Bourbon Street (Allen, Les & His Band).
Album: released on Nola in Apr'79. Distributed by: JSU, Jazz Music, Cadillac, Chris Wellard

Allen, Marcus

Breathe (Allen, Marcus / John Bernoff).

Petals (Allen, Marcus / John Bernoff / Dallas Smith / Eja Bell).
Album: released on Rising Sun (Holland) in Dec'84

Musicassette: released on Rising Sun (Holland) in Dec'84

Allen, Patrick

Odessa file, The Forsyth, Frederick.
Musicassette: released on Listen For Pleasure in Jul'78 by MFP Records. Distributed by: EMI

Allen, Pete

Dixie date (Allen, Pete Band).
Album: released on Black Lion in Jul'86 by Black Lion Records. Distributed by: Jazz Music, Chris Wellard, Taylor, H.R., Counterpoint, Cadillac

Gonna build a mountain (Allen, Pete Jazz Band).
Tracks: / Gonna build a mountain / Livery stable blues / I ain't gonna give nobody none of my jelly roll / Seagull strut / My little Bimbo / Louisiana / Chimes blues / Snake rag / I've got a feeling I'm falling / Potato head blues / I'm slapping Seventh Avenue with the sole of my shoe / T'ain't no sin to take off your skin / West End blues / 1919 march.
Album: released on Platform in '82. Distributed by: Jazz Music, Wellard, Chris

Musicassette: released on Platform in '82. Distributed by: Jazz Music, Wellard, Chris

Jazzin' around II (Allen, Pete Band).
Album: released on ARB in Nov'85. Distributed by: Conifer

While we danced at the Mardi Gras (Allen, Pete Jazz Band).
Album: released on Jazz Club U.K. in Mar'87

Allen, Peter

I could have been a sailor.
Tracks: / I could have been a sailor / Don't wish too hard / Two boys / Angels with dirty faces / Don't cry out loud / If you were wondering / Don't leave me now / I'd rather leave while I'm in love / We've come to an understanding / Paris at 21.
Album: released on A&M in Mar'79 by A&M Records. Distributed by: Polygram

Musicassette: released on A&M in Mar'79 by A&M Records. Distributed by: Polygram

Not the boy next door.
Tracks: / Just another make-out song / Not the boy next door / You'll always get your way / You and me (we had it all) / Fade to black / Somebody's got your love / You haven't heard the last of me / Easy on the weekend / Once before I go.

Notes: Peter Allen was born in Australia although now lives in New York. He was discovered by Judy Garland and formerly married Lisa Minnelli. He has written: "I honestly love you" (Olivia Newton-John), "I'd rather leave while I'm in love" (Rita Coolidge), "Don't cry out loud" (Elkie Brooks and Melissa Manchester), "You and me" (Sinatra). The album was produced by Richard Landis and Allen co-wrote 7 tracks, with the cream of American writers: Tom Snow, Eric Kaz, Carole Bayer-Sager, David Foster, Dean Pitchford.
Album: released on Arista in Apr'83 by Arista Records. Distributed by: RCA

Taught by experts.
Tracks: / Puttin' out roots / She loves to hear the music / Back doors crying / I go to Rio / Planes / Quiet please, there's a lady on stage / This time around / More I see you, The / Harbour / I've been taught by experts / Six-thirty Sunday morning / New York, I don't know about you.
Album: released on A&M in Sep'76 by A&M Records. Distributed by: Polygram

Allen, Red

Red Allen & George Lewis (With George Lewis Quartet).
Album: released on Hot Society in Dec'82. Distributed by: Jazz Music, Chris Wellard

Red Allen meets Kid Ory (Allen, Red & Kid Ory).
Album: released on Verve (France) in Oct'82

Red Allen & The Blues Singers (Allen, Red & The Blues Singers).
Album: released on Jazz Archives in Jul'86 by Jazz Archives Records. Distributed by: Jazz Music

Allen, Rex

Boney kneed, hairy legged cowboy songs.
Tracks: / Little Joe / Wrangler, The / Moonshine steer / Firemen Cowboy, The / Braggin / Drunk from Wilcox / Fiddlin / Medley / Tyin / Knots in the Devil's tail / Droop ears / Windy Bill / When the work's all done this fall / Streets of Laredo.
Album: released on Bear Family in Jul'84 by Bear Family Records. Distributed by: Rollercoaster Distribution, Swift

Hawaiian Cowboy.
Picture disc album: released on Bear Family in Apr'86 by Bear Family Records. Distributed by: Rollercoaster Distribution, Swift

Under western skies.
Album: released on Stetson in Nov'85 by Hasmick Promotions Ltd.. Distributed by: Counterpoint Distribution, H.R. Taylor Distribution, Swift Distribution, Chris Wellard Distribution

Musicassette: released on Stetson in Nov'85 by Hasmick Promotions Ltd.. Distributed by: Counterpoint Distribution, H.R. Taylor Distribution, Swift Distribution, Chris Wellard Distribution

Voice of the West, The.
Tracks: / Tyin' knots in the devil's tail / Moonshine steer / Fireman cowboy, The / Today I started loving you today.
Compact disc: released on Bear Family in Aug'86 by Bear Family Records. Distributed by: Rollercoaster Distribution, Swift

Allen, R. Justice

Crackin' up.
Tracks: / Crackin' up / Crackin' up (dub version).
Single (7"): released on Lisson in Oct'86. Distributed by: PRT

Single (12"): released on Lisson in Oct'86. Distributed by: PRT

Allen, Rodney

Happy sad.
Album: released on Subway Organisation in Feb'87. Distributed by: Revolver, Cartel

Allen, Steve

All star Jazz concert vol 2.
Album: released on Jasmine in Jun'84 by Jasmine Records. Distributed by: Counterpoint, Lugtons, Taylor, H.R., Wellard, Chris, Swift, Cadillac

Jazz for tonight.
Tracks: / S'posin I should fall in love with you / Chicken wire blues / Body & soul / I thought about you / Limehouse blues / Tea for two / Lover man / Poor butterfly.
Album: released on Jasmine in Jun'83 by Jasmine Records. Distributed by: Counterpoint, Lugtons, Taylor, H.R., Wellard, Chris, Swift, Cadillac

Love is in the air.
Single (7"): released on WEA in May'87 by WEA Records. Distributed by: WEA

Single (12"): released on WEA in May'87 by WEA Records. Distributed by: WEA

Steve Allen's all star Jazz concert vol 1.
Tracks: / I want to be happy / Sweet Georgia Brown / I can't get started / Big noise from Winnetka / Love me or leave me / Swing that music / Big town boogie / That's a plenty / Long gone.
Album: released on Jasmine in Dec'83 by Jasmine Records. Distributed by: Counterpoint, Lugtons, Taylor, H.R., Wellard, Chris, Swift, Cadillac

Allen, Terry

Bloodlines.
Album: released on Spindrift in Nov'85. Distributed by: Roots

Allen, Tony

N.E.P.A. (Allen, Tony / Afrobeat 2000).
Album: released on Earthworks in Dec'84 by Earthworks Records. Distributed by: Earthworks Distributors, Rough Trade, Cartel, Projection

Allen, Verden

About tomorrow.
Single (7"): released on Spirit in Feb'85 by Spirit Records. Distributed by: WEA

Come on back Sweet sweet girl.
Single (7"): released on Spirit in Mar'84 by Spirit Records. Distributed by: WEA

Alley, Patrick

Just another night You're all I need.
Single (12"): released on Tabs in Jul'82

Allez Allez

Allez allez African queen.
Single (7"): released on Kamera in Jun'82

Flesh and blood Time you cost me.
Single (7"): released on Virgin in Jan'83 by Virgin Records. Distributed by: EMI, Virgin Distribution

Single (12"): released on Virgin in Jan'83 by Virgin Records. Distributed by: EMI, Virgin Distribution

Promises.
Album: released on Virgin in Nov'82 by Virgin Records. Distributed by: EMI, Virgin Distribution

Musicassette: released on Virgin in Nov'82 by Virgin Records. Distributed by: EMI, Virgin Distribution

All Fall Down

Arecibo.
Single (7"): released on Confidential in Jul'83 by Confidential Records. Distributed by: Pinnacle

Allies

Virtues.
Notes: This, the second album by Allies, paints a clearer picture of the band's identity and potential than their self-titled debut. Stronger production (produced by Dino Elephante and Randy Thomas) superbly crafted pop songs and crisp, effective performances characterise "Virtues". An up-tempo pop/rock album with a lot going for it. That Allies has a lot to offer is apparent on every track.
Album: released on Light in Feb'87 by Mainline Record Company. Distributed by: Mainline

Musicassette: released on Light in Feb'87 by Mainline Record Company. Distributed by: Mainline

Allington, Valerie

Stop.
Single (7"): released on Carrere in Apr'83 by Carrere Records. Distributed by: PRT, Spartan

Single (12"): released on Carrere in Apr'83 by Carrere Records. Distributed by: PRT, Spartan

Allison, Clay

Clay Allison.
Album: released on Rough Trade in Jun'84 by Rough Trade Records. Distributed by: Rough Trade Distribution, Cartel Distribution

Allison, George

Afraid of love Little girl.
Single (12"): released on Red Man in Dec'82 by Red Man Records. Distributed by: Jetstar

No one else.
Single (12"): released on Gibbous in Oct'82 by Gibbous Records. Distributed by: Jetstar

You will never know.
Single (12"): released on Buzzin in Sep'83. Distributed by: DMS, RCA, Pinnacle
o

Allison, Luther

Blues nebulae.
Album: . Distributed by: Projection, Swift, Cadillac

Let's have a natural ball.
Tracks: / You're all I need / Let's have a natural ball / Sit & talk / Funkin' it / I have the same old blues / Get out of my life / You're gonna need my help / Let me love you baby.
Album: released on JSP in Aug'84 by JSP Records. Distributed by: Swift, Projection

Power wire blue.
Tracks: / Dust my broom / I got worries / You don't love me / Going down / I'm gonna leave you alone / Sweet home Chicago.
Album: released on Charly in '86 by Charly Records. Distributed by: Charly, Cadillac

Southside safari.
Album: released on Red Lightnin' in Aug'83 by Red Lightnin' Records. Distributed by: Roots, Swift, Jazz Music, JSU, Pinnacle, Cartel, Wynd-Up Distribution

Allison, Mose

Back country suite.
Tracks: / Back country suite (for piano, bass & drums) / New ground / Train / Warm night / Blues / Saturday / Scamper / January / Promised land / Spring song / Highway 49 / Blueberry Hill / I thought about you / In Salah / You won't let me go / One room country shack.
Album: released on Prestige (USA) in Feb'84

Mose alive.
Album: released on Edsel in Jul'85 by Demon Records. Distributed by: Pinnacle, Jazz Music, Projection

Seventh son.
Tracks: / Seventh son, (The) / Eyesight to the blind / Do nothin' till you hear from me / Lost mind / I got a right to cry baby / Baby let me hold your hand / Parchman Farm / If you live / Don't get around much anymore / One room country shack / I hadn't anyone till you / Young man, (A) / That's all right.
Album: released on Prestige (USA) in May'84

Allisons

Biographical Details: John Alford and Bob Day became honorary Allison 'brothers' in 1961, when they represented the United Kingdom in the Eurovision Song Contest. Their self-penned entry 'Are You Sure' came second both in the contest and in the charts. Two smaller hits followed, then the Allisons drifted into obscurity. (Bob McDonald)

Are you sure.
Single (7"): released on Old Gold in Jul'82 by Old Gold Records. Distributed by: Lightning, Jazz Music, Spartan, Counterpoint

Inside and out.
Notes: A country gem by the European pop duo.
Album: released on Elecstar in Dec'85 by Elecstar Records. Distributed by: PRT

Sings Christmas.
Album: released on Aim in Feb'83. Distributed by: H.R. Taylor

Allman Brothers

Beginnings.
Tracks: / Black hearted woman / Trouble no more / Every hungry woman / Dreams / Whipping post / Revival / Don't keep me wonderin' / Midnight rider / In memory of Elizabeth Reed / I'm your hoochie coochie man / Please call home / Leave my blues at home / Don't want you no more / It's not my cross to bear.
Compact disc: by Polydor Records. Distributed by: Polygram, Polydor

Brothers and Sisters.
Tracks: / Wasted words / Ramblin' man / Come and go blues / Jelly jelly / Southbound / Jessica / Pony boy / Wasted words / Ramblin man / Come and go blues / Jelly jelly / Southbound / Jessica / Pony boy.
Compact disc: released on Polydor in '86 by Polydor Records. Distributed by: Polygram, Polydor

Compact disc: released on Capricorn in 20 Jun'87 by Polydor Records. Distributed by: Polygram

Brothers and sisters (Allman Brothers Band).
Album: released on Capricorn in Jun'81 by Polydor Records. Distributed by: Polygram

Eat a peach.
Tracks: / Ain't wastin' time no more / Le bers in A minor / Melissa / Mountain jam / One way out / Trouble no more / Stand back / Blue sky / Little Martha / Mountain jam.
Compact disc: released on Polydor in '86 by Polydor Records. Distributed by: Polygram, Polydor

Jessica Ramblin' man (Allman Brothers Band).
Single (12"): released on Polydor in Sep'82 by Polydor Records. Distributed by: Polygram, Polydor

Jessica.
Notes: Long version
Single (7"): released on Old Gold in Jul'84 by Old Gold Records. Distributed by: Lightning, Jazz Music, Spartan, Counterpoint

Live At Fillmore.
Compact disc: released on Polydor in '86 by Polydor Records. Distributed by: Polygram, Polydor

Allman Brothers, The

Win, lose or draw,.
Compact disc: released on Capricorn in Aug'87 by Polydor Records. Distributed by: Polygram

Allman, Gregg

I'm no angel.
Tracks: / I'm no angel / Anything goes / Evidence of love / Yours for the asking / Things that might have been / Can't keep running / Faces without names / Lead me on / Don't want you no more / It's not my cross to bear / I'm no angel / Lead me on.
Album: released on Epic in May'87 by CBS Records. Distributed by: CBS

Musicassette: released on Epic in May'87 by CBS Records. Distributed by: CBS

Compact disc: released on Epic in May'87 by CBS Records. Distributed by: CBS

Laid back.
Compact disc: released on Capricorn in Aug'87 by Polydor Records. Distributed by: Polygram

All My...

All my appointed time Various artists (Various Artists).
Tracks: / Standing by the bedside of a neighbour / Listen to the lambs / Precious lord / God shall wipe all tears away / I'm bound for Canaan land / Standing out on the highway / Well well well / I'm gonna tell god / Here I am, do lord send me / Where the sun will never go down / Bessie Griffin; the lord will make a way / Any stars in my crown / I'll make it somehow / They led my lord away / All my appointed time / Lord will make a way, The.
Double Album: released on Stash in Apr'81. Distributed by: Swift Distribution, Jazz Music Distribution, Jazz Horizons Distribution, Celtic Music Distribution, Cadillac, JSU Distribution, Zodiac Distribution

All my favourite nursery rhymes Various artists (Various Artists).
Album: released on Premier in May'84 by Premier Records. Distributed by: CBS

Musicassette: released on Premier in May'84 by Premier Records. Distributed by: CBS

All my loving Various artists (Various Artists).
Tracks: / All my loving / Fool on the hill / Guantanamera / More I see you, (The) / Quando m'innamora / Our day will come / Mas que nada / Where have all the flowers gone / There will never be another you / Girl from Ipanema, (The) / Goin out of my head / Misty roses / When a man loves a woman / Sunny / Yesterday / Don't go breaking my heart / Fly me to the moon / Chelsea morning / What now my love.
Album: released on MFP in Sep'81 by EMI Records. Distributed by: EMI

Musicassette: released on MFP in Sep'81 by EMI Records. Distributed by: EMI

Single (7"): released on Voyage International in Feb'81 by Code Records. Distributed by: PRT

Single (12"): released on Voyage International in Feb'81 by Code Records. Distributed by: PRT

All New Leeds...

All new Leeds top of the iceberg Various artists (Various Artists).
Tracks: / On the ground / This girl / I wanna be loved by you / Lights of Tokyo / I've got some / It's hard to believe it / All the night / War of the world / Crimson red / Colours turn to grey / Dreaming the night away / Misplaced ideals / Live by the sword / Berlin nuns / Imagine by a song / Tramp, (The).
Musicassette: released on Bomb in Jul'85. Distributed by: Menace Breaker Distributors

All Night Band

Joker,The(The Wigan Joker).
Single (7"): released on Casino Classics in Feb'79 by RK Records. Distributed by: PRT

Allnighters

Love and affection.
Single (7"): released on A.1 in Jul'84 by A.1 Records. Distributed by: PRT

Single (7"): released on A.1 in Jul'84 by A.1 Records. Distributed by: PRT

Allons au Fais Do-Do

Allons au Fais Do-Do Various artists (Various Artists).
Album:

All Soul's Orchestra

Sing a new song.
Tracks: / Sing a new song to the lord / Blessed is the man / Lord is king!, THe / Stand up,o god / O righteous lord / O lord I love you / May god be gracious / Mary sang a song / Safe in the shadow of the lord / Fool has been gracious, The / O praise god / Angels praise him / Sing a song / Listen to my prayer,Lord / God of gods,we sound his praises.
Album: released on Word in May'82 by Word Records. Distributed by: Word Distribution, CBS

Musicassette: released on Word in May'82 by Word Records. Distributed by: Word Distribution, CBS

Song's of worship.
Tracks: / My lord of light / Canticle of the gift, The / We come as guests / Make me a channel of your peace / We have a gospel to proclaim / Freedom song / Jubilate everybody / Come,christians,join to sing / He gave his life / Calypso Carol / Jesus is lord / O lamb of god / Alleluia, alleluia,give thanks / Lord of all hopefulness.
Album: released on Word in May'82 by Word Records. Distributed by: Word Distribution, CBS

Musicassette: released on Word in May'82 by Word Records. Distributed by: Word Distribution, CBS

All Star...

All Star Country Music Fair (Various Artists).
Video-cassette (VHS): released on RCA/Columbia in May'87

All star country round up Various Artists (Various Artists).
Tracks: / Oh lonesome me / Geisha girl / Six days on the road / What am I worth / Things go better with love / Mississippi woman / Jambalaya / Pick me up on your way down / DJ for a day / Night life / Flyin' south / Yes Mr. Peters / Sixteen tons / Folsom Prison blues.
Album: released on Spot in Feb'83 by Pickwick Records. Distributed by: H.R. Taylor, Lugtons

Musicassette: released on Spot in Feb'83 by Pickwick Records. Distributed by: H.R. Taylor, Lugtons

All star swing Various artists (Various Artists).
Double Album: released on Savoy (France) in Oct'85

All star trombone spectacular Various artists (Various Artists).
Album: released on Progressive in Aug'82 by Progressive Records. Distributed by: Jetstar

All star trumpet spectacular Various artists (Various Artists).
Album: released on Progressive in Apr'81 by Progressive Records. Distributed by: Jetstar

All Stars...

All star's at newport Various artists (Various Artists).
Album: released on Verve in Aug'81 by Phonogram Records. Distributed by: Polygram

All star sax spectacular Various artists (Various Artists).
Album: released on Progressive in Apr'81 by Progressive Records. Distributed by: Jetstar

All star's Vol.1 Various artists (Various Artists).
Musicassette: released on Gold in Apr'81 by Gold Records. Distributed by: President Distribution, Taylors

All star's Vol.2 Various artists (Various Artists).
Musicassette: released on Gold in Apr'81 by Gold Records. Distributed by: President Distribution, Taylors

All star swing groups Various artists (Various Artists).
Double Album: released on Savoy (USA) in Mar'85 by Arista Records. Distributed by: Polygram, Swift

Double Album: released on Savoy in '78

Live European concert.
Tracks: / Bauhaus / Tenderly / Makin' whoppee / C jam blues / Yardbird suite / Sunday / Willow weep for me / This can't be love.
Album: released on Unique Jazz in Apr'81. Distributed by: Swift, Jazz Music, Jazz Horizons

Newport Jazz Festival.
Album: released on Avan-Guard in Aug'86 by Vanguard Records. Distributed by: Conifer, Discovery

All's Well That Ends Well

All's well that ends well (complete text)

All the Rage

Concrete city.
Single (7"):

Allyn, Dave

Dave Allyn sings Jerome Kern.
Album: released on Discovery (USA) in Apr'84 by Discovery Records (USA). Distributed by: Swift, Flexitron-Audio, Jazz Music

Sings Jerome Kern/Sure thing.
Tracks: / Sure thing / Dearly beloved / I'm old fashioned / Lovely to look at / The way you look tonight / The folks who live on the hill / Long ago and far away / I've told every little star / All in fun / In love in vain.
Album: released on Discovery (USA) in Apr'84 by Discovery Records (USA). Distributed by: Swift, Flexitron-Audio, Jazz Music

Almario, Justo

Forever friends.
Notes: Colombian-born flute and tenor sax player Justo Almerio hes over 40 albums to his credit, two of them with Koinonia. He is helped out on this 'peacful yet rhythmic' album by Koinonia friends Abraham Laboriel, Alex Acuna and Hadley Hockensmith, and producer Bill Maxwell.
Album: released on Meadowlark in Mar'86 by Sparrow Records. Distributed by: Word Distribution

Musicassette: released on Meadowlark in Mar'86 by Sparrow Records. Distributed by: Word Distribution

Almeida, Laurindo

Artistry in rhythm (Almeida, Laurindo Trio).
Tracks: / Charriots of fire / Astronauta / Andante / Te amo / Artistry in rhythm / Always on my mind / Slaughter on 10th avenue / Up where we belong / Almost a heartful / Liza / Puka shells in a whirl.
Notes: This is a beautiful collection of melodies performed in the soft and serious manner that Brazilian guitarist Laurindo Almeida is known for. Artistry in rhythm is an appropriate name for this recording...Laurindo was a member of the Stan Kenton orchestra in 1947 when he just came to North America in 1953, this album is latin-laced with samba rhythms. A true listening delight.
Album: released on Concord Jazz (USA) in Apr'84 by Concord Jazz Records (USA). Distributed by: IMS, Polygram

Brazilian soul (Almeida, Laurindo & Charlie Byrd).
Album: released on Concord Jazz (USA) in May'81 by Concord Jazz Records (USA). Distributed by: IMS, Polygram

Latin Odyssey (Almeida, Laurindo & Charlie Byrd).
Tracks: / Memory (from cats) / Zum and ressurection / El nino / Gitanerias / Adios / El cavilan / Estrellita / Turbilhao / Intermezzo malinconico.
Notes: More offerings from two of the greatest exponents of Brazillian/jazz guitar
Album: released on Concord Jazz (USA) in May'83 by Concord Jazz Records (USA). Distributed by: IMS, Polygram

Musicassette: released on Concord Jazz (USA) in May'83 by Concord Jazz Records (USA). Distributed by: IMS, Polygram

New directions.
Album: released on Crystal Clear in Dec'80 by Crystal Records. Distributed by: Revolver, Cartel

Selected classical works for guitar and flute (Almeida, Laurendo / Bud Shank).
Album: released on Concord Jazz (USA) in Jul'82 by Concord Jazz Records (USA). Distributed by: IMS, Polygram

Tango (Almeide, Laurindo & Charlie Byrd).
Tracks: / Orchids in the moonlight / Blue tango / Jalousie / Los enamorados / La Rosita / Tanog alegre / La cumparsita / Moon was yellow, The / Hernando's hideaway / Tanguero.
Compact disc: released on Concord Jazz (USA) in Jan'87 by Concord Jazz Records (USA). Distributed by: IMS, Polygram

Album: released on Concord Jazz (USA) in Dec'85 by Concord Jazz Records (USA). Distributed by: IMS, Polygram

Musicassette: released on Concord Jazz (USA) in Dec'85 by Concord Jazz Records (USA). Distributed by: IMS, Polygram

Virtuoso guitar.
Notes: Direct cut
Album: released on Crystal Clear in Aug'78 by Crystal Records. Distributed by: Revolver, Cartel

Almond, Marc

Boy who came back (The).
Single 10": released on Some Bizarre in Jun'84 by Virgin Records. Distributed by: EMI, CBS, Polygram

House is haunted, The.
Tracks: / House is haunted, The / Broken bracelet / Cara a cara / Unchain my heart / Burning boat.
Single (7"): released on Some Bizzare in Dec'85 by Charisma Records. Distributed by: EMI, CBS, Polygram

Single (12"): released on Some Bizzare in Dec'85 by Charisma Records. Distributed by: EMI, CBS, Polygram

Love letter.
Single (7"): released on Some Bizzare in Oct'85 by Charisma Records. Distributed by: EMI, CBS, Polygram

Single (12"): released on Some Bizzare in Oct'85 by Charisma Records. Distributed by: EMI, CBS, Polygram

Compact disc: released on Some Bizarre in Oct'85 by Virgin Records. Distributed by: EMI, CBS, Polygram

Mother fist.
Tracks: / Mother fist / Two sailors on a beach / Hustler, The.
Single (12"): released on Some Bizzare in Mar'87 by Charisma Records. Distributed by: EMI, CBS, Polygram

Other people's room.
Album: released on Horizon in Jan'79 by A&M Records. Distributed by: CBS

Ruby red.
Tracks: / Ruby red / I'm sick of your tasting of somebody else / Anarcoma / Broken hearted and beautiful / Jackal jackal.
Single (7"): released on Some Bizzare in Oct'86 by Charisma Records. Distributed by: EMI, CBS, Polygram

Single (12"): released on Some Bizzare in Oct'86 by Charisma Records. Distributed by: EMI, CBS, Polygram

Stories of Johnny.
Tracks: / Traumas, traumas, traumas / Stories of Johnny / The house is haunted / Love letters / The flesh is willing / Always / Contempt / I who never / My candle burns / Love and little white lies.
Musicassette: released on Some Bizarre in Oct'85 by Virgin Records. Distributed by: EMI, CBS, Polygram

Album: released on Some Bizarre in Oct'85 by Virgin Records. Distributed by: EMI, CBS, Polygram

Single (7"): released on Some Bizzare in Aug'85 by Charisma Records. Distributed by: EMI, CBS, Polygram

Single (12"): released on Some Bizzare in Aug'85 by Charisma Records. Distributed by: EMI, CBS, Polygram

Vermine in ermine.
Tracks: / Shining sinners / Hell was a city / You have / Crime sublime / Gutter hearts / Ugly head / The boy who came back / Solo adultos / Tenderness is a weakness.
Notes: 9 new Marc Almond songs
Compact disc: by Charisma Records. Distributed by: EMI, CBS, Polygram

Album: released on Some Bizarre in Oct'84 by Virgin Records. Distributed by: EMI, CBS, Polygram Deleted Jun'87.

Musicassette: released on Some Bizarre in Oct'84 by Virgin Records. Distributed by: EMI, CBS, Polygram Deleted Jun'87.

Woman's story, A.
Tracks: / Woman's story, A / For one moment / Some songs to take to the tomb.
Single (7"): released on Some Bizzare in May'86 by Charisma Records. Distributed by: EMI, CBS, Polygram

Single (12"): released on Some Bizzare in May'86 by Charisma Records. Distributed by: EMI, CBS, Polygram

Single (cassette): released on Some Bizzare in May'86 by Charisma Records. Distributed by: EMI, CBS, Polygram

Almost Brothers

Almost Brothers.
Extended-play record: released on Rat Race in Oct'82

Bum's rush.
Single (7"): released on Rat Race in Jan'82

Almost Summer

Almost summer Original soundtrack.
Album: released on MCA in Jun'78 by MCA Records. Distributed by: Polygram, MCA

Musicassette: released on MCA in Jun'78 by MCA Records. Distributed by: Polygram, MCA

Almost There

Almost there A collection of British no.2 hits (Various Artists).
Tracks: / Little arrows / Ride a white swan / Jeepster / Rocket man / My coo ca choo / Come back my love / Boy from New York City / It's raining / Love is a many splendoured thing / Tear fell, A / Tammy / Baby face / I'm gonna be strong / Heartful of soul / Wild thing / Night of fear / Nobody needs your love / I can't control myself / Flowers in the rain.
Notes: Compiled by John Howard.It has been siad that those records that reached no.2 in the charts were often better than those which held them off the top spot.There are many no.1 collections but poor old no.2 tends to be forgotten. This album is a tribute to those smash hits which didn't quite make it. Dating from 1955-1978, it covers nearly 25 years of the hits that were 'Almost there - but not quite'
Double Album: released on Cambra in Sep'86 by Cambra Records. Distributed by: IDS, Conifer

Double musicassette: released on Cambra in Sep'86 by Cambra Records. Distributed by: IDS, Conifer

Alone again

Dream come true (Alone Again Or).
Single (7"): released on Polydor in Mar'85 by Polydor Records. Distributed by: Polygram, Polydor

Drum the beat.
Single (7"): released on All One in Dec'84

Aloopa

Aloopa (Devon childrens' rhyme games).
Musicassette: released on Folktracks in Nov'79 by Folktracks Cassettes. Distributed by: Folktracks

Alper, Greg

Fat doggie (Alper, Greg Band).
Album: released on Adelphi(USA) in May'81 by Adelphi Records (USA). Distributed by: Projection, Swift

Alpert, Herb

Blow your own horn.
Tracks: / Red hot / True confessions / Blow your

own horn / Gently / The midnight tango / Garden party / Paradise cove / Latin lady / Oriental eyes / Shundown.
Notes: "Blow your own horn" the follow up release to "Fandango", is an album of many flavours renowned Latin producer Jose Quintana co-producer "Latin lady, "Oriental eyes" and "Sundown" whilst Motown's legendary Holland-Dozier-Holland wrote and co-produced two tracks including the title cut. The album was re-mixed by Bruce Swedien, who worked on Michael Jackon's "Thriller". It features Herb Alpert's version of Mezzaforte's "Garden Party".

Blow your own horn.
Album: released on A&M in Sep'83 by A&M Records. Distributed by: Polygram

Musicassette: released on A&M in Sep'83 by A&M Records. Distributed by: Polygram

Compact disc: released on A&M in Jun'84 by A&M Records. Distributed by: Polygram

Bullish.
Tracks: / Bullish / Always have a dream / Make a wish / Maniac / Struttin on five / Love without words / Passion play / Life is my song.
Notes: Herb Alpert has set records in his field which continue to endure. At one point in his career with the Tijuana Brass, five of their albums were ranked in the U.S top 20 - a feat never to have been equalled. He has achieved sales 73 million records, and represents one of the most outstanding musical sucess stories of all time. The new album "Bullish" marks the reunion or Herb Alpert and the Tijuana Brass, and features an electrifying blend of synthesisers and accoustic sounds, plus of course, the outfit's unmistakeable brass sound.
Album: released on A&M in Sep'84 by A&M Records. Distributed by: Polygram

Musicassette: released on A&M in Sep'84 by A&M Records. Distributed by: Polygram

Closer you get.
Tracks: / Closer you get / Lady down on love / She put the sad in all his songs / Red river / What in the name of love / Dixieland delight / Alabama sky / Very special love / Dixie boy / Lovin' man.
Album: by RCA Records. Distributed by: RCA, Roots, Swift, Wellard, Chris, I & B, Solomon & Peres Distribution

Musicassette: by RCA Records. Distributed by: RCA, Roots, Swift, Wellard, Chris, I & B, Solomon & Peres Distribution

Diamonds.
Tracks: / Diamonds / Rocket to the moon.
Single (7"): released on Breakout in May'87 by A&M Records. Distributed by: Polygram
Cat.no ....USA 605
Single (12"): released on Breakout in May'87 by A&M Records. Distributed by: Polygram
Cat.no ....USAT 605
Single (cassette): released on Breakout in May'87 by A&M Records. Distributed by: Polygram

Diamonds (cool summer mix).
Tracks: / Diamonds (cool summer mix) / Diamonds (12" dance mix) / Rocket to the moon.
Single (12"): released on Breakout in 6 Jun'87 by A&M Records. Distributed by: Polygram

Fandango.
Tracks: / Fandango / Margarita / Push and pull / California blues / Quiereme tal como soy (Love me the way I am) / Route 101 / Coco loco (La grajira) / Aria / Angel / Sugarloaf / Latin medley (frenesai) / Bahia / Moliando cafe (El porompompero.
Notes: Herb celebrates 20 years of hit recordinf with a contemporary sounding re-visit to his latin to his latin influenced origins. Marvellous, joyous music that showcases a man whose talent transcends time.
Album: released on A&M in Jun'82 by A&M Records. Distributed by: Polygram

Musicassette: released on A&M in Jun'82 by A&M Records. Distributed by: Polygram

Greatest hits: Herb Alpert (Alpert, Herb / Tijuana Brass).
Tracks: / Lonely bull / Spanish flea / My favourite things / If I were a rich man / Up cherry street / Marjorine / Wade in the water / Cabaret / Taste of honey / Tijuana taxi / Hello Dolly / A banda / Lollipops and roses / So whats new / Zorba the Greek.
Album: released on Pickwick (A&M) in May'84

Musicassette: released on Pickwick (A&M) in May'84

Greatest hits:Herb Alpert (Alpert, Herb / Tijuana Brass).
Album: released on A&M in Mar'82 by A&M Records. Distributed by: Polygram

Musicassette: released on A&M in Mar'82 by A&M Records. Distributed by: Polygram

Album: released on Pickwick in May'84 by Pickwick Records. Distributed by: Pickwick Distribution, Prism Leisure Distribution, Lugtons

Musicassette: released on Pickwick in May'84 by Pickwick Records. Distributed by: Pickwick Distribution, Prism Leisure Distribution, Lugtons

Keep your eye on me.
Tracks: / Keep your eye on me / Our song / Hot shot / Pillow / Diamonds / Stranger on the shore / Traffic jam / Rocket to the moon / Making love in the rain.
Album: released on A&M in Mar'87 by A&M Records. Distributed by: Polygram

Musicassette: released on A&M in Mar'87 by A&M Records. Distributed by: Polygram

Compact disc: released on A&M in Mar'87 by A&M Records. Distributed by: Polygram

Single (7"): released on A&M in Mar'87 by A&M Records. Distributed by: Polygram

Single (12"): released on A&M in Mar'87 by A&M Records. Distributed by: Polygram

Making love in the rain.
Single (7"): released on Breakout in Aug'87 by A&M Records. Distributed by: Polygram

Single (12"): released on Breakout in Aug'87 by A&M Records. Distributed by: Polygram

Rise.
Tracks: / 1980 / Rise / Behind the rain / Rotations / Street life / Love is / Angelina / Aranjuez (mon amour).
Compact disc: released on A&M in Apr'84 by A&M Records. Distributed by: Polygram

Album: released on Hallmark in Feb'85 by Pickwick Records. Distributed by: Pickwick Distribution, PRT, Taylors

Musicassette: released on Hallmark in Feb'85 by Pickwick Records. Distributed by: Pickwick Distribution, PRT, Taylors

Rise (single).
Single (7"): released on Old Gold in Sep'85 by Old Gold Records. Distributed by: Lightning, Jazz Music, Spartan, Counterpoint

Wild Romance.
Tracks: / "8" ball / You are the one / Lady love / It's all for you / Catch me / African flame / Dancin in the light / No time for time.
Notes: Ever since the release of The Lonely Bull in the early 60's, Herb Alpert has continued to break musical ground as a trumpeter, producer, songwriter and recording artists selling literally millions of records in the process. Wild Romance is Alpert's latest A & M album, on which he has featured as a producer, a co-producer and a performer. His principal collaborators on this superbly contemporary album include bassist/co-producer Romeo Williams and keyboard player John Barnes (who co-produced Alpert's last album Bullish). The album features a strong rhythmic foundation, with emphasis on bass and a spectrum on computerised drum sounds, plus a very distinctive rock jazz flavour.
Compact disc: by A&M Records. Distributed by: Polygram

Wild romance.
Album: released on A&M in Aug'85 by A&M Records. Distributed by: Polygram

Musicassette: released on A&M in Aug'85 by A&M Records. Distributed by: Polygram

Alpha

Blondy-rasta poue.
Single (12"): released on Syllart in Mar'85 by Earthworks Records. Distributed by: Earthworks Distributors

We keep on rocking.
Single (12"): released on Ambassador in Mar'82 by Ambassador Records. Distributed by: Pinnacle, Jetstar

Alphaville

Afternoons in Utopia.
Tracks: / I A O / Fantastic dream / Jerusalem / Dance with me / Afternoons in Utopia / Sensations / 20th century / Voyager, The / Carol Masters / Universal daddy / Lassie come home / Red rose / Lady bright.
Album: released on WEA in Jul'86 by WEA Records. Distributed by: WEA

Musicassette: released on WEA in Jul'86 by WEA Records. Distributed by: WEA

Compact disc: released on WEA in Aug'86 by WEA Records. Distributed by: WEA

Big in Japan.
Single (7"): released on WEA International in May'84 by WEA Records. Distributed by: WEA

Single (12"): released on WEA International in May'84 by WEA Records. Distributed by: WEA

Dance with me.
Single (7"): released on WEA in Apr'86 by WEA Records. Distributed by: WEA

Single (12"): released on WEA in Apr'86 by WEA Records. Distributed by: WEA

Forever young.
Tracks: / Victory of love / Summer in Berlin / Big in Japan / To Germany with love / Fallen angel / Forever young / In the mood / Sounds like a melody / Jet set, The / Lies.
Compact disc: released on WEA in Feb'85 by WEA Records. Distributed by: WEA

Album: released on WEA in Nov'84 by WEA Records. Distributed by: WEA

Musicassette: released on WEA in Nov'84 by WEA Records. Distributed by: WEA

Forever young (single).
Single (7"): released on WEA in Oct'84 by WEA Records. Distributed by: WEA

Single (12"): released on WEA in Oct'84 by WEA Records. Distributed by: WEA

Next generation.
Single (7"): released on WEA in Nov'86 by WEA Records. Distributed by: WEA

Single (12"): released on WEA in Nov'86 by WEA Records. Distributed by: WEA

Universal daddy.
Tracks: / Universal daddy / Next generation.
Single (7"): released on WEA in Nov'86 by WEA Records. Distributed by: WEA

Single (12"): released on WEA in Nov'86 by WEA Records. Distributed by: WEA

Alphonso, Rolando

Roll on.
Album: released on Wackies in Jul'85 by Wackies Records. Distributed by: Jetstar

Alpine

Georgetown girl.
Single (7"): released on Hive in Sep'85. Distributed by: PRT

Single (12"): released on Hive in Sep'85. Distributed by: PRT

Alston

Try again.
Single (7"): released on Sonet in Apr'85 by Sonet Records. Distributed by: PRT

Alston, Frank

Superlover.
Single (12"): released on Move in Aug'86 by Charly Records. Distributed by: Charly Distribution, Fast Forward Distribution, Cartel Distribution

Altar Boys

Be bop a lula.
Single (7"): released on Sundance in Nov'82 by Sundance Records. Distributed by: PRT Distribution

You really got me.
Single (7"): released on Sundance in May'83 by Sundance Records. Distributed by: PRT Distribution

Altar Ego

War.
Single (7"): released on Round World Discs in Sep'86. Distributed by: DMS-RCA

Altena, Maarten

Miere (Altena, Maarten Quartet).
Tracks: / Monks measure / London 72 / Something / Miere / Amsterdam 83 / Ciao.
Album: released on Nato (France) in Sep'86 by Disques Nato. Distributed by: Essex Record Distributors Ltd.

Alterations

My favourite animals.
Tracks: / Sleeping beauty / Segue to my heart / Adios half cow-boy / Up in the paint cards / Ca n'est pas mon chat / Thru and thru / Cat's whiskers / Calamity Joan / Emus in the zone / Nopan kissa / Horse with no hooves, A / Hank's pantry / Old coffity pot, The / Burning rosebush, The / Yes, sir.
Notes: With: Steve Beresford/Peter Cusack/Terry Day/David Toop.

Album: released on Nato (France) in Sep'86 by Disques Nato. Distributed by: Essex Record Distributors Ltd.

Single (7"): released on Beat-The-System in Nov'83 by Lightbeat Records. Distributed by: Pinnacle

Altered Images

Bring me closer.
Single (7"): released on Epic in May'83 by CBS Records. Distributed by: CBS

Single (12"): released on Epic in May'83 by CBS Records. Distributed by: CBS

Picture disc single: released on Epic in Jun'83 by CBS Records. Distributed by: CBS

Picture disc single: released on Epic in Jun'83 by CBS Records. Distributed by: CBS

Collected images.
Album: released on Epic in May'84 by CBS Records. Distributed by: CBS

Album: released on Epic in May'84 by CBS Records. Distributed by: CBS

Greatest original hits.
Extended-play record: released on Epic in Mar'83 by CBS Records. Distributed by: CBS

Happy birthday.
Tracks: / Happy birthday / I could be happy.

I could be happy.
Single (7"): released on Old Gold in Jan'87 by Old Gold Records. Distributed by: Lightning, Jazz Music, Spartan, Counterpoint

Alternative

If they treat you.....

Alternative Cabaret

Alternative cabaret.
Album: released on Original in Oct'81. Distributed by: RCA Distribution, Jazz Music Distribution, PRT Distribution

Musicassette: released on Original in Oct'81. Distributed by: RCA Distribution, Jazz Music Distribution, PRT Distribution

Alternative Radio

First night (LP).
Album: released on Cold Harbour in Mar'87. Distributed by: Pinnacle, Probe Plus Distribution, Cartel, M.I.S., EMI, DMS, RCA, Ariola

Musicassette: released on Cold Harbour in Mar'87. Distributed by: Pinnacle, Probe Plus Distribution, Cartel, M.I.S., EMI, DMS, RCA, Ariola

First night (Single).
Tracks: / First night / Emotional disaster.
Single (7"): released on Cold Harbour in May'86. Distributed by: Pinnacle, Probe Plus Distribution, Cartel, M.I.S., EMI, DMS, RCA, Ariola

Strangers in love.
Tracks: / Strangers in love / Summer '85.
Single (7"): released on Towerbell in Jul'86 by Towerbell Records. Distributed by: EMI

Valley of evergreen.
Tracks: / What a dream / Valley of evergreen / Summer 85.
Single (7"): released on Cold Harbour in Jan'87. Distributed by: Pinnacle, Probe Plus Distribution, Cartel, M.I.S., EMI, DMS, RCA, Ariola

Single (12"): released on Cold Harbour in Jan'87. Distributed by: Pinnacle, Probe Plus Distribution, Cartel, M.I.S., EMI, DMS, RCA, Ariola

Alternatives To Marriage

Alternatives to marriage Rogers, Carol (Rogers, Carol).
Musicassette: released on Psychology in Oct'81

Alternative TV

Image has cracked, (The).
Album: released on Deptford Fun City in Jan'79 by Faulty Products Records. Distributed by: Faulty Products Records, Pinnacle

Love & sex.
Single (12"): released on Noiseville in Jun'86. Distributed by: Rough Trade, Cartel

My baby's laughing.

Single (7"): released on Anagram in Aug'87 in Cherry Red Records. Distributed by: Pinnacle

Strange kicks.
Album: released on IRS in Jul'81. Distributed by: Polygram

Vibing up the Senile man (Part 1).
Album: released on Deptford Fun City in Jan'79 by Faulty Products Records. Distributed by: Faulty Products Records, Pinnacle

Welcome to the end of fun.
Single (12"): released on Noiseville in Mar'86. Distributed by: Rough Trade, Cartel

What you see is what you are.
Album: released on Deptford Fun City in Jan'79 by Faulty Products Records. Distributed by: Faulty Products Records, Pinnacle

Althia and Donna

Uptown top ranking.
Single (7"): released on Lightning in Jan'78 by Lightning Records. Distributed by: Jetstar

Altman, Laurie

For now at least (Altman, Laurie Quintet).
Tracks: / Song for Charles Mingus / Often enough / Lonely woman(Elusive form) / Song for Oliver / Pirate, The / Salut, Ma Femme / Colour me.
Notes: Artists: Laurie Altman/Mack Goldsbury/George Naha/Tom Marvel/Bill DiMartino. Recorded Dec.29th 1981
Album: released on Progressive in Dec'82 by Progressive Records. Distributed by: Jetstar

Altogether Now

Sing-Along Party Pack

Altogether now (sing-along party pack) Various Artists (Various Artists).
Album: released on Royal in Nov'82 by Royal Records. Distributed by: Stage One Distribution

Alton, Roy

Carnival disco.
Album: released on Tackle in Aug'78

Carnival in Ladbroke Grove.
Album: released on Tackle in Mar'78

Don't gamble with love.
Single (12"): released on Sunburn in Oct'83 by Orbitone Records. Distributed by: Jetstar Distribution

Don't stop the carnival.
Album: released on Tackle in Mar'78

Girl I love you.
Single (12"): released on Sunburn in Jul'83 by Orbitone Records. Distributed by: Jetstar Distribution

In the grove.
Album: released on Tackle in Feb'78

Iron lady.
Single (12"): released on Sunburst in May'82. Distributed by: Sunburst Records

My mistake.
Single (12"): released on Sunburn in Nov'83 by Orbitone Records. Distributed by: Jetstar Distribution

Stay alive.
Single (7"): released on Sunburn in Aug'85 by Orbitone Records. Distributed by: Jetstar Distribution

Tell them.
Single (12"): released on Sunburn in May'83 by Orbitone Records. Distributed by: Jetstar Distribution

We shall overcome.
Single (12"): released on Sunburn in Jan'85 by Orbitone Records. Distributed by: Jetstar Distribution

Album: released on President in Mar'85 by President Records. Distributed by: Taylors, Spartan

Altschul, Barry

Brahma (Altschul, Barry, Trio).
Album: released on Sackville in Apr'81. Dis-

---

tributed by: JSU, Jazz Music, Jazz Horizons, Cadillac Music, Celtic Music, Swift

You can't name your own tune.
Album: released on Muse in Apr'81 by Peerless Records. Distributed by: Lugtons Distributors

Alveoli

How many sugars.
Single (7"): released on Paladin in Jun'85 by Paladin Records. Distributed by: Rough Trade, Pinnacle

Single (12"): released on Paladin in Jun'85 by Paladin Records. Distributed by: Rough Trade, Pinnacle

Alvie

I'll go to (Alvie & The Alviettes).
Single (7"): released on 46 Records (Germany) in Aug'83 by 46 Records (Germany). Distributed by: Rough Trade

Alvim, Cesarius

Jean Pierre Mas & Cesarius Alvim (Alvim, Cesarius & Jean Pierre Mas).

Alvin, Dave

Every night about this time.
Tracks: / Every night about this time / Fourth of July / Long white cadillac / Romeo's escape / Brother (on the line) / Jubilee train / Border radio / Fire away / New tattoo / You got me / I wish it were saturday night.
Compact disc: released on Demon in Apr'87 by Demon Records. Distributed by: Pinnacle

Album: released on Demon in Apr'87 by Demon Records. Distributed by: Pinnacle

Musicassette: released on Demon in Apr'87 by Demon Records. Distributed by: Pinnacle

Fourth of July.
Tracks: / Fourth of July / You got me.
Single (7"): released on Demon in May'87 by Demon Records. Distributed by: Pinnacle

Alvin, Phil

Unsung stories.
Tracks: / Someone stole Gabriels horn / Next week sometime / Ballad of Smoky Joe, The / Death in the morning / Old man of the mountain, The / Daddy rollin' stone / Titanic blues / Brother can you spare a dime / Collins cave / Gangsters blues.
Notes: Phil Alvin is best known for his work as lead vocalist with the Slash band The Blasters, who have built up a small UK following. This solo album is very jazz influenced and features Sun Ra & The Arkestra as well as The Dirty Dozen Brass Band
Album: released on Slash in Sep'86 by London Records. Distributed by: Polygram

Always

Ariel atlas.
Tracks: / Dreams of leaving / Morning heights / Heavens / Flying display, The.
Single (12"): released on EL in Oct'86 by EL Records. Distributed by: Rough Trade, Cartel, Pinnacle

Metroland.
Tracks: / Metroland / Arcade (The) / W.C..
Single (12"): released on EL in Mar'87 by EL Records. Distributed by: Rough Trade, Cartel, Pinnacle

Always August

Black pyramid.
Album: released on SST in Aug'87 by SST Records. Distributed by: Pinnacle. Estim retail price in Sep'87 was £6.49.

Always & Forever

Always and forever Various Artists (Various Artists).
Tracks: / Still / Lovely day / Heartbreaker / If you don't know me by now / You make me feel brand new / You'll never find another love like mine / Touch me in the morning / Three times a lady / Jack & Jill / Me and Mrs. Jones / Tears on my pillow (I can't take it) / How 'bout us / Always and forever / Theme from mahogany (do you know where you're going to).
Album: released on Impression in Aug'84. Distributed by: CBS

Musicassette: released on Impression in Aug'84. Distributed by: CBS

Always Rockin'

Always rockin' Various Artists (Various Artists).
Album: released on White Label (Holland) in

Feb'85. Distributed by: CSA, PRT

Always The Now

From dawn till dusk.
Single (7"): released on Mayday in Jun'83. Distributed by: Rough Trade

Aly

Kiss in the dark.
Single (7"): released on Raffia in Nov'82. Distributed by: Spartan

You were my everything.
Single (7"): released on Raffia in Nov'82. Distributed by: Spartan

Amadeus

Amadeus Original Soundtrack.
Double compact disc: released on London in Jan'85 by London Records. Distributed by: Polygram

Amadeus Original motion picture soundtrack (Various Artists).
Double Album: released on London in Feb'85 by London Records. Distributed by: Polygram

Double musicassette: released on London in Feb'85 by London Records. Distributed by: Polygram

Compact disc: released on London in Feb'85 by London Records. Distributed by: Polygram

Amalgam

Innovation.
Album: released on Tangent in Apr'81. Distributed by: Roots Distribution, Lugtons Distributors, Taylors, JSU Distribution, Spartan Distribution

Amanda

Cry out in the night.
Tracks: / Cry out in the night.
Single (12"): released on Rise in Aug'87 by Steve O'Donnell/Colin Jennings. Distributed by: Pinnacle

Amara, Adrian

Diamonds.
Single (7"): released on Diamonds in Aug'84 by President Records. Distributed by: H.R. Taylor

Amarcord Nino Rota

Amarcord Nino Rota Fellini film themes (Bley, Carla/Byard/Carter/Marsalis/Lacy etc).
Notes: Other info. Fellini film interpreted by a variety artiste.
Album: released on Hannibal in Jan'87 by Hannibal Records. Distributed by: Charly, Harmonia Mundi, Projection, Celtic Music, Roots

Amaro, Eugene

Owl, The (Amaro, Eugene Quartet).
Album: released on Innovation (Canada) in Sep'84. Distributed by: Mole Jazz

Amazing Bavarian Stompers

Liberty bell/Colonel Bogey.
Single (7"): released on Penthouse in Dec'81 by Penthouse Records. Distributed by: Pinnacle

Amazing Grace

Amazing Grace Various artists (Various Artists).
Album: released on K-Tel (Era) in Jun'83 by K-Tel Records. Distributed by: K-Tel

Musicassette: released on K-Tel (Era) in Jun'83 by K-Tel Records. Distributed by: K-Tel

Amazing Grace Original version (Various Artists).
Musicassette: released on RCA/Camden in Jan'79

Amazing Grace (see Dessau, Joanna).

Amazing Monsters

Amazing monsters Jim Slater- Read by Martin Jarvis (Martin Jarvis).
Musicassette: released on MacMillan in Oct'81

Amazing Noel Bon Band

Grandma got run over by a reindeer/Lonely.

Single (7"): released on A2B in Nov'83 by A2B. Distributed by: Spartan

Amazulu

All over the world.
Tracks: / All over the world / Moonlight romance (dub) / After tonight.
Single (7"): released on Island in Nov'86 by Island Records. Distributed by: Polygram

Single (12"): released on Island in Nov'86 by Island Records. Distributed by: Polygram

Amazulu.
Tracks: / Too good to be forgotten / Excitable / After tonight / All over the world / Things the lonely do, The / Montego Bay / Don't you just know it / Cairo / Moonlight romance / Upright forward.

Cairo.
Single (7"): released on Towerbell in Feb'83 by Towerbell Records. Distributed by: EMI

Single (12"): released on Towerbell in Feb'83 by Towerbell Records. Distributed by: EMI

Don't you just know it.
Single (7"): released on Island in Nov'85 by Island Records. Distributed by: Polygram

Single (12"): released on Island in Nov'85 by Island Records. Distributed by: Polygram Deleted Jun'87.

Excitable.
Single (7"): released on Island in Aug'85 by Island Records. Distributed by: Polygram Deleted Jun'87.

Picture disc single: released on Island in Aug'85 by Island Records. Distributed by: Polygram Deleted Jun'87.

Single (12"): released on Island in Aug'85 by Island Records. Distributed by: Polygram Deleted Jun'87.

Single (12"): released on Island in Aug'85 by Island Records. Distributed by: Polygram Deleted Jun'87.

Montego bay.
Tracks: / Montego bay / Only love.
Single (7"): released on Island in Aug'86 by Island Records. Distributed by: Polygram

Single (12"): released on Island in Aug'86 by Island Records. Distributed by: Polygram

Moonlight romance.
Single (7"): released on Island in Oct'84 by Island Records. Distributed by: Polygram Deleted Jun'87.

Single (12"): released on Island in Oct'84 by Island Records. Distributed by: Polygram Deleted Jun'87.

Smiley stylee.
Single (7"): released on Towerbell in Jul'83 by Towerbell Records. Distributed by: EMI

Things the lonely do, The.
Tracks: / Things the lonely do / Sez who.
Single (7"): released on Island in Mar'86 by Island Records. Distributed by: Polygram

Picture disc single: released on Island in Mar'86 by Island Records. Distributed by: Polygram

Single (12"): released on Island in Mar'86 by Island Records. Distributed by: Polygram

Gatefold sleeve: released on Island in Mar'86 by Island Records. Distributed by: Polygram

To good to be forgotten.
Tracks: / Too good to be forgotten / Too good to be forgotten (megamix) / Too good to be forgotten (hitmix) / Sez who.
Picture disc single: released on Island in Jun'86 by Island Records. Distributed by: Polygram

Double-pack single: released on Island in Jun'86 by Island Records. Distributed by: Polygram

Ambassadeur International

Mandjou.
Album: released on Celluloid (France) in Jul'85 by Island. Distributed by: Polygram

Ambassador

Life's riddle.
Single (12"): released on Dubplate in Mar'85 by Dubplate Records. Distributed by: Jetstar

Ambassadors Male Chorus

It is well with my soul.
Tracks: / Worthy is the lamb / It is well / Song & melody I bring / Purer in heart / Behold the wonderous love / Crown of thorns, A / I am so glad that Jesus loves me / Ring the bells of heaven / When I think / The saviour with me / Yes he did / Then the lord stood by me / This love is mine / He set me free.
Album: released on Word in May'82 by Word Records. Distributed by: Word Distribution, CBS

Musicassette: released on Word in May'82 by Word Records. Distributed by: Word Distribution, CBS

Ambatone

Party time.
Tracks: / Party time / Saxaphone party.
Single (12"): released on Firm in Aug'86 by Firm Records. Distributed by: Jetstar

Ambience

Miss you.
Tracks: / Miss you / Gone.
Single (7"): released on Mr. Sam in Aug'86

Amboy Dukes

Call of the & tooth fang (Amboy Dukes & Ted Nugent).

Ambrose

Ambrose and His Orchestra - 1929.
Album: released on Halcyon in Dec'82 by Halcyon Records. Distributed by: Jazz Music

Ambrose, Bert Orchestra

Ambrose 1928-1932.
Album: released on World in Jan'74. Distributed by: Jetstar

Ambrose & His Orchestra

Ambrose and His Orchestra.
Album: released on Monmouth in Mar'79

Ambrose & His Orchestra.
Notes: See under *British Dance Bands of the Forties*

Faithfully yours.
Tracks: / Please (8/11/32) / I'm just wearing out my heart for you (21/2/31) / Have a little faith in me (28/3/30) / If they ever had an income take on love (22/9/31) / Till tomorrow (22/11/32) / Livin' in the sunlight, lovin' in the moonlight (19/6/30) / For you, just you my baby (28/7/32) / Laughing at the rain (7/4/31) / Little girl (1/9/31) / Just like in a story book (24/4/30) / Loving you the way I do (15/1/31) / Humming to myself (17/6/32) / Kss by kiss (9/3/32) / Love, you funny thing (6/5/32) / I'm in the market for you (24/$/30) / What good am I without you (18/11/30) / One little raindrop (21/4/31) / Here lies love (8/11/32) / Faithfully yours (19/6/31) / Please / Wearing my heart out for you / I found you / Have a little faith in me / If ever they ever had a income tax on love / Til tomorrow / Livin in the sunlight / For you just you / Laughing at

the rain / Little girl / Just like in a story book / Loving you the way I do / Humming to myself / Kiss by kiss / Love you funny thing / I'm in the market for you / What good am I without you / One little raindrop here lies love / Faithfully yours.
Album: released on Saville in '86 by Conifer Records. Distributed by: Conifer

Musicassette: released on Saville in '86 by Conifer Records. Distributed by: Conifer

Golden age of Ambrose and His Orchestra (The).
Tracks: / I don't know why (I just do) / Dancin in the dark / Soft lights and sweet music / When yuba plays the rumba on the tuba / Isn't it romantic / Pu-leeze mister Hemmingway / Too

many tears / Lets put out the lights / Leven thirsty Saturday night / Cryin for the Carolines / The free and easy / Stardust / Blue again / Bye bye blues / Yes yes(my baby says yes) / Whistling in the dark.
Notes: 16 great tracks from the man who went to become a great impresario, furthering the career of Kathy Kirby in the later years of his life. Recorded during his heyday in the late 20's and early 30's at the Ritzy nite spot in London this LP contains amongst other, "Stardust", "Dancin in the dark", "Isn't it romantic", and his theme tune "Leven thirty Saturday night". While reading the interesting sleeve note, take a listen to "Let's put out the lights" Surely a risky for 1932?
Album: released on Golden Age in Apr'85 by Music For Pleasure Records. Distributed by: EMI

Musicassette: released on Golden Age in Apr'85 by Music For Pleasure Records. Distributed by: EMI

Happy days.
Musicassette: released on Saville in Jan'86 by Conifer Records. Distributed by: Conifer

Happy days (1929-30).
Album: released on Saville in Jun'82 by Conifer Records. Distributed by: Conifer

Heart & soul.
Tracks: / Stormy weather / There's a cabin in the pines / You've got me cryin' again / Punch and Judy show, The / Lazybones / I can't remember / Body and soul / Goodnight but not goodbye / Cupid / It's the talk of the town / Stay as sweet as you are / Last round-up, The / College rhythm / Willow weep for me / I couldn't be mean to you / Who's been polishing the sun.
Album: released on Conifer in Jan'86 by Conifer Records. Distributed by: Conifer

Musicassette: released on Conifer in Jan'86 by Conifer Records. Distributed by: Conifer

Hits of 1931.
Album: released on World (Retrospect Series) in Feb'84

Musicassette: released on World (Retrospect Series) in Feb'84

I only have eyes for you.
Tracks: / It's an old southern custom / According to the moonlight / Top hat, white tie and tails / Isn't this a lovely day / How could we be wrong / Because it's love / Tick tock town / Stars fell on Alabama / I travel alone / Lost in a fog / I only have eyes for you / Dames / Winter wonderland / If I had a million dollars / If I love again / London on a rainy night / Maracas / Copenhagen.
Notes: Personnels: (a) Bert Ambrose directing Max Goldberg and Harry Owen (trumpets); Ted Heath and Tony Thrpe (trombones; Danny Polo (clarinet, alto and baritone saxs); Sid Phillips (clarinet, alto and baritone saxs and arranger);Joe Jeannette(alto saxs and flute); Billy Amstell (clarinet and tenor sax); Ernie Lewis and Reg Pursglove, sometimes others (violins when used); Bert Read (Piano and arranger); Joe Brannely (guitar); Dick Ball (string bass); Max Bacon (drums, maracas etc). London 2 / 1 1 / 3 3 (b) As for (a) London 8/3/34. (c) As for (a) but Bert Barnes (piano and arranger) replaces Read. London 12/6/34. (d) as for (c) London 24/10/34. (e) As for (d) London 25/10/34. (f) As for (c), plus Lew Davis (trombone) London 8/11/34. (g) As for (f) London 14/12/34. (h) As for (f) London 20/3/35. (i) As for (f) plus Tony Thorpe (trombone) London 30/3/35. (j) As for (i) London 9/9/35. (k) As for (i) London 10/10/35 Publishers: Chappell Music Ltd. Dash Music Co. Ltd, Campbell Connelly & Co., FDH, B Feldman & Co., Sterling Music Pub. Co., Darewski Music Pub. Co. , K Prowse. Produced and transferred by John Wadley. Sleeve design: John R. Bennett. Co-ordinator: Franke Greene. MONO
Album: released on Old Bean in Sep'86. Distributed by: Jazz Music

Musicassette: released on Old Bean in Sep'86. Distributed by: Jazz Music

Recollections.
Tracks: / If I didn't care / What do we care / I'm in love for the last time / Let there be love / You made me care / No mama no / Two sleepy people / The continental / I threw a kiss in the ocean / My own / I have eyes / Sympathy / How about you / Cinderella / Sweetheart / I got love

/ That lovely weekend / Scatter brain / An apple for the teacher.
Notes: Featuring Vera Lynn
: released on Decca in Jun'81 by Decca Records. Distributed by: Polygram

Soft light and sweet music.
Tracks: / I'll guess I'll have to change my plan / Moon / You brought a new kind of love to me / After tonight we say goodbye / You forgot your gloves / When mother played her organ / I don't want to go to bed / Let's all sing like the birdies sing / Lullaby of the leaves / I'm an unemployed sweetheart / I'm gonna get you / You rascal you / Trees / All of me / Aboard the lugger.
Album: released on Joy in Apr'83 by President Records. Distributed by: Jazz Music, Swift, President Distribution

S'Wonderful.
Album: released on Saville in Jan'87 by Conifer Records. Distributed by: Conifer

Musicassette: released on Saville in Jan'87 by Conifer Records. Distributed by: Conifer

Tribute to Cole Porter.
Tracks: / Night and day / I get a kick out of you / I've got my eyes on you / Thank you so much missus Lowsborough Goodbye / Begin the beguine / After you / Anything goes / I've got you on my mind / Easy to love / I've got you under my skin / Just one of those things / My heart belongs to daddy / You're the top / You'd be so nice to come home to.
Album: released on Jasmine in Mar'83 by Jasmine Records. Distributed by: Counterpoint, Lugtons, Taylor, H.R., Wellard, Chris, Swift, Cadillac

Ambrosetti, Franco

Close encounter.
Album: released on Enja (Germany) in Jan'82 by Enja Records (W.Germany). Distributed by: Cadillac Music

Heart bop.
Album: released on Enja (Germany) in Jan'82 by Enja Records (W.Germany). Distributed by: Cadillac Music

Wings.
Album: released on Enja (Germany) in Nov'84 by Enja Records (W.Germany). Distributed by: Cadillac Music

Ambrosia

How can you love me.
Picture disc single: released on Warner Bros in May'82 by Warner Bros Records. Distributed by: WEA

Amebix

Arise.
Album: released on Alternative Tentacles in Jul'85 by Alternative Tentacles Records. Distributed by: Rough Trade, Pinnacle

Enemy (The).
Single (7"): released on Spiderleg in Sep'82. Distributed by: Rough Trade

Monolith.
Tracks: / Monolith / Nobody's driving / Power remains, The / Time bomb / Last will and testament / I.C.B.M. / Chain reaction / Fallen from

grace / Coming home.
Album: released on Heavy Metal in Aug'87 by FM-Revolver Records. Distributed by: EMI Estim retail price in Sep'87 was £6.29.

No sanctuary.
Album: released on Spiderleg in Oct'83. Distributed by: Rough Trade

Winter.
Single (7"): released on Spiderleg in Feb'83. Distributed by: Rough Trade

Ameling, Elly

After hours (classic 20th century popular songs).
Tracks: / Embraceable you / I got rhythm / With a song in my heart / Man I love / Body and soul / My cousin in Milwaukee.
Album: released on Philips in Jan'83. Distributed by: IMS-Polygram

Musicassette: released on Philips in Jan'83. Distributed by: IMS-Polygram

Sentimental me.
Tracks: / I get a kick out of you / Night and day / All the things you are / Begin the Beguine / In a sentimental mood / Can that boy foxtrot / But not for me / You do something for me.
Compact disc: released on Philips in Nov'85. Distributed by: IMS-Polygram

America

Biographical Details: America were formed in 1971, all three members having been based with their parents at a US Air Force base in Britain. Their acoustic soft rock sound, a direct imitation of the then red-hot Crosby, Stills & Nash, was an instant success. 'A Horse With No Name' went to no.1 in the US and no.3 in the UK in 1972. Their self-titled debut LP also sold well. It featured all three writing, singing and playing guitar. Thereafter America's following shrank into a small hard core in Britain, but they continued to be strong sellers in their native land. 'I need you', 'Tin Man' and 'Lonely People' were all top 10 singles and albums such as 'Hat Trick' and 'Hearts' made them firm favourites amongest the easy rock fraternity. 1975 saw them score a second US no.1 single, 'Sister Golden Hair'. In 1977 Dan Peek departed and America sank into oblivion. They bounced back five years later as a duo, achieving a new Stateside top ten single, 'You Can Do Magic', composed by Russ Ballard.(BM 84)

Alibi.
Album: released on EMI (Germany) in Aug'83 by EMI Records. Distributed by: Conifer

America.
Tracks: / Riverside / Sandman / Three roses / Children / Here / I need you / Rainy day / Never found the time / Clarice / Donkey jaw / Pigeon song.
Album: by Warner Bros Records. Distributed by: WEA

America live.
Musicassette: released on Warner Brothers in Jan'78 by Warner Bros Records. Distributed by: WEA

American blues legends Various artists (Various Artists).
Album: released on Big Bear in '74 by Big Bear Records. Distributed by: Big Bear, Swift

American samoa (American Samoa Arts Choir).
Album: released on Viking in Nov'77. Distributed by: Harmonia Mundi Distributors

Border/Sometimes lovers.
Single (7"): released on Capitol in Jul'83 by Capitol Records. Distributed by: EMI

Border, The/ Sometimes lovers.
Single (7"): released on Capitol in Jul'83 by Capitol Records. Distributed by: EMI

Harbor.
Musicassette: released on Warner Brothers in Mar'77 by Warner Bros Records. Distributed by: WEA

Hat trick.
Tracks: / Muskrat love / Wind wave / She's gonna let you down / Rainbow song / Submarine ladies / It's life / Hat trick / Molten love / Green monkey / Willow tree lullaby / Goodbye.
Album: released on Warner Brothers in '73 by Warner Bros Records. Distributed by: WEA

Hdeaway.
Album: released on Warner Brothers in Apr'76 by Warner Bros Records. Distributed by: WEA

Hideaway.
Tracks: / Lovely night / Amber cascades / Don't let it get you down / Can't see you / Watership down / She's beside you / Hideaway part 1 / She's a liar / Letter / Today's the day / Jet boy blue / Who loves you / Hideaway part 2.
Album: released on Warner Brothers in Apr'76 by Warner Bros Records. Distributed by: WEA

History-America's greatest hits.
Album: released on Warner Brothers in '75 by Warner Bros Records. Distributed by: WEA

Musicassette: released on Warner Brothers in '75 by Warner Bros Records. Distributed by: WEA

History- America's Greatest Hits.
Tracks: / Horse with no name, (A) / I need you Sandman / Ventura highway / Don't cross the river / Only in your heart / Muskrat love / Tin man / Lonely people / Sister golden hair / Daisy Jane / Woman tonight.
Compact disc: released on Warner Bros. in Jan'87 by Warner Bros Records. Distributed by: WEA

Horse with no name, A.
Single (7"): released on Old Gold in Sep'85 by Old Gold Records. Distributed by: Lightning, Jazz Music, Spartan, Counterpoint

Live in Central Park.
Video-cassette (VHS): released on PMI in Jun'86 by PMI Records. Distributed by: EMI

Video-cassette [Betamax]: released on PMI in Jun'86 by PMI Records. Distributed by: EMI

Silent letter, (The).
Tracks: / Only game in town / All around / Tall

treasures / 1960 / And forever / Foolin' / All night / No fortune / All my life / One morning / HiHgHh in the city.
Album: released on Fame (Capitol) in Nov'83 by Music For Pleasure Records. Distributed by: EMI

Musicassette: released on Fame (Capitol) in Nov'83 by Music For Pleasure Records. Distributed by: EMI

View from the ground.
Tracks: / You can do magic / Never be lonely / You girl / Inspector Mills / Love on the vine / Desperate love / Right before your eyes / Jody / Sometimes lovers / Even the score.
Album: released on Capitol in Nov'82 by Capitol Records. Distributed by: EMI

Musicassette: released on Capitol in Nov'82 by Capitol Records. Distributed bv: EMI

American All Stars

American All Stars with Keith Smith 1966.
Album: released on Hefty Jazz in Apr'79. Distributed by: JSU, Swift, Wellard, Chris, Jazz Music, Cadillac Music

American Anthem

American Anthem Original Soundtrack.

Tracks: / Two hearts / Run to her / Same direction / Battle of the dragon / Wings to fly / Take it easy / Wings of love / Love and lonliness / Angel eyes / Arthur's theme.
Album: released on Atlantic in Aug'86 by WEA Records. Distributed by: WEA

Musicassette: released on Atlantic in Aug'86 by WEA Records. Distributed by: WEA

Compact disc: by WEA Records. Distributed by: WEA

American Authentic...

American authentic square dances Various artist (Various Artists).
Album: released on Melodisc in Jan'80 by Spartan Records. Distributed by: Spartan Distribution

American Blues...

American Blues Legends 79 Various artists (Various Artists).
Tracks: / Love with you baby / Look what you done / High rise blues / 480 pounds / I wish I had somebody / I'm goin' home where women got meat on their bones / Buzzard luck / Conjured / Don't throw your love on me so strong / All your love / I'm tryin' / No peace.
Album: released on Big Bear in '82 by Big Bear Records. Distributed by: Big Bear, Swift

American blues legends 75 Various artists (Various Artists).
Album: released on Big Bear in Apr'75 by Big Bear Records. Distributed by: Big Bear, Swift

Doin' their thing.
Album: released on See For Miles in Jul'87 by See For Miles Records. Distributed by: Pinnacle

American Buzz

Queen of illusion.
Single (7"): released on Plaza in Jul'84 by Plaza Records. Distributed by: Spartan

Single (12"): released on Plaza in Jul'84 by Plaza Records. Distributed by: Spartan

American Dance Band

Sweet sweet music/Get it on.
Single (7"): released on DJM in May'83 by DJM Records. Distributed by: CBS, Polygram

Single (12"): released on DJM in May'83 by DJM Records. Distributed by: CBS, Polygram

American Dances

American dances Various artists (Various Artists).
Album: released on Unidisc (France) in May'85. Distributed by: Discovery

American Dream

American Dream Various artists (Various Artists).
Album: released on Pickwick in Sep'80 by Pickwick Records. Distributed by: Pickwick Distribution, Prism Leisure Distribution, Lugtons

American Dreams

American dreams Various artists (Various Artists).
Notes: Featuring Iron Butterfly, Gary Pucket, Del Shannon, The Chrystals, The Coasters etc.
Compact disc: released on Delta in Apr'87 by Delta Records. Distributed by: Target

American Dreams Various artists (Various Artists).
Tracks: / Song for America / Joker, (The) / Read 'em & weep / Born to be wild / Stage fright / Keep on loving you / Do you believe in love / Foolish heart / She's not there / White rabbit / More than a feeling / Heart like a wheel / Even the nights are better / We belong / I can't hold back / American Woman / Don't stop believing / She's gone / Sylvia's mother / Trouble / Missing you / Rosana / Because the night / Miracles / Nobody but you / Freebird / Feels so right / Here comes that feeling.
Double Album: released on Starblend in Jun'85 by Starblend Records. Distributed by: PRT Distribution

Double musicassette: released on Starblend in Jun'85 by Starblend Records. Distributed by: PRT Distribution

American Fade

I'm alive.
Single (7"): released on Proto in Mar'83 by Proto Records. Distributed by: WEA

Single (12"): released on Proto in Feb'83 by Proto Records. Distributed by: WEA

American Festival...

American Festival folk blues Various artists (Various Artists).
Double Album: released on Musidisc (France) in Jun'84. Distributed by: Discovery Distribution, Swift Distribution

American Flyer

American Flyer.
Album: released on United Artists in Sep'76

American Folk Blues..

American folk blues festival '66 (Various Artists).
Notes: Artists include: Otis Rush, Big Joe Turner & Junior Wells.
Album: released on Amiga in Jul'87

American Gigolo

American Gigolo Original film soundtrack (Various Artists).
Album: released on Polydor in '80 by Polydor Records. Distributed by: Polygram, Polydor

Musicassette: released on Polydor in '80 by Polydor Records. Distributed by: Polygram, Polydor

American Girls

American girls.
Tracks: / American girls / Androgynous zone / Last prayer / Stay with me / Out on my own / Goodbye, amen / Blind ambition / Take the night / Sarkskin suit / Practice (what you preach).
Album: released on I.R.S.(Independent Record Syndicate) in Jun'86 by I.R.S.. Distributed by: MCA

Musicassette: released on I.R.S.(Independent Record Syndicate) in Jun'86 by I.R.S.. Distributed by: MCA

American girls (single).
Single (7"): released on I.R.S.(Independent Record Syndicate) in Aug'86 by I.R.S.. Distributed by: MCA

Single (12"): released on I.R.S.(Independent Record Syndicate) in Aug'86 by I.R.S.. Distributed by: MCA

American Graffiti

American Graffiti Vol.1 Various Artists (Various Artists).
Tracks: / Rock around the clock (We're gonna....) / Sixteen candles / Runaway / Why do fools fall in love / That'll be the day / Maybe baby / Fanny Mae / At the hop / She's so fine / Goodnight well it's time to go / See you in September / Surfin' safari / All summer long / He's the great imposter / Almost grown / Johnny B. Goode / Smoke gets in your eyes / Only you / Great pretender, (The) / Little darlin' / Stroll, (The) / Peppermint twist / Ya, Ya / Ain't that a shame / I only have eyes for you / Get a job / To the aisle / Do you wanna dance / Party doll / Come go with me / You're sixteen, you're beautiful (& you're mine) / Love potion number 9 / Since I don't have you / Chantilly lace / Teen angel / Crying in the chapel / Thousand miles away, (A) / Heart & soul / Green onions / Barbara Ann / Book of love.
Double Album: released on MCA in '74 by MCA Records. Distributed by: CBS

Double musicassette: released on MCA in '74 by MCA Records. Distributed by: CBS

Double Album: released on MCA in Sep'85 by MCA Records. Distributed by: Polygram, MCA

Double musicassette: released on MCA in Sep'85 by MCA Records. Distributed by: Polygram, MCA

American Graffiti Vol.2 Various Artists (Various Artists).
Tracks: / See you later alligator / Maybe / Bony Maronie / Shoop shoop song, (The) / Teenager in love, (A) / Ready, Teddy / Tutti Frutti / Stagger Lee / Gee / My heart is an open book / Oh boy / Happy happy birthday baby / Louie Louie / It might as well rain until September / Peggy Sue / Locomotion, (The) / He will break your heart / Twilight time / Will you still love me tomorrow / Could this be magic / Poison Ivy / I'm sorry / Speedo / Duke of Earl / One summer night.
Double Album: released on MCA in Sep'85 by MCA Records. Distributed by: Polygram, MCA

Double musicassette: released on MCA in Sep'85 by MCA Records. Distributed by: Polygram, MCA

American Graffiti Vol.3 Various Artists (Various Artists).
Tracks: / Surfer girl surfin' / Lucille / Good golly Miss Molly / At my front door / For your precious love / Endless sleep / Wake up little Susie / Bye bye love / You talk too much / Mary Lou / Poetry in motion / Donna / Bamba, (La) / Honeycomb / Since I fell for you / Kansas City / Hey little one / To know him is to love him / Thousand stars, (A) / Alley oop / Shimmy shimmy ko ko pop / Western movies / Mule skinner blues / Rave on / Birds & the bees, (The) / Let's dance / My special angel / Mountains of love / Baby what you want me to do / Big hurt, (The).
Double Album: released on MCA in Sep'85 by MCA Records. Distributed by: Polygram, MCA

Double musicassette: released on MCA in Sep'85 by MCA Records. Distributed by: Polygram, MCA

American Graffiti Vol.4 Various artists (Various Artists).
Album: released on MCA in '85 by MCA Records. Distributed by: Polygram, MCA

Musicassette: released on MCA in '85 by MCA Records. Distributed by: Polygram MCA

American Greats

100 minutes Original artists (Various Artists).
Musicassette: released on PRT in '82 by PRT Records. Distributed by: PRT

American Heart and Soul

American heart and soul (Various Artists).

American Heartbeat

American Heartbeat Various Artists (Various Artists).
Tracks: / Eye of the tiger / American heartbeat / Rosanna / Africa / Hold the line / Who's crying now? / Don't fear the reaper / Babe / Take it on the run / Keep on loving you / Dance hall days / More than a feeling / Harden my heart / Carry on wayward son / I got you / Heat of the moment.
Video-cassette (VHS): released on CBS in Oct'84 by CBS Records. Distributed by: CBS

Album: released on Epic in '84 by CBS Records. Distributed by: CBS

Musicassette: released on Epic in '84 by CBS Records. Distributed by: CBS

American Heroes

(Just) Walkaway.
Single (7"): released on GFM in Aug'87 by GFM Records. Distributed by: Fast Forward, Cartel, PRT, Projection

Single (12"): released on GFM in Aug'87 by GFM Records. Distributed by: Fast Forward, Cartel, PRT, Projection

American Hot Wax

American hot wax Various original artists (Various original artists).
Album: released on A&M in '78 by A&M Records. Distributed by: Polygram

American Indian Legends

American indian legends (volume 1).
Musicassette: released on Anvil in '83. Distributed by: Anvil

American indian legends Vol.1 Various artists (Various Artists).
Musicassette: released on Anvil in '81. Distributed by: Anvil

American Indian Legends Vol.2 Various artists (Various Artists).
Musicassette: released on Anvil in '81. Distributed by: Anvil

American Jazz

American Jazz Series 12 (Various Artists).
Notes: Includes: McKinneys Cotton Pickers etc.
Musicassette: released on Emporium Cassettes in Jul'86 by Emporium Cassettes Records. Distributed by: Jazz Music

American Jazz Series 13 (Various Artists).
Notes: Includes: The Arcadian Seranaders/Fess Williams
Musicassette: released on Emporium Cassettes in Jul'86 by Emporium Cassettes Records. Distributed by: Jazz Music

American Jazz Rarities

American Jazz Rarities no.11 (Various Artists).
Notes: Includes: New Orleans Rhythm Kings etc.
Musicassette: released on Emporium Cassettes in Jul'86 by Emporium Cassettes Records. Distributed by: Jazz Music

American Military Band

Sousa marches.
Tracks: / Hands across the sea / Bells of Chicargo, The / Thunderer, The / Stars and stripes forever / Semper Fidelis / Crusader, The / Gladiators, The / Washington Post March / High school Cadets, The / El captain / King cotton.
Notes: Sousa Marches played with all the vigour and vitality one would expect from an American Military Band.
Album: released on Austrophon Diepholz(Germany) in Jul'83

Musicassette: released on Austrophon Diepholz(Germany) in Jul'83

American Musicological...

American Musicological Society presents.. Various artists (Various Artists).
Tracks: / Balkan fantasy solo / Greek dancerama / Variations on twinkle star / Russian pear tree / Variations on "Father John" / You'll never know just how much I love you / Sunnyside of the street / Poinciana / This is a lovely way to spend an evening / Twilight time / All the things you are.
Notes: Fearturing Father Stanley Kloskowski, Stanley Darrow and Joanne Arnold. Mail order distribution address: Accordian Record Club, 146 Birmingham Road ,Kidderminster, Worcs. DY10 2SL. Tel. 0562-746105

Album: released on ARC (Accordion Records) in '84. Distributed by: Accordion Record Club

American Neo-Rockabillies

American neo-rockabillies Various artists (Various Artists).
Album: released on Rockhouse(USA) in Nov'82

American Ram Jam

American Ram Jam.
Album: by CBS Records. Distributed by: CBS

Americans

Disneyworld.
Single (7"): released on Eagle (West Germany) in Feb'82 by Bear Family Records. Distributed by: Stage One

American School Choir

Save the animals.
Album: released on Ears And Eyes in Apr'83 by Ears And Eyes Records. Distributed by: Taylors, Ears And Eyes Records

Musicassette: released on Ears And Eyes in Apr'83 by Ears And Eyes Records. Distributed by: Taylors, Ears And Eyes Records

Americans In Europe

Americans In Europe Vol.1 Various artists (Various Artists).
Tracks: / No smokin' / Low life / I can't get started / Freeway / Pyramid / Round midnight.
Album: released on Jasmine in Mar'83 by Jasmine Records. Distributed by: Counterpoint, Lugtons, Taylor, H.R., Wellard, Chris, Swift, Cadillac

Americans In Europe Vol.2 Various artists (Various Artists).
Album: released on Jasmine in Mar'83 by Jasmine Records. Distributed by: Counterpoint, Lugtons, Taylor, H.R., Wellard, Chris, Swift, Cadillac

American Tail

American Tail Original Soundtrack.
Album: released on MCA in Jun'87 by MCA Records. Distributed by: Polygram, MCA

Musicassette: released on MCA in Jun'87 by MCA Records. Distributed by: Polygram, MCA

American Youth Report

American youth report Various USA groups (Various Artists).
Album: released on Bomp International in Nov'82

Amiet, Julie

Music is our freedom.
Single (7"): released on Precious in Jun'83 by Precious Records. Distributed by: CBS, Polygram

Tonight.
Single (7"): released on Precious in Sep'81 by Precious Records. Distributed by: CBS, Polygram

Amin Peck

Girls on me.
Single (12"): released on Connection in Jun'82 by Connection Records. Distributed by: Pinnacle

Love disgrace.
Single (7"): released on Connection in Mar'82 by Connection Records. Distributed by: Pinnacle

Amion

I hear you knocking.
Tracks: / I hear you knocking / Pizza walk.
Single (7"): released on Uptown (USA) in 23 May'87 by Uptown Records. Distributed by: Jazz Music

Single (12"): released on Uptown (USA) in 23 May'87 by Uptown Records. Distributed by: Jazz Music

Amir

Lines of Love.
Single (12"): released on Pink Pop in Feb'87. Distributed by: Red Rhino, Cartel

Amir, Mr.

No place to go.
Album: released on Probe Plus in Mar'85 by Probe Plus Records. Distributed by: Probe Plus Distribution

Amitri, Del

Del Amitri.
Album: released on Chrysalis in May'85 by Chrysalis Records. Distributed by: CBS

Sense sickness.
Single (7"): released on No Strings in Aug'83. Distributed by: Rough Trade, Cartel

Amlak

Christmas is here.
Single (7"): released on Roots Music in Dec'83 by Roots Music Records. Distributed by: PRT Distribution

Single (12"): released on Roots Music in Dec'83 by Roots Music Records. Distributed by: PRT Distribution

Ammons, Albert

Boogie woogie and the blues (Ammons, Albert & His Rhythm Kings).
Tracks: / Bugle boogie / Revelle boogie / Blues in the groove / Breaks, The / Jammin the boogie / Bottom blues / Albert's special boogie / Boogie rocks, The / Blues on my mind.
Album: released on Commodore Classics (USA) in Nov'86 by Teldec Records (Germany). Distributed by: Conifer, IMS, Polygram

Compact disc: released on Commodore Classics in May'87 by Teldec Records (Germany). Distributed by: Conifer, IMS, Polygram

Boogie woogie classics (Ammons, Albert & Pete Johnson).
Album: released on Blue Note (USA Import) in Sep'84

Boogie woogie masters (Ammons, Albert/Pete Johnson/Meade Lux Lewis).
Album: released on Affinity in Apr'84 by Charly Records. Distributed by: Charly, Cadillac

Boogie woogie woogie piano stylings.
Tracks: / Swanee River boogie / Boogie woogie at the Civic Opera / S.P.Blues / Sheik of Araby, The / St.Louis Blues / You are my sunshine / Shufflin' the boogie / Twelfth St.Boogie.
Notes: Artists include: Marvin Randolph/Gene Ammons/Ike Perkins/Israel Crosby/Al Burroughs/Jack Cooley. Recorded between 1947-1949
Album: released on Mercury Jazz Masters in Dec'83

Giants of boogie woogie (Ammons, Albert/Pete Johnson/Meade Lux Lewis).
Tracks: / St.Louis blues / Mecca flat blues / Bass goin' crazy / Closing hour blues / Messin' around / Deep fives / Blues de luxe / Let 'em jump / Pete's blues / B & O blues.
Album: released on Joker in Apr'81. Distributed by: Counterpoint, Mainline, Record Services Distribution (Ireland)

With Rhythm Kings & piano solos -1944 (Ammons, Albert & His Rhythm Kings).
Tracks: / Blues in the groove / Breaks, The / Jammin' the boogie / Bottom blues / Albert's special boogie / Boogie rocks, The / Blues on my mind / Bugle boogie / Reveille boogie.
Album: released on Commodore Classics in Aug'82 by Teldec Records (Germany). Distributed by: Conifer, IMS, Polygram

Ammons, Gene

All Stars Sessions (Ammons, Gene All Stars).
Album: released on Original Jazz Classics (USA) in Jun'86. Distributed by: Fantasy (USA) Distribution, Chris Wellard Distribution, IMS-Polygram Distribution

Early visions.
Tracks: / Swinging for Xmas / Talk of the town, The / Battle, The / Jam for boppers / Do you really mean it? / Bless you / Stuffy / Once in a while / Pennies from heaven / Cha bootie / More moon / Last mile, The / Goodbye / Ten or eleven / It's you or no one / My foolish heart / Jug head ramble / You go to my head / Baby won't you please say yes / Don't do me wrong / Prelude to a kiss / Can anyone explain / You're not the kind / Happiness is a thing called Joe.
Notes: A collecters item of recordings made between 1948 and 1951 in Chicago.Some of the personnel are,unfortunately, unidentified but is known on some of the sessions feature Christine Chatman on piano who also sings on the 'Do You Realy Mean It'track.Leo Blevins on guitar,Llowell POinter on bass,Ike Day on drums. But this double set is really about the fine tenor sax playing og Gene Ammons (son of the great boogie pianist Albert Ammons,as it is history of his evolvementr during his early twenties
Album: released on Chess Jazz in Oct'84 by Charly Records. Distributed by: Charly, Swift, PRT

Musicassette: released on Chess Jazz in Oct'84 by Charly Records. Distributed by: Charly, Swift, PRT

Album:

Gene Ammons.
Album: released on Jazz Reactivation in Jul'82. Distributed by: PRT

Happy blues, The (Ammons, Gene All Stars).
Album:

In Sweden.
Album: released on Enja (Germany) in Feb'82 by Enja Records (W.Germany). Distributed by: Cadillac Music

Jammin' with Gene (Ammons, Gene All Stars).
Album:

Juganthology.
Double Album: released on Prestige in May'74 by Prestige Records (USA). Distributed by: RCA, JSU, Swift

Juggin' around (Ammons, Gene and Benny Green).
Tracks: / Juggin' around / Sermonette / Swinging for Benny / Little ditty / Going south / Jim dog.
Album: released on Charly in Dec'86 by Charly Records. Distributed by: Charly, Cadillac

Musicassette: released on Charly in Dec'86 by Charly Records. Distributed by: Charly, Cadillac

Amnesty International

Amnesty International- Conspiracy Of Hope Various Artists.
Album: released on Mercury in Nov'86 by Phonogram Records. Distributed by: Polygram Distribution

Musicassette: released on Mercury in Nov'86 by Phonogram Records. Distributed by: Polygram Distribution

Compact disc: by Phonogram Records. Distributed by: Polygram Distribution

Amon Duul

Airs on a shoe string.
Tracks: / Hymn for the hardcore / Pioneer / One moments anger is two pints of blood / Marcus Leid / Olaf.
Album: released on Thunderbolt in Jul'87 by Magnum Music Group Ltd. Distributed by: Magnum Music Group Ltd, PRT Distribution, Spartan Distribution

Musicassette: released on Thunderbolt in Jul'87 by Magnum Music Group Ltd. Distributed by: Magnum Music Group Ltd, PRT Distribution, Spartan Distribution

Compact disc: released on Thunderbolt in Jul'87 by Magnum Music Group Ltd. Distributed by: Magnum Music Group Ltd, PRT Distribution, Spartan Distribution. Estim retail price in Aug'87 was £11.99.

Anthology (Amon Duul II).
Tracks: / Soap shock rock / Burning sister / Halluzination guillotine / Gulp a sonata / Flesh coloured anti-aircraft alarm / Kanaan / Trap / Phallus dei / Yeti (improvisation) / Wolf city / C.I.D. in uruk / Morning excuse / Apocalyptic bore / Jailhouse frog.
Album: released on Raw Power in Mar'87. Distributed by: Pinnacle

Hawk meets penguin vol.1.
Tracks: / One moment of anger is two pints of blood / Meditative music from the third o before the producers.
Album: released on Demi-Mode in '86

Hawk meets penguin (Amon Duul II).
Album: released on Illuminated in Jan'83 by IKF Records. Distributed by: Pinnacle, Cartel, Jetstar

Meetings with menmachines unremarkable heroes of the past.
Tracks: / Pioneer / Old one, The / Marcus lied / Song, The / Things aren't always what they seem / Burundi drummer's nightmare.
Notes: All Weinzier/Anderson/Wareing-Charly Publishing Ltd.
Album: released on Demi Monde in Jul'85. Distributed by: Charly

Meetings with menmachines in glorious heroes of the past (Amon Duul II).
Album: released on Illuminated in Jan'85 by IKF Records. Distributed by: Pinnacle, Cartel, Jetstar

Minnelied.
Album: released on Brain in Jul'80

Monde meets penguin Vol.1.
Tracks: / One moment of anger is two pints of blood / Meditative music from the third o before the producers part1 / Meditative music from the third o before the producers part2.
Notes: Both sides licenced from Charly Records International APS,Copenhagen,Denmark (P)1985 Charly Holding Inc. (C) 1985 Charly Records Ltd.
Album: released on Demi-Mode in Sep'85

Yeti.
Double Album: released on Telefunken (Germany) in Apr'84. Distributed by: Decca Distribution, IMS, Polygram
Cat.no **DT6 28521**
Double Album: released on Teldec (Germany) in Mar'84 by Import Records. Distributed by: IMS Distribution, Polygram Distribution

Yeti (Amon Duul II).
Double Album: released on Liberty in '70 by Liberty-United. Distributed by: EMI

Among the Northumbrian...

Among the Northumbrian hills Various artists (Various Artists).
Album: released on Viking in May'82. Distributed by: Harmonia Mundi Distributors

Amoo, Chris

No choir of angels (Amoo, Chris & Debby Bishop).
Single (7"): released on EMI in Mar'84 by EMI Records. Distributed by: EMI

Amos, Adam

Adam Amos & Noel Rocks (Amos, Adam & Noel Rocks).
Album: released on Celtic Music in Mar'84 by Celtic Music Distribution. Distributed by: Celtic Music, Jazz Music, Projection, Roots

Casual on the balcony (Amos, Adam & Noel Rocks).
Album: released on Celtic Music in Sep'85 by Celtic Music Distribution. Distributed by: Celtic Music, Jazz Music, Projection, Roots

Amphibious

Twighlight smile.
Single (7"): released on Crammed Discs in Sep'82. Distributed by: Rough Trade, Nine Mile, Cartel

Amps, Kym

You don't know my name.
Single (7"): released on Division in Feb'85 by Division Records. Distributed by: Pinnacle

Amstell, Billy

Billy amstell's Dixielanders session after midnight.
Album: released on Zodiac in Apr'81. Distributed by: Jazz Music

Jewish Party, dances & stories.
Album: released on Zodiac in May'81. Distributed by: Jazz Music

Session after midnight (Amstell, Billy, Dixielanders).
Album: released on Zodiac in May'81. Distributed by: Jazz Music

Amuzement Park

Groove your blues away.
Single (7"): released on Satril in Aug'82 by Satril Records. Distributed by: PRT

Single (12"): released on Satril in Aug'82 by Satril Records. Distributed by: PRT

Amy, Curtis

Katanga (Amy, Curtis & Dupree Bolton).
Album: released on Affinity in Nov'84 by Charly Records. Distributed by: Charly, Cadillac

Ana

Shy boys.
Tracks: / Shy boys / Love is the winner.
Single (12"): released on Epic in Jul'87 by CBS Records. Distributed by: CBS

Shy boys.
Single (7"): released on Epic in Aug'87 by CBS Records. Distributed by: CBS

Anabas

Barricades/Dream dance.
Single (7"): released on Flame On in Nov'83 by Flame On Records. Distributed by: Cartel

Analysis

Surface tension/Connections.

An American In Paris

An American in Paris Original soundtrack (Various Artists).
Compact disc: released on CBS in May'87 by CBS Records. Distributed by: CBS

An American in Paris/Les girls (Various Artists).
Tracks: / Why am I so gone / C'est l'amour, A / S'Wonderful / Love is here to stay / I'll build a stairway to paradise / I got rhythm / An American in Paris Ballet / Les Girls / You're just too, too / A, C'est l'amour / Ladies in waiting.
Album: released on CBS in Feb'87 by CBS Records. Distributed by: CBS

Musicassette: released on CBS in Feb'87 by CBS Records. Distributed by: CBS

An American tail

An American tail Original soundtrack (Original Soundtrack).
Album: released on MCA in Jun'87 by MCA Records. Distributed by: Polygram, MCA

Musicassette: released on MCA in Jun'87 by MCA Records. Distributed by: Polygram, MCA

Compact disc: released on MCA in Jun'87 by MCA Records. Distributed by: Polygram, MCA

Ananda

Amazonia.
Compact disc: released on Sonic Atmospheres in Jun'86. Distributed by: Target

Anastasia

Anastasia: The Mystery of Anna Original TV soundtrack (Rosenthal, Laurence).
Album: released on Silva Screen in May'87 by Silva Screen Records. Distributed by: Silva Screen

Musicassette: released on Silva Screen in May'87 by Silva Screen Records. Distributed by: Silva Screen

Ancient Evenings

Ancient evenings Norman Mailer (Mailer, Norman).
Musicassette: released on Caedmon(USA) in '84 by Caedmon (USA) Records. Distributed by: Gower, Taylors, Discovery

Ancient Ways...

Ancient ways to new freedom Doris Lessing.
Musicassette: released on Seminar Cassettes in Oct'81 by Seminar Cassettes. Distributed by: Davidson Distribution, Eastern Educational Products Distrib., Forlaget Systime Distribution, Laser Books Ltd Distribution, MacDougall Distribution, Talktapes Distribution, Watkins Books Ltd Distribution, Norton, Jeff Distribution

And Also The Trees

And Also The Trees.

Album: released on Reflex in Mar'84

Critical distance, The.
Tracks: / Critical distance, The / Scythe and spade, The / Renegade, The.
Single (12"): released on Reflex in Jun'87

Single (12"): released on Reflex in 13 Jun'87

Night of the 24th,The.
Album: released on Reflex in 30 May'87

Retrospective 1983-1986, A.
Tracks: / Shantell / Talk without words / Shrine / Midnight garden / Impulse of man / Twilights pool / Room lives in Lucy, A / Scarlet arch / Slow pulse boy / Maps in her wrists and arms / Dwelling place, The / Vincent craine / Gone like the swallows / Virus meadow.
Compact disc: released on Reflex in May'87

Room lives in Lucy (3-track EP),A.
Single (12"): released on Reflex in Jan'85

Secret sea, (The).
Single (7"): released on Reflex in May'84

Single (12"): released on Reflex in Jun'84

Shantell.
Single (7"): released on Reflex in Nov'84

Virus meadow.
Tracks: / Slow pulse boy / Maps in her wrists and arms / Dwelling place, The / Vincent Crane / Jack / Headless clay woman, The / Gone...like the swallows / Virus meadow.
Notes: Composers: Burrows,Jones,Havas,Jones. Pub: Flex Music
Album: released on Reflex in Jun'86

And A Nightingale Sang

And a nightingale sang

Andante

Andante Various artists (Various Artists).
Album: released on Celestial Harmonies in Feb'87 by TM Records. Distributed by: PRT

Musicassette: released on Celestial Harmonies in Feb'87 by TM Records. Distributed by: PRT

Anders, Bob

Dancing a-go-go..In strict tempo rhythm.
Album: released on Condor(Germany) in Jul'85

Anders, Christoph

Es herrscht uhu im land (Anders, C/H.Goebels/A.Harth/P.Lovens/R.Riehm/A.M.Roelofs).
Album: released on Japo in Nov'81

Andersen, Arild

Bande a part (Andersen, Arild Quintet).
Tracks: / 3 for 5 / Natt / Sort of / Vanilje / Ball / Tutte / No soap / Nyl.
Notes: During his long association with EMC Norwegian bass player Arild Anderson has introduced a number of new young musicians from his country to an international audience.His new quintet Masquelero live up to this reputation, presenting one of the freshest, most exciting sounds in modern jazz. This music is for the head, heart and feet.Personnel: Nils Petter Molvaer-trumpet/Tore Brunborg-tenor & sop. sax/Jon Balke-acoustic & electric keyboards/Arild Anderson-acoustic & electric bass/Jon Christensen-drums,percussion
Album: released on ECM (Germany) in Apr'86 by ECM Records. Distributed by: IMS, Polygram, Virgin through EMI

Compact disc: released on ECM (Germany) in Apr'86 by ECM Records. Distributed by: IMS, Polygram, Virgin through EMI

Bande A Parte.

Lifelines.
Album: released on ECM in May'81 by ECM Records. Distributed by: IMS, Polygram, Virgin through EMI

Molde concert, A.
Album: released on ECM (Germany) in Oct'82 by ECM Records. Distributed by: IMS, Polygram, Virgin through EMI

Andersen, Lale

Drei rote rosen.
Album: released on EMI (Germany) in '83 by EMI Records. Distributed by: Conifer

Supergold.
Album: released on EMI (Germany) in '83 by EMI Records. Distributed by: Conifer

Anderson

Afric popperbird

Anderson, Alistair

Alistair Anderson plays English concertina.
Album: released on Leader in '81. Distributed by: Jazz Music, Projection

Concertina workshop.
Tracks: / Dancing tailor, The / O'Carolan's fancy / Blarney Pigrim, The / Barrington hornpipe, The / Cliff hornpipe, The / Recruited colliers, The / Sir Sydney Smith's march / Flannel jacket, The / Scholar, The / Joe Burke's hornpipe / Fairy queen, The / Jenny Linn polka / One horned sheep, The / Turnpike side / Sunbeam, The / Admiral Cole / Derwentwater's farewell / Jimmy Allen / Herd on the hill, The / King's favourite, The / Tipsy sailor, The / Aith rant, The / Framm upon him / Da south end / Fateful head, The / Randy wives of Greenlaw, The / John McNeil's reel / Kick the world before you / Come upstairs with me / Malt man comes on monday.
Album: released on Free Reed in '81 by Free Reed Records. Distributed by: Roots, Projection, Hobgoblin Records, Oblivion

Corby crag.
Tracks: / Hawk polka, The / Thrunton woods / Keelman's petition, The / Tipp staff, The / La fille de Lyon / Cotillon des marionettes / Blakes hornpipe / President Garfield's hornpipe / Bonny broom hill / Felton lonnin / Kirden fair / Tich Richardson's favourite / Hey to the camp / Brosehill / Alistair Anderson's favourite / Old french / Belfast hornpipe, The / Prize potato, The / Trip to Carlisle, The / Corby crag / Ali Anderson / Henry Atkinson / Blayton flats / Whittingham games / James Brown / Derwent water's bonny lord / Bride's favourite, The / Remember me / Left handed fiddler, The / Geld him lasses, geld him / Uncle John / Darkening, The.
Album: released on Topic in '81. Distributed by: Roots Distribution

Dookin' for apples.
Tracks: / Culloden day / Kaspar's rant / New moon, The / Curds and cream / Crooked bawbee / Carrick hornpipe / Weddings bes / Number 28 / Highland reel / West indian, The / Stage hornpipe, The / Johnson's hornpipe / White meadow, The / Simonside reel, The / Wedderburn's cave / Dookin' for apples / Mayday / Penicuick hornpipe / Silver tassle / Flowers of the forest, The / Hold on / Miss Fenwick's reel / Lads of Leith / Up and run away / Whittle dean hornpipe / Pet of the pipers / Bob Johnson's reel / Miss soutar of plains / Great Eastern reel / Jack's gettin' a wife / New way of gettin' bairns, A / Carding and spinning / Polly the lass.
Album: released on Topic in '81. Distributed by: Roots Distribution

Plays traditional music on the English concertina.
Album: released on Topic in Sep'86. Distributed by: Roots Distribution

Steel skies.
Tracks: / First light / Rhymeside 1,2 / Mountain stream, The / Rhymeside 3 / First light / Road to the north, The / Clennel street / Franklin river, The / Air of Maurice Ogg, The / Jumping Jack / Green ginger / Ironbridge, The / Eynhallow / In trim / Mount Hooley / Lemington bank / Kestral, The / High force / Dog leap stairs / Hot rivets / Seven gate road, The / When the frosts are setting in / East winds / Millstream, The / Centenary pack.
Album: released on Topic in '83. Distributed by: Roots Distribution

Anderson, Anders

Help me make it through the night.
Musicassette: released on Chevron in Nov'84. Distributed by: Multiple Sound Distributors

Anderson Band

Scapa flow Orkney instrumentals.
Musicassette: released on Folktracks in Nov'79 by Folktracks Cassettes. Distributed by: Folktracks

Anderson, Bill

Bill Anderson Story.
Tracks: / Bright lights and country music / No one's gonna hurt you anymore / I get the fever / Mama sang a song / I love you drops / Tip of my fingers, The / Po' folks / City lights / Get while the gettin's good / 8 x 10 / That's what it's like to be lonesome / For loving you / Still / Easy come - easy go / Once a day / I can do nothing alone / Cincinnati / Golden guitar / Wild week-end / Think I'll go somewhere and cry myself to sleep / Ninety nine / Papa / Happiness / Five little fingers.

Double Album: released on MCA Import in Mar'86 by MCA Records. Distributed by: Polygram, IMS

Bill Anderson story, The.
Tracks: / Bright lights and country music / No ones gonna hurt you anymore / I get the fever / Mama sang a song / I love you drops / Tip of my fingers, The / Still / Easy come easy go / Once a day / I can do nothing alone / Cincinnati / Ohio / Golden guitar / Wild week-end / Think i'll go somewhere and cry myself to sleep / Ninety-nine / Papa / Happiness / Five little fingers / Po' folks / City lights / Get while the gettin's good / Eight by ten / That's what it's like to be lonesome / For loving you.

Double Album: released on MCA in '74 by MCA Records. Distributed by: Polygram, MCA

Billy Boy and Mary Lou (Anderson, Bill & Mary Lou Turner).
Tracks: / Country lay on my mind / I'm way ahead of you / What we're taking here tonight / Just enough to make me want it all / I've been lovin' you too long / Building fires / Children / We made love (but where's the love we made) / Where are you going, Billy boy / Sad ole shade of grey / Sometimes / Circle in a triangle / Gone at last / Gone at last / Come walk with me / Can we still be friends / That's what made me love you / Without / Charlie, Mary and us / I can't sleep with you / Let me take you away.

Bright lights and country music (Anderson, Bill & The PO Boys).
Album: released on Stetson in Nov'85 by Hasmick Promotions Ltd.. Distributed by: Counterpoint Distribution, H.R. Taylor Distribution, Swift Distribution, Chris Wellard Distribution

Musicassette: released on Stetson in Nov'85 by Hasmick Promotions Ltd.. Distributed by: Counterpoint Distribution, H.R. Taylor Distribution, Swift Distribution, Chris Wellard Distribution

Golden greats: Bill Anderson.
Album: released on MCA in Oct'85 by MCA Records. Distributed by: Polygram, MCA

Musicassette: released on MCA in Oct'85 by MCA Records. Distributed by: Polygram, MCA

Greatest hits:Bill Anderson.
Tracks: / I get the fever / Tip of my fingers, The / Bright lights and country music / Mama sang a song / Easy come - easy go / Still / I love you drops / 8 x 10 / Po' folks / Five little fingers / Three A.M. / Golden guitar.
Album: released on MCA Import in Mar'86 by MCA Records. Distributed by: Polygram, IMS

Ladies choice.
Tracks: / Trust me / One more sexy lady / This is a love song / Rememering the good / Ladies get lonesome too / I can't wait any longer / Kiss you all over / Doubles / Married lady / Stay with me / Three times a lady.
Album: released on Bulldog in Jul'82 by Bulldog Records. Distributed by: President Distribution, Spartan, Swift, Taylor, H.R.

Album: released on Bulldog in Jul'82 by Bulldog Records. Distributed by: President Distribution, Spartan, Swift, Taylor, H.R.

Scotland now Albany (Anderson, Billy Band & Margaret Macleod).
Tracks: / 6 / 8 Marches / Bonawe highlanders, The / Joan C.Mackenzie / Dark island, The / Mull of cool high bens irish jigs / Thady you gandy / Cobbler, The / Drops O brandy / Queen Maries, The / Galway shawl, The / Blackbird, The / Nickels and dimes / Till the end of the day 'Orange blossom special / Bernera barn dance, The / Fire hose reel, The / Albany reel, The / Boatie rows, The / Military two step / Household Brigade, The / Culloden medley / Cumha uillean siosal / Hale O Scotland, The / Come boat me o'er / Mouth music / Need na circe fraoiche / Carson carson a Mhorag bheag / Fear an duin' Mhor / Mingulay boat song, The / Aodann strathbhain / St. Andrews medley / Square tower, The / Pends, The / Bottle dungeon, The.
Album: released on Academy Sound & Vision in May'82 by Academy Sound & Vision Records. Distributed by: Pinnacle

Musicassette: released on Academy Sound & Vision in May'82 by Academy Sound & Vision Records. Distributed by: Pinnacle

Anderson, Carl

Carl Anderson.
Tracks: / Friends and lovers / C'est la vie / First time on a ferris wheel / Buttercup / Can't stop this feeling / Mr. V J / You are my shining star / Just a little love / Woman in love, A.
Album: released on Epic in Sep'86 by CBS Records. Distributed by: CBS

Musicassette: released on Epic in Sep'86 by CBS Records. Distributed by: CBS

Protocol.
Tracks: / Can't stop this feeling / Let's talk / Still thinking of you / What will happen now / Buttercup / Somebody up there likes me / One more time with feeling / Love on ice / Girl'I won't take no / Saving my love for you.
Album: released on Epic in Aug'85 by CBS Records. Distributed by: CBS

Musicassette: released on Epic in Aug'85 by CBS Records. Distributed by: CBS

Anderson, Cat

Cat Anderson & Les Four Bones.
Album: released on Barclay in Nov'79 by Decca Records. Distributed by: Polygram, Discovery, Conifer, IMS, Swift

Paris - 1958 and 1964 (Anderson, Cat & The Duke Ellington All Stars).
Album: released on Ace in Oct'86 by Ace Records. Distributed by: Pinnacle, Swift, Hotshot, Cadillac

Anderson, Ernestine

Be mine tonight.
Tracks: / Sunday in New York / In a Mellotone / I'm comin' home again / Christopher Columbus / London by night / Little bird / Be mine (tonight) / Lend me your life / Sack full of dreams.
Notes: Personnel: Ernestine Anderson - vocals / Ray Brown - bass / Benny Carter - alto sax / Ron Eschete - guitar / Marshall Otwell - piano / Jimmie Smith - drums.
Album: released on Concord Jazz (USA) in Jul'87 by Concord Jazz Records (USA). Distributed by: IMS, Polygram

Musicassette: released on Concord Jazz (USA) in Jul'87 by Concord Jazz Records (USA). Distributed by: IMS, Polygram

Compact disc: released on Concord Jazz (USA) in Jul'87 by Concord Jazz Records (USA). Distributed by: IMS, Polygram

Big city.
Tracks: / All I need is you / Sping is here / 59th street bridge song, The / Spring is here / I'll never pass this way again / Big city / All blues / Welcome to the club / I didn't know what time it was.
Notes: Ernestine Anderson -Vocals/Hank Jones -piano/Monty Budwig -Bass/Jeff Hamilton- Drums
Album: released on Concord Jazz (USA) in May'83 by Concord Jazz Records (USA). Distributed by: IMS, Polygram

Musicassette: released on Concord Jazz (USA) in May'83 by Concord Jazz Records (USA). Distributed by: IMS, Polygram

Miss Ernestine Anderson.
Tracks: / Let's get away from it all / End of a love affair / So nice / Funny how time slips away / Talk to me baby / Tears have to fall / Big spender / What did I have that I don't have / On a clear day / I fall in love too easily / Feeling good / Make it another old fashioned please.
Notes: Johnnie Scott & His Orchestra/Bill Oliver &His Orchestra A good selection of classics on this, Ernestine Anderson's only British recorded album. this fine singer works her way through favourites such as 'Let's get away from it all','Big spender' and 'On a clear day you can see forever' in a style comparable to Sarah Vaughn. A good collectors album.
Album: released on Capitol in Jan'86 by Capitol Records. Distributed by: EMI

Musicassette: released on Capitol in Jan'86 by Capitol Records. Distributed by: EMI

Never make your move too soon.
Album: released on Concord Jazz (USA) in May'81 by Concord Jazz Records (USA). Distributed by: IMS, Polygram

When the sun goes down.

Tracks: / Someone else is steppin' / In the evenin' when the sun goes down / I love being here with you / Down home blues / I'm just a lucky so and so / Alone on my own / Mercy, mercy, mercy / Goin to Chicago blues.
Notes: American singer Ernestine Anderson had to go Sweden to gain sucess and recognition .Having formerly worked with Johnny Otis and Lionel Hampton, it wasn't until her album 'Hot Chicago' recorded in Sweden with the Harry Arnold Band wasreleased that she gained acceptance in her own country. She won the 'New Star' award in Down Beat's critics poll in 1959. This album, her seventh for concord, features blues and blues related songs, and includes pieces from Count Basie, Peggy Lee ,and Duke Ellinton. Personnel: Ernestine Anderson -Vocals/Ray Brown - Bass/Gene Harris - Piano/Red Holloway - Tenor Saxophone/Gerryck King - Drums
Album: released on Concord Jazz (USA) in Apr'85 by Concord Jazz Records (USA). Distributed by: IMS, Polygram

Musicassette: released on Concord Jazz (USA) in Apr'85 by Concord Jazz Records (USA). Distributed by: IMS, Polygram

Anderson, Ian

Walk into light.
Tracks: / Fly by night / Made in England / Walk Into Light / Trains / End game / Black and White Television / Toad in the hole / Looking for Eden

/ User-Friendly / Different Germany.
Album: released on Chrysalis in Nov'83 by Chrysalis Records. Distributed by: CBS

Musicassette: released on Chrysalis in Nov'83 by Chrysalis Records. Distributed by: CBS

Anderson, John

Big bands are back.
Single (7"): released on Emerald (Ireland) in Jun'84 by Emerald Records. Distributed by: I & B, Ross, PRT

Cage of freedom.
Single (7"): released on CBS in Dec'84 by CBS Records. Distributed by: CBS

Single (12"): released on CBS in Dec'84 by CBS Records. Distributed by: CBS

Glenn Miller medley, The (Anderson, John Band).
Single (7"): released on Priority in Nov'85 by Priority Records. Distributed by: RCA

Single (12"): released on Priority in Nov'85 by Priority Records. Distributed by: RCA

Greatest hits:John Anderson.
Tracks: / Swingin' / I just came home to count the memories / 1959 / She just started likin' cheatin' songs / Chicken truck / I'm just an old chunk of coal / Would you catch a falling star / Wild and blue / Your lying blue eyes / Black sheep.
Musicassette: released on Warner Bros. in '86 by Warner Bros Records. Distributed by: WEA

Swingin'.
Single (7"): released on Warner Bros. in Jul'83 by Warner Bros Records. Distributed by: WEA

Anderson, Jon

3 ships.
Tracks: / Three ships / Forest of fire / Ding dong merrily on high / Save all your love / Holly and the ivy / Day of days / 2,000 years / Where were you / Oh holy night / How it hits you / Jingle bells / Save all your love / Easier said than done.
Album: released on Elektra (USA) in Dec'85 by Elektra/Asylum/Nonesuch Records. Distributed by: WEA

Easier said than done.
Single (7"): released on Elektra (USA) in Nov'85 by Elektra/Asylum/Nonesuch Records. Distributed by: WEA

Single (12"): released on Elektra (USA) in Nov'85 by Elektra/Asylum/Nonesuch Records. Distributed by: WEA

Olias of sunhillow.
Tracks: / Ocean song / Meeting (Garden of Geda) / Sound out the Galleon / Dance of Ranyart Olias(To build the Moorglade) / Qoquaq en transic naon transic to (Flight of the moorglade) / Solid space / Moon ra chords song of search / To the runner.
Album: released on Atlantic in Jun'76 by WEA Records. Distributed by: WEA

Song of seven.
Tracks: / For you for me / Some are born / Don't forget / Heart of the matter / Hear it / Everybody loves you / Take your time / Days / Song of seven.
Album: released on Atlantic in Oct'80 by WEA Records. Distributed by: WEA

Anderson, Laurie

Big Science.
Tracks: / From the air / Big science / Sweaters / Walking and falling / Born' never asked / O superman / Example 22 / Let X=X / It tango.
Notes: Digital Stereo
Compact disc: released on Warner Bros. in Apr'84 by Warner Bros Records. Distributed by: WEA

Musicassette: released on WEA in Apr'82 by WEA Records. Distributed by: WEA

Compact disc: released on Warner Bros. in Apr'82 by Warner Bros Records. Distributed by: WEA

Album: released on Warner Bros. in Apr'82 by Warner Bros Records. Distributed by: WEA

Home Of The Brave.
Tracks: / Smoke rings / White lily / Late show / Talk normal / Language is a virus from outer space / Radar / Sharkey's night / Credit racket.
Album: by WEA Records. Distributed by: WEA

Musicassette: by WEA Records. Distributed by: WEA

Compact disc: by WEA Records. Distributed by: WEA

Language is a virus from outer space.
Tracks: / Language is a virus from outer space (edit) / White.
Single (7"): released on Warner Bros. in May'86 by Warner Bros Records. Distributed by: WEA

Single (12"): released on Warner Bros. in May'86 by Warner Bros Records. Distributed by: WEA

Let X=X.
Single (7"): released on Warner Bros. in Jun'82 by Warner Bros Records. Distributed by: WEA

Mister Heartbreak.
Tracks: / Sharkey's day / Langue d'armour / Gravity's angel / Blue lagoon / Excellent birds / Sharkey's night.
Notes: Digital Stereo
Compact disc: released on Warner Bros. in Jul'84 by Warner Bros Records. Distributed by: WEA

Album: released on WEA in Feb'84 by WEA Records. Distributed by: WEA

Musicassette: released on WEA in Feb'84 by WEA Records. Distributed by: WEA

Oh superman.
Single (7"): released on Warner Bros. in Oct'81 by Warner Bros Records. Distributed by: WEA

O superman.
Single (7"): released on Warner Bros. in Oct'81 by Warner Bros Records. Distributed by: WEA

United States live.
Boxed set: released on Warner Bros. in Jan'85 by Warner Bros Records. Distributed by: WEA

Anderson, Lynn

Best of Lynn Anderson, The.
Album: released on K-Tel in Oct'82 by K-Tel Records. Distributed by: Record Merchandisers Distribution, Taylors, Terry Blood Distribution, Wynd-Up Distribution, Relay Distribution, Pickwick Distribution, Solomon & Peres Distribution, Polygram

Musicassette: released on K-Tel in Oct'82 by K-Tel Records. Distributed by: Record Merchandisers Distribution, Taylors, Terry Blood Distribution, Wynd-Up Distribution, Relay Distribution, Pickwick Distribution, Solomon & Peres Distribution, Polygram

Musicassette: released on K-Tel Goldmasters in Aug'84 by K-Tel Records. Distributed by: K-Tel

Country girl.
Album: released on Embassy in Jul'77 by CBS Records. Distributed by: CBS

Greatest hits:Lynn Anderson.
Tracks: / Rose garden / Cry / Can I unlove you / Stay there til I get there / That's what loving you has meant to me / Listen to a country song / You're my man / No love at all / Don't say things you don't mean / I'm gonna write a song / Nothing between us.
Album: released on CBS in Mar'86 by CBS Records. Distributed by: CBS

Musicassette: released on CBS in Mar'86 by CBS Records. Distributed by: CBS

Her top hits.
Musicassette: released on Timeless Treasures in Jul'86. Distributed by: Counterpoint Distribution

Listen to a country song.
Album: released on Hallmark in Apr'79 by Pickwick Records. Distributed by: Pickwick Distribution, PRT, Taylors

Musicassette: released on Hallmark in Apr'79 by Pickwick Records. Distributed by: Pickwick Distribution, PRT, Taylors

Lynn Anderson.
Tracks: / (I never promised you a) rose garden / I still belong to you / Another lonely night / It's only make believe / Your sweet love lifted me / You're my man / Help me make it through the night / I'm gonna write a song / Cy, cry again / I might as well be here alone / Flying machine.
Musicassette: released on Pickwick in '83 by Pickwick Records. Distributed by: Pickwick Distribution, Prism Leisure Distribution, Lugtons

Rose garden.
Musicassette: released on Pickwick in Jan'83 by Pickwick Records. Distributed by: Pickwick Distribution, Prism Leisure Distribution, Lugtons

Single (7"): released on CBS in Apr'82 by CBS Records. Distributed by: CBS

Single (7"): released on Old Gold in Jun'84 by Old Gold Records. Distributed by: Lightning, Jazz Music, Spartan, Counterpoint

Anderson, Michael

Lovers harmony.
Single (12"): released on JD in Mar'83

Anderson, Moira

Favourite Scottish songs.
Album: released on Waverley in Mar'80 by EMI Records. Distributed by: EMI

Focus on Moira Anderson.
Musicassette: released on Decca in May'78 by Decca Records. Distributed by: Polygram

Golden memories (Anderson, Moira & Harry Secombe).
Album: released on Warwick in Sep'81. Distributed by: Multiple Sound Distributors

Musicassette: released on Warwick in Sep'81. Distributed by: Multiple Sound Distributors

Love of God, The.
Notes: During her hugely successful cerreer Moira has often been asked if she has recorded certain hymns or gospel songs. Gradually the idea of recording an album of sacred songs crystallised. Moira has had ample opportunity to share her Christian beliefs, not only on record and cassette, but also on radio and TV. Consistently during her career she has been forthright in stating her christian stand. Her reason for recording gospel songs such as these is: 'When I go to church these days these are the kind og hymns I like to hear...I think they convey the Christian message most effectively'
Album: released on Word in Jun'86 by Word Records. Distributed by: Word Distribution, CBS

Musicassette: released on Word in Jun'86 by Word Records. Distributed by: Word Distribution, CBS

Sings operetta.
Tracks: / Laughing song, The / Don't be cross / Chambre separee / Vilia / Though they say that love is blind / On my lips every kiss is like wine / Letter song, The / My hero / Some day I'll find him.
Notes: Track One: from Die Fleidermaus Track Two: from Merry Widow Track Three:from Der Obersteiger Track Four:from The Opera all Track Five: from Gypsy Love Track seven:from La Perichole Track Nine:from The Chocolate Soldier
Album: released on PRT in Oct'85 by PRT Records. Distributed by: PRT

Musicassette: released on PRT in Oct'85 by PRT Records. Distributed by: PRT

Star for Sunday, A.
Album: released on MFP in Apr'79 by EMI Records. Distributed by: EMI

Musicassette: released on MFP in Apr'79 by EMI Records. Distributed by: EMI

World of Moira Anderson volume 1.
Album: released on Decca in Jul'74 by Decca Records. Distributed by: Polygram

World of Moira Anderson volume 4.
Musicassette: released on Decca in Apr'76 by Decca Records. Distributed by: Polygram

World of Moira Anderson volume 5.
Musicassette: released on Decca in Sep'76 by Decca Records. Distributed by: Polygram

World of Moira Anderson volume 2.
Musicassette: released on Decca in Nov'74 by Decca Records. Distributed by: Polygram

Anderson, Pink

Carolina blues man vol.1.
Tracks: / My baby left me this morning / Baby please don't go / Mama where did you stay last night / Big house blues / Meet me in the bottom / Weeping willow blues / Baby I'm going away / I had my fun / Everyday in the week.
Album: released on Prestige in Jun'84 by Prestige Records (USA). Distributed by: RCA, JSU, Swift

Anderson, Ray

Right Down Your Alley.
Compact disc: released on Soul Note (Italy) in Dec'86. Distributed by: Harmonia Mundi Distributors

Anderson, Ricky

I don't want to lose your love.
Single (7"): released on Creole in Aug'83 by Creole Records. Distributed by: Rhino, PRT

Nite spot.
Single (7"): released on Creole in Nov'84 by Creole Records. Distributed by: Rhino, PRT

Andersons

Boogie woogie bugle boy.
Single (7"): released on President in May'83 by President Records. Distributed by: Taylors, Spartan

Tin pan alley.
Tracks: / Love me forever / Thanks for the mem'ries / Talking in your sleep / Boogie woogie bugle boy / Reason to believe / Tin pan alley / Daddy / Baby come back / You never done it like that / We don't make each other laugh anymore / It won't be easy / Show me the way to go home.
Album: released on President in Mar'83 by President Records. Distributed by: Taylors, Spartan

Anderson, Sherwood

Winesburg, Ohio (The conscience of Winesburg).
Musicassette: released on Caedmon(USA) in '84 by Caedmon (USA) Records. Distributed by: Gower, Taylors, Discovery

Anderson, Stuart

'A' side 'B' side.
Album: released on Country House in Jun'81 by BGS Productions Ltd. Distributed by: Taylor, H.R., Record Merchandisers Distribution, Pinnacle, Sounds of Scotland Records

Musicassette: released on Country House in Jun'81 by BGS Productions Ltd. Distributed by: Taylor, H.R., Record Merchandisers Distribution, Pinnacle, Sounds of Scotland Records

On top of the world.
Tracks: / Millbank cottage etc. / Hawaiian tattoo / John MacFadyan etc. / Dumfries polka etc, The / Horee Horro etc. / Brig'Motel etc, The / Bandboys:Murdo's wedding etc. / Reine de mussette / Heroes of Kohima etc, The / Pipers weird crying time & On top of the world / Eight men of Moidart etc, The / Donald Maclean's farewell to Oban, etc..
Album: by Lismor Records. Distributed by: Lismor, Roots, Celtic Music

Stuart Anderson.
Tracks: / Orange blossom special / Mist covered mountains / My own land / Diggy liggy lo / Norman's telly tune / Jaqueline waltz, The / Happy accordion / Shetland two step / Lord Lovat's lament / Losefalter's / Mr.A'Spink Snr. / Dancing fingers / Mary of Skye / Circassion circle.
Album: released on Country House in Dec'80 by BGS Productions Ltd. Distributed by: Taylor, H.R., Record Merchandisers Distribution, Pinnacle, Sounds of Scotland Records

Musicassette: released on Country House in Dec'80 by BGS Productions Ltd. Distributed by: Taylor, H.R., Record Merchandisers Distribution, Pinnacle, Sounds of Scotland Records

Stuart Anderson's welcome.
Tracks: / Donald Ian Rankie etc. / My Florence / Captain Lumsden / Skyline of Skye, The / Spanish eyes / Cuckoo waltz / Flett from Flotta etc. / Helen Black etc. / Triumph march / Mingulay boat song etc. / Crusader's march etc. / Double eagle / Harvest home etc. / Mull of the coal / High Bens.
Album: released on Lismor in Nov'76 by Lismor Records. Distributed by: Lismor, Roots, Celtic Music

Anderson, Tom

Shetland folk fiddling (Anderson, Tom & Aly Bain).
Album: released on Topic in May'78. Distributed by: Roots Distribution

Andes

Guaranis, (Les).
Compact disc: released on Musidisc (France) in Dec'86. Distributed by: Discovery Distribution, Swift Distribution

And Indians

Opera of love.
Single (7"):

Andi, Patrick

Don't waste yourself.
Single (12"): released on Jedi in Oct'84. Distributed by: Jetstar

Andi Sex Gang

Amants d'un jour, (Les).

Single (12"): released on Illuminated in Sep'84 by IKF Records. Distributed by: Pinnacle, Cartel, Jetstar

Blind.
Album: released on Illuminated in Dec'84 by IKF Records. Distributed by: Pinnacle, Cartel, Jetstar

Ida-ho.
Single (7"): released on Illuminated in Feb'85 by IKF Records. Distributed by: Pinnacle, Cartel, Jetstar

Single (12"): released on Illuminated in Feb'85 by IKF Records. Distributed by: Pinnacle, Cartel, Jetstar

Naked and the dead.
Tracks: / Naked and the dead, The / You don't know me / Quick and the dead, The.
Single (12"): released on Revolver in Sep'86 by Revolver Records. Distributed by: Revolver, Cartel

Andreou, Petros

Classic bouzouki, The.
Album: released on Classic Bouzouki in Nov'85. Distributed by: M.I.S.

Andrew, Elvis

Just a lonely man.
Single (12"): released on Antigua's in Oct'83. Distributed by: Jetstar, Rough Trade

Andrews, Catherine

Fruits.
Album: released on Cat Tracks in Nov'82. Distributed by: Pinnacle

Andrews, Chris

20 golden pieces of Chris Andrews.
Tracks: / Yesterday man / To whom it concerns / Pretty Belinda / Something on my mind / Stop that girl / I love ya / Whatcha gonna do now / Long live love / They've all got their eyes on you / First time / Brown eyes / Silver lining / Sugar daddy / Lazy days / Carole O.K. / Too bad you don't want me / Message understood / Lady oh lady / It's all coming back to me / I'll walk to you.
Album: released on Bulldog in Jun'87 by Bulldog Records. Distributed by: President Distribution, Spartan, Swift, Taylor, H.R.

20 golden pieces of Chris Andrews.
Album: released on Bulldog in Jul'87 by Bulldog Records. Distributed by: President Distribution, Spartan, Swift, Taylor, H.R

Amazing grace.
Single (7"): released on Klub in Apr'79

To whom it concerns.
Extended-play record: released on Scoop 33 in Oct'84 by Pickwick Records. Distributed by: H.R. Taylor

Yesterday man.
Single (7"): released on Decca in Sep'65 by Decca Records. Distributed by: Polygram

Single (7"): released on Old Gold in Sep'85 by Old Gold Records. Distributed by: Lightning, Jazz Music, Spartan, Counterpoint

Andrews, Elaine

Amazing Elaine Andrews, The.
Musicassette: released on Klub in Apr'79

Album: released on Klub in Apr'79

In the beginning.
Album: released on Klub in Apr'79

Andrews, Harvey

Friends of mine.
Album: released on Beeswing in '85 by Broadside Records. Distributed by: Roots, Jazz Music, Celtic Music, Pinnacle, Projection

Golden pennies theme.
Single (7"): released on Telebell in Nov'85 by Towerbell Records. Distributed by: EMI

Margarita.
Tracks: / My little boy / Dear Miss Allyson / Lot 204 / Margarita / Long ago, far away / Pinball / Able baker / Hey, old friend.
Album: released on Beeswing in May'85 by Broadside Records. Distributed by: Roots, Jazz Music, Celtic Music, Pinnacle, Projection

Musicassette: released on Beeswing in May'85 by Broadside Records. Distributed by: Roots, Jazz Music, Celtic Music, Pinnacle, Projection

Me mom / We were there.
Single (7"): released on Dingles in Jul'83 by Dingles Records. Distributed by: Projection

Old mother earth.
Album: released on Beeswing in Feb'85 by Broadside Records. Distributed by: Roots, Jazz Music, Celtic Music, Pinnacle, Projection

PG.
Tracks: / Bruges / Cheeky young lad / Yesterdays' Bread / Songs that Harry wrote / Take a little time / Please don't get on the plane / Room service / She saw him smile / First you lose the rhyming / PG / Binges.
Album: released on Beeswing in Aug'87 by Broadside Records. Distributed by: Roots, Jazz Music, Celtic Music, Pinnacle, Projection

Writer of songs.
Album: released on Beeswing in May'85 by Broadside Records. Distributed by: Roots, Jazz Music, Celtic Music, Pinnacle, Projection

Single (7"): released on Modtone in May'86. Distributed by: EMI, Priority Distribution

Single (12"): released on Modtone in May'86. Distributed by: EMI, Priority Distribution

Andrew, Simon

Call me now (Don't).
Tracks: / Call me now (Don't) / So confused.
Single (7"): released on Epic in Sep'86 by CBS Records. Distributed by: CBS

Single (12"): released on Epic in Sep'86 by CBS Records. Distributed by: CBS

So confused.
Single (7"): released on Ideal Music in Oct'85 by Ideal Music Records. Distributed by: Ideal Music

Single (12"): released on Ideal Music in Oct'85 by Ideal Music Records. Distributed by: Ideal Music

Andrew Sisters, The

20 greatest hits.
Compact disc: released on The Compact Collection in Sep'87 by Conifer Records. Distributed by: Conifer Distribution

Andrews, Julie

Broadway's Fair.

Love me tender.
Tracks: / Crazy / Some days are diamonds / See the funny little clown / When I dream (Hey won't you play) / Another somebody done somebody wrong song / You don't bring me flowers / I wish I could hurt that way again / The valley that time forget / Blanket on the ground / Love is a place where two people fall / We love each other / Lyin' in my arms.
Album: released on Peach River in Jul'83 by Peach River Records. Distributed by: PRT

Album: released on Splash in Mar'85 by Splash Records. Distributed by: CBS

Musicassette: released on Splash in Mar'85 by Splash Records. Distributed by: CBS

Secret of Christmas, The.
Album: released on Embassy in Nov'77 by CBS Records. Distributed by: CBS

Andrews Sisters

20 greatest hits.
Album: released on Nostalgia (USA) in Dec'85 by Sonic Arts Corporation

Musicassette: released on Nostalgia (USA) in Dec'85 by Sonic Arts Corporation

Andrews Sisters.
Album: released on Magic(UK) in Apr'85

Musicassette: released on Magic(UK) in Apr'85

Album: released on EMI (Holland) in '83 by EMI Records. Distributed by: Conifer

Andrews Sisters, The.
Tracks: / Beimir bist du chon / Rum and coca cola / Beer barrel polka / Begin the beguine.
Album: released on Music For Pleasure (Holland) in '86 by EMI Records. Distributed by: EMI

Musicassette: released on Music For Pleasure (Holland) in '86 by EMI Records. Distributed by: EMI

At the microphone.
Album: released on Take 2 in Jun'87. Distributed by: Swift Distribution, Jazz Music Distribution

Beat me daddy eight to the bar.
Tracks: / Beat me daddy, eight to the bar / Boogie woogie bugle boy / I'll be with you in apple blossom time / Beer barrel polka / I can dream, can't I? / Pennsylvania polka / Hold tight (want some sea food mama) / Oh Johnny, Oh Johnny / Rum and coca-cola / Down in the valley / Bei mir du schon / The shrine of saint Cecilia / Rhumboogie / Joseph! Joseph! / South American way / Strip polka.
Album: released on MFP in May'82 by EMI Records. Distributed by: EMI

Musicassette: released on MFP in May'82 by EMI Records. Distributed by: EMI

Best of the Andrews Sisters, The.
Tracks: / The woodpeck song / Daddy / Elmer's tune / I love you much too much / The house of blue lights / Aurora / Straighten up and fly right / Down in the valley (hear that train blow) / Lullaby of Broadway / Down by the o-hi-o / Alexander's ragtime band / Let a smile be your umberella / The blond sailor / I remember mama / Too fat polka / A bushel and a peck / Rumours are flying / When the midnight choo choo leaves for Alabama / It never entered my head / Your red wagon.
Double Album: released on MCA Coral in Oct'81 by MCA Records. Distributed by: Polygram

Boogie woogie bugle boy.
Single (7"): released on Revival in Jul'82. Distributed by: Lightning, Swift

Single (7"): released on Old Gold in Nov'83 by Old Gold Records. Distributed by: Lightning, Jazz Music, Spartan, Counterpoint

Golden greats: Andrews Sisters.
Tracks: / Boogie woogie bugle boy / Beimir bist du schon / Don't sit under the apple tree / Rum and coca-cola / Beat me daddy eight to the bar.
Album: released on MCA in Jul'85 by MCA Records. Distributed by: Polygram, MCA

Musicassette: released on MCA in Jul'85 by MCA Records. Distributed by: Polygram, MCA

Jumpin' jive, The.
Tracks: / Jumpin' jive, The / Tu-li-tulip time / Oooo-oh boom / Tuxedo junction / I got Johhny Peddler / Daddy / Coffee song, The / Straighten up and fly right / Three little sisters / I'll pray for you / Pennsylvania 6-5000 / Rainy night in Rio, A / Mister five by five / Money is the root of all evil / Rancho pillow / Massachusetts.
Album: released on MCA in Apr'84 by MCA Records. Distributed by: Polygram, MCA

Musicassette: released on MCA in Apr'84 by MCA Records. Distributed by: Polygram, MCA

Sing the dancing 20's.
Tracks: / Last night on the back porch / When Francis dances with me / Back in your own back yard / Keep your skirts down / Mary Ann / The Japanese sandman / Show me the way to go home / Don't bring Lulu / Me too / That naughty waltz / A smile will go a long long way / Barney Google / Collegiate.
Notes: Mono. Nostalgia existed even in the 50's. On this light-hearted album, the Andrews Sisters revive the carefree days of he 20's with tunes such as 'Don't Bring Lulu','Keep your skirts down, Mary Ann','When Francis Dances with me' and many more, all with orchestrarion by Billy May.
Album: by Capitol Records. Distributed by: EMI

Musicassette: released on Capitol in Apr'85 by Capitol Records. Distributed by: EMI

Very best of the Andrew Sisters.
Tracks: / Booglie - wooglie piggy, The / Beat me daddy eight to the bar / Rhumboogie / House of blue light, The / Say si si / Oh Johnny oh Johnny oh / Boogie woogie bugle boy / Don't sit under the apple tree / Rum and coca cola / Beer barrel polka / South American way / Bei mir bist du schon / Shoo shoo baby / Strip polka / I'll be with you in apple blossom time / Hold tight.
Album: released on MCA in Dec'81 by MCA Records. Distributed by: Polygram, MCA

Musicassette: by MCA Records. Distributed by: Polygram, MCA

Worth remembering.
Album: released on Magic in Oct'84. Distributed by: Jazz Music, Submarine, Swift, Chris Wellard, Conifer

Musicassette: released on Magic in Oct'84. Distributed by: Jazz Music, Submarine, Swift, Chris Wellard, Conifer

Andrews-Walsh

Classics of Irish piping vol 2.
Tracks: / The portlaw reel / The faithful brown cow / Billy Taylor's fancy / The garden of daisies / The bank of the Suir / The mountain lark / Dan McCarthy's fancy / The cliffs of Moher / Saddle the pony (Walsh) / Yellow John / Kitty's rambles / Speed the plough / Johnny Gorman / Two single jigs / May day / The cuckoo's nest / Smash the windows / Rocky road to Dublin / Bonny Kate / The first house of Connaught / Munster buttermilk (Andrew's).
Album: released on Topic in '81. Distributed by: Roots Distribution

Andreyev, V

Suite (Andreyev, V & Russian Folk Orchestra).
Album: released on Melodiya (USSR) in May'78. Distributed by: T.B.C Distribution

Andros, Dede

Master of the game.
Single (7"): released on BBC in Aug'84 by BBC Records & Tapes. Distributed by: EMI, PRT, Pye

Andrzej Wajda Trilogy

Andrzej Wajda Trilogy Original soundtrack recordings (Various Artists).
Album: released on TER in Dec'83. Distributed by: Pinnacle

And So To Bed

And so to bed (Vocal selection from the show by the original cast) (Various Artists).
Album: . Distributed by: Polygram

And So To Bed - The EP.
Single (7"): released on Timebox in Sep'87 by Timebox records. Distributed by: Pinnacle

Just desserts/ Plaindom.
Single (7"): released on Timebox in Aug'87 by Timebox records. Distributed by: Pinnacle

And The Bands Played On

And the bands played on Various artists-music from the ATV series) (Various dance bands).
Album: released on Decca in Aug'80 by Decca Records. Distributed by: Polygram

And the bands played on Various original 1930's bands (Various Artists).
Musicassette: released on Decca in Aug'80 by Decca Records. Distributed by: Polygram

And the bands played on Various original artists (Various original artists).
Double Album: released on Decca in May'77 by Decca Records. Distributed by: Polygram

And The Ship Sails On

And the ship sails on Original soundtrack (Various Artists).
Tracks: / Convoi funebre, Le / Depart, Le / De la cuisine au salon / Le cygne / Pas de trois / L'escalier d'honneur / Valse de l'archiduchesse, La / Glass-concertino / Clare de lune / Kolo vlah.
Notes: This latest Fellini film, currently showing in London and scheduled for nation release, has received much critical acclaim. Featured in the cast is Italian soprano Mara Zampieri who makes her debute with the Royal Opera House, Covent Garden in the title role of Tosca, On 8 June.
Album: released on Milan in Jun'84, IMS Distribution, Conifer Distribution, Discovery Distribution

And Would You...

And would you believe yet another 100 comedy DJ inserts

Andy, Bob

Friends.
Album: released on I-Anka in Nov'83 by I-Anka Records. Distributed by: Revolver, Cartel, Jetstar

Honey.
Single (12"): released on I-Anka in Jul'83 by I-Anka Records. Distributed by: Revolver, Cartel, Jetstar

Just for a time.
Tracks: / Just for a time / Life.
Single (12"): released on Anka in Aug'86. Distributed by: Jetstar

Lot's of love & I.
Album: released on Skynote in Aug'78. Distributed by: Sidewalk Records

Music inside me, the.

Album: released on Tropical Soundtracks in Jan'77

Super powers Dark clouds.
Single (12"): released on I-Anka in Jul'87 by I-Anka Records. Distributed by: Revolver, Cartel, Jetstar

Andy Capp

Andy Capp Original cast with Tom Courtenay (Various Artists).
Album: released on Key in Feb'83 by Key Records. Distributed by: Spartan

Andy & Chris

Unrest work & play (EP).
Single (7"): released on Art House in Nov'82

Andy, Horace

Ain't no love.
Single (12"): released on Tads in Jan'84 by Tads Records. Distributed by: Jetstar Distribution

Best of Horace Andy.
Album: released on Culture Press in Jun'85 by Vista Sounds Records. Distributed by: Jetstar, Rough Trade

Big bad man, The.
Album: released on Rockers Forever in 9 May'87. Distributed by: Jetstar Distribution

Clash of the Andys (Andy, Horace & Patrick).
Album: released on Thunderbolt in Oct'85 by Magnum Music Group Ltd. Distributed by: Magnum Music Group Ltd, PRT Distribution, Spartan Distribution

Confusion.
Album: released on Music Hawk in Jul'85 by Music Hawk Records. Distributed by: Jetstar Distribution

Single (12"): released on Music Hawk in Jun'84 by Music Hawk Records. Distributed by: Jetstar Distribution

Cool & deadly.
Single (12"): released on Tads in Oct'83 by Tads Records. Distributed by: Jetstar Distribution

Cus cus.
Single (12"): released on Scom in Jan'85 by Scom Records. Distributed by: Jetstar

Dance hall style.
Album: released on Wackies in Jul'85 by Wackies Records. Distributed by: Jetstar

Elementary (Andy, Horace & The Rhythm Queen).
Album: released on Rough Trade in Dec'85 by Rough Trade Records. Distributed by: Rough Trade Distribution, Cartel Distribution

Elementary.
Single (12"): released on Rough Trade in Apr'85 by Rough Trade Records. Distributed by: Rough Trade Distribution, Cartel Distribution

Eternal love.
Single (12"): released on Tads in Apr'84 by Tads Records. Distributed by: Jetstar Distribution

Exclusively.
Album: released on Solid Groove in Oct'82. Distributed by: Jetstar, Pinnacle

Gateman (Andy, Horace/Percy Clark & Reprobates(b-side)).
Single (12"): released on Fashion in Aug'85 by Fashion Records. Distributed by: PRT, Jetstar

Get down.
Single (12"): released on Rough Trade in Jul'85 by Rough Trade Records. Distributed by: Rough Trade Distribution, Cartel Distribution

Gun shot.
Single (12"): released on Taxi in Sep'84 by Taxi Records. Distributed by: Jetstar Distribution

Haul and jack up.
Album: released on Live & Love in Jul'87 by Third World Records. Distributed by: Jetstar

Hypocrites.
Tracks: / Hypocrites / Diplomatic dance / Hypocrites / Diplomatic Don.
Single (12"): released on Fashion in May'86 by Fashion Records. Distributed by: PRT, Jetstar

I'm in love.
Single (7"): released on Oval in May'82. Distributed by: Projection

Love hangover.
Single (12"): released on S.Groove in Jul'82

Must have to get it.
Single (12"): released on Live & Love in May'87 by Third World Records. Distributed by: Jetstar

One more night.
Single (12"): released on Money Disc in Nov'85. Distributed by: Jetstar Distribution

Ramm dancemaster.
Single (12"):

Reggae superstar's meet

Showcase.
Album: released on Vista Sounds in '83 by Vista Sounds Records Distributed by: Jetstar

Sweet music.
Single (12"): released on Music Hawk in Nov'83 by Music Hawk Records. Distributed by: Jetstar Distribution

Things for you & I.
Album: released on Striker Lee in Mar'85 by Striker Lee Records. Distributed by: Jetstar Distribution

User.
Tracks: / User / User (version).
Single (12"): released on Music Hawk in Feb'86 by Music Hawk Records. Distributed by: Jetstar Distribution

Watch your step.
Tracks: / Watch your step / Strange thing.
Single (12"): released or Ragin' Lion in Feb'86

You are my angel.
Single (12"): released on Tads in Jul'84 by Tads Records. Distributed by: Jetstar Distribution

Andy Pandy

Andy Pandy & Teddy at the zoo Churchmen, Ysanne (Churchman, Ysanne).
Musicassette: released on Look & Listen in Nov'84 by Listen For Pleasure. Distributed by: EMI

Andy Pandy & the badger Churchmen, Ysanne (Churchman, Ysanne).
Musicassette: released on Look & Listen in Nov'84 by Listen For Pleasure. Distributed by: EMI

Andy Pandy & the dovecot Various artists (Various Artists).
Musicassette: released on Listen For Pleasure in Jun'84 by MFP Records. Distributed by: EMI

Andy Pandy & the ducklings Various artists (Various Artists).
Musicassette: released on Listen For Pleasure in Jun'84 by MFP Records. Distributed by: FMI

Andy Pandy & the red motor car Various artists (Various Artists).
Musicassette: released on Listen For Pleasure in Jun'84 by MFP Records. Distributed by: EMI

Andy Pandy & the spotted cow Various artists (Various Artists).
Musicassette: released on Listen For Pleasure in Jun'84 by MFP Records. Distributed by: EMI

Andy Pandy & the willow tree Various artists (Various Artists).
Musicassette: released on Listen For Pleasure in Jun'84 by MFP Records. Distributed by: EMI

Andy, Patrick

Cow horn chalice.
Single (7"): released on Ujama in Oct'84 by Ujama Records. Distributed by: Spartan, Jetstar

Cry for me.

Single (12"): released on Crystal in Nov'85 by Crystal Records. Distributed by: Jetstar, Revolver, Cartel

Don't worry yourself.
Single (12"): released on Jedi in Jan'85. Distributed by: Jetstar

Get up,stand up.
Single (12"): released on Greensleeves in Aug'84 by Greensleeves Records. Distributed by: BMG, Jetstar, Spartan

Neat si sweet.
Single (12"): released on Tonof in Mar'85 by Tonof Records. Distributed by: Jetstar Distribution

Pretty me.
Single (12"): released on Jedi in Nov'84. Distributed by: Jetstar

Sting me a sting,shock me a shock.
Single (12"): released on Greensleeves in Mar'85 by Greensleeves Records. Distributed by: BMG, Jetstar, Spartan

Struggle (Andy, Patrick & Aswad).
Single (12"): by Simba Records. Distributed by: Jetstar

Two new superstars (Andy, Patrick & Frankie Jones).
Album: released on Burning Sounds in Sep'85 by Ross, Bill/Burning Sounds Records. Distributed by: PRT

Andy T

Weary of the flesh(EP).
Single (7"): released on Crass in Nov'82 by Exitstencil Music. Distributed by: Rough Trade, Cartel

Aneka

Biographical Details: Despite appearing on "Top Of The Pops" with kimono and Japanese wig, Aneka was, in fact, a Scottish folk singer usually known as Mary Sandeman. Deciding to record a pop single purely for fun, she cut a Eurodisco record and entitled "Japanese Boy" for the German - based Hansa company, best known for its Boney M hits. The song went to No.1 in the UK and was also a sizeable Continental hit. Several follow-ups were tried, but Sandeman soon returned to her Gaelic folk singing-Anekan had only been a hobby.

Heart to beat.
Single (7"): released on Ariola in Feb'83. Distributed by: RCA, Ariola

Japanese boy.
Tracks: / Japanese boy / I lost my heart to a starship trooper.
Notes: Double 'A' side
Single (7"): released on Hansa in Sep'82 by Hansa Records. Distributed by: Polygram

Single (7"): released on Old Gold in Apr'87 by Old Gold Records. Distributed by: Lightning, Jazz Music, Spartan, Counterpoint

Ooh shooby doo doo lang.
Single (7"): released on Hansa in Sep'82 by Hansa Records. Distributed by: Polygram

An Evening With...

An evening with Windham Hill Various artists (Various Artists).
Compact disc: . Distributed by: AM

Angel

Do it.
Single (7"): released on Rainbow in Nov'85. Distributed by: I & B, CBS

Single (12"): released on Rainbow in Nov'85. Distributed by: I & B, CBS

Driving (down).
Single (7"): released on Teddy Bear Records in Aug'82

It's gonna come back to you.
Tracks: / It's gonna come back to you / Tomorrow night.
Single (7"): released on Rainbow in Jun'86. Distributed by: I & B, CBS

Single (12"): released on Rainbow in Jun'86. Distributed by: I & B, CBS

Angel Chorus

Devil on my shoulder.
Tracks: / Devil on my shoulder / Can't you see / Devil on my shoulder (dub).

Single (7"): released on 10 in Jan'86 by 10 Records. Distributed by: Virgin, EMI

Single (12"): released on 10 in Jan'86 by 10 Records. Distributed by: Virgin, EMI

Angel Corpus Christi

I love New York.
Album: released on Criminal Damage in Aug'85 by Criminal Damage Records. Distributed by: Backs, Cartel

Wake up and cry.
Album: released on Criminal Damage in Aug'86 by Criminal Damage Records. Distributed by: Backs, Cartel

Angel Eek

Look at me now.
Single (7"): released on Playfair in Mar'83

Angelic Upstarts

Angel dust(The collected highs).
Tracks: / The murder of Liddel Towers / Police oppression / I'm an upstart / Teenage warning / Never 'ad nothin' / Shotgun solution / Last night another soldier / Two million voices / Kids on the street / England / Hearts lament / Shotgun solution / Never say die / Woman in disguise / Solidarity / Lust for glory / Never give up / Waiting hating / Reason why? / Nobody was saved / Geordies wife / Loneliness of the long distance runner / 42nd street / The burglar / Fire flew over the cuckoo's nest / As the passion / A young punk / Where we started.
Album: released on Anagram in Sep'83 by Cherry Red Records. Distributed by: Pinnacle

Musiccassette: released on Anagram in Sep'83 by Cherry Red Records. Distributed by: Pinnacle

Bootlegs and Rarities.
Tracks: / Kids on the street / Stick's diary / Last night another soldier - Police oppression / I'm an upstart / Student power / Teenage warning / Liddle Towers (Who killed) / We are the people / Tommy, never again / Box on / Solidarity (Polish folk song) / Tut tut shuffle, The / Gonna be a star.
Album: released on Dojo in Apr'86 by Castle Communications Records. Distributed by: Cartel

Brighton bomb.
Single (12"): released on Gas in Jun'85 by Gas Records. Distributed by: Pinnacle

Burglar, The.
Single (7"): released on Anagram in Jul'83 by Cherry Red Records. Distributed by: Pinnacle

Last tango in Moscow.
Album: released on Picasso in Sep'85 by Picasso Records. Distributed by: Pinnacle

Live in Yugoslavia.
Album: released on Picasso in Sep'85 by Picasso Records. Distributed by: Pinnacle

Machine gun Kelly.
Single (12"): released on Picasso in Jul'85 by Picasso Records. Distributed by: Pinnacle

Not just a name.
Single (7"): released on Anagram in Sep'83 by Cherry Red Records. Distributed by: Pinnacle

Single (12"): released on Anagram in Sep'83 by Cherry Red Records. Distributed by: Pinnacle

Power of the press.
Album: released on Gas in Jan'86 by Gas Records. Distributed by: Pinnacle

Solidarity.
Single (7"): released on Anagram in May'83 by Cherry Red Records. Distributed by: Pinnacle

Single (12"): released on Anagram in May'83 by Cherry Red Records. Distributed by: Pinnacle

Teenage warning.
Album: released on Warner Bros. in Aug'79 by Warner Bros Records. Distributed by: WEA

Musiccassette: released on Warner Bros. in Aug'79 by Warner Bros Records. Distributed by: WEA

We gotta get out of this place.
Album: by WEA Records. Distributed by: WEA

Woman in disguise.
Single (7"): released on Anagram in Nov'82 by Cherry Red Records. Distributed by: Pinnacle

Single (12"): released on Anagram in Nov'82 by Cherry Red Records. Distributed by: Pinnacle

Angelo, Bobby

Baby sittin'.
Single (7"): released on Old Gold in Oct'83 by Old Gold Records. Distributed by: Lightning, Jazz Music, Spartan, Counterpoint

Angelo, Don

Bietcle move.
Single (12"): released on R & M in Oct'84 by R & M Records. Distributed by: Jetstar

Clash

Golden hen (The)

Reggae music we want.
Tracks: / Reggae music we want / Petty robber.
Single (12"): released on Unity Sound in Feb'86. Distributed by: Jetstar

Angels

Biographical Details: The Angels were a vocal trio from New Jersey consisting of two sister Barbara and Jiggs plus another girl Peggy. The group formed in 1961, and achieved two US Top 40 hits with "Til" and "Cry Baby Cry". The big one came in the autumn of '63 when they hit No.1 with "My Boyfriend's Back", a song written by Richard Gottehrer (later known for his production work with Blondie and the Go-Gos), Gerald Goldstein and Robert Fieldman. Britain, by this time, was caught up in Beatlemania and was no longer interested in theis rapidly dating early Sixties girl-group sound, unless it was produced by Phil Spector. The record had just one week on the UK Top 50, at No.50. The girls could only manage one more American success before the Beatles conquered that country too.

My boyfriend's back.
Single (7"): released on Creole in Aug'82 by Creole Records. Distributed by: Rhino, PRT

Angels Are Coming

Angels are coming Various Artists (Various Artists).
Musicassette: released on Sunset Gun in Nov'83

Angels In The...

Angels In The Architecture Various Artists (Angels In The Architecture).
Notes: Over 50 minutes of music on LP or cassette and almost one hour on Compact Disc. Compact Disc and Cassette feature an extra track. 'Angels in Architecture' fea tures the very best of artists who record for Editions EG.
Album: released on E.G. in Mar'87 by Virgin Records. Distributed by: Virgin, EMI

Musicassette: released on E.G. in Mar'87 by Virgin Records. Distributed by: Virgin, EMI

Compact disc: by Virgin Records. Distributed by: EMI

Angels Of Light

Godstar

Angels With Dirty Faces

Angels with dirty faces Various Artists (Various Artists).
Album: released on Future-No-Future in Dec'83. Distributed by: Pinnacle

Angel Witch

Biographical Details: This British three-piece band are one of rhe acts who share the dubious distinction of being the Least Successful Chart Act on the singles list. "Sweet Danger", their only chart single, enjoyed just one week of glory in 1980-at No.75.

Angel Witch.
Album: released on Bronze in Dec'80 by Polygram Records. Distributed by: Polydor

Musicassette: released on Bronze in Dec'80 by Polygram Records. Distributed by: Polydor

Doctor Phibes.
Tracks: / Angel witch / Atlantis / White witch / Confused / Sorcerer / Loser / Docter Phibes / Gorgon / Sweet danger / Free man / Angel of death / Devil's tower / Suffer.
Notes: K. Heybourne/Hit Songs Ltd except track 7 K. Heybourne/Riddles/Dufort/Hit Songs Ltd. Produced by Martin Smith
Album: released on Raw Power in Sep'86. Distributed by: Pinnacle

Frontal assault.
Album: released on Killerwatt in May'86. Distributed by: Kingdom Records, Pinnacle

Goodbye.
Single (7"): released on Killerwatt in Jul'85. Distributed by: Kingdom Records, Pinnacle

Screamin' 'n'bleedin'.
Album: released on Killerwatt in Jul'85. Distributed by: Kingdom Records, Pinnacle

Anger, Darol

Chiaroscuro (Anger, Darol & Mike Marshall).

Live at Montreux (Anger, Darol/Barbera Higbie Quintet).
Album: released on Windham Hill (Germany) in Aug'85

Live At Montreux (Anger, Darol/Barbera Higbie Quintet).
Album: released on Windham Hill in May'86. Distributed by: AM

Musicassette: released on Windham Hill in May'86. Distributed by: AM

Compact disc: . Distributed by: AM

Tideline (Anger, Darol & Barbara Higbie).
Notes: Darol Anger - violin/Barbara Higbie - acoustic piano/Mike Marshall - multi instrumentation/Michael Manring - bass/Andy Narrell - steel drums. The music is a wonderful melting pot of classical, pop, jazz, r'n'b and bluegrass, incorporating Western, African and Caribbean styles.
Album: released on Windham Hill in May'86. Distributed by: AM

Musicassette: released on Windham Hill in May'86. Distributed by: AM

Tidelines (Anger, Darol & Barbara Higbie).
Album: released on Windham Hill (Germany) in Sep'84

Angers, Daryl

Fiddlesticks.
Album: released on Kaleidoscope in Sep'79

Angie

Don't let it break your heart.
Single (7"): released on Lamborghini in Jun'84 by Lamborghini Records. Distributed by: PRT

Anglaspel

Lappland.
Album: released on Dragon in Jul'87 by Dragon Records. Distributed by: Jazz Music, Projection, Cadillac

Angola-Bonga

Noir ton pay.
Album: . Distributed by: Conifer, Discovery

Angola Prisoner's Blues

Angola prisoner's blues Various artists (Various Artists).
Album: released on Arhoolie in May'81 by Arhoolie Records. Distributed by: Projection, Topic, Jazz Music, Swift, Roots

Angst

Angst Original soundtrack (Various Artists).
Notes: Music by Karl Schulz
Album: released on Thunderbolt in Feb'86 by Magnum Music Group Ltd. Distributed by: Magnum Music Group Ltd, PRT Distribution, Spartan Distribution

Angus

Papa don't freak.
Single (12"): released on Megaton in Jul'87 by Megaton Records. Distributed by: Rough Trade Distribution, Cartel Distribution

Track of doom.
Album: released on Megaton in Jul'86 by Megaton Records. Distributed by: Rough Trade Distribution, Cartel Distribution

An Hour Of...

An hour of golden songs of stage and screen (Various Artists).
Tracks: / Around the world / Somewhere my love (Lara's theme from Dr. Zhivago) / Evergreen / Day by day/Prepare ye the way of the Lord (from Godspell) / Summer knows, The (from Summer of '42) / Send in the clowns (from A little night music) / Edelweiss / Somewhere (from West side story) / Long ago and far away (from No, no Nanette) / People (from Funny Girl) / Don't cry for me Argentina (from Evita) / Soliloquy (My boy Bill) (from Carousel) / Where do I begin / Gonna build a mountain (from Stop the world ...) / Alfie (From Alfie) / How to handle a woman / Sunrise, sunset (from Fiddler on the Roof).
Musicassette: released on Hour Of Pleasure in Aug'86 by Music For Pleasure Records. Distributed by: EMI. Estim retail price in Sep'87 was £1.99.

An hour of Sousa Marches (Various Artists).
Tracks: / Stars and stripes forever / King Cotton / National fencibles / High school cadets / Manhattan beach / Semper fidelis / Invincible eagle / Gladiator, The / Washington post / Hands across the sea / Royal Welsh Fusileirs, The / Legionaires, The / Daughters of Texas / Gallant seventh, The / Golden jubillee / Pride of the wolverines, The / Hail to the spirit of liberty / Kansas wildcats / Sound off / Thunderer, The.
Notes: Composer: Sousa Tracks 1-11 conducted by Major Trevor L Sharpe, MBE LROM ARCM Psm. Tracks 12-22 Band of HM Royal Marines conducted by Lt. Col. G.A.C. Hoskins MVO LRAM RM
Musicassette: released on Hour Of Pleasure in Aug'86 by Music For Pleasure Records. Distributed by: EMI. Estim retail price in Sep'87 was £1.99.

An hour of the hits of 1962 (Various Artists).
Tracks: / When my little girl is smiling / Softly as I leave you / Cindy's birthday / Little Miss Lonely / Guitar tango / What now my love / Lovesick blues / Hole in the ground, The / Must be Madison / Baby take a bow / Let's talk about love / Our favourite melodies / Nut rocker / Drums are my beat / Jambalaya (on the bayou) / Clown shoes / Sharing you / James Bond theme (from Dr. No) / Norman / As you like it / Up on the roof / I remember you / Tell me what he said / Wonderful land / Theme from Dr. Kildare.
Musicassette: released on Hour Of Pleasure in Aug'86 by Music For Pleasure Records. Distributed by: EMI

An hour of the hits of 1963 (Various Artists).
Tracks: / Do you want to know a secret / If you've got to make a fool of somebody / Stay / Hippy hippy shake, The / I'll never get over you / Hello little girl / Foot tapper / Night has a thousand eyes / My way / My little girl / Surfin' USA / Little town flirt / We are in love / Hungry for love / Searchin' / First time / Dance on / Don't you think it's time / I'll keep you satisfied / Confession (that I love you) / I like it / bad to me / Cruel sea, The / I (who have nothing) / I'm telling you now / I'm in love / From Russia with love / How do you do it.
Musicassette: released on Hour Of Pleasure in Aug'86 by Music For Pleasure Records. Distributed by: EMI

An hour of the hits of 1964 Various artists (Various Artists).
Tracks: / Hungry for love / Poison ivy / Little children / Anyone who had a heart / Just one look / World without love, A / Little loving, A / Don't let the sun catch you crying / Rise and fall of Flingel Bunt (The) / You're no good / Do wah diddy diddy / Message to Martha, A (Kentucky blubird) / One way love / Golfinger / I'm the one / I'm into something good / 5-4-3-2-1 / House of the rising sun (The) / We're through / Over you / Nobody I know / I'm in love / Rhythm and greens / Good golly miss Molly / Message to Martha, A (Kentucky blubird) / I understand / Little loving, A.
Musicassette: released on Hour Of Pleasure in May'87 by Music For Pleasure Records. Distributed by: EMI. Estim retail price in Sep'87 was £1.99.

An hour of the hits of 1965 Various artists (Various Artists).
Musicassette: released on Hour Of Pleasure in Sep'87 by Music For Pleasure Records. Distributed by: EMI. Estim retail price in Sep'87 was £1.99.

An hour of your favourite hymns Various artists (Various Artists).
Tracks: / Onward christian soldiers / I will sing the wondrous story / What a friend we have in Jesus / In the bleak midwinter / Tell me the old, old story / Lord of all hopefulness / Lord's my shepherd, The / Abide with me / In the sweet by and by / Holy city, The / Paise my soul / Steal away / My Jesus I love thee / O come all ye faithful (Adeste Fideles) / Who is he? (In yonder stall) / Just a closer walk with thee / Faith can move mountains / Sweet hour of prayer / Behold me standing at the door / Old rugged cross.
Musicassette: released on Hour Of Pleasure in Sep'87 by Music For Pleasure Records. Distributed by: EMI. Estim retail price in Sep'87 was £1.99.

Anhrefn

Sheep skateboards & wellies.
Album: released on Workers Playtime in Jul'87

An Imaginative Woman

An imaginative woman Hardy, Thomas (Morant, Richard).
Musicassette: released on Talking Tape in '84

Animal Farm

Model soldier.
Single (7"): released on Rot in Mar'84 by Rot Records. Distributed by: Red Rhino Through Cartel Distributions

Animal House

Animal house Original soundtrack (Original Soundtrack).
Tracks: / Faber College theme / Louie, Louie / Twistin' the night away / Tossin' and turnin' / Shama lama ding dong / Hey Paula / Animal house / Money (that's what I want) / Let's dance / Dream girl / (What a) wonderful world / Shout.
Compact disc: released on MCA in Sep'87 by MCA Records. Distributed by: Polygram, MCA

Animal Hysteria

Jingle bells.
Single (7"): released on Look in Dec'83. Distributed by: R. Smith & Co. Records, H.R. Taylor

Animal Liberation

Animal Liberation (Various Artists).
Album: released on Waxtrax in Jul'87 by Jungle Records. Distributed by: PRT

Animal Magic

Doo doo dooley.
Single (7"): released on Sniff in Apr'83 by Sniff Records. Distributed by: Stiff

Get it right.
Single (7"): released on Record Shack in Feb'82 by Record Shack Records. Distributed by: PRT

Single (12"): released on Record Shack in Feb'82 by Record Shack Records. Distributed by: PRT

Standard man.
Single (7"): released on Recreational in May'82 by Revolver Records. Distributed by: Rough Trade

Welcome to the monkey house.
Single (12"): released on EMI in Nov'81 by EMI Records. Distributed by: EMI

Animal Nightlife

Love is just the great pretender.
Single (7"): released on Island in Jun'85 by Island Records. Distributed by: Polygram

Double-pack single: released on Island in Jun'85 by Island Records. Distributed by: Polygram

Picture disc single: released on Island in Jul'85 by Island Records. Distributed by: Polygram

Musicassette: released on Island in Jul'85 by Island Records. Distributed by: Polygram

Love is just the great pretender 'undressing'.
Single (12"): released on Island in Jul'85 by Island Records. Distributed by: Polygram

Mighty hands of love.
Single (7"): released on Inner Vision in Mar'83 by CBS Records. Distributed by: CBS

Single (12"): released on Inner Vision in Mar'83 by CBS Records. Distributed by: CBS

Mr. Solitaire.
Single (7"): released on Island in Jul'84 by Island Records. Distributed by: Polygram

Picture disc single: released on Island in Jul'84 by Island Records. Distributed by: Polygram

Musicassette:

Preacher, preacher.

Single (7"): released on Island in Sep'85 by Island Records. Distributed by: Polygram

Musicassette: released on Island in Oct'85 by Island Records. Distributed by: Polygram

Preacher preacher remix.
Single (12"): released on Island in Oct'85 by Island Records. Distributed by: Polygram

Shangri-la.
Album: released on Island in Aug'85 by Island Records. Distributed by: Polygram

Musicassette: released on Island in Aug'85 by Island Records. Distributed by: Polygram

Animals

Biographical Details: The Animals had their roots in an early Sixties jazz trio, the Alan Price Combo. They became the Animals when Burdon and Valentine were recruited in 1962. Having gigged around their native Newcastle, they cut their own EP and sold five hundred copies. Pop producer Mickie Most, who had recently returned from being a recording star in South Africa, was impressed and brought them down to London. Success was immediate. The band remade "Baby Let Me Follow You Down", a track from Bob Dylan's debut album, and called it "Baby Let Me Take You Home". It reached No.21. In a move that was as obvious as it was brilliant, they followed that initial hit with a version of the very next track on the Dylan album. The traditional blues number "House Of The Rising Sun" proved perfect for the Animals' bluesy style. It shot to No.1 not only in Britain but also in the States, wherethe Beatles were leading the famous British invasion. Burdon's passionate vocals combined with the eerie organ arrangement of Alan Price, made it quite unlike anything else being played on pop radio at the time. In this regard, it broke an important barrier in Britain by being over four minutes in length, far longer than the conventional 2:30 - 3 minute pop single (though in America an edited version was usually played). "House Of The Rising Sun's" all - time classic status was reaffirmed in 1972 and 1982, when it hit the British Top 30 for the second and third times. Having made the major contributions to the appeal of "House", Burdon and Price wrote its follow-up themselves. "I'm Crying" reached No.8 in the UK and No.19 in the US. The Animals' self-titled debut LP established the group as one of the greatest white exponents of black rhythm and blues; it featured a mix of originals and blues standards, all sung convincingly and powerfully by Burdon. Having become international stars in '64, they continued in '65 withthe hits "Don't Let Me Be Misunderstood", "Bring It On Home To Me" and "We've Gotta Get Out Of This Place", all Top 10 in Britain and Top 40 in America. About this time, Price quit the group, citing not only musical differences but a manic fear of flying. He went on to have hits in the Sixties and Seventies with the Alan Price Set, with Georgie Fame and as a solo artist. The Animals continued having hits for a year without Price but, following the departure of John Steel in '66 the group broke up. Burdon embarked on a solo career but, on record company insistence used the billing 'Eric Burdon and the Animals'. Hits followed for a couple of years, "San Franciscan Nights" being the biggest on both sides of the Atlantic. In 1970, as one of the greatest white r'n'b singers, he teamed up with US soul act War for a one-off American hit. Meanwhile Chas Chandler, having been Jimi Hendrix's manager, was about to guide slade to the top. The Animals have released two reunion albums, in 1977 and 1983, but neither were of any great musical value. (Bob McDonald 1984)

All time greatest hits.
Tracks: / I'm crying / House of the rising sun / Boom boom / I'm mad again / Bring it on home to me / We've gotta get out of this place / Story of Bo Diddley / How you've changed / Bright lights big city / Road runner / Worried life blues / It's my life / Bury my body / I've been around / Dimples / I'm in love again / Girl can't help it, The / For Miss Caulker / Talkin' about you / She said yeah.
Double Album: released on EMI (Germany) in '83 by EMI Records. Distributed by: Conifer

Animals, The.
Album: released on Charly in Feb'81 by Charly Records. Distributed by: Charly, Cadillac

Animal tracks.
Tracks: / Mess around / How you've changed / Hallelujah / I love her so / I love her so / I believe to my soul / Worried life blues / Roberta / I ain't got you / Bright lights big city / Let the good times roll / For Miss Caulker / Roadrunner.
Album: released on Fame (Columbia) in Sep'84 by Music For Pleasure Records. Distributed by: EMI

Musicassette: released on Fame (Columbia) in Sep'84 by Music For Pleasure Records. Distributed by: EMI

Before we were so rudely interrupted.
Tracks: / Last clean shirt / It's all over now, baby blue / Fire on the sun / As the crow flies / Please send me someone to love / Many rivers to cross / Just a little bit / Riverside County / Lonely avenue / Fool, The.
Album: released on Polydor (Italy) in Jun'83

Musicassette: released on Polydor (Italy) in Jun'83

Greatest hits live: Animals.
Tracks: / It's too late / House of the rising sun / It's my life / Don't bring me down / Don't let me be misunderstood / I'm crying / Bring it on home to me / O lucky man / Boom boom / We've gotta get out of this place.
Album: released on I.R.S.(Independent Record Syndicate) in Sep'84 by I.R.S.. Distributed by: MCA

Musicassette: released on I.R.S.(Independent Record Syndicate) in Sep'84 by I.R.S.. Distributed by: MCA

House of the rising sun (3LP set).
Triple album / cassette: released on Capitol(USA) in Jan'85 by Capitol (USA) Records. Distributed by: EMI

House of the rising sun.
Tracks: / House of the rising sun / Don't let me be misunderstood / I'm crying / It's my life.
Album: released on European Import in Jun'83. Distributed by: Conifer

Musicassette: released on European Import in Jun'83. Distributed by: Conifer

House of the rising sun (single).
Single (7"): released on Rak Replay in Sep'82

Picture disc single: released on Rak Replay in Sep'82

Single (7"): released on EMI (France) in Apr'83 by EMI Records. Distributed by: Conifer

Most of the animals.
Album: released on Music For Pleasure in Aug'81 by EMI Records. Distributed by: EMI

Musicassette: released on Music For Pleasure in Aug'81 by EMI Records. Distributed by: EMI

Newcastle December 1963 (Animals/Sonny Boy Williamson).
Tracks: / Sonny's slow walk / Pontiac blues / My babe / I don't care no more / Baby don't you worry / Night time is the right time / I'm gonna put you down / Fattening frogs for snakes / Nobody but you / Bye bye sonny / Bye bye coda.
Album: released on Charly in '82 by Charly Records. Distributed by: Charly, Cadillac

not on file (Animals/Eric Burdon).
Album: released on Charly in Mar'83 by Charly Records. Distributed by: Charly, Cadillac

Animal Sampler

Animal sampler Various Artists (Various Artists).
Tracks: / Run through the jungle / Dancing in Heaven / Pantherman / Horse song, The / Like calling up thunder / I'm on this rocket / Villagers, The / All the way / I don't know samba / Twitch, The / Babylon under pressure / Irresistable impulse.
Album: released on Animal in Feb'83 by Chrysalis Records. Distributed by: Polygram

Musicassette: released on Animal in Feb'83 by Chrysalis Records. Distributed by: Polygram

Animals & Men

New age.
Single (7"): released on T.W. in May'82 by T.W. Records. Distributed by: Cartel

Animal Tales

Animal tales Various Artists (Various Artists).
Musicassette: released on Invicta in Jul'84 by Audio-Visual Productions. Distributed by: Spartan

Animotion

I engineer.
Tracks: / I engineer / Essence, The / I engineer (remix) / Obsession (remix).
Single (7"): released on Philips in Apr'86. Distributed by: IMS-Polygram

Single (12"): released on Philips in Apr'86. Distributed by: IMS-Polygram

Obsession.
Tracks: / Obsession / Let him go / Everything's leading / Turn around / Fn fun fun / Tremble / Holding you / Run to me / Open door.
Compact disc: released on Mercury in Jul'85 by Phonogram Records. Distributed by: Polygram Distribution

Obsession (single).
Single (7"): released on Mercury in Apr'85 by Phonogram Records. Distributed by: Polygram Distribution

Single (12"): released on Mercury in Apr'85 by Phonogram Records. Distributed by: Polygram Distribution

Strange behavior.
Tracks: / I want you / I engineer / Strange behavior / Stealing time / Anxiety / Out of control / Stranded / ssence, The / One step ahead / Staring down the demons.
Album: released on Mercury in Jun'86 by Phonogram Records. Distributed by: Polygram Distribution

Musicassette: released on Mercury in Jun'86 by Phonogram Records. Distributed by: Polygram Distribution

Compact disc: released on Mercury in Jun'86 by Phonogram Records. Distributed by: Polygram Distribution

Strange Behaviour.

An Invitation To...

An invitation to Windham Hill Various artists (Various Artists).
Notes: Artists include: Scott Cossu, Dave Valentin, Mark Egan, Gottlieb, Eugene Friesen, George Winston, Will Ackerman and Mark Isham.
Compact disc: released on Windham Hill in Jan'86. Distributed by: AM

Anka, Paul

21 golden hits.
Album: by RCA Records. Distributed by: RCA, Roots, Swift, Wellard, Chris, I & B, Solomon & Peres Distribution

Musicassette: by RCA Records. Distributed by: RCA, Roots, Swift, Wellard, Chris, I & B, Solomon & Peres Distribution

Compact disc: by RCA Records. Distributed by: RCA, Roots, Swift, Wellard, Chris, I & B, Solomon & Peres Distribution

21 golden hits.
Tracks: / Diana / Put your head on my shoulder / Lonely boy / Time to cry / Puppy love / I love you in the same old way / You are my destiny / Cazy love / Don't ever leave me / Summer's gone / Adam and Eve / Don't gamble with love / I'm still waiting for you / I love you baby / It doesn't matter anymore / Tonight my love, tonight / My home town / Cinderella / Loveland / Dance on little girl / Longest day, The / Cinderella / Loveland / Don't ever leave me.
Compact disc: by RCA Records. Distributed by: RCA, Roots, Swift, Wellard, Chris, I & B, Solomon & Peres Distribution

3 great guys (see 3 Great Guys) (Anka, Paul/Sam Cooke/Neil Sedaka).

Best of.
Album: released on Buddah in Jul'85. Distributed by: Swift, Jazz Music, PRT

Musicassette: released on Buddah in Jul'85. Distributed by: Swift, Jazz Music, PRT

Best of Paul Anka, The.
Tracks: / My way / Yesterday my life / Do I love you? / That's what living's about / We make it happen / Filles de Paris, Les / She's a lady / Jubilation / Something good is coming / Love is / Let me be the one.
Album: released on Rhino (USA) in May'86 by Rhino Records (USA)

Diana.
Tracks: / Diana / Put your head on my shoulder / Lonely boy / Time to cry / I love you in the same way / You are my destiny / Crazy love / I love you baby / Adam and Eve / Tonight my love, tonight.
Notes: All titles by Paul Anka. Tracks 1,6,7,8, - EMI Music Pub. Ltd/2,3,4,11 - Sparta Florida Music Group/5,9,10,12,13,14 - Spanka Music Ltd

Album: released on MFP in Sep'86 by EMI Records. Distributed by: EMI

Musicassette: released on MFP in Sep'86 by EMI Records. Distributed by: EMI

Single (7"): by Old Gold Records. Distributed by: Lightning, Jazz Music, Spartan, Counterpoint

Golden highlights of....
Album: released on CBS(Import) in Jun'86 by CBS Records. Distributed by: Conifer, Discovery, Swift

Musicassette: released on CBS(Import) in Jun'86 by CBS Records. Distributed by: Conifer, Discovery, Swift

Greatest hits:Paul Anka.
Compact disc: . Distributed by: Target

Picture disc album: released on Astan in Dec'85 by Astan Records. Distributed by: Counterpoint

Hold me 'til the morning comes.
Single (7"): by CBS Records. Distributed by: CBS

In concert - 16 hits.
Album: released on Masters (Holland) in Jan'87

Musicassette: released on Masters (Holland) in Jan'87

Lonely boy.
Single (7"): by Old Gold Records. Distributed by: Lightning, Jazz Music, Spartan, Counterpoint

My way.
Compact disc: by RCA Records. Distributed by: Pickwick Distribution, Taylors, Swift

Album:

Original hits of Paul Anka, The.
Album: by CBS Records. Distributed by: CBS

Musicassette: by CBS Records. Distributed by: CBS

Second chance.
Single (7"): by CBS Records. Distributed by: CBS

Songs.
Album:

Walk a fine line.
Tracks: / Second chance / Hold me 'til the morning comes / Darlin' darlin' / No way out / Walk a fine line / Take me in your arms / This is the first time / Gimme the world / Golden boy.
Notes: Paul Anka is back and has assembled quite a variety of talent to complete his first album in quite a few years. Songwriters, writing with Paul include David Foster, Michael McDonald, Steve Kipner and Jay Graydon. Musicians include members of Toto Paulinho de Costa and Ernie Watts. Special guest vocalist include Kenny Loggins, Peter Ceters from Chicago, Michael McDonald from the Doobie Brothers and karlo De Vito of Meat Loaf fame.
Album: by CBS Records. Distributed by: CBS

Musicassette: by CBS Records. Distributed by: CBS

Ankh

Still life before success.
Single (7"):

Anna

Nothing can make me feel (the way you do).
Tracks: / Nothing can make me feel (the way you do) / Love in command.
Single (7"): released on No-Go in Aug'86. Distributed by: EMI

Annabas

Start of our lives, The.
Single (7"):

Single (12"):

Annabella

Don't dance with a stranger.
Single (7"): by RCA Records. Distributed by: RCA, Roots, Swift, Wellard, Chris, I & B, Solomon & Peres Distribution

Single (12"): by RCA Records. Distributed by: RCA, Roots, Swift, Wellard, Chris, I & B, Solomon & Peres Distribution

Fever.
Tracks: / School's out / Under the gun / Desire / Nightmare / Magdalen / War boys / High powered girl / Fever / Marry for love / Wild in me.
Compact disc: released on RCA in Jun'86 by RCA Records. Distributed by: RCA, Roots, Swift, Wellard, Chris, I & B, Solomon & Peres Distribution

Album: released on RCA in Jun'86 by RCA Records. Distributed by: RCA, Roots, Swift, Wellard, Chris, I & B, Solomon & Peres Distribution

Musicassette: released on RCA in Jun'86 by RCA Records. Distributed by: RCA, Roots, Swift, Wellard, Chris, I & B, Solomon & Peres Distribution

Fever (single).
Tracks: / Fever / War boys (rough & tough mix).
Single (7"): released on RCA in Apr'86 by RCA Records. Distributed by: RCA, Roots, Swift, Wellard, Chris, I & B, Solomon & Peres Distribution

Single (12"): released on RCA in Apr'86 by RCA Records. Distributed by: RCA, Roots, Swift, Wellard, Chris, I & B, Solomon & Peres Distribution

War boys.
Single (7"): released on RCA in Feb'86 by RCA Records. Distributed by: RCA, Roots, Swift, Wellard, Chris, I & B, Solomon & Peres Distribution

Single (12"): released on RCA in Feb'86 by RCA Records. Distributed by: RCA, Roots, Swift, Wellard, Chris, I & B, Solomon & Peres Distribution

Anne, Shirley

Growing up is hard.
Single (7"): by Greenhill Records. Distributed by: PRT

Annette

I'm alone (Annette & The Roots Radics).
Single (12"): by New Talents Records. Distributed by: Jetstar

Love affair.
Single (12"): by New Talents Records. Distributed by: Jetstar

Annie

Annie Original broadway cast.
Musicassette: by CBS Records. Distributed by: CBS

Annie Original childrens soundtrack and story.
Tracks: / Tomorrow / The hard knock life / Maybe / Sandy / I think I'm gonna like it here / We got Annie / You're never fully dressed without a smile / Easy street / Maybe (reprise) / Finale: I don't need anything but you/ Tomorrow.
Notes: This record tells the entire story of the film with music, dialogue and sound effect highlights complete with additional narration. The album comes in a very special package containing an illustration of the films popular cast, plus a special Annie board game for children to play as they listen.
Album: by CBS Records. Distributed by: CBS

Annie Original London cast.
Tracks: / Overture / Maybe / The hard-knock life / Tomorrow / We'd like to thank you / Herbert Hoover / Little girls / I think I'm going to like it here / NYC / Easy street / You won't be an orphon for long / You're never fully dressed without a smile / Tomorrow, reprise / Something was missing / I don't need anything but you / Annie / A new deal for Christmas.

Annie Original London cast recording.
Musicassette: by CBS Records. Distributed by: CBS

Annie Original motion picture sondtrack.
Tracks: / Tomorrow / It's the hard-knock / Maybe / Dumb dog / Sandy / I think I'm gonna like it here / Little girls / We got Annie / Let's go to the movies / Sign / You're never fully dressed without a smile / Easy street / Tomorrow reprise / Maybe / Finale-I don't need anything but you-We got Annie-Tomorrow..
Notes: The stage play that shook the world and that has played to full houses on both sides of the Atlantic for five years is now a major motion picture 'Annie'. It's one of the best entertainment films for all the family. The soundtrack features five new songs.
Album: by CBS Records. Distributed by: CBS

Musicassette: by CBS Records. Distributed by: CBS

Annie Get Your Gun

Annie Get Your Gun Various Artists.
Compact disc: released on First Night in Aug'86 by Safari Records. Distributed by: Pinnacle

Album: released on First Night in Aug'86 by Safari Records. Distributed by: Pinnacle

Musicassette: released on First Night in Aug'86 by Safari Records. Distributed by: Pinnacle

Annie get your gun orginal cast.
Tracks: / Doin' what comes natur'lly / Moonshine lullaby / You can't get a man with a gun / I'm an Indian too / They say it's wonderful / Anything you can do / I got lost in his arms / I got the sun in the morning / Girl that I marry, The / My defences are down / Who do you love I hope / There's no business like show business.
Album: by MCA Records. Distributed by: Polygram, MCA

Musicassette: by MCA Records. Distributed by: Polygram, MCA

Annihilated

Path to destruction.
Single (12"): released on Annihilated in Oct'86. Distributed by: Backs, Cartel

Anno Domini

Anno Domini (Various Artists).
Album: released on BBC in Mar'86 by BBC Records & Tapes. Distributed by: EMI, PRT, Pye

Musicassette: released on BBC in Mar'86 by BBC Records & Tapes. Distributed by: EMI, PRT, Pye

Ann & Sonya

Hey little boy.
Tracks: / Hey little boy / Start all over again.
Single (12"): released on BB in Feb'87. Distributed by: Jetstar

Anorexia

Anorexia.
Extended-play record:

Anorexic Dread

Tracey's burning.
Single (12"): by Criminal Damage Records. Distributed by: Backs, Cartel

Another Camera

Halluncination spires.
Single (12"): by Altered States Records. Distributed by: Red Rhino, Cartel

Another Cinema

Midnight blue oceans.
Single (7"): by Altered States Records. Distributed by: Red Rhino, Cartel

Single (12"): by Altered States Records. Distributed by: Red Rhino, Cartel

Another Feast Of...

Another feast of Irish folk (Various Artists).
Tracks: / Rare oul times, The / Do you want your lobby washed con shine? / Glenbeigh Hornpipe / Mountain lark / Musical priest, The (De Danann) / Tipping it up to fancy / Kid on the mountain, The / An phis fhiliuch (slip jigs) / Boys of Killybegs, The / Thios chios na tra domh / Lanigans ball / Snowy breasted pearl / Green fields of France, The / Boys of Fiarhill / Seven drunken nights / Pretty Peg / Craig's pipes / Shipward slips / Johnny Cope song and hornpipe / Weila weila waile.
Album: released on Polydor (Ireland) in Aug'86 by Polydor Records. Distributed by: Polygram, I & B

Musicassette: released on Polydor (Ireland) in Aug'86 by Polydor Records. Distributed by: Polygram, I & B

Another Saturday night

Another Saturday night Various original artists (Various original artists).
Album: . Distributed by: Projection

Another Spark Number 1

Another spark number 1 various artists (Various Artists).
Musicassette: . Distributed by: Cartel

Another Time...

Another time, another place original soundtrack.
Single (12"): . Distributed by: Pinnacle

Ansell, Martin

Eighth wonder.
Single (7"): by Island Records. Distributed by: Polygram

Single (12"): by Island Records. Distributed by: Polygram

Anselm Gets His Chance

Anselm gets his chance Wodehouse, P.G. (Carlton, Timothy).
Musicassette:

Ansil Meditation

Quiet woman.
Tracks: / Quiet woman / Reggae crazy.
Single (12"): released on Paradise in Dec'85. Distributed by: Jetstar, JSU, WEA

Anson

Knock you out (Anson & the Rockets).
Album: . Distributed by: Roots

Ant, Adam

Goody two shoes.
Single (7"): by CBS Records. Distributed by: CBS

Hits.
Tracks: / Kings of the wild frontier / Dog eat dog / Ant music / Stand and deliver / Prince Charming / Ant rap / Goody two shoes / Friend or foe / Desperate but not serious / Puss'n'boots / Strip / Apollo 9 / Vive le rock.
Album: released on CBS in Sep'86 by CBS Records. Distributed by: CBS

Musicassette: released on CBS in Sep'86 by CBS Records. Distributed by: CBS

Hits 1980 - 86.
Video-cassette (VHS): released on CBS in Oct'86 by CBS Records. Distributed by: CBS

Nine to five (Ant, Adam & Toyah).
Single (7"): by Virgin Records. Distributed by: Virgin, EMI

Strip.
Tracks: / Baby let me scream at you / Libertine / Spanish games / Vanity / Puss 'n' boots / Playboy / Strip / Montreal / Naval to neck / Amazon.
Compact disc: by CBS Records. Distributed by: CBS

Single (7"): by CBS Records. Distributed by: CBS

Single (12"): by CBS Records. Distributed by: CBS

Picture disc single: by CBS Records. Distributed by: CBS

Vive le rock.
Tracks: / Vive le rock / Miss thing / Razor keen / Rip down / Scorpio rising / Apollo 9 / Hell's eight acres / Mohair lockeroom pin-up boys / No zap / P.O.E. / Human bondage den (cassette only).
Single (12"): by CBS Records. Distributed by: CBS

Antena

Seaside weekend.
Single (7"): released on Les Disques Du Crepuscule in Feb'86. Distributed by: Rough Trade, Pinnacle, Island, Polygram

Single (12"): released on Les Disques Du Crepuscule in Feb'86. Distributed by: Rough Trade, Pinnacle, Island, Polygram

Antena, Isabelle

En cavale.
Album: released on Les Disques Du Crepuscule in Apr'86. Distributed by: Rough Trade, Pinnacle, Island, Polygram

Hoping for love.
Album: released on Crepescule in Apr'87 by Island Records. Distributed by: Polygram, Pinnacle

Laying on the sofa.
Single (7"): released on Les Disques Du Crepuscule in Aug'87. Distributed by: Rough Trade, Pinnacle, Island, Polygram

Single (7"): released on Les Disques Du Crespuscle in 15 Aug'87. Distributed by: Rough Trade, Pinnacle, Island, Polygram

Le poisson des mers du sud.
Single (12"): released on Les Disques Du Crepuscule in Aug'87. Distributed by: Rough Trade, Pinnacle, Island, Polygram

Antenna

B-bop.
Single (7"): by Phonogram Records. Distributed by: Polygram Distribution

Single (12"): by Phonogram Records. Distributed by: Polygram Distribution

Boy from Ipanema.
Single (7"):

Camino del sol.
Album: . Distributed by: Rough Trade, Pinnacle, Island, Polygram

Anthologie Gregorienne

Anthologie Gregorienne Various Artists.
Compact disc: released on Musidisc (France) in Dec'85. Distributed by: Discovery Distribution, Swift Distribution

Anthology Of...

Antholgy of traditional Irish music various artists (Various Artists).
Album: by Clair Records. Distributed by: Jetstar

Cryin' in the morning Various artists (Various Artists).
Tracks: / Got a get a gettin' / Pig 'N' whistle Red / A to Z blues / She don't treat me good no more / Poor little angel girl / You're gonna weep & moan / When my wife quit me / Kidman blues / I'm a country boy / Cryin' in the morning / Trying to change my ways / Orphan boy blues / Ooh wee baby.
Album: released on Muse in Apr'81 by Peerless Records. Distributed by: Lugtons Distributors

Dancing bow, The Various artists (Various Artists).
Album: by Sonet Records. Distributed by: PRT

Anthony And The Camp

What I like.
Tracks: / What I like / What I like (inst).
Single (7"): released on Warner Bros. in Jun'86 by Warner Bros Records. Distributed by: WEA

Single (12"): released on Warner Bros. in Jun'86 by Warner Bros Records. Distributed by: WEA

Anthony, Carlton

Nightwalk.
Tracks: / Nightwalk / Nightwalk (version).
Single (12"): released on Water Mount in May'86. Distributed by: ILA, Jetstar

Anthony, Charles

Breakthrough.
Single (7"): by Musical Characters Records. Distributed by: Spartan

Anthony, Chris

Chances are gone.
Tracks: / Chances are gone / Chances are gone (inst).
Single (12"): released on Unit 7 in May'86 by Greensleeves Records. Distributed by: RCA

Anthony, John

Guitar goes travelling.
Tracks: / Maria Elena / Zorba's dance / South of the border / Stairway to the sea / Don't cry for me Argentina / Summertime in Venice / Have nagila / African sunset / Shenandoah / Annie's song / Tokyo melody.
Album: by President Records. Distributed by: Taylors, Spartan

Guitar talk.
Tracks: / Main theme (Star wars) / Evergreen / Somewhere my love / Albatross / James Bond theme (From Russia with love) / Granada / Speak softly / Just a little note / Rodrigo guitar concerto / Catari.
Album: by President Records. Distributed by: Taylors, Spartan

Midnight guitar serenade.
Musicassette: by Pickwick Records. Distributed by: H.R. Taylor

Anthony, Mike

Why can't we live together.
Single (7"): . Distributed by: RCA, Ariola

Single (12"): . Distributed by: RCA, Ariola

Anthony, Pad

Carrot and onion.
Tracks: / Carrot and onion.
Single (12"): by CSA Records. Distributed by: PRT, Jetstar

Champion bubbler (Anthony, Pad & Tonto Irie).
Single (12"): by Greensleeves Records. Distributed by: BMG, Jetstar, Spartan

Hell in the dance (Anthony, Pad/Frankie Jones).
Tracks: / Long run short catch / Love just a fool / Flash it mash it / She's in love with me / Way dem a do fe we / Me a know / Run come / Hell in the dance / Stay on your corner / Niceness.
Album: released on CSA in Apr'86 by CSA Records. Distributed by: PRT, Jetstar

Money problem.
Single (12"): by Reggae Rock Records. Distributed by: Jetstar

No world without you.
Tracks: / No world without you / Loving stylee (Tonto irie).
Single (12"): released on Wheely Connexion in Sep'86. Distributed by: Jetstar

P A meets K E (Anthony, Pad & King Everald).
Album: by Sun Set Records. Distributed by: Jetstar Distribution

Respect you.
Single (12"): by Greensleeves Records. Distributed by: BMG, Jetstar, Spartan

What's your name.
Single (12"): by Right Track Records. Distributed by: Cartel, Jetstar

Anthony, Pat

Moving forward.
Tracks: / Moving forward / Moving forward (version).
Single (12"): released on Super Power in Jun'87 by Super Power Records. Distributed by: Jetstar Distribution

Anthony, Patrick

Kusupeng.
Single (12"): by RM Records. Distributed by: Jetstar

Anthony, Peter

Song for Fescon.
Single (7"): by Clay Records. Distributed by: Pinnacle

Anthony, Ray

Big Band Singer.
Album: released on Aerospace in May'86. Distributed by: Swift

Brass Galore.
Album: released on Aerospace in May'86. Distributed by: Swift

Dancing alone together (Anthony, Ray & His Orchestra).
Tracks: / My funny valentine / Guess 'Il hang my tears out to dry / To love and be loved / I should care / Party's over, The / Here's that rainy day / What's new / Misty / Like someone in love / Alone together / All the way.
Album: released on Capitol in Jun'86 by Capitol Records. Distributed by: EMI

Musicassette: released on Capitol in Jun'86 by Capitol Records. Distributed by: EMI

Dream dancing medley (Anthony, Ray & His Orchestra).
Tracks: / As time goes by / Soon / Where am I ? / I'll string along with you / Of thee I sing / It had to be you / Auf wiedersehen, my dear / Can't we be friends? / Heaven can wait / Too marvellous for words / When your lover has gone / The love nest / Dancing on the ceiling / Sweet madness / S'wonderful / With a song in my heart / The very thought of you / The boulevard of broken dreams / Autumn in New York / The man I love / Tis' autumn / Please be king / Ev'ry day / If there is someone lovelier than you / September in the rain / My heart stood still / Dancing in the dark / Something to remember you by / Oh! You crazy moon / Mine.
Notes: The smooth, sentimental sound of Ray Anthony's Orchestra playing a lush medley of thirty famous tunes including, 'As time goes by', 'With a song in my heart', 'Autumn in New York','The man I love','Please be kind' and many more. Ideal for dancing!
Album: by Capitol Records. Distributed by: EMI

Musicassette: by Capitol Records. Distributed by: EMI

Houseparty hop (Anthony, Ray & His Orchestra).
Tracks: / I get a kick out of you / Houseparty hop / Begin the beguine / Perdido / The bunny hop / The darktown strutters' ball / Dinah / Sentimental journey / My blue heaven / Wagon wheels / Rockin' in rhythm / Bandstand matinee.
Album: by Capitol Records. Distributed by EMI

Musicassette: by Capitol Records. Distributed by: EMI

I remember Glenn Miller.
Tracks: / Tuxedo junction / Chattanooga choo choo / Serenade in blue / Elmer's tune / Sunrise serenade / Song of the Volga boatman / In the mood / I know why (and so do you) / Sweet as apple cider / At last / Little Brown jug / Moonlight serenade.
Album: by Capitol (USA) Records. Distributed by: EMI

More dream dancing.
Tracks: / April in Paris / Blue Hawaii / There's a small hotel / I cover the waterfront / Meet me tonight in dreamland / Venezuela / East of the sun / Along the Sante Fe / Palm springs / Home Monika / Dream while you dance.
Album: by Capitol (USA) Records. Distributed by: EMI

Musicassette: by Capitol (USA) Records. Distributed by: EMI

Plays for dream dancing.
Tracks: / This love is mine / Dream dancing / I'll never smile again / Out of nowhere / I only have eyes for you / Embraceable you / Street of dreams / Stars fell on Alabama / I don't know why (I just do) / Laura / Moonlight in Vermont / September song.
Notes: Ray Anthony, who served his apprenticeship with the Glen Miller Orchestra became famous for his 'Dream Dancing' albums-collections of well known songs lushly arranged for dancing cheek to cheek. This is the classic first album of that series and has not been available for a number of years.
Album: by Capitol Records. Distributed by: EMI

Musicassette: by Capitol Records. Distributed by: EMI

Swing goes on, The (vol 10).
Tracks: / What can I say / I wonder what's become of Sally / Idaho / Blue moon / Dancing over the waves / It's de-lovely / The man with the horn / For dancers only / Jeepers creepers / My blue heaven / Amor / Dinah / Sentimental journey / Begin the beguine / I get a kick out of you / Houseparty hop.
Album: by EMI Records. Distributed by: Conifer

Swingin' on campus.
Tracks: / What can I say after I say I'm sorry / On the Alamo / I've found a new baby / Chloe / At sundown / Pick yourself up / Ain't misbehavin' / Lady is in love with you, The / Am I blue / If I had you / Undecided / Swing on campus.
Notes: A good set of swinging standards in the same vein as 'Houseparty Hop' - the sucessful multi-tempo album.
Album: released on Capitol in Dec'85 by Capitol Records. Distributed by: EMI

Musicassette: released on Capitol in Dec'85 by Capitol Records. Distributed by: EMI

Anthony, Richard

Disque d'or.
Tracks: / J'Entends siffler le train / Donne-moi ma chance / C'est ma fete / A present, tu peux t'en aller / Ce monde / Je me suis souvent demande / Le deserteur / Sunny / Arranguez, mon amour / Les mains dans les poches / Il faut croire aux etoiles / L'ete / Les ballons / Le sirop typhon.
Album: by EMI Records. Distributed by: Conifer

Anthony, Tad

Bomb, The.
Single (12"): . Distributed by: Jetstar

Anthrax

Among the living.
Picture disc album: released on Island in Apr'87 by Island Records. Distributed by: Polygram

Armed and dangerous.
Album: released on Megaforce (USA) in Aug'87 by Megaforce Records (USA). Distributed by: Pinnacle

Picture disc album: released on Megaforce (USA) in Aug'87 by Megaforce Records (USA). Distributed by: Pinnacle

Capitalism is cannibalism.
Extended-play record: by Exitstencil Music. Distributed by: Rough Trade, Cartel

Fistful of metal.
Notes: Limited edition pic disc
Album: released on MFN in Apr'87 by Music For Nations Records. Distributed by: Pinnacle

Album: by Music For Nations Records. Distributed by: Pinnacle

I am the law.
Tracks: / Bud.E.Luvbomb and satan's lounge band.
Single (7"): released on Island in Feb'87 by Island Records. Distributed by: Polygram

Single (12"): released on Island in Feb'87 by Island Records. Distributed by: Polygram

Indians.
Tracks: / Indians / Sabbath bloody sabbath / Taint.
Single (7"): released on Island in 13 Jun'87 by Island Records. Distributed by: Polygram

Single (12"): released on Island in 13 Jun'87 by Island Records. Distributed by: Polygram

Picture disc single: released on Island in 13 Jun'87 by Island Records. Distributed by: Polygram

Single (cassette): released on Island in Jul'87 by Island Records. Distributed by: Polygram

Mad House.
Tracks: / Madhouse / A.I.R. / God save the Queen.
Picture disc single: released on Island in May'86 by Island Records. Distributed by: Polygram

Single (12"): released on Island in Sep'86 by Island Records. Distributed by: Polygram

Single (12"): released on Island in Sep'86 by Island Records. Distributed by: Polygram

Single (12"): released on Island in Sep'86 by Island Records. Distributed by: Polygram

Single (12"): released on Island in Sep'86 by Island Records. Distributed by: Polygram

Single (12"): released on Island in Sep'86 by Island Records. Distributed by: Polygram

Single (7"): released on Island in Sep'86 by Island Records. Distributed by: Polygram

Spreading the disease.
Album: released on Music For Nations in Feb'86 by Music For Nations Records. Distributed by: Pinnacle

Musicassette: released on Music For Nations in Sep'87 by Music For Nations Records. Distributed by: Pinnacle. Estim retail price in Sep'87 was £5.99.

They've got it all wrong.
Single (7"): by Small Wonder Records. Distributed by: Cartel, Indies

Anti-Cimex

Anti-Cimex.
Album: released on Skysaw in Oct'86 by Skysaw Records. Distributed by: Red Rhino, Cartel

Distraught.
Single (12"): released on Skysaw in 6 Jun'87 by Skysaw Records. Distributed by: Red Rhino, Cartel

Anti Establishment

Anti men.
Single (7"): by Glass Records. Distributed by: Nine Mile, Rough Trade, Red Rhino, Play It Again Sam

Future girl.
Single (7"): by Glass Records. Distributed by: Nine Mile, Rough Trade, Red Rhino, Play It Again Sam

Antietam

Antietam.
Album: released on Homestead in Jul'85. Distributed by: Rough Trade, Cartel, Shigaku

Music from Elba.
Album: released on Homestead in Sep'86. Distributed by: Rough Trade, Cartel, Shigaku

Until now.
Single (7"): released on Homestead in Sep'86. Distributed by: Rough Trade, Cartel, Shigaku

Anti Group

Big sex, The.
Single (7"): released on Sweatbox in Aug'87 by Sweatbox Records. Distributed by: Rough Trade, Cartel

Single (12"): released on Sweatbox in Aug'87 by Sweatbox Records. Distributed by: Rough Trade, Cartel

Ha.
Single (12"): by Sweatbox Records. Distributed by: Rough Trade, Cartel

Ha-Zulu.
Single (12"): released on Sweatbox in Jan'86 by Sweatbox Records. Distributed by: Rough Trade, Cartel

Antigua

Antigua Various Artists (Various Artists).
Album: released on Playasound (France) in May'85

Musicassette: released on Playasound (France) in May'85

Antilles

I've got to have you.
Single (7"): released on Creole in Apr'83 by Creole Records. Distributed by: Rhino, PRT

Single (12"): released on Creole in Apr'83 by Creole Records. Distributed by: Rhino PRT

Anti-Nowhere League

For you.
Single (7"):

I hate people.
Single (7"):

Live in Yugoslavia.
Album: released on I.D. in Oct'83 by I.D. Records. Distributed by: Revolver, Cartel

Long live the league.
Tracks: / For you / We will survive / Out on the wasteland / On the waterfront / Queen & country / We're the league / Streets of London / So what / Let's break the law / Ballad of JJ Decay, The / Woman / Snowman / Wreck a nowhere / Let the country feed you / Going down / I hate people.
Album: released on Dojo in Apr'86 by Castle Communications Records. Distributed by: Cartel

Out on the wasteland.
Single (7"): released on ABC in Dec'84. Distributed by: CBS, Pinnacle

Single (12"): released on ABC in Dec'84. Distributed by: CBS, Pinnacle

Picture disc single: released on ABC in Dec'84. Distributed by: CBS, Pinnacle

Perfect crime, The.
Album: released on GWR in May'87 by GWR Records. Distributed by: RCA

Musicassette: released on GWR in May'87 by GWR Records. Distributed by: RCA

R.I.P..
Album: released on Dojo in Oct'85 by Castle Communications Records. Distributed by: Cartel

Musicassette: released on Dojo in Oct'85 by Castle Communications Records. Distributed by: Cartel

We are...the league.
Tracks: / Roll on world war three / So what / Wreck a nowhere / Let's break the law / Woman / Streets of London / For you.
Album: released on WXYZ in Apr'82

Album: released on WXYZ in Jun'82

We are the League.
Album: released on I.D Noise in Nov'85. Distributed by: Revolver, Cartel

Woman.
Single (7"): released on WXYZ in Jun'82

Picture disc single: released on WXYZ in Jun'82

Anti Pasti

Anti pasti.
Album: released on Rondelet Music And Records in Sep'83 by Rondelet Music And Records. Distributed by: Pinnacle, Cartel Distribution, Rondelet Music And Records Distribution

Caution in the wind.
Tracks: / Caution in the wind / One friday night / X affair / Get out now / Mr. Mystery / East to the West / See how they run / Hate circulation / Agent ABC / The best of us / Guinea pigs / Beyond belief.
Album: released on Rondelet Music And Records in Jun'82 by Rondelet Music And Records. Distributed by: Pinnacle, Cartel Distribution, Rondelet Music And Records Distribution

Musicassette: released on Rondelet Music And Records in Jun'82 by Rondelet Music And Records. Distributed by: Pinnacle, Cartel Distribution, Rondelet Music And Records Distribution

Single (7"): released on Rondelet Music And Records in Sep'82 by Rondelet Music And Records. Distributed by: Pinnacle, Cartel Distribution, Rondelet Music And Records Distribution

East to the west.
Single (7"): released on Rondelet Music And Records in May'82 by Rondelet Music And Records. Distributed by: Pinnacle, Cartel Distribution, Rondelet Music And Records Distribution

Four sore points.
Single (7"): released on Rondelet Music And Records in Nov'80 by Rondelet Music And Records. Distributed by: Pinnacle, Cartel Distribution, Rondelet Music And Records Distribution

Last call, The.
Tracks: No government / Brew your own / Another dead soldier / Call the army (I'm alive) / City below / 24 hours / Night of the war cry / Freedom row / St. George (Get's his gun) / The last call / Ain't got me / Truth and justice / Hell / I wanna be your dog.
Album: released on Rondelet Music And Records in Jul'81 by Rondelet Music And Records. Distributed by: Pinnacle, Cartel Distribution, Rondelet Music And Records Distribution

Musiccassette: released on Rondelet Music And Records in Jul'81 by Rondelet Music And Records. Distributed by: Pinnacle, Cartel Distribution, Rondelet Music And Records Distribution

Let them free.
Single (7"): released on Rondelet Music And Records in Jan'81 by Rondelet Music And Records. Distributed by: Pinnacle, Cartel Distribution, Rondelet Music And Records Distribution

Six guns.
Single (7"): released on Rondelet Music And Records in Oct'81 by Rondelet Music And Records. Distributed by: Pinnacle, Cartel Distribution, Rondelet Music And Records Distribution

Antisect

In darkness there is no choice.
Album: released on Spiderleg in Jan'84. Distributed by: Rough Trade

Out from the void.
Single (7"): released on Endangered Musik in Oct'85 by Endangered Musik Records. Distributed by: Revolver

Anti Social

Made in England.
Extended-play record: released on Lightbeat in Jul'82 by Lightbeat Records. Distributed by: Pinnacle

Too many people.
Single (7"): released on Beat-The-System in Oct'82 by Lightbeat Records. Distributed by: Pinnacle

Anti Social Workers

Punky reggae party positive style.
Album: released on Arewa in Aug'83. Distributed by: Indies, Cartel

Anti-System

Defence of the realm.
Extended-play record: released on Paragon in Jun'83 by Paragon Records. Distributed by: Paragon

High society.
Album: released on Reconciliation in Apr'86 by Anti system. Distributed by: Red Rhino, Cartel

Look at life, A.
Album: released on Reconciliation in May'86 by Anti system. Distributed by: Red Rhino, Cartel

No laughing matter.
Album: released on Recordian Sgwar in Jan'85. Distributed by: Independents Distribution

Strange love.
Single (7"): released on Recordian Sgwar in Apr'85. Distributed by: Independents Distribution

Antix

Get up get happy.
Album: released on Heavy Metal America in Oct'85 by FM-Revolver Records. Distributed by: EMI

Antlers

It looks like reindeer.
Single (7"): released on Kingdom Records in Dec'82 by Kingdom Records. Distributed by: Kingdom Records

Antolini, Charly

Special delivery.
Album: released on MPS Jazz in May'81

Antonia

Bamba, Le.
Single (7"): released on Calibre in Oct'83 by Calibre Records. Distributed by: PRT

Single (12"): released on Calibre in Oct'83 by Calibre Records. Distributed by: PRT

Antonio

Restless fingers.
Tracks: Cin cin polka / Cuballero / Caprice / Marsala bella / Simple et musette / Samba polka / Restless fingers / Luci e ombra dark eyes / Interrogation / Bouquet / Valse des as.
Notes: Mail order distribution address: Accordion Record Club, 146 Birmingham Road, Kidderminster, Worcs. DY10 2SL. Tel:(0562) 746105.
Album: released on ARC (Accordion Record Club) in '84. Distributed by: Accordion Record Club

Antoniou, Tony

Can't give you all my love.
Single (7"): released on Adventures In Clubland in Jul'86. Distributed by: DMS, RCA

Single (12"): released on Adventures In Clubland in Jul'86. Distributed by: DMS, RCA

Lifeline.
Send in the night.
Single (7"): released on Spartan in Jul'84 by Spartan Records. Distributed by: Spartan

Street sound.
Single (12"): released on Elite in Dec'82. Distributed by: PRT

Antrobus,Frosdsham

Step in wild horse (Soul Caring).
Musiccassette: released on Folktracks in Nov'79. Distributed by: Roots

Ants' hillvania

Ants' hillvania various artists (Various Artists).
Tracks: Ant's hillvania / Work song / Independ-ant's song / All it really is / Mr. Worm / Seeds / Choice is up to you, The / Toast of the town, The / Riddle, The / Repent-ants song / Come on home / Ants' hillvania.
Album: released on Birdwing in May'82 by Word Records. Distributed by: Word Distribution

Musiccassette: released on Birdwing in May'82 by Word Records. Distributed by: Word Distribution

Antz Avenue

Cheers club, The.
Extended-play record: released on Boulevard in Nov'85. Distributed by: Pinnacle

Anusia

Imagination.
Single (7"): released on Metropolis (France) in Oct'82 by Island Records. Distributed by: EMI

Single (12"): by Island Records. Distributed by: EMI

Anvil

Backwaxed.
Album: released on Roadrunner (Dutch) in Jun'85. Distributed by: Pinnacle

Forged in fire.
Album: released on Attic in May'83. Distributed by: Pinnacle

Musiccassette: released on Attic in May'83. Distributed by: Pinnacle

Hard & heavy.
Album: released on Attic in Jan'82. Distributed by: Pinnacle

Musiccassette: released on Attic in Jan'82. Distributed by: Pinnacle

Make it up to you.
Single (7"): released on Attic in Jun'83. Distributed by: Pinnacle

Single (12"): released on Attic in Jun'83. Distributed by: Pinnacle

Metal on metal.
Album: released on Attic in May'82. Distributed by: Pinnacle

Musiccassette: released on Attic in Jul'82. Distributed by: Pinnacle

Steamin.
Single (7"): released on Attic in Aug'82. Distributed by: Pinnacle

Single (12"): released on Attic in Aug'82. Distributed by: Pinnacle

Strength of steel.
Album: released on Metal Blade in Jun'87. Distributed by: Enigma Distribution

Anvil Bitch

Rise to offend.
Album: released on New Renaissance (USA) in Aug'87

Anxiety, Annie

As I lie in your arms.
Single (7"): released on One Little Indian in Jul'87 by One Little Indian Records. Distributed by: Nine Mile Distribution, Cartel Distribution

Soul possession.
Album: released on Corpus Christi in Feb'84 by Exitstencil Music. Distributed by: Cartel

Anya

One word.
Single (7"): released on Rocket in Apr'87 by Phonogram Records. Distributed by: Polygram Distribution

Single (12"): released on Rocket in Apr'87 by Phonogram Records. Distributed by: Polygram Distribution

Any Day Now

I'll be waiting.
Tracks: I'll be waiting / Under your spell.
Single (7"): released on A&M in Oct'86 by A&M Records. Distributed by: Polygram

Show me the way (Grand groove).
Tracks: Show me the way (Grand groove) / Shock tactic / Show me the way (No Derek).
Single (7"): released on A&M in Apr'86 by A&M Records. Distributed by: Polygram

Single (12"): released on A&M in Apr'86 by A&M Records. Distributed by: Polygram

Any Old Time String Band

Any old time string band.
Album: released on Arhoolie in May'81 by Arhoolie Records. Distributed by: Projection, Topic, Jazz Music, Swift, Roots

Anyone For Dennis

Anyone for Dennis Original London cast.
Album: released on RCA in Oct'81 by RCA Records. Distributed by: RCA, Roots, Swift, Wellard, Chris, I & B, Solomon & Peres Distribution

Musiccassette: released on RCA in Oct'81 by RCA Records. Distributed by: RCA, Roots, Swift, Wellard, Chris, I & B, Solomon & Peres Distribution

Anyone's Daughter

Adonis.
Album: released on Brain in Feb'80

Anything Goes

Anything goes Revival 1969 London cast (Various Artists).
Album: released on That's Entertainment in Sep'84 by That's Entertainment Records. Distributed by: Pinnacle, PRT

Musiccassette: released on That's Entertainment in Sep'84 by That's Entertainment Records. Distributed by: Pinnacle, PRT

Any Trouble

Girls are always right.
Single (7"): released on Stiff in Sep'80 by Stiff Records. Distributed by: EMI, Record Services Distribution (Ireland)

I'll be your man.
Single (7"): released on EMI America in Sep'83 by EMI Records. Distributed by: EMI

Single (12"): released on EMI America in Sep'83 by EMI Records. Distributed by: EMI

Live at the venue.
Album: released on Teldec (West Germany) in Jan'85

Nice girls.
Single (7"): released on Stiff in Feb'80 by Stiff Records. Distributed by: EMI, Record Services Distribution (Ireland)

Single (7"): released on Arista in Jan'83 by Arista Records. Distributed by: RCA

Open fire.
Single (7"): released on EMI America in Jun'84 by EMI Records. Distributed by: EMI

Second choice.
Single (7"): released on Stiff in Jun'80 by Stiff Records. Distributed by: EMI, Record Services Distribution (Ireland)

Touch and go.
Single (7"): released on EMI America in May'83 by EMI Records. Distributed by: EMI

Single (12"): released on EMI America in May'83 by EMI Records. Distributed by: EMI

Trouble with love.
Single (7"): released on Stiff in Jul'81 by Stiff Records. Distributed by: EMI, Record Services Distribution (Ireland)

Wheels in motion.
Tracks: Trouble with love / Open fire / As lovers do / Walking in chains / Dimming of the day / Another heartache / To be a king / Power cut / Eastern promise / Sun never sets, The.
Album: released on Stiff in Jul'81 by Stiff Records. Distributed by: EMI, Record Services Distribution (Ireland)

Where are all the nice girls.
Tracks: Second choice / Playing Bogart / No idea / Foolish pride / Nice girls / Turning up the heat / Romance / Hurt, The / Girls are always right / Growing up / Honolulu / (Get you off) the hook.
Album: released on Stiff in Oct'80 by Stiff Records. Distributed by: EMI, Record Services Distribution (Ireland)

Musiccassette: released on Stiff in Oct'80 by Stiff Records. Distributed by: EMI, Record Services Distribution (Ireland)

AOA

Unlimited genocide (AOA & Oi Polloi).
Album: released on Children Of The Revolution in Jul'86 by Revolver Records. Distributed by: Revolver, Cartel

Who are they trying to con.
Single (12"): released on Children Of The Revolution in May'85 by Revolver Records. Distributed by: Revolver, Cartel

AP50

I've got an AP50 and I'm gonna thrash it.
Tracks: Sixty kit I see, A / Nearly at 350000 / Sixty kit I see, A.
Single (7"): released on Audiophile in Apr'87 by Jazzology Records (USA). Distributed by: Jazz Music, Swift

Apache moon

Apache moon Durham, John (Horne, David).
Boxed set: released on Soundings in Mar'85. Distributed by: Soundings

Apartments

All you wanted.
Tracks: All you wanted / Sunset Hotel / What's the morning for / Black road shines, The.
Single (7"): released on Rough Trade in Mar'86 by Rough Trade Records. Distributed by: Rough Trade Distribution, Cartel Distribution

Single (12"): released on Rough Trade in Mar'86 by Rough Trade Records. Distributed by: Rough Trade Distribution, Cartel Distribution

Evening visits, The.
Album: released on Rough Trade in Oct'85 by Rough Trade Records. Distributed by: Rough Trade Distribution, Cartel Distribution

APB

Chain reaction.
Single (7"): released on Oily in Jul'81 by Oily Records. Distributed by: Fast Distribution

Cure for the blues.
Album: released on Red River in Apr'86. Distributed by: Fast Forward, Cartel

Danceability.

Single (12"): released on Albion Records in
Apr'84

One day.
Single (7"): released on Oily in Aug'83 by Oily
Records. Distributed by: Fast Distribution

Open your eyes.
Tracks: / Open your eyes / Sunset song.
Single (7"): released on Red River in Apr'86.
Distributed by: Fast Forward, Cartel

Single (12"): released on Red River in Apr'86.
Distributed by: Fast Forward, Cartel

Palace filled with love.
Single (7"): released on Oily in Apr'82 by Oily
Records. Distributed by: Fast Distribution

Rainy day.
Single (7"): released on Oily in Oct'82 by Oily
Records. Distributed by: Fast Distribution

Shoot you down.
Single (7"): released on Oily in Oct'81 by Oily
Records. Distributed by: Fast Distribution

Something to believe in.
Single (7"): released on Red River in Oct'85.
Distributed by: Fast Forward, Cartel

Single (12"): released on Red River in Oct'85.
Distributed by: Fast Forward, Cartel

Summer love.
Single (7"): released on Red River in Jul'85.
Distributed by: Fast Forward, Cartel.l

Single (12"): released on Red River in Jul'85.
Distributed by: Fast Forward, Cartel

What kind of girl.
Single (7"): released on Albion in Jun'84 by Albion Records. Distributed by: Spartan, Pinnacle

Single (12"): released on Albion Records in
Jun'84

Aphrodites Child

666.
Tracks: / Aegean sea / All the seats were occupied / Altomont / Babylon / Battle of the beast
/ Beast,The / Break / Capture of the beast / Do
it / Four horesmen,The / Hic-et-nunc / Infinity /
Lamb,The / Lament / Loud loud / Marching
beast,The / Ofis / Seven trumpets / Seventh
seal,The / System,The / Tribulation / Wakening
beast,The / Wedding of the lamb,The.
Notes: From the group which spawned Demis
Roussos, this is the only complete Aphrodites
album still available.   Issued in its original
sleeve.
Album: released on Philips (Import) in May'83

Musicassette: released on Philips Import in
May'83

Aphrodites child   Greatest hits
(Aphrodites Child, Greatest Hits).
Album: released on Mercury in Aug'81 by Phonogram Records. Distributed by: Polygram Distribution

Musicassette: released on Mercury in Aug'81
by Phonogram Records. Distributed by: Polygram Distribution

Album: released on Impact in Jul'78 by Ace
Records. Distributed by: Rough Trade, Pinnacle, Swift, Backs, Counterpoint, Jungle, Hotshot, Cartel

Apocalypse

Teddy.
Single (7"): released on Jamming in Sep'82

Single (12"): released on Jamming in Sep'82

Apocalypse 84

**Apocalypse 84 various artists (Various
Artists).**
Tracks: / Gimme more / Cold sweat / Out for
blood / Don't talk to strangers / Analog kid, The
/ Trashed / Trop fou pour yoi / Devil made me
do it, The / Don't say make me / Whippin' boy.
Album: released on Phonogram Import in
May'84

Musicassette: released on Phonogram Import
in May'84

Apocalypse Jive

Life the outcome.
Single (7"): released on Company in Nov'82 by
Company Records. Distributed by: Swift, Jazz
Music, Chris Wellard

Apoicalypse Now

**Apocalypse now   original motion sound-
track.**
Album: released on Elektra (USA) in Dec'79 by
Elektra/Asylum/Nonesuch Records. Distributed by: WEA

Apollo 100

Classical gas.
Album: released on MFP in Sep'81 by EMI
Records. Distributed by: EMI

Musicassette: released on MFP in Sep'81 by
EMI Records. Distributed by: EMI

Apollonia 6

Apollonia 6.
Tracks: / Happy birthday, Mr. Christian / Sex
shooter / Blue limousine / Million miles, A / Ooo
she she wa wa / Some kind of lover / In a Spanish villa.
Album: released on Warner Bros. in Oct'84 by
Warner Bros Records. Distributed by: WEA

Sex shooter.
Single (7"): released on Warner Bros. in Oct'84
by Warner Bros Records. Distributed by: WEA

Apology For Innocence

Across the wire.
Single (7"): released on Illusive in May'82 by
Pauline Murray. Distributed by: RSO, Polygram

Single (12"): released on Illusive in May'82 by
Pauline Murray. Distributed by: RSO, Polygram

A-Pop

Art of persuasion.
Tracks: / Art of persuasion (radio mix) /
Rock'n'roll.
Single (12"): released on Jungle in Oct'86 by
Jungle Records. Distributed by: Jungle, Cartel

Apostles

Curse of the creature.
Single (7"): released on Pigs For Slaughter in
Jun'84 by Pigs For Slaughter Records. Dis-
tributed by: Rough Trade, Cartel

Single (7"): released on Scum in Jun'84. Distributed by: Rough Trade, Cartel

Fifth apostle, The.
Extended-play record: released on Mortarhate in Mar'85 by Dorane Ltd

Lives and times of the Apostles, The.
Album: released on Children Of The Revolution in May'86 by Revolver Records. Distributed by: Revolver, Cartel

Rising from the ashes.
Single (7"): released on Scum in Dec'83. Distributed by: Rough Trade, Cartel

Appalacia-Old Traditions

**Appalacia-The old Traditions   Blue
Ridge Mountain Music (Various Artists).**
Album: released on Home Made Music in '85.
Distributed by: Celtic Distributions, Projection

Appice Carmine

Be my baby.
Single (7"): released on Riva in Feb'82. Distributed by: PRT

Carmine Appice.
Album: released on Riva in Mar'82. Distributed
by: PRT

Apple Jack

Beatles magic.
Album: released on Dansan in Jul'80 by Spartan Records. Distributed by: Spartan

Applejacks

Tell me when/Baby Jane.
Single (7"): released on Decca-Originals in
May'82 by Decca Records. Distributed by: Poly-
gram, I.S

Tell me when/Just like Eddie.
Single (7"): released on Old Gold in Oct'83 by
Old Gold Records. Distributed by: Lightning,
Jazz Music, Spartan, Counterpoint

Apple Mosaic

Honey if.

Tracks: / Honey if / Mary Hell / Me, myself and
I."
Single (7"): released on MDM in Jul'87. Dis-
tributed by: Siren, Virgin, EMI

Single (12"): released on MDM in Jul'87. Distributed by: Siren, Virgin, EMI

Appreciations

I can't hide it.
Single (7"): released on Soul Supply in Jan'85
by High Energy Records. Distributed by: Charly

Appropriate Noise

Deception.
Musicassette: by Dead Happy Records. Distributed by: Mason's Music Distributors/Whole-
salers, Rough Trade

April

Boys come and go.
Single (7"): released on Record Shack in
Apr'85 by Record Shack Records. Distributed
by: PRT

Single (12"): released on Record Shack in
Apr'85 by Record Shack Records. Distributed
by: PRT

April In Managua

April In Managua (Various Artists).
Musicassette: released on LMS in Jun'84. Distributed by: Rough Trade, Cartel

April Moon

Reckless Heart.
Single (7"): released on Red Bus in May'84 by
Red Bus Records. Distributed by: PRT

April Showers

Abandoned ship.
Single (7"): released on Big Star in Jun'84

Single (12"): released on Big Star in Jun'84

April Wine

Animal grace.
Tracks: / This could be the right one / Sons of
the pioneers / Without your love / Rock tonite /
Hard rock kid / money talks / Gimme that thing
called love / Last time I'll ever sing the blues.
Album: released on Capitol in Apr'84 by Capitol Records. Distributed by: EMI Deleted '86.

Musicassette: released on Capitol in Apr'84 by
Capitol Records. Distributed by: EMI

Harder faster.
Album: released on Capitol in Nov'79 by Capitol Records. Distributed by: EMI

Live In London.
Video-cassette (VHS): released on PMI in
Jun'86 by PMI Records. Distributed by: EMI

Video-cassette [Betamax]: released on PMI in
Jun'86 by PMI Records. Distributed by: EMI

Aquai

Shades of moods.
Album: released on Equatone in May'87

Aquila

Fail/Threatened.
Single (7"): released on Graphic in Oct'82 by
Graphic Records

Aquino, Leo

Leo Aquino.
Tracks: / Carnival of Venice / Brave matador,
The / Florrette / Dizzy accordion / Mazurka / Hot
points / Olive blossoms / Internat patrol / Jolly
Caballero / Comedians / Presto / Malaguena /
Gitarerias / La cumparsa / Acquarelli Cubani /
Waltz (Khachaturian).
Notes: Accordion Record Club, 146 Birminham
Road, Kidderminster, Worcs. DY 10 2SL Tel:
0562 746105 Price excluding P & P 6.50
Musicassette: released on Accordion Record
Club in Jul'86 by Accordion Record Club Rec-
ords. Distributed by: Accordion Record Club

Leo Aquino 11.
Tracks: / Dance of the swans / Claire de lune /
Prayer hora staccato / Sleeping beauty waltz /
Hungarian rhapsody no.2 / Dizzy fingers / Valse
arabesque / Flight of the bumble bee / Win-
women and song / Pizzicato polka / Impromptu
EF1 / Perpetual motion / Rondo capriccioso.
Notes: Details as for vol.1
Musicassette: released on Accordion Record
Club in Jul'86 by Accordion Record Club Rec-
ords. Distributed by: Accordion Record Club

Leo Aquino 111.
Tracks: / Glocca morra / Dizzy fingers / Noia /
Miglia vacca / Flight of the bumle bee / Fiddle
faddle / Wooden soldiers / Sole mio / Torna sur-
riento / Funiclli / Barber of Seville / Carnival of
Venice / Summer night (Greig) / Anitra's dance
/ March of the dwarfs.
Notes: Details as for vol.1
Musicassette: released on Accordion Record
Club in Jul'86 by Accordion Record Club Rec-
ords. Distributed by: Accordion Record Club

Aquizim

African connection/African voyage.
Single (12"): released on Ariwa in Aug'83 by
Ariwa Records. Distributed by: Revolver, Car-
tel, Jetstar, Rough Trade

African dream/English girl.
Single (12"): released on Jah Shaka in Oct'82
by Jah Shaka Records. Distributed by: Jetstar

Kunte Kinte.
Single (12"): released on Ariwa in Feb'83 by
Ariwa Records. Distributed by: Revolver, Car-
tel, Jetstar, Rough Trade

Time of my life/Sheila.
Single (12"): released on Ariwa in Sep'82 by
Ariwa Records. Distributed by: Revolver, Car-
tel, Jetstar, Rough Trade

True true loving/Concrete sleaveship.
Single (12"): released on Ariwa in May'82 by
Ariwa Records. Distributed by: Revolver, Car-
tel, Jetstar, Rough Trade

Arabeque

Time to say goodbye.
Single (12"): released on ZYX (Germany) in
Nov'85 by ZYX Records. Distributed by: Grey-
hound

Arabia

Ancient Egypt.
Album: released on Lyrichord (USA) in Oct'81
by Lyrichord Records (USA). Distributed by:
Flexitron Distributors Ltd

Musicassette: released on Lyrichord (USA) in
Aug'82 by Lyrichord Records (USA). Distributed by: Flexitron Distributors Ltd

Arab music.
Double Album: released on Lyrichord (USA) in
Oct'81 by Lyrichord Records (USA). Distributed
by: Flexitron Distributors Ltd

Arab music volume 2.
Album: released on Lyrichord (USA) in Oct'81
by Lyrichord Records (USA). Distributed by:
Flexitron Distributors Ltd

Exotic music for the oud.
Notes: H Aram Gulezyan - oud, sultania, Indian
sarod   plus instrumental
group
Album: released on Lyrichord (USA) in Oct'81
by Lyrichord Records (USA). Distributed by:
Flexitron Distributors Ltd

Fantasie Arabe.
Album: released on Lyrichord (USA) in Oct'81
by Lyrichord Records (USA). Distributed by:
Flexitron Distributors Ltd

Oud, (The).
Notes: H. Aram Gulezyan
Album: released on Lyrichord (USA) in Oct'81
by Lyrichord Records (USA). Distributed by:
Flexitron Distributors Ltd

Musicassette: released on Lyrichord (USA) in
Aug'82 by Lyrichord Records (USA). Distributed by: Flexitron Distributors Ltd

Arabia, Tales From

Tales from Arabia.
Musicassette: released on Anvil in Apr'80. Distributed by: Anvil

Arabic

Arabic.
Notes: See under language courses.

Aragorn

Black ice.
Single (7"): released on Neat in Feb'81 by Neat
Records. Distributed by: Pinnacle, Neat

Aram, Vikki

**Sings & plays the great songs (Aram,
Vikki Plus Her All Star Band).**
Album: released on Zodiac in May'81. Dis-

tributed by: Jazz Music

Aran, Duncan

Teach me how to dance.
Single (7"): released on Pulsar in Apr'81 by Lismor Records. Distributed by: Lismor

Arase, Randy

Hollywood fantasia.
Tracks: / There will never be another you / Someone to watch over me / Three coins in the fountain / Foggy day, A / Boy next door, The / Hollywood fantasia / American in Japan, The / Sonata di bravura.
Album: released on ARC (Accordion Records) in '84. Distributed by: Accordion Record Club

Arawaks & Friends

Caribbean experience.
Album: released on Caribana in Oct'81. Distributed by: Pinnacle

Arbeid Adelt

Dag dat het zonlich niet meer scheen, (De).
Single (7"): released on Parsley (Belgium) in Aug'82. Distributed by: Pinnacle, Rough Trade

Ar Bras, Dan

Acoustic.
Album: released on FLVM (France) in Jun'84. Distributed by: Projection

Allez dire a la ville.
Album: released on Hexagone in Sep'79. Distributed by: Projection

Musiques pour les silence a venir.
Album: released on Celtic Music in Jul'86 by Celtic Music Distribution. Distributed by: Celtic Music, Jazz Music, Projection, Roots

Terre nouvelle.
Album: released on Hexagone in Sep'79. Distributed by: Projection

Arc

War of the ring.
Single (7"): released on Slipped Discs in Nov'81 by Slipped Discs Records. Distributed by: PRT, Self Distribution

Arcadia

Arcadia.
Tracks: / Election day / Promise (The) / Goodbye is forever / Flame, The / Missing.
Notes: A superb collection of moody, expressive videos which perfectly match the music. Plus fascinating on location material of the filming of the videos in London, Paris and the South of France. Number of tracks: 5. Total playing time : 56 minutes approx.
Video-cassette [Betamax]: released on PMI in Feb'87 by PMI Records. Distributed by: EMI

Election day.
Single (7"): released on EMI in Oct'85 by EMI Records. Distributed by: EMI

Single (12"): released on EMI in Oct'85 by EMI Records. Distributed by: EMI

Election day cryptic cut.
Notes: Cryptic cut - no voice
Single (12"): released on Parlophone Odeon in Nov'85

Flame, The.
Tracks: / Flame, The / Flame game / Election day.
Single (7"): released on Parlophone Odeon in Jul'86

Single (12"): released on Parlophone Odeon in Jul'86

Promise, The.
Tracks: / Promise, The / Rose Arcana / Promise, The (ext).
Single (7"): released on Parlophone Odeon in Jan'86

Single (12"): released on Parlophone Odeon in Jan'86

So red the rose.
Tracks: / Election day / Keep me in the dark / Goodbye is forever / Flame, The / Missing / Rose arcana / Promise, The / El diablo / Lady Ice.
Notes: Arcadia: Rhodes/Le Bon/Taylor. Features Sting/David Gilmour/Andy Mackay/Masami Tsuchiaya.
Album: released on Parlophone in Dec'85 by EMI Records. Distributed by: EMI

Arcadians

With all our loving.
Single (7"): released on Les Disques Du Crepuscule in Dec'84. Distributed by: Rough Trade, Pinnacle, Island, Polygram

Arcainians

Christmas in Jamaica.
Tracks: / Christmas in Jamaica / Christmas in Jamaica (dub).
Single (12"): released on Jama in Jan'86 by Jama Records

Arceneaux, Fernest

From the heart of the bayous.
Tracks: / Mother's love / Last night / It's alright / You don't have to go / I don't want nobody / Mean woman blues / London zydeco / Every day I have the blues / Chains of love / Reconsider, baby.
Album: released on JSP in Jan'84 by JSP Records. Distributed by: Swift, Projection

Archangel, Natalie

Mr Perfect for me.
Tracks: / Mr Perfect for me / Let's make love.
Single (7"): released on CBS in Aug'87 by CBS Records. Distributed by: CBS

Single (12"): released on CBS in Aug'87 by CBS Records. Distributed by: CBS

Nathalie Archangel.
Tracks: / Mr Perfect / I can't reached you / Diamonds in the rough / Let's make love / What I'd do / Never be the same / Pledge my time / It was us / La vie continue / Never let me down again.
Album: released on CBS in Sep'87 by CBS Records. Distributed by: CBS

Musicassette: released on CBS in Sep'87 by CBS Records. Distributed by: CBS

Archer, Jeffrey

Matter of honour, A.
Notes: Read by Martin Jarvis. Adam Scott listens to the reading of his father's will, aware that the financial benefit can only be pitiful. The colonel, after all, had nothing to leave - except a letter he had never opened. Should Adam open the letter and discover what had caused his father to leave the regiment in discrace and force him to resign his commission - his mother begs him not to, but the moment he does he realises his life can never be the same again. Running time: 3 hours approx.
Musicassette: released on Listen For Pleasure in Feb'87 by MFP Records. Distributed by: EMI

Matter Of Honour, A.
Notes: Full details see under Archer, Jeffrey

Not a penny more, not a penny less.
Musicassette: released on Listen For Pleasure in Nov'86 by MFP Records. Distributed by: EMI

Archer, Robyn

Star is torn , (A) (Excerpts from).
Extended-play record: released on Cube in Aug'82 by Dakota Records. Distributed by: PRT

Archers

Stand up!.
Tracks: / Only His love / We're all gonna leave here / Fool's paradise / Moments with you / Stand up! / Blame it on the one I love / More (so much more) / Livin' in your love / God loves you / Pickin' up the pieces.
Album: released on Light in May'82 by Mainline Record Company. Distributed by: Mainline

Musicassette: released on Light in May'82 by Mainline Record Company. Distributed by: Mainline

Archer, Yvonne

Ain't nobody.
Single (12"): released on Virgo Stomach in Dec'84 by Virgo Stomach Records. Distributed by: Jetstar

Archibald

Ballin' with Archie.
Tracks: / Great big eyes / Early morning blues / Ballin' with Archie / Little Miss Muffet / Stack-a-lee / Crescent City bounce / Shake baby shake / Soon as I go home / House party blues / My gal / She's scattered everywhere.
Album: released on Krazy Kat in Mar'83. Distributed by: Jazz Music, Swift, Chris Wellard, H.R. Taylor, Charly, Hotshot, IRS Distribution

Archies

Sugar sugar.
Tracks: / Sugar sugar / Sugar and spice / Jingle jangle.
Single (7"): released on Old Gold in Jul'82 by Old Gold Records. Distributed by: Lightning, Jazz Music, Spartan, Counterpoint

Single (7"): released on Debut in Jul'87 by Skratch Music. Distributed by: PRT

Single (12"): released on Debut in Jul'87 by Skratch Music. Distributed by: PRT

Architects Of Disaster

Cucumber sandwich.
Single (7"): released on Neuter in Nov'82

Ardelles

Tribute to the police, (A).
Musicassette: released on Kingfisher Cassettes in Nov'81 by Fraser-Peacock Associates Ltd. Distributed by: PRT

Ardley, Neil

Kaleidoscope of rainbows.
Tracks: / Prologue / Rainbow 1 / Rainbow 2 / Rainbow 3 / Rainbow 4 / Rainbow 5 / Rainbow 6 / Rainbow 7 / Epilogue.
Album: released on Gull in Sep'77 by Gull Records. Distributed by: Pinnacle

Ardoin Family Orchestra

Couple of Cajuns, (A).
Tracks: / Grande Mamou / Grande prairie waltz / Two step de lans prie noir / I went to the dance last night / Cher tout tout / Two step a mama's / Morris special / Valse de meche, (La) / Cucaracha, (La) / Valse de gros garcon, (La) / Johnny can't dance / Valse fonce, (La).
Album: released on Sonet in Nov'81 by Sonet Records. Distributed by: PRT

Ardoin, Lawrence 'Black'

Zydeco.
Album: released on Arhoolie in Mar'85 by Arhoolie Records. Distributed by: Projection, Topic, Jazz Music, Swift, Roots

Areety, Colin

Love and pain.
Single (7"): released on Troubadour in Dec'82

Arena

Back a yard.
Single (12"): released on City Boy in Jul'82 by City Boy Records. Distributed by: Jetstar

Blow my mind.
Single (12"): released on City Boy in Nov'82 by City Boy Records. Distributed by: Jetstar

Love is here.
Single (12"): released on City Boy in Jan'84 by City Boy Records. Distributed by: Jetstar

Turn around.
Single (12"): released on City Boy in Apr'83 by City Boy Records. Distributed by: Jetstar

Are You Lonesome Tonight

Are you lonesome tonight (Various Artists).
Album: released on Safari in Dec'85 by Safari Records. Distributed by: Pinnacle

Musicassette: released on Safari in Dec'85 by Safari Records. Distributed by: Pinnacle

Argent

Biographical Details: This four-piece British group was formed in 1969 by former Zombie Rod Argent. A track from their eponymous debut album, a song called 'Lair', became an American top 10 hit for Three Dog Night in 1971. Argent introduced their third album 'All Together Now' with a transatlantic top 5 single in their own right, 'Hold Your Head Up'. After a second UK top 20 single, 'God Gave Rock And Roll To You', the band went into commercial decline. Russ Ballard quit in 1974 and pursued a solo career. While being relatively unsuccessful as a performer, he established an astonishing reputation as a song-writer, and composed numerous hits over the following decade. Among the acts who have charted in the UK and/or US with his songs are Rainbow, Santana, America, Frida and Agnetha, to name just five. The band folded in 1976 and Rod Argent commenced a solo career encompassed various diverse activities. (BM 84)

Anthology/best of.
Album: released on Epic in Sep'84 by CBS Records. Distributed by: CBS

Musicassette: released on Epic in Sep'84 by CBS Records. Distributed by: CBS Deleted '86.

Hold your head up.
Single (7"): released on Old Gold in Jul'82 by Old Gold Records. Distributed by: Lightning Jazz Music, Spartan, Counterpoint

Argentina

Argentine folk music.
Album: released on Lyrichord (USA) in Oct'81 by Lyrichord Records (USA). Distributed by Flexitron Distributors Ltd

Guitar of the pampas, (The).
Notes: Roberto Lara - Guitar.
Album: released on Lyrichord (USA) in Oct'81 by Lyrichord Records (USA). Distributed by Flexitron Distributors Ltd

Indians of the Gran Chaco, (The).
Album: released on Lyrichord (USA) in Oct'81 by Lyrichord Records (USA). Distributed by Flexitron Distributors Ltd

Argyle Arms Ceilidh, The

Argyle Arms Ceilidh, The (Various Artists).
Album: released on Lapwing in Jul'86 by Lapwing Records Ltd. Distributed by: Celtic Music Projection, Roots Records, Ross, Gordon Duncan Distribution, Graham Tosh Distribution Chans Records

Arhams, Muhal Richard

Blues forever.
Compact disc: released on Black Saint (Italy) in Jun'86. Distributed by: Target, Jazz Music Harmonia Mundi

View from within.
Compact disc: released on Black Saint (Italy) in Jun'86. Distributed by: Target, Jazz Music, Harmonia Mundi

Ariel

Ariel.
Album: released on Move in Jan'86 by Charly Records. Distributed by: Charly Distribution Fast Forward Distribution, Cartel Distribution

Arima, Susumu

Super touch.
Album: released on JVC in '78. Distributed by Target

Arista Funksters

Arista funksters Various Artists (Various Artists).
Extended-play record: released on Arista in Sep'81 by Arista Records. Distributed by: RCA

Ariwa Hits

Ariwa Hits (Various Artists).
Album: released on Ariwa in Jul'86 by Ariwa Records. Distributed by: Revolver, Cartel, Jetstar, Rough Trade

Ariwa Posse

Ariwa posse Various Artists (Various Artists).
Album: released on Ariwa in Jul'84 by Ariwa Records. Distributed by: Revolver, Cartel, Jetstar, Rough Trade

Arizona

Arizona.
Tracks: / Sweet fantasy / Let go yer lowdowns / So hard living without you / Dance if you wanna dance / Strugglin' singers / Gamblin' man / Johnny O / Tomorrow's picture / Don't it feel good / Mary's waltz (if you believe in me) / Too late to begin.
Album: released on RCA in Mar'76 by RCA Records. Distributed by: RCA, Roots, Swift Wellard, Chris, I & B, Solomon & Peres Distribution

Low down.
Tracks: / Low down music / Like can turn to love / Got no business (bein' that funky) / Wind wishin' / Music ship / Aberration / Go down town / Love take over / Play a little music / Don't let it get you down.
Album: released on RCA in Oct'77 by RCA Records. Distributed by: RCA, Roots, Swift Wellard, Chris, I & B, Solomon & Peres Distribution

Arizona Smoke Revue

All fall down.
Single (7"): released on Rola in Mar'81 by Rola Records. Distributed by: Roots Distribution Spartan Distribution

Arizona Smoke Revue, (The).
Tracks: / Take me back to my last life / January second / Football Phil / In the real old style / Same old man / Good morning stranger / Ava-on town / No-one to blame but yourself / Par-don me while I smoke / Stockade / Prison / Sweet home.
Album: released on Avada in '73. Distributed by: Roots

Don't look back.
Single (7"): released on Rola in Sep'81 by Rola Records. Distributed by: Roots Distribution, JSU Distribution, Spartan Distribution

Factory.
Single (7"): released on Rola in Apr'82 by Rola Records. Distributed by: Roots Distribution, JSU Distribution, Spartan Distribution

Mohammeds radio.
Single (7"): released on Rola in Apr'83 by Rola Records. Distributed by: Roots Distribution, JSU Distribution, Spartan Distribution

Smokin'.
Extended-play record: released on Avada in Aug'80. Distributed by: Roots

Thundering on the horizon, (A).
Album: released on Rola in Mar'81 by Rola Records. Distributed by: Roots Distribution, JSU Distribution, Spartan Distribution

Arka

In Paradisum.
Single (12"): released on IG in Apr'87. Distributed by: Rough Trade, Cartel

Arkangelsk

Arkangelsk.
Album: released on Leo in Oct'85. Distributed by: Recommended

Arkin, Alan

Catch 22.
Musicassette: released on Listen For Pleasure in Aug'85 by MFP Records. Distributed by: EMI

Ark Royal

Biographical Details: The ship's company and Royal Marine band of H.M.S Ark Royal had a minor Christmas hit in 1978 with their rendition of 'The Last Farewell'. It peaked at no.46, 44 places lower than the origianl 1975 version by Roger Whittaker.

Last farewell, (The).
Album: by BBC Records & Tapes. Distributed by: EMI, PRT

Musicassette: released on BBC in May'79 by BBC Records & Tapes. Distributed by: EMI, PRT

Arky's Toast

From the Half Moon to the Rising Sun.
Tracks: / From the half moon to the rising sun / Summer sketch / Arky's people / April / Cold's the wind / Child's dream, A / Tree I love best, The / Merry haymakers / Acrobats / Sir Marmaduke / Balaclave charge, The / Hunting song / Village pub / Plastic's all the go / Arky's toast.
Notes: Arky's Toast the Sussex based trio, give their own tribute to Arthy Arky standing of Charkwood with songs directly connected with him and the village.
Album: released on Greenwich Village in May'81 by Sweet Folk All Records. Distributed by: Roots, Projection, Lightning, Celtic Music, Wellard, Chris

Arlana

You can't keep breaking my heart.
Single (12"): released on Hitman in Aug'83 by Hitman Records. Distributed by: Pinnacle

Arlen, Harold

Harold Arlen in Hollywood.
Tracks: / Out of this world / It's only a paper moon / Ac-cent-tchu-ate the positive / Last night when we were young / This time the dream's on me / That old black magic / Medley "The Wizard of Oz" / Now I know / Let's fall in love / What's good about goodbye / One for my baby / Rusty Dedrick and the winds of change.
Album: released on Monmouth in Mar'79

Harold sings Arlen.
Tracks: / Blues in the night / Little biscuit / Ding-dong! The witch is dead / Sleepin' Bee, A / In the shade of the new apple tree / Hit the road to Dreamland / Ac-cent-tchu-ate the positive / My shining hour / Today I love everybody / House of flowers / For every man there is a woman / That's a fine kind O' freedom.
Album: released on CBS Cameo in Jul'83 by CBS Records. Distributed by: CBS

Ar-Log

Ar-Log.
Album: released on Dingles in Mar'79 by Dingles Records. Distributed by: Projection

Ar-Log II.
Album: released on Dingles in '83 by Dingles Records. Distributed by: Projection

Ar-Log III.
Album: released on Dingles in '83 by Dingles Records. Distributed by: Projection

Carmarthen Oak.
Single (7"): released on Dingles in Nov'80 by Dingles Records. Distributed by: Projection

Meillionen (The Clover).
Album: released on Dingles in '83 by Dingles Records. Distributed by: Projection

Pedawar.
Album: released on Recordiau Ar-Log in Feb'85

Arlott, John

Talks cricket.
Album: released on Charisma in Sep'83 by Virgin Records. Distributed by: EMI

Musicassette: released on Charisma in Sep'83 by Virgin Records. Distributed by: EMI

World of the countryside.
Album: released on World of Learning in Jul'74 by World Of Learning Records. Distributed by: World Of Learning

Armalite

Living on the edge.
Single (7"): released on Sonar in Apr'84 by Sonar Records. Distributed by: Sonar

Armatrading, Joan

Biographical Details: Born in St. Kitts, West Indies, Joan Armatrading emigrated to Birmingham with her family at the age of eight. In the early Seventies she cut her first album "Whatever's For Us" - this was in fact a collaboration with the uncredited Pam Nester. Going fully solo in the middle of the decade, her second album "Back To The Night" won sufficient acclaim to build up a cult following. Teaming up with mega-producer Glyn Johns (famed for his work with the Stones, Who, Eagles and many others), Armatrading issued a self-titled third album in '76. This LP transformed her into a major artist, logging six months on the album chart yielding a Top 21 single "Love And Affection"/ The fact that this was her first foray into either chart, combined with the LP's simple "Joan Armatrading" title, led many new fans to believe that this was a debut album-they only later became aware of her previous platters. "Love And Affection" was an extraordinarily individual single, in a differnent musical catergory from anything else on the charts at the time. Armatrading was to wait until 1980 for her next chart single, but it did not matter. The intervening albums "Show Some Emotion" and "To The Limit" continued her unique fusion of sparsely arranged acoustic funk, passionate but uncluttered love songs, perceptive lyrics and deep vocals, and were well received. Cutting the tie with Glyn Johns, she enlisted Richard Gottehrer to produce her 1980 album "Me Myself I". The title track was a hit single in Britan, while the album continued to widen her audience in both the UK and US. Subsequent albums "Walk Under Ladders" and "The Key", produced by Steve Lillywhite, have continued the musical pattern, though a rockier, electric-based feel has gradually been worked in. In 1983 "Drop The Pilot" reached No.11 on the single chart, the closest Armatrading has ever come to repeating the Top 10 success of "Love And Affection".
B.M 85

Back to the night.
Tracks: / No love for free / Travelled so far / Steppin' out / Dry land / Cool blue stole my heart / Get in touch with Jesus / Body to dust / Back to the night / So good / Let's go dancing / Come when you need me.
Notes: Original released 1975.
Album: released on Hallmark in Sep'84 by Pickwick Records. Distributed by: Pickwick Distribution, PRT, Taylors

Musicassette: released on Hallmark in Sep'84 by Pickwick Records. Distributed by: Pickwick Distribution, PRT, Taylors

Jesse.
Tracks: / Jesse / Don Juan / Love and affection / Willow.
Single (7"): released on A&M in Sep'86 by A&M Records. Distributed by: Polygram

Single (12"): released on A&M in Sep'86 by A&M Records. Distributed by: Polygram

Double-pack single: released on A&M in Sep'86 by A&M Records. Distributed by: Polygram

Key, The.
Tracks: / I love it when you call me names / Foolish pride / Drop the pilot / Key, The / Everybody gotta know / Tell tale / What do boys dream / Game of love, The / Dealer, The / Bad habits / I love my baby.
Compact disc: released on A&M in Jun'86 by A&M Records. Distributed by: Polygram

Key, (The).
Album: released on A&M in Mar'83 by A&M Records. Distributed by: Polygram

Musicassette: released on A&M in Mar'83 by A&M Records. Distributed by: Polygram

Kind words (and a real good heart).
Tracks: / Kind words (and a real good heart) / Figure of speech.
Single (7"): released on A&M in Apr'86 by A&M Records. Distributed by: Polygram

Single (12"): released on A&M in Apr'86 by A&M Records. Distributed by: Polygram

Lonely lady.
Single (7"): released on Cube in Jun'82 by Dakota Records. Distributed by: PRT

Mean old man.
Album: released on Platinum (W.Germany) in Oct'85. Distributed by: Mainline

Musicassette: released on Platinum (W.Germany) in Oct'85. Distributed by: Mainline

Me, myself, I.
Album: released on A&M in May'80 by A&M Records. Distributed by: Polygram

Musicassette: released on A&M in May'80 by A&M Records. Distributed by: Polygram

Me myself I.
Tracks: / Me, myself, I / Ma-me-o-beach / Friends / Is it tomorrow yet / Turn out the light / When you kissed me / All the way from America / Feeling in my heart (for you) / Simon / I need you / Me, myself, I / Ma-me-o-beach / Friends / Is it tomorrow yet / Turn out the light / When you kissed me / All the way from America / Feeling in my heart (for you) / Simon / I need you.
Album: released on A&M in Sep'86 by A&M Records. Distributed by: Polygram

Musicassette: released on A&M in Sep'86 by A&M Records. Distributed by: Polygram

Reach out.
Tracks: / Reach out / Rivers on fire.
Single (7"): released on A&M in Jul'86 by A&M Records. Distributed by: Polygram

Replay of Joan Armatrading.
Album: released on Sierra in Feb'85 by Sierra Records. Distributed by: WEA

Musicassette: released on Sierra in Feb'85 by Sierra Records. Distributed by: WEA

Secret secrets.
Tracks: / Persona grata / Temptation / Moves / Talking to the wall / Love by you / Thinking man / Friends not flowers / One night / Secret secrets / Strange / Persona grata / Temptation / Moves / Talking to the wall / Love by you / Thinking man / Friends not flowers / One night / Secret secrets / Strange.
Notes: At last after two years, the long-awaited new studio album from one of the world's foremost artists - Joan Armatrading. "Secret secrets" is possibly Joan's finest album to date, featuring her ever-distinctive voice, spanning the whole range of emotions, from the opening ballad "Persona Grate" through to the superb up-tempo "Temptation" - forthcoming single. This is Joan's first new album for two years, and her first album since the successful compilation "Track Record". Produced by Mike Howlet (Blancmange, Flock Of Seagulls, Tears For Fears etc) it features a stunning line-up of musicians, including Joe Jackson, Westley Magoogan and Dave Betelli.
Compact disc: released on A&M in Feb'85 by A&M Records. Distributed by: Polygram

Album: released on A&M in Feb'85 by A&M Records. Distributed by: Polygram

Musicassette: released on A&M in Feb'85 by A&M Records. Distributed by: Polygram

Show some emotion.
Tracks: / Get in the sun / Willow / Kissin' and a hugging / Woncha come on home / Show some emotion / Warm love / Never is too late / Peace in mind / Opportunity / Mama mercy / Woncha come on home / Show some emotion / Warm love / Never is too late / Peace in mind / Opportunity / Mama mercy / Get in the sun / Willow / Kissin' and a hugging.
Album: released on A&M in Apr'86 by A&M Records. Distributed by: Polygram

Musicassette: released on A&M in Sep'77 by A&M Records. Distributed by: Polygram

Sleight of hand.
Tracks: / Kind words (and a real good heart) / Killing time / Reach out / Angel man / Laurel and the rose / One more chance / Russian roulette / Jesse / Figure of speech / Don Juan.
Notes: The new album, featuring 10 new songs from one of the UK's most talented singer/songwriters. Includes the up tempo single "Kind words" as well as ballads like "Jesse" which are destined to join the list of Armatrading classics. Written, produced and arranged by Joan Armatrading; mixed by Steve Lillywhite.
Album: released on A&M in May'86 by A&M Records. Distributed by: Polygram

Musicassette: released on A&M in May'86 by A&M Records. Distributed by: Polygram

Compact disc: released on A&M in May'86 by A&M Records. Distributed by: Polygram

Steppin' out.
Tracks: / Mama mercy / Cool blue stole my heart / How cruel / Love song / Love and affection / Steppin' out / You rope you tied me / Kissin' and hugging / Tall in the saddle.
Album: released on A&M in Aug'79 by A&M Records. Distributed by: Polygram

Musicassette: released on A&M in Aug'79 by A&M Records. Distributed by: Polygram

Album: released on Hallmark in Sep'85 by Pickwick Records. Distributed by: Pickwick Distribution, PRT, Taylors

Musicassette: released on Hallmark in Sep'85 by Pickwick Records. Distributed by: Pickwick Distribution, PRT, Taylors

Temptation.
Single (7"): released on A&M in Feb'85 by A&M Records. Distributed by: Polygram

Musicassette: released on A&M in Feb'85 by A&M Records. Distributed by: Polygram

Thinking man.
Single (7"): released on A&M in May'85 by A&M Records. Distributed by: Polygram

To the limit.
Tracks: / Barefoot and pregnant / Your letter / Am I blue for you / You rope tied me / Baby I / Bottom to the top / Taking my baby uptown / What do you want / Wishing / Let it last.
Album: released on A&M in Sep'78 by A&M Records. Distributed by: Polygram

Musicassette: released on A&M in Sep'78 by A&M Records. Distributed by: Polygram

Track Record.
Tracks: / Drop the pilot / I love it when you call me names / Frustration / When I get it right / I'm lucky / Me myself I / Weakness in me, The / Heaven / Down to Sero / Love and affection / Show some emotion / Willow / Rosie / Drop the pilot / I love it when you call me names / Frustration / When I get it right / I'm lucky / Me myself I / Weakness in me, The / Heaven / Down to zero / Love and affection / Show some emotion / Willow / Rosie.
Compact disc: released on A&M in Oct'84 by A&M Records. Distributed by: Polygram

Track record.
Album: released on A&M in Nov'83 by A&M Records. Distributed by: Polygram

Musicassette: released on A&M in Nov'83 by A&M Records. Distributed by: Polygram

Compact disc: released on A&M in Oct'84 by A&M Records. Distributed by: Polygram

Walk under ladders.
Tracks: / I'm lucky / When I get it right / Romancers / I wanna hold you / Weakness in me, The / No love / At the hop / I can't lie to myself / Eating the bear / Only one.
Album: released on A&M in Sep'81 by A&M Records. Distributed by: Polygram

Musicassette: released on A&M in Sep'81 by A&M Records. Distributed by: Polygram

Whatever's for us.
Tracks: / My family / City girl / Spend a little time / Whatever's for us / Child star / Visionary mountains / It could have been better / Head of the table / Mister remember me / Gave it a try / Alice / Conversation / Mean old man / All the king's gardens.
Album: released on Cube in Oct'81 by Dakota Records. Distributed by: PRT

Musicassette: released on Cube in Oct'81 by Dakota Records. Distributed by: PRT

Armenta

I wanna be with you.
Single (7"): released on Savoir Faire in Nov'83

Musicassette: released on Savoir Faire in Nov'83

Armoured Saint

Delirious nomad.
Tracks: / Long before I die / Nervous man / Over the edge / Laugh, Te / Conqueror / For the sake / Aftermath / In the hole / You're never alone / Released.
Album: released on Chrysalis in Jan'86 by Chrysalis Records. Distributed by: CBS

Musicassette: released on Chrysalis in Jan'86 by Chrysalis Records. Distributed by: CBS

March of the saints.
Tracks: / March of the saint / Can u deliver / Mad house / Take a turn / Seducer / Mutiny on the world / Glory hunter / Stricken by fate / Envy / False alarm.
Album: released on Chrysalis in Oct'84 by Chrysalis Records. Distributed by: CBS

Musicassette: released on Chrysalis in Oct'84 by Chrysalis Records. Distributed by: CBS

Armour, Matt

On the morning tide.
Tracks: / Trawlerman, The / On the morning tide / Isle of May, The / Wild white rose, The / Greytown / Harvest home, The / Deep sea fishermen, The / Lammasfair, The / Reyjavic / Head for home / Shores of the Forth, The / Hills of Caithness, The.
Album: released on Sweet Folk All in May'81 by Sweet Folk All Records. Distributed by: Sweet Folk All, Roots, Celtic Music, Dragon, Impetus, Projection, Chris Wellard, Festival Records

Armoury Show

Castles in Spain.
Tracks: / Castles in Spain / Gathering, A / Ring those bells.
Single (7"): released on Parlophone in Jan'86 by EMI Records. Distributed by: EMI

Single (12"): released on Parlophone in Jan'86 by EMI Records. Distributed by: EMI

Single (7"): released on Parlophone in Aug'84 by EMI Records. Distributed by: EMI

Single (12"): released on Parlophone in Aug'84 by EMI Records. Distributed by: EMI

Glory of love.
Single (12"): released on EMI in Jul'85 by EMI Records. Distributed by: EMI

New York City.
Tracks: / New York City / Whirlwind.
Single (7"): released on Parlophone in Apr'87 by EMI Records. Distributed by: EMI

Single (12"): released on Parlophone in Apr'87 by EMI Records. Distributed by: EMI

New York City (Dance version).
Tracks: / New York City (Dance version) / New York City (New York a go go version).
Single (12"): released on Parlophone in Apr'87 by EMI Records. Distributed by: EMI

Waiting for the floods.
Tracks: / Castles in Spain / Kyrie / Feeling, A / Jungle of cities / We can be brave again / Higher than the world / Glory of love / Waiting for the floods / Sense of freedom / Sleep city sleep / Avalanche.
Album: released on Parlophone in Sep'85 by EMI Records. Distributed by: EMI

Musicassette: released on Parlophone in Sep'85 by EMI Records. Distributed by: EMI

Arms

Complete concert, The.
Video-cassette (VHS): released on Channel 5 in Jun'86. Distributed by: W.H. Smiths

Royal Albert Hall concert (The) - part 1.
Video-cassette (VHS): released on Videoform in Oct'84

Royal Albert Hall concert (The) - part 2.
Video-cassette (VHS): released on Videoform in Oct'84

Armstead, J

Louis vol.4: Savoy blues.
Album: released on Joker in Apr'81. Distributed by: Counterpoint, Mainline, Record Services Distribution (Ireland)

Arms & The Man

Arms and the man **Shaw, Bernard.**
Musicassette: released on Talking Tape Company in '84 by Talking Tape Company Records

Armstrong, Billy

Billy, don't sell your fiddle.
Tracks: / Fraulein / Truck driving man / San Antonia medley / Kind of love I can't forget, The / Six days on the road / Roly poly / Last letter, The / Take me back to Tulsa / Liberty.
Album: released on Westwood in '82 by Westwood Records. Distributed by: Jazz Music, H.R. Taylor, Pinnacle Ross Records

Mr. Fiddle.
Album: released on Westwood in '76 by Westwood Records. Distributed by: Jazz Music, H.R. Taylor, Pinnacle, Ross Records

Armstrong & Ellington

Reunion Concert.
Notes: See under Ellington and Armstrong

Armstrong, Frankie

Bird in the bush.

Birds in the bush.
Album: . Distributed by: Roots Distribution

Frankie Armstrong.
Tracks: / Little Duke Arthur's nurse / Pitmen's union, The / Lady Diamond / Lament for the Hull trawlers / Month of January, The / Three drunken maidens / Jack the lad / Whore's lament, The / Little musgrave / Collier lass, The / Female drummer, The.
Album: released on Topic in '81. Distributed by: Roots Distribution

I heard a woman singing.
Notes: Artists also include Roy Bailey/Leon Rossleton
Album: released on Fuse in May'86 by Fuse Records. Distributed by: Projection

Album: released on Flying Fish (USA) in Oct'85 by Flying Fish Records (USA). Distributed by: Roots, Projection

Lovely on the water.
Tracks: / Tarry trousers / Green valley, The / Low down in the broom / Cruel mother, The / Crafty maid's policy, The / Maid on the shore, The / Frog and the mouse, The / Lovely on the water / Brown girl, The / Young girl cut down in her prime, The / Unquiet grave, The / Saucy sailor, The / Two sisters, The.
Album: released on Topic in '81. Distributed by: Roots Distribution

Tamlin.
Album: released on Plant Life in Feb'85. Distributed by: Roots

Armstrong, Herbie

Back Against The Wall.
Tracks: / Josie / Horses of stream / Friday's child / Haven only knows / You take me up / Back against the wall / Losing you / Let it run / Save the last dance / Coming in from the rain / Do.
Compact disc: released on MMC in '86 by MMC Records. Distributed by: PRT Distribution, Pinnacle

Back against the wall.
Tracks: / Josie / Horses of steam / Friday's child / Heaven only knows / You take me up / Back against the wall / Losing you / Let it run / Save the last dance / Coming in from the rain / Do you.
Album: released on MMC in Nov'83 by MMC Records. Distributed by: PRT Distribution, Pinnacle

Here comes the night.
Tracks: / Here comes the night / Back against the wall.
Single (7"): released on Making Waves in May'86 by Making Waves Records

Josie.
Single (7"): released on MMC in Jan'83 by MMC Records. Distributed by: PRT Distribution, Pinnacle

Real real gone.
Single (7"): released on Avatar in Aug'81 by Avatar Communications. Distributed by: CBS

Save the last dance for me.
Single (7"): by PRT Records. Distributed by: PRT

Save the last dance.
Single (7"): released on MMC in Mar'84 by MMC Records. Distributed by: PRT Distribution, Pinnacle

Armstrong, Jack

Celebrated minstrel.
Album: released on Saydisc in Jul'77 by Saydisc Records. Distributed by: Essex, Harmonia Mundi, Roots, H.R. Taylor, Jazz Music, Swift, Projection, Gamut

Armstrong, Kevin

How the west was won.
Single (7"): released on Oval in May'82. Distributed by: Projection

Armstrong, Louis

1924 (Armstrong, Louis/Red Onion Jazz Babies/Freddie Keppard/Doc C).
Tracks: / Everybody loves my baby / Texas moaner blues / Of all the wrongs you've done to me / Terrible blues / Santa Claus blues / Nobody knows the way I feel this morning / Early early morn / Cake walking babies from home / Scissor grinder Joe / Lonely little wallflower / So this is Venice / Moanful man / Memphis maybe man, (The) / One I love belongs to somebody else, (The) / Stock yards strut / Salty dog.
Album: released on Swaggie (Australia) in Jan'83

1944-51.
Tracks: / Blues in the night / Pretty girl is like a melody, (A) / Baby don't you cry / Coquette / Dear old Southland / Lazy river / I've got a girl in Kalamazoo / Ain't misbehavin' / Is you is or is you ain't my baby / Perdido / Accentuate the positive / Always / Back o' town blues / Basin St. blues / Black & blue / Do you know what it means to miss New Orleans / I got a right to sing the blues / I'm confessin' that I love you / You rascal you / Lazy river / Some day you'll be sorry / Panama / Struttin' with some barbecue.
Album: released on Joker in Apr'81. Distributed by: Counterpoint, Mainline, Record Services Distribution (Ireland)

19 Historical tracks.
Compact disc: released on Delta in Apr'87 by Delta Records. Distributed by: Target

20 golden pieces of...
Tracks: / Someday (you'll be sorry) / Heebie Jeebies / I can't give you anything but love baby / Muskrat ramble / Dear old southland / That lucky old sun / Black & blue / Panama / Royal garden blues / Chinatown my Chinatown / Swing that music / Tiger rag / Baby won't you please come home / Storyville blues / Jeepers creepers / Do you know what it means to miss New Orleans / Brother Bill / Old rockin' chair / Way down yonder in New Orleans / I'm not so rough.
Album: released on Bulldog in Jul'82 by Bulldog Records. Distributed by: President Distribution, Spartan, Swift, Taylor, H.R.

20 greatest hits.
Album: released on Astan in Nov'84 by Astan Records. Distributed by: Counterpoint

Musicassette: released on Astan in Nov'84 by Astan Records. Distributed by: Counterpoint

20 unforgettable hits (Armstrong, Louis & His All Stars).
Musicassette: released on Astan in Jun'86 by Astan Records. Distributed by: Counterpoint

All stars vol 11.
Tracks: / High society / I cried for you / Whispering / Me & Brother Bill / Don't fence me in / Basin Street blues / I gotta right to sing the blues / Jack Armstrong blues / Mop mop.
Notes: Note: "I cried for you","Don't fence me in" &"Basin Street blues" were issued by this group on a major label.Other titles appear for the first time on record.
Album: released on Unique Jazz in Apr'81. Distributed by: Swift, Jazz Music, Jazz Horizons

Ambassador satch.
Album: released on CBS(France) in May'85 by CBS Records. Distributed by: Conifer, Discovery, Swift

Musicassette: released on CBS(France) in May'85 by CBS Records. Distributed by: Conifer, Discovery, Swift

Armed forces radio service (Armstrong, Louis & His Orchestra).
Album: released on Duke in Jun'86 by Melodisc Records. Distributed by: Jazz Horizons, Jazz Music, Celtic Music, JSU, Swift

At his rarest of all rare performances vol 2.
Album: released on Kings Of Jazz in Jul'82. Distributed by: Jazz Horizons, Jazz Music, Celtic Music

At the Carnegie Hall **February 8th, 1947.**
Tracks: / Black & blue / I'm confessin' that I love you / Up the lazy river / You rascal you / Save it, pretty mama / Ain't misbehavin' / Struttin' with some barbecue / Dippermouth blues / Mahogany Hall stomp / Muskrat ramble / St. Louis blues / Rockin' chair / Tiger rag.

Album: released on Joker in Apr'81. Distributed by: Counterpoint, Mainline, Record Services Distribution (Ireland)

At the Eddie Condon floor show vol 1.
Tracks: / When it's sleepy time down south / Them there eyes / St. James' Infirmary / Sweethearts on parade / Do you know what it means to miss New Orleans / Struttin' with some barbecue / Sweet Georgia Brown / After you've gone / Royal Garden blues / Back o' town blues / Me & Brother Bill / Blues in b-flat.
Album: released on Queen-Disc in Apr'81. Distributed by: Celtic Music, JSU, Jazz Horizons, Jazz Music

At the Eddie Condon floor show vol 2.
Tracks: / Walking my baby back home / Fine & mellow / I love you Porgy / Them there eyes / Running wild / These foolish things / Swing that music / Aunt Hagar's blues / Heebie jeebies / Farewell to Storyville / I love my man / Ole Miss.
Album: released on Queen-Disc in Apr'81. Distributed by: Celtic Music, JSU, Jazz Horizons, Jazz Music

Back O'Town Blues.
Album: released on Pathe MarconiFrance) in Feb'87

Basin street blues.
Album: released on EMI (France) in Mar'84 by EMI Records. Distributed by: Conifer

Musicassette: released on EMI (France) in Mar'84 by EMI Records. Distributed by: Conifer

Best of Louis Armstrong.
Album: released on Music For Pleasure (Holland) in Apr'83 by EMI Records. Distributed by: EMI

Musicassette: released on Music For Pleasure (Holland) in Apr'83 by EMI Records. Distributed by: EMI

Best of Satchmo.
Tracks: / On the sunny side of the street / Lazy river / Georgia on my mind / I surrender dear / Exactly like you / Some of these days / Kiss to build a dream on, A / La vien rose / Blueberry Hill / Whiffenpoof song, The / Shadrack / When it's sleepy time down south / I can't give you anything but love / If I could be with you one hour tonight / When you're smiling.
Album: released on MCA Coral in Aug'81 by MCA Records. Distributed by: Polygram

Musicassette: released on MCA Coral in Aug'81 by MCA Records. Distributed by: Polygram

Big bands, The.
Album: released on Swaggie (Australia) in Jan'83

Blues in the night.
Tracks: / Blues in the night / Pretty girl is like a melody, A / Baby don't you cry / Coquette / Dear old Southland / Lazy river / I've got a girl in Kalamazoo / Ain't misbehavin' / Is you is or is you ain't my baby / Perdido / Accentuate the positive / Always.
Album: released on Joker in Apr'81. Distributed by: Counterpoint, Mainline, Record Services Distribution (Ireland)

Bunny Berigan, Louis Armstrong and Mills Brothers 1937 (Armstrong, Louis/Bunny Berigan/Mills Brothers).

Carnegie Hall concert **February 8th, 1947.**
Tracks: / New Orleans function / Free as a bird / Oh didn't he ramble? / Dippermouth blues / Mahogany Hall stomp / Muskrat ramble / St Louis blues / Rockin' chair / Tiger rag / Black and blue / I'm confessin' / Struttin' with some barbecue / Up a lazy river / You rascal you / Save it, pretty mama / Ain't misbehavin'.
Album: released on Connoisseur Rarities in Apr'81. Distributed by: Jazz Horizons, Jazz Music

Carnegie Hall, New York City **February 8th 1947.**
Tracks: / Black and blue / I'm confessing / Struttin' with some barbecue / Up a lazy river / You rascal you / Save it, pretty mama / Ain't misbehavin' / Dippermouth blues / Mahogany Hall stomp / Muskrat ramble / St Louis blues / Rockin' chair / Tiger rag.
Album: released on Kings Of Jazz in Apr'81. Distributed by: Jazz Horizons, Jazz Music, Celtic Music

Chicago concert 1956.
Tracks: / Memphis blues, The / Frankie & Johnny / Tiger rag / Do you know what it means to miss New Orleans / Basin Street blues / Black & blue / West End blues / On the sunny side of the street / Struttin' with some barbecue / Manhattan / When it's sleepy time down south / Indiana / Gypsy, The / Faithful Hussar, The / Rockin' chair / Bucket's got a hole in it / Perdido / Clarinet marmalade / Mack the knife / Tenderly / You'll never walk alone / Stompin' at the Savoy / Margie / Mama's back in town / That's my desire / Ko ko mo / I love you so.
Double Album: released on CBS in '84 by CBS Records. Distributed by: CBS

Double musicassette: released on CBS in '84 by CBS Records. Distributed by: CBS

Chinatown my Chinatown.
Album: released on Astan in Nov'84 by Astan Records. Distributed by: Counterpoint

Musicassette: released on Astan in Nov'84 by Astan Records. Distributed by: Counterpoint

Complete Town Hall Concert, The (vols.1&2).
Tracks: / Cornet chop suey / Our monday date / Dear old Southland / Big butter and egg man / Tiger rag / Struttin' with some barbecue / Sweethearts on parade / St. Louis blues / Pennies from heaven / On the sunny side of the street / I can't give you anything but love / Back o'town blues / Ain't misbehavin' / Rockin' chair / Muskrat ramble / Save it pretty mama / St. James Infirmary / Royal garden blues / Do you know what it means to be Miss New Orleans / Jack Armstrong blues.
Album: released on RCA in Mar'86 by RCA Records. Distributed by: RCA, Roots, Swift, Wellard, Chris, I & B, Solomon & Peres Distribution

Musicassette: released on RCA in Mar'86 by RCA Records. Distributed by: RCA, Roots, Swift, Wellard, Chris, I & B, Solomon & Peres Distribution

Ella and Louis again (Armstrong, Louis & Ella Fitzgerald).
Notes: For full information see Fitzgerald, Ella & Louis Armstrong

Ella and Louis again Vol 1.
Album: released on Verve in Aug'81 by Phonogram Records. Distributed by: Polygram

Essence of Louis Armstrong, The.
Album: released on Phontastic in Jul'87. Distributed by: Wellard, Chris

Evening with Louis Armstrong (An).
Musicassette: released on Vogue in Oct'77. Distributed by: Discovery, Jazz Music, PRT, Swift

First recorded concert 1932/1933.
Tracks: / I cover the waterfront / Dinah / Tiger rag / Chinatown / You rascal you / On the closet / Dinah / Harlem stomp / When it's sleepy time down south.
Album: released on Jazz Anthology in May'85. Distributed by: Discovery, Swift

From the Big Band to the All Stars.
Tracks: / Long long journey / Linger in my arms / Back 'o town blues / Where the blues were born in New Orleans / I believe / You don't learn that in school / Rockin' chair / I never saw a better day / Hobo you can't ride this train.
Album: released on RCA (France) in Feb'86 by RCA Records. Distributed by: Discovery

Golden greats: Louis Armstrong.
Tracks: / What a wonderful world / Hello Dolly / Cabaret / On the sunny side of the street / Lazy river.
Album: released on MCA in Jul'85 by MCA Records. Distributed by: Polygram, MCA

Musicassette: released on MCA in Jul'85 by MCA Records. Distributed by: Polygram, MCA

Greatest concert, The.
Tracks: / Rose room / Back 'o' town blues / C'est si bon / Way down yonder in New Orleans / Stardust / Rockin' chair / Where did you stay last night / Baby it's cold outside / C jam blues / Stomping at the Savoy / I used to love you / La vie en rose / Lover / That's my desire / Royal garden blues / Ain't misbehavin' / Love me or leave me / How high the moon / Tea for two / Hucklebuck.
Notes: Louis Armstrong with all star band recorded live in Toronto during 1951. All thefavourites are here.Collective Personnel Louis Armstrong-Trumpet & Vocals/ Barney Bigard -Clarinet/Jack Teagarden -Trombone & Vocals/Arvell Shaw -String Bass/Cozy Cole -Drums/Earl "Fartha" Himes Piano/Velma Middleton -Vocals.
Album: released on Festival (France) in Nov'84. Distributed by: Discovery, Red Lightnin' Distribution, Swift

Greatest hits:Louis Armstrong.
Tracks: / Mack the Knife (Threepenny Opera) / Back o' town blues / Black & blue / Ain't misbehavin' / Basin Street blues / Cabaret / Honeysuckle Rose / When it's sleepy time down south / All of me / West End blues / Struttin' with some barbecue / Indiana / Tin roof blues.
Album: released on CBS in May'83 by CBS Records. Distributed by: CBS

Musicassette: released on CBS in May'83 by CBS Records. Distributed by: CBS

Album: released on CBS in '84 by CBS Records. Distributed by: CBS

Musicassette: released on CBS in '84 by CBS Records. Distributed by: CBS

Album: released on K-Tel in Aug'85 by K-Tel Records. Distributed by: Record Merchandisers Distribution, Taylors, Terry Blood Distribution, Wynd-Up Distribution, Relay Distribution, Pickwick Distribution, Solomon & Peres Distribution, Polygram

Musicassette: released on K-Tel in Aug'85 by K-Tel Records. Distributed by: Record Merchandisers Distribution, Taylors, Terry Blood Distribution, Wynd-Up Distribution, Relay Distribution, Pickwick Distribution, Solomon & Peres Distribution, Polygram

* * * * *

Great Original Performances 1923-1931.
Notes: Features Louis Armstrong's Hot Five and Hot Seven, Johny Dodds, Earl Hinesand Jack Teagarden
Album: released on BBC in Aug'86 by BBC Records & Tapes. Distributed by: EMI, PRT,

Musicassette: released on BBC in Aug'86 by BBC Records & Tapes. Distributed by: EMI, PRT

Great Reunion.
Compact disc:

Great reunion.
Compact disc: released on Roulette/Vogue in May'85

His immortal concert series.
Tracks: / Back o' town blues / Do you know what it means to miss New Orleans / Black & blue / Basin Street blues / I gotta right to sing the blues / I'm confessin' that I love you / You rascal you / Lazy river / Someday you'll be sorry / Panama / Struttin' with some barbecue.
Album: released on Joker in Apr'81. Distributed by: Counterpoint, Mainline, Record Services Distribution (Ireland)

His last recordings - 1970.
Tracks: / Boy from New Orleans / What a wonderful world / Mood indigo / Give peace a chance / Creator has a master plan, The / My one and only love / Everybody's talkin' / His father wore long hair / This black cat has nine lives / We shall overcome.
Album: released on RCA (France) in '83 by RCA Records. Distributed by: Discovery

Hot Five (1925-26).
Album: released on Swaggie (Australia) in Jan'83

Hot Five (1928).
Album: released on Swaggie (Australia) in Jan'83

Hot fives and sevens complete.
Tracks: / My heart / Yes I'm in the barrel / Gut bucket blues / Come back sweet papa / Georgia grind / Heebie jeebies / Cornet chop suey / Oriental strut / You're next / Muskrat ramble / Don't forget to mess around / I'm gonna getcha / Dropping shucks / Who's it? / King of the Zulus, The / Big fat ma and skinny pa / Lonesome blues / Sweet little papa / Jazz lips / Skid dat de dat / Big butter and egg man / Sunset cafe stomp / You made me love you / Irish black bottom / Willie the weeper / Wild man blues / Chicago breakdown / Alligator crawl / Potato head blues / Melancholy blues / Weary blues / Twelfth Street rag / Keyhole blues / SOL blues / Gully low blues / That's when I'll come back to you / Put 'em down blues / Ory's Creole trombone / Last time, The / Struttin' with some barbecue / Got no blues / Once in a while / I'm not rough / Hotter than that / Savoy blues / Fireworks / Skip the gutter / Monday date, A / Don't jive me / West End blues / Sugar foot strut / Two deuces / Squeeze me / Knee drops / Symphonic raps / Savoyagers' stomp / No papa no / Basin Street blues / No one else but you / Bean koo jack / Save it, pretty mama / Weather bird / Muggles / Heah me talkin' to ya / St James' Infirmary / Tight like this / Knockin' a jug.

Hot Five/Seven (1926-27).
Album: released on Swaggie (Australia) in Jan'83

Hot Fives & Sevens complete (SH 405).
Album: released on World in Jan'81. Distributed by: Jetstar

Hot Fives & Sevens complete (SH 407).
Album: released on World in Mar'81. Distributed by: Jetstar

Hot Fives & Sevens complete (SH 405).
Album: released on World in Mar'81. Distributed by: Jetstar

Hot Fives & Sevens complete (SH 404).
Album: released on World in Mar'81. Distributed by: Jetstar

Hot Fives & Sevens complete (set of 4).
Album: released on World in Mar'81. Distributed by: Jetstar

Hot Fives & Sevens complete (SH 406).
Album: released on World in Mar'81. Distributed by: Jetstar

Hot Seven/Five (1927-28).
Album: released on Swaggie (Australia) in Jan'83

In Sweden.
Album: released on Route 66 in Oct'86

Integral Nice concert 1948 - volume 1.
Tracks: / Panama / Black and blue / Velma's blues / Monday date, 1 / Monday date, 2 / Royal Garden blues, 1 / Royal Garden blues, 2 / Someday / Muskrat ramble / I cried last night, 1 / I cried last night, 2.
Album: released on Jazz Anthology in Jun'85. Distributed by: Discovery, Swift

Jam session broadcast 1938 (Armstrong/Waller/Teagarden).
Album: released on Swaggie (Australia) in Jan'83

Jazz greats.
Album: released on RCA (Germany) in Jan'85

July 4, 1900 - July 6, 1971.
Double Album:

Live from Hollywood 1949.
Album: released on Swinghouse in Apr'79. Distributed by: Jazz Music Distribution, Swift Distribution, Chris Wellard Distribution

Live in Yokohama.
Tracks: / When it's sleepy time down south / Indiana / Kiss to build a dream on, A / Tea for two / My bucket's got a hole in it / Margie / Velma's blues / C'est si bon / Stompin' at The Savoy.
Album: released on Queen-Disc in Apr'81. Distributed by: Celtic Music, JSU, Jazz Horizons, Jazz Music

Louis Armstrong.
Tracks: / Hello Dolly / Sit down, you're rocking the boat / I'm confessin' / Jeepers creepers / Swing that music / That's my desire / On the sunny side of the street / When the saints go mraching in / Cabaret / Heebie jeebies / I'll string along with you / West End blues / Down by the riverside / Among my souvenirs / It's wonderful / Georgia on my mind / What a wonderful world / High society / Mahogany Hall blues stomp / Carry me back to old Virginny / When you're smiling / I can't give you anything but love / Alexander's ragtime band / Blueberry Hill / Naturally / That lucky old sun / Dippermouth blues / Ain't misbehavin' / Basin Street blues / When it's sleepy time down south.
Notes: Artists include: Red Onion Jazz Babies & Freddie Keppard, Doc. Cooks Dreamland Orchestra & His Jazz Cardinals.
Album: released on Fountain in May'86 by Retrieval Records. Distributed by: Jazz Music, Swift, VJM, Wellard, Chris, Retrieval

Album: released on Dakota (Countdown series) in Oct'82 by Dakota Records. Distributed by: PRT

Musicassette: released on Dakota (Countdown series) in Oct'82 by Dakota Records. Distributed by: PRT

Musicassette: released on Cambra in '83 by Cambra Records. Distributed by: IDS, Conifer

Musicassette: released on Audio Fidelity in Oct'84. Distributed by: PRT

Louis Armstrong All Stars 1948-1949 vol 2.
Album: released on Jazz Connoisseur in Apr'79. Distributed by: Jazz Horizons, Jazz Music, Swift, Wellard, Chris

Louis Armstrong All Stars Philadephia (August 7 and 9, 1949).
Album: released on Jazz Connoisseur (Italy) in Apr'79. Distributed by: Jazz Horizons, Jazz Music, Swift, Wellard, Chris

Louis Armstrong All Stars.
Album: released on Storyville in May'86 by Storyville Records. Distributed by: Jazz Music Distribution, Swift Distribution, Chris Wellard Distribution, Counterpoint Distribution

Musicassette: released on Ditto in Mar'86 by Pickwick Records. Distributed by: H.R. Taylor

Louis Armstrong and King Oliver.
Tracks: / Just gone / Canal Street blues / Mandy Lee blues / I'm going to wear you off my mind / Chimes blues / Weather bird rag / Dipper mouth blues / Froggie Moore / Snake rag / Alligator hop / Zulu's ball / Working man blues / Krooked blues / Mabel's dreams(take 1) / Mabel's dreams(take 2) / Southern stomps (take 1) / Southern stomps (take 2) / Riverside blues / King Oliver / Jeely Roll Morton -King porter stomp / Tom cat blues / Terrible blues / Santa Claus blues / Texas moaner blues / Of all the wrongs you've done to me / Nobody knows the way I feel this morning / Early every morn / Cake walking.
Double Album: released on Milestone in Aug'80 by Ace Records. Distributed by: PRT

Louis Armstrong and His All Stars.
Musicassette: released on Swinghouse in Oct'84. Distributed by: Jazz Music Distribution, Swift Distribution, Chris Wellard Distribution

Louis Armstrong and his all stars.
Double Album: released on Joker in Apr'81. Distributed by: Counterpoint, Mainline, Record Services Distribution (Ireland)

Louis Armstrong and His All Stars (Armstrong, Louis & His All Stars).
Tracks: / When it's sleepy time down south / Hello Dolly / Blueberry Hill / Volare(Nel blu dipinto di blu) / St. James' Infirmary / Girl from Impanema / Indiana / Muskrat ramble / Mack the knife / I love Paris / Time after time / Cabaret / Tiger rag / When the saints go marching in / This could be the start of something big / Please don't talk about me when I'm gone / Stompin' at the Savoy / That's my desire / Closer walk with thee, A / Them there eyes / Avalon / Kiss to build a dream on, A / Ole miss.
Album: released on Storyville in May'86 by Storyville Records. Distributed by: Jazz Music Distribution, Swift Distribution, Chris Wellard Distribution, Counterpoint Distribution

Louis Armstrong and Duke Ellington vol 1.

Louis Armstrong and His Orchestra 1935-1944.
Album: released on Swaggie (Australia) in Jan'83

Louis Armstrong collection.
Album: by Deja Vu Records. Distributed by: Counterpoint Distribution, Record Services Distribution (Ireland)

Musicassette: released on Deja Vu in Aug'85 by Deja Vu Records. Distributed by: Counterpoint Distribution, Record Services Distribution (Ireland)

Compact disc: released on Deja Vu in Jul'87 by Deja Vu Records. Distributed by: Counterpoint Distribution, Record Services Distribution (Ireland)

Louis Armstrong/Fletcher Henderson Orchestra (Armstrong, Louis/Fletcher Henderson Orchestra).
Album: released on VJM in '79 by Wellard, Chris Distribution. Distributed by: Wellard, Chris Distribution

Louis Armstrong July 4 - July 6, 1971.
Double Album: released on RCA (Germany) in Jan'85

Louis Armstrong legend 1926-27.
Tracks: / Lonesome blues / Sweet little Papa / Jazz lips / Skid-dat-de-dat / I want a big butter & egg man / Sunset cafe stomp / You made me love you / Irish black bottom / Willie the weeper / Wild man blues / Chicago breakdown / Alligator crawl / Potato head blues / Melancholy / Weary blues / Twelfth Street rag.
Album: released on EMI Retrospect in Mar'85 by EMI Records. Distributed by: EMI

Musicassette: by EMI Records. Distributed by: EMI

Louis Armstrong legend (SH 404).
Tracks: / My heart / Yes I'm in the barrel / Cut bucket blues / Come back, sweet Papa / Georgia grind / Heebie Jeebies / Cornet chop suey / Oriental strut / You're next / Muskrat ramble / Don't forget to mess around / I'm gonna gitcha / Dropping shucks / Who sit / King of the Zulus, (The) / Big fat ma & skinny pa.
Musicassette: released on World (Retrospect Series) in Feb'84

Louis Armstrong Legend, The 1927-1928.
Tracks: / Put 'em down blues / Ory's creole trombone / Last time, The / Struttin' with some barbecue / Got no blues / Once in a while / I'm not rough / Hotter than that / Savoy blues / Fireworks / Skip the gutter / Monday date, A / Don't jive me / Keyhole blues / SOL blues / Gully low blues / That's when I'll come back to you.
Notes: The third re-issue due to popular demand, from 'The Louis Armstrong Legend' collection - only latterly available in a four record box set.This album displays Armstrong's unquestionable talent and familiar style through from up tempo New Orleans jives to the ever popular sophisticated blues sound of the 20's, illustrating beautidully this important transitional period of his career.

Album: released on Retrospect in Jan'86 by World Records

Louis Armstrong Legend, The 1928-1929.
Tracks: / West end blues / Sugar foot strut / Two deuces / Squeeze me / Knee drops / Symphonic raps / Savoyages stomp / No papa, no / Basin street blues / No one else but you / Beau koo Jack / Save it pretty mama / Weather bird / Muggles / Heah me talking to ya / St. James infirmary / Tight like this / Knockin' a jug.
Notes: Tracks 1-9 Louis Armstrong and His Hot Five/*=Carroll Dickerson and his Orchestra/**=Louis Armstrong and His Orchestra/***=Louis Armstrong and His Savoy Ballroom Five
Album: released on Retrospect in Nov'86 by World Records

Musicassette: released on Retrospect in Nov'86 by World Records

Louis Armstrong legend.
Album: released on World in Mar'79. Distributed by: Jetstar

Louis Armstrong & Luis Russell 1929-1930.
Notes: MONO
Album: released on Swaggie (Australia) in Jan'83

Louis Armstrong Meets Oscar Peterson The Silver Collection (Armstrong, Louis & Oscar Peterson).
Compact disc: by Phonogram Records. Distributed by: Polygram

Louis Armstrong meets Oscar Peterson (Armstrong, Louis & Oscar Peterson).
Tracks: / That old feeling / I'll never be the same / How long has this been going on / I was doing all right / Moon song / There's no you / Sweet Lorraine / Let's fall in love / Blues in the night / What's new / Just one of those things / You go to my head.
Album: released on Verve (USA) in Mar'83 by Polydor. Distributed by: Polygram

Louis Armstrong/Sidney Bechet (Armstrong, Louis & Sidney Bechet).
Tracks: / On the sunny side of the street / King Porter stomp* / Dutch Swing College blues* / St.Louis blues / Tiger rag / Pretty little missy / Bye'n'bye / Tyree's blues / Short but sweet / Tin roof blues / Circle of your arms, The / When the saints go marching in.
Notes: Louis Armstrong & His Orchestra. Sidney Bechet featured on two tracks with the Dutch Swing College Band. Recorded:May 1951,November 1964,September 1964,October 1965,April 1966.
Album: released on Jazz Masters in '83. Distributed by: IMS-Polygram

Louis Armstrong story.
Album: released on CBS(France) in Feb'85 by CBS Records. Distributed by: Conifer, Discovery, Swift

Louis Armstrong & The All Stars Philadelphia 1948.
Tracks: / Just you, just me / Boogie woogie on St.Louis blues / Struttin' with some barbecue / St. Louis blues / Someday / Together / That's a plenty / East of the sun / St. James' infirmary / Panama / Maybe you'll be there / Lazy river / Muskrat ramble.
Notes: Line-up: Armstrong,Teagarden,Bigard,Hines,Shaw,Catlett,V.Middleton.
Album: released on Queen-Disc in '81. Distributed by: Celtic Music, JSU, Jazz Horizons, Jazz Music

Louis Armstrong vol 2.
Album: released on Jazz Reactivation in May'83. Distributed by: PRT

Louis Armstrong vol 1.
Album: released on Jazz Reactivation in Jan'82. Distributed by: PRT

Louis' Blues.
Album: released on Astan in '84 by Astan Records. Distributed by: Counterpoint

Musicassette: released on Astan in '84 by Astan Records. Distributed by: Counterpoint

Louis in Los Angeles.
Album: released on Swaggie (Australia) in Jan'83

Louis' Love Songs.
Tracks: / Among my souveniers / I'm confessing / It's all in the game / Only you (and you only) / I'll string along with you / I'm in the mood for love / Dream a little dream of me / You are my lucky star / Gypsy, The / Be my life's companion / Your cheatin' heart / I guess I'll get the papers and go home / Ramona / April in Portugal.

Album: released on MCA in May'86 by MCA Records. Distributed by: Polygram, MCA

Louis vol 10: Orch 1931.
Album: released on Joker in Apr'81. Distributed by: Counterpoint, Mainline, Record Services Distribution (Ireland)

Louis vol 11: Orch. 1932-33.
Album: released on Joker in Apr'81. Distributed by: Counterpoint, Mainline, Record Services Distribution (Ireland)

Louis vol 12: Orch. 1933.
Album: released on Joker in Apr'81. Distributed by: Counterpoint, Mainline, Record Services Distribution (Ireland)

Louis vol.3: Potato head blues.
Album: released on Joker in Apr'81. Distributed by: Counterpoint, Mainline, Record Services Distribution (Ireland)

Louis vol.5: West End blues.
Album: released on Joker in Apr'81. Distributed by: Counterpoint, Mainline, Record Services Distribution (Ireland)

L:ouis vol.6: Savoy Ballroom Five & His Orch..
Album: released on Joker in Apr'81. Distributed by: Counterpoint, Mainline, Record Services Distribution (Ireland)

Louis vol.7: Orch. 1929-30.
Album: . Distributed by: Counterpoint, Mainline, Record Services Distribution (Ireland)

Louis vol.8: Sebastian New Cotton Club Orch..
Album: released on Joker in Apr'81. Distributed by: Counterpoint, Mainline, Record Services Distribution (Ireland)

Louis vol.9: Orch 1931.
Album: released on Joker in Apr'81. Distributed by: Counterpoint, Mainline, Record Services Distribution (Ireland)

Masters of jazz.
Album: released on RCA (Germany) in '83

Masters of jazz vol.1.
Album: released on Storyville in May'86 by Storyville Records. Distributed by: Jazz Music Distribution, Swift Distribution, Chris Wellard Distribution, Counterpoint Distribution

Music for the millions.
Tracks: / Stompin' at the savoy / Do nothing till you hear from me / Just one of those things / Foggy day, A / Uncle Satchmo's lullaby / When the saints go marchin' in / Someday you'll be sorry / Nobody knows the trouble I've seen / Top hat, white tie and tails / Blues in the night.
Album: released on Mercury (Holland) in Feb'86 by Phonogram Records. Distributed by: Polygram Distribution

Musicassette: released on Mercury (Holland) in Feb'86 by Phonogram Records. Distributed by: Polygram Distribution

New Orleans function.
Tracks: / When it's sleepy time down south / Indiana / Give me a kiss to build a dream on / My bucket's got a hole in it / Mack the knife / Ole Miss / C'est si bon / Vie en rose, La / New Orleans function / Free as a bird / Oh didn't he ramble?.
Album: released on Black Lion in Oct'82 by Black Lion Records. Distributed by: Jazz Music, Chris Wellard, Taylor, H.R., Counterpoint, Cadillac

New Orleans masters volume 2.
Album: released on Swinghouse in '84. Distributed by: Jazz Music Distribution, Swift Distribution, Chris Wellard Distribution

Musicassette: released on Swinghouse in '84. Distributed by: Jazz Music Distribution, Swift Distribution, Chris Wellard Distribution

On stage.
Tracks: / Jubilee / Do you know what it means / I'm confessin' / Panama rag stomp / Struttin' with some barbecue / Muskrat ramble / High society / Basin St. blues.
Album: released on Jazz Live in Oct'86

On stage (1937).
Album: released on Jazz Live in Apr'81

Pasadena Concert.
Tracks: / Some day / Ole Miss / Tin roof blues / My bucket's got a hole in it / Dardenella / Gypsy, The / Undecided / Blues / That's my desire / Didn't he ramble / Sleepytime down south (2 takes) / Indiana.
Compact disc: . Distributed by: Discovery, Jazz Music, PRT, Swift

Porgy and Bess (Armstrong, Louis & Ella Fitzgerald).
Album: released on Verve in Jan'78 by Phonogram Records. Distributed by: Polygram

Musicassette: released on Verve in Jan'78 by Phonogram Records. Distributed by: Polygram

Compact disc: released on Verve in '83 by Phonogram Records. Distributed by: Polygram

Porgy & Bess.
Tracks: / Summertime / I loves you Porgy / My man's gone now / I got plenty of nuttin' / Bess you is my woman / It ain't necessarily so / Woman is a sometime thing / There's a boat that's leavin' soon for New York / Where's my Bess / I'm on my way.

Rare Louis Armstrong volume 3 The Big Band 1943-44.
Tracks: / I can't give you anything but love / If I could be with you one hour tonight / I'm confessing that I love you / In the mood / I never knew / What's the good word / Lost my sugar in Salt Lake City / Lazy river / On the sunny side of the street / King Porter stomp / It's love love love / Ain't misbehavin' / Barrelhouse Bessie from Basin Street / Peanut vendor / Slender, tender & tall / Coquette.
Album: released on Rarities in Apr'81

Rare performances of the 50's & 60's.
Tracks: / 'Tain't wat'cha do / Back o'town blues / Mack the knife / Mack the knife (inst) / Indiana / Six foot four / When the red red robin comes bob bob bobbin' along / Way down yonder in New Orleans / Blueberry hill / Mack the knife (concert version) / Tin roof blues / My bucket's got a hole in it / Whispering / Bugle blues - Ole Miss / Kokomo / Basin Street blues / Mahogany hall stomp / St. Louis blues / Rockin' chair / On the sunny side of the street / Nomad / Lonesome / You swing baby / Canal Street blues.
Album: released on CBS in Jul'86 by CBS Records. Distributed by: CBS

Red onion jazz babies.
Album: released on Fountain in '73 by Retrieval Records. Distributed by: Jazz Music, Swift, VJM, Wellard, Chris, Retrieval

Reminiscin' with Louis.
Tracks: / Ain't misbehavin' / When the saints go marching in / I cried for you / Boogie woogie on St. Louis / When it's sleepy time down south / I cried last night / Steak face.
Album: released on Queen-Disc in Apr'81. Distributed by: Celtic Music, JSU, Jazz Horizons, Jazz Music

Replay on.
Album: released on Sierra in May'86 by Sierra Records. Distributed by: WEA

Musicassette: released on Sierra in May'86 by Sierra Records. Distributed by: WEA

Rockin' chair (Armstrong, Louis & His All Stars).
Tracks: / Rockin' chair / Where did you stay last night / Baby, it's cold outside / C Jam Blues / Stomping at the Savoy / I used to love you / La vie en rose / Lover / I love the guy / That's my desire / Royal Garden blues / Ain't misbehavin' / Rose room / Back o' town blues / Rose room / C'est ci bon / Way down yonder in New Orleans / Stardust / Rockin' chair / Where did you stay last night / Baby, it's cold outside / C jam blues / Stomping at the Savoy.
Album: released on Topline in Apr'87 by Charly Records. Distributed by: Charly Distribution

Rockin' chair.
Album: released on Topline in Jan'85 by Charly Records. Distributed by: Charly Distribution

Musicassette: released on Topline in Jan'85 by Charly Records. Distributed by: Charly Distribution

Rock it for me.
Album: released on Phontastic in Jul'87. Distributed by: Wellard, Chris

Satchmo in Stockholm.
Tracks: / When it's sleepy time down south / Indiana / Tin roof blues / Basin street blues / Sweet Georgia Brown / Struttin' with some barbecue / Gipsy, The / Pretty little missy / When the saints go marchin' in / When it's sleepy time down south.
Album: released on Queendisc (Import) in '81. Distributed by: Cadillac

Satchmo's Greatest Hits.
Tracks: / I gotta right to sing the blues / High society / When you're smiling / St. James Infirmary / Dinah / Basin Street blues / You rascal you / Seepytime down south / Nobody's sweetheart / Mahogany hall stomp / Do you know what it means to be Miss New Orleans / St. Louis blues / Sweet Sue / Back o'town blues / Jack Armstrong blues / Where the blues were born in New Orleans.
Album: released on RCA in Jun'86 by RCA Records. Distributed by: RCA, Roots, Swift, Wellard, Chris, I & B, Solomon & Peres Distribution

Musicassette: released on RCA in Jun'86 by RCA Records. Distributed by: RCA, Roots, Swift, Wellard, Chris, I & B, Solomon & Peres Distribution

Satch plays Fats.
Tracks: / Honeysuckle rose / Blue turning grey over you / I'm crazy 'bout my baby and my baby's crazy 'bout me / I've got a feeling I'm falling / Keepin' out of mischief now / All that meat and no potatoes / Squeeze me / Black and blue / Ain't misbehavin'.
Album: released on CBS in '84 by CBS Records. Distributed by: CBS

Musicassette: released on CBS in '84 by CBS Records. Distributed by: CBS

Silver collection.
Compact disc: released on Verve in Nov'84 by Phonogram Records. Distributed by: Polygram

Silver Collection, The Compilation.
Tracks: / Top hat white tie and tails / Have you met Miss Jones / I only have eyes for you / Stormy weather / Home / I only have eyes for you / Stormy weather / East of the sun (and west of the moon) / You're blase / Body and soul / When your lover has gone / You're the top / Nobody knows the trouble I've seen / We'll be together again / I've got the world on a string / Do nothin' till you hear from me / I gotta right to sing the blues.
Compact disc: released on Verve in Nov'84 by Phonogram Records. Distributed by: Polygram

Soundtrack New Orleans (Armstrong, Louis & Billie Holiday).
Album: released on Giants of Jazz in Jul'84 by Hasmick Promotions Ltd.. Distributed by: Counterpoint, Jazz Music, Taylors, Swift, Mainline, Wellard, Chris

Special magic (Armstrong, Louis & Ella Fitzgerald).
Musicassette: released on Verve in Aug'76 by Phonogram Records. Distributed by: Polygram

St. Louis blues.
Tracks: / Tiger rag / Maine / So long dearie / Cheesecake / Pretty little miss / Short and sweet / When the saints go marching in / St. Louis blues / Circle of your arms, The / Tin roof blues / Tyrees blues / Bye n bye / On the sunny side of the street / Black and blue / I'm confessin' that I love you / Struttin' with some barbecue / Up a lazy river / Save it pretty mama / Ain't misbehavin' / St. Louis blues / Rocking chair / Rocking chair / Tiger rag / Dippermouth blues / Mahongany hall stomp / Muskrat ramble.
Album: released on Black Lion-Intercord in '82

Musicassette: released on Black Lion-Intercord in '82

St. Louis blues (1960's).
Album: released on Mercury (USA) in Mar'83 by Import Records. Distributed by: IMS Distribution, Polygram Distribution

Album: released on Mercury (USA) in Mar'83 by Import Records. Distributed by: IMS Distribution. Polygram Distribution

St. Louis blues (CBS).
Album: released on CBS(France) in Feb'85 by CBS Records. Distributed by: Conifer, Discovery, Swift

Musicassette: released on CBS(France) in Feb'85 by CBS Records. Distributed by: Conifer, Discovery, Swift

Story vol.1.
Notes: 4 LP set.
Album: released on CBS(Import) in Jun'86 by CBS Records. Distributed by: Conifer, Discovery, Swift

Struttin' with some barbecue.
Tracks: / Struttin with some barbecue / What is this thing called swing? / Jeepers creepers / Lyin' to myself / Shoe shine boy / I hope Gabriel likes my music / Perdido St. blues / 2.19 blues / Swing that music / Down in honky tonk / Coal cart blues / Ev'ntide / Dippermouth blues / Solitude / Jubilee / Mahogany hall stomp.
Album: released on Affinity in Jun'86 by Charly Records. Distributed by: Charly, Cadillac

Swing that music Satchmo.
Tracks: / Swing that music / Dippermouth blues / I've got a heart full of rhythm / On the sunny side of the street / Struttin' with some barbecue / When the Saints go marching in / Flat foot boogie, The / Ain't misbehavin' / Jeepers creepers / What is this thing called swing? / Savoy blues / West-End blues.
Album: released on Joker Import in '81

That old feeling (Armstrong, Louis & Billie Holiday).
Notes: Special price 'double star' album including material from Bing Crosby's last album which is no longer available
Album: released on Polydor (Import) in Feb'82

Musicassette: released on Polydor (Import) in Feb'82

That rhythm man.
Album: released on American Recollections in Dec'84 by London Records. Distributed by: Polygram

Town hall concert plus.
Tracks: / Rockin' chair / Ain't misbehavin' / Back o town blues / Long long journey / I want a little girl / Mahogany / Pennies from heaven / St. James Infirmary / Save it pretty mama / Someday you'll be sorry / Sugar / Snafu.
Album: released on RCA International in Nov'84

Musicassette: released on RCA International in Nov'84

V Disc All Stars (Armstrong, Louis/Jack Teagarden).
Album: released on Pumpkin in Apr'79. Distributed by: Jazz Music, Wellard, Chris, Cadillac

Volume 1: Muskrat ramble.
Tracks: / My heart / Yes, I'm in the barrel / Gut bucket blues / Come back sweet Papa / Georgia grind / Heebie jeebies / Cornet chop suey / Oriental Strut / You're next / Muskrat ramble / Don't forget to mess around / I'm gonna gitcha.
Album: released on Joker in Apr'81. Distributed by: Counterpoint, Mainline, Record Services Distribution (Ireland)

Volume 2: Irish black bottom.
Tracks: / Droppin' sucks / Who's it / King of the Zulus, (The) / Big fat me & skinny pa / Lonesome blues / Sweet little papa / Jazz lips.
Album: . Distributed by: Counterpoint, Mainline, Record Services Distribution (Ireland)

What a wonderful world/Hello Dolly.
Single (7"): released on MCA in Jul'86 by MCA Records. Distributed by: Polygram, MCA Deleted '86.

What a wonderful world.
Single (7"): released on Old Gold in Jul'84 by Old Gold Records. Distributed by: Lightning, Jazz Music, Spartan, Counterpoint

When the saints go marching in.
Album: released on Astan in Nov'84 by Astan Records. Distributed by: Counterpoint

Musicassette: released on Astan in Nov'84 by Astan Records. Distributed by: Counterpoint

Young Louis Armstrong (1930-1933).
Album: released on RCA (France) in '83 by RCA Records. Distributed by: Discovery

Young Louis Armstrong (1930-1933).
Tracks: / Blue yodel No. 9 (Standing on the corner) / That's my home - 1 / Hobo, you can't ride this train / I hate to leave you now - 2 / I hate to leave you now - 1 / That's my home - 2 / You'll wish you'd never been born / When you're smiling / St. James' Infirmary / Dinah / You rascal, you / When it's sleepy time down south / Nobody's sweetheart / I've got the world on a string / I gotta right to sing the blues / Hustlin' and bustlin' for a baby / Sittin' in the dark / High Society / He's a son of the south / Some sweet day / Basin Street blues / Sittin' in the dark / He's a son of the south / Some sweet day / Basin Street blues / Honey do / Snowball / Mahogany hall stomp / Swing, you cats / Honey don't you love me anymore? / Mississippi Basin / Laughin' Louie / Tomorrow night / Dusky stevedore / There's a cabin in the pines / Mighty river / Sweet Sue, just you / I wonder who / St. Louis blues / Don't play me cheap.
Double Album: released on RCA in Jan'87 by RCA Records. Distributed by: RCA, Roots, Swift, Wellard, Chris, I & B, Solomon & Peres Distribution

Double musicassette: released on RCA in Jan'87 by RCA Records. Distributed by: RCA, Roots, Swift, Wellard, Chris, I & B, Solomon & Peres Distribution

Armstrong, Louis Satchmo

20 unforgettable hits.
Compact disc: released on The Compact Collection in Sep'87 by Conifer Records. Distributed by: Conifer Distribution

Armstrong, Tommy

Tommy Armstrong of Tyneside.
Album: released on Topic in '81. Distributed by: Roots Distribution

Armstrong Twins

Armstrong Twins.
Album: released on Old Timey in May'79

Just country boys.
Album: released on Arhoolie in May'81 by Arhoolie Records. Distributed by: Projection, Topic, Jazz Music, Swift, Roots

Arnez, Chico

From Chico with love (Arnez, Chico & His Orchestra).
Album: released on Dansan in Nov'81 by Spartan Records. Distributed by: Spartan

Arnie's Love

Biographical Details: Arnie's Love are one of the numerous anonymous, faceless acts to have made the disco/dance charts. 'I'm Out Of Your Life' scored a minor national chart placing in late 1983, having been issued by Morgan Khan's Streetwave label, an outlet for many club favourites in the Eighties. (BM 84)

Natural wish.
Tracks: / Natural wish / Natural wish (inst).
Single (7"): released on PRT in Mar'86 by PRT Records. Distributed by: PRT

Single (12"): released on PRT in Mar'86 by PRT Records. Distributed by: PRT

Arnold, Billy Boy

Blow the back off it.
Tracks: / I'm sweet on you baby / You got to love me baby / I wish you would / I was fooled / Don't stay out all night / I ain't got you / Hello stranger / Here's my picture / You've got me wrong / My heart is crying / Kissing at midnight / Prisoners plea / Rockinitis.
Album: released on Red Lightnin' in Sep'82 by Red Lightnin' Records. Distributed by: Roots, Swift, Jazz Music, JSU, Pinnacle, Cartel, Wynd-Up Distribution

Checkin' it out.
Tracks: / Dirty mother fucker / Don't stay out all night / 1-2-99 / Riding the el / Just to know / Christmas time / I wish you would / Ah'w baby / Sweet Miss Bea / Blue & lonesome / Eldorado Cadillac / Mary Bernice.
Album: released on Red Lightnin' in Sep'82 by Red Lightnin' Records. Distributed by: Roots, Swift, Jazz Music, JSU, Pinnacle, Cartel, Wynd-Up Distribution

Crying and pleading.
Album: released on Charly in Mar'81 by Charly Records. Distributed by: Charly, Cadillac

I wish you would.
Single (7"): released on Charly in Jul'80 by Charly Records. Distributed by: Charly, Cadillac

Johnny Jones & Billy Boy Arnold (see Jones, Johnny) (Arnold, Billy Boy & Johnny Jones).

Sinners prayer.
Tracks: / I was fooled / Hi heel sneakers / Back door friend / Tomorrow night / Annie Lee / Ooh Wee / Blues in A natural / I'm gonna move / Sinners prayer.
Album: released on Red Lightnin' in Sep'82 by Red Lightnin' Records. Distributed by: Roots, Swift, Jazz Music, JSU, Pinnacle, Cartel, Wynd-Up Distribution

Arnold, Dave

Affair of chemistry.
Video-cassette (VHS): released on Dead Happy in '86 by Dead Happy Records. Distributed by: Mason's Music Distributors/Wholesalers, Rough Trade

Conjuring images.
Musicassette: released on Dead Happy in '86 by Dead Happy Records. Distributed by: Mason's Music Distributors/Wholesalers, Rough Trade

For all and sundry.
Musicassette: released on Dead Happy in '86 by Dead Happy Records. Distributed by: Mason's Music Distributors/Wholesalers, Rough Trade

Frustration of economy.
Musicassette: released on Dead Happy in '86 by Dead Happy Records. Distributed by: Mason's Music Distributors/Wholesalers, Rough Trade

I'm a natural candidate for the tortured artists.
Musicassette: released on Dead Happy in Nov'82 by Dead Happy Records. Distributed by: Mason's Music Distributors/Wholesalers, Rough Trade

Spotlight on Dave Arnold.
Musicassette: released on Plato Tapes in '82 by Plato Tapes. Distributed by: Plato Tapes

Arnold, Eddy

20 of the best.
Tracks: / Make the world go away / Cattle call / Just call me lonesome / What's he doing in my world / I really don't want to know / I want to go with you / Somebody like me / Lonely again / Turn the world around / Then you can tell me goodbye / I'll hold you in my heart / Bouquet of roses / Anytime / Just a little lovin' (will go a long way) / Don't rob another mans castle / I'm throwing rice at the girl I love / There's been a change in me / Kentucky waltz / I wanna play house with you / Eddy's song.
Album: released on RCA in '82 by RCA Records. Distributed by: RCA, Roots, Swift, Wellard, Chris, I & B, Solomon & Peres Distribution

Musicassette: released on RCA in '82 by RCA Records. Distributed by: RCA, Roots, Swift, Wellard, Chris, I & B, Solomon & Peres Distribution

All-time favorites.
Tracks: / Moonlight and roses (bring mem'ries of you) / Missouri waltz, The (Hus-a-bye, ma baby) / I'm gonna lock my heart (and throw away the key) / You always hurt the one you love / I'm thinking tonight of my blue eyes / It makes no difference now / I'm waiting for ships that never come in / I'm gonna sit right down and write myself a letter / When your hair has turned to silver / Angry / Prisoner's song, The / Seven years with the wrong woman.
Album: released on RCA in Jan'87 by RCA Records. Distributed by: RCA, Roots, Swift, Wellard, Chris, I & B, Solomon & Peres Distribution

Musicassette: released on RCA in Jan'87 by RCA Records. Distributed by: RCA, Roots, Swift, Wellard, Chris, I & B, Solomon & Peres Distribution

Make the world go away.
Tracks: / Make the world go away / End of the world.
Single (7"): released on Old Gold in Oct'86 by Old Gold Records. Distributed by: Lightning, Jazz Music, Spartan, Counterpoint

Arnold, Kokomo

Kokomo Arnold - Master of the bottleneck guitar 1930-38.
Album: released on Document in Jul'87

Arnold, P.P.

Biographical Details: P.P. Arnold was born in Los Angeles, but settled in Britain in 1966 when she arrived here as a member of the Ikettes, Ike and Tina Turner's backing group. The Turners were flopping in their native land with 'River Deep Mountain High' but were in demand in Britain in the wake of the single's big UK success. Arnold recorded a Cat Stevens song 'The First Cut Is The Deepest' and took it to no.18 on the British charts. (Exactly ten years later Rod Stewart was to take the song to no.1). Her first cut was the biggest. A year later, in the summer of '68, she hit the top 30 with 'Angel Of The Morning', but her pleasant voice failed to grace the charts again, at least in her own name. An album called 'Kafunta' aroused little interest, despite being produced by Mick Jagger and Steve Marriott. She has subsequently pursued a career as a session singer, and is still active in the music business.

Angel of the morning.
Single (7"): released on Immediate in Apr'82 by Castle Communications. Distributed by: Cartel

Electric dreams.
Single (7"): released on Ten in Aug'84

Single (12"): released on Ten in Aug'84

First cut is the deepest, The.
Single (7"): released on Immediate in Dec'82 by Castle Communications. Distributed by: Cartel

Single (7"): released on Old Gold in Jan'85 by Old Gold Records. Distributed by: Lightning, Jazz Music, Spartan, Counterpoint

Greatest hits:P P Arnold.
Tracks: / First cut is the deepest / Dreaming / Would you believe / To love somebody / Born to be together / Eleanor Rigby / Angel of the morning / As tears go by / Am I still dreaming / Though it hurts me badly / Speak to me / If you think you're groovy.
Album: released on Immediate in Jan'78 by Castle Communications. Distributed by: Cartel

Little pain (A).
Single (7"): released on 10 in Sep'85 by 10 Records. Distributed by: Virgin, EMI

Single (12"): released on 10 in Sep'85 by 10 Records. Distributed by: Virgin, EMI

Supergrass.
Single (7"): released on Island in Dec'85 by Island Records. Distributed by: Polygram

Aroma Di Amore

Deskeer van grote bagen.
Album: released on Play It Again Sam in Jun'85. Distributed by: Red Rhino, Cartel

Koude oorlog.
Single (12"): released on Play It Again Sam in Jun'84. Distributed by: Red Rhino, Cartel

Zonder omzien.
Single (12"): released on Play It Again Sam in Jan'86. Distributed by: Red Rhino, Cartel

Arpeggio

Featuring Quartario

Love and desire.
Album: released on Polydor in Apr'79 by Polydor Records. Distributed by: Polygram, Polydor

Musicassette: released on Polydor in Apr'79 by Polydor Records. Distributed by: Polygram, Polydor

Arran, John

Castles of Spain.
Album: released on Response in Feb'81 by Priority Records. Distributed by: BMG

Arrington, Steve

Dancin' in the key of life.
Tracks: / Feel so real / Dancin' in the key of life / She just don't know / Willie Mae / Gasoline / Stand with me / Brown baby boy / Turn up love.
Album: released on Atlantic in Apr'85 by WEA Records. Distributed by: WEA

Musicassette: released on Atlantic in May'85 by WEA Records. Distributed by: WEA

Single (7"): released on Atlantic in Jun'85 by WEA Records. Distributed by: WEA

Single (12"): released on Atlantic in Jun'85 by WEA Records. Distributed by: WEA

Feel so real.
Single (7"): released on Atlantic in Apr'85 by WEA Records. Distributed by: WEA

Single (12"): released on Atlantic in Apr'85 by WEA Records. Distributed by: WEA

Hump to the bump.
Single (12"): released on Atlantic in Mar'84 by WEA Records. Distributed by: WEA

Jammin' National Anthem, The (single).
Tracks: / Jammin' National Anthem, The / Racial jammin'.
Single (7"): released on Atlantic in Apr'86 by WEA Records. Distributed by: WEA

Single (12"): released on Atlantic in Apr'86 by WEA Records. Distributed by: WEA

Jammin' National Anthem, The.
Tracks: / Jammin' National Anthem, The / Holiday / Teenage jazz / One of a kind / Paradise / Everybody's got to be free / Homeboy / Like it loud / Have a heart / Homeboy / Like it loud / Have a heart.
Album: released on Atlantic in May'86 by WEA Records. Distributed by: WEA

Musicassette: released on Atlantic in May'86 by WEA Records. Distributed by: WEA

Positive power.
Tracks: / 15 rounds / Money on it / Sugar momma baby / What do you want from / Young and ready / Mellow as a cello / Hump to the bump / Positive power.
Album: released on Atlantic in Feb'84 by WEA Records. Distributed by: WEA

Arrow

Deadly.
Album: released on Deadly Arrow in Jan'86. Distributed by: Jetstar

Hot hot hot.
Single (7"): released on Chrysalis in Jun'84 by Chrysalis Records. Distributed by: CBS

Single (12"): released on Chrysalis in Jun'84 by Chrysalis Records. Distributed by: CBS

Long time.
Single (7"): released on London in Jun'85 by London Records. Distributed by: Polygram

Single (12"): released on London in Jun'85 by London Records. Distributed by: Polygram

Single (cassette): released on London in Aug'85 by London Records. Distributed by: Polygram

Soca savage.
Tracks: Long time / Columbia rock / Hot hot hot.
Album: released on Dynamic in Dec'84 by Creole Records. Distributed by: CBS, Essex
Album: released on London in Aug'85 by London Records. Distributed by: Polygram

Arrows

Talk talk.
Tracks: Talk talk / Easy street.
Single (7"): released on A&M in Feb'86 by A&M Records. Distributed by: Polygram

Single (12"): released on A&M in Feb'86 by A&M Records. Distributed by: Polygram

Arrowsmith, Eugenie

Dancing in my heart.
Tracks: Dancing in my heart / Talk talk about.
Single (7"): released on 10 in Feb'86 by 10 Records. Distributed by: Virgin, EMI

Single (12"): released on 10 in Feb'86 by 10 Records. Distributed by: Virgin, EMI

Promises.
Tracks: Promises / Try.
Single (7"): released on 10 in Apr'86 by 10 Records. Distributed by: Virgin, EMI

Single (12"): released on 10 in Apr'86 by 10 Records. Distributed by: Virgin, EMI

Arsenal F.C.

Arsenal centennial album.
Picture disc album: released on GB Football in Apr'87 by GB Football Records. Distributed by: GB Football Distribution

Art Bears

Winter songs.
Album: released on Recommended in Oct'79 by Recommended Records. Distributed by: Recommended, Impetus, Rough Trade

Art Company

Get it out of your head.
Single (7"): released on Epic in Jul'84 by CBS Records. Distributed by: CBS

Susannah.
Single (7"): released on Epic in Apr'81 by CBS Records. Distributed by: CBS

Single (12"): released on Epic in Apr'84 by CBS Records. Distributed by: CBS

Art Deco Orchestra

There is always a place for the past.
Album: released on Raphaele in Oct'82 by Mozart Edition (Music Publishers). Distributed by: Wellard, Clink, Jazz Music, Swift

Art Ensemble of Chicago

A.A.C.M.: great black music.
Tracks: Waltz (The) / Ericka / Song for Charles / Jackson in your house, A / Jackson in your house, A / Get in line / Waltz Ericka, The / Song for Charles.
Notes: Full title: "A.A.C.M. Great Black Music - A Jackson in Your House".
Compact disc: released on Charly in Mar'87 by Charly Records. Distributed by: Charly, Cadillac
Album: released on Affinity in Feb'78 by Charly Records. Distributed by: Charly, Cadillac

Among the people.

Album: released on Praxis (Greece) in May'84. Distributed by: Mole Jazz

Fanfare for warriors.
Album: released on Atlantic in Mar'77 by WEA Records. Distributed by: WEA

Full Force.
Compact disc: released on ECM (Germany) in Oct'86 by ECM Records. Distributed by: IMS, Polygram, Virgin through EMI

Kabbalaba live at Montreux.
Album: released on Aeco in May'81. Distributed by: Projection

Live.
Album: released on Affinity in Feb'80 by Charly Records. Distributed by: Charly, Cadillac

Message to our folks.
Tracks: Old time religion / Dexterity / Rock out / Brain for the Seine.
Album: released on Affinity in Mar'83 by Charly Records. Distributed by: Charly, Cadillac

Nice Guys.
Tracks: Ja / Nice guys / Folkus / 597-59 / Cyp / Dreaming of the master.
Compact disc: released on ECM (Germany) in Jun'86 by ECM Records. Distributed by: IMS, Polygram, Virgin through EMI

Paris session (The).
Double Album: released on Freedom in Jun'79 by Logo Records. Distributed by: RCA, Discovery, Wellard, Chris

People in sorrow.
Album: released on Nessa in Mar'79. Distributed by: Projection, Swift

Rosse and the smooth ones.
Album: released on Affinity in May'79 by Charly Records. Distributed by: Charly, Cadillac

Stances a Sophie, (Les).
Album: released on Nessa in Mar'79. Distributed by: Projection, Swift

Third Decade.
Compact disc: released on ECM (Germany) in Apr'85 by ECM Records. Distributed by: IMS, Polygram, Virgin through EMI

Third decade (The).
Album: released on ECM (Germany) in Feb'85 by ECM Records. Distributed by: IMS, Polygram, Virgin through EMI

Tutenkhamun.
Album: released on Black Lion in Sep'85 by Black Lion Records. Distributed by: Jazz Music, Chris Wellard, Taylor, H.R., Counterpoint, Cadillac

Urban bushmen.
Album: released on ECM (Germany) in May'82 by ECM Records. Distributed by: IMS, Polygram, Virgin through EMI

Musicassette: released on ECM (Germany) in Jul'85 by ECM Records. Distributed by: IMS, Polygram, Virgin through EMI

Artery

Afterwards.
Single (7"): released on Armageddon in Nov'81 by Armageddon Records. Distributed by: Revolver, Cartel, Pinnacle

Alabama song.
Single (7"): released on Red Flame in Nov'83 by Red Flame Records. Distributed by: Nine Mile, Cartel

Single (12"): released on Red Flame in Nov'83 by Red Flame Records. Distributed by: Nine Mile, Cartel

Big machine.
Single (12"): released on Golden Dawn in May'84 by Artery Records. Distributed by: Cartel

Clown (The).
Single (7"): released on Red Flame in Aug'82 by Red Flame Records. Distributed by: Nine Mile, Cartel

Diamonds in the mine field.

Single (7"): released on Golden Dawn in Oct'84 by Artery Records. Distributed by: Cartel

Single (12"): released on Golden Dawn in Oct'84 by Artery Records. Distributed by: Cartel

Oceans.
Album: released on Red Flame in Oct'82 by Red Flame Records. Distributed by: Nine Mile, Cartel

Slide (The).
Single (12"): released on Red Flame in Jun'82 by Red Flame Records. Distributed by: Nine Mile, Cartel

Terminal.
Album: released on Golden Dawn in Nov'84 by Artery Records. Distributed by: Cartel

Unbalanced.
Single (7"): released on Aardvark in Nov'80 by Aardvark. Distributed by: Aardvark

Artful Dodger

Honour among thieves.
Album: released on CBS(Import) in Aug'86 by CBS Records. Distributed by: Conifer, Discovery, Swift

Arthey, Johnny

Sentimental journey (Arthey, Johnny Orchestra).
Album: released on K-Tel in Apr'80 by K-Tel Records. Distributed by: Record Merchandising, Taylors, Terry Blood Distribution, Wynd-Up Distribution, Relay Distribution, Pickwick Distribution, Solomon & Peres Distribution, Polygram

Musicassette: released on Lotus in May'80. Distributed by: Counterpoint

Arthur

Rocking with the Doggies (Arthur & His Rocking Doggies).
Single (7"): released on Lampost in Jun'85

Arthur, Charline

Welcome to the club.
Tracks: / Welcome to the club / Burn that candle / What about tomorrow / Honey bun / Kiss the baby goodnight / Just look don't touch, he's mine / How many would there be / Later on / I heard about you / Anything can happen / Lookin at the moon wishin on a star / I'm having a party all by myself / Leave my man alone / Please darlin' please / Hartbreak ahead / I was wrong / Count your blessings / Real love / Nobody walks in LA / How does it fit / Relations / What becomes of love / Way ahead / 10th round.
Notes: Produced by Steve Sholes and Chet Atkins. Re-issue produced by Richard Weize. Thanks to Charline Arthur. Mastering by Bob Jones at CTS Studios, Wembley. This record is produced from digital tapes without any quality loss.
Album: released on Bear Family in Jun'86 by Bear Family Records. Distributed by: Rollercoaster Distribution, Swift

Arthur, Dave & Toni

Harken to the witches rune.
Album: released on Leader in '81. Distributed by: Jazz Music, Projection

Lark in the morning, The.
Tracks: / All frolicking I'll give over / Death of Queen Jane, The / Creeping Jane / Merchant's daughter of Bristol, The / Bold dragoon, The / Cold blows the winter's wind / Lark in the morning, The / Poor old horse / Hey John Barleycorn / Bedlam / Admiral Benbow / Father father build me a boat / Press gang, The / Six jolly miners.
Album: released on Topic in '81. Distributed by: Roots Distribution

Artillery

Artillery.
Album: released on Neat in Nov'86 by Neat Records. Distributed by: Pinnacle, Neat

Fear of the dark.
Musicassette: released on Neat in Jul'86 by Neat Records. Distributed by: Pinnacle, Neat

Terror Squad.
Album: released on Neat in Apr'87 by Neat Records. Distributed by: Pinnacle, Neat
Musicassette: released on Neat in May'87 by Neat Records. Distributed by: Pinnacle, Neat

Art In The Dark

Art In The Dark.
Single (12"): released on Press in Sep'85 by Press Records

Icons, The.
Album: released on Press in Nov'85 by Press Records

Musicassette: released on Press in Nov'85 by Press Records

In colour.
Tracks: Tell me / In colour / Calling anyone / Answer / Tell me / In colour / Calling anyone / Answer.
Album: released on Press in Jul'86 by Press Records
Album: released on Press in Jul'85 by Press Records

Artists

Artist Various artists (Various Artists).
Album: released on Streetwave in May'84 by Streetwave Records. Distributed by: PRT Distribution

Musicassette: released on Streetwave in Sep'84 by Streetwave Records. Distributed by: PRT Distribution

Artists and songs that inspired the Motown 25th anniversary (Various original artists (Various original artists).
Notes: Full title: Artists and songs that inspired the Motown 25th anniversary TV special.
Album: released on Motown in Oct'83 by Motown Records. Distributed by: BMG Distribution

Musicassette: released on Motown in Oct'83 by Motown Records. Distributed by: BMG Distribution

Artists Vol.1, The Various artists (Various Artists).
Compact disc: released on Streetsounds in Mar'86

Artists Vol.2, The Various artists (Various Artists).
Album: released on Streetsounds in Jun'85

Artists Vol.4, The Various artists (Various Artists).
Notes: Full title: Isley Brothers/ Isley, Jasper, Isley/ Quincy Jones
Album: released on Streetsounds in Mar'86

Musicassette: released on Streetsounds in Mar'86

Playing games.
Single (7"): released on Bulrush in May'83. Distributed by: Pinnacle

Artists Against Apartheid

Sun City.
Notes: Concieved by Little Steven aka Stevie Van Zandt, formerly og Bruce Springsteen's E St. Band, Sun City is an anti-apartheid protest against those performers who played at the sun City resort, ignoring the racist rule in South AfricaCo-produced by remix-master Arthur Baker, the project has united more than 3 dozen artists from an immense variety of musical areas, such as Africa Bambaata, Pat Benetar, Kurtis Blow, Jackson Browne, Darlene Love, John Oates, Joey Ramone, Lou Reed, Gil Scott Heron, Bruce Springsteen, Ringo Starr, Pete Townshend and Bobby Womack. Artist royalties will go to the Africa Fund, a charitable trust based in NY and registered with the United Nations. The income will benefit political prisoners and their families in SA and educational work of anti-apartheid groups in the US.
Album: released on Manhattan in Dec'85 by President Records. Distributed by: Jazz Music, Swift, Taylors, Chris Wellard

Musicassette: released on Manhattan in Dec'85 by President Records. Distributed by: Jazz Music, Swift, Taylors, Chris Wellard

Single (7"): released on Manhattan in Nov'85 by President Records. Distributed by: Jazz Music, Swift, Taylors, Chris Wellard

Single (12"): released on Manhattan in Nov'85 by President Records. Distributed by: Jazz Music, Swift, Taylors, Chris Wellard

Artists Mean

Love.
Single (7"): released on Social in Mar'83 by Social Records. Distributed by: Rough Trade

Artman, Gilbert

Urban sax 2.
Album: released on Celluloid (France) in Jul'85 by Island. Distributed by: Polygram

Art Objects

Showing off to impress the girls.
Single (7"): released on Heartbeat in '81. Distributed by: Revolver, Pinnacle

Art Of Mechanical Music

Gavioli organ at the throne fairground.
Album: released on Arion in Mar'79. Distributed by: Discovery

Art Of Noise

Art Of Noise.
Extended-play record: released on ZTT in Oct'83 by Island Records. Distributed by: Polygram

Album: released on ZTT in Nov'84 by Island Records. Distributed by: Polygram

Musicassette: released on ZTT in Nov'84 by Island Records. Distributed by: Polygram

Beat box.
Single (7"): released on ZTT in Mar'84 by Island Records. Distributed by: Polygram

Close (to the edit).
Single (7"): released on ZTT in Oct'84 by Island Records. Distributed by: Polygram

Single (12"): released on ZTT in Nov'84 by Island Records. Distributed by: Polygram

Picture disc single: released on ZTT in Feb'85 by Island Records. Distributed by: Polygram

Dragnet.
Tracks: / Dragnet / Dragnet (aon mix).
Single (7"): released on China in Jul'87 by Chrysalis Records. Distributed by: Chrysalis

Single (12"): released on China in Jul'87 by Chrysalis Records. Distributed by: Chrysalis

Single (cassette): released on China in Jul'87 by Chrysalis Records. Distributed by: Chrysalis

Into trouble.
Single (7"): released on Ying Yang Yum in May'85. Distributed by: Polygram

In Visible Silence.
Tracks: / Opus 4 / Paranoimia / Eye of a needle / Legs / Slip of the tongue / Backbeat / Instruments of darkness / Peter Gunn / Camilla / Chameleon's dish / Backbeat.
Compact disc: by Chrysalis Records. Distributed by Chrysalis

Legacy.
Tracks: / Legacy / Opus 111.
Single (7"): released on China in Oct'86 by Chrysalis Records. Distributed by: Chrysalis

Single (12"): released on China in Oct'86 by Chrysalis Records. Distributed by: Chrysalis

Legs.
Single (7"): released on China in Oct'85 by Chrysalis Records. Distributed by: Chrysalis

Single (12"): released on China in Oct'85 by Chrysalis Records. Distributed by: Chrysalis

Moments in love.
Tracks: / Moments in love / Love beat.
Single (7"): released on ZTT in May'87 by Island Records. Distributed by: Polygram

Single (12"): released on ZTT in 30 May'87 by Island Records. Distributed by: Polygram

Single (7"): released on ZTT in Mar'85 by Island Records. Distributed by: Polygram

Single (12"): released on ZTT in Mar'85 by Island Records. Distributed by: Polygram

Picture disc single: released on ZTT in Mar'85 by Island Records. Distributed by: Polygram

Musicassette: released on ZTT in Mar'85 by Island Records. Distributed by: Polygram

Paranoimia (Art Of Noise with Max Headroom).
Single (7"): released on China in May'86 by Chrysalis Records. Distributed by: Chrysalis

Single (12"): released on China in May'86 by Chrysalis Records. Distributed by: Chrysalis

Peter Gunn (Art Of Noise With Duane Eddy).

Tracks: / Peter Gunn / Something always happens.
Single (7"): released on China in Mar'86 by Chrysalis Records. Distributed by: Chrysalis

Single (12"): released on China in Mar'86 by Chrysalis Records. Distributed by: Chrysalis

Single (7"): released on London in May'68 by London Records. Distributed by: Polygram

Who's Afraid Of....
Compact disc: released on ZTT in Dec'85 by Island Records. Distributed by: Polygram

Art Of Selections

Art of selections Various artists (Various Artists).
Album: released on Out Of Town in Jun'82

Art Of Suburban Dancing

Art of suburban dancing Various artists (Various Artists).
Album: released on PRT in Feb'84 by PRT Records. Distributed by: PRT

Musicassette: released on PRT in Feb'84 by PRT Records. Distributed by: PRT

Art Of Survival

Art of survival Various artists (Various Artists).
Album: released on Survival in Nov'84 by Survival Records. Distributed by: Backs, Cartel Distribution

Art Of The Musical Box

Art of the musical box Various works and composers (Various Artists).
Album: released on Arion in Mar'79. Distributed by Discovery

Art School

Lovin' you.
Single (7"): released on RAK in Apr'83 by RAK. Distributed by: EMI

Artwoods

100 Oxford Street.
Tracks: / Sweet Mary / If I ever get my hands on you / Goodbye sisters / Oh my love / I take what I want / Big city / She knows what to do / I'm looking for a saxophonist / Keep lookin' / I keep forgettin' / I feel good / One more heartache / Down in the valley / Be my lady / Stop and think it over / Don't cry no more.
Album: released on Edsel in Mar'83 by Demon Records. Distributed by: Pinnacle, Jazz Music, Projection

Arvo Part

Tabula rasa.
Tracks: / Fratres / Cantus in memory of Benjamin Britten / Fratres / Tabula rasa.
Notes: Gidon Kremer/Tatjana Grindenko/Alfred Schnittke/Lithuanian Chamber Orchestra(cond.Saulus Sondeckis),Staats Orchestra Stuttgart(Cond.Dennis Russell Davis),Keith Jarrett,The 12 Cellists of the Berlin Philharmonic Orchestra.
Album: released on ECM (Germany) in Nov'84 by ECM Records. Distributed by: IMS, Polygram, Virgin through EMI

Ash 48

Ash 48.
Tracks: / Ash 48 (remix) / 137 Disco heaven.
Single (12"): released on Sedition in Jan'86. Distributed by: PRT

Ash 48 (part 2).
Single (12"): released on Sedition in Oct'85. Distributed by: PRT

Ashantis

Life could be a dream.
Single (12"): released on Tree Roots in Feb'83 by Tree Roots Records. Distributed by: Jetstar

Ashanti Waugh

Party time loving.
Single (12"): released on Youth In Progress in Jun'83 by Youth In Progress Records. Distributed by: Jetstar

Ashaye

Michael Jackson medley.
Single (7"): released on Record Shack in Oct'83 by Record Shack Records. Distributed by: PRT

Single (12"): released on Record Shack in Oct'83 by Record Shack Records. Distributed by: PRT

Ashby, Dorothy

Concierto de Aranjuez.
Tracks: / Concierto de Aranjuez / Gypsy airs / Greensleeves / Gershwin medley / Autumn leaves / Dear old Stockholm / Yesterday.
Notes: America's leading jazz harpist Dorothy Ashby with a fine selection from 'Concierto de Aranjuez'to'Yesterday'.
Compact disc: by Phonogram Records. Distributed by: Polygram

Django - Misty.
Tracks: / Django / Softly, as in morning sunrise / Round midnight / Blues for Mr. K / Favourite things / September in the rain / Misty / Amor en paz.
Compact disc: released on Emarcy(USA) in Apr'85 by Emarcy Records(USA). Distributed by: Polygram

Ashby, Harold

Candy (Ashby, Harold/Don Friedman/George Mraz/Ronnie Bedford).
Tracks: / Candy / Quickie / There is no greater love / Dainty / Over the rainbow / Pleading / Days of wine & roses / Cous cous.
Album: released on Progressive (Import) in '81

Ashcroft, Peggy

World of... (The).
Album: released on Decca in Apr'80 by Decca Records. Distributed by: Polygram

Ash, Daniel

Burning skies.
Single (7"): released on Situation 2 in May'83. Distributed by: Cartel, Pinnacle

Single (12"): released on Situation 2 in May'83. Distributed by: Cartel, Pinnacle

There's only one.
Single (12"): released on Beggars Banquet in Sep'82 by Beggars Banquet Records. Distributed by: WEA

Tones on tail.
Extended-play record: released on 4AD in Apr'82 by 4AD Records. Distributed by: Rough Trade

Ashdown, Doug

Winter in America.
Musicassette: released on Decca in Nov'77 by Decca Records. Distributed by: Polygram

Asher, Ras Imru

Marshall.
Single (12"): released on Jah Shaka Music in Jun'82

Asher Senator

Abreviation qualification.
Single (12"): released on Fashion in Aug'85 by Fashion Records. Distributed by: PRT, Jetstar

Ashes & Diamonds...

Ashes and Diamonds, Generation A, Canal Original Soundtracks (Ashes & Diamonds, Generation A, Canal).
Album: released on That's Entertainment in Apr'83 by That's Entertainment Records. Distributed by: Pinnacle, PRT

Ashes & Stars

Going home (2 parts).
Single (7"): released on Satril in Nov'82 by Satril Records. Distributed by: PRT

Single (12"): released on Satril in Nov'82 by Satril Records. Distributed by: PRT

Ashford & Simpson

Ashford and Simpson Video, The.
Notes: They are one of musics most celebrated performing and songwriting teams. This video is a soul spectacular, full of energy from the opening credits and introduction of 'I need your light' to the finale of 'Ain't no mountain high enough'.
Video-cassette (VHS): released on EMI in Nov'82 by EMI Records. Distributed by: EMI

Video-cassette (Betamax): released on EMI in Nov'82 by EMI Records. Distributed by: EMI

Count your blessings.

Tracks: / Count your blessings / Side effect.
Single (7"): released on Capitol in Aug'86 by Capitol Records. Distributed by: EMI

Single (12"): released on Capitol in Aug'86 by Capitol Records. Distributed by: EMI

High rise.
Single (7"): released on Capitol in Aug'83 by Capitol Records. Distributed by: EMI

Single (12"): released on Capitol in Jul'83 by Capitol Records. Distributed by: EMI

Musical affair (A).
Musicassette: released on Warner Brothers in Sep'80 by Warner Bros Records. Distributed by: WEA

Real Love.
Notes: All tracks written/composed/produced/arranged by Ashford and Simpson
Compact disc: by EMI Records. Distributed by: EMI

Album: released on Capitol in Aug'86 by Capitol Records. Distributed by: EMI

Musicassette: released on Capitol in Aug'86 by Capitol Records. Distributed by: EMI

Solid.
Tracks: / Solid / Jungle (The) / Honey I love you / Babies / Closest to love / Cherish forever more / Tonight we escape (we make love) / Solid / Outta the world / Jungle, The (from the film'Body Rock') / Honey I love you / Babies / Close to love (from film'Body Rock') / Cherish forever more / Tonight we escape(we make love).
Notes: Staff writers & producers for Motown in the 1960's,Ashford & Simpson composed & produced many classic hits from that era for Diana Ross & The Supremes,Marvin Gaye & Tammi Terrell & many others.Their more recent work includes compositions for Chaka Khan, Quincy Jones & Gladys Knight.The title track of the album exemplifies the immense talent & musical experience this duo possesses,and the track was released as the first single from the album.It was re-mixed by Francois Kevorkian.Featured musicians include Michael Brecker & Ralph McDonald as well as the usual cast of first-class session players.
Compact disc: released on Capitol in Apr'87 by EMI Records. Distributed by: EMI

Album: released on Capitol in Nov'84 by Capitol Records. Distributed by: EMI

Musicassette: released on Capitol in Nov'84 by Capitol Records. Distributed by: EMI

Single (7"): released on Capitol in Oct'84 by Capitol Records. Distributed by: EMI

Single (12"): released on Capitol in Jan'85 by Capitol Records. Distributed by: EMI

Solid (video).
Notes: 4 tracks
Video-cassette (VHS): released on Video Collection in May'87 by Video Collection Records. Distributed by: Counterpoint

Time talking.
Tracks: / Time talking / Time talking (ext mix) / Flying / Flying (inst).
Single (7"): released on EMI in Mar'86 by EMI Records. Distributed by: EMI

Single (12"): released on EMI in Mar'86 by EMI Records. Distributed by: EMI

Ashington, Carl

Photo in a frame.
Tracks: / Photo in a frame.
Single (7"): released on WBL in Aug'87 by WBL (White Bell Records Ltd.). Distributed by: WBL (White Bell Records Ltd.)

Why.
Tracks: / Why.
Notes: 'Why' is an old Anthony Newley song revived in an up-tempo reggae/disco type version.
Single (7"): released on WBL in Sep'87 by WBL (White Bell Records Ltd.). Distributed by: WBL (White Bell Records Ltd.)

Ash, Leslie

Don't call me baby (I'm a woman).
Single (7"): released on Jive in May'86 by Zomba Records. Distributed by: RCA, PRT, CBS

Single (12"): released on Jive in May'86 by Zomba Records. Distributed by: RCA, PRT, CBS

Ashley, Steve

Family album (The).
Album: released on Woodworm in Sep'84 by Charly Records. Distributed by: Charly

Speedy return.
Tracks: / None can tell / Don't forget / Wll, well,well / Good enemies / Lazy lament / Speedy return / Old John England / Cynical sam / Travelling through the night / Broken wing / Well at the world's end / Duke of Cambridge / First thing.
Album: released on Gull in May'78 by Gull Records. Distributed by: Pinnacle

Stroll on.
Tracks: / Fire & wine / Finite time / Silly summer games / Spring song / Monkey puzzle tree / Farewell green leaves / Morris minor / Candlemas carol / John Donne song / Lord Bateman / Follow on.
Album: released on Gull in May'78 by Gull Records. Distributed by: Pinnacle

Ashra

Correlations.
Album: released on Virgin in Mar'79 by Virgin Records. Distributed by: EMI, Virgin Distribution

New age of earth.
Album: released on Virgin in Mar'84 by Virgin Records. Distributed by: EMI, Virgin Distribution

Ashton & Hayes

Resurrection shuffle.
Single (7"): released on Safari in May'83 by Safari Records. Distributed by: Pinnacle

Single (12"): released on Safari in May'83 by Safari Records. Distributed by: Pinnacle

Ashwell, Julia

Fugitive from love.
Notes: Read by Elizabeth Proud
Musicassette: released on Cover to Cover in Nov'86 by Cover to Cover Cassettes. Distributed by: Conifer

Asia

Biographical Details: Asia represent one of the most carefully contrived projects in the history of rock. Their story began in 1980 when Yes decided to disband. Long-serving member Steve Howe and Buggle Geoff Downes (recruited by the group mere months before) were looking for outlets for their musicianship, now that their band was folded. Howe met & teamed up with John Wetton and then suggested that Downes join them in a new group. Wetton had, at various times played with Family, King Crimson, Roxy Music and Uriah Heep. The quartet was completed in 1981 when Carl Palmer, one third of Emerson, Lake and Palmer(and another former Crimson) joined the band. A supergroup had been assembled. With unashamed calculation, the four set about making an LP that would be 99% certain of US success, one that would be ideally suited for rock and AOR (adult oriented rock) radio in the States. They even reportedly, hired a professional American radio consultant to advise them while recording. Rock critics en masse were pre-judging the record, arguing that, in an age of new and exciting techno-rock, this amalgamation of old seventies megastars was a total irrelevance. When the 'Asia'LP was released in april 82 the reviews were predictable. But if the band had aimed squarely at the USA, even they could not have forseen the sheer scale of their success. Asia held the no.1 spot on the Billboard album chart for nine weeks and ended up as America's biggest selling album for 1982. It's first two tracks, 'Heat Of The Night' and Only Time Will Tell' were both top 20 singles. The group was less well recieved in their native country, though it should be noted that 'Asia' was a steady but unspectacular seller, remaining on the UK top 100 albums for 36 weeks. A supergroup whose four superstars had all previously had more success in the UK than the US, now had there position reversed.

Alpha.
Tracks: / Don't cry / Smile has left your eyes, The / Never in a million years / My own time (I'll do what I want) / Heat goes on, The / Eye to eye / Last to know, The / True colours / Midnight sun / Open your eyes.
Album: released on Geffen in Sep'86 by Geffen Records. Distributed by: WEA, CBS

Musicassette: released on Geffen in Sep'86 by Geffen Records. Distributed by: WEA, CBS

Asia.
Tracks: / Go / Voice of America / Hard-on me / Wishing / Rock and roll dream / Countdown to zero / Love now till eternity / Too late / Suspicion / After the war / Heat of the moment / Only time will tell / Sole survivor / Time again / One step closer / Wildest dreams / Without you / Cutting it fine / Here comes the feeling.
Compact disc: by Geffen Records. Distributed by: WEA, CBS

Album: released on Geffen in Sep'86 by Geffen Records. Distributed by: WEA, CBS

Musicassette: released on Geffen in Sep'86 by Geffen Records. Distributed by: WEA, CBS

Compact disc: released on Geffen in Feb'87 by Geffen Records. Distributed by: WEA, CBS

Asia In Asia.
Notes: Tee British superstar studded band featured live on stage in the Far East
Video-cassette (VHS): released on Vestron in Sep'84

Astra.
Tracks: / Go / Voice of America / Hard on me / Wishing / Rock and roll dream / Countdown to zero / Love now till eternity / Too late / Suspicion / After the war.
Compact disc: by Geffen Records. Distributed by: WEA, CBS

Album: released on Geffen in Dec'85 by Geffen Records. Distributed by: WEA, CBS

Musicassette: released on Geffen in Dec'85 by Geffen Records. Distributed by: WEA, CBS

Asimov, Isaac

Foundations Edge.
Musicassette: released on Caedmon(USA) in Apr'83 by Caedmon (USA) Records. Distributed by: Gower, Taylors, Discovery

Asinovi, Jon

Dream reggae music (Asinovi, Jon & Isho Kan).
Single (7"): released on Edit in Aug'83 by Edit Records. Distributed by: Stage One

Asinov, Isaac

Mule, (The) Foundation & Empire.
Musicassette: released on Caedmon(USA) in Oct'81 by Caedmon (USA) Records. Distributed by: Gower, Taylors, Discovery

Askey, Arthur

Golden age of Arthur Askey, The.
Tracks: / Bee song, The / Chirrup / Only a glass of champagne / Ding dong bell / All to specification / Turn on the old music box / Proposal, The (inc. Let the people sing) / Sarah Sarah / Cuckoo, The / Give a little whistle / Talking shop / She was very very shy / Destiny waltz - At the piano / Rachmaninov prelude in C sharp major - At the piano / September in the rain - At the piano / Now is the moment.
Notes: Tracks 1-2-4 with piano accompaniment by Eric Fowler/Tracks 3-8-12 with orchestra/Tracks 5-9 with orchestra conducted by Ronnie Monro/Tracks 6-10 with orchestra conducted by George Scott-Wood/Tracks 7-11 with Richard Murdoch Recorded from a broadcast concert for Britsish troops "Somewhere in France" Produced, compiled and transferred by Chris Ellis. Engineered by Peter Brown.n
Album: released on Golden Age in Aug'86 by Music For Pleasure Records. Distributed by: EMI

Musicassette: released on Golden Age in Aug'86 by Music For Pleasure Records. Distributed by: EMI

Aslan

This Is Aslan.
Tracks: / This is... / Please don't stop.
Single (7"): released on Reekus in Jul'86 by Reekus Records. Distributed by: Nine Mile, Cartel

Single (12"): released on Reekus in Jul'86 by Reekus Records. Distributed by: Nine Mile, Cartel

Asleep At The Wheel

Collision course.
Album: released on Capitol in Jul'78 by Capitol Records. Distributed by: EMI

Comin' right at ya'.
Album: released on Edsel in May'86 by Demon Records. Distributed by: Pinnacle, Jazz Music, Projection

Musicassette: released on Edsel in May'86 by Demon Records. Distributed by: Pinnacle, Jazz Music, Projection

Framed.
Tracks: / Midnight in Memphis / Lonely avenue revisited / Slow dancing / Cool as a breeze / You wanna give me a lift / Don't get caught out in the rain / Whatever it takes / Fiddle funk - corn fusion / Up up up / Musical talk.
Album: released on MCA Import in Mar'86 by MCA Records. Distributed by: Polygram, IMS

Jumping at the woodside.
Album: released on Edsel in Feb'86 by Demon Records. Distributed by: Pinnacle, Jazz Music, Projection

Pasture prime.
Album: released on Demon in Apr'85 by Demon Records. Distributed by: Pinnacle

Musicassette: released on Demon in Apr'85 by Demon Records. Distributed by: Pinnacle

Ten.
Tracks: / Way down Texas way / Tulsa straight ahead / Coast to coast / House of blue lights / Blowin' like a bandit / I want a new drug / Big foot stomp / Boogie back to Texas / String of pars / Blues stay away from me.
Album: released on Epic in Jun'87 by CBS Records. Distributed by: CBS

Musicassette: released on Epic in Jun'87 by CBS Records. Distributed by: CBS

Very best of Asleep At The Wheel.
Tracks: / Cherokee Boogie / I'll never get out of this world alive / Space Buggy / Letter that Jonny Walker read (The) / Let me go home whiskey / Trouble in mind / Runnin' after fools / Miles and miles of Texas / (Get your kicks on) Route 66 / My baby thinks she's a train / Am I high? / Ragtime Annie / Somebody stole his body / When love goes wrong / Louisiana 1927 / Ain't nobody here but us chickens / One O'clock jump.
Album: released on See For Miles in Feb'87 by See For Miles Records. Distributed by: Pinnacle

Wheel, The.
Album: released on Capitol in Apr'77 by Capitol Records. Distributed by: EMI

Asmussen, Sven

1937-44 Danish jazz Vol. 6.
Album: released on Storyville in Jul'82 by Storyville Records. Distributed by: Jazz Music Distribution, Swift Distribution, Chris Wellard Distribution, Counterpoint Distribution

June night.
Tracks: / June night / Sweet Georgia Brown / Lazy River / Ladja / Blue prelude / Just a gigolo / Careless love / Pretty girl is like a melody, A / When day is done / Hush-a-bye.
Notes: Featuring: Derek Smith, Bucky Pizzarelli, Oliver Jackson Jr and Milt Hinton. Active on the jazz scene since the '30s, violinist Asmussen is one of Benny Goodman's favourite musicians. Here is a very new recording - it was recorded August 1983 in New York City. The trio accompanying Sven are Britisher Derek Smith on piano who settled in the US in 1957 and Bucky Pizzarelli guitar, Milt Hilton bass and Oliver Jackson drums. Asmussen's experience in jazz going back to the 30's is amazing. He has worked with the Who's Who of Jazz including Fats Waller, The Mills Brothers, Josephine Baker, MJQ Pianist John Lewis, Lionel Hampton and Toots Thielmans, which is a good enough pedigree for any jazz musician.
Album: released on Doctor Jazz (USA) in Apr'84 by Doctor Jazz Records. Distributed by: CBS

Musicassette: released on Doctor Jazz (USA) in Apr'84 by Doctor Jazz Records. Distributed by: CBS

Asmussen, Svend

Biographical Details: seeunder - Lionel Hampton.

Two of a kind (Asmussen, Svend & Stephane Grappelli).
Album: released on Storyville in May'86 by Storyville Records. Distributed by: Jazz Music Distribution, Swift Distribution, Chris Wellard Distribution, Counterpoint Distribution

Asmus Tietchens

Litia.
Album: released on Sky (Germany) in Mar'84

Asmus Tietdiens

Seuchengbiete.
Album: released on Emission in Nov'85. Distributed by: Red Rhino, Cartel

Aspey, Gary

Don't get married girl (Aspey, Gary & Vera).
Single (7"): released on Dingles in Jul'81 by Dingles Records. Distributed by: Projection

From the north (Aspey, Gary & Vera).
Tracks: / From the north / parting, The / Coal picking / three foot seam, The / Mill girls lullaby / King cotton / Auntie Ketyll / Cum t'thi tay / cradle song, The / Roving navvy, The / Ship canal song, The / Hailey go / Tuppence on the rope / Bit of a sing, A.
Notes: Vera Aspey vocal, concertina, guitar, Gary Aspey vocal, Bernard Wrigley concertinas, Wilf Darlington mandolin.
Album: released on Topic in '81. Distributed by: Roots Distribution

Seeing double (Aspey, Gary & Vera).
Tracks: / Seeing double / My goodlooking man / Miss tickle toby / Dowie dens of Yarrow, The / cruise of the calibar, The / Hounds and horn together / bolinder boatman, The / testimony of Patience kershaw, The / July wakes / Knocker upper man / price of coal, The / Coal and Albert Berry, The.
Album: released on Topic in '81. Distributed by: Roots Distribution

Stories,songs & humour (Aspey, Gary & Vera).
Album: released on Dingles in '83 by Dingles Records. Distributed by: Projection

Taste of hotpot, A (Aspey, Gary & Vera).
Tracks: / Eskdale and Ennerdale hunt song, The / Weepin' an' wailin' away / Shuttle kissing song, The / Foddered me yowes / Nightingale, The / Don't get married girls / Kids songs / Coal hole cavalry, The / Morning stands on tiptoe.
Notes: Vera Aspey vocal, accordion, concertina, guitar, Gary Aspey vocal.
Album: released on Topic in '81. Distributed by: Roots Distribution

Aspeys

Come on home (Aspeys with Bayou Brothers).
Single (7"): released on Dingles in Jul'82 by Dingles Records. Distributed by: Projection

Aspey, Vera

Blackbird, The.
Tracks: / Blackbird, The / Owd Betty Barlow / Ladybird / Maypole Inn, The / Pit brow lassies, The / My Johnny was a shoemaker / Coal black faces / Highwayman, The / Shule agra / Aggie bell / sprig of thyme, The.
Notes: Vera Aspey with own guitar, concertina, John Luce guitar, bass, Dave Gotliffe piano.
Album: released on Topic in '81. Distributed by: Roots Distribution

Assad, Sergio Odair

Brazilian guitar music for 2 guitars.
Album: released on Nonesuch in Mar'86

As Seen On TV

Summer holiday.
Single (7"): released on Empire in Jun'83 by Empire Records. Distributed by: Backs, Cartel, Jetstar

Assistants

Down at the superstore.
Single (7"): released on BBC in Oct'82 by BBC Records & Tapes. Distributed by: EMI, PRT,

Associated Rediffusion's.

Associated Rediffusion's,Ready Steady Go Various artists (Various Artists).
Album: released on Decca (Rock Echoes) in Dec'82 by Decca Records. Distributed by: Polygram, IMS

Musicassette: released on Decca (Rock Echoes) in Dec'82 by Decca Records. Distributed by: Polygram, IMS

Associates

Biographical Details: Billy Mackenzie and Alan Rankine were a cabaret outfit in their native Scotland in 1976. Over the next few years they experimented with various group line-ups, finally reverting to a duo but with backing musicians. Their debut LP "The Affectionate Punch" came out in 1980 and received wide acclaim in the rock press. A series of indie single hits and 1981's "Fourth Drawer Down" album further enhanced their 'press darlings' status. 1982 saw the release of "Party Fears Two", a single that combined the latest aspects of British rock vocalising, with a catchy keyboard hook. It reached No.9 on the national charts and was followed by "Club Country" at No.13. Both were issued on their own eponymous label, which also released the pair's third album 'Sulk", a Top 10 LP. Having cracked both singles and album charts for the first time in '82, the Associates failed to consolidate the following year. Alan Rankine quit, leaving Mackenzie to form a new Associates group. The new line-up's first singles, "Those First Impressions" and "Waiting For The Love Boat", scored minor chart placings in 1984.

Affectionate punch, The.
Tracks: / Logan time / Paper house / Deeply concerned / Even dogs in the wild / Transport to central / Amused as always / Affectionate punch, The / Matter of gender, A / Would I ....bounce back.
Album: released on Fiction in Aug'83 by Fiction Records. Distributed by: Polygram

Musicassette: released on Fiction in Aug'83 by Fiction Records. Distributed by: Polygram

Kitchen person.
Single (7"): released on Situation 2 in Nov'82. Distributed by: Cartel, Pinnacle

Single (12"): released on Situation 2 in Nov'82. Distributed by: Cartel, Pinnacle

Message oblique speech.
Single (7"): released on Situation 2 in Nov'82. Distributed by: Cartel, Pinnacle

Single (12"): released on Situation 2 in Nov'82. Distributed by: Cartel, Pinnacle

Perhaps.
Tracks: / Those first impressions / Waiting for the Loveboat / Perhaps / Schampout / Helicopter helicopter / Breakfast / Thirteen feelings / Stranger in your voice, The / Best of you, The / Don't give me that I told you so look.
Album: released on WEA in Feb'85 by WEA Records. Distributed by: WEA

Musicassette: released on WEA in Feb'85 by WEA Records. Distributed by: WEA

Q quarters.
Single (7"): released on Situation 2 in Nov'82. Distributed by: Cartel, Pinnacle

Sulk.
Tracks: / It's better this way / Party fears two / Club country / Love hangover / 18 carat love affair / Arrogance gave him up / No / Skipping / White car in Germany / Gloomy Sunday / Associate, The.
Album: released on WEA in Oct'82 by WEA Records. Distributed by: WEA

Musicassette: released on WEA in Oct'82 by WEA Records. Distributed by: WEA

Take me to the girl.
Single (7"): released on WEA in Oct'85 by WEA Records. Distributed by: WEA

Single (12"): released on WEA in Oct'85 by WEA Records. Distributed by: WEA

Single 10": released on WEA in Nov'85 by WEA Records. Distributed by: WEA

Tell me Easter's on friday.
Single (12"): released on Situation 2 in Nov'82. Distributed by: Cartel, Pinnacle

White car in Germany.
Single (7"): released on Situation 2 in Nov'82. Distributed by: Cartel, Pinnacle

Single (12"): released on Situation 2 in Nov'82. Distributed by: Cartel, Pinnacle

Association

Biographical Details: The Association were a six-man vocal harmony group who sang straightforward late Sixties pop but with tinges of flower power. Hailing from California, their first big hit was "Along Comes Mary" in the summer of 1966. This reached No.7 on the US charts despite alleged drug references. It was followed by the No.1 smash "Cherish". Questions were again asked about the next single "Pandora's Golden Heebie Jeebies", a smaller hit and their last on Valiant Records before switching to Warner Bros. Once with this major company, their records became totally conventional love songs. "Windy" was their biggest single, logging four weeks at No. 1 in the US in the summer of '67. It was followed by two more Top Tenners, "Never My Love" and "Everything That Touches You". The Association's final American Top 40 record, "Time For Livin'", was their only hit in Britain, where the commercial pop market was already well catered for.

Association and the Kingston Trio (Association/Kingston Trio).
Musicassette: released on Timeless Treasures in Jul'86. Distributed by: Counterpoint Distribution

Never my love.
Single (7"): released on Old Gold in Jul'82 by Old Gold Records. Distributed by: Lightning, Jazz Music, Spartan, Counterpoint

Assyne

Call it a day.
Single (7"): released on Zone To Zone in Apr'83 by Zone To Zone Records. Distributed by: Pinnacle

Leaving.
Single (7"): released on Zone To Zone in Oct'83 by Zone To Zone Records. Distributed by: Pinnacle

Astaire

Anglia remix Vol.2 (Astaire/Angle Gold/Toto Coelo).
Single (12"): released on ZYX (Germany) in Nov'85 by ZYX Records. Distributed by: Greyhound

Born to dance.
Tracks: / Born to dance / Shame / Love Trap / In the name of love / Skratch Music Publishing / Keep Movin' / Get that girl / Feelings for me / Lazy days, magical nights / You were made to love me / Treat me like a fool / Creatures of the night / Because we've got the love / Dancing my way to the top / Living as one.
Album: released on Passion in Nov'83 by Skratch Records. Distributed by: PRT

Single (7"): released on Passion in Oct'83 by Skratch Records. Distributed by: PRT

Single (12"): released on Passion in Oct'83 by Skratch Records. Distributed by: PRT

Fire in my heart.
Tracks: / Fire in my heart / Fire in my heart (inst).
Single (12"): released on Passion in Jun'86 by Skratch Records. Distributed by: PRT

Fire me up.
Tracks: / Fire me up / Fire me up (inst).
Single (12"): released on Passion in Feb'86 by Skratch Records. Distributed by: PRT

In the name of love.
Single (12"): released on Passion in Feb'85 by Skratch Records. Distributed by: PRT

Love trap.
Single (12"): released on Passion in Feb'84 by Skratch Records. Distributed by: PRT

Power of love, The.
Single (12"): released on Passion in Oct'84 by Skratch Records. Distributed by: PRT

Turn me on again.
Tracks: / Turn me on again / Turn me on again (inst).
Single (12"): released on Passion in Jul'87 by Skratch Records. Distributed by: PRT

Astaire, Fred

An evening with....
Double Album: released on Nostalgia in Jun'86. Distributed by: Jazz Music, Counterpoint

Chante ses plus grandes success.
Album: released on WEA in Jun'86 by WEA Records. Distributed by: WEA

Crazy feet.
Tracks: / Night and day / My one and only / Fascinating rhythm / New sun in the sky / Louisiana / Swiss miss / I'd rather Charleston / High hat / Whichness of the whatness / I've got you on my mind / Puttin' on the Ritz / White heat / Dancing in the dark / Hang on to me / Oh hee oh gosh / Not my girl / Half of it dearie blues / Babbitt and the bromide / I love Louisa / Funny face / Crazy feet.
Compact disc: by Academy Sound & Vision Records. Distributed by: Pinnacle

Album: released on ASV Living Era in Mar'83 by ASV Records. Distributed by: PRT

Musicassette: released on ASV Living Era in Mar'83 by ASV Records. Distributed by: PRT

Fred & Adele Astaire.
Album: released on Monmouth in Jun'79

Fred Astaire Original recordings 1935-40.
Album: released on CBS(Import) in Jun'86 by CBS Records. Distributed by: Conifer, Discovery, Swift

Fred Astaire Collection.
Album: released on Deja Vu in Nov'85 by Deja Vu Records. Distributed by: Counterpoint Distribution, Record Services Distribution (Ireland)

Musicassette: released on Deja Vu in Nov'85 by Deja Vu Records. Distributed by: Counterpoint Distribution, Record Services Distribution (Ireland)

Fred Astaire sings his greatest hits.
Album: released on C5 in Jul'87 by See For Miles Records. Distributed by: Countemoint

Funny face (Astaire, Fred & Adele).
Album: released on World in '70. Distributed by: Jetstar

Golden age of Fred Astaire Vol.2.
Album: released on Golden Age in Jul'85 by Music For Pleasure Records. Distributed by: EMI

Musicassette: released on Golden Age in Jul'85 by Music For Pleasure Records. Distributed by: EMI

Golden age of Fred Astaire.
Tracks: / Top hat, white tie and tails / Fine romance, A / Cheek to cheek / I wanna be a dancin' man / They can't take that away from me / One for my baby (and one more for the road) / Night and day / Something's gotta give / Foggy day, A / Isn't this a lovely day / They all laughed / That's entertainment.
Notes: Licensed from Liberty Records, the great Fred Astaire with recordings made in 1976. Each track was featured in one of Astaire's many successful films, including titles written by Irving Berlin, Gershwin, Cole Porter and Johnny Mercer.
Album: released on Golden Age in Jul'83 by Music For Pleasure Records. Distributed by: EMI

Musicassette: released on Golden Age in Jul'83 by Music For Pleasure Records. Distributed by: EMI

Irving Berlin Songbook.
Compact disc: by Polydor Records. Distributed by: Polygram, Polydor

Special magic of Fred Astaire Vol.2.
Musicassette: released on Verve in Aug'77 by Phonogram Records. Distributed by: Polygram

Special magic of Fred Astaire.
Album: released on Polydor in Mar'84 by Polydor Records. Distributed by: Polygram, Polydor
Deleted '87.

Musicassette: released on Polydor in Mar'84 by Polydor Records. Distributed by: Polygram, Polydor

Starring Fred Astaire.
Tracks: / No strings / Isn't this a lovely day / Top hat, white tie and tails / Cheek to cheek / Piccolino, the / We saw the sea / Let yourself go / I'd rather lead a band / I'm putting all my eggs in one basket / Let's face the music and dance / I'm building up to an awful let-down / Pick yourself up / Way you look tonight, The / Waltz in swing time, The / Fine romance, A / Bojangles of Harlem / Never gonna dance / Slap that bass / Beginners luck / They all laughed / Let's call the whole thing off / They can't take that away from me / Shall we dance / I can't be bothered now / Things are looking up / Nice work if you can get it / Foggy day, A / Iused to be colour blind / Change partners / Yam, The / Yam step, The / No strings / Isn't this a lovely day / Top hat, white tie and tails / Cheek to cheek / Piccolino, The / We saw the sea / Let yourself go / I'd rather lead a band / I'm putting all my eggs in one basket / Let's face the music and dance / I'm building up to an awful let down / Pick yourself up / Way you look tonight, The / Waltz in swing time, The / Fine romance, A / Bojangles of Harlem / Never gonna dance / Slap the bass / Beginner's luck / They all laughed / Let's call the whole thing off / They can't take that away from me / Shall we dance / I can't be bothered now / Things are looking up / Foggy day (in London town), A / Nice work if you can get it / I used to be color blind / Change partners / Yam, The / Yam step, The.
Notes: Featuring the orchestras of Johnny Green, Ray Noble and Leo Reisman. Double LP. Tracks 1-4 Top Hat Irving Berlin. June 1935/6-11 Follow the Fleet. Irving Berlin. Jan. 1936/12-17 Swing Time. Dorothy Fields & Jerome Kern. July 1936/18-23 Shall We Dance. George & Ira Gershwin. March 1937/24-27 A Damsel in Distress. George and Ira Gershwin. Oct. 1937/28-31 Carefree. Irving Berlin. March 1938
Album: released on Avan-Guard (CBS Recordings) in Aug'86. Distributed by: Conifer, Discovery

Album: released on CBS in Aug'87 by CBS Records. Distributed by: CBS

Musicassette: released on CBS in Aug'87 by CBS Records. Distributed by: CBS

Story of Vernon & Irene Castle (Astaire, Fred & Ginger Rogers).
Album: released on Video Collection in Jul'87 by Video Collection Records. Distributed by: Counterpoint

Aster, Andre

Ballade en Quercy (Aster, Andre & Andre Roques).
Tracks: / Bon vin de cahors / Quercy mon beau pays / Les filles de Montauban / Querca querla / Lapelleto / De Mauriac a rodez / Plaisirs de quercy / Le grand pere / Potpourri de valses / Aio de rosta / Chez la mere Antoine a pas legers / Bourees / Polka piquee.
Notes: Accordion Record Club, 146 Birmingham Road, Kidderminster, Worcs. Tel:0562 746105. 5.95 exc. P&P
Musicassette:

Asteriks

So Confusion vol.4.
Album: released on Striker in May'87 by Striker Records. Distributed by: Jetstar Distribution

Asterisks

Darling cool it.
Single (12"): released on Sunburn in Mar'83 by Orbitone Records. Distributed by: Jetstar Distribution

Asterix

Asterix the Gladiator (Rushton, Willie).
Notes: Asterix and Obelix set off to Rome to rescue the village bard Cacofonix, who is about to be thrown to the lions in Caesar's Circus Maximus. Adapted by Anthea Bell, read by William Rushton, text by Goscinny.
Musicassette: released on Listen For Pleasure in Feb'86 by MFP Records. Distributed by: EMI

Asterix In Britain

Asterix in Britain Goscinny (Rushton, Willie).
Notes: This recording of Astrix in Britain is adapted from its well-known comic strip format by Anthea Bell, who together with Derek Hockridge translated the stories.William Rushton adds his considerable skill as a storyteller in this hilarious adventure guaranteed to delight listeners of all ages. The year if 50BC, Gaul isentirely occupied by the Romans. Well not entirely ... One small village of indomitable Gauls still holds out led by Asterix, the hero of the story, accompaniedby his trusty warriors Getafix, Vitalstatistix, Obelix and Cacofonix. Running time: 2 hours approx. Drawings: Uderzo.
Musicassette: released on LFP in Jun'87

As Time Goes By

As time goes by (a collection of timeless love songs) (Various original artists).
Tracks: / Way I want to touch you, The / Dedicated to the one I love / Sad sweet dreamer / Hey there lonely girl / You keep me steady / So sad the song / Tired of being alone / Can't get by without you / Two people in the morning / I wanna get next to you / Best thing that ever happened to me, The / Let's stay together / Suspicious minds / I feel love coming on / Nobody needs your love / Stardust / Melodie d'amour / On the street where you live / My heart cries for you / Never my love / Arriverderci,my love.
Album: released on Cambra in '83 by Cambra Records. Distributed by: IDS, Conifer

Musicassette: released on Cambra in '83 by Cambra Records. Distributed by: IDS. Conifer

Astley, John

Everyone loves the pilot except the crew.
Tracks: / Jane's getting serious / Lipservice / Target practise / Suffering fools / Animal,The / Jumping in the deep end / Better never than later / I want to dance / Disclaimer / Emperor,The.
Album: released on Atlantic in Jun'87 by WEA Records. Distributed by: WEA

Musicassette: released on Atlantic in Jun'87 by WEA Records. Distributed by: WEA

Astley, Jon

Everyone loves the pilot Except the crew.
Album: released on Atlantic in Jun'87 by WEA Records. Distributed by: WEA

Musicassette: released on Atlantic in Jun'87 by WEA Records. Distributed by: WEA

Astley, Rick

Never gonna give you up.
Tracks: / Never gonna give you up / Never gonna give you up (inst).
Single (12"): released on RCA in Jul'87 by RCA Records. Distributed by: RCA, Roots, Swift, Wellard, Chris, I & B, Solomon & Peres Distribution

Single (7"): released on RCA in Jul'87 by RCA Records. Distributed by: RCA, Roots, Swift, Wellard, Chris, I & B, Solomon & Peres Distribution

Astley, Tyrone

Just another Rumour.
Tracks: / Just another rumour (inst).

Single (12"): released on Nightmare Gold in Feb'87. Distributed by: PRT

Astley, Virginia

Abao aqu.
Single 10": released on Why-Fi in Jan'82 by Why-Fi Records. Distributed by: RCA, Indies

Darkness has reached it's end.
Single (7"): released on Elektra (USA) in Nov'85 by Elektra/Asylum/Nonesuch Records. Distributed by: WEA

Single (12"): released on Elektra (USA) in Nov'85 by Elektra/Asylum/Nonesuch Records. Distributed by: WEA

From the gardens where we feel secure.
Album: released on Rough Trade in Aug'83 by Rough Trade Records. Distributed by: Rough Trade Distribution, Cartel Distribution

Hope in a darkened heart.
Compact disc: by WEA Records. Distributed by: WEA

Love's a lonely place to be.
Single (7"): released on Why-Fi in Jan'83 by Why-Fi Records. Distributed by: RCA, Indies

Single (12"): released on Why-Fi in Jan'83 by Why-Fi Records. Distributed by: RCA, Indies

Melt the snow EP.
Single (12"): released on Rough Trade in Feb'85 by Rough Trade Records. Distributed by: Rough Trade Distribution, Cartel Distribution

Promise nothing.
Album: released on Les Disques Du Crepuscule in Dec'84. Distributed by: Rough Trade, Pinnacle, Island, Polygram

Some Small Hope.
Tracks: / So like Dorian / Summer long since past, A.
Notes: "So like Dorian" on 12" version only.
Single (7"): released on WEA in Feb'87 by WEA Records. Distributed by: WEA

Single (12"): released on WEA in Feb'87 by WEA Records. Distributed by: WEA

Tender.
Single (7"): released on Elektra (USA) in Sep'85 by Elektra/Asylum/Nonesuch Records. Distributed by: WEA Deleted '86.

Single (12"): released on Elektra (USA) in Sep'85 by Elektra/Asylum/Nonesuch Records. Distributed by: WEA

Aston, John

You take the blame for the roses.
Album: released on Happy Face in Oct'80 by Happy Face Records. Distributed by: Red Rhino, Bullet Distribution, Pinnacle, PRT, Birds Nest

Aston Manor School

David.
Album: by Pilgrim Records. Distributed by: Rough Trade, Cartel

Jerusalem joy.
Tracks: / To Jerusalem / Palm Sunday / In the temple / Let's get rid of him / Last supper, The / Gethsemane / Peter's denial / trial, The / Don't let Him go / Crucifixion, The / It is over now / He's not here (for He is risen) / David, you're gonna be King / Samuel, we're waiting for you / Lord's my shepherd, The / David and Goliath / Look out, David / I will bless the Lord / David and Jonathan / Mighty are fallen, The / David is the one / Praise the Lord.
Album: by Pilgrim Records. Distributed by: Rough Trade, Cartel

Stargazers, The.
Tracks: / Let's take a trip / Farewell home / Riding high / Are we in the right place / Bethlehem (That's the place) / Look here, wise guys / In search of love / Look at the star / Jesus, baby Jesus / Just you / As with gladness / Band 2 Psalm 100 / Band 3 How sweet the name.
Album: by Pilgrim Records. Distributed by: Rough Trade, Cartel

Astra

Wake up to my love.
Tracks: / Wake up to my love (ballroom mix) / Wake up to my love (bathroom mix) / Wake up to my love (bedroom mix).
Single (7"): released on Adventures In Clubland in Jul'86. Distributed by: DMS, RCA

Single (12"): released on Adventures In Clubland in Jul'86. Distributed by: DMS, RCA

Astronauts

Bye bye girl.
Single (12"): released on Thunderbolt in Jun'82 by Magnum Music Group Ltd. Distributed by: Magnum Music Group Ltd, PRT Distribution, Spartan Distribution

Darling Jamaica.
Single (7"): released on Thunderbolt in Oct'83 by Magnum Music Group Ltd. Distributed by: Magnum Music Group Ltd, PRT Distribution, Spartan Distribution

I'm your astronaut.
Single (7"): released on Stiff in Apr'82 by Stiff Records. Distributed by: EMI, Record Services Distribution (Ireland)

It's all done with mirrors.
Notes: Features Lol Coxhill
Album: released on All The Madmen in Oct'86 by All The Madmen Records. Distributed by: Rough Trade, Cartel

Mek we jam.
Single 10": released on Pama in Aug'82 by Pama Records. Distributed by: Pama, Enterprise, Jetstar

Pranksters in revolt (EP).
Single (7"): released on Bugle in Oct'80. Distributed by: Rough Trade

Pretty island.
Single (12"): released on Thunderbolt in May'83 by Magnum Music Group Ltd. Distributed by: Magnum Music Group Ltd, PRT Distribution, Spartan Distribution

Aswad

Biographical Details: One of Britain's foremost reggae bands, Aswad released their debut self-titled album in 1976. After much gigging, a second LP 'Hulet' finally came out in 1980.After switching from Island to CBS they released 'New Chapter' in 81 and 'Not Satisfied' their first chart album in 82. Aswad's story has been one of hard gigging and gradually building up greater support with each LP release. 1984 saw themmake their long overdue singles chart debut, with two minor hits 'Chasing For The Breeze' and '54-46 (Was My Number)'.

54-46(was my number).
Single (7"): released on Island in Sep'84 by Island Records. Distributed by: Polygram

Single (12"): released on Island in Sep'84 by Island Records. Distributed by: Polygram

Aswad.
Album: released on Island in Jun'76 by Island Records. Distributed by: Polygram

Bubbling.
Single (12"): released on Simba in Oct'85 by Simba Records. Distributed by: Jetstar

Chasing for the breeze.
Single (7"): released on Island in Mar'84 by Island Records. Distributed by: Polygram

Single (12"): released on Island in Mar'84 by Island Records. Distributed by: Polygram

Don't bite the hand

Hooked On You.
Tracks: / Hooked on you (Version).
Single (12"): released on Simba in Feb'87 by Simba Records. Distributed by: Jetstar

Hulet.
Album: released on Island in Jun'80 by Island Records. Distributed by: Polygram

Jah Shaka meets Aswad in Addis Ababa Studio.
Album: released on Jah Shaka in Nov'85 by Jah Shaka Records. Distributed by: Jetstar

Kool noh.
Tracks: / Kool noh / Free Azania.
Single (12"): released on Simba in Dec'85 by Simba Records. Distributed by: Jetstar

Live & direct.
Tracks: / Not guilty / Not satisfied / Your recipe / Roots rocking drum & bass line / African children / Soca rumba / Rockers medley / Love fire.
Album: released on Island in Dec'83 by Island Records. Distributed by: Polygram

Musicassette: released on Island in Dec'83 by Island Records. Distributed by: Polygram

Need you by my side.
Single (12"): released on World Enterprise in Dec'84. Distributed by: Jetstar

Need your love (each & every day).
Single (7"): released on Island in Mar'85 by Island Records. Distributed by: Polygram

New chapter.
Tracks: / African children / Natural progression / Ways of the Lord / I will keep on loving you / He gave the sun to shine / Tuff we tuff / Didn't know at the time / Zion / In a your rights / Candles / Love fire.
Album: released on CBS in Jun'84 by CBS Records. Distributed by: CBS

Musicassette: released on CBS in Jun'84 by CBS Records. Distributed by: CBS

Not satisfied.
Tracks: / Drum & bass line / Not satisfied / Reality / African children (part 2) / Pass the cup / I need your love / No more living a lie / Down the line / Your recipe / Girl's got to know.
Album: released on CBS in Feb'85 by CBS Records. Distributed by: CBS

Musicassette: released on CBS in Feb'85 by CBS Records. Distributed by: CBS

Promised land

Pull up.
Tracks: / Pull up / Dub up.
Single (7"): released on Simba in Jun'86 by Simba Records. Distributed by: Jetstar

Single (12"): released on Simba in Jun'86 by Simba Records. Distributed by: Jetstar

Rebel souls.
Album: released on Island in Oct'84 by Island Records. Distributed by: Polygram

Musicassette: released on Island in Oct'84 by Island Records. Distributed by: Polygram

Roots rockin'.
Single (7"): released on Simba in Jun'83 by Simba Records. Distributed by: Jetstar

Single (12"): released on Simba in Jun'83 by Simba Records. Distributed by: Jetstar

To the top.
Album: released on Simba in Jun'86 by Simba Records. Distributed by: Jetstar

Compact disc: released on Simba in Mar'87 by Simba Records. Distributed by: Jetstar

As You Like It

As you like it Shakespeare, William.
Musicassette: released on Argo (Spokenword) in Jul'82 by Decca Records. Distributed by: Polygram

Atari-Sci/Fi Adventures

Atari-sci-fi adventures in sound Various artists (Various Artists).
Musicassette: released on Pickwick Talking Books in Mar'84

A-Team

A-Team, The Original Score.
Tracks: / Theme from the A-team / Young Hannibal / B. A. 's ride / A-team in New York City, (The) / Bandits! / Taxi chase / A-team escape, (The) / A-team prepare for war, (The) / Showtime! / Move sucker! / Let's get busted / Murdock's "face" / Helicopters / More bandits / Theme from the A-team.
Album: released on MFP in Oct'85 by EMI Records. Distributed by: EMI

Musicassette: released on MFP in Oct'85 by EMI Records. Distributed by: EMI

Athens, GA

Athens, GA - Inside out Original soundtrack (Various Artists).
Notes: Inc REM, Love Tractor, Time Toys
Album: released on I.R.S.(Independent Record Syndicate) in May'87 by I.R.S.. Distributed by: MCA

Musicassette: released on I.R.S.(Independent Record Syndicate) in May'87 by I.R.S.. Distributed by: MCA

Atkins

Atkins.
Album: released on Warner Bros. in Jun'82 by Warner Bros Records. Distributed by: WEA

Atkins, Chet

Biographical Details: Born in Tennessee in 1924, Chet Atkins successfully combined careers as musician, producer and executive. Learning to play fiddle and then guitar, he signed to RCA Records in 1946. He established himself as a leading session guitarist, moved to Nashville in 1950 and helped make the town the centre of country music. During the early fifties Atkins was living a double life, he became artists and repertoire assistant to RCA's Steve Sholes while simultaneously commencing a solo recording career. His debut album 'Gallopin' shoes' was the first of numerous strong selling country LP's that dotted his career. In the mid-fifties he played sessions with RCA's new signing Elvis Presley, he was soon assigned by the companyto supervise Elvis's recording career. In 1960 he became RCA's head of NashvilleA & R. As well as steering the careers of many fledgling country singers who were to become major artists, he played on many of their records himself, together with pianist Floyd Cramer. Atkin's guitar and Cramer's piano characterised many country records of the period. By both playing on so many Nashville hits and supervising the artists involved, Atkins became all powerful. He created the Nasville Sound- the familiar pedal steel guitars, the massed strings. The style evolved not only from traditional country, but also from Atkin's interests in jazz androck. Having been responsible for such a distinctive sound, however, he became less and less interested in progression. The Nashville establishment grew more and more conservative in a attempt to preserve their musical trademark. Their output becane samey. Having gained further promotion within his record company, Atkins was elected to the Country Music Association Hall of Fame in 1973. As guitarist, writer, producer, executive and above all, catalyst, he was the man most resposible for bringing about RCA's dominance of the US country charts. He was an important figure in the careers of Elvis Presley, Jim Reeves, Charley Pride, Jerry Reed and numerous others. As far as UK recognition is concerned, Chet Atkins scored three top 20 albums in the early sixties, also a minor chart single called'Teensville'.

20 of the best.
Tracks: / Yakety ake / Yankee doodle Dixie / Galloping on the guitar / Walkin' on strings / You're just in love / In the mood / Whispering / Theme from 'A summer place' / Hidden charm / Heartaches / When you wish upon a star / Over the rainbow / Music to watch girls by / Siboney / El relicario / Early dawn (La madrugada) / Steeplechase lane / Funky junk / Cascade / Black Mountain rag.
Album: released on RCA in Mar'86 by RCA Records. Distributed by: RCA, Roots, Swift, Wellard, Chris, I & B, Solomon & Peres Distribution

Musicassette: released on RCA in Mar'86 by RCA Records. Distributed by: RCA, Roots, Swift, Wellard, Chris, I & B, Solomon & Peres Distribution

Best of Chet Atkins and Friends, The (Atkins, Chet & Friends).
Tracks: / Terry on the turnpike / Sail along silv'ry moon / Sweet Georgia Brown / Avalon / Sugarfoot rag / Battle of New Orleans / Do I ever cross your mind / Frog kissin' / Twichy / Fiddlin' around / Poison love / I'll see you in my dreams.
Album: released on MFP in Sep'86 by EMI Records. Distributed by: EMI

Musicassette: released on MFP in Sep'86 by EMI Records. Distributed by: EMI

Best of Chet Atkins, The.
Album: released on RCA/Camden in Jul'86

Musicassette: released on RCA/Camden in Jul'86

Best of Chet Atkins, The.
Album: released on RCA International in Oct'80

Musicassette: released on RCA International in Oct'80

Christmas album.
Album: released on CBS in Dec'83 by CBS Records. Distributed by: CBS

Musicassette: released on CBS in Dec'83 by CBS Records. Distributed by: CBS

Famous country music makers.
Tracks: / Yakety axe / Walking on strings / Bells of Saint Mary's / Corrine, Corrine / Amazing grace / Theme from "The Third Man" / Little bit of blues, (A) / Dill pickle rag / Country style / Django's castle / Glow worm / Stephen Foster medley / Trambone / Remembering / Prisoner's song / Country gentleman / Oh by jingo / Will the circle be unbroken / Greensleeves / Windy & warm / Arkansas traveller / Squirrelly / Red wing / Twelfth Street rag / Get on with it / Little Rock getaway / South / When you wish upon a star / Whispering / Halacious / Main street breakdown.

Double Album: released on RCA in Mar'76 by RCA Records. Distributed by: RCA, Roots, Swift, Wellard, Chris, I & B, Solomon & Peres Distribution

Guitar pickin' man.
Double Album: released on Cambra in '83 by Cambra Records. Distributed by: IDS, Conifer

Double musicassette: released on Cambra in '83 by Cambra Records. Distributed by: IDS, Conifer

Man & his guitar, A.
Album: released on RCA (Germany) in Jan'85

Musicassette: released on RCA (Germany) in Jan'85

Nashville gold.
Album: released on RCA (Germany) in Oct'84

Sails.
Tracks: / Sails / Why worry / Sometime, someplace / Up in my treehouse / Waltz for the lonely / Laffin' at life / On a roll / My song / Wobegon (the way it used to be).
Album: released on CBS in Jun'87 by CBS Records. Distributed by: CBS

Musicassette: released on CBS in Jun'87 by CBS Records. Distributed by: CBS

Solid gold guitar.
Musicassette: released on RCA International in Jun'82

Stay tuned.
Album: released on CBS in May'85 by CBS Records. Distributed by: CBS

Musicassette: released on CBS in May'85 by CBS Records. Distributed by: CBS

Street dreams (Atkins, Chet C.G.P.).
Tracks: / Spat'n'hats / Cystal in the light, The / Official beach music, The / Street dreams / Stay a little longer (If you'll) / Classical gas / Last farewell, The / Alisha / Homecoming anthem, The / Honolulu blue.
Album: released on CBS in Jun'86 by CBS Records. Distributed by: CBS

Musicassette: released on CBS in Jun'86 by CBS Records. Distributed by: CBS

Atkins, Chet C.G.P.

East Tennessee Christmas.
Tracks: / Jingle bell rock / White Christmas / Let it snow / Winter wonderland / Christmas song, (The) / I'll be home for Christmas / East Tennessee Christmas / Do you hear what I hear? / Little drummer boy, (The) / God rest ye merry, Gentlemen / Silent night / Away in a manger.
Musicassette: released on CBS in Dec'83 by CBS Records. Distributed by: CBS

Atkinson, Lisle

Lisle Atkinson Grady Tate etc.... (Atkinson, Lisle/Grady Tate etc.).
Notes: See under McGhee, Howard etc....

Midnight creeper

Atkinson, Rowan

Biographical Details: Star of BBC TV's 'Not The Nine O'Clock News,a satirical show that always included a high musical element, Rowan Atkinson proceeded in the early eighties to pursue a career as one of Britain's top one-man comedians. His album 'Live In Belfast' reached no.44 in 1981, a respectable placing for a comedy LP though not the top 5 status that he was able to achieve as part of the 'Nine O'Clock' team. Atkinson's ultra-flexible facial features and hands have made him an engaging visual performancer. (BM 84)

Live in Belfast.
Album: released on Arista in Aug'83 by Arista Records. Distributed by: RCA

Musicassette: released on Arista in Aug'83 by Arista Records. Distributed by: RCA

Atlain

Living in the dark.
Album: released on Mausoleum in Mar'85 by Mausoleum Records. Distributed by: Pinnacle

Atlanta

Atlanta.
Tracks: / Can't you hear that whistle blow / She will / Dancin' on the Bayou / Long ago shoes / We're history / Why not tonight / She's the best friend I've ever had / One jump ahead of the storm / My sweet-eyed Georgia girl / Good time chariot.

Album: released on MCA Import in Mar'86 by MCA Records. Distributed by: Polygram, IMS

Pictures.
Tracks: / Dixie dreaming / Wishful drinkin' / Pictures / Sweet was our rose / Blue side of the grey / Atlanta burned again last night / Sweet country music / But Alabama (Nothing left between us) / You are the wine / Long cool woman in a black dress.
Album: released on MCA Import in Mar'86 by MCA Records. Distributed by: Polygram, IMS

Album: released on MCA in Apr'84 by MCA Records. Distributed by: Polygram, MCA

Musicassette: released on MCA in Apr'84 by MCA Records. Distributed by: Polygram, MCA Deleted '85.

Single (7"): released on WEA in Nov'84 by WEA Records. Distributed by: WEA

Atlanta Brass Ensemble

Sonic fireworks Vol.1.
Album: released on Metrosound Audio in Sep'79

Sonic fireworks Vol.2.
Album: released on Metrosound Audio in Sep'79

Atlanta Rhythm Section

Biographical Details: This group of Atlanta studio musicians released their debut eponymous album in 1972. Two years on, their second set "Back Up Against The Wall" yielded the US Top 40 single "Doraville". For a three year period, from 1977-9, thier brand of soft adult rock brought American radio and album success. The LPs "Rock 'n' Roll Alternative" and "Champagne Jam" were strong sellers, and the band chalked up five top 20 singles. The last of these, a remake of late Sixties hit "Spooky", was a piece of deja vu for guitarist Cobb; he had played on the original version by Classic IV. "Spooky" was the Section's only taste of British chart success, peaking at No.48 in the autumn of '79.

Best of..., The.
Album: released on Polydor (Import) in Nov'82

Musicassette: released on Polydor (Import) in Nov'82

Boys from Doraville.
Album: released on Polydor in Sep'80 by Polydor Records. Distributed by: Polygram, Polydor

Red tape.
Album: released on Polydor in Jul'76 by Polydor Records. Distributed by: Polygram, Polydor

Underdog.

Atlantic...

Atlantic blues (Various Artists).
Album: released on Atlantic in Feb'87 by WEA Records. Distributed by: WEA

Musicassette: released on Atlantic in Feb'87 by WEA Records. Distributed by: WEA

Atlantic Blues.
Boxed set: released on Atlantic in '87 by WEA Records. Distributed by: WEA

Atlantic blues: Chicago (Various Artists).
Tracks: / Chicago blues / Hoy hoy / Play on little girl / T-bone blues special / Poor man's plea / My baby she left me / T-bone shuffle / I wonder why / Play it cool / Woke up this morning / Gambler's blues / Feel so bad / Reap what you sow / Highway 49 / Honey bee / Wang dang doodle / Dust my broom / Goin' down / Please send me someone to love / Walkin' the dog / Feel so good.

Atlantic blues: guitar (Various Artists).
Tracks: / Broke down engine / Shake 'em on down / My baby don't love me / Tall pretty woman / Blues rock / There goes the blues / Bongo boogie / Two bones and a pick / Mean old world / Let me know / It hurts to love someone / Down through the years / Okie dokie stomp / Blues nocturne / TV mama / Reconsider baby / Midnight midnight / I smell trouble / Why I sing the blues / Crosscut saw / Angels of mercy / Can't be satisfied / Flood down in Texas.

Atlantic blues: piano.
Tracks: / Yancey special / Talkin' boogie / Mournful blues / Farish street jive / Salute to pinetop / Vicksburg blues / Shave 'em dry / Frankie & Johnny / T.B.Blues / Strollin' / Boogie woogie / Tipitina / Blue sender / After midnight / Roll 'em Pete / Fore day rider / Cherry red / My chile / Cow cow blues / Albert's blues / Honky tonk train / Ray's blues / Low society / Bit of soul, A / Hey bartender / Floyd's blues / After hours blues / Junco partner / I don't know.

Atlantic blues: Vocalists (Various Artists).
Tracks: / You got to know how / Suitcase blues / Mighty tight woman / How long blues / In the evenin' / Gimmie a pigfoot / Make me a pallet on the floor / St.Louis blues / Oke-she-mokeshe-pop / I've got that feelin / Destination love / Tell a whale of a tale / Rain is a bringdown / R.B.Blues / I don't want to be president / Nothing stays the same / River's invitation / Just like a fish / Pouring water on a drowning man / Did you ever love a woman / Baby girl parts 1 & 2 / Ain't that lovin' you / It's my own tears / Cheatin' woman / I had a dream / Takin' another mans place / It's a hang up / Home ain't home at suppertime.

Atlantic history 20 original tracks (Various Artists).
Musicassette: released on WEA in Apr'83 by WEA Records. Distributed by: WEA

Atlantic jazz (Various Artists).
Tracks: / Hard times (no one knows better than i) / I want a little girl / T'aint nobody's bizness / Have you met Miss Jones / Empty bed blues / I can't dream, can't i / Any time / Crazy he calls me / Love is a word for the blues / Your mind on vacation / Whisper not / Tain't nobody's bizness if i do / Desafinado / Good life, The / Salty papa blues / Confessin' the blues / There's no you / I got it bad and that ain't good / Do nothin' till you hear from me / Moody's Mood / Don't let me be lonely tonight / Something / Lonely woman / Sing joy Spring / Way you look tonight, The / In the purple grotto / Line up / Celia / Sweet sixteen bars / In walked Bud / Delaunay's dilemma / One for fun / Night in Tunisia, A / Lazy bird / Nirvana / Blues for five reasons / Young soul / My one and only love / Sweet Georgia Brown / Einbahnstrasse / Blues 2 / Pardon my rags / Koto song / Last year's lies and tomorrow's promises / Acorn / State trooper / Think / Twist city / Broasted or fried / Wade in the water / How long blues / Comin' home baby / Russell and Eliot / Burnin coal / Listen hear / Comapared to what / Compared to what / You're the one / Jive samba / Money in the pocket / Memphis soul stew / Black mystery has been revealed / Wednesday night prayer meeting / Eventually / Cherryco / Countdown / Inflated tear, The / Nonaah / Yoruba / Tones for Joan's bones / Forest flower/sunrise / In a silent way / Standing outside / Chega De Saudade (no more blues) / Fortune smiles / Freedom jazz dance / Beaux J. Pooboo / Quadrant 4 / Beneath the earth / Homunculus / Egocentric molecules.
Album: released on Atlantic in Feb'87 by WEA Records. Distributed by: WEA

Musicassette: released on Atlantic in Feb'87 by WEA Records. Distributed by: WEA

Atlantic Jazz Aarious artists (Various Artists).
Tracks: / Bourbon Street Parade / Burgundy Street Blues / My bucket's got a hole in it / Cielito Lindo / Salty dog / Eh La Bas / Maple leaf rag, The / Eureka brass band, The / Nobody knows the way i feel this morning / Shreveport Stomp / Sing on / Shake it and break it / Tiger rag / You're driving me crazy / Lamp is low, The / Hootie blues / E-Flat boogie / Confessin' the blues / Jumpin' at the woodside / Until the real thing comes along / Undecided / Evenin' / Buster's tune / Piney brown blues / Our love is here to stay / Evidence / Bebop / Ko-Ko / Salt peanuts / Almost like me / Allen's alley / Sa-Frantic / Not really the blues / Paradox / Cheremoya / Blues way up high / Song is you, The / Topsy / Triplin' awhile / You name it / I'll be seeing you / Ain't misbehavin' / Stuffy / Django / Daphne / Perdio / Embraceable you / Four brothers / Everthing happens to me / Speedy reeds / Lydian M-1 / I can't get started / Bag's groove / This 'n' that / Giant steps / Sister salvation / White sand / Misty / Thoroughbred.
Notes: Off all the post-war labels involved in jazz, few can compete with Atlantic when it comes to the scope their recordings have covered or the number of sessions they have conducted. In its 39-year existence, Atlantic has built one of America's finest jazz catalogues. This sweeping retrospective, comprising three double and nine single albums (available as a 15-disc boxed set), is the first attempt by the company to anthologize its great wealth of material in this field. 141 cuts, recorded from the label's inception in 1947 up to this year, are arranged according to style in 12 volumes. Every major stylistic development is represented, from avant-garde to mainstream, from fusion to New Orleans. Digital re-mastering guarentees the best sound quality possible, while extensive liner notes and track-by-track credits will satisfy the most avid jazz buff. Rarely has America's classical music received such splendid treatment.
Boxed set: released on All Atlantic in Apr'87

Atlantic masters startracks,Part 1 Various artists (Various Artists).
Album: released on Atlantic in Jun'80 by WEA Records. Distributed by: WEA

Atlantic masters startracks, Part2 Various artists (Various Artists).
Album: released on Atlantic in Jun'80 by WEA Records. Distributed by: WEA

Atlantic Records history of r&b vocal groups Various artists (Various Artists).
Album: released on Atlantic in Mar'84 by WEA Records. Distributed by: WEA

Atlantic Rhythm and Blues 1947-1974 (Various Artists).
Notes: Box set of **seven** double albums & cassettes **186** tracks
Album: released on Atlantic in Jul'86 by WEA Records. Distributed by: WEA

Musicassette: released on Atlantic in Jul'86 by WEA Records. Distributed by: WEA

Atlantic rhythm & blues, 1947-74 various artists (Various Artists).
Tracks: / Lowe groovin' / That old black magic / Annie Laurie / Midnight special / Applejack, The / Drinkin wine spo-dee-0-dee / Cole slaw / So long / I'll get along somehow (parts 1&2) / Hey little girl / Mardi gras in New Orleans / Tee nah nah / Anytime, anyplace, anywhere / Teardrops from my eyes / One monkey don't stop the show / Don't you know i love you / Shouldn't i know / Chil is on, The / Chains of love / Fool, fool, fool / One mint julep / Wheel of fortune / Sweet sixteen / 5-10-15 Hours / Ting-a-ling / Gator's groove / Daddy daddy / Midnight hour, The / Beggar for your kisses, A / Mama, he treats your daughter mean / Good lovin / Wild wild young men / Mess around / Hush hush / Soul on fire / Money honey / Such a night / Tipitina / White Christmas / Honey love / Watcha gonna do / Shake, rattle & roll / Sh'boom / Jam up / Tommorow night / Tweedlee dee / I got a woman / Door is still open, The / Flip flop & fly / Fool for you, A / This little girl of mine / Play it fair / Adorable / Smokey Joe's cafe / Ruby baby / In paradise / Chicken and the hawk, The / Devil or angel / Drown in my own tears / Hallelujah, i love her so / Jim Dandy / Down in Mexico / Corrine Corrina / Treasure of love / Love, love, love / It's too late / Lonely avenue / Since i met you baby / Lucky lips / Without love (there is nothing) / Fools fall in love / Midnight special train / Empty arms / C.C Rider / Betty & Dupree / What am i livin for? / Hang my rock and roll shoes / Yakety yak / Lover's question / I cried a tear / Right time,The / What'd say (parts 1&2) / There goes my baby / There goes my baby / Along came Jones / Let the good times roll / Poison ivy / Dance with me / Just for a thrill / This magic moment / Save the last dance for me / Shopping for clothes / Spanish harlem / Young boy blues / Stand by me / Gee whiz / Saved / Just out of reach (of my two open arms) / Little Egypt / Amor / Last night / I'm blue (the gong-gong song) / You don't miss your water / I found a love / Cry to me / Don't play that song (you lied) / Green onions / Up on the roof / See see rider / I (what have nothing) / If you need me / These arms of mine / Hello stranger / On Broadway / Just one look / Do the mashed potatoes (parts 1&2) / Land of 1000 dances / Walkin' the dog / Release me / Mercy, mercy / Under the boardwalk / I love him, And / Hold what you've got / Mr. Pitiful / Baby i'm yours / Teasin' you / I've been loving you too long / In the midnight hour / See-saw / Respect / You don't know like i know / When a man loves a woman / Hold on, i'm comin' / Cool jerk / Neighbor, neighbor / Land of 1000 dances / Knock on wood / Try a little tenderness / Mustang Sally / When something is wrong with my baby / Sweet soul music / Soul man / I never loved a man (the way i loved you) / Do right woman-do right man / Show me / Tramp / Funky Broadway / Hip hug-her / Respect / You make me feel like a natural woman / Soul finger / Baby i love you / Skinny legs and all / Chain of fools / I'm in love / Memphis soul stew / Sittin' on the dock of the bay / Tighten up / Slip away / Think / First time ever i saw your face, The / Take a letter, Maria / Rainy night in Georgia / Ghetto, The / Turn back the hands of time / Compared to what / Don't play that song (you lied) / Groove me / Patches / Funky Nassau (parts 1&2) / Thin line between love and hate / Rock steady / Youv'e got a friend / Clean up woman / Could it be i'm falling in love / Killing me softly with his song / Where is the love / I'll be around / Feel lide makin' love / Mighty love / Love won't let me wait.
Notes: 38 years ago, a gradute student in philosophy named Ahmet Ertegun decided to supplement his allowance by making and selling a few records. What began as a part-time avocation quickly grew into a full-time enterprise, as Atlantic became an aggressive, independent force in contemporary music. From the outset, Atlantic was a pioner in the new musical hybrid known as rhythm and blues. By the mid-1950's, it had become the premiere R&R label, releasing records that were to have a profound impact on the course of contemporary music. This album is an incredible labor of love, it is a collection which will be cherished by serious collectors and casual listers alike. This extraordinary compilation of 186 Classic songs is available as a complete box set (14 records), and features in-depth liner notes detailing the history of each recording. Documenting the first 27 yearsof Atlantic Black Music, it is the definitive history of a musical revolution.
Album: released on Atlantic in Apr'87 by WEA Records. Distributed by: WEA

Musicassette: released on Atlantic in Apr'87 by WEA Records. Distributed by: WEA

Compact disc: released on Atlantic in Apr'87 by WEA Records. Distributed by: WEA

Atlantic rhythm & blues, 1947-1974, Vol. 1 various artists (Various Artists).

Atlantic rhythm & blues, 1947-1974, Vol. 2 various artists (Various Artists).
Compact disc: released on Atlantic in Apr'87 by WEA Records. Distributed by: WEA

Atlantic rhythm & blues, 1947-1974, Vol. 3 various artists (Various Artists).
Compact disc: released on Atlantic in Apr'87 by WEA Records. Distributed by: WEA

Atlantic rhythm & blues, 1947-1974, Vol. 4 various artists (Various Artists).
Compact disc: released on Atlantic in Apr'87 by WEA Records. Distributed by: WEA

Atlantic rhythm & blues, 1947-1974, Vol. 5 various artists (Various Artists).
Compact disc: released on Atlantic in Apr'87 by WEA Records. Distributed by: WEA

Atlantic rhythm & blues, 1947-1974, Vol. 6 various artists (Various Artists).
Compact disc: released on Atlantic in Apr'87 by WEA Records. Distributed by: WEA

Atlantic rhythm & blues, 1947-1974, Vol. 7 various artists (Various Artists).
Compact disc: released on Atlantic in Apr'87 by WEA Records. Distributed by: WEA

Atlantic Soul Classics (Various Artists).
Tracks: / Sweet soul music / In the midnight hour / Knock on wood / Soul man / Respect / See Saw / Everybody needs somebody to love / Soul finger / Stand by me / B-A-B-Y / Under the boardwalk / Tramp / Green onions / When a man loves a woman / Tribute to a king, A / Dock of the bay, The (Sittin' on).
Album: released on Atlantic in May'87 by WEA Records. Distributed by: WEA

Musicassette: released on Atlantic in May'87 by WEA Records. Distributed by: WEA

Atlantic Soul Classics Various Artists (Various Artists).
Compact disc: released on Atlantic in Jul'87 by WEA Records. Distributed by: WEA

Album: released on Atlantic in Jul'87 by WEA Records. Distributed by: WEA

Musicassette: released on Atlantic in Jul'87 by WEA Records. Distributed by: WEA

Atlantics

Passion Blue.
Tracks: / Passion blue / 7 roads to heaven.
Single (7"): released on Delightful in May'86 by Delightful Records. Distributed by: Red Rhino

Atlantic Starr

Biographical Details: Atanitc Starr, an American funk band featuring lead singer Sharon Bryant, had a small chart single in the UK in 1978 with their disco hit 'Gimme Your Lovin'. Since then they have been increasing their status in the US black charts, most notably with 1982's 'Circles'. This single also reached no,38 on the Billboard pop chart an area that they would penetrate far more frequently wre it not for the fact that American radio's format/crossover system tends to ghetto-ize black soul music.(BM 84)

4-leaf clover.
Single (7"): released on A&M in Oct'83 by A&M Records. Distributed by: Polygram

Single (12"): released on A&M in Oct'83 by A&M Records. Distributed by: Polygram

All in the name of love.
Tracks: / One lover at a time / You belong with me / Females / Don't take me for granted / Always / Let the sun in / Thankful / All in the name of love / My mistake / Interlude.
Notes: This recording is a digital one.
Album: released on Warner Bros. in Apr'87 by Warner Bros Records. Distributed by: WEA

Musicassette: released on Warner Bros. in Apr'87 by Warner Bros Records. Distributed by: WEA

Compact disc: released on Warner Bros. in May'86 by Warner Bros Records. Distributed by: WEA

Always.
Tracks: / Always / Always (inst).
Single (7"): released on Warner Bros. in 30 May'87 by Warner Bros Records. Distributed by: WEA

Single (12"): released on Warner Bros. in 30 May'87 by Warner Bros Records. Distributed by: WEA

As the band turns.
Album: released on A&M in Jun'85 by A&M Records. Distributed by: Polygram

Musicassette: released on A&M in Jun'85 by A&M Records. Distributed by: Polygram

Freak-a-ristic.
Single (7"): released on A&M in Apr'85 by A&M Records. Distributed by: Polygram

Single (12"): released on A&M in Apr'85 by A&M Records. Distributed by: Polygram

If your heart isn't in it.
Tracks: / If your heart isn't in it / Let's start it over / Stand up.
Single (7"): released on A&M in May'86 by A&M Records. Distributed by: Polygram

Single (12"): released on A&M in May'86 by A&M Records. Distributed by: Polygram

One love.
Single (7"): released on A&M in Aug'85 by A&M Records. Distributed by: Polygram

Single (12"): released on A&M in Aug'85 by A&M Records. Distributed by: Polygram

One lover at a time.
Tracks: / I'm in love.
Single (7"): released on Warner Brothers in Aug'87 by Warner Bros Records. Distributed by: WEA

Single (12"): released on Warner Brothers in Aug'87 by Warner Bros Records. Distributed by: WEA

Secret lovers.
Tracks: / Secret lovers / When love calls.
Single (7"): released on A&M in Feb'86 by A&M Records. Distributed by: Polygram

Single (12"): released on A&M in Feb'86 by A&M Records. Distributed by: Polygram

Secret lovers - The very best of....
Notes: Inc: Silver shadow/Circles/Touch a four feather clover/If your heart isn't in it/Secret lovers. 12 tracks in all. 2 extra tracks on cassette.
Album: released on A&M in Oct'86 by A&M Records. Distributed by: Polygram

Musicassette: released on A&M in Oct'86 by A&M Records. Distributed by: Polygram

Silver shadow.
Tracks: / Silver shadow / Cool calm collected / Cool calm collected (LP version remix) / Cool calm collected (US club mix).
Single (7"): released on A&M in Aug'86 by A&M Records. Distributed by: Polygram

Single (12"): released on A&M in Aug'86 by A&M Records. Distributed by: Polygram

Yours forever.
Tracks: / Yours forever / Touch a four leaf clover / More more more / I want your love / Second to none / Island dreams / Who could love you better / More time for me / Tryin'.
Album: released on A&M in Nov'85 by A&M Records. Distributed by: Polygram

Musicassette: released on A&M in Nov'85 by A&M Records. Distributed by: Polygram

Atlantis

Atlantis.
Album: released on Vertigo in '73 by Phonogram Records. Distributed by: Polygram

Musicassette: released on Vertigo in '73 by Phonogram Records. Distributed by: Polygram

Atmosfear

Biographical Details: Atmosfear, an all-male British disco band, hit no.46 on the charts in 1979 with 'Dancing In Outer Space'. Subsequent club-oriented singles hace included 'Invasion', 'Motivation' and 'What Do We Do'.

First/Fourmost.
Album: released on Elite in Jan'84. Distributed by: PRT

Interplay.
Single (12"): released on Elite in Oct'81. Distributed by: PRT

Invasion.
Single (7"): released on MCA in Jul'81 by MCA Records. Distributed by: Polygram, MCA

Single (12"): released on MCA in Jul'81 by MCA Records. Distributed by: Polygram, MCA

Personal column.
Tracks: / Personal column / Dancing in outer space.
Single (12"): released on Elite in Mar'86. Distributed by: PRT

Telepathy.
Single (12"): released on Elite in Dec'84. Distributed by: PRT

What do we do.
Single (7"): released on Chrysalis in Aug'83 by Chrysalis Records. Distributed by: CBS

Single (12"): released on Chrysalis in Aug'83 by Chrysalis Records. Distributed by: CBS

When tonight is over.
Single (7"): released on Elite in Jun'84. Distributed by: PRT

Single (12"): released on Elite in Mar'84. Distributed by: PRT

Xtra special.
Single (12"): released on Elite in Apr'82. Distributed by: PRT

Atmospheres

Atmospheres Software compilation (Various Artists).
Album: released on CBS(Import) in Sep'86 by CBS Records. Distributed by: Conifer, Discovery, Swift

Musicassette: released on Epic in Sep'86 by CBS Records. Distributed by: CBS

Atomcraft

Conductors of noize.
Album: released on Neat in Jul'87 by Neat Records. Distributed by: Pinnacle, Neat

Future warriors.
Album: released on Neat in Sep'85 by Neat Records. Distributed by: Pinnacle, Neat

Atomic Rooster

Biographical Details: British group Atomic Rooster were formed at the beginning of the seventies. Vincent Crane had played keyboards on 'Fire' the 1968 no.1 by the Crazy World Of Arthur Brown. The new band's debut LP had just one week on the charts in 1970 at no.49. Their next set 'Death Walks Behind You' hit the top 20 the following year to be quickly succeeded by 'In Hearing Of Atomic Rooster'. 1971 also yielded two hit 45's :'Tomorrow Night' reached no.11, to be bettered by 'The Devil's Answer' at no.4. However, many other bands were also doing the same kind of riff-laden rock material, and Atomic Rooster floundered. Cann and Hammond went on to form an unsuccessful band called Hard Stuff.(BM 84)

Atomic Rooster.
Tracks: / They took control of you / She's my woman / He did it again / Where's the show / In the shadows / Do you know who's looking for you / Don't lose your mind / Watch out I can't stand it / Lost in space.
Album: released on Charisma in Oct'86 by Virgin Records. Distributed by: EMI

Devils' answer.
Single (7"): released on Old Gold in Jun'84 by Old Gold Records. Distributed by: Lightning, Jazz Music, Spartan, Counterpoint

Headline news.
Album: released on Towerbell in Jun'83 by Towerbell Records. Distributed by: EMI

Musicassette: released on Towerbell in Jun'83 by Towerbell Records. Distributed by: EMI

Home to roost.
Tracks: / Death walks behind you / V.U.G. / Seven streets / sleeping for years / Can't take no more / Nobody else / Friday 13th / And so to bed / Broken wings / Before tomorrow / Banstead / Winter / Breakthrough / Descision/Indescision / Devils answer / Spoonful of bromide helps the pulse rate go down, A / Black snake / Head inthe sky / Spoonfull of bromide helps the pulse rate go down, A / Tomorrow night / Break the ice.
Compact disc: released on Raw Power in Apr'87 Distributed by: Pinnacle

Double Album: released on Raw Power in Dec'86 Distributed by: Pinnacle

Musicassette: released on Raw Power in Dec'86. Distributed by: Pinnacle

Double Album: released on Mooncrest in '83 by Mooncrest Records. Distributed by: PRT Distribution

Atom Kraft

Queen of Death.
Single (12"): released on Neat in Oct'86 by Neat Records. Distributed by: Pinnacle, Neat

At Pepper's Lounge...

At Pepper's Lounge,Chicago Vol.2 Various artists (Various Artists).
Tracks: / Off the wall / Pepper's other thing / You're so fine / Rocker / Pepper's Boogie Woogie / How long can this thing go on? / These ole cotton pickin' blues / Left me alone / Every day I have the Blues / Dynamite.
Notes: Personnel: Featuring Little Walter, Ear Hooker, Louis Myers, Dave Myers, Fred Bellow, Eddie Taylor, John 'Big Moose' Walker, Pau Askell, Geno Skaggs, Little Mac Roosevel Shaw, B. B. King Junior (Andre Odom). Recorded: A fabulous live recording - early 1960's in Chicago, Illinois.
Album: released on Rarities in Apr'81

Attacco Decente

Trojan horse.
Single (7"): released on Timber in Mar'84. Distributed by: ILA Distribution

Attack

Murder in the subway.
Single (7"): released on No Future in Sep'82 by No Future Records. Distributed by: Pinnacle Rough Trade, Cartel

Ooin' in the moonlight.
Single (7"): released on Towerbell in Jul'82 by Towerbell Records. Distributed by: EMI

Todays generation.
Single (7"): released on No Future in Jul'82 by No Future Records. Distributed by: Pinnacle, Rough Trade, Cartel

Zombies.
Album: released on No Future in May'83 by No Future Records. Distributed by: Pinnacle, Rough Trade, Cartel

Attacker

Battle at Helms Deep.
Album: released on Roadrunner (Dutch) in Sep'85. Distributed by: Pinnacle

Attack From Downunda

Attack from Downunda (Various Artists).
Album: released on Receiver in Sep'86 by Receiver Records. Distributed by: Pinnacle

Attaco Decente

United kingdom of america.
Album: released on All Or Nothing in Nov'86. Distributed by: Red Rhino

Atterson, Alex

Pushing the business on.
Tracks: / Johnny alleluia / Three masts / O Billy do ye hear that bell / Nelson Gardens / Hawthorn white / Billy medals / Two corbies, The / Reaper, The / Wimbledon wag / In the wee midnight hour / Pass the bottle round.
Notes: Alex Atterson is a name well known of the British and European folk scene. One side of third record features Alex singing and playing some of the songs and tunes from his current club reportoire, the other showcases six of Alex's settings to music of works by the celebrated Cornish Poet, Charles Causley.
Album: released on Plant Life in Nov'81. Distributed by: Roots

At The Cavern

At the cavern (Various Artists).
Tracks: / Keep on rolling / She's sure the girl I love / You've really got a hold on me / Everybody loves a loser / Devoted to you / You better move on / Somebody to love / Little Queenie / Diddley Diddley daddy / Bring it on home to me / Skinny Minnie / Jezebel / Im talking about you / Little Egypt / Don't start running away / Zip-a-dee-doo-dah / Reelin' and rockin'.
Notes: Artists include Dave Berry & The Cruisers/Beryl Marsden/The Big Three/The Fortunes/Heinz Bern/Elliott & The Fen men/The Marauders/The Dennisons/Lee Curtis & The All-Stars
Album: released on See For Miles in Jul'86 by See For Miles Records. Distributed by: Pinnacle

At The Hop

At the hop 15 rockin million sellers of the 50's (Various Artists).
Album: released on Pickwick in Mar'87 by Pickwick Records. Distributed by: Pickwick Distribution, Prism Leisure Distribution, Lugtons

Musicassette: released on Pickwick in Mar'87 by Pickwick Records. Distributed by: Pickwick Distribution, Prism Leisure Distribution, Lugtons

At The Rockhouse

At the Rockhouse Vol.10 Various artists (Various Artists).
Album: released on Eagle (West Germany) in Feb'84 by Bear Family Records. Distributed by: Stage One

Attila The Stockbroker

Cocktails (EP).
Single (7"): released on Cherry Red in Oct'82 by Cherry Red Records. Distributed by: Pinnacle

Libyan students from hell.
Tracks: / Libyan students from Hell / I'm so miserable / Ballad of Comrade Enver, The / Flapping mole! / Radio rap / Airstrip one / Green fields of France, The / Another country / Glanendes Empire.
Album: released on Plastic Head in Feb'87. Distributed by: Pinnacle, Rough Trade, Cartel

Radio rap.
Tracks: / Radio rap! / Everytime I eat vegetables...let the drain take the strain / Vomit on a viking / Take a leak on a Greek / Albanian rifle poem / Nigel want's to join the S.A.S / I don't tak o pop stars / Love and herpes / Letter from Nigel's mum, A / Russians versus the tetley bitermen / Poetry requiem.
Single (12"): released on Cherry Red in Aug'84 by Cherry Red Records. Distributed by: Pinnacle

Ranting at the nation.
Tracks: / Awayday / Night I slept with seething wells, The / Contributory negligence / Nigel wants to go to C&A's / Albanian football / Perils of stealing half a bottle of wine, The / They must be Russians / Russians in the DHSS / Russians in MacDonalds / Oracle, The / Death in Bromley / Band & a Wimpey, A / Nigel wants to go and see Depeche Mode / Russians at the Henley regatta / Russsians on the centre court / Fifth column / Fall of King Zog, The / Holiday in Albania / Burn it down / England are back (Luxembourg where are you) / Where you goin' with that flounder? / Hands off our halibuts / Flappin' in the wind / Gentlemen o the wrist / Eros products commercial / Spencers croft cat, The (dead cat strut) / Very silly East European propaganda station / Fall of King Zog, The (reprise).
Notes: All tracks on this album by John Baine and Published by Cherry Red Music Limited.
Album: released on Cherry Red in Apr'83 by Cherry Red Records. Distributed by: Pinnacle

Sawdust and empire.
Tracks: / March of the Levellers / Sawdust & empire / Alone in the Sidco / Recession / Spare a thought / Nigel's revenge / Holiday in Albania / Boadicea uber alles / Factory gods / Midas the grand / Ghosts of the levellers.
Notes: Original sound recording made by Anagram Records-a division of Cherry Red Records Limited.
Album: released on Anagram in Mar'84 by Cherry Red Records. Distributed by: Pinnacle

Attitude Adjustment

American paranoia.
Album: released on Pusmort in Jan'87

Attractions

Mad about the wrong boy.
Album: released on Demon in Jun'84 by Demon Records. Distributed by: Pinnacle

Musicassette: released on F-Beat in Aug'80 by F-Beat Records. Distributed by: RCA, Pinnacle

Attrition

Action and reaction.
Musicassette: released on Adventures In Reality in Jul'84 by Backs Records. Distributed by: Cartel

Attrition of reason, (The).
Album: released on Third Mind in Aug'84 by Third Mind Records. Distributed by: Backs, Cartel Distribution

Death house.
Musicassette: released on Adventures In Reality in Oct'84 by Backs Records. Distributed by: Cartel

Album: released on Hamster in Jun'87 by Hamster Records And Tapes. Distributed by: Backs, Cartel

In the realm of the hungry ghosts.
Album: released on Third Mind in Jun'86 by Third Mind Records. Distributed by: Backs, Cartel Distribution

Monkey in a bin.
Single (12"): released on Uniton Records in Mar'84. Distributed by: Cartel

Shrinkwrap.
Single (12"): released on Third Mind in May'85 by Third Mind Records. Distributed by: Backs, Cartel Distribution

Smiling, at the Hypergonder Club.
Album: released on Third Mind in Nov'85 by Third Mind Records. Distributed by: Backs, Cartel Distribution

Voice of God, (The).
Single (12"): released on Third Mind in Dec'84 by Third Mind Records. Distributed by: Backs, Cartel Distribution

Atwell, Winifred

Around the world of ....
Musicassette: released on Decca in Oct'72 by Decca Records. Distributed by: Polygram

It's ragtime.
Tracks: / Raggin' the scale / Entertainer, The / Kitten on the keys / Glad rag / Russian rag / Jubilee rag / Doll dance / Maple leaf rag / Black and white rag / Down yonder / Hunting rag / Flirtation rag / South Rampant Street parade / Grizzly bear rag / Dizzy fingers / Vamp, The / Rialto ripples / Steamboat rag / Flapper rag / Temptation rag.
Album: released on RCA in '84 by RCA Records. Distributed by: RCA, Roots, Swift, Wellard, Chris, I & B, Solomon & Peres Distribution

Musicassette: released on RCA in '84 by RCA Records. Distributed by: RCA, Roots, Swift, Wellard, Chris, I & B, Solomon & Peres Distribution

Piano party.
Tracks: / Poor people of Paris, The / Plink plank plunk / Flirtation waltz / Maple leaf rag / Britannia rag / Left bank, The / Cross hands boogie / Twelfth Street rag / Coronation rag / Jubilee rag / Port au Prince / Summer of the seventeenth doll / Dixie boogie / Black and white rag.
Album: released on Decca (Elite) in May'84 by Decca Records. Distributed by: Polygram, IMS

Seven rags, seven boogies.
Album: released on Eclipse in Oct'75 by Decca Records. Distributed by: Polygram

Winifred Atwell.
Tracks: / Cross hands boogie / Dixie boogie / Tattoo samba / Swannee river boogie / Big Ben boogie / Bounce the boogie / Bumble bee boogie / Hamps boogie.
Album: released on Philips Import in May'83

Musicassette: released on Philips Import in May'83

Winifred Atwell plays 50 all-time greats.
Tracks: / On your toes / It's D lovely / I won't dance / Goody goody / Shall we dance / April in Portugal / Wish you were here / C'est magnifique / I talk to the trees / Cherry pink & apple blossom white / Bewitched / I couldn't sleep a wink / Bill / Can't help lovin' that man of mine / Californ-I-Ay / Falling in love with love / It's a grand night for singing / Best things in life are free, The / Look for the silver lining / Lady is a tramp, The / I love Paris / My heart belongs to daddy / How high the moon / I whistle a happy tune / People will say we're in love / Bluebird of happiness / Harry Lime theme, The / Life is just a bowl of cherries / Blueberry hill / It might as well be spring / Young and foolish / Room five hundred and four / Sea, The / Darn ya smile, The / Smoke gets in your eyes / Lovely to look at / Long ago (and far away) / Dearly beloved / Good morning / June is bustin' out all over / Pedro the fisherman / We'll gather lilacs / Make believe / How are things in Glocco Morra / This is my lovely day / Some enchanted evening.
Album: released on President in Nov'83 by President Records. Distributed by: Taylors, Spartan

Musicassette: released on President in Jan'84 by President Records. Distributed by: Taylors, Spartan

Winifred Atwell's piano party.
Tracks: / Carolina in the morning / Get out and under the moon / Sleepy time gal / Chicago / Cecilia / My sweetie went away / Sweet Georgia Brown / Broadway melody / Lullaby of Broadway / Bye bye blues / Let's fall in love / After you've gone / I cried for you / By the light of the silvery moon / I'm sorry I made you cry / Dark Town strutters ball / Alexander's ragtime band / Bill Bailey won't you please come home? / My blue heaven / Am I blue? / Some of these days / It had to be you / I'm sitting on top of the world / Crying for the Carolines / Tiptoe through the tulips / Me and my shadow / Them there eyes / Five foot two, eyes of blue / Dinah / A tisket, a tasket / If you were the only girl in the world / I don't know why.
Album: released on Flashback in Nov'85 by Flashback Records/PRT Records. Distributed by: Mainline, PRT

Musicassette: released on Flashback in Nov'85 by Flashback Records/PRT Records. Distributed by: Mainline, PRT

Atwood, Margaret

Poetry and voice of Margaret Atwood.
Musicassette: released on Caedmon(USA) in Aug'79 by Caedmon (USA) Records. Distributed by: Gower, Taylors, Discovery

Auden, W.H.

Four twentieth century poets.
Tracks: / Homage to Clio / The shield of Achilles / Sext / Nones / Vespers / Compline / Metaloque to the magic flute / The hard question / Song / Lady weeping at the crossroads / The more loving one / A walk after dark / The Wanderer / First things first / Alonso to Ferdinand.
Double musicassette: released on Argo in May'85 by Decca Records. Distributed by: Polygram

Audience

House on the hill, The.
Tracks: / Jackdaw / You're not smiling / I had a dream / Raviole / Eye to eye / I put a spell on you / House on the hill, The.
Album: released on Charisma in Sep'83 by Virgin Records. Distributed by: EMI

Musicassette: released on Charisma in Sep'83 by Virgin Records. Distributed by: EMI

Audio

Love on your mind.
Single (7"): released on Rex in Apr'83 by Decca

Audion Sampler

Audion sampler Various artists (Various Artists).
Compact disc: by Pacific Records (USA). Distributed by: Atlantic

Audio/Visual

Audio/Visual Abstract no.6 (Various Artists).
Album: released on Sweatbox in Mar'86 by Sweatbox Records. Distributed by: Rough Trade, Cartel

Auerbach, Loren

After the long night (Auerbach, Loren/Bert Jansch with Presence).
Album: released on Christabel in Mar'85 by Gerard Management. Distributed by: Projection

Musicassette: released on Christabel in Mar'85 by Gerard Management. Distributed by: Projection

Playing the game.
Tracks: / Carousel / Weeping willow blues / Give me love / I can't go back / Smiling faces / Yarrow / Playing the game / Is it real / Sorrow / Days and nights.
Album: released on Christabel in Oct'85 by Gerard Management. Distributed by: Projection

Musicassette: released on Christabel in Oct'85 by Gerard Management. Distributed by: Projection

Aufray, Hughes

Chante Dylan.
Album: released on Barclay in Feb'77 by Decca Records. Distributed by: Polygram, Discovery, Conifer, IMS, Swift

Auf Wiedersehn Pet

Auf wiedersehn pet TV soundtrack.
Album: released on Towerbell in Jan'84 by Towerbell Records. Distributed by: EMI

Musicassette: released on Towerbell in Jan'84 by Towerbell Records. Distributed by: EMI

Auger, Brian

Encore (Auger, Brian & Julie Tippetts).
Tracks: / Spirit / Don't let me be misunderstood / Git up / Freedom highway / Future pilot / Rope ladder to the moon / No time to live / Nothing will be as it was / Lock all the gates.
Album: released on Warner Brothers in Apr'78 by Warner Bros Records. Distributed by: WEA

Here and now.
Tracks: / Hurricane, The / Call me / Happiness is just around the bend / Downtown hookup / Seeker, The / They say nothing lasts forever / Let's keep this love together / Heart of the hunter.
Notes: Jazz organist Brian Auger was one of the most respected musicians of the 60's R&B scene. Together with Julie Driscoll he led the group The Trinity which spawned the classic 'This wheel's on fire'. This new album recorded in Italy during 1984 features contemporary dance disco/funk music with vocals reminiscent of Level 42.
Album: released on Polydor (France) in Jul'85. Distributed by: Polygram

Musicassette: released on Polydor (France) in Jul'85. Distributed by: Polygram

Jam sessions (Auger, Brian/Jimmy Page/Sonny Boy Williamson).
Album: released on Charly in '82 by Charly Records. Distributed by: Charly, Cadillac

London 1964/1967 (Auger, Brian & Julie Driscoll).
Album: released on Charly in Jan'77 by Charly Records. Distributed by: Charly, Cadillac

Augins, Charles

Baby I need your loving/Baby dub.
Single (7"): released on Malaco in Nov'82 by Malaco Records. Distributed by: Charly

Single (12"): released on Malaco in Nov'82 by Malaco Records. Distributed by: Charly

Augustine, Nat

Ego.
Tracks: / Ego / I'll rescue you.
Single (7"): released on A&M in Aug'86 by A&M Records. Distributed by: Polygram

Single (12"): released on A&M in Aug'86 by A&M Records. Distributed by: Polygram

Summer is here again.
Single (7"): released on Debut in Jul'85 by Skratch Music. Distributed by: PRT

Single (12"): released on Debut in Jul'85 by Skratch Music. Distributed by: PRT

Augustin, Nat

That girl.
Single (7"): released on Breakout in Aug'87 by A&M Records. Distributed by: Polygram

Single (12"): released on Breakout in Apr'87 by A&M Records. Distributed by: Polygram

August, Joseph

Rock my soul (August, Joseph 'Mr. Google Eyes').
Album: released on Route 66 in Oct'86

Auld, George

George Auld Vol 1 1945.
Album: released on Musicraft in Apr'79

Auld, Georgie

By George.
Album: released on Swinghouse in '84. Distributed by: Jazz Music Distribution, Swift Distribution, Chris Wellard Distribution

Homage.
Album:

I've got you under my skin.
Tracks: / I've got you under my skin / S'posin / I cover the waterfront / I didn't know what time it was / Stairway to the stars, A / Body and soul / I don't stand a ghost of a chance with you / Take care / Smoke gets in your eyes / All the things you are / Someone to watch over me.
Album: released on Jasmine in Feb'83 by Jasmine Records. Distributed by: Counterpoint, Lugtons, Taylor, H.R., Wellard, Chris, Swift, Cadillac

Jump Georgie jump.
Tracks: / Short circuit / Mandrake root / Poinciana / Jivin with the jug / Yesterdays / I'll always be in love with you / Stomping at the Savoy / Sentimental journey / Jump Georgie jump / I'm always chasing rainbows / I can't get started / Taps Miller / Concerto for tenor.
Album: released on Hep in Jan'83 by H.R. Taylor Records. Distributed by: Jazz Music, Cadillac Music, JSU, Taylors, Wellard, Chris, Zodiac, Swift, Fast Forward

Auld Meal Mill

Auld meal mill (Various Artists).
Notes: John Mearns and others
Album: released on Ross in Jun'86 by Ross Records. Distributed by: Ross Distribution, Roots Distribution

Musicassette: released on Ross in Jun'86 by Ross Records. Distributed by: Ross Distribution, Roots Distribution

Auldridge, Mike

An old dog.
Album: released on Flying Fish (USA) in Feb'79 by Flying Fish Records (USA). Distributed by: Roots, Projection

Dobro.
Tracks: / Hillbilly hula / Tennessee stud / It's over / It's over / Pickaway / Rolling fog / Dobro island train 451-2 / Take me / Greensleeves / Silver threads / Rockbottom / Jamboree / House of the rising sun.
Album: released on Sonet in '74 by Sonet Records. Distributed by: PRT

Mike Auldridge.
Album: released on Flying Fish (USA) in Feb'79 by Flying Fish Records (USA). Distributed by: Roots, Projection

Auld Triangle

Auld Triangle.
Tracks: / Old miner, The / Do you love an apple / Wee room, The / No man's land / Saturday's cowboys / Ryebuck shearer / Coal black faces / Now I'm easy / May, and might never / Leaving Nancy / B.U.D.G.I.E..

Album: released on Castle Studio in '81 by Castle Studio Records

Aungier, Cliff

Full moon.
Album: released on ALP in Nov'84. Distributed by: Projection

Au Pairs

Inconvenience/Pretty boys.
Single (7"): released on Human in Jul'81. Distributed by: Roots, Stage One

Musicassette: released on Human in Jul'81. Distributed by: Roots, Stage One

It's obvious/Diet.
Single (7"): released on Human in Nov'80. Distributed by: Roots, Stage One

Live in Berlin.
Album: released on AKA in Aug'83. Distributed by: Stage One, IDS, Indies, Cartel

Playing with a different sex.
Album: released on Human in May'81. Distributed by: Roots, Stage One

Sense and sensuality.
Album: released on Kamera in Aug'82

You.
Single (7"): released on 021 in Jun'81 by 021 Records. Distributed by: Spartan

Auracle

Auracle.
Album: released on Chrysalis in Mar'78 by Chrysalis Records. Distributed by: CBS

Musicassette: released on Chrysalis in '79 by Chrysalis Records. Distributed by: CBS

City slickers.
Album: by Chrysalis Records. Distributed by: CBS

Musicassette: released on Chrysalis in '79 by Chrysalis Records. Distributed by: CBS

Aural Exciters

Chinese rap.
Single (12"): released on Move in Apr'83 by Charly Records. Distributed by: Charly Distribution, Fast Forward Distribution, Cartel Distribution

Aural John

Reason.
Single (12"): released on Joint Effort in May'83

Aural wax

Aural wax (Various Artists).
Album: released on Aura in Jan'86 by Hollywood Nites Distribution. Distributed by: Pinnacle

Album: released on Aura in Feb'80 by Hollywood Nites Distribution. Distributed by: Pinnacle

Aurora

I'll be your fantasy/If I really knew ....
Single (7"): released on Aurora in Mar'83. Distributed by: Neon Distribution

Aurra

Happy feeeling.
Single (7"): released on 10 in Jul'85 by 10 Records. Distributed by: Virgin, EMI

Single (12"): released on 10 in Jul'85 by 10 Records. Distributed by: Virgin, EMI

Like I like it.
Tracks: / You and me tonight / Keep on dancing / Hooked on you / Talking in your sleep / Bedtime story / Like I like it / Living inside yourself / Happy feelings / I'll keep waiting / I love myself.
Album: released on 10 in Sep'86 by 10 Records. Distributed by: Virgin, EMI

Musicassette: released on 10 in Sep'86 by 10 Records. Distributed by: Virgin, EMI

Album: released on 10 in Jul'85 by 10 Records. Distributed by: Virgin, EMI

Musicassette: released on 10 in Jul'85 by 10 Records. Distributed by: Virgin, EMI

Single (7"): released on 10 in Apr'85 by 10 Records. Distributed by: Virgin, EMI

Single (12"): released on 10 in Apr'85 by 10 Records. Distributed by: Virgin, EMI

Like I like it (single).
Tracks: / Like I like it (remix) / I love myself.
Single (7"): released on 10 in Jun'86 by 10 Records. Distributed by: Virgin, EMI

Little love, (A).
Single (12"): released on Battersea in Jun'82 by Battersea Records. Distributed by: Pinnacle

Live and let live.
Album: released on Salsoul in Mar'83

Send your love.
Album: released on Salsoul in Jun'81

You and me tonight (midnight mix).
Single (12"): released on 10 in May'86 by 10 Records. Distributed by: Virgin, EMI

You & me tonight.
Tracks: / You and me tonight / You and me tonight (inst) / Keep on dancing.
Single (7"): released on 10 in Apr'86 by 10 Records. Distributed by: Virgin, EMI

Single (12"): released on 10 in Apr'86 by 10 Records. Distributed by: Virgin, EMI

Ausberg Orchestra

Accordion in Concert.
Tracks: / Sinfonietta concertante / Dorische suite / Scherzino / Sinfonietta / Burleske auf eine speilmannweise.
Album: released on Accordion Record Club in Jul'86 by Accordion Record Club Records. Distributed by: Accordion Record Club

Ausgang

Head on.
Tracks: / Head on / Sink into your luck / If that's your bat / I'm leaving you.
Single (12"): released on Criminal Damage in Dec'84 by Criminal Damage Records. Distributed by: Backs, Cartel

Here it comes.
Single (12"): released on Heavy Metal in Oct'85 by FM-Revolver Records. Distributed by: EMI

Manipulate.
Album: released on FM in Jan'86 by FM-Revolver Records. Distributed by: EMI

Solid glass spine.
Single (7"): released on Criminal Damage in Jun'84 by Criminal Damage Records. Distributed by: Backs, Cartel

Teaching of web (4 track EP).
Single (12"): released on Criminal Damage in Feb'84 by Criminal Damage Records. Distributed by: Backs, Cartel

Think in to you.
Single (12"): released on Criminal Damage in Oct'84 by Criminal Damage Records. Distributed by: Backs, Cartel

Aussiebilly

Aussiebilly (Various Artists).
Album: released on Nervous in Jun'86 by Nervous Records. Distributed by: Nervous, Rough Trade

Austen, Jane

Sense and sensibility.
Musicassette: released on Cover to Cover in Feb'87 by Cover to Cover Cassettes. Distributed by: Conifer

Austin, Charles

Allana (Austin, Charles & Joe Gallivan - The New Orchestra).
Album: released on Hannibal in Aug'85 by Hannibal Records. Distributed by: Charly, Harmonia Mundi, Projection, Celtic Music, Roots

Home from home.
Album: released on Ogun in Sep'79. Distributed by: Jazz Music, JSU, Cadillac

Miami.
Tracks: / Moods / To Shoenberg / Motions in blue and red / Michelle / Compositions for our peers / Absolute end, almost, The / Birds, The / Tuning fork / Reflective thinking, Parts 1 & 2 / Little train, The / Speedway.

Album: released on Atmosphere in Jul'79 by E.S.S.P.

Austin, Claire

1954 (Austin, Claire (with Kid Ory)).
Album: released on Hot Society in Dec'82. Distributed by: Jazz Music, Chris Wellard

Austin, David

This boy loves the sun.
Single (7"): released on Parlophone in Aug'84 by EMI Records. Distributed by: EMI

Single (12"): released on Parlophone in Aug'84 by EMI Records. Distributed by: EMI Deleted '86.

Turn to gold.
Single (7"): released on Parlophone in May'84 by EMI Records. Distributed by: EMI

Single (12"): released on Parlophone in May'84 by EMI Records. Distributed by: EMI

Austin, Dean

Share my music.

Tracks: / Country comfort / Change places with me / Old Shep / Home to Emma Jane / Three good reasons / Greyhounds and trailways / She's free but she's not easy / Working in the diner / Before this day ends / Heartbreak hotel.
Album: released on Champ in '82 by Champ Records. Distributed by: Champ

Austin, Lovie

Lovie Austin's blues serenaders 1924-26 (Austin, Lovie & His Blue Serenaders).
Album: released on Fountain in Apr'79 by Retrieval Records. Distributed by: Jazz Music, Swift, VJM, Wellard, Chris, Retrieval

Austin, Michel

Out tonight.
Single (7"): released on Chrysalis in Oct'84 by Chrysalis Records. Distributed by: CBS

Single (12"): released on Chrysalis in Oct'84 by Chrysalis Records. Distributed by: CBS

Picture disc single: released on Chrysalis in Oct'84 by Chrysalis Records. Distributed by: CBS

Austin, Patti

Biographical Details: Quincy Jones, producer of the world's biggest ever album 'Thriller', cities Pattie Austin as his favourite singer. The two have worked extensively together, with Austin singing backing vocals on many of the stars records that Jones has produced and with Jones producing her own work. The first Patti Austin album 'End Of A Rainbow' was issued in 1976, to be followed in '77 by Havana Candy and in '80 by 'Body Language'. The first LP to make a real impact was 1981's 'Every Home Should Have One', a slow but steady seller in her native US. It appeared that not every British home had one, for it managed just one week on the UK album chart, at no.99. Austin did score a British top 20 single that year, however, singing lead on Quincy Jones,'Razzamatazz. In 1982 she teamed with another of Jones stalwart singers, James Ingram, for a 45 entitled 'Baby Come To Me'. The record proved to be a sleeper smash, having hovered in the being used regularly on a TV series. It hit no.1 in February to be deposed by the Jones-produced 'Billie Jean' by Michael Jackson. The success of 'Baby' crossed the Atlantic, and the song hit no.11 in the UK. Patti Austin's dual career is continuing apace. (BM 84)

Baby come to me (Austin, Patti & James Ingram).
Single (7"): released on Warner Bros. in Feb'83 by Warner Bros Records. Distributed by: WEA Deleted '86.

Single (12"): released on Warner Bros. in Feb'83 by Warner Bros Records. Distributed by: WEA

Every home should have one.
Tracks: / Do you love me / Love me to death / Way I feel, The / Every home should have one / Baby, come to me / Genie, The / Stop look listen / Symphony of love / Oh no, Margerita / Island, The.
Compact disc: by Quincy Jones. Distributed by: Warner Brothers, WEA

Gettin' away with murder.
Tracks: / Talkin' 'bout my baby / Big bad world / Heat of heat, The / If I believe / Honey for the bees / Gettin' away with murder / Anything can happen here / Only a breath away / Summer is the coldest time of year.
Album: released on Qwest in Oct'85 by WEA Records. Distributed by: WEA

Musicassette: released on Qwest in Oct'85 by WEA Records. Distributed by: WEA

Heat of heat, The.
Tracks: / Heat of heat, The / Hot in the heat of love / All behind us now.
Single (7"): released on Warner Bros. in Mar'86 by Warner Bros Records. Distributed by: WEA

Single (12"): released on Warner Bros. in Mar'86 by Warner Bros Records. Distributed by: WEA

How do you keep the music play (Austin, Patti & James Ingram).
Single (7"): released on Warner Bros. in May'83 by Warner Bros Records. Distributed by: WEA

Single (12"): released on Warner Bros. in May'83 by Warner Bros Records. Distributed by: WEA

Live at the Bottom Line.
Musicassette: released on CTI (Musidisc France) in Feb'84 by Polydor Records. Distributed by: IMS, Polygram

Patti Austen.

Patti Austin.
Tracks: / It's gonna be special / Rhythm of the street / All behind us now / Hot in flames of love / Change your attitude / Shoot the moon / I've got my heart set on you / Fine fine fella / Starstruck / Any way you can.
Compact disc: by Quincy Jones. Distributed by: Warner Brothers, WEA

Compact disc: released on Qwest (USA) in Jul'84 by Quincy Jones. Distributed by: Warner Brothers, WEA

Album: released on Qwest in Feb'84 by WEA Records. Distributed by: WEA

Musicassette: released on Qwest in Feb'84 by WEA Records. Distributed by: WEA Deleted '86.

Austin, Rockin' Johnny

City lights.
Single (7"): released on Nervous in Jun'81 by Nervous Records. Distributed by: Nervous, Rough Trade

Meets the feds.
Single (7"): released on Nervous in Jun'81 by Nervous Records. Distributed by: Nervous, Rough Trade

Austin, Steve

Kiss and tell (Austin, Steve Band).

Single (7"): released on Parlophone in Jul'85 by EMI Records. Distributed by: EMI

Single (12"): released on Parlophone in Jul'85 by EMI Records. Distributed by: EMI

Australia

Australia Come listen to Australia (Various Artists).
Tracks: / Didjeridu solo / No more boomerang / Cartain Cook / Girls from the Shamrock Shore, The / Tent poles are rotten, The / Teams, The / Come listen / 1,000 miles away / Australia Square / Mullimbmy madness million are / Wimmins ball, The / F1 11 / Aussie medley / Red dust.
Notes: Traditional music of the Aborigine and settler, country music, didjridu and folk songs.
Album: released on Teldec (Germany) in Nov'85 by Import Records. Distributed by: IMS Distribution, Polygram Distribution

Australia down under country (Various Artists).
Album: released on Magic in May'83. Distributed by: Jazz Music, Submarine, Swift, Chris Wellard, Conifer

Musicassette: released on Magic in May'83. Distributed by: Jazz Music, Submarine, Swift, Chris Wellard, Conifer

Australian Army tour (Australian Army, Band of).
Album: released on Vikings in '78

Musicassette: released on Vikings in '78

Old England (for Mom).
Single (7"): released on Magic in Apr'83. Distributed by: Jazz Music, Submarine, Swift, Chris Wellard, Conifer

Songs of the Aborigines.
Album: released on Lyrichord (USA) in Oct'81 by Lyrichord Records (USA). Distributed by: Flexitron Distributors Ltd

Australian Broadcasting...

Music From Great Australian Films.
Tracks: / Newsfront / Gallipoli / My brilliant career / Tall timbers / Cathy's child / Eliza Fraser / Breaker Morrant / Child of Jimmy Blacksmith / Picture show man / Picnic at Hanging Rock / Mango tree (The) / Dimboola / Dimboola / Caddie.
Notes: Arranged & conducted by: William Motzing Featuring: Mark Isaacs,Bob Barnard,Tony Ansell & Erroll Buddle Orchestra leader: Robert Ingram MBE Producer: Peter Wall Music from great Australian films by the Australian Broadcasting Commission Philharmonic Orchestra
Compact disc: released on DRG (USA) in May'87 by DRG Records. Distributed by: Conifer, RCA

Australian Crawl

Boys light up.
Single (7"): released on Geffen in Jan'84 by Geffen Records. Distributed by: WEA, CBS

Single (12"): released on Geffen in Jan'84 by Geffen Records. Distributed by: WEA, CBS

Downhearted.
Single (7"): released on EMI in Feb'83 by EMI Records. Distributed by: EMI

Reckless.
Single (7"): released on Geffen in Feb'84 by Geffen Records. Distributed by: WEA, CBS

Single (12"): released on Geffen in Feb'84 by Geffen Records. Distributed by: WEA, CBS

Australian Rock 84

Australian rock 84 (Various Artists).
Album: released on Epic in Sep'84 by CBS Records. Distributed by: CBS

Musicassette: released on Epic in Sep'84 by CBS Records. Distributed by: CBS

Austrian Folk Music

East Provinces vol.1.
Album: released on Arhoolie in May'81 by Arhoolie Records. Distributed by: Projection Topic, Jazz Music, Swift, Roots

Wstern Provinces vol.2.
Album: released on Arhoolie in May'81 by Arhoolie Records. Distributed by: Projection, Topic, Jazz Music, Swift, Roots

Austria, Songs Of

Sing children sing.
Musicassette: released on Caedmon(USA) in Dec'79 by Caedmon (USA) Records. Distributed by: Gower, Taylors, Discovery

Ausweis

A victimes.
Single (12"): released on Chainsaw in Nov'85 by Chainsaw Records. Distributed by: Red Rhino, Cartel

Jours de haine.
Single (12"): released on Ediesta in May'86 by Ediesta Records. Distributed by: Red Rhino, Cartel

Auto Da Fe

All is yellow (hot, hot, hot).
Single (7"): released on Spartan in Feb'85 by Spartan Records. Distributed by: Spartan

Single (12"): released on Spartan in Feb'85 by Spartan Records. Distributed by: Spartan

Magic moments.
Single (7"): released on Spartan in Dec'85 by Spartan Records. Distributed by: Spartan

Man of mine.
Single (7"): released on Rewind in Apr'83 by Rewind Records. Distributed by: Spartan

November November.
Single (7"): released on Rewind in Oct'83 by Rewind Records. Distributed by: Spartan

Something's gotten hold of my heart.
Single (7"): released on Rewind in Apr'84 by Rewind Records. Distributed by: Spartan

Autograph

Sign in please.
Tracks: / Send her to me / Turn up the radio / Nineteen and non-stop / Cloud 10 / Deep end / My girlfriend's boyfriend isn't me / Thrill of love / Friday in the night / All I'm gonna take.
Album: released on RCA in Mar'85 by RCA Records. Distributed by: RCA, Roots, Swift, Wellard, Chris, I & B, Solomon & Peres Distribution

Musicassette: released on RCA in Mar'85 by RCA Records. Distributed by: RCA, Roots, Swift, Wellard, Chris, I & B, Solomon & Peres Distribution

Turn up the radio.
Single (7"): released on RCA in Mar'85 by RCA Records. Distributed by: RCA, Roots, Swift, Wellard, Chris, I & B, Solomon & Peres Distribution

Single (12"): released on RCA in Mar'85 by RCA Records. Distributed by: RCA, Roots, Swift, Wellard, Chris, I & B, Solomon & Peres Distribution

Automatic Diamini

Crazy supper, The.
Extended-play record:

I don't know you but....
Tracks: / I don't know you but....
Single (7"): released on D for Drum in Mar'87 Distributed by: Revolver, Cartel

Automatic Slim

Slim live.
Album: released on Square One in Nov'86

Automaton

Dancing in outer space 84 rap.
Single (12"): released on Jungle Rhythm in Sep'84

Autopilot

Rapid eye movements.
Double Album: released on Chrysalis in Sep'81 by Chrysalis Records. Distributed by: CBS

Double musicassette: released on Chrysalis in Sep'81 by Chrysalis Records. Distributed by: CBS

Autry, Gene

20 golden pieces of Gene Autrey.
Tracks: / Dixie cannon ball / My old Kentucky home / Down in the valley / Cowboy blues / Boy from Texas, a girl from Tennesse, A / west a nest and you, The / Don't bite the hand that's feeding you / Missouri waltz / There's no back door to heaven / Kentucky babe / You're the only good thing / When day is done / You are my sunshine / I hang my head and cry / San Antonio rose / Goodbye little darling / I hang my head and cry / San Antonio rose / Goodbye little darling / Trouble in mind / Lonely river / You're the only star (in my blue heaven) / Tweedle-o-twill.
Album: released on Bulldog in Jul'82 by Bulldog Records. Distributed by: President Distribution, Spartan, Swift, Taylor, H.R.

Best of....
Musicassette: released on Creole (Everest-Europa) in Jul'84 by Creole Records. Distributed by: PRT, Rhino

Gene Autry.
Tracks: / Tumbling tumbleweeds / I'll go riding down that old Texas trail / It makes no difference now / There's a new moon over my shoulder / Amapola / Ridin' down the canyon / Deep in the heart of Texas / Same old fashioned hoedown / Don't fence me in.
Album: released on CBS in Sep'82 by CBS Records. Distributed by: CBS

Gene Autry 50th Anniversary.
Double Album: released on Republic in Jan'79 by Code Records. Distributed by: Bulldog

Live from Madison Square Garden.
Tracks: / Down yonder / Anytime / My lazy day / Someday you'll want me to want you / Silver haired daddy of mine / Last letter, The / Let me cry on your shoulders / Half as much / Blue Canadian rockies / I was just walking out the door / Rounded up in glory / There's goldmine in the sky.
Album: released on Bulldog in Jul'82 by Bulldog Records. Distributed by: President Distribution, Spartan, Swift, Taylor, H.R.

Sings south of the border.
Tracks: / El rancho grande / You belong to my heart / In a little Spanish town / My abode hacienda / Under fiesta stars / Vaya con dios / Gay ranchero, A / It happened in old Monterey / Rancho pillow / Mexicali rose / Serenade of the bells / South of the border.
Album: released on Bulldog in Jul'82 by Bulldog Records. Distributed by: President Distribution, Spartan, Swift, Taylor, H.R.

Yellow rose of Texas, The.
Tracks: / Yellow rose of texas / Little ranch house on the old circle B (The) / Louisiana moon / Cow boy's heaven / Kentucky lullaby / Black bottom blues / That ramshackle shack / Back home in the blue ridge mountain / Do right daddy blues / Money ain't no use anyway / That's how i got my start / Bear cat papa blues / Don't do me that way / High steppin' mama / There's a good gal in the mountains / My dreaming of you.
Album: released on Bear Family in Nov'86 by Bear Family Records. Distributed by: Rollercoaster Distribution, Swift

Autumn Records Story

Autumn Records Story (Various Artists).
Album: released on Edsel in May'86 by Demon Records. Distributed by: Pinnacle, Jazz Music, Projection

Musicassette: released on Edsel in May'86 by Demon Records. Distributed by: Pinnacle, Jazz Music, Projection

Avalanche

Pray for the summer.
Album: released on Road Runner in Nov'85

Avalon

Rocky roads.
Tracks: / Overture / Jack in irons / Traveller's tale / Greenpeace / Bruntsfield link / Leith walk / Open roads / Ballrooms of romance / Another encore / Blue highways / Road to Dingwall/Arran more.
Notes: New departures in Celtic folk culture. Strong influences in a near rock setting. A great concept album.
Album: released on Lismor in May'86 by Lismor Records. Distributed by: Lismor, Roots, Celtic Music

Musicassette: released on Lismor in May'86 by Lismor Records. Distributed by: Lismor, Roots, Celtic Music

Avalon, Frankie

Best of....
Musicassette: released on Creole (Everest-Europa) in Jul'84 by Creole Records. Distributed by: PRT, Rhino

Bobby sox to stockings.
Album: released on Ace in Nov'84 by Ace Records. Distributed by: Pinnacle, Swift, Hotshot, Cadillac

Frankie Avalon.
Album: released on Bison Bop in Jan'85. Distributed by: Swift

Teen kings.
Notes: See under Fabian & Franfie Avalon

Venus/Why.
Single (7"): released on Old Gold in Jul'82 by Old Gold Records. Distributed by: Lightning, Jazz Music, Spartan, Counterpoint

Avant Gardeners

Church of the inner cosmos, The.
Album: released on Appaloosa in Jan'84. Distributed by: Roots, Folksound, JSU, Projection, Celtic Music, Chris Wellard

Deadwood stage.
Single (7"): released on Speed in Dec'83

Avenger

Blood sports.
Tracks: / Enforcer / You'll never make me (alive) / Matriarch / Warfare / On the rocks / Rough ride / Victims of force / Death race 2000 / Night of the jackal.
Album: released on Neat in '85 by Neat Records. Distributed by: Pinnacle, Neat

Bloodsports.
Album: released on Neat in Jul'84 by Neat Records. Distributed by: Pinnacle, Neat

Killer elite.
Tracks: / Revenge attack / Run for your life / Brand of torture / Steel on steel / Right to rock (Fight for the) / Hard times / Under the hammer / Face to the ground / Dangerous games / Yesterdays hero / M.M.85 / Saw mill.
Album: released on Neat in '85 by Neat Records. Distributed by: Pinnacle, Neat

Killer Elite.
Album: released on Neat in Sep'85 by Neat Records. Distributed by: Pinnacle, Neat

Too wild to tame.
Single (7"): released on Neat in Aug'83 by Neat Records. Distributed by: Pinnacle, Neat

Avengers

Avengers, The.
Album: released on CD Presents in Aug'86. Distributed by: IMS, Polygram

Oh baby.
Single (7"): released on MCA in Jul'84 by MCA Records. Distributed by: Polygram, MCA

Avenue

Three cheers.
Album: released on Boulevard in Sep'83. Distributed by: Pinnacle

Average Buss Cue

Whenever I'm with you.
Single (7"): released on Swagman in Mar'84. Distributed by: Pinnacle

Average White Band

Average white band.
Tracks: / You got it / Got the love / Pick up the pieces / Person to person / Nothing you can do / Work to do / Just want to love you tonight / Keepin' it to myself / I just can't give you up / There's always someone waiting.
Notes: Publisher: AWB Music Ltd, except 'Work to do' - Carlin Music Corp.
Album: released on Fame in Jun'86 by Music For Pleasure Records. Distributed by: EMI

Musicassette: released on Fame in Jun'86 by Music For Pleasure Records. Distributed by: EMI

Benny & Us.
Tracks: / Get it up for love / Fool for your anyway / Star in the Guetto, A / Message, The / What is soul / Someday we'll be free / Imagine / Keepin' it to myself.
Album: released on Atlantic in Jul'77 by WEA Records. Distributed by: WEA

Musicassette: released on Atlantic in Jul'77 by WEA Records. Distributed by: WEA

Best of....
Album: released on RCA International (USA) in '84 by RCA Records. Distributed by: RCA

Musicassette: released on RCA International (USA) in '84 by RCA Records. Distributed by: RCA

Cupid's in fashion.
Tracks: / You're my number one / Easier said than done / You wanna belong / Cupids in fashion / Theatre of excess I believe / Is it love that you're running from / Reach out I'll be there / Isn't it strange / Love's a heartache.
Album: released on RCA in Sep'82 by RCA Records. Distributed by: RCA, Roots, Swift, Wellard, Chris, I & B, Solomon & Peres Distribution

Musicassette: released on RCA in Sep'82 by RCA Records. Distributed by: RCA, Roots, Swift, Wellard, Chris, I & B, Solomon & Peres Distribution

Cut the cake.
Album: released on Atlantic in Jun'75 by WEA Records. Distributed by: WEA

Feel no fret.
Tracks: / When will you be mine / Please don't fall in love / Walk on by / Feel no fret / Stop the rain / Atlantic Avenue / Too late to cry / Ace of hearts / Too late to cry / Fire burning / Cut the cake / School boy crush / It's a mystery / Groovin' the night away / If I ever lose this heaven / Why / High flyin' woman / Cloudy / How sweet can you get / When they bring down the curtain.
Album: released on RCA International (USA) in Sep'81 by RCA Records. Distributed by: RCA

Musicassette: released on RCA International (USA) in Sep'81 by RCA Records. Distributed by: RCA

I believe.
Single (7"): released on RCA in Sep'82 by RCA Records. Distributed by: RCA, Roots, Swift, Wellard, Chris, I & B, Solomon & Peres Distribution

Single (12"): released on RCA in Sep'82 by RCA Records. Distributed by: RCA, Roots, Swift, Wellard, Chris, I & B, Solomon & Peres Distribution

Person to person.
Tracks: / Person to person / Cut the cake / If I ever lose this heaven / Cloudy / T.L.C. / I'm the one / Pick up the pieces / Love you life / School boy crush / I heard it through the grapevine.
Double Album: released on Atlantic in Jan'77 by WEA Records. Distributed by: WEA

Double musicassette: released on Atlantic in Jan'77 by WEA Records. Distributed by: WEA

Page 59

Pick up the pieces.
Single (7"): released on RCA Golden Grooves in Jul'81 by RCA Records. Distributed by: RCA

Show your hand.
Tracks: / Jugglers, Try / This world has music / Twilight zone / Put it where you want it / Show your hand / Back in '67 / Reach out / T.L.C..
Notes: Originally MCA: MCF 2514 Released 1973
Album: released on Fame in May'83 by Music For Pleasure Records. Distributed by: EMI

Musicassette: released on Fame in May'83 by Music For Pleasure Records. Distributed by: EMI

Soul searching.
Album: released on RCA International (USA) in Nov'80 by RCA Records. Distributed by: RCA

Musicassette: released on RCA International (USA) in Nov'80 by RCA Records. Distributed by: RCA

Poo poo lala.
Single (7"): released on CBS in Feb'85 by CBS Records. Distributed by: CBS

Single (12"): released on CBS in Feb'85 by CBS Records. Distributed by: CBS Deleted '86.

Running away.
Single (12"): released on Polydor in Mar'80 by Polydor Records. Distributed by: Polygram, Polydor Deleted '80.

Silver vibrations.
Album: released on Uno Melodic in Jul'83

Musicassette: released on Uno Melodic in Jul'83

Single (7"): released on Uno Melodic in Jul'83

Single (12"): released on Uno Melodic in Jul'83

Vibrations (Ayers, Roy Ubiquity).
Musicassette: released on Polydor in Feb'77 by Polydor Records. Distributed by: Polygram, Polydor

You might be surprised.
Tracks: / Hot / Programmes for love / Virgo / You might be surprised / Night flyte / Can I see you? / For you / Slip 'n' slide.
Album: released on CBS in Oct'85 by CBS Records. Distributed by: CBS

Musicassette: released on CBS in Oct'85 by CBS Records. Distributed by: CBS

You send me.
Album: released on Spring in '78 by Polydor Inc.. Distributed by: Polygram Distribution

Ayler, Albert

Albert Aylor.
Album: released on ESP in Apr'81 by ESP Records. Distributed by: Jazz Horizons, Jazz Music

At Slug's Saloon (Ayler, Albert Quintet).
Album: released on Base in Oct'82. Distributed by: Jazz Horizons

At Slug's Saloon vol.2, May 1st 1966 (Ayler, Albert Quintet).
Album: released on Base in Oct'82. Distributed by: Jazz Horizons

Awakening, The.
Album: released on MCA in Oct'85 by MCA Records. Distributed by: Polygram, MCA

First recordings.
Album: by Sonet Records. Distributed by: PRT

In Greenwich Village.
Tracks: / For John Coltrane / Change has come / Truth is marching in / Our prayer.
Album: released on Jasmine in Mar'83 by Jasmine Records. Distributed by: Counterpoint, Lugtons, Taylor, H.R., Wellard, Chris, Swift, Cadillac

New York eye & ear control.
Album: released on ESP in Apr'81 by ESP Records. Distributed by: Jazz Horizons, Jazz Music

Nuits de la fondation.
Album: released on Shandar in Mar'78

Prophecy.
Album: released on Uni/Base in Apr'81. Distributed by: Jazz Music, Jazz Horizons

Spiritual unity (Ayler, Albert Trio).

Witches and devils.
Album: released on Freedom in Jan'79 by Logo Records. Distributed by: RCA, Discovery, Wellard, Chris

Ayre Rayde

Sock it to me.
Single (7"): released on Cherry Red in Jun'86 by Cherry Red Records. Distributed by: Pinnacle

Single (12"): released on Cherry Red in Jun'86 by Cherry Red Records. Distributed by: Pinnacle

Ayres, Pam

Biographical Details: The comical poetry of Pam Ayres, satirising the everyday lives of ordinary folk, shot her to TV stardom in the mid-Seventies. "Some Of Me Poems And Songs" capitalised on her fame, reaching No.13 on the album chart with 14 weeks on the list, in 1976. The formula was repeated later in the year, but with less success: "Some More Of Me Poems And Songs" peaked at No.23 with a six-week run. Ayres has not graced the album chart since, but her nauseating or refreshing way with words (depending on taste) has continued to sell well in book form throughout her native Britain. (Bob McDonald 1984)

Please will you take your children.
Single (7"): released on Honest Penny in Nov'81. Distributed by: Pinnacle

Some more of me poems & songs.
Album: released on Galaxy in Oct'76 by Galaxy Records. Distributed by: RCA, Red Lightnin' Distribution, Discovery, Swift

Musicassette: released on Galaxy in Oct'76 by Galaxy Records. Distributed by: RCA, Red Lightnin' Distribution, Discovery, Swift

Some of me poems & songs.
Album: released on MFP in Jan'80 by EMI Records. Distributed by: EMI

Musicassette: released on MFP in Jan'80 by EMI Records. Distributed by: EMI

Thoughts of a late night knitter.
Album: by EMI Records. Distributed by: EMI

Will anybody marry me.
Album: by EMI Records. Distributed by: EMI

Azaad

Nachdi Jawani.
Album: released on Multitone in Mar'86

Azana

Runaway woman.
Tracks: / Runaway woman / Runaway woman (version).
Single (12"): released on UK Bubblers in Apr'87 by Greensleeves Records. Distributed by: RCA, Jetstar

Azare

Love's gone.
Single (7"): released on TVM in May'85. Distributed by: Gipsy, CBS

Azimuth

Azimuth '85.
Tracks: / Adios lony / Dream - lost song / Who are you / Breathtaking / Potion 1 / Februery daze / Til bakeblikk / Potion 2.
Album: released on ECM (Germany) in Dec'85 by ECM Records. Distributed by: IMS, Polygram, Virgin through EMI

Compact disc: by ECM Records. Distributed by: IMS, Polygram, Virgin through EMI

Aznavour, Charles

1980...A l'olympia.
Triple album / cassette: released on Import Music Service (IMS) in Mar'81. Distributed by: Concord Jazz Distributions, Pablo, Polygram

30 carats.
Album: released on EMI (France) in '83 by EMI Records. Distributed by: Conifer

Amour toujours.
Tracks: / Hier encore / Tu t'laisses aller / She / Il fait savoir / Et pourtant / La mama / Comme ils disent / Les plaisirs demodes / Com'e triste Venezia / Desormais / Non je n'ai rien oublie / Une premiere danse.

Amour Toujours.
Tracks: / Hier encore / Tu t'laisses aller / She / Il fait savoir / Et pourtant / La mama / Comme ils disent / Les plaisirs demodes / Com'e triste Venezia / Desormais / Non, je n'ai rien oublie / Une premiere danse.
Compact disc: released on Barclay (France) in '84 by Decca Records. Distributed by: IMS, Discovery, Conifer, Swift, Polygram

Best of Aznavour, The.
Album: released on Barclay in Nov'79 by Decca Records. Distributed by: Polygram, Discovery, Conifer, IMS, Swift

Best of Sampler.
Album: released on Barclay in Nov'79 by Decca Records. Distributed by: Polygram, Discovery, Conifer, IMS, Swift

Boheme, La.
Album: released on Barclay in Nov'79 by Decca Records. Distributed by: Polygram, Discovery, Conifer, IMS, Swift

Charles Aznavour collection vol.1, The.
Tracks: / Old fashioned way, The / Women of today / Love is new everyday / Between us / How sad Venice can be / Town, The / It will be my day / Yesterday when I was young / Ciao, always ciao / All those pretty girls / What makes a man.
Album: released on Barclay in Feb'82 by Decca Records. Distributed by: Polygram, Discovery, Conifer, IMS, Swift

Musicassette: released on Barclay in Feb'82 by Decca Records. Distributed by: Polygram, Discovery, Conifer, IMS, Swift

Charles Aznavour collection vol.2, The.
Tracks: / She / Sunday is not my day / Happy anniversary / C'est fini / I live for you / Sound of your name, The / After loving you / From today / My hand needs your hand / You've got to learn / Slowly / La boheme (en Francais).
Album: released on Barclay in Oct'82 by Decca Records. Distributed by: Polygram, Discovery, Conifer, IMS, Swift

Musicassette: released on Barclay in Oct'82 by Decca Records. Distributed by: Polygram, Discovery, Conifer, IMS, Swift

Comme ils disent.
Album: released on Barclay in Nov'79 by Decca Records. Distributed by: Polygram, Discovery, Conifer, IMS, Swift

Desrmais.
Album: released on Barclay in Nov'79 by Decca Records. Distributed by: Polygram, Discovery, Conifer, IMS, Swift

Emmez moi.
Album: released on Barclay in Nov'79 by Decca Records. Distributed by: Polygram, Discovery, Conifer, IMS, Swift

Enregistrements originaux.
Compact disc: . Distributed by: Swift

Face au public.
Album: released on Barclay in Nov'79 by Decca Records. Distributed by: Polygram, Discovery, Conifer, IMS, Swift

Grands succes, Les.
Album: released on Barclay in Nov'79 by Decca Records. Distributed by: Polygram, Discovery, Conifer, IMS, Swift

Hier encore.
Album: released on Barclay in Nov'79 by Decca Records. Distributed by: Polygram, Discovery, Conifer, IMS, Swift

His greatest love songs.
Album: released on K-Tel in Jul'80 by K-Tel Records. Distributed by: Record Merchandisers Distribution, Taylors, Terry Blood Distribution, Wynd-Up Distribution, Relay Distribution, Pickwick Distribution, Solomon & Peres Distribution, Polygram

Musicassette: released on K-Tel in '83 by K-Tel Records. Distributed by: Record Merchandisers Distribution, Taylors, Terry Blood Distribution, Wynd-Up Distribution, Relay Distribution, Pickwick Distribution, Solomon & Peres Distribution, Polygram

Il faut savoir.
Album: released on Barclay in Nov'79 by Decca Records. Distributed by: Polygram, Discovery, Conifer, IMS, Swift

In times to be.
Tracks: / I'll be there / In your room / Hold back the night / To be a soldier / I didn't see the time go / In times to be / Somewhere out of town / We / Daydreaming / I act as if.
Single (7"): released on Barclay in Apr'83 by Decca Records. Distributed by: Polygram, Discovery, Conifer, IMS, Swift

Musicassette: released on Barclay in May'83 by Decca Records. Distributed by: Polygram, Discovery, Conifer, IMS, Swift

Je m'voyais deja.
Album: released on Barclay in Nov'79 by Decca Records. Distributed by: Polygram, Discovery, Conifer, IMS, Swift

Je n'ai pas vu le temps passer.
Album: released on Barclay in Nov'79 by Decca Records. Distributed by: Polygram, Discovery, Conifer, IMS, Swift

Mama, La.
Album: released on Barclay in Nov'79 by Decca Records. Distributed by: Polygram, Discovery, Conifer, IMS, Swift

My Christmas album.
Album: released on Hallmark in Oct'81 by Pickwick Records. Distributed by: Pickwick Distribution, PRT, Taylors

Musicassette: released on Hallmark in Oct'81 by Pickwick Records. Distributed by: Pickwick Distribution, PRT, Taylors

Non Je n'ai rien oublie.
Album: released on Barclay in Nov'79 by Decca Records. Distributed by: Polygram, Discovery, Conifer, IMS, Swift

Paris au mois d'aout.
Album: released on Barclay in Nov'79 by Decca Records. Distributed by: Polygram, Discovery, Conifer, IMS, Swift

Plein feu sur Aznavour.
Album: released on Barclay in Nov'79 by Decca Records. Distributed by: Polygram, Discovery, Conifer, IMS, Swift

Premiere danse, The.
Album: released on Barclay (France) in Mar'83 by Decca Records. Distributed by: IMS, Discovery, Conifer, Swift, Polygram

Musicassette: released on Barclay (France) in Mar'83 by Decca Records. Distributed by: IMS, Discovery, Conifer, Swift, Polygram

Private Christmas, A.
Tracks: / Very private Christmas, A / Christmas calypso / Tell me who was born / Christmas Eve in gambling town / My own child for Christmas from you / Ave Maria / I don't understand / Goodbye Christmas past / Snowball / Hosanna.
Album: released on M.A.M. in Dec'82 by M.A.M. Records. Distributed by: T.B.C

Qui.
Album: released on Barclay in Nov'79 by Decca Records. Distributed by: Polygram, Discovery, Conifer, IMS, Swift

Reste.
Album: released on Barclay in Nov'79 by Decca Records. Distributed by: Polygram, Discovery, Conifer, IMS, Swift

She.
Musicassette: released on Music For Pleasure in Dec'79 by EMI Records. Distributed by: EMI

Temps, Le.
Album: released on Barclay in Nov'79 by Decca Records. Distributed by: Polygram, Discovery, Conifer, IMS, Swift

Visages de l'amour.
Album: released on Barclay in Nov'79 by Decca Records. Distributed by: Polygram, Discovery, Conifer, IMS, Swift

Azrie, Abed

Epic of Gilgamesh.
Album: released on Shandar in Mar'78

Aztec Camera

Biographical Details: This Scottish band are very much dominated by frontman Roddy Frame, vocalist, guitarist and songwriter. Originally formed in January 1980 while still at school, they released their first single "Just Like Gold" in March 1981. The record that began attracting attention was their '82 single, the Sixties-inflected "Pillar To Post". The band scored their first minor hit in early '83 with "Oblivious", from the debut album "High Land Hard Rain". The highly melodic next single failed when issued that May - hardly a sensible time to release a song called "Walk Out To Winter". Later in the year they were snapped up by WEA, having previously recorded for Postcard and Rough Trade, and the new company promptly re-issued "Oblivious" and made it into a Top 20 hit. In 1984 the "Knife" album and its first single "All I Need Is Everything" both charted respectably, but Roddy Frame's nifty songs and group's attractive acoustic-based sound probably have greater sales potential than thus far achieved. (Bob McDonald 1984)

All I need is everthing.
Single (7"): released on WEA in Aug'84 by WEA Records. Distributed by: WEA

Single (12"): released on WEA in Aug'84 by WEA Records. Distributed by: WEA Deleted '86.

Highland hard rain.
Album: released on Rough Trade in '83 by Rough Trade Records. Distributed by: Rough Trade Distribution, Cartel Distribution

High Land, Hard Rain.
Tracks: / Oblivious / Boy wonders, The / Walk out to Winter / We could send letters / Bugle sounds again, The / Pillar to Post / Release / Lost outside the tunnel / Back on board / Down the dip.
Compact disc: released on Rough Trade in Feb'87 by Rough Trade Records. Distributed by: Rough Trade Distribution, Cartel Distribution

Just like gold.
Single (7"): released on Postcard in Mar'81 by Alan Horne. Distributed by: Rough Trade

Album: released on WEA in Sep'84 by WEA Records. Distributed by: WEA

Musicassette: released on WEA in Sep'84 by WEA Records. Distributed by: WEA

Compact disc: released on WEA in Sep'84 by WEA Records. Distributed by: WEA

Knife.
Tracks: / Just like the USA / Head is happy (heart's insane) / Backdoor to heaven / All I need is everything / Backwards and forwards / Birth of the true / Knife / Still on fire.

Compact disc: released on WEA in Aug'84 by WEA Records. Distributed by: WEA

Mattress of wire.
Single (7"): released on Postcard in Jul'81 by Alan Horne. Distributed by: Rough Trade

Oblivious.
Single (7"): released on Rough Trade in Jan'83 by Rough Trade Records. Distributed by: Rough Trade Distribution, Cartel Distribution

Single (12"): released on Rough Trade in Jan'83 by Rough Trade Records. Distributed by: Rough Trade Distribution, Cartel Distribution

Pillar to post.
Single (7"): released on Rough Trade in Aug'82 by Rough Trade Records. Distributed by: Rough Trade Distribution, Cartel Distribution

Still on fire.
Single (7"): released on WEA in Nov'84 by WEA Records. Distributed by: WEA

Single (12"): released on WEA in Nov'84 by WEA Records. Distributed by: WEA Deleted '86.

Walk out to winter.
Single (7"): released on Rough Trade in May'83 by Rough Trade Records. Distributed by: Rough Trade Distribution, Cartel Distribution

Single (12"): released on Rough Trade in May'83 by Rough Trade Records. Distributed by: Rough Trade Distribution, Cartel Distribution

A-Z & The Girl Guides

Love is blind.
Single (7"): released on Mordant Music in Feb'85

Azure

Azure Various artists (Various Artists).
Album: released on Shout in Sep'84 by Shout Records. Distributed by: Rough Trade, Cartel

Azymuth

Depart (Azymuth with Ralph Towner).
Album: released on ECM in Nov'80 by ECM Records. Distributed by: IMS, Polygram, Virgin through EMI

Flame.
Album: released on Milestone in Sep'84 by Ace Records. Distributed by: PRT

Rapid transit.
Tracks: / Make mine guarana / Afternoon / Missing doto / Somewhere in Brazil / I'm just looking around / Montreux / Gate of time.
Album: released on Milestone in Mar'84 by Ace Records. Distributed by: PRT

Spectrum.
Compact disc: released on Carrere in Apr'87 by Carrere Records. Distributed by: PRT, Spartan

Azzola, Marcel

Trois temps pour bien faire

B

B-52'S

B-52'S.
Tracks: / Planet Claire / 52 Girls / Dance this mess around / Rock lobster / Lava / There's a moon in the sky (called moon) / Hero worship / 6060-842 / Downtown.
Compact disc: released on Island in Jan'87 by Island Records. Distributed by Polygram

Album: released on Island in Oct'86 by Island Records. Distributed by: Polygram

Cassette: released on Island in Oct'86 by Island Records. Distributed by: Polygram

BOUNCING OFF THE SATELLITES.
Tracks: / Summer of love / Girl from Ipanema goes to Greenland / Housewax / Detour thru your mind / Wig / Theme for a nude beach / Theme to a nude beach / Juicy jungle / Comminicate / She brakes for rainbows.
Album: released on Island in Aug'87 by Island Records. Distributed by: Polygram

Cassette: released on Island in Aug'87 by Island Records. Distributed by: Polygram

FUTURE GENERATION, INSTRUMENTAL.
Single (7"): released on Island in Apr'83 by Island Records. Distributed by: Polygram

FUTURE GENERATION.
Single (7"): released on Island in Apr'83 by Island Records. Distributed by: Polygram

GIVE ME BACK MY MAN.
Single (7"): released on Island in Sep'81 by Island Records. Distributed by: Polygram

MISOPOTAMIA.
Album: released on Island in Feb'82 by Island Records. Distributed by: Polygram

Cassette: released on Island in Feb'82 by Island Records. Distributed by: Polygram

PARTY MIX.
Tracks: / Party out of bounds / Private Idaho / Give me back / My man / Lava / Dance this mess a-round / 52 girls.
Album: released on Island in Jun'81 by Island Records. Distributed by: Polygram

Cassette: released on Island in Jun'81 by Island Records. Distributed by: Polygram

PLANET CLAIR.
Single (7"): released on Island in Jul'81 by Island Records. Distributed by: Polygram

Single (7"): released on Island in Jul'81 by Island Records. Distributed by: Polygram

ROCK LOBSTER.
Tracks: / Rock lobster / Panet Claire / Song for a future generation*+ / Give me back my man* / 52 Girl+.
Notes: *=Extra tracks on 12" only. +=Extra tracks on double pack only.
Single (7"): released on Island in Apr'86 by Island Records. Distributed by: Polygram

Double-pack single: released on Island in Apr'86 by Island Records. Distributed by: Polygram

Single (12"): released on Island in Apr'86 by Island Records. Distributed by: Polygram

Picture disc single: released on Island in May'86 by Island Records. Distributed by: Polygram

WHAMMY!.
Tracks: / Legal tender / Whammy kiss / Song for a future generation / Butterbean / Trism / Queen of Las Vegas / Don't worry / Big bird / Work that skirt.
Album: released on Island in May'83 by Island Records. Distributed by: Polygram

Cassette: released on Island in May'83 by Island Records. Distributed by: Polygram

WIG.
Tracks: / Wig / Summer of love / Song for a future generation.
Single (7"): released on Island in 6 Jun'87 by Island Records. Distributed by: Polygram

Single (12"): released on Island in 6 Jun'87 by Island Records. Distributed by: Polygram

Picture disc single: released on Island in 20 Jun'87 by Island Records. Distributed by: Polygram

Cassette single: released on Island in Jul'87 by Island Records. Distributed by: Polygram

WILD PLANET.
Tracks: / Party out of bounds / Private Idaho / Running around / Give me back my man / Private Idaho / Quiche lorraine / Strobelight / 53 miles west of Venus / Devils in my car, The.
Album: released on Island in Sep'80 by Island Records. Distributed by: Polygram

Cassette: released on Island in Apr'81 by Island Records. Distributed by: Polygram

Baa Baa Black Sheep

BAA BAA BLACK SHEEP Various artists (Various Artists).
Cassette: released on Storyteller in Jun'86

Babakoto

LOVE HAS GOT A HOLD ON ME.
Tracks: / Love has got a hold on me / Special lady.
Single (7"): released on Mr. Sam in Mar'87

Babar The Little Elephant

BABAR THE LITTLE ELEPHANT (Rippon, Angela).
Album: released on ASV in Oct'81 by Academy Sound & Vision Records. Distributed by: Pinnacle

Cassette: released on ASV in Oct'81 by Academy Sound & Vision Records. Distributed by: Pinnacle

Babatunde

DANCE TO THE BEAT OF MY DRUM
Featuring Carlos Santana.
Tracks: / Beat of my drum, The / Loyin, loyin / Ife l'oju l'aiye / Akiwowo / Se eni a fe l'amo- kere kere.
Notes: Exciting African percussion album from Babatunde, famous West African drummer. If you look at the personnel detail you will notice that this is no ordinary African percussion project. As well as being engineered by Mickey Hart of the band The Greatful Dead, also featured throughout as lead guitarist is the one and only Carlos Santana.
Album: released on Blue Heron in Apr'87

Babbacombe Lee...

BABBACOMBE LEE & WIDECOMBE FAIR (Various Artists).
Cassette: released on Folktracks in Nov'79 by Folktracks Cassettes. Distributed by: Folktracks

Babe Ruth

BEST OF BABE RUTH, THE.
Tracks: / Wells Fargo (single version) / Ain't that livin' / Theme from 'For a few dollars more' / Private number (single version) / Joker / Dancer / Duchess of Orleans (The) / Black dog / If heaven's on beauty's side / Lady / Jack o'lantern.
Cassette: released on FM in Aug'86 by FM-Revolver Records. Distributed by: EMI

Album: released on FM in Mar'87 by FM-Revolver Records. Distributed by: EMI

FIRST BASE.
Album: released on EMI in '72 by EMI Records. Distributed by: EMI

Bables

I'M FALLING.
Tracks: / I'm falling / Time on my hands / Do it nice ** / Jack the lad ** / Bitch or angel **.
Single (7"): released on Pow Wop in Oct'86

Single (12"): released on Pow Wop in Oct'86

Babs, Alice

FAR AWAY STAR (Babs, Alice with Duke Ellington & Nils Lindberg Orchestras).
Tracks: / Far away star / Serenade to Sweden / Spaceman / Jeep's blues / Day dream / Is god a three letter word for love / Jump for joy / Warm valley / Blues for the maestro.
Cassette: released on Phontastic in '82. Distributed by: Wellard, Chris

Album: released on Phontastic (Sweden) in '82 by Wellard, Chris Distribution. Distributed by: Wellard, Chris Distribution

Babson, Monty

ONE FOR MY BABY (AND ONE MORE FOR THE ROAD).
Single (7"): released on Mr. Sam in Aug'85

Baby

BABY Original Broadway cast (Various Artists).
Compact disc: released on TER in Oct'84. Distributed by: Pinnacle

Album: released on TER in Mar'84. Distributed by: Pinnacle

Cassette: released on TER in Mar'84. Distributed by: Pinnacle

Baby Amphetamine

CHERNOBYL BABY (Who needs the government).
Tracks: / Chernobyl baby (who needs the government) / Cheque it out.
Single (7"): released on Creation in Apr'87. Distributed by: Rough Trade, Cartel

Single (12"): released on Creation in Apr'87. Distributed by: Rough Trade, Cartel

Baby Go Boom

LIFE (CAN BE A HURTFUL THING).
Tracks: / Life (can be a hurtful thing) / Perfect thing / Life (can be a hurtful thing)(US remix) **
Single (7"): released on Island in Mar'86 by Island Records. Distributed by: Polygram

Single (12"): released on Island in Mar'86 by Island Records. Distributed by: Polygram

LIFE CAN BE A HURTFUL THING.
Single (7"): released on Inner Vision in May'84 by CBS Records. Distributed by: CBS Deleted '86.

Single (12"): released on Inner Vision in May'84 by CBS Records. Distributed by: CBS

Baby Lemonade

SECRET GOLDFISH, THE.
Single (7"): released on Narodnik in 30 May'87. Distributed by: Fast Forward, Cartel

Babylon

BABYLON Original soundtrack (Various Artists).
Tracks: / Deliver me from my enemies / Turn me loose / Free Africa / Whap 'n'bap 'n' / Beefy's tune / Thank you for the many things you've done / Hey jah children / Manhunter / Jazterpiece / Warrior change.
Album: released on Chrysalis in Oct'80 by Chrysalis Records. Distributed by: CBS

Baby Love

BABY LOVE Original soundtrack to Lemon Popsicle 5.
Tracks: / Take good care of my baby / Summertime blues / Teen beat / You send me / Sweet little sixteen / Dream lover / Rescue me / Locomotion,The / Maybelline / Sixteen candles / Spilsh splash / He's so fine / Keep a knockin' / Crazy love / Apache / What a wonderful world / Multiplication / Pretty little angel eyes / Speedy Gonzales / Wanderer, The / Girl can't help it,The / Raunchy / Twilight time / Who put the bomp in the bomp bomp bomp/ Rhythm of the rain / Only sixteen / Silence is golden / Ginny come lately / Tiger / End of the world / Bend me shape me / Wipe out.
Notes: Double LP. Single Cassette.

Double Album: released on Red Bus in Nov'85 by Red Bus Records. Distributed by: PRT

Cassette: released on Red Bus in Nov'85 by Red Bus Records. Distributed by: PRT

BABY LOVE (Various Artists).
Album: released on Ronco in Mar'84

Cassette: released on Ronco in Mar'84

Babymen

FOR KING WILLY.
Single (12"): released on One Little Indian in Feb'87 by One Little Indian Records. Distributed by: Nine Mile Distribution, Cartel Distribution

Single (12"): released on One Little Indian in Aug'87 by One Little Indian Records. Distributed by: Nine Mile Distribution, Cartel Distribution

Baby 'n' The Monsters

I'D RATHER NOT/STOOD.
Single (7"): released on Mean in Oct'81 by Mean Records. Distributed by: Spartan

Babys

BABY'S ANTHOLOGY, THE.
Tracks: / Head first / Isn't it time / Midnight rendezvous / Money / Back on my feet again / Give me your love / Turn and walk away / Everytime I think of you / If you've got the time / Sweet 17.
Album: released on Chrysalis in Oct'81 by Chrysalis Records. Distributed by: CBS

Cassette: released on Chrysalis in Oct'81 by Chrysalis Records. Distributed by: CBS

Baby's Got A Gun

SUICIDE GIRL.
Single (12"): released on McDonald Bros. in Apr'87

Babysitters

BABYSITTERS, THE.
Tracks: / Here we is / American toys / No particular place / Beard song, The / I wanna be on T.V. / Rock and roll chicken / Alright O.K.
Album: released on Heavy Metal in Jun'85 by FM-Revolver Records. Distributed by: EMI

Cassette: released on Heavy Metal in Jun'85 by FM-Revolver Records. Distributed by: EMI

I WANNA BE ON THE TV.
Single (7"): released on Jun'85 by FM-Revolver Records. Distributed by: EMI

LIVE AT THE MARQUEE.
Tracks: / Live at the Marquee (EP) / Picking up the blues / Can you hear it / Overkill / Big girls / Frank Bough.
Single (12"): released on Killerwatt in Nov'86. Distributed by: Kingdom Records, Pinnacle

Baby Soother

BABY SOOTHER, (THE) (Unknown).
Cassette: released on Unknown in Sep'83

Baby Soother Tape

BABY SOOTHER TAPE Various artists (Various Artists).
Cassette: released on Conifer in Oct'86 by Conifer Records. Distributed by: Conifer

Baby Tuckoo

FIRST BORN.
Tracks: / Hot wheels / Things (ain't always what they seem) / Holdin' on / Mony mony / A.W.O.L. / Baby's rocking tonight / Broken heart / Sweet rock'n'roll.
Notes: Produced and engineered by: John Verity Recorded : Yorkshire Baby's rocking tonight Mastered by: Ray Staff at Trident Sax on 'Things' by: Tony Siwek

Album: released on Castle Communications in Jul'86 by Castle Communications. Distributed by: Cartel, Pinnacle, Counterpoint

Cassette: released on Castle Communications in Jul'86 by Castle Communications. Distributed by: Cartel, Pinnacle, Counterpoint

Album: released on Albion in Mar'84 by Albion Records. Distributed by: Spartan, Pinnacle

FORCE MAJEURE.
Album: released on Music For Nations in Feb'86 by Music For Nations Records. Distributed by: Pinnacle

Cassette: released on Music For Nations in Feb'86 by Music For Nations Records. Distributed by: Pinnacle

MONY MONY.
Single (7"): released on Albion in Mar'84 by Albion Records. Distributed by: Spartan, Pinnacle

ROCK ROCK.
Tracks: / Rock rock.
Single (12"): released on Music For Nations in May'86 by Music For Nations Records. Distributed by: Pinnacle

TEARS OF A CLOWN, THE.
Tracks: / Tears of a clown, The / Over you / Lights go down, The **.
Single (7"): released on Fun After All in Aug'86. Distributed by: Pinnacle

Single (12"): released on Fun After All in Aug'86. Distributed by: Pinnacle

Bacall, Warren

BRIEF ENCOUNTER.
Single (7"): released on Pilot in Oct'84 by New Music Records. Distributed by: New Music Distribution

CRYSTAL TEARS.
Single (7"): released on Pilot in Mar'85 by New Music Records. Distributed by: New Music Distribution

Baccara

YES SIR, I CAN BOOGIE.
Tracks: / Yes sir, I can boogie / Sorry, I'm a lady.
Single (7"): released on Old Gold in Apr'87 by Old Gold Records. Distributed by: Lightning, Jazz Music, Spartan, Counterpoint

YES SIR I CAN BOOGIE/SORRY I'M A LADY.
Single (7"): released on RCA Golden Grooves in Jul'81 by RCA Records. Distributed by: RCA

Bacharach, Burt

BURT BACHARACH'S GREATEST HITS.
Tracks: / I'll never fall in love again / What the world needs now is love / (They long to be) close to you / This guy's in love with you / Wives and lovers / Reach out for me / Look of love, The / I say a little prayer / Rain drops keep falling on my head / Make it easy on yourself / Alfie / Living together growing together.
Album: by A&M Records. Distributed by: Polygram

Cassette: by A&M Records. Distributed by: Polygram

GREATEST HITS:BURT BACHARACH.
Cassette: released on Pickwick in Mar'84 by Pickwick Records. Distributed by: Pickwick Distribution, Prism Leisure Distribution, Lugtons

Bach-a-Telle

GET BACK TO BACH/JAPANESE NIGHTS.
Single (7"): released on Paro in May'83 by Paro Records. Distributed by: Spartan

Bachdenkel

LEMMINGS.
Album: released on Initial in Sep'81 by Initial Records. Distributed by: Pinnacle

STALINGRAD.
Tracks: / With the whole world looking over my shoulder / After the fall / Seven times tomorrow / For you to live with me / Tournament, The / Easy to be hard / Xenophon / Stalingrad (1) / Stalingrad (2).
Album: released on Initial in Sep'81 by Initial Records. Distributed by: Pinnacle

Bachelet, Pierre

MUSIC FROM THE STORY OF O.
Single (7"): released on Byron Lane in Dec'83

Bachelor Party

BACHELOR PARTY Original soundtrack (Various Artists).
Tracks: / American heartbeat '84 / Something isn't right / Crazy over you / Little demon / Wind out / Bachelor party / What kind of Hell / Alley oop / Why do good girls like bad boys / Dream of the west / Translation / Equals / Appointment with the master, An / Settlement song, The / Long time living / Strangerstill / Come all ye faces.
Album: released on I.R.S.(Independent Record Syndicate) in Dec'84 by I.R.S.. Distributed by: MCA

Bachelors

BACHELORS COLLECTION, THE.
Tracks: / Cecilia / Gonna build a mountain / Cecillia / Gonna build a mountain / Walk with faith in your heart / Marie / Well respected / Sound of silence, The / Elusive butterfly / Chapel in the moonlight / You'll never walk alone / Mame / Marta / My foolish heart.
Double cassette: released on Pickwick in Jul'82 by Pickwick Records. Distributed by: Pickwick Distribution, Prism Leisure Distribution, Lugtons

BEST OF THE BACHELORS, THE.
Tracks: / Diana / The impossible dream / Edelweiss / With these hands / Carmaine / When the saints go marching in / No arms can ever hold you / Marie / Whispering grass / I wouldn't trade you in for the world / Ramona / By the light of the silvery moon.
Notes: Originally released between 1962 and 1971, this track selection includes most of their hit singles during that period with such classic titles as 'Diane','Charmaine' and 'I believe' standing out as probably their most memorable but it is also worth recalling that these three titles were by no means the sum total of their success at that time. Few of the other eleven titles failed to achieve top ten status at a time when the Bachelors could apparently, do nothing wrong.
Album: released on Decca in Sep'81 by Decca Records. Distributed by: Polygram

Cassette: released on Decca in Sep'81 by Decca Records. Distributed by: Polygram

CHARMAINE.
Tracks: / Charmaine / I'm yours / I wouldn't trade you for the world / You're breaking my heart / I wish you love / Ramona / Diane / I believe / Heartaches / Mistakes / No arms could ever hold you / Whispering.
Album: released on Spot in Feb'83 by Pickwick Records. Distributed by: H.R. Taylor, Lugtons

Cassette: by Pickwick Records. Distributed by: H.R. Taylor, Lugtons

CHARMAINE/RAMONA.
Single (7"): released on Decca in Mar'82 by Decca Records. Distributed by: Polygram

DIANE.
Single (7"): released on Decca in Jan'64 by Decca Records. Distributed by: Polygram

DIANE/I BELIEVE.
Single (7"): released on Old Gold in Oct'83 by Old Gold Records. Distributed by: Lightning, Jazz Music, Spartan, Counterpoint

I BELIEVE.
Single (7"): released on Decca in Mar'64 by Decca Records. Distributed by: Polygram

SIX TRACK HITS.
Tracks: / The sound of silence / Marie / Hello Dolly / Me with all your heart / Marta / Mame.
Double compact disc: released on Scoop 33 in Sep'83 by Pickwick Records. Distributed by: H.R. Taylor

Cassette: released on Scoop 33 in Sep'83 by Pickwick Records. Distributed by: H.R. Taylor

SUFFER LITTLE CHILDREN.
Single (7"): released on President in Nov'81 by President Records. Distributed by: Taylors, Spartan

WORLD OF THE BACHELORS, (THE).
Tracks: / Charmaine / If ever I would leave you / Mame / My foolish heart / Marie / Love isn't love / Diane / No arms can ever hold you / He's got the whole world in his hands / You were meant for me / The sound of silence / The unicorn.
Album: released on Decca in '68 by Decca Records. Distributed by: Polygram Deleted '81.

Cassette: released on Decca in '68 by Decca Records. Distributed by: Polygram

Bachman Turner Overdrive

B T O.
Tracks: / For the weekend / Just look at me now / My sugaree / City's still growin' / Another fool / Lost in a fantasy / Toledo / Service with a smile.
Notes: This album commemorates the end of the re-formed Bachman Turner Overdrive. In the summer of 1983 Randy Bachman met again with Garry Peterson and Burton Cummings, former members of the Guess Who, and they went on to mount a reunion tour, and the band then went into studios in Vancouver and recorded the album.
Album: released on Compleat in Nov'84 by Compleat Records. Distributed by: PRT

Cassette: released on Compleat in Nov'84 by Compleat Records. Distributed by: PRT

FOR THE WEEKEND.
Single (7"): released on Compleat in Sep'84 by Compleat Records. Distributed by: PRT

GREATEST HITS:BACHMAN TURNER OVERDRIVE.
Album: released on Mercury in Aug'81 by Phonogram Records. Distributed by: Polygram Distribution

Cassette: released on Mercury in Aug'81 by Phonogram Records. Distributed by: Polygram Distribution

LIVE FOR LIFE.
Album: released on MCA in Aug'86 by MCA Records. Distributed by: Polygram, MCA

Cassette: released on MCA in Aug'86 by MCA Records. Distributed by: Polygram, MCA

OVERDRIVE- GREATEST HITS.
Compact disc: by Phonogram Records. Distributed by: Polygram Distribution

YOU AIN'T SEEN NOTHING YET.
Tracks: / Four wheel drive / She's a devil / You ain't seen nothing yet / Gimme your money please / Free wheelin' / Not fragile / Roll on down the highway / My wheels won't turn / Take it like a man.
Album: released on Mercury in Oct'83 by Phonogram Records. Distributed by: Polygram Distribution

Cassette: released on Mercury in Oct'83 by Phonogram Records. Distributed by: Polygram Distribution

Single (7"): released on Mercury in Oct'84 by Phonogram Records. Distributed by: Polygram Distribution

Bach, Othello

LILLY, WILLY AND THE MAIL-ORDER WITCH.
Cassette: released on Caedmon(USA) in '84 by Caedmon (USA) Records. Distributed by: Gower, Taylors, Discovery

WHOEVER HEARD OF A FIRD? Performed by Joel Grey.
Cassette: released on Caedmon(USA) in '84 by Caedmon (USA) Records. Distributed by: Gower, Taylors, Discovery

Bach's Greatest Hits

BACH'S GREATEST HITS (Various Artists).
Cassette: released on CBS in Jul'83 by CBS Records. Distributed by: CBS

Back Bite Band

THRU THE MIDDLE OF THE HOUSE.
Single (7"): released on Savoir Faire in Oct'84

Back Door

ANOTHER FINE MESS.
Album: released on Warner Brothers in Jan'75 by Warner Bros Records. Distributed by: WEA

Backhouse, Miriam

GYPSY WITHOUT A ROAD.
Album: released on Mother Earth in Aug'77 Distributed by: Folksound Distribution, JSU Distribution, Jazz Music Distribution, Projection Distribution, Celtic Music Distribution

Back In The Saddle Again

BACK IN THE SADDLE AGAIN Various artists (Various Artists).
Tracks: / Old Chisholm trail, The / Pot wrassler, The / Gol-durned wheel, The / When the work's all done this fall / Streets of Laredo / Sioux Indians / Dying cowboy, The / Tying a knot in the devils tail / Strawberry Road / Lone Star Trail, The / Ridge runnin' road / Whoopee-ti-yi-yo / Cowhand's last ride / Little old log shack I always call my home / A-ridin' old paint / I want to be a cowboy's sweetheart / Cattle call / One more ride / Dim narrow trail / I want to be a real cowboy girl / Back in the saddle again / My dear old Arizona home / Cowboy stomp / D-Bar-2 horse wrangler / City boarders / Cowboys, The / Rusty spurs / Cowboy song.
Notes: Mono recording Producer and program consultant: Charlie Seermann
Double Album: released on New World (USA) in Sep'86 by New World Records (USA). Distributed by: Conifer

Back In Your Own Backyard

BACK IN YOUR OWN BACKYARD (Various Artists).
Cassette: released on Dansan in Jan'80 by Spartan Records. Distributed by: Spartan

Backlash

BACKLASH (Various Artists).
Album: released on Criminal Damage in May'85 by Criminal Damage Records. Distributed by: Backs, Cartel

Back o' Benachie

BACK O' BENACHIE Songs and ballads from the lowland east of Scotland.
Album: Distributed by: Roots Distribution

Backstage

BACKSTAGE.
Tracks: / Tell me / Movin' on / This kind of blues / keep on lovin' / I'll never get there / Let your daddy role / You get me like you want / Cold water flat blues / That's wrong / Going back on the road / Boogie woogie.
Album: released on Sonet in Jan'81 by Sonet Records. Distributed by: PRT

Back To Buchan

BACK TO BUCHAN (Various Artists).
Cassette: released on Ross in Jun'86 by Ross Records. Distributed by: Ross Distribution, Roots Distribution

Back To The Future

BACK TO THE FUTURE Soundtrack (Various Artists).
Tracks: / Johnny B. Goode / Power of love, The / Time bomb town / Back to the future / Heaven is one step away / Back in time / Back to the future overture / Wallflower(dance with me Henry),The / Night train / Earth angel (will you be mine).
Album: released on MCA in Feb'86 by MCA Records. Distributed by: Polygram, MCA

Cassette: released on MCA in Feb'86 by MCA Records. Distributed by: Polygram, MCA

Compact disc: released on MCA in Feb'86 by MCA Records. Distributed by: Polygram, MCA

Backus, Gus

DAMALS.
Tracks: / Wooden heart (Muss I denn zum Stadtele hinaus) / Sieben susse girls (Seven little girls) / Hatt' ich dock ein girl (If I had a girl) / Brauner Bar und weisse Taube (Running Bear) / Ab und zu (A fool such as I) / Das ist viel zu schon, um wahr zu sein / Baby deine beine (Lyin' kisses) / Ich bin traurig, wenn du gehst (Have you ever had the blues) / Damals (Your love) / Wein' nicht mehr (Teenage tears) / Blue boy (Lonely blue boy) / Ich leibe dich so sehr (A story of my love) / Ich steh' an der Bar und habe kein geld (A pub with no beer) / Da sprach der alte hauptling / Big Willie broke jail tonight (Englischer Gersang) / Short on love (Englischer Gesang).
Album: released on Polydor (Germany) in '80. Distributed by: IMS-Polygram

Bacon Fat

GREASE ONE FOR ME.
Album: released on Line (Germany) in Feb'84

Badarou, Wally

BACK TO SCALES TONIGHT.
Album: released on Polydor in May'82 by Polydor Records. Distributed by: Polygram, Polydor

CHEIF INSPECTOR.
Single (12"): released on Fourth & Broadway in Nov'85 by Island Records. Distributed by: Polygram, EMI

CHIEF INSPECTOR.
Single (7"): released on Fourth & Broadway in Oct'85 by Island Records. Distributed by: Polygram, EMI

Single (12"): released on Fourth & Broadway in Oct'85 by Island Records. Distributed by: Polygram, EMI

COUNTRYMAN THEME.
Single (7"): released on Island in Apr'82 by Island Records. Distributed by: Polygram

Album: released on Island in May'85 by Island Records. Distributed by: Polygram

Cassette: released on Island in May'85 by Island Records. Distributed by: Polygram

Compact disc: released on Island in May'85 by Island Records. Distributed by: Polygram

ECHOES.
Tracks: / Keys / Hi life / Mambo / Voices / Canyons / Endless race / Chief inspector / Waltz / Jungle / Rain.
Notes: Known as the Profit for his pioneering work with his particular keyboard. Wally Badarou has provided keyboard arrangements and compositions for various soundtracks and prominent artists including Level 42's first two albums and Nightclubbing for Grace Jones.
Compact disc: by Island Records. Distributed by: Polygram

HI-LIFE.
Tracks: / Hi-life (radio edit).
Single (7"): released on Fourth & Broadway in Oct'86 by Island Records. Distributed by: Polygram, EMI

NOVELA DAS NOVE.
Tracks: / Novela das nove / Chief Inspector (precinct 13) / Endless race **.
Single (7"): released on Fourth & Broadway in Mar'86 by Island Records. Distributed by: Polygram, EMI

Bad Boys Blue

YOU'RE A WOMAN.
Single 7": released on Zaytron, Oct'86 by Zaytron Records. Dist: Spartan

Single 12": released on Zaytron, Oct'86 by Zaytron Records. Dist: Spartan

Bad Brains

BAD BRAINS.
Cassette: Dist: Red Rhino, Cartel

Single 12": released on Alternative, Jun'82

I AGAINST I.
Album: released on SST (USA), Nov'86 Dist: Pinnacle

I AND I SURVIVE/DESTROY BABYLON.
Single 12": released on Food For Thought, Mar'83 by Music For Nations Records. Dist: Pinnacle

ROCK FOR LIGHT.
Album: released on PVC, '87 Dist: Pacific

Album: released on PVC, '87 Dist: Pacific

Bad Breed Band

HEY LITTLE GIRL.
Single 12": released on Bad Breed, Apr'83 by Bad Breed Records. Dist: Jetstar

Bad Caesar

DADDY'S BEEN WORKING.
Tracks: / Daddy's been working / Demon lover
Single 7": released on GFM, 13 Jun'87 by GFM Records. Dist: Fast Forward, Cartel, Cadillac, Jazz Music

Single 12": released on GFM, 13 Jun'87 by GFM Records. Dist: Fast Forward, Cartel, Cadillac, Jazz Music

Bad Company

10 FROM 6.
Tracks: / Can't get enough / Feel like makin' love / Run with the pack / Shooting star / Movin' on / Bad company / Rock 'n' roll fantasy / Electric land / Ready for love / Live for the music
Cassette: released on Atlantic, Jan'86 by WEA Records. Dist: WEA, Swift, Celtic Music

Compact disc: released on Atlantic, Jan'86 by WEA Records. Dist: WEA, Swift, Celtic Music

BAD COMPANY.
Album: released on Island, Jan'78 by Island Records. Dist: Polygram, Celtic Music

Cassette: released on Island, Jun'81 by Island Records. Dist: Polygram, Celtic Music Deleted '85.

BURNIN' SKY.
Album: released on Island, Mar'77 by Island Records. Dist: Polygram, Celtic Music

DESOLATION ANGELS.
Album: released on Swansong, Mar'79

FAME & FORTUNE.
Tracks: / Burning up / This love / Fame & fortune / Long walk / Valerie / Hold on my heart / That girl / When we made love / If I'm sleeping / Tell it like it is
Album: released on Atlantic, Oct'86 by WEA Records. Dist: WEA, Swift, Celtic Music

Cassette: released on Atlantic, Oct'86 by WEA Records. Dist: WEA, Swift, Celtic Music

Compact disc: released on Atlantic, Oct'86 by WEA Records. Dist: WEA, Swift, Celtic Music

Single 7": released on Atlantic, Feb'87 by WEA Records. Dist: WEA, Swift, Celtic Music

RUN WITH THE PACK.
Tracks: / Live for the music / Simple man / Honey child / Love me somebody / Run with the pack / Silver blue and gold / Young blood / Do right by your woman / Sweet lil' sister / Fade away
Album: released on Island, Jan'78 by Island Records. Dist: Polygram, Celtic Music

Cassette: released on Island, Jun'81 by Island Records. Dist: Polygram, Celtic Music

STRAIGHT SHOOTER.
Tracks: / Good lovin' gone bad / Feel like makin' lov / Weep no more / Shooting star / Deal with the preacher / Wild fire women / Anna / Call on me
Album: released on Island, Jan'78 by Island Records. Dist: Polygram, Celtic Music Deleted '85.

THIS LOVE.
Tracks: / This love / Tell it like it is / Burning up ** / Fame & fortune **
Single 7": released on Atlantic, Nov'86 by WEA Records. Dist: WEA, Swift, Celtic Music

Single 12": released on Atlantic, Nov'86 by WEA Records. Dist: WEA, Swift, Celtic Music
Media Note: "**" = extra track on 12" only

Bad Dress Sense

GOODBYE...IT WAS FUN.
Album: released on Vinyl Solution, Jul'87 Dist: Pinnacle

Bad Girls

CONGA/IT'S NOT THE ROCK.
Single 7": released on Spinach, Nov'81

Bad Karma Beckons

MUTATE AND SURVIVE.
Tracks: / Mutate and survive
Album: released on Media Burn, Dec'86 by Rocks Off Record Emporium. Dist: Rough Trade, Cartel

Bad Lizard

POWER OF DESTRUCTION.
Album: released on Roadrunner(Germany), Jan'86 by Roadrunner Records (Germany). Dist: Pinnacle, Celtic Music

Bad Luck 'N' Trouble

BAD LUCK 'N TROUBLE (Various artists).
Album: by Arhoolie Records. Dist: Jazz Music, Projection, Roots, Celtic Music, Cadillac, Ross, Duncans, Impetus

Bad Manners

CAN CAN.
Tracks: / Lorraine / Can can / My girl lollipop / Walking in the sunshine / Special brew / Runaway / Echo 4-2 / El pussy cat / Here comes the major / Lip up fatty / Lorraine / Ivor the engine / Tequila / Never will change
Single 7": released on Old Gold, Jan'87 by Old Gold Records. Dist: PRT, Counterpoint, Lightning, Jazz Music, Taylors

Single 12": released on Old Gold, Jan'87 by Old Gold Records. Dist: PRT, Counterpoint, Lightning, Jazz Music, Taylors*

Album: released on Pickwick, Apr'84 by Pickwick Records. Dist: PRT, Clyde Factors

Cassette: released on Pickwick, Apr'84 by Pickwick Records. Dist: PRT, Clyde Factors

Single 7": released on Magnet, Nov'85 by Magnet Records. Dist: BMG

FORGING AHEAD (IV FOR ENTERTAINMENT).
Tracks: / Salad bar / Tonight is your night / Samson and Delilah / Exodus / Got no brains / Rose of Italy / My girl lollipop / Falling our of love / Seventh heaven
Recording Notes: originally issued November, 1982.
Album: released on Magnet, Jul'83 by Magnet Records. Dist: BMG

Cassette: released on Magnet, Jul'83 by Magnet Records. Dist: BMG

GOSH IT'S BAD MANNERS.
Tracks: / Walking in the sunshine / Dansetta / Can-can / Weeping and wailing / Casablanca / Don't be angry / Ben. E. Wriggle / Runaway / Never change / Only funkin' / End of the world / Gherkin
Recording Notes: Originally released September, 1981. Produced by Roger Lomas.
Album: released on Magnet, '83 by Magnet Records. Dist: BMG

Cassette: released on Magnet, '83 by Magnet Records. Dist: BMG

HEIGHT OF, THE.
Tracks: / Special brew / Ne-ne-na-na-na-nu-nu / Lip up fatty / Woolly bully / Lorraine / Just a feeling / Inner London violence / Buona sera / Walking in the sunshine / Can-can / Samson and Delilah / My girl lollipop / Got no brains / Elizabethan reggae / Falling out of love / That'll do nicely
Album: released on Telstar, Apr'83 by Telstar Records. Dist: BMG

Cassette: released on Telstar, Apr'83 by Telstar Records. Dist: BMG

LOONEE TUNES.
Tracks: / Echo / Just a feeling / El pussy cat / Doris / Spy I / Tequila / Lorraine / Echo gone wrong / Suicide / The under sea adventures of Ivor the engine / Back in '60 / Just pretendin'
Recording Notes: Originally issued October, 1980.
Album: released on Magnet, '83 by Magnet Records. Dist: BMG

Cassette: released on Magnet, '83 by Magnet Records. Dist: BMG

SKA 'N' B.
Tracks: / Ne-ne-na-na-na-na-nu-nu / Here comes the major / Fattie fattie / King ska fa / Monster mash / Calonia / Magnificent 7 / Woolly bully / Lip up fatty / Special brew / Inner London violence
Recording Notes: Originally issued in April, 1980.
Album: released on Magnet, '83 by Magnet Records. Dist: BMG

Cassette: released on Magnet, '83 by Magnet Records. Dist: BMG

SPECIAL BREW.
Tracks: / Lip up fatty
Single 7": released on Old Gold, Jan'87 by Old

Gold Records. Dist: PRT, Counterpoint, Lightning, Jazz Music, Taylors

Bad News

BAD NEWS.
Tracks: / Hey hey bad news / Warriors of Ghengis Khan / Bohemian rhapsody / Bad News / Masturbike / Drink 'til I die
Compact disc: released on EMI, Sep'87 by EMI Records(UK). Dist: EMI

Compact disc: released on EMI, Oct'87 by EMI Records(UK). Dist: EMI

Album: released on EMI, 10 Oct'87 by EMI Records(UK). Dist: EMI

Cassette: released on EMI, 10 Oct'87 by EMI Records(UK). Dist: EMI

BOHEMIAN RHAPSODY.
Tracks: / Bohemian rhapsody / Life with Brian
Picture disc single: released on EMI, Sep'87 by EMI Records(UK). Dist: EMI

Single 7": released on EMI, Sep'87 by EMI Records(UK). Dist: EMI Media Note: Scratch & sniff pic bag.

Single 7": released on EMI, Aug'87 by EMI Records(UK). Dist: EMI

Video-cassette (VHS): released on EMI, Oct'87 by EMI Records(UK). Dist: EMI

CASHING IN ON CHRISTMAS.
Tracks: / Cashing in on Christmas (7" version) / Cashing in on Christmas (Let's Bank mix) / Bad News
Single 7": released on EMI, Nov'87 by EMI Records(UK). Dist: EMI

Single 12": released on EMI, Nov'87 by EMI Records(UK). Dist: EMI

Single 7": released on EMI, 28 Nov'87 by EMI Records(UK). Dist: EMI

Bad River Band

WHISTLE STOP.
Cassette: released on VFM Cassettes, May'85 by VFM Records., Wynd-Up

Bad Seed

J-BECK STORY, THE.
Album: released on Eva-Lolita, Feb'84 Dist: Pinnacle

Bad Spell...

BAD SPELL FOR THE WORST WITCH, A (Murphy, Jill).
Recording Notes: For full details see under - Murphy, Jill

Bad Steve

KILLING THE NIGHT.
Album: released on Mausoleum, May'85 by Mausoleum Records. Dist: Pinnacle

Bad Tune Men

DO THE SWAMP.
Single 7": released on Nonchalant, Jul'85 Dist: Revolver*

Bad Tuneman

JAILHEAD RACK.
Single 12": released on Nonchalant, Jan'87 Dist: Revolver*

Badge

SILVER WOMAN.
Single 7": released on Metal Minded, Oct'81 by Neat Records. Dist: Bullet

Badi, Mark

CHANGES.
Single 7": released on Sour Grape, May'85 by Sour Grape Records. Deleted '87.

Badoo

I GOT LOVE IN THE MORNING.
Single 12": released on Yah Congo, Nov'82 by Yah Congo Records. Dist: Jetstar

Baez, Joan

100 MINUTES OF JOAN BAEZ.
Cassette: released on PRT, Jun'82 by PRT Records.

ANY DAY NOW.
Tracks: / Love minus zero / No limit / You ain't goin' nowhere / Drifter's escape / I pity the poor immigrant / Tears of rage / Sad eyed lady of the lowlands / Love is just a four letter word / I dreamed I saw St. Augustine / Walls of red wing, The / Dear Landlord / One too many mornings / I shall be released / Boots of Spanish leather / Walkin' down the line / Restless farewell
Album: by PRT Records.

BALLAD BOOK.
Tracks: / Fare thee well
Recording Notes: 2LP set. A definitive collection of Joan Baez's most beautiful and haunting early performances of the classic British and American ballads and folksongs   tracks :same as 'Joan Baez ballad book'except 10,000 miles replaced by   'Fare thee well'

Gold Records. Dist: PRT, Counterpoint, Lightning, Jazz Music, Taylors

TOSSING IN MY SLEEP.
Tracks: / Tossing in my sleep / Louie louie
Single 7": released on Portrait (USA), Feb'86 by CBS Records. Dist: CBS

Double Album: released on Vanguard(USA), Apr'84 Dist: IMS, Polygram

BEST OF JOAN BAEZ.
Cassette: released on Pickwick, Mar'84 by Pickwick Records. Dist: PRT, Clyde Factors

Album: released on Hallmark, Aug'85 by Pickwick Records.

Cassette: released on Hallmark, Aug'85 by Pickwick Records.

Album: released on A&M, Mar'82 by A&M Records. Dist: Polygram

Cassette: released on A&M, Mar'82 by A&M Records. Dist: Polygram

BLESSED ARE.
Tracks: / Blessed are... / Night they drove old Dixie down, The / Salt of the earth, The / Three horses / Brand new Tennessee waltz, The / Last lonely and wretched / Lincoln freed me today / Otside the Nashville City Limits / San Francisco Mabel Joy / When time is stolen / Heaven help us all / Angeline / Help me make it through the night / Let it be / Put your hand in the hand / Gabriel / And me / Milanese waltz / Marie Flora / Hitch-hikers song, The / 33rd of August, The / Fifteen months
Double Album: by PRT Records.

CONTEMPORARY BALLAD BOOK.
Tracks: / North country blues / It ain't me babe / Children of darkness / E'era un ragazzo che come me amaya / Beatles E I Rolling stones / I am a poor way farin' stranger / Birmingham Sunday / San Francisco Mabel Joy / Be not too hard / Restless farewell / Rangers command / Long black veil / Hickory wind / Lady came from Baltimore, The / I dreamed I saw St. Augustine / Tramp on the street / Saigon bride / Donna Donna / Song in the blood / Magic wood, The / Babe I'm gonna leave you
Double Album: released on Vanguard, Nov'74 by PRT Records.

COUNTRY MUSIC.
Double Album: released on Vanguard, Oct'79 by PRT Records.

Album: by PRT Records.

FAREWELL ANGELINA.
Tracks: / Farewell Angelina / Daddy, you've been on my mind / It's all over now / Baby blue / Will you go laddie go / Rangers command, The / Colours / Satisfied mind / A/ River in the pines, The / Pauvre rutebauf / Sagt mir wo die blumen sind(Where have all the flowers gone) / Hard rains a gonna fall, A
Recording Notes: Digital Stereo
Compact disc: released on Accord(France), Jun'84 Dist: Discovery

FIRST 10 YEARS.
Tracks: / Ghetto, The / If I were a carpenter / Silver dagger / Love is a four letter word / There but for fortune / Will the circle be unbroken / John Riley / You ain't goin' nowhere / Mary Hamilton / Carry it on / Manha de carnavl / If I knew
Double Album: by PRT Records.

GOLDEN HOUR: JOAN BAEZ VOL.3.
Cassette: released on Golden Hour, Apr'77 by PRT Records.

GOLDEN HOUR PRESENTS JOAN BAEZ
Album: released on Golden Hour, Mar'76 by PRT Records.

Album: released on Golden Hour, Mar'76 by PRT Records.

GREATEST HITS:JOAN BAEZ.
Tracks: / Night they drove old Dixie down, The / Help me make it through the night / It's all over now, baby blue / If I were a carpenter / Put your hand in the hand / House of the rising sun / Will the circle be unbroken / Let it be / Farewell Angelina / Sagt mir wo die blumen sind(Where have all the flowers gone)
Compact disc: released on IMS, '84 by Polydor Records. Dist: IMS, Polygram

HITS GREATEST & OTHERS.
Tracks: / Night they drove old Dixie down, The / Dangling conversation / Help me make it through the night / Blessed are... / Eleanor Rigby / Let it be / There but for fortune / Brand new Tennessee waltz, The / I pity the poor immigrant / Love is a four letter word / Heaven help us all
Album: released on Vanguard, '73 by PRT Records.

JOAN BAEZ.
Tracks: / Silver dagger / East Virginia / Ten thousand miles / House of the rising sun / All my trials / Wildwood flower / Donna donna / John Riley / Rake and the rambling boy / Little moses / Mary Hamilton / Henry Martin / El preso numero nuevo / We real cowboy / There but for the fortune / Plasir d'armour / Babe I'm gonna leave you / Night they drove old dixie down, The / Don't think twice it's alright / Long black veil / Hard rain s gonna fall, A / It ain't me babe / Black is the colour / Last thing on my mind, The / Help me make it through the night / Farewell Angelina / Bachianas Brasilias No.5 / Lady came from Baltimore / It's all over now baby blue / Hush little baby
Album: by PRT Records.

JOAN BAEZ BALLAD BOOK, THE.
Tracks: / East Virginia / Henry Martin / All my trials / Old blue / House of rising son / Wagoner's lad / Black is the colour of my true love's hair / Lily of the West / Silkie / House carpenter / Trees they do grow high, The / 10,000 miles / Barbara Allen / Jackaroe / John Riley / Matty Groves / Queen of hearts / Fe-nario / Go way from my window / Railroad boy / Mary Hamilton / Once I had a sweetheart / Silver dagger
Double Album: by PRT Records.

JOAN BAEZ IN CONCERT.
Double Album: released on Musidisc(France), Jun'84 Dist: Discovery, Swift

---

JOAN BAEZ IN CONCERT.
Tracks: / Babe / I'm gonna leave you / Geordie / Copper Kettle / Kubaya / What have they done to the rain / Black is the colour of my true love's hair / Danger water / Gospel ship / House carpenter, The / Pretty boy floyd / Lady Mary / Ate amanha / Matty Groves
Album: by PRT Records.

JOAN BAEZ IN CONCERT VOL.2.
Tracks: / Once I had a sweetheart / Jackaroe / Don't think twice it's alright / We shall overcome / Portland Town / Queen of hearts / Manha de carnaval / Te ador / Long black veil / Fennario / Ne belle cardillo / With god on our side / Three fishers / Hush little baby / Battle Hymn of the republic
Album: by PRT Records.

JOAN BAEZ LOVESONG ALBUM, THE.
Tracks: / Come all ye fair and tender ladies / No limit / Sweet Sir Galahad / Love is just a four-letter word / Wild mountain thyme, The / Lass from the low country, The / Sad eyes lady of the lowlands / Plaisir d'armour
Double Album: released on Vanguard, Oct'76 by PRT Records.

Cassette: released on Vanguard, Oct'76 by PRT Records.

JOAN BAEZ VOL.5.
Tracks: / There but for fortune / Stewball / It ain't me babe / Death of Queen Jane, The / Child No.170 / Bachianas Brasileires No.5 -Aria / Go 'way from my window / I still miss someone / When you hear them cuckoos hollerin' / Birmingham Sunday / So we'll go no more a- roving / O'Cangaceiro / Unquiet grave,The / Child No. 78
Album: by PRT Records

NIGHT THEY DROVE OLD DIXIE DOWN.
Single 7": released on Flashback, Jan'83 by Flashback Records/PRT Records. Dist: Mainline

---

ONE DAY AT A TIME.
Tracks: / Sweet Sir Gallahad / No expectations / Long black veil / Ghetto / Carry it on / Take me back to the sweet sunny south / Seven bridges road / Jolie blonde / Joe Hill / Song for David / One day at a time
Album: by PRT Records.

SPOTLIGHT ON JOAN BAEZ.
Tracks: / There but for fortune / Lady came from Baltimore / Suzanne / Don't think twice / All my trials / We shall overcome / It's all over now baby blue / Farewell Angelina / It ain't me babe / If I were a carpenter / Joe Hill / Long black veil / Love's just a four letter word / Love minus zero / No limit / Blessed are / What have they done to rain / I shall be released / Sagt Mir wo die blumen sind(Where have all the flowers gone) / Night they drove old Dixie down / Eleanor Rigby / Donna donna / Colours / Let it be / Hush little baby
Double Album: released on PRT, '80 by PRT Records.

Cassette: released on PRT, '80 by PRT Records.

VERY EARLY JOAN.
Tracks: / Last night I had the strangest dream / Willie Moore / She's a trouble maker / Tears in my eyes / Somebody got lost in a storm / Water is wide, The / Man of constant sorrow / Freight train / Lady gay / Johnny Cuckoo / Lonesome valley / Riddle song, The / Streets of Laredo / Railroad Bill / My good old man / Little darlin' / In the pines / Pilgrim of sorrow / Where have all the flowers gone / Rambler gambler / Come all ye fair and tender maidens / Hallowed by thy name / Twelves gates to the city / Silver dagger
Recording Notes: During the early 1960's, at the outset of Joan Baez's remarkable career,VanguardRecords released but one long playing record per year of her performances .The inclusions were lovinly culled from numerous recording sessions and from on- location recordings of 45 full length concerts presented at auditoriums in major cities and universities in every region of North America. Both Joan and her record producer well known that many of the unreleased performanceswere equal in quality to those which were actually issued ;and it was their hope that those performances would eventuasilt appear. But events rapidly overtook and nullified their expectations.By the mid 1960's the unaccompanied folksinger was quickly becoming anachronistic -well- loved but somehow prehistoric.Folk ballads and folksongs were giving way to folk style contempory songs, at first discreetly accompanied by traditional and acoustic instruments, but very soon to be clothed in full-scale arrangements in varied styles -country,rock,popular .So many classic early Joan Baez performances remained on the shore, awaiting a more fav-ourable time.This double album is evidence that that time has now arrived. It cantains 24 performances of Joan Baez' favourites -including a couple of affect-ionate rock n roll parodies-recorded at 15 concerts through out the Continental United States between November 11th, 1961 (Town hall) and August 17th, 1963 (Forest Hill Stadium). Included are two extraordinary duets by Joan and Pete Seeger-an historic and bbeautiful collabration - recorded on November 16th 1962 , at Bushnell Auditorium in Hartford.
Double Album: released on Vanguard, Jan'83 by PRT Records.

Double cassette: released on Vanguard, Jan'83 by PRT Records.

WHERE ARE YOU NOW MY SON.
Album: released on A&M, '73 by A&M Records. Dist: Polygram

Bag Of Sleepers

FRIDAY NIGHT Vol 1 1927-32.
Album: released on Arcadia, Apr'79 Dist: Cartel

HOT LICKS Vol 2 1927-30.
Album: released on Arcadia, Apr'79 Dist: Cartel

SPIKED BEER Vol 3 1927-30.
Album: released on Arcadia, Apr'79 Dist: Cartel

Bagatelle

DON'T SAY NO.
Tracks: / Don't say no / Golden days
Single 7": released on Roxy, May'86 by Ritz Records. Dist: Spartan*

Compact disc: released on Capitol, Apr'87 by Capitol Records. Dist: EMI

GOLD.
Tracks: / Summer in Dublin / Love is the reason / Is it raining in Paris tonight? / Jersey girl / Lesson street lady / Rock 'n' roll fantasy / Outrageous / Second violin / Trump card / Johnny set 'em up tonight / Baby's looking good tonight / I need you / Hurting inside / All fall down Philadelphia
Recording Notes: Popular Irish pop group Bagatelle with a new compilation of their best known numbers.including their 1981 hit single "Second violin" and their new single "Hurting Inside".
Album: released on Polydor(Ireland), Sep'85 by Polydor Records. Dist: Polygram, I & B, Celtic Music, Jazz Music

Cassette: released on Polydor(Ireland), Sep'85 by Polydor Records. Dist: Polygram, I & B, Celtic Music, Jazz Music

---

GOLD - THE BEST OF BAGATELLE.
Tracks: / Summer in Dublin / Love is the reason / Is it raining in Paris to-night / Jersey girl / Leeson street lady / Rock 'n' roll fantasy / Outrageous / Second violin / Trump card / Johnny set them up tonight / Baby's looking good tonight / I need you / Hurting inside / All fall down Philadelphia
Album: released on Polydor(Ireland), Jul'85 by Polydor Records. Dist: Polygram, I & B, Celtic Music, Jazz Music

Cassette: released on Polydor(Ireland), Jul'85 by Polydor Records. Dist: Polygram, I & B, Celtic Music, Jazz Music

Compact disc: released on Polydor(Ireland), Jul'85 by Polydor Records. Dist: Polygram, I & B, Celtic Music, Jazz Music

Bagga Puss & Curlew

PARTY INNA CHELSEA.
Tracks: / Party inna Chelsea / Party inna Chelsea (version)
Single 12": released on Street Beat, Aug'86 by Decca Records. Dist: Polygrama*

Baghdad Five

LOVIN' AFFECTION.
Single 7": released on Risky, Jan'84 Dist: Pinnacle

Bagley, Desmond

RUNNING BLIND.
Recording Notes: This two-&-half hour adventure read by Martin Jarvis begins as a simple task & gradually becomes more complicated as Alan Stewart is asked to deliver a parcel to Iceland.As he speaks the language and knows the country well,there seems to be no problem until an attempt is made on his life at Jeykjavik Airport and he begins to suspect he has been double-crossed.
Cassette: released on Listen For Pleasure, Feb'86 Dist: EMI

Baglin, Lyndon

BEST OF BRASS.
Album: released on Saydisc, Sep'85 by Saydisc Records. Dist: Taylors, Jazz Music, Swift, Projection, Essex, Gamut, Harmonia Mundi, Celtic Music

Cassette: released on Saydisc, Sep'85 by Saydisc Records. Dist: Taylors, Jazz Music, Swift, Projection, Essex, Gamut, Harmonia Mundi, Celtic Music

Bagpipe

IRELAND, SCOTLAND, BRITTANY AND GALICIA.
Album: released on Lyrichord(USA), Oct'81 by Lyrichord Records(USA). Dist: Flexitron Ltd., Roots

Bagpipe In Canada

BAGPIPE IN CANADA.
Album: released on Lyrichord(USA), Oct'81 by Lyrichord Records(USA). Dist: Flexitron Ltd., Roots

Bagpipe In Italy

BAGPIPE IN ITALY.
Album: released on Lyrichord(USA), Oct'81 by Lyrichord Records(USA). Dist: Flexitron Ltd., Roots

Bahatia, Amin

INTER STELLAR SUITE, THE.
Compact disc: released on Blue Note, Sep'87 by EMI Records(UK). Dist: EMI

Bailey, Benny

BIG BRASS.
Album: released on Candid, Dec'85 Dist: Counterpoint, Cadillac, Jazz Music, Wellard

Compact disc: released on Candid, Nov'87 Dist: Counterpoint, Cadillac, Jazz Music, Wellard

Compact disc: released on Candid, Dec'87 Dist: Counterpoint, Cadillac, Jazz Music, Wellard

---

EAST OF ISAR (Bailey, Benny/Sal Nistico).
Album: released on Ego, Oct'79 by Ego Records. Dist: Cadillac

---

ISLANDS.
Album: released on Enja(Germany), Jan'82 by Enja Records (W.Germany). Dist: Cadillac, Jazz Music

---

SERENADE TO A PLANET.
Album: released on Ego, Oct'79 by Ego Records. Dist: Cadillac

Bailey & Bridges

COME AND GET MY LOVE.
Recording Notes: Pic bag
Single 7": released on Rhythm King, Apr'87 by Mute. Dist: Rough Trade, Cartel

Single 12": released on Rhythm King, Apr'87 by Mute. Dist: Rough Trade, Cartel

Bailey, Buster

ALL ABOUT MEMPHIS.
Tracks: / Bear wallow / Hatton avenue and Gayoso street / Sunday parade / Beale street blues / Memphis blues / Chicasaw bluff / Hot water ba you
Album: released on Affinity, Oct'86 by Charly Records. Dist: Charly, Cadillac, Swift

---

COMPLETE RECORDINGS 1934-1940.
Tracks: / Call of the Delta / Shanghai shuffle / Afternoon in Africa / Dizzy Debutante / Planters Punch / Sloe Jam fizz / Chained to a dream / Light up / Man with a horn goes berzerk / Should I / Blue room, The / April in Paris / Am I blue / Seems like a month of Sundays / Fable of roses / Pinetop's boogie woogie / Eccentric rag
Album: released on Rarities, Apr'81 Dist: Wellard, Swift **Media Note:** Mono.

Album: released on Saydisc, Apr'87 by Saydisc Records. Dist: Taylors, Jazz Music, Swift, Projection, Essex, Gamut, Harmonia Mundi, Celtic Music

---

VARISITY SESSIONS VOL 1, THE (Bailey, Buster & His Orchestra).
Album: released on Storyville, Jul'81 by Storyville Records. Dist: Swift, Wellard

Bailey, Deford

HARMONICA SHOWCASE (Bailey, Deford & D.H. 'Bert' Bilbro).
Album: released on Matchbox, Oct'85 Dist: Projection, Roots, Jazz Music, Celtic Music, Taylors

Bailey, Derek

COMPANY 3 (Bailey, Derek & Hans Bennink).
Album: released on Incus, May'78 by Cadillac Music. Dist: Recommended, Cadillac, Jazz Music

---

COMPANY 5.
Album: released on Incus, '78 by Cadillac Music. Dist: Recommended, Cadillac, Jazz Music

---

CONCERT... (Bailey, Derek & Tristan Honsinger).
Album: released on Incus, Nov'76 by Cadillac Music. Dist: Recommended, Cadillac, Jazz Music

---

DROPS (Bailey, Derek & Andrea Centazzo).
Album: released on Incus, Dec'77 by Cadillac Music. Dist: Recommended, Cadillac, Jazz Music

---

LIVE FROM VERITY'S PLACE (Bailey, Derek & Hans Bennink).
Album: released on Incus, Nov'76 by Cadillac Music. Dist: Recommended, Cadillac, Jazz Music

---

LONDON CONCERT (Bailey, Derek & Evan Parker).

Album: released on Incus, Nov'76 by Cadillac Music. Dist: Recommended, Cadillac, Jazz Music

---

LOT 74-SOLO IMPROVISATIONS.
Album: released on Incus, Nov'76 by Cadillac Music. Dist: Recommended, Cadillac, Jazz Music

---

SOLO.
Album: released on Incus, Nov'76 by Cadillac Music. Dist: Recommended, Cadillac, Jazz Music

Bailey, Errol

DANCE TO REGGAE MUSIC.
Single 12": released on Foundation, Oct'83 by Foundation Records, The. Dist: Jetstar

Bailey, James

I'M YOUR SUGAR.
Tracks: / I'm your sugar (Dub Mix)
Single 12": released on Willow Tree, Feb'87 Dist: Jetstar

Bailey, Mildred

ALL OF ME.
Album: released on Monmouth Evergreen, May'79 Dist: Jazz Music, Swift

---

MILDRED BAILEY 1938/39.
Album: released on Jazz Document, Jul'82 Dist: Jazz Music

MILDRED BAILEY WITH THE PAUL BARONS ORCHESTRA 1944.
Album: released on London, Oct'79 by London Records. Dist: Polygram

---

RARE OF ALL RAREST PERFORMANCES VOL 1.
Album: released on Kings Of Jazz, Jul'82 Dist: Jazz Horizons, Jazz Music, Celtic Music

---

UNCOLLECTED MILDRED BAILEY, THE (CBS Radio Show).
Tracks: / Please don't talk about me / St. Louis blues / I'll get by / Someday sweetheart / From the land of the sky-blue water / Body & soul / China boy / It had to be you / I'll never be the same / Man I love, The / I dream of you / Four in a bar / Lover come back / I didn't know / Evelina / I never knew
Album: released on Hindsight(UK), May'79 Dist: Jazz Music

Bailey, Pearl

LENA HORNE & PEARL BAILEY.
Album: released on Jazz Greats, Jan'79 Dist: Swift

Bailey, Phillip

CHINESE WALL.
Tracks: / Photogenic memory / I go crazy / Walking on the Chinese wall / For every heart that's been broken / Go / Easy lover / Show you the way to love / Time is a woman / Woman / Children of the Ghetto
Album: released on CBS, Nov'86 by CBS Records. Dist: CBS

Cassette: released on CBS, Nov'86 by CBS Records. Dist: CBS

Compact disc: by CBS Records. Dist: CBS **Media Note:** AAD

Album: released on CBS, Nov'84 by CBS Records. Dist: CBS Deleted '87.

Cassette: released on CBS, Nov'84 by CBS Records. Dist: CBS Deleted '87.

CONTINUATION.
Tracks: / I know / It's our time / Desire / I'm waiting for your love / Vaya (go with love) / Good guy's supposed to get the girls, The / Your boyfriend's back / I know / Trapped / It's our time / Desire / I'm waitin' for your love / Vaya (go with love) / Good guy's supposed to get the girls, The / Your boyfriend's back
Album: released on CBS, Feb'86 by CBS Records. Dist: CBS **Media Note:** Re-issue

Cassette: released on CBS, Feb'86 by CBS Records. Dist: CBS **Media Note:** Re-issue

Album: released on CBS, Sep'83 by CBS Records. Dist: CBS Deleted '85.

Cassette: released on CBS, Sep'83 by CBS Records. Dist: CBS

ECHO MY HEART.
Tracks: / Echo my heart / Take this with you / Walking on the Chinese Wall ** / Children of the ghetto **
Single 7": released on CBS, Jul'86 by CBS Records. Dist: CBS

Single 12": released on CBS, Jul'86 by CBS Records. Dist: CBS **Media Note:** Extra tracks on 12" only

INSIDE OUT.
Tracks: / Welcome to the club / State of the heart / Long distance love / Echo my heart / Don't leave me baby / Special effect / Because of you / Back it up / Take this with you / Day will come, The.
Album: released on CBS in May'86 by CBS Records. Distributed by: CBS

Cassette: released on CBS in May'86 by CBS Records. Distributed by: CBS

Compact disc: by CBS Records. Distributed by: CBS

STATE OF THE HEART.
Tracks: / State of the heart / Take this with you.
Single (7"): released on CBS in May'86 by CBS Records. Distributed by: CBS

Single (12"): released on CBS in May'86 by CBS Records. Distributed by: CBS

TRIUMPH.
Notes: Philip Bailey's first step into the Christian music field was with the album "The Wonders of His Love" which sold a quarter of a million copies,establishing Bailey as an artist with a following among christian listeners.This second album blends his varied musical talents."Triumph" is an aptly named mix of pop,R&B &gospel traditions,with performances by Greg Philinganes,Paul Jackson Jnr.,Andrew Woolfok (from Earth Wind & Fire).Freddie Washington,& George Duke who also wrote and played all the music on the track 'Marvellous',providing an ideal counterpart for Bailey's patented falsetto vocals.
Album: released on Myrrh in Nov'86 by Word Records. Distributed by: Word Distribution

Cassette: released on Myrrh in Nov'86 by Word Records. Distributed by: Word Distribution

WONDERS OF HIS LOVE.
Tracks: / I will no wise cast you out / I want to know you / God is love / Sing a new song / Safe in god's love / I am gold / He don't lie / Make us one / Wonders of his love.
Notes: Already picked as Time Out's album choice, this first solo Gospel release from the dynamic lead singer of Earth Wind and Fire is set to make a big impression .It's different from EW&F, more thoughtful and thought-provoking, and with a strong scriptural basis, but still with a thoroghly contemporary soul sound.
Album: released on Myrrh in Feb'85 by Word Records. Distributed by: Word Distribution

Cassette: released on Myrrh in Feb'85 by Word Records. Distributed by: Word Distribution

Bailey, Phillip

EASY LOVER (Bailey, Phillip & Phil Collins).
Single (7"): released on CBS in Mar'85 by CBS Records. Distributed by: CBS

Single (12"): released on CBS in Mar'85 by CBS Records. Distributed by: CBS Deleted '86.

Bailey, Razzy

FEELIN' RIGHT.
Tracks: / She left love all over me / I've had my limit (Of two timing women) / Blaze of glory / Travelin' time / Night life / Bad news look / Everytime you cross my mind(You break my heart) / Sittin' here wishing (I was someplace else) / I loved 'em all / Your momma and daddy sure did something right.
Album: released on RCA International in '82

Cassette: released on RCA International in '82

MAKIN' FRIENDS.
Tracks: / Friend's too far gone and much too close to you / Scratch my back and whisper in my ear / Best kept secret in town, The / Spending my nights with you / Midnight hauler / Blind faith and the naked truth / Anywhere there's a duke box / Old no Homer / Late night honky tonk country song.
Album: released on RCA in Jul'81 by RCA Records. Distributed by: RCA, Roots, Swift, Wellard, Chris, I & B, Solomon & Peres Distribution

Cassette: released on RCA in Jul'81 by RCA Records. Distributed by: RCA, Roots, Swift, Wellard, Chris, I & B, Solomon & Peres Distribution

STILL GOING STRONG.
Tracks: / Still going strong / Susie Q / Mona Lisa / Loki / Lover please come back / Let the good times roll / Linda Lou / Pretend / Sunshine / High heel sneakers.
Album: released on Sundown in Jul'87 by Magnum Music Group Ltd. Distributed by: Magnum Music Group Ltd, PRT Distribution, Spartan Distribution

Bailey, Roy

FREEDOM PEACEFULLY.
Album: released on Fuse in Aug'85 by Fuse Records. Distributed by: Projection

HARD TIMES.
Album: released on Fuse in May'86 by Fuse Records. Distributed by: Projection

IF I KNEW WHO THE ENEMY WAS... (Bailey, Roy/Leon Rosselson).
Album: released on Fuse in May'86 by Fuse Records. Distributed by: Projection

LOVE,LONELINESS,LAUNDRY (Bailey, Roy/Leon Rosselson).
Notes: Artists include Martin Carthy
Album: released on Fuse in May'86 by Fuse Records. Distributed by: Projection

NEW BELL WAKE.
Album: released on Fuse in May'86 by Fuse Records. Distributed by: Projection

ROY BAILEY.
Album: released on Fuse in May'86 by Fuse Records. Distributed by: Projection

Album: released on Leader in '81. Distributed by: Jazz Music, Projection

Baillies Mills

100,000 WELCOMES (Baillies Mills Accordian Band).
Tracks: / It's a long way to Tipperary / Pack up your troubles / Keep the home fires burning / My bonnie / Daisy, Daisy / Bunch of violets blue / If you're Irish / With my shilleleagh under my arm / McNamara's Band / My love is like a red red rose / Rowan tree / Ballad of Glencoe / Bonnie lass of Fife / Scotland the brave / I love a lassie / Home on the range / Tulips from Amsterdam / When it's springtime in The Rockies / Hiking song, The / Mitchell march, The / Westering home / Doonaree / When Irish eyes are smiling / Morningtide ride / World of our own / Carnival is over, The / Dark island / Northern lights, The / I belong to Glasgow / Dancing in the Clyde / Green glens of Antrim / Boys from Co Armagh / Mountains of Mourne / Will ye no come back again? / Shepherd's boy / Nut brown maiden.
Album: released on Homespun(Ireland) in Jun'84 by Outlet Records. Distributed by: Outlet

Cassette: released on Homespun(Ireland) in Jun'84 by Outlet Records. Distributed by: Outlet

Baily, Marcie

PLANNING TO GO.
Tracks: / Planning to go / Man can't hold a woman, A.
Single (12"): released on Technique in Aug'86 by Technique. Distributed by: CBS

Bain, Aly

ALY BAIN.
Cassette: released on Whirlie in Mar'85 by Whirlie Records. Distributed by: Roots, Projection

MIKE WHELLANS & ALY BAIN (see Whellans, Mike) (Bain, Aly & Mike Whellans).

SHETLAND FOLK FIDDLING (Bain, Aly & Tom Anderson).
Album: released on Topic in '78. Distributed by: Roots Distribution

SILVER BOW, THE (Bain, Aly & Tom Anderson).
Cassette: released on Topic in Jun'85. Distributed by: Roots Distribution

Baine, John

RANTING AT THE NATION.
Tracks: / Awayday / Contributory negligence / Albanian football / They must be Russians / Oracle / Fifth column / Fall of King Zog / Burn it down / Hands off our halibuts / Eros Products commercial / Very silly East European propaganda station.
Album: released on Cherry Red in Apr'83 by Cherry Red Records. Distributed by: Pinnacle

Baines, Murray

ON MY OWN (Baines, Murray & George Faith).
Single (12"): released on Joe Frazer in Jun'86 by Joe Frazer Records. Distributed by: Jetstar

SECRET LOVER (Baines, Murray & Bobby Floyd).
Tracks: / Secret lover / Loving mood.
Single (12"): released on Joe Frazer in Feb'86 by Joe Frazer Records. Distributed by: Jetstar

TOGETHER FOREVER (Baines, Murray & George Faith).
Tracks: / Together forever.
Album: released on Joe Frazer in Nov'86 by Joe Frazer Records. Distributed by: Jetstar

Balser

SUMMER BREEZE.
Single (7"): released on Malaco in Jun'84 by Malaco Records. Distributed by: Charly

Single (12"): released on Malaco in Jun'84 by Malaco Records. Distributed by: Charly

Baisiks

THINK ABOUT THAT.
Single (7"): released on Musician Survival in Apr'82

Baiza, Joe

CERTAIN WAY (Baiza, Joe & The Universal Congress).
Single (12"): released on SST in Aug'87 by SST Records. Distributed by: Pinnacle

Baker, Adrian

I GET AROUND (Baker, Adrian & Gidea Park).
Single (7"): released on Creole in Aug'85 by Creole Records. Distributed by: Rhino, PRT

Single (12"): released on Creole in Aug'85 by Creole Records. Distributed by: Rhino, PRT

Baker, Anita

CAUGHT UP IN A RAPTURE.
Tracks: / Mystery.
Single (7"): released on Elektra (USA) in Jan'87 by Elektra/Asylum/Nonesuch Records. Distributed by: WEA

Single (12"): released on Elektra (USA) in Jan'87 by Elektra/Asylum/Nonesuch Records. Distributed by: WEA

RAPTURE.
Tracks: / Sweet love / You bring me joy / Caught up in the rapture / Been so long / Mystery / No one in the world / Same ole love / Watch your step.
Album: released on Elektra (USA) in Apr'86 by Elektra/Asylum/Nonesuch Records. Distributed by: WEA

Cassette: released on Elektra (USA) in Apr'86 by Elektra/Asylum/Nonesuch Records. Distributed by: WEA

Compact disc: released on Elektra (USA) in Aug'86 by Elektra/Asylum/Nonesuch Records. Distributed by: WEA

SAME OLE LOVE.
Tracks: / Same ole love / Been so long.
Single (7"): released on Elektra (USA) in 30 May'87 by Elektra/Asylum/Nonesuch Records. Distributed by: WEA

Single (12"): released on Elektra (USA) in 30 May'87 by Elektra/Asylum/Nonesuch Records. Distributed by: WEA

SONGSTRESS.
Compact disc: by Pacific Records (USA). Distributed by: Atlantic

SWEET LOVE.
Tracks: / Sweet love / No one in the world / Watch your step * / Same ole love (live) ** / You bring me joy (live) ** / Watch your step (inst.) **.
Single (7"): released on Elektra (USA) in Jun'86 by Elektra/Asylum/Nonesuch Records. Distributed by: WEA

Single (12"): released on Elektra (USA) in Jun'86 by Elektra/Asylum/Nonesuch Records. Distributed by: WEA

Double-pack single: released on Elektra (USA) in Oct'86 by Elektra/Asylum/Nonesuch Records. Distributed by: WEA

Baker, Ann

Rare Louis Armstrong volume 3

Baker, Carrol

HEARTBREAK TO HAPPINESS.
Tracks: / I found a l-i-e in the middle of believe / I'm an old rock'n'roller(dancin'to a different beat) / Too late for the two of us / You are my everything / Arms that love(hearts that don't) / It always hurts like the first time / Star in momma's eyes, A / You still excite me / I'm taking care of myself / If you can't stand the heat don't light the fire / Anything but hearts.
Notes: Carrol Baker is Canada's undisputed Queen of Country Music.Achievements to date :-1million album sales & 2 platinum LP's/1 gold LP/5 gold singles/14 no.1 singles on RPM's Country Music chart.In September 1985 Carrol won the Canadian Country Music Award for Top Female Country Vocalist,the 8th time in the past eleven years she has won this award.
Album: released on Tembo in Feb'86 by Tembo (Canada). Distributed by: IMS Distribution, Polygram Distribution

Cassette: released on Tembo in Feb'86 by Tembo (Canada). Distributed by: IMS Distribution, Polygram Distribution

IT ALWAYS HURTS LIKE THE FIRST TIME.
Tracks: / It always hurts like the first time.
Single (7"): released on Tembo UK in Mar'86

Baker, Cheryl

IF PARADISE IS HALF AS NICE.
Single (7"): released on WEA in Aug'87 by WEA Records. Distributed by: WEA

Single (12"): released on WEA in Aug'87 by WEA Records. Distributed by: WEA

Baker, Chet

ALL TOGETHER (Baker, Chet, Lee Konitz & Keith Jarrett).
Album: released on Jazz Connoisseur in Apr'79. Distributed by: Jazz Horizons, Jazz Music, Swift, Wellard, Chris

BALLADS FOR TWO.
Album: released on Sandra in Sep'79

CANDY.
Album: released on Sonet in Jan'87 by Sonet Records. Distributed by: PRT

CHET.
Album: released on Riverside (USA) in Feb'84. Distributed by: Fantasy (USA) Distribution

CHET BAKER.
Album: released on Horizon in Jan'78 by A&M Records. Distributed by: CBS

CHET BAKER AND STRINGS: FEATURING ZOOT SIMS.
Tracks: / You don't know what love is / I'm thru with love / Love walked in / You better go now / I married an angel / Love / I love you / What a difference a day makes / Why should't I / Little duet, A / Wind, The / Trickledidlier.
Album: released on CBS in Jul'87 by CBS Records. Distributed by: CBS

Cassette: released on CBS in Jul'87 by CBS Records. Distributed by: CBS

CHET BAKER IN PARIS VOL 3.
Album: released on Barclay in Nov'79 by Decca Records. Distributed by: Polygram, Discovery, Conifer, IMS, Swift

CHET BAKER SEXTET & QUARTET
(Baker, Chet Sextet & Quartet).
Tracks: / Ladybird / Cheryl / Tune up / Line for Lyons / Pent up house / My old flame / Indian summer / Look for the silver lining.
Album: released on Up International in Apr'81

CHET BAKER SINGS AGAIN.
Compact disc: released on RCA Jazz (Japan) in Jun'86

CHET IS BACK.
Album: released on RCA (Germany) in Jan'85

Album: released on RCA (France) in Oct'85 by RCA Records. Distributed by: Discovery

COOL BLUES Unissued live recordings vol.2 (Baker, Chet Quintet).
Album: released on Replica in Mar'87. Distributed by: Jazz Music

COOLS OUT (Baker, Chet Quintet).
Album: released on Boplicitya in Nov'86 by Boplicity Records. Distributed by: Ace Records, Pinnacle

DAYBREAK (Baker, Chet Trio).
Album: released on Steeplechase in Apr'81

EVERYTHING HAPPENS TO ME
(Baker, Chet Trio).
Cassette: released on Timeless in Oct'86

EXITUS Unissued live recordings vol.1 (Baker, Chet Quintet).
Album: released on Replica in Mar'87. Distributed by: Jazz Music

IN CONCERT (Baker, Chet & Lee Konitz).
Album: released on India Navigation in May'84 by India Navigation Records. Distributed by: Cadillac, Projection, Swift

IN NEW YORK.
Compact disc: released on Carrere in Apr'87 by Carrere Records. Distributed by: PRT, Spartan

IN NEW YORK.
Album: released on Original Jazz Classics (USA) in Jun'86. Distributed by: Fantasy (USA) Distribution, Chris Wellard Distribution, IMS-Polygram Distribution

LIVE AT NICK'S.
Album: released on Criss Cross in Jul'87. Distributed by: Jazz Music, Jazz Horizons, Cadillac

LIVE IN SWEDEN.
Album: released on Dragon in Jun'86 by Dragon Records. Distributed by: Jazz Music, Projection, Cadillac

MR B (Baker, Chet Trio).
Tracks: / Dolphin dance / Ellen and David / Ellen and David / Strollin' / In your own sweet way / Mister B / Beatrice.
Album: released on Timeless (Holland) in Aug'85. Distributed by: JSU Distribution, Jazz Music Distribution, Jazz Horizons Distribution, Cadillac, Celtic Music Distribution

NEW BLUE HORNS (Baker, Chet/Kenny Dorham).
Tracks: / New blue horns.
Album:

PLAYBOYS (Baker, Chet & Art Pepper).
Tracks: / For minors only / Original Pepper / Resonant emotions / Tynan time / Pictures of Heath / For miles and miles / C.T.A..
Album: released on Boplicitya in Oct'83 by Boplicity Records. Distributed by: Ace Records, Pinnacle

PLAYS VLADIMIR COSMA.
Compact disc: released on Carrere in Apr'87 by Carrere Records. Distributed by: PRT, Spartan

TOUCH OF YOUR LIPS, THE (Baker, Chet Trio).
Album: released on Steeplechase in Sep'79

WITCH DOCTOR (Baker, Chet & Lighthouse All Stars).
Tracks: / Witch Doctor.
Album: released on Contemporary in Nov'86 by Contemporary Records. Distributed by: Pinnacle

Baker, Duck

FINGER STYLE JAZZ GUITAR.
Album: released on Kicking Mule in Sep'79 by Sonet. Distributed by: Roots, PRT

KING OF BONGO BONG, THE.
Tracks: / New righteous blues / Crazy rhythm / I found a new baby / No love / There'll be some changes made / See you in my dreams / I ain't go nobody / Mama's getting younger / Papa's getting older each day / Immaculate Conception rag / River blues / Chicken ain't nothing but a bird / King of bongo bong / Business as usual.
Album: released on Kicking Mule in Jan'78 by Sonet. Distributed by: Roots, PRT

THERE'S SOMETHING FOR EVERYONE IN AMERICA.
Tracks: / Jackson stomp, The / Mission street blues, The / Allegheny county / Matty powell / Zebra blues / Wolverine blues / Melancholy baby / Medley / The Jackson stomp / The mission street blues / Allegheny county / Matty Powell / Zebra blues / Wolverine blues / Melancholy baby / Take me out to the ball game / America / Temperence reel / Pineapple rag / Hicks farewell / Doctor jazz / The old folks polka / There'll be a happy meeting / The wreck of old 97.
Album: by Sonet. Distributed by: Roots, PRT-

WHEN YOU WORE A TULIP.
Tracks: / You took advantage of me / Grace street / Was / Liza (all the clouds'll roll away) / Boys from blue hill / Back home in Indiana / Rapid transit blues / Two cats with new shoes / Angeline the baker / Plymouth rock / Honeysuckle rose / Cousin / Lazy river / Drunken wagoner / When you wore a tulip / Thou swell / Boys from blue hill / Back home in Indiana / Rapid transit blues / Two cats with new shoes / Angeline the baker / Plymouth rock / Honey suckle rose / Cousin lazy / Drunken wagoner / When you wore a tulip / Thou swell.
Album: released on Kicking Mule in Jan'78 by Sonet. Distributed by: Roots, PRT-

Baker, Earl

LEGENDARY EARL BAKER CYLANDERS, THE.
Album: released on Jazz Archives in Jan'80 by Jazz Archives Records. Distributed by: Jazz Music

Baker, Ginger

FROM HUMBLE ORANGES (Baker, Ginger & Band).
Tracks: / Eleventh hour, The / Too many apples / IT / Uder the sun / On the road to granma's house / Land of mordor, The / This planet / Sore head in the morning blues / Wasting time / Lament.
Notes: A new album from legendary drummer Ginger Baker. This his first recording with his nnew band.Recorded in Italy 1982. The other members of the band are Doug Brockie -Guitars and lead Vocals, Karl Hill-Bass guitar and Vocals
Album: released on CDG(Italy) in Jun'83. Distributed by: IMS, Polygram

Cassette: released on CDG(Italy) in Jun'83. Distributed by: IMS, Polygram

GINGER BAKER IN CONCERT.
Notes: Recent live album: includes some Cream and Airforce material.
Album: released on Onsala in Apr'87. Distributed by: Making Waves, Pinnacle

Baker, Glen

BRIEF ENCOUNTER.
Album: released on Stand in Jun'85

Baker, Josephine

50 YEARS OF SONG.
Album: released on Pathe MarconiFrance) in Jan'85

DIS MOI JOSEPHINE BAKER?.
Tracks: / J'ai deux amours / Le petite tonkinoise / Voulez-vous de la canne a sucre? / Dis moi Josephine / You're driving me crazy / My fate is in your hands / Si j'etais blanche / Sans amour / Madiana / Haiti / C'est lui (pour moi y qu'un homme dans Paris) / Vous faites partie de moi (I've got you under my skin) / C'est un nid charmant (There's a small hotel) / I'm feelin' like a million / Message from the man in the moon, A / Afraid to dream / Loveliness of you, The / De temps en temps / Brazil / Piel canela.
Album: released on Retrospect Series in Jun'87

Cassette: released on Retrospect in Jul'87 by World Records

JOSEPHINE BAKER.
Tracks: / J'ai deux amours / Dis moi Josephine / Voulez vous de la canne a sucre / Haiti / C'est un nid charmant / Pardon si je t'importune / La petite tonkinoise / Piel canela / Dans mon village / Sur deux notes / Demain / La vie en rose / Hello Dolly / Quand ja pense a ca.
Album: released on Deja Vu in Jan'87 by Deja Vu Records. Distributed by: Counterpoint Distribution, Record Services Distribution (Ireland)

Cassette: released on Deja Vu in Jan'87 by Deja Vu Records. Distributed by: Counterpoint Distribution, Record Services Distribution (Ireland)

Album: released on Columbia in Apr'87 by EMI Records. Distributed by: EMI

Cassette: released on Columbia in Apr'87 by EMI Records. Distributed by: EMI

Album: released on Monmouth in Mar'79

Baker, Lavern

REAL GONE GAL.
Tracks: / How can you leave a man like this / Jim dandy / My happiness for ever / Fee fee fi fo fum / Jim Dandy got married / Subsitute / Whipper snapper / Voodoo voodoo / I cried a tear / He's a real gone guy / I waited too long / Tiny tim / Shake a hand / Bumble bee / Hey memphis / See see rider.
Notes: A sister release to our Ruth Brown compilation(CRB 1069).Lavern was Atlantic Record's other great female R&B starof the fifties,and this album presents 16 other humdingers from 1953-62, three or four of which have never previously appeared on album.They weren't all hits: despite her great popularity Lavern's chart sucess was erratic and, any way ,we have deliberately omitted some hit titles, some of the poppier items, in favour of grittier tracks; The result has much thesame sort of musical balance as the Ruth Brown album: one or two of her best ballad performances, one or two of her bouncy but brittle finger snappers, a bitof blues and a whole lotta good-time rick and rolling. Irrestible stuff then and now..
Album: released on Charly(R&B) in Apr'84 by Charly Records. Distributed by: Charly, Cadillac

Cassette: released on Charly(R&B) in '85 by Charly Records. Distributed by: Charly, Cadillac

TWEEDLE DEE.
Single (7"): released on Revival in Jul'82. Distributed by: Lightning, Swift

Baker, Legendary Earl

CYLINDERS.
Notes: Mono recording
Album: released on Jazz Archives in Jul'86 by Jazz Archives Records. Distributed by: Jazz Music

Baker, Lloyd

BISI.
Single (7"): released on Sunburst in May'82. Distributed by: Sunburst Records

Bakerloo Junction

IRISH SONGS AND BALLADS.
Album: released on Emerald (Ireland) in Dec'84 by Emerald Records. Distributed by: I & B. Ross. PRT

Cassette: released on Emerald (Ireland) in Dec'84 by Emerald Records. Distributed by: I & B. Ross, PRT

IRISH SONGS & BALLADS.
Tracks: / When I grow too old to dream / Lassie from sweet Aghalee / Isle of Innisfree / Girl I left behind me, The / Shimna, The / Green fields of France / Dunmurry Mill / Wild mountain thyme / Farewell to you my lovely rose / Dark island / I'll tell me ma / Reap the wild harvest.
Notes: Produced by : George Doherty at Hydepark Studios
Album: released on Emerald (Ireland) in Dec'84 by Emerald Records. Distributed by: I & B. Ross. PRT

MY IAGAN SOFTLY FLOWING.
Single (7"):

REMEMBER GREEN.
Single (7"):

WINDS OF CHANGE.
Single (7"):

Baker, Marilyn

AN EVENING WITH MARILYN BAKER.
Tracks: / He's my saviour,my friend and my Lord / What a great day / Jesus is alive in me / Rest in my love.
Notes: Marilyn Baker's second album to be released by Word is a live album recorded during a concert in Jersey this year and features material written by Marilyn.Backing vocals are provided by Lovelight.
Album: released on Word in Aug'86 by Word Records. Distributed by: Word Distribution, CBS

Cassette: released on Word in Aug'86 by Word Records. Distributed by: Word Distribution, CBS

CLOSE TO HIS HEART.
Album: released on Word in Aug'87 by Word Records. Distributed by: Word Distribution, CBS

Cassette: released on Word in Aug'87 by Word Records. Distributed by: Word Distribution,

MARILYN BAKER.
Notes: Formerly available through Window Records,this is the first album Word are releasing since Marilyn signed to Word at the beginning of the year.At the time of signing David Payne commented on behalf of Window 'Having been involved in Marilyn's ministry since 1977 I rarely come across an artist who has more impact on the lives of people through her music than Marlin'.Word are delighted to be able to offer another opportunity to obtain this album from one of Britain's leading praise and worship singer/songwriters.
Album: released on Word in Jun'86 by Word Records. Distributed by: Word Distribution, CBS

Cassette: released on Word in Jun'86 by Word Records. Distributed by: Word Distribution, CBS

Baker, Michael

DON'T YOU WANT MY LOVIN.
Single (12"): released on SMP in Mar'84. Distributed by: Jetstar

Baker, Mickey

BLUES & JAZZ GUITAR.
Tracks: / Corrina corrina / Zanzie / Belzona blues / Got the blues / Spoonful / Lord ,have mercy / Hello world / Stack o'lee / Baby please don't go / Town's east end, The / Juicy Lucy / Love in vain.
Album: released on Kicking Mule in Aug'77 by Sonet. Distributed by: Roots, PRT-Pye Distribution

JAZZ ROCK GUITAR.
Album: released on Kicking Mule in '78 by Sonet. Distributed by: Roots, PRT

TAKE A LOOK INSIDE.
Tracks: / Make your bed up mamma / Take a look inside / Blues fell this morning / Diggin' in my potatoes / Playing with danger / I'll always be in love with you / She brings out the animal / New York New York / Tight ropes and bumpy roads / Bewidered.
Album: released on Big Bear in '82 by Big Bear Records. Distributed by: Big Bear, Swift

Baker, Richard

KID ON THE MOUNTAIN (Baker, Richard Royal).
Tracks: / Wicklow hornpipe, The / Proudlock's horn pipe / Blind Mary / Blarney pilgrim, The / Duke of Fife's welcome to Deeside / Sir Sidney Smith's march / Bantry bay / Morgan Magan / Kid on the mountain / Rights of man / Fantelada, Boys of Ballisodore / Elsie Marley / Sheebeg an sheemor / Lament of Limerick.
Album: released on Kicking Mule in Nov'80 by Sonet. Distributed by: Roots, PRT-

LET'S BEGIN AGAIN (See Kings Singers).

RICHARD BAKER'S MUSICAL MENAGERIE.
Album: released on Unicorn in Nov'82. Distributed by: Nine Mile, Cartel

Cassette: released on Unicorn in Dec'82. Distributed by: Nine Mile, Cartel

WIND IN THE WILLOWS AND THE RELUCTANT DRAGON (See Kings Singers) (Baker, Richard & Kings Singers).

Baker, Sam

BRINGING YOU SOME SOUL.
Tracks: / Coming to bring you some soul / Hold back girl / I love you / I can't breakaway / Let me come on home / Sometimes you have to cry / What did sister do / Don't feel rained on / Sugarman / I believe in you / I'm number one / It's all over / Strange sensation / Something tells me / You can't see the blood / Sunny.
Album: released on Charly in Oct'86 by Charly Records. Distributed by: Charly, Cadillac

Bakers Dozen...

BAKERS DOZEN FROM VINDALOO
Various artists (Various Artists).
Tracks: / Rockin' with Rita / Let's surf / XX Sex / Open up she said / Driving down the road / Down in the dumps / Aaarrrggghhh / Keep lying I love it / She loves you / Buck up / Fever / At the end of the day / Rockin' with Rita.
Album: released on WEA in Sep'86 by WEA Records. Distributed by: WEA

Cassette: released on WEA in Sep'86 by WEA Records. Distributed by: WEA

Baker, Shorty

SUMMER CONCERT 1960 (Baker, Shorty & Bud Freeman).
Album: released on Jazz Archives in Jan'80 by Jazz Archives Records. Distributed by: Jazz Music

Balaam & The Angel

DAY AND NIGHT.
Single (7"): released on Chapter 22 in Sep'85 by Chapter 22 Records. Distributed by: Nine Mile, Cartel

Single (12"): released on Chapter 22 in Sep'85 by Chapter 22 Records. Distributed by: Nine Mile, Cartel

GREATEST STORY EVER TOLD, THE.
Album: released on Virgin in Aug'86 by Virgin Records. Distributed by: EMI, Virgin Distribution

Cassette: released on Virgin in Aug'86 by Virgin Records. Distributed by: EMI, Virgin Distribution

Compact disc: released on Virgin in Jul'87 by Virgin Records. Distributed by: EMI, Virgin Distribution

LIGHT OF THE WORLD.
Tracks: / Light of the world / Day & night,family & friends / She knows * / Love *.
Single (7"): released on Virgin in Aug'86 by Virgin Records. Distributed by: EMI, Virgin Distribution

Single (12"): released on Virgin in Aug'86 by Virgin Records. Distributed by: EMI, Virgin Distribution

LOVE ME.
Single (12"): released on Chapter 22 in Apr'85 by Chapter 22 Records. Distributed by: Nine Mile, Cartel

SHE KNOWS.
Tracks: / She knows / Dreams wide awake / Sister moon ** / Warm again ** / 2 into 1 * / Darklands *.
Double-pack single: released on Virgin in Mar'86 by Virgin Records. Distributed by: EMI, Virgin Distribution

Single (12"): released on Virgin in Mar'86 by Virgin Records. Distributed by: EMI, Virgin Distribution

SLOW DOWN.
Tracks: / Slow down / Walk away / Travel on * / In the morning *.
Single (7"): released on Virgin in Jun'86 by Virgin Records. Distributed by: EMI, Virgin Distribution

Single (12"): released on Virgin in Jun'86 by Virgin Records. Distributed by: EMI, Virgin Distribution

SOMETHING SPECIAL.
Tracks: / Something special / I feel love / Let it happen* / You took my soul*.
Single (7"): released on Virgin in Jun'87 by Virgin Records. Distributed by: EMI, Virgin Distribution

Single (12"): released on Virgin in Jun'87 by Virgin Records. Distributed by: EMI, Virgin Distribution

WORLD OF LIGHT.
Single (7"): released on Chapter 22 in Nov'84 by Chapter 22 Records. Distributed by: Nine Mile, Cartel

Single (7"): released on True Friends in Mar'84 by True Friends Records. Distributed by: Cartel

Balalaika Trio

TRIANGLE.
Tracks: / Katusha / Song of the plains / Moscow nights romance / If I were a rich man / Brightly shines the moon / Narybalke / Kalinka / Cliff on Volga / In the garden / Ochi chorniye / Play my pipes / Kasbek.
Notes: Retail price given by ARC excluding p&p (via mail order) is 5.49 Mail order distribution address: Accordian Record Club,146 Birmingham Road Kidderminster,Worcs. DY10 2SL Tele: 0562 746105

Album: released on Accordion Record Club in Jul'86 by Accordion Record Club Records. Distributed by: Accordion Record Club

Balance

RUSSIAN TRAIN.
Tracks: / Russian Train / River ghosts.
Single (7"): released on Siren in Jun'87 by Virgin Records. Distributed by: EMI

Single (12"): released on Siren in Jun'87 by Virgin Records. Distributed by: EMI

Balcony

PORTRAIT.
Cassette: released on Balcony in Apr'85 by Probe Records. Distributed by: Cartel

REDDER THAN BURNING COALS.
Single (12"): released on Pink Pop in Feb'87. Distributed by: Red Rhino, Cartel

SURPRISE AFTER SURPRISE.
Single (7"): released on Praxis in Aug'82

Baldry, Long John

LET THE HEARTACHES BEGIN.
Single (7"): released on Flashback in Jan'83 by Flashback Records/PRT Records. Distributed by: Mainline, PRT

MEXICO.
Tracks: / Mexico / Let the heartaches begin.
Single (7"): released on PRT in Jun'86 by PRT Records. Distributed by: PRT

Baldwin, Clive

HIS MAJESTY THE BABY.
Single (7"): released on Pantoni in Jun'83 by Pantoni Records. Distributed by: Pinnacle

Baldwin, Stephen

ENGLISH VILLAGE FIDDLER.
Double Album: released on Leader in '81. Distributed by: Jazz Music, Projection

Baldwyn, Richard

YOUR FAVOURITE FAIRY STORIES.
Tracks: / Cinderella / 3 little pigs / Rapunzel / Goldilocks & the 3 bears / Snow White & the 7 dwarfs / Jack & the beanstalk / Gingerbread man / Dick Whittington / Beauty & the beast / Hansel & Gretel / Little Red Ridinghood / Rumpelstiltskin / Hare & the Hedgehog / Sleeping beauty.
Notes: Read by Wendy Craig & Richard Briers .Adapted and produced by Richard Baldwyn. Fourteen of the most well-known and loved fairy stories are gathered together to provide almost three hours of enchantment,adventure,mystery and magic. Adults and children alike will find them compelling listening on holiday,at home or in the car.
Cassette: released on Listen For Pleasure in Sep'86 by MFP Records. Distributed by: EMI

Bales, Bert

NEW ORLEANS RAGTIME.
Album: released on Euphonic in Apr'79 by Euphonic Records. Distributed by: Jazz Music, Swift

Balfa Brothers

ARCADIAN MEMORIES.
Album: released on Ace in Nov'86 by Ace Records. Distributed by: Pinnacle, Swift, Hotshot, Cadillac

CAJUN DAYS.
Album: released on Sonet in Jun'80 by Sonet Records. Distributed by: PRT

CAJUNS, THE Vol. 1 (Balfa Brothers Orchestra).
Tracks: / Acadian two step / La valise de grand bois / J'ai passe devant ta porte / Pine groove blues / Les veuves de Basile / Lacassine special / Mon chapeau / Apres du midi / Johnny ne pas danse / La valse de la prison / Ce voulait separe / Mamou hot step.
Album: released on Sonet in '73 by Sonet Records. Distributed by: PRT

MORE TRADITIONAL CAJUN MUSIC.
Album:

NEW YORK CONCERTS, THE.
Album:

TRADITIONAL CAJUN MUSIC.
Album:

UNDERNEATH THE GREEN OAK TREE.
Album: released on Arhoolie in May'81 by Arhoolie Records. Distributed by: Projection, Topic, Jazz Music, Swift, Roots

Balfa, Dewey

Couple of Cajuns, (A)

DEWEY BALFA & FRIENDS FAIT A LA MAIN!.
Album:

FAIT A LA MAIN (Balfa, Dewey & Friends).
Album: released on Swallow in Jun'87

SOUVENIRS.
Album:

Balham Alligators

BALHAM ALLIGATORS, THE.
Tracks: / Balham 2-step / Hey,hey,ho,ho / Malheureuse / Sugar bee / Tennessee blues / Johnny B.Goode / Oh Siobhan-let's dance / Louisiana / Scotland / Allons a Lafayette / Tacos / Little Liza Jane / Hobo blues / Balham 2-step(reprise).
Album: released on Special Delivery in May'87. Distributed by: Nine Mile, Cartel

Cassette: released on Special Delivery in May'87. Distributed by: Nine Mile, Cartel

LET'S DANCE.
Single (7"): released on Mays in Jan'87 by Mays Records. Distributed by: Roots, Spartan, Projection

Single (7"): released on Special Delivery in Aug'87. Distributed by: Nine Mile, Cartel

OH MARIE.
Single (7"): released on Sweet Heart in Aug'84 by Sweet Heart Records. Distributed by: Rough Trade Distribution, Cartel Distribution

Ball

GAMELAN MUSIC OF BALI.
Album: released on Lyrichord (USA) in Oct'81 by Lyrichord Records (USA). Distributed by: Flexitron Distributors Ltd

MAGIC MALI.
Compact disc: . Distributed by: IMS-Polygram Distribution

SCINILLATING SOUNDS OF BALI.
Album: released on Lyrichord (USA) in Oct'81 by Lyrichord Records (USA). Distributed by: Flexitron Distributors Ltd

Balkana

MUSIC OF BULGARIA, THE.
Album: released on Hannibal in Oct'87 by Hannibal Records. Distributed by: Charly, Harmonia Mundi, Projection, Celtic Music, Roots. Estim retail price in Sep'87 was £5.99.

Ballad Hits Mid 50's

BALLAD HITS MID 50'S (Various Artists).
Tracks: / Unchained Melody / Cool Water / Mangos / Magic Moments / Look Homeward Angel / Big Man / My Prayer / Memories are Made of This / Passing Strangers / We Will Make Love / Island in the Sun / Wayward wind (The) / Twelfth of Never / When I Fall in Love.
Album: released on Old Gold in Nov'86 by Old Gold Records. Distributed by: Lightning, Jazz Music, Spartan, Counterpoint

Cassette: released on Old Gold in Nov'86 by Old Gold Records. Distributed by: Lightning, Jazz Music, Spartan, Counterpoint

Ballads Of...

BALLAD OF THE BLACK COUNTRY various artists (Various Artists).
Tracks: / John Hobbs / Nine times a night / All bells of paradise / Brave collier lads / John Wilkinson / Wedgebury cocking / Funny rigs of good and tender hearted masters, The / Tommy Note, The / Nailmakers strike, The / Jews they crucified him, The / Brave Dudley boys, The / Souling, clemency, gooding / Oxford and Hampton railway, The / Perry Croft's bull-bait / Song of the Staffordshire men, The.
Album: released on Broadside in Jun'81 by Broadside Records. Distributed by: Celtic Distributions, H.R. Taylor, Jazz Music, Projection, Jazz Services Unlimited Dist. (JSU)

Cassette: released on Broadside in Jun'81 by Broadside Records. Distributed by: Celtic Distributions, H.R. Taylor, Jazz Music, Projection, Jazz Services Unlimited Dist. (JSU)

BALLADS OF BRITAIN & IRELAND Classic ballads, vol 2-child nos 2-84.

BALLADS OF BRITAIN & IRELAND, VOL 1 Classic ballads, child nos 2-84.
Cassette: released on Folktracks in Nov'79 by Folktracks Cassettes. Distributed by: Folktracks

BALLADS OF BRITAIN & IRELAND, VOL 2 Classic ballads, vol 2-nos 85-215.
Cassette: released on Folktracks in Nov'79 by Folktracks Cassettes. Distributed by: Folktracks

BALLADS OF BRITAIN & IRELAND, VOL 3 classic ballads, vol 3.
Cassette: released on Folktracks in Nov'79 by Folktracks Cassettes. Distributed by: Folktracks

Ballard, Hank

LET'S GO, LET'S GO, LET'S GO (Ballard, Hank & The Midnighters).
Tracks: / Twist, The (ext.version).
Single (12"): released on Charly in Jan'87 by Charly Records. Distributed by: Charly, Cadillac

Single (12"): released on Charly in Jul'85 by Charly Records. Distributed by: Charly, Cadillac

LIVE AT THE PALAIS (Ballard, Hank & The Midnighters).
Tracks: / Lucille (Instrumental) / Hoochi coochi coo (The) / Work with Annie / Tore up over you / Teardrops on you letter / Look at little sister / Annie had a baby / My girl / Girl's alright with me (The) / You're all I need to get by / I'll try something new / Stand by me / Hold on I'm coming / Soul man / Sky is crying (The) / Sugaree / It's love baby (24 hours a day) / Sexy ways / Deep blue sea / Baby workout / Your love keeps lifting me (higher and higher) / Christmas time for everyone but me / Finger poppin' time / Let's go, let's go', let's go / Twist (The).
Notes: Tracks 2-6, 16-19 Carlin Music Corp. 7 - Jobete Music (UK) Ltd. Tracks 1, 11, 14, 15, on album and cassette only.
Album: released on Charly in Apr'87 by Charly Records. Distributed by: Charly, Cadillac

Cassette: released on Charly in Apr'87 by Charly Records. Distributed by: Charly, Cadillac

Compact disc: released on Charly in Apr'87 by Charly Records. Distributed by: Charly, Cadillac

WHAT YOU GET WHEN THE GOING GETS GOOD (Ballard, Hank & The Midnighters).
Tracks: / Sexy ways / Don't change your pretty ways / Rock and roll wedding / Open up the back door / Rock, granny, roll / Tore up over you / Is your love for real? / Twist, The / Teardrops on your letter / Kansas City / Sugaree / Finger poppin' time / Let's go, let's go, let's go / What is this I see / I'm gonna miss you / Work with me Annie.
Compact disc: released on Charly in Oct'86 by Charly Records. Distributed by: Charly, Cadillac

WHAT YOU GET WHEN THE GETTIN' GETS GOOD (Ballard, Hank & The Midnighters).
Album: released on Charly(R&B) in Jul'85 by Charly Records. Distributed by: Charly, Cadillac

Cassette: released on Charly(R&B) in Jul'85 by Charly Records. Distributed by: Charly, Cadillac

Ballard, Russ

FIRE STILL BURNS, THE.
Tracks: / Once a rebel / Omen, The / Hey Bernadette / Searching / Time / Your time is gonna come / Dream on / Fire still burns, The.
Album: released on EMI America in Jul'85 by EMI Records. Distributed by: EMI

Cassette: released on EMI America in Jul'85 by EMI Records. Distributed by: EMI

RUSS BALLARD.
Tracks: / I can't hear you no more / In the night / Two silhouettes / Voices / Woman like you, A / Day to day / Playing with fire / Last time, The.
Album: released on EMI America in Jul'84 by EMI Records. Distributed by: EMI

Cassette: released on EMI America in Jul'84 by EMI Records. Distributed by: EMI

TWO SILHOUETTES.
Single (7"): released on EMI America in Jun'84 by EMI Records. Distributed by: EMI

VOICES.
Tracks: / Voices / Living without you.
Single (7"): released on EMI America in Jan'86 by EMI Records. Distributed by: EMI

Ball, Barber

LIVE AT THE ROYAL FESTIVAL HALL (Ball, Barber & Bilk).
Album: released on Cambra in Apr'85 by Cambra Records. Distributed by: IDS, Conifer

Cassette: released on Cambra in Apr'85 by Cambra Records. Distributed by: IDS, Conifer

Ball, Dave

IN STRICT TEMPO.
Tracks: / Mirrors / Sincerity / Passion of a primitive / Strict tempo / Man in the man / Only time / Life of love / Rednecks / American stories.
Notes: The debut album from Soft Cell's multi-instrumentalist.
Album: released on Some Bizzare in Nov'83 by Charisma Records. Distributed by: EMI, CBS, Polygram

Cassette: released on Some Bizzare in Nov'83 by Charisma Records. Distributed by: EMI, CBS, Polygram

Ballet Shoes

BALLET SHOES Noel Streatfield (Shearer, Moira).
Cassette: released on Argo in Apr'84 by Decca Records. Distributed by: Polygram

Ballistic Kisses

DOMESTIC SERVANTS.
Single (7"): released on Don't Fall Off The Mountain in Jan'82 by Don't Fall Off The Mountain Records. Distributed by: Pinnacle, Rough Trade, Nine Mile, Indies

FIVE O'CLOCK WORLD.
Single (7"): released on Ensign in Apr'82 by Ensign Records. Distributed by: CBS Distribution

Single (12"): released on Ensign in Apr'82 by Ensign Records. Distributed by: CBS Distribution

SHARECROP THE NIGHT.
Single (12"): released on Don't Fall Off The Mountain in Feb'84 by Don't Fall Off The Mountain Records. Distributed by: Pinnacle, Rough Trade, Nine Mile, Indies

TOTAL ACCESS.
Tracks: / Whose mama is this / Recipe for revolt / Workaholic / Five o'clock world / Black and broke / Domestic servants / Body rhymes / Tough shit / Samurai toys.
Album: released on Don't Fall Off The Mountain in Apr'82 by Don't Fall Off The Mountain Records. Distributed by: Pinnacle, Rough Trade, Nine Mile, Indies

WET MOMENTS.
Album: released on Don't Fall Off The Mountain in Sep'83 by Don't Fall Off The Mountain Records. Distributed by: Pinnacle, Rough Trade, Nine Mile, Indies

Ball, Kenny

AT THE MOVIES.
Tracks: / Raiders of the lost ark / Mrs. Robinson / As time goes by / Arthur's theme / I love you, Samantha / Cavatina / March of the Siamese children, The / Mona Lisa / When you wish upon a star / Hello Dolly / Green leaves of summer / Ben / Bare necessities / I wanna be like you.
Album: released on MFP in Sep'87 by EMI Records. Distributed by: EMI

Cassette: released on MFP in Sep'87 by EMI Records. Distributed by: EMI

CLAP TRAP (Ball, Kenny & His Jazzmen).
Single (7"): released on Mont in Jul'82 by Mont Records. Distributed by: Spartan Distribution

COTTON CLUB.
Tracks: / Minnie the moocher / Midnight in Moscow / I wanna be like you / Scorpio blues / March of the Siamese children / You are my sunshine / Sailing / Samantha / Eyes / It's life / So do I / One night stand / Annie's song / Is that the human thing to do.
Album: released on Conifer in Apr'86 by Conifer Records. Distributed by: Conifer

Cassette: released on Conifer in Apr'86 by Conifer Records. Distributed by: Conifer

GOLDEN HITS: KENNY BALL (Ball, Kenny & His Jazzmen).
Tracks: / Midnight in Moscow / So do I / March of the Siamese children / Someday you'll be sorry / 55 Days at Peking / Rondo a la turk / Sukiyaki / I still love you all / Green leaves of summer / I love you Samantha.
Album: released on PRT Flashback in Jul'86

Cassette: released on PRT Flashback in Jul'86

GOLDEN HOUR: KENNY BALL with his Jazzmen.
Cassette: released on Golden Hour in '71 by PRT Records. Distributed by: PRT

GREENSLEEVES (Ball, Kenny & His Jazzmen).
Tracks: / Flow gently sweet afternoon / Nobody knows when you're down and out / I've got rhythm / Ostrich walk / I shall not be moved / St Louis blues / Greensleeves / My mothers eyes / I wanna be like you / Mood indigo / Them there eyes / Old folks / Sweet Georgia Brown.
Notes: Personnel: Kenny Ball- trumpet and vocals; John Fenner- guitar, banjo and vocals John Bennett- trombone and vocals; Ron Bowden- drums; Andy Cooper- clarinet and vocals; Duncan Swift- piano; John Benson- bass and vocal. Recorded November 1982.
Album: released on Timless (Holland) in Sep'86

Cassette: released on Timeless in Sep'86

Cassette: released on T.I.M. Records in Aug'85

HELLO DOLLY.
Album: released on Golden Hour in Sep'77 by PRT Records. Distributed by: PRT

I WANNA BE LIKE YOU (Ball, Kenny & His Jazzmen).

Single (7"): released on PRT in Oct'83 by PRT Records. Distributed by: PRT

KENNY BALL IN CONCERT Live.
Album: released on Nevis in Jul'78. Distributed by: H.R. Taylor

KENNY IN CONCERT IN THE USA Vol. 1.
Album: released on Jazzology in Aug'79. Distributed by: Jazz Music, Swift

MIDNIGHT IN MOSCOW (Ball, Kenny & His Jazzmen).
Single (7"): released on Old Gold in Jul'82 by Old Gold Records. Distributed by: Lightning, Jazz Music, Spartan, Counterpoint

SATURDAY NIGHT AT THE MILL.
Tracks: / Saturday night at the mill / Sunday / Sweet painted lady / Feline stomp / Them there eyes / You can't get to heaven by livin like hell / Lady of Spain / I've got plenty of nuttin / Bess you is my woman / Tain't what you do / Lili Marlene / Down by the river.
Album: released on Spiral in May'77 by President Records. Distributed by: Jazz Music

SATURDAY NIGHT AT THE MILL (Ball, Kenny & His Jazzmen).
Album: released on Spiral in Nov'86 by President Records. Distributed by: Jazz Music

SOAP.
Cassette: released on AMI in Sep'81 by AMI Records

SUNSHINE.
Single (7"): released on American Phonogram in Dec'84 by PRT Records. Distributed by: PRT

WAY DOWN YONDER (Ball, Kenny & His Jazzmen).
Album: released on Nevis in Nov'80. Distributed by: H.R. Taylor

Cassette: released on Nevis in Nov'80. Distributed by: H.R. Taylor

Ball, Marcia

HOT TAMALE BABY.
Album: released on Rounder Europa in Mar'87

Album: released on Rounder Europa in Jul'86

SOULFUL DRESS.
Album: released on Rounder (USA) in Apr'84. Distributed by: Mike's Country Music Room Distribution, Jazz Music Distribution, Swift Distribution, Roots Records Distribution, Projection Distribution, Topic Distribution

Ballot, Errol

WICKED AND WILD.
Single (12"): released on Unity Sound in Nov'85. Distributed by: Jetstar

Ballou, Classie

ALL NIGHT MAN.
Album: released on Krazy Kat in Feb'86. Distributed by: Jazz Music, Swift, Chris Wellard, H.R. Taylor, Charly, Hotshot, IRS Distribution

Ballou, Monte

THEY'RE MOVING WILLIE'S GRAVE (Ballou, Monte & His New Castle Jazz Band).
Album: released on GHB in Mar'87. Distributed by: Jazz Music, Swift

Ball, Patrick

CELTIC HARP VOL.2.
Compact disc: released on Fortuna in 6 Jun'87 by TM Records. Distributed by: PRT

CELTIC HARP VOLUME ONE.
Album: released on Fortuna in Feb'87 by TM Records. Distributed by: PRT

Cassette: released on Fortuna in Feb'87 by TM Records. Distributed by: PRT

Compact disc: released on TM Records in Jun'86

Bally

LUCIFER IN POWDER FORM.
Tracks: / All woman nice.
Single (12"): released on Hot Vinyl in Dec'86 by Hot Vinyl Records. Distributed by: Jetstar

Ballykeigle...

FIFTY YEARS OF MARCHING (Ballykeigle Accordion Band).
Album: released on Outlet in Jul'79 by Outlet Records. Distributed by: Outlet Distribution

Ballymena...

VARIOUS SONGS OF PRAISE (Ballymena West Church Choir).
Album: released on Praise in Nov'79. Distributed by: Outlet

Baltimora

TARZAN BOY.
Single (7"): released on Columbia in Aug'85 by EMI Records. Distributed by: EMI

Single (12"): released on Columbia in Aug'85 by EMI Records. Distributed by: EMI

TARZAN BOYS.
Single (7"): released on Columbia in May'85 by EMI Records. Distributed by: EMI

Single (12"): released on Columbia in May'85 by EMI Records. Distributed by: EMI

Bambaataa, Afrika

BAMBAATAA'S THEME(ASSAULT ON PRECINCT 13).
Tracks: / Bambaataa's theme(assault on precinct 13) / Tension.
Single (12"): released on WEA Int in Aug'86

BEWARE(THE FUNK IS EVERYWHERE).
Tracks: / Funk jam party / Funk you / Bionic kats / What time is it / Beware(the funk is everywhere) / Banbaataa's theme / Tension / Rock America / Kick out the jams.
Album: released on WEA in Oct'86 by WEA Records. Distributed by: WEA

Cassette: released on WEA in Oct'86 by WEA Records. Distributed by: WEA

DEATH MIX THROWDOWN.
Album: released on Blatant in Jul'87 by Castle Communications. Distributed by: PRT

Cassette: released on Blatant in Jul'87 by Castle Communications. Distributed by: PRT

LOOKING FOR THE PERFECT BEAT (Bambaataa, Afrika & the Soul Sonic Force).
Single (12"): released on 21 Records in Jul'84 by Polydor Records. Distributed by: Polydor

PLANET ROCK (Bambaataa, Afrika & the Soul Sonic Force).
Single (12"): released on 21 Records in Jul'84 by Polydor Records. Distributed by: Polydor

Bam bam

POLKA DOT.
Single (7"): released on Vox Populi in May'82

Bambi

BAMBI various artists (Various Artists).
Album: released on Disneyland in Dec'82 by Disneyland-Vista Records (USA). Distributed by: BBC Records & Tapes, Rainbow Communications Ltd(Distribution)

Cassette: released on Disneyland in Dec'82 by Disneyland-Vista Records (USA). Distributed by: BBC Records & Tapes, Rainbow Communications Ltd(Distribution)

Album: released on Disneyland in Dec'82 by Disneyland-Vista Records (USA). Distributed by: BBC Records & Tapes, Rainbow Communications Ltd(Distribution)

Picture disc album: released on Disneyland in Dec'82 by Disneyland-Vista Records (USA). Distributed by: BBC Records & Tapes, Rainbow Communications Ltd(Distribution)

BAMBI Film sound track.
Tracks: / Love is a song / Little April shower / Let's sing a gay little spring song / Looking for romance (I bring you a song).
Album: released on Disney in Oct'84 by BBC Records & Tapes. Distributed by: BBC Records & Tapes, PRT

Cassette: released on Disney in Oct'84 by BBC Records & Tapes. Distributed by: BBC Records & Tapes, PRT

BAMBI Felix Salten (Bartlett, Peter).
Cassette: released on Tellastory in Apr'84 by Bartlett Bliss Productions. Distributed by: PRT Distribution, Hayward Promotions Distribution, H.R. Taylor Distribution

BAMBI Felix Salter (Kendall, Felicity).
Cassette: released on Pickwick in '83 by Pickwick Records. Distributed by: Pickwick Distribution, Prism Leisure Distribution, Lugtons

Bambi Slam

BAMP-BAMP.
Tracks: / Hit me with your hairbrush / Awful flute song (first half) The.
Single (7"): released on Product Inc. in Feb'87. Distributed by: Cartel

Single (12"): released on Product Inc. in Feb'87. Distributed by: Cartel

DON'T IT MAKE YOU FEEL.
Single (7"): released on Product Inc. in May'87. Distributed by: Cartel

Single (12"): released on Product Inc. in May'87. Distributed by: Cartel

Bam-Boo

GIVE YOUR LOVE TO ME.
Single (7"): released on Funzone in Aug'83 by Funzone Records

Single (12"): released on Funzone in Aug'83 by Funzone Records

IT'S ALL IN YOUR MIND.
Single (12"): released on Fourth Floor (USA) in Aug'87

Bamboo Blue

SCARLET ON A THURSDAY.
Single (7"): released on Variety in Nov'82 by Variety Records. Distributed by: PRT

Bamboo Fringe

DORIAN GRAY.
Single (7"): released on Probe Plus in Jun'83 by Probe Plus Records. Distributed by: Probe Plus Distribution

LIFE AND TIMES OF THE BAMBOO FRINGE.
Album: released on Skysaw in Apr'85 by Skysaw Records. Distributed by: Red Rhino, Cartel

Bamboola

BAMBOOLA.
Album: released on Plastic Head in Jul'86. Distributed by: Pinnacle, Rough Trade, Cartel

BILLY HART.
Tracks: / Billy Hart / Window.
Single (7"): released on Plastic Head in May'86. Distributed by: Pinnacle, Rough Trade, Cartel

Banana Boat Company

HURTING NEVER STOPS, THE.
Tracks: / Hurting never stops, The.
Single (7"): released on La Fillette in Sep'86. Distributed by: Revolver

Bananamen

CRUSHER, THE.
Single (7"): released on Big Beat in Jul'83 by Ace Records. Distributed by: Projection, Pinnacle

Bananarama

AIE A MWANA.
Single (7"): released on Deram in Sep'81 by Decca Records. Distributed by: Polygram

Single (12"): released on Deram in Sep'81 by Decca Records. Distributed by: Polygram

BANANARAMA.
Tracks: / Cruel summer / Rough justice / Robert de Niro's waiting / Hot line to heaven.
Notes: A compilation of 10 promo hits by the girl trio,including their latest single 'Hotline to Heaven' and all their previous hits.1984 Production. number of tracks:10 Type of recording: Compilation Total playing time: 30 minutes.
Compact disc: released on London in May'84 by London Records. Distributed by: Polygram

Album: released on London in Apr'84 by London Records. Distributed by: Polygram

Cassette: released on London in Apr'84 by London Records. Distributed by: Polygram

Compact disc: released on London in Apr'84 by London Records. Distributed by: Polygram

BANANARAMA (VIDEO).
Video-cassette (VHS): released on Polygram in Oct'84 by Polygram Records. Distributed by: Polygram

CHEERS THEN.
Single (7"): released on London in Nov'82 by London Records. Distributed by: Polygram

Single (12"): released on London in Nov'82 by London Records. Distributed by: Polygram

CRUEL SUMMER.
Single (7"): released on London in Jul'83 by London Records. Distributed by: Polygram

Single (12"): released on London in Jul'83 by London Records. Distributed by: Polygram

DEEP SEA SKIVING.
Tracks: / He was really saying something / Boy trouble / What a shambles / Young at heart / Na na hey hey kiss him good bye / Shy boy.
Album: released on London in Apr'83 by London Records. Distributed by: Polygram

Cassette: released on London in Apr'83 by London Records. Distributed by: Polygram

DO NOT DISTURB.
Single (7"): released on London in Aug'85 by London Records. Distributed by: Polygram

Single (12"): released on London in Aug'85 by London Records. Distributed by: Polygram

Picture disc single: released on London in Aug'85 by London Records. Distributed by: Polygram

HOTLINE TO HEAVEN.
Single (7"): released on London in Oct'84 by London Records. Distributed by: Polygram

Single (12"): released on London in Oct'84 by London Records. Distributed by: Polygram

I HEARD A RUMOUR.
Tracks: / I heard a rumour / Clean cut boy (Party size) / I heard a rumour (Horoscope mix) / I heard a rumour (Dub).
Single (7"): released on London in Jul'87 by London Records. Distributed by: Polygram

Single (12"): released on London in Jul'87 by London Records. Distributed by: Polygram

MORE THAN PHYSICAL.
Tracks: / More than physical.
Single (7"): released on London in Aug'86 by London Records. Distributed by: Polygram

Single (12"): released on London in Aug'86 by London Records. Distributed by: Polygram

NANA HEY HEY KISS HIM GOODBY.
Single (7"): released on London in Feb'83 by London Records. Distributed by: Polygram

Single (12"): released on London in Feb'83 by London Records. Distributed by: Polygram

REALLY SAYING SOMETHING (Bananarama & Fun Boy 3).
Single (7"): released on Deram in Apr'82 by Decca Records. Distributed by: Polygram

Single (12"): released on Deram in Apr'82 by Decca Records. Distributed by: Polygram

ROBERT DE NIRO'S WAITING.
Single (7"): released on Decca in Apr'84 by Decca Records. Distributed by: Polygram

Single (7"): released on Decca in Apr'84 by Decca Records. Distributed by: Polygram

SHY BOY.
Single (7"): released on London in Jun'82 by London Records. Distributed by: Polygram

Single (12"): released on London in Jun'82 by London Records. Distributed by: Polygram

TRICK OF THE NIGHT.
Tracks: / Tricky mix / Set on you.
Single (7"): released on London in Jan'87 by London Records. Distributed by: Polygram

Single (12"): released on London in Jan'87 by London Records. Distributed by: Polygram

TRUE CONFESSIONS.
Tracks: / True confessions / Ready or not / Trick of the night, A / Dance with a stranger / In a perfect world / Venus / Do not disturb / Cut above the rest / Promised land / More than physical / Hooked on love.
Notes: Produced by: Swain & Jolley with 2 tracks produced by Stock/Aitken/Waterman
Album: released on London in Jul'86 by London Records. Distributed by: Polygram

Compact disc: released on London in Jul'86 by London Records. Distributed by: Polygram

VENUS.
Tracks: / Venus / White train / More than physical ** / Scarlet **.
Single (7"): released on London in May'86 by London Records. Distributed by: Polygram

Single (12"): released on London in May'86 by London Records. Distributed by: Polygram

Double-pack single: released on London in Aug'86 by London Records. Distributed by: Polygram

VIDEOSINGLES, THE.
Notes: Released on Channel 5 Video

WOW.
Compact disc: released on London in Jul'87 by London Records. Distributed by: Polygram

Banbarra

SHACK UP.
Single (7"): released on Stateside in Jul'85. Distributed by: EMI Deleted '86.

Single (12"): released on Stateside in Jul'85. Distributed by: EMI

Banchory Strathspey...

BANCHORY STRATHSPEY & REEL SOCIETY.
Album: released on Country House in Dec'83 by BGS Productions Ltd. Distributed by: Taylor, H.R., Record Merchandisers Distribution, Pinnacle, Sounds of Scotland Records

Cassette: released on Country House in Dec'83 by BGS Productions Ltd. Distributed by: Taylor, H.R., Record Merchandisers Distribution, Pinnacle, Sounds of Scotland Records

Bancroft, Armsbee

CINEMA ORGAN ENCORES.
Album: released on Derry in Jun'81 by Outlet Records. Distributed by: Outlet Records

Band

ANTHOLOGY 1.
Cassette: released on EMI (Italy) in Feb'87 by EMI Records. Distributed by: Conifer

ANTHOLOGY 2.
Cassette: released on EMI (Italy) in Feb'87 by EMI Records. Distributed by: Conifer

BAND, THE.
Tracks: / Across the great divide / Rag mama rag / Night they drove old dixie down / When you awake / Up on Cripple Creek / Whispering pines / Jemima surrender / Rockin' chair / Look out Cleveland / Jawbone / Unfaithful servant, The / King harvest (has surely come).
Notes: Tracks 1-6 total time 22.07 /7-12,22.04
Album: released on Capitol in Aug'86 by Capitol Records. Distributed by: EMI

Cassette: released on Capitol in Aug'86 by Capitol Records. Distributed by: EMI

Compact disc: released on Capitol in Apr'87 by Capitol Records. Distributed by: EMI

BAND,THE.

BEFORE THE FLOOD (Band, The & Bob Dylan).
Album: released on Island in Jun'74 by Island Records. Distributed by: Polygram

BEST OF THE BAND, THE.
Compact disc: released on Capitol in '87 by Capitol Records. Distributed by: EMI

ISLANDS.
Tracks: / Right as rain / Street walker / Let the night fall / Ain't that a lot of love / Christmas must be tonight / Islands / Saga of Pepote Rouge, The / Georgia on my mind / Livin' in a dream / Knockin' lost John.
Album: released on Capitol in Apr'77 by Capitol Records. Distributed by: EMI

LAST WALTZ, THE.
Tracks: / Theme from the last waltz / Up on cripple creek / Who do you love / Helpless / Stage fright / Coyote / Dry your eyes / It makes no difference / Such a night / Night they drove old Dixie down, The / Mystery train / Mannish boy / Further on up the road / Shape I'm in / Down south in New Orleans / Ophelia / Tura lura larai (That's an Irish lullaby) / Caravan / Life is a carnival / Baby let me follow you down / I don't believe you (she acts like we never have met) / Forever young / Baby let me follow you down (reprise) / I shall be released / Last waltz suite, The / Well, The / Evangeline / Out of the blue / Weight, The / Last waltz, The (refrain) / Theme from the last waltz (with orchestra).
Boxed set: released on Warner Brothers in Apr'78 by Warner Bros Records. Distributed by: WEA

Cassette: released on Warner Brothers in Apr'78 by Warner Bros Records. Distributed by: WEA

MOONDOG MATINEE.
Album: released on EMI (Import) in Feb'84 by EMI Records. Distributed by: Conifer

MUSIC FROM BIG PINK.
Album: released on Greenlight-Capitol in Jun'81 by Capitol Records. Distributed by: EMI

MUSIC FROM BIG PINK.
Tracks: / Tears of rage / To Kingdom come / In a station / Caledonia mission / Weight, The / We can talk / Long black veil / Chest fever / Lonesome Suzie / This wheels on fire / I shall be released.
Cassette: released on Greenlight-Capitol in Jun'81 by Capitol Records. Distributed by: EMI

MUSIC FROM BIG PINK.
Compact disc: released on Capitol in May'87 by Capitol Records. Distributed by: EMI

ROCK OF AGES.
Tracks: / Don't do it / King Harvest / Caledonia Mission / Get up Jake / W.S. Walcott medicine / Stage fright / Night they drove old Dixie down, The / Across the great divide / Wheels on fire / Rag Mama rag / Weight, The / Shape I'm in, The / Unfaithful servant / Life is a carnival / Gentle method, The / I don't want to - Hang up my rock & roll shoes.
Album: released on EMI Europe in Feb'87 by EMI Records. Distributed by: Conifer

Album: released on EMI (Italy) in Mar'87 by EMI Records. Distributed by: Conifer

Cassette: released on EMI (Italy) in Mar'87 by EMI Records. Distributed by: Conifer

ROCK OF AGES.
Album: released on EMI in Jul'83 by EMI Records. Distributed by: EMI

ROCK OF AGES.
Tracks: / Don't do it / King Harvest (has surely come) / Caledonia mission / Get up, Jake / W.S. Wallcott medicine show / Stage fright / Night they drove old dixie down, The / Across the great divide / This wheel's on fire / Rag mama rag / Weight, The / Shape I'm in, The / Unfaithful servant / Life is a carnival / Chest fever / Hang up my rock and roll shoes (I don't want to).
Compact disc: released on Capitol in Apr'87 by Capitol Records. Distributed by: EMI

STAGE FRIGHT.
Tracks: / Strawberry wine / Sleeping time to kill / Just another whistle stop / All la glory / Shape I'm in, The / W.S. Walcott medicine show, The / Daniel and the sacred harp / Stage fright / Rumor, The.
Album: released on Greenlight-Capitol in Jun'81 by Capitol Records. Distributed by: EMI

Band Aid

DO THEY KNOW IT'S CHRISTMAS.
Video-cassette (VHS): released on Polygram in Jan'86 by Polygram Records. Distributed by: Polygram

Single (7"): released on Polygram in Dec'84 by Polygram Records. Distributed by: Polygram

Single (12"): released on Polygram in Dec'84 by Polygram Records. Distributed by: Polygram

DO THEY KNOW IT'S CHRISTMAS?.
Single (7"): released on Mercury in Nov'85 by Phonogram Records. Distributed by: Polygram Distribution

Single (12"): released on Mercury in Nov'85 by Phonogram Records. Distributed by: Polygram Distribution

Band A.K.A

IF YOU WANT TO HEAR.
Single (7"): released on Epic in Apr'83 by CBS Records. Distributed by: CBS

Single (12"): released on Epic in Apr'83 by CBS Records. Distributed by: CBS

MEN OF THE MUSIC.
Tracks: / If you want to know / Joy / Men of the music / Work me all over / You got it all / It must be love / It's you that I need.
Album: released on Epic in Apr'83 by CBS Records. Distributed by: CBS

Cassette: released on Epic in Apr'83 by CBS Records. Distributed by: CBS

Bandana

SENORITA (HOLIDAY GIRL).
Tracks: / Senorita (holiday girl) / Wish you were here.
Single (7"): released on Tembo in Jun'86 by Tembo (Canada). Distributed by: IMS Distribution, Polygram Distribution

Band Apart

BAND APART.
Album: released on Crammed UK in Sep'84. Distributed by: Rough Trade, Nine Mile, Cartel

MARSEILLE.
Album: released on Crammed in Sep'83. Distributed by: Rough Trade, Nine Mile, Cartel

Band, Barratt

Friends on tour

Bandera R & B & Doo Wop

HYPE YOU INTO SELLING YOUR HEAD.
Album: released on JSP in Jan'82 by JSP Records. Distributed by: Swift, Projection

Bandera Rockabillies

BANDERA ROCKABILLIES (Various Artists).
Album: released on JSP in Jan'82 by JSP Records. Distributed by: Swift, Projection

Band'Its at ten o'clock

BAND'ITS AT TEN O'CLOCK (Various Artists).
Album: released on Polydor in Sep'80 by Polydor Records. Distributed by: Polygram, Polydor

Bandleader Digital

BANDLEADER DIGITAL SPECTACULAR Various military & brass bands (Various bands).
Tracks: / Berne patrol / Thunderbirds / Royal salute / Regimental slow march / Motorcycle display / Chocolate dancing / Shepherd's song / Music box dancer / Canter / St.Louis blues march / Caesar's romp / Concerto for clarinet / Mount Longden / Drum beating / Rule Britannia / Jerusalem / Last post / Auld lang syne / Colonel Bogey / Artillery salvo / Fanfare / God save the Queen / Bugle flute & drum calls / Precision in percussion / Tornado, The / Artillery salvo / Fanfare / God save the queen / Bugle flute and drum calls / Precision in percussion / Tornado, The / Bernie patrol / Thunderbirds / Royal salute / Regimental slow march / Motor cycle display / Chocolate dancing / Shepherd's song / Music box dancer / Canter / St. Louis blues march / Caesar's romp / Concerto for clarinet / Mount Longden / Drum beating / Rule Britannia / Jerusalem / Last post / Auld lang syne / Colonel Bogey.
Compact disc: released on Bandleader in Feb'85 by Bandleader Records. Distributed by: PRT

Band of Angels

ACCEPT MY INVITATION.
Single (7"): released on Soul Supply in Oct'83 by High Energy Records. Distributed by: Charly

Single (12"): released on Soul Supply in Oct'83 by High Energy Records. Distributed by: Charly

Band of Blacky Ranchette

BAND OF BLACKY RANCHETTE.
Album: released on New Rose in Jun'85. Distributed by: Rough Trade, Cartel

HEARTLAND.
Album: released on Zippo in Sep'86

Band of Glory

DOWN BY THE SEA/SWEET SWEET LOVER.
Single (7"): released on V-Tone in Jul'82 by Relic. Distributed by: Swift

Band of Gold

IN LOVE AGAIN (MEDLEY).
Single (7"): released on RCA in Jan'85 by RCA Records. Distributed by: RCA, Roots, Swift, Wellard, Chris, I & B, Solomon & Peres Distribution

Single (12"): released on RCA in Jan'85 by RCA Records. Distributed by: RCA, Roots, Swift, Wellard, Chris, I & B, Solomon & Peres Distribution

LOVE SONGS ARE BACK AGAIN.
Tracks: / Love songs are back again / Let's put it all together / Betcha by golly wow / Side show / Have you seen her / Reunited / You make me feel brand new / Kiss & say goodbye / Just to say / In love again.
Album: released on RCA in Jan'85 by RCA Records. Distributed by: RCA, Roots, Swift, Wellard, Chris, I & B, Solomon & Peres Distribution

Cassette: released on RCA in Jan'85 by RCA Records. Distributed by: RCA, Roots, Swift, Wellard, Chris, I & B, Solomon & Peres Distribution

Cassette: released on RCA in Sep'84 by RCA Records. Distributed by: RCA, Roots, Swift, Wellard, Chris, I & B, Solomon & Peres Distribution

THIS IS OUR TIME.
Single (7"): released on RCA in Jun'85 by RCA Records. Distributed by: RCA, Roots, Swift, Wellard, Chris, I & B, Solomon & Peres Distribution

Single (12"): released on RCA in Jun'85 by RCA Records. Distributed by: RCA, Roots, Swift, Wellard, Chris, I & B, Solomon & Peres Distribution

Band Of Holy Joy

BIG SHIP SAILS, THE.
Notes: Mini LP
Album: released on Flim Flam in May'86 by Flim Flam Productions. Distributed by: Pinnacle

HAD A MOTHER WHO WAS PROUD.
Single (12"): released on Flim Flam in Oct'85 by Flim Flam Productions. Distributed by: Pinnacle

WHO SNATCHED THE BABY.
Tracks: / Who snatched the baby.
Single (7"): released on Flim Flam in Oct'86 by Flim Flam Productions. Distributed by: Pinnacle

Single (12"): released on Flim Flam in Oct'86 by Flim Flam Productions. Distributed by: Pinnacle

Band of Joy

24 K.
Tracks: / 3 A.m in the city / Woman / Overseer / So cold / Live bait / Like a river / Please call home / She's the one / Shock house.
Notes: Band of Joy featuring Robert Plant with John Bonham, Paul Lockey, Michael Chetwood, Kevin Hammond, Francesco Nizza, John Pasternak.
Album: released on Thunderbolt in Sep'83 by Magnum Music Group Ltd. Distributed by: Magnum Music Group Ltd, PRT Distribution, Spartan Distribution

Album: released on Thunderbolt in Sep'83 by Magnum Music Group Ltd. Distributed by: Magnum Music Group Ltd, PRT Distribution, Spartan Distribution

Band of Outsiders

I WISH I WAS YOUR KID.
Single (12"): released on Flicknife in Sep'85 by Flicknife Records. Distributed by: Spartan

UP THE RIVER.
Album: by Flicknife Records. Distributed by: Spartan

Band Of The...

BOOTS AND SADDLES (Band of the Life Guards).
Album: released on Bandleader in Feb'86 by Bandleader Records. Distributed by: PRT

Cassette: released on Bandleader in Feb'86 by Bandleader Records. Distributed by: PRT

DANKE SCHON (Band of the RAF Germany).
Tracks: / Stage centre / Avengers / Walk in the Black Forest / Swinging safari / Beer barrel polka / Danke schoen / War of the worlds / Wonderland by night / Old comrades / Country gardens / Skyrider / Colonel bogey / Elizabethan serenade / Carmina burana.
Album: released on Polyphonic Digital in Aug'86

Cassette: released on Polyphonic Digital in Aug'86

IN CONCERT (Band of the 2nd Battalion, Light Infantry).
Album: released on Music Masters in Jun'82 by Music Masters Records. Distributed by: Taylors

MARCHES FROM THE CLASSICS (Band of the Irish Guards).
Album: released on Bandleader in Feb'85 by Bandleader Records. Distributed by: PRT

Cassette: released on Bandleader in Feb'85 by Bandleader Records. Distributed by: PRT

MARCHING THROUGH THE YEARS (Band of the Grenadier Guards).
Album: released on Grasmere in Jul'87 by Grasmere Records. Distributed by: EMI

Cassette: released on Grasmere in Jul'87 by Grasmere Records. Distributed by: EMI

MEN OF ACTION (Band of the Royal Marines).
Album: released on Bandleader in Aug'85 by Bandleader Records. Distributed by: PRT

Cassette: released on Bandleader in Aug'85 by Bandleader Records. Distributed by: PRT

SCOTCH ON THE ROCKS (Band of the Black Watch).
Single (7"): released on RK in May'84

Bandoggs

BANDOGGS (Various Artists).
Album: released on Leader in May'78. Distributed by: Jazz Music, Projection

Band, Richard

REANIMATOR, THE.
Album: released on Vinilo Spain in Aug'86 by Vinilo Spain Records. Distributed by: Silva Screen

Bandstand Grand

BANDSTAND GRAND (Various bands).
Tracks: / Greensleeves / Spitfire prelude / Cockles and mussels / Trumpet voluntary / Sullivan at sea / Spirt of pageantry / Farandole / Yeoman of the guard overture, The / Tannhauser grand march / Birdie's song / Caesar's camp / Policeman's holiday / Concerto for two trumpets / Musical joke / Pique dame / Great war medley / Skye boat song / Frensham.
Double Album: released on Cambra in '83 by Cambra Records. Distributed by: IDS, Conifer

Double cassette: released on Cambra in '83 by Cambra Records. Distributed by: IDS, Conifer

Bandy, Moe

20 GREAT SONGS OF THE AMERICAN COWBOY.
Tracks: / Springtime in the rockies / Red river valley / Take me back to Tulsa / Bury me not on the lone prairie / Don't fence me in / Tumbling tumbleweed / San Antonio Rose / I'm an old cowhand / Oklahoma hills / Old faithful / Home on the range / Sioux City Sue / Deep in the heart of Texas / Cool water / Good old paint / Back in the saddle again / Streets of Laredo / High noon (do not forsake me) / Strawberry roan, The / Old Chisholm trail, The.
Album: released on Warwick in Mar'82. Distributed by: Multiple Sound Distributors

Cassette: released on Warwick in Mar'82. Distributed by: Multiple Sound Distributors

AT THE COUNTRY STORE.
Album: released on Starblend Country Store in Aug'86 by Starblend Records. Distributed by: PRT Distribution

Cassette: released on Starblend Country Store in Aug'86 by Starblend Records. Distributed by: PRT Distribution

CHAMP, THE.
Tracks: / Champ, The / Cowboy's a kitten at home, The / Wild side of life, The / Beethoven was before my time / Giver took all she could stand, The / Yesterday once more / I just can't leave those honky tonks alone / She took out the outlaw in me / Like some good ol' boy / Accidently on purpose tonight.
Album: released on CBS in Aug'80 by CBS Records. Distributed by: CBS

Cassette: released on CBS in Aug'80 by CBS Records. Distributed by: CBS

GOOD OL' BOYS - ALIVE AND WELL, THE See Stampley, Joe (Bandy, Moe & Joe Stampley).
Album: released on CBS in Aug'84 by CBS Records. Distributed by: CBS

Cassette: released on CBS in Aug'84 by CBS Records. Distributed by: CBS

MOE BANDY I love country.
Tracks: / Wound time can't erase, A / Barroom is my battleground tonight, The / Wound time can't erase, A / Barroom Roses / There's nobody home on the range anymore / That's as close to cheatin' as I came / Yippi Cry Yi / Yesterday Oncemore / Two Lonely People / Soft Lights and Hard Country Music / Jambalaya (on the Bayou) / One Of A Kind / Barstool Mountain / It's A Cheatin' Situation / Would You Mind If I Just Called You Julie / My woman loves the devil out of me / I Cheated Me Right Out Of You.
Album: released on CBS in Mar'87 by CBS Records. Distributed by: CBS

Cassette: released on CBS in Mar'87 by CBS Records. Distributed by: CBS

SHE'S NOT REALLY CHEATIN' (SHE'S JUST GETTIN' EVEN).
Tracks: / She's not really cheatin' (she's just gettin' even) / He's taking my place at your place / Can I pick you up / Hank and Leftyh raised my country soul / All American dream, The / Only if there is another you / Our love could burn Atlanta down again / Your memory is showing all over me / An angel like you / Jesus in a Nashville jail.
Album: released on CBS in Jul'82 by CBS Records. Distributed by: CBS

WHERE'S THE DRESS? (Bandy, Moe & Joe Stampley).
Single (7"): released on CBS in Aug'84 by CBS Records. Distributed by: CBS

YOU HAVEN'T HEARD THE LAST OF ME.
Album: released on MCA in Mar'87 by MCA Records. Distributed by: Polygram, MCA

Bandzi

ZIG ZAG/SOLID SECURITY.
Single (7"): released on Flipdisc in Dec'82 by Menace Breaker Distributors. Distributed by: Menace Breaker Distributors, Cartel

Bandzilla

BANDZILLA.
Album: released on Rainbow in Jun'87. Distributed by: I & B, CBS

Cassette: released on Rainbow in Jul'87. Distributed by: I & B, CBS

DON'T TOUCH THAT DIAL.
Tracks: / Don't touch that dial / Blue movies.
Single (7"): released on Rainbow in May'87. Distributed by: I & B, CBS

Bane

WHAT HAPPENS NEXT.....
Cassette: released on Bane in Dec'86. Distributed by: Rough Trade, Cartel, Backs

Bane, Honey

DIZZY DREAMERS.
Single (7"): released on Zonophone in Feb'83 by EMI Records. Distributed by: EMI

YOU CAN BE YOU.
Single (7"): released on Crass in Oct'81 by Exitstencil Music. Distributed by: Rough Trade, Cartel

Banger, Ed

KINNEL TOMMY.
Single (7"): released on Rabid in Sep'83 by Rabid Records. Distributed by: Pinnacle, Rough Trade

POOR PEOPLE.
Single (7"): released on Cloud Nine in Dec'82 by Cloud Nine Records. Distributed by: Silva Screen, Harmonia Mundi

Bangesters

ESCAPE FROM BUBBLEGUM LAND.
Album: released on New Rose in Dec'84. Distributed by: Rough Trade, Cartel

Bangles

ALL OVER THE PLACE.
Tracks: / Hero takes a fall / Live / James / All about you / Dover beach / Tell me / Restless / Going down to liverpool / He's got a secret / Silent treatment / More than meets the eye.
Album: released on CBS in Nov'86 by CBS Records. Distributed by: CBS

Cassette: released on CBS in Nov'86 by CBS Records. Distributed by: CBS

DIFFERENT LIGHT.
Tracks: / Manic monday / In a different light / Walking down your street / Walk like an Egyptian / Standing in the hallway / Return post / If she knew what she wants / Let it go / September girl / Angels don't fall in love / Following / Not like you.
Album: released on CBS in Mar'86 by CBS Records. Distributed by: CBS

Cassette: released on CBS in Mar'86 by CBS Records. Distributed by: CBS

Compact disc: released on CBS in Mar'86 by CBS Records. Distributed by: CBS

FOLLOWING.
Single (7"): released on CBS in Apr'87 by CBS Records. Distributed by: CBS

GOING DOWN TO LIVERPOOL.
Tracks: / Going down to Liverpool / Let it go.
Single (7"): released on CBS in Jun'85 by CBS Records. Distributed by: CBS

Single (12"): released on CBS in Jun'85 by CBS Records. Distributed by: CBS

IF SHE KNEW WHAT SHE WANTS.
Tracks: / If she knew what she wants / Angels don't fall in love / Hero takes a fall * / James *.
Single (7"): released on CBS in May'86 by CBS Records. Distributed by: CBS

Double-pack single: released on CBS in May'86 by CBS Records. Distributed by: CBS

Single (12"): released on CBS in May'86 by CBS Records. Distributed by: CBS

MANIC MONDAY.
Tracks: / Manic Monday / In a different light / Going down to Liverpool * / Dover beach *.
Single (7"): released on CBS in Nov'85 by CBS Records. Distributed by: CBS

Single (7"): released on CBS in Nov'85 by CBS Records. Distributed by: CBS

Single (12"): released on CBS in Nov'85 by CBS Records. Distributed by: CBS

WALKING DOWN YOUR STREET.
Tracks: / Return post.
Single (7"): released on CBS in Dec'86 by CBS Records. Distributed by: CBS

Single (12"): released on CBS in Nov'86 by CBS Records. Distributed by: CBS

WALK LIKE AN EGYPTIAN.
Tracks: / Walk like an Egyptian / Not like you.
Single (7"): released on CBS in Sep'86 by CBS Records. Distributed by: CBS

Bang On The Drum

BANG ON A DRUM AGAIN (Various Artists).

Tracks: / Head and shoulders, knees and toes / How do you feel today / Paddle your own canoe / Paddle your own canoe / Hey you! / Elephants on a piece of string / Hokey cokey / Spells / Wiggle my ears / Stand up sit down / Zoom / Step aside / How high does a fly fly / Well Jemima, let's go shopping / Share / Wouldn't it be funny / Rain makes all things beautiful.
Album: released on BBC in Jul'83 by BBC Records & Tapes. Distributed by: EMI, PRT

Cassette: released on BBC in Jul'83 by BBC Records & Tapes. Distributed by: EMI, PRT,

BANG ON THE DRUM (Various Artists).
Tracks: / Early in the morning / Brush, brush, brush / Sunbeams play / I am here / Caterpillars only crawl / Wheels keep turning / I like peace, I like quiet / Building up my house / Fidget / Israeli boat song / One potato, two potato / Bang on a drum / Jump / Paper song / Down on the farm / Fidget / Come to the shops / What do we do with this and that / Circus is coming / Build it up / I think I've got a cold / You can stamp your feet / Playaway.
Album: released on BBC in Oct'76 by BBC Records & Tapes. Distributed by: EMI, PRT,

Cassette: released on BBC in Oct'76 by BBC Records & Tapes. Distributed by: EMI, PRT,

Bangor

TERRAS BANGKOK.
Album: released on Bang in May'86. Distributed by: Red Rhino, Cartel

Bang Orchestra

SAMPLE THAT.
Tracks: / Sample that (short house mix).
Single (7"): released on Geffen in Oct'86 by Geffen Records. Distributed by: WEA, CBS

Single (12"): released on Geffen in Oct'86 by Geffen Records. Distributed by: WEA, CBS

Bangor Parish...

CAROLS BY CANDLELIGHT (Bangor Parish Church Choir).
Tracks: / O little town of Bethlehem / Adam lay abounden / Ding dong merrily on high / Gabriel's message / Away in a manger / Blessed son of God / As with gladness men of old / Sussex carol / We've been awhile a wondering / Still still still / As I outrode this enderes night / Tender shoot / Stille nacht / Chester carol / Joseph and the angel / Lute book lullaby / Psallite unigenito / O come all ye faithful / Over the hills / While shepherds watched their flocks.
Album: released on Alpha in Dec'82 by Alpha Records. Distributed by: H.R. Taylor,

Banjo In The Hills

BANJO IN THE HILLS (Various Artists).
Album: released on Starday in Apr'87

Cassette: released on Starday in Apr'87

Banjo Kings

FAVOURITES.
Compact disc: released on London in Apr'87 by London Records. Distributed by: Polygram

Banjo Man

BANJO MAN Original soundtrack.
Album: released on Sire in Feb'79

Bank Robbers

JENNY.
Single (7"): released on Good Vibration in May'83 by Good Vibrations Records. Distributed by: Pinnacle, Rough Trade

Banks, Bessie

GO NOW.
Tracks: / Go now / It sounds like my baby.
Notes: An original Tiger recording. Arranged by Gerry Sherman. Produced by Jerry Leiber & Mike Stoller. This release C 1987 Charly Records Ltd.
Single (7"): released on Charly in May'87 by Charly Records. Distributed by: Charly, Cadillac

Banks, Bosca

BAM BAM BOLERO.
Single (12"): released on Roke in Aug'83. Distributed by: Roke Distribution

Banks, Tony

CURIOUS FEELING, A.
Notes: Originally released in 1979
Album: released on Charisma in Oct'86 by Virgin Records. Distributed by: EMI

FUGITIVE, THE.
Tracks: / This is love / Man of spells / And the wheels keep turning / Say you'll never leave me / Thirty three's / By you / At the edge of night / Charm / Moving under.
Notes: Originally released in 1983
Cassette: released on Charisma in Oct'86 by Virgin Records. Distributed by: EMI

Album: released on Charisma in Oct'86 by Virgin Records. Distributed by: EMI

SHORT CUT TO SOMEWHERE (Banks, Tony Featuring Fish).
Tracks: / Short cut to somewhere / Smilin' Jack / K2.
Single (7"): released on Charisma in Oct'86 by Virgin Records. Distributed by: EMI

Single (12"): released on Charisma in Oct'86 by Virgin Records. Distributed by: EMI

Album: released on Charisma in May'86 by Virgin Records. Distributed by: EMI

Cassette: released on Charisma in May'86 by Virgin Records. Distributed by: EMI

SOUNDTRACKS.
Compact disc: released on Charisma in Jul'87 by Virgin Records. Distributed by: EMI

TONY BANKS (EP) (Banks, Tony/Jim Diamond/Toyah).
Single (7"): released on Charisma in Sep'85 by Virgin Records. Distributed by: EMI

WICKED LADY.
Single (7"): released on Atlantic in May'83 by WEA Records. Distributed by: WEA

Banna Spar

CHANGES COMING.
Single (7"): released on Oraima in Sep'82

Banned From U.N.C.L.E.

CLOCKWORK ORANGE.
Single (7"): released on AMF in Jun'85 by AMF Records. Distributed by: M.I.S., EMI

Bannerman, Helen

STORY OF LITTLE BLACK SAMBO AND OTHERS.
Tracks: / Story of little black Quibba (The) / Story of little black Quasha (The) / Story of Sambo and the twins (The) / Story of little black Bobtail(The) / Story of little black Mingo (The).
Cassette: released on Tellastory in Dec'86 by Bartlett Bliss Productions. Distributed by: PRT Distribution, Hayward Promotions Distribution, H.R. Taylor Distribution

B, Annette

CASANOVA.
Tracks: / Casanova / Casanova (P.A Mix) (bubblers Crew).
Single (7"): released on Greensleeves in Jan'87 by Greensleeves Records. Distributed by: BMG, Jetstar, Spartan

GIVE HER THE LOVE THAT'S RIGHT.
Tracks: / Give her the love that's right / Give her the love that's right (version).
Single (12"): released on UK Bubblers in 13 Jun'87 by Greensleeves Records. Distributed by: RCA, Jetstar

I FOUND LOVE.
Tracks: / I found love / I found love (version).
Single (12"): released on UK Bubblers in Sep'86 by Greensleeves Records. Distributed by: RCA, Jetstar

Banquet Scene, The

BANQUET SCENE, (THE) From Dune, by Frank Herbert (Not shown).
Cassette: released on Caedmon(USA) in Jan'78 by Caedmon (USA) Records. Distributed by: Gower, Taylors, Discovery

Banton, Evans, Jackson

GENTLEMEN PREFER BLUES.
Notes: For full details see under Jackson,Banton,Evans

Banton, George

FAITHFUL AND TRUE.
Single (12"): released on Londis in Oct'85

Single (7"): released on Londisc in Oct'85 by Londisc Records

SOCA MEDLEY.
Single (12"): released on Londisc in Oct'84 by Londisc Records

Banton, Pato

BAD MAN & WOMAN.
Tracks: / Bad man & woman / Bad man & woman (dub mix).
Single (12"): released on Movin Music in Oct'86

BOSS, (THE).
Single (12"): released on Fashion in Jul'85 by Fashion Records. Distributed by: PRT, Jetstar

DOG IS A MAN'S BEST FRIEND, A.
Tracks: / Dog is a man's best friend, A / Dog is a man's best friend, A (version).
Single (12"): released on UK Bubblers in 13 Jun'87 by Greensleeves Records. Distributed by: RCA, Jetstar

MASH UP THE TELLY.
Single (7"): released on UK Bubblers in Sep'85 by Greensleeves Records. Distributed by: RCA, Jetstar

PROFESSOR CAPTURES PATO BANTON (See Mad Professor) (Banton, Pato & Mad Professor).

SECRET THUNDERBIRD DRINKER.
Tracks: / Secret thunderbird drinker / Don't sniff coke.
Single (12"): released on UK Bubblers in May'86 by Greensleeves Records. Distributed by: RCA, Jetstar

Bantu

ENGLAND TO HER SONGS.
Single (7"): released on Peninsula in Aug'85 by Prism Records. Distributed by: Various Distribution

VIEW OF JERUSALEM (EP) (Bantu/Vicious Circle/Fish Shoots Man).
Single (7"): released on Wounded Knee in Aug'86 by Endangered Musik Records. Distributed by: Revolver

Banzai

RUNAWAY.
Single (7"): released on Groove PR in Oct'81 by Beggars Banquet Records. Distributed by: WEA, PRT

Single (12"): released on Groove PR in Oct'81 by Beggars Banquet Records. Distributed by: WEA, PRT

Bap

KRISTALLNACHT.
Tracks: / Alexandra, nit nur do / Bahnhofsino / Drei wunsch frei / Sendelschlub / Kristallnaach / Diess nach ess alles drin / Deshav'spill mer he / Zofall un'e janz klei bessje glock / Do kans zaubere.
Album: released on EMI in Jun'85 by EMI Records. Distributed by: EMI

Bappi Bappi, K

MOVIN' ON.
Tracks: / Movin' on / Tell me.
Single (7"): released on BL in Jul'86. Distributed by: Spartan

Single (12"): released on BL in Jul'86. Distributed by: Spartan

Baptist Beat

BAPTIST BEAT (THE) Various artists (Various Artists).
Tracks: / Rev. Moses / Jody grind (The) / Turnaround (The) / Fungii mama / Baptist beat, A / Sara's dance / Party time / Good gracious.
Album: released on EMI America in Apr'87 by EMI Records. Distributed by: EMI

Cassette: released on EMI America in Apr'87 by EMI Records. Distributed by: EMI

Baptiste, Denise

WEAK AT THE KNEES (PART 2).
Single (12"): released on Gi Gi in Jul'83 by Gi Gi Records. Distributed by: Jetstar

Baraka, Imamu Amiri

New York Quartet & Imamu Amiri Baraka

Baranco, Wilbert

GROOVIN' HIGH (see Wilson, Gerald) (Baranco, Wilbert/Gerald Wilson/Jimmy Mundy).

Baranoo, Wilbert

Groovin high

Barb

BOUQUET OF BARBS.
Album: released on Magnet in Dec'84 by Magnet Records. Distributed by: BMG

Cassette: released on Magnet in Dec'84 by Magnet Records. Distributed by: BMG

I WANT MY MONEY BACK.
Single (7"): released on Magnet in Dec'83 by Magnet Records. Distributed by: BMG

Single (12"): released on Magnet in Dec'83 by Magnet Records. Distributed by: BMG

TELL ME WHY/SUGAR CANE.
Single (7"): released on Magnet in Sep'83 by Magnet Records. Distributed by: BMG

Single (12"): released on Magnet in Sep'83 by Magnet Records. Distributed by: BMG

YEAH.
Single (7"): released on Magnet in May'84 by Magnet Records. Distributed by: BMG

Single (12"): released on Magnet in May'84 by Magnet Records. Distributed by: BMG

Barbara...

BARBARA OF THE HOUSE OF GREBE Hardy, Thomas (Morant, Richard).
Cassette:

Cassette: released on Talking Tape Company in '84 by Talking Tape Company Records

Barbarin, Paul

STREETS OF THE CITY (Barbarin, Paul & His New Orleans Band 1950).
Album: released on 504 in Sep'86 by 504 Records. Distributed by: Chris Wellard, Jazz Music

Cassette: released on 504 in Sep'86 by 504 Records. Distributed by: Chris Wellard, Jazz Music

Barbary Coast

CLEAN UP.
Tracks: / Last ride, The / Rollin' on / Take me home truck / Toe the line / Many roads I ride / Truck drivers blues / Truckers life, A / God bless the truckers bike / Rockabilly trucker / Breakers blues.
Album: released on Champ in '82 by Champ Records. Distributed by: Champ

Cassette: released on Champ in '82 by Champ Records. Distributed by: Champ

COASTLINES.
Tracks: / Did it rain / Fool such as I / Leave them with a smile / Living on sunshine / Give my love to Rose / If this is just a game / Blowin' away / You only live once in a while / Old five and dimers like me / Long gone.
Album: released on Champ in '82 by Champ Records. Distributed by: Champ

FISTFUL OF ROSES.
Album: released on Tank in Jun'79 by Tank Records

HEARTS ON FIRE (ROCK MIX).
Single (7"): released on MDE in Apr'84 by MDE Records. Distributed by: MDE Distribution

LONG VEHICLE.
Tracks: / Son of a son of a trucker / Ridin' rubber / Move on down the road / Don's cafe / Keep those wheels a rollin' / High rollin' lonesome / Truck stop woman / Queen of the road / Joe's rig road / Reversing song, The / Pedal to the medal.
Album: released on Champ in '82 by Champ Records. Distributed by: Champ

Cassette: released on Champ in '82 by Champ Records. Distributed by: Champ

Barbecue Bob

REMAINING TITLES, THE 1927-30.
Tracks: / Good time rounder / Yo Yo blues / Darktown gamblin' / Easy rider don't you deny my name / Cold wave blues.
Album: released on Saydisc in Apr'87 by Saydisc Records. Distributed by: Essex, Harmonia Mundi, Roots, H.R. Taylor, Jazz Music, Swift, Projection, Gamut

Barbed Wire

AGE THAT DIDN'T CARE, THE.
Album: released on Oi! in Aug'86. Distributed by: Revolver Distribution

Skins'n'Punks volume 4

Barbee, John Henry

BLUES LIVE (Barbee, John Henry/Sleepy John Estes).
Album: released on Storyville in Sep'86 by Storyville Records. Distributed by: Jazz Music Distribution, Swift Distribution, Chris Wellard Distribution, Counterpoint Distribution

Barber, Billy

LIGHTHOUSE.
Notes: Billy Barker plays Hamburg Steinway grand Piano and uses IBM & Macintosh Computers MIDI interfaced to Kurzeil, Prophet & Yamaha Synthesizers.
Compact disc: released on DMP in Jun'86 by DMP Records. Distributed by: Venture

SHADES OF GREY.
Compact disc: released on DMP in Jun'86 by DMP Records. Distributed by: Venture

Barber, Chris

BARBER/BUE BESTSELLERS (Barber, Chris/Papa Bue).
Notes: 6 tracks each
Compact disc: released on Storyville in Jun'87 by Storyville Records. Distributed by: Jazz Music Distribution, Swift Distribution, Chris Wellard Distribution, Counterpoint Distribution

BARBER'S BEST.
Tracks: / Bobby Shaftoe / Martinique, The / Chimes blues / Merry down rag / Skokiaan / St.Louis blues / It's tight like that / Ice cream / Oh, didn't he ramble / Storyville blues / World is waiting for the sunshine, The / Reckless blues.
Album: released on Jasmine in Mar'85 by Jasmine Records. Distributed by: Counterpoint, Lugtons, Taylor, H.R., Wellard, Chris, Swift, Cadillac

BARBER'S CHOICE.
Album: released on Teldec (Germany) in Jul'84 by Import Records. Distributed by: IMS Distribution, Polygram Distribution

BARBICAN BLUES.
Tracks: / Bourbon Street Parade / Mary had a little Lamb / Perdido Street Blues / Spanish Castles / Barbican Blues / Bugle Boy March / Good Queen Bess / Wild Cat Blues / Rose Room / Basin Street Blues / Ice Cream.
Notes: Recorded at Barbican Centre on April 20, 1982.

Double Album: released on Black Lion in Feb'83 by Black Lion Records. Distributed by: Jazz Music, Chris Wellard, Taylor, H.R., Counterpoint, Cadillac

BEST OF CHRIS BARBER, (THE).
Tracks: / Bobby Shaftoe / Rock Island line / New Orleans / John Henry / Stevedore stomp / Merrydown blues / I'd love it / Storyville blues / Girls go crazy about the way I walk, The / I hat a man like you / Alution March / Weeping willow blues.
Album: released on Decca in Jun'85 by Decca Records. Distributed by: Polygram

CAN'T WE GET TOGETHER?.
Album: released on Timeless (Holland) in Aug'85. Distributed by: JSU Distribution, Jazz Music Distribution, Jazz Horizons Distribution, Cadillac, Celtic Music Distribution

CAN'T WE GET TOGETHER (Barber, Chris Jazz & Blues Band).
Tracks: / Holiday / Double check stomp / Here come my blackbird / I wish I could shimmy like my sister Kate / Over the waves / Everybody love my baby / Whistlin' Rufus / Can't we get together / Good time tonight / High Society / Bobby Saftoe / New Orleans Ceremony / Just a little while to stay here / Oration by Chris Barber / Just a closer walk with thee / When the saints go marching in / A the jazzband ball / Good Queen Bess / Easter Parade / Isle of Capri, The / Wabas blues / Sheik of Araby, The / Goin' home / Old rugged cross, The / Too busy.
Notes: Double Album. Personnel includes: Pat Halcox - trumpet/Chris Barber - trombone/Eddie Smith - banjo/Dick Smith - bass/Ron Bowden - drums with special guests Ottilie Patterson, Monty Sunshine, Ken Colyer and Dr John. Recordings made between November 1954 and October 1984.
Double Album: released on Timeless in Sep'86

Cassette: released on Timeless in Sep'86

CHRIS BARBER AND DR JOHN (VOL 1) (Barber, Chris & Dr John).
Album: released on Black Lion in '83 by Black Lion Records. Distributed by: Jazz Music, Chris Wellard, Taylor, H.R., Counterpoint, Cadillac

CHRIS BARBER & DR JOHN (VOL 2) (Barber, Chris & Dr John).
Album: released on Black Lion in '83 by Black Lion Records. Distributed by: Jazz Music, Chris Wellard, Taylor, H.R., Counterpoint, Cadillac

CHRIS BARBER IN NEW ORLEANS.
Tracks: / Shake it or break it / Eh la bas / It's right here for you / High society / You can't depend on me / Hindustan / Mama's in the racket / Billies' boogie / Gulf coast blues / Dippermouth blues / Billie's blues / All of me / Love song of the Nile / Love song of the Nile.
Album: released on Hefty Jazz in Sep'79. Distributed by: JSU, Swift, Wellard, Chris, Jazz Music, Cadillac Music

CHRIS BARBER JAZZ BAND, (THE) Creole love call.
Tracks: / Stevedore stomp / Come Friday / Sweet Sue / Wild cat blues / St Louis Blues / Alligator hop / Queen Bess / Creole Love Call / South Rampart Street parade / Snag it / Easter parade.
Notes: Artists: Chris Barber/Ian Wheeler/ John Croker/Johnny McCallum/Roger Hill/ Vic Pitt/Norman Emberson.
Double Album: released on Timeless in Mar'83

CONCERT FOR THE BBC (Barber, Chris Jazz & Blues Band).
Compact disc: by Bellaphon Records. Distributed by: IMS-Polygram

Double Album: released on Timeless in Sep'86

Compact disc: released on Timeless in Sep'86

CREOLE LOVE CALL.
Album: released on Timeless in Mar'83

CREOLE LOVE CALL (Barber, Chris Band).
Tracks: / Stevedore stomp / Come Friday / Sweet Sue / Wild cat clues / St. Louis blues / Alligator hop / Queen Bess / Creole love call / South Rampart street parade / Snag it / Easter parade.
Double Album: released on Timeless in Sep'86

ECHOES OF HARLEM.
Album: released on Dormouse in Nov'86 by Dormouse Records. Distributed by: Swift

EVERYBODY KNOWS.
Compact disc: released on The Compact Collection in Sep'87 by Conifer Records. Distributed by: Conifer Distribution

ICE CREAM.
Tracks: / Wild cat blues / Old rugged cross, The / Over in the gloryland / Canal Street blues / Muskrat ramble / High society / Jazz me blues / New Orleans wiggle / London blues / Ice cream.
Notes: Personnel: Pat Halcox/Monty Sunshine/Eddie Smith/Dick Smith/Graham Burbidge/Ian Wheeler/Stu Morrison/Jackie Flavelle/John Slaughter/Steve Hammond/Johnny McCallum.
Album: released on Black Lion-Intercord in '82

Cassette: released on Black Lion-Intercord in '82

IN BUDAPEST.
Notes: Recorded July 7th 1962
Compact disc: released on Storyville in Jun'87 by Storyville Records. Distributed by: Jazz Music Distribution, Swift Distribution, Chris Wellard Distribution, Counterpoint Distribution

Album: released on Storyville in Jan'85 by Storyville Records. Distributed by: Jazz Music Distribution, Swift Distribution, Chris Wellard Distribution, Counterpoint Distribution

JAZZ HOLIDAY Meets Rod Mason's Hot Five (Barber, Chris/Rod Mason's Hot Five).
Album: released on Timeless in Sep'86

JUBILEE ALBUM.
Tracks: / Savoy blues / Doctor jazz / Baby won't you please come home / Star of the country down / Bill Bailey won't you please come home / Please don't talk about me when I'm gone / Oro / Give me an old fashioned swing in the evening / It's tight like that / New Orleans wiggle / I'm slapping Seventh Avenue with the sole of my shoe / I think it's going to rain today / Jazz me blues / What' cha gonna do / Canal Street blues / Muskrat ramble / Ice cream / Goodbye, goodbye, goodbye.
Notes: Personnel: Pat Halcox/John Crocker/John Slaughter/Stu Morrison/Jackie Flavelle/Graham Burbidge/Ottilie Patterson/Steve Hammond/Stig Praestvang/Johnny McCallum. Recorded: 1970-1974.
Album: released on Black Lion-Intercord in '82

LIVE IN '85 (Barber, Chris Jazz & Blues Band).
Album: released on Timeless in Sep'86

MUSIC FROM THE LAND OF DREAMS.
Tracks: / Music from the land of dreams / Goin' up the river / Nobody knows you when you're down & out / New Orleans Louisiana / Big bass drum (on a mardi gras day) / Beg,steal or borrow / Whose blues / New York town / Second line saints.
Notes: Produced by Tony Atkins for Chris Barber Productions Personnel: Chris Barber-trombone & vocals/Pat Halcox-trumpet/Ian Wheeler-clarinet,alto,harmonica/John Crocker-tenor,alto ,"New York Town"/Roger Hill-guitar/ Johnny McCalham - banjo,guitar/Vic Pitt-string bass,tuba/Norman Emberson-drums
Compact disc: released on Sonet in Jun'86 by Sonet Records. Distributed by: PRT

Album: released on Sonet in Sep'86 by Sonet Records. Distributed by: PRT

Single (7"): released on Sonet in Oct'85 by Sonet Records. Distributed by: PRT

REUNION.
Tracks: / Bourbon Street parade / Saturday night function / Martinque, The / Isle of Capri, The / Hushabye / It's tight like that / Fairfield reunion blues / Bobby Shaftoe / On a Monday / Bury my body / Long gone lost John / Jenny's ball / Chimes blues / Whistlin' Rufus / Jazz me blues / Just a sittin' and a rockin' / Stevedore stomp / Jack-ass blues / New Orleans stomp / Maryland my Maryland / When you wore a tulip / Panama rag.
Album: released on Black Lion-Intercord in '82

SPECIAL.
Tracks: / Dardanella / Jazz lips / Original Charleston strut / Lonesome Road / Eh La bas / I wish I could shimmy like my sister Kate / Makin' whoopee / Clarinet Marmalade / Precious lord, take my hand / Colla voce / High society / I'm looking for a four leaf clover / Panama rag / From me to you / Money can't buy me love / Over in the gloryland / Tiger rag / South Rampart Street Parade / Easter Parade / All my loving.
Double Album: released on Black Lion-Intercord in '82

STAR PORTRAIT.
Tracks: / Down by the riverside / Burgandy Street blues / Phil's late / Sweet Lorraine / Blueberry Hill / When the saints go marching in / Whistlin' Rufus / Lazy River / St. Georges rag / Creole song / Gonna build a mountain / Stevedore stomp / Ice cream / Baby won't you please come home / I can't escape from you / Canal Street blues / Running wild / Just a closer walk with me / Muskrat ramble / Savoy blues / When you and I were young, Maggie / Bourbon Street Parade / Oh Didn't he ramble / Goodbye, goodbye, goodbye.
Notes: Personnel: Pat Halcox/Ian Wheeler/Eddie Smith/Dick Smith/Graham Burbidge/ Ottilie Patterson/Monty Sunshine/Edmond Hall/Joe Marshall/Hanc Duncan/Hayes Alvis/John Crocker/Johnny McCallum/Dickie Hawdon/Ben Cohen/Brylo Ford.
Double Album: released on Black Lion-Intercord in '82

TAKE ME BACK TO NEW ORLEANS (Barber, Chris & Dr John).
Double Album: released on Black Lion in Feb'83 by Black Lion Records. Distributed by: Jazz Music, Chris Wellard, Taylor, H.R., Counterpoint, Cadillac

Double Album: released on Black Lion-Intercord in '82

Album: released on Black Lion-Intercord in '82

UP JUMPED THE BLUES.
Album: released on Hefty Jazz in Sep'79. Distributed by: JSU, Swift, Wellard, Chris, Jazz Music, Cadillac Music

Barber, Frank

BARBER CUTS.
Tracks: / James Bond medley / If only I could talk to you / Michel Le Grand Medley / Charlie Chaplin Medley / Richard Rodgers Medley / Henry Mancini Medley / I know I'm lucky / John Williams Medley / Where are you now / Dicing

with disco / Bond Medley (Vocal).
Notes: Following on Frank Barber's world success and his success with the Disco Bond 12" and 7" single, this album features many of the great film themes by some of the finest composers and four of Frank's own compositions. As always, Frank hasarranged all the tracks and the Orchestra features many of the top session musicians in the UK, including - Trombonist Don Lusher and Trumpeter Kenny Baker.
Album: released on PRT in Oct'83 by PRT Records. Distributed by: PRT

Cassette: released on PRT in Oct'83 by PRT Records. Distributed by: PRT

BIG BANDS ARE BACK.
Tracks: / One o'clock jump / 9.20 special / Jumpin' at the Woodside / Lil' darlin' / Lester leaps in / Swingin' the blues / Lil' darlin' (reprise) / Song on India / Marie / At the fat mans / Liebstraum / Chloe / Tuxedo junction / String of pearls / When Johnny comes marching home / Serenade in blues / Son of the Volga boatman / On the Atcheson and Santa Fe / Woodchoppers ball / Four brothers / Your fathers moustache / Good earth, The / Northwest passage / Skyliner / Cherokee / Redskin rhumba / Pompton turnpipe / Skyliner (reprise) / Artistry in rhythm / Intermission riff / Southern scandal / Eager beaver / Painted rhythm.
Album: released on PRT in Oct'82 by PRT Records. Distributed by: PRT

Cassette: released on PRT in Oct'82 by PRT Records. Distributed by: PRT

DALLAS.
Single (7"): released on BBC in Jan'80 by BBC Records & Tapes. Distributed by: EMI, PRT, Pye

GLENN MILLER TODAY (VOL 2).
Single (7"): released on PRT in Jan'83 by PRT Records. Distributed by: PRT

Single (12"): released on PRT in Jan'83 by PRT Records. Distributed by: PRT

MEDDLIN' WITH MILLER (Barber, Frank & His Orchestra).
Tracks: / In the mood / Pennsylvania 6 5000 / I've got a gal in Kalamazoo / Moonlight serenade / Little brown jug / Chattanooga choo choo / At last / American patrol / In the mood / Perdido / Take the 'A' train / C Jam blues / Satin doll / Things ain't what they used to be / I'm beginning to see the light / Begin the beguine / Back bay shuffle / What is this thing called love / Frenesi / My heart stood still / Johnson rag / Tangerine / So rare / I'm getting sentimental over you / On the sunny side of the street / Opus one / Hello dolly / When it's sleepy time down south / What a wonderful world / Struttin' with some barbecue / Rockin' chair / Mack the knife / Hello Dolly / Sing sing sing / Stompin' at the Savoy / Don't be that way / Jersey bounce / Christopher Columbus / And the angels sing.
Album: released on PRT in Mar'82 by PRT Records. Distributed by: PRT

Cassette: released on PRT in Mar'82 by PRT Records. Distributed by: PRT

Barber, Tony

SOMEDAY ... NOW.
Album: released on Rebel (Australia) in Feb'84. Distributed by: Swift

Barbieri

Worlds in a small room

Barbieri, Gato

APASIONADO.
Tracks: / Latin lovers / Que pasa / Last tango in Paris / Terra me siente / Angel / Tiempo buono / Habanera.
Album: released on Polydor (Italy) in Feb'84

Cassette: released on Polydor (Italy) in Feb'84

Compact disc: released on Polydor (Italy) in Feb'84

CHAPTER FOUR - ALIVE IN NEW YORK.
Tracks: / Milonga triste / La China leoncia / Baihia / Lluvia azul.
Album: released on Jasmine in Sep'82 by Jasmine Records. Distributed by: Counterpoint, Lugtons, Taylor, H.R., Wellard, Chris, Swift, Cadillac

Cassette: released on Jasmine in Sep'82 by Jasmine Records. Distributed by: Counterpoint, Lugtons, Taylor, H.R., Wellard, Chris, Swift, Cadillac

CONFLUENCE (Barbieri, Gato & Dollar Brand).
Album: released on Black Lion in Sep'85 by Black Lion Records. Distributed by: Jazz Music, Chris Wellard, Taylor, H.R., Counterpoint, Cadillac

GATO, EL.
Album: released on RCA (France) in '83 by RCA Records. Distributed by: Discovery

GATO...PARA LOS AMIGOS!.
Tracks: / Llamerito tango / Carnavalito / Brazil / Viva emilliano zapata / Encuentros / Latino america / El arriero / Bolivia / Finale medley.

Album: released on Doctor Jazz (USA) in Apr'84 by Doctor Jazz Records. Distributed by: CBS

Cassette: released on Doctor Jazz (USA) in Apr'84 by Doctor Jazz Records. Distributed by: CBS

HAMBA KHALE (Barbieri, Gato/Dollar Brand).
Compact disc: released on Charly in Mar'87 by Charly Records. Distributed by: Charly, Cadillac

HAMBE KHALE.
Album: released on Affinity in Oct'79 by Charly Records. Distributed by: Charly, Cadillac

OBSESSION.
Album: released on Affinity in '78 by Charly Records. Distributed by: Charly, Cadillac

VIVA EMILIANO ZAPATA.
Album: released on Impulse in Oct'85 by Impulse Records. Distributed by: MCA, Polygram

Barbosa-Lima, Carlos

IMPRESSIONS.
Tracks: / Sicilienne / Gymopedie No.3 / Girl with the flaxen hair, The / Three pieces from 'childrens corner' / Pavane pour une enfant defunte / New York rush / Lost child, The / Kerry morn / Prelude-introduction / Sentimental melody / Baa-too-kee-al almeida.
Notes: A beautiful classical solo guitar album highlighting French impressionist composers and contemporary pieces from North & South American composers. All the music is arranged by Carlos Barbosa-Lima,as on his previous three recordings on the Concord Concerto label. This digitally recorded album captures Barbosa-Lima's unique orchestral approach.
Album: released on Concord Concerto (USA) in Dec'85

PLAYS LUIZ BONFA & COLE PORTER.
Tracks: / Amor fascinante (love fascination) / Manha de carnival (morning of the carnival) / Xango / Sambolero / Na sombra da mangue - IRA (in the shade of the mango tree) / Passeio no Rio (a walk in Rio) / It's a lovely day / Where or when / Begin the beguine / Let's do it / Still of the night, The / Night and day / Love for sale.
Album: released on Concord Concerto (USA) in Nov'84

PLAYS THE ENTERTAINER and selected works by Scott Joplin.
Tracks: / Entertainer, The / Heliotrope bouquet / Weeping willow / Solace / Maple leaf rag / Surag cane / Chrysanthemum, The / Pleasant moments / Easy winners, The / Cascades, The.
Album: released on Concord Jazz (USA) in Sep'83 by Concord Jazz Records (USA). Distributed by: IMS, Polygram

Barchester Towers

BARCHESTER TOWERS Anthony Trollope (Hawthorne, Nigel).
Cassette: released on Argo (Spokenword) in Oct'83 by Decca Records. Distributed by: Polygram

Barclay, Bill

HALF A LIVE.
Album: released on Safari in Nov'79 by Safari Records. Distributed by: Pinnacle

I AIN'T GONNA DRINK ANYMORE.
Single (7"): released on G&M in May'81. Distributed by: PRT

Barclay James Harvest

BABY JAMES HARVEST.
Tracks: / Moonwater / Crazy (over you) / Delph Town Morn / Summer soldier / Thank you / One hundred thousand smiles out.
Album: released on Fame in Mar'87 by Music For Pleasure Records. Distributed by: EMI

Cassette: released on Fame in Mar'87 by Music For Pleasure Records. Distributed by: EMI

Album: released on Harvest in '85 by EMI Records. Distributed by: Roots, EMI

Cassette: released on Harvest in '85 by EMI Records. Distributed by: Roots, EMI

BERLIN-A CONCERT FOR THE PEOPLE.
Tracks: / Loving is easy / Mockingbird / Berlin / Sip of wine / Nova Lepidoptera / In memory of the martyrs.

BERLIN - A CONCERT FOR THE PEOPLE.
Compact disc: released on Polydor in '83 by Polydor Records. Distributed by: Polygram, Polydor

BEST OF BARCLAY JAMES HARVEST - VOL.2.
Tracks: / Early morning / She said / Lady loves / Crazy (over you) / When the city sleeps / Medicine man / Mother dear / Vanessa Simmons / One hundred thousand miles out / Mr. Sunshine / Taking some time out / Breathless.

Album: released on Harvest in '82 by EMI Records. Distributed by: Roots, EMI

Cassette: released on Harvest in '82 by EMI Records. Distributed by: Roots, EMI

BEST OF BARCLAY JAMES HARVEST, THE.
Tracks: / Medicine man / Iron maiden / Moonwater / Ursula / Brother thrush / Poor wages / Child of man / Joker, The / Rock 'n' roll woman / Good love child / Mockingbird / Galadriel.
Cassette: released on Harvest in Aug'86 by EMI Records. Distributed by: Roots, EMI

BEST OF BARCLAY JAMES HARVEST, THE.
Tracks: / Ursula / Child of man.
Album: released on Harvest in Jan'77 by EMI Records. Distributed by: Roots, EMI

COLLECTION: BARCLAY JAMES HARVEST.
Album: released on EMI (Germany) in '83 by EMI Records. Distributed by: Conifer

COMPACT STORY OF BARCLAY JAMES HARVEST.
Compact disc: by Polydor Records. Distributed by: Polygram, Polydor

CONCERT FOR THE PEOPLE (BERLIN), A.
Tracks: / Berlin / Loving is easy / Mockingbird / Sip of wine / Nova Lepidopter / In memory of the martyrs / Life is for living / Child of the universe / Hymm.
Album: released on Polydor in Jul'82 by Polydor Records. Distributed by: Polygram, Polydor

Cassette: released on Polydor in Jul'82 by Polydor Records. Distributed by: Polygram, Polydor

EARLY MORNING ONWARDS.
Tracks: / Early morning / Poor wages / Brother thrush / Mr Sunshine / Taking some time on / Mother dear / Mocking bird / Song with no meaning / I'm over you / Child of man / After the day.
Album: released on EMI (Germany) in '83 by EMI Records. Distributed by: Conifer

EVERYONE IS EVERYBODY ELSE.
Album: released on Polydor in Aug'83 by Polydor Records. Distributed by: Polygram, Polydor

Cassette: released on Polydor in Aug'83 by Polydor Records. Distributed by: Polygram, Polydor

EYES OF THE UNIVERSE.
Tracks: / Alright get down boogie / Capricorn / Love on the line / Play to the world / Rock 'n' Roll Lady / Skin flicks / Song they love to sing, The / Sperratus / Child of the Universe / Negative earth / Paper wings / Great 1974 mining disaster, The / Crazy city / See me, see you / Poor boy blues / Mill boys / For no one.
Notes: Digital stereo
Album: released on Polydor in Nov'79 by Polydor Records. Distributed by: Polygram, Polydor

Cassette: released on Polydor in Nov'79 by Polydor Records. Distributed by: Polygram, Polydor Deleted '83.

Compact disc: released on Polydor in Jun'84 by Polydor Records. Distributed by: Polygram, Polydor

FACE TO FACE.
Album: released on Polydor in Jan'87 by Polydor Records. Distributed by: Polygram, Polydor

Cassette: released on Polydor in Jan'87 by Polydor Records. Distributed by: Polygram, Polydor

Compact disc: released on Polydor in Jan'87 by Polydor Records. Distributed by: Polygram, Polydor

GONE TO EARTH.
Tracks: / Hymn / Love is like a violin / Friend of mine / Poor man's moody blues / Hard-hearted woman / Sea of tranquility / Spirit on the water / Leper's song / Taking me higher.
Compact disc: by Polydor Records. Distributed by: Polygram, Polydor

Album: released on Polydor in Sep'77 by Polydor Records. Distributed by: Polygram, Polydor

Cassette: released on Polydor in Sep'77 by Polydor Records. Distributed by: Polygram, Polydor Deleted '83.

Compact disc: released on Polydor in '83 by Polydor Records. Distributed by: Polygram, Polydor

HE SAID LOVE.
Tracks: / He said love / On the wings of love / Hymn (Live) *.
Single (7"): released on Polydor in Nov'86 by Polydor Records. Distributed by: Polygram, Polydor

Single (12"): released on Polydor in Nov'86 by Polydor Records. Distributed by: Polygram, Polydor

JUST A DAY AWAY.
Single (7"): released on Polydor in May'83 by Polydor Records. Distributed by: Polygram, Polydor

Picture disc single: released on Polydor in May'83 by Polydor Records. Distributed by: Polygram, Polydor

LIVE TAPES.
Double Album: released on Polydor in Apr'78 by Polydor Records. Distributed by: Polygram, Polydor

Double compact disc: released on Polydor in Apr'78 by Polydor Records. Distributed by: Polygram, Polydor

Cassette: released on Polydor in Apr'78 by Polydor Records. Distributed by: Polygram, Polydor Deleted '83.

LIVE TAPES.
Tracks: / Child of the universe / Rock'n'roll star / Poor man's Moody Blues / Mockingbird / Hard hearted woman / One night / Taking me higher / Suicide / Crazy city / Jonathan / For no-one / Polk Street rag / Hymn.
Double compact disc: by Polydor Records. Distributed by: Polygram, Polydor

MOCKING BIRD Early years, The.
Tracks: / Mocking bird / Joker, The / Rock and roll woman / 100,000 miles out / Thank you / Medicine man / Ursula / Song for dying / Crazy / She said / Galadriel.
Album: released on EMI (Germany) in '83 by EMI Records. Distributed by: Conifer

OCTOBERON.
Tracks: / World goes on, The / May day / Ra / Rock'n'Roll / Star / Polk street rag / Believe in me / Suicide.
Notes: Digital Stereo.
Album: released on Polydor in '76 by Polydor Records. Distributed by: Polygram, Polydor

Cassette: released on Polydor in '76 by Polydor Records. Distributed by: Polygram, Polydor Deleted '86.

Compact disc: released on Polydor in Jun'84 by Polydor Records. Distributed by: Polygram, Polydor

ONCE AGAIN.
Tracks: / She said / Happy old world / Song for dying / Galadriel / Mocking bird / Vanessa Simmons / Ball and chain / Lady loves.
Album: released on Fame in Jul'83 by Music For Pleasure Records. Distributed by: EMI

Cassette: released on Fame in Jul'83 by Music For Pleasure Records. Distributed by: EMI

RING OF CHANGES.
Tracks: / Fifties child / Looking from the outside / Teenage heart / High wire / Midnight drug / Waiting for the right time / Just a day away / Paraiso des cavalos / Ring of changes.
Compact disc: released on Polydor in '83 by Polydor Records. Distributed by: Polygram, Polydor

TIME HONOURED GHOSTS.
Tracks: / In my life / Sweet Jesus / Titles / Jonathan / Beyond the grave / Song for you / Hymm for the children / Moon girl / One night.
Compact disc: by Polydor Records. Distributed by: Polygram, Polydor

Album: released on Polydor in Aug'83 by Polydor Records. Distributed by: Polygram, Polydor

Cassette: released on Polydor in Aug'83 by Polydor Records. Distributed by: Polygram, Polydor

TURN OF THE TIDE.
Tracks: / Waiting on the borderline / How do you feel now / Back to the wall / Highway for fools / Echoes and shadows / Death of a city / I'm like a train / Doctor doctor / Life is for living / In memory of the martyrs.
Album: released on Polydor in May'81 by Polydor Records. Distributed by: Polygram, Polydor

Cassette: released on Polydor in May'81 by Polydor Records. Distributed by: Polygram, Polydor

Compact disc: released on Polydor in '83 by Polydor Records. Distributed by: Polygram, Polydor

Album: released on Polydor in '78 by Polydor Records. Distributed by: Polygram, Polydor Deleted '86.

VICTIMS OF CIRCUMSTANCE.
Tracks: / Sideshow / Hold on / Rebel woman / Say you'll stay / For your love / Victims of circumstance / Inside my nightmare / Watching you / I've got a feeling.
Compact disc: by Polydor Records. Distributed by: Polygram, Polydor

XII.
Tracks: / Loving is easy / Tale of two sixties, A / Turning in circles / Closed shop, The / In search of England / Sip of wine / Harbour / Nova lepidoptera / Giving it up / Streets of San Francisco, The.
Compact disc: by Polydor Records. Distributed by: Polygram, Polydor

Bardens, Pete

SEEN ONE EARTH.

Tracks: / Seascape / Man alive / Seen one earth / Home thoughts / Prelude / In dreams / Stargate, The / Many happy returns / Seascape / Man alive / Seen on earth / Home thoughts / Prelude / In dreams / Stargate, The / Many happy returns.
Compact disc: released on Capitol in Sep'87 by Capitol Records. Distributed by: EMI

Bardo

HANG ON TO YOUR HEAT.
Single (7"): released on Epic in Jan'83 by CBS Records. Distributed by: CBS

Bardot

ROCKING IN RHYTHM.
Album: released on RCA in May'78 by RCA Records. Distributed by: RCA, Roots, Swift, Wellard, Chris, I & B, Solomon & Peres Distribution

Bardot, Brigitte

DISQUE D'OR, THE.
Album: released on Disc AZ (France) in Aug'84. Distributed by: Discovery

Cassette: released on Disc AZ (France) in Aug'84. Distributed by: Discovery

Bards Of The Barleycorn

WHEN GRANDMA USED....
Album: released on Beet in Mar'78

Bare Bill's...

BARE BILL'S HARD LUCK BLUES
Various artists (Various Artists).
Notes: Artists include: Ed Bell/John Lee/Pillie Bolling/Mat Armstrong/Sonny Scott etc.
Album: released on Mamlish in Oct'86. Distributed by: Swift, Making Waves

Bare, Bobby

20 OF THE BEST.
Tracks: / All american boy / Detroit City / 500 miles away from home / Four strong winds / Millers cave / It's alright shame on me / The streets of baltimore / Come kiss me love / Charlestone railroad tavern / Have I stayed away too long / The piney wood hills / Find out whats happening (Margies at) the Lincoln inn / You know who / I hate goodbyes / The winner / Signing in the kitchen / Daddy what if / Where'd I come from.
Notes: Originally released in August 1982 on INTS 5187/INTK 5187
Album: released on RCA International in '84

Cassette: released on RCA International in '84

AT THE COUNTRY STORE.
Album: released on Starblend Country Store in Aug'86 by Starblend Records. Distributed by: PRT Distribution

Cassette: released on Starblend Country Store in Aug'86 by Starblend Records. Distributed by: PRT Distribution

BEST OF BOBBY BARE, THE.
Album: released on Nightflite in Aug'87 by Adrian Owlett. Distributed by: Charly, Spartan. Estim retail price in Sep'87 was £5.99.

Cassette: released on Nightflite in Aug'87 by Adrian Owlett. Distributed by: Charly, Spartan. Estim retail price in Sep'87 was £5.99.

BETTER NOT LOOK DOWN.
Tracks: / Better not look down / Wait until tomorrow.
Single (7"): released on EMI America in May'86 by EMI Records. Distributed by: EMI

BOBBY BARE I love country.
Tracks: / Gambler, The / Jogger, The / Last time, The / Numbers / Tequial Sheila / Let Him Roll / Goin' up's easy, comin' down's harder / Praise The Lord and send me the money / Goodnight Irene / I've never gone to bed with an ugly woman / Food Blues / Desperados waiting for the train / Three-legged man / Finger on the button / Greasy grit gravy / Big dupree / Finger on the button / Yard full of rusty cars / Too many nights alone / Childhood hero / February snow / This guitar is for sale / Sing for the song.
Album: released on CBS in Mar'87 by CBS Records. Distributed by: CBS

Cassette: released on CBS in Mar'87 by CBS Records. Distributed by: CBS

Album: released on CBS in Nov'81 by CBS Records. Distributed by: CBS

Cassette: released on CBS in Nov'81 by CBS Records. Distributed by: CBS

CITY BOY.
Tracks: / Fool / Fallen star / Hello darling / Lonely street / Under it all / Crazy arms / Alabama rose / High and dry / City boy country born / New york city snow / Leaving on a jet plane.
Notes: 2 LP set 2 Cassettes 28 other titles included
Double Album: released on Cambra in Apr'85 by Cambra Records. Distributed by: IDS, Conifer

Double cassette: released on Cambra in Apr'85 by Cambra Records. Distributed by: IDS, Conifer

COUNTRY SUPERSTARS (Bare, Bobby & Don Williams).
Compact disc: . Distributed by: CD Centre Distribution, Pinnacle, Target

DETROIT CITY.
Album: released on RCA (Germany) in Oct'84

DOWN & DIRTY.
Album: released on CBS in Mar'80 by CBS Records. Distributed by: CBS

DRUNK AND CRAZY.
Cassette: released on CBS in Dec'80 by CBS Records. Distributed by: CBS

ENCORE.
Tracks: / Number / On a real good night / Healin / Gambler, The / Food blues / Willie Jones / Sleep tight / Good night man / Tequila Sheila / I can almost see Houston from here / Too many nights alone.
Album: released on CBS in '84 by CBS Records. Distributed by: CBS

Cassette: released on CBS in '84 by CBS Records. Distributed by: CBS

FAMOUS COUNTRY MUSIC MAKERS.
Tracks: / Don't turn out the light / Somebody bought my old home town / Chester / (There was a) tall oak tree / Ride me down easy / Salt lake city.
Double Album: by RCA Records. Distributed by: RCA, Roots, Swift, Wellard, Chris, I & B, Solomon & Peres Distribution

LULLABYS, LEGENDS AND LIES.
Tracks: / Lullabys, legends and lies / Paul / Marie Laveau / Daddy what if / Winner, the / In the hills of Shiloh / She's my ever lovin' machine / Mermaid, The / Rest awhile / Bottomless well / Wonderful soup stone, The / True story / Sure hit songwriters pen / Rosalie's good eats cafe.
Album: released on RCA in Jan'87 by RCA Records. Distributed by: RCA, Roots, Swift, Wellard, Chris, I & B, Solomon & Peres Distribution

Cassette: released on RCA in Jan'87 by RCA Records. Distributed by: RCA, Roots, Swift, Wellard, Chris, I & B, Solomon & Peres Distribution

MORE TUNES FOR TWO (Bare, Bobby & Skeeter Davis).
Tracks: / Your husband my wife / Before the sunrise / A true love you'll never find / I'm so afraid of losing you again / Dream baby (how long must I dream) / My elusive dreams / Let's make love not war / I got you / Jackson / There was never a time.
Album: released on RCA International in Nov'80

THIS IS BARE.
Album: released on RCA (Germany) in Oct'84

TUNES FOR TWO.
Album: by RCA Records. Distributed by: RCA, Roots, Swift, Wellard, Chris, I & B, Solomon & Peres Distribution

Bare Bones

BARE BONES Various artists (Various Artists).
Tracks: / Rakes of mallow, The / Ewe, The / Earl's chair, The / Boys around Tantarageo / Cork hornpipe / Limerick slides / Wearing of the britches, The / My love is in America / Pigeon on the gate / Tramps and hawkers / Charlie Chaplin / Musical priest, The / Sailor on the rock / Union, The / Navvy on the line / Maggie in the wood / Tralee jail / Four-hand reel / Delahunty's hornpipe / Girl I left behind me, The / Sporting races of Galway, The.
Album: released on Greenwich Village in May'81 by Sweet Folk All Records. Distributed by: Roots, Projection, Lightning, Celtic Music, Wellard, Chris

Bare Essentials

REBEL TOUR.
Single (12"): released on Sunburn in Jul'83 by Orbitone Records. Distributed by: Jetstar Distribution

Barefoot Bill's...

BAREFOOT BILL'S HARD LUCK BLUES Various artists (Various Artists).
Album: released on Mamlish (USA) in Mar'84. Distributed by: Swift

Barefoot, Jerry

WATCHING TV.
Album: released on Houdini in Jan'80 by Criminal Records. Distributed by: Spartan

Barenberg, Russ

CALYPSO COWBOY.
Album: released on Rounder in Sep'79. Distributed by: Roots Distribution

Barflies

DOWN TO THE BONE.
Notes: Mini LP Self- 78 Breakspears Road,Brockley,London SE4 1TX
Album: released on Fly Boy in Dec'85 by Fly Boy Records. Distributed by: Fly Boy Records

THERE'S A FIRE.
Single (7"): released on Barflies in Sep'84 by Barflies Records. Distributed by: ILA

Barin Or Morbis

NEIGHBOURS.
Tracks: / Neighbours.
Single (12"): released on Flim Flam in May'86 by Flim Flam Productions. Distributed by: Pinnacle

Barinov, Valeri

TRUMPET CALL, THE.
Notes: 'The Trumpet Call',a rock musical was written by Valeri Barinov and recorded secretly inside the Soviet Union.The original recording in English of this opera about the Second Coming of Jesus Christ is now available through Word records distribution.As a company Word R1ecords feels that the message contained within 'The Trumpet Call' is as important as it was when it was first recorded.From a contribution point of view,Word are releasing this cassette to financially help Valeri and his family in their current plight.The situation for Valeri and his family is far from good despite the fact that he is now out of prison.We need to support him both in prayer and finacially for many years to come.Therefore,all profits from the sale of this cassette will be channelled to Valeri and his family in some form.'The Trumpet Call' is available in cassette form only ,and because it has been taken from the original recording,the quality is poor.Uderstandably this would not be really suitable for radio broadcast,but if you feel you could use a copy of this cassette any publicity or exposure will help Valeri,and we would be happy to supply you with a copy.'The Trumpet Calls'is widely available throughout Christian Bookshops and through the Word record Club.
Cassette: released on Myrrh in Nov'86 by Word Records. Distributed by: Word Distribution

Bar-Kays

BANGING THE WALL.
Album: released on Mercury (Holland) in Nov'85 by Phonogram Records. Distributed by: Polygram Distribution

Cassette: released on Mercury (Holland) in Nov'85 by Phonogram Records. Distributed by: Polygram Distribution

DANGEROUS.
Tracks: / Dangerous / Dirty dancer / Make-believe lover / Dance party / Freakshow on the dance floor / Lovers should never fall in love / Loose talk / Sexomatic.
Album: released on Mercury (Holland) in Jul'84 by Phonogram Records. Distributed by: Polygram Distribution

PROPOSITIONS.
Tracks: / Propositions / Tripping out / Anticipations (busted) / Do it (let me shake you) / She talks to me with her body / I can't believe you're leaving me / You made a change in my life.
Album: released on Mercury (Import) in Feb'83

Barker, Dave

COOL OFF WOMAN.
Single (12"): released on Striker Lee in May'85 by Striker Lee Records. Distributed by: Jetstar Distribution

CURIOUS.
Single (12"): released on Paradise in Apr'85. Distributed by: Jetstar, JSU, WEA

GET HIGH EVERYBODY.
Single (12"): released on Striker Lee in Mar'85 by Striker Lee Records. Distributed by: Jetstar Distribution

PRISONER OF LOVE.
Single (12"): released on Sunsplash in Apr'84 by Sunsplash Records. Distributed by: Jetstar Distribution

TILL I KISS YOU (Barker, Dave & Natural Mystics).
Single (12"): released on Terminal in Mar'85 by Terminal. Distributed by: Jetstar Distribution

Barker, Les

MRS.ACKROYDS ROCK'N'ROLL SHOW.
Album: released on Mrs.Ackroyd in '85. Distributed by: Folksound Distribution, Mrs.Ackroyd

MRS ACKROYD - SUPERSTAR.
Album: released on Free Reed in Aug'77 by Free Reed Records. Distributed by: Roots, Projection, Hobgoblin Records, Oblivion

NIGEL'S BLUES.
Single (7"): released on Mrs.Ackroyd in Jun'84. Distributed by: Folksound Distribution, Mrs.Ackroyd

Barker, Ronnie

PORRIDGE With original cast.
Cassette: released on BBC in Apr'77 by BBC Records & Tapes. Distributed by: EMI, PRT, Pye

TWO RONNIES (Barker, Ronnie & Ronnie Corbett).
Album: released on BBC in Oct'76 by BBC Records & Tapes. Distributed by: EMI, PRT, Pye

Cassette: released on BBC in Oct'76 by BBC Records & Tapes. Distributed by: EMI, PRT, Pye

TWO RONNIES VOL 2 (Barker, Ronnie & Ronnie Corbett).
Album: released on BBC in Nov'77 by BBC Records & Tapes. Distributed by: EMI, PRT, Pye

Cassette: released on BBC in Nov'77 by BBC Records & Tapes. Distributed by: EMI, PRT, Pye

Barker, Tim

LOOKING GOOD.
Single (7"): released on Keswick in '80 by Loose Records. Distributed by: Pinnacle

Barley

REMEMBER REMEMBER.
Album: released on SRT in '75 by SRT Records. Distributed by: Pinnacle, Solomon & Peres Distribution, SRT Distribution, H.R. Taylor Distribution, PRT Distribution

Barleypop

HOOKED ON SCOTCH.
Single (7"):

Barley Wine

THAT TRAIN (Barley Wine featuring Saxa).
Single (7"): released on Black Vinyl in Sep'83

Barleywine, Mr.

REGGAE MUSIC 1 (Barleywine, Mr. & The B.W. Band).
Single (7"): released on Top Dog in Jan'85 by Top Dog Records. Distributed by: Jetstar Distribution

Barlow, Charles

24 BALLROOM DANCING FAVOURITES.
Album: released on Note in Jan'80 by EMI Records. Distributed by: EMI

Album: released on Acorn in Jun'79. Distributed by: Folksound, Jazz Music

DANCE ON & ON (Barlow, Charles & His Orchestra).
Tracks: / Bring me sunshine / All my loving / When Irish eyes are smiling / Cavatina / Rocking chair / As time goes by / Remordimiento / Super trouper / Chacharini / Caprice / I'll never love this way again / All the things you are are mine / Exotica / On and on.
Album: released on ASV in Jun'81 by Academy Sound & Vision Records. Distributed by: Pinnacle

MEMORIES (Barlow, Charles & His Orchestra).
Tracks: / Sing sing sing / Perdido / Lester leaps in / Back home in Tennessee / Play fiddly play / Thorn birds / Don't tell a soul / Hold me / Anientamento / Shy serenade / Sam baba / Memory / Woman in love / Here comes the toreador.
Album: released on Dansan in Jun'84 by Spartan Records. Distributed by: Spartan

Barlow, Eric

BALLROOM FAVOURITES.
Notes: Eric Barlow at the mighty Wurlitzer organ
Cassette: released on Lancastrian Organ Trust in Sep'86. Distributed by: Jazz Music

BALLROOM MAGIC Eric Barlow plays the wonder Wurlitzer.
Album: released on Lancastrian Organ Trust in Sep'86. Distributed by: Jazz Music

Barlow, Randy

ARRIVAL.
Album:

Barnabas

FEEL ON FIRE.
Album: released on Light in May'85 by Mainline Record Company. Distributed by: Mainline

Cassette: released on Light in May'85 by Mainline Record Company. Distributed by: Mainline

Barnard, Bob

AT BIX FESTIVAL 1976 (Barnard, Bob & His Australian Jazz Band).
Album: released on BBMS in Apr'79. Distributed by: Swift

BUD FREEMAN WITH THE BOB BARNARD JAZZBAND (see Freeman, Bud) (Barnard, Bob Jazzband with Bud Freeman).

COUNT 'EM (Barnard, Bob, Jazz Orchestra).
Album: released on Swaggie (Australia) in Jan'83

FIRST UP (1975-76) (Barnard, Bob & His Jazz Band).
Album: released on Swaggie (Australia) in Jan'83

NED KELLY JAZZ SUITE (Barnard, Bob & Friends).
Album: released on Swaggie (Australia) in Jan'83

RIVERBOAT DAYS (Barnard, Bob & Friends).
Album: released on Swaggie (Australia) in Jan'83

Barnard, Len

Partners in crime

Barnback

WHEN I WAS A LAD.
Tracks: / Old MacDonald had a farm.
Single (7"): released on Homespun(Ireland) in Dec'86 by Outlet Records. Distributed by: Outlet

Barnbrack

BARNBRACK.
Tracks: / Unicorn / Jug of punch / Home boys home / Coortin' in the kitchen / As I roved out / Postman pat / I'll take you home again Kathleen / Star of the county down / Mother's love is a blessing, A / Goodbye Johnny dear / Gentle mother / Will you go Lassie go / Whiskey on a sunday / Belfast.
Album: released on Homespun(Ireland) in Jul'85 by Outlet Records. Distributed by: Outlet

Cassette: released on Homespun(Ireland) in Jul'85 by Outlet Records. Distributed by: Outlet

BELFAST.
Single (7"): released on Homespun(Ireland) in Jan'85 by Outlet Records. Distributed by: Outlet

CHILDRENS PARTY.
Tracks: / Teddy bears' picnic / Mickey Marley's roundabout / Yellow submarine / Matchstalk men & matchstalk cats & dogs / Old MacDonald had a farm / When I was a lad / Postman Pat / Puff the magic dragon / Big rock candy mountain / Unicorn, The / Big ship sails on the alley.... / Mama will you buy me a banana / Happy wanderer, The.
Album: released on Homespun(Ireland) in Dec'86 by Outlet Records. Distributed by: Outlet

Cassette: released on Homespun(Ireland) in Dec'86 by Outlet Records. Distributed by: Outlet

FEAST OF IRISH FOLK SONGS VOL.2.
Tracks: / Westmeath bachelor / If you're Irish / Dear oul donegal / Blacksmith / Old flames / Doonaree / Butcher boy / Green glams of Antrim / Boys from Co. Armargh / Irish eyes are smiling / Nancy Spain / Leaving of Liverpool / Mursheen Durkin / Belfast mill / Boston burgaler / Moonshine / Hills of Connemara / Mountains of Mourne / Three countries meet / My Eileen is waiting for me / Homes of Donegal / My aunt Jane / Al lammas fair / Gentle Annie / Spancil hill / Village where I went to school / Any dream will do / Mickey Marley's roundabout.
Album: released on Homespun(Ireland) in May'84 by Outlet Records. Distributed by: Outlet

Cassette: released on Homespun(Ireland) in May'84 by Outlet Records. Distributed by: Outlet

IRISH FOLK PUB SING-A-LONG.
Album: released on Homespun(Ireland) in Jul'83 by Outlet Records. Distributed by: Outlet

Cassette: released on Homespun(Ireland) in Jul'83 by Outlet Records. Distributed by: Outlet

Album: released on Homespun(Ireland) in Jul'83 by Outlet Records. Distributed by: Outlet

Cassette: released on Homespun(Ireland) in Jul'83 by Outlet Records. Distributed by: Outlet

MICKEY MARLEY'S ROUNDABOUT.
Single (7"): released on Homespun(Ireland) in Mar'84 by Outlet Records. Distributed by: Outlet

MY LOVELY IRISH ROSE.
Tracks: / My lovely Irish rose / Irish rover / Goodbye Mick, goodbye Pat / Ma Ma will you buy me a banana.
Single (12"): released on Homespun(Ireland) in Feb'87 by Outlet Records. Distributed by: Outlet

POSTMAN PAT.
Single (7"): released on Homespun(Ireland) in Dec'84 by Outlet Records. Distributed by: Outlet

PUNCH & JUDY MAN.
Tracks: / Punch & Judy man / Phil the fluter / Come back Paddy Reilly / Slatter's mounted fut.
Single (7"): released on Homespun(Ireland) in Mar'86 by Outlet Records. Distributed by: Outlet

WORLD OF BARNBRACK.
Tracks: / Irish rover / Goodbye Mick & goodbye Pat / Mama will you will buy me a banana / Punch & Judy / Moon behind the hill / Alley alley O / Uncle Nobby's steamboat / Love's old sweet song / Swallow (La golondrina), The / Wedding prayer, The / B for Barney / Doffer, The / My lovely Irish rose / More than yesterday / Love is teasing / Phil the fluters ball / Come back Paddy Reilly / Slattery's mounted fut.
Album: released on Homespun(Ireland) in May'86 by Outlet Records. Distributed by: Outlet

Cassette: released on Homespun(Ireland) in May'86 by Outlet Records. Distributed by: Outlet

Barnes-Bocage Big Five

BARNES-BOCAGE BIG FIVE.
Album: released on Nola in Apr'79. Distributed by: JSU, Jazz Music, Cadillac, Chris Wellard

Barnes, Emile

EMILE BARNES & HIS NEW ORLEANS MUSIC (Barnes, Emile & His New Orleans Music).

N.O.-THE LEGENDS LIVE (Barnes, Emile & His New Orleans Music).
Album: released on Jazzology in Jun'86. Distributed by: Jazz Music, Swift

Barnes, George

GEORGE BARNES (Barnes, George & His Octet).
Tracks: / I can't give you anything but love / South side blues / Somebody loves me / Smoke gets in your eyes / Zebra's derby / September in the rain / Chicago / Aren't you glad you're you / Starlight interlude.
Album: released on Hindsight(UK) in Mar'79. Distributed by: Jazz Music

Barnes, [illegible]

SCHOOL G[illegible] it.
Single (7"): released [illegible] Distributed by: Pinnacle

Barnes, Jimmy

JIMMY BARNES.
Tracks: / No second prize / I'd die to be with you tonight / Working class man / Promise me you'll call / Boys cry out for war / Paradise / Without your love / American heartbeat / Thick skinned / Ride the night away / Daylight.
Album: released on Geffen in May'86 by Geffen Records. Distributed by: WEA, CBS

Cassette: released on Geffen in May'86 by Geffen Records. Distributed by: WEA, CBS

WORKING CLASS MAN.
Tracks: / Working class man (Remix) / Boys cry out for war.
Single (7"): released on Geffen in May'86 by Geffen Records. Distributed by: WEA, CBS

Single (12"): released on Geffen in May'86 by Geffen Records. Distributed by: WEA, CBS

WORLD OF BUDDY BOLDEN, THE
see under Lyttleton, Humphrey.

Barnes, J.J.

COMPETITION AIN'T NOTHING.
Single (7"): released on Inferno Soul Club in May'84 by Inferno Records. Distributed by: Inferno, Cartel, Pinnacle

Picture disc single: released on Inferno in Jul'84 by Inferno Records. Distributed by: Inferno, Cartel, Pinnacle

GUESS I'LL TRY IT AGAIN.
Single (12"): released on Inferno in Mar'85 by Inferno Records. Distributed by: Inferno, Cartel, Pinnacle

SWEET SHERRY.
Single (7"): released on Inferno in Dec'83 by Inferno Records. Distributed by: Inferno, Cartel, Pinnacle

Barnes, Johnny

JAZZ MASTERS (Barnes, Johnny & Bruce Turner).
Album: released on Cadillac in Feb'77 by Cadillac Records. Distributed by: Cadillac

Barnes, Max D.

PIECES OF MY LIFE.
Album: released on Country Roads Records in Nov'81 by Country Roads Records. Distributed by: Stage One

Album: released on No Label in Apr'79. Distributed by: Fast Distribution

Barnes, Paul

PAUL BARNES.
Notes: Also featuring Louis Nelson, Joe Harris, Sing Miller.
Album: released on CSA in Jan'87 by CSA Records. Distributed by: PRT, Jetstar

PAUL BARNES QUARTETS (Barnes, Paul Quartets).
Cassette: released on Nola in May'87. Distributed by: Jazz Music, Cadillac, Chris Wellard

PAUL "POLO" BARNES, INTERNATIONAL JAZZ BAND.
Album: released on CSA in Jan'87 by CSA Records. Distributed by: PRT, Jetstar

VIOL, THE VIOLET & THE VINE, THE (Barnes, Paul & His Polo Players).
Album: released on Jazzology in Feb'87. Distributed by: Jazz Music, Swift

Barnes, Walter

1928-29 (Barnes, Walter & His Royal Creolins).
Album: released on Fountain-Retrieval in Sep'86 by Retrieval Records. Distributed by: Retrieval, VJM, Swift, Jazz Music, Wellard, Chris

RUFF SCUFFLIN' (Barnes, Walter/George E. Lee).
Album: released on Retrieval in Jun'87 by Retrieval Records. Distributed by: Retrieval, VJM, Swift, Record Sales(Chris Wellard), Jazz Music

WALTER BARNES/GEORGE E. LEE (Barnes, Walter/George E. Lee).
Album: released on Fountain in Mar'87 by Retrieval Records. Distributed by: Jazz Music, Swift, VJM, Wellard, Chris, Retrieval

Barnet, Charlie

APRIL 1938 (Barnet, Charlie & His Orchestra).
Tracks: / Make believe ballroom / Lullaby in rhythm / Stop, look & listen / In a jam / Prelude in C sharp minor / Chatterbox / Blue turning grey over you / Undecided / Harmony in Harlem / I let a song go out of my heart / You go to my head / Rock it for me / Prelude to a kiss / Ya got me / Jump jump's here.
Album: released on Jazz Live in Apr'81

AT BASIN STREET EAST.
Tracks: / Rabble rouser / It had to be you / Mumbles / I can't get started / Cottontail / Satin doll / Bali bali buck dance / Basieville / Mad medley / Introduction to an ending.
Album: released on Hep in Apr'81 by H.R. Taylor Records. Distributed by: Jazz Music, Cadillac Music, JSU, Taylors, Wellard, Chris, Zodiac, Swift, Fast Forward

CHARLIE BARNET (Barnet, Charlie Orchestra).
Album: released on Bright Orange in Apr'79. Distributed by: Swift

CHARLIE BARNET & HIS ORCHESTRA (Barnet, Charlie & His Orchestra).
Album: released on First Heard in Apr'79 by Submarine Records. Distributed by: Conifer, Taylors

CHARLIE BARNET ON THE AIR VOL 1.
Album: released on Aircheck in Apr'79

CHARLIE BARNET ORCHESTRA, THE.
Album: released on Jazz Live in Oct'86

CHARLIE BARNET VOL 1 1933/6.
Album: released on Ajax in Apr'79

CHARLIE BARNET VOL 18.
Album: released on Ajax in Apr'79

CHARLIE BARNET VOL 2 1936/7.
Album: released on Ajax in Apr'79

CHARLIE BARNET VOL 17 1944.
Album: released on Ajax in Apr'79

CHARLIE BARNET VOL 16 1942/3.
Album: released on Ajax in Apr'79

DANCE BASH.
Tracks: / Jubilee junp / Charleston alley / Gal from Joes / Deep purple / Blue Lou / Southern fried / Cherokee / Skyliner / Fur trappers boogie / Wosie posie / Let's blow the blues / Rhubarb / St. Louis blues / Swinging down the lane / Who's sorry now.
Album: released on Verve in May'82 by Phonogram Records. Distributed by: Polygram

DANCE DATE (Barnet, Charlie & His Orchestra).
Album: released on Swinghouse in Apr'79. Distributed by: Jazz Music Distribution, Swift Distribution, Chris Wellard Distribution

DUKE'S IDEAS 1939/41 VOL 1.
Album: released on Black & White in Nov'77

FILM TRACKS OF..., THE.
Album: released on Joyce in Jul'82

...& HIS ORCHESTRA 1945/47.
Album: released on First Heard in Jul'77 by Submarine Records. Distributed by: Conifer, Taylors

IN DISCO ORDER VOL 1.
Album: released on Ajax in Jul'77

IN DISCO ORDER VOL 2.
Album: released on Ajax in Jul'77

INDISPENSABLE CHARLIE BARNET VOLS.3/4 (1940-42).
Tracks: / Comanche war dance / Tappin' at the tappa / Southland shuffle / Lover's lullaby, A / Leapin' at the Lincoln / Wanderin' blues / Shake rattle & roll (afternoon of a moax) / Lament for May / Flyin' home / No name jive, part 1&2 / Reverie of a moax(oh Claire the goon), The / It's the last time i'll fall in love / Rockin' in rhythm / Pompton turnpike / Ring dem bells / Sergeant was shy, The / Wild Mab of the fishpond / Night & day / Redskin rhumba / Lumby / Phyllysee / Blue juice / Charleston alley / Little John ordinary / Haunted town / Merry-go-round / Birmingham breakdown / Ponce de leon / Little dip / Harlem speaks / I can't get started.
Double Album: released on Jazz Tribune (USA) in Sep'86. Distributed by: Discovery

Cassette: released on Jazz Tribune (USA) in Sep'86. Distributed by: Discovery

INDISPENSABLE CHARLIE BARNET VOLS 1/2 (1935-39).
Tracks: / Echoes of Harlem / Scotch & soda / Miss Annabelle Lee / Lazy bug / Midweek function / I never knew / Ebony rhapsody / Lament for a lost love / Cherokee / All-night record man, The / Last jump,The / Duke's idea, The / Count's idea, The / Ogoun badagris / Oh what you said / Wrong idea, The / Right idea, The / Night glow / Between 18th & 19th on Chestnut Street / Clap hands here comes Charlie / Growlin' / Nagasaki / On a holiday / Always / I'm praying humble / Tin roof blues / Knocking at the famous door / Gal from Joe's, The / Jump session / Swing street strut / Night song / Some like it hot / Only a rose.
Double Album: released on Jazz Tribune (USA) in Sep'86. Distributed by: Discovery

Double cassette: released on Jazz Tribune (USA) in Sep'86. Distributed by: Discovery

INDISPENSABLE, VOLUME'S 3/4, THE.
Album: released on RCA (France) in Feb'85 by RCA Records. Distributed by: Discovery

LIVE AT BASIN ST. EAST.
Album: released on Hep in Jan'80 by H.R. Taylor Records. Distributed by: Jazz Music, Cadillac Music, JSU, Taylors, Wellard, Chris, Zodiac, Swift, Fast Forward

ONE FOR MY BABY.
Cassette: released on Astan in Jun'86 by Astan Records. Distributed by: Counterpoint

ON STAGE WITH CHARLIE BARNET ORCHESTRA.
Album: released on Bright Orange in Apr'79. Distributed by: Swift

SHOWCASE.
Album: released on First Heard in '84 by Submarine Records. Distributed by: Conifer, Taylors

SKYLINER (Barnet, Charlie & His Orchestra).
Tracks: / Skyliner / Flat top flips his lid / Andy's boogie / Gulf coast blues / E-bob-o-lee-bob / Pow! Wow / Drop me off in Harlem / Xango / Washington whirligig / Moose / Sharecroppin' blues / Thing's ain't what they used to be / West End blues / Great lie / Strollin' / Just a sittin' & a rockin'.
Album: released on Affinity (MCA) in Sep'83

Barnett, Al

IN MY DREAM.
Tracks: / My life.
Single (12"): released on Ade J. in Nov'86 by Ade J., Records. Distributed by: Jetstar, Rough Trade, Jungle

Barnett, Janice

JANICE.
Tracks: / Wake up smiling / Goody two-shoes / Told you so / Take me away / Him / If I had known (I'd be gone) / Love on the line / You're letting me go / I should have left you / I should have left you.

Notes: American soul singer Janice Barnett is little known here in the UK, except for two songs which are currently very popular in the clubs. Both these songs are contained on this reissued album, "Goody Two Shoes" and "I Told You So". The album was first issued in 1975.
Album: released on Stax in Nov'86 by Ace Records. Distributed by: Pinnacle, Chris Wellard, IMS-Polygram

Barnett, Ricky

YOU MAKE IT HAPPEN.
Single (12"): released on Hawkeye in Jun'83 by Hawkeye Records. Distributed by: Hawkeye, Lightning (WEA) Distribution, Jetstar, PRT

Barnum

BARNUM Oringinal London stage cast.
Album: released on Chrysalis in '81 by Chrysalis Records. Distributed by: CBS

Cassette: released on Chrysalis in '81 by Chrysalis Records. Distributed by: CBS

Barnwell, Bobbie

BOBBIE.
Album: released on Westwood in '78 by Westwood Records. Distributed by: Jazz Music, H.R. Taylor, JSU, Pinnacle, Ross Records

Barod Am Roc

BAROD AM ROC.
Album: released on Sain in '85. Distributed by: Roots

Barone

SHAKE IT UP.
Single (12"): released on Jungle Rhythm in '85

Barone Brothers

BLUES & OTHER HAPPY MOMENTS.
Album: released on Palo Alto (Italy) in '84

Baron, Paul

ONE DEEP BREATH.
Album: released on Swinghouse in '84. Distributed by: Jazz Music Distribution, Swift Distribution, Chris Wellard Distribution

Baron Rojo

BARON AL ROJO VIVI.
Album: released on Mausoleum in '84 by Mausoleum Records. Distributed by: Pinnacle

BRUTAL VOLUME.
Album: released on Mausoleum in '84 by Mausoleum Records. Distributed by: Pinnacle

LARGA VIDA AL ROCK AND ROLL.
Album: released on Mausoleum in '84 by Mausoleum Records. Distributed by: Pinnacle

METAL MORFOSIS.
Album: released on Mausoleum in '84 by Mausoleum Records. Distributed by: Pinnacle

VOLUMEN ROJO (SPANISH VERSION).
Album: released on Mausoleum in '84 by Mausoleum Records. Distributed by: Pinnacle

Baroque...

BEATLES SEASONS, THE (Baroque Chamber Orchestra).
Compact disc: released on EMI in Jun'87 by EMI Records. Distributed by: EMI

Album: released on EMI in Jun'87 by EMI Records. Distributed by: EMI

Cassette: released on EMI in Jun'87 by EMI Records. Distributed by: EMI

Baroque Beatles Book

BAROQUE BEATLES BOOK,THE.
Album:

Barracudas

BIG GAP,THE.
Album: released on Coyote in '84 by Rough Trade Records. Distributed by: Cartel

DROP OUT WITH THE BARRACUDAS.
Tracks: / I can't pretend / We're living in violent times / Don't let go / Codeine / This ain't my time / I saw my death in a dream last night / Somewhere outside / Summer fun / His last summer / Somebody / Campus tramp / On the strip / California lament / I wish it could be 1965 again.
Album: released on Zonophone in '81 by EMI Records. Distributed by: EMI

Cassette: released on Zonophone in '81 by EMI Records. Distributed by: EMI

ENDEAVOUR TO PERSEVERE.
Album: released on Closer (France) in '84. Distributed by: Nine Mile, Cartel

HOUSE OF KICKS.
Single (12"): released on Flicknife in '83 by Flicknife Records. Distributed by: Spartan

INSIDE MINE/HOUR OF DEGRADATION.
Single (7"): released on Flicknife in '82 by Flicknife Records. Distributed by: Spartan

I WANT MY WOODY BACK/SUBWAY SURFIN.
Single (7"): released on Cells in '79 by Cells Records. Distributed by: Rough Trade

LIVE 1983.
Album: released on Coyote in '83 by Rough Trade Records. Distributed by: Cartel

MEANTIME.
Tracks: / Grammar of misery / Bad news / I ain't no miracle worker / Be my friend again / Shades of today / Dead skin / Middle class blues / You've come a long way / Ballad of a liar / When I'm gone / Eleventh hour / Hear me calling.
Album: released on Import Music Service (IMS) in '83. Distributed by: Concord Jazz Distributions, Pablo, Polygram

STOLEN HEART.
Single (7"): released on Closer (France) in '84. Distributed by: Nine Mile, Cartel

Single (12"): released on Closer (France) in '84. Distributed by: Nine Mile, Cartel

THEY SAY WE'VE CHANGED/LAUGHING AT YOU.
Single (7"): released on Closer (France) in '84. Distributed by: Nine Mile, Cartel

WORLD'S A BURN,THE.
Album: released on Trust in '85 by Fast. Distributed by: Cartel Distribution

Barratt Band

PLAYING IN THE CITY.
Tracks: / Only one / Not the way / Your love / Playing in the city / Coming of the man / Bad mean world / My spirit's free / Voice in the night / Never seen your face.
Album: released on Chapel Lane in '83. Distributed by: RCA

Cassette: released on Chapel Lane in '83. Distributed by: RCA

VOICE.
Tracks: / Descender / Stereo / Computer failure / Loud silence / Play my guitar / Exit through exit / Being alive / Voice.
Album: released on Chapel Lane in '83. Distributed by: RCA

Cassette: released on Chapel Lane in '83. Distributed by: RCA

Barratt, Norman

ROCK FOR ALL AGES.
Album: released on Chapel Lane in '84. Distributed by: RCA

Cassette: released on Chapel Lane in '84. Distributed by: RCA

Barrax, Andrew

JUST CAN'T SEEM TO FORGET.
Tracks: / Just can't seem to forget (instrumental) / Just can't seem to forget / Just can't seem to forget (vocal edit).
Single (12"): released on Expansion in Apr'86. Distributed by: PRT

Barreka...

BARREKA,INSANITY,PROFANITY
Vaious artists (Various Artists).
Album: released on A Killer in Apr'86. Distributed by: Pinnacle

Barrelhouse...

BARRELHOUSE BLUES & STOMPS-VOL.4 Various artists (Various Artists).
Album: released on Euphonic in '79 by Euphonic Records. Distributed by: Jazz Music, Swift

BARRELHOUSE BLUES & STOMPS-VOL.5 Various artists (Various Artists).
Album: released on Euphonic in '79 by Euphonic Records. Distributed by: Jazz Music, Swift

DRIVING HOT JAZZ FROM THE 20'S (Barrelhouse Jazz Band).
Album: released on GHB in Jun'86. Distributed by: Jazz Music, Swift

MAKIN' WHOOPEE (Barrelhouse Mob...).
Album: released on Dansan in '85 by Spartan Records. Distributed by: Spartan

TICKLED PINK (Barrelhouse Mob...).
Tracks: / Tickled pink / True love / Always / Together / Carolina moon / Singin' in the rain / Goodnight Vienna / Margie / Baby face / You were meant for me / Diane / Ramona / Gharmaine / Harry Lime theme / You'll never know / Sally / Peg o' my heart.
Notes: Feat. Tony Harrison
Album: released on Dansan in '84 by Spartan Records. Distributed by: Spartan

Barrell, Roland

LOVE BOAT.
Single (12"): released on Gamble in '84 by Gamble Records. Distributed by: Jetstar

Barrere, Paul

ON MY OWN TWO FEET.
Tracks: / Sweet coquette / High roller / Fool for you / Love sweet love / Who knows for sure / She lays down the beat / Fortune cookie / Along this lane.
Cassette: released on WEA International in '83 by WEA Records. Distributed by: WEA

Barres, Michael Des

OBSESSION.
Single (7"): released on A&M in '84 by A&M Records. Distributed by: Polygram

Single (12"): released on A&M in '84 by A&M Records. Distributed by: Polygram

Barreta

BARRETA.
Album: released on Tank in '77 by Tank Records

Barrett, Al Linemen

DEEP WATER.
Tracks: / Miles of Texas / Heart, The / Rodeo clown man / Drifter / Faded love / Pure love / Sweet dreams / Why ask why / Deep water / Desperation.
Cassette: released on Champ in '82 by Champ Records. Distributed by: Champ

DON'T GET AROUND MUCH ANYMORE.
Tracks: / Rollin' with the flow / Do you right tonight / When loves goes wrong / Don't get around much anymore / Harder times / Vincent / I changed everything but my mind / Two dollars in the jukebox.
Album: released on Champ in '82 by Champ Records. Distributed by: Champ

Cassette: released on Champ in '82 by Champ Records. Distributed by: Champ

OPEN COUNTRY.
Tracks: / Muddy Mississippi line / Take me / I still miss someone / Hawaiian wedding song / Everything a man could ever need / Break my mind / Dear God / I fall to pieces / Truck driving man / Twelfth of never / Last thing on my mind / Crazy / Try a little kindness / Buckaroo.
Album: released on Sweet Folk All in '81 by Sweet Folk All Records. Distributed by: Sweet Folk All, Roots, Celtic Music, Dragon, Impetus, Projection, Chris Wellard, Festival Records

OPEN COUNTRY - VOL.2.
Tracks: / See you in the windshield / Drinking again / Corine Corina / Streets of Larado / Pop a top / I forget you everyday / Streets of Baltimore / Drinking champagne / Back of my hand / Games that people play, The / Every fool has a rainbow / Where love used to live.
Album: released on Sweet Folk All in '81 by Sweet Folk All Records. Distributed by: Sweet Folk All, Roots, Celtic Music, Dragon, Impetus, Projection, Chris Wellard, Festival Records

Barrett, Anne

STAY.
Single (7"): released on Loose in '84 by Loose Records. Distributed by: Nine Mile, Cartel

Barrett, Jack

CEILI TIME IN IRELAND.
Album: released on Shamrock (Ireland) in '75. Distributed by: I & B, EMI (Ireland), Swift, Chris Wellard, Solomon & Peres Distribution, Jazz Music

Barretto, Ray

BARRETTO,RAY Best of.
Album: released on Vogue (France) in '84. Distributed by: Discovery, Jazz Music, PRT, Swift

CUNA, (LA).
Cassette: released on CTI (Musidisc France) in '84 by Polydor Records. Distributed by: IMS, Polygram

LIVE IN NEW YORK CITY.
Tracks: / Intro / Vaya / Ahora si que vamo a gozar / Bab ban quere / Guarare / Night Flowers (flores de noche) / Slo flo / Cocinando / Que viva la musica.
Album: released on Messidor (Germany) in Jan'87. Distributed by: IMS Distribution, Polygram

QUE VIVA LA MUSICA.
Album: released on Salsa in '82

Barrett Sisters

PRECIOUS LORD.
Album: released on Auvidis (France) in '85. Distributed by: Discovery

Album: released on Auvidis (France) in '85. Distributed by: Discovery

Cassette: released on Auvidis (France) in '85. Distributed by: Discovery

Barrett, Syd

BARRETT.
Tracks: / Baby lemonade / Love song / Dominoes / It is obvious / Rats / Maisie / Gigolo aunt / Waving my arms in the air / Wined and dined / Wolfpack / Effervescing elephant / Baby lemonade / Love song / Dominoes / It is obvious / Rats / Maisie / Gigolo Aunt / Waving my arms in the air / I never lied to you / Wined and dined / Wolfpack / Effervescing elephant.
Notes: Produced by David Gilmour and Richard Wright.
Compact disc: released on EMI in May'87 by EMI Records. Distributed by: EMI

Album: released on Harvest in '85 by EMI Records. Distributed by: Roots, EMI

Cassette: released on Harvest in '85 by EMI Records. Distributed by: Roots, EMI

MADCAP LAUGHS, THE.
Tracks: / Terrapin / No good trying / Love you / No man's land / Here I go / Dark globe / Octopus / Golden hair / Long gone / She took a long cool look / Feel / If it's in you / Late night.
Compact disc: released on Harvest in May'87 by EMI Records. Distributed by: Roots, EMI

SYD BARRETT.
Album: released on Harvest in '74 by EMI Records. Distributed by: Roots, EMI

Barrett, Wild Willie

GONE WITH THE BIN Best of Otway & Barrett.
Album: released on Polydor in '81 by Polydor Records. Distributed by: Polygram Polydor

Cassette: released on Polydor in '81 by Polydor Records. Distributed by: Polygram, Polydor

HITCHHIKER & THE PUNK.
Single (7"):

KRAZY KONG ALBUM.
Album: released on Black Eyes in '81. Distributed by: Rough Trade

OLD JOE CLARK/RABBIT IN BOSTON.
Single (7"): released on Carrere in '83 by Carrere Records. Distributed by: PRT, Spartan

Single (12"): released on Carrere in '83 by Carrere Records. Distributed by: PRT, Spartan

ORGANIC BONDAGE.
Album: released on Galvanised in May'86. Distributed by: Rough Trade, Cartel

Album: released on Galvanised in May'86. Distributed by: Rough Trade, Cartel

TALES FROM THE RAJ.
Single (7"): released on Black Eyes in '81. Distributed by: Rough Trade

WE'VE GOTTA GET OUT OF THIS PLACE.
Single (7"): released on Black Eyes in '81. Distributed by: Rough Trade

WRAPPING ON A MOUNTAIN/SIDE SOUNDING.
Single (7"): released on Carrere in '83 by Carrere Records. Distributed by: PRT, Spartan

Barrie, J.J

BUENOS DIAS SENORITA.
Single (7"): released on Monarch in '82 by Chart Records. Distributed by: Pinnacle

CALL MY NAME.
Album: released on RCA in '78 by RCA Records. Distributed by: RCA, Roots, Swift, Wellard, Chris, I & B, Solomon & Peres Distribution

CHRISTMAS/SSSSCROOGE'XMAS.
Single (7"): released on Monarch in '81 by Chart Records. Distributed by: Pinnacle

ESPECIALLY FOR YOU.
Album: released on Starblend in '84 by Starblend Records. Distributed by: PRT Distribution

Cassette: released on Starblend in '84 by Starblend Records. Distributed by: PRT Distribution

FORTY AND FADING.
Single (7"): released on Magic in '84. Distributed by: Jazz Music, Submarine, Swift, Chris Wellard, Conifer

IF I COULD ONLY LOVE YOU ONCE MORE.
Single (7"): released on Magic in '83. Distributed by: Jazz Music, Submarine, Swift, Chris Wellard, Conifer

I'M JUST FALLING IN LOVE AGAIN.
Single (7"): released on Monarch in '82 by Chart Records. Distributed by: Pinnacle

LOVE 'N' COUNTRY.
Album: released on Monarch in '82 by Chart Records. Distributed by: Pinnacle

LUCILLE/WHERE'S THE REASON.
Single (7"): released on Magic in '83. Distributed by: Jazz Music, Submarine, Swift, Chris Wellard, Conifer

MY SON.
Album: released on Magic in '83. Distributed by: Jazz Music, Submarine, Swift, Chris Wellard, Conifer

Cassette: released on Magic in '83. Distributed by: Jazz Music, Submarine, Swift, Chris Wellard, Conifer

MY SON/WHY DID YOU HAVE TO GO AND DO IT.
Single (7"): released on Magic in '83. Distributed by: Jazz Music, Submarine, Swift, Chris Wellard, Conifer

NO CHARGE.
Single (7"): released on Magic in '85. Distributed by: Jazz Music, Submarine, Swift, Chris Wellard, Conifer

SINGS SONGS FROM FRAGGLE ROCK.
Album: released on Cherry Lane in '84 by Cherry Lane Productions. Distributed by: PRT

Cassette: released on Cherry Lane in '84 by Cherry Lane Productions. Distributed by: PRT

WHERE'S THE REASON/WHEN I'VE GOT....
Single (7"): released on Magic in '83. Distributed by: Jazz Music, Submarine, Swift, Chris Wellard, Conifer

WHILE THE FEELINGS GOOD.
Single (7"): released on Starblend in '84 by Starblend Records. Distributed by: PRT Distribution

Barrie, Ken

LAZY.
Single (7"): released on Go Ahead in '84 by Go Ahead Records. Distributed by: Go Ahead

POSTMAN PAT/HANDYMAN SONG.
Single (7"):

Barrie, Mike

GIRLS.
Tracks: / Secondhand Rose / Sweet Lorraine / Pretty girl is like a melody, A / Louise / Lady they call the gypsy, The / Ramona / Irene / Dance my darlings / Sweetheart of all my dreams / I'm thinking tonight of my blue eyes / No no Nanette / Waltz for Sarah / Emily / Mary Rose / Barbara Allen / Josephine / When Joanna left me / Woman in love, A / Laura / Rio Rita / Darling / Anastasia.
Album: released on Sounds Ultimate in Jun'86. Distributed by: PRT, H.R. Taylor

GOLDEN SOUVENIRS.
Tracks: / Pick yourself up / So do I / Have you met miss Jones / I've got my eyes on you / Take me to the dance / I apologise / Isle of my golden dreams / Sleepy lagoon / Silence is golden / Golden souvenirs / Cherie amour / You make me feel brand new / I'm beginning to see the light / Sentimental journey / An apple for the teacher / Yes we have no bananas / El cumbanchero / Nice work if you can get it / Camptown races / Nic-nac-paddy-wac / Lady be good / 12th street rag.
Album: released on Sounds Ultimate in Jul'87. Distributed by: PRT, H.R. Taylor

MY SOUVENEIRS (Barrie, Mike With The Starlight Sound).
Tracks: / Canadian capers / 57 Chevrolet / Tears / Among my souvenirs / Danke schoen / My baby just cares for me / Daddy's little girl / Sweet heart land / Mistakes / Always there / Mamselle / All I ask of you / Habanera / Who can I turn to / Tales from the Vienna woods / Lilli / Strauss theme / Little boxes / Cuckoo waltz / Till the time when you're with me / Consider yourself at home / Round the Marble Arch / Two little boys / Susan slept here / I love the way you say goodnight / Shores of Ballachulish / Loch Lomond.
Album: released on Sounds Ultimate in Nov'86. Distributed by: PRT, H.R. Taylor

PARADISE.
Tracks: / So in love / You do something to me / When the poppies bloom again / We just couldn't say goodbye / It looks like rain in Cherry Blossom lane / You are my sunshine / If I should fall in love again / Paradise waltz / When my sugar walks down the street / Met a gal in Calico / Stranger in paradise / Mind if I make love to you / Latin touch-down / Suagr, sugar / Bambino de los playa.
Album: released on Sounds Ultimate in '85. Distributed by: PRT, H.R. Taylor

SAY IT WITH FLOWERS.
Tracks: / Three little words / Oh what a beautiful morning / Apple blossom time / We'll gather lilacs / Moonlight and roses / Lambeth walk / This is my lovely day / Red roses for a blue lady / Rose in a garden of weeds, A / Eidelweiss / I got the sun in the mornin' / Cherry / I won't send roses / Say it with flowers / Lavender blue / Where have all the flowers gone / Begin the beguine / Azalae delicado / Orchids in the moonlight / Oh! Rosalita.
Album: released on Sounds Ultimate in '85. Distributed by: PRT, H.R. Taylor

Barron, Blue

UNCOLLECTED BLUE BARRON, THE - VOL.2 1938-39.
Tracks: / Teacher's pet / Garden of the moon / Yam, The / Love of my life / No wonder / Somebody nobody knows / That's right, I'm wrong / Roller skating on a rainbow / Goody goodbye / Does your heart beat for me / Scatterbrain / Faithful forever / I wanna wrap you up / Make with the kisses / I'm fit to be tied / It's a whole new thing.
Album: released on Hindsight(UK) in '79. Distributed by: Jazz Music

Barrone, Nick

BLUES IN THE CITY.
Single (7"): released on Blue August in Aug'87. Distributed by: Pinnacle

Single (12"): released on Blue August in Aug'87. Distributed by: Pinnacle

Barron, Kenny

1+1+1+1.
Album: released on Blackhawk in Aug'86 by Blackhawk Records (USA). Distributed by: IMS-Polygram

Cassette: released on Blackhawk in Aug'86 by Blackhawk Records (USA). Distributed by: IMS-Polygram

GOLDEN LOTUS.
Album: released on Muse in '82 by Peerless Records. Distributed by: Lugtons Distributors

IN TANDEM (Barron, Kenny & Ted Dunbar).
Album: released on Muse in '75 by Peerless Records. Distributed by: Lugtons Distributors

LUCIFER.
Tracks: / Spirits / Firefly / Ethereally / Yours / Hellbound / Lucifer / Oleo.
Album: released on Muse in '81 by Peerless Records. Distributed by: Lugtons Distributors

SPIRAL.
Album: released on East Wind in '85 by East Wind Records. Distributed by: PRT

SUNSET TO DAWN.
Tracks: / Sunset / Flower, A / Swamp demon / Al-Kifha / Delores St. S.F. / Dawn.
Album: released on Muse in '81 by Peerless Records

Barron Knights

BARRON KNIGHTS.
Tracks: / Call up the groups / Pop go the workers / Under new management / Come to the dance / Round the world / Rhythm and blues / Return my love / Big girls don't cry / Sphinx won't tell, The / She's a woman / Merry minuet / Knock knock / Let her go.
Album: released on Contour in '82 by Pickwick Records. Distributed by: Pickwick Distribution, PRT

Cassette: released on Contour in '82 by Pickwick Records. Distributed by: Pickwick Distribution, PRT

BEST OF THE BARRON KNIGHTS.
Album: released on Warwick in '82. Distributed by: Multiple Sound Distributors

Cassette: released on Warwick in '82. Distributed by: Multiple Sound Distributors

BUFFALO BILL'S LAST LAMENT.
Single (7"): released on Epic in '83 by CBS Records. Distributed by: CBS

Single (12"): released on Epic in '83 by CBS Records. Distributed by: CBS

CHURCHILL RAP,THE.
Single (7"): released on Towerbell in '84 by Towerbell Records. Distributed by: EMI

Single (12"): released on Towerbell in '84 by Towerbell Records. Distributed by: EMI

FULL CIRCLE/EYE OF THE HURRICANE.
Single (7"): released on Epic in '83 by CBS Records. Distributed by: CBS

I'D LIKE TO TEACH THE WORLD TO LAUGH.
Album: released on Spot in '84 by Pickwick Records. Distributed by: H.R. Taylor,

Cassette: released on Spot in '84 by Pickwick Records. Distributed by: H.R. Taylor, Lugtons

KNIGHTS OF LAUGHTER.
Album: released on Pickwick in '79 by Pickwick Records. Distributed by: Pickwick Distribution, Prism Leisure Distribution, Lugtons

Cassette: released on Pickwick in '79 by Pickwick Records. Distributed by: Pickwick Distribution, Prism Leisure Distribution, Lugtons

LIVE IN TROUBLE.
Tracks: / Live in trouble / You make me feel like dancing / Angelo / D i v o r c e / Lucille / Float on / Telephone man / Ernie / Clair / Amazing Grace / 1358 number song / Linking - Incidental music / Space Oddity / Autograph hunter / Loving you / What is a pop star? / Three finger picker / Any old iron.
Album: released on Spot in '83 by Pickwick Records. Distributed by: H.R. Taylor Lugtons

Cassette: released on Spot in '83 by Pickwick Records. Distributed by: H.R. Taylor, Lugtons

MR BRONSKI MEETS MR EVANS.
Single (7"): released on Spartan in '85 by Spartan Records. Distributed by: Spartan

R-R-ROCK ME FATHER CHRISTMAS.
Tracks: / R-r-rock me Father Christmas / Big bad band (big bad John).
Single (7"): released on WEA in Nov'86 by WEA Records. Distributed by: WEA

Single (12"): released on WEA in Nov'86 by WEA Records. Distributed by: WEA

TEACH THE WORLD TO LAUGH.
Cassette: released on Epic in '79 by CBS Records. Distributed by: CBS

TWO SIDES OF BARRON KNIGHTS, THE.
Tracks: / Ballad of Frank Spencer / You know what / Cold in my nose / Couldn't spell / Popumentry '71 (Part 1) / Banner man / Grandad / Did you ever / 1358 into Beetroot song / Green knickers / I'm a nut / Head tucked underneath her arm / Popumentry '71 (Part 2) / Chirpy chirpy cheep cheep / Resurrection shuffle, The / Knock thre time / You're all I need / Before you leave / Bottle on the shelf / Lonely / You know what I mean / Don't let it die / Turning my back on you / Oh little girl / To the wood / Peaceful life.
Double Album: released on Pickwick in '80 by Pickwick Records. Distributed by: Pickwick Distribution, Prism Leisure Distribution, Lugtons

Cassette: released on Pickwick in '80 by Pickwick Records. Distributed by: Pickwick Distribution, Prism Leisure Distribution, Lugtons

Barron, Ronnie

BON TON ROULETTE.
Tracks: / Bon ton roulette / Carry on / Fever / Boney Moronie / Rock and roll dream / Lights out / Life is just a struggle / Pixie / Maybellene / Cha dooky-doo.
Album: released on Ace in Aug'83 by Ace Records. Distributed by: Pinnacle, Swift, Hotshot, Cadillac

Barrow Boys

WALLY RAP.
Single (7"): released on Creole in '84 by Creole Records. Distributed by: Rhino, PRT

Single (12"): released on Creole in '84 by Creole Records. Distributed by: Rhino, PRT

Barr, Walt

ARTFUL DANCER.
Album: released on Muse (Import) in '81

Barry, Claudja

CAN'T YOU HEAR MY HEARTBEAT.
Single (7"): released on Epic in Apr'87 by CBS Records. Distributed by: CBS

Single (12"): released on Epic in Apr'87 by CBS Records. Distributed by: CBS

CLAUDJA.

DOWN & COUNTING.
Tracks: / Down & counting.
Single (7"): released on Epic in Oct'86 by CBS Records. Distributed by: CBS

Single (12"): released on Epic in Oct'86 by CBS Records. Distributed by: CBS

I, CLAUDJA.
Tracks: / Down and counting / Can't you feel my heart beat / Dance for your life / Give me a sign / Hot to the touch / Dead or alive (I don't know if you are) / Secret affair / You've got me jumpin' / Change of heart / Show me another way.
Album: released on Epic in Aug'87 by CBS Records. Distributed by: CBS

Cassette: released on Epic in Aug'87 by CBS Records. Distributed by: CBS

I WILL FOLLOW HIM/WORK ME OVER.
Single (7"): released on Excaliber in '83 by Red Bus Records. Distributed by: PRT

Single (12"): released on Excaliber in '83 by Red Bus Records. Distributed by: PRT

TRIPPIN' ON THE MOON.
Single (7"): released on Personal in '84 by Personal Records. Distributed by: PRT

Single (12"): released on Personal in '84 by Personal Records. Distributed by: PRT

Barry, D

CRAZY FOR YOUR LOVE.
Single (12"): released on Viking in '85. Distributed by: Harmonia Mundi Distributors

HERE I GO AGAIN.
Tracks: / Still falling (Class One Crew) / Here I go again.
Single (12"): released on Class One in Nov'86

Barry-Gorman

HER MANTLE SO GREEN.
Tracks: / Cycling champion of Ulster, The / Flower of sweet Strabane, The / Dr. Gilbert / Turfman from Ardee, The / Galway shawl, The / Maguire's favourite / Tralee gaol / Maggie in the wood / Wild colonial boy, The / My lagan love / Hornpipe / Boys of blue hill, The / Factory girl, The / Her mantle so green / Bunch of keys, The / Heather breeze, The.
Album: released on Topic in '81. Distributed by: Roots Distribution

Barry, Harry

GOD BLESS YOU/IN WINTER.
Single (7"): released on Coochly St. in '82

OLD WAYS NEW BEGINNINGS.
Tracks: / Symphony of love / In Winter / Lonely in the night / All I need is you / Give your loce a chance / Your cheating heart / God bless you / See what we can do / Building a wall of love / It doesn't matter anymore / Happy in love again.
Album: released on OK in '84. Distributed by: Stage One Distribution

Cassette: released on OK in '84. Distributed by: Stage One Distribution

Barry, John

BIG SCREEN HITS OF JOHN BARRY, THE.
Tracks: / Thunderball / Theme from born free / Theme from the persuaders / Midnight cowboy / Ipress file, The / We have all the time in the world / Lion in winter, The / Goldfinger / You only live twice / Girl with the sun in her hair / More things change, The / Fun city / James Bond theme, The.
Cassette: released on CBS in Aug'84 by CBS Records. Distributed by: CBS

GOLDFINGER Original soundtrack.
Tracks: / Goldfinger / Into Miami / Alpine drive-Aurics factory / Oddjobs pressing engagement / Bond in action again / Teasing the Korean / Gassing the gangsters / Goldfinger / Dawn raid on Fort Knox / Arrival of the bomb and count-down, The / Death of Goldfinger.
Album: released on EMI (Italy) in May'87 by EMI Records. Distributed by: Conifer

Cassette: released on EMI (Italy) in May'87 by EMI Records. Distributed by: Conifer

MIDNIGHT COWBOY.
Single (7"): released on United Artists in Sep'80

MUSIC FROM THE BIG SCREEN.
Cassette: released on Ditto in Mar'86 by Pickwick Records. Distributed by: H.R. Taylor

MUSIC OF....
Tracks: / Born free / You only live twice / Goldfinger / Whisperers / From Russia with love / Wednesday's child / Quiller memorandum / Space march (Capsule in space) / Girl with the sun in her hair, The / Thunderball / Wrong box, The / James Bond theme, The / 007 / Mister kiss kiss bang bang / Chase, The / King rat / Seance on a wet afternoon / Ipcress file, The / Midnight cowboy / Theme from 'Romance for guitar & orchestra' / On Her Majesty's secret service / Theme from 'The appointment' / Lion in winter, The.
Double Album: released on CBS in Jun'76 by CBS Records. Distributed by: CBS

STRINGBEAT.
Tracks: / It doesn't matter anymore / Sweet talk / Moody river / Moody river / There's life in the old boy yet / Handful of songs, A / Like waltz / Rodeo / Donna's theme / Star fire / Baubles, bangles and beads / Zapata / Rum-de-dum-de-da / Spanish harlem / Man from Madrid / Challenge, The.
Album: released on Cherry Red in Aug'83 by Cherry Red Records. Distributed by: Pinnacle

VERY BEST OF JOHN BARRY.
Cassette: released on Polydor in Jun'81 by Polydor Records. Distributed by: Polygram, Polydor

Barry, John Seven

HIT & MISS (Barry, John Seven & Orchestra).
Tracks: / Hit & miss / Big guitar / Rodeo / Big fella / Walk don't run / Bess's knees / Ev'ry which way / Beat girl / Human jungle / I'm moving on / Zapata / Like waltz / Black stockings / James Bond theme, The / Lost patrol / Magnificent seven / Hideaway / Menace / Never let go / Sharks.
Album: released on See For Miles in Mar'82 by See For Miles Records. Distributed by: Pinnacle

Cassette: released on See For Miles in Mar'82 by See For Miles Records. Distributed by: Pinnacle

Barry, Len

1-2-3.
Single (7"): released on Old Gold in Jul'82 by Old Gold Records. Distributed by: Lightning, Jazz Music, Spartan, Counterpoint

MORE FROM THE 1-2-3 MAN.
Tracks: / Bob, Carool, Ted and Alice / Christopher Columbus / Now I'm alone / Spread it on like butter / This old world / Funky nite / Put out the fire / You're my picasso baby / In my present state of mind / Wouldn't it be beautiful / Keem-o-sabe.
Album: released on Bulldog in Jul'82 by Bulldog Records. Distributed by: President Distribution, Spartan, Swift, Taylor, H.R.

Barry, Margaret

HER MANTLE SO GREEN.
Album: . Distributed by: Roots Distribution

IRELAND'S OWN STREET SINGER.
Album: released on Outlet in Jul'76 by Outlet Records. Distributed by: Outlet Distribution

SHE MOVES THROUGH THE FAIR.
Cassette: released on Folktracks in Nov'79 by Folktracks Cassettes. Distributed by: Folktracks

Barrymore, Michael

DO THE CRAB.
Tracks: / Do the crab.
Single (7"): released on Candy (USA) in 20 Jun'87 by Candy (USA) Records

Barry Sisters

WHEN THE BOAT COMES IN.
Album: released on MWM in Jun'82 by Mawson & Wareham. Distributed by: Spartan Distribution, Jazz Music Distribution, JSU Distribution

Cassette: released on MWM in Jun'82 by Mawson & Wareham. Distributed by: Spartan Distribution, Jazz Music Distribution, JSU Distribution

Barth, Bobby

DON'T COME TO ME.
Tracks: / Don't come to me / Sara.
Single (7"): released on Atco in May'86 by Atlantic Records. Distributed by: WEA

TWO HEARTS-ONE BEAT.
Tracks: / Stop in the name of love / Sara / Knifes edge / I don't want to be alone tonight / Burn me once, burn me twice / Once in a lifetime / Dangerous games / Don't come to me.
Album: released on Atco in May'86 by Atlantic Records. Distributed by: WEA

Cassette: released on Atco in May'86 by Atlantic Records. Distributed by: WEA

Bartholomew, Dave

JUMP CHILDREN.
Album: released on Pathe Marconi in Sep'84. Distributed by: Swift

MONKEY,THE.
Album: released on Pathe MarconiFrance) in Apr'85

Bartle, Peter

PLAYS SIMPLY HAMMOND.

Barton, Edward

ME & MINNIE.
Tracks: / Me & Minnie / I've got no chicken but I got wooden chairs.
Single (7"): released on Wooden in Nov'86

Barton & Harry

MULCH.
Extended-play record: released on Fever in Aug'84 by Fever Records. Distributed by: Red Rhino, Cartel

Barton, Tony

STONED.
Tracks: / Blueberry Hill / He'll have to go / Green green grass of home / When I fall in love / Ernie / Last one home (Mr.Toad), The / Dave, Stones bitter & me.

Notes: Recorded live at the Belvedere
P 1986 President Records Ltd
C 1986 President Records Ltd
Introduction by Jim Davidson
Album: released on President in Apr'86 by President Records. Distributed by: Taylors, Spartan

Cassette: released on President in Apr'86 by President Records. Distributed by: Taylors, Spartan

Bartram, Dave

BLACK ICE.
Single (7"): released on Utopia in Dec'82

Baseball Boys

NEVER TOLD LIES.
Single (7"): released on Radio in Sep'83 by Radio Records. Distributed by: Pinnacle

Baselli, Joss

CLASSIC JAZZ (Baselli, Joss & His Quartet).
Tracks: / Mozart march turque / Albino adagio / Bach choral de veilleur / Mozart menuet / Chopin mazurka / Grieg danse d'anitra / Mozart sonate / Bach Italian concerto / Adante & Presto (1st movement) / De falla danse du feu.
Notes: Mail order distribution address: Accordian Record Club,146 Birmingham Road, Kidderminster, Worcs. DY10 2SL Tel: 0562 746105
Cassette: released on Accordion Record Club in Jul'86 by Accordion Record Club Records. Distributed by: Accordion Record Club

Album: released on CBS in Jul'86 by CBS Records. Distributed by: CBS

DOIGTS D'OR, (LES).
Tracks: / Piccola rag / Multi faces / La polka suedoise / La balocharde / Rock minuer / Passymusette / Les doigts d'or / Via Rio / L'avignonnaise / Campans de fiesta / Pour une valse / Accordion rag.
Notes: Mail order distribution address: Accordian Record Club,146 Birmingham Road, Kidderminster,Worcs. DY10 2SL Tel 0562 746105
Album: released on Accordion Record Club in Jul'86 by Accordion Record Club Records. Distributed by: Accordion Record Club

Cassette: released on Accordion Record Club in Jul'86 by Accordion Record Club Records. Distributed by: Accordion Record Club

Album: released on ARC (Accordion Records) in May'84. Distributed by: Accordion Record Club

INOUBLIABLE.
Tracks: / Geraldine / Mazureva / Minousette / Marquisette / La corsette / Belina / Basquaise la rivale / La galliniere / Corisette / Lori Lori / L'oiseleur.
Notes: Mail order distribution address: Accordian Record Club,146 Birmingham Road, Kidderminster, Worcs. DY10 2SL Tel: 0562 746105
Cassette: released on Accordion Record Club in Jul'86 by Accordion Record Club Records. Distributed by: Accordion Record Club

Album: released on Accordion Record Club in Jul'86 by Accordion Record Club Records. Distributed by: Accordion Record Club

PERLES D'ACCORDEON.
Tracks: / Feu vert / Pietro's return / La migliavacca / Perles de cristal / Aubade d'oiseaux / Mille accordeon / Jeanette les troilets / Brazil accordeon / Indifference / Croma duet / Perles d'accordeon / Boutade / Roba / Accordeon holiday / Electro ballade.
Notes: Mail order distribution address : Accordian Record Club,146 Birmingham Road, Kidderminster,Worcs. DY 10 2SL Tel: 0562 746105
Album: released on Accordion Record Club in Jul'86 by Accordion Record Club Records. Distributed by: Accordion Record Club

Cassette: released on Accordion Record Club in Jul'86 by Accordion Record Club Records. Distributed by: Accordion Record Club

Basement 5

1965-1980.
Album: released on Island in Jan'81 by Island Records. Distributed by: Polygram

Basement Walls

BASEMENT WALLS 14 US oil slickers &garage mechanics from the mid 60's (Various Artists).
Album: released on Antar in Feb'86 by Bam Caruso Records. Distributed by: Rough Trade, Revolver

Base Team

CHANGE OF HABIT (Base Team Featuring T.C. Curtis).
Tracks: / Change of habit / Change of habit (melt down dub mix).
Single (12"): released on Hot Melt in Apr'87 by Hot Melt Records. Distributed by: Pinnacle, Spartan

Bashful Brother Oswald

BASHFUL BROTHER OSWALD.
Album: released on Starday in Apr'87

Cassette: released on Starday in Apr'87

Bashville

BASHVILLE Original Cast Recording (Various Artists).
Album: released on TER in Jan'84. Distributed by: Pinnacle

Cassette: released on TER in Jan'84. Distributed by: Pinnacle

Basia

NEW DAY FOR YOU.
Tracks: / New day for you / Forgive and forget.
Single (7"): released on Portrait in 13 Jun'87 by CBS Records. Distributed by: CBS

Single (12"): released on Portrait in 13 Jun'87 by CBS Records. Distributed by: CBS

NEW DAY FOR YOU (TAKE 2).
Tracks: / New day for you / Prime time TV.
Single (12"): released on Portrait in Jul'87 by CBS Records. Distributed by: CBS

PRIME TIME TV.
Tracks: / Prime time TV / Freeze thaw.
Single (7"): released on Portrait in Jul'86 by CBS Records. Distributed by: CBS

RUN FOR COVER.
Tracks: / Run for cover / From now on.
Single (7"): released on Portrait in Oct'86 by CBS Records. Distributed by: CBS

Single (12"): released on Portrait in Oct'86 by CBS Records. Distributed by: CBS

TIME AND TIDE.
Tracks: / Promises / Run for cover / Time and tide / Freeze thaw / From now on / New day for you / Prime time TV / Astrud / How dare you / Miles away / Forgive and forget.
Single (7"): released on Portrait in Feb'87 by CBS Records. Distributed by: CBS

Single (12"): released on Portrait in Feb'87 by CBS Records. Distributed by: CBS

Album: released on Portrait in Apr'87 by CBS Records. Distributed by: CBS

Cassette: released on Portrait in Apr'87 by CBS Records. Distributed by: CBS

Compact disc: released on Portrait in Apr'87 by CBS Records. Distributed by: CBS

Basie, Count

Biographical Details: Born William Basie in New Jersey in 1904, Count Basie learned to play the piano from his mother and then studied informally with famous pianist Fats Waller. When turning professional, he began as a pianist on the vaudeville circuit, then joined the Blue Devils, many of whose members went on to play in Basie's own ensemble. When the Blue Devils broke up, a large proportion of their players joined a band under the leadership of Bennie Moten. With Moten passing away in 1935, the nucleus of his band became the first Basie outfit. It was when this ensemble began recording in '37 that Basie became an enormous star in the jazz fiueld. His band gained international recognition for its hard-seinging style and freewheeling solo playing. Throughout the Fories and Fifties Count Basie consolidated on his reputation, always recruiting players of the highest musical calibre. Among his big band's most played numbers were "Swingin' At The Daisy Chain", "Every Tub", "One O'Clock Jump" and "Jumpin' At The Woodside". He was still able to hit the US Top 30 at the start of the rock'n'roll era, reaching No.28 in early 1956 with "April In Paris". In April 1960 he hit the UK albums Top 20 with Chairman Of The Board", though most of his greatest triumphs had occurred before the inception of the British charts. The Count Basie.

14 CLASSICS.
Tracks: / Hollywood jump / I never knew / Tickle toe / Let me see / Blow top / What's your number / Five o'clock whistle / Broadway / Stampede in G minor / Rockin' the blues / Wiggle woogie / Jitters / Tuesday at ten / I do mean you.
Album: released on CBS in Jul'86 by CBS Records. Distributed by: CBS

Cassette: released on CBS in Jul'86 by CBS Records. Distributed by: CBS

1938-39.
Album: released on Jazz Archives in Jul'86 by Jazz Archives Records. Distributed by: Jazz Music

1944.
Album: released on Circle(USA) in Jun'84 by Jazzology Records (USA). Distributed by: Jazz Music, Swift, Chris Wellard

1946.
Album: released on First Heard in '84 by Submarine Records. Distributed by: Conifer, Taylors

Cassette: released on First Heard in '84 by Submarine Records. Distributed by: Conifer, Taylors

20 GOLDEN PIECES OF COUNT BASIE.
Tracks: / One o'clock jump / Motem swing / Study in brown / Dinah / Good morning blues / Lady be good / Flat foot foogie / Every tub / Boogie woogie blues / Lullaby of birdland / Summertime / These foolish things / One note samba / Makin' whoopee / April in Paris / Jumpin' at the woodside / Ain't misbehavin' / Shake rattle and roll / I got it bad (and that ain't good) / Lester leaps in.
Album: released on Bulldog in Jul'82 by Bulldog Records. Distributed by: President Distribution, Spartan, Swift, Taylor, H.R.

88 BASIE STREET (Basie, Count & His Orchestra).
Tracks: / Bluesville / 88 Basie Street / Contractor's blues / Blues machine, The / Katy / Sunday at the Savoy.
Album: released on Pablo (USA) in May'84 by Pablo Records (USA). Distributed by: Wellard, Chris, IMS-Polygram, BMG

Cassette: released on Pablo (USA) in May'84 by Pablo Records (USA). Distributed by: Wellard, Chris, IMS-Polygram, BMG

AFRIQUE.
Album: released on Doctor Jazz (USA) in Mar'85 by Doctor Jazz Records. Distributed by: CBS

Cassette: released on Doctor Jazz (USA) in Mar'85 by Doctor Jazz Records. Distributed by: CBS

AIRSHOTS BIRDLAND, JAN. 1953 VOL. 1.
Album: released on Unique Jazz in Nov'86. Distributed by: Swift, Jazz Music, Jazz Horizons

AIR SHOTS,BIRDLAND-JANUARY 1953 VOL.1.
Album: released on Unique Jazz in Apr'79. Distributed by: Swift, Jazz Music, Jazz Horizons

APRIL IN PARIS.
Compact disc: released on Polygram/Verve (W.Germany) in Jun'86 by Polygram Records. Distributed by: Polygram

AT BIRDLAND.
Album: released on Vogue in Mar'80. Distributed by: Discovery, Jazz Music, PRT, Swift

ATOMIC BASE.
Album: released on Vogue (France) in May'84. Distributed by: Discovery, Jazz Music, PRT, Swift

Cassette: released on Vogue (France) in May'84. Distributed by: Discovery, Jazz Music, PRT, Swift

ATOMIC MR.BASIE (Basie, Count & His Orchestra).
Compact disc: released on Roulette (USA) in May'85 by Sunnyview Records Inc.(USA)

ATOMIC MR.BASIE, THE.
Album: released on PRT in Jul'84 by PRT Records. Distributed by: PRT

Cassette: released on PRT in Jul'84 by PRT Records. Distributed by: PRT

ATOMIC MR. BASIE, THE.
Tracks: / Kid from the Red Bank, The / Dust / After supper / Flight of the foo birds / Double - O / Teddy the Toad / Whirly bird / Midnight blue / Splanky / Fantail / Li'l darlin'.
Notes: A re-release of the classic Count Basie album of the late 50's. This is from the original mono masters, as it was first heard in the UK,when both the album & the single 'Li'l Darlin'' were both enormous hits. A great tribute to Count Basie.
Compact disc: released on Vogue in May'87. Distributed by: Discovery, Jazz Music, PRT, Swift

ATOMIC MR.CHAIRMAN, THE.
Tracks: / Kid from Red Bank, (The) / Duet / After supper / Flight of the foo birds / Double-O / Teddy the toad / Whirly-bird / Midnite blue / Splanky / Fantail / Lil' darling / Blues in Hoss's flat / H.R.H. / Segue in C / Kansas City shout / Speaking of sounds / T.V. time / Who, me? / Deacon, (The) / Half Moon Street / Mutt and Jeff.
Album: released on Vogue Jazz (France) in May'83

Cassette: released on Vogue Jazz (France) in May'83

ATOMIC PERIOD, THE (Basie, Count Orchestra).
Tracks: / Shiny stockings / HRH / Bag of bones / Deacon, The / Whirley bird / In a mellow tone / Midgets, The / Basie boogie / Old man river / Sisteen men a'swinging.
Album: released on Rarities in Apr'81

AT THE BLUENOTE (Basie, Count & His Orchestra).
Tracks: / Fancy meeting you / Basie English / Everyday / Basses loaded / April in Paris / Peace pipe / Cherry point / Smack dab in the middle / Jumpin' at the woodside / Teach me tonight / How high the moon.

Page 79

Notes: Personnel: Trumpets-Thad Jones,Joe Newman,Wendell Culley,Reunald Jones. Trombones-Henry Coker,Benny Powell,Bill Hughes. Saxes-Marshall Royal(cl,as),Frank Wess(fl,ts,as),Frank Foster & Bill Graham(ts),Charlie Fowlkes(bs). Rhythm:Freddie Green(guitar),Eddie Jones(bass),Sonnie Payne(drums) William'Count'Basie(piano & leader). Vocals: Joe Williams
Album: released on Magic in Sep'86. Distributed by: Jazz Music, Submarine, Swift, Chris Wellard, Conifer

Cassette: released on Magic in Sep'86. Distributed by: Jazz Music, Submarine, Swift, Chris Wellard, Conifer

AT THE MONTREUX JAZZ FESTIVAL 1975.
Album: released on Pablo (USA) in May'82 by Pablo Records (USA). Distributed by: Wellard, Chris, IMS-Polygram, BMG

Cassette: released on Pablo (USA) in May'82 by Pablo Records (USA). Distributed by: Wellard, Chris, IMS-Polygram, BMG

AUTUMN IN PARIS.
Album: released on Magic in Jun'85. Distributed by: Jazz Music, Submarine, Swift, Chris Wellard, Conifer

Cassette: released on Magic in Jun'85. Distributed by: Jazz Music, Submarine, Swift, Chris Wellard, Conifer

BASIC BASIE.
Tracks: / Idaho / Blues in my heart / I don't stand a ghost of a chance with you / Red roses for a blue lady / Moonglow / Ma he's making eyes at me / M-squad / Sweet Lorraine / Ain't misbehavin' / Don't worry about me / As long as I live / Don't worry 'bout me / As long as I live / As long as I live / I've got the world on a string.
Compact disc: released on Verve in Nov'84 by Phonogram Records. Distributed by: Polygram

Album: released on MPS (Germany) in Sep'84. Distributed by: IMS-Polygram Distribution, Parnote Distribution (Formerly MDC)

BASIE AND ZOOT (Basie, Count and Zoot Sims).
Album: released on Pablo (USA) in May'82 by Pablo Records (USA). Distributed by: Wellard, Chris, IMS-Polygram, BMG

Cassette: released on Pablo (USA) in May'82 by Pablo Records (USA). Distributed by: Wellard, Chris, IMS-Polygram, BMG

BASIE AND ZOOT (see Sims, Zoot) (Basie, Count & Zoot Sims).

BASIE BIG BAND.
Album: released on Pablo (USA) in May'82 by Pablo Records (USA). Distributed by: Wellard, Chris, IMS-Polygram, BMG

Cassette: released on Pablo (USA) in May'82 by Pablo Records (USA). Distributed by: Wellard, Chris, IMS-Polygram, BMG

BASIE BLUES.
Album: released on MFP (France) in May'84 by EMI Records. Distributed by: EMI

Cassette: released on MFP (France) in May'84 by EMI Records. Distributed by: EMI

BASIE BOOGIE (Basie, Count & His Orchestra).
Cassette: released on CBS in May'83 by CBS Records. Distributed by: CBS

BASIE DOUBLE.
Double Album: released on Vogue in Jun'75. Distributed by: Discovery, Jazz Music, PRT, Swift

BASIE JAM.
Album: released on Pablo (USA) in May'82 by Pablo Records (USA). Distributed by: Wellard, Chris, IMS-Polygram, BMG

Album: released on Pablo (USA) in May'82 by Pablo Records (USA). Distributed by: Wellard, Chris, IMS-Polygram, BMG

BASIE JAM.
Tracks: / Doubling blues / Hanging out / Red bank blues / One nighter / Freeport blues.
Compact disc: released on Pablo (USA) in Jul'86 by Pablo Records (USA). Distributed by: Wellard, Chris, IMS-Polygram, BMG

BASIE JAM AT MONTREUX 1975.
Tracks: / Billie's bounce / Festival blues / Lester leaps in.
Compact disc: by Pablo Records. Distributed by: Wellard, Chris, IMS-Polygram, BMG

BASIE JAM NO.2.
Album: released on Pablo (USA) in May'82 by Pablo Records (USA). Distributed by: Wellard, Chris, IMS-Polygram, BMG

Cassette: released on Pablo (USA) in May'82 by Pablo Records (USA). Distributed by: Wellard, Chris, IMS-Polygram, BMG

BASIE JAM NO.3.
Album: released on Pablo (USA) in May'82 by Pablo Records (USA). Distributed by: Wellard, Chris, IMS-Polygram, BMG

Album: released on Pablo (USA) in May'82 by Pablo Records (USA). Distributed by: Wellard, Chris, IMS-Polygram, BMG

BASIE RIDES AGAIN.
Album: released on Polydor (Import) in Feb'82

BASIE'S BASEMENT (Basie, Count & His Orchestra).
Tracks: / Bill's mill / Swingin' the blues / Basie's basement / I never knew / Sugar / South / Seventh Avenue express / Your red wagon / Just a minute / Bye bye baby / Shoutin' blues / Rat race.
Album: released on RCA in Jul'86 by RCA Records. Distributed by: RCA, Roots, Swift, Wellard, Chris, I & B, Solomon & Peres Distribution

Cassette: released on RCA in Jul'86 by RCA Records. Distributed by: RCA, Roots, Swift, Wellard, Chris, I & B, Solomon & Peres Distribution

BASIE & ZOOT (Basie, Count & Zoot Sims).
Tracks: / I never knew / Its only a paper moon / Blues for Nat Cole / Captain Bligh / Honeysuckle rose / Hardav / Mean to me / Surrender dear.
Compact disc: released on Pablo (USA) in Jul'86 by Pablo Records (USA). Distributed by: Wellard, Chris, IMS-Polygram, BMG

BEST OF BASIE.
Tracks: / Jumpin' at the Woodside / Blue & sentimental / Red bank boogie / Shorty George / Rock-a-bye Basie / Every tub / Swingin' the blues / Sent for you yesterday / Boogie woogie / Broadway / Texas shuffle / Tickle toe / Doggin' around / Dickie's dream / Topsy / Topsy / Lester leaps in / Out the window.

BEST OF BASIE, THE.
Compact disc: released on Vogue in '86. Distributed by: Discovery, Jazz Music, PRT, Swift

BEST OF COUNT BASIE, THE.
Tracks: / Tree frog / Swee' pea / Ticker / Flirt / Blues for Alfie / Billie's bounce / Festival blues.

BEST OF, THE.
Album: released on Pablo Jazz (USA) in Oct'84 by United Artists. Distributed by: Swift

Cassette: released on Pablo Jazz (USA) in Oct'84 by United Artists. Distributed by: Swift

BIG BAND, VOL.1, THE (Basie, Count & Milt Jackson).

BIG BAND VOL.2, THE (Basie, Count & Milt Jackson).
Album: released on Pablo (USA) in '82 by Pablo Records (USA). Distributed by: Wellard, Chris, IMS-Polygram, BMG

Cassette: released on Pablo (USA) in '82 by Pablo Records (USA). Distributed by: Wellard, Chris, IMS-Polygram, BMG

BIG BASIE.
Album: released on Queen-Disc in Apr'81. Distributed by: Celtic Music, JSU, Jazz Horizons, Jazz Music

BIRDLAND ERA VOL.1, THE (Basie, Count & His Orchestra).
Album: released on Duke in Jun'86 by Melodisc Records. Distributed by: Jazz Horizons, Jazz Music, Celtic Music, Swift

BIRDLAND ERA VOL.2, THE (Basie, Count & His Orchestra).
Tracks: / One o'clock jump / Why not? / Out of nowhere / How high the moon / Hobnail boogie / Jumpin' at The Woodside / Blee blop blues / Basie blues / Every tub / You're not the kind / Paradise squat / Lullaby of Birdland.
Album: released on Duke in Jun'86 by Melodisc Records. Distributed by: Jazz Horizons, Jazz Music, Celtic Music, Swift

BIRDLAND ERA VOLUME 2, THE (Basie, Count Orchestra).
Album: released on Duke in May'83 by Melodisc Records. Distributed by: Jazz Horizons, Jazz Music, Celtic Music, Swift

BOSSES, THE (Basie, Count & Joe Turner).
Tracks: / Honeydripper / Honey hush / Cherry red / Night time is the right time / Blues around the clock / Since I fell for you / Flip, flop and fly / Wee baby blues / Good mornin' blues / Roll 'em Pete.

CHAPTER FIVE (Basie, Count Orchestra).
Album: released on Queen-Disc in Apr'81. Distributed by: Celtic Music, Jazz Horizons, Jazz Music

CHAPTER FOUR.
Album: released on Queen-Disc in Apr'81. Distributed by: Celtic Music, Jazz Horizons, Jazz Music

CHAPTER SIX (Basie, Count Orchestra).
Album: released on Queen-Disc in Apr'81. Distributed by: Celtic Music, Jazz Horizons, Jazz Music

CHAPTER THREE (Basie, Count Orchestra).
Album: released on Queen-Disc in Apr'81. Distributed by: Celtic Music, Jazz Horizons, Jazz Music

CHICAGO (Basie, Count & Tony Bennett).
Album: released on Astan in Nov'84 by Astan Records. Distributed by: Counterpoint

Cassette: released on Astan in Nov'84 by Astan Records. Distributed by: Counterpoint

COMPACT JAZZ.
Compact disc: released on Verve in Jul'87 by Phonogram Records. Distributed by: Polygram

COUNT BASIE.
Tracks: / Moten swing / Shout & feel it / Me and you that used to be, The / Count steps in, The / I'll always be in love with you / When my dreamboat comes home / Swing brother swing / Down for the double / Rockin' the blues / Wiggle woogie / Andy's blues / I've found a new baby / Basie boogie.
Album: released on Queendisc (Import) in Apr'81. Distributed by: Cadillac

Album: released on Phoenix in Oct'82 by Audio Fidelity Enterprises. Distributed by: Stage One,

COUNT BASIE, 1937 - 44.
Album: released on Joker Import in '81

COUNT BASIE AND THE KANSAS CITY SEVEN.
Tracks: / I'll always be in love with you / Snooky / Blues for Charlie Christian / Jaws / I'm confessin' that I love you / I want a little girl / Blues in C / Brio.
Compact disc: released on Impulse in Feb'87 by Impulse Records. Distributed by: MCA, Polygram

COUNT BASIE AND THE KANSAS CITY SEVEN (Basie, Count & The Kansas City Seven).
Album: released on Jasmine in Jun'82 by Jasmine Records. Distributed by: Counterpoint, Taylor, H.R., Wellard, Chris, Swift, Cadillac

Cassette: released on Jasmine in Jun'82 by Jasmine Records. Distributed by: Counterpoint, Taylor, H.R., Wellard, Chris, Swift, Cadillac

COUNT BASIE BIG BAND.
Tracks: / Heat's on, The / Freckle face / Splanky / More I see you, The / Night in Tunisia / Hittin' twelve / Bag of dreams / Things ain't what they used to be / I needs to be'd with / Li'l darlin' / Jumpin' at the Woodside / One o'clock jump.
Album: released on Pablo (USA) in May'82 by Pablo Records (USA). Distributed by: Wellard, Chris, IMS-Polygram, BMG

Cassette: released on Pablo (USA) in May'82 by Pablo Records (USA). Distributed by: Wellard, Chris, IMS-Polygram, BMG

COUNT BASIE BIG BAND + MILT JACKSON VOL 2-1978 (Basie, Count Big Band & Milt Jackson).
Notes: See under Jackson ,Milt + Count Basie & The Big Band

COUNT BASIE COLLECTION.
Album: released on Deja Vu in Aug'85 by Deja Vu Records. Distributed by: Counterpoint Distribution, Record Services Distribution (Ireland)

Cassette: released on Deja Vu in Aug'85 by Deja Vu Records. Distributed by: Counterpoint Distribution, Record Services Distribution (Ireland)

COUNT BASIE & HIS ORCHESTRA (Basie, Count & His Orchestra).
Album: released on Jazz Archives in Jul'86 by Jazz Archives Records. Distributed by: Jazz Music

COUNT BASIE JAM.
Tracks: / Bookie blues / She's funny that way / These foolish things / Kidney stew / Trio blues / I got it bad / Jumpin' at the Woodside.
Album: released on Pablo (USA) in May'82 by Pablo Records (USA). Distributed by: Wellard, Chris, IMS-Polygram, BMG

Cassette: released on Pablo (USA) in May'82 by Pablo Records (USA). Distributed by: Wellard, Chris, IMS-Polygram, BMG

COUNT BASIE/JOE WILLIAMS (Basie, Count & Joe Williams).
Double Album: released on Vogue Jazz (France) in May'83

COUNT BASIE ORCHESTRA.
Tracks: / Good morning blues / What comes up, must come down / Baby don't tell on me / Sub dab blues / Moonlight serenade / I can't believe that you're in love with me / Between the devil & the deep blue sea / Let's make hay while the moon shines / Blow top / Gone with 'what' wind / Do I mean you? / When the sun goes down / Royal flush / I got rhythm / How long blues / Farewell blues.
Album: released on Queen-Disc in Apr'81. Distributed by: Celtic Music, Jazz Horizons, Jazz Music

COUNT BASIE VOL.1.
Album: released on Jazz Reactivation in Jul'82. Distributed by: PRT

COUNT BASIE VOL.2.
Tracks: / Not now, i'll tell you when / Swingin' at the Waldorf / Quince / Vine Street rumble / Square at the Roundtable / Brotherly shove / Blue five jive / Rare butterfly / Jackson County Jubilee / Big walk.
Album: released on Jazz Reactivation in May'83. Distributed by: PRT

COUNT BASIE VOL.2 1937/8.
Album: released on Ajax (USA) in Apr'79. Distributed by: Swift

COUNT BASIE VOL.3 1938.
Album: released on Ajax (USA) in Apr'79. Distributed by: Swift

COUNT BASIE VOL 4 1938/9.
Album: released on Ajax (USA) in Apr'79. Distributed by: Swift

COUNT BASIE VOL.5 1939.
Album: released on Ajax (USA) in Apr'79. Distributed by: Swift

COUNT BASIE VOL.6 1939.
Album: released on Ajax (USA) in Apr'79. Distributed by: Swift

COUNT BASIE VOL.7 1939.
Album: released on Ajax (USA) in Apr'79. Distributed by: Swift

COUNT ON THE COAST.
Album: released on Phontastic (Sweden) in Jan'85 by Wellard, Chris Distribution. Distributed by: Wellard, Chris Distribution

COUNT ON THE COAST VOL. 3.
Album: released on Phontastic in Jan'87. Distributed by: Wellard, Chris

DECEMBER 1962 (Basie, Count & His Orchestra).
Tracks: / Just before midnight / Comin' through the rye / Sometimes I feel like a motherless child / Evil weevil / Basically blue / Splash / Danny boy / Wash / Clementine Annie Laurie / Swing low sweet chariot.
Album: released on Jazz Vault in Oct'80. Distributed by: Jazz Music, Taylor, H.R.

DOCUMENT.
Tracks: / Moten swing / One o'clock jump / I can't get started / Study in brown, A / Rhythm in nursery rhymes / John's idea / Good morning blues / Dinah / Every tub / Song of the wanderer / Flat foot floogie / Boogie woogie blues / One o'clock jump.
Album: released on Nostalgia (Sweden) in May'82 by Wellard, Chris Distribution. Distributed by: Wellard, Chris Distribution

DOWN FOR TROUBLE.
Tracks: / Something new / I struck a match in the dark / Platterbrains / All of me / Feather merchant / Down for double / Down for double / My old flame / Fiesta in blue / To Thumb.
Album: released on Showdown in Apr'86

Cassette: released on Showdown in Apr'86

ELLA & BASIE (Basie, Count & Ella Fitzgerald).
Album: released on Verve (USA) in Oct'84 by Polydor. Distributed by: Polygram

Cassette: released on Verve (USA) in Oct'84 by Polydor. Distributed by: Polygram

Album: released on Verve (USA) in Oct'84 by Polydor. Distributed by: Polygram

Cassette: released on Verve (USA) in Oct'84 by Polydor. Distributed by: Polygram

E= MC2.
Compact disc: . Distributed by: Discovery, Jazz Music, PRT, Swift

FANCY PANTS (Basie, Count & His Orchestra).
Album: released on Pablo (USA) in Dec'86 by Pablo Records (USA). Distributed by: Wellard, Chris, IMS-Polygram, BMG

Cassette: released on Pablo (USA) in Dec'86 by Pablo Records (USA). Distributed by: Wellard, Chris, IMS-Polygram, BMG

FANCY PANTS.
Compact disc: released on Pablo (USA) in Apr'87 by Pablo Records (USA). Distributed by: Wellard, Chris, IMS-Polygram, BMG

FARMERS MARKET BARBEQUE.
Tracks: / Way out Basie / St.Louis blues / Beaver Junction / Lester leaps in / Blues for the barbeque / I don't know yet / Ain't that something / Jumpin' at the Woodside.
Compact disc: released on Pablo Jazz (USA) in Apr'86 by United Artists. Distributed by: Swift

FIRST RECORDS HE EVER MADE, THE.
Album: released on Sandy Hook in Aug'79

Cassette: released on Sandy Hook in Aug'79

FIRST TIME WITH DUKE ELLINGTON.
Album: released on CBS(Import) in Jun'86 by

CBS Records. Distributed by: Conifer, Discovery, Swift

Cassette:

FOR THE FIRS'. TIME (Basie, Count Trio).
Album: released on Pablo Jazz (USA) in May'82 by United Artists. Distributed by: Swift

Cassette: released on Pablo Jazz (USA) in May'82 by United Artists. Distributed by: Swift

FOR THE FIRST TIME.
Tracks: / Baby Lawrence / Pres / I'll always be in love with you / Blues in the church / Lady be good / Lady be good (concept II) / Blues in the alley / As long as I live / Song of the island / Royal Garden blues / Un-easy does it / O.P.
Notes: Personnel: Count Basie- piano organ/Ray Brown- bass/Louis Bellson-drums.
Compact disc: released on Pablo Jazz (USA) in Apr'86 by United Artists. Distributed by: Swift

FOR THE SECOND TIME (Basie, Count /Kansas City 3).
Tracks: / Sandman / If I could be with you one hour tonight / Draw / On the sunny side of the street / One I love belongs to somebody else, The / Blues for Eric / I surrender dear / Race-horse.
Album: released on Pablo in Mar'83 by Pablo Records. Distributed by: Wellard, Chris, IMS-Polygram, BMG

Cassette: released on Pablo in Mar'83 by Pablo Records. Distributed by: Wellard, Chris, IMS-Polygram, BMG

GET TOGETHER.
Compact disc: released on Pablo (USA) in Apr'87 by Pablo Records (USA). Distributed by: Wellard, Chris, IMS-Polygram, BMG

GIFTED ONES, THE (Basie, Count & Dizzy Gillespie).
Tracks: / Back to the land / Constantinople / You got it / St James Infirmary / Follow the leader / Ow.

GOLDEN YEARS 1937-38, THE (Basie, Count & His Orchestra).
Notes: Featuring Lester Young
Album: released on Nostalgia in May'86. Distributed by: Jazz Music, Counterpoint

GREAT CONCERT OF COUNT BASIE & HIS ORCHESTRA, THE (Basie, Count & His Orchestra).
Tracks: / All of me / Flight of the foo birds / Boone blues / Stormy Monday blues / Magic flea, The / Wee baby blues / In a mellow town / Whirly bird / Night in Tunisia / Hittin' twelve / Cherokee / Midnight sun will never set, The / Blues for Eileen / Jumpin' at the woodside / April in Paris / I got rhythm / I need's to be deed with / Lil' darlin' / All heart / One o'clock jump.
Double Album: released on Music Disc (France) in Apr'84. Distributed by: IMS-Polygram Distribution

HAVE A NICE DAY.
Tracks: / Have a nice day / Plunger, The / Jamie / It's about time / This way / Scott's place / Doin' Basie's thing / Spirit is willing / Small talk / You'n'me / Feelin' free.
Notes: Personnel: Paul Cohen/George'Sonny' Cohn/George Minger/Waymond Reed/Al Grey/Bill Hughes/Grover Mitchell/Melvin Wanzo/John Watson Sr./Bobby'Jersey Boun-ce'Plater/Eric Dixon/Curtis Peagler/J.C.Williams/Eddie 'Lockjaw'Davis/Count William Basie/Freddie Green/Norman'Dewey'Keenan/Harold Jones.
Compact disc: released on Verve (USA) in Dec'85 by Polydor. Distributed by: Polygram

HIGH VOLTAGE.
Compact disc: released on Polydor in Aug'85 by Polydor Records. Distributed by: Polygram, Polydor

I GOT RHYTHM.
Album: released on Affinity in Jan'81 by Charly Records. Distributed by: Charly, Cadillac

IN DISCO ORDER VOL.1.
Album: released on Ajax in Feb'78

INDISPENSABLE COUNT BASIE, THE.
Tracks: / Bill's mill / Brand new wagon / One o'clock boogie / Futuile frustration / Swingin' the blues / St. Louis boogie / Basie's basement / Backstage at Stuff's / My buddy / Shine on harvest moon / Lopin' / I never knew / Sugar / Jungle king, The / I ain't mad at you / After you've gone / House rent boogie / South / Don't you want a man like me / Seventh Avenue express / Sophisticated swing / Guest in a nest / Your red wagon / Money is honey / Just a minute / Robbin's nest / Hey pretty baby / Bye bye baby / Just an old manuscript / She's a wine-o / Shoutin' blues / Wonderful thing / Mine too / Walking slow behind you / Normania / Rat race / Sweets.
Double Album: released on RCA (France) in '83 by RCA Records. Distributed by: Discovery

I TOLD YOU SO (Basie, Count & His Orchestra).
Album: released on Pablo (USA) in May'82 by Pablo Records (USA). Distributed by: Wellard, Chris, IMS-Polygram, BMG

Cassette: released on Pablo (USA) in May'82 by Pablo Records (USA). Distributed by: Wellard, Chris, IMS-Polygram, BMG

I TOLD YOU SO.
Tracks: / Tree frog / Flirt / Blues for Alfy / Something to live for / Plain brown wrapper / Swee' pea / Too close for comfort / Told you so / Git, The.
Compact disc: released on Pablo (USA) in Jul'86 by Pablo Records (USA). Distributed by: Wellard, Chris, IMS-Polygram, BMG

JITTERS - 1939/41, (THE).
Album: released on Tax in Mar'77. Distributed by: Jazz Music Distribution, Swift

KANSAS CITY 5.
Tracks: / Jive at five / One o'clock jump / No special thing / Memories of you / Frog's blues / Rabbit / Perdido / Timekeeper / Mean to me / Blues for Joe Turner.
Album: released on Pablo (USA) in May'82 by Pablo Records (USA). Distributed by: Wellard, Chris, IMS-Polygram, BMG

Cassette: released on Pablo (USA) in May'82 by Pablo Records (USA). Distributed by: Wellard, Chris, IMS-Polygram, BMG

KANSAS CITY 6.
Tracks: / Walking the blues / Blues for little jazz / Vegas drag / Wee baby / Scooter / St. Louis blues / Opus six.
Album: released on Pablo in Sep'82 by Pablo Records. Distributed by: Wellard, Chris, IMS-Polygram, BMG

Cassette: released on Pablo in Sep'82 by Pablo Records. Distributed by: Wellard, Chris, IMS-Polygram, BMG

KANSAS CITY 7.
Tracks: / Oh, lady,be good / Secrets / I want a little girl / Shoe shine boy / Count's place / Senator Whitehead / Tally-ho Mr. Basie! / What'cha talkin'?.
Compact disc: by Pablo Records. Distributed by: Wellard, Chris, IMS-Polygram, BMG

Album: released on Pablo (USA) in Dec'84 by Pablo Records (USA). Distributed by: Wellard, Chris, IMS-Polygram, BMG

Cassette: released on Pablo (USA) in Dec'84 by Pablo Records (USA). Distributed by: Wellard, Chris, IMS-Polygram, BMG

KANSAS CITY 8 Get together.
Tracks: / Ode to Pres / Basie's bag / Swinging on the cusp / Like it used to be / My main men / Pretty time / I can't get started / What will I tell my heart / Talk of the town / I can't give you anything but love / I'm confessing that I love you.
Album: released on Pablo (USA) in Jan'87 by Pablo Records (USA). Distributed by: Wellard, Chris, IMS-Polygram, BMG

KANSAS CITY SHOUT (Basie, Count, Joe Turner, Eddie Vinson).
Tracks: / My jug & I / Cherry red / Apollo daze / Standing on the corner / Stormy Monday / Signifying / Just a dream on my mind / Blues for Joe Turner / Blues for Joel / Every day I have the blues / Blues au four.
Album: released on Pablo in '82 by Pablo Records. Distributed by: Wellard, Chris, IMS-Polygram, BMG

Cassette: released on Pablo in '82 by Pablo Records. Distributed by: Wellard, Chris, IMS-Polygram, BMG

KANSAS CITY STYLE.
Album: released on Giants of Jazz in Jun'86 by Hasmick Promotions Ltd.. Distributed by: Counterpoint, Jazz Music, Taylors, Swift, Mainline, Wellard, Chris

KANSAS CITY SUITE.
Compact disc: released on Vogue in '86. Distributed by: Discovery, Jazz Music, PRT, Swift

LAST DECADE, THE.
Double Album: released on Artistry in Sep'86. Distributed by: Jazz Music

LESTER VISITS BASIE VOL.2 Air Shots Birdland,Jan. 1953 (Basie, Count Orchestra).
Tracks: / Basie English / Basie blues / Paradise squat / Every tub.
Notes: Personnel: Trumpets: W.Culley,R.Jones,J.Newman,P.Campbell/Alto sax: H.Coker,B.Powell,J.Wilkins,M.Royal,E.Wilkins/ Tenor sax: P.Quinchette,Eddie 'Lockjaw'Davis,Lester Young/ Baritone sax: C.Fowlkes/ Guitar: F.Greene/ Bass: G.Ramsey/ Piano: Count Basie/ Drums: G.Johnson.
Album: released on Unique Jazz in Apr'81. Distributed by: Swift, Jazz Music, Jazz Horizons

LESTER VISITS BASIE Air Shots Birdland,Jan. 1953 (Basie, Count Orchestra).
Tracks: / Theme & prevue / Jingle bells / Why not? / Hob nail boogie / Perdido / Fancy meeting you / Basie kicks / Jumpin' at the Woodside / Bread / Smooth sailing.
Notes: Trumpets: W.Culley/R.Jones/P.Campbell/J.Newman/ Trombones: H.Coker/B.Powell/J.Wilkins/ Alto sax: M.Royal/E.Wilkins/ Tenor sax: P.Quinchette/Eddie'Lockjaw'Davis/Lester Young/ Baritone sax: C.Fowlkes/ Guitar: F.Greene/ Bass: G.Ramsey/Piano: Count Basie/ Drums: G.Johnson.
Album: released on Unique Jazz in Apr'81. Distributed by: Swift, Jazz Music, Jazz Horizons

LET'S JUMP - 1943/44 (Basie, Count & His Orchestra).
Album: released on Golden Era in Jul'82 by Import Records. Distributed by: Wellard, Chris, Swift

LIL' OL' GROOVEMASTER.
Tracks: / Pleasingly plump / Body rumble / Belly roll / Count 'em / Nasty Magnus / Dum dum / Lullaby for Jolie / Kansa City wrinkles / Li'l ol' groovemaker...Basie.
Compact disc: released on Verve in Sep'86 by Phonogram Records. Distributed by: Polygram

LIVE AT MONTREUX '77 (Basie Big Band).
Compact disc: by Pablo Records (USA). Distributed by: Wellard, Chris, IMS-Polygram, BMG

LIVE AT THE SAVOY BALLROOM.
Album: released on Astan in Nov'84 by Astan Records. Distributed by: Counterpoint

Cassette: released on Astan in Nov'84 by Astan Records. Distributed by: Counterpoint

LIVE FROM BIRDLAND.
Album: released on Vogue in May'80. Distributed by: Discovery, Jazz Music, PRT, Swift

LIVE IN JAPAN '78.
Tracks: / Heat's on ,The / Freckle face / Ja-da / Things ain't what they used to be / Bit of this & a bit of that, A / All of me / Shiny stockings / Left hand funk / John the III / Basie / Black velvet / Jumpin' at the Woodside.
Notes: Personnel: Count Basie/Waymon Reed/Pete Minger/Sonny Cohns/Noran Smith Jr/Mel Wanzo/Bill Hughes/ Dennis Wilson/Alonzo Wesley Jnr./Bobby Plater/ Danny Turner/Kenny Hing/Eric Dixon/Charlie Fowlkes/Freddie Greene/ John Clayton/Butch Miles. A well balanced programme from the basie book,with contributions from side man Frank Foster-'Shiny stockings',Ernie Wilkins' Basie' & sam Nestico who wrote prolifically for the Basie Band.As well as these there are favourites like 'Jumpin' at the Woodside' & 'All of me' which was often used to spotlight singer Joe Williams.We expect good reviews for this previously unreleased album.

LIVE IN JAPAN 78.
Compact disc: released on Pablo (USA) in Jul'86 by Pablo Records (USA). Distributed by: Wellard, Chris, IMS-Polygram, BMG

Album: released on Pablo (USA) in Sep'85 by Pablo Records (USA). Distributed by: Wellard, Chris, IMS-Polygram, BMG

Cassette: released on Pablo (USA) in Sep'85 by Pablo Records (USA). Distributed by: Wellard, Chris, IMS-Polygram, BMG

LIVE IN PERSON (Basie, Count Orchestra).
Album: released on Natural Organic (USA) in '79. Distributed by: Jazz Horizons, JSU, Swift

LONG LIVE THE CHIEF (Basie, Count & His Orchestra).
Tracks: / You got it / April in Paris / Misunderstood Blues / Autumn leaves / Foggy day / Hey! See you over there / Lil' darlin' / Bus dust / Corner pocket / Dr. Feelgood / Four five six / Shiny stockings.
Notes: Hayden Labs. Tel.: 0753 888447. Hayden Labs. Tel: 0753 888447.
Compact disc: released on Denon in Jan'87 by Denon Records. Distributed by: Harmonia Mundi

MASTERS OF JAZZ.
Album: released on RCA (Germany) in '83

ME AND YOU.
Compact disc: released on Pablo (USA) in May'86 by Pablo Records (USA). Distributed by: Wellard, Chris, IMS-Polygram, BMG

MEMORIAL.
Album: released on First Heard in '84 by Submarine Records. Distributed by: Conifer, Taylors

Cassette: released on First Heard in Oct'84 by Submarine Records. Distributed by: Conifer, Taylors

MONTREUX 77 (Basie, Count Big Band).
Compact disc: released on Pablo (USA) in May'86 by Pablo Records (USA). Distributed by: Wellard, Chris, IMS-Polygram, BMG

MOSTLY BLUES AND SOME OTHERS (Basie, Count Kansas City Seven).
Tracks: / I'll always be in love with you / Snooky / Blues for Charlie Christian / Jaws / I'm confessing that I love you / I want a little girl / Blues in C / Brio.
Compact disc: released on Pablo (USA) in Feb'87 by Pablo Records (USA). Distributed by: Wellard, Chris, IMS-Polygram, BMG

Cassette: released on Pablo (USA) in Jul'86 by Pablo Records (USA). Distributed by: Wellard, Chris, IMS-Polygram, BMG

Album: released on Pablo (USA) in Jul'86 by Pablo Records (USA). Distributed by: Wellard, Chris, IMS-Polygram, BMG

MOTEN SWING (Basie, Count Orchestra).
Tracks: / Moten swing / Bugle call rag / Lady be good / Darn that dream / Sent for you yesterday & here you come today / I'm gonna sit right down & write myself a letter / Jumpin' at the Woodside / 9.20 Special / Avenue C / Blue Lou / One o'clock jump.
Album: released on Joker in Apr'81. Distributed by: Counterpoint, Mainline, Record Services Distribution (Ireland)

NIGHT RIDER (Basie, Count & Oscar Peterson).
Tracks: / Night rider / Memories of you / 9.20 Special / Sweet Lorraine / It's a wonderful world / Blues for Pamela.
Album: released on Pablo (USA) in '82 by Pablo Records (USA). Distributed by: Wellard, Chris, IMS-Polygram, BMG

Cassette: released on Pablo (USA) in '82 by Pablo Records (USA). Distributed by: Wellard, Chris, IMS-Polygram, BMG

ONE O'CLOCK JUMP.
Album: released on Black Lion-Intercord in '82

Cassette: released on Black Lion-Intercord in '82

ONE O'CLOCK JUMP.
Tracks: / One o'clock jump / When my dream-boat comes home / I got rhythm in my nursery rhymes / John's idea / Good morning blues / Dinah / Shout & fell about / I'll always be in love with you / Count steps in, The / I got rhythm / Study in brown, A / Bugle blues.
Notes: Personnel: Buck Clayton/Eddie Durham/Earle warren/Lester Young/Freddie greene/Walter Page/Jo Jones. Recorded 1939.
Cassette: released on Astan in Jun'86 by Astan Records. Distributed by: Counterpoint

ON THE ROAD.
Tracks: / Wind machine / Blues for Stephanie / John the III / There'll never be another you / Bootie's blues / Splanky / Basie / Whatch what happens / Work song / In a mellow tone.
Compact disc: by Pablo Records (USA). Distributed by: Wellard, Chris, IMS-Polygram, BMG

Album: released on Pablo (USA) in '82 by Pablo Records (USA). Distributed by: Wellard, Chris, IMS-Polygram, BMG

Cassette: released on Pablo (USA) in '82 by Pablo Records (USA). Distributed by: Wellard, Chris, IMS-Polygram BMG

ON THE ROAD 79.
Compact disc: released on Pablo (USA) in May'86 by Pablo Records (USA). Distributed by: Wellard, Chris, IMS-Polygram, BMG

PERFECT MATCH, A (Basie, Count & Ella Fitzgerald).
Notes: See also under Fitzgerald, Ella & Count Basie
Compact disc: by Pablo Records. Distributed by: Wellard, Chris, IMS-Polygram, BMG

Album: released on Pablo (USA) in May'82 by Pablo Records (USA). Distributed by: Wellard, Chris, IMS-Polygram, BMG

Cassette: released on Pablo (USA) in May'82 by Pablo Records (USA). Distributed by: Wellard, Chris, IMS-Polygram, BMG

PLAYS BENNY CARTER'S KANSAS CITY SUITE.
Tracks: / Vine Street rumble / Katy-do / Miss Missouri / Jackson County Jubilee / Sunset glow / Wiggle walk / Meetin' time / Paseo promenade / Blue five jive / Rompin' at the Reno / Trot, The / Easy money / Amoroso / Goin' on / Swizzle / Legend, The / Who's blues / Turnabout.
Album: released on Vogue Jazz (France) in May'83

Cassette: released on Vogue Jazz (France) in May'83

PLAYS QUINCY JONES & NEAL HEFTI.
Compact disc: released on Vogue in Dec'86. Distributed by: Discovery, Jazz Music, PRT, Swift

PLAYS QUINCY JONES & NEAL HEFTI.
Album: released on Vogue in '78. Distributed by: Discovery, Jazz Music, PRT, Swift

PRIME TIME.
Tracks: / Prime time / Bundle o'funk / Sweet Georgia Brown / Featherweight / Reachin' out / Ja-da / Great debate, The / Ya gotta try.
Compact disc: released on Pablo (USA) in Jul'86 by Pablo Records (USA). Distributed by: Wellard, Chris, IMS-Polygram, BMG

PRIME TIME (Basie, Count & His Orchestra).
Album: released on Pablo (USA) in '82 by Pablo Records (USA). Distributed by: Wellard, Chris, IMS-Polygram, BMG

Cassette: released on Pablo (USA) in '82 by Pablo Records (USA). Distributed by: Wellard, Chris, IMS-Polygram, BMG

RHYTHM MEN.
Album: released on Swinghouse in '84. Dis-

tributed by: Jazz Music Distribution, Swift Distribution, Chris Wellard Distribution

Cassette: released on Swinghouse in '84. Distributed by: Jazz Music Distribution, Swift Distribution, Chris Wellard Distribution

ROCK-A-BYE BASIE.
Tracks: / Jumping at the Woodside / Blue & sentimental / Red Bank boogie / Sent for you / Yesterday / Shorty George / Rock-a-bye Basie / Every tub / Jive at five / Down for trouble / Boogie woogie / Taps Miller / Swinging the blues / Broadway / Texas shuffle / Tickle toe / Doggin' around / Dickie's dream / Topsy / Lester leaps in / Time out / 9.20 Special / Avenue C / Out the window.
Album: released on Vogue Jazz (USA) in Jun'83

SATCH AND JOSH (Basie, Count & Oscar Peterson).
Album: released on Pablo (USA) in '82 by Pablo Records (USA). Distributed by: Wellard, Chris, IMS-Polygram, BMG

Cassette: released on Pablo (USA) in '82 by Pablo Records (USA). Distributed by: Wellard, Chris, IMS-Polygram, BMG

Album: released on Pablo (USA) in '82 by Pablo Records (USA). Distributed by: Wellard, Chris, IMS-Polygram, BMG

SEND IN THE CLOWNS (Basie, Count & Sarah Vaughan).
Album: released on Pablo (USA) in '82 by Pablo Records (USA). Distributed by: Wellard, Chris, IMS-Polygram, BMG

Cassette: released on Pablo (USA) in '82 by Pablo Records (USA). Distributed by: Wellard, Chris, IMS-Polygram, BMG

SING ALONG WITH BASIE.
Compact disc: released on Vogue in Dec'86. Distributed by: Discovery, Jazz Music, PRT, Swift

SOUTHLAND CAFE (Basie, Count Orchestra & Chick Webb Orchestra).
Tracks: / One o'clock jump / Ebony rhapsody / Riff interlude / Take it Prez / Baby don't you tell on me / Breakin' 'em down / If I didn't care / Stars & stripes forever / My wild Irish rose / Chew,chew,chew,chew (your bubble gum).
Album: released on Joker in Apr'81. Distributed by: Counterpoint, Mainline, Record Services Distribution (Ireland)

STANDING OVATION - THREE ERAS OF BASIE.
Tracks: / Down for trouble / Li'l darlin' / Broadway / Jive at five / Cherry Point / Jumpin' at the Woodside / One o'clock jump / Shiny stockings / Blue & sentimental / Every tub / Corner pocket / Kid from Red Bank, The / One o'clock jump.
Album: released on Jasmine in Jun'82 by Jasmine Records. Distributed by: Counterpoint, Lugtons, Taylor, H.R., Wellard, Chris, Swift, Cadillac

Cassette: released on Jasmine in Jun'82 by Jasmine Records. Distributed by: Counterpoint, Lugtons, Taylor, H.R., Wellard, Chris, Swift, Cadillac

STEREO SOUND OF COUNT BASIE, (THE).
Album: released on Orange (US) in Apr'79

SWINGIN' AT THE DAISY CHAIN.
Tracks: / Swingin' at the Daisy Chain / Glory of love, The / My heart belongs to daddy / Cherokee / How long,how long blues / Dirty dozens,The / Honeysuckle rose / Thursday / One o'clock jump / Sing for your supper / Your red wagon / Smarty(you know it all) / Dark rapture / Dupree blues / When the sun goes down / Roseland shuffle.
Album: released on Affinity in '86 by Charly Records. Distributed by: Charly, Cadillac

SWINGING THE BLUES.
Album: released on Swaggie (Australia) in Jan'83

SWINGIN' THE BLUES.
Tracks: / Swingin' the blues / John's idea / Blue & sentimental / Texas shuffle / Panassie stomp / Sent for you yesterday / You can depend on me / Every tub / Jumpin' at the Woodside / Time out / Jive at five / Oh, lady be good / Shorty George / Out of the window / Topsy / Doggin' around.
Album: released on Affinity in Sep'83 by Charly Records. Distributed by: Charly, Cadillac

THIS AND THAT.
Tracks: / Basie boogie / Sent for you yesterday / Gotta be this or that / An old manuscript / Just sittin' & rockin' / Andy's blues / I ain't mad about you / My silent love / Lady be good / Theme / Move / One o'clock jump / One golden bullet,(Theme from) / Basie boogie, The / Sent for you yesterday / Gotta be this or that / Old manuscript, An / Just a sittin' and rockin' / Andy's blues / I ain't mad at you / My silent love / Lady be good / Theme / Move / One O'clock jump / One golden bullet, Theme from.
Album: released on Swinghouse in Jul'86. Distributed by: Jazz Music Distribution, Swift Distribution, Chris Wellard Distribution

Cassette: released on Swinghouse in Jul'86. Distributed by: Jazz Music Distribution, Swift Distribution, Chris Wellard Distribution

Single (7"): released on Limelight in Oct'80

V DISCS VOL. 2.
Album: released on Jazz Society in Mar'87. Distributed by: Jazz Music, Swift

VERY BEST OF COUNT BASIE, THE.
Tracks: / St. Louis blues / Can't buy me love / Basie love / Dee Dee / Long night, The / Belly roll / Nasty Magnus / Help / Do you want to know a secret / Frankie and Johnny / I'm walking / Oh, lonesome me.
Album: released on Swinghouse in May'86. Distributed by: Jazz Music Distribution, Swift Distribution, Chris Wellard Distribution

Cassette: released on Swinghouse in May'86. Distributed by: Jazz Music Distribution, Swift Distribution, Chris Wellard Distribution

VOICES.
Compact disc: released on Vogue in Dec'86. Distributed by: Discovery, Jazz Music, PRT, Swift

VOLUME 5.
Double Album: released on CBS in Sep'86 by CBS Records. Distributed by: CBS

Cassette: released on CBS in Sep'86 by CBS Records. Distributed by: CBS

VOLUME 6.
Double Album: released on CBS in Sep'86 by CBS Records. Distributed by: CBS

Cassette: released on CBS in Sep'86 by CBS Records. Distributed by: CBS

VOLUME III-DON FOR PREZ.
Tracks: / World is mad (ptl),The / World is mad (pt2),The / Moten swing / It's torture / I want a little girl / All or nothing at all / Moon fell in the river, The / What's your number / Draftin' blues / Five o'clock whistle / Love jumped out / My wandering man / Broadway / It's the same old south / Stampede in G minor / Who am I? / Rockin' the blues / It's square but it rocks / I'll forget / I'll forget-2 / You lied to me / Wiggle woogie / Beau Brummel / Music makers / Jump the blues away / Jump the blues away / Deep in the blues / Jitters / Tuesday at ten / Undecided blues / I do mean you / 9.20 Special / H & J feeding the bean.
Double Album: released on CBS in Jul'86 by CBS Records. Distributed by: CBS

Cassette: released on CBS in Jul'86 by CBS Records. Distributed by: CBS

VOLUME II-LESTER LEAPS IN.
Tracks: / Moonlight serenade / Song of the islands / I can't believe that you're in love with me / Clap hands here comes Charlie / Dickie's dream / Lester leaps in / Apple jump, The / I left my baby / Riff interlude / Volcano / Between the devil & the deep blue sea / Ham'n'eggs / Hollywood jump / Someday sweetheart / I never knew / Tickle -toe / Let's make hay while the sun shines / Louisiana / Easy does it / Let me see / Blues (still think of her) / Somebody stole my girl / Blow top / Gone with what wind / Super chief / You can't run around / Evenin'.
Double Album: released on CBS in Jul'86 by CBS Records. Distributed by: CBS

Cassette: released on CBS in Jul'86 by CBS Records. Distributed by: CBS

VOLUME I-THE COUNT & THE PRESIDENT.
Tracks: / Shoe shine boy / Evenin' / Boogie woogie / Oh,lady be good / I ain't got nobody / Going to Chicago / Live & love tonight / love me or leave me / What goes up must come down / Rock-a-bye Basie / Baby you don't tell on me / If I could be with you / One house tonight / Taxi war dance / Don't worry about me / Jump for me / And the angels sing / If I didn't care / Twelth street rag / Miss thing(ptl) / Miss thing(pt2) / Lonesome & pretty / Bolero at the Savoy / Nobody knows / Pound cake / You can count on me / You can count on me / You & your love / How long blues / Sub-deb blues.
Double Album: released on CBS in Jul'86 by CBS Records. Distributed by: CBS

Cassette: released on CBS in Jul'86 by CBS Records. Distributed by: CBS

VOLUME IV-ONE O'CLOCK JUMP.
Tracks: / Going to Chicago blues / You betcha my life / Down down down / Tune town shuffle / I'm tired of waiting for you / One-two-three O'Lairy / Basie boogie / Fancy meeting you / Diggin' for Dex / My old flame / Fiesta in blue / Tom Thumb / Take me back baby / King Joe (pt.l) / King Joe (pt.2) / Moon nocturne / Something new / I struck a match / In the dark / Platterbrains / All of me / Feather merchant / Down for double / More than you know / Harvard blues / Coming out party / One o'clock jump / Blue shadows & white gardenias / Ay now / Basie blues.
Double Album: released on CBS in Jul'86 by CBS Records. Distributed by: CBS

Cassette: released on CBS in Jul'86 by CBS Records. Distributed by: CBS

WALKMAN JAZZ.
Cassette: released on Polydor in Jun'87 by Polydor Records. Distributed by: Polygram, Polydor

WARM BREEZE.
Tracks: / C.B. express / After the rain / Warm breeze / Cookie / Flight to Nassau / How sweet it is / Satin doll.
Compact disc: released on Pablo (USA) in May'86 by Pablo Records (USA). Distributed by: Wellard, Chris, IMS-Polygram, BMG

Album: released on Pablo in '82 by Pablo Records. Distributed by: Wellard, Chris, IMS-Polygram, BMG

Cassette: released on Pablo in '82 by Pablo Records. Distributed by: Wellard, Chris, IMS-Polygram, BMG

YESSIR THAT'S MY BABY (Basie, Count & Oscar Peterson).
Notes: See also under Oscar Peterson.

Basil, Toni

Biographical Details: When Toni Basil hit with "Mickey" in 1982, she was heavily made up to look like a new up-and -coming star. Her publicists did not seem particularly keen to point out that she cut her first record in 1966. In the intervening years she spent her time as a successful dancer and choreographer. She appeared as a dancer in the 1968 Monkees' movie "Head" and then, having taken small acting parts in "Easy Rider" and "Five Easy Pieces", choreographed and appeared in the 1973 film "American Graffiti". Basil subsequently worked wtih David Bowie and Bette Midler. Always primarily interested in the visual side of the entertainment business, she became involved in the video boom of the early Eighties. The return to singing came about while making a videocassette called "Word Of Mouth" - this featured Basil performing a Nicky Chinn/Mike Chapman song called "Mickey". The track was released as a single in the spring of '81 without success. Then the BBC showed "Word Of Mouth" on television, the record was repromoted, and went to No.2 almost a year after its original issue. However, Basil was not cut out for recording stardom. Although the "Word Of Mouth" album sold well, reaching No 15 on the LP chart, the next single "Nobody" could climb no higher than No. 52. Months later, in December '82, "Mickey" hit No.1 in the US. But Toni Basil could not follow it up in her native America, any more than she could in Britain. (BM 1984)

MICKEY.
Single (7"): released on Radial Choice in Jan'82

TONI BASIL.
Album: released on Virgin in Apr'84 by Virgin Records. Distributed by: EMI, Virgin Distribution

Cassette: released on Virgin in Apr'84 by Virgin Records. Distributed by: EMI, Virgin Distribution Deleted '85.

WORD OF MOUTH.
Album: released on Radial Choice in May'81

Cassette: released on Radial Choice in May'81

Basking Sharks

DIAMOND AGE.
Single (7"): released on Fin in Dec'83 by Posh Records. Distributed by: Pinnacle

THRILL OF THE GAME (EP).
Single (7"): released on Small Run in Mar'83 by Small Run Records. Distributed by: Pinnacle

Basque Country

BASQUE COUNTRY 1:Biaritz & Pampona (Various Artists).
Cassette: released on Folktracks in Nov'79 by Folktracks Cassettes. Distributed by: Folktracks

Basque Songs & Dances

BASQUE SONGS & DANCES Various artists (Various Artists).
Album: released on Lyrichord (USA) in Oct'81 by Lyrichord Records (USA). Distributed by: Flexitron Distributors Ltd

Bassey, Shirley

21 HIT SINGLES.
Tracks: / I(who have nothing) / As long as he needs me / My special dream / Kiss me honey honey kiss me / Tonight / Banana boat song / With these hands / What now my love / Climb every mountain / as I love you / I'll get by(as long as I have you) / Gone / Fire down below / No regrets / Ave Maria / You'll never know / Far away / Goldfinger / Wat kind of fool am I / Reach for the stars / You you Romeo.
Album: released on EMI in Jan'79 by EMI Records. Distributed by: EMI

Cassette: released on EMI in Jan'83 by EMI Records. Distributed by: EMI

25TH ANNIVERSARY ALBUM.
Tracks: / Fire down below / As I love you / Banana boat song / You you Romeo / Kiss me honey honey kiss me / With these hands / As long as he needs me / Reach for the stars / You'll never know / I'll get by (as long as I have you) / Climb every mountain / Far away / Ave Maria / What now my love / Tonight / What kind of fool am I / I (who have nothing) / My special dream / Gone / Goldfinger / No regrets / Big spender / Does anybody miss me / This is my life / Something / Fool on the hill, The / Diamonds are forever / Where do I begin / For all we know / And I love you so / Make the world a little younger / Never never never / Nobody does it like me / Send in the clowns / Emotion / Good bad but beautiful / Way we were, The / What I did for love / Feelings / If I never sing another song.
Double Album: released on United Artists in '78 Deleted '85.

Cassette: released on United Artists in '78

ALL BY MYSELF.
Tracks: / All by myself / This masquerade / If & when / He's out of my life / New York state of mind / Can you read my mind / Only when I laugh / Solitaire / New York medley / We don't cry out loud.
Compact disc: released on Vogue (France) in Jun'84. Distributed by: Discovery, Jazz Music, PRT, Swift

ALL BY MYSELF (SINGLE).
Single (7"): released on Applause in Mar'82 by Riva Records. Distributed by: WEA, Discovery

AS I LOVE YOU.
Album: released on Philips in Nov'84. Distributed by: IMS-Polygram

Cassette: released on Philips in Nov'84. Distributed by: IMS-Polygram

AS LONG AS HE NEEDS ME.
Tracks: / As long as he needs me(from 'Oliver') / What now my love / In the still of the night / Moon river / Come back to me / Who can I turn to / With these hands / Tonight / Somewhere / Let there be love / What kind of fool am I / I'll get by (as long as I have you) / I who have nothing / You'll never know / Goldfinger / All of me / I get a kick out of you / He loves me / You'll never walk alone / People / Don't rain on my parade / Ev'ry time we say goodbye.
Cassette: released on Ideal(Tapes) in Apr'80. Distributed by: EMI

AS TIME GOES BY.
Tracks: / Big spender / It must be him / As time goes by / I'll never fall in love again / If you go away / Funny girl / On a clear day you can see forever / Look of love, The / It's impossible / Bridge over troubled water / My way / Impossible dream, The / Hold me thrill me kiss me / You made me love you / Time after time / Softly as I leave you / For all we know / Breakfast in bed / One less bell to answer / That's life.
Album: released on Music For Pleasure in Oct'80 by EMI Records. Distributed by: EMI

Cassette: released on Music For Pleasure in Oct'80 by EMI Records. Distributed by: EMI

EMOTIONS.
Album: released on Platinum (W.Germany) in Oct'85. Distributed by: Mainline

Cassette: released on Platinum (W.Germany) in Oct'85. Distributed by: Mainline

FABULOUS SHIRLEY BASSEY, (THE).
Tracks: / Foggy day in London town, A / I've got you under my skin / Cry me a river / April in Paris / I've never been in love before / Man that got away, The / She's wonderful / I'll remember april / Easy to love / No one ever tells you / They can't take that away from me / Party's over, The.
Album: released on Capitol(USA) in Mar'84 by Capitol (USA) Records. Distributed by: EMI

GOLDEN HITS: SHIRLEY BASSEY.
Tracks: / Who can I turn to / As long as he needs me / Goldfinger / I (Who have nothing) / You'll never know / What now my love / What kind of fool am I / Once in a lifetime / Climb every mountain / Till / Reach for the stars / Party's over, The / With these hands / No regrets.
Cassette: released on Columbia in '68 by EMI Records. Distributed by: EMI

GOOD BAD BUT BEAUTIFUL.
Tracks: / Emotion / Send in the clowns / Good bad but beautiful / Sing / Way we were, The / I'll be your audience / Feel like making love / All in love is fair / Run on and on and on / Other side of me, The / Jesse / Living.
Album: released on United Artists in Oct'75 Deleted '80.

Cassette: released on United Artists in Oct'75

I AM WHAT I AM.
Tracks: / Gold finger / I who have nothing / As long as he needs me / Big spender / Something / For all we know / Send in the clowns / What know my love.

I AM WHAT I AM.
Single (7"): released on Towerbell in Nov'84 by Towerbell Records. Distributed by: EMI

Notes: Digitally recorded with the London Symphony Orchestra conducted by Carl Davis
Album: released on Towerbell in Oct'84 by Towerbell Records. Distributed by: EMI

Cassette: released on Towerbell in Oct'84 by Towerbell Records. Distributed by: EMI

I AM WHAT I AM.
Tracks: / Something / As long as he needs me / Big spender / Goldfinger / I (who have nothing) / And I love you so / This is my life.
Notes: Greatest hits including -

Page 82

Compact disc: released on Ariola in Apr'87. Distributed by: RCA, Ariola

I'M IN THE MOOD FOR LOVE.
Tracks: / What now my love / Moon river / Fools rush in / No regrets / I wish you love / Liquidator, The / Nearness of you, The / This love of mine / Where are you / If love were all / There will never be another you / Days of wine and roses, The / People / Second time around, The / Tonight / Strange how love can be / I'm in the mood for love / I get a kick out of you / Angel eyes / To be loved by a man / Hold me tight / I believe in you / Let's start all over again / I'm a fool to want you.
Double Album: released on Music For Pleasure in Oct'81 by EMI Records. Distributed by: EMI

Double cassette: released on Music For Pleasure in Oct'81 by EMI Records. Distributed by: EMI

I'VE GOT YOU UNDER MY SKIN.
Picture disc album: released on Astan in Dec'85 by Astan Records. Distributed by: Counterpoint

LIVE-YOU AIN'T HEARD NOTHING YET.
Video-cassette (VHS): released on Video Gems in Aug'86

LOVE SONGS.
Tracks: / All by myself / This masquerade / If Hand when / He's out of my life / New York state of mind / Can you read my mind / Only when I laugh / Solitare / New York medley / We don't cry out loud.
Album: released on Applause in Jun'82 by Riva Records. Distributed by: WEA, Discovery

Cassette: released on Applause in Jun'82 by Riva Records. Distributed by: WEA, Discovery

MEMORY.
Single (12"): released on Meteor in Nov'84 by Magnum Music Group Ltd. Distributed by: Magnum Music Group Ltd, PRT Distribution, Spartan Distribution

MOTIVE SERIES.
Tracks: / Banana boat song / Kiss me honey / As I love you.
Notes: Mid price compilation includes Shirley Bassey's first three top 10 hits aswell as others
Album: released on Philips (Germany) in Jul'82

Cassette: released on Philips (Germany) in Jul'82

Album: released on Philips (Germany) in Jul'82

Cassette: released on Philips (Germany) in Jul'82

NATALIE.
Single (7"): released on Towerbell in Oct'84 by Towerbell Records. Distributed by: EMI

NEW YORK, NEW YORK.
Compact disc: by President Records. Distributed by: Taylors, Spartan

PLAYING SOLITAIRE.
Album: released on President in Mar'85 by President Records. Distributed by: Taylors, Spartan

Cassette: released on President in Mar'85 by President Records. Distributed by: Taylors, Spartan

SHIRLEY BASSEY.
Tracks: / Let me sing and I'm happy / And I love you so / You're gonna hear from me / Strangers in the night / Where do I begin (love story) / Way a woman loves, The / Without you / Light of my life / Sound of music, The / I've never been a woman before / Baby I'm a want you / Killing me softly with his song / Yesterday I heard the rain / And we were lovers / You are the sunshine of my life / Spinning wheel.
Album: released on Hallmark in Feb'82 by Pickwick Records. Distributed by: Pickwick Distribution, PRT, Taylors

Cassette: released on Hallmark in Feb'82 by Pickwick Records. Distributed by: Pickwick Distribution, PRT, Taylors

SHIRLEY BASSEY SINGLES ALBUM, (THE).
Tracks: / Something theme (Where do I begin) / Diamonds are forever / Fool on the hill, The / Make the world a little younger / Big spender / Never never never / When you smile / If you go away / And I love you so / Does anybody miss me / For all we know.
Album: released on United Artists in Feb'75

Cassette: released on United Artists in Feb'75

Cassette: released on MFP in Sep'85 by EMI Records. Distributed by: EMI

Album: released on MFP in Sep'85 by EMI Records. Distributed by: EMI

SHIRLEY BASSEY - SOLITAIRE.
Tracks: / All by myself / This masquerade / If and when / He's out of my life / New York state of mind / Can you read my mind / Only when I laugh / Solitaire / New York Medley-New York New York / New York Medley-New York New York 2 / We don't cry out loud.

Notes: Licensed from San Juan Music Group USA. (P) & (C) 1987 K-Tel International (UK) Ltd.
Compact disc: released on K-Tel in Jun'87 by K-Tel Records. Distributed by: Record Merchandisers Distribution, Taylors, Terry Blood Distribution, Wynd-Up Distribution, Relay Distribution, Pickwick Distribution, Solomon & Peres Distribution, Polygram

SINGLES ALBUM, THE.
Album: released on Music For Pleasure (Holland) in '86 by EMI Records. Distributed by: EMI

Cassette: released on Music For Pleasure (Holland) in '86 by EMI Records. Distributed by: EMI

SOLITAIRE.
Compact disc: released on K-Tel in May'87 by K-Tel Records. Distributed by: Record Merchandisers Distribution, Taylors, Terry Blood Distribution, Wynd-Up Distribution, Relay Distribution, Pickwick Distribution, Solomon & Peres Distribution, Polygram

SOMETHING.
Single (7"): released on United Artists in May'70

SOMETIMES.
Single (7"): released on Towerbell in Mar'84 by Towerbell Records. Distributed by: EMI

SONGS FROM THE SHOWS.
Tracks: / Moon river / People / Tonight / If love were all / Days of wine & roses / I believe in you / I've never been in love before / Long ago and far away / Lady is a tramp, The / Somewhere / It might as well be spring / Don't rain on my parade / I get a kick out of you / Just one of those things / As long as he needs me / Where or when / 'S wonderful / Everything's coming up roses / He loves me / If ever I would leave you / You'll never walk alone.
Cassette: released on Hour Of Pleasure in '86 by Music For Pleasure Records. Distributed by: EMI

THERE'S NO PLACE LIKE LONDON.
Tracks: / There's no place like London / Born to sing.
Single (7"): released on Towerbell in Jun'86 by Towerbell Records. Distributed by: EMI

THIS IS MY LIFE.
Tracks: / Goldfinger / Light my fire / Never never never.
Album: released on Music For Pleasure (Holland) in '86 by EMI Records. Distributed by: EMI

Cassette: released on Music For Pleasure (Holland) in '86 by EMI Records. Distributed by: EMI

Album: released on EMI Europe in Mar'83 by EMI Records. Distributed by: Conifer

Cassette: released on EMI Europe in Mar'83 by EMI Records. Distributed by: Conifer

THOUGHTS OF LOVE.
Tracks: / Send in the clowns / Killing me softly with his song / Feelings / What are you doing the rest of your life / What I did for love / All that love went to waste / Way we were, The / If you go away / Alone again / Jesse / I won't last a day without you / You are the sunshine of my life.
Album: released on United Artists in Nov'76

Cassette: released on United Artists in Nov'76

TO ALL THE MEN I'VE LOVED BEFORE.
Tracks: / To all the men i've loved before.
Single (7"): released on Towerbell in Mar'86 by Towerbell Records. Distributed by: EMI

TONIGHT.
Tracks: / Tonight / On a wonderful day like today / You'll never know / Who can I turn to / As long as he needs me / Party's over, The / Cry me a river / Goldfinger / I (Who have nothing) / I'll get by (As long as I have you) / You'd better love me / Imagination / All of me / Climb every mountain / What now my love / Second time around, The.
Notes: Specially compiled for Music For Pleasure another great album from Shirley Basey -Tonight!. Taken from her 60's recordings for EMI Records many favourites are featured including "As long as she needs me","The partry's over","Golfinger","I'll get by" and her first No.1, for EMI "climb every mountain".Also included are several "live" tracks from her show at the Pigalle Night Club in 1965 part- icularly a fine sensitive version of "The second time around".The sleeve is a different, exciting shot of this talented Superstar who always sells records!.
Album: released on Music For Pleasure in Jul'84 by EMI Records. Distributed by: EMI

Cassette: released on Music For Pleasure in Jul'84 by EMI Records. Distributed by: EMI

VERY BEST OF SHIRLEY BASSEY, (THE).
Tracks: / Goldfinger / Fly me to the moon / Let there be love / What now my love / I've got you under my skin / No regrets / You'll never walk alone / What kind of fool am I / I wish you love / Who can I turn to / Party's over, The / Just one of those things / I get a kick out of you / I (who have nothing) / Love is a many splendoured thing / Days of wine and roses, The / Easy to love / If you love me / Liquidator, The / As long as he needs me.
Album: released on Columbia in Oct'74 by EMI Records. Distributed by: EMI Deleted '86.

Cassette: released on Columbia in Oct'74 by EMI Records. Distributed by: EMI

Bass, Fontella

RESCUE ME.
Single (7"): released on Old Gold in Jul'84 by Old Gold Records. Distributed by: Lightning, Jazz Music, Spartan, Counterpoint

Single (7"): released on Chess in Jul'85 by Charly Records. Distributed by: Charly, Swift, PRT, Discovery, IMS, Polygram

Bass Is

BASS IS.
Album: released on Enja (Germany) in Jan'82 by Enja Records (W.Germany). Distributed by: Cadillac Music

Bass Line

WIMBLEDON BREAK POINT.
Single (7"): released on BBC in Jun'85 by BBC Records & Tapes. Distributed by: EMI, PRT,

Basso, Gianni

LUNET (Basso, Gianni European Quartet).
Album: released on Splash in Oct'86 by Splash Records. Distributed by: CBS

Bass Tone Tap

TRAPPING.
Album: released on BTT in Mar'84 by BTT Records. Distributed by: Red Rhino, Cartel

Bass Wingates Band

SPARKLING BRASS.
Album: released on Look in Feb'81. Distributed by: R. Smith & Co. Records, H.R. Taylor

Cassette: released on Look in Feb'81. Distributed by: R. Smith & Co. Records, H.R. Taylor

Bata Drum

PASSION.
Tracks: / Passion / This way.
Single (7"): released on Champion in Feb'86 by Champion Records. Distributed by: RCA

Single (12"): released on Champion in Feb'86 by Champion Records. Distributed by: RCA

Bat Cave

BAT CAVE YOUNG LIMBS & NUMB HYMNS Various Artists (Various Artists).
Album: released on London in May'83 by London Records. Distributed by: Polygram

Cassette: released on London in May'83 by London Records. Distributed by: Polygram

Batchelor, Johnny

MUMBLE.
Single (7"): released on Northwood in Mar'84 by Northwood Records. Distributed by: Backs-Cartel

Batchelor Pad

AN ALBUM OF JACKS.
Tracks: / An album of jacks.
Single (12"): released on Warhold Sound in 20 Jun'87

Bates, Blaster

1001 GELIGNITES (Blaster Bates volume 2).
Album: released on Big Ben in Nov'80 by Big Ben Records. Distributed by: Spartan, Taylor, H.R.

Cassette: released on Big Ben in Nov'80 by Big Ben Records. Distributed by: Spartan, Taylor, H.R.

BLASTERMINED (Blaster Bates volume 7).
Album: released on Big Ben in Nov'80 by Big Ben Records. Distributed by: Spartan, Taylor, H.R.

Cassette: released on Big Ben in Nov'80 by Big Ben Records. Distributed by: Spartan, Taylor, H.R.

GELLY BABE (Blaster Bates volume 6).
Album: released on Big Ben in Nov'80 by Big Ben Records. Distributed by: Spartan, Taylor, H.R.

Cassette: released on Big Ben in Nov'80 by Big Ben Records. Distributed by: Spartan, Taylor, H.R.

HUNTING & SHOOTING STORIES (Blaster Bates volume 8).
Album: released on Big Ben in Nov'84 by Big Ben Records. Distributed by: Spartan, Taylor,

Cassette: released on Big Ben in Nov'84 by Big Ben Records. Distributed by: Spartan, Taylor,

LAUGHTER WITH A BANG (Blaster Bates volume 1).
Album: released on Big Ben in Nov'80 by Big Ben Records. Distributed by: Spartan, Taylor,

Cassette: released on Big Ben in Nov'80 by Big Ben Records. Distributed by: Spartan, Taylor,

LIFT OFF (Blaster Bates volume 5).
Album: released on Big Ben in Nov'80 by Big Ben Records. Distributed by: Spartan, Taylor,

Cassette: released on Big Ben in Nov'80 by Big Ben Records. Distributed by: Spartan, Taylor,

TNT FOR TWO (Blaster Bates volume 3).
Album: released on Big Ben in Oct'80 by Big Ben Records. Distributed by: Spartan, Taylor,

Cassette: released on Big Ben in Oct'80 by Big Ben Records. Distributed by: Spartan, Taylor,

WATCH OUT FOR THE BITS (Blaster Bates volume 4).
Album: released on Big Ben in Nov'80 by Big Ben Records. Distributed by: Spartan, Taylor,

Cassette: released on Big Ben in Nov'80 by Big Ben Records. Distributed by: Spartan, Taylor,

Bates, Django

HUMAN CHAIN (Bates, Djanjo & Steve Arguelles).
Album: released on Loose Tubes in Nov'86. Distributed by: IMS-Polygram

Bate, Seldiy

PAGAN EASTER (Bate, Seldiy/Nigel Bourne).
Album: released on Temple in Apr'87 by Temple Records. Distributed by: Roots Distribution, Folksound Distribution, Celtic Music Distribution, Projection Distribution

Bates, Martyn

LETTERS WRITTEN.
Tracks: / Morning singing / Cut like sunset / In June / Mirrored in me / Overflowing look / Aftertaste of old / Jagged tears of words / Letters from yesterday / Calls of birds / Hungry like sharp desire.
Album: released on Cherry Red in Oct'82 by Cherry Red Records. Distributed by: Pinnacle

Batey, Derek

WORDS & MUSIC FOR EVERY MR. & MRS..
Tracks: / Mr and Mrs / Play the game - at home / High hopes / Swinging on a star / What a wonderful world / Tie a yellow ribbon / Day's end, The / Music hall medley / Sing / Funny thing happened, A / King of the road / You are the sunshine of my life / Everything is beautiful / Marriage lines / Mr and Mrs (reprise).
Album: released on Look in Nov'79. Distributed by: R. Smith & Co. Records, H.R. Taylor

Cassette: released on Look in Nov'79. Distributed by: R. Smith & Co. Records, H.R. Taylor

Batfish Boys

CROCODILE TEARS (EP).
Single (12"): released on Batfish in Apr'86. Distributed by: Red Rhino, Cartel

GODS HATE KANSAS, (THE).
Album: released on Batfish in Jul'85. Distributed by: Red Rhino, Cartel

HEAD.
Album: released on Batfish in Sep'86. Distributed by: Red Rhino, Cartel

JUSTINE.
Single (7"): released on Batfish in Nov'86. Distributed by: Red Rhino, Cartel

SWAMP LIQUOR.
Single (7"): released on Batfish in Apr'85. Distributed by: Red Rhino, Cartel

Single (12"): released on Batfish in Apr'85. Distributed by: Red Rhino, Cartel

Bathory

BATHORY.
Album: released on Under One Flag in Mar'87.

Distributed by: Pinnacle

RETURN (THE).
Album: released on Under One Flag in Mar'87. Distributed by: Pinnacle

UNDER THE SIGN OF THE BLACK MARK.
Cassette: released on Under One Flag in Jun'87. Distributed by: Pinnacle

Album: released on Under One Flag in Jun'87. Distributed by: Pinnacle

Batish Family

NORTH INDIAN FOLK AND CLASSICAL MUSIC.
Tracks: / Folk music northwest frontier dance / Kashmiri hill song / Punjabi love song / Punjabi lyrical song / Urban folksong / Punjabi women's song / Central Indian melody / Raga pat multani / Raga todi / Raga shudh sarang / Raga khamaj.
Notes: S D Batish - sitar, vichitra vina, dilruba, harmonium, vocal Shanta Batish - vocal, harmonium Vijay Batish - vocal Ashwin Batish - sitar, ghungroo bells Ravi Batish - tambourine Mohamad Ismail - tabla, dholak
Album: released on Topic in '81. Distributed by: Roots Distribution

Batman.....

BATMAN IN RHYMES, RIDDLES & RIOTS Various Artists (Various Artists).
Notes: From the Super Heroes series.
Cassette: released on MFP in Oct'85 by EMI Records. Distributed by: EMI

Batmobile

BAMBOO LAND.
Album: released on Count Orlok in Jul'87

BATMOBILE.
Album: released on Kix 4 U in Dec'85 by Kix 4u Records. Distributed by: Pinnacle

Baton Rouge Blues

BATON ROUGE BLUES Various artists (Various Artists).
Tracks: / I'm a kingbee / It's half past midnight / Draft board blues / Sittin' here wonderin' / Cigarettes / G.I.blues / Cold chills / I'm a lucky man / Hoodoo party / Bloodstains / Oh baby / I need your love / I don't know why.
Album: released on Flyright in Oct'86 by Flyright Records. Distributed by: Krazy Kat, Swift, Jazz Music

BATON ROUGE BLUES Various Artists.

Bats

MADE UP IN BLUE.
Tracks: / Made up in blue.
Single (12"): released on Flying Nun in Oct'86. Distributed by: Rough Trade, Cartel

Batson, Slim

RUNNING AWAY.
Single (12"): released on Ruff Cut in Nov'83 by Ruff Cut Records. Distributed by: Jetstar Distribution

Batson, Whitfield

I WILL ALWAYS LOVE YOU.
Single (12"): released on Ruff Cut in Aug'83 by Ruff Cut Records. Distributed by: Jetstar Distribution

I will always love you

Batstone,Bill

ONE BY ONE.
Album: released on Word in Jul'85 by Word Records. Distributed by: Word Distribution, CBS

Cassette: released on Word in Jul'85 by Word Records. Distributed by: Word Distribution, CBS

Batterie, (La)

LET THERE BE DRUMS.
Single (7"): released on Polo in Jan'83 by Polo Records. Distributed by: PRT

Single (12"): released on Polo in Jan'83 by Polo Records. Distributed by: PRT

Battiato, Alice

I TRENI DI TOZEUR.
Single (7"): released on EMI in May'84 by EMI Records. Distributed by: EMI

Battin, Skip

EX BYRDS.
Album: released on Appaloosa (Italy) in Feb'85

Battin' The Boogie

BATTIN' THE BOOGIE Various artists (Various Artists).
Tracks: / One note boogie / Good morning Mary / What'd he say / Rock-a-beating boogie / Kiss me / Off and on / Do it easy / Restum in peace blues / Save me a boogie / Hello / You're breaking my heart no more / It's over / Rock it Davy Crockett / Battin' the boogie / Ramblin' woman / Your love has me rockin' and reelin'.
Album: released on Charly in Aug'86 by Charly Records. Distributed by: Charly, Cadillac

Battisti, Lucio

GREATEST HITS:LUCIO BATTISTI.
Album: released on RCA (France) in Dec'84 by RCA Records. Distributed by: Discovery

Cassette: released on RCA (France) in Dec'84 by RCA Records. Distributed by: Discovery

IMAGES.
Album: released on RCA in Mar'78 by RCA Records. Distributed by: RCA, Roots, Swift, Wellard, Chris, I & B, Solomon & Peres Distribution

Battle...

BATTLE OF THE BANDS Various Bands (Various bands).
Album: released on RCA in Mar'82 by RCA Records. Distributed by: RCA, Roots, Swift, Wellard, Chris, I & B, Solomon & Peres Distribution

Cassette: released on RCA in Mar'82 by RCA Records. Distributed by: RCA, Roots, Swift, Wellard, Chris, I & B, Solomon & Peres Distribution

BATTLE OF THE BIG BANDS - VOLUME 1 Various Artists (Various Artists).
Album: released on Bright Orange in Apr'79. Distributed by: Swift

BATTLE OF THE BIG BANDS - VOLUME 2 Various Artists (Various Artists).
Album: released on Bright Orange in Apr'79. Distributed by: Swift

Battleaxe

BURN THIS TOWN.
Album: released on Music For Nations in Jul'83 by Music For Nations Records. Distributed by: Pinnacle

POWER FROM THE UNIVERSE.
Album: released on Music For Nations in Jul'84 by Music For Nations Records. Distributed by: Pinnacle

Battlefield Band

ANTHEM FOR THE COMMON MAN.
Album: released on Temple in Jun'84 by Temple Records. Distributed by: Roots Distribution, Folksound Distribution, Celtic Music Distribution, Projection Distribution

AT THE FRONT.
Tracks: / Lady Carmichael / South of the Grampians / Mickie Ainsworth / Bachelor, The / Ge do theid mi do m'leabradh / Battle of harlaw, The / Jenny Nettles / Grays of tongside, The / Tae the beggin' / Tamosher, The / Blackbird and the trush, The / Moray club, The / Lang Johnnie moir / Brown milkmaid, The / Dunnottar castle / Maid of Glengarrysdale / Disused railways / Lady Leroy, The / Stirling castle / Earl of Mansfield.
Notes: Brian McNeill - vocal, fiddle, mandolin, bouzouki, cittern, concertina Jamie McMenemy - vocal, mandolin, cittern, bouzouki, whistle Alan Reid - vocal, pedal organ, electric piano, piano Pat Kilbride - vocal, guitar, cittern, bodhran
Album: released on Topic in '81. Distributed by: Roots Distribution

BATTLEFIELD BAND, (THE).
Tracks: / Silver spear / Humours of Tulla / Shipyard apprentice, The / Crossing the Minch / Minnie Hynd / Glasgow Gaelic Club / Brisk young lad, The / Birnie bouzle / Compliments of the band / A.A. Cameron's strathspey / Scott Skinner's compliments to Dr MacDonald / Bonnie Jean / Paddy Fahey's reel / Joseph's fancy / Hog's reel, The / It was all for our rightful king / Inverness gathering, The / Marquis of Huntley's strathspey / John MacNeil's reel / Miss Margaret Brown's favourite / Deserts of Tulloch / Cruel brother, The.
Notes: Brian McNeill - vocal, fiddle, viola, mandolin, cittern, concertina Jamie McMenemy - vocal, cittern, guitarra Alan Reid - vocal, organ, guitar John Gahagan - whistle, concertina
Album: released on Topic in '81. Distributed by: Roots Distribution

HOME IS WHERE THE VAN IS.
Album: released on Temple in Jan'83 by Temple Records. Distributed by: Roots Distribution, Folksound Distribution, Celtic Music Distribution, Projection Distribution

ON THE RISE.
Album: released on Temple in Mar'86 by Temple Records. Distributed by: Roots Distribution, Folksound Distribution, Celtic Music Distribution, Projection Distribution

Cassette: released on Temple in Mar'86 by Temple Records. Distributed by: Roots Distribution, Folksound Distribution, Celtic Music Distribution, Projection Distribution

STAND EASY.
Tracks: / Miss Drummond of Perth / Fiddler's joy / Trad reels, parts 3 & 4 / Shetland fiddler, The / Seven braw gowns / Miss Drummond of Perth's favourite Scotch measure / Miss MacLeod's minuet / My last farewell to Stirling / Cuidich'n righ / I hae a herrin' in salt / My wife's a wanton wee thing / Banks of Allan, The / Battle of Falkirk Muir / John D. Burgess / Braemar gathering, The / I hae nae with I hae nae kin / Miss Lyall / Small coals for nailers / Bleaton gardens / Christ has my heart ay / Joe McGann's fiddle / Center's bonnet.
Album: released on Topic in '81. Distributed by: Roots Distribution

STORY SO FAR..., (THE).
Album: released on Temple in '82 by Temple Records. Distributed by: Roots Distribution, Folksound Distribution, Celtic Music Distribution, Projection Distribution

THERE'S A BUZZ.
Album: released on Temple in Dec'82 by Temple Records. Distributed by: Roots Distribution, Folksound Distribution, Celtic Music Distribution, Projection Distribution

WINTERFOLK 80.
Notes: Featuring Melanie Harrold Band, Dommelvolk, Silly Wizard, Sonerien Du
Album: released on Stoof in '82. Distributed by: Roots Distribution

Battle, Kathleen

CHRISTMAS CELEBRATION, A.
Tracks: / O come all ye faithful / O holy night / Un flambeau,Janette,Isabelle / Fum,fum,fum / How a rose e'er blooming / Ave Maria / Gesu bambino / I saw three ships / First nowell / Holly & the ivy, The / Away in the manger / Silent night / Hark the herald angel sing / Marie Wiegenlied / Zither carol / I wonder as I wonder / Mary had a baby / Rise up shepherd / What child is this? / Ave Maria / Veni,veni, Emanuelle / It came upon a midnight clear / O little town of Bethlehem / Silent night / O come all ye faithful.
Notes: Kathleen Battle, New York Choral Artists,The Boy's Choir of Harlem,The Orchestra of St.Lukes conducted by Leonard Slatkin. Producer/arranger: Anthony Caronia/John Newton
Album: released on H.M.V. in Nov'86 by EMI Records. Distributed by: EMI

Cassette: released on H.M.V. in Nov'86 by EMI Records. Distributed by: EMI

Battle of...

BATTLE OF BRITAIN Various Sounds (Battle of Britain).
Double Album: released on Flightstream in Jun'83 by Flightstream Records. Distributed by: Taylo

Double cassette: released on Flightstream in Jun'83 bv Flightstream Records. Distributed by: Taylor

BATTLE OF WATERLOO (A Guards live recording) (Guards Live Recording).
Album: released on Major Richards in Oct'77 by Major Richards Records. Distributed by: Taylors

Battle of Dune

BATTLE OF DUNE Herbert, Frank (Herbert, Frank).
Cassette: released on Caedmon(USA) in Oct'70 by Caedmon (USA) Records. Distributed by: Taylors, Discovery

Battleship Galactica

BATTLESHIP GALACTICA (Original Soundtrack).
Album: released on MCA in Apr'79 by MCA Records. Distributed by: Polygram, MCA Deleted '83.

Cassette: released on MCA in Apr'79 by MCA Records. Distributed by: Polygram, MCA

Batt, Mike

Biographical Details: Mike Batt started life as staff songwriter at Liberty Records eventually progressing to A & R manager. Going freelance, he was responsible for various junk albums such as budget price orchestral renditions of Beatles songs. His big break came in the early Seventies when he wrote the theme song for the children's TV series 'The Wombles'. 'The Wombling Song' was a neat pop ditty, full of McCartney -type irresistable melody. As a single it reached no.4 on the chart 1974 with an impressive run of 23 weeks on the list. To promote the record, Batt assembled a phoney 'group' called the Wombles with him-self dressed as the programme's leading character Orinoco. He was at the forefront of a major marketing campaign which included not only the Womble records, but also Womble books, models, key rings, etc. When the Womble novelty was wearing off in 1975, Batt wrote the theme for the television show 'Seaside Special'. Under the title 'Summertime City', he released the song under his own name and reached no.4. Despite a series of quality singles and albums, which included some experimental orchestral arrangements, Mike Batt the artist never penetrated the charts again. Instead he became known as a writer, arranger and producer of hits for other acts. The biggest of these was 'Bright Eyes' the 'Watership Down', theme sung by Art Garfunkel. This was Britain's biggest selling single of 1979, becoming the last 45 for four years to log six weeks at no.1. In the Eighties Batt collaborated with fellow British writer Tim Rice on 'A Winter's Tale' a no.2 hit for David Essex, and then proceeded to write 'I Feel Like Buddy Holly' for Alvin Stardust. The latter epitomised Mike Batt's style - strong melodies with neat, uncluttered lyrics, twee but tasteful. Less successful was 1983's 'Zero Zero' full - length video/TV project, which attempted to put Batt back in the spotlight. His forte is behind the scenes work. (BM 84)

CHILDREN OF THE SKY.
Single (7"):

Single (12"): released on Starblend in Nov'86 by Starblend Records. Distributed by: PRT Distribution

Album: released on Epic in Oct'86 by CBS Records. Distributed by: CBS

Cassette: released on Epic in Oct'86 by CBS Records. Distributed by: CBS

DRAGON DANCE (Batt, Mike/London Philharmonic Orchestra).
Single (7"): released on Chrysalis in Dec'84 by Chrysalis Records. Distributed by: CBS

HUNTING OF THE SNARK, THE.
Album: released on Starblend in Nov'86 by Starblend Records. Distributed by: PRT Distribution

Cassette: released on Starblend in Nov'86 by Starblend Records. Distributed by: PRT Distribution

LOVE MAKES YOU CRAZY.
Single (7"): released on Epic in Jan'83 by CBS Records. Distributed by: CBS

WHISPERING FOOLS.
Single (7"): released on Epic in Mar'83 by CBS Records. Distributed by: CBS

ZERO ZERO.
Tracks: / Introduction (The birth of No 17) / System 605 / Love makes you crazy / Delirium / Whispering fools / Zero zero / Dance of the neurosurgeons / No lights in my eyes / Love makes you crazy (instrumental reprise).
Album: released on Epic in Jan'83 by CBS Records. Distributed by: CBS Deleted '85.

Cassette: released on Epic in Jan'83 by CBS Records. Distributed by: CBS

Batwing Chaps

CRAVE.
Single (7"): released on Full Moon in Jul'84 by Epic. Distributed by: CBS

Bauerle, Dick

DICK BAUERLE GROUP (Bauerle, Dick Group).
Album: released on MCA in Feb'87 by MCA Records. Distributed by: Polygram MCA

Cassette: released on MCA in Feb'87 by MCA Records. Distributed by: Polygram, MCA

Bauhaus

Biographical Details: Named after Germany's Bauhaus art movement of the Twenties, this Northampton quartet released their debut record in 1979, the 12-inch EP "Bela Lugosi's Dead". A much praised session on the John Peel show helped to make it an underground classic, selling in small but steady quantities over months, even years. In November 1980 their first album "In The Flat Field" made a brief appearance on the national album chart, a toehold that was exploited the following year. 1981 brought the band their first two minor hit singles, "Kick In The Eye" and "The Passion Of Lovers", plus a Top 30 LP "Mask". The former re-surfaced in '82 on a chart EP, to be followed by the "Spirit" single. Bauhaus were now cult favourites, but were criticised by the music press for being a dated rehash of both Bowie and punk. These complaints were brought to a head in late '82 when the group scored their only Top 20 single, a carbon copy cover version of Bowie's "Ziggy Stardust". The success of this record boosted their third album "The Sky's Gone Out" to No.4 on the LP charts. 1983 saw the group chalk up two more chart singles "Lagartija Nick" and "She's In Parties" plus the Top 20 album "Burning From The Inside". At the end of that year Bauhaus fell apart. Lead vocalist and main spokesman went on to form Dali's Car, a partnership with ex-Japan man Mick Karn. B.M. 84

1979-1983 VOL.1.

BAUHAUS 1979-1983.
Tracks: / Kick in the eye / Hollow hills / In fear of fear / Ziggy Stardust / Silent hedges / Lagartija Nick / Third uncle / Spirit / All we ever wanted was everything / She's in parties / Sanity assassin, The / Crowds / Double dare / In the flat field / Stigmata martyr / Bela Lugosi's dead / Telegram Sam / St.Vitus dance / Spy in the cab, A / Terror couple kill colonel / Passions of lovers / Mask.

Double Album: released on Beggars Banquet in Dec'85 by Beggars Banquet Records. Distributed by: WEA

Cassette: released on Beggars Banquet in Dec'85 by Beggars Banquet Records. Distributed by: WEA

BAUHAUS 1979-1983 VOL.1.
Compact disc: released on Beggars Banquet in Apr'86 by Beggars Banquet Records. Distributed by: WEA

BELA LUGOSI'S DEAD.
Tracks: / Bela Lugosi's dead / Boys.
Single (12"): released on Small Wonder in Sep'86 by Small Wonder Records. Distributed by: Cartel, Indies

BURNING FROM THE INSIDE.
Tracks: / She's in parties / Hope / Burning from the inside.
Album: released on Beggars Banquet in Jul'83 by Beggars Banquet Records. Distributed by: WEA

Cassette: released on Beggars Banquet in Jul'83 by Beggars Banquet Records. Distributed by: WEA

DARK ENTRIES.
Single (12"): released on 4AD in Sep'83 by 4AD Records. Distributed by: Rough Trade

KICK IN THE EYE.
Single (7"): released on Beggars Banquet in Feb'82 by Beggars Banquet Records. Distributed by: WEA

Single (12"): released on Beggars Banquet in Feb'82 by Beggars Banquet Records. Distributed by: WEA

LARGARTIJA NICK.
Single (7"): released on Beggars Banquet in Jan'83 by Beggars Banquet Records. Distributed by: WEA

Single (12"): released on Beggars Banquet in Jan'83 by Beggars Banquet Records. Distributed by: WEA

MASK.
Tracks: / Hair of the dog / Passion of lovers / Of lilies and remains / Hollow hills / Dancing / Kick in the eyes / Muscle in plastic / In fear of fear / Man with the X-ray eyes, The / Mask.
Album: released on Beggars Banquet in Oct'81 by Beggars Banquet Records. Distributed by: WEA

Cassette: released on Beggars Banquet in Oct'81 by Beggars Banquet Records. Distributed by: WEA

PASSION OF LOVERS.
Single (7"): released on Beggars Banquet in Jun'81 by Beggars Banquet Records. Distributed by: WEA

PASSION OF LOVERS (12").
Single (12"): released on Beggars Banquet in Oct'83 by Beggars Banquet Records. Distributed by: WEA

SHADOW OF LIGHT.
Video-cassette (VHS): released on Kace International Products in Jan'84. Distributed by: Gold & Sons

SHE'S IN PARTIES.
Single (7"): released on Beggars Banquet in Apr'83 by Beggars Banquet Records. Distributed by: WEA

Single (12"): released on Beggars Banquet in Apr'83 by Beggars Banquet Records. Distributed by: WEA

Picture disc single: released on Beggars Banquet in Aug'84 by Beggars Banquet Records. Distributed by: WEA

SINGLES 1981-1983, (THE).
Single (12"): released on Beggars Banquet in Aug'84 by Beggars Banquet Records. Distributed by: WEA

SKY'S GONE OUT, (THE).
Tracks: / Third uncle / Silent hedges / In the night / Swing the heartache / Spirit / Three shadows, part 1 / Three shadows, part 2 / Three shadows, part 3 / All we ever wanted was everything / Exquisite corpse.
Notes: The cassette, BEGC 42, is double-titled, containing both The sky's gone out and Press the eject and give me the tape.
Album: released on Beggars Banquet in Nov'82 by Beggars Banquet Records. Distributed by: WEA

SKY'S GONE OUT, (THE)/PRESS THE EJECT & GIVE ME THE TAPE.
Tracks: / In the flat field / Rosegarden funeral of sores / Dancing / Man with the X-ray eyes, The / Bela Lugosi's dead / Spy in the cab, The / Kick in the eye / In fear of fear / Hollow hills / Stigmata martyr / Dark entries.
Notes: Double-title cassette.
Cassette: released on Beggars Banquet in Nov'82 by Beggars Banquet Records. Distributed by: WEA

SPIRIT.
Single (7"): released on Beggars Banquet in Jun'82 by Beggars Banquet Records. Distributed by: WEA

TELEGRAM SAM.
Single (7"): released on 4AD in Oct'80 by 4AD Records. Distributed by: Rough Trade

Single (12"): released on 4AD in Nov'80 by 4AD Records. Distributed by: Rough Trade

ZIGGY STARDUST.
Single (7"): released on Beggars Banquet in Sep'82 by Beggars Banquet Records. Distributed by: WEA

Single (12"): released on Beggars Banquet in Oct'82 by Beggars Banquet Records. Distributed by: WEA

Baumann, Peter

REPEAT REPEAT.
Notes: Produced by Robert Palmer
Album: released on Virgin in Sep'81 by Virgin Records. Distributed by: EMI, Virgin Distribution

ROMANCE 76.
Album: released on Virgin in Feb'77 by Virgin Records. Distributed by: EMI, Virgin Distribution

TRANS-HARMONIC NIGHTS.
Album: by Virgin Records. Distributed by: EMI, Virgin Distribution

Bavan

At Newport '63

Havin' a ball at the village gate

Bavaria

BAVARIAN FOLK MUSIC Various Artists (Various Artists).
Album: released on Telefunken (Germany) in Jun'81. Distributed by: Decca Distribution, IMS, Polygram

BAVARIAN MUSIC Songs from the October Festival (Various Artists).
Album: released on Polydor in Jul'87 by Polydor Records. Distributed by: Polygram, Polydor

Cassette: released on Polydor in Jul'87 by Polydor Records. Distributed by: Polygram, Polydor

BAVARIAN MUSIC (24 GOLDEN FOLK SONGS - WINE SONGS) Various Artists (Various Artists).
Cassette: released on Philips (Germany) in Apr'85

BAVARIAN MUSIC (ALPINE SONGS & BRASS MUSIC) Various Artists (Various Artists).
Cassette: released on Philips (Germany) in Apr'85

BAVARIAN MUSIC (ALPINE SONGS ON A ZITHER) Various Artists (Various Artists).
Cassette: released on Philips (Germany) in Apr'85

BAVARIAN MUSIC (BEER FESTIVAL SONGS) Various Artists (Various Artists).
Cassette: released on Philips (Germany) in Apr'85

BAVARIAN MUSIC (BRASS MUSIC) Various Artists (Various Artists).
Cassette: released on Philips (Germany) in Apr'85

BAVARIAN MUSIC (EDELWEISS ACCORDION PLAYERS-SNOW WALTZ) Various Artists (Various Artists).
Cassette: released on Philips (Germany) in Apr'85

BAVARIAN MUSIC (FOLK SONGS FROM THE EGER COUNTRY) Various Artists (Various Artists).
Cassette: released on Philips (Germany) in Apr'85

BAVARIAN MUSIC (GOLDEN SOUNDS FROM THE LAND OF CASTLES) Various artists (Various Artists).
Cassette: released on Philips (Germany) in Apr'85

BAVARIAN MUSIC (SCHUPLATTEN MUSIC-KNEE SLAPPING BRASS MUSIC) Various Artists (Various Artists).
Cassette: released on Philips (Germany) in Apr'85

BAVARIAN MUSIC (YODELLING SONGS FROM THE ALPS) Various Artists (Various Artists).
Cassette: released on Philips (Germany) in Apr'85

BAVARIAN OOMPAH BAND (Bavarian Oompah Band).
Album: released on Oak in Jul'83 by Oak Records. Distributed by: Spartan Distribution, Pinnacle

KINGS OF BRASS MUSIC (Bavarian Brass Bands).
Album: released on Polydor (Germany) in Jul'87. Distributed by: IMS-Polygram

Cassette: released on Polydor (Germany) in Jul'87. Distributed by: IMS-Polygram

OOMPAH STRIKES BACK, THE (Bavarian Steinswingers).
Notes: Mail order & distribution address: Accordion Record Club, 146 Birmingham Road Kidderminster, Worcs. DY10 2SL Tel: 0562 746105
Album: released on Accordion Record Club in Jul'86 by Accordion Record Club Records. Distributed by: Accordion Record Club

Baxon, Bill

SUPERMAN.
Single (7"): released on Roxon in May'81 by Roxon Records. Distributed by: Pinnacle

Baxter, Bruce

POP GUITAR EXTRAVAGANZA (Baxter, Bruce Orchestra).
Tracks: / Alone again (naturally) / Let it be / Don't give up on us / Yesterday / Little bit more, A / Sailing / Don't cry for me, Argentine / Tie a yellow ribbon / Stand by your man / You are the sunshine of my life / Save your kisses for me / Summer of '42.
Double cassette: released on Pickwick (Ditto series) in Jul'82

Baxters

ERA BUFFET.
Notes: Baxters: John Lopinski-vocals,guitar,keyboards/Steve Arnold-vocals,guitars,harmonicas/Baker Rorick-bass,vocals/Jack de Pietro- drums. Produced & engineered by: Doug Epstein:262 Rio Circle Decatur,GA 30030 USA-29 Beethoven Street London W10 4LG. UK. Assistant engineers: Vic Daglio,'Ahm'Ed O'Connor, Alexander Haes Recorded at Media Sounds,NYC/Grog Kill Studio,Willow, NY. Cover photos by Steve Pavlovic,Back cover photo by:Cindy Grossman Execution by: Peter Dyer. Special thanks to: Michael Mograve-ro(drums)Vic Daglio,Michael Hektoen,Carla Bley & Mike Mantler
Album: released on Press in Jun'86 by Press Records

Cassette: released on Press in Jun'86 by Press Records

Baxter, Screamin' Tony

GET UP OFFA THAT THING.
Single (7"): released on Fourth & Broadway in Aug'85 by Island Records. Distributed by: Polygram, EMI

Single (12"): released on Fourth & Broadway in Aug'85 by Island Records. Distributed by: Polygram, EMI

Bay Area Blues Blasters

BAY AREA BLUES BLASTERS (Various Artists).
Album: released on Ace in 7 Sep'87 by Ace Records. Distributed by: Pinnacle, Swift, Hotshot, Cadillac

Bayer Sager, Carole

Biographical Details: Singer/songwriter Carole Bayer Sager was born in New York in 1947, and began writing at 15. She signed as a writer with Don Kirshner's Screen Gems and her first demo, "Groovy Kind Of Love" (co-written with Tony Wein) was a no. 2 hit in both USA and UK by the Mindbenders in 1966; but her greatest success began in the 1970's.
She was the youngest lyricist ever to write a Broadway musical, but **Gregory** flopped in 1970, but she has co-written dozens of hits with Melissa Manchester, Peter Allen, film composer Marvin Hamlisch (born in New York 2 June 1944), others; she and Hamlisch wrote songs for Neil Simon's musical **They're Playing Our Song** in 1979, said to have been loosely based on their relationship; married Burt Bacharach in 1982. Her albums have always been critically praised; Bacharach collaborated on her third album, **Sometimes Late At Night** in 1981, the first to reach Billboard's album chart, including a top 30 hit "Stronger Than Before". [Donald Clarke, April 87]

I DON'T KNOW ONE.
Notes: Carole Bayer Sager is a singer songwriter from the USA.

Baylis, Chris

HEART OF STONE.
Tracks: / Heart of stone / Closer to the heart.
Single (7"): released on VM in Oct'86 by VM Records. Distributed by: PRT

Single (12"): released on VM in Oct'86 by VM Records. Distributed by: PRT

Bayne, Pam & Phil

BORDER COUNTRY.
Album: released on Neptune in Apr'78 by Lismor. Distributed by: Spartan

Cassette: released on Neptune in Apr'78 by Lismor. Distributed by: Spartan

Bayou Beat

BAYOU BEAT Various artists (Various Artists).
Album: released on Flyright in Sep'86 by Flyright Records. Distributed by: Krazy Kat, Swift, Jazz Music

Bayou Boogie

BAYOU BOOGIE Various Artists (Various Artists).
Album: released on Ace in Jul'85 by Ace Records. Distributed by: Pinnacle, Swift, Hotshot, Cadillac

Bayou Brothers

SUNNY WEATHER.
Single (7"): released on Dingles in Aug'83 by Dingles Records. Distributed by: Projection

YOU'VE GOT A WAY WITH YOU.
Single (7"): released on Dingles in Jun'82 by Dingles Records. Distributed by: Projection

Baysal, Salih

MYTH, (THE).
Album: by Sonet Records. Distributed by: PRT

Bazza Bawdy

RUN FOR YOUR LIFE.
Single (7"): released on Peak Records in Oct'82 by Peak Records. Distributed by: MIS-EMI Distribution

Bazzar, Thereza

BIG KISS, (THE).
Album: released on MCA in Oct'85 by MCA Records. Distributed by: Polygram, MCA

Cassette: released on MCA in Oct'85 by MCA Records. Distributed by: Polygram, MCA

BB Allstars...

BB ALLSTARS SUPERHITS VOLUME 1 Various Artists (Various Artists).
Album: released on BB in Dec'84. Distributed by: Jetstar

B B Band

DUKE (THE).
Single (7"): released on AVM in Jan'83. Distributed by: PRT

BBC...

BBC CHILDREN'S TV THEMES Various artists (BBC Children's TV Themes).
Tracks: / Dr Who / Captain Zep / Magic roundabout / Paddington bear / Animal magic / The dukes of hazzard / Watch / Trumpton / Monkey / Camberwick green / Heads and tails / Saturday superstore / Blue peter / Willo the wisp / Grand hill / The pink panther / Swap shop / Take heart / The monkee's theme / Mr men / Think again / Playschool.
Single (7"): released on BBC in Oct'83 by BBC Records & Tapes. Distributed by: EMI, PRT,

Single (12"): released on BBC in Oct'83 by BBC Records & Tapes. Distributed by: EMI, PRT,

BBC'S FOLK ON 2 PRESENTS NORTHUMBRIAN FOLK (Various Artists).
Album: by BBC Records & Tapes. Distributed by: EMI, PRT,

CARDIFF SINGERS OF THE WORLD, THE (BBC Welsh Orchestra).
Album: released on BBC Artium in Aug'85

Cassette: released on BBC Artium in Aug'85

DOCTOR WHO The music 11 (BBC Radiophonic Workshop).
Album: released on BBC in Feb'85 by BBC Records & Tapes. Distributed by: EMI, PRT,

Cassette: released on BBC in Feb'85 by BBC Records & Tapes. Distributed by: EMI, PRT,

DR WHO (BBC Radiophonic Workshop).
Single (7"): released on Decca in Feb'84 by Decca Records. Distributed by: Polygram

LAST NIGHT OF THE PROMS '82 (BBC Symphony Orchestra).
Album: released on K-Tel in Nov'82 by K-Tel Records. Distributed by: Record Merchandisers Distribution, Taylors, Terry Blood Distribution, Wynd-Up Distribution, Relay Distribution, Pickwick Distribution, Solomon & Peres Distribution, Polygram

Cassette: released on K-Tel in Nov'82 by K-Tel Records. Distributed by: Record Merchandisers Distribution, Taylors, Terry Blood Distribution,

Wynd-Up Distribution, Relay Distribution, Pickwick Distribution, Solomon & Peres Distribution, Polygram

LIVING PLANET, (THE) Music from the television series (BBC Radiophonic Workshop).
Album: released on BBC in Jan'84 by BBC Records & Tapes. Distributed by: EMI, PRT,

Cassette: released on BBC in Jan'84 by BBC Records & Tapes. Distributed by: EMI, PRT,

SOUND HOUSE (BBC Radiophonic Workshop).
Tracks: / Radiophonic rock, The / Lascaux / Computers in the real world / Seascape / Whale, The / Rallyman / Catch the wind / Believe it or not / Planet earth / Dawn / Mainstream / Unseeing eye / Fancy fish / Brighton pier / Amagiddean war games / Yellow moon / Radio Blackburn / Macrocosm / Land and people / Housin's musical box / Ghost in the water / Milonga, The.
Album: released on BBC in Apr'83 by BBC Records & Tapes. Distributed by: EMI, PRT,

Cassette: released on BBC in Apr'83 by BBC Records & Tapes. Distributed by: EMI, PRT,

VOICES FROM THE HOLY LAND (BBC Welsh Chorus).
Tracks: / Let us break bread together / Ave Marie / My Lord' what a mornin' / Deep river / Holy City, The / There is a green hill far away / How beautiful are the feet (From 'Mesiah) / Ave Verum Corpus / Easty hymn / Jesu joy of man's desiring / Little road to Bethlehem, The / Shepherds farewell, The (From 'Childhood of Christ') / Ave Maria / O for a closer walk with God / O for the wings of a dove (From'Hear My Prayer') / Tua Bethlem Dref / O Holy Night / Virgin Mary had a baby boy.
Notes: Choral favourites from the highly acclaimed BBC Welsh Chorus featuring Aled Jones.
Album: released on BBC in Apr'85 by BBC Records & Tapes. Distributed by: EMI, PRT,

Cassette: released on BBC in Apr'85 by BBC Records & Tapes. Distributed by: EMI, PRT,

BBC English Course

TAKE A BREAK Various artists (Various Artists).
Triple album / cassette: released on BBC English in '78

B-Biz-R

SUCKER FOR LOVE.
Single (7"): released on Magnet in Aug'84 by Magnet Records. Distributed by: BMG

Single (12"): released on Magnet in Aug'84 by Magnet Records. Distributed by: BMG

B Boys

START WREKKIN'.
Tracks: / Start wrekkin' / Start wrekkin' (demolition version).
Single (7"): released on Debut in Jul'87 by Skratch Music. Distributed by: PRT

Single (12"): released on Debut in Jul'87 by Skratch Music. Distributed by: PRT

B.B.& Q

DREAMER, (I'M A).
Tracks: / Dreamer, (I'm a) / Dreamer,(I'ma) (Instrumental).
Single (7"): released on Cool Tempo in Aug'86 by Chrysalis Records. Distributed by: CBS

Single (12"): released on Cool Tempo in Aug'86 by Chrysalis Records. Distributed by: CBS

MINUTES AWAY (Brooklyn Bronx & Queens).
Single (7"): released on Cool Tempo in Aug'85 by Chrysalis Records. Distributed by: CBS

Single (12"): released on Cool Tempo in Aug'85 by Chrysalis Records. Distributed by: CBS

B B & Q Band

GENIE.
Tracks: / Genie / Main attraction / Won't you be with me tonight? / Don't force it / Minutes away / On the shelf / Dreamer / Riccochet.
Album: released on Cool Tempo in Jul'85 by Chrysalis Records. Distributed by: CBS

Cassette: released on Cool Tempo in Jul'85 by Chrysalis Records. Distributed by: CBS

GENIE (SINGLE).
Single (7"): released on Cool Tempo in Jun'85 by Chrysalis Records. Distributed by: CBS Deleted '86.

Single (12"): released on Cool Tempo in Jun'85 by Chrysalis Records. Distributed by: CBS

BB'S

HORROR MOVIES.
Single (7"): released on Charly in Jan'83 by Charly Records. Distributed by: Charly, Cadillac

B. Bumble & The Stingers

BUMBLE BOOGIE.
Single (7"): released on Creole in Aug'82 by Creole Records. Distributed by: Rhino, PRT

NUT ROCKER.
Single (7"): released on Creole in Aug'82 by Creole Records. Distributed by: Rhino, PRT

Single (7"): released on EMI (France) in Apr'83 by EMI Records. Distributed by: Conifer

NUT ROCKER/BUMBLE BOOGIE.
Single (7"): released on Old Gold in Aug'82 by Old Gold Records. Distributed by: Lightning, Jazz Music, Spartan, Counterpoint

Single (7"): released on EMI Golden 45's in Feb'85 by EMI Records. Distributed by: EMI

Beach Boys

15 GREATEST HITS, THE (Beach Boys/Jan & Dean).
Tracks: / Surfin' safari / Surfer girl / Surfin' / Judy / Barbee / Luau / What is a young girl / Surf city / Little old lady from pasadena,The / Dead man's curve / Drag city / Little deuce coupe / Heart and soul / Ride the wild surf / Sidewalk surfin'.
Compact disc: released on Bescol in May'87. Distributed by: Target

20 GOLDEN GREATS.
Tracks: / Surfin' USA / Fun,fun,fun / I get around / Don't worry baby / Little deuce coupe / When I grow up(to be a man) / Help me Rhonda / California girls / Barbara Ann / Sloop John B. / You're so good to me / God only knows / Wouldn't it be nice / Good vibrations / Then I kissed her / Heroes & villains / Darlin' / Do it again / I can hear music / Breakaway.
Album: released on Capitol in Aug'79 by Capitol Records. Distributed by: EMI

Cassette: released on Capitol in Aug'79 by Capitol Records. Distributed by: EMI

40 GREATEST HITS.
Tracks: / Surfin' surfari / 409 / 10 Little indians / Surfin' USA / Shut down / Farmer's daughter / Hawaii / Surfer girl / Little deuce coupe / Be true to your school / In my room / Fun,fun,fun / I get around / Don't worry baby / When I grow up (to be a man) / Wendy / Little Honda / Dance, dance, dance / Do you wanna dance? / Please let me wander / Help me Rhonda / California girls / Little girl, The / Barbara Ann / Sloop John B. / Wouldn't it be nice / God only knows / You're so good to me / Good vibrations / Then I kissed her / Heroes & villains / Gettin' hungry / Wild honey / Darlin' / Friends / Do it again / Bluebirds.
Album: released on EMI (Holland) in '83 by EMI Records. Distributed by: Conifer

ALL SUMMER LONG.
Tracks: / I get around / All summer long / Hushabye / Little Honda / We'll run away / Carl's big chance / Wendy / Do you remember? / Girls on the beach / Drive-in / Our favourite recording session / Don't back down.
Notes: Total time tracks 1-6= 12.42, tracks 7 - 12 = 10.02
Album: released on Capitol in Jun'86 by Capitol Records. Distributed by: EMI

Cassette: released on Capitol in Jun'86 by Capitol Records. Distributed by: EMI

BARBARA ANN.
Single (7"): released on EMI Golden 45's in Mar'84 by EMI Records. Distributed by: EMI

BEACH BOYS.
Tracks: / Getch back / It's gettin' late / Crack at your love / Maybe I don't know / She believes in love again / California calling / Passing friend I'm so lonely / Where I belong / I do love you / It's just a matter of time / Add some music to your day / Roller skating child / Disney girls / It's a beautiful day / California saga / Wontcha come out tonight / Marcella / Rock and roll music / Goin' on / It's ok / Cool cool water / San Miquel / School day / Good timin' / Sail on sailor / Darlin' / Lady Lyndia / Sea cruise / Trader, The / This whole world / Don't go near the water / Surf's up / Come go with me / Diedre / She's got rhythm / River song / Long promised road / Feel flow's / Til I die / Surfin' USA / Then I kissed her / I can hear music / Fun, fun, fun / Don't worry baby / Cottonfield / Dance, dance, dance / Barbara Ann / Good vibrations / You're so good to me / Little deuce coupe / Surfer girl / When I grow up (to be a man) / In my room / Do you wanna dance / God only knows / Do it again / California girls / You still believe in me / Wendy / Help me Rhonda / Break away / Wouldn't it be nice / I get around / Darlin' / Here today / Sloop John B / Surfing safari / Good to my baby / Heroes and villains.
Notes: 105 Tracks including: Fun fun fun; Barbara Ann; Wouldn't it be nice; Help me Rhonda; Good Vibrations plus 100 more. Presentation box with free book - Free 17 track collectors album 'The Brian Wilson Productions'. These albums (or cassettes) available only by mail order direct from World Records, Freepost, Richmond, Surrey TW9 1BH.
Album: released on Caribou in Jun'85 by Epic Records. Distributed by: CBS

Cassette: released on Caribou in Jun'85 by Epic Records. Distributed by: CBS

Compact disc: released on Caribou in Jun'85 by Epic Records. Distributed by: CBS

Double cassette: released on Cambra in '83 by Cambra Records. Distributed by: IDS, Conifer

Album: released on Music For Pleasure (Holland) in Apr'83 by EMI Records. Distributed by: EMI

Cassette: released on Music For Pleasure (Holland) in Apr'83 by EMI Records. Distributed by: EMI

Cassette: released on Audio Fidelity in Oct'84. Distributed by: PRT

Compact disc: released on Intertape in Jul'87. Distributed by: Target

BEACH BOYS CONCERT.
Tracks: / Fun fun fun / Little old lady from Pasadena / Little deuce coupe / Long tall Texan / In my room / Monster mash / Let's go tripping / Papa oom mow mow / Wanderer / Hawaii / Graduation day / Johnny B.Goode.
Cassette: released on Capitol in Jun'81 by Capitol Records. Distributed by: EMI

BEACH BOYS MEDLEY.
Single (7"): released on Capitol in Jul'83 by Capitol Records. Distributed by: EMI

BEACH BOY'S PARTY.
Tracks: / Baby hully gully / I should have known better / Tell me why / Papa-oom-mow-mow / Mountain of love / You've got to hide your love away / Devoted to you / Alley oop / There's no other (like my baby) / I get around / Little deuce coupe / Times they are a changing, The / Barbara Ann.
Album: released on Capitol in Jul'86 by Capitol Records. Distributed by: EMI

Cassette: released on Capitol in Jul'86 by Capitol Records. Distributed by: EMI

BEACH BOYS RARITIES.
Tracks: / With a little help from my friends / Letter, The / I was made to love her / You're welcome / Lord's prayer / Bluebirds over the mountain / Celebrate the news / Good vobrations / Land ahoy / In my room / Cotton fields / All I want to do / Auld lang syne.
Album: released on Capitol in '85 by Capitol Records. Distributed by: EMI

Cassette: released on Capitol in '85 by Capitol Records. Distributed by: EMI

BEACH BOYS (THE).
Album: released on World Records in Dec'81. Distributed by: Polygram

Cassette: released on World Records in Dec'81. Distributed by: Polygram

BEACH BOYS, THE.
Tracks: / Betcha back / It's getting late / Crack at your love / Maybe I don't know / She believes in love again / California calling / Passing friend / I'm so lonely / I do love you / Where I belong / It's just a matter of time / Fun fun fun / Barbara Ann / Wouldn't it be nice / Help me Rhonda / Good vibrations.

BEACH BOYS VS. JAN & DEAN 15 greatest hits (Beach Boys/Jan & Dean).
Compact disc: released on Bescol in Jul'87. Distributed by: Target

CALIFORNIA DREAMING.
Tracks: / California dreaming / Lady liberty / Beach Boy's ballads (medley).
Single (7"): released on Capitol in Sep'86 by Capitol Records. Distributed by: EMI

Single (12"): released on Capitol in Sep'86 by Capitol Records. Distributed by: EMI

CAPITOL YEARS (THE).
Album: released on Pathe MarconiFrance) in Jun'85

COLLECTION: BEACH BOYS.
Album: released on EMI (Germany) in '83 by EMI Records. Distributed by: Conifer

Album: released on EMI (Germany) in '83 by EMI Records. Distributed by: Conifer

DISQUE D'OR.
Tracks: / I get around / Fun fun fun / Surfin' USA / Shut down / Little deuce coupe / Dance dance dance / California girls / Barbara Ann / Then I kissed her / Sloop John B. / God only knows / Good vibrations / Do it again / I can hear music.
Album: released on EMI (France) in '83 by EMI Records. Distributed by: Conifer

DO IT AGAIN.
Tracks: / Warmth of the sun / 409 / Catch a wave / Lonely sea / Do it again / Long tall Texan / Wild honey / Darlin' / Please let me wonder / Let him run wild / Country air / I know there's an answer / Friends / Heroes and villains.
Album: released on MFP in Oct'86 by EMI Records. Distributed by: EMI

Cassette: released on Music For Pleasure in Oct'86 by EMI Records. Distributed by: EMI

ENDLESS SUMMER.
Tracks: / Surfin' safari / Surfer girl / Catch a wave / Warmth of the sun (The) / Surfin' USA / Be true to your school / Little deuce coupe / In my room / Shut down / Fun fun fun / I get around / Girls on the beach (The) / Wendy / Let him run wild / Don't worry baby / California girls / Girl don't tell me / Help me Rhonda / You're so good to me / All summer long / Good vibrations.
Compact disc: released on EMI in Mar'87 by EMI Records. Distributed by: EMI

Album: released on Music For Pleasure (Holland) in Sep'81 by EMI Records. Distributed by: EMI

Cassette: released on Music For Pleasure (Holland) in Sep'81 by EMI Records. Distributed by: EMI

GETCHA BACK.
Single (12"): released on Caribou in Jul'85 by Epic Records. Distributed by: CBS

GIRLS ON THE BEACH.
Tracks: / Girls on the beach / In my room / Hushabye / We'll run away / California girls / Surfer girl / God only knows / Caroline no.
Cassette: released on Capitol in Jun'80 by Capitol Records. Distributed by: EMI

GOOD VIBRATIONS.
Single (7"): released on Capitol in Jun'79 by Capitol Records. Distributed by: EMI

Single (7"): released on EMI (France) in Apr'83 by EMI Records. Distributed by: Conifer

Album: released on Capitol in Nov'81 by Capitol Records. Distributed by: EMI

Cassette: released on Capitol in Nov'81 by Capitol Records. Distributed by: EMI

L.A. (LIGHT ALBUM).
Tracks: / Shortenin' bread / Good Timin' / Lady Lynda / Full sail / Angel come home / Love surrounds me / Sumahama / Here comes the night / Baby blue / Goin' south / Good timin' / Lady Lynda / Full sail / Angel come home / Love surrounds me / Sumahmama / Here comes the night / Baby blue / Goin' South / Shortenin bread.
Album: released on Caribou in Aug'86 by Epic Records. Distributed by: CBS

Cassette: released on Caribou in Aug'86 by Epic Records. Distributed by: CBS

LITTLE DEUCE COUPE.
Tracks: / Little deuce coupe / Ballad of 'ole Betsy / Be true to your school / Car crazy cutie / Cherry cherry coupe / 409 / Shut down / Spirit of America / Our car club / No-go showboat / Young man is gone, A / Custom machine.
Album: released on Capitol in Jul'86 by Capitol Records. Distributed by: EMI

Cassette: released on Capitol in Jul'86 by Capitol Records. Distributed by: EMI

MADE IN THE USA.
Tracks: / Surfin' safari / 409 / Surfin' U.S.A. / Be true to your school / Surfer girl / Dance dance dance / Fun fun fun / I get around / Help me Rhonda / Don't worry baby / California girls / When I grow up to be a man / Barbara Ann / Good vibrations / Heroes & villains / Wouldn't it be nice / Sloop John B / God only knows / Caroline no / Do it again.
Compact disc: by Capitol Records. Distributed by: EMI

Album: released on Capitol in Aug'86 by Capitol Records. Distributed by: EMI

Cassette: released on Capitol in Aug'86 by Capitol Records. Distributed by: EMI

PET SOUNDS.
Tracks: / Caroline no / Wouldn't it be nice / You still believe in me / That's not me / Don't talk (put your head on my shoulder) / I'm waiting for the day / Let's go away for a while / Sloop John B / God only knows / I know there's an answer / Here today / I just wasn't made for these times / Pet sounds.
Album: released on Capitol in Jun'86 by Capitol Records. Distributed by: EMI

Cassette: released on Capitol in Jun'86 by Capitol Records. Distributed by: EMI

PROFILE.
Tracks: / Surfin' safari / Judy / 409 / Beach boy stomp / What is a young girl / Surfer girl / Barbee / Ludy / Surfin' / Little deuce coop.
Album: released on Teldec (Germany) in Jun'82 by Import Records. Distributed by: IMS Distribution, Polygram Distribution

Cassette: released on Teldec (Germany) in Jun'82 by Import Records. Distributed by: IMS Distribution, Polygram Distribution

ROCK'N'ROLL TO THE RESCUE.
Tracks: / Rock'n'roll to the rescue / Good vibrations / Rock'n'roll to the rescue (radio version).
Single (7"): released on Capitol in Jul'86 by Capitol Records. Distributed by: EMI

Single (12"): released on Capitol in Aug'86 by

Capitol Records. Distributed by: EMI

SLOOP JOHN B.
Single (7"): released on Capitol (Holland) in Jul'84 by Capitol Records. Distributed by: Conifer

SPIRIT OF AMERICA.
Tracks: / Dance dance dance / Break away / Young man is gone, A / 409 / Little girl I once knew (The) / Spirit of America / Little Honda / Hushabye / Hawaii / Drive-in / Good to my baby / Teel me why / Do you remember? / This car of mine / Please let me wonder / Why do fools fall in love / Custom machine / Barbara Ann / Salt Lake City / Don't back down / When I grow up (to be a man) / Do you wanna dance / Graduation day.

SPIRIT OF AMERICA,THE.
Compact disc: released on Capitol in '87 by Capitol Records. Distributed by: EMI

SUMMER DAYS (AND SUMMER NIGHTS).
Tracks: / Girl from New York City, The / Amusement park U.S.A. / Then I kissed her / Salt Lake City / Girl don't tell me / Help me Rhonda / California girls / Let him run wild / You're so good for me / Summer means new love / I'm bugged at my ol' man / And your dreams come true.
Album: released on Capitol in Jun'86 by Capitol Records. Distributed by: EMI

Cassette: released on Capitol in Jun'86 by Capitol Records. Distributed by: EMI

SUPERGOLD.
Double Album: released on EMI (Germany) in '83 by EMI Records. Distributed by: Conifer

SURFER GIRL.
Tracks: / Surfer girl / Catch a wave / Surfer moon, The / South bay surfer / Rocking surfer, The / Little deuce coupe / In my room / Hawaii / Surfer's rule / Our car club / Your summer dream / Boogie woogie / Surfin' / Barbi / Karate / Luan / Surfer girl / Surfer's stomp / Balboa blue / Surfin' safari / What is a young girl made of / Wipe out / Don't go near the water.
Album: released on Capitol in Jul'86 by Capitol Records. Distributed by: EMI

Cassette: released on Capitol in Jul'86 by Capitol Records. Distributed by: EMI

Album: released on Topline in Nov'84 by Charly Records. Distributed by: Charly Distribution

Cassette: released on Topline in Nov'84 by Charly Records. Distributed by: Charly Distribution

SURFIN' SAFARI.
Single (7"): released on Creole Replay in Aug'84 by Creole Records. Distributed by: PRT, Rhino

SURF'S UP.
Tracks: / Long promised road / Long promised road / Take a load off your feet / Disney girls / Students demonstration time / Feel flows / Lookin at tomorrow / Day in the life of a tree, A / Till I die / Surf's up.
Album: released on Caribou in Nov'81 by Epic Records. Distributed by: CBS

TEN YEARS OF HARMONY.
Album: released on CBS in Sep'84 by CBS Records. Distributed by: CBS

Cassette: released on CBS in Sep'84 by CBS Records. Distributed by: CBS

VERY BEST OF THE BEACH BOYS.
Tracks: / Surfin' safari / Surfin' USA / Shutdown / Little deuce coupe / In my room / Fun,fun,fun / I get around / Don't worry baby / When I grow up(to be a man) / Wendy / Little Honda / Dance dance dance / All summer long / Do you wanna dance / Help me Rhonda / California girls / Little girl I once knew / Barbara Ann / You're so good for me / Then I kissed her / Sloop John B / God only knows / Wouldn't it be nice / Here today / Good vibrations / Heroes & villains / Wild honey / Darlin' / Country air / Here comes the night / Friends / Do it again / Bluebirds over the mountains / I can hear music / Breakaway / Cottonfields.
Notes: This is a 36 track compilation of the Beach Boys classic Capitol record hits.
Album: released on EMI (Capitol) in Jul'83 by Capitol Records. Distributed by: EMI

Cassette: released on EMI (Capitol) in Jul'83 by Capitol Records. Distributed by: EMI

WIPE OUT.
Album: released on Meteor in Oct'86 by Magnum Music Group Ltd. Distributed by: Magnum Music Group Ltd, PRT Distribution, Spartan Distribution

Beach Coma

SHOTGUN.
Single (7"): released on Baskerville in Jul'84. Distributed by: Pinnacle

Beach-la-Mar

BREAKDOWN.
Tracks: / While the beat goes on.
Single (7"): released on Pure Joy in Dec'86

Beachnuts

RAVING ON THE BEACH.
Single (7"): released on Vista Sounds in Sep'83 by Vista Sounds Records. Distributed by: Jetstar

Single (12"): released on Vista Sounds in Sep'83 by Vista Sounds Records. Distributed by: Jetstar

Beacon, Kim

TALKING TO MYSELF.
Album: released on Rialto in Dec'81 by Rialto Records. Distributed by: Pinnacle

Cassette: released on Rialto in Dec'81 by Rialto Records. Distributed by: Pinnacle

Beadle, Rob

ROB AND HIS MUSIC.
Tracks: / At the Woodchoppers Ball / Try a little tenderness / Lady be good / Somebody loves me / Lady is a tramp, The / Don't get around much anymore / Sunny side of the street / Time after time / I'll string along with you / Whiffenpoof song / Umberella man, The / Around the world / Whispering / Yours / Can't buy me love / All my loving / Hello Dolly / It's de lovely / Mame / Cabaret / New York, New York / I don't want to set the world on fire / I'm always chasing rainbows / Amor amor amor / Brazil / What I did for love / I left my heart in San Francisco / We'll meet again.
Notes: Rob Beadle playing the Elka X 705 Electronic Organ.
Album: released on Grosvenor in Sep'83 by Grosvenor Records. Distributed by: Taylors

Beamer, Kapono

DAYDREAMS.
Album: released on Intersound in Dec'86 by Intersound Records. Distributed by: Jazz Music

Bean, Billy

BEAN BAG (an album of Adult Humour).
Album: released on Climber in May'85 by Climber Records. Distributed by: PRT

Cassette: released on Climber in May'85 by Climber Records. Distributed by: PRT

Bearburger

BEARBURGER.
Cassette: released on Uniton Records in Sep'84. Distributed by: Cartel

Bear, George

BEAR RAP.
Single (7"): released on Cambra in Nov'83 by Cambra Records. Distributed by: IDS, Conifer

Bearman, Louisa

POEMS IN THE LANCASHIRE DIALECT.
Album: released on Big Ben in Apr'81 by Big Ben Records. Distributed by: Spartan, Taylor,

Bears

BEAR ESSENTIALS.
Tracks: / He's gonna get me / Back to the drawing board / Happy go lucky / Newsman / Quiet one, The / Anorak city / Cruising down the Rhine / Roundabout romeoes / Whistling in the dark / Donny Rimshott / Blood will run / I like dogs / After eights / Putting on the style.
Album: released on OK in May'81. Distributed by: Stage One Distribution

Cassette: released on OK in May'81. Distributed by: Stage One Distribution

INSANE.
Album: released on Tigerbeat in 11 Apr'87

Bearz

DARWIN.
Single (7"): released on Occult in Apr'84. Distributed by: Cartel Distribution

Beasley, Jimmy

JIMMY'S HOUSEPARTY.
Album: released on Ace in Jan'87 by Ace Records. Distributed by: Pinnacle, Swift, Hotshot, Cadillac

Beasley, Paul

MY SOUL IS FREE.
Album: released on Myrrh in Aug'84 by Word Records. Distributed by: Word Distribution

Cassette: released on Myrrh in Aug'84 by Word Records. Distributed by: Word Distribution

Beast

BEAST HAS ARRIVED, THE.
Album: released on Flame in Jul'86 by Nimbus Records. Distributed by: Nimbus, Swift

NEW MOONE.
Single (7"): released on I.D. in Dec'83 by I.D. Records. Distributed by: Revolver, Cartel

Single (12"): released on I.D. in Dec'83 by I.D. Records. Distributed by: Revolver, Cartel

Beastie Boys

COOKY PUSS (EP).
Tracks: / Cooky dub / Bonus batter / Beastie revolution / Cooky puss censored.
Extended-play record: released on Rat Cage in Jul'87

FIGHT FOR YOUR RIGHT (TO PARTY)-(YOU GOTTA).
Tracks: / Time to Get Ill.
Single (7"): released on Def Jam (USA) in Feb'87 by CBS Records. Distributed by: CBS

Single (12"): released on Def Jam (USA) in Feb'87 by CBS Records. Distributed by: CBS

HOLD IT,NOW HIT IT.
Tracks: / Hold it,now hit it / Accapulco.
Single (7"): by CBS Records. Distributed by: CBS

Single (12"): released on Def Jam (USA) in May'87 by CBS Records. Distributed by: CBS

INTERVIEW PICTURE DISC.
Album: released on Baktabak in Jun'87 by Baktabak Records. Distributed by: Arabesque

IT'S THE NEW STYLE.
Tracks: / It's the new style / Paul Revere.
Single (12"): released on Def Jam (USA) in Nov'86 by CBS Records. Distributed by: CBS

LICENSED TO ILL.
Tracks: / Rhymin and stealin' / New Style (The) / She's crafty / Posse in effect / Slow ride / Girls / Fight for your right / No sleep till Brooklyn / Paul Revere / Hold it, now hit it. / Brass monkey / Slow and low / Time to get ill.
Album: released on Def Jam (USA) in Apr'87 by CBS Records. Distributed by: CBS

Cassette: released on Def Jam (USA) in Apr'87 by CBS Records. Distributed by: CBS

Compact disc: released on Def Jam (USA) in May'87 by CBS Records. Distributed by: CBS

NO SLEEP TILL BROOKLYN.
Tracks: / No sleep till Brooklyn / Posse in effect.
Single (7"): released on Def Jam (USA) in 23 May'87 by CBS Records. Distributed by: CBS

Picture disc single: released on Def Jam (USA) in 23 May'87 by CBS Records. Distributed by: CBS

Single (12"): released on Def Jam (USA) in 23 May'87 by CBS Records. Distributed by: CBS

POLLY WOG STEW.
Single (7"): released on Rat Cage in Nov'82

SHE'S ON IT.
Tracks: / She's on it / Slow'n'low / Hold it now hit it.
Single (7"): released on Def Jam (USA) in Sep'86 by CBS Records. Distributed by: CBS

Single (12"): released on Def Jam (USA) in Sep'86 by CBS Records. Distributed by: CBS

Single (7"): released on Def Jam (USA) in Jul'87 by CBS Records. Distributed by: CBS

Single (12"): released on Def Jam (USA) in Jul'87 by CBS Records. Distributed by: CBS

Single (7"): released on Def Jam (USA) in Jul'87 by CBS Records. Distributed by: CBS

Beasts Of Bourbon

AXEMAN'S JAZZ (THE).
Album: released on Hybrid in Oct'85 by Statik Records. Distributed by: Pinnacle

Beat

HAND'S OFF SHE'S MINE.
Single (7"): released on Go Feet in Feb'80 by Arista Records. Distributed by: RCA

I JUST CAN'T STOP IT.
Tracks: / Mirror in the bathroom / Hands off-she's mine / Two swords / Twist & crawl / Rough rider / Click click / Big shot / White & grine / Stand down Margaret / Noise in this world / Can't get used to losing you / Best friend / Jackpot.
Album: released on Go Feet in May'80 by Arista Records. Distributed by: RCA

Cassette: released on Go Feet in May'80 by Arista Records. Distributed by: RCA

Album: released on Fame (Arista) in Mar'84 by Music For Pleasure Records. Distributed by: EMI

Cassette: released on Fame (Arista) in Mar'84 by Music For Pleasure Records. Distributed by: EMI

Cassette: released on Go Feet in Aug'83 by Arista Records. Distributed by: RCA

MIRROR IN THE BATHROOM.
Single (7"): released on Go Feet in Apr'80 by Arista Records. Distributed by: RCA

SPECIAL BEAT SERVICE.
Tracks: / I confess / Jeanette / Sorry / Sole salvation / Spar wid me / Rotating head / Save it for later / She's going / Ago talk / Sugar & stress / End of the party / Acke 123.
Album: released on Go Feet in Sep'82 by Arista Records. Distributed by: RCA

Cassette: released on Go Feet in Sep'82 by Arista Records. Distributed by: RCA

TEARS OF A CLOWN.
Single (7"): released on Two-Tone in Dec'79 by Chrysalis Records. Distributed by: H.R. Taylor

THESE NIGHTS.
Single (7"): released on New Town in Mar'83

WHA'PPEN.
Tracks: / Door of your heart / All out to get you / Monkey murders / I am your flag / French toast / Drowning / Dreamhome in N-Z / Walk away / Over & over / Cheated / Get a job / Limits we set, The.
Album: released on Go Feet in May'81 by Arista Records. Distributed by: RCA

Cassette: released on Go Feet in May'81 by Arista Records. Distributed by: RCA

WHAT IS BEAT? (the best of Beat).
Tracks: / Tears of a clown / Hands off ...she's mine / Mirror in the bathroom / Stand down Margaret / Twist and crawl / Doors of your heart / Save it for later / Too nice to talk to / I confess / Best friend / Drowning / Ackee 1-2-3 / Can't get used to losing you / Rankin' full stop.
Notes: Following the Top 5 success of "Can't get used to losing you", Arista release "What is beat?", a compilation of The Beat's greatest hits. This is the definitive collection, including their first hit single on Two-Tone, "Tears of a clown". A special 'double-take' cassette carries the full album on one side, and on the reverse, features extended remixes of some of the hits for life.
Album: released on Go Feet in May'83 by Arista Records. Distributed by: RCA

Cassette: released on Go Feet in May'83 by Arista Records. Distributed by: RCA

Beatboy A

HONEYDRIPPER, THE.
Tracks: / Please please 82.
Single (7"): released on Waterloo Sunset in 30 May'87 by Waterloo Sunset Records. Distributed by: MIS-EMI Distribution, Backs

Beat Boys

B BOP ROCK (2 parts).
Single (12"): released on I.R.S.(Independent Record Syndicate) in Jul'83 by I.R.S.. Distributed by: MCA

Beat Direction

LONG DISTANT BEAT.
Album: released on Hi-Lo in Feb'85 by Hi-Lo Records. Distributed by: Nine Mile, Cartel

Beat Farmers

BIGGER STONES.
Single (7"): released on Demon in Jul'85 by Demon Records. Distributed by: Pinnacle

GLAD 'N' GREASY.
Album: released on Demon in Apr'86 by Demon Records. Distributed by: Pinnacle

POWDER FINGER.
Tracks: / Powder finger / Big ugly wheels / Come sail at the church / Come sail at the church.
Single (7"): released on MCA in Jun'86 by MCA Records. Distributed by: Polygram, MCA

Single (12"): released on MCA in Jun'86 by MCA Records. Distributed by: Polygram, MCA

TALES OF THE NEW WEST.
Album: released on Demon in Feb'85 by Demon Records. Distributed by: Pinnacle

VAN GO.
Tracks: / Riverside / Deceiver / Powderfinger / Seven year blues / Blue Chevrolet / I want you too / Road of ruin / Buy me a car / Gun sale at the church / Bigger fool than me / Big ugly wheels.
Notes: San Diego's finest rock'n'roll band presented in all their glory on their first MCA album.The album was produced by Craig Leon,most recently responsible for "Spirit in the sky".
Album: released on MCA in Jul'86 by MCA Records. Distributed by: Polygram, MCA

Cassette: released on MCA in Jul'86 by MCA Records. Distributed by: Polygram, MCA

Beat Freaks

NATIONAL ANTHEM, THE.
Tracks: / National anthem / Government don't care (dub).
Single (12"): released on Supreme in Jun'86 by Supreme Records. Distributed by: PRT Distribution

Beat Generation...

BEAT GENERATION AND THE ANGRY YOUNG MEN Various artists (Various Artists).
Album: released on Well Suspect in Dec'84 by Well Suspect Records. Distributed by: Pinnacle

Beat Girl

BEAT GIRL Soundtrack various artists (Soundtrack various artists).
Album: released on Big Beat in Mar'85 by Ace Records. Distributed by: Projection, Pinnacle

Beat Happening

BEAT HAPPENING.
Album: released on Rough Trade in Nov'86 by Rough Trade Records. Distributed by: Rough Trade Distribution, Cartel Distribution

Beating Hearts

LOVE BEAT KID On the nod.
Cassette: released on Stupid Rabbit Tapes in '83. Distributed by: Stupid Rabbit Tapes

RETROSPECTIVE JEALOUSY.
Cassette: released on Stupid Rabbit Tapes in '82. Distributed by: Stupid Rabbit Tapes

Beating the meat...

BEATING THE MEAT... Various artists (Various Artists).
Album: released on Xcentric Noise in Sep'84 by Xcentric Noise Records & Tapes Records. Distributed by: Cartel

Beat Is On

BEAT IS ON, THE (Various Artists).
Album: released on Stateside in Jul'87. Distributed by: EMI

Cassette: released on Stateside in Jul'87. Distributed by: EMI

Beatitudes

HOME ALONE.
Single (7"): released on Exile in May'87 by Exile Records. Distributed by: Pinnacle

Beatles

1962-1966.
Tracks: / Love me do / Please please me / From me to you / She loves you / I want to hold your hand / All my loving / Can't buy me love / Hard days night, A / And I love her / Eight days a week / I feel fine / Ticket to ride / Yesterday / Help / You've got to hide your love away / We can work it out / Day tripper / Drive my car / Norwegian wood(this bird has flown) / Nowhere man / Michelle / In my life / Girl / Paperback writer / Eleanor Rigby / Yellow Submarine.
Album: released on Parlophone in Jun'73 by EMI Records. Distributed by: EMI

Cassette: released on Parlophone in Jun'73 by EMI Records. Distributed by: EMI

1967-1970.
Tracks: / Strawberry fields forever / Penny lane / Sgt. Pepper's lonely hearts club / With a little help from my friends / Lucy in the sky with diamonds / Day in the life, A / All you need is love / I am the walrus / Hello goodbye / Fool on the hill, The / Magical mystery / Lady Madonna / Hey Jude / Revolution / Back in the U.S.S.R. / While my guitar weeps / Ob la di ob la da / Get back / Don't let me down / Ballad of John & Yoko, The / Old brown shoe / Here comes the sun / Come together / Something / Octopus's garden / Let it be / Across the universe / Long and winding road, The.
Album: released on Parlophone in Jun'73 by EMI Records. Distributed by: EMI

Cassette: released on Parlophone in Jun'73 by EMI Records. Distributed by: EMI

20 GOLDEN HITS.
Tracks: / She loves you / I want to hold your hand / Can't buy me love / Hard day's night, A / Ticket to ride / Help / Something / We can work it out / Michelle / Hey Jude / All you need is love / Penny Lane / With a little help from my friends / Lady Madonna / Paperback writer / Ob-la-di,ob-la-da / Yesterday / Get back / Here comes the sun / Let it be.
Album: released on EMI (France) in '83 by EMI Records. Distributed by: Conifer

26 SINGLES (THE).
Single (7"): released on Parlophone in Dec'82 by EMI Records. Distributed by: EMI

ABBEY ROAD.
Tracks: / Come together / Something / Maxwell's silver hammer / Oh darling / Octopus's garden / I want you (she's so heavy) / Here comes the sun / Because / You never give me your money / Sun king / Mean Mr Mustard / Polythene Pam / She came in through the bathroom window / Golden slumbers / Carry the weight / End of her majesty The.
Album: released on Parlophone in Nov'69 by EMI Records. Distributed by: EMI

Cassette: released on Parlophone in Nov'69 by EMI Records. Distributed by: EMI

Compact disc: released on Parlophone in Oct'87 by EMI Records. Distributed by: EMI. Estim retail price in Sep'87 was £11.99.

ALL MY LOVING.
Extended-play record: released on Parlophone in Feb'64 by EMI Records. Distributed by: EMI

ALL YOU NEED IS LOVE.
Tracks: / All you need is love / Baby, you're a rich man.
Picture disc single: released on Parlophone in Jul'87 by EMI Records. Distributed by: EMI

Single (12"): released on Parlophone in Jul'87 by EMI Records. Distributed by: EMI

Cassette single: released on EMI in Jul'87 by EMI Records. Distributed by: EMI

ALL YOU NEED IS LOVE.
Single (7"): released on Parlophone in Jul'67 by EMI Records. Distributed by: EMI

BACK IN THE USSR.
Single (7"): released on Parlophone in Jun'76 by EMI Records. Distributed by: EMI

BALLAD OF JOHN AND YOKO.
Single (7"): released on Apple in May'69. Distributed by: EMI

BEATLE INTERVIEWS (THE).
Album: released on Premier in '84 by Premier Records. Distributed by: CBS

Cassette: released on Premier in '84 by Premier Records. Distributed by: CBS

BEATLES.
Extended-play record: released on Parlophone in Dec'81 by EMI Records. Distributed by: EMI

Album: released on Contour in Jun'76 by Pickwick Records. Distributed by: Pickwick Distribution, PRT

Cassette: released on Contour in Jun'76 by Pickwick Records. Distributed by: Pickwick Distribution, PRT

BEATLES '65.
Tracks: / She's a woman / I'm a loser / I feel fine.
Notes: A European compilation aimed mainly towards collectors of the Fab Four's rarest issues. Tracks include :'She's a woman' 'I'm a loser' & 'I feel fine'.
Album: released on EMI Electrola (Germany) in Jul'83 by EMI Records. Distributed by: Conifer

Cassette: released on EMI Electrola (Germany) in Jul'83 by EMI Records. Distributed by: Conifer

BEATLES AT THE HOLLYWOOD BOWL (THE).
Tracks: / Twist & shout / She's a woman / Dizzy Miss Lizzy / Ticket to ride / Can't buy me love / Things we said today / Roll over Beethoven / Boys / Hard day's night, A / Help / All my loving / She loves you / Long tall sally.
Notes: On Music For Pleasure-the unique record of the Beatles at The Hollywood Bowl. Reproduced in the original sleeve,the excitement of the occasion leaps from the grooves as the Beatles perform all their early hits including 'Help','Hard day's night', 'Roll over Beethoven' and many more.
Album: released on Music For Pleasure in Sep'84 by EMI Records. Distributed by: EMI

Cassette: released on Music For Pleasure in Sep'84 by EMI Records. Distributed by: EMI

BEATLES BALLADS.
Tracks: / Yesterday / Norweigan wood (this bird has flown) / Do you want to know a secret / For no one / Michelle / You've got to hide your love away / Across the universe / Herecomes the sun / Blackbird / And I love her / She's leaving home / Here an there and everywhere / let it be me.
Album: released on Parlophone in Oct'80 by EMI Records. Distributed by: EMI

Cassette: released on Parlophone in Oct'80 by EMI Records. Distributed by: EMI

BEATLES BEAT (THE).
Tracks: / She loves you / Thank you girl / From me to you / I'll get you / I want to hold your hand / Hold me tight / Can't buy me love / You can't do that / Roll over Beethoven / Till there was you / Money / Please Mr. Postman.
Album: released on EMI (Germany) in '83 by EMI Records. Distributed by: Conifer

BEATLES BOX SET.
Album: released on Parlophone in Dec'78 by EMI Records. Distributed by: EMI

Cassette: released on Parlophone in Dec'78 by EMI Records. Distributed by: EMI

BEATLES BOX (THE).
Album: released on World Records in '81. Distributed by: Polygram

Cassette: released on World Records in '81. Distributed by: Polygram

BEATLES FOR SALE.
Tracks: / No Reply / I'm A Loser / Baby's In Black / Rock And Roll Music / I'll Follow The Sun / Mr Moonlight / Kansas City/Hey, Hey, Hey / Eight Days A Week / Words Of Love / Honey Don't / Every Little Thing / Don't Want To Spoil The Party / What You're Doing / Everybody"s Trying To Be My Baby.
Compact disc: by EMI Records. Distributed by: EMI

BEATLES FOR SALE.
Album: released on Parlophone in Jan'65 by EMI Records. Distributed by: EMI

Album: released on Parlophone in Jun'81 by EMI Records. Distributed by: EMI

Cassette: released on Parlophone in Jan'65 by EMI Records. Distributed by: EMI

BEATLES FOR SALE NO 2.
Extended-play record: released on Parlophone in Jun'65 by EMI Records. Distributed by: EMI

BEATLES FOR SALE NO 1.
Extended-play record: released on Parlophone in Apr'65 by EMI Records. Distributed by: EMI

BEATLES GREATEST HITS, THE.
Tracks: / Love me do / From me to you / She loves you / I want to hold your hand / Can't buy me love / Hard day's night / I feel fine / Ticket to ride / Help / Day tripper / We can work it out / Paperback writer / Yellow Submarine / Eleanor Rigby / All you need is love / Hello goodbye / Lady Madonna / Hey Jude / Get back / Ballad of John & Yoko.
Notes: 20 of the Fab Four's all-time best sellers combined for the first time ever on one record since it all began 20 years ago.
Album: released on Parlophone in Oct'82 by EMI Records. Distributed by: EMI

Cassette: released on Parlophone in Oct'82 by EMI Records. Distributed by: EMI

BEATLES' HITS.
Single (7"): released on Parlophone in Sep'63 by EMI Records. Distributed by: EMI

BEATLES IN ITALY (THE).
Album: released on EMI (Holland) in '83 by EMI Records. Distributed by: Conifer

BEATLES-LIVE Ready steady go! (special).
Video-cassette (VHS): released on PMI in Jun'86 by PMI Records. Distributed by: EMI

Video-cassette [Betamax]: released on PMI in Jun'86 by PMI Records. Distributed by: EMI

BEATLES MILLION SELLERS.
Extended-play record: released on Parlophone in Dec'85 by EMI Records. Distributed by: EMI

BEATLES MOVIE MEDLEY.
Single (7"): released on Parlophone in May'82 by EMI Records. Distributed by: EMI

BEATLES NO 1.
Extended-play record: released on Parlophone in Nov'63 by EMI Records. Distributed by: EMI

BEATLES TALK DOWNUNDER - AUSTRALIA 1964 (THE).
Album: released on Goughsound in May'82 by Goughsound. Distributed by: Counterpoint

Cassette: released on Goughsound in May'82 by Goughsound. Distributed by: Counterpoint

Picture disc single: released on Goughsound in Feb'84 by Goughsound. Distributed by: Counterpoint

BEATLES TAPES/INTERVIEWS WITH DAVID WIGG.
Tracks: / Interview(part I) June 1969 / Give peace a chance / Interview(Part 2)June 1969 / Imagine / Interview (Part 3)June 1969 / Come together / Interview October 1971 / Interview(Part 1)March 1970 / Because / Interview(Part 2)March 1970 / Hey Jude / Interview(Part 1)March 1969 / Here comes the sun / Interview(Part 2)March 1969 / Something / Interview December 1968 / Interview July 1970 / Interview (Part 1)December 1973 / Octopus's Garden / Interview(Part 2)December 1973 / Yellow Submarine.
Cassette: released on Polydor in Oct'84 by Polydor Records. Distributed by: Polygram, Polydor

BEATLES (THE) (The White Album).
Tracks: / Back in the U.S.S.R. / Dear Prudence / Glass onion / Ob-la-di, ob-la-da / Wild honey pie / Continuing story of Bungalow Bill, The / While my guitar gently weeps / Happiness is a warm gun / Martha my dear / I'm so tired / Blackbird / Piggies / Rocky raccoon / Don't pass me by / Why don't we do it in the road / I will / Julia / Birthday / Yer blues / Mother nature's son / Everybody's got something to hide except me & my monkey / Sexy Sadie / Helter skelter / Long long ago / Revolution 1 / Honey pie / Savoy truffle / Cry baby cry / Revolution 9 / Good night / Back in the U.S.S.R / Dear Prudence / Glass onion / Ob-la-di, ob-la-da / Wild honey pie / Continuing story of bungalow Bill / While my guitar gently weeps / Happiness is a warm gun / Martha my dear / I'm so tired / Blackbird / Piggies / Rocky raccoon / Don't pass me by / Why don't we do it in the road / I will / Julia / Yer blues / Mother nature's son / Everybody's got something to hide except me and my donkey / Sexy Sadie / Helter skelter / Long long long / Revolution 1 / Honey pie / Savoy truffle / Cry baby cry / Revolution 9 / Good night.
Double Album: released on Parlophone in Dec'68 by EMI Records. Distributed by: EMI

Double Album: released on Parlophone in Jun'81 by EMI Records. Distributed by: EMI

Double cassette: released on Parlophone in Feb'68 by EMI Records. Distributed by: EMI

Compact disc: released on Parlophone in Aug'87 by EMI Records. Distributed by: EMI

BEATLES VOL 1 (THE).
Cassette: released on Audio Fidelity in Oct'84. Distributed by: PRT

BEATLES VOLUME 111 (THE).
Cassette: released on Audio Fidelity in Oct'84. Distributed by: PRT

BEATLES VOLUME 11 (THE).
Cassette: released on Audio Fidelity in Oct'84. Distributed by: PRT

BEATLES VOLUME IV (THE).
Cassette: released on Audio Fidelity in Oct'84. Distributed by: PRT

CAN'T BUY ME LOVE.
Single (7"): released on Parlophone in Mar'84 by EMI Records. Distributed by: EMI

Picture disc single: released on Parlophone in Mar'84 by EMI Records. Distributed by: EMI

COLLECTION: BEATLES.
Notes: The Beatles/the collection is much more than an assemblage of original master recordings by the Beatles. In the interests of the total authenticity, mobile fidelity sound lab has exclusively licensed the total album repertoire that the Beatles originally in England through EMI records limited. These LP's were issued from March, 1963 through May, 1970 and include 192 indiidual Beatles songs. It is a true limited edition collectors library. Each set includes a certificateof authenticity, hand numbered and signed to guarantee its enduring value. only a very limited number of these sets will be pressed and assembled by Mobile Fideltiy sound lab. Once total quantities are sold out, each set will rapidly increase in value (several of mobile fidelity sound lab's out of print original master recordings are now commanding prices among collectors of more than five times their original selling price). Each collection includes a large format artbook recounting the graphic history of original Beatles album covers artwork in beautiful colou. A chronological and technological account of the making of TheBeatles/The collection is also included, written by mobile fidelity sound lab's senior technical staff.
Album: released on Mobile Fidelity Sound Lab in Nov'82 by Mobile Fidelity Records

COLLECTION OF BEATLES OLDIES.
Tracks: / She loves you / From me to you / We can work it out / Help / Michelle / Yesterday / I feel fine / Yellow submarine / Can't buy me love / Bad boy / Hard days night A (from the film) / Ticket to ride / Paperback writer / Eleanor Rigby / I want to hold your hand.
Album: released on Fame (Parlophone) in Nov'83 by Music For Pleasure Records. Distributed by: EMI

Cassette: released on Fame (Parlophone) in Nov'83 by Music For Pleasure Records. Distributed by: EMI

COMPLEAT BEATLES, THE.
Video-cassette (VHS): released on MGM/UA in '86. Distributed by: Pickwick Distribution

COMPLETE SILVER BEATLES, THE.
Tracks: / Three cool cats / Crying, waiting, hoping / Besame mucho / Searchin' / Sheik of Araby / Money / To know him is to love him / Take good care of my baby / Memphis / Sure to fall / Till there was you / September in the rain.
Notes: 'The one that got away'-12 tracks from the tapes of the Beatles audition with Decca with Pete Best as drummer.
Album: released on Audio Fidelity in Sep'82. Distributed by: PRT

Cassette: released on Audio Fidelity in Sep'82. Distributed by: PRT

DAY TRIPPER.
Single (7"): released on Parlophone in Dec'65 by EMI Records. Distributed by: EMI

EARLY BEATLES VOL 1.
Tracks: / I saw her standing there / Roll over Beethoven / Hippy hippy shake / Sweet little shake / Gotta go home / Twist and shout / Mr moonlight / Taste of honey, A / Besame mucho / Reminiscing.
Album: released on Phoenix in Jul'81 by Audio Fidelity Enterprises. Distributed by: Stage One, Lugtons

EARLY BEATLES VOL 2.
Tracks: / Ain't nothing shakin (like leaves on a tree) / To know her is to love her / Little Queenie / Falling in love again / Ask me way / Red sails in the sunset / Everybody trying to be my baby / You ain't no friend / Talking about you / Shimmy shake.
Album: released on Phoenix in Jul'81 by Audio Fidelity Enterprises. Distributed by: Stage One, Lugtons

FIRST.
Tracks: / Ain't she sweet / Cry for a shadow / When the saints go marching in / Why / If you love me baby / What'd I say / Sweet Georgia Brown / Ruby baby / My Bonnie / Nobody's child / Ready teddy / Ya ya / Kansas City stomps.
Compact disc: released on Polydor in Dec'84 by Polydor Records. Distributed by: Polygram, Polydor

FROM ME TO YOU.
Single (7"): released on Parlophone in Apr'83 by EMI Records. Distributed by: EMI

Picture disc single: released on Parlophone in Apr'83 by EMI Records. Distributed by: EMI

GET BACK.
Single (7"): released on Apple in Apr'69. Distributed by: EMI

GOLDEN BEATLES (INTERVIEWS) (THE).

Album: released on Silhouette (USA) in Aug'85. Distributed by: Swift

GREATEST.
Tracks: / I want to hold your hand / Twist and shout / Hard day's night, A / 8 day's a week / I should have known better / Long tall Sally / She loves you / Please Mr postman / I feel fine / Rock and roll music / Ticket to ride / Please please me / It won't be long / From me to you / Can't buy me love / All my loving.
Album: released on EMI (Germany) in '83 by EMI Records. Distributed by: Conifer

HAMBURG 1961 Featuring Tony Sheridan (Beatles & Tony Sheridan).
Tracks: / Why (can't you love me again) / Cry for a shadow / Let's dance / Ya, ya / What'd I say / Ruby baby / Take out some insurance / Sweet Georgia Brown.
Compact disc: released on Topline in Apr'87 by Charly Records. Distributed by: Charly Distribution

HAMBURG 1961.
Album: released on Topline in Nov'84 by Charly Records. Distributed by: Charly Distribution

Cassette: released on Topline in Nov'84 by Charly Records. Distributed by: Charly Distribution

HARD DAY'S NIGHT, A.
Tracks: / I should have known better / If I fell / I'm happy just to dance with you / And I love her / Tell me why / Can't buy me love / Hard day's night, A / Anytime at all / I'll cry instead / Things we said today / When I get home / You can't do that / I'll be back.
Video-cassette (VHS): released on Vestron in Oct'84

Compact disc: released on EMI in Feb'87 by EMI Records. Distributed by: EMI

Single (7"): released on Parlophone in Jul'64 by EMI Records. Distributed by: EMI

Picture disc single: released on Parlophone in Jul'84 by EMI Records. Distributed by: EMI

Album: released on Parlophone in Aug'64 by EMI Records. Distributed by: EMI

Album: released on Parlophone in Jun'81 by EMI Records. Distributed by: EMI

Cassette: released on Parlophone in Aug'64 by EMI Records. Distributed by: EMI

Extended-play record: released on Parlophone in Nov'64 by EMI Records. Distributed by: EMI

Single (7"): released on Parlophone in Dec'64 by EMI Records. Distributed by: EMI

HARD DAY'S NIGHT, A (VIDEO).
Released by Vestron Video

HEAR THE BEATLES TELL ALL (a unique collectors item).
Notes: The album contains interviews with the Beatles made at the end of their second American tour in Los Angeles in 1965. Side one is taken up by a long interview with john Lennon, while the other Beatles are featured on side two
Album: released on Charly in Jan'81 by Charly Records. Distributed by: Charly, Cadillac

HELLO GOODBYE.
Single (7"): released on Parlophone in Nov'67 by EMI Records. Distributed by: EMI

HELP.
Tracks: / Help / Night before (The) / You've got to hide your love away / I need you / Another girl / You're going to lose that girl / Ticket to ride / Act naturally / It's only love / You like me too much / Tell me what you see / I've just seen a face / Yesterday / Dizzy Miss Lizzy.
Compact disc: released on Parlophone in Apr'87 by EMI Records. Distributed by: EMI

Album: released on Parlophone in Sep'65 by EMI Records. Distributed by: EMI

Album: released on Parlophone in Jun'81 by EMI Records. Distributed by: EMI

Cassette: released on Parlophone in Sep'65 by EMI Records. Distributed by: EMI

Single (7"): released on Parlophone in Jul'85 by EMI Records. Distributed by: EMI

Single (12"): released on Parlophone in Jul'85 by EMI Records. Distributed by: EMI

HEY JUDE.
Tracks: / Can't buy me love / I should have known / Rain / Lady Madonna / Hey Jude / Old brown shoe / Don't let me down.
Album: released on Parlophone in May'79 by EMI Records. Distributed by: EMI

Cassette: released on Parlophone in May'79 by EMI Records. Distributed by: EMI

Single (7"): released on Apple in Aug'68. Distributed by: EMI

HISTORY OF THE BEATLES.
Album: released on Masters (Holland) in Apr'87

Cassette: released on Masters (Holland) in Apr'87

I FEEL FINE.
Single (7"): released on Parlophone in Nov'84 by EMI Records. Distributed by: EMI

Picture disc single: released on Parlophone in Nov'84 by EMI Records. Distributed by: EMI

INTERVIEWS VOLUME 2.
Album:

Cassette: released on Premier in Feb'87 by Premier Records. Distributed by: CBS

I WANT TO HOLD YOUR HAND.
Single (7"): released on Parlophone in Nov'63 by EMI Records. Distributed by: EMI

Picture disc single: released on Parlophone in Nov'83 by EMI Records. Distributed by: EMI

LADY MADONNA.
Single (7"): released on Parlophone in Mar'68 by EMI Records. Distributed by: EMI

LET IT BE.
Tracks: / Two of us / Dig a pony / Across the universe / I me mine / Dig it / Let it be / Maggie Mae / I've got a feeling / One after 909 / The long and winding road / Get back.
Album: released on Parlophone in Jun'70 by EMI Records. Distributed by: EMI

Cassette: released on Parlophone in Jun'70 by EMI Records. Distributed by: EMI

Single (7"): released on Apple in Mar'70. Distributed by: EMI

LIVE AT THE STAR CLUB HAMBURG.
Tracks: / I saw here standing there / Roll over Beethoven / Hippy hippy shake / Sweet little sixteen / Lend me your comb / Your feets too big / Twist and shout / Mr moonlight / A taste of honey / Besame mucho / Reminicising / Medley: Kansas city / Hey hey hey / Ain't nothing shakin / To know her is to love her / Little Queenie / Falling in love again / Ask me why / Be bop a lula / Hallelujah / I love her so / Red sails in the sunset / Everybody's trying to be my baby / Matchbox / Talking about you / Shimmy shake / Long tall Sally / I remember you.
Album: released on Lingasong in May'77

LIVE -VOLUME 1.
Tracks: / I'm gonna sit right down & cry over you / Roll over Beethoven / Hippy hippy shake / Sweet little sixteen / Lend me your comb / Your feets too big / Where have you been all my life / Mr Moonlight / Taste of honey, A / Besame mucho / Til there was you / Kansas City / Hey hey hey hey.
Album: released on Showcase in Apr'86. Distributed by: Counterpoint

Cassette: released on Showcase in Apr'86. Distributed by: Counterpoint

LIVE- VOLUME 2.
Tracks: / Ain't nothing shakin'(but the leaves on the trees) / To know her is to love her / Little Queenie / Falling in love again / Sheila / Be-bop-a lula / Hallelujah I just love her so / Red sails in the sunset / Everybody's trying to be my baby / Match box / Talking about you / Shimmy shake / Long tall sally / I remember you.
Album: released on Showcase in Apr'86. Distributed by: Counterpoint

Cassette: released on Showcase in Apr'86. Distributed by: Counterpoint

LONG TALL SALLY.
Extended-play record: released on Parlophone in Aug'64 by EMI Records. Distributed by: EMI

LONG TALL SALLY (Beatles & Tony Sheridan).

LOVE AT THE STAR CLUB, HAMBURG.
Double Album: released on Lingasong in May'77

LOVE ME DO.
Single (7"): released on Parlophone in Oct'62 by EMI Records. Distributed by: EMI

Single (7"): released on Parlophone in Oct'62 by EMI Records. Distributed by: EMI

Single (12"): released on Parlophone in Nov'82 by EMI Records. Distributed by: EMI

LOVE SONGS.
Tracks: / Yesterday / I'll follow the sun / I'll get by / Girl in my life / Words of love / Here, there and everywhere / Something / I love her / If I fell / I'll be back / Tell me what you see / Yes it is / Michelle / It's only love / You're going to lose that girl / Every little thing I do / For no one / She's leaving home / Long and winding road, The / This boy / Norwegian wood / You've got to hide your love away / I will / PS I love you.
Double Album: released on Parlophone in Dec'77 by EMI Records. Distributed by: EMI

Double cassette: released on Parlophone in Dec'77 by EMI Records. Distributed by: EMI

MAGICAL MYSTERY TOUR (EP).
Tracks: / Magical mystery tour / Your mother should know / I am the walrus / Fool on the hill, The / Flying / Bue Jay Way.
Extended-play record: released on Parlophone in Dec'67 by EMI Records. Distributed by: EMI

MAGICAL MYSTERY TOUR.
Tracks: / Magical mystery tour / Fool on the hill, The / Flying / Blue jay way / Your mother should know / I am the walrus / Hello, goodbye / Strawberry fields forever / Penny Lane / Baby you're a rich man / All you need is love / Magical mystery tour / Fool in the hill, The / Flying / Blue jay way / Your mother should know / I am the walrus / Hello goodbye / Strawberry fields forever / Penny lane / Baby you're a rich man / All you need is love.
Album: released on Parlophone in Nov'76 by EMI Records. Distributed by: EMI

Cassette: released on Parlophone in Nov'76 by EMI Records. Distributed by: EMI

Compact disc: released on Parlophone in Sep'87 by EMI Records. Distributed by: EMI

NOWHERE MAN.
Single (7"): released on Parlophone in Jul'66 by EMI Records. Distributed by: EMI

PAPERBACK WRITER.
Tracks: / Paperback writer / Rain.
Single (7"): released on Parlophone in Jun'86 by EMI Records. Distributed by: EMI

Picture disc single: released on Parlophone in Jun'86 by EMI Records. Distributed by: EMI

Single (7"): released on Parlophone in Jun'66 by EMI Records. Distributed by: EMI

PLEASE PLEASE ME.
Album: released on Parlophone in May'63 by EMI Records. Distributed by: EMI

Album: released on Parlophone in Jun'81 by EMI Records. Distributed by: EMI

Cassette: released on Parlophone in May'63 by EMI Records. Distributed by: EMI

Single (7"): released on Parlophone in Jan'83 by EMI Records. Distributed by: EMI

Picture disc single: released on Parlophone in Jan'83 by EMI Records. Distributed by: EMI

PLEASE PLEASE ME.
Tracks: / Taste of honey, A / I Saw Her Standing There / Misery / Anna (Go To Him) / Chains / Boys / Ask Me Why / Please Please Me / Love Me Do / I Love You / Baby It's You / Do You Want To Know A Secret / There's a place / Twist And Shout.
Compact disc: released on EMI in Feb'87 by EMI Records. Distributed by: EMI

RARE BEATLES.
Album: released on Phoenix in '81 by Audio Fidelity Enterprises. Distributed by: Stage One, Lugtons

REEL MUSIC.
Album: released on Parlophone in Mar'82 by EMI Records. Distributed by: EMI

Cassette: released on Parlophone in Mar'82 by EMI Records. Distributed by: EMI

REVOLVER.
Tracks: / Taxman / Eleanor Rigby / I'm only sleeping / Love you too / Here, there and everywhere / Yellow submarine / She said she said / Good day sunshine / And your bird can sing / For no one / Doctor Robert / I want to tell you / Got to get you into my life / Tomorrow never knows.
Compact disc: released on Parlophone in Apr'87 by EMI Records. Distributed by: EMI

Album: released on Parlophone in Sep'66 by EMI Records. Distributed by: EMI

Album: released on Parlophone in Jun'81 by EMI Records. Distributed by: EMI

Cassette: released on Parlophone in Sep'86 by EMI Records. Distributed by: EMI

ROCK 'N' ROLL VOL 1.
Triple album / cassette: released on EMI Europe in Mar'83 by EMI Records. Distributed by: Conifer

Triple album / cassette: released on EEC Imports in Dec'82. Distributed by: IMS, Polygram

Album: released on MFP in Oct'80 by EMI Records. Distributed by: EMI

Cassette: released on MFP in Oct'80 by EMI Records. Distributed by: EMI

ROCK 'N' ROLL VOL 2.
Album: released on MFP in Oct'80 by EMI Records. Distributed by: EMI

Cassette: released on MFP in Oct'80 by EMI Records. Distributed by: EMI

RUBBER SOUL.
Tracks: / Drive my car / Norwegian wood (this bird has flown) / You won't see me / Nowhere man / Think for yourself / Word (The) / Michelle / What goes on / Girl / I'm looking through you / In my life / Wait / If I needed someone / Run for your life.
Compact disc: released on Parlophone in Apr'87 by EMI Records. Distributed by: EMI

Album: released on Parlophone in Feb'66 by EMI Records. Distributed by: EMI

Album: released on Parlophone in Jun'81 by EMI Records. Distributed by: EMI

Cassette: released on Parlophone in Feb'66 by EMI Records. Distributed by: EMI

SAVAGE YOUNG BEATLES, THE.
Tracks: / Why? / Cry for a shadow / Let's dance / Ya ya / What'd I say / Ruby baby / Take out some insurance / Sweet Georgia Brown.
Notes: Recorded by the Beatles in Hamburg, Germany 1961.
Album: released on Charly in '82 by Charly Records. Distributed by: Charly, Cadillac

SEARCHIN'.
Single (7"): released on Audio Fidelity in Nov'82. Distributed by: PRT

SERGEANTS PEPPER'S LONELY HEARTS CLUB BAND.
Album: released on Parlophone in Jun'67 by EMI Records. Distributed by: EMI

Album: released on Parlophone in Jun'81 by EMI Records. Distributed by: EMI

Cassette: released on Parlophone in Jun'67 by EMI Records. Distributed by: EMI

Single (7"): released on Parlophone in Sep'78 by EMI Records. Distributed by: EMI

SGT. PEPPER'S LONELY HEARTS CLUB BAND.
Tracks: / Within you, without you / When I'm 64 / Lovely Rita / Good morning good morning / Sgt. Pepper's Lonely Hearts Club Band / Day in the life / With a little help from my friends / Lucy in the sky with diamonds / Getting better / Fixing a hole / She's leaving home / Being for the benefit of Mr. Kite.
Compact disc: released on Parlophone in Jun'87 by EMI Records. Distributed by: EMI

SHE LOVES YOU.
Single (7"): released on Parlophone in Sep'83 by EMI Records. Distributed by: EMI

Picture disc single: released on Parlophone in Aug'83 by EMI Records. Distributed by: EMI

SILVER BEATLES BLACK & WHITE.
Picture disc album: released on Astan in Dec'86 by Astan Records. Distributed by: Counterpoint

SILVER BEATLES FULL COLOUR.
Picture disc album: released on Astan in Dec'85 by Astan Records. Distributed by: Counterpoint

SOMETHING.
Single (7"): released on Apple in Oct'69. Distributed by: EMI

SOMETHING NEW.
Album: released on EMI (Germany) in '83 by EMI Records. Distributed by: Conifer

STRAWBERRY FIELDS FOREVER.
Tracks: / Penny Lane.
Single (7"): released on Parlophone in Feb'87 by EMI Records. Distributed by: EMI

STRAWBERRY FIELDS FOREVER.
Single (7"): released on Parlophone in Feb'67 by EMI Records. Distributed by: EMI

TICKET TO RIDE.
Single (7"): released on Parlophone in Apr'85 by EMI Records. Distributed by: EMI

Picture disc single: released on Parlophone in Apr'85 by EMI Records. Distributed by: EMI

TIMELESS.
Picture disc album: released on Astan in Dec'85 by Astan Records. Distributed by: Counterpoint

TWIST AND SHOUT.
Single (7"): released on Parlophone in Sep'63 by EMI Records. Distributed by: EMI

WE CAN WORK IT OUT.
Single (7"): released on Parlophone in Nov'85 by EMI Records. Distributed by: EMI

Picture disc single: released on Parlophone in Nov'85 by EMI Records. Distributed by: EMI

WITH THE BEATLES.
Album: released on Parlophone in Dec'63 by EMI Records. Distributed by: EMI

Album: released on Parlophone in Jun'81 by EMI Records. Distributed by: EMI

Cassette: released on Parlophone in Dec'63 by EMI Records. Distributed by: EMI

WITH THE BEATLES.
Tracks: / It Won't Be Long / All I've Got To Do / All My loving / Don't Bother Me / Little Child / Till There Was You / Please Mr Postman / Roll Over Beethoven / Hold Me Tight / You Really Got A Hold On Me / I Wanna Be Your Man / Devil In Her Heart / Not a second time / Money.
Compact disc: released on EMI in Feb'87 by EMI Records. Distributed by: EMI

WORDS AND MUSIC.
Double Album: released on Cambra in Mar'85 by Cambra Records. Distributed by: IDS, Conifer

Double cassette: released on Cambra in Mar'85 by Cambra Records. Distributed by: IDS, Conifer

YELLLOW SUBMARINE.
Album: released on Parlophone in Jan'69 by EMI Records. Distributed by: EMI

Album: released on Parlophone in Jun'81 by EMI Records. Distributed by: EMI

Cassette: released on Parlophone in Jan'69 by EMI Records. Distributed by: EMI

Single (7"): released on Parlophone in Aug'66 by EMI Records. Distributed by: EMI

YELLOW SUBMARINE (7").
Tracks: / Yellow Submarine / Eleanor Rigby.
Single (7"): released on Parlophone in Aug'86 by EMI Records. Distributed by: EMI

Picture disc single: released on Parlophone in Aug'86 by EMI Records. Distributed by: EMI

Compact disc: released on Parlophone in Aug'87 by EMI Records. Distributed by: EMI

YELLOW SUBMARINE (CD).
Tracks: / Yellow submarine / Only a northern song / All together now / Hey bulldog / It's all too much / All you need is love / Pepperland / Sea of time / Sea of holes / Sea of monsters / March of the meanies / Pepperland laid waste / Yellow submarine in Pepperland.

YELLOW SUBMARINE (LP) Film soundtrack.
Tracks: / Yellow Submarine / Only a Northern Song / All you need is love / Hey bulldog / It's all too much / All together now / Pepperland / Sea of time / Sea of holes / Sea of monsters / March of the meanies / Pepperland laid to waste / Yellow submarine in Pepperland.
Album: released on Parlophone in '69 by EMI Records. Distributed by: EMI

Cassette: released on Parlophone in '69 by EMI Records. Distributed by: EMI

Album: released on Parlophone in Jun'81 by EMI Records. Distributed by: EMI

YESTERDAY.
Single (7"): released on Parlophone in Mar'76 by EMI Records. Distributed by: EMI

Extended-play record: releas ...n Parlophone in Mar'66 by EMI Records. Distributed by: EMI

Beatmasters

ROK DA HOUSE (Beatmasters & The Cookie Crew).
Single (7"): released on Rhythm King in Jul'87. Distributed by: Rough Trade, Cartel

Single (12"): released on Rhythm King in Jul'87. Distributed by: Rough Trade, Cartel

Beat Necessity

PLEASURE.
Single (7"): released on New Town in Feb'82

Beatniks

BEATNIKS (THE).
Album: released on Statik in Oct'82. Distributed by: Rough Trade Distribution, Stage One Distribution

Beat Poets

GLASGOW, HOWARD MISSOURI.
Extended-play record: released on 53rd & 3rd in 30 May'87 by Fast Forward Records. Distributed by: Fast Forward, Cartel

Beat Rodeo

EVERYTHING I'M NOT.
Tracks: / Everything I'm not / New love / True / Still in Hollywood.
Single (12"): released on IRS in Feb'87. Distributed by: Polygram

HOME IN THE HEART OF THE BEAT.
Tracks: / Twin Home Towns / Everything I'm Not / New Love / It Could Happen Here / (I Have) Everything I Need / I'm Not Afraid (Doesn't Matter To Me) / In The Summertime / Home In The Heart Of The Beat / Song For An Angry Young Man / It's Been Too Long / While We're Apart.
Album: released on I.R.S.(Independent Record Syndicate) in Feb'87 by I.R.S.. Distributed by: MCA

Cassette: released on I.R.S.(Independent Record Syndicate) in Feb'87 by I.R.S.. Distributed by: MCA

STAYING OUT LATE WITH THE BEAT RODEO.
Album: released on Zensor in Dec'84 by Zensor Records. Distributed by: Rough Trade

Beatroots

UNNECESSARY WAR.
Single (7"): released on Beatroot in Feb'82. Distributed by: Indies, Rough Trade

Beat Runs Wild

BEAT RUNS WILD Various artists (Various Artists).
Notes: Artists include: Hipsway,Wet Wet Wet,Tom Verlaine,Pete Shelley,Swing Out Sister, Love & Money,Brandon Cooke,Topper Headon,Zerra One,Curiosity Killed the Cat.
Album: released on Mercury in Jul'86 by Phonogram Records. Distributed by: Polygram Distribution

Beat Sharks

RUN AWAY.
Single (7"): released on Sedition - Pure Trash in Aug'85

Single (12"): released on Sedition - Pure Trash in Aug'85

Beatstreet

BEATSTREET Original Soundtrack.
Tracks: / Beat street breakdown / Baptize the beat / Strangers in a strange world / Frantic situation / Beat street strut / Us girls / This could be the night / Breaker's revenge / Tu carino - carmen's theme.
Compact disc: by WEA Records. Distributed by: WEA

BEAT STREET Original motion picture soundtrack.
Tracks: / Beat street breakdown / Baptize the beat / Strangers in a strange world / Frantic situation / Beat Street strut / US girls / This could be the night / Breaker's revenge / Tu Carino - Carmen's theme.
Album: released on Atlantic in Jul'84 by WEA Records. Distributed by: WEA

Cassette: released on Atlantic in Jul'84 by WEA Records. Distributed by: WEA

Compact disc: released on Atlantic in Jul'84 by WEA Records. Distributed by: WEA

BEATSTREET Original film soundtrack.
Compact disc: released on Atlantic in Sep'84 by WEA Records. Distributed by: WEA

BEAT STREET VOLUME 2 Original soundtrack (Various Artists).
Tracks: / Son of beat street / Give me all / Nothin's gonna come easy / Santa's rap / It's alright by me / Battle cry / Phony four MC's-wappin' / Into the night.
Album: released on Atlantic in Oct'84 by WEA Records. Distributed by: WEA

Cassette: released on Atlantic in Oct'84 by WEA Records. Distributed by: WEA

Beat Street Band

BEAT STREET.
Single (7"): released on Legacy in Jul'83. Distributed by: PRT

Single (12"): released on Legacy in Jul'83. Distributed by: PRT

Beat Temptation

BEAT TEMPTATION.
Album: released on Homestead in Aug'86. Distributed by: Rough Trade, Cartel, Shigaku

Beat The Drum

THIS CITY.
Single (7"): released on Loose in Oct'84 by Loose Records. Distributed by: Nine Mile, Cartel

Single (12"): released on Loose in Oct'84 by Loose Records. Distributed by: Nine Mile, Cartel

TRY.
Single (7"): released on Loose in Mar'84 by Loose Records. Distributed by: Nine Mile, Cartel

Single (12"): released on Loose in Mar'84 by Loose Records. Distributed by: Nine Mile, Cartel

Beattie, Johnny

GLASGOW RAP.
Single (7"): released on Klub in Nov'83

SINOOKER.
Single (7"): released on Klub in Nov'85

WELCOME TO THE CEILIDH.
Album: released on Nevis in Jul'81. Distributed by: H.R. Taylor

Cassette: released on Nevis in Jul'81. Distributed by: H.R. Taylor

Beau, Heinie

HEINIE BEAU & HIS HOLLYWOOD JAZZ QUARTET (Beau, Heinie & His Hollywood Jazz Quartet).
Album: released on Unknown in Jun'81

Beau Leisure

AMERICAN BEAT.
: released on W.O.R. in Jul'83 by Wor Records. Distributed by: Pinnacle

Beaumont, Howard

AS TIME GOES BY VOL.2 (Beaumont, Howard & John Taylor).
Album: released on Grosvenor in Sep'85 by Grosvenor Records. Distributed by: Taylors

CHRISTMAS MAGIC.
Tracks: / Sleigh ride / Mary's boy chid / In dulci jubilo / Winter wonderland / Let it snow, let it snow, let it snow / Christmas medley / Good King Wenceslas / Jingle bells / Rudolph the red nosed reindeer / Frosty the snowman / Christmas carols / Hark the herald angels sing / Away in a manger / Once in Royal David's city / While shepherds watched / Silent night / Ding dong merrily on high / When a child is born / When a child is born / I saw Mommy kissing Santa Claus / Christmas melody / Holly and the ivy / Joy to the world / God rest ye merry gentlemen / Christmas song / Ave Maria.
Album: released on Grosvenor in '78 by Grosvenor Records. Distributed by: Taylors

ELECTRIFYING.
Tracks: / Without a song / Bermuda triangle / You needed me / Dallas hoedown - Turkey in the straw / Jambalaya / Theme from Juliet Bravo / Hungry years / String of pearls / Continental, The / Piccolino, The / Somewhere over the rainbow / Romance / Love theme from Superman / Just the way you are / Star wars - vidor toccato.
Album: released on Grosvenor in Jun'81 by Grosvenor Records. Distributed by: Taylors

EMINENT ARTISTRY.
Tracks: / Skyliner / Arthurs theme / Tomorrow / Tomorrow / Waltz ballszene / Makin' whoopee / They can't take that away from me / Ease on down the road / Lonely sheperd / Easier said than done / Chopin nocturne op 27 no.2 / We're all alone / Samba medley / Samba medley - Brazil / Cavaquino / Wedding samba / Zambezi / To hell with him / Boomerang / Ride like the wind / Let it run / Love party / Listen to your heart / Kiss it (make it better) / I saw him first.
Album: released on Grosvenor in Jul'82 by Grosvenor Records. Distributed by: Taylors

Cassette: released on Grosvenor in Jul'82 by Grosvenor Records. Distributed by: Taylors

FASCINATING RHYTHM.
Tracks: / Fascinating rhythm / Crazy rhythm / I've got rhythm / Way you look tonight (The) / Time was / I'm gonna wash that man / Cock eyed optimist, A / Many a newday / Whisper not / Our love is here to stay / Perdido / Undecided / Amazing grace / Best of times (The) / I am what I am / Other side of me (The) / Early autumn / Poor butterfly / Harlem nocturne / Triste / Quiet nights / Days of wine and roses (The) / Just for you.
Notes: Electronic Keyboard Series
Cassette: released on Grosvenor in May'87 by Grosvenor Records. Distributed by: Taylors

HOWARD BEAUMONT PLAYS....
Album: released on Grosvenor in Jan'78 by Grosvenor Records. Distributed by: Taylors

IT TAKES TWO TO TEMPO (Beaumont, Howard & John Taylor).
Album: released on Grosvenor in Dec'86 by Grosvenor Records. Distributed by: Taylors

PLAYS WURLITZER.
Album: released on Grosvenor in Sep'81 by Grosvenor Records. Distributed by: Taylors

PLAY THE WURLITZER AT COTTON (Beaumont, Howard/Bryan Jones).
Album: released on Grosvenor in Jul'86 by Grosvenor Records. Distributed by: Taylors

SOUNDS NEW.
Notes: Howard Beaumont plays the Eminent B85
Cassette: released on Grosvenor in May'86 by Grosvenor Records. Distributed by: Taylors

Beausoleil

BAYOU BOOGIE.
Album: released on Rounder Europe in Aug'87

SPIRIT OF CANUN MUSIC.
Album:

ZYDECO GRIS GRIS.
Album:

Beautiful Bend

BEAUTIFUL BEND.
Album: released on TK in Feb'79. Distributed by: CBS Distribution

Beautiful Dreams

BEAUTIFUL DREAMS Various artists (Various Artists).
Tracks: / My way / Whiter shade of pale / Greensleeves / My funny valentine / Plaisir d'amour / I'll never fall in love again / Yesterday / Vergi b mein nicht / Nearness of you / Santa lucia / Fur elise / You stepped out of a dream.
Album: released on Karussell (Germany) in May'82

Cassette: released on Karussell (Germany) in May'82

Beautiful Music

BEAUTIFUL MUSIC (Session Orchestra).
Tracks: / Bright eyes / More than I can say / Theme from the'Deer Hunter'(cavatina), The / Suddenly / Lately / Keep on loving you / Do that to me one more time / Theme from 'MASH'(suicide is painless),The / Woman in love / I made it through the rain / Imagine / Bermuda triangle / One day in your life / Woman / sailing / Winner takes it all / With you i'm born again / For your eyes only / Theme from 'Rich Man Poor Man', The / Chariots of fire / North star / Crystal mountain / Crying / Chi mai (Theme from'Lloyd George') / Xanadu / All out of love / I love a rainy night / Sleepy shores / Little in love / Angel of the morning.
Double Album: released on Cambra in Sep'86 by Cambra Records. Distributed by: IDS, Conifer

Double cassette: released on Cambra in Sep'86 by Cambra Records. Distributed by: IDS, Conifer

BEAUTIFUL MUSIC (1) Various classical performers (Various Artists).
Album: released on ASV in May'82 by Academy Sound & Vision Records. Distributed by: Pinnacle

Cassette: released on ASV in May'82 by Academy Sound & Vision Records. Distributed by: Pinnacle

BEAUTIFUL MUSIC (2) Various classical performers (Various Artists).
Album: released on ASV in Sep'82 by Academy Sound & Vision Records. Distributed by: Pinnacle

Cassette: released on ASV in Sep'82 by Academy Sound & Vision Records. Distributed by: Pinnacle

MORE BEAUTIFUL MUSIC Various Artists (Various Artists).
Double Album: released on Cambra in '83 by Cambra Records. Distributed by: IDS, Conifer

Double cassette: released on Cambra in '83 by Cambra Records. Distributed by: IDS, Conifer

Beautiful Pea Green Boat

CHANCE.
Single (12"): released on Rough Trade in

Nov'84 by Rough Trade Records. Distributed by: Rough Trade Distribution, Cartel Distribution

OBSESSIONS.
Album: released on Third Mind in 30 May'87 by Third Mind Records. Distributed by: Backs, Cartel Distribution

Beauty

BEAUTY Various artists (Various Artists).
Album: released on Pink in Feb'87 by Pink Records. Distributed by: Rough Trade

Single (7"): released on Occult in '82. Distributed by: Cartel Distribution

Beauty & The Beast

BEAUTY & THE BEAST Various artists (Various Artists).
Cassette: released on Pickwick (Ladybird) in Feb'83

Cassette: released on Tellastory in Apr'81 by Bartlett Bliss Productions. Distributed by: PRT Distribution, Hayward Promotions Distribution, H.R. Taylor Distribution

Beauty The Beat...

BEAUTY THE BEAT ON BROADWAY Various artists (Various Artists).
Album: released on Fourth & Broadway in Nov'85 by Island Records. Distributed by: Polygram, EMI

Cassette: released on Fourth & Broadway in Nov'85 by Island Records. Distributed by: Polygram, EMI Deleted '87.

Beauvoir, Jean

DRUM ALONG THE MOHAWK.
Tracks: / Feel the heat / Never went down / Missing the young days / Rockin' in the street / Sorry I missed your wedding day / Drive you home / Sam's songs play on & on / This is our house / If I was me / Nina.
Album: released on Virgin in '86 by Virgin Records. Distributed by: EMI, Virgin Distribution

Cassette: released on Virgin in '86 by Virgin Records. Distributed by: EMI, Virgin Distribution

Compact disc: released on Virgin in '86 by Virgin Records. Distributed by: EMI, Virgin Distribution

FEEL THE HEAT.
Tracks: / Feel the heat / Standing in the line of fire.
Single (7"): released on Virgin in Aug'86 by Virgin Records. Distributed by: EMI, Virgin Distribution

Single (7"): released on Virgin in Aug'86 by Virgin Records. Distributed by: EMI, Virgin Distribution

MISSING THE YOUNG DAYS.
Tracks: / Crazy / Crazy.
Single (7"): released on Virgin in Jan'87 by Virgin Records. Distributed by: EMI, Virgin Distribution

Single (12"): released on Virgin in Jan'87 by Virgin Records. Distributed by: EMI, Virgin Distribution

MISSING THE YOUNG DAYS.

Beau Weevil

WOOLY BULLY.
Single (7"): released on Forever in Jun'82 by Forever Records. Distributed by: Pinnacle

Beavl & Hippy Dread

HEROES.
Tracks: / Heroes / Wolf & sheep.
Single (12"): released on Mega in Apr'86. Distributed by: Jetstar

Bebo

BEBO IN A DUB STYLE.
Album: released on Bebo's Music in Apr'85

Bebop Bebop

BEBOP BEBOP Various artists (Various Artists).
Tracks: / Congo Blues / You're not the kind / Shaw 'nuff / Parkers mood / Things to come / Relaxin' at Camarillo / Embraceable you / Ko Ko / Lemon drop / Un poco loco / Jahbero / Misterioso / What is this thing called love / Stop time.
Notes: Full archival information and a complete list of the performers of each selection may be found within the individual discussion of each work in the liner notes.Producer: Michael Brooks
Sound equalization:Doug Pomeroy Researchers:Dan Morgenstern,Michael Brooks Cover by Elaine Sherer Cox Historical chart & bibliography compiled by Arthur E Scherr Library of Congress Card no. 75-751058
P & C 1976 Recorded Anthology of American Music Inc.

Album: released on New World (USA) in Sep'86 by New World Records (USA). Distributed by: Conifer

Bebop & Beyond Sextet

BEBOP & BEYOND.
Album: released on Concord (USA) in Sep'84. Distributed by: IMS, Polygram

Bebop Boys

ANTHOLOGY Various artists.
Double Album: released on Savoy in '78

Be Bop DeLuxe

Biographical Details: This British band, dominated by vocalist and guitarist Bill Nelson, released their first album "Axe Victim" in 1974. "Sunburst Finish" gave them their first chart album, reaching No. 17 with 12 weeks on the list, in early '76 and yielded aTop 30 single "Ships In The Night". Later in the year they issued their fourth album "Modern Music" and had a Top 40 EP "Hot Valves". The group were a diversemixture of early Seventies rock, heavy metal, glitter rock and futurist pop. On stage they wore suits and ties, while presenting a quietly rebellious face to the music press. This eclecticism meant that they fell between various musical stools, and remained on the fringes of the big league of rock bands without actually entering it. Their only Top 10 LP came in 1977 with the live double set "Live! In The Air Age". It was followed by 1978's less successful "Drastic Plastic", then the group folded. Their leader formed the partially accepted Bill Nelson's Red Noise, before going solo in 1980. "Do You Dream In Colour", a single issued on his own Cocteau lable, was an airplay favourite but could only reach No.52. 1981's LP "Quit Dreaming And Get On The Beam" reached No. 7 his highest ever plaing. He has kept a low profile in the Eighties, his occasional records always being too left-field to sell in large quantities. In the autumn of '84 he released a strong rock/dance single "Acceleration". (BM 1984)

AXE VICTIM/FUTURAMA.
Tracks: / Axe victim / Love is swift arrows / Jet silver and the dolls of Venus / Third floor heaven / Night creatures / Rocket cathedrals / Adventures in a Yorkshire landscape / Jets at dawn / No trains to heaven / Darkness / Stage whispers / Love with the madman / Maid in heaven / Sister seagull / Sound track / Music in dreamland / Jean Cocteau / Between the worlds / Swan song.
Album: released on Harvest in Sep'83 by EMI Records. Distributed by: Roots, EMI

BE BOP DELUXE SINGLES A'S & B'S.
Tracks: / Jet silver and the dolls of Venus / Between the worlds / Maids in heaven / Ships in the night / Kiss of light / Japan / Panic in the wHold / Electrical language / Third floor heaven / Lights / Crying to the sky / Shine / Futurist manifesto / Blue as a jewel / Surreal / Surreal / Estate.
Album: released on Harvest in May'81 by EMI Records. Distributed by: Roots, EMI

Cassette: released on Harvest in May'81 by EMI Records. Distributed by: Roots, EMI

BEST OF BE BOP DE LUXE (THE).
Tracks: / Jet Silver and the Dolls of Venus / Adventures in a Yorkshire Landscape / Maid in Heaven / Ships in the night / Life in the Air Age / Kiss of light / Sister Seagull / Modern Music / Japan / Panic In The World / Bring Back The Spark / Forbidden Lovers / Electrical Language.
Notes: A new compilaton of 13 classic tracks from Be Bop De Luxe featuring the inimitable Bill Nelson. Spans the group's highly successful career during the 70's, combining their original, progressive sound with Bill Nelson's impressive guitar sound gleaned from artists such as Duane Eddy and Hank Marvin to Jimi Hendrix and Jeff Beck. A striking sleeve design depicting Nelson and guitar in classic pose, is complimented by detailed sleeve notes giving a brief history on all tracks. As well as ever popular songs it contains the track 'Japan' only previously available as a single - a hint of things to come in Nelson's future of oriental styling.
Album: released on Harvest in Feb'87 by EMI Records. Distributed by: Roots, EMI

Cassette: released on Harvest in Feb'87 by EMI Records. Distributed by: Roots, EMI

BOP TO THE RED NOISE.
Tracks: / Ships in the night / Life in the air age / Maid in heaven / Jean Cocteau / 3rd floor heaven / Rocket cathedrals / No trains to heaven / Orphans of Babylon / Modern music / New precision / Don't touch me (i'm electric) / For young moderns.
Album: released on Dojo in Aug'86 by Castle Communications Records. Distributed by: Cartel

ELECTRICAL LANGUAGE (EP).
Single (12"): released on Cocteau in Feb'83 by Cocteau Records. Distributed by: Pinnacle, IDS

PANIC IN THE WORLD.
Single (7"): released on Cocteau in Aug'83 by Cocteau Records. Distributed by: Pinnacle, IDS

SHIPS IN THE NIGHT.
Single (7"): released on EMI Golden 45's in Apr'84 by EMI Records. Distributed by: EMI

SUNBURST FINISH.
Tracks: / Fair exchange / Heavenly homes / Ships in the night / Crying to the sky / Sleep that burns / Beauty secrets / Life in the air-age / Like an old blues / Crystal glazing / Blazing apostles.
Notes: Originally released by EMI Records Ltd on the album 'Sunburst Finish' Catalogue No. SHSP 4653
Album: released on Revolver in Jun'86 by Revolver Records. Distributed by: Revolver, Cartel

Cassette: released on Revolver in Jun'86 by Revolver Records. Distributed by: Revolver, Cartel

Bebop Is Where It's At

BEBOP IS WHERE IT'S AT VOL.1 Various artists (Various Artists).
Album: released on Honeydew in Oct'79. Distributed by: Swift,

BEBOP IS WHERE IT'S AT VOL.2 Various artists (Various Artists).
Album: released on Honeydew in Oct'79. Distributed by: Swift,

Be-Bop Keyboard Masters

BE-BOP KEYBOARD MASTERS feat: Geo.Wallington/Al Haig/Duke Jordan/Wade Leege (Various Artists).
Tracks: / Fairyland / Woody'n'you / Just one of those things / Honeysuckle rose / Star eyes / N.Y. / Day in Paris, A / These foolish things / Just one of those things / Yardbird suite / Taboo / Mighty like a rose / S'wonderful / Just you and me / Moon was yellow, The / 'Round about midnight / Just one of those things / Embraceable you / Scotch blues / Confirmation / Darn tha dream / They can't take that away from me / Wait and see / Perdido / Dream a little dream of me / Wade Legge's blues / Swedish folk song / Dance of the infidels / Aren't you glad you're you / These foolish things / Why don't you believe me.
Double Album: released on Vogue in May'81. Distributed by: Discovery, Jazz Music, PRT, Swift

Bebop Preservation...

PIED PIPER OF HAMELIN SUITE.
Tracks: / Hamelin / Council Cakewalk / Rats / Pied piper / Mayor's got the blues / Little boy lost / Town band birthday.
Notes: Hank Shaw (trumpet)/Peter King(Alto sax)/Bill Le Sage(piano, Composer)/Spike Heatley (Bass)/Martin Drew (Drums)
Album: released on Spotlite in '83 by Spotlite Records. Distributed by: Cadillac, Jazz Music, Spotlite

Be-Bop Vocals

BE-BOP VOCALS Various artists (Various Artists).
Tracks: / I don't want love / Bye bye blackbird / Sugar Ray / Cool whalin' / But beautiful(1) / Gambler's blues / Let there be love / But beautiful (2) / Bless my soul / Beautiful memories / I'll remember April / Gone with the wind / Oop-bop-a-da / Especially to you / Nobody knows / Searching blues / Nightingale.
Notes: For lovers of vocal jazz this is a must.Featured here are:-Babs Gonzales, Joe Carroll, Kenny 'Pancho'Hagood,Eddie Jefferson, Earl Coleman and Frankie Passions
Album: released on Spotlite in '83 by Spotlite Records. Distributed by: Cadillac, Jazz Music, Spotlite

Becaud, Gilbert

Biographical Details: This MoR singer is a long-standing major star in his native France, and normally records in his native tongue. A brief 1975 excursion in English language yielded a one-off British Top 10 single "A Little Love And Understanding". Being part of the insular French music business, however, he has stuck to his tried and tested market ever since. B.M. 84

AL'OLYMPIA.
Tracks: / Y'a pas d'lapin dans le chapeau / So far away from Courbevoie / Viens nous aider / C'est en Septembre / Toi et moi / Credo / Chaque enfant qui nait, A / Les tantes Jeannes / Quand Jules est an violon / Le pommier a pommes / L'orange / Le pianiste de Varsovie.
Album: released on EMI (France) in '83 by EMI Records. Distributed by: Conifer

COLLECTION: GILBERT BECAUD.
Cassette: released on EMI (Germany) in '83 by EMI Records. Distributed by: Conifer

DISQUE D'OR VOL. 1.
Tracks: / Le train de la vie / C'est en Septembre / Un peu d'amour et d'amitie / Charlie, t'iras pas au paradis / L'important c'est la rose / Mademoiselle Lise / Nathalie / Et maintenant / Le jour ou la pluie viendra / Les marches de provence / La corrida / Alors raconte... / Quand tu dances / Viens.
Album: released on EMI (France) in '83 by EMI Records. Distributed by: Conifer

DISQUE D'OR VOL. 2.
Tracks: / Mes mains / Le pianiste de Varsovie / L'absent / Quand Jules est au violin / Les tantes Jeanne / T'es venu de loin / Quand il est mort le poete / Les petites mad'maselles / Je reviens te chercher / Les cerisier's sont blancs / La vente aux encheres / La solitude, ca n'existe pas / Chante / Et le spectacle continue.
Album: released on EMI (France) in '83 by EMI Records. Distributed by: Conifer

GILBERT BECAUD.
Album: released on EMI (France) in '83 by EMI Records. Distributed by: Conifer

LITTLE LOVE AND UNDERSTANDING, A.
Tracks: / Little love and understanding, A / Masquerade, The / Something missing / If only I could live my life again / It's wonderful to be alive / What now my love / Importance of your love, The / Mexican singing bird, The / Sand and sea / Days the rains came, The / My pretty summer princess / Living.
Single (7"): released on Old Gold in Sep'85 by Old Gold Records. Distributed by: Lightning, Jazz Music, Spartan, Counterpoint

LITTLE LOVE & UNDERSTANDING, A.
Album: released on Decca in Apr'75 by Decca Records. Distributed by: Polygram Deleted '81.

Cassette: released on Decca in Apr'75 by Decca Records. Distributed by: Polygram

MOI JE VEUX CHANTER.
Album: released on EMI (France) in '83 by EMI Records. Distributed by: Conifer

Bechet/Bunk

BOSTON 1945.
Album: released on Jazz Archives in Jul'86 by Jazz Archives Records. Distributed by: Jazz Music

Bechet Legacy

Ode to Bechet

On the road

Bechet-Mezzrow

KING JAZZ VOL.5 (Bechet-Mezzrow Quintet\Septet).
Notes: For full info. see: Mezzrow-Bechet Quintet\Septet

Bechet, Sidney

1947

BECHET - THE THIRTIES.
Tracks: / Black stick blues / Loveless love - first version / Basement blues (The) / Roll on, M Mississippi, roll on / Viper mad / When the sun sets down south / Sweet patootie / Uncle Joe / Freight train blues / My daddy rocks me - part 1 / My daddy rocks me - part 2 / You can't live in Harlem / Tain't a fit night / Rhthym of Broadway moon / Loveless love - second version / Polka dot stomp.
Album: released on Affinity in May'86 by Charly Records. Distributed by: Charly, Cadillac

BECHET VOLUME 5 (1941-43) The Panassie session (Bechet, Sidney, Mezzrow & T. Ladnier).
Tracks: / Mood indigo (pt.1) / Mood indigo (pt.2) / Rose room / Lady be good / Lady be good (pt 2) / What is this thing called love? / After you've gone / Bugle call rag / Ole miss rag / St.Louis blues / Revolutionary blues / Comin' on with the come on (pt.1) / Comin' on with the come on (pt.2) / Careless love (swingin' for Mezz) / Careless love (swingin' for Mezz) (pt.2) / Royal garden blues (pt 1) / Royal garden blues (pt 2) / Everybody loves my baby (pt1) / Everybody loves my baby (pt2) / I ain't gonna give nobody any of this jelly roll(pt.1) / I ain't gonna give nobody any of this jelly roll(pt.2) / If you see me comin' (pt1) / If you see me comin' (pt2) / Gettin' together (pt.1) / Gettin' together (pt.2) / Rosetta / Minor jive / World is waiting for the sunrise, The / Who? / Blues my baby gave to me, The / Rompin'.
Double Album: released on RCA in Mar'86 by RCA Records. Distributed by: RCA, Roots, Swift, Wellard, Chris, I & B, Solomon & Peres Distribution

Double cassette: released on RCA in Mar'86 by RCA Records. Distributed by: RCA, Roots, Swift, Wellard, Chris, I & B, Solomon & Peres Distribution

BIG FOUR(WITH MUGGSY SPANIER 1940).
Album: released on Swaggie (Australia) in Jan'83

COMPLETE SIDNEY BECHET VOLS.1/2 1932-41.
Tracks: / One o'clock jump / Preachin' blues / Old man blues / Blues in thirds / Ain't misbehavin' / Save it pretty mama / Stomp Jones / Muskrat ramble / Coal black shine / Sweetie dear / Lay your racket / Maple leaf rag / Ja-da / Really the blues / Weary blues / Indian summer / Sweetie dear / I want you tonight / I've found a new baby / Lay your racket / Maple leaf rag / Shag-ja-da / Really the blues / When you and I were young / Maggie / Weary blues / Indian summer / One o'clock jump / Preachin' the blues / Sidney's blues / Shake it and break it / Old man blues / Wild man blues / Nobody know the way I feel dis mornin' / Make a pallet on the floor / Saint Louis blues / Blues in third / Blues for you / Johnny / Ain't misbehavin' / Save it, pretty mama / Stompy Jones / Muskrat ramble / Coal black shine / Eygptian fantasy.
Notes: 28 tracks including ones listed in tracks session
Double Album: released on RCA in Jul'86 by RCA Records. Distributed by: RCA, Roots, Swift, Wellard, Chris, I & B, Solomon & Peres Distribution

Double cassette: released on RCA in Jul'86 by RCA Records. Distributed by: RCA, Roots, Swift, Wellard, Chris, I & B, Solomon & Peres Distribution

COMPLETE SIDNEY BECHET, VOLS. 3/4.
Tracks: / I'm coming Virginia - 1 / I'm coming Virginia - 2 / Limehouse blues / Geogia cabin - 1 / Geogia cabin - 2 / Texas moaner - 1 / Texas moaner - 2 / Strange fruit / You're the limit - 1 / You're the limit - 2 / Rip up the joint / Suey - 1 / Suey - 2 / Blues in the air - 1 / Blues in the air - 2 / Mooche, The - 1 / Mooche, The - 2 / Laughin' in rhythm / 12th Street rag - 1 / 12th Street rag - 2 / I know that you know - 3 / Egyptian fantasy / Baby, won't you please come home? / Slippin' and slidin' / Sheik of Araby / Blues of Bechet / Swing parade - 1 / Swing parade - 2 / I know that you know - 1 / I know that you know - 2 / When it's sleepy time down south / I ain't gonna give nobody none o' this jelly roll / I ain't gonna give nobody none o' this jelly roll - 2.
Double Album: released on RCA in Jan'87 by RCA Records. Distributed by: RCA, Roots, Swift, Wellard, Chris, I & B, Solomon & Peres Distribution

Double cassette: released on RCA in Jan'87 by RCA Records. Distributed by: RCA, Roots, Swift, Wellard, Chris, I & B, Solomon & Peres Distribution

COMPLETE SIDNEY BECHET (1941) VOL.3/4, THE.
Tracks: / Baby, won't you please come home / Slippin' and slidin' / Sheik of Araby, (The) / Blues of Bechet / Swing parade / I know that you know / When it's sleepy time down south / I ain't gonna give noboby none of this jelly role / I'm coming Virginia / Limehouse blues / Georgia cabin / Texas moaner blues / Strange fruit / You're the limit / Rip up the joint / Blues in the air / Mooche, (The) / Laughin' in rhythm / Twelfth street rag.
Double Album: released on RCA (France) in '83 by RCA Records. Distributed by: Discovery

COMPLETE SIDNEY BECHET(1932-1941) VOL.1/2, THE.
Double Album: released on RCA (France) in '83 by RCA Records. Distributed by: Discovery

CONCERT INEDITS VOL.2.
Album: released on Vogue (France) in Jan'85. Distributed by: Discovery, Jazz Music, PRT, Swift

DJANGO REINHARDT/SIDNEY BECHET (Bechet, Sidney & Django Reinhardt).
Notes: Full details see under REINHARDT, Django
Compact disc: . Distributed by: Discovery, Jazz Music, PRT, Swift

FABULOUS SIDNEY BECHET,THE.
Tracks: / Original Dixieland one-step / Blues my naughty sweetie gives to me / That's a plenty / Ballin' the Jack / Avalon / Rose of Rio Grande / Black and blue(What did I do to be so) / Sweet Georgia Brown / All of me / Ding dong daddy.
Album: released on Blue Note in Oct'84 by EMI Records. Distributed by: EMI

GIANT OF JAZZ VOL.1.
Album: released on Blue Note (USA Import) in Sep'84

Cassette: released on Blue Note (France) in Mar'84. Distributed by: Conifer

HIS WAY 1951.
Album: released on Pumpkin in Apr'79. Distributed by: Jazz Music, Wellard, Chris, Cadillac

HOUSE PARTY (Bechet, Sidney & Mezz Mezzrow).
Tracks: / House party / Perido St.stomp / Minor swoon / Sheik of Araby, The / Breathless blues / Really the blues(Parts 1 & 2) / Ole miss / Bowin' the blues / I'm gonna give nobody to my Jelly Roll / Perdido St. stomp / Old school / Gone away blues / De lux stomp / Out of the Gallion.
Notes: Tracks relesed between 1945 and 1947
Album: released on Joker in Apr'81. Distributed by: Counterpoint, Mainline, Record Services Distribution (Ireland)

IN PHILADELPHIA VOL.2.
Album: released on Jazz Archives in Oct'79 by Jazz Archives Records. Distributed by: Jazz Music

JAZZ CLASSICS VOL.2.
Album: released on Blue Note (USA Import) in Sep'84

LIVE IN NEW YORK.
Album: released on EMI (Continental) in Apr'84 by EMI Records. Distributed by: Conifer

Cassette: released on EMI (Continental) in Apr'84 by EMI Records. Distributed by: Conifer

LOUIS ARMSTRONG/ SIDNEY BECHET (Bechet, Sidney & Louis Armstrong).
Album: released on Mercury Jazz Masters in Dec'83

MASTERS OF JAZZ VOL.4.
Album: released on Storyville in May'86 by Storyville Records. Distributed by: Jazz Music Distribution, Swift Distribution, Chris Wellard Distribution, Counterpoint Distribution

MEMORIAL SET VOL.2 (Bechet, Sidney & Mezz Mezzrow Quintet).
Tracks: / Groovin' the minor / Where am I / Tommy's blues / Revolutionary blues / I want some / I'm speaking my mind / Kaiser's last break / Funky butt / Delta mood / Blues of the roaring twenties.
Album: released on Joker in Apr'81. Distributed by: Counterpoint, Mainline, Record Services Distribution (Ireland)

NEW ORLEANS STYLE OLD & NEW (Bechet, Sidney & N.O.Footwarmers/Bob Wilber & Wildcats).
Album: released on Teldec (Germany) in Sep'83 by Import Records. Distributed by: IMS Distribution, Polygram Distribution

NEW ORLEANS STYLE OLD AND NEW (Bechet, Sidney & Bob Wilber).
Tracks: / Jelly roll blues / At a Georgia camp meeting / National emblem march / Hindustan / I'll take New Orleans music / Willie the weepie / Willie the weeper no.2 / Mabel's dream / Mabel's dream no.2 / Wild cat blues / Wild cat blues no.2 / Blues for fowler / Blues for fowler no.2.
Album: released on Commodore Classics in May'87 by Teldec Records (Germany). Distributed by: Conifer, IMS, Polygram

OLYMPIA CONCERT.
Compact disc: released on Vogue (France) in Jun'84. Distributed by: Discovery, Jazz Music, PRT, Swift

Tracks: / Indicatif/Buddy Bolden Stomp / Montmatre Boogie Woogie / At-tu Le Cafard / Riverboat Shuffle Montmatre / Halle Hallelujah/When The Saints Go Marching In / Temperamental / Sobbin' and Cryin' / Muskrat Ramble / On The Sunny Side Of The Street / Indicatif / Buddy bolden stomp / Monmartre boogie woogie / As-tu le cafard / River boat shuffle Monmartre / Halle Hallelujah-When the saints go marchin' in / Temperamental / Sobbin' and cryin' / Muskrat ramble / On the sunnyside of the street.

PARISIAN ENCOUNTER (Bechet, Sidney & Teddy Buckner).
Tracks: / Bravo / Aubergines / I Can't Get Started / Souvenirs / Blue Festival / Weary Blues / Ain't Misbehavin' / Sugar / Who's Sorry Now / All Of Me.
Compact disc: released on Vogue in Jun'86. Distributed by: Discovery, Jazz Music, PRT, Swift

PLATINUM FOR....
Tracks: / Petite fleur / Promenade aux Champs D'Elysee / A-tu le cafard / Passport to paradise / Marchand de poissant / Si tu vois ma mere / Ce moissieu qui parle / Bechet creole blues / Madame Becassine / Blues in Paris / Moulin a cafe / Sobbin' & cryin' / Les oignons / Premier bal / Egyptian fantasy / Temperamental / Buddy Bolden story / Dans les rue's d'Antibes.
Compact disc: released on Vogue in '86. Distributed by: Discovery, Jazz Music, PRT, Swift

PLATINUM FOR SIDNEY BECHET.
Album: released on Vogue (France) in Jun'84. Distributed by: Discovery, Jazz Music, PRT, Swift

Cassette: released on Vogue (France) in Jun'84. Distributed by: Discovery, Jazz Music, PRT, Swift

PLEYEL CONCERTS 1952.
Compact disc: released on Vogue in Jun'86. Distributed by: Discovery, Jazz Music, PRT, Swift

RARE OF ALL RAREST PERFORMANCES VOL.2.
Album: released on Kings Of Jazz in Jul'82. Distributed by: Jazz Horizons, Jazz Music, Celtic Music

REFRESHING TRACKS - 1958 VOL.1.
Tracks: / I only have eyes for you / Man I love, (The) / Exactly like you / These foolish things / Once in a while / Jeepers creepers / I never knew / All the things you are / All of me / Embraceable you / Wrap your troubles in dreams / Rose room / I don't mean a thing / Pennies from heaven / Rosetta / Once in a while / Sweet Georgia Brown / St. Louis Blues / On the sunny side of the street / Sister Kate / I'm coming Virginia.
Double Album: released on Vogue in Nov'77. Distributed by: Discovery, Jazz Music, PRT, Swift

REFRESHING TRACKS VOL.2.
Double Album: released on Vogue in '78. Distributed by: Discovery, Jazz Music, PRT, Swift

SIDNEY BECHET COLLECTION, THE.
Album: released on Deja Vu in Jul'86 by Deja Vu Records. Distributed by: Counterpoint Distribution, Record Services Distribution (Ireland)

Cassette: released on Deja Vu in Jul'86 by Deja Vu Records. Distributed by: Counterpoint Distribution, Record Services Distribution (Ireland)

SIDNEY BECHET & HIS AMERICAN FRIENDS.
Compact disc: released on Vogue in Dec'86. Distributed by: Discovery, Jazz Music, PRT, Swift

SIDNEY BECHET & MUGGSY SPANIER BIG FOUR (Bechet, Sidney & Muggsy Spanier Big Four).
Tracks: / Sweet Lorraine / Lazy river, The / China boy / Four or five times / That's plenty / If I could be with you / Squeeze me / Sweet Sue, just you.
Notes: With Carmen Maestren gt;Wellman Braud bs
Album: released on Joker in Apr'81. Distributed by: Counterpoint, Mainline, Record Services Distribution (Ireland)

SIDNEY BECHET SESSIONS With Mezzrow & Joe Sullivan (Bechet, Sidney, Mezzrow & Joe Sullivan).
Album: released on Storyville in Sep'86 by Storyville Records. Distributed by: Jazz Music Distribution, Swift Distribution, Chris Wellard Distribution, Counterpoint Distribution

SIDNEY BECHET & THE NEW ORLEANS FEETWARMERS VOL.3 (Bechet, Sidney & New Orleans Footwarmers).
Tracks: / I'm coming Virginia / Limehouse blues / Georgia cabin / Texas moaner / Strange fruit / You're the limit / Rip up the joint / Blues in the air / Mooche, The / Laughin' in rhythm / Twelfth street rag / Mood indigo / Rose room / Oh, lady be good / What is this thing called love?.
Album: released on Joker in Apr'81. Distributed by: Counterpoint, Mainline, Record Services Distribution (Ireland)

SIDNEY BECHET & THE NEW ORLEANS FOOTWARMERS VOL.1 (Bechet, Sidney & New Orleans Footwarmers).
Tracks: / Sweetie dear / I want you tonight / I've found a new baby / Lay your racket / Maple leaf rag / Shag / Indian summer / One O' clock jump / Sidney blues / Shake it and break it / Old man blues / Wild man blues / Nobody knows the way I feel this morning / Make me a pallet on the floor / Blues in thirds / Sweetie dear.
Album: released on Joker in Apr'81. Distributed by: Counterpoint, Mainline, Record Services Distribution (Ireland)

SIDNEY BECHET & THE NEW ORLEANS FEETWARMERS VOL.2 (Bechet, Sidney & New Orleans Footwarmers).
Tracks: / Blues for you, Johnny / Ain't misbehavin' 1&2 / Save it pretty mama / Coal black shine / Egyptian fantasy / Baby won't you please come home / Slippin' and slidin' / Sheik of Araby, The / Blues of bechet / Swing parade / I know that you know / When it's sleepy time down south / I ain't gonna give nobody none of this Jellyroll.
Album: released on Joker in Apr'81. Distributed by: Counterpoint, Mainline, Record Services Distribution (Ireland)

SIDNEY BECHET VOL.1.
: released on Jazz Reactivation in Jul'82. Distributed by: PRT

SIDNEY BECHET WITH EDDIE CONDON ALL STARS.
Tracks: / Buddy Bolden stomp / Black & blue / Summertime / Honeysuckle Rose / Argone stomp / High society / Blues in my heart / Sweet Georgia Brown / September song / Just one of those things / Blues / Ole Miss.
Album: released on Queen-Disc in Apr'81. Distributed by: Celtic Music, Jazz Horizons, Jazz Music

SIDNEY BECHET WITH.....
Tracks: / Blues, The / Baby won't you please come home / Charleston / I know that you know / That's a plenty / Black & blue / You are some pretty doll / Farewell blues / Summertime / Sensation rag.
Notes: Sidney bechet with Mugsy Spanier, George brunis,Albert Nicholas,Danny Parker, Pops Foster, Johnson,Baby Dodds
Album: released on Jazz Archives in Jul'86 by Jazz Archives Records. Distributed by: Jazz Music

Album: released on Kings Of Jazz in Apr'81. Distributed by: Jazz Horizons, Jazz Music, Celtic Music

SIDNEY'S BLUES.
Tracks: / Sweetie dear / Maple leaf rag / Shag / Ja-da / Really the blues / Indian summer / Sidney's blues / Blues in thirds / Blues in the air / Suey / Mooche / Mood indigo.
Album: released on RCA in Jul'86 by RCA Records. Distributed by: RCA, Roots, Swift, Wellard, Chris, I & B, Solomon & Peres Distribution

Cassette: released on RCA in Jul'86 by RCA Records. Distributed by: RCA, Roots, Swift, Wellard, Chris, I & B, Solomon & Peres Distribution

Sissle and his Sizzling Syncopators

SUPERB SIDNEY.
Album: released on CBS(France) in Feb'85 by CBS Records. Distributed by: Conifer, Discovery, Swift

Cassette: released on CBS(France) in Feb'85 by CBS Records. Distributed by: Conifer, Discovery, Swift

THIRTIES, THE.
Tracks: / Black stick blues / Loveless love / Basement blues / Roll on,Mississippi,roll on / Viper mad / When the sun sets south / Sweet patootie / Uncle Joe / Freight train blues / My daddy rocks me / You can't live in Harlem / Tain't a fit night out for man or beast / Rhythm of Broadway moon / Polka dot rag.
Album: released on Affinity in Jul'86 by Charly Records. Distributed by: Charly, Cadillac

Beck, Bogart, Appice

BECK, BOGART, APPICE.
Tracks: / Black cat moan / Lady / Oh to love you / Superstition / Sweet sweet surrender / Why should I care about you / Lose myself with love / Livin' alone / I'm so proud.
Album: released on Epic in Sep'84 by CBS Records. Distributed by: CBS

Cassette: released on Epic in Sep'84 by CBS Records. Distributed by: CBS

Becker, David

LONG PETER MADSEN.
Album: released on MCA in Feb'87 by MCA Records. Distributed by: Polygram, MCA

Cassette: released on MCA in Feb'87 by MCA Records. Distributed by: Polygram, MCA

Becker, Ernest

EVERYDAY HEROICS OF LIVING & DYING.
Cassette: released on Psychology in Oct'81

Beckers, Chris

HIGH TENSION.
Tracks: / Blow back,buddy / Seven star motel / Gentle grande / Funky red shoes / Metal bass / Cafe solo(por dos) / South Avenue.
Notes: This is guitarist Chris Becker's 4th solo album on his own Cris Crazz Recrds. Chris first gained success with his album'Night Move'.Key tracks on 'High Tension'are 'Seven Star Motel','Gentle Grande' and 'Funky Red Shoes'. Personnel includes: Ernie Watts-tenor sax/Abraham Laboriel-bass/Alex Acuna-drums/Eddie Conrad-percussion.
Album: released on Cris Crazz in Dec'85 by Beckers, Chris. Distributed by: IMS, Polygram

Cassette: released on Cris Crazz in Dec'85 by Beckers, Chris. Distributed by: IMS, Polygram

KEEP ON DANCING (Beckers, Chris Splash).
Single (7"): released on Steinar in Oct'84

Single (12"): released on Steinar in Oct'84

Becker, Walter

STEELY DAN- THE EARLY YEARS (Becker, Walter & Donald Fagen).
Album: released on Teldec (Germany) in May'84 by Import Records. Distributed by: IMS Distribution, Polygram Distribution

Becket

SOCA.
Tracks: / Soca / Soca (dance mix).
Single (7"): released on Bumble Bee in Aug'86 by CSA Records. Distributed by: PRT, Jetstar, CSA

Single (12"): released on Bumble Bee in Aug'86 by CSA Records. Distributed by: PRT, Jetstar, CSA

TENTH ANNIVERSARY.
Album: released on Cocoa in Aug'85. Distributed by: Jetstar

VINCYMAS.
Album: released on Sunburn in Sep'84 by Orbitone Records. Distributed by: Jetstar Distribution

Beckett, Chris

SHE WEARS MY RING.
Single (7"): released on Homespun(Ireland) in Jun'81 by Outlet Records. Distributed by: Outlet

Beckett, Harry

PICTURES OF YOU.
Album: released on Palladin in Apr'85 by Paladin Records. Distributed by: Cartel

Beckett, Peter

I'M CRYING.
Single (7"): released on MCA in Apr'85 by MCA Records. Distributed by: Polygram, MCA

Beckford, Keeling

BIG WHEEL (SPINNING WHEEL).
Single (12"): released on Vista Sounds in Dec'82 by Vista Sounds Records. Distributed by: Jetstar

Beckford, Vincent

YOU.
Single (12"): released on BWB in Jun'85. Distributed by: Jetstar

Beck, Jeff

AMBITIOUS.
Tracks: / Ambitious / Escape.
Single (7"): released on Epic in Mar'86 by CBS Records. Distributed by: CBS

Single (12"): released on Epic in Mar'86 by CBS Records. Distributed by: CBS

BECKOLA.
Album: released on Columbia (France) in '83. Distributed by: EMI

BEST OF JEFF BECK (1967-69) FEAT.ROD STEWART.
Tracks: / Shapes of things / Morning dew / You shook me / I ain't superstitious / All shook up / Jailhouse rock / Plynth (water down the drain) / Hi ho silver lining / Tallyman / Love is blue / I've been drinking / Rock my plimsoul / Beck's bolero / Rice pudding.
Album: released on Fame in May'85 by Music For Pleasure Records. Distributed by: EMI

Cassette: released on Fame in May'85 by Music For Pleasure Records. Distributed by: EMI

BLOW BY BLOW.
Tracks: / It doesn't really matter / She's a woman / Constipated duck / Air blower / Scatterbrain / Cause we've ended as lovers / Thelonius / Freeway jam / Diamond dust.
Album: released on Epic in Sep'83 by CBS Records. Distributed by: CBS

Cassette: released on Epic in Sep'83 by CBS Records. Distributed by: CBS Deleted '87.

COSA NOSTRA BECK-OLA.
Tracks: / All shook up / Spanish boots / Girl from mill valley / Jailhouse rock / Plynth (water down the drain) / Hangman's knee / Rice pudding.
Album: released on RAK in Jul'85 by RAK. Distributed by: EMI

Cassette: released on RAK in Jul'85 by RAK. Distributed by: EMI

FLASH.
Tracks: / Ambitious / Gets us all in the end / Escape / People get ready / Stop, look and listen / Get workin' / Ecstacy / Night after night / You know, we know.
Compact disc: by CBS Records. Distributed by: CBS

Album: released on Epic in Jul'85 by CBS Records. Distributed by: CBS

Cassette: released on Epic in Jul'85 by CBS Records. Distributed by: CBS

HI HO SILVER LINING.
Single (7"): released on RAK Replay in Sep'82

Single (12"): released on RAK Replay in Sep'82

Picture disc single: released on RAK Replay in Oct'82

LIVE (Beck, Jeff with Jan Hammer Group).
Tracks: / Freeway jam / Earth (still our only home) / She's a woman / Full moon boogie / Darkness earth in search of sun / Scatterbrain / Blue wind.
Album: released on Epic in Jun'85 by CBS Records. Distributed by: CBS

Cassette: released on Epic in Jun'85 by CBS Records. Distributed by: CBS Deleted '87.

PEOPLE GET READY (Beck, Jeff & Rod Stewart).
Tracks: / People get ready / Back on the street.
Single (7"): released on Epic in Dec'85 by CBS Records. Distributed by: CBS

ROCK GIANTS.
Album: released on CBS(Holland) in Jun'84 by CBS Records. Distributed by: Discovery

ROUGH AND READY.
Tracks: / Got the feeling / Situation / Short business / Max's tune / I've been used / New ways / Train train / Jody.
Album: released on CBS in '84 by CBS Records. Distributed by: CBS Deleted '87.

Cassette: released on CBS in Aug'84 by CBS Records. Distributed by: CBS

THERE & BACK.
Album: released on Epic in Aug'84 by CBS Records. Distributed by: CBS

Cassette: released on Epic in Aug'84 by CBS Records. Distributed by: CBS Deleted '86.

TRUTH.
Tracks: / Shapes of things / Let me love you / Morning dew / You shook me / Ol' man river / Greensleeves / Rock my plimsoul / Beck's bolero / Blue deluxe / I ain't superstitious / Shape of things / Let me love you / Morning dew / You shook me / Ol' man river / Greensleeves / Rock my plimsoul / Beck's bolero / Blues de luxe / I ain't superstitious.
Notes: P 1968 Original Sound Recordings made by EMI Records Ltd.except'Beck's Bolero' P 1967
Album: released on Fame in Jun'86 by Music For Pleasure Records. Distributed by: EMI

Cassette: released on Fame in Jun'86 by Music For Pleasure Records. Distributed by: EMI

Cassette: released on Columbia in '85 by EMI Records. Distributed by: EMI

Cassette: released on Columbia in '85 by EMI Records. Distributed by: EMI

WILD THING.
Tracks: / Wild thing / Get us all in the end / Night hawk.
Single (7"): released on Epic in Jul'86 by CBS Records. Distributed by: CBS

Single (12"): released on Epic in Jul'86 by CBS Records. Distributed by: CBS

WIRED.
Tracks: / Led boots / Come dancing / Goodbye pork pie hat / Head for backstage pass / Blue wind / Sophie / Play with me / Love is green.
Album: released on Epic in Mar'82 by CBS Records. Distributed by: CBS

Cassette: released on Epic in Mar'82 by CBS Records. Distributed by: CBS

Beck, Joe

FRIENDS.
Compact disc: released on DMP in Jun'86 by DMP Records. Distributed by: Venture

RELAXIN'.
Compact disc: released on DMP in Jun'86 by DMP Records. Distributed by: Venture

Bedford, David

RIGEL 9, THE (Bedford, David & Ursula Le Guinn).
Album: released on Charisma in Jun'85 by Virgin Records. Distributed by: EMI

Cassette: released on Charisma in Jun'85 by Virgin Records. Distributed by: EMI

Bedlem

BEDLEM.
Album: released on Razor in Jun'85 by Razor. Distributed by: Pinnacle

Bednarczyk, Stefan

LIVE AT THE MORGUE.
Tracks: / Pusillaninimity / Sunny view rest home commercial / Taboo / N.W.3 / Gold day of youth / Seance humoresque / Visual aids / Dinasaur can-can / The champagne aria / With a charm that is all your own / Valentines song / Twelve days of warning / Young executives square dance / Children's action workshop.
Notes: Stefan Bednarczyk has been variously described as the most talented singer/ songwriter of his generation (by Sheridan morley) the cream of the perrier generation (by Gyles brandeth) and "A right little chain smoker" (by his mother). His first one man show of which the Sunday times critic said. It rolled us in the aisle for an hour and half, is now captured on this well produced, live EP.
Album: released on Academy Sound & Vision in Oct'83 by Academy Sound & Vision Records. Distributed by: Pinnacle

Cassette: released on Academy Sound & Vision in Oct'83 by Academy Sound & Vision Records. Distributed by: Pinnacle

WHEN SANTA KISSED THE FAIRY ON THE CHRISTMAS TREE.
Single (7"): released on ASV in Nov'83 by Academy Sound & Vision Records. Distributed by: Pinnacle Deleted Jul'87.

Bedtime for Bonzo

HAVE A NICE DAY.
Album: released on Scarface in Aug'85 by Scarface Records. Distributed by: Cartel

Bee Gees

Biographical Details: Barry Gibb and his younger non-identical twin brothers Robin and Maurice, formedas a child group in Manchester, before emigrating to Australia with their parents in 1958. In the mid-Sixties, while still in their teens, they became radio and TV favourites in Australia and established themselves as one of that country'smajor chart acts. They had taken their name from the eldest brother's initials.Australian entrepreneur Robert Stigwood figured that they would do well in theirnative Britian. Thus they returned in 1967, just as "Spicks and Specks" was hitting No.1 downunder. They were now a five-piece, having recruited guitarist Vince Melouney and drummer Colin Petersen. Manager Stigwood's prediction proved correct, and the group quickly achieved their first British and American hit. "New York Mining disaster 1941" made the Top 20 on both sides of the Atlantic. Written by the three brothers, it was one of the strangest debut hits in chart histroy - here was a group establishing themselves in the late Sixties pop market with a sombre, doomy piece about a catastrophe from another era. The next two singles, "To Love Somebody" and "Holiday", both made the US Top 20 but fared badly in Britain. This situation was quickly rectified by "Massachusetts," a four week UK No. 1 in the autumn of '67.It was to be their longest run at the top, though three further numbers ones were later achieved. By the end of '67 the Bee Gees were recognised as highly talented singers and songwriters. Two more UK Top Tenners, "World" and "Words", were followed by the less successful double A side"Jumbo"/"The Singer Sang His song". The group were adept at responding to the occasional stiff, and the next 45 "I've Gotta Get A Message To You" gave them their second British No. 1 and their first American Top 10 hit. It was another doom-laden song, this time about a murderer on Death Row desperate to communicate with his woman. "I Started A Joke" was an even bigger US hit, but internal frictions were now starting to emerge within the group. Few were aware that their 1969 hit "First Of May", though composed by all three Gibbs, featured only Barry and Maurice on vocals - Robin had been on holiday at the time of recording, and the others had simply gone ahead without him. This was a sympton of the animositythat was growing between Robin and his two brothers; he left and went solo, obtaining a big hit with "Saved By The Bell", but he could not sustain his success. The two sidesmen, Melouney and Petersen, also left within a short space of one another. In similar style to Robin's one-off smash, the Bee Gees duo managed oneNo.2 hit with "Don't Forget To Remember" but soon floundered. The music press had had a field day reporting every acrimonious twist and turn of the group's breakup, and the strain was showing. The Bee Gees went for over a year without a Top 40 single, either in Britain or the States; and whereas their previous five albums had all hit the UK Top 20, 1970's "Cucumber Castle" could do no better thanNo. 57. Failure brought the brothers back together.Barry, Maurice and Robin reformed as a trio in late '70, and scored their biggest US hit so far with "LonelyDays". Though hitting No.3 Stateside, it peaked at No.33 in Britain, and this sudden difference was even more pronounced with "How Can You Mend A Broken Heart' - this ballad was the Gibb's first American No.1 but failed to chart at all in Britain. Two 1972 singles, "My World" and "Run To Me", reached the Top 20 in both countries, but the brothers spent the next three years in the wilderness. Itseemed that the end had come; but in fact it was merely the end of their first era. That era had been full of dramatic ballads, strong story songs boldly sung and plaintively written. The second era began in 1975 and could hardly have been more different. Riding the mid-Seventies disco and sweet soul boom, the Gibbsused funky rhythms and emasculated harmony vocals to begin a historic string of danceable hits. From 1975 until the end of the decade, virtually every record was bigger in the US than the UK. While enormously popular at home, it was in the United States that the reborn trio found its greatest success. The albums "Main Course" and "Children Of The Universe". "Fanny (Be Tender With Love)" and "Love So Right" proved that the funky Bee Gees' could still come up with strong love ballads when they wanted to. One such ballad was "How Deep Is Your Love", a pivotal single in the group's career. Released at the end of '77, it had the honour of dethroning Debby Boone's "You Light Up My Life", a 10 week American No. 1. It also began a string of six consecutive Bee Gee No. 1s in the States. But most importantly, it ushered in the "Saturday Night Fever" soundtrack.

1967-70.
Tracks: / Massachusetts / Don't forget to remember / Words / Lonely days / August October / Spicks & specks / I.O.I.O. / To love somebody / I can't see nobody / World / I've gotta get a message to you / New York mining disaster 1941.
Album: released on RSO-Polydor in Dec'85

Cassette: released on RSO-Polydor in Dec'85

BEE GEES BEST 1967-70.
Album: released on Karussell (Import) in Mar'82

Cassette: released on Karussell (Import) in Mar'82

BEST OF THE BEE GEES VOL.1.
Tracks: / Holiday / I've gotta get a message to you / I've gotta get a message to you / I can't see nobody / Words / I started a joke / Spicks & specks / Spicks & specks / First of May / World / Massachusetts / To love somebody / Every christian lion-hearted man / New York mining disaster 1941.
Notes: Originally RSO 2394 113 released 1977.
Album: released on RSO in Nov'84

: released on RSO in Nov'84

BEST OF THE BEE GEES.
Album: released on Impact (import) in Feb'77. Distributed by: IMS, Polygram

BEST OF THE BEE GEES VOL.2.
Tracks: / How can you mend a broken heart / I.O.I.O. / Don't wanna live inside myself / Don't wanna live inside myself / Melody fair / My world / Let there be love / Saved by the bell / Lonely days / Morning of my life / Don't forget to remember / And the sun will shine / Run to me / Man for all seasons / Alive.
Album: released on RSO in '77

Cassette: released on RSO in '77

BEST OF, VOLUME 1.
Compact disc: by Polydor Records. Distributed by: Polygram, Polydor

DON'T FORGET TO REMEMBER.
Tracks: / Don't forget to remember / First of May.
Single (7"): released on Old Gold in Mar'86 by Old Gold Records. Distributed by: Lightning, Jazz Music, Spartan, Counterpoint

EARLY DAYS, THE.
Tracks: / Where are you / Spicks and specks / Playdown / Big chance / Glass house / How many birds / Secondhand people / I don't know why I bother with myself / Monday's rain / Tint of blue / Jingle jangle / Born a man.
Double cassette: released on Pickwick in Jul'82 by Pickwick Records. Distributed by: Pickwick Distribution, Prism Leisure Distribution, Lugtons

FIRST.
Tracks: / Close another door / Craise Frinton Kirk-Royal Academy of Arts / Cucumber Castle / Every christian lion-hearted man / I can't see nobody / I close my eyes / In my own time / New York mining disaster 1941 / One minute woman / Please read me / Red chair fade away / To love somebody / Turn of the century.

FIRST CD.
Compact disc: by Polydor Records. Distributed by: Polygram Distribution

GREATEST HITS: BEE GEES.
Tracks: / Child of the world / Don't throw it all away / Fanny / How deep is your love / If I can't have you / Jive talkin' / Love me / Love so right / Love you inside out / More than a woman / Night fever / Nights on Broadway / Rest of your love on me / Spirits(having flown) / Stayin' alive / Too much heaven / Tragedy / Wind of change / You should be dancing / You stepped into my life.
Album: released on RSO in Oct'79

Cassette: released on RSO in Oct'79

Compact disc: released on RSO in '83

GREATEST HITS: BEE GEES VOL.1.
Tracks: / Massachusetts / To love somebody / Holiday / I can't see nobody / Don't forget to remember / Words / I started a joke / Saved by the bell / World / New York mining disaster 1941 / I've gotta get a message to you / Tomorrow, tomorrow / First of May / How can you mend a broken heart / My world / Lonely days.
Notes: 16 tracks: 11 chart singles:2 number 1's:Over 50 minutes playing time.
Album: released on RSO (Holland) in Feb'84

Cassette: released on RSO in Feb'84

HERE AT LAST - BEE GEES LIVE.
Tracks: / I've gotta get a message to you / Love so right / Edge of the universe / Come on over / Can't keep a good man down / New York mining disaster 1941 / Run to me / World / Holiday / Can't see nobody / I started a joke / Massachusetts / How can you mend a broken heart / To love somebody / You should be dancing / Boogie child / Down the road / Words / Wind of change / Nights on Broadway / Jive talkin' / Lonely days.
Notes: Album: 2658 120 deleted 1983.
Double cassette: released on RSO in Jun'77

I'VE GOTTA GET A MESSAGE TO YOU.
Tracks: / To love somebody / I've gotta get a message to you / I've gotta get a message to you / My life has been a song / I am the world / World one million years / It doesn't matter much to me.
Single (7"): released on Old Gold in Mar'86 by Old Gold Records. Distributed by: Lightning, Jazz Music, Spartan, Counterpoint

Cassette: released on Contour in Nov'77 by Pickwick Records. Distributed by: Pickwick Distribution, PRT

Album: released on Contour in Nov'77 by Pickwick Records. Distributed by: Pickwick Distribution, PRT

JIVE TALKING.
Tracks: / Jive talking / You should be dancing.
Single (7"): released on Old Gold in Mar'86 by Old Gold Records. Distributed by: Lightning, Jazz Music, Spartan, Counterpoint

LIVING EYES.
Compact disc: by Polydor Records. Distributed by: Polygram Distribution

Album: released on RSO in Aug'83

Cassette: released on RSO in Aug'83 Deleted '87.

Tracks: / Living eyes / He's a liar / Paradise / Don't fall in love with me / Soldiers / I still love you / Wild flower / Nothing could be good / Cryin' every day / Be who you are / Living eyes / He's a liar / Paradise / Don't fall in love with me / Soldiers / I still love you / Wild flower / Nothing could be good / Cryin' every day / Be who you are.
Notes: Originally RSO: RSBG 002 released October 1981.

MASSACHUSETTES.
Tracks: / Massachusettes / New York mining disaster (1941).
Single (7"): released on Old Gold in Mar'86 by Old Gold Records. Distributed by: Lightning, Jazz Music, Spartan, Counterpoint

MASSACHUSETTS.
Album: released on Contour in Aug'85 by Pickwick Records. Distributed by: Pickwick Distribution, PRT

Cassette: released on Contour in Aug'85 by Pickwick Records. Distributed by: Pickwick Distribution, PRT

MUSIC FOR THE MILLIONS.
Tracks: / Holiday / I can't see nobody / I started a joke / First of May / Massachusettes / Every Christian lionhearted man / New York mining disaster / I've gotta get a message to you / Words / Turn of the century / World / To love somebody.
Album: released on RSO in Mar'83

Cassette: released on RSO in Mar'83

ODESSA.
Tracks: / Odessa (city on the Black Sea) / You'll never see my face again / Marley Purt Drive / Black diamond / Melody fair / Suddenly / Whisper whisper / Lamplight / Sound of love / Give your best / Seven sea symphony / With all nations (international anthem) / Laugh in your face / never say never again / First of May / British opera,The / Odessa (city on the black sea) / You'll never see my face again / Black diamond / Marley purt drive / Edison / Edison / Melody fair / Suddenly / Whisper shipser / Lamplight / Sound of love / Give your best / Seven sea symphony / With all nations (international anthem) / Laugh in your face / Never say never again / First Of May / British opera, The.
Compact disc: released on Polydor (Germany) in May'85. Distributed by: IMS-Polygram

Album: released on Polydor (Germany) in Sep'84. Distributed by: IMS-Polygram

Cassette: released on Polydor (Germany) in Sep'84. Distributed by: IMS-Polygram

SATURDAY NIGHT FEVER.
Double compact disc: released on RSO in '83

SPIRITS HAVING FLOWN.
Tracks: / Tragedy / Too much heaven / Love you inside out / Reaching out / Spirits(having flown) / Living together / I'm satisfied / Until.
Notes: Originally RSO: RSBG 001 released February 1979.
Album: released on RSO in Sep'83 Deleted '86.

Cassette: released on RSO in Sep'83

STAYING ALIVE.
Album: released on RSO in Jul'83

Cassette: released on RSO in Jul'83

Compact disc: released on RSO in Jul'83

Tracks: / Woman in you / Love you too much / Breakout / Someone belonging to someone / Life goes on / Stayin' alive / Far from over / Look out for number one / Finding out the hard way / Moody girl / (We dance) so close to the fire / I'm never gonna give you up.

Beerdrop Explodes

BEERDROP EXPLODES (Various Artists).
Album: released on Abstract in Aug'83 by Abstract. Distributed by: Pinnacle

Beer, Mark

PRETTY.
Single (7"): released on Rough Trade in Mar'81 by Rough Trade Records. Distributed by: Rough Trade Distribution, Cartel Distribution

Beer Parlor Jive

BEER PARLOR JIVE Western Swing 1935-1941 (Various Artists).
Tracks: / Yes sir! / Draggin' the bow / Chicken reel stomp / Settle down blues / Train song / Joe Turner blues / When you're smiling / Somebody's been using that thing / Hi flyer stomp / Sally's got a wooden leg / Sundown blues / Sallys got a wooden leg / Sundown blues / Black and white rag / Holding the sack / Beer parlor jive.
Album: released on String in '81 by Topic Records. Distributed by: Roots Distribution, Jazz Music Distribution, JSU Distribution, Projection Distribution, Swift Distribution

Beer, Phil

DANCE WITH ME.
Single (7"): released on Avada in Aug'80. Distributed by: Roots

MANDOLIN.
Tracks: / Dan Tucker / Morning sky / Banks of the Bann / Three pretty maidens / Good King Arthur's days / Green rag / Up to the rigs / Buddy can you spare a dime.
Album: released on Greenwich Village in May'81 by Sweet Folk All Records. Distributed by: Roots, Projection, Lightning, Celtic Music, Wellard, Chris

Beeta

MEMORIES.
Single (7"): released on Omega in Feb'85 by Omega Records. Distributed by: Jetstar Distribution

Beethoven's Greatest Hits

BEETHOVEN'S GREATEST HITS (Various Artists).
Double cassette: released on CBS in Jul'83 by CBS Records. Distributed by: CBS

Bee Vamp

OUR EYES MET ACROSS THE DISCO FLOOR.
Single (12"): released on Red Flame in Jun'82 by Red Flame Records. Distributed by: Nine Mile, Cartel

VALIUM GIRLS.
Single (7"): released on Monsters In Orbit in Dec'81. Distributed by: Rough Trade Distribution

Beggar & Co

Biographical Details: Having evolved from various soul outfits, British funk band Beggar and Co hit the Top 20 in early 1981 with"(Somebody) Help Me Out". Their horn section backed Spandau Ballet later in the year, and helped give them a British Top 3 smash andan international dance hit with "Chant No. 1 (I Don't Need This Pressure On)". Asequel entitled "Mule (Chant No.2)"came out in Beggar and Co's own name, and peaked at No. 37 in the autumn of '81. Subsequent releases, such as December 1981's"Monument" LP and July 1983's single "Anybody See My Trial", have found a club audience but have not crossed over to the pop charts. (BM 1984)

LIFE.
Tracks: / Life / Life (instrumental).
Single (7"): released on Total Control in Jun'86

Single (12"): released on Total Control in Jun'86

MONUMENT.
Tracks: / You need love / Laughing on / (Somebody) help me out / Mule (chant no.2) / Break it up / Got to get away / Bahia de palma / I tried to write a song / That's life / Keep on writing.
Album: released on RCA in Dec'81 by RCA Records. Distributed by: RCA, Roots, Swift, Wellard, Chris, I & B, Solomon & Peres Distribution

Cassette: released on RCA in Dec'81 by RCA Records. Distributed by: RCA, Roots, Swift, Wellard, Chris, I & B, Solomon & Peres Distribution

Beggars Mantle

HOME THAT I LOVE.
Tracks: / Home that I love / Gentle Annie / All Gods creatures / Broom o' the Cowdenknowes / Friends of mine / Carrick hills / Beggars mantle / Whiskey on a sunday / Rantin' rovin' Robin / Love's the rising sun / Rolling hills of the border / Will ye no come back again.
Album: released on Lochshore in Oct'85 by Klub Records. Distributed by: PRT

Cassette: released on Lochshore in Oct'85 by Klub Records. Distributed by: PRT

MILESTONE.
Tracks: / Barnyards of delgatie / Massacre of Glencoe / Roses of Prince Charlie / Jock o' Hazeldean / Wee china pig / Loch Lomond / Wee Scots lad / My wee laddie / Aye waukin' o / Braes o' mar / No mans land / Mingula boat song / Staying alive.
Album: released on Lochshore in Apr'85 by Klub Records. Distributed by: PRT

Cassette: released on Lochshore in Apr'85 by Klub Records. Distributed by: PRT

Beggar's Opera

ACT ONE.
Tracks: / Poet and peasant / Passacaglia / Memory / Raymond's road / Light cavalry.
Album: released on Vertigo (Germany) in Apr'85

Begley, Philomena

BEST OF PHILOMENA BEGLEY.
Album: released on Ritz in Mar'84 by Outlet Records. Distributed by: Outlet, Prism Leisure Distribution, Record Services Distribution (Ireland), Roots

Cassette: released on Ritz in Mar'84 by Outlet Records. Distributed by: Outlet, Prism Leisure Distribution, Record Services Distribution (Ireland), Roots

BLANKET ON THE GROUND.
Album: released on Topspin (Ireland) in Jan'76. Distributed by: I & B, Outlet, Shannon Distribution, S & P Distribution

Cassette: released on Topspin (Ireland) in Jan'76. Distributed by: I & B, Outlet, Shannon Distribution, S & P Distribution

COUNTRY STARS (Begley, Philomena & Ray Lynam).
Tracks: / You're the one I can't live without / Papa's wagon / You never were mine / My elusive dreams / Truck driving woman / Door is always open, (The) / You & me, her & him / What's your mama's name / I can't believe that you stopped loving me / Jeannie's afraid of the dark / Gypsy Joe & Me / Here today & gone tomorrow.
Album: released on Homespun(Ireland) in May'84 by Outlet Records. Distributed by: Outlet

Cassette: released on Homespun(Ireland) in May'84 by Outlet Records. Distributed by: Outlet

Ireland's own

IRISH COUNTRY QUEEN.
Album: released on Topspin (Ireland) in Jan'77. Distributed by: I & B, Outlet, Shannon Distribution, S & P Distribution

Cassette: released on Topspin (Ireland) in Jan'77. Distributed by: I & B, Outlet, Shannon Distribution, S & P Distribution

Album: released on Ritz in Apr'84 by Outlet Records. Distributed by: Outlet, Prism Leisure Distribution, Record Services Distribution (Ireland), Roots

Cassette: released on Ritz in Apr'84 by Outlet Records. Distributed by: Outlet, Prism Leisure Distribution, Record Services Distribution (Ireland), Roots

MORE ABOUT LOVE.
Album: released on Ritz in Feb'87 by Outlet Records. Distributed by: Outlet, Prism Leisure Distribution, Record Services Distribution (Ireland), Roots

Cassette: released on Ritz in Feb'87 by Outlet Records. Distributed by: Outlet, Prism Leisure Distribution, Record Services Distribution (Ireland), Roots

NASHVILLE COUNTRY.
Album: released on Shannon in '78

ONE LOVE AT A TIME.
Tracks: / One love at a time / Real men don't make quiche.
Single (7"): released on Ritz in Feb'87 by Outlet Records. Distributed by: Outlet, Prism Leisure Distribution, Record Services Distribution (Ireland), Roots

PHILOMENA.
Album: released on Ritz in Apr'84 by Outlet Records. Distributed by: Outlet, Prism Leisure Distribution, Record Services Distribution (Ireland), Roots

Cassette: released on Ritz in Apr'84 by Outlet Records. Distributed by: Outlet, Prism Leisure Distribution, Record Services Distribution (Ireland), Roots

QUEEN OF THE SILVER DOLLAR.
Album: released on Topspin (Ireland) in May'76. Distributed by: I & B, Outlet, Shannon Distribution, S & P Distribution

SIMPLY DEVINE (Begley, Philomena & Ray Lynam).
Album: released on Ritz in Apr'85 by Outlet Records. Distributed by: Outlet, Prism Leisure Distribution, Record Services Distribution (Ireland), Roots

Cassette: released on Ritz in Apr'85 by Outlet Records. Distributed by: Outlet, Prism Leisure Distribution, Record Services Distribution (Ireland), Roots

TOGETHER AGAIN (Begley, Philomena & Ray Lynam).
Album: released on Release in Nov'76 by Release Records. Distributed by: I & B, Wynd-Up Distribution, Taylors, Solomon & Peres Distribution

TRUCK DRIVING WOMAN.
Tracks: / Never again / Truck driving woman / I'll be all smiles / I really think I'm crying / How can I face tomorrow / Here today & gone tomorrow / Ramblin' man / Darling are you ever coming home / Philadelphia lawyer / Village in country Tyrone, A / My little son (England's motorway) / Old Arboe.
Album: released on Homespun(Ireland) in May'84 by Outlet Records. Distributed by: Outlet

Cassette: released on Homespun(Ireland) in May'84 by Outlet Records. Distributed by: Outlet

TRUCKIN' QUEEN.
Album: released on Topspin (Ireland) in Apr'78. Distributed by: I & B, Outlet, Shannon Distribution, S & P Distribution

Cassette: released on Ritz in Apr'84 by Outlet Records. Distributed by: Outlet, Prism Leisure Distribution, Record Services Distribution (Ireland), Roots

Album: released on Ritz in Apr'84 by Outlet Records. Distributed by: Outlet, Prism Leisure Distribution, Record Services Distribution (Ireland), Roots

Album: released on Ritz in Dec'84 by Outlet Records. Distributed by: Outlet, Prism Leisure Distribution, Record Services Distribution (Ireland), Roots

Cassette: released on Ritz in Dec'84 by Outlet Records. Distributed by: Outlet, Prism Leisure Distribution, Record Services Distribution (Ireland), Roots

WAY OLD FRIENDS DO.
Single (7"): released on Ritz in Apr'84 by Outlet Records. Distributed by: Outlet, Prism Leisure Distribution, Record Services Distribution (Ireland), Roots

Behan, Dominic

EASTER WEEK & AFTER.
Album: released on Topic in '81. Distributed by: Roots Distribution

STREETS OF SONG.
Album: released on Topic in '81. Distributed by: Roots Distribution

Behaviour Red

KE KE KE KE KE.
Single (7"): released on Dining Out in Apr'82 by Dining Out Records. Distributed by: IKF, Independent

Behemoth

DEATHWINGS.
Single (7"): released on Bullet Continental in Apr'84 by Neon Records. Distributed by: Neon Distribution

Beiderbecke, Bix

1924.
Album: released on Swaggie (Australia) in Jan'83

BIX AND HIS GANG (1927 - 28).
Album: released on Swaggie (Australia) in Jan'83

BIX AND TRAM (1927) (Beiderbecke, Bix & Frankie Trumbauer).
Album: released on Swaggie (Australia) in Jan'83

BIX AND TRAM (1928) (Beiderbecke, Bix & Frankie Trumbauer).
Album: released on BBMS in Apr'79. Distributed by: Swift

BIX BEIDERBECKE.
Album: released on Deja Vu in Nov'85 by Deja Vu Records. Distributed by: Counterpoint Distribution, Record Services Distribution (Ireland)

Cassette: released on Deja Vu in Nov'85 by Deja Vu Records. Distributed by: Counterpoint Distribution, Record Services Distribution (Ireland)

BIX BEIDERBECKE JAZZ FESTIVAL, IOWA, 1974 Various artists (Various Artists).
Album: released on BBMS in Apr'79. Distributed by: Swift

Album: released on BBMS in Apr'79. Distributed by: Swift

BIX BEIDERBECKE JAZZ FESTIVAL, IOWA, 1976 Various artists (Various Artists).
Album: released on BBMS in Apr'79. Distributed by: Swift

Album: released on BBMS in Apr'79. Distributed by: Swift

BIX BEIDERBECKE JAZZ FESTIVAL, IOWA, 1972 Various artists (Various Artists).
Album: released on BBMS in Apr'79. Distributed by: Swift

Album: released on BBMS in Apr'79. Distributed by: Swift

BIX BEIDERBECKE JAZZ FESTIVAL, IOWA, 1975 Various artists (Various Artists).
Album: released on BBMS in Apr'79. Distributed by: Swift

Album: released on BBMS in Apr'79. Distributed by: Swift

BIX BEIDERBECKE STORY.
Notes: 3 LP set
Album: released on CBS(Import) in Jun'86 by CBS Records. Distributed by: Conifer, Discovery, Swift

BIX 'N' BING (Beiderbecke, Bix & Bing Crosby).
Tracks: / Changes / Mary / There ain't no sweet man that's worth the salt of my tears / Sunshine / Mississippi mud / High water / From Monday on / Loveable / My pet / Louisiana / Do I hear you saying "I love you"? / You took advantage of me / Tain't so, honey tain't so / That's my weakness now / Because my baby don't mean maybe now / I'm in the seventh heaven / Reaching for someone(and not finding anyone there) / Oh, Miss Hannah / Your mother and mine / Waiting at the end of the road.
Notes: See also under Bing Crosby. With The Paul Whiteman Orchestra. A twenty trace disc.
Compact disc: by Academy Sound & Vision Records. Distributed by: Pinnacle

Album: released on ASV in Aug'81 by Academy Sound & Vision Records. Distributed by: Pinnacle

Cassette: released on ASV in Aug'81 by Academy Sound & Vision Records. Distributed by: Pinnacle

DAVENPORT BLUES Bix Beiderbecke Vol 2.
Tracks: / Flock o' blues / I'm glad I didn't know / Toddling blues / Idolizing / Hush-a-bye / I'd rather be the girl in your arms / Sunday / Cover me up with sunshine / Just one more kiss.
Album: released on Joker Import in Apr'81

FIDGETY FEET.
Tracks: / Fidgety feet / Jazz me blues / Copenhagen / Riverboat shuffle / Oh baby / Susie / Sensation rag / Lazy daddy / Tiger rag / Big boy / Tia juana.
Album: released on Joker Import in Apr'81

Album: released on Saar Giants Of Jazz (Italy) in Sep'85. Distributed by: Mainline

Cassette: released on Saar Giants Of Jazz (Italy) in Sep'85. Distributed by: Mainline

FUTURISTIC RHYTHM Bix Beiderbecke Vol 13.
Tracks: / Futuristic rhythm / Raisin' the roof / Louise / Wait till you see Ma Cherie / Baby won't you please come home / No one can take your place / I like that / When my dreams come true / Reaching for someone / China boy / Oh misss Hanna / Waiting at the end of the road / When you're counting the stars alone.
Album: released on Joker Import in Apr'81

GEORGIA ON MY MIND Bix Beiderbecke Vol 14.
Tracks: / Rockin chair / Barnacle Bill the sailor / Loved one / Loved one B / Deep harlem / Strutt Miss Lizzie / Deep south (takes 1&2) / I don't mind walking in the rain / I'll be a friend with pleasure (takes 2&3) / Georgia on my mind / One night in Havana / Bessie couldn't help it (takes 1&2).
Album: released on Joker Import in Apr'81

GOLDEN AGE OF BIX BEIDERBECKE, (THE).
Tracks: / Singin' the blues / Riverboat shuffle / I'm coming Virginia / Way down yonder in New Orleans / There ain't no land like Dixieland to me / I'm wondering who / At the jazz band ball / Sorry / Cryin' all day / Since my best girl let me down / Royal Garden blues / Humpty Dumpty / In a mist / Trumbology.
Album: released on Golden Age in Jul'83 by Music For Pleasure Records. Distributed by: EMI

Cassette: released on Golden Age in Jul'83 by Music For Pleasure Records. Distributed by: EMI

GOOD MAN IS HARD TO FIND, A Bix Beiderbecke Vol 6.
Tracks: / Three blind mice / Clorinda / I'm more than satisfied / Goose pimples / Sorry / Crying all day / Good man is hard to find, A / Since my best gal turned me down.
Album: released on Joker Import in Apr'81

IN A MIST Bix Beiderbecke Vol 5.
Tracks: / In a mist / Blue river / Clementine / Wringin' & twistin' / Humpty dumpty / Krazy kat / Baltimore / There ain't no land like Dixie / There's a crandle Caroline / Just an hour of love / I'm wandering who / At the jazz ball / Royal Garden blues / Jazz me blues.
Album: released on Joker Import in Apr'81

INDISPENSABLE BIX BEIDERBECKE (1924-30).
Tracks: / I didn't know / Idolizing / Sunday / I'm proud of a baby like you / I'm looking over a four-leaf clover / I'm gonna meet my sweetie now / Hoosier sweetheart / My pretty girl / Slow river / In my merry Oldsmobile / Clementine (from New Orleans) / Washboard blues / Changes / Mary / Lonely melody / San / Back in your own back yard / There ain't no sweet man that's worth the salt of my tears / Dardanella / From Monday on / Mississippi Mud / Sugar / Coquette / When / Lovable / My pet / For get-me-not / Louisiana / You took advantage of me / Rockin' chair / Barnacle Bill the sailor / Deep down south / I don't mind walking in the rain / I'll be a friend with pleasure / Georgia on my mind / Bessie couldn't help it.
Double Album: released on Jazz Tribune (USA) in Sep'86. Distributed by: Discovery

Double cassette: released on Jazz Tribune (USA) in Sep'86. Distributed by: Discovery

Double Album: released on RCA in Jan'87 by RCA Records. Distributed by: RCA, Roots, Swift, Wellard, Chris, I & B, Solomon & Peres Distribution

JAZZ CLASSICS IN DIGITAL STEREO.
Tracks: / Take Your Tomorrow / Goose Pimples / Wa-da-da / Rhythm King / Since My Best Girl Turned Me Down / There'll Come A Time / Barnacle Bill The Sailor / Deep Harlem / Rockin' Chair / I Like That / Jazz Me Blues / At The Jazz Band Ball / Copenhagen / Royal Garden Blues / Mississippi Mud / Sorry.
Album: released on BBC in Aug'86 by BBC Records & Tapes. Distributed by: EMI, PRT, Pye

Cassette: released on BBC in Aug'86 by BBC Records & Tapes. Distributed by: EMI, PRT, Pye

Compact disc: released on BBC in Aug'86 by BBC Records & Tapes. Distributed by: EMI, PRT, Pye

LONELY MELODY Bix Beiderbecke Vol 7.
Tracks: / Washboard blues / Changes / Mary (who are you waiting for) / Lonely melody / Smile / There'll come a time / Jubilee / Ol' man river / San 6 / San 7.
Album: released on Joker Import in Apr'81

LOUISIANA Bix Beiderbeck Vol.9.
Tracks: / Borneo / My pet / Somebody stole my gal / Thou swell / My pet & I / It was the dawn of love / Forget me not / Louisiana / You took advantage of me.
Album: released on Joker Import in Apr'81

MISSISSIPPI MUD Bix Beiderbecke Vol 8.
Tracks: / Mississippi mud / Smile / Make believe / Darndanella / There ain't no sweet man / Back in your own backyard / Love nest, The / From Monday to Mississippi mud / From Monday on.
Album: released on Joker Import in Apr'81

MY PRETTY GIRL Bix Beiderbecke Vol 3.
Tracks: / I'm proud of a baby like you / I'm looking over a four leaf clover / I'm gonna meet my sweetie now / Hoosier sweetheart / Look at the world & smile / My pretty girl / Sunny disposish / Lane in Spain, A.
Album: released on Joker Import in Apr'81

OL' MAN RIVER Bix Beiderbecke Vol 11.
Tracks: / My melancholy / Is it gonna be long / Get out and get under the moon / Oh you have no idea / Felix the cat / Taint't so honey / I'd rather cry over you / That's my weakness now / Georgie porgie / Because my baby don't mean "Maybe" now / Out of town gal / Bless your sister / Dusty Stevedore / Ol man river / Wa-da-da.
Album: released on Joker Import in Apr'81

RARE BIX, 1927-29, (THE).
Album: released on Swaggie (Australia) in Jan'82

RHYTHM KING Bix Beiderbecke Vol 12.
Tracks: / Concerto in F (2nd movement pt 1) / Gipsy / Sweet sue, just you / Take your tomorrow / Love affairs / Rhythm king / Louisianna / Margie / The love nest / The Japenese sandman / High upon a hilltop / Sentimental baby.
Album: released on Joker Import in Apr'81

RIVERBOAT SHUFFLE Bix Beiderbecke Vol 1.
Tracks: / Jazz me blues, The / Fidgety feet / Oh babe / Copenhagen / Riverboat shuffle / Susie - A / Susie - B / I need some pettin' / Royal Garden blues / Tiger rag / Sensation / Lazy Daddy - A / Lazy Daddy - B / Tia Juana / Big boy.
Album: released on Joker Import in Apr'81

SHOWBOAT Bix Beiderbecke Vol 9.
Tracks: / Why do I love you / Can't help lovin that man / You are my love / Make belives / Cocuette / When / Metropolis / Lovable / Our bungalow of dreams / Lila.
Album: released on Joker Import in Apr'81

SINGING THE BLUES.
Cassette: released on Astan in Jun'86 by Astan Records. Distributed by: Counterpoint

SINGIN' THE BLUES Bix Beiderbecke Vol 4.
Tracks: / Trumbology / Clarinet marmalade / Singin' the blues / Slow river / Ostrich walk / Riverboat shuffle / I'm coming Virginia / Way down yonder in New Orleans / For no reason at all in 'C' / In my merry oldsmobile / Three blind mice / Blue river / There's a cradle in Caroline.
Album: released on Joker Import in Apr'81

STUDIO GROUPS - 1927 , THE.
Tracks: / Trumbology / Clarinet marmalade / Singin' the blues / Ostrich walk / Riverboat shuffle / I'm coming Virginia / Way down yonder New Orleans / For no reason at all in C / Three blind mice / Blue river / There's a cradle in Carolina / In a mist / Wringin' an' twistin' / Humpty Dumpty / Krazy Kat / Baltimore.
Album: released on EMI Retrospect in Apr'85 by EMI Records. Distributed by: EMI

Cassette: released on EMI Retrospect in Apr'85 by EMI Records. Distributed by: EMI

STUDIO GROUPS-LATE 1927 (VOL 2), THE.
Tracks: / There ain't no land like dixieland / There's a cradle in Caroline / Just an hour of love / I'm wondering who / At the jazz band ball / Royal garden blues / Jazz me blues / I'm more than satisfied (Take 1) / I'm more than satisfied (Take 2) / Clorinda (Take 1) / Clorinda (Take 2) / Three blind mice (Take 1) / Three blind mice (Take 2) / Goose pimples / Sorry / Cryin' all day / Good man is hard to find, A / Since my best girl turned me down.
Notes: The second volume from Bix Beiderbecke & His Gang and friends to follow up from last year's successful re-issue of Volume 1,released to co-incide with 'The Beiderbecke Affair' TV series.Extensive sleeve notes by Brian Rust and detailed personnels make this an excellent purchase for the authentic enthusiast,while also containing the trad-jazz flavour so much in vogue today. A MONO recording
Album: released on Retrospect in Jan'86 by World Records

Cassette: released on Retrospect in Jan'86 by World Records

UNHEARD BIX (Beiderbecke, Bix/Various Artists).
Album: released on Broadway (USA) in '79

YOUNG MAN WITH A HORN.
Tracks: / Jazz me blues / Louisiana / Sorry / Thou swell / Ol' man river / Somebody stole my gal / Royal Garden blues / At the jazz band ball / Since my best gal turned me down / Wa-da-da (everybody's doin' it now) / Goose pimples / Rhythm King / Singin' the blues / Clarinet marmalade / Way down yonder in New Orleans / Mississippi mud / For no reason at all in C / There'll come a time (wait and see) / I'm comin' Virginia / Ostrich walk / Good man is hard to find, A / Wringin' and twistin' / Cryin' all day / Riverboat shuffle.
Double Album: released on CBS in Mar'85 by CBS Records. Distributed by: CBS

Cassette: released on CBS in Mar'85 by CBS Records. Distributed by: CBS

Beirach, Richard

Double edge

Beki

OUT OF THE DARKNESS.
Tracks: / Out of the darkness.
Single (7"): released on Communacate in Mar'86. Distributed by: Revolver, Cartel

Single (12"): released on Communacate in Mar'86. Distributed by: Revolver, Cartel

Cassette single: released on Communacate in Mar'86. Distributed by: Revolver, Cartel

Single (12"): released on Communique in Jul'86. Distributed by: Backs, Cartel

Belafonte, Harry

24 HITS.
Album: released on RCA (Germany) in '83

BANANA BOAT SONG, THE.
Tracks: / Mary's boy child.
Single (7"): released on Old Gold in Oct'86 by Old Gold Records. Distributed by: Lightning, Jazz Music, Spartan, Counterpoint

EVENING WITH BELAFONTE & MAKEBA, AN Songs from Africa (Belafonte, Harry & Miriam Makeba).
Tracks: / Train song / In the land of the Zulus / Hush, hush / To those we love / Give us our land / Beware Verwoerd / Gone are my children / Hurry, mama, hurry / My Angel / Cannon / Lullaby / Show me the way / My brother.
Album: released on RCA (Germany) in '83

FABULOUS, THE.
Tracks: / Day 0 / Island in the sun / Fox, The / Come back Liza / Wedding song / Jumpdown spin around / Man piaba / John Henry / Soldier, soldier / Shenandoah / Scratch, scratch / Jamaica farewell / Matilda, Matilda / Judy drowned / Turn around / Mama look a boo-boo / Danny boy / Try to remember / Coconut woman / Scarlet ribbons / Man smart / Abraham, Martin and John.
Double Album: released on Cambra in May'85 by Cambra Records. Distributed by: IDS, Conifer

Double cassette: released on Cambra in May'85 by Cambra Records. Distributed by: IDS, Conifer

FOLK SONGS.
Album: released on RCA (Germany) in '83

GREATEST HITS:HARRY BELAFONTE.
Picture disc album: released on Astan in Dec'85 by Astan Records. Distributed by: Counterpoint

HARRY BELAFONTE COLLECTION, (THE).
Album: released on Deja Vu in Aug'85 by Deja Vu Records. Distributed by: Counterpoint Distribution, Record Services Distribution (Ireland)

Cassette: released on Deja Vu in Aug'85 by Deja Vu Records. Distributed by: Counterpoint Distribution, Record Services Distribution (Ireland)

HARRY B & MIRIAM M (Belafonte, Harry & Miriam Makeba).
Album: released on RCA (France) in Oct'85 by RCA Records. Distributed by: Discovery

Cassette: released on RCA (France) in Oct'85 by RCA Records. Distributed by: Discovery

ISLAND IN THE SUN.
Tracks: / Island in the sun / Scarlet ribbons.
Single (7"): released on Old Gold in Nov'86 by Old Gold Records. Distributed by: Lightning, Jazz Music, Spartan, Counterpoint

MIDNIGHT SPECIAL.
Album: released on RCA (Germany) in Dec'84

Cassette: released on RCA (Germany) in Dec'84

MIDNIGHT SPECIAL, THE.
Tracks: / Midnight special / Crawdad song / Memphis Tennessee / Gotta travel on / Did you hear about Jerry / On top of Old Smokey / Muleskinner / Makes a long time man feel bad / Michael row the beat.
Album: released on RCA International in Jul'80

Cassette: released on RCA International in Jul'80

TO WISH YOU A MERRY CHRISTMAS.
Album: released on RCA in Nov'83 by RCA Records. Distributed by: RCA, Roots, Swift, Wellard, Chris, I & B, Solomon & Peres Distribution

Cassette: released on RCA in Nov'83 by RCA Records. Distributed by: RCA, Roots, Swift, Wellard, Chris, I & B, Solomon & Peres Distribution

VERY BEST OF HARRY BELAFONTE, THE.
Tracks: / Banana boat song (day o) / Island in the sun / Scarlet ribbons (for her hair) / Mary's boy child / Shenandoah / Jamaica farewell / Mama look a boo boo / Danny boy / Matilda Matilda / Swing dat hammer / There's a hole in my bucket / Angelina / Unchained melody / Coconut woman / Waltzing Matilda / Michael row the boat ashore / Boat, The.
Album: released on RCA in '84 by RCA Records. Distributed by: RCA, Roots, Swift, Wellard, Chris, I & B, Solomon & Peres Distribution

Cassette: released on RCA in '84 by RCA Records. Distributed by: RCA, Roots, Swift, Wellard, Chris, I & B, Solomon & Peres Distribution

Belew, Adrian

BIG ELECTRIC CAT.
Single 10": released on Island in Jun'82 by Island Records. Distributed by: Polygram

TWANG BAR KING.
Album: released on Island in Sep'83 by Island Records. Distributed by: Polygram

Cassette: released on Island in Sep'83 by Island Records. Distributed by: Polygram

Belfairs

DRY BONES.
Single (7"): released on Channel Music in Apr'82. Distributed by: Pinnacle

Belfast Gypsies

BELFAST GYPSIES.
Tracks: / Gloria's dream / Crazy world inside me, The / Midnight train / Aria of the fallen angels / Baby blue / People, let's freak out / Boom boom / Last will and testament, The / Portland town / Hey Gyp, dig the slowness / Suicide song / Secret police.
Album: by Sonet Records. Distributed by: PRT

Belfegore

BELFEGORE.
Single (12"): released on Pure Freude in Jan'84. Distributed by: Swift

Belgian Bitch

SAME TIME, SAME FACE.
Single (7"): released on Out Of Town in Jun'82

Belgique

CASABLANCA.
Single (7"): released on Out Of Town in Jun'82

Belgrano, Matt

HERE'S LOOKING AT YA (Belgrano, Matt & Roy Gale).
Tracks: / Here's looking at ya.
Single (7"): released on Music UK in Nov'86. Distributed by: PRT Distribution

Single (12"): released on Music UK in Nov'86. Distributed by: PRT Distribution

Belgravia

TALKING STRANGERS.
Single (7"): released on Phatom in Feb'82

Bella Donna

I REMEMBER.
Single (7"): released on Firebird in May'83 by Pinnacle Records. Distributed by: Pinnacle

Single (12"): released on Firebird in May'83 by Pinnacle Records. Distributed by: Pinnacle

Bell, Alan

MINSTREL, THE.
Tracks: / All in our north country / Windmills / Good shepherd, The / Two thousand years ago

/ Alice White / Band in the park, The / Ballad of a working man, The / Gypsy lad, The / Bread & fishes / Weaver's song, The / Packman, The / Minstrel's song, The.
Album: released on Folk Heritage in Jul'82 by Folk Heritage Records. Distributed by: Roots, Wynd-Up Distribution, Jazz Music, Folk Heritage

Cassette: released on Folk Heritage in Jul'82 by Folk Heritage Records. Distributed by: Roots, Wynd-Up Distribution, Jazz Music, Folk Heritage

Bellamy Brothers

BEAUTIFUL FRIENDS.
Album: released on Warner Brothers in Jun'78 by Warner Bros Records. Distributed by: WEA

BEST OF THE BELLAMY BROTHERS, (THE).
Album: released on MCA in Mar'85 by MCA Records. Distributed by: Polygram, MCA

Cassette: released on MCA in Mar'85 by MCA Records. Distributed by: Polygram, MCA

GREATEST HITS: BELLAMY BROTHERS VOL.2.
Tracks: / Feelin' the feelin' / When i'm away from you / Old hippie / I'd lie to you for your love / Too much is not enough / Forget about me / World's greatest lover / I need more of you / Strong weakness / I love her mind.

HOWARD & DAVID.
Tracks: / Wheels / Season of the wind / Single man & his wife,The / I'm gonna hurt her on the radio / Feelin' the feelin' / You're my favourite waste of time / Lie to you for your love / Old hippie / Everybody's somebody's darling / Jeannie Rae.
Album: released on MCA Import in Mar'86 by MCA Records. Distributed by: Polygram, IMS

IF I SAID YOU HAD A BEAUTIFUL BODY.
Single (7"): released on Old Gold in Sep'85 by Old Gold Records. Distributed by: Lightning, Jazz Music, Spartan, Counterpoint

I NEED MORE OF YOU.
Single (7"): released on MCA in Aug'84 by MCA Records. Distributed by: Polygram, MCA

LET YOUR LOVE FLOW.
Tracks: / Satin sheets / Nothin' heavy / Rainy,windy,sunshine / Rodeo Road / Let fantasy live / Highway 2-18(Hang on to your dreams) / Let your love flow / Livin' in the west / I'm the only sane man left alive / Inside of my guitar / Hell cat.
Album: released on Warner Brothers in Jun'76 by Warner Bros Records. Distributed by: WEA

Single (7"): released on Warner Brothers in Mar'76 by Warner Bros Records. Distributed by: WEA

OLD HIPPIE.
Single (7"): released on MCA in Oct'85 by MCA Records. Distributed by: Polygram, MCA

RESTLESS.
Tracks: / Forget about me / World's greatest lover / Down to you / We're having some fun now / Rock-a-billy / Restless / I love it / Diesel cafe / Tragedy / I need more of you.
Album: released on MCA Import in Mar'86 by MCA Records. Distributed by: Polygram, IMS

SONS OF THE SUN.
Tracks: / Lovers live longer / Do you love as good as you look / It's hard to be a cowboy these days / Dancin' romance / Endangered species / Givin' in to love again / Honey, we don't know no one in Nashville / Spiders & snakes / Classic case of the blues / Illusions of love.
Album: released on Warner Brothers in Nov'80 by Warner Bros Records. Distributed by: WEA

Bellamy Brothers,The

GREATEST HITS: BELLAMY BROTHERS VOL.1.
Compact disc: released on MCA in Jun'87 by MCA Records. Distributed by: Polygram, MCA

Album: released on MCA in Jun'87 by MCA Records. Distributed by: Polygram, MCA

Cassette: released on MCA in Jun'87 by MCA Records. Distributed by: Polygram, MCA

Bellamy, David

BRONTOSAURUS WILL YOU WAIT FOR ME.
Single (7"): released on MD in Apr'83 by MD Records

Bellamy, Peter

BOTH SIDES THEN.
Tracks: / Barbaree / Trees they do grow high, (The) / Lord will provide, (The) / Gallant frigate Amphitite, (The) / Roving on a winter's day, (The) / Derry gaol / Long time travelling / Shepherd of the downs, (The) / Housecarpenter, (The) / When I die / Edmund in the lowlands / Around cape horn / Turfman from Ardee, (The) / Amazing grace.
Album: released on Topic in '81. Distributed by: Roots Distribution

FOX JUMPS OVER THE PARSON'S GATE, THE.
Tracks: / Spotted cow, (The) / Two pretty boys (The two brothers) / Femal drummer, (The) / Here's adieu, sweet lovely nancy / Ghost's song, The-The cruel ship's carpenter / Carnal and crane, (The) / Little black horse, (The)-The penny wager / Barley and the Rye, (The) / Turkish lady, (The) / Warlike seamen,(The Irish captain) / Blackberry fold, (The) / Saint Stephen / Rigs of London town, (The) / Fox jumps over the parson's gate, (The).
Album: released on Topic in '81. Distributed by: Roots Distribution

KEEP ON KIPLING.
Tracks: / Pilgrims way, A / Cuckoo song / Blue roses / Ford O'kabul river / Land, (The) / Daysping mishandled / Roll down to Rio / Liner she's a lady, (The) / Anchor song / Minesweepers / My lady's law / Coiner, (The) / My boy Jack / Follow me 'ome / Cities and thrones and powers.
Album: by Fellside Records. Distributed by: Roots, Jazz Music, Celtic Music, Projection

SECOND WIND.
Album: released on E.F.D.S.S. in Oct'85 by E.F.D.S.S. Records. Distributed by: Projection, Roots

SINGS THE 'BARRACK-ROOM BALLADS' OF RUDYARD KIP LING.
Album: released on Free Reed in Jan'87 by Free Reed Records. Distributed by: Roots, Projection, Hobgoblin Records, Oblivion

TELL IT LIKE IT WAS.
Album: released on Leader in '81. Distributed by: Jazz Music, Projection

TRANSPORTS, THE.
Notes: A Ballad Opera by Peter Bellamy with Martin Carthy/Nic Jones/Dave Swarbrick/June Tabor/Cyril Tawney/etc. etc. Other information; A double album.
Album: released on Free Reed in Jan'87 by Free Reed Records. Distributed by: Roots, Projection, Hobgoblin Records, Oblivion

Bell, Andy

Who needs love like that

Bell, Archie

ARTISTS SHOWCASE: ARCHIE BELL.
Album: released on Streetsounds in Oct'86

Cassette: released on Streetsounds in Oct'86

DON'T LET LOVE LET YOU DOWN (Bell, Archie & The Drells).
Tracks: / Don't let love get you down / Where will you go when the party's over.
Single (7"): released on Portrait in Jun'86 by CBS Records. Distributed by: CBS

HERE I GO AGAIN (Bell, Archie & The Drells).
Single (7"): released on Old Gold in Jul'72 by Old Gold Records. Distributed by: Lightning, Jazz Music, Spartan, Counterpoint

Single (7"): released on Atlantic in Sep'72 by WEA Records. Distributed by: WEA

I NEVER HAD IT SO GOOD.
Tracks: / Don't wait for the world / Anytime is right / I never made love I never had it so good / Why didja do me / Good guys / Harder and harder / Without you.
Album: released on Becket in Jul'81

LOOK BACK OVER YOUR SHOULDER (Bell, Archie & The Drells).
Tracks: / Look back over your shoulder / Look back over your shoulder(Instrumental version).
Single (7"): released on Nightmare in Mar'87 by Nightmare Records. Distributed by: PRT

Single (12"): released on Nightmare in Mar'87 by Nightmare Records. Distributed by: PRT

WHERE WILL YOU GO WHEN THE PARTY'S OVER (Bell, Archie & The Drells).
Tracks: / Don't let love get you down / Where will you go when the party's over / Right here is where I want to be / Dancin' man / Everybody have a good time / I swear you're beautiful / Nothing comes easy / I bet I can do that dance you're doing.
Album: released on Portrait in Aug'86 by CBS Records. Distributed by: CBS

Cassette: released on Portrait in Aug'86 by CBS Records. Distributed by: CBS

Bell, Beckie

LET ME KNOW.
Notes: Pic bag
Single (12"): released on Carrere in Apr'87 by Carrere Records. Distributed by: PRT, Spartan

Bell, Book and Candle

BELL, BOOK AND CANDLE Film soundtrack (Duning, George).
Album: released on Citadel in Mar'79. Distributed by: Swift

Bell, Carey & Lurrie

SON OF A GUN.
Album: released on Rooster (USA) in Feb'84. Distributed by: Swift Distribution, Projection Distribution

Bell, Crawford

ANGELINE.
Single (7"): released on Homespun(Ireland) in Jan'81 by Outlet Records. Distributed by: Outlet

ANOTHER TEXAS SONG.
Tracks: / (When you're in love) everything's a waltz / Learning to live again / Lullaby's legends & lies / Three / Another Texas song / Stay a little longer / Queen Bee / Texas when I die / Somedays are diamonds (somedays are stones).
Album: released on Homespun(Ireland) in '82 by Outlet Records. Distributed by: Outlet

Cassette: released on Homespun(Ireland) in '82 by Outlet Records. Distributed by: Outlet

C B COUNTRY.
Cassette: released on Homespun(Ireland) in Nov'79 by Outlet Records. Distributed by: Outlet

COWBOY SINGER.
Tracks: / Union mare & Confederate grey, The / Ozark mountain / Tequila Sheila / Cowboy singer, The / Old flames (can't hold a candle to you) / Angelina / Hard to be humble / Littlest cowboy rides again, The / Mississippi you're on my mind / Leaving Louisiana in broad daylight / Evangelina / Mother of a wandering boy.
Album: released on Homespun(Ireland) in '82 by Outlet Records. Distributed by: Outlet

Cassette: released on Homespun(Ireland) in '82 by Outlet Records. Distributed by: Outlet

EVERYTHING'S A WALTZ.
Single (7"): released on Homespun(Ireland) in Sep'81 by Outlet Records. Distributed by: Outlet

HYMNS & SONGS FROM THE FAMILY ALBUM.
Tracks: / Where the soul never dies / Softly & tenderly / Let the lower lights keep burning / Tell mother I'll be there / Angel band / In the garden / Life's railway to Heaven / Jesus tender shepherd / He's the one / Jesus hold my hand / Precious memories / At the end of the day / Another bridge to burn / I dreamed I saw our country on her knees / Peace of mind.
Album: released on Homespun(Ireland) in Dec'83 by Outlet Records. Distributed by: Outlet

Cassette: released on Homespun(Ireland) in Dec'83 by Outlet Records. Distributed by: Outlet

SIOUX CITY SIOUX.
Single (7"): released on Homespun(Ireland) in Feb'83 by Outlet Records. Distributed by: Outlet

STAY A LITTLE LONGER.
Single (7"): released on Homespun(Ireland) in Feb'82 by Outlet Records. Distributed by: Outlet

THERE'S A STAR SPANGLED BANNER.
Tracks: / There's a star spangled banner waving somewhere / Have I stayed away too long / Down the trail of aching hearts / Sioux city Sue / Vaya con dios / Molly darling / Blue moon of Kentucky / Down in the little green valley / Can I sleep in your arms tonight / Lamplighting time in the valley / Sweetheart of the valley / Three little bells (Jimmy Brown song).
Album: released on Homespun(Ireland) in Dec'82 by Outlet Records. Distributed by: Outlet

Cassette: released on Homespun(Ireland) in Dec'82 by Outlet Records. Distributed by: Outlet

Bell, Dee

LET THERE BE LOVE (Bell, Dee with Stan Getz & Eddie Duran).
Tracks: / There's a lull in my life / Let there be love / This life we've led / Waltz for Debbie / You must believe in Spring / Give me one more chance / Reminiscing in Tempo / Living inside my mind / Just because we're kids.
Album: released on Concord Jazz (USA) in Apr'83 by Concord Jazz Records (USA). Distributed by: IMS, Polygram

ONE BY ONE (Bell, Dee & Eddie Duran).
Tracks: / What a little moonlight can do / This time the dream's on me / One by one / Please / Estate / Don't be that way / All my tears / Wonder why / Let's fall in love / Zingaro.
Album: released on Concord Jazz (USA) in Jul'85 by Concord Jazz Records (USA). Distributed by: IMS, Polygram

Cassette: released on Concord Jazz (USA) in Jul'85 by Concord Jazz Records (USA). Distributed by: IMS, Polygram

Bell, Della

FEW DOLLARS MORE, A (Bell, Delia & Bill Grant).
Album: released on Rounder (USA) in Jun'86. Distributed by: Mike's Country Music Room Distribution, Jazz Music Distribution, Swift Distribution, Roots Records Distribution, Projection Distribution, Topic Distribution

Bell, Derek

CAROLAN'S RECEIPT.
Cassette: released on Claddagh in Mar'77 by Claddagh Records. Distributed by: I & B, Record Services Distribution (Ireland), Roots, Topic, Impetus, Projection, CM

Belle

BELLE Original London cast.
Album: released on That's Entertainment in Apr'83 by That's Entertainment Records. Distributed by: Pinnacle, PRT

Bell, Eja

Petals

Belle, Lulu & Scotty

SWEETHEARTS OF COUNTRY MUSIC.
Album: released on Starday in Apr'87

Cassette: released on Starday in Apr'87

SWEETHEARTS STILL.
Album: released on Starday in Apr'87

Cassette: released on Starday in Apr'87

Belle, Regina

ALL BY MYSELF.
Tracks: / Show me the way / Take your love away / Please be mine / After the love has lost its shine / Intimate relations / You got the love / How could you do it to me / Gotta give it up / So many tears.
Album: released on CBS in Jul'87 by CBS Records. Distributed by: CBS

Cassette: released on CBS in Jul'87 by CBS Records. Distributed by: CBS

SHOW ME THE WAY.
Tracks: / Show me the way / Show me the way (inst) / How could you do it to me*.
Single (7"): released on CBS in Jun'87 by CBS Records. Distributed by: CBS

Single (12"): released on CBS in Jun'87 by CBS Records. Distributed by: CBS

Single (12"): released on CBS in Jul'87 by CBS Records. Distributed by: CBS

Belle Stars

80'S ROMANCE.
Single (7"): released on Stiff in Jun'84 by Stiff Records. Distributed by: EMI, Record Services Distribution (Ireland)

Single (12"): released on Stiff in Jun'84 by Stiff Records. Distributed by: EMI, Record Services Distribution (Ireland)

ANOTHER LATIN LOVE SONG.
Single (7"): released on Stiff in Oct'81 by Stiff Records. Distributed by: EMI, Record Services Distribution (Ireland)

CLAPPING SONG.
Single (7"): released on Stiff in Jul'82 by Stiff Records. Distributed by: EMI, Record Services Distribution (Ireland)

Picture disc single: released on Stiff in Jul'82 by Stiff Records. Distributed by: EMI, Record Services Distribution (Ireland)

Single (12"): released on Stiff in Jul'82 by Stiff Records. Distributed by: EMI, Record Services Distribution (Ireland)

ENTERTAINER, THE.
Single (7"): released on Stiff in Sep'83 by Stiff Records. Distributed by: EMI, Record Services Distribution (Ireland)

Single (12"): released on Stiff in Sep'83 by Stiff Records. Distributed by: EMI, Record Services Distribution (Ireland)

HIAWATHA.
Single (7"): released on Stiff in May'81 by Stiff Records. Distributed by: EMI, Record Services Distribution (Ireland)

IKO IKO.
Single (7"): released on Stiff in Jun'82 by Stiff Records. Distributed by: EMI, Record Services Distribution (Ireland)

INDIAN SUMMER.
Single (7"): released on Stiff in Jul'83 by Stiff Records. Distributed by: EMI, Record Services Distribution (Ireland)

Single (12"): released on Stiff in Jul'83 by Stiff Records. Distributed by: EMI, Record Services Distribution (Ireland)

LIVE SIGNS,LIVE TIMES.
Tracks: / Sign of the times / Mockingbird / Entertainer, The / Indian summer.
Notes: The all-girl group recorded live at the Marquee Club early in 1984,playing 16 songs including most of their hits-'Sign of the Times','The Clapping Song'etc. Number of tracks: 16 Type of recording: Live Total playing time: 60 minutes
Video-cassette (VHS): released on Polygram Music in Oct'84 by Polygram Records. Distributed by: Polygram

Video-cassette [Betamax]: released on Polygram Music in Oct'84 by Polygram Records. Distributed by: Polygram

MOCKING BIRD.
Single (7"): released on Stiff in Sep'82 by Stiff Records. Distributed by: EMI, Record Services Distribution (Ireland)

SIGN OF THE TIMES.
Tracks: / Sign of the times / Ci Ya Ya / Clapping song, (The) / Indian Summer / Harlem Shuffle / Reason, (The) / Iko Iko / Baby I'm yours / Mockingbird / Snake, (The) / Burning / Needle in a haystack.
Album: released on Stiff in Jan'82 by Stiff Records. Distributed by: EMI, Record Services Distribution (Ireland)

Single (7"): released on Stiff in Nov'82 by Stiff Records. Distributed by: EMI, Record Services Distribution (Ireland)

Single (7"): released on Stiff in Jan'83 by Stiff Records. Distributed by: EMI, Record Services Distribution (Ireland)

SLICK TRICK.
Single (7"): released on Stiff in Jul'81 by Stiff Records. Distributed by: EMI, Record Services Distribution (Ireland)

SWEET MEMORY.
Single (7"): released on Stiff in Apr'83 by Stiff Records. Distributed by: EMI, Record Services Distribution (Ireland)

Single (12"): released on Stiff in Apr'83 by Stiff Records. Distributed by: EMI, Record Services Distribution (Ireland)

WORLD DOMINATION.
Tracks: / World domination / just a minute / Rock me to the top.
Single (12"): released on Stiff in Apr'86 by Stiff Records. Distributed by: EMI, Record Services Distribution (Ireland)

Single (7"): released on Stiff in Apr'86 by Stiff Records. Distributed by: EMI, Record Services Distribution (Ireland)

Belle & The Devotions

Biographical Details: Belle and the Devotions represented their native Britain in the 1984 Eurovision Song Contest. Having released a couple of flop 45's in '83, they thus became the UK's first Eurovision act of the Eighties not to be specially formed for the event. But this did not make much difference-for the third consecutive year Britain failed to make the top 5 in the contest. The BBC then decided to alter their 'Song For Europe' rules to improve the UK's chances. Indeed, so turgid was Belle And The Devotions 'Love Games' - a Sixties Supremes pastiche in the style of 'Baby Love - that the Labour Party were prompted to launch a 'Better Song For Europe, as a vehicle for promoting their Euro-election campaign. At least Belle's girls had the consolation of reaching no.11 on the UK charts, ten places higher than the previous year's entry by Sweet Dreams (who?). However, rumours abounded that the group were not even singing on the single, even if this untrue, this record served to underline the lack of creativity and imagination shown by UK entrants to Eurovision in the Eighties.

ALL THE WAY UP.
Single (7"): released on CBS in Aug'84 by CBS Records. Distributed by: CBS

GOT TO LET YOU KNOW.
Cassette: released on That's Entertainment in Apr'83 by That's Entertainment Records. Distributed by: Pinnacle, PRT

Single (7"): released on DJM in Aug'83 by DJM Records. Distributed by: CBS, Polygram

Single (12"): released on DJM in Aug'83 by DJM Records. Distributed by: CBS, Polygram

LOVE GAMES.
Single (7"): released on CBS in Apr'84 by CBS Records. Distributed by: CBS Deleted Dec'85.

Single (12"): released on CBS in Apr'84 by CBS Records. Distributed by: CBS

LOVE LIKE THAT.
Single (7"): released on DJM in Jan'84 by DJM Records. Distributed by: CBS, Polygram

WHERE DID LOVE GO WRONG.
Single (7"): released on DJM in Apr'83 by DJM Records. Distributed by: CBS, Polygram

Single (12"): released on DJM in Apr'83 by DJM Records. Distributed by: CBS, Polygram

Bell For Adano, A

BELL FOR ADANO, (A) Hersey, John (Marshall, E.G.).
Cassette: released on Caedmon(USA) in Aug'83 by Caedmon (USA) Records. Distributed by: Gower, Taylors, Discovery

Bell, Freddy

GIDDY UP A DING DONG (Bell, Freddy & The Bellboys).
Single (7"): released on Old Gold in Jan'85 by Old Gold Records. Distributed by: Lightning, Jazz Music, Spartan, Counterpoint

Bell, Graeme

CZECHOSLOVAK JOURNEY.
Album: released on Swaggie (Australia) in Jan'83

CZECHOSLOVAK RECORDINGS.
Album: released on Dawn Club in '74. Distributed by: Cadillac, Swift, JSU

GRAEME BELL ALL STARS.
Album: released on Jazzology (USA) in Mar'84. Distributed by: Jazz Music, Swift

GRAEME BELL & HIS AUSTRALIAN JAZZ BAND (LONDON, 1951).
Album: released on Swaggie (Australia) in Jan'83

GRAEME BELL & HIS AUSTRALIAN JAZZ BAND (1949).
Album: released on Swaggie (Australia) in Jan'83

GRAEME BELL & HIS AUSTRALIAN JAZZ BAND (1948-49).
Album: released on Swaggie (Australia) in Jan'83

GRAEME BELL & HIS AUSTRALIAN JAZZ BAND (1949-50).
Album: released on Swaggie (Australia) in Jan'83

GRAEME BELL & HIS AUSTRALIAN JAZZ BAND (1949-52).
Album: released on Swaggie (Australia) in Jan'83

GRAEME BELL & JAZZ BAND 1947-51 (Bell, Graeme & Jazz Band).
Notes: Featuring previously unissued "See see rider" and "Way down yonder in New Orleans".
Cassette: released on Swaggie (Australia) in Jun'87

GREAT REVIVAL, THE (Bell, Graeme/Ken Colyer/Christie Brothers).
Album: released on Esquire in May'81 by Titan International Productions. Distributed by: Jazz Music, Cadillac Music, Swift, Wellard, Chris, Backs, Rough Trade, Revolver, Nine Mile

IN CZECHOSLOVAKIA (Bell, Graeme & His Dixieland Jazz Band).
Album: released on Dawn Club in Dec'86. Distributed by: Cadillac, Swift, JSU

PARIS (1948).
Album: released on Swaggie (Australia) in Jan'83

Bellls, Arthur D.

500 AS ONE.
Album: released on Dene in Jan'87. Distributed by: Jazz Music

Bell, Jim

PITTER PATTER (Bell, Jim Collection).
Single (7"): by Target Records. Distributed by: Spartan Distribution

Bell, Jimmie

STRANGER IN YOUR TOWN.
Album: released on Enja (Germany) in Oct'79 by Enja Records (W.Germany). Distributed by: Cadillac Music

Bell, Lloyd

SHE WILL BE WAITING.
Single (12"): released on Copasetic in Nov'82. Distributed by: Stage One

Bell, Madelaine

EAST SIDE, WEST SIDE (Bell, Madelaine & David Martin).
Single (7"): released on Deb in Apr'82 by Deb Records. Distributed by: Spartan

I'M NOT REALLY ME WITHOUT YOU (Bell, Madelaine & David Martin).
Single (7"): released on Deb in Jan'82 by Deb Records. Distributed by: Spartan

RUBADUB-POP GOES THE NURSERY RHYMES (Bell, Madelaine & John Telfer).
Album: released on Rubber Band in Nov'84

THIS IS ONE GIRL.
Album: released on PRT in Feb'76 by PRT Records. Distributed by: PRT

Bell, Maggie

GOOSE BUMPS.
Single (7"): released on Swan Song USA in Sep'82 by Atlantic Records. Distributed by: WEA Distribution, Atlantic Distribution

HAZELL.
Single (7"): released on Swan Song USA in Mar'78 by Atlantic Records. Distributed by: WEA Distribution, Atlantic Distribution

Bell & Martin

TOGETHER AGAIN.
Single (7"): released on Rampage in Mar'81

WHO'S KIDDING WHO?.
Single (7"): released on Deb in Jan'83 by Deb Records. Distributed by: Spartan

Bell Notes

I'VE HAD IT.
Album: released on Time in Jun'87. Distributed by: Jetstar Distribution

Bellot, Errol

SOUND IN A FURY.
Tracks: / Sound in a fury / Trouble make.
Single (12"): released on Jah Tubbys in Jun'86 by Jah Tubbys Records. Distributed by: Jetstar

Bellott, Errol

DON'T JOKE WITH LOVE.
Single (12"): by Jet Sounds Records. Distributed by: Jetstar Deleted Feb'83.

GIMMIE.
Single (12"): released on S&G in Sep'81. Distributed by: Pinnacle

IS THAT ALRIGHT GIRL.
Single (12"): released on S&G in May'82. Distributed by: Pinnacle

Bell, Paddie

IN RETROSPECT (Bell, Paddie & Corrie Folk Trio).
Album: released on Talisman in '70 by EMI (Ireland) Records. Distributed by: EMI (Ireland) Distribution, I & B Distribution

Bell, Ritchie

YOUR LOVE IS ECSTASY.
Tracks: / Your love is ecstasy / Your love is ecstasy (dub).
Notes: Essex record distributors- 02774 56196
Single (7"): released on Somar in May'86. Distributed by: Essex Record Distributors Ltd.

Bell, Roger

MAPLE LEAF RAG.
Album: released on Swaggie (Australia) in Jan'83

Bells

AULD LANG SYNE.
Single (7"): released on Klub in Nov'85

CHANGE RINGING From St. Mary Redcliffe, Bristol.
Album: released on Saydisc in May'79 by Saydisc Records. Distributed by: Essex, Harmonia Mundi, Roots, H.R. Taylor, Jazz Music, Swift, Projection, Gamut

HOKEY COKEY.
Single (7"): released on Klub in Nov'81

Single (12"): released on Klub in Nov'85

SOUNDS OF THE CARILLONN (Bells with Bournville & Loughborough Carillons).
Album: released on Saydisc in May'79 by Saydisc Records. Distributed by: Essex, Harmonia Mundi, Roots, H.R. Taylor, Jazz Music, Swift, Projection, Gamut

Bells Are Ringing

BELLS ARE RINGING Original Broadway Cast.
Tracks: / Overture / Bells are ringing / It's a perfect relationship / On my own / It's a simple little system / It is a crime / Hello, hello there / I met a girl / Long before I knew you / Mu-cha-cha / Just in time / Drop that name / Party's over, (The) / Saltzburg / Midas touch, (The) / I'm goin' back.
Album: released on CBS Cameo in Apr'83 by CBS Records. Distributed by: CBS

Cassette: released on CBS Cameo in Apr'83 by CBS Records. Distributed by: CBS

Bell Sisters

HIS BANNER OVER ME IS LOVE.
Album: released on Homespun(Ireland) in Oct'79 by Outlet Records. Distributed by: Outlet

Cassette: released on Homespun(Ireland) in Oct'79 by Outlet Records. Distributed by: Outlet

Bells of...

BELLS OF FROME A campanology LP special (Bells of Frome).
Album: released on Grosvenor in Jun'77 by Grosvenor Records. Distributed by: Taylors

BELLS OF LONDON (CHANGE RINGING) various artists (Various Artists).
Tracks: / St. Vedast / St. Lawrence Jewry / St. Giles Cripplegate / St. Clement Danes / St. Sepulchre / St. Mary-le-bow / St. Olave / St. Michael Cornhill / St. Bartholomew / Westminster Abbey / St. Martin-in-the-fields.
Album: released on Saydisc in Nov'83 by Saydisc Records. Distributed by: Essex, Harmonia Mundi, Roots, H.R. Taylor, Jazz Music, Swift, Projection, Gamut

Cassette: released on Saydisc in Nov'83 by Saydisc Records. Distributed by: Essex, Harmonia Mundi, Roots, H.R. Taylor, Jazz Music, Swift, Projection, Gamut

BELLS OF THE COTSWOLDS Bells of eight Cotswold churches (Bells of The Cotswolds).
Album: released on Saydisc in May'79 by Saydisc Records. Distributed by: Essex, Harmonia Mundi, Roots, H.R. Taylor, Jazz Music, Swift, Projection, Gamut

Cassette: released on Saydisc in '79 by Saydisc Records. Distributed by: Essex, Harmonia Mundi, Roots, H.R. Taylor, Jazz Music, Swift, Projection, Gamut

Bellson, Louis

COOL, COOL BLUE.
Tracks: / Tapooze don.
Album: released on Pablo Jazz (USA) in Oct'84 by United Artists. Distributed by: Swift

ECUE (Bellson, Louis & Walfredo De Los Reyes).
Tracks: / Javille / Sentifo en seis (six feeling) / Para buenos bailarines (for good dancers) / Salsa en cinco (salsa in five) / Ecue (folder sleeve).
Album: released on Pablo in '82 by Pablo Records. Distributed by: Wellard, Chris, IMS-Polygram, BMG

Cassette: released on Pablo in '82 by Pablo Records. Distributed by: Wellard, Chris, IMS-Polygram, BMG

London concert, The

LONDON CONCERT, THE (Bellson, Louis/Peterson/Heard).
Album: released on Pablo in '82 by Pablo Records. Distributed by: Wellard, Chris, IMS-Polygram, BMG

Cassette: released on Pablo in '82 by Pablo Records. Distributed by: Wellard, Chris, IMS-Polygram, BMG

LONDON GIG, THE (Bellson, Louis & Big Band).
Tracks: / Sing a song of love / My mother / Drum squad / Blues for Freddy / Jus fer us / We've come a long way together / Put it right here / Santos.
Album: released on Pablo in May'83 by Pablo Records. Distributed by: Wellard, Chris, IMS-Polygram, BMG

Cassette: released on Pablo in May'83 by Pablo Records. Distributed by: Wellard, Chris, IMS-Polygram, BMG

LONDON SCENE (Bellson, Louis & Big Band).
Album: released on Concord Jazz (USA) in Nov'81 by Concord Jazz Records (USA). Distributed by: IMS, Polygram

LOUIS BELLSON BIG BAND.
Tracks: / Intimacy of the bands / Quiet riots / Carnaby street / Beyond category / Chameleon / Open your window / Movin' on / Groove blues / La banda grande.
Album: released on Pablo in '82 by Pablo Records. Distributed by: Wellard, Chris, IMS-Polygram, BMG

Cassette: released on Pablo in '82 by Pablo Records. Distributed by: Wellard, Chris, IMS-Polygram, BMG

LOUIS BELLSON JAM.
Tracks: / Melody for Thelma / Stein on vine / Shave tail / Gonga din / I wonder why / Ballad medley-All the way home / Time to ride a moonbeam / Bye bye to all the birds / Blue invasion / Gush of periwinkles, A.
Album: released on Pablo in '82 by Pablo Records. Distributed by: Wellard, Chris, IMS-Polygram BMG

Cassette: released on Pablo in '82 by Pablo Records. Distributed by: Wellard, Chris, IMS-Polygram, BMG

MATTERHORN.

Tracks: / Matterhorn suite for drums (The)-Entrance / Knuf brothers (The) / Conversations / Then and now / War bird.
Album: released on Pablo in '82 by Pablo Records. Distributed by: Wellard, Chris, IMS-Polygram, BMG

Cassette: released on Pablo in '82 by Pablo Records. Distributed by: Wellard, Chris, IMS-Polygram, BMG

ORIGINALS (Bellson, Louis/Malach/Pizzapelli/Jones).
Album: released on Stash in Apr'81. Distributed by: Swift Distribution, Jazz Music Distribution, Jazz Horizons Distribution, Celtic Music Distribution, Cadillac, JSU Distribution, Zodiac Distribution

SIDE TRACK.
Album: released on Concord in Apr'81 by Import Records. Distributed by: IMS, Polygram

SUNSHINE ROCK (Bellson, Louis & The Explosion Orchestra).
Tracks: / Sunshine swing / Mid-eastern spango / Night birds / Feels so good / Hawk talks, The / Rich outing / Niles blues / Numero uno.
Album: released on Pablo in '82 by Pablo Records. Distributed by: Wellard, Chris, IMS-Polygram, BMG

Cassette: released on Pablo in '82 by Pablo Records. Distributed by: Wellard, Chris, IMS-Polygram, BMG

THUNDERBIRD.
Tracks: / Thunderbird / Little pixie, (The) / Nails / Serenade in blues.
Album: released on Jasmine in Aug'82 by Jasmine Records. Distributed by: Counterpoint, Lugtons, Taylor, H.R., Wellard, Chris, Swift, Cadillac

Cassette: released on Jasmine in Aug'82 by Jasmine Records. Distributed by: Counterpoint, Lugtons, Taylor, H.R., Wellard, Chris, Swift, Cadillac

WITH BELLS ON!.
Tracks: / Who's who / Cool / Amoroso / Prelude / Gumshoe / Blitzen / St. Louis / Moon is low / Doozy / Lou's blues / With bells on / Diplomat speaks, The / Mighty two, The / Paradiddle song / Rolls a la bossa nova / More flams / Swinging the rudiments / Que sticks / Two in one / Rhythmic excursion / Slides and hides.
Album: released on Vogue Jazz (France) in May'83

Bell, Teja

SUMMER SUITE (Bell, Teja/Dallas Smith/John Bernoff).
Album: released on Rising Sun (Holland) in Dec'84

Cassette: released on Rising Sun (Holland) in Dec'84

Bell, Vanessa

FOLLOWING JESUS (Bell Armstrong, Vanessa).
Album: released on Malaco in Oct'87 by Malaco Records. Distributed by: Charly

Bell, William

DO RIGHT MAN.
Album: released on Charly(R&B) in Apr'84 by Charly Records. Distributed by: Charly, Cadillac

Cassette: released on Charly(R&B) in Apr'84 by Charly Records. Distributed by: Charly, Cadillac

FEELING GUILTY.
Tracks: / Feeling guilty / Headline news.
Single (7"): released on Tout Ensemble in Feb'87. Distributed by: Pinnacle

Single (12"): released on Tout Ensemble in Feb'87. Distributed by: Pinnacle

I FORGOT TO BE YOUR LOVER.
Single (7"): released on Stax in Oct'87 by Ace Records. Distributed by: Pinnacle, Chris Wellard, IMS-Polygram

PASSION.
Tracks: / Passion.
Album: released on Tout Ensemble in Aug'86. Distributed by: Pinnacle

Cassette: released on Tout Ensemble in Aug'86. Distributed by: Pinnacle

Single (7"): released on Tout Ensemble in Jun'86. Distributed by: Pinnacle

Single (12"): released on Tout Ensemble in Jun'86. Distributed by: Pinnacle

Belly Dance Nights

BELLY DANCE NIGHTS Layale burg el haman-vol 1.
Cassette: released on EMI in May'79 by EMI Records. Distributed by: EMI

LAYALE BURG EL HAMAN - VOL 2.
Cassette: released on EMI in May'79 by EMI Records. Distributed by: EMI

Bel, M'Bilia

BA GERANTS.
Album: released on Genidia (Zaire) in Jul'84. Distributed by: Earthworks Distributors, Rough Trade

BEMALI SOY.
Album: released on Shanachie in Jun'85. Distributed by: Sterns/Triple Earth Distribution, Roots

Cassette: released on Shanachie in Jun'85. Distributed by: Sterns/Triple Earth Distribution, Roots

BOYA YE (ZAIRE).
Tracks: / Boya ye / Maeta vi / Shawuri yako / Tonton skoll.
Notes: The irrisistable charms of Africa's favourite lady in one of her most enticing moods. Guaranteed to please. "...monsters of slick studio soukous"(Blues & Soul).
Album: released on Sterns in Sep'86 by Sterns Records. Distributed by: Sterns/Triple Earth Distribution

Belmonde, Pierre

THEMES FOR DREAMS.
Compact disc: released on K-Tel in Nov'86 by K-Tel Records. Distributed by: Record Merchandisers Distribution, Taylors, Terry Blood Distribution, Wynd-Up Distribution, Relay Distribution, Pickwick Distribution, Solomon & Peres Distribution, Polygram

Compact disc: by K-Tel Records. Distributed by: Record Merchandisers Distribution, Taylors, Terry Blood Distribution, Wynd-Up Distribution, Relay Distribution, Pickwick Distribution, Solomon & Peres Distribution, Polygram

Belmont School Choir

ROBIN SONG.
Single (7"): released on Dakota in Dec'82 by Dakota Records. Distributed by: PRT

Belouis Some

BELOUIS SOME.
Notes: Full details see under: Some, Belious

SOME PEOPLE.
Album: released on Parlophone in Aug'85 by EMI Records. Distributed by: EMI

Cassette: released on Parlophone in Aug'85 by EMI Records. Distributed by: EMI

TARGET PRACTICE.
Single (7"): released on EMI in Jun'84 by EMI Records. Distributed by: EMI

Single (12"): released on EMI in Jun'84 by EMI Records. Distributed by: EMI Deleted '86.

Beloved

HAPPY NOW.
Single (12"): released on Flim Flam in 7 Mar'87 by Flim Flam Productions. Distributed by: Pinnacle

HUNDRED WORDS, A.
Single (12"): released on Flim Flam in Mar'86 by Flim Flam Productions. Distributed by: Pinnacle

SURPRISE ME.
Single (7"): released on Flim Flam in 13 Jun'87 by Flim Flam Productions. Distributed by: Pinnacle

Single (12"): released on Flim Flam in 13 Jun'87 by Flim Flam Productions. Distributed by: Pinnacle

THIS MEANS WAR.
Single (7"): released on Flim Flam in Aug'86 by Flim Flam Productions. Distributed by: Pinnacle

Single (12"): released on Flim Flam in Aug'86 by Flim Flam Productions. Distributed by: Pinnacle

Beloved Screen Music

BELOVED SCREEN MUSIC Various artists (Various Artists).
Tracks: / Over the rainbow / Gonna fly now / Speak softly love / Ben Hur love theme / Raindrops keep falling on my head / Summertime in Venice / Theme from East of Eden / Tara's theme / From Russia with love / Plein soleil / Love is many splendored thing.
Album: released on Denon in Mar'82 by Denon Records. Distributed by: Harmonia Mundi

Beltane Fire

CAPTAIN BLOOD.
Tracks: / Captain Blood / Further up,further in.
Single (7"): released on CBS in Dec'85 by CBS Records. Distributed by: CBS

DIFFERENT BREED.
Tracks: / Captain Blood / Fortune favours the brave / Night fishing / Poacher, The / Excalibur (I believe) / King Arthur's cave / Different breed / Run (light the Beltane Fire).

Album: released on CBS in Feb'86 by CBS Records. Distributed by: CBS

Cassette: released on CBS in Feb'86 by CBS Records. Distributed by: CBS

EXCALIBUR.
Tracks: / Excalibur / Uther 11.
Single (7"): released on CBS in Mar'86 by CBS Records. Distributed by: CBS

Single (12"): released on CBS in Mar'86 by CBS Records. Distributed by: CBS

Belton, Richard

RICHARD, BELTON & HIS MUSICAL ACES (Belton, Richard & His Musical Aces).
Album:

Belverderes

Jane Aire & Belverderes

Belvin, Jesse

JUST JESSE BELVIN.
Album: released on RCA in Nov'85 by RCA Records. Distributed by: RCA, Roots, Swift, Wellard, Chris, I & B, Solomon & Peres Distribution

Cassette: released on RCA in Nov'85 by RCA Records. Distributed by: RCA, Roots, Swift, Wellard, Chris, I & B, Solomon & Peres Distribution

MEMORIAL ALBUM.
Tracks: / Goonight my love, pleasant dreams / You send me / Let me love you tonight / Senorita / I'm in love(with a girl) / Girl of my dreams / My desire / (I love you)for sentimental reasons / Dream house / Just to say hello / I wanna know why / Sad & Lonesome / I need you so / I'll mess you up.
Notes: Side one: All tracks Copyright Control except track 1 Chappell Morris Ltd. Track 2 Burlington Music Ltd. & Track 7 Modern Music Pub Co. Ltd. **Side two:**All tracks Copyright Control except track 1 Peter Maurice Music Co Ltd /EMI Music
Album: released on Ace in Apr'84 by Ace Records. Distributed by: Pinnacle, Swift, Hotshot, Cadillac

Benatar, Pat

CRIMES OF PASSION.
Tracks: / Treat Mr.Right / You better run / Never wanna leave you / Hit me with your best shot / Hell is for children / Prisoner of love / Out a touch / Little paradise / I'm gonna follow you / Wuthering heights.
Album: released on Chrysalis in Sep'80 by Chrysalis Records. Distributed by: CBS

Cassette: released on Chrysalis in Sep'80 by Chrysalis Records. Distributed by: CBS

Compact disc: released on Chrysalis in Sep'80 by Chrysalis Records. Distributed by: CBS

Album: released on That's Entertainment in Jun'87 by That's Entertainment Records. Distributed by: Pinnacle, PRT

GET NERVOUS.
Tracks: / Shadows of the night / I want out / Looking for a stranger / Anxiety (get nervous) / Fight it out / Victim, The / Little too late / I'll do it / Tell it to her / Silent partner.
Album: released on Chrysalis in Nov'82 by Chrysalis Records. Distributed by: CBS

Picture disc album: released on Chrysalis in Nov'82 by Chrysalis Records. Distributed by: CBS

Cassette: released on Chrysalis in Nov'82 by Chrysalis Records. Distributed by: CBS

Compact disc: released on Chrysalis in Nov'82 by Chrysalis Records. Distributed by: CBS

HIT ME WITH YOUR BEST SHOT.
Tracks: / Promises in the dark / Fire & ice / Just like me / Precious / Hit me with your best shot.
Single (7"): released on Chrysalis in May'86 by Chrysalis Records. Distributed by: CBS

Single (12"): released on Chrysalis in May'86 by Chrysalis Records. Distributed by: CBS

IN THE HEAT OF THE NIGHT/CRIMES OF PASSION.
Cassette: released on Chrysalis in Dec'82 by Chrysalis Records. Distributed by: CBS

IN THE HEAT OF THE NIGHT.
Compact disc: released on Chrysalis in Jun'85 by Chrysalis Records. Distributed by: CBS

IN THE HEAT OF THE NIGHT.
Tracks: / Heartbreaker / I need a lover / If you think you know how to love me / In the heat of the night / My clone sleeps alone / We live for love / Rated X / Don't let it show / No you don't / So sincere / Heartbreaker / I need a lover / I you think you know how to love / In the heat of the night / My clone sleeps alone / We live for love / Rated X / Don't let it show / No you don't / So sincere.
Album: released on Chrysalis in Jun'85 by Chrysalis Records. Distributed by: CBS

Compact disc: released on Chrysalis in Jun'85 by Chrysalis Records. Distributed by: CBS

LIVE FROM EARTH.
Tracks: / Lookin' for a stranger / I want out / We live for love / Hell is for children / Hit me with your best shot / Promises in the dark / Heartbreaker / Love is a battlefield / Lipstick lies / Fire and ice.
Album: released on Chrysalis in Oct'83 by Chrysalis Records. Distributed by: CBS

Cassette: released on Chrysalis in Oct'83 by Chrysalis Records. Distributed by: CBS

Picture disc album: released on Chrysalis in Oct'83 by Chrysalis Records. Distributed by: CBS

Compact disc: released on Chrysalis in Oct'83 by Chrysalis Records. Distributed by: CBS

LOVE IS A BATTLEFIELD.
Single (7"): released on Chrysalis in Feb'85 by Chrysalis Records. Distributed by: CBS

Single (12"): released on Chrysalis in Feb'85 by Chrysalis Records. Distributed by: CBS

PRECIOUS TIME.
Tracks: / Promises in the dark / Fire and ice / Just like me / Precious time / It's a tuff life / Take it any way you want it / Hard to believe / Helter skelter.
Album: released on Chrysalis in Jul'81 by Chrysalis Records. Distributed by: CBS

Cassette: released on Chrysalis in Jul'81 by Chrysalis Records. Distributed by: CBS

Compact disc: released on Chrysalis in Jul'81 by Chrysalis Records. Distributed by: CBS

SEVEN THE HARD WAY.
Tracks: / Sex as a weapon / Le bel age / Walking in the underground / Big life / Red version / Seven rooms of gloom / Invincible / Run between the raindrops / Art of letting go.
Compact disc: released on Chrysalis in Apr'86 by Chrysalis Records. Distributed by: CBS

SEVEN THE HARD WAY.
Tracks: / Sex as a weapon / Le bel age / Walking in the underground / Big life / Red version / 7 rooms of gloom / Run between the raindrops / Invincible (Theme from the "Legend of Billie Jean") / Sex as a weapon / Le bel age / Walking in the underground / Big life / Red version / 7 rooms of gloom / Run between the raindrops / Invincible / Legend of Billy Jean, The / Art of letting go, The.
Album: released on Chrysalis in Nov'85 by Chrysalis Records. Distributed by: CBS

Cassette: released on Chrysalis in Nov'85 by Chrysalis Records. Distributed by: CBS

SEX AS A WEAPON.
Tracks: / Sex as a weapon / Red vision.
Single (7"): released on Chrysalis in Feb'86 by Chrysalis Records. Distributed by: CBS

Single (12"): released on Chrysalis in Feb'86 by Chrysalis Records. Distributed by: CBS

SHADOWS OF THE NIGHT (4 TRACK EP).
Tracks: / Diamond field / We belong / Painted desert / Temporary heroes / Love in the ice age / Ooh ooh song / Outlaw blues / Suburban king / Crazy world like this, A / Takin' it back.
Single (7"): released on Chrysalis in Feb'83 by Chrysalis Records. Distributed by: CBS

TROPICO.
Tracks: / Diamond field / We belong / Painted desert / Temporary heroes / Love in the ice age / Ooh ooh song / Outlaw blues, The / Suburban king / Crazy world like this, A / Takin' it back / Diamond field / We belong / Painted desert / Temporary heroes / Love in the ice age / Ooh ooh song / Outlaw blues, The / Surburban king / Crazy world like this, A / Takin' it back.
Cassette: released on Chrysalis in Nov'84 by Chrysalis Records. Distributed by: CBS

Compact disc: released on Chrysalis in Nov'84 by Chrysalis Records. Distributed by: CBS

Album: released on Chrysalis in Nov'84 by Chrysalis Records. Distributed by: CBS

WE BELONG.
Tracks: / We belong / Suburban king / We live for love.
Single (7"): released on Chrysalis in Dec'84 by Chrysalis Records. Distributed by: CBS

Single (12"): released on Chrysalis in Dec'84 by Chrysalis Records. Distributed by: CBS

Benbow, Steve

SONGS OF IRELAND (Benbow, Steve & The Strawberry Hill Boys).
Tracks: / O'Reilly's daughter / Banks of roses / Bould thady quill / Little beggar man / Mush, mush / Spanish lady / I'm a rambler / Holy ground / Irish Rover, The / She moved through the fair / Finnegan's wake / Green grows the laurel / Bennan on the moor / Hot asphalt / Brian O'Linn / Wiuld colonial boy / O'Reilly's daughter / Banks of the roses / Bould thady quill / Little beggar man / Mush, mush / Spanish lady / I'm a rambler / Holy ground / Irish rover, The / She moved through the fair / Finnegan's wake /

Green grows the laurel / Brennan on the moor / Hot asphalt / Brian O'Linn / Wild colonial boy.
Album: released on Bulldog in Jul'82 by Bulldog Records. Distributed by: President Distribution, Spartan, Swift, Taylor, H.R.

Benchley, Robert

BEST OF BENCHLEY.
Notes: Read by Bob Elliott
Cassette: released on Caedmon(USA) in '84 by Caedmon (USA) Records. Distributed by: Gower, Taylors, Discovery

Bendalls Box

NIGHTMARES/GAMES TODAY.
Single (7"): released on Circus in Apr'81. Distributed by: Circus, Recommended

Benders

DISTANCE.
Album: released on Hot in Aug'85 by Hot Records. Distributed by: Rough Trade, Cartel

Bendeth, David

Biographical Details: This Canadian vocalist and multi-instrumentalist had a minor British hit in 1979, reaching No.44 with the single "Feel the real". It was taken from his album "Adrenalin". A sequal, "Feel the real (again)", popped up on 1981's follow-up album "Just dessert", but Bendeth did not appear on the charts again. (Bob McDonald 1984).

JUST DESSERT.
Tracks: / Make it pop / Goldmine / I was there / Love collects / Rollin' / Feel the real (again) / Colourful dream, A / Risque rock / Better believe it / Acapulco.
Album: released on Ensign in Mar'81 by Ensign Records. Distributed by: CBS Distribution

Cassette: released on Ensign in Mar'81 by Ensign Records. Distributed by: CBS Distribution

Bendix, Ralf

SINGT ROCK AND ROLL.
Tracks: / Buona sera / Wirfahr'n nach San Fernando / Weit von Alaska / Hotel zur einsamkeit / Mona Lisa / Hey Joe / Heute geh ich nicht nach haus / 99 Jahr'(Geht meine post jetzt nach sing sing / Rock a beatin' boogie / See you later alligator / Shake rattle and roll- medley / Ich liebe ein Hassliches madchen / Sputnick rock / At the hop / So geht das jede nacht / Babysitter boogie / Du bist ja so schon / Minne haha / Buona sera / Wir fahr'n nach san Fernando / Weit von Alaska / Hotel zur einsamkeit / Mona Lisa / Hey Joe / Heute geh nicht nach haus / 99 Jah / See you later alligator / Shake rattle and roll / Ich leibe ein Hassliches madchen / Sputnick rock / At the hop / Babysitter boogie / Du bist ja so schon / Minne haha.
Album: released on Electrola in Sep'81 by Bear Family Records. Distributed by: Rollercoaster Distribution, Swift

Bene Jesserit

FASHION IS A DIRTY WORD.
Tracks: / Gloria / I had taken a few minutes to go... / Kidnapping / I could feel a pulse hammering in... / No rule for a dream: Peking (with rain) / Room had faded from her mind / Words / Il serait peu t'etre judicieux / You can dance if you want it... / Band was playing some unfamiliar... / La chanson d'ugly / Joyeux poeme / This guy was so made he stuttered as... / Femmes aux yeux d'argile / She was never so beautiful as then... / So far from Asia / Watching watching the world move / Derisoire / She had faded blondish hair... / Be happy / Little lady.
Album: released on Deadman's Curve in Feb'87 by Dave Henderson

Beneke, Tex

BENEKE ON BROADWAY (Beneke, Tex & The Glenn Miller Sound).
Tracks: / More I see you, The / Hello Dolly / I left my heart in San Francisco / My favourite things / Lemon tree, The / I wish you love.
Album: released on Bulldog in Apr'82 by Bulldog Records. Distributed by: President Distribution, Spartan, Swift, Taylor, H.R.

Cassette: released on Bulldog in Aug'82 by Bulldog Records. Distributed by: President Distribution, Spartan, Swift, Taylor, H.R.

MEMORIES.
Notes: Mono
Album: released on First Heard in Oct'84 by Submarine Records. Distributed by: Conifer, Taylors

Cassette: released on First Heard in Oct'84 by Submarine Records. Distributed by: Conifer, Taylors

SHOOTING STAR (1948) (Beneke, Tex Orchestra).
Tracks: / Shooting star / Now is the hour / Over the rainbow / Whistler, The / Dreamy lullaby / 18th century drawing room / Thoughtless / Things ain't what they used to be / Rhapsody in blue / That feathery feeling / Sabre dance / Pianissimo / Saturday date / Body and soul / Cherokee canyon / Beyond the sea / All the things you are.
Notes: The music on this record comes from radio programmes recorded whilst the band played for dancing on locations as far apart as New York City, Iowa, The Meadowbrook in New Jersey and the Capitol Theatre in Washington D.C. These recordings are of particular interest being 1948 items, as a studio recording ban existed for that year. Several ex "Glenn Miller Band" men were still in the orchestra in 1948. Bobby Nicholas and Whitey Thomas were in the trumpet section and Jimmy Priddy and Paul Tanner in the trombone section. The drummer was Jack Sperling- Arrangements by Henry Mancini, Jerry Gray and Norman Leyden were still being used.
Album: released on Magic in Jun'83. Distributed by: Jazz Music, Submarine, Swift, Chris Wellard, Conifer

Cassette: released on Magic in Jun'83. Distributed by: Jazz Music, Submarine, Swift, Chris Wellard, Conifer

UNDER THE RAINBOW.
Album: released on Artistic in Oct'84 by Submarine Records. Distributed by: JSU, Chris Wellard, Jazz Music, Swift, Clyde Factors Distributors

Cassette: released on Artistic in Oct'84 by Submarine Records. Distributed by: JSU, Chris Wellard, Jazz Music, Swift, Clyde Factors Distributors

WITH NO STRINGS (Beneke, Tex Orchestra).
Tracks: / What can you do / What's new / Begin the beguine / Devil and the deep blue sea / Blue moon / Cock a doodle / Way you look tonight / Java junction / Look up / La Rosita / Castle rock / Horses / Dancer's delight / Hop scotch / Baby O / World on a string.
Album: released on Hep in Apr'81 by H.R. Taylor Records. Distributed by: Jazz Music, Cadillac Music, JSU, Taylors, Wellard, Chris, Zodiac, Swift, Fast Forward

Benford, Mac

BACKWOOD BANJO.
Album: released on Rounder in Sep'79. Distributed by: Roots Distribution

Bengal Minstrel

MUSIC OF THE BAULS.
Album:

Bengal Tigers

METAL FETISH.
Album: released on Heavy Metal Worldwide in Sep'84 by FM-Revolver Records. Distributed by: EMI

Bengimani, Earl

HEALTH AND SORROW.
Single (12"): released on Negus Roots in Apr'82 by Negus Roots Records. Distributed by: Jetstar

Ben Hur

BEN HUR Original Soundtrack (Various Artists).
Tracks: / Fanfare to prelude / Star of Bethlehem and the adoration of the Magi / Friendship / Burning desert (The) / Arrius' party / Rowing of the galley slaves / Parade of the charioteers / Mother's love (The) / Return to Judes / Ring for freedom / Leper's search for the Christ / Procession to Calvary / Miracle and finale (The).
Notes: Rome Symphony Orchestra. National Philharmonic Orchestra conducted by Miklos Rozsa, composed by Miklos Rozsa.
Compact disc: released on London in '86 by London Records. Distributed by: Polygram

Compact disc: by CBS Records. Distributed by: CBS

BEN HUR (ORIG. SOUNDTRACK) (Various Artists).
Tracks: / Prelude / Miracle and finale, The / Procession to Calvary, The / Leper's search for the christ, The / Mother's love / Victory parade / Return of Judea / Naval battle / Rowing of the galley slaves / Burning desert, The / Love theme of Ben Hur / Roman march / Adoration of the Magi, The.
Album: released on CBS in Jul'86 by CBS Records. Distributed by: CBS

Cassette: released on CBS in Jul'86 by CBS Records. Distributed by: CBS

Benie Man

OVER THE SEA.
Single (12"): released on Jah Observers in Apr'83 by Jah Observers Records. Distributed by: Ruff Lion Distribution

Benjahman, I

HOLD ME TIGHT.
Tracks: / Jah World Will Keep On Turning.
Single (12"): released on Lion Kingdom in Feb'87 by Lion Kingdom Records. Distributed by: Jetstar, Pinnacle

Benjamin, Floella

REGGAE RITA.
Single (7"): released on BBJ International in Apr'84. Distributed by: PRT

Benjamin, Sathima Bea

MEMORIES AND DREAMS.
Album: released on Ekapa (USA) in Nov'84 by Ekapa Records. Distributed by: IMS, Polygram

Benjamin, Shani

LOOK AFTER YOU.
Single (12"): released on Ariwa in Apr'84 by Ariwa Records. Distributed by: Revolver, Cartel, Jetstar, Rough Trade

Benjamin, Tony

GO 'PON DE LAND.
Single (12"): released on Ariwa in Nov'82 by Ariwa Records. Distributed by: Revolver, Cartel, Jetstar, Rough Trade

SIT ALONE AGAIN.
Tracks: / Sit alone again / Dub for company.
Single (12"): released on Soundgrip in Jul'86 Distributed by: Jetstar

TREASURES IN THE WORLD.
Single (12"): released on Ariwa in Apr'84 by Ariwa Records. Distributed by: Revolver, Cartel, Jetstar, Rough Trade

TWILIGHT SMILE (Benjamin, Tony /Heiloo/Schnellinx).
Single (7"): released on Ample Productions in '82. Distributed by: Fresh

Benjax

WAITING FOR YOU (Benjax & Ulynis Brown).
Single (7"): released on Orbitone in Feb'84 by Orbitone Records. Distributed by: Jetstar Distribution

Ben, Jorge

MARAVILHAS 78/85.
Compact disc: by Island. Distributed by: Polygram

SONSUAL.
Album: released on Sign (France) in Apr'86. Distributed by: Greyhound

Ben, Mohammed Malcolm

AFRICAN FEELING.
Tracks: / Preservation of humanity / Zimbabwe / Turn me loose (The cry of a Namibian) / Reconciliation.
Album: released on Sterns African in Sep'83 by Sterns African Records. Distributed by: Stern's Distribution, Rough Trade Distribution

AFRICAN FEELING (GHANA).
Tracks: / Preservation of humanity / Zimbabwe / Turn me loose / Reconciliation.
Notes: Guitar band highlife from one of Ghana's top songwriters/producers.A plea for justice & humanity,sung in English. '.....the sound is roots,the message radical' (Black Music)
Album: released on Sterns in Sep'86 by Sterns Records. Distributed by: Sterns/Triple Earth Distribution

Bennett, Alan

FORTY YEARS ON.
Cassette: released on BBC in May'84 by BBC Records & Tapes. Distributed by: EMI, PRT, Pye

Bennett & Basie

BENNETT & BASIE.
Album: released on Jazz Reactivation in Jul'82. Distributed by: PRT

Bennett, Billy

ALMOST A GENTLEMAN.
Album: released on Topic in '81. Distributed by: Roots Distribution

Bennett, Brian

VOYAGE.
Cassette: released on DJM in May'78 by DJM Records. Distributed by: CBS, Polygram

Bennett, Cliff

GOT TO GET YOU INTO MY LIFE (Bennett, Cliff & The Rebel Rousers).
Tracks: / Use me / Hold on. I'm coming / C.C. Rider blues / One way love / Beautiful dreamer / Ain't that lovin' you baby / Ain't love good, ain't love good / Got to get you into my life / I take what I want / Back in the USSR / Three rooms with running water / I'll take good care of you / Said I weren't gonna tell nobody / It's all right / I'll take you home / Barefootin' / Hurtin' inside / That's what I said / I'm in love with you / You got what I like.
Album: released on See For Miles in Oct'86 by See For Miles Records. Distributed by: Pinnacle

Cassette: released on See For Miles in Oct'86 by See For Miles Records. Distributed by: Pinnacle

Album: released on See For Miles in Mar'82 by See For Miles Records. Distributed by: Pinnacle

Cassette: released on See For Miles in Mar'82 by See For Miles Records. Distributed by: Pinnacle

SLOW DOWN (Bennett, Cliff & The Rebel Rousers).
Album: released on Edsel in Dec'85 by Demon Records. Distributed by: Pinnacle, Jazz Music, Projection

Bennett, Errol

DON'T JOKE WITH LOVE.
Single (12"): released on Jet Sounds in Dec'82 by Jet Sounds Records. Distributed by: Jetstar

Bennett, Jim

BUMP AND ROLL Give up the funk (Bennett, Jim & His Bumpin' Crew).
Tracks: / Bump and roll (give up the funk) / Bump and roll (give up the funk)(Inst.).
Single (12"): released on Bluebird in Apr'87 by Bluebird Records. Distributed by: EMI, Jetstar

Bennett, Joe

BLACK SLACKS (Bennett, Joe & Sparkletones).
Album: released on Revival in Jul'82. Distributed by: Lightning, Swift

Bennett, Richard Rodney

HAROLD ARLEN'S SONGS.
Album: released on Audiophile in Jul'87 by Jazzology Records (USA). Distributed by: Jazz Music, Swift

LITTLE JAZZ BIRD.
Album: released on EMI in Aug'83 by EMI Records. Distributed by: EMI

Puttin' on the Ritz
Suprise suprise
Town & country

Bennett, Steve

COMEDY.
Album: released on Smallville in Sep'84 by Smallville Records. Distributed by: Smallville

Bennett, Tony

16 GOLDEN CLASSICS.
Tracks: / They'll be some changes made / Blue moon / Lady is a tramp, The / Lover / Manhattan / Spring is here / I could write a book / Child is born / Make someone happy / Life is beautiful / Maybe september / Lonely girl / You don't know what love is / Thou swell / There's a small hotel / As time goes by.
Notes: All tracks licensed from CBS Special Products: Design shoot that tiger!/(c) 1986/ Castle Communications Place, Units 7, 271 Merton Road, London SW18 5JS: BAR CODE 5/013428/920190
Album: released on Unforgettable in Dec'86 by Castle Communications Records. Distributed by: Counterpoint

Cassette: released on Unforgettable in Oct'86 by Castle Communications Records. Distributed by: Counterpoint

Compact disc: released on Unforgettable in '86 by Castle Communications Records. Distributed by: Counterpoint

ANYTHING GOES (Bennett, Tony & The Count Basie Big Band).
Album: released on Bulldog in Oct'85 by Bulldog Records. Distributed by: President Distribution, Spartan, Swift, Taylor, H.R.

Cassette: released on Bulldog in Oct'85 by Bulldog Records. Distributed by: President Distribution, Spartan, Swift, Taylor, H.R.

ART OF EXCELLENCE, THE.
Tracks: / Why do people fall in love/people (medley) / Moments like this / What are you afraid of? / When love was all we had / Everybody has the blues / How do you keep the music playing? / City of the angels / Forget the woman / I got lost in her arms / Day you leave me, The.
Album: released on CBS in Oct'86 by CBS Records. Distributed by: CBS

Cassette: released on CBS in Oct'86 by CBS Records. Distributed by: CBS

BEST OF.
Cassette: released on Creole (Everest-Europa) in Jul'84 by Creole Records. Distributed by: PRT, Rhino

CHICAGO (Bennett, Tony & Count Basie).
Album: released on Astan in Nov'84 by Astan Records. Distributed by: Counterpoint

Cassette: released on Astan in Nov'84 by Astan Records. Distributed by: Counterpoint

Compact disc: released on Dunhill Compact Classics (USA) in Jun'86

I LEFT MY HEART IN SAN FRANCISCO.
Tracks: / I left my heart in San Francisco / Once upon a time / Tender is the night / Smile / Love for sale / Taking a chance on love / Candy kisses / Have I told you lately? / Rules of the road / Marry young / I'm always chasing rainbows / Best is yet to come, The.
Notes: Re-issue
Album: released on CBS in Mar'86 by CBS Records. Distributed by: CBS

Cassette: released on CBS in Mar'86 by CBS Records. Distributed by: CBS

Single (7"): released on Old Gold in Jul'82 by Old Gold Records. Distributed by: Lightning, Jazz Music, Spartan, Counterpoint

IN PERSON (Bennett, Tony & Count Basie).
Album: released on CBS Cameo in Nov'83 by CBS Records. Distributed by: CBS

JAZZ.
Tracks: / I can't believe that you're in love with me / Don't get around much anymore / Stella by starlight / On green dolphin street / Let's face the music and dance / I'm thru with love / Solitude / Lullaby of Broadway / Dancing in the dark / I let a song go out of my heart / When lights are low / Just one of those things / Crazy rhythm / Judy / Give me the simple life / Street of dreams / Love scene / While the music plays on / Close your eyes / Out of this world / Just friends / Have you met Miss Jones? / Danny boy / Sweet Lorraine.
Album: released on CBS in Jun'87 by CBS Records. Distributed by: CBS

Cassette: released on CBS in Jun'87 by CBS Records. Distributed by: CBS

LIFE IS A SONG (Bennett, Tony & Count Basie).
Album: released on Topline in '86 by Charly Records. Distributed by: Charly Distribution

Cassette: released on Topline in '86 by Charly Records. Distributed by: Charly Distribution

Album: released on Topline in Aug'87 by Charly Records. Distributed by: Charly Distribution

Cassette: released on Topline in Aug'87 by Charly Records. Distributed by: Charly Distribution

RODGERS AND HART SONGBOOK (THE).
Tracks: / This can't be love / Blue moon / Lady is a tramp (The) / Lover / Manhattan / Spring is here / Have you met Miss Jones? / Isn't it romantic / Wait 'till you see her / I could write a book / Thou swell / Most beautiful girl in the world (The) / There's a small hotel / I've got five dollars / You took advantage of me / I wish I were in love again / This funny world / My heart stood still / My romance / Mountain greenery.
Notes: Recorded at CBS Studios, New York City, September 28-30, 1973. Engineer: Frank Laico. Musicians: Ruby Braff, Cornet/George Barnes,Guitar/Wayne Wright,guitar/ John Giuffrida,Bass.
Compact disc: by DRG Records. Distributed by: Conifer, RCA

SAN FRANCISCO.
Cassette: released on Pickwick (Ditto series) in Jan'83

TO MY WONDERFUL ONE.
Cassette: released on CBS(Blue Diamond) in Jun'85 by CBS Records. Distributed by: CBS

Album: released on Deja Vu in Nov'85 by Deja Vu Records. Distributed by: Counterpoint Distribution, Record Services Distribution (Ireland)

TONY BENNETT COLLECTION, THE.
Cassette: released on Deja Vu in Aug'85 by Deja Vu Records. Distributed by: Counterpoint Distribution, Record Services Distribution (Ireland)
Cat.no .... DVMC 2026
Album: released on Topline in Sep'85 by Charly Records. Distributed by: Charly Distribution

Cassette: released on Topline in Sep'85 by Charly Records. Distributed by: Charly Distribution

Benoit, David

FREEDOM AT MIDNIGHT.
Tracks: / Freedom at midnight / Along the Milky Way / Kei's song / Man with the panama hat, The / Pieces of time / Morning sojourn / Tropical breeze / Passion walk / Del sasser / Last goodbye, The".
Notes: Pianist David Benoit has already proven his ability to chart and sell records. His first album,'This Side Up' on the Spindletop label in the US was one of the top selling jazz albums of '86. The LP's solid success attracted GRP and licensed this album for Europe.Benoit,now signed exclusively to GRP,presents his debut for them with strong star support from Sam Riney,tenor sax;Dan Huff,guitar; Abraham Laboriel,bass & Tony Morales,drums.
Album: released on GRP (USA) in May'87 by GRP Records (USA). Distributed by: IMS, Polygram

Cassette: released on GRP (USA) in May'87 by GRP Records (USA). Distributed by: IMS, Polygram

Compact disc: released on GRP (USA) in May'87 by GRP Records (USA). Distributed by: IMS, Polygram

THIS SIDE UP.
Tracks: / Beach trails / Stingray / Land of the loving / Linus & Lucy / Sunset island / Hymn for Aquino / Santa Barbara / Waltz for Debbie.
Notes: A young & talented keyboard player,David Benoit,somewhat fits the description of being a "young Dave Grusin",he writes,arranges & plays his own compositions. This particular album will only be available from GRP Europe,for the USA,the rights will remain with his former label Spindletop.Nevertheless GRP Inc. is about to produce his first GRP album,so this LP may serve as introductory material far greater things to come.
Compact disc: released on GRP (USA) in Mar'87 by GRP Records (USA). Distributed by: IMS, Polygram

Album: released on GRP (USA) in Mar'87 by GRP Records (USA). Distributed by: IMS, Polygram

Benson, Cy

CY BENSON & FAIRWIND.
Album: released on Bullseye in Jul'79. Distributed by: Bullseye Music

Benson & Farrell

BENSON & FARRELL.
Album: by Polydor Records. Distributed by: IMS, Polygram

Benson, Gary

DYING TO LIVE WITH YOU.
Single (7"): released on Aura in Jan'81 by Hollywood Nites Distribution. Distributed by: Pinnacle

Benson, George

20/20.
Tracks: / No one emotion / Please don't walk away / I just wanna hang around you / Nothing's gonna change my love for you / La mere / 20-20 / New day / You are the love of my life / Hold me / Stand up / 20/20 / Shark bite.
Album: released on Warner Bros. in Jan'85 by Warner Bros Records. Distributed by: WEA

Cassette: released on Warner Bros. in Jan'85 by Warner Bros Records. Distributed by: WEA

Compact disc: released on Warner Bros. in Jan'85 by Warner Bros Records. Distributed by: WEA

20/20 (7").
Single (7"): released on Warner Bros. in Jan'85 by Warner Bros Records. Distributed by: WEA

Single (12"): released on Warner Bros. in Jan'85 by Warner Bros Records. Distributed by: WEA

BEST OF....
Album: released on A&M in Mar'82 by A&M Records. Distributed by: Polygram

Cassette: released on A&M in Mar'82 by A&M Records. Distributed by: Polygram

BEST OF GEORGE BENSON The early years.
Tracks: / White rabbit / somewhere in the east / Body talk / Take five / California dreamin' / Full compass.
Compact disc: released on CTI in Sep'84 by Polydor Records. Distributed by: IMS, Polygram

BEYOND THE SEA.
Single (7"): released on Warner Brothers in Apr'85 by Warner Bros Records. Distributed by: WEA

Single (12"): released on Warner Brothers in Apr'85 by Warner Bros Records. Distributed by: WEA

BLUE BENSON.
Album: released on Polydor (Italy) in Jun'83

Cassette: released on Polydor (Italy) in Jun'83

BODY TALK.
Compact disc: released on Musidisc (France) in Dec'86. Distributed by: Discovery Distribution, Swift Distribution

BODY TALK.
Cassette: released on CTI (Musidisc France) in Feb'84 by Polydor Records. Distributed by: IMS, Polygram

BREEZIN'.
Tracks: / This masquerade / Six to four / Breezin' / Affirmation / So this is love / Lady.
Compact disc: released on Warner Bros. in '83 by Warner Bros Records. Distributed by: WEA

Album: released on Warner Brothers in Sep'76 by Warner Bros Records. Distributed by: WEA

Cassette: released on Warner Brothers in Oct'82 by Warner Bros Records. Distributed by: WEA

COLLABORATION (Benson, George/Earl Klugh).
Tracks: / Mt.Airy road / Mimosa / Brazilian stomp / Dreamin' / Since you're gone / Collaboration / Jamaica / Love theme from "Romeo & Juliet".
Album: released on Warner Bros. in Jul'87 by Warner Bros Records. Distributed by: WEA

Cassette: released on Warner Bros. in Jul'87 by Warner Bros Records. Distributed by: WEA

Compact disc: released on Warner Bros. in Jul'87 by Warner Bros Records. Distributed by: WEA

COLLECTION: GEORGE BENSON.
Album: released on Deja Vu in Aug'86 by Deja Vu Records. Distributed by: Counterpoint Distribution, Record Services Distribution (Ireland)
Cat.no .... DVLP 2076
Cassette: released on Deja Vu in Aug'86 by Deja Vu Records. Distributed by: Counterpoint Distribution, Record Services Distribution (Ireland)

EARLY YEARS.
Tracks: / White rabbit / Somewhere in the east / Take five / California dreaming / Body talk / Full compass.
Album: released on CTI in Nov'83 by Polydor Records. Distributed by: IMS, Polygram

Cassette: released on CTI in Nov'83 by Polydor Records. Distributed by: IMS, Polygram

Compact disc: released on CTI in Nov'83 by Polydor Records. Distributed by: IMS, Polygram

ELECTRIFYING GEORGE BENSON, THE (Benson, George Quartet).
Tracks: / All the things you are / Love For Sale / Oleo / All Blues / The Masquerade Is Over (I'm afraid) / Invitation / Li'l Darlin'.
Notes: Licensed from Charly Records International APS. P 1986 Charly Holdings Inc. C 1986 Charly Records Ltd
Compact disc: released on Charly in Mar'86 by Charly Records. Distributed by: Charly, Cadillac

Album: released on Affinity in May'85 by Charly Records. Distributed by: Charly, Cadillac
Cat.no .... AFFD 140
Compact disc: released on Intertape in Jul'87. Distributed by: Target

GENIUS OF GEORGE BENSON.
Tracks: / California dreaming / Shell of a man / Summer knows, The / Summertime / Cast your fate to the wind / No sooner said than done / Changing world, The / Take five.
Album: released on Hallmark in Nov'83 by Pickwick Records. Distributed by: Pickwick Distribution, PRT, Taylors

Cassette: released on Hallmark in Nov'83 by Pickwick Records. Distributed by: Pickwick Distribution, PRT, Taylors

GEORGE BENSON COLLECTION.
Tracks: / Turn your love around / Love all the hurt away / Give me the night / Cast your fate to the wind / Love ballad / Nature boy / Last train to Clarksville / Livin' inside your love / Never give up on a good thing / On Broadway / White rabbit / This masquerade / Here comes the sun / Breezin' / Moody's mood / We got the love / Greatest love of all, The.
Album: released on Warner Bros. in Nov'81 by Warner Bros Records. Distributed by: WEA

Cassette: released on Warner Bros. in Nov'81 by Warner Bros Records. Distributed by: WEA

GEORGE BENSON IN CONCERT.
Album: released on Premier in '84 by Premier Records. Distributed by: CBS

Cassette: released on Premier in '84 by Premier Records. Distributed by: CBS

GEORGE BENSON & JACK MCDUFF (Benson, George & Jack McDuff).
Double Album: released on Prestige in Jul'77 by Prestige Records (USA). Distributed by: RCA, JSU, Swift

GEORGE BENSON LIVE IN CONCERT.
Album: released on Design in Apr'84 by Breakaway Records. Distributed by: PRT, Stage One

Cassette: released on Design in Apr'84 by Breakaway Records. Distributed by: PRT, Stage One

GIVE ME THE NIGHT.
Album: released on Warner Brothers in Jul'80 by Warner Bros Records. Distributed by: WEA

Cassette: released on Warner Brothers in Jul'80 by Warner Bros Records. Distributed by: WEA

Compact disc: released on Warner Brothers in '83 by Warner Bros Records. Distributed by: WEA

Single (7"): released on Warner Brothers in Aug'80 by Warner Bros Records. Distributed by: WEA

GREATEST LOVE OF ALL (OLD GOLD).
Single (7"): released on Old Gold in Jul'84 by Old Gold Records. Distributed by: Lightning, Jazz Music, Spartan, Counterpoint

GREATEST LOVE OF ALL.
Single (7"): released on Arista in Nov'80 by Arista Records. Distributed by: RCA

IN CONCERT.
Album: released on Premier in May'85 by Premier Records. Distributed by: CBS

Cassette: released on Premier in May'85 by Premier Records. Distributed by: CBS

IN CONCERT - CARNEGIE HALL.
Album: released on CTI in May'77 by Polydor Records. Distributed by: IMS, Polygram

IN FLIGHT.
Album: released on Warner Brothers in Jan'77 by Warner Bros Records. Distributed by: WEA

Cassette: released on Warner Brothers in Jan'77 by Warner Bros Records. Distributed by: WEA

INSIDE LOVE.
Single (7"): released on Warner Brothers in Dec'83 by Warner Bros Records. Distributed by: WEA

IN YOUR EYES.
Album: released on Warner Brothers in Jun'83 by Warner Bros Records. Distributed by: WEA

Cassette: released on Warner Brothers in Jun'83 by Warner Bros Records. Distributed by: WEA

Single (7"): released on Warner Brothers in Sep'83 by Warner Bros Records. Distributed by: WEA

IT'S UPTOWN/G BENSON COOKBOOK.
Double Album: released on CBS(Blue Diamond) in Jun'85 by CBS Records. Distributed by: CBS

Double cassette: released on CBS(Blue Diamond) in Jun'85 by CBS Records. Distributed by: CBS

KISSES IN THE MOONLIGHT.
Tracks: / Kisses in the moonlight / Open your eyes(instrumental).
Single (7"): released on Warner Bros. in Jul'86 by Warner Bros Records. Distributed by: WEA

LATE AT NIGHT.
Single (7"): released on WEA in Mar'84 by WEA Records. Distributed by: WEA

Single (12"): released on WEA in Mar'84 by WEA Records. Distributed by: WEA

LIVIN' INSIDE YOUR LOVE.
Album: released on Warner Brothers in Mar'79 by Warner Bros Records. Distributed by: WEA

Cassette: released on Warner Brothers in Mar'79 by Warner Bros Records. Distributed by: WEA

LOVE ALL THE HURT AWAY.
Single (7"): released on Arista in Aug'81 by Arista Records. Distributed by: RCA

Single (12"): released on Arista in Aug'81 by Arista Records. Distributed by: RCA

LOVE SONGS, THE.
Tracks: / Give me the night / Lady love me (one more time) / Love X love / New day / Feel like makin' love / 20/20 / Never give up on a good thing / Inside love (so personal) / No one emotion / In your eyes / Turn your love around / Greatest love of all, The.
Album: released on K-Tel in Oct'85 by K-Tel Records. Distributed by: Record Merchandisers Distribution, Taylors, Terry Blood Distribution, Wynd-Up Distribution, Relay Distribution, Pickwick Distribution, Solomon & Peres Distribution, Polygram

Cassette: released on K-Tel in Oct'85 by K-Tel Records. Distributed by: Record Merchandisers Distribution, Taylors, Terry Blood Distribution, Wynd-Up Distribution, Relay Distribution, Pickwick Distribution, Solomon & Peres Distribution, Polygram

LOVE WALKED IN.
Album: released on Platinum (W.Germany) in Oct'85. Distributed by: Mainline

Cassette: released on Platinum (W.Germany) in Oct'85. Distributed by: Mainline

LOVE X LOVE.
Single (7"): released on Warner Bros. in Sep'80 by Warner Bros Records. Distributed by: WEA

Single (12"): released on Warner Bros. in Sep'80 by Warner Bros Records. Distributed by: WEA

NEVER GIVE UP ON A GOOD THING.
Single (7"): released on Warner Bros. in Jan'82

by Warner Bros Records. Distributed by: WEA

Single (12"): released on Warner Bros. in Jan'82 by Warner Bros Records. Distributed by: WEA

NO ONE EMOTION (Benson, George/Roberta Flack).
Single (7"): released on Warner Bros. in Oct'85 by Warner Bros Records. Distributed by: WEA

Single (12"): released on Warner Bros. in Oct'85 by Warner Bros Records. Distributed by: WEA

ON BROADWAY/LOVE WILL COME AGAIN.
Single (7"): released on Warner Bros. in Nov'83 by Warner Bros Records. Distributed by: WEA

Single (12"): released on Warner Bros. in Nov'83 by Warner Bros Records. Distributed by: WEA

REPLAY ON...
Album: released on Sierra in Aug'85 by Sierra Records. Distributed by: WEA

Cassette: released on Sierra in Aug'85 by Sierra Records. Distributed by: WEA

SHIVER.
Tracks: / Shiver / Love is here tonight.
Single (7"): released on Warner Bros. in Nov'86 by Warner Bros Records. Distributed by: WEA

Single (12"): released on Warner Bros. in Nov'86 by Warner Bros Records. Distributed by: WEA

SILVER COLLECTION, THE.
Tracks: / Billie's bounce / Low down and dirty / Thunder walk / Doobie doobie blues / What's new / I remember Wes / Windmills of your mind / Song for my father / Carnival joys / Giblet gravy / Walk on by / Sack o' woe / Groovin' / Billie's bounce / Low down and dirty / Thunder walk / Doobie doobie blues / What's new? / I remember Wes / Windmills of your mind / Song for my father / Carnival joys / Giblet gravy / Walk on by / Sack o' woe / Groovin'.

SILVER COLLECTION.
Compact disc: released on Polydor in Nov'85 by Polydor Records. Distributed by: Polygram, Polydor

STORMY WEATHER.
Tracks: / Clockwise / Big fat lady / Hammond's bossa nova / Stormy weather / Slow scene / Jumpin' with symphony Sid / Cooker, The / Push push / Bullfight / Ready 'n' able / Bossa rocka / Flamingo.
Album: released on CBS in '84 by CBS Records. Distributed by: CBS Deleted '86.

Cassette: released on CBS in '84 by CBS Records. Distributed by: CBS

SUMMERTIME.
Album: released on Epic in Sep'82 by CBS Records. Distributed by: CBS

Cassette: released on Epic in Sep'82 by CBS Records. Distributed by: CBS

TEASER.
Tracks: / Did you hear the thunder.
Single (12"): released on Warner Bros. in Feb'87 by Warner Bros Records. Distributed by: WEA

Single (7"): released on Warner Bros. in Jan'87 by Warner Bros Records. Distributed by: WEA

WEEKEND IN LA.
Album: released on Warner Bros. in Jan'78 by Warner Bros Records. Distributed by: WEA

WHAT'S ON YOUR MIND?.
Tracks: / What's on your mind? / Turn out the light.
Single (7"): released on Warner Bros. in Feb'81 by Warner Bros Records. Distributed by: WEA

Single (12"): released on Warner Bros. in Feb'81 by Warner Bros Records. Distributed by: WEA

WHILE THE CITY SLEEPS.
Tracks: / Shiver / Love is here tonight / Teaser / Secrets in the night / Too many times / Did you hear thunder / While the city sleeps / Kisses in the moonlight.
Album: released on Warner Bros. in Sep'86 by Warner Bros Records. Distributed by: WEA

Cassette: released on Warner Bros. in Sep'86 by Warner Bros Records. Distributed by: WEA

Compact disc: released on Warner Bros. in Sep'86 by Warner Bros Records. Distributed by: WEA

WONDERFUL YEARS, THE.
Album: released on Proto in Mar'84 by Proto Records. Distributed by: WEA

Benson, Ivy

IVY BENSON & HER ORCHESTRA (Benson, Ivy & Her Orchestra).
Album: released on SJB Records in Jul'77

Benson, Jo Jo

Soul shake

Benson, Sharon

FIGHTING CHANCE.
Tracks: / Fighting chance / When love's so right.
Single (7"): released on Sedition in Sep'86. Distributed by: PRT

Single (12"): released on Sedition in Sep'86. Distributed by: PRT

IN YOUR EYES.
Single (7"): released on Starlite in Mar'84. Distributed by: Swift Distribution, PRT Distribution

Benson, Shaw

SECLUSION.
Tracks: / Seclusion / Seclusion(instrumental).
Single (12"): released on Priority in Jul'86 by Priority Records. Distributed by: RCA

Benson, Vicki

EASY LOVE.
Single (7"): released on Bronze in Sep'84 by Polygram Records. Distributed by: Polydor

Single (12"): released on Bronze in Sep'84 by Polygram Records. Distributed by: Polydor Deleted '85.

PASSION.
Single (7"): released on Bronze in Feb'85 by Polygram Records. Distributed by: Polydor

Cassette: released on Bronze in Feb'85 by Polygram Records. Distributed by: Polydor

Bensusan, Pierre

SOLILAI.
Compact disc: released on Rounder (USA) in Dec'86. Distributed by: Mike's Country Music Room Distribution, Jazz Music Distribution, Swift Distribution, Roots Records Distribution, Projection Distribution, Topic Distribution

Bentine, Michael

BEST OF BENTINE, (THE).
Album: released on BBC in Jan'84 by BBC Records & Tapes. Distributed by: EMI, PRT, Pye

Cassette: released on BBC in Jan'84 by BBC Records & Tapes. Distributed by: EMI, PRT, Pye

SQUARE BASHING.
Album: released on RCA International in Nov'80

Cassette: released on RCA International in Nov'80

Bentley, Earlene

CAUGHT IN THE ACT.
Single (7"): released on Record Shack in Jun'84 by Record Shack Records. Distributed by: PRT

Single (12"): released on Record Shack in Jun'84 by Record Shack Records. Distributed by: PRT

DON'T DELAY.
Tracks: / Don't delay / Don't delay (instrumental).
Single (7"): released on Nightmare in Nov'86 by Nightmare Records. Distributed by: PRT

Single (12"): released on Nightmare in Nov'86 by Nightmare Records. Distributed by: PRT

I GOT YOU COVERED.
Tracks: / I got you covered / I got you covered (inst).
Single (7"): released on Nightmare in Apr'87 by Nightmare Records. Distributed by: PRT

Single (12"): released on Nightmare in Apr'87 by Nightmare Records. Distributed by: PRT

I'M LIVING MY OWN LIFE.
Single (7"): released on Record Shack in Feb'84 by Record Shack Records. Distributed by: PRT

Single (12"): released on Record Shack in Feb'84 by Record Shack Records. Distributed by: PRT

LET THE NIGHT TAKE THE BLAME.
Tracks: / Let the night take the blame.
Single (12"): released on Rise in Aug'86 by Steve O'Donnell/Colin Jennings. Distributed by: Pinnacle

POINT OF NO RETURN.
Tracks: / Point of no return / Point of no return (dub mix).
Single (7"): released on Champion in May'86 by Champion Records. Distributed by: RCA

Single (12"): released on Champion in May'86 by Champion Records. Distributed by: RCA

STARGAZING.
Single (12"): released on Record Shack in Jan'85 by Record Shack Records. Distributed by: PRT

WHEN THE BOYS COME TO TOWN.
Single (7"): released on Soho in Aug'83

Single (12"): released on Soho in Aug'83

Bentley, John

JOHN BENTLEY & HIS BUDDIES
Various artists (Bentley, John & His Buddies).
Album: released on Euphonic in Apr'79 by Euphonic Records. Distributed by: Jazz Music, Swift

Bentley & The Bear

MOSTLY BLUES.
Album: released on Euphonic in Apr'79 by Euphonic Records. Distributed by: Jazz Music, Swift

Benton, Brook

16 GOLDEN CLASSICS.
Tracks: / Kiddio / It's just a matter of time / My true confession / Frankie and Johnny / Think twice / Hotel happiness / Thank you pretty baby / Boll weevil song, The / Rainy night in Georgia / Lie to me / Revenge / So many ways / I got what I wanted / Ties that bind (The) / Shadrack / For my baby.
Notes: All tracks licensed from CBS Special Products Recordings: Design: Shoot that Tiger! (c) 1986, Castle Communications Place, Unit 7, 271 Merton Road, London SW18 5JS: Bar Code 5/013428/920107.
Album: released on Unforgettable in Dec'86 by Castle Communications Records. Distributed by: Counterpoint

Cassette: released on Unforgettable in Dec'86 by Castle Communications Records. Distributed by: Counterpoint

20 GOLDEN PIECES OF BROOK BENTON.
Album: released on Bulldog in Mar'84 by Bulldog Records. Distributed by: President Distribution, Spartan, Swift, Taylor, H.R.

BACK TO BACK (Benton, Brook & Dinah Washington).
Double Album: released on Mercury in '78 by Phonogram Records. Distributed by: Polygram Distribution

Double cassette: released on Mercury in '78 by Phonogram Records. Distributed by: Polygram Distribution

BEST OF BROOK BENTON, (THE).
Album: released on Mercury in Jul'84 by Phonogram Records. Distributed by: Polygram Distribution

Cassette: released on Mercury in Jul'84 by Phonogram Records. Distributed by: Polygram Distribution

Cassette: released on K-Tel Goldmasters in Aug'84 by K-Tel Records. Distributed by: K-Tel

BEST OF BROOK BENTON, VOL 1.
Album: released on Phoenix in Oct'82 by Audio Fidelity Enterprises. Distributed by: Stage One, Lugtons

BROOK BENTON.
Cassette: released on Audio Fidelity in Oct'84. Distributed by: PRT

BROOK BENTON SINGS THE STANDARDS.
Album: released on RCA in '84 by RCA Records. Distributed by: RCA, Roots, Swift, Wellard, Chris, I & B, Solomon & Peres Distribution

Cassette: released on RCA in '84 by RCA Records. Distributed by: RCA, Roots, Swift, Wellard, Chris, I & B, Solomon & Peres Distribution

ENDLESSLY.
Tracks: / Its Just A Matter Of Time / Boll weevil song, The / Baby (You Got What It Takes) / Lie to me / So many ways / Hotel happiness / Kiddio / Endlessly / Revenge / Same one, The / Think Twice / Rockin' good way, A.
Album: released on Topline in Jan'87 by Charly Records. Distributed by: Charly Distribution

Cassette: released on Topline in Jan'87 by Charly Records. Distributed by: Charly Distribution

Cassette: released on K-Tel Goldmasters in Aug'84 by K-Tel Records. Distributed by: K-Tel

HIS GREATEST HITS.
Album: released on Mercury (USA) in Aug'87 by Import Records. Distributed by: IMS Distribution, Polygram Distribution

Cassette: released on Mercury (USA) in Aug'87 by Import Records. Distributed by: IMS Distribution, Polygram Distribution

HIS TOP HITS.
Cassette: released on Timeless Treasures in Jul'86. Distributed by: Counterpoint Distribution

INCOMPARABLE BROOK BENTON, (THE).
Album: released on Audio Fidelity in Oct'82. Distributed by: PRT

MAGIC MOMENTS WITH BROOK BENTON.
Cassette: released on RCA in May'85 by RCA Records. Distributed by: RCA, Roots, Swift, Wellard, Chris, I & B, Solomon & Peres Distribution

ROCKIN' GOOD WAY See Washington, Dinah (Benton, Brook & Dinah Washington).
Single (7"): released on Mercury in Jul'77 by Phonogram Records. Distributed by: Polygram Distribution

SONGS I LOVE TO SING.
Tracks: / Moonlight in Vermont / It's been a long long time / Lover come back to me / If you are but a dream / Why try to change me now / September song / Oh what it seemed to be / Baby won't you please come home / They can't take that away from me / I'll be around / I don't know enough about you / Fools rush in.
Album: released on Memoir in Dec'85 by Memoir Records. Distributed by: PRT Distribution

Cassette: released on Memoir in Dec'85 by Memoir Records. Distributed by: PRT Distribution

SPOTLIGHT ON BROOK BENTON.
Double Album: released on Philips in Jun'77. Distributed by: IMS-Polygram

TWO OF US, THE See Washington, Dinah (Benton, Brook & Dinah Washington).
Double Album: released on Mercury in '78 by Phonogram Records. Distributed by: Polygram Distribution

Double cassette: released on Mercury in '78 by Phonogram Records. Distributed by: Polygram Distribution

Benton, Buster

BLUESBUSTER.
Album: released on Red Lightnin' in Sep'82 by Red Lightnin' Records. Distributed by: Roots, Swift, Jazz Music, JSU, Pinnacle, Cartel, Wynd-Up Distribution

FIRST TIME IN EUROPE.
Album: released on Blue Phoenix (France) in Jan'85

SWEET 94.
Single (7"): released on Charly in Jul'80 by Charly Records. Distributed by: Charly, Cadillac

Benton, Marv

BEST OF MARV BENTON.
Album: released on Rebel (Australia) in Feb'84. Distributed by: Swift

Bentzon, Adrian

DANISH JAZZ, VOL 7.
Album: released on Storyville in Jul'82 by Storyville Records. Distributed by: Jazz Music Distribution, Swift Distribution, Chris Wellard Distribution, Counterpoint Distribution

Beresford

BEOWULF AND OTHER OLD ENGLISH POEMS (Various Artists).
Cassette: released on Argo (Spokenword) in Jul'83 by Decca Records. Distributed by: Polygram

Beresford Band

YORKSHIRE DALES DANCE NIGHT.
Album: released on Leader in '81. Distributed by: Jazz Music, Projection

Beresford, Steve

Dancing the line

DEADLY WEAPONS (Beresford, Steve/David Topp/John Zorn/Tonie Marshall).
Album: released on Nato (France) in Apr'87 by Disques Nato. Distributed by: Essex Record Distributors Ltd.

ELEVEN SONGS FOR DORIS DAY.
Tracks: / I was there / Secret love / Let it ring / Serenade in blue / Sentimental journey / Black hills of Dakota / It's magic / Que sera sera / At last / I'm beginning to see the light / Back in Cincinnati.
Notes: With Deb Bora/Tony Coe/Terry Day
Album: released on Chabada(France) in Sep'86. Distributed by: Essex

TEA TIME.
Album: released on Incus in Nov'76. Distributed by: Jazz Music, Cadillac

Beretta, Anne Marie

DANCING THE LINE.
Tracks: / Comfortable gestures / Ata 82 / Gift of linen / Horse tail / Tendance / Sand from the desert / Hiver 83/84 / Lover of paradox / Snap / Un aimant vivant / Altitude / Clins d'oeil.
Notes: Lyrics by Andrew Brenner
Album: released on Nato (France) in Sep'86 by Disques Nato. Distributed by: Essex Record Distributors Ltd.

Bergali, G

SOUL TRAIN (Bergali, G/Koverhult/Larson/Janson etc.).
Notes: For full info. see under: JANSON, Claes/BERGALI/etc.

Berg, Bob

STEPPIN - LIVE IN EUROPE.
Album: released on Red in Jan'87. Distributed by: Projection, Jazz Horizons

Berger, Bengt

BENGT BERGER.
Album: released on Dragon in Jul'87 by Dragon Records. Distributed by: Jazz Music, Projection, Cadillac

BITTER FUNERAL BEER.
Album: released on ECM in May'82 by ECM Records. Distributed by: IMS, Polygram, Virgin through EMI

Berger, Karl

ALL KINDS OF TIME (Berger, Karl & David Holland).
Album: released on Sackville in Apr'81. Distributed by: JSU, Jazz Music, Jazz Horizons, Cadillac Music, Celtic Music, Swift

WITH SILENCE.
Album: released on Enja (Germany) in Jan'82 by Enja Records (W.Germany). Distributed by: Cadillac Music

Bergeyk Van, Ton

FAMOUS RAGTIME GUITAR SOLOS.
Album: by Sonet. Distributed by: Roots, PRT-

FROM SOUP TO NUTS.
Album: by Sonet. Distributed by: Roots, PRT-

I GOT RHYTHM.
Album: by Sonet. Distributed by: Roots, PRT-

LULU'S BACK IN TOWN Hot Guitar Solos.
Album: released on Kicking Mule in '81 by Sonet. Distributed by: Roots, PRT

Bergman, Bill

MIDNIGHT SAX.
Compact disc: by Pacific Records (USA). Distributed by: Atlantic

B, Eric

I KNOW YOU GOT SOUL.
Single (7"): released on Chrysalis in 6 Jun'87 by Chrysalis Records. Distributed by: CBS

Single (12"): released on Chrysalis in 6 Jun'87 by Chrysalis Records. Distributed by: CBS

B, Eric & Rakim

PAID IN FULL.
Tracks: / I' ain't no joke / Eric B - is on the cut / My melody / I know you got soul / Move the crowd / Paid in full / As the rhyme goes on / Chines arithmetic / Eric B - is president / Extended beat.
Album: released on Fourth & Broadway in Aug'87 by Island Records. Distributed by: Polygram, EMI

Cassette: released on Fourth & Broadway in Aug'87 by Island Records. Distributed by: Polygram, EMI

Compact disc: released on Fourth & Broadway in Aug'87 by Island Records. Distributed by: Polygram, EMI

Berigan, Bunny

1931.
Album: released on Shoestring in '83 by Shoestring Records. Distributed by: Shoestring

1936 VOLUME 1.
Album: released on Jazz Information in May'86. Distributed by: Swift

BUNNY BERIGAN.
Tracks: / Shanghai shuffle / Devils holiday / Sing you sinners / Sunday / 'Taint so honey, 'taint so / I'll always be in love with you / Frankie & Johnny / Flat foot floogie / Peg O' my heart / Mahogany hall blues stomp / Wearin' of the green / Dardanella (Blues).
Album: released on Charly in Dec'86 by Charly Records. Distributed by: Charly, Cadillac

Cassette: released on Charly in Dec'86 by Charly Records. Distributed by: Charly, Cadillac

BUNNY BERIGAN 1937/40 Vol.2.
Album: released on Shoestring in '81 by Shoestring Records. Distributed by: Shoestring

BUNNY BERIGAN BAND 1938/9 (Berigan, Bunny & His Orchestra).
Album: released on Shoestring in '81 by Shoestring Records. Distributed by: Shoestring

BUNNY BERIGAN & HIS ORCHESTRA (Berigan, Bunny, Louis Armstrong & His orchestra).
Album: released on Shoestring in '81 by Shoestring Records. Distributed by: Shoestring

BUNNY BERIGAN & HIS ORCHESTRA (Berigan, Bunny & His Orchestra).
Album: released on Jazz Archives in Jul'86 by Jazz Archives Records. Distributed by: Jazz Music

BUNNY BERIGAN/LOUIS ARMSTRONG/MILLS BROTHERS, 1937 (Berigan, Bunny, Louis Armstrong, Mills Brothers).
Album: released on Shoestring in Apr'79 by Shoestring Records. Distributed by: Shoestring

Bunny Berigan, Louis Armstrong & Mills Brothers 1937

BUNNY BERIGAN WITH 1936 STUDIO BANDS.
Album: released on Shoestring in '81 by Shoestring Records. Distributed by: Shoestring

BUNNY BERIGAN WITH HAL KEMP & HIS ORCHESTRA 1930 Vol.1.
Album: released on Shoestring in '81 by Shoestring Records. Distributed by: Shoestring

INDISPENSABLE, 1937-39 (Berigan, Bunny & His Orchestra).
Tracks: / Swanee river / Frankie & Johnnie / Study in brown / I can't get started / Prisoner's song / Black bottom / Azure / Russian lullaby / High society / Sobbin' blues / In a mist / Flashes / Candlelights / In the dark / Blue Lou / Jazz me blues / Night song.
Notes: 34 titles including those listed in tracks
Double cassette: released on RCA in Jul'86 by RCA Records. Distributed by: RCA, Roots, Swift, Wellard, Chris, I & B, Solomon & Peres Distribution

INDISPENSABLE BUNNY BERIGAN,THE (1937-1939).
Album: released on RCA (France) in '83 by RCA Records. Distributed by: Discovery

LEADER & SIDEMAN.
Album: released on Meritt in Jan'87. Distributed by: Jazz Music Distribution

Berk, Dick

BIG JAKE (Berk, Dick & The Jazz Adoption Agency).
Album: released on Discovery (USA) in '84 by Discovery Records (USA). Distributed by: Swift, Flexitron-Audio, Jazz Music

MORE BIRDS, LESS FEATHERS (Berk, Dic/Jazz Adopt.Agency/N.Brignola).
Compact disc: released on Discovery (USA) in Dec'86 by Discovery Records (USA). Distributed by: Swift, Flexitron-Audio, Jazz Music

RARE ONE (Berk, Dick & The Jazz Adoption Agency).
Album: released on Discovery in '83. Distributed by: PRT

Berkeley Blues Festival

BERKELEY BLUES FESTIVAL Various artists.
Album: released on Arhoolie in '81 by Arhoolie Records. Distributed by: Projection, Topic, Jazz Music, Swift, Roots

Berkeley Rhythm

BERKELEY RHYTHM.
Album: released on Berkeley Rhythm in '82. Distributed by: Jazz Music

Album: released on Berkeley Rhythm in '82. Distributed by: Jazz Music

Berk, Lotte

LOTTE BERK EXERCISE RECORD,THE -GET PHYSICAL.
Album: released on Warwick in '82. Distributed by: Multiple Sound Distributors

Cassette: released on Warwick in '82. Distributed by: Multiple Sound Distributors

Berkshire Bell Ringers

BELLS OF CHRISTMAS, THE.
Album: released on Audio Fidelity in '84. Distributed by: PRT

Cassette: released on Audio Fidelity in '84. Distributed by: PRT

Berlin

COUNT THREE AND PRAY.
Tracks: / Will I ever understand you / You don't know / Like flames / Heartstrings / Take my breath away / Trash / When love goes to war / Hideaway / Sex me,talk me / Pink & velvet.
Compact disc: released on Mercury in Dec'86 by Phonogram Records. Distributed by: Polygram Distribution

Album: released on Mercury in Nov'86 by Phonogram Records. Distributed by: Polygram Distribution

Cassette: released on Mercury in Nov'86 by Phonogram Records. Distributed by: Polygram Distribution

DANCING IN BERLIN.
Single (7"): released on Mercury in '84 by Phonogram Records. Distributed by: Polygram Distribution

Single (12"): released on Mercury in '84 by Phonogram Records. Distributed by: Polygram Distribution

LIKE FLAMES.
Tracks: / Like flames / Trash.
Single (7"): released on Mercury in Feb'87 by Phonogram Records. Distributed by: Polygram Distribution

Single (12"): released on Mercury in Feb'87 by Phonogram Records. Distributed by: Polygram Distribution

LOVE LIFE.
Compact disc: released on Mercury in Aug'84 by Phonogram Records. Distributed by: Polygram Distribution

LOVE LIFE.

NO MORE WORDS.
Single (7"): released on Mercury in '84 by Phonogram Records. Distributed by: Polygram Distribution

Single (12"): released on Mercury in '84 by Phonogram Records. Distributed by: Polygram Distribution

SEX (I'M A...)/PLEASURE VICTIM.
Single (7"): released on Mercury in '83 by Phonogram Records. Distributed by: Polygram Distribution

Single (12"): released on Mercury in '83 by Phonogram Records. Distributed by: Polygram Distribution

TAKE MY BREATH AWAY.
Tracks: / Take my breath away / Radar radio / You've lost that loving feeling.
Single (7"): released on CBS in Oct'86 by CBS Records. Distributed by: CBS

Single (12"): released on CBS in Oct'86 by CBS Records. Distributed by: CBS

YOU DON'T KNOW.
Tracks: / Hide away / Dancing the Berlin (remix).
Single (7"): released on Mercury in Nov'86 by Phonogram Records. Distributed by: Polygram Distribution

Single (12"): released on Mercury in Nov'86 by Phonogram Records. Distributed by: Polygram Distribution

Berlin Blondes

MARSEILLES/THE POET.
Single (7"): released on Scratch in '81

Berline, Byron

DAD'S FAVORITES.
Album: released on Rounder in Jan'87. Distributed by: Roots Distribution

FIDDLER'S DREAM (Berline, Byron & Sundance).
Album: released on Appaloosa (Italy) in '85

Berlin, Irving

GOLDEN AGE OF IRVING BERLIN,THE.
Album: released on Golden Age in '84 by Music For Pleasure Records. Distributed by: EMI

Cassette: released on Golden Age in '84 by Music For Pleasure Records. Distributed by: EMI

SAY IT WITH MUSIC (1923-1933).
Double Album: released on Monmouth in '79

Berlin, Jeff

CHAMPION (Berlin, Jeff & Vox Humana).
Compact disc: by Pacific Records (USA). Distributed by: Atlantic

PUMP IT.
Compact disc: by Pacific Records (USA). Distributed by: Atlantic

Berlin P.O.

BEATLES (Berlin Philharmonic orchestra).
Album: released on Teldec (Germany) in '84 by Import Records. Distributed by: IMS Distribution, Polygram Distribution

Cassette: released on Teldec (Germany) in '84 by Import Records. Distributed by: IMS Distribution Polygram Distribution

EINSTEIN IN EDEN (Berlin Philharmonic orchestra).
Album: released on D.G.G.-Polydor in '82

Cassette: released on D.G.G.-Polydor in '82

Berlin Walls

NIGHT AND DAY.
Single (7"): released on La Rondie in '84. Distributed by: Pinnacle

Berman, Sonny

CONFIRMATION (Berman, Sonny/Dizzy Gillespie).
Album: released on Spotlite in '83 by Spotlite Records. Distributed by: Cadillac, Jazz Music, Spotlite

Album: released on Spotlite in '83 by Spotlite Records. Distributed by: Cadillac, Jazz Music, Spotlite

Bernadette

BACK ON THE ROAD AGAIN.
Album: released on Lismor in '84 by Lismor Records. Distributed by: Lismor, Roots, Celtic Music

Cassette: released on Lismor in '84 by Lismor Records. Distributed by: Lismor, Roots, Celtic Music

SING ME A SONG.
Single (7"): released on Polydor in '83 by Polydor Records. Distributed by: Polygram, Polydor

Bernard, Len

TAKE ME TO THE CIRCUS.
Album: released on Swaggie (Australia) in '83

Bernard, Rod

Boogie in black and white

BOOGIE IN BLACK & WHITE (Bernard, Rod & Clifton Chenier).

COUNTRY LOVIN'.
Album: released on Jin in '79. Distributed by: Swift

NIGHT LIGHTS & LOVE SONGS.
Album: released on Jin in '79 by Priority Records. Distributed by: EMI

ROD BERNARD.
Album: released on Jin in '79 by Priority Records. Distributed by: EMI

THIS SHOULD GO ON FOREVER.
Tracks: / Pardon Mr. Gordon / Colinda forgive / Fais do do / I might as well / Who's gonna rock my baby / Diggy liggy / Loneliness / My joile blonde / Congratulations to you / Cajun honey / Take her back / Boss man's son.
Album: released on Ace in '85 by Ace Records. Distributed by: Pinnacle, Swift, Hotshot, Cadillac

Berne, Jaqui

DON'T GET SERIOUS.
Tracks: / Don't get serious / I'll be your angel.
Single (7"): released on Hi-Hat in Jul'87 by Hi-Hat Records. Distributed by: Pinnacle

Single (12"): released on Hi-Hat in Jul'87 by Hi-Hat Records. Distributed by: Pinnacle

Bernelle, Agnes

FATHER LYING DEAD ON THE IRONING BOARD.
Album: released on Imp in '85 by Demon. Distributed by: Pinnacle

TOOTSIES.
Single (7"): released on Imp in '85 by Demon. Distributed by: Pinnacle

Bernhardt, Clyde

CLYDE BERNHARDT & THE HARLEM BLUES JAZZ BAND.
Album: released on Barron in '79

MORE BLUES & JAZZ FROM HARLEM.
Album: released on Barron in '79

Bernhardts

I HEAR YOU CALLING.
Single (7"): released on Parlophone in '84 by EMI Records. Distributed by: EMI

Bernhardt, Warren

HANDS ON.
Compact disc: released on DMP in Jan'87 by DMP Records. Distributed by: Venture

WARREN BERNHARDT TRIO (Bernhardt, Warren Trio).
Compact disc: released on DMP in Jun'86 by DMP Records. Distributed by: Venture

Bernoff, John

BREATHE (Bernoff, John/Marcus Allen).
Album: released on Rising Sun (Holland) in '84

Cassette: released on Rising Sun (Holland) in '84

Bernsen, Randy

MUSIC FOR PLANETS, PEOPLE AND WASHING MACHINES.
Album: released on Zebra in Feb'87 by Cherry Red Records. Distributed by: Pinnacle

Cassette: released on Zebra in Feb'87 by Cherry Red Records. Distributed by: Pinnacle

Bernstein, Elmer

MAGNIFICENT 7 Return of the Magnificent 7.
Album: released on Sun Set in '70 by Sun Set Records. Distributed by: Jetstar Distribution

MIDAS RUN,THE Film soundtrack.
Album: released on Citadel in '79. Distributed by: Swift

Bernstein on Broadway

BERNSTEIN ON BROADWAY Various artists (Various Artists).
Album: released on CBS in '85 by CBS Records. Distributed by: CBS

Cassette: released on CBS in '85 by CBS Records. Distributed by: CBS

Berntholer

MY SUITOR.
Single (7"): released on Blanco Y Negro in '85 by WEA Records. Distributed by: WEA

Berry, Bill

SHORTCAKE.
Tracks: / Avalon / Betty / Bloose / I didn't know about you / Royal garden blues / Moon song / I'm getting sentimental over you / I hadn't anyone till you....
Album: released on Concord in '79 by Import Records. Distributed by: IMS, Polygram

Berry, Chu

GIANT OF THE TENOR SAX, A.
Tracks: / Blowin' up a breeze (2) / On the sunny side of the street (2) / On the sunny side of the street / Monday at Minton's (2) / Monday at Minton's / Gee baby,ain't I good to you / Gee baby,ain't I good to you (2) / Sittin in / Sittin in (2) / Stardust / Body & soul / Forty six west fifty two / Forty six west fifty two (2) / Blowin' up a breeze.
Album: released on Commodore Classics (USA) in Nov'86 by Teldec Records (Germany). Distributed by: Conifer, IMS, Polygram

Compact disc: released on Commodore Classics in May'87 by Teldec Records (Germany). Distributed by: Conifer, IMS, Polygram

INDISPENSABLE, THE.
Album: released on RCA (France) in '85 by RCA Records. Distributed by: Discovery

RAREST...,THE 1037/40.
Album: released on Everybody's in '82 by Everybody's Records. Distributed by: Jazz Music, Swift

WITH LITTLE JAZZ ENSEMBLE 1938 & 1941.
Tracks: / Sitting in / Stardust / Body and soul / Forty six west fifty two / Blowing up a breeze / On the sunny side of the street / Monday at Minton's / Gee baby ain't I good to you.
Album: released on Commodore Classics (USA) in '82 by Teldec Records (Germany). Distributed by: Conifer, IMS, Polygram

Berry, Chuck

Biographical Details: BIOGRAPHICAL DETAILS: As well as being one of the greatest of the fifties rock 'n' rollers, Chuck Berry stands among the most influential artists in the entire history of rock music.

100 MINUTES.
Cassette: released on PRT (100 Minute Series) in '82

16 GREATEST HITS.
Compact disc: released on Bescol in Aug'87. Distributed by: Target

20 SUPER HITS.
Notes: Includes all hi biggies dating from the halcyon rock'n'roll days to his more recent success in the 70's
Album: released on Chess in Dec'85 by Charly Records. Distributed by: Charly, Swift, PRT, Discovery, IMS, Polygram

Cassette: released on Chess in Dec'85 by Charly Records. Distributed by: Charly, Swift, PRT, Discovery, IMS, Polygram

21 GREATEST HITS,THE.
Tracks: / Maybelline / Seet little sixteen / School days / Rock and roll music / Johnny b. good / Carol / Reelin' and rockin' / Memphis Tennessee / Bring another drink / Good lovin' woman / Roll over Beethoven / Back in the USA / Sweet little rock 'n' roller / Oh baby doll / CC rider / Thirty days / Goodnight,well its time to go / Back to memphis / Check me out / My heart will always belong to you / I really do love you.
Compact disc: released on Bescol in May'87. Distributed by: Target

BACK IN THE U.S.A..
Picture disc album: released on Astan in Dec'85 by Astan Records. Distributed by: Counterpoint

BERRY IS ON TOP.
Album: released on Chess in Oct'87 by Charly Records. Distributed by: Charly, Swift, PRT, Discovery, IMS, Polygram

Cassette: released on Chess in Oct'87 by Charly Records. Distributed by: Charly, Swift, PRT, Discovery, IMS, Polygram

BEST OF CHUCK BERRY (THE).

CHESS MASTERS.
Tracks: / Maybellene / Wee wee hours / You can't catch me / Downbound train / No money down / Brown eyed handsome man / Roll over Beethoven / Too much monkey business / Havana moon / School days / La Juanda / Rock an roll music / Oh baby doll / Sweet little sixteen / Johnny B.Goode / Round and round / Carol / Jo Jo Gunne / Bautiful Delilah / House of blue lights / Memphis / Sweet little rock 'n' roller / Johnny B Goode / Sweet little sixteen / Nadine / In the wee wee hours / Rock and roll music / Mabellene / Too much monkey business / Hail,hail,rock and roll / My ding-a-ling.
Album: released on Chess in '83 by Charly Records. Distributed by: Charly, Swift, PRT, Discovery, IMS, Polygram

CHUCK BERRY.
Picture disc album: released on Astan in Dec'85 by Astan Records. Distributed by: Counterpoint

Cassette: released on Audio Fidelity in '84. Distributed by: PRT

CHUCK BERRY,BEST OF.
Cassette: released on Creole (Everest-Europa) in '84 by Creole Records. Distributed by: PRT, Rhino

CHUCK BERRY COLLECTION, THE.
Album: released on Deja Vu in Jul'86 by Deja Vu Records. Distributed by: Counterpoint Distribution, Record Services Distribution (Ireland)

Cassette: released on Deja Vu in Jul'86 by Deja Vu Records. Distributed by: Counterpoint Distribution, Record Services Distribution (Ireland)

DUCKWALKING.
Album: released on Chess in '83 by Charly Records. Distributed by: Charly, Swift, PRT, Discovery, IMS, Polygram

Cassette: released on Chess in '83 by Charly Records. Distributed by: Charly, Swift, PRT, Discovery, IMS, Polygram

GREATEST HITS: CHUCK BERRY (CD).
Tracks: / Little Queenie.
Notes: Original Chess Recordings Licensed from Sugarhill Records Inc.
Compact disc: released on Charly in Jul'86 by Charly Records. Distributed by: Charly, Cadillac

GREATEST HITS:CHUCK BERRY.
Tracks: / Sweet little sixteen / Carol / Route 66 / Back in the USA / No particular place to go / Nadine / Roll over Beethoven / Too much monkey business / Sweet little rock'n'roller / Reelin' & rockin' / Johnny B. Goode / Promised land ,The / Maybelline / Rock'n'roll music / School days / Little Queenie.
Album: released on Showcase in Apr'86. Distributed by: Counterpoint

Cassette: released on Showcase in Apr'86. Distributed by: Counterpoint

GREATEST HITS LIVE: CHUCK BERRY.
Tracks: / Johnny B Goode / Sweet little sixteen / In the wee wee hours / Rock and roll music / Maybelline / Too much monkey business / Hail hail / My ding-a-ling.
Album: released on Spot in '83 by Pickwick Records. Distributed by: H.R. Taylor, Lugtons

Cassette: released on Spot in '83 by Pickwick Records. Distributed by: H.R. Taylor, Lugtons

LIVE.
Tracks: / No particular place to go / Hail hail rock and roll / In the wee wee hours / Johnny B Goode / Promised land / Hoochie kootchie man / Sweet little sixteen / Memphis tennessee / My ding-a-ling.
Notes: Previously released on the Everest label.
Album: released on Premier in '84 by Premier Records. Distributed by: CBS

Cassette: released on Premier in '84 by Premier Records. Distributed by: CBS

LONDON CHUCK BERRY SESSIONS,THE.
Album: released on Chess (France) in '84 by Charly Records. Distributed by: Charly, Swift, PRT

MEMPHIS TENNESSEE/NO PARTICULAR.
Single (7"): released on Old Gold in '83 by Old Gold Records. Distributed by: Lightning, Jazz Music, Spartan, Counterpoint

MOTIVE SERIES.
Tracks: / Louis to Frisco / Sweet little rock and roll / Roll over Beethoven / Back to Memphis / Wee baby blues / Johnny B Goode / Club nitty gritty / Sweet little sixteen / School days(Ring goes the bell) / Feelin' it / Let it rock / Carol.
Album: released on Mercury in '82 by Phonogram Records. Distributed by: Polygram Distribution

Cassette: released on Mercury in '82 by Phonogram Records. Distributed by: Polygram Distribution

MY DIG-A-LING.
Single (7"): released on SMP in '84. Distributed by: Jetstar

NEW JUKE BOX HITS.
Album: released on Chess in Aug'86 by Charly Records. Distributed by: Charly, Swift, PRT, Discovery, IMS, Polygram

Cassette: released on Chess in Aug'86 by Charly Records. Distributed by: Charly, Swift, PRT, Discovery, IMS, Polygram

NO PARTICULAR PLACE TO GO Sweet.
Single (7"): released on Flashback in '83 by Flashback Records/PRT Records. Distributed by: Mainline, PRT

PROFILE.
Cassette: released on Teldec in '81

PROFILE OF CHUCK BERRY.
Album: released on Teldec (Germany) in '81 by Import Records. Distributed by: IMS Distribution, Polygram Distribution

REELIN' AND ROCKIN'.
Tracks: / Bonsoir cherie / Carol / Hail hail rock and roll / Hoochie kootchie man / In the wee wee hours / Johnny B Goode / Johnny B Goode(Encore) / Maybelline / Sweet little sixteen / Too much monkey business.
Album: released on Topline in '85 by Charly Records. Distributed by: Charly Distribution

Cassette: released on Topline in Jan'85 by Charly Records. Distributed by: Charly Distribution

REELIN' AND ROCKIN' (LIVE).
Tracks: / Reelin' and rockin' / School days / My ding-a-ling / Too much monkey business / Memphis / Maybellene / Nadine.
Notes: Some of chuck Berry's greatest hits recorded live at the Toronto Rock and Roll festival including a seventeen minute version of "My ding-a-ling".
Album: released on Magnum Force in '84 by Magnum Music Group Ltd. Distributed by: Magnum Music Group Ltd, PRT, Spartan

REELING, ROLLING & ROCKING.
Tracks: / Memphis Tennessee / Too much monkey business / My ding a ling / Reeling & rockin' / Johnny Be Goode / Maybellene / Nadine (is it you) / Hail, hail rock and roll / Sweet little sixteen.
Album: released on Bulldog in Nov'83 by Bulldog Records. Distributed by: President Distribution, Spartan, Swift, Taylor, H.R.

ROCKIN' AT THE HOPS.
Album: released on Chess (France) in '84 by Charly Records. Distributed by: Charly, Swift, PRT

ROCKIN' AT THE TOP.
Album: released on Chess in Oct'87 by Charly Records. Distributed by: Charly, Swift, PRT, Discovery, IMS, Polygram

Cassette: released on Chess in Oct'87 by Charly Records. Distributed by: Charly, Swift, PRT, Discovery, IMS, Polygram

ROCKING WITH CHUCK BERRY.
Album: released on Mercury in '81 by Phonogram Records. Distributed by: Polygram Distribution

Cassette: released on Mercury in '81 by Phonogram Records. Distributed by: Polygram Distribution

ROCK 'N' ROLL HITS.
Tracks: / Johnny Be Goode / Rock and roll music / School day / Maybelline / Back in the USA / Sweet little sixteen / Memphis / Roll over Beethoven / Forty days / Carol / Club nitty gritty.
Notes: 3 UK singles hit plus 8 other classics
Album: released on Mercury (USA) in '83 by Import Records. Distributed by: IMS Distribution, Polygram Distribution

Cassette: released on Mercury (USA) in '83 by Import Records. Distributed by: IMS Distribution, Polygram Distribution

ROCK 'N' ROLL RARITIES.
Compact disc: released on Vogue in Dec'86. Distributed by: Discovery, Jazz Music, PRT, Swift

Double Album: released on Chess in Aug'87 by Charly Records. Distributed by: Charly, Swift, PRT, Discovery, IMS, Polygram

Double cassette: released on Chess in Aug'87 by Charly Records. Distributed by: Charly, Swift, PRT, Discovery, IMS, Polygram

SPOTLIGHT ON CHUCK BERRY.
Tracks: / Schooldays / Sweet little sixteen / Carol / Route 66 / Back in the USA / Rock and roll music / Promised land, The / Let it rock / Brown eyed handsom man / Maybelline / Round and round / Run Rudolph run / No particular place to go / You never can tell / Nadine / Roll over Beethoven / Too much monkey business / Go go go / Reelin and rockin / Memphis / Johnny Be Goode / Tulane / Come on / My ding a ling.
Album: released on PRT in '80 by PRT Records. Distributed by: PRT

Cassette: released on PRT in '80 by PRT Records. Distributed by: PRT

ST LOUIS TO FRISCO TO MEMPHIS (Berry, Chuck & Steve Miller band).
Album: released on Karussell (Germany) in '82

Cassette: released on Karussell (Germany) in '82

ST. LOUIS TO LIVERPOOL.
Album: released on Chess in Aug'86 by Charly Records. Distributed by: Charly, Swift, PRT, Discovery, IMS, Polygram

Cassette: released on Chess in Aug'86 by Charly Records. Distributed by: Charly, Swift, PRT, Discovery, IMS, Polygram

SWEET LITTLE ROCK 'N' ROLLER.
Album: released on Mercury (Holland) in '84 by Phonogram Records. Distributed by: Polygram Distribution

Cassette: released on Mercury (Holland) in '84 by Phonogram Records. Distributed by: Polygram Distribution

SWEET LITTLE SIXTEEN.
Single (7"): released on SMP in '84. Distributed by: Jetstar

Single (7"): released on Chess in '85 by Charly Records. Distributed by: Charly, Swift, PRT, Discovery, IMS, Polygram

TWO DOZEN BERRYS.
Compact disc: released on Vogue in '86. Distributed by: Discovery, Jazz Music, PRT Swift

Berry, Dave

CRYING GAME.
Single (7"): released on Decca-Originals in Mar'82 by Decca Records. Distributed by: Polygram, IMS

Single (7"): released on Old Gold in Jun'84 by Old Gold Records. Distributed by: Lightning, Jazz Music, Spartan, Counterpoint

HOSTAGE TO THE BEAT.
Tracks: / Searchlight / Love from Johnny / Heart of stone / Love is a killer / Bring my cadillac back / God bless the child / Mountains of the moon / On the waterfront / My baby left me / For a Knight to win his spurs / Boppin' the blues / Tracks of my tears.
Album: released on Butt in Jan'87 by Butt Records. Distributed by: Counterpoint

LITTLE THINGS.
Single (7"): released on Dakota in Mar'83 by Dakota Records. Distributed by: PRT

STRANGE EFFECT, THE.
Tracks: / I love you babe / Go on home / You're gonna need someone / Don't gimme no lip child / My baby left me / Memphis Tennessee / Hoochie coochie man / St. James infirmary / Diddley daddy / Alright baby / Same game / One heart between two / I'm gonna take you there / Mama / This strange effect / Forever / Crying game / Baby it's you / Little things / Picture me gone.
Album: released on See For Miles in Oct'86 by See For Miles Records. Distributed by: Pinnacle

THIS STRANGE EFFECT.
Album: released on See For Miles in Dec'83 by See For Miles Records. Distributed by: Pinnacle

Berry Gordy...

BERRY GORDY'S THE LAST DRAGON original soundtrack (Various Artists).
Album: released on Motown in May'85 by Motown Records. Distributed by: BMG Distribution

Cassette: released on Motown in May'85 by Motown Records. Distributed by: BMG Distribution

Berry, Len & Barbara

LEN & BARBARA BERRY.
Album: released on Greenwich Village in Jan'87 by Sweet Folk All Records. Distributed by: Roots, Projection, Lightning, Celtic Music, Wellard, Chris

Berry, Mike

EVERY LITTLE WHILE.
Single (7"): released on Rockney in May'83 by Rockney Records. Distributed by: EMI

HOLLY.
Single (7"): released on Switchback in Nov'85

MEMORIES.
Album: released on Polydor in Mar'82 by Polydor Records. Distributed by: Polygram, Polydor

Album: released on Polydor in Mar'82 by Polydor Records. Distributed by: Polygram, Polydor

SUNSHINE OF YOUR SMILE.
Single (7"): released on Polydor in Jun'80 by Polydor Records. Distributed by: Polygram, Polydor

SUNSHINE OF YOUR SMILE, THE.
Cassette: released on Polydor in Dec'80 by Polydor Records. Distributed by: Polygram, Polydor

SUNSHINE OF YOUR SMILE,THE/MEMORIES.
Double cassette: released on Polydor in Jun'83 by Polydor Records. Distributed by: Polygram, Polydor

TRIBUTE TO BUDDY HOLLY.
Tracks: / Tribute to Buddy Holly.
Album: released on Silver Star in Nov'86

Cassette: released on Silver Star in Nov'86

TRIBUTE TO BUDDY HOLLY (SINGLE).
Tracks: / Tribute to Buddy Holly / Look for a star.
Single (7"): released on Old Gold in Mar'87 by Old Gold Records. Distributed by: Lightning, Jazz Music, Spartan, Counterpoint

Berry, Nick

EVERY LOSER WINS.
Tracks: / Every loser wins / Every loser wins (instrumental).
Single (7"): released on BBC in Oct'86 by BBC Records & Tapes. Distributed by: EMI, PRT,

NICK BERRY.
Album: released on BBC in Feb'87 by BBC Records & Tapes. Distributed by: EMI, PRT,

Berry, Richard

GET OUT OF THE CAR.
Album: released on Ace in Sep'82 by Ace Records. Distributed by: Pinnacle, Swift, Hotshot, Cadillac

Bertei, Adele

WHEN IT'S OVER.

Bertha

BERTHA Children's TV series (Various Artists).
Album: released on BBC in Oct'85 by BBC Records & Tapes. Distributed by: EMI, PRT,

Cassette: released on BBC in Oct'85 by BBC Records & Tapes. Distributed by: EMI, PRT,

Berwick Speedway Club

COLORADO.
Cassette: released on Trimtop in Jun'87

Beserkley Chartbusters

BESERKLEY CHARTBUSTERS, VOL.1 various original artists (Various Artists).
Album: released on Beserkley (USA) in Jan'79 by Beserkley Records. Distributed by: DMS, RCA

Cassette: released on Beserkley (USA) in Jan'79 by Beserkley Records. Distributed by: DMS, RCA

Beshara

OH NO.
Single (12"): released on Mass Media Music in May'82

SHADOW OF LOVE.
Single (12"): released on Sub-Zero Music in Nov'84. Distributed by: PRT Distribution

WON'T LET YOU GO.
Single (12"): released on Mass Media Music in Jul'82

Beshera

GLORY GLORY.
Single (12"): released on Homespun(Ireland) in Jun'83 by Outlet Records. Distributed by: Outlet

Besserman, Martin

HIGH CLASS DINNER PARTY.
Tracks: / High class dinner party.
Single (7"): released on Awesome in May'86 by Awesome Records. Distributed by: Rough Trade, Cartel

Single (12"): released on Awesome in May'86 by Awesome Records. Distributed by: Rough Trade, Cartel

Besses Boys Band

OUR BOY'S WILL SHINE TONIGHT.
Album: released on Look in Feb'84. Distributed by: R. Smith & Co. Records, H.R. Taylor

Cassette: released on Look in Feb'84. Distributed by: R. Smith & Co. Records, H.R. Taylor

Besses o' Th' Barn Band

ALEX OWEN 60TH ANNIVERSARY.
Album: released on Chandos in Aug'81 by Chandos Records. Distributed by: Harmonia Mundi, Taylors

Cassette: released on Chandos in Aug'81 by Chandos Records. Distributed by: Harmonia Mundi, Taylors

BESSES IN AUSTRALIA.
Album: released on Chandos in Aug'81 by Chandos Records. Distributed by: Harmonia Mundi, Taylors

Cassette: released on Chandos in Aug'81 by Chandos Records. Distributed by: Harmonia Mundi, Taylors

ENGLISH BRASS, VOL.1.
Album: released on Top Brass in Apr'78 by PRT Records. Distributed by: PRT Distribution

ENGLISH BRASS, VOL.2.
Album: released on Top Brass in Apr'78 by PRT Records. Distributed by: PRT Distribution

SHOWCASE FOR BRASS.
Album: released on Chandos in Apr'83 by Chandos Records. Distributed by: Harmonia Mundi, Taylors

Cassette: released on Chandos in Apr'83 by Chandos Records. Distributed by: Harmonia Mundi, Taylors

Best Disco...

BEST DISCO ALBUM IN THE WORLD various original artists (Various Artists).
Album: released on WEA in Jul'79 by WEA Records. Distributed by: WEA

Cassette: released on WEA in Jul'79 by WEA Records. Distributed by: WEA

Best Foot Forward

BEST FOOT FORWARD original off-Broadway cast.
Album: released on DRG (USA) in Jul'79 by DRG Records. Distributed by: Conifer, RCA

Best Friends

BEST FRIENDS various artists (Various Artists).
Album: released on Impression in Nov'82. Distributed by: CBS

Cassette: released on Impression in Nov'82. Distributed by: CBS

Best From McTavish...

BEST FROM MCTAVISH'S KITCHENS various original artists (Various Artists).
Double Album: released on Charivari in '76 by Canon Records. Distributed by: Polygram, Jazz Music

Best, George

IT TAKES TWO (Best, George & Mary Stavin).

Single (12"): released on Lifestyle in Mar'84 by Zomba Records. Distributed by: CBS, PRT, RCA

Single (7"): released on Lifestyle in Mar'84 by Zomba Records. Distributed by: CBS, PRT, RCA

Best In Scottish...

BEST IN SCOTTISH DANCE MUSIC VOL.1, THE various artists (Various Artists).
Tracks: / Hamilton House / MacPhail's reels / Polka / Duke of Perth / Scottish waltz / Scottish reform / Marching with Robin / Bagpipe medley / Highland laddie / Lea rig / Hesitation waltz / Isle of Skye / Maxwell's rant / Dunoon barn dance.
Notes: Mail order distribution address is:Accordion Record Club, 146 Birmingham Road, Kidderminster, Worcs. DY10 2SL Tel. 0562 746105 Retail price supplied by ARC is 4.99 excluding P&P (via mail order)
Album: released on Accordion Record Club in Jul'86 by Accordion Record Club Records. Distributed by: Accordion Record Club

Cassette: released on Accordion Record Club in Jul'86 by Accordion Record Club Records. Distributed by: Accordion Record Club

Album: released on ARC (Accordion Records) in '84. Distributed by: Accordion Record Club

Album: released on ARC (Accordion Records) in '84. Distributed by: Accordion Record Club

BEST IN SCOTTISH DANCE MUSIC VOL.2, THE various artists (Various Artists).
Tracks: / Highland laddie / Blue bonnets / Reels / Waltz / Duncan barn dance / Scottish ramble / Trip to Bavaria / Eva three-step / Dundee whaler / Waltzes / Two & two / Polka / New Ashludie rant / Scottish waltz selection.
Notes: Retail price given by ARC is 4.99 excluding p&p(via mail order) Mail order dist. address is:Accordion Record Club,146 Birmingham Road, Kidderminster,Worcs.DY10 2SL Tel: 0562 746105
Album: released on Accordion Record Club in Jul'86 by Accordion Record Club Records. Distributed by: Accordion Record Club

Cassette: released on Accordion Record Club in Jul'86 by Accordion Record Club Records. Distributed by: Accordion Record Club

Best Little Whorehouse...

BEST LITTLE WHOREHOUSE IN TEXAS Original soundtrack.
Album: released on MCA in Mar'81 by MCA Records. Distributed by: Polygram, MCA

Cassette: released on MCA in Mar'81 by MCA Records. Distributed by: Polygram, MCA

Best, Martin

ART OF MINSTREL (Best, Martin & E. Flower).
Album: by Grosvenor Records. Distributed by: Taylors

KNIGHTS ON THE ROAD.
Tracks: / American dream / Cambric shirt / Elfin Knight, The / Love death / Banks of the Ohio / Close up the gate / Yesterday / Knight on the road / Peace of mind / City is a woman / Weary man / Two ravens / Ballad of the dead man.
Album: released on EMI in Jun'77 by EMI Records. Distributed by: EMI

KNIGHT'S ON THE ROAD.

Best Of...

BEST OF 80'S COUNTRY (THE) Various artists (Various Artists).
Tracks: / Stranger in my house / John deere tractor / From where I stand / Read all about it / Stand on it / Out goin' cattin' / Jagged edge of a broken heart / Out on the front line / Feels so right / Then it's love / Memphis roots / You're still new to me / I tell it like it used to be / Letter from home / Turn me loose / Just another love.
Album: released on MFP in Mar'87 by EMI Records. Distributed by: EMI

Cassette: released on MFP in Mar'87 by EMI Records. Distributed by: EMI

BEST OF THE TRUCK DRIVER SONGS (Various Artists).
Album: released on Starday in Apr'87

Cassette: released on Starday in Apr'87

Best Of Abba

BEST OF ABBA various artists (Various Artists).
Cassette: released on AIM (Budget Cassettes) in Feb'83

Best Of Ace Rockabilly

BEST OF ACE ROCKABILLY Various artists (Various Artists).

Best Of A Swinging Era

BEST OF A SWINGING ERA various artists (Various Artists).

Album: released on RCA (Germany) in Jul'83

Cassette: released on RCA (Germany) in Jul'83

Best Of Baton R & B

BEST OF BATON R & B (Various Artists).
Notes: with Marie Knight, Ann Cole etc.
Album: released on Flyright in Feb'87 by Flyright Records. Distributed by: Krazy Kat, Swift, Jazz Music

Best Of Beverlys

BEST OF BEVERLEYS Masterpieces from the works of Leslie Kong (Various Artists).
Album: released on Trojan in Oct'81 by Trojan Records. Distributed by: PRT, Jetstar

Best Of Black Country

BEST OF THE BLACK COUNTRY NIGHT OUT SHOW Various artists (Various Artists).
Album: released on Jester's Court in '81 by Broadside Records. Distributed by: Pinnacle

Cassette: released on Jester's Court in '81 by Broadside Records. Distributed by: Pinnacle

Best Of Blue Note

BEST OF BLUE NOTE various artists (Various Artists).
Album: released on Blue Note in May'85 by EMI Records. Distributed by: EMI

BEST OF BLUE NOTE VOL. 2 various artists (Various Artists).
Tracks: / Blue Harlem / Our delight / Round midnight / Gears, The / Collard greens & black eyed peas / Senor blues / Brownie speaks / Three o'clock in the morning / Lou's blues / Blues march / Wadin' / Rumproller, The / Something else / Blues bossa / Watermelon man.
Notes: The first collection of the Best of Blue Note,which commemorated the initial year of Blue Note's reactivation,met with surprising success.Our second year brings a second collection from the rich & vast Blue Note vaults,bringing together more of the labels most popular and significant recordings.
Double Album: released on Blue Note in May'86 by EMI Records. Distributed by: EMI

Best Of Blues & Soul

BEST OF BLUES AND SOUL, THE (Various Artists).
Compact disc: released on Malaco in Apr'87 by Malaco Records. Distributed by: Charly

Best Of Brass

BEST OF BRASS 1982 Highlights from the BBC TV brass band contest 1982 (Various Artists).
Album: released on Polyphonic in Feb'83 by Polyphonic Records. Distributed by: Taylors

Cassette: released on Polyphonic in Feb'83 by Polyphonic Records. Distributed by: Taylors

BEST OF BRASS 1983 Various artists (Various Artists).
Album: released on Polyphonic in Mar'84 by Polyphonic Records. Distributed by: Taylors

Cassette: released on Polyphonic in Mar'84 by Polyphonic Records. Distributed by: Taylors

BEST OF BRASS 1984 various artists (Various Artists).
Album: released on Polyphonic in Feb'85 by Polyphonic Records. Distributed by: Taylors

Cassette: released on Polyphonic in Feb'85 by Polyphonic Records. Distributed by: Taylors

Best Of Brass, The

BEST OF BRASS, THE various artists (Various Artists).
Cassette: released on Ditto in May'86 by Pickwick Records. Distributed by: H.R. Taylor

Album: released on Polyphonic Digital in Aug'86

Cassette: released on Polyphonic Digital in Aug'86

Cassette: released on EMI (Miles Of Music) in Nov'83 by EMI Records. Distributed by: EMI

Best Of British...

BEST OF BRITISH various artists (Various Artists).
Cassette: released on Collectors Music in Jul'86. Distributed by: Conifer

Album: released on Zebra in Apr'85 by Cherry Red Records. Distributed by: Pinnacle

BEST OF BRITISH BARBERSHOP various artists (Various Artists).
Tracks: / I'd give a million tomorrows / Darkness on the delta / Berkeley square / Let the rest of the world go by / Muskrat ramble / Carolina in the morning / Sam the accordian man / What a

wonderful world / Don't bring Lulu / Sweet and lovely / Over the rainbow / Do you remember / Born free / I believe / 76 trombones / Wonderful guy, A / Oh Susannah / Swing low sweet chariot / Daddy sang bass / Pollution.
Album: released on MWM in Jun'82 by Mawson & Wareham. Distributed by: Spartan Distribution, Jazz Music Distribution, JSU Distribution

BEST OF BRITISH COMEDY SONGS Various artists (Various Artists).
Album: released on Lamborghini in Nov'84 by Lamborghini Records. Distributed by: PRT

Cassette: released on Lamborghini in Nov'84 by Lamborghini Records. Distributed by: PRT

BEST OF BRITISH COUNTRY Various artists (Various Artists).
Album: released on Silver Dollar in Mar'79 by VFM Records

BEST OF BRITISH DANCE BANDS various artists (Various Artists).
Tracks: / Happy days are here again / After the sun's kissed the world goodbye / It's the girl / By the river Sainte Marie / My baby just cares for me / Crazy rhythm / How can you say no / My silent love / I'm in the market for you / Too many tears / Good little,bad little you / Any times the time to fall in love / Honeymoon hotel / Wind's in the west, The / Baby face / Like taking candy from a baby / Say it / Play to me gypsy / Kiss me dear / For all we know.
Album: released on Saville in Jul'86 by Conifer Records. Distributed by: Conifer

Cassette: released on Saville in Jul'86 by Conifer Records. Distributed by: Conifer

BEST OF BRITISH FILM MUSIC Various artists (Various Artists).
Compact disc: by Decca Records. Distributed by: Polygram

BEST OF BRITISH FOLK Various artists (Various Artists).
Album: released on Cambra in Apr'85 by Cambra Records. Distributed by: IDS, Conifer

Cassette: released on Cambra in Apr'85 by Cambra Records. Distributed by: IDS, Conifer

BEST OF BRITISH FOLK VOL. 2 various artists (Various Artists).
Album: released on Cambra in Jun'85 by Cambra Records. Distributed by: IDS, Conifer

Cassette: released on Cambra in Jun'85 by Cambra Records. Distributed by: IDS, Conifer

BEST OF BRITISH FUNK VOL.2 Various Artists (Various Artists).
Tracks: / I'm for real / Body shake / One to one / You and me just started / Magic / Somebody help me out / Play the game / Love train / Come and get me / Don't be mistaken / You're lying / North London boy / Tarantula walk / Time's running out.
Album: released on Beggars Banquet in Oct'82 by Beggars Banquet Records. Distributed by: WEA

Cassette: released on Beggars Banquet in Oct'82 by Beggars Banquet Records. Distributed by: WEA

BEST OF BRITISH FUNK Various Artists (Various Artists).
Tracks: / Love games / Starchild / Feels like the right time / Easier said than done / Can't keep holding on / Fall in love / Walking into sunshine / Mama used to say.
Album: released on Polydor in May'82 by Polydor Records. Distributed by: Polygram, Polydor

Cassette: released on Polydor in May'82 by Polydor Records. Distributed by: Polygram, Polydor

BEST OF BRITISH ROCKABILLY various artists (Various Artists).
Notes: Artists include: Blue Cat Trio/Shotgun/Dave Phillips & the Hot Rod Gang/Deltas /Restless/Ray Neale & the All Stars.
Album: released on Rockhouse in Jul'86 by Rockhouse Records. Distributed by: Swift Distribution, Charly Distribution

Album: released on Sonet in Jan'79 by Sonet Records. Distributed by: PRT

BEST OF BRITISH ROCKABILLIES Various artists (Various Artists).
Album: released on Charly(R&B) in Feb'79 by Charly Records. Distributed by: Charly, Cadillac

BEST OF BRITISH TRADITIONAL JAZZ Various Artists (Various Artists).
Tracks: / St. George's rag / Lazy river / Stevedore stomp / Phil's late / Tuxedo rag / Creole love call / 1919 rag / Oh Monah / Wild man blues / Nagasaki / Dardanella / Monmartre / Hindustan / Creole jazz / Perdido street blues / Papa dip / South / Mabel's dream / Sweet Sue.
Compact disc: released on Polydor in Jul'84 by Polydor Records. Distributed by: Polygram, Polydor

ENCHANTED EVENINGS.
Album: released on Sweet Folk All in May'81 by Sweet Folk All Records. Distributed by: Sweet Folk All, Roots, Celtic Music, Dragon, Impetus, Projection, Chris Wellard, Festival Records

VERY BEST OF BRITISH JAZZ, THE (Various Artists).

Best Of Chess...

BEST OF CHESS, CHECKER, CADET.....ROCKABILLIES Various artists (Various Artists).
Album: released on Chess in '84 by Charly Records. Distributed by: Charly, Swift, PRT, Discovery, IMS, Polygram

Best Of Chicago Blues

BEST OF THE CHICAGO BLUES Various artists (Various Artists).
Tracks: / Love me or leave me / Next time you see me / Rocket 88 / Vietcong blues / When my baby left me / Spaan's stomp / Twisted snake / One room country country shack / Sweet little angel / I had a dream last night / Somebody been talkin' / Mule kicking in my stall / Blues is a botheration / S.P blues someday / Blues keep falling, The / Rockin' my boogie / Five long years / Checking on my baby / Tobacco road / Money (that's all I want) / Stealin' back.
Album: released on Vanguard (USA) in '83

Best Of Christmas

BEST OF CHRISTMAS Various artists (Various Artists).
Album: released on Audio Fidelity Enterprises in Oct'84. Distributed by: PRT

Cassette: released on Audio Fidelity Enterprises in Oct'84. Distributed by: PRT

Best Of Country

BEST OF COUNTRY VOL.1 various artists (Various Artists).
Album: released on RCA in Oct'84 by RCA Records. Distributed by: RCA, Roots, Swift, Wellard, Chris, I & B, Solomon & Peres Distribution

Cassette: released on RCA in Oct'84 by RCA Records. Distributed by: RCA, Roots, Swift, Wellard, Chris, I & B, Solomon & Peres Distribution

BEST OF COUNTRY VOL.2 various artists (Various Artists).
Album: released on RCA in Oct'84 by RCA Records. Distributed by: RCA, Roots, Swift, Wellard, Chris, I & B, Solomon & Peres Distribution

Cassette: released on RCA in Oct'84 by RCA Records. Distributed by: RCA, Roots, Swift, Wellard, Chris, I & B, Solomon & Peres Distribution

BEST OF COUNTRY VOL.3 various artists (Various Artists).
Album: released on RCA in Oct'84 by RCA Records. Distributed by: RCA, Roots, Swift, Wellard, Chris, I & B, Solomon & Peres Distribution

Cassette: released on RCA in Oct'84 by RCA Records. Distributed by: RCA, Roots, Swift, Wellard, Chris, I & B, Solomon & Peres Distribution

Best Of Country & Western

BEST OF COUNTRY & WESTERN VOL.4 various artists (Various Artists).
Tracks: / Distant drums / Rose garden / All I ever need is you / Taker, The / Just for what I am / Never ending song of love / Four strong winds / Morning / Snowbird / One tin soldier / Thing called love, A / I'm movin' on.
Album: released on RCA in Aug'84 by RCA Records. Distributed by: RCA, Roots, Swift, Wellard, Chris, I & B, Solomon & Peres Distribution

Cassette: released on RCA in Aug'84 by RCA Records. Distributed by: RCA, Roots, Swift, Wellard, Chris, I & B, Solomon & Peres Distribution

Cassette: released on Aim in Feb'83. Distributed by: H.R. Taylor

BEST OF COUNTRY & WESTERN various artists (Various Artists).

Best Of Disney

BEST OF DISNEY Songs From Original Soundtracks (Various Artists).
Tracks: / Dream is a wish your heart makes, A / When you wish upon a star / Supercalifragilisticexpialidocius / When I see an elephant fly / I've got no strings / Bella Notte / Creulla de ville / Some day my prince will come / Bare necessities, The / Give a little whistle / Jolly 'Oliday / Bibbidi-bobbidi-boo / Trust in me / Second star to the right (The) / Little April shower / Spoonful of sugar / He's a tramp / Appreciate the lady / Chim-Chim-Cher-ee / Dream is a wish your heart makes, A / Following the leader / I wanna be like you / Feeds the birds / Whistle while you work / Look out for Mr. Stork / Heigh Ho! / Hi-diddle-dee-dee / When you wish upon a star (recap.) / When you wish upon a star.
Album: released on MFP in Feb'87 by EMI Records. Distributed by: EMI

Cassette: released on MFP in Feb'87 by EMI Records. Distributed by: EMI

Album: released on BBC in Oct'85 by BBC Records & Tapes. Distributed by: EMI, PRT, Pye

Cassette: released on BBC in Oct'85 by BBC Records & Tapes. Distributed by: EMI, PRT, Pye

Best of Dixieland

BEST OF DIXIELAND (Various Artists).
Cassette: released on Polydor in Jun'87 by Polydor Records. Distributed by: Polygram, Polydor

Album: released on RCA Australia in Apr'83

Compact disc: released on Verve in Jul'87 by Phonogram Records. Distributed by: Polygram

Album: released on RCA in Aug'85 by RCA Records. Distributed by: RCA, Roots, Swift, Wellard, Chris, I & B, Solomon & Peres Distribution

Cassette: released on RCA in Aug'85 by RCA Records. Distributed by: RCA, Roots, Swift, Wellard, Chris, I & B, Solomon & Peres Distribution

Best Of Dixie Records

BEST OF DIXIE RECORDS VOL.5 50's rockabilly (Various Artists).
Album: released on Million (Holland) in Jul'84. Distributed by: Swift Distribution

BEST OF DIXIE RECORDS VOL. 6 50's rockabilly (Various Artists).
Album: released on Million (Holland) in Jul'84. Distributed by: Swift Distribution

Best of easystreet, The

BEST OF EASYSTREET, THE Various artists (Various Artists).
Album: released on Streetsounds in Aug'87

Cassette: released on Streetsounds in Aug'87

Best Of English Folk

BEST OF ENGLISH FOLK Various artists (Various Artists).
Cassette: released on Autograph in Apr'85. Distributed by: Record Services Distribution (Ireland)

Best Of High Energy

BEST OF HIGH ENERGY Various artists (Various Artists).
Album: released on Electricity in Dec'84 by Electricity Records. Distributed by: PRT

Cassette: released on Electricity in Dec'84 by Electricity Records. Distributed by: PRT

Best Of House

BEST OF HOUSE, THE Volume 1 (Various Artists).
Notes: Including : House Master Boyz ; Raze
Album: released on Serious in Jun'87 by Serious Records. Distributed by: PRT
Cat.no ....
Cassette: released on Serious in Jun'87 by Serious Records. Distributed by: PRT

Best Of I Love Jazz

BEST OF I LOVE JAZZ Various artists (Various Artists).
Album: released on CBS(Import) in Aug'84 by CBS Records. Distributed by: Conifer, Discovery, Swift

Cassette: released on CBS(Import) in Aug'84 by CBS Records. Distributed by: Conifer, Discovery, Swift

Best Of Irish...

BEST OF IRISH BALLADS VOL 1 Various artists (Various Artists).

BEST OF IRISH BALLADS, THE Various artists (Various Artists).
Album: released on Polydor (Ireland) in Oct'83 by Polydor Records. Distributed by: Polygram, I & B

Cassette: released on Polydor (Ireland) in Oct'83 by Polydor Records. Distributed by: Polygram, I & B

Cassette: released on Tara (Ireland) in Oct'85 by Tara Records. Distributed by: I & B Records Distribution, Record Services Distribution (Ireland), Roots Distribution

BEST OF IRISH FOLK Various artists (Various Artists).
Cassette: released on Autograph in Apr'85. Distributed by: Record Services Distribution (Ireland)

Album: released on Cambra in Jun'85 by Cambra Records. Distributed by: IDS, Conifer

Cassette: released on Cambra in Jun'85 by Cambra Records. Distributed by: IDS, Conifer

BEST OF IRISH JIGS AND REELS VOL.2, THE Various artists (Various Artists).

BEST OF IRISH JIGS AND REELS VOL.1, THE Various artists (Various Artists).
Cassette: released on Tara (Ireland) in Oct'85 by Tara Records. Distributed by: I & B Records Distribution, Record Services Distribution (Ireland), Roots Distribution

Cassette: released on Tara (Ireland) in Oct'85 by Tara Records. Distributed by: I & B Records Distribution, Record Services Distribution (Ireland), Roots Distribution

BEST OF IRISH TRADITIONAL MUSIC & BALLADS Various artists (Various Artists).
Tracks: / Shores of Lough Bran, The / O'Carolan tribute / Nancy Spain / Brian Boru's march / Danny boy / Leaving of Nancy, The / Cill Aodain / Paddy's green shamrock shore / Gipsy Davey / Glenbeigh hornpipe / Mountain lark / Musical priest / Old rustic bridge, The / Nil se ina la / Cill chais / Fanny Poer (Carolan slow air) / Banks of Claudy, The.
Cassette: released on Polydor (Eire) in '85

Best Of Italo

BEST OF ITALO VOLUME 9 Various artists (Various Artists).
Album: released on ZYX (Germany) in Aug'87 by ZYX Records. Distributed by: Greyhound. Estim retail price in Sep'87 was £5.75.

Best Of Italo-Disco

BEST OF ITALO-DISCO VOL.1 various artists (Various Artists).
Double Album: released on ZYX (West Germany) in Feb'86

BEST OF ITALO-DISCO VOL.2 various artists (Various Artists).
Double Album: released on ZYX (West Germany) in Feb'86

BEST OF ITALO-DISCO VOL.3 various artists (Various Artists).
Double Album: released on ZYX (West Germany) in Feb'86

BEST OF ITALO-DISCO VOL.4 various artists (Various Artists).
Double Album: released on ZYX (West Germany) in Feb'86

BEST OF ITALO-DISCO VOL.5 various artists (Various Artists).
Double Album: released on ZYX (West Germany) in Apr'86

BEST OF ITALO DISCO - VOL. 9 Various artists (Various Artists).
Compact disc: released on ZYX (Germany) in Aug'87 by ZYX Records. Distributed by: Greyhound

Best Of Music & Rhythm

BEST OF MUSIC AND RHYTHM Womad (Various Artists).
Compact disc: by Pacific Records (USA). Distributed by: Atlantic

Best of New Orleans R & B

BEST OF NEW ORLEANS R & B Various artists (Various Artists).
Album: released on Chess in Oct'84 by Charly Records. Distributed by: Charly, Swift, PRT, Discovery, IMS, Polygram

Best Of Pebbles

BEST OF PEBBLES, THE Various artists (Various Artists).
Album: released on Hit in Sep'86 by Hit Records. Distributed by: Pinnacle, Backs, Cartel

Best of Pietro Frosini

BEST OF PIETRO FROSINI Various artists (Various Artists).
Tracks: / Jolly Caballero / Love smiles, skippin' along / Serenata Primaverile / Swedish Italian Mazurka / Rag in D Minor / Olive blossoms / Hot points / Carmelita / Bel viso / La Mariposita / Dizzy accordion.
Notes: Mail order distribution: Accordion Record Club, 146 Birmingham Road, Kidderminster, Worcs. DY10 2SL. Tel 0562-746105.
Album: released on ARC (Accordion Records) in '84. Distributed by: Accordion Record Club

Best Of Praise

BEST OF PRAISE Various artists (Various Artists).
Album: released on Maranatha in May'82

Cassette: released on Maranatha in May'82

BEST OF PRAISE VOL.2 Various artists (Various Artists).
Album: released on Maranatha in Mar'84

Cassette: released on Maranatha in Mar'84

Best Of Rockabilly

BEST OF ROCKABILLY various artists (Various Artists).
Album: released on Ace in Dec'81 by Ace Records. Distributed by: Pinnacle, Swift, Hotshot, Cadillac

Best of Rock Legends

BEST OF ROCK LEGENDS (Various Artists).
Compact disc: released on Telstar in Jul'87 by Telstar Records. Distributed by: RCA Distribution

Best Of Rock'N'Roll

BEST OF ROCK 'N' ROLL Various artists (Various Artists).
Notes: Featuring: Jerry Lewis, Little Richard, Bill Haley, Roy Orbison, Charlie Rich etc..
Compact disc: released on Bellaphon in Dec'86 by Bellaphon Records. Distributed by: IMS-Polygram

Best Of Salsa

BEST OF SALSA Various artists (Various Artists).
Album: released on Vogue (France) in Dec'84. Distributed by: Discovery, Jazz Music, PRT, Swift

Best Of Scandinavian Rock

BEST OF SCANDINAVIAN ROCK Various artists (Various Artists).
Album: released on Music For Nations-Sword in '85

Best Of Scottish Folk

BEST OF SCOTTISH FOLK Various artists (Various Artists).
Cassette: released on Autograph in '85. Distributed by: Record Services Distribution (Ireland)

Best Of Sixties Mania

BEST OF SIXTIES MANIA Various artists (Various Artists).
Compact disc: released on Telstar in Mar'87 by Telstar Records. Distributed by: RCA Distribution

Best of Smash Hits

BEST OF SMAH TRACKS FROM THE 80'S Various artists (Various Artists).
Cassette: released on AIM (Budget Cassettes) in '83

BEST OF SMASH HITS Various artists (Various Artists).
Tracks: / House of fun / Do you really want to hurt me / Africa / Down under / Chariots of fire / Rock the boat / She means nothing to me / Arthur's theme.
Cassette: released on AIM (Budget Cassettes) in '83

BEST OF SMASH HITS OF 1981 Various artists (Various Artists).
Cassette: released on AIM (Budget Cassettes) in '83

Best Of Studio One

BEST OF STUDIO ONE Various artists (Various Artists).
Album: released on Rounder (USA) in '84. Distributed by: Mike's Country Music Room Distribution, Jazz Music Distribution, Swift Distribution, Roots Records Distribution, Projection Distribution, Topic Distribution

Album: released on Heartbeat in '85. Distributed by: Revolver, Pinnacle

BEST OF STUDIO ONE VOL. 2 Various artists (Various Artists).

Best Of Sun Rockabilly

BEST OF SUN ROCKABILLY VOL.2 various artists (Various Artists).
Tracks: / Got love if you want it / That don't move me / Itchy / Drinkin' wine / How come you do me / Gimme some lovin' / Johnny Valentine / Baby please don't go / Sentimental fool / Rebound / Miss Froggie / Rock around the town / Wild one(real wild child) / My baby don't rock / Find my baby for me / My gal Mary Ann / Me and my rhythm guitar / All night rock / Your loving man / Mad man / Fairlane rock / I need your loving kiss / Perkins wiggle / Ain't got a thing.
Notes: Original Sun recordings. Licensed from Charly Records International APS.
Compact disc: released on Sun in Nov'86 by Charly Records. Distributed by: Charly Distribution

BEST OF SUN ROCKABILLY VOL. 1 Various artists (Various Artists).
Tracks: / Ten cats down / Jump right out of this jukebox / Gonna romp & stomp / Domino / Rakin' & scrapin' / Slow down / Red Cadillac & a black moustache / Break up / Greenback dollar / Red headed woman / Flyin' saucer rock'n'roll / Crawdad hole, The / Love my baby / Red hot / We wanna boogie / Come on little mama / Right behind you baby / Ubangi stomp / Let's bop / Rabbit action / Put your cat clothes on / Rocking with my baby.
Compact disc: released on Sun/Charly in Apr'86

Best Of The Blues, The

BEST OF THE BLUES, THE various artists (Various Artists).
Notes: With Big Joe Williams/Memphis Slim/Broonzy etc.
Album: released on Storyville in May'86 by Storyville Records. Distributed by: Jazz Music Distribution, Swift Distribution, Chris Wellard Distribution, Counterpoint Distribution

Best Of The Sweet Bands

BEST OF THE SWEET BANDS,THE various artists (Various Artists).
Album: released on Hindsight(UK) in Apr'86. Distributed by: Jazz Music

Best Of Welsh folk

BEST OF WELSH FOLK Various artists (Various Artists).
Album: released on Sain in '85. Distributed by: Roots

Best Of West Coast Hip Hop

BEST OF WEST COAST HIP HOP Various artists (Various Artists).
Album: released on Macola in Aug'87 by Streetsounds Records. Distributed by: PRT

Cassette: released on Macola in Aug'87 by Streetsounds Records. Distributed by: PRT

Best Party Album...

BEST PARTY ALBUM IN THE WORLD Various artists (Various Artists).
Album: released on K-Tel in '83 by K-Tel Records. Distributed by: Record Merchandisers Distribution, Taylors, Terry Blood Distribution, Wynd-Up Distribution, Relay Distribution, Pickwick Distribution, Solomon & Peres Distribution, Polygram

Cassette: released on K-Tel in '83 by K-Tel Records. Distributed by: Record Merchandisers Distribution, Taylors, Terry Blood Distribution, Wynd-Up Distribution, Relay Distribution, Pickwick Distribution, Solomon & Peres Distribution, Polygram

Best shot

BEST SHOT Original soundtrack (Original Soundtrack).
Album: released on That's Entertainment in Aug'87 by That's Entertainment Records. Distributed by: Pinnacle, PRT

Cassette: released on That's Entertainment in Aug'87 by That's Entertainment Records. Distributed by: Pinnacle, PRT

Compact disc: released on That's Entertainment in Aug'87 by That's Entertainment Records. Distributed by: Pinnacle, PRT

Best, Tony

BY REQUEST.
Tracks: / San Antonio rose / You're my best friend / Words / One day at a time / I don't want to cry / Turn out the light (love me tonight) / Old rugged cross, The / Love or something like it / Legend in my time, A / Today I started love you again / Crazy / Some broken hearts never mend / Nobody's child / China doll.
Album: released on ARC (Accordion Records) in '84. Distributed by: Accordion Record Club

DOING WHAT I LIKE DOING.
Tracks: / Doing what I like doing / Mansion on the hill / Great El Tigre, The / Let's keep it that way / Some days are diamonds / Angelean / Jimmy Brown song, The / Do what you do do well / Catfish John / Who were you thinking of / Drinking them beers / Smooth sailing.
Album: released on ARC (Accordion Records) in '84. Distributed by: Accordion Record Club

Best Way To Walk

UNBELIEVABLE.
Single (12"): released on Two Bad in Mar'87

Best Years Of Our Lives

BEST YEARS OF OUR LIVES Original soundtrack.
Album: released on Entr'Acte (France) in '80. Distributed by: Unicorn

Bethel

BETHEL Various artists (Various Artists).
Cassette: released on Bethel in '84 by Bethel Records. Distributed by: Cartel

Bethnal

MORNING CHILD.
Single (7"): released on Magic Moon in '80. Distributed by: Pinnacle

Betjeman, Sir John

BETJEMAN READS BETJEMAN.
Tracks: / Middlesex / Harrow-on-the-hill / Upper Lambourne / Wantage bells / Trebetherick / heart of Thomas Hardy, The / Arrest of Oscar Wilde, The / I.M.Walter Ramsden / Devonshire Street W.1. / In a bath teashop / Attempt, The / Irish unionist's farewell, The / Lincolnshire church, The / Pot-pourri from a Surrey garden / Henley-on-Thames / Diary of a church mouse / In the public gardens / Eunice / Last of her order, The / Matlock bath.
Notes: John Bejeman, the poet Laureate, here reads a selection of his best-loved poems, and excerpts from his autobiographical work ,"Summoned by Bells"
Cassette: released on Argo (Spokenword) in '83 by Decca Records. Distributed by: Polygram

BETJEMAN'S BRITAIN, VARSITY RAG.
Cassette: released on Charisma in '83 by Virgin Records. Distributed by: EMI

LATE FLOWERING LOVE, BANANA BLUSH.
Tracks: / Narcissus / Olympic girl / Invasion exercise on the poultry farm / Licorice fields at Pontefact, The / Russell flint, A / Station syren / Myfanwy and Myfanwy at Oxford / In the public gardens / Eunice / Senex / Late flowering lust / Sun and fun / Indoor games near Newbury / Business girls / Agricultural caress / Youth and age on Beaulieu River / Arrest of Oscar Wilde at the Cadogen Hotel, The / Lenten thoughts / Cockney amorist, The / Long fellow's visit to Venice / Flight from Bootle, The / Shropshire lad, A / On a portrait of a deaf man / Child ill, A.
Cassette: released on Charisma in '83 by Virgin Records. Distributed by: EMI

SIR JOHN BETJEMAN.
Cassette: released on Talking Tape in '82

Cassette: released on Caedmon(USA) in '78 by Caedmon (USA) Records. Distributed by: Gower, Taylors, Discovery

Album: released on Caedmon(USA) in '78 by Caedmon (USA) Records. Distributed by: Gower, Taylors, Discovery

Cassette: released on Talking Tape Company in '84 by Talking Tape Company Records

Bet Lynch's Legs

RIDERS IN THE SKY.
Single (7"): released on Absurd in '83 by Absurd. Distributed by: Pinnacle, Rough Trade

SOME LIKE IT HOT.
Single (7"): released on Absurd in '83 by Absurd. Distributed by: Pinnacle, Rough Trade

Betmead, Jon

VISION OF HEAVEN, A.
Album: released on Plant Life in '81. Distributed by: Roots

Betrayed

SKINS AND PUNKS VOLUME 2 (Betrayed/Oi Polloi).
Notes: For full information see under: OI POLLOI/BETRAYED

Better An Old Demon...

BETTER AN OLD DEMON THAN A NEW GOD various artists (Various Artists).
Album: released on Giorno Poetry System in '84. Distributed by: Rough Trade, Cartel

Better Class Of Folk

BETTER CLASS OF FOLK various artists (Various Artists).
Album: by Lismor Records. Distributed by: Lismor, Roots, Celtic Music

Betty Blue

BETTY BLUE Original soundtrack.
Album: released on Virgin in Sep'86 by Virgin Records. Distributed by: EMI, Virgin Distribution

Cassette: released on Virgin in Sep'86 by Virgin Records. Distributed by: EMI, Virgin Distribution

Compact disc: released on Virgin in Oct'86 by Virgin Records. Distributed by: EMI, Virgin Distribution

Between

CONTEMPLATION.
Album: released on Wergo in '78

DHARANA.
Album: released on Wergo in '78

HESS BETWEEN MUSIC.
Album: released on Wergo in '78

Bevan, Bob

ONE FLEW OVER THE BAR - SIX FLEW INTO THE NET.
Album: released on Red Bus in '82 by Red Bus Records. Distributed by: PRT

Beverley Sisters

SISTERS.
Single (7"): released on Hippodrome in '85. Distributed by: EMI

Single (12"): released on Hippodrome in '85. Distributed by: EMI

SPARKLE.
Album: released on K-Tel in Nov'85 by K-Tel Records. Distributed by: Record Merchandisers Distribution, Taylors, Terry Blood Distribution, Wynd-Up Distribution, Relay Distribution, Pickwick Distribution, Solomon & Peres Distribution, Polygram

Cassette: released on K-Tel in Nov'85 by K-Tel Records. Distributed by: Record Merchandisers Distribution, Taylors, Terry Blood Distribution, Wynd-Up Distribution, Relay Distribution, Pickwick Distribution, Solomon & Peres Distribution, Polygram

TOGETHER.
Tracks: / Together / Hold me / English muffins and Irish stew / We have to be so careful / Green fields / Skye boat song / Oh wishing star / Water or the wine, The / Sultan, The / Sphinx won't tell, The / I never was loved by anyone / Undecided / Teasin' / Yell for your mama / String along / I wish I wuz / Wheel of fortune / Poor whip-poor will / For you / In the wee small hours of the morning / Once in a while / When the boys talk about the girls / I'm always chasing rainbows / No one but you / Mother never told me (it was anything like this) / Goodnight my someone / Nearness of you, The / Tammy / It takes so long (to say goodbye) / Beneath the lights of home / It's no sin / Wyoming lullaby.
Album: released on Music For Pleasure (Holland) in '85 by EMI Records. Distributed by: EMI

Cassette: released on Music For Pleasure in '85 by EMI Records. Distributed by: EMI

Beverly, Frank

IF THAT'S WHAT YOU WANTED.
Single (7"): released on Neil Rushton in '83

Single (7"): released on Neil Rushton in '83

Beverly Hills Cop

BEVERLY HILLS COP Original Film Soundtrack (Various Artists).
Tracks: / New attitude / Don't get stopped in Beverly Hills / Do you really (want my love) / Emergency / Neutron dance / Heat is on, The / Gratitude / Stir it up / Rock'n'roll me again / Axel F.
Compact disc: released on MCA in Aug'85 by MCA Records. Distributed by: Polygram, MCA

Album: released on MCA in '85 by MCA Records. Distributed by: Polygram, MCA

Cassette: released on MCA in '85 by MCA Records. Distributed by: Polygram, MCA

Compact disc: released on MCA in '85 by MCA Records. Distributed by: Polygram. MCA

BEVERLY HILLS COP LL Original Film Soundtrack (Various Artists).
Tracks: / Shakedown / Be there / In deep / Hold on / I want your sex / Better way / Love/Hate / Cross my broken heart / 36 lovers / I can't stand it / All revved up.
Album: released on MCA in Jul'87 by MCA Records. Distributed by: Polygram, MCA

Cassette: released on MCA in Jul'87 by MCA Records. Distributed by: Polygram, MCA

Compact disc: released on MCA in Jul'87 by MCA Records. Distributed by: Polygram, MCA

Bevis Marks Synagogue

SEPHARDI MELODIES LIVE.
Cassette: released on B'nai B'rith in '85

Bevoir, Paul

HAPPIEST DAY OF YOUR LIFE, THE.
Album: released on Dance Network in '85 by Dance Network Records. Distributed by: Backs, Cartel

Beyond

EPISCENE.
Album: released on Midnight Music in May'87 by Midnight Music Records. Distributed by: Rough Trade Distribution, Cartel Distribution

Beyond Possession

IS BEYOND POSSESSION.
Album: released on Road Runner in Jan'87

Beyond The Planets

BEYOND THE PLANETS Various artists (Various Artists).
Tracks: / Waves / Journey, The / Mars, the bringer of war / Venus, the bringer of peace / Mercury, the winged messenger / Jupiter, the bringer of jollity / Circles / Saturn, the bringer of old age / Uranus, the magician / Neptune, the

mystic / Heavens reply, The / Beyond.
Notes: Interpretation of Holst's **The Planets**. Artists include Rick Wakeman, Jeff Wayne, and Kevin Peek. Narrated by: Patrick Allen.
Compact disc: released on Telstar in '86 by Telstar Records. Distributed by: RCA Distribution

Album: released on Telstar in '84 by Telstar Records. Distributed by: RCA Distribution

Cassette: released on Telstar in '84 by Telstar Records. Distributed by: RCA Distribution

Beyond The River

BEYOND THE RIVER Various artists (Various Artists).
Album: released on Open Door in '83 by Open Door Records. Distributed by: Open Door Distribution

Beyond The Southern Cross

BEYOND THE SOUTHERN CROSS Various Artists (Various Artists).
Double Album: released on Ink in Jan'85 by Red Flame. Distributed by: Rough Trade, Cartel Pinnacle

Beyond The Wildwood

BEYOND THE WILDWOOD (Various Artists).
Album: released on Imaginary in 30 May'87 by Imaginary Records. Distributed by: Fast Forward

Beytelman

BORDONA, (LA) (Beytelman;Caratini;Mosalini).
Tracks: / La bordona / El choclo / Cardo y malvon / Nocturna / La cumparista / Inspiracion / Palomita blanca / Contrajeando la cumparsita / Inspiracion (2) / Palomita blanca (2).
Notes: Retail price given by ARC is 6.00 excluding p&p(via mail order). Mail order address: Accordion Record Club,146 Birmingham Road,Kidderminster Worcs. DY10 2SL. Tele:0562 746105
Album: released on Accordion Record Club in Jul'86 by Accordion Record Club Records. Distributed by: Accordion Record Club

Bezis Frond

MIASMA, THE.
released on Woronzow in Mar'87

B. Fats

B. FATS, THE.
Single (12"): released on Rooftop (USA) in Aug'87. Distributed by: Pinnacle

BG & The Mouse

BREAKER ONE FOUR.
Single (7"): released on Maestro in Nov'81 by Maestro Records

DA DOO RON RON.
Single (7"): released on Maestro in Jun'82 by Maestro Records

Bhamra, Mohinder Kalir

HIT SELECTION OF MODERN PUNJABI SONGS, A.

PUNJABI DISCO.
Tracks: / Disco Wich Aa / Par Toon Ki Janay / Pyar Mainu Kar / Ve Toon Jaldi Jaldi Aa / Aye Diwane / Chum Chum Dil Nal / Mainu Apne Dyar Wich / Nainan Da Pyar Degaya / Sohnia Mukh Tera.
Cassette: released on EMI (India) in Dec'82 by EMI Records. Distributed by: Conifer, Sterns, Triple Earth

PUNJABI FOLK DANCE SONGS.
Tracks: / Giddha Pao Haan Dio / Lutley Toon Jindri / Kurhi Patli Patang Wargi / Dil Kadke Toon Baliye / Hogya Ni Chit Chor / Kurhi Southall Di / Ton Patli Patang / Chardi Umar Jawani / Maan Kari Na / Is Joban De Din Char / Terian Dil Jani / Aari Aari Aari.
Album: released on Indiana in May'85. Distributed by: PRT

PUNJABI GEET.
Tracks: / Rahia Ve Haria / Hara Ni Koi Karlo Chara / Mere Nach Di Jawani / Mach Gai Dohai / Kuri Ne Sawaya / Ve Sadi Sajnan Tu Yard / Papoo Diay Amma / Dhand Mere Eun Hassde / Kurti Sawaday Kutmi / Toon Vidah Hoaya / Menu Tilley Dar Jutti / Raatan Chhad De Ve.
Album: released on Bhamra in Dec'78 by Bhamra Records. Distributed by: Bhamra Records

Bhundu Boys

BHUNDU BOYS & AFRICAN HERB.
Single (12"): released on Discafrique in Oct'85 by Discafrique Records. Distributed by: Sterns, Triple Earth

JIT JIVE.
Single (7"): released on WEA in Aug'87 by WEA Records. Distributed by: WEA

Single (12"): released on WEA in Aug'87 by WEA Records. Distributed by: WEA

SHABINI.
Album: released on Discafrique in Sep'86 by Discafrique Records. Distributed by: Sterns, Triple Earth

Cassette: released on Discafrique in 11 Apr'87 by Discafrique Records. Distributed by: Sterns, Triple Earth

Album: released on Discafrique in Jul'87 by Discafrique Records. Distributed by: Sterns, Triple Earth

TSVIMBO-DZE-MOTO Sticks on fire.
Album: released on Discafrique in Jun'87 by Discafrique Records. Distributed by: Sterns, Triple Earth

Cassette: released on Discafrique in Jun'87 by Discafrique Records. Distributed by: Sterns, Triple Earth

Bianca

WHERE THE BEAT MEETS THE STREET.
Single (7"): released on EMI in Apr'84 by EMI Records. Distributed by: EMI

Single (12"): released on EMI in Apr'84 by EMI Records. Distributed by: EMI Deleted '86.

Bibi Dans Tsibaya

BEST AMBIENCE.
Single (7"): released on Earthworks in Jan'84 by Earthworks Records. Distributed by: Earthworks Distributors, Rough Trade, Cartel, Projection

Bible

GRACELAND.
Tracks: / Glory Band (Live) / High Wide* / Slow drag down (The) * / Walking The Ghost Back Home*.
Single (7"): released on Chrysalis in Feb'87 by Chrysalis Records. Distributed by: CBS

Single (12"): released on Chrysalis in Feb'87 by Chrysalis Records. Distributed by: CBS

GRACELANDS.
Tracks: / Gracelands / Glory bound / High wide & handsome *.
Single (7"): released on Chrysalis in Aug'86 by Chrysalis Records. Distributed by: CBS

Single (12"): released on Chrysalis in Aug'86 by Chrysalis Records. Distributed by: CBS

MAHALIA.
Tracks: / Mahalia / Spend spend spend / Sweetness *.
Single (7"): released on Backs in Nov'86 by Backs Records. Distributed by: Backs, Cartel

Single (12"): released on Backs in Nov'86 by Backs Records. Distributed by: Backs, Cartel

WALKING THE GHOST BACK HOME.
Album: released on Backs in Mar'86 by Backs Records. Distributed by: Backs, Cartel

Bible stories

BIBLE STORIES Various artists (Various Artists).
Cassette: released on Audiocord Cassettes in May'83

Bic

MUSICA POP.
Single (7"): released on Pop in Oct'83 by Magnet Records. Distributed by: RCA

Single (12"): released on Pop in Oct'83 by Magnet Records. Distributed by: RCA

Bicat, Nick

CLEOPATRA'S.
Single (7"): released on BBC in Jan'83 by BBC Records & Tapes. Distributed by: EMI, PRT, Pye

IRISH RM (THEME).
Single (7"): released on Ritz in Feb'83 by Outlet Records. Distributed by: Outlet, Prism Leisure Distribution, Record Services Distribution (Ireland), Roots

Bickert, Ed

BORDER CROSSING.
Album: released on Concord Jazz (USA) in Jun'83 by Concord Jazz Records (USA). Distributed by: IMS, Polygram

DANCE TO THE LADY (Bickert, Ed/Don Thompson).
Album: released on Sackville in Apr'83. Distributed by: JSU, Jazz Music, Jazz Horizons, Cadillac Music, Celtic Music, Swift

FROM CANADA WITH LOVE.
Album: released on PMR in Oct'79

IN CONCERT AT THE GARDEN PARTY (Bickert, Ed/Don Thompson).
Album: released on Sackville (Import) in Apr'81. Distributed by: Cadillac

I WISHED ON THE MOON (Bickert, Ed Quartet).
Tracks: / CTA / Easy street / Somewhere along the way / Blues for Tommy / Blues my naughty sweetie gives to me / Handful of stars, A / I wished on the moon / I'll never stop loving you.
Notes: This lyrical Canadian guitarist is joined by three fellow alumni from Rob McConnell's Boss Brass,to present some of the loveliest,yet rarely heard,standards. Personnel: Ed Bickert-guitar/Terry Clarke- drums/Steve Wallace-bass/Rick Wilkins- tenor sax.
Compact disc: released on Concord Jazz (USA) in Nov'86 by Concord Jazz Records (USA). Distributed by: IMS, Polygram

Album: released on Concord Jazz (USA) in Dec'85 by Concord Jazz Records (USA). Distributed by: IMS, Polygram

Bid

REACH FOR YOUR GUNS.
Tracks: / Reach for your guns / Sweet chariots / Love *.
Single (7"): released on EL in Jun'86 by El Records. Distributed by: Rough Trade, Cartel, Pinnacle

Single (12"): released on EL in Jun'86 by El Records. Distributed by: Rough Trade, Cartel, Pinnacle

Biddu

NIRVANA.
Album: released on Heaven in Oct'84 by Heaven Records

Cassette: released on Heaven in Oct'84 by Heaven Records

Biddu Orchestra

DANCE OF SHIVA.
Compact disc: released on Bellaphon in Dec'86 by Bellaphon Records. Distributed by: IMS-Polygram

SERENADE FOR LOVERS.
Album: released on Hallmark in Mar'81 by Pickwick Records. Distributed by: Pickwick Distribution, PRT, Taylors

Cassette: released on Hallmark in Mar'81 by Pickwick Records. Distributed by: Pickwick Distribution, PRT, Taylors

Bid for Power

BID FOR POWER BBC English Course.

Biff Bang Pow

50 YEARS OF FUN.
Single (7"): released on Creation Artefact in Feb'84. Distributed by: Rough Trade, Cartel

CHOCOLATE ELEPHANT MAN,(THE).
Single (7"): released on Creation Artefact in Jun'84. Distributed by: Rough Trade, Cartel

GIRLS WHO RUNS THE BEAT HOTEL, THE Pass the paintbrush honey.
Double cassette: released on Creation in Mar'87. Distributed by: Rough Trade, Cartel

LOVE'S GOING OUT OF FASHION.
Tracks: / Love's going out of fashion.
Single (7"): released on Creation in Apr'86. Distributed by: Rough Trade, Cartel

Single (12"): released on Creation in Apr'86. Distributed by: Rough Trade, Cartel

PASS THE PAINTBRUSH HONEY.
Album: released on Creation in Feb'85. Distributed by: Rough Trade, Cartel

SOMEONE STOLE MY WHEELS.
Tracks: / Someone stole my wheels.
Single (7"): released on Creation in Nov'86. Distributed by: Rough Trade, Cartel

Single (12"): released on Creation in Nov'86. Distributed by: Rough Trade, Cartel

WORLD'S TURNING BROUCHARD, THE.
Tracks: / Death of England, The.
Single (7"): released on Creation in Feb'87. Distributed by: Rough Trade, Cartel

Big Amongst Sheep

ASTRO POP.
Single (12"): released on Rock Solid in Jun'83 by Rock Solid Records. Distributed by: Neon Distribution

Bigard, Barney

BARNEY BIGARD & THE PELICAN TRIO (Bigard,Barney & The Pelican Trio).
Album: released on Crescent Jazz Prods in Apr'79

BUCKET'S GOT A HOLE IN IT.
Tracks: / I'll be back.
Album: . Distributed by: Projection, Swift, Cadillac

Big Audio Dynamite

BOTTOM LINE, (THE).
Single (7"): released on CBS in Oct'85 by CBS Records. Distributed by: CBS

C'MON EVERY BEAT BOX.
Tracks: / C'mon every beatbox.
Single (7"): released on CBS in Sep'86 by CBS Records. Distributed by: CBS

E= MC2.
Tracks: / E = MC2 / This is Big Audio Dynamite.
Single (7"): released on CBS in Mar'86 by CBS Records. Distributed by: CBS

Single (12"): released on CBS in Mar'86 by CBS Records. Distributed by: CBS

MEDICINE SHOW.
Tracks: / Medicine show / Party, A.
Single (7"): released on CBS in May'86 by CBS Records. Distributed by: CBS

Single (12"): released on CBS in May'86 by CBS Records. Distributed by: CBS

NO. 10 UPPING STREET.
Tracks: / C'mon every beatbox / Beyond the pale / Limbo the law / Sambadrome / V. thirteen / Ticket / Hollywood Boulevard / Dial a hitman / Sightsee M.C. / Ice cool killer * / Big V, The *.
Compact disc: by CBS Records. Distributed by: CBS

Album: released on CBS in Oct'86 by CBS Records. Distributed by: CBS

Cassette: released on CBS in Oct'86 by CBS Records. Distributed by: CBS

SIGHTSEE M.C..
Single (12"): released on CBS in Jul'87 by CBS Records. Distributed by: CBS

THIS IS BIG AUDIO DYNAMITE.
Tracks: / Medicine show / Sony / E = MC2 / Bottom line / Sudden impact / Stone Thames / B.A.D..
Compact disc: released on CBS in '86 by CBS Records. Distributed by: CBS

Album: released on CBS in Nov'85 by CBS Records. Distributed by: CBS

Cassette: released on CBS in Nov'85 by CBS Records. Distributed by: CBS

V13.
Tracks: / Hollywood Boulevard.
Single (7"): released on Barbarella in Feb'87. Distributed by: Rough Trade

Single (12"): released on CBS in Feb'87 by CBS Records. Distributed by: CBS

Big Band Classics

BIG BAND CLASSICS Various artists (Various Artists).
Album: released on Telstar in Nov'84 by Telstar Records. Distributed by: RCA Distribution

Cassette: released on Telstar in Nov'84 by Telstar Records. Distributed by: RCA Distribution

Big Band Jazz...

BIG BAND JAZZ FROM JOE DAVIS 1940-1952 various artists (Various Artists).
Notes: Artists: Walter Thomas, Fred Norman, Frankie Trumbauer,Harry James. MONO Recording
Album: released on Harlequin in Jun'86 by Harlequin Records. Distributed by: Swift, Jazz Music, Wellard, Chris, IRS, Taylor

Big Bands...

BIG BANDS FROM THE SWING ERA Various artists (Various Artists).
Album: released on Jazz Live in Apr'81

BIG BANDS ON THE AIR 1938-46 Various artists (Various Artists).
Album: released on Solid Sender in Apr'81. Distributed by: Jazz Music

GOLDEN AGE,(THE).
Cassette: released on Creole (Everest-Europa) in Jul'84 by Creole Records. Distributed by: PRT, Rhino

SWEET AND LOW BLUES (Various Artists).
Tracks: / Static strut / Symphonic raps / Boy in the boat,The / That's how I feel today / Sweet and low blues / Till times get better / Willow tree / What is this thing called love / Starvation blues / Blue devil blues / There's a squabblin' / Dreamland blues / Dreamland blues II / Ruff scuffling / Black and blue rhapsody / After you've gone / I've found a new baby.
Notes: Mono recording.

Album: released on New World (USA) in Sep'86 by New World Records (USA). Distributed by: Conifer

Big Band Treasures

BIG BAND TREASURES Various artists.
Compact disc: released on Dunhill Compact Classics (USA) in Dec'86

Big Beat Beach Party

BIG BEAT BEACH PARTY various artists (Various Artists).
Notes: Artists include: Del-Monas/Prisoners/Larry & Blue Notes/Mighty Ceasars/Screaming Blue Messiahs/Joe King Carrasco/Pride of the Cross/Surfin' LUngs/Lash Lariat/ Restless/Sugar Ray Ford/Hasil Adkins/Legendary Stardust Cowboy/Tall Boys/Sting- Rays/Turkey Bones & Wild Dogs.
Album: released on Big Beat in Jan'86 by Ace Records. Distributed by: Projection, Pinnacle

Big Ben Banjo Band

BIG BEN BANJO BAND.
Double cassette: released on Pickwick (Ditto series) in Jul'82

DANCIN' BANJOS.
Album: released on EMI Retrospect in May'84 by EMI Records. Distributed by: EMI

Cassette: released on EMI Retrospect in May'84 by EMI Records. Distributed by: EMI

RAGS & TATTERS.
Album: released on PRT in Sep'78 by PRT Records. Distributed by: PRT

Big Ben Hawaiian Band

BIG BEN HAWAIIAN BAND.
Cassette: released on Ideal(Tapes) in Feb'81. Distributed by: EMI

Big Black

ATOMISER.
Album: released on Blast First in Nov'86 by Sonic Youth Records. Distributed by: Rough Trade, Nine Mile, Red Rhino, Cartel

Album: released on Homestead in Sep'86. Distributed by: Rough Trade, Cartel, Shigaku

HAMMER PARTY.
Album: released on Homestead in Dec'86. Distributed by: Rough Trade, Cartel, Shigaku

HEADACHE.
Single (12"): released on Blast First in Jun'87 by Sonic Youth Records. Distributed by: Rough Trade, Nine Mile, Red Rhino, Cartel

HEADACHE (LP).
Album: released on Blast First in Jul'87 by Sonic Youth Records. Distributed by: Rough Trade, Nine Mile, Red Rhino, Cartel

IL DUCE.
Tracks: / Il Duce.
Single (7"): released on Homestead in Sep'86. Distributed by: Rough Trade, Cartel, Shigaku

RACER X.
Album: released on Homestead in May'85. Distributed by: Rough Trade, Cartel, Shigaku

SOUND OF IMPACT.
Album: released on Blast First in Jul'87 by Sonic Youth Records. Distributed by: Rough Trade, Nine Mile, Red Rhino, Cartel

Big Bob

WE'VE MADE MEMORIES (Big Bob & The Fugitives).
Cassette: released on Ardvene in Jun'87 by Ardvene Records. Distributed by: Ross

Big Bopper

CHANTILLY LACE.
Album: released on Mercury in Nov'81 by Phonogram Records. Distributed by: Polygram Distribution

Cassette: released on Mercury in Nov'81 by Phonogram Records. Distributed by: Polygram Distribution

Single (7"): released on Swift in Mar'83. Distributed by: Swift Distribution

Single (7"): released on Old Gold in Jan'85 by Old Gold Records. Distributed by: Lightning, Jazz Music, Spartan, Counterpoint

Big Brother

BIG BROTHER.
Single (7"): released on Code in Oct'84 by Code Records. Distributed by: Jetstar, EMI

CHEAPER THRILLS (Big Brother & The Holding Company).
Album: released on Edsel in Jan'84 by Demon Records. Distributed by: Pinnacle, Jazz Music, Projection

CHEAP THRILLS (Big Brother & The Holding Company).
Album: released on CBS in '84 by CBS Records. Distributed by: CBS

Cassette: released on CBS in '84 by CBS Records. Distributed by: CBS

JOSEPH'S COAT (Big Brother & Holding Co.).
Album: released on Edsel in Apr'86 by Demon Records. Distributed by: Pinnacle, Jazz Music, Projection

Big Chalk

IN THE COLD WINTERS NIGHT.
Single (7"): released on A & R in Mar'83. Distributed by: Spartan

Big Chill

BIG CHILL, THE Original Soundtrack.
Compact disc: released on Motown in Jun'85 by Motown Records. Distributed by: BMG Distribution

Album: released on Motown in Jul'84 by Motown Records. Distributed by: BMG Distribution

Cassette: released on Motown in Jul'84 by Motown Records. Distributed by: BMG Distribution

Compact disc: released on Motown in Jul'84 by Motown Records. Distributed by: BMG Distribution

Big City Soul Sound

BIG CITY SOUL SOUND various artists (Various Artists).
Album: released on Kent in Dec'86 by Ace Records. Distributed by: Pinnacle

Big Country

BIG COUNTRY LIVE.
Notes: Number of tracks: 15
Type of recording: Live
Total playing time: 75mins
Video-cassette (VHS): released on Channel 5 in Apr'86. Distributed by: W.H. Smiths

CHANCE.
Single (12"): released on Mercury in Jun'84 by Phonogram Records. Distributed by: Polygram Distribution

Single (7"): released on Mercury in Aug'83 by Phonogram Records. Distributed by: Polygram Distribution

CROSSING, THE.
Compact disc: released on Mercury in '83 by Phonogram Records. Distributed by: Polygram Distribution

Album: released on Mercury in Jul'83 by Phonogram Records. Distributed by: Polygram Distribution

Cassette: released on Mercury in Jul'83 by Phonogram Records. Distributed by: Polygram Distribution

FIELDS OF FIRE.
Single (7"): released on Mercury in Feb'83 by Phonogram Records. Distributed by: Polygram Distribution

FIELDS OF FIRE(ALTERNATIVE MIX).
Single (12"): released on Mercury in Jun'84 by Phonogram Records. Distributed by: Polygram Distribution

HARVEST HOME.
Single (7"): released on Mercury in Feb'83 by Phonogram Records. Distributed by: Polygram Distribution Deleted '87.

Single (12"): released on Mercury in Jun'84 by Phonogram Records. Distributed by: Polygram Distribution

HOLD THE HEART.
Tracks: / Honky tonk woman.
Single (7"): released on Mercury in Nov'86 by Phonogram Records. Distributed by: Polygram Distribution

Single (12"): released on Mercury in Nov'86 by Phonogram Records. Distributed by: Polygram Distribution

IN A BIG COUNTRY.
Single (7"): released on Mercury in Oct'84 by Phonogram Records. Distributed by: Polygram Distribution

Single (12"): released on Mercury in Oct'84 by Phonogram Records. Distributed by: Polygram Distribution

JUST A SHADOW.
Single (7"): released on Mercury in Jan'85 by Phonogram Records. Distributed by: Polygram Distribution Deleted '86.

Single (12"): released on Mercury in Jan'85 by Phonogram Records. Distributed by: Polygram Distribution

LOOK AWAY.
Tracks: / Look away / Restless natives.
Single (7"): released on Mercury in Mar'86 by Phonogram Records. Distributed by: Polygram Distribution

Single (12"): released on Mercury in Mar'86 by Phonogram Records. Distributed by: Polygram Distribution

ONE GREAT THING.
Tracks: / One great thing / Song of the south / Porroh man * / Champs * / Flame of the west.
Single (7"): released on Mercury in Aug'86 by Phonogram Records. Distributed by: Polygram Distribution

Single (12"): released on Mercury in Aug'86 by Phonogram Records. Distributed by: Polygram Distribution

Double-pack single: released on Mercury in Aug'86 by Phonogram Records. Distributed by: Polygram Distribution

SEER, THE.
Album: released on Mercury in Jul'86 by Phonogram Records. Distributed by: Polygram Distribution

Cassette: released on Mercury in Jul'86 by Phonogram Records. Distributed by: Polygram Distribution

Compact disc: by Phonogram Records. Distributed by: Polygram Distribution

STEELTOWN.
Tracks: / East of Eden / Steeltown / Where the rose is sown / Come back to me / Tall ships go / Girl with grey eyes / Rain dance / Great divide, The / Just a shadow.
Compact disc: released on Mercury in Oct'84 by Phonogram Records. Distributed by: Polygram Distribution

Album: released on Mercury in Oct'84 by Phonogram Records. Distributed by: Polygram Distribution

Cassette: released on Mercury in Oct'84 by Phonogram Records. Distributed by: Polygram Distribution

TEACHER, THE.
Tracks: / Teacher, The / Home came the angel / Of the restless angel *.
Single (7"): released on Mercury in Jun'86 by Phonogram Records. Distributed by: Polygram Distribution

Single (12"): released on Mercury in Jun'86 by Phonogram Records. Distributed by: Polygram Distribution

WONDERLAND (EXT.VERSION).
Single (12"): released on Mercury in Jun'84 by Phonogram Records. Distributed by: Polygram Distribution

Big country collection

BIG COUNTRY COLLECTION Various artists (Various Artists).
Album: released on Cambra in Feb'85 by Cambra Records. Distributed by: IDS, Conifer

Cassette: released on Cambra in Feb'85 by Cambra Records. Distributed by: IDS, Conifer

Big Country, The

BIG COUNTRY, THE Original soundtrack (Moross, Jerome).
Album: released on Hallmark in Jan'79 by Pickwick Records. Distributed by: Pickwick Distribution, PRT, Taylors

Cassette: released on Hallmark in Jan'79 by Pickwick Records. Distributed by: Pickwick Distribution, PRT, Taylors

Big Daddy

BIG DADDY.
Album: released on Making Waves in Mar'85 by Making Waves Records

Cassette: released on Making Waves in Mar'85 by Making Waves Records

BIG DADDY SUN AND ... (Big Daddy & The Outer Planets).
Album: released on Nervous in Aug'84 by Nervous Records. Distributed by: Nervous, Rough Trade

EYE OF THE TIGER.
Single (7"): released on Making Waves in Sep'84 by Making Waves Records

I WRITE THE SONGS.
Single (7"): released on Making Waves in Jun'85 by Making Waves Records

Big Dave

ARTHUR MURRAY ROCK & ROLL.
Album: released on Pathe MarconiFrance) in Apr'85

Big Dipper

BOO-BOO.
Album: released on Homestead in Apr'87. Distributed by: Rough Trade, Cartel, Shigaku

Big Dish

CHRISTINA'S WORLD (SINGLE).
Tracks: / Everlasting faith / She say's nothing.
Single (7"): released on Virgin in Jan'87 by Virgin Records. Distributed by: EMI, Virgin Distribution

Single (12"): by Virgin Records. Distributed by: EMI, Virgin Distribution

PROSPECT STREET.
Tracks: / Prospect street / From the neighbourhood.
Single (7"): released on Virgin in Oct'86 by Virgin Records. Distributed by: EMI, Virgin Distribution

Single (12"): released on Virgin in Oct'86 by Virgin Records. Distributed by: EMI, Virgin Distribution

SLIDE.
Tracks: / Slide / Reverend killer / Presence *.
Single (7"): released on Virgin in Aug'86 by Virgin Records. Distributed by: EMI, Virgin Distribution

Single (12"): released on Virgin in Aug'86 by Virgin Records. Distributed by: EMI, Virgin Distribution

Compact disc single: released on Virgin in May'87 by Virgin Records. Distributed by: EMI, Virgin Distribution

SWIMMER.
Tracks: / Prospect street / Christina's world / Slide / Big new beginning / Another people's palace / Swimmer / Lonliest man in the world (The) / Jealous / Her town / Beyond the pale / Second swimmer.
Album: released on Virgin in Dec'86 by Virgin Records. Distributed by: EMI, Virgin Distribution

Cassette: released on Virgin in Dec'86 by Virgin Records. Distributed by: EMI, Virgin Distribution

Compact disc: released on Virgin in Dec'86 by Virgin Records. Distributed by: EMI, Virgin Distribution

Big Ed

BINGO (Big Ed & The Rockin' Rattlesnakes).
Album: released on Black Lagoon in Sep'86 by Black Lagoon Records. Distributed by: Red Rhino, Cartel

Big Flame

CUBIST POP MANIFESTO.
Single (7"): released on Ron Johnson in Feb'87 by Ron Johnson Records. Distributed by: Nine Mile Distribution, Cartel Distribution

DEBRA.
Single (7"): released on Ron Johnson in Mar'85 by Ron Johnson Records. Distributed by: Nine Mile Distribution, Cartel Distribution

POPSTARS.
Tracks: / Popstars.
Single (7"): released on Ron Johnson in Mar'86 by Ron Johnson Records. Distributed by: Nine Mile Distribution, Cartel Distribution

SINK.
Single (7"): released on Plaque in Apr'84 by Red Rhino Records. Distributed by: Cartel

TOUGH.
Single (7"): released on Ron Johnson in Sep'85 by Ron Johnson Records. Distributed by: Nine Mile Distribution, Cartel Distribution

TWO KAN GURU (EP).
Tracks: / Two kan guru / Sink / Sometimes / Man of few syllables / Sargasso / All the Irish / Cuba.
Single 10": released on Ron Johnson in Jul'86 by Ron Johnson Records. Distributed by: Nine Mile Distribution, Cartel Distribution

XPZWRTX.
Single (12"): released on Ron Johnson in Feb'87 by Ron Johnson Records. Distributed by: Nine Mile Distribution, Cartel Distribution

Bigger Than God

BIGGER THAN GOD Variuos artists (Various Artists).
Tracks: / Bigger than god.
Single (12"): released on Bunker in Feb'86. Distributed by: Red Rhino, Cartel

Biggest band...

BIGGEST BAND SPECTACULAR IN THE WORLD Various artists (Various Artists).
Album: released on Bandleader in Aug'85 by Bandleader Records. Distributed by: PRT

Page 108

Cassette: released on Bandleader in Aug'85 by Bandleader Records. Distributed by: PRT

Biggles

BIGGLES Capt. W.E Johns (York, Michael).
Cassette: released on Listen For Pleasure in '83 by MFP Records. Distributed by: EMI

SOUNDTRACK, THE.
Tracks: / Do you want to be a hero / Chock's away / Big hot blues / Knocking at your back door / Knock 'em dead kid / No turning back / Music soundtrack / Ariel pursuit / Discovery / Biggles theme / Maria's theme.
Notes: From the motion picture 'Biggles', tracks by Jon Anderson, Deep Purple, Motley Crewand The Immortales(featuring John Deacon from Queen).
Album: released on MCA in Jun'86 by MCA Records. Distributed by: Polygram, MCA

Cassette: released on MCA in Jun'86 by MCA Records. Distributed by: Polygram, MCA

Biggs, Barry

ALL I HAVE TO DO IS DREAM.
Single (7"): released on Revue in Dec'86 by Revue Records. Distributed by: Creole

BARRY BIGGS & THE INNER CIRCLE.
Tracks: / Stoned in love with you / Side show / Westbound train / Your kiss is sweet / Burial / Love grows / Why must you cry / Got to be mellow / Natty dread / orward jah jah children / One bad apple / T.S.O.P..
Album: released on Trojan in '83 by Trojan Records. Distributed by: PRT, Jetstar

CONVERSATION.
Tracks: / Wide awake in a dream.
Single (7"): released on Revue in Aug'85 by Revue Records. Distributed by: Creole

DON'T CRY BABY.
Tracks: / Don't cry baby / Exclusively yours.
Single (12"): released on Revue in Dec'85 by Revue Records. Distributed by: Creole

IF YOU WANNA MAKE LOVE.
Tracks: / If you wanna make love / Girl I really love you.
Single (7"): released on Revue in Mar'87 by Revue Records. Distributed by: Creole

Single (12"): released on Revue in Mar'87 by Revue Records. Distributed by: Creole

IF YOU WERE NOT HERE.
Tracks: / If you were not here / If you were not here.
Single (12"): released on Starlight in Jun'86 by Starlight Records. Distributed by: Jetstar Distribution

ILLUSION.
Single (12"): released on Bullet in Jul'83. Distributed by: Bullet Distribution

LOVE COME DOWN.
Single (7"): released on Afrik in Feb'83 by Afrik Records. Distributed by: Jetstar

PROMISE IS A COMFORT TO A FOOL.
Single (12"): released on Afrik in Jun'82 by Afrik Records. Distributed by: Jetstar

REFLECTION (Biggs, Barry/Rudy Thomas).
Single 10": released on Mobiliser in Dec'82 by Jetstar Records. Distributed by: Jetstar Distribution

SIDE SHOW.
Single (7"): released on Creole in Aug'84 by Creole Records. Distributed by: Rhino, PRT

Single (12"): released on Creole in Aug'84 by Creole Records. Distributed by: Rhino, PRT

SIDESHOW.
Tracks: / Sideshow / Hurt So good.
Single (7"): released on Old Gold in Nov'86 by Old Gold Records. Distributed by: Lightning, Jazz Music, Spartan, Counterpoint

SIDE SHOW (87 MIX).
Tracks: / Side show (87 mix) / Wide awake in a dream / Work all day.
Single (7"): released on Dynamic in May'87 by Creole Records. Distributed by: CBS, Essex

Single (12"): released on Dynamic in May'87 by Creole Records. Distributed by: CBS, Essex

WORK ALL DAY.
Single (12"): released on Dynamic in May'83 by Creole Records. Distributed by: CBS Essex

Big Gun

YOU'LL ALWAYS GIVE YOUR BEST.
Tracks: / Basil Peironi / Don't ever go away again.
Single (7"): released on Hi-Fibre in Jan'87. Distributed by: Fast Forward, Cartel

Biggun, Ivor

MAJORCA SONG,THE.
Tracks: / Majorca song,The / Great big filthy disco version.
Single (7"): released on Dead Badger in 20 Jun'87 by Dead Badger Records. Distributed by: Beggars Banquet, WEA

Single (12"): released on Dead Badger in 20 Jun'87 by Dead Badger Records. Distributed by: Beggars Banquet, WEA

MORE FILTH DIRT CHEAP.
Tracks: / Cockerel song, The / My shirt collar (it won't go stiff) / Southern breeze / Burglars holler, The / Gums and plums / John Thomas Allcock / I have a dog his name is Rover / My brothers magazine / Richard the third / Walking your blues away / Are mice electric / I can be the hot dog and you can be the bun / I wanna be a bear / A woke up dis moanin' / Terrific Teddy sings the blues / Ah feel so bad / Other educated monkey.
Album: released on Beggars Banquet in Jul'81 by Beggars Banquet Records. Distributed by: WEA

Cassette: released on Beggars Banquet in Jul'81 by Beggars Banquet Records. Distributed by: WEA

WINKERS ALBUM, THE.
Album: released on Beggars Banquet in Nov'79 by Beggars Banquet Records. Distributed by: WEA

Big hits...

BIG HITS OF THE 40'S AND 50'S Various artists (Various Artists).
Cassette: released on RCA International (USA) in Jun'82 by RCA Records. Distributed by: RCA

Big Jim

BIG JIM.
Album: released on Homespun(Ireland) in Aug'82 by Outlet Records. Distributed by: Outlet

Cassette: released on Homespun(Ireland) in Aug'82 by Outlet Records. Distributed by: Outlet

REQUESTS.
Tracks: / Sweet forget me not / Amazing grace / She wears my ring / Did your mother come from Ireland / I will love you all my life / Jerusalem / When your old wedding ring was new / Way love's supposed to be, The / Old pals of yesterday / Baby blue / Veil of white lace / Mother of mine.
Album: released on Homespun(Ireland) in Oct'86 by Outlet Records. Distributed by: Outlet

Cassette: released on Homespun(Ireland) in Oct'86 by Outlet Records. Distributed by: Outlet

SWEET FORGET ME NOT.
Tracks: / Sweet forget me not / When your old wedding ring was new.
Single (7"): released on Homespun(Ireland) in Oct'86 by Outlet Records. Distributed by: Outlet

Big John's Yoppers

YOPPER'S DREAM.
Cassette: released on JTN in Oct'83

Big Mac

ROUGH DRIED WOMAN.
Single (7"): released on Charly in Jul'80 by Charly Records. Distributed by: Charly, Cadillac

Big Maceo

KING OF CHICAGO BLUES PIANO,VOL 1, (THE).
Album: released on Blues Classics (USA) in May'84 by Arhoolie Records. Distributed by: Topic, Jazz Music, Projection

KING OF CHICAGO BLUES PIANO, VOLUME 2.
Album: released on Blues Classics (USA) in May'84 by Arhoolie Records. Distributed by: Topic, Jazz Music, Projection

Big Maybelle

ROOTS OF R&R AND EARLY SOUL.
Album:

Big Motown Hits...

BIG MOTOWN HITS & HARD TO FIND CLASICS VOL. 1 Various artists (Various Artists).
Tracks: / Helpless / You've made me so very happy / Love's gone bad / I got a feeling / Baby I'm for real / Does your mama know about me / Bells, The / What becomes of the brokenhearted / I've passed this way before / Walk away from love / My world ended (the moment you left me) / Get ready / I'm losing you, (I know) / War / Twenty-five miles / It's a shame / I'll always love you / Darling baby / Heaven must have sent you / Just look what you've done Love's gone bad.
Compact disc: released on Motown in Jan'87 by Motown Records. Distributed by: BMG Distribution

BIG MOTOWN HITS & HARD TO FIND CLASSICS VOL.2 various artists (Various Artists).
Tracks: / When i'm gone / Jamie / River deep mountain high / Smiling faces sometimes / I can't believe you love me / Indiana wants me / Function at the junction / He was really saying something / I guess I'll always love you / I've never been to me / Born to wander / With you i'm born again / Every little bit hurts / When I'm gone / Needle in a haystack / Lonely, lonely girl am I / I can't believe you love me / Money (that's what I want) / Jamie / Take me in your arms (rock a little while) / I guess I'll always love you / Here comes the judge / Function at the junction / Smiling faces sometimes / I just want to celebrate / Born to wander / River deep - mountain high / Indiana wants me / I've neveer been to me / With you I'm born again / What the world needs now is love/Abraham, Martin and John.
Album: released on Tamla Motown in Jun'86 by Motown Records. Distributed by: RCA Distribution

Cassette: released on Tamla Motown in Jun'86 by Motown Records. Distributed by: RCA Distribution

Compact disc: released on Motown in Jan'87 by Motown Records. Distributed by: BMG Distribution

Double compact disc: released on Motown in 20 Jun'87 by Motown Records. Distributed by: BMG Distribution

Big Music

COLD EMOTION.
Tracks: / Cold emotion / Hard rain's gonna fall, A.
Single (7"): released on RCA in Sep'86 by RCA Records. Distributed by: RCA, Roots, Swift, Wellard, Chris, I & B, Solomon & Peres Distribution

Single (12"): released on RCA in Sep'86 by RCA Records. Distributed by: RCA, Roots, Swift, Wellard, Chris, I & B, Solomon & Peres Distribution

Big Noise

BIG NOISE COMPILATION (Various Artists).
Tracks: / Land and life / Alone / Now I ride alone / Quiet lives / Boy's town work song / Chilli part two / Juice squeezer / Love is you.
Album: released on Big Time in Jun'87 by Mainline Record Company. Distributed by: Mainline

Cassette: released on Big Time in Jun'87 by Mainline Record Company. Distributed by: Mainline

Big noise from Northwood

BIG NOISE FROM NORTHWOOD Various artists (Various Artists).
Album: released on Northwood in Mar'85 by Northwood Records. Distributed by: Backs-Cartel

Big Outdoor Type

CALL YOU ON SUNDAY.
Single (7"): released on Havasac in Jul'84 by Havasac Records. Distributed by: Revolver, Cartel

Big Pete

ORIGINAL SLOBB, THE (Big Pete & The Wooden Pickles).
Single (7"): released on Stan Ollie in Jul'84

Big Red Boat

FAREWELL MY LOVELY.
Single (7"): released on Elastic Music in Mar'85 by Elastic Records. Distributed by: Revolver, Cartel

Big River

BIG RIVER Adventures of Hukleberry Finn (Various Artists).
Tracks: / Overture / Do you wanna go to heaven? / Boys, The / Waitin' for the light to shine / Guv'ment / Hand for the hog / I, Huckleberry, me / Muddy water / Crossing, The / River in the rain / When the sun goes down in the south / Entracte / Royal nonesuch,The / Worlds apart / Arkansas / How blest we are / You oughta be here with me / Leavin's not the only way to go / Waitin' for the light to shine(reprise) / Free at last / Muddy water (reprise).
Notes: Winner of seven Tony Awards in 1985 including that of Best Musical,The Original Broadway Cast album of "Big River" is now set for UK release.The absorbing Mark Twain tale of Huckleberry Finn is brilliantly illuminated by Roger Miller's exciting score and the heartfelt performance of the Big River Company Cast.A delightful album bound to be sought out by many collectors of quality cast recordings.
Album: released on MCA in Feb'86 by MCA Records. Distributed by: Polygram, MCA

Big Self

DON'T TURN AROUND.
Single (7"): released on Reekus in Mar'82 by Reekus Records. Distributed by: Nine Mile, Cartel

GHOST SHIRT.
Single (7"): released on Reekus in Mar'84 by Reekus Records. Distributed by: Nine Mile, Cartel

Single (12"): released on Reekus in Mar'84 by Reekus Records. Distributed by: Nine Mile, Cartel

REASON SMILES.
Single (12"): released on Reekus in Apr'85 by Reekus Records. Distributed by: Nine Mile, Cartel

STATELESS.

SURPRISE SURPRISE.
Single (7"): released on Reekus in Sep'81 by Reekus Records. Distributed by: Nine Mile, Cartel

VISION.
Single (7"): released on Reekus in Aug'85 by Reekus Records. Distributed by: Nine Mile, Cartel

Big Sleep

BIG SLEEP, (THE) Chandler, Raymond (Massey, Daniel).
Cassette: released on Listen For Pleasure in Apr'83 by MFP Records. Distributed by: EMI

Big soul sound

BIG SOUL SOUND Various artists (Various Artists).
Album: released on K-Tel (Era) in Jun'83 by K-Tel Records. Distributed by: K-Tel

Cassette: released on K-Tel (Era) in Jun'83 by K-Tel Records. Distributed by: K-Tel

Album: released on K-Tel (Era) in Jun'83 by K-Tel Records. Distributed by: K-Tel

Big Sound Authority

BAD TOWN.
Single (7"): released on MCA in May'85 by MCA Records. Distributed by: Polygram, MCA

Single (12"): released on MCA in May'85 by MCA Records. Distributed by: Polygram, MCA

Single (1[illegible]): released [illegible] in May'85 by MCA Records. Distributed by: Polygram, MCA

Single (7"): released on Source in Jun'85 by SMP Records. Distributed by: PRT

DON'T LET OUR LOVE START A WAR.
Tracks: / Don't let our love strat a war / Moving heaven & earth (revisited) / Family thing *.
Single (7"): released on MCA in Aug'86 by MCA Records. Distributed by: Polygram, MCA

Single (12"): released on MCA in Aug'86 by MCA Records. Distributed by: Polygram, MCA

INWARD REVOLUTION.
Tracks: / (Call me)soulman / Be true to yourself / Moving heaven & earth / My hell shaped room / This is the day / I'm stronger now / This house (is where your love stands) / Bad town, A / Loverama / Let's hold together / When things fall apart.
Album: released on MCA in Nov'85 by MCA Records. Distributed by: Polygram, MCA

Cassette: released on MCA in Nov'85 by MCA Records. Distributed by: Polygram, MCA

Big Star

NO. 1 ALBUM.
Cassette: released on Big Beat in Mar'87 by Ace Records. Distributed by: Projection, Pinnacle

NO.1 ALBUM/RADIO CITY.
Notes: 70 minutes playing time. 23 tracks from both the recently reissued Big Star albums. Big Beat booklet containg full sleeve notes.

NO.1 RECORD/RADIO CITY.
Notes: With Alex Chilton
Compact disc: released on Big Beat in Jun'87 by Ace Records. Distributed by: Projection, Pinnacle

NO I RECORD.
Album: released on Big Beat in Nov'86 by Ace Records. Distributed by: Projection, Pinnacle

RADIO CITY.
Cassette: released on Big Beat in Mar'87 by Ace Records. Distributed by: Projection, Pinnacle

RADIO CITY.
Album: released on Big Beat in Nov'86 by Ace Records. Distributed by: Projection, Pinnacle

Big Stick

DRAG RACING.
Tracks: / Drag racing.
Single (12"): released on Blast First in Jun'86 by Sonic Youth Records. Distributed by: Rough Trade, Nine Mile, Red Rhino, Cartel

Big Supreme

DON'T WALK.
Tracks: / Don't walk / My addiction.
Single (7"): released on Polydor in Aug'86 by Polydor Records. Distributed by: Polygram, Polydor

Single (12"): released on Polydor in Aug'86 by Polydor Records. Distributed by: Polygram, Polydor

LET'S TURN OUR LOVE AROUND.
Tracks: / Let's turn our love around / He'll deceive.
Single (7"): released on Polydor in May'86 by Polydor Records. Distributed by: Polygram, Polydor

Single (12"): released on Polydor in May'86 by Polydor Records. Distributed by: Polygram, Polydor

PLEASE YOURSELF.
Tracks: / Keep On Pushing.
Single (7"): released on Polydor in Feb'87 by Polydor Records. Distributed by: Polygram, Polydor

Single (12"): released on Polydor in Feb'87 by Polydor Records. Distributed by: Polygram, Polydor

REMIND ME.
Tracks: / Remind me / What love means / Remind me (I don't wanna see no panties).
Single (7"): released on Polydor in Apr'87 by Polydor Records. Distributed by: Polygram, Polydor

Single (12"): released on Polydor in Apr'87 by Polydor Records. Distributed by: Polygram, Polydor

Single (12"): released on Polydor in Apr'87 by Polydor Records. Distributed by: Polygram, Polydor

Big Sur

DANCING ON THE HIGH WIRE.
Single (12"): released on Hands Like Feet in Aug'87 by Hands Like Feet Records. Distributed by: Fast Forward, Cartel

Big Three

AT THE CAVERN (EP).
Single (7"): released on Decca in Jun'81 by Decca Records. Distributed by: Polygram

CAVERN STOMP.
Album: released on Edsel in Nov'82 by Demon Records. Distributed by: Pinnacle, Jazz Music, Projection

I FEEL LIKE STEPPIN' OUT (Big Three Trio, The).
Album: released on Route 66 in Oct'86

Big Tom

ALL TIME HITS OF.... (Big Tom & The Mainliners).
Album: released on Emerald (Ireland) in Oct'81 by Emerald Records. Distributed by: I & B, Ross, PRT

Cassette: released on Emerald (Ireland) in Oct'81 by Emerald Records. Distributed by: I & B, Ross, PRT

LITTLE BIT OF COUNTRY & IRISH (Big Tom & The Mainliners).
Tracks: / Isle of Innisfree, The / Don't be angry / My world's come down / Guess things happened / Back in my babys arms / Tears on a bridal bouquet / She's gone / Cold hard facts of life, The / Before(I met you) / Gentle mother.
Album: released on Emerald (Ireland) in Nov'84 by Emerald Records. Distributed by: I & B, Ross, PRT

Cassette: released on Emerald (Ireland) in Nov'84 by Emerald Records. Distributed by: I & B, Ross, PRT

LITTLE BIT OF COUNTRY (Big Tom & The Mainliners).
Cassette: released on Emerald (Ireland) in Oct'81 by Emerald Records. Distributed by: I & B, Ross, PRT

Big Tony

CAN'T GET ENOUGH OF YOUR LOVE BABE.
Tracks: / Can't get enough of your love babe / I miss you.
Single (7"): released on Lisson in Jul'86. Distributed by: PRT

Single (12"): released on Lisson in Jul'86. Distributed by: PRT

Big Town Playboys

DOWN THE ROAD APIECE.
Tracks: / Down the road apiece.
Single (7"): released on Pinnacle in Jan'86 by Pinnacle Records. Distributed by: Pinnacle

Single (7"): released on Making Waves in Sep'85 by Making Waves Records

PLAYBOY BOOGIE.
Tracks: / Hurry Baby / Chicken Shack Boogie / Happy Pay Day / Walkin' / She walks right in / What more do you want me to do ? / Playboy Boogie / Come on / Down the road apiece / Don Done it,I / Shake your hips / Roomin' house boogie / Driftin'.
Album: released on Spindrift in Sep'85. Distributed by: Roots

Big Trouble...

BIG TROUBLE IN LITTLE CHINA Original soundtrack (Coup De Villes).
Tracks: / Big trouble in little China / Pork chop.
Cassette: released on Silva Screen in Nov'86 by Silva Screen Records. Distributed by: Silva Screen

Album: released on Silva Screen in Nov'86 by Silva Screen Records. Distributed by: Silva Screen

Big Twist

300 POUNDS OF HEAVENLY JOY (Big Twist & the Mellow Fellows).
Single (7"): released on Sonet in Jan'84 by Sonet Records. Distributed by: PRT

BIG TWIST AND THE MELLOW FELLOWS (Big Twist & the Mellow Fellows).
Album: released on Sonet in Oct'83 by Sonet Records. Distributed by: PRT

ONE TRACK MIND (Big Twist & the Mellow Fellows).
Album: released on Red Lightnin' in Sep'82 by Red Lightnin' Records. Distributed by: Roots, Swift, Jazz Music, JSU, Pinnacle, Cartel, Wynd-Up Distribution

Big View

AUGUST GRASS.
Single (7"): released on Point in Aug'82. Distributed by: PRT

Big Walter

JOHNNY YOUNG AND BIG WALTER See Young, Johnny (Big Walter/ Johnny Young).
Album: released on Arhoolie in '81 by Arhoolie Records. Distributed by: Projection, Topic, Jazz Music, Swift, Roots

Big Western Film Themes

BIG WESTERN FILM THEMES Various artists (Various Artists).
Cassette: released on AIM (Budget Cassettes) in Sep'83

Big Wheels Of Motown

BIG WHEELS OF MOTOWN Various artists (Various Artists).
Album: released on Motown in Oct'81 by Motown Records. Distributed by: BMG Distribution

Cassette: released on Motown in Oct'81 by Motown Records. Distributed by: BMG Distribution

Big Youth

A LUTA CONTINUA.
Album: released on Heartbeat (USA) in Sep'85. Distributed by: Mike's Country Music Room Distribution, Swift, Projection, Topic, Jetstar, Ruff Lion Distribution

CHANTING DREAD INNA FINE STYLE.
Album: released on Blue Moon in Jun'85. Distributed by: Magnum Music Group Ltd, PRT, Spartan

Cassette: released on Blue Moon in Jun'85. Distributed by: Magnum Music Group Ltd, PRT, Spartan

DREADLOCKS DREAD.
Album: released on Virgin (Front Line) in Apr'83

EVERYDAY SKANK BEST OF BIG YOUTH.
Tracks: / S.90 / One of these fine days / Pride & joy rag / So we stay / Cool breeze / Can you keep a secret / Screaming target / Killer / Give praise / Hell is for heroes / Natty / Cultural dread / 10 against.
Album: released on Trojan in '83 by Trojan Records. Distributed by: PRT, Jetstar

HIT THE ROAD JACK.
Tracks: / What's going on / Hit the road Jack / Wake up everybody / Get up stand up / Jah man of Syreen / Ten against one / Hotter fire / Way of the light, The / Dread high ranking / Dread is the best.
Album: released on Trojan in '83 by Trojan Records. Distributed by: PRT, Jetstar

LIVE AT THE REGGAE SUNSPLASH.
Album: released on Vista Sounds in Jul'84 by Vista Sounds Records. Distributed by: Jetstar

NATTY CULTURAL DREAD.
Tracks: / Wolf in sheep clothing / Natty cultural dread / Hell is for heroes / Jim Squashey / Touch me in the morning / Every nigger is a star / I love the way you love.
Album: released on Trojan in '83 by Trojan Records. Distributed by: PRT, Jetstar

SCREAMING TARGET.
Tracks: / Lee a low / Concrete jungle / Screaming target / Pride and joy rock / Be careful / Tippertone rock / One of these fine days / Screaming target (vers 2) / Killer, The / Solomon a Gunday / Honesty / I am alright / Screaming target / Pride and joy rock / Be careful / Tippertone rock / One of these fine / Screaming target (Vers 2) / Killer, The / Solomon A Gunday / Honesty / I am alright / Lee A Low / Concrete jungle.
Album: released on Trojan in '83 by Trojan Records. Distributed by: PRT, Jetstar

SOME GREAT BIG YOUTH.
Album: released on Blue Moon in Mar'85. Distributed by: Magnum Music Group Ltd, PRT, Spartan

TROUBLE ON THE ROAD.
Single (12"): released on Judge Dread in May'87

Big Zap!

PSYCHEDELIC SHACK.
Tracks: / Psychedelic shack / Zap attack / Psychedelic shack / Zap attack.
Single (7"): released on T.I.M. in 13 Jun'87 by T.I.M. Records. Distributed by: Backs, Cartel Distribution

Single (12"): released on T.I.M. in Jul'87 by T.I.M. Records. Distributed by: Backs, Cartel Distribution

Bikini Atoll

TRIBAL RADIO.
Single (7"): released on Ready Go in Jul'82. Distributed by: Pinnacle

WALL,(THE).
Single (7"): released on Ready Go in Nov'81. Distributed by: Pinnacle

Bilbo

SEX MACHINE.
Tracks: / Relax.
Single (7"): released on All Boys in Aug'83

Single (12"): released on All Boys in Aug'83

Bilbro, D.H. 'Bert'

HARMONICA SHOWCASE (see Bailey, Deford & D.H. 'Bert' Bilbro) (Bilbro, D.H 'Bert' & Deford Bailey).

Bilbrough, Dave

DAVE BILBOROUGH & FRIENDS.
Album: released on Dove in May'79 by Dove Records. Distributed by: Jetstar

Bileams asna

BILEAMS ASNA.
Album: released on Cantio(Sweden) in Aug'82. Distributed by: Plankton Distribution

SAAB TURBO.
Tracks: / Passive so long.
Single (7"): released on Cantio(Sweden) in May'84. Distributed by: Plankton Distribution

Bilitis

BILITIS Original Soundtrack.
Tracks: / Bilitis-main theme / Promenade / Les 2 nudites / Spring time ballet / L'abre / I need a man / Melissa / La Campagne / Scene d'amour / Rainbow / Bilitis-main theme and end titles.
Album: released on United Artists in Apr'78

Cassette: released on United Artists in Apr'78

Bilk, Acker

100 MINUTES.
Cassette: released on PRT (100 Minute Series) in Jun'82

ACKER BILK IN HOLLAND.
Tracks: / I can't believe that you're in love with me / Clarinet marmalade / Mood indigo / Them there eyes / Take the A train / World is waiting for the sunshine, The / Just a closer walk with thee / Jeepers creepers / Lover man / Watermelon man / I don't want to set the world on fire / St.Thomas / Georgia / Senora Signora / Blues walks / Stranger on the shore / Nobody's sweetheart / Once in a while / Old music master, The.
Compact disc: released on Timeless (Holland) in Nov'86. Distributed by: JSU Distribution, Jazz Music Distribution, Jazz Horizons Distribution, Cadillac, Celtic Music Distribution

Double Album: released on Timeless (Holland) in Aug'85. Distributed by: JSU Distribution, Jazz Music Distribution, Jazz Horizons Distribution, Cadillac, Celtic Music Distribution

Double cassette: released on Timeless (Holland) in Aug'85. Distributed by: JSU Distribution, Jazz Music Distribution, Jazz Horizons Distribution, Cadillac, Celtic Music Distribution

ACKER BILK SAGA, THE.
Tracks: / Perdido street blues / Papa dip / South / Summerset / Snag it / Should I / Acker's personal jungle / Royal garden blues / Blues for this year / Blues for last year / Acker raga / La paloma / Soho blues / Bustamento / Adios mi chaparita / Irish lullaby / Petit fleur / Honeysuckle rose / Basin street blues / Georgia on my mind / Creole love call / Dinah / Stranger on the shore.
Double Album: released on Polydor in Jul'79 by Polydor Records. Distributed by: Polygram, Polydor

ACKER'S CHOICE.
Album: released on Teldec (West Germany) in Jan'85

ACKER'S LULLABY.
Single (7"): released on PRT in Jun'84 by PRT Records. Distributed by: PRT

ARIA.
Single (7"): released on PRT in Jun'76 by PRT Records. Distributed by: PRT

BEST OF ACKER BILK VOLUME 2.
Cassette: released on Golden Hour in Mar'79 by PRT Records. Distributed by: PRT

COLLECTION: ACKER BILK.
Special: released on PRT in Sep'78 by PRT Records. Distributed by: PRT

DREAMING IN THE SUN (Bilk, Acker & Norman Candler).
Album: released on Intersound in Dec'86 by Intersound Records. Distributed by: Jazz Music

EXTREMELY LIVE IN STUDIO 1.
Cassette: released on PRT in Jul'78 by PRT Records. Distributed by: PRT

FINEST MOMENTS.
Tracks: / Stranger on the shore / Send in the clowns / Night that made me forget,The / Red haired girl / August evening / Fond memories / Just for you / Birchtree road / Aria / Fool on the hill / Autumn Evening / Goodbye / You won't see a tear / Western Farm / Dusk / Windharp.
Album: released on Showdown in Apr'86

Cassette: released on Showdown in Apr'86

FREE.
Cassette: released on PRT in Feb'78 by PRT Records. Distributed by: PRT

GOLDEN HOUR OF THE BEST OF ACKER BILK.
Cassette: released on Golden Hour in Nov'76 by PRT Records. Distributed by: PRT

I'M IN THE MOOD FOR LOVE.
Tracks: / Stranger on the shore / Frenesi / I'm in the mood for love / La paloma / Petite fleur / Scarlet ribbons / Georgia on my mind / Taste of honey, A / Greensleeves / Non dimenticar / Nature boy / Perhaps, perhaps perhaps / Meraviegliose labbra / Moon river.
Album: released on Philips (Italy) in Aug'83

Cassette: released on Philips (Italy) in Aug'83

IN HOLLAND (Bilk, Acker & His Paramount Jazzband).
Compact disc: released on Timeless in Oct'86

INVITATION.
Cassette: released on PRT in Feb'77 by PRT Records. Distributed by: PRT

JOHN HENRY.
Single (7"): released on PRT in Jul'83 by PRT Records. Distributed by: PRT

JOHN, PAUL AND ACKER (Bilk, Acker, His Clarinet & Strings).
Tracks: / Norwegian wood / With a little luck / Imagine / Michelle / World without love / Mull of Kintyre / Fool on the hill / Ebony and ivory / Nowhere man / Yesterday / She's leaving home / Here, there and everywhere / Pipes of peace.
Album: released on PRT in Nov'86 by PRT Records. Distributed by: PRT

Cassette: released on PRT in Nov'86 by PRT Records. Distributed by: PRT

Compact disc: released on PRT in Nov'86 by PRT Records. Distributed by: PRT

LOVE SONGS.
Tracks: / Stranger on the shore / Eros Tu(Touch The Wind).
Compact disc: released on Bridge in Feb'86. Distributed by: CD Centre Distribution, Pinnacle, Target

Album: released on Charly in Nov'86 by Charly Records. Distributed by: Charly, Cadillac

Cassette: released on Charly in Nov'86 by Charly Records. Distributed by: Charly, Cadil-

Compact disc: released on PRT in Nov'85 by PRT Records. Distributed by: PRT

LOVE SONGS.
Tracks: / Strangers on the shore / We've only just begun / Morning has broken / Ramblin' Rose / My way.
Album: released on Bridge in Jun'87. Distributed by: CD Centre Distribution, Pinnacle, Target

MADE IN HUNGARY.
Cassette: released on PRT in May'80 by PRT Records. Distributed by: PRT

MAGIC CLARINET OF ACKER BILK.
Compact disc: released on K-Tel in Nov'86 by K-Tel Records. Distributed by: Record Merchandisers Distribution, Taylors, Terry Blood Distribution, Wynd-Up Distribution, Relay Distribution, Pickwick Distribution, Solomon & Peres Distribution, Polygram

MAMA TOLD ME SO (Bilk, Acker & His Paramount Jazzband).
Tracks: / Mama told me so / Chips are down, The / Gee baby ain't I good to you / Time's a wastin' / Bloodshot eyes / Um / Liza / Someday you'll be sorry / Gospel truth, The.
Album: released on Flashback in Nov'85 by Flashback Records/PRT Records. Distributed by: Mainline, PRT

Cassette: released on Flashback in Nov'85 by Flashback Records/PRT Records. Distributed by: Mainline, PRT

Cassette: released on Flashback in Nov'85 by Flashback Records/PRT Records. Distributed by: Mainline, PRT

MOMENT I'M WITH YOU, THE.
Tracks: / Norwegian wood / Colours of my life, The / Bilitis / Little green apples / How does it feel / Imagine / Chi mai / Spanish harlem / First of spring, The / Moment I'm with you, The / Chariots of fire / Pechel canon / Missing you ain't easy / Love letters / For the good times / Soap.
Cassette: released on PRT in Oct'81 by PRT Records. Distributed by: PRT

Cassette: released on PRT in Oct'81 by PRT Records. Distributed by: PRT

MY WAY.
Tracks: / Let it be me / First time ever I saw your face / Rose, The / My Way / Hey Jude / Never my Love / Ramblin'Rose / We've only just begun / Morning has broken / Can't stop loving you,I / Stranger On The Shore / (Eres Tu) Touch The Wind / Let It Be Me / First Time Ever I Saw Your Face / Rose (The) / My Way / Hey Jude / Never My Love / Ramblin Rose / We've Only Just Begun / Morning Has Broken / I Can't Stop Loving You.
Album: released on Topline in Jan'87 by Charly Records. Distributed by: Charly Distribution

Cassette: released on Topline in Jan'87 by Charly Records. Distributed by: Charly Distribution

NATURE BOY.
Compact disc: released on PRT in Oct'85 by PRT Records. Distributed by: PRT

ONE FOR ME, THE.
Cassette: released on PRT in Jul'86 by PRT Records. Distributed by: PRT

RELAXIN.
Tracks: / Verde / One more time / Minuetto / Stay / Cavatina / I'm happy when I'm dancing with you / Volveras / On Sunday / Theme from the Incredible Hulk / Piccolina / Back to you / Summer never came / Aranjuez mon amour / Best out of me, The.
Cassette: released on Picadilly in Feb'81

Album: released on Picadilly in Feb'81

SMILE SAM SMILE.
Tracks: / Smile sam smile / Smile sam smile (Instrumental).
Single (7"): released on PRT in Jun'86 by PRT Records. Distributed by: PRT

SOME OF MY FAVOURITE THINGS.
Tracks: / Stranger on the shore / What are you doing the rest of your life / Folks who live on the hill,The / Makin' Whoppee / Misty / Close to you / Raindrops keep faling on my head / This guys in love with you / Sugar / What a wonderful world / Hundred years from today, A / Going home / Stranger on the shore / What are you doing the rest of your life / Folks who live on the hill, The / Makin' whoopee / Misty / Close to you / Summer knows, The.
Album: released on PRT in '73 by PRT Records. Distributed by: PRT

Cassette: released on PRT in '73 by PRT Records. Distributed by: PRT

SOME OF MY FAVOURITE THINGS.
Compact disc: by PRT Records. Distributed by: PRT

SPOTLIGHT ON ACKER BILK VOL.2.
Album: released on PRT (Spotlight) in Oct'82 by PRT Records. Distributed by: PRT

Cassette: released on PRT (Spotlight) in Oct'82 by PRT Records. Distributed by: PRT

SPOTLIGHT ON ACKER BILK.
Tracks: / Verde / Universe / Incontro / Volveras / Canio's tune / Theme from Swan Lake / Stranger on the shore / Bridge over troubled water / Fool on the hill / Close to you (They long to be) / Clair / Way we were, The / Aria Sailing / Amazing grace / We're all alone / Fire and rain / Aranjuez mon amour (based on the 'Concerto de Aranjuez) / Cavatina / Where do I begin (Love story) / Miss you nights / Don't cry for me Argentina / Song I wrote to you, The / I don't want to talk about it.
Double Album: released on PRT in '80 by PRT Records. Distributed by: PRT

Cassette: released on PRT in '80 by PRT Records. Distributed by: PRT

STRANGER ON THE SHORE (Bilk, Acker with Leon Young String Chorale).
Tracks: / Stranger on the shore / It had to be you / Petite fleur / Ain't misbehavin' / Greensleeves / Only you / Sentimental journey / I'm in the mood for love / La mer / Moon river / Shenandoah / I left my heart in San Francisco.

STRANGER ON THE SHORE.
Tracks: / When I need you / Amazing grace / Down in nempnett thrumbwell / If / Together we are beautiful / Stranger on the shore / Fool on the hill / Up in the world / First of spring / Norwegian wood / You are the sunshine of my life / On Sunday.
Album: released on PRT Flashback in Jul'86

Cassette: released on PRT Flashback in Jul'86

Cassette: released on Polydor in Nov'80 by Polydor Records. Distributed by: Polygram, Polydor

Single (7"): released on Old Gold in Jul'82 by Old Gold Records. Distributed by: Lightning, Jazz Music, Spartan, Counterpoint

Album: released on Polydor in Nov'80 by Polydor Records. Distributed by: Polygram, Polydor

UNISSUED ACKER.
Tracks: / Dauphine street blues / Corrine corrina / Gloryland / Trouble in mind / Travelling blues / Salutation march / Monday date / King Joe / Lou - easy - an - I - a / Darkness on the delta / Careless love / Deep bayou blues.
Album: released on Harlequin in Mar'85 by Harlequin Records. Distributed by: Swift, Jazz Music, Wellard, Chris, IRS, Taylor, H.R.

VERY BEST OF ACKER BILK.
Album: released on Pickwick in May'85 by Pickwick Records. Distributed by: Pickwick Distribution, Prism Leisure Distribution, Lugtons

Cassette: released on Pickwick in May'85 by Pickwick Records. Distributed by: Pickwick Distribution, Prism Leisure Distribution, Lugtons

WERELDSUCCESSEN.
Tracks: / Stranger on the shore / Petite fluer / Summer set / White cliffs of Dover.
Double Album: released on Philips (Germany) in Jul'82

Cassette: released on Philips (Germany) in Jul'82

Bilko
CRAIG AND BENTLEY.
Single (7"): released on Bilko in Apr'83 by Red Admiral Records. Distributed by: Pinnacle

Bill & Benns
WAKE UP AND DRESS FUNNY.
Notes: No catalogue numbers.Bill Zorn an American from Arizona and Jon Benns,a home grown Englishman,have only been together little more than a year,yet their act runs smoothly at a brisk pace.Both have been in the business all their lives. They have known eachother a long time and written for thei own entertainment as well as for other groups including The Flying Pickets.When Jon became bored and Bill was at a loose end they decided to work up an act together and I predict weshall be hearing alot more from these two talented boys. Availible from:Sunrise Music,2 Oakbank,19 Hayes Road,Cheltenham,Glos.

Billberg, Rolf
RARE DANISH RECORDINGS.
Album: released on Storyville in Jul'82 by Storyville Records. Distributed by: Jazz Music Distribution, Swift Distribution, Chris Wellard Distribution, Counterpoint Distribution

Bill Evans - A Tribute
BILL EVANS - A TRIBUTE (Various Artists).
Album: released on Palo Alto (USA) in Jan'84 by Palo Alto Records. Distributed by: Conifer

Billie
NOBODY'S BUSINESS.
Tracks: / Nobody's Business (Instrumental-Club Mix) / Nobody's Business.
Single (7"): released on Club in Oct'86 by Phonogram Records. Distributed by: Polygram

Single (12"): released on Club in Oct'86 by Phonogram Records. Distributed by: Polygram

Billington, Mike
BALLAD OF THE BLACK COUNTRY.
Album: released on Broadside in Jun'81 by Broadside Records. Distributed by: Celtic Distributions, H.R. Taylor, Jazz Music, Projection,

Cassette: released on Broadside in Jun'81 by Broadside Records. Distributed by: Celtic Distributions, H.R. Taylor, Jazz Music, Projection,

Bill Stickers Banned
CHRISTMAS WRAPPING.
Single (7"): released on Wombat in Dec'83 by Wombat Records. Distributed by: Stage One

Bill The Galactic Hero
BILL THE GALACTIC HERO various artists (Various Artists).
Album: released on BBC in Oct'84 by BBC Records & Tapes. Distributed by: EMI, PRT,

Cassette: released on BBC in Oct'84 by BBC Records & Tapes. Distributed by: EMI, PRT,

Billy And Blaze
BILLY AND BLAZE Anderson, C.W. (Cassidy, David).
Cassette: released on Caedmon(USA) in Sep'84 by Caedmon (USA) Records. Distributed by: Gower, Taylors, Discovery

Billy Boyo
BUSHMASTER CONNECTION (Billy Boyo & Little John).

Billy Pilgrim
THEY ARE COMING TO GET US.
Single (7"): released on Zone To Zone in Oct'83 by Zone To Zone Records. Distributed by: Pinnacle

Binary
MEANING, THE.
Single (7"): released on Cocteau in Feb'85 by Cocteau Records. Distributed by: Pinnacle, IDS

Single (12"): released on Cocteau in Feb'85 by Cocteau Records. Distributed by: Pinnacle, IDS

Bingert, Hector
JARDINS.
Album: released on Sonet in Jun'87 by Sonet Records. Distributed by: PRT

Bingo Brothers
RUSSIANS ARE COMING (THE).
Tracks: / Russians are coming(The) / Asleep at the wheel.
Single (7"):

Bingy Bunny
HUSH (Bingy Bunny & Morwells).
Single (7"): released on Carib Jems in Jun'82 by Carib Jems. Distributed by: Spartan, Jetstar

LONELY WIDOW (Bingy Bunny & Morwells).
Single (12"): released on Number 1 in Jun'82

ME AND JANE.
Single (12"): released on Cha-Cha in Jan'82 by Cha Cha. Distributed by: Jetstar

STREET LOVER.
Single (12"): released on Cha-Cha in Mar'82 by Cha Cha. Distributed by: Jetstar

TRAIN TO ZION (Bingy Bunny & Lee Van Cleef).
Single (12"): released on Top Ranking in Jul'82

Binky Boy
EVERYBODY.
Single (7"): released on Proto in May'83 by Proto Records. Distributed by: WEA

Single (12"): released on Proto in May'83 by Proto Records. Distributed by: WEA

Bino
DREAM for my sake.
Single (7"): released on Upper Class in Feb'81 by Chinless Productions. Distributed by: Spartan, Music Galore

Biocar
HERO.
Single (7"): released on No Bad in Aug'80 by No Bad Records. Distributed by: Pinnacle, Wynd-Up Distribution (Scotland)

Biograph girl
BIOGRAPH GIRL Original soundtrack.
Album: released on That's Entertainment in Apr'83 by That's Entertainment Records. Distributed by: Pinnacle, PRT

Biondi, Dick
CRUISIN' 1960 WKBW Buffalo.
Cassette: released on Increase(USA) in Jun'87 by Quicksilver Records (USA)

Bioscope Memories
BIOSCOPE MEMORIES.
Album: released on Saydisc in Jul'81 by Saydisc Records. Distributed by: Essex, Harmonia Mundi, Roots, H.R. Taylor, Jazz Music, Swift, Projection,

Biota
RACKABONES.
Notes: Double Album,includes set of prints.
Album: released on Recommended in Mar'86 by Recommended Records. Distributed by: Recommended, Impetus, Rough Trade

Birdhouse
BURNIN'UP.
Notes: Mini LP.
Album: released on Vinyl Solution in Jun'87. Distributed by: Pinnacle

MY BIRDMAN.
Tracks: / My Birdman.
Single (7"): released on Power House in Jul'86 by Power House Records. Distributed by: Jetstar

Bird, John
COLLECTED BROADCASTS OF IDI AMIN.
Album: released on Transatlantic in Jul'81 by Logo Records. Distributed by: Roots Distribution. RCA Distribution

COLLECTED BROADCASTS OF IDI AMIN, THE.
Cassette: released on Transatlantic in Jul'81 by Logo Records. Distributed by: Roots Distribution, RCA Distribution

Birdland All Stars...
BIRDLAND ALL STARS AT THE CARNEGIE HALL Various artists (Various Artists).
Compact disc: released on Vogue in Dec'86. Distributed by: Discovery, Jazz Music, PRT, Swift

Birdmen Of Alcatraz
GLIDING OFF.
Album: released on Electric Eye in Mar'87 by Electric Eye Records. Distributed by: Red Rhino, Cartel

Birds
THESE BIRDS ARE DANGEROUS.
Album: released on Demon in Mar'85 by Demon Records. Distributed by: Pinnacle

Birds & Ballads
BIRDS & BALLADS Various artists (Various Artists).
Notes: Art Pepper, Johnny Griffin,Joe Farrell,Joe Henderson,Harold Land etc.
Compact disc: released on JVC Fantasy (Japan) in May'87

Birds, beasts & flowers
BIRDS, BEASTS & FLOWERS (Princess Grace of Monaco & Pasco, Richard).
Album: released on Nimbus (USA) in Oct'82. Distributed by: Cadillac

BIRDS, BEASTS & FLOWERS (see Princess Grace of Monaco) (Pasco, Richard & Princess Grace of Monaco).

Bird's Night
BIRD'S NIGHT: A CELEBRATION OF THE MUSIC OF CHARLIE PARKER Various artists (Various Artists).
Album:

Bird Songs
BIRD SONGS (CASSETTE BOX 1) BBC/Swedish Radio Production (Various birds).
Boxed set: released on BBC/SRP in Jul'82

BIRD SONGS (CASSETTE BOX 2) BBC/Swedish Radio Production (Various birds).
Boxed set: released on BBC/SRP in Jul'82

BIRD SONGS (CASSETTE BOX 3) BBC/Swedish Radio Production (Various birds).
Boxed set: released on BBC/SRP in Jul'82

BIRD SONGS (CASSETTE BOX 4)
BBC/Swedish Radio Production (Various birds).
Boxed set: released on BBC/SRP in Jul'82

BIRD SONGS (VOL.1) BBC/Swedish Radio Production (Various birds).
Album: released on BBC-Swedish Radio in Jul'82

BIRD SONGS (VOL.10) BBC/Swedish Radio Production (Various birds).
Album: released on BBC-Swedish Radio in Jul'82

BIRD SONGS (VOL.11) BBC/Swedish Radio Production (Various birds).
Album: released on BBC-Swedish Radio in Jul'82

BIRD SONGS (VOL.12) BBC/Swedish Radio Production (Various birds).
Album: released on BBC-Swedish Radio in Jul'82

BIRD SONGS (VOL.13) BBC/Swedish Radio Production (Various birds).
Album: released on BBC-Swedish Radio in Jul'82

BIRD SONGS (VOL.14) BBC/Swedish Radio Production (Various birds).
Album: released on BBC-Swedish Radio in Jul'82

BIRD SONGS (VOL.15) BBC/Swedish Radio Production (Various birds).
Album: released on BBC-Swedish Radio in Jul'82

BIRD SONGS (VOL.2) BBC/Swedish Radio Production (Various birds).
Album: released on BBC-Swedish Radio in Jul'82

BIRD SONGS (VOL.3) BBC/Swedish Radio Production (Various birds).
Album: released on BBC-Swedish Radio in Jul'82

BIRD SONGS (VOL.4) BBC/Swedish Radio Production (Various birds).
Album: released on BBC-Swedish Radio in Jul'82

BIRD SONGS (VOL.5) BBC/Swedish Radio Production (Various birds).
Album: released on BBC-Swedish Radio in Jul'82

BIRD SONGS (VOL.6) BBC/Swedish Radio Production (Various birds).
Album: released on BBC-Swedish Radio in Jul'82

BIRD SONGS (VOL.7) BBC/Swedish Radio Production (Various birds).
Album: released on BBC-Swedish Radio in Jul'82

BIRD SONGS (VOL.8) BBC/Swedish Radio Production (Various birds).
Album: released on BBC-Swedish Radio in Jul'82

BIRD SONGS (VOL.9) BBC/Swedish Radio Production (Various birds).
Album: released on BBC-Swedish Radio in Jul'82

Bird Spot
BIRD SPOT More British wild birds in stereo (Various birds).
Album: released on BBC in Apr'82 by BBC Records & Tapes. Distributed by: EMI, PRT, Pye

Cassette: released on BBC in Apr'82 by BBC Records & Tapes. Distributed by: EMI, PRT, Pye

Birds With Ears
MR SNEED.
Single (7"): released on Laughing Man in Aug'83. Distributed by: Backs, Cartel

Birgitta
WHAT A DIFFERENCE.
Tracks: / We owe it all to you / What a difference you've made / Take my life / It wouldn't be joy / Mother prays. A / How many more / Jesus is here in my heart / Highest praise. The / My love song / Be exalted / Majesty / We owe it all to you / What a difference you've made / Take my life / It wouldn't be joy / Mother prays / How many more / Jesus is here in my heart / Highest praise. The / My love song / Be exalted / Majesty.
Album: released on Word in May'82 by Word Records. Distributed by: Word Distribution, CBS

Birgitta and Swante
UP WHERE WE BELONG.

Page 112

Album: released on Word in May'85 by Word Records. Distributed by: Word Distribution, CBS

Cassette: released on Word in May'85 by Word Records. Distributed by: Word Distribution, CBS

Birkin, Jane
JE T'AIME MOI NON PLUS (Birkin, Jane/ Serge Gainsbourgh).
Single (7"): released on Antic in Jul'81 by WEA. Distributed by: WEA

Birthday Party
BAD SEED.
Single (12"): released on 4AD in Feb'83 by 4AD Records. Distributed by: Rough Trade

BIRTHDAY PARTY (EP).
Single (12"): released on 4AD in Jun'83 by 4AD Records. Distributed by: Rough Trade

FRIEND CATCHER.
Single (7"): released on 4AD in Oct'80 by 4AD Records. Distributed by: Rough Trade

JUNKYARD.
Album: released on 4AD in May'82 by 4AD Records. Distributed by: Rough Trade

Cassette: released on 4AD in Sep'82 by 4AD Records. Distributed by: Rough Trade

MR CLARINET.
Single (7"): released on 4AD in Oct'81 by 4AD Records. Distributed by: Rough Trade

MUTINY.
Album: released on Mute in Nov'83. Distributed by: Spartan Distribution, Rough Trade Distribution, Cartel Distribution

MUTINY 1983.
Single (12"): released on Mute in Dec'83. Distributed by: Spartan Distribution, Rough Trade Distribution, Cartel Distribution

PEEL SESSION 28.4.81.
Single (12"): released on Strange Fruit in Jan'87 by Clive Selwood. Distributed by: Pinnacle

RELEASE THE BATS.
Single (7"): released on 4AD in Aug'81 by 4AD Records. Distributed by: Rough Trade

Birth of the Y
BIRTH OF THE Y Various artists (Various Artists).
Album: released on Y/Y in Nov'82

Biscuit, Karl
REGRET ETERNELS.
Album: released on Crammed Discs in Oct'84. Distributed by: Rough Trade, Nine Mile, Cartel

SECRET LOVE.
Single (12"): released on Crammed Discs in Feb'87. Distributed by: Rough Trade, Nine Mile, Cartel

Bishop, Eddie
CALL ME.
Tracks: / Darkest days.
Single (7"): released on Kent in Apr'85 by Ace Records. Distributed by: Pinnacle

Bishop, Randy
TWO HEARTS ON THE LOOSE.
Tracks: / If I was a fool.
Single (7"): released on Aura in Oct'85 by Hollywood Nites Distribution. Distributed by: Pinnacle

UNDERDOG.
Single (7"): released on Aura in Aug'85 by Hollywood Nites Distribution. Distributed by: Pinnacle

Bishop, Stephen
BISH.
Album: released on MCA in Mar'87 by MCA Records. Distributed by: Polygram, MCA

Cassette: released on MCA in Mar'87 by MCA Records. Distributed by: Polygram, MCA

Cassette: released on ABC in Aug'78. Distributed by: CBS, Pinnacle

CARELESS.
Tracks: / Never letting go / Careless / Sinking in an ocean of tears / Madge / Every minute / Little Italy / One more night / Guitar interlude / Save it for a rainy day / Rock and roll slave / Same old tears on a new backround / On and on.
Album: released on Fame (MCA) in '82 by Music For Pleasure Records. Distributed by: EMI

Cassette: released on Fame (MCA) in '82 by Music For Pleasure Records. Distributed by: EMI

RED CAB TO MANHATTAN.
Tracks: / Big house / Don't you worry / Thief in the night / Send a little love my way (like always) / Let her go / Little moon / Story of a boy in love. The / Living in the land of Abe Lincoln / Red cab to Manhattan / Sex kittens go to college / City girl / My clarinet.
Album: released on WEA in Oct'80 by WEA Records. Distributed by: WEA

Bishop, Walter Jnr.
CUBICLE.
Tracks: / My little suede shoes / Valley land / Those who chant / Summertime / Now, now that you've left me / Cubicle.
Album: released on Muse in Apr'81 by Peerless Records.

HOT HOUSE.
Tracks: / Sophisticated lady / Dahoud / Time for love. A / Hot house / Move / My little suede shoes / Wave / All god's children.
Album: released on Muse in Apr'81 by Peerless Records.

SOUL VILLAGE.
Tracks: / Soul turnaround / Valerie / Sweet Rosa Rosa / Philadelphia bright / Coral keys / Soul village.
Album: released on Muse in Apr'81 by Peerless Records.

SPEAK LOW.
Tracks: / Blues in the closet / Green Dolphin street / Alone together / Milestones / Speak low / Sometimes I'm happy / Sometimes I'm happy / Blues in the closet / Green Dolphin Street / Alone together / Milestones / Speak low.
Album: released on Muse (Import) in Apr'81

VALLEY LAND.
Tracks: / Sam's blues / You stepped out of a dream / Invitation / Lush life / Valley land / Killer Joe / Make someone happy.
Album: released on Muse (Import) in Apr'81

Bison Bop
BISON BOP Various artists (Various Artists).
Album: released on Bison Bop in Jul'79. Distributed by: Swift

BISON BOP STRICTLY INSTRUMENTAL Various artists (Various Artists).
Album: released on Bear Family in Oct'81 by Bear Family Records. Distributed by: Rollercoaster Records

BISON BOP VOL.2 Various artists (Various Artists).
Album: released on Bison Bop in Jul'79. Distributed by: Swift

BISON BOP VOL.33 Various artists (Various Artists).
Album: released on Bison Bop(West Germany) in Jan'85

BISON BOP VOL.34 Various artists (Various Artists).
Album: released on Bison Bop(West Germany) in Jan'85

B.I.T.B
NOCTURNAL.
Single (7"): released on Blue Rhythm in Aug'82. Distributed by: Swift

Bitch
BITCH IS BACK.
Album: released on Metal Blade in Jun'87. Distributed by: Enigma Distribution

Bitches Sin
ALWAYS READY(FOR LOVE).
Single (7"): released on Neat in Apr'81 by Neat Records. Distributed by: Pinnacle, Neat

NO MORE CHANCES.
Album: released on QT in Dec'83. Distributed by: Pinnacle

Single (7"): released on QT in Nov'83. Distributed by: Pinnacle

OUT OF MY MIND.
Single (7"): released on Terminal in Aug'83 by Terminal. Distributed by: Jetstar Distribution

PREDATOR.
Album: released on Heavy Metal in Jun'82 by FM-Revolver Records. Distributed by: EMI

Bitelli, Dave
FOOT IN THE DOOR.
Single (12"): released on Palladin in Oct'83 by Palladin Records. Distributed by: Cartel

---

Bite, Pete
ONE MORE BITE OF MY HEART.
Single (7"): released on Loose in Sep'85 by Loose Records. Distributed by: Nine Mile, Cartel

Single (12"): released on Loose in Apr'84 by Loose Records. Distributed by: Nine Mile, Cartel

Bites and Stabs
Northern Bands
BITES AND STABS (NORTHERN BANDS) Various artists (Various Artists).
Album: released on Torpedo in Aug'85 by President Records

Biting Tongues
COMPRESSOR.
Single (12"): released on Factory in 30 May'87 by Factory Records. Distributed by: Cartel, Pinnacle

FEVERHOUSE.
Album: released on Factory in Apr'85 by Factory Records. Distributed by: Cartel, Pinnacle

LIBREVILLE.
Album: released on Paragon in '84 by Paragon Records. Distributed by: Paragon

TROUBLE HAND.
Single (12"): released on Factory in Nov'85 by Factory Records. Distributed by: Cartel, Pinnacle

Bitter withy sampler
BITTER WITHY SAMPLER Various artists (Various Artists).
Album: released on Nevis in May'77. Distributed by: H.R. Taylor

BIZ
FALLING.
Single (7"): released on Midas in Feb'83 by Magnet Records. Distributed by: PRT Distribution

Single (12"): released on Midas in Feb'83 by Magnet Records. Distributed by: PRT Distribution

WE'RE GONNA GROOVE TONIGHT.
Single (7"): released on Midas in Jul'83 by Magnet Records. Distributed by: PRT Distribution

Bizarre Boy's
HOP OFF YOU FROGS.
Tracks: / Hop off you frogs / Electro frog.
Single (12"): released on Creole in Feb'86 by Creole Records. Distributed by: Rhino, PRT

Bjoerling & Merrill
PEARL FISHERS ACT 1 PART.
Single (7"): released on Red Seal in Jun'78 by RCA Records. Distributed by: RCA

Bjornstad, Ketil
PRELUDE.
Album: released on Uniton Records in Nov'84. Distributed by: Cartel

Black
EVERYTHING'S COMING UP ROSES.
Tracks: / Everything's coming up roses / Ravel in the rain / It's not you Lady Jane.
Notes: Limited edition White Vinyl in gatefold sleeve with booklet.
Single (7"): released on A&M in Mar'87 by A&M Records. Distributed by: Polygram

Single (12"): released on A&M in Mar'87 by A&M Records. Distributed by: Polygram

MORE THAN THE SUN.
Single (7"): released on Wonderful in Oct'82. Distributed by: Spartan

SWEETEST SMILE.
Tracks: / Sweetest smile / Sixteens / Leave yourself alone / Hardly star crossed lovers'.
Single (7"): released on A&M in Jun'97 by A&M Records. Distributed by: Polygram

Single (12"): released on A&M in Jun'87 by A&M Records. Distributed by: Polygram

WONDERFUL LIFE.
Tracks: / Wonderful life.
Single (12"): released on Ugly Man in Aug'86. Distributed by: Cartel

Single (7"): released on A&M in Aug'87 by A&M Records. Distributed by: Polygram

Single (12"): released on A&M in Aug'87 by A&M Records. Distributed by: Polygram

Cassette single: released on A&M in Aug'87 by A&M Records. Distributed by: Polygram

Compact disc single: released on A&M in Aug'87 by A&M Records. Distributed by: Polygram

Black Ace

BLACK ACE & HIS STEEL GUITAR.
Album: released on Arhoolie in May'81 by Arhoolie Records. Distributed by: Projection, Topic, Jazz Music, Swift, Roots

Black Alice

ENDANGERED SPECIES.
Album: released on Street Tunes in Sep'83 by Street Tunes Records. Distributed by: Pinnacle

NO WARNING.
Single (12"): released on Street Tunes in Apr'84 by Street Tunes Records. Distributed by: Pinnacle

Black Angels

KICK DOWN.
Album: released on Gull in Apr'84 by Gull Records. Distributed by: Pinnacle

Black Bands

ON FILM 1928-1935.
Album: released on Harlequin in May'86 by Harlequin Records. Distributed by: Swift, Jazz Music, Wellard, Chris, IRS, Taylor

Blackbeard

STRICTLY DUBWISE.
Album: released on Liberty in Jan'80 by Liberty-United. Distributed by: EMI

Black Beauty

BLACK BEAUTY Sewell, Anna (Rippon, Angela).
Double cassette: released on Argo in Jul'82 by Decca Records. Distributed by: Polygram

BLACK BEAUTY Sewell, Anna (Davis, David).
Cassette: released on Pinnacle in '79 by Pinnacle Records. Distributed by: Pinnacle

BLACK BEAUTY Sewell, Anna (Mills, Hayley).
Double cassette: released on Listen For Pleasure in Apr'78 by MFP Records. Distributed by: EMI

Cassette: released on Listen For Pleasure in Sep'84 by MFP Records. Distributed by: EMI

BLACK BEAUTY & OTHER FAVOURITE STORIES For children aged 3-7 (Various Artists).
Cassette: released on VFM in Jul'85 by VFM Records. Distributed by: Taylors, Wynd-Up Distribution

Black, Bill

Biographical Details: Born in Memphis, Tennessee in 1926, Bill Black joined Memphis' Sun label in the fifties as a session bass guitar player. It was with Sun Records that the young **Elvis Presley** cut his first series of singles in 1954, before being signed by RCA in '56 and turned into a massive star. Black played with Presley in both Sun and RCA days, backing him on the vast majority of his discs between 1955 & 1958. His driving, pulsating bass was perfectly suited to Elvis' powerful singing.

FIRST YEAR, THE (Black, Bill/Elvis Presley/Scotty Moore).
Album: released on Charly in '83 by Charly Records. Distributed by: Charly, Cadillac

SHEPHERD'S CHOICE, THE (Black, Bill & His Scottish Dance Band).
Album: released on Springthyme in '83 by Springthyme Records. Distributed by: Jazz Music Distribution, Projection Distribution, Roots Distribution

Cassette: released on Springthyme in '83 by Springthyme Records. Distributed by: Jazz Music Distribution, Projection Distribution, Roots Distribution

UNTOUCHABLE (THE) (Black, Bill Combo).
Cassette: released on Hi in Jul'86 by Demon Records. Distributed by: Pinnacle

Black Bottom Stompers

BLACK BOTTOM STOMPERS.
Tracks: / Weatherbird rag / Shout 'em,Aunt Tillie / Wild man blues / Cornet chop suet / Sidewalk blues / Garittin' with some barbeque / Hiawatha rag / Blue blood blues / Mahogany hall stomp / Where did you stay last night / Potato head blues / Alligator hop.
Album: released on Stomp Off in Jun'86 by Stomp Off Records. Distributed by: Jazz Music Distribution

Cassette: released on VJM in Apr'86 by Wellard, Chris Distribution. Distributed by: Wellard, Chris Distribution

Black Britain

AIN'T NO ROCKIN'IN A POLICE STATE.
Tracks: / Ain't no rockin'in police state / Cold on the streets.
Single (7"): released on 10 in Mar'86 by 10 Records. Distributed by: Virgin, EMI

Single (12"): released on 10 in Mar'86 by 10 Records. Distributed by: Virgin, EMI

FUNKY NASSAU.
Tracks: / Funky Nassau / Runaway.
Single (7"): released on 10 in May'86 by 10 Records. Distributed by: Virgin, EMI

Single (12"): released on 10 in May'86 by 10 Records. Distributed by: Virgin, EMI

NIGHT PEOPLE.
Tracks: / Night people (remix) / Night people.
Single (7"): released on 10 in Mar'87 by 10 Records. Distributed by: Virgin, EMI

Single (12"): released on 10 in Mar'87 by 10 Records. Distributed by: Virgin, EMI

OBVIOUS.
Album: released on 10 in Jul'87 by 10 Records. Distributed by: Virgin, EMI

Cassette: released on 10 in Jul'87 by 10 Records. Distributed by: Virgin, EMI

Blackbyrds

WALKING IN RHYTHM.
Single (7"): released on Streetwave in Sep'85 by Streetwave Records. Distributed by: PRT Distribution

Black California

BLACK CALIFORNIA various artists (Various Artists).
Album:

Black Cat

DANCE WITH THE DOLLY.
Single (7"): released on Peach River in Oct'83 by Peach River Records. Distributed by: PRT

Black Cauldron

BLACK CAULDRON,(THE) Original Soundtrack.
Notes: Elmer Bernstein-Composer.
Album: released on Colosseum (West Germany) in Jan'86. Distributed by: Silva Screen

Album: released on BBC in Oct'85 by BBC Records & Tapes. Distributed by: EMI, PRT, Pye

Cassette: released on BBC in Oct'85 by BBC Records & Tapes. Distributed by: EMI, PRT, Pye

Black, Cilla

LOVE SONGS.
Tracks: / Baby don't change your mind / Sometimes when we touch / Just the way you are / Talking in your sleep / You don't bring me flowers / How deep is your love / Bright eyes / Don't cry for me Argentina / When will I see you again / You needed me / If you leave me now / When I need you / Knowing me knowing you / Still / When a child is born / Do that to me one more time.
Notes: (P) & (C) 1987 K-Tel International (UK) Ltd.
Compact disc: released on K-Tel in May'87 by K-Tel Records. Distributed by: Record Merchandisers Distribution, Taylors, Terry Blood Distribution, Wynd-Up Distribution, Relay Distribution, Pickwick Distribution, Solomon & Peres Distribution, Polygram

SURPRISE SURPRISE.
Single (7"): released on Towerbell in Dec'85 by Towerbell Records. Distributed by: EMI

SURPRISINGLY CILLA.
Album: released on Towerbell in Oct'85 by Towerbell Records. Distributed by: EMI

Cassette: released on Towerbell in Oct'85 by Towerbell Records. Distributed by: EMI

THERE'S A NEED IN ME.
Single (7"): released on Towerbell in Sep'85 by Towerbell Records. Distributed by: EMI

VERY BEST OF CILLA BLACK.
Tracks: / Love of the loved / Anyone who had a heart / You're my world / It's for you / You've lost that lovin' feelin' / I've been wrong before / Love's just a broken heart / Alf / Don't answer me / Fool am I, A / What good am I / I only live to love you / Step inside love / Where is tomorrow / Surround yourself with sorrow / Conversations / If I thought you'd ever change your mind / Something tells me (Something's gonna happen tonight) / Baby we can't go wrong / Liverpool lullaby.
Album: released on Music For Pleasure (Holland) in May'84 by EMI Records. Distributed by: EMI

Cassette: released on Music For Pleasure in May'84 by EMI Records. Distributed by: EMI

YOU'RE MY WORLD.
Single (7"): released on EMI in Oct'77 by EMI Records. Distributed by: EMI

Black Cillas

SEBASTIAN.
Single (7"): released on Cillagram in Nov'86. Distributed by: Pinnacle

Blackcountrymen

FIRST TIME OUT.
Tracks: / Cradley Heath song / Slapbum tailor / Arthur McBride / Perry Croft bull bait / John O' Dreams / Cuckoo's nest / Can't find Brummagen / July wakes / Y viva Morris / Gornal nailmakers carol / Spotted cow, The / Punk folkers / I don't belong to Glasgow.
Album: released on Folk Heritage in Jul'82 by Folk Heritage Records. Distributed by: Roots, Wynd-Up Distribution, Jazz Music, Folk Heritage

Black Country Night Out

BLACK COUNTRY NIGHT OUT, VOL.1 various artists (Various Artists).
Album: released on Broadside in Jun'81 by Broadside Records. Distributed by: Celtic Distributions, H.R. Taylor, Jazz Music, Projection,

Cassette: released on Broadside in Jun'81 by Broadside Records. Distributed by: Celtic Distributions, H.R. Taylor, Jazz Music Projection,

BLACK COUNTRY NIGHT OUT, VOL.2 various artists (Various Artists).
Album: released on Broadside in Jun'81 by Broadside Records. Distributed by: Celtic Distributions, H.R. Taylor, Jazz Music, Projection,

Cassette: released on Broadside in Jun'81 by Broadside Records. Distributed by: Celtic Distributions, H.R. Taylor, Jazz Music, Projection,

BLACK COUNTRY NIGHT OUT, VOL.3 various artists (Various Artists).
Album: released on Broadside in Jun'81 by Broadside Records. Distributed by: Celtic Distributions, H.R. Taylor, Jazz Music, Projection,

Cassette: released on Broadside in Jun'81 by Broadside Records. Distributed by: Celtic Distributions, H.R. Taylor, Jazz Music, Projection,

Black Crucial

MR. SUNNY.
Album: released on Jamming in Aug'85

Black Diamond Orchestra

PLAY TED HEATH HITS Big Bands Vol.2.
Cassette: released on Bi Bi(Budget Cassettes) in Jan'83

Black, Dick

KEEP ON DANCING (Black, Dick & His Dance Band).
Cassette: released on Igus in Nov'86 by Klub. Distributed by: PRT, Musac Distribution Ltd (Scotland)

LET'S DANCE (Black, Dick & His Dance Band).
Cassette: released on Igus in Nov'86 by Klub. Distributed by: PRT, Musac Distribution Ltd (Scotland)

MODERN SEQUENCE DANCING (Black, Dick & His Dance Band).
Cassette: released on Igus in Nov'86 by Klub. Distributed by: PRT, Musac Distribution Ltd (Scotland)

SOUND OF THE LOTHIANS (Black, Dick & His Dance Band).
Tracks: / La-va / Tom burns polka / Blue violets / New high level / Scotland well / By yon baonnie border burn / Morman braes / Fitba crazy / North lands, The / Old rustic brig.
Cassette: released on Klub in Nov'85

Black, Donald

DANCING HAZARDS.
Album: released on Lismor in Jun'85 by Lismor Records. Distributed by: Lismor, Roots, Celtic Music

Cassette: released on Lismor in Jun'85 by Lismor Records. Distributed by: Lismor, Roots, Celtic Music

Black Dyke Mills Band

BLACK DYKE IN DIGITAL.
Album: released on Chandos in Oct'81 by Chandos Records. Distributed by: Harmonia Mundi, Taylors

Cassette: released on Chandos in Oct'81 by Chandos Records. Distributed by: Harmonia Mundi, Taylors

BLACK DYKE KINGS OF BRASS.
Tracks: / Hungarian rhapsody no.2 / Carnival of Venice / Scherzo from Borodin's symphony no.2 / Serenade / Millions d'arlequin, Les / Finale from Richard Strauss' horn concerto no.1 / Roi d'ys overture, Le.
Album: released on Chandos in Aug'81 by Chandos Records. Distributed by: Harmonia Mundi, Taylors

Cassette: released on Chandos in Aug'81 by Chandos Records. Distributed by: Harmonia Mundi, Taylors

BLACK DYKE PLAYS ROSSINI.
Album: released on Chandos in Sep'83 by Chandos Records. Distributed by: Harmonia Mundi, Taylors

Cassette: released on Chandos in Sep'83 by Chandos Records. Distributed by: Harmonia Mundi, Taylors

BLACK DYKE PLAYS WINGS.
Album: released on Chandos in Aug'81 by Chandos Records. Distributed by: Harmonia Mundi, Taylors

Cassette: released on Chandos in Aug'81 by Chandos Records. Distributed by: Harmonia Mundi, Taylors

BLITZ.
Tracks: / Blitz / Pageantry / Journey into freedom / Tam O'Shanter's ride.
Compact disc: released on Chandos in Aug'85 by Chandos Records. Distributed by: Harmonia Mundi, Taylors

CHAMPIONS, THE.
Album: by PRT Records. Distributed by: PRT

COMPLETE CHAMPIONS, THE.
Compact disc: released on Chandos in '86 by Chandos Records. Distributed by: Harmonia Mundi, Taylors

GREAT BRITISH TRADITION, THE.
Album: released on Chandos in May'84 by Chandos Records. Distributed by: Harmonia Mundi, Taylors

Cassette: released on Chandos in May'84 by Chandos Records. Distributed by: Harmonia Mundi, Taylors

LIFE DIVINE.
Tracks: / Labour and love / Kenilworth / Life Divine / Three Musketeers,(The).
Notes: Black Dyke Mills Band(John Foster & Son PLC).Conducted by Major Peter Parkes andDerek Broadbent.
Album: released on Chandos in Nov'85 by Chandos Records. Distributed by: Harmonia Mundi, Taylors

Cassette: released on Chandos in Nov'85 by Chandos Records. Distributed by: Harmonia Mundi, Taylors

MORE OF THE WORLD'S MOST BEAUTIFUL MELODIES.
Notes: Philip McCann on cornet.
Compact disc: released on Chandos in '87 by Chandos Records. Distributed by: Harmonia Mundi, Taylors

PLAYS ROSSINI.
Compact disc: released on Chandos in '86 by Chandos Records. Distributed by: Harmonia Mundi, Taylors

RUSSIAN FESTIVAL, A.
Tracks: / Festival overture / Vocalise / Gopak / Scheherazade love theme / Montagues and Capulets from "Romeo and Juliet" / Russian and Ludmilla overture / Nocturne / Khovantschina prelude / Little Russian, The.
Album: released on Chandos in Aug'81 by Chandos Records. Distributed by: Harmonia Mundi, Taylors

Cassette: released on Chandos in Aug'81 by Chandos Records. Distributed by: Harmonia Mundi, Taylors

THEMES FROM FILMS,TV & STAGE.
Album: released on RCA in Jul'79 by RCA Records. Distributed by: RCA, Roots, Swift, Wellard, Chris, I & B, Solomon & Peres Distribution

TRADITIONALLY BRITISH.
Album: released on RCA in '84 by RCA Records. Distributed by: RCA, Roots, Swift, Wellard, Chris, I & B, Solomon & Peres Distribution

Cassette: released on RCA in '84 by RCA Records. Distributed by: RCA, Roots, Swift, Wellard, Chris, I & B, Solomon & Peres Distribution Deleted '85.

TRIUMPHANT BRASS.
Album: by PRT Records. Distributed by: PRT

VOLCANO.
Album: released on Chandos in Aug'81 by Chandos Records. Distributed by: Harmonia Mundi, Taylors

Cassette: released on Chandos in Aug'81 by Chandos Records. Distributed by: Harmonia Mundi, Taylors

WORLD CHAMPION BRASS.
Album: by PRT Records. Distributed by: PRT

WORLD'S MOST BEAUTIFUL MELODIES.
Tracks: / Songs my mother taught me / Ave Maria / Lullaby / Passing by / One fine day / None but the lonely heart / Rusalka's bist die ruh' / Girl with the flaxen hair / O my beloved father / Non so plu / Lost chord.
Compact disc: released on Chandos in May'86 by Chandos Records. Distributed by: Harmonia Mundi, Taylors

Black Dynamites

READY TO ROCK WITH THE BLACK DYNAMITES.
Album: released on Redita (Holland) in Jun'85

Black Eagle Jazz Band

BLACK EAGLE JAZZ BAND 1981 with Rudi Ballieu & Butch Thompson.
Album: released on Stomp Off in Jan'84 by Stomp Off Records. Distributed by: Jazz Music Distribution

B.Thompson and the Black Eagle Jazz Band

TIGHT LIKE THIS.
Album: released on Stomp Off in Jan'84 by Stomp Off Records. Distributed by: Jazz Music Distribution

Black Easter

READY TO ROT (EP).
Single (7"): released on Carnage in Oct'82. Distributed by: Cartel, Pinnacle

Blackett, Anthony

MY LITTLE WOMAN.
Single (12"): released on JR in Oct'82

Black Family

BLACK FAMILY, THE.
Notes: The Black family have been performing traditional folk music together on and offsince 1978 under various formats and personnel changes. Mary Black is the only one who has made a solo career in folk music.
Album: released on Dara in Apr'87 by CML Distributors. Distributed by: MK, Projection

Cassette: released on Dara in Apr'87 by CML Distributors. Distributed by: MK, Projection

BLACK'S FAMILY FAVOURITES.
Album: released on ARC (Accordion Records) in '84. Distributed by: Accordion Record Club

Black Flag

EVERYTHING WENT BLACK.
Compact disc: released on SST in Sep'87 by SST Records. Distributed by: Pinnacle.

FAMILY MAN.
Album: released on SST in Sep'84 by SST Records. Distributed by: Pinnacle

Single (12"): released on SST in Oct'84 by SST Records. Distributed by: Pinnacle

IN MY HEAD.
Album: released on SST in Sep'85 by SST Records. Distributed by: Pinnacle

JEALOUS AGAIN (EP).
Single (12"): released on SST in Mar'83 by SST Records. Distributed by: Pinnacle

LIVE 84.
Cassette: released on SST in Dec'84 by SST Records. Distributed by: Pinnacle

LOOSE NUT.
Album: released on SST in Jun'85 by SST Records. Distributed by: Pinnacle

MY WAR.
Album: released on SST in Mar'84 by SST Records. Distributed by: Pinnacle

PROCESS OF WEEDING OUT.
Single (12"): released on SST in Mar'86 by SST Records. Distributed by: Pinnacle

Single (12"): released on SST in Oct'85 by SST Records. Distributed by: Pinnacle

Compact disc: released on SST in Sep'87 by SST Records. Distributed by: Pinnacle. Estim retail price in Sep'87 was £13.12.

SIX PACK(EP).
Single (7"): released on Alternative Tentacles in Dec'81 by Alternative Tentacles Records. Distributed by: Rough Trade, Pinnacle

SLIP IT IN.
Album: released on SST in Sep'84 by SST Records. Distributed by: Pinnacle

Single (12"): released on SST in Aug'84 by SST Records. Distributed by: Pinnacle

WHO'S GOT THE 10%.
Compact disc: released on SST in Aug'87 by SST Records. Distributed by: Pinnacle

Blackfoot

FOUR FROM BLACKFOOT.
Single (7"): released on Atco in Mar'82 by Atlantic Records. Distributed by: WEA

HIGHWAY SONG.
Single (7"): released on Atco in Aug'82 by Atlantic Records. Distributed by: WEA

MARAUDER.
Tracks: / Good morning / Paying for it / Diary of a working man / Too hard to hand / Fly away / Dry country / Fire of the dragon / Rattlesnake rock 'n' roller / Searchin'.
Album: released on Atco in Jul'81 by Atlantic Records. Distributed by: WEA

Cassette: released on Atco in Jul'81 by Atlantic Records. Distributed by: WEA Deleted '86.

MORNING DEW.
Single (7"): released on Atlantic in Jun'85 by WEA Records. Distributed by: WEA Deleted '86.

Single (12"): released on Atlantic in Jun'85 by WEA Records. Distributed by: WEA Deleted '86.

SEND ME AN ANGEL.
Single (12"): released on Atco in May'83 by Atlantic Records. Distributed by: WEA

Single (12"): released on Atco in May'83 by Atlantic Records. Distributed by: WEA

Picture disc single: released on Atco in May'83 by Atlantic Records. Distributed by: WEA

SIOGO.
Tracks: / Send me an angel / Crossfire / Heart's grown cold / We're goin' down / Teenage idol / Goin' in circles / Run for cover / White man's land / Sailaway / Drivin' fool.
Album: released on Atco in Jun'83 by Atlantic Records. Distributed by: WEA

Cassette: released on Atco in Jun'83 by Atlantic Records. Distributed by: WEA Deleted '85.

STRIKES.
Tracks: / Road fever / I got a line on you / Left turn on a red light / Pay my dues / Baby blue / Wishing well / Run and hide / Train train / Highway song.
Album: released on Atlantic in Aug'79 by WEA Records. Distributed by: WEA

TEENAGE IDOL.
Single (7"): released on Atco in Jul'83 by Atlantic Records. Distributed by: WEA

Single (12"): released on Atco in Jul'83 by Atlantic Records. Distributed by: WEA

TOMCATTIN'.
Tracks: / Warped / On the run / Dream on / Street fighter / Gimme gimme gimme / Every man should know / In the night / Reckless daughter / Spendin' cabbage / Fox chase.
Album: released on Atlantic in Jul'80 by WEA Records. Distributed by: WEA

VERTICAL SMILES.
Tracks: / Morning dew / Living in the limelight / Ride with you / Get it on / Young girl summer days / Legend never dies, A / Heartbeat and heels / In for the kill.
Album: released on Atco in Oct'84 by Atlantic Records. Distributed by: WEA

Cassette: released on Atco in Oct'84 by Atlantic Records. Distributed by: WEA Deleted '86

Blackfoot, J.

CITY SLICKER.
Tracks: / Way of the city, The / Taxi / Street girl / One of those parties / Where is love? / I stood on the sidewalk / City slicker / All because of what you did to me / Can you hang?.
Album: released on Allegiance in Mar'84 by PRT Records. Distributed by: PRT

Cassette: released on Allegiance in Mar'84 by PRT Records. Distributed by: PRT

TAXI.
Single (7"): released on Allegiance in Feb'84 by PRT Records. Distributed by: PRT

WHAT YOU DID TO ME LAST NIGHT.
Single (7"): released on Allegiance in Aug'84 by PRT Records. Distributed by: PRT

Single (12"): released on Allegiance in Aug'84 by PRT Records. Distributed by: PRT

Blackfoot Sue

STANDING IN THE ROAD.
Single (7"): released on Old Gold in Jul'82 by Old Gold Records. Distributed by: Lightning, Jazz Music, Spartan, Counterpoint

Black Gospel

BLACK GOSPEL.
Album: released on MCA in May'85 by MCA Records. Distributed by: Polygram, MCA

Cassette: released on MCA in May'85 by MCA Records. Distributed by: Polygram MCA

Black Harmony

EVERYTHING TO ME (Black Harmony & Unity Rockers).
Single (12"): released on Blue Inc in May'82

LET'S BE LOVERS.
Single (12"): released on Cyprian in Dec'83 by Cyprian Records. Distributed by: Jetstar

YOU SHOULD NEVER RUN AWAY FROM LOVE.
Single (12"): released on Regal in Apr'82

Black Hole

BLACK HOLE various artists (Various Artists).
Album: released on Disneyland in Dec'82 by Disneyland-Vista Records (USA). Distributed by: BBC Records & Tapes, Rainbow Communications Ltd(Distribution)

Cassette: released on Disneyland in Dec'82 by Disneyland-Vista Records (USA). Distributed by: BBC Records & Tapes, Rainbow Communications Ltd(Distribution)

Black, Ika

CRUCIAL WORLD.
Single (7"): released on Keyman in Oct'83 by Keyman Records. Distributed by: Keyman, Revolver

SPECIAL LOVE.
Album: released on Keyman in May'86 by Keyman Records. Distributed by: Keyman, Revolver

Cassette: released on KM in May'86. Distributed by: PRT

Single (12"): released on Keyman in Nov'85 by Keyman Records. Distributed by: Keyman, Revolver

SPECIAL LOVE (SINGLE).
Single (12"): released on Keyman in Sep'86 by Keyman Records. Distributed by: Keyman, Revolver

Black Lace

PARTY CRAZY.
Album: released on Telstar in Nov'86 by Telstar Records. Distributed by: RCA Distribution

Cassette: released on Telstar in Nov'86 by Telstar Records. Distributed by: RCA Distribution

VIVA LA MEXICO.
Tracks: / So now the hurting starts.
Picture disc single: released on Flair in May'86 by Flair Records. Distributed by: Pinnacle

Single (7"): released on Flair in May'86 by Flair Records. Distributed by: Pinnacle

WIG-WAM BAM.
Tracks: / Soaking up the sun / So now the hurting starts / Clap clap sound / We dance we dance.
Single (7"): released on Flair in Aug'86 by Flair Records. Distributed by: Pinnacle

Single (12"): released on Flair in Aug'86 by Flair Records. Distributed by: Pinnacle

Double-pack single: released on Flair in Aug'86 by Flair Records. Distributed by: Pinnacle

Black Lace (UK)

AGADOO.
Single (7"): released on Flair in May'84 by Flair Records. Distributed by: Pinnacle

Single (12"): released on Flair in May'84 by Flair Records. Distributed by: Pinnacle

DO THE CONGA.
Single (7"): released on Flair in Dec'84 by Flair Records. Distributed by: Pinnacle

Single (12"): released on Flair in Dec'84 by Flair Records. Distributed by: Pinnacle

EL VINO COLLAPSO.
Single (7"): released on Flair in May'85 by Flair Records. Distributed by: Pinnacle

Single (12"): released on Flair in May'85 by Flair Records. Distributed by: Pinnacle

HEY YOU.
Single (7"): released on Flair in Dec'83 by Flair Records. Distributed by: Pinnacle

Single (12"): released on Flair in Dec'83 by Flair Records. Distributed by: Pinnacle

HOKEY COKEY.
Single (7"): released on Flair in Nov'85 by Flair Records. Distributed by: Pinnacle

Single (12"): released on Flair in Nov'85 by Flair Records. Distributed by: Pinnacle

Single (12"): released on Flair in Nov'85 by Flair Records. Distributed by: Pinnacle

I SPEAKA DA LINGO.
Single (7"): released on Flair in Aug'85 by Flair Records. Distributed by: Pinnacle

Single (12"): released on Flair in Aug'85 by Flair Records. Distributed by: Pinnacle

PARTY PARTY.
Tracks: / Agadoo / Hands up / Ob-la-di-ob-la-da / Birdie song, The / Locomotion, The / This ole house / Dancing party / Rock around the clock / Wig wham bam / Do the conga / Knock three times / Super man / Hi ho silver lining / Simon says / Bump, The / Fiddling / Let's twist again / Sailing / You'll never walk alone.
Album: released on Telstar in Dec'84 by Telstar Records. Distributed by: RCA Distribution

Cassette: released on Telstar in Dec'84 by Telstar Records. Distributed by: RCA Distribution

PARTY PARTY 2.
Tracks: / Y.M.C.A. - In the navy / Brown girl in the ring / Rivers of Babylon / Hooray hooray it's a holi-holiday / D.i.s.c.o. / Ghostbusters / Come on Eileen / Let's dance / Leap up and down (wave your knickers in the air) / Y viva Espania / Hokey cokey / Atmosphere / Dancing in the street / Doo wah diddy diddy / Hippy hippy shake / Good golly Miss Molly / Twist and shout / Do you love me / Clapping song, The / I speaka da lingo / Can can - Knees up mother brown.
Album: released on Telstar in Dec'85 by Telstar Records. Distributed by: RCA Distribution

Cassette: released on Telstar in Dec'85 by Telstar Records. Distributed by: RCA Distribution

TEARDROPS.
Single (7"): released on Flair in Jul'83 by Flair Records. Distributed by: Pinnacle

Single (12"): released on Flair in Jul'83 by Flair Records. Distributed by: Pinnacle

Black Lace (USA)

GET IT WHILE IT'S HOT.
Notes: American group from the Bronx (New York,USA) comprising: Maryann Scandiffio-vocals/Carl Fragnito-guitar/Anthony Fragnito-Bass/Steve Werner-Drums.
Album: released on Mausoleum in Jul'85 by Mausoleum Records. Distributed by: Pinnacle

UNLACED.

Black Lion All Stars

BLACK LION ALL STARS (Various Artists).
Album: released on Black Lion in Jul'87 by Black Lion Records. Distributed by: Jazz Music, Chris Wellard, Taylor, H.R., Counterpoint, Cadillac

Black Magic

BLACK MAGIC Various artists (Various Artists).
Album: released on Stylus in Sep'86. Distributed by: Pinnacle, Terry Blood Distribution, Stylus Distribution

Cassette: released on Stylus in Sep'86. Distributed by: Pinnacle, Terry Blood Distribution, Stylus Distribution

Blackman, Honor

EVERYTHING I'VE GOT.
Tracks: / Kinky boots / Everything I've got / Darling,je vous aime beaucoup / Men will decieve you / I wish I'd never loved you / Den of iniquity / World without love / Remind me / To keep my love alive / C'est drole / I wouldn't walk across the street / Tomorrow is my turn / I want a fair and square man.
Album: released on Cherry Red in Jul'83 by Cherry Red Records. Distributed by: Pinnacle

KINKY BOOTS (Blackman, Honor & Patrick MacNee).
Single (7"): released on Cherry Red in May'83 by Cherry Red Records. Distributed by: Pinnacle

Single (12"): released on Cherry Red in Jul'83 by Cherry Red Records. Distributed by: Pinnacle

Black, Mary

COLLECTED.
Album: released on Dara in Jun'85 by CML Distributors. Distributed by: MK, Projection

Cassette: released on Dara in Jun'85 by CML Distributors. Distributed by: MK, Projection

MARY BLACK.
Album: released on Dara in Mar'86 by CML Distributors. Distributed by: MK, Projection

WITHOUT THE FANFARE.
Album: released on Dara in Jan'86 by CML Distributors. Distributed by: MK, Projection

Blackmore, George

GOODBYE (Blackmore, George & David Shepherd).

Blackmore, R.H.

LORNA DOONE.
Notes: Read by Peter Gilmore: R.D.Blackmore's romantic story of love, adventure, gallantry and treachery is set on Exmoor in the 17th century. The feared Doone family have killed John Ridd's father yet, despite this brutality, John falls in love with Lorna Doone and determines to rescue her from Doone valley. Running time approximately 3 hours.
Cassette: released on Listen For Pleasure in Jul'86 by MFP Records. Distributed by: EMI

Blackmore's Rainbow

Biographical Details: Ace guitarist Ritchie Blackmore was a founder member of Deep Purple in 1968 and played a pivotal role in helping them to become one of Britain's most successful rock groups from the early Seventies. He left in 1975 to form Rainbow, taking members from a New York band called Elf. The line up consisted of Blackmore, Ronnie James Dio, Gary Gruber and Mickey Lee Soule. Their debut album 'Ritchie Blackmore's Rainbow' reached no.11 on the British LP charts in the autumn of '75. In 1976 Blackmore sacked the whole group save vocalist Dio, and recruited Jimmy Bain, Tony Carey and well known Cozy Powell (who had scored three UK hit singles in 1974). This line up's album reached no.11 also, but had a much longer chart run, it was entitled 'Rainbow Rising' and featured some surprise contributions form the Munich Philharmonic Orchestra. From '77 onwards, the band were known simply as Rainbow. Blackmore's domineering and demanding personality resulted in numerous personnal changes over the following years , but the group's sound did not change radically. They remanied hard rockers, but gradually added more melody, resulted in several hit singles as well as albums. (BM 84)

RAINBOW RISING.
Album: released on Oyster in Aug'93 by Oyster Records. Distributed by: Polygram Distribution

Cassette: released on Oyster in Aug'93 by Oyster Records. Distributed by: Polygram Distribution

RITCHIE BLACKMORE'S RAINBOW.
Album: released on Oyster in Aug'83 by Oyster Records. Distributed by: Polygram Distribution

Cassette: released on Oyster in Aug'83 by Oyster Records. Distributed by: Polygram Distribution

Black Music In Britain

BLACK MUSIC IN BRITAIN, THE EARLY FIFTIES Vol. 1 - Port of Spain shuffle (Various Artists).
Tracks: / Underground train, The / Dollar and the pound, the / General election / Iere / Man smart and woman smarter / Federation / Port of Spain shuffle / Ugly woman / Tick' tick' (the story of the lost watch) / King Porter stomp / Fat Tuesday / Daddy gone / London blues / Sightseeing in the UK / Mamzelle Josephine / Linstead Market.
Album: released on New Cross in May'87 by Charly Records. Distributed by: Charly

BLACK MUSIC IN BRITAIN, THE EARLY FIFTIES Vol. 2 -Caribbean Connections (Various Artists).
Tracks: / Nora / I will die a bachelor / Rum more rum / Breakaway / Mary Ann / Weed woman / Calypso be / Mattie rag / Massa Johnnie / Fire fire / Trinidad land of calypso / Trouble in Arima / Trinidad / Mikes Tangana / Baionga / Kalenda March (J'Ouvert Barriot).
Album: released on New Cross in May'87 by Charly Records. Distributed by: Charly

Black'n'Blue

BLACK'N'BLUE.
Tracks: / Strong will rock, The / School of hard knocks / Autoblast / Hold onto 18 / Wicked bitch / Action / Show me the night / One for the money / I'm the king / Chains around heaven.
Album: released on Geffen in Sep'84 by Geffen Records. Distributed by: WEA, CBS

Cassette: released on Geffen in Sep'84 by Geffen Records. Distributed by: WEA, CBS

NASTY NASTY.
Tracks: / Nasty nasty / I want it all / Des she or doesn't she / Kiss of death / 12 o'clock high / Do what you wanna do / I'll be there for you / Rules / Best of the west.
Album: released on Geffen in Oct'86 by Geffen Records. Distributed by: WEA, CBS

Cassette: released on Geffen in Oct'86 by Geffen Records. Distributed by: WEA, CBS

Black Oak Arkansas

JIM DANDY.
Album: released on Heavy Metal America in Apr'86 by FM-Revolver Records. Distributed by: EMI

Cassette: released on Heavy Metal America in Apr'86 by FM-Revolver Records. Distributed by: EMI

Black Orpheus

BLACK ORPHEUS (ORFEU NEGRO)
Original soundtrack.
Album: released on Philips (France) in Sep'83

Cassette: released on Philips (France) in Sep'83

Blackout

CITY, (THE).
Single (7"): released on Green Flag in Jan'84 by Green Flag Records. Distributed by: Cartel

Blackouts

EXCHANGE OF GOODS.
Single (7"): released on Situation 2 in Nov'81. Distributed by: Cartel, Pinnacle

Black, Pauline

PIRATES ON THE AIRWAVES (Black, Pauline with Sunday Best).
Single (7"): released on Chrysalis in Apr'84 by Chrysalis Records. Distributed by: CBS

Single (12"): released on Chrysalis in Apr'84 by Chrysalis Records. Distributed by: CBS

Blackpool Rockers

SAN FRANCISCO DISCO DANCING SCHOOL.
Single (7"): released on Sunny in Oct'82 by Sunny Records. Distributed by: PRT Distribution

Black Roots

BLACK ROOTS.
Album: released on Kick in Nov'83 by Mike Collier. Distributed by: Pinnacle

Album: released on BBC in Dec'84 by BBC Records & Tapes. Distributed by: EMI, PRT, Pye

Cassette: released on BBC in Dec'84 by BBC Records & Tapes. Distributed by: EMI, PRT, Pye

CHANTING FOR FREEDOM.
Single (12"): released on Nubian in Dec'81

FRONT LINE.
Album: released on BBC in Dec'84 by BBC Records & Tapes. Distributed by: EMI, PRT, Pye

Cassette: released on BBC in Dec'84 by BBC Records & Tapes. Distributed by: EMI, PRT, Pye

Album: released on Kick in Nov'84 by Mike Collier. Distributed by: Pinnacle

Single (7"): released on BBC in Nov'84 by BBC Records & Tapes. Distributed by: EMI, PRT, Pye

IN SESSION.
Tracks: / Confusion / Survival / Juvenile delinquent / What them a do / Move on / Opportunity / Tribal war / Africa / Father, The / Chanting for freedom.
Album: released on BBC in Sep'85 by BBC Records & Tapes. Distributed by: EMI, PRT, Pye

Cassette: released on BBC in Sep'85 by BBC Records & Tapes. Distributed by: EMI, PRT, Pye

JUVENILE DELINQUENT.
Single (7"): released on Joy in May'84 by President Records. Distributed by: Jazz Music, Swift, President Distribution

Single (12"): released on Joy in May'84 by President Records. Distributed by: Jazz Music, Swift, President Distribution

MOVE ON.
Single (12"): released on Silvertown in Jan'83 by Silvertown Records

SEEN YOUR FACE.
Tracks: / Conman.
Single (12"): released on Nubian in Jul'86

SUZY WONG.
Single (7"): released on Nubian in Apr'87

Single (12"): released on Nubian in Apr'87

Black Rose

BOYS WILL BE BOYS.
Album: released on Bullet in Apr'84. Distributed by: Bullet Distribution

Single (7"): released on Bullet in May'84. Distributed by: Bullet Distribution

NIGHTMARE.
Single (12"): released on Neat in Jun'85 by Neat Records. Distributed by: Pinnacle, Neat

NO POINT RUNNING.
Single (7"): released on Teesbeat in Aug'82 by Smellytapes. Distributed by: Red Rhino Distribution, Indies Distribution, Self Distribution, Bullet Distribution

ROCK ME HARD.
Single (12"): released on Neat in Mar'85 by Neat Records. Distributed by: Pinnacle, Neat

WALK IT HOW YOU TALK IT.
Album: released on Neat in Apr'87 by Neat Records. Distributed by: Pinnacle, Neat

Cassette: released on Neat in May'87 by Neat Records. Distributed by: Pinnacle, Neat

WE GONNA ROCK YOU (EP).
Single (12"): released on Bullet in Sep'83. Distributed by: Bullet Distribution

Black Russian

BLACK RUSSIAN.
Tracks: / Move together / 'Cause I love you / Love's enough / Leave me now / Mystified / New York City / Life is too short / Emptiness.
Album: released on Motown in Oct'81 by Motown Records. Distributed by: BMG Distribution

Black Sabbath

BLACK SABBATH.
Tracks: / Black Sabbath / Wizard (The) / Behind The Wall Of Sleep / N.I.B / Evil Woman / Sleeping Village / Warning / Black Sabbath / Wizard, The / Behind the walls of sleep / N.I.B. / Evil woman / Sleeping village / Warning.
Compact disc: released on Castle in Dec'86 by Castle Records. Distributed by: Pinnacle

Album: released on Castle in Nov'85 by Castle Records. Distributed by: Pinnacle

Album: released on Nems in Nov'80. Distributed by: Castle Communications Records, Pinnacle Records

BLACK SABBATH - LIVE AT LAST.
Cassette: released on Stage One in Jul'80 by Stage One Records. Distributed by: Stage One Distribution

BLACK SABBATH VOLUME 4.
Tracks: / Wheels of confusion / Tomorrow's dream / Changes / FX / Supernaut / Snowblind / Cornucopia / Laguna sunrise / St.Vitas dance / Under the sun.
Compact disc: by Castle Records. Distributed by: Pinnacle

Album: released on Nems in Nov'80. Distributed by: Castle Communications Records, Pinnacle Records

BOX SET.
Album: by Castle Records. Distributed by: Pinnacle

COLLECTION: BLACK SABBATH.
Tracks: / Paranoid / Behind the wall of sleep / Sleeping village / Warning / Warpigs / Hand of doom / Planet caravan / Electric funeral / Rat salad / Iron man / After forever / Supernaut / St.Vitas dance / Wheels of confusion / Snowblind / Killing yourself to live / Sabra cadabra / Writ, The / Paranoid / Snowblind / Writ (The) / Warpigs / Sabra Cadabra / Killing Yourself to Live / Supernaut / St. Vitus Dance / After Forever / Rat Salad / Electric Funeral / Planet Caravan / Hand of Doom / Sleeping Village / Behind the Wall of Sleep / Wheels of Confusion / Warning / Iron Man.
Album: released on Castle Communications in Nov'85 by Castle Communications. Distributed by: Cartel, Pinnacle, Counterpoint

Cassette: released on Castle Communications in Nov'85 by Castle Communications. Distributed by: Cartel, Pinnacle, Counterpoint

GREATEST HITS:BLACK SABBATH.
Tracks: / Paranoid / Changes / Sabbath bloody sabbath / Iron man / Black Sabbath / War pigs / Laguna sunrise / Tomorrows dream / Sweet leaf / N.I.B. / Paranoid / N.I.B. / Changes / Sabbath bloody Sabbath / Iron man / Black Sabbath / War pigs / Laguna sunrise / Tomorrow's dream / Sweet leaf.
Compact disc: released on Castle in Nov'85 by Castle Records. Distributed by: Pinnacle

Album: released on Nems in Nov'80. Distributed by: Castle Communications Records, Pinnacle Records

HEAVEN AND HELL.
Tracks: / Neon knights / Children of the sea / Lady evil / Heaven and hell / Wishing well / Die young / Walk away / Lonely is the world / Tomorrow dream.

Album: released on Vertigo in May'83 by Phonogram Records. Distributed by: Polygram

Cassette: released on Vertigo in May'83 by Phonogram Records. Distributed by: Polygram

LIVE AND EVIL.
Tracks: / E 5 150 / Neon knights / N.I.B. / Children of the sea / Voodoo / Black Sabbath / War pigs / Iron man / Mob rules / Heaven and hell / Sign of southern cross / Sign of southern cross / Paranoid / Children of the grave / Fluff.
Album: released on Vertigo in Apr'86 by Phonogram Records. Distributed by: Polygram

Cassette: released on Vertigo in Apr'86 by Phonogram Records. Distributed by: Polygram

LIVE AT LAST.
Tracks: / Tomorrow's dream / Sweet leaf / Killing yourself to live / Cornucopia / War pigs / Wicked world / Paranoid / Sweet leaf / Killing yourself to live / Cornucopia / War pigs / Wicked world / Paranoid.
Compact disc: released on Castle in Nov'86 by Castle Records. Distributed by: Pinnacle

Video-cassette [Betamax]: released on Nems in Nov'80. Distributed by: Castle Communications Records, Pinnacle Records

MASTER OF REALITY.
Tracks: / Sweet leaf / After forever / Embryo / Children of the grave / Lord of this world / Solitude / Into the void / Sweet leaf / After forever / Embryo / Children of the grave / Orchid / Lord of this world / Solitude / Into the void.
Album: released on Castle in Nov'85 by Castle Records. Distributed by: Pinnacle

Album: released on Nems in Nov'80. Distributed by: Castle Communications Records, Pinnacle Records

MASTERS OF REALITY.
Compact disc: by Castle Records. Distributed by: Pinnacle

MOB RULES.
Tracks: / Turn up the night / Voodoo / Sign of the Southern Cross / E 5150 / Mob rules / Country girl / Slippin' away / Falling off the edge of the world / Over and over.
Album: released on Vertigo in Jan'85 by Phonogram Records. Distributed by: Polygram

Cassette: released on Vertigo in Jan'85 by Phonogram Records. Distributed by: Polygram

NEVER SAY DIE Live in concert.
Tracks: / Black sabbath / Dirty women / Rock and roll doctor / Electric funeral / Children of the grave / Paranoid / Snowblind / Never say die / Johnny Blade / Junior eyes / Hard road / Shock wave / Air dance / Over to you / Breakout / Swinging the chain.
Notes: Introduction and symptom of the universe. The raw energy of Black Sabbath live in concert at the Hammersmith Odeon. A devastating performance from the archetypal "Heavy Band".
Video-cassette (VHS): released on VCL in Sep'86 by Elecstar Records. Distributed by: PRT

Album: released on Vertigo in May'83 by Phonogram Records. Distributed by: Polygram

Cassette: released on Vertigo in May'83 by Phonogram Records. Distributed by: Polygram

PARANOID.
Tracks: / War pigs / Planet caravan / Iron man / Electric funeral / Hand of doom / Rat salad / Fairies wear boots.
Album: released on Castle in Nov'85 by Castle Records. Distributed by: Pinnacle

Compact disc: released on Castle in Jan'86 by Castle Records. Distributed by: Pinnacle

Single (7"): released on Nems in Sep'80. Distributed by: Castle Communications Records, Pinnacle Records

Single (7"): released on Nems in Sep'82. Distributed by: Castle Communications Records, Pinnacle Records

Single (12"): released on Archive 4 in Aug'86 by Castle Communications Records. Distributed by: Nine Mile, Cartel

PARANOID (7").
Single (7"): released on Old Gold in Jan'85 by Old Gold Records. Distributed by: Lightning, Jazz Music, Spartan, Counterpoint

SABBATH BLOODY SABBATH.
Tracks: / Sabbath bloody sabbath / National acrobat, A / Fluff / Sabbra Cadabra / Killing yourself to live / Who are you / Looking for today / Spiral architect.
Album: released on Castle in Nov'85 by Castle Records. Distributed by: Pinnacle

Compact disc: released on Castle in Nov'85 by Castle Records. Distributed by: Pinnacle

SABOTAGE.
Tracks: / Hole in the Sky / Don't Start (Too Late) / Symtom of the Universe / Megalomania / Thrill of it all / Superzar / Am I Going Insane? / Writ (The) / Hole in the sky / Don't start (too late) / Symptom of the universe / Megalomania / Thrill of it all / Superzar / Am I going insane / Writ, The.

Album: released on Castle in Nov'85 by Castle Records. Distributed by: Pinnacle

Compact disc: released on Nems in Jan'86. Distributed by: Castle Communications Records, Pinnacle Records

Album: released on Nems in Nov'80. Distributed by: Castle Communications Records, Pinnacle Records

SEVENTH STAR.
Tracks: / In for the kill / No stranger to love / Turn to stone / Sphinx (The guardian) / Seventh star / Danger zone / Heart like a wheel / Angry heart / I memory....
Notes: Produced by: Jeff Glixman... A new album featuring Tony Lommo-founder member of Black Sabbath and guitar hero a generation of young guitarists. New line-up includes: Glenn Hughes- vocals/David Spitz-Bass/Eric Singer- Drums/Geoff Nichols-Keyboards.
Album: released on Vertigo in Feb'86 by Phonogram Records. Distributed by: Polygram

Cassette: released on Vertigo in Feb'86 by Phonogram Records. Distributed by: Polygram

Compact disc: released on Vertigo in Feb'86 by Phonogram Records. Distributed by: Polygram

TECHNICAL ECSTASY.
Tracks: / All moving parts / Back street kids / Dirty woman / Gypsy / It's alright / Rock 'n' roll doctor / She's gone / You won't change me.
Album: released on Vertigo in Aug'83 by Phonogram Records. Distributed by: Polygram

Cassette: released on Vertigo in Aug'83 by Phonogram Records. Distributed by: Polygram

TURN UP THE NIGHT.
Single (7"): released on Vertigo in Jan'82 by Phonogram Records. Distributed by: Polygram

TURN UP THE NIGHT (PICTURE DISC).
Single (7"): released on Vertigo in Jan'82 by Phonogram Records. Distributed by: Polygram

Single (12"): released on Vertigo in Jan'82 by Phonogram Records. Distributed by: Polygram

VOL.4.
Tracks: / Wheels of confusion / Tommorows dream / Changes / FX / Supernaut / Snowblind / Cornucopia / Laguna sunrise / St.Vitus dance / Under the sun.
Album: released on Castle in Nov'85 by Castle Records. Distributed by: Pinnacle

Compact disc: released on Castle in Nov'85 by Castle Records. Distributed by: Pinnacle

WE SOLD OUR SOUL FOR ROCK'N'ROLL.
Tracks: / Black Sabbath / Wizard, The / Warning / Paranoid / Wicked world / Tommorrow's dream / Fairies wear boots / Changes / Sweat leaf / Children of the grave / Sabbath bloody sabbath / Am I going insane (radio) / Laguana sunrise / Snowblind.
Album: released on Raw Power in Apr'86. Distributed by: Pinnacle

Cassette: released on Raw Power in Apr'86. Distributed by: Pinnacle

WE SOLD OUR SOUL FOR ROCK 'N' ROLL.
Album: released on Nems in Nov'80. Distributed by: Castle Communications Records, Pinnacle Records

Black satin

BLACK SATIN Various artists (Various Artists).
Tracks: / When a man loves woman / Hold on I'm coming / Heatwave / Knock on wood / Up on the roof / Rescue me / Do the funky chicken / Hey there lonely girl / Everlasting love / Jimmy Mack / If loving you is wrong / Hey girl don't bother me / B.A.B.Y. / Patches / I heard it through the grapevine / Sitting on the dock of the bay / Harlem shuffle / Lovers concerto / Best thing that happened to me / Under the boardwalk / Softly whispering I love you / Da do ron ron / Midnight train to Georgia / Try a little tenderness / My guy / You little trustmaker / Soul man / Quicksand / Then he kissed me / Tighten up.
Cassette: released on Cambra in '83 by Cambra Records. Distributed by: IDS, Conifer

Black September

RAINBOW KISS.
Single (12"): released on Lost Moment in May'86

Black, Sharon

I JUST HAD YOU ON MY MIND.
Single (12"): released on Real Wax in Jul'84

SLOW HAND.
Single (12"): released on Clintones in May'84 by Clintones Records. Distributed by: Jetstar

Black Sheep

BLACK SHEEP.
Album: released on Razor in Jun'85 by Razor. Distributed by: Pinnacle

Black Slate

BLACK SLATE.
Album: released on Sierra in Apr'85 by Sierra Records. Distributed by: WEA

Cassette: released on Sierra in Apr'85 by Sierra Records. Distributed by: WEA

BLACK SLATE DUB.
Single (12"): released on Top Ranking in Nov'82

LOOK WHAT LOVE HAS DONE.
Single (7"): released on Top Ranking in Oct'82

Single (12"): released on Top Ranking in Oct'82

NO JUSTICE FOR THE POOR.
Single (7"): released on Sierra in May'85 by Sierra Records. Distributed by: WEA

Single (12"): released on Sierra in May'85 by Sierra Records. Distributed by: WEA

RASTA REGGAE.
Single (7"): released on Top Ranking in May'82

Single (12"): released on Top Ranking in May'82

SIRENS IN THE CITY.
Tracks: / Sirens in the city / Live a life / I love you still / Reggae everytime / Message to Mr Sus Man / Dread in the house / Winners / Rocker's palace / Zion.
Album: released on Ensign in Aug'81 by Ensign Records. Distributed by: CBS Distribution

Cassette: released on Ensign in Aug'81 by Ensign Records. Distributed by: CBS Distribution

SIX PLUS ONE.
Album: released on Top Ranking in Sep'82

STICKS MAN.
Single (12"): released on Top Ranking in Jul'82

Single (7"): released on Top Ranking in Jul'82

Single (12"): released on Port in Sep'85

WISER THAN BEFORE.
Single (7"): released on Sir George in May'84 by Sir George Records. Distributed by: Jetstar, Pinnacle

Blackslate, Keith

DAYLIGHT COME.
Single (12"): released on Uptempo in May'85 by Uptempo Records. Distributed by: Jetstar Distribution

Blacksmiths

MERRILY KISSED THE QUAKER.
Album: released on Aran in Jan'76. Distributed by: EMI (Ireland)

Black soul

BLACK SOUL Various artists (Various Artists).
Album: released on Creole in Nov'83 by Creole Records. Distributed by: Rhino, PRT

Black, Stanley

DIGITAL MAGIC (Black, Stanley and His Orchestra).
Tracks: / Chiquitita / California suite / Bilitis / Tomorrow / Just when I needed you most / I will survive / Here's that rainy day / Way we were / Cavatina.
Compact disc: by London Records. Distributed by: Polygram

Album: released on Decca in Dec'79 by Decca Records. Distributed by: Polygram

Black Steel

DANCING THE REGGAE.
Single (12"): released on Ariwa in Jul'85 by Ariwa Records. Distributed by: Revolver, Cartel, Jetstar, Rough Trade

GROOVIN' IN LOVE.
Single (12"): released on Ariwa in Apr'85 by Ariwa Records. Distributed by: Revolver, Cartel, Jetstar, Rough Trade

Blackstock, Wayne

BLACK STAR LINER Various African artists (Various Artists).
Album: released on Rounder (USA) in Jan'84. Distributed by: Mike's Country Music Room Distribution, Jazz Music Distribution, Swift Distribution, Roots Records Distribution, Projection Distribution, Topic Distribution

MR. OFFICER.
Single (12"): released on Tonof in Mar'85 by Tonof Records. Distributed by: Jetstar Distribution

Blackstone, Eddie

LIGHT AND SHADE OF EDDIE BLACKSTONE, THE.
Tracks: / After dark / 1643 Pennsylvania Boulevard / Spencer Walker Rose / Dolly McGraw / Never let a dream go by / Blues for a weirdo / You never left me side / Turn back the years / Lay my feet down on the street / Hero of the dreamers.
Album: released on T.W. in May'83 by T.W. Records. Distributed by: Cartel

LIGHT & SHADE OF EDDIE BLACKSTONE, THE.

NEVER LET A DREAM GO BY.

Blackstones

AIN'T SHE LOOKING FINE.
Single (12"): released on Live & Love in Nov'82 by Third World Records. Distributed by: Jetstar

CREATED BY ONE.
Single (12"): released on KG in Apr'82

FIGHTING TO THE TOP.
Single (12"): released on Easy Street in Nov'83 by Easy Street Records. Distributed by: Jetstar

I'LL BE THERE.
Tracks: / I'll be there (acapella).
Single (12"): released on Blackstones in May'86. Distributed by: Jetstar

I'M THE ONE FOR YOU.
Single (12"): released on Sir George in Nov'86 by Sir George Records. Distributed by: Jetstar, Pinnacle

IT'S ALL IN THE GAME.
Single (7"): released on Riff-Raff in Dec'81. Distributed by: Jetstar

JEALOUSY.
Single (12"): released on Live & Love in May'82 by Third World Records. Distributed by: Jetstar

MIGHTY LONG TIME.
Single (7"): released on PRT in Oct'84 by PRT Records. Distributed by: PRT

Single (12"): released on PRT in Oct'84 by PRT Records. Distributed by: PRT

NOTHING YOU CAN DO ABOUT LOVE.
Tracks: / Take another look at love.
Single (7"): released on PRT in Apr'86 by PRT Records. Distributed by: PRT

Single (12"): released on PRT in Apr'86 by PRT Records. Distributed by: PRT

NOTHIN' YOU CAN DO ABOUT LOVE.
Single (7"): released on PRT in Oct'85 by PRT Records. Distributed by: PRT

Single (12"): released on PRT in Oct'85 by PRT Records. Distributed by: PRT

SATURDAY NITE.
Single (12"): released on Hep To Hep in Jun'85 by Hep To Hep Records. Distributed by: Jetstar

SOULED OUT OF LOVE.
Single (12"): released on Blackstones in Aug'84. Distributed by: Jetstar

SWEET FEELINGS.
Tracks: / Riding high.
Single (12"): released on War International in Feb'86 by War International Records. Distributed by: Jetstar

TAKE ANOTHER LOOK AT LOVE.
Album: released on Pressure Recordings in Nov'83

Blackstones, Leon

ROCKERS MEDLEY.
Single (12"): released on Music Force in Jul'83

Blackstuff Lads

GIS A JOB.

Black Swing Tradition

BLACK SWING TRADITION Various artists (Various Artists).
Album:

Black Symbol

BLACK SYMBOL PRESENTS HANSWORTH EXPLOSION VOL 2.
Album: released on Black Symbol in Feb'85. Distributed by: Jetstar

LOVING JAH.
Single (12"): released on Black Symbol in Dec'82. Distributed by: Jetstar

SOLIDARITY.
Tracks: / Tension.
Single (12"): released on Black Symbol in Aug'86. Distributed by: Jetstar

Black Task

LONG AFTER MIDNIGHT.
Album: released on Eva-Lolita in Jul'86. Distributed by: Pinnacle

Blackthorn

BELFAST MARATHON.
Single (7"):

BLACKTHORN.
Album: released on Homespun(Ireland) in Jul'86 by Outlet Records. Distributed by: Outlet

PADDY LIE BACK, KATIE LIE OVER.
Album: released on Glen in Mar'80. Distributed by: EMI, Outlet

Black UA Singles

BLACK UA SINGLES - '59-'67 From Motor City to Central Park (Various Artists).
Tracks: / Tell him / Cry baby / I love the way you love / Bells / Who's that lady / You're so fine / Everybody's going / You got what it takes / Love potion No. 9 / Masquerade is over, The (I'm afraid) / Wonder of it all, The / I'll take good care of you / Till the end / Come to me.
Album: released on Stateside in Jul'87. Distributed by: EMI

Cassette: released on Stateside in Jul'87. Distributed by: EMI

Black Uhuru

BLACK SOUNDS OF FREEDOM.
Tracks: / I love King Selassie / Satan army band / Time to unite / Natural mystic / Edan out deh / Love crisis / African love / Hard ground / Willow tree / Sorry for the man.
Album: released on Greensleeves in Jul'81 by Greensleeves Records. Distributed by: BMG, Jetstar, Spartan

BLACK UHURU.
Album: released on Virgin in Aug'81 by Virgin Records. Distributed by: EMI, Virgin Distribution

BRUTAL.
Tracks: / Let us Pray / Dread in the Mountain / Brutal / City Vibes / Great Train Robbery / Uptown Girl / Vision / Reggae with You / Conviction or a Fine / Fit you Haffe Fit.
Notes: The album co produced by Arthur Baker, and all tracks are backed by Sly and Robbie.
Compact disc: released on Ras in Feb'87 by Real Authentic Sound. Distributed by: Greensleeves Records, RCA, Jetstar

Album: released on Ras in May'86 by Real Authentic Sound. Distributed by: Greensleeves Records, RCA, Jetstar

BRUTAL DUB.
Album: released on Ras in Nov'86 by Real Authentic Sound. Distributed by: Greensleeves Records, RCA, Jetstar

CHILL OUT.
Album: released on Island in Jun'82 by Island Records. Distributed by: Polygram

Cassette: released on Island in Jun'82 by Island Records. Distributed by: Polygram

CONQUER THE TANKER.
Single (7"): released on Real Authentic Sound in 23 May'87

CONVICTION OR FINE.
Tracks: / Conviction or fine (version).
Single (12"): released on Ras in Jan'85 by Real Authentic Sound. Distributed by: Greensleeves Records, RCA, Jetstar

DARKNESS.
Single (7"): released on Island in Jun'82 by Island Records. Distributed by: Polygram

Single 10": released on Island in Jun'82 by Island Records. Distributed by: Polygram

GREAT TRAIN ROBBERY.
Tracks: / Great train robbery (dub).
Single (12"): released on Real Authentic Sound in Apr'86

REGGAE GREATS.
Tracks: / Happiness / World in Africa / Sponji reggae / Youth of Eglington / Darkness / What is life? / Bull in the pen / Elements / Push push / Right stuff.
Album: released on Island in May'85 by Island Records. Distributed by: Polygram

Cassette: released on Island in May'85 by Island Records. Distributed by: Polygram

SINSEMILLA.
Tracks: / Happiness / World is Africa / Push push / There is fire / No loafing / Sinsemilla / Every dreadlocks / Vampire.
Album: released on Island in Feb'81 by Island Records. Distributed by: Polygram

Cassette: released on Island in Feb'81 by Is-

land Records. Distributed by: Polygram

SIT U HAFFY SIT.
Single (12"): released on Taxi in Jul'85 by Taxi Records. Distributed by: Jetstar Distribution

SOUNDS OF FREEDOM.
Compact disc: released on Greensleeves in Feb'87 by Greensleeves Records. Distributed by: BMG, Jetstar, Spartan

TEAR IT UP.
Album: released on Island in Feb'82 by Island Records. Distributed by: Polygram

Cassette: released on Island in Feb'82 by Island Records. Distributed by: Polygram

UHURU IN DUB/OSBOURNE IN DUB (Black Uhuru & Johnny Osbourne).
Cassette: released on CSA in Jun'85 by CSA Records. Distributed by: PRT, Jetstar

WHAT IS LIFE?.
Single (12"): released on Island in Oct'84 by Island Records. Distributed by: Polygram

Single (7"): released on Island in Aug'84 by Island Records. Distributed by: Polygram

Single (12"): released on Island in Aug'84 by Island Records. Distributed by: Polygram

Black, Vince

BACK OFF.
Single (12"): released on 1 Tone in Jun'82

Black Watch

PAPA'S GOT A BRAMD NEW BAGPIPE.
Single (7"): released on Sunny in Oct'83 by Sunny Records. Distributed by: PRT Distribution

Single (12"): released on Sunny in Oct'83 by Sunny Records. Distributed by: PRT Distribution

Black Watch Band

ON THE MARCH, VOL 3.
Album: released on Major Richards in Jul'81 by Major Richards Records. Distributed by: Taylors

Cassette: released on Major Richards in Jul'81 by Major Richards Records. Distributed by: Taylors

ON THE MARCH, VOL 4.
Tracks: / Glorious victory / Action front / Gridiron club, The / Under the banner of victory / Festjubel / Argancab bavarda / Army of the Nile.
Album: released on Major Richards in Apr'83 by Major Richards Records. Distributed by: Taylors

Cassette: released on Major Richards in Apr'83 by Major Richards Records. Distributed by: Taylors

ON THE MARCH, VOL 5.
Album: released on Major Richards in Nov'82 by Major Richards Records. Distributed by: Taylors

ON THE MARCH, VOL 6.
Album: released on Major Richards in Jul'83 by Major Richards Records. Distributed by: Taylors

Cassette: released on Major Richards in Jul'83 by Major Richards Records. Distributed by: Taylors

ON THE MARCH, VOL 7.
Tracks: / Liberty bell / Graf Zeppelin / Radetzky march / St. Julien / Ambassador, The / Laridah.
Album: released on Major Richards in Aug'83 by Major Richards Records. Distributed by: Taylors

Cassette: released on Major Richards in Aug'83 by Major Richards Records. Distributed by: Taylors

RED HACKLE, (THE).
Album: released on RK in Nov'79

SANDS OF TIME.
Single (7"): released on Sunny in Oct'82 by Sunny Records. Distributed by: PRT Distribution

SCOTCH ON THE ROCKS.
Album: released on Spark in Jan'76 by Spark Records. Distributed by: PRT

Cassette: released on Spark in Jan'76 by Spark Records. Distributed by: PRT

SPIRIT OF THE ISLES.
Tracks: / Spirit of the Isles / O bla di o bla da / Country roads / Africana / Our gracious Queen / Banner man / Jigger of whiskey / Miller Cha's in the mood / Chatnuga chu chu / Hackle red / Blueberry hill / Put your hand in the hand / Soul finger.
Album:

STRIKE UP THE BAND.
Album: released on Spark in Aug'76 by Spark Records. Distributed by: PRT

VIVA SCOTLAND.
Single (7"): released on RK in Apr'82

Blackwell, Debbie

ONCE YOU GOT ME GOING.
Tracks: / Once you got me going.
Single (7"): released on 10 in Jul'86 by 10 Records. Distributed by: Virgin, EMI

Single (12"): released on Ten in Jul'86

Blackwell, Ed

EL CORAZON (Blackwell, Ed and Don Cherry).
Compact disc: released on ECM (Germany) in Oct'86 by ECM Records. Distributed by: IMS, Polygram, Virgin through EMI

OLD AND NEW DREAMS (Blackwell, Ed, Don Cherry & Redman).
Compact disc: . Distributed by: Projection, IMS, Polygram, Chris Wellard, Harmonia Mundi, Swift

Blackwell,Jill & Bernard

ADVENTURES OF NOTION.
Album: released on Fellside in Jul'86 by Fellside Records. Distributed by: Roots, Jazz Music, Celtic Music, Projection

Blackwell, Otis

SINGIN' THE BLUES.
Album: released on Flyright in Oct'86 by Flyright Records. Distributed by: Krazy Kat, Swift, Jazz Music

Black & White Blues

BLACK & WHITE BLUES Various artists (Various Artists).
Boxed set: released on Teldec (Germany) in Apr'84 by Import Records. Distributed by: IMS Distribution, Polygram Distribution

Black & White Minstrels

BLACK & WHITE MINSTRELS & THE JOE LOSS ORCHESTRA.
Album: released on MFP in Sep'85 by EMI Records. Distributed by: EMI

Cassette: released on MFP in Sep'85 by EMI Records. Distributed by: EMI

Blackwych

OUT OF CONTROL.
Album: released on Metal Masters in Apr'86 by Razor Records. Distributed by: Pinnacle

Blade Runner

BACK STREET LADY.
Single (7"): released on Ebony in Jan'85 by Ebony Records. Distributed by: Pinnacle, Ebony

WARRIORS OF ROCK.
Album: released on Ebony in Mar'86 by Ebony Records. Distributed by: Pinnacle, Ebony

Blades

DOWNMARKET (Blades,The Featuring Paul Cleary).
Tracks: / Downmarket / Truth don't hurt.
Single (7"): released on Reekus in Jul'86 by Reekus Records. Distributed by: Nine Mile, Cartel

LAST MAN IN EUROPE,(THE).
Tracks: / Last man in Europe,(The) / Downmarket / That's not love / Talk about listening / Got soul / Chance to stop / Don't break the silence / Those were the days / Pride / Boy one / Waiting.
Album: released on Reekus in Sep'86 by Reekus Records. Distributed by: Nine Mile, Cartel

Cassette: released on Reekus in Sep'86 by Reekus Records. Distributed by: Nine Mile, Cartel

RAYTOWN REVISITED.
Album: released on Reekus in Mar'86 by Reekus Records. Distributed by: Nine Mile, Cartel

Blades, Ruben

AGUA DE LUNA.
Tracks: / Isobel / No te Duermas / Blackaman / Ojos de Perro Azul / Claro Oscuro / Laura Farina / La cita / Agua de luna.
Album: released on Elektra (USA) in Jul'87 by Elektra/Asylum/Nonesuch Records. Distributed by: WEA

Cassette: released on Elektra (USA) in Jul'87 by Elektra/Asylum/Nonesuch Records. Distributed by: WEA

BUSCANDO AMERICA.
Album: released on WEA (Import) in Aug'84

BUSCANDO AMERICA (SEARCHING FOR AMERICA).
Tracks: / Decisiones / G D B D / Desapariciones / Todos Vuelven / Caminos Verdes / El Padre Antonio y el Monaguillo Andres / Buscando America.
Compact disc: released on Messidor (Germany) in Jan'87. Distributed by: IMS Distribution, Polygram

ESCENAS.
Album: released on Elektra (USA) in Oct'85 by Elektra/Asylum/Nonesuch Records. Distributed by: WEA

ESCENAS (SCENES).
Compact disc: released on Messidor (Germany) in Jan'87. Distributed by: IMS Distribution. Polygram

MOVE ON (MUEUETE).
Tracks: / Move on (Mueuete) / Mueuete.
Single (7"): released on Elektra (USA) in May'86 by Elektra/Asylum/Nonesuch Records. Distributed by: WEA

Single (12"): released on Elektra (USA) in May'86 by Elektra/Asylum/Nonesuch Records. Distributed by: WEA

Blah Blah Blah

BLAH BLAH BLAH.
Album: released on Trans Universal in Mar'82

IN THE ARMY.
Single (7"): released on Absurd in Sep'82 by Absurd. Distributed by: Pinnacle, Rough Trade

Blair, Alex

ESPECIALLY FOR YOU.
Album: released on Denon in Mar'82 by Denon Records. Distributed by: Harmonia Mundi

Blair, Douglas

CELTOLOGY.
Album: released on Redburn in Dec'84 by Redburn Records. Distributed by: Celtic Music

Blair, Lionel

LIONEL BLAIR'S AEROBIC DANCE LP.
Album: released on Dureco Benelux (Holland) in Jul'83

Blake, Blind

1926-29: THE REMAINING TITLES.
Album: released on Matchbox in May'85. Distributed by: Projection

RAGTIME GUITAR'S FOREMOST FINGERPICKER.
Album: released on Yazoo(USA) in Feb'85

Blake, Howard

SNOWMAN, (THE).
Album: released on CBS in Dec'83 by CBS Records. Distributed by: CBS

Cassette: released on CBS in Dec'83 by CBS Records. Distributed by: CBS

Blake, John

MAIDEN DANCE.
Album: released on Gramavision (USA) in Jun'84 by Gramavision Records (USA). Distributed by: PRT, IMS, Polygram

Cassette: released on Gramavision (USA) in Jun'84 by Gramavision Records (USA). Distributed by: PRT, IMS, Polygram

TWINKLING OF AN EYE.
Album: released on Gramavision (USA) in Dec'85 by Gramavision Records (USA). Distributed by: PRT, IMS, Polygram

Blake, Karl

PREHENSILE TALES, (THE).
Album: released on Normal in Jun'83. Distributed by: Red Lightnin' Distribution, Rough Trade Distribution, Cartel Distribution

Blake, Norman

BLACKBERRY BLOSSOM.
Album: released on Flying Fish (USA) in Feb'79 by Flying Fish Records (USA). Distributed by: Roots, Projection

HOME IN SULPHUR SPRINGS.
Album: released on Rounder in Jan'87. Distributed by: Roots Distribution

LIGHTHOUSE ON THE SHORE.
Album: released on Rounder (USA) in Dec'85. Distributed by: Mike's Country Music Room Distribution, Jazz Music Distribution, Swift Distribution, Roots Records Distribution, Projection Distribution, Topic Distribution

Cassette: released on Rounder (USA) in Dec'85. Distributed by: Mike's Country Music Room Distribution, Jazz Music Distribution, Swift Distribution, Roots Records Distribution, Projection Distribution, Topic Distribution

NASHVILLE BLUES.
Album: released on Rounder (USA) in Sep'84. Distributed by: Mike's Country Music Room Distribution, Jazz Music Distribution, Swift Distribution, Roots Records Distribution, Projection Distribution, Topic Distribution

Blake, Paul

EVERY POSSE GET FLAT (Blake, Paul & The Blood Fire Posse).
Single (12"): released on Rass in Mar'85. Distributed by: Jetstar

RUB A DUB SOLDIER (Blake, Paul & The Blood Fire Posse).
Single (7"): released on Review in May'84. Distributed by: Jetstar

Single (12"): released on Review in May'84. Distributed by: Jetstar

Blake, Ron

DUKE DREAMS, THE LEGACY OF STRAYHORN-ELLINGTON.
Album: released on Soul Note in Jul'82. Distributed by: Harmonia Mundi Distributors

Improvisations

Blake, Sonny

MY SPECIAL ANGEL.
Tracks: / My special angel / Curiosity.
Single (7"): released on Creole in May'87 by Creole Records. Distributed by: Rhino, PRT

Blake, Tim

BLAKE'S NEW JERSUALEM.
Album: released on Barclay in '78 by Decca Records. Distributed by: Polygram, Discovery, Conifer, IMS, Swift

CRYSTAL MACHINE.
Album: released on Egg in Nov'79. Distributed by: Red Rhino, Cartel

NEW JERUSALEM.
Album: released on Egg in Nov'79. Distributed by: Red Rhino, Cartel

Blakey, Art

AIN'T LIFE GRAND? (Blakey, Art Big Band & Quintet).
Album: released on Affinity in Nov'83 by Charly Records. Distributed by: Charly, Cadillac

ALBUM OF THE YEAR (Blakey, Art & The Jazz Messengers).
Tracks: / Cheryl / MS BC / In case you missed it / Little man / Witch hunt / Soulful Mr. Timmons.
Compact disc: released on Timeless in Oct'86

Album: released on Timeless (Holland) in Aug'85. Distributed by: JSU Distribution, Jazz Music Distribution, Jazz Horizons Distribution, Cadillac, Celtic Music Distribution

ALL STAR JAZZ MESSENGER, (THE).
Album: released on RCA (France) in '83 by RCA Records. Distributed by: Discovery

ART BLAKEY & HIS JAZZ MESSENGERS (Blakey, Art & The Jazz Messengers).
Album: released on Lotus in Apr'81. Distributed by: Counterpoint

ART BLAKEY IN SWEDEN 1959.
Album: released on Dragon in Jul'87 by Dragon Records. Distributed by: Jazz Music, Projection, Cadillac

ART BLAKEY'S JAZZ MESSENGERS (Blakey, Art & The Jazz Messengers).
Album: released on RCA (Germany) in Aug'83

ART BLAKEY & THE JAZZ MESSENGERS (Blakey, Art & The Jazz Messengers).
Cassette: released on Timeless in Oct'86

Compact disc: released on RCA Jazz (Japan) in Jan'86

Album: released on Jasmine in Mar'83 by Jasmine Records. Distributed by: PRT

Album: released on Kings Of Jazz in '81. Distributed by: Jazz Horizons, Jazz Music, Celtic Music

ART'S BREAK (Blakey, Art & The Jazz Messengers).
Album: released on Lotus in Sep'86. Distributed by: Counterpoint

ASCENSEUR PUR L'ECHAFAUD (see Davis, Miles).

AT THE CAFE BOHEMIA, VOL 1 (Blakey, Art & The Jazz Messengers).
Album: released on Blue Note in Oct'85 by EMI

Records. Distributed by: EMI

BACKGAMMON (Blakey, Art & The Jazz Messengers).
Album: released on Carosello in Jan'83. Distributed by: Jazz Music, Jazz Horizons

BIG BEAT (Blakey, Art & The Jazz Messengers).

BIG BEAT, THE (Blakey, Art & The Jazz Messengers).
Tracks: / Chess players (The) / Sakeena's vision / Politely / Dat dere / Lester left town / It's only a paper moon / It's only a paper moon (alternate take).
Compact disc: released on EMI in Mar'87 by EMI Records. Distributed by: EMI

Compact disc: by EMI Records. Distributed by: EMI

Cassette: released on Blue Note in Apr'87 by EMI Records. Distributed by: EMI

Album: released on Blue Note in Apr'87 by EMI Records. Distributed by: EMI

Album: released on Blue Note in Apr'85 by EMI Records. Distributed by: EMI

BIG BEAT, (THE) (Blakey, Art & The Jazz Messengers).

BLUE NIGHT (Blakey, Art & The Jazz Messengers).
Tracks: / Two of a kind / Blue minor / Blue night / Body & soul / Mr.Combinated.
Notes: Latest offering from legendary drummer Art Blakey and his young Jazz Messengers.Featuring Terrence Blanchard on trumpet(some believe him to be better than Wynton Marsalis) and Donald Harrison on alto,this is the same group that appeared at Ronnie Scott's & jazz festivals here last year. Personnel:Art Blakey-drums/Terrence Blanchard-trumpet/Donald Harrison-alto sax/ Julgrew Miller-piano/Lonnie Plaxico-bass.
Album: released on Timeless(USA) in Feb'86

BLUES BAG (Blakey, Art & Buddy De Franco).
Tracks: / Blues bag / Rain dnce / Straight no chaser / Cousin Mary / Blues connotation / Kush / Twelve tone blues.
Album: released on Charly in Dec'86 by Charly Records. Distributed by: Charly, Cadillac

Cassette: released on Charly in Dec'86 by Charly Records. Distributed by: Charly, Cadillac

Album: released on Affinity in Jan'81 by Charly Records. Distributed by: Charly, Cadillac

BLUES MARCH (Blakey, Art & The Jazz Messengers).
Tracks: / Blues march / Uranus / Whisper not / Backgammon / Georgia on my mind / Third world express / Nam fulay / I can't get started.
Compact disc: released on Rouelette-Vogue in May'85

BUTTERCORN LADY (Blakey, Art & The Jazz Messengers).
Tracks: / Buttercorn lady / Recuederdo / Theme,The / Between races / My romance / Secret love.
Compact disc: released on Emarcy(USA) in Apr'85 by Emarcy Records(USA). Distributed by: Polygram

CARAVAN.
Album: released on RCA (France) in Jun'84 by RCA Records. Distributed by: Discovery

DAY WITH ART BLAKEY, A - VOLUME 1.
Tracks: / Summit, The / Breeze and I, The / Blues March / Moanin' / It's Only a Paper Moon.
Compact disc: released on East Wind in Jan'86 by East Wind Records. Distributed by: PRT

DAY WITH ART BLAKEY, A - VOLUME 2.
Tracks: / Night in Tunisia, A / Nelly Bly / Dat Dere / Round About Midnight / Night in Tunisia, A.
Compact disc: released on East Wind in Jan'86 by East Wind Records. Distributed by: PRT

DAY WITH ART BLAKEY, VOL 2, (A).
Album: released on East Wind in Apr'85 by East Wind Records. Distributed by: PRT

DRUM NIGHT AT BIRDLAND.
Notes: With Art Blakey, Philly Joe Jones, Charlie Persip & Elvin Jones.
Compact disc: released on Vogue in '86. Distributed by: Discovery, Jazz Music, PRT, Swift

DRUM SOUNDS (Blakey, Art & The Jazz Messengers).
Tracks: / New world / Angel eyes / Slide No.2 / Theme.
Album: released on Star Jazz USA in Apr'86 by Charly Records. Distributed by: Charly Distribution

Cassette: released on Star Jazz USA in Apr'86 by Charly Records. Distributed by: Charly Distribution

Album: released on Chase Music in Nov'84 by Chase Records. Distributed by: PRT

Cassette: released on Chase Music in Nov'84 by Chase Records. Distributed by: PRT

DRUM SUITE.
Album: released on CBS in May'83 by CBS Records. Distributed by: CBS Deleted '86

Cassette: released on CBS in May'83 by CBS Records. Distributed by: CBS

FOR MINORS ONLY (Blakey, Art & The Jazz Messengers).
Tracks: / Right down front / Deo X / For minors only / Sweet Sakeena / For miles & miles / Krafty / Late spring / Tippin' / Pristine.
Compact disc: released on Charly in '86 by Charly Records. Distributed by: Charly, Cadillac

INDESTRUCTABLE (Blakey, Art & The Jazz Messengers).
Tracks: / Egyptian,The / Sortie / Calling Miss Kahdija / When love is new / Mr.Jin / Egyptian, The / Sortie / Calling Miss Khadija / When love is new / Mr. Jin / It's a long way down.
Notes: This is the only album of Blakey's classic sextet band of the early sixties on which Lee Morgan returns to the Jazz Messengers to replace Freddie Hiubbard. Wayne Shorter,Curtis Fuller,Cedar Walton & Reggie Wormans complete the band. Walton's tender'When Love is New'is a lyrical showcase for Morgans trumpet. 'The Egyptian' is pure charging Jazz Messenger music.
Album: released on Blue Note in Dec'85 by EMI Records. Distributed by: EMI

Compact disc: released on Blue Note in Aug'87 by EMI Records. Distributed by: EMI

Cassette: released on Blue Note in Sep'87 by EMI Records. Distributed by: EMI. Estim retail price in Sep'87 was £5.99.

IN MY PRIME, VOL 1 (Blakey, Art & The Jazz Messengers).
Album: released on Timeless in Apr'81

IN MY PRIME VOL.2 (Blakey, Art & The Jazz Messengers).
Album: released on Timeless in Sep'86

IN SWEDEN (Blakey, Art & The Jazz Messengers).
Album: released on Amigo in Jul'82. Distributed by: Red Rhino, Cartel

JAZZ MESSAGE.
Album: released on Jasmine in Feb'84 by Jasmine Records. Distributed by: Counterpoint, Lugtons, Taylor, H.R., Wellard, Chris, Swift, Cadillac

JAZZ MESSAGE, A (Blakey, Art Quartet).
Tracks: / Cafe / Just knock on my day / Summertime / Blues back / Sunday / Song is you (The).

JAZZ MESSENGER (Blakey, Art Quartet).
Compact disc: released on MCA in Jul'87 by MCA Records. Distributed by: Polygram, MCA

JAZZ MESSENGERS, (THE) (Blakey, Art Percussion Ensemble).
Album: released on CBS in '84 by CBS Records. Distributed by: CBS

Cassette: released on CBS in '84 by CBS Records. Distributed by: CBS

KILLER JOE (Blakey, Art & George Kawaguchi).
Album: released on Storyville (USA) in Jun'86 by Moss Music Group Records (USA). Distributed by: Discovery Distribution, Jazz Music Distribution, Swift Distribution, Chris Wellard Distribution, JSU Distribution, Celtic Music Distribution

LIAISONS DANGEREUSES 1960, (LES) (Blakey, Art & The Jazz Messengers).
Album: released on Phonogram (France) in Aug'83

Cassette: released on Phonogram (France) in Aug'83

LIVE (Blakey, Art & The Jazz Messengers).
Album: released on Carrere(France) in Apr'84 by Carrere Records (France). Distributed by: PRT

LIVE AT BUBBA'S.
Album: released on Gateway (USA) in Sep'83 by Gemcom Inc.(USA) Records

LIVE AT KIMBALL'S (Blakey, Art & The Jazz Messengers).
Tracks: / Second Thoughts / I Love You / Jody / Old Folks / You and the Night and the Music / Polka Dots and Moonbeams / Dr. Jekyl.
Album: released on Concord Jazz (USA) in Dec'86 by Concord Jazz Records (USA). Distributed by: IMS, Polygram

Cassette: released on Concord Jazz (USA) in Dec'86 by Concord Jazz Records (USA). Distributed by: IMS, Polygram

LIVE AT MONTREAUX & NORTH-SEA (Blakey, Art & The Jazz Messengers Big Band).

Album: released on Timeless(import) in '81. Distributed by: Cadillac

LIVE AT RONNIE SCOTT'S (Blakey, Art & The Jazz Messengers).
Notes: Art Blakey and the Jazz Messengers includes the virtuoso trumpet of Terence Blanchard, and the tenor saxophone of Jean Toussaint, in a memorable set which will be remembered for it's spontaneous clarity.
Compact disc: released on Heron in May'87

LIVE AT SWEET BASIL (Blakey, Art & The Jazz Messengers).
Tracks: / Jodi / Blues march / Mr.Babe / Moanin'.
Notes: Album recorded in March 1985,Blakey's current Messengers,as featured on this album,need no introduction.They have been frequent visitors to the UK over the past three years,packing them in down at Ronnie Scotts.Straight ahead be-bop featuring two of Blakey's most popular vehicles'Blues March'&'Moanin''.
Album: released on King (Japan) in Jul'86. Distributed by: IMS, Polygram

MESSAGES (Blakey, Art & The Jazz Messengers).
Album: released on Vogue Jazz in Feb'79

MOANIN' (Blakey, Art & The Jazz Messengers).
Album: released on Blue Note (USA Import) in Sep'84

MOSAIC (Blakey, Art & The Jazz Messengers).
Tracks: / Mosaic / Down under / Children of the night / Arabia / Crisis.
Compact disc: released on Manhattan-Blue Note in May'87 by EMI America Records (USA). Distributed by: EMI

NEW YEAR'S EVE AT SWEET BASIL (Blakey, Art & The Jazz Messengers).
Tracks: / Hide and seek / Little man / New York / I want to talk about you.
Notes: Recorded 1985/6.
Album: released on King (USA) in Apr'87. Distributed by: Gusto Distribution

NEW YORK SCENE.
Tracks: / Oh,by the way / Ballad medley:(my one & only love) / It's easy to remember / Who cares / Controversy / Tenderly / Falafel.
Compact disc: released on Concord Jazz (USA) in Sep'86 by Concord Jazz Records (USA). Distributed by: IMS, Polygram

Album: released on Concord Jazz (USA) in Nov'84 by Concord Jazz Records (USA). Distributed by: IMS, Polygram

Cassette: released on Concord Jazz (USA) in Nov'84 by Concord Jazz Records (USA). Distributed by: IMS, Polygram

NIGHT AT BIRDLAND, A - VOL. ONE (Blakey, Art Quintet).
Tracks: / Split kick / Once in a while / Quicksilver / Wee-dot / Blues / Night in Tunisia, A / Mayreh.
Compact disc: released on Manhattan-Blue Note in May'87 by EMI America Records (USA). Distributed by: EMI

NIGHT AT BIRDLAND, A VOL.1.
Cassette: released on Blue Note in Apr'87 by EMI Records. Distributed by: EMI

Album: released on Blue Note in Apr'87 by EMI Records. Distributed by: EMI

NIGHT AT BIRDLAND, A VOL.2.
Cassette: released on Blue Note in Apr'87 by EMI Records. Distributed by: EMI

Album: released on Blue Note in Apr'87 by EMI Records. Distributed by: EMI

Album: released on Blue Note in Jul'85 by EMI Records. Distributed by: EMI

NIGHT IN TUNISIA (Blakey, Art & The Jazz Messengers).
Compact disc: released on Philips in '83. Distributed by: IMS-Polygram

Album: released on Import Music Service (IMS) in Apr'81. Distributed by: Concord Jazz Distributions, Pablo, Polygram

Compact disc: released on Philips in '83. Distributed by: IMS-Polygram

NIGHT IN TUNISIA, A (Blakey, Art & The Jazz Messengers).
Tracks: / Night in Tunisia, A / Sincerely Diana / So tired / Yama / Kozo's waltz.
Notes: P 1987 Manhattan Records,a division of Capitol records Inc.
Compact disc: released on Manhattan-Blue Note in May'87 by EMI America Records (USA). Distributed by: EMI

Album: released on Blue Note in Sep'84 by EMI Records. Distributed by: EMI

Cassette: released on Blue Note in Mar'84 by EMI Records. Distributed by: EMI

OH BY THE WAY (Blakey, Art & The Jazz Messengers).

Album: released on Timeless in Aug'82

ONE BY ONE (Blakey, Art & The Jazz Messengers).
Album: released on Palcoscenico (Italy) in '81. Distributed by: Jazz Music

ORGY IN RHYTHM, VOL 1.
Album: released on Blue Note (USA) in Sep'84

PERCUSSION DISCUSSION (Blakey, Art & Max Roach).

REFLECTIONS IN BLUE (Blakey, Art & The Jazz Messengers).
Album: released on Timeless in Apr'81

STRAIGHT AHEAD.
Album: released on Concord in Dec'81 by Import Records. Distributed by: IMS, Polygram

UGETSU.
Album: released on Prestige in Jun'84 by Prestige Records (USA). Distributed by: RCA, JSU, Swift

Blam Blam

SUMMER HOLIDAY.
Single (7"): released on Kak in Jun'85. Distributed by: M.I.S., EMI

Blanchard, Terence

DISCERNMENT.
Tracks: / Worth the Pain / When The Saints Go Marching In / When I Fall in Love / Directions / Discernment / Are You Sleeping? / Akira / Dorchester House.
Album: released on George Wein Concord Jazz (USA) in Apr'86 by Concord Jazz Records (USA). Distributed by: IMS, Polygram

Cassette: released on George Wein Concord Jazz (USA) in Apr'86 by Concord Jazz Records (USA). Distributed by: IMS, Polygram

Compact disc: released on Concord Jazz (USA) in Jan'86 by Concord Jazz Records (USA). Distributed by: IMS, Polygram

NEW YORK SECOND LINE.
Album: released on George Wein Concord Jazz (USA) in Apr'84 by Concord Jazz Records (USA). Distributed by: IMS, Polygram

Blanchart, Dirk

COCKPIT.
Single (7"): released on Statik in Jan'85. Distributed by: Rough Trade Distribution, Stage One Distribution

Single (12"): released on Statik in Jan'85. Distributed by: Rough Trade Distribution, Stage One Distribution

DROP ME IN A CITY.
Single (7"): released on Statik in Jun'84. Distributed by: Rough Trade Distribution, Stage One Distribution

I DON'T MIND IF THE SPUTNIK LANDS.
Single (7"): released on Statik in Jan'84. Distributed by: Rough Trade Distribution, Stage One Distribution

Single (12"): released on Statik in Jan'84. Distributed by: Rough Trade Distribution, Stage One Distribution

Blancmange

BELIEVE YOU ME.
Tracks: / Lose your love / What's your problem? / Paradise / Why don't they leave things alone / 22339 / Don't you love it all / Believe / Lorraine's my nurse / Other animals / No wonder they never made it / John.
Compact disc: released on London in Nov'85 by London Records. Distributed by: Polygram

Album: released on London in Oct'85 by London Records. Distributed by: Polygram

Cassette: released on London in Oct'85 by London Records. Distributed by: Polygram

BLIND VISION.
Single (7"): released on London in May'83 by London Records. Distributed by: Polygram

Single (12"): released on London in May'83 by London Records. Distributed by: Polygram

DAY BEFORE YOU CAME,(THE).
Single (7"): released on London in Jun'84 by London Records. Distributed by: Polygram

Single (12"): released on London in Jun'84 by London Records. Distributed by: Polygram

Single (7"): released on London in Jul'84 by London Records. Distributed by: Polygram

Single (12"): released on London in Jul'84 by London Records. Distributed by: Polygram

DON'T TELL ME.
Single (12"): released on London in Mar'84 by London Records. Distributed by: Polygram

Single (7"): released on London in Mar'84 by London Records. Distributed by: Polygram

HAPPY FAMILIES.
Album: released on London in Sep'82 by London Records. Distributed by: Polygram

Cassette: released on London in Sep'82 by London Records. Distributed by: Polygram

HELLO,GOOD EVENING (VIDEO).
Tracks: / Blind vision / That's love that it is / Don't tell me / Living on the ceiling.
Notes: A live recording from the Hammersmith Palais interspersed with other footage, and featuring 13 songs in all by the duo, including their singles. Number of tracks: 13 Type of recording: Live Total playing time: 60mins
Video-cassette (VHS): released on Polygram Music in Oct'84 by Polygram Records. Distributed by: Polygram

Video-cassette [Betamax]: released on Polygram Music in Oct'84 by Polygram Records. Distributed by: Polygram

I CAN SELL IT.
Tracks: / I can sell it / Scream down the house.
Single (7"): released on London in Apr'86 by London Records. Distributed by: Polygram

Single (12"): released on London in Apr'86 by London Records. Distributed by: Polygram

LIVING ON THE CEILING.
Single (7"): released on London in Oct'82 by London Records. Distributed by: Polygram

Single (12"): released on London in Oct'82 by London Records. Distributed by: Polygram

LOSE YOUR LOVE.
Single (12"): released on London in Oct'85 by London Records. Distributed by: Polygram

MANGE TOUT.
Tracks: / Don't tell me / Blind vision / That's love that is / Day before you came, The.
Compact disc: released on London in Jun'84 by London Records. Distributed by: Polygram

Album: released on London in May'84 by London Records. Distributed by: Polygram

Cassette: released on London in May'84 by London Records. Distributed by: Polygram

THAT'S LOVE THAT IT IS.
Single (7"): released on London in Nov'83 by London Records. Distributed by: Polygram

Single (12"): released on London in Nov'83 by London Records. Distributed by: Polygram

Picture disc single: released on London in Nov'83 by London Records. Distributed by: Polygram

WHAT'S YOUR PROBLEM?.
Single (7"): released on London in Aug'85 by London Records. Distributed by: Polygram

Single (12"): released on London in Aug'85 by London Records. Distributed by: Polygram

Blanc, Richard De
HUSH.
Single (7"): released on Avatar in Apr'84 by Avatar Communications. Distributed by: CBS

Bland, Billy
BLUES CHICKEN, FRIENDS AND RELATIVES.
Album: released on Ace in Jun'87 by Ace Records. Distributed by: Pinnacle, Swift, Hotshot, Cadillac

LET THE LITTLE GIRL DANCE.
Single (7"): released on Old Gold in Jul'82 by Old Gold Records. Distributed by: Lightning, Jazz Music, Spartan, Counterpoint

Bland, Bobby
AFTER ALL.
Album: released on Malaco in Dec'86 by Malaco Records. Distributed by: Charly

AIN'T NOTHING YOU CAN DO.
Album: released on Duke in '77. Distributed by: Swift Distribution

BAREFOOT, ROCK, (THE) (Bland, Bobby & Junior Parker).
Album: released on Duke in '77. Distributed by: Swift Distribution

BEST OF BOBBY BLAND, (THE).
Album: released on ABC in Apr'82. Distributed by: CBS, Pinnacle

Cassette: released on ABC in Apr'82. Distributed by: CBS, Pinnacle

BLUES IN THE NIGHT.
Album: released on Ace in May'85 by Ace Records. Distributed by: Pinnacle, Swift, Hotshot, Cadillac

Cassette: released on Ace in May'85 by Ace Records. Distributed by: Pinnacle, Swift, Hotshot, Cadillac

CALL ON ME.
Album: released on Duke in '77. Distributed by: Swift Distribution

FOOLIN' WITH THE BLUES.
Album: released on Charly(R&B) in '83 by Charly Records. Distributed by: Charly, Cadillac

Album: released on ABC in Jun'78. Distributed by: CBS, Pinnacle

HERE'S THE MAN.
Album: released on Duke in '77. Distributed by: Swift Distribution

INSTRUMENTAL ALBUM.
Album:

INTROSPECTIVE OF THE EARLY YEARS.
Album: released on Duke in '77. Distributed by: Swift Distribution

LIKE 'ER RED HOT.
Album: released on Duke in '77. Distributed by: Swift Distribution

MEMBERS ONLY.
Tracks: / Members only / In the ghetto / I've just got to know / Straight / From the shoulder / Sweet woman's love / Can we make love tonight / Sweet surrender / I need your love so bad / Heart open up again.
Album: released on Malaco in Nov'85 by Malaco Records. Distributed by: Charly

MEMBERS ONLY (12").
Tracks: / Members only / Straight from the shoulder / Sweet surrender.
Single (12"): released on Malaco in Mar'86 by Malaco Records. Distributed by: Charly

REFLECTIONS IN BLUE.
Album: released on ABC in May'77. Distributed by: CBS, Pinnacle

SHOES.
Single (7"): released on Kent in Jun'85 by Ace Records. Distributed by: Pinnacle. Estim retail price in Sep'87 was £9.62.

SOULFUL SIDE OF BOBBY BLAND, THE.
Tracks: / Getting used to the blues / Yum yum tree / These hands(small but mighty) / Back in the same old bag again / Keep on loving me(you'll see the change) / Honey child / Wouldn't you rather have me / Call on me / Dear Bobby / How does a cheating woman feel / I ain't myself anymore / That did it / Ain't doing too bad(pt.1) / Love with a reputation / Good time Charlie / Ain't nothing you can do.
Album: released on Kent in Oct'86 by Ace Records. Distributed by: Pinnacle

Album: released on Kent in Oct'85 by Ace Records. Distributed by: Pinnacle

SOUL OF THE MAN, (THE).
Album: released on Duke in '77. Distributed by: Swift Distribution

SPOTLIGHTING THE MAN B.B..
Album: released on Duke in '77. Distributed by: Swift Distribution

TOGETHER AGAIN - LIVE (Bland, Bobby & B.B. King).
Album: released on Impulse in Jul'76 by Impulse Records. Distributed by: MCA, Polygram

TOUCH OF THE BLUES.
Album: released on Duke in '77. Distributed by: Swift Distribution

TWO STEPS FROM THE BLUES.
Album: released on Duke in '77. Distributed by: Swift Distribution

WOKE UP SCREAMING.
Album: released on Ace in Oct'81 by Ace Records. Distributed by: Pinnacle, Swift, Hotshot, Cadillac

Bland, Paula Ann
LOCOMOTION.
Single (7"): released on Kay-Drum in Sep'83 by Kay-Drum Records. Distributed by: Pinnacle

Blank, Stu
NO FAT ON THE BONE (Blank, Stu & His Nasty Habits).
Album: released on Move in Jun'86 by Charly Records. Distributed by: Charly Distribution, Fast Forward Distribution, Cartel Distribution

Blarney Lads
FOLK SONGS FROM THE EMERALD ISLE.
Album: released on Music Masters in Mar'82 by Music Masters Records. Distributed by: Taylors

Blast
BLAST (Various Artists).
Album: released on Criminal Damage in Nov'86 by Criminal Damage Records. Distributed by: Backs, Cartel

IT'S IN MY BLOOD.
Album: released on SST in Aug'87 by SST Records. Distributed by: Pinnacle

POWER OF EXPRESSION, THE.
Album: released on Road Runner in Apr'86

Blast, C.L.
BOOMERANG LOVE.
Album: released on Charly in Nov'86 by Charly Records. Distributed by: Charly, Cadillac

I WANNA GET DOWN.
Album: released on Timeless in Aug'87

LAY ANOTHER LOG ON THE FIRE.
Tracks: / Lay another log on the fire / Somebody shot my eagle.
Single (12"): released on Charly in Feb'87 by Charly Records. Distributed by: Charly, Cadillac

Blasters
HARD LINE.
Album: released on Slash in May'85 by London Records. Distributed by: Polygram

Cassette: released on Slash in May'85 by London Records. Distributed by: Polygram

Blast Furnace
CAN'T STOP THE BOY.
Single (7"): released on Nighthawk in Aug'80 by Faulty Products Records. Distributed by: Pinnacle, Swift

SOUTH OF THE RIVER.
Single (7"): released on Nighthawk in Feb'79 by Faulty Products Records. Distributed by: Pinnacle, Swift

Blasting Concept
BLASTING CONCEPT COL. 2, THE
Various Artists (Various Artists).
Compact disc: released on SST in Aug'87 by SST Records. Distributed by: Pinnacle

BLASTING CONCEPT, (THE) Various artists.
Album: released on SST in Dec'83 by SST Records. Distributed by: Pinnacle

BLASTING CONCEPT VOL.2, (THE)
various artists (Various Artists).
Album: released on SST in Jul'86 by SST Records. Distributed by: Pinnacle

Blaze
WHATCHA GONNA DO.
Tracks: / Whatcha Gonna Do / Whatcha Gonna Do (Dub mix).
Single (7"): released on Champion in Feb'87 by Champion Records. Distributed by: RCA

Single (12"): released on Champion in Feb'87 by Champion Records. Distributed by: RCA

Blazing Apostles
DAY OF DESCENT.
Notes: Distributor: Broken Records,37 Dollar Crescent,Kircaldy,Fife,Scotland.
Single (7"): released on Broken in Mar'86 by Broken Records. Distributed by: Stiff Records, EMI

DAY OF DESCENT, (THE).
Single (7"): released on Broken in Oct'84. Distributed by: Fast Forward

IT'S SO EASY.
Tracks: / It's so easy / Comfort.
Single (7"): released on KDY in Feb'86. Distributed by: Fast Forward, Cartel

Blazin' Son
CHANT DOWN NATIONAL FRONT.
Single (7"): released on Cool Ghoul in Jul'83 by Cool Ghoul Records. Distributed by: Rough Trade, Cool Ghoul

Bleeched Black
BLEECHED BLACK.
Album: released on Relativity (USA) in Aug'87. Distributed by: Pinnacle

Blegvad, Peter
NAKED SHAKESPEARE, (THE).
Album: released on Virgin in Dec'83 by Virgin Records. Distributed by: EMI, Virgin Distribution

NIGHTS LIKE THIS KNIGHT.
Album: released on Virgin in Aug'85 by Virgin Records. Distributed by: EMI, Virgin Distribution

Cassette: released on Virgin in Aug'85 by Virgin Records. Distributed by: EMI, Virgin Distribution

SPECIAL DELIVERY.
Single (12"): released on Virgin in Jul'85 by Virgin Records. Distributed by: EMI, Virgin Distribution

Blenner, Serge
DIMENSION PROCHAINE, (LA).
Album: released on Sky (Germany) in Aug'86

PLAISIR ARDENT.
Album: released on Sky (Germany) in Aug'85

Bless Me Father
BLESS ME FATHER Boyd, Neil (Wheeler, Peter).
Cassette: released on Soundings in Mar'85. Distributed by: Soundings

Blevins, Alan
SMILE WITH US.
Tracks: / Smile with us.
Single (7"): released on Neat in Aug'86 by Neat Records. Distributed by: Pinnacle, Neat

Bley, Carla
DINNER MUSIC.
Cassette: released on ECM (Germany) in Jul'85 by ECM Records. Distributed by: IMS, Polygram, Virgin through EMI

ESCALATOR OVER THE HILL.
Album: released on ECM in Dec'81 by ECM Records. Distributed by: IMS, Polygram, Virgin through EMI

EUROPEAN TOUR 1977.
Compact disc: released on ECM (Germany) in Jul'87 by ECM Records. Distributed by: IMS, Polygram, Virgin through EMI

HEAVY HEART.
Tracks: / Light or dark / Talking hearts / Joyful noise / Ending it / Starting again / Heavy heart.
Album: released on Watts in Mar'84

Cassette: released on Watts in Jul'85

I HATE TO SING.
Album: released on ECM (Germany) in Jan'85 by ECM Records. Distributed by: IMS, Polygram, Virgin through EMI

LIVE.
Tracks: / Blunt object / Lord is listenin' to ya,hallelujah, The / Time & us / Still in the room / Real life hits / Song sung long.
Compact disc: released on ECM (Germany) in Feb'86 by ECM Records. Distributed by: IMS, Polygram, Virgin through EMI

Album: released on ECM (Germany) in May'82 by ECM Records. Distributed by: IMS, Polygram, Virgin through EMI

Cassette: released on ECM (Germany) in Jun'84 by ECM Records. Distributed by: IMS, Polygram, Virgin through EMI

MORTELLE RANDONNEE.
Tracks: / Musique mecanique / Whistling palomino / Morning / Death rolls / Los Palominos / Sad Paloma / Paloma, La / Some dirge / Teenage Paloma / Grown-up Paloma / Blunt object.
Album: released on Phonogram in Jun'83 by Phonogram Records. Distributed by: Polygram

Album: released on Phonogram in Jun'83 by Phonogram Records. Distributed by: Polygram

MUSIQUE MECANIQUE.
Cassette: released on ECM (Germany) in Jul'85 by ECM Records. Distributed by: IMS, Polygram, Virgin through EMI

NIGHT-GLO.
Tracks: / Pretend you're in love / Night-glo / Rut / Crazy with you / Wildlife:horns-paws without claws-sex with birds.
Notes: With her new album 'Night-Glo' Carla Bley moves clearly into the direction already indicated on 'Heavy Heart'. With a slightly reduced line up of excellent musicians she sticks closely to fixed musical structures, rather than leaving spacefor extended improvisations. The album is built around the bass of Steve Swallow. Her instruction for the album shows her intentions; 'Slip into something comfortable, make yourself a cool drink, turn down the lights and and put on 'Night-Glo". With its perfect mixture of melancholy and subtle humour this new albumis another example of Carla Bley's musical flexibility. Personnel: Carla Bley -organ, synthesizers/Steve Swallow-bass/Larry Willis-piano, electric piano/Hiram Bullock-guitar/Victor Lewis-drums/Manolo Badrena-percussion.
Compact disc: released on ECM (Germany) in Dec'85 by ECM Records. Distributed by: IMS, Polygram, Virgin through EMI

Album: released on ECM (Germany) in Dec'85 by ECM Records. Distributed by: IMS, Polygram, Virgin through EMI

SEXTET.
Tracks: / More Brahms / Houses and people /

Girl who cried champagne, The / Brooklyn bridge / Lawns / Healing power.
Notes: With 'Sextet' Carla Bley continues along the musical road she set out on with "Heavy Heart" and "Night-Glo" (WATT 14 & 16). Putting aside the avantgarde, shehas developed a style that is accessible to a large audience.
Album: released on ECM (Germany) in Apr'87 by ECM Records. Distributed by: IMS, Polygram, Virgin through EMI

Compact disc: released on ECM (Germany) in Apr'87 by ECM Records. Distributed by: IMS, Polygram, Virgin through EMI

SOCIAL STUDIES.
Album: released on ECM (France) in Jun'81 by ECM Records. Distributed by: IMS, Polygram, Virgin through EMI

Compact disc: released on ECM (Germany) in Jul'87 by ECM Records. Distributed by: IMS, Polygram, Virgin through EMI

Bley, Paul

ALONE AGAIN.
Album: released on Impro-arts in Jul'78. Distributed by: Projection

BALLADS (Bley, Paul, Altschul & Peacock).

FRAGMENTS.
Compact disc: released on ECM (Germany) in Sep'86 by ECM Records. Distributed by: IMS, Polygram, Virgin through EMI

Album: released on ECM (Germany) in Sep'86 by ECM Records. Distributed by: IMS, Polygram, Virgin through EMI

JAPAN SUITE.
Album: released on Impro-arts in Jul'78. Distributed by: Projection

OPEN TO LOVE.
Tracks: / Closer / Ida Lupino / Open to love / Started / Harlem / Seven / Nothing ever was anyway.
Compact disc: by ECM Records. Distributed by: IMS, Polygram, Virgin through EMI

QUIET SONG (Bley, Paul, Connors & Guiffre).
Album: released on Impro-arts in Jul'78. Distributed by: Projection

RAMBLING.
Album: released on Affinity in Jan'80 by Charly Records. Distributed by: Charly, Cadillac

SONOR.
Tracks: / Little bells / Landscape / Speed / Recollection / Joined / Sonor / Waltz / Set / Darkness / Tightrope.
Album: released on Soul Note in May'85. Distributed by: Harmonia Mundi Distributors

TURNING POINT (Bley, Paul & various artists).
Album: released on Impro-arts in '78. Distributed by: Projection

VIRTUISI (Bley, Paul, Altschul & Peacock).
Album: released on Impro-arts in Jul'78. Distributed by: Projection

Blind Blake

BOOTLEG RUM DUM BLUES.
Album: released on Blue Moon in Jun'87. Distributed by: Magnum Music Group Ltd, PRT, Spartan

Blind Date

BLIND DATE Original Soundtrack.
Album: released on Silva Screen in Aug'87 by Silva Screen Records. Distributed by: Silva Screen

Cassette: released on Silva Screen in Aug'87 by Silva Screen Records. Distributed by: Silva Screen

HEY DAD.
Tracks: / Hey dad.
Single (7"): released on Mak in Jan'86 by Mak. Distributed by: Pinnacle

TOO HOT TO HANDLE.
Single (7"): released on Mak in Aug'85 by Mak. Distributed by: Pinnacle

Single (12"): released on Mak in Aug'85 by Mak. Distributed by: Pinnacle

YOUR HEART KEEPS BURNING.
Tracks: / Your heart keeps burning / Feel my love.
Single (7"): released on Arista in Feb'86 by Arista Records. Distributed by: RCA

Blind Faith

BLIND FAITH.
Tracks: / Had to cry today / Can't find my way home / Well alright / Presence of the Lord / Sea of joy / Do what you like.

Compact disc: released on Polydor in Apr'86 by Polydor Records. Distributed by: Polygram, Polydor

Album: released on RSO in Aug'83

Cassette: released on RSO in Aug'83 Deleted '86.

Blind Fury

OUT OF REACH.
Album: released on Road Runner in Jun'85

Blind Idiot God

BLIND IDIOT GOD.
Album: released on SST in Jul'87 by SST Records. Distributed by: Pinnacle

Cassette: released on SST in Jul'87 by SST Records. Distributed by: Pinnacle

Blinding Tears

BLINDING TEARS.
Compact disc: . Distributed by: PRT

Album: released on Riva in Mar'87. Distributed by: PRT

Cassette: released on Riva in Mar'87. Distributed by: PRT

HEAVEN ONLY KNOWS.
Tracks: / Heaven only knows / Call of the wild.
Single (7"): released on Riva in Feb'87. Distributed by: PRT

Bliss

I HEAR YOU CALL.
Single (12"): released on Sermon in Jan'87. Distributed by: Backs, Cartel

Blistering Moments

THERAPEUTIC DREAMS.
Album: released on Deadman's Curve in Nov'86 by Dave Henderson

Blitz

ALL OUT ATTACK.
Single (7"): released on No Future in Jul'82 by No Future Records. Distributed by: Pinnacle, Rough Trade, Cartel

BLITZ original London cast.
Album: released on That's Entertainment in Apr'83 by That's Entertainment Records. Distributed by: Pinnacle, PRT

Cassette: released on That's Entertainment in Apr'83 by That's Entertainment Records. Distributed by: Pinnacle, PRT

NEVER SURRENDER.
Single (7"): released on No Future in Jul'82 by No Future Records. Distributed by: Pinnacle, Rough Trade, Cartel

NEW AGE.
Single (7"): released on Future in Jan'83. Distributed by: Pinnacle

SECOND EMPIRE JUSTICE.
Album: released on Future in May'83. Distributed by: Pinnacle

SOLAR.
Single (7"): released on No Future in Oct'83 by No Future Records. Distributed by: Pinnacle, Rough Trade, Cartel

Single (12"): released on No Future in Oct'83 by No Future Records. Distributed by: Pinnacle, Rough Trade, Cartel

TELECOMMUNICATIONS (EP).
Single (7"): released on No Future in Apr'83 by No Future Records. Distributed by: Pinnacle, Rough Trade, Cartel

TELECOMMUNICATION.
Single (12"): released on No Future in Apr'83 by No Future Records. Distributed by: Pinnacle, Rough Trade, Cartel

VOICE OF A GENERATION.
Tracks: / Warriors / Propaganda / Time bomb / Criminal damage / Fuck you / We are the boys / Bleed / I don't need you / Your revolution / Moscow.
Album: released on No Future in Oct'82 by No Future Records. Distributed by: Pinnacle, Rough Trade, Cartel

WARRIORS.
Single (7"): released on No Future in Jul'82 by No Future Records. Distributed by: Pinnacle, Rough Trade, Cartel

Blitzkrieg

BLITZKRIEG.
Album: released on Neat in Mar'85 by Neat Records. Distributed by: Pinnacle, Neat

BURIED ALIVE.
Single (7"): released on Neat in Oct'81 by Neat Records. Distributed by: Pinnacle, Neat

CONCIOUS PRAYER.
Single (7"): released on Sexual Phonograph in Mar'83 by Sexual Phonograph Records. Distributed by: Stage One

LEST WE FORGET.
Single (7"): released on No Future in Jul'82 by No Future Records. Distributed by: Pinnacle, Rough Trade, Cartel

READY FOR ACTION.
Album: released on Roadrunner (Dutch) in Nov'85. Distributed by: Pinnacle

TIME OF CHANGES, A.
Tracks: / Ragnarok / Inferno / Blitzkreig / Pull the trigger / Armageddon / Hell to pay / Vikings / Time of changes, A / Saviour.
Album: released on Neat in '85 by Neat Records. Distributed by: Pinnacle, Neat

Blitz One

BLITZ ONE (Various Artists).
Album: released on Hallmark in Jan'87 by Pickwick Records. Distributed by: Pickwick Distribution, PRT, Taylors

Cassette: released on Hallmark in Jan'87 by Pickwick Records. Distributed by: Pickwick Distribution, PRT, Taylors

Block, Rory

HOW TO PLAY BLUES GUITAR (Block, Rory/Stefan Grossman).
Album: released on Kicking Mule in '78 by Sonet. Distributed by: Roots, PRT

RHINESTONE & STEEL STRINGS.
Album: released on Rounder (USA) in Jul'84. Distributed by: Mike's Country Music Room Distribution, Jazz Music Distribution, Swift Distribution, Roots Records Distribution, Projection Distribution, Topic Distribution

YOU'RE THE ONE.
Tracks: / You're the one / Askin' for more / Someone like you / I can't believe in you no more / Please put out the fire / Love at first sight / If I can't have good love / Movin' up / Movin' out.
Album: by Chrysalis Records. Distributed by: CBS

Blondel

BLONDEL Original soundtrack (Rice, Tim).
Album: released on MCA in Nov'83 by MCA Records. Distributed by: Polygram, MCA

Cassette: released on MCA in Nov'83 by MCA Records. Distributed by: Polygram, MCA

Blondell, Joan

Bing Crosby and Joan Blondell

Blondie

BEST OF BLONDIE.
Tracks: / Denis / Tide is high, The / In the flesh / Sunday girl / I'm always touched by your presence dear / Dreaming / Hanging on the telephone / Rapture / Picture this / Union City blues / Call me / Atomic / Rip her to shreds / Heart of glass.
Album: released on Chrysalis in Oct'81 by Chrysalis Records. Distributed by: CBS

Cassette: released on Chrysalis in Oct'81 by Chrysalis Records. Distributed by: CBS

Compact disc: released on Chrysalis in Oct'81 by Chrysalis Records. Distributed by: CBS

BLONDIE.
Tracks: / X offender / Rifle range / Look good in blue / In the sun / Shark in jets clothing, A / Man overboard / Rip her to shreds / Little girl lies / In the flesh / Kung fu girls / Attack of the giant ants, The.
Album: released on Hallmark in Oct'82 by Pickwick Records. Distributed by: Pickwick Distribution, PRT, Taylors

Cassette: released on Hallmark in Oct'82 by Pickwick Records. Distributed by: Pickwick Distribution, PRT, Taylors

Album: released on MFP in Apr'85 by EMI Records. Distributed by: EMI

Cassette: released on MFP in Apr'85 by EMI Records. Distributed by: EMI

BLONDIE- LIVE(VIDEO).
Tracks: / Heart of glass / Call me / Tide is high, The.
Notes: Type of recording: Live
Total playing time: 53minutes.
Debbie Harry and band filmed at their final live concert,and featuring 5 years worth of hits like'Heart of Glass','Call Me' and 'The Tide Is High'.
Video-cassette (VHS): released on CIC Video in Oct'86 by CBS Records. Distributed by: CBS, Pickwick Distribution

CALL ME.
Tracks: / Call Me / Union City Blue.
Single (7"): released on Old Gold in Feb'87 by Old Gold Records. Distributed by: Lightning, Jazz Music, Spartan, Counterpoint

DENIS.
Single (7"): released on Chrysalis in Feb'78 by Chrysalis Records. Distributed by: CBS

Single (12"): released on Chrysalis in Dec'81 by Chrysalis Records. Distributed by: CBS

DREAMING.
Tracks: / Dreaming / Atomic.
Single (7"): released on Old Gold in Feb'87 by Old Gold Records. Distributed by: Lightning, Jazz Music, Spartan, Counterpoint

EAT TO THE BEAT.
Tracks: / Dreaming / Hardest part, The / Union city blues / Shayla / Eat to the beat / Accidents never happen / Die young stay pretty / Slow motion / Atomic / Sound asleep / Victor / Living in the real world.
Compact disc: released on Chrysalis in Jun'87 by Chrysalis Records. Distributed by: CBS

HEART OF GLASS.
Tracks: / Heart of Glass / Tide is high (The).
Compact disc: released on Old Gold in Feb'87 by Old Gold Records. Distributed by: Lightning, Jazz Music, Spartan, Counterpoint

Single (7"): released on Chrysalis in Jan'79 by Chrysalis Records. Distributed by: CBS

Single (12"): released on Chrysalis in Jan'79 by Chrysalis Records. Distributed by: CBS

ISLAND OF LOST SOULS.
Single (7"): released on Chrysalis in Apr'82 by Chrysalis Records. Distributed by: CBS

PARALLEL LINES.
Tracks: / Fade away & radiate / Hanging on the telephone / One way or another / Picture this / Pretty baby / I know but I don't know / 11.59 / Will anything happen / Sunday girl / Heart of glass / I'm gonna love you too / Just go away.
Album: released on Fame (Chrysalis) in Nov'83 by Music For Pleasure Records. Distributed by: EMI

Cassette: released on Fame (Chrysalis) in Nov'83 by Music For Pleasure Records. Distributed by: EMI

Compact disc: released on Fame (Chrysalis) in Nov'83 by Music For Pleasure Records. Distributed by: EMI

RAPTURE.
Single (12"): released on Chrysalis in Jan'81 by Chrysalis Records. Distributed by: CBS

SUNDAY GIRL.
Tracks: / Sunday Girl / Hanging on the Telephone.
Single (7"): released on Old Gold in Feb'87 by Old Gold Records. Distributed by: Lightning, Jazz Music, Spartan, Counterpoint

Single (7"): released on Chrysalis in May'79 by Chrysalis Records. Distributed by: CBS

Single (12"): released on Chrysalis in Dec'81 by Chrysalis Records. Distributed by: CBS

Blondy, Alpha

JAH GLORY (Blondy, Alpha & The Natty Rebels).
Album: released on Celluloid (France) in Aug'85 by Island. Distributed by: Polygram

RASTA POUE.
Single (12"): released on Syllart in Aug'84 by Earthworks Records. Distributed by: Earthworks Distributors

Blonker

HOMELAND.
Tracks: / African kalimba / Morning breeze / Sleep walk / Perpetuum motion / Blue horizon / Here there and everywhere / Alhambra / Maria Elena / Homeland / When a man loves a woman.
Album: released on German Import in Nov'83. Distributed by: IMS, Polygram

Cassette: released on German Import in Nov'83. Distributed by: IMS, Polygram

Blood

FALSE GESTURES FOR A DEVIOUS PUBLIC.
Tracks: / Done some brain cells last night / Degenerate / Gestapo khazi / Well sick / Sewer brain / Sucker / Mesrine / Rule 43 / Joys of noise / Waste of flesh and bones / Throttle you blue.
Album: released on Noise in Nov'83 by Dorane. Distributed by: Revolver, Cartel

MEGLOMANIA.
Single (7"): released on No Future in Mar'83 by No Future Records. Distributed by: Pinnacle, Rough Trade, Cartel

SICK KICKS FOR SHOCK ROCKERS.

Album: released on Conquest in Jun'85. Distributed by: Red Rhino, Cartel

STARK RAVING NORMAL.
Single (7"): released on Noise in Oct'83 by Dorane. Distributed by: Revolver, Cartel

Blood Brothers

BLOOD BROTHERS Original cast feat.Barbara Dickson (Various Artists).

Blood Donor

DOCTOR?.
Single (7"): released on Safari in May'85 by Safari Records. Distributed by: Pinnacle

Bloodfire Posse

ARE YOU READY.
Tracks: / Are you ready / Rub a dub soldier / Pink panther (The) / Nuclear weapons / Every posse get flat / Suddenly / Coconut water / Be / I should have known better / Are you ready.
Album: released on CBS in Nov'86 by CBS Records. Distributed by: CBS

Cassette: released on CBS in Nov'86 by CBS Records. Distributed by: CBS

Album: released on Synergy in Dec'85. Distributed by: Jetstar Distribution

ARE YOU READY (SINGLE).
Tracks: / Are you ready / Coconut water / Every posse gets flat.
Single (12"): released on CBS in Sep'86 by CBS Records. Distributed by: CBS

Single (7"): released on CBS in Aug'86 by CBS Records. Distributed by: CBS

EVERY POSSE GET FLAT.
Tracks: / Every posse get flat / Pink Panther.
Single (7"): released on CBS in Oct'86 by CBS Records. Distributed by: CBS

Single (12"): released on CBS in Oct'86 by CBS Records. Distributed by: CBS

Bloodied Sword, (The)

BLOODIED SWORD, (THE) Langdown, Maxwell (Ure, Midge & Chris Cross).
Album: released on Chrysalis in Apr'83 by Chrysalis Records. Distributed by: CBS

Cassette: released on Chrysalis in Apr'83 by Chrysalis Records. Distributed by: CBS

Blood, James

TALES OF CAPTAIN BLACK.
Album: released on Artists House in May'81. Distributed by: JSU, Swift

Bloodlust

GUILTY AS SIN.
Album: released on Roadrunner (Dutch) in Aug'86. Distributed by: Pinnacle

Blood On The Cats

BLOOD ON THE CATS various artists (Various Artists).
Album: released on Anagram in Sep'83 by Cherry Red Records. Distributed by: Pinnacle

BLOOD ON THE CATS/REVENGE OF THE KILLER PUSSIES Various artists (Various Artists).
Double Album: released on Anagram in May'86 by Cherry Red Records. Distributed by: Pinnacle

BLOOD ON THE CATS(VIDEO) Various artists (Various Artists).
Notes: A compilation of 17acts from the flourishing indie label music scene,many recorded live on stage.Mostly punk-oriented,but in all covering a range from Alien Sex Fiend to Lord S u t c h
Number of tracks: 17
Type of recording: Compilation
Total playing time: 55minutes.
Video-cassette (VHS): released on Jettisoundz in Oct'84. Distributed by: Red Rhino, Cartel

Blood On The Roq

BLOOD ON THE ROQ various artists (Various Artists).
Album: released on Quiet in Sep'83 by Quiet Records. Distributed by: Nine Mile, Cartel

Blood On The Saddle

BLOOD ON THE SADDLE.
Album: released on New Alliance (USA) in Apr'84 by SST Records. Distributed by: Rough Trade

POISON LOVE.
Album: released on Gates of Heaven in Apr'86. Distributed by: Stiff Records, EMI

Blood On The Sun

BLOOD ON THE SUN Original soundtrack.
Album: released on Citadel in Mar'79. Distributed by: Swift

Blood & Roses

ENOUGH IS NEVER ENOUGH.
Album: released on Audiodrome in Feb'85. Distributed by: Backs, Cartel

LIFE AFTER DEATH.
Cassette: released on 96 Tapes in Mar'85 by 96 Tapes Records. Distributed by: Rough Trade, Cartel

NECRO MANTRA.
Single (12"): released on Kamera in Feb'83

SOME LIKE IT HOT.
Single (7"): released on Audiodrome in Jun'85. Distributed by: Backs, Cartel

Single (12"): released on Audiodrome in Jun'85. Distributed by: Backs, Cartel

Bloods

BUTTON UP.
Single (7"): released on Exit International in Apr'82 by Phonogram Records. Distributed by: Polygram

Bloodshed & Butchery

BLOODSHED & BUTCHERY Various artists (Various Artists).
Album: released on Criminal Damage in '83 by Criminal Damage Records. Distributed by: Backs, Cartel

Blood Sisters

MY GUY.
Single (12"): released on Sound City in Mar'82 by Sound City Records. Distributed by: Jetstar

NIGHTS ARE SO LONELY.
Single (12"): released on Sound City in Sep'82 by Sound City Records. Distributed by: Jetstar

RING MY BELL.
Single (12"): released on Sound City in Jun'83 by Sound City Records. Distributed by: Jetstar

Bloodsport

AGENT.
Tracks: / Agent / On ice.
Single (7"): released on Quiet in Jan'86 by Quiet Records. Distributed by: Nine Mile, Cartel

CLASS STRUGGLE.
Single (12"): released on Quiet in Aug'85 by Quiet Records. Distributed by: Nine Mile, Cartel

Bloodstone

BLOODSTONE.
Album: released on Decca in '72 by Decca Records. Distributed by: Polygram

INSTANT LOVE.
Single (7"): released on Epic in Jun'84 by CBS Records. Distributed by: CBS

NATURAL HIGH.
Single (7"): released on Old Gold in Oct'83 by Old Gold Records. Distributed by: Lightning, Jazz Music, Spartan, Counterpoint

Blood, Sweat & Tears

CHALLENGE, (THE).
Album: released on Astan in Nov'84 by Astan Records. Distributed by: Counterpoint

Cassette: released on Astan in Nov'84 by Astan Records. Distributed by: Counterpoint

GREATEST HITS:BLOOD, SWEAT & TEARS.

LATIN FIRE.
Album: released on Platinum (W.Germany) in Oct'85. Distributed by: Mainline

Cassette: released on Platinum (W.Germany) in Oct'85. Distributed by: Mainline

Blood Uncles

BEATHAG.
Tracks: / Beathag / God says no / Broken town*.
Single (7"): released on Virgin in Jul'87 by Virgin Records. Distributed by: EMI, Virgin Distribution

Single (12"): released on Virgin in Jul'87 by Virgin Records. Distributed by: EMI, Virgin Distribution

CRASH.
Tracks: / Crash / Caravan / Never happy man.
Single (7"): released on Virgin in May'87 by Virgin Records. Distributed by: EMI, Virgin Distribution

Single (12"): released on Virgin in May'87 by Virgin Records. Distributed by: EMI, Virgin Distribution

PETROL.
Tracks: / Petrol (4-track EP).
Single (12"): released on Drastic Plastic in Apr'86. Distributed by: Fast Forward

Blood Uncles, The

LIBERTINE.
Album: released on Virgin in Aug'87 by Virgin Records. Distributed by: EMI, Virgin Distribution

Cassette: released on Virgin in Aug'87 by Virgin Records. Distributed by: EMI, Virgin Distribution

Bloody Marys

PARIS.
Tracks: / Paris / Party hair.
Single (12"): released on Mess in Sep'86. Distributed by: Revolver Distribution, Cartel Distribution

STAIN.
Tracks: / Stain / Suspicion.
Single (7"): released on Meff in May'87

Bloody Six

IN THE NAME OF BLOOD.
Album: released on Mausoleum in May'85 by Mausoleum Records. Distributed by: Pinnacle

Bloom, Bobby

MONTEGO BAY.
Tracks: / Montego Bay / Try a little harder.
Single (7"): released on Polydor in Oct'86 by Polydor Records. Distributed by: Polygram, Polydor

Single (7"): released on Old Gold in Jul'84 by Old Gold Records. Distributed by: Lightning, Jazz Music, Spartan, Counterpoint

Bloomfield, Hammond

TRIUMPIRATE.
Album: released on Edsel in Jun'87 by Demon Records. Distributed by: Pinnacle, Jazz Music, Projection

Bloomfield, Mike

AMERICAN HERO.
Album: released on Thunderbolt in Apr'84 by Magnum Music Group Ltd. Distributed by: Magnum Music Group Ltd, PRT Distribution, Spartan Distribution

ANALINE.
Album: released on Sonet in Jan'78 by Sonet Records. Distributed by: PRT

BLOOMFIELD.
Double Album: released on CBS in Jan'84 by CBS Records. Distributed by: CBS Deleted '85.

Double cassette: released on CBS in Jan'84 by CBS Records. Distributed by: CBS

BLOOMFIELD & HARRIS (Bloomfield, Mike & Woody Harris).
Album: released on Kicking Mule in Apr'80 by Sonet. Distributed by: Roots, PRT

CRUISIN' FOR A BRUISIN'.
Album: released on Sonet (Takoma USA) in Jun'81 by Sonet Records. Distributed by: PRT

IF YOU LOVE THESE BLUES....
Album: released on Sonet in Aug'77 by Sonet Records. Distributed by: PRT

I'M WITH YOU ALWAYS.
Album: released on Demon in Jun'87 by Demon Records. Distributed by: Pinnacle

LIVING IN THE FAST LANE.
Album: released on Waterhouse in Apr'82

TRIUMVIRATE (Bloomsfield / Hammond / Doctor John).
Album: released on Edsel in May'87 by Demon Records. Distributed by: Pinnacle, Jazz Music, Projection

Bloomfield, Steve

ROCKABILLY ORIGINALS.
Album: released on Charly in '78 by Charly Records. Distributed by: Charly, Cadillac

Bloom, Rube

RUBE BLOOM & OTHERS (Bloom, Rube & His Bayou Boys).
Album: released on VJM in Apr'79 by Wellard, Chris Distribution. Distributed by: Wellard,

Bloomsbury Set

DRESS PARADE.
Single (7"): released on Stiletto in Aug'83 by Fast Records. Distributed by: Cartel Distribution

Single (12"): released on Stiletto in Aug'83 by Fast Records. Distributed by: Cartel Distribution

HANGING AROUND WITH THE BIG BOYS.
Single (7"): released on Stiletto in Apr'83 by Fast Records. Distributed by: Cartel Distribution

Single (12"): released on Stiletto in Apr'83 by Fast Records. Distributed by: Cartel Distribution

SWEET EUROPEANS.
Single (7"): released on Disques Blue in Nov'82 by Disques Bleu

THIS YEAR NEXT YEAR.
Single (7"): by Graduate Records. Distributed by: Nine Mile, Cartel

Bloss, Rainer

AMPSY.
Tracks: / From long ago / Energy / Adoring multitude, The / Psyche / I'm the heat / He's an angel / Who the hell is she? / Lights out baby / Oracle, The / Love is the beginning.
Compact disc: by Magnum Music Group Ltd. Distributed by: Magnum Music Group Ltd, PRT Distribution, Spartan Distribution

Album: released on Thunderbolt in Jun'86 by Magnum Music Group Ltd. Distributed by: Magnum Music Group Ltd, PRT Distribution, Spartan Distribution

Album: released on Team (W. Germany) in Feb'85

Drive Inn

Bloss, Rainier

APHRICA (see Schulze, Klaus) (Bloss, Rainier/Klaus Schulze/Ernst Such).

Blotto Otto

LAST ORDERS.
Tracks: / Last orders / Blotto's blues.
Single (7"): released on Crystal in Jul'87 by Crystal Records. Distributed by: Spartan

Blount, Chris

MAYBE ANOTHER DAY (Blount, Chris New Orleans Jazz Band).
Album: released on Lake in Nov'86 by Fellside Recordings. Distributed by: Jazz Music, Fellside

TELL ME YOUR DREAMS (Blount, Chris New Orleans Jazz Band).
Album: released on Rainbow Sound in Oct'86. Distributed by: Jazz Music

Blow Fly

BUSINESS DEAL.
Single (12"): released on Red Rooster in Nov'83 by Red Rooster Records. Distributed by: Pinnacle

ELECTRONIC BANANA.
Album: released on Red Lightnin' in Nov'84 by Red Lightnin' Records. Distributed by: Roots, Swift, Jazz Music, Pinnacle, Cartel, Wynd-Up Distribution

Blow, Kurtis

AMERICA.
Tracks: / America / America dub mix / Super sperm / Aj meets Davy mix / Hello baby / If I ruled the world / Respect to the king / Aj is cool / Summertime groove MC lullaby / Don"t cha feel like making love.
Album: released on Club in Dec'85 by Phonogram Records. Distributed by: Polygram

Cassette: released on Club in Dec'85 by Phonogram Records. Distributed by: Polygram

EGO TRIP.
Album: released on Mercury (USA) in Nov'84 by Import Records. Distributed by: IMS Distribution, Polygram Distribution

Cassette: released on Mercury (USA) in Nov'84 by Import Records. Distributed by: IMS Distribution, Polygram Distribution

IF I RULED THE WORLD.
Tracks: / If I ruled the world / If I ruled the world(dub) / If I ruled the world(inst.)*.
Single (7"): released on Club in Dec'85 by Phonogram Records. Distributed by: Polygram

Single (12"): released on Club in Dec'85 by Phonogram Records. Distributed by: Polygram

I'M CHILLIN'.
Tracks: / I'm chillin' / Don't cha feel like making love.
Single (7"): released on Club in Oct'86 by Phonogram Records. Distributed by: Polygram

Single (12"): released on Club in Oct'86 by Phonogram Records. Distributed by: Polygram

KINGDOM BLOW.

Notes: Kurtis' new LP features Trouble Funk, George Clinton, Bob Dylan and classic rap from the original and best rap artist.
Album: released on Club in Nov'86 by Phonogram Records. Distributed by: Polygram

Cassette: released on Club in Nov'86 by Phonogram Records. Distributed by: Polygram

Compact disc: by Phonogram Records. Distributed by: Polygram

PARTY TIME.
Single (7"): released on Club in Feb'85 by Phonogram Records. Distributed by: Polygram

Single (12"): released on Club in Feb'85 by Phonogram Records. Distributed by: Polygram

RAPPER IN TOWN, (THE).
Album: released on Mercury (USA) in Oct'84 by Import Records. Distributed by: IMS Distribution, Polygram Distribution

Cassette: released on Mercury (USA) in Oct'84 by Import Records. Distributed by: IMS Distribution, Polygram Distribution

TOUGH.
Album: released on Mercury in Oct'82 by Phonogram Records. Distributed by: Polygram Distribution

Cassette: released on Mercury in Oct'82 by Phonogram Records. Distributed by: Polygram Distribution

Blow Monkeys

ANIMAL MAGIC.
Tracks: / Digging your scene / Animal magic / Wicked ways / Sweet murder / Aeroplane city lovesong / I nearly died laughing / Don't be scared of me / Burn the rich / I backed a winner(in you) / Forbidden fruit / Heaven is a place i'm moving to.
Compact disc: by RCA Records. Distributed by: RCA, Roots, Swift, Wellard, Chris, I & B, Solomon & Peres Distribution

Album: released on RCA in '86 by RCA Records. Distributed by: RCA, Roots, Swift, Wellard, Chris, I & B, Solomon & Peres Distribution

Cassette: released on RCA in '86 by RCA Records. Distributed by: RCA, Roots, Swift, Wellard, Chris, I & B, Solomon & Peres Distribution

ATOMIC LULLABY.
Single (7"): released on RCA in Sep'84 by RCA Records. Distributed by: RCA, Roots, Swift, Wellard, Chris, I & B, Solomon & Peres Distribution

Single (12"): released on RCA in Sep'84 by RCA Records. Distributed by: RCA, Roots, Swift, Wellard, Chris, I & B, Solomon & Peres Distribution Deleted '85.

DAY AFTER YOU (THE).
Single (7"): released on RCA in May'87 by RCA Records. Distributed by: RCA, Roots, Swift, Wellard, Chris, I & B, Solomon & Peres Distribution

Single (12"): released on RCA in May'87 by RCA Records. Distributed by: RCA, Roots, Swift, Wellard, Chris, I & B, Solomon & Peres Distribution

DIGGING YOUR SCENE.
Tracks: / Digging your scene / I backed a winner(in you).
Single (7"): released on RCA in Feb'86 by RCA Records. Distributed by: RCA, Roots, Swift, Wellard, Chris, I & B, Solomon & Peres Distribution

Single (12"): released on RCA in Feb'86 by RCA Records. Distributed by: RCA, Roots, Swift, Wellard, Chris, I & B, Solomon & Peres Distribution

DON'T BE SCARED OF ME.
Tracks: / Don't be scared of me / Superfly.
Single (7"): released on RCA in Jun'86 by RCA Records. Distributed by: RCA, Roots, Swift, Wellard, Chris, I & B, Solomon & Peres Distribution

Single (12"): released on RCA in Jun'86 by RCA Records. Distributed by: RCA, Roots, Swift, Wellard, Chris, I & B, Solomon & Peres Distribution

FORBIDDEN FRUIT.
Single (7"): released on RCA in Sep'85 by RCA Records. Distributed by: RCA, Roots, Swift, Wellard, Chris, I & B, Solomon & Peres Distribution

Single (12"): released on RCA in Sep'85 by RCA Records. Distributed by: RCA, Roots, Swift, Wellard, Chris, I & B, Solomon & Peres Distribution

GO PUBLIC.
Single (7"): released on RCA in Mar'84 by RCA Records. Distributed by: RCA, Roots, Swift, Wellard, Chris, I & B, Solomon & Peres Distribution

Single (12"): released on RCA in Mar'84 by RCA Records. Distributed by: RCA, Roots, Swift, Wellard, Chris, I & B, Solomon & Peres Distribution

IT DOESN'T HAVE TO BE THAT WAY.
Tracks: / Ask for more.
Single (7"): released on RCA in Jan'87 by RCA Records. Distributed by: RCA, Roots, Swift, Wellard, Chris, I & B, Solomon & Peres Distribution

Single (12"): released on RCA in Jan'87 by RCA Records. Distributed by: RCA, Roots, Swift, Wellard, Chris, I & B, Solomon & Peres Distribution

LIMPING FOR A GENERATION.
Album: released on RCA in Oct'84 by RCA Records. Distributed by: RCA, Roots, Swift, Wellard, Chris, I & B, Solomon & Peres Distribution

Cassette: released on RCA in Oct'84 by RCA Records. Distributed by: RCA, Roots, Swift, Wellard, Chris, I & B, Solomon & Peres Distribution

LIVE TODAY LOVE TOMORROW.
Single (7"): released on Parasol in Jun'82 by Parasol Records. Distributed by: Pinnacle

MAN FROM RUSSIA.
Single (7"): released on RCA in Jun'84 by RCA Records. Distributed by: RCA, Roots, Swift, Wellard, Chris, I & B, Solomon & Peres Distribution

Single (12"): released on RCA in Jun'84 by RCA Records. Distributed by: RCA, Roots, Swift, Wellard, Chris, I & B, Solomon & Peres Distribution

OUT WITH HER.
Tracks: / Out with her / Grantham Groover (The).
Single (7"): released on RCA in Mar'87 by RCA Records. Distributed by: RCA, Roots, Swift, Wellard, Chris, I & B, Solomon & Peres Distribution

Single (12"): released on RCA in Mar'87 by RCA Records. Distributed by: RCA, Roots, Swift, Wellard, Chris, I & B, Solomon & Peres Distribution

SHE WAS ONLY A GROCER'S DAUGHTER.
Tracks: / It doesn't have to be this way / Sme kind of wonderful / Out with her / How long can a bad thing last / Man at the end of his tether / Rise above / Rise above / Day after you, The / Checking out / Don't give it up / Cash / Beautiful child / This is the way it has to be / Grantham grizzler, The.
Album: released on RCA in Jan'87 by RCA Records. Distributed by: RCA, Roots, Swift, Wellard, Chris, I & B, Solomon & Peres Distribution

Cassette: released on RCA in Jan'87 by RCA Records. Distributed by: RCA, Roots, Swift, Wellard, Chris, I & B, Solomon & Peres Distribution

Compact disc: released on RCA in Jan'87 by RCA Records. Distributed by: RCA, Roots, Swift, Wellard, Chris, I & B, Solomon & Peres Distribution

SOME KIND OF WONDERFUL.
Tracks: / Some kind of wonderful / Sweet obsession / Huckleberry*.
Single (7"): released on RCA in Jul'87 by RCA Records. Distributed by: RCA, Roots, Swift, Wellard, Chris, I & B, Solomon & Peres Distribution

Single (12"): released on RCA in Jul'87 by RCA Records. Distributed by: RCA, Roots, Swift, Wellard, Chris, I & B, Solomon & Peres Distribution

WICKED WAYS.
Tracks: / Wicked ways / Walking the bluebeat.
Single (7"): released on RCA in Apr'86 by RCA Records. Distributed by: RCA, Roots, Swift, Wellard, Chris, I & B, Solomon & Peres Distribution

Single (12"): released on RCA in Apr'86 by RCA Records. Distributed by: RCA, Roots, Swift, Wellard, Chris, I & B, Solomon & Peres Distribution

WILD FLOWER.
Single (7"): released on RCA in Jan'85 by RCA Records. Distributed by: RCA, Roots, Swift, Wellard, Chris, I & B, Solomon & Peres Distribution

Single (12"): released on RCA in Jan'85 by RCA Records. Distributed by: RCA, Roots, Swift, Wellard, Chris, I & B, Solomon & Peres Distribution

Blow the wind southerly

BLOW THE WIND SOUTHERLY Various artists (Various Artists).
Album: released on Viking Publications in May'82 by Viking Publications. Distributed by: Viking Publications, Harmonia Mundi Distributors, Banks Music publications

Blow Up

GOOD FOR ME.
Single (7"): released on Creation in 13 Jun'87. Distributed by: Rough Trade, Cartel

Single (12"): released on Creation in 13 Jun'87. Distributed by: Rough Trade, Cartel

Blowzabella

BLOWZABELLA.
Album: released on Plant Life in Sep'84. Distributed by: Roots

BLOWZABELLA IN COLOUR.
Album: released on Plant Life in May'83. Distributed by: Roots

BLOWZABELLA WALL OF SOUND, THE.
Album: released on Plant Life in Sep'86. Distributed by: Roots

BOBITTYSHOOTY.
Album: released on Plant Life in Jul'84. Distributed by: Roots

Blubbery Hellbellies

BLUBBERY HELLBELLIES,THE.
Album: released on Upright in Jun'86 by Upright Records. Distributed by: Cartel, Rough Trade

BLUBBERY HELLBELLIES, (THE).
Album: released on Upright in Aug'84 by Upright Records. Distributed by: Cartel, Rough Trade

CAFE BLUR.
Album: released on Flicknife in Mar'86 by Flicknife Records. Distributed by: Spartan

FLABBERGASTED.
Album: released on Upright in Mar'87 by Upright Records. Distributed by: Cartel, Rough Trade

PLASTIC PONY.
Tracks: / Plastic pony / Bar of soap / Sex gods cometh.
Single (12"): released on I.D. in Nov'86 by I.D. Records. Distributed by: Revolver, Cartel

Bludgeoned

BLUDGEONED (Various Artists).
Tracks: / BLUD 1.
Album: released on Bludgeon in Sep'86 by Bludgeon Records. Distributed by: Cartel

Cassette: released on Bludgeon in Sep'86 by Bludgeon Records. Distributed by: Cartel

Bludgeon Meat

POTTED TROTTER.
Single (7"): released on Bludgeon in Sep'84 by Bludgeon Records. Distributed by: Cartel

Blue

DON'T WANNA MAKE YOU CRY.
Single (7"): released on Zuma in Jan'85 by Zuma Records. Distributed by: CBS, PRT

I WANNA GO TO NEW YORK.
Single (7"): released on Zuma in Mar'84 by Zuma Records. Distributed by: CBS, PRT

Blue Aeroplane

BOP ART.
Album: released on Abstract in Apr'84 by Abstract. Distributed by: Pinnacle

Blue Aeroplanes

ACTION PAINTING.
Single (12"): released on Fire in Feb'85 by Twist and Shout Music. Distributed by: Nine Mile, Rough Trade, Cartel

LOVER AND CONFIDANTE.
Tracks: / Lover and confidante.
Single (12"): released on Fire in Mar'86 by Twist and Shout Music. Distributed by: Nine Mile, Rough Trade, Cartel

TOLERANCE.
Tracks: / Tolerance / When the wave comes down.
Single (7"): released on Fire in Oct'86 by Twist and Shout Music. Distributed by: Nine Mile, Rough Trade, Cartel

Single (12"): released on Fire in Oct'86 by Twist and Shout Music. Distributed by: Nine Mile, Rough Trade, Cartel

Single (7"): released on Fire in Oct'86 by Twist and Shout Music. Distributed by: Nine Mile, Rough Trade, Cartel

Single (12"): released on Fire in Oct'86 by Twist and Shout Music. Distributed by: Nine Mile, Rough Trade, Cartel

Blue Angel

BLUE ANGEL.
Album: released on Polydor in Feb'81 by Polydor Records. Distributed by: Polygram, Polydor

Blue August Project

OXYGEN.
Single (7"): released on Blue August in 13 Jun'87. Distributed by: Pinnacle

Single (12"): released on Blue August in 13 Jun'87. Distributed by: Pinnacle

Blue, Barry

DANCIN' ON A SATURDAY NIGHT.
Single (7"): released on Old Gold in Jul'82 by Old Gold Records. Distributed by: Lightning, Jazz Music, Spartan, Counterpoint

DO YOU WANNA DANCE?.
Single (7"): released on Old Gold in Jul'82 by Old Gold Records. Distributed by: Lightning, Jazz Music, Spartan, Counterpoint

Blue Bay

BLUE BAY Various artists (Various Artists).
Album: released on Messaround in Apr'79

Blue Beard

BLUE BEARD Various artists (Various Artists).
Cassette: released on Anvil in Jan'81. Distributed by: Anvil

Bluebells

ALL I AM (IS LOVING YOU).
Single (7"): released on London in Jan'85 by London Records. Distributed by: Polygram

Single (12"): released on London in Jan'85 by London Records. Distributed by: Polygram

CATH.
Single (7"): released on London in Jan'83 by London Records. Distributed by: Polygram

Single (12"): released on London in Jan'83 by London Records. Distributed by: Polygram

Single (7"): released on London in Sep'84 by London Records. Distributed by: Polygram

Single (12"): released on London in Sep'84 by London Records. Distributed by: Polygram

FOREVER MORE.
Single (7"): released on London in Oct'82 by London Records. Distributed by: Polygram

Single (12"): released on London in Oct'82 by London Records. Distributed by: Polygram

I'M FALLING.
Single (7"): released on Decca in Mar'84 by Decca Records. Distributed by: Polygram

Single (12"): released on Decca in Mar'84 by Decca Records. Distributed by: Polygram

SISTERS.
Album: released on London in Aug'84 by London Records. Distributed by: Polygram

Cassette: released on London in Aug'84 by London Records. Distributed by: Polygram

SUGAR BRIDGE (IT WILL STAND).
Single (7"): released on London in Jun'83 by London Records. Distributed by: Polygram

Single (12"): released on London in Jun'83 by London Records. Distributed by: Polygram

WILL SHE ALWAYS BE WAITING.
Single (7"): released on London in Aug'84 by London Records. Distributed by: Polygram

Single (12"): released on London in Aug'84 by London Records. Distributed by: Polygram

YOUNG AT HEART.
Single (12"): released on London in Aug'84 by London Records. Distributed by: Polygram

Bluebell & The Shamrock

BLUEBELL AND THE SHAMROCK (Various Artists).
Notes: Gordon Pattullo, Robbie Shepherd, Angus Cameron, Anne Byrne, etc.
Album: released on Ross in Jan'86 by Ross Records. Distributed by: Ross Distribution, Roots Distribution

Cassette: released on Ross in Jan'86 by Ross Records. Distributed by: Ross Distribution, Roots Distribution

Blue, Bill

GIVING GOOD BOYS A BAD NAME.
Album: released on Adelphi in May'81 by Adelphi Records. Distributed by: Jetstar

SING LIKE THUNDER (Blue, Bill Band).
Album: released on Adelphi in May'81 by Adelphi Records. Distributed by: Jetstar

Blue Blood

BLUE BLOOD.
Album: by Sonet Records. Distributed by: PRT

Blue Bop

BLUE BOP (Various Artists).
Tracks: / Dem tambourines / True blue / Jeannie / So tired / Nica's dream / Happy Johnny.
Notes: Artists include: Don Wilkerson, Tina Brooks, Donald Byrd, Art Blakey, Horace Silver.
Album: released on Blue Note in Oct'86 by EMI Records. Distributed by: EMI

Cassette: released on Blue Note in Oct'86 by EMI Records. Distributed by: EMI

Blue Bossa

BLUE BOSSA Various artists (Various Artists).
Tracks: / Congalegre / Latona / Back down to the tropics / Sandalia dela / Afrodisia / Mambo Inn / Cape Verdean blues, The / You're everything.
Notes: Transfer engineer: Ron McMaster All tracks are stereo except'Afrodisia' which is presented in its original monaural form.
Album: released on Blue Note in Jun'86 by EMI Records. Distributed by: EMI

Cassette: released on Blue Note in Jun'86 by EMI Records. Distributed by: EMI

BLUE BOSSA II Various Artists (Various Artists).
Tracks: / Recako bossa nova / Samba De Orfes / Mira / Stormy / South of the border / Brazil / Ghana / Old devil moon.
Album: released on Blue Note in Aug'87 by EMI Records. Distributed by: EMI

Cassette: released on Blue Note in Aug'87 by EMI Records. Distributed by: EMI

Blue Boy

BLUE FEVER.
Album: released on Culture House in Dec'86. Distributed by: Jetstar

Blue Caps

BLUE CAPS UNLEASHED.
Album: released on Magnum Force in Feb'83 by Magnum Music Group Ltd. Distributed by: Magnum Music Group Ltd, PRT, Spartan

ON THE ROAD AGAIN.
Album: released on Magnum Force in Aug'84 by Magnum Music Group Ltd. Distributed by: Magnum Music Group Ltd, PRT, Spartan

Blue Cats

BLUE CATS, (THE).
Album: released on Rockhouse in Apr'84 by Rockhouse Records. Distributed by: Swift Distribution, Charly Distribution

Album: released on Charly in Feb'81 by Charly Records. Distributed by: Charly, Cadillac

EARLY DAYS: VOLS 1 & 2.
Double Album: released on Nervous in Jul'84 by Nervous Records. Distributed by: Nervous, Rough Trade

FIGHT BACK.
Album: released on Rockhouse(USA) in Nov'82

Blue Cheer

BEST OF BLUE CHEER.
Album: released on Philips Import in Oct'82

Cassette: released on Philips Import in Oct'82

Blue Diamonds

RAMONA.
Album: released on Music For Pleasure (Holland) in '86 by EMI Records. Distributed by: EMI

Cassette: released on Music For Pleasure (Holland) in '86 by EMI Records. Distributed by: EMI

Blue Feather

FEATHER FUNK.
Album: released on Philips Import in Aug'82

LET IT OUT.
Single (7"): released on Mercury in Mar'83 by Phonogram Records. Distributed by: Polygram Distribution

Single (12"): released on Mercury in Mar'83 by Phonogram Records. Distributed by: Polygram Distribution

Blue Flames

My favourite songs

Blue Fly

X-RATED.
Album: released on Red Rooster in Nov'83 by Red Rooster Records. Distributed by: Pinnacle

Bluegrass Albums Vol. 4

BLUEGRASS ALBUMS VOL. 4 Various artists (Various Artists).
Album: released on Rounder (USA) in Dec'85. Distributed by: Mike's Country Music Room Distribution, Jazz Music Distribution, Swift Distribution, Roots Records Distribution, Projection Distribution, Topic Distribution

Blue Grass Cardinals

HOME IS WHERE THE HEART IS.
Album: released on Sugarhill (USA) in Mar'85 by PRT Records. Distributed by: PRT Distribution

Bluegrass Compact Disc

BLUEGRASS COMPACT DISC (Various Artists).
Compact disc: released on Rounder (USA) in Dec'86. Distributed by: Mike's Country Music Room Distribution, Jazz Music Distribution, Swift Distribution, Roots Records Distribution, Projection Distribution, Topic Distribution

Bluegrass Hall Of Fame

BLUEGRASS HALL OF FAME (Various Artists).
Album: released on Starday in Apr'87

Cassette: released on Starday in Apr'87

Blue in Heaven

ACROSS MY HEART.
Single (7"): released on Island in Sep'84 by Island Records. Distributed by: Polygram

Single (12"): released on Island in Sep'84 by Island Records. Distributed by: Polygram Deleted '87.

ALL THE GODS MEN.
Tracks: / Sometimes / Big beat, The / It's Saturday / Old Ned / All you fear / Julie cries / Like a child / In your eyes / Slowly.
Album: released on Island in May'85 by Island Records. Distributed by: Polygram

Cassette: released on Island in May'85 by Island Records. Distributed by: Polygram

EXPLICIT MATERIAL.
Tracks: / Change your mind / Tell me / Just another day / Sister / Be your man / I just wanna / Close your eyes / Rolling in the crowd / Hope to God.
Notes: Album produced by Chris Blackwell,Eric Thorngren & Blue In Heaven.
Album: released on Island in Aug'86 by Island Records. Distributed by: Polygram

Cassette: released on Island in Aug'86 by Island Records. Distributed by: Polygram

I JUST WANNA.
Tracks: / I just wanna / Beating in my head(Little flower).
Single (12"): released on Island in May'86 by Island Records. Distributed by: Polygram

JULIE CRIES.
Single (7"): released on Island in Jul'84 by Island Records. Distributed by: Polygram

Single (12"): released on Island in Jul'84 by Island Records. Distributed by: Polygram

Blue, Jimmy

BRAND NEW FROM ANDY (Blue, Jimmy Band & Andy Stewart).
Album: released on Pye in Apr'75

FAVOURITE SCOTTISH DANCE MUSIC VOL.1 (Blue, Jimmy & His Scottish Band).
Album: released on RCA International (USA) in '84 by RCA Records. Distributed by: RCA

Cassette: released on RCA International (USA) in '84 by RCA Records. Distributed by: RCA

HIS SCOTTISH DANCE BAND VOL.1 (Blue, Jimmy & His Scottish Dance Band).
Cassette: released on PRT in Jun'77 by PRT Records. Distributed by: PRT

SATURDAY BARN DANCE (Blue, Jimmy Band & Various artists).
Cassette: released on PRT in Jan'78 by PRT Records. Distributed by: PRT

Blue Letter

BLUE LETTER.
Tracks: / Blue letter / Antenna's up.

Blue, Little Joe

BLUE'S BLUE'S.
Tracks: / Right there where you left it / Little Joe Blue / Sometime Tomorrow / Encourage Me Baby / Don't Stop Loving Me / Fool is what you wanted, A / Southern Country Boy / Just Love Won't Do / If You'd Only Let Me Love You / I'm Not Your First Love / Loose Me / Gonna Walk On / If There's a Better Way / Fool is what you wanted, A.
Notes: Original Jewel Recordings licensed from Charly Int. APS.
Album: released on Charly in Jan'87 by Charly Records. Distributed by: Charly, Cadillac

Blue Magic

GREATEST HITS:BLUE MAGIC.
Tracks: / Sideshow / Stop to Start / Spell / What's Come Over Me / Three Ring Circus / Tear it Down / Look me up / Welcome to the club / Chasing rainbows / Just don't want to be lonely / Summer snow / Where have you been.
Album: released on Streetwave in Nov'86 by Streetwave Records. Distributed by: PRT Distribution

Blue Mathue

PERFECT PICTURES.
Single (12"): released on Uniton Records in Jan'84. Distributed by: Cartel

Blue Max

BLUE MAX Film soundtrack.
Album: released on Citadel in Mar'79. Distributed by: Swift

BLUE MAX, THE.
Tracks: / Dream machine / Sing song blues / Bad bad Amigo / Hangman, The / Need your love / Flying to Moscow / Paid assassin / Camera, camera / Photographing Gold / Murder at the movies / I know you're there / Wait for the new one.
Album: released on Charisma in Jan'79 by Virgin Records. Distributed by: EMI

Blue Meeting in...

BLUE MEETING IN CHICAGO Various artists (Various Artists).
Album: released on Strawberry in Apr'84. Distributed by: Pinnacle

Blue Mink

BANNER MAN.
Single (7"): released on Old Gold in Apr'83 by Old Gold Records. Distributed by: Lightning, Jazz Music, Spartan, Counterpoint

BLUE MINK - THE COLLECTION.
Album: released on Action Replay in Nov'86 by Action Replay Records. Distributed by: PRT

Cassette: released on Action Replay in Nov'86 by Action Replay Records. Distributed by: PRT

HIT MAKING SOUNDS.
Tracks: / Melting pot / Can you feel it / Our world / We have all been saved / Cat house / Gasoline alley bred / Good morning freedom / Bang bang Johnny's gang is after me / World (you're closing in on me) / Gimme reggae / Gap, The / Jubilation.
Album: released on Gull in Sep'77 by Gull Records. Distributed by: Pinnacle

MELTING POT.
Single (7"): released on Old Gold in Jul'82 by Old Gold Records. Distributed by: Lightning, Jazz Music, Spartan, Counterpoint

Blue Moderne

THROUGH THE NIGHT.
Tracks: / Through the night.
Single (7"): released on Sure Delight in Jul'86. Distributed by: Jetstar Distribution

Single (12"): released on Sure Delight in Jul'86. Distributed by: Jetstar Distribution

Blue Monday

MURDERED BY LOVE.
Tracks: / Murdered by love / She's so fine / Thrill is gone, The / Old fashioned funny feeling / What do you want / Bad is bad / Chocolate cookie / Every time I get wasted I take it out on you / She's gone / I'm the blues / Gas, food & lodging / Nothin' left but the blues.
Compact disc: released on Hermes in Jun'87 by Nimbus Records. Distributed by: Target

Blue Murder

BLUE MURDER AT HOME.
Album: released on Roadrunner (Dutch) in Aug'87. Distributed by: Pinnacle. Estim retail price in Sep'87 was £5.99.

ENERGISE.
Album: released on Blue Murder in Mar'85 by Great Divide Records. Distributed by: Backs, Cartel

TALK TALK TALK.
Tracks: / Talk talk talk / Mr.Soul.
Single (7"): released on WEA International in Jun'86 by WEA Records. Distributed by: WEA

Blue Nile

STAY.
Single (7"): released on Linn in Oct'84 by Virgin Records. Distributed by: EMI

Single (12"): released on Linn in Oct'84 by Virgin Records. Distributed by: EMI

TINSELTOWN.
Single (7"): released on Linn in Jul'84 by Virgin Records. Distributed by: EMI

Single (12"): released on Linn in Jul'84 by Virgin Records. Distributed by: EMI

WALK ACROSS THE ROOFTOPS, A.
Tracks: / Walk across the rooftops, A / Tinsel Town in the rain / From rags to riches / Stay / Easter parade / Heatwave / Automobile noise.
Compact disc: by Virgin Records. Distributed by: EMI

Album: released on Linn in Apr'84 by Virgin Records. Distributed by: EMI

Cassette: released on Linn in Apr'84 by Virgin Records. Distributed by: EMI

Blue Note '86

BLUE NOTE '86 Various artists.
Album: released on Blue Note in Aug'86 by EMI Records. Distributed by: EMI

Blue On Shock

HEAVEN WON HERE.
Single (7"): released on Trigger Happy in Mar'87

Blue Orchids

AGENTS OF CHANCE.
Single (12"): released on Rough Trade in Nov'82 by Rough Trade Records. Distributed by: Rough Trade Distribution, Cartel Distribution

DISNEY BOYS.
Single (7"): released on Rough Trade in Nov'80 by Rough Trade Records. Distributed by: Rough Trade Distribution, Cartel Distribution

GREATEST HITS: BLUE ORCHIDS.
Album: released on Rough Trade in '84 by Rough Trade Records. Distributed by: Rough Trade Distribution, Cartel Distribution

WORK.
Single (7"): released on Rough Trade in Mar'81 by Rough Trade Records. Distributed by: Rough Trade Distribution, Cartel Distribution

Blue Oyster Cult

BLUE OYSTER CULT.
Tracks: / Transmission MC / I'm the lamb but I ain't no sheep / Then came the last days of May / Stairway to the stars / Before the kiss / Redcap, A / Screams / She's as beautiful as a foot / Cities on flame with rock and roll / Workshop of the telescopes / Redeemed.
Album: released on CBS in Mar'81 by CBS Records. Distributed by: CBS

CLUB NINJA.
Tracks: / Madness to the method / White flags / Dancin' in the ruins / Rock not war / Perfect water / Spy in the house of the night / Beat 'em up / When the war comes / Shadow warrior / White flags / Dancin' in the ruins / Rock not war / Perfect water / Spy in the house of the night / Beat 'em up / When the war comes / Shadow warrior / Madness to the method.
Compact disc: by CBS Records. Distributed by: CBS

Album: released on CBS in Dec'85 by CBS Records. Distributed by: CBS

Cassette: released on CBS in Dec'85 by CBS Records. Distributed by: CBS

CULTOSAURUS ERECTUS.
Tracks: / Black blade / Monsters / Divine wind / Deadlines / Marshall plan, The / Hungry boys / Fallen angel / Lips in the hills / Unknown tongue.
Album: released on CBS in Jul'80 by CBS Records. Distributed by: CBS

(DON'T FEAR) THE REAPER.
Single (7"): released on CBS in Jul'84 by CBS Records. Distributed by: CBS

E.T.I..
Tracks: / Dominance and submission / Cities on flame / Dr. Music / Red and the black, The / Joan Crawford / Burnin' for you / Roadhouse blues / Black blade / Hot rails to Hell / Godzilla / Veteran of the Psychic wars / E.T.I. / Don't fear the Reaper.
Double Album: released on CBS in May'82 by CBS Records. Distributed by: CBS

ON YOUR FEET OR ON YOUR KNEES.
Tracks: / Subhuman / Harvester of eyes / Hot rails to hell / Red and the black, The / 7 screaming diz-busters / Buck's boogie / Then came the last days of May / Cities on flame / Me 262 / Before the kiss (a redcap) / I ain't got you / Born to be wild.
Album: released on CBS in Sep'87 by CBS Records. Distributed by: CBS

SHOOTING SHARK.
Single (7"): released on CBS in Jan'84 by CBS Records. Distributed by: CBS

Single (12"): released on CBS in Jan'84 by CBS Records. Distributed by: CBS

SOME ENCHANTED EVENING.
Tracks: / R U ready 2 rock / E.T.I. (Extra terrestrial intelligence) / Astronomy / Kick out the jams / Godzilla / Don't fear the reaper / We gotta get out of this place.
Album: released on CBS in Sep'78 by CBS Records. Distributed by: CBS

Cassette: released on CBS in Sep'78 by CBS Records. Distributed by: CBS

SPECTRES.
Tracks: / Godzilla / Golden age of leather / Death Valley nights / Searchin' for Celine / Fireworks / R.U. ready / Rock / Celestial the queen / Goin' through the motions / I love the night / Nosferatu / Godzilla / Golden age of leather / Death valley nights / Searchin for Celine / Fireworks / R U ready 2 rock / Celestial the Queen / Going through the motions / I love the night / Nosferatu.
Album: released on CBS in Feb'86 by CBS Records. Distributed by: CBS

Cassette: released on CBS in Feb'86 by CBS Records. Distributed by: CBS

Album: released on CBS in Jan'78 by CBS Records. Distributed by: CBS

Blue Print Sampler
BLUE PRINT SAMPLER Various artists (Various Artists).
Album: released on Blue Print in Feb'80. Distributed by: PRT

Blue Rhythm Boys
ROLLIN' 'N' TUMBLIN'.
Single (7"): released on Backs in Mar'84 by Backs Records. Distributed by: Backs, Cartel

THAT DON'T MOVE ME.
Single (7"): released on Backs in Mar'84 by Backs Records. Distributed by: Backs, Cartel

Blue Ribbon Boogie
BLUE RIBBON BOOGIE Various artists (Various Artists).
Tracks: / Paper boy boogie / Barbershop boogie / Blue ribbon bboogie / Cherokee boogie / Long John boogie / Big bear boogie / All nite boogie / Elevator boogie / Too hot to handle / Juke joint Johnny / I'm a ding dong daddy (from Dumas) / Baby you should live so long / I ain't got time / Bloodshot eyes.
Album: released on Charly in Jul'85 by Charly Records. Distributed by: Charly, Cadillac

Blue Ridge Corn Shuckers
Ernest V. Stoneman & Blue Ridge Corn Shuckers

Blue Ridge Mountain...
BLUE RIDGE MOUNTAIN FIELD TRIP Various artists (Various Artists).
Album: released on Leader in Jun'86. Distributed by: Jazz Music, Projection

Album: released on Leader in '81. Distributed by: Jazz Music, Projection

Blue Ridge Rangers, The
BLUE RIDGE RANGERS, THE.
Album: released on Fantasy in Oct'87 by Ace Records. Distributed by: Pinnacle. Estim retail price in Sep'87 was £4.90.

Compact disc: released on Fantasy in Oct'87 by Ace Records. Distributed by: Pinnacle. Estim retail price in Sep'87 was £11.99.

Blue River Show Band
TOGETHER AGAIN.
Cassette: released on BRS in Jan'87. Distributed by: Ross

Blue Rondo
BEES KNEES AND CHICKENS ELBOWS.
Album: released on Virgin in Jul'84 by Virgin Records. Distributed by: EMI, Virgin Distribution

TOO SOON TO COME.
Album: released on Virgin in Nov'86 by Virgin Records. Distributed by: EMI, Virgin Distribution

Cassette: released on Virgin in Nov'86 by Virgin Records. Distributed by: EMI, Virgin Distribution

Blue Rondo A La Turk
CARIOCA.
Single (7"): released on Virgin in Oct'82 by Virgin Records. Distributed by: EMI, Virgin Distribution

HEAVENS ARE CRYING (PARTS 1 & 2).
Single (7"): released on Virgin in Aug'82 by Virgin Records. Distributed by: EMI, Virgin Distribution

Single (12"): released on Virgin in Aug'82 by Virgin Records. Distributed by: EMI, Virgin Distribution

KLACTO VE SEDTSTEIN.
Single (7"): released on Virgin in Feb'82 by Virgin Records. Distributed by: EMI, Virgin Distribution

Single (12"): released on Virgin in Feb'82 by Virgin Records. Distributed by: EMI, Virgin Distribution

Blue, Ruby
GIVE US OUR FLAG BACK.
Single (7"): released on Red Flame in Jul'87 by Red Flame Records. Distributed by: Nine Mile, Cartel

Blues
100 MINUTES.
Cassette: released on PRT (100 Minute Series) in Jun'82

AIM FOR THE EYES.
Single (7"): released on Precious in Jun'82 by Precious Records. Distributed by: CBS, Polygram

BLUES VOL.1, THE (Various Artists).
Album: released on Chess in Apr'87 by Charly Records. Distributed by: Charly, Swift, PRT, Discovery, IMS, Polygram

Cassette: released on Chess in Apr'87 by Charly Records. Distributed by: Charly, Swift, PRT, Discovery, IMS, Polygram

BLUES VOLUME 3, THE Various artists (Various Artists).
Album: released on Big Bear in '82 by Big Bear Records. Distributed by: Big Bear, Swift

BLUES VOLUME 4, THE Various artists (Various Artists).
Album: released on Big Bear in '82 by Big Bear Records. Distributed by: Big Bear, Swift

Blues Alive(video)
BLUES ALIVE(VIDEO) Various artists (Various Artists).
Notes: A reunion concert by John Mayall and former members of his Bluesbreakers like John McVie and Mick Taylor plus guest bluesmen Albert King, Buddy Guy and Junior Wells filmed in 1982.
Total playing time: 58minutes.
Video-cassette (VHS): released on RCA in Oct'84 by RCA Records. Distributed by: RCA, Roots, Swift, Wellard, Chris, I & B, Solomon & Peres Distribution

Blues Band
BLUES BAND OFFICIAL BOOTLEG ALBUM.
Tracks: / Talk To Me Baby / Flatfoot Sam / Two bones and a pick / Someday baby / Boom boom (Out go the lights) / Come on in / Death letter / Going home / I don't know / Diddy Wah Diddy.
Notes: (Originally Arista:BBBP 101 Released 1980)
Album: released on Fame (Arista) in Jan'83 by Music For Pleasure Records. Distributed by: EMI

Cassette: released on Fame (Arista) in Jan'83 by Music For Pleasure Records. Distributed by: EMI

BRAND LOYALTY.
Tracks: / Seemed like a good idea at the time / Rolling log / I want to be loved / Might as well be / What do you want / Big fine girl / Sure feels good / Little baby / Grits ain't groceries / Funny money / Take me home / Oo-oo-ee.
Album: released on Arista in Sep'82 by Arista Records. Distributed by: RCA

Cassette: released on Arista in Sep'82 by Arista Records. Distributed by: RCA

BYE BYE BLUES.
Tracks: / Hey hey little girl / Death letter / Grits ain't groceries / Flat foot Sam / Don't lie to me / Can't hold on much longer / It might as well be me / Nadine / Big boss man / Maggie's farm / Treat her right.
Notes: This is the Blue Band's fourth and farewell album and their first (and only) live album featuring almost an hour of music with guest appearances from Jo Ann Kelly, Phil May and Ian Stewart. 12 tracks including one previously unrecorded song.

COME ON.
Single (7"): released on Arista in Nov'81 by Arista Records. Distributed by: RCA

ITCHY FEET.
Tracks: / Talkin woman blues / Who's right who's wrong / Rock'n'roll radio / Itchy feet / Ultimatum time / So lonely / Come on / Turn around / I can't be satisfied / Got to love you baby / Nothin but the blues / Let your bucket down.
Notes: Latest album from the Blues Band is Itchy Feet, eight out of the twelve tracks have been written by the band, and the others are Lowell Fulsom's 'Talkin woman blues', Chuck Berry's 'Come on', Muddy Water's 'I can't be satisfied' and Willie Dixon's 'Got to love you baby'
Album: released on Arista in Sep'81 by Arista Records. Distributed by: RCA

Cassette: released on Arista in Sep'81 by Arista Records. Distributed by: RCA

READY.
Tracks: / Twenty-nine ways / I'm ready / Hallelujah I love her so / Sus blues / Noah Lewis blues / Treat her right / Lonely Avenue / Find yourself another fool / Hey hey little girl / Green stuff / Can't hold on / cat, The.
Album: released on Arista in Oct'80 by Arista Records. Distributed by: RCA

Cassette: released on Arista in Oct'80 by Arista Records. Distributed by: RCA

WHO'S RIGHT WHO'S WRONG.
Single (7"): released on Arista in Sep'81 by Arista Records. Distributed by: RCA

Blues Brothers
BEST OF....
Album: released on Atlantic in Jan'82 by WEA Records. Distributed by: WEA

BLUES BROTHERS original soundtrack recording.
Album: released on Atlantic in Oct'80 by WEA Records. Distributed by: WEA

BLUES BROTHERS Original soundtrack.
Compact disc: released on Atlantic in Jan'87 by WEA Records. Distributed by: WEA

BLUES BROTHERS (THE) Original soundtrack (Various Artists).
Tracks: / Shake a tail feather / Think / Minnie the moocher / Rawhide everybody needs somebody to love / Jailhouse rock / She caught the Katy / Gimme some lovin' / Old landmark / Sweet home Chicago / Peter Gunn.
Compact disc: released on Atlantic in Feb'87 by WEA Records. Distributed by: WEA

BRIEFCASE FULL OF BLUES.
Tracks: / I can't turn you loose / Hey bartender / Messin' with the kid / I got everything I need almost / Shot gun blues / Rubber biscuit / Groove me / Soul man / Flip, flop and fly / B movie box car blues.
Compact disc: released on Atlantic in Mar'87 by WEA Records. Distributed by: WEA

MADE IN AMERICA.
Tracks: / Soul finger / Funky Broadway / Who's making love / Do you love me / Guilty / Perry Mason theme / Riot in cell block number nine / Green onions / I ain't got you / From the bottom / Going to Miami.
Album: released on Atlantic in Feb'81 by WEA Records. Distributed by: WEA

Cassette: released on Atlantic in Feb'81 by WEA Records. Distributed by: WEA

Blues Burglars
BREAKIN' IN.
Tracks: / Feels so good / Up and down the avenue / Sugar Mama / Shake your money maker / Built for comfort / Hoochie coochie man / Trouble no more / Don't start me talking / Mojo working / Spaced out / Evening / Walkin' / Whoppin.
Album: released on Red Lightnin' in Nov'86 by Red Lightnin' Records. Distributed by: Roots, Swift, Jazz Music, Pinnacle, Cartel, Wynd-Up Distribution

Blues Busters
ACCEPT NO SUBSTITUTE.
Album: released on Landslide in Oct'86 by Dorane Ltd

Cassette: released on Landslide in Oct'86 by Dorane Ltd

CLOSER I GET TO YOU.
Tracks: / Closer I get to you / Midnight.
Single (12"): released on Spank in Sep'86. Distributed by: Jetstar

MERRY CHRISTMAS.
Album: released on Tower in Dec'84 by Tower Records. Distributed by: Jungle, Cartel

PHILLIP & LLOYD.
Album: released on Dynamic in Dec'76 by Creole Records. Distributed by: CBS, Essex

THIS TIME.
Notes: Features: Paul Barrere, guitars/vocals (Little Feat), Catfish Hodge, guitars/vocal (Legendary Washington Bluesman), T. Lavitz, (The Dregs), Freebo, bass (Bonnie Raitt), Larry Zack (drums).
Album: released on Landslide (USA) in Aug'87. Distributed by: Compendium, Rough Trade, Cartel

TOP OF THE POPS.
Album: released on Vista Sounds in '83 by Vista Sounds Records. Distributed by: Jetstar

Blues Came Down...
BLUES CAME DOWN FROM MEMPHIS Various original artists (Various Artists).
Tracks: / We all gotta go sometime / She maybe yours (but she comes to see me sometimes) / Keep your arms around me / Tiger man (king of thejungle) / Come back baby / That ain't right / Take a little chance / Wolf call boogie / Easy / West winds / Walter's instrumental swing / Seems like a million years / Baker shop boogie / Take a little walk with me / Bear cat / Cotton crop blues / Feelin' good / Mystery train / Love my baby / Carry my busines on / I feel so worried / So long baby goodbye.
Compact disc: released on Charly in Apr'87 by Charly Records. Distributed by: Charly, Cadillac

Album: released on Charly in Sep'77 by Charly Records. Distributed by: Charly, Cadillac

Blues Deluxe
BLUES DELUXE Various artists (Various Artists).
Album: released on XRT-Sonet in Jan'81

Blue Section Two
STRANGE FASCINATION.
Single (7"): released on EMI in Mar'84 by EMI Records. Distributed by: EMI

Blues EP
BLUES EP, THE Various artists (Various Artists).
Single (7"): released on Chess in Jul'85 by Charly Records. Distributed by: Charly, Swift, PRT, Discovery, IMS, Polygram

Blues From...
BLUES FROM BIG BILL'S COPACABANA Various artists (Various Artists).
Album: released on Chess (France) in Oct'85 by Charly Records. Distributed by: Charly, Swift PRT

Blues From Fields
BLUES FROM THE FIELDS TO THE TOWNS Various artists (Various Artists).
Album: released on Fontana (Europe) in Feb'83 by Phonogram Records. Distributed by: Polygram

Cassette: released on Fontana (Europe) in Feb'83 by Phonogram Records. Distributed by: Polygram

BLUES FROM THE FIELDS (VOLUME 2) Various artists (Various Artists).
Album: released on Fontana (Europe) in May'83 by Phonogram Records. Distributed by: Polygram

Cassette: released on Fontana (Europe) in May'83 by Phonogram Records. Distributed by: Polygram

BLUES FROM THE FIELDS INTO THE TOWN (VOLUME 3) Various artists (Various Artists).
Album: released on Happy Bird (Germany) in Jun'84. Distributed by: Polygram, IMS

Cassette: released on Happy Bird (Germany) in Jun'84. Distributed by: Polygram, IMS

Blues From S. Carolina..
BLUES FROM SOUTH CAROLINA & GEORGIA 1924/32 Various artists (Various Artists).
Album: released on Heritage (USA) in May'84. Distributed by: Mike's Country Music Room Distribution, I & B

Blues Giants
MASTERS OF JAZZ.
Album: released on RCA (Germany) in '83

Blues Girls From
BLUES GIRLS FROM THE '40'S Various artists (Various Artists).
Album: released on Pathe MarconiFrance) in Apr'85

Blues Guitar
BLUES GUITAR ALBUM Various artists (Various Artists).
Album: released on JSP in Mar'82 by JSP Records. Distributed by: Swift, Projection

Album: released on JSP in Feb'83 by JSP Records. Distributed by: Swift, Projection

Blues Guitar Workshop
BLUES GUITAR WORKSHOP Various artists (Various Artists).
Album: released on Kicking Mule in Jan'80 by Sonet. Distributed by: Roots, PRT

Blues In D Natural

BLUES IN D NATURAL - ANTHOLOGY Various artists (Various Artists).
Album: released on Red Lightnin' in Sep'82 by Red Lightnin' Records. Distributed by: Roots, Swift, Jazz Music Pinnacle, Cartel, Wynd-Up Distribution

Blues Is Alright

BLUES IS ALRIGHT, THE Various artists (Various Artists).
Tracks: / Down home blues / Blues is alright, The / Your husband is cheatin' on us / End of the rainbow, The / Misty blue / Lady,my whole world is you / Down home blues(x-rated) / Two steps from the blues / I'm a bluesman / Bad risk.
Album: released on Malaco in Feb'86 by Malaco Records. Distributed by: Charly

BLUES IS ALRIGHT VOLUME 2 (Various Artists).
Album: released on Malaco in Dec'86 by Malaco Records. Distributed by: Charly

Blues Is Killing

BLUES IS KILLING Various artists (Various Artists).
Album: released on Juke Joint in Apr'79. Distributed by: Swift

Blues Jam In Chicago

BLUES JAM IN CHICAGO Various artists (Various Artists).
Double Album: released on Epic in Feb'83 by CBS Records. Distributed by: CBS

Blues Legend

BLUES LEGEND, THE (VOL.1) Various artists (Various Artists).
Boxed set: released on Happy Bird (Germany) in Aug'83. Distributed by: Polygram, IMS

BLUES LEGEND, THE (VOL.2) Various artists (Various Artists).
Boxed set: released on Happy Bird (Germany) in Aug'83. Distributed by: Polygram, IMS

BLUES LEGEND, THE (VOL.3) Various artists (Various Artists).
Boxed set: released on Happy Bird (Germany) in Aug'83. Distributed by: Polygram, IMS

Blues'n'Trouble

BLUES'N'TROUBLE.
Album: released on Ammunition Communications in Nov'85. Distributed by: Pinnacle, Fast Forward, Cartel, M.I.S., EMI

BLUES'N'TROUBLE Various artists (Various Artists).
Album: released on Arhoolie in '81 by Arhoolie Records. Distributed by: Projection, Topic, Jazz Music, Swift, Roots

BLUES'N'TROUBLE (VOLUME 2) Various artists (Various Artists).
Album: released on Arhoolie in '81 by Arhoolie Records. Distributed by: Projection, Topic, Jazz Music, Swift, Roots

FINE,FINE,FINE.
Tracks: / Fine,fine,fine / Free to ride / Red hot.
Single (7"): released on Ammunition Communications in Feb'86. Distributed by: Pinnacle, Fast Forward, Cartel, M.I.S., EMI

HAT TRICK.
Album: released on Blue Horizon in Aug'87 by Ace Records. Distributed by: Pinnacle. Estim retail price in Sep'87 was £5.67.

NO MINOR KEYS.
Album: released on Ammunition Communications in May'86. Distributed by: Pinnacle, Fast Forward, Cartel, M.I.S., EMI

Cassette: released on Ammunition Communications in May'86. Distributed by: Pinnacle, Fast Forward, Cartel, M.I.S., EMI

OLD TIME BOOGIE.
Single (7"): released on Castle Rock in Oct'83. Distributed by: Indies, Cartel

THANK YOU AND GOODNIGHT.
Album: released on Ammunition Communications in Jul'87. Distributed by: Pinnacle, Fast Forward, Cartel, M.I.S., EMI

Blues Piano Greats

BLUES PIANO GREATS Various artists (Various Artists).
Album: released on JSP in Jun'83 by JSP Records. Distributed by: Swift, Projection

Blues Project

BLUES PROJECT, THE.
Album: released on Polydor in Aug'86 by Polydor Records. Distributed by: Polygram, Polydor

Cassette: released on Polydor in Aug'86 by Polydor Records. Distributed by: Polygram, Polydor

Blues Rarities

BLUES RARITIES Various artists (Various Artists).
Album: released on Chess in Mar'85 by Charly Records. Distributed by: Charly, Swift, PRT, Discovery, IMS, Polygram

Blues/Rock Avalanche

BLUES/ROCK AVALANCHE Various artists (Various Artists).
Album: released on Chess in Mar'85 by Charly Records. Distributed by: Charly, Swift, PRT, Discovery, IMS, Polygram

Blues Roots

BLUES ROOTS Various artsits (Various Artists).
Album: released on Tomato in Mar'79

BLUES ROOTS VOL. 1 Mississippi blues (Various Artists).
Notes: Artists include : Big Joe Williams, Johnny Young.
Album: released on Storyville (USA) in Jun'86 by Moss Music Group Records (USA). Distributed by: Discovery Distribution, Jazz Music Distribution, Swift Distribution, Chris Wellard Distribution, Celtic Music Distribution

BLUES ROOTS VOL. 2 Blues all around my bed (Various Artists).
Notes: Artists include: Leroy Dalls, Carl Hodges etc.
Album: released on Storyville (USA) in Jun'86 by Moss Music Group Records (USA). Distributed by: Discovery Distribution, Jazz Music Distribution, Swift Distribution, Chris Wellard Distribution, Celtic Music Distribution

BLUES ROOTS VOL. 3 I ain't gonna pick no more cotton (Various Artists).
Album: released on Storyville (USA) in Jun'86 by Moss Music Group Records (USA). Distributed by: Discovery Distribution, Jazz Music Distribution, Swift Distribution, Chris Wellard Distribution, JSU Distribution, Celtic Music Distribution

BLUES ROOTS VOL. 4 Dirty dozen, The (Various Artists).
Notes: Artists: Speckled Red
Album: released on Storyville (USA) in Jun'86 by Moss Music Group Records (USA). Distributed by: Discovery Distribution, Jazz Music Distribution, Swift Distribution, Chris Wellard Distribution, Celtic Music Distribution

BLUES ROOTS VOL. 5 Ramblin' & wanderin' blues (Various Artists).
Notes: Artists: Big Joe Williams
Album: released on Storyville (USA) in Jun'86 by Moss Music Group Records (USA). Distributed by: Discovery Distribution, Jazz Music Distribution, Swift Distribution, Chris Wellard Distribution, Celtic Music Distribution

BLUES ROOTS VOL. 6 I'm growing older everyday (Various Artists).
Notes: Artists: Champion Jack Dupree
Album: released on Storyville (USA) in Jun'86 by Moss Music Group Records (USA). Distributed by: Discovery Distribution, Jazz Music Distribution, Swift Distribution, Chris Wellard Distribution, Celtic Music Distribution

BLUES ROOTS VOL. 7 Good morning Mr. Blues (Various Artists).
Notes: Artists: Otis Spann
Album: released on Storyville (USA) in Jun'86 by Moss Music Group Records (USA). Distributed by: Discovery Distribution, Jazz Music Distribution, Swift Distribution, Chris Wellard Distribution, JSU Distribution, Celtic Music Distribution

BLUES ROOTS VOL. 8 Swingin' with Lonnie (Various Artists).
Notes: Artist: Lonnie Johnson.
Album: released on Storyville (USA) in Jun'86 by Moss Music Group Records (USA). Distributed by: Discovery Distribution, Jazz Music Distribution, Swift Distribution, Chris Wellard Distribution, Celtic Music Distribution

BLUES ROOTS VOL. 9 Sad & lonesome blues (Various Artists).
Notes: Artist: Sunnyland Slim
Album: released on Storyville (USA) in Jun'86 by Moss Music Group Records (USA). Distributed by: Discovery Distribution, Jazz Music Distribution, Swift Distribution, Chris Wellard Distribution, Celtic Music Distribution

BLUES ROOTS VOL.TEN(10) I'm so alone (Various Artists).
Notes: Artist: Memphis Slim
Album: released on Storyville (USA) in Jun'86 by Moss Music Group Records (USA). Distributed by: Discovery Distribution, Jazz Music Distribution, Swift Distribution, Chris Wellard Distribution, Celtic Music Distribution

Blues Singers

BLUES SINGERS OF THE 20'S SERIES 3 Various artists (Various Artists).
Notes: MONO Recording Artists include: Edna Hicks,Rosa Henderson etc.
Cassette: released on Emporium Cassettes in Jul'86 by Emporium Cassettes Records. Distributed by: Jazz Music

JAZZ SOUNDS OF THE TWENTIES.
Album: released on Swaggie (Australia) in Jan'82

Blues & Soul Power

BLUES & SOUL POWER Various artists (Various Artists).
Notes: Selection of tracks from original U.S Kent and Modern Record labels:Include;Johnny Otis-'Signifying Monkey',Lowell Fulson-'Tramp',Ikettes-'Peaches and Cream',Ike and Tina Turner-'Chicken Shack' etc.
Album: released on Kent in Jun'87 by Ace Records. Distributed by: Pinnacle

Blues Southside Chicago

BLUES SOUTHSIDE CHICAGO Various artists (Various Artists).
Album: released on Decca (Rock Echoes) in Feb'83 by Decca Records. Distributed by: Polygram, IMS

Album: released on Flyright in Jul'87 by Flyright Records. Distributed by: Krazy Kat, Swift, Jazz Music

Blues Summit...

BLUES SUMMIT LIVE AT NEWPORT Various artists (Various Artists).
Double compact disc: released on Mobile Fidelity in Oct'86 by Mobile Fidelity Records

Blues & The Abstract...

BLUES AND THE ABSTRACT TRUTH Various artists (Various Artists).
Tracks: / Stolen moments / Hoe down / Cascades / Yearnin' / Butch butch / Teenie's blues.
Notes: Featuring : Bill Evans, Roy Hanes, Oliver Nelson, Eric Dolphy, Paul Chambers and Freddie Hubbard.
Album: released on Jasmine in Jun'82 by Jasmine Records. Distributed by: Counterpoint, Taylor, H.R., Wellard, Chris, Swift

Cassette: released on Jasmine in Jun'82 by Jasmine Records. Distributed by: Counterpoint, Taylor, H.R., Wellard, Chris, Swift,

Blues & Trouble

CADILLAC.
Single (7"): released on Ammunition Communications in Sep'85. Distributed by: Pinnacle, Fast Forward, Cartel, M.I.S., EMI

MYSTERY TRAIN.
Single (7"): released on Plus One in Aug'84 by Plus One Records. Distributed by: Cartel

Blues Upside Your Head

BLUES UPSIDE YOUR HEAD Various artists (Various Artists).
Tracks: / I'm goin' upside your head / I'm gonna love you / Two steps from the blues / House rent boogie / Strange angels / Those lonely, lonely feelings / Have you ever loved a woman / Southern country boy / I ain't got you / Messin' around / Reconsider Baby / Stroll out west / Gangster of love / Booze in the bottle / Jelly roll king / I wish you would / You've got to love her with a feeling / Steppin' out / Mama, you got a daughter / Put it all in there / Look on yonder wall / When you're doing alright (don't say nothing).
Notes: Tracks 1,2,4,9,10,12,16,18,19,22: Original Vee-Jay recordings. Licensed from Charly Records International APS. Tracks 6,7,13,17: Original King recordings. Licensed from Gusto Records Inc. Tracks 8,14,20: Original Jewel recordings. Licensed from Charly Records International APS. Tracks 3,11: Original Duke recordings. Licensed from MCA Records Ltd. Tracks 5,21: Original Fury recordings via Sansu Enterprises. Licensed from Charly Records International APS. Track 15: Original Sun recording. Licensed from Charly Records International APS.
Compact disc: released on Charly in Oct'87 by Charly Records. Distributed by: Charly, Cadillac

Bluesville

BLUESVILLE Various artists (Various Artists).
Album: released on Goldband in Feb'79 by Charly Records. Distributed by: Charly

Blues Women

BLUES WOMEN Various artists (Various Artists).
Album: released on Krazy Kat (USA) in Apr'85

Blue Train

LAND OF GOLD.
Single (12"): released on Dreamworld in Mar'87 by TV Personalities, The. Distributed by: Rough Trade

Blue Velvet

BLUE VELVET Original soundtrack.
Album: released on That's Entertainment in May'87 by That's Entertainment Records. Distributed by: Pinnacle, PRT

Cassette: released on That's Entertainment in May'87 by That's Entertainment Records. Distributed by: Pinnacle, PRT

Blue Yonder

BLUE YONDER.
Tracks: / Windsong / House of love / When grace is falling / In the rain / Still I love / Long haul, The / Something for the pain / Indigo / Secret miracle.
Album: released on Atlantic in 11 Apr'87 by WEA Records. Distributed by: WEA

Cassette: released on Atlantic in 11 Apr'87 by WEA Records. Distributed by: WEA

Blue Zone

FINEST THING.
Tracks: / Finest thing / Love will wait / Finest thing(US remix)* / Finest thing(instr.)*.
Single (7"): released on Rockin' Horse in Jun'86 by Arista Records. Distributed by: RCA Distribution

Single (12"): released on Rockin' Horse in Jun'86 by Arista Records. Distributed by: RCA Distribution

Single (12"): released on Rockin' Horse in Jun'86 by Arista Records. Distributed by: RCA Distribution

LOVE WILL WAIT.
Tracks: / Love will wait / There was I / Dirty tale*.
Single (7"): released on Rockin' Horse in Mar'86 by Arista Records. Distributed by: RCA Distribution

Single (12"): released on Rockin' Horse in Mar'86 by Arista Records. Distributed by: RCA Distribution

Single (12"): released on Rockin' Horse in Mar'86 by Arista Records. Distributed by: RCA Distribution

Blue Zoo

CRY BOY CRY.
Single (7"): released on Magnet in Sep'82 by Magnet Records. Distributed by: BMG

Single (12"): released on Magnet in Sep'82 by Magnet Records. Distributed by: BMG

FORGIVE AND FORGET.
Single (7"): released on Magnet in Apr'83 by Magnet Records. Distributed by: BMG

Single (12"): released on Magnet in Apr'83 by Magnet Records. Distributed by: BMG

Picture disc single: released on Magnet in Apr'83 by Magnet Records. Distributed by: BMG

LOVED ONE'S AN ANGEL.
Single (7"): released on Magnet in Jan'83 by Magnet Records. Distributed by: BMG

Single (12"): released on Magnet in Jan'83 by Magnet Records. Distributed by: BMG

SOMEWHERE IN THE WORLD THERE'S A COWBOY SMILING.
Single (7"): released on Magnet in Oct'83 by Magnet Records. Distributed by: BMG

Single (12"): released on Magnet in Oct'83 by Magnet Records. Distributed by: BMG

TWO BY TWO.
Tracks: / Cry boy cry / John's Lost / Far cry / Count On Me (You Can) / In love and in life / Love moves in strange ways / Somewhere in the world there's a cowboy smiling / Forgive and forget (I just can't) / I'm your man / Open up / Can't hold me down / Something familiar.
Album: released on Magnet in Nov'83 by Magnet Records. Distributed by: BMG

Cassette: released on Magnet in Nov'83 by Magnet Records. Distributed by: BMG

Bluiett, Hamiet

EBU.
Compact disc: released on Soul Note (Italy) in Jan'86. Distributed by: Harmonia Mundi Distributors

Blume, Judy

DEENIE.
Notes: Read by Kim Braden. Running for over three hours, this is Judy Blume's story of 'Deenie', unabridged & sensitively read by Kim Braden. 'Deenie' a young teenager has to wear an ugly black brace just when she is dreaming of a relationship with Buddy Braden and when she has hopes of becoming a cheerleader. Her self-centred mother and devoted, but weak father

make up the background to this moving story of a girl's very personal feelings about herself and those around her. Running time: 3 hours approx.
Cassette: released on Listen For Pleasure in Feb'87 by MFP Records. Distributed by: EMI

Blunsdon, Ian
CUT ME DOWN.
Single (7"): released on Climber in Aug'85 by Climber Records. Distributed by: PRT

Single (12"): released on Climber in Aug'85 by Climber Records. Distributed by: PRT

Blunstone, Colin
MILES AWAY.
Single (7"): released on Panache in Sep'81 by Panache Records. Distributed by: Island

SAY YOU DON'T MIND.
Single (7"): released on Epic in Apr'82 by CBS Records. Distributed by: CBS

SHE'S NOT THERE.
Tracks: / She's not there / Who fires the gun.
Single (7"): released on Sierra in Oct'86 by Sierra Records. Distributed by: WEA

Single (12"): released on Sierra in Oct'86 by Sierra Records. Distributed by: WEA

WHERE DO WE GO FROM HERE.
Tracks: / Where do we go from here / Helen loves Paris.
Single (7"): released on Sierra in May'86 by Sierra Records. Distributed by: WEA

Single (12"): released on Sierra in May'86 by Sierra Records. Distributed by: WEA

Blu, Peggi
BLU BLOWIN'.
Tracks: / Tender moments / Love's just a mystery / Once had your love (and I can't let go) / All the way with you / Over and over / Mesmorize me / Feels good to me / All and all / Two can play at that game / Valentine to you.
Album: released on Capitol in Jan'87 by Capitol Records. Distributed by: EMI

Cassette: released on Capitol in Jun'87 by Capitol Records. Distributed by: EMI

Blurt
IN BERLIN.
Album: released on Armageddon in Apr'84 by Armageddon Records. Distributed by: Revolver, Cartel, Pinnacle

POPPYCOCK.
Album: released on Toeblock in Jan'86. Distributed by: Revolver Distribution

RUMINANT PLINTH.
Single (12"): released on Red Flame in May'82 by Red Flame Records. Distributed by: Nine Mile, Cartel

WHITE LINE FEVER.
Single (12"): released on Another Side in Feb'85 by Les Disques Du Crepuscule Records. Distributed by: Rough Trade, Cartel

Blush On Black
BLUSH ON BLACK Various artists (Various Artists).
Album: released on Blush in Jan'85

Blythe, Arthur
DA-DA.
Tracks: / Odessa / Spain thang / Esquinas (corners) / Crescent / Break tune / After Paris.
Album: released on CBS in Jun'86 by CBS Records. Distributed by: CBS

Cassette: released on CBS in Jun'86 by CBS Records. Distributed by: CBS

GRIP, THE.
Album: released on India Navigation in May'78 by India Navigation Records. Distributed by: Cadillac, Projection, Swift

LIGHT BLUE.
Album: released on CBS in Jun'83 by CBS Records. Distributed by: CBS

Cassette: released on CBS in Jun'83 by CBS Records. Distributed by: CBS

PUT SUNSHINE IN IT.
Album: released on CBS in Mar'85 by CBS Records.

Records. Distributed by: CBS

Cassette: released on CBS in Mar'85 by CBS Records. Distributed by: CBS

Blythe, Jimmy
STOMP YOUR STUFF (1927-31).
Album: released on Swaggie (Australia) in Jan'83

Blyth Power
CHEVY CHASE.
Single (12"): released on All The Madmen in Sep'85 by All The Madmen Records. Distributed by: Rough Trade, Cartel

JUNCTION SIGNAL.
Tracks: / Junction signal / Bind their kings in chains & the nobles with links of iron / Tribute to Admiral Byng * / Ffucke masticke room*.
Single (7"): released on All The Madmen in May'86 by All The Madmen Records. Distributed by: Rough Trade, Cartel

Single (12"): released on All The Madmen in May'86 by All The Madmen Records. Distributed by: Rough Trade, Cartel

LITTLE TOUCH OF HARRY IN THE MIDDLE OF THE NIGHT, A.
Cassette: released on 96 Tapes in Mar'85 by 96 Tapes Records. Distributed by: Rough Trade, Cartel

Blyton, Enid
ENID BLYTON-15 MINUTE TALES.
Cassette: released on Pickwick Talking Books in '84

FIVE GO TO MYSTERY MOOR.
Notes: Read by Sarah Greene
Double cassette: released on Listen For Pleasure in Aug'86 by MFP Records. Distributed by: EMI

B Mania
BACK IN THE USSR.
Tracks: / Back in the USSR / Love game.
Single (7"): released on Epic in Aug'87 by CBS Records. Distributed by: CBS

Single (12"): released on Epic in Aug'87 by CBS Records. Distributed by: CBS

B-Movie
FOREVER RUNNING.
Tracks: / Forever running / Heart og gold / My ship of dreams / Just an echo / Remembrance day / Switch on - Switch off / Blind allegiance / Arctic Summer / Nowhere girl.
Album: released on Sire in Nov'85

Cassette: released on Sire in Nov'85

LETTER FROM AFAR/NO JOY IN HEAVEN.
Single (7"): released on Sire in Jan'84

REMEMBERANCE DAY.
Tracks: / Rememberance day / Marilyn dreams / Nowhere girl.
Notes: Nowhere Girl is an extra track on the 12" version.
Single (7"): released on Wax in Mar'87 by Wax Records. Distributed by: Pinnacle

Single (12"): released on Wax in Mar'87 by Wax Records. Distributed by: Pinnacle

SWITCH ON SWITCH OFF.
Single (7"): released on Sire in Sep'85

Single (12"): released on Sire in Sep'85

BMX Bandits
CAT FROM OUTER SPACE, THE.
Tracks: / Cat from outer space, the / Strawberry Sunday.
Single (12"): released on 53rd & 3rd in Oct'86 by Fast Forward Records. Distributed by: Fast Forward, Cartel

E 102.
Tracks: / E 102 / Sad?.
Single (7"): released on 53rd & 3rd in May'86 by Fast Forward Records. Distributed by: Fast Forward, Cartel

WHAT A WONDERFUL WORLD.
Tracks: / Day before tomorrow, The / Johnny Alucard / Sad.
Single (12"): released on 53rd & 3rd in Jan'87 by Fast Forward Records. Distributed by: Fast Forward, Cartel

Boa, Philip
ARISTOCRACIE (Boa, Philip & The Voodoo Club).
Album: released on Red Flame in Feb'87 by Red Flame Records. Distributed by: Nine Mile, Cartel

FOR WHAT BASTARDS. (Boa, Philip & The Voodoo Club).
Single (12"): released on Red Flame in 23 May'87 by Red Flame Records. Distributed by: Nine Mile, Cartel

Boardman, Harry
BALLADS, SONGS & RECITATIONS.
Album: released on Topic in '81. Distributed by: Roots Distribution

STEAM BALLADS.
Album: released on Broadside in Jun'81 by Broadside Records. Distributed by: Celtic Distributions. H.R. Taylor, Jazz Music, Projection,

Cassette: released on Broadside in Jun'81 by Broadside Records. Distributed by: Celtic Distributions. H.R. Taylor, Jazz Music, Projection,

Boardman-Hillery
TRANS-PENNINE.
Album: released on Topic in '81. Distributed by: Roots Distribution

Boardman, Phil
MUCH MISSED MAN.
Single (7"): released on Mayfield in Jan'82 by Mayfield Records. Distributed by: PRT

Boat
BOAT, THE Original soundtrack.
Album: released on WEA in Apr'82 by WEA Records. Distributed by: WEA

Boateng, Kwabena
ME DOFO WUO.
Album: released on Asaase Music Production in Jul'86. Distributed by: Jetstar

Boatman, Tooter
FOR TOOTER BOATMAN FANS ONLY.
Album: released on White in Jul'87

RARE ORIGINAL 50'S RECORDINGS.
Album: released on White Label (Holland) in Feb'84. Distributed by: CSA, PRT

TOOTER BOATMAN AND FRIENDS.
Album: released on White in Feb'87

TOOTER BOATMAN SOUND, THE.
Album: released on White Label (Holland) in Feb'85. Distributed by: CSA, PRT

Boatmen
STRAIGHT FROM THE TUNNELS MOUTH.
Album: released on Sweet Folk All in May'81 by Sweet Folk All Records. Distributed by: Sweet Folk All, Roots, Celtic Music, Dragon, Impetus, Projection, Chris Wellard, Festival Records

Bobbettes
MR LEE.
Single (7"): released on Revival in Jul'82. Distributed by: Lightning, Swift

Bobby M
LET'S STAY TOGETHER.
Single (7"): released on Gordy (USA) in Jan'83 by Motown Records. Distributed by: RCA

Single (12"): released on Gordy (USA) in Jan'83 by Motown Records. Distributed by: RCA

Bobby 'O'
I'M SO HOT FOR YOU.
Single (7"): released on O in Oct'82 by Vanguard (USA). Distributed by: PRT Distribution

Single (12"): released on O in Oct'82 by Vanguard (USA). Distributed by: PRT Distribution

SHE HAS A WAY.
Single (7"): released on O in Feb'83 by Vanguard (USA). Distributed by: PRT Distribution

Single (12"): released on O in Feb'83 by Vanguard (USA). Distributed by: PRT Distribution

Single (7"): released on BMC Imp in Sep'84

Bobby's Boys
BOBBY CAN'T DANCE.
Tracks: / Bobby can't dance / Bobby can't dance (dub) / Bobby can't dance (radio version).
Single (12"): released on Oval in Aug'86. Distributed by: Projection

BOBBY CAN'T DANCE (RE-ISSUE).
Tracks: / Bobby can't dance / No way Jose (King size enigma mix).
Single (7"): released on Oval in 13 Jun'87. Distributed by: Projection

Single (12"): released on Oval in 13 Jun'87. Distributed by: Projection

Bobby Socks
LET IT SWING.
Single (7"): released on RCA in May'85 by RCA Records. Distributed by: RCA, Roots, Swift, Wellard, Chris, I & B, Solomon & Peres Distribution

Bobby Sox
WAITING FOR THE MORNING.
Tracks: / Waiting for the morning / Working heart.
Single (7"): released on Sonet in Jun'86 by Sonet Records. Distributed by: PRT

Bob & Earl
HARLEM SHUFFLE.
Album: released on Line (West Germany) in Feb'84

Single (7"): released on Old Gold in Jul'82 by Old Gold Records. Distributed by: Lightning, Jazz Music, Spartan, Counterpoint

Bob Hope To Die
LIVING EMBODIEMENT OF JIMI HENDRIX.
Album: released on Backs in Jun'86 by Backs Records. Distributed by: Backs, Cartel

SHITE.
Album: released on Backs in Jul'85 by Backs Records. Distributed by: Backs, Cartel

Bob, Ken
IN DANGER.
Single (12"): released on Dynamic in Jun'84 by Creole Records. Distributed by: CBS

Bob, Lil
SWEET SOUL SWINGER.
Album: . Distributed by: Swift

Bob & Marcia
YOUNG, GIFTED AND BLACK.
Single (7"): released on Trojan in Oct'83 by Trojan Records. Distributed by: PRT Jetstar

Single (12"): released on Sunset in Jul'83. Distributed by: EMI

Single (7"): released on Old Gold in Jul'84 by Old Gold Records. Distributed by: Lightning, Jazz Music, Spartan, Counterpoint

Bobo Zero
CRIME OF EMOTION.
Single (7"): released on Safari in Jun'85 by Safari Records. Distributed by: Pinnacle

Bobs
BOBS, THE.
Album: released on Kaleidoscope (USA) in Nov'85 by Flying Fish Records (USA). Distributed by: Flying Fish (USA)

Bob & Vi
KEEP LYING, I LOVE IT.
Tracks: / Keep lying, I love it / O boy.
Single (7"): released on Vindaloo in Feb'86 by Vindaloo Records. Distributed by: WEA. Cartel

Bocage, Peter
AT SAN JACINTO HALL (Bocage, Peter with George Lewis/Louis Nelson).
Notes: With George Lewis/Louis Nelson. MONO recording.
Album: released on Jazzology in Jun'86. Distributed by: Jazz Music, Swift

Album: released on Jazzology in Jun'86. Distributed by: Jazz Music, Swift

NEW ORLEANS- THE LEGENDS LIVE (Bocage, Peter & His Creole Serenaders).
Notes: MONO recording
Album: released on Jazzology in Jun'86. Distributed by: Jazz Music, Swift

Bocquet, Didler
PICTURES OF LIFE.
Album: released on Pulse in Mar'84 by Pulse Records

Bodast
BODAST TAPES, THE.
Tracks: / Do you remember / Beyond winter / Once in a lifetime / Black leather gloves / Tired towers / Mr. Jones / 1,000 years / Nether street.
Album: released on Cherry Red in '82 by Cherry Red Records. Distributed by: Pinnacle

Boddy, Ian
CLIMB, (THE).

Album: released on Volume in '84 by Volume Records. Distributed by: Pinnacle

SPIRIT.
Album: released on The Newcastle Media Workshop in Apr'85

BoDeans

LOVE & HOPE & SEX & DREAMS.
Tracks: / She's a runaway / Fadeaway / Still the night / Rickshaw riding / Angels / Misery / Strangest kind, The / Say you will / Ultimately fine / That's all / Lookin' for me somewhere.
Notes: BoDeans are Slash Records newest sure-fired find,ready to start a stampede in your heart.Hailing like those fabulous Femmes,from the metropolis of Milwaukee,their debut album is set for release in early April.It's a no foolin'record,serving up mighty portions of those things attendant to the heart,like love & hope & sex & dreams.This is one of those rare rock'n'roll bands who pull no punches,squaring off against the modern world with equal parts fiery passion and honest attitude.And like fellow label mates,Los Lobos,BoDeans LP features T-Bone Burnett's spirited production ,which combined with David Tickle's mixing wizardry(Split Enz,Blondie,Prince,& Peter Gabriel among others),has produced an American rock & roll-mantic feast.. This record is guaranteed to jump start his/her heart.
Album: released on Slash in Apr'86 by London Records. Distributed by: Polygram

Cassette: released on Slash in Apr'86 by London Records. Distributed by: Polygram

Bodle, Ian

PHOENIX.
Album: released on Something Else in Sep'86

Bodines

HEARD IT ALL.
Tracks: / Heard it alll / William Shatner / Clear.
Single (7"): released on Creation in Aug'86. Distributed by: Rough Trade, Cartel

Single (12"): released on Creation in Aug'86. Distributed by: Rough Trade, Cartel

PLAYED, THE.
Album: released on Magnet in Aug'87 by Magnet Records. Distributed by: BMG

Cassette: released on Magnet in Aug'87 by Magnet Records. Distributed by: BMG

SKANKIN QUEENS.
Tracks: / Skankin queens / 1000 times / My remarkable mind.
Single (7"): released on Pop in Jul'87 by Magnet Records. Distributed by: RCA

Single (12"): released on Pop in Jul'87 by Magnet Records. Distributed by: RCA

THERESE.
Tracks: / Therese (new Mix) / Heard it all Pop.
Single (7"): released on Pop in Feb'87 by Magnet Records. Distributed by: RCA

Single (12"): released on Pop in Feb'87 by Magnet Records. Distributed by: RCA

THERESE (NEW MIX).
Tracks: / Therese (new mix) / Heard it all.
Single (7"): released on Pop in Feb'87 by Magnet Records. Distributed by: RCA

Single (12"): released on Pop in Feb'87 by Magnet Records. Distributed by: RCA

Bodiness

GOD BLESS.
Single (7"): released on Creation in Sep'85. Distributed by: Rough Trade, Cartel

Body

BODY Film soundtrack.
Tracks: / Our song / Sea shell & stone / Red stuff writhe / Gentle breeze blew through life, A / Lick your partner / Bridge passage for three plastic teeth / Chain of life / Womb bit, The / Embryo thought / March past of the Embryos / More than seven dwarfs in penis land / Dance of the red corpuscles / Body transport / Hand dance-full evening dress / Breathe / Old folks ascension / Bed-time dream-clime / Piddle in perspex / Embryonic womb walk / Mrs. Throat goes walking / Sea shell & soft stone / Give birth to a smile.
Notes: Music from the film with Ron Geesin & Roger Walters.
Album: released on Harvest in '70 by EMI Records. Distributed by: Roots, EMI

Body Heat

NO NO MR. BOOM BOOM.
Tracks: / No no Mr. Boom Boom / No no Mr. Boom Boom (version).
Single (7"): released on Diamond in Jul'87 by Revolver Records. Distributed by: Cartel

Single (12"): released on Diamond in Jul'87 by Revolver Records. Distributed by: Cartel

Body Music

BODY MUSIC (VIDEO) (Rainbow, Chris).
Notes: Song & music by Chris Rainbow,accompanying photos by Brian Aris of six of the world's top nude models in exotic locations.

Total playing time: 30 minutes.
Video-cassette (VHS): released on PMI in Sep'86 by PMI Records. Distributed by: EMI

Body Snatcher, The

BODY SNATCHER, (THE) (Shedden, John).
Double cassette: released on Colophone in Feb'81 by Audio-Visual Library Services. Distributed by: Audio-Visual Library Services

Boeing Boeing

UP SHE RISES.
Single (7"): released on Mont in Dec'82 by Mont Records. Distributed by: Spartan Distribution

Bofill, Angela

BEST OF ANGELA BOFILL, THE.
Tracks: / I try / This time / I'll be sweeter / What I wouldn't do (for the love of you) / Still in love / I'm on your side / Time to say goodbye / Something about you / Let me be the one / Tonight I give in / Call of the wild / Break it to me gently / Angel of the night.
Album: released on Arista in Aug'86 by Arista Records. Distributed by: RCA

Cassette: released on Arista in Aug'86 by Arista Records. Distributed by: RCA

SOMETHING ABOUT YOU.
Tracks: / Something about you / Break it to me gently / On and on / Tropical love / You should know by now / Only love / Holdin' out for love / Stop look listen / I do love you / Three blind mice / Time to say goodbye.
Notes: Produced by Narada Michael Walden (Sister Sledge) this is Angela Bofill's third Arista LP following 'Angie' and 'Angel of the night'
Album: released on Arista in Feb'82 by Arista Records. Distributed by: RCA

TELL ME TOMORROW.
Tracks: / Generate love / Tell me tomorrow / Midnight shine / I don't wanna come down(From love) / First time / This change of yours / Still in love / Woman't intuition / If you wanna love me, you're on..
Notes: Produced by George Duke
Album: released on Arista in Nov'85 by Arista Records. Distributed by: RCA

Cassette: released on Arista in Nov'85 by Arista Records. Distributed by: RCA

TOO TOUGH.
Tracks: / Too tough / Ain't nothing like the real thing(Duet with Boz Scaggs) / Tonight I give in / You could come take me home / Love you too much / Is this a dream / Song for a rainy day / I can see it in your eyes / Accept me / Rainbow inside my heart.
Notes: "Too tough" is Angela Bofill's fourth album.The first side is produced by NaradaMichael Walden, while Angela herself has written and produced Side 2.
Album: released on Arista in Feb'83 by Arista Records. Distributed by: RCA

Cassette: released on Arista in Feb'83 by Arista Records. Distributed by: RCA

Single (7"): released on Arista in Feb'83 by Arista Records. Distributed by: RCA

Single (12"): released on Arista in Feb'83 by Arista Records. Distributed by: RCA

Bogaert, Joe

NONE OF THEM ARE GREEN.
Album: released on Whale in Feb'84. Distributed by: Rough Trade, Cartel

Bogarde, Dirk

LYRICS FOR LOVERS.
Tracks: / Foggy day, A / Way you look tonight, The / Our love affair / You go to my head / Can't we be friends / Smoke gets in your eyes / Just one of those things / Get out of town / I get along without you very well / These foolish things / Where or when / As time goes by.
Notes: This LP is now re-released in its original form. 1.For many weeks,the record enjoyed regular plays on Radio two's David Jacob's show, 2. The David Jacobs show claim to have recieved more correspondance and enquiries regarding this LP than any other record they have played on the show.With the additional exposure which will result from the re-release of this unique album, especially on such shows as 'The Kenny Everett' and 'John Peel' shows,dealers should be ready for the rush.
Album: released on Decca in Dec'81 by Decca Records. Distributed by: Polygram

Bogaz

I'VE GOT LOVE.
Single (7"): released on AGR in Oct'83 by AGR Records. Distributed by: PRT

Single (12"): released on AGR in Oct'83 by AGR Records. Distributed by: PRT

Bogdan

OH EDDIE.
Single (7"): released on Black Label (USA) in Jul'81 by HSE Of America Records (USA)

WHO DO YOU THINK YOU ARE?.
Single (7"): released on Brilliant in Nov'81 by PVK. Distributed by: Spartan

Bogle, Eric

DOWN UNDER.
Album: released on Autogram in '82. Distributed by: Projection

IN CONCERT.
Album: released on Larrikin (Australia) in Jan'86. Distributed by: Roots

Cassette: released on Larrikin (Australia) in Jan'86. Distributed by: Roots

IN PERSON.
Album: released on Autogram in '82. Distributed by: Projection

PURE.
Album: released on Autogram in '82. Distributed by: Projection

SINGING THE SPIRIT HOME.
Tracks: / Singing the spirit home / Australian through and through.
Single (7"): released on Sonet in Apr'87 by Sonet Records. Distributed by: PRT

SINGING THE SPIRIT HOME.
Tracks: / An old song / Lifeline / Singing the spirit home / Twenty years ago / All the fine young men / Leaving the land / Australian through and through / Lancelot and Guinevere / Silo / Shelter.
Notes: Featuring: Eric Bogle, Brent Miller, Andy McGloin, John Munro, Phil Cuneen, Quentin Eyers and John Schumann.
Album: released on Sonet in Jun'87 by Sonet Records. Distributed by: PRT

WHEN THE WIND BLOWS.
Album: released on Topic in Nov'86. Distributed by: Roots Distribution

WHEN THE WIND BLOWS.
Album: released on Topic in Mar'85. Distributed by: Roots Distribution

Bognermay/Zuschrader

BERGPREDICT.
Album: released on Erdenklang (Germany) in Jun'84

Bogshed

BRUTAL.
Album: released on Shellfish in Aug'87 by Bogshed Records. Distributed by: Backs, Cartel

LET THEM EAT BOGSHED.
Single (12"): released on Vinyl Drip in Sep'85. Distributed by: Backs, Cartel

MORNING SIR.
Tracks: / Morning sir.
Single (7"): released on Shellfish in May'86 by Bogshed Records. Distributed by: Backs, Cartel

STEP ON IT BOGSHED.
Album: released on Help Shellfish in Aug'86. Distributed by: Backs, Cartel

TRIED AND TESTED PUBLIC SPEAKER (THE PEEL SESSION).
Tracks: / Champion love shoes / Little grafter / Morning Sir / Fastest legs / Adventure of dog.
Single (12"): released on Shellfish in Jan'87 by Bogshed Records. Distributed by: Backs, Cartel

Bohannon

BOHANNON DRIVE, (THE).
Tracks: / Rock your body / Wake up / Running from yourlove / Do it Goo / Lets start the dance III / Tell me you'll wait / Enjoy your day.
Album: released on Compleat in Oct'83 by Compleat Records. Distributed by: PRT

LET'S START THE DANCE 111.
Single (7"): released on Compleat in Jun'83 by Compleat Records. Distributed by: PRT

Single (12"): released on Compleat in Jun'83 by Compleat Records. Distributed by: PRT

MAKE YOUR BODY MOVE.
Tracks: / Make your body move / Wrong number / Don't leave me / B.T. is doing the reggae / School girl / Funkville / Come back my love / Make your body move (instrumental).
Album: released on Compleat in Aug'83 by Compleat Records. Distributed by: PRT

WAKE UP/ ENJOY YOUR DAY.
Single (7"): released on Compleat in Sep'83 by Compleat Records. Distributed by: PRT

Single (12"): released on Compleat in Sep'83 by Compleat Records. Distributed by: PRT

Bohannon, Hamilton

BOHANNON MIX/DISCO STOMP/SOUTH AFRICAN MAN.
Single (12"): released on Passion in Jan'84 by Skratch Records. Distributed by: PRT

LET'S START TO DANCE AGAIN(RAP).
Tracks: / Let's start to dance again(rap) / Let's start to dance again(party version).

Single (12"): released on Domino in Jul'86 by Domino Records. Distributed by: Charly

LET'S START TO DANCE AGAIN.
Single (7"): released on London in Jul'83 by London Records. Distributed by: Polygram

Single (12"): released on London in Jul'83 by London Records. Distributed by: Polygram

Bohard

MAYBE TOMORROW.
Tracks: / Maybe tomorrow / Maybe tomorrow (mega mix).
Single (12"): released on Seahorse in Apr'87. Distributed by: PRT

Single (7"): released on Atlantic in Jan'82 by WEA Records. Distributed by: WEA

QUITE A FEELING.
Tracks: / Quite a Feeling / Heaven.
Single (7"): released on Seahorse in Feb'87. Distributed by: PRT

Single (12"): released on Seahorse in Feb'87. Distributed by: PRT

Bohemian Girl

BOHEMIAN GIRL various artists (Various Artists).
Album: released on H.M.V. in Jan'68 by EMI Records. Distributed by: EMI

Bolarsky, Andrew

PLAYS SOUTH THE BORDER.
Tracks: / Sudam / Despidiendome de ti (sleeping on the beach) / Ritmo da ruas (street rhythm) / Latinum plus / Durmiendo en la playa / Chapter one / Feijoada.
Album: released on Spotlite in Jan'83 by Spotlite Records. Distributed by: Cadillac, Jazz Music, Spotlite

Bolzee

WINTER IS.
Single (7"): released on State in Nov'82 by State Records

Bokoor

HIP HIP HOP (EP).
Single (12"): released on Keynote in Dec'82 by Keynote Records. Distributed by: Cartel

Boland, Francy

AT HER MAJESTY'S PLEASURE (see Clarke, Kenny) (Boland, Francy Big Band & Kenny Clarke).
OPEN DOOR.
Tracks: / New box / A Rose Negra / Duas rosas / Milkshake / Open door / Dia blues / Total blues.
Album: released on Muse in Apr'81 by Peerless Records. Distributed by: Lugtons Distributors

Bolan, Marc

20TH CENTURY BOY Video.
Notes: Released on Channel 5 Video

ACROSS THE AIRWAVES.
Tracks: / Misty coast of Albany / Iscariot / Once upon the seas of Abyssinia / Misty mist / Chariots of silk / Scenescof / Girl / Life's a gas / Jeepster / Beltane walk / Jewel / Sailors of the highway / Suneye / Daye laye, A / Wind cheetah / By the light of the magical moon / Hot love / First heart might dawn dart / Summertime blues / Pavilions of sun / Ride a white swan.
Album: released on Cube in Jan'82 by Dakota Records. Distributed by: PRT

BEST OF 20TH CENTURY BOY (Bolan, Marc & T.Rex).
Compact disc: released on K-Tel in '86 by K-Tel Records. Distributed by: Record Merchandisers Distribution, Taylors, Terry Blood Distribution, Wynd-Up Distribution, Relay Distribution, Pickwick Distribution, Solomon & Peres Distribution, Polygram

Tracks: / Groover, The / Jeepster / Dreamy lady / Get it on / I love to boogie / One inch rock / Sunken rags / Telegram Sam / Debora / Laser love / Summertime blues / Light of love / New York City / Soul of my suit, The / 20th century boy / By the light of the magical moon / Truck

on(tyke) / Ride a white swan / Zip gun boogie / Teenage dream / Hot love / King of the rumblin' spires / Children of the revolution / London boys / Jitterbug love / Metal guru / Solid gold easy action / Cosmic dancer.

BEST OF THE 20TH CENTURY BOY.
Album: released on K-Tel in Apr'85 by K-Tel Records. Distributed by: Record Merchandisers Distribution, Taylors, Terry Blood Distribution, Wynd-Up Distribution, Relay Distribution, Pickwick Distribution, Solomon & Peres Distribution, Polygram

Cassette: released on K-Tel in Apr'85 by K-Tel Records. Distributed by: Record Merchandisers Distribution, Taylors, Terry Blood Distribution, Wynd-Up Distribution, Relay Distribution, Pickwick Distribution, Solomon & Peres Distribution, Polygram

BEYOND THE RISING SUN.
Album: released on Cambra in Apr'84 by Cambra Records. Distributed by: IDS, Conifer

Cassette:

BILLY SUPER DUPER.
Album: released on Marc On Wax in Apr'85. Distributed by: RCA, Spartan

Cassette: released on Marc On Wax in Apr'85. Distributed by: RCA, Spartan

BOLAN'S ZIP GUN.
Album: released on Marc On Wax in Apr'85. Distributed by: RCA, Spartan

Cassette: released on Marc On Wax in Apr'85. Distributed by: RCA, Spartan

CAT BLACK.
Single (7"): released on Cherry Red in Nov'81 by Cherry Red Records. Distributed by: Pinnacle

CHILDREN OF RARN SUITE (THE).
Album: released on Marc On Wax in Jun'82. Distributed by: RCA, Spartan

CHRISTMAS BOP.
Single (7"): released on Marc in Dec'82. Distributed by: Pinnacle

CROWN OF JEWELS, A (Bolan, Marc & T.Rex).
Tracks: / Slider, The / Buick McKane / Country honey / Mad Donna / Chance / Liquid gang / Token of my love / I really love you baby / My little baby / Dawn storm / Visions of Domino / Teen riot structure / Depth charge / Dance in the midnight.
Album: released on Dojo in Apr'86 by Castle Communications Records. Distributed by: Cartel

Cassette: released on Dojo in Apr'86 by Castle Communications Records. Distributed by: Cartel

DANCE IN THE MIDNIGHT.
Album: released on Marc On Wax in Apr'85. Distributed by: RCA, Spartan

Cassette: released on Marc On Wax in Apr'85. Distributed by: RCA, Spartan

DANDY IN THE UNDERWORLD.
Album: released on Marc On Wax in Apr'85. Distributed by: RCA, Spartan

Cassette: released on Marc On Wax in Apr'85. Distributed by: RCA, Spartan

DEEP SUMMER.
Single (7"): released on Marc On Wax in Jul'82. Distributed by: RCA, Spartan

FUTURISTIC DRAGON.
Album: released on Marc On Wax in Apr'85. Distributed by: RCA, Spartan

Cassette: released on Marc On Wax in Apr'85. Distributed by: RCA, Spartan

GET IT ON (Bolan, Marc & T.Rex).
Tracks: / Get it on / Ride a white swan / Jeepster / One inch rock / King of the rumbling spires / Cosmic dancer / Jewel / Telegram Sam / Metal guru / Solid gold easy action / 20th century boy / Groover, The / Truck on(tyke) / I love to boogie.
Album: released on Fame in Jun'86 by Music For Pleasure Records. Distributed by: EMI

Cassette: released on Fame in Jun'86 by Music For Pleasure Records. Distributed by: EMI

LIFE'S A GAS.
Single (12"): released on Marc On Wax in Jun'82. Distributed by: RCA, Spartan

LOVE AND DEATH.
Tracks: / You scare me to death / You've got the power / Eastern spell / Charlie / I'm weird / Hippy gumbo / Mustang Ford / Observations / Jasmin '49 / Cat black / Black & white incident / Perfumed garden of Gulliver Smith / Wizard, The / Beyond the rising sun / Rings of fortune / Recorded quotes from the book(You scare me to death).
Compact disc: by Cherry Red Records. Distributed by: Pinnacle

MAIN MAN (THE).
Double Album: released on Cambra in May'85 by Cambra Records. Distributed by: IDS, Conifer

Double cassette: released on Cambra in May'85 by Cambra Records. Distributed by: IDS, Conifer

MARC BOLAN WITH T.REX.
Compact disc: released on The Collection in Jul'87 by Object Enterprises Ltd. Distributed by: Counterpoint Distribution

MEGAREX 1.
Single (7"): released on Marc On Wax in Apr'85. Distributed by: RCA, Spartan

Single (12"): released on Marc On Wax in Apr'85. Distributed by: RCA, Spartan

Picture disc single: released on Marc On Wax in Apr'85. Distributed by: RCA, Spartan

ON VIDEO.
Tracks: / Metal guru / Ride a white swan / Telegram Sam.
Notes: A compilation of Marc Bolan & T.Rex performing some of their biggest hit singles of the 1970's
Total playing time: 60minutes.
Video-cassette (VHS): released on Videoform Music in Dec'84. Distributed by: EMI

Video-cassette [Betamax]: released on Videoform Music in Dec'84. Distributed by: EMI

SAILOR OF THE HIGHWAY.
Single (7"): released on Dakota in Jun'84 by Dakota Records. Distributed by: PRT

S BOLAN 13.
Single (7"): released on Marc On Wax in Feb'82. Distributed by: RCA, Spartan

Single (12"): released on Marc On Wax in Feb'82. Distributed by: RCA, Spartan

SING ME A SONG.
Single (7"): released on Rarn in Mar'81 by Rarn. Distributed by: Greensleeves Records, RCA

Picture disc single: released on Rarn in Jul'82 by Rarn. Distributed by: Greensleeves Records, RCA

SLIDER (THE).
Album: released on Marc On Wax in Apr'85. Distributed by: RCA, Spartan

Cassette: released on Marc On Wax in Apr'85. Distributed by: RCA, Spartan

SOLID GOLD BOOGIE BOY (Bolan, Marc & T.Rex).
Tracks: / Hot love / Ride a white swan / Debora / Motivator, The / Beltane walk, The / Woodland rock / Summertime blues / Telegram Sam / Solid gold easy action / 20th century boy / I love to boogie / Chariot choogle / Tenement lady / Casual agent.
Notes: The Official Marc Bolan Fan Club: P.O. Box 10,Bath,Avon,BA1 1YH,England. Bar code:5 012106 220072
Album licensed from Philip H.A. Bailey (PHAB). Tracks by kind permission of C/Era Records Ltd./Cube Records Ltd. and Marc On Wax Ltd.
Album: released on Warwick Reflections in Jun'86 by Warwick Records

Cassette: released on Warwick Reflections in Jun'86 by Warwick Records

SUNKEN RAGS.
Single (7"): released on Marc On Wax in Jul'85. Distributed by: RCA, Spartan

Single (12"): released on Marc On Wax in Jul'85. Distributed by: RCA, Spartan

TANX.
Compact disc: . Distributed by: RCA, Spartan

Album: released on Marc On Wax in Apr'85. Distributed by: RCA, Spartan

Cassette: released on Marc On Wax in Apr'85. Distributed by: RCA, Spartan

THINK ZINC.
Single (7"): released on Marc On Wax in Jun'83. Distributed by: RCA, Spartan

Picture disc single: released on Marc On Wax in Jun'83. Distributed by: RCA, Spartan

Single (12"): released on Marc On Wax in Jun'83. Distributed by: RCA, Spartan

T-REX COLLECTION.
Double cassette: released on Pickwick in Jul'80 by Pickwick Records. Distributed by: Pickwick Distribution, Prism Leisure Distribution, Lugtons

WIZARD.
Single (7"): released on Cherry Red in Apr'82 by Cherry Red Records. Distributed by: Pinnacle

WORDS AND MUSIC OF MARC BOLAN (1947-1977).
Tracks: / Afghan woman / One inch rock / Stacey grove / Eastern spell / Salamanda palaganda / Cat black the wizards hat / She was born to be a unicorn / Warlord of the royal crocodiles / Woodland bop / By the light of the magical moon / Great horse / Elemental child / Cosmic dancer / King of the rumbling spires / Beltane walk / Ride a white swan / Hot love / Get it on / Jeepster / Frowning atchuallpa / Children of ran suite.
Album: released on Cube in '82 by Dakota Records. Distributed by: PRT

YOU SCARE ME TO DEATH.
Album: released on Cherry Red in Oct'81 by Cherry Red Records. Distributed by: Pinnacle

Cassette: released on Cherry Red in Oct'81 by Cherry Red Records. Distributed by: Pinnacle

Single (7"): released on Cherry Red in Aug'81 by Cherry Red Records. Distributed by: Pinnacle

ZINC ALLOY AND THE HIDDEN RIDERS OF TOMORROW.
Album: released on Marc On Wax in Apr'85. Distributed by: RCA, Spartan

Cassette: released on Marc On Wax in Apr'85. Distributed by: RCA, Spartan

Bolan, Marc & T.Rex

SLIDER.
Compact disc: released on Marc On Wax in Nov'86. Distributed by: RCA, Spartan

TILL DAWN.
Album: released on Marc On Wax in Nov'85. Distributed by: RCA, Spartan

Cassette: released on Marc On Wax in Nov'85. Distributed by: RCA, Spartan

VERY BEST OF VOLUME 1, THE.
Notes: See also listings under T.Rex
Album: released on Hallmark in Jan'87 by Pickwick Records. Distributed by: Pickwick Distribution, PRT, Taylors

Cassette:

ZINC ALLOY.
Compact disc: . Distributed by: RCA, Spartan

Bold Navigators

BOLD NAVIGATORS Various artists (Various Artists).
Album: released on Tradition in '76. Distributed by: JSU, Cassion Distribution, Celtic Music, Jazz Music, Projection, Roots Records

Bolger, Ray

LAND OF OZ.
Cassette: released on Caedmon(USA) in May'80 by Caedmon (USA) Records. Distributed by: Gower, Taylors, Discovery

Bolivia

BOLIVIA (music from) (Wayra, Pukaj).
Album: released on Lyrichord in May'83. Distributed by: Roots

Bolland

DOMINO THEORY.
Album: released on Moon in May'82 by Moon Records. Distributed by: PRT Distribution

Bolling, Claude

JAZZ A LA FRANCAIS (Bolling, Claude Trio).
Album: released on CBS in Mar'85 by CBS Records. Distributed by: CBS

Cassette: released on CBS in Mar'85 by CBS Records. Distributed by: CBS

JAZZ A LA FRANCAISE.
Tracks: / A la Francaise / Garnerama / Bach to swing / Etue in blue not this time / Blue kiss from Brazil / Fiancees en folie / A La Francaise / Garnerama / Bach to swing / Etude in blue / Not this time / Blue kiss from Brazil / Fiancees en folie.
Compact disc: by CBS Records. Distributed by: CBS

LIVE AT THE MERIDIEN (Bolling Claude, Big Band).
Album: released on CBS(France) in Oct'85 by CBS Records. Distributed by: Conifer, Discovery, Swift

RAGTIME - BOOGIE WOOGIE.
Tracks: / 3-4 6-8 boogie / Mississippi rag / Death ray boogie / On the Mississippi / Louisiana glide / Maple leaf rag / Tiger rag / Man that got away, The / Yesterdays / Begin the beguine / Tea for two / Dardanella / Honky tonk train blues / Harlem strut / Pinetop's boogie woogie / Entertainer's rag, The / Waiting for the Robert E. Lee / Perfect rag.

RAGTIME-BOOGIE WOOGIE.
Tracks: / 3-4-6-8 Boogie / Mississippi rag / Death ray boogie / On the Mississippi / Louisiana glide / Maple leaf rag / Tiger rag / Man that got away, The / Yesterday's / Begin the beguine / Tea for two / Dardanella / Honky tonk train blues / Harlem strut / Pinetop's boogie woogie / Entertainer's rag / Waiting for the Robert E.Lee / Perfect rag.
Compact disc: by Phonogram Records. Distributed by: Polygram

Bollock Brothers

77, 78, 79.
Album: released on Mausoleum in Apr'85 by Mausoleum Records. Distributed by: Pinnacle

ACT BECOMES REAL.
Single (7"): released on MacDonald-Lydon in Mar'81 by MacDonald-Lydon Records. Distributed by: Pinnacle

BUNKER.
Single (7"): released on Charly in Apr'83 by Charly Records. Distributed by: Charly, Cadillac

DRAC'S BACK.
Tracks: / Drac's back / Horror movies.
Single (7"): released on Charly in Apr'86 by Charly Records. Distributed by: Charly, Cadillac

Single (12"): released on Charly in Apr'86 by Charly Records. Distributed by: Charly, Cadillac

FAITH HEALER/RETURN TO THE GARDEN OF EDEN.
Album: released on Charly in Oct'86 by Charly Records. Distributed by: Charly, Cadillac

FOUR HORSEMEN OF THE APOCALYPSE (THE).
Album: released on Charly in Jul'85 by Charly Records. Distributed by: Charly, Cadillac

FOUR HORSEMEN OF THE APOCALYPSE, THE.
Tracks: / Legend of the snake / Mistress of the macabre / Woke up this morning and found myself dead / Faith healer / King rat / Loud, loud, loud / Four horsemen of the apocalypse, The / Seventh seal, The / Return to the garden of Eden.
Compact disc: released on Charly in Mar'87 by Charly Records. Distributed by: Charly, Cadillac

HARLEY DAVIDSON.
Tracks: / Harley Davidson.
Single (12"): released on Play It Again Sam in Sep'86. Distributed by: Red Rhino, Cartel

LAST SUPPER (THE).
Tracks: / Horror movies / Enchantment / Reincarnation of / Save our souls / Face in the mirror / Last Supper, The / Act became real, The / Gift, The.
Album: released on Charly in '83 by Charly Records. Distributed by: Charly, Cadillac

LIVE - IN PUBLIC IN PRIVATE.
Tracks: / Woke up this morning (found myself dead) / Drac's back / Four horsemen of the Apocalypse / Count Dracula where's yar troosers / King Rat / Midnight Moses / Faith healer / Rock and roll.
Album: released on Charly in Jan'87 by Charly Records. Distributed by: Charly, Cadillac

LIVE PERFORMANCES (the official bootleg).
Double Album: released on Charly in Dec'83 by Charly Records. Distributed by: Charly, Cadillac

NEVER MIND THE BOLLICKS '83.
Album: released on Charly in Jul'83 by Charly Records. Distributed by: Charly, Cadillac

PRINCE AND THE SHOWGIRL.
Single (12"): released on Disc (Brussels) in Aug'84

ROCK AND ROLL 2001.
Single (12"): released on Charly in Sep'82 by Charly Records. Distributed by: Charly, Cadillac

ROCK'N'ROLL SUICIDE.
Album: released on Konnexion in Feb'86. Distributed by: Roots, Pinnacle

SLOW REMOVAL OF V V GOGH'S LEFT EAR.
Single (7"): released on Charly in Sep'82 by Charly Records. Distributed by: Charly, Cadillac

Bollox To The Gonads

BOLLOX TO THE GONADS-HERE'S THE TESTICLES (Various Artists).
Tracks: / Mau Maus / Anti-system / Xtract / Repulsive alien / Skeptix / Legion of parasites / Savage circle.
Album: released on Pax in Oct'83 by Pax Records. Distributed by: Red Rhino, Cartel

Boll Weevils

Farm Blues Bossmen & Boll Weevils

Bolshol

A AWAY II.
Tracks: / Black black black.
Single (7"): released on Beggars Banquet in Jan'87 by Beggars Banquet Records. Distributed by: WEA

Single (12"): released on Beggars Banquet in Jan'87 by Beggars Banquet Records. Distributed by: WEA

AWAY.
Tracks: / Away.
Single (12"): released on Beggars Banquet in Mar'86 by Beggars Banquet Records. Distributed by: WEA

Single (7"): released on Beggars Banquet in Mar'86 by Beggars Banquet Records. Distributed by: WEA

BOOKS ON THE BONFIRE.
Tracks: / Books on the bonfire / Boss / Funny thing, A.
Single (7"): released on Beggars Banquet in Aug'86 by Beggars Banquet Records. Distributed by: WEA

Single (12"): released on Beggars Banquet in Aug'86 by Beggars Banquet Records. Distributed by: WEA

FRIENDS.
Tracks: / Away / Modern man / Someones daughter / Sunday morning / Looking for a life to lose / Romeo in clover / Books on the bonfire / Pardon me / Fat and jealous / Waspy.
Album: released on Beggars Banquet in Nov'86 by Beggars Banquet Records. Distributed by: WEA

Cassette: released on Beggars Banquet in Nov'86 by Beggars Banquet Records. Distributed by: WEA

Compact disc: released on Beggars Banquet in Dec'86 by Beggars Banquet Records. Distributed by: WEA

GIANT.
Album: released on Situation 2 in Jul'85. Distributed by: Cartel, Pinnacle

HAPPY BOY.
Single (7"): released on Situation 2 in Oct'85. Distributed by: Cartel, Pinnacle

Single (12"): released on Situation 2 in Oct'85. Distributed by: Cartel, Pinnacle

ITV MAN.
Single (7"): released on Beggars Banquet in Aug'87 by Beggars Banquet Records. Distributed by: WEA

Single (12"): released on Beggars Banquet in Aug'87 by Beggars Banquet Records. Distributed by: WEA

PLEASE.
Tracks: / Please / West of London town.
Single (7"): released on Beggars Banquet in May'87 by Beggars Banquet Records. Distributed by: WEA

Single (12"): released on Beggars Banquet in May'87 by Beggars Banquet Records. Distributed by: WEA

SOB STORY.
Single (7"): released on Situation 2 in Mar'85. Distributed by: Cartel, Pinnacle

Single (12"): released on Situation 2 in Mar'85. Distributed by: Cartel, Pinnacle

SUNDAY MORNING.
Tracks: / Sunday morning / Foxes / Musak *.
Single (7"): released on Beggars Banquet in Oct'86 by Beggars Banquet Records. Distributed by: WEA

Single (12"): released on Beggars Banquet in Oct'86 by Beggars Banquet Records. Distributed by: WEA

Bolstertone Choir

VILLAGE OF SONG (THE) (Bolstertone Male Voice Choir).
Tracks: / Morning has broken / Llanfair / With catlike tread / Go down Moses / Mull of Kintyre / When a child / Sound an alarm / Uist tramping song, The / Sunrise, sunset / John Peel / Kalinka / Old woman, The / Stout-hearted men / Gwahoddiad.
Album: released on Look in Nov'79. Distributed by: R. Smith & Co. Records, H.R. Taylor

VILLAGE SONG (THE) (Bolstertone Male Voice Choir).
Cassette: released on Look in Nov'79. Distributed by: R. Smith & Co. Records, H.R. Taylor

Bolt From The Block

BOLT FROM THE BLOCK Various artists (Various Artists).
Album: released on Thunderbolt in Nov'84 by Magnum Music Group Ltd. Distributed by: Magnum Music Group Ltd, PRT Distribution, Spartan Distribution

Bolton, Cecil

SERENADE IN SEQUENCE.
Album: released on Dansan in Apr'79 by Spartan Records. Distributed by: Spartan

Bolton, Michael

MICHAEL BOLTON.
Tracks: / Fool's game / She did the same thing / Hometown hero / Can't hold on / Can't let go / Fighting for my life / Paradise / Back in my arms again / Carrie / I almost believed you.
Album: released on CBS in Jul'83 by CBS Records. Distributed by: CBS

Bomans, Godfried

GODFRIED BOMANS.
Album: released on Music For Pleasure (Holland) in '86 by EMI Records. Distributed by: EMI

Cassette: released on Music For Pleasure (Holland) in '86 by EMI Records. Distributed by: EMI

Bombay

BREAKING THE RULES.
Single (12"): released on Music For Nations in Apr'84 by Music For Nations Records. Distributed by: Pinnacle

Bombay Ducks

DANCE MUSIC.
Album: released on United Dairies in Mar'86. Distributed by: Rough Trade, Indies

Bomb Drugs

DRUGS.
Album: released on Abstract in May'86 by Abstract. Distributed by: Pinnacle

Bomb Party

LAST SUPPER, THE.
Album: released on Abstract in Jun'87 by Abstract. Distributed by: Pinnacle

LIFE'S A BITCH.
Single (7"): released on Abstract in Dec'85 by Abstract. Distributed by: Pinnacle

NEW MESSIAH.
Extended-play record: released on Abstract in Jul'85 by Abstract. Distributed by: Pinnacle

RAY GUN.
Extended-play record: released on Abstract in May'85 by Abstract. Distributed by: Pinnacle

Bonano, Sharkey

SHARKEY BONANO & HIS NEW ORLEANS BOYS & SHARKS OF RHYTHM (Bonano, Sharkey & His New Orleans Boys & Sharks of Rhythm).
Cassette: released on Holmia Cassettes in Jun'86. Distributed by: Jazz Music, Wellard,

Boncher, Judy

LOVELY PARADISE.
Tracks: / Lovely paradise / Lovely paradise(version).
Single (12"): released on Orbitone in May'86 by Orbitone Records. Distributed by: Jetstar Distribution

Bond

BOYS TOYS.
Tracks: / Boys toys / Do you really want to hide.
Single (7"): released on Arista in Apr'87 by Arista Records. Distributed by: RCA

Single (12"): released on Arista in Apr'87 by Arista Records. Distributed by: RCA

Bondage, Beki

DON'T TURN AWAY.
Single (7"): released on Communique in Nov'85. Distributed by: Backs, Cartel

Single (12"): released on Communique in Nov'85. Distributed by: Backs, Cartel

WHEEL OF FORTUNE (THE).
Single (12"): released on Communique in Oct'85. Distributed by: Backs, Cartel

Bond, Eddie

EDDIE BOND Original Early Recordings.
Album: released on White in Dec'86

ORIGINAL EARLY RECORDINGS.
Album: released on White Label (Holland) in Feb'85. Distributed by: CSA, PRT

ROCKING DADDY FROM MEMPHIS VOL 2.
Album: released on Rockhouse in Sep'84. Distributed by: Pinnacle

Bond, Gary

CROSS MY PAWS AND HOPE TO DIE.
Single (7"): released on TV Records in Jan'83 by TV Records. Distributed by: Virgin

Bond, Graham

BEGINNING OF JAZZ-ROCK.
Tracks: / Wade in the water / Big boss man / Early in the morning / Person to person blues / Spanish blues / First time I met the blues, The / Stormy Monday / Train time / What'd I say?.
Album: released on Charly in Jan'77 by Charly Records. Distributed by: Charly, Cadillac

Bondi Beat Poets

BALTIMORE (behold the precious stupa).
Album: released on Cherry Red in Mar'84 by Cherry Red Records. Distributed by: Pinnacle

Bond, Jane

POLITICALLY CORRECT (Bond, Jane & the Undercover Men).
Album: released on Dreamworld in Sep'86 by TV Personalities, The. Distributed by: Rough Trade

Bond, Johnny

BEST OF....
Notes: 10 Tracks
Album: released on Starday in Apr'87

Cassette: released on Starday in Apr'87

Bond, Peter

IT'S ALL RIGHT FOR SOME.
Tracks: / Baron and the busker, The / Afrika '65 / Category D / Some you win, some you lose / Letter from Sunderland / Birthday cake city / No coals off / Lark across the vapour train, The / Let it be on your mind / It's all right for some / Joe Peel / Joker, The.
Album: released on Highway in '81 by Highway Records. Distributed by: Roots, Projection, Ross

SE ME UP SEE ME DOWN.
Album: released on Highway in '81 by Highway Records. Distributed by: Roots, Projection, Ross

Bonds, Gary U.S.

DEDICATION.
Tracks: / Jole Blon / This little girl / Your love / Dedication / Daddy's come home / It's only love / Pretender, The / Way back when / From a Buick 6 / Just like a child.
Album: released on EMI America in Sep'85 by EMI Records. Distributed by: EMI

Cassette: released on EMI America in Sep'85 by EMI Records. Distributed by: EMI

Album: released on Fame (EMI) America in Nov'83 by Music For Pleasure Records. Distributed by: EMI

Cassette: released on Fame (EMI) America in Nov'83 by Music For Pleasure Records. Distributed by: EMI

GARY U.S. BONDS.
Album: released on K-Tel in Aug'84 by K-Tel Records. Distributed by: Record Merchandisers Distribution, Taylors, Terry Blood Distribution, Wynd-Up Distribution, Relay Distribution, Pickwick Distribution, Solomon & Peres Distribution, Polygram

GARY U.S. BONDS MEETS CHUBBY CHECKER.
Album: released on EMI (France) in '83 by EMI Records. Distributed by: Conifer

Gary US Bonds meets Chubby Checker

GREATEST HITS:GARY U.S. BONDS.
Tracks: / New Orleans / Quarter to three / Not me / Dear lady twist / Mixed up faculty / School is out / School is in / Having so much fun / Twist twist Senora / Where did that naughty girl go? / I dig this station / Take me back to New Orleans.
Album: released on Ensign in Sep'81 by Ensign Records. Distributed by: CBS Distribution

Cassette: released on Ensign in Sep'81 by Ensign Records. Distributed by: CBS Distribution

NEW ORLEANS.
Single (7"): released on Creole in Oct'80 by Creole Records. Distributed by: Rhino, PRT

ON THE LINE.
Album: released on EMI (Germany) in Apr'84 by EMI Records. Distributed by: Conifer

QUARTER TO THREE.
Single (7"): released on Creole in Oct'80 by Creole Records. Distributed by: Rhino, PRT

STANDING IN THE LINE OF FIRE.
Album: released on Making Waves in Aug'85 by Making Waves Records

Cassette: released on Making Waves in Aug'85 by Making Waves Records

Single (7"): released on Making Waves in Jul'85 by Making Waves Records

Single (12"): released on Making Waves in Jul'85 by Making Waves Records

STAR (THE).
78 rpm record: released on Charly in Nov'81 by Charly Records. Distributed by: Charly, Cadillac

TWIST UP CALYPSO.
Tracks: / Calypso / Scratch me back / Coconut woman / Day O / Twist, twist, senora.
Album: released on Teldec (Germany) in Dec'81 by Import Records. Distributed by: IMS Distribution, Polygram Distribution

Boneless Ones

SKATE FOR THE DEVIL.
Album: released on Boner in Jan'87. Distributed by: Revolver

Bone Orchard

JACK.
Album: released on Jungle in Nov'84 by Jungle Records. Distributed by: Jungle, Cartel

Single (7"): released on Jungle in Sep'84 by Jungle Records. Distributed by: Jungle, Cartel

PENTHOUSE POULTRY.
Album: released on Vax in Nov'85. Distributed by: Red Rhino

PRINCESS EPILEPSY.
Single (12"): released on Jungle in Jun'85 by Jungle Records. Distributed by: Jungle, Cartel

STUFFED TO THE GILLS.
Album: released on Jungle in Mar'85 by Jungle Records. Distributed by: Jungle, Cartel

Extended-play record: released on Jungle in Nov'83 by Jungle Records. Distributed by: Jungle, Cartel

SWALLOWING HAVOC.
Extended-play record: released on Jungle in Apr'84 by Jungle Records. Distributed by: Jungle, Cartel

Bone, Richard

BEAT IS ELITE (THE).
Single (12"): released on Survival in Sep'82 by Survival Records. Distributed by: Backs, Cartel Distribution

BRAVE TALES.
Album: released on Survival in Jul'83 by Survival Records. Distributed by: Backs, Cartel Distribution

DIGITAL DAYS.
Single (7"): released on Survival in Apr'82 by Survival Records. Distributed by: Backs, Cartel Distribution

EXSPECTABLE.
Album: released on Survival in Feb'85 by Survival Records. Distributed by: Backs, Cartel Distribution

JOY OF RADIATION.
Single (7"): released on Survival in Feb'83 by Survival Records. Distributed by: Backs, Cartel Distribution

Single (12"): released on Survival in Feb'83 by Survival Records. Distributed by: Backs, Cartel Distribution

LIVING IN PARTY TOWN.
Single (12"): released on Survival in Mar'84 by Survival Records. Distributed by: Backs, Cartel Distribution

REAL THING.
Single (12"): released on Survival in Nov'84 by Survival Records. Distributed by: Backs, Cartel Distribution

Bones, Elbow

HAPPY BIRTHDAY BABY.
Single (7"): released on EMI America in Apr'84 by EMI Records. Distributed by: EMI

Single (12"): released on EMI America in Apr'84 by EMI Records. Distributed by: EMI

MAMA'S IN LOVE AGAIN.
Single (7"): released on EMI America in Aug'84 by EMI Records. Distributed by: EMI

NIGHT IN NEW YORK.
Single (12"): released on EMI America in Nov'83 by EMI Records. Distributed by: EMI

Bone Symphony

IT'S A JUNGLE OUT THERE.
Single (12"): released on Capitol in Feb'84 by Capitol Records. Distributed by: EMI

Boney M

Biographical Details: Hailing from various West Indian Islands but permanently based in West Germany, this three woman one-man quartet have always been little more than the good-looking vocal puppets of their producer, Frank Farian. From the start of 1977 until the end of the Seventies, they were one of the hottest acts throughout Europe, with success on a scale rivalled only by Abba and by the Bee Gees/John Travolta-inspired "Saturday night Fever"/"Grease" boom. Nowhere was Boney M's success more pronounced than in Britain. They opened their UK chart career with nine consecutive Top 10 singles. The first was "Daddy Cool", a banal and repetitive but highly danceable disc that peaked at No.6. It was followed by "Sunny", a No.3 remake of a 1966 Bobby Hebb/Georgie Fame hit. "Ma Baker" hit No.2 and cemented their status, but "Belfast" (No.8) gained little airplay due to its lyrics concerning the Northern Ireland conflict. Nevertheless, the fact that it was able to collect a Top 10 placing despite lack of radio support, confirmed that Boney M were a popular group who were here to stay. In April 1978 their fifth hit was released. "Rivers of Babylon" was a traditional song that had previously been best known through two early Seventies renditions: a reggae version by the Melodians and a folky version by Don McLean on his "American pie" album, Boney M and Farian recorded the song in the style that had become their trademark, bouncy melodic Eurodisco (a style that they helped to invent). It was a runaway hit right across the Continent. In the UK the single logged five weeks at No.1; by the end of its chart-topping run it had sold well over a million copies. On its way down, however, discos and radio stations suddenly picked up on its B side "Brown girl in the ring", a singalong ditty ideal for parties. Having descended to No.20, "Babylon", was transformed into a double A sided hit and climbed up the chart again, this time peaking at No.2. In total "Rivers of Babylon"/"Brown girl in the ring" logged 40 weeks on the UK chart, one of the all-time longest unbroken runs. It is Britain's second biggest single in history, one of only two 45's to sell more than two million copies in the UK alone. Boney M's disc is bettered soley by Wings' "Mull of Kintyre/"Girls' school", which had been a monster hit just a few months earlier. It should be added that there was strong evidence that many consumers purchased the Boney M single twice, unaware that their 'new hit' "Brown girl in the ring" had been on the B side of "Babylon"!. By the time this historic 45 fell off the British chart in early '79, the group had had two follow-up successes. "Rasputin" reached no.2, then came their second and final UK No. 1 single: "Mary's boy child - oh my Lord" was the Chrismas chart-topper of '78. The principal portion of this medley single was a remake of Harry Belafonte's 1957 winner. However the ever-crafty Frank Farian added a section entitled "Oh my Lord" and thus won a share in the compser's royalties. Those royalties were lucrative indeed, for the disc was another phenomenal success. It is ranked as Britain's fifth best-selling single of all time, thereby giveng Boney M the extraordinary honour of scoring two out of the UK's all-time Top 5. The platinum touch of Farian and his group (that helped to make 1978 one of Britain's hottest years ever for singles sales) diminished slightly in '79, but nevertheless yielded two final UK Top Tenner, plus a second No.1 album with "Oceans of fantasy" (the first having been 1978's "Night flight to Venus") May 1980 brought a third and a final No.1 album with a compilation entitled "The magic of Boney M". But by this time, the hit singles were dramatically tailing off in both Britain and Continental Europe. Their last British chart gasp was breathed in late '81 with the No.39 placing of "We kill the world (don't kill the world)", then the lean years began. Despite their exceptional record sales (though they never conquered America), Boney M have been dismissed by many as purveyors of throwaway disco fodder. Yet a survey of their lists of hits reveals that a notorious Yankee criminal, Ulster, a famous Russian casanova and the perils of modern technology have all been subjects covered in their singles. Indeed, the Soviet authorities ordered "Rasputin" to be deleted from their repertoire, when the group toured Russia! Boney M have also been criticised for being merely the faces and voices fronting a manipulative business team. This charge is undoubtedly true, but at least they had faces. B.M. 84

BABY DO YOU WANNA BUMP?.
Single (7"): released on Creole in May'78 by Creole Records. Distributed by: Rhino, PRT

BANG BANG LULU.
Tracks: / Bang bang Lulu / Young free & single.
Single (12"): released on Carrere in Jul'86 by Carrere Records. Distributed by: PRT, Spartan

BELFAST.
Single (7"): released on Atlantic in Oct'77 by WEA Records. Distributed by: WEA

BEST OF TEN YEARS.
Tracks: / Daddy cool / Ma Baker / Rivers of Babylon / Belfast / Rasputin / Brown girl in the ring / Sunny / Happy song.
Compact disc: . Distributed by: Pinnacle, Terry Blood Distribution, Stylus Distribution

Album: released on Stylus in Aug'86. Distributed by: Pinnacle, Terry Blood Distribution, Stylus Distribution

Cassette: released on Stylus in Aug'86. Distributed by: Pinnacle, Terry Blood Distribution, Stylus Distribution

BROWN GIRL IN THE RING.
Single (7"): released on Atlantic in Mar'78 by WEA Records. Distributed by: WEA

CARNIVAL IS OVER.
Single (7"): released on Atlantic in Dec'82 by WEA Records. Distributed by: WEA

EYE DANCE.
Album: released on Carrere in Mar'86 by Carrere Records. Distributed by: PRT, Spartan

Cassette: released on Carrere in Mar'86 by Carrere Records. Distributed by: PRT, Spartan

HOORAY HOORAY IT'S A HOLIDAY.
Single (7"): released on Atlantic in Apr'79 by WEA Records. Distributed by: WEA

JAMBO-HAKUMA-MATATA.
Single (7"): released on Atlantic in Sep'83 by WEA Records. Distributed by: WEA

MA BAKER.
Single (7"): released on Atlantic in Jun'77 by WEA Records. Distributed by: WEA

MAGIC OF BONEY M, (THE).
Tracks: / Daddy cool / Rivers of Babylon / Sunny / Belfast / El lute / No woman no cry / Rasputin / Painter man / Ma baker / Gotta go home / My friend Jack / I see a boat on the river / Brown girl in the ring / Mary's boy child / Bahama mama / I'm born again / Oceans of fantasy / Ribbons of blue / Still I'm sad / Hooray hooray it's a holi-day.
Album: released on Atlantic in Apr'80 by WEA Records. Distributed by: WEA

Cassette: released on Atlantic in Apr'80 by WEA Records. Distributed by: WEA

MARY'S BOY CHILD.
Single (7"): released on Atlantic in '78 by WEA Records. Distributed by: WEA

PAINTER MAN.
Single (7"): released on Atlantic in May'82 by WEA Records. Distributed by: WEA

RIVERS OF BABYLON.
Single (7"): released on Atlantic-Hansa in Jul'81

WE KILL THE WORLD (DON'T KILL THE WORLD).
Single (7"): released on Atlantic in Nov'81 by WEA Records. Distributed by: WEA

Single (12"): released on Atlantic in Nov'81 by WEA Records. Distributed by: WEA

YOUNG FREE & SINGLE.
Tracks: / Young free & single / Chica da Silva.
Single (7"): released on Carrere in Mar'86 by Carrere Records. Distributed by: PRT, Spartan

Single (12"): released on Carrere in Mar'86 by Carrere Records. Distributed by: PRT, Spartan

Bonfa, Luiz

JAZZ SAMBA ENCORE (Bonfa, Luiz/Stan Getz).
Notes: Classic Verve re-issue featuring the compositions of Luiz Bonfa & Antonio Carlos Jobim. Latin jazz at it's best. Stan Getz-tenor sax/Luiz Bonfa-guitar/Antonio Carlos Jobim-guitar,piano/george Duvivier-bass/Tommy Williams- bass/Paulo ferreira-drums/Jose Carlos-drums/Don Payne-bass/dave Bailey-drums.
Album: released on Verve (USA) in May'84 by Polydor. Distributed by: Polygram

Bonfires In The Sky

MACHINES.
Single (7"): released on Writers Reign in Jun'85. Distributed by: Red Rhino, Cartel

Bonga

MARIKA.
Tracks: / Marika / Makongo / Espende / NH'Guvulu / Cambomborinho / Lamento de garina / Camin longe / Oma.
Notes: The music of Angola is rich in its African tradition & Portugese influence brought about by colonialism. This music is a direct link to todays popular Brazilian music.Bonga is a leading exponent of this music & has performed extensively around the world.
Album: released on Sunset (France) in Mar'85. Distributed by: IMS-Polygram Distribution

Bongos

BONGOS.
Album: released on Fetish in '81 by Fetish Records. Distributed by: Cartel, Pinnacle

BULLRUSHES.
Single (7"): released on Fetish in Dec'81 by Fetish Records. Distributed by: Cartel, Pinnacle

IN THE CONGO.
Single (12"): released on Fetish in May'81 by Fetish Records. Distributed by: Cartel, Pinnacle

MAMBO SUN.
Single (7"): released on Fetish in Apr'82 by Fetish Records. Distributed by: Cartel, Pinnacle

Single (12"): released on Fetish in Apr'82 by Fetish Records. Distributed by: Cartel, Pinnacle

TELEPHOTO LENS.
Single (7"): released on Fetish in May'81 by Fetish Records. Distributed by: Cartel, Pinnacle

TIME AND RIVER.
Album: released on Fetish in Feb'82 by Fetish Records. Distributed by: Cartel, Pinnacle

ZEBRA CLUB.
Single (7"): released on Fetish in Feb'82 by Fetish Records. Distributed by: Cartel, Pinnacle

Bonham, Debbie

FOR YOU AND THE MOON.
Album: released on Carrere in Sep'85 by Carrere Records. Distributed by: PRT, Spartan

Cassette: released on Carrere in Sep'85 by Carrere Records. Distributed by: PRT, Spartan

ON THE AIR TONIGHT.
Single (7"): released on Carrere in Aug'85 by Carrere Records. Distributed by: PRT, Spartan

Single (12"): released on Carrere in Aug'85 by Carrere Records. Distributed by: PRT, Spartan

SANCTUARY.
Single (7"): released on Carrere in Jul'85 by Carrere Records. Distributed by: PRT, Spartan

Single (12"): released on Carrere in Jul'85 by Carrere Records. Distributed by: PRT, Spartan

Bon Jovi

7800 DEGREES FAHRENHEIT.
Tracks: / In and out of love / Price of love, The / Only lonely / King of the mountains / Silent night / Tokyo road / Hardest part of the night / Always run to you / To the fire / Secret dreams / In and out of love / Price of love, The / Only lonely / King of the mountain / Silent night / Tokyo road / Hardest part of the night / Always run to you / To the fire / Secret dreams.
Compact disc: by Phonogram Records. Distributed by: Polygram

Album: released on Vertigo in May'85 by Phonogram Records. Distributed by: Polygram

Cassette: released on Vertigo in May'85 by Phonogram Records. Distributed by: Polygram

BON JOVI.
Tracks: / Runaway / She didn't know me / Shot through the heart / Love lies / Burning for love / Breakout / Come back / Get ready.
Album: released on Vertigo in Apr'84 by Phonogram Records. Distributed by: Polygram

Cassette: released on Vertigo in Apr'84 by Phonogram Records. Distributed by: Polygram

Compact disc: released on Vertigo in Jul'84 by Phonogram Records. Distributed by: Polygram

BREAKOUT (VIDEO).
Notes: A 6-track set from the U.S. heavy rock band named after leader and songwriter Jon Bon Jovi,and including current album material. 1985 Production. Total playing time 27 minutes. Number of tracks: 6
Video-cassette (VHS): released on Polygram in Jun'86 by Polygram Records. Distributed by: Polygram

Video-cassette [Betamax]: released on Polygram in Jun'86 by Polygram Records. Distributed by: Polygram

HARDEST PART IS THE NIGHT.
Single (12"): released on Vertigo in Aug'85 by Phonogram Records. Distributed by: Polygram

IN AND OUT OF LOVE.
Single (12"): released on Vertigo in May'85 by Phonogram Records. Distributed by: Polygram

LIVIN' ON A PRAYER.
Tracks: / Livin' on a prayer / Wild in the streets / Edge of a broken heart* / Livin' on a prayer(remix)**.
Single (12"): released on Vertigo in Oct'86 by Phonogram Records. Distributed by: Polygram

Single (12"): released on Vertigo in Oct'86 by Phonogram Records. Distributed by: Polygram

Single (7"): released on Vertigo in Oct'86 by Phonogram Records. Distributed by: Polygram

NEVER SAY GOODBYE.
Tracks: / Never say goodbye / Raise your hands.
Single (7"): released on Vertigo in Aug'87 by Phonogram Records. Distributed by: Polygram

Single (12"): released on Vertigo in Aug'87 by Phonogram Records. Distributed by: Polygram

SHE DOESN'T KNOW ME.
Single (7"): released on Vertigo in May'84 by Phonogram Records. Distributed by: Polygram

Single (12"): released on Vertigo in May'84 by Phonogram Records. Distributed by: Polygram

SLIPPERY WHEN WET.
Tracks: / Let it rock / You give love a bad name / Livin' on a prayer / Social disease / Wanted dead or alive / Raise your hands / Without love / I'd die for you / Never say goodbye / Wild in the streets.
Compact disc: by Phonogram Records. Distributed by: Polygram

Album: released on Vertigo in Sep'86 by Phonogram Records. Distributed by: Polygram

Cassette: released on Vertigo in Sep'86 by Phonogram Records. Distributed by: Polygram

Album: released on Vertigo in Aug'87 by Phonogram Records. Distributed by: Polygram

WANTED DEAD OR ALIVE.
Tracks: / Wanted dead or alive / Shot through the heart / Social Disease / Silent night / Get ready.
Single (7"): released on Mercury in Mar'87 by Phonogram Records. Distributed by: Polygram Distribution

Single (12"): released on Mercury in Mar'87 by Phonogram Records. Distributed by: Polygram Distribution

Double-pack single: released on Mercury in Mar'87 by Phonogram Records. Distributed by: Polygram Distribution

YOU GIVE LOVE A BAD NAME.
Tracks: / You give love a bad name / Let it rock / Borderline *.
Single (7"): released on Vertigo in Jul'86 by Phonogram Records. Distributed by: Polygram

Single (12"): released on Vertigo in Jul'86 by Phonogram Records. Distributed by: Polygram

Bonnay, Max

ACCORDEON.
Album: released on ARC (Accordion Records) in '84. Distributed by: Accordion Record Club

ACCORDEON CLASSIQUE.
Tracks: / Suite gothique / Espiegle / De profundis / Choral en si mineur / Mobile / Valeur de la transcription.
Notes: Retail price given by ARC excl.p&p(via mail order)is 6.99. Mail order distribution address: Accordian Record Club,146 Birmingham Road, Kidderminster,Worcs.DY10 2SL. Tele: 0562 746105
Album: released on Accordion Record Club in Jul'86 by Accordion Record Club Records. Distributed by: Accordion Record Club

Bonner Brothers

NOW AND FOREVER.
Tracks: / 1-2-3-4 / All we've got is each other / Rivers of Babylon / EH viva Espana / Now and forever / Knock on my door / Any way you want me / Mull of Kintyre / Brown girl in the ring / Nobody / Beautiful Sunday / Song for Guy.
Album: released on President in Jul'79 by President Records. Distributed by: Taylors, Spartan

Bonner, Joe

LIFESAVER (THE).
Tracks: / Bonner's bounce / Tattoo / Little chocolate boy / Lifesaver, The / Native son / Observer.
Album: released on Muse in Apr'81 by Peerless Records. Distributed by: Lugtons Distributors

Bonner, Juke Boy

GOING BACK TO THE COUNTRY.
Album: released on Arhoolie in May'81 by Arhoolie Records. Distributed by: Projection, Topic, Jazz Music, Swift, Roots

LEGACY OF THE BLUES VOL 5.
Tracks: / I'm a bluesman / Problems all round / Trying to get ahead / If you don't want to get mistreated / Lonesome ride back home / Funny money / I'm lonely too / Real good money / Come to me / Yammin' the blues / Better place to go / Tired of the greyhound blues.
Album: by Sonet Records. Distributed by: PRT

ONE MAN TRIO (THE).
Album: released on Flyright in Oct'79 by Flyright Records. Distributed by: Krazy Kat, Swift, Jazz Music

STRUGGLE (THE).
Album: released on Arhoolie in May'81 by Arhoolie Records. Distributed by: Projection, Topic, Jazz Music, Swift, Roots

Bonner, Les

STRICTLY INSTRUMENTAL (farfisa coronet organ).
Tracks: / Sing / Long ago and far away / Madrugada / Music maestro please / Affair to remember, An / What I did for love / Honeysuckle rose / Sweet Georgie Fame / One morning in May / Cavantina / Nature boy.
Album: released on Grosvenor in Mar'78 by Grosvenor Records. Distributed by: Taylors

Bonnie Scotland

BONNIE SCOTLAND Various artists (Various Artists).
Cassette: released on Ditto in May'86 by Pickwick Records. Distributed by: H.R. Taylor

Bonnie Scotland Show

BONNIE SCOTLAND SHOW Various artists (Various Artists).
Album: by Lismor Records. Distributed by: Lismor, Roots, Celtic Music

Bonnie,Tyler

VERY BEST OF BONNIE TYLER,THE.
Album: released on RCA in '84 by RCA Records. Distributed by: RCA, Roots, Swift, Wellard, Chris, I & B, Solomon & Peres Distribution

Cassette: released on RCA in '84 by RCA Records. Distributed by: RCA, Roots, Swift, Wellard, Chris, I & B, Solomon & Peres Distribution

WORLD STARTS TONIGHT,THE.
Album: released on RCA (Germany) in Mar'84

Cassette: released on RCA (Germany) in Mar'84

Bonn, Issy

BLESS YOU.
Tracks: / That lovely weekend / My little sailor man / Bless you / Some day / My Yiddisha Momma / Every night about this time / If I had my way / Shrine of St Cecilia.
Album: released on Decca in Apr'85 by Decca Records. Distributed by: Polygram

PAL FOREVER, A.
Tracks: / Here in my heart / My mother's lullaby / Pal must be a pal forever, A / Who knows / As sure as there's a heaven / My-na shay-na tyra(my sweet & dear one) / Bells of home, The / Humble people / Somewhere,someone(is saying a prayer) / Mom-e-le / My friend / I went to my mother / When you're home with the ones you love / Little boy that Santa Claus forgot, The / Home for Christmas.
Notes: A timely re-issue by the popular singer/comedian of the 20's-40's,Issy Bonn. Contains most of his material recorded for EMI and was originally issued due to massive public demand in 1981.Many tracks also feature Eddie calvert,along with a star studded array of popular conductors and their orchestras including Norrie Paramor and Ron Goodwin.
Album: released on EMI Retrospect in May'86 by EMI Records. Distributed by: EMI

Cassette: released on EMI Retrospect in May'86 by EMI Records. Distributed by: EMI

WHISPERING GRASS (Bonn, Issy/Dorothy Carless/Benny Lee/Adelaide Hall).
Notes: For full details see under Dorothy Carless.

Bonny Lass...

BONNY LASS COME O'ER THE BURN Various artists (Various Artists).
Album: released on Topic in '81. Distributed by: Roots Distribution

Bonny, Lauren

INVASION.
Single (7"): released on S&G in Jan'82. Distributed by: Pinnacle

Bonny North Tyne

NORTHUMBRIAN COUNTRY.
Album: released on Topic in '81. Distributed by: Roots Distribution

Bonoff, Karla

SOMEBODY'S EYES.
Single (7"): released on CBS in Jun'84 by CBS Records. Distributed by: CBS

Bon Rock

B BOY.
Single (12"): released on Beau-Jolly in Feb'84 by Nouveau Records. Distributed by: PRT

Bonsall, Joe

CAJUN JAMBOREE.
Album: released on Swallow in Feb'82

CAJUN JAMBOREE VOL 2.
Album: released on Swallow in Feb'79

JOE BONSALL'S GREATEST HITS.
Album:

Bon temps rouler

BON TEMPS ROULER Various artists (Various Artists).
Album:

Bonzo Dog Band

DOUGHNUTS IN GRANNY'S GREENHOUSE.
Notes: Re-release in original sleeve.
Album: released on Edsel in Mar'87 by Demon Records. Distributed by: Pinnacle, Jazz Music, Projection

GORILLA.
Tracks: / Cool Britannia / Equestrian statute, (The) / Jollity farm / I left my heart in San Francisco / Look out there's a monster coming / Jazz delicious hot disgusting cold / Death cab for a cutie / Narcissus / Intro and the outro / Mickey's son and daughter / Big shot / Music for head ballet / Piggy bank love / I'm bored / Sound of music, (The).
Album: released on Liberty-United in Aug'80 by EMI Records. Distributed by: EMI

HISTORY OF BONZOS.
Tracks: / Sport (the odd boy) / Noises for the leg / King of scurf / Labio dental fricative / Hello Mabel / Look at my, I'm wonderful / Canyons of your mind / Jolity farm / You done my brain in / My pink half of the drainpipe / Mr. Apollo / Hunting Tigers out in India / Suspicion / Mr Slater's parrot / Narcissus / I'm the urban spaceman / Bad blood / I left my heart in San Francisco / Tent / Can blue men sing with the whites / 9-5 pollution blues / Big shot / Release me / We are normal / Sound of music, (The) / Kama Sutra / Rhinocratic oaths / Straight from my heart / Mickey's son and daughter / Blind date / Trouser press, (The) / Slush.
Album: released on United Artists in '74

I'M THE URBAN SPACEMAN.
Single (7"): released on EMI Golden 45's in Jul'84 by EMI Records. Distributed by: EMI

LET'S MAKE UP AND BE FRIENDLY.
Tracks: / Strain, The / Turkeys / King of scurf / Waiting for the wardrobe / Straight from my heart / Rusty / Rawlinson end / Fresh wound / Slush / Bad blood.
Album: released on Awareness in Apr'87 by Awareness. Distributed by: EMI

TADPOLES.
Album: released on Edsel in May'86 by Demon Records. Distributed by: Pinnacle, Jazz Music, Projection

VERY BEST OF BONZO DOG DOO DAH BAND.
Tracks: / I'm the urban spaceman / Jollity farm / Mr. Apollo / Can blue men sing the whites / Death cab cutie / Trouser press, The / We are normal / Look out there's a monster coming / Intro & the outro, The / Hunting tigers out in Africa / Canyons of your mind / Equestrian statue, The / Mickey's son & daughter / Humanoid boogie / Monster mash / My pink half of the drain pipe.
Notes: Especially compiled for MFP, this album features the very best of the Bonzo Dog Doo Dah Band. Compiled from the Liberty Catalogue,this album features 16 tracks that hopefully capture the essence of this surrealist & anarchic collection of loonies. An interesting sleeve note outlines the history of this 60's outfit who made us laugh with tracks like 'I'm the urban spaceman','Jollity Farm','The intros & the outros' &'Hunting tigers out in India'.-all packaged in a superb sleeve.
Album: released on Music For Pleasure in Oct'84 by EMI Records. Distributed by: EMI

Cassette: released on Music For Pleasure in Oct'84 by EMI Records. Distributed by: EMI

Boogie Blues

BOOGIE BLUES (women sing and play the Boogie Woogie) (Various Artists).
Album: released on Rosetta (USA) in Mar'84

Boogie Box High

JIVE TALKIN'.
Tracks: / Jive talkin' / Rhythm talking (part 1).
Single (7"): released on Hardback in 20 Jun'87 by Streetwave Records. Distributed by: PRT, Priority, DMS, RCA

Single (12"): released on Hardback in 20 Jun'87 by Streetwave Records. Distributed by: PRT, Priority, DMS, RCA

Boogie Boys

DEALIN' WITH LIFE.
Tracks: / Dealin' with life / Fly girl.
Single (7"): released on Capitol in Aug'86 by Capitol Records. Distributed by: EMI

Single (12"): released on Capitol in Aug'86 by Capitol Records. Distributed by: EMI

Boogie Kings

Clint West & the Boogie Kings

Boogie Men

CURLY SHUFFLE.
Single (12"): released on Crash in Jan'84 by Satril Records. Distributed by: PRT

Boogie T

JULIA.
Tracks: / Julia / Love of my people.
Single (12"): released on Hawkeye in Aug'86 by Hawkeye Records. Distributed by: Hawkeye, Lightning (WEA) Distribution, Jetstar, PRT

Boogie Woogie

BOOGIE WOOGIE Various artists (Various Artists).
Notes: MONO production. With Meade Lux Lewis,Pete Johnson,Albert Ammons.
Album: released on Storyville in May'86 by Storyville Records. Distributed by: Jazz Music Distribution, Swift Distribution, Chris Wellard Distribution, Counterpoint Distribution

BOOGIE WOOGIE A LA PARISIENNE Various artists (Various Artists).
Album: released on Pathe MarconiFrance) in Sep'84

GREATEST HITS:BOOGIE WOOGIE Various artists (Various Artists).
Album: released on Boogie Woogie in Feb'82. Distributed by: Chris Wellard, Jazz Music

Boogie Woogie Fever

BOOGIE WOOGIE FEVER Various artists (Various Artists).
Tracks: / Barracuda / Catfish boogie / Juke box boogie / Louisiana boogie / I'm a do right daddy / Blackberry boogie / Cash on the barrel-head / Downtown boogie / Boogie woogie fever / Shotgun boogie / Hot rod race / Texas boogie / Honky tonkin' all the time / Baby buggy boogie / Slow down sweet mama / Jump rope boogie.
Album: released on Charly in May'82 by Charly Records. Distributed by: Charly, Cadillac

Boogie Woogie Hits

BOOGIE WOOGIE HITS Various artists (Various Artists).
Tracks: / Honky tonk train blues / Yancey stomp / Roll 'em / Boogie woogie man / Barrel-house boogie / Boogie woogie / Boogie woogie on St.Louis blues / Whiskey & gin blues / One o'clock boogie / Chicago breakdown / Rooming house boogie / Hey ba-ba-re-bop / Hamps boogie woogie.
Album: released on RCA in Jul'86 by RCA Records. Distributed by: RCA, Roots, Swift, Wellard, Chris, I & B, Solomon & Peres Distribution

Cassette: released on RCA in Jul'86 by RCA Records. Distributed by: RCA, Roots, Swift, Wellard, Chris, I & B, Solomon & Peres Distribution

Boogie Woogie Kings

BOOGIE WOOGIE KINGS Various artists (Various Artists).
Album: released on Euphonic in Apr'79 by Euphonic Records. Distributed by: Jazz Music, Swift

Album: released on Euphonic in Apr'79 by Euphonic Records. Distributed by: Jazz Music, Swift

Boogie Woogie Masters

BOOGIE WOOGIE MASTERS Various artists (Various Artists).
Album: released on Affinity in Aug'86 by Charly Records. Distributed by: Charly, Cadillac

Cassette: released on Affinity in Aug'86 by Charly Records. Distributed by: Charly, Cadillac

Boo-Hooray

HEP CAT GLOSS.
Single (12"): released on Gone in Jun'84 by Gone Records. Distributed by: Fast Forward, Cartel

Boo Hoos

SUN, THE SNAKE AND THE HOO (THE).
Single (12"): released on Electric Eye in Apr'87 by Electric Eye Records. Distributed by: Red Rhino, Cartel

Bookbinder, Roy

RAGTIME MILLIONAIRE.
Album: released on Blue Goose in May'79. Distributed by: Projection, Swift

TRAVELLIN' MAN.
Album: released on Adelphi in May'81 by Adelphi Records. Distributed by: Jetstar

Album: released on Adelphi in May'81 by Adelphi Records. Distributed by: Jetstar

Booker, James

BOOGIE WOOGIE AND RAGTIME PIANO CONTEST.
Album: released on Gold in Apr'79 by Gold Records. Distributed by: President Distribution, Taylors

CLASSIFIED.
Tracks: / All around the world / One for the highway / King of the road / Bald head Tipitina / Baby face / Swedish rhapsody / Classified / Lawdy Miss Clawdy / Angel eyes / Hound dog / If you're lonely / Three keys.
Album: released on Demon in Jul'83 by Demon Records. Distributed by: Pinnacle

KING OF THE NEW ORLEANS KEYBOARD.
Tracks: / How do you feel / Going down slow / Classified / One hell of a nerve / Blues rhapsody / Rockin' pneumonia / Please send me someone to love / All by myself / Ain't nobody's business / Something you got / Harlem in Hamburg.
Album: released on JSP in Dec'84 by JSP Records. Distributed by: Swift, Projection

KING OF THE NEW ORLEANS KEYBOARD VOL 2.
Album: released on JSP in Mar'85 by JSP Records. Distributed by: Swift, Projection

MR MYSTERY.
Album: released on Sundown (Holland) in Feb'85

Booker, Steve

GET UP STAND UP.
Single (7"): released on Ram in Mar'84 by Ram. Distributed by: PRT

Single (12"): released on Ram in Mar'84 by Ram. Distributed by: PRT

LEAN ON ME.
Single (7"): released on Ram in Oct'83 by Ram. Distributed by: PRT

Booker T

BEST OF BOOKER T & THE MG'S (THE) (Booker T & The MGs).
Tracks: / Green onions / Green onions / Slim Jenkins place / Hip hug-her / Soul dressing / Summertime / Bootleg / Jellybread / Tic-tac-toe / Can't be still / Groovin' / Mo' onions / Red beans and rice.
Album: released on Atlantic in Jul'84 by WEA Records. Distributed by: WEA

Cassette: released on Atlantic in Jul'84 by WEA Records. Distributed by: WEA

GREEN ONIONS.
Album: released on Atlantic in Feb'80 by WEA Records. Distributed by: WEA

Cassette: released on Pickwick in May'80 by Pickwick Records. Distributed by: Pickwick Distribution, Prism Leisure Distribution, Luctons

Single (7"): released on Atlantic in Jun'86 by WEA Records. Distributed by: WEA

Single (12"): released on Atlantic in Apr'80 by WEA Records. Distributed by: WEA

Single (7"): released on Old Gold in Jan'85 by Old Gold Records. Distributed by: Lightning, Jazz Music, Spartan, Counterpoint

SOUL LIMBO.
Single (7"): released on Stax in Aug'82 by Ace Records. Distributed by: Pinnacle, Chris Wellard, IMS-Polygram

SOUL LIMBO (Booker T & The MGs).
Single (7"): released on Stax in Aug'87 by Ace Records. Distributed by: Pinnacle, Chris Wellard, IMS-Polygram

TIME IS TIGHT.
Single (7"): released on Stax in Mar'82 by Ace Records. Distributed by: Pinnacle, Chris Wellard, IMS-Polygram

UNIVERSAL LANGUAGE.
Tracks: / Sticky stuff / Grab bag / Space nuts / Love wheels / Moto cross / Last tango in Memphis / MG's salsa / Tie stick / Reincarnation.
: released on Asylum in Mar'77 by WEA Records. Distributed by: WEA

Booker T & The MGs

BEST OF, THE.
Compact disc: released on London in Apr'87 by London Records. Distributed by: Polygram

BOOKER T SET (THE).
Cassette: released on Stax in Dec'86 by Ace Records. Distributed by: Pinnacle, Chris Wellard, IMS-Polygram

Album: released on Stax in Dec'86 by Ace Records. Distributed by: Pinnacle, Chris Wellard,

IMS-Polygram

Bookins, Robert

IN THE NIGHT.
Album: released on MCA in Jun'87 by MCA Records. Distributed by: Polygram, MCA

Cassette: released on MCA in Jun'87 by MCA Records. Distributed by: Polygram, MCA

Compact disc: released on MCA in Jun'87 by MCA Records. Distributed by: Polygram, MCA

Book Of Love

BOOK OF LOVE.
Album: released on WEA in Apr'86 by WEA Records. Distributed by: WEA

BOY.
Single (7"): released on Sire in Jun'85

I TOUCH ROSES.
Tracks: / I touch roses / Lost souls / Happy day*.
Single (7"): released on Sire in Jan'86

Single (12"): released on Sire in Jan'86

Books

EXPERTISE.
Tracks: / Spillane / Metaphysic / Hirohito / Osterreich / Rain / Expertise / Ballroom debut / Dusters / I'll be your friend.
Album: released on Logo in Oct'80 by Logo Records. Distributed by: Roots, BMG

Boom, Barry

COME FOLLOW ME.
Tracks: / When you smile.
Single (12"): released on On Top in Dec'86

Boom, Bobby

MISTER INFORMER.
Single (7"): released on London Gemi in Apr'84. Distributed by: Pinnacle

Boom Boom Room

HERE COMES THE MAN.
Tracks: / Here comes the man / Here comes the man(remix).
Single (7"): released on Fun After All in Jan'86. Distributed by: Pinnacle

Single (12"): released on Fun After All in Jan'86. Distributed by: Pinnacle

Single (7"): released on Epic in Aug'86 by CBS Records. Distributed by: CBS

Single (12"): released on Epic in Aug'86 by CBS Records. Distributed by: CBS

LOVE YOUR FACE.
Tracks: / Love your face / Texas blood.
Single (7"): released on Epic in Jul'87 by CBS Records. Distributed by: CBS

Single (7"): released on Epic in Jul'87 by CBS Records. Distributed by: CBS

Single (12"): released on Epic in Jul'87 by CBS Records. Distributed by: CBS

TAKE YOUR TIME.
Tracks: / Take your time / Mgic boy / Future king*.
Single (7"): released on Epic in Oct'86 by CBS Records. Distributed by: CBS

Single (12"): released on Epic in Oct'86 by CBS Records. Distributed by: CBS

Boomerang

BOOMERANG.
Tracks: / Boomerang fanfare / Boomerang / These boots are made for walking / When the phone stops ringing / Night train / Guess you'll know i'll be around / Baby i'm back in love again / In the darkness / Money, men and make-up / Stowaway.
Album: released on Atlantic in Aug'86 by WEA Records. Distributed by: WEA

Cassette: released on Atlantic in Aug'86 by WEA Records. Distributed by: WEA

Boomerang Gang

DR. JONES.
Tracks: / Dr, Jones / Inspiration.
Single (7"): released on WEA in Jan'86 by WEA Records. Distributed by: WEA

ROCK OUT WHEN YOU CLOCK IN.
Single (7"): released on Survival in May'85 by Survival Records. Distributed by: Backs, Cartel Distribution

Single (12"): released on Survival in May'85 by Survival Records. Distributed by: Backs, Cartel Distribution

Boom, Taka

BOOMERANG.
Cassette: released on Calibre in Jun'83 by Calibre Records. Distributed by: PRT

MIDDLE OF THE NIGHT.
Compact disc: by Polydor Records. Distributed by: Polygram, Polydor

MIDDLE OF THE NIGHT.
Tracks: / Middle of the night / Rock yo' world / Wait & see / Love on the side / Climate for love / Butter me up / Pleasure unit / Love bank.
Album: released on Polydor in Mar'86 by Polydor Records. Distributed by: Polygram, Polydor

Cassette: released on Polydor in Mar'86 by Polydor Records. Distributed by: Polygram, Polydor

TO HELL WITH HIM.
Single (7"): released on Casablanca in May'83. Distributed by: Polygram, Phonogram

Single (12"): released on Casablanca in May'83. Distributed by: Polygram, Phonogram

Single (7"): released on Casablanca in May'83.

Boomtown Rats

BOOMTOWN RATS.
Tracks: / Close as you'll ever be / Do you in / I can make it if you can / Joey / Kicks / Kicks / Lookin' after number 1 / Mary of the 4th form / Neon heart / Never bite the hand that feeds.
Album: released on Mercury in Dec'83 by Phonogram Records. Distributed by: Polygram Distribution

Cassette: released on Mercury in Dec'83 by Phonogram Records. Distributed by: Polygram Distribution

DAVE.
Single (7"): released on Mercury in Jan'85 by Phonogram Records. Distributed by: Polygram Distribution

FINE ART OF SURFACING.
Tracks: / Having my picture taken / Nothing happened today / I don't like Mondays / Someone's looking at you / Diamond smiles.
Album: released on Ensign in Nov'84 by Ensign Records. Distributed by: CBS Distribution

Cassette: released on Ensign in Nov'84 by Ensign Records. Distributed by: CBS Distribution

TONIC FOR THE TROOPS, A(VIDEO)
Live in concert.
Tracks: / Blind date / I never loved Eva Braun / Me & Howard Hughes / Don't believe what you read / Rat trap / Kicks / Joey's on the street again / She's gonna do you in / Like clockwork / She's so modern / Looking after no.1 / Do the rat.
Notes: In this explosive concert recorded live at the Hammersmith Odeon,the Boomtown Rats vividly demonstrate that they are the most energetic and articulate group to emerge from the'new wave'.
Number of tracks: 12
Total playing time: 50 minutes
Type of recording: Live
Video-cassette (VHS): released on VCL in Sep'86 by Elecstar Records. Distributed by: PRT

TONIC FOR THE TROOPS (A).
Album: released on Mercury in Dec'82 by Phonogram Records. Distributed by: Polygram Distribution

Cassette: released on Mercury in Dec'82 by Phonogram Records. Distributed by: Polygram Distribution

TONIGHT.
Single (7"): released on Mercury in Jan'84 by Phonogram Records. Distributed by: Polygram Distribution

Single (12"): released on Mercury in Jan'84 by Phonogram Records. Distributed by: Polygram Distribution

V DEEP.
Tracks: / Never in a million years / Bitter end / Talking in code / He watches all / Storm breaks / House on fire / Up all night / Skin on skin / Little death / House burned down / Never in a million years / Bitter end, The.

V DEEP.
Cassette: released on Mercury in Mar'82 by Phonogram Records. Distributed by: Polygram Distribution

Compact disc: released on Mercury in '83 by Phonogram Records. Distributed by: Polygram Distribution

Boone Creek

BOONE CREEK.
Album: released on Sundown in May'85 by Magnum Music Group Ltd. Distributed by: Magnum Music Group Ltd, PRT Distribution, Spartan Distribution

ONE WAY TRACK.
Album: released on Sugar Hill USA in Jun'79 by MCA Records. Distributed by: Roots Distribution, Mike's Country Music Room Distribution, Projection Distribution, PRT Distribution

Boone, Daniel

BEAUTIFUL SUNDAY.
Single (7"): released on Old Gold in Jul'82 by Old Gold Records. Distributed by: Lightning, Jazz Music, Spartan, Counterpoint

I'M ONLY LOOKING.
Tracks: / Sweet conversation / I'm only looking / Man on the other side of the moon / Street fighters / One more night / Sanctuary / Total reaction / VCR's and space invaders / Trouble in the family / I'm only looking (album) / Life line / Not me / Sweet conversation (album) / Why not.
Single (7"): released on Swoop in Aug'83. Distributed by: Le Matt Music Distribution

Album: released on PVK in Jan'87

I'VE REALLY GOT YOU.
Single (7"): released on WEA in Jan'80 by WEA Records. Distributed by: WEA

STREET FIGHTERS.
Tracks: / Street fighters / Trouble in the family.
Single (7"): released on Swoop in Sep'86. Distributed by: Le Matt Music Distribution

TOTAL REACTION.
Tracks: / Total reaction / Sanctuary.
Single (7"): released on Brilliant in Nov'83 by PVK. Distributed by: Spartan

TROUBLE IN THE FAMILY.

Boone, Debby

CHOOSE LIFE.
Album: released on Lamb & Lion in Jul'85 by Word Records. Distributed by: Word Distribution

Cassette: released on Lamb & Lion in Jul'85 by Word Records. Distributed by: Word Distribution

SURRENDER.
Compact disc: released on Word in Aug'85 by Word Records. Distributed by: Word Distribution, CBS

Album: released on Lamb & Lion in Aug'84 by Word Records. Distributed by: Word Distribution

Cassette: released on Lamb & Lion in Aug'84 by Word Records. Distributed by: Word Distribution

Boone Girls

HEAVENLY LOVE.
Tracks: / Heavenly love / He lives / He lives / My sisters and brothers / Praise the Lord / No I've never / Because I love him / You came softly / No I can't stop / Your love / Fairest Lord Jesus.
Album: released on Lamb & Lion in May'82 by Word Records. Distributed by: Word Distribution

Cassette: released on Lamb & Lion in May'82 by Word Records. Distributed by: Word Distribution

Boone, Pat

16 CLASSIC TRACKS.
Tracks: / April love / Don't forbid me / I almost lost my mind / At my front door / Friendly persuasion / Sugar moon / Moody river / I'll be home / Love letters in the sand / Gospel boogie / Remember you're mine / Ain't that a shame / Main attraction, The / It's too soon to know / Why baby why? / Speedy Gonzales.
Album: released on ABC in Apr'82. Distributed by: CBS, Pinnacle

Cassette: released on ABC in Apr'82. Distributed by: CBS, Pinnacle

20 BEST LOVED GOSPEL SONGS.
Tracks: / Down from his glory / He touched me / Whispering hope / It's free / Answer, The / I'm coming home / Thank you / Woman at the well, The / Do Lord / Lord's prayer, The / There's a song in my heart / Face to face / Saved by grace / Man called Billy, A / Yesterday, today and tomorrow / How great thou art / Heaven is my home / Lead the way Lord / My wish my prayer / Lead the way Lord.
Album: by Pilgrim Records. Distributed by: Rough Trade, Cartel

20 GOLDEN PIECES OF PAT BOONE.
Album: released on Bulldog in Nov'86 by Bulldog Records. Distributed by: President Distribution, Spartan, Swift, Taylor, H.R.

ALL THE GREATEST HITS.
Album: released on Topline in Dec'86 by Charly Records. Distributed by: Charly Distribution

Cassette: released on Topline in Dec'86 by Charly Records. Distributed by: Charly Distribution

ALL THE HITS.
Tracks: / Speedy Gonzales / Ain't that shame / Love letters in the sand / Johnny Will / April love / I'll be home / Moody river / Don't forbid me / Remeber you're mine / I almost lost my mind / Why baby why / Wonderful time up there.
Notes: Licensed from Kilo Music Lt. This compilation: P 1986 Charly Records Ltd C 1986 Charly records Ltd
Album: released on Topline in May'87 by Charly Records. Distributed by: Charly Distribution

Cassette: released on Topline in May'87 by Charly Records. Distributed by: Charly Distribution

ALL-TIME FAVOURITES.
Cassette: released on K-Tel Goldmasters in Aug'84 by K-Tel Records. Distributed by: K-Tel

APRIL LOVE.
Single (7"): released on Old Gold in Jul'82 by Old Gold Records. Distributed by: Lightning, Jazz Music, Spartan, Counterpoint

BABY OH BABY.
Tracks: / Baby,oh baby / Rosemarie / Baby sonnenschein / Wie eine lady / Ein goldener stern / Komm zu mir wenn du einsam bist / Oh lady / Nein nein valentina / Mary Lou / Wo find ich meine traume / Que pasa contigo / Y te quiero / Recuerdame siempre / Amor al reves / En cualquier lugar / Cartas en la arena / Tu che non hai amato mai / E fuori la pioggia cade / Se tu non fossi qui.
Album: released on Bear Family in Feb'86 by Bear Family Records. Distributed by: Rollercoaster Distribution, Swift

BEST OF PAT BOONE.
Album: released on Warwick in Jan'81. Distributed by: Multiple Sound Distributors

Cassette: released on Warwick in Jan'81. Distributed by: Multiple Sound Distributors

COME TOGETHER (Boone, Pat & Carol Owens).
Tracks: / Come together / His name is Jesus / He his here / Turn your hearts / Come together / Clap your hands / Hallulujah, his blood avails for me / Doxology / Holy, holy / Greet somebody in Jesus' name / People of God / Blest be the tie that binds / May I introduce you to a friend / All we like sheep / God so loved the world / Is he coming for you? / Finale.

FRIENDLY PERSUASION..
Single (7"): released on Old Gold in Jul'82 by Old Gold Records. Distributed by: Lightning, Jazz Music, Spartan, Counterpoint

FRIENDLY PERSUASION.
Tracks: / Ain't that a shame / I'll be home / I almost lost my mind / Friendly persuasion / No other arms / Gee Whittakers / Love letters in the sand / Spring rain / Don't forbid me / A wonderful time up there / Cherie I love you / Moody river / Long tall Sally / Why baby why? / Mona Lisa / It's too soon / Are you lonesome tonight / Deep purple / When I fall in love / Speedy Gonzales / Tutti frutti / Johnny will / When the swallows come back to Capistrane / Fools hall of fame / The wang dang taffy apple / I'll see you in my dreams / Bernadine.
Double Album: released on Cambra in Apr'85 by Cambra Records. Distributed by: IDS, Conifer

Double cassette: released on Cambra in Apr'85 by Cambra Records. Distributed by: IDS, Conifer

GOLDEN GREATS: PAT BOONE.
Tracks: / I'll be home / Love letters in the sand / Friendly persuasion / Speedy Gonzales / April love.
Notes: Tracks on the album include those listed above.
Album: released on MCA in Jul'85 by MCA Records. Distributed by: Polygram, MCA

Cassette: released on MCA in Jul'85 by MCA Records. Distributed by: Polygram, MCA

GREATEST HITS:PAT BOONE.
Compact disc: released on Card/Grand Prix in Dec'86. Distributed by: Target

Compact disc: released on MCS Look Back in Jul'87

Picture disc album: released on Astan in Dec'85 by Astan Records. Distributed by: Counterpoint

HIS TOP HITS.
Cassette: released on Timeless Treasures in Jul'86. Distributed by: Counterpoint Distribution

JIVIN' PAT.
Tracks: / Good rockin' tonight / For my good fortune / Flip,flop,fly / Shotgun boogie / Hoboken baby / Fat man, the / Tutti frutti / Two hearts / Rock boll weevil / Honey hush / Bingo / Rock around the clock / I'm in love with you / Money honey / Wonderful time up there / Ain't nobody here but us chickens.
Album: released on Bear Family in Feb'86 by Bear Family Records. Distributed by: Rollercoaster Distribution, Swift

LOVE LETTERS.
Compact disc: released on K-Tel in Jan'86 by K-Tel Records. Distributed by: Record Merchandisers Distribution, Taylors, Terry Blood Distribution, Wynd-Up Distribution, Relay Distribution, Pickwick Distribution, Solomon & Peres Distribution, Polygram

LOVE LETTERS IN THE SAND.
Single (7"): released on Old Gold in Jul'82 by Old Gold Records. Distributed by: Lightning, Jazz Music, Spartan, Counterpoint

LOVE SONGS.
Tracks: / Who's sorry now / It's a sin to tell a lie

/ True in my dreams / True love / Secret love / I'm in the mood for love / I'll see you in my dreams / Deep purple / Ebb tide / Stardust / Send me the pillow that you dream on / Blue moon / Misty / Night and day / Yesterday / He'll have to go / Are you lonesome to night.
Notes: Original sound recordings made by ABC Records Inc. MCA Records Ltd. are the exclusive licensees for the U.K. This compilation : P 1986 MFP Ltd.
Album: released on MFP in Aug'86 by EMI Records. Distributed by: EMI

Cassette: released on MFP in Aug'86 by EMI Records. Distributed by: EMI

SPEEDY GONZALES.
Single (7"): released on Old Gold in Jul'82 by Old Gold Records. Distributed by: Lightning, Jazz Music, Spartan, Counterpoint

SUGAR MOON.
Tracks: / Beach girl / Anastasia / Exodus / Dear John / Welcome new lovers / 500 miles / Blueberry hill / For a penny / Candy sweet / Sugar moon / Ten lonely guys / Twist 12 & 20 / At my front door.
Notes: 29 tracks including those listed above.
Double cassette: released on Cambra in May'84 by Cambra Records. Distributed by: IDS, Conifer

WHAT I BELIEVE.
Notes: Here's Pat, now a grandfather with a brand new release in the style of Ralph Carmichael or Jimmy Owens, and the songs are statements of faith, a declare of belief. So there are old familiar hymns- 'The old rugged cross','Softly and tenderly','Onward Christian Soldiers','Wonderful words of life','How a firm foundation',and there are newer titles-'It was his love','People need the Lord','Let me live', and the title song "What I believe".
Album: released on Lamb & Lion in Aug'85 by Word Records. Distributed by: Word Distribution

Cassette: released on Lamb & Lion in Aug'85 by Word Records. Distributed by: Word Distribution

WHISPERING HOPE Whispering hope.
Tracks: / Whispering hope / Mine eyes have seen the glory / Yield not to temptation / I love to tell the story / Have thine own way Lord / take the name of Jesus with you / He (can turn the tide) / I walked today where Jesus walked / Saviour like a shepherd lead us / It's no secret / How great thou art / Softly and tenderly / Abide with me / Let the lower lights be burning / The old rugged cross / Blessed assurance / Blessed assurance Jesus is mine / I believe / What a friend we have in Jesus / God be with you 'til we meet again / Will the circle be unbroken.
Album: released on Word 20 in May'82

Cassette: released on Word 20 in May'82

Boothe, Ken

ARCHIBELLA.
Single (12"): released on Small Axe in Oct'84 by Small Axe Records. Distributed by: Jetstar

BABY I LOVE YOU TOO.
Single (12"): released on Tads in Sep'83 by Tads Records. Distributed by: Jetstar Distribution

BAD RISK.
Tracks: / Bad risk / Sitting on a mountain top.
Single (7"): released on Silverman in Aug'87 by Priority Records. Distributed by: BMG

Single (12"): released on Silverman in Aug'87 by Priority Records. Distributed by: BMG

BRING IT ON HOME TO ME.
Tracks: / We'll understand.
Single (7"): released on Trojan in Nov'86 by Trojan Records. Distributed by: PRT, Jetstar

EVERYTHING I OWN.
Tracks: / Everything I own / Crying over you / It's the way nature planned it (Part 1/2).
Single (12"): released on Trojan in Mar'87 by Trojan Records. Distributed by: PRT, Jetstar

EVERYTHING I OWN.
Album: released on Trojan in Feb'85 by Trojan Records. Distributed by: PRT, Jetstar

EVERYTHING I OWN..
Single (7"): released on Old Gold in Apr'83 by Old Gold Records. Distributed by: Lightning, Jazz Music, Spartan, Counterpoint

IF I HAD KNOWN.
Single (12"): released on Greensleeves in Jul'83 by Greensleeves Records. Distributed by: BMG, Jetstar, Spartan

IMAGINE.
Album: released on Park Heights in Feb'86. Distributed by: Jetstar Distribution

KEN BOOTHE COLLECTION.
Album: released on Trojan in May'87 by Trojan Records. Distributed by: PRT, Jetstar

Cassette: released on Trojan in May'87 by Trojan Records. Distributed by: PRT, Jetstar

LOVE IS REAL.
Single (12"): released on White Label in Nov'84 by White Label Records. Distributed by: Jetstar

OH WHAT A SMILE.
Tracks: / Oh what a smile / Open the door.
Single (12"): released on Blue Mountain in Aug'86. Distributed by: Jetstar

THINKING.
Single (12"): released on Greensleeves in Mar'84 by Greensleeves Records. Distributed by: BMG, Jetstar, Spartan

Booth, Patrick

EASIER SAID THAN DONE.
Single (7"): released on Supreme in Jul'87 by Supreme Records. Distributed by: PRT Distribution

Single (12"): released on Supreme in Jul'87 by Supreme Records. Distributed by: PRT Distribution

Booth, Webster

GOLDEN AGE OF WEBSTER BOOTH, THE.
Tracks: / Roses of Picardy / Vienna, city of my dreams / Drink to me only with thine eyes / Sweethearts / On the wings of song / Nirvana / Fairy song, The / Perfect day, A / Serenade / Passing by / Everywhere I go / Come into the garden Maude / Eleanore / Song of the vagabonds / I leave my heart in an English garden / At the end of the day.
Notes: P Original sound recordings made by EMI Records Ltd. This compilation P 1986 EMI Records Ltd.
Album: released on Golden Age in Aug'86 by Music For Pleasure Records. Distributed by: EMI

Cassette: released on Golden Age in Aug'86 by Music For Pleasure Records. Distributed by: EMI

Bootleggers

HOT MIX 1.
Single (7"): released on Polo in Aug'87 by Polo Records. Distributed by: PRT

Single (12"): released on Polo in Aug'87 by Polo Records. Distributed by: PRT

Boots For Dancing

OOH BOP SH'BANG.
Single (7"): released on Fast in Apr'82 by Fast Forward Communications (Scotland). Distributed by: Cartel

RAIN SONG.
Single (7"): released on Pop Aural in Nov'80. Distributed by: Fresh, Rough Trade, Swift, Spartan, Virgin

Bootsy's Rubber Band

AHH.. THE NAME IS BOOTSY.
Tracks: / Ahh the name is Bootsy, baby / The Pinnochio theory / Rubber dickie / Preview side too / What's a telephone bill / Munchies for your love / Can't stay away / Reprise; we want Bootsy.
Album: released on Warner Bros. in Jan'77 by Warner Bros Records. Distributed by: WEA

BOOTSY PLAYER OF THE YEAR.
Album: released on Warner Bros. in Feb'78 by Warner Bros Records. Distributed by: WEA

STRETCHIN' OUT.
Tracks: / Stretchin' out (In a rubber band) / Psychotic bum school / Another point of view / I'd rather be with you / Love vibes / Physical love / Vanish in our sleep.
Album: released on Warner Bros. in Aug'76 by Warner Bros Records. Distributed by: WEA

Boottee Duke

BROADWAY.
Tracks: / Broadway (inst.).
Single (7"): released on Hardback in Nov'86 by Streetwave Records. Distributed by: PRT, Priority, DMS, RCA

Single (12"): released on Hardback in Nov'86 by Streetwave Records. Distributed by: PRT, Priority, DMS, RCA

Booty, Charlie

BOOGIE WOOGIE 8-TO-THE-BAR (Booty, Charlie & Ben Conroy).
Album: released on Jazzology in Feb'87. Distributed by: Jazz Music, Swift

Boozoo Chavis

LOUISIANA ZYDECO MUSIC.
Album: released on Maison de Soul in May'86. Distributed by: Swift

Bop

TOO YOUNG TO KNOW.
Single (7"): released on EMI in Feb'84 by EMI Records. Distributed by: EMI

Bop Boogie In The Dark

BOP BOOGIE IN THE DARK Various artists.
Album: released on Goldband in Sep'84 by Charly Records. Distributed by: Charly

Bopcats

BLACK STOCKING ROCK.
Album: released on Magnum Force in May'83 by Magnum Music Group Ltd. Distributed by: Magnum Music Group Ltd, PRT, Spartan

BOP CATS, THE.
Album: released on Attic in Apr'82. Distributed by: Pinnacle

ROCK'N'ROLL GRAFFITI.
Tracks: / Tennessee border / Rock it Pete / Bobpcat boogie / Night riding / M.T's boogie / Good rockin boogie / Doodle eye bop bop / Tore up / Dr rock 'n' roll / Rockin daddy / Down on the line.
Album: released on Magnum Force in '81 by Magnum Music Group Ltd. Distributed by: Magnum Music Group Ltd, PRT, Spartan

Bop City

BOP CITY: EVIDENCE Various artists.
Album: released on Boplicitya in Sep'85 by Boplicity Records. Distributed by: Ace Records, Pinnacle

BOP CITY: MIDNIGHT Barious artists (Various Artists).
Album: released on Boplicitya in Sep'85 by Boplicity Records. Distributed by: Ace Records, Pinnacle

BOP CITY: STRAIGHT AHAED Various artists (Various Artists).
Album: released on Boplicitya in Sep'85 by Boplicity Records. Distributed by: Ace Records, Pinnacle

BOP CITY: THINGS ARE GETTING BETTER Various artists (Various Artists).
Album: released on Boplicitya in Sep'85 by Boplicity Records. Distributed by: Ace Records, Pinnacle

Bop Natives

ON THE CASE.
Single (7"): released on King (USA) in Sep'81 by Gusto Records. Distributed by: Gusto Distribution, IMS, Swift

Bop'n'Roll Party

BOP'N'ROLL PARTY Various artists (Various Artists).
Double Album: released on Rock Star in Sep'82. Distributed by: Lightning, Swift Distribution, Superdisc Distribution

Bopol

HELENA.
Album: released on Syllart(Zaire) in Sep'84

Bop Session

BOP SESSION Various artists (Various Artists).
Tracks: / Blues 'n' boogie / Confirmation / Groovin' high / Lover man / All the things you are are mine / Lady bird.

Bop Session, The

BOP SESSION, THE (Various Artists).
Notes: Dizzy/Stitt/Max Roach/Hank Jones etc.
Album: released on Sonet in Mar'87 by Sonet Records. Distributed by: PRT

Bop Stop Rock

BOP STOP ROCK Various artists (Various Artists).
Album: released on Goldband in Sep'84 by Charly Records. Distributed by: Charly

Bop,Stroll,Roll

BOP,STROLL,ROLL Various artists (Various Artists).
Album: released on CBS in Dec'81 by CBS Records. Distributed by: CBS

Bop That Never Stopped

BOP THAT NEVER STOPPED FOR REAL ROCKIN' VOL.29 Various artists (Various Artists).
Album: released on Bison Bop(West Germany) in Mar'84

Boray, Lisa

TONIGHT.
Single (7"): released on Albion in Oct'83 by Albion Records. Distributed by: Spartan, Pinnacle

Single (12"): released on Albion in Oct'83 by Albion Records. Distributed by: Spartan, Pinnacle

Borbetomagus & Friends

INDUSTRIAL STRENGTH.
Album: released on Leo in Sep'84. Distributed by: Recommended

Border Boys

TRIBUTE(EP),THE.
Single (12"): released on Les Disques Du Crepuscule in Nov'83. Distributed by: Rough Trade, Pinnacle, Island, Polygram

Border Country

BORDER COUNTRY DANCE BAND, THE (Border Country Dance Band).
Tracks: / Trip to Bavaria / Bill sutherland / Cadum woods / Kenmay house / Dennis Murphy's / Athlone, The / Sherlock's / Davy's brae / Iain's hunting horn / 19th hole, The / Donald Ian Rankie / Dancing fingers(accordian solo) / Braes of breadalbane / Cambleton Kiltie ball / Capt. Home / Maguire's / Rattigan's / Jackie coleman's / Mr and Mrs Mac Rogerson / Pig that shakes the piggery, The / Mr and Mrs T M Robertson / Bratch bana / Highland Donald / Black bear / Airlie Bobbies / Lassie come dance with me / Hot potato, The / Morpeth rant / Miss K Rose / Miss C M Barfour / New high level / When you and I were round / Maggie dear / Castle, The.
Notes: Artists include: Alan Coulson -accordian/Geoff Purvis -fiddle/Ian Murray -drums.Recorded October 1977.Produced by Paul Adams
Album: released on Fellside in '83 by Fellside Records. Distributed by: Roots, Jazz Music, Celtic Music, Projection

Border Dance Band

BORDER DANCE BAND AT GRETNA HALL, THE.
Album: released on Fellside in '83 by Fellside Records. Distributed by: Roots, Jazz Music, Celtic Music, Projection

Borderline

ENGLISH PEOPLE.
Tracks: / Little flower / Yellow hill / Rip rap / I want to talk about you / Diggin' the parch / English People(The Subterranean life at..) / The impossible question.
Album: released on Spotlight in '83 by PRT Records. Distributed by: PRT

Border Strathspey

RINGING STRINGS OF THE BORDER.
Album: released on Springthyme in '83 by Springthyme Records. Distributed by: Jazz Music Distribution, Projection Distribution, Roots Distribution

Border Town Jive

BORDER TOWN JIVE-CHICAGO R&B FROM SAN ANTONIO 1960'S various artists (Various Artists).
Notes: Full title: Border Town Jive-Chicago R&B From San Antonio 1960's
Album: released on Krazy Kat (USA) in Nov'85

Borge, Victor

BORGERING ON GENIUS.
Tracks: / Charmaine / Inflationary language / The blue Danube / Fascination / British Grenadier / Anchors away / Summertime / Tea for two / Cheek to cheek / I could have danced all night.
Album: released on MGM in Oct'75. Distributed by: Polygram Distribution, Swift Distribution

Cassette: released on MGM in Oct'75. Distributed by: Polygram Distribution, Swift Distribution

CAUGHT IN THE ACT.
Tracks: / Requests-Tea for two / Malaguena / Stardust / Nola / Trees / One fine dfay / Tales from the Vienna woods / Third man theme / Nocturne Blue Danube Waltz / a)Tango b)Minute Waltz c)Liebestraum / Family background / Phonetic punctuation.
Album: released on CBS Cameo in Jul'84 by CBS Records. Distributed by: CBS

COMEDY IN MUSIC.
Tracks: / Happy birthday / Alexander's Ragtime Band / Medley of popular songs / Warsaw concerto.
Album: released on CBS Cameo in Nov'83 by CBS Records. Distributed by: CBS

Cassette: released on CBS Cameo in Nov'83 by CBS Records. Distributed by: CBS

LIVE AT THE LONDON PALADIUM.
Tracks: / Night and day / Happy birthday to you / Chopsticks / Hungarian rhapsody / Folk song, The / Russian opera, The.
Album: released on Pye in '73

MY FAVOURITE THINGS Excerpts.
Tracks: / Borge on Bach and Beethoven / Borge on Handel / Borge on Mozart and Offenbach / Borge on Rossini.
Album: released on Pye in Jun'75

Borka & Other Stories

BORKA & OTHER STORIES Various artists (Burningham, John).
Cassette: released on Tellastory in Jul'82 by

Bartlett Bliss Productions. Distributed by: PRT Distribution, Hayward Promotions Distribution, H.R. Taylor Distribution

Born B.C

POWER AND PRIVILEGE.
Single (7"): released on Expertise Noise & Tapes in Oct'83. Distributed by: Cartel

Borneo

ASIAN TRADITIONAL MUSIC VOL 6.
Album: . Distributed by: Conifer, Discovery

Born Free

BORN FREE (see under Adamson, Joy).

Born On The Bayou

BORN ON THE BAYOU Various artists (Various Artists).
Tracks: / Born on the bayou / Knock on wood / 96 tears / Summertime blues / Nadine / You really got a hold on me / I don't want to discuss it / Boogie chillun / Soul man / Out of sight / Good good lovin / Sugar bee / Harlem shuffle / I've been lovin' you too long / Treat her right / Night owl.
Album: released on Charly in '83 by Charly Records. Distributed by: Charly, Cadillac

Borofsky, Johnathan

RADICAL SONGBIRDS OF ISLAM.
Cassette: released on Roir in Jun'87 by Reach Out International Records. Distributed by: Red Rhino Distribution, Cartel Distribution

Borrowed Plumes

BORROWED PLUMES Various artists (Various Artists).
Cassette: released on Candlelight in Jun'81 by Audio-Visual Library Services. Distributed by: Audio-Visual Library Services

Borsig, Alexander Von

HIROSHIMA.
Single (12"): released on Supermax (Germany) in Aug'83. Distributed by: Cartel Distribution, Rough Trade Distribution

Zuden Anderson Gerolt

Bosca

WE'LL BE TOGETHER.
Single (12"): released on Oval in May'85. Distributed by: Projection

Bose, Miguel

LIVING ON THE WIRE.
Tracks: / living on the wire / Up to the up.
Single (7"): released on WEA Int in 20 Jun'87
Cat.no . . . . **X 8561**
Single (12"): released on WEA Int in 20 Jun'87

MADE IN SPAIN.
Tracks: / Fuego / Sin ton ni son / La chula / Septiembra / Panama connection / Snack bar / Por un amor relampago / Te quiero amor / Los ojos del miedo / Twenty three horas al dia.
Album: released on CBS(Spain) in Jan'84 by CBS Records. Distributed by: Conifer, Discovery, Swift

Cassette: released on CBS(Spain) in Jan'84 by CBS Records. Distributed by: Conifer, Discovery, Swift

SALAMANDRA.
Tracks: / Heaven / Up to the up / Living on the wire / You live in me / Amazonas / Over / Town of gold / Catch the season / Amapola besame.
Album: released on WEA in Apr'87 by WEA Records. Distributed by: WEA

Cassette: released on WEA in Apr'87 by WEA Records. Distributed by: WEA

Bosho

BOSHO.
Album: released on Dossier in Jun'87. Distributed by: Red Rhino, Cartel

Boss

DANCING IN THE U.S.A...MEDLEY.
Tracks: / Dancing in the U.S.A...medley / Lonely heart.
Single (7"): released on WEA in Feb'86 by WEA Records. Distributed by: WEA

Single (12"): released on WEA in Feb'86 by WEA Records. Distributed by: WEA

Bossa Nova

BOSSA NOVA Various Brazilian artists (Various Artists).
Tracks: / Chega de saudade / Brigas nuncha mais / Coisa mais Linda / Este teu olhar / So em teus bracos / Garota de Ipanema / Ela e carioca / Flaso baiana / E eu / Surf board / Desafinada / O Barquinho / Voce.
Notes: Historic collection of Bossa Nova hits from some of the best known artists of Brazil.The material on this album is authentic and well known.It features some of the most famous Brazilian artists-including Sergio Mendes,Joao Gilberto and Gal Costa.
Album: released on Polydor (France) in Sep'86. Distributed by: Polygram

Cassette: released on Polydor (France) in Sep'86. Distributed by: Polygram

Bossbone, Pat

BREAKAWAY MUSIC.
Single (12"): released on Sunburn in Apr'83 by Orbitone Records. Distributed by: Jetstar Distribution

BREAKAWAY SESSION (see Breakaway music).

LITTLE MISS HARD TO GET.
Single (12"): released on Sunburn in Jul'83 by Orbitone Records. Distributed by: Jetstar Distribution

SOCA MAGIC.
Single (12"): released on Sunburn in Mar'83 by Orbitone Records. Distributed by: Jetstar Distribution

Boss Twang

BOSS TWANG Various artists (Various Artists).
Tracks: / Twangin' fool / Duanes stroll / Fool's blues, A / Juice / Freight train / 5.17 / Put a little love in your heart / Something / Boss / Thing / Nut cracker / Never on sunday / Guitar boogie / Raunchy / Groovy grubworm / Goodnight sweetheart.
Album: released on Charly in Sep'86 by Charly Records. Distributed by: Charly, Cadillac

Cassette: released on Charly in Sep'86 by Charly Records. Distributed by: Charly, Cadillac

Boss Vocal Groups...

BOSS VOCAL GROUPS OF THE 60'S (Various Artists).
Tracks: / Daddy rollin'stone / Ol' man river / Deep river / Homesick / Homesick / Oh' what a feeling / You've got just what I need / Poor baby / Sincerley / Some of this, some of that / So long / Night and day / Love bound / Kisses / In my dream / Dreaming.
Notes: Various groups featuring: The Ravens, The Clovers, The Orioles and Sonny Til. All record track selections produced by Herb Abramson.
Album: released on Red Lightnin' in Jan'87 by Red Lightnin' Records. Distributed by: Roots, Swift, Jazz Music, JSU, Pinnacle, Cartel, Wynd-Up Distribution

Bostic, Earl

16 SWEET TUNES OF THE 50'S.
Album: released on Starday in Apr'87

Cassette: released on Starday in Apr'87

BLOWS A FUSE.
Tracks: / Night train / 8.45 stomp / That's the groovy thing / Special delivery stomp / Moonglow / Mambostic / Earl blows a fuse / Harlem nocturne / Who snuck the wine in the gravy / Don't you do it / Disc jockey's nightmare / Flamingo / Steam whistle jump / What! No pearls / Tuxedo junction.
Album: released on Charly(R&B) in Jul'85 by Charly Records. Distributed by: Charly, Cadillac

Cassette: released on Charly(R&B) in Jul'85 by Charly Records. Distributed by: Charly, Cadillac

SAX 'O' BOOGIE.
Album: released on Oldie Blues Holland in May'84

TRADING LICKS (Bostic, Earl & Bill Doggett).
Tracks: / Honky Tonk Pt 1 & 2 / Big Boy / Buttered Popcorn / Backwoods / Slow Walk / Quaker City / Night Train / Ram Bunk Shush / Peacock Alley / Hold It / Rainbow Riot Pt 1 & 2 / Flamingo / Steam Whistle Jump / What, No Pearls / Don't you do it / Moonglow / Special Delivery Stomp / Harlem Nocturne / Mambostic.
Compact disc: released on Charly in Feb'87 by Charly Records. Distributed by: Charly, Cadillac

Boston

AMANDA.
Tracks: / My Destination.
Single (7"): released on MCA in Jan'87 by MCA Records. Distributed by: Polygram, MCA

Single (12"): released on MCA in Jan'87 by MCA Records. Distributed by: Polygram, MCA

BOSTON.
Tracks: / More than a feeling / Peace of mind / Foreplay/long time / Rock and roll band / Smokin' / Hitch a ride / Something about you / Let me take you home tonight / More than a feeling.
Compact disc: released on Epic in Mar'87 by CBS Records. Distributed by: CBS

Cassette: released on Epic in Mar'81 by CBS Records. Distributed by: CBS

Album: released on Epic in Mar'81 by CBS Records. Distributed by: CBS

Cassette: released on CBS in Aug'83 by CBS Records. Distributed by: CBS

CAN'TCHA SAY (YOU BELIEVE IN ME).
Tracks: / Can'tcha say (you believe in me) / Still in love / Call the engines / Launch (The):Countdown/Ignition/Third stage.
Single (7"): released on MCA in May'87 by MCA Records. Distributed by: Polygram, MCA

Single (12"): released on MCA in May'87 by MCA Records. Distributed by: Polygram, MCA

Compact disc single: released on MCA in May'87 by MCA Records. Distributed by: Polygram, MCA

DON'T LOOK BACK.
Tracks: / Journey / It's easy / Man I'll never be / Feelin' satisfied / Party / Used to bad news / Don't look back / Don't be afraid.
Compact disc: released on Epic in Mar'87 by CBS Records. Distributed by: CBS

DON'T LOOK BACK.
Album: released on Epic in Jun'81 by CBS Records. Distributed by: CBS

Cassette: released on Epic in Jun'81 by CBS Records. Distributed by: CBS

MORE THAN A FEELING.
Single (7"): released on Old Gold in May'83 by Old Gold Records. Distributed by: Lightning, Jazz Music, Spartan, Counterpoint

THIRD STAGE.
Compact disc: by MCA Records. Distributed by: Polygram, MCA

Album: released on MCA in Oct'86 by MCA Records. Distributed by: Polygram, MCA

Cassette: released on MCA in Oct'86 by MCA Records. Distributed by: Polygram, MCA

Bostonians

BOSTONIANS Various artists (Various Artists).
Album: released on Audiotrax in Jan'85 by Audiotrax. Distributed by: PRT

Cassette: released on Audiotrax in Jan'85 by Audiotrax. Distributed by: PRT

Boston Pops

AMERICA, THE DREAM GOES ON (Boston Pops Orchestra).
Tracks: / American salute / America the beautiful / New York,New York / Lonely town / When the saints / Battle hymn of the Republic / This land is your land / America the dream goes on / Hoe down / Fanfare for the common man / America / Prayer of thanksgiving.
Compact disc: . Distributed by: IMS-Polygram

POPS IN SPACE (Boston Pops Orchestra).
Tracks: / Superman march / Superman love theme / Empire strikes back-excerpts / Star Wars -excerpts / Close Encounters of the Third Kind suite.
Compact disc: released on Philips in Jan'86. Distributed by: IMS-Polygram

POPS ON THE MARCH.
Album: released on Import Music Service (IMS) in Apr'81. Distributed by: Concord Jazz Distributions, Pablo, Polygram

SATURDAY NIGHT FIEDLER (Boston Pops Orchestra).
Tracks: / Saturday night fever medley / Saturday Night Fever medley / Stayin alive / Night fever / Manhattan skyline / Night on disco mountain / Disco inferno / Bachmania.
Album: released on Bulldog in Apr'81 by Bulldog Records. Distributed by: President Distribution, Spartan, Swift, Taylor, H.R.

STOMPIN' AT THE SAVOY (Boston Pops, John Williams).

TWO SOUNDS OF FIEDLER, THE (Boston Pops Orchestra).
Album: released on Decca in Sep'79 by Decca Records. Distributed by: Polygram

Boston Pops Orchestra

Out of this world

Boswell, Connie

ON THE AIR (Boswell, Connie & Boswell Sisters).
Album: released on Totem in Jun'79. Distributed by: Jazz Music, Projection, Swift

SAND IN MY SHOES.
Tracks: / Top hat, white tie and tails / Cheek to cheek / I'm gonna sit right down and write me a letter / Music goes round and round / Let yourself go / I'm putting all my eggs in one basket / Between 18th and 19th on Chestnut Street / Yes indeed / Trust in me / Mama don't allow / Martha ah so pure / Fare thee, honey, fare thee well / Sand in my shoes / I hear a rhapsody / I let a song go out of my heart / That old feeling / Mr.Freddie blues / Sunrise serenade / Home on the range / Home on the range / Blueberry hill.
Album: released on MCA in Jun'82 by MCA Records. Distributed by: Polygram, MCA

Cassette: released on MCA in Jun'82 by MCA Records. Distributed by: Polygram, MCA

Boswell, Eric

LEFT TO WRITE (Boswell, Eric & Various artists).
Tracks: / Golden voice of Bobby, The / Welcome to Geordieland / You'll never find a woman like me / North of the Tyne / Sweet waters of Tyne / Take me up the Tyne / I've got a little whippet / First footin' song / They don't write songs like these / Ballad of George Washington, The / Bird fly high / No one else for me / Wi me pit claes on / There's more to life than woman and beer.
Album: released on MWM in Jun'82 by Mawson & Wareham. Distributed by: Spartan Distribution, Jazz Music Distribution, JSU Distribution

Boswell Sisters

IT'S THE GIRLS (Boswell Sisters & Connie Boswell).
Tracks: / It's the girls / That's what I like about you / Heebie jeebies / Concentratin' on you / Wha'd ja do to me? / I'm all dressed up with a broken heart / When I take sugar in my tea / Don't tell him what happened to me / Roll on, Mississippi, roll on / I'm gonna cry (cryin' blues) / This is the missus / That's love / Life is just a bowl of cherries / My future just passed / What is it? / Shine on, harvest moon / Gee, but I'd like to make you happy / We're on the highway to heaven / Time on my hands / Nights when I'm lonely / Shout, sister, shout / It's you!.
Album: released on Academy Sound & Vision in Jun'82 by Academy Sound & Vision Records. Distributed by: Pinnacle

Cassette: released on Academy Sound & Vision in Jun'82 by Academy Sound & Vision Records. Distributed by: Pinnacle

On the air

YOU OUGHTA BE IN PICTURES.
Tracks: / Alexander's ragtime band / You oughta be in pictures / Doggone i've done it / I hate myself / Goin' home / Louisiana hayride / If I had a million dollars / Object of my affection, The / Old Yazoo / Sentimental gentleman from Georgia / It don't mean a thing (if it ain't got that swing) / Rock & roll / Minnie the moocher's wedding day / If it ain't love / Lonesome road / There'll be some changes made / Stop the sun,stop the moon / Mood indigo.
Notes: MONO recording.
Album: released on Conifer Happy Days in Sep'86 by Conifer Records. Distributed by: Conifer, Chris Wellard, Swift, Jazz Music

Cassette: released on Conifer Happy Days in Sep'86 by Conifer Records. Distributed by: Conifer, Chris Wellard, Swift, Jazz Music

Botany 500

BULLY BEEF.
Tracks: / Bully beef / Chill shake / My secret love.
Single (12"): released on Supreme in Jul'86 by Supreme Records. Distributed by: PRT Distribution

Botham, Ian

Take time to care

Both Sides Of The Downs

BOTH SIDES OF THE DOWNS(KENT & SUSSEX) Various artists (Various Artists).
Tracks: / Lord Thomas & fair Eleanor / Sheep stealer, The / William Bowmaneer / Rigs of Rye / Fiddlers Green.
Notes: Crayfolk (North Downs):Vic & Christine Smith (South Downs): Gwyllam Wake. Morris tunes;traditional songs with bowed psalteries,dulzaine etc. Eron Records,27 Balmoral Road,Kingsdown,Deal, Kent CT 14 8BX
Album: released on Eron in Sep'85 by Eron Records. Distributed by: Eron Records

Cassette: released on Eron in Sep'85 by Eron Records. Distributed by: Eron Records

Bothy Ballads

SCOTTISH TRADITION VOLUME 1 (Bothy Ballads-Music from the N.E.).
Album: released on Tangent in Apr'81. Distributed by: Roots Distribution, Lugtons Distributors, Taylors, JSU Distribution, Spartan Distribution

Bothy Band

AFTERHOURS Recorded live in Paris.
Cassette: released on Polydor in Mar'79 by Polydor Records. Distributed by: Polygram, Polydor

Casadh ant sugain / Msic in the glen / Fionnghuala / Old hag you have killed me / Do you love an apple / Rip the calico / Death of Queen Jane, The / Green groves of Erin, The / Flowers of Red Hill, The.
Album: released on Mulligan (Ireland) in Aug'86 by Topic Records. Distributed by: Roots Distribution, Jazz Music Distribution, JSU Distribution, I & B Distribution, Projection Distribution, Wynd-Up Distribution, Celtic Distributions

Cassette: released on Mulligan (Ireland) in Aug'86 by Topic Records. Distributed by: Roots Distribution, Jazz Music Distribution, JSU Distribution, I & B Distribution, Projection Distribution, Wynd-Up Distribution, Celtic Distributions

BOTHY BAND 1975, THE.
Cassette: released on Mulligan in Sep'78 by Topic Records. Distributed by: Roots Distribution, Jazz Music Distribution, JSU Distribution, I & B Distribution, Projection Distribution, Wynd-Up Distribution, Celtic Distributions

BOTHY BAND, THE.
Tracks: / Kesh jig, The / Give us a drink of water / Flowers of the flock / Famous Ballymote / Green groves of Erin, The / Flowers of Red Hill, The / Do you love an apple / Julia Delaney / Patsy Geary's / Coleman's cross / Is trua nack bhfuil me in Eirinn / Navvy on the line, The / Rainy day, The / Tar road to slingo, The / Paddy Clancy's / Martin Wynn's / Lonford tinker, The / Pretty peg / Craigs pipes / Hector the hero / Laird of Drumblaire, The / Traveller, The / Humors of Lissade, The / Butterfly, The / Salamanca, The / Banshee, The / Sailor's bonnet, The.
Album: released on Polydor in Mar'76 by Polydor Records. Distributed by: Polygram, Polydor

OLD HAG YOU HAVE KILLED ME.
Cassette: released on Mulligan in Sep'78 by Topic Records. Distributed by: Roots Distribution, Jazz Music Distribution, JSU Distribution, I & B Distribution, Projection Distribution, Wynd-Up Distribution, Celtic Distributions

Bothy Greats

BOTHY GREATS Various artists (Various Artists).
Album: released on Springthyme in Oct'86 by Springthyme Records. Distributed by: Jazz Music Distribution, Projection Distribution, Roots Distribution

Cassette: released on Springthyme in Oct'86 by Springthyme Records. Distributed by: Jazz Music Distribution, Projection Distribution, Roots Distribution

BOTHY GREATS Various artists (Various Artists).
Album: released on Springthyme in May'85 by Springthyme Records. Distributed by: Jazz Music Distribution, Projection Distribution, Roots Distribution

Bottle Boys

BOTTLE BOYS.
Single (7"): released on Sierra in Sep'84 by Sierra Records. Distributed by: WEA

Bottles

CRASH HELMET.
Single (7"): released on Waterfront in Jun'84 by Waterfront Records. Distributed by: Rough Trade, Cartel, Projection, Roots

Bouche, (La)

ROMANTIC LOVE.
Single (7"): released on Safari in Mar'85 by Safari Records. Distributed by: Pinnacle

STEP TIME.
Album: released on Singing Dog in Oct'85

Boucher, Judy

CAN'T BE WITH YOU TONIGHT (SINGLE).
Tracks: / Dreaming of a little island.
Single (7"): released on Orbitone in Dec'86 by Orbitone Records. Distributed by: Jetstar Distribution

Single (12"): released on Orbitone in Dec'86 by Orbitone Records. Distributed by: Jetstar Distribution

CAN'T BE WITH YOU TONIGHT (LP).
Album: released on Orbitone in Sep'86 by Orbitone Records. Distributed by: Jetstar Distribution

DREAMING OF A LITTLE ISLAND.
Single (12"): released on Orbitone in Aug'85 by Orbitone Records. Distributed by: Jetstar Distribution

MY HEART IS YEARNING.
Tracks: / My heart is yearning / My heart is yearning (version).
Single (12"): released on Orbitone in Oct'86 by Orbitone Records. Distributed by: Jetstar Distribution

YOU CAUGHT MY EYE.
Single (12"): released on Orbitone in Jul'87 by Orbitone Records. Distributed by: Jetstar Distribution

Single (7"): released on Orbitone in Jul'87 by Orbitone Records. Distributed by: Jetstar Distribution

Boudet, Michele

MULTIFACES.
Tracks: / Emotion / Monsieur Baselli / Ca marche / Chatoyante / Le marin a casquette / En Java / Multifaces / 1st of Mai / Caresse Andalouse / Bric-a-brac / Super favourite / Cristaline, Cristaline.
Notes: Retail price given by ARC excluding p&p(via mail order) is 5.95 Mail order distribution address:146 Birmingham Road,Kidderminster,Worcs.DY10 2SL Telephone: 0562 746105.
Album: released on Accordion Record Club in Jul'86 by Accordion Record Club Records. Distributed by: Accordion Record Club

Cassette: released on Accordion Record Club in Jul'86 by Accordion Record Club Records. Distributed by: Accordion Record Club

Boudoir

GO TO SLEEP MY BABY.
Single (7"): released on V-Tone in Nov'82 by Relic. Distributed by: Swift

Boulaye, Patti

SWINGING ON A STAR (Boulaye, Patti & Georgie Fame).
Single (7"): released on Hollywood in Oct'84 by Hollywood Records. Distributed by: Pinnacle

THAT'S MY MAN.
Single (7"): released on Shell in Sep'82 by Shell Records

TRY ME I'M A WOMAN.
Single (7"): released on Shell in Feb'83 by Shell Records

Boulle, Piere

BRIDGE OVER THE RIVER KWAI, THE (Read by Robert Hardy).
Cassette: released on Listen For Pleasure in May'84 by MFP Records. Distributed by: EMI

Bouncer, Peter

READY FOR THE DANCE HALL TONIGHT.
Tracks: / Don't test.
Single (12"): released on Unity Sounds in Dec'86

Bouncing Czechs

I'M A LITTLE CHRISTMAS CRACKER.
Single (7"): released on RCA in Nov'84 by RCA Records. Distributed by: RCA, Roots, Swift, Wellard, Chris, I & B, Solomon & Peres Distribution

LOOKING FOR A MAN.
Single (7"): released on Pretentious in Apr'82

Bouncy Bouncy

100TH MONKEY EFFECT.
Single (7"): released on Wooltown in Jan'85 by Wooltown Records. Distributed by: M.I.S.

Bourbonese Quaik

BOURBONESE QUALK.
Album: released on New International in Mar'87

HOPE.
Album: released on Recloose in Sep'84

LAUGHING AFTERNOON.
Album: released on Recloose Organisation in Dec'83 by Recloose Organisation. Distributed by: Cartel, Rough Trade

PREPARING FOR POWER.
Album: released on Recloose Organisation in Jan'86 by Recloose Organisation. Distributed by: Cartel, Rough Trade

Bourgie Bourgie

BREAKING POINT.
Single (7"): released on MCA in Feb'84 by MCA Records. Distributed by: Polygram, MCA

Single (12"): released on MCA in Feb'84 by MCA Records. Distributed by: Polygram, MCA

CARELESS.
Single (7"): released on MCA in Apr'84 by MCA Records. Distributed by: Polygram, MCA

Single (12"): released on MCA in Apr'84 by MCA Records. Distributed by: Polygram, MCA

Bourvil

C'ETAIT BIEN.
Album: released on EMI (France) in '83 by EMI Records. Distributed by: Conifer

Boustedt, Christer

PLAYS THELONIOUS MONK.
Tracks: / Trinkle tinkle / Pannonica / Straight, no chaser / Reflections / Gallop's gallop / Ruby my dear / We'll you need'nt.
Album: released on Dragon in Jun'83 by Dragon Records. Distributed by: Jazz Music, Projection, Cadillac

Boutte, Lillian

MUSIC IS MY LIFE (Boutte, Lillian & Her Music Friends).
Album: released on Timeless in Oct'86

Bouw Kool

MERRY CHRISTMAS.
Single (7"): released on Master Funk in Nov'84 by Master Funk Records. Distributed by: PRT

Single (12"): released on Master Funk in Nov'84 by Master Funk Records. Distributed by: PRT

Bouzouki At The Bridge

BOUZOUKI AT THE BRIDGE Various artists (Various Artists).
Cassette: released on Plato Tapes in '82 by Plato Tapes. Distributed by: Plato Tapes

Bovell, Dennis

I WAH DUB.
Album: released on More Cut in Feb'80

Bowater, Chris

DO SOMETHING NEW LORD.
Notes: Word are delighted to present their first live recording with Chris on the Spirit of Praise label-a first class recording of a large youth celebration held in October last year in St.David's Hall,Cardiff.Chris led the worship and the album features a variety of songs,many of them new and written during the'Seasons of the Soul' experiences in Lincoln.
Album: released on Spirit of Praise in Feb'86

Cassette: released on Spirit of Praise in Feb'86

Bowens, Bobby

GOTTA KEEP REACHING FOR THE TOP (Bowens, Bobby & The Shades Of Magic).
Album: released on Move in Apr'86 by Charly Records. Distributed by: Charly Distribution, Fast Forward Distribution, Cartel Distribution

Bowie, Angie

CRYING (IN THE DARK) (Bowie, Angie & Chico Rey).
Single (7"): released on Sierra in Oct'85 by Sierra Records. Distributed by: WEA

Single (12"): released on Sierra in Oct'85 by Sierra Records. Distributed by: WEA

Bowie, David

ABSOLUTE BEGINNERS.
Tracks: / Absolute beginners / Absolute beginners(dub).
Single (7"): released on Virgin in Mar'86 by Virgin Records. Distributed by: EMI, Virgin Distribution

Picture disc single: released on Virgin in Mar'86 by Virgin Records. Distributed by: EMI, Virgin Distribution

Single (12"): released on Virgin in Mar'86 by Virgin Records. Distributed by: EMI, Virgin Distribution

Single (12"): released on Virgin in Mar'86 by Virgin Records. Distributed by: EMI, Virgin Distribution

ALABAMA SONG.
Album: released on RCA (Special Imports Service) in Jul'84

Single (7"): released on RCA in Feb'80 by RCA Records. Distributed by: RCA, Roots, Swift, Wellard, Chris, I & B, Solomon & Peres Distribution

Single (12"): released on RCA (Germany) in May'83

ALADDIN SANE.
Album: released on RCA International in '84

Cassette: released on RCA International in '84

Picture disc album: released on RCA International in '84

ALADDIN SANE.
Tracks: / Watch that man / Aladdin Sane (1913-1938-197?) / Drive in saturday / Panic in Detroit / Cracked actor / Time / Prettiest star, The / Let's spend the night together / Jean Genie, The / Lady grinning soul / Watch that man / Alladdin sane / (1913 - 1938 - 197?) / Drive in saturday / Panic in Detroit / Cracked actor / Time / Prettiest star, The / Lets spend the night together / Jean Genie, The / Lady grinning soul.
Notes: Original released in February 1981 on INTS 5067/ INTK 5067.
Compact disc: released on RCA in Jun'85 by RCA Records. Distributed by: RCA, Roots, Swift, Wellard, Chris, I & B, Solomon & Peres Distribution

ANOTHER FACE.
Tracks: / Rubber band / London boys, The / Gospel according Tony Day, The / There is a happy land / Maid of Bond Street / When I live my dream / Liza Jane / Laughing gnome, The / In the heat of the morning / Did you ever have a dream / Please Mr. Gravedigger / Join the gang / Love you till Tuesday / Louie louie go home.
Album: released on Decca in Apr'81 by Decca Records. Distributed by: Polygram

Cassette: released on Decca in Apr'81 by Decca Records. Distributed by: Polygram

ARNOLD CORNS AND THE SPIDERS FROM MARS.
Single (7"): released on Strawberry in Feb'84. Distributed by: Pinnacle

ASHES TO ASHES.
Tracks: / Ashes to ashes / Alabama song.
Single (12"): released on RCA (Import) in Mar'86

Album: released on RCA (Special Imports Service) in Jul'84

Single (7"): released on RCA in Aug'80 by RCA Records. Distributed by: RCA, Roots, Swift, Wellard, Chris, I & B, Solomon & Peres Distribution

BAAL.
Single (12"): released on RCA in Jul'83 by RCA Records. Distributed by: RCA, Roots, Swift, Wellard, Chris, I & B, Solomon & Peres Distribution

BEAUTY AND THE BEAST.
Single (7"): released on RCA in Jun'83 by RCA Records. Distributed by: RCA, Roots, Swift, Wellard, Chris, I & B, Solomon & Peres Distribution

BE MY WIFE.
Single (7"): released on RCA in Jun'83 by RCA Records. Distributed by: RCA, Roots, Swift, Wellard, Chris, I & B, Solomon & Peres Distribution

BLUE JEANS.
Single (7"): released on EMI America in Sep'84 by EMI Records. Distributed by: EMI

Single (12"): released on EMI America in Sep'84 by EMI Records. Distributed by: EMI

BOYS KEEP SWINGING.
Single (7"): released on RCA in Apr'79 by RCA Records. Distributed by: RCA, Roots, Swift, Wellard, Chris, I & B, Solomon & Peres Distribution

BREAKING GLASS.
Single (7"): released on RCA in Jun'83 by RCA Records. Distributed by: RCA, Roots, Swift, Wellard, Chris, I & B, Solomon & Peres Distribution

CAT PEOPLE.
Single (12"): released on MCA in Dec'83 by MCA Records. Distributed by: Polygram, MCA

CHANGESONEBOWIE.
Tracks: / Space oddity / John,i'm only dancing / Changes / Ziggy Stardust / Suffragette city / Jean Genie, The / Diamond dogs / Rebel,rebel / Young Americans / Fame / Golden years.
Compact disc: released on RCA in Dec'84 by RCA Records. Distributed by: RCA, Roots, Swift, Wellard, Chris, I & B, Solomon & Peres Distribution

Album: released on RCA in May'84 by RCA Records. Distributed by: RCA, Roots, Swift, Wellard, Chris, I & B, Solomon & Peres Distribution

Cassette: released on RCA in May'84 by RCA Records. Distributed by: RCA, Roots, Swift, Wellard, Chris, I & B, Solomon & Peres Distribution

CHANGESTWOBOWIE.
Tracks: / Aladdin sane / Oh you pretty things / Starman / 1984 / Ashes to ashes / Sound and vision / Fashion / Wild is the wind / John I'm only dancing / DJ / John I'm only dancing (again 1975).
Album: released on RCA in May'84 by RCA Records. Distributed by: RCA, Roots, Swift, Wellard, Chris, I & B, Solomon & Peres Distribution

Cassette: released on RCA in May'84 by RCA Records. Distributed by: RCA, Roots, Swift, Wellard, Chris, I & B, Solomon & Peres Distribution

Compact disc: released on RCA in May'84 by RCA Records. Distributed by: RCA, Roots, Swift, Wellard, Chris, I & B, Solomon & Peres Distribution

CHINA GIRL.
Single (7"): released on EMI America in May'83 by EMI Records. Distributed by: EMI

Single (12"): released on EMI America in May'83 by EMI Records. Distributed by: EMI

CHRISTIANE F.WIR KINDER VOM BAHNOF ZOO.
Tracks: / V-2 Schneider / TVC-15 / Heroes / Helden / Boys keep swinging / Sense of double / Station to station / Look back in anger / Stay / Warszawa.
Album: released on RCA in May'81 by RCA Records. Distributed by: RCA, Roots, Swift, Wellard, Chris, I & B, Solomon & Peres Distribution

Cassette: released on RCA in May'81 by RCA Records. Distributed by: RCA, Roots, Swift, Wellard, Chris, I & B, Solomon & Peres Distribution

COLLECTION: DAVID BOWIE.
Tracks: / Laughing gnome, The / Rubber band / Love you till Tuesday / Maid of Bond Street / Sell me a coat / In the heat of the morning / Maka man / Please Mr. Gravedigger / London boys, The / She's got medals / Silly boy blue / Join the gang / Did you ever had a dream / Gospel according to Tony Day, The / I'm not losing sleep / I dig everything / Can't help thinking about me / Do anything you say / Good morning girl / And I say to myself.
Album: released on Castle Communications in Nov'85 by Castle Communications. Distributed by: Cartel, Pinnacle, Counterpoint

Double cassette: released on Castle Communications in Nov'85 by Castle Communications. Distributed by: Cartel, Pinnacle, Counterpoint

DANCING IN THE STREET (Bowie, David/Mick Jagger).
Single (7"): released on EMI America in Aug'85 by EMI Records. Distributed by: EMI

Single (12"): released on EMI America in Aug'85 by EMI Records. Distributed by: EMI

DAVID BOWIE.
Tracks: / Uncle Arthur / Sell me a coat / Rubber band / Love you till tuesday / There is a happy land / We are hungry men / When I live my dream / Little bombadier / Silly boy blue / Come and buy my toys / Join the gang / She's got medals / Maids of Bond street / Please Mr. gravedigger.
Album: released on Deram in Aug'84 by Decca Records. Distributed by: Polygram

Compact disc: released on London in May'83 by London Records. Distributed by: Polygram

DAVID BOWIE - VIDEO EP.
Video-cassette (VHS): released on PMI in Aug'87 by PMI Records. Distributed by: EMI

DAVID LIVE.
Album: released on RCA (Germany) in Nov'83

DAVID LIVE At Tower theatre philadelphia.
Tracks: / 1984 / Rebel rebel / Moonage daydream / Sweet thing / Changes / Suffragette city / Aladdin Sane / 1913-1938-197? / All the young dudes / Cracked actor / Rock 'n' roll with me / Watch that man / Knock on wood / Diamond dogs / Big brother / Width of the circle / Jean Genie, The / Rock 'n' suicide.
Album: released on RCA in May'84 by RCA Records. Distributed by: RCA, Roots, Swift, Wellard, Chris, I & B, Solomon & Peres Distribution

Cassette: released on RCA in May'84 by RCA Records. Distributed by: RCA, Roots, Swift, Wellard, Chris, I & B, Solomon & Peres Distribution

DAY-IN, DAY-OUT.
Tracks: / Day-in, day-out / Julie.
Single (7"): released on EMI America in Mar'87 by EMI Records. Distributed by: EMI

Single (12"): released on EMI America in Mar'87 by EMI Records. Distributed by: EMI

DAY-IN DAY-OUT (REMIX).
Tracks: / Day-in Day-out (remix) / Day-in Day-out (ext dub mix) / Julie.
Single (12"): released on EMI America in Apr'87 by EMI Records. Distributed by: EMI

DAY IN DAY OUT(VIDEO).
Tracks: / Day in day out(7"version) / Loving the alien / Day in day out(ext.dance version).
Notes: Both versions of 'Day in day out' were directed by David Bowie together with Julian Temple,whose previous work with Bowie has included the video for'Jazzin' For Blue Jeans' and the feature film'Absolute Beginners'.'Day in day out' is the first single taken from Bowie's album'Never let me down'.'Loving the Alien' was also co-directed by Bowie,the other director in this case being David Mallet well known for his work with Tina Turner,Freddie Mercury et al.The audio track comes from Bowie's last studio album'Tonight'.
Video-cassette (VHS): released on Picture Music International in May'87 by Picture Music International. Distributed by: EMI

DIAMOND DOGS.
Tracks: / Future legend / Diamond dogs / Sweet thing / Candidate / Sweet thing / Rebel rebel / Rock 'n' with me / We are the dead / 1984 / Big brother / Chant of the ever circling skeletal family.
Compact disc: by RCA Records. Distributed by: RCA, Roots, Swift, Wellard, Chris, I & B, Solomon & Peres Distribution

Album: released on RCA in May'84 by RCA Records. Distributed by: RCA, Roots, Swift, Wellard, Chris, I & B, Solomon & Peres Distribution

Cassette: released on RCA in May'84 by RCA Records. Distributed by: RCA, Roots, Swift, Wellard, Chris, I & B, Solomon & Peres Distribution

Picture disc album: released on RCA in May'84 by RCA Records. Distributed by: RCA, Roots, Swift, Wellard, Chris, I & B, Solomon & Peres Distribution

DIAMOND DOGS (SINGLE).
Single (7"): released on RCA in Jun'83 by RCA Records. Distributed by: RCA, Roots, Swift, Wellard, Chris, I & B, Solomon & Peres Distribution

DJ.
Single (7"): released on RCA in Jun'83 by RCA Records. Distributed by: RCA, Roots, Swift, Wellard, Chris, I & B, Solomon & Peres Distribution

DON'T BE FOOLED BY THE NAME.
Tracks: / I'm not losing sleep / Dig everything / Can't help thinking about me / I do anything you say / Good morning girl / And I say to myself.
Album: released on PRT in Jun'81 by PRT Records. Distributed by: PRT

Cassette: released on PRT in Jun'81 by PRT Records. Distributed by: PRT

DRIVE IN SATURDAY.
Single (7"): released on RCA in Jun'83 by RCA Records. Distributed by: RCA, Roots, Swift, Wellard, Chris, I & B, Solomon & Peres Distribution

EARLY YEARS.
Tracks: / Watch that man / Aladdin Sane / Drive-in Saturday / Panic in Detroit / Cracked actor / Time / Prettiest star, The / Let's spend the night together / Jean Genie,The / Lady grinning soul / Width of a circle,The / All the madmen / Black country rock / After all / Running gun blues / Saviour machine / She shook me cold / Man who sold the world, The / Supermen,The / Changes / Oh you pretty thing / Eight line poem / Life on Mars / Kooks / Quicksand / Fill your heart / Andy Warhol / Song for Bob Dylan / Queen Bitch / Bewlay Brothers, The.
Notes: 3 LP set 3 Casstette sety
Album: released on RCA (France) in '86 by RCA Records. Distributed by: Discovery

Cassette: released on RCA (France) in '86 by RCA Records. Distributed by: Discovery

FAME.
Single (7"): released on RCA in Jun'83 by RCA Records. Distributed by: RCA, Roots, Swift, Wellard, Chris, I & B, Solomon & Peres Distribution

FAME & FASHION.
Tracks: / Space oddity / Changes / Starman / 1984 / Young Americans / Young Americans / Golden years / TVC 15 / Heroes / DJ / Fashion / Ashes to ashes / Space oddity / Changes / Starman / 1984 / Young Americans / Fame / Golden years / TVC 15 / Heroes / D.J / Fashion / Ashes to Ashes.
Compact disc: by RCA Records. Distributed by: RCA, Roots, Swift, Wellard, Chris, I & B, Solomon & Peres Distribution

FASHION.
Album: released on RCA (Special Imports Service) in Jul'84

Single (7"): released on RCA in Oct'80 by RCA Records. Distributed by: RCA, Roots, Swift, Wellard, Chris, I & B, Solomon & Peres Distribution

Single (12"): released on RCA in Oct'80 by RCA Records. Distributed by: RCA, Roots, Swift, Wellard, Chris, I & B, Solomon & Peres Distribution

Single (12"): released on RCA (Germany) in May'83

FASHIONS.
Picture disc single: released on RCA in Nov'82 by RCA Records. Distributed by: RCA, Roots, Swift, Wellard, Chris, I & B, Solomon & Peres Distribution

GOLDEN YEARS.
Tracks: / Fashion / Red sails / Look back in anger / I can't explain / Ashes to Ashes / Golden Years / Joe the lion / Scary monsters (and super creeps) / Wild is the wind.
Album: released on RCA in Jul'83 by RCA Records. Distributed by: RCA, Roots, Swift, Wellard, Chris, I & B, Solomon & Peres Distribution

Cassette: released on RCA in Jul'83 by RCA Records. Distributed by: RCA, Roots, Swift, Wellard, Chris, I & B, Solomon & Peres Distribution

GOLDEN YEARS (SINGLE).
Single (7"): released on RCA in Jun'83 by RCA Records. Distributed by: RCA, Roots, Swift, Wellard, Chris, I & B, Solomon & Peres Distribution

HEROES.
Tracks: / Beauty & the beast / Joe the lion / Sons of the silent age / Black out / V-2 Schneider / Sense of double / Moss garden / Neukoln / Secret live of Arabia, The / There ain't no good chain gang / Beauty and the beast / Heroes / Joe the lion / Sons of the silent age / Black out / V-2 Schneider / Sense of double / Moss garden / Neukoln / Secret life of Arabia, (The).
Compact disc: by RCA Records. Distributed by: RCA, Roots, Swift, Wellard, Chris, I & B, Solomon & Peres Distribution

Album: released on RCA (Germany) in Mav'83

Album: released on RCA (Special Imports Service) in Jul'84

Album: released on RCA International in Nov'84

Cassette: released on RCA International in Nov'84

Compact disc: released on RCA International in Nov'84

Single (7"): released on RCA in Jun'83 by RCA Records. Distributed by: RCA, Roots, Swift, Wellard, Chris, I & B, Solomon & Peres Distribution

Single (12"): released on RCA (Germany) in Mav'83

HEROES (12").
Tracks: / Heroes / Helden.
Single (12"): released on RCA (Import) in Mar'86

HEROES (BOX SET).
Triple album / cassette: released on RCA (Germany) in Aug'83

HUNKY DORY.
Tracks: / Changes / Oh,you pretty thing / Eight line poem / Life on Mars / Kooks / Quicksand / Fill your heart / Andy Warhol / Songs for Bob Dylan / Queen bitch / Bewlay Brothers, The / Changes / Oh pretty thing / Eight line poem / Life on mars / Queen bitch / Kooks quicksand / Fill your heart / Andy Warhol / Song for Bob Dylan / Bewley brothers, (The) / There is a happy land.
Compact disc: by RCA Records. Distributed by: RCA, Roots, Swift, Wellard, Chris, I & B, Solomon & Peres Distribution

Album: released on RCA International in Nov'84

Cassette: released on RCA International in Nov'84

Picture disc album: released on RCA International in Nov'84

Compact disc: released on RCA International in Nov'84

IMAGES.
Tracks: / Rubber band / Maid of Bond Street / Sell me a coat / Love you till tuesday / There is a happy land / Laughing gnome, (The) / Gospel according to Tony Day, (The) / Did you ever have a dream / Uncle Arthur / We are hungry men / When I live me dream / Join the gang / Little bombadier / Come and buy my toys / Silly boy blue / She's got medals / Please Mr. Gravedigger / London boys / Karma man / Let me sleep beside you / In the heat of the morning.
Double Album: released on Deram in May'75 by Decca Records. Distributed by: Polygram

JAZZIN' FOR BLUE JEAN (VIDEO).
Video-cassette (VHS): released on Video Collection in May'87 by Video Collection Records. Distributed by: Counterpoint

JAZZING FOR BLUE JEAN(VIDEO).
Notes: This is the full length twenty minute Blue Jean video.The film was made in London and directed by Julian Temple(previous credits include Rolling Stones'Under Cover'video and'The Great Rock'n'Roll Swindle').The video was show-cased on Channel 4 at 11.20pm on September 28th and is currently on general theatrical release with 'Company of Wolves'.Both of these events,coupled with Bowie's current record success,will enhance public awareness and sales potential of this video release. Total playing time: 20minutes. Type of recording : Film
Video-cassette (VHS): released on PMI in Nov'84 by PMI Records. Distributed by: EMI

Video-cassette [Betamax]: released on PMI in Nov'84 by PMI Records. Distributed by: EMI

JEAN GENIE.
Single (7"): released on RCA in Jun'83 by RCA Records. Distributed by: RCA, Roots, Swift, Wellard, Chris, I & B, Solomon & Peres Distribution

JOHN I'M ONLY.
Single (7"): released on RCA in Jun'83 by RCA Records. Distributed by: RCA, Roots, Swift, Wellard, Chris, I & B, Solomon & Peres Distribution

KNOCK ON WOOD.
Single (7"): released on RCA in Jun'83 by RCA Records. Distributed by: RCA, Roots, Swift, Wellard, Chris, I & B, Solomon & Peres Distribution

LABRYRINTH.
Tracks: / Opening titles-including Underground / Into the labyrinth / Magic dance / Sarah / Chilly down / Hallucination / As the world falls down / Goblin battle, The / Within you / Thirteen o'clock / Home at last / Underground.
Album: released on EMI America in Jun'86 by EMI Records. Distributed by: EMI

Cassette: released on EMI in Jun'86 by EMI Records. Distributed by: EMI

LAUGHING GNOME.
Single (7"): released on Decca-Originals in May'82 by Decca Records. Distributed by: Polygram, IMS

LET'S DANCE.
Tracks: / Modern love / China girl / Let's dance / Without you / Ricochet / Criminal world / Cat people (putting out fire) / Shake it / Modern love / China girl / Without you / Ricochet / Criminal world / Cat people (putting out fires) / Shake it.
Compact disc: by EMI Records. Distributed by: EMI

Album: released on EMI in Apr'83 by EMI Records. Distributed by: EMI

Cassette: released on EMI in Apr'83 by EMI Records. Distributed by: EMI

Picture disc single: released on America in Oct'83. Distributed by: Discovery, Swift

Compact disc: released on EMI America in May'83 by EMI Records. Distributed by: EMI

Single (7"): released on EMI America in Mar'83 by EMI Records. Distributed by: EMI

Single (12"): released on EMI America in Mar'83 by EMI Records. Distributed by: EMI

Cassette single: released on EMI America in Mar'83 by EMI Records. Distributed by: EMI

LIVE(VIDEO).
Tracks: / Space oddity / Rebel rebel / Fame / Ashes to ashes / Interview.
Notes: The follow up to 'Serious Moonlight'offers live versions from last year's tour of 9 more Bowie classics like'Space Oddity','Rebel Rebel','Fame' & 'Ashes To Ashes',plus an interview
Number of tracks: 9
Type of recording: live
Video-cassette (VHS): released on Videoform in Sep'84

LODGER.
Tracks: / Fantastic voyage / African night flight / Move on / Yass assin / Red sails / DJ / Look back in anger / Boys keep swinging / Repitition / Red money.
Compact disc: by RCA Records. Distributed by: RCA, Roots, Swift, Wellard, Chris, I & B, Solomon & Peres Distribution

Album: released on RCA International in May'84

Cassette: released on RCA International in May'84

Compact disc: released on RCA International in May'84

LONDON BOYS.
Single (7"): released on Decca-Originals in Mar'82 by Decca Records. Distributed by: Polygram, IMS

LONDON BOYS.
Tracks: / London boys / Love you till Tuesday / Laughing gnome / Maid of Bond Street.
Notes: Written by David Bowie Licensed from the Decca Record Co.Ltd. Limited edition release.
Single (12"): released on Archive 4 in Aug'86 by Castle Communications Records. Distributed by: Nine Mile, Cartel

LOVE YOU TILL TUESDAY.
Tracks: / Love you till tuesday / London boys, (The) / Ching-a-long / Laughing gnome, (The) / Liza Jane / When I'm five / Space oddity / Sell me a coat / Rubber band / Let me sleep beside you / When I live my dream.
Album: released on Deram in May'84 by Decca Records. Distributed by: Polygram

Cassette: released on Deram in May'84 by Decca Records. Distributed by: Polygram

LOVING THE ALIEN.
Single (7"): released on EMI America in May'85 by EMI Records. Distributed by: EMI

Single (12"): released on EMI America in May'85 by EMI Records. Distributed by: EMI

Single (12"): released on EMI America in Jun'86 by EMI Records. Distributed by: EMI

LOW.

Tracks: / Speed of life / Breaking glass / What in the world / Sound and vision / Always crashing in the same car / Be my wife / New career in a mew town, A / Warswawa / Art decade / Weeping wall / Subterraneans.
Notes: Originally released in 12/80 on INTS 5065/INTK 5065
Compact disc: by RCA Records. Distributed by: RCA, Roots, Swift, Wellard, Chris, I & B, Solomon & Peres Distribution

Album: released on RCA International in Oct'84

Cassette: released on RCA International in Oct'84

Compact disc: released on RCA International in Oct'84

MAN WHO SOLD THE WORLD, THE.
Tracks: / Width of the circle / All the madmen / Black country rock / After all / Running gun blues / Saviour machine / She shook me cold / Man who sold the world, The / Supermen, The.
Album: released on RCA (Germany) in '83

Cassette: released on RCA (Germany) in '83

MODERN LOVE (2 PARTS).
Single (7"): released on EMI America in Aug'83 by EMI Records. Distributed by: EMI

Single (12"): released on EMI America in Aug'83 by EMI Records. Distributed by: EMI

NEVER LET ME DOWN.
Tracks: / New York's in love / '87 and cry / Too dizzy / Bang bang / Day-in day-out / Time will crawl / Beat of your drum / Never let me down / Zeroes / Glass spider / Shining star (making my love) / Time will crawl / 87 and cry / Never let me down (7" version) / Time will crawl (Ext. dance mix) / Day 'n day out (Groucho mix) / 87 and cry (single version).
Notes: *Never let me down* is the first studio album from David Bowie for 2 1/2 years, following a period of film-orientated projects including *Absolute beginners* and *Labyrinth*, where he had both acting and musical involvement. The ever-shifting Mr. Bowie returns with the emphasis firmly on the music. [EMI release sheet, April 87].
Album: released on EMI America in Jan'87 by EMI Records. Distributed by: EMI

Cassette: released on EMI America in Jan'87 by EMI Records. Distributed by: EMI

Compact disc: released on EMI America in Jan'87 by EMI Records. Distributed by: EMI

Single (7"): released on EMI America in Aug'87 by EMI Records. Distributed by: EMI

Single (12"): released on EMI America in Aug'87 by EMI Records. Distributed by: EMI

Cassette single: released on EMI America in Aug'87 by EMI Records. Distributed by: EMI

Picture disc single: released on EMI America in Aug'87 by EMI Records. Distributed by: EMI

PETER AND THE WOLF Young person's guide to the orchestra.
Compact disc: released on RCA in '86 by RCA Records. Distributed by: RCA, Roots, Swift, Wellard, Chris, I & B, Solomon & Peres Distribution

PIN UPS.
Tracks: / Rosalyn / Here comes the night / I wish you would / See Emily play / Everything's alright / I can't explain / Friday on my mind / Sorrow / Don't bring me down / Shapes of things / Anyway anyhow anywhere / Where have all the good times gone.
Compact disc:

Album: released on RCA in Sep'81 by RCA Records. Distributed by: RCA, Roots, Swift, Wellard, Chris, I & B, Solomon & Peres Distribution

Picture disc album: released on RCA in Sep'81 by RCA Records. Distributed by: RCA, Roots, Swift, Wellard, Chris, I & B, Solomon & Peres Distribution

Cassette: released on RCA in Sep'81 by RCA Records. Distributed by: RCA, Roots, Swift, Wellard, Chris, I & B, Solomon & Peres Distribution

PORTRAIT OF A STAR.
Triple album / cassette: released on RCA (Special Imports Service) in Jul'84

RARE TRACKS.
Tracks: / I'm not sleeping / I dig everything / Can't help thinking about me / Do anything you say / Good morning girl / And I say to myself.
Album: released on Showcase in Apr'86. Distributed by: Counterpoint

REBEL REBEL.
Single (7"): released on RCA in Jun'83 by RCA Records. Distributed by: RCA, Roots, Swift, Wellard, Chris, I & B, Solomon & Peres Distribution

RISE & FALL OF ZIGGY STARDUST.
Tracks: / Five years / Soul love / Moonage daydream / Starman / It ain't easy / Lady stardust / Star / Hang on to yourself / Ziggy Stardust / Suffragette city / Rock'n'roll suicide.
Cassette: released on RCA in '86 by RCA Records. Distributed by: RCA, Roots, Swift, Wellard, Chris, I & B, Solomon & Peres

RISE & FALL OF ZIGGY STARDUST AND THE SPIDERS FROM MARS.
Album: released on RCA International in Oct'84

Cassette: released on RCA International in Oct'84

Compact disc: released on RCA International in Oct'84

ROCK GALAXY.
Double Album: released on RCA in '83 by RCA Records. Distributed by: RCA, Roots, Swift, Wellard, Chris, I & B, Solomon & Peres Distribution

Double cassette: released on RCA in '83 by RCA Records. Distributed by: RCA, Roots, Swift, Wellard, Chris, I & B, Solomon & Peres Distribution

ROCK'N'ROLL SUICIDE.
Single (7"): released on RCA in Jun'83 by RCA Records. Distributed by: RCA, Roots, Swift, Wellard, Chris, I & B, Solomon & Peres Distribution

SCARY MONSTERS.
Tracks: / It's no game / Up the hills backwards / Scary monsters and super creeps / Ashes to ashes / Fashion / Teenage wildlife / Scream like a baby / Kingdom come / Because you're young / It's no game (no.2).
Compact disc: by RCA Records. Distributed by: RCA, Roots, Swift, Wellard, Chris, I & B, Solomon & Peres Distribution

Album: released on RCA (Special Imports Service) in Jul'84

Album: released on RCA in Oct'84 by RCA Records. Distributed by: RCA, Roots, Swift, Wellard, Chris, I & B, Solomon & Peres Distribution

Cassette: released on RCA in Oct'84 by RCA Records. Distributed by: RCA, Roots, Swift, Wellard, Chris, I & B, Solomon & Peres Distribution

Single (7"): released on RCA in Jan'81 by RCA Records. Distributed by: RCA, Roots, Swift, Wellard, Chris, I & B, Solomon & Peres Distribution

Single (12"): released on RCA (Germany) in May'83

SCARY MONSTERS(12").
Tracks: / Scary monsters / Because you're young.
Single (12"): released on RCA (Import) in Mar'86

SERIOUS MOONLIGHT 2(VIDEO).
Video-cassette (VHS): released on Channel 5 in Oct'86. Distributed by: W.H. Smiths

SERIOUS MOONLIGHT (VIDEO).
Video-cassette (VHS): released on Videoform in Oct'84

SORROW.
Single (7"): released on RCA in Jun'83 by RCA Records. Distributed by: RCA, Roots, Swift, Wellard, Chris, I & B, Solomon & Peres Distribution

SOUND AND VISION.
Single (7"): released on RCA in Jun'83 by RCA Records. Distributed by: RCA, Roots, Swift, Wellard, Chris, I & B, Solomon & Peres Distribution

SPACE ODDITY.
Album: released on RCA in Oct'84 by RCA Records. Distributed by: RCA, Roots, Swift, Wellard, Chris, I & B, Solomon & Peres Distribution

Cassette: released on RCA in Oct'84 by RCA Records. Distributed by: RCA, Roots, Swift, Wellard, Chris, I & B, Solomon & Peres Distribution

Single (7"): released on RCA in Jun'83 by RCA Records. Distributed by: RCA, Roots, Swift, Wellard, Chris, I & B, Solomon & Peres Distribution

SPACE ODDITY.
Tracks: / Space oddity / Unwashed and somewhat slightly dazed / Letter to Hermione / Cygnet committee / Janine an occasional dream / Wild eyed boy from Freecloud, The / God knows I'm good / Memory of a free festival.
Compact disc: by RCA Records. Distributed by: RCA, Roots, Swift, Wellard, Chris, I & B, Solomon & Peres Distribution

STAGE.
Double compact disc: by RCA Records. Distributed by: RCA, Roots, Swift, Wellard, Chris, I & B, Solomon & Peres Distribution

Album: released on RCA (Germany) in May'83

Cassette: released on RCA (Germany) in May'83

Album: released on RCA in Jul'84 by RCA Records. Distributed by: RCA, Roots, Swift, Wellard, Chris, I & B, Solomon & Peres Distribution

STARMAN.
Single (7"): released on RCA in '74 by RCA Records. Distributed by: RCA, Roots, Swift, Wellard, Chris, I & B, Solomon & Peres Distribution

STATION TO STATION.
Tracks: / Station to station / Golden years / Word on a wing / TVC15 / Stay / Wild is the wind.
Compact disc: by RCA Records. Distributed by: RCA, Roots, Swift, Wellard, Chris, I & B, Solomon & Peres Distribution

Album: released on RCA in Oct'84 by RCA Records. Distributed by: RCA, Roots, Swift, Wellard, Chris, I & B, Solomon & Peres Distribution

Cassette: released on RCA in Oct'84 by RCA Records. Distributed by: RCA, Roots, Swift, Wellard, Chris, I & B, Solomon & Peres Distribution

THIS IS NOT AMERICA (Bowie, David/Pat Metheny Group).
Single (7"): released on EMI America in Jan'85 by EMI Records. Distributed by: EMI

Single (12"): released on EMI America in Jan'85 by EMI Records. Distributed by: EMI

TIME WILL CRAWL (DANCE CREW MIX).
Tracks: / Time will crawl (dance crew mix) / Time will crawl (dub) / Girls (Japanese version).
Single (12"): released on EMI America in Jul'87 by EMI Records. Distributed by: EMI

TIME WILL CRAWL (SINGLE VERSION).
Tracks: / Time will crawl (single version) / Girls (single edit).
Single (7"): released on EMI America in 13 Jun'87 by EMI Records. Distributed by: EMI

Single (12"): released on EMI America in 13 Jun'87 by EMI Records. Distributed by: EMI

Single (7"): released on EMI America in 27 Jun'87 by EMI Records. Distributed by: EMI

TONIGHT.
Tracks: / Loving the alien / Don't look down / God only knows / Tonight / Neighbourhood threat / Blue Jeans / Tumble and twirl / I keep forgetting / Dancing with the big boys.
Compact disc: by EMI Records. Distributed by: EMI

Cassette: released on EMI America in '86 by EMI Records. Distributed by: EMI

Cassette: released on EMI America in '86 by EMI Records. Distributed by: EMI

Single (7"): released on EMI America in Nov'84 by EMI Records. Distributed by: EMI

Single (12"): released on EMI America in Nov'84 by EMI Records. Distributed by: EMI

TVC 15.
Single (7"): released on RCA in Jun'83 by RCA Records. Distributed by: RCA, Roots, Swift, Wellard, Chris, I & B, Solomon & Peres Distribution

UNDERGROUND.
Tracks: / Underground / Underground(instrumental).
Single (7"): released on EMI America in Jun'86 by EMI Records. Distributed by: EMI

Single (12"): released on EMI America in Jun'86 by EMI Records. Distributed by: EMI

Under pressure / Soul brother

UP THE HILL BACKWARDS.
Single (7"): released on RCA in Mar'81 by RCA Records. Distributed by: RCA, Roots, Swift, Wellard, Chris, I & B, Solomon & Peres Distribution

VIDEO EP.
Video-cassette (VHS): released on PMI in Jun'86 by PMI Records. Distributed by: EMI

Video-cassette [Betamax]: released on PMI in Jun'86 by PMI Records. Distributed by: EMI

WHEN THE WIND BLOWS.
Tracks: / When the wind blows / When the wind blows(dub).
Single (7"): released on Virgin in Oct'86 by Virgin Records. Distributed by: EMI, Virgin Distribution

Single (12"): released on Virgin in Oct'86 by Virgin Records. Distributed by: EMI, Virgin Distribution

WILD IS THE WIND.
Tracks: / Wild is the wind / Golden years.
Single (12"): released on RCA (Import) in Mar'86

Single (12"): released on RCA in Jul'84 by RCA Records. Distributed by: RCA, Roots, Swift, Wellard, Chris, I & B, Solomon & Peres Distribution

Single (7"): released on RCA in Nov'81 by RCA Records. Distributed by: RCA, Roots, Swift, Wellard, Chris, I & B, Solomon & Peres Distribution

Single (12"): released on RCA in Nov'81 by RCA Records. Distributed by: RCA, Roots, Swift, Wellard, Chris, I & B, Solomon & Peres Distribution

WORLD OF DAVID BOWIE, THE.
Tracks: / Uncle Arthur / Love you till Tuesday / There is a happy land / Little bombardier / Sell me a coat / Silly boy blue / London boys, The / Karma man / Rubber band / Let me sleep beside you / Come and buy my toys / She's got medals / In the heat of the morning / When I live my dream.
Album: released on Decca in '70 by Decca Records. Distributed by: Polygram

Cassette: released on Decca in '70 by Decca Records. Distributed by: Polygram

YOUNG AMERICANS.
Tracks: / Young Americans / Win / Fascination / Right / Somebody up there likes me / Across the universe / Can you hear me / Fame / Young Americans / Win / Fascination / Right / Somebody up there likes me / Across the universe / Can you hear me / Fame.
Compact disc: by RCA Records. Distributed by: RCA, Roots, Swift, Wellard, Chris, I & B, Solomon & Peres Distribution

Album: released on RCA in Oct'84 by RCA Records. Distributed by: RCA, Roots, Swift, Wellard, Chris, I & B, Solomon & Peres Distribution

Cassette: released on RCA in Oct'84 by RCA Records. Distributed by: RCA, Roots, Swift, Wellard, Chris, I & B, Solomon & Peres Distribution

Single (7"): released on RCA in Jun'83 by RCA Records. Distributed by: RCA, Roots, Swift, Wellard, Chris, I & B, Solomon & Peres Distribution

ZIGGY STARDUST & THE SPIDERS FROM MARS(VIDEO).
Video-cassette (VHS): released on Thorn-Emi in Oct'84

ZIGGY STARDUST THE MOTION PICTURE.
Tracks: / Watch that man / Moonage daydream / Suffragette city / Changes / Time / All the young dudes / Space oddity / White light white heat / My death / Wild eyed boy / Oh, you pretty things / Hang onto yourself / Ziggy Stardust / Cracked actor / Time / Width of a circle / Let's spend the night together / Rock 'n' roll suicide.
Double Album: released on RCA in Nov'83 by RCA Records. Distributed by: RCA, Roots, Swift, Wellard, Chris, I & B, Solomon & Peres Distribution

Double cassette: released on RCA in Nov'83 by RCA Records. Distributed by: RCA, Roots, Swift, Wellard, Chris, I & B, Solomon & Peres Distribution

Bowie, Lester

ALL THE MAGIC.
Album: released on ECM (Germany) in Apr'83 by ECM Records. Distributed by: IMS, Polygram, Virgin through EMI

AVANT POP (Bowie, Lester, Brass Fantasy).
Album: released on ECM (Germany) in Sep'86 by ECM Records. Distributed by: IMS, Polygram, Virgin through EMI

Compact disc: released on ECM (Germany) in Sep'86 by ECM Records. Distributed by: IMS, Polygram, Virgin through EMI

DUET (Bowie, Lester & Philip Wilson).
Album: released on Impro-arts in Jul'78. Distributed by: Projection

DUET (Bowie, Lester & Nobuyoshi Ino).
Album: released on King (Japan) in Feb'87. Distributed by: IMS, Polygram

FAST LAST.
Album: released on Muse in Apr'81 by Peerless Records. Distributed by: Lugtons Distributors

FIFTH POWER, THE (Bowie, Lester with Various artists).
Album: released on Black Saint Import in Jul'78

GREAT PRETENDER, THE.
Album: released on ECM (Germany) in Mar'82 by ECM Records. Distributed by: IMS, Polygram, Virgin through EMI

I ONLY HAVE EYES FOR YOU.
Album: released on ECM (Germany) in Nov'85 by ECM Records. Distributed by: IMS, Polygram, Virgin through EMI

NOS. 1 & 2.
Album: released on Nessa in Mar'79. Distributed by: Projection, Swift

ROPE-A-DOPE.
Album: released on Muse in Apr'81 by Peerless Records.

TWILIGHT DREAM (Bowie, Lester, Brass Fantasy).
Album: released on Venture in Jul'87. Distributed by: Revolver, Cartel

Cassette: released on Venture in Jul'87. Distributed by: Revolver, Cartel

Bowlly, Al

1931 SESSIONS.
Cassette: released on Saville in Jan'86 by Conifer Records. Distributed by: Conifer

20 PIECES OF.
Cassette: released on Collectors Music in Jul'86. Distributed by: Conifer

AL BOWLLY CIRCLE, THE.
Tracks: / Cuddle up close - You'll never understand / Torn sails / Moon / Gone forever / If you were only mine / Call it a day / Sweeping the clouds away / Who'll buy an old ring / Foolish facts / Eleven more months and ten more days / Minnie the moocher's wedding day / Roy Fox's commentary on the wedding reception / Lazy Louisiana moon / Moonlight on the Colorado / Dark clouds / Save the last dance.
Album: released on Joy in Feb'84 by President Records. Distributed by: Jazz Music, Swift, President Distribution

AL BOWLLY IN NEW YORK.
Tracks: / Say When / When love comes singing along / Be still my heart / My melancholy baby / St. Louis blues / Way back home / If I had a million dollars / You and the night and the music / You were there / Little white gardenia, A / Piccolino / Everything's been done before / Little gypsy tearoom, A / Red sails in the sunset / Dinner for one please James.
Album: released on President in Jan'87 by President Records. Distributed by: Taylors, Spartan

AMBASSADOR OF SONG.
Tracks: / Fancy our meeting / My canary has circles under his eyes / Judy / I'm thru' with love / Be still, my heart / Roll on Mississippi, roll on / Heartaches / Maria, my own / If I had a million dollars / Miss Elizabeth Brown / If anything happened to you / Got a date with an angel / There's rain in my eyes / Night and day / Brother, can you spare a dime.
Album: released on Ace Of Clubs in '66 by Decca Records. Distributed by: Polygram

DANCE BAND DAYS, THE.
Tracks: / Time on my hands / Can't get Mississippi off my mind / Tell me (you love me) / Moon / Linda / I'm glad I waited / Heartaches / Goodnight sweetheart / Waltz you saved for me, The / Life is meant for love / We've got the moon and sixpence / Longer that you linger in Virginia, The / Roll on Mississippi, roll on / Lady, play your mandoline / Time alone will tell / Can't we be friends / Girl in the upstairs flat, The / Trusting my luck / I'm saving the last waltz for you / Somebody's thinking of you to-night / Louisiana hayride / It's a long way to your heart / There's a gold mine in the sky / Proud of you / Souvenir of love / Waves of the ocean are whisp'ring goodnight / Little lady make-believe / Fare thee well / Sweet Genevieve / Because it's love / In my little red book / In a shelter from a shower / I won't tell a soul / Riding on a haycart home / Say goodnight to your old fashioned mother.
Album: released on Decca (Recollections) in Nov'84 by Decca Recollections. Distributed by: Polygram, IMS

GERALDO & AL BOWLLY (Bowlly, Al & Geraldo).
Cassette: released on Halcyon in Aug'87 by Halcyon Records. Distributed by: Jazz Music. Estim retail price in Sep'87 was £5.25.

GOLDEN AGE OF AL BOWLLY, THE.
Tracks: / Love is the sweetest thing / Bei mur bist du schoen (Means that you're grand) / Marie / In my little red book / Something to sing about / Walkin' thru Mockin' Bird Lane / My Melancholy baby / Blow, thou winter wind / It was a lover and his lass / Have you ever been lonely? / You're a sweetheart / I'll string along with you / Only forever / Goodnight sweetheart.
Notes: Al Bowlly represented the sound that won the hearts of the public during the 30's and would have gone onto greater things had his life not been brought to a sudden end in 1943.
Album: released on Golden Age in Jul'83 by Music For Pleasure Records. Distributed by: EMI

Cassette: released on Golden Age in Jul'83 by Music For Pleasure Records. Distributed by: EMI

GOODNIGHT SWEETHEART.
Tracks: / I'm telling the world she's mine / Goodnight sweetheart / Lazy day / Hang out the stars in Indiana / There's a ring around the moon / Goodnight Vienna / I'll do my best to make you happy / Love is the sweetest thing / Wanderer / Maybe I love you too much / Shadow waltz / I've got to sing a torch song / Close your eyes / Unless / Who walks in when I walk out / Very thought of you, The / I'll string along with you / Grinzing / Dreaming a dream / Sing as we go.
Notes: A new 20 track compilation of great tracks from the incomparable Al Bowlly.It includes many of his all-time classics such as 'Love is the sweetest thing','The very thought of you' and of course'Goodnight sweetheart'.On most titles,Al Bowlly is accompanied by Ray Noble & His Orchestra,the partnership which is regarded as producing the best Bowlly material of all time.This release coincides with the launch of a new biography of Al Bowlly written by Ray Pallett,called'Al Bowlly',who also provides the informative sleeve notes on this album.
Album: released on EMI Retrospect in Mar'86 by EMI Records. Distributed by: EMI

Cassette: released on EMI Retrospect in Mar'86 by EMI Records. Distributed by: EMI

Album: released on Saville in Jun'82 by Conifer Records. Distributed by: Conifer

LONDON SESSIONS(1928-1930),THE.
Tracks: / Just imagine / Wherever you are / If I had you / Misery farm / I'm sorry Sally / When the lilac blooms again / Up in the clouds / After the sun's kissed the world goodbye / If anything happened to you / Happy days are here again / On the sunny side of the street / Sweepin' the clouds away / Dancing with tears in my eyes / Adeline / Beware of love / Frankie & Johnnie / By the old oak tree / Never swat a fly / Sunny days / Roamin' through the roses.
Album: released on Saville in '86 by Conifer Records. Distributed by: Conifer

Cassette: released on Saville in '86 by Conifer Records. Distributed by: Conifer

MILLION DREAMS, A.
Tracks: / Moonstruck / Maria my own / Love looked out / Cabin in the pines / Night and day / Learn to croon / I'm getting sentimental over you / I'll follow you / Million dream / My romance / Keep your last goodnight for me / There's goodbye.
Album: released on Saville in Mar'84 by Conifer Records. Distributed by: Conifer

MY SONG GOES ROUND THE WORLD (Bowlly, Al & Ray Noble).
Tracks: / Wanderer / Just and echo in the valley / Can't we meet again / When you've fallen in love / Let me give my happiness to you / Hustling and bustling for my baby / Waltzing in a dream / It's within your power / Hiawatha's lullaby / Couple of fools in love, A / On the other side of lover's lane / It's bad for me / Dinner at eight / Experiment / Weep no more my baby / Thanks / Oceans of time / On a steamer coming over / Did you ever see a dream walking / Couple of fools in love, A / My song goes round the world.
Cassette: released on Halcyon (USA) in Mar'87 by Halcyon Records (USA). Distributed by: Jazz Music, Conifer, Taylors

Album: released on Halcyon (USA) in Oct'86 by Halcyon Records (USA). Distributed by: Jazz Music, Conifer, Taylors

ON THE SENTIMENTAL SIDE.
Double Album: released on Decca in '78 by Decca Records. Distributed by: Polygram

SENTIMENTALLY YOURS.
Tracks: / Modonna mine / I'm getting sentimental over you / Judy / Everything I have is yours / Glorious Devon / Isle of Capri / Lover come back to me / There's a cabin in the pines / If I had a million dollars / True / It's all forgotten now / That's me without you / Fancy our meeting / Learn to croon / Night & day / Love locked out / Be still my heart.
Notes: MONO recording.
Album: released on Conifer in Jan'86 by Conifer Records. Distributed by: Conifer

Cassette: released on Conifer in Jan'86 by Conifer Records. Distributed by: Conifer

SOMETHING TO SING ABOUT.
Tracks: / Hometown / Grandma said / Deep in a dream / You're a sweet little headache / I'm madly in love with you / Same old story (The) / Could be / Between a kiss and a sigh / To mother with love / Thanks for ev'rything / I miss you in the morning / Small town / What do you know about love / Moon love / Au revoir but not goodbye / Vieni, vieni / Le Touquet / Smile when you say goodbye / Something to sing about / In my little red book.
Notes: Produced, compiled and transferred by Chris Ellis
Album: released on Retrospect in Jun'87 by World Records

Cassette: released on Retrospect in Jun'87 by World Records

SWEET AS A SONG.
Tracks: / Carelessly / On a little dream ranch / Blue Hawaii / Sweet is the word for you / Bei mir bist du schoen / Marie / You're a sweetheart / Pretty little patchwork quilt, The / Sweet as a song / Sweet someone / Goodnight Angel / When the organ played 'O promise me / Romany / Lonely / I miss you in the morning / Violin in Vienna / What do you know about love / Hey gypsy, play gypsy / South of the border / Dark eyes.
Notes: A brand new compilation of titles sung by the legendary Al Bowlly. These tracks from between 1937 and 1939, were recorded as solos for Browlly, most accompanied by Ronnie Munro and his Orchestra. The original 78 rpm issue of these tracks have long been highly treasured and highly priced collectors pieces, and on this rcecord appear in LP form for the first time. Bowlly is accompanied on piano on two tracks on this album by Violet Carson - Coronation Street's Ena Sharples.

Album: released on EMI Retrospect in Jun'85 by EMI Records. Distributed by: EMI

Cassette: released on EMI Retrospect in Jun'85 by EMI Records. Distributed by: EMI

Bown, Alan

HELP ME.
Single (7"): released on EMI in Mar'83 by EMI Records. Distributed by: EMI

KICK ME OUT.
Tracks: / My friend / Strange little friend / Elope / Perfect day / All I can do / Friends in St Louis / Still as stone / Prisoner The / Kick me out / Children of the night / Gypsy girl / Wrong idea.
Album: released on See For Miles in Jan'85 by See For Miles Records. Distributed by: Pinnacle

Bow, Trevor

WOMAN.
Single (12"): released on 24 Karat in Dec'84 by 24 Karat Records. Distributed by: Jetstar

Bow Wow

WARNING FROM STARDUST.
Tracks: / You're mine / Jets / Clean machine / Can't get back to you / Heels of the wind / Poor man's Eden / 20th century child / Abnormal weather / Welcome to the monster city / Breakout the trick / Warning from stardust.
Album: released on Heavy Metal in Apr'83 by FM-Revolver Records. Distributed by: EMI

YOU'RE MINE.
Single (7"): released on Heavy Metal Worldwide in Nov'83 by FM-Revolver Records. Distributed by: EMI

Bow Wow Wow

BOW WOW WOW.
Tracks: / I want candy / See jungle / Go wild in the country / Chihuahua.
Cassette single: released on RCA in May'83 by RCA Records. Distributed by: RCA, Roots, Swift, Wellard, Chris, I & B, Solomon & Peres Distribution

C30 C60 C90 GO.
Single (7"): released on EMI in Jul'80 by EMI Records. Distributed by: EMI

Single (12"): released on EMI in Jul'80 by EMI Records. Distributed by: EMI

CHIHAUHUA.
Single (7"): released on RCA in Oct'81 by RCA Records. Distributed by: RCA, Roots, Swift, Wellard, Chris, I & B, Solomon & Peres Distribution

Single (12"): released on RCA in Oct'81 by RCA Records. Distributed by: RCA, Roots, Swift, Wellard, Chris, I & B, Solomon & Peres Distribution

DO YOU WANNA HOLD ME.
Single (7"): released on RCA in Feb'83 by RCA Records. Distributed by: RCA, Roots, Swift, Wellard, Chris, I & B, Solomon & Peres Distribution

Single (12"): released on RCA in Feb'83 by RCA Records. Distributed by: RCA, Roots, Swift, Wellard, Chris, I & B, Solomon & Peres Distribution

FOOLS RUSH IN.
Single (7"): released on EMI in Sep'82 by EMI Records. Distributed by: EMI

GO WILD IN THE COUNTRY.
Tracks: / Go wild in the country / I want candy.
Single (7"): released on Old Gold in Nov'86 by Old Gold Records. Distributed by: Lightning, Jazz Music, Spartan, Counterpoint

Single (7"): released on RCA in Jan'82 by RCA Records. Distributed by: RCA, Roots, Swift, Wellard, Chris, I & B, Solomon & Peres Distribution

Single (12"): released on RCA in Jan'82 by RCA Records. Distributed by: RCA, Roots, Swift, Wellard, Chris, I & B, Solomon & Peres Distribution

I WANT CANDY.
Album: released on RCA (Germany) in Mar'84

Cassette: released on RCA (Germany) in Mar'84

Single (7"): released on RCA in May'82 by RCA Records. Distributed by: RCA, Roots, Swift, Wellard, Chris, I & B, Solomon & Peres Distribution

LOUIS QUARTORZE.
Single (7"): released on RCA in Jul'82 by RCA Records. Distributed by: RCA, Roots, Swift, Wellard, Chris, I & B, Solomon & Peres Distribution

PRINCE OF DARKNESS.
Single (7"): released on RCA in Jul'81 by RCA Records. Distributed by: RCA, Roots, Swift, Wellard, Chris, I & B, Solomon & Peres Distribution

Single (12"): released on RCA in Aug'81 by RCA Records. Distributed by: RCA, Roots, Swift, Wellard, Chris, I & B, Solomon & Peres Distribution

SEE JUNGLE (JUNGLE BOY).
Single (7"): released on RCA in Apr'82 by RCA Records. Distributed by: RCA, Roots, Swift, Wellard, Chris, I & B, Solomon & Peres Distribution

Single (12"). released on RCA in Apr'82 by RCA Records. Distributed by: RCA, Roots, Swift, Wellard, Chris, I & B, Solomon & Peres Distribution

SEE JUNGLE! SEE JUNGLE! GO JOIN YOUR GANG YEAH, CITY ALL....
Tracks: / Jungle boy / Chihuahua / Sinner sinner sinner / Mickey put it down / I'm a TV savage / Elimination dancing / Golly golly / Go buddy / King Kong / Go wild in the country / I am not a know it all / Why are babies so wise? / Orang-utang / Hello hello daddy.
Notes: Full Title **See jungle! See jungle! Go join your gang yeah, city all over! Go ape crazy**
Album: released on RCA in Oct'81 by RCA Records. Distributed by: RCA, Roots, Swift, Wellard, Chris, I & B, Solomon & Peres Distribution

Cassette: released on RCA in Oct'81 by RCA Records. Distributed by: RCA, Roots, Swift, Wellard, Chris, I & B, Solomon & Peres Distribution

WHEN THE GOING GETS TOUGH THE TOUGH GET GOING.
Tracks: / Aphrodosiac / Do you wanna hold me / Roustabout / Lonesome tonight / Love me / What the time (hey buddy) / Mario (your own way to paradise) / Quiver (Arrows in my) / Man mountain, (The) / Rikki Dee / Tommy Tucker / Love, peace and harmony.
Album: released on RCA in Feb'83 by RCA Records. Distributed by: RCA, Roots, Swift, Wellard, Chris, I & B, Solomon & Peres Distribution

Cassette: released on RCA in Feb'83 by RCA Records. Distributed by: RCA, Roots, Swift, Wellard, Chris, I & B, Solomon & Peres Distribution

WORK (NO NAH NO NO MY...).
Single (7"): released on EMI in Mar'81 by EMI Records. Distributed by: EMI

Single (12"): released on EMI in Mar'81 by EMI Records. Distributed by: EMI

Box

EP.
Single (12"): released on Double Vision in Oct'84 by Double Vision Records. Distributed by: Rough Trade, Cartel

GREAT MOMENTS IN BIG SLAM.
Tracks: / Walls come down / Flatstone, The / Big slam / Stop / Low line / Breaking stream / Small blue car / Still in the woodwork.
Album: released on Go Discs in Jun'84 by Go Discs Records. Distributed by: CBS Distribution Deleted '86

Cassette: released on Go Discs in Jun'84 by Go Discs Records. Distributed by: CBS Distribution

MUSCLE OUT.
Album: released on Double Vision in Sep'85 by Double Vision Records. Distributed by: Rough Trade, Cartel

Single (12"): released on Double Vision in Dec'84 by Double Vision Records. Distributed by: Rough Trade, Cartel

NO TIME FOR TALK.
Single (12"): released on Go Discs in Jan'83 by Go Discs Records. Distributed by: CBS Distribution

OLD STYLE DROP DOWN.
Single (7"): released on Go Discs in May'83 by Go Discs Records. Distributed by: CBS Distribution

Single (12"): released on Go Discs in May'83 by Go Discs Records. Distributed by: CBS Distribution

SECRETS OUT.
Album: released on Go Discs in Jun'83 by Go Discs Records. Distributed by: CBS Distribution

Box and Banjo Band

AT THE MOVIES.
Album: released on Lismor in Dec'86 by Lismor Records. Distributed by: Lismor, Roots, Celtic Music

Album: released on Lismor in Dec'86 by Lismor Records. Distributed by: Lismor, Roots, Celtic Music

GREAT SCOTTISH SINGALONG.
Album: released on Lismor in Nov'85 by Lismor Records. Distributed by: Lismor, Roots, Celtic Music

Cassette: released on Lismor in Nov'85 by Lismor Records. Distributed by: Lismor, Roots, Celtic Music

GO DANCING.
Album: released on Lismor in '84 by Lismor Records. Distributed by: Lismor, Roots, Celtic Music

Cassette: released on Lismor in '84 by Lismor Records. Distributed by: Lismor, Roots, Celtic Music

Boxcar Willie

Biographical Details: This American singer has spent his career in the second division of country music, without ever breaking into the big league. His brand of humorous country enjoys more popularity in Britain than at home. His TV advertised "King of the road" compilation gave him a one-off chart album, reaching No.5 on the UK list. B.M 84

20 GREAT HITS.
Tracks: / I've got a bad case of feeling sorry for me / The lord made a hobo out of me / Blue-eyed girl of Berlin / Six pound fish / The fragrance of her perfume / Daddy was a railroad man / The day Elvis died / Hot box blues / I'm going back to Texas / I can'thelpit if I'm stillin love with you / I'm so lonesome I could cry / Lonesome whistlee / Waitin' for a train / TB blues / Cold windy city of Chicago / Take me home / I wake up every morning with a smile on my face / Trouble / Train medley.
Album: released on Big R in Sep'81 by Big R Records. Distributed by: Pinnacle, Wynd-Up Distribution, Solomon & Peres Distribution, I & B, Swift, Record Merchandisers Distribution, Spartan

Cassette: released on Big R in Sep'81 by Big R Records. Distributed by: Pinnacle, Wynd-Up Distribution, Solomon & Peres Distribution, I & B, Swift, Record Merchandisers Distribution, Spartan

AT THE COUNTRY STORE.
Album: released on Starblend Country Store in Aug'86 by Starblend Records. Distributed by: PRT Distribution

Cassette: released on Starblend Country Store in Aug'86 by Starblend Records. Distributed by: PRT Distribution

BOXCAR WILLIE.
Tracks: / Songs of songs / Dreary days / Gypsy lady & the hobo / Honey I love you / Cheating wife / Boxcar's my home / My hearts deep in the heart of Texas / Hobo heaven / Big freight train carry me home / Ain't gonna be your day.
Notes: The album is produced by Boxcar Willie & features two tracks with Willie Nelson, 'Songs of Songs' & 'Boxcar's My Home'. Since his memorable Wembley appearance,Boxcar has become a firm favourite with British audiences.
Album: released on MCA in Mar'86 by MCA Records. Distributed by: Polygram, MCA

Cassette: released on MCA in Mar'86 by MCA Records. Distributed by: Polygram, MCA

Album: released on Big R in Nov'80 by Big R Records. Distributed by: Pinnacle, Wynd-Up Distribution, Solomon & Peres Distribution, I & B, JSU, Swift, Record Merchandisers Distribution, Spartan

BOXCAR WILLIE COLLECTION, THE.
Tracks: / Lost highway / We made memories / S.U.C.K.E.R. / Living it up in Washington D.C. / Blue, blue days / Tennessee rain / Atomic bum / I was kind of in the neighbourhood / Streamline cannon ball.
Double Album: released on Castle Collectors in Jul'87 by Castle Communications Records. Distributed by: Pinnacle

Cassette: released on Castle Collectors in Jul'87 by Castle Communications Records. Distributed by: Pinnacle

Compact disc: released on Collectors Series in '86 by Castle Communications Records. Distributed by: PRT, Pinnacle, RCA, Ariola

COLLECTION: BOXCAR WILLIE.
Album: released on Spartan in Jan'86 by Spartan Records. Distributed by: Spartan

Cassette: released on Spartan in Jan'86 by Spartan Records. Distributed by: Spartan

DADDY WAS A RAILROAD MAN.
Album: released on Big R in Nov'80 by Big R Records. Distributed by: Pinnacle, Wynd-Up Distribution, Solomon & Peres Distribution, I & B, Swift, Record Merchandisers Distribution, Spartan

Cassette: released on Big R in Nov'80 by Big R Records. Distributed by: Pinnacle, Wynd-Up Distribution, Solomon & Peres Distribution, I & B, Swift, Record Merchandisers Distribution, Spartan

FREIGHT TRAIN BLUES.
Tracks: / Last train to heaven / Bummin' around / Bad news / Keep on rollin' down the line / Freight train blues / Lonesome blues / We made memories / You got the kind of love that grass a hold / To my baby I'm a big star all the time / Don't blame me for what happened last night / There's nothing like a good old country song / Lefty left us lonely.
Album: released on Colorado in Apr'85

GOOD HEARTED WOMAN.
Single (7"): released on Big R in Mar'81 by Big R Records. Distributed by: Pinnacle, Wynd-Up Distribution, Solomon & Peres Distribution, I & B, Swift, Record Merchandisers Distribution, Spartan

GOOD OL' COUNTRY SONGS.
Tracks: / Bummin' around / Bad news / That sinking feeling / Keep on rollin' down the line / Freight train blues / Lefty left us lonely / Eagle, The / Lonesome Joe / Alligator song, The / To my baby I'm a big star all the time / You got the kind of love that grabs a hold... / We made memories / Dearest darling / Don't blame me for what happened last night / There's nothing like a good of' country song.
Album: released on K-Tel in Apr'82 by K-Tel Records. Distributed by: Record Merchandisers Distribution, Taylors, Terry Blood Distribution, Wynd-Up Distribution, Relay Distribution, Pickwick Distribution, Solomon & Peres Distribution, Polygram

Cassette: released on K-Tel in Apr'82 by K-Tel Records. Distributed by: Record Merchandisers Distribution, Taylors, Terry Blood Distribution, Wynd-Up Distribution, Relay Distribution, Pickwick Distribution, Solomon & Peres Distribution, Polygram

KING OF THE ROAD.
Tracks: / King of the road / Wabash cannonball / You are my sunshine / Don't let the stars get in your eye / San Antonio rose / You're cheatin' / I saw the light / Peace in the valley / Kaw Lige / Heaven / Mule train / Hey good lookin' / Move it on over / London leaves / Rolling in my sweet baby's arms / Boxcar blues / Wreck of the old '97 / Hand and the hobo / Divorce me C.O.D. / Red river valley.
Cassette: released on Colorado (USA) in Dec'85

Album: released on Colorado in Apr'85

LIVE IN CONCERT.
Album: released on Pickwick in Apr'84 by Pickwick Records. Distributed by: Pickwick Distribution, Prism Leisure Distribution,

Cassette: released on Pickwick in Apr'84 by Pickwick Records. Distributed by: Pickwick Distribution, Prism Leisure Distribution,

MAN I USED TO BE, THE.
Single (7"): released on Spartan in Apr'85 by Spartan Records. Distributed by: Spartan

NO MORE TRAINS TO RIDE.
Tracks: / The man I used to be / Not on the bottom yet / Watching a new love grow / I just gotta go / Luther / Whine whistle / Daddy played over the waves / It ain't no record / Hobo's lament / Mister can you spare a dime / No more trains to ride.
Album: released on Colorado in Apr'85

SINGS HANK WILLIAMS & JIMMIE RODGERS.
Album: released on Big Red Group in Nov'80 by Big Red Group Records. Distributed by: PRT

Cassette: released on Big Red Group in Nov'80 by Big Red Group Records. Distributed by: PRT

TAKE ME HOME.
Tracks: / Train medley / From a boxcar door / Take me home / Cold windy city of Chicago / Hank,you still make me cry / Country music nightmare / I can't help it (I'm still in love with you) / I love the sound of a whistle / Blue blue days,Blue blue nights / Six pound fish / 'T' for Texas.
Album: released on Colorado in Apr'85

Album: released on Big R in Nov'80 by Big R Records. Distributed by: Pinnacle, Wynd-Up Distribution, Solomon & Peres Distribution, I & B, Swift, Record Merchandisers Distribution, Spartan

Cassette: released on Big R in Nov'80 by Big R Records. Distributed by: Pinnacle, Wynd-Up Distribution, Solomon & Peres Distribution, I & B, Swift, Record Merchandisers Distribution, Spartan

WATCHING NEW LOVE GROW.
Single (7"): released on Spartan in Dec'85 by Spartan Records. Distributed by: Spartan

Boxers

WATCH IT(DO ME A FAVOUR).
Single (7"): released on Gipsy in Aug'83 by Gipsy Records. Distributed by: PRT

Single (12"): released on Gipsy in Aug'83 by Gipsy Records. Distributed by: PRT

Box Of Frogs

AVERAGE.
Tracks: / Average / Strange lands / Keep calling*.
Notes: *Extra track on 12" only

Single (7"): released on Epic in Jun'86 by CBS Records. Distributed by: CBS

Single (12"): released on Epic in Jun'86 by CBS Records. Distributed by: CBS

BACK WHERE I STARTED.
Single (7"): released on Epic in Jun'84 by CBS Records. Distributed by: CBS

Single (12"): released on Epic in Jun'84 by CBS Records. Distributed by: CBS

BOX OF FROGS.
Album: released on Epic in Jul'84 by CBS Records. Distributed by: CBS

Cassette: released on Epic in Jul'84 by CBS Records. Distributed by: CBS Deleted '86.

INTO THE DARK.
Single (7"): released on Epic in Aug'84 by CBS Records. Distributed by: CBS

Single (12"): released on Epic in Aug'84 by CBS Records. Distributed by: CBS Deleted '85.

STRANGE LAND.
Tracks: / Get it while you can / You mix me up / Average / House on fire / Hanging from the wreckage / Heart full of soul / Asylum / Strange land / Strange land.
Album: released on Epic in Jun'86 by CBS Records. Distributed by: CBS

Cassette: released on Epic in Jun'86 by CBS Records. Distributed by: CBS

Box Of Toys

I'M THINKING OF YOU NOW.
Single (7"): released on Inevitable in Aug'83 by Inevitable Records. Distributed by: Rough Trade

PRECIOUS IS THE PEARL.
Single (7"): released on Inevitable in Mar'84 by Inevitable Records. Distributed by: Rough Trade

Single (12"): released on Inevitable in Mar'84 by Inevitable Records. Distributed by: Rough Trade

Box, Robin

I AIN'T GOT YOU.
Single (7"): released on Punchline in Nov'82

Box Tops

Biographical Details: This American group consisted of Alex Chilton, Bill Cunningham, John Evans, Danny Smythe and Gary Talley. The five members met while in collage and formed the group in 1965. Hailing from Memphis, Tennessee, they were one of the few white acts of the Sixties to score success from that City's soul studios. Their first success was the biggest : 'The Letter', a powerful, intense and very catchy pop single was no.1 for four week's in the States in the autumn of 1967. It reached at no.2 in the US , no.15 in the UK. Their only other 45 to hit the top 20 on either side of the Atlantic was 1969's 'Soul Deep', no.18 in the US. Several other records were American top 40 hits, but the Box Tops will always be best remembered for 'The Letter'. Joe Cocker's remake of this single reached the US top 10 in the summer of 1970, but by this time the Box Tops had disbanded.(BM 84)

CRY LIKE A BABY.
Single (7"): released on Creole in Aug'82 by Creole Records. Distributed by: Rhino, PRT

LETTER, THE.
Single (7"): released on Creole in Aug'82 by Creole Records. Distributed by: Rhino, PRT

Single (7"): released on Juke Box in Mar'82

Single (7"): released on Old Gold in Jul'82 by Old Gold Records. Distributed by: Lightning, Jazz Music, Spartan, Counterpoint

Boyce, Jesse

IT'S YOUR CHANCE(TO BREAK DANCE).
Single (12"): released on Compleat in Aug'84 by Compleat Records. Distributed by: PRT

Boyce, Kim

KIM BOYCE.
Album: released on Myrrh in May'87 by Word Records. Distributed by: Word Distribution

Cassette: released on Myrrh in May'87 by Word Records. Distributed by: Word Distribution

Boyce, Max

IN CONCERT.
Album: released on Spot in Sep'85 by Pickwick Records. Distributed by: H.R. Taylor,

Cassette: released on Spot in Sep'85 by Pickwick Records. Distributed by: H.R. Taylor

INCREDIBLE PLAN, THE.
Album: released on MFP (EMI) in Nov'82 by EMI Records. Distributed by: EMI

Cassette: released on MFP (EMI) in Nov'82 by EMI Records. Distributed by: EMI

IN TOUCH WITH MAX BOYCE.
Album: released on One Up in Mar'80 by EMI Records Deleted '86.

Cassette: released on One Up in Mar'80 by EMI Records

LIVE AT TREORCHY.
Tracks: / 9-3 / The Scottish trip / The ballad of Morgan the moon / The Outside-Half factory / Asso asso yogishi / Duw it's hard / Ten thousand instant Christians / Did you understand? / Hymns and arias.
Album: released on One Up in May'74 by EMI Records

Cassette: released on One Up in Jul'81 by EMI Records Deleted '83.

Album: released on Music For Pleasure (Holland) in Jun'85 by EMI Records. Distributed by: EMI

Boyd, Carole

TALES FROM TEN IN A BED Spoken Word.
Cassette: released on Tellastory in Mar'84 by Bartlett Bliss Productions. Distributed by: PRT Distribution, Hayward Promotions Distribution, H.R. Taylor Distribution

Boyd, Eddie

EDDIE BOYD & HIS BLUES BAND FEAT.PETER GREEN (Boyd, Eddie & His Blues Band/Peter Green).
Tracks: / Too bad / Dust my broom / Unfair lovers / Key to the highway / Vacation from the blues / Steakhouse rock / Letter missin' blues / Ain't doin' too bad / Blue coat man / Save her doctor / Rack 'em back / Too bad part 2 / Big bell / Pinetops boogie / Night time is the right time / Train is coming.
Album: by IMS-Polygram Records. Distributed by: IMS, Polygram, Rollercoaster Distribution

LEGACY OF THE BLUES VOL.10.
Tracks: / I'm a fool / Kindness for weakness / Tell the truth / Cannonball / Black, brown and white / Do yourself a favour / Dedication to my baby / Zip code.
Album: released on Sonet in '75 by Sonet Records. Distributed by: PRT

LOVERS PLAYGROUND.
Album: released on Stockholm in Feb'85. Distributed by: Swift Distribution

Meat and gravy from cadillac baby - Vol.3

Boyd, Kay

FIRST SLICE.
Tracks: / This could be the start of something / Love is here to stay / For once in my life / I'm gonna sit right down and write myself a letter / My way / Sometimes when I'm happy / When I fall in love / Teach me tonight / My funny Valentine.
Album: released on Spotlite in Nov'83 by Spotlite Records. Distributed by: Cadillac, Jazz Music, Spotlite

Boyd Rice

BOYD RICE.
Album: released on Mute in '81. Distributed by: Spartan Distribution, Rough Trade Distribution, Cartel Distribution

Boyer, Lucienne

50 YEARS OF SONG.
Double Album: released on EMI (France) in '83 by EMI Records. Distributed by: Conifer

Boyfriend Cast

IT'S NEVER TOO LATE IN LOVE.
Single (7"): released on That's Entertainment in Dec'84 by That's Entertainment Records. Distributed by: Pinnacle, PRT

Boyfriends

BOYFRIEND.
Single (7"): released on Plastic in Jan'83 by Plastic Records. Distributed by: Pinnacle

Boyfriends & Love

BOYFRIENDS AND LOVE Girl Groups of the Sixties (Various Artists).
Tracks: / My Boyfriend's Back / Sally Go Round the Roses / Remember Walkin' in the Sand / He's So Fine / Party Lights / I wanna love him so bad / Chapel of Love / Goodnight Baby / Dedicated to the One I Love / Will You Love Me Tomorrow / Boy From New York City / I Can't Let Him Go.
Album: released on Charly in Jan'87 by Charly Records. Distributed by: Charly, Cadillac

Cassette: released on Charly in Nov'86 by Charly Records. Distributed by: Charly, Cadillac

Boyfriend, The

BOYFRIEND, THE Various artists (Various Artists).
Compact disc: released on TER in Apr'85. Distributed by: Pinnacle

BOYFRIEND, THE Various artists (Revival 1967 London Cast).
Album: released on That's Entertainment in Sep'84 by That's Entertainment Records. Distributed by: Pinnacle, PRT

Cassette: released on That's Entertainment in Sep'84 by That's Entertainment Records. Distributed by: Pinnacle, PRT

BOYFRIEND, THE Original 1984 London cast (Various Artists).

Album: released on That's Entertainment in Dec'84 by That's Entertainment Records. Distributed by: Pinnacle, PRT

Cassette: released on That's Entertainment in Dec'84 by That's Entertainment Records. Distributed by: Pinnacle, PRT

Compact disc: released on That's Entertainment in Dec'84 by That's Entertainment Records. Distributed by: Pinnacle, PRT

Boy George

EVERYTHING I OWN.
Tracks: / Everything I Own / Use Me.
Single (7"): released on Virgin in Feb'87 by Virgin Records. Distributed by: EMI, Virgin Distribution

Single (12"): released on Virgin in Feb'87 by Virgin Records. Distributed by: EMI, Virgin Distribution

KEEP ME IN MIND.
Tracks: / Keep me in mind / State of love / I pray".
Single (7"): released on Virgin in 23 May'87 by Virgin Records. Distributed by: EMI, Virgin Distribution

Single (12"): released on Virgin in 23 May'87 by Virgin Records. Distributed by: EMI, Virgin Distribution

Cassette single: released on Virgin in 20 Jun'87 by Virgin Records. Distributed by: EMI, Virgin Distribution

SOLD.
Tracks: / Sold / Are you too afraid.
Single (7"): released on Virgin in Jul'87 by Virgin Records. Distributed by: EMI, Virgin Distribution

Single (12"): released on Virgin in Jul'87 by Virgin Records. Distributed by: EMI, Virgin Distribution

Cassette single: released on Virgin in Jul'87 by Virgin Records. Distributed by: EMI, Virgin Distribution

SOLD (LP).
Compact disc: released on Virgin in Jun'87 by Virgin Records. Distributed by: EMI, Virgin Distribution

Album: released on Virgin in Jun'87 by Virgin Records. Distributed by: EMI, Virgin Distribution

Cassette: released on Virgin in Jun'87 by Virgin Records. Distributed by: EMI, Virgin Distribution

Boy Growing Up, A

BOY GROWING UP, A Thomas, Dylan (Williams, Emlyn).
Tracks: / Introduction / Memories of childhood / Who do you wish was with us / The fight / The outing / The reminiscence of a schoolmaster / Just like little dogs / Self portrait / Adventures in the skin trade / Child's Christmas, A / A visit to America / A visit to grandpa's.
Cassette: released on Argo (Spokenword) in Mar'83 by Decca Records. Distributed by: Polygram

Boyle, Maggie

REACHING OUT.
Album: released on Run River in Feb'87

Boyle, Neil

MOVING CLOUDS, THE.
Cassette: released on Folktracks in Nov'79 by Folktracks Cassettes. Distributed by: Folktracks

Boy Meets Girl

EMPTY BED.
Single (7"): released on Chromozone in Aug'82. Distributed by: Cartel

OH GIRL.
Single (7"): released on A&M in May'85 by A&M Records. Distributed by: Polygram

Single (12"): released on A&M in May'85 by A&M Records. Distributed by: Polygram

Boyo, Billy

BILLY BOYO ON THE GO.
Single (12"): released on Greensleeves in Nov'82 by Greensleeves Records. Distributed by: BMG, Jetstar, Spartan

D.J.CLASH VOL. 2 (Boyo, Billy & Little Harry).
Album: released on Greensleeves in Jan'83 by Greensleeves Records. Distributed by: BMG, Jetstar, Spartan

Album: released on Greensleeves in Jan'83 by Greensleeves Records. Distributed by: BMG, Jetstar, Spartan

Boys

Biographical Details: Their debut self-titled album reached No.50 on the UK chart in October 1977. Its solitary week of glory was the group's only success-they did not achieve a hit single, and subsequent albums failed to chart. These LPs included the 1978 offering "Alternative Chartbusters" and "To hell with the boys" (1979). The band continued recording into the early Eighties. B.M. 84

ALTERNATIVE CHARTBUSTERS.
Album: released on Nems in Mar'78. Distributed by: Castle Communications Records, Pinnacle Records

BOYS ONLY.
Album: released on Safari in Feb'81 by Safari Records. Distributed by: Pinnacle

KAMIKAZE.
Single (7"): released on Safari in '80 by Safari Records. Distributed by: Pinnacle

LET IT RAIN.
Single (7"): released on Safari in Feb'81 by Safari Records. Distributed by: Pinnacle

TERMINAL LOVE.
Single (7"): released on Safari in Jan'80 by Safari Records. Distributed by: Pinnacle

TO HELL WITH THE BOYS.
Album: released on Safari in Nov'79 by Safari Records. Distributed by: Pinnacle

WEEKEND.
Single (7"): released on Safari in '81 by Safari Records. Distributed by: Pinnacle

YOU BETTER MOVE ON.
Single (7"): released on Safari in '80 by Safari Records. Distributed by: Pinnacle

Boy's Brigade

OLD FATHER TIME.
Single (7"): released on Thaw in Aug'83

PASION OF LOVE.
Single (7"): released on Capitol in Feb'84 by Capitol Records. Distributed by: EMI

Single (12"): released on Capitol in Feb'84 by Capitol Records. Distributed by: EMI Deleted '85.

Boy's Brigade Band

BOY'S BRIGADE CENTENARY ALBUM, THE.
Album: released on Lismor in Nov'82 by Lismor Records. Distributed by: Lismor, Roots, Celtic Music

Cassette: released on Lismor in Nov'82 by Lismor Records. Distributed by: Lismor, Roots, Celtic Music

Boy's Choir of Vienna

CHRISTMAS VOICES & BELLS.
Album: released on Audio Fidelity in Oct'84. Distributed by: PRT

Cassette: released on Audio Fidelity in Oct'84. Distributed by: PRT

Boys Don't Cry

12" MEGAMIX ALBUM.
Album: released on Legacy in Nov'86. Distributed by: PRT

BOYS DON'T CRY.
Compact disc: released on Legacy in Jan'86. Distributed by: PRT

Album: released on Legacy in Jan'86. Distributed by: PRT

Cassette: released on Legacy in Jan'86. Distributed by: PRT

CITIES ON TIME, THE.
Tracks: / Cities on time, The.
Single (7"): released on Legacy in Oct'86. Distributed by: PRT

Single (12"): released on Legacy in Oct'86. Distributed by: PRT

DON'T TALK TO STRANGERS.
Single (7"): released on Legacy in Mar'84. Distributed by: PRT

Single (12"): released on Legacy in Mar'84. Distributed by: PRT

HEARTS BEEN BROKEN.
Tracks: / Hearts been broken.
Single (7"): released on Legacy in Aug'86. Distributed by: PRT

Single (12"): released on Legacy in Aug'86. Distributed by: PRT

HEART'S BIN BROKEN.
Single (7"): released on Legacy in Apr'83. Distributed by: PRT

I WANNA BE A COWBOY.
Tracks: / I wanna be a cowboy / Turn over(I like it better that way).
Picture disc single: released on Legacy in May'86. Distributed by: PRT

Single (7"): released on Legacy in Sep'85. Distributed by: PRT

Single (12"): released on Legacy in Sep'85. Distributed by: PRT

LIPSTICK.
Single (7"): released on Legacy in Mar'85. Distributed by: PRT

TURN OVER(I LIKE IT BETTER THAT WAY).
Single (12"): released on Legacy in Jul'84. Distributed by: PRT

WHO THE AM DAM DO YOU THINK YOU AM.
Tracks: / Who the am dam do you think you am / Cure (The).
Single (7"): released on Legacy in Apr'87. Distributed by: PRT

Single (12"): released on Legacy in Apr'87 Distributed by: PRT

Boys From Brazil

BOYS FROM BRAZIL Original motion picture soundtrack (Various Artists).
Album: released on A&M in Mar'79 by A&M Records. Distributed by: Polygram

Boys From Syracuse

BOYS FROM SYRACUSE Original London Cast.
Album: released on TER in Apr'85. Distributed by: Pinnacle

Cassette: released on TER in Apr'85. Distributed by: Pinnacle

I'LL CRY FOR YOU.
Tracks: / I'll cry for you.
Single (7"): released on New England in Jul'86. Distributed by: RCA,

Single (12"): released on New England in Jul'86. Distributed by: RCA,

Boys From The East

BRILLIANT.
Single (7"): released on Final Cut in Jun'87 by Final Cut Records. Distributed by: Red Rhino, Cartel

Boys In Darkness

HEART OF DARKNESS.
Single (7"): released on Parlophone in Jun'84 by EMI Records. Distributed by: EMI

Single (12"): released on Parlophone in Jun'84 by EMI Records. Distributed by: EMI Deleted '86.

Boys Of The Lough

BOYS OF THE LOUGH.
Tracks: / Da lerwick lasses / Da Scalloway lasses / Da underhill / Da valley watch / An goirtin eornan / Sally Monroe / Patsy C Campbell / Gravel walk / Lough erne / Gold ring / Halting march / Lovely Nancy / Merrily kiss the quakers wife / Padriac O'Keefe / Yow cam tir wir door yarmin / Christmas day Ida moarning / Lass with the bonny brown hair / Lowrie Tarrell / Masons apron / Lovesick soul.
Album: released on Leader in '81. Distributed by: Jazz Music, Projection

FAR FROM HOME.
Album: released on Auk in Nov'86. Distributed by: Jazz Music, Projection

IN THE TRADITION.
Cassette: released on Ross in Jan'86 by Ross Records. Distributed by: Ross Distribution, Roots Distribution

LIVE AT PASSIM.
Album: released on Philo in May'79. Distributed by: Roots

OPEN ROAD.
Tracks: / Calliope house / Jerry O'Connor's jig in A / Harvest home-toss the feathers / Clay of Kilcreggan / On Raglan Road / Dying year-Madame Vanoni / Big Terry McAloon's-Tommy Peoples'-Jenny Dang the weaver / Flower of the quern etc / Trotting to the larne-Spey in spate / Black cock of Whickham / Lough erne / Gates of the yellow town / Petticoat loose etc..
Album: released on Topic in Nov'86. Distributed by: Roots Distribution

Cassette: released on Topic in Apr'84. Distributed by: Roots Distribution

REGROUPED.
Cassette: released on Ross in Jan'86 by Ross Records. Distributed by: Ross Distribution, Roots Distribution

Album: released on Topic in '81. Distributed by: Roots Distribution

SECOND ALBUM.
Album: released on Leader in '81. Distributed by: Jazz Music, Projection

WELCOMING PADDY HOME.
Album: released on Lough in Nov'86 by Lough Records. Distributed by: Roots, Celtic Distributions, Jazz Music, Projection

Boystown

BOYSTOWN Various artists (Various Artists).
Album: released on Streetsounds in Jan'84

Cassette: released on Streetsounds in Jan'84

Boystown Gang

Biographical Details: This mixed group of American vocalists were, as their name suggests, at the forefront of the boystown disco scene of the Eighties, later called 'high energy' music (or 'Hi-NRG). This style is perhaps best described as a gay version of the Eurovision Song Contest. Material consisted either of cover versions, or of supposedly original material that borrowed heavily from other songs: it was usually embellished with a 'pots and pans' percussion sound and amateurish production. But for all its shortcomings, the boystown genre had a significant pop appeal, allowing some of its singles to cross over from their original homosexual audience into the national disco and pop charts, especially in Britain. The Boystown Gang's output has mainly consisted of remakes. They first hit the UK pop charts with their 1981 renditin of Diana Ross' 1970 hit "Ain't no mountain high enough" peaking at No.46. Their only major hit was "Can't take my eyes off you", a reworking of the familiar late Sixties smash. The Gang took its bland but irrestible catchy version to No.4 on the British chart, one place higher than Andy Williams had managed. They followed it with a No.50 remake of Stevie Wonder's "Signed sealed delivered (i'm yours)". As 'boystown' gradually became a dated word the Gang faded B.M 84

AIN'T NO MOUNTAIN HIGH ENOUGH.
Single (7"): released on Moby Dick in Sep'8[illegible] by ERC Records. Distributed by: PRT Distribution

Single (12"): released on Moby Dick in Sep'8[illegible] by ERC Records. Distributed by: PRT Distribution

BRAND NEW ME.
Single (7"): released on Rich & Famous in Sep'84 by Rich & Famous Records. Distributed by: PRT

Single (12"): released on Rich & Famous in Sep'84 by Rich & Famous Records. Distributed by: PRT

CAN'T TAKE MY EYES OFF YOU.
Single (7"): released on ERC in Jul'82 by ERC Records. Distributed by: PRT

Single (12"): released on ERC in Jul'82 by ERC Records. Distributed by: PRT

CAST OF THOUSANDS, A.
Tracks: / Good man (is hard to find), A / Brand new me / In and out of love / (Here I am) waiting for you / I just can't help believing / Dance trance medley / Yester-me, yester-you, yesterday / When will I see you again.
Album: released on Rich & Famous in Oct'8[illegible] by Rich & Famous Records. Distributed by: PR[illegible]

Cassette: released on Rich & Famous in Oct'[illegible] by Rich & Famous Records. Distributed by: PR[illegible]

CRUISIN' THE STREETS.
Tracks: / Remember me / Ain't no mountain high enough / Reprise / Finale / Cruisin' the streets / Cruisin' / Rejected / Pick up, The Busted.
Album: released on Moby Dick in Aug'81 by ERC Records. Distributed by: PRT Distribution

DISCHARGE.
Album: released on ERC in Aug'82 by ERC Records. Distributed by: PRT

Cassette: released on ERC in Aug'82 by ERC Records. Distributed by: PRT

I JUST CAN'T HELP BELIEVIN'.
Single (7"): released on ERC in Jul'83 by ERC Records. Distributed by: PRT

Single (12"): released on ERC in Jul'83 by ERC Records. Distributed by: PRT

REMEMBER ME.
Tracks: / Remember me / Ain't no mountain high enough / Cruising in the streets / You do it for me.
Single (12"): released on Record Shack in Aug'86 by Record Shack Records. Distributed by: PRT

SIGNED, SEALED, DELIVERED (I'M YOURS).
Single (7"): released on ERC in Sep'82 by ERC Records. Distributed by: PRT

Single (12"): released on ERC in Sep'82 by ERC Records. Distributed by: PRT

YESTER-ME, YESTER-YOU, YESTERDAY.
Single (7"): released on Rich & Famous in Jan'85 by Rich & Famous Records. Distributed by: PRT

Single (12"): released on Rich & Famous in Dec'84 by Rich & Famous Records. Distributed by: PRT

Boys White Teeth

PRICES (WILL BE QUOTED).
Single (7"): released on T.W. in Jul'82 by T.W. Records. Distributed by: Cartel

Single (12"): released on T.W. in Jul'82 by T.W. Records. Distributed by: Cartel

Boys Wonder

NOW WHAT EARTHMAN.
Tracks: / Now what earthman / 10 million ton headache.
Single (12"): released on Sire in 13 Jun'87

Single (7"): released on Sire in 13 Jun'87

Boy Tronic

YOU.
Single (7"): released on Magic in Feb'84. Distributed by: Jazz Music, Submarine, Swift, Chris Wellard, Conifer

Single (12"): released on Magic in Feb'84. Distributed by: Jazz Music, Submarine, Swift, Chris Wellard, Conifer

Boyzone

LAST ADVENTURE.
Single (7"): released on Topland in Dec'84

Single (12"): released on Topland in Dec'84

B.P.M. Volume 2

B.P.M. VOLUME 2 Various artists (Various Artists).
Album: released on Carrere in Oct'85 by Carrere Records. Distributed by: PRT, Spartan

Cassette: released on Carrere in Oct'85 by Carrere Records. Distributed by: PRT, Spartan

B Project

WAR THEME FROM ROCKY IV.
Tracks: / War theme from Rocky IV / War-the fanfare.
Single (7"): released on Certain in Mar'86. Distributed by: Priority, EMI, Pinnacle

Single (12"): released on Certain in Mar'86. Distributed by: Priority, EMI, Pinnacle

Brackeen, Joanne

AFT.
Tracks: / Haiti B / Charlotte's dream / Dreamers Aft / Winter is here / Green voices of play air.
Album: released on Timeless(import) in Sep'86. Distributed by: Cadillac

AFT.
Album: released on Timeless in Apr'81

FI-FI GOES TO HEAVEN.
Tracks: / Estilo magnifico / Stardust / Fi-Fi goes to heaven / Zingaro / I hear a rhapsody / Cosmonaut / Dr Chang.
Notes: Personnel: Joanne Brackeen - piano / Terance Blanchard - trumpet / Branford Marsalis - alto & soprano sax / Cecil McBee - bass / Al Foster - drums.
Album: released on Concord Jazz in Jul'87 by Concord Jazz Records (USA). Distributed by: IMS, Polygram

Cassette: released on Concord Jazz in Jul'87 by Concord Jazz Records (USA). Distributed by: IMS, Polygram

Compact disc: released on Concord Jazz (USA) in Jul'87 by Concord Jazz Records (USA). Distributed by: IMS, Polygram

HAVIN' FUN (Brackeen, Joanne Trio).
Tracks: / Breaking Up The House / Walk That Mess / Train kept a rollin' (The) / Bradshaw Boogie / Walkin' The Chalk Line / Mailman's Sack / Snaggle Tooth Ruth / Rippin' And Runnin' / Blues came pouring down, The / Two Dry Bones On the Pantry Shelf / Brad's Blues / Boodie Green / Well Oh Well / Newspaper Boy Blues / One, Two, Three, Kick Blues.
Compact disc: released on Concord Jazz (USA) in Jan'87 by Concord Jazz Records (USA). Distributed by: IMS, Polygram

Album: released on Concord Jazz (USA) in Dec'85 by Concord Jazz Records (USA). Distributed by: IMS, Polygram

INVITATION.
Album: released on Freedom in '78 by Logo Records. Distributed by: RCA, Discovery, Wellard, Chris

NEW TRUE ILLUSION (Brackeen, Joanne & Clint Houston).
Tracks: / Steps what was / Search for peace / New true illusion / My romance / Freedent / Solar.
Album: released on Timeless in Apr'81
Cat.no

TRINKETS & THINGS (Brackeen, Joanne & Ryo Kawaski).
Tracks: / Trinkets & things / Showbrook air / Winnie & Woodstock / Fair weather / Whim within / Spring of things / Haiti B.
Album: released on Timeless in Apr'81

Braddeley, John

WIND IN THE WILLOWS.. Spoken Word.
Cassette: released on Tempo in Aug'84. Distributed by: MSD Distribution

WIND IN THE WILLOWS: THE OPEN ROAD Spoken Word.
Cassette: released on Tempo in Aug'84. Distributed by: MSD Distribution

WIND IN THE WILLOWS: THE WILD WOOD Spoken Word.
Cassette: released on Tempo in Aug'84. Distributed by: MSD Distribution

Bradenburg, Helmuth

BABYLON AMC.

Notes: For full information see: RIAS ORCHESTRA, The/Helmuth Bradenburg

Bradford, Geoff

MAGNOLIA.
Album: released on Christabel in Jul'86 by Gerard Management. Distributed by: Projection

Brad Is Sex

GENTLEMEN START YOUR SHEEP.
Album: released on Bam Caruso in Jun'87 by Bam Caruso Records. Distributed by: Rough Trade, Revolver, Cartel

Bradley

I AM WHAT I AM.
Single (7"): released on Hippodrome in Apr'84. Distributed by: EMI

Bradley, Brian

PRINCE BORN TODAY.
Single (7"): released on Zodiac in Sep'84. Distributed by: Jazz Music

Bradley, Martyn

TIME CAN'T STAND STILL.
Tracks: / Burkes jig / Hardiman / Paddy be aisy / Sligo fair / Helas medame / Humors of tullacreen / Rakes of Brandenburg / Spot the tune rag / McKinnons march / Lord Mayo / Sonato in F major, (The)- G.F Handel / South wind, (The) / Planxty hewlet / Playfords / Empty days.
Album: released on Greenwich Village in May'81 by Sweet Folk All Records. Distributed by: Roots, Projection, Lightning, Celtic Music, Wellard, Chris

Bradley, Owen

BIG GUITAR.
Tracks: / Big guitar / Cannonball / Rumble / Ramrod / Tequila / Tricky / Raunchy / Blueberry hill / Honky Tonk / Five o'clock jump / Hound dog / Stroll, (The) / Cool daddy / Funky.
Album: released on Charly in Jun'84 by Charly Records. Distributed by: Charly, Cadillac

Bradley & The Boys

DYNA-DALL.
Single (7"): released on Hippodrome in Jan'85 Distributed by: EMI

Single (12"): released on Hippodrome in Dec'84. Distributed by: EMI

Bradley, Tommie

JAMES COLE GROUPS (1930-33).
Album: released on Matchbox in May'83 by Saydisc Records. Distributed by: Roots, Projection, Jazz Music, JSU, Celtic Music

Tommie Bradley - James Cole

Bradley, Will

IN DISCO ORDER VOL 1.
Album: released on Ajax Import in Jul'77

IN DISCO ORDER VOL 2.
Album: released on Ajax Import in Dec'77

IN DISCO ORDER VOL 3.
Album: released on Ajax Import in Dec'77

WILL BRADLEY & RAY MCKINLEY, 1940-41 (Bradley, Will & Ray McKinley).
Album: released on Aircheck in Apr'79

WILL BRADLEY - VOL 4, 1940.
Album: released on Ajax in Apr'79

WILL BRADLEY - VOL 5, 1940-41.
Album: released on Ajax in Apr'79

WILL BRADLEY - VOL 6, 1941.
Album: released on Ajax in Apr'79

WILL BRADLEY - VOL 7, 1941.
Album: released on Ajax in Apr'79

WILL BRADLEY - VOL 8, 1941-46.
Album: released on Ajax in Apr'79

WINGY MANONE & WILL BRADLEY (Bradley, Will & Wingy Manone).
Album: released on Harlequin in Jul'82 by Harlequin Records. Distributed by: Swift, Jazz Music, Wellard, Chris, IRS, Taylor, H.R.

Bradshaw, Tiny

BREAKING UP THE HOUSE.
Tracks: / Breaking up the house / Walk that mess / Train kept a-rollin, (The) / T-99 / Bradshaw boogie / Walkin' the chalk line / Mailman's sack / Snaggle tooth ruth / Rippin' and runnin' / Blues came pouring down, (The) / Two dry bones on the pantry shelf / Brad's blues / Boodie green / Well oh well / Newspaper boy blues / One,two,three, kick blues.
Compact disc: by Charly Records. Distributed by: Charly, Cadillac

Album: released on Charly(R&B) in Jul'85 by Charly Records. Distributed by: Charly, Cadillac

Cassette: released on Charly(R&B) in Jul'85 by Charly Records. Distributed by: Charly, Cadillac

STOMPING ROOM ONLY.
Tracks: / Walk that mess / Bradshaw boogie / T.99 / Breaking up the house / Well oh well / Train kept a-rollin' / Cat fruit / Stomping room only / Gravy train / Newspaper boy blues / I'm gonna have myself a ball / Long time baby / Mailman's sack / Blues came pouring down / Heavy juice / Cat nap.
Album: released on Krazy Kat in Jan'84. Distributed by: Jazz Music, Swift, Chris Wellard, H.R. Taylor, Charly, Hotshot, IRS Distribution

TINY BRADSHAW 1934/TEDDY HILL 1935-1936 (Bradshaw, Tiny/Hill, Teddy).
Album: released on Harlequin in Jan'87 by Harlequin Records. Distributed by: Swift, Jazz Music, Wellard, Chris, IRS, Taylor, H.R.

Brady, Paul

ANDREW I & PAUL B (Brady, Paul & Andrew Irvine).
Cassette: released on Mulligan in Sep'78 by Topic Records. Distributed by: Roots Distribution, Jazz Music Distribution, I & B Distribution, Projection Distribution, Wynd-Up Distribution, Celtic Distributions

BACK TO THE CENTRE.
Notes: It's something out of the ordinary when an artiste whose songs,and live performances are publicly admired by Bob Dylan,Eric Clapton,U2'sBono and Dire Strait's Mark Knopfler;and whose songs have been covered by Tina Turner,Dave Edmunds & Santana to name but three,is still a closely guarded secret in the record business.1986 is the year that the'best kept secret in rock' will come out into the open! This fabulous album contains great songs and excellent performances by Brady and his

band,which includes Eric Clapton,Loudon Wainwright III,Phil Saatchi and Larry Mullen Jnr.
Compact disc: by Phonogram Records. Distributed by: Polygram Distribution

Album: released on Mercury in Apr'86 by Phonogram Records. Distributed by: Polygram Distribution

Cassette: released on Mercury in Apr'86 by Phonogram Records. Distributed by: Polygram Distribution

BACK TO THE CENTRE(WALK THE WHITE LINE).
Tracks: / Back to the centre (walk the white line) / Airwaves / Lakes of Pontchartrain*.
Single (7"): released on Mercury in Jun'86 by Phonogram Records. Distributed by: Polygram Distribution

Single (12"): released on Mercury in Jun'86 by Phonogram Records. Distributed by: Polygram Distribution

DEEP IN YOUR HEART.
Tracks: / Deep in your heart / Follow on / Cold cold night*.
Single (7"): released on Mercury in Mar'86 by Phonogram Records. Distributed by: Polygram Distribution

Single (12"): released on Mercury in Mar'86 by Phonogram Records. Distributed by: Polygram Distribution

EAT THE PEACH.
Tracks: / Eat the peach (7"version) / In case of accidents / Loving of a srtanger, The / Eat the peach (12" extended mix).
Compact disc single: released on Mercury in Apr'87 by Phonogram Records. Distributed by: Polygram Distribution

EAT THE PEACH (SINGLE).
Tracks: / Eat the peach.
Single (7"): released on Mercury in Mar'87 by Phonogram Records. Distributed by: Polygram Distribution

Single (12"): released on Mercury in Mar'87 by Phonogram Records. Distributed by: Polygram Distribution

FULL MOON.
Compact disc: by Demon Records. Distributed by: Pinnacle

FULL MOON.
Album: released on Demon in Nov'84 by Demon Records. Distributed by: Pinnacle

Cassette: released on Demon in Nov'84 by Demon Records. Distributed by: Pinnacle

HARD STATION.
Tracks: / Crazy dreams / Road to the promised land / Busted loose / Cold cold night / Hard station / Dancer in the fire / Night hunting time / Nothing but the same old story.
Album: released on 21 Records in Aug'82 by Polydor Records. Distributed by: Polydor

Cassette: released on 21 Records in Aug'82 by Polydor Records. Distributed by: Polydor

HIGH PART OF ROAD.
Cassette: released on Shanachie (Ireland) in May'77

ISLAND, THE.
Tracks: / Island, The / Great pretender, The / Dance the romance*.
Notes: * Extra track on 12" only
Single (7"): released on Mercury in Sep'86 by Phonogram Records. Distributed by: Polygram Distribution

Single (12"): released on Mercury in Sep'86 by Phonogram Records. Distributed by: Polygram Distribution

PRIMITIVE DANCE.
Tracks: / Steal your heart away / Soul commotion (The) / Paradise is here / It's gonna work out fine / Awakening (The) / Eat the peach / Don't start knocking / Just in case of accidents / Game of love (The).
Notes: Paul Brady is no longer 'the best kept secret in rock' known only to dedicated fans and other musicians.**Primitive dance** is a superb album of great songs and a fine performance. In short a very enjoyable experience for the **Brady** fan and all lovers of adult contempory music.
Album: released on Mercury in Apr'87 by Phonogram Records. Distributed by: Polygram Distribution

Cassette: released on Mercury in Apr'87 by Phonogram Records. Distributed by: Polygram Distribution

Compact disc: released on Mercury in Apr'87 by Phonogram Records. Distributed by: Polygram Distribution

STEAL YOUR HEART AWAY.
Tracks: / Steal your heart away / Soul commotion, The / Awakening, The*.
Single (7"): released on Mercury in 30 May'87 by Phonogram Records. Distributed by: Polygram Distribution

Single (12"): released on Mercury in 30 May'87 by Phonogram Records. Distributed by: Polygram Distribution

TRUE FOR YOU.
Tracks: / Great pretender, (The) / Let it happen / Helpless heart / Dance the romance / Steel claw / Take me away / Not the only one / Interlude / Trouble round the bend.
Album: released on 21 Records in May'83 by Polydor Records. Distributed by: Polydor Deleted Dec'85.

Cassette: released on 21 Records in May'83 by Polydor Records. Distributed by: Polydor

WELCOME HERE KIND STRANGER.
Album: released on Mulligan in Nov'79 by Topic Records. Distributed by: Roots Distribution, Jazz Music Distribution, , I & B Distribution, Projection Distribution, Wynd-Up Distribution, Celtic Distributions

Cassette: released on Mulligan in Sep'78 by Topic Records. Distributed by: Roots Distribution, Jazz Music Distribution, & B Distribution, Projection Distribution, Wynd-Up Distribution, Celtic Distributions

Brady, Phil

LIVERPOOL SOUNDS.
Album: released on Sweet Folk and Country in Dec'77. Distributed by: Chris Wellard Distribution

Brady, Sean

TAOISEACH'S HOOLEY.
Single (7"): released on Crubeen in Mar'84 by Crubeen Records (Ireland). Distributed by: Kay's Irish Music Distributors

THATCHER SONG.
Album: released on Crubeen in Dec'84 by Crubeen Records (Ireland). Distributed by: Kay's Irish Music Distributors

Cassette: released on Crubeen in Dec'84 by Crubeen Records (Ireland). Distributed by: Kay's Irish Music Distributors

Single (7"): released on IMI in Mar'84 by IMI Records. Distributed by: Kay's Irish Music Distributions

Brafa Team

LET'S MAKE AFRICA GREEN AGAIN.
Single (7"): released on Island in Apr'85 by Island Records. Distributed by: Polygram

Single (12"): released on Island in Apr'85 by Island Records. Distributed by: Polygram

Braff, Ruby

AMERICA THE BEAUTIFUL (Braff, Ruby & Dick Hyman).
Tracks: / When it's sleepy time down south / When my sugar walks down the street / When I fall in love / As long as I live / America the beautiful / Louisiana / High society / I'll be with you in apple blossom time / I ain't got nobody / This is all I ask.
Album: released on George Wein Concord Jazz (USA) in Jul'84 by Concord Jazz Records (USA). Distributed by: IMS, Polygram

BEST I'VE HEARD, (THE).
Tracks: / Our love is here to stay / On the sunny side of the street / It don't mean a thing / It don't mean a thing if it ain't got that swing / You're a lucky guy / Strutting with some barbeque / Rockin' in rhythm / Body and soul / Sugar.
Album: released on Vogue Jazz in Jan'83

Cassette: released on Vogue Jazz in Jan'83

BRAFF PLAYS BING.
Album: released on Pizza Express in Oct'79 by Pizza Express Records. Distributed by: Wellard, Chris

Cassette: released on Pizza Express in Nov'79 by Pizza Express Records. Distributed by Wellard, Chris

EASY NOW.
Tracks: / My walking stick / Willow weep for me / When my sugar walks down the street / Song is ended but the melody lingers on, (The) / Give my regard to broadway / This is my lucky day / This is my lucky day / Someday you'll be sorry / Yesterdays / For now / I just couldn't take it,baby / Little man, you've a busy day / Swinging on a star / Old folks / Did you ever see a dream walking / Pocketful of dreams / Moonlight becomes you / Pennies from heaven / Go fly a kite / Please / All alone / You're sensational / Too ra loo ra loo ral / White Christmas.
Album: released on RCA (France) in '83 by RCA Records. Distributed by: Discovery

FINE MATCH, A (Braff, Ruby & Scott Hamilton).
Tracks: / Romance in the dark / When a woman love's a man / Rockin' chair / Dinah / All my life / Shine / If you were mine** / I wished on the moon** / Bugle blues**.
Notes: This is the first time that Scott Hamilton's group and Ruby Braff have been heard together on record,although Scott & Ruby have appearedtogether several times since 1979.
Album: released on Concord Jazz (USA) in Dec'85 by Concord Jazz Records (USA). Distributed by: IMS, Polygram

HEAR ME TALKING.
Album: released on Black Lion in Jan'85 by Black Lion Records. Distributed by: Jazz Music, Chris Wellard, Taylor, H.R., Counterpoint, Cadillac

MIGHTY BRAFF, (THE).
Tracks: / When you're smiling / Easy livin' / Pullin' through / You're a lucky guy / Blue room / I can't get started / This can't be love / Flowers for a lady / Foolin' myself / I'll be around / It's easy to blame the weather / Struttin' with some barbeque / Mean to me / Ellie / You're a sweetheart / Blue and sentimental.
Album: released on Affinity in May'83 by Charly Records. Distributed by: Charly, Cadillac

ON SUNNIE'S SIDE OF THE STREET (Braff, Ruby & Ralph Sutton).
Album: released on BAJC in Apr'79. Distributed by: Swift

PRETTIES.
Album: released on Sonet in Jun'79 by Sonet Records. Distributed by: PRT

RUBY BRAFF, FEATURING DAVE MCKENNA.
Tracks: / Dancing in the dark / Blue prelude / Why was I born / Blue / If I could be you / I'm crazy about my baby / Louisiana / It's wonderful / Almost like being in love / Love come back to me / I must have that man.
Album: released on Jasmine in Jun'84 by Jasmine Records. Distributed by: Counterpoint, Taylor, H.R., Wellard, Chris, Swift,

RUBY BRAFF & SCOTT HAMILTON (Braff, Ruby & Scott Hamilton).
Album: released on Phontastic in Nov'86. Distributed by: Wellard, Chris

RUBY BRAFF WITH THE ED BICKERT TRIO (Braff, Ruby & the Ed Bickert Trio).
Tracks: / True love / I've got a feeling I'm falling / This year's kisses / World is waiting for the sunrise, (The) / Very thought of you, (The) / After a while / What is there to say / My funny valentine / Song is ended, (The) / When I fall in love.
Album: released on Sackville in Apr'81. Distributed by: Jazz Music, Jazz Horizons, Cadillac Music, Celtic Music, Swift

RUBY GOT RHYTHM.
Album: released on Black Lion in '78 by Black Lion Records. Distributed by: Jazz Music, Chris Wellard, Taylor, H.R., Counterpoint, Cadillac

Album: released on Black Lion in '78 by Black Lion Records. Distributed by: Jazz Music, Chris Wellard, Taylor, H.R., Counterpoint, Cadillac

SAILBOAT IN THE MOONLIGHT (Braff, Ruby & Scott Hamilton).
Tracks: / Lover Come Back To Me / Where Are You? / Deed I Do / When Lights Are Low / Jeepers Creepers / Milkman's Matinee (The) / Sweethearts On Parade / Sailboat in the moonlight,A.
Compact disc: released on Concord Jazz (USA) in Nov'86 by Concord Jazz Records (USA). Distributed by: IMS, Polygram

Album: released on Concord Jazz (USA) in Apr'86 by Concord Jazz Records (USA). Distributed by: IMS, Polygram

Cassette: released on Concord Jazz (USA) in Apr'86 by Concord Jazz Records (USA). Distributed by: IMS, Polygram

SWING THAT MUSIC (Braff, Ruby & Red Norvo).
Album: released on Affinity in Feb'80 by Charly Records. Distributed by: Charly, Cadillac

THEM THERE EYES.
Tracks: / Swinging on a star / Same old south / Yesterdays / Medley: I'm pulling through / It's the little things that mean so much / Them there eyes / I've grown accustomed to her face / Why was I born / Dream dancing / Love lies / Tea for two.
Notes: with J. Rowles, Vic Dickenson, B. Pizzarelli.

Album: released on Sonet in Mar'87 by Sonet Records. Distributed by: PRT

Bragg, Billy

Biographical Details: This singer and songwriter from the east end of London survived the pressure of being widely tipped as 'Brightest Hope for 1984'. During 1983 he had established himself on Britain's independent charts with the mini-album "Life's a riot with Spy vs Spy". It had also given Bragg his debut entry on the UK's national LP charts. It was a collection of witty, uncluttered songs delivered by one man and his guitar, placing Bragg in the folk tradition despite being the darling of the rock press. The standout cuts were "The milkman of human kindness" and "A new England". Bragg was originally in a Peterborough band called Riff Raff, and later spent an abortive three-month spell in the army. He consolidated his position as a solo recording artist in late '84 with "Brewing up with Billy Bragg" another UK chart LP. Bragg was proving a success, but his style was too far removed from conventional pop to make him the major star that some had predicted. B.M. 84

BACK TO BASICS.
Tracks: / Milkman of human kindness, The / To have and to have not / Richard / Lovers town revisited / New England, A / Man in the iron mask, The / Busy girl buys beauty, The / It says here / Love gets dangerous / From a Vauxhall Velox / Myth of trust, The / Saturday boy, The / Saturday boy, The / Island of no return, The / This guitar says sorry / Like soldiers do / St.Swithins day / Strange things happen / Lover sings, A / Between the wars / World turned upside down, The / Which side are you on.
Double Album: released on Go Discs in May'87 by Go Discs Records. Distributed by: CBS Distribution

Cassette: released on Go Discs in May'87 by Go Discs Records. Distributed by: CBS Distribution

Compact disc: released on Go Discs in May'87 by Go Discs Records. Distributed by: CBS Distribution

BETWEEN THE WARS.
Single (7"): released on Go Discs in Feb'85 by Go Discs Records. Distributed by: CBS Distribution

BREWING UP WITH BILLY BRAGG.
Tracks: / It says here / Love gets dangerous / Myth of trust, The / From a vauxhall velox / Saturday boy, The / Island of no return / St.Swithin's day / Like soldiers do / This guitar says sorry / Strange things happen / Lover sings, A.
Album: released on Go Discs in Oct'84 by Go Discs Records. Distributed by: CBS Distribution

Cassette: released on Go Discs in Oct'84 by Go Discs Records. Distributed by: CBS Distribution

DAYS LIKE THESE.
Tracks: / Days like these / I don't need this pressure Ron / Scholarship is the enemy of romance.
Single (7"): released on Go Discs in Dec'85 by Go Discs Records. Distributed by: CBS Distribution

LEVI STUBB'S TEARS.
Tracks: / Levi Stubb's tears / Think again / Walk away Renee / Between the wars(live)*.
Notes: *=Extra track on 12" only
Single (7"): released on Go Discs in Jun'86 by Go Discs Records. Distributed by: CBS Distribution

Single (12"): released on Go Discs in Jun'86 by Go Discs Records. Distributed by: CBS Distribution

LIFE'S A RIOT WITH SPY VS. SPY.
Tracks: / Milkman of human kindness, The / To have and have not / New England, A / Man in the iron mask, The / Busy girl buys beauty, The / Lovers town revisited.
Album: released on Go Discs in Jun'84 by Go Discs Records. Distributed by: CBS Distribution

Cassette: released on Go Discs in Jun'84 by Go Discs Records. Distributed by: CBS Distribution

NEW ENGLAND, A.
Single (7"): released on Go Discs in Jan'85 by Go Discs Records. Distributed by: CBS Distribution

PEEL SESSION 27.3.83.
Single (12"): released on Strange Fruit in Jun'87 by Clive Selwood. Distributed by: Pinnacle

TALKING WITH THE TAXMAN ABOUT POETRY.
Tracks: / Greetings to the new brunette / Train train / Marriage, The / Ideology / Levi Stubbs tears / Honey I'm a big boy now / There is power in a union / Help save the youth of America / Wishing the days away / Passion, The / Warmest room, The / Home front, The.
Notes: Produced by John Porter and Kenny Jones
Compact disc: released on Go Discs in May'87 by Go Discs Records. Distributed by: CBS Distribution

Album: released on Go Discs in Sep'86 by Go Discs Records. Distributed by: CBS Distribution

Cassette: released on Go Discs in Sep'86 by Go Discs Records. Distributed by: CBS Distribution

Braille Party

WELCOME TO MARYLAND.
Album: released on Fountain Of Youth in Aug'85. Distributed by: Rough Trade, Cartel

Brain, Brian

CULTURE.
Single (12"): released on Secret in Dec'80 by Secret Records. Distributed by: EMI

FUNKY ZOO.
Single (7"): released on Secret in Oct'82 by Secret Records. Distributed by: EMI

Single (12"): released on Secret in Oct'82 by Secret Records. Distributed by: EMI

JIVE JIVE.
Single (7"): released on Secret in Jul'82 by Secret Records. Distributed by: EMI

Brains

DANCING UNDER STREET.
Notes: Strong and memorable music.
Album: released on LM/LD in Jul'86. Distributed by: Compendium International Distribution

DANCING UNDER THE STREET-LIGHTS.
Tracks: / Dancing under the streetlights / Danya / Read my mind / Don't give yourself away.
Album: released on Landslide in Jul'85 by Dorane Ltd

Brainstorm

BRAINSTORM Original film score.
Album: released on TER in Nov'83. Distributed by: Pinnacle

Brainstormers

BRAINSTORMERS (Various Artists).
Album: released on Kent in Aug'85 by Ace Records. Distributed by: Pinnacle

Brains Trust

UNEARTHLY POWERS.
Single (7"): released on Trust in Mar'84 by Fast. Distributed by: Cartel Distribution

Braithwaite, Norman..

CAN'T FINISH THE SONG.
Single (7"): released on Solid in Jul'82 by Solid Records. Distributed by: Graduate, Spartan

Bramble, Mark

IN WITH THE OLD (Bramble, Mark/BBC Radio 2 Cast).
Cassette: released on That's Entertainment in Dec'86 by That's Entertainment Records. Distributed by: Pinnacle, PRT

Album: released on That's Entertainment in Jan'87 by That's Entertainment Records. Distributed by: Pinnacle, PRT

Brammer, Junior

CRUISIN'.
Single (12"): released on High Power in Nov'85 by High Power Records. Distributed by: Jetstar

HOLD YOUR LOVER.
Album: released on Live & Learn in 30 May'87. Distributed by: Jetstar

I CAN'T STAND THE PAIN.
Tracks: / I can't stand the pain / I can't stand the pain(version).
Single (12"): released on John Dread Production in Jul'86. Distributed by: Jetstar

IF YOU SHOULD LOSE ME.
Single (12"): released on High Power in Nov'85 by High Power Records. Distributed by: Jetstar

TELEPHONE LINE.
Album: released on John Dread Production in Nov'86. Distributed by: Jetstar

Cassette: released on John Dread Production in '86. Distributed by: Jetstar

Brammer, Phil

LONDON PLEASURES.
Single (7"): released on Paperback in Ap.'82

MUSIC BY NUMBERS.
Album: released on Zoometronome in Jul'81

Brancaster Musicale

DREAMS.
Tracks: / Greensleeves / London by night / Songs of the seas / Irish prelude / Strawberry fair / English country / Dream of the isles / My love is like a red red rose / David of the white rock / Banks of the Cam / Scarborough fair / Ash grove, The / To a wild rose / Cornish floral, The / Windmills of my mind, The / Hunting the hare / Winter melody, A / Blowing in the wind / Dawn chorus / Watermill, The / September, song / Oranges and lemons / Theme from "Elvira Madigan" / Lark in the clear air / How deep is the ocean / Ship of dreams / Stratford on Avon / Ebb tide.
Album: released on Cambra in '83 by Cambra Records. Distributed by: IDS, Conifer

Cassette: released on Cambra in '83 by Cambra Records. Distributed by: IDS, Conifer

Brancaster Studio...

MIDNIGHT.
Tracks: / Imagine / I just called to say I love you / Woman / Cavatina / Bright eyes / Cariots of fire / Chi mai / Do you know where / Do you know where you're going to / For your eyes only / MASH / Arthur's theme / Bermuda triangle / Careless whisper / Hello / Hill Street Blues / If you leave me now / Jewel in the crown / Lately / Up where we belong / I'd rather leave while I'm in love.
Compact disc: released on The Collection in Apr'87 by Object Enterprises Ltd. Distributed by: Counterpoint Distribution

Brancaster Symphony...

WARM & TENDER MOMENTS.
Tracks: / All the love in the world / Begin the beguine / Can't smile without you / One more night / Crying / I made it through the rain / Imagine / Lately / Do that to me one more time / First time ever I saw your face, The / Hello / If you leave me now / I write the songs / Just when I needed you most / Lara's theme / More than a lover / One day I'll fly away.
Notes: All tracks licensed from Coombe Music International Ltd. C 1986
Matrix number 0 13428 111512
Album: released on Showcase in Sep'86. Distributed by: Counterpoint

Cassette: released on Showcase in Sep'86. Distributed by: Counterpoint

Brand, Dollar

AFRICAN PIANO.
Tracks: / Bra Joe from Kilimnjaro / Selby that the eternal spirit / Is the only reality / Moon, The / Xaba / Sunset in the blue / Kippy / Jabulani-easter joy / Tintiy ana.
Album: released on ECM (Germany) in Apr'84 by ECM Records. Distributed by: IMS, Polygram, Virgin through EMI

AFRICAN PORTRAITS.
Tracks: / Cherry / Bra joe from Kilimanjaro / Blues for Hughie / Kipoie gafsa / Life is for the living / Death is for us all / Gwangwas / Little boy / Easter joy / Jabulani / Xaba.
Album: released on Sackville in Apr'81. Distributed by: Jazz Music, Jazz Horizons, Cadillac Music, Celtic Music, Swift

AFRICAN SKETCH BOOK.
Album: released on Enja (Germany) in Jan'82 by Enja Records (W.Germany). Distributed by Cadillac Music

AFRICAN SPACE PROGRAMME.
Album: released on Enja (Germany) in Jan'82 by Enja Records (W.Germany). Distributed by: Cadillac Music

AFRICA - TEARS AND LAUGHTER (Brand, Dollar Quartet).
Album: released on Enja (Germany) in Jan'82 by Enja Records (W.Germany). Distributed by: Cadillac Music

ANCIENT AFRICA.
Tracks: / Bra Joe from Kilimanjaro / Mamma / Tokai / Ilanga / Cherry / African sun / Tintinyana / Xaba / Peace-Salaam air.
Album: released on ECM (Germany) in Apr'84 by ECM Records. Distributed by: IMS, Polygram, Virgin through EMI

ANTHEM FOR THE NEW NATION.
Tracks: / Anthem of the New Nations / Biral / Liberation dance / Trial, The / Cape town / Wedding suite, The / Wedding, The / Lovers / I surrender dear / One day when we were yound / Thaba Nchu.
Album: released on Denon in Mar'82 by Denon Records. Distributed by: Harmonia Mundi

CHILDREN OF AFRICA.
Album: released on Enja (Germany) in Jan'82 by Enja Records (W.Germany). Distributed by: Cadillac Music

DUET (Brand, Dollar & Archie Shepp).
Tracks: / Fortunato / Barefoot boy from Queens Town / Left alone / Theme from proof of the man / Ubu saku / Moniebah.

DUKES' MEMORIES (Brand, Dollar/Abdullah Ibrahim).
Notes: For full details see under Abdullah Ibrahim.

ECHOES FROM AFRICA.
Album: released on Enja (Germany) in Jan'82 by Enja Records (W.Germany). Distributed by: Cadillac Music

GOOD NEWS FROM AFRICA (Brand, Dollar Duo).
Album: released on Enja (Germany) in Jan'82 by Enja Records (W.Germany). Distributed by: Cadillac Music

LIVE AT MONTREUX.
Album: released on Enja (Germany) in Jan'82 by Enja Records (W.Germany). Distributed by: Cadillac Music

MATSIDISO.
Compact disc: . Distributed by: Projection, Celtic Music, Cadillac

SANGOMA (VOLUME 1).
Album: released on Sackville in Jul'86. Distributed by: Jazz Music, Jazz Horizons, Cadillac Music, Celtic Music, Swift

SOUTH AFRICAN SUNSHINE.
Compact disc: . Distributed by: Projection, Celtic Music, Cadillac

Brandes, Will

KING CREOLE.
Tracks: / Wunderbares madchen / Wach auf little Susie / Ahoi-ohe / O Judy / Komm / Marina / Ich mocht mit dir traumen / Kiss me, honey honey, kiss me / King Creole / Die musik ist gut / Die boys und die girls von heute / Teenager melodie / Du bist schon / Du bist schon / In Toni's pizzeria / Was war das alles ohne dich.
Album: released on Bear Family in Mar'84 by Bear Family Records. Distributed by: Rollercoaster Distribution, Swift

Brand, Oscar

BILLY THE KID IN SONG & STORY.
Album: released on Caedmon(USA) in Jan'78 by Caedmon (USA) Records. Distributed by: Taylors, Discovery

Brandt's, Pete Method

POSITIVE THINKING.
Single (7"): released on Fried Egg in Jul'81 by Fried Egg Records. Distributed by: Rough Trade, Cartel

Brand X

Biographical Details: The group's first album "Unorthodox behaviour" was released in 1976. Their most famous member was Phil Collins, who in the same year took over the lead vocals in Genesis. Brand X's second album "Moroccan roll" gave them their first British chart appearance, peaking at No.37 in 1977. Subsequent LPs have been issued regularly, though only 1982's "Is there anything about?" made the UK chart. Their jazz-flavoured style has never been intended to be commercial however. For Collins, Brand X represents an enjoyable diversion from his mainstream work with Genesis and as a solo artist. B.M. 84.

BRAND X LIVESTOCK.
Tracks: / Nightmare patrol / Ish / Euthanasia waltz / Isis mourning / Malaga virgen.
Album: released on Charisma in Sep'83 by Virgin Records. Distributed by: EMI

MOROCCAN ROLL.
Album: released on Charisma in Oct'86 by Virgin Records. Distributed by: EMI

PRODUCT.
Tracks: / Don't make waves / Dance of the illegal aliens / Soho / Not good enough - see me / Algon / Rhesus perplexus / Wal to wal / And so to f....
Album: released on Charisma in Sep'83 by Virgin Records. Distributed by: EMI

Cassette: released on Charisma in Sep'83 by Virgin Records. Distributed by: EMI

UNORTHODOX BEHAVIOUR.
Tracks: / Nuclear burn / Euthanasia waltz / Born ugly / Smacks of euphoric hysteria / Unorthodox behaviour / Running on three / Touch wood / Sun in the night / Why should I lend you mine / Maybe I'll lend you mine after all / Hate zone / Collapsar / Disco suicide / Orbits / Malaga virgen / Macrocosm.
Album: released on Charisma in Oct'86 by Virgin Records. Distributed by: EMI

Compact disc: by Pacific Records (USA). Distributed by: Atlantic

Cassette: released on Charisma in Mar'83 by Virgin Records. Distributed by: EMI

X TRACKS (BEST OF).
Compact disc: by Pacific Records (USA). Distributed by: Atlantic

Brandy & Pope

GETTIN' HIGH WITH BRANDY & POPE.
Tracks: / I've been loving you so long now / Evangelina / Kate & Edith / Everybody sings the blues / Idol of the band / Honky tonk heroes / Gettin' high, by, and strange / Train of life / Heaven is my woman's love / Hello darlin' / Me and Paul / I'll break out again tonight.
Album: released on Folk Heritage in Jul'82 by Folk Heritage Records. Distributed by: Roots, Wynd-Up Distribution, Jazz Music, Folk Heritage

Braniffs

WHY SHOULD I BE LONELY.
Single (7"):

Branigan, Laura

Biographical Details: This American pop singer came to fame in 1982 with the single "Gloria". This Italian song had originally been a hit in Continental Europe in the late Seventies, but had been ignored in the UK and US, save for a minor British hit version by the irrepressible Jonathan King. When Branigan recorded it in '82 (with a different English lyric from the King version), it was a sleeper smash, eventually climbing to No.2 in the States. Her powerful voice breathed new life into this catchy song, sung in a Donna Summer vein. It was also Branigan's first UK hit, peaking at No.6 in early '83. Its follow-up "Solitaire" was another Top Tenner in America, though not a major British success. In 1984 she recorded another Italian song and scored another international smash. "Self control" reached No.4 in the US, was a huge hit, in complex structure but still with a broad pop appeal. The most extraordinary example of its success was in West Germany, where the Branigan version went to No.1 while the original Italian disc by co-writer Raffaele Riefcoli was simultaneously at the No.2. Raff's original had the disadvange of lacking the Branigan vocal performance, which was once again power-packed. The next single "The Lucky one" was a Top 20 hit in the States. Her LPs are patchy in their choice of material, but her voice is good enough that, when she has the right song, Branigan will sell many singles. B.M. 84

BRANIGAN.
Tracks: / All night with me / Gloria / Lovin' you baby / Living a lie / If you loved me / Please stay,go away / I wish I could be alone / Down like a rock / Maybe I love you / All night with me.
Compact disc: by WEA Records. Distributed by: WEA

Album: released on Atlantic in Feb'83 by WEA Records. Distributed by: WEA

Cassette: released on Atlantic in Feb'83 by WEA Records. Distributed by: WEA

BRANIGAN 2.
Tracks: / Solitaire / Deep in the dark / Close enough / Sueeze box / Gloria / How am I supposed to live without you / I'm not the only one / Mama / Don't show your love / Find me.
Compact disc: by WEA Records. Distributed by: WEA

BRANIGAN TWO.
Tracks: / Solitaire / Deep in the dark / Close enough / Lucky / Squeeze box / Gloria / How am I supposed to live with you / I'm not the only one / Mama / Find me / Don't show your love.
Album: released on Atlantic in Apr'83 by WEA Records. Distributed by: WEA

Cassette: released on Atlantic in Apr'83 by WEA Records. Distributed by: WEA

DEEP IN THE DARK.
Single (7"): released on Atlantic in Aug'83 by WEA Records. Distributed by: WEA

Single (12"): released on Atlantic in Aug'83 by WEA Records. Distributed by: WEA

GLORIA.
Single (7"): released on Atlantic in Aug'82 by WEA Records. Distributed by: WEA

Single (12"): released on Atlantic in Aug'82 by WEA Records. Distributed by: WEA

HOLD ME.
Tracks: / Hold me / Maybe tonight / Maybe tonight / Foolish lullaby / Spanish Eddie / Forever young / When i'm with you / I found someone / Sanctuary / Tenderness / When the heart hits the streets.
Compact disc: by WEA Records. Distributed by: WEA

Album: released on Atlantic in Aug'85 by WEA Records. Distributed by: WEA

Cassette: released on Atlantic in Aug'85 by WEA Records. Distributed by: WEA

LAURA BRANIGAN (VIDEO).
Video-cassette (VHS): released on RCA/Columbia in May'87

SELF CONTROL.
Tracks: / Lucky one / Self control / Ti amo / Heart / Heart / Will you still love me tomorrow / Satisfaction / Silent partners / Breaking out / Take me / With ever beat of my heart.
Compact disc: by WEA Records. Distributed by: WEA

Album: released on Atlantic in '86 by WEA Records. Distributed by: WEA

Single (7"): released on Atlantic in Jun'84 by WEA Records. Distributed by: WEA

SHATTERED GLASS.
Tracks: / Shattered glass / Statue in the rain.
Single (7"): released on Atlantic in Jul'87 by WEA Records. Distributed by: WEA

Single (12"): released on Atlantic in Jul'87 by WEA Records. Distributed by: WEA

SOLITAIRE.
Single (7"): released on Atlantic in Apr'83 by WEA Records. Distributed by: WEA

Single (12"): released on Atlantic in Apr'83 by WEA Records. Distributed by: WEA

Brannigan, Owen

BRANNIGAN'S NORTHUMBRIA.
Album: released on MWM in Jun'82 by Mawson & Wareham. Distributed by: Spartan Distribution, Jazz Music Distribution.

EVERGREEN.
Double Album: released on MFP in Apr'81 by EMI Records. Distributed by: EMI. Estim retail price in Jul'87 was £2.25.

Branscombe, Alan

SWINGIN' ON THE SOUND STAGE (Branscombe, Alan and Friends).
Tracks: / On green dolphin street / Rose room / Blues for Alan, The / Out of nowhere / For Pete's sake / On the Alamo / Tangerine / Close your eyes.
Notes: A tribute to Alan Branscombe with Kenny Wheeler, Bob Efford, Duncan Lamont, Eddie Blair and Stan Roderick.
Album: released on Esquire in Jul'87 by Titan International Productions. Distributed by: Jazz Music, Cadillac Music, Swift, Wellard, Chris, Backs, Rough Trade, Revolver, Nine Mile

Brard, Patty

TENDER LOVE (Brard, Patti & Eddie Kendricks).
Tracks: / Tender love / Mystery theme.
Notes: See also listing under Eddie Kendricks.
Single (7"): released on Spartan in Feb'87 by Spartan Records. Distributed by: Spartan

Single (12"): released on Spartan in Feb'87 by Spartan Records. Distributed by: Spartan

TENDER LOVER (Brard, Patty & Eddy Hendrix).
Tracks: / Mystery theme (Patty Brard).
Single (7"): released on Spartan in Jan'87 by Spartan Records. Distributed by: Spartan

Brasil

BRASIL Various artists (Various Artists).
Compact disc: by Polydor Records. Distributed by: Polygram, Polydor

Brasil Original

BRASIL ORIGINAL (Various Artists).
Album: released on RCA in Apr'84 by RCA Records. Distributed by: RCA, Roots, Swift, Wellard, Chris, I & B, Solomon & Peres Distribution

Brasil, Vera

BRAZIL - JUNE 1964.
Album: released on Revelation in Apr'81

Brass Band Concert

BRASS BAND CONCERT 1984 Various Brass Bands (Various bands).
Album: released on Polyphonic in Apr'85 by Polyphonic Records. Distributed by: Taylors

Brass Band Festival

BRASS BAND FESTIVAL 1982 (HIGHLIGHTS) various brass bands (Various bands).
Album: released on Chandos in Nov'82 by Chandos Records. Distributed by: Taylors

Cassette: released on Chandos in Nov'82 by Chandos Records. Distributed by: Taylors

Brass Bands

BRASS BANDS OF FODENS, FAREY AVIATION & MORRIS MTRS (VOL 3) various brass bands (Various bands).
Cassette: released on Decca in '74 by Decca Records. Distributed by: Polygram

Brass Britannia

BRASS BRITANNIA Best of British brass (Various bands).
Tracks: / Rule britannia / Jerusalem / Dambusters march / Largo / Trumpet voluntary / Jesu, joy of mans desiring / Liberty bell / Berecuse / Superman suite / Floral dance / Greensleeves / Theme from Ordinary People / John Barleycorn / Take a pair of sparkling eyes / Onward Christian soldiers / Radetsky march / Ash grove / Pomp and circumstance march no.1.
Album: released on Ronco in Mar'83

Cassette: released on Ronco in Mar'83

Brass Connection

BRASS CONNECTION, THE.
Album: released on Innovation in Sep'84 by Innovation Records. Distributed by: Jetstar

BRASS CONSTRUCTION 5.
Album: released on Liberty-United in Jan'80 by EMI Records. Distributed by: EMI

NEW LOOK, THE.
Album: released on Innovation in Sep'84 by Innovation Records. Distributed by: Jetstar

Brass Construction

Biographical Details: Formed in 1975, Brass Construction hit big the following year with their debut self-titled album. Following its disco success, it became a transatlantic Top 10 seller. It was an important LP as it was one of the first to make a successful fusion between jazz and R & B, and the group were one of the pioneers of the form later known as jazz-funk. A single from the album "Movin" went to No. 14 in the US and No.23 in the UK. Up to and including their sixth album, 1981's "Brass Constrution 6", asll their albums were simply named after the band, with the appropriatenumber added. None sold as well as their first outing, however. Like many acts who score major successes with their debut, they were unable to maintain their momentum. This was particularly the case in Britain, where they never

entered the album chart again, after their first offering. "Brass Construction 5" yielded the UK Top 40 single "Music makes you feel like dancing", but the LP failed to chart. Nevertheless the group continue to please their own specialist audience with albums such as 1982's "Attitudes" and 1983's "Conversations", and they are still competent exponents of the music that they helped to launch. B.M. 84

CONQUEST.
Tracks: / Goodnews / Modern touch / Give and take / Startin' all over again / Comeback / Zig zag / Secret lover / My place / Conquest.
Album: released on Capitol in Aug'85 by Capitol Records. Distributed by: EMI

Cassette: released on Capitol in Aug'85 by Capitol Records. Distributed by: EMI

Single (7"): released on Capitol in Aug'85 by Capitol Records. Distributed by: EMI

Single (12"): released on Capitol in Aug'85 by Capitol Records. Distributed by: EMI

GIVE AND TAKE.
Single (7"): released on Capitol in Oct'85 by Capitol Records. Distributed by: EMI

Single (12"): released on Capitol in Oct'85 by Capitol Records. Distributed by: EMI

INTERNATIONAL.
Single (7"): released on Capitol in Oct'84 by Capitol Records. Distributed by: EMI

Single (12"): released on Capitol in Oct'84 by Capitol Records. Distributed by: EMI Deleted '86.

PARTYLINE.
Single (12"): released on Capitol in Jun'84 by Capitol Records. Distributed by: EMI Deleted '86.

WALKIN' THE LINE.
Single (7"): released on Capitol in May'83 by Capitol Records. Distributed by: EMI

Single (12"): released on Capitol in May'83 by Capitol Records. Distributed by: EMI Deleted '85.

WE CAN WORK IT OUT.
Single (7"): released on Capitol in Jul'83 by Capitol Records. Distributed by: EMI

Single (12"): released on Capitol in Jul'83 by Capitol Records. Distributed by: EMI

Brassens, Georges

GEORGES BRASSENS.
Tracks: / Les compains d'abord / La demande en mariage / Le petit joueur de flateau / La route aux 4 chansons / Les 4 z'arts / Le pornographe / Le temps ne fait rien a l'affaire / Supplique pour etre enterre a la plaga de sete / Le trompettes de la renommee / Jeanne / Dans l'eau de la Claire Fontaine / Lew quarte bacheliers / Au bois de mon coeur / Le grand chene / Aupres de mon arbre / Chanson pour l'auvergnat.
Cassette: released on Philips (France) in Sep'86

Brass Fiddle

BRASS FIDDLE, THE (Various Artists).
Album: released on Claddagh in Jul'87 by Claddagh Records. Distributed by: I & B, Record Services Distribution (Ireland), Roots, Topic, Impetus, Projection, CM

Brass Impact

BRASS IMPACT.
Album: released on Coda in Feb'85 by Coda Records. Distributed by: Pinnacle, Cartel, WEA, Roots

Cassette: released on Coda in Feb'85 by Coda Records. Distributed by: Pinnacle, Cartel, WEA, Roots

Brass Monkey

BRASS MONKEY.
Tracks: / Watermans hornpipe / Fable of the wings / Millers three sons / Maid and the palmer / Bad news / Sovay / Tip top hornpipe-Primrose polka / Jolly bold robber / Old grenadier.
Album: released on Topic in '83. Distributed by: Roots Distribution

SEE HOW IT RUNS.
Tracks: / Wailing On The Wire / Count On Angels / Warmest kiss (The).
Album: released on Topic in Nov'86. Distributed by: Roots Distribution

Brass Target

BRASS TARGET Film soundtrack.
Album: released on Varese in Mar'79. Distributed by: Swift

Bratter, Henri

MADAME LEROY.
Single (7"): released on Red Bus in Jun'84 by Red Bus Records. Distributed by: PRT

Brat, The

CHALK DUST - THE UMPIRE STRIKES BACK.
Single (7"): released on Ariola in Sep'82. Distributed by: RCA,

Braun, Steve

LOVE COULD BE SO GOOD.
Tracks: / Love could be so good / Red light districts.
Single (7"): released on Numa in Jun'86 by Numa Records. Distributed by: PRT Distribution

Single (12"): released on Numa in Jun'86 by Numa Records. Distributed by: PRT Distribution

OUT TO PLAY (Braun, Steve Universe).
Single (7"): released on Universe in Mar'82

WHEN I SEE YOUR EYES.
Tracks: / When I see your eyes / Out to play.
Single (7"): released on Numa in Jan'86 by Numa Records. Distributed by: PRT Distribution

Single (12"): released on Numa in Jan'86 by Numa Records. Distributed by: PRT Distribution

Brave Combo

PEOPLE ARE STRANGE.
Notes: 6-track 12" 45
Single (12"): released on Rogue in Jan'86 by Fast Forward Records. Distributed by: Nine Mile Distribution, Cartel Distribution

Brave Little Tailor

BRAVE LITTLE TAILOR (Pleasance, Donald).
Cassette: released on Kiddy Kassettes in Aug'77

Brave New World

SUPERHERO.
Single (7"): released on Tristar in Jul'83 by Tristar Records. Distributed by: Pinnacle

Braxton, Anthony

1-OQA + 19.
Album: released on Black Saint in Jul'78. Distributed by: Projection, IMS, Polygram, Chris Wellard, Harmonia Mundi, Swift

3 COMPOSITIONS OF NEW JAZZ.
Album: . Distributed by: Projection, Swift, Cadillac

ANTHONY BRAXTON.
Album: released on Affinity in '78 by Charly Records. Distributed by: Charly, Cadillac

CREATIVE CONSTRUCTION COMPANY.
Album: released on Muse in Apr'81 by Peerless Records. Distributed by: Lugtons Distributors

CREATIVE CONSTRUCTION COMPANY VOL 2.
Album: released on Muse in Apr'81 by Peerless Records.
tors

CREATIVE MUSIC ORCHESTRA.
Triple album / cassette: released on Ring in Jul'78. Distributed by: Cadillac

FOUR COMPOSITIONS (1973).
Album: released on Denon in Mar'82 by Denon Records. Distributed by: Harmonia Mundi

LIVE - MOERS FESTIVAL 74.
Double Album: released on Ring in Jul'78. Distributed by: Cadillac

MAX ROACH & ANTHONY BRAXTON (Braxton, Anthony & Max Roach).
Tracks: / Birth / Magic and music / Tropical forest / Dance griot / Spirit possession / Soft show / Rebirth.
Notes: Anthony Braxton-saxaphone and clarinet. Max Roach-drums
Album: released on Black Saint in Apr'79. Distributed by: Projection, IMS, Polygram, Chris Wellard, Harmonia Mundi, Swift

ROYAL VOL 1 (Braxton, Anthony & Derek Bailey).
Album: released on Incus in '84. Distributed by: Jazz Music, Cadillac

SIX COMPOSITIONS (QUARTET) 1984.
Compact disc: released on Black Saint (Italy) in Jan'86. Distributed by: Target, Jazz Music,

SOLO - LIVE AT MOERS FESTIVAL, 74.
Album: released on Ring in Jul'78. Distributed by: Cadillac

THIS TIME.
Album: released on Affinity in Jan'80 by Charly Records. Distributed by: Charly, Cadillac

TOGETHER ALONE (Braxton, Anthony & J. Jarman).
Album: released on Delmark in Jul'75. Distributed by: Projection, Swift, Cadillac

TRIO & DUET.
Notes: Artists include: D.Holland/Leo Smith/R.Teitelbaum
Album: released on Sackville in Jul'86. Distributed by: Jazz Music, Jazz Horizons, Cadillac Music, Celtic Music, Swift

Braxton, Dhar

JUMP BACK (SET ME FREE).
Tracks: / Jump back (set me free) / Jump back (set me free)(backappella).
Single (7"): released on Fourth & Broadway in May'86 by Island Records. Distributed by: Polygram, EMI

Single (12"): released on Fourth & Broadway in May'86 by Island Records. Distributed by: Polygram, EMI

Brazil

BLACK MUSIC OF BAHAI (Various Artists).
Album: released on Albatross(Italy) in Jul'84

Cassette: released on Albatross(Italy) in Jul'84

NUTS FROM BRAZIL/GIVE YOUR LOVE.
Single (7"): released on Spellbound in May'83 by Spellbound Records. Distributed by: CBS

SLIP AWAY.
Single (7"): released on G.A.P. in Aug'85 by G.A.P. Records. Distributed by: Revolver, Cartel

WHO'S GONNA LOVE YOU NOW.
Single (7"): released on MCA in Oct'80 by MCA Records. Distributed by: Polygram, MCA

Brazil Today

BRAZIL TODAY (Various Artists).
Album: released on Polydor (Holland) in Dec'83

Cassette: released on Polydor (Holland) in Dec'83

BRAZIL TODAY VOLUME 2 (Various Artists).
Album: released on Verve (USA) in Mar'85 by Polydor. Distributed by: Polygram

Cassette: released on Verve (USA) in Mar'85 by Polydor. Distributed by: Polygram

Brazil, Tom

SIVUCA.
Album: released on Sonet in Nov'85 by Sonet Records. Distributed by: PRT

B & R Brass Band

IN A CLASSICAL MOOD.
Cassette: released on Autograph in May'86. Distributed by: Record Services Distribution (Ireland)

Bread

BABY I'M A WANT YOU.
Album: released on Elektra (USA) in Nov'76 by Elektra/Asylum/Nonesuch Records. Distributed by: WEA

BABY I'M A WANT YOU (7").
Single (7"): released on Old Gold in Sep'85 by Old Gold Records. Distributed by: Lightning, Jazz Music, Spartan, Counterpoint

BEST OF BREAD VOL.1.
Album: released on Elektra (USA) in Nov'76 by Elektra/Asylum/Nonesuch Records. Distributed by: WEA

Cassette: released on Elektra (USA) in Nov'76 by Elektra/Asylum/Nonesuch Records. Distributed by: WEA

BEST OF BREAD VOL.2.
Album: released on Elektra (USA) in Nov'76 by Elektra/Asylum/Nonesuch Records. Distributed by: WEA

Cassette: released on Elektra (USA) in Nov'76 by Elektra/Asylum/Nonesuch Records. Distributed by: WEA

BEST OF VOL 1/VOL 2.
Cassette: released on Elektra (USA) in Nov'83 by Elektra/Asylum/Nonesuch Records. Distributed by: WEA

GUITAR MAN.
Album: released on Elektra (USA) in Nov'76 by Elektra/Asylum/Nonesuch Records. Distributed by: WEA

GUITAR MAN/BABY I'M A WANT YOU.
Single (7"): released on Elektra (USA) in Sep'76 by Elektra/Asylum/Nonesuch Records. Distributed by: WEA

IF/SWEET SURRENDER.
Single (7"): released on Elektra (USA) in Sep'76 by Elektra/Asylum/Nonesuch Records. Distributed by: WEA

LOST WITHOUT YOUR LOVE.
Album: released on Elektra (USA) in Jan'77 by Elektra/Asylum/Nonesuch Records. Distributed by: WEA

Cassette: released on Elektra (USA) in Jan'77 by Elektra/Asylum/Nonesuch Records. Distributed by: WEA

MAKE IT WITH YOU.
Single (7"): released on Old Gold in Sep'85 by Old Gold Records. Distributed by: Lightning, Jazz Music, Spartan, Counterpoint

MAKE IT WITH YOU/EVERYTHING I OWN.
Single (7"): released on Elektra (USA) in Sep'76 by Elektra/Asylum/Nonesuch Records. Distributed by: WEA

SOUND OF BREAD.
Album: released on Elektra (USA) in Oct'77 by Elektra/Asylum/Nonesuch Records. Distributed by: WEA

Cassette: released on Elektra (USA) in Oct'77 by Elektra/Asylum/Nonesuch Records. Distributed by: WEA

Compact disc: released on Elektra (USA) in Jan'87 by Elektra/Asylum/Nonesuch Records. Distributed by: WEA

Breakdance

BREAKDANCE Various artists (Various Artists).
Notes: The feature film about a young girl dancer and two hot black break-dancers who climbed to fame on a new music and dance style,with plenty of hip-hop music. Type of recording: Film
Total playing time: 88minutes.
Video-cassette (VHS): released on Guild in Sep'84 by Guild Records.

BREAKDANCE (SOUNDTRACK) (Various Artists).
Album: released on Polydor in Jun'87 by Polydor Records. Distributed by: Polygram,

Cassette: released on Polydor in Jun'87 by Polydor Records. Distributed by: Polygram,

YOU CAN DO IT.
Video-cassette (VHS): released on K-Tel in Sep'84 by K-Tel Records. Distributed by: Record Merchandisers Distribution, Taylors, Terry Blood Distribution, Wynd-Up Distribution, Relay Distribution, Pickwick Distribution, Solomon & Peres Distribution, Polygram

Breakdance 2

BREAKDANCE 2 - ELECTRIC BOOGALOO Various artists (Various Artists).
Tracks: / Electric boogaloo / Radiotron / Din daa daa / When I.C.U. / Gotta have the money / Believe in the beat / Set it out / I don't wanna come down / Stylin' profilin' / Oye Mamacita.
Compact disc: released on Polydor in Dec'84 by Polydor Records. Distributed by: Polygram,

Breakdance Fever

BREAKDANCE FEVER (Various Artists).
Album: released on Jive in Aug'84 by Zomba Records. Distributed by: RCA, PRT, CBS

Cassette: released on Jive in Aug'84 by Zomba Records. Distributed by: RCA, PRT, CBS

Breakdancing

BREAKDANCING (Various Artists).
Album: released on CBS in Feb'85 by CBS Records. Distributed by: CBS

Cassette: released on CBS in Feb'85 by CBS Records. Distributed by: CBS

Breakfast Band

DOLPHIN RIDE.
Album: released on Breakfast Music Records in Feb'82. Distributed by: PRT, Greyhound

FUNKSTERS/SUCH A FEELING.
Single (12"): released on Breakfast Music Records in Nov'83. Distributed by: PRT, Greyhound

SUCH A FEELING/DOZEN TIME DRAGON.
Single (7"): released on Breakfast Music Records in Sep'82. Distributed by: PRT, Greyhound

Single (12"): released on Breakfast Music Records in Sep'82. Distributed by: PRT, Greyhound

TOKYO SHUFFLE/BROADSIDE RHUMBA.
Single (7"): released on Breakfast Music Records in Mar'82. Distributed by: PRT, Greyhound

Single (12"): released on Breakfast Music Records in Mar'82. Distributed by: PRT, Greyhound

WATER'S EDGE.
Album: released on Making Waves in Sep'85 by Making Waves Records

Breakfast Club

BREAKFAST CLUB.
Tracks: / Never be the same / Right on track / Kiss and tell / Always be like this / Rico mambo / Express way to your heart / Speciality / Standout / Tongue tied.
Album: released on A&M in May'85 by A&M Records. Distributed by: Polygram

Cassette: released on A&M in May'85 by A&M Records. Distributed by: Polygram

Cassette: released on MCA in Mar'87 by MCA Records. Distributed by: Polygram, MCA

Album: released on MCA in Mar'87 by MCA Records. Distributed by: Polygram, MCA

Compact disc: released on MCA in Apr'87 by MCA Records. Distributed by: Polygram, MCA

RIGHT ON TRACK.
Tracks: / Right on track / Right on track (local mix).
Single (7"): released on MCA in 23 May'87 by MCA Records. Distributed by: Polygram, MCA

Single (12"): released on MCA in 23 May'87 by MCA Records. Distributed by: Polygram, MCA

Breakfast Of Champions

BREAKFAST OF CHAMPIONS (Vonnegut, Kurt).
Notes: Very funny book. Read by the author.
Cassette: released on Caedmon(USA) in Oct'79 by Caedmon(USA) Records. Distributed by: Taylors, Discovery

Breaking Circus

ICE MACHINE, THE.
Album: released on Homestead in Apr'87. Distributed by: Rough Trade, Cartel,

VERY LONG FUSE.
Album: released on Homestead in Jun'85. Distributed by: Rough Trade, Cartel,

Breaking Glass

BREAKING GLASS (O'Connor, Hazel).
Notes: Breaking Glass is the story of one girl's meteoric rise to stardom from the rock pubs of London to Bowie-style status.Kate(Hazel O'Connor) meets(Phil Daniels) in a back alley and offers his services as manager.Finally rock-stardom with it's demands and pressures bring Kate ,drugged and alone,to the brink,ready to c r a c k . Type of recording: Film
Total playing time: 104 minutes
Video-cassette (VHS): released on Picture Time Video in Sep'86. Distributed by: VCL

Breaking The Back Of Love

BREAKING THE BACK OF LOVE (Various Artists).
Album: released on Saderal in Aug'85. Distributed by: Nine Mile, Cartel

Breakin' In The U.S.A.

BREAKIN' IN THE U.S.A. Various artists (Various Artists).
Notes: A visual guide to the body-taxing art of break dancing,how to do it and how to look the part,courtesy of Shuzan Studios in New York. A 1985 production.
Total playing time: 60 minutes
Video-cassette (VHS): released on Central Communications in Jul'86 by Central Communications Records. Distributed by: Central Communications Records

Break Machine

ARE YOU READY.
Single (7"): released on Record Shack in Jul'84 by Record Shack Records. Distributed by: PRT

Single (12"): released on Record Shack in Jul'84 by Record Shack Records. Distributed by: PRT

BREAK MACHINE.
Album: released on Record Shack in '84 by Record Shack Records. Distributed by: PRT

Cassette: released on Record Shack in '84 by Record Shack Records. Distributed by: PRT

LET'S HAVE A BREAK DANCE PARTY.
Single (7"): released on Record Shack in May'84 by Record Shack Records. Distributed by: PRT

Single (12"): released on Record Shack in May'84 by Record Shack Records. Distributed by: PRT

STREET DANCE.
Single (7"): released on Record Shack in Jan'84 by Record Shack Records. Distributed by: PRT

Single (12"): released on Record Shack in Jan'84 by Record Shack Records. Distributed by: PRT

Breakout

BREAKOUT 22 roaring great hits by various original artists (Various Artists).
Album: released on Ronco in Aug'82

Cassette: released on Ronco in Aug'82

Breakwater

SAY YOU LOVE ME GIRL.
Tracks: / Say you love me girl / Work it out.
Single (7"): released on Arista in Sep'86 by Arista Records. Distributed by: RCA

Single (12"): released on Arista in Sep'86 by Arista Records. Distributed by: RCA

Bream, Julian

MUSIC OF SPAIN VOLS. 7 & 8.
Album: released on Red Seal in Jul'83 by RCA Records. Distributed by: RCA

Cassette: released on Red Seal in Jul'83 by RCA Records. Distributed by: RCA

PLAYS GRANADOS & ALBENIZ.
Compact disc: by RCA Records. Distributed by: RCA, Roots, Swift, Wellard, Chris, I & B, Solomon & Peres Distribution

Breant, Francois

SONS OPTIQUES.
Album: released on Egg in Nov'79. Distributed by: Red Rhino, Cartel

Breathe

DON'T TELL ME LIES.
Tracks: / Don't tell me lies / Moments.
Single (7"): released on Siren in Jan'86 by Virgin Records. Distributed by: EMI

Single (12"): released on Siren in Jan'86 by Virgin Records. Distributed by: EMI

JONAH.
Tracks: / Jonah / In all honesty.
Single (7"): released on Siren in 30 May'87 by Virgin Records. Distributed by: EMI

Single (12"): released on Siren in 30 May'87 by Virgin Records. Distributed by: EMI

Breathers

LIVIN' IN THE AGE AGE.
Single (7"): released on Diversion in Dec'80 by Dingle's

Breathless

2 DAYS FROM EDEN.
Single (12"): released on Tenor Vossa in Aug'85. Distributed by: Rough Trade Distribution

GLASS BEAD GAME, THE.
Album: released on Tenor Vossa in Jun'86. Distributed by: Rough Trade Distribution

NAILING COLOURS TO THE WHEEL (EP).
Tracks: / Bad Blood.
Single (12"): released on Tenor Vossa in Nov'86. Distributed by: Rough Trade Distribution

WATERLAND.
Single (7"): released on Tenor Vossa in Apr'84. Distributed by: Rough Trade Distribution

Brecker, Michael

MICHAEL BRECKER Z.
Tracks: / Sea glass / Syzygy / Choices / Nothing personal / Cost of living / Original rays.
Album: released on MCA in Jun'87 by MCA Records. Distributed by: Polygram, MCA

Cassette: released on MCA in Jun'87 by MCA Records. Distributed by: Polygram, MCA

Brecker, Randy

AMANDA (Brecker, Randy & Eliane Elias).
Tracks: / Splash / Para nada / Pandamandium / Samba de bamba / Amandamada / Guaruja.
Notes: P 1985 Randal E. Brecker. C 1986 Sonet Records Ltd.
Album: released on Sonet in Jul'86 by Sonet Records. Distributed by: PRT

AMANDA.
Compact disc: by Pacific Records (USA). Distributed by: Atlantic

Breen, Ann

ANN BREEN.
Album: released on Homespun(Ireland) in Nov'84 by Outlet Records. Distributed by: Outlet

Cassette: released on Homespun(Ireland) in Nov'84 by Outlet Records. Distributed by: Outlet

BLUE VIOLETS AND RED ROSES/TEDDY.
Single (7"): released on Homespun(Ireland) in Feb'83 by Outlet Records. Distributed by: Outlet

BREAKAWAY.
Single (7"): released on Homespun(Ireland) in Feb'85 by Outlet Records. Distributed by: Outlet

BUNCH OF VIOLETS BLUE.
Single (7"): released on Homespun(Ireland) in Nov'83 by Outlet Records. Distributed by: Outlet

BY THE SILVERY LIGHT OF THE MOON.
Single (7"): released on Homespun(Ireland) in Sep'82 by Outlet Records. Distributed by: Outlet

COLLECTION: ANN BREEN.
Cassette: released on Play in Nov'86 by Play Records. Distributed by: Spartan

Album: released on Play in Nov'86 by Play Records. Distributed by: Spartan

COUNTRY SONG BIRD.
Album: released on Homespun(Ireland) in '82 by Outlet Records. Distributed by: Outlet

Cassette: released on Homespun(Ireland) in '82 by Outlet Records. Distributed by: Outlet

DEAR LITTLE BOY OF MINE.
Single (7"): released on Homespun(Ireland) in Jul'82 by Outlet Records. Distributed by: Outlet

DIVIDED WE FALL.
Tracks: / Divided we fall / Divided we fall (instrumental).
Single (7"): released on Play in Mar'87 by Play Records. Distributed by: Spartan

DOMINO.
Tracks: / Domino (easy listening mix) / Domino (slap remix).
Single (7"): released on Play in Sep'86 by Play Records. Distributed by: Spartan

Single (12"): released on Play in Sep'86 by Play Records. Distributed by: Spartan

GENTLE MOTHER/BUNCH OF VIOLETS BLUE.
Single (7"): released on Homespun(Ireland) in Oct'83 by Outlet Records. Distributed by: Outlet

GIVE ME ONE GOOD REASON.
Single (7"): released on Homespun(Ireland) in May'84 by Outlet Records. Distributed by: Outlet

IF I HAD MY LIFE TO LIVE OVER.
Tracks: / If I had my life to live over / When you & I were young Maggie / Walk right back / I'll be your sweetheart / Will you still love me tomorrow / Save the last dance for me / Have you ever been lonely / I just called to say I love you / Who's sorry now / It's a sin to tell a lie / Among my souvenirs / You always hurt the one you love.
Album: released on Homespun(Ireland) in May'87 by Outlet Records. Distributed by: Outlet

Cassette: released on Homespun(Ireland) in May'87 by Outlet Records. Distributed by: Outlet

I'LL BE YOUR SWEETHEART.
Album: released on Homespun(Ireland) in Sep'85 by Outlet Records. Distributed by: Outlet

Cassette: released on Homespun(Ireland) in Sep'85 by Outlet Records. Distributed by: Outlet

IRISH STYLE.
Tracks: / Gentle mother / Noreen Bawn / Two loves / Cottage by the lee / Moon behind the hill / I'll remember you love in my prayers / Sninning wheel / Bunch of violets blue / Too ra loo ra loo ra (That's an Irish lullaby) / Old rustic bridge by the mill / When you and I were young Maggie / By the light of the silvery moon / Spinning wheel / Bunch of violets blue / By the bright silvery light of the moon.
Album: released on Homespun(Ireland) in Jun'87 by Outlet Records. Distributed by: Outlet

Cassette: released on Homespun(Ireland) in Jun'87 by Outlet Records. Distributed by: Outlet

LOVE BY LOVE.
Single (7"): released on Homespun(Ireland) in Sep'84 by Outlet Records. Distributed by: Outlet

MEDALS FOR MOTHERS.
Tracks: / Pal of my cradle days / Among my souvenirs / Gentle mother / It's a sin to tell a lie / What a friend we have in mother / Noreen Bawn / Medals for mothers / Two loves / When you & I were young Maggie / If I had my life to live over / Carolina moon / Boy of mine,(Dear little).
Album: released on Homespun(Ireland) in Nov'86 by Outlet Records. Distributed by: Outlet

Cassette: released on Homespun(Ireland) in Nov'86 by Outlet Records. Distributed by: Outlet

PAL OF MY CRADLE DAYS(SINGLE).
Tracks: / Pal of my cradle days / Love is teasin'.
Single (7"): released on Homespun(Ireland) in Mar'86 by Outlet Records. Distributed by: Outlet

PAL OF MY CRADLE DAYS.
Tracks: / Those brown eyes / Who's sorry now / Blue Kentucky girl / You needed me / Two loves / What a friend we have in mother / Walk right back / Save the last dance for me / Love is teasin' / Pal of my cradle days / Hey good looking / Heart you break will be your own.
Album: released on Homespun(Ireland) in Aug'86 by Outlet Records. Distributed by: Outlet

Cassette: released on Homespun(Ireland) in Aug'86 by Outlet Records. Distributed by: Outlet

QUE SERA SERA.
Single (7"): released on Homespun(Ireland) in Oct'84 by Outlet Records. Distributed by: Outlet

SAVE THE LAST DANCE FOR ME/RUSTIC BRIDGE.
Single (7"): released on Homespun(Ireland) in Jan'84 by Outlet Records. Distributed by: Outlet

TEDDY BEAR/BLUE VIOLETS & RED ROSES.
Single (7"): released on Homespun(Ireland) in Nov'82 by Outlet Records. Distributed by: Outlet

THIS ALBUM IS JUST FOR YOU.
Album: released on Homespun(Ireland) in Aug'84 by Outlet Records. Distributed by: Outlet

Cassette: released on Homespun(Ireland) in Aug'84 by Outlet Records. Distributed by: Outlet

THOSE BROWN EYES/LOVE IS TEASIN'.
Single (7"): released on Homespun(Ireland) in Jul'81 by Outlet Records. Distributed by: Outlet

TWO LOVES/HEART YOU BREAK WILL.....
Single (7"): released on Homespun(Ireland) in Sep'82 by Outlet Records. Distributed by: Outlet

WHAT A FRIEND WE HAVE IN MOTHER.
Single (7"): released on Homespun(Ireland) in Sep'82 by Outlet Records. Distributed by: Outlet

YOU ALWAYS HURT THE ONE YOU LOVE.
Single (7"): released on Homespun(Ireland) in Jun'83 by Outlet Records. Distributed by: Outlet

Breen, Paddy

RAMBLING IRISHMAN.
Cassette: released on Folktracks in Nov'79 by Folktracks Cassettes. Distributed by: Folktracks

Breeze

MIDNIGHT LADIES.
Single (7"): released on Breeze in Aug'83 by Pinnacle Records. Distributed by: Pinnacle

Single (12"): released on Breeze in Aug'83 by Pinnacle Records. Distributed by: Pinnacle

Breeze From Erin

BREEZE FROM ERIN Irish folk music on wind instruments (Various Artists).
Album: released on Topic in '81. Distributed by: Roots Distribution

Brel, Jacques

BREL ALIVE IN PARIS.

Double Album: released on Vanguard in Aug'86 by PRT Records. Distributed by: PRT

CHANSON FRANCAISE, (LA).
Tracks: / J'aimais / Vasoul / Ces gens la / Amsterdam / Chanson des vieux amants, (La) / Flamendes, (Les) / Plat pays, (La) / Quand on n'a que l'amour / Paumes du petit matin, (Les) / Jef.
Album: released on Barclay in Nov'79 by Decca Records. Distributed by: Polygram, Discovery, Conifer, IMS, Swift

JACQUES BREL.
Tracks: / Les prenoms de Paris / Clara / On n'oublie rien / Les singes / Madeleine / Les biches / Les paumes du petit matin / Zangra / La statue / Les bourgeois / Marieke / Ne me quitte pas / Le prochain amour / Le morribond / Au printemps / La colombe / Les flamandes / L'Ivrogne / La valse a mille temps / Mivre debout.
Cassette: released on Philips (France) in Sep'86

MARQUISES, (LES).
Tracks: / Jaures / Ville s'endormait, (La) / Vieilir / Bon dieu, (Le) / F... Orly / Remparts de varsovie, (Les) / Voir un ami pleurer / Knokke-le-zoute tango / Jojo / Lion, (Le) / Marquises, (Les).
Compact disc: released on Phonogram in '84 by Phonogram Records. Distributed by: Polygram

MUSIC FOR THE MILLIONS.
Album: released on Philips Import in Apr'83

Cassette: released on Philips Import in Apr'83

NE ME QUITTE PAS.
Tracks: / Ne me quitte pas / Marieke / On n'oublie rien / Les flamandes / Les prenoms de Paris / Quand on n'a l'amour / Les biches / Le prochain amour / Le moribond / La valise a mille temps / Je ne sais pas.
Compact disc: by Phonogram Records. Distributed by: Polygram

Compact disc: released on Phonogram Import in Jul'85

SES PLUS GRANDES CHANSONS.
Tracks: / Madeleine / L'Ivrogne / La valise a mille temps / Ne me quitte pas / Le moribond / Les bourgeois / Les flamandes / Marieke / Buxelles / Le plat pays / La Dame Patronesse / Les vieux / Rosa / Mathilde / I'l neige sur liege / J'aimais / Amsterdam.
Album:

Cassette:

Bremner, Billy

ENDLESS SLEEP.
Single (7"): released on Rock City in Feb'85 by Brian Adams. Distributed by: Pinnacle

LAUGHTER TURNS TO TEARS.
Single (7"): released on Stiff in Feb'82 by Stiff Records. Distributed by: EMI, Record Services Distribution (Ireland)

LOUD MUSIC IN CARS.
Single (7"): released on Stiff in Sep'81 by Stiff Records. Distributed by: EMI, Record Services Distribution (Ireland)

LOVE GOES TO SLEEP.
Single (7"): released on Arista in Apr'84 by Arista Records. Distributed by: RCA

Single (12"): released on Arista in Apr'84 by Arista Records. Distributed by: RCA

MEEK POWER.
Single (7"): released on Demon in Aug'82 by Demon Records. Distributed by: Pinnacle

SHATTERPROOF.
Single (7"): released on Arista in Feb'84 by Arista Records. Distributed by: RCA

Single (12"): released on Arista in Feb'84 by Arista Records. Distributed by: RCA

Brenda & The Big Dudes

AMALAHLE.
Tracks: / Amalahle / Bongani / Weekend special (ext. version).
Notes: Weekend special (Ext. Version) is an extra track only available on 12" version.
Single (7"): released on EMI in Mar'87 by EMI Records. Distributed by: EMI

Single (12"): released on EMI in Mar'87 by EMI Records. Distributed by: EMI

BONGANI.
Tracks: / Bongani(remix) / Higher.
Single (7"): released on Family in Feb'86 by Priority Records. Distributed by: Priority, EMI

Single (12"): released on Family in Feb'86 by Priority Records. Distributed by: Priority, EMI

WEEKEND SPECIAL.
Tracks: / Weekend special / Weekend special(instrumental).
Single (7"): released on EMI in Jul'86 by EMI Records. Distributed by: EMI

Single (12"): released on EMI in Jul'86 by EMI Records. Distributed by: EMI

Brennan, Dave

AMAZING GRACE.
Album: by Wellard, Chris Distribution. Distributed by: Wellard, Chris Distribution

BOUNCING AROUND.
Album: by Wellard, Chris Distribution. Distributed by: Wellard, Chris Distribution

Brennan, Lee

SHUT YER GOB.
Single (7"): released on Rox in Apr'81 by Rox Records. Distributed by: Spartan Distribution

Brent, Michael

SWEET SENSATION.
Tracks: / From this moment on / Certain smile, A / Vienna,city of my dreams / Under Paris skies / Tulips from Amsterdam / Country gardens / Misty / Stairway to the stars / You made me love you / Time after time / I got rhythm / Liza / Someone to watch over me / Why did I choose you / Scotland the brave / Ash grove, The / Come to the food / Londonderry / One note samba / Wish me luck as you wave me goodbye.
Album: released on Grosvenor in Oct'81 by Grosvenor Records. Distributed by: Taylors

Cassette: released on Grosvenor in Oct'81 by Grosvenor Records. Distributed by: Taylors

Brett, Adrian

MELLOW MUSIC (Brett, Adrian & The Brian Rogers Orchestra).
Tracks: / Cavatina / Portsmouth / Scarborough Fair / New World theme / Don't cry for me Argentina / Danny boy / Shepherd song / Yesterday once more / Scarlet ribbons / Mull of Kintyre / Elizabethan serenade / Yesterday / Morning has broken / Sleepy shores / Greensleeves / Sailing / Dance to your daddy / Send in the clowns / Skye boat song, The / Annie's song.
Notes: Bar code 5 012106 220133
Compact disc: released on Warwick Reflections in Jun'86 by Warwick Records

Album: released on Warwick Reflections in Jun'86 by Warwick Records

Cassette: released on Warwick Reflections in Jun'86 by Warwick Records

Brett, Ann & Ray

SOMEBODY LOVES YOU.
Album: released on Sweet Folk Country in Nov'76. Distributed by: Chris Wellard Distribution

THERE'S NO MORE YOU AND ME.
Single (7"): released on A & R in Jun'83. Distributed by: Spartan

Brewer, Jim

JIM BREWER.
Album: released on Philo in May'79. Distributed by: Roots

Brewer, Teresa

BEST OF TERESA BREWER, THE.
Tracks: / Till I waltz again with you / Let me go love / You send me / Empty arms / Jilted / Empty arms / Jilted / Mutal admiration society / Sweet old fashioned girl / Pledging my love / A tear fell / I gotta go get my baby / Bell bottom blues / Bo weevil / The Hula Hoop song / Richochet / Anymore / Music music music.
Album: released on MCA in Dec'81 by MCA Records. Distributed by: Polygram, MCA

Cassette: released on MCA in Dec'81 by MCA Records. Distributed by: Polygram, MCA

GOLDEN GREATS: TERESA BREWER.
Tracks: / Music music music / Let me go lover / Till I waltz again with you / A tear fell / A sweet old fashioned girl.
Album: released on MCA in Jul'85 by MCA Records. Distributed by: Polygram, MCA

Cassette: released on MCA in Jul'85 by MCA Records. Distributed by: Polygram, MCA

GOOD NEWS.
Tracks: / Good news / I want to be bad / Button up your overcoat / Sunny-side up / Lucky in love / Varsity drag / Just imagine / Together / You're the cream in my coffee / The best things in life are free.
Album: released on Doctor Jazz (USA) in Jun'84 by Doctor Jazz Records. Distributed by: CBS

Album: released on Doctor Jazz (USA) in Jun'84 by Doctor Jazz Records. Distributed by: CBS

I DIG BIG BAND SINGERS.
Tracks: / Classic medley(A tisket A Tasket) / Got a date with an angel / Goo-hoo / I'm looking over a four leaf clover / Glenn Miller Medley / Chattanooga Choo-Choo / Juke box Saturday night / Pennsylvania 6-5000 / (I've got a girl in)Kalamazoo / Elmer's tune / Don't sit under the apple tree / Benny Goodman medley / And the Angels sing / Why don't you do right / Goody goody / Goodnight my love / Gotta be this or that / Loch Lomond / Jimmy Dorsey Medley / Tangerine / Amapola / Besame mucho / Green eyes / Classic Medley / I've heard that song before / In a shanty in old Shanty town / Daddy / Ragtime Cowby Joe / 'taint what you do (It's the way that you do it) / I'm beginning to see the light / Tommy Dorsey Medley / On the sunny side of the street / Oh look at me now / Chicago / Yes indeed / Let's get away from it all / Deed I do / Marie.
Album: released on Doctor Jazz (USA) in Oct'83 by Doctor Jazz Records. Distributed by: CBS

Cassette: released on Doctor Jazz (USA) in Oct'83 by Doctor Jazz Records. Distributed by: CBS

LIVE AT CARNEGIE HALL & MONTREUX, SWITZERLAND.
Tracks: / It don't mean a thing if it ain't got that swing / Breakin' up is hard to do / St. Louis Blues / After you've gone / It had to be you / I've got a crush on you / Romance in the dark / Mood indigo / Some songs / That's when the music takes me / I ain't got nobody / Baby won't you please come home / We love you Fats / Ain't misbehavin' / Find out what they like / The joint is jumping / Come on and drive me crazy / It don't mean a thing if it ain't got that swing / Mood indigo / St Louis Blues / New Orleans.
Album: released on Doctor Jazz (USA) in May'85 by Doctor Jazz Records. Distributed by: CBS

Cassette: released on Doctor Jazz (USA) in May'85 by Doctor Jazz Records. Distributed by: CBS

ON THE ROAD AGAIN (Brewer, Teresa & Stephane Grappelli).
Tracks: / On the road again / It had to be you / Come on and drive me crazy / Them there eyes / Smile / After you've gone / I love a violin / Don't take your love from me / As time goes by.
Album: released on Doctor Jazz (USA) in Jan'84 by Doctor Jazz Records. Distributed by: CBS

Cassette: released on Doctor Jazz (USA) in Jan'84 by Doctor Jazz Records. Distributed by: CBS

TERESA BREWER.
Cassette: released on Audio Fidelity in Oct'84. Distributed by: PRT

TERESA BREWER IN LONDON.
Tracks: / Music music music / The pilgrim-chapter 23 / Another useless day / Up on cripple creek / Music to the man / Come running / Saturday night / Hot damn home made wine / School days / Whupin' it.
Album: released on Signature in Oct'84 by PRT Records. Distributed by: PRT

Cassette: released on Signature in Oct'84 by PRT Records. Distributed by: PRT

WHEN YOUR LOVER HAS GONE.
Tracks: / When your lover has gone / Maybe you'll be there / I had the craziest dream / Darn that dream / Baby don't be mad at me / Faded Summer dream / Mixed emotions / You go to my head / More than you know / Music Maestro please / Time out for tears / Fools rush in.
Album: released on Jasmine in Oct'84 by Jasmine Records. Distributed by: Counterpoint, Taylor, H.R., Wellard, Chris, Swift, Cadillac

Brian & Michael

MAMA (Brian & Michael with St Winifred's School Choir).
Single (7"): released on RCA in Nov'83 by RCA Records. Distributed by: RCA, Roots, Swift, Wellard, Chris, I & B, Solomon & Peres Distribution

MATCHSTALK MEN AND MATCHSTALK CATS AND DOGS.
Single (7"): released on Old Gold in Apr'83 by Old Gold Records. Distributed by: Lightning, Jazz Music, Spartan, Counterpoint

Single (7"): released on PRT in Dec'77 by PRT Records. Distributed by: PRT

Brian & Zan

PUMP YOUR BODY.
Single (7"): released on Sound Of New York in Jul'83 by Sound Of New York Records. Distributed by: PRT

Single (12"): released on Sound Of New York in Jul'83 by Sound Of New York Records. Distributed by: PRT

Briar

EDGE OF A BROKEN HEART.
Tracks: / Edge of a broken heart / Don't forget me when you're on your island / Boys are back in town, The*.
Single (7"): released on PRT in Jul'87 by PRT Records. Distributed by: PRT

EDGE OF A BROKEN HEART (ROCK MIX).
Tracks: / Edge of a broken heart (rock mix) / Edge of a broken heart (radio mix) / Boys are back in town, (The).
Single (12"): released on PRT in Jul'87 by PRT Records. Distributed by: PRT

EDGE OF A BROKEN HEART.
Single (7"): released on PRT in Aug'87 by PRT Records. Distributed by: PRT

Picture disc single: released on PRT in Aug'87 by PRT Records. Distributed by: PRT

ONE MORE CHANCE.
Single (7"): released on FM in Aug'85 by FM-Revolver Records. Distributed by: EMI

TOO YOUNG.
Album: released on Heavy Metal in Aug'85 by FM-Revolver Records. Distributed by: EMI

Brideshead Revisited

BRIDESHEAD REVISITED Waugh, Evelyn (Gielgud, Sir John).
Cassette: released on Argo (Spokenword) in Jul'82 by Decca Records. Distributed by: Polygram

BRIDESHEAD REVISITED Original Soundtrack.
Compact disc: released on Chrysalis in May'87 by Chrysalis Records. Distributed by: CBS

Album: released on Chrysalis in Nov'81 by Chrysalis Records. Distributed by: CBS

Cassette: released on Chrysalis in Nov'81 by Chrysalis Records. Distributed by: CBS

Bride, The

BRIDE, THE Original soundtrack (Various Artists).
Album: released on Colosseum (West Germany) in Jan'86. Distributed by: Silva Screen

Bridge

BABY DON'T HOLD YOUR LOVE BACK.
Single (7"): released on Atlantic in Jul'85 by WEA Records. Distributed by: WEA Deleted '86.

Single (12"): released on Atlantic in Jul'85 by WEA Records. Distributed by: WEA

INDUSTRIAL LOVE DANCE.
Single (7"): released on Second Vision in May'84 by Second Vision Records. Distributed by: Pinnacle

Single (12"): released on Second Vision in May'84 by Second Vision Records. Distributed by: Pinnacle

SALT IN MY WOUNDS.
Single (12"): released on Legacy in Aug'87. Distributed by: PRT

SHAME IS A GIRL.
Tracks: / Shame is a girl / Loveless (The).
Single (7"): released on Backs in Mar'87 by Backs Records. Distributed by: Backs, Cartel

Bridge Ceili Band

BRIDGE CEILI BAND.
Cassette: released on Hawk in Mar'77 by Dolphin Records. Distributed by: I & B, Celtic Music, Solomon & Peres Distribution

Bridge on the River Kwai

BRIDGE ON THE RIVER KWAI Boulle, Pierre (Mills, Sir John).
Cassette: by Chivers Sound & Vision. Distributed by: Chivers Sound & Vision

Bridges, Alicia

I LOVE THE NIGHTLIFE.
Single (7"): released on Polydor in Aug'87 by Polydor Records. Distributed by: Polygram, Polydor

Single (12"): released on Polydor in Aug'87 by Polydor Records. Distributed by: Polygram, Polydor

Bridges, Calvin

ROSE OF SHARON.
Tracks: / Rose of Sharon / Rse of Sharon (inst).
Single (7"): released on Bluebird in Apr'87 by Bluebird Records. Distributed by: EMI, Jetstar

Bridges, Slim

ROCKING GOOSE.
Single (7"): released on Circus in Nov'81. Distributed by: Circus, Recommended

Bridgewater Brothers

GENERATIONS SUITE.

Tracks: / African sunrise / Bororo / Sade / Synapse / Your ballad / Something I saw thru my mind / Samba para ustedos dos.
Album: released on Denon in Mar'82 by Denon Records. Distributed by: Harmonia Mundi

LIGHTNING AND THUNDER.
Tracks: / Silent rain / Dear trane / Lightning and thunder.
Album: released on Denon in Mar'82 by Denon Records. Distributed by: Harmonia Mundi

Bridgewater, Dee Dee

LIVE IN PARIS.
Tracks: / All blues / Misty / On a clear day / Dr. Feelgood / There is no greater love / Here's that rainy day / Medley blues / Cherokee.
Album: released on Affinity in Apr'87 by Charly Records. Distributed by: Charly, Cadillac

Compact disc: released on Charly in Jun'87 by Charly Records. Distributed by: Charly, Cadillac

Cassette: released on Affinity in Apr'87 by Charly Records. Distributed by: Charly, Cadillac

Brief Lives

BRIEF LIVES Aubrey, John (Dotrice, Roy).
Double cassette: released on Argo (Spokenword) in Jul'83 by Decca Records. Distributed by: Polygram

Brigade of Brass

FIRST IN LINE.
Single (7"): released on Bulldog in Jul'82 by Bulldog Records. Distributed by: President Distribution, Spartan, Swift, Taylor, H.R.

Brigadier Jerry

JAH JAH YOU PAIN.
Single (12"): released on Jwyanza in Dec'82. Distributed by: Jetstar

JAMAICA JAMAICA.
Tracks: / Jamaica Jamaica / Jah jah move / Jah love music / Give thanks & praise / Everyman a me brethren / Kushunpeng / Armagiddeon style / Three blind mice.
Notes: This long-awaited LP is entitled 'Jamaica Jamaica'.As the top ranking DJ on the Jah Love Sound System in Kingston for many years,Brigadier Jerry has been perhaps the most popular of all DJ's on the dance hall cassettes which are so sought after,and it is perhaps surprising that this is ,in fact,his first studio album.
Album: released on RAS in Jan'86

Single (12"): released on Jah Love in Sep'84 by Jah Love Records. Distributed by: Jetstar

LIVE AT THE CONTROLS.
Album: released on Vista Sounds in '83 by Vista Sounds Records. Distributed by: Jetstar

Brigadoon

BRIGADOON (Various Artists).
Tracks: / Almost Like Being in Love / There But For You Go I / Brigadoon / Prologue / Down on Mac Connachy Square / Heather on the hill, The / Waitin' for my Dearie / I'll go Home with Bonnie Jean / Come to me, Bend me.
Album: released on CBS in Feb'87 by CBS Records. Distributed by: CBS

Cassette: released on CBS in Feb'87 by CBS Records. Distributed by: CBS

Brigandage

PRETTY LITTLE THING.
Album: released on Gungho in Nov'86. Distributed by: Pinnacle

Briggs, Anne

ANNE BRIGGS.
Tracks: / Blackwater side / The snow it melts the soonest / Willie o'Winsbury / Go your way / Thorneymoor woods / The cuckoo / Reynardine / Young tambling / Living by the water / Maa bonny lad.
Album: released on Topic in '81. Distributed by: Roots Distribution

BIRD IN THE BUSH (Briggs, Anne, Lloyd & Armstrong).
Album: . Distributed by: Roots Distribution

Briggs, Brian

BRIAN DAMAGE.
Tracks: / Lookin' out / Nervous breakdown / See you on the other side / AEO (parts 1 & 2) / Psyclone / Goin' out of my head / Spy vs spy / Let me hear me talkin' / Lifer.
Album: released on Bearsville (USA) in Dec'81 by Warner Bros Records. Distributed by: WEA

Cassette: released on Bearsville (USA) in Dec'81 by Warner Bros Records. Distributed by: WEA

COMBAT ZONE.
Album: released on Bearsville (USA) in Jun'82 by Warner Bros Records. Distributed by: WEA

Cassette: released on Bearsville (USA) in Jun'82 by Warner Bros Records. Distributed by: WEA

LOOKIN' OUT.
Single (7"): released on Avatar in Jan'82 by Avatar Communications. Distributed by: CBS

Briggs, Lloyd

BIRDS IN THE BUSH (see under Armstrong, Frankie) (Briggs, Lloyd/Frankie Armstrong).

Brighouse...

BRASS MASTERPIECES (Brighouse & Rastrick Band).
Notes: 3 albums of brass band recordings including many classical and other favourites from the brass band repertoire. 3 albums.3 cassettes.
Triple album / cassette: released on Avon in Nov'85 by Avon Records. Distributed by: Counterpoint

Triple album / cassette: released on Avon in Nov'85 by Avon Records. Distributed by: Counterpoint

Brighten The Corner...

BRIGHTEN THE CORNER WHERE YOU ARE Various artists (Various Artists).
Tracks: / God shall wipe all tears away / Canaan land / Walk around / Tree of level / Yield not to temptation / Daniel in the lions den(he locked the lion's jaw) / Give me wings / They led my Lord away / We're marching to Zion / Jesus is all the world to me / Ninety & nine, The / To God be the glory / Brighten the corner where you are / In the garden / Nearer,my God to thee(Bethany) / Saved by grace / Just as I am, without one plea(Woodworth).
Notes: MONO recording.
Album: released on New World (USA) in Jul'86 by New World Records (USA). Distributed by: Conifer

Bright, Greg

I'M A BELIEVER.
Single (7"): released on Rat Race in Aug'80

Bright, June

NO PLACE CALLED HOME.
Single (7"): released on In Tape in Nov'85 by In Tape Records. Distributed by: Red Rhino, Cartel

Single (12"): released on In Tape in Nov'85 by In Tape Records. Distributed by: Red Rhino, Cartel

Bright, Len Combo

LEN BRIGHT COMBO PRESENTS...,THE.
Notes: Full title :'The Len Bright Combo presents the Len Bright Combo'
Album: released on Empire in Feb'86 by Empire Records. Distributed by: Backs, Cartel, Jetstar

SOMEONE MUST HAVE NAILED US TOGETHER.
Tracks: / Someone must have nailed us together / Mona.
Single (7"): released on Empire in Apr'86 by Empire Records. Distributed by: Backs, Cartel, Jetstar

Brightman, Sarah

MUSIC OF THE NIGHT, THE (Brightman, Sarah & Micheal Crawford).
Notes: For full information see CRAWFORD, Micheal & Sarah Brightman

MY BOYFRIENDS BACK.
Single (7"): released on Whisper in Jul'81 by Whisper Records. Distributed by: Spartan

NOT HAVING THAT.
Single (7"): released on Whisper in Oct'81 by Whisper Records. Distributed by: Spartan

PHANTOM OF THE OPERA (Brightman, Sarah & Steve Harley).
Tracks: / Phantom of the opera, The / Overture-The phantom of the opera.
Single (7"): released on Polydor in Nov'85 by Polydor Records. Distributed by: Polygram, Polydor

Single (12"): released on Polydor in Nov'85 by Polydor Records. Distributed by: Polygram, Polydor

ROOM WITH A VIEW, A The theme from....
Single (7"): released on Polydor in May'87 by Polydor Records. Distributed by: Polygram, Polydor

UNEXPECTED SONG.
Single (7"): released on RCA in Sep'84 by RCA Records. Distributed by: RCA, Roots, Swift, Wellard, Chris, I & B, Solomon & Peres Distribution

Brighton Beach Memoirs

BRIGHTON BEACH MEMOIRS Original soundtrack (Various Artists).
Album: released on MCA in Feb'87 by MCA Records. Distributed by: Polygram, MCA

Cassette: released on MCA in Feb'87 by MCA Records. Distributed by: Polygram, MCA

Brighton Football Club

BOYS IN THE OLD BRIGHT BLUE (Brighton & Hove Albion Football Club).
Single (7"): released on Energy in May'83 by Energy Records. Distributed by: Jazz Music

Single (12"): released on Energy in May'83 by Energy Records. Distributed by: Jazz Music

Brighton, Ian

MARSH GAS.
Album: released on Bead in Nov'77. Distributed by: Cadillac

Brighton Rock

BRIGHTON ROCK.
Album: released on Atlantic in Feb'87 by WEA Records. Distributed by: WEA

Cassette: released on Atlantic in Feb'87 by WEA Records. Distributed by: WEA

YOUNG WILD AND FREE.
Tracks: / We Came To Rock / Game Of Love / Change Of Heart / Can't Wait For The Night / Assault Attack / Jack Is Back / Save Me / Nobody's Hero / Barricade / Rock 'N' Roll.
Album: released on WEA in Jan'87 by WEA Records. Distributed by: WEA

Brightsteen, Bill

IF IT MOVES FUNK IT.
Single (7"): released on Green Pea in Jul'85 by Green Pea Records. Distributed by: Pinnacle

Single (12"): released on Green Pea in Jul'85 by Green Pea Records. Distributed by: Pinnacle

Brightwell, Jumbo

SONGS FROM THE EEL'S FOOT.
Tracks: / Flower of London, The / Derby miller, The / Loss of the ramillies, The / Green mossy banks of the lea, The / Blow the candle out / Bold princess royal, The / Newry town / Indian lass, The / Muddley barracks / False hearted knight / Lost heiress, The / Down in the fields where the butter cups grow / Rumbleaway / Life of a man, The.
Album: released on Topic in Jan'81. Distributed by: Roots Distribution

Brignola, Nick

SIGNALS...IN FROM SOMEWHERE (Brignola, Nick Quartet).
Tracks: / In from somewhere / Brother John / Night song / Tadd's delight / Signals / Frame, The / Once upon a samba / Fun.
Album: released on Discovery (USA) in Jan'84 by Discovery Records (USA). Distributed by: Swift, Flexitron-Audio, Jazz Music

Cassette: released on Discovery (USA) in Jan'84 by Discovery Records (USA). Distributed by: Swift, Flexitron-Audio, Jazz Music

Brilliant

COLOURS.
Single (12"): released on Risk in Jun'83 by Rough Trade Records. Distributed by: Rough Trade

END OF THE WORLD, THE.
Tracks: / End of the world, the / How high the sun / Crash the car* / Ruby fruit jungle*.
Notes: Extra track on 12" only*
Single (7"): released on Food For Thought in Nov'86 by Food For Thought Records. Distributed by: Pinnacle

Single (12"): released on Food For Thought in Nov'86 by Food For Thought Records. Distributed by: Pinnacle

IT'S A MAN'S MAN'S MAN'S WORLD.
Single (7"): released on Food in Sep'85 by Food Records. Distributed by: Rough Trade, Cartel, WEA

KISS THE LIPS OF LIFE.
Tracks: / It's a man's,man's,man's world / Somebody / Ruby fruit jungle / How high the sun / Kiss the lips of life / Love is war / Crash the car / I'll be your lover / End of the world, The.
Album: released on Food in Sep'86 by Food Records. Distributed by: Rough Trade, Cartel, WEA

Cassette: released on Food in Sep'86 by Food Records. Distributed by: Rough Trade, Cartel, WEA

LOVE IS WAR.
Tracks: / Love is war / Red red groovy, The / Ruby fruit jungle*.
Single (7"): released on Food in Feb'86 by Food Records. Distributed by: Rough Trade, Cartel, WEA

Single (12"): released on Food in Feb'86 by Food Records. Distributed by: Rough Trade, Cartel, WEA

SOMEBODY.
Tracks: / Somebody / Burning necklace, The / Love is war*.
Single (7"): released on Food For Thought in Jul'86 by Food For Thought Records. Distributed by: Pinnacle

Single (12"): released on Food For Thought in Jul'86 by Food For Thought Records. Distributed by: Pinnacle

Single (7"): released on Mute in '84. Distributed by: Spartan Distribution, Rough Trade Distribution, Cartel Distribution

Brilliant Corners

BRIAN RIX.
Tracks: / Brian Rix / Trudy is a squeal.
Single (7"): released on SS20 in Apr'87 by Brilliant Corners. Distributed by: Revolver Distribution, Cartel Distribution

FRUIT MACHINE.
Tracks: / Fruit machine (EP).
Single (7"): released on SS in May'86 by SS Records. Distributed by: Bullet Distribution, Fresh Distribution, Inferno Distribution, Red Rhino Distribution, Rough Trade Distribution

Single (12"): released on SS in May'86 by SS Records. Distributed by: Bullet Distribution, Fresh Distribution, Inferno Distribution, Red Rhino Distribution, Rough Trade Distribution

GROWING UP ABSURD.
Album: released on SS20 in Oct'85 by Brilliant Corners. Distributed by: Revolver Distribution, Cartel Distribution

MY BABY IN BLACK.
Single (12"): released on SS20 in Oct'84 by Brilliant Corners. Distributed by: Revolver Distribution, Cartel Distribution

SHE'S GOT FEVER.
Single (7"): released on SS20 in Jan'84 by Brilliant Corners. Distributed by: Revolver Distribution, Cartel Distribution

Brim, John

JAMES/BRIM/JONES (Brim, John/Floyd Jones/Elmore James).
Notes: For full details see under Elmore James.

JOHN BRIM & LITTLE HUDSON (Brim, John & Little Hudson).
Album: released on Flyright in Oct'86 by Flyright Records. Distributed by: Krazy Kat, Swift, Jazz Music

Brim, John & Grace

JOHN & GRACE BRIM WITH LITTLE HUDSON.
Album: released on Flyright in Jun'81 by Flyright Records. Distributed by: Krazy Kat, Swift, Jazz Music

Brimmer, Charles

BRIMFUL OF SOUL.
Tracks: / I love her / Dedicating my love to you / With you in mind / My sweet thing / That's how strong my love is / I want to be your breadwinner / Play something sweet / Don't break my heart / We've only just begun / Your man's gonna be in trouble.
Notes: Licensed from Charly Records International APS This compilation P 1986 Charly Holdings Inc. C 1986 Charly Records Ltd.
Album: released on Charly in Apr'86 by Charly Records. Distributed by: Charly, Cadillac

Brimstone

WINNER, THE.
Single (12"): released on London Gemi in Jun'84. Distributed by: Pinnacle

Brimstone, Derek

CHEAPO ALBUM.
Album: released on Brimstone in '85 by Brimstone records. Distributed by: Folksound

SHUFFLEBOAT RIVER FAREWELL.
Tracks: / Fairytale lullaby / Suffleboat farewell / To Althea from prison / Wheel The / Oh lord how happy I am / Make me a pallet on your floor / Blues run the game The / Columbine / Won't you come along / Silver coin / Scarlet town.

Album: released on Rubber in Jun'82 by Rubber Records. Distributed by: Roots Distribution, Projection Distribution, Jazz Music Distribution, Celtic Music Distribution, JSU Distribution, Spartan Distribution

VERY GOOD TIME.
Tracks: / Very good time / March rain / Mrs Fisher / Ain't it a shame / All those songs / Bimbles rags / Sing a song of summer / When the music starts to play / Piss off / Gavotte in H / I live not where I love / River The / Gnome The.
Album: released on Rubber in Jun'82 by Rubber Records. Distributed by: Roots Distribution, Projection Distribution, Jazz Music Distribution, Celtic Music Distribution, JSU Distribution, Spartan Distribution

Brimstone & Treacle
BRIMSTONE & TREACLE Original soundtrack (Various Artists).
Tracks: / When the roll is called up yonder / Brimstone and Treacle / Narration / How stupid Mr Bates / Only you / I burn for you / Spread a little happiness / We got the beat / You know I had the strangest dreams / Up the junction / Bless this house / Kind of loving A / Brimstone.
Notes: This month of September sees the release of the film "Brimstone & Treacle" that will positively establish Sting as a sucessful actor. On A&M is the soundtrack album that features the music of Sting, The Police and even cut from the Go Go's and Squeeze. Include on the album is the massive hit single "Spread a little happiness" and four other solo sting tracks, with six brand new police tracks, a rare collection indeed. Brimstone & Treacle will be supported by a massive advertising campaign.
Album: released on A&M in Sep'82 by A&M Records. Distributed by: Polygram

Cassette: released on A&M in Sep'82 by A&M Records. Distributed by: Polygram

Bringing On Back...
BRINGING ON BACK THE GOOD TIMES The collection (Various Artists).
Tracks: / Crying game, The / Little things / Tell him / Angel of the morning / Same old feeling / Honey honey / Bringing on back the good times / Everlasting love / Sorrow / How do you do what you do to me / Miss Grace / People / Here it comes again / You've got your troubles / Somewhere / Those were the days / You'll never walk alone / Hold me.
Compact disc: by Object Enterprises Ltd. Distributed by: Counterpoint Distribution

Bring On The Empty Horses
BRING ON THE EMPTY HORSES (David Niven).
Cassette: released on Listen For Pleasure in Oct'80 by MFP Records. Distributed by: EMI

Brinsley Schwarz
SILVER PISTOL.
Album: released on Edsel in May'86 by Demon Records. Distributed by: Pinnacle, Jazz Music, Projection

Cassette: released on Edsel in May'86 by Demon Records. Distributed by: Pinnacle, Jazz Music, Projection

Brio
TWO SIDE TO LOVE.
Single (7"): released on Essel in Sep'86. Distributed by: Priority, RCA

Brisker, Gordon
ABOUT CHARLIE.
Compact disc: released on Discovery (USA) in Dec'86 by Discovery Records (USA). Distributed by: Swift, Flexitron-Audio, Jazz Music

Brissett, Annette
HARD TO FIND.
Single (12"): released on Wackies in Aug'84 by Wackies Records. Distributed by: Jetstar

Bristol
CHANGE RINGING (Bristol: Bells Of St Mary Redcliffe, Bristol).
Album: released on Saydisc in May'79 by Saydisc Records. Distributed by: Essex, Harmonia Mundi, Roots, H.R. Taylor, Jazz Music, Swift, Projection, Gamut

Bristol, Johnny
HANG ON IN THERE BABY.
Single (7"): released on Old Gold in Jul'84 by Old Gold Records. Distributed by: Lightning, Jazz Music, Spartan, Counterpoint

Britain, Chris
FOREVER.
Single (7"): released on Raffia in Jul'82. Distributed by: Spartan

British...
BRITISH MILITARY BANDS ON PARADE Various artists (Various Artists).
Notes: A box set containing 4 albums of military bands material from selections in the Decca catalogue: Bands Include:- Royal Marines/Coldstream guards/Royal Anglican Regiment/Band of the Black Watch/Grenadier Guards/Band of the Scots Guards/2nd Btll. Royal Green Jackets/Duke of Wellingtons Regiment/Royal Army Medical Corps./Staffordshire Ragiment etc.
Special: released on Decca in Jun'79 by Decca Records. Distributed by: Polygram

Special: released on Decca in Jun'79 by Decca Records. Distributed by: Polygram

BRITISH MOTORCYCLE INDUSTRY, THE Various artists (Various Artists).
Cassette: released on Audiocord Cassettes in May'83

BRITISH R & B SCENE Various artists (Various Artists).
Album: released on See For Miles in Jan'85 by See For Miles Records. Distributed by: Pinnacle

BRITISH ROCK HISTORY (THE VERY BEST OF...) Various artists (Various Artists).
Tracks: / Ferry across the Mersey / With a girl like you / Wild thing / I understand / If you gotta make a fool of somebody / I'm telling you now / Here comes my baby / Silence is golden.
Notes: 14 tracks including the above
Album: released on EEC Imports in Dec'82. Distributed by: IMS, Polygram

BRITISH ROCK'N'ROLL Various artists (Various Artists).
Tracks: / Don't let nobody move / Rock 'n' roll opera / Mercy, mercy / Cool shake / Rough and smooth / Slim Jim tie / Ain't that a shame / Ninety -nine ways / Baby talk / Cool cool / Betty betty / Five days / Summertime blues / If your so smart / Later / Lots more love / Living doll / Dynamo / Crazy little daisy / No more.
Notes: 'British rock'n'roll' Includes tracks by Larry Page, Vince Eager, Ray Ellington,Etc..)
Album: released on See For Miles in Jan'85 by See For Miles Records. Distributed by: Pinnacle

GOLDEN AGE OF BRITISH DANCE BANDS, THE (British Dance Bands).
Special: released on World Records in '81. Distributed by: Polygram

Special: released on World Records in '81. Distributed by: Polygram

Double Album: released on World in '69. Distributed by: Jetstar

Album: released on World in Jan'79. Distributed by: Jetstar

British Brass Bands
BRITISH BRASS BANDS Various artists (Various Artists).
Album: released on Royal in Jan'85 by Royal Records. Distributed by: Stage One Distribution

British Colony
HAVE YOU SEEN ME DANCING.
Single (7"): released on Carrere in Nov'83 by Carrere Records. Distributed by: PRT, Spartan

Single (12"): released on Carrere in Nov'83 by Carrere Records. Distributed by: PRT, Spartan

British Dance Bands
BRITISH DANCE BANDS Various artists (Various Artists).
Album: released on Saville in Jul'86 by Conifer Records. Distributed by: Conifer

Cassette: released on Saville in Jul'86 by Conifer Records. Distributed by: Conifer

BRITISH DANCE BANDS OF THE FORTIES Various bands (Various dance bands).
Tracks: / If I had my way / More & more / Cookhouse serenade / Better not roll those blue blue eyes / An hour never passes / I threw a kiss in the ocean / Shrine of Saint Cecilia, The / My wubba dolly / Coming in on a wing and a prayer / It's a blue world / In a little rocky valley / There's nothing new to tell you / Sing a round up song / Too romantic / Hut sut song,The / Mother's prayer at twilight, A / And so do I / We'll meet again / Keep an eye on your heart / Blue champagne / It's foolish but it's fun / Out of nowhere / There I go / Whistler's mother-in-law, The / Lover's lullaby / All our tomorrows / You started something / An apple for the teacher / You're mine / When the night is thru' / Sometimes / Man & his dream, A / Moonlight avenue / When the rose of Tralee met Danny boy / Basin Street ball / Sing,everybody,sing.
Notes: Setting the style for the future double album multi-artists format:each act having one complete side of the release.This thirty six track value-for-money package features four of Britain's top dance bands of the 1940's,with an impressive line-up of vocalists interpreting many big hits of the decade. Featured vocalists with Ambrose & His Orchestra. Ann Shelton/Leslie Douglas/George Melachrino/Doroty Carless/Denny Dennis/Evelyn Dall. Featured vocalists with Lew Stone & His Band. Sam Browne/Rita Carr/Wendy Claire/Carl Barriteau. Featured vocalists with The Royal Airforce Dance Orchestra. Sid Collin/Jimmy Miller/Doroty Carless. Featured vocalists with Oscar Rabin & His Band. Beryl Davis/Garry Gowan/Diane/Bob Dale/terry Devon/Benny Lee.
A MONO recording.
Double Album: released on Recollections in Sep'86

Double cassette: released on Recollections in Sep'86

British Dance Team
180.
Single (7"): released on Smile in Apr'82 by Smile Records. Distributed by: Spartan

British guide To C.B.
TEACH YOURSELF C.B..
Cassette: released on Bridair in Sep'80

British Hot Bands...
PICCADILLY NIGHTS (British Hot Bands Of The Twenties).

British Invaders
BRITISH INVADERS Various artists (Various Artists).
Tracks: / Do you want to know a secret / I'm telling you now / Hello little girl / Sorrow / Tobacco road / Hippy hippy shake / How do you do it / Baby come back / Game of love / You've got your troubles / Baby now that I've found you / In the summertime.
Album: released on Topline in Feb'87 by Charly Records. Distributed by: Charly Distribution

Cassette: released on Topline in Feb'87 by Charly Records. Distributed by: Charly Distribution

British Isles
MUSIC OF THE BRITISH ISLES Various Artists (Various Artists).
Cassette: released on EMI (Miles Of Music) in Nov'83 by EMI Records. Distributed by: EMI

British Lions
TROUBLE WITH WOMEN.
Album: released on Cherry Red in '82 by Cherry Red Records. Distributed by: Pinnacle

British Piano Recordings
MECHANICAL MEMORIES.
Cassette: released on PRT in Oct'76 by PRT Records. Distributed by: PRT

MUSICAL MEMORIES.

British Psychedelic Trip
BRITISH PSYCHEDELIC TRIP VOL. 1 Various artists (Various Artists).
Cassette: released on See For Miles in Sep'87 by See For Miles Records. Distributed by: Pinnacle. Estim retail price in Sep'87 was £5.67.

British Psychedlic Trip
BRITISH PSYCHEDELIC TRIP VOL. 2 1965-1970 (Various Artists).
Tracks: / My White Bicycle / Skeleton And The Round About / In The Land Of The Few / Kites / Mr. Armageddan / You've Got A Habit Of Leaving / Excerpt From A Teenage Opera / Rumours / It's So Nice To Come Home / Real Love Guaranteeed / We Are The Moles Part 1 / Friendly Man / Sorrow / I See / Lady On A Bicycle / On A Saturday / Worn Red Carpet / Strawberry Fields Forever / She Says Good Morning / Hey Bulldog!.
Album: released on See For Miles in Nov'87 by See For Miles Records. Distributed by: Pinnacle

BRITISH PSYCHEDELIC TRIP, THE (VOL.3) Various artists (Various Artists).
Tracks: / Renaissance Fair / Miss Pinkerton / Toffee apple Sunday / Green plant / Follow me / Just one more chance / Heavenly club / 'Cos I'm lonely / Turquoise tandem cycle / Jenny Artichoke / Magic potion / Cast a spell / Deep inside your mind / Elf, The / Happy castle / Death at the seaside / Secret / In my magic garden / Woodstock / Desdemona.
Album: released on See For Miles in Aug'87 by See For Miles Records. Distributed by: Pinnacle. Estim retail price in Sep'87 was £5.67.

British Rock'n'Roll..
BRITISH ROCK'N'ROLL 1955-1960 Various artists (Various Artists).
Tracks: / Don't let nobody move / Rock'n'roll opera / Mercy mercy / Cool shake / Rough & smooth / Slim Jim tie / Ain't that a shame / Ninety nine ways / Baby talk / Cool gool / Betty Betty / Five days,five days / If you're so smart / Summertime blues / Later / Lot's more love / Living doll / Dynamo / Crazy little daisy.
Album: released on See For Miles in Aug'86 by See For Miles Records. Distributed by: Pinnacle

British Soul Of R'N'B...
BRITISH SOUL OF R'N'B 1962/69, THE Various artists (Various Artists).
Album: released on See For Miles in Apr'86 by See For Miles Records. Distributed by: Pinnacle

British Steel
BRITISH STEEL Various artists (Various Artists).
Notes: Artists include: Venom,Motorhead, Hawkwind etc.
Album: released on Steeltrax in Nov'85 by Steeltrax Records. Distributed by: PRT Distribution

Cassette: released on Steeltrax in Nov'85 by Steeltrax Records. Distributed by: PRT Distribution

British Summer Time Ends
POP OUT EYES.
Album: released on Nato (France) in Jul'86 by Disques Nato. Distributed by: Essex Record Distributors Ltd.

British Wild Birds...
BRITISH WILD BIRDS IN STEREO Burton, J.F. (Burton, John & David Tombs).
Album: released on BBC in Jan'75 by BBC Records & Tapes. Distributed by: EMI, PRT, Pye

Brittany
CHANTS PROFONDS VOLUME 2 (Jean-Francois Quemener).
Cassette: released on Arion in May'79. Distributed by: Discovery

DIR HA TAN-VOL.4 Dances du Pays de Vannes.
Album: released on Arion in May'79. Distributed by: Discovery

Cassette: released on Arion in May'79. Distributed by: Discovery

Britt, Elton
BEST OF BRITT.
Tracks: / There's a star spangled banner waving somewhere / Blue eyes crying in the rain / Mockin' Bird hill / I almost lost my mind / Rovin' gambler, The (a lover's hand in hearts) / It is no secret (what God can do) / Someday (you'll want me to want you) / Detour / I get the blues when it rains / Candy kisses / I hung my head and cried / Beyond the sunset.
Album: released on RCA in Jan'87 by RCA Records. Distributed by: RCA, Roots, Swift, Wellard, Chris, I & B, Solomon & Peres Distribution

Cassette: released on RCA in Jan'87 by RCA Records. Distributed by: RCA, Roots, Swift, Wellard, Chris, I & B, Solomon & Peres Distribution

Britten, Benjamin
Britten,Benjamin

FOLK SONGS (Britten, Benjamin & Peter Pears).
Album: released on Decca in Jun'84 by Decca Records. Distributed by: Polygram

Cassette: released on Decca in Jun'84 by Decca Records. Distributed by: Polygram

Britton, Maggie
BRIGHT WATER.
Single (7"): released on Songwriters Workshop in Apr'80. Distributed by: PRT

MAGGIE BRITTON.
Album: released on Monarch in Dec'80 by Chart Records. Distributed by: Pinnacle

Britton, Tony
STUDY IN SCARLET, A (Sir A.Conan Doyle).
Cassette: released on Listen For Pleasure in '83 by MFP Records. Distributed by: EMI

Brixton, Webby J
READY.
Single (12"): released on Spiderweb in Dec'82

Broadbent, Alan
EVERYTHING I LOVE.
Compact disc: released on Discovery (USA) in Dec'86 by Discovery Records (USA). Distributed by: Swift, Flexitron-Audio, Jazz Music

Broadbent, Tim
SONGS OF THIS THAT AND THE OTHER.
Tracks: / City Of New Orleans / Petit garcon / Adieu sweet Nancy / I want to see the bright lights tonight / Lah di dah di dah / Andrew roses / Dorset four hand reel, The / I'm on myown grandpa / Great fish finger disaster, The / Ball of yarn / I had to say I loved you in a song / Wildwood flower / Town loved so well / Lord of the dance, The.

Album: released on Sweet Folk All in May'81 by Sweet Folk All Records. Distributed by: Sweet Folk All, Roots, Celtic Music, Dragon, Impetus, Projection, Chris Wellard, Festival Records

Broadbery, Jo

REGGAE TREASURE (Broadbery, Jo & The Standouts).
Album: released on Chinless in '83 by Chinless Productions. Distributed by: Music Galore, Spartan

Broadhurst, Phil

SUSTENANCE (Broadhurst, Phil Quartet).
Album: released on Kiwi-Pacific (New Zealand) in '84. Distributed by: Flexitron Distributors Ltd

Cassette: released on Kiwi-Pacific (New Zealand) in '84. Distributed by: Flexitron Distributors

Broads

SING SING SING.
Single (7"): released on Proto in Oct'83 by Proto Records. Distributed by: WEA

Single (12"): released on Proto in Oct'83 by Proto Records. Distributed by: WEA

Broadside

MOON SHONE BRIGHT, THE.
Tracks: / Seventeen come Sunday / Lincolnshire wedding song / Bold grenadier, The / Gardener and the ploughman, The / Free and easy / Outlandish knight, The / Caister fair / Dicky Turpin / Lisbon / American stranger, The / Maria Marten / Poacher, The / Creeping Jane / Banks of sweet Dundee, The.
Notes: John Connoly vocal guiotar, whistle melodeon, Brian Dawson vocal accordion, Fiddle, Mike Lee vocal, guitar, dulcimer, Bill Meek vocal, Tom Smith banjo, mandolin.
Album: released on Topic in '81. Distributed by: Roots Distribution

Broadside Band

J. PLAYFORD'S POPULAR TUNES.
Notes: The Broadside Band playing original instruments.
Album: released on Amon Ra in Sep'86 by Saydisc Records. Distributed by: H.R. Taylor, PRT, Jazz Music, Essex Record Distributors Ltd., Projection, Swift

Broadway Blockbusters

BROADWAY BLOCKBUSTERS Various artists (Various Artists).
Cassette: released on Ditto in May'86 by Pickwick Records. Distributed by: H.R. Taylor

Broadway Hits

BROADWAY HITS Various artists (Various Artists).
Cassette: released on Bravo in Feb'80 by Pickwick Records

Brock, Dave

EARTHED TO THE GROUND.
Tracks: / Earthed to the ground / Assassination / Green finned demon / Spirits / Sweet obsession / Oscillations / Machine dream / Now is the winter of our discontent / On the case.
Album: released on Flicknife in Apr'86 by Flicknife Records. Distributed by: Spartan

SOCIAL ALLIANCE.
Single (7"): released on Flicknife in Sep'83 by Flicknife Records. Distributed by: Spartan

Picture disc single: released on Flicknife in Sep'83 by Flicknife Records. Distributed by: Spartan

Brody, Saul

TRAVELS WITH BRODY.
Album: released on Adelphi(USA) in May'81 by Adelphi Records (USA). Distributed by: Projection, Swift

Broggs, Peter

INTERNATIONAL FARMER.
Single (12"): released on Ras in Oct'84 by Real Authentic Sound. Distributed by: Greensleeves Records, RCA, Jetstar

RASTAFARI LIVETH.
Album: released on Rastafari in Jun'83

RISE & SHINE.
Album: released on RAS in Feb'86

Brogue

BROGUE (Saki-Read by Hugh Burden).
Cassette: by Talking Tape Company Records

Broken Bones

CRUCIFIX.
Single (7"): . Distributed by: Swift, Red Rhino, Cartel

DECAPITATED.
Single (7"): released on Scarlet in Jan'84 by Scarlet Records. Distributed by: Cartel

Single (12"): released on Fall Out in Jun'85. Distributed by: Swift, Red Rhino, Cartel

Album: released on Fall Out in Aug'87. Distributed by: Swift, Red Rhino, Cartel

DEM' BONES.
Album: released on Fall Out in Jul'84. Distributed by: Swift, Red Rhino, Cartel

FOAD.
Album: released on Fall Out in Feb'87. Distributed by: Swift, Red Rhino, Cartel

LIVE AT LEEDS.
Notes: Another strong punk act,recorded live on stge early 84. Type of recording: Live
Total playing time: 50 minutes.
Video-cassette (VHS): released on Jettisoundz in Oct'84. Distributed by: Red Rhino, Cartel

NEVER SAY DIE.
Tracks: / Never say die.
Single (12"): released on Fall Out in Jul'86. Distributed by: Swift, Red Rhino, Cartel

SEEING THROUGH MY EYES.
Single (7"): released on Fall Out in Jun'85. Distributed by: Swift, Red Rhino, Cartel

TRADERS IN DEATH.
Single (12"): released on RFB in 13 Jun'87

Broken Dreams

BROKEN DREAMS Various artists (Various Artists).
Tracks: / She's out of my life / You needed me / Love so right / One of us / Almost over you / Wedding bells / Rose, The / Love will tear us apart / Love is a stranger / Just another winter's tale / In a broken dream / So sad(to watch love go bad) / Tell me it's all over / Sometimes when we touch / I guess that's why they call it the blues / Time after time / I'd really love to see you tonight / Breaking up is hard to do / When I stop dreaming / Lately / Best thing we can do is say goodbye / I'm not in love / Your love is king / Superstar/Until you come back / To me(that's what i'm gonna do) / Wonderful tonight / Diary / Broken dreams / I will always love you.
Double Album: released on Starblend in Feb'85 by Starblend Records. Distributed by: PRT Distribution

Double cassette: released on Starblend in Feb'85 by Starblend Records. Distributed by: PRT Distribution

Broken English

COMIN' ON STRONG.
Tracks: / Comin' on strong (fallout mix) / Suffer in silence / Comin' on strong / Fire me up (long version).
Single (7"): released on EMI in May'87 by EMI Records. Distributed by: EMI

Single (12"): released on EMI in May'87 by EMI Records. Distributed by: EMI

Compact disc single: released on EMI in May'87 by EMI Records. Distributed by: EMI

Picture disc single: released on EMI in 30 May'87 by EMI Records. Distributed by: EMI

COMIN' ON STRONG (ALT VERSION).
Single (7"): released on EMI in Jun'87 by EMI Records. Distributed by: EMI

Broken Glass

STYLE OF THE STREET.
Tracks: / Style of the street / Style of the street(original mix).
Single (12"): released on Streetwave in Jul'84 by Streetwave Records. Distributed by: PRT Distribution

Bron Area

DIFFERENT PHASES.
Single (12"): released on Glass in Feb'82 by Glass Records. Distributed by: Nine Mile, Rough Trade, Red Rhino, Play It Again Sam

TREES AND THE VILLAGES, (THE).
Album: released on Glass in May'83 by Glass Records. Distributed by: Nine Mile, Rough Trade, Red Rhino, Play It Again Sam

Bronski Beat

AGE OF CONSENT, THE.
Tracks: / Why / Ain't neccessarily so / Screaming / No more war / Love & money / Smalltown boy / Heatwave / Junk / Need a man blues / I feel love.

AGE OF CONSENT ,(THE).
Compact disc: released on Forbidden Fruit in Nov'84 by London Records. Distributed by: Polygram

Album: released on Forbidden Fruit in Oct'84 by London Records. Distributed by: Polygram

Cassette: released on Forbidden Fruit in Oct'84 by London Records. Distributed by: Polygram

C'MON,C'MON.
Tracks: / C'mon, c'mon / Something special / Drum majors*.
Single (7"): released on Forbidden Fruit in Mar'86 by London Records. Distributed by: Polygram

Single (12"): released on Forbidden Fruit in Mar'86 by London Records. Distributed by: Polygram

FIRST CHAPTER, THE.
Notes: Number of tracks: 4 Type of recording: EP
Total playing time: 20 minutes.
Video-cassette (VHS): released on Channel 5 in Mar'86. Distributed by: W.H. Smiths

HIT THAT PERFECT BEAT.
Single (7"): released on Forbidden Fruit in Nov'85 by London Records. Distributed by: Polygram

Single (12"): released on Forbidden Fruit in Nov'85 by London Records. Distributed by: Polygram

HUNDREDS AND THOUSANDS.
Tracks: / Cadillac car / Heatwave (remix) / Why (remix) / Run from love / Hard rain / Smalltown boy (remix) / Junk / Infatuation/ Memories / Close to the edge / I feel love/ Love to love you baby/ Johnny remember me.
Album: released on Forbidden Fruit in Sep'85 by London Records. Distributed by: Polygram

Cassette: released on Forbidden Fruit in Sep'85 by London Records. Distributed by: Polygram

Compact disc: released on Forbidden Fruit in Sep'85 by London Records. Distributed by: Polygram

HUNDREDS AND THOUSANDS.
Tracks: / Heatwave (Remix) / Why? (Remix) / Run From Love / Hard Rain / Smalltown Boy / Junk / Infatuation/Memories / Close To The Edge / I Feel Love/Love To Love You Baby/Johnny Remember Me / Cadillac Car.
Compact disc: released on Forbidden Fruit in Nov'86 by London Records. Distributed by: Polygram

I FEEL LOVE.
Single (7"): released on Forbidden Fruit in Apr'85 by London Records. Distributed by: Polygram

IT AIN'T NECESSARILY SO.
Single (7"): released on Forbidden Fruit in Nov'84 by London Records. Distributed by: Polygram

Single (12"): released on Forbidden Fruit in Nov'84 by London Records. Distributed by: Polygram

SMALLTOWN BOY.
Single (7"): released on Forbidden Fruit in Jun'84 by London Records. Distributed by: Polygram

Single (12"): released on Forbidden Fruit in Jun'84 by London Records. Distributed by: Polygram

THIS HEART.
Tracks: / This heart / What are you going to do about it.
Single (7"): released on Forbidden Fruit in Aug'86 by London Records. Distributed by: Polygram

Single (12"): released on Forbidden Fruit in Aug'86 by London Records. Distributed by: Polygram

TRUTHDARE DOUBLEDARE.
Tracks: / Hit that perfect beat / Truthdare doubledare / C'mon, c'mon / Punishment for love / We know how it feels / This heart / Do it / Dr John / In my dreams / What are you going to do about it*.
Compact disc: released on Forbidden Fruit in May'86 by London Records. Distributed by: Polygram

Album: released on Forbidden Fruit in May'86 by London Records. Distributed by: Polygram

Cassette: released on Forbidden Fruit in May'86 by London Records. Distributed by: Polygram

WHY.
Single (7"): released on Forbidden Fruit in Sep'84 by London Records. Distributed by: Polygram

Single (12"): released on Forbidden Fruit in Sep'84 by London Records. Distributed by: Polygram

Bronstein, Stan

LIVING ON THE AVENUE.
Album: released on Muse in Jun'77 by Peerless Records.

Bronte, Charlotte

JANE EYRE.
Cassette: released on Listen For Pleasure in Jul'84 by MFP Records. Distributed by: EMI

Album: released on That's Entertainment in Apr'83 by That's Entertainment Records. Distributed by: Pinnacle, PRT

Bronte, Emily

WUTHERING HEIGHTS.
Cassette: released on Listen For Pleasure in Sep'84 by MFP Records. Distributed by: EMI

Bronx

MIDNIGHT QUEEN.
Album: released on Strawberry in Mar'84. Distributed by: Pinnacle

Bronz

SEND DOWN AN ANGEL.
Single (7"): released on Bronze in Aug'84 by Polygram Records. Distributed by: Polydor

Single (12"): released on Bronze in Aug'84 by Polygram Records. Distributed by: Polydor

TAKEN BY STORM.
Tracks: / Send down an angel / Heat of the night / Cold truth, The / Night runner / Taken by storm / Don't ever wanna lose ya / Sweet lady / Harder than diamond / Tiger / Loneliness is mine.
Album: released on Bronze in Mar'84 by Polygram Records. Distributed by: Polydor

Bronze Rocks

BRONZE ROCKS Various artists (Various Artists).
Notes: Artists include: Motorhead,Girlsschool,Robin George etc. Number of tracks: 12
Total playing time: 45 minutes.
Video-cassette (VHS): released on Virgin in Apr'86 by Virgin Records. Distributed by: EMI, Virgin Distribution

Brook Brothers

WARPAINT.
Single (7"): released on Flashback in Apr'80 by Flashback Records/PRT Records. Distributed by: Mainline, PRT

Brooker, Gary

CYCLE Let it flow.
Single (7"): released on Mercury in Mar'82 by Phonogram Records. Distributed by: Polygram Distribution

LEAD ME TO THE WATER.
Tracks: / Mineral man / Another way / Hang on rose / Home loving / Cycle, The / Lead me to the water / Angler, The / Low flying birds / Sympathy for the hard of hearing.
Album: released on Mercury in Feb'82 by Phonogram Records. Distributed by: Polygram Distribution

Cassette: released on Mercury in Feb'82 by Phonogram Records. Distributed by: Polygram Distribution

TWO FOOLS IN LOVE.
Single (7"): released on Mercury in Apr'85 by Phonogram Records. Distributed by: Polygram Distribution

Brookes, Jacqui

SOB STORIES.
Tracks: / Lost without your love / One that got away, The / Cold light of day, The / Another place for a dreamer / Trains and boats and planes / Haunted cocktails / Just another / I'm not ashamed / Thin air / Departures.
Album: released on MCA in Jan'84 by MCA Records. Distributed by: Polygram, MCA

Cassette: released on MCA in Jan'84 by MCA Records. Distributed by: Polygram, MCA

TRAINS AND BOATS AND PLANES.
Single (7"): released on MCA in Jan'84 by MCA Records. Distributed by: Polygram, MCA

Brookins, Robert

IF ONLY YOU KNEW.
Tracks: / If only you knew / Sensuality.
Single (7"): released on MCA in Apr'87 by MCA Records. Distributed by: Polygram, MCA

Single (12"): released on MCA in Apr'87 by MCA Records. Distributed by: Polygram, MCA

IN THE NIGHT.
Album: released on MCA in Jun'87 by MCA Records. Distributed by: Polygram, MCA

Cassette: released on MCA in Jun'87 by MCA Records. Distributed by: Polygram, MCA

OUR LIVES.
Tracks: / Our lives / Incredulous.
Single (7"): released on MCA in Jul'87 by MCA Records. Distributed by: Polygram, MCA

Single (12"): released on MCA in Jul'87 by MCA Records. Distributed by: Polygram, MCA

Brooklyn
YOU NEVER KNOW WHAT YOU'LL FIND.
Tracks: / Two wheels / Breaking up / You never know what you'll find / Can't we be lovers / Hollywood / I wanna be a detective / Born to win / No replay / Late again / Rainbows end.
Album: released on Rondelet in Nov'80. Distributed by Spartan Distribution

Brooklyn Dreams
SLEEPLESS NIGHTS.
Tracks: / Make it last / That's not the way your mama taught you to be / Sleepless nights / Send me a dream / Fashion for me / First love / Street man / Touching in the dark / Long distance / Coming up the hard way / Heaven knows.
Album: released on RCA in May'79 by RCA Records. Distributed by: RCA, Roots, Swift, Wellard, Chris, I & B, Solomon & Peres Distribution

Brookmeyer, Bob
AT THE VILLAGE VANGUARD (Brookmeyer, Bob with Mel Lewis & The Jazz Orchestra).
Tracks: / Ding dong ding / First love song / Hello and goodbye / Skylark / El co / Fan club.
Album: released on Rhapsody in Apr'81 by President Records. Distributed by: Taylors, Swift, Jazz Music, Wellard, Chris

BLUES HOT & COLD (Brookmeyer, Bob Quartet).
Tracks: / Languid blues / On the sunny side of the street / Stoppin' at the Savoy / I got rhythm / Smoke gets in your eyes / Hot and cold blues.
Album: released on Verve (USA) in Oct'84 by Polydor. Distributed by: Polygram

OSLO (Brookmeyer, Bob Quartet).
Tracks: / With the wind & the rain in your hair / Oslo / Later blues / Detour ahead / Tootsie samba / Alone together / Who could care / Caravan.
Notes: Personnel: Bob Brookmeyer - valve trombone / Alan Broadbent - piano and synthesizer / Eric von Essen - bass / Michael Stephans - drums
Album: released on Concord Jazz (USA) in Feb'87 by Concord Jazz Records (USA). Distributed by: IMS, Polygram

Compact disc: released on Concord Jazz (USA) in Jul'87 by Concord Jazz Records (USA). Distributed by: IMS, Polygram

TRADITIONALISM REVISITED.
Album: released on Affinity in Nov'84 by Charly Records. Distributed by: Charly, Cadillac

ZOOT SIMS WITH THE BOB BROOKMEYER QUINTET (see Sims, Zoot) (Brookmeyer, Bob Quintet & Zoot Sims).

Brookmeyer, Bobby
BOBBY BROOKMEYER AND HIS ORCHESTRA (Brookmeyer, Bobby & His Orchestra).
Tracks: / Oh Jane snavely / Nature boy / Just you, just me / I'm old fashioned / Gone latin / Zing went the strings of my heart / Big city life / Confusion blues / Open country.
Album: released on RCA (France) in Jan'83 by RCA Records. Distributed by: Discovery

Brook, Michael
HYBIRD.
Album: released on Editions EG in Nov'86 by Virgin Records. Distributed by: EMI

Cassette: released on Editions EG in Nov'86 by Virgin Records. Distributed by: EMI

HYBIRD (Brook, Michael & Brian Eno).
Album: released on E.G. in Aug'85 by Virgin Records. Distributed by: Virgin, EMI

Cassette: released on E.G. in Aug'85 by Virgin Records. Distributed by: Virgin, EMI

Brook, Mike
DARLING I LOVE YOU.
Single (12"): released on Music Rock in May'85

Brooks, Dave
VOX POP.
Single (7"): released on BBC in Jan'83 by BBC Records & Tapes. Distributed by: EMI, PRT

Brooks, Elkie
BREAK THE CHAIN.
Tracks: / Break the chain (ext mix) / Break the chain (Edit/The Groove) / Break the chain / Groove (The).
Single (7"): released on Legend in Feb'87 by Legend Records. Distributed by: EMI, Legend Distribution, Island

Single (12"): released on Legend in Feb'87 by Legend Records. Distributed by: EMI, Legend Distribution, Island

Compact disc single: released on Legend in Apr'87 by Legend Records. Distributed by: EMI, Legend Distribution, Island

I JUST CAN'T GO ON.
Single (7"): released on A&M in Feb'83 by A&M Records. Distributed by: Polygram

LILAC WINE.
Single (7"): released on A&M in Jan'78 by A&M Records. Distributed by: Polygram

LIVE AND LEARN.
Tracks: / Viva la money / On the horizon / He could have been an army / Rising cost of love, The / Dream dealer / Who's making love? / If you can't beat me rocking / Heartache is on, The / Not enough lovin' yet / Falling star.
Album: released on A&M in Mar'82 by A&M Records. Distributed by: Polygram

Cassette: released on A&M in Mar'82 by A&M Records. Distributed by: Polygram

LIVE & LEARN.
Album: released on Pickwick in May'84 by Pickwick Records. Distributed by: Pickwick Distribution, Prism Leisure Distribution, Lugtons

Cassette: released on Pickwick in May'84 by Pickwick Records. Distributed by: Pickwick Distribution, Prism Leisure Distribution, Lugtons

MINUTES.
Tracks: / Minutes / Driftin' / Night run / Take your freedom / Growing tired / Born lucky / I've been in love before / Too heavy, too strong / Crossfire / Work pay.
Album: released on A&M in Jul'84 by A&M Records. Distributed by: Polygram

Cassette: released on A&M in Jul'84 by A&M Records. Distributed by: Polygram

NO MORE THE FOOL.
Tracks: / No more the fool / City lights / Blue jay".
Notes: =extra track on 12" only
Cassette: released on Legend in Dec'86 by Legend Records. Distributed by: EMI, Legend Distribution, Island

Compact disc: released on Legend in Dec'86 by Legend Records. Distributed by: EMI, Legend Distribution, Island

Single (7"): released on Legend in Nov'86 by Legend Records. Distributed by: EMI, Legend Distribution, Island

Single (12"): released on Legend in Nov'86 by Legend Records. Distributed by: EMI, Legend Distribution, Island

Album: released on Legend in Dec'86 by Legend Records. Distributed by: EMI, Legend Distribution, Island

NO MORE THE FOOL (VIDEO).
Video-cassette (VHS): released on Gold Rushes in Mar'87 by Video Collection Records. Distributed by: Counterpoint

ONLY LOVE CAN BREAK YOUR HEART.
Single (7"): released on A&M in Apr'78 by A&M Records. Distributed by: Polygram

Album: released on A&M in Nov'81 by A&M Records. Distributed by: Polygram

Cassette: released on A&M in Nov'81 by A&M Records. Distributed by: Polygram

PEARLS.
Tracks: / Superstar / Fool if you think it's over / Givin' it up for your love / Sunshine after the rain / Warm and tender love / Lilac wine / Pearl's a singer / Don't cry out loud / Too busy thinking about my baby / If you leave me now / Paint your pretty picture / Dance away.
Compact disc: by A&M Records. Distributed by: Polygram

PEARL'S A SINGER.
Single (7"): released on Old Gold in Sep'85 by Old Gold Records. Distributed by: Lightning, Jazz Music, Spartan, Counterpoint

PEARLS 2.

Brooks, Hadda
QUEEN OF THE BOOGIE.
Album: released on Oldie Blues Holland in Feb'84

Brooks, John Benson
FOLK JAZZ USA.
Tracks: / New saints, The / Venezuela / Black is the colour / Betsy / Randall my son / Turtle dove / Shenandoah / Joe's old folks / Sara Jane / Scarlet Town / Wayfarin' stranger / Darling Corey.
Album: released on RCA (France) in Jan'83 by RCA Records. Distributed by: Discovery

Brooks, Karen
I WILL DANCE WITH YOU.
Tracks: / Nobody's angel / I'll dance with you / Hard way, The / Have a heart / Last time, The / I do blues / Last one to know, The / Other night, The / Too bad for love / Great divide, The.
Cassette: released on Warner Bros. in Jun'85 by Warner Bros Records. Distributed by: WFA

I WILL DANCE WITH YOU (Brooks, Karen & Johnny Cash).
Single (7"): released on Warner Bros. in Aug'85 by Warner Bros Records. Distributed by: WEA

Brooks, Leonard
CHIAPPA FAIRGROUND ORGAN VOL.1.
Album: released on Response in Feb'81 by Priority Records. Distributed by: BMG

CHIAPPA FAIRGROUND ORGAN VOL 2.

Album: released on Response in Feb'81 by Priority Records. Distributed by: BMG

LEONARD BROOKS & HIS CHIAPPA FAIRGROUND ORGAN.
Album: by Priority Records. Distributed by: BMG

Brooks, Lonnie
BAYOU LIGHTENING.
Album: released on Sonet in Sep'79 by Sonet Records. Distributed by: PRT

BAYOU LIGHTNING.
Tracks: / Voodoo daddy / Figure head / Watch dog / Breakfst in bed / Worked up woman / Alimony / Watch what you got / I ain't superstitious / You know what my body needs / In the dark.
Compact disc: by Sonet Records. Distributed by: PRT

BROKE AN' HUNGRY.
Tracks: / Wee, wee hours / Things they used to do / Go to the Mardi Gras / Texas flood / Tom cat blues / Rooster blues / Train and the horse, The / Broke an' hungry / When there's no way out / Don't touch me,baby / Red bug blues.
Album: released on Cross Cut in Apr'84

CRAWL, (THE).
Album: released on Charly(R&B) in Apr'84 by Charly Records. Distributed by: Charly, Cadillac

HOT SHOT.
Album: released on Sonet in Oct'83 by Sonet Records. Distributed by: PRT

LIVE AT PEPPERS.
Album: released on Black Magic (Holland) in Feb'85

TURN ON THE NIGHT.
Album: released on Sonet in May'81 by Sonet Records. Distributed by: PRT

WOUND UP TIGHT.
Tracks: / Got lucky last night / Jealous man / Belly rubbin' music / Bewitched / End of the rope / Wound up tight / Boomerang / Musta' been dreaming / Skid row / Hush mouth money.
Album: released on Sonet in Jan'87 by Sonet Records. Distributed by: PRT

Brooks, Mel
GREATEST HITS:MEL BROOKS featuring the fabulous film scores of John Morris.
Album: released on Asylum in May'78 by WEA Records. Distributed by: WEA

IT'S GOOD TO BE THE KING RAP.
Single (7"): released on Luggage in Oct'81 by Luggage. Distributed by: Multicord

Brooks, Mike
BEYOND THE HILLS (Brooks, Mike & the Investigators).
Single (12"): released on Music Rock in Feb'85

COME SISTER COME.
Single (12"): released on Coptic Lion in Jun'83.

NIGHT RAVER.
Single (7"): released on Coptic Lion in Jun'84. Distributed by: Jetstar

Brooks, Mikie
ONE LOVE.
Album: released on Vista Sounds in Jan'83 by Vista Sounds Records. Distributed by: Jetstar

Brooks, Nigel
HYMNS AT HOME (Brooks, Nigel Singers).
Tracks: / Through all the changing scenes of life / Dear lord and father of mankind / O love that wilt not let me go / O thou who camest from above / Nearer still nearer / How I praise thee, precious saviour / Old rugged cross, The / Pleasant are thy courts above / Just as I am / Lead kindly light / God be with you till we meet again / Glory to thee my god this night.
Album: by Pilgrim Records. Distributed by: Rough Trade, Cartel

Brooks, Randy
1945-1947 (Brooks, Randy & His Orchestra).
Album: released on Circle(USA) in Jun'86 by Jazzology Records (USA). Distributed by: Jazz Music, Swift, Chris Wellard

RADIO DISCS OF .... 1945, THE.
Album: released on Joyce in Jul'82

Brooks, Ray
SONGS WITHIN (Brooks, Ray & Full Force).
Album: released on Timeless in Aug'87

Brooks, Terry & Strange
RAW POWER.
Album: . Distributed by: Funhouse, Rough Trade

Album: released on CBS in Nov'81 by CBS Records. Distributed by: CRS

Cassette: released on CBS in Nov'81 by CBS Records. Distributed by: CBS

TRANSLUCENT WORLD.
Album: released on Psycho in Feb'85. Distributed by: Funhouse, Rough Trade

Broonzy, Big Bill
1927 - 32.
Album: released on Matchbox in Sep'85. Distributed by: Projection

1934-47 VOL.1.
Album: released on Document in Jul'87

BACKWATER BLUES.
Album: released on Joker Import in Apr'81

BIG BILL BROONZY & WASHBOARD SAM (Broonzy, Big Bill/Washboard Sam).
Album: released on Chess in Apr'87 by Charly Records. Distributed by: Charly, Swift, PRT, Discovery, IMS, Polygram

Cassette: released on Chess in Apr'87 by Charly Records. Distributed by: Charly, Swift, PRT, Discovery, IMS, Polygram

BIG BILL'S BLUES.
Compact disc: . Distributed by: Discovery, Jazz Music, PRT, Swift

Album: released on CBS(France) in May'85 by CBS Records. Distributed by: Conifer, Discovery, Swift

Cassette: released on CBS(France) in May'85 by CBS Records. Distributed by: Conifer, Discovery, Swift

BLACK, BROWN, & WHITE.
Notes: MONO recording.
Album: released on Storyville in Jun'86 by Storyville Records. Distributed by: Jazz Music Distribution, Swift Distribution, Chris Wellard Distribution, Counterpoint Distribution

LAST SESSION VOL 2.
Album: released on Polydor (France) in Oct'83. Distributed by: Polygram

Album: released on Polydor (France) in Oct'83. Distributed by: Polygram

MIDNIGHT STEPPERS.
Album: released on Bluetime in Aug'86 by Charly Records. Distributed by: Charly

MY GAL IS GONE.
Album: released on Manhattan Italy in Mar'87

TROUBLE IN MIND.
Album: released on Spotlite in '83 by Spotlite Records. Distributed by: Cadillac, Jazz Music, Spotlite

STORY VOL. 3.
Album: released on Verve (France) in Apr'84

LAST SESSION VOL 1.
Album: released on Verve (Import) in Oct'82

Bros
I OWE YOU NOTHING.
Single (7"): released on CBS in Aug'87 by CBS Records. Distributed by: CBS

Single (12"): released on CBS in Aug'87 by CBS Records. Distributed by: CBS

Brother...
BROTHER, CAN YOU SPARE A DIME? Various artists (Various Artists).
Tracks: / Brother can you spare a dime? / Boulevard of broken dreams, The / Life is just a bowl of cherries / In the still of the night / Love walked in / On the good ship lollipop / Unemployment stomp / Gold diggers song. The / All in down & out blues / Fifteen miles from Birmingham / Coal loading machine, The / NRA blues / I ain't got no home in this world no more / Death of Mrs. Jones / All I want / White Cliffs of Dover, The.
Notes: Full title: "Brother can you spare a dime?"/American song during the Great Depression)
MONO recording.
Album: released on New World (USA) in Aug'86 by New World Records (USA). Distributed by: Conifer

Brother Beyond
CHAIN GANG SMILE.
Tracks: / Chain gang smile / Sometimes good sometimes bad (sometimes better) / Chaingang smile / Sometimes good, sometimes bad (sometimes better).

Single (7"): released on Parlophone in Jul'87 by EMI Records. Distributed by: EMI

Single (12"): released on Parlophone in Jul'87 by EMI Records. Distributed by: EMI

Special: released on Parlophone in Aug'87 by EMI Records. Distributed by: EMI

Single (12"): released on Parlophone in Aug'87 by EMI Records. Distributed by: EMI

GET EVEN.
Tracks: / Chain-gang smile / Somebody, somewhere / Restless / Shipwrecked / Sunset bars / I should have lied / How many times / Sometimes good, sometimes bad, (sometimes better) / Think of you / King of blue / Act for love (Ext. version)* / Chain-gang smile (Stephen Haque remix)* / Chain-gang smile.
Notes: * Extra tracks on cassette.
Compact disc: released on Parlophone in Sep'87 by EMI Records. Distributed by: EMI

Album: released on Parlophone in Sep'87 by EMI Records. Distributed by: EMI. Estim retail price in Sep'87 was £5.99.

Cassette: released on Parlophone in Sep'87 by EMI Records. Distributed by: EMI. Estim retail price in Sep'87 was £5.99.

HOW MANY TIMES.
Tracks: / How many times / How many times (more) / How many times (John Robie remix) / Give it all back.
Compact disc single: released on EMI in May'87 by EMI Records. Distributed by: EMI

HOW MANY TIMES (MORE).
Tracks: / How Many Times (More) / Give It All Back (Loveline).
Single (7"): released on EMI in Feb'87 by EMI Records. Distributed by: EMI

Single (12"): released on EMI in Feb'87 by EMI Records. Distributed by: EMI

I SHOULD HAVE LIED.
Tracks: / I should have lied / Act for love.
Single (7"): released on EMI in Aug'86 by EMI Records. Distributed by: EMI

Single (12"): released on EMI in Aug'86 by EMI Records. Distributed by: EMI

Brother Choice
HOW I FEEL.
Tracks: / How I feel.
Single (7"): released on Bluebird in Jul'86 by Bluebird Records. Distributed by: EMI, Jetstar

Single (12"): released on Bluebird in Jul'86 by Bluebird Records. Distributed by: EMI, Jetstar

Brother D
NENGEH NENGEH.
Tracks: / Nengeh nengeh / Private image.
Single (12"): released on Blue Trac in Apr'86 by Blue Mountain Records. Distributed by: Jetstar

UP AGAINST THE BEAST (Brother D and Silver Fox).
Cassette: released on Reach Out International in Jan'84. Distributed by: Red Rhino, Cartel

Brother Dee
PRIVATE ENEMY NO 1.
Single (12"): released on Big Brother in Nov'84 by Big Brother Records

Brotherhood Of Man
100 MINUTES.
Cassette: released on PRT in Jun'82 by PRT Records. Distributed by: PRT

20 LOVE SONGS AND 20 DISCO GREATS.
Album: released on Warwick in Oct'81. Distributed by: Multiple Sound Distributors

BEST OF BROTHERHOOD OF MAN, THE.
Album: released on Spot in Feb'83 by Pickwick Records. Distributed by: H.R. Taylor

Cassette: released on Spot in Feb'83 by Pickwick Records. Distributed by: H.R. Taylor

SAVE YOUR KISSES FOR ME.
Album: released on Flashback in Nov'85 by Flashback Records/PRT Records. Distributed by: Mainline, PRT

Cassette: released on Flashback in Nov'85 by Flashback Records/PRT Records. Distributed by: Mainline, PRT

Single (12"): released on Old Gold in Jul'82 by Old Gold Records. Distributed by: Lightning, Jazz Music, Spartan, Counterpoint

SING 20 SMASH HITS.
Cassette: released on Ditto in Sep'83 by Pickwick Records. Distributed by: H.R. Taylor

---

SPOTLIGHT ON BROTHERHOOD OF MAN.
Album: released on PRT in '80 by PRT Records. Distributed by: PRT

Cassette: released on PRT in '80 by PRT Records. Distributed by: PRT

WHEN THE KISSING STOPS.
Single (7"): released on EMI in Jun'83 by EMI Records. Distributed by: EMI

Brother Lees
DID YOU HEAR WHAT TERRY WOGAN SAID.
Single (7"): released on Go Ahead in Dec'82 by Go Ahead Records. Distributed by: Go Ahead

Brother Resistance
RAPSO TAKE OVER.
Album: released on Masimba Collection in Aug'86

RING DE BELL.
Single (7"): released on Bumble Bee in Aug'87 by CSA Records. Distributed by: PRT, Jetstar, CSA

Single (12"): released on Bumble Bee in Aug'87 by CSA Records. Distributed by: PRT, Jetstar, CSA

Brothers
LOUD, PROUD AND PUNK - LIVE.
Album: released on Syndicate in Sep'84

MONTEGO BAY.
Single (7"): released on Paro in Sep'83 by Paro Records. Distributed by: Spartan

NIGHTSCHOOL.
Single (7"): released on TVM in Aug'85. Distributed by: Gipsy, CBS

SUNNY WEATHER.
Single (7"): released on Dingles in Aug'82 by Dingles Records. Distributed by: Projection

Brothers Christ
ECHOES OF LOST SOULS.
Album: released on Colony in Jun'87 by Colony Records. Distributed by: Backs, Cartel

Brothers Four
GREATEST HITS: BROTHERS FOUR.
Album: released on CBS(France) in Mar'84 by CBS Records. Distributed by: Conifer, Discovery, Swift

Cassette: released on CBS(France) in Mar'84 by CBS Records. Distributed by: Conifer, Discovery, Swift

THIS LAND IS YOUR LAND.
Album: released on MFP in Sep'81 by EMI Records. Distributed by: EMI

Cassette: released on MFP in '81 by EMI Records. Distributed by: EMI

Brothers Grimm
GRIMMS FAIRY TALES (Hancock, Sheila).
Cassette: released on Listen For Pleasure in '83 by MFP Records. Distributed by: EMI

Brothers Johnson
LOOK OUT FOR NUMBER ONE.
Album: released on A&M in Mar'82 by A&M Records. Distributed by: Polygram

Cassette: released on A&M in Mar'82 by A&M Records. Distributed by: Polygram

STOMP.
Tracks: / Get The Funk Outer My Face / So Fine / Dynomite.
Single (12"): released on Old Gold in Jan'87 by Old Gold Records. Distributed by: Lightning, Jazz Music, Spartan, Counterpoint

STOMP (THE BROTHERS JOHNSON'S GREATEST HITS).
Album: released on Funk America in Dec'84 by A&M Records. Distributed by: CBS

Cassette: released on Funk America in Dec'84 by A&M Records. Distributed by: CBS

Brothers Of Craig
TOSSING & TURNING.
Tracks: / Tossing & turning.
Single (7"): released on Brotherhood in Aug'86. Distributed by: Fast Forward, Cartel

Brothers & Other...
BROTHERS & OTHER MOTHERS Various Artists (Various Artists).

Album:

BROTHERS & OTHER MOTHERS VOL. 2 Various artists (Various Artists).
Album:

Broughton, Edgar Band
BUNCH OF 45'S, A.
Album: released on Harvest in Apr'75 by EMI Records. Distributed by: Roots, EMI

LEGENDARY, THE.
Album: released on Music 2000(Germany) in Sep'84

OUT DEMONS OUT Best of the Edgar Broughton Band.
Tracks: / Out demons out / Love in the rain / Green lights / I got mad / Hotel room / Poppy / Evening over rooftops / Apache/Dropout boogie / Moth, The* / People* / Peter* / Gone blue / Why can't somebody love me / Capers.
Notes: Compilation including several of the favourites they used to perform on tour. Their first minor hit single reached No.39 in April 1970, followed about a year later by 'Apache Dropout', a track which was based on a marriage between The Shadows hit 'Apache' & Captain Beefheart's 'Dropout Boogie' which spent 3 months of 1971 in and out of the top 40. Likely album for the rock collectors market. Informative sleeve notes.
Album: released on Harvest in Apr'86 by EMI Records. Distributed by: Roots, EMI

Cassette: released on Harvest in Apr'86 by EMI Records. Distributed by: Roots, EMI

WASA WASA.
Album: released on EMI (Germany) in '83 by EMI Records. Distributed by: Conifer

Broughtons
SUPER CHIP.
Album: released on Sheet in Jun'82. Distributed by: Rough Trade

Broussard, Alex
Cajun & country songs

Broussard, Van
MORE BAYOU BOOGIE.
Album: . Distributed by: Swift

VAN BROUSSARD.
Album: . Distributed by: Swift

Brown, A. J
HUMAN NATURE.
Single (7"): released on Sunset in Dec'83. Distributed by: Jetstar

JUST CAN'T GET YOU OUT OF MY MIND.
Single (12"): released on Level Vibes in Dec'84 by Level Vibes Records. Distributed by: Jetstar

LOVE PEOPLE.
Album: released on Unknown in Jun'85

Brown, Al
CARIBBEAN QUEEN.
Single (12"): released on Jedi in Nov'84. Distributed by: Jetstar

NO SOUL TODAY.
Single (12"): released on Ethnic in Aug'84. Distributed by: Kingdom

Brown, Ale
IT'S ONLY A WIND UP (MAKING YOUR MIND UP).
Single (7"): released on Radioactive in Mar'82

Brown, Alex
COME ON AND SHOUT.

Brown, Andrew
BIG BROWN'S CHICAGO BLUES.
Album: released on Black Magic in Oct'82. Distributed by: Swift

Brown, Arthur
CAZY WORLD OF ARTHUR BROWN, THE.
Album: released on Track (Import) in Oct'82

Album: released on Polydor (Holland) in Feb'84

CHISHOLM IN MY BOSOM.
Album: released on Gull in Feb'78 by Gull Records. Distributed by: Pinnacle

CRAZY WORLD OF ARTHUR BROWN, THE.
Tracks: / Nightmare / Fanfare - fire poem / Fire / Come and buy / Time / I put a spell on you /

Spontaneous apple creation / Rest cure / I've got money / Child of my kingdom.

DANCE.
Tracks: / We've gotta get out of this place / Helen with the sun / Take a chance / Crazy / Hearts and minds / Dance / Out of time / Quietly with tact / Soul garden / Lord will find a way, The / Is there nothing beyond God?.
Album: released on Gull in May'78 by Gull Records. Distributed by: Pinnacle

FIRE.
Single (7"): released on Old Gold in Jul'84 by Old Gold Records. Distributed by: Lightning, Jazz Music, Spartan, Counterpoint

FIRE (Crazy World of Arthur Brown).
Single (7"): released on Track in Jan'74 by Polydor Records. Distributed by: Polygram

LOST EARS, THE.
Tracks: / Internal messenger / Space plucks / Trouble / Brains / Night of the pigs / Creep / Creation / Gypsy escape / Love is a spirit / Experiment, The / Hymn, The / Traffic light song, The / Spirit of joy / Time captives / Conception / Come alive / Sunrise / Triangles / Metal monster / Space plucks, including Dem bones / So high up here / Through the planets.
Double Album: released on Gull in Sep'77 by Gull Records. Distributed by: Pinnacle

Brown, A. S

SUNSHINE FOR ME.
Single (12"): released on Level Vibes in Sep'85 by Level Vibes Records. Distributed by: Jetstar

Brown, Barry

BELLY MOVE.
Single (12"): released on Greensleeves in Jun'84 by Greensleeves Records. Distributed by: BMG, Jetstar, Spartan

BEST OF BARRY BROWN.
Album: released on Culture Press in Mar'85 by Vista Sounds Records. Distributed by: Jetstar, Rough Trade

FREE AGAIN.
Single (12"): released on Lix in Dec'84 by Lix Records. Distributed by: Jetstar

LADY.
Single (12"): released on Lix in Dec'84 by Lix Records. Distributed by: Jetstar

OVER ME.
Single 10": released on Hitbound in Jul'83 by Hitbound Records. Distributed by: Jetstar

RIGHT NOW.
Album: released on Time in Apr'84. Distributed by: Jetstar Distribution

ROOTS AND CULTURE (Brown, Barry & Willie Williams).
Album: released on Uptempo in Aug'85 by Uptempo Records. Distributed by: Jetstar Distribution

TANK YOU MAMA.
Single (12"): released on Observers in Jul'83

THEM A FIGHT.
Single (12"): released on Joe Gibbs in Mar'83 by Joe Gibbs Records. Distributed by: Jetstar

TOURIST SEASON.
Single (12"): released on Real Wax in Jun'84

YOUR STEP.
Single 10": released on Hitbound in May'83 by Hitbound Records. Distributed by: Jetstar

Brown, Betty

I GOT A DREAM.
Tracks: / I got a dream.
Single (12"): released on L.I.S. in Jul'86. Distributed by: Pinnacle

Brown, Bobby

CANADA ON TOUR (Brown, Bobby & The Scottish Accent).
Notes: With the Cape Breton Symphony Fiddle.
Album: released on Ross in Jan'86 by Ross Records. Distributed by: Ross Distribution, Roots Distribution

Cassette: released on Ross in Jan'86 by Ross Records. Distributed by: Ross Distribution, Roots Distribution

GIRLFRIEND.
Tracks: / Girlfriend / King of stage.
Single (7"): released on MCA in Apr'87 by MCA Records. Distributed by: Polygram, MCA

Single (12"): released on MCA in Apr'87 by MCA Records. Distributed by: Polygram, MCA

GIRL NEXT DOOR, A.
Tracks: / Girl next door, A / Girl next door, A (inst).
Single (7"): released on MCA in May'87 by MCA Records. Distributed by: Polygram, MCA

Single (12"): released on MCA in May'87 by MCA Records. Distributed by: Polygram, MCA

ISLAND FLING, THE (Brown, Bobby & The Scottish Accent).

KINGS OF STAGE.
Album: released on MCA in Jan'87 by MCA Records. Distributed by: Polygram, MCA

Cassette: released on MCA in Jan'87 by MCA Records. Distributed by: Polygram, MCA

MAID OF THE MILL, THE (Brown, Bobby & The Scottish Accent).

PRESENTS A SALUTE TO SCOTLAND.
Album: released on Ross in Aug'84 by Ross Records. Distributed by: Ross Distribution, Roots Distribution

Cassette: released on Ross in Aug'84 by Ross Records. Distributed by: Ross Distribution, Roots Distribution

ROCK FROM ARKANSAS (Brown, Bobby & Friends).
Album: released on White in Apr'87

SALUTE TO SCOTLAND, A.
Album: released on Ross in Jan'86 by Ross Records. Distributed by: Ross Distribution, Roots Distribution

Cassette: released on Ross in Jan'86 by Ross Records. Distributed by: Ross Distribution, Roots Distribution

TARRY A WHILE WITH.... (Brown, Bobby & The Scottish Accent).
Album: released on Ross in Jan'86 by Ross Records. Distributed by: Ross Distribution, Roots Distribution

Cassette: released on Ross in Jan'86 by Ross Records. Distributed by: Ross Distribution, Roots Distribution

Brown, Boe

CHINATOWN.
Tracks: / Chinatown / Dancer man.
Single (7"): released on President in Aug'86 by President Records. Distributed by: Taylors, Spartan

SOUND THAT FUNKY HORN (Brown, Boe & Uptown Horns).
Single (7"): released on President in Sep'85 by President Records. Distributed by: Taylors, Spartan

Single (12"): released on President in Sep'85 by President Records. Distributed by: Taylors, Spartan

Brown, Boots

Rockin"n'ravin'

Brown, Bus

PORTRAIT (Brown, Bus & Driftwood).
Album: released on Tank in Dec'77 by Tank Records

Brown, Carol

COME LOVE ME.
Tracks: / Come love me / Version love.
Single (12"): released on Rhythm Gits in Apr'86 by Rhythm Gits Records. Distributed by: Jetstar

FEEL SO GOOD.
Single (12"): released on UK Bubblers in Sep'84 by Greensleeves Records. Distributed by: RCA, Jetstar

Single (12"): released on Revue in Jan'85 by Revue Records. Distributed by: Creole

I WON'T HURT YOUR FEELINGS.
Tracks: / I won't hurt your feelings / Whistling Willie / Little action, A / Little action, A (instrumental).
Single (12"): released on CSA in Sep'87 by CSA Records. Distributed by: PRT, Jetstar

THIS USED TO BE YOUR HOUSE.
Single (12"): released on Rhythm Gits in Jun'85 by Rhythm Gits Records. Distributed by: Jetstar

Brown, Chad

I'M SORRY.
Tracks: / I'm sorry.
Single (7"): released on Bonaire in Mar'86. Distributed by: RCA, Ariola

Brown, Charles

DRIFTIN' BLUES.
Album: released on Pathe Marconi in Sep'84. Distributed by: Swift

GREAT RHYTHM AND BLUES VOL.2.
Album: released on Bulldog Records in Jul'82

SUNNYLAND (Brown, Charles & Johnny Moore's Three Blazers).
Album: released on Route 66 in Apr'79

SUNNY ROAD.
Album: released on Route 66 in Jun'80

Brown, Charlie

CHARLIE BROWN'S ALL STARS.
Cassette: released on Polydor in Nov'80 by Polydor Records. Distributed by: Polygram, Polydor

HE'S YOUR DOG,CHARLIE BROWN.
Cassette: released on Polydor in Nov'80 by Polydor Records. Distributed by: Polygram, Polydor

IT'S THE GREAT PUMPKIN,CHARLIE BROWN.

YOU'RE IN LOVE CHARLIE BROWN.
Cassette: released on Polydor in Nov'80 by Polydor Records. Distributed by: Polygram, Polydor

Brown, Chris

FORTUNE MY FOE (Brown, Chris/Andrew Geuter).
Album: released on Broadside in Jun'81 by Broadside Records. Distributed by: Celtic Distributions, H.R. Taylor, Jazz Music, Projection,

Cassette: released on Broadside in Jun'81 by Broadside Records. Distributed by: Celtic Distributions, H.R. Taylor, Jazz Music, Projection,

Brown, Chuck

BUSTIN' LOOSE (Brown, Chuck & Soul Searchers).
Album: released on EMI in Mar'85 by EMI Records. Distributed by: EMI

Cassette: released on EMI in Mar'85 by EMI Records. Distributed by: EMI

Single (12"): released on Source in Feb'85 by SMP Records. Distributed by: PRT

Single (7"): released on Source in Mar'85 by SMP Records. Distributed by: PRT Deleted May'86.

WE NEED SOME MONEY (Brown, Chuck & Souls).
Single (12"): released on Greyhound in Aug'84 by Greyhound Records. Distributed by: Greyhound

Brown, Clarence

ALRIGHT AGAIN (Brown, Clarence Gatemouth).
Album: released on Demon in May'82 by Demon Records. Distributed by: Pinnacle

ATOMIC ENERGY (Brown, Clarence Gatemouth).
Album: released on Blues Boy (Sweden) in Mar'84

CLARENCE 'GATEMOUTH' BROWN Original Peacock Recordings (Brown, Clarence Gatemouth).
Album: released on Rounder (USA) in Jan'84. Distributed by: Mike's Country Music Room Distribution, Jazz Music Distribution, Swift Distribution, Roots Records Distribution, Projection Distribution, Topic Distribution

CLARENCE GATEMOUTH BROWN (Brown, Clarence Gatemouth).
Album: released on Rounder Europa in Mar'87

GATE'S ON HEAT VOL.3.
Album: released on Barclay in Nov'79 by Decca Records. Distributed by: Polygram, Discovery, Conifer, IMS, Swift

MORE STUFF (Brown, Clarence Gatemouth).
Album: released on Black & Blue (France) in Jan'85. Distributed by: Swift, Target, Discovery

ONE MORE MILE (Brown, Clarence Gatemouth).
Album: released on Demon in Jul'83 by Demon Records. Distributed by: Pinnacle

SAN ANTONIO BALLBUSTER (Brown, Clarence Gatemouth).
Tracks: / Gate's salty blues / It never can be that way / I've been mistreated / She winked her eye / Win with me baby / She walked right in / Boogie uproar / Baby take it easy / Just got lucky / Didn't reach my goal / You got money / Okie dokie stomp / Just before dawn / Dirty work at the crossroads / Sad hour / Rock my blues away.
Album: released on Red Lightnin' in Sep'82 by Red Lightnin' Records. Distributed by: Roots, Swift, Jazz Music Pinnacle, Cartel, Wynd-Up Distribution

TEXAS GUITARMAN (Duke-Peacock Story Vol.1) (Brown, Clarence Gatemouth).
Tracks: / Boogie rambler / Justice blues / Atomic energy / Two o'clock in the morning / Mary is fine / Didn't reach my goal / Ilive the life / My time is expensive / She walks right in / I've been mistreated / Win with me baby / Just got lucky / Mercy on me / Too late baby / Taking my chances / It can never be that way.
Album: released on Ace in Jan'86 by Ace Records. Distributed by: Pinnacle, Swift, Hotshot, Cadillac

Brown, Clifford

ALTERNATE TAKES.
Album: released on Blue Note in Apr'85 by EMI Records. Distributed by: EMI

ARR: BY QUINCY JONES (Brown, Clifford Big Band).
Compact disc: . Distributed by: Discovery, Jazz Music, PRT, Swift

AT BASIN STREET (Brown, Clifford & Max Roach).
Tracks: / What is this thing called love? / Love is a many-splendoured thing / I'll remember April / Powell's prences / Time / Scene is clean, The / Gertrude's bounce.
Album: released on Mercury (Emarcy)_ in Dec'83

Compact disc: released on Mercury (Emarcy)_ in Dec'83

CLIFFORD BROWN, VOL.2.
Album: released on Jazz Reactivation in May'83. Distributed by: PRT

CLIFFORD BROWN QUARTET (Brown, Clifford Quartet).
Compact disc: released on Vogue in Dec'86. Distributed by: Discovery, Jazz Music, PRT, Swift

CLIFFORD BROWN, VOL.1.
Album: released on Jazz Reactivation in Jan'82. Distributed by: PRT

CLIFFORD BROWN, VOL.4.
Album: released on Jazz Reactivation in May'83. Distributed by: PRT

CLIFFORD BROWN, VOL.3.
Album: released on Jazz Reactivation in May'83. Distributed by: PRT

JAZZ IMMORTAL.
Album: released on Affinity in Nov'84 by Charly Records. Distributed by: Charly, Cadillac

LIVE AT BASIN STREET-1956 (Brown, Clifford & Max Roach).
Tracks: / Valse hot / I feel a song coming on / Sweet Georgia Brown / What's new? / Daahoud - drum conversation.
Album: released on Ingo in Apr'81. Distributed by: Jazz Horizons, Jazz Music, Celtic Music

MEMORIAL.
Album: released on Original Jazz Classics (USA) in Jun'86. Distributed by: Fantasy (USA) Distribution, Chris Wellard Distribution, IMS-Polygram Distribution

Album: released on Blue Note (USA Import) in Sep'84

MEMORIAL ALBUM.
Tracks: / Hymn of the Orient / Easy living / Minor mood / Cherokee (Indian love song) / Wail bait / Brownie speaks / De-dah / Cookin' you go to my head / Carvin' the rock.
Cassette: released on Blue Note in Apr'87 by EMI Records. Distributed by: EMI

Album: released on Blue Note in Apr'87 by EMI Records. Distributed by: EMI

MORE STUDY IN BROWN.
Tracks: / I'll remember April / Junior's arrival / Flossie Lou / Mildama / Jordu / These foolish things / Lands End / Blues walk, The.
Compact disc: by Emarcy Records(USA). Distributed by: Polygram

PURE GENIUS (Brown, Clifford & Max Roach).
Album: released on Elektra(Musician) in Jun'82 by WEA Records. Distributed by: WEA

STUDY IN BROWN (see also Max Roach) (Brown, Clifford & Max Roach).
Tracks: / Cherokee / Jacqui / Lands End / George's dilemma / Sandu / Gherkin for Perkin / If I love again / Take the A train.
Compact disc: by Emarcy Records(USA). Distributed by: Polygram

Album: released on Mercury (Emarcy)_ in Dec'83

Compact disc: released on Mercury (Emarcy)_ in Dec'83

TRUMPET MASTERS (Brown, Clifford & D.Gillispie).
Single (7"): released on Vogue in Mar'75. Distributed by: Discovery, Jazz Music, PRT, Swift

WITH STRINGS.

Tracks: / Yesterdays / Laura / What's new? / Blue moon / Can't help lovin' dat man / Embraceable you / Willow weep for me / Smoke gets in your eyes / Portrait of Jenny / Where or when / Stardust.
Album: released on Mercury (Emarcy) in Dec'83

Compact disc: released on Mercury (Emarcy) in Dec'83

WITH STRINGS.
Compact disc: by Phonogram Records. Distributed by: Polygram Distribution

Brown, Dennis

20 CLASSIC REGGAE TRACKS.
Album: released on Meteor in Apr'85 by Magnum Music Group Ltd. Distributed by: Magnum Music Group Ltd, PRT Distribution, Spartan Distribution

ALL FOR ONE,ONE FOR ALL (Brown, Dennis & Leroy Sibble).
Tracks: / All for one,one for all / All for one,one for all(version).
Single (12"): released on Charm in May'86. Distributed by: Jetstar

AMAGIDEON.
Single (12"): released on Tads in Jul'84 by Tads Records. Distributed by: Jetstar Distribution

ANYWAY YOU WANT IT.
Tracks: / Anyway you want it / Anyway you want it(version).
Single (12"): released on Tads in Sep'86 by Tads Records. Distributed by: Jetstar Distribution

BAALGAD (Brown, Dennis & Enos the Clown).
Album: released on Goodies in Aug'86. Distributed by: Jetstar

BEST OF DENNIS BROWN, THE.
Album: released on Blue Moon in Jun'83. Distributed by: Magnum Music Group Ltd, PRT, Spartan

Cassette: released on Blue Moon in Jun'83. Distributed by: Magnum Music Group Ltd, PRT, Spartan

BEST, THE.
Notes: Previously unavailable album specially compiled for the Pricebusters series.This is the definitive album from one of the all-time reggae greats.14 songs including'Love Has Found It's Way' and 'The Profit Rides Again'.The album features production credits by the legendary Joe Gibbs and boasts a stunning array of musicians(including Robbie Shakespeare & Sly Dunbar).
Album: released on A&M in Sep'86 by A&M Records. Distributed by: Polygram

Cassette: released on A&M in Sep'86 by A&M Records. Distributed by: Polygram

BLACK MAGIC WOMAN.
Single (12"): released on Phil Pratt in Apr'84

BREAKING DOWN THE BARRIERS.
Single (12"): released on Natty Congo in Nov'83 by Natty Congo Records. Distributed by: Jetstar

BROWN SUGAR.
Album: released on Taxi in Aug'86 by Taxi Records. Distributed by: Jetstar Distribution

DECEIVING GIRL.
Single (12"): released on Yucca Ur in Apr'84 by Revolver Records. Distributed by: Cartel

DEEPEST LOVE.
Tracks: / Deepest love / Deep music.
Single (12"): released on Natty Congo in May'86 by Natty Congo Records. Distributed by: Jetstar

DENNIS BROWN COLLECTION, THE.
Album: released on Dennis Ting in Jan'85 by Dennis Ting Records. Distributed by: Jetstar

EASY TAKE IT EASY.
Single (12"): released on Tads in Jun'83 by Tads Records. Distributed by: Jetstar Distribution

EXIT, THE.
Album: released on Trojan in Nov'86 by Trojan Records. Distributed by: PRT, Jetstar

Cassette: released on Trojan in Nov'86 by Trojan Records. Distributed by: PRT, Jetstar

EXIT,THE.
Tracks: / Exit, The / Exit, The(version).
Single (12"): released on Unity Sound in Dec'85. Distributed by: Jetstar

FLY ME AWAY.
Single (12"): released on Jah Shaka in Dec'82 by Jah Shaka Records. Distributed by: Jetstar

FUNNY FEELING (Brown, Dennis & Trinity).
Single (12"): released on Hawkeye in Apr'84 by Hawkeye Records. Distributed by: Hawkeye, Lightning (WEA) Distribution, Jetstar, PRT

GO NOW.
Single (7"): released on Oval in May'82. Distributed by: Projection

HALFWAY UP HALFWAY DOWN.
Single (7"): released on A&M in Aug'82 by A&M Records. Distributed by: Polygram

Single (12"): released on A&M in Aug'82 by A&M Records. Distributed by: Polygram Deleted '84.

HERE I COME.
Single (12"): released on Tads in Aug'85 by Tads Records. Distributed by: Jetstar Distribution

HISTORY.
Album: released on World Enterprise in Nov'86. Distributed by: Jetstar

HOLD ON TO WHAT YOU GOT.
Single (12"): released on Power House in Jul'82 by Power House Records. Distributed by: Jetstar

HOLD TIGHT.
Tracks: / Hold tight / Indiscioline woman / Footstool / Let him go / When spring is around / I've got your number / Worried man / Things in life.
Album: released on Live & Love in Sep'86 by Third World Records. Distributed by: Jetstar

Cassette: released on Live & Love in Sep'86 by Third World Records. Distributed by: Jetstar

HOLD TIGHT(12").
Tracks: / Hold tight / Hold tight(version).
Single (12"): released on Live & Learn in Apr'86. Distributed by: Jetstar

HOW CAN I LEAVE.
Single (12"): released on Real Wax in Aug'84

I CAN'T STAND IT.
Single (12"): released on Joe Gibbs in Apr'84 by Joe Gibbs Records. Distributed by: Jetstar

IF I DON'T LOVE YOU.
Single (12"): released on Thompson Sound in Dec'82 by Thompson Sound Records. Distributed by: PRT Distribution

IF THIS WORLD WAS MINE.
Single (12"): released on Tads in Nov'82 by Tads Records. Distributed by: Jetstar Distribution

I LIKE IT LIKE THAT.
Single (12"): released on Yvonne's in Jun'83 by Special Records. Distributed by: Jetstar

ISRAEL.
Single (12"): released on Natty Congo in Nov'85 by Natty Congo Records. Distributed by: Jetstar

IT'S MAGIC.
Single (12"): released on Greensleeves in Dec'84 by Greensleeves Records. Distributed by: BMG, Jetstar, Spartan

I'VE GOT TO FIND YOU.
Single (12"): released on Black Joy in Feb'82. Distributed by: Jetstar

JOSEPH'S COAT OF MANY COLOURS.
Album: released on Blue Moon in Apr'84. Distributed by: Magnum Music Group Ltd, PRT, Spartan

JUDGE NOT (Brown, Dennis/Gregory Isaacs).
Album: released on Greensleeves in Oct'84 by Greensleeves Records. Distributed by: BMG, Jetstar, Spartan

JUST DENNIS.
Tracks: / Show us the way / Cassandra / Run too tuff / Westbound train / Africa / Love jah / No more will I roam / Some like it hot / Conquerer / Only a smile / Silver words / Yagga yagga you'll suffer).
Album: released on Trojan in May'83 by Trojan Records. Distributed by: PRT, Jetstar

LET OFF SUPM (Brown, Dennis/Gregory Isaacs).
Single (12"): released on Greensleeves in Jun'85 by Greensleeves Records. Distributed by: BMG, Jetstar, Spartan

LIVE AND LOVE.
Single (12"): released on Greensleeves in Nov'85 by Greensleeves Records. Distributed by: BMG, Jetstar, Spartan

LIVE AT MONTREUX.
Album: released on Blue Moon in Aug'84. Distributed by: Magnum Music Group Ltd, PRT, Spartan

LOVE HAS FOUND IT'S WAY.
Tracks: / Love has found it's way / Get high on your love / Handwriting on the wall / Weep and moan / Bood sweat and tears / Halfway up halfway down / Any day now / I couldn't stand losing you / Why baby why / Get up.
Notes: Getting to be reggae's acknowledged crown prince is not an easy business. Dennischildhood included not just the lunchtime vocalising but serious professional work with Kingston's popular Bryon Lee & The Dragonaires. by the time he was out of his teens, he performed extensively throughout the West Indies and developed one of the freshest, and most distictive style in rteggae music. In 1979 he starred at montreaux's prestigious jazz festival, and followed it up with his first hit, Money in my pocket. It's sucess led to brown's signing with A & M and the January 1981 release of his first LP Foul Play.
Album: released on A&M in Jun'82 by A&M Records. Distributed by: Polygram

LOVELY FEELING.
Tracks: / Lovely feeling.
Single (12"): released on Blue Mountain in Aug'86. Distributed by: Jetstar

LOVE ME FOREVER.
Single (12"): released on Paradise in Mar'86. Distributed by: Jetstar

LOVE'S GOT A HOLD ON ME.
Album: released on Joe Gibbs in Sep'84 by Joe Gibbs Records. Distributed by: Jetstar

LOVE'S GOTTA HOLD ME.
Album: released on Blue Moon in Oct'86. Distributed by: Magnum Music Group Ltd, PRT, Spartan

MADONNA.
Single (7"): released on Chartsounds in Aug'85 by Chartsounds Records. Distributed by: Jetstar

MISCHIEF.
Single (12"): released on Live & Learn in May'87. Distributed by: Jetstar

MONEY IN MY POCKET.
Tracks: / Money in my pocket / Ah so we stay(Big Youth) / Changing times / Silhouettes / Africa / Yagga-yagga / I am the conqueror / Show us the way / Cassandra / No more will I roam.
Album: released on Trojan in Feb'86 by Trojan Records. Distributed by: PRT, Jetstar

Cassette: released on Trojan in Feb'86 by Trojan Records. Distributed by: PRT, Jetstar

Cassette: released on Trojan in May'83 by Trojan Records. Distributed by: PRT, Jetstar

MR BOJANGLES.
Single (12"): released on Maccabees in Jul'85 by Maccabees Records. Distributed by: Jetstar

NOWHERE WILL I ROAM.
Single (12"): released on Time in Dec'84. Distributed by: Jetstar Distribution

OH GIRL.
Single (12"): released on Natty Congo in Oct'82 by Natty Congo Records. Distributed by: Jetstar

Single (12"): released on Natty Congo in Sep'85 by Natty Congo Records. Distributed by: Jetstar

OLE MAN RIVER.
Single (12"): released on Maccabees in Apr'85 by Maccabees Records. Distributed by: Jetstar

PROMISED LAND (Brown, Dennis & Aswad).
Single (12"): released on Simba in Apr'83 by Simba Records. Distributed by: Jetstar

PROPHET RIDES AGAIN, THE.
Tracks: / Out of the funk / Jasmine my way to fame / Save a little love for me / Wonders of the world / Too hot / Prophet rides again, The / Historical places / This love of mine / Shashamane living (country living) / Storms are raging.
Notes: The second A & M album from reggae giant Dennis Brown, once again produced by the legendary Jamaican soundman, Joe Gibbs. The Prophet rides again has a decidely "Funkier" sound than his previous recordings, fusing contemporary black music with Dennis Brown's traditional reggae roots.
Album: released on A&M in Aug'83 by A&M Records. Distributed by: Polygram

Cassette: released on A&M in Aug'83 by A&M Records. Distributed by: Polygram

RAGGAMUFFIN' (Brown, Dennis/Freddie MacGregor).
Single (12"): released on Greensleeves in Sep'85 by Greensleeves Records. Distributed by: BMG, Jetstar, Spartan

REBEL WITH A CAUSE (Brown, Dennis & Jackie Mitoo).
Tracks: / Rebel with a cause.
Single (12"): released on Jakki in Jun'86. Distributed by: Jetstar

REGGAE SUPERSTARS MEET (Brown, Dennis/Horace Andy).
Album: released on Striker Lee in Jun'86 by Striker Lee Records. Distributed by: Jetstar Distribution

REVOLUTION.
Album: released on Yvonne's Special in Jan'85

REVOLUTION (PART 2).
Single (12"): released on Taxi in Apr'85 by Taxi Records. Distributed by: Jetstar Distribution

SATISFACTORY FEELING.
Tracks: / Revolution / If this world were mind / Oh girl / Easy take it easy / Rub-a-dub / Unite brotherman / Praise without raise / Money in my pocket.
Album: released on Tads-Yvonne Special in Jun'83

SLAVE DRIVER.
Single (12"): released on Blue Moon in Jan'84. Distributed by: Magnum Music Group Ltd, PRT, Spartan

SLOW DOWN.
Tracks: / Slow Down / Woman / Joy in the Morning / They Fight / Let's Build Our Dreams / Love by the Score / Can't Keep a Good Man Down / Icy Road / Now and Forever / Come on Over / Africa We Want To Go.
Compact disc: released on Greensleeves in Feb'87 by Greensleeves Records. Distributed by: BMG, Jetstar, Spartan

SLOW DOWN.
Album: released on Greensleeves in Jul'85 by Greensleeves Records. Distributed by: BMG, Jetstar, Spartan

Cassette: released on Greensleeves in Jul'85 by Greensleeves Records. Distributed by: BMG, Jetstar, Spartan

SLOW DOWN WOMAN.
Single (12"): released on Greensleeves in Apr'85 by Greensleeves Records. Distributed by: BMG, Jetstar, Spartan

SMILE LIKE AN ANGEL.
Album: released on Blue Moon in Nov'86. Distributed by: Magnum Music Group Ltd, PRT, Spartan

Cassette: released on Blue Moon in Nov'86. Distributed by: Magnum Music Group Ltd, PRT, Spartan

SPELLBOUND.
Album: released on Blue Moon in Sep'85. Distributed by: Magnum Music Group Ltd, PRT, Spartan

STEP BY STEP.
Tracks: / Step by step / Stepping.
Single (12"): released on Diamond C in May'86 by Diamond C Records. Distributed by: Jetstar

SUPER HITS.
Tracks: / Concentration (ver 1) / Concentration (ver 2) / Silhouettes / Witchita line man / How he can't spell / Musical heatwave / I didn't know (ver 1) / I didn't know (ver 2) / How could I let you get away / Lips of wine / Let me down easy / Changing times.
Album: released on Trojan in May'83 by Trojan Records. Distributed by: PRT, Jetstar

TIME AND PLACE.
Single (12"): released on Clock Tower in Feb'84

VISIONS.
Tracks: / Deliverence will come / Oh mother / Love me always / Concrete castle / Malcolm X / Repatriation / Jah can do it / Milk and honey / Stay at home / Say what you say.
Album: released on Lightning in Jul'78 by Lightning Records. Distributed by: Jetstar

Album: released on Blue Moon in Apr'85. Distributed by: Magnum Music Group Ltd, PRT, Spartan

WAKE UP.
Album: released on Natty Congo in Dec'85 by Natty Congo Records. Distributed by: Jetstar

WALLS AND LETTERS.
Album: released on Joe Gibbs in Aug'84 by Joe Gibbs Records. Distributed by: Jetstar

WHIP THEM JAH.
Single (12"): released on Hawkeye in Sep'81 by Hawkeye Records. Distributed by: Hawkeye, Lightning (WEA) Distribution, Jetstar, PRT

WOLF & LEOPARDS.
Cassette: released on EMI in Jun'79 by EMI Records. Distributed by: EMI

WOLVES AND LEOPARDS.
Album: released on Blue Moon in 11 Apr'87. Distributed by: Magnum Music Group Ltd, PRT, Spartan

Cassette: released on Blue Moon in 11 Apr'87. Distributed by: Magnum Music Group Ltd, PRT, Spartan

WORDS OF WISDOM.
Tracks: / So Jah say / Don't feel no way / Words of wisdom / Should I? / True / Ain't that lovin' you / Cassandra / Love.
Album: released on Blue Moon in Dec'82. Distributed by: Magnum Music Group Ltd, PRT, Spartan

YESTERDAY, TODAY & TOMORROW.
Album: released on Blue Moon in Aug'86. Distributed by: Magnum Music Group Ltd, PRT,

YOU ARE.
Single (7"): released on Tads in Dec'83 by Tads Records. Distributed by: Jetstar Distribution

YOUR LOVE GOTTA HOLD ON ME.
Single (7"): released on Joe Gibbs in May'83 by Joe Gibbs Records. Distributed by: Jetstar

Single (12"): released on Joe Gibbs in Jun'83 by Joe Gibbs Records. Distributed by: Jetstar

YOUR LOVE IS A BLESSING.
Single (12"): released on Yvonne's Special in Nov'83

Brown, Dougie

PRESENCE.
Tracks: / Reigning in all splendour / All because of your love / Lord and father / For thou O lord / Jesus, we enthrone you / River, wash over me / Living under the shadow / We worship and adore you / We place you on the highest place / Father's love / You laid aside your majesty / Father, we love you / I love you lord / Lord, we want to thank you / When I look into your holiness.
Album: released on Spirit of Praise in Jul'87

Cassette: released on Spirit of Praise in Jul'87

Browne, Duncan

MUSIC FROM THE TRAVELLING MAN (Browne, Duncan & Graham Jones).
Tracks: / Max's theme / Steve's theme / Lament for Billie / Andrea's theme / Berceuse / Family, The / Winter / Chase, The / Day for night / Morag / Zoot / Travelling man / Old flames / End of the line.
Album: released on Towerbell in Sep'86 by Towerbell Records. Distributed by: EMI

Cassette: released on Towerbell in Sep'86 by Towerbell Records. Distributed by: EMI

PLANET EARTH.
Tracks: / American heartbeat / Things to come / Wild places, The / Planet earth / Fauvette / Streets of fire / Child of change,(Restless) / She's just a fallen angel / Crash, The / Cancion de cuna:street echoes.
Album: released on Conifer in May'86 by Conifer Records. Distributed by: Conifer

Cassette: released on Conifer in May'86 by Conifer Records. Distributed by: Conifer

THEME FROM TRAVELLING MAN.
Single (7"): released on Towerbell in Jul'85 by Towerbell Records. Distributed by: EMI

Browne, Jackson

EGO MANIAC.
Tracks: / Ego maniac / Love's gonna get you.
Single (7"): released on Warner Brothers in Feb'87 by Warner Bros Records. Distributed by: WEA

Single (12"): released on Warner Brothers in Feb'87 by Warner Bros Records. Distributed by: WEA

FOR AMERICA.
Tracks: / For America / Till I go down.
Single (7"): released on Elektra (USA) in Feb'86 by Elektra/Asylum/Nonesuch Records. Distributed by: WEA

FOR EVERYMAN.
Tracks: / Take it easy / Our Lady of the Well / Colours of the sun / I thought I was a child / These days / Redneck friend / Times you come, The / Ready or not / Sing my songs to me / For Everyman.
Compact disc: released on Asylum in Jan'87 by WEA Records. Distributed by: WEA

HOLD OUT.
Album: released on Elektra (USA) in Jul'80 by Elektra/Asylum/Nonesuch Records. Distributed by: WEA

Cassette: released on Elektra (USA) in Aug'80 by Elektra/Asylum/Nonesuch Records. Distributed by: WEA

HOLD OUT.
Tracks: / Disco Apocalypse / Hold On, Hold Out / Of Missing Persons / Call It A Loan / That Girl Could Sing / Hold Out / Boulevard / Disco apocalypse / Hold out / That girl could sing / Boulevard / Oh missing persions / Call it a loan / Hold on hold out / Disco apocalypse / Hold out / That girl could sing / Boulevard / Oh missing persons / Call it a loan / Hold on hold out.
Compact disc: released on Asylum in Jan'87 by WEA Records. Distributed by: WEA

IN THE SHAPE OF A HEART.
Tracks: / In the shape of a heart(Edited remix) / Voice.
Single (7"): released on Elektra (USA) in '86 by Elektra/Asylum/Nonesuch Records. Distributed by: WEA

JACKSON BROWNE.
Tracks: / Jamaica say you will / Child in these hills, A / Song for Adam / Doctor my eyes / From silver lake / Something fine / Under the falling sky / Looking into you / Rock me on the water / My opening farewell / Jamaica say you will / Child in these hills, A / Song for Adam / Doctor my eyes / From Silver Lake / Something fine / Under the falling sky / Looking into you / Rock me on the water / My opening farewell.
Compact disc: released on Asylum in Dec'86 by WEA Records. Distributed by: WEA

Album: released on Asylum in Jun'76 by WEA Records. Distributed by: WEA

JACKSON BROWNE/RUNNING ON EMPTY.
Double cassette: released on Asylum in Nov'83 by WEA Records. Distributed by: WEA

LATE FOR THE SKY.
Tracks: / Late for the sky / Fountain of sorrow / Farther on / Late show, The / Road and the sky, The / For a dancer / Walking slow / Before the deluge / Late for the sky / Fountain of sorrow / Further on / Late show, The / Road and the sky, The / For a dancer / Walking slow / Before the deluge.
Album: released on Asylum in Jun'76 by WEA Records. Distributed by: WEA

LAWYERS IN LOVE.
Tracks: / For a rocker / Lawyers in love / On the day / Cut it away / Downtown / Tender is the night / Knock on any door / Say it isn't true.
Compact disc: by WEA Records. Distributed by: WEA

Album: released on Asylum in Sep'83 by WEA Records. Distributed by: WEA

Cassette: released on Asylum in Sep'83 by WEA Records. Distributed by: WEA

Single (7"): released on Elektra (USA) in Jul'83 by Elektra/Asylum/Nonesuch Records. Distributed by: WEA

LIVES IN THE BALANCE.
Tracks: / For America / Soldier of plenty / In the shape of a heart / Candy / Lawless avenue / Lives in the balance / Till I go down / Black & white.
Compact disc: by Elektra/Asylum/Nonesuch Records. Distributed by: WEA

Album: released on Elektra (USA) in Mar'86 by Elektra/Asylum/Nonesuch Records. Distributed by: WEA

Cassette: released on Elektra (USA) in Mar'86 by Elektra/Asylum/Nonesuch Records. Distributed by: WEA

PRETENDER/LATE FOR THE SKY.
Cassette: released on Asylum in Oct'82 by WEA Records. Distributed by: WEA

PRETENDER, THE.
Tracks: / Fuse, The / Your bright baby blues / Linda Paloma / Here come those tears again / Only child, The / Daddy's time / Sleep's dark and silent gate / Pretender, The.
Compact disc: released on Asylum in Dec'86 by WEA Records. Distributed by: WEA

Album: released on Asylum in Nov'76 by WEA Records. Distributed by: WEA

Cassette: released on Asylum in Nov'76 by WEA Records. Distributed by: WEA

RUNNING ON EMPTY.
Compact disc: released on Asylum in Jan'87 by WEA Records. Distributed by: WEA

RUNNING ON EMPTY.
Tracks: / Running on empty / Road, The / Rosie / You love the thunder / Cocaine / Shaky town / Love needs a heart / Nothing but time / Load out, The / Stay / Running on empty.
Album: released on Asylum in Jan'78 by WEA Records. Distributed by: WEA

Cassette: released on Asylum in Jan'78 by WEA Records. Distributed by: WEA

Brown, Errol

PERSONAL TOUCH.
Tracks: / Personal touch / Why don't you call me.
Single (7"): released on WEA in Jun'87 by WEA Records. Distributed by: WEA

Single (12"): released on WEA in Jun'87 by WEA Records. Distributed by: WEA

Browne, Tom

FUNKIN' FOR JAMAICA.
Single (7"): released on Arista in Jun'80 by Arista Records. Distributed by: RCA

Single (12"): released on Arista in Jun'80 by Arista Records. Distributed by: RCA

Single (7"): released on Old Gold in Jul'84 by Old Gold Records. Distributed by: Lightning, Jazz Music, Spartan, Counterpoint

LOVE APPROACH.
Album: released on GRP (USA) in Jul'80 by GRP Records (USA). Distributed by: IMS, Polygram

MAGIC.
Single (7"): released on Arista in Jan'81 by Arista Records. Distributed by: RCA

Single (12"): released on Arista in Jan'81 by Arista Records. Distributed by: RCA

ROCKIN' RADIO.
Album: released on Arista in Oct'83 by Arista Records. Distributed by: RCA

Cassette: released on Arista in Oct'83 by Arista Records. Distributed by: RCA

TOMMY GUN.
Album: released on Arista in Oct'84 by Arista Records. Distributed by: RCA

Cassette: released on Arista in Oct'84 by Arista Records. Distributed by: RCA

YOURS TRULY.
Tracks: / Fungi mama (beebopafunkadiscolypso) / Bygonnes / Charisma / Can't can't give it away / Lazy bird / Naima / Come for a ride / My latin sky / Message, A: pride and pity.
Notes: Yours Truly is tom Browne's fourth arista/GRP album and follows Browne Sugar, "Love Approach" and "Magic". On his new album Browne and his band pay homage to their jazz influences, while also continuing their funk explosion and gettingfarther into dance rhythms. yours Truly conains two compositions by the immortanJohn Coltrane (Lazy bird and Naima) one by Lonnie Smith (My latin sky and some tom Browne originals.
Album: released on GRP (USA) in Dec'81 by GRP Records (USA). Distributed by: IMS, Polygram

Brown, Floyd

BROWN, FLOYD.
Album: . Distributed by: Swift

Brown, Gabriel

GABRIEL BROWN.
Album: released on Krazy Kat (USA) in Nov'84

Brown, Gatemouth

DUKE PEACOCKS STORY VOL. 1 (THE).
Album: released on Ace in Dec'86 by Ace Records. Distributed by: Pinnacle, Swift, Hotshot, Cadillac

Brown, Gerry

IT'S ALRIGHT.
Single (7"): released on AOR in Apr'84. Distributed by: PRT

MARY SAID.
Single (7"): released on AOR in Aug'84. Distributed by: PRT,

Brown, Glen

YOU'RE BREAKING MY HEART.
Tracks: / (Hi-Tech Dub).
Single (12"): released on Hi-Tech in Nov'86. Distributed by: Jetstar

Brown, Graham. T.

I TELL IT LIKE IT USED TO BE.
Tracks: / Say when / Don't go to strangers / Rock it, Billy / I tell it like it used to be / I wish that I could hurt that way again / Later train / You're trying to hard / Hell and high water / Don't make a liar out of me / Is there anything I can do.
Notes: Soulful Country Stylist T. Graham Brown makes his Capitol album debut in the UK with a Rhythm and Blues flavoured country album. The album contains a well balanced mix of soulful ballads and rousing country rockers and is produced by the noted Nashville producer Bud Logan. Featuring the excellent guitar work of Brent Rowan, one of Nashville's top session musicians who has performed with virtually every top country name.
Album: released on Capitol in Mar'87 by Capitol Records. Distributed by: EMI

Cassette: released on Capitol in Mar'87 by Capitol Records. Distributed by: EMI

SAY WHEN.
Tracks: / Say When / She's Mine.
Single (7"): released on Capitol in Feb'87 by Capitol Records. Distributed by: EMI

TALKIN' TO IT.
Single (7"): released on Capitol in Aug'87 by Capitol Records. Distributed by: EMI

Brown, Greg

BABY TALK.
Single (7"): released on Beau-Jolly in Jun'84 by Nouveau Records. Distributed by: PRT

Single (12"): released on Beau-Jolly in Jun'84 by Nouveau Records. Distributed by: PRT

Brown, Hylo

HYLO BROWN MEETS THE LONESOME PINE FIDDLERS (Brown, Hylo/Lonesome Pine Fiddlers).
Album: released on Starday in Apr'87

Cassette: released on Starday in Apr'87

Browning Version, The

BROWNING VERSION, THE Terence Rattigan (Roundabout Theatre Company).
Double cassette: released on Caedmon(USA) in Aug'83 by Caedmon (USA) Records. Distributed by: Gower, Taylors, Discovery

Brown, James

BEST OF JAMES BROWN, THE.
Tracks: / Say it loud, I'm black and I'm proud / Please please please / Try me / Lost someone / Papa's got a brand new bag, Part 1 / It's a man's man's man's world / Cold sweat / There was a time / Popcorn, The / Hot pants / Sex machine.
Album: released on Polydor in Jul'82 by Polydor Records. Distributed by: Polygram, Polydor

Cassette: released on Polydor in Jul'82 by Polydor Records. Distributed by: Polygram, Polydor

Cassette: released on K-Tel in Oct'87 by K-Tel Records. Distributed by: Record Merchandisers Distribution, Taylors, Terry Blood Distribution, Wynd-Up Distribution, Relay Distribution, Pickwick Distribution, Solomon & Peres Distribution, Polygram

Cassette: released on K-Tel in Oct'87 by K-Tel Records. Distributed by: Record Merchandisers Distribution, Taylors, Terry Blood Distribution, Wynd-Up Distribution, Relay Distribution, Pickwick Distribution, Solomon & Peres Distribution, Polygram

Compact disc: released on K-Tel in Aug'87 by K-Tel Records. Distributed by: Record Merchandisers Distribution, Taylors, Terry Blood Distribution, Wynd-Up Distribution, Relay Distribution, Pickwick Distribution, Solomon & Peres Distribution, Polygram. Estim retail price in Sep'87 was £6.99.

BODY HEAT.
Album: released on Phonogram in Oct'82 by Phonogram Records. Distributed by: Polygram

BRING IT ON.
Album: released on Sonet in Sep'83 by Sonet Records. Distributed by: PRT

BRING IT ON,BRING IT ON.
Tracks: / Bring it on,bring it on / Night time is the right time, The.
Single (7"): released on Sonet in Mar'86 by Sonet Records. Distributed by: PRT

Single (12"): released on Sonet in Mar'86 by Sonet Records. Distributed by: PRT

COLD SWEAT.
Album: released on Polydor in Nov'83 by Polydor Records. Distributed by: Polygram, Polydor

Album: released on Polydor in Nov'83 by Polydor Records. Distributed by: Polygram, Polydor

COLD SWEAT LIVE.
Notes: Recorded live in concert. Includes 'Papa's got a brand new bag', 'Get up off of that thing', 'Sex machine', 'Please please please', 'This is a man's world', 'Cold sweat'.
Album: released on Perfect in Apr'87

COMPACT DISC OF JAMES BROWN, THE.
Tracks: / Doing it to death / Super bad / Soul power / Think / It's a man's man's man's world / Try me (I need you) / Bewildered / Out of sight / I got you / Prisoner of love / I got the feelin' / Maybe the last time / Licking stick, licking stick / Mother popcorn / Papa's got a brand new bag / Sex machine / Payback, The / Please please please.
Compact disc: released on Polydor in Sep'85 by Polydor Records. Distributed by: Polygram, Polydor

DEAD ON THE HEAVY FUNK 74-76.
Tracks: / Superbad,superslick / Your love / Body-heat(Part 1) / Hot (I need to be loved,loved,loved) / Get up offa that thing / Funky president (people it's bad) / Don't tell it / Future shock of the world / Woman.
Album: released on Polydor in Mar'86 by Polydor Records. Distributed by: Polygram, Polydor

Cassette: released on Polydor in Mar'86 by Polydor Records. Distributed by: Polygram, Polydor

EXCITEMENT.
Album: released on Polydor in Nov'83 by Polydor Records. Distributed by: Polygram, Polydor

FEDERAL YEARS VOL.1.
Album: released on Solid Smoke (USA) in Jul'84. Distributed by: Rhino

FEDERAL YEARS VOL.2 (Maag, Peter & The London Symphony Orchestra).
Album: released on Solid Smoke (USA) in Jul'84. Distributed by: Rhino

FROGGY MIX.
Single (7"): released on Boiling Point in Apr'85 by Polydor Records. Distributed by: Polygram

Single (12"): released on Boiling Point in Apr'85 by Polydor Records. Distributed by: Polygram

GET UP, GET INTO IT, GET INVOLVED.
Tracks: / Get up, get into it, get involved (pt.I) / Get up, get into it, get involved (pt.II).
Single (7"): released on King (USA) in Mar'87 by Gusto Records. Distributed by: Gusto Distribution, IMS, Swift

GET UP I FEEL LIKE BEING A SEX MACHINE (PART 1).
Single (7"): released on Boiling Point in Jun'85 by Polydor Records. Distributed by: Polygram

Single (12"): released on Boiling Point in Jun'85 by Polydor Records. Distributed by: Polygram

GET UP I FEEL LIKE BEING A SEX MACHINE.
Single (7"): released on Old Gold in Jul'84 by Old Gold Records. Distributed by: Lightning, Jazz Music, Spartan, Counterpoint

GET UP I FEEL LIKE BEING A SEX MACHINE(PART 1).
Tracks: / Get up I feel like being a sex machine(part 1) / Papas got a brand new bag / Get up I feel like being a sex machine(part 2)* / Get on the good foot* / Get up offa that thing* / Get up I feel like being a sex machine (part 1) / Papa's got a brand new bag / Get up I feel like being a sex machine (part 2) / Get on the good foot / Get up offa that thing (release the pressure).
Notes: *=Extra track on 12" only.
Single (7"): released on Boiling Point in Feb'86 by Polydor Records. Distributed by: Polygram

Single (12"): released on Boiling Point in Feb'86 by Polydor Records. Distributed by: Polygram

GRAVITY.
Tracks: / How do you stop / Turn me loose, I'm Dr. Feelgood / Living in America / Goliath / Repeat the beat (faith) / Return to me / Gravity / Let's get personal / Gravity / How do you stop / Turn me loose / I'm Dr.Feelgood / Living in America / Goliath / Repeat the beat(Faith) / Return to me.
Compact disc: released on Scotti Brothers in Mar'87 by Scotti Brothers Records. Distributed by: CBS

Album: released on Scotti Brothers in Oct'86 by Scotti Brothers Records. Distributed by: CBS

Cassette: released on Scotti Brothers in Oct'86 by Scotti Brothers Records. Distributed by: CBS

GRAVITY (S).
Tracks: / Gravity / Gravity(dub).
Single (7"): released on Scotti Brothers in Oct'86 by Scotti Brothers Records. Distributed by: CBS

Single (12"): released on Scotti Brothers in Oct'86 by Scotti Brothers Records. Distributed by: CBS

GREATEST HITS:JAMES BROWN.
Tracks: / Please,please,please / Try me / Think / Papa's got a brand new bag / I got you (I feel good) / It's a man's man's man's world / Bring it up / Cold sweat / There was a time / I got the feelin' / Say it loud-I'm black & I'm proud / Sex machine / Hot pants / My thang / Funky President (people it's bad) / Get up offa that thing.
Double Album: released on Polydor in Nov'80 by Polydor Records. Distributed by: Polygram, Polydor

Album: released on Polydor (France) in Feb'85. Distributed by: Polygram

Cassette: released on Polydor (France) in Feb'85. Distributed by: Polygram

HOW DO YOU STOP.
Tracks: / How do you stop / Repeat the beat.
Single (7"): released on Scotti Brothers in Apr'87 by Scotti Brothers Records. Distributed by: CBS

Single (12"): released on Scotti Brothers in Apr'87 by Scotti Brothers Records. Distributed by: CBS

HOW DO YOU STOP (SPECIAL EXTENDED REMIX).
Tracks: / Goliath (Message House Mix) / Repeat The Beat (Faith).
Single (12"): released on Scotti Brothers in Dec'86 by Scotti Brothers Records. Distributed by: CBS

I GOT YOU.
Tracks: / I got you (I feel good) / Good good lovin' / Lost someone / I can't help it / You've got the power / Night train / I've got money / Dancin' little thing / Think / Three hearts in a tangle / Suds / Love don't love nobody.
Album: released on Polydor in Nov'83 by Polydor Records. Distributed by: Polygram, Polydor

IN THE JUNGLE GROOVE.
Compact disc:

IN THE JUNGLE GROOVE.
Tracks: / It's a new day / Funky drummer / Give it up or turn it loose(remix) / I got to move* / Talking loud & saying nothing(remix) / Get up,get into it, get involved / Soul power(re-edit) / Hot pants / Funky drummer(bonus beats).
Notes: Two record set containing over an hour of full length,full strength funk.There are two brand new remixes,a previously unreleased master piece,and two new re-edits. All other tracks are presented in their original full-length versions,many for the first time.
Double Album: released on Polydor (USA) in Sep'86

Cassette: released on Polydor (USA) in Sep'86

IT'S A MAN'S MAN'S MAN'S WORLD.
Tracks: / It's a man's man's man's world / Is it yes or is it no / Ain't that a groove (parts 1 & 2) / Scratch, (The) / Bewildered / Bells in the wee wee hours, (The) / Come over here / I don't mind / Just you and me / I love you, yes I do.
Album: released on Polydor in Nov'83 by Polydor Records. Distributed by: Polygram,

IT'S A MAN'S WORLD.
Tracks: / It's a man's world / Sex machine.
Single (12"): released on Konnexion in May'86 Distributed by: Roots, Pinnacle

JAMES BROWN IN CONCERT.
Tracks: / Papa's got a brand new bag / It's a man's,man's world.
Notes: The funk-master recorded on stage at Hammersmith Odeon. 1985 Production.Type of recording: Live Total playing time: 60minutes.
Video-cassette (VHS): released on Virgin in Apr'86 by Virgin Records. Distributed by: EMI, Virgin Distribution

JAMES BROWN LIVE AND LOW-DOWN AT THE APOLLO VOL.1.
Tracks: / I'll go crazy / Try me / Think / I don't mind / Lost someone / Please,please,please / You've got the power / I found someone / Why do you do me like you do / I want you so bad / I love you, yes I do / Why does everything happen to me / Bewildered / Please don't go / Night train.
Album: released on Polydor in Sep'83 by Polydor Records. Distributed by: Polygram, Polydor

JAMES BROWN'S FUNKY PEOPLE.
Tracks: / Gimme some more / Pass the peas / Think (about it) / Givin' up food for funk / Mama feelgood / Hot pants road / Rock me again & again & again..... / Damn right,I am somebody(pt.1) / Take me just as I am / If you don't get it the first time....... / Parrty (Part 1) / It's the JB's monaurail(It's not the express).
Notes: Superb compilation from James Brown's People label.With tracks dating from between '71-'75 this material is in great demand from the new generation of James brown fans.Each of the tracks are prized gems for which DJ's have paid high prices for original copies of the singles. As well as producing,writing and co-writing James Brown also performs on seven of the twelve tracks.
Album: released on People in Aug'86. Distributed by: Trojan

Cassette: released on People in Aug'86. Distributed by: Trojan

LIVE AT THE APOLLO VOLUME 1.
Compact disc:

LIVE AT THE APPOLLO (PART 2).
Album: released on Rhino (USA) in Jan'86 by Rhino Records (USA)

LIVE AT THE APPOLLO (PART 1).
Album: released on Rhino (USA) in Jan'86 by Rhino Records (USA)

LIVE IN LONDON.
Notes: Number of tracks: 12 Type of recording: Live Total playing time: 60 minutes.
Video-cassette (VHS): released on Virgin in May'86 by Virgin Records. Distributed by: EMI, Virgin Distribution

LIVE IN NEW YORK.
Tracks: / Too funky in here / Funky good time / Get up off that thing / Body heat / Sex machine / Try me / Brown's inferno / Papa's got a brand new bag / Good foot / This is a man's world / Got that feeling / Cold sweat / Please, please, please / Jam / Bay ridge boogy / Payback / Too funky in here.
Double Album: released on SPI Milan (France) in Apr'87. Distributed by: Silva Screen

Album: released on Audio Fidelity in Dec'81. Distributed by: PRT

Cassette: released on SPI Milan (France) in Jul'87. Distributed by: Silva Screen

Compact disc: released on SPI Milan (France) in Jul'87. Distributed by: Silva Screen

LIVING IN AMERICA.
Tracks: / Living in America / Farewell(Vince Di Cola).
Single (7"): released on Scotti Brothers in Jan'86 by Scotti Brothers Records. Distributed by: CBS

Single (12"): released on Scotti Brothers in Jan'86 by Scotti Brothers Records. Distributed by: CBS

LP OF J.B., THE
Sex machine & other soul classics.
Album: released on Polydor in Apr'86 by Polydor Records. Distributed by: Polygram, Polydor

Cassette: released on Polydor in Apr'86 by Polydor Records. Distributed by: Polygram, Polydor

MEAN ON THE SCENE.
Tracks: / Too funky here / Please please please / Good foot / Get up offa that thing / Cold sweat / Browns inferno (instrumental).
Album: released on Phoenix in Oct'82 by Audio Fidelity Enterprises. Distributed by: Stage One,

PAPA'S GOT A BRAND NEW BAG.
Tracks: / Mashed potatoes / Papa's got a brand new bag / USA / This old heart / Cross firing / Doin' the limbo / Baby, you're right / Love don't love nobody / Have mercy baby / And I do just what I want / I stay in the Chapel every night / You don't have to go.
Single (12"): released on Perfect in May'87

Album: released on Polydor in Nov'83 by Polydor Records. Distributed by: Polygram, Polydor

Single (12"): released on Polydor in Oct'82 by Polydor Records. Distributed by: Polygram, Polydor

PLEASE, PLEASE, PLEASE.
Tracks: / Please please please / Try me / I feel that old feeling coming on / Tht's when I lost my heart / Chonnie on chon / Hold my baby's hand / Tell me what I did wrong / Baby cries over the ocean / Begging,begging / No,no,no,no / That dood it / I don't know / I walked alone / Love or a game / Let's make it / Just won't do right.
Album: released on Polydor in Nov'83 by Polydor Records. Distributed by: Polygram, Polydor

PRISONER OF LOVE.
Tracks: / Wait in the rain / Again / Lost someone / Bewildered / So long / Signed sealed and delivered / Try me, can you (feel it part 1) / How long darling / Thing in 'G', (The).
Album: released on Polydor in Nov'83 by Polydor Records. Distributed by: Polygram, Polydor

ROOTS OF A REVOLUTION.
Tracks: / I feel that old feeling coming on again / Hold my baby's hand / Chonnie-on-chon / Just won't do right / Let's make it / Fine old foxy self / Why does everything happen to me / Begging, begging / That dood it / There must be a reason / I want you so bad / Bewildered / Doodle bug / This old heart / You've got the power / Baby you're right / I don't mind / Come over here / And I do just what I want / Tell me what you're gonna do / Hold it / Dancin' little thing / You don't have to go / Lost someone / Shout and shimmy / I found you / I don't care / I've got money / Mashed potatoes USA / Prisoner of love / Oh baby don't you weep / Maybe the last time.
Album: released on Polydor in Jan'84 by Polydor Records. Distributed by: Polygram,

SEX MACHINE AND OTHER SOUL CLASSICS.
Compact disc:

SOLID GOLD.
Tracks: / Please please please / Try me / Try me / Good good lovin' / I'll go crazy / Think / Night train / Out of sight / Papa's got a brand new bag / I got you / It's a mans mans world / Cold sweat / There was a time / I got the feelin' / Say it loud-I'm black and I'm proud / Give it up or turn it loose / Mother popcorn / Get up, I feel like being a sex machine / Call me superbad / Soul power / Hot pants / Make it funky / Talking loud and saying nothing / Honky tonk / Get on the good foot / Payback, (The) / My thang / Papa don't take no mess / Funky president / Hot / Get up offa that thing.
Single 10": released on Polydor in May'77 by Polydor Records. Distributed by: Polygram,

SOUL CLASSICS.
Tracks: / Get up, I feel like a sex machine / My part / Cold sweat / I got you (I feel good) / Night train / Papa's got a brand new bag / Soul power / It's a man's man's man's world / Hot pants / Make it funky, Part 3 / Call me super bad / Money won't change you / Make it funky, Part 1 / Give it up and turn it loose / Out of sight.
: released on Polydor (Germany) in Apr'83. Distributed by: IMS-Polygram

SOUL POWER (PART 1).
Tracks: / Soul power (part 1) / It's a man's world / King heroin* / Don't tell it*.
Single (7"): released on Boiling Point in Apr'86 by Polydor Records. Distributed by: Polygram

Single (12"): released on Boiling Point in Apr'86 by Polydor Records. Distributed by: Polygram

SOUL SYNDROME.
Tracks: / Rapp payback / Mashed potatoes / Funky men / Smokin' and drinkin' / Stay with me / Honky tonk.
Album: released on RCA in Sep'81 by RCA Records. Distributed by: RCA, Roots, Swift, Wellard, Chris, I & B, Solomon & Peres Distribution

Cassette: released on RCA in Sep'81 by RCA Records. Distributed by: RCA, Roots, Swift, Wellard, Chris, I & B, Solomon & Peres Distribution

SPECIAL.
Album: released on Polydor in Sep'81 by Polydor Records. Distributed by: Polygram,

Cassette: released on Polydor in Sep'81 by Polydor Records. Distributed by: Polygram, Polydor

SUPERBAD.
Tracks: / Superbad (pt.I) / Superbad (Pt.II).
Single (7"): released on King (USA) in Mar'87 by Gusto Records. Distributed by: Gusto Distribution, IMS, Swift

TAKE A LOOK AT THOSE CAKES.
Tracks: / For goodness sakes, look at those cakes / Man understands, A / Someone to talk to / Spring / As long as I love you.
Album: released on Polydor in Jan'79 by Polydor Records. Distributed by: Polygram,

UNBEATABLE 16 HITS.
Tracks: / Try me / I've got to change / Strange things happen / I've got to cry / There must be a reason / Why do you do me? / Don't let it happen to me / Can't be the same / It hurts to tell you / Gonna try / You're mine / Fine old foxy self / I won't please no more / Messing with the blues / It was you / I want you so bad.
Album: released on Polydor in Nov'83 by Polydor Records. Distributed by: Polygram,

Brown, Jeff

FLAT STANLEY.
Cassette: released on Cover to Cover in Jun'85 by Cover to Cover Cassettes. Distributed by: Conifer

Brown, Jim

CUFE FOR FEVER.
Single (12"): released on Studio Worx in Sep'84 by Studio Worx Records. Distributed by: Jetstar Distribution

GREATEST HITS:JIM BROWN & HELEN CORNELIUS (Brown, Jim & Helen Cornelius).
Tracks: / I don't want to have to marry you / If the world ran out of love tonight / Bedroom, The / Morning comes to early / Born believer / Lying in love with you / You don't bring me flowers / Saying hello, saying I love you, saying goodbye / Fools / Don't bother to knock.
Album: released on RCA International (USA) in Oct'81 by RCA Records. Distributed by: RCA

Cassette: released on RCA International (USA) in Oct'81 by RCA Records. Distributed by: RCA

IN TIME.
Single (12"): released on Midnight Rock in Oct'83. Distributed by: Jetstar Distribution, Kingdom Distribution

Brown, Jocelyn

I WISH YOU WOULD.
Single (7"): released on Fourth & Broadway in Sep'84 by Island Records. Distributed by: Polygram, EMI

Single (12"): released on Fourth & Broadway in Sep'84 by Island Records. Distributed by: Polygram, EMI Deleted '87.

Single (12"): released on Fourth & Broadway in Oct'84 by Island Records. Distributed by: Polygram, EMI

LOVE'S GONNA GET YOU.
Tracks: / Love's gonna get you / Love's gonna get you(fun house mix).
Single (7"): released on Warner Bros. in Feb'86 by Warner Bros Records. Distributed by: WEA

Single (12"): released on Warner Bros. in Feb'86 by Warner Bros Records. Distributed by: WEA

ONE FROM THE HEART.
Tracks: / Ego maniac / Love's gonna get you / Living without your love / I cry real tears / Caught in the act / My time will come / True love / Whatever satisfies you.
Album: released on Warner Bros. in Apr'87 by Warner Bros Records. Distributed by: WEA

Cassette: released on Warner Bros. in Apr'87 by Warner Bros Records. Distributed by: WEA

SOMEBODY ELSE'S GUY.
Single (7"): released on Fourth & Broadway in Apr'84 by Island Records. Distributed by: Polygram, EMI

Single (12"): released on Fourth & Broadway in Apr'84 by Island Records. Distributed by: Polygram, EMI

TO THROUGH.
Single (7"): released on Excaliber in Aug'85 by Red Bus Records. Distributed by: PRT

Single (12"): released on Excaliber in Aug'85 by Red Bus Records. Distributed by: PRT

Brown, Joe

GIVE US A BREAK.
Single (7"): released on BBC in Sep'83 by BBC Records & Tapes. Distributed by: EMI, PRT,

HEY MAMA.
Single (7"): released on TFI in Apr'81. Distributed by: Revolver Distribution, Cartel Distribution

LITTLE CHILDREN (Brown, Joe & The Family).
Single (7"): released on Solid Gold in Nov'81. Distributed by: MCA

Brown, J.T

ROCKIN' WITH J.T (Brown, J.T & His Boogie Boys).
Album: released on Krazy Kat in May'84. Distributed by: Jazz Music, Swift, Chris Wellard, H.R. Taylor, Charly, Hotshot,

Brown, Julie

GODDESS IN PROGRESS.
Album: released on Rhino (USA) in Feb'85 by Rhino Records (USA)

Brown, June

JUNGLE BEWARE.
Single (12"): released on Bolts in Feb'85 by Bolts Records. Distributed by: PRT, Pinnacle

LONDON.
Tracks: / Where Is Love?.
Single (7"): released on MBS in Jan'87. Distributed by: PRT

Brown, Junior

KNOCK KNOCK KNOCK.
Single (12"): released on London Gemi in Apr'84. Distributed by: Pinnacle

LONG TIME ME CALL YOU.
Single (12"): released on Fashion in Dec'83 by Fashion Records. Distributed by: PRT, Jetstar

LOVE ME DARLING.
Single (12"): released on Natty Congo in Nov'85 by Natty Congo Records. Distributed by: Jetstar

MY DEVOTION.
Single (12"): released on CSA in Dec'82 by CSA Records. Distributed by: PRT, Jetstar

OH NO NOT MY BABY.
Single (12"): released on Broadway in Oct'85. Distributed by: Jetstar

REGGAE MELODY.
Single 10": released on Roots Music in Nov'82 by Roots Music Records. Distributed by: PRT Distribution

ROCKERS.
Single (12"): released on Solid Groove in Apr'82. Distributed by: Jetstar, Pinnacle

SHOW THE YOUTH THE WAY.
Single (12"): released on Kingdom Records in Dec'81 by Kingdom Records. Distributed by: Kingdom Records

WARRIOR.
Single (12"): released on Jah Shake in Apr'82

Brown, Laverne

I GOT THE WILL.
Single (7"): released on Big Beat in May'81 by Ace Records. Distributed by: Projection, Pinnacle

WORDS ARE IMPOSSIBLE.
Single (7"): released on Chiswick-Ace in May'82 by Ace Records. Distributed by: Pinnacle

Brown, Lawrence

INSPIRED ABANDON (Brown, Lawrence All Stars/Johnny Hodges).
Album: released on Jasmine in Apr'83 by Jasmine Records. Distributed by: Counterpoint, Taylor, H.R., Wellard, Chris, Swift, Cadillac

Brown, Leroy

IT'S ALRIGHT.
Single (7"): released on Creole in Sep'80 by Creole Records. Distributed by: Rhino, PRT

Single (12"): released on Creole in Sep'80 by Creole Records. Distributed by: Rhino, PRT

TAXI.
Single (12"): released on Revue in Jan'85 by Revue Records. Distributed by: Creole

Brown, Les

1943 BAND, THE.
Tracks: / OK for baby / I heard you cried last night / Canteen bounce, The / Baby knock me a kiss / Takin' a chance on love / Later tonight / What's the good word Mr. Bluebird / Things ain't what they used to be.
Notes: With Randy Brooks, Hal Derwin, Town Criers.
Album: released on Fanfare in Jun'79 by Feroway/Fanfare Records. Distributed by: PRT

1946 (Brown, Les & His Orchestra).
Notes: With Doris Day, Butch Stone, Jack Haskell. Mono.
Album: released on Circle(USA) in Dec'86 by Jazzology Records (USA). Distributed by: Jazz Music, Swift, Chris Wellard

1956/7 VOL.4.
Album: released on Hindsight(USA) in Apr'84 by Hindsight Records (USA). Distributed by: Swift, Charly

20 GOLDEN PIECES OF LES BROWN (Brown, Les & His Band Of Renown).
Tracks: / Strictly instrumental / You made me love you / Blue flame / So rare / Lazy river / How high the moon / Baby elephant walk / Gentle on my mind / Sentimental journey / Pink panther theme, The / Let's dance / Jersey bounce / Moonglow / At the woodchopper's ball / On the sunnyside of the street / Ballin' the jack / A pretty girl is a melody / Softly as in a morning sunrise / I want to hold your hand / Walk on by.
Album: released on Bulldog in Nov'81 by Bulldog Records. Distributed by: President Distribution, Spartan, Swift, Taylor, '

Cassette: released on Bulldog in Feb'82 by Bulldog Records. Distributed by: President Distribution, Spartan, Swift, Taylor, H.R.

ALL WEATHER MUSIC (Brown, Les & His Band Of Renown).
Album: released on Jasmine in Jun'83 by Jasmine Records. Distributed by: Counterpoint, Taylor, H.R., Wellard, Chris, Swift, Cadillac

COMPLETE LES BROWN-VOL.2, THE.
Album: released on Ajax (USA) in Apr'84. Distributed by: Swift

CONCERT AT THE HOLLYWOOD PALLADIUM.
Album: released on Jasmine in Feb'83 by Jasmine Records. Distributed by: Counterpoint, , Taylor, H.R., Wellard, Chris, Swift, Cadillac

CONCERT AT THE HOLYWOOD PALLADIUM.
Album: released on Jasmine in Feb'83 by Jasmine Records. Distributed by: Counterpoint, Taylor, H.R., Wellard, Chris, Swift, Cadillac

DANCE TO SOUTH PACIFIC (Brown, Les & His Band Of Renown).
Tracks: / Honey bun / Happy talk / Some enchanted evening / Loneliness of evening / Wonderful guy, A / Bloody Mary / Bali ha'i / Dites-moi / Younger than spring time / This nearly was mine / There is nothing like a dame / I'm gonna wash that man right out of my hair.
Notes: A highly dancealbe album from Les Brown and his Band of Renown. Arrangements designed for dancing of popular titles from the South Pacific such as 'Bali Ha'i','I'm gonna wash that man right out of my hair','Some enchanted evening' and more...
Album: released on Capitol in Apr'85 by Capitol Records. Distributed by: EMI

Cassette: released on Capitol in Apr'85 by Capitol Records. Distributed by: EMI

DOUBLE DATE (Brown, Les/Sam Donahue).
Album: released on Hep in Dec'77 by H.R. Taylor Records. Distributed by: Jazz Music, Cadillac Music, Taylors, Wellard, Chris, Zodiac, Swift, Fast Forward

DUKE BLUE DEVILS, THE.
Album: released on Golden Era in Jul'82 by Import Records. Distributed by: Wellard, Chris, Swift

FROM THE CAFE ROUGE.
Album: released on Giants of Jazz in Oct'84 by Hasmick Promotions Ltd.. Distributed by: Counterpoint, Jazz Music, Taylors, Swift, Mainline, Wellard, Chris

JAZZ SONG BOOK, THE.
Tracks: / King Phillip stomp / Willow weep for me / Don't get around much anymore / Wonderful / Apple honey / I remember you / Claw / Let's get away from it all / Pizza boy & love is here to stay / I only have eyes for you / Chelsea bridge.
Album: released on Jasmine in Apr'84 by Jasmine Records. Distributed by: Counterpoint, Taylor, H.R., Wellard, Chris, Swift, Cadillac

LES BROWN & HIS ORCHESTRA 1946-50 (Brown, Les & His Orchestra).
Album: released on First Heard in Oct'79 by Submarine Records. Distributed by: Conifer, Taylors

LES BROWN'S IN TOWN.
Tracks: / Just you, just me / Harlem nocturne / Checkin' in / Moonlight in Vermont / Continental, The / Spanish monster / Meanwhile back on the bus / Ridin' high / Nina never knew / On a little street in Singapore / Piccolino, The.
Album: released on Capitol(USA) in Apr'84 by Capitol (USA) Records. Distributed by: EMI

LES BROWN WITH ROSEMARY CLOONEY (Brown, Les & Rosemary Clooney).
Album: released on Artistic in Jun'85 by Submarine Records. Distributed by: Chris Wellard, Jazz Music, Swift, Clyde Factors Distributors

Cassette: released on Artistic in Jun'85 by Submarine Records. Distributed by: Chris Wellard, Jazz Music, Swift, Clyde Factors Distributors

ONE NIGHT STAND (Brown, Les/Krupa/Osborne).
Album: released on Joyce (USA) in Apr'84. Distributed by: Swift

ONE & ONLY, THE.
Tracks: / On a sunny day / One more blues / Holiday in big band land / Say what? / Turn around / Perky / Bruised bones / Summer talk / LB special / Boogie train blues / Goldfish / Swing flow.
Notes: Born in 1912,Les Brown started his musical career in 1935 at Duke University leading the'Duke Blue Devils'dance band.In 1937 he was writing arrangements for Ruby Newman,Isham Jones,Jimmy Dorsey,Larry Clinton and Red Nichols,and a year later formed the big band which became known as 'Les Brown & His Band Of Renown'.A clean-cut,hard swinging band playing outstanding arrangements which quickly established an international reputation,performing at the 'New York World's Fair' in 1939 and recording the million-sales record hit'Sentimental Journey'sung by Doris Day in 1944.This is a new recording and features 3 original Les Brown compositions.The album also has the benefit of Direct Metal Mastering.
Album: released on Intercord (Germany) in Aug'86 by Intercord Records. Distributed by: IMS, Polygram

RHAPSODY IN BLUE (Brown, Les/Day, Doris).
Tracks: / Dig it / While the music played on / Celery talks at midnight / Easy as pie / Keep cool fool / Come to baby do / We'll be together again / My dreams are getting better / Let's be buddies between friends / Boogie woogie piggy / Hotch kiss corner / I'd rather be with you / Last time I saw you / Till the end of time / Rhapsody in blue.
Notes: Miss Day in her original role. A delightful trip into Yesteryear.
Album: released on Astan (USA) in May'85

Album: released on First Heard in Nov'79 by Submarine Records. Distributed by: Conifer, Taylors

SENTIMENTAL THING.
Cassette: released on First Heard in Oct'84 by Submarine Records. Distributed by: Conifer, Taylors

SWEETEST SOUNDS (Brown, Les & Rosemary Clooney).
Tracks: / Sweetest sounds, The / How am I to know / My funny valentine / Why shouldn't I? / My romance / I get along without you very well / Angry / Some people / Man with a horn / Show me / Have you met Miss Jones? / Little Brown jug / Sleepy time girl / I didn't know what time it was.
Album: released on Artistic in '84 by Submarine Records. Distributed by: Chris Wellard, Jazz Music, Swift, Clyde Factors Distributors

Cassette: released on Artistic in '84 by Submarine Records. Distributed by: Chris Wellard, Jazz Music, Swift, Clyde Factors Distributors

Album: released on Artistic in '84 by Submarine Records. Distributed by: Chris Wellard, Jazz Music, Swift, Clyde Factors Distributors

SWING GOES ON, THE-VOL 5.
Tracks: / Ridin' high / Just you, just me / Swingin' down the lane / Checkin' in / Stardust / My melancholy baby / Piccolino, The / I've got my love to keep me warm / Sentimental journey / Happy talk / Continental, The / Sophisticated swing / Josephine / Leap frog.
Album: released on EMI (Germany) in '83 by EMI Records. Distributed by: Conifer

SWING SONG BOOK (Brown, Les & His Band Of Renown).
Album: released on Jasmine in '83 by Jasmine Records. Distributed by: Counterpoint, , Taylor, H.R., Wellard, Chris, Swift, Cadillac

THAT SOUND OF RENOWN.
Album: released on Jasmine in Feb'83 by Jasmine Records. Distributed by: Counterpoint, Taylor, H.R., Wellard, Chris, Swift, Cadillac

Brown, Marion

LA PLACITA (LIVE IN WILLISAU) (Brown, Marion Quartet).
Album: released on Timeless in Sep'86

Brown, Maxine

IT'S TORTURE.
Tracks: / It's torture / I got love.
Single (7"): released on Kent in Mar'86 by Ace Records. Distributed by: Pinnacle

LIKE NEVER BEFORE.
Album: released on Kent in Nov'85 by Ace Records. Distributed by: Pinnacle

ONE IN A MILLION.
Tracks: / One in a million / Since I found you / Let me give you my lovin' / Little girl lost / I wonder what my baby's doing tonight / Yesterday's kisses / One step at a time / It's gonna be alright / Oh no not my baby / Anything for a laugh / Put yourself in my place / I cry alone / You're in love / I don't need anything / Funny / All in my mind.
Album: released on Kent in Oct'84 by Ace Records. Distributed by: Pinnacle

Brown, Milton

DANCE-O-RAMA (Brown, Milton & The Brownies).
Tracks: / St.Louis blues / Sweet Jennie Lee / Texas hambone blues / Brownie special / Right or wrong / Washington & Lee Swing / Beautiful Texas / Little Betty Brown.
: released on Rambler in Jul'81. Distributed by: Swift

EASY RIDIN' PAPA (Brown, Milton & The Brownies).
Tracks: / Down by the O-H-I-O / Easy Ridin' Papa / Sweet Jenny Lee / Ida Sweet as Apple Cider / Little Betty Brown / Black and White Rag / Brownie Special / Wabash Blues / Hesitation blues / St. Louis Blues / I've Got the Blues for my Mamy / Texas hambone blues / Beautiful Texas / Right or wrong.
Album: released on Charly in Mar'87 by Charly Records. Distributed by: Charly, Cadillac

FALLING FROM A GREAT HEIGHT.
Tracks: / Falling from a great height / Falling from a great height (inst.).
Single (7"): released on Nightmare in Mar'87 by Nightmare Records. Distributed by: PRT

Single (12"): released on Nightmare in Mar'87 by Nightmare Records. Distributed by: PRT

TAKING OFF (Brown, Milton & The Brownies).
Tracks: / Chinatown, my Chinatown / St.Louis blues / In El Rancho Grande / Taking off / If you can't get five take two / Fan it / Little Betty Brown / Some of these days / Sweet Georgia Brown / Texas hambone blues / Washington & Lee Swing / My Mary / Goofus / Honky tonk blues / Sweet Jennie Lee / There'll be some changes made.
Album: released on String in '81 by Topic Records. Distributed by: Roots Distribution, Jazz Music Distribution, Projection Distribution, Swift Distribution

Brown, Miquel

BLACK LEATHER.
Single (12"): released on Record Shack in Sep'84 by Record Shack Records. Distributed by: PRT

CLOSE TO PERFECTION (SINGLE).
Single (7"): released on Record Shack in Aug'85 by Record Shack Records. Distributed by: PRT

Single (12"): released on Record Shack in Aug'85 by Record Shack Records. Distributed by: PRT

CLOSE TO PERFECTION.
Album: released on Record Shack in Oct'85 by Record Shack Records. Distributed by: PRT

Cassette: released on Record Shack in Oct'85 by Record Shack Records. Distributed by: PRT

FOOTPRINTS IN THE SAND.
Tracks: / Footprints In The Sand (Inst.).
Single (7"): released on Nitemare in Jan'87

Single (12"): released on Nightmare in Jan'87 by Nightmare Records. Distributed by: PRT

HE'S A SAINT HE'S A SINNER.
Single (7"): released on Record Shack in Feb'84 by Record Shack Records. Distributed by: PRT

Single (12"): released on Record Shack in Feb'84 by Record Shack Records. Distributed by: PRT

MANPOWER.
Album: released on Record Shack in Nov'83 by Record Shack Records. Distributed by: PRT

ON THE RADIO.
Single (7"): released on Record Shack in Nov'85 by Record Shack Records. Distributed by: PRT

Single (12"): released on Record Shack in Nov'85 by Record Shack Records. Distributed by: PRT

SO MANY MEN SO LITTLE TIME.
Single (7"): released on Record Shack in Jun'83

Single (12"): released on Record Shack in Jun'83

Single (7"): released on Record Shack in Apr'84

Single (12"): released on Record Shack in Apr'84

Brown, Nappy

DON'T BE ANGRY.
Album:

I GOT DONE OVER (Brown, Nappy/The Roosters).

Page 156

Album: released on Stockholm (Sweden) in Jun'85. Distributed by: Swift Distribution

TORE UP (Brown, Nappy with The Heartfixers).
Notes: O.I.D. = Oasis Independent Distribution. Tel: 0428 4001
Album: released on Nightflite in Jun'86 by Adrian Owlett. Distributed by: Charly, Spartan. Estim retail price in Sep'87 was £5.99.

Brown, Neville

I'M A SUPERMAN.
Single (12"): released on Negus Roots in Mar'85 by Negus Roots Records. Distributed by: Jetstar

SCIENTIST PRESENTS.
Tracks: / Right one, The / Where did she go / Friend indeed, A.
Notes: Tracks include: (as listed in tracks).
Album: released on Vista Sounds in '83 by Vista Sounds Records. Distributed by: Jetstar

Brown, Noreen

I'D RATHER GO BLIND.
Single (12"): released on Three Kings in Apr'85 by Three Kings Records. Distributed by: Jetstar Distribution

Brown, O'Chi

100% PURE PAIN.
Tracks: / 100% pure pain / I just want to be loved.
Single (7"): released on Magnet in Jul'86 by Magnet Records. Distributed by: BMG

Single (12"): released on Magnet in Jul'86 by Magnet Records. Distributed by: BMG

100% PURE PAIN(US EXT.REMIX).
Tracks: / 100% pure pain(US ext.remix) / I just want to be loved.
Single (12"): released on Magnet in Aug'86 by Magnet Records. Distributed by: BMG

CAN'T SAY GOODBYE TO YOU.
Single (12"): released on Carib Jems in May'82 by Carib Jems. Distributed by: Spartan, Jetstar

I GOT A FEELING.
Single (7"): released on Magnet in Aug'87 by Magnet Records. Distributed by: BMG

Single (12"): released on Magnet in Aug'87 by Magnet Records. Distributed by: BMG

O'CHI.
Tracks: / Whenever You Need Somebody / Fantasy / 100% pure pain / Caught in a life / Lady / Two hearts beating as one / Learning to live (without your love) / Call me up / Another broken heart.
Compact disc: released on Magnet in Nov'86 by Magnet Records. Distributed by: BMG

Album: released on Magnet in Nov'86 by Magnet Records. Distributed by: BMG

Cassette: released on Magnet in Nov'86 by Magnet Records. Distributed by: BMG

ROCK YOUR BABY (EDIT).
Tracks: / Rock your baby (edit) / Another broken heart.
Single (7"): released on Magnet in Feb'87 by Magnet Records. Distributed by: BMG

Single (12"): released on Magnet in Feb'87 by Magnet Records. Distributed by: BMG

TWO HEARTS BEATING AS ONE.
Tracks: / Two hearts beating as one.
Single (7"): released on Magnet in Oct'86 by Magnet Records. Distributed by: BMG

Single (12"): released on Magnet in Oct'86 by Magnet Records. Distributed by: BMG

UNCHAINED MELODY.
Single (7"): released on DBM in Jun'84 by DBM Records. Distributed by: RCA

WHENEVER YOU NEED SOMEBODY.
Tracks: / Whenever you need somebody(cool & deadly mix) / I play games / Whenever you need somebody(7" mix).
Single (12"): released on Magnet in Jan'86 by Magnet Records. Distributed by: BMG

Single (7"): released on DBM in Dec'85 by Magnet Records. Distributed by: BMG

Single (12"): released on Magnet in Dec'85 by Magnet Records. Distributed by: BMG

WHITER SHADE OF PALE.
Single (7"): released on Romantic in Sep'83. Distributed by: MCA Distribution

Single (12"): released on Romantic in Sep'83. Distributed by: MCA Distribution

WHY CAN'T WE BE FRIENDS.
Single (7"): released on DBM in Jul'85 by DBM Records. Distributed by: RCA

Single (12"): released on DBM in Jul'85 by DBM Records. Distributed by: RCA

Brown/Orpheus

CHAOCHAMBER, (THE).
Cassette: released on Complex in Mar'85

Brown, Patrick

ON THE RIGHT TRACK.
Single (12"): released on Kufe in Oct'84 by Kufe Records. Distributed by: Pinnacle

Brown, Paul

WE'RE HAVIN' FUN.
Single (7"): released on Carrere in Jun'84 by Carrere Records. Distributed by: PRT, Spartan

Single (12"): released on Carrere in Jun'84 by Carrere Records. Distributed by: PRT, Spartan

Brown, Pete

BEFORE SINGING LESSONS.
Tracks: / Week looked good on paper, The / Station song / High flying electric bird / Things may come & things may go / High sorrow / Raining pins and needles / Station song platform two / Thousands on a raft / Broken magic / My last band / Aeroplane head woman / Lost tribe / Mass debate / Spend my nights in armour / Night at Joan & Ray's / She used to come and see me when I slept on the floor / Late Fiona / Cange of heart / Old rocksinger, The / Barbed wire nightdress / Big city cowboy.
Double Album: released on Decal in Mar'87 by Charly Records. Distributed by: Charly

HARLUM JUMP AND SWING (Brown, Pete Sextet & Jonah Jones Sextet).
Album: released on Affinity in May'83 by Charly Records. Distributed by: Charly, Cadillac

PARTY IN THE RAIN (Brown, Pete & Ian Lynn).
Tracks: / Broken windscreen dance / White room / Big city cowboy / Walk into the sun / Comeback, The / Still have the love / I read the funky times / Party in the rain.
Notes: all published by Tonechild, Intersong except White Room Dratleaf
Album: released on Discs International in Aug'82 by Discs International Records. Distributed by: Pinnacle

Brown, Peter

BABY GETS HIGH.
Single (7"): released on RCA in Feb'83 by RCA Records. Distributed by: RCA, Roots, Swift, Wellard, Chris, I & B, Solomon & Peres Distribution

DO YA WANNA GET FUNKY WITH ME.
Single (7"): released on TK in May'82. Distributed by: CBS Distribution

THEY ONLY COME OUT AT NIGHT.
Single (7"): by CBS Records. Distributed by: CBS

Single (12"): by CBS Records. Distributed by: CBS

Brown, Polly

BELIEVE IN ME.
Single (7"): released on Witch in Oct'82 by Witch Records. Distributed by: PRT

BEWITCHED.
Single (7"): released on Witch in Aug'80 by Witch Records. Distributed by: PRT

Single (12"): released on Witch in Aug'80 by Witch Records. Distributed by: PRT

I'LL NEVER BE THE SAME.
Single (7"): released on Witch in Feb'82 by Witch Records. Distributed by: PRT

LOVE TO GIVE.
Single (7"):

PRECIOUS ME.
Single (7"): released on Witch in May'81 by Witch Records. Distributed by: PRT

YOU'VE GOT IT ALL (Brown, Polly/P.J Proby).
Single (7"): released on Rooster in Oct'81 by Rooster Records. Distributed by: PRT Distribution

Brown, Randy

CHECK IT OUT.
Tracks: / Sweet to the bone / Heaven knows / If it's love that you want / Two fools / If I had to do it all over / Thank you for the happiness / Without you / Smoking room.
Notes: Memphis singer song writer Randy Brown was a leading figure with the '60's Stax label as one of their session singers & house writers.His warm seductive voice borrows much from two other Memphis greats-Otis Redding & Al Green.
Album: released on MPS(USA) in Jun'86

INTIMATELY.
Tracks: / You say it's all / I'm here / I was blessed / Day I found you, The / I thought of you today / You make me happy / It scares me so / Use it / I wanna baby you / Crazy about you baby.
Album: released on Parachute (USA) in Jul'79. Distributed by: Polygram

WELCOME TO MY ROOM.
Album: released on Parachute (USA) in May'78. Distributed by: Polygram

Album: released on Threeway in Oct'87 by Charly Records. Distributed by: Charly Distribution

Brown, Ray

AIN'T BUT A FEW OF US (see Jackson, Milt) (Brown, Ray/ Milt Jackson/ Grady Tate/ Ocsar Peterson).

BYE BYE BLACKBIRD (Brown, Ray Trio).
Tracks: / Bye bye blackbird / Everything happens to me / Mean to me / Things ain't what they used to be / Te Rev. / I remember / I should care / Blue & sentimental.
Notes: Eight popular and jazz standards tastefully performed by the excellent Ray Brown Trio & featuring two of Japan's best musicians, Ichiro Mauda on vibraphone & Emi Nakajima on vocals.
Album: released on King (Japan) in Jul'86. Distributed by: IMS, Polygram

DON'T FORGET THE BLUES (Brown, Ray All Stars).
Tracks: / Blues'd Out / Jim / Night Train / If I Could Be With You (One Hour Tonight) / Rocks in my Bed / You Don't Know Me / Jumpin' the Blues / Don't Forget the Blues.
Notes: Personnel: Ray Brown-Bass/Ron Eschete-Guitar/Al Grey-Trombone/Gene Harris-piano and fender Rhodes/Grady Tate-Drums.
Compact disc: released on Concord Jazz (USA) in Jan'87 by Concord Jazz Records (USA). Distributed by: IMS, Polygram

Album: released on Concord Jazz (USA) in Feb'86 by Concord Jazz Records (USA). Distributed by: IMS, Polygram

Cassette: released on Concord Jazz (USA) in Feb'86 by Concord Jazz Records (USA). Distributed by: IMS, Polygram

GIANTS, THE (Brown, Ray, Oscar Peterson & Joe Pass).
Album: released on Pablo (USA) in '82 by Pablo Records (USA). Distributed by: Wellard, Chris, IMS-Polygram, BMG

Cassette: released on Pablo (USA) in '82 by Pablo Records (USA). Distributed by: Wellard, Chris, IMS-Polygram, BMG

I FEEL THAT YOUNG MAN'S RHYTHM.
Album: released on Route 66 (Sweden) in Apr'85 by Mr. R&B Records. Distributed by: Swift Distribution, Cadillac, Jazz Music Distribution

MILT JACKSON/RAY BROWN JAM (Brown, Ray & Milt Jackson).
Album: released on Pablo (USA) in May'82 by Pablo Records (USA). Distributed by: Wellard, Chris, IMS-Polygram, BMG

Cassette: released on Pablo (USA) in May'82 by Pablo Records (USA). Distributed by: Wellard, Chris, IMS-Polygram, BMG

ONE O'CLOCK JUMP 1953 (Brown, Ray, Ben Webster & Oscar Peterson).
Album: released on Verve in Apr'84 by Phonogram Records. Distributed by: Polygram

Cassette: released on Verve in Apr'84 by Phonogram Records. Distributed by: Polygram Deleted '85.

Poll winners, The

RAY BROWN THREE, A (Brown, Ray, Monty Alexander & Sam Most).
Tracks: / I wish you love / I can't stop loving you / Jamento / Blue monk / Candy man The / Too late now / You're my everything / There is no greater love.
Notes: Sam Most has appeared on many Contemporary albums and has recently been involved with Bobby Hutcherson's group. Artists include Ray Brown Bass Monty Alexander piano Sam Most flute
Album: released on Concord Jazz in May'83 by Concord Jazz Records (USA). Distributed by: IMS, Polygram

Cassette: released on Concord Jazz in May'83 by Concord Jazz Records (USA). Distributed by: IMS, Polygram

RED HOT RAY BROWN TRIO, THE.
Tracks: / Have you met Miss Jones? / Meditation / Street of dreams / Lady be good / That's all / Love me tender / How could you do a thing like this to me? / Captain Bill.
Notes: Recorded live at the Blue Note, New York. Personnel : Ray Brown - bass / Gene Harris - piano / Mickey Roker - drums.
Album: released on Concord Jazz (USA) in Jul'87 by Concord Jazz Records (USA). Distributed by: IMS, Polygram

Cassette: released on Concord Jazz (USA) in Jul'87 by Concord Jazz Records (USA). Distributed by: IMS, Polygram

SOMETHING FOR LESTER (Brown, Ray Trio).
Notes: With Cedar Walton and Elvin Jones.
Compact disc: released on JVC Fantasy (Japan) in Jan'86

SOULAR ENERGY (Brown, Ray Trio).
Tracks: / Exactly like you / Cry me a river / Teach me tonight / Take the 'A' train / Mistreated but undefeated blues / That's all / Easy does it / Sweet Georgia Brown / Exactly like you / Cry me a river / Teach me tonight / Take the 'A' train / Mistreated but undefeated blues / That's all / Easy does it / Sweet georgia brown.
Notes: The chemisrtry between bassit Ray Brown and pianist Gene Harris is amazing. Their soulful approach makes the most mainstream theme sound bluesy. These fine artists are masters of rhythm and melody, as well as dynamics and mood. Red Rolloway and Emily Remler contributed fire breathing solos on "Mistreated But Undefeated Blues". Personnel: Ray Brown-bass/Gene Harris-piano/Gerryck King-drums Emily Remler- guitar/Red Holloway-tenor saxophone.
Compact disc: by Concord Jazz Records (USA). Distributed by: IMS, Polygram

SOULAR ENERGY (Brown, Ray Trio).
Album: released on Concord Jazz (USA) in Jul'85 by Concord Jazz Records (USA). Distributed by: IMS, Polygram

Cassette: released on Concord Jazz (USA) in Jul'85 by Concord Jazz Records (USA). Distributed by: IMS, Polygram

THIS ONE'S FOR BLANTON (Brown, Ray & Duke Ellington).
Album: released on Pablo (USA) in May'82 by Pablo Records (USA). Distributed by: Wellard, Chris, IMS-Polygram, BMG

Cassette: released on Pablo (USA) in May'82 by Pablo Records (USA). Distributed by: Wellard, Chris, IMS-Polygram, BMG

Brown, Reuben

STARBUST.
Album: released on Adelphi in May'81 by Adelphi Records. Distributed by: Jetstar

Brown, Roy

Battle of the blues

BOOGIE AT MIDNIGHT.
Tracks: / Mighty mighty man / Boogie at midnight / Cadillac baby / Hard luck blues / Love don't love nobody / Too much lovin' ain't no good / Big town / Rock-a-bye-baby / Answer to big town / Ain't no rockin' no more / My gal from kokomo / Fannie Brown got married / Black diamond / Shake em up baby / Adorable one / Good looking and foxy too.
Notes: In some respects Roy Brown's jumping R & B style was similar to that of Tiny Bradshaw, Wyonie Harris and others, i.e he was another of the hot R & B acts that immediately preceeded and help to shape the rock 'n' roll boom of the mid fifties. However, unlike Bradshaw and Harris, Brown was a quality cry style singer rather than an R & B shouter he had a lot of gospel inflections in his voicethat would surface more noticeably still in the next generation of early soul singers. This difference is evident in the untempo ravers such as Mighty Mighty Man Love don't Love nobody My gal from Kokomo Black diamond and many more but it's particularly blatent in the dramatic Hard luck blues (1950) and a 1959 ballad "Adorable one" on the latter Brown sounds astonishingly like Jackie Wilson, whomof course he influenced. Essential stuff from a key figure in the development of R & B.
Album: released on Charly(R&B) in Jul'85 by Charly Records. Distributed by: Charly, Cadillac

Cassette: released on Charly(R&B) in Jul'85 by Charly Records. Distributed by: Charly, Cadillac

CHEAPEST PRICE IN TOWN.
Album: released on Faith in Feb'79 by Faith Records. Distributed by: Jazz Music, Swift

GOOD ROCKING TONIGHT.
Album: released on Route 66 in Jun'80

GOOD ROCKIN' TONIGHT.
Tracks: / Travellin blues / Let the four winds blow / Love for sale / Boogie woogie blues / Good rockin' tonight / Boogie at midnight / Love don't love nobody / Losing hand / Tin pan alley.
Notes: Writer of the classic Good Rockin' tonight featured here in is own performance
Album: released on Magnum Force in Jun'84 by Magnum Music Group Ltd. Distributed by: Magnum Music Group Ltd, PRT, Spartan

LAUGHING BUT CRYING.
Album: released on Route 66 in Jun'80

Brown, Roy 'Chubby'

I'M LOOKING SICK.
Single (7"): released on Really Rude in Jan'82

Brown, Rula

I DON'T WANNA LIVE MY LIFE WITHOUT YOU.
Single (12"): released on Revue in Dec'84 by Revue Records. Distributed by: Creole

MANY A TIME.
Album: released on Bee Cap in Nov'86 by Bee Cap Records. Distributed by: Jetstar

Brown, Russ

GOTTA FIND A WAY.
Tracks: / Gotta find a way.
Single (7"): released on 10 in Apr'86 by 10 Records. Distributed by: Virgin, EMI

Single (12"): released on 10 in Apr'86 by 10 Records. Distributed by: Virgin, EMI

TAKE MY LOVE.
Tracks: / Take my love / Got to find a way.
Single (7"): released on 10 in Jun'87 by 10 Records. Distributed by: Virgin, EMI

Single (12"): released on 10 in Jun'87 by 10 Records. Distributed by: Virgin, EMI

Brown, Ruth

BLACK IS BROWN AND BROWN IS BEAUTIFUL.
Tracks: / Yesterday / Please send me someone to love / Looking back / Try me and see / Miss Browns blues / My prayer / Since I fell for you / This bitter earth.
Album: released on Rhapsody in May'81 by President Records. Distributed by: Taylors, Swift, Jazz Music, Wellard, Chris

BROWN SUGAR.
Tracks: / Sugar baby / Stop knocking / Old fashioned good time / I love my man / My old bed / Brown sugar / I want to sleep with you / What colour is blue / Lot more of me leaving / Life ain't no piece of cake.
Album: released on Topline in May'86 by Charly Records. Distributed by: Charly Distribution

Cassette: released on Topline in May'86 by Charly Records. Distributed by: Charly Distribution

ROCKIN' WITH RUTH.
Tracks: / Teardrops from my eyes / 5-10-15 hours / Daddy daddy / Mamma he treats your daughter mean / Wild wild young men / Love contest / Hello littlt boy / Oh what a deam / Somebody touched me / Bye bye you -ng men / I can see everybody's baby / As long as I'm moving / This little girls gone rockin / I can't hear a word you say / Papa daddy / Don't decieve me.
Notes: Ruth "miss rhythm" brown was Atlantic Records first real star signing and was unquestionably the most popular and sucessful female R 'N' B star on the fifties. This compilation amply covers those glorious years, from her first R 'n' B number 1 (teardrops october 19500 to her last atlantic hit (don't decieve me April 1960) including the majority of her most significant recordings in betweenHowever, like all the albums in the series this isn't just a Greatest Hit package, we have omitted certain hits which , we feel, haven't stood the test of time (i.e her first opo hit "Lucky dips) allowing more room for several excellent R 'n' B/R 'n' R tracks such as "Love contest, "Hello little boy", "As long as I'm moving" and others. The last mentioned title and "This little girl's gone rockin have been much in demand (but well nigh impossible to find) with modern fans of prime - vintage R 'n' B over the last few years: the rest of the album- a solid sender from start to finish- willbe recieved with equal enthusiasm.
Album: released on Charly(R&B) in Mar'84 by Charly Records. Distributed by: Charly, Cadillac

Cassette: released on Charly(R&B) in Mar'84 by Charly Records. Distributed by: Charly, Cadillac

SUGAR BABE.
Tracks: / Sugar babe / Stock knocking / Old fashioned good time / I love my man / Old bed / Brown sugar / I want to sleep with you / What colour is blue / You're gonna see a lot more of me / Leaving / Life ain't no piece of cake.
Album: released on President in Jan'77 by President Records. Distributed by: Taylors, Spartan

TAKING CARE OF BUSINESS.
Album: released on Stockholm (Sweden) in Mar'84. Distributed by: Swift Distribution

Browns

20 OF THE BEST.
Tracks: / I take the chance / I heard the bluebirds sing / Would you care / Beyond the shadow / Three bells / Scarlet ribbons / Teen ex / Old lamplighter / Ground hog / Blue christmas / Send me the pillow / Oh no / Then I'll stop loving you / Every body's darlin' plus mine / Meadow green / I'd just be fool enough / Coming back to you / I hear it now / Big daddy / I will bring you water.
Album: released on RCA International in Apr'85

Cassette: released on RCA International in Apr'85

LOOKING BACK TO SEE.
Tracks: / Lookin' back to see / Rio De Janeiro / Draggin' main street / You thought, I thought / Itsy witsy bitsy me / Your love is as wild as the west wind / Grass is green, The / Lookin' on / Jungle magic / Set the dawgs on 'em" / I'm your man,i'm your gal" / Why am I falling / Do memories haunt me / It's love,I guess" / Here today and gone tomorrow / Cool green.
Notes: Original Fabor Recordings
Album: released on Bear Family in Sep'86 by Bear Family Records. Distributed by: Rollercoaster Distribution, Swift

ROCKIN' ROLLIN' BROWNS.
Tracks: / Three bells, The (Les trois cloches) / Teen-ex / Blue bells ring / This time I would know / Heaven fell last night / Beyond a shadow / Margo (The ninth of May) / You're so much apart of me / Bye bye love / Only one way to love you / Button and bows / Brighton the corner where you are / Dream on (she'll break your heart) / Oh no / Tobacco road.
Album: released on Bear Family in Sep'84 by Bear Family Records. Distributed by: Rollercoaster Distribution, Swift

THREE BELLS, THE.
Tracks: / Three bells, The / Lion sleeps tonight, The.
Single (7"): released on Old Gold in Nov'86 by Old Gold Records. Distributed by: Lightning, Jazz Music, Spartan, Counterpoint

Brown, Sandy

IN THE EVENING (Brown, Sandy/Brian Lemon Trio).
Album: released on Hep in Mar'84 by H.R. Taylor Records. Distributed by: Jazz Music, Cadillac Music, Taylors, Wellard, Chris, Zodiac, Swift, Fast Forward

MCJAZZ (Brown, Sandy Jazz Band).
Album: released on Dormouse in May'86 by Dormouse Records. Distributed by: Swift

SANDY BROWN QIUNTET, THE.
Album: released on Spotlite in Jan'80 by Spotlite Records. Distributed by: Cadillac, Jazz Music, Spotlite

SPLANKY.
Tracks: / Splanky / In the evening (Vcl) / Roll em Pete (Vcl) / I got it bad / Royal garden blues.
Album: released on Spotlite in May'83 by Spotlite Records. Distributed by: Cadillac, Jazz Music, Spotlite

Brown, Savoy

Biographical Details: Savoy Brown was a British blues-rock quintet with constantly changing personnel that was more popular in USA than at home: nine musicians passed through the first four albums. Originally Savoy Brown Blues Band, formed '66 by guitarist/vocalist/harmonica Kim Simmonds, the only constant factor. [Donald Clarke, April 87]

BEST OF SAVOY BROWN.
Tracks: / Train to nowhere / Mr Downchild / Stay with me baby / Shake 'em on down / Leavin' again / Needle and spoon / Hellbound train / Coming your way / Made up my mind / Let it rock / Highway blues.
Album: released on C5 in Jul'87 by See For Miles Records. Distributed by: Counterpoint

Brown, Sawyer

SHAKIN'.
Tracks: / When your heart goes(woo,woo,woo) / Secretary's song, The / Heart don't fall now / Shakin' / Sharin' the moonshine / Betty's being bad / I believe / Lonely girls / That's a no no / Billy does your bulldog bite.
Album: released on Capitol in Mar'86 by Capitol Records. Distributed by: EMI

Album: released on Capitol in Mar'86 by Capitol Records. Distributed by: EMI

Brown, Scott-Wesley

KINGDOM OF LOVE.
Album: released on Sparrow in Jun'85 by Word Records. Distributed by: Spartan

Cassette: released on Sparrow in Jun'85 by Word Records. Distributed by: Spartan

LANGUAGE OF JESUS IS LOVE, THE.
Album: released on Birdwing in Aug'87 by Word Records. Distributed by: Word Distribution. Estim retail price in Sep'87 was £5.99.

Cassette: released on Birdwing in Aug'87 by Word Records. Distributed by: Word Distribution. Estim retail price in Sep'87 was £5.99.

SOMEBODY'S BROTHER.
Notes: Scott's seventh album for Sparrow contains ten all-new selections from some of the best song writers in Christian music:Gloria Gaither,Michael W.Smith and Greg Nelson.
Album: released on Birdwing in Oct'86 by Word Records. Distributed by: Word Distribution

Brown's Ferry Four

16 GREATEST HITS.
Album: released on Starday in Apr'87

Cassette: released on Starday in Apr'87

Brown, Sharon

I SPECIALISE IN LOVE.
Single (7"): released on Virgin in Aug'85 by Virgin Records. Distributed by: EMI, Virgin Distribution Deleted '86.

Single (12"): released on Virgin in Aug'85 by Virgin Records. Distributed by: EMI, Virgin Distribution

LOVE DON'T HURT PEOPLE.
Single (7"): released on Virgin in Aug'82 by Virgin Records. Distributed by: EMI, Virgin Distribution

Single (12"): released on Virgin in Aug'82 by Virgin Records. Distributed by: EMI, Virgin Distribution

Brown, Shirley

BOYFRIEND.
Single (7"): released on Fourth & Broadway in Jul'85 by Island Records. Distributed by: Polygram, EMI

Single (12"): released on Fourth & Broadway in Jul'85 by Island Records. Distributed by: Polygram, EMI Deleted '87.

INTIMATE STORM.
Tracks: / Boyfriend / I don't play that / Looking for the real thing / This love / I'm up to no good / Love fever / This used to be your house / Leave the bridges standing.
Notes: produced by: Homer Banks and Chuck Brooks
Album: released on Fourth & Broadway in Jun'85 by Island Records. Distributed by: Polygram, EMI

Cassette: released on Fourth & Broadway in Jun'85 by Island Records. Distributed by: Polygram, EMI

LOVE FEVER.
Single (7"): released on Fourth & Broadway in Jun'85 by Island Records. Distributed by: Polygram, EMI

Single (12"): released on Fourth & Broadway in Jun'85 by Island Records. Distributed by: Polygram, EMI

WOMAN TO WOMAN.
Tracks: / Woman to woman / Yes sir brother / It ain't no fun / Long as you love me / Stay with me baby / I've got to go on without you / It's worth a whipping / Woman to woman / So glad to have you / Passion / I can't give you up / I need you tonight / Between you and me.
Single (7"): released on Stax in 13 Jun'87 by Ace Records. Distributed by: Pinnacle, Chris Wellard, IMS-Polygram

Album: released on Stax in Aug'81 by Ace Records. Distributed by: Pinnacle, Chris Wellard, IMS-Polygram

Cassette: released on Stax in Aug'81 by Ace Records. Distributed by: Pinnacle, Chris Wellard, IMS-Polygram

Single (7"): released on Stax in Mar'82 by Ace Records. Distributed by: Pinnacle, Chris Wellard, IMS-Polygram

Album: released on Ace in Aug'87 by Ace Records. Distributed by: Pinnacle, Swift, Hotshot, Cadillac

Album: released on Stax in Aug'87 by Ace Records. Distributed by: Pinnacle, Chris Wellard, IMS-Polygram

Brown, Simon

AULD BROON FAE FOGGIE TOON.
Cassette: released on Ross in Jan'86 by Ross Records. Distributed by: Ross Distribution, Roots Distribution

Brown, Steven

Douzieme journee: le verbe, la parure, l'amour

LAST RENDEZVOUS, THE.
Single (7"): released on Play It Again Sam in 20 Jun'87. Distributed by: Red Rhino, Cartel

ME & YOU & THE LICORICE STICK.
Single (12"): released on Sub Rosa in Jul'87 by Sub Rosa Records. Distributed by: Red Rhino Distribution, Cartel Distribution

SEARCHING FOR CONTACT.
Album: released on Play It Again Sam in Jun'87. Distributed by: Red Rhino, Cartel

Brown Sugar

GO NOW.
Single (12"): released on El Jay in Jul'83 by El Jay Records. Distributed by: Jetstar

Brownsville Banned

IN ANY CASE.
Tracks: / Bad again / Come back, Corinna / I'm in the mood for love / Banjoreno / Emeline / Hot patella swing / Juggae, juggae / Dust / Longin' blues / Cabaret time / Norman Mills live at the Conogo-Hogolo / Kick out your can.
Album: released on Sweet Folk All in May'81 by Sweet Folk All Records. Distributed by: Sweet Folk All, Roots, Celtic Music, Dragon, Impetus, Projection, Chris Wellard, Festival Records

THAT'S SHOEBIZ.
Tracks: / Charles Lennon / Doc Roberts / Van blues / Mrs Tas Pronk musical sink / Hang fire / Pick up / Julie the schoolie / Getting older / Norman Mills at the Halltappers and Shouters / Six feet tall / Gordon.
Album: released on Sweet Folk All in May'81 by Sweet Folk All Records. Distributed by: Sweet Folk All, Roots, Celtic Music, Dragon, Impetus, Projection, Chris Wellard, Festival Records

Brown, Ted

TED BROWN & JIMMY RAINEY (Brown, Ted/ Jimmy Rainey).
Album: released on Criss Cross in Jul'86. Distributed by: Jazz Music, Jazz Horizons, Cadillac

Brown, T Graham

BRILLIANT CONVERSATIONALIST.
Album: released on Capitol in Sep'87 by Capitol Records. Distributed by: EMI. Estim retail price in Sep'87 was £5.99.

Cassette: released on Capitol in Sep'87 by Capitol Records. Distributed by: EMI. Estim retail price in Sep'87 was £5.99.

Compact disc: released on Capitol in Sep'87 by Capitol Records. Distributed by: EMI. Estim retail price in Sep'87 was £11.99.

ROCK IT BILLY.
Tracks: / Rock it, Billy / Later train.
Single (7"): released on Capitol in May'87 by Capitol Records. Distributed by: EMI

Brown, Tom

NORFOLD DRIFTERMAN VOL.1.
Cassette: released on Folktracks in Nov'79 by Folktracks Cassettes. Distributed by: Folktracks

VOLUME 2 (Brown, Tom/Bertha Brown).
Cassette: released on Folktracks in Nov'79 by Folktracks Cassettes. Distributed by: Folktracks

Brown, U

JAM IT TONIGHT.
Tracks: / Jam it tonight / Take your time / Get it in the line / Tu-sheng-peng / Walk with Jah love / Me have to get you / Stop your bouncing / Get ready shank steady / Gimme the music / Jah is my father still.
Album: released on CSA in Jul'83 by CSA Records. Distributed by: PRT, Jetstar

OUT OF HAND.
Single (12"): released on Taxi in Aug'82 by Taxi Records. Distributed by: Jetstar Distribution

RAVERS PARTY.
Album: released on Trojan in May'83 by Trojan Records. Distributed by: PRT, Jetstar

THINGS A COME UP TO GO BUMP.
Single (12"): released on Midnight Rock in Sep'83. Distributed by: Jetstar Distribution, Kingdom Distribution

TU SHENG PENG.
Album: released on Vista Sounds in May'83 by Vista Sounds Records. Distributed by: Jetstar

Brown, Veda

SHORT STOPPIN'.
Single (7"): released on Stax in Aug'87 by Ace Records. Distributed by: Pinnacle, Chris Wellard, IMS-Polygram

SHORT STOPPING.
Single (7"): released on Stax in Mar'82 by Ace Records. Distributed by: Pinnacle, Chris Wellard, IMS-Polygram

Brown, Walter

CONFESSIN' THE BLUES.
Album: released on Affinity in Sep'81 by Charly Records. Distributed by: Charly, Cadillac

Brown, Winston 'Axeman'

AFRICA.
Tracks: / Africa.
Single (12"): released on Fashion in '86 by Fashion Records. Distributed by: PRT, Jetstar

SAFER WITH YOU.
Tracks: / Safer with you.
Single (12"): released on Fashion in Aug'86 by Fashion Records. Distributed by: PRT, Jetstar

Single (12"): released on Fine Style in 13 Jun'87 by Fine Style Records. Distributed by: Revolver, Jetstar, PRT, Cartel

Brown, Yvonne

MY WORLD IS EMPTY WITHOUT YOU.
Single (12"): released on Buzz Int. in Apr'84

Brozman, Bob

HELLO CENTRAL-GIVE ME DR. JAZZ (Brozman, Bob with George Winston).

Album: released on Rounder (USA) in Sep'85. Distributed by: Mike's Country Music Room Distribution, Jazz Music Distribution, Swift Distribution, Roots Records Distribution, Projection Distribution, Topic Distribution

Brubeck, Dave

1954-1972.
Album: released on CBS in Jan'87 by CBS Records. Distributed by: CBS

1975 THE DUETS (Brubeck, Dave/Paul Desmond).
Album: released on Ode in Jan'76 by Epic Records. Distributed by: CBS Distribution

25TH ANNIVERSARY REUNION CONCERT.
Album: released on Horizon in Mar'77 by A&M Records. Distributed by: CBS

ALL TOGETHER AGAIN.
Compact disc: released on Atlantic Jazz in Jul'87 by WEA Records. Distributed by: WEA

CONCORD ON A SUMMER NIGHT (Brubeck, Dave Quartet).
Tracks: / Benjamin / Koto Song / Black And Blue / Take Five / Softly, William, Softly.
Compact disc: released on Concord Jazz (USA) in Nov'86 by Concord Jazz Records (USA). Distributed by: IMS, Polygram

DAVE BRUBECK COLLECTION, THE.
Cassette: released on Deja Vu in Aug'85 by Deja Vu Records. Distributed by: Counterpoint Distribution, Record Services Distribution (Ireland)

DAVE BRUBECK OCTET, THE (Brubeck, Dave Octet).
Album: released on Riverside (USA) in Aug'84. Distributed by: Fantasy (USA) Distribution

DAVE BRUBECK/PAUL DESMOND.
Tracks: / Jeepers creepers / On a little street in Singapore / Trolly song (rehearsal) / Trolly song / I may be wrong / Blue moon / My heart stood still / Let's fall in love / Over he rainbow / You go to my head / Crazy ghris / Give a little whistle / Oh lady be good / Tea for two / This can't be love / Jeepers creepers / On a little street in Singapore / Trolley song / I may be wrong / Blue moon / My heart stood still / Let's fall in love / Let's fall in love / Over the rainbow / You go to my head / Crazy Chris / Give a little whistle / Lady be good / Tea for two / This can't be love.
Notes: 2 LP set
Double Album: released on Prestige (USA) in May'84

Double Album: released on Prestige (USA) in May'84

DAVE BRUBECK'S GREATEST HITS.
Tracks: / Take five / I'm in a dancing mood / In your own sweet way / Campton races / Duke, The / It's a raggy waltz / Bossa nova USA / Trolly song, The / Unsquare dance / Blue rondo a la turk / Theme from Mr Broadway / Take five / I'm in a dancing mood / In your own sweet way / Camptown races / Duke, The / It's a raggy waltz / Bossanova USA / Trolley song / Unsquare dance / Blue rondo a la turk / Theme from Mr Broadway.
Album: released on CBS in Jun'81 by CBS Records. Distributed by: CBS

Cassette: released on CBS in Jun'81 by CBS Records. Distributed by: CBS

FOR IOLA (Brubeck, Dave Quartet).
Tracks: / Polly / I hear a rhapsody / Thank you / Big bad Basie / For Iola / Summer song / Pange lingua march / Polly / I hear a rapshody / Thank you / Big bad baise / For iola / Summer song / Pange lingua march / Polly / I hear a rhapsody / Thank you / Big bad Basie / For Iola / Summer song / Pange lingua march.
Notes: Personnel: Dave Brubeck - piano/Chris brubeck - bass & trombone/Randy Jones drums/Bill Smith - clarinet
Compact disc: by Concord Jazz Records (USA). Distributed by: IMS, Polygram

Album: released on Concord Jazz (USA) in Feb'85 by Concord Jazz Records (USA). Distributed by: IMS, Polygram

Cassette: released on Concord Jazz (USA) in Feb'85 by Concord Jazz Records (USA). Distributed by: IMS, Polygram

IN CONCERT (Brubeck, Dave Quartet).
Compact disc: released on London in Apr'87 by London Records. Distributed by: Polygram

LAST SET AT NEWPORT.
Compact disc: released on Atlantic Jazz in Jul'87 by WEA Records. Distributed by: WEA

Compact disc: released on Atlantic Jazz in Jul'87 by WEA Records. Distributed by: WEA

MUSIC FROM WEST SIDE STORY..... (Brubeck, Dave with New York Philharmonic).
Tracks: / Maria / I feel pretty / Somewhere / Quiet girl, A / Tonight / Allegro I / Andante-ballad II / Adagio-ballad III / Allegro-blues IV.
Notes: Full title: Dave Brubeck with the New York Philharmonic(Bernstein)-Music from 'West Side Story''Wonderful Town'& Dialogues for Jazz Combo & Orchestra.

Album: released on CBS in Mar'86 by CBS Records. Distributed by: CBS

Cassette: released on CBS in Mar'86 by CBS Records. Distributed by: CBS

NEAR-MYTH.
Album: released on Original Jazz Classics (USA) in Apr'86. Distributed by: Fantasy (USA) Distribution, Chris Wellard Distribution, IMS-Polygram Distribution

NEWPORT '58.
Tracks: / Things ain't what they used to be / Jump for joy / Perdido / Liberian suite dance No. 3 / Duke, The / Flamingo / C Jam blues.
Album: released on CBS in Jul'87 by CBS Records. Distributed by: CBS

Cassette: released on CBS in Jul'87 by CBS Records. Distributed by: CBS

PAPER MOON.
Tracks: / Music maestro please / I hear a rhapsody / Symphony / I thought about you / It's only a paper moon / Long ago and far away / St Louis blues.
Album: released on Concord Jazz in Apr'82 by Concord Jazz Records (USA). Distributed by: IMS, Polygram

Cassette: released on Concord Jazz in Apr'82 by Concord Jazz Records (USA). Distributed by: IMS, Polygram

PLACE IN TIME, A (Brubeck, Dave Quartet).
Tracks: / Audrey / Jeepers creepers / Pennies from heaven / Why do I love you / Stompin' for Milli / Keepin' out of mischief now / Fine romance, A / Brother can you spare a dime.
Notes: Featuring Paul Desmind -sax/Bob Bates-bass/Joe Dodge-drums.
Album: released on Avan-Guard (CBS Recordings) in Aug'86. Distributed by: Conifer, Discovery

PLAYS WEST SIDE STORY/PLAYS MY FAIR LADY Dave Brubeck /Andre Previn (Brubeck, Dave/ Andre Previn).
Album: released on CBS in May'83 by CBS Records. Distributed by: CBS Deleted '86.

Cassette: released on CBS in May'83 by CBS Records. Distributed by: CBS

REFLECTIONS (Brubeck, Dave Quartet).
Tracks: / Reflections of you / Misty morning, A / I'd walk a country mile / My one bad habit / Blues for Newport / We will remember Paul / Michael,my second son / Blue Lake Tahoe / Reflections of you / Misty morning, A / I'd walk a country mile / My one bad habit / Blues for Newport / We will remember Paul / Michael, my second son / Blue Lake Tahoe.
Notes: Personnel: Dave Brubeck -piano Bill Smith -clarinet Chris Brubeck-electric bass,bass trombone Randy Jones -drums
Compact disc: released on Concord Jazz (USA) in Mar'87 by Concord Jazz Records (USA). Distributed by: IMS, Polygram

Album: released on Concord Jazz (USA) in Jun'86 by Concord Jazz Records (USA). Distributed by: IMS, Polygram

Cassette: released on Concord Jazz (USA) in Jun'86 by Concord Jazz Records (USA). Distributed by: IMS, Polygram

SEE HOW IT FEELS (Brubeck, Dave Quartet).
Album: released on Blackhawk in Aug'86 by Blackhawk Records (USA). Distributed by: IMS-Polygram

SHISH KEBAB.
Tracks: / Shish kebab / Fairy day / Don't worry about me / Lover come back to me / Royal garden blues / Love walked in / How high the moon / Shish kebab / Fairy day / Don't worry about me / Lover come back to me / Royal Garden blues / Love walked in / How high the moon.
Album: released on Joker in Apr'81. Distributed by: Counterpoint, Mainline, Record Services Distribution (Ireland)

SOUTHERN SCENE (Brubeck, Dave with Quartet/Trio/Duo).
Album: released on Japanese Import in Apr'79

TAKE FIVE.
Tracks: / Take five / Bossa nova USA / Unsquare dance / Someday my prince will come / I'm in a dancing mood / It's a raggy waltz / Blue rondo a la turk / Kathy's waltz / My favourite things / Castilian drums / Duke, The / Trolley song.
Album: released on CBS in Nov'81 by CBS Records. Distributed by: CBS

Cassette: released on CBS in Nov'81 by CBS Records. Distributed by: CBS

Single (7"): released on Old Gold in Apr'83 by Old Gold Records. Distributed by: Lightning, Jazz Music, Spartan, Counterpoint

TIME OUT.
Tracks: / Blue Rondo a la Turk / Take five / Strange meadowlark / Blue rondo a la turk / Strange meadowlark / Take five / Three to get ready / Kathy's waltz / Everybody's jumpin' / Pick up sticks / It's a raggy waltz / Bluesette / Charles Matthew Halleluya / Far more blue / Far more drums / Maori blues / Unsquare dance / Bru's boogie woogie / Blue shadows in the street.
Compact disc: by CBS Records. Distributed by: CBS

TIME OUT/TIME FURTHER OUT.
Tracks: / Blue rondo a la turk / Strange meadow lark / Take five / Three to get ready / Kathy's waltz / Everybody's jumpin' / Pick up sticks / It's a raggy waltz / Bluette / Charles Matthew hallelujah / Far more blue / Far more drums / Maori blues / Unsquare dance / Bru's boogie woogie / Blue shadows in the street.
Double Album: released on CBS in May'82 by CBS Records. Distributed by: CBS

Double cassette: released on CBS in May'82 by CBS Records. Distributed by: CBS

Brubeck, Dave Quartet

BLUE RONDO.
Tracks: / How does your garden grow? / Festival hall / Easy as you go / Blue Rondo a la turk / Dizzy's dream / I see, Satie / Swing bells / Strange meadowlark / Elana Joy.
Notes: Personnel: Dave Brubeck - piano / Bill Smith - clarinet / Chris Brubeck - electric bass & bass trombone / Randy Jones - drums.
Album: released on Concord Jazz (USA) in Jul'87 by Concord Jazz Records (USA). Distributed by: IMS, Polygram

Cassette: released on Concord Jazz (USA) in Jul'87 by Concord Jazz Records (USA). Distributed by: IMS, Polygram

Compact disc: released on Concord Jazz (USA) in Jul'87 by Concord Jazz Records (USA). Distributed by: IMS, Polygram

Bruce & Bongo

GEIL.
Tracks: / Geil / Geil (Bruce & Bongo dub).
Single (7"): released on Columbia in Jun'86 by EMI Records. Distributed by: EMI

Single (12"): released on Columbia in Jun'86 by EMI Records. Distributed by: EMI

Bruce, Ed

DIANE.
Single (7"): released on MCA in Apr'83 by MCA Records. Distributed by: Polygram, MCA

ED BRUCE.
Tracks: / Last thing she said, The / Last cowboy song, The / Red doggin' again / Love ain't something I can do alone / Girls,women & ladies / Neon fool / Blue umbrella / I still wish / Outlaw & the stranger, The.
Album: released on MCA Import in Mar'86 by MCA Records. Distributed by: Polygram, IMS

GREATEST HITS:ED BRUCE.
Tracks: / Last cowboy song, The / Girls,women & ladies / Everything's a waltz (When you fall in love) / You're the best break this old heart ever had / Love's found you & me / Ever,never lovin' you / My first taste of Texas / You're not leavin' here tonight / If it was easy / After all.
Album: released on MCA Import in Mar'86 by MCA Records. Distributed by: Polygram, IMS

I WRITE IT DOWN.
Tracks: / My first taste of texas / Ever,never lovin' you / Somebody's crying / One more shot of old back home again / Songwriter(I write it down), The / Bret Maverick(Theme from) / Memories can't stand to be alone / Your jukebox could use a few more sad songs / Babe in arms / Mammas don't let your babies grow up to be cowboys / My first taste of Texas / Ever, never lovin' you / Somebody's crying / One more shot of "old back home again" / Songwriter, The (I write it down) / Theme from Bret maverick / Memories can't stand to be alone / Your jukebox could use a few more sad songs / Babe in arms / Mammas don't let your babies grow up to be cowboys / My first taste of Texas / Ever, never lovin' you / Somebody's crying / One more shot of "Old back home again" / Songwriter, The (I write it down) / Theme from "Bret Maverick" / Memories can't stand to be alone / Your jukebox could use a few more sad songs / Babe in arms / Mammas, don't let your babies grown up to be cowboys.
Album: released on MCA Import in Mar'86 by MCA Records. Distributed by: Polygram, IMS

Album: released on MCA in Apr'83 by MCA Records. Distributed by: Polygram, MCA

Cassette: released on MCA in Apr'83 by MCA Records. Distributed by: Polygram, MCA

LAST TRAIN TO CLARKESVILLE.
Tracks: / I know better / Why can't I come home / Walker's woods / Ninety seven more to go / I could just go home / By route of New Orleans / Shadows of her mind / Lonesome is me / I'm getting better / Her sweet love and the baby / I'll take yu away / Last train to Clarkesville / I'd best be leaving you / Tiny golden locket / Ballad of he drummer boy, The / Something else to mess your mind / Puzzles / Memphis morning / Painted girls and wine / Blue bayou / I know better / Why can't I come home? / Walker's woods / Ninety-seven more to go / I could just go home / By route of New Orleans / Shadows of her mind / Lonesome is me / I'm getting better / Her sweet love and the baby / I'll take you away / Last train to Clarkesville / I'd best be leaving you / Tiny golden locket / Ballad of the drummer boy, The / Something else to mess your mind / Puzzles / Memphis morning / Painted girls and wine / Blue bayou.

Album: released on RCA International in May'82

Cassette: released on RCA International in May'82

ONE TO ONE.
Tracks: / When you fall in love(everything's a waltz) / Evil angel / You're the best break this old heart ever had / It just makes me want you more / Hundred dollar lady / Love's found you and me / I take the chance / No regrets / Thirty nine & holding / Easy temptations.
Album: released on MCA Import in Mar'86 by MCA Records. Distributed by: Polygram, IMS

ROCK BOPPIN' BABY.
Tracks: / Rock boppin' baby / More than yesterday / Eight wheel* / Ballad of Ringo* / King of fools* / Just being with you* / Alone with a broken heart* / You come to me* / Sweet woman / Doll baby* / King of fools* / Flight 303 / Sun gold.
Notes: Original Sun/RCA recordings. Contains previously un-issued tracks(marked*).
Album: released on Bear Family in Apr'86 by Bear Family Records. Distributed by: Rollercoaster Distribution, Swift

TELL 'EM I'VE GONE CRAZY.
Tracks: / If I just knew what she said / She never could dance / It's all in your mind / Straight shooter / Devil inside, The / Tell 'em I've gone crazy / Old time's sake / Birds of paradise / Someone who would care / If she just helps me get over you.
Album: released on MCA Import in Mar'86 by MCA Records. Distributed by: Polygram, IMS

YOU'RE NOT LEAVIN' HERE TONIGHT.
Tracks: / You're not leavin' here tonight / It would take a fool / In Mexico / If it was easy / It's the lovers(who give love a bad name) / After all / Lucky arms / You've got her eyes / I think I'm in love / I'll be there to catch you / You're not leaving here tonight / It would take a fool / In Mexico / It it was easy / Lovers give love a bad name / After all / Lucky arms / You've got her eyes / I'll be there to catch you / You're not leavin' here tonight / It would take a fool / In Mexico / It was easy / Lovers give love a bad name / After all / Lucky arms / You've got her eyes / I'll be there to catch you.
Album: released on MCA Import in Mar'86 by MCA Records. Distributed by: Polygram, IMS

Album: released on MCA in '83 by MCA Records. Distributed by: Polygram, MCA

Cassette: released on MCA in '83 by MCA Records. Distributed by: Polygram, MCA

Bruce, Fraser

FAREWELL TAE TARWATHIE.
Album: released on Nevis in May'77. Distributed by: H.R. Taylor

MRS. BRUCE'S BOYS VOL.1 (Bruce, Fraser & Ian).
Tracks: / Ryebuck shearers / Leaving the Dales / King's shilling, The / Rise up Jack / Ring a rosie / Cape Ann / Walking song, The / New railroad, The / Isle of Haut / Down where the drunkards roll / Gadie rins, The.
Album: released on Lochshore in May'81 by Klub Records. Distributed by: PRT

Cassette: released on Lochshore in May'81 by Klub Records. Distributed by: PRT

MRS. BRUCE'S BOYS VOL.2 (Bruce, Fraser & Ian).
Tracks: / Idiot, The / Western boat / Man you don't meet every day, A / Catch me if you can / Tatties and herring / Edinburgh / Mrs MacDonald's lament / Waiting for the lark / Deportees / Bonny Susie Clelland / Wedding, The / Tak' a dram.
Album: released on Lochshore in Oct'84 by Klub Records. Distributed by: PRT

Cassette: released on Lochshore in Oct'84 by Klub Records. Distributed by: PRT

SHAMROCK & HEATHER.
Album: released on Nevis in May'77. Distributed by: H.R. Taylor

VEIL OF THE AGES (Bruce, Fraser & Ian).
Tracks: / Nostradamus / John O'Dreams / I don't belong to Glasgow / Can ye saw cushions / Crey funnel line / Hagged man, The / Sally Wheatley / Roll on the day / Roseville faire / Stumpy / Farewell to gold / Aye's the boy.
Album: released on Lochshore in Oct'82 by Klub Records. Distributed by: PRT

Cassette: released on Lochshore in Oct'82 by Klub Records. Distributed by: PRT

Bruce, Ian

GOSPEL ACCORDION (Bruce, Ian/May).
Tracks: / Amazing grace / Since Jesus came into my heart / Sweet by-and-by, The / This is the day / Wide, wide as the ocean / Running over / Whosoever will / Still sweeter everyday / Bringing in the sheaves / For God so loved the world / Somewhere beyond the blues / Jesus loves even me / Isn't he wonderful / What a frind we have in Jesus / Give me oil in my lamp / Thou art worthy / Hallelujah / There's something about that name / Old rugged cross, The / It is

Page 159

no secret / Whispering hope / This world is not my home / Thank you, lord / All that thrills my soul / Sing when the day is bright / Christ is the answer / Windows of heaven are open, The / Bringing in the sheaves.
Album: by Pilgrim Records. Distributed by: Rough Trade, Cartel

Bruce, Jack

AUTOMATIC.
Tracks: / Make Love Part II / Uptown Breakdown / Travelling Child / New World / E. Boogie / Green And Blue / Swarm / Encore / Automatic Pilot.
Notes: (P) Edward Kassner Music Co. Ltd
Album: released on President in Jan'87 by President Records. Distributed by: Taylors, Spartan

Cassette: released on President in Jan'87 by President Records. Distributed by: Taylors, Spartan

GREATEST HITS:JACK BRUCE.
Double Album: released on Polydor in Nov'80 by Polydor Records. Distributed by: Polygram, Polydor

Double cassette: released on Polydor in Nov'80 by Polydor Records. Distributed by: Polygram, Polydor

I FEEL FREE.
Tracks: / I feel free / Make love.
Single (7"): released on Virgin in Jun'86 by Virgin Records. Distributed by: EMI, Virgin Distribution

Single (12"): released on Virgin in Jun'86 by Virgin Records. Distributed by: EMI, Virgin Distribution

I'VE ALWAYS WANTED TO DO THIS.
Cassette: released on Epic in Dec'80 by CBS Records. Distributed by: CBS

SONGS FOR A TAILOR.
Tracks: / Never tell your mother / She's out of tune / Theme of an imaginary western / Tickets to water falls / Weird of Hermiston / Rope ladder to the moon / Ministry of bag, The / He the Richmond / Boston ball game, 1967 / To Isengard / Clearout, The.
Notes: After Cream break-up in 1969, Bruce recorded this much praised album with all star support from Dick Heckstall-Smith, John Hiseman, Chris Spedding, John Marshall and others.
Album: released on Polydor (Germany) in May'84. Distributed by: IMS-Polygram

TRUCE (Bruce, Jack & Robin Trower).
Tracks: / Gonna shut you down / Gone too far / Thin ice / Last train to the stars / Take good care of yourself / Falling in love / Fat gut / Shadows touching / Little boy lost.
Album: released on Chrysalis in Jan'82 by Chrysalis Records. Distributed by: CBS

Cassette: released on Chrysalis in Jan'82 by Chrysalis Records. Distributed by: CBS

Bruce, Lenny

CARNEGIE HALL.
Tracks: / Introduction- Don Friedman / Miracle on 57th street / Arlines, The / Sound / Kidnap, The / Point of view / Ku Klux Klan / What's it mean, A / Kennedy acceptance speech / On humour / Nightclubs / Dykes and faggots / Homosexuality / Girl ringing / Flag and communism, The / Dear Abbey / Las Vegas tits and ass / Clap, The / Christ and moses / Equality / Interval revenue / Pills / Burlesque house / Judge Saperstein decision / On contemporaries / Shelley Berman / Operation, The / Joke, The / End, The.
Triple album / cassette: released on United Artists in Sep'75

IN CONCERT.
Album: released on Demon in Jul'86 by Demon Records. Distributed by: Pinnacle

SICK HUMOUR OF LENNY BRUCE.
Album: released on Demon in Jun'84 by Demon Records. Distributed by: Pinnacle

UNEXPURGATED..THE VERY BEST OF...
Tracks: / Airplane glue / How to relax your coloured friends at parties / Fathe Flotski's triumph / Commercials / Religions, inc; Dijinni in the candy store / Psychpathia sexualis / White collar drunks / Three message movies (Naracotics, truth, tolerence) / Esther Costello story / Marriage, divorce and motels / Non skeldo flies again.
Album: released on Fantasy in '82 by RCA Records. Distributed by: RCA, Jetstar

Cassette: released on Fantasy in '82 by RCA Records. Distributed by: RCA, Jetstar

Bruce, Tommy

GREATEST HITS:TOMMY BRUCE.
Cassette: released on Autograph in Apr'85. Distributed by: Record Services Distribution (Ireland)

Bruce, Vin

CAJUN COUNTRY.
Album: released on Swallow in Feb'79

GREATEST HITS:VIN BRUCE.
Album: released on Swallow in Feb'79

VIN BRUCE SINGS COUNTRY.
Album: released on Swallow in Feb'79

VIN BRUCE SINGS JOLE BLON.
Album: released on Swallow in Feb'79

Bruford, Bill

EARTHWORKS.
Album: released on E.G. in Mar'87 by Virgin Records. Distributed by: Virgin, EMI

Cassette: released on E.G. in Mar'87 by Virgin Records. Distributed by: Virgin, EMI

FEELS GOOD TO ME.
Tracks: / Beelzebub / Back to the beginning / Seems like a lifetime ago / Sample and hold / Feels good to me / Either end of August / If you can't stand the heat / Springtime in Siberia / Adios in pasade / Adios la pasade.
Album: released on Polydor in Jan'78 by Polydor Records. Distributed by: Polygram, Polydor

GRADUALLY GOING TORNADO.
Album: released on E.G. in Jan'80 by Virgin Records. Distributed by: Virgin, EMI

MASTER STROKES.
Album: released on E.G. in Dec'86 by Virgin Records. Distributed by: Virgin, EMI

Compact disc: by Virgin Records. Distributed by: Virgin, EMI

MUSIC FOR PIANO AND DRUMS (Bruford, Bill & Patrick Moraz).
Notes: For full information see under MORAZ, Patrick & Bill Bruford.

Bruford Tapes

BRUFORD TAPES, THE.
Album: released on Canadian Imps in Jan'80. Distributed by: IMS

Brum Beat...

BRUMBEAT LIVE AT THE BARRELL ORGAN Various artists (Various Artists).
Double Album: released on Big Bear in Sep'80 by Big Bear Records. Distributed by: Big Bear, Swift

Brummagem Ballads

FARRIERS & KEMPION.
Album: released on Broadside in Jun'81 by Broadside Records. Distributed by: Celtic Distributions, H.R. Taylor, Jazz Music, Projection,

Cassette: released on Broadside in Jun'81 by Broadside Records. Distributed by: Celtic Distributions H.R. Taylor, Jazz Music, Projection,

Brummel, Beau

AUTUMN IN SAN FRANCISCO.
Album: released on Edsel in Jul'85 by Demon Records. Distributed by: Pinnacle, Jazz Music, Projection

BRADLEY'S BARN.
Album: released on Edsel in Apr'85 by Demon Records. Distributed by: Pinnacle, Jazz Music, Projection

HOT GEORGE.
Single (7"): released on Moonlight in Sep'82 by Lithon Recording & Music Publishing

Bruna, Dick

MIFFY AND OTHER STORIES.
Tracks: / Other Stories (Cont.).
Cassette: released on Tellastory in Dec'86 by Bartlett Bliss Productions. Distributed by: PRT Distribution, Hayward Promotions Distribution, H.R. Taylor Distribution

Brunes, Cliff

WATCH OUT FOR CLIFF.
Album: released on Showtime in Sep'79 by Relic. Distributed by: Swift

Brunies, Albert

NEW ORLEANS SHUFFLE 1925-28 (Brunies, Albert & Halfway House Orchestra).
Cassette: released on VJM in Jun'87 by Wellard, Chris Distribution. Distributed by: Wellard, Chris Distribution

Bruninghaus, Ranier

CONTINUUM.
Album: released on ECM (Germany) in Mar'84 by ECM Records. Distributed by: IMS, Polygram, Virgin through EMI

FREIGEWEHT (BLOWN FREE).
Album: released on ECM in May'81 by ECM Records. Distributed by: IMS, Polygram, Virgin through EMI

Brunious, Wendell

IN THE TRADITION.
Notes: with J. Kimball, Louis Nelson, S. Rimington, Frank Fields, Barry Martyn.
Album: released on GHB in Feb'87. Distributed by: Jazz Music, Swift

Brunis, George

KING OF TAILGATE TROMBONE.
Album: released on Commodore Classics in '87 by Teldec Records (Germany). Distributed by: Conifer, IMS, Polygram

TIN ROOF BLUES Commodore classics (Brunis, George & Wild Bill Davison).
Tracks: / Royal Garden blues / Royal garden blues(2) / Ugly child / Ugly child (2) / Tin roof blues / Tin roof blues(2) / That da da strain / That da da strain(2) / High society / High society(2) / Wrap your troubles in dreams / Wrap your troubles in dreams(2) / I'm coming Virginia / I'm coming Virginia(2) / Wabash blues / Wabash blues(2).
Album: released on Commodore in Mar'83. Distributed by: Swift

Brunis, Merritt

1924-26 (Brunis, Merritt & His Friars Inn Orchestra).
Album: released on Fountain-Retrieval in Sep'86 by Retrieval Records. Distributed by: Retrieval, VJM, Swift, Jazz Music, Wellard,

Brunis, Wendell

IN THE TRADITION.
Notes: With Jeanette Kimball, Louis Nelson Nelson, Frank Fields, Sammy Rimmington, and also Barry Martin.
Album: released on GHB in Jan'87. Distributed by: Jazz Music, Swift

Brunning Band

DREAM POLICE.
Single (7"): released on Technical in Feb'83. Distributed by: Stage One Distribution

Brunning Sunflower...

I WISH YOU WOULD.
Album: released on Appaloosa in Jan'84. Distributed by: Roots, Folksound, Projection, Celtic Music, Chris Wellard

Brunskill, Bill

30 YEARS ON (Brunskill, Bill Jazzmen).
Tracks: / Marie / Kitchen man / Ampola / Coney Island / Washboard / Down in Honky Tonk Town / If you're a viper / Mamas gone goodbye.
Notes: Artists include: Mike Pointon, Hugh Crozier, Bill Stagg, Jim Bray, Les Allen, Dave Jenkins. A celebration of 30 years in jazz.
Album: released on VLP in Jul'82

Brunson, Tyrone

LOVE TRIANGLE.
Tracks: / Love triangle / Tell me why / Free bee / Method, The / Lot of pop, A / Tender touch / Knucklehead syndrome / Space boy / Love triangle / Tell me why / Free bee / Method, The / Lot of pop, A / Tender touch / Knuckle syndrome / Space boy.
Album: released on MCA in Jun'87 by MCA Records. Distributed by: Polygram, MCA

Cassette: released on MCA in Jun'87 by MCA Records. Distributed by: Polygram, MCA

STICKY SITUATION.
Tracks: / Sticky situation / I need love / Go for it / Don't you want it / Smurf, The / Hot line / New wave disco punk funk rock.
Album: released on Epic in Feb'83 by CBS Records. Distributed by: CBS Deleted '85.

Cassette: released on Epic in Feb'83 by CBS Records. Distributed by: CBS

Brush Arbor

HERO.
Tracks: / Only for the love of the lord / Come back home / Witness / All I want to be / Hero / Hey there stranger / Running / Trust in the lord / God is good / St. Peter / Rescue me.
Album: released on Myrrh in May'82 by Word Records. Distributed by: Word Distribution

Cassette: released on Myrrh in May'82 by Word Records. Distributed by: Word Distribution

Brush Shiels

BETTER THAN I EXPECTED BUT NOT MUCH.
Single (7"): released on Bruised in Aug'80

Brutus

EXCITATION.
Single (7"): released on Philly Wood in Jul'83

Single (12"): released on Philly Wood in Jul'83

Brutus, Tony

WATER PISTOL.
Single (12"): released on Intense in Jan'84 by Intense Records. Distributed by: PRT, Kingdom

Bryan, Ashley

DANCING GRANNY & OTHER AFRICAN STORIES, THE.
Cassette: released on Caedmon(USA) in Sep'85 by Caedmon (USA) Records. Distributed by: Taylors, Discovery

Bryan, Carlton

NUCLEAR YARD.
Album: released on Roots Invasion in Aug'85. Distributed by: Jetstar Distribution

Bryan, James

FIRST OF MAY, THE.
Album: released on Rounder (USA) in Jun'86. Distributed by: Mike's Country Music Room Distribution, Jazz Music Distribution, Swift Distribution, Roots Records Distribution, Projection Distribution, Topic Distribution

Bryant, Felice

ALL I HAVE TO DO IS DREAM (Bryant, Felice & Boudleaux).
Tracks: / All I have to do is dream / Love hurts / Raining in my heart / Yeh bye love / Wake up little Susie.
Album: released on DB in Nov'80 by DB Records. Distributed by: Pinnacle

Bryant, Jimmy

TWO GUITARS COUNTRY STYLE (Bryant, Jimmy & Speedy West).
Album: released on Pathe MarconiEMI Europe) in Jun'84

Bryant, Lynn

YOU ARE.
Single (12"): released on Vista Sounds in May'83 by Vista Sounds Records. Distributed by: Jetstar

Bryant, Marie

DON'T TOUCH MY NYLONS.
Album: released on Spartan in Feb'87 by Spartan Records. Distributed by: Spartan

Cassette: released on Spartan in Feb'87 by Spartan Records. Distributed by: Spartan

Bryant, Ray

ALL BLUES (Bryant, Ray Trio).
Tracks: / All blues / C-jam blues / Please send me someone to love / Jumpin' with symphony Sid / Blues changes / Billie's bounce / Stick with it.
Album: released on Pablo (USA) in '82 by Pablo Records (USA). Distributed by: Wellard, Chris, IMS-Polygram, BMG

Cassette: released on Pablo (USA) in '82 by Pablo Records (USA). Distributed by: Wellard, Chris, IMS-Polygram, BMG

ALONE WITH THE BLUES.
Album:

BEST OF RAY BRYANT.
Tracks: / Stick with it / Girl talk / In de back room / Please send me someone to love / Li'l darlin' / All blues / Moanin' / Good morning heartache.
Album: released on Pablo (USA) in '82 by Pablo Records (USA). Distributed by: Wellard, Chris, IMS-Polygram, BMG

Cassette: released on Pablo (USA) in '82 by Pablo Records (USA). Distributed by: Wellard, Chris, IMS-Polygram, BMG

HERE'S RAY BRYANT.
Tracks: / Girl talk / Good morning heartache / Manteca / When sunny gets blue / Hold back mon / Li'l darlin' / Cold turkey / Prayer song.
Album: released on Pablo (USA) in '82 by Pablo Records (USA). Distributed by: Wellard, Chris, IMS-Polygram, BMG

Cassette: released on Pablo (USA) in '82 by Pablo Records (USA). Distributed by: Wellard, Chris, IMS-Polygram, BMG

POTPOURRI (Bryant, Ray Trio).
Tracks: / D.B. blues / One o' clock jump / Milestones / Undecided / In walked Bud / In a mellow tone / My one and only love / Night in Tunisia.
Album: released on Pablo (USA) in '82 by Pablo Records (USA). Distributed by: Wellard, Chris, IMS-Polygram, BMG

Cassette: released on Pablo (USA) in '82 by Pablo Records (USA). Distributed by: Wellard, Chris, IMS-Polygram, BMG

RAY BRYANT.
Tracks: / Take the 'A' train / Georgia on my mind / Jungle town jubilee / If I could just make it to

heaven / Django / Blues No. 6 / Satin doll / Sometimes I feel like a motherless child / St. Louis blues / Things ain't what they used to be.
Album: released on Pablo (USA) in '82 by Pablo Records (USA). Distributed by: Wellard, Chris, IMS-Polygram, BMG

Cassette: released on Pablo (USA) in '82 by Pablo Records (USA). Distributed by: Wellard, Chris, IMS-Polygram, BMG

RAY BRYANT TRIO (Bryant, Ray Trio).

RAY BRYANT TRIO (Bryant, Ray Trio).
Compact disc: released on JVC Fantasy (Japan) in Apr'87

SOLO FLIGHT.
Tracks: / In de back room / What are you doing the rest of your life / Monkey business / Blues in de big brass bed / Moanin' / St. Louis blues / Take the 'A' train / Lullaby.
Album: released on Pablo (USA) in '82 by Pablo Records (USA). Distributed by: Wellard, Chris, IMS-Polygram, BMG

Cassette: released on Pablo (USA) in '82 by Pablo Records (USA). Distributed by: Wellard, Chris, IMS-Polygram, BMG

TRIO.
Compact disc: released on Carrere in Apr'87 by Carrere Records. Distributed by: PRT, Spartan

Bryant, Rusty

RUSTY BRYANT WITH THE BOSS 4.
Tracks: / Getting in the groove / Soft winds / St. Thomas / Rusty rides again / Entertainer, The / I'm old fashioned.
Album: released on Phoenix in May'81 by Audio Fidelity Enterprises. Distributed by: Stage One,

Bryars, Gavin

SINKING OF THE TITANIC, THE.
Album: released on Editions EG in Jan'87 by Virgin Records. Distributed by: EMI

SINKING OF THE TITANIC.
Album: released on Obscure in Apr'78 by Polydor Records. Distributed by: Polygram Distribution

THREE VIENNESE DANCERS.
Compact disc: by ECM Records. Distributed by: IMS, Polygram, Virgin through EMI

Album: released on ECM (Germany) in Sep'86 by ECM Records. Distributed by: IMS, Polygram, Virgin through EMI

Brygada Kryzys

BRYGADA KRYZYS.
Album: released on Fresh in May'82. Distributed by: Jetstar

CRISIS BRIGADE.
Album: released on Fresh in Jan'87. Distributed by: Jetstar

Bryner, Yul

GYPSY & I.
Album: released on Vanguard in Jul'79 by PRT Records. Distributed by: PRT

Bryson, Peabo

BORN TO LIVE (Bryson, Peabo & Roberta Flack).
Tracks: / Tonight, I celebrate my love / Blame it on me / Heaven above me / Born to love / Maybe / I just came here to dance / Comin' alive / Your looking like love to me / Can we find love again'.
Notes: This is the first album on Capitol from this dynamic new combination. Amongst the songwriting/-production credits are Burt Bacharch, Carol Bayer-Sager, MarvinHamlisch, Bob Gaudio, Bob Crewe and Michael Masser, who together with Gerry Goffin wrote the single "Tonight I celebrate my love".
Album: released on Capitol in '85 by Capitol Records. Distributed by: EMI

Cassette: released on Capitol in '85 by Capitol Records. Distributed by: EMI

HEAVEN ABOVE ME (Bryson, Peabo & Roberta Flack).
Single (7"): released on Capitol in Oct'83 by Capitol Records. Distributed by: EMI

Single (12"): released on Capitol in Oct'83 by Capitol Records. Distributed by. EMI

QUIET STORM.
Tracks: / Since i've been in love / Somebody in your life / Good combination / If you love me(let me know) / Higher you climb, The / Catch 22 / Only at night / After you.
Album: released on Elektra (USA) in Oct'86 by Elektra/Asylum/Nonesuch Records. Distributed by: WEA

Cassette: released on Elektra (USA) in Oct'86 by Elektra/Asylum/Nonesuch Records. Distributed by: WEA

STRAIGHT FROM THE HEART.
Tracks: / Slow dancin' / If ever you're ever in my arms again / Straight from the heart / There's no getting over you / I get nervous / Learning the ways of love / Real deal / Love means forever.
Cassette: released on Elektra (USA) in May'84 by Elektra/Asylum/Nonesuch Records. Distributed by: WEA

Album: released on Elektra (USA) in May'84 by Elektra/Asylum/Nonesuch Records. Distributed by: WEA Deleted '86.

Compact disc: released on Elektra (USA) in May'84 by Elektra/Asylum/Nonesuch Records. Distributed by: WEA

TAKE NO PRISONERS.
Tracks: / Take no prisoners / There ain't nothing out there / Let's apologise / Irresistable / Love always finds a way / Falling for you / I'm in love / Talk to me / She's over me.
Compact disc: by Elektra/Asylum/Nonesuch Records. Distributed by: WEA

Album: released on Elektra (USA) in Jun'85 by Elektra/Asylum/Nonesuch Records. Distributed by: WEA

Cassette: released on Elektra (USA) in Jun'85 by Elektra/Asylum/Nonesuch Records. Distributed by: WEA

Tonight I celebrate my love for you

BSWG Ensemble

ANIMALS WENT IN TWO BY TWO.
Single (7"): released on International Discs in May'83 by International. Distributed by: Pinnacle

JINGLE BELLS.
Single (7"): released on International Discs in May'83 by International. Distributed by: Pinnacle

B. Team

ALL BECAUSE (I LOVE YOU).
Single (7"): released on Mainfeature in Feb'87. Distributed by: Gold & Sons, Cartel, O.I.D, Backs

ALL I EVER WANTED.
Single (7"): released on Diamond in Sep'85 by Revolver Records. Distributed by: Cartel

B.T.Express

MIDNIGHT BEAT.
Single (7"): released on Excaliber in Mar'81 by Red Bus Records. Distributed by: PRT

Single (12"): released on Excaliber in Mar'81 by Red Bus Records. Distributed by: PRT

OLD GOLD FUTURE GOLD.
Tracks: / Stretch / Peace pipe (remix) / Shout it out (remix) / Let me be the one / Express (remix) / Do it (till you are satisfied) / I wanna hold you / Midnight beat.
Album: released on Excaliber in Jan'81 by Red Bus Records. Distributed by: PRT

THIS MUST BE THE NIGHT.
Single (7"): released on Record Shack in Feb'83 by Record Shack Records. Distributed by: PRT

Single (12"): released on Record Shack in Feb'83 by Record Shack Records. Distributed by: PRT

B, Tina

NOTHING'S GONNA COME EASY.
Single (7"): released on Atlantic in Jan'85 by WEA Records. Distributed by: WEA

B.T.O.

STREET ACTION.
Album: released on Mercury in Apr'78 by Phonogram Records. Distributed by: Polygram Distribution

B. Troop

EUROPEANS.
Album: released on KSV in Nov'81 by Kingsley Sound & Vision. Distributed by: Kingsley Sound & Vision Distribution

Buarque, Chico

OPERA DO MALANDRO.
Tracks: / A volta do Malandro / Las muchachas de Copacabana / Tema da repressao / Aquela mulher / Viver do amor / Sentimental / Desafio do Malandro / O ultimo blues / Palavra de mulher / O meu amor / Tango do covil / Uma cancao desnaturada / Rio / Pedaco de mim.
Notes: A satirical opera based on Kurt Weill and Bert Brecht's 'The Threepenny Opera' composed by one of Brazil's best known composers and intellectuals,Chico Buarqua. Chico's revolutionary songs which deal with social injustice are known the world over.During the period of the military junta,his songs were constantly banned.'Opera do malandro'features Elba Ramalho,one of Brazil's top female singers and well known in Europe through her appearances at the Montreux Jazz festival.'Opera do malandro' was originally written for the stage and had it's premiere in Brazil some eight years ago.
Album: released on Polydor (France) in Sep'86. Distributed by: Polygram

Cassette: released on Polydor (France) in Sep'86. Distributed by: Polygram

Bubba Lou

LOVE ALL OVER THE PLACE (Bubba Lou & The Highballs).
Single (7"): released on Stiff in Mar'81 by Stiff Records. Distributed by: EMI, Record Services Distribution (Ireland)

Bubble Gum Biggies

BUBBLE GUM BIGGIES (Nineteen Ten Fruitgum Co/Ohio Express).
Single (7"): released on Flashback in Jul'80 by Flashback Records/PRT Records. Distributed by: Mainline, PRT

Bubblegum Splash

SPLASHDOWN EP.
Extended-play record: released on Subway in Aug'87. Distributed by: Revolver Distribution, Spartan Distribution

Bubble Puppy

WHEELS GO ROUND.
Album: released on One Big Guitar in Aug'87 by One Big Guitar Records. Distributed by: Revolver Distribution, Cartel Distribution, Pinnacle

Bubblers Rock

BUBBLERS ROCK VOL.1 Various artists (Various Artists).
Album: released on Tom Tom in Sep'85 by Tom Tom Records. Distributed by: Jetstar Distribution

Bubbles, John W.

BACK ON BROADWAY.
Tracks: / It ain't necessarily so / Belitting me / Somebody's gonna make you fall / Why was I born / Sweet mama / On the unny side of the street / Bubbles blue / Wrap your troubles in dreams / Lady be good / Nobody knows / My mother's eyes / Somebody loves me.
Album: released on Uptown (USA) in Feb'83 by Uptown Records. Distributed by: Jazz Music

Bubblies

BUBBLIES, THE.
Cassette: released on PRT in '83 by PRT Records. Distributed by: PRT

Bubblies & Friends

PLEASE COME HOME FOR CHRISTMAS.
Tracks: / Please come home for Christmas / Christmas story.
Single (7"): released on Snowbow in Nov'86. Distributed by: PRT

Bubbling Brown Sugar

BUBBLING BROWN SUGAR Original London cast (Various Artists).
Double Album: released on Pye in Oct'77

Buchanan, Gilly

ME NO ME (Buchanan, Gilly & Patrick Anderson).
Single (12"): released on Toe in Sep'85 by Toe Records. Distributed by: Jetstar Distribution

Buchanan, Jack

ELEGANCE.
Tracks: / Night time / Living in clover / Fancy our meeting / Oceans of time / Like Monday follows Sunday / We get our divorce / Not bad / Dancing honeymoon / And her mother came too / Who / Now that I've found you / You forgot your gloves / One I'm looking for The / Sweet so an so / I think I can / Dapper Dan / Alone with my dreams / Two little bluebirds / Goodnight Vienna / It's not you / There's always tomorrow.
Notes: Britain's answer to Fred Astaire' was one label frequently tagged to Jack Buchanan. Six foot height and with a flair to casual elegance, Buchanan in fact had no formal training in dance or song, but went on to become the great singer, dancer and actor who charmed audiences on both sides of the Atlantic - a man whose bearing, sparkle and polish made him the personification of elegance in the inter-war years.
Album: released on ASV Living Era in Jun'85 by ASV Records. Distributed by: PRT

Cassette: released on ASV Living Era in Jun'85 by ASV Records. Distributed by: PRT

GOLDEN AGE OF JACK BUCHANAN, THE.
Tracks: / Two little birds / It's not you / There's always tomorrow / Dancing honeymoon / And her mother came too / Who take a step / Alone with my dreams / You forgot your gloves / Leave a little for me / Yes Mr brown / Now that I've found you / In clover / Goodnight Vienna / Fancy our meeting / Weep no more my baby / One good tune deserves another / I think I can / So green / Oo la la / Adapted from the French.
Notes: A superb album from the charming deboniar heart - throb of the 30's stage and screen, Jack Buchanan. In the 20's & 30's he soared to sucess with his talent for singing and dancing and light comedy. featured titles "Goodnight vienna" "Yes Mr Brown" "You forgot your gloves" and "Fancy our meeting" Also available on cassette.
Album: released on Golden Age in Jul'84 by Music For Pleasure Records. Distributed by: EMI

Cassette: released on Golden Age in Jul'84 by Music For Pleasure Records. Distributed by: EMI

THAT'S A GOOD GIRL.
Cassette: released on World in Jul'79. Distributed by: Jetstar

Buchanan, Kingsley

I'LL GET AWAY (AND BE FREE).
Single (12"): released on Mikey in Jun'82

Buchanan, Margo

KEEP ON.
Single (7"): released on London in Dec'86 by London Records. Distributed by: Polygram

Single (12"): released on London in Dec'86 by London Records. Distributed by: Polygram

Buchanan, Roy

DANCING ON THE EDGE.
Tracks: / Peter Gunn / Chokin' kind, The / Jungle Gym / Drowning on dry land / Petal to the metal / You can't judge a book by the cover / Cream of the crop / Beer drinking woman / Whiplash / Baby, baby, baby / Mathew.
Album: released on Sonet in Jan'87 by Sonet Records. Distributed by: PRT

RESCUE ME.
Tracks: / Rescue me / I'm a ram / In the beginning / C.C Rider / Country preacher / You're killing my love / She can't say no / Wayfairing pilgrim.
Album: released on Polydor in Feb'75 by Polydor Records. Distributed by: Polygram, Polydor

ROY BUCHANAN.
Tracks: / Sweet dreams / Tribute to Elmore James / Roys bluz / Cajun / Country preacher / After hours / Messiah will come again The / Filthy teddy / Wayfairing pilgrim / Please don't turn me away / She once lived here / In the beginning.
Album: released on Polydor in Apr'76 by Polydor Records. Distributed by: Polygram, Polydor

SWEET DREAMS.
Single (7"): released on Old Gold in Jul'84 by Old Gold Records. Distributed by: Lightning, Jazz Music, Spartan, Counterpoint

WHEN A GUITAR PLAYS THE BLUES.
Tracks: / When a guitar plays the blues / Mrs. Pressure / Nickel and a nail, A / Short fuse / Why don't you want me? / Country boy / Sneaking Godzilla through the alley / Hawaiian punch.
Compact disc: by Sonet Records. Distributed by: PRT

Album: released on Sonet in Jun'86 by Sonet Records. Distributed by: PRT

YOU CAN'T JUDGE A BOOK BY THE COVER.
Tracks: / You can't judge a book by the cover / Choking kind, The.
Single (7"): released on Sonet in Jul'86 by Sonet Records. Distributed by: PRT

Buck, Bobby

TAKE TIME TO CARE (Buck, Bobby, Ian Botham & Poacher).
Tracks: / Take time to care / Ian,Viv & Me.
Notes: All A-side royalties to leukaemia research.
Single (7"): released on Spartan in Mar'86 by Spartan Records. Distributed by: Spartan

Buck Clayton

TRUMPET SUMMIT 1967 (Buck Clayton meets Roy Eldridge).
Album: released on Pumpkin in Apr'79. Distributed by: Jazz Music, Wellard, Chris, Cadillac

Buck, George

JAZZOLOGY ALL-STARS.
Album: released on Jazzology in Feb'87. Distributed by: Jazz Music, Swift

Buckingham, Lindsey

GO INSANE.
Tracks: / I want you / Go insane / Slow dancing / I must go / Play in the rain(parts 1& 2) / Loving cup / Bang the drum / D.W. suite.

Cassette: released on Mercury in Sep'84 by Phonogram Records. Distributed by: Polygram Distribution Deleted '85.

GO INSANE.
Compact disc: by Phonogram Records. Distributed by: Polygram Distribution

Album: released on Mercury in Sep'84 by Phonogram Records. Distributed by: Polygram Distribution Deleted '85.

Single (7"): released on Mercury in Aug'84 by Phonogram Records. Distributed by: Polygram Distribution Deleted '85.

Single (12"): released on Mercury in Aug'84 by Phonogram Records. Distributed by: Polygram Distribution

LAW AND ORDER.
Tracks: / Bwana / Trouble / Mary Lee Jones / I'll tell you now / It was I / September song / Shadow of the west / That's how we do it in LA / Johnny stew / Love from here love from there / Satisfied mind A.
Compact disc: by Phonogram Records. Distributed by: Polygram Distribution

Cassette: released on Mercury in Nov'81 by Phonogram Records. Distributed by: Polygram Distribution

Album: released on Mercury in Nov'81 by Phonogram Records. Distributed by: Polygram Distribution

Buckley, Lord

BLOWING HIS MIND AND YOURS TOO.
Album: released on Demon Verbals in Sep'84 by Demon Records. Distributed by: Demon Records, Pinnacle

Buckley, Paul

SHINING BRIGHT.
Album: released on Fun in Jul'85 by Fun Records. Distributed by: Projection

Buckley, Tim

GOODBYE AND HELLO.
Tracks: / No man can find the war / Carnival song / Pleasant street / Hallucinations / I never asked to be your mountain / Once I was / Plantasmagoria in two / Knightterrant / Goodbye and hello / Morning glory.
Album: by Elektra/Asylum/Nonesuch Records. Distributed by: WEA

GREETINGS FROM L.A..
Album: by Warner Bros Records. Distributed by: WEA

SEFRONIA.
Tracks: / Dolphins / Honey man / Because of you / Peanut man / Martha / Quicksand I know I'd recognise your face / Stone in love / Sefronafter asklepiades after Kafka / Sefronia- The kings chain / Sally go round the roses.
Album: released on Discreet (USA) in May'74 by Warner Bros Records. Distributed by: Warner Bros.

Buckner, Milt

ROCKIN HAMMOND.
Album: released on Capitol (France) in '83 by Capitol Records. Distributed by: Conifer

Buckner, Teddy

TEDDY BUCKNER 1955.
Album: released on Aircheck (USA) in Apr'79. Distributed by: Swift, Jazz Music

Buck Rogers

BUCK ROGERS Soundtrack from TV series.
Album: released on MCA in Apr'81 by MCA Records. Distributed by: Polygram, MCA

Bucks Fizz

ARE YOU READY.
Tracks: / Land of make believe The / My camera never lies / Now those day's are gone / Easy love / Love dies hard / One way love / Are you ready / Breaking and entering / 20th century hero / Another night.
Album: released on RCA in '82 by RCA Records. Distributed by: RCA, Roots, Swift, Wellard, Chris, I & B, Solomon & Peres Distribution

Cassette: released on RCA in '82 by RCA Records. Distributed by: RCA, Roots, Swift, Wellard, Chris, I & B, Solomon & Peres Distribution

BUCKS FIZZ.
Tracks: / Making your mind up / Piece of the action / My camera never lies / Land of make believe / Midnight reservation / It's got to be love / Took it to the limit / One of those nights / Lady of the night / Getting kinda lonely / Shine on / Right situation The.
Cassette: released on RCA in May'83 by RCA Records. Distributed by: RCA, Roots, Swift, Wellard, Chris, I & B, Solomon & Peres Distribution

Album: released on RCA in '84 by RCA Records. Distributed by: RCA, Roots, Swift, Wellard, Chris, I & B, Solomon & Peres Distribution

Cassette: released on RCA in '84 by RCA Records. Distributed by: RCA, Roots, Swift, Wellard, Chris, I & B, Solomon & Peres Distribution

Album: released on RCA in Oct'85 by RCA Records. Distributed by: RCA, Roots, Swift, Wellard, Chris, I & B, Solomon & Peres Distribution

Cassette: released on RCA in Oct'85 by RCA Records. Distributed by: RCA, Roots, Swift, Wellard, Chris, I & B, Solomon & Peres Distribution

GREATEST HITS:BUCKS FIZZ.
Tracks: / My camera never lies / London town / Piece of the action / Now those day's are gone / Making your mind up / When we were young / Land of make believe / Of one of nights / Oh Suzanne / If you can't stand the heat / Run for your life / Rules of the game.
Album: released on RCA in Nov'83 by RCA Records. Distributed by: RCA, Roots, Swift, Wellard, Chris, I & B, Solomon & Peres Distribution

Cassette: released on RCA in Nov'83 by RCA Records. Distributed by: RCA, Roots, Swift, Wellard, Chris, I & B, Solomon & Peres Distribution

Compact disc: released on RCA in Apr'84 by RCA Records. Distributed by: RCA, Roots, Swift, Wellard, Chris, I & B, Solomon & Peres Distribution

GREATEST HITS VIDEO: BUCKS FIZZ.
Notes: The promos for 14 tracks by the group,including most of their hit singles such as 'Making Your Mind Up' and 'Land of Make Believe'.A 1986 compilation. Number of tracks:14. Type of recording: Compilation.Total playing time: 52mins.
Video-cassette (VHS): released on RCA in Jun'86 by RCA Records. Distributed by: RCA, Roots, Swift, Wellard, Chris, I & B, Solomon & Peres Distribution

HAND CUT.
Tracks: / Run for your life / 10,9,8,7,6,5,4 / I do it all for you / Where the ending starts / Surrender your heart / If you can't stand the heat / I'd like to say I love you / You love love / Shot me through the heart / Running out of time.
Album: released on RCA in Mar'83 by RCA Records. Distributed by: RCA, Roots, Swift, Wellard, Chris, I & B, Solomon & Peres Distribution

Cassette: released on RCA in Mar'83 by RCA Records. Distributed by: RCA, Roots, Swift, Wellard, Chris, I & B, Solomon & Peres Distribution

IF YOU CAN'T STAND THE HEAT.
Single (7"): released on RCA in Nov'82 by RCA Records. Distributed by: RCA, Roots, Swift, Wellard, Chris, I & B, Solomon & Peres Distribution

Single (12"): released on RCA in Nov'82 by RCA Records. Distributed by: RCA, Roots, Swift, Wellard, Chris, I & B, Solomon & Peres Distribution

Picture disc single: released on RCA in Dec'82 by RCA Records. Distributed by: RCA, Roots, Swift, Wellard, Chris, I & B, Solomon & Peres Distribution

I HEAR TALK.
Tracks: / I hear the talk / Indebted to you / Tears on the ballroom floor / Cold war / Golden days / Talking in your sleep / Breaking me up / January's gone / She cries / Thief in the night.
Album: released on RCA in Nov'84 by RCA Records. Distributed by: RCA, Roots, Swift, Wellard, Chris, I & B, Solomon & Peres Distribution

Cassette: released on RCA in Nov'84 by RCA Records. Distributed by: RCA, Roots, Swift, Wellard, Chris, I & B, Solomon & Peres Distribution

Single (7"): released on RCA in Dec'84 by RCA Records. Distributed by: RCA, Roots, Swift, Wellard, Chris, I & B, Solomon & Peres Distribution

Single (12"): released on RCA in Dec'84 by RCA Records. Distributed by: RCA, Roots, Swift, Wellard, Chris, I & B, Solomon & Peres Distribution

KEEP EACH OTHER WARM.
Tracks: / Give A Little Love.
Single (7"): released on Polydor in Nov'86 by Polydor Records. Distributed by: Polygram,

Single (7"): released on Polydor in Nov'86 by Polydor Records. Distributed by: Polygram,

Single (12"): released on Polydor in Nov'86 by Polydor Records. Distributed by: Polygram,

LAND OF MAKE BELIEVE, THE.
Tracks: / Land of make believe, The / My camera never lies / Run for your life / I do it all for you / When we were young / Thief in the night / Running out of time / Indebted to you / Januarys gone / Breaking me up.

Album: released on Music For Pleasure in Jun'86 by EMI Records. Distributed by: EMI

Cassette: released on Music For Pleasure in Jun'86 by EMI Records. Distributed by: EMI

LAND OF MAKE BELIEVE.
Tracks: / Land of make believe / Making your mind up.
Single (7"): released on Old Gold in Oct'86 by Old Gold Records. Distributed by: Lightning, Jazz Music, Spartan, Counterpoint

LAND OF MAKE BELIEVE, THE.
Single (7"): released on RCA in Nov'81 by RCA Records. Distributed by: RCA, Roots, Swift, Wellard, Chris, I & B, Solomon & Peres Distribution

LONDON TOWN.
Single (7"): released on RCA in Sep'83 by RCA Records. Distributed by: RCA, Roots, Swift, Wellard, Chris, I & B, Solomon & Peres Distribution

Single (12"): released on RCA in Sep'83 by RCA Records. Distributed by: RCA, Roots, Swift, Wellard, Chris, I & B, Solomon & Peres Distribution

LOVE THE ONE YOUR WITH.
Tracks: / Love the one your with / Too hard / I hear talk*.
Single (7"): released on Polydor in Aug'86 by Polydor Records. Distributed by: Polygram, Polydor

Single (12"): released on Polydor in Aug'86 by Polydor Records. Distributed by: Polygram, Polydor

MAGICAL.
Single (7"): released on RCA in Aug'85 by RCA Records. Distributed by: RCA, Roots, Swift, Wellard, Chris, I & B, Solomon & Peres Distribution

Single (12"): released on RCA in Aug'85 by RCA Records. Distributed by: RCA, Roots, Swift, Wellard, Chris, I & B, Solomon & Peres Distribution

MAKING YOUR MIND UP.
Album: released on RCA/Camden in Nov'85

Cassette: released on RCA/Camden in Nov'85

Single (7"): released on RCA in Mar'81 by RCA Records. Distributed by: RCA, Roots, Swift, Wellard, Chris, I & B, Solomon & Peres Distribution

MY CAMERA NEVER LIES.
Single (7"): released on RCA in Mar'82 by RCA Records. Distributed by: RCA, Roots, Swift, Wellard, Chris, I & B, Solomon & Peres Distribution

Single (12"): released on RCA in Mar'82 by RCA Records. Distributed by: RCA, Roots, Swift, Wellard, Chris, I & B, Solomon & Peres Distribution

NEW BEGINNING.
Tracks: / New beginning(mamba seyra) / In your eyes / I need your love*.
Notes: Extra track on 12" only.
Single (7"): released on Polydor in May'86 by Polydor Records. Distributed by: Polygram, Polydor

Single (7"): released on Polydor in May'86 by Polydor Records. Distributed by: Polygram, Polydor

Single (12"): released on Polydor in May'86 by Polydor Records. Distributed by: Polygram, Polydor

NOW THOSE DAYS ARE GONE.
Single (7"): released on RCA in Jun'82 by RCA Records. Distributed by: RCA, Roots, Swift, Wellard, Chris, I & B, Solomon & Peres Distribution

Picture disc single: released on RCA in Jun'82 by RCA Records. Distributed by: RCA, Roots, Swift, Wellard, Chris, I & B, Solomon & Peres Distribution

ONE OF THOSE NIGHTS.
Single (7"): released on RCA in Jul'82 by RCA Records. Distributed by: RCA, Roots, Swift, Wellard, Chris, I & B, Solomon & Peres Distribution

PIECE OF THE ACTION.
Single (7"): released on RCA in May'81 by RCA Records. Distributed by: RCA, Roots, Swift, Wellard, Chris, I & B, Solomon & Peres Distribution

RULES OF THE GAME.
Single (7"): released on RCA in Nov'83 by RCA Records. Distributed by: RCA, Roots, Swift, Wellard, Chris, I & B, Solomon & Peres Distribution

Single (12"): released on RCA in Nov'83 by RCA Records. Distributed by: RCA, Roots, Swift, Wellard, Chris, I & B, Solomon & Peres Distribution

RUN FOR YOUR LIFE.
Single (7"): released on RCA in Feb'83 by RCA Records. Distributed by: RCA, Roots, Swift, Wellard, Chris, I & B, Solomon & Peres Distribution

WHEN WE WERE YOUNG.
Single (7"): released on RCA in Jun'83 by RCA Records. Distributed by: RCA, Roots, Swift, Wellard, Chris, I & B, Solomon & Peres Distribution

Single (12"): released on RCA in Jun'83 by RCA Records. Distributed by: RCA, Roots, Swift, Wellard, Chris, I & B, Solomon & Peres Distribution

Picture disc single: released on RCA in Jun'83 by RCA Records. Distributed by: RCA, Roots, Swift, Wellard, Chris, I & B, Solomon & Peres Distribution

WRITING ON THE WALL, THE.
Compact disc: by Polydor Records. Distributed by: Polygram, Polydor

YOU AND YOUR HEART OF BLUE.
Single (7"): released on RCA in Jun'85 by RCA Records. Distributed by: RCA, Roots, Swift, Wellard, Chris, I & B, Solomon & Peres Distribution

Single (12"): released on RCA in Jun'85 by RCA Records. Distributed by: RCA, Roots Swift, Wellard, Chris, I & B, Solomon & Peres Distribution

Bucktown Five

BUCKTOWN FIVE, STOMP SIX, JUNGLE KINGS, ETC, THE (Bucktown Five & Others).
Album: released on Fountain in Apr'79 by Retrieval Records. Distributed by: Jazz Music, Swift, VJM, Wellard, Chris, Retrieval

Buckwheat Zydeco

BUCKWHEAT ZYDECO.
Album: released on Rounder Europa in Apr'86

MARIE MARIE.
Tracks: / Marie Marie / Time is tight / Buckwheat's special.
Single (7"): released on Island in Jul'87 by Island Records. Distributed by: Polygram

Single (12"): released on Island in Jul'87 by Island Records. Distributed by: Polygram

ON A NIGHT LIKE THIS.
Tracks: / On a night like this / Time is tight / Space Zydeco / Hot Tamale baby / People's choice / Ma 'tit fille / Buckwheat's special / Zydeco honky tonk / Marie, Marie / Ma 'Tit Fille / Buckwheats special / Zydeco Honky Tonk / Marie Marie / On a night like this / Time is tight / Space zydeco / Hot tamale baby / People's choice.
Album: released on Island in Jul'87 by Island Records. Distributed by: Polygram

Compact disc: released on Island in Jul'87 by Island Records. Distributed by: Polygram

Cassette: released on Island in Jul'87 by Island Records. Distributed by: Polygram

Budd

MOON AND THE MELODIES, THE (Budd/Fraser/Guthrie/Raymonde).
Album:

Cassette: released on 4AD in Nov'86 by 4AD Records. Distributed by: Rough Trade

Compact disc: released on 4AD in Nov'86 by 4AD Records. Distributed by: Rough Trade

Buddah All Stars

BUDDAH ALL STARS Various artists (Various Artists).
Album: released on Buddah in May'80. Distributed by: Swift, Jazz Music, PRT

Budd, Harold

LOVELY THUNDER.
Album: released on Editions EG in Oct'86 by Virgin Records. Distributed by: EMI

Cassette: released on Editions EG in Oct'86 by Virgin Records. Distributed by: EMI

Compact disc: released on Editions EG in Oct'86 by Virgin Records. Distributed by: EMI

PAVILION OF DREAMS, THE.
Album: released on Obscure in Mar'78 by Polydor Records. Distributed by: Polygram Distribu-

PLATEAUX OF MIRROR (Budd, Harold & Brian Eno).
Cassette: released on Editions EG in '78 by Virgin Records. Distributed by: EMI

PAVILION OF DREAMS & PLATEAUX OF MIRROR.
Tracks: / PAVILION - bismallahi rrahani rrahim / Let us go into the house of the lord / Butterfly Sunday / Mandrigals of the rose angel / Juno / PLATEAUX OF MIRROR First light / Steal away / Plateaux of mirror The / Above chiangmai / An arc of doves / Not yet remembered / Chill air, The / Among fields of crystal / Wind in lonely fences / Failing light.
Double cassette: released on Editions EG in Apr'82 by Virgin Records. Distributed by: EMI

PAVILLION OF DREAMS, THE.
Tracks: / Bismiliah / Rrahmani / Let Us Go Into The House Of The Lord / Butterfly Sunday / Madrigals Of The Rose Angel / Rrahmani / Let us go into the house of the lord / Butterfly Sunday / Madrigals of the rose angel-(a) rosetta noise / Madrigals of the rose angel-(b) the crystal garden / Juno.
Album: released on Editions EG in Jan'87 by Virgin Records. Distributed by: EMI

Cassette: released on Editions EG in Jan'87 by Virgin Records. Distributed by: EMI

PEARL (THE) (Budd, Harold & Brian Eno).
Tracks: / Stram With Bright Fish, A / Late October / Stream with bright fish A / Silver ball, The / Against the sky / Lost in the humming air / Darkeyed sister / Their memories / Pearl, The / Foreshadowed / Echo of the night / Still returned.
Notes: Re-issue.
See also under Brian Eno.
Cassette: released on Editions EG in Jan'87 by Virgin Records. Distributed by: EMI

Album: released on Editions EG in Jan'87 by Virgin Records. Distributed by: EMI

Compact disc: released on Editions EG in Jan'87 by Virgin Records. Distributed by: EMI

Budd, Roy

FINAL FRONTIER, THE.
Notes: Double album.
Compact disc: released on Mobile Fidelity in Jan'86 by Mobile Fidelity Records

SPACE MOVIE THEMES (Budd, Roy & London Symphony Orchestra).
Notes: Full details see under LONDON SYMPHONY ORCHESTRA

Budgie

BEST OF BUDGIE.
Tracks: / Whisky river / Guts / Rolling home again / Homicidal suicidal / Hot as a docker's armpit / Drugstore woman / Rocking man / You and I / Stranded.
Album: released on Cube in '82 by Dakota Records. Distributed by: PRT

Album: released on MCA in Feb'82 by MCA Records. Distributed by: Polygram, MCA

Cassette: released on MCA in Feb'82 by MCA Records. Distributed by: Polygram, MCA

BEST OF BUDGIE(ORIGINAL SOUND RECORDING).
Tracks: / Breadfan / I ain't no mountain / I can't see my feelings / Baby please don't go / Zoom club / Breaking all the house rules / Parents / In for the kill / In the grip of a tyre-fitter's hand.

BORED WITH RUSSIA.
Single (7"): released on RCA in Sep'82 by RCA Records. Distributed by: RCA, Roots, Swift, Wellard, Chris, I & B, Solomon & Peres Distribution

DELIVER US FROM EVIL.
Tracks: / Bored with Russia / Don't cry / Truth drug / Young girl / Flowers in the atic / N.O.R.A.D.(domesday city) / Give me the truth / Alison / Finger on the button / Hold on to love.
Album: released on RCA in Oct'82 by RCA Records. Distributed by: RCA, Roots, Swift, Wellard, Chris, I & B, Solomon & Peres Distribution

Cassette: released on RCA in Oct'82 by RCA Records. Distributed by: RCA, Roots, Swift, Wellard, Chris, I & B, Solomon & Peres Distribution

NEVER TURN BACK.
Tracks: / Breadfan / Baby please don't go / You're the biggest thing since powdered milk / You know I'll always love you / In the grip of a tyres fitter's hand / Riding my nightmare / Parents / Apparatus / Superstar / Change your ways / Untitled lullaby.
Album: released on MCA in Aug'87 by MCA Records. Distributed by: Polygram, MCA

Cassette: released on MCA in Aug'87 by MCA Records. Distributed by: Polygram, MCA

NIGHT FLIGHT.
Tracks: / I turned to stone / Keeping a rendezvous / Reaper of glory / She used me up / Don't lay down and die / Apparatus / Superstar / Change your ways / Untitled lullaby.
Album: released on RCA in Oct'81 by RCA Records. Distributed by: RCA, Roots, Swift, Wellard, Chris, I & B, Solomon & Peres Distribution

Cassette: released on RCA in Oct'81 by RCA Records. Distributed by: RCA, Roots, Swift, Wellard, Chris, I & B, Solomon & Peres Distribution

POWER SUPPLY.
Tracks: / Forearm smash / Hellbender / Heavy revolution / Gunslinger / Power supply / Secrets in my head / Time to remember / Crimes against the world.
Album: released on RCA in Sep'81 by RCA Records. Distributed by: RCA, Roots, Swift, Wellard, Chris, I & B, Solomon & Peres Distribution

Cassette: released on RCA in Sep'81 by RCA Records. Distributed by: RCA, Roots, Swift, Wellard, Chris, I & B, Solomon & Peres Distribution

Budimir, Dennis

ALONE TOGETHER.
Tracks: / Blues for ray / Embraceable you / East of the sun / No cover, no minimum / I can't get started / All the things you are.
Album: released on Revelation in Apr'81

SECOND COMING, A.
Tracks: / Some day my prince will come / For every man there's a woman / Woodyn you / All the things you are / There is no greater love.
Album: released on Revelation in Apr'81

SESSION WITH ALBERT.
Tracks: / Warm up / Warm up blues / Au privave / There is no freater love.
Album: released on Revelation in Apr'81

SPRUNG FREE.
Tracks: / Blues sprung free, The / East of the sun / Sultry serenade / Blues by the bags.
Album: released on Revelation in Apr'81

Budwig, Monte/7 others

Discoveries

Budwig, Monty

DIG.
Album: released on Concord (USA) in Mar'79. Distributed by: IMS, Polygram

Buell, Bebe

LITTLE BLACK EGG.
Single (7"): released on Moonlight in May'82 by Lithon Recording & Music Publishing

Buen, Hauk

RINGING STRINGS (FIDDLE MUSIC OF NORWAY) (Buen, Hauk/Knut Buen/Tom Anderson/Vidar Lande).
Album: released on Topic in May'83

Buen,Knut

Ringing strings (Fiddle music of Norway)

Bue, Papa

DANISH JAZZ VOL.8 1957-77.
Album: released on Storyville in Jul'82 by Storyville Records. Distributed by: Jazz Music Distribution, Swift Distribution, Chris Wellard Distribution, Counterpoint Distribution

NEW ORLEANS (Bue, Papa Viking Jazz Band).
Album: released on Storyville in Jun'86 by Storyville Records. Distributed by: Jazz Music Distribution, Swift Distribution, Chris Wellard Distribution, Counterpoint Distribution

ON STAGE (Bue, Papa Viking Jazz Band).
Compact disc: released on Timeless (Holland) in Jan'86. Distributed by: Jazz Music Distribution, Jazz Horizons Distribution, Cadillac, Celtic Music Distribution

Album: released on Timeless in Sep'86

PAPA BUE'S VIKING JAZZ BAND (Bue, Papa Viking Jazz Band).
Notes: MONO Production. Jazzband with friends,George Lewis/Art Hodes
Album: released on Storyville in Jun'86 by Storyville Records. Distributed by: Jazz Music Distribution, Swift Distribution, Chris Wellard Distribution, Counterpoint Distribution

PAPA BUE'S VIKING JAZZ BAND WITH WINGY MANONE (Bue, Papa Viking Jazz Band & Wingy Manone).
Notes: MONO production
Album: released on Storyville in Jun'86 by Storyville Records. Distributed by: Jazz Music Distribution, Swift Distribution, Chris Wellard Distribution, Counterpoint Distribution

WITH FRIENDS (Bue, Papa Viking Jazz Band).
Notes: Friends include: George Lewis/Edmond Hall/Wingy Manone/Art Hodes/Albert Nicholas/Wild Bill/Jack Dupree etc.
Album: released on Storyville in Jun'86 by Storyville Records. Distributed by: Jazz Music Distribution, Swift Distribution, Chris Wellard Distribution, Counterpoint Distribution

Buffalo Soldier

HI-JACKER.
Single (12"): released on Pinnacle in Apr'84 by Pinnacle Records. Distributed by: Pinnacle

Buffalo

BATTLE TORN HEROES.
Single (7"): released on Heavy Metal in Sep'81 by FM-Revolver Records. Distributed by: EMI

MEAN MACHINE.
Single (7"): released on Heavy Metal in Nov'82 by FM-Revolver Records. Distributed by: EMI

Buffalo Bop

BUFFALO BOP VOLUME 35 Various artists (Various Artists).
Album: released on Bison Bop (Germany) in Jul'85

BUFFALO BOP VOLUME 38 Various artists (Various Artists).
Album: released on Bison Bop (Germany) in Jul'85

BUFFALO BOP VOLUME 37 Various artists (Various Artists).
Album: released on Bison Bop (Germany) in Jul'85

BUFFALO BOP, VOLUME 39 Various artists (Various Artists).
Album: released on Buffalo Bop(Germany) in Jan'86.

BUFFALO BOP, VOLUME 40 Various artists (Various Artists).
Album: released on Buffalo Bop(Germany) in Jan'86.

BUFFALO BOP, VOLUME 41 Various artists (Various Artists).
Album: released on Buffalo Bop(Germany) in Jan'86.

Buffalo Rhythm

BUFFALO RHYTHM Various dance bands of the 1920's (Various Artists).
Tracks: / Since my best gal turned me down / Back in your own back yard / I'm tickled pink / Breakaway / Charleston baby o' mine / Baby's blue / Sitting on top of the world / Voice of the Southland, The / Nobody but you / Waitin' for Katy / Say it again / Buffalo rhythm / True blue Lou / Tin ear / Dusky stevedore / When sweet Suzie goes steppin' by / I'm riding to glory / Say, who is that baby doll? / Lazy weather / Suzie's feller.
Notes: Hot performances by famous dance bands of the 1920's. Jan Garber & His Orchestra,Fred Rich & His Orchestra,The Georgians,Don Voorhees & His Orchestra,Ipana Troubadours,Guy Lombardo & His Royal Canadians,Ted Wallace& His Orchestra,Californian Ramblers,Thelma Terry & Her Playboys,Ross Gorman's Earl Carroll Vanities Orchestra. MONO recording.
Album: released on VJM in Apr'86 by Wellard, Chris Distribution. Distributed by: Wellard, Chris Distribution

Buffalo Springfield

RETROSPECTIVE.
Tracks: / For what it's worth / Hello Mr Soul / Sit down I think I love you / Kind woman / Blue bird / On the way home / Nowaday's Clarence can't even sing / Broken arrow / Rock and roll woman / I am a child / Go and say goodbye / Expecting to fly.
Album: by WEA Records. Distributed by: WEA

Buffet, Jimmy

CHANGES IN LATTITUDE, CHANGES IN ATTITUDE.
Tracks: / Wonder Why We Ever Go Home / Banana Republic / Tampico Trauma / Tampico Trauma / Lovely Cruise / Margaritaville / In The Shelter / Miss You So Badly / Biloxi / Landfall.
Album: released on MCA Import in Mar'86 by MCA Records. Distributed by: Polygram, IMS

Cassette: released on MCA Import in Mar'86 by MCA Records. Distributed by: Polygram, IMS

CREOLA.
Tracks: / Creola / You'll never work in dis bidness again.
Single (7"): released on MCA in Oct'86 by MCA Records. Distributed by: Polygram, MCA

Single (12"): released on MCA in Oct'86 by MCA Records. Distributed by: Polygram, MCA

Album: released on MCA in Aug'86 by MCA Records. Distributed by: Polygram, MCA

Cassette: released on MCA in Aug'86 by MCA Records. Distributed by: Polygram, MCA

FLORIDAYS.
Tracks: / Creola / I love the now / First look / Meet me in Memphis / Nobody speaks to the captain no more / Floridays / If it all falls down / No plane on Sunday / When the coast is clear / You'll never work in dis bisness again.

Compact disc: released on MCA in Feb'87 by MCA Records. Distributed by: Polygram, MCA

LIVE BY THE BAY.
Notes: The laid-back countryish singer-songwriter filmed in concert at Marine Stadium in Miami, with 18 songs including his biggest hit "Margaritaville" 1985 production. Cert 15. Number of tracks: 18. Type of recording: live. Total playing time 85 mins.
Video-cassette (VHS): released on CIC Video in Nov'86 by CBS Records. Distributed by: CBS, Pickwick Distribution

LIVING AND DYING IN 3/4 TIME.
Tracks: / Pencil Thin Moustache / Come Monday / Ringling, Ringling / Brahma Fear / Brand New Country Star / Livinston's Gone To Texas / Wino and I know (The) / West Nashville Grand Ballroom Gown / Ballard Of Spider John / God's Own Drunk.
Album: released on MCA Import in Mar'86 by MCA Records. Distributed by: Polygram, IMS

Cassette: released on MCA Import in Mar'86 by MCA Records. Distributed by: Polygram, IMS

Buffett, Jimmy

LAST MANGO IN PARIS.
Tracks: / Everybody on the run / Frank and Loia / Perfect partner (The) / Please bypass this heart / Gypsies in the palace / Deperation Samba(Halloween in Tijuana) / Last mango in Paris / Jolly mon sing / Beyond the end.
Compact disc: released on MCA in '87 by MCA Records. Distributed by: Polygram, MCA

MANGO.
Compact disc: released on MCA in Jul'87 by MCA Records. Distributed by: Polygram. MCA

Buggles

ADVENTURES IN MODERN RECORDING.
Tracks: / Adventures in modern recording / Beatnik / Vermillion sands / I am a camera / On TV / Inner city / Lenny rainbow warrior.
Album: released on Carrere in Mar'82 by Carrere Records. Distributed by: PRT, Spartan

Cassette: released on Carrere in Mar'82 by Carrere Records. Distributed by: PRT, Spartan

AGE OF PLASTIC.
Tracks: / Plastic age, The / Video killed the radio star / Kid dynamo / I love you / Clean, clean / Elstree / Astro boy / Johnny on the mono rail.
Cassette: released on Island in Apr'87 by Island Records. Distributed by: Polygram

Album: released on Island in Apr'87 by Island Records. Distributed by: Polygram

LIVING IN THE PLASTIC AGE.
Tracks: / Plastic cage, The / Video killed the radio star / Kid dynamo / I live you / Clean clean / Elstree / Astro boy / Johnny on the mono rail.
Album: released on Island in Jan'80 by Island Records. Distributed by: Polygram

VIDEO KILLED THE RADIO STAR.
Single (7"): released on Island in Jul'81 by Island Records. Distributed by: Polygram

Bugs

DARKSIDE.
Album: released on Big Beat in Aug'87 by Ace Records. Distributed by: Projection, Pinnacle

LEAVING HERE.
Tracks: / Leaving here / Leave us alone / See if I care.
Single (7"): released on Hit in Feb'87 by Hit Records. Distributed by: Pinnacle, Backs, Cartel

Bugs On The Wire

BUGS ON THE WIRE (Various Artists).
Album: released on Foghorn Leghorn in Jun'87 by Foghorn Leghorn Records. Distributed by: Red Rhino, Cartel

Bugs, The

DARKSIDE.
Album: released on Big Beat in Aug'87 by Ace Records. Distributed by: Projection, Pinnacle

Bugsy Malone

BUGSY MALONE Original soundtrack (Various Artists).
Tracks: / Bad guys / Bugsy Malone / Down Had out / Fat Sam's grand slam / I'm feeling fine / My name is Tallalah / Ordinary fool / So you wanna be a boxer / Tommorow / You give a little love.
Notes: Film directed by Alan Parker. Words and music by Paul Williams. Originally released August 1976.
Album: released on Polydor in Jun'83 by Polydor Records. Distributed by: Polygram, Polydor

Cassette: released on Polydor in Jun'83 by Polydor Records. Distributed by: Polygram, Polydor

Buhl, J.D.
5 O'CLOCK WORLD (Buhl, J.D. & Believers).
Single (7"): released on Rag Baby in Aug'81. Distributed by: Pinnacle, Red Lightnin' Distribution

Buhrman, Bert
BERT BUHRMAN.
Notes: Bert Buhrman gives a concert at Paramount Organ Works, Bolton, UK.
Album: released on Deroy in May'86 by Deroy Records. Distributed by: Jazz Music, Swift

CINEMA ORGAN ENCORES.
Album: released on Deroy in Jun'81 by Deroy Records. Distributed by: Jazz Music, Swift

Builders
NO MORE PROMISES.
Single (7"): released on Tunnel in Nov'84 by Tunnel Records. Distributed by: Tunnel

Bulgarian Folk Music
FOLK HEROES AND RUCHENITSAS.
Album: released on Balkanton in Mar'79

Bulgarian Music
MYSTERE DES VOIX BULGARES, (LE) (Various artists (Various Artists).
Album: released on 4AD in Dec'86 by 4AD Records. Distributed by: Rough Trade

Cassette: released on 4AD in May'86 by 4AD Records. Distributed by: Rough Trade

Compact disc: released on 4AD in May'87 by 4AD Records. Distributed by: Rough Trade

Bullamakanka
DOCTOR WHO IS GONNA FIT IT.
Single (7"): released on BBC in Nov'83 by BBC Records & Tapes. Distributed by: EMI, PRT, Cartel

Bullaweyo
FALLING APART.
Single (7"): released on Shout in Dec'81 by Shout Records. Distributed by: Rough Trade, Cartel

Bull City Blues
BULL CITY BLUES.
Album: released on Magpie in Jul'79. Distributed by: Projection

Bulldozer
DAY OF WRATH.
Album: released on Road Runner in Jun'85

FINAL SEPARATION, THE.
Tracks: / Final separation, The / Ride hard,die fast / Cave, The / Sex symbol's bullshit / Don Andras / Never relax / Don't trust the saint / Death of the gods, The.
Album: released on Roadrunner (Dutch) in Jul'86. Distributed by: Pinnacle

Bullets Won't Stop Us Now
BULLETS WON'T STOP US NOW Various Artists (Various Artists).
Album: released on Konkurrel in Aug'87

Cassette: released on Konkurrel in Aug'87

Bullett
NO MERCY.
Album: released on Heavy Metal Worldwide in Mar'84 by FM-Revolver Records. Distributed by: EMI

Bull, Geoff
IN NEW ORLEANS.
Album: released on GHB in Jul'87. Distributed by: Jazz Music, Swift

Bull, Johnny
BATTLE OF THE FALKLANDS.
Single (7"): released on Victory in Dec'82

Bullock, Chick
CHICK BULLOCK & HIS LEVEE LOUNGERS. (Bullock, Chick & His Levee Loungers).
Album: released on Everybody's in Jul'82 by Everybody's Records. Distributed by: Jazz Music, Swift

Bullock, Hiram
FOM ALL SIDES.

Album: released on Atlantic in Feb'87 by WEA Records. Distributed by: WEA

Cassette: released on Atlantic in Feb'87 by WEA Records. Distributed by: WEA

Bullshit Detector
BULLSHIT DETECTOR Various artists (Various Artists).
Album: released on Crass in Nov'82 by Exit-stencil Music. Distributed by: Rough Trade, Cartel

BULLSHIT DETECTOR VOLUME II.
Album: released on Crass in Dec'84 by Exit-stencil Music. Distributed by: Rough Trade, Cartel

Bulluck, Janice
DON'T START A FIRE.
Album: released on Wilbe (USA) in Aug'87

Cassette: released on Wilbe (USA) in Aug'87

DO YOU REALLY LOVE ME.
Single (7"): released on Ichiban in Aug'87. Distributed by: PRT

Bully Wee Band
MADMAN OF GOTHAM, THE.
Album: released on Jigsaw in May'81. Distributed by: Roots, Pinnacle, Projection

Bulpitt, Chris
GAMES OF CHANCE.
Cassette: released on Cockpit in Apr'84. Distributed by: Vibes

SURFACE TENSION.
Cassette single: released on Cockpit in Apr'84. Distributed by: Vibes

SURFACE TENSION/GAMES OF CHANCE.
Cassette single: released on Cockpit in Jul'83. Distributed by: Vibes

Bumble & The Beez
MY LIFE.
Single (7"): released on Zonophone in Jan'83 by EMI Records. Distributed by: EMI

Bumbry, Grace
NATALIE.
Single (7"): released on Multi-Media in Jun'81 by Multi Media Tapes Records. Distributed by: Pinnacle, Conifer Distribution, H.R. Taylor Distribution, Stage One Distribution

Bumper 2 Bumper
BUMPER 2 BUMPER Various artists (Various Artists).
Tracks: / Flashback / Breakin' up(The best part of) / Nice & slow (US Remix) / Every way but loose / Ease your mind / Why can't we live together / Thanks to you / Puerto Rico(US Remix) / Like the way(You funk with me) / Over like a fat rat / Never let you go / You don't like my music.
Notes: 'Bumper 2 bumper' is a double album package containing the 12 outstanding disco singles from PRT and licensed lables.All the tracks are the 12" versions and in certain cases they are the US Remixed versions.With thanks to you-Sinnamon and Illusions 'Why can't we live together'
Album: released on Calibre in Aug'82 by Calibre Records. Distributed by: PRT

Cassette: released on Calibre in Aug'82 by Calibre Records. Distributed by: PRT

BUMPER 2 BUMPER VOL.2 Various artists (Various Artists).
Tracks: / Just an illusion / Touch / Work me over / Do it anyway you wanna / Let's do it / I'd like to / That's when (we'll be free) / He's gonna take you home (to his houser) / Mirda Rock / Rock your baby / Pull our love together / Tell tale heart.
Notes: Follow up to a very succesful Bumper 2 Bumper Vol 1 contains many dance classics including "Just An Illusion" - Imagination"Rock Your Baby" -Disco Connection "Do It Anyway You Wanna" - Cashmere Please note that all versions contained in this package are full lenght 12" versions
Album: released on Calibre in Jun'83 by Calibre Records. Distributed by: PRT

Cassette: released on Calibre in Jun'83 by Calibre Records. Distributed by: PRT Deleted '85.

Bumper Roots
COUNTRY MAN.
Tracks: / Country man / Give the youth a chance.
Single (12"):

Bun Burys
WE'RE THE BUN BURYS.

Tracks: / We're the Bun Bury's / Record breakers(chapter 1).
Single (7"): released on Enterprises Ltd-Island in Aug'86 by Island Records. Distributed by: Polygram

Cassette single: released on Enterprises Ltd-Island in Aug'86 by Island Records. Distributed by: Polygram

Bunch Of 5's
MASTERGROOVE (WILDEBEEST MIX).
Tracks: / Mastergroove (wildebeest mix) / Mastergroove (master mix).
Single (12"): released on Production House in 13 Jun'87. Distributed by: Bluebird, Revolver, Cartel

SHAK RENDEZVOUS.
Tracks: / Shak Rendezvous (Inst.).
Single (12"): released on Production House in Jan'87. Distributed by: Bluebird, Revolver, Cartel

Bunena, Richard
ATOMIC TWIST.
Single (12"): released on Survival in Jun'82 by Survival Records. Distributed by: Backs, Cartel Distribution

Bunker, Larry
Discoveries

Bunnicula
BUNNICULA (Howe, Deborah & James).
Cassette: released on Caedmon(USA) in Sep'82 by Caedmon (USA) Records. Distributed by: Taylors, Discovery

Bunny
SHAKE YOU BATTY.
Single (12"): released on Right Sounds in Dec'83 by Right Sounds Records. Distributed by: Mojo Distribution

Bunny Lie Lie
ITIE-TITIE GIRL.
Single (12"): released on Greensleeves Records in May'82 by Greensleeves Records. Distributed by: BMG, Jetstar, Spartan

MR DYNAMITE (Bunny Lie Lie & Lee Van Cleef).
Single (12"): released on Greensleeves in Apr'83 by Greensleeves Records. Distributed by: BMG, Jetstar, Spartan

Bunny/Louie
3 COMPLETE RADIO SHOWS.
Album: released on Shoestring in Sep'79 by Shoestring Records. Distributed by: Shoestring

Bunny Rugs
LET LOVE TOUCH US NOW.
Single (12"): released on Black Ark in May'82

Bunyan, John
PILGRIM'S PROGRESS, THE (Geilgud, Sir John).
Cassette: released on Argo (Spokenword) in Jun'84 by Decca Records. Distributed by: Polygram

PILGRIM'S PROGRESS, THE (Mason, James).
Cassette: released on Caedmon(USA) in Oct'81 by Caedmon (USA) Records. Distributed by: Taylors, Discovery

Buongiorno Italia
BUONGIORNO ITALIA New beginners' course in Italian.
Special: released on BBC Publications in Apr'82. Distributed by: Record and Tape Sales Distribution, Taylor,H.R., Solomon & Peres Distribution

Burbank, Albert
CREOLE CLARINET.
Album: released on Smokey Mary in Apr'79. Distributed by: Swift

Burch, Nigel
FACISTS IN THE SNUG BAR.
Single (7"): released on Cheapsound in Apr'87 by Cheapsound Records. Distributed by: Backs, Cartel

Burden, Ernest
MR PLOD AND LITTLE NODDY.
Album: released on Golden Wand in Nov'83. Distributed by: Taylors

Cassette: released on Golden Wand in Nov'83. Distributed by: Taylors

NODDY AND THE TOOTLES.
Album: released on Children's Wand in Jan'84 by Children's Wand Records. Distributed by: Pinnacle

NODDY GOES TO SEA.
Album: released on Golden Wand in Nov'83. Distributed by: Taylors

Cassette: released on Golden Wand in Nov'83. Distributed by: Taylors

NODDY HAS AN ADVENTURE.
Album: released on Golden Wand in Nov'83. Distributed by: Taylors

Cassette: released on Golden Wand in Nov'83. Distributed by: Taylors

TALE OF THE CUDDLY TOYS, THE.
Album: released on Golden Wand in Nov'83. Distributed by: Taylors

Cassette: released on Golden Wand in Nov'83. Distributed by: Taylors

Burden Of Population
BURDEN OF POPULATION Peking, Tokyo, Unesco.
Cassette: released on International Report in Oct'81 by Seminar Cassettes. Distributed by: Audio-Visual Library Services, Davidson Distribution, Eastern Educational Products Distribution, Forlaget Systime Distribution, MacDougall Distribution, Talktapes Distribution, Watkins Books Ltd Distribution, Norton, Jeff Distribution

Burdick, Kathy
HEART BEATER.
Single (7"): released on Sesame in Jan'84 by Sesame Records. Distributed by: PRT

Burdon, Eric
ERIC BURDON & THE ANIMALS (Burdon, Eric & The Animals).
Tracks: / Don't bring me down / One monkey don't stop no show / Maudie / Sweet little sixteen / You're on my mind / Clapping / Inside looking-out / Outcast / I put a spell on you / Cheating / Gin House blues / CC Rider / Boom boom / I just want to make love to you / That's all I am to you / She'll return it / Help me girl / Mama told me not to come / Squeeze her, tease her / What a living for / Big boss man / Pretty thing / Let it rock / Gotta find my baby / Bo Diddley / I'm almost grown / Dimples / Boom boom / C jam blues.
Notes: A compilation of the groups later material.
Album: released on Charly in Mar'83 by Charly Records. Distributed by: Charly, Cadillac

Cassette: released on Polydor in Sep'83 by Polydor Records. Distributed by: Polygram, Polydor

Album: released on Teldec (Germany) in Oct'83 by Import Records. Distributed by: IMS Distribution, Polygram Distribution

GOOD TIMES (Burdon, Eric & The Animals).
Single (7"): released on MGM in Nov'82. Distributed by: Polygram Distribution, Swift Distribution

GREATEST HITS:ERIC BURDON.
Double Album: released on Polydor in Nov'80 by Polydor Records. Distributed by: Polygram, Polydor

Cassette: released on Polydor in Nov'80 by Polydor Records. Distributed by: Polygram, Polydor

GREATEST HITS:ERIC BURDON & THE ANIMALS (Burdon, Eric & The Animals).
Album: released on Astan in Nov'84 by Astan Records. Distributed by: Counterpoint

Cassette: released on Astan in Nov'84 by Astan Records. Distributed by: Counterpoint

HOUSE OF THE RISING SUN (Burdon, Eric & The Animals).
Album: released on Platinum (W.Germany) in Oct'85. Distributed by: Mainline

Cassette: released on Platinum (W.Germany) in Oct'85. Distributed by: Mainline

Compact disc: released on Intertape in Jul'87. Distributed by: Target

POWER COMPANY.
Tracks: / Power company / Devil's daughter / You can't kill my spirit / Do you feel it(today) / Wicked man / Heart attack / Who gives a f--k / Sweet blood call / House of the Rising Sun / Comeback.
Album: released on President in 2 Mar'84 by President Records. Distributed by: Taylors, Spartan

PROFILE (Burdon, Eric & The Animals).
Tracks: / I put a spell on you / Help me girl / Don't bring me down.
Notes: Includes chart hits listed in tracks.
Album: released on Teldec (Germany) in Dec'81 by Import Records. Distributed by: IMS Distribution, Polygram Distribution

Cassette: released on Teldec (Germany) in Dec'81 by Import Records. Distributed by: IMS Distribution, Polygram Distribution

ROAD, THE.
Tracks: / Wall of silence / Streetwalker / It hurts me too / Lights out / Bird on the beach / No more Elmore / Road, The / Crawling king snake / Take it easy / Dey don't.
Notes: Tremendous blues/rock album from the gravel-voiced British born former leader of the Animals
Album: released on Thunderbolt in Jun'84 by Magnum Music Group Ltd. Distributed by: Magnum Music Group Ltd, PRT Distribution, Spartan Distribution

SAN FRANCISCAN NIGHTS (Burdon, Eric & The Animals).
Album: released on Karussell (Germany) in Nov'85

Cassette: released on Karussell (Germany) in Nov'85

STAR PORTRAIT.
Tracks: / Good times / Sky pilot / We love you Lil / Hey Gyp / San Franciscan nights / Paint it black / When I was young / See see rider / Ring of fire / River deep,mountain high / True love(comes only once in a lifetime) / Inside-looking out / I'm an animal / Monterey / To love somebody / Anything / I'm dying,or am I?.
Double compact disc: by Polydor Records. Distributed by: Polygram, Polydor

WINDS OF CHANGE.
Tracks: / Winds of change / Poem by the sea / Paint it black / Black plague, The / Yes I am experienced / San Francisco nights / Man-woman / Hotel hell / Good times / Anything / It's all meat.
Compact disc: released on Polydor in Oct'85 by Polydor Records. Distributed by: Polygram, Polydor

Burdon, Eric & The Animals

GREATEST HITS: ERIC BURDON.
Compact disc: released on The Compact Collection in Sep'87 by Conifer Records. Distributed by: Conifer Distribution

Burge, Greg

SURPRISE SURPRISE.
Tracks: / Surprise surprise / I can do that.
Single (7"): released on Casablanca in Jan'86. Distributed by: Polygram, Phonogram

Single (12"): released on Casablanca in Jan'86. Distributed by: Polygram, Phonogram

Burge, Jon

Fair was the city

Burgess, John

ART OF THE HIGHLAND BAGPIPE,THE.
Album: released on Topic in '81. Distributed by: Roots Distribution

Album: released on Topic in '81. Distributed by: Roots Distribution

Album: released on Topic in '83. Distributed by: Roots Distribution

KING OF HIGHLAND PIPERS,THE.
Album: released on Topic in '81. Distributed by: Roots Distribution

PLAYS THE GREAT HIGHLAND BAGPIPE (Burgess, Pipe Major John D).
Album: released on Lismor in '83 by Lismor Records. Distributed by: Lismor, Roots, Celtic Music

Cassette: released on Lismor in '83 by Lismor Records. Distributed by: Lismor, Roots, Celtic Music

Burgess, Sonny

I NEED A MAN (Burgess, Sonny/Barbara Pittman/Warren Smith/M.Yelvington).
Album: released on Charly in Sep'81 by Charly Records. Distributed by: Charly, Cadillac

LEGENDARY SUN PERFORMERS.
Tracks: / Red headed woman / Restless / Going home / Ain't got a thing / Find my baby for me / Tomorrow night / You're not the one for me / Thunderbirds / We wanna boogie / Feel so good / Y.O.U / My bucket's got a hole in it / All my sins taken away / Sally Brown / I love you so / Sadie's back in town.
Album: released on Charly in '77 by Charly Records. Distributed by: Charly, Cadillac

OLD GANG,THE.
Album: released on Charly in '81 by Charly Records. Distributed by: Charly, Cadillac

ROCK ROCK-A-BILLY (Burgess, Sonny & Larry Donn).
Album: released on White in Apr'87

SONNY BURGESS & THE PACERS (Burgess, Sonny & The Pacers).
Album: released on Sun in '85 by Charly Records. Distributed by: Charly Distribution

SONNY BURGESS VOLUME 3.
Tracks: / Itchy / Always will / Little town baby / Changed my mind / Kiss goodnight, A / Sadie's back in town / Thunderbird / So soon / Smootchin' Jill / Sweet Jenny / Tomorrow never comes / Ootchie cootchie / You're not the one for me.
Album: released on Sun in Oct'86 by Charly Records. Distributed by: Charly Distribution

SPELLBOUND.
Album: released on Off-Beat in Sep'86 by Off-Beat Records. Distributed by: Jetstar Distribution

WE WANNA BOOGIE (Burgess, Sonny & The Pacers).
Album: released on Sun in '85 by Charly Records. Distributed by: Charly Distribution

Burgon, Geoffrey

BRIDESHEAD THEME.
Single (7"): released on Chrysalis in '81 by Chrysalis Records. Distributed by: CBS

Buritz

SLEEP SOFTLY MARY.
Single (7"): released on Spartan in '84 by Spartan Records. Distributed by: Spartan

Single (12"): released on Spartan in '84 by Spartan Records. Distributed by: Spartan

Burke, Chris

CHRIS BURKE & HIS NEW ORLEANS MUSIC (Burke, Chris & His New Orleans Music).
Notes: Featuring Emery Thompson MONO recording.
Album: released on GHB in Jun'86. Distributed by: Jazz Music, Swift

Burke & Hodge

INDEED.
Single (7"): released on Orchid in Aug'87. Distributed by: Impetus Distribution, Orchid

Single (12"): released on Orchid in Aug'87. Distributed by: Impetus Distribution, Orchid

Burke, Jo

HAPPY TO MEET, SORRY TO PART.
Album: released on Green Linnet(USA) in Mar'87 by Green Linnet Records (USA). Distributed by: Projection

Cassette: released on Green Linnet(USA) in Mar'87 by Green Linnet Records (USA). Distributed by: Projection

Burke, Joe

GALWAY'S OWN.
Notes: Retail price given by ARC,excluding p&p (via mail order)is 5.75. Mail order distribution address: Accordian record Club,146 Birmingham Road, Kidderminster,Worcs. DY10 2SL. Tel: 0562 746105
Cassette: released on Accordion Record Club in Jul'86 by Accordion Record Club Records. Distributed by: Accordion Record Club

Burke, Keni

ARTISTS SHOWCASE: KENI BURKE.
Album: released on Streetsounds in Nov'86

Cassette: released on Streetsounds in Nov'86

Burke, Kevin

EAVESDROPPER,THE (Burke, Kevin/Jackie Daly).
Album: released on Mulligan in '80 by Topic Records. Distributed by: Roots Distribution, Jazz Music Distribution, I & B Distribution, Projection Distribution, Wynd-Up Distribution, Celtic Distributions

Cassette: released on Mulligan in '80 by Topic Records. Distributed by: Roots Distribution, Jazz Music Distribution, I & B Distribution, Projection Distribution, Wynd-Up Distribution, Celtic Distributions

IF THE CAPS FITS.
Album: released on Mulligan in '78 by Topic Records. Distributed by: Roots Distribution, Jazz Music Distribution, I & B Distribution, Projection Distribution, Wynd-Up Distribution, Celtic Distributions

Cassette: released on Mulligan in '78 by Topic Records. Distributed by: Roots Distribution, Jazz Music Distribution, I & B Distribution, Projection Distribution, Wynd-Up Distribution, Celtic Distributions

PROMENADE.
Album: released on Mulligan in '79 by Topic Records. Distributed by: Roots Distribution, Jazz Music Distribution, JSU Distribution, I & B Distribution, Projection Distribution, Wynd-Up Distribution, Celtic Distributions

UP CLOSE.
Album: released on WEA Ireland in Mar'87 by WEA Records. Distributed by: Celtic Distributions, Projection, I & B

Cassette: released on WEA Ireland in Mar'87 by WEA Records. Distributed by: Celtic Distributions, Projection, I & B

Burke, Ray

RAY BURKE SPEAKEASY BOYS (Burke, Ray Speakeasy Boys).
Album: released on New Orleans in Sep'86. Distributed by: Swift, Zodiac Distribution, Jazz Music,

Burke, Solomon

CHANGE IS GONNA COME, A.
Album: released on Rounder Europa in Feb'87

Compact disc: released on Rounder (USA) in Dec'86. Distributed by: Mike's Country Music Room Distribution, Jazz Music Distribution, Swift Distribution, Roots Records Distribution, Projection Distribution, Topic Distribution

CHANGE IS GONNA COME, A.
Album: released on Rounder Europa(USA) in Apr'86

CRY TO ME.
Tracks: / Be bop grandma / Just out of reach / Cry to me / Down in the valley / I'm hanging up my heart for you / Stupidity / Can't nobody love you / If you need me / Won't you give him(One more chance) / You're good for me / Goodbye baby(Baby goodbye) / Everybody needs somebody to love / Yes I do / Price, The / Got to get you off my mind / Maggie's farm.
Notes: If chuck Willis was in first division of fities R&B, the mighty Solomon Burke was right near the top of the premier division of Sixties soul.During the first half of the Sixties (the period of this compilation) he was definitely at the front line. Like any other musical category "Soul Music" means different things to different people.And so it should :different strokes for different times and places.But when if first started to be used in references to popular black music."Soul" referred specifically to a particular ggheneration and style of urban singers who, in musical setting, were far more "Pop" than the earthier "R&B" records, but,in singing style, were far too black gospel-Influenced to be calledpop singers.The earliest three most influencial, Urban exponents of the 'Soul' style of singing, before the discription came into common usage, are generally said to have been Clyde McPhatter, Sam Cooke,and Jackie Wilson. Along with CookeSolomon Burke wasone of the first of the generation to actually be called a'SoulSinger'.This compilation, Selectivly covering Solomon Burke's first five momentuous years with Atlantic Records,contains all of his recordings for which(eitherdirectly or via cover versions) he is best known in Britain, plus many equally great tracks, a couple of which have never never previously appeared on album. These originals such as "Cry to me","Down in the valley","Stupidity", "If you need me","Everybody needs somebody to love" and "Got to get you off my mind",were some of the earlist Soul hits to inspire and influence white R&B/Soulgroups of the Sixties,and to start the soul train rolling.They sound great today
Album: released on Charly(R&B) in '84 by Charly Records. Distributed by: Charly, Cadillac

Cassette: released on Charly(R&B) in '84 by Charly Records. Distributed by: Charly, Cadillac

KING OF ROCK 'N' SOUL FROM THE HEART.
Album: released on Charly in '81 by Charly Records. Distributed by: Charly, Cadillac

LOVE TRAP.
Tracks: / Love trap / Do you believe in the hereafter / Every breath you take / Daddy love bear / Isis / Nothing but the truth / Only God knows / Drive / Sweet spirit.
Notes: Solomon Burke was dubbed 'King Of Rock & Soul' by his record company Atlantic. During his eight year tenure with the label which began in 1960 he notched up a large number of quality hits. These included "Cry to me", "Just Out Of Reach", "Everybody needs somebody to love" and "Down in the valley" to name just a few. "Love Trap" was recorded in 1987 and is Solomon's first album for several years.With the current interest in revival sixties Soul hits (Percy Sledge, Ben E King, Jackie Wilson etc) this album is sure to find a ready market.
Album: released on Polygram in Jul'87 by Polygram Records. Distributed by: Polygram

Cassette: released on Polygram in Jul'87 by Polygram Records. Distributed by: Polygram

Compact disc: released on Polygram in Jul'87 by Polygram Records. Distributed by: Polygram

REST OF SOLOMON BURKE,THE.
Album: released on Atlantic in '85 by WEA Records. Distributed by: WEA

SOUL ALIVE!.
Album: released on Rounder (USA) in '84. Distributed by: Mike's Country Music Room Distribution, Jazz Music Distribution, Swift Distribution, Roots Records Distribution, Projection Distribution, Topic Distribution

Album: released on Demon in '85 by Demon Records. Distributed by: Pinnacle

YOU SEND ME.
Single (12"): released on Perfect in May'87

Burland, Dave

DALESMAN'S LITANY,A.
Album: released on Leader in '81. Distributed by: Jazz Music, Projection

DAVE BURLAND.
Album: released on Leader in '81. Distributed by: Jazz Music, Projection

DAVE BURLAND DOUBLE ALBUM.
Tracks: / Cruel mother / Banks of the Bann / King George hunt, The / Lakes of shilin / Bitter withy / Brave wolfe / Old changing way, The / I am a Rover / Great silkie, The / His name is Andrew / Bright Phoebus Lambkin / Shooting of his dear, The / Farmer is the man / Collier Laddie / Shaky nancy / Haul away for rosie / Grey funnel line / Edward Hollander / Wllie o' winebury / You can't fool the fat man.
Album: released on Rubber in '83 by Rubber Records. Distributed by: Roots Distribution, Projection Distribution, Jazz Music Distribution, Celtic Music Distribution, Spartan Distribution

SONGS OF EWAN MACCOLL (Burland, Dave, Dick Gaughan & Tony Capstick).
Album: released on Rubber in '82 by Rubber Records. Distributed by: Roots Distribution, Projection Distribution, Jazz Music Distribution, Celtic Music Distribution, Spartan Distribution

SONGS OF EWAN MACCOLL (See Gaughan, Dick) (Burland, Dave, Dick Gaughan & Tony Capstick).

YOU CAN'T FOOL THE FAT MAN.
Tracks: / Lamkin / Shooting of his dear, The / Farmer is the man / Collier laddie / Shaky Nancy / Haul away for Rosie / Grey funnel line / Edward Hollander / Willie O'Winsbury / You can't fool the fat man.
Album: released on Rubber in '82 by Rubber Records. Distributed by: Roots Distribution, Projection Distribution, Jazz Music Distribution, Celtic Music Distribution, Spartan Distribution

Compact disc: released on Rubber in '82 by Rubber Records. Distributed by: Roots Distribution, Projection Distribution, Jazz Music Distribution, Celtic Music Distribution, Spartan Distribution

Burmoe Brothers

SKIN.
Single (12"): by Virgin Records. Distributed by: EMI, CBS, Polygram

Burne, Keni

RISIN' TO THE TOP(GIVE IT ALL YOU GOT).
Single (7"): released on RCA in '83 by RCA Records. Distributed by: RCA, Roots, Swift, Wellard, Chris, I & B, Solomon & Peres Distribution

Single (12"): released on RCA in '83 by RCA Records. Distributed by: RCA, Roots, Swift, Wellard, Chris, I & B, Solomon & Peres Distribution

SHAKIN' Night dress.
Single (7"): released on RCA in '82 by RCA Records. Distributed by: RCA, Roots, Swift, Wellard, Chris, I & B, Solomon & Peres Distribution

Single (12"): released on RCA in '82 by RCA Records. Distributed by: RCA, Roots, Swift, Wellard, Chris, I & B, Solomon & Peres Distribution

YOU'RE THE BEST.
Tracks: / Let somebody love you / Gotta find my way back in your heart / Love is the answer / You're the best / Paintings of love / Night rides / Never stop loving me.
Album: released on RCA in '81 by RCA Records. Distributed by: RCA, Roots, Swift, Wellard, Chris, I & B, Solomon & Peres Distribution

Cassette: released on RCA in '81 by RCA Records. Distributed by: RCA, Roots, Swift, Wellard, Chris, I & B, Solomon & Peres Distribution

Burnel, Jean-Jacques

EUROMAN COMETH.
Tracks: / Euroman / Jellyfish / Freddie Laker (concord and eurobus) / Euromess / Deutschi and nicht uber alles / Do the European / Tout comprendez / Triumph (of the good city) / Pretty face / Crabs / Eurospeed / Your own speed.

FIRE AND WATER.
Album: released on Epic in '83 by CBS Records. Distributed by: CBS

Cassette: released on Epic in '83 by CBS Records. Distributed by: CBS

FIRE AND WATER (see Greenfield, Dave).

RAIN, DOLE AND TEA (see Greenfield, Dave).
Notes: Long deleted, reissued in original sleeve with insert. The bassist of The Stranglers features Lords Of New Church and ex-damned guitarist Brian James.
Album: released on Demon in Sep'87 by Demon Records. Distributed by: Pinnacle. Estim retail price in Sep'87 was £5.99.

Cassette: released on Under One Flag in Sep'87. Distributed by: Pinnacle. Estim retail price in Sep'87 was £5.99.

Burnet, R

Free fair

Burnette

RUNNING BEAR.
Tracks: / Running bear / Dance, dance, dance (shall we).
Single (7"): released on Hot Lead in Feb'87 by Hot Lead Records. Distributed by: Hot Lead

Burnette, Charmaine

AM I THE SAME GIRL.
Single (12"): released on Pro in '81

Burnette, Dorsey

DORSEY BURNETTE VOL.1 Great shakin' fever.
Album: released on Hollywood in Jul'87 by Hollywood Records. Distributed by: Pinnacle

DORSEY BURNETTE VOL.2 Keep a knockin'.
Album: released on Hollywood in Jul'87 by Hollywood Records. Distributed by: Pinnacle

Burnette, Hank C.

DON'T MESS WITH MY DUCKTAIL.
Tracks: / Spinning rock boogie / Your driving licence please / Riders in the sky / Blue moon / Hank's 97 / Come on little mama / Don't mess with my ducktail / Fools like me / Gold in the morning sun / Rocking daddy / Peggy Sue / Rock-Ola jive.
Album: released on Sonet in Mar'87 by Sonet Records. Distributed by: PRT

ROCKABILLY GASSEROONIE.
Tracks: / Dirty Boogie / Pony tail girl / Guitar Nellie / Red Cadillac and a black moustache / Sweet skinny Jenny / Patsy / Good good lovin' / Connie Lou / Too much / Rakin' and scrapin' / Over the rainbow / Sneaky Pete / Rocky road blues / Miss froggie.
Album: released on Dirty Boogie in Jan'78

Cassette: released on Sonet in Jan'78 by Sonet Records. Distributed by: PRT

Burnette, Johnny

10TH ANNIVERSARY ALBUM.
Album: released on Liberty (France) in '83

20 ROCK'N'ROLL HITS.
Tracks: / You're 16 / Little boy sad / You're the reason / Settin' the woods on fire / Walk on by / Fool, The / Why don't you haul off and love me / Me & the bear / Clown shoes / Cincinnati fireball / Lovesick blues / Finders keepers / Mona Lisa / Fool of the year, The / Just out of reach / Poorest boy in town, The / Moody river / Girl of my best friend / In the chappel in the moonlight / Me & the bear / Settin' the woods on fire / Dreamin' / Hello walls / Why don't you haul off and love me / Fool, The / My honey / Clown shoes / Cincinnati fireball / Little bitty tear / Moody river / Big,big world / God,country and my baby / You're the reason / You're 16 / Little boy sad.
Album: released on EMI (Germany) in '83 by EMI Records. Distributed by: Conifer

ALL BY MYSELF (Burnette, Johnny & R & R Trio).
Single (7"): released on Revival in Jul'82. Distributed by: Lightning, Swift

JOHNNY BURNETTE ROCK 'N' ROLL TRIO, THE.
Album: released on Solid Smoke in Apr'79. Distributed by: Projection, Swift

JOHNNY & DORSEY BURNETTE (Burnette, Johnny & Dorsey).
Album: released on Rockhouse(USA) in Nov'82

LEGENDARY JOHNNY BURNETTE ROCK 'N' ROLL TRIO (Burnette, Johnny & R & R Trio).
Tracks: / Tear it up / You're undecided / Oh baby babe / Midnight train / Shattered dreams / Train kept a rollin', The / Blues stay away from me / All by myself / Drinkin' wine spodee-o-dee / Chains of love / Honey hush / Lonsome tears in my eyes / I just found out / Please don't leave me / Rock therapy / Rockabilly boogie / Lonsome train(on a lonsome track) / Sweet love or my mind / My love you're a stranger / I love you so / Your baby blue eyes / Touch me / If you want it enough / Butterfingers / Eager beaver baby / On baby babe.
Album: released on Charly(R&B) in Jun'84 by Charly Records. Distributed by: Charly, Cadillac

LEGENDARY JOHNNY BURNETTE, THE (Burnette, Johnny & R & R Trio).
Cassette: released on Charly(R&B) in Jun'84 by Charly Records. Distributed by: Charly, Cadillac

LONESOME TRAIN (Burnette, Johnny & R & R Trio).
Single (7"): released on Revival in Jul'82. Distributed by: Lightning, Swift

PLEASE DON'T LEAVE ME (Burnette, Johnny & R & R Trio).
Single (7"): released on Revival in Jul'82. Distributed by: Lightning, Swift

ROCKABILY BOOGIE (Burnette, Johnny & R & R Trio).
Single (7"): released on Revival in Jul'82. Distributed by: Lightning, Swift

SINGS COLLECTABLE RECORDINGS.
Album: released on Musketeer in Jan'87

TOGETHER AGAIN (Burnette, Johnny & R & R Trio).
Album: released on Rollercoaster in Sep'82 by Rollercoaster Records. Distributed by: Swift Distribution, Rollercoaster Distribution

TRAIN KEPT A ROLLIN (Burnette, Johnny & R & R Trio).
Single (7"): released on Revival in Jul'82. Distributed by: Lightning, Swift

Burnette, Rocky

SON OF ROCK 'N' ROLL, THE.
Cassette: released on EMI in Apr'80 by EMI Records. Distributed by: EMI Deleted '82.

Burnette, T. Bone

BABY FALL DOWN Art movies.
Single (7"): released on Demon in '83 by Demon Records. Distributed by: Pinnacle

Burnett, Howard

DANCE OF THE DUCKS.
Single (7"): released on Smile in '81 by Smile Records. Distributed by: Spartan

Burnett, Paul

FUN AT 1 Various artists (Various Artists).
Album: released on BBC in '79 by BBC Records & Tapes. Distributed by: EMI, PRT,

Burnett, Richard

FINCHCOCKS COLLECTION OF HISTORIC KEYBOARD INSTRUMENTS,THE.
Album: released on Amon Ra in '82 by Saydisc Records. Distributed by: H.R. Taylor, PRT, Jazz Music, Essex Record Distributors Ltd., Projection, Swift

Cassette: released on Amon Ra in '82 by Saydisc Records. Distributed by: H.R. Taylor, Gamut, PRT, Jazz Music, Essex Record Distributors Ltd., Projection, Swift

ROMANTIC FORTEPIANO,THE.
Album: released on Amon Ra in '82 by Saydisc Records. Distributed by: H.R. Taylor, PRT, Jazz Music, Essex Record Distributors Ltd., Projection, Swift

Cassette: released on Amon Ra in '82 by Saydisc Records. Distributed by: H.R. Taylor, PRT, Jazz Music, Essex Record Distributors Ltd., Projection, Swift

Compact disc: released on Amon Ra in Sep'87 by Saydisc Records. Distributed by: H.R. Taylor, PRT, Jazz Music, Essex Record Distributors Ltd., Projection, Swift

Burnett, T-Bone

BEHIND THE TRAP DOOR.
Album: released on Side Effects in '84 by SPK Records. Distributed by: Rough Trade, Cartel

PROOF THROUGH THE NIGHT.
Album: released on Demon in '83 by Demon Records. Distributed by: Pinnacle

T-BONE BURNETT.
Notes: This is the fourth solo album from this aclaimed singer-songwriter. T-Bone is probably best known for his production work - recent projects have included Elvis Costello, Los Lobos, Marshall Crenshaw, Bodeans and Peter Case. This album was recorded in one frentic four-day period in Nashville, and the musicians roped in to help include David Hidalgo of Los Lobos (also Paul Simon's new album), Jerry Douglas, Jerry Scheff and Ron Berline. There are six of T-Bone's own songs here, as well as tunes by Tom Waites, Billy Swann and the Johnny and Jack classic 'Poison Love'.
Album: released on MCA in Dec'86 by MCA Records. Distributed by: Polygram, MCA

Cassette: released on MCA in Dec'86 by MCA Records. Distributed by: Polygram, MCA

TRUTH DECAY.
Album: released on Demon in Jul'86 by Demon Records. Distributed by: Pinnacle

Cassette: released on Demon in Jul'86 by Demon Records. Distributed by: Pinnacle

TRUTH DECAY.
Compact disc: released on Demon in Nov'86 by Demon Records. Distributed by: Pinnacle

Burnett, Watty

DANCING SHOES Congo dubba.
Single (12"): released on Dread At The Controls in '82. Distributed by: Dub Vendor, Virgin Records, EMI

Burnham, Alan

MUSIC TO SAVE THE WORLD BY.
Single (7"): released on Cherry Red in Jan'81 by Cherry Red Records. Distributed by: Pinnacle

Burning

THROUGH THE DARKNESS.
Tracks: / Touch Me / Feeling Your Bite.
Single (12"): released on Bang Bang in Nov'86. Distributed by: Red Rhino, Cartel

Burning Ambitions

BURNING AMBITIONS-A HISTORY OF PUNK various artists (Various Artists).
Album: released on Cherry Red in Nov'82 by Cherry Red Records. Distributed by: Pinnacle

Burning Bush

GO TO SCHOOL.
Single (12"): released on Kongo in Jul'84 by Kongo Records. Distributed by: Jetstar

Burning Illusion

SO LONELY.
Tracks: / So lonely / Worries in the dark.
Single (12"): released on Melody in Dec'85 by Melody Records. Distributed by: Jetstar Distribution

Burning Sensations

BELLY OF THE WHALE.
Single (7"): released on Capitol in Jun'83 by Capitol Records. Distributed by: EMI

Single (12"): released on Capitol in Jun'83 by Capitol Records. Distributed by: EMI

Burning Spear

DRY AND HEAVY.
Tracks: / Any river / Sun, The / It's a long way around / I.W.I.N. / Throw down your arms / Dry and heavy / Wailing / Disciples / Shout it out.
Album: released on Mango in Jul'77 by Inferno Records. Distributed by: Inferno

FITTEST OF THE FITTEST, THE.
Tracks: / Fittest of the fittest, The / Fire man / Bad to worst / Repatriation / Old Boy Garvey / 2,000 years / For you / In Africa / Vision.
Notes: Brand new studio recordings from Jamaica.Very strong ethnic and reghgae interestin Spear.Fourth album for EMI. Superb sleeve painting by french artist Frederic Voisin.
Album: released on Radic in Sep'83 by Radic. Distributed by: EMI

Cassette: released on Radic in Sep'83 by Radic. Distributed by: EMI

GARVEY'S GHOST.
Tracks: / Ghost, The(Marcus Garvey) / I and I survive(Slavery days) / Black wa-da-da(Invasion) / John Burns shank(Live good) / Brian food(give me) / Father east of Jack(Old Marcus Garvey) / 2000 years(Tradition) / Dread river(Jordan river) / Workshop(Red,green,and gold) / Reggaelation(Resting place).
Album: released on Island in Apr'76 by Island Records. Distributed by: Polygram

HAIL H.I.M.
Album: released on EMI in Apr'80 by EMI Records. Distributed by: EMI

Album: released on EMI (France) in May'84 by EMI Records. Distributed by: Conifer

Cassette: released on EMI (France) in May'84 by EMI Records. Distributed by: Conifer

HARDER THAN THE BEAT.
Tracks: / Marcus Garvey / Dry and heavy / Throw down your arms / Social living / Invasion / Black we-da-da / Slavery days / Old Marcus Garvey / Man in the hills / Sun, The / Civilised Reggae.
Album: released on EMI in Aug'79 by EMI Records. Distributed by: EMI

MAN IN THE HILLS.
Tracks: / Man in the hills / It's good / No more way / Black soul / Lion / People get ready / Children / Mother / Door peep / Groovy.
Album: released on Island in Aug'76 by Island Records. Distributed by: Polygram

MARCUS GARVEY.
Tracks: / Marcus Garvey / Slavery days / Invasion / Live good / Give me / Old Marcus Garvey / Tradition / Jordan river / Red, gold and green / Resting place.
Album: released on Island in Dec'75 by Island Records. Distributed by: Polygram

Single (12"): released on Island in Aug'87 by Island Records. Distributed by: Polygram

Compact disc: released on Island in Aug'87 by Island Records. Distributed by: Polygram

PEOPLE OF THE WORLD.
Tracks: / People of the world / I'm not the worst / Seville land / Who's the winner / Distant drum / We are going / This experience / Built this city / No worry you'self / Little love song.
Notes: Produced by Burning Spear & Nelson Miller.
Compact disc: by Greensleeves Records. Distributed by: BMG, Jetstar, Spartan

Album: released on Greensleeves in Oct'86 by Greensleeves Records. Distributed by: BMG, Jetstar, Spartan

Cassette: released on Greensleeves in Oct'86 by Greensleeves Records. Distributed by: BMG, Jetstar, Spartan

REGGAE GREATS.
Tracks: / Door peep / Scavery days / Lion / Black disciples / Man in the hill / Tradition / Throw down your arms / Social living / Marcus Garvey / Dry & heavy / Black wa-da-da(Invasion) / Sun, The.
Album: released on Island in Jul'85 by Island Records. Distributed by: Polygram

Cassette: released on Island in Jul'85 by Island Records. Distributed by: Polygram

RESISTANCE.
Album: released on Heartbeat (USA) in Sep'85. Distributed by: Mike's Country Music Room Distribution, Swift, Projection, Topic, Jetstar, Ruff Lion Distribution

ROCKING TIME.
Album: released on Studio Worx in Sep'84 by Studio Worx Records. Distributed by: Jetstar Distribution

SOCIAL LIVING.
Tracks: / Marcus children suffer / Social living / Nayah Keith / Insitution / Marcus senior / Civilised reggae / Mister Garvey / Come / Marcus say Jah no dead.
Album: released on Island in Jul'80 by Island Records. Distributed by: Polygram

Burning The Midnight Sun

BURNING THE MIDNIGHT SUN various artists (Various Artists).
Album: released on Uniton Records in Sep'84. Distributed by: Cartel

Cassette: released on Uniton Records in Sep'84. Distributed by: Cartel

Burning up

BURNING UP, VOL, 1 various artists (Various Artists).
Album: released on Burning Sounds in Apr'84 by Ross, Bill/Burning Sounds Records. Distributed by: PRT

Cassette: released on Burning Sounds in Apr'84 by Ross, Bill/Burning Sounds Records. Distributed by: PRT

BURNING UP, VOL. 2 various artists (Various Artists).
Album: released on Burning Sounds in Apr'84 by Ross, Bill/Burning Sounds Records. Distributed by: PRT

Cassette: released on Burning Sounds in Apr'84 by Ross, Bill/Burning Sounds Records. Distributed by: PRT

BURNING UP, VOL.3 various artists (Various Artists).
Album: released on Burning Sounds in Nov'84 by Ross, Bill/Burning Sounds Records. Distributed by: PRT

BURNING UP, VOLS 1 & 2 various artists (Various Artists).
Album: released on Burning Sounds in Jul'85 by Ross, Bill/Burning Sounds Records. Distributed by: PRT

Burns, David

SONG FROM THE KNEE PLAYS.
Album: released on EMI in Jul'85 by EMI Records. Distributed by: EMI

Album: released on EMI in Jul'85 by EMI Records. Distributed by: EMI

Burns, Eddie

DETROIT BLACK BOTTOM (Burns, Eddie 'guitar').
Album: released on Big Bear in Apr'79 by Big Bear Records. Distributed by: Big Bear, Swift

TREAT ME LIKE I TREAT YOU.
Album: released on Moonshine (Belgium) in Dec'85. Distributed by: Projection Distribution

Burns, Eddy

BY THE WAY.
Album: released on Tartan Hippo in Aug'85 Distributed by: Fast Forward Distribution, Cartel Distribution

Burns, Gill

SIGHT MORE CURIOUS, A.
Album: released on Nosuch in '85 by Nosuch Records

Burnside, R.L

PLAYS AND SINGS THE MISSISSIPPI DELTA BLUES.
Album: released on Swingmaster in Oct'82. Distributed by: Jazz Music Distribution

Burns, Jake

BREATHLESS (Burns, Jake & The Big Wheel).
Tracks: / Breathless / Valentines day.
Single (7"): released on Jive in Feb'87 by Zomba Records. Distributed by: RCA, PRT, CBS

ON FORTUNE STREET (Burns, Jake & The Big Wheel).
Single (7"): released on Rigid Digits in Jul'85. Distributed by: PRT

Single (12"): released on Survival in Jul'85 by Survival Records. Distributed by: Backs, Cartel Distribution

SHE GREW UP (Burns, Jake & The Big Wheel).
Tracks: / She grew up / Race you to the grave.
Single (7"): released on Survival in Mar'86 by Survival Records. Distributed by: Backs, Cartel Distribution

Single (12"): released on Survival in Mar'86 by Survival Records. Distributed by: Backs, Cartel Distribution

Burns, Jethro

BACK TO BACK.
Album: released on Kaleidoscope in Sep'79

Burns, Laura

LIGHT THIS NIGHT.
Album: released on Flying Fish (USA) in Apr'86 by Flying Fish Records (USA). Distributed by: Roots, Projection

Burns, R.L.

PLAYS & SINGS MISSISSIPPI BLUES.
Album: released on Swingmaster in May'86. Distributed by: Jazz Music Distribution

Burns, Robert

JOHN CAIRNEY TELLS THE STORY OF ROBERT BURNS.
Double Album: released on Talking Tape Company in May'79 by Talking Tape Company Records

ROBERT BURNS SONGBOOK various artists (Various Artists).
Tracks: / Happy are we all together / Oh lovely Polly Stewart / Ca'the ewes / De'il's awa' with the exciseman, The / My heart's in the highlands / Of a' the airts / Oh, whistle and I'll come to you / My lad / Ae fond kiss / Highland lad, A / Rosebud by my early walk, A / John Anderson / My jo / I'll aye ca'in by yon toon / My love she's but a lassie yet / Ye banks and braes.
Album: by Lismor Records. Distributed by: Lismor, Roots, Celtic Music

Cassette: released on Lismor in Jan'78 by Lismor Records. Distributed by: Lismor, Roots, Celtic Music

Album: released on Lismor in Jan'78 by Lismor Records. Distributed by: Lismor, Roots, Celtic Music

SONGS OF... (Burns, Robert & Redpath, Jean).
Album: released on Philo in May'79. Distributed by: Roots

Burns, Steve

WHISPERING WINDS.
Album: released on BGS Chord in Sep'79

Burns Supper, A

BURNS SUPPER, A Various artists (Various Artists).
Notes: Artists include:Kenneth McKellar/Andy Stewart/Moira Anderson/Ian Powne & His Band/John Cairney/Jean Anderson/Russell Hunter/John Carmichael & His Band/Iain McFayden/Joe Campbell/Lionel Daiches/George Younger etc.
Album: released on Lismor in Jul'86 by Lismor Records. Distributed by: Lismor, Roots, Celtic Music

Cassette: released on Lismor in Jul'86 by Lismor Records. Distributed by: Lismor, Roots, Celtic Music

Buro

BURO.
Tracks: / Better than the rest / I can't take the runnings in a Babylon / If me a chat / Out of hand / Jolly bus / Tenament / Tell me what you want / Stumbling block / Rose Marie / Modulla.
Album: released on CSA in Jan'83 by CSA Records. Distributed by: PRT, Jetstar

Burrage, Harold

SHE KNOCKS ME OUT 1956-58.
Album: released on Flyright in Jun'81 by Flyright Records. Distributed by: Krazy Kat, Swift, Jazz Music

Burrell, Dave

ECHO.
Album: released on Affinity in Sep'79 by Charly Records. Distributed by: Charly, Cadillac

LUSH LIFE.
Tracks: / In a sentimental mood / Lush life / Come sunday / Flower is a loversome thing / Mexico city / Trade winds / Crucificade / Budapest conclusion.
Album: released on Denon in Mar'82 by Denon Records.

ROUND MIDNIGHT.
Tracks: / Straight no chaser / Round midnight / Blue monk / Black roberts / No games / New York.
Album: released on Denon in Mar'82 by Denon Records.

Burrell, Kenny

A LA CARTE.
Tracks: / I've been in love before / Dreamy / Our love / St.Thomas / Tenderly / I thought about you / A la carte.
Notes: Produced by: Helen Keane./Recorded by: Malcom Addey./recorded live at Village West-NYC August 23rd. 1983. Kenny Burrell-guitar/Rufus Reid-bass
Album: released on Muse Jazz (USA) in Jan'86

AT THE FIVE SPOT CAFE, VOLUME 1.
Tracks: / Birk's work / Hallelujah / Lady be good / Lover man / 36-23-36.
Notes: Guitar master Kenny Burrell was a 1956 Blue Note discovery who is back on the label in 1986! This live session at New York's legendary Five Spot took place in 1959 with a swinging cast that included Art Blakey,saxophonist Tina Brooks and alternating pianists Roland Hanna & Bobby Timmons. The tone is definitely straight ahead jazz with rousing versions of 'Lady Be Good' & 'Birk's Work' as well as funky originals such as 'Hallelujah' & '36-23-36'.
Album: released on Blue Note in May'86 by EMI Records. Distributed by: EMI

AT THE FIVE SPOT CAFE.
Tracks: / Birk's work / Lady be good / Lover man / Swingin' / hallelujah / Beef stew blues / If you could see me now / 36-23-36.
Compact disc: released on Manhattan-Blue Note in May'87 by EMI America Records (USA). Distributed by: EMI

BLUESIN' AROUND.
Album: released on CBS(France) in Jan'84 by CBS Records. Distributed by: Conifer, Discovery, Swift

FOR CHARLIE CHRISTIAN & BENNY GOODMAN.
Notes: Performance dedicated to the memory of Charlie Christian & the Benny Goodman small groups. Recorded between December 1966 & March 1967. This CD has 3 additional tracks which were not on the original album.
Compact disc: released on Verve (USA) in May'87 by Polydor. Distributed by: Polygram

FREIGHT TRAIN (Burrell, Kenny & John Coltrane).
Compact disc: released on Carrere in Apr'87 by Carrere Records. Distributed by: PRT, Spartan

GENERATION.
Tracks: / Generation / High-fly / Jumpin' the blues / Lover man / Mark I / So little time / Fungii mama / Generation / Hi-fly / Jumpin' the blues / Lover man / Dolphin dance * / Naima * / Star crossed * / Just friends * / Mark 1 * / So little time / Fungii mama.
Notes: Kenny Burrell, fresh from Detroit, made his very first album for Blue Note in 1956. He has recorded as a leader for the label many times since then in many settings. One of his loveliest efforts was the exciting live album "At The Five Spot" from 1959. On his latest album, he is heard with a very different band live at the Village Vanguard. The electricity of the live event is evident throughout. This album is called "Generation" because it features this great guitarist with two fine guitarists of the next generation Bobby Broom and Rodney Jones. Backed only by bass and drums, the three guitarists weave arrangements that are intricate and almost orchestral, but they swing! The album features a blend of new compositions with jazz standards such as Jay McShann's "Jumpin' The Blues" as well as the pop standard "Lover Man", which coincidentally also appears on "At The Five Spot". [EMI release shet, May 1987] * medley
Album: released on Blue Note in May'87 by EMI Records. Distributed by: EMI

Album: released on Blue Note in May'87 by EMI Records. Distributed by: EMI

Compact disc: released on Manhattan-Blue Note in Jun'87 by EMI America Records (USA). Distributed by: EMI

GROOVIN' HIGH.
Tracks: / Peace / Someone to light up my life / Lament / If I Love Again / Spring can really hang you up the most / Secret love / Groovin' high.
Album: released on Muse (USA) in Feb'87 by Muse Records (USA). Distributed by: Conifer Distribution, Jazz Music Distribution

GUITAR FORMS (Burrell, Kenny & Gil Evans).
Tracks: / Geensleeves / Last night when we were young / Breadwinner / Downstairs / Lotus land / Prelude No.2(Gershwin) / Moon and sand / Loie / Terrace theme.
Notes: Kenny Burrell one of today's finest jazz guitarists,teamed with Gil Evans for this 1965 recording.
Album: released on Verve in Aug'81 by Phonogram Records. Distributed by: Polygram

Compact disc: released on Verve in Aug'81 by Phonogram Records. Distributed by: Polygram

HANDCRAFTED.
Tracks: / You and the night & the music / So little time / I'm glad there is you / All blues / It could happen to you.
Album: released on Muse in Apr'81 by Peerless Records.

KENNY BURRELL.
Album: released on Jazz Reactivation in Jul'82. Distributed by: PRT

KENNY BURRELL IN NEW YORK.
Tracks: / Pent up house / But beautiful / Begs groove / Makin' whoopee / Come rain or come shine / Love your magic spell is everywhere.
Notes: Artists: Larry Gales, Sherman (Recorded at The Villiage Vanguard, New York City)
Album: released on Muse (Import) in '81

KENNY BURRELL & JOHN COLTRANE (Burrell, Kenny & John Coltrane).
Compact disc: released on JVC Fantasy (Japan) in Nov'86

LISTEN TO THE DAWN.
Tracks: / Yours is my heart / Alone / My one & only love / You're my everything / Listen to the dawn / Isabella / It amazes me / Never let me go / Papa Joe.
Notes: Artists: Kenny Burrell/Rufus Reid/Ben Rilet. Recorded December 9th & 10th 1980
Album: released on Muse in Feb'83 by Peerless Records

LIVE AT THE VANGUARD (Burrell, Kenny Trio).
Compact disc: released on Greenline in May'87 by Charly Records. Distributed by: Charly

LIVE AT THE VILLAGE VANGUARD (Burrell, Kenny Trio).
Tracks: / All night long / Will you still be in my mind / I'm a fool to want to / Trio / Broadway / Soft winds / Just a sittin' & a rockin' / Well you needn't.
Album: released on Arco in May'86 by Charly Records. Distributed by: Charly

LIVE AT THE VILLAGE VANGUARD.
Tracks: / Second balcony jump / Willow weep for me / Work song / Woodyn' you / In the still of the night / Don't you know I care / Love you madly / It's getting dark.
Album: released on Muse in Apr'81 by Peerless Records.

MIDNIGHT BLUE.
Tracks: / Chitlins con carne / Mule / Soul lament / Midnight blue / Wavy gravy / Gee baby ain't I good to you / Saturday night blues.
Notes: This soulful, after hours album couples Stanley Turrentine and Kenny Burrell with a pianoless rhythm section.The performances range from the sensitive guitarsolo 'Soul Lament' to the full blown, hard cooking 'Chitlins Con Carne' with thewhole band.Another highlight in there reading of Don Redman's 'Gee baby ain't I good to you'
Compact disc: released on EMI in Mar'87 by EMI Records. Distributed by: EMI

Album: released on Blue Note in Oct'85 by EMI Records. Distributed by: EMI

Cassette: released on Blue Note in Sep'87 by EMI Records. Distributed by: EMI. Estim retail price in Sep'87 was £5.99.

Cassette: released on Blue Note in Sep'87 by EMI Records. Distributed by: EMI. Estim retail price in Sep'87 was £5.99.

NIGHT SONG.
Tracks: / Night song / Blues for lues / Namely you / Love you madly / Just a-sittin' and a-rockin' / Shadow of your smile / Brother where are you / Night hawk / Teach me tonight.
Album: released on Verve in May'82 by Phonogram Records. Distributed by: Polygram

TOGETHERING (Burrell, Kenny & Grover Washington Jr.).
Tracks: / Soulero / Sails of your soul / Daydream / Beautiful friendship, A / Togethering / Romance dance / Asphalt canyon blues / What am I here for.
Notes: 'Togethering' is a distinctly straight-ahead album, teaming two of Jazz's most distinguished and popular instrumentalists and designed to be accessible to all fans of contemporary instrumental music.The pairing of washington & Burrell was the brainchild of Bruce Lundvall, the renowned record executive vehind the re- launch of the Blue Note label and founder of the Electra Musician label, for which this album was originally recorded.Backed by Ron Carter, Jack De Johnette and Ralph MacDonald, this is the first jazz record that Grover Wahington has made for quite some time.
Album: released on Blue Note in Apr'85 by EMI Records. Distributed by: EMI

TWO GUITARS (Burrell, Kenny & Jimmy Rainey).
Album:

Burrell, Roland

BLOODSHOT EYES.
Single (12"): released on Music Hawk in Dec'83 by Music Hawk Records. Distributed by: Jetstar Distribution

Burris, J.C.

ONE OF THESE MORNINGS.
Album: released on Arhoolie in Jan'81 by Arhoolie Records. Distributed by: Projection, Topic, Jazz Music, Swift, Roots

Burrito Brothers

ALMOST SATURDAY NIGHT.
Single (7"): released on MCA in Jan'84 by MCA Records. Distributed by: Polygram, MCA

Burrough, Roslyn

LOVE IS HERE.
Tracks: / Devil may care / Love is here(lonely tears) / Song for Jean-Gene / If I were a bell / Never let me go / Did he ever love me / All the things you are / So much in love / I want to make you smile / Youngfolks.
Notes: Personnel:Kevin Ewbanks-elec,& acoustic guitars/Eddie Gladden-drums/Jerry Gladden-percussions & trumpet/Onaje Allan Cumbs-piano & synthesiser/Kirk Lightsey-piano/Rufus Reid-acoustic bass/Warren Smith-vibraphone/Akira Tana-drums.
Album: released on Sunnyside Jazz (USA) in Jan'86

Burroughs, William

BREAKTHROUGH IN GREY ROOM.
Album: released on Sub Rosa in Feb'87 by Sub Rosa Records. Distributed by: Red Rhino Distribution, Cartel Distribution

DOCTOR IS ON THE MARKET (THE).

Burrows, Stuart

SONGS FOR YOU.
Double Album: released on Decca in Sep'78 by Decca Records. Distributed by: Polygram

Double cassette: released on Decca in Sep'78 by Decca Records. Distributed by: Polygram

TO THE LAND OF DREAMS.
Tracks: / Marie my girl / Passing by / Oh, promise me / Trees / Gortnamona / I heard you singing / Kerry dance / Dry those tears / Smilin' thro / Parted / Dearest of all / Sitting by the windows / Gloaming, The.
Album: released on L'Oiseau-Lyre in Jun'80 by Decca Records. Distributed by: Conifer

WORLD OF THE SACRED SONGS.
Album: released on World of Learning in Jan'72 by World Of Learning Records. Distributed by: World Of Learning

Cassette: released on Rex in Jan'79 by Decca

Burrows, Terry

Watching the burning bride

Bursens & Verbek Organ

TURNERS MERRY-GO-ROUND VOL.2.
Album: released on Grosvenor in May'83 by Grosvenor Records. Distributed by: Taylors

Cassette: released on Grosvenor in May'83 by Grosvenor Records. Distributed by: Taylors

Burton, G

PASSENGERS (Burton, G & Eberhard Weber).
Album: released on ECM in Apr'77 by ECM Records. Distributed by: IMS, Polygram, Virgin through EMI

Burton, Garry

PARIS ENCOUNTER (Burton, Garry/Stephane Grappelli).

Burton, Gary

COUNTRY ROADS AND OTHER PLACES (Burton, Gary Quartet).
Album: released on RCA (France) in Jan'83 by RCA Records. Distributed by: Discovery

EASY AS PIE (Burton, Gary Quartet).
Album: released on ECM (France) in Jun'81 by ECM Records. Distributed by: IMS, Polygram, Virgin through EMI

IN CONCERT (Burton, Gary & Ahmad Jamal).

LYRIC SUITE FOR SEXTET (Burton, Gary & Chick Corea).

MATCHBOOK (see Towner, Ralph) (Burton, Gary/Ralph Towner).

PICTURE THIS (Burton, Gary Quartet).
Album: released on ECM (Germany) in Mar'83 by ECM Records. Distributed by: IMS, Polygram, Virgin through EMI

REAL LIFE HITS (Burton, Gary Quartet).
Album: released on ECM (Germany) in Mar'85 by ECM Records. Distributed by: IMS, Polygram, Virgin through EMI

REAL LIFE HITS.
Tracks: / Syndrome / Beatle, The / Fleurette Africaine / Ladies in Mercedes / Real life hits / I need you here / Ivanushka Durachok.
Notes: 'Real Life Hits' is probably Gary Burton's most coherent and vital record in a long time.In his quartet,Burton introduces the young talented Japanese piano player Makoto Ozone who with this recording,proves a unique and adequate partner for Burton.'Real Life Hits' comprises compositions by Carla Bley,Duke Ellington, John Scofield,Makoto Ozone and the Quartet's bassist Steve Swallow.He in particular contributes to the group's overall sound.
Compact disc: by ECM Records. Distributed by: IMS, Polygram, Virgin through EMI

RING.
Compact disc: released on ECM (Germany) in Oct'86 by ECM Records. Distributed by: IMS, Polygram, Virgin through EMI

SOMETHING'S COMING.
Album: released on RCA (France) in Nov'84 by RCA Records. Distributed by: Discovery

Album: released on ECM (Germany) in Nov'84 by ECM Records. Distributed by: IMS, Polygram, Virgin through EMI

Compact disc: released on ECM (Germany) in Nov'84 by ECM Records. Distributed by: IMS, Polygram, Virgin through EMI

WHIZ KIDS (Burton, Gary Quartet).
Notes: Gary Burton back again with a great line-up of tremendous new talent.British tenor sax player Tommy Smith has already caused quite a stir along with American drummer Martin Richards,Japanese pianist Makoto Ozone has already recorded with Burton on "Real Life Hits" in 1984.Steve Swallow on bass needs no introduction as their musical partnership goes back to the very beginning of Burton's recording career.
Personnel:Gary Burton-vibraphone/Makoto Ozone-piano/Tommy Smith-saxaphone/Steve Swallow -bass/ Martin Richards-drums.
Compact disc: released on ECM (Germany) in Mar'87 by ECM Records. Distributed by: IMS, Polygram, Virgin through EMI

Album: released on ECM (Germany) in Feb'87 by ECM Records. Distributed by: IMS, Polygram, Virgin through EMI

WORKS.
Tracks: / Olhos de gato / Desert air / Tunnel of love / Vox humana / Three / Brotherhood / Chelsea Bells / Coral / Domino biscuit.
Compact disc: by ECM Records. Distributed by: IMS, Polygram, Virgin through EMI

ZURICH CONCERT (Burton, Gary & Chick Corea).

Burton, James

CORN PICKIN & SLICK SLIDIN (Burton, James/ Ralph Mooney).

Burton, Jay Arthur

MIDNIGHT.
Album: released on President in Oct'80 by President Records. Distributed by: Taylors, Spartan

Burton, Jenny

BAD HABITS.
Single (7"): released on Atlantic in Jun'85 by WEA Records. Distributed by: WEA

Single (12"): released on Atlantic in Jun'85 by WEA Records. Distributed by: WEA

DO YOU WANT IT BAD ENUFF.
Tracks: / Call Me Anytime.
Single (7"): released on Atlantic in Jan'87 by WEA Records. Distributed by: WEA

Single (12"): released on Atlantic in Jan'87 by WEA Records. Distributed by: WEA

JENNY BURTON.
Cassette: released on Atlantic in Apr'85 by WEA Records. Distributed by: WEA

REMEMBER WHAT YOU LIKE.
Single (7"): released on Atlantic in Apr'84 by WEA Records. Distributed by: WEA

Single (12"): released on Atlantic in Mar'84 by WEA Records. Distributed by: WEA

SOUVENIRS.
Album: released on Atlantic in Feb'87 by WEA Records. Distributed by: WEA

Cassette: released on Atlantic in Feb'87 by WEA Records. Distributed by: WEA

Burton, Tommy

IT AIN'T EXACTLY BACKGROUND.
Album: released on Unit in May'85 by Unit Records. Distributed by: PRT

TOMMY BURTON'S SPORTING-HOUSE QUARTET PLUS ONE (Burton, Tommy Quartet).
Album: released on Lost in Jul'87

Burtussi, Ann

I'M NUMBER ONE.
Single (7"): released on Speed in Feb'83

Burundi Black

BURUNDI BLACK.
Single (7"): released on Barclay in Jul'81 by Decca Records. Distributed by: Polygram, Discovery, Conifer, IMS, Swift

Single (12"): released on Barclay in Jul'81 by Decca Records. Distributed by: Polygram, Discovery, Conifer, IMS, Swift

Bus Boys

AMERICAN WORKER.
Album: released on Arista in Aug'82 by Arista Records. Distributed by: RCA

BOYS ARE BACK IN TOWN.
Single (7"): released on Arista in Apr'83 by Arista Records. Distributed by: RCA

Busby, Colin

BIG SWING BAND FAVOURITE (Busby, Colin Big Swing Band).
Album: released on Horatio Nelson in Nov'85. Distributed by: PRT

Cassette: released on Horatio Nelson in Nov'85. Distributed by: PRT

TEN GREAT TV THEMES (Busby, Colin Swinging Brass).
Notes: Includes Dynasty, Dallas, Soap
Album: released on Horatio Nelson in Jul'86. Distributed by: PRT

Cassette: released on Horatio Nelson in Jul'86. Distributed by: PRT

Busch, Lou

ZAMBESI.
Tracks: / Zambesi / Sixteen tons.
Notes: Also contains:"Sixteen tons" by Tennessee Ernie Ford
Single (7"): released on Old Gold in Apr'87 by Old Gold Records. Distributed by: Lightning, Jazz Music, Spartan, Counterpoint

Bush, Blake

COUNTRY BLUE GRASS (Bush, Blake & Taylor).
Album: released on Sonet in Oct'76 by Sonet Records. Distributed by: PRT

Bush, Charlie

LOCAL LIVING LEGEND.
Album: released on Revelation in Apr'81

Bushido

AMONG THE RUINS.
Single (12"): released on Third Mind in Nov'84 by Third Mind Records. Distributed by: Backs, Cartel Distribution

DELIVERANCE.
Album: released on Third Mind in May'85 by Third Mind Records. Distributed by: Backs, Cartel Distribution

SANDS OF NAKAJIMA, THE.
Album: released on Third Mind in Jan'85 by Third Mind Records. Distributed by: Backs, Cartel Distribution

VOICES.
Single (12"): released on Third Mind in Oct'85 by Third Mind Records. Distributed by: Backs, Cartel Distribution

Bush, Kate

ARMY DREAMERS.
Single (7"): released on EMI in Sep'80 by EMI Records. Distributed by: EMI

BIG SKY, THE.
Tracks: / Big sky, The (single mix) / Not this time / Morning fog, The*.
Single (7"): released on EMI in Apr'86 by EMI Records. Distributed by: EMI

Single (12"): released on EMI in Apr'86 by EMI Records. Distributed by: EMI

CLOUDBURSTING.
Single (7"): released on EMI in Oct'85 by EMI Records. Distributed by: EMI

Single (12"): released on EMI in Oct'85 by EMI Records. Distributed by: EMI

DREAMING, THE.
Tracks: / Sat in your lap / There goes a tenner / Pull out the pin / Suspended in Gaffa / Leave it open / Dreaming, The / Night of the swallow / All the love / Houdini / Get out of my house.
Compact disc: released on EMI in Jan'87 by EMI Records. Distributed by: EMI

HAIR OF THE HOUND, THE.
Tracks: / Running up that hill / Hounds of love / Big sky, The / Cloudbusting.
Notes: Her first video release for over 2 years.Includes 4 tracks from the'A' side of her album'The Hounds of Love',which have not been commercially available before now.The single 'Cloudbusting' was specially re-mixed for the video.This remix is not available on any form of vinyl.Also includes the single 'The Big Sky' directed by Kate Bush herself. Total playing time: 30 minutes. Type of recording : Compilation.
Video-cassette (VHS): released on PMI in Jun'86 by PMI Records. Distributed by: EMI

Video-cassette [Betamax]: released on PMI in Jun'86 by PMI Records. Distributed by: EMI

HOUNDS OF LOVE.
Album: released on EMI in Sep'85 by EMI Records. Distributed by: EMI

Cassette: released on EMI in Sep'85 by EMI Records. Distributed by: EMI

Compact disc: released on EMI in Sep'85 by EMI Records. Distributed by: EMI

Album: released on Fame (EMI) in Apr'84 by Music For Pleasure Records. Distributed by: EMI

Cassette: released on Fame (EMI) in Apr'84 by Music For Pleasure Records. Distributed by: EMI

Compact disc: released on Fame (EMI) in Apr'84 by Music For Pleasure Records. Distributed by: EMI

HOUNDS OF LOVE.
Tracks: / Hounds of love / Handsome cabin boy, The / Hounds of love(Del Palmer remix)* / Jig of love*.
Single (7"): released on EMI in Feb'86 by EMI Records. Distributed by: EMI

Single (12"): released on EMI in Feb'86 by EMI Records. Distributed by: EMI

KATE BUSH INTERVIEW PICTURE DISC.
Album: released on Baktabak in Apr'87 by Baktabak Records. Distributed by: Arabesque

KICK INSIDE, THE.
Compact disc: by EMI Records. Distributed by: EMI

Album: released on EMI in Feb'78 by EMI Records. Distributed by: EMI

Cassette: released on EMI in Feb'78 by EMI Records. Distributed by: EMI

LIONHEART.
Compact disc: by EMI Records. Distributed by: EMI

LIVE AT HAMMERSMITH ODEON.
Video-cassette (VHS): released on PMI in Jun'86 by PMI Records. Distributed by: EMI

Video-cassette [Betamax]: released on PMI in Jun'86 by PMI Records. Distributed by: EMI

NE T'ENFUIS PAS.
Single (7"): released on EMI (Import) in Aug'83 by EMI Records. Distributed by: Conifer

NEVER FOR EVER.
Album: released on EMI in Sep'80 by EMI Records. Distributed by: EMI

Cassette: released on EMI in Sep'80 by EMI Records. Distributed by: EMI

NEVER FOREVER.
Tracks: / Babooshka / Delius / Blow away / All we ever look for / Egypt / Wedding list (The) / Violin / Infant kiss (The) / Night scented stock / Army dreamers / Breathing.
Compact disc: released on EMI in Mar'87 by EMI Records. Distributed by: EMI

ON STAGE.
Album: released on EMI (Holland) in Aug'83 by EMI Records. Distributed by: Conifer

RUNNING UP THAT HILL.
Single (7"): released on EMI in Aug'85 by EMI Records. Distributed by: EMI

Single (12"): released on EMI in Aug'85 by EMI Records. Distributed by: EMI

SINGLE FILE BOX SET.
Boxed set: released on EMI in Jan'84 by EMI Records. Distributed by: EMI

SINGLE FILE, THE.
Notes: Number of tracks: 12 Type of recording: Compilation Total playing time: 50minutes.
Video-cassette (VHS): released on PMI in Jun'86 by PMI Records. Distributed by: EMI

Video-cassette [Betamax]: released on PMI in Jun'86 by PMI Records. Distributed by: EMI

WHOLE STORY, THE.
Tracks: / Wuthering Heights / Cloudbusting / Man with the child in his eyes / Breathing / Wow / Hounds of love / Running up that hill / Army Dreamers / Sat in your lap / Experiment IV / Dreaming, the / Babooshka / Big sky, the.
Album: released on EMI in Nov'86 by EMI Records. Distributed by: EMI

Cassette: released on EMI in Nov'86 by EMI Records. Distributed by: EMI

Compact disc: released on EMI in Nov'86 by EMI Records. Distributed by: EMI

Video-cassette (VHS): released on PMI in Nov'86 by PMI Records. Distributed by: EMI

Video-cassette [Betamax]: released on PMI in Nov'86 by PMI Records. Distributed by: EMI

WUTHERING HEIGHTS.
Single (7"): released on EMI in Feb'83 by EMI Records. Distributed by: EMI. Estim retail price in Jul'87 was £3.99.

Bushkin, Joe

World is waiting, The

Bushmen

SEAT IT OUT.
Single (12"): released on Uptight in Jun'85

Bush, Sam

LATE AS USUAL.
Album: released on Rounder (USA) in Jun'85. Distributed by: Mike's Country Music Room Distribution, Jazz Music Distribution, Swift Distribution, Roots Records Distribution, Projection Distribution, Topic Distribution

Bush, Stan

TOUCH, THE.
Tracks: / Dare to be stupid.
Single (7"): released on Epic in Nov'86 by CBS Records. Distributed by: CBS

Bush Tetras

BOOM.
Single (7"): released on Fetish in May'81 by Fetish Records. Distributed by: Cartel, Pinnacle

RITUALS.
Single (12"): released on Fetish in Dec'81 by Fetish Records. Distributed by: Cartel, Pinnacle

Album: released on ECM (Germany) in Apr'85 by ECM Records. Distributed by: IMS, Polygram, Virgin through EMI

WILD THINGS.
Cassette: released on Reach Out Int in Jan'83

Bush Twangers

HERE WE GO AGAIN.
Album: released on Amigo in May'86. Distributed by: Red Rhino, Cartel

Busia, Kofi

HOLD SOMEBODY.
Tracks: / Hold somebody / Nelson Mandela Quintet.
Single (12"): released on African Records International in Jul'87 by African Records International. Distributed by: Jetstar, EMI. Estim retail price in Jul'87 was £3.99.

Single (12"): released on African International in Aug'87

HOLD SOMEBODY.
Single (12"): released on African in Aug'87. Distributed by: Self

OH AFRICA.
Tracks: / Oh Africa / Child of a survivor / Scramble / One day (The mountains) / There can be no blues / Deathless one, The / Missionary, The / Thirty men / Traveller, The / Green green green / N.M.Q. (Nelson Mandela Quintet) / Hold somebody.
Album: released on African Records International in Jul'87 by African Records International. Distributed by: Jetstar, EMI

Cassette: released on African Records International in Jul'87 by African Records International. Distributed by: Jetstar, EMI

Compact disc: released on African Records International in Jul'87 by African Records International. Distributed by: Jetstar, EMI

Business

1980-81 THE OFFICIAL BOOTLEG.
Album: released on Syndicate in Dec'83

DRINKING AND DRIVING.
Single (7"): released on Diamond in Dec'85 by Revolver Records. Distributed by: Cartel

Single (12"): released on Diamond in Dec'85 by Revolver Records. Distributed by: Cartel

GET OUT OF MY HOUSE.
Tracks: / Get out of my house / All out tonight / Foreign girl / Outlaw.
Single (7"): released on Link in Aug'86. Distributed by: DMS, RCA

HARRY MAY.
Single (7"): released on Secret in Jul'82 by Secret Records. Distributed by: EMI

OFFICIAL BOOTLEG BACKED WITH LOUD, THE.
Album: released on Wonderful World in Sep'85. Distributed by: M.I.S., EMI, Stage One

SATURDAY'S HEROES.
Album: released on Harry May in Jan'86. Distributed by: Red Rhino, Cartel

SINGALONG A BUSINESS The best of the Business.
Tracks: / Suburban rebels / Blind justice / Loud proud & punk / Real enemy / Spanish jails / Product / National insurance blacklist(Employers blacklist) / Get out of my house / Saturday's heroes / Out in the cold / Smash the discos / Harry May / Drinking and driving / Hurry up Harry.
Notes: Sleeve notes by: Harry May's best friends next door neighbours cousins parole officer.
Album: released on Dojo in Aug'86 by Castle Communications Records. Distributed by: Cartel

SMASH THE DISCOS.
Single (7"): released on Secret in Jul'82 by Secret Records. Distributed by: EMI

SUBURBAN REBELS.
Album: released on Secret in Mar'83 by Secret Records. Distributed by: EMI

Business Connection

BRING YOU DOWN.
Tracks: / Bring you down / Connections.
Single (7"): released on Hippodrome in Jan'86. Distributed by: EMI

Single (12"): released on Hippodrome in Jan'86. Distributed by: EMI

Business Trading Ethics

BUSINEES TRADING ETHICS.
Cassette: released on International Report in Oct'81 by Seminar Cassettes. Distributed by: Audio-Visual Library Services, Davidson Distribution, Eastern Educational Products Distrib., Forlaget Systime Distribution, MacDougall Distribution, Talktapes Distribution, Watkins Books Ltd Distribution, Norton, Jeff Distribution

Business Unusual

BUSINESS UNUSUAL various artists (Various Artists).
Tracks: / C.I.D / 19 and mad / Just another teenage rebel / Justifiable homicide / Consequences / M.O.R. / 01-01-212 / Private plane / A.C.C. / United / Do the Mussonlini.
Album: released on Cherry Red in Jan'82 by Cherry Red Records. Distributed by: Pinnacle

Busker

HOME NEWCASTLE.
Single (7"): released on Lynx in Aug'81

Buskers

BUSKERS, THE.
Tracks: / Mary McMahon / Drowsy / Maggie / Life of a man / Pretty Susan the pride of Kildare / Piper on the hob / Bill hearts / Beggarman, The / Off to sea once more / Fahey's No. 1 / Humours of tulla / Lord of the dance / Banish misfortune / Job of journeywork / Job of journeywork / Spancill hill / New York girls / Jack in the fog / Yellow tinker, The / Mary McMahon / Drowsy Maggie / Life of a man / Pretty Susan, the pride of Kildare / Piper on the hob / Bill hearts / Beggarman, The / Off to sea once more / Fahey's No 1 / Humours of Tulla / Lord of the dance / Banish misfortune / Night visiting song / Spancill Hill / New York girls / Jack in the fog / Yellow tinker, The.
Album: released on Rubber in Aug'82 by Rubber Records. Distributed by: Roots Distribution, Projection Distribution, Jazz Music Distribution, Celtic Music Distribution, Spartan Distribution

Buskin, Joe

WORLD IS WAITING 1942-46 (Buskin, Joe & Mel Powell).

Busse, Henry

1941/44 VOL 2 (Busse, Henry & His Shuttle Rhythm Orchestra).
Album: released on Hindsight(USA) in Mar'84 by Hindsight Records (USA). Distributed by: Swift, Charly

1949 (Busse, Henry & His Orchestra).
Notes: Mono.
Album: released on Circle(USA) in Jan'87 by Jazzology Records (USA). Distributed by: Jazz Music, Swift, Chris Wellard

Buster, Prince

AL CAPONE.
Single (7"): released on Blue Beat in Sep'81 by Blue Beat. Distributed by: Spartan

Single (12"): released on Blue Beat in Sep'81 by Blue Beat. Distributed by: Spartan

BIG 5.
Single (7"): released on P. Buster in Sep'81

Single (12"): released on P. Buster in Sep'81

CLEOPATRA.
Single (7"): released on P. Buster in Sep'81

Single (12"): released on P. Buster in Sep'81

FABULOUS GREATEST HITS.
Album: released on Spartan in Feb'87 by Spartan Records. Distributed by: Spartan

Cassette: released on Spartan in Feb'87 by Spartan Records. Distributed by: Spartan

JUDGE DREAD.
Single (7"): released on P. Buster in Sep'81

Single (12"): released on P. Buster in Sep'81

MEMORY LANE.
Album:

PRINCE BUSTER'S FABULOUS GREATEST HITS.
Album: released on Melodisc in Jan'80 by Spartan Records. Distributed by: Spartan Distribution

SHE WAS A ROUGH RIDER.
Album: released on Melodisc in Apr'78 by Spartan Records. Distributed by: Spartan Distribution

TEN COMMANDMENTS OF MEN.
Single (7"): released on Blue Beat in Sep'81 by Blue Beat. Distributed by: Spartan

Single (12"): released on Blue Beat in Sep'81 by Blue Beat. Distributed by: Spartan

WRECK A PUM PUM.
Album: released on Blue Beat in Jul'76 by Blue Beat. Distributed by: Spartan

Single (7"): released on P. Buster in Sep'81

Single (12"): released on P. Buster in Sep'81

Butch & Bucky

LADY BE GOOD.
Album: released on Dreamstreet in Apr'79. Distributed by: Swift

Butcher

ON THE GROUND.
Single (7"): released on Inept in Feb'83. Distributed by: Jetstar, Cartel

STAND AND FIGHT.
Single (12"): released on Inept in Oct'83. Distributed by: Jetstar, Cartel

Butcher, Eddie

I ONCE WAS A DAYSMAN.
Album: released on Free Reed in Jan'87 by Free Reed Records. Distributed by: Roots, Projection, Hobgoblin Records, Oblivion

SHAMROCK ROSE & THISTLE.
Double Album: released on Leader in Jan'81. Distributed by: Jazz Music, Projection

Butler, Billy

RIGHT TRACK.
Single (7"): released on Skratch in Mar'85 by Skratch Records. Distributed by: PRT

Single (12"): released on Skratch in Mar'85 by Skratch Records. Distributed by: PRT

RIGHT TRACK, THE (Butler, Billy & The Enchanters).
Album: released on Edsel in Sep'85 by Demon Records. Distributed by: Pinnacle, Jazz Music, Projection

Butler, Frank

STEPPER,THE.
Album: released on Xanadu in Mar'79. Distributed by: Discovery, Jazz Horizons, Jazz Music, Swift

Butler, George

OPEN UP BABY.
Album: released on Charly(R&B) in Apr'85 by Charly Records. Distributed by: Charly, Cadillac

Butler, Henry

FIVIN' AROUND.
Album: released on MCA in Aug'86 by MCA Records. Distributed by: Polygram, MCA

Cassette: released on MCA in Aug'86 by MCA Records. Distributed by: Polygram, MCA

Butler, Jerry

HE WILL BREAK YOUR HEART.
Single (7"): released on Charly in Jul'80 by Charly Records. Distributed by: Charly, Cadillac

JERRY & BETTY (Butler, Jerry & Betty Everett).

LEGENDARY PHILADELPHIA HITS, THE.
Album: released on Mercury (USA) in Aug'87 by Import Records. Distributed by: IMS Distribution, Polygram Distribution

Cassette: released on Mercury (USA) in Aug'87 by Import Records. Distributed by: IMS Distribution, Polygram Distribution

ONLY THE STRONG SURVIVE.
Tracks: / Send a telegram (western union man) / Only the strong survive / Lost / Don't let love hang you up / Got to see if I can get mommy (to come back home) / Just because I really love you / I could write a book / Whats the use of breaking up / Since I lost you baby / Been a long time / Moody woman / Brand new me / Can't forget about you baby / Are you happy / Go away - find yourself / Never give you up.
Notes: Full title Only the strong survive (The best of Philedelphia years) Great value mid price compilation. Includes all the best Gamble-Huff tracks from his two best selling albums Ice-On-Ice and The ice man cometh.
Album: released on Club in May'85 by Phonogram Records. Distributed by: Polygram

Cassette: released on Club in May'85 by Phonogram Records. Distributed by: Polygram

SOUL WORKSHOP - JERRY BUTLER.
Tracks: / I stand accused.
Notes: Original Vee Jay recordings.
Compact disc: released on Charly in Jan'86 by Charly Records. Distributed by: Charly, Cadillac

WHATEVER YOU WANT.
Tracks: / Rainbow Valley / Lonely soldier / Thanks to you / When trouble calls / Aware of love / Isle of sirens / It's too late / Moon River / Woman with soul / Let it be whatever it is / I almost lost my mind / Good times / Give it YP / Believe in me / Just for you / For your precious love.

Notes: Licensed from Charly records international APS. This compilation: P 1986 Charly Holdings Inc. C 1986 Charly Records Ltd.
Album: released on Charly in Mar'86 by Charly Records. Distributed by: Charly, Cadillac

Butler, Jonathan

BABY PLEASE DON'T TAKE IT.
Tracks: / Baby please don't take it / Haunted by your love / Gentle love*.
Single (7"): released on Jive in May'86 by Zomba Records. Distributed by: RCA, PRT

Single (12"): released on Jive in May'86 by Zomba Records. Distributed by: RCA, PRT

INTRODUCING JONATHAN BUTLER.
Album: released on Jive in Mar'86 by Zomba Records. Distributed by: RCA, PRT,

Cassette: released on Jive in Mar'86 by Zomba Records. Distributed by: RCA, PRT

JONATHAN BUTLER.
Album: released on Jive in Oct'87 by Zomba Records. Distributed by: RCA, PRT

Cassette: released on Jive in Oct'87 by Zomba Records. Distributed by: RCA, PRT,

LIES.
Single (7"): released on Jive in Jul'87 by Zomba Records. Distributed by: RCA, PRT,

Single (12"): released on Jive in Jul'87 by Zomba Records. Distributed by: RCA, PRT,

LIVE.
Tracks: / Live / Haunted by you love.
Single (7"): released on Jive in 13 Jun'87 by Zomba Records. Distributed by: RCA, PRT,

Single (12"): released on Jive in 13 Jun'87 by Zomba Records. Distributed by: RCA, PRT,

Cassette single: released on Jive in 13 Jun'87 by Zomba Records. Distributed by: RCA, PRT,

Butler, Marty

LOOKS LIKE LOVE THIS TIME.
Single (7"): released on Gipsy in Jan'84 by Gipsy Records. Distributed by: PRT

Butler, Richard

PERFECT TRIANGLE, THE.
Notes: Piper to His Grace the Duke of Northumberland,Northumbrian Small Pipes.
Album: released on Saydisc in Nov'85 by Saydisc Records. Distributed by: Essex, Harmonia Mundi, Roots, H.R. Taylor, Jazz Music, Swift, Projection,

Cassette: released on Saydisc in Nov'85 by Saydisc Records. Distributed by: Essex, Harmonia Mundi, Roots, H.R. Taylor, Jazz Music, Swift, Projection,

Butler, Steve

WAVING AND DROWNING.
Album: released on Sticky Music in Jun'84 by Sticky Music Records. Distributed by: Fast Forward Distributors, Cartel Distribution

Butler, Tara

MISCHIEF.
Single (12"): released on Illuminated in May'85 by IKF Records. Distributed by: Pinnacle, Cartel, Jetstar

UP AGAINST THE WALL.
Single (7"): released on Illuminated in Feb'85 by IKF Records. Distributed by: Pinnacle, Cartel, Jetstar

Single (12"): released on Illuminated in Feb'85 by IKF Records. Distributed by: Pinnacle, Cartel, Jetstar

Butter'd Please

BUTTER'D PLEASE Yorkshire country dances. Fiddle, accordion etc. (Various Artists).
Cassette: released on Folktracks in Nov'79 by Folktracks Cassettes. Distributed by: Folktracks

Butterfield, Billy

RAPPORT.
Album: released on 77 in Sep'79 by 77 Records. Distributed by: Chris Wellard, Cadillac Music, Jazz Music

WATCH WHAT HAPPENS.
Album: released on Flyright in Aug'79 by Flyright Records. Distributed by: Krazy Kat, Swift, Jazz Music

Butterfield Blues Band

EAST WEST.
Album: released on Edsel in Feb'87 by Demon Records. Distributed by: Pinnacle, Jazz Music, Projection

PAUL BUTTERFIELD BLUES BAND.
Album: released on Edsel in Mar'85 by Demon Records. Distributed by: Pinnacle, Jazz Music, Projection

Butterfield, Erskine

1944 & 1956, PIANO SOLOS.
Album: released on Harlequin in Sep'86 by Harlequin Records. Distributed by: Swift, Jazz Music, Wellard, Chris, Taylor, H.R.

Butterfield, Paul

AN OFFER YOU CAN'T REFUSE (Butterfield, Paul & Walter Horton).
Album: released on Red Lightnin' in Sep'82 by Red Lightnin' Records. Distributed by: Roots, Swift, Jazz Music, Pinnacle, Cartel, Wynd-Up Distribution

Butthole Surfers

BUTTHOLE SURFERS.
Album: released on Alternative Tentacles in Apr'84 by Alternative Tentacles Records. Distributed by: Rough Trade, Pinnacle

CREAMED CORN FROM THE SOCKET OF DAVIS EP.
Single (12"): released on Fundamental in Oct'85 by Fundamental Records. Distributed by: Red Rhino, Cartel

LIVE POP EP.
Album: released on Alternative Tentacles in Jan'85 by Alternative Tentacles Records. Distributed by: Rough Trade, Pinnacle

LOCUST ABORTION TECHNICIAN.
Tracks: / Sweat loaf / Graveyard (1) / Graveyard (2) / Pittsburgh to Lebanon / Weber / Hay / Human cannonball / USSA / O-men, The / Kuntz / 22 going on 23.
Album: by Sonic Youth Records. Distributed by: Rough Trade, Nine Mile, Red Rhino, Cartel

Compact disc: released on Blast First in Jun'87 by Sonic Youth Records. Distributed by: Rough Trade, Nine Mile, Red Rhino, Cartel

PSYCHIC POWERLESS ANOTHER MAN SAC.
Album: released on Fundamental in Jul'85 by Fundamental Records. Distributed by: Red Rhino, Cartel

REMBRANDT PUSSY HOUSE.
Album: released on Red Rhino (Europe) in Apr'86

Button Down Brass

GOLDEN HOUR OF BUTTON DOWN BRASS.
Album: released on Golden Hour in Oct'74 by PRT Records. Distributed by: PRT

Buttons And Bows

BUTTONS AND BOWS.
Album: released on Dambuster in Jun'84 by Dambuster Records. Distributed by: Projection, Celtic Music, Roots

BUTTONS AND BOWS (Buttons And Bows volume 2).
Album: released on Dambuster in Jun'85 by Dambuster Records. Distributed by: Projection, Celtic Music, Roots

Butzman, Frieder

DAS MADCHEN AUF DER SCHAUKER.
Album: released on Zensor in Apr'85 by Zensor Records. Distributed by: Rough Trade

WAR PUR WAR (Butzman, Frieder & Thoma Kapir).
Album: released on Zensor in Jul'87 by Zensor Records. Distributed by: Rough Trade

Buy Off The Bar

MY LIFE IS LIKE A STANLEY KNIFE(EP) (Buy Off The Bar/Golden Strings).
Extended-play record: released on Deng Deng Deng in Jun'86. Distributed by: Backs, Cartel

Buzby

BIRDS DANCE/DISNEYLAND.
Single (7"): released on Flair in Sep'81 by Flair Records. Distributed by: Pinnacle

Buzz And The Flyers

BUZZ AND THE FLYERS.
Album: released on Nervous in Jul'84 by Nervous Records. Distributed by: Nervous, Rough Trade

GO CAT WILD/DANCE TO THE BOP.
Single (7"): released on Hot Rock in Mar'81 by Hot Rock Records. Distributed by: Hot Rock

Buzzcocks

ANOTHER MUSIC IN A DIFFERENT KITCHEN.
Tracks: / Fast cars / No reply / You tear me up / Get on your own / Love battery / 16 / I don't mind / Fiction romance / Autonomy / I need / Moving away from the pulsebeat.
Notes: Original catalogue number: UAG 30159(album);TCK 30159(cassette).
Album: released on Liberty in Aug'85 by Liberty-United. Distributed by: EMI

Cassette: released on Liberty in Aug'85 by Liberty-United. Distributed by: EMI

Album: released on Fan Club in Jun'87 by New Rose. Distributed by: Rough Trade, Cartel

DIFFERENT KIND OF TENSION, A.
Album: released on Fan Club in Jun'87 by New Rose. Distributed by: Rough Trade, Cartel

LOVE BITES.
Tracks: / Real world / Ever fallen in love (with somone you shouldn't've) / Operator's manual / Nostalgia / Just lust / Sixteen again / Walking distance / Love is lies / Nothing left / E.S.P. / Late for the train.
Notes: Originally released in 1978.
Album: released on Fame in Mar'87 by Music For Pleasure Records. Distributed by: EMI

Cassette: released on Fame in Mar'87 by Music For Pleasure Records. Distributed by: EMI

Album: released on Fan Club in Jun'87 by New Rose. Distributed by: Rough Trade, Cartel

SINGLES GOING STEADY.
Tracks: / Orgasm addict / What do I get / I don't mind / Love you more / Ever fallen in love(with someone you shouldn't've) / Promises / Everybody's happy nowadays / Harmony in my head / Whatever happened to / Oh shit! / Autonomy / Noise annoys / Just lust / Lipstick / Why can't I touch it / Somethings gone wrong again.
Notes: Original catalogue number:LBR 1043(album);TCLBR 1043(cassette).
Album: released on Liberty in Nov'81 by Liberty-United. Distributed by: EMI

Cassette: released on Liberty in Nov'81 by Liberty-United. Distributed by: EMI

Compact disc: released on EMI in Jul'87 by EMI Records. Distributed by: EMI

SPIRAL SCRATCH (EP).
Single (7"): released on New Hormones in Jul'81 by New Hormones Records

TOTAL POP.
Album: released on Wierd Systems in 11 Apr'87

Cassette: released on Wierd Systems in 11 Apr'87

Buzzz

HIT THE ROAD JACK.
Single (7"): released on RCA in Jul'82 by RCA Records. Distributed by: RCA, Roots, Swift, Wellard, Chris, I & B, Solomon & Peres Distribution

Single (12"): released on RCA in Jul'82 by RCA Records. Distributed by: RCA, Roots, Swift, Wellard, Chris, I & B, Solomon & Peres Distribution

OBSESSION/I LIKE IT LIKE THAT.
Single (7"): released on RCA in Nov'82 by RCA Records. Distributed by: RCA, Roots, Swift, Wellard, Chris, I & B, Solomon & Peres Distribution

Single (12"): released on RCA in Nov'82 by RCA Records. Distributed by: RCA, Roots, Swift, Wellard, Chris, I & B, Solomon & Peres Distribution

SORRY MY DEAR/BUZZY.
Single (7"): released on RCA in Jan'82 by RCA Records. Distributed by: RCA, Roots, Swift, Wellard, Chris, I & B, Solomon & Peres Distribution

Single (12"): released on RCA in Jan'82 by RCA Records. Distributed by: RCA, Roots, Swift, Wellard, Chris, I & B, Solomon & Peres Distribution

BVO

PINK PUNKER/KYOTO.
Single (7"): released on EMI in May'83 by EMI Records. Distributed by: EMI

Bwchadanas

CARIAD CYWIR.
Album: released on Sain in Jul'85. Distributed by: Roots

Byard, Jaki

FAMILY MAN.
Tracks: / Just rollin' along / Mood indigo / Chelsea bridge / L.H gatewalk rag / Ballad to Louise / Family Suite:Prelude/Gaeta/Garr/Emil/John Arthur.
Album: released on Muse (Import) in Apr'81

IMPROVISATIONS (Byard, Jaki & Ran Blake).
Album: released on Soul Note in Jul'82.

PHANTASIES (Byard, Jaki & The Apollo Stompers).
Compact disc: released on Soul Note (Italy) in Dec'86. Distributed by: Harmonia Mundi Distributors

THERE'LL BE SOME CHANGES MADE.
Tracks: / There'll be some changes made / Lonely town / Blues au gratin / Excerpts from songs of proverbs-Toni / Besame mucho / Spanish tinge / Journey-Night of departure / To Bob Vatel of Paris-Blues for Jennie / Some other spring-Every year / Tribute to Jimmy Slide.
Album: released on Muse (Import) in Apr'81

Byas, Don

AMBIENCES ET SLOWS.
Album: released on Barclay (Import) in Nov'79

ANTHROPOLOGY.
Album: released on Black Lion in Apr'85 by Black Lion Records. Distributed by: Jazz Music, Chris Wellard, Taylor, H.R., Counterpoint, Cadillac

DANISH BREW (see Moore,Brew/Don Byas) (Byas, Don/Brew Moore).

DON BYAS MEETS THE GIRLS.
Album: released on Jazz Legacy (France) in Sep'79. Distributed by: Discovery, Jazz Music, Swift

SAVOY JAM PARTY.
Album: released on Savoy Jazz (USA) in Mar'85

TENDERLY (Byas, Don Trios & Quartet).
Compact disc: released on Vogue in Dec'86. Distributed by: Discovery, Jazz Music, PRT, Swift

TWO KINGS OF THE TENOR SAX (Byas, Don & Ben Webster).
Album: released on Commodore Classics in May'87 by Teldec Records (Germany). Distributed by: Conifer, IMS, Polygram

By Chance

SOUL KITCHEN.
Single (7"): released on Crammed UK in May'87. Distributed by: Rough Trade, Nine Mile, Cartel

Single (12"): released on Crammed UK in May'87. Distributed by: Rough Trade, Nine Mile, Cartel

Byfield, Rockin' Jimmy

RAGING STORM/CAN'T JIVE ENOUGH.
Single (7"): released on Sonet in Oct'81 by Sonet Records. Distributed by: PRT

STAND BACK/ANOTHER CHANCE.
Single (7"): released on Sonet in May'81 by Sonet Records. Distributed by: PRT

YOU GOT ME AND I GOT YOU.
Single (7"): released on Sonet in Oct'82 by Sonet Records. Distributed by: PRT

Byfield, Ziggy

RUNNING.
Album: released on PVK in May'80

Bygraves, Max

100 GOLDEN GREATS.
Album: released on Ronco in Nov'81

Cassette: released on Ronco in Nov'81

100 MINUTES.
Cassette: released on PRT in '82 by PRT Records. Distributed by: PRT

BEST OF MAX.
Album: released on Spot in May'84 by Pickwick Records. Distributed by: H.R. Taylor,

Cassette: released on Spot in May'84 by Pickwick Records. Distributed by: H.R. Taylor,

BLUE EYES DON'T MAKE AN ANGEL.
Single (7"): released on Monarch in Sep'82 by Chart Records. Distributed by: Pinnacle

CLASSICS.
Tracks: / Cowpuncher's cantata / True loves and false lovers / Little Sir Echo / Big head (big 'ead) / You're a pink toothbrush / I wish I could sing like Al Jolson / (Gang that sang, The) heart of my heart / Friends and neighbours / Gilly Gilly Ossenfeffer Katzenellenbogen by the sea / Mister sandman / Pendulum song, The / Gretna Green / Meet me on the corner / Little Laplander, The / Out of town / Ballad of Davy Crockett, The / Dummy song, The / Nothin' to do / Try another cherry tree / By the light of the silvery moon / Peggy O'neil (Medley) / When you wore a tulip (and I wore a red, red rose) / If you were the only girl in the world / For me and my girl / Good idea son, A / Seventeen tons / Lovely dolla lolly / Chip chopper Charlie / Tomorrow / Say Si-Si / She's a lassie from Lancashire (Medley) / When Irish eyes are smiling / I belong to Glasgow / Any old iron.
Album: released on MFP in Oct'84 by EMI Records. Distributed by: EMI

Cassette: released on MFP in Oct'84 by EMI Records. Distributed by: EMI

COLLECTION: MAX BYGRAVES.
Cassette: released on PRT in Nov'86 by PRT Records. Distributed by: PRT

Album: released on PRT in Nov'86 by PRT Records. Distributed by: PRT

COSTA DEL SOL.
Single (7"): released on Lantern in Jul'85 by Lantern Records. Distributed by: Stage One

DECK OF CARDS.
Tracks: / Tie a yellow ribbon round an old oak tree / Little green apples / Heartbreaker / What a wonderful world / Kite, The (new version from single) / Mack the knife / Deck of cards / Whose sorry now / Singing the blues / Ramblin' Rose / Messing around on the river / You say something nice about everybody.
Album: released on Flashback in Oct'85 by Flashback Records/PRT Records. Distributed by: Mainline, PRT

Cassette: released on Flashback in Oct'85 by Flashback Records/PRT Records. Distributed by: Mainline, PRT

DECK OF CARDS (7").
Single (7"): released on PRT in '74 by PRT Records. Distributed by: PRT

DISCOLONGAMAX.
Tracks: / Get me to the church on time / How ya gonna keep down on the farm / You need hands / Autumn leaves / Moonlight serenade / Won't you come home Billy Bailey / Ma (he's making eyes at me) / My mammy / Tulips from Amsterdam / Love is a song / Somebody stole my gal / Feelings.
Album: released on PRT in Oct'79 by PRT Records. Distributed by: PRT

Cassette: released on PRT in Oct'79 by PRT Records. Distributed by: PRT

FAMILY FAVOURITES.
Album: released on Lantern in Jan'85 by Lantern Records. Distributed by: Stage One

Cassette: released on Lantern in Jan'85 by Lantern Records. Distributed by: Stage One

FOCUS ON MAX BYGRAVES.
Tracks: / Heart / Whiffenpoof song, The / Over the rainbow / Oh my papa / Don't bring Lulu / Get me to the church on time (medley) / Tonight / June is bustin' out all over / There is nothin like a dame / You need hands / Riders in the sky / Lazybones / I whistle a happy tune / Whatever will be will be / It's all right with me (Medley) / People will say we're in love / So in love / Shall we dance / Peg O my heart / My Ukelele / Gilly gilly ossen feffer katzenellenbogen by the sea / Did you ever see a dream walking / Down the lane / Oh what a beautiful morning (Medley) / On the street where you live / I love Paris / Sit down you're rockin' the boat / Swinging on a star / Paddlin Madelin home / Who made the morning / Consider yourself / I'd do anything / What noise annoys an oyster / Standing on the corner (medley) / Hey look me over (medley) / Oklahoma / Seventy six trombones.
Album: released on Decca in Sep'78 by Decca Records. Distributed by: Polygram Deleted '83.

Cassette: released on Decca in Sep'78 by Decca Records. Distributed by: Polygram

GOLDEN GREATS OF THE 40'S.
Tracks: / Good morning / Jingle jangle / I've got sixpence / Bless em all / Maizy doats and dozy doats / You always hurt the one you love / Tangerine / Old black magic, The / You'll never know / Boogie woogie bugle boy / Little on the lonely side, A / I can't love you anymore / Only forever / Don't sit under the apple tree / Five minutes more / That's the moon my son / There I've said it again / That lovely weekend / I'll never smile again until I smile at you / Heartbreaker / Far away places / You don't have to tell me I know / Let bygones be bygones / A-you're adorable.
Album: released on PRT in Jun'77 by PRT Records. Distributed by: PRT

Cassette: released on PRT in Jun'77 by PRT Records. Distributed by: PRT

GOLDEN GREATS OF THE 30'S.
Tracks: / We'll all go riding on a rainbow / Sunnyside up / When the guards are on parade / I don't why / Dancing in the dark / Way you look

tonight, The / Life is nothing without music / Red sails in the sunset / You brought a new kind of love to me / Dream a little dream of me / Love is the sweetest thing / Play me gypsy / Shoe shine boy / We just couldn't say goodbye / Glory of love, The / Once in a while / Song of the Islands / Blue Hawaii / Harbour lights / I only have eyes for you / Three little words / Exactly like you / I may be wrong / Wish me luck as you wave me goodbye.
Album: released on PRT in Jun'77 by PRT Records. Distributed by: PRT

Cassette: released on PRT in Jun'77 by PRT Records. Distributed by: PRT

GOLDEN GREATS OF THE 50'S.
Tracks: / Mack the knife / Tennessee waltz / Hi lilli hi lo / My heart cries for you / Three coins in a fountain / Mister sandman / Who wants to be millionaire / It's a lovely day today / Singin' the blues / Dear hearts and gentle people / Young and foolish / Sugar hush / Music music music / She wears red feathers / Too young / Unforgettable / That doggie in the window / Moments to remember / Blueberry hill / Chanson d'armour / Because of you / My foolish heart / When I fall in love / Memories are made of this.
Album: released on PRT in Nov'77 by PRT Records. Distributed by: PRT

Cassette: released on PRT in Nov'77 by PRT Records. Distributed by: PRT

HAPPY HITS.
Tracks: / Back in my childhood days / Let me call you sweetheart / Girl of my dreams / Where the blue of the night / Me and my shadow / Moonlight and roses / You were meant for me / You are my sunshine / Let the rest of the world go by / Say, has anybody seen my sweet Gypsy Rose? / Tie a yellow ribbon round the old oak tree / Back in my young man's days / Happy days are here again / Powder your face with sunshine / I'm looking over a four-leaf clover / When you're smiling / Put your arms around me, honey / It had to be you / I'll get by / I'll string along with you / I'll be seeing you / Bye bye blues / I'll see you in my dreams / It's time to say goodnight / Goodnight sweetheart / I love to play my ukelele / I can't stop loving you / Those were the days / Old straw hat, The / Little green apples / Ramblin' rose.
Album: released on Spot in Feb'83 by Pickwick Records. Distributed by: H.R. Taylor,

Cassette: released on Spot in Feb'83 by Pickwick Records. Distributed by: H.R. Taylor,

LINGALONGAMAX Vol 2.
Tracks: / Roll roll roll / Broadway melody / Chicago / 42nd Street / Lullaby of Broadway / Kite, The / Picking up pebbles / Dance in the old-fashioned way / You won't find another fool like me / Last farewell, The / Please do it again / Second-hand Rose / Somebody loves me / Hard day's night / Shoeshine boy / We just couldn't say goodbye / Glory of love / Every now and then / What a rainy day / Sound of music / Climb every mountain / You'll never walk alone.
Album: released on PRT in Jun'80 by PRT Records. Distributed by: PRT

Cassette: released on PRT in Jun'80 by PRT Records. Distributed by: PRT

MAX BYGRAVES.
Tracks: / You're my everything / Gentle on my mind / Deck of cards / Walk right back / For the good times / Rolling 'round the world / You're my everything / Charley girl / One of those songs / Rolling around the world / Out of town / Hello Dolly.
Cassette: released on Pickwick (Ditto series) in Jul'82

MAX BYGRAVES (II).
Cassette: released on Pickwick (Ditto series) in Mar'83

MAX BYGRAVES (PREMIER).
Album: released on Premier in Dec'84 by Premier Records. Distributed by: CBS

Cassette: released on Premier in Dec'84 by Premier Records. Distributed by: CBS

MAX SINGS WHILE TED SWINGS (Bygraves, Max & Ted Heath).
Tracks: / It is true what they say about Dixie / Underneath the arches / Did you ever see a dream walking / Ten pretty girls / It's a sin to tell a lie / Oh ma-ma (the butcher boy) / Back to those happy days / Lazybones / You're driving me crazy / What did I do / All I do is dream of you / Scatterbrain / When my dream boat comes home.
Album: released on President in Nov'83 by President Records. Distributed by: Taylors, Spartan

Cassette: released on President in Nov'83 by President Records. Distributed by: Taylors, Spartan

SINGALONGAMAX.
Tracks: / Cockney medley / Al Johson medley / Sentimental medley / Marching medley / Max's medley / Beatles medley / One for the road medley.
Album: released on MFP in Nov'82 by EMI Records. Distributed by: EMI

Cassette: released on MFP in Nov'82 by EMI Records. Distributed by: EMI

SINGALONGAMAX-MAS.
Tracks: / We wish you a merry Christmas / O come all ye faithful / Once in royal David's city / While shepherds watched their flocks by night / First Noel, The / Good King Wenceslas / Hark the herald angels sing / Christmas island / I saw mommy kissing Santa Claus / Rudolph the red nosed reindeer / Have yourself a merry little Christmas / Christmas alphabet / Just a wee deoch and Doris / Here's to the good old beer / Mop it down / Let's have another one / Rolling home / Little drummer boy / Winter wonderland / White Christmas / Merry Christmas everybody / I wish it could be Christmas everyday / Silver bells / Mary's boy child / Auld lang syne.
Album: released on PRT in Nov'74 by PRT Records. Distributed by: PRT

Cassette: released on PRT in Nov'74 by PRT Records. Distributed by: PRT

SINGALONGAPARTYSONG.
Tracks: / Medley(1) / Medley(2) / Medley(3) / Medley(4) / Medley(5) / Medley(6) / Medley(7) / Medley(8).
Album: released on PRT in '73 by PRT Records. Distributed by: PRT

Cassette: released on PRT in '73 by PRT Records. Distributed by: PRT

SINGALONGWITHMAX.
Album: released on PRT in '83 by PRT Records. Distributed by: PRT

Cassette: released on PRT in '83 by PRT Records. Distributed by: PRT

SING ALONG WITH MAX.
Tracks: / Medley (1) / Medley (2) / Medley (3) / Medley (4) / Medley (5) / Medley (6).
Compact disc: released on PRT in Jan'86 by PRT Records. Distributed by: PRT

SINGALONGWITHMAX VOL.2.
Tracks: / Medley(1) / Medley(2) / Medley(3) / Medley(4) / Medley(5) / Medley(6).
Album: released on PRT in '83 by PRT Records. Distributed by: PRT

Cassette: released on PRT in '83 by PRT Records. Distributed by: PRT

SING IT AGAIN MAX.
Tracks: / Somebody stole my gal / Put on your old grey bonnet / Goodbye-ee / Bye bye blackbird / Bill bailey won't you please come home / Ma (he's making eyes at me) / Oh you beautiful doll / Alexanders ragtime band / Rolling around the world / Dance in the old-fashioned way / You won't find another fool like me / Is it true what they say about Dixie / Home in Pasedena / Deep in the heart of Texas / Sweet gypsy rose / Tie a yellow ribbon around the old oak tree / If you were the only girl in the world / Marie / Mary's a grand old name / Daisy daisy / For me and my gal / I'll be with you in apple blossom time / If I have my way / Edelweiss / Whiffenpoef song, The / Pack up your troubles / Tavern in the town / It's a long way to tipperary / Goodbye Dolly Gray / Roll out the barrel.
Album: released on Picadilly in Nov'80

Cassette: released on Picadilly in Nov'80

SIX TRACK HIS.
Special: released on Scoop 33 in Sep'83 by Pickwick Records. Distributed by: H.R. Taylor

Cassette: released on Scoop 33 in Sep'83 by Pickwick Records. Distributed by: H.R. Taylor

SONG AND DANCE MEN (Bygraves, Max & Victor Silvester).
Tracks: / Tie a yellow ribbon / Dancing in the dark / Let the rest of the world go by / Edelweiss / Is it true what they say about Dixie? / Deep in the heart of Texas / What now my love / How wonderful to know / Old-fashioned way / After you've gone / Everybody loves my baby / I could have danced all night / Tea for two / Oh you beautiful doll / What'll I do? / Last waltz.
Compact disc: by PRT Records. Distributed by: PRT

SPOTLIGHT ON MAX BYGRAVES VOL 2.
Album: released on PRT (Spotlight) in Oct'82 by PRT Records. Distributed by: PRT

Cassette: released on PRT (Spotlight) in Oct'82 by PRT Records. Distributed by: PRT

SPOTLIGHT ON MAX BYGRAVES.
Tracks: / Tie a yellow ribbon round the old oak tree / Ramblin rose / Whispering grass / Cabaret / Snowbird / What a wonderful world / Mack the knife / I only have eyes for you / When I'm 64 / Remember when / Feelings / Deck of cards / Gentle on my mind / Singin' the blues / Any dream will do / You say something nice about everybody / Little green apples / Memories are made of this / Hello dolly / Messing around on the river / Heart breaker / I don't know why / Who's sorry now / Kite, The.
Album: released on PRT in Oct'81 by PRT Records. Distributed by: PRT

Cassette: released on PRT in Oct'81 by PRT Records. Distributed by: PRT

TIME,TIME,TIME.
Tracks: / Time,time,time / When you were young.
Single (7"): released on Spartan in Jan'86 by Spartan Records. Distributed by: Spartan

TOGETHER (Bygraves, Max & Acker Bilk).
Tracks: / Together(Ackerlongamax) / You say something nice about everybody / Who wants to be a millionaire / I like beer / Harmonise medley / Civilisation / Home town / Movies, The / Crazy / Stranger on the shore / Guilty / Love theme from the prisoner(On the inside) / Dreaming my dreams / Tonight you belong to me.
Compact disc: by PRT Records. Distributed by: PRT

Byles, Junior

BETTER BE CAREFUL.
Single (12"): released on Carib Jems in Jun'82 by Carib Jems. Distributed by: Spartan, Jetstar

Byrd, Bobby

I KNOW YOU GOT SOUL.
Tracks: / Hot pants...I'm coming, coming I'm coming.
Single (7"): released on Urban in Aug'87 by Polydor Records. Distributed by: Polygram

Single (12"): released on Urban in Aug'87 by Polydor Records. Distributed by: Polygram

Byrd, Charlie

BRAZILVILLE (Byrd, Charlie, Bud Shank).
Tracks: / Zingaro / Brazilville / Saquarema / Speak low / Yesterdays / Charlotte's fancy / What are you doing the rest of your life.

BYRD AT THE GATE.
Album:

CHRISTMAS ALBUM.
Tracks: / O come all ye faithful / Deck the halls / Hark the herald angel sing / Christmas song, The / In the bleak mid winter / God rest ye merry gentlemen / Holly and the Ivy, The.
Album: released on Concord Classics in Nov'82

DESAFINADO.
Compact disc: by Phonogram Records. Distributed by: Polygram

Compact disc: released on Verve in '83 by Phonogram Records. Distributed by: Polygram

Album: released on Verve (France) in '84

Tracks: / Samba dessa day's / O pata / Samba triste / Samba de una nota / E luxo so / Baia / Desafinado.

GREAT GUITARS AT THE WINERY (Byrd, Charlie/ Herb Ellis/ Barney Kessel).

HOLLYWOOD BIRD.
Cassette: released on CBS in Aug'84 by CBS Records. Distributed by: CBS

ISN'T IT ROMANTIC (Byrd, Charlie Trio).
Tracks: / Isn't it romantic / I could write a book / Cheek to cheek / Very thought of you, The / Thou swell / One morning in May / I didn't know what time it was / There's a small hotel / Someone to watch over me / Thought about me.
Notes: A superb set of love songs, skillfully interpreted by the Charlie Byrd Trio. Collection of romantic ballads from the pens of Roger & Hart, Hoagy Carmichael Johnny Mercer & Jimmy van heusen, Cole Porter, George Gershwin, and Irvin BerlinPersonnel; Charlie Byrd - Guitar/Joe Byrd - Bass/Chuck riggs-Drums.
Album: released on Concord Jazz (USA) in Nov'84 by Concord Jazz Records (USA). Distributed by: IMS, Polygram

LATIN BYRD.
Double Album: released on Milestone in Nov'80 by Ace Records. Distributed by: PRT

LATIN ODYSSEY (Byrd, Charlie & Laurindo Almeida).
Album: released on Concord Jazz in May'83 by Concord Jazz Records (USA). Distributed by: IMS, Polygram

Cassette: released on Concord Jazz in May'83 by Concord Jazz Records (USA). Distributed by: IMS, Polygram

MEDITATION.
Album: released on Riverside (USA) in Aug'84. Distributed by: Fantasy (USA) Distribution

TAMBU (Byrd, Charlie & Cal Tjader).
Notes: For full information see: Tjader, Cal & Charlie Byrd.
Compact disc: released on Fantasy (USA) in Jun'87 by Fantasy Inc USA Records. Distributed by: IMS, Polygram

Byrd, Donald

AT THE HALF NOTE CAFE,VOLUME 1.
Tracks: / My girl Shirl / Soulful kiddy / Portrait of Jennie, A / Cecile / Theme:Pure D funk / Child's play / Chant.
Notes: After graduating from the Jazz Messengers and before pioneering a variety of jazz-fusion successes,Donald Byrd & Pepper Adams co-led a beautifully relaxed and lyrical quintet that often included another Blue Note artist Duke Pearson as pianist and musical director.Their live Half Note recordings are generally considered to be their finest.A secret to their success was the quality and appeal of their material as"My Girl Shirl""Soulful Kiddy" and "A Portrait Of Jenny" amply prove here. P 1986 Manhattan Records,a division of Capitol Records Inc.
Album: released on Blue Note in Apr'86 by EMI Records. Distributed by: EMI

Compact disc: released on Manhattan-Blue Note in Jun'87 by EMI America Records (USA). Distributed by: EMI

BYRD IN HAND.
Tracks: / Witchcraft / Here am I / Devil whip / Bronze dance / Clarion calls / Injuns, The.
Notes: With a sextet that includes his long time partner Pepper Adams as well as Charlie Rouse and Walter Davis, the trumpeter presents a straight ahead program of sixpieces with great varity. The breakneck paced "Devil Whip" Witchcraft and two Walter Davis compositions (Bronze dance and clarion calls) stand out.
Album: released on Blue Note in Jul'85 by EMI Records. Distributed by: EMI

CAT WALK, THE.
Tracks: / Say you're mind / Duke's mixture / Each time I think of you / Cat walk, The / Cute / Hello bright sunflower.
Album: released on Blue Note in Oct'84 by EMI Records. Distributed by: EMI

DOMINOES.
Tracks: / Dominoes / Change (Makes you want to hustle).
Single (12"): released on Domino in Feb'87 by Domino Records. Distributed by: Charly

DOMINOES(LIVE).
Tracks: / Dominoes(live) / Wind parade.
Notes: DJ limited edition
Single (12"): released on Streetwave in Mar'86 by Streetwave Records. Distributed by: PRT Distribution

FREE FORM.
Tracks: / Pentecostal feelin' / Night flower / Nai nai / French spice / Free form.
Notes: With Wayne Shorter,Herbie Hancock,Dutch Warren and Billy Higging,Donald Byrd introduced a variety of excellent material on the forward looking 1962 date. Highlights include the adventurous title tune,Hancock's lovely ballad'Night Flower',the gospel-like'Pentecostal Feelin'' and the funky'Nai Nai'.
Album: released on Blue Note in Dec'85 by EMI Records. Distributed by: EMI

FUEGO.
Tracks: / Fuego / Bup a loup / Funky mama / Lament / Amen.
Notes: P 1987 Manhattan Records,a division of Capitol records Inc.
Compact disc: released on Manhattan-Blue Note in May'87 by EMI America Records (USA). Distributed by: EMI

I'LL ALWAYS LOVE YOU.
Single (7"): released on Elektra (USA) in Jan'82 by Elektra/Asylum/Nonesuch Records. Distributed by: WEA

I'M TRYING TO GET HOME.
Tracks: / Brother Isaac / Noah / I'm tryin' to get home / I've longed and searched for my mother / March children / Parly gates.
Album: released on Manhattan in Nov'86 by President Records. Distributed by: Jazz Music, Swift, Taylors, Chris Wellard

LOVE FOR SALE.
Single (7"): released on Elektra (USA) in Apr'82 by Elektra/Asylum/Nonesuch Records. Distributed by: WEA

NEW FORMULAS FROM THE JAZZ LAB (Byrd, Donald & Gigi Gryce).
Album: released on RCA (France) in Jan'83 by RCA Records. Distributed by: Discovery

NEW PERSPECTIVE , A.
Tracks: / Elijah / Beast of burden / Cristo redentor / Black discipline, The / Chant.
Album: released on Blue Note in Apr'85 by EMI Records. Distributed by: EMI

SEPTEMBER AFTERNOON.
Tracks: / Stardust / Indian summer / I'm a fool to want you / Someday my prince will come / Moon mist / I get along without you very well / Touch of your lips / Lazy afternoon / Varmeland / Love is the sweetest thing / September afternoon / Dearly beloved.
Album: released on Discovery (USA) in Jun'83 by Discovery Records (USA). Distributed by: Swift, Flexitron-Audio, Jazz Music

STAR TRIPPIN.
Single (12"): released on Elektra (USA) in Nov'82 by Elektra/Asylum/Nonesuch Records. Distributed by: WEA

Byrd, Gary

CROWN, THE 2 Parts (Byrd, Gary & The G.B.Experience).
Single (12"): released on Motown in Jul'83 by Motown Records. Distributed by: BMG Distribution

RAP THE WORLD(IN YOUR LOVE).
(Byrd, Gary & The G.B.Experience).
Tracks: / Rap the world(in your love) / Rap the world(in your love)(club version).
Single (7"): released on In Recordings in Oct'86. Distributed by: RCA, DMS

Single (12"): released on In Recordings in Oct'86. Distributed by: RCA, DMS

Byrds

6 TRACK HITS.
Tracks: / Lay lady lay / Turn turn turn / Gon'back / So you want to be a rock 'n' roll star / Chestnut mare / All I really want to do.
Extended-play record: released on Scoop 33 in Aug'83 by Pickwick Records. Distributed by: H.R. Taylor

Cassette: released on Scoop 33 in Aug'83 by Pickwick Records. Distributed by: H.R. Taylor

BYRDS COLLECTION PARTS 1&2, THE.
Tracks: / Lady friend / Chestnut mare / Bells of Rhymeny, The / He was a friend of mine / Why / Everybody's been burned / Eight miles high / Girl with no name / Goin' back / So you want to be a rock'n'roll star / 5D (fifth dimension) / Old John Robertson / Here without you / Wasn't born to follow / Draft morning / It won't be wrong / John Riley / My back pages / Mr. Tambourine man / Turn,turn,turn / Feel a whole lot better / Have you seen her face / All I really want to do / You ain't goin' nowhere.
Notes: All tracks licensed from CBS Records. Matrix number:5 013428 131510
Double cassette: released on Castle Collectors in Sep'86 by Castle Communications Records. Distributed by: Pinnacle
Double cassette: released on Castle Collectors in Sep'86 by Castle Communications Records. Distributed by: Pinnacle

BYRDS PLAY DYLAN, THE.
Tracks: / Mr tambourine man / All I really want to do / Chimes of freedom / Spanish harlem incident / Time they are a changin', The / Lay down your weary tune / My back pages / You ain't going nowhere / Nothing was delivered / This wheel's on fire / It's all over now / Baby blue / Lay lady lay / Positively 4th street.
Album: released on CBS in Feb'80 by CBS Records. Distributed by: CBS Deleted '86.

Cassette: released on CBS in Feb'80 by CBS Records. Distributed by: CBS

CHESTNUT MARE.
Single (7"): released on Old Gold in Jul'82 by Old Gold Records. Distributed by: Lightning, Jazz Music, Spartan, Counterpoint

GOLDEN HIGHLIGHTS.
Album: released on CBS(Import) in Jun'86 by CBS Records. Distributed by: Conifer, Discovery, Swift

Cassette: released on CBS(Import) in Jun'86 by CBS Records. Distributed by: Conifer, Discovery, Swift

GREATEST HITS:BYRDS.
Tracks: / Mr tambourine man / I'll feel a whole lot better / Bells of rhymney, The / Turn turn turn / All I really want to do / Chimes of freedom / Eight miles high / Mr spaceman / 5D(fifth dimension) / So you want to be a rock 'n' roll star / My back pages.
Album: released on CBS in Jan'84 by CBS Records. Distributed by: CBS

Cassette: released on CBS in Jan'84 by CBS Records. Distributed by: CBS

HISTORY OF THE BYRDS.
Tracks: / Mr tambourine man / Turn turn turn / She don't care about time / Wild mountain thyme / Eight miles high / Mr spaceman / 5D(fifth dimension) / So you wanna be a rock 'n' roll star / Time between / My back pages / Lady friend / Goin back / Old John Robertson / Wasn't born to follow / You ain't goin nowhere / Hickory wind / Nashville west / Drug store truck driving man / Gunga din / Jesus is just alright / Ballad of easy rider / Chestnut mare / Yesterday's train / Just the season / Citizen Kane / Jamaica(Say you will) / Tiffany queen / America's great national pastime / Mr. Tambourine man / Turn turn turn / She don't care about time / Wild mountain thyme / Eight miles high / Mr. Spaceman / 5D (fifth dimension) / So you wanna be a rock 'n' roll star / Time between / My back pages / Lady friend / Goin' back / Old John Robertson / Wasn't born to follow / You ain't goin' nowhere / Hickory wind / Nashville West / Drug store truck drivin' man / Gunga Din / Jesus is just alright / Ballad of easy rider / Chestnut mare / Yesterday's train / Just a season / Citizen Kane / Jamaica (say you will) / Tiffany queen / America's great national pastime.
Album: released on CBS in '73 by CBS Records. Distributed by: CBS

Cassette: released on CBS in '73 by CBS Records. Distributed by: CBS Deleted '85.

Album: released on CBS in Sep'87 by CBS Records. Distributed by: CBS

Cassette: released on CBS in Sep'87 by CBS Records. Distributed by: CBS

MR TAMBOURINE MAN.
Tracks: / Mr tambourine man / I'll feel a whole lot better / Spanish harlem incident / You won't have to cry / Here without you / Bells of rhymney, The / All I really want to do / I knew I'd want you / It's no use / Don't doubt yourself babe / Chimes of freedom / We'll meet again.
Album: released on CBS in Jul'77 by CBS Records. Distributed by: CBS

Cassette: released on CBS in Jul'77 by CBS Records. Distributed by: CBS

ORIGINAL SINGLES-VOL 2, THE.
Tracks: / My back pages / Renaissance fair / Have you seen her face / Don't make waves / Lady friend / Old John Robertson / Going back / Change is now / You ain't going nowhere / Artificial energy / I am a pilgrim / Pretty Boy Floyd / Bad night at the whiskey / Drug store truck driving man / Lay lady lay / Old blue.
Album: released on CBS in Apr'82 by CBS Records. Distributed by: CBS

Cassette: released on CBS in Apr'82 by CBS Records. Distributed by: CBS Deleted '85.

SWEETHEART OF THE RODEO.
Notes: From 1968,originally from CBS.
Album: released on Edsel in May'87 by Demon Records. Distributed by: Pinnacle, Jazz Music, Projection

Compact disc: released on Edsel in Jul'87 by Demon Records. Distributed by: Pinnacle, Jazz Music, Projection

YOUNGER THAN YESTERDAY.
Album: released on Edsel in May'87 by Demon Records. Distributed by: Pinnacle, Jazz Music, Projection

Cassette: released on Edsel in May'87 by Demon Records. Distributed by: Pinnacle, Jazz Music, Projection

Compact disc: released on Edsel in Aug'87 by Demon Records. Distributed by: Pinnacle, Jazz Music, Projection

BYRDS COLLECTION, THE.
Compact disc: by Castle Communications Records. Distributed by: Pinnacle

FIFTH DIMENSION.
Tracks: / 5D(Fifth dimension) / Wild mountain thyme / Mr space-man / I see you / What's happening?!?! / I come and stand at every door / Eight miles high / Hey Joe / Captain soul / John Riley / 2-4-2 Foxtrot(the lear jet song).
Album: released on CBS in '84 by CBS Records. Distributed by: CBS

Cassette: released on CBS in '84 by CBS Records. Distributed by: CBS

SWEETHEART OF THE RODEO.
Cassette: released on Edsel in May'87 by Demon Records. Distributed by: Pinnacle, Jazz Music, Projection

Compact disc: released on Edsel in Aug'87 by Demon Records. Distributed by: Pinnacle, Jazz Music, Projection

Byrne, Anne
FROM BUNCLODY TO AVONDALE.
Album: released on Harp(Ireland) in Feb'82 by Pickwick Records. Distributed by: Taylors

Cassette: released on Harp(Ireland) in Feb'82 by Pickwick Records. Distributed by: Taylors

Byrne, Bryan
SWEET CARNLOCH BAY.
Album: released on Harp(Ireland) in Feb'82 by Pickwick Records. Distributed by: Taylors

Cassette: released on Harp(Ireland) in Feb'82 by Pickwick Records. Distributed by: Taylors

Byrne, David
CATHERINE WHEEL, THE songs from.
Tracks: / His wife refused / Two soldiers / Red house, The / My big hands(Fall through the cracks) / Big business / Eggs in a briar patch / Poison / Cloud chamber / What a day that was / Big blue Plymouth(eyes wide open) / Light bath.
Album: released on Sire in Nov'81

Cassette: released on Sire in Nov'81 Deleted '85.

MUSIC FOR THE KNEE PLAYS.
Tracks: / In the upper room / Tree(Today is an important occasion) / Sound of business, The / Social studies / (The sound)where the sun never goes down / Theadora is dozing / Admiral Perry I bid you goodnight / I've tried / Winter / Jungle book / In the future.
Album: released on EMI Regal Zonophone in Sep'85 by EMI Records. Distributed by: EMI

Cassette: released on EMI Regal Zonophone in Sep'85 by EMI Records. Distributed by: EMI

Byrne, Julie
COUNTRY.
Cassette: released on Aim in Feb'83. Distributed by: H.R. Taylor

RAMBLIN' ROUND.
Tracks: / Route 65 to Nashville / Legend in my time / King of country music / I'm easy / I can't stop loving you / It don't worry me / Talk talk / Crazy arms / I'd like to go to Memphis / Ramblin'round / Honey / My babe.
Album: released on Folk Heritage in Jul'82 by Folk Heritage Records. Distributed by: Roots, Wynd-Up Distribution, Jazz Music, Folk Heritage

Byrne, Packie
HALF DOOR, THE (Byrne, Packie & Bonnie Shaljean).
Album: released on Dingles in Apr'79 by Dingles Records. Distributed by: Projection

ROUNDTOWER (Byrne, Packie & Bonnie Shaljean).
Album: released on Dingles in '83 by Dingles Records. Distributed by: Projection

SONGS OF A DONEGAL MAN.
Tracks: / John and the farmer / Rich man's daughter, The / Holland hankerchief, The / Molly bawn / Jolly ploughboy, The / Young Alvin Johnny O' Hazelgreen / Lament to the moon / Creel, The.
Album: released on Topic in '81. Distributed by: Roots Distribution

Byrnes, Martin
MARTIN BYRNES.
Tracks: / Duke of Leinster, The / Duke of Leinster's wife, The / Paddy Fahey's / Cliffs of Moher, The / Tarbolton / Longford collector, The / Sailors's bonnet, The / Bantry bay / Shack of barley, The / Farewell to Ireland / Irish Molly / Ashplant, The / Liffey banks, The / Shaskeen, The / Hitler's downfall / Battle of Aughrium, The / Humours of Lissadel, The / Blackbird, The / Rodney's glory / Collier's, The / Bucks of Oranmore, The.
Album: released on Leader in '81. Distributed by: Jazz Music, Projection

Byron Band
EVERY INCH OF THE WAY.
Single (7"): released on Creole in Apr'81 by Creole Records. Distributed by: Rhino, PRT

NEVER SAY DIE.
Single (7"): released on Creole in Oct'81 by Creole Records. Distributed by: Rhino, PRT

Single (7"): released on Creole in Jul'81 by Creole Records. Distributed by: Rhino, PRT

ON THE ROCKS.
Album: released on Creole in Oct'81 by Creole Records. Distributed by: Rhino, PRT

Cassette: released on Creole in Oct'81 by Creole Records. Distributed by: Rhino, PRT

Bywaters
BIG BLUE PLYMOUTH (Bywaters/Greening/Hoggins/Marchant).
Single (7"): released on Sire in Dec'81

Single (12"): released on Sire in Dec'81

Byzantine Omelette
BYZANTINE OMELETTE.
Cassette: released on Talking Tape Company in Aug'81 by Talking Tape Company Records

BZN
BEST OF BZN, THE.
Album: released on Music For Pleasure (Holland) in '86 by EMI Records. Distributed by: EMI

Cassette: released on Music For Pleasure (Holland) in '86 by EMI Records. Distributed by: EMI

C

Cabaret

CABARET Original soundtrack (featuring Wayne Sleep) (Various Artists).
Album: released on First Night in Aug'86 by Safari Records. Distributed by: Pinnacle

Cassette: released on First Night in Aug'86 by Safari Records. Distributed by: Pinnacle

Compact disc: released on CBS in May'87 by CBS Records. Distributed by: CBS

CABARET original film soundtrack.
Album: released on ABC in Apr'82. Distributed by: CBS, Pinnacle

Cassette: released on ABC in Apr'82. Distributed by: CBS, Pinnacle

CABARET (ORIGINAL LONDON CAST) various artists.
Cassette: released on Embassy in Jul'77 by CBS Records. Distributed by: CBS

Cabaret Voltaire

2 X 45.
Tracks: / Protection / Get out of my face.
Album: released on Rough Trade in Jun'82 by Rough Trade Records. Distributed by: Rough Trade Distribution, Cartel Distribution

BRAIN TRAIN (THE).
Single (12"): released on Double Vision in Jun'86 by Double Vision Records. Distributed by: Rough Trade, Cartel

CODE.
Tracks: / Don't argue / Sex money freaks . Thank you America / Here to go / Trouble (won't stop) / White car / No one here / Life slips by . Code + / Hey hey / Here to go (little dub) / Don't argue / Sex money freaks / Thank you America / Here to go / Trouble (won't stop) / White car / No one here / Life slips by / Code.
Album: released on Parlophone in Sep'87 by EMI Records. Distributed by: EMI

Cassette: released on Parlophone in Sep'87 by EMI Records. Distributed by: EMI

Compact disc: released on Parlophone in Sep'87 by EMI Records. Distributed by: EMI Estim retail price in Sep'87 was £11.99.

CONVENANT, THE, THE SWORD AND THE ARM OF THE LAW, THE.
Album: released on Some Bizzare in Oct'85 by Charisma Records. Distributed by: EMI, CBS, Polygram

Cassette: released on Some Bizzare in Oct'85 by Charisma Records. Distributed by: EMI, CBS, Polygram

COVENANT, THE SWORD AND ARM OF THE LORD (THE).
Tracks: / L21st / I want you / Hell's home / Kick back / Arm of the lord / Warm / Golden halos / Motion rotation / Whip blow / Web.
Compact disc: released on Virgin in Feb'86 by Virgin Records. Distributed by: EMI, Virgin Distribution

CRACKDOWN (THE).
Tracks: / Why kill time (when you can kill yourself) / Haiti / Crackdown / 24-24 / In the shadows / Taking time / Over and over / Animation / Just facination.
Notes: This is a re-issue.
Compact disc: released on Some Bizzare in Apr'86 by Charisma Records. Distributed by: EMI, CBS, Polygram

Album: released on Some Bizzare in Apr'86 by Charisma Records. Distributed by: EMI, CBS, Polygram

Cassette: released on Some Bizzare in Apr'86 by Charisma Records. Distributed by: EMI, CBS, Polygram

DON'T ARGUE.
Tracks: / Don't argue / Don't argue (Who's arguing).
Single (7"): released on Parlophone in Jul'87 by EMI Records. Distributed by: EMI

Single (12"): released on Parlophone in Jul'87 by EMI Records. Distributed by: EMI

Cassette single: released on Parlophone in Jul'87 by EMI Records. Distributed by: EMI

DON'T ARGUE (DANCE MIX).
Tracks: / Don't argue (dance mix) / Don't argue (dub).
Single (12"): released on Parlophone in Jul'87 by EMI Records. Distributed by: EMI

DRINKING GASOLINE.
Single (7"): released on Virgin in May'85 by Virgin Records. Distributed by: EMI, Virgin Distribution

Cassette: released on Virgin in May'85 by Virgin Records. Distributed by: EMI, Virgin Distribution

Single (12"): released on Some Bizzare in Jul'85 by Charisma Records. Distributed by: EMI, CBS, Polygram

EDDIE'S OUT.
Single (7"): released on Rough Trade in Dec'81 by Rough Trade Records. Distributed by: Rough Trade Distribution, Cartel Distribution

HAI.
Album: released on Rough Trade in Nov'82 by Rough Trade Records. Distributed by: Rough Trade Distribution, Cartel Distribution

HERE TO GO.
Tracks: / Here to go (extended mix) / Here to go (space dub) / Here to go.
Compact disc single: released on Parlophone in Sep'87 by EMI Records. Distributed by: EMI

I WANT YOU.
Single (7"): released on Some Bizzare in Sep'85 by Charisma Records. Distributed by: EMI, CBS, Polygram

Single (12"): released on Some Bizzare in Sep'85 by Charisma Records. Distributed by: EMI, CBS, Polygram

JAMES BROWN.
Single (7"): released on Some Bizzare in Jan'85 by Charisma Records. Distributed by: EMI, CBS, Polygram

Single (12"): released on Some Bizzare in Jan'85 by Charisma Records. Distributed by: EMI, CBS, Polygram

JAZZ THE GLASS.
Single (12"): released on Rough Trade in Oct'81 by Rough Trade Records. Distributed by: Rough Trade Distribution, Cartel Distribution

JOHNNY YES NO.
Album: released on Double Vision in Nov'83 by Double Vision Records. Distributed by: Rough Trade, Cartel

LIVE AT THE YMCA.
Album: released on Rough Trade in Jan'80 by Rough Trade Records. Distributed by: Rough Trade Distribution, Cartel Distribution

MICRO-PHONIES.
Album: released on Some Bizzare in Nov'84 by Virgin Records. Distributed by: EMI, CBS, Polygram

Cassette: released on Some Bizzare in Nov'84 by Virgin Records. Distributed by: EMI, CBS, Polygram

MICROPHONIES.
Tracks: / Do right / Operative (The) / Digital Rasta / Spies in the wires / Theme from earthshaker / James Brown / Slammer / Blue heat / Sensoria.
Compact disc: released on Some Bizzare in '86 by Charisma Records. Distributed by: EMI, CBS, Polygram

MIX UP.
Album: released on Rough Trade in Oct'79 by Rough Trade Records. Distributed by: Rough Trade Distribution, Cartel Distribution

NAG NAG NAG.
Single (7"): released on Rough Trade in Jun'79 by Rough Trade Records. Distributed by: Rough Trade Distribution, Cartel Distribution

RED MECCA.
: released on Rough Trade in '81 by Rough Trade Records. Distributed by: Rough Trade Distribution, Cartel Distribution

SECONDS TOO LATE.
Single (7"): released on Rough Trade in Nov'80 by Rough Trade Records. Distributed by: Rough Trade Distribution, Cartel Distribution

SENSORIA.
Single (7"): released on Some Bizarre in Sep'84 by Virgin Records. Distributed by: EMI, CBS, Polygram Deleted '85.

Single (12"): released on Some Bizzare in Sep'84 by Virgin Records. Distributed by: EMI, CBS, Polygram

SILENT COMMAND.
Single (7"): released on Rough Trade in Nov'79 by Rough Trade Records. Distributed by: Rough Trade Distribution, Cartel Distribution

TALKOVER.
Single (7"): released on Rough Trade in Jan'79 by Rough Trade Records. Distributed by: Rough Trade Distribution, Cartel Distribution

THREE MANTRAS.
Single (12"): released on Rough Trade in Apr'80 by Rough Trade Records. Distributed by: Rough Trade Distribution, Cartel Distribution

VOICE OF AMERICA, THE.
Album: released on Rough Trade in '84 by Rough Trade Records. Distributed by: Rough Trade Distribution, Cartel Distribution

Cabinet

LANGUAGE AND WORDS.
Single (7"): released on Sharp in Nov'83 by Sharp Records. Distributed by: Red Rhino, Cartel

STILL TEARS.
Single (12"): released on Sharp in Feb'83 by Sharp Records. Distributed by: Red Rhino, Cartel

Cabo Frio

JUST HAVING FUN.
Album: released on Zebra in Feb'87 by Cherry Red Records. Distributed by: Pinnacle

Cassette: released on Zebra in Feb'87 by Cherry Red Records. Distributed by: Pinnacle

Cabo Verde Show

DESTINO.
Album: released on Syllart (Cape Verde) in Aug'84

Cabrera, Jorge

CHARANGA VALLENATA.
Album: released on Globestyle in Apr'87 by Ace Records. Distributed by: Projection

Cache

WHERE IS MY SUNSHINE?.
Single (7"): released on Groove PR in Nov'81 by Beggars Banquet Records. Distributed by: WEA, PRT

Single (12"): released on Groove PR in Nov'81 by Beggars Banquet Records. Distributed by: WEA, PRT

Cacique

DEVOTED TO YOU.
Single (7"): released on Diamond Duel in May'85 by Diamond Duel Records. Distributed by: Priority

Single (12"): released on Diamond Duel in May'85 by Diamond Duel Records. Distributed by: Priority

DRESSED TO KILL.
Tracks: / Dressed to kill / Dressing up mix.
Single (7"): released on Point Sound in 2' May'87

Cactus World News

BRIDGE (THE).
Cassette single: released on MCA in Sep'86 by MCA Records. Distributed by: Polygram, MCA

BRIDGE, (THE).
Single (7"): released on Mother in Nov'85. Distributed by: Island Distribution

Single (12"): released on Mother in Nov'85. Distributed by: Island Distribution

URBAN BEACHES.
Tracks: / Works apart / In a whirlpool / Promise (The) / Bridge (The) / State of emergency / Years later / Church of the cold / Pilots of beka / Jigsaw street / Maybe this time / Cashen bay strand.
Notes: Debut album from much acclaimed Dublin band.
Compact disc: released on MCA in '86 by MCA Records. Distributed by: Polygram, MCA

Album: released on MCA in May'86 by MCA Records. Distributed by: Polygram, MCA

Cassette: released on MCA in May'86 by MCA Records. Distributed by: Polygram, MCA

WORLDS APART.
Tracks: / Worlds apart / Cashen bay strand.
Single (7"): released on MCA in Apr'86 by MCA Records. Distributed by: Polygram, MCA

Single (12"): released on MCA in Apr'86 by MCA Records. Distributed by: Polygram, MCA

YEARS LATER.
Tracks: / Years later / Hurry back / Third one live.
Single (7"): released on MCA in Jan'86 by MCA Records. Distributed by: Polygram, MCA

Single (12"): released on MCA in Jan'86 by MCA Records. Distributed by: Polygram, MCA

Caddick, Bill

REASONS BRIEFLY SET DOWN.
Album: released on Highway in '81 by Highway Records. Distributed by: Roots, Projection, Ross

ROUGH MUSIC.
Album: released on Highway in '81 by Highway Records. Distributed by: Roots, Projection, Ross

SUNNY MEMORIES.
Album: released on Leader in '81. Distributed by: Jazz Music, Projection

WILD WEST SHOW, THE.
Album: released on Topic in Nov'86. Distributed by: Roots Distribution

Caddy, Alan

PIANO SERENADE.
Cassette: released on Aim in Feb'83. Distributed by: H.R. Taylor

Cadets

CADETS MEET THE JACKS, THE.
Album: released on Ace in Jan'87 by Ace Records. Distributed by: Pinnacle, Swift, Hotshot, Cadillac

Cadillac

MARCH OF THE ROCKERS.
Album: released on Nevis in Aug'77. Distributed by: H.R. Taylor

Cadillacs

BILLY.
Single (7"): released on Red Eye in Sep'80

CADILLAC WALK.
Single (7"): released on Red Eye in Oct'81

PLEASE MR JOHNSON.
Album: released on Dr. Horse (Sweden) in Mar'84. Distributed by: Swift

Cadillac, Vince
MODERN BOY.
Album: released on Satril in Aug'78 by Satril Records. Distributed by: PRT

Cadman, John
ALHAMBRA (CAN FEEL YOUR LOVE).
Single (7"): released on Black Eyes in May'81. Distributed by: Rough Trade

EL CAD.
Album: released on Plant Life in Oct'83. Distributed by: Roots

Cadogan, Susan
CAUSE YOU LOVE ME BABY.
Single (12"): released on Hawkeye in Sep'84 by Hawkeye Records. Distributed by: Hawkeye, Lightning (WEA) Distribution, Jetstar, PRT

HURT SO GOOD.
Tracks: / Hurt so good / Sideshow.
Single (7"): released on Old Gold in Nov'86 by Old Gold Records. Distributed by: Lightning, Jazz Music, Spartan, Counterpoint

LOVE ME.
Single (7"): released on Hawkeye in Jan'83 by Hawkeye Records. Distributed by: Hawkeye, Lightning (WEA) Distribution, Jetstar, PRT

Single (12"): released on Hawkeye in Jan'83 by Hawkeye Records. Distributed by: Hawkeye, Lightning (WEA) Distribution, Jetstar, PRT

LOVE TRILOGY (Cadogan, Susan & Rudy Thomas).
Tracks: / Love trilogy / Curfew.
Single (7"): released on Solid Gold - Revue in Jun'86. Distributed by: MCA

Single (12"): released on Solid Gold - Revue in Jun'86. Distributed by: MCA

NOBODY WINS.
Tracks: / Nobody wins (Version).
Single (12"): released on C & E in Nov'86. Distributed by: Jetstar

PIECE OF MY HEART.
Single (12"): released on Cartridge in May'82 by Cartridge. Distributed by: Jetstar

SUSAN CADOGAN.
Album: released on Trojan-PRT-Jetstar Distribution in Feb'85

TRACKS OF MY TEARS.
Single (12"): released on GG'S in Jun'82 by GG'S Records. Distributed by: Jetstar

Caedmon Players
PEOPLE IN THE WIND.
Cassette: released on Caedmon(USA) in Sep'85 by Caedmon (USA) Records. Distributed by: Taylors, Discovery

Caesar, Shirley
REJOICE.
Album: released on Myrrh in May'82 by Word Records. Distributed by: Word Distribution

Cassette: released on Myrrh in May'82 by Word Records. Distributed by: Word Distribution

Cafe
WANT ADS.
Single (12"): released on Malaco in Oct'83 by Malaco Records. Distributed by: Charly

Cafe Creme
CAFE CREME.
Album: released on RSO in '78

UNLIMITED CITATIONS.
Album: by EMI Records. Distributed by: Roots, EMI

Cafe Society
RELIGHT MY FIRE.
Single (12"): released on Passion in Dec'84 by Skratch Records. Distributed by: PRT

SOMEBODY TO LOVE.
Single (7"): by Skratch Records. Distributed by: PRT

Single (12"): by Skratch Records. Distributed by: PRT

Cafferty, John
HEARTS ON FIRE (Cafferty, John & The Beaver Brown Band).
Single (12"): released on Scotti Brothers in Mar'86 by Scotti Brothers Records. Distributed by: CBS

ON THE DARK SIDE (Cafferty, John & The Beaver Brown Band).
Single (7"): released on Scotti Brothers (USA) in Apr'85 by Epic Records. Distributed by: CBS

Album: released on Scotti Brothers (USA) in Jul'85 by Epic Records. Distributed by: CBS

Cassette: released on Scotti Brothers (USA) in Jul'85 by Epic Records. Distributed by: CBS

TOUGH ALL OVER (Cafferty, John & The Beaver Brown Band).
Compact disc: released on Bellaphon in Dec'86 by Bellaphon Records. Distributed by: IMS-Polygram

VOICE OF AMERICA'S SON (Cafferty, John & The Beaver Brown Band).
Tracks: / Voice of America's son / Dixie land.
Single (7"): released on Scotti Brothers in Aug'86 by Scotti Brothers Records. Distributed by: CBS

Cage, Butch
RAISE A RUCKUS TONIGHT.
Album: released on Flyright in Feb'79 by Flyright Records. Distributed by: Krazy Kat, Swift, Jazz Music

Cage, John
JOHN CAGE.
Album: released on Tomato in Mar'79

VOICES & INSTRUMENTS.
Album: released on Obscure in Nov'76 by Polydor Records. Distributed by: Polygram Distribution

Cagliostra
LIBERA ME.
Tracks: / Madmen and lovers.
Single (7"): released on EL in Dec'86 by El Records. Distributed by: Rough Trade, Cartel, Pinnacle

Cahill, Eddie
AH-SURLEY (Cahill, Eddie & Mick Moloney).
Album: released on Shanachie in Sep'79. Distributed by: Sterns/Triple Earth Distribution, Roots

YOU DON'T KNOW ME.
Single (7"): released on Dibble in Jun'84 by Dibble Records

Single (12"): released on Dibble in Jun'84 by Dibble Records

Cahn, Sammy
I'VE HEARD THAT SONG BEFORE.
Album: . Distributed by: Polygram

Cahoot
ARE YOU READY.
Tracks: / Are you ready / Gimme some sign.
Single (12"): released on Haj in Nov'86. Distributed by: Jetstar

Cain, David
DAVID CAIN'S MUSIC.
Album: by BBC Records & Tapes. Distributed by: EMI, PRT,

Caine, Andrew
ONE.
Tracks: / What kind of world / What do we say to each other / New blood (this time tomorrow) / Talkin' / Watchin' the world go by / Move it / Wilderness years / Cathy come home / Physical contact / Still the night.
Album: released on Epic in Sep'86 by CBS Records. Distributed by: CBS

Cassette: released on Epic in Sep'86 by CBS Records. Distributed by: CBS

Single (12"): released on Epic in Aug'86 by CBS Records. Distributed by: CBS

WHAT DO WE SAY TO EACH OTHER.
Tracks: / What do we say to each other / Dance under a midnight sun.
Single (7"): released on Epic in Aug'86 by CBS Records. Distributed by: CBS

Single (12"): released on Epic in Aug'86 by CBS Records. Distributed by: CBS

WHAT KIND OF WORLD.
Tracks: / What kind of world / Tearing me apart.
Single (7"): released on Epic in Oct'86 by CBS Records. Distributed by: CBS

WHAT KIND OF WORLD?.
Single (7"): released on Epic in Jun'85 by CBS Records. Distributed by: CBS Deleted '86.

Single (12"): released on Epic in Jun'85 by CBS Records. Distributed by: CBS

Caine, Daniel
A-TEAM, (THE).
Album: released on Indiana in Aug'84. Distributed by: PRT

Cassette: released on Indiana in Aug'84. Distributed by: PRT

CAGNEY AND LACEY.
Album: released on Indiana in Nov'85. Distributed by: PRT

Cassette: released on Indiana in Nov'85. Distributed by: PRT

HILL STREET BLUES.
Album: released on Indiana in Feb'85. Distributed by: PRT

Cassette: released on Indiana in Feb'85. Distributed by: PRT

THEME FROM THE A-TEAM.
Single (7"): released on Indiana in Sep'84. Distributed by: PRT

Caine, Marti
BEHIND THE SMILE.
Album: released on Pye in May'78

LADY'S GONNA SING, THE.
Album: released on Pye in Sep'79

NOBODY DOES IT LIKE MARTI.
Album: released on Pye in Jun'76

Cain, Jackie
WE'VE GOT IT - THE MUSIC OF CY COLEMAN (Cain, Jackie & Roy Kral).
Album: released on Discovery (USA) in Nov'84 by Discovery Records (USA). Distributed by: Swift, Flexitron-Audio, Jazz Music

Cain, Tane
TANE CAIN.
Tracks: / Temptation / Danger zone.
Album: released on RCA in Mar'83 by RCA Records. Distributed by: RCA, Roots, Swift, Wellard, Chris, I & B, Solomon & Peres Distribution

Cassette: released on RCA in Mar'83 by RCA Records. Distributed by: RCA, Roots, Swift, Wellard, Chris, I & B, Solomon & Peres Distribution

Calphus Semenya
ANGELINA.
Single (7"): released on Jive in Jul'83 by Zomba Records. Distributed by: RCA, PRT, CBS

Single (12"): released on Jive in Jul'83 by Zomba Records. Distributed by: RCA, PRT, CBS

Single (7"): released on Jive in Jun'85 by Zomba Records. Distributed by: RCA, PRT, CBS

Single (12"): released on Jive in Jun'85 by Zomba Records. Distributed by: RCA, PRT, CBS

Cairney, John
ROBERT BURNS STORY, THE.
Cassette: released on REL in '76. Distributed by: Roots

ROBERT SERVICE STORY, THE.
Album: released on REL in '79. Distributed by: Roots

Cassette: released on REL in '79. Distributed by: Roots

WILLIAM MCGONAGALL STORY, THE.
Cassette: released on REL in '82. Distributed by: Roots

Cairns, Forrie
GOLDEN CLARINET, (THE).
Album: released on Country House in Sep'84 by BGS Productions Ltd. Distributed by: Taylor, H.R., Record Merchandisers Distribution, Pinnacle, Sounds of Scotland Records

Cairo
I WANT YOU IN MY LIFE.
Tracks: / Uncle Charlie.
Single (7"): released on Citybeat in Aug'87. Distributed by: WEA

Single (12"): released on Citybeat in Aug'87. Distributed by: WEA

ON THE REBOUND.
Single (7"): released on Champion in Jul'85 by Champion Records. Distributed by: RCA

Single (12"): released on Champion in Jul'85 by Champion Records. Distributed by: RCA

YOU ARE.
Single (12"): released on Vista Sounds in May'83 by Vista Sounds Records. Distributed by: Jetstar

Calr Paravel
WISE MAN.
Single (7"): released on Multi Media Tapes in Apr'82 by Multi Media Tapes Records. Distributed by: Stage One Distribution, Conifer Distribution, H.R. Taylor Distribution, Pinnacle

Cajun ...
14 CAJUN HITS Various artists (Various Artists).
Album:

BEST OF THE CAJUN HITS Various artists (Various Artists).
Album:

CAJUN HITS - VOL. 3 Various artists (Various Artists).
Album:

CAJUN HITS - VOLUME 2 Various artists (Various Artists).
Album:

CAJUN HITS - VOLUME 4 Various artists (Various Artists).
Album:

CAJUN TREAT Various artists.
Album:

LOUISIANA'S CAJUN-FRENCH VERSIONS OF POPULAR HITS Various artists (Various Artists).
Album:

MERRY CAJUN CHRISTMAS Various artists (Various Artists).
Album:

Cajun Aces
DEAF HEIGHTS.
Album: released on Temple in Jul'87 by Temple Records. Distributed by: Roots Distribution, Folksound Distribution, Celtic Music Distribution, Projection Distribution

Cajun Country
Jimmy C. Newman & Cajun Country

Cajun Cruisin'
CAJUN CRUISIN' VOL 1 (Various Artists).
Album: released on Sonet in Jun'80 by Sonet Records. Distributed by: PRT

CAJUN CRUISIN' VOL 2 (Various Artists).
Album: released on Sonet in Jun'80 by Sonet Records. Distributed by: PRT

Cajun Fair Do Do
CAJUN FAIS DO DO Various artists (Various Artists).
Album: released on Arhoolie in May'81 by Arhoolie Records. Distributed by: Projection, Topic, Jazz Music, Swift, Roots

Cajun Music
CAJUN MUSIC: MARDI GRAS IN MAMOU, LOUISIANA, USA Various artists (Various Artists).
Album: released on IMS in Sep'85 by Polydor Records. Distributed by: IMS, Polygram

CAJUN MUSIC: THE EARLY 50'S Various artists (Various Artists).
Album: released on Arhoolie in May'81 by Arhoolie Records. Distributed by: Projection, Topic, Jazz Music, Swift, Roots

Cajun, R
BAYOU RHYTHMS.
Album: released on Moonraker in Oct'85, Projection Distribution

Cajun Rendezvous
CAJUN RENDEZVOUS Various artists (Various Artists).
Album: released on Swallow in Feb'79

Cajuns

CAJUNS: VOL 1.
Album: released on Sonet in '73 by Sonet Records. Distributed by: PRT

CAJUNS: VOL 2.
Album: released on Sonet in '73 by Sonet Records. Distributed by: PRT

Calamites, Les

LES CALCHAKIS SING NERUDA, GUILLEN, JARA.
Album: released on Arion in Jun'79. Distributed by: Discovery

PAS LA PEINE.
Single (7"): released on New Rose in Jan'85. Distributed by: Rough Trade, Cartel

Calchakis, Los

AFRICAN ROOTS.
Album: released on Arion (France) in Feb'85. Distributed by: Conifer, Discovery

Cassette: released on Arion (France) in Feb'85. Distributed by: Conifer, Discovery

Calder, Adrian

STORY BOOK OF CHILDRENS' SONGS.
Tracks: / Lavender's blue / I had a little nut tree / Twinkle little star / This old man.
Notes: A great favourite with children including the above songs plus some excellent new songs for kiddies accompanied on guitar with some harmonizing by Hazel SmithEron Records, 27 Balmoral Road, Kingsdown, Deal, Kent CT14 8BX.
Cassette: released on Eron in Sep'85 by Eron Records. Distributed by: Eron Records

Caldwell, Bobby

WHAT YOU WON'T DO FOR LOVE.
Tracks: / What you won't do for love (edit) / Down for the third time (edit).
Single (7"): released on Magnetic Dance in 13 Jun'87 by Magnetic Dance Records. Distributed by: BMG

Single (12"): released on Magnetic Dance in 13 Jun'87 by Magnetic Dance Records. Distributed by: BMG

Caledonian Companion

INSTRUMENTAL MUSIC FROM SCOTLAND.
Single (12"): released on Topic in '81. Distributed by: Roots Distribution

Cale, J.J

8.
Compact disc: by Phonogram Records. Distributed by: Polygram Distribution

Album: released on Mercury in Sep'83 by Phonogram Records. Distributed by: Polygram Distribution Deleted '85.

Cassette: released on Mercury in Sep'83 by Phonogram Records. Distributed by: Polygram Distribution Deleted '85.

FEMME DE MON POTE, (LA).
Album: released on Mercury (France)_ in Jun'84

Cassette: released on Mercury (France)_ in Jun'84

FIVE.
Album: released on Shelter in Oct'83

Cassette: released on Shelter in Oct'83

GRASSHOPPER.
Tracks: / City girls / Devil in disguise / One step ahead of the blues / You keep me hangin' on / Downtown L.A. / Can't live here / Grasshopper / Drifter's wife / Thing going on, A / Nobody but you / Mississippi river / Does your mama like to reggae / Dr. Jive.
Compact disc: released on Mercury in '83 by Phonogram Records. Distributed by: Polygram Distribution

Album: released on Ensign in Nov'84 by Ensign Records. Distributed by: CBS Distribution

Cassette: released on Ensign in Nov'84 by Ensign Records. Distributed by: CBS Distribution

NATURALLY.
Compact disc: released on Shelter in Jan'87

SHADES.
Album: released on Philips in May'84. Distributed by: IMS-Polygram

Cassette: released on Philips in May'84. Distributed by: IMS-Polygram

Compact disc: released on Mercury in '83 by Phonogram Records. Distributed by: Polygram Distribution

SPECIAL EDITION.
Tracks: / Cocaine / Don't wait / Magnolia / Devil in disguise / Sensitive kind / Carry on after midnight / Money talks / Call me the breeze / Lies / City girls / Cajun moon / Don't cry sister / Crazy mama.
Album: released on Mercury in Jun'84 by Phonogram Records. Distributed by: Polygram Distribution

Cassette: released on Mercury in Jun'84 by Phonogram Records. Distributed by: Polygram Distribution

Compact disc: released on Mercury in Jun'84 by Phonogram Records. Distributed by: Polygram Distribution

TROUBADOUR.
Compact disc: released on Mercury in '83 by Phonogram Records. Distributed by: Polygram Distribution

Album: released on Shelter in Aug'83

Cassette: released on Shelter in Aug'83

Cale, John

ACADEMY IN PERIL.
Album: released on Edsel in Apr'86 by Demon Records. Distributed by: Pinnacle, Jazz Music, Projection

ARTIFICIAL INTELLIGENCE.
Album: released on Beggars Banquet in Oct'85 by Beggars Banquet Records. Distributed by: WEA

Cassette: released on Beggars Banquet in Oct'85 by Beggars Banquet Records. Distributed by: WEA

BLACK ROSE.
Album: released on Beggars Banquet in Aug'85 by Beggars Banquet Records. Distributed by: WEA

Cassette: released on Beggars Banquet in Aug'85 by Beggars Banquet Records. Distributed by: WEA

CARIBBEAN SUNSET.
Album: released on ZE in Jan'84 by Island Records. Distributed by: Polygram

Cassette: released on ZE in Jan'84 by Island Records. Distributed by: Polygram Deleted '87.

CHURCH OF ANTHRAX (Cale, John & Terry Riley).
Album: by CBS Records. Distributed by: CBS

DYING ON THE VINE.
Single (7"): released on Beggars Banquet in Jul'85 by Beggars Banquet Records. Distributed by: WEA

Single (12"): released on Beggars Banquet in Jul'85 by Beggars Banquet Records. Distributed by: WEA

FEAR.
Album: released on Island in Sep'74 by Island Records. Distributed by: Polygram

GUTS.
Album: released on Island in Feb'77 by Island Records. Distributed by: Polygram

JOHN CALE COMES ALIVE.
Album: released on ZE in Sep'84 by Island Records. Distributed by: Polygram Deleted '87.

Cassette: released on ZE in Sep'84 by Island Records. Distributed by: Polygram

JUNE 1, 1974.
Album: released on Island in Jun'74 by Island Records. Distributed by: Polygram

MUSIC FOR A NEW SOCIETY.
Album: released on ZE in Sep'82 by Island Records. Distributed by: Polygram

Cassette: released on ZE in Sep'82 by Island Records. Distributed by: Polygram

SATELLITE WALK.
Single (12"): released on Beggars Banquet in Nov'85 by Beggars Banquet Records. Distributed by: WEA

SLOW DAZZLE.
Tracks: / Mr.Wilson / Taking it all away / Dirty-ass rock & roll / Darling I need you / Rollaroll / Heartbreak Hotel / Ski patrol / I'm not the loving kind / Guts / Jeweller,The.
Compact disc: released on Island in '87 by Island Records. Distributed by: Polygram

SLOW DAZZLE.
Album: by Island Records. Distributed by: Polygram

VINTAGE VIOLENCE.
Album: released on Edsel in May'87 by Demon Records. Distributed by: Pinnacle, Jazz Music, Projection

Calendar Crowd

LISTEN TO THE HEART.
Single (12"): released on Production Line in Jun'85 by Calendar Crowd. Distributed by: Cartel

PERFECT HIDEAWAY.
Single (7"): released on Romantic in Dec'82. Distributed by: MCA Distribution

Calendar, Phil

ISLAND MUSIC.
Single (12"): released on Revue in May'85 by Revue Records. Distributed by: Creole

Calening

SONGS AND TUNES FROM WALES.
Album: released on Greenwich Village in May'81 by Sweet Folk All Records. Distributed by: Roots, Projection, Lightning, Celtic Music, Wellard, Chris

Calennig

CALENNIG.
Album: released on Greenwich Village in Jan'87 by Sweet Folk All Records. Distributed by: Roots, Projection, Lightning, Celtic Music, Wellard, Chris

Cale's Dubset, Grace

HITTIES AND KASSITES.
Album: released on Janaow in Apr'84 by Janaow Records. Distributed by: Jetstar

California

CALIFORNIA The Collection (Various Artists).
Tracks: / Surfin' safari / Little darlin' / Little old lady from Pasadena, The / Da doo ron ron / Surfer girl / Happy together / Deadman's curve / Stroll, The / Louie louie / Help me Rhonda / Leader of the pack / Sweet talkin' guy / Remember (walkin' in the sand).
Compact disc: released on The Collection in Apr'87 by Object Enterprises Ltd. Distributed by: Counterpoint Distribution

HE'S ALMOST THERE.
Single (7"): released on RCA in Feb'83 by RCA Records. Distributed by: RCA, Roots, Swift, Wellard, Chris, I & B, Solomon & Peres Distribution

California Collection

CALIFORNIA COLLECTION Various artists (Various Artists).
Album: released on Rounder (USA) in Jan'84. Distributed by: Mike's Country Music Room Distribution, Jazz Music Distribution, Swift Distribution, Roots Records Distribution, Projection Distribution, Topic Distribution

California Dreamin'

CALIFORNIA DREAMIN' Various artists (Various Artists).
Album: released on K-Tel in Aug'81 by K-Tel Records. Distributed by: Record Merchandisers Distribution, Taylors, Terry Blood Distribution, Wynd-Up Distribution, Relay Distribution, Pickwick Distribution, Solomon & Peres Distribution, Polygram

Cassette: released on K-Tel in Aug'81 by K-Tel Records. Distributed by: Record Merchandisers Distribution, Taylors, Terry Blood Distribution, Wynd-Up Distribution, Relay Distribution, Pickwick Distribution, Solomon & Peres Distribution, Polygram

California Jump Blues

CALIFORNIA JUMP BLUES Various artists (Various Artists).
Tracks: / Rockola / Take a ride / Mardi Gras / Rag mop / Wino / Have you ever been in love / KC Limited Part 2 / Rampart street blues / Mary Sue / Bayou bounce / Blues has got me, The / I want to rock 'n' roll / Flirting blues / KC Limited Part 1.
Album: released on Ace(Cadet) in Jul'83 by Ace Records. Distributed by: Pinnacle, Swift, Hotshot

California Ramblers

1920'S FLAPPER PARTY.
Tracks: / Ev'rything is hotsy totsy now / Sweet Georgia Brown / I'm gonna charleston back to Charleston / Show me the way to go home / No foolin' / Girl friend, The / Ya gotta know how to love / Stockholm stomp / We love the college girls / Yes she do - no she don't / Vo-do-do-de-o blues / Nothin' does-does like it used to do-do-do / Make my cot where the cot-cot cotton grows / Mine - all mine / Singapore sorrows / Pay-off, The.
Cassette: released on Halcyon (USA) in May'87 by Halcyon Records (USA). Distributed by: Jazz Music, Conifer, Taylors

CALIFORNIA RAMBLERS.
Album: released on Jazz Supreme in Dec'86. Distributed by: Jazz Music

California, Randy

ALL ALONG THE WATCHTOWER.
Single (7"): released on Beggars Banquet in Sep'82 by Beggars Banquet Records. Distributed by: WEA

Single (12"): released on Beggars Banquet in Sep'82 by Beggars Banquet Records. Distributed by: WEA

EURO AMERICAN.
Tracks: / Easy love / Fearless leader / Five in the morning / Skull and crossbones / Breakout / Toy guns / This is the end / Mon ami / Rude creation / Calling you / Wild thing.
Album: released on Beggars Banquet in Apr'82 by Beggars Banquet Records. Distributed by: WEA

Cassette: released on Beggars Banquet in Apr'82 by Beggars Banquet Records. Distributed by: WEA

JACK RABBIT.
Single (7"): released on Vertigo in Jun'85 by Phonogram Records. Distributed by: Polygram

Single (12"): released on Vertigo in Jun'85 by Phonogram Records. Distributed by: Polygram

KAPTAIN KOPTER & HIS TWIRLY BIRDS.
Cassette: released on Demon in Nov'85 by Demon Records. Distributed by: Pinnacle

WATCHTOWER.
Album: released on Teldec (Germany) in Apr'84 by Import Records. Distributed by: IMS Distribution, Polygram Distribution

California Sound Of The

CALIFORNIA SOUND OF THE 60'S,THE Original artists (Original artists).
Compact disc: released on The Compact Collection in Sep'87 by Conifer Records. Distributed by: Conifer Distribution

California Strings...

ROUND MIDNIGHT.
Cassette: released on VFM in May'85 by VFM Records. Distributed by: Taylors, Wynd-Up Distribution

California Suite

CALIFORNIA SUITE Original film soundtrack (Various Artists).
Tracks: / California main title / Love theme from California Suite / Black battle / Hannah's daughter / Black folks / Academy awards / Beverly Hills / California end credits.
Album: released on CBS in Mar'79 by CBS Records. Distributed by: CBS

Cassette: released on CBS in Mar'79 by CBS Records. Distributed by: CBS

Call

EVERYWHERE I GO.
Tracks: / Everywhere I go / Tore the old place down.
Single (7"): released on Elektra (USA) in May'86 by Elektra/Asylum/Nonesuch Records. Distributed by: WEA

Single (12"): released on Elektra (USA) in May'86 by Elektra/Asylum/Nonesuch Records. Distributed by: WEA

I DON'T WANNA.
Tracks: / I don't wanna / Day or night.
Single (12"): released on Elektra in Jul'87 by WEA Records. Distributed by: WEA

Single (12"): released on Elektra in Jul'87 by WEA Records. Distributed by: WEA

INTO THE WOODS.
Tracks: / I don't wanna / In the river / It could have been me / Woods, The / Day or night / Memory / Too many tears / Expecting / Walk walk.
Album: released on Elektra (USA) in Jul'87 by Elektra/Asylum/Nonesuch Records. Distributed by: WEA

Cassette: released on Elektra (USA) in Jul'87 by Elektra/Asylum/Nonesuch Records. Distributed by: WEA

Compact disc: released on Elektra (USA) in Jul'87 by Elektra/Asylum/Nonesuch Records. Distributed by: WEA

MODERN ROMANS.
Tracks: / Walls came down, The / Turn a blind eye / Time of your life / Modern Romans / Back from the front / Destination / Violent times / Face to face / All about you.
Album: released on Metronome (Germany) in Sep'83. Distributed by: Jazz Music Distribution

RECONCILED.
Tracks: / Everywhere I go / I still believe (great design) / Blood red (America) the morning / Oklahoma / With or withour reason / Sanctuary / Tore the old place down / Even now.
Album: released on Elektra (USA) in May'86 by Elektra/Asylum/Nonesuch Records. Distributed by: WEA

Cassette: released on Elektra (USA) in May'8€ by Elektra/Asylum/Nonesuch Records. Distributed by: WEA

SCENE BEYOND DREAMS.
Tracks: / Scene beyond dreams / Burden, The / Tremble / Delivered / Heavy hand / Promise and threat / One life leads to another / Apocalypse / Notified.
Album: released on Phonogram (France) in Oct'84

Cassette: released on Phonogram (France) in Oct'84

WALLS CAME DOWN.
Single (7"): released on London in Jul'83 by London Records. Distributed by: Polygram

Cassette: released on London in Jul'83 by London Records. Distributed by: Polygram

Callas, Maria

MARIA CALLAS COLLECTION,THE.
Double Album: released on Stylus in 30 May'87. Distributed by: Pinnacle, Terry Blood Distribution, Stylus Distribution

Cassette: released on Stylus in 30 May'87. Distributed by: Pinnacle, Terry Blood Distribution, Stylus Distribution

Caller, Terry

FIRE ON ICE.
Tracks: / Be a believer / Holdin' on (To your love) / Street fever / Butterfly / I been doin' alright Part II (Everything's gonna be alright) / Disco in the sky / American violet / Love two tone / Martin St Martin.
Album: released on Elektra (USA) in Aug'78 by Elektra/Asylum/Nonesuch Records. Distributed by: WEA

TURN YOU TO LOVE.
Tracks: / Sign of the times / Pyramids of love / Turn you to love / Do it again / Ordinary Joe / Occasional rain / Still water (Love) / You and me (Will always be in love) / Mother's love, A.
Album: released on Elektra (USA) in May'85 by Elektra/Asylum/Nonesuch Records. Distributed by: WEA

Callies

ON YOUR SIDE.
Tracks: / Rocking chair / January man / Monty's song / Make me happy / Reason to believe / Home town / Peggy Gordon / Is it surprising / Change of mind, A / Turning into winter / Top 40.
Album: released on Rubber in Jun'82 by Rubber Records. Distributed by: Roots Distribution, Projection Distribution, Jazz Music Distribution, Celtic Music Distribution, Spartan Distribution

Calling Hearts

RETURN TO BASE.
Single (7"): released on Illuminated in Sep'81 by IKF Records. Distributed by: Pinnacle, Cartel, Jetstar

Call It Love

CALL IT LOVE Original London cast.
Album: released on TER in Mar'85. Distributed by: Pinnacle

Call Me Madam

CALL ME MADAM Original cast, featuring Ethel Merman (Various Artists).
Tracks: / Hostess with the mostest on the ball.

Calloway, Cab

1933/4 COTTON CLUB ORCHESTRA SESSIONS.
Recording Notes: This is a double album and a double cassette.
Album: released on RCA(France), Oct'85 by RCA Records. Dist: Discovery, Silva Screen Records

Cassette: released on RCA(France), Oct'85 by RCA Records. Dist: Discovery, Silva Screen Records

CAB CALLOWAY.
Album: released on Giants of Jazz, Apr'79 by Hasmick Promotions Ltd.. Dist: Counterpoint, Taylors, Wellard, Swift, Crusader, Jazz Music

CLUB ZANZIBAR BROADCASTS.
Tracks: / For a little rally / Russian lullaby / I was here when you left me / St. Louis blues / Frantic on the Atlantic / 9/20 special / Great lie, The / I can't give you anything but love / Rosemarie / I'm not ashamed of my tears / One o'clock jump
Album: released on Unique Jazz, Apr'81 Dist: Swift, Jazz Music, Jazz Horizons, Cadillac

COLLECTION: CAB CALLOWAY.
Cassette: released on Deja Vu, May'86 by Deja Vu Records. Dist: Counterpoint, Jazz Music

Album: released on Deja Vu, May'86 by Deja Vu Records. Dist: Counterpoint, Jazz Music

FRANTIC IN THE ATLANTIC.
Album: released on Dance Band Days, Oct'87 by Prism Leisure. Dist: Prism Leisure, Jazz Music, Taylors

Cassette: released on Dance Band Days, Oct'87 by Prism Leisure. Dist: Prism Leisure, Jazz Music, Taylors

GET WITH IT.
Album: released on Swinghouse, '84 Dist: Jazz Music, Swift, Wellard, Celtic Music
Cat. no: **SWH 38**

Cassette: released on Swinghouse, '84 Dist: Jazz Music, Swift, Wellard, Celtic Music

HI-DE-HO MAN, THE.
Tracks: / Jumping jive, The / Minnie the moocher / It ain't necessarily so / Saint James infirmary / I see a million people / Hi-de-ho man, The / Summertime / Kickin' the gong around / Stormy weather / You rascal you
Album: released on RCA(France), '83 by RCA Records. Dist: Discovery, Silva Screen Records

JAZZ OF THE AIR (VOL 4).
Tracks: / We the cats / Dawn time / Minnie the moocher / Rhythm cocktail / Very thought of you, The / Foo a little bally hoo / Is you is or is you ain't my baby / Frantic in the Atlantic / Blue skies / Cruisin' with Cab / Body and soul / Minnie the moocher / Rhythm cocktail / Kabla / Lammar's boogie / Coastin' with JC
Recording Notes: Another band that not all could make. Featuring Ike Quebec, Jonah Jones, Ilinois Jacquet and Benny Carter.
Album: released on Spotlite, '83 by Spotlite Records. Dist: Cadillac, Jazz Music, Spotlite

JUMPIN' STUFF.
Album: by Import Records. Dist: Wellard, Swift, Zodiac

JUMPING JIVE.
Album: released on Swinghouse, '84 Dist: Jazz Music, Swift, Wellard, Celtic Music

Cassette: released on Swinghouse, '84 Dist: Jazz Music, Swift, Wellard, Celtic Music

Album: released on CBS, Aug'84 by CBS Records. Dist: CBS

Cassette: released on CBS, Aug'84 by CBS Records. Dist: CBS

JUMPING & JIVING 1930-37.
Album: released on Swingtime, Jan'86 Dist: Jazz Music, Charly, Swift, Zodiac

KICKING THE GONG AROUND.
Tracks: / Minnie the moocher / Without rhythm / Aw you dog / Bugle call rag / Downhearted blues / Night mare, The / Black rhyhtm / Yaller / Between the Devil and the deep blue sea / Nobody's sweetheart / Trickeration / St. Louis blues / Mood indigo / Farewell blues / You rascal you / My honey's lovin' / Some of these days / Six or seven times / Somebody stole my gal / Kicking the gong around
Album: released on ASV(Academy Sound & Vision), May'82 by Academy Sound & Vision Records. Dist: Pinnacle

Cassette: released on ASV(Academy Sound & Vision), May'82 by Academy Sound & Vision Records. Dist: Pinnacle

MAN FROM HARLEM, (THE).
Album: Dist: Jazz Music, Swift

MINNIE THE MOOCHER.
Tracks: / Scat song, The / You rascal you / Nobody's sweetheart / Between the devil and the deep blue sea / Kicking the gong around / Hotcha razz-ma-tazz / Jitterbug / Harlem hospitality / Lady with the fan, The / Zaz zuh zaz / Fathers got his glasses on / Liutle town girl / There's a cabin in the cotton / Harlem camp meeting / Minnie the moocher / Long about midnight / Moonglow / Margie
Recording Notes: All vocals by Cab Calloway except on track 17 - Cab Calloway and Bennie Payne. Recorded in mono.
Cassette: released on Astan, Jun'86 by Astan Records.

Album: released on President, Sep'86 by President Records. Dist: President, Jazz Music, Taylors, Spartan

Album: released on RCA, '84 by RCA Records. Dist: BMG

Cassette: released on RCA, '84 by RCA Records. Dist: BMG Deleted '85.

MISSOURIANS.
Tracks: / Market street stomp / Ozark mountain blues / You'll cry for me but I'll be gone / Missouri moan / I've got someone / 400 hop / Vine street drag / Scotty blues / Two hundred squabble / Swingin' dem cats / Stoppin' the traffic / Prohibition blues / Gotta darn good reason now / St. Louis blues / Sweet Jennie Lee / Happy feet / Yaller / Viper's drag / Is that religion? / Some of these days
Recording Notes: Recorded: 1929 - 1930 in mono.
Album: released on VJM(Vintage Jazz Music), Jul'86 by Vintage Jazz Music Society(VJM). Dist: Wellard, Jazz Music, Swift, Taylors, VJM

ON FILM.
Tracks: / Minnie the moocher / Rail rhythm / Zaz zuh zaz / Lady with the fan / Got a right to sing the blues / Hi-de-ho miracle man / Frisco Flo / Some of these days / Skunk song / Virginia, Georgia and Caroline / Blues in the night / Jumpin' jive / Sunday in Savannah / Geechie Joe / Calloway boogie
Album: released on Harlequin, Jan'84 by Flyright Records. Dist: Swift, Jazz Music, Wellard, Cadillac, Taylors

Calloways

WENT THATAWAY.
Single 7": released on Wonderful World Of, Jun'84 by Wonderful World Of Records. Dist: Fast Forward, Cartel

Calvert, Eddie

20 GOLDEN TRUMPET GREATS.
Cassette: released on EMI, Sep'79 by EMI Records(UK). Dist: EMI

GOLDEN TRUMPET GREATS.
Album: released on Polydor, '79 by Polydor Records. Dist: Polygram

MAN WITH THE GOLDEN TRUMPET, THE.
Album: released on One Up, Jan'78 by EMI Records(UK). Dist: EMI

Album: released on MFP, Jun'85 by Music For Pleasure Records. Dist: EMI

Cassette: released on MFP, Jun'85 by Music For Pleasure Records. Dist: EMI

O MEIN PAPA.
Single 7": released on H.M.V., Nov'80 by EMI Records(UK). Dist: EMI

Calvert, Robert

FREQ.
Album: released on Flicknife, Sep'84 by Flicknife Records. Dist: Spartan

LUCKY LEIF & THE LONGSHIPS.
Recording Notes: Robert Calvert's second solo album, originally released by EMI in the summer of 1975 recorded during his first split from Hawkwind. Produced by Brian Eno featuring other Hawkwind members.
Album: released on Beat Goes On, Ma''87 Dist: Pinnacle

TEST TUBE CONCEIVED.
Tracks: / Telekinesis / I hear voices / Fanfare for the perfect race / On line / Save them from the scientists / Fly on the wall / Thanks to the scientists / Test tube conceived
Album: released on Demi-Monde, Apr'86 by Charly Records. Dist: Charly

Compact disc: released on The CD Label, Aug'87. Estim retail price in Sep'87 was £11.99.

Calypso Rose

LEH WE PUNTA.
Album: released on Striker, May'87 by Striker Records. Dist: Jetstar

Calzado, Rudy

RICA CHARANGA.
Album: released on Globestyle, Nov'87 by Ace Records. Dist: Projection, Celtic Music, Pinnacle, Cadillac, Jazz Music, Wellard. Estim retail price in Sep'87 was £5.67

Camarata Symphony Orc.

VIENNA OF J STRAUSS (Camarata & Kungsway Symphony Orc.).
Album: released on Phase 4, '72

Camarque

HOWL OF THE PACK.
Single 7": released on Clubland, Jun'84 by Clubland Records. Dist: EMI, Pinnacle

Cambell, Carol

BETWEEN ME AND YOU (Cambell, Carol & Les Cliff).
Single 12": released on Sea View, Oct'83 by Sea View Records. Dist: Jetstar

Camberwell Now

GHOST TRAIN, THE.
Album: released on Ink, Mar'86 by Red Flame. Dist: Rough Trade, Cartel, Pinnacle

GREENFINGERS.
Single 12": released on Ink, Feb'87 by Red Flame. Dist: Rough Trade, Cartel, Pinnacle

Cambridge Buskers

SOAP OPERA.
Album: released on DGG, Apr'83 by Polydor Records. Dist: Polygram

Cassette: released on DGG, Apr'83 by Polydor Records. Dist: Polygram

Cambridge City Jassband

CAMBRIDGE BLUES.
Recording Notes: "Jassband" is correct spelling.
Album: released on Plant Life Jazz, Nov'81 Dist: Jazz Music, Projection, Swift, Celtic Music, Cadillac, Ross, Duncans, Impetus

Cambridge Youth Choir

SONG FOR ALL SEASONS, A (Cambridge Silver Jubilee Youth Choir).
Album: released on Plant Life, Nov'81 Dist: Jazz Music, Projection, Swift, Celtic Music, Cadillac, Ross, Duncans, Impetus

Camel

BREATHLESS.
Album: released on Decca, Sep'78 by Decca Records. Dist: Polygram

Cassette: released on Decca, Sep'78 by Decca Records. Dist: Polygram

CAMEL.
Album: released on MCA, Aug'81 by MCA Records. Dist: Polygram

Cassette: released on MCA, Sep'81 by MCA Records. Dist: Polygram

CHAMELEON.
Album: released on Decca, Sep'81 by Decca Records. Dist: Polygram

Cassette: released on Decca, Sep'81 by Decca Records. Dist: Polygram

CLOAK & DAGGER MAN.
Single 7": released on Decca, Apr'84 by Decca Records. Dist: Polygram

Single 12": released on Decca, Apr'84 by Decca Records. Dist: Polygram

COLLECTION: CAMEL.
Tracks: / Aristillus / Freefall / Supertwister / Spirit of the water / Lunar Sea / White rider / Earthrise / Song within a song / Rhayader goes to town / Migration / Rhayader alone / La princesse perdue / Great marsh, The / Drafted / Captured / Sasquatch / Rain dances / Highways of the sun / First Light
Compact disc: released on Collector Series, Jan'86 by Castle Communications Records. Dist: BMG

Album: released on Castle Communications, Nov'85 by Castle Communications. Dist: PRT, Pinnacle

Cassette: released on Castle Communications, Nov'85 by Castle Communications. Dist: PRT, Pinnacle

I CAN SEE YOUR HOUSE FROM HERE.
Album: released on Decca, Sep'79 by Decca Records. Dist: Polygram

Cassette: released on Decca, Sep'79 by Decca Records. Dist: Polygram

LIVE RECORD, THE.
Double Album: released on Decca, Apr'78 by Decca Records. Dist: Polygram

Cassette: released on Decca, Apr'78 by Decca Records. Dist: Polygram

MIRAGE.
Tracks: / Freefall / Supertwister / Nimrodel / Procession, The / White rider, The / Earthrise / Lady Fantasy / Encounter / Smiles for you / Lady Fantasy
Album: released on Deram, '74 by London Records. Dist: Polygram

MOON MADNESS.
Tracks: / Aristillus / Song within a song / Chord change / Spirit of the water / Another night / Air born / Lunar sea
Album: released on Decca, Apr'76 by Decca Records. Dist: Polygram

Cassette: released on Decca, Apr'76 by Decca Records. Dist: Polygram

Compact disc: released on Decca, '83 by Decca Records. Dist: Polygram **Media Note:** AAD

Compact disc: released on Decca, '83 by Decca Records. Dist: Polygram

NUDE.
Tracks: / City life / Nude / Drafted / Dock's / Beached / Landscape / Changing places / Pomp and circumstance / Please come home / Reflections / Captures / Homecoming, The / Lies / Last farewell, The / Birthday cake, The / Nude's return / Changing places / Promp and circumstance
Album: released on Decca, Jan'81 by Decca Records. Dist: Polygram

Cassette: released on Decca, Jan'81 by Decca Records. Dist: Polygram

Compact disc: released on Decca, '83 by Decca Records. Dist: Polygram

PRESSURE POINTS Camel live.
Tracks: / Drafted / Captured / Lies / Sasquatch / West Berlin / Fingertips / Wait / Rhayader / Rhayader goes to town / Waltzing frauleins / Stationary traveller
Recording Notes: Live recording of highlights from Camel's concert at Hammersmith Odeon on May 11th 1984. This concert is also available as a full length Polygram Music Videocassette which was also recorded live at Hammersmith Odeon and includes 14 tracks in all, plus conceptual linking film. Total playing time 80 minutes.
Album: released on Decca, Nov'84 by Decca Records. Dist: Polygram

Cassette: released on Decca, Nov'84 by Decca Records. Dist: Polygram

Page 176

Video-cassette (VHS): released on Polygram Music, Oct'84 by Polygram Records. Dist: Polygram

Video-cassette [Betamax]: released on Polygram Music, Oct'84 by Polygram Records. Dist: Polygram

Compact disc: released on Decca, Nov'84 by Decca Records. Dist: Polygram **Media Note:** AAD

RAIN DANCES.
Album: released on Decca, Sep'77 by Decca Records. Dist: Polygram Deleted '86.

Cassette: released on Decca, Sep'77 by Decca Records. Dist: Polygram

SINGLE FACTOR.
Tracks: / No easy answer / You are the one / Heroes / Selva / Lullabye / Sasquatch / Manic / Camelogue / Today's goodbye / Heart's goodbye / Heart's desire, A / End piece
Album: released on Decca, May'82 by Decca Records. Dist: Polygram

Cassette: released on Decca, May'82 by Decca Records. Dist: Polygram

Compact disc: released on Decca, '83 by Decca Records. Dist: Polygram

SNOW GOOSE.
Tracks: / Great marsh, The / Rhayader / Rhayader goes to town / Sanctuary / Fritha / Snow goose, The / Friendship / Rhayader alone / Flight of the snow goose / Preparation / Preparation / Dunkirk / Epitaph / Fritha alone / La Princess Perdue / Great marsh, The / Pressure points / Refugee / Stationary traveller
Album: released on Decca, Nov'76 by Decca Records. Dist: Polygram Deleted Dec'77.

Cassette: released on Decca, Nov'76 by Decca Records. Dist: Polygram

Compact disc: released on Decca, '83 by Decca Records. Dist: Polygram

STATIONARY TRAVELLER.
Tracks: / Pressure points / Refugee / Vopos / Cloak and dagger man / Stationary traveller / West Berlin / Fingertips / Missing / Long goodbye / After words / Fingertips / Stationary traveller / Pressure points / Copos
Album: released on Decca, Apr'84 by Decca Records. Dist: Polygram

Cassette: released on Decca, Apr'84 by Decca Records. Dist: Polygram Deleted '86.

Compact disc: released on Decca, Apr'84 by Decca Records. Dist: Polygram

Camelia Jazz Band

...WITH HERB HALL.
Album: released on New Orleans, Aug'81 Dist: Swift, Jazz Music

Camelot

CAMELOT Revival London cast (Various artists).
Tracks: / Overture - prologue / Camelot / Simple joys of maidenhood / I wonder what the king is doing tonight / C'est moi / Follow me / Joust, The / Lusty month of May, The / Resolution / Then you may take me to the fair / How to handle a woman / Entracte madrigal / Before I gaze at you again / Fie on goodness! / If ever I would leave you / I loved you once in silence / Seven deadly virtues, The / What do the simple folks do? / Guenevere / Finale
Album: released on That's Entertainment, Apr'83 by That's Entertainment Records. Dist: Pinnacle

Cassette: released on That's Entertainment, Apr'83 by That's Entertainment Records. Dist: Pinnacle

Compact disc: released on That's Entertainment, Apr'83 by That's Entertainment Records. Dist: Pinnacle

CAMELOT Original London cast (Various artists).
Compact disc: Dist: Pinnacle **Media Note:** DDD

Cameo

ALLIGATOR WOMAN.
Album: released on Casablanca, May'82 Dist: Polygram **Media Note:** Note

Album: released on Casablanca, May'82 Dist: Polygram

ATTACK ME WITH YOUR LOVE.
Single 7": released on Club, Jun'85 by Phonogram Records. Dist: Polygram Deleted '86.

Single 12": released on Club, Jun'85 by Phonogram Records. Dist: Polygram

BABY, NOW THAT I'VE FOUND YOU.
Single 7": released on Loose, Jul'83 by Loose Records. Cartel

BACK AND FORTH.
Tracks: / Back and forth / You can have the world
Single 7": released on Club, Apr'87 by Phonogram Records. Dist: Polygram

Single 12": released on Club, Apr'87 by Phonogram Records. Dist: Polygram

CANDY.
Single 7": released on Club, Nov'86 by Phonogram Records. Dist: Polygram

Single 12": released on Club, Nov'86 by Phonogram Records. Dist: Polygram

Double-pack single: released on Club, Nov'86 by Phonogram Records. Dist: Polygram

FOUR FROM CAMEO (EP).
Single 7": released on Casablanca, May'82 Dist: Polygram

Single 12": released on Casablanca, May'82 Dist: Polygram

GOODBYE, A.
Tracks: / Goodbye, A / I've got your image / On the one / Goodbye, A (long version) / Just be yourself / It's serious
Recording Notes: On The One - only on 12" version. A Goodbye(long version)/Just Be Yourself/ It's Serious - only on 12" double pack edition.
Single 7": released on Club, Mar'86 by Phonogram Records. Dist: Polygram

Single 12": released on Club, Mar'86 by Phonogram Records. Dist: Polygram

Double-pack single: released on Club, Mar'86 by Phonogram Records. Dist: Polygram **Media Note:** This is a 12" double pack single

HANGIN' DOWNTOWN.
Single 7": released on Club, May'84 by Phonogram Records. Dist: Polygram

Single 12": released on Club, May'84 by Phonogram Records. Dist. Polygram

SHE'S MINE.
Tracks: / Flirt* / Knights of the sound table*
Recording Notes: *Available on 12" only.
Single 7": released on Club, Sep'87 by Phonogram Records. Dist: Polygram

Single 12": released on Club, Sep'87 by Phonogram Records. Dist: Polygram **Media Note:** 12" Picture bag.

SHE'S MINE - THE CAMEO MEGAMIX 2.
Tracks: / She's mine - The Cameo Megamix / She's mine
Single 12": released on Club, Sep'87 by Phonogram Records. Dist: Polygram

SHE'S STRANGE.
Tracks: / She's strange / Love you anyway / Talkin' out the side of your neck / Tribute to Bob Marley / Groove with you / Hangin' downtown / Leve tol
Single 7": released on Club, Nov'85 by Phonogram Records. Dist: Polygram Deleted '87

Single 12": released on Club, Nov'85 by Phonogram Records. Dist: Polygram Deleted '87.

Extended-play record: released on Club, Nov'85 by Phonogram Records. Dist: Polygram

Compact disc: Dist: Polygram **Media Note:** AAD

SINGLE LIFE.
Tracks: / Attack me with your love / Single life / I've got your image / Goodbye, A / I'll never look for love / Little boys-dangerous toys / Attack me with you love / Single life / I've got your image / Good-bye, A / I'll never look for love / Little boys-dangerous toys
Album: released on Club, Aug'85 by Phonogram Records. Dist: Polygram

Cassette: released on Club, Aug'85 by Phonogram Records. Dist: Polygram

Compact disc: released on Club, Aug'85 by Phonogram Records. Dist: Polygram

Single 12": released on Club, Sep'85 by Phonogram Records. Dist: Polygram

STYLE.
Tracks: / Aphrodisiac / This life is not for me / You're a winner / Can't help falling in love / Interlude / Serenity / Cameo's dance / Let's not talk shop / Slow movin' / Heaven only knows
Recording Notes: This is Cameo's eighth album and their second for Casablanca. They have had many American chart success, including the singles 'We're going out tonight', 'One the one', 'Shake your pants' and 'Freaky dancing'.
Album: released on Casablanca(Holland), Sep'83 Dist: IMS, Polygram

VIDEOSINGLES.
Video-cassette (VHS): released on Channel 5, '87 Dist: W.H. Smiths

WORD UP.
Tracks: / Word up / Urban warrior / Candy / Back and forth / Don't be lonely / She's mine / Fast, fierce and funny / You can have the world
Recording Notes: Produced by Larry Blackmon. Features guest appearances by Charlie Singleton andThe Brecker Brothers.
Single 7": released on Club, Aug'86 by Phonogram Records. Dist: Polygram

Single 12": released on Club, Aug'86 by Phonogram Records. Dist: Polygram

Album: released on Club, Sep'86 by Phonogram Records. Dist: Polygram

Cassette: released on Club, Sep'86 by Phonogram Records. Dist: Polygram

Compact disc: released on Club, Sep'86 by Phonogram Records. Dist: Polygram

Camera Obscura

DESTITUTION.
Single 7": released on Small Wonder, Apr'83 by Small Wonder Records. Dist: Indies, Cartel

Cameron, Andy

ALLY'S TARTAN ARMY.
Single 7": released on Klub, Apr'78 by Klub Records. Dist: Celtic Music, Musac(Scotland)Ltd., Ross

ANDY'S TARTAN ALBUM.
Album: released on Klub, Apr'78 by Klub Records. Dist: Celtic Music, Musac(Scotland)Ltd., Ross

WE'RE ON THE MARCH AGAIN].
Single 7": released on Klub, Apr'82 by Klub Records. Dist: Celtic Music, Musac(Scotland)Ltd., Ross

Cameron, Argo

TOAST TO THE HIGHLANDS.
Album: released on Ross, Jan'86 by Ross Records. Dist: Ross, Taylors, Celtic Music, Roots

Cassette: released on Ross, Jan'86 by Ross Records. Dist: Ross, Taylors, Celtic Music, Roots

Cameron, Chris

IS THIS LOVE.
Single 7": released on Steinar, Jun'85

Single 12": released on Steinar, Jun'85

WRITTEN IN YOUR HEART.
Single 7": released on Steinar, Sep'85

Single 12": released on Steinar, Sep'85

Cameron, Christel

GIVE ME ONE MORE CHANCE.
Tracks: / Give me one more chance / Return fom exile
Single 12": released on Jam Star, Jul'86 Dist: Jetstar

Cameron, Debbie

YOU TO ME ARE EVERYTHING (Cameron, Debbie/Plateau).
Single 7": released on Artistic, Oct'84 by Submarine Records. Dist: Wellard, Swift, Jazz Music, Clyde Factors

Cameron, G.C.

HEARTS AND FLOWERS.
Single 7": released on Malaco, Apr'83 by Malaco Records. Dist: PRT, Charly, Celtic Music

Cameron, Ian

POP UP THE AISLE (Cameron, Ian/Marching up and down band).
Single 7": released on Pip, Jul'81 by PRT Records.

Cameron, Jim

COME SCOTTISH DANCING (Cameron, Jim Scottish Dance Band).
Recording Notes: Retail price given by ARC excluding P & P (via mail order) is 4.99. Mail order distribution address: Accordion Record Club, 146 Birmingham Road, Kidderminster, Worcs DY10 2SL. Tel 0562 746105.
Album: released on Ross, Jan'86 by Ross Records. Dist: Ross, Taylors, Celtic Music, Roots

Cassette: released on Accordion Record Club, Jul 86 by Accordion Record Club. Dist: Accordion Record Club

Cameron Men

CAMERON MEN Classic Scots fiddle recordings from the thirties (Various artists).
Album: released on Topic, '81 Dist: Projection

Cameron, Rafael

CAMERONS IN LOVE.
Album: released on Salsoul (USA), Sep'81 Dist: BMG

Cameroon

MUSIC FROM THE FULANI OF THE NORTH.
Album: released on Lyrichord(USA), Oct'81 by Lyrichord Records(USA). Dist: Flexitron Ltd., Roots

Camillo

SAG WARUM.
Single 7": released on EMI(France), Apr'83 by EMI Records(UK). Dist: Conifer

Camillo, Tony Bazuka

DYNOMITE.
Recording Notes: For full detials see under BROTHER JOHNSON 'Stomp'

Camilo, Michel

IN TRIO.
Tracks: / We three / Tombo in 7 / 4 / Las Olas / Cha-cha (used to be a) / Suntan
Recording Notes: Personnel: Michel Camilo/Anthony Jackson/Dave Weckl/Joel Rosenblaf. Recorded in June 1986.
Album: released on King(USA), Apr'87 by Gusto Records (USA). Dist: Gusto. IMS, Swift

Compact disc: released on King (Japan), Oct'87 Dist: IMS, Polygram

WHY NOT?.
Tracks: / Just kiddin' / Hello and goodbye / Thinking of you / Why not? / Not yet / Suite sandrine part V
Recording Notes: New York pianist and composer. Latin jazz in the style and tradition of Titi Puente and others. All compositions by Michel Camilo.
Album: released on King (Japan), Jul'86 Dist: IMS, Polygram

Camia, Stan

SO VERY FIN DE SIECLE.
Cassette: released on Slob, Feb'84 by Slob Records. Dist: Falling A

Camouflage

SAMANTHA.
Single 7": released on Homespun(Ireland), Sep'84 by Homespun Records. Dist: Homespun, Outlet

Campaign

TRY AGAIN.
Single 7": released on CBS, Apr'83 by CBS Records. Dist: CBS

Campbell, Al

AIN'T THAT LOVING YOU.
Album: released on Vista Sounds, '83 by Vista Sounds Records. Dist: Jetstar

ALL KINDS OF PEOPLE.
Single 12": released on Greensleeves, May'83 by Greensleeves Records. Dist: BMG, Jetstar, Spartan

BABY BOY.
Single 12": released on CSA, Feb'84 by CSA Records. Dist: PRT, Jetstar, CSA

BAD BOY.
Album: released on CSA, May'84 by CSA Records. Dist: PRT, Jetstar, CSA

BEING WITH YOU.
Single 12": released on Greensleeves, Feb'82 by Greensleeves Records. Dist: BMG, Jetstar, Spartan

CAN'T TAKE THE PRESSURE.
Tracks: / Can't take the pressure / Police in England (computerised version)
Single 12": released on Greensleeves, Mar'86 by Greensleeves Records. Dist: BMG, Jetstar, Spartan

COLLIE HERB.
Single 12": released on Jah Life, May'85 by Jah Life Records. Dist: Jetstar

DANCE HALL STYLEE.
Single 12": released on Greensleeves, Jun'82 by Greensleeves Records. Dist: BMG, Jetstar, Spartan

DOWN IN BABYLON.
Single 12": released on Ethnic, Jun'84 Dist: Kingdom

EVERYBODY NEEDS LOVE.
Single 12": released on Striker Lee, Sep'85 by Striker Lee Records. Dist: Jetstar

Album: released on Motown, Apr'82 by Motown Records. Dist: BMG

Cassette: released on Motown, Apr'82 by Motown Records. Dist: BMG

FENCE TOO TALL.
Album: released on Live & Learn, May'87 Dist: Jetstar

FOWARD NATTY (Campbell, Al/Triston Palmer).
Album: released on Move, Mar'85 by Charly Records. Dist: Charly, Fast Forward, Cartel

Single 12": released on Live & Learn, Jun'85 Dist: Jetstar

FREEDOM STREET.
Album: released on Londisc, Aug'84 by Londisc Records. Dist: Jetstar

GEE BABY.
Single 12": released on Solomonic, Nov'83 by Solomonic Records. Dist: Jetstar, Pinnacle

GIMME WEH ME WANT.
Tracks: / Gimme weh me want / Gimme weh me want (version)

Single 12": released on Greensleeves, Jul'87 by Greensleeves Records. Dist: BMG, Jetstar, Spartan

GIVE ME LOVE.
Single 12": released on Mobiliser, Jan'84 by Jetstar Records. Dist: Jetstar

HOLD YOUR CORNER.
Tracks: / Hold your corner / Jammys posse
Single 12": released on Jammy's, Oct'86 by Jammy's Records. Dist: Jetstar

I CAN'T STOP LOVING YOU.
Tracks: / I can't stop loving you / I can't stop loving you (Version)
Single 12": released on Hands & Hearts, May'86 Dist: Jetstar

I SHOULD BE YOUR LOVER.
Single 12": released on J.B., Oct'82 Dist: Jetstar

I'VE GOT TO GET YOUR LOVING.
Single 12": released on Music Maker, Oct'82 by Music Maker Records. Dist: Jetstar

JUGGLING IN THE FRONT LINE.
Single 12": released on FMJ, Jun'85 by FMJ Records. Dist: Jetstar

JUST MY IMAGINATION.
Single 12": released on Exclusive, Dec'82 Dist: Jetstar

LAMBS BREAD.
78 rpm record: released on Silver Camel, Apr'82 Dist: Jetstar, Rough Trade

LET ME INTO YOUR WORLD.
Single 12": released on Music Works, Dec'82 Dist: Jetstar

LET THEM PROSPER.
Single 12": released on Black Solidarity, Nov'84 by Black Solidarity Records. Dist: Jetstar

LOVE AGAIN.
Tracks: / Love again
Single 7": released on Mix Music, 10 Oct'87 Dist: Jetstar

MASH IT ALREADY (Campbell, Al & Little John).
Single 12": released on Arrival, Sep'84 by Arrival Records. Dist: Revolver, Cartel

MORE SHOWCASE.
Album: released on Ethnic, May'84 Dist: Kingdom

OTHER SIDE OF LOVE, THE.
Tracks: / Old-time loving / Land of the living / If you want my love / Keep moving / Come let me hold your hand / Being with you / Other side of love, The / Don't tell me / You've changed / Hello stranger
Album: released on Greensleeves, Dec'81 by Greensleeves Records. Dist: BMG, Jetstar, Spartan

POLITICIANS.
Single 12": released on Move, Jul'86 by Charly Records. Dist: Charly, Fast Forward, Cartel

REGGAE '85 (Campbell, Al/Triston Palmer).
Recording Notes: See also under Triston Palmer.
Album: released on Blue Mountain, Nov'85 Dist: Jetstar

RIOT.
Single 12": released on John Dread Production, Nov'85 Dist: Charly, Jetstar

SHE NUH READY.
Single 12": released on Tads, Jul'84 by Tads Records. Dist: Jetstar*

STYLE & FASHION.
Single 12": released on Greensleeves, Aug'84 by Greensleeves Records. Dist: BMG, Jetstar, Spartan

TALK ABOUT LOVE.
Single 12": released on Scom, Apr'85 by Scom Records. Dist: Jetstar

TRY MY LOVE.
Tracks: / Try my love / Official fashion
Single 12": released on Fashion, May'86 by CSA Records. Dist: PRT, Jetstar, Revolver, Cartel

WHEN THE LIGHTS ARE LOW.
Single 12": released on Taxi, Apr'85 by Taxi Records. Dist: Jetstar

Campbell, Alex

CRM (Campbell, Alex/Alan Roberts/Dougie Maclean).
Tracks: / Trooper and the maid, The / I lo'e nae a lassie but ane / Jute mill song / Her fa la la lo / Wha widna fecht for Charlie / Leis a lurighan / Bonnie Mary / Rattlin' roarin' Willie / John Anderson my Jo / Miss Elspeth Campbell / Alick C. MacGregor / Jock Stewart / Little song
Recording Notes: Alex Campbell has well earned his nickname of the "Big daddy of Folk Music' having been one of the stalwarts of the scene for over 20 years. He has started and encouraged many of the familiar folk 'names' we know today, and he is joined by Alan Roberts and Dougie MacLean, whose singing and playing of Scottish songs and tunes is rapidly making their own reputation.
Album: released on Burlington, Nov'81 by Plant Life Records. Dist: Jazz Music, Projection, Swift, Celtic Music, Cadillac, Ross, Duncans, Impetus

LIVE IN BELGIUM.
Album: released on CCC, Feb'82 Dist: Folksound, Jazz Music

TRADITIONAL BALLADS OF SCOTLAND.
Tracks: / Battle of Otterbourne, The / Twa corbies, The / Bonnie James Campbell / Wae's me for Charlie / King Farewell / I will go / Bonnie Bessie Logan / Gypsy laddie, The / Bonnie Glenshee / Lord Gregory / Farewell farewell / Scotish settlers lament
Album: released on Sweet Folk All, '81 by Sweet Folk All Records. Dist: Sweet Folk All, Projection, Celtic Music, Jazz Music, Impetus, Wellard, Festival Records

Campbell, Barbara

I'M A WOMAN.
Single 12": by Red Rose Records. Dist: Jetstar

Campbell, Bill

ENDLESS LOVE (Campbell, Bill & Valerie Harrison).
Single 12": released on BB, Oct'81 Dist: Jetstar

LET ME HAVE THE CHANCE (Campbell, Bill & Lillie Welsh).
Tracks: / Guilty
Single 12": released on Backbeat, Nov'86 Dist: Jetstar

ON MY OWN (Campbell, Bill & Valerie Harrison).
Tracks: / On my own / For the love of you
Recording Notes: See also under Valerie Harrison.
Single 12": released on Blackbeat, May'86 Dist: Jetstar

TAKE ME AND MAKE ME.
Single 12": released on Cima, Oct'84 by Cima Records. Dist: Jetstar

TONIGHT I CELEBRATE MY LOVE (Campbell, Bill & Valerie Harrison).
Single 12": released on BB, Oct'83 Dist: Jetstar

WE ARE (FUNKY).
Tracks: / We are (funky) / We are (funky) part 2
Single 12": released on BB, Feb'86 Dist: Jetstar

WHO TOUCHED SHE BAM BAM.
Single 12": released on Blackbeat, Aug'86 Dist: Jetstar

Campbell, Carol

EVERYHTHING I LOVE SEEMS TO DIE.
Single 12": released on Sea View, Apr'84 by Sea View Records. Dist: Jetstar

GOT TO LET YOU KNOW.
Tracks: / Got to let you know / Got to let you know (Nightflight Band)

I'M IN LOVE.
Single 7": released on Sea View, Nov'85 by Sea View Records. Dist: Jetstar

IT'S REAL.
Single 12": released on Sea View, Jan'85 by Sea View Records. Dist: Jetstar

LET'S KISS AND MAKE UP.
Single 12": released on Jenieves, Dec'82 by Jenieves Records. Dist: Jetstar

LET'S TRY AGAIN.
Single 12": released on Sea View, Aug'84 by Sea View Records. Dist: Jetstar

Campbell, Colin

COLLECTION OF SONGS, A.
Cassette: released on Ross, Jan'86 by Ross Records. Dist: Ross, Taylors, Celtic Music, Roots

HIGHLAND STYLE (Campbell, Colin & his Highland Band).
Album: released on Lismor, '73 by Lismor Records. Dist: Projection, Celtic Music, Taylors, Cadillac, Outlet, Roots, Ross

LET'S ALL DANCE AND SING (Campbell, Colin & His Highland Band).
Album: released on Beltona, '72 by Decca Records. Dist: Polygram

LOCAL RADIO.
Cassette: released on Ross, Jan'86 by Ross Records. Dist: Ross, Taylors, Celtic Music, Roots

LOCAL RADIO VOL.2.
Cassette: released on Ross, Jan'86 by Ross Records. Dist: Ross, Taylors, Celtic Music, Roots

Campbell, Cornell

CONSCIOUS LOVER.
Single 12": Dist: Jetstar

CORNELL CAMPBELL MEETS THE GAYLADS.
Album: released on Culture Press, Mar'85 by Vista Sounds Records. Dist: Cadillac, Rough Trade, Jetstar, Celtic Music, Jazz Music

FIGHT AGAINST CORRUPTION.
Album: released on Vista Sounds, '83 by Vista Sounds Records. Dist: Jetstar

HUNDRED POUNDS OF COLLIE (Campbell, Cornell & Pappa Tullo).
Single 12": released on Black Joy, Jun'82 Dist: Jetstar

I AM A MAN.
Single 12": released on Black Music, Jul'82 by Black Music Records. Dist: Jetstar

JOHNNIE CLARK MEETS CORNELL CAMPBELL IN NEW STYLE (see Clark, Johnnie) (Campbell, Cornell & Johnnie Clark).
Album: released on Vista Sounds, '83 by Vista Sounds Records. Dist: Jetstar

LOVE THAT'S TRUE.
Single 12": released on Kingdom Records, Jun'81 by Kingdom Records. Dist: Kingdom, PRT, Wellard

LOVE TRAP (Campbell, Cornell & Raymond Naptali).
Single 12": released on Shuttle, Apr'83 Dist: BMG

NEVER LET IT GO.
Single 12": released on Greensleeves, Nov'83 by Greensleeves Records. Dist: BMG, Jetstar, Spartan

TURN BACK THE HANDS OF TIME.
Album: released on Third World, Dec'77 Dist: Jetstar*

UNFAIR GAME.
Tracks: / Unfair game
Single 12": released on Live & Love, Mar'87 by Third World Records. Dist: Jetstar

WE A BOOBLING.
Single 12": released on Striker, Oct'84 by Striker Records. Dist: Jetstar

WHAT KIND OF WORLD ARE WE LIVING IN? (Campbell, Cornell & Peter Metro).
Single 12": released on Mobiliser, Jan'84 by Jetstar Records. Dist: Jetstar

YOU ARE MY LADY.
Single 12": released on Guidance, Apr'83 Dist: Jetstar

YOU WALKING.
Single 12": released on Earthquake, Mar'83 by Earthquake Records. Dist: Jetstar

Campbell, Del

POWER.
Album: released on BB, May'86 Dist: Jetstar

Campbell, Dudley

BAPTISM.
Single 12": released on Cartridge, May'82 by Cartridge. Dist: Jetstar

GETTING STRONGER.
Single 12": released on Cartridge, May'82 by Cartridge. Dist: Jetstar

Campbell, Eddie

BADDEST CAT ON THE BLOCK, (THE).
Tracks: / Hye baby / 19 years old / I'm in love with you baby / Tears are for losers / Early in the morning / Same thing / Cha cha blues / Cheaper to keep her
Album: released on JSP, Feb'85 by JSP Records. Dist: Taylors, Hotshot, Conifer, Jazz Music, Swift, Wellard

KING OF THE JUNGLE.
Album: released on Rooster, Apr'86 by Rooster Records. Dist: Celtic Music, Projection, Roots, Cadillac, Topic, Ross, Duncans, Impetus

LET'S PICK IT.
Album: released on Black Magic, Feb'85 Dist: Cadillac, Projection, Swift, Celtic Music, Topic, Ross, Duncans, Impetus

Campbell, Ethna

FOR THE GOOD TIMES.
Tracks: / All my trials / Early morning rain / For the good times / From clare to here / Hallelujah I love him so / I'll be your baby tonight / I'm so lonesome I could cry / Isn't it funny / Love is strange / Lovin' you / Song of evening / Til tomorrow
Album: released on Philips, '77 Dist: IMS-Polygram

OLD RUGGED CROSS, (THE).
Tracks: / Airport song / Boulder to Birmingham / By the time I get to Phoenix / Going my way / House of gold / How great thou art / It's no secret / Jeannie's affraid of the dark / Old rugged cross, The / Try to remember / Wedding song, The / Wichita lineman
Album: released on Philips, Apr'86 Dist: IMS-Polygram

PEACE IN THE VALLEY.
Album: released on Scotdisc, Oct'87 by Scotdisc Records. Dist: Duncans, Sounds of Scotland

Cassette: released on Scotdisc, Oct'87 by Scotdisc Records. Dist: Duncans, Sounds of Scotland

Campbell, Evrol

NEAREST TO MY HEART.
Single 7": released on Stiff, Feb'83 by Stiff Records. Dist: EMI, Record Services(Ireland), Jazz Music

Campbell Family

SINGING CAMPBELLS, (THE).
Album: released on Topic, '81 Dist: Projection

Campbell, Glen

20 CLASSIC TRACKS: GLEN CAMPBELL.
Album: released on MFP, Sep'81 by Music For Pleasure Records. Dist: EMI

Cassette: released on MFP, Sep'81 by Music For Pleasure Records. Dist: EMI

20 GOLDEN GREATS: GLEN CAMPBELL.
Album: released on EMI(Capitol), Oct'76 by Capitol Records. Dist: EMI

Cassette: released on EMI(Capitol), Oct'76 by Capitol Records. Dist: EMI

Compact disc: released on EMI, Nov'87 by EMI Records(UK). Dist: EMI

20 GOLDEN PIECES: GLEN CAMPBELL.
Album: released on Bulldog Records, Oct'82 Dist: President, Jazz Music, Taylors, Spartan

Cassette: released on Bulldog Records, Nov'82 Dist: President, Jazz Music, Taylors, Spartan

ALL I HAVE TO DO IS DREAM (Campbell, Glen & Bobbie Gentry).
Tracks: / All I have to do is dream / Less of me / Gentle on my mind / Heart to heart talk / My elusive dreams / Let it be me / Little green apples / Mornin' glory / Terrible tangled web / Sunday mornin' / (It's only your) imagination / Scarborough fair / Canticle
Album: released on MFP, Jan'83 by Music For Pleasure Records. Dist: EMI

Cassette: released on MFP, Jan'83 by Music For Pleasure Records. Dist: EMI

COLLECTION: GLEN CAMPBELL.
Album: released on EMI(Germany), '83 by EMI Records(UK). Dist: Pinnacle

Boxed set: released on Ember, Sep'78 by Bulldog Records. Dist: President, Spartan, Swift

COUNTRY.
Album: released on MFP, Jan'85 by Music For Pleasure Records. Dist: EMI

Cassette: released on MFP, Jan'85 by Music For Pleasure Records. Dist: EMI

COUNTRY FAVOURITES.
Album: released on Capitol, Apr'84 by Capitol Records. Dist: EMI

Cassette: released on Capitol, Apr'84 by Capitol Records. Dist: EMI

GLEN CAMPBELL SINGS WITH ANNE MURRAY & BOBBIE GENTRY.
Album: released on MFP(Holland), Mar'84 by Music For Pleasure Records. Dist: Conifer

Cassette: released on MFP(Holland), Mar'84 by Music For Pleasure Records. Dist: Conifer

GLEN CAMPBELL STORY, THE.
Compact disc: released on K-Tel, Jan'86 by K-Tel Records. Dist: K-Tel, Celtic Music, Terry Blood, Wynd-Up, Taylors, Pickwick, Solomon & Peres, Polygram

GLEN CAMPBELL'S GREATEST HITS.
Tracks: / Honey come back / Gentle on my mind / Everything a man could need / Galveston / Try a little kindness / Dreams of the everyday housewife / By the time I get to Phoenix / Where's the playground Susi / It's only make believe / Wichita lineman / All I have to do is dream
Recording Notes: Original catalogue number ST 21885 (album); TCST 21885 (cassette).
Album: released on Capitol, Mar'85 by Capitol Records. Dist: EMI

Cassette: released on Capitol, Mar'85 by Capitol Records. Dist: EMI

IF YOU WERE MY LADY (Campbell, Glen & Diane Solomon).
Single 7": released on Energy, Oct'82 by Energy Records. Dist: President, Jazz Music, Taylors, Spartan

IT'S JUST A MATTER OF TIME.
Tracks: / It's just a matter of time / Wild winds / Cowboy hall of fame / Rag doll / Call home / Do what you gotta do / Cowpoke / Shattered / Sweet sixteen / Gene Autry, my hero
Album: released on Atlantic, Jan'86 by WEA Records. Dist: WEA, Swift, Celtic Music

Cassette: released on Atlantic, Jan'86 by WEA Records. Dist: WEA, Swift, Celtic Music

IT'S THE WORLD GONE CRAZY.
Tracks: / Why don't we just sleep on it tonight / I don't want to know your name / In cars / It's the world gone crazy / Rollin' / Nothing quite like love / Daisy a day, A / Any which way you want / It's your world
Album: released on Capitol, Apr'81 by Capitol Records. Dist: EMI Deleted '83.

Cassette: released on Capitol, Apr'81 by Capitol Records. Dist: EMI

JUST A MATTER OF TIME.
Tracks: / Just a matter of time / Gene Autry, my hero
Single 7": released on Atlantic, Mar'86 by WEA Records. Dist: WEA, Swift, Celtic Music

LETTING GO.
Single 7": released on Compleat, Apr'84 by Compleat Records. Dist: PRT

LIVE: GLEN CAMPBELL.
Album: released on RCA, Dec'81 by RCA Records. Dist: BMG

Cassette: released on RCA, Dec'81 by RCA Records. Dist: BMG Deleted '83.

Album: released on EEC Imports, Jan'83 Dist: IMS, Polygram

Cassette: released on EEC Imports, Jan'83 Dist: IMS, Polygram

RHINESTONE COWBOY.
Single 7": released on Capitol, May'75 by Capitol Records. Dist: EMI

SOUTHERN NIGHTS.
Album: released on Capitol(Greenlight), Jun'81 by Capitol Records. Dist: Conifer Deleted '83.

Cassette: released on Capitol(Greenlight), Jun'81 by Capitol Records. Dist: Conifer

Single 7": released on Capitol, Sep'85 by Capitol Records. Dist: EMI

STILL WITHIN THE SOUND OF MY VOICE.
Tracks: / I'm a one woman man / Still within the sound of my voice / Hand that rocks the cradle, The / For sure, for certain, forever, for always / I have you / You are / Arkansas / In my life / Leavin's not the only way to go / I remember you
Compact disc: released on MCA, Oct'87 by MCA Records. Dist: Polygram

Album: released on MCA, Oct'87 by MCA Records. Dist: Polygram

Cassette: released on MCA, Oct'87 by MCA Records. Dist: Polygram

THAT CHRISTMAS FEELING.
Album: released on MFP, Dec'82 by Music For Pleasure Records. Dist: EMI

Cassette: released on MFP, Dec'82 by Music For Pleasure Records. Dist: EMI

THEY STILL DANCE TO WALTZES IN ENGLAND.
Single 7": released on Atlantic, May'84 by WEA Records. Dist: WEA, Swift, Celtic Music

TOGETHER (Campbell, Glen & Anne Murray).
Album: released on MFP(Holland), Jan'85 by Music For Pleasure Records. Dist: Conifer

Cassette: released on MFP, Jan'85 by Music For Pleasure Records. Dist: EMI

Album: released on MFP, Jan'85 by Music For Pleasure Records. Dist: EMI

TWENTY GOLDEN GREATS.
Tracks: / Rinestone cowboy / Both sides now / By the time I get to Phoenix / Gentle on my mind / Too many mornings / Wichita lineman / One last time / Don't pull your love, then tell me goodbye / Reason to believe / It's only make believe / Honey come back / Give me back that old familiar feeling / Galveston / Dreams of the everyday housewife / Last thing on my mind, The / Where's the playground, Susie / Try a little kindness / Country boy (you got your feet in L.A.) / All I have to do is dream / Amazing Grace
Compact disc: released on Capitol, Nov'87 by Capitol Records. Dist: EMI

Album: released on Capitol(Greenlight), Jun'81 by Capitol Records. Dist: Conifer Deleted '83.

Cassette: released on Capitol(Greenlight), Jun'81 by Capitol Records. Dist: Conifer

VERY BEST OF GLEN CAMPBELL.
Tracks: / Rhinestone cowboy / Wichita lineman / Galveston / By the time I get to Phoenix / Try a little kindness / My little one / Where' the playground Susie / Gentle on my mind / Dreams of the everyday housewife / All I have to do is dream / Dream baby (How long must I dream) / It's only make believe / Sunflower / Southern nights / Country boy (you got your feet in L.A.)
Compact disc: released on EMI, Jul'87 by EMI Records(UK). Dist: EMI

WOMAN'S TOUCH.
Single 7": released on Atlantic, Oct'82 by WEA Records. Dist: WEA, Swift, Celtic Music

Campbell, Gloria

ONE OF US.
Single 12": released on Pioneer International, Aug'85 by Pioneer International Records. Dist: Jetstar

TONIGHT IS MY NIGHT OUT.
Single 12": released on Disco Rocker, Apr'82 by BMD. Dist: Echo

Campbell, Gordon

I WOULD LOVE YOU.
Single 7": released on Holyrood, May'85 Dist: Pinnacle Deleted '87.

JUST LET ME.
Tracks: / Just let me / Miss miss miss
Single 7": released on Rocket, May'87 by Phonogram Records. Dist: Polygram

WITH A WOMAN LIKE YOU.
Single 7": released on Holyrood, Jul'83 Dist: Pinnacle Deleted '87.

YOU ARE MY WOMAN.
Album: released on Holyrood, Oct'83 Dist: Pinnacle Deleted '87.

YOU CAN'T ALWAYS WANT WHAT YOU GET.
Single 7": released on Holyrood, Oct'84 Dist: Pinnacle Deleted '87.

Campbell, Ian

LIVE: IAN CAMPBELL (Campbell, Ian Folk Group).
Recording Notes: Mono production.
Album: released on Storyville, May'86 by Storyville Records. Dist: Swift, Wellard

Campbell, James

NASHVILLE STREET BAND (Campbell, Blind James).
Album: released on Arhoolie(USA), May'81 by Arhoolie Records. Dist: Jazz Music, Projection, Roots, Celtic Music, Cadillac, Ross, Duncans, Impetus

Campbell, Jo Ann

FOR TWISTIN' & LISTENIN'.
Album: released on ABC, Oct'87 by MCA Records. Dist: Polygram

MISS REET PETITE.
Tracks: / Crazy Daisy / Motorcycle Michael / I changed my mind Jack / Mr Lee / Dance with me Henry / Willie and the hand jive / Duane / Mama don't want no twistin' / Kookie little paradise, A / I wish it would rain all summer / You made me love you / Eddie my love / Bobby Bobby Bobby / Amateur night / Goodbye Jimmy goodbye / Puka puka pants
Recording Notes: Licensed from MCA Records Ltd. This compilation (P) 1986, 1986 Charly Records Ltd.
Album: released on Charly, Apr'86 by Charly Records. Dist: Charly, Cadillac, Swift

Campbell, John

WISPS OF BALLADS.
Album: released on Outlet, Oct'79 by Outlet Records. Dist: Projection, Duncans, Outlet, Celtic Music, Roots

Cassette: released on Outlet, Oct'79 by Outlet Records. Dist: Projection, Duncans, Outlet, Celtic Music, Roots

Campbell, Junior

HALLELUJAH FREEDOM.
Single 7": released on Old Gold, Oct'83 by Old Gold Records. Dist: PRT, Counterpoint, Lightning, Jazz Music, Taylors

Campbell, Malcolm

BUCK UP.
Single 12": released on Solid Groove, Feb'82 Dist: Jetstar, Pinnacle

Campbell, Mike

SECRET FANTASY.
Album: released on Palo Alto (Italy), Jan'84

Campbell, Pat

JUST A QUIET CONVERSATION.
Album: released on Release(Ireland), Jan'78 Dist: I & B, Solomon & Peres, Wynd-Up

Campbell, Patrick

WAVING ALL EXCUSES.
Cassette: released on Listen Productions, Nov'84, Hayward Promotions

Campbell, Pete

CARIBBEAN CIRCUS SHOW.
Single 12": released on B.B. Music, Mar'85 by B.B. Music Records. Dist: Jetstar

HOLDING BACK THE YEARS.
Tracks: / Holding back the years / Blue music
Single 12": released on PC, Aug'86 Dist: Jetstar

I WANT TO WAKE UP WITH YOU.
Tracks: / I want to wake up with you / I want to wake up with you (version)
Single 12": released on Blackbeat, Aug'86 Dist: Jetstar

LET'S MAKE A BABY.
Single 12": released on PC, Nov'84 Dist: Jetstar

RED RED WINE.
Single 12": released on Caribbean Echo, Oct'83 Dist: Jetstar

SHAVING CREAM.
Tracks: / Shaving cream (instrumental)
Single 12": released on PC, Nov'86 Dist: Jetstar

Campbell & Reid

SWEET VIBRATIONS.
Album: released on Sweet Folk & Country, '78 Dist: Wellard, Cadillac

Campbell, Ricky

DON'T BLAME ME FOR YOUR MISTAKE.
Tracks: / Other side (The)
Single 12": released on Time, Jan'87 Dist: Jetstar

Campbell, Robert

LIVING IN THE SHADOW OF A DOWNTOWN MOVIE SHOW.
Album: by Decca Records. Dist: Polygram

Campbell, Rocky

BUONA SERA.
Single 12": released on Sunburn, Dec'83 by Orbitone Records. Dist: Jetstar

FATHER BEG YOUR PARDON.
Single 12": released on Cartridge, May'82 by Cartridge. Dist: Jetstar

RHYTHM AND ROCK.
Album: released on Orbitone, '78 by Orbitone Records. Dist: Jetstar

Campbell, Shona

SCOTLAND MY HOME.
Album: released on Lismor, Nov'82 by Lismor Records. Dist: Projection, Celtic Music, Taylors, Cadillac, Outlet, Roots, Ross

Cassette: released on Lismor, Nov'82 by Lismor Records. Dist: Projection, Celtic Music, Taylors, Cadillac, Outlet, Roots, Ross

Campbell, Stan

CRAWFISH.
Tracks: / Crawfish / Till we meet again
Single 7": released on WEA, Mar'87 by WEA Records. Dist: WEA

Single 12": by WEA Records. Dist: WEA

KNOCKING ON HEAVENS DOOR.
Single 7": released on WEA, Aug'87 by WEA Records. Dist: WEA

Single 12": released on WEA, Aug'87 by WEA Records. Dist: WEA

STAN CAMPBELL.
Tracks: / Years go by / Crawfish / Seven more days / Save the world / Dancing troupe / Little more faith / You'll never know / Don't let me be misunderstood / Can't get enough / Strange fruit
Album: released on WEA, Apr'87 by WEA Records. Dist: WEA

Cassette: released on WEA, Apr'87 by WEA Records. Dist: WEA

Compact disc: released on WEA, Apr'87 by WEA Records. Dist: WEA

YEARS GO BY.
Tracks: / Years go oy / Seven more days
Single 7": released on WEA, May'87 by WEA Records. Dist: WEA

Single 12": released on WEA, May'87 by WEA Records. Dist: WEA

Campbell Town Band

MULL OF KINTYRE.
Compact disc: released on Chrysalis, Jun'87 by Chrysalis Records. Dist: CBS

Campbell, Trevor 'Big T'

DESIDERATA.
Tracks: / Desiderata / Desiderata (instrumental)
Single 7": released on Mint, Dec'83 by Emerald Records. Dist: Ross, Solomon & Peres

Campbell-Lyons

NAKED ROBOTS WATCHING BREAKFAST TV (Campbell-Lyons, Patrick).
Single 7": released on Public, Nov'81 by Patrick Cambell-Lyons. Dist: Spartan

Campbeltown Pipe Band

MULL OF KINTYRE.
Tracks: / Mull of Kintyre / Lara's theme / Legion's last patrol / Drummer's call / My land / Battle's o'er, The / Green hills of Tyrol, The / Liberton pipe band / Floral dance, The / Kilberry ball / Highland Mary / Wee Highland laddie, The / Soldier's return / Malcolm Lang / Kyle sku / Flower of Scotland / Serenade of Heyken / Murray's welcome / Men of Argyle / Haughs of Cromdale, The / Rhodesian regiment, The / Colin's cattle / Sheiling, The / Braes of Tullymet, The / Munlochy Bridge / Bogallan / Raven's rock, The / Banks of the Avon / Connaught man's rambles, The
Album: released on MFP, Jun'85 by Music For Pleasure Records. Dist: EMI

Cassette: released on MFP, Jun'85 by Music For Pleasure Records. Dist: EMI

Camper Van Beethoven

GOOD BUYS AND BAD GUYS.
Album: released on Rough Trade, 21 Nov'87 by Rough Trade Records. Dist: Rough Trade, Cartel

Single 12": released on Rough Trade, Oct'87 by Rough Trade Records. Dist: Rough Trade, Cartel

II & III & PLUS.
Recording Notes: White vinyl edition.
Double Album: released on Line(W.Germany), Nov'87 Dist: Pinnacle

III.
Recording Notes: Includes Take the Skinheads Bowling.
Compact disc: released on Line(W.Germany), Nov'87 Dist: Pinnacle

TAKE THE SKINHEADS BOWLING.
Tracks: / Take the skinheads bowling
Single 7": released on Rough Trade, Mar'87 by Rough Trade Records. Dist: Rough Trade, Cartel

Single 12": released on Rough Trade, Mar'87 by Rough Trade Records. Dist: Rough Trade, Cartel

TELEPHONE FREE LANDSLIDE VICTORY.
Album: released on Rough Trade, Apr'86 by Rough Trade Records. Dist: Rough Trade, Cartel

THIRD LP, THE.
Album: released on Rough Trade, Dec'86 by Rough Trade Records. Dist: Rough Trade, Cartel

VAMPIRE CAN MATING OVEN.
Album: released on Pitch-A-Tent (USA), Nov'87 Dist: Pinnacle. Estim retail price in Nov'87 was £6.49.

Camper Van Chadbourne

CAMPER VAN CHADBOURNE.
Album: released on Fundamental, Dec'87 by Fundamental Records. Dist: Red Rhino, Cartel

Campi, Ray

BOOZE IT.
Single 7": released on Rollin' Rock, Jun'80 Dist: Jazz Music, Pinnacle, Swift

CATERPILLAR.
Single 7": released on Rollin' Rock, Jul'81 Dist: Jazz Music, Pinnacle, Swift

EAGER BEAVER BOY.
Album: released on Rollin' Rock, Jun'80 Dist: Jazz Music, Pinnacle, Swift

EAGER BEAVER BOY.
Single 7": released on Rollin' Rock, Jun'80 Dist: Jazz Music, Pinnacle, Swift

GONE, GONE, GONE.
Album: released on Rollin' Rock, Oct'86 Dist: Jazz Music, Pinnacle, Swift

MY BABY LEFT ME.
Single 7": released on Rollin' Rock, Jun'80 Dist: Jazz Music, Pinnacle, Swift

NEWEST WAVE.
Single 7": released on Rollin' Rock, Jun'80 Dist: Jazz Music, Pinnacle, Swift

NEWEST WAVE, THE (Campi, Ray & His Rockabilly Rebels).
Tracks: / Newest wave, The / Lucky to be in love / Rockabilly music / Boo hoo / Cruisin / Once is enough / Will of love, The / I've been around / Sweet woman blues / You nearly lose your mind / Sweet mama baby / Do what you did / She don't belong to me / My heart's on fire / Right back where we started from
Album: released on Rondelet Music & Records, Apr'81 Dist: Pinnacle, Cartel, Rondelet

PLAY IT COOL (Campi, Ray & His Snappers).
Single 7": released on Rollercoaster, Sep'81 by Rollercoaster Records. Dist: Swift, Rollercoaster

RAY CAMPI ROLLIN' ROCK SINGLES COLLECTION 1971-1978, THE.
Tracks: / Eager boy / Tore up / If it's all the same to you / Pan American boogie / Sixteen chicks / Baby left me / Lil bit of heartache, A / Booze it / Wrong wrong wrong / Rockin' at the Ritz / Quit your triffin / Rattlin daddy / Wild one
Album: released on Rondelet Music & Records, Nov'81 Dist: Pinnacle, Cartel, Rondelet

RAY CAMPI ROLLIN' ROCK SINGLES COLLECTION 1971-1978, THE.
Tracks: / Eager boy / Tore up / If it's all the same to you / Pan American boogie / Sixteen chicks / Baby left me / Lil bit of heartache, A / Booze it / Wrong wrong wrong / Rockin' at the Ritz / Quit your triffin / Rattlin daddy / Wild one.
Album: released on Rondelet in Nov'81. Distributed by: Spartan Distribution

ROCKABILLY LIVES.
Album: released on Rollin' Rock in Jun'80

ROCKABILLY MAN (Campi, Ray & His Rockabilly Rebels).
Tracks: / Rockabilly man / Love and lots more love / No way out / Don't come knockin' / Don't let the bad times let you down / Give me a taste / Can't you Yodel blues / Hollywood cats / Recipe for love / Soul sisters / Little love lies / Hold that train / It's blowin away.
Album: released on Rondelet in Nov'81. Distributed by: Spartan Distribution

ROCKABILLY REBELLION.
Album: released on Rollin' Rock (USA) in Oct'86 by Rondelet Music And Records. Distributed by: Jazz Music Distribution, Pinnacle, Swift Distribution

Album: released on Rollin' Rock in Jun'80

ROCKABILLY ROCKET.
Album: released on Rollin' Rock in Jun'80

ROCKIN' AT THE RITZ (Campi, Ray & His Rockabilly Rebels).
Single (7"): released on Rondelet in Dec'81. Distributed by: Spartan Distribution

SIXTEEN CHICKS.
Single (7"): released on Rollin' Rock in Jun'80

TORE UP.
Single (7"): released on Rollin' Rock in Jun'80

Camp Sophisto

SONGS IN PRAISE OF THE REVOLUTION.
Single (7"): released on Pure Freude in Aug'83. Distributed by: Swift

Camp, Steve

FOR EVERY MAN.
Album: released on Myrrh in May'82 by Word Records. Distributed by: Word Distribution

Cassette: released on Myrrh in May'82 by Word Records. Distributed by: Word Distribution

ONE ON ONE.
Notes: Steve Camp is back with another exciting album. His last album 'Shake Me To Wake Me' took his 80's pop/rock artist in new directions both musically and spiritually. 'One On One' does not deviate from this. Steve has brought together the strengths of previous endeavours in a solid and consistently recognisable form. 'One On One' extends and improves upon his now established formula.
Album: released on Sparrow in Jan'87 by Word Records. Distributed by: Spartan

Cassette: released on Sparrow in Jan'87 by Word Records. Distributed by: Spartan

SAYIN IT WITH LOVE.
Album: released on Myrrh in May'82 by Word Records. Distributed by: Word Distribution

Cassette: released on Myrrh in May'82 by Word Records. Distributed by: Word Distribution

SHAKE ME TO WAKE ME.
Album: released on Sparrow in Aug'85 by Word Records. Distributed by: Spartan

Cassette: released on Sparrow in Aug'85 by Word Records. Distributed by: Spartan

Can

EGE BAMYASI.
Album: released on United Artists in '72

FLOW MOTION.
Tracks: / I want more / Cascade waltz / Laugh till you cry / Live till you die / And more / Babylonian pearl / Smoke (E.F.S. No.59) / Flow motion.
Compact disc: released on Virgin in 20 Jun'87 by Virgin Records. Distributed by: EMI, Virgin Distribution

Album: released on Virgin in Oct'76 by Virgin Records. Distributed by: EMI, Virgin Distribution

Album: released on EMI (Germany) in Aug'83 by EMI Records. Distributed by: Conifer

FUTURE DAYS.
Album: released on United Artists in '74

Album: released on Thunderbolt in Feb'85 by Magnum Music Group Ltd. Distributed by: Magnum Music Group Ltd, PRT Distribution, Spartan Distribution

INNER SPACE.
Compact disc: by Magnum Music Group Ltd. Distributed by: Magnum Music Group Ltd, PRT Distribution, Spartan Distribution

LANDED.
Compact disc: released on Virgin in Jun'87 by Virgin Records. Distributed by: EMI, Virgin Distribution

LIMITED EDITION.
Album: released on United Artists in Aug'74

MOONSHAKE.
Single (12"): released on Cherry Red in Mar'83 by Cherry Red Records. Distributed by: Pinnacle

OUT OF REACH.
Album: released on Thunderbolt in Jun'86 by Magnum Music Group Ltd. Distributed by: Magnum Music Group Ltd, PRT Distribution, Spartan Distribution

Cassette: released on Thunderbolt in Jun'86 by Magnum Music Group Ltd. Distributed by: Magnum Music Group Ltd, PRT Distribution, Spartan Distribution

PREHISTORIC FUTURE.
Cassette: released on Tago Mago in Jan'85. Distributed by: Rough Trade Distribution, Cartel Distribution

SAW DELIGHT.
Compact disc: released on Virgin in 20 Jun'87 by Virgin Records. Distributed by: EMI, Virgin Distribution

SOON OVER BABALUMA.
Album: released on United Artists in Nov'74

SOUNDTRACKS.
Album: released on United Artists in '73

Canadian Brass

MOSTLY FATS Fats Waller's greatest hits.
Album: released on Red Seal in Jul'80 by RCA Records. Distributed by: RCA

Canal

CANAL Original soundtrack.
Album: released on That's Entertainment in Apr'83 by That's Entertainment Records. Distributed by: Pinnacle, PRT

Canal Street Jazz Band

NEW ORLEANS STOMP.
Album: released on Stomp Off in Sep'86 by Stomp Off Records. Distributed by: Jazz Music Distribution

Can-can

CALL ME MADAM Berlin.
Album:

CAN-CAN Original soundtrack.
Album: released on Capitol in May'85 by Capitol Records. Distributed by: EMI

Cassette: released on Capitol in May'85 by Capitol Records. Distributed by: EMI

Album: released on EMI (Germany) in '83 by EMI Records. Distributed by: Conifer

INFORMER, THE.
Single (12"): released on Illegal in Nov'12 by Faulty Products Records. Distributed by: Pinnacle, Lightning, Cartel

Candice

MY HEART.
Tracks: / No, no sin, no sin at all / My Heart.
Single (12"): released on TR in Nov'86

Candido

DANCIN' & PRANCIN'.
Album: released on Salsoul in Sep'79

JINGO.
Single (12"): released on Streetwave in Nov'86 by Streetwave Records. Distributed by: PRT Distribution

Candle

ANIMALS AND OTHER THINGS (Candle & The Agapeland Singers).
Album: released on Birdwing in May'82 by Word Records. Distributed by: Word Distribution

Cassette: released on Birdwing in May'82 by Word Records. Distributed by: Word Distribution

BIRTHDAY PARTY.
Album: released on Birdwing in May'82 by Word Records. Distributed by: Word Distribution

Cassette: released on Birdwing in May'82 by Word Records. Distributed by: Word Distribution

BULLFROGS AND BUTTERFLIES (Candle & The Agape Force Prep. School).
Album: released on Birdwing in May'82 by Word Records. Distributed by: Word Distribution

Cassette: released on Birdwing in May'82 by Word Records. Distributed by: Word Distribution

MUSIC MACHINE, THE Children's musical, A.
Tracks: / Land called love / Music machine, The / Whistle song / Smile / String song, The / Patience / Gentleness / Faith / Joy / Peace / Goodness / Love / Self-control / Kindness / Reprise.
Album: released on Birdwing in May'82 by Word Records. Distributed by: Word Distribution

Cassette: released on Birdwing in May'82 by Word Records. Distributed by: Word Distribution

SIR OLIVER'S SONG (Candle & The Agape Force Prep. School).
Album: released on Birdwing in May'82 by Word Records. Distributed by: Word Distribution

Cassette: released on Birdwing in May'82 by Word Records. Distributed by: Word Distribution

TO THE CHIEF MUSICIAN CHAPTER II.
Tracks: / Come on rejoice / Simple song / Surely goodness and mercy / Alpha and Omega / Love from the father / Lord, show me what it means / Whom have I in heaven / Talk with me / Not to us / I trust you / In love / Holy is the lord / I will praise thee / Freely sing / All I want to do / Voice of thankfulness / Greatest thing, The / Press on.
Album: released on Birdwing in May'82 by Word Records. Distributed by: Word Distribution

Cassette: released on Birdwing in May'82 by Word Records. Distributed by: Word Distribution

WITHIN THE GATE.
Tracks: / Soldiers of the army / Stay on the battlefield / I will sing / Scripture reading / Fill me now / Lord of hosts / Glory to God in the highest / Glory, Jesus glory / I want to be in service for Jesus / Lord is my strength, The / Lay hold / Steadfast love, The / Living fire / Hallelujah song / Scripture reading / Worthy / Greatest thing, The / Higher,higher.
Album: released on Birdwing in May'82 by Word Records. Distributed by: Word Distribution

Cassette: released on Birdwing in May'82 by Word Records. Distributed by: Word Distribution

Candlelight Dancing

CANDLELIGHT DANCING Various artists (Various Artists).
Album: released on Karussell (Germany) in May'82

Cassette: released on Karussell (Germany) in May'82

Candler, Norman

Dreaming In the sun

TRIBUTE TO JOHN LENNON, A.
Tracks: / Mind games / (Just like) Starting over / Woman / Whatever gets you thru' the night / Mother / Oh my love / Tribute to John, a / Oh Yoko / Happy X-mas(war is over) / Imagine / Power to the people.
Notes: Since his tragic murder in New York, John Lennon's songs, already well loved and acclaimed during his lifetime have assumed a new level of significance for millions of people throughout the world. This selection of new recordings from Norman Candler consists of eleven classic Lennon compositions and one by Candler himself (titled 'A tribute to John')
Album: released on Telefunken in Oct'81

Cassette: released on Telefunken in Oct'81

Candoli, Conte

FINE AND DANDY.
Tracks: / Fine and dandy / I'm getting sentimental over you / Night flight / I can't get started / On the Alamo / Groovin' higher / Tune for Tex / My funny Valentine / They can't take that away from me / Everything happens to me / Toot suite / I'll remember April.
Notes: A Bethlehem recording. Licenced from International Jazz Emporium Inc.
Album: released on Affinity in Jan'87 by Charly Records. Distributed by: Charly, Cadillac

GETTIN' TOGETHER See under Pepper, Art.

GROOVIN' HIGHER (Candoli, Conte Quintet).
Tracks: / Toot suite / Jazz city blues / My old flame / Full count / I'm getting sentimental over you / Four / Groovin higher.
Album: released on Affinity in May'82 by Charly Records. Distributed by: Charly, Cadillac

Candy

BABY BABY I STILL LOVE YOU.
Single (7"): released on Speed in Sep'83

Candy From...

CANDY (Candy From Peppermint Rock).
Single (7"): released on KA in Feb'83

Candy Girls

NO ONE'S GONNA LOVE YOU.
Single (12"): released on Record Shack in Sep'84 by Record Shack Records. Distributed by: PRT

Candy Roxx

SEX AND LEATHER.
Single (12"): released on Sword in Feb'85 by Sword Records. Distributed by: Pinnacle

Candy & The Kisses

MR CREATOR.
Single (7"): released on Kent in Apr'85 by Ace Records. Distributed by: Pinnacle

Canedy Feinstein

HOLLYWOOD (Canedy Feinstein, Bordonaro & Caudle).
Album: released on Zebra in May'86 by Cherry Red Records. Distributed by: Pinnacle

Canevony Y Sireodd

CANEVONY Y SIREODD Various artists (Various Artists).
Album: released on Sain in Jul'85. Distributed by: Roots

Cann, Bob

WEST COUNTRY MELODEON.
Album: released on Topic in '81. Distributed by: Roots Distribution

Canned Heat

BOOGIE WITH CANNED HEAT.
Tracks: / Evil woman / My crime / On the road again / World in a jug / Turpentine moan / Whiskey headed woman / Amphetamine Annie / An owl song / Marie / Laveau / Fried hookie boogie / Evil woman / My crime / On the road again / World in a jug / Turpentine moan / Whiskey-headed woman No 2 / Amphetamine Annie / Owl song, An / Marie Laveau / Fried hookey boogie.
Album: released on See For Miles in Feb'86 by See For Miles Records. Distributed by: Pinnacle

Cassette: released on EMI (Italy) in Feb'87 by EMI Records. Distributed by: Conifer

Album: released on EMI (Germany) in Aug'83 by EMI Records. Distributed by: Conifer

HOOKER 'N' HEAT.
Double Album: released on Liberty in '71 by Liberty-United. Distributed by: EMI

HUMAN CONDITION, THE.
Album: released on Sonet in Jan'79 by Sonet Records. Distributed by: PRT

KINGS OF THE BOOGIE.
Album: released on Platinum (W.Germany) in Oct'85. Distributed by: Mainline

Cassette: released on Platinum (W.Germany) in Oct'85. Distributed by: Mainline

LIVING THE BLUES.
Album: released on See For Miles in Jul'87 by See For Miles Records. Distributed by: Pinnacle

MASTER OF ROCK.
Album: released on EMI (Holland) in '83 by EMI Records. Distributed by: Conifer

ON THE ROAD AGAIN.
Single (7"): released on EMI (France) in Apr'83 by EMI Records. Distributed by: Conifer

Single (7"): released on EMI Golden 45's in May'84 by EMI Records. Distributed by: EMI

SUPER PACK.
Album: released on EMI (Holland) in '83 by EMI Records. Distributed by: Conifer

Canned Rock

CANNED ROCK LIVE.
Album: released on Canned Rock in Nov'79. Distributed by: Pinnacle

KINETIC ENERGY.
Album: released on Canned Rock in Jun'79 Distributed by: Pinnacle

Cannibals

CHRISTMAS ROCK'N ROLL.
Tracks: / New Year's Eve song.
Single (7"): released on Hit Freebee in Dec'86. Distributed by: Backs, Cartel

CHRISTMAS ROCK 'N' ROLL.
Single (7"): released on Hit in Nov'85 by Hit Records. Distributed by: Pinnacle, Backs, Cartel

CRASH FOR TRASH.
Album: released on Hit in Feb'85 by Hit Records. Distributed by: Pinnacle, Backs, Cartel

FEED THE CANNIBALS.
Album: released on Scarface in Feb'86 by Scarface Records. Distributed by: Cartel

LED ASTRAY mumbo jumbo.
Single (7"): released on Hit in '82 by Hit Records. Distributed by: Pinnacle, Backs, Cartel

REST OF THE CANNIBALS, THE.
Album: released on GMG in Mar'86. Distributed by: Rough Trade, Cartel

RUN CHICKEN RUN VOLUME 1 (Cannibals/Surfadelics).
Album: released on Run Chicken Run in Nov'86

Canning, Francis

BLACK AND WHITE RAG.
Tracks: / Black and white rag / Root beet rag.
Single (7"):

Cannon & Ball

BOYS IN BLUE Big star.
Single (7"): released on MFP in '83 by EMI Records. Distributed by: EMI

EVERYBODY'S MAKING IT BIG BUT ME.
Single (7"): released on MFP in '82 by EMI Records. Distributed by: EMI

HOLD ME IN YOUR ARMS Crying.
Single (7"): released on Fame in '82 by Music For Pleasure Records. Distributed by: EMI

IT'S ALL IN THE GAME.
Single (7"): released on Relax in '84. Distributed by: CBS

LET YOUR BRACES DOWN.
Single (7"): released on SRT in '81 by SRT Records. Distributed by: Pinnacle, Solomon & Peres Distribution, SRT Distribution, H.R. Taylor Distribution, PRT Distribution

ROCK ON TOMMY.
Album: released on SRT in '80 by SRT Records. Distributed by: Pinnacle, Solomon & Peres Distribution, SRT Distribution, H.R. Taylor Distribution, PRT Distribution

Cassette: released on SRT in '80 by SRT Records. Distributed by: Pinnacle, Solomon & Peres Distribution, SRT Distribution, H.R. Taylor Distribution, PRT Distribution

Single (7"): released on SRT in '80 by SRT Records. Distributed by: Pinnacle, Solomon & Peres Distribution, SRT Distribution, H.R. Taylor Distribution, PRT Distribution

TOGETHER.
Tracks: / Together we'll be ok / Crying / Hold me in your arms / Everybody's making it big but me / Let me rock you / Bandido / Sun ain't gonna shine anymore, The / Dreamin' / Dream baby / Dream lover / Nellie the elephant / Remember the stars / Better love next time / This time.
Album: released on Music For Pleasure (Holland) in '82 by EMI Records. Distributed by: EMI

Cassette: released on Music For Pleasure (Holland) in '82 by EMI Records. Distributed by: EMI

Single (7"): released on SRT in '81 by SRT Records. Distributed by: Pinnacle, Solomon & Peres Distribution, SRT Distribution, H.R. Taylor Distribution, PRT Distribution

Cannon, Freddie

EXPLOSIVE FREDDY CANNON,THE.
Tracks: / Abigail Beechet / Action / Buzz buzz a-diddle-it / California here I come / Chattanooga shoe shine boy / Dedication song, The / For me and my gal / Happy shades of blue / If you were a rock and roll record / Muskrat ramble / Oke-fen-oke / Palisades park / Tallahassee lassie / Teen Queen of the week / Transistor sister / Way down yonder in New Orleans.
Album: released on Sonic in '76

HEY PUNK ROCKER At the disco.
Single (7"): released on Hot Rock in '80 by Hot Rock Records. Distributed by: Hot Rock

PALISADES PARK Beachwood City.
Single (7"): released on Old Gold in '82 by Old Gold Records. Distributed by: Lightning, Jazz Music, Spartan, Counterpoint

TALLAHASSEE LASSIE.
Single (7"):

Single (7"): released on Old Gold in '82 by Old Gold Records. Distributed by: Lightning, Jazz Music, Spartan, Counterpoint

WAY DOWN YONDER.
Single (7"): released on Old Gold in '82 by Old Gold Records. Distributed by: Lightning, Jazz Music, Spartan, Counterpoint

WAY DOWN YONDER IN NEW ORLEANS.
Single (7"): released on Creole in '82 by Creole Records. Distributed by: Rhino, PRT

Single (7"): released on Creole Replay in '84 by Creole Records. Distributed by: PRT, Rhino

Cannon, Noel

YOUR CAROLINA BUDDY.
Album: released on Ross in Oct'86 by Ross Records. Distributed by: Ross Distribution, Roots Distribution

Cassette: released on Ross in Oct'86 by Ross Records. Distributed by: Ross Distribution, Roots Distribution

Canny Cummerland

CANNY CUMBERLAND Songs & tales in Cumbrian dialect.
Tracks: / Canny aul Cummerlan' / To t'milken / Shades o' John Peel / Dinah Grayson / Oyster girl, The / Willie whoar's ta bin? / Straw rope / Hoo happy we lived then / Branthet neuk boggle / Tarry woo' / Sally Gray / Cumberland reel, The / It's winter.
Notes: Cumbrian dialect performed by Linda Adams, Robbie Ellis, Angil Marchant, Derwent Pickering and Hodgett's Barnstromers.
Album: released on Fellside in '83 by Fellside Records. Distributed by: Roots, Jazz Music, Celtic Music, Projection

CANNY CUMMERLAND Various artists (Various Artists).
Album: released on Fellside in '81 by Fellside Records. Distributed by: Roots, Jazz Music, Celtic Music, Projection

Canny Fettle

VARRY CANNY.
Album: released on Tradition in '76. Distributed by: Cassion Distribution, Celtic Music, Jazz Music, Projection, Roots Records

Cassette: released on Tradition in '76. Distributed by: Cassion Distribution, Celtic Music, Jazz Music, Projection, Roots Records

Canny Newcassel

BALLADS & SONGS From Newcastle & therabouts.
Album: released on Topic in '81. Distributed by: Roots Distribution

Canoldir Choir

HOW SWEET THE SOUND (Canoldir Male Voice Choir).
Tracks: / Arwlfa / Holy City, The / Nant y mynydd / Thanks be to God / Prayer / King of Glory / Jack was every inch a sailor / O Isis and Osiris / Amazing grace / Eia Eia / Bridge over troubled water / Pilgrim's chorus.
Album: released on Grosvenor in '82 by Grosvenor Records. Distributed by: Taylors

LET ME SING AGAIN (Canoldir Male Voice Choir).
Tracks: / Soldier's chorus (Faust) / Angel and the stranger, The / Gwahoddiad / Flight of ages, The / Vive l'amour / Virgin of the Angel Host, The / Battle Hymn, The / Llanfair / Impossible Dream, The (Man of La Mancha) / De animals a-comin' / Lost chord, The / Sospan Fach / Take me home / There is nothin' like a dame / Hallelujah Amen.
Album: released on Grosvenor in '78 by Grosvenor Records. Distributed by: Taylors

WE RAISE OUR VOICES HIGH (Canoldir Male Voice Choir).
Tracks: / Roman war song from 'Rienzi', A / What shall we do with the drunken sailor? / Memory from 'Cats' / We'll keep a welcome / Finnish forest, The / Shepherd, shepherd / Lord's prayer, The / How great thou art / Calm is the sea / Little innocent lamb / Eli Jenkins prayer from 'Under milk wood' / Speed your journey / My love is like a red red rose / Maja moja / Bryn myrddin.
Notes: Conductor: D. Clive Griffiths L.T.C.L. The Canoldir Male Choir are based in Birmingham and have an interesting tale to tell, being a mixture of Welsh exiles and Midlands men interested in choral singing of the highest standard. A fine choir, they understandably have a large following in the industrial heartland of England. (Indeed, Canoldir can be freely translated from the Welsh as 'Midlands'). They have had many successful albums on sale, but this is their first for Grasmere records. As a result, they have chosen the content as items from their repertoire which the public have requested and enjoyed at concerts.
Album: released on Grasmere in '84 by Grasmere Records. Distributed by: EMI

Cassette: released on Grasmere in '84 by Grasmere Records. Distributed by: EMI

Cantabile

BEAUTIFUL MEXICAN LADY Aubade.
Single (7"): released on Zonk in '83. Distributed by: PRT

HEAR NO EVIL.
Album: released on Plant Life in '85. Distributed by: Roots

OVERTURE.
Album: released on Plant Life in '81. Distributed by: Roots

Canterbury Choir

BRIDGE THROUGH TIME (Canterbury Cathedral Choir).
Album: by Grosvenor Records. Distributed by: Taylors

CHRISTMAS CAROLS (Canterbury Cathedral Choir).
Album: released on Abbey in '83 by Abbey. Distributed by: PRT, Taylors,

Cassette: released on Abbey in '83 by Abbey. Distributed by: PRT, Taylors, Gamut

CHRISTMAS CAROLS AT CANTERGURY CATHEDRAL (Canterbury Cathedral Choir).
Album: released on Abbey in Nov'83 by Abbey. Distributed by: PRT, Taylors,

Cassette: released on Abbey in Nov'83 by Abbey. Distributed by: PRT, Taylors,

IN QUIRES & PLACES (Canterbury Cathedral Choir).
Album: released on Abbey in '80 by Abbey. Distributed by: PRT, Taylors,

Canterbury Clerkes

FILL YOUR GLASSES.
Tracks: / Fill your glasses / Push about the bottle boys / When gen'rous wind expands my soul / There behold the mighty bowl / Life's a bumper / Sportive little trifler / How merrily we live / Breathe softly ye winds / Time has not thinned.
Notes: The Glee is a particularly English phenomenon which was so popular in the 18th and 19th century's. Glees are basically part-songs with words of a more light- hearted nature. The Canterbury Clerkes, specialise in Glee Songs and the theme of this album is mainly convivial. The Clerkes are joined by that enigmatic group, The London Serpent Trio, for the second airing in this month's releases of that much maligned instrument usually regarded as obsolete.
Compact disc: released on Saydisc in Dec'86 by Saydisc Records. Distributed by: Essex, Harmonia Mundi, Roots, H.R. Taylor, Jazz Music, Swift, Projection

Album: released on Syadisc in Oct'86

Cassette: released on Syadisc in Oct'86

Compact disc: released on Saydisc in Jun'87 by Saydisc Records. Distributed by: Essex, Harmonia Mundi, Roots, H.R. Taylor, Jazz Music, Swift, Projection,

Canterbury Tales

CANTERBURY TALES Geoffrey Chaucer (Various Artists).
Cassette: released on Listen For Pleasure in '82 by MFP Records. Distributed by: EMI

CANTERBURY TALES Prologue & The Pardoner's Prologue & tale (Chaucer, Geoffrey).
Cassette: released on Argo (Spokenword) in '82 by Decca Records. Distributed by: Polygram

CANTERBURY TALES Various (Various Artists).
Album: released on That's Entertainment in '84 by That's Entertainment Records. Distributed by: Pinnacle, PRT

Cassette: released on That's Entertainment in '84 by That's Entertainment Records. Distributed by: Pinnacle, PRT

CANTERBURY TALES Nun's Priest's tale,The/The Knight's Tale (Various Artists).
Notes: Read in middle English By: Nevill Cogill/Norman Davis/Lena Davis/John Burrow/Roy Spencer/Richard Bebb/Frank Duncan/Peter Orr/Denis McCarthy/Prunella Scales. Following the highly sucessful release of the Prologue and the Pardoner's Tale from Cahucer's Canterbury Tales on SAY 24, this new release includes two equallypopular tales. The distinguished cast as that used on SAY 24,and again the talesare read in Middle English are read in Middle English.Chaucer's Canterbury Talesappear on almost every GCE Examination list for 1984.
Album: released on Argo (Spokenword) in '83 by Decca Records. Distributed by: Polygram

Canterville Ghost

CANTERVILLE GHOST (Wilde, Oscar).
Cassette: released on Talking Tape Company in '84 by Talking Tape Company Records

Cantico Del Sole, Canto 99

CANTICO DEL SOLE,CANTO 99... And other poems (Pound,Ezra).
Cassette: released on Caedmon(USA) in '83 by Caedmon (USA) Records. Distributed by: Taylors, Discovery

Canton

PLEASE DON'T STAY.
Single (7"): released on Creole in '85 by Creole Records. Distributed by: Rhino, PRT

Cantor, Eddie

CANTOR,EDDIE The best of.
Tracks: / If you knew Susie (like I know Susie) / Josephine please no lean on my bell / Makin whoopee / Margie / Baby face / Ida sweet as apple cider / Yes sir that's my baby / How ya gonna keep em down on the farm / Ma (she's making eyes at me) / Waiting for Robert E Lee / Ballin the jack / Ain't she sweet.
Album: released on RCA International in '81

Cassette: released on RCA International in '81

Cantorial & Choral Music

CANTORIAL & CHORAL MUSIC Various artists (Various Artists).
Tracks: / Yehi Ratson / Anna Avada / Kohanecha / Ladonai Ha'Aretz / Acheinu do beit yisrael / Kiddush / Uvashofar gadol / B'rosh hashanah / Uv'chien yitkadash / Se'u she'arim.
Notes: (Yehi Ratzon- Charles Lowy) On the shabbat preceeding the New Moon, this prayeris recited. It also contains an expression of Messianic hopes/(Anna Avda- Charles Lowy) Part of a meditation in aramaic, beginning: Blessed be the Name of the Sovereign of the universe. It is a noble passage, deprived from the Zohar, and stressed direct communion between god and man. It is full of ecsratic devotion/ (Kohanecha - Ernest Kaye) This collection of verse from various parts of the Hebrew scriptures is recited while placing the scrolls of the Torah in the holy arkafter reading of the scriptual lesson./(Sim Shalom - Samuel Almon) This lituricaQ prayer for peace has its origin in the Talmud: It follows the priestly bene- diction which ends with the word "Peace"(Acheinu Kol Beit Yisrael- Lazar Lowy)An impassioned plea for mercy on behalf of are brethern who suffer persecution Ofcaptivity, recited on Monday's and Thursday's: Cantor Lowy heated this movingcomposition from his grandfather Lazar Lowy who was an eminent Chazen in Hungaryandalso from his father who was known as Chazan of great ability.(Ladonai Ha'Aretz - Lewandowski) Psalm 24, sun at the return of the scroll to t~he ark. Who shall ascend the mountain of the lord" ..he that has clean hands.." is a s fine summing of the noble character (Kiddush (Rosh Hashanah- Samuel Alman) Kiddush or sancitification with the cup of wine on New Year's eve. Apart from the specificreference to the festival of Rosh Hashanah, it is also recall s the departure from Egypt.//(Uvashofar Gadol Arr Dudley Cohen) One of the most moving prayers onRosh Hashanah, refering to the solemn sound of the ~shofar which reminds us thatGod remembers all creatures in mercy and in judgement (B'Rosh Hashanah - Naumbourg) In the words of his prayer God remembers each man's deeds and destiny; hisworks and ways. The devout jew sends his supplication to God to remember him with kindness and mercy(Uv'Chein Yitkadash Goldstein) Arecitative following the Kedushah(sanctification) with many references to the people of Israel,, and the holy city over which the name of the holy one should be hallowed (Se'u She'Arim-Naumbourg)This latter part of psalm 24 is a triunphal choral first sung according to the Talmud, when Solomon brought the Ark into holy holies of the newlyerected temple.Composers: (Samuel Alman) Liturgical composer. Born in Russia, hewas former choirmaster in the Hampstead Synagogue. He published 2 volumes of synagogue music)-(Dudley Cohen) Former choirmaster of the Hampstead Synagogue and of the Zemel choir) (Mali goldstein) Chazen in Hungary and composer of synagoguemusic) (Ernest Kaye) composer. grandson of the late Chazen ben Zoin Hoffman formerly Chazen ofthe Adath Yisrael, London)(Louis Lewandowski) German liturgicalcomposer and conductor. He composed and arranged traditional music in the sytle of his own period.)(Lazar Lowy) Grandfather of cantor lowy, cheif cantor of papaHungary for forty years. Recieved official letter of recognition from the Hungarian ministry of culturefor his devoted services.) Samuel Naumbourg) German musicologist and cantor in paris. Published Zemirot Yisrael, settings for the entire liturgical cyclefor cantor, choir andorgan) (Cantor Charles Lowy) Was born in Pressburg (Bratislava) into a family of Chazanim. He studied music in Vienna, Budapest and at the state conservatoire in Munich and at the Rombach synagogue inBudapet. He gave recitals of litugicalmusic on radio Budapest, and also officiated at the famous Tabak-temple in that city. He joined Hampstead synagogue in 1959)(Willie Scharf)first studied the violin nd for several years was professionalviolinist and played under many famous conductors. His interest then switched toconducting which he studied at the Guildhall school of music being sung as written by the composer(if the original manuscripts are available)(The Hampstead Synagogue) has a tradition of fine choral singing and all the items are for the reoertoire. To retain the atmosphere of dedication the recording was made speciallyin the synagogue bythe regular chorists (with no ending). In its 93 years the most notable

choirmaster has been Samuel Alman who for 31 years was in charge ofthemusic. The congregation includes some well known musicians some of whom have written works especially for the choir and we are proud to include one of these items in this selection. Allitems are sung in the Israeli pronunciation which isused throughout the service. produced by: Warren Records NW4 4LP Compatioble with Dolby(P) Hampstead synagogue 1972(C) Hampstead synagogue and Jewish music productions 1985 Disrtributed by: Jewish music: (distribution) Po Box 232 Harrow Middlesex, HA1 2NN Full title Cantorial And Choral music From Hampstead Synagogue.
Cassette: released on B'nai B'rith in '85

Cantorion Creigiau

CANTORION CREIGIAU.
Album: released on Black Mountain in '82 by Black Mountain Records

Can't Sit Down

CAN'T SIT DOWN Hot blues guitar (Various Artists).
Notes: Full title: Can't sit down (hot blues guitar with Jimmy Dawkins, Lowell Fulson etc.).
Album: released on JSP in Dec'85 by JSP Records. Distributed by: Swift, Projection

Can't Stop The Music

CAN'T STOP THE MUSIC Original motion picture soundtrack (Various Artists).
Cassette: released on Mercury in '80 by Phonogram Records. Distributed by: Polygram Distribution

Can't Stop The Party

CAN'T STOP THE PARTY - VOLUME 1 Various artists (Various Artists).
Compact disc: released on Record Shack in Jan'87 by Record Shack Records. Distributed by: PRT

CAN'T STOP THE PARTY VOLS 1 & 2 Various artists (Various Artists).
Album: released on Record Shack in Oct'86 by Record Shack Records. Distributed by: PRT

Cassette: released on Record Shack in Oct'86 by Record Shack Records. Distributed by: PRT

CAN'T STOP THE PARTY - VOLUME 2 Various artists (Various Artists).
Compact disc: released on Record Shack in Jan'87 by Record Shack Records. Distributed by: PRT

Canute

NO LOOKING BACK.
Single (7"): released on EMI in '85 by EMI Records. Distributed by: EMI

Single (12"): released on EMI in '85 by EMI Records. Distributed by: EMI

Can You Pooker Romany

CAN YOU POOKER ROMANY?.
Cassette: released on Folktracks in Nov'79 by Folktracks Cassettes. Distributedby: Folktracks

Can You Spare A Dime

CAN YOU SPARE A DIME (Various Artists).
Album: released on New World (USA) in Aug'86 by New World Records (USA). Distributed by: Conifer

Capaldi, Jim

CHILD IN THE STORM Bright fighter.
Single (7"): released on Carrere in '81 by Carrere Records. Distributed by: PRT, Spartan

CONTENDER,THE.
Tracks: / Dirty business / Sealed with a kiss / Daughter of the night / You burn me / Game of love / Contender, the / Elixir of life / Short ends / Hunger and greed.
Album: released on Polydor in '78 by Polydor Records. Distributed by: Polygram, Polydor

ELECTRIC NIGHTS.
Album: released on Polydor in '79 by Polydor Records. Distributed by: Polygram, Polydor

I'LL KEEP HOLDING ON.
Single (7"): released on WEA Int in '84

LET THE THUNDER CRY.
Tracks: / Let the thunder cry / Favella music / Child in the storm / Only love / Louie louie / Warm / Dreams do come true / Old photographs / We don't need / Anxiety.
Album: released on Carrere in '81 by Carrere Records. Distributed by: PRT, Spartan

Cassette: released on Carrere in '81 by Carrere Records. Distributed by: PRT, Spartan

LIVING ON THE EDGE Gifts.
Single (7"): released on WEA Int in '83

OH,HOW WE DANCED.
Album: by Island Records. Distributed by: Polygram

ONE MAN MISSION.
Tracks: / One man mission of love / Tonight / lost inside your love / I'll keep holding on / Nobody loves you / Young Savages / Tales of power / Warriors of love / Ancient highway / Let the thunder cry / Favella music / Child in the storm / Only love / Louie louie / Warm / Dreams do come true / Old photographs / We don't need / Anxiety.
Cassette: released on WEA in '84 by WEA Records. Distributed by: WEA

SHORT CUT DRAW BLOOD.
Tracks: / Goodbye love / It's all up to you / Love hurts / Johnny too bad / Short cut draw blood / Living on a marble / Boy with a problem / Keep on tryin' / Seagull / Goodbye love.
Album: released on Island in '75 by Island Records. Distributed by: Polygram

SWEET SMELL OF SUCCESS, THE.
Tracks: / Hold on to your love / Take me how you find me girl / Sweet smell of sucess, The / Every man must march to the beat of his own drum / Tonight etc..
Album: released on Carrere in '80 by Carrere Records. Distributed by: PRT, Spartan

Cassette: released on Carrere in '80 by Carrere Records. Distributed by: PRT, Spartan

THAT'S LOVE Runaway.
Single (7"): released on WEA Int in '83

Single (12"): released on WEA Int in '83

TONITE YOU'RE MINE Back at my place.
Single (7"): released on WEA in '83 by WEA Records. Distributed by: WEA

Cape Breton...

CAPE BRETON VOL.1 Various artists (Various Artists).
Album: released on Topic in '81. Distributed by: Roots Distribution

Album: released on Ross in Jan'86 by Ross Records. Distributed by: Ross Distribution, Roots Distribution

Cassette: released on Ross in Jan'86 by Ross Records. Distributed by: Ross Distribution, Roots Distribution

CAPE BRETON VOL.2 Various artists (Cape Breton Symphony Fiddle).
Album: released on Topic in '81. Distributed by: Roots Distribution

Album: released on Ross in Jan'86 by Ross Records. Distributed by: Ross Distribution, Roots Distribution

Cassette: released on Ross in Jan'86 by Ross Records. Distributed by: Ross Distribution, Roots Distribution

SALUTE TO SCOTLAND,A (Cape Breton Symphony Fiddle).
Album: released on Ross in '84 by Ross Records. Distributed by: Ross Distribution, Roots Distribution

Cassette: released on Ross in '84 by Ross Records. Distributed by: Ross Distribution, Roots Distribution

Capella Nova

CAPELLA NOVA.
Album: released on Aloi in Jan'87 by Aloi Records. Distributed by: Aloi Records, Chris Wellard, IRS

Capercaillie

CASCADE.
Album: released on Etive in Jun'86

Album: released on SRT in '84 by SRT Records. Distributed by: Pinnacle, Solomon & Peres Distribution, SRT Distribution, H.R. Taylor Distribution, PRT Distribution

CROSSWINDS.
Album: released on WEA Ireland in Jul'87 by WEA Records. Distributed by: Celtic Distributions, Projection, I & B

Cassette: released on WEA Ireland in Jul'87 by WEA Records. Distributed by: Celtic Distributions, Projection, I & B

Capital Letters

HEADLINE NEWS.
Album: released on Greensleeves in '79 by Greensleeves Records. Distributed by: BMG, Jetstar, Spartan

Capitals

COOL JERK.
Single (7"): released on Creole Classics in Aug'87 by Creole Records. Distributed by: PRT, Rhino

Single (12"): released on Creole Classics in Aug'87 by Creole Records. Distributed by: PRT, Rhino

Capitol...

CAPITOL BLACK MUSIC 82 Various artists (Various Artists).
Album: released on Capitol (France) in '83 by Capitol Records. Distributed by: Conifer

CAPITOL CLASSICS (1942-1958) (Various Artists).
Album: released on Music For Pleasure in '83 by EMI Records. Distributed by: EMI

Cassette: released on Music For Pleasure in '83 by EMI Records. Distributed by: EMI

CAPITOL COUNTRY CRUISIN' Various original artists (Various original artists).
Album: released on Capitol in '78 by Capitol Records. Distributed by: EMI

CAPITOL COUNTRY GEMS various original artists (Various original artists).
Tracks: / Long black limousine / Loving him was easier / San Antonio Rose / Radiator man from Wasco / Good hearted woman / I got a new field to plough / Jambalaya (on the Bayou) / Take me home country roads / Stand by your man / Just a strand from a yellow curl / Sad situation / Wabash cannon ball / Lay some happiness on me / To hear the family sing.
Album: released on MFP in '82 by EMI Records. Distributed by: EMI

Cassette: released on MFP in '82 by EMI Records. Distributed by: EMI

CAPITOL COUNTRY KICKS various artists (Various original artists).
Album: released on Capitol in '77 by Capitol Records. Distributed by: EMI

CAPITOL ROCKABILLY ORIGINALS Various original artists (Various original artists).
Album: released on Capitol in '77 by Capitol Records. Distributed by: EMI

Capitol Collectables

CAPITOL COLLECTABLES (Various Artists).
Tracks: / I'm in love / Why should I cry / All because of you / If you want me / Take it to the limit / Betcha don't know / If you were mine / Working up a sweat / Tender moments / Little bit more, A / Don't take my love away.
Album: released on Capitol in Jul'87 by Capitol Records. Distributed by: EMI

Cassette: released on Capitol in Jul'87 by Capitol Records. Distributed by: EMI

Compact disc: released on Capitol in Aug'87 by Capitol Records. Distributed by: EMI

Capitol Pops Orchestra

BOLERO.
Single (7"): released on Sirocco in '84 by Sirocco Records. Distributed by: Pinnacle

Capitol Punishment

WHEN PUTSCH COMES TO SHOVE.
Album: released on Destiny in Nov'86 by Destiny Records. Distributed by: Red Rhino, Cartel

Capitol Regiment Band

JOHN PHILIP SO USA Greatest hits of.
Cassette: released on Oak in '82 by Oak Records. Distributed by: Spartan Distribution, Pinnacle

Capitols

COOL JERK.
Tracks: / It's my party.
Album: released on Solid Smoke (USA) in '84. Distributed by: Rhino

Single (7"): released on Creole Replay in '84 by Creole Records. Distributed by: PRT, Rhino

COOL JERK/COOL PEARL.
Single (7"): released on Old Gold in '82 by Old Gold Records. Distributed by: Lightning, Jazz Music, Spartan, Counterpoint

Capone's Treatment, Eddie

I WON'T GIVE YOU UP.
Single (7"): released on Treatment in '85 by Treatment Records. Distributed by: Pinnacle

Capon, Galliano

GALLIANO CAPON & PERRIN (Capon, Galliano & Perrin).
Tracks: / Musique / Blue rondo a la turk / Sing me so softly of the blues / Spain / Violette / Point d'interrogation / Funky accordion / Blues ah bill.
Notes: Artists -Richard Galliano, Jean-Charles Capon, Gilles Perrin.Mail order distrib-ution address: Accordion Rcord Club, 146 Birmingham Road, Kidderminster, Worcs DY10 2SL. Tel: 0562 746105
Album: released on Accordion Record Club in Jul'86 by Accordion Record Club Records. Distributed by: Accordion Record Club

Capp, Frankie

JUGGERNAUT STRIKES AGAIN (Capp, Frankie & Nat Pierce).
Tracks: / One for Marshall / I remember Clifford / New York shuffle / Chops, fingers & sticks / You are so beautiful / Parker's mood / Word from Bird / Charade / Things ain't what they used to be / Little Pony.
Album: released on Concord in '82 by Import Records. Distributed by: IMS, Polygram

Capp Pierce Juggernaut

CAPP PIERCE JUGGERNAUT.
Album: released on Concord in '79 by Import Records. Distributed by: IMS, Polygram

Caprice

100%.
Single (7"): released on Lovebeat Int. in '85. Distributed by: Gipsy, Spartan

Single (12"): released on Lovebeat Int. in '85. Distributed by: Gipsy, Spartan

100% (TAKE IT TO THE MAX).
Tracks: / 100% (take it to the max) / Voiceless.
Single (12"): released on Lovebeat Int. in Jan'86. Distributed by: Gipsy, Spartan

Capstick, Tony

HIS ROUND.
Tracks: / I drew my ship / Foggy dew, The / Rambling royal, The / Arthur McBride / To Ramona / Lloyd George / Sir thomas of Winesberry / Hello Hans / Captain Grant / Goodnight Irene.
Album: released on Rubber in '82 by Rubber Records. Distributed by: Roots Distribution, Projection Distribution, Jazz Music Distribution, Celtic Music Distribution
Spartan Distribution

SHEFFIELD GRINDER Capstick comes home.
Single (7"): released on Dingles in '81 by Dingles Records. Distributed by: Projection

Songs of Ewan MacColl

SONGS OF EWAN MACCOLL (See Gaughan, Dick) (Capstick, Tony, Dick Gaughan & Dave Burland).

TONY CAPSTICK DOES A TURN.
Tracks: / Dolphin, The / Donkey, The / Seeds of love / Moving-on song, Tghe / Twins / Coat she wore, The / If I had a boat / Flock of lobsters, A / Casey's last ride / Scarecrow, The / Red wine and promises / Twelsh joke / They don't write like that anymore.
Album: released on Rubber in '82 by Rubber Records. Distributed by: Roots Distribution, Projection Distribution, Jazz Music Distribution, Celtic Music Distribution
Spartan Distribution

Captain Beaky Stories

CAPTAIN BEAKY STORIES (Lloyd, Jeremy).
Cassette: released on Pickwick Talking Books in '83

Captain Beefheart

ABBA-ZABBA.
Album: released on Masters (Holland) in Jan'87

Cassette: released on Masters (Holland) in Jan'87

BLUEJEANS AND MOONBEAMS.
Tracks: / Party of special things to do / Same old blues / Observatory quest / Pompadour swamp / Captain's holiday / Rock'n'roll's evil doll / Further than we've gone / Twist ah luck / Bluejeans and moonbeams / Party of special things to do / Same old blues / Observatory crest / Pompadour swamp / Captain's holiday / Rock 'n' roll's evil doll / Further than we've gone / Twist ah luck / Bluejeans and moonbeams.
Compact disc: released on Virgin in Jun'87 by Virgin Records. Distributed by: EMI, Virgin Distribution

BLUE JEANS & MOONBEAMS.
Album: released on Virgin in '84 by Virgin Records. Distributed by: EMI, Virgin Distribution

CAPTAIN BEEFHEART FILE,THE.
Tracks: / Sure 'nuff 'n yes I do / Zig-zag wanderer / Call on me / Dropout boogie / I'm glad / Electricity / Yellow brick road / Abba zaba / Plastic factory / Where there's woman / Grown so ugly / Autumn's child / Tarotplane / Kandy korn / 25th century quaker / Mirror man.
Album: released on Buddah in '77. Distributed by: Swift, Jazz Music, PRT

CLEAR SPOT.
Tracks: / Low yo yo stuff / Nowadays a woman's gotta hit a man / Too much time / Circumstances / My head is my only house unless it rains / Sun zoom spark / Clear spot / Crazy little thing / Long-neck bottles / Her eyes are a blue million miles / Big-eyed beans from Venus / Golden birdies.
Album: by WEA Records. Distributed by: WEA

Page 182

DOC AT THE RADAR STATION.
Compact disc: released on Virgin in Feb'87 by Virgin Records. Distributed by: EMI, Virgin Distribution

LEGENDARY A & M SESSIONS.
Single (12"): released on A&M in '84 by A&M Records. Distributed by: Polygram

MIRROR MAN.
Album: released on PRT in '82 by PRT Records. Distributed by: PRT

MIRROR MAN.
Tracks: / Tarotplane / Kandy korn / 25th century quaker / Mirror man.
Album: released on Edsel in Apr'86 by Demon Records. Distributed by: Pinnacle, Jazz Music, Projection

MUSIC IN SEA MINOR.
Tracks: / Electricity / Yellow brick road / Zig-zag wanderer / Kandy korn / Abba zaba / Dropout boogie / I'm glad / 25th century quaker.
Album: released on Buddah in '83. Distributed by: Swift, Jazz Music, PRT

Cassette: released on Buddah in '83. Distributed by: Swift, Jazz Music, PRT

SAFE AS MILK.
Album: released on PRT in '82 by PRT Records. Distributed by: PRT

SAFE AS MILK.
Tracks: / Sure 'nuff 'n yes I do / Zig-zag wanderer / Call on me / Dropout boogie / I'm glad / Electricity / Yellow brick road / Abba zaba / Plastic factory / Where there's woman / Grown so ugly / Autumn's child.
Album: released on Buddah in '85. Distributed by: Swift, Jazz Music, PRT

Cassette: released on Buddah in '85. Distributed by: Swift, Jazz Music, PRT

SHINY BEAST.
Compact disc: released on Virgin in Jul'87 by Virgin Records. Distributed by: EMI, Virgin Distribution

TOP SECRET.
Album: released on Design in '84 by Breakaway Records. Distributed by: PRT, Stage One

TROUT MASK REPLICA.
Album: released on Reprise in '75 by WEA Records. Distributed by: WEA

TWO ORIGINALS OF CAPTAIN BEEFHEART Spotlight Kid/Lick my decals off, baby.
Tracks: / Spotlight Kid, The / I'm gonna booglarize you, baby / White jam / Blabber 'n' smoke / When it blows its stacks / Alice in blunderland / Click clack / Grow fins / There ain't no Santa Claus on the evenin' stage / Lick my decals off, baby / Doctor Dark / I love you, you big dummy / Peon / Ellerin' plain / Woe-is-uh-me-bop / Japan in a dishpan / I wanna find a woman that'll hold my big toe till I go / Petrified forest / One rose that I mean / Buggy boogie woogie / Smithsonian Institute blues / Space-age couple / Clouds are full of wine (not whiskey or rye) / Flash Gordon's apple.
Album: by WEA Records. Distributed by: WEA

UNCONDITIONALLY GUARANTEED.
Compact disc: released on Virgin in May'87 by Virgin Records. Distributed by: EMI, Virgin Distribution

Captain Kremmen

CAPTAIN KREMMEN Greatest adventure yet (Everett, Kenny).
Compact disc: released on CBS in '80 by CBS Records. Distributed by: CBS

Captain Rapp

BAD TIMES (I CAN'T STAND IT) Instrumental.
Single (12"): released on Becket in '84

Captain Rock

LOT OF FIST, A.
Album: released on Hardcore in Aug'87 by Hardcore Records. Distributed by: PRT. Estim retail price in Sep'87 was £4.99.

Captain Sensible

GLAD IT'S ALL OVER.
Single (7"): released on A&M in '84 by A&M Records. Distributed by: Polygram

Picture disc single: released on A&M in '84 by A&M Records. Distributed by: Polygram

JET BOY JET GIRL.
Single (7"): released on Big Beat in '82 by Ace Records. Distributed by: Projection, Pinnacle

Picture disc single: released on Big Beat in '82 by Ace Records. Distributed by: Projection, Pinnacle

ONE CHRISTMAS CATALOGUE.
Single (7"): released on A&M in '84 by A&M Records. Distributed by: Polygram

Single (12"): released on A&M in '84 by A&M Records. Distributed by: Polygram

POWER OF LOVE,THE.
Album: released on A&M in '83 by A&M Records. Distributed by: Polygram

Cassette: released on A&M in '83 by A&M Records. Distributed by: Polygram

REVOLUTION NOW!.
Tracks: / Revolution now / Coward of treason grove, The.
Single (7"): released on A&M in 13 Jun'87 by A&M Records. Distributed by: Polygram

Single (12"): released on A&M in 13 Jun'87 by A&M Records. Distributed by: Polygram

SENSIBLE SINGLES.
Album: released on A&M in '84 by A&M Records. Distributed by: Polygram

Cassette: released on A&M in '84 by A&M Records. Distributed by: Polygram

THERE ARE MORE SNAKES THAN LADDERS.
Single (7"): released on A&M in '84 by A&M Records. Distributed by: Polygram

Single (12"): released on A&M in '84 by A&M Records. Distributed by: Polygram

THIS IS YOUR CAPTAIN SPEAKING.
Single (7"): released on Crass in '81 by Exitstencil Music. Distributed by: Rough Trade, Cartel

WOMEN AND CAPTAINS FIRST.
Album: released on A&M in '82 by A&M Records. Distributed by: Polygram

WOT NO MEAT.
Tracks: / Wot no meat / Meat sandwich.
Single (7"): released on Animus in Nov'86. Distributed by: Rough Trade, Cartel

WOT - NO MEAT?.
Single (7"): released on Animus in '85. Distributed by: Rough Trade, Cartel

Captain Sinbad

DALLAS.
Single (12"): released on Mab in '85 by Mab Records. Distributed by: Jetstar

SEVEN VOYAGES OF CAPTAIN SINBAD,THE.
Album: released on Greensleeves in '82 by Greensleeves Records. Distributed by: BMG, Jetstar, Spartan

SINBAD AND METRIC SYSTEM (Captain Sinbad & Peter Metro).
Album: released on CSA in '83 by CSA Records. Distributed by: PRT, Jetstar

SISTER MIRACLE Funny love.
Single (12"): released on Rusty International in '83 by Rusty International Records. Distributed by: Jetstar Distribution

Captain Sky

DON'T TOUCH THAT DIAL Natural high.
Single (7"):

Single (12"):

Captains of Industry

LIFELINE.
Single (7"): released on Go Discs in '84 by Go Discs Records. Distributed by: CBS

ROOMFUL OF MONKEYS,A.
Album: released on Chrysalis in '85 by Chrysalis Records. Distributed by: CBS

Album: released on Tank in Dec'77 by Tank Records

Captain & Tennille

20 GREATEST HITS.
Tracks: / Love will keep us together / You never done it like that / Shop around / You need a woman tonight / Lonely nights / Love is spreading over the world / Good enough / Dixie hummingbird / Sweet love / Can't stop dancin' / I write the songs / Wedding song / Way I want to touch you, The / Muskrat love / Circles / Come in from the rain / Disney girls / Sing a song of joy / Dream / We never really say goodbye.
Album: released on MFP in '80 by EMI Records. Distributed by: EMI

CAPTAIN & TENNILLE.
Cassette: released on Ditto in '85 by Pickwick Records. Distributed by: H.R. Taylor

Album: released on A&M in '82 by A&M Records. Distributed by: Polygram

Cassette: released on A&M in '82 by A&M Records. Distributed by: Polygram

LOVE WILL KEEP US TOGETHER.
Single (7"): released on Scoop in '84

Cassette: released on Scoop in '84

MAKE YOUR MOVE.
Tracks: / Love on a shoestring / No love in the morning / Deep in the dark / How can you be so cold? / Do that to me one more time / Happy together / Baby you still got it / Never make your move too soon.
Album: released on Casablanca in '82. Distributed by: Polygram, Phonogram

C.A Quintet

TRIP THRU HELL.
Album: released on Psycho in Sep'83. Distributed by: Funhouse, Rough Trade

Cara, Irene

ANYONE CAN SEE.
Album: released on Epic in '82 by CBS Records. Distributed by: CBS

Cassette: released on Epic in '82 by CBS Records. Distributed by: CBS

BREAKDANCE.
Single (7"): released on Epic in '84 by CBS Records. Distributed by: CBS

Single (12"): released on Epic in '84 by CBS Records. Distributed by: CBS

CARASMATIC.
Tracks: / Get a grip / Give me love / We're gonna get up / Now that it's over / Say goodnight Irene / Don't wanna let go / Girlfriends / Be your number one / Falling in love.
Album: released on Elektra (USA) in Jul'87 by Elektra/Asylum/Nonesuch Records. Distributed by: WEA

Cassette: released on Elektra (USA) in Jul'87 by Elektra/Asylum/Nonesuch Records. Distributed by: WEA

DREAM,THE.
Single (7"): released on Network in '84 by Epic. Distributed by: PRT, CBS

Single (12"): released on Network in '84 by Epic. Distributed by: PRT, CBS

FAME.
Compact disc: released on Polydor in '83 by Polydor Records. Distributed by: Polygram,

FLASHDANCE WHAT A FEELING.
Single (7"): released on Casablanca in '84. Distributed by: Polygram,

Caramba

FEDORA (I'LL BE YOUR DAWG) Ralph & Rolph.
Single (7"): released on Billco in '83 by Billco Records

Single (12"): released on Billco in '83 by Billco Records

Caratini, Patrice

3 TEMPS POUR BIEN FAIRE (Caratini; Azzola; Fosset).
Tracks: / Azzola 2,000 / Monsieur Astor / Majeur / Lise & Fatty / Quartier saint-merri / Beguine des lavandieres / Index / Double scotch / Pouce / Canal saint-martin / Valse des crayons / Trois temps bien faire.
Notes: Retail price give by ARC excluding P & P (via mail order) is 6.00. Mail order distribution address: Accordion Record Club, 146 Birmingham Road, Kidderminster,Worcs. DY10 2SL. Tel: 0562 746105.
Album: released on Accordion Record Club in Jul'86 by Accordion Record Club Records. Distributed by: Accordion Record Club

TROIS TEMPS POUR BIEN FAIRE (Caratini, Patrice & Marcel Azzola).
Album: released on ARC (Accordion Records) in '84. Distributed by: Accordion Record Club

Carats

CARATS Various original artists (Various Artists).
Cassette: released on Polydor in '82 by Polydor Records. Distributed by: Polygram, Polydor

Caravan

ALBUM,THE.
Tracks: / Heartbreaker / Corner of my eye / Watcha gonna tell me / Piano player / Make yourself at home / Golden mile / Bright shiny day / Clear blue sky / Keepin' up de fences.
Album: released on Kingdom in '83 by Kingdom Records. Distributed by: Kingdom

Cassette: released on Kingdom in '83 by Kingdom Records. Distributed by: Kingdom

BACK TO FRONT.
Tracks: / Back to Herne bay front / Bet you wanna take it all / Hold on hold on A.A man / Videos of Hollywood / Sally don't change it / Take my breath away / Proper job / Back to front.
Album: released on Kingdom Records in '83 by Kingdom Records. Distributed by: Kingdom Records

BEST OF CARAVAN.
Tracks: / And I wish I were stoned again don't worry / Can't be long now (medley) / Francoise (medley) / For Richard (medley) / Warlock / No backstage pass / Dog, the dog, he's at it again, The / Love in your eye (medley - 2) / To catch me a brother / Subsultus (medley - 2) / Debouchement (medley - 2) / Tilbury kecks (medley - 2) / In the land of grey and pink / Memory lain, Hugh.
Album: released on C5 in Jul'87 by See For Miles Records. Distributed by: Counterpoint

BLIND DOG AT ST.DUNSTAN'S.
Tracks: / Here I am / Chiefs and indians / Very smelly, grubby little oik, A / Bobbing wide / Come on back / Very smelly, grubby little oik, A (reprise) / Jack and Jill / Can you hear me / All the way.
Album: released on BTM in '76. Distributed by: BMG Distribution

CANTERBURY COLLECTION (THE).
Compact disc: released on Kingdom Records in Jan'87 by Kingdom Records. Distributed by: Kingdom Records

COLLECTION: CARAVAN.
Album: released on Kingdom in '84 by Kingdom Records. Distributed by: Kingdom

HEARTBREAKER It's never to late.
Single (7"): released on Kingdom Records in '80 by Kingdom Records. Distributed by: Kingdom Records

IF I COULD DO IT ALL OVER AGAIN.
Tracks: / If I could do it all over again I'd do it all over you / And I wish I was stoned / Don't worry / As I feel I die / With an ear to the ground I can make it / Martinian / Only cox / Reprise / Hello, hello / Asforteri / Can't be long now / Francoise / For Richard / Warlock / Limits.
Album: released on Decca in '70 by Decca Records. Distributed by: Polygram

IN THE LAND OF GREY & PINK.
Tracks: / Golf girl / Winter wine / Love to love you / In the land of grey and pink / Nine feet underground: Nigel blows a tune / Love's a friend / Make it 76 / Dance of the seven paper hankies- hold grandad by the nose / Honest I did- disassociation / 100% proof.
Album: released on Deram in '71 by Decca Records. Distributed by: Polygram

I WISH I WERE STONED DON'T WORRY,AND.
Album: released on See For Miles in '85 by See For Miles Records. Distributed by: Pinnacle

KEEPING UP DEFENCES.
Single (7"): released on Kingdom in '81 by Kingdom Records. Distributed by: Kingdom

SHOW OF OUR LIVES,THE.
Album: released on Decca in '81 by Decca Records. Distributed by: Polygram

WATERLOO LILY.
Tracks: / Waterloo Lily / Nothing at all / It's coming soon / Nothing at all / Song and signs / Aristocracy / Love in your eye, The / To catch me a brother / Subsultus / Debouchement / Tilbury kecks / World is yours, The.
Album: released on Deram in '72 by Decca Records. Distributed by: Polygram

Caravelli

BEST OF (Caravelli Orchestra).
Compact disc: released on CBS in '83 by CBS Records. Distributed by: CBS

Caravelli Orchestra

CARAVELLI Best of.
Compact disc: released on CBS in '83 by CBS Records. Distributed by: CBS

Carbia Ole

CARBIA OLE Happy South America for dancing (Various Orchestras).
Album: released on Polydor (Germany) in '83. Distributed by: IMS-Polygram

Cassette: released on Polydor (Germany) in '83. Distributed by: IMS-Polygram

Car Crash International

ALL PASSION SPENT.
Single (12"): released on Crammed in '84. Distributed by: Rough Trade, Nine Mile, Cartel

WHIP,THE/GHOSTMAN/TV SHOCK THEATRE.
Single (12"): released on Crammed in '83. Distributed by: Rough Trade, Nine Mile, Cartel

Cardell, Vince

LIBERANCE PRESENTS....

Album: released on Pye International in '78

Cardenas, Luis

ANIMAL INSTINCT.
Album: released on Car in Nov'86 by Car Records. Distributed by: Pinnacle

RUNAWAYS.
Tracks: / Runaways / Still waiting / Let it out (live).
Notes: Let it out (live) is an extra track on 12" version.
Single (7"): released on Consolidated Allied in Aug'86. Distributed by: Pinnacle

Single (12"): released on Consolidated Allied in Aug'86. Distributed by: Pinnacle

Picture disc single: released on Consolidated Allied in Aug'86. Distributed by: Pinnacle

Cardiacs

BIG SHIP.
Album: released on Alphabet in Jan'87. Distributed by: Pinnacle

SEASIDE TREATS.
Single (12"): released on Jettisoundz in May'86. Distributed by: Red Rhino, Cartel

THERE'S TOO MANY IRONS IN THE FIRE.
Single (7"): released on Alphabet in Aug'87. Distributed by: Pinnacle

Cardiff...

CARDIFF POLPHONIC CHOIR (Cardiff Polphonic Choir).
Album: released on Black Mountain in '82 by Black Mountain Records

CARDIFF SEARCHLIGHT TATTOO 1983 (Cardiff Searchlight Tattoo 1983).
Album: released on Bandleader in '83 by Bandleader Records. Distributed by: PRT

COME ALIVE (Cardiff City Temple Youth Choir).
Tracks: / Come alive / Our God is marching on / I'm gonna keep on singing / Blood will never lose it's power, The / Walk with him in white / Come holy spirit / Never in a million years / Let me touch him / That'a the way to find happiness / Why should I worry or fret / It's God who watches / King of kings / I cannot fail the lord.
Album: by Pilgrim Records. Distributed by: Rough Trade, Cartel

Card, Joy

SUPER STATIC MAGIC MYSTERY.
Single (12"): released on Wackies in '84 by Wackies Records. Distributed by: Jetstar

Card, Michael

KNOWN BY THE SCARS.
Album: released on Birdwing in '84 by Word Records. Distributed by: Word Distribution

Cassette: released on Birdwing in '84 by Word Records. Distributed by: Word Distribution

SCANDALON.
Notes: Second album by co-writer of Amy Grant's famous song 'El Shaddai'.
Album: released on Sparrow in Apr'86 by Word Records. Distributed by: Spartan

Cassette: released on Sparrow in Apr'86 by Word Records. Distributed by: Spartan

Care

WHATEVER POSESSED YOU.
Single (7"): released on Arista in '84 by Arista Records. Distributed by: RCA

Single (12"): released on Arista in '84 by Arista Records. Distributed by: RCA

Care Bears

CARE BEARS MOVIE.
Album: released on Cherry Lane in '85 by Cherry Lane Productions. Distributed by: PRT

Cassette: released on Cherry Lane in '85 by Cherry Lane Productions. Distributed by: PRT

CARE BEARS TO THE RESCUE.
Album: released on Cherry Lane in Nov'85 by Cherry Lane Productions. Distributed by: PRT

Cassette: released on Cherry Lane in Nov'85 by Cherry Lane Productions. Distributed by: PRT

Carefree

CAREFREE Musical (Various Artists).
Notes: Fred and Ginger at the peak of their careers.
Video-cassette (VHS): released on Video Collection in May'87 by Video Collection Records. Distributed by: Counterpoint

Careless Hands

LOOKING FOR A SECRET.
Single (7"): released on Flying Kites in '82. Distributed by: Indies, Cartel

Carey, Tony

IT'S A FINE DAY.
Single (7"): released on MCA in '84 by MCA Records. Distributed by: Polygram, MCA

SOME TOUGH CITY.
Album: released on MCA in '84 by MCA Records. Distributed by: Polygram, MCA

Cassette: released on MCA in '84 by MCA Records. Distributed by: Polygram, MCA

Cargo

DO IT.
Single (12"): released on Cargogold Productions in '84. Distributed by: RCA,

Single (12"): released on Cargogold Productions in Jul'87. Distributed by: RCA,

DON'T STOP YOUR LOVE.
Tracks: / Don't stop your love / Cover me.
Single (7"): released on WEA in Apr'86 by WEA Records. Distributed by: WEA

Single (12"): released on WEA in Apr'86 by WEA Records. Distributed by: WEA

Single (12"): released on Cargogold Productions in '86. Distributed by: RCA,

HOLDING ON FOR LOVE.
Single (12"): released on Cargogold Productions in '82. Distributed by: RCA,

Single (7"): released on Zonophone in '82 by EMI Records. Distributed by: EMI

Single (12"): released on Zonophone in '82 by EMI Records. Distributed by: EMI

JAZZ RAP.
Single (7"): released on Calibre in '85 by Calibre Records. Distributed by: PRT

Single (12"): released on Calibre in '85 by Calibre Records. Distributed by: PRT

Single (12"): released on Cargogold Productions in '85. Distributed by: RCA, Ariola

LADY'S MAN.
Tracks: / Fill your glass / Push about the bottle boys / When Bibo thought fit / Foresters sound cheerful horn / When gen'rous wine expands my soul / We're three poor mariners / Hark the hollow woods resounding / There behold the mighty bowl / Life's a bumper / Music's the language of the blest above / Fear no danger to ensue / Peace to the souls of my heroes / Sportive little trifler / How merrily we live / Fair Aurora / Fear no more the heat of the sun / O sweetly Delia sings / Breathe soft ye winds / Of all the brave birds / Time has not thinned / Sleep while the soft evening etc..
Single (12"): released on Cargogold Productions in Mar'87. Distributed by: RCA,

LOVELY SUMMERS DAY.
Tracks: / Lovely summers day / You bring the sunshine / Without you / Holding on for love / Ladys man / Lovely summers day (inst.) / Sunshine / Do it (inst.) / You make my wsorld / Without you.
Album: released on Cargogold Productions in Aug'87. Distributed by: RCA

LOVE YOU SO (WITHOUT YOU) (Cargo, featuring Dave Collins).
Tracks: / Love you so (without you) / Love you so (instrumental).
Single (7"): released on Streetwave in Aug'86 by Streetwave Records. Distributed by: PRT Distribution

Single (12"): released on Streetwave in Aug'86 by Streetwave Records. Distributed by: PRT Distribution

SUNNY LOVE AFFAIR.
Tracks: / Sunny love affair / Drifter, The.
Single (12"): released on Cargogold Productions in '81. Distributed by: RCA, Ariola

TENDER TOUCH.
Single (7"): released on Korova in '84. Distributed by: WEA

Single (12"): released on Korova in '84. Distributed by: WEA

Single (12"): released on Cargogold Productions in '83. Distributed by: RCA,

Caribbean...

CARIBBEAN COCKTAIL Various artists (Various Artists).
Album: released on BBC in '85 by BBC Records & Tapes. Distributed by: EMI, PRT,

Cassette: released on BBC in '85 by BBC Records & Tapes. Distributed by: EMI, PRT,

CARIBBEAN SONGS & DANCES Harious artists (Various Artists).

Album: released on Nonesuch Explorer (USA) in '84

Caribbean Caper

SUNSHINE BOY Hold me.
Single (7"): released on Rooster in '83 by Rooster Records. Distributed by: PRT Distribution

Carillons Of Scotland

CARILLONS OF SCOTLAND Various artists (Various Artists).
Album: released on Saydisc in '84 by Saydisc Records. Distributed by: Essex, Harmonia Mundi, Roots, H.R. Taylor, Jazz Music, Swift, Projection, Gamut

Cassette: released on Saydisc in '84 by Saydisc Records. Distributed by: Essex, Harmonia Mundi, Roots, H.R. Taylor, Jazz Music, Swift, Projection,

Carle, Frankie

1944-1946 (Carle, Frankie & His Orchestra).
Album: released on Circle(USA) in Jun'86 by Jazzology Records (USA). Distributed by: Jazz Music, Swift, Chris Wellard

Carless, Dorothy

WHISPERING GRASS (Carless, Dorothy/Benny Lee/Adelaide Hall/Issy Bonn).
Tracks: / I hear a rhapsody / Lonely serenade / As if you didn't know / We both told a lie / Why don't we do this more often / When they sound the last 'all clear' / What more can I say / I don't want anybody at all (if I can't have you) / Who told you I cared? / Careless / I'm getting sentimental over you / Don't make me laugh / I heard you cried last night (and so did I) / Ain't it a shame about mame / Serenade in blue / Sophisticated lady / There I've said it again / It's a wonderful world (after all) / Across the bridge of gold / Some day you'll want me to want you / Somewhere beyond the stars / Goodnight till tomorrow / Waiting / Till then / My little sailor man / Whispering grass / Autumn nocturne / Jim / How about you / Do you care? / I'll always remember / We three (my echo, my shadow and me) / Beat me daddy, eight to a bar / Five o'clock whistle, The / Number ten lullaby lane / I guess I'll have to dream the rest.
Notes: This is a double album and a double cassette. See also under Benny Lee, Adelaide Hall, Issy Bonn.
Double Album: released on Decca (London) in Mar'87 by Decca Records. Distributed by: Polygram, IMS

Cassette: released on Decca (London) in Mar'87 by Decca Records. Distributed by: Polygram, IMS

Carley, Raymond

BEAUTIFUL WEEKEND.
Album: released on Night Owl in '78

Carlin, Bob

BANGING AND SAWING.
Album: released on Rounder (USA) in '85. Distributed by: Mike's Country Music Room Distribution, Jazz Music Distribution, Swift Distribution, Roots Records Distribution, Projection Distribution, Topic Distribution

Carlisle, Belinda

BELINDA.
Tracks: / Mad about you / I need a disguise / Since you've gone / I feel the magic / I never wanted a rich man / Band of gold / Gotta get to you / From the heart / Shot in the dark / Stuff and nonsense.
Notes: Former lead singer with the Go-Go's, Belinda Carlisle, releases her first solo album on IRS Records.
Album: released on I.R.S.(Independent Record Syndicate) in Jul'86 by I.R.S.. Distributed by: MCA

Cassette: released on I.R.S.(Independent Record Syndicate) in Jul'86 by I.R.S.. Distributed by: MCA

MAD ABOUT YOU.
Tracks: / Mad about you / I never wanted a rich man.
Single (7"): released on I.R.S.(Independent Record Syndicate) in Jun'86 by I.R.S.. Distributed by: MCA

Single (12"): released on I.R.S.(Independent Record Syndicate) in Jun'86 by I.R.S.. Distributed by: MCA

Carlisle, Elsie

SHE'S THE TALK OF THE TOWN.
Tracks: / It's the talk of the town / One little kiss / When a woman loves a man / Home James and don't spare the horses / Snowball / Porter's love song, The / I cover the waterfront / I'm gonna wash my hands of you / We just could't say goodbye / Smoke gets in your eyes / Place in your heart, A / Girl next door, The / No, no, a thousand times no / Clouds will soon roll by, The / You're my everything / No more love / There's no more you can say / Show is over, The.
Cassette: released on Happy Days in Jul'86 by Conifer Records. Distributed by: Conifer

Album: released on Saville in Jan'86 by Conifer Records. Distributed by: Conifer

STAR GAZING 1932-1936.
Album: released on Old Bean in Mar'87. Distributed by: Jazz Music

Cassette: released on Old Bean in Mar'87. Distributed by: Jazz Music

STAR GAZING (1932-1936).
Tracks: / Star gazing / Solitude / Mama I long for a sweetheart / Dancing with my shadow / Place in your heart, A / Conversation for two / Poor butterfly / You try somebody else / When a man loves a woman / Whisper sweet / Making conversation / Up the wooden hill to Bedfordshire / To be worthy of you / Deep water / Come up and see me sometime / My shadow's where my sweetheart used to be / He wooed her and wooed her and wooed her.
Notes: In that marvelous pre-TV era of the Big Bands their broadcasts were listened to by millions, and beacause of those broadcasts the names of the artists concerned were house-old ones. Can one really think of Lew Stone without immediately linking him with Al Bowlly? is it possible to recall Roy Fox without also recalling Mary Lee? and is there any way that the magical name of Ambrose can be conjured up without remembering the lady who, for so long, gave so much pleasure to so many by her sheer talent and professionalism - Elsie Carlisle? Elsie, along with Sam Browne, made up one of the most successful singing partnerships of that golden age, but the fact that the lassie from Lancashire also made many solo recordings show that although she was capable of being the eual half of a famous duo, she was also more than capable of having an appreciative audience in her own right. Ambrose paid for, and usually got, the best in the business, and his battery of vocalists was no exception: Evelyn Dall, Anne Shelton, and Vera Lynn being but three of the singers who sang with the maestro. To hold your own with that kind of competition you have to be good, and Elsie was.
Album: released on Old Bean in Apr'87. Distributed by: Jazz Music

Cassette: released on Old Bean in Apr'87. Distributed by: Jazz Music

THAT'S LOVE.
Album: released on ASV Living Era in '82 by ASV Records. Distributed by: PRT

Cassette: released on ASV Living Era in '82 by ASV Records. Distributed by: PRT

Carlisles

BUSY BODY BOOGIE.
Album: released on Bear Family in '85 by Bear Family Records. Distributed by: Rollercoaster Distribution, Swift

Carlisle's Folk Workshop

CARLISLE'S FOLK WORKSHOP Best of (Various Artists).
Album: released on Fellside in '77 by Fellside Records. Distributed by: Roots, Jazz Music, Celtic Music, Projection

Carlisle, Una Mae

UNA MAE CARLISLE Savannah Churchill 1944 (Carlisle, Una Mae & Savannah Churhill 1944).
Album: released on Harlequin in '82 by Harlequin Records. Distributed by: Swift, Jazz Music, Wellard, Chris, IRS, Taylor, H.R.

Carlo's Chicagoans

CARLO KRAHMER MEMORIAL ALBUM,THE.
Album: released on Esquire in '79 by Titan International Productions. Distributed by: Jazz Music, Cadillac Music, Swift, Wellard, Chris, Backs, Rough Trade, Revolver, Nine Mile

Carlos, Don

CAN'T WASTE TIME Waste dub.
Single 10": released on Cha-Cha in '82 by Cha Cha. Distributed by: Jetstar

COME IN Special request.
Single (12"): released on Greensleeves in '83 by Greensleeves Records. Distributed by: BMG, Jetstar, Spartan

DANCE GATES 12 tribes of Israel.
Single (12"): released on Rusty International in '83 by Rusty International Records. Distributed by: Jetstar Distribution

DAY TO DAY LIVING.
Tracks: / Hog and goat / I like it / Dice cups / Roots man party / Hey Mr Babylon / Street life / English woman / I'm not crazy / At the bus stop.
Album: released on Greensleeves in '82 by Greensleeves Records. Distributed by: BMG, Jetstar, Spartan

FIND YOURSELF A FOOL (Carlos, Don & Gold).
Single (12"): released on Kingdom in '84 by Kingdom Records. Distributed by: Kingdom

FROM CREATION.
Single (12"): released on Blacker Dread in '84

GRIEF MY HEART Spread out.
Single (12"): released on Ethnic in '83. Distributed by: Kingdom

ISOBEL One morning(Silly boys).
Single (12"): released on Rusty International in '82 by Rusty International Records. Distributed by: Jetstar Distribution

JORDAN RIVER Reason (Little John).
Single (12"): released on Youth In Progress in '83 by Youth In Progress Records. Distributed by: Jetstar

JUST A PASSING GLANCE.
Album: released on RAS in '85

MAGIC MAN Magic rhythm.
Single (12"): released on Negus Roots in '82 by Negus Roots Records. Distributed by: Jetstar

MONEY & WOMEN Keeping on working (Carlos, Don & John Wayne).
Single (12"): released on Shuttle in '83. Distributed by: RCA

MR BIG MAN Runaround.
Single (12"): released on Black Roots in '83 by Black Roots Records. Distributed by: Jetstar

NEVER RUN AWAY (Carlos, Don & Gold).
Album: released on Kingdom in '84 by Kingdom Records. Distributed by: Kingdom

NICE TIME (LATE NIGHT BLUES) Get up.
Single (12"): released on CSA in '83 by CSA Records. Distributed by: PRT, Jetstar

PEACE AND LOVE Lock and keys.
Single 10": released on Nice 'n' Nasty in '83

PLANTATION (Carlos, Don & Gold).
Album: released on CSA in '84 by CSA Records. Distributed by: PRT, Jetstar

PURE GOLD.
Album: released on Vista Sounds in '84 by Vista Sounds Records. Distributed by: Jetstar

RASTA BROTHERS.
Album: released on Dancefloor in '85 by Dancefloor Records. Distributed by: Vista Sounds Records, Jetstar

RAVING TONIGHT (Carlos, Don & Gold).
Album: released on RAS in '84

ROCK THIS HERE MUSIC.
Single (12"): released on Shuttle in '83. Distributed by: RCA

SHOWDOWN VOL.II.
Album: released on Empire in '84 by Empire Records. Distributed by: Backs, Cartel, Jetstar

SRICTLY CULTURE.
Single (12"): released on Scom in '85 by Scom Records. Distributed by: Jetstar

UNTRUE GIRL.
Single (12"): released on EAD in '84 by EAD Records. Distributed by: Jetstar

YOU ARE MY SUNSHINE.
Single (12"): released on Tads in '84 by Tads Records. Distributed by: Jetstar Distribution

Carlos, Roberto

CARLOS, ROBERTO.
Album: released on CBS(Spain) in '84 by CBS Records. Distributed by: Conifer, Discovery, Swift

Cassette: released on CBS(Spain) in '84 by CBS Records. Distributed by: Conifer, Discovery, Swift

ROBERTO CARLOS.
Album: released on CBS(Holland) in '84 by CBS Records. Distributed by: Discovery

Carlos, Walter

WALTER CARLOS-BY REQUEST.
Cassette: released on CBS in '77 by CBS Records. Distributed by: CBS

Carlos, Wendy

BEST OF CARLOS.
Tracks: / Title music theme from clockwork orange / What's new pussycat / Eleanor Rigby / Gazza ladra, La / Water music / Scarlatti sonatas / Jesu joy of man's desiring / Air on a G string / Brandenberg No. 3.
Album: released on CBS in '83 by CBS Records. Distributed by: CBS

Carlson, Pete

YOU WERE THERE.
Tracks: / In this quiet hour / He promise / Evermore / Tell me all your troubles / Hope of my salvation / You were there / Jesus is all the world me / Simple story / You ask me why / I don't wanna go home.
Album: by Pilgrim Records. Distributed by: Rough Trade, Cartel

Carl 'That man'...

GRAND NATIONAL (Carl 'That man' Progression All Stars).
Single (12"): released on Big Ship in '84 by Big Ship Records. Distributed by: Jetstar

Carlton, Carl

CARL CARLTON.
Album: released on 20th Century in '81. Distributed by: RCA, IMS-Polygram

Cassette: released on 20th Century in '81. Distributed by: RCA, IMS-Polygram

Carlton & His Shoes

MOOD FOR LOVE Carlton's mood.
Single (7"): released on Fashion in '82 by Fashion Records. Distributed by: PRT, Jetstar

Single (7"): released on Fashion in '82 by Fashion Records. Distributed by: PRT, Jetstar

Carlton, Larry

ALONE BUT NEVER ALONE.
Tracks: / Smiles and smiles to go / Perfect peace / Carrying you / Lord's prayer (The) / High Steppin' / Whatever happens / Pure delight / Alone/but never alone / Smiles and smiles to go / Perfect peace / Carrying you / Lord's prayer, The / High steppin' / Whatever happens / High steppin' / Whatever happens / Pure delight / Alone, but never alone.
Notes: Larry Carlton - Long recognised as probably the best guitarist in the States, Larry has recorded over a long and distinguished career with Steely Dan, The Crusaders, Joni Mitchell, Bill Withers and many, many others.
Album: released on MCA in Jul'87 by MCA Records. Distributed by: Polygram, MCA

Cassette: released on MCA in Jul'87 by MCA Records. Distributed by: Polygram, MCA

Compact disc: released on MCA in Jul'87 by MCA Records. Distributed by: Polygram, MCA

FRIENDS.
Tracks: / Breaking ground / South town / Tequila / Blues for TJ / Song in the 5th grade / Crusin' / L A N Y / Friends.
Album: released on Warner Brothers in '83 by Warner Bros Records. Distributed by: WEA

Cassette: released on Warner Brothers in '83 by Warner Bros Records. Distributed by: WEA

LARRY CARLTON.
Album: released on Warner Brothers in '79 by Warner Bros Records. Distributed by: WEA

LAST NITE.
Album: released on MCA in Jan'87 by MCA Records. Distributed by: Polygram, MCA

Cassette: released on MCA in Jan'87 by MCA Records. Distributed by: Polygram, MCA

LIVE IN JAPAN.
Album: released on Flyover in '79 by Flyover Records. Distributed by: Flyover Records

SLEEPWALK.
Tracks: / Last nite / Blues bird / Song for Katie / Frenchman's flat / Upperkern / 10.00 p.m / You gotta get it while you can / Sleepwalk.
Album: released on Warner Brothers in '82 by Warner Bros Records. Distributed by: WEA

Cassette: released on Warner Brothers in '82 by Warner Bros Records. Distributed by: WEA

Carlton, Little Carl

COMPETITION AIN'T NOTHING.
Single (7"): released on Kent in '85 by Ace Records. Distributed by: Pinnacle

Carlton Main Frickley...

BANDING WITH BALL.
Album: released on Amberlee in '79 by Amberlee Records. Distributed by: Amberlee Records, H.R. Taylor

CARLTON MAIN FRICKLEY COLLIERY BAND Best of.
Album: released on Decca in '79 by Decca Records. Distributed by: Polygram

LABOUR & LOVE.
Cassette: released on Grosvenor in '74 by Grosvenor Records. Distributed by: Taylors

: by Grosvenor Records. Distributed by: Taylors

Carlton Sisters

JUMP.
Cassette: released on Chevron in '84. Distributed by: Multiple Sound Distributors

Carlton, Steve

EASY.
Tracks: / Easy / Back to square one / Baby's good to me.
Notes: Baby's good to me - extra track on 12".
Single (7"): released on RCA in Aug'86 by RCA Records. Distributed by: RCA, Roots, Swift, Wellard, Chris, I & B, Solomon & Peres Distribution

Single (12"): released on RCA in Aug'86 by RCA Records. Distributed by: RCA, Roots, Swift, Wellard, Chris, I & B, Solomon & Peres Distribution

KEEP ON WALKING.
Tracks: / Keep on walking / Goodbye / Keep on walking (inst).
Notes: Keep on walking (inst) is an extra track on 12".
Single (7"): released on RCA in Apr'86 by RCA Records. Distributed by: RCA, Roots, Swift, Wellard, Chris, I & B, Solomon & Peres Distribution

Single (12"): released on RCA in Apr'86 by RCA Records. Distributed by: RCA, Roots, Swift, Wellard, Chris, I & B, Solomon & Peres Distribution

Carluke Primrose...

IN CONCERT (Carluke Primrose Flute Band).
Album: released on Country House in '82 by BGS Productions Ltd. Distributed by: Taylor, H.R., Record Merchandisers Distribution, Pinnacle, Sounds of Scotland Records

Carman

CHAMPION, THE.
Notes: Carman has proved himself to be a top contender, particularly in the US, for contemporary Christian music interest. He presents his message in an innovativepackage of street-smart storytelling and humour, but always with a decisive punch. With his new release Carman steps into the ring to challenge us to a deeper commitment. His songs take aim at significant spiritual principles, ranging from pop to ballad.
Album: released on Myrrh in Jun'86 by Word Records. Distributed by: Word Distribution

Cassette: released on Myrrh in Jun'86 by Word Records. Distributed by: Word Distribution

COMIN' ON STRONG.
Album: released on Myrrh in '85 by Word Records. Distributed by: Word Distribution

Cassette: released on Myrrh in '85 by Word Records. Distributed by: Word Distribution

Carman, Pauli

DIAL MY NUMBER.
Tracks: / Dial my number / Flashback / You impress me / Big on pleasure / Lose control / High and low / Close to the bone / Dangerous.
Album: released on CBS in Jul'86 by CBS Records. Distributed by: CBS

Cassette: released on CBS in Jul'86 by CBS Records. Distributed by: CBS

Single (7"): released on CBS in May'86 by CBS Records. Distributed by: CBS

Single (12"): released on CBS in May'86 by CBS Records. Distributed by: CBS

Carmel

6 TRACK EP.
Single (12"): released on Red Flame in '82 by Red Flame Records. Distributed by: Nine Mile, Cartel

BAD DAY Lament.
Single (12"): released on London in '83 by London Records. Distributed by: Polygram

BAD DAY/RUE ST.DENIS/BAD DAY.
Single (12"): released on London in '83 by London Records. Distributed by: Polygram

CARMEL.
Tracks: / Tracks of my tears / Sugar daddy / Guilty / Thunder / Love affair / Storm.
Album: released on Red Flame in '82 by Red Flame Records. Distributed by: Nine Mile, Cartel

DRUM IS EVERYTHING,THE.
Album: released on London in '84 by London Records. Distributed by: Polygram

Cassette: released on London in '84 by London Records. Distributed by: Polygram

Compact disc: released on London in '84 by London Records. Distributed by: Polygram

FALLING, THE.
Compact disc: released on London in Jun'86 by London Records. Distributed by: Polygram

Album: released on London in Sep'86 by London Records. Distributed by: Polygram

Cassette: released on London in Sep'86 by London Records. Distributed by: Polygram

I'M NOT AFRAID OF YOU.
Single (7"): released on London in '85 by London Records. Distributed by: Polygram

Single (12"): released on London in '85 by London Records. Distributed by: Polygram

IT'S ALL IN THE GAME.
Single (7"): released on London in Aug'87 by London Records. Distributed by: Polygram

IT'S ALL THE GAME.
Tracks: / It's all the game / More, more, more / Tracks of my tears*.
Single (7"): released on London in Jul'87 by London Records. Distributed by: Polygram

Single (12"): released on London in Jul'87 by London Records. Distributed by: Polygram

MERCY.
Tracks: / Mercy / What a story.
Single (7"): released on London in Sep'86 by London Records. Distributed by: Polygram

Single (12"): released on London in Sep'86 by London Records. Distributed by: Polygram

MORE MORE MORE Hot Day (version).
Single (7"): released on London in '84 by London Records. Distributed by: Polygram

Single (12"): released on London in '84 by London Records. Distributed by: Polygram

MY HEART SINGS COUNTRY.
Single (7"): released on Superbad in '85

SALLY.
Tracks: / Sally / Hymn of love.
Single (7"): released on London in May'86 by London Records. Distributed by: Polygram

Single (12"): released on London in May'86 by London Records. Distributed by: Polygram

STORM Can't stand the rain,I.
Single (7"): released on Red Flame in '82 by Red Flame Records. Distributed by: Nine Mile, Cartel

WILLOW WEEP FOR ME That's cool that's neat.
Single (7"): released on London in '83 by London Records. Distributed by: Polygram

Single (12"): released on London in '83 by London Records. Distributed by: Polygram

Carmen

CARMEN Original Motion Picture Soundtrack (Various Artists).
Tracks: / Search for Carmen, The / Introduction / Stop crying / Bulerias (Seguidillas) / Adagio / Womens knife fight in La Tabacalera de Sevilla, The / Soldiers arrest Carmen, The / Intermezzo / Habanero / Fiesta popular / Guitar strumming / Company rehearses, The / Love theme and premonition / Fight with sticks / Carmen's infidelity / El Gato montes / Show down between Escamillo and Don Jose / Cante Gitano / Mirabras / Finale.
Notes: Recorded in digital stereo.
Compact disc: released on Polydor in Feb'84 by Polydor Records. Distributed by: Polygram, Polydor

Compact disc: by Erato Records. Distributed by: Conifer

CARMEN Original Soundtrack.
Notes: Digital Stereo.
Compact disc: released on Polydor in Feb'84 by Polydor Records. Distributed by: Polygram, Polydor

CARMEN (3 DISC SET) Original soundtrack (Various Artists).
Notes: Digital stereo.
Triple album / cassette: released on Erato (France) in Mar'85 by Erato Records. Distributed by: Conifer

Carmen, Eric

ALL BY MYSELF.
Single (7"): released on Old Gold in Jul'82 by Old Gold Records. Distributed by: Lightning, Jazz Music, Spartan, Counterpoint

ERIC CARMEN (Different album).
Tracks: / Sunrise / That's rock 'n' roll / Never gonna fall in love / Last night / All by myself / My girl.
Album: released on Fame (Arista) in Nov'82 by Music For Pleasure Records. Distributed by: EMI

Cassette: released on Fame (Arista) in Nov'82 by Music For Pleasure Records. Distributed by: EMI

ERIC CARMEN.
Tracks: / I wanna hear it from your lips / I'm through with love / American as apple pie / Living without your love / Come back to my love / She remembered / Maybe my baby / Spotlight / Way we used to be, The.

Album: released on Geffen in Feb'85 by Geffen Records. Distributed by: WEA, CBS

Cassette: released on Geffen in Feb'85 by Geffen Records. Distributed by: WEA, CBS

I WANT TO HEAR IT FROM YOUR LIPS.
Single (7"): released on Geffen in Jan'85 by Geffen Records. Distributed by: WEA, CBS

Single (12"): released on Geffen in Jan'85 by Geffen Records. Distributed by: WEA, CBS

Carmen Jones

CARMEN JONES Original Soundtrack.
Album: by RCA Records. Distributed by: RCA, Roots, Swift, Wellard, Chris, I & B, Solomon & Peres Distribution

Carmen, Tracey

RESCUE ME.
Tracks: / Rescue me / Infrarfni (infra) / Summertime.
Notes: Summertime - extra track on 12".
Single (7"): released on Infrastructure in Jan'86 by Label City Buildings. Distributed by: M.I.S., EMI

Single (12"): released on Infrastructure in Jan'86 by Label City Buildings. Distributed by: M.I.S., EMI

Carmichael, Hoagy

16 CLASSIC TRACKS.
Tracks: / I may be wrong, but, I think you're wonderful / Talking is a woman / Sh-h the old man's sleepin' / Don't forget to say NO baby / Casanova cricket / Man could be a wonderful thing, A / Put yourself in my place baby / Tune for humming, A / That's a plenty / Gonnna get a girl / For every man there's a woman / Ten to one it's Tennessee / Coney island washboard / Some days there just ain't no fish / Monkey song, The / Rogue river valley.
Album: released on MCA in Jun'82 by MCA Records. Distributed by: Polygram, MCA

Cassette: released on MCA in Jun'82 by MCA Records. Distributed by: Polygram, MCA

BALLADS FOR DANCING.
Tracks: / I walked with music / Sky lark / I get along without you very well / Two sleepy people / Lamplighter's serenade, The / Heart and soul / Narness of you, The / Ivy / One morning in May / How little we know / Blue orchids / Star dust.
Notes: A strong addition to MCA's terrific nostalgia releases, "Ballads for Dancing" features many of the great Hoagy Carmichael's best works.
Album: released on MCA in May'86 by MCA Records. Distributed by: Polygram, MCA

CURTIS HITCH & HOAGY CARMICHAEL 1923-28 (Carmichael, Hoagy & Curtis Hitch).

HOAGY.
Tracks: / Rockin' chair / Georgia on my mind / Sing it way down low / Lazybones / March of the hoodlums / Snowball / Walkin' the dog / Pap's gone goodbye / Bessie couln't help it / One morning in May / Washboard blues / Moon country / Cosmics / Sittin' and whittlin' / Stardust / Lazy river / Judy / Barnacle Bill the sailor.
Album: released on RCA International in Mar'82

Cassette: released on RCA International in Mar'82

Album: released on RCA International in Mar'82

Cassette: released on RCA International in Mar'82

HOAGY CARMICHAEL.
Notes: Piano solos with whistling and singing. Not all the old warhorses. Recorded privately in 1951.
Album: released on Harlequin in Jul'82 by Harlequin Records. Distributed by: Swift, Jazz Music, Wellard, Chris Taylor,

HOAGY CARMICHAEL SINGS HOAGY CARMICHAEL.
Tracks: / Old music master, The / Hong Kong blues / Memphis in June / Ode buttermilk sky / My resistance is low / Rockin' chair / Riverboat shuffle / Georgia on my mind / Lazy river / Judy / Stardust / In the cool, cool, cool of the evening / Moon country / Baltimore oriole / Little old lady / Washboard blues.
Album: released on MCA in Aug'81 by MCA Records. Distributed by: Polygram, MCA

Cassette: released on MCA in Aug'81 by MCA Records. Distributed by: Polygram, MCA

HOAGY SINGS CARMICHAEL.
Tracks: / Georgia on my mind / Winter moon / New Orleans / Memphis in June / Skylark / Two sleepy people / Baltimore oriole / Rockin' chair / Ballad in blue / Lazy river.
Notes: Recorded in 1956. Art Pepper - alto saxophone Harry Edison
Album: released on EMI Retrospect in Oct'84 by EMI Records. Distributed by: EMI

Cassette: released on EMI Retrospect in Oct'84 by EMI Records. Distributed by: EMI

Carmichael, John

HOP SCOTCH (Carmichael, John/Accordion Bonanza Band).
Album: released on ARC (Accordion Records) in '84. Distributed by: Accordion Record Club

JOHN CARMICHAEL'S CEILIDH BAND.
Tracks: / Swinging westward (Highland Lassie going to the fair etc.) / Shetland reel (Shetland etc.) / Sicilian dance - Hebridean waltz (Where I was Yestreen etc.) / Strathspey and reel (Monymusk etc.) / Marches 2/4 and 6/8 time (Leaving Lunga etc.) / Gaelic medley (Ballachulish Glen etc.) / Looking lively (C.M. Hall etc.) / Jigtime (Skyeman's jig etc.) / Barn dance (The Hen's march etc.) / Irish reels (Peeler's jacket etc.) / Continental waltz (Gay Bavarian) / Toast to Nova Scotia, A (Canadian jig etc.) / Slow air and jig (Paddy's leather breeches).
Album: by Lismor Records. Distributed by: Lismor, Roots, Celtic Music

TUNES OF THE GAELN (Carmichael, John & His Band).
Cassette: released on Lochshore in Apr'87 by Klub Records. Distributed by: PRT

YOURS ACCORDIONLY.
Tracks: / Punch bowl reel / French-Canadian medley / Pipers delight / Norman's waltz / Jan's dance / Gaelic medley / March, strathspey and reel / Fiona Carmichael / Russe reel, La / Irish jigs / Farewell medley / Highland Schottische / Pipe jigs / Jole Bion / Marches 2/4 & 6/8 / Gaelic waltz.
Album: released on Country House in Aug'80 by BGS Productions Ltd. Distributed by: Taylor, H.R., Record Merchandisers Distribution, Pinnacle, Sounds of Scotland Records

Cassette: released on Country House in Aug'80 by BGS Productions Ltd. Distributed by: Taylor, H.R., Record Merchandisers Distribution, Pinnacle, Sounds of Scotland Records

Carmichael, Judy

PEARLS.
Notes: With Warren Vache Jr./Red Callender/H. Alden.
Album: released on Statiras in May'86 by Statiras Records. Distributed by: Jazz Music Distribution

TWO HANDED STRIDE.
Tracks: / Christopher Columbus / Viper's drag / Ja-Da / Honeysuckle Rose / Ain't misbehavin' / Handful of keys, A / I ain't got nobody / (I would do) anything for you.
Notes: Recorded 4/4/1980 & 29/4/1980 Judy Carmichael Marshall Royal Freddie Greene Red Callender Harold Jones
Album: released on Progressive in Nov'82 by Progressive Records. Distributed by: Jetstar

Carmichael, Ralph

CHRISTMAS JOYS (Carmichael, Ralph Orchestra & Chorus).
Tracks: / Wonderful world of Christmas, The / Caroling, caroling / Silent night / Birthday of a king / O holy night / Messiah medley / Inspirational world of Christmas, The / Ove in Bethlehem / Little drummer boy, The / Some children see him / Christmas joys medley.
Album: released on Light in May'82 by Mainline Record Company. Distributed by: Mainline

Cassette: released on Light in May'82 by Mainline Record Company. Distributed by: Mainline

I'M HERE, GOD'S HERE, NOW WE CAN START (Carmichael, Ralph & Kurt Kaiser).
Tracks: / Let it ring / God is here right now / Lookin' for the man called Jesus / Now we can start to hear music / Are you in control Lord? / Now we can start to be thankful / Nothing but amazing / Now we can start to have peace / Symbols and tokens / Now we can start to be free / I will lift up my eyes / Now we can start to love / God loved so much / Rough old roads / Road to glory, The / Come as you are / He'll go with you now.
Album: released on Light in May'82 by Mainline Record Company. Distributed by: Mainline

Cassette: released on Light in May'82 by Mainline Record Company. Distributed by: Mainline

Carmody, Simon

LAST BANDITS IN THE (THE) (Carmody, Simon, Nikki Sudden, Johnny Fean).
Album: released on Hotwire (Ireland) in May'86. Distributed by: Rough Trade, Cartel

YOU CAN'T ALWAYS GET WHAT YOU WANT See Friday, Gavin (Carmody, Simon & Gavin Friday).
Single (7"): released on Baby in Aug'87 by New Rose Records. Distributed by: Cartel

Single (12"): released on Baby in Aug'87 by New Rose Records. Distributed by: Cartel

Carnage

ALL THE SAD PEOPLE.
Single (7"): released on Creative Reality in Nov'83. Distributed by: Cartel

FACE THE FACTS.
Album: released on Creative Reality in Feb'85. Distributed by: Cartel

LIARS AND HYPOCRITES.
Single (7"): released on Creative Reality in Jul'84. Distributed by: Cartel

MAY THE FARCE BE WITH YOU.
Album: released on Creative Reality in May'86. Distributed by: Cartel

OUR LIFE IN THEIR HANDS.
Single (7"): released on Creative Reality in Jun'85. Distributed by: Cartel

Carnegie

JO STREET MACHINE.
Tracks: / Jo street machine (ext street mix) / Road machine (ext road mix).
Single (7"): released on Dove in Apr'87 by Dove Records. Distributed by: Jetstar

Single (12"): released on Dove in Apr'87 by Dove Records. Distributed by: Jetstar

Carne, Jean

ARTISTS SHOWCASE: JEAN CARNE.
Tracks: / We got some catching up to do / Lonely girl in a cold cold world / My love don't come easy / Trust me / I'm in love once again / No no you can't come back now / Bet your lucky star / Start the fire / When I find you love / Love don't love nobody / Free love / If you wanna go back / Sweet and wonderful / Was that all it was / You got a problem / Dindi / If you don't know me by now / Don't let it go to your head / Mystic stranger / Let's stay together / Happy to be with you.
Album: released on Streetsounds in Sep'87

Cassette: released on Streetsounds in Sep'87

CLOSER THAN CLOSE.
Album: released on Omni in Sep'86. Distributed by: Pinnacle

Single (7"): released on Omni in Aug'86. Distributed by: Pinnacle

Single (12"): released on Omni in Aug'86. Distributed by: Pinnacle

Carnes, Kim

ABADABADANGO.
Single (7"): released on EMI America in Oct'85 by EMI Records. Distributed by: EMI

BETTE DAVIS EYES.
Single (7"): released on EMI America in Apr'81 by EMI Records. Distributed by: EMI

CAFE RACERS.
Compact disc: released on EMI America in Mar'84 by EMI Records. Distributed by: EMI

DIVIDED HEARTS.
Tracks: / Divided Hearts / You say you love me (but I know better).
Single (7"): released on EMI America in Jul'86 by EMI Records. Distributed by: EMI

Single (12"): released on EMI America in Jul'86 by EMI Records. Distributed by: EMI

LIGHTHOUSE.
Tracks: / Divided hearts / I'd lie to you for your love / Black and white / Piece of the sky / You say you love me (but I know you don't) / Dancin' at the lighthouse / Love me like you never did before / Along with the radio / Only lonely lore / That's where the trouble lies.
Album: released on EMI America in Aug'86 by EMI Records. Distributed by: EMI

Cassette: released on EMI America in Aug'86 by EMI Records. Distributed by: EMI

MAKE NO MISTAKE, HE'S MINE (see Streisand, Barbra) (Carnes, Kim & Barbra Streisand).

MISTAKEN IDENTITY.
Tracks: / Bette Davis eyes / Hit and run / Mistaken identity / When I'm away from you / Draw of the cards / Break the rules tonite / Still hold on / Don't call it love / Miss you tonite / My old pals.
Notes: Originally released in June 1981.
Album: released on Fame in '85 by Music For Pleasure Records. Distributed by: EMI

Cassette: released on Fame in '85 by Music For Pleasure Records. Distributed by: EMI

Carney, Jack

CRUISIN' 1958 WIL St Louis.
Cassette: released on Increase(USA) in Jun'87 by Quicksilver Records (USA)

Carnival

WAKE UP (Don't be sheep).
Single (7"): released on Allemande in Apr'83

Carnival of....

CARNIVAL OF BRAZIL Various Artists (Various Artists).
Tracks: / Imperatriz Leopoldinesse / Primeira de Mangueira / Em cima da hora / Porteia / Imperio Serrano / Traz os montes / Samba de Roda / Capoeira / Makulele / Frevo / Maracatu / Caboclinhos / Ursos.
Album: released on IMS in Sep'85 by Polydor Records. Distributed by: IMS, Polygram

SQUARE DANCES (Carnival of Chicoutimi, Quebec).
Tracks: / Reel du diable, Le / Reel des nocus d'or, Le / Carnival du bout du monde / Samba Murielle / Reel des montagnes, Le / Reel des rioux, Le / Granda vaise, Le / Reel des Toussex, Le / Bastringue / Reel du chemin de fer, Le / Reel de ste-anne, The / Chant de l'alouette / Mouchoirs, Les / Brandy / Reel de l'oiseau moqueur, Le / Reel de St. Isidor, Le / Plongeuse, La.
Album: released on Sunset (France) in Sep'84. Distributed by: IMS-Polygram Distribution

Carnival Season

PLEASE DON'T SEND ME TO HEAVEN.
Tracks: / Please don't send me to heaven / Wondering about the.
Single (12"): released on What Goes On in Feb'87. Distributed by: Rough Trade, Cartel, Shigaku

Carnivore

CARNIVORE.
Album: released on Road Runner in Apr'86

Carn, Jean

IF YOU DON'T KNOW ME BY NOW.
Single (7"): released on Motown in Jul'82 by Motown Records. Distributed by: BMG Distribution

TRUST ME.
Tracks: / Steady on my mind / Don't let me slip away / Trust me / Super explosion / My baby loves me / If you don't know me by now / Completeness / Better to me.
Album: released on Motown in Aug'82 by Motown Records. Distributed by: BMG Distribution

Carnyx

SOUNDS OF THE ROMAN WORLD.
Tracks: / Lacrimosa / In the forum / Lutatia's dance / Outpost / Reflections / Gladiators, The.
Notes: Artists include Graeme Lawson - lute reed pipes/ Wendy Lawson - panpipes,trumpet
Cassette: released on Archaic in Oct'86. Distributed by: Archaeologia Musica

SOUNDS OF THE VIKING AGE.
Tracks: / Watchman / Lamentation / Ut-re-mi / Pilgrim song / Nightingale, The / Come sweet love.
Notes: Artists include: Graeme Lawson-lyre-bone flute/Wendy Lawson-panpipes.
Cassette: released on Archaic in Oct'86. Distributed by: Archaeologia Musica

Carola

LOVE ISN'T LOVE.
Single (7"): released on Towerbell in May'83 by Towerbell Records. Distributed by: EMI

RUNAWAY.
Tracks: / Runaway / So far.
Single (7"): released on Polydor in Aug'86 by Polydor Records. Distributed by: Polygram, Polydor

Carolan, Mary-Ann

SONGS FROM THE IRISH TRADITION.
Tracks: / Bold Doherty / Maid of Ballymore, The / Bob Riddley / Old oak tree, The / Tinker's old budget, The / Bonny light horseman, The / In London so fair / My father's a hedger and a ditcher / Highland Mary / Wedding at baltray, The.
Album: released on Topic in '82. Distributed by: Roots Distribution

Carolina Slim

CAROLINA BLUES AND BOOGIE (1950-1952).
Tracks: / Money blues / Mama's boogie / Black chariot / Worrying blues / One more drink / Carolina boogie / I'll get by somehow / Rag mama / Sugarfree / Blues go away from me / Blues knockin' at my door / Worry you off my mind / Wine head baby / Slo freight blues.
Album: released on Travelin' Man (USA) in Mar'85

Carols, Christmas

CAROLING AT CHRISTMAS Various Artists (Various Artists).
Cassette: released on Ampro Cassettes in Sep'81

CAROLS FOR CHRISTMAS Various Artists (Various Artists).
Video-cassette (VHS): released on PMI in

Jun'86 by PMI Records. Distributed by: EMI

Video-cassette [Betamax]: released on PMI in Jun'86 by PMI Records. Distributed by: EMI

Carousel

CAROUSEL Original film soundtrack (Various Artists).
Tracks: / Carousel waltz (The) / You're a queer one Julie Jordan / Mister Snow / If I loved you / When the children are asleep / When the children are asleep / June is bustin' out all over / Soliloquy / Blow high blow low / Real nice clambake, A / Stonecutters cut it in stone / What's the use in wondering / You'll never walk alone / Carousel waltz, The / You're a queer one / Julie Jordan / Mister Snow / If I loved you / When the children are asleep / June is bustin' out all over / Soliloquoy / Blow high, blow low / Real nice clambake, A / Stonecutters cut it on stone / What's the use of wondering? / You'll never walk alone.
Compact disc: released on Capitol in Apr'87 by Capitol Records. Distributed by: EMI

CAROUSEL (Original cast) (Various Artists).
Album: released on MCA in Mar'82 by MCA Records. Distributed by: Polygram, MCA

Cassette: released on MCA in Mar'82 by MCA Records. Distributed by: Polygram, MCA

CAROUSEL (Soundtrack).
Album: released on Capitol in '58 by Capitol Records. Distributed by: EMI

Cassette: released on Capitol in '61 by Capitol Records. Distributed by: EMI

Carousel Van Der Beek

MARCHING & WALTZING.
Album: released on Eclipse in '71 by Decca Records. Distributed by: Polygram

Carpendale, Howard

HELLO AGAIN.
Single (7"): released on Juice in Dec'84 by IRS. Distributed by: A&M, CBS

SHINE ON.
Single (7"): released on Juice in Jul'85 by IRS. Distributed by: A&M, CBS

Single (12"): released on Juice in Jul'85 by IRS. Distributed by: A&M, CBS

Carpenter, Richard

TIME.
Tracks: / Say yeah! / Who do you love? / Something in your eyes / When time was all we had / Time / Calling your name again / In love alone / Remind me to tell you / That's what I believe / I'm still not over you.
Album: released on A&M in Oct'87 by A&M Records. Distributed by: Polygram

Cassette: released on A&M in Oct'87 by A&M Records. Distributed by: Polygram

Compact disc: released on A&M in Sep'87 by A&M Records. Distributed by: Polygram

Carpenters

BEST OF..., THE.
Boxed set: released on World Records in Dec'81. Distributed by: Polygram

CARPENTER COLLECTION (THE).
Tracks: / Yesterday once more / Hurting each other / Please Mr. Postman / I need to be in love / Make believe it's your first time / Sing / Only yesterday / Back in my life again (want you) / Ticket to ride / Sweet sweet smile / I won't last a day without you / Now / For all we know / Touch me when we're dancing / Top of the world / Calling occupants of interplanetary craft / Solitaire / Don't cry for me Argentina (from Evita) / We've only just begun / Those good old dreams / There's a kind of hush / Jambalaya / Close to you (they long to be) / Superstar / Rainy days and Mondays / Goodbye to love.
Notes: Digital stereo. Double compact disc.
Compact disc: released on EMI in Oct'84 by EMI Records. Distributed by: EMI

COLLECTION: CARPENTERS.
Tracks: / Close to you / Jambalaya / Bless the beasts and children / Saturday / Help / For all we know / Song for you, A / Sing / Let me be the one / Mr Guder / I'll never fall in love again / Goodbye to love / Rainy days and Mondays / Love is surrender / Heather / Maybe it's you / Druscilla Penny / This masquerade / Superstar / Flat baroque / I won't last a day without you / I keep on loving you / Crystal lullaby / I can't make music / Yesterday once more / Bacharach / Knowing when to leave / Make it easy on yourself / Always something there to remind me / I'll never fall in love again / Walk on by / Do you know the way to San Jose? / Baby it's hurting you / Hurting each other / Reason to believe / Sometimes / We've only just begun / Top of the world / One love / It's going to take some time / Hideaway / Another song.
Triple album / cassette: released on A&M in Mar'76 by A&M Records. Distributed by: Polygram

KIND OF HUSH, (A).
Tracks: / There's a kind of hush / You / Sandy / Goofus / Can't smile without you / I need to be in love / One more time / Boat to sail / I have you / Breaking up is hard to do.
Album: released on A&M in Mar'82 by A&M Records. Distributed by: Polygram

Cassette: released on A&M in Mar'82 by A&M Records. Distributed by: Polygram

LIVE AT THE PALLADIUM.
Tracks: / Flat baroque / There's a kind of hush / Jambalaya / Piano picker / Strike up the band / S'wonderful / Fascinating rhythm / Warsaw concerto / From this moment on / Carpenters' medley / We've only just begun.
Album: released on Pickwick (A&M) in May'84

Cassette: released on Pickwick (A&M) in May'84

NOW AND THEN.
Tracks: / Sing / This masquerade / Heather / Jambalaya / I can't make music / Yesterday once more / Fun, fun, fun / End of the world, The / Da doo ron ron / Deadman's curve / Johnny angel / Night has a thousand eyes, The / Our day will come / One fine day.
Album: released on A&M in Nov'85 by A&M Records. Distributed by: Polygram

Cassette: released on A&M in Nov'85 by A&M Records. Distributed by: Polygram

Album: released on MWM in Jun'82 by Mawson & Wareham. Distributed by: Spartan Distribution, Jazz Music Distribution,

Cassette: released on MWM in Jun'82 by Mawson & Wareham. Distributed by: Spartan Distribution, Jazz Music Distribution,

OLD-FASHIONED CHRISTMAS, AN.
Tracks: / It came upon a midnight clear / Overture / Old-fashioned Christmas, An / O holy night / Home for the holidays / Medley / Little altar boy / Do you hear what I hear? / My favourite things / He came here for me / Santa Claus is coming to town / What are you doing New Year's Eve? / Selections from The Nutcracker / I heard the bells on Christmas Day.
Album: released on A&M in Dec'84 by A&M Records. Distributed by: Polygram

Cassette: released on A&M in Dec'84 by A&M Records. Distributed by: Polygram

SINGLES 1969-1973, (THE).
Album: released on A&M in '74 by A&M Records. Distributed by: Polygram

Cassette: released on A&M in '74 by A&M Records. Distributed by: Polygram

Compact disc: released on A&M in Jun'84 by A&M Records. Distributed by: Polygram

SINGLES 1969-73, THE.
Tracks: / We've only just begun / Top of the world / Ticket to ride / Superstar / Rainy days and Mondays / Goodbye to love / Yesterday once more / It's going to take some time / Sing / For all we know / Hurting each other / Close to you.
Compact disc: released on A&M in Jun'84 by A&M Records. Distributed by: Polygram

SINGLES 1974-1978.
Tracks: / Sweet sweet smile / Jambalaya / Can't smile without you / I won't last a day without you / All you get from love is a love song / Only yesterday / Solitaire / Please Mister Postman / I need to be in love / Happy / There's a kind of hush / Calling occupants of interplanetary craft.
Album: released on A&M in '78 by A&M Records. Distributed by: Polygram

Cassette: released on A&M in '78 by A&M Records. Distributed by: Polygram

TICKET TO RIDE.
Cassette: released on Music For Pleasure in Jul'79 by EMI Records. Distributed by: EMI

VOICE OF THE HEART.
Tracks: / Now / Sailing on the tide / Make believe it's your first time / Two lives / At the end of a song / Ordinary fool / Your baby doesn't love you anymore / Look to your dreams.
Compact disc: by A&M Records. Distributed by: Polygram

YESTERDAY ONCE MORE (SINGLE).
Single (7"): released on Old Gold in Sep'85 by Old Gold Records. Distributed by: Lightning, Jazz Music, Spartan, Counterpoint

YESTERDAY ONCE MORE.
Video-cassette (VHS): released on A&M in Dec'86 by A&M Records. Distributed by: Polygram

Carpetbaggers

SORRY.
Single (7"): released on Page One in Nov'82 by Page, Larry. Distributed by: PRT, Spartan

Carpettes

HOW ABOUT ME AND YOU.
Single (7"): released on Small Wonder in Jan'78 by Small Wonder Records. Distributed by: Cartel, Indies

Carrack, Paul

EVERY TIME YOU WALK IN THE ROOM.
Tracks: / How long* / Album medley* / Every time you walk in the room / Collraine.
Notes: * = Extra track on 12" only.
Single (7"): released on Chrysalis in Apr'87 by Chrysalis Records. Distributed by: CBS

Single (12"): released on Chrysalis in Apr'87 by Chrysalis Records. Distributed by: CBS

LITTLE UNKIND.
Single (7"): released on Epic in Feb'83 by CBS Records. Distributed by: CBS

NIGHTBIRD.
Tracks: / Beauty's only skin deep / There's a good chance / In love with me / Love is all it takes / Where you going babe / Foregone conclusion / Bet you never been in love / Nightbird.
Album: released on Vertigo in Jul'80 by Phonogram Records. Distributed by: Polygram

WHEN YOU WALK IN THE ROOM.
Compact disc single: released on Chrysalis in May'87 by Chrysalis Records. Distributed by: CBS

Carrageen

FROM CLARE TO HERE.
Cassette: released on Homespun(Ireland) in May'79 by Outlet Records. Distributed by: Outlet

Carra, Raffaella

RAFFAELLA.
Tracks: / Do it,do it again / Black cat / Sono nera / Dancin' in the sun / Tango / California / Rumore / Tanti Auguri / Luca / Amoa, Ci Vidiamo Domani / Million dollars, A.
Album: released on Epic in May'78 by CBS Records. Distributed by: CBS

Carrasco, Joe 'King'

BORDER TOWN (Carrasco, Joe 'King' & The Crowns).
Album: released on Big Heat in Oct'84

Cassette: released on Big Heat in Oct'84

CORONAS BANDIDO ROCK, (LAS).
Album: released on New Rose in Jun'87. Distributed by: Rough Trade, Cartel

EL MOLINO.
Album: released on Big Heat in Sep'79

JOE 'KING' CARRASCO (Carrasco, Joe 'King' & The Crowns).
Tracks: / Buena / Betty's world / I get my kicks on you / One more time / Don't bug me baby / Nervoused out / Caca de vaca / Susan friendly / Party doll / Federals / Wild 14 / Let's get pretty.
Album: released on Stiff in Sep'80 by Stiff Records. Distributed by: EMI, Record Services Distribution (Ireland)

SYNAPSE GAP Mundo total (Carrasco, Joe 'King' & The Crowns).
Album: released on MCA in Jun'82 by MCA Records. Distributed by: Polygram, MCA Deleted '83.

Cassette: released on MCA in Jun'82 by MCA Records. Distributed by: Polygram, MCA Deleted '83.

TALES FROM THE CRYPT.
Cassette: released on Reach Out International in Aug'84. Distributed by: Red Rhino, Cartel

Carr, Dave

CARR FOR SALE.
Album: released on SRT in Mar'77 by SRT Records. Distributed by: Pinnacle, Solomon & Peres Distribution, SRT Distribution, H.R. Taylor Distribution, PRT Distribution

Carre, John Le

SPY WHO CAME IN FROM THE COLD, THE.
Cassette: released on LFP in May'85

Carreras, Jose

LOVE IS (Carreras, Jose with Robert Farnon Orchestra).
Tracks: / My own true love / Because you're mine / My way / Tonight / Tenderly / Summer knows / Love is a many splendoured thing / As time goes by / Way we were / Shadow of your smile / Memory / Impossible dream.
Compact disc: released on Philips in Jun'84. Distributed by: IMS-Polygram

Compact disc: released on Philips in Jun'84. Distributed by: IMS-Polygram

SOME ENCHANTED EVENING.
Tracks: / This nearly was mine.
Single (7"): released on CBS in Nov'86 by CBS Records. Distributed by: CBS

YOU BELONG TO MY HEART.
Tracks: / You belong to my heart / Mattinata / El dia que me quieras / Fenesta che lucive / Concerto d'autojno / Siboney / Te quiero, dijiste / Because / Quiereme mucho / Anema e core / La danza / Aquellos ojos verdes / You belong to my heart / Mattinata / El dia me quieras / Fenesta che lucive / Concerto d'autojno / Siboney / Te quiero dijiste / Because / Quiereme mucho / Anema e core / La danza / Aquellos ojos verdes.
Compact disc: released on Philips in Nov'84. Distributed by: IMS-Polygram

Album: released on Philips in Nov'84. Distributed by: IMS-Polygram

Cassette: released on Philips in Nov'84. Distributed by: IMS-Polygram

Carrere B.P.M.

CARRERE B.P.M. Various artists (Various Artists).
Album: released on Carrere in Dec'84 by Carrere Records. Distributed by: PRT, Spartan

Carr, Georgia

SOFTLY BABY.
Tracks: / Softly / Is that bad / Sun forgot to shine, The / I don't know any better / I'm not gonna letcha in / Whispering serenade / You made me love you / I dream of you / From man to man / Wasted tears / Lonely / Make me a present of you / Laugh / Why darling why / All of me / Gimme the simple life.
Notes: A new compliation of songs including a good selection of Capitol classics alongwith some previously unreleased material by Geogia Carr, on of the lesser known ladies of the 50's era. Orchestra is conducted by the late Nelson Riddle.
Album: released on Capitol in Jan'86 by Capitol Records. Distributed by: EMI

Cassette: released on Capitol in Jan'86 by Capitol Records. Distributed by: EMI

Carr, Ian

DIRECT HIT (Carr, Ian Nucleus).
Album: released on Vertigo in Mar'76 by Phonogram Records. Distributed by: Polygram

IN FLAGRANTE DELICTO (Carr, Ian Nucleus).
Tracks: / Gestalt / Mysteries / Heyday / In flagrante delicto.
Album: released on Capitol in Jul'78 by Capitol Records. Distributed by: EMI

OUT OF THE LONG DARK (Carr, Ian Nucleus).
Tracks: / Gone with the weed / Lady bountiful / Solar wind / Selina / Out of the long dark / Sassy (American girl) / Simply this (The human condition) / Black ballad (Ecdodomina) / For Liam.
Album: released on Capitol in Feb'79 by Capitol Records. Distributed by: EMI

Carr, John

PENNY ARCADE.
Single (7"): released on Dual Purpose in Dec'82. Distributed by: Pinnacle

Carr, Johnny

COME SHARE MY LOVE.
Single (7"): released on Dual Purpose in Aug'84. Distributed by: Pinnacle

IF EVER I SEE YOU AGAIN.
Single (7"): released on Dual Purpose in Mar'84. Distributed by: Pinnacle

Carr, Larry

FIT AS A FIDDLE.
Album: released on Audiophile in Jul'87 by Jazzology Records (USA). Distributed by: Jazz Music, Swift

Carr, Leroy

LEROY CARR (1928).
Tracks: / My own lonesome blues / How long how long blues / Broken spoke blues / Tennessee blues / Truthful blues / Mean old train blues / You got to reap what you sow / Low down dirty blues / How long how long blues no.2 and part 3 / Baby don't you love me no more / Tired of your low down ways / I'm going away and leave my baby / Prison bound blues / You don't mean me no good.
Album: released on Matchbox (Bluesmaster) in May'83

Carr, Melinda

ENDLESS LOVE.
Cassette: released on Chevron in Feb'85. Distributed by: Multiple Sound Distributors

Carr, Mike

LIVE AT RONNIE SCOTT'S (Carr, Mike Trio).
Tracks: / Claremont avenue / Teach me tonight / Shaw 'nuff / It's impossible / Footloose.
Album: released on Spotlite in '83 by Spotlite Records. Distributed by: Cadillac, Jazz Music, Spotlite

Carroll, Barbara

JULY 24TH, 1959 (Carroll, Barbara Trio).
Album: released on From The Jazz Vault in Oct'80 by Damont Records. Distributed by: Swift, Taylor, H.R.

Carroll, Diahann

DIAHANN CARROLL.
Tracks: / Perfect love / I can't give back the love I feel for you / I mean to shine / Somewhere between love and tomorrow / Sweet sweet candy / I've never been a fool like this before / Easy to love / Anybody else / After being your lover / I've been there before.
Album: released on Motown in Aug'86 by Motown Records. Distributed by: BMG Distribution

Cassette: released on Motown in Aug'86 by Motown Records. Distributed by: BMG Distribution

Carroll, Jim

CATHOLIC BOY (Carroll, Jim Band).
Album: released on CBS in Jun'81 by CBS Records. Distributed by: CBS

Carroll, Johnnie

TEXABILLY.
Album: released on Rollin' Rock in Jun'80

Carroll, Johnny

CRAZY HOT ROCK.
Album: released on Charly in Jul'85 by Charly Records. Distributed by: Charly, Cadillac

RATTLE MY BONES.
Single (7"): released on Seville in Jul'83 by President Records. Distributed by: Jazz Music, Swift

ROCK BABY, ROCK IT.
Album: released on Magnum Force in Aug'86 by Magnum Music Group Ltd. Distributed by: Magnum Music Group Ltd, PRT, Spartan

SCREAMIN' DEMON HEATWAVE.
Album: released on Seville in Jul'83 by President Records. Distributed by: Jazz Music, Swift

SHADES OF VINCENT (Carroll, Johnny & Judy Lindsey).
Tracks: / Rock road blues / I gotta baby / Git it / Dance to the bop / Wear my ring / Lotta loving / Maybe / Swing, The / Dance at Billy Bob's / Honey don't / Baby let's play house / I've had it / Savin' my love / I want you to be my baby / What I'd say / Hurt so good / Love me up.
Notes: Licensed from Dave Travis. This compilation: (P) 1986 Charly Records Ltd. (C) 1986 Charly Records Ltd.
Album: released on Charly in '86 by Charly Records. Distributed by: Charly, Cadillac

Carroll, Lewis

ALICE IN WONDERLAND (Scott, Margaretta & Jane Asher).
Cassette: released on Argo (Spokenword) in '82 by Decca Records. Distributed by: Polygram

ALICE IN WONDERLAND.
Album: released on BBC in May'85 by BBC Records & Tapes. Distributed by: EMI, PRT,

Cassette: released on BBC in May'85 by BBC Records & Tapes. Distributed by: EMI, PRT,

Cassette: released on Caedmon(USA) in Sep'85 by Caedmon (USA) Records. Distributed by: Taylors, Discovery

ALICE'S ADVENTURES IN WONDERLAND.
Cassette: released on Cover to Cover in Jun'85 by Cover to Cover Cassettes. Distributed by: Conifer

HUNTING OF THE SNARK, THE.
Cassette: released on Anvil in Apr'80. Distributed by: Anvil

Carroll, Liz

FRIEND INDEED, A.
Album: released on Shanachie in Sep'79. Distributed by: Sterns/Triple Earth Distribution, Roots

KISS ME KATE (Carroll, Liz & Tommy McGuire).
Album: released on Shanachie in Sep'79. Distributed by: Sterns/Triple Earth Distribution, Roots

Carrot, Jasper

COSMIC CARROT.
Tracks: / 60's, The / Cowards / Alternatives / Plumbers / Mechanics / Boy scouts / Store detectives / Cruise missiles / More cars / Fear / Animals / Xmas time.
Album: released on Portrait in Dec'86 by CBS Records. Distributed by: CBS

Cassette: released on Portrait in Dec'86 by CBS Records. Distributed by: CBS

LIVE IN AMERICA.
Album: released on Rhino (USA) in Jan'86 by Rhino Records (USA)

Carrott, Jasper

BEAT THE CARROTT.
Tracks: / Introduction / Television / Scunthorpe baths / Acne / Australian sticky tape / Car insurance (Australian style) / Driving lesson / Pets / Truck driving / Biffer / Day trip to Blackpool.
Album: released on DJM in Sep'81 by DJM Records. Distributed by: CBS, Polygram

Cassette: released on DJM in Sep'81 by DJM Records. Distributed by: CBS, Polygram

BEST OF JASPER CARROTT, THE.
Tracks: / Bastity Chelt / Jersey / Football match, The / America / Zits / Number plates / Bus trip, The / Car insurance / Magic roundabout.
Album: released on DJM in '78 by DJM Records. Distributed by: CBS, Polygram

Cassette: released on DJM in '78 by DJM Records. Distributed by: CBS, Polygram

BEST OF..., THE/CARROTT IN NOTTS.
Double cassette: released on DJM in May'81 by DJM Records. Distributed by: CBS, Polygram

CARROTTS IN NOTTS.
Tracks: / Give me an 'F' / Top of the pops / My cottage / New faces / Now all join in / Bastity chelt / Mal's shirt / Wor Malcolm / Radio adverts / My mate Jake / Bantam cock / Football news / European cup / Cup final 76 / I'm a goalie / You know / What sa teem / Complete C & W, The / Dem blues / Blue goldfish / French O level / Hava Nagila.
Album: released on DJM in Oct'76 by DJM Records. Distributed by: CBS, Polygram

Cassette: released on DJM in Oct'76 by DJM Records. Distributed by: CBS, Polygram

CARROTT'S LIB.
Album: released on DJM in Nov'82 by DJM Records. Distributed by: CBS, Polygram

Cassette: released on DJM in Nov'82 by DJM Records. Distributed by: CBS, Polygram

PAIN IN THE ARM, A.
Tracks: / Introduction / Hangman / Getting here / Football match, The / Local radio promotion / Hari Krishna / America / Zits / Number plates / Bus trip, The / Car insurance / Twelve days of christmas.
Album: released on DJM in Jan'78 by DJM Records. Distributed by: CBS, Polygram

Cassette: released on DJM in Jan'78 by DJM Records. Distributed by: CBS, Polygram

RABBITTS ON AND ON AND ON....
Tracks: / Introduction / Spaghetti junction / Boggery, The / Sex supermarket / In concert / Local radio / BBC medical / Magic roundabout / Jersy / Waggy's testimonial / Learner driver / Tribute to Eric Idle my idol.
Album: released on DJM in Nov'76 by DJM Records. Distributed by: CBS, Polygram

Cassette: released on DJM in Nov'76 by DJM Records. Distributed by: CBS, Polygram

RABBITTS ON & ON/PAIN IN THE ARM.
Double cassette: released on DJM in May'81 by DJM Records. Distributed by: CBS, Polygram

STUN-CARROTT TELLS ALL, THE.
Album: released on DJM in Oct'83 by DJM Records. Distributed by: CBS, Polygram

Cassette: released on DJM in Oct'83 by DJM Records. Distributed by: CBS, Polygram

UNRECORDED JASPER CARROTT, THE.
Tracks: / Introduction / Muppets / Gleemodemt / Zits / Mole, The / Microphones / Punk rock / Local radio / Nutter on the bus, The / Mug job / Explosive gasses.
Album: released on DJM in Oct'79 by DJM Records. Distributed by: CBS, Polygram

Cassette: released on DJM in Oct'79 by DJM Records. Distributed by: CBS, Polygram

Carrou, Johnny

ROCK (see Curtis, Mac) (Carrou, Johnny/Mac Curtis).

Carr, Richard

STRING VIBRATIONS (Carr, Richard & Pro Bow Trio).
Album: released on Progressive in Jan'87 by Progressive Records. Distributed by: Jetstar

Carr, Vikki

IT MUST BE HIM.
Tracks: / It must be him / Hurt.
Notes: Also contains:"Hurt" by Timi Yuro
Single (7"): released on Old Gold in Apr'87 by Old Gold Records. Distributed by: Lightning, Jazz Music, Spartan, Counterpoint

Carr, Wynona

HIT THAT JIVE, JACK.
Tracks: / Jump Jack jump / Till the well runs dry / Boppity bop / Should I ever love again / I'm mad at you / Old fashioned love / Hurt me / It's raining outside / Nursery rhyme rock / Ding dong daddy / Somebody somewhere somehow / Act right / What do you know about love / Now that I'm free / Heartbreak melody / Please Mr. Jailer.
Album: released on Ace in Mar'85 by Ace Records. Distributed by: Pinnacle, Swift, Hotshot, Cadillac

Carry On Oi

CARRY ON OI Various artists (Various Artists).
Album: released on Secret in Jun'82 by Secret Records. Distributed by: EMI

Cars

CANDY O.
Compact disc: by Elektra/Asylum/Nonesuch Records. Distributed by: WEA

CANDY O.
Tracks: / Let's go / Since I held you / It's all I can do / Double life / Shoo be doo / Candy O / Nightspots / You can't hold on too long / Lust for kicks / Got a lot on my head / Dangerous type.
Album: released on Elektra (USA) in Jun'79 by Elektra/Asylum/Nonesuch Records. Distributed by: WEA Deleted '83.

Cassette: released on Elektra (USA) in Jun'79 by Elektra/Asylum/Nonesuch Records. Distributed by: WEA

Compact disc: released on Elektra (USA) in Jun'79 by Elektra/Asylum/Nonesuch Records. Distributed by: WEA

CARS (THE).
Album: released on Elektra (USA) in '78 by Elektra/Asylum/Nonesuch Records. Distributed by: WEA

Compact disc: released on Elektra (USA) in Jan'84 by Elektra/Asylum/Nonesuch Records. Distributed by: WEA

Cassette: released on Elektra (USA) in Aug'78 by Elektra/Asylum/Nonesuch Records. Distributed by: WEA

CARS (THE).
Tracks: / Good times roll / My best friend's girl / Just what I needed / I'm in touch with your world / Don't cha stop / You're all I've got tonight / Bye bye love / Moving in stereo / All mixed up.
Compact disc: released on Elektra (USA) in '84 by Elektra/Asylum/Nonesuch Records. Distributed by: WEA

DOOR TO DOOR.
Album: released on Elektra in Aug'87 by WEA Records. Distributed by: WEA

Cassette: released on Elektra in Aug'87 by WEA Records. Distributed by: WEA

DRIVE.
Single (7"): released on Elektra (USA) in Aug'84 by Elektra/Asylum/Nonesuch Records. Distributed by: WEA

Single (12"): released on Elektra (USA) in Aug'84 by Elektra/Asylum/Nonesuch Records. Distributed by: WEA

GREATEST HITS:CARS.
Tracks: / Just what I needed / Since you're gone / You might think / Good time roll / Touch and go / Drive / Tonight she comes / My best friend's girl / Heartbeat city / Let's go / Magic / Shake it up.
Album: released on Elektra (USA) in Nov'85 by Elektra/Asylum/Nonesuch Records. Distributed by: WEA

Cassette: released on Elektra (USA) in Nov'85 by Elektra/Asylum/Nonesuch Records. Distributed by: WEA

Compact disc: released on Elektra (USA) in Nov'85 by Elektra/Asylum/Nonesuch Records. Distributed by: WEA

HEARTBEAT CITY.
Album: released on Elektra (USA) in Feb'84 by Elektra/Asylum/Nonesuch Records. Distributed by: WEA

Cassette: released on Elektra (USA) in Feb'84 by Elektra/Asylum/Nonesuch Records. Distributed by: WEA

Compact disc: released on Elektra (USA) in Jul'84 by Elektra/Asylum/Nonesuch Records. Distributed by: WEA

Single (7"): released on Elektra (USA) in Sep'85 by Elektra/Asylum/Nonesuch Records. Distributed by: WEA Deleted '86.

Single (12"): released on Elektra (USA) in Sep'85 by Elektra/Asylum/Nonesuch Records. Distributed by: WEA

HEARTBEAT CITY.
Tracks: / Looking for love / Jackie / Not the night / Shooting for you / Why can't I / Magic / You might think / I do refuse / Stranger eyes / Hello again / Who's going to drive you home.
Notes: Recorded in digital stereo.
Compact disc: released on Elektra (USA) in Jul'84 by Elektra/Asylum/Nonesuch Records. Distributed by: WEA

Video-cassette (VHS): released on Warner in Dec'84 by Warner Bros Records. Distributed by: WEA

I'M NOT THE ONE.
Tracks: / I'm not the one (remix) / Since you've gone / Shake it up.
Single (7"): released on Elektra (USA) in Apr'86 by Elektra/Asylum/Nonesuch Records. Distributed by: WEA

Single (12"): released on Elektra (USA) in Apr'86 by Elektra/Asylum/Nonesuch Records. Distributed by: WEA

PANORAMA.
Tracks: / Panorama / Touch an go / Gimme some slack / Don't tell me no / Getting through / Misfit kid / Down boys / You wear those eyes / Running to you / Up and down.
Album: released on Elektra Asylum in Sep'80 by Elektra/Asylum/Nonesuch Records. Distributed by: WEA

Cassette: released on Elektra Asylum in Sep'80 by Elektra/Asylum/Nonesuch Records. Distributed by: WEA

Album: released on Elektra (USA) in Nov'81 by Elektra/Asylum/Nonesuch Records. Distributed by: WEA

Cassette: released on Elektra (USA) in Nov'81 by Elektra/Asylum/Nonesuch Records. Distributed by: WEA

Compact disc: released on Elektra (USA) in Nov'81 by Elektra/Asylum/Nonesuch Records. Distributed by: WEA

Single (7"): released on Elektra (USA) in Nov'81 by Elektra/Asylum/Nonesuch Records. Distributed by: WEA

SHAKE IT UP.
Tracks: / Since you're gone / Shake it up / I'm not the one / Victim of love / Cruiser / Dream away, A / Think it over / This could be love / May be baby.
Compact disc: by Elektra/Asylum/Nonesuch Records. Distributed by: WEA

SINCE YOU'RE GONE.
Single (7"): released on Elektra (USA) in May'82 by Elektra/Asylum/Nonesuch Records. Distributed by: WEA

THINK IT OVER.
Single (7"): released on Elektra (USA) in Aug'82 by Elektra/Asylum/Nonesuch Records. Distributed by: WEA

TONIGHT SHE COMES.
Single (7"): released on Elektra (USA) in Nov'85 by Elektra/Asylum/Nonesuch Records. Distributed by: WEA

Single (12"): released on Elektra (USA) in Nov'85 by Elektra/Asylum/Nonesuch Records. Distributed by: WEA

WHY CAN'T I HAVE YOU.
Single (7"): released on Elektra (USA) in Apr'84 by Elektra/Asylum/Nonesuch Records. Distributed by: WEA

Single (7"): released on Elektra (USA) in Feb'85 by Elektra/Asylum/Nonesuch Records. Distributed by: WEA

Single (12"): released on Elektra (USA) in Feb'85 by Elektra/Asylum/Nonesuch Records. Distributed by: WEA

Carson, Ernie

ERNIE CARSON & HIS CAPITOL CITY JAZZ BAND (Carson, Ernie & His Capitol City Jazz Band).
Album: released on Jazzology in Jun'86. Distributed by: Jazz Music, Swift

Carson, Joe

IN MEMORIAM.
Album: released on Pathe MarconiEMI Europe) in Jun'84

Carson, John

TALE OF TWO CITIES Spoken Word.
Double cassette: released on Listen For Pleasure in '80 by MFP Records. Distributed by: EMI

Carson, Martha

MUSIC DRIVES ME CRAZY.
Tracks: / Music drives me crazy, especially rock'n'roll / Dixieland roll / Let the light shine on me / O.K. amen / Now stop / Get on board little children / Saints and chariot / Let's talk about that old time religion / Just whistle or call / Rocka my soul / This ole house / I'm gonna walk and

Page 188

talk with the lord / All these things / Satisfied / Be not disencouraged / Get that golden key.
Notes: Track 4 previously unissued. Original RCA Victor Recordings.
Album: released on Bear Family in Sep'86 by Bear Family Records. Distributed by: Rollercoaster Distribution, Swift

Carson, Mike

Midem-Live 80

Carson, Tee

BASICALLY COUNT (Carson, Tee & The Basie Bandsmen).
Album: released on Palo Alto (Italy) in Jan'84

Carstairs

IT REALLY HURTS ME GIRL.
Single (7"): released on Inferno in Jul'80 by Inferno Records. Distributed by: Inferno, Cartel, Pinnacle

Single (12"): released on Inferno in Jul'80 by Inferno Records. Distributed by: Inferno, Cartel, Pinnacle

Carter, Anita

FOLK SONGS OLD AND NEW.
Tracks: / Love's ring of fire / All my trials / Sour grapes / Fair and tender ladies / My love / Voice of the Bayous / Fly pretty swallow / Johnny I hardly knew you / Satan's child / Few short years ago, A / Kentuckian song, The / Brian running back / As the sparrow goes.
Album: released on Mercury (USA) in Sep'84 by Import Records. Distributed by: IMS Distribution, Polygram Distribution

Carter, Benny

ADDITIONS TO FURTHER DEFINITIONS.
Tracks: / Fantastisc that's you / Come on back / We were in love / If dreams come true / Prohibido / Doozy / Rock bottom / Titmouse.
Album: released on Jasmine in Sep'82 by Jasmine Records. Distributed by: Counterpoint, Taylor, H.R., Wellard, Chris, Swift, Cadillac

Cassette: released on Jasmine in Sep'82 by Jasmine Records. Distributed by: Counterpoint, Taylor, H.R., Wellard, Chris, Swift, Cadillac

ALONE TOGETHER (Carter, Benny & Oscar Peterson).
Tracks: / Isn't it romantic / Long ago and far away / Alone together / Bewitched etc..
Album: released on Verve in Dec'81 by Phonogram Records. Distributed by: Polygram

BENNY CARTER, 1928-1952.
Double Album: released on RCA (France) in '83 by RCA Records. Distributed by: Discovery

BENNY CARTER 1945: THE METRONOME ALL STARS.
Album: released on Queen-Disc in Apr'81. Distributed by: Celtic Music, Jazz Horizons, Jazz Music

BENNY CARTER ALL STARS Featuring Nat Adderley and Red Norvo.
Tracks: / Easy money / Memories of you / Here's that rainy day / Blues for lucky lovers / Work song / When lights are low.
Notes: Produced by Rune Ofwerman.
Album: released on Sonet in Sep'86 by Sonet Records. Distributed by: PRT

BENNY CARTER FOUR.
Tracks: / Three little words / In a mellow tone / Wave / Undecided / Body and soul / On green dolphin street / Here's that rainy day.
Album: released on Pablo in '82 by Pablo Records. Distributed by: Wellard, Chris, IMS-Polygram, BMG

Cassette: released on Pablo in '82 by Pablo Records. Distributed by: Wellard, Chris, IMS-Polygram, BMG

BEST OF BENNY CARTER, (THE).
Album: released on Pablo (USA) in '82 by Pablo Records (USA). Distributed by: Wellard, Chris, IMS-Polygram, BMG

Cassette: released on Pablo (USA) in '82 by Pablo Records (USA). Distributed by: Wellard, Chris, IMS-Polygram, BMG

CARTER, GILLESPIE INC (Carter, Benny & Dizzy Gillespie).
Tracks: / Sweet and lovely / Broadway / Courtship, The / Constantinople / Nobody knows the trouble I've seen / Night in tunisia / Three little words / In a mellow tone / Waves / Undecided / Body and soul / On green dolphin street / Here's that rainy day.
Album: released on Pablo in '82 by Pablo Records. Distributed by: Wellard, Chris, IMS-Polygram, BMG

Cassette: released on Pablo in '82 by Pablo Records. Distributed by: Wellard, Chris, IMS-Polygram, BMG

Album: released on Pablo in '82 by Pablo Records. Distributed by: Wellard, Chris, IMS-Polygram, BMG

FURTHER DEFINITIONS.
Tracks: / Honeysuckle rose / Midnight sun will never set (The) / Crazy rhythm / Blue star / Cotton tail / Body & soul / Cherry / Doozy.
Compact disc: released on MCA in Jul'87 by MCA Records. Distributed by: Polygram, MCA

FURTHER DEFINITIONS (Carter, Benny & His Orchestra).
Album: released on Jasmine in Jun'82 by Jasmine Records. Distributed by: Counterpoint, Taylor, H.R., Wellard, Chris, Swift, Cadillac

Cassette: released on Jasmine in Jun'82 by Jasmine Records. Distributed by: Counterpoint, Taylor, H.R., Wellard, Chris, Swift, Cadillac

GENTLEMAN AND HIS MUSIC, A.
Tracks: / Sometimes I'm happy / Blues for George / Things ain't what they used to be / Lover man / Idaho / Kiss from you, A.
Notes: The great Benny Carter has created a masterpiece here, gathering an all star cast. Complimenting the informative liner notes is a special insert with photosand an in depth essay by Leonard Feather.
Compact disc: released on Concord Jazz (USA) in Jan'87 by Concord Jazz Records (USA). Distributed by: IMS, Polygram

Album: released on Concord Jazz (USA) in Dec'85 by Concord Jazz Records (USA). Distributed by: IMS, Polygram

JAZZ GIANT.
Album: released on Contemporary in Mar'86 by Contemporary Records. Distributed by: Pinnacle

JAZZ OFF THE AIR (VOL 3) (Carter, Benny & His Orchestra).
Album: released on Spotlite in '83 by Spotlite Records. Distributed by: Cadillac, Jazz Music, Spotlite

KING, (THE).
Album: released on Pablo (USA) in '82 by Pablo Records (USA). Distributed by: Wellard, Chris, IMS-Polygram, BMG

Single 10": released on Pablo (USA) in '82 by Pablo Records (USA). Distributed by: Wellard, Chris, IMS-Polygram, BMG

LIVE AND WELL IN JAPAN.
Compact disc: released on Pablo (USA) in May'86 by Pablo Records (USA). Distributed by: Wellard, Chris, IMS-Polygram, BMG

Album: released on Pablo (USA) in '82 by Pablo Records (USA). Distributed by: Wellard, Chris, IMS-Polygram, BMG

Cassette: released on Pablo (USA) in '82 by Pablo Records (USA). Distributed by: Wellard, Chris, IMS-Polygram, BMG

SOMEBODY LOVES ME (Carter, Benny & His Orchestra).
Album: released on Magic in Jul'87. Distributed by: Jazz Music, Submarine, Swift, Chris Wellard, Conifer. Estim retail price in Sep'87 was £5.25.

Cassette: released on Magic in Jul'87. Distributed by: Jazz Music, Submarine, Swift, Chris Wellard, Conifer. Estim retail price in Sep'87 was £5.25.

SUMMER SERENADE (Carter, Benny Quartet).
Notes: Mono production.
Album: released on Storyville in Jun'86 by Storyville Records. Distributed by: Jazz Music Distribution, Swift Distribution, Chris Wellard Distribution, Counterpoint Distribution

SWINGIN' AT MAIDA VALE (Carter, Benny & His Orchestra).
Album: released on Jasmine in Feb'83 by Jasmine Records. Distributed by: Counterpoint, Taylor, H.R., Wellard, Chris, Swift, Cadillac

SWINGIN' THE 20'S.
Album: released on Contemporary Jazz in Jul'81

Carter, Betty

1.
Tracks: / By the bend of the river / Ego / Body and soul / Heart and soul / Surrey with the fringe on top / Girl talk / I didn't know what time it was / All the things you are / I could write a book / Sun dies, The / Please do something.
Album: released on Bet-Car in Jul'82

2.
Tracks: / You're a sweetheart / I can't help it / What is it? / On our way up / We tried / Happy / Sunday, Monday or always / Tight / Children learn what they live / Sounds.
Album: released on Bet-Car in Jul'82

AUDIENCE WITH BETTY CARTER.
Double Album: released on Bet-Car in Jul'82

WHATEVER HAPPENED TO LOVE?.
Album: released on Import Music Service (IMS) in Mar'83. Distributed by: Concord Jazz Distributions, Pablo, Polygram

Carter, Bo

BANANA IN YOUR FRUIT BASKET.
Album: released on Yazoo in Jan'79. Distributed by: Swift, Projection

Carter Brothers

SOUTHERN COUNTRY BOY.
Single (7"): released on Charly in Jul'80 by Charly Records. Distributed by: Charly, Cadillac

Carter, Carlene

CARLENE CARTER.
Album: released on Warner Brothers in Jun'78 by Warner Bros Records. Distributed by: WEA

C'EST SI BON.
Tracks: / Meant it for a minute / Heart to heart / Third time charm / Heart's in traction / I'm the kind a sugar daddy likes / Love like a glove / Cool reaction / Don't give my heart a break / That boy / One-way ticket / Patient love.
Album: released on Epic in Aug'83 by CBS Records. Distributed by: CBS Deleted '85.

Cassette: released on Epic in Aug'83 by CBS Records. Distributed by: CBS

Carter, Chris

MONDO BEAT.
Album: released on Conspiracy International in Aug'85. Distributed by: Cartel

Carter, Clarence

DOCTOR CC.
Album: released on Tout Ensemble in Jul'86. Distributed by: Pinnacle

DR. CC.
Album: released on Ichiban in Aug'87. Distributed by: PRT

Cassette: released on Ichiban in Aug'87. Distributed by: PRT

I WAS IN THE NEIGHBOURHOOD.
Single (7"): released on Tout Ensemble in May'86. Distributed by: Pinnacle

Single (12"): released on Tout Ensemble in May'86. Distributed by: Pinnacle

MESSIN' WITH MY MIND.
Single (7"): released on Certain in Oct'85. Distributed by: Priority, EMI, Pinnacle

Cassette: released on Certain in Oct'85. Distributed by: Priority, EMI, Pinnacle

PATCHES.
Single (7"): released on Creole in Aug'82 by Creole Records. Distributed by: Rhino, PRT

SOUL DEEP.
Album: released on Edsel in Apr'84 by Demon Records. Distributed by: Pinnacle, Jazz Music, Projection

Carter, Diane

IF YOU TAKE THE TIME (Carter, Diane & Ed Welch).
Single (7"): released on Tycos in Aug'83 by Tycos Records. Distributed by: Tycos

IF YOU WOULD TAKE THE TIME / MAKE A FRIEND OF YOU (Carter, Diane & Ed Welch).

LITTLE BOY LOST.
Single (7"): released on Beebee in Dec'83 by Grasmere Records. Distributed by: EMI

Carter Family

20 OF THE BEST.
Tracks: / Keep on the sunnyside / Little darling pal of mine / John Hardy was a desperate little man / Wildwood flower / Sweet fern / My Clinch Mountain home / I'm thinking of my blue eyes / Lula Wall / Foggy mountain top / Jimmy Brown the newsboy / Carters' blues / Wabash cannonball / Diamonds in the rough / Kitty waltz / Cannonball, The / Worried man blues / Lonesome valley / Lonesome pine special / Church in the wildwood / I never will marry.
Album: released on RCA in Mar'84 by RCA Records. Distributed by: RCA, Roots, Swift, Wellard, Chris, I & B, Solomon & Peres Distribution

Cassette: released on RCA in Mar'84 by RCA Records. Distributed by: RCA, Roots, Swift, Wellard, Chris, I & B, Solomon & Peres Distribution

COLLECTION OF FAVOURITES BY..., A.
Album: released on Stetson in Oct'86 by Hasmick Promotions Ltd.. Distributed by: Counterpoint Distribution, H.R. Taylor Distribution, Swift Distribution, Chris Wellard Distribution

Cassette: released on Stetson in Oct'86 by Hasmick Promotions Ltd.. Distributed by: Counterpoint Distribution, H.R. Taylor Distribution, Swift Distribution, Chris Wellard Distribution

Carter, Goree

ROCK A WHILE (Carter, Goree & His Hepcats).
Album: released on Blues Boy (Sweden) in Mar'84

Carter/Hancock/Williams

THIRD PLANE.
Compact disc: by Carrere Records. Distributed by: PRT, Spartan

Carter, Joe

CHESTNUT (Carter, Joe & Lee Konitz).
Album: released on Empathy (USA) in May'84 by Empathy Records (USA). Distributed by: Mole Jazz

ORIGINAL CHICAGO BLUES (Carter, Joe & Kansas City Red).
Album: released on JSP in Aug'82 by JSP Records. Distributed by: Swift, Projection

TOO MARVELLOUS FOR WORDS (Carter, Joe & Rufus Reid).
Album: released on Empathy (USA) in May'84 by Empathy Records (USA). Distributed by: Mole Jazz

Carter, John

SECRETS (Carter, John & Bobby Bradford).
Album: released on Revelation in Apr'81

Carter, Mike

MY TRUE LOVE (Carter, Mike & Dragonfly).
Single (7"): released on Button in Jun'84 by Musical Characters Records. Distributed by: Spartan

Carter, Mrs Mabel

NEAR THE CROSS.
Album: released on Nola in Dec'77. Distributed by: Jazz Music, Cadillac, Chris Wellard

Carter, Nina

FOLIES BERGERE.
Single (7"): released on Moon in Nov'81 by Moon Records. Distributed by: PRT Distribution

THESE BOOTS ARE MADE FOR WALKIN'.
Single (7"): released on Moon in Mar'83 by Moon Records. Distributed by: PRT Distribution

Carter, Ralph

YOUNG AND IN LOVE.
Album: released on Mercury in Jun'76 by Phonogram Records. Distributed by: Polygram Distribution

Carter, Ron

ALL BLUES.
Album: released on CTI (Musidisc France) in Feb'84 by Polydor Records. Distributed by: IMS, Polygram

ETUDES.
Tracks: / Last resort / Bottoms up / Arboretum / Rufus / Echoes / Doctors' Row.
Album: released on Elektra(Musician) in Feb'83 by WEA Records. Distributed by: WEA

HEART AND SOUL (Carter, Ron & Cedar Walton).
Album:

LIVE AT VILLAGE WEST (Carter, Ron & Jim Hall).
Tracks: / Bag's groove / All the things you are / Blue Monk / New waltz / St Thomas / Embraceable you / Laverne Walk / Baubles, bangles and beads.
Album: released on Concord Jazz (USA) in Jul'84 by Concord Jazz Records (USA). Distributed by: IMS, Polygram

Album: released on Concord (USA) in Jul'84. Distributed by: IMS, Polygram

MAN WITH THE BASS, THE.
Compact disc: released on JVC Fantasy (Japan) in May'87

PASTELS.
Compact disc: released on JVC Fantasy in Nov'86. Distributed by: Target

PICK 'EM.
Album: released on RCA in Jun'80 by RCA Records. Distributed by: RCA, Roots, Swift, Wellard, Chris, I & B, Solomon & Peres Distribution

TELEPHONE (Carter, Ron & Jim Hall).
Tracks: / Telephone / Indian summer / Candlelight / Chorale and dance / Alone together / Stardust / Two's blues.
Compact disc: released on Concord Jazz (USA) in Sep'86 by Concord Jazz Records (USA). Distributed by: IMS, Polygram

Album: released on Concord Jazz (USA) in Jul'85 by Concord Jazz Records (USA). Distributed by: IMS, Polygram

Cassette: released on Concord Jazz (USA) in Jul'85 by Concord Jazz Records (USA). Distributed by: IMS, Polygram

THIRD PLANE (Carter, Ron, Tony Williams & Herbie Hancock).
Notes: For full details see under Herbie Hancock.

Carter Sisters

CARTER SISTERS.
Album: released on CBS(USA) in Sep'84 by Bear Family Records. Distributed by: Rollercoaster Distribution, Swift

Carter, Sydney

LOVELY IN THE DANCES.
Album: released on Plant Life in Nov'81. Distributed by: Roots

Carter, Valerie

JUST A STONE'S THROW AWAY.
Album: released on CBS in Jun'77 by CBS Records. Distributed by: CBS

Carter, Wilf

MONTANA SLIM (Carter, Wilf (Montana Slim)).
Album: released on Starday in Apr'87

Cassette: released on Starday in Apr'87

Carthy, Martin

BECAUSE IT'S THERE.
Tracks: / Nothing rhymed / May song / Swaggering Boney / Lord Randal / Long John, old John and Jackie North / Jolly tinker / Lovely Joan / Three cripples / Siege of Delhi / Death of young Andrew.
Album: released on Topic in '81. Distributed by: Roots Distribution

BYKER HILL.
Tracks: / Man of Burnham Town, The / Fowler, The / Gentleman soldier / Brigg Fair / Bloody gardener / Barley straw, The / Byker Hill / Davy Lowston / Our captain cried all hands / Domeama / Wife of the soldier, The / John Barleycorn / Lucy Wan / Bonny black hare, The.
Album: released on Topic in '81. Distributed by: Roots Distribution

CROWN OF HORN.
Tracks: / Bedmaking, The / Locks and bolts / King Knapperty / Geordie / Willie's lady / Virginny / Worcestershire wedding, The / Bonny lass of Anglesey / William Taylor the poacher / Old Tom of Oxford / Palaces of gold.
Album: released on Topic in '81. Distributed by: Roots Distribution

LANDFALL.
Tracks: / Here's adieu to all judges and juries / Brown Adam / O'er the hills / Cruel mother / Cold haily windy night / His name is Andrew / Bold poachers / Dust to dust / Broomfield hill, The / January man.
Album: released on Topic in '81. Distributed by: Roots Distribution

MARTIN CARTHY.
Tracks: / High Germany / Trees they do grow high / Sovay / Ye mariners all / Queen of hearts, The / Broomfield hill / Springhill mine disaster / Scarborough fair / Lovely Joan / Barley and the rye, The / Wind that shakes the barley, The / Two magicians / Handsome cabin boy, The / And a begging I will go.
Notes: With Dave Swarbrick on fiddle and mandolin.
Album: released on Topic in '81. Distributed by: Roots Distribution

OUT OF THE CUT.
Tracks: / Devil and the feathery wife, The / Reynard the fox / Song of the lower classes, The / Rufford park poachers / Molly Oxford / Rigs of the time / I sowed some seeds / Frair in the well, The / Jack Rowland / Old horse.
Notes: First published by Topic 1982. Produced by Jerry Boys and Martin Carthy for GamaRecords Ltd. Recorded at Gateway Studio, London. Engineered by Jerry Boys. Sleeve
Album: released on Topic in '82. Distributed by: Roots Distribution

SECOND ALBUM.
Tracks: / Two butchers / Ball 'o' yarn / Farewell Nancy / Lord Franklin / Ramblin' sailor / Lowlands of Holland / Fair maid on the shore / Bruton town / Box on her head / Newlyn town / Brave Wolfe / Peggy and the soldier / Sailor's life.
Album: released on Topic in '81. Distributed by: Roots Distribution

SHEARWATER.
Album: released on Mooncrest in Mar'76 by Mooncrest Records. Distributed by: PRT Distribution

SWEET WIVELSFIELD.
Album: released on Topic Records in Jul'81

THIS IS MARTIN CARTHY.
Tracks: / Barley straw, The / Bonny black hare, The / Brigg fair / Byker hill / Fowler Jack, The / Orion / John Barleycorn / Lord of the dance / Poor murdered woman / Ship in distress / Streets of Forbes / White hare.
Album: released on Philips in '72. Distributed by: IMS-Polygram

WORD IS ...THE (Carthy, Martin & Leon Rosselson).
Album: . Distributed by: Jazz Music, Celtic Music, JSU

Carthy-Swarbrick

BUT TWO CAME BY.
Tracks: / Ship in distress / Banks of sweet primroses / Long lankin / Brass band music.
Album: released on Topic in '81. Distributed by: Roots Distribution

PRINCE HEATHEN.
Tracks: / Arthur McBride and the sergeant / Salisbury plain / Polly on the shore / Rainbow, The / Died for love / Staines Morris / Reynardine / Seven yellow gypies / Little Musgrave and Lady Barnard / Wren, The.
Album: released on Topic in '81. Distributed by: Roots Distribution

Cartland, Barbara

ALBUM OF LOVE SONGS (Cartland, Barbara with the LPO).
Album: released on Multi-Media in Apr'82 by Multi Media Tapes Records. Distributed by: Pinnacle, Conifer Distribution, H.R. Taylor Distribution, Stage One Distribution

Cassette: released on Multi-Media in Apr'82 by Multi Media Tapes Records. Distributed by: Pinnacle, Conifer Distribution, H.R. Taylor Distribution, Stage One Distribution

Cartoons

BEEP BEEP LOVE.
Single (7"): released on Hot in Oct'81 by Hot Records. Distributed by: Rough Trade, Cartel

GEE GEORGE.
Single (7"): released on Stiletto in Aug'83 by Fast Records. Distributed by: Cartel Distribution

LUNCHTIME LOVE AFFAIR.
Single (7"): released on Hot in Apr'80 by Hot Records. Distributed by: Rough Trade, Cartel

ONCE THE VICTOR.
Single (7"): released on Another Fabulous Production in Jun'84. Distributed by: Fast, Cartel

Car Trouble

CAR TROUBLE Soundtrack (Various Artists).
Tracks: / Car trouble / Hearts of fire / Unchained melody / Mated / Second choice / Send my heart / Mony mony / Break these chains / Only ones / Stay away / True love ways.
Notes: Produced y Meatloaf, Alan Tarney, Derek Bramble, Flesh and Bob Sargeant.
Album: released on Chrysalis in Feb'86 by Chrysalis Records. Distributed by: CBS

Cassette: released on Chrysalis in Feb'86 by Chrysalis Records. Distributed by: CBS

Cartwright, Dave

DON'T LET YOUR FAMILY DOWN.
Album: released on Transatlantic in Sep'74 by Logo Records. Distributed by: Roots Distribution. RCA Distribution

Carty, J.J.

ACCORDION ESPECIALLY RECORDED FOR IRISH DANCERS (1).
Tracks: / Beginners reel / Introduction(O'Neill's march) / Advanced reel / Slip jig / Light jig / Single jig / Three tunes, The / Trip to the cottage / Blackbird, The / Garden of daisies, The / Job of journeyword / Jocky to the fair / St.Patrick's day.
Album: released on Outlet (Ireland) in Mar'82

Cassette: released on Outlet (Ireland) in Mar'82

ACCORDION ESPECIALLY RECORDED FOR IRISH DANCERS (2).
Tracks: / Introduction (O'neills march) / Fairy reel, The / High cauled cap, The / Planxty drury / Three sea captains, The / Double jig / Hornpipe / Kilkenny races / Blackthorn stick, The / Downfall of Paris, The / Orange rouge, The.
Album: released on Outlet (Ireland) in Mar'82

Cassette: released on Outlet (Ireland) in Mar'82

Caruso, Enrico

VOLUME ONE.
Album: released on Bulldog in Sep'85 by Bulldog Records. Distributed by: President Distribution, Spartan, Swift, Taylor, H.R.

Car Wash

BEST OF CAR WASH,THE (FILM) (Royce,Rose).
Tracks: / Car wash / Zig zag / Water / Doin' what comes naturally / I'm going down / Put your money where your mouth is / I wanna get next to you / Daddy rich / Yo yo / Sunrise.
Album: released on MCA in '81 by MCA Records. Distributed by: Polygram, MCA

Cassette: released on MCA in '81 by MCA Records. Distributed by: Polygram, MCA

Casablanca

WITH LOVE.
Single (7"): released on RCA in Mar'83 by RCA Records. Distributed by: RCA, Roots, Swift, Wellard, Chris, I & B, Solomon & Peres Distribution

Casal

BEWITCHED (Embrujada).
Single (7"): released on EMI in Jul'83 by EMI Records. Distributed by: EMI

Casa Loma Orchestra

CASA LOMA STOMP.
Album: released on Hep in Aug'86 by H.R. Taylor Records. Distributed by: Jazz Music, Cadillac Music, Taylors, Wellard, Chris, Zodiac, Swift, Fast Forward

Cascade Orchestra

SPRING RAIN.
Single (12"): released on Passion in Nov'83 by Skratch Records. Distributed by: PRT

Cascades

RHYTHM OF THE RAIN.
Single (7"): released on Old Gold in Jul'82 by Old Gold Records. Distributed by: Lightning, Jazz Music, Spartan, Counterpoint

Case

OH.
Single (7"): released on SUS in Aug'83 by Sus Records

Case, Connie

SOONER OR LATER (Case, Connie/Kouchie Klan).
Single (12"): released on Vista Sounds in Dec'82 by Vista Sounds Records. Distributed by: Jetstar

Case, Peter

PETER CASE.
Tracks: / Echo wars / Steel strings / Three days straight / More than curious / I shook his hand / Small town spree / Old blue car / Walk in the woods / Horse and crow / Ice water / Satellite beach / Brown eyes.
Album: released on Geffen in Jul'86 by Geffen Records. Distributed by: WEA, CBS

Cassette: released on Geffen in Jul'86 by Geffen Records. Distributed by: WEA, CBS

STEEL STRINGS.
Tracks: / Steel strings / Small town spree.
Single (7"): released on Geffen in Oct'86 by Geffen Records. Distributed by: WEA, CBS

Single (12"): released on Geffen in Oct'86 by Geffen Records. Distributed by: WEA, CBS

Casey, Al

AL CASEY.
Notes: Mono production. Al Casey & George kelly with Fessords Session Boys.
Album: released on Storyville in Jun'86 by Storyville Records. Distributed by: Jazz Music Distribution, Swift Distribution, Chris Wellard Distribution, Counterpoint Distribution

AL CASEY REMEMBERS KING CURTIS.
Album: released on JSP in Dec'85 by JSP Records. Distributed by: Swift, Projection

BEST OF FRIENDS (Casey, Al/Jay McShann).
Album: released on JSP in Aug'82 by JSP Records. Distributed by: Swift, Projection

GENIUS OFTHE JAZZ GUITAR.
Album: released on JSP in Jan'84 by JSP Records. Distributed by: Swift, Projection

SIX SWINGING STRINGS.
Album: released on JSP in Jul'81 by JSP Records. Distributed by: Swift, Projection

Casey, Terence

LITTLE BIT OF HEAVEN, (A).
Album: released on Deroy in Jun'81 by Deroy Records. Distributed by: Jazz Music, Swift

Cash, Bernie

CONTRA BACH.
Album: released on Wave in Apr'79 by Wave Records. Distributed by: Swift, Jazz Music, Cadillac, Chris Wellard

Cashflow

CAN'T LET LOVE PASS US BY.
Tracks: / Can't let love pass us by / Can't let love pass us by (remix) / Can't let love pass us by (remix)(dub version) / I need your love / Spending money.
Single (7"): released on Club in Jul'86 by Phonogram Records. Distributed by: Polygram

Single (12"): released on Club in Jul'86 by Phonogram Records. Distributed by: Polygram

Single (12"): released on Club in Jul'86 by Phonogram Records. Distributed by: Polygram

CASHFLOW.
Tracks: / Party Freak / Mine all mine / Can't let love pass us by / Spending money / Reach out / I need your love / Just a dream / Party freak / Mine all mine / Can't let love pass us by / Spending money / Reach out / I need your love / Just a dream.
Compact disc: released on Club in Jan'87 by Phonogram Records. Distributed by: Polygram

Album: released on Club in Jun'86 by Phonogram Records. Distributed by: Polygram

Cassette: released on Club in Jun'86 by Phonogram Records. Distributed by: Polygram

MINE ALL MINE.
Tracks: / Mine all mine / Party freak / It's just a dream.
Single (7"): released on Club in May'86 by Phonogram Records. Distributed by: Polygram

Single (12"): released on Club in May'86 by Phonogram Records. Distributed by: Polygram

Single (12"): released on Club in May'86 by Phonogram Records. Distributed by: Polygram

Cash, Johnny

18 LEGENDARY PERFORMANCES.
Album: released on Premier in '84 by Premier Records. Distributed by: CBS

Cassette: released on Premier in '84 by Premier Records. Distributed by: CBS

1958-1986 THE CBS YEARS.
Tracks: / Oh, what a dream / I still miss someone / Pickin' time / Don't take your guns to town / Five feet high and rising / Seasons of my heart / Legend of John Henty's hammer / Ring of fire / Ballad of Ira Hayes / Orange Blossom special / Folsom Prison blues / San Quinten / Boy named Sue / Sunday morning coming down / Man in black / One piece at a time / Riders in the sky / Without love / Baron, The / Highway Patrolman.
Album: released on CBS in Apr'87 by CBS Records. Distributed by: CBS

Compact disc: released on CBS in May'87 by CBS Records. Distributed by: CBS

Compact disc: released on CBS in May'87 by CBS Records. Distributed by: CBS

20 FOOT TAPPIN' GREATS.
Album: released on CBS in Aug'78 by CBS Records. Distributed by: CBS

Cassette: released on CBS in Aug'78 by CBS Records. Distributed by: CBS

6 TRACK HITS.
Single (7"): released on Scoop 33 in Sep'83 by Pickwick Records. Distributed by: H.R. Taylor

Cassette: released on Scoop 33 in Sep'83 by Pickwick Records. Distributed by: H.R. Taylor

AT FOLSOM PRISON.
Tracks: / Folsom prison blues / Dark as the dungeon / I still miss someone / Cocaine blues / Twenty-five minutes to go / Orange blossom special / Long black veil, The / Send a picture of mother / Wall, The / Dirty old egg-sucking dog / Flushed from the bathroom of your heart / Jackson / Give my love to Rose / I got stripes / Green green grass of home / Greystone Chapel.
Album: by CBS Records. Distributed by: CBS

Cassette: by CBS Records. Distributed by: CBS

AT THE COUNTRY STORE.
Album: released on Country Store in Dec'85 by Starblend Records. Distributed by: PRT, Prism Leisure

Cassette: released on Country Store in Dec'85 by Starblend Records. Distributed by: PRT, Prism Leisure

BELIEVE IN HIM.
Notes: Believe In Him communicates the Gospel in songs that Johnny Cash has personally chosen, including several that he has written himself. It's an expression of his Faith, sung in his own musical style.
Album: released on Word in Sep'86 by Word Records. Distributed by: Word Distribution, CBS

Cassette: released on Word in Sep'86 by Word Records. Distributed by: Word Distribution, CBS

BEST OF.
Cassette: released on Creole (Everest-Europa) in Jul'84 by Creole Records. Distributed by: PRT, Rhino

BIGGEST HITS.
Tracks: / Don't take your guns to town / Ring of fire / Understand your man / One on the right is on the life, The / Rosanna's going wild / Folsom prison blues / Baddy sand bass / Boy named Sue, A / Sunday morning coming down / Flesh and blood / Thing called love, A / One piece at a time / There ain't no good chain gang / Riders in the sky / Baron, The.
Album: released on CBS in Mar'83 by CBS Records. Distributed by: CBS

Cassette: released on CBS in Mar'83 by CBS Records. Distributed by: CBS

BITTER TEARS.
Tracks: / Big foot / As long as the grass shall grow / Apache tears / Custer / Talking leaves, The / Ballad of Ira Hayes, The / Drums / White girl / Old Apache squaw / Vanishing race, The.
Album: released on Bear Family in Jul'84 by Bear Family Records. Distributed by: Rollercoaster Distribution, Swift

BOY NAMED SUE.
Single (7"): released on CBS in Apr'82 by CBS Records. Distributed by: CBS

BOY NAMED SUE, (A).
Tracks: / Boy named Sue, A / Green green grass of home / Still in town / Peace in the valley / When papa played the dobro / Tall men / After taxes / Pick the wild wood flowers / Praise The Lord and pass the soup / Old Shep / Keep on the sunny side / Time changes everything / Second honeymoon / Diamonds in the rough / Whirl and the suck, The / San Quentin.
Album: released on CBS in '84 by CBS Records. Distributed by: CBS

Cassette: released on CBS in '84 by CBS Records. Distributed by: CBS

BOY NAMED SUE, (A) (SINGLE).
Single (7"): released on Old Gold in Jul'82 by Old Gold Records. Distributed by: Lightning Jazz Music, Spartan, Counterpoint

COUNTRY BOY.
Tracks: / I walk the line / Wide open road / Cry, cry, cry / Hey porter / Folsom prison blues / Get rhythm / Luther played the boogie / There you go / Train of love / Straight A's in love / Give my love to Rose / Goodnight Irene / Rock island line / Country boy / If the lord's willing / Big river / Ballad of a teenage queen / Come in stranger / Guess things happen that way / Life goes on / Blue train / Katy too / Ways of a woman in love, The / Thanks a lot.
Compact disc: released on Charly in Apr'86 by Charly Records. Distributed by: Charly, Cadillac

COWBOYS, THE (Cash, Johnny & Marty Robbins).
Tracks: / Dont' take your guns to town / Big iron / Twenty five minutes to go / Hangin' tree, The / Cottonwood tree, The / Long black veil, The / Bury me not on the lone prairie / Cool water / Riders in the sky / Red river valley / Old Doc Brown / Meet me tonight in Laredo / Bonanza / Take me back to the prairie / Ira Hayes / Running gun / Ballad of Boot hill, The / Mr Garfield / El Paso / Billy the Kid / Streets of Laredo, The / Five brothers / Last gunfighter ballad, The / Shifting, whispering sands, The / Saddle tramp / Remember the Alamo / Sweet Betsy from Pike / Little Joe the wrangler / Give my love to Rose / Stampede.
Notes: Tracks by either artist, no duets.
Album: released on Ronco in Mar'82

Cassette: released on Ronco in Mar'82

DIAMOND IN THE ROUGH, (A).
Tracks: / Jesus / Preacher said "Jesus said" / That's enough / Miracle man, The / I never met a man like you before / Look for me / I talk to Jesus every day / Peace in the valley / Pie in the sky / Supper time / Far banks of Jordan / Matthew 24 (is knocking at the door) / Diamonds in the rough / I'm just an old chunk of coal.
Album: released on Word in May'85 by Word Records. Distributed by: Word Distribution, CBS

Cassette: released on Word in May'85 by Word Records. Distributed by: Word Distribution, CBS

FIRST YEARS, (THE).
Tracks: / Folsom prison blues / I can't help it / You win again / Mean eyed cat / My treasure / Hey porter / Straight a's in love / Two timin' woman / Oh lonesome me / Sugartime.
Album: released on Allegiance in Apr'84 by PRT Records. Distributed by: PRT

Cassette: released on Allegiance in Apr 84 by PRT Records. Distributed by: PRT

FOLSOM PRISON BLUES.
Tracks: / Ways of a woman in love, The / If the good Lord's willing / I was there when it happened / Down the street to 301 / Blue train / Don't make me go / I could never be ashamed of you / There you go / Thanks a lot / I couldn't keep fom crying / Just about time / Straight A's in love / I just thought you'd like to know / You're the nearest thing to heaven / Rock island line / Cold cold heart / Folsom prison blues / Hey good lookin'.

Album: released on Showcase in Apr'86. Distributed by: Counterpoint

Cassette: released on Showcase in Apr'86. Distributed by: Counterpoint

GREATEST HITS: JOHNNY CASH VOL.2 A Johnny Cash portrait.
Tracks: / Boy named Sue, A / Hey porter / Guess things happen that way / Blistered / Big river / Long legged guitar pickin' man / Folsom prison blues / Sunday morning coming down / If I were a carpenter / Frankie's man Johnny / Daddy sang bass.
Album: released on CBS in Mar'86 by CBS Records. Distributed by: CBS

Cassette: released on CBS in Mar'86 by CBS Records. Distributed by: CBS

GREATEST HITS: JOHNNY CASH VOL.1.
Tracks: / Jackson / I walk the line / Ballad of Ira Hayes, The / Orange blossom special / One on the right is on the left, The / Ring of fire / It ain't me babe / Understand you man / Rebel, The - Johnny Yuma / Five feet high and rising / Don't take your guns to town.
Album: released on CBS in Feb'85 by CBS Records. Distributed by: CBS

GREATEST HITS: JOHNNY CASH VOL.2.
Cassette: released on CBS in '73 by CBS Records. Distributed by: CBS

GREAT JOHNNY CASH, (THE).
Cassette: released on Bravo in Feb'80 by Pickwick Records. Distributed by: Lugtons

GREAT JOHNNY CASH, THE.
Cassette: released on Ditto in Sep'86 by Pickwick Records. Distributed by: H.R. Taylor

GREAT SONGS OF.
Tracks: / I walk the line / Rock island line / Sugartime / Folsom prison blues / Born to lose / Remember me / Wreck of the old 97, The / Ballad of a teenage queen / I heard that lonsome whistle / Home of the blues, The.
Picture disc album: released on Astan in Dec'85 by Astan Records. Distributed by: Counterpoint

GREAT SONGS OF JOHNNY CASH.
Album: released on IMS(Import) in Oct'82 by Polydor Records. Distributed by: IMS, Polygram

Cassette: released on IMS(Import) in Oct'82 by Polydor Records. Distributed by: IMS, Polygram

Album: released on Astan in Nov'84 by Astan Records. Distributed by: Counterpoint

Cassette: released on Astan in Nov'84 by Astan Records. Distributed by: Counterpoint

HEROES (Cash, Johnny & Waylon Jennings).
Tracks: / Folks out on the road / I'm never gonna roam again / American by birth / Field of diamonds / Heroes / Even cowgirls get the blues / Love is the way / Ballad of forty dollars, The / I'll always love you - in my own crazy way / One too many mornings.
Notes: See also under Waylon Jennings.
Album: released on CBS in Jun'86 by CBS Records. Distributed by: CBS

Cassette: released on CBS in Jun'86 by CBS Records. Distributed by: CBS

HOME OF THE BLUES.
Tracks: / Port of lonely hearts, The / My treasure / So doggone lonesome / Goodbye little darling / I love you because / Next in line / Don't make me go / Home of the blues / Belshazar / Leave that junk alone / Story of a broken heart, The / You win again / I could never be ashamed of you / It's just about time / I just thought you might like to know / I forgot to remember to forget.
Notes: original Sun recordings. Licensed from Charly Records International APS. This CD (P) 1987 Charly Holdings Ltd. (C) Charly Records Ltd.
Compact disc: released on Top Notch in May'87

I'M SO LONESOME I COULD CRY.
Cassette: released on Hallmark in Apr'80 by Pickwick Records. Distributed by: Pickwick Distribution, PRT, Taylors

INSIDE A SWEDISH PRISON.
Tracks: / Orleans parish prison / Jacob green / Me and Bobby McGee / Prisoners song, The / Invertebraes, The / That silver haired daddy of mine / City jail of a prisoner / Looking back in anger / Looking back in anger / Nobody cared / Help me make it throught the night / I saw a man.
Album: released on Bear Family in Oct'82 by Bear Family Records. Distributed by: Rollercoaster Distribution, Swift

IS COMING TO TOWN.
Tracks: / Big light, The / Ballad of Barbara, The / I'd rather have you / Let him roll / Night Hank Williams came to town, The / Sixteen tons / Letters from home / W.Lee O'Daniel / Heavy metal (don't mean rock & roll to me) / My ship will sail.
Album: released on Mercury in Jun'87 by Phonogram Records. Distributed by: Polygram Distribution

Cassette: released on Mercury in Jun'87 by Phonogram Records. Distributed by: Polygram Distribution

Compact disc: released on Mercury in Jun'87 by Phonogram Records. Distributed by: Polygram Distribution

Album: by Phonogram Records. Distributed by: Polygram Distribution

Cassette: released on Mercury in 13 Jun'87 by Phonogram Records. Distributed by: Polygram Distribution

I WALK THE LINE.
Tracks: / I walk the line / Ballad of a teenage queen / Big river / Wreck of the old 97 / Guess things happen that way / Born to lose / Folsom prison blues / Give my love to Rose / Rock Island line / Luther played the boogie / Straight A's in love / Get rhythm.
Album: released on Topline in '86 by Charly Records. Distributed by: Charly Distribution

Cassette: released on Topline in '86 by Charly Records. Distributed by: Charly Distribution

Compact disc: released on Intertape in Jul'87. Distributed by: Target

I WILL DANCE WITH YOU (Cash, Johnny & Karen Brooks).

JOHNNY AND JUNE (Cash, Johnny, June Carter & Anita Carter).
Tracks: / (I'm proud) the baby is mine / Cotton pickin' hands / Thunderball / One too many mornings / Wer kennt wer weg (I walk the line) / Smiling Bill McCall / In Virginia / Close the door lightly / Adios aloha / Ain't you ashamed / That's what it's like to be lonesome / How did you get away from me.
Album: released on Bear Family (CBS) in Sep'84

JOHNNY CASH I love country.
Tracks: / Boy named Sue, A / Boy named Sue A / Ghost Riders in the sky.
Album: released on CBS in Mar'87 by CBS Records. Distributed by: CBS

Cassette: released on CBS in Mar'87 by CBS Records. Distributed by: CBS

Compact disc: released on Pickwick in Apr'86 by Pickwick Records. Distributed by: Pickwick Distribution, Prism Leisure Distribution, Lugtons

JOHNNY CASH.
Tracks: / Just about time / Straight as in love / I just thought you'd like to know / You're the nearest thing to heaven / Rock island line / Cold cold heart / Folsom prison blues / Hey good lookin' / I love you because / Big river / Ballad of a teenage queen / Goodbye little darling / I could ever be ashamed of you / Next in line / Port of lonely hearts / Sugar-time / There you go / Two timin' woman.
Album: released on Premier in May'85 by Premier Records. Distributed by: CBS

Cassette: released on Premier in May'85 by Premier Records. Distributed by: CBS

JOHNNY CASH Original golden hits Vol 1.
Compact disc: released on Bellaphon in Nov'86 by Bellaphon Records. Distributed by: IMS-Polygram

JOHNNY CASH AT SAN QUENTIN.
Album: by CBS Records. Distributed by: CBS Deleted '86.

Cassette: by CBS Records. Distributed by: CBS

JOHNNY CASH COLLECTION, (THE).
Tracks: / Folsom prison blues / Country boy / Doin' my time / Cold cold heart / Sugar time / Wide open road / I walk the line / There you go.
Double cassette: released on Pickwick (Ditto series) in Jul'82

Cassette: released on Pickwick in Dec'79 by Pickwick Records. Distributed by: Pickwick Distribution, Prism Leisure Distribution,

JOHNNY CASH COLLECTION, THE.
Tracks: / Wide open road / Cry, cry, cry, / Folsom prison blues / So doggone lonesome / Mean eyed cat / New Mexico / I walk the line / I love you because / Straight A's in love / Home of the blues / Rock island line / Country boy / Doin' my time / Big river / Ballad of a teenage queen / Oh lonesome me / You're the nearest thing to heaven / Always alone / You win again / Hey good lookin' / Blue train / Katy too / Fools hall of fame / Ways of a woman in love, The / Down the street to 301.
Double Album: released on Collectors in '86 by Castle Communications Records. Distributed by: PRT, Pinnacle, Jazz Music

Cassette: released on Collectors in '86 by Castle Communications Records. Distributed by: PRT, Pinnacle, Jazz Music

JOHNNY CASH COLLECTION.
Double cassette: released on Pickwick in Jul'80 by Pickwick Records. Distributed by: Pickwick Distribution, Prism Leisure Distribution,

JOHNNY CASH (NOT SUBTITLED).
Tracks: / I walk the line / Street of Laredo, The / Don't take your guns to town / Five feet high and rising / I promise you / I'm gonna try to be that way / Don't think twice / It's alright / Hey porter / Give my love to Rose / Big river / I still miss someone / All god's children ain't free.
Album: released on Embassy in Jul'77 by CBS Records. Distributed by: CBS

Cassette: released on Embassy in Jul'77 by CBS Records. Distributed by: CBS Deleted '83.

LADY.
Album: released on Premier in Feb'87 by Premier Records. Distributed by: CBS

Cassette: released on Premier in Feb'87 by Premier Records. Distributed by: CBS

LAST GUNFIGHTER BALLAD, (THE).
Cassette: released on CBS in Feb'77 by CBS Records. Distributed by: CBS

LIVE IN LONDON (VIDEO).
Notes: Released by BBC/Screen Legends

LOVE ME TENDER (Cash, Johnny & Julie Andrews).
Single (7"): released on Peach River in Aug'83 by Peach River Records. Distributed by: PRT

MORE OF OLD GOLDEN THROAT.
Tracks: / Bottom of a mountain / You beat all I ever saw / Put the sugar to bed / Girl from Saskatoon / Time and time again / Honky tonk girl / Locomotive man / Second honeymoon / I'll remember you / Lorena / Roll call / Blues for two / Jeri and Nina's melody / Bandana / Wabash blues.
Album: released on Bear Family in Sep'82 by Bear Family Records. Distributed by: Rollercoaster Distribution, Swift

NIGHT HANK WILLIAMS CAME TO TOWN, THE.
Single (7"): released on Mercury in Aug'87 by Phonogram Records. Distributed by: Polygram Distribution

OLD GOLDEN THROAT.
Tracks: / I got stripes / Certain kinda hurtin', A / Little at a time, A / All over again / Still in town / Smiling Bill McCall / Wind changes, The / Sons of Katie Elder, The / Dark as a dungeon / Tennessee flat top / Matador, The / Send a picture of mother / You dreamer you / Red Velvet.
Album: released on Charly in Oct'75 by Charly Records. Distributed by: Charly, Cadillac

OLD GOLDEN THROAT (COMPLETELY DIFFERENT ALBUM).
Tracks: / Big river / Luther's boogie / You are my baby / Folsom prison / Hey porter / Next in line / Oh lonesome me / Belshazzar / Get rhythm / Rock island line / Country boy / Train of love / I walk the line / Katy too / Ballad of a teenage queen / Mean eyed cat.
Album: released on Bear Family in Sep'82 by Bear Family Records. Distributed by: Rollercoaster Distribution, Swift

ONE PIECE AT A TIME.
Tracks: / Let there be a country / One piece at a time / In a young girl's mind / Mountain lady / Michigan city howdy do / Sold out of flagpoles / Committed to Parkview / Daughter of a railroad man / Love has lost again / Go on blues.
Album: released on Hallmark in Sep'85 by Pickwick Records. Distributed by: Pickwick Distribution, PRT, Taylors

Cassette: released on Hallmark in Sep'85 by Pickwick Records. Distributed by: Pickwick Distribution, PRT, Taylors

ORIGINAL JOHNNY CASH (THE).
Tracks: / Don't make me go / Next in line / Home of the blues / Give my love to Rose / Guess things happen that way / Come in stranger / Ways of a woman (The) / You're the nearest thing to heaven / I just thought you'd like to know / It's just about time / You tell me / Goodbye little darling / Story of a broken heart / Down the street to 301 / Blue train / Born to lose.
Cassette: released on Charly in Sep'86 by Charly Records. Distributed by: Charly, Cadillac

ORIGINAL JOHNNY CASH, (THE).
Album: released on Charly in '80 by Charly Records. Distributed by: Charly, Cadillac

RAINBOW.
Tracks: / I'm leaving now / Here comes that rainbow again / They're all the same / Easy street / Have you ever seen the rain / You beat all I ever saw / Unwed fathers / Love me like you used to / Casey's last ride / Borderline (A musical whodunit).
Album: released on CBS in Dec'85 by CBS Records. Distributed by: CBS

Cassette: released on CBS in Dec'85 by CBS Records. Distributed by: CBS

RAMBLER, (THE).
Cassette: released on CBS in Aug'77 by CBS Records. Distributed by: CBS

RIDING THE RAILS.
Double cassette: released on CBS in '79 by CBS Records. Distributed by: CBS

RING OF FIRE.
Cassette: released on Hallmark in Apr'79 by Pickwick Records. Distributed by: Pickwick Dis-

tribution, PRT, Taylors

ROCKABILLY BLUES.
Tracks: / Cold lonesome morning / Without love / W.O.M.A.N. / Cowboy who started the fight, The / Twentieth century is almost over, The / Rockabilly blues (Texas 1955) / Last time, The / She's a go-er / It ain't nothing new babe / One way rider.
Album: released on CBS in Dec'80 by CBS Records. Distributed by: CBS

Cassette: released on CBS in Dec'80 by CBS Records. Distributed by: CBS Deleted '83.

SILVER.
Album: released on CBS in Sep'79 by CBS Records. Distributed by: CBS

Cassette: released on CBS in Sep'79 by CBS Records. Distributed by: CBS Deleted '83

STORYTELLER.
Album: released on I Love Country in Sep'86. Distributed by: Counterpoint

SUN SOUNDS SPECIAL.
Tracks: / Cry cry cry / I'm so doggone lonesome / There you go / I heard that lonesome whistle blow / Doin' my time / If the good Lord's willing / Wide open road / Two timin' woman / Cold cold heart / Hey good lookin' / I could never be ashamed of you / Always alone / Thanks a lot / I forgot to remember to forget / New Mexico / I couldn't keep from crying.
Album: released on Charly in '78 by Charly Records. Distributed by: Charly, Cadillac

SUN YEARS, (THE).
Tracks: / Wide open road / You're my baby / Folsom Prison blues / Two-timin' woman / Goodnight Irene / Port of lonely hearts / My treasure / Cry cry cry / Hey porter / Luther played the boogie / So doggone lonesome / Mean-eyed cat / I couldn't keep from crying / New Mexico / Rock 'n' roll Ruby / Get rhythm / I walk the line / Train of love / There you go / One more ride / Goodbye little darling / I love you because / Straight A's in love / Don't make me go / Next in line / Give my love to Rose / Home of the blues / Wreck of the old '97, The / Rock Island line / Belshazar / Leave that junk alone / Country boy / Doin' my time / If the good Lord's willing / I heard that lonesome whistle blow / Remember me / I was there when it happened / Come in stranger / Big river / Ballad of a teenage queen / Oh lonesome me / Guess things happen that way / You're the nearest thing to Heaven / Sugartime / Born to lose / Always alone / Story of a broken heart, The / You tell me / Life goes on / You win again / I could never be ashamed of you / Cold cold heart / Hey good lookin' / I can't help it / Blue train / Katy too / Ways of a woman in love, The / Thanks a lot / It's just about time / I just thought you'd like to know / I forgot to remember to forget / Down the street to 301.
Notes: Also contains large booklet
Boxed set: released on Sun in Mar'84 by Charly

Survivors, The

SURVIVORS, (THE) (Cash, Johnny, Jerry Lee Lewis & Carl Perkins).
Album: released on CBS in May'82 by CBS Records. Distributed by: CBS

Cassette: released on CBS in May'82 by CBS Records. Distributed by: CBS

Album: released on Hallmark in Sep'85 by Pickwick Records. Distributed by: Pickwick Distribution, PRT, Taylors

Cassette: released on Hallmark in Sep'85 by Pickwick Records. Distributed by: Pickwick Distribution, PRT, Taylors

TALL MAN.
Tracks: / Tall man / Foolish questions / Pick a bale o' cotton / I tremble for you / Besser so, Jenny Joe / My old faded rose / Kleine Rosmarie / Rodeo hand / Sound of laughter, The / Hammer & nails / Engine 143 / On the line.
Album: released on Bear Family (CBS) in Sep'84

THING CALLED LOVE, (A).
Single (7"): released on Old Gold in Jul'82 by Old Gold Records. Distributed by: Lightning, Jazz Music, Spartan, Counterpoint

UNISSUED JOHNNY CASH, (THE).
Album: released on Bear Family (CBS) in Sep'84

UP THROUGH THE YEARS '1955 - 1957'.
Tracks: / Cry cry cry / Hey Porter / Folsom prison blues / Luther played the boogie / So doggone lonesome / I walk the line / Get rhythm / Train of love / There you go / Goodbye little darling goodbye / I love you because / Straight A's in Love / Next in line / Don't make me go / Home of the blues / Give my love to Rose / Rock is-land line / Wreck of the old '97 / Ballads of a teenage queen / Big river / Guess things happen that way / Come in stranger / You're the nearest thing to heaven / Blue train.
Compact disc: released on Bear Family in Nov'86 by Bear Family Records. Distributed by: Rollercoaster Distribution, Swift

VERY BEST OF JOHNNY CASH.
Tracks: / What is truth / All over again / I'm so lonesome I could cry / Understand your man / Daddy sang bass / Busted / Let there be country / Ghost riders in the sky / Thing called love, A / It ain't me babe / Don't take your guns to town / Wreck of the old '97 / Ring of fire / If I were a carpenter.
Album: released on Hallmark in Jul'84 by Pickwick Records. Distributed by: Pickwick Distribution, PRT, Taylors

Cassette: released on Hallmark in Jul'84 by Pickwick Records. Distributed by: Pickwick Distribution, PRT, Taylors

WELCOME FRIEND.
Album: released on Word in May'85 by Word Records. Distributed by: Word Distribution, CBS

Cassette: released on Word in May'85 by Word Records. Distributed by: Word Distribution, CBS

...WITH HIS HOT & BLUE GUITAR.
Album: released on Charly in Feb'81 by Charly Records. Distributed by: Charly, Cadillac

WORLD OF..., THE.
Cassette: released on CBS in '74 by CBS Records. Distributed by: CBS

Cashmere

CAN I.
Single (7"): released on Fourth & Broadway in Jan'85 by Island Records. Distributed by: Polygram, EMI

Single (12"): released on Fourth & Broadway in Jan'85 by Island Records. Distributed by: Polygram, EMI

CASHMERE.
Album: released on Fourth & Broadway in Feb'85 by Island Records. Distributed by: Polygram, EMI

DO IT ANY WAY YOU WANNA.
Single (7"):

Single (12"):

LET THE MUSIC TURN YOU ON.
Single (7"):

Single (12"):

TRY YOUR LOVIN'.
Single (7"):

Single (12"):

WE NEED LOVE.
Single (7"): released on Fourth & Broadway in Mar'85 by Island Records. Distributed by: Polygram, EMI

Single (12"): released on Fourth & Broadway in Mar'85 by Island Records. Distributed by: Polygram, EMI Deleted '87.

Cash, Rosanne

I DON'T KNOW WHY.
Tracks: / I don't know why / You don't want me / What you gonna do about it.
Single (7"): released on CBS in Feb'86 by CBS Records. Distributed by: CBS

KING'S RECORD SHOP.
Tracks: / Rosie strikes back / Way we make a broken heart, The / If you change your mind / Real me, The / Somewhere sometime / Runaway train / Tennessee flat top box / I don't have to crawl / Green, yellow and red / Why don't you quit leaving me alone.
Album: released on CBS in Aug'87 by CBS Records. Distributed by: CBS

Cassette: released on CBS in Aug'87 by CBS Records. Distributed by: CBS

RHYTHM AND ROMANCE.
Tracks: / Hold on / I don't know why you don't want me / Never be you / Second to no one / Halfway house / Pink bedroom / Never alone / My old man / Never gonna hurt / Closing time.
Album: released on CBS in Mar'86 by CBS Records. Distributed by: CBS

Cassette: released on CBS in Mar'86 by CBS Records. Distributed by: CBS

Casino Classics

CASINO CLASSICS Various artists (Various Artists).
Album: released on Casino Classics in Feb'83 by RK Records. Distributed by: PRT

Casinos

THEN YOU CAN TELL ME GOODBYE.
Single (7"): released on Old Gold in Jul'82 by Old Gold Records. Distributed by: Lightning, Jazz Music, Spartan, Counterpoint

Casino Steel

RUBY (DON'T TAKE YOUR LOVE TO TOWN) (Casino Steel & Gary Holton).

Casiopea

DOWN UPBEAT.
Album: released on Sonet in Nov'84 by Sonet Records. Distributed by: PRT

SOUNDOGRAPHY, THE.
Tracks: / Asayake / Mid-Manhattan / Looking up / Misty lady / What can't speak a lie / Fabbydabby / Soundography, The / Gypsy wind / Eyes of the mind / Sunnyside feeling.
Compact disc: released on Sonet in Oct'86 by Sonet Records. Distributed by: PRT

SOUNDOGRAPHY, (THE).
Single (7"): released on Sonet in Jun'84 by Sonet Records. Distributed by: PRT

Casket and Crush

YOUNG GUYS WILL DO ANYTHING.
Album: released on Mekano in Jul'86. Distributed by: Red Rhino Distribution

Cassady, Linda

CB WIDOW.
Single (7"): released on Amigo in Nov'81. Distributed by: Red Rhino, Cartel

DUSTY RAVEN.
Single (7"): released on Amigo in Nov'81. Distributed by: Red Rhino, Cartel

INTRODUCING LINDA CASSADY.
Album: released on Amigo in Nov'81. Distributed by: Red Rhino, Cartel

Cassandra

IF YOU WANT ME.
Single (12"): released on Cima in Dec'84 by Cima Records. Distributed by: Jetstar

LOVE ME SWEETER TONIGHT.
Single (7"): released on Red Nails in Jun'82

Cassandra Complex

DATA KILL.
Single (12"): released on Rouska in Jul'86. Distributed by: Red Rhino Distribution, Cartel Distribution

GRENADE.
Album: released on Rouska in Sep'86. Distributed by: Red Rhino Distribution, Cartel Distribution

Cassette: released on Rouska in Sep'86. Distributed by: Red Rhino Distribution, Cartel Distribution

HELLO AMERICA.
Album: released on Rouska in May'87. Distributed by: Red Rhino Distribution, Cartel Distribution

LIVE IN LEATHER.
Cassette: released on Complex in Apr'85

MARCH.
Single (7"): released on Complex in Apr'85

MOSCOW IDAHO.
Single (12"): released on Rouska in Sep'85. Distributed by: Red Rhino Distribution, Cartel Distribution

Cassandra Crossing

CASSANDRA CROSSING Film soundtrack.
Album: released on Citadel in Mar'79. Distributed by: Swift

Cass Cass

CASS CASS.
Album: released on Sterns in Jul'87 by Sterns Records. Distributed by: Sterns/Triple Earth Distribution

Cassel, Justin

WHO IS THE MAN.
Tracks: / Who is the man / Who is the man (version).
Single (12"): released on Hero in Feb'86. Distributed by: Jetstar

Cassiber

PERFECT WORLD.
Album: released on Recommended in Dec'86 by Recommended Records. Distributed by: Recommended, Impetus, Rough Trade

Cassidy, David

EP, THE.
Single (7"): released on Starblend in Nov'86 by Starblend Records. Distributed by: PRT Distribution

Single (12"): released on Starblend in Nov'86 by Starblend Records. Distributed by: PRT Distribution

GREATEST HITS:DAVID CASSIDY.
Album: released on MFP in Mar'77 by EMI Records. Distributed by: EMI

HIS GREATEST HITS-LIVE.
Compact disc: released on Starblend in Jan'86 by Starblend Records. Distributed by: PRT Distribution

HIS GREATEST HITS - LIVE.
Album: released on Starblend in Nov'86 by Starblend Records. Distributed by: PRT Distribution

Cassette: released on Starblend in Nov'86 by Starblend Records. Distributed by: PRT Distribution

LAST KISS, (THE).
Single (7"): released on Arista in Feb'85 by Arista Records. Distributed by: RCA

Single (12"): released on Arista in Feb'85 by Arista Records. Distributed by: RCA

Picture disc single: released on Arista in Feb'85 by Arista Records. Distributed by: RCA

ROMANCE.
Tracks: / Letter (The) / Heart of emotion / Tenderly / She knows all about boys / Remember me / Romance (let your heart go) / Touched by the lightning / Last kiss (The) / Thin ice / Someone.
Compact disc: released on Arista in Mar'87 by Arista Records. Distributed by: RCA

Album: released on Arista in May'85 by Arista Records. Distributed by: RCA

Cassette: released on Arista in May'85 by Arista Records. Distributed by: RCA

Compact disc: released on Arista in May'85 by Arista Records. Distributed by: RCA

ROMANCE (LET YOUR HEART GO).
Single (7"): released on Arista in Apr'85 by Arista Records. Distributed by: RCA

Single (12"): released on Arista in Apr'85 by Arista Records. Distributed by: RCA

SOMEONE.
Single (7"): released on Arista in Aug'85 by Arista Records. Distributed by: RCA

Single (12"): released on Arista in Aug'85 by Arista Records. Distributed by: RCA

Cassidy, Jane

EMPTY ROAD, (THE).
Album: released on Claddagh in Oct'85 by Claddagh Records. Distributed by: I & B, Record Services Distribution (Ireland), Roots, Topic, Impetus, Projection, CM

Cassidy, Shaun

UNDER WRAPS.
Album: released on Atlantic in Jun'79 by WEA Records. Distributed by: WEA

Cassie

CHANGE MY IMAGE.
Single (7"): released on AKA in Sep'82. Distributed by: Stage One, IDS, Indies, Cartel

Cast

GALLERY.
Tracks: / Multi storey car park / Out of my mind / Trains / Sharp bends / Lullaby / Juliet / Willow / Procession.
Notes: The Cast are Dave Kent and Keith Rodway. This recording consists of several instrumentals recorded for an exhibition of landscapes at The Church Gallery, Marble Arch; plus several songs. Musicians include: Dave Kent: Vocal, guitar, glock, keyboards, percussion/Keith Rodway: Vocal, bass, keyboards, flexatone/Geoff Andrew, Flute/Carl Turner: Percussion, vocal/Gary Blakeley: Violin/Ernie Block-Sage: Drums/Danny Treger: Sax/Bill Clements: Guitar/Tom Hickmore: Guitar/Mick Hutchinson: Guitar/Dave Arnold: Treatments/Touch Eleven: Effects. Engineered by Clive Drew-Clifton, mixed by The Cast. All enquiries to: Rana Records, 96, Kenilworth Road, St Leonards-On-Sea, East Sussex.
Cassette: released on Rana in Jun'86

HOME.
Tracks: / Home (theme from Bread) / Red bricks.
Single (7"): released on BBC in May'86 by BBC Records & Tapes. Distributed by: EMI, PRT,

TUTTI FRUTTI.
Single (7"): released on BBC in Nov'86 by BBC Records & Tapes. Distributed by: EMI, PRT,

Castaway

CASTAWAY Original Soundtrack (Various Artists).
Tracks: / Be kind to my mistakes / Catamaran / Chemistry / Clair de lune / Fata Morgana / End titles / Island (The) / Memories of tango / Healing / Castaway.
Album: released on EMI in Mar'87 by EMI Records. Distributed by: EMI

Cassette: released on EMI in Mar'87 by EMI Records. Distributed by: EMI

Castaways
DREAM MAKER.
Single (7"): released on Virgin in Sep'82 by Virgin Records. Distributed by: EMI, Virgin Distribution

Castell, Lacksley
JOHNNY BROWN.
Single (12"): released on Negus Roots in Aug'83 by Negus Roots Records. Distributed by: Jetstar

TUG-O-WAR GAMES.
Single (12"): released on CSA in Nov'83 by CSA Records. Distributed by: PRT, Jetstar

Castell, Lesley
SEAK SOFTLY.
Single (7"): released on Negus Roots in Sep'82 by Negus Roots Records. Distributed by: Jetstar

Castille, Hadley J.
Going back to Louisiana

Castle Blak
BABES IN TOYLAND.
Album: released on Heavy Metal America in Jan'86 by FM-Revolver Records. Distributed by: EMI

Castle, David
CASTLE IN THE SKY.
Album: Distributed by: Polygram

Castle, Lee
DIXIELAND HEAVEN.
Album: released on Harlequin in Jan'84 by Harlequin Records. Distributed by: Swift, Jazz Music, Wellard, Chris, Taylor, H.R.

Castle Of The Golden Sun
CASTLE OF THE GOLDEN SUN (Reeves, James).
Cassette: released on Talking Tape Company in '84 by Talking Tape Company Records

Castle, Pete
RAMBLING ROBIN.
Album: released on Burlington in Oct'86 by Giant Life Records. Distributed by: Jazz Music, Celtic Music, Clyde Factors Distributors, I.R.S., Projection, Wellard, Chris, Roots

TRADITIONAL ENGLISH FOLK SONGS VOLUME 1.
Cassette: released on VFM in May'79 by VFM Records. Distributed by: Taylors, Wynd-Up Distribution

Castlereagh Choir
LET'S BE SINGING (Castlereagh Male Testimony Choir).
Album: by Pilgrim Records. Distributed by: Rough Trade, Cartel

LIGHT OF THE WORLD, THE (Castlereagh Male Testimony Choir).
Album: by Pilgrim Records. Distributed by: Rough Trade, Cartel

Castle, Roy
RECORD BREAKERS.
Album: released on Glenmore in Nov'81. Distributed by: Pinnacle

Cast of 1000's
NOTHING IS FOREVER.
Tracks: / Nothing is forever (7" mix) / New tomorrow.
Single (7"): released on Fun After All in 30 May'87. Distributed by: Pinnacle

Single (12"): released on Fun After All in 30 May'87. Distributed by: Pinnacle

Cast Of The Bike Shed
BEHIND THE BIKE SHED.
Single (7"): released on MCA in Feb'85 by MCA Records. Distributed by: Polygram, MCA

Cast of Thousands
NOTHING IS FOREVER.
Single (7"): released on Fun After All in June 87. Distributed by: Pinnacle

Casualeers
DANCE DANCE DANCE.
Single (7"): released on Disco Demand in '74.

Distributed by: PRT

Casuals
JESAMINE.
Single (7"): released on Creole in Aug'82 by Creole Records. Distributed by: Rhino, PRT

Single (7"): released on Old Gold in Oct'83 by Old Gold Records. Distributed by: Lightning, Jazz Music, Spartan, Counterpoint

Caswell, Johnny
YOU DON'T LOVE ME ANYMORE.
Single (7"): released on Kent in Apr'85 by Ace Records. Distributed by: Pinnacle

Catapult
SUMMARY.
Single (7"): released on SST in Apr'87 by SST Records. Distributed by: Pinnacle

Catch
25 YEARS.
Single (7"): released on Carrere in Apr'84 by Carrere Records. Distributed by: PRT, Spartan

Single (12"): released on Carrere in Apr'84 by Carrere Records. Distributed by: PRT, Spartan

Single (7"): released on Stiff in Jul'84 by Stiff Records. Distributed by: EMI, Record Services Distribution (Ireland)

Single (12"): released on Stiff in Aug'84 by Stiff Records. Distributed by: EMI, Record Services Distribution (Ireland)

FIND THE LOVE.
Single (7"): released on Stiff in Apr'85 by Stiff Records. Distributed by: EMI, Record Services Distribution (Ireland)

Single (12"): released on Stiff in Apr'85 by Stiff Records. Distributed by: EMI, Record Services Distribution (Ireland)

Catch 22
FREEWAY TO PARADISE.
Tracks: / Freeway to paradise / Truth conquers all.
Notes: Self - 01 534 8500.
Single (7"): released on Plankton in Sep'86 by Plankton Records. Distributed by: Cantio (Sweden)

GET CLOSE TO ME.
Single (7"): released on Rimshot in Feb'85 by Rimshot Records. Distributed by: Cartel

MARATHON MAN.
Single (7"): released on Applause in May'82 by Riva Records. Distributed by: WEA, Discovery

Catch This Beat
CATCH THIS BEAT - THE ROCK-STEADY YEARS Various artists (Various Artists).
Album: released on Island in Apr'80 by Island Records. Distributed by: Polygram

Cat Club, The
ONE LAST KISS.
Tracks: / Wild.
Single (7"): released on Jive in Aug'87 by Zomba Records. Distributed by: RCA, PRT.

Cate Bros.
CATE BROS..
Album: by WEA Records. Distributed by: WEA

Cateran
LAST BIG LIE.
Tracks: / Difficult days.
Single (7"): released on DDT in Jan'87 by D.D.T Records. Distributed by: Fast Forward, Cartel

LITTLE CIRCLES.
Album: released on DDT in Jul'86 by D.D.T Records. Distributed by: Fast Forward, Cartel

Cates, Demo
CHARIOTS OF FIRE.
Album: released on Vista Sounds in '83 by Vista Sounds Records. Distributed by: Jetstar

IN FLIGHT.
Album: released on Abraham in Dec'85. Distributed by: Jetstar

Catfish Hodge Band
EYE WITNESS BLUES.
Album: released on Adelphi in May'81 by Adelphi Records. Distributed by: Jetstar

Catheads
HUBBA.
Album: released on Enigma in May'87 by Enigma Records. Distributed by: Rough Trade, Cartel, EMI

Cathedral Choir
CHRISTMAS CAROLS FROM GUILDFORD CATHEDRAL.
Album: released on MFP in Sep'85 by EMI Records. Distributed by: EMI

Cassette: released on MFP in Sep'85 by EMI Records. Distributed by: EMI

Catherine, Philippe
GUITARS.
Album: by WEA Records. Distributed by: WEA

SPLENDID.
Album: released on Elektra (USA) in Aug'78 by Elektra/Asylum/Nonesuch Records. Distributed by: WEA

TWIN HOUSE.
Album: released on Atlantic in May'77 by WEA Records. Distributed by: WEA

Cathleen
BABY ME.
Single (12"): released on Another Side in Mar'86 by Les Disques Du Crepuscule Records. Distributed by: Rough Trade, Cartel

Catley, Marc
THIS IS THE BIRTH OF CLASSICAL ACOUSTIC ROCK.
Tracks: / Love / Write your will on my heart / Help me-peace the answer / New life / Hosea.
Cassette: released on Plankton in Jan'86 by Plankton Records. Distributed by: Cantio (Sweden)

Cat People
CAT PEOPLE Original soundtrack.
Album: released on Backstreet in Apr'82

Cassette: released on Backstreet in Apr'82

Cats
CATS Various artists (Various Artists).
Double compact disc: released on Polydor in Jun'84 by Polvdor Records. Distributed by: Polygram

CATS Original London cast.
Double Album: released on Polydor in Jun'81 by Polydor Records. Distributed by: Polygram,

Double cassette: released on Polydor in Jun'81 by Polydor Records. Distributed by: Polygram,

SUPERGOLD.
Album: released on EMI (Germany) in '83 by EMI Records. Distributed by: Conifer

Cats Can Fly
FLIPPIN' TO THE A SIDE.
Tracks: / Flippin' to the A side / One way or the other.
Single (7"): released on Epic in Sep'86 by CBS Records. Distributed by: CBS

Single (12"): released on Epic in Sep'86 by CBS Records. Distributed by: CBS

Catsfield Steamers
HOME BOYS HOME.
Single (7"): released on Dandelion in Jul'82. Distributed by: WEA

Cat Trance
DREAMS OF LIVING.
Single (12"): released on Ink in Mar'84 by Red Flame. Distributed by: Rough Trade, Cartel, Pinnacle

ISHTA BIL HABUL (CREAM GALORE!).
Tracks: / Ishta bil habul (cream galore!) / Ishta bil habul (dance mix) / Ishta bil habul (edit mix).
Notes: With the St. Louis Symphony Orchestra, conducted by Slatkin. Artists include Lieberman
Single (12"): released on Ink in Apr'87 by Red Flame. Distributed by: Rough Trade, Cartel, Pinnacle

ISHTA BILL HABUL.
Tracks: / Ishta Bill Habul.
Single (12"): released on Ink in Mar'87 by Red Flame. Distributed by: Rough Trade, Cartel, Pinnacle

KHAMU.
Album: released on Ink in '85 by Red Flame. Distributed by: Rough Trade, Cartel, Pinnacle

SCREAMING TO BE WITH YOU.

Single (12"): released on Ink in Oct'86 by Red Flame. Distributed by: Rough Trade, Cartel, Pinnacle

SHE STEALS CARS.
Single (12"): released on Ink in '85 by Red Flame. Distributed by: Rough Trade, Cartel, Pinnacle

ZOUAVE.
Album: released on Ink in Dec'86 by Red Flame. Distributed by: Rough Trade, Cartel, Pinnacle

Catullus
CATULLUS Poetry of Catullus read by James Mason.
Cassette: released on Caedmon(USA) in Oct'79 by Caedmon (USA) Records. Distributed by: Gower, Taylors, Discovery

Catwax Axe Co
25 GALLONS OF PARANOIA.
Single (12"): released on Fever in Aug'84 by Fever Records. Distributed by: Red Rhino, Cartel

WAX WALK.
Single (7"): released on Rondelet in Mar'82. Distributed by: Spartan Distribution

Single (7"): released on Doila in Oct'81

Caudel, Stephen
WINE DARK SEA.
Tracks: / Wine dark sea (the outward journey) / Wine dark sea (the return journey).
Compact disc: released on Coda in Jul'86 by Coda Records. Distributed by: Pinnacle, Cartel, WEA, Roots
Album: released on Coda Landscape in Feb'86 by Coda Records. Distributed by: WEA

Cassette: released on Coda Landscape in Feb'86 by Coda Records. Distributed by: WEA

Caught In The Act
WALK ON WATER/BLIND LOVE.
Tracks: / Walk on water / Blind love.
Single (7"): released on Works in Feb'86. Distributed by: PRT

Caution
SHOULD I (Caution & Maxi Priest).
Single (12"): released on Level Vibes in Dec'84 by Level Vibes Records. Distributed by: Jetstar

Cautionary Verses
CAUTIONARY VERSES Belloc-Various artists (Belloc-Various artists).
Cassette: released on Anvil in Jan'81. Distributed by: Anvil

Cava Cava
BROTHER BRIGHT.
Single (7"): released on Regard in Jan'83

Picture disc single: released on Regard in Jan'83

BURNING BOY.
Single (7"): released on Regard in May'83

Single (12"): released on Regard in May'83

Picture disc single: released on Regard in Jun'83

WHERE'S ROMEO.
Single (7"): released on Regard in Aug'82

Cavaliers
IT'S A BEAUTIFUL GAME.
Tracks: / It's a beautiful game / I.T. Man.
Single (7"): released on EL in Jul'86 by El Records. Distributed by: Rough Trade, Cartel, Pinnacle

Cavallaro, Carmen
DANCING IN A DREAM.
Album: released on Jasmine in Oct'84 by Jasmine Records. Distributed by: Counterpoint, Lugtons, Taylor, H.R., Wellard, Chris, Swift, Cadillac

Cavello, Jimmy
ROCK ROCK ROCK.
Single (7"): released on Revival in Jul'82. Distributed by: Lightning, Swift

Cave, Nick
FIRST BORN IS DEAD, THE (Cave, Nick & The Bad Seeds).
Album: released on Mute in Jun'85. Distributed

by: Spartan Distribution, Rough Trade Distribution, Cartel Distribution

Cassette: released on Mute in Jun'85. Distributed by: Spartan Distribution, Rough Trade Distribution, Cartel Distribution

FROM HER TO ETERNITY (Cave, Nick & The Bad Seeds).
Album: released on Mute in Jun'84. Distributed by: Spartan Distribution, Rough Trade Distribution, Cartel Distribution

IN THE GHETTO (Cave, Nick & The Bad Seeds).
Single (7"): released on Mute in Jun'84. Distributed by: Spartan Distribution, Rough Trade Distribution, Cartel Distribution

KICKING AGAINST THE PRICKS (Cave, Nick & The Bad Seeds).
Compact disc: . Distributed by: Spartan Distribution, Rough Trade Distribution, Cartel Distribution

Album: released on Mute in Aug'86. Distributed by: Spartan Distribution, Rough Trade Distribution, Cartel Distribution

Cassette: released on Mute in Aug'86. Distributed by: Spartan Distribution, Rough Trade Distribution, Cartel Distribution

SINGER, THE (Cave, Nick & The Bad Seeds).
Tracks: / Singer, The / Running scared / Black betty.
Single (7"): released on Mute in Jun'86. Distributed by: Spartan Distribution, Rough Trade Distribution, Cartel Distribution

Single (12"): released on Mute in Jun'86. Distributed by: Spartan Distribution, Rough Trade Distribution, Cartel Distribution

TUPELO (Cave, Nick & The Bad Seeds).
Single (7"): released on Mute in Aug'85. Distributed by: Spartan Distribution, Rough Trade Distribution, Cartel Distribution

YOUR FUNERAL MY TRIAL (Cave, Nick & The Bad Seeds).
Album: released on Mute in Nov'86. Distributed by: Spartan Distribution, Rough Trade Distribution, Cartel Distribution

Cassette: released on Mute in Nov'86. Distributed by: Spartan Distribution, Rough Trade Distribution, Cartel Distribution

YOUR FUNERAL, MY TRIAL.
Compact disc: released on Mute in Feb'87. Distributed by: Spartan Distribution, Rough Trade Distribution, Cartel Distribution

Cavern
IT MIGHT AS WELL RAIN UNTIL SEPTEMBER.
Single (7"): released on Kay-Drum in Jun'83 by Kay-Drum. Distributed by: Pinnacle

NO REASON TO CRY.
Single (7"): released on KA Drum in Nov'82

Cawood, Garth
GARTH CAWOOD'S FUNHOUSE.
Album: released on SRT in Dec'76 by SRT Records. Distributed by: Pinnacle, Solomon & Peres Distribution, SRT Distribution, H.R. Taylor Distribution, PRT Distribution

Cayenne
CAYENNE.
Album: released on Groove PR in '81 by Beggars Banquet Records. Distributed by: WEA, PRT

CROSS THE CHANNEL FERRY.
Single (7"): released on Coda in Aug'86 by Coda Records. Distributed by: Pinnacle, Cartel, WEA, Roots

Single (12"): released on Coda in Aug'86 by Coda Records. Distributed by: Pinnacle, Cartel, WEA, Roots

EVENING IN JAFFA.
Album: released on Coda in '84 by Coda Records. Distributed by: Pinnacle, Cartel, WEA, Roots

Cassette: released on Coda in '84 by Coda Records. Distributed by: Pinnacle, Cartel, WEA, Roots

HOT NIGHTS.
Album: released on Coda in Sep'86 by Coda Records. Distributed by: Pinnacle, Cartel, WEA, Roots

Cassette: released on Coda in Sep'86 by Coda Records. Distributed by: Pinnacle, Cartel, WEA, Roots

ROBERTO WHO?
Album: released on Groove PR in '84 by Beggars Banquet Records. Distributed by: WEA, PRT

Single (7"): released on Groove PR in '81 by

Beggars Banquet Records. Distributed by: WEA, PRT

Single (12"): released on Groove PR in '81 by Beggars Banquet Records. Distributed by: WEA, PRT

Cazazza, Monte
SOMETHING FOR NOBODY.
Single (7"): released on Industrial in '80 by Industrial Records. Distributed by: Rough Trade

C-Bank
GET WET.
Single (12"): released on Elite in '83. Distributed by: PRT

CBS...
CBS ARTISTS VOL 1 various artists (Various Artists).
Cassette: released on CBS in Aug'82 by CBS Records. Distributed by: CBS

CBS ARTISTS VOL 2 Various artists (Various Artists).
Cassette: released on CBS in Aug'82 by CBS Records. Distributed by: CBS

CBS Rockabilly
CBS ROCKABILLY Various artists (Various Artists).
Album: released on CBS in '79 by CBS Records. Distributed by: CBS

Cassette: released on CBS in '79 by CBS Records. Distributed by: CBS

Album: released on CBS in '79 by CBS Records. Distributed by: CBS

Cassette: released on CBS in '77 by CBS Records. Distributed by: CBS

Album: released on CBS in '78 by CBS Records. Distributed by: CBS

CCCP
1964-1984.
Album:

CC Frost
ACE OF HEARTS.
Single (7"): released on After Hours in '82. Distributed by: CBS

CCS
CCS Best of.
Album: released on RAK in '77 by RAK. Distributed by: EMI

WHOLE LOTTA LOVE.
Single (7"): released on EMI Golden 45's in '84 by EMI Records. Distributed by: EMI

CD III
SUCCESS.
Single (12"): released on Prelude in '84. Distributed by: CBS

Cecchetto, Claudio
GIOCA JOUER (Superman).
Single (7"): released on Banana in '83. Distributed by: Pinnacle, Fresh

Single (12"): released on Banana in '83. Distributed by: Pinnacle, Fresh

Cedar Roots
NIGHT CLUB Fight them.
Single (12"): released on Live & Love in '83 by Third World Records. Distributed by: Jetstar

Ceejay
COULD THIS BE LOVE.
Tracks: / Could this be love / Hammer to my head.
Single (7"): released on Noir in Feb'87. Distributed by: Pinnacle, Jetstar, PRT

Single (12"): released on Noir in Feb'87. Distributed by: Pinnacle, Jetstar, PRT

Ceilidh
CUED MILE FAILTE (Various Artists).
Album: released on Lismor in '74 by Lismor Records. Distributed by: Lismor, Roots, Celtic Music

Celebrated Ratliffe Stout Band
BEHIND THE MASK.
Album: released on Plant Life in '81. Distributed by: Roots

VANLAG.
Album: released on Plant Life in '81. Distributed by: Roots

Celebration
CELEBRATION GOLD.
Single (7"): released on Polo in '82 by Polo Records. Distributed by: PRT

Single (12"): released on Polo in '82 by Polo Records. Distributed by: PRT

Celebration Of Duke
CELEBRATION OF DUKE Various artists (Various Artists).
Album: released on Pablo in '82 by Pablo Records. Distributed by: Wellard, Chris, IMS-Polygram, BMG

Cassette: released on Pablo in '82 by Pablo Records. Distributed by: Wellard, Chris, IMS-Polygram, BMG

Celebrity Selection Rhymes
CELEBRITY SELECTION RHYMES Various artists.
Album: released on Warwick (Super Tempo) in '83

CELEBRITY SELECTION OF CHILDREN'S STORIES (Various Artists).
Album: released on Super Tempo in May'84 by Multiple Sounds Records. Distributed by: Multiple Sound Distributors

Cassette: released on Super Tempo in May'84 by Multiple Sounds Records. Distributed by: Multiple Sound Distributors

Celentano, Adriano
LANGUAGE OF LOVE (PRISENCO-LINENSINAINCIUSOL).
Tracks: / Disc Jockey.
Single (7"): released on Clan in Aug'87

Celestin, Papa
PAPA CELESTIN & HIS NEW ORLEANS RAGTIME BAND (Celestin, Papa, & His New Orleans Ragtime Band).
Notes: With Alphonse Picou. Recorded in mono.
Album: released on Jazzology in Jun'86. Distributed by: Jazz Music, Swift

PAPA CELESTIN & HIS NEW ORLEANS JAZZ BAND (Celestin, Papa, & His New Orleans Jazz Band).
Album: released on Folklyric (USA) in Dec'86 by Arhoolie Records. Distributed by: Topic, Projection

Celibate Rifles
KISS KISS BANG BANG.
Album: released on What Goes On in Apr'87. Distributed by: Rough Trade, Cartel, Shigaku

MINA, MINA, MINA,.
Album: released on What Goes On in Jul'86. Distributed by: Rough Trade, Cartel, Shigaku

PRETTY PICTURE.
Single (7"): released on Homestead in 30 May'87. Distributed by: Rough Trade, Cartel, Shigaku

PRETTY PICTURES.
Tracks: / Pretty pictures / Kent theme.
Single (7"): released on Shigaku in Apr'87

QUITESSENTIALLY YOURS.
Album: released on What Goes On in Jul'85. Distributed by: Rough Trade, Cartel, Shigaku

TURGID MIASMA OF EXISTENCE, THE.
Album: released on Hot in Jun'86 by Hot Records. Distributed by: Rough Trade, Cartel

Cell, Bee
ALTERNATING CURRENTS (Cell, Bee & The Buzzy Bunch).
Cassette: released on TK in Jun'78. Distributed by: CBS Distribution

Celtic Frost
EMPEROR'S RETURN.
Picture disc album: released on Noise in Sep'86 by Dorane. Distributed by: Revolver, Cartel

EMPERORS RETURN.
Album:

INTO THE PANDEMONIUM.
Album: released on Noise in Apr'87 by Dorane. Distributed by: Revolver, Cartel

Cassette: released on Noise in Jun'87 by Dorane. Distributed by: Revolver, Cartel

Compact disc: released on Noise International in Jul'87. Distributed by: Revolver, Cartel

MORBID TALES.

Album:
TO MEGA THERION.
Album: released on Noise in Dec'85 by Dorane. Distributed by: Revolver, Cartel

Central Avenue blues
CENTRAL AVENUE BLUES (Various Artists).
Album: released on Ace Of Spades in Apr'79 by Decca Records. Distributed by: Polygram, Swift

Central Council
BELLS-THE RHYTHM OF THE BELLS (Central Council Of Church Bell Ringers).
Album: released on Saydisc in May'79 by Saydisc Records. Distributed by: Essex, Harmonia Mundi, Roots, H.R. Taylor, Jazz Music, Swift, Projection, Gamut

Central Line
BETCHA GONNA.
Single (7"): released on Mercury in Feb'84 by Phonogram Records. Distributed by: Polygram Distribution

Single (12"): released on Mercury in Feb'84 by Phonogram Records. Distributed by: Polygram Distribution

BREAKING POINT.
Album: released on Mercury in Jan'82 by Phonogram Records. Distributed by: Polygram Distribution

Cassette: released on Mercury in Jan'82 by Phonogram Records. Distributed by: Polygram Distribution

SURPRISE SURPRISE.
Single (7"): released on Mercury in Mar'83 by Phonogram Records. Distributed by: Polygram Distribution

Single (12"): released on Mercury in Mar'83 by Phonogram Records. Distributed by: Polygram Distribution

Centrefold
DICTATOR.
Tracks: / Dictator / Dictator (inst).
Single (7"): released on Carrere in May'87 by Carrere Records. Distributed by: PRT, Spartan

Single (12"): released on Carrere in May'87 by PRT Spartan

Century Of Sound
CENTURY OF SOUND 1877-1974 (Various Artists).
Double Album: released on RCA in '77 by RCA Records. Distributed by: RCA, Roots, Swift, Wellard, Chris, I & B, Solomon & Peres Distribution

Century Steel Band
BABY DONT WANT YOU.
Single (7"): released on Glasshouse in Dec'82. Distributed by: Cartel

Cerrone
CERRONE'S PARADISE.
Album: released on Atlantic in Aug'77 by WEA Records. Distributed by: WEA

CLUB UNDERWORLD.
Single (7"): released on Personal in Aug'84 by Personal Records. Distributed by: PRT

LOVE IN 'C' MINOR.
Single (7"): released on Atlantic in Feb'77 by WEA Records. Distributed by: WEA

SUPERNATURE.
Album: released on Atlantic in Feb'78 by WEA Records. Distributed by: WEA

SUPERNATURE 86.
Single (7"):

SUPERNATURE (SINGLE).
Single (7"): released on Atlantic in Mar'78 by WEA Records. Distributed by: WEA

WHERE ARE YOU NOW.
Single (7"): released on Record Shack in Nov'83 by Record Shack Records. Distributed by: PRT

Single (12"): released on Record Shack in Nov'83 by Record Shack Records. Distributed by: PRT

Certain General
LIFE'S A SCREAM.
Single (12"): released on Factory in Dec'84 by Factory Records. Distributed by: Cartel, Pinnacle

SEXTET.
Album: released on Factory in Sep'81 by Factory Records. Distributed by: Cartel, Pinnacle

Cassette: released on Factory in Sep'81 by Factory Records. Distributed by: Cartel, Pinnacle

THESE ARE THE DAYS.
Album: released on New Rose in Mar'86. Distributed by: Rough Trade, Cartel

Certain Ratio

BRAZILIA.
Single (12"): released on Factory Benelux in Feb'85 by Rough Trade Records. Distributed by: Cartel

FLIGHT, A.
Single (7"): released on Factory in Nov'80 by Factory Records. Distributed by: Cartel, Pinnacle

FORCE.
Tracks: / Only together / Bootsy / Fever 103 degrees / Naked and white / Mickey way / And then she smiled / Take me down / Anthem / Si fermi o gredo*.
Album: released on Factory in Nov'86 by Factory Records. Distributed by: Cartel, Pinnacle

Cassette: released on Factory in Nov'86 by Factory Records. Distributed by: Cartel, Pinnacle

Compact disc: released on Factory in Nov'86 by Factory Records. Distributed by: Cartel, Pinnacle

GRAVEYARD & THE BALLROOM, THE.
Cassette: released on Factory in Nov'85 by Factory Records. Distributed by: Cartel, Pinnacle

GREETINGS TOO.
Tracks: / Greetings too.
Single (7"): released on Materiali Sonori Maso in 20 Jun'87

GUESS WHO.
Single (12"): released on Factory Benelux in Jul'82 by Rough Trade Records. Distributed by: Cartel

I'D LIKE TO SEE YOU AGAIN.
Album: released on Factory in Nov'82 by Factory Records. Distributed by: Cartel, Pinnacle

I NEED SOMEONE TONIGHT.
Single (7"): released on Factory in Jul'83 by Factory Records. Distributed by: Cartel, Pinnacle

Single (12"): released on Factory in Jul'83 by Factory Records. Distributed by: Cartel, Pinnacle

KNIFE SLITS WATER EP.
Single (7"): released on Factory in Oct'82 by Factory Records. Distributed by: Cartel, Pinnacle

Single (12"): released on Factory in Oct'82 by Factory Records. Distributed by: Cartel, Pinnacle

LIVE IN AMERICA.
Album: released on Dojo in Feb'87 by Castle Communications Records. Distributed by: Cartel

MICKEY WAY.
Single (12"): released on Factory in Sep'86 by Factory Records. Distributed by: Cartel, Pinnacle

OLD AND THE NEW, THE.
Album: released on Factory in Jan'86 by Factory Records. Distributed by: Cartel, Pinnacle

Cassette: released on Factory in Jan'86 by Factory Records. Distributed by: Cartel, Pinnacle

THERE'S ONLY THIS.
Single (12"): released on Factory in Sep'84 by Factory Records. Distributed by: Cartel, Pinnacle

WATERLINE.
Single (7"): released on Factory in Dec'81 by Factory Records. Distributed by: Cartel, Pinnacle

WILD PARTY.
Single (12"): released on Factory in Jun'85 by Factory Records. Distributed by: Cartel, Pinnacle

Single (12"): released on Factory in Jun'85 by Factory Records. Distributed by: Cartel, Pinnacle

Cervenka, Exene

TWIN SISTERS (Cervenka, Exene & Wanda Coleman).
Album: released on Rhino (USA) in Jan'86 by Rhino Records (USA)

Cetera, Peter

GLORY OF LOVE.
Tracks: / Glory of love / On the line.
Single (7"): released on Warner Bros. in Jul'86 by Warner Bros Records. Distributed by: WEA

Single (12"): released on Warner Bros. in Jul'86 by Warner Bros Records. Distributed by: WEA

NEXT TIME I FALL, THE (Cetera, Peter & Amy Grant).
Tracks: / Next time I fall, The / Holy Moly.
Single (7"): released on Full Moon in Oct'86 by Epic. Distributed by: CBS

SOLITUDE/SOLITAIRE.
Tracks: / They don't make 'em like they used to / Glory of love / Queen of the masquerade ball / Daddy's girl / Next time I fall, The / Wake up to love / Solitude/solitaire / Only love knows why / Big mistake.
Album: released on Warner Bros. in Jul'86 by Warner Bros Records. Distributed by: WEA

Cassette: released on Warner Bros. in Jul'86 by Warner Bros Records. Distributed by: WEA

SOLITUDE/SOLITAIRE.
Tracks: / Big mistake / They don'y make 'em like they used to / Glory of love / Queen of the masquerade ball / Daddy's girl / Next time I fall (The) / Wake up love / Solitude/Solitaire / Only love knows why.
Compact disc: released on Warner Brothers in Nov'86 by Warner Bros Records. Distributed by: WEA

Ceud Mile Failte

CEUD MILE FAILTE Gaelic ceilidh (Various Artists).
Album: released on Lismor in Jun'74 by Lismor Records. Distributed by: Lismor, Roots, Celtic Music

Chacksfield, Frank

CHARIOTS OF FIRE.
Album: released on Premier in '84 by Premier Records. Distributed by: CBS

Cassette: released on Premier in '84 by Premier Records. Distributed by: CBS

COULD I HAVE THIS DANCE.
Album: released on Dansan in May'81 by Spartan Records. Distributed by: Spartan

LIMELIGHT AND OTHER FAVOURITES.
Album: released on President in Sep'85 by President Records. Distributed by: Taylors, Spartan

LITTLE MORE LOVE, A.
Album: released on Premier in Feb'87 by Premier Records. Distributed by: CBS

Cassette: released on Premier in Feb'87 by Premier Records. Distributed by: CBS

LOVE IS IN THE AIR.
Album: released on Premier in Dec'84 by Premier Records. Distributed by: CBS

Cassette: released on Premier in Dec'84 by Premier Records. Distributed by: CBS

LOVE IS IN THE AIR - BOX SET.
Boxed set: released on Everest (Premier) in '82 by Everest Records. Distributed by: Pinnacle

NICE'N'EASY.
Album: released on Premier in '84 by Premier Records. Distributed by: CBS

Cassette: released on Premier in '84 by Premier Records. Distributed by: CBS

NOBODY DOES IT BETTER.
Album: released on Spot in Jun'85 by Pickwick Records. Distributed by: H.R. Taylor.

Cassette: released on Spot in Jun'85 by Pickwick Records. Distributed by: H.R. Taylor,

STARDUST.
Album: released on Contour in Jun'81 by Pickwick Records. Distributed by: Pickwick Distribution, PRT

Cassette: released on Contour in Jun'81 by Pickwick Records. Distributed by: Pickwick Distribution, PRT

WORLD OF....
Album: released on World of Learning in '69 by World Of Learning Records. Distributed by: World Of Learning

Chadbourne, Eugene

CORPSES OF FOREIGN WARS.
Notes: Featuring Brian and Richie from Violent Femmes.
Album: released on Fundamental in Jun'86 by Fundamental Records. Distributed by: Red Rhino, Cartel

COUNTRY PROTEST.
Single (7"): released on Fundamental in Nov'85 by Fundamental Records. Distributed by: Red Rhino, Cartel

VERMIN OF THE BLUES.
Album: released on Fundamental in Jun'87 by Fundamental Records. Distributed by: Red Rhino, Cartel

Chadbournes, The

LSD C & W, THE.
Double Album: released on Fundamental in Jun'87 by Fundamental Records. Distributed by: Red Rhino, Cartel

Chad Tree

SWEET JESUS BLUE EYES.
Single (12"): released on Hot in Nov'86 by Hot Records. Distributed by: Rough Trade, Cartel

Chadwick, Doreen

DOREEN CHADWICK IN MANCHESTER.
Album: released on Acorn in Jun'79. Distributed by: Folksound, Jazz Music

PRINCESS OF THE THEATRE ORGAN.
Album: released on Doric in Sep'80 by Amberlee Records. Distributed by: H.R. Taylor

Chai Am

DANCE CRAZY.
Single (7"): released on Illuminated in Aug'85 by IKF Records. Distributed by: Pinnacle, Cartel, Jetstar

Single (12"): released on Illuminated in Aug'85 by IKF Records. Distributed by: Pinnacle, Cartel, Jetstar

FASCINATION.
Tracks: / Fascination / Far away.
Single (7"): released on GC in Aug'86 by GC Recordings. Distributed by: DMS, RCA

Single (12"): released on GC in Aug'86 by GC Recordings. Distributed by: DMS, RCA

ME AND BABY BROTHER.
Single (7"): released on Illuminated in Oct'85 by IKF Records. Distributed by: Pinnacle, Cartel, Jetstar

Single (12"): released on Illuminated in Oct'85 by IKF Records. Distributed by: Pinnacle, Cartel, Jetstar

Chain

BANGING ON THE HOUSE CHAIN (Chain & Peter Hope).
Single (12"): released on Native in Sep'85 by Native Records. Distributed by: Red Rhino, Cartel

Chain Gang

LONG TIME GONE.
Single (12"): released on Idea in 30 May'87 by Idea Records. Distributed by: Rough Trade, Cartel

MORE THAN A DREAM.
Tracks: / More than a dream / Ridin' down the line / Long time gone / Fight for your life.
Single (12"): released on Troll Kitchen in Mar'87

Chain Reaction

CHANGE OF ACTION.
Album: released on Vista in '83 by Vista Records. Distributed by: H.R. Taylor Distribution

CHASE A MIRACLE.
Album: released on Vista Sounds in '83 by Vista Sounds Records. Distributed by: Jetstar

INDEBTED TO YOU.
Album: released on Gull in Jul'77 by Gull Records. Distributed by: Pinnacle

X RATED DREAM.
Album: released on Attic in Jul'82. Distributed by: Pinnacle

Chain, Ruby

SHARON'S SMILE.
Album: released on Ruby in '86. Distributed by: Red Rhino Distribution, Cartel Distribution

Chainsaw

HELL'S BURNIN' UP.
Tracks: / Hell's burnin' up / Dungeon, The / Last fortress / Cut loose / Rage and revenge / Midnight hunter / Born to kill / He knows you are alone / Ageless force.
Album: released on Bonebreaker (Germany) in Apr'86. Distributed by: IMS, Polygram

MASSACRE.
Album: released on Thunderbolt in Dec'84 by Magnum Music Group Ltd. Distributed by: Magnum Music Group Ltd, PRT Distribution, Spartan Distribution

Chairmen Of The Board

AGM.
Album: released on HDH(Holland/Dozier/Holland) in Jul'85 by Demon Records. Distributed by: Pinnacle

GIVE ME JUST A LITTLE MORE TIME.
Single (7"): released on HDH(Holland/Dozier/Holland) in Oct'84 by Demon Records. Distributed by: Pinnacle

GIVE ME JUST A LITTLE MORE TIME (EP).
Single (7"): released on Inferno in Jan'80 by Inferno Records. Distributed by: Inferno, Cartel, Pinnacle

LOVERBOY.
Tracks: / Loverboy / Loverboy-instrumental / Give me just a little more time / You've got me dangling on a string / Loverboy - Ian levine Remix / Loverboy - 7" version / Loverboy - original 12" version / Everything is Tuesday.
Single (7"): released on EMI in Aug'86 by EMI Records. Distributed by: EMI

Single (12"): released on EMI in Aug'86 by EMI Records. Distributed by: EMI

Double-pack single: released on EMI in Aug'86 by EMI Records. Distributed by: EMI

Single (12"): released on EMI in Oct'86 by EMI Records. Distributed by: EMI

LOVER BOY (MEDLEY).
Single (12"): released on EMI in Aug'87 by EMI Records. Distributed by: EMI

Cassette single: released on EMI in Aug'87 by EMI Records. Distributed by: EMI

SALUTE THE GENERAL.
Album: released on HDH(Holland/Dozier/Holland) in Apr'84 by Demon Records. Distributed by: Pinnacle

SKIN I'M IN.
Album: released on Invictus in Nov'74 by CBS Records. Distributed by: CBS

YOU'VE GOT ME DANGLING ON A STRING.
Album: released on HDH(Holland/Dozier/Holland) in Mar'84 by Demon Records. Distributed by: Pinnacle

Chakachas

JUNGLE FEVER.
Single (7"): released on Old Gold in Jul'84 by Old Gold Records. Distributed by: Lightning, Jazz Music, Spartan, Counterpoint

Chakk

BIG HOT BLUES.
Tracks: / Big hot blues / Cut the dust / Big hot blues - big blue mix.
Single (7"): released on MCA in May'86 by MCA Records. Distributed by: Polygram, MCA

Single (12"): released on MCA in May'86 by MCA Records. Distributed by: Polygram, MCA

IMAGINATION.
Tracks: / Imagination - who needs a better life / Imagination - who needs a better life (inst) / Imagination - who needs a better life (dub).
Single (7"): released on MCA in Mar'86 by MCA Records. Distributed by: Polygram, MCA

Single (12"): released on MCA in Mar'86 by MCA Records. Distributed by: Polygram, MCA

MURDERER.
Tracks: / Murderer / Big hot mix / Stare me out - crash mix / Cut the dust.
Single (7"): released on Fon in Jun'86 by Fon Records. Distributed by: Rough Trade, Red Rhino, Cartel

OUT OF THE SLUSH.
Single (12"): released on Double Vision in Sep'84 by Double Vision Records. Distributed by: Rough Trade, Cartel

TEN DAYS IN AN ELEVATOR.
Tracks: / Stare me out / Imagination / Big hot blues / Over the edge / Lovetrip / She conceives destruction / Falling / Years I worked / Murder / Big hot mix / Stare me out - crash mix / Cut the dust.
Notes: Special package including 12" E.P. WITH THE LP.
Album: released on MCA in Jun'86 by MCA Records. Distributed by: Polygram, MCA

Cassette: released on MCA in Jun'86 by MCA Records. Distributed by: Polygram, MCA

Compact disc: released on MCA in '86 by MCA Records. Distributed by: Polygram, MCA

TIMEBOMB.
Tracks: / Take your time (earth coming) / Just

pieces bumper bomb bonus bomb-bay mix bouncing beats.
Single (7"): released on Fon in Mar'87 by Fon Records. Distributed by: Rough Trade, Red Rhino, Cartel

Single (12"): released on Fon in Feb'87 by Fon Records. Distributed by: Rough Trade, Red Rhino, Cartel

Double-pack single: released on Fon in 30 May'87 by Fon Records. Distributed by: Rough Trade, Red Rhino, Cartel

YOU.
Single (7"): released on Fon in Mar'85 by Fon Records. Distributed by: Rough Trade, Red Rhino, Cartel

Single (12"): released on Fon in Mar'85 by Fon Records. Distributed by: Rough Trade, Red Rhino, Cartel

Chako, Lori

GLOSSY MAGAZINES.
Single (7"): released on Boadicea in Apr'83

Chaksfield, Frank

LITTLE MORE LOVE, A (Chaksfield, Frank Orchestra).
Album: released on Premier in '84 by Premier Records. Distributed by: CBS

Chalice

DANGEROUS DISTURBANCES.
Single (12"): released on Pipe in Oct'84 by Cherry Red Records. Distributed by: Pinnacle

LIVE AT REGGAE SUNSPLASH.
Album: released on Vista Sounds in Feb'84 by Vista Sounds Records. Distributed by: Jetstar

STAND UP.
Tracks: / Hit you like a bomb / Dangerous disturbances / Wicked intentions / Back way evil forces / Stand up / Go slow / Point dem finger / Easy street / Shine on / I never knew love.
Album: released on CSA in Jun'85 by CSA Records. Distributed by: PRT, Jetstar

WICKED INTENTION.
Single (12"): released on Diamond C in Apr'85 by Diamond C Records. Distributed by: Jetstar

Chalkdust

PORT OF SPAIN GONE INSANE.
Album: released on Ebony in Jul'86 by Ebony Records. Distributed by: Pinnacle, Ebony

Chalker, Bryan

CROSS TRACKIN'.
Album: released on Emerald (Ireland) in '78 by Emerald Records. Distributed by: I & B, Ross, PRT

EARLY DAYS.
Album: released on Sweet Folk and Country in Nov'76. Distributed by: Chris Wellard Distribution

I CAN'T READ THE THOUGHTS IN YOUR MIND.
Single (7"): released on Acuff-Rose in Aug'83 by Acuff-Rose. Distributed by: Pinnacle

SONGS AND BALLADS.
Tracks: / Going from Cotton fields / Molly darling / Great titanic, The / Give me your love / When I swim the Golden river / Rosewood casket, The / Wreck on the highway / Long black veil, The / Mary on the wild moore / Legend of the Irish rebel / Ballad of the blue tail fly / Blue ridge mountain blues.
Album: released on Sweet Folk All in May'81 by Sweet Folk All Records. Distributed by: Sweet Folk All, Roots, Celtic Music, Dragon, Impetus, Projection, Chris Wellard, Festival Records

Chalker, Curly

NASHVILLE SUNDOWN.
Album: by Sonet Records. Distributed by: PRT

SONGS OF GORDON LIGHTFOOT.
Album: released on Sonet in Apr'85 by Sonet Records. Distributed by: PRT

Challengers

HE'LL BE THERE.
Single (7"): released on Out Of Town in Jun'82

Single (7"): released on Out Of Town in Jun'82

SURF BEAT.
Album: released on Edsel in Aug'85 by Demon Records. Distributed by: Pinnacle, Jazz Music, Projection

Chalmers, Lloyd

IF LEAVING ME IS EASY.
Single (7"): released on KR in Jun'82 by KR Recordings Ltd. Distributed by: RCA, Revolver, Cartel

Single (12"): released on KR in Jun'82 by KR Recordings Ltd. Distributed by: RCA, Revolver, Cartel

IF YOU WERE HERE TONIGHT.
Tracks: / If you were here tonight / Galveston Bay.
Single (12"): released on Sarge in Jun'86 by Sarge Records. Distributed by: Jetstar

SO SOON WE CHANGE.
Album: released on Sarge in Sep'85 by Sarge Records. Distributed by: Jetstar

SWEET MEMORIES VOL.3 (REMIX).
Album: released on Sarge in Nov'84 by Sarge Records. Distributed by: Jetstar

Chaloff, Serge

BLUE SERGE.
Tracks: / Handful of stars, A / Goof and I, the / Thanks for the memory / All the things you are / I've got the world on a string / Susie's blues / Stairway to the stars.
Album: released on Affinity in '86 by Charly Records. Distributed by: Charly, Cadillac

BOSTON BLOW UP (Chaloff, Serge Sextet).
Album: released on Affinity in Apr'81 by Charly Records. Distributed by: Charly, Cadillac

BOSTON BLOW-UP (Chaloff, Serge Sextet).
Tracks: / Bob, the robin / Yesterday's gardenias / Sergical / What's new / J.R. / Body and soul / Kip / Diana's melody / Unison.
Compact disc: released on Affinity in Apr'87 by Charly Records. Distributed by: Charly, Cadillac

Chaloner, Susan

MISSING MR. MARLEY.
Single (7"): released on Fearless in Apr'84 by Fearless Records. Distributed by: Spartan, Cartel

Chamber Jazz Sextet

PLAY PAL JOEY.
Album: released on Candid in Jul'87. Distributed by: Counterpoint, Cadillac

Chamberland, Linc

YET TO COME.
Tracks: / I hear a rhapsody / Virgo / Have you met Miss Jones / Footprints / Yet to come / Autumn leaves.
Notes: Artists: Linc Chamberland/David Friesen/Gary Hobbs.
Album: released on Muse in May'83 by Peerless Records

Chamberpot

CHAMBERPOT Free improvised avant garde music (Various Artists).
Album: released on Bead in Jan'77. Distributed by: Cadillac

Chambers, Dave

DON'T LET IT GO TO YOUR HEAD.
Single (12"): released on Elite in Mar'83. Distributed by: PRT

Chambers, Joe

SUPER JAZZ TRIO, THE (Chambers, Joe and Tommy Flanagan and Reggie Workman).

Chambers, Paul

BASS ON TOP.
Tracks: / Yesterdays / You'd be so nice to come home to / Chasin' the bird / Dear old Stockholm / Theme, The / Confessin' / Chamber mates.
Album: released on Manhattan-Blue Note in Jun'87 by EMI America Records (USA). Distributed by: EMI

BRASS ON TOP.
Tracks: / Yesterdays / You'd be so nice to come home to / Chasin' the bird / Dear old Stockholm / Theme, The / Confessin' (that I love you) / Chamber mates.
Compact disc: released on Manhattan-Blue Note in May'87 by EMI America Records (USA). Distributed by: EMI

EASE IT (Chambers, Paul & Cannonball Adderly).
Tracks: / Ease it / Just friends / I got rhythm / Julie Ann / Awful mean / There is no greater love.
Notes: This original Vee Jay Album presents a fascinating combination of top flight jazz stars from the early sixties. In the front line we have Cannonball Adderly, the number one soul jazz alto player of the era, teamed with a young Freddie Hubbard, who just started to make his mark in the jazz world at the time this album was recorded. The rhythm section was at the time propelling the famous Miles Davis Quintet. This album has been long unavailable in the world and solid sales are to be expected, since the upturn in interest in hardbop music is definitely here.
Album: released on Affinity in Mar'84 by Charly Records. Distributed by: Charly, Cadillac

West Coast conference

WE THREE (Chambers, Paul, Roy Haynes & Phineas Newborn).
Compact disc: released on JVC Fantasy (Japan) in Nov'86

Chameleons

AS HIGH AS YOU CAN GO.
Single (12"): released on Statik in Feb'83. Distributed by: Rough Trade Distribution, Stage One Distribution

FAN AND THE BELLOWS, THE.
Album: released on Hybrid in Mar'86 by Statik Records. Distributed by: Pinnacle

Cassette: released on Hybrid in Mar'86 by Statik Records. Distributed by: Pinnacle

NOSTALGIA.
Single (7"): released on Statik in Feb'85. Distributed by: Rough Trade Distribution, Stage One Distribution

Single (12"): released on Statik in Feb'85. Distributed by: Rough Trade Distribution, Stage One Distribution

PARADISE.
Single (7"): released on Model in May'82. Distributed by: T.B.C Distribution

PERSON ISN'T SAFE ANYWHERE THESE DAYS.
Single (7"): released on Statik in Jun'83. Distributed by: Rough Trade Distribution, Stage One Distribution

SCRIPT OF THE BRIDGE.
Tracks: / Don't fall / Here today / Monkeyland / Seal skin / Up the down escalator / Less than human / Pleasure and pain / Thursday's child / As high as you can go / Person isn't safe anywhere these days, a / Paper tiger / View from a hill / Nostalgia / In shreds.
Compact disc: released on Statik in '86. Distributed by: Rough Trade Distribution, Stage One Distribution

Album: released on Statik in Oct'85. Distributed by: Rough Trade Distribution, Stage One Distribution

Cassette: released on Statik in Oct'85. Distributed by: Rough Trade Distribution, Stage One Distribution

SINGING RULE BRITANNIA While the walls close in.
Single (7"): released on Statik in Aug'85. Distributed by: Rough Trade Distribution, Stage One Distribution

Single (12"): released on Statik in Aug'85. Distributed by: Rough Trade Distribution, Stage One Distribution

STRANGE TIMES.
Tracks: / Mad Jack / Caution / Tears / Soul in isolation / Swamp thing / Time / End of time, The / Seriocity / In answer / Childhood / I'll remember.
Album: released on Geffen in Sep'86 by Geffen Records. Distributed by: WEA, CBS

Cassette: released on Geffen in Sep'86 by Geffen Records. Distributed by: WEA, CBS

Compact disc: released on Geffen in Mar'87 by Geffen Records. Distributed by: WEA, CBS

SWAMP THING.
Tracks: / Swamp thing / John, I'm only dancing / Tears - original arrangement.
Single (7"): released on Geffen in Aug'86 by Geffen Records. Distributed by: WEA, CBS

Single (12"): released on Geffen in Aug'86 by Geffen Records. Distributed by: WEA, CBS

TEARS.
Tracks: / Tars / Paradiso / Inside out (W).
Single (7"): released on Geffen in Jun'86 by Geffen Records. Distributed by: WEA, CBS

Single (12"): released on Geffen in Jun'86 by Geffen Records. Distributed by: WEA, CBS

WHAT DOES ANYTHING MEAN? BASICALLY.
Compact disc: released on Statik in Feb'86. Distributed by: Rough Trade Distribution, Stage One Distribution

Album: released on Statik in Oct'85. Distributed by: Rough Trade Distribution, Stage One Distribution

Cassette: released on Statik in Oct'85. Distributed by: Rough Trade Distribution, Stage One Distribution

Champagne Country

CHAMPAGNE COUNTRY (Various Artists).
Album: released on Hallmark in Feb'86 by Pickwick Records. Distributed by: Pickwick Distribution, PRT, Taylors

Cassette: released on Hallmark in Feb'86 by Pickwick Records. Distributed by: Pickwick Distribution, PRT, Taylors

Champagne Kindergarten

I WANT TO MARRY HARRY WHEN I'M GROWN UP.
Single (7"): released on EMI in Sep'85 by EMI Records. Distributed by: EMI

Champagne & Roses

CHAMPAGNE & ROSES (Various Artists).
Album: released on Polystar in Jun'80. Distributed by: Polygram

Champaign

HOW ABOUT US.
Single (7"): released on Old Gold in Sep'85 by Old Gold Records. Distributed by: Lightning, Jazz Music, Spartan, Counterpoint

Single (12"): released on Black Jack in Dec'82. Distributed by: Jetstar, Spartan

MODERN HEART.
Album: released on CBS in May'83 by CBS Records. Distributed by: CBS

Cassette: released on CBS in May'83 by CBS Records. Distributed by: CBS

Champion String Band

CHAMPION STRING BAND.
Album: released on Black Crow in Aug'81 by Mawson & Wareham Records. Distributed by: Projection

Cassette: released on Black Crow in Aug'81 by Mawson & Wareham Records. Distributed by: Projection

Champs, The

TEQUILA.
Album: released on Ace in Oct'87 by Ace Records. Distributed by: Pinnacle, Swift, Hotshot, Cadillac. Estim retail price in Sep'87 was £6.49.

Chan

CHAN THEME SHIMBA.
Single (7"): released on CSB London in Dec'81. Distributed by: CSB London, S. Gold Distribution

Chance

MODERN TV.
Single (7"): released on Fortune (USA) in Nov'82 by Fortune Records (USA). Distributed by: Swift

Chance, James

LIVE IN NEW YORK (Chance, James & the Contortions).
Cassette: released on Reach Out Int in '83

Chance, Trevor

EVERYTHING MUST CHANGE.
Album: released on Lee Lambert in Dec'81 by Lee Lambert Records. Distributed by: Cadillac

LOVE IS....
Album: released on Simon in Feb'79 by Supertunes Records. Distributed by: Pinnacle

Chandell, Tim

LITTLE LOVE, A.
Album: released on Imperial in Jun'86 by K-Tel Records. Distributed by: K-Tel, Taylors, Polygram

LOVE MUSIC.
Album: released on Skynote in Nov'84. Distributed by: Sidewalk Records

LOVING MOODS OF TIM CHANDELL.
Album: released on Orbitone in Jul'77 by Orbitone Records. Distributed by: Jetstar Distribution

Cassette: released on Orbitone in Jul'77 by Orbitone Records. Distributed by: Jetstar Distribution

OH WHAT A SMILE CAN DO.
Single (12"): released on Orbitone in May'82 by Orbitone Records. Distributed by: Jetstar Distribution

SEND ME SOME LOVING.
Album: released on Imperial in Dec'85 by K-Tel Records. Distributed by: K-Tel, Taylors, Polygram

SWEETER THAN HONEY.
Single (12"): released on Freedom in Jun'82 by Logo Records. Distributed by: RCA, Discovery, Wellard, Chris

TOGETHER AGAIN (Chandell, Tim & Ornell Hinds).

TRUE LOVE.
Single (12"): released on Orbitone in May'82 by Orbitone Records. Distributed by: Jetstar Distribution

YOU'RE GONNA HURT ME SO.
Album: released on Orbitone in Jun'78 by Orbitone Records. Distributed by: Jetstar Distribution

Cassette: released on Orbitone in '78 by Orbitone Records. Distributed by: Jetstar Distribution

Chandler, E.J.

I CAN'T STAND TO LOSE YOU.
Single (7"): released on Destiny in Feb'80 by Destiny Records. Distributed by: Red Rhino, Cartel

Chandler, Gene

60'S SOUL BROTHER.
Tracks: / If you can't be true (find a part time love) / Bet you never thought / Gonna be good times / Nothing can stop me / There goes the lover / I'm just a fool for you / What now / Girl don't care, The / There was a time / From the teacher to the preacher / Those were the good old days / Little like lovin', A / Pretty little girl / My baby's gone / Tell me what I can do / Here comes the tears.
Album: released on Kent in Jan'86 by Ace Records. Distributed by: Pinnacle

80.
Album: released on 20th Century in Jul'80. Distributed by: RCA, IMS-Polygram

DUKE OF EARL.
Single (7"): released on Old Gold in Jul'82 by Old Gold Records. Distributed by: Lightning, Jazz Music, Spartan, Counterpoint

DUKE OF SOUL, THE.
Album: released on Chess in Oct'84 by Charly Records. Distributed by: Charly, Swift, PRT, Discovery, IMS, Polygram

GET DOWN.
Single (7"):

Single (7"): released on Old Gold in Jan'85 by Old Gold Records. Distributed by: Lightning, Jazz Music, Spartan, Counterpoint

LIVE AT THE REGAL.
Tracks: / Rainbow / If you can't be true / Soul hootenanny / Monkey time, The / What now / Just be true / Ain't no use / Bless our love / Song called soul, A.
Album: released on Charly in '86 by Charly Records. Distributed by: Charly, Cadillac

STAND BY ME.
Tracks: / Duke of Earl / Big lie (The) / Nite owl / Festival of love / Stand by me / Thousand miles away / I wake up crying / Turn on your lovelight / Tear for tear / You threw a lucky punch / Rainbow / Check yourself / Baby that's love / Man's temptation / It's no good for me / Think nothing about it / Song called soul, A / Just be true / What now / You can't hurt me no more / Nothing can stop me / Good times (Gonna be).
Compact disc: released on Charly in Apr'87 by Charly Records. Distributed by: Charly, Cadillac

Chandler, Norman

SUPER DOUBLE DISC OF NORMAN CHANDLER.
Double Album: released on A&M in Apr'79 by A&M Records. Distributed by: Polygram

Chandra, Sheila

NADA BRAHMA.
Album: released on Indipop in Jun'85 by Indipop Records. Distributed by: Independent

OUT ON MY OWN.
Album: released on Indipop in Jan'84 by Indipop Records. Distributed by: Independent

QUIET.
Album: released on Indipop in Aug'84 by Indipop Records. Distributed by: Independent

STRUGGLE, THE.
Album: released on Indipop in May'85 by Indipop Records. Distributed by: Independent

Chanel

YOU'VE GOT A GIFT.
Single (12"): released on Mass Media Music in Apr'82

Chaney, Allen

SOUND OF MUZAK.
Single (7"): released on Albion in Jan'82 by Albion Records. Distributed by: Spartan, Pinnacle

Change

ALRIGHT LET'S GO.
Single (7"): released on Cool Tempo in Mar'85 by Chrysalis Records. Distributed by: CBS Deleted '86.

Single (12"): released on Chrysalis in Mar'85 by Chrysalis Records. Distributed by: CBS

CHANGE OF HEART.
Album: released on WEA International in Jun'84 by WEA Records. Distributed by: WEA

Cassette: released on WEA International in Jun'84 by WEA Records. Distributed by: WEA

MUTUAL ATTRACTION.
Single (7"): released on Cool Tempo in Jun'85 by Chrysalis Records. Distributed by: CBS

Single (12"): released on Cool Tempo in Jun'85 by Chrysalis Records. Distributed by: CBS Deleted '86.

OH WHAT A FEELING.
Single (7"): released on Cool Tempo in Apr'85 by Chrysalis Records. Distributed by: CBS

Single (12"): released on Cool Tempo in Apr'85 by Chrysalis Records. Distributed by: CBS Deleted '86.

Single (12"): released on Cool Tempo in Apr'85 by Chrysalis Records. Distributed by: CBS

SHARING YOUR LOVE.
Album: released on London in Jun'82 by London Records. Distributed by: Polygram

Cassette: released on London in Jun'82 by London Records. Distributed by: Polygram

TURN ON THE RADIO.
Album: released on Chrysalis in Apr'85 by Chrysalis Records. Distributed by: CBS

Cassette: released on Chrysalis in Apr'85 by Chrysalis Records. Distributed by: CBS

Change Ringing

CHANGE RINGING St.Mary Redcliffe, Bristol.
Album: released on Saydisc in Apr'78 by Saydisc Records. Distributed by: Essex, Harmonia Mundi, Roots, H.R. Taylor, Jazz Music, Swift, Projection,

CHANGE RINGING ON HANDBELLS (Various Artists).
Album: released on Saydisc in Mar'81 by Saydisc Records. Distributed by: Essex, Harmonia Mundi, Roots, H.R. Taylor, Jazz Music, Swift, Projection,

Cassette: released on Saydisc in Mar'81 by Saydisc Records. Distributed by: Essex, Harmonia Mundi, Roots, H.R. Taylor, Jazz Music, Swift, Projection,

Changing Face Of Harlem

CHANGING FACE OF HARLEM.
Double Album:

CHANGING FACE OF HARLEM VOL.2 (Various Artists).
Album: released on Savoy in '78

Chan, Jackie

NO ONE MOVE.
Single (12"): released on Crown H.I.M. in Nov'84 by Crown H.I.M. Records. Distributed by: Jetstar

Channel 3

I'VE GOT A GUN.
Album: released on No Future in Sep'82 by No Future Records. Distributed by: Pinnacle, Rough Trade, Cartel

Single (7"): released on No Future in Jan'84 by No Future Records. Distributed by: Pinnacle, Rough Trade, Cartel

WHEN THE LIGHTS GO OUT.
Album: released on No Future in Aug'83 by No Future Records. Distributed by: Pinnacle, Rough Trade, Cartel

Channel, Bruce

HEY BABY.
Single (7"): released on Old Gold in Jul'82 by Old Gold Records. Distributed by: Lightning, Jazz Music, Spartan, Counterpoint

Channel Islands...

CHANNEL ISLAND FOLK MUSIC Volume 2 - Jersey (Various Artists).
Cassette: released on Folktracks in Nov'79 by Folktracks Cassettes. Distributed by: Folktracks

CHANNEL ISLANDS FOLK MUSIC Volume 1 - Guernsey & Sark (Various Artists).
Cassette: released on Folktracks in Nov'79 by Folktracks Cassettes. Distributed by: Folktracks

Channing, Carol

KIDDING AROUND WITH CAROL CHANNING.
Album: released on Caedmon(USA) in Aug'77 by Caedmon (USA) Records. Distributed by: Taylors, Discovery

PETER AND THE WOLF.
Cassette: released on Caedmon(USA) in May'80 by Caedmon (USA) Records. Distributed by: Taylors, Discovery

PETER & THE WOLF & TUBBY THE TUBA.
Album: released on Caedmon(USA) in Jan'81 by Caedmon (USA) Records. Distributed by: Taylors, Discovery

POOH SONG BOOK.
Cassette: released on Caedmon(USA) in Aug'83 by Caedmon (USA) Records. Distributed by: Gower, Taylors, Discovery

Chantays

PIPELINE.
Single (7"): released on Creole in Aug'82 by Creole Records. Distributed by: Rhino, PRT

Single (7"): released on MCA in Jul'80 by MCA Records. Distributed by: Polygram, MCA

Single (7"): released on Old Gold in Jul'82 by Old Gold Records. Distributed by: Lightning, Jazz Music, Spartan, Counterpoint

Chantell

DESPERATE TIME.
Single (12"): released on Phaze One in Mar'85 by Phaze One Records. Distributed by: Jetstar

Chantelle

I LOVE EVERY LITTLE THING ABOUT YOU.
Tracks: / I love every little thing about you / Over-world.
Single (7"): released on T-Mac in Jul'86 by T-Mac Records. Distributed by: PRT Distribution

Chantels

CHANTELS, THE.
Album: released on End in Apr'79 by End Records. Distributed by: Swift

Chanter Sisters

CAN'T STOP DANCING.
Single (7"): released on Safari in '79 by Safari Records. Distributed by: Pinnacle

READY FOR LOVE.
Tracks: / You've lost that lovin' feeling / Never thought fall in love (could be so wild) / Dance, dance, dance / Talking too much about my baby / When the lights go out / Na na hey hey (Kiss him goodbye) / It's too late now / Just your fool / Sunshiny day / Nashville.
Album: released on Safari in Jun'78 by Safari Records. Distributed by: Pinnacle

SHOULDER TO SHOULDER.
Tracks: / Shoulder to shoulder / Oh what a shame / I wanna get closer / I love you / Born to lose / Can't stop dancing / Carrie Blue / I'll be there / I've got your number / Thanks to you.
Album: released on Safari in '79 by Safari Records. Distributed by: Pinnacle

Chant Of Barry Flynn

SMILE AND THE KISS.
Tracks: / Smile and the kiss / Big love theme.
Single (7"): released on Ensign in Apr'84 by Ensign Records. Distributed by: CBS Distribution

Single (12"): released on Ensign in Apr'84 by Ensign Records. Distributed by: CBS Distribution

Chant Village Stories

CHANT VILLAGE STORIES (Isla St.Clair).
Special: released on Tempo Storytime in May'84

MORE CHANT VILLAGE STORIES (St.Clair, Isla).
Cassette: released on Tempo Storytime in May'84

Chaos In Europe

CHAOS IN EUROPE (Various Artists).
Album: released on Chaos in Jun'85 by Backs Records. Distributed by: Nine Mile, Cartel

Chaos UK

BURNING BRITAIN (EP).
Single (7"): released on Riot City in Mar'82 by Riot City Records. Distributed by: Revolver

EAR SLAUGHTER (Chaos UK & Extreme Noise Terror).
Album: released on Manic Ears in Nov'86

LAWLESS BRITAIN.
Album: released on Children Of The Revolution in Nov'84 by Revolver Records. Distributed by: Revolver, Cartel

LOUD, POLITICAL AND UNCOMPROMISING.
Single (7"): released on Riot City in Jul'82 by Riot City Records. Distributed by: Revolver

SHORT SHARP SHOCK.
Album: released on Children Of The Revolution in Jul'86 by Revolver Records. Distributed by: Revolver, Cartel

SINGLES EP.
Single (12"): released on Riot City in Sep'84 by Riot City Records. Distributed by: Revolver

SINGLES, THE.
Single (12"): released on Riot City in Apr'86 by Riot City Records. Distributed by: Revolver

Chaotic Dischord

CHAOTIC DISCORD LIVE.
Album: released on Riot City in Sep'84 by Riot City Records. Distributed by: Revolver

F*CK RELIGION, F*CK POLITICS AND F*CK THE LOT OF YOU.
Album: released on Riot City in Aug'83 by Riot City Records. Distributed by: Revolver

F*CK THE WORLD.
Single (7"): released on Riot City in Jul'82 by Riot City Records. Distributed by: Revolver

FINAL CURTAIN.
Single (7"): released on Riot City in Jan'84 by Riot City Records. Distributed by: Revolver

FK OFF YOU C**T WHAT A LOAD OF B******S.**
Album: released on Syndicate in Aug'84

GOAT F**** VIRGIN KILLERZ FROM HELL.**
Album: released on Not Very Nice-Children Of The Revolution in Nov'86

NEVER TRUST A FRIEND (3 TRACK EP).
Single (7"): released on Riot City in May'83 by Riot City Records. Distributed by: Revolver

NEW IMPROVED.
Album: released on Riot City in May'84 by Riot City Records. Distributed by: Revolver

NOW THAT'S WHAT I CALL A ...... RACKET VOL.1.
Album: released on Not Very Nice in Jun'85. Distributed by: Revolver Distribution, Cartel Distribution

Chaotic Youth

SAD SOCIETY (EP).
Single (7"): released on Lightbeat in May'83 by Lightbeat Records. Distributed by: Pinnacle

Chapel Choir...

CHAPEL CHOIR OF BLUECOAT SCHOOL (Chapel Choir of Bluecoat School).
Album: by Abbey. Distributed by: PRT, Taylors,

Chapin, Harry

ANTHOLOGY.
Tracks: / W.O.L.D / Any old kind of day / Cats in the cradle / 30,000 Pounds of bananas / Taxi / She is always seventeen / Sunday morning sunshine / I wanna learn a love song / Better place to be / Song man.
Album: released on Elektra (USA) in Nov'85 by Elektra/Asylum/Nonesuch Records. Distributed by: WEA

Cassette: released on Elektra (USA) in Nov'85 by Elektra/Asylum/Nonesuch Records. Distributed by: WEA

GREATEST STORIES-LIVE.
Tracks: / Dreams go by / W.O.L.D. / Saturday morning / I wanna learn a love song / Mr. Tanner / Better place to be, A / Let time go lightly / Cats in a cradle / Taxi / Circle / 30,000 Pounds of bananas / She is always seventeen / Love is just another world / Shortest story, The.
Album: released on Elektra (USA) in Apr'86 by Elektra/Asylum/Nonesuch Records. Distributed by: WEA

LIVING ROOM SUITE.
Album: released on Elektra (USA) in May'78 by Elektra/Asylum/Nonesuch Records. Distributed by: WEA

Cassette: released on Elektra (USA) in May'78 by Elektra/Asylum/Nonesuch Records. Distributed by: WEA

ON THE ROAD TO KINGDOM COME.
Cassette: released on Elektra (USA) in Oct'76 by Elektra/Asylum/Nonesuch Records. Distributed by: WEA

PORTRAIT GALLERY.
Tracks: / Dreams go by / Tangled up puppet / Star tripper / Babysitter / Someone keeps calling my name / Rock, The / Sandy / Dirt gets under the fingernails / Summer / Stop singing those sad songs / Dancin' boy / If you want to feel / Poor damned fool / I wonder what happened to this world / Jenny / It seems you only love me when it rains / Why do little girls / Flowers are red / Somebody said.
Album: released on Elektra (USA) in Nov'76 by Elektra/Asylum/Nonesuch Records. Distributed by: WEA

SEQUEL.
Compact disc: released on Epic in May'81 by CBS Records. Distributed by: CBS

WOLD/CAT'S IN THE CRADLE.
Single (7"): released on Elektra (USA) in Sep'76 by Elektra/Asylum/Nonesuch Records. Distributed by: WEA

Chaplain, Paul

MR NICOTINE (Chaplain, Paul & The Emeralds).
Album: released on White in May'87

Chaplin, Charlie

BOYIE BOYIE.
Single (12"): released on Horseshoe in Nov'85. Distributed by: Jetstar

COME BACK CHARLIE.
Single (12"): released on Winner in Apr'86 by Creole Records. Distributed by: Jetstar, PRT

DANCE HALL ROCKERS.
Album: released on Sun Set in Mar'85 by Sun Set Records. Distributed by: Jetstar Distribution

KILLER.
Single (12"): released on Power House in Oct'84 by Power House Records. Distributed by: Jetstar

KNEE AFRICA.
Album: released on Power House in Jun'87 by Power House Records. Distributed by: Jetstar

ONE OF A KIND.
Album: released on Trojan in Sep'83 by Trojan Records. Distributed by: PRT, Jetstar

PRESENTING CHARLIE CHAPLIN.
Tracks: / Mother-in-law / Now leave me chalwa / Air is polluted / Chaplin's chant / Ann Marie / Youthman / Fussing and fighting / Jamaican callie / Electric shrank.
Album: released on Kingdom in Sep'83 by Kingdom Records. Distributed by: Kingdom

ROOTS OF CULTURE.
Album: released on Vista Sounds in Jul'84 by Vista Sounds Records. Distributed by: Jetstar

SOUND SYSTEM.
Album: released on Arrival in Dec'84 by Arrival. Distributed by: Revolver, Cartel

UNITY IN STRENGTH (Chaplin, Charlie & Don Carlos).
Single (12"): released on CSA in Apr'83 by CSA Records. Distributed by: PRT, Jetstar

Yellowman meets Charlie Chaplin

Chapman, Michael

ALMOST ALONE.
Tracks: / Dogs got more sense / Fireside hound / I'm sober now / Theme from the movie of the same name / Nuages / Deal gone down / SHC / Kodak ghosts / Waiting for Miguel: Northern lights / Fahey's flag / No thanks to me / Falling apart / Among the trees / In the trees.
Album: released on Black Crow in Nov'81 by Mawson & Wareham Records. Distributed by: Projection

FULLY QUALIFIED SURVIVOR.
Tracks: / Aviator / Naked ladies and electric ragtime / Stranger in the room / Postcards of Scarborough / Fishbeard sunset / Soulful lady / Rabbit hills / March rain / Kodak ghosts / Andru's easy rider / Trinkets and rings.
Notes: Previously: Criminal: Take 3 and Harvest: TPS 7003
Album: released on Cube in '82 by Dakota Records. Distributed by: PRT

HEARTBEAT.
Compact disc: released on Coda in Jun'87 by Coda Records. Distributed by: Pinnacle, Cartel, WEA, Roots

Compact disc: released on Coda in Jun'87 by Coda Records. Distributed by: Pinnacle, Cartel, WEA, Roots

Album: released on Coda in Jun'87 by Coda Records. Distributed by: Pinnacle, Cartel, WEA, Roots

Cassette: released on Coda in Jun'87 by Coda Records. Distributed by: Pinnacle, Cartel, WEA, Roots

LIFE ON THE CEILING.
Album: released on Criminal in '78 by Criminal Records. Distributed by: Jetstar

MAN WHO HATED MORNINGS.
Album: released on Criminal in Aug'78 by Criminal Records. Distributed by: Jetstar

MICHAEL CHAPMAN LIVED HERE FROM 1968-72.
Tracks: / Naked ladies and electric ragtime / Rainmaker / You say / In the valley / Kodak ghosts / Postcards of Scarborough / It didn't work out / Last lady song / Wrecked again / First leaf of autumn, The / Soulful lady.
Album: released on Cube in '82 by Dakota Records. Distributed by: PRT

ORIGINAL OWNERS (Chapman, Michael & Rick Kemp).
Album: released on Konexion in Mar'84 by Konexion Records. Distributed by: Pinnacle

PLAY THE GUITAR THE EASY WAY.
Album: released on Criminal in Jun'78 by Criminal Records. Distributed by: Jetstar

PLEASURES OF THE STREET.
Album: released on Telefunken in Feb'76

Chapman, Morris

VOICE OF PRAISE (Chapman, Morris & Friends).
Notes: Who is Morris Chapman? He's a mixture of the majestic and the humble in a single package, and despite a Grammy award nomination, three popular albums and a worldwide ministry, he still hasn't lost that gracious spririt. Morris writes and performs songs that consistently reach the hearts of Christians everywhere. His unassuming nature and warm vocal quality blend beautifully - always a compelling combination. In VOICE OF PRAISE, his debut album for Maranatha Music, Morris joins with the Maranatha Singers and several other friends to create a moving celebration of worship and praise. Morris Chapman was the guest soloist at Filey at Skegness Bible Week in September 1986.
Album: released on Maranatha Music in Aug'86

Cassette: released on Maranatha Music in Aug'86

Chapman, Roger

CHAPPO.
Tracks: / Midnite child / Hang on to a dream / Face of stone / Pills / Always gotta pay in the end / Moth to a flame / Shape of things.
Album: released on Acrobat in Feb'79 by Acrobat Records. Distributed by: Polygram, Red Rhino, Cartel

HE WAS SHE WAS YOU WAS WE WAS.
Album: released on Polydor (Import) in Oct'82

HYENAS ONLY LAUGH FOR FUN.
Album: released on Teldec (Germany) in Oct'81 by Import Records. Distributed by: IMS Distribution, Polygram Distribution

Cassette: released on Teldec (Germany) in Oct'81 by Import Records. Distributed by: IMS Distribution, Polygram Distribution

LIVE IN HAMBURG.
Album: released on Teldec (Germany) in Sep'81 by Import Records. Distributed by: IMS Distribution, Polygram Distribution

MAIL ORDER MAGIC.
Album: released on Kamera in Sep'81

SHADOW KNOWS, THE.
Album: released on RCA in May'85 by RCA Records. Distributed by: RCA, Roots, Swift, Wellard, Chris, I & B, Solomon & Peres Distribution

Cassette: released on RCA in May'85 by RCA Records. Distributed by: RCA, Roots, Swift, Wellard, Chris, I & B, Solomon & Peres Distribution

Chapman, Toby

ALWAYS.
Tracks: / Always / Give it a little time.
Single (7"): released on Tembo in Sep'86 by Tembo (Canada). Distributed by: IMS Distribution, Polygram Distribution

Single (7"): released on Klub in Sep'81

THAT'S HOW HEARTS BREAK.
Tracks: / That's how hearts break / Forever.
Single (7"): released on Tembo in Feb'87 by Tembo (Canada). Distributed by: IMS Distribution, Polygram Distribution

Chapman/Whitney

STREETWALKERS.
Album: by WEA Records. Distributed by: WEA

Chappelat, Jean-Robert

PRINCE DE L'ACCORDEON.
Tracks: / Polka satellite / Belle et sentimentale / Toboggan rag / Shocking valse / Senhor sivuca / Matins qui chantant / Accordeon Bresilien / Cornaline / Drole de rigolade / System A / L'oiseau mouche / Slalom tres special.
Notes: Retail price given by ARC excluding P & P (via mail order) is 5.95. Mail order distribution address: Accordion Record Club, 146 Birmingham Road, Kidderminster, Worcs. DY10 2SL. Tel: 0562 746105
Album: released on Accordion Record Club in Jul'86 by Accordion Record Club Records. Distributed by: Accordion Record Club

Cassette: released on Accordion Record Club in Jul'86 by Accordion Record Club Records. Distributed by: Accordion Record Club

Chaps

LEGEND OF ROBIN HOOD.
Single (7"): released on Dakota in Mar'84 by Dakota Records. Distributed by: PRT

RAWHIDE.
Picture disc single: released on Stiff in Sep'82 by Stiff Records. Distributed by: EMI, Record Services Distribution (Ireland)

RAWHIDE/GHOST RIDERS IN THE SKY.
Single (7"): released on Stiff in Sep'82 by Stiff Records. Distributed by: EMI, Record Services Distribution (Ireland)

Chapter House Choir

TEDDY BEAR'S PICNIC.
Tracks: / Teddy bears' picnic / Christopher Robin is saying his prayers / Lullaby of Birdland / Moon river / Bluebell polka / Sweet and low / Over the rainbow / Night and day / Shenandoah / I got shoes / Summertime / Radetzky march / Ev'ry time we say goodbye / Autumn leaves / Deep purple / Feller from fortune.
Album: released on Music From York in Jun'81. Distributed by: H.R. Taylor Distribution

Cassette: released on Music From York in Jun'81. Distributed by: H.R. Taylor Distribution

Characters

LOVE TALK.
Tracks: / Love talk / Where's all the love gone.
Single (7"): released on Characters in Oct'86. Distributed by: Big Ears Music Distribution

Charade

BREAK ME (Charade (Featuring Norma Lewis)).
Single (12"): released on Passion in Aug'84 by Skratch Records. Distributed by: PRT

GOT TO GET TO YOU.
Single (7"): released on Passion in Aug'83 by Skratch Records. Distributed by: PRT

Single (12"): released on Passion in Aug'83 by Skratch Records. Distributed by: PRT

Charge

DESTROY THE YOUTH (EP).
Single (7"): released on Kamera in Feb'82

FASHION/UGLY.
Single (7"): released on Kamera in May'82

LUXURY/MADMAN IN THE NORTH.
Single (7"): released on Kamera in Sep'82

PERFECTION.
Album: released on Kamera in '82

Charig, Marc

PIPEDREAM.
Album: released on Ogun in Sep'77. Distributed by: Jazz Music, Cadillac

Chariot

ALL ALONE AGAIN.
Single (12"): released on Shades in Mar'85. Distributed by: Pinnacle

BURNING AMBITION.
Album: released on Shades in Mar'86. Distributed by: Pinnacle

WARRIOR.
Album: released on Shades in Jul'84. Distributed by: Pinnacle

WARRIOR. THE.
Album: released on Mausoleum in Jun'85 by Mausoleum Records. Distributed by: Pinnacle

Charisma...

CHARISMA REPEAT PERFORMANCE (Various Artists).
Tracks: / Theme one / Lady Eleanor / Gaye / Sympathy / It's a game / Liar / America / I know what I like / I get a kick out of you / Spanish wine / Solsbury hill / It's all over now / Everyday / Reggae for it now.
Notes: Sampler. Artists recorded on Charisma label.
Album: released on Charisma in Sep'80 by Virgin Records. Distributed by: EMI

Cassette: released on Charisma in Sep'80 by Virgin Records. Distributed by: EMI

EVERYTHING IS FIN/EVERY DUB.
Single (12"): released on King & City in Sep'82. Distributed by: Jetstar

LOVE IS JUST AROUND THE CORNER.
Single (12"): released on MK in Aug'84

ONE FOR THE ROAD.
Album: released on SRT in Dec'76 by SRT Records. Distributed by: Pinnacle, Solomon & Peres Distribution, SRT Distribution, H.R. Taylor Distribution, PRT Distribution

OPEN UP THE DOOR/IT'S A SIN.
Single (12"): released on King & City in Feb'82. Distributed by: Jetstar

Single (12"): released on King & City in Feb'82. Distributed by: Jetstar

SOMETHING ABOUT YOU.
Single (12"): released on Neville King in Jan'85 by Neville King Records. Distributed by: Jetstar

Charjan, Papa

ONE SCOTCH, ONE LAGER, ONE BREW (Charjan, Papa & Jack Reuben).
Tracks: / One scotch, one lager, one brew / Moany, moany.
Single (7"): released on Shuttle in May'86. Distributed by: RCA

Single (12"): released on Shuttle in May'86. Distributed by: RCA

ONE SCOTCH, ONE TENNANTS, ONE BREW (Charjan, Papa & Jack Reuben).
Tracks: / One scotch, one tennants, one brew / One scotch, one lager, one brew / Moany, moany / Drinking spree.
Single (12"): released on Shuttle in Jun'86. Distributed by: RCA

Charlemagne Palestine

STRUMMING MUSIC.
Album: released on Shandar in Mar'78

Charlene

HIT AND RUN LOVER.
Album: released on Motown in Oct'84 by Motown Records. Distributed by: BMG Distribution

Cassette: released on Motown in Oct'84 by Motown Records. Distributed by: BMG Distribution

IF YOU TAKE AWAY THE PAIN UNTIL THE...
Single (7"): released on Motown in Aug'83 by Motown Records. Distributed by: BMG Distribution

IT AIN'T EASY COMIN' DOWN.
Single (7"): released on Motown in Aug'82 by Motown Records. Distributed by: BMG Distribution

I'VE NEVER BEEN TO ME.
Tracks: / I've never been to me / It ain't easy comin' down / Can't we try / Hungry / Hey mama / I won't remember ever loving you / Johnny doesn't live here anymore / After the ball / I need a man / If I could see myself.
Album: released on Motown in Jul'82 by Motown Records. Distributed by: BMG Distribution

Cassette: released on Motown in Jul'82 by Motown Records. Distributed by: BMG Distribution

I'VE NEVER BEEN TO ME/SOMEWHERE.
Album: released on Motown in Mar'82 by Motown Records. Distributed by: BMG Distribution

SKY IS THE LIMIT.
Tracks: / Sky is the limit / Living still goes on / Rise up / I want the world to know he's mine / There was nothing to believe in / Jesus is love / Prayer, The / You knew just what I needed / Cover me.
Album: released on Chapel Lane in Dec'83. Distributed by: RCA

Cassette: released on Chapel Lane in Dec'83. Distributed by: RCA

USED TO BE.
Tracks: / If you take away the pain until the morning / Used to be / Heaven help us all / I want to go back there again / Rainbows / Last song, The / Some things never change / Richie's song / You're home.
Album: released on Motown in Dec'82 by Motown Records. Distributed by: BMG Distribution

Cassette: released on Motown in Dec'82 by Motown Records. Distributed by: BMG Distribution

USED TO BE (see Wonder, Stevie) (Charlene & Stevie Wonder).

USED TO BE/I WANT TO COME (Charlene & Stevie Wonder).
Single (7"): released on Motown in Nov'82 by Motown Records. Distributed by: BMG Distribution

WE'RE BOTH IN LOVE WITH YOU.
Single (7"): released on Motown in Oct'84 by Motown Records. Distributed by: BMG Distribution

Charles, Alex

COME ON OVER.
Tracks: / Come on over / Come on over (version).
Single (12"): released on New York in 30 May'87 by New York Records. Distributed by: Jetstar

Single (7"): released on New York in Jul'87 by New York Records. Distributed by: Jetstar

Charles Augustus...

CHARLES AUGUSTUS MILVERTON (Various Artists).
Cassette: released on Anvil in Jan'81. Distributed by: Anvil

Charles, Bobby

BOBBY CHARLES.
Tracks: / Watch it sprocket / Yeah yeah / You know I love you / Good loving / I'd like to know / Ain't got no home / Time will tell / Take it easy greasy / You can suit yourself / See you later alligator / On bended knee / I'll turn square for you / Put your arms around me / I ain't gonna do it no more / Lonely street / Mr Moon / One eyed Jack / Hey good looking.
Album: released on Chess(USA) in Apr'83 by Sugar Hill (USA). Distributed by: PRT, Swift

Charles, C.August

GET UP GET WITH IT.
Tracks: / Getup get with it / Get up get with it (dub inst).
Single (7"): released on Champion in Mar'87 by Champion Records. Distributed by: RCA

Single (12"): released on Champion in Mar'87 by Champion Records. Distributed by: RCA

Charles, Clare

TOO MUCH.
Tracks: / One step closer / Too much.
Single (7"): released on IBE in Jan'87 by IBE Records. Distributed by: B & E Promotions

Charles, Evan

ASK YOURSELF.
Single (7"): released on Naive in Aug'82 by Naive. Distributed by: Spartan

INTIMACY.
Single (7"): released on Naive in May'83 by Naive. Distributed by: Spartan

Charles, Julie

AS LONG AS YOU LOVE ME.
Single (12"): released on Body Music in Jan'83 by Body Music Records. Distributed by: Jetstar

Charles, Kenny

TONGUE TIED.
Single (7"): released on MCA in Mar'86 by MCA Records. Distributed by: Polygram, MCA

Charles, Phil

JOKER, THE/DJ VERSION.
Single (7"): released on Fun in Sep'82 by Fun Records. Distributed by: Projection

Charles, Ray

1950.
Album: . Distributed by: Discovery, Jazz Music, PRT, Swift

20 GOLDEN PIECES OF....
Album: released on Bulldog in Jul'82 by Bulldog Records. Distributed by: President Distribution, Spartan, Swift, Taylor, H.R.

20 GREATEST HITS.
Album: released on Masters (Holland) in Jan'87

Cassette: released on Masters (Holland) in Jan'87

25TH ANNIVERSARY IN SHOW BUSINESS.
Album: by WEA Records. Distributed by: WEA

CAN'T STOP LOVING YOU.
Album: released on Platinum (W.Germany) in Oct'85. Distributed by: Mainline

Cassette: released on Platinum (W.Germany) in Oct'85. Distributed by: Mainline

C.C. RIDER.
Tracks: / C.C rider / I wonder who's kissing her now / Going down slow / Lovin' the girls / Kiss me baby / All alone / Sitting on top of the world / Tell me baby / Baby let me hold your hand / Hey now / All to myself alone / Walkin' & Talkin'.
Album: released on Premier in Jun'85 by Premier Records. Distributed by: CBS

Cassette: released on Premier in Jun'85 by Premier Records. Distributed by: CBS

COLLECTION: RAY CHARLES.
Album: released on Star Jazz USA in Apr'86 by Charly Records. Distributed by: Charly Distribution

Cassette: released on Star Jazz USA in Apr'86 by Charly Records. Distributed by: Charly Distribution

COME LIVE WITH ME.
Album: released on London in '74 by London Records. Distributed by: Polygram

COUNTRY SIDE OF RAY CHARLES, THE.
Album: released on Arcade Music Gala in Apr'86. Distributed by: Stage One

Cassette: released on Arcade Music Gala in Apr'86. Distributed by: Stage One

DO I EVER CROSS YOUR MIND.
Album: released on CBS in Jul'84 by CBS Records. Distributed by: CBS

Cassette: released on CBS in Jul'84 by CBS Records. Distributed by: CBS

EVERYTHING.
Tracks: / Kiss me baby / Sitting on top of the world / I'm gonna drown myself / All alone again / Lovin' the girls / I will not let you go / I'm glad for your sake / Walkin' and talkin'.
Album: released on Manhattan in Sep'80 by President Records. Distributed by: Jazz Music, Swift, Taylors, Chris Wellard

FANTASTIC RAY CHARLES, THE.
Double Album: released on Musidisc (France) in Mar'85. Distributed by: Discovery Distribution, Swift Distribution

FRIENDSHIP.
Tracks: / Two old cats like us / This old heart / We didn't see a thing / Who cares / Rock and roll shoes / Friendship / It ain't gonna worry my mind / Little hotel room / Crazy old soldier / Seven Spanish angels.
Album: released on CBS in Oct'84 by CBS Records. Distributed by: CBS

Cassette: released on CBS in Oct'84 by CBS Records. Distributed by: CBS

Album: released on Charly in Sep'83 by Charly Records. Distributed by: Charly, Cadillac

FROM THE PAGES OF MY MIND.
Tracks: / Pages of my mind, The / Slip away / Anybody with the blues / Class reunion / Caught a touch of your love / Little bit of heaven, A / Dixie moon / Over and over (again) / Beaucoup love / Love is worth the pain.
Album: released on CBS in Aug'86 by CBS Records. Distributed by: CBS

Cassette: released on CBS in Aug'86 by CBS Records. Distributed by: CBS

GOIN' DOWN SLOW.
Tracks: / Goin' down slow / Alone in the city / Now she's gone / Rockin' chair blues / Can anyone ask for more / Let's have a ball / This love of mine / Can't see you darling? / If I give you my love.
Album: released on Meteor in Jun'84 by Magnum Music Group Ltd. Distributed by: Magnum Music Group Ltd, PRT Distribution, Spartan Distribution

GREAT HITS.
Tracks: / Going down slow / All night long / I'm givin' up / Guitar blues / Talkin' 'bout you / I found my baby there / I'm wonderin' & wonderin' / By myself / Snowfall.
Album: released on Phoenix in '82 by Audio Fidelity Enterprises. Distributed by: Stage One, Lugtons

HERE AM I.
Tracks: / Easy riding gal / Tapeworld / Ray's blues / Here am I / Blow my baby back home / Blues is my middle name.
Album: released on Barclay (Import) in Apr'83

Cassette: released on Barclay (Import) in Apr'83

HIT THE ROAD JACK.
Album: released on Platinum (W.Germany) in Oct'85. Distributed by: Mainline

Cassette: released on Platinum (W.Germany) in Oct'85. Distributed by: Mainline

I CAN'T STOP LOVING YOU.
Tracks: / Hit the road Jack / Hallelujah I love her so / Mess around / Let's go get stoned / Don't let the sun catch you cryin' / What'd I say / Georgia on my mind / I got a woman / Drown in my own tears / Night time is the right time / Eleanor Rigby / I can't stop loving you.
Album: released on Picture Disc in Sep'80. Distributed by: Jazz Music

IF I GIVE YOU MY LOVE.
Tracks: / Alone in the city / Can anyone ask for more / Rocking chair blues / Let's have a ball / If I give you my love / Can't see you darling? / This love of mine / Sentimental blues, A / Now she's gone / Going down slow.
Album: released on IMS(Import) in Oct'82 by Polydor Records. Distributed by: IMS, Polygram

Cassette: released on IMS(Import) in Oct'82 by Polydor Records. Distributed by: IMS, Polygram

I WISH YOU WERE HERE TONIGHT.
Single (7"): released on CBS in May'83 by CBS Records. Distributed by: CBS

I WONDER WHO'S KISSING HER NOW.
Tracks: / I wonder who's kissing her now / She's on the ball / Baby won't you please come home.
Single (12"): released on Charly in Feb'87 by Charly Records. Distributed by: Charly, Cadillac

JAMMIN' THE BLUES.
Album: released on Astan in Nov'84 by Astan Records. Distributed by: Counterpoint

Cassette: released on Astan in Nov'84 by Astan Records. Distributed by: Counterpoint

KING OF THE BLUES.
Cassette: released on Ampro Cassettes in May'79

Cassette: released on Ampro Cassettes in Sep'81

RAY CHARLES.
Cassette: released on Pickwick in Sep'80 by Pickwick Records. Distributed by: Pickwick Distribution, Prism Leisure Distribution, Lugtons

Cassette: released on Audio Fidelity in Oct'84. Distributed by: PRT

RAY CHARLES BLUES.
Album: released on Astan in Nov'84 by Astan Records. Distributed by: Counterpoint

Cassette: released on Astan in Nov'84 by Astan Records. Distributed by: Counterpoint

RAY CHARLES (CD).
Compact disc: released on Deja Vu in Jul'87 by Deja Vu Records. Distributed by: Counterpoint Distribution, Record Services Distribution (Ireland)

RAY CHARLES COLLECTION, THE.
Album: released on Deja Vu in Aug'85 by Deja Vu Records. Distributed by: Counterpoint Distribution, Record Services Distribution (Ireland)

Cassette: released on Deja Vu in Aug'85 by Deja Vu Records. Distributed by: Counterpoint Distribution, Record Services Distribution (Ireland)

RAY CHARLES VOL.2.
Tracks: / Alone in the city / Can anyone ask for more / Rocking chair blues / Let's have a ball / If I give you my love / Can't see you darling? / This love of mine / Sentimental blues, A / Now she's gone / Going down slow.
Album: released on Joker in Apr'81. Distributed by: Counterpoint, Mainline, Record Services Distribution (Ireland)

RAY OF HOPE.
Album: released on Manhattan in Aug'80 by President Records. Distributed by: Jazz Music, Swift, Taylors, Chris Wellard

RIGHT TIME,THE.
Album: released on Atlantic in 30 May'87 by WEA Records. Distributed by: WEA

Cassette: released on Atlantic in 30 May'87 by WEA Records. Distributed by: WEA

Compact disc: released on Atlantic in Jul'87 by WEA Records. Distributed by: WEA

RIGHT TIME, THE.
Tracks: / Leave my woman alone / My Bonnie / That's enough / Drown in my own tears / Fool for you, A / Hallelujah I love her so / This little girl of mine / Mary Ann / I got a woman / Yes indeed / Swanee river rock / Lonely avenue / I had a dream / Early in the mornin' / Right time, The / I'm moving on / What kind of man are you / I want to know / What'd I say part 1 / What'd I say part II / Jumpin' in the mornin'.
Album: released on Atlantic in Jul'87 by WEA Records. Distributed by: WEA

Cassette: released on Atlantic in Jul'87 by WEA Records. Distributed by: WEA

Compact disc: released on Atlantic in Jul'87 by WEA Records. Distributed by: WEA

SEE SEE RIDER.
Album: released on Premier in Dec'84 by Premier Records. Distributed by: CBS

Cassette: released on Premier in Dec'84 by Premier Records. Distributed by: CBS

SIMPLY RAY.
Album: released on Manhattan in May'80 by President Records. Distributed by: Jazz Music, Swift, Taylors, Chris Wellard

SOUL MEETING (Charles, Ray & Milt Jackson).
Tracks: / Hallelujah I love her so / Blue genius / X-ray blues / Soul meeting / Love on my mind / Bags of blues.
Album: released on Atlantic in Jul'76 by WEA Records. Distributed by: WEA

SPIRIT OF CHRISTMAS, THE.
Cassette: released on CBS in Dec'85 by CBS Records. Distributed by: CBS

Album: released on CBS in Dec'85 by CBS Records. Distributed by: CBS Deleted '87.

TELL THE TRUTH.
Album: released on Charly(R&B) in Mar'84 by Charly Records. Distributed by: Charly, Cadillac

Cassette: released on Charly(R&B) in Mar'84 by Charly Records. Distributed by: Charly, Cadillac

THIS LOVE OF MINE.
Tracks: / Kiss me baby / Baby let me hold your hand / C. C. Rider / I wonder who's kissing her now / I'm going down to the river / They're crazy about me / Goin' down slow / Sentimental blues, A / Can anyone ask for more / Rocking chair blues / If I give you my love / This love of mine.
Compact disc: released on Topline in Apr'87 by Charly Records. Distributed by: Charly Distribution

Album: released on Topline in '86 by Charly Records. Distributed by: Charly Distribution

Cassette: released on Topline in '86 by Charly Records. Distributed by: Charly Distribution

TRUE TO LIFE.
Album: released on London in Jan'78 by London Records. Distributed by: Polygram

WHAT IS LIFE.
Album: released on Barclay (Import) in Apr'83

Cassette: released on Barclay (Import) in Apr'83

WISH YOU HERE HERE TONIGHT.
Album: released on CBS in Mar'83 by CBS Records. Distributed by: CBS

Cassette: released on CBS in Mar'83 by CBS Records. Distributed by: CBS Deleted '85.

Charles, Ronnie

HANDS OFF.
Album: released on Telaeg in May'84 by Telaeg Records. Distributed by: Gipsy Distribution, CBS Distribution

Charles, Tina

DANCE LITTLE LADY DANCE.
Cassette: released on RCA/Camden in Apr'81

Album: released on Hallmark in Apr'81 by Pickwick Records. Distributed by: Pickwick Distribution, PRT, Taylors

Album: released on CBS in Nov'76 by CBS Records. Distributed by: CBS

HEART'N'SOUL.
Album: released on CBS in Sep'77 by CBS Records. Distributed by: CBS

I LOVE TO LOVE.
Tracks: / I love to love (teenage mix) / Biddu Orchestra, The.
Single (7"): released on Disco Mix in Aug'86 by DMS Records. Distributed by: DMS

Single (12"): released on Disco Mix in Aug'86 by DMS Records. Distributed by: DMS

Single (12"): released on Disco Mix in Aug'86 by DMS Records. Distributed by: DMS

Single (7"): released on CBS in Apr'82 by CBS Records. Distributed by: CBS

Single (7"): released on Old Gold in Jul'82 by Old Gold Records. Distributed by: Lightning, Jazz Music, Spartan, Counterpoint

Album: released on CBS in Mar'76 by CBS Records. Distributed by: CBS

Single (7"): released on DMC in Aug'87. Distributed by: Red Rhino, Cartel

Single (12"): released on DMC in Aug'87. Distributed by: Red Rhino, Cartel

LOVE HUNGER.
Single (7"): released on Sonet in Feb'85 by Sonet Records. Distributed by: PRT

Single (12"): released on Sonet in Feb'85 by Sonet Records. Distributed by: PRT

RUNNING INTO DANGER.
Single (7"): released on Sonet in Sep'85 by Sonet Records. Distributed by: PRT

Single (12"): released on Sonet in Sep'85 by Sonet Records. Distributed by: PRT

SECOND TIME AROUND.
Tracks: / Second time around / Played for a fool.
Single (7"): released on Sonet in Sep'86 by Sonet Records. Distributed by: PRT

TINA SINGS.
Album: released on M.A.M. in Apr'77 by M.A.M. Records. Distributed by: T.B.C

Charleston Chasers

CHARLESTON CHASERS 1925/28.
Album: released on VJM in Apr'79 by Wellard, Chris Distribution. Distributed by: Wellard, Chris Distribution

CHARLESTON CHASERS 1929/31.
Album: released on VJM in Apr'79 by Wellard, Chris Distribution. Distributed by: Wellard, Chris Distribution

Charleston Days

CHARLESTON DAYS 1923-29 Various artists (Various Artists).
Album: released on Pearl in Mar'83 by Pavilion (USA). Distributed by: Taylors, Swift

Charlie

GERMAN PROPAGANDA SWING:1940-1941 VOL.1 (Charlie & His Orchestra).
Tracks: / Stormy weather / It's a long way to Tipperary / You're driving me crazy / You can't stop me from dreaming / With a smile and a song / St. Louis blues / Slumming on Park Avenue / Adieu mon pere / Dinah / Daisy / I'm playing with fire / Goody goody / F.D.R. Jones / After you've gone / Who'll buy my bublitchky / Sketch uber das abhorverbot auslandischer sender.
Notes: This is the first of four albums in which German propoganda in World War II isinvestigated in depth, concentrating on the swing band arrangements of Charlie(Karl Schedler) & His Orchestra. Often these open with lyrics sung "straight",part-way through becoming anti-American or anti-British, with anti-"Winnie" oranti-"Frankie" lyrics. Often titles are played quite straight, with no specificpropoganda use. These are very rare recordings; their possession after 1945 in the Russian sector carried the death sentence.
Album: released on Harlequin in Aug'87 by Harlequin Records. Distributed by: Swift, Jazz Music, Wellard, Chris, IRS, Taylor, H.R.

GOOD MORNING AMERICA.
Album: released on RCA in Sep'81 by RCA Records. Distributed by: RCA, Roots, Swift, Wellard, Chris, I & B, Solomon & Peres Distribution

Cassette: released on RCA in Sep'81 by RCA Records. Distributed by: RCA, Roots, Swift, Wellard, Chris, I & B, Solomon & Peres Distribution

HERE COMES TROUBLE.
Album: released on Polydor in Mar'82 by Polydor Records. Distributed by: Polygram, Polydor

LINES.
Album: by Polydor Records. Distributed by: Polygram, Polydor

OUR EARTH.
Single (7"): released on President in Feb'83 by President Records. Distributed by: Taylors, Spartan

Charlie Girl

CHARLIE GIRL New London Cast Recording (Defilm).
Album: released on First Night in Jul'87 by Safari Records. Distributed by: Pinnacle

Cassette: released on First Night in Jul'87 by Safari Records. Distributed by: Pinnacle

Charlie's Brothers

WISHING TREE.
Single (7"): released on Lost Moments in Mar'85. Distributed by: Backs, Cartel

Single (12"): released on Lost Moments in Mar'85. Distributed by: Backs, Cartel

Charlie & Sgt.Pepper

GIRL IS MINE.
Single (12"): released on Holly Cone in Apr'83 by Ariwa Records. Distributed by: Jetstar, Rough Trade

Charlie & The Chocolate..

CHARLIE & THE CHOCOLATE FACTORY Roald Dahl (Dahl, Roald).
Cassette: released on Listen For Pleasure in Sep'82 by MFP Records. Distributed by: EMI

Charlotte

PICTURE OF A CLOWN.
Single (12"): released on Tropical Sunset in Jun'85 by Tropical Sunset Records. Distributed by: Jetstar

Charlton, George

STRICTLY FOR DANCING (Charlton, George & Peter Scatter).
Album: released on MWM in Jun'82 by Mawson & Wareham. Distributed by: Spartan Distribution, Jazz Music Distribution,

Charly...

CHARLY BLACK MUSIC SAMPLER Various artists (Various Artists).

CHARLY DANCE PARTY Harious artists (Various Artists).
Tracks: / Let's go, let's go, let's go / Shake your moneymaker / I'm gonna love you / Stormy weather / Rebound / Surely I love you / Feelin' good / Look out Mabel / Convention, The / She's the most / Sapphire / I wanna know / Wildcat tamer / Black diamond / Breaking up the house.
Album: released on Charly in Oct'86 by Charly Records. Distributed by: Charly, Cadillac

CHARLY R & B PARTY (Various Artists).
Tracks: / Barefootin' / Ride your pony / Picking wild mountain berries / Neighbour neighbour / I stand accused / Shame, shame, shame / If you gotta make a fool of somebody / Let's stick together / It's alright / Hey girl don't bother me / Tell it like it is / Get out of my life woman / Boom boom / Dust my broom / Nothing can stop me / It's in his kiss.
Album: released on Charly in Jun'85 by Charly Records. Distributed by: Charly, Cadillac

Cassette: released on Charly in Jun'85 by Charly Records. Distributed by: Charly, Cadillac

CHARLY R&B SAMPLER This is Charly Blues (Various Artists).
Album: released on Charly in Aug'87 by Charly Records. Distributed by: Charly, Cadillac

Cassette: released on Charly in Aug'87 by Charly Records. Distributed by: Charly, Cadillac

CHARLY R&B SAMPLER-THIS IS CHARLY SOUL Various Artists (Various Artists).
Album: released on Charly in Aug'87 by Charly Records. Distributed by: Charly, Cadillac

Cassette: released on Charly in Aug'87 by Charly Records. Distributed by: Charly, Cadillac

Charly's Angels

CHARLY'S ANGELS Various artists (Various Artists).
Album: released on Charly in Sep'78 by Charly Records. Distributed by: Charly, Cadillac

Charme

GEORGY PORGY.
Single (7"): released on RCA in Nov'84 by RCA Records. Distributed by: RCA, Roots, Swift, Wellard, Chris, I & B, Solomon & Peres Distribution

Charmers, Lloyd

GREATEST INSPIRATION.
Single (12"): released on Sarge in Apr'83 by Sarge Records. Distributed by: Jetstar

OH ME, OH LADY.
Tracks: / Oh me, oh lady / Colour him father.
Single (12"): released on Charmers in Sep'86. Distributed by: Jetstar

Charms

I CAN'T LET GO.
Tracks: / I can't let go / One step closer.
Single (7"): released on WEA Int in Apr'87

Single (12"): released on WEA Int in Apr'87

Charm School

DANCER / PULLING ME UNDER.
Single (7"): released on WEA in Aug'87 by WEA Records. Distributed by: WEA

Single (12"): released on WEA in Aug'87 by WEA Records. Distributed by: WEA

KARMA CHAMELEON.
Cassette: released on Chevron in Nov'84. Distributed by: Multiple Sound Distributors

LIFE'S A DECEIVER.
Single (7"): released on Zarjazz in Mar'85 by Virgin. Distributed by: EMI

Single (12"): released on Zarjazz in Mar'85 by Virgin. Distributed by: EMI

SUN.
Single (7"): released on Button in Jan'84 by Musical Characters Records. Distributed by: Spartan

Charney, Marlene Roots

IT'S TOO LATE.
Single (12"): released on Esso Jaxxon in Jul'85 by Esso Jaxxon. Distributed by: Jetstar

Charon

CHARON.
Album: released on Heavy Metal Worldwide in Sep'84 by FM-Revolver Records. Distributed by: EMI

Charquet & Co

DANS LES JUNGLES DU POITOU.
Album: released on Pragmaphone in Aug'77. Distributed by: Cadillac

LIVE AT THE JOSEPH LAM JAZZ CLUB.
Album: released on Stomp Off in Jan'84 by Stomp Off Records. Distributed by: Jazz Music Distribution

VOLUME 3.
Album: released on Stomp Off in Jun'86 by Stomp Off Records. Distributed by: Jazz Music Distribution

VOLUME 4.
Album: released on Stomp Off in Jun'86 by Stomp Off Records. Distributed by: Jazz Music Distribution

Chart

CHART.
Single (7"): released on The Chart in Sep'84 by Chart Records. Distributed by: Pinnacle

Chart Action

CHART ACTION 1 Various original artists (Various Artists).
Boxed set: released on Pickwick in Jun'82 by Pickwick Records. Distributed by: Pickwick Distribution, Prism Leisure Distribution,

Cassette: released on Pickwick in Jun'82 by Pickwick Records. Distributed by: Pickwick Distribution, Prism Leisure Distribution,

CHART ACTION 2 Various original artists (Various Artists).
Tracks: / Fame / Use it up wear it out / Funky town / Good thing going / Hi fidelity / Shirley / Instant replay / Rabbit / I don't like Mondays / Einstein a go go / Never knew love like this before / Going back to my roots / Love come down / Thunder in the mountains / Oh Julie / Wedding bells / I only want to be with you / Danger games / I want to be free / Waiting for an alibi / This ole house / Don't leave me this way / Inside out / Every day hurts / Land of make believe / Don't stop the music / Night birds / Everlasting love / Hold on to my love / You're looking for a way out / Ain't no pleasing you / Shuffle, The.
Boxed set: released on Pickwick in Jul'83 by Pickwick Records. Distributed by: Pickwick Distribution, Prism Leisure Distribution

Cassette: released on Pickwick in Jul'83 by Pickwick Records. Distributed by: Pickwick Distribution, Prism Leisure Distribution

CHART ACTION 3 Various original artists (Various Artists).

Chart Attack

CHART ATTACK Various original artists (Various Artists).
Album: released on Telstar in Sep'82 by Telstar Records. Distributed by: RCA Distribution

Cassette: released on Telstar in Sep'82 by Telstar Records. Distributed by: RCA Distribution

Chart Beat, Chart Heat

CHART BEAT, CHART HEAT Various original artists (Various Artists).
Double Album: released on K-Tel in Sep'82 by K-Tel Records. Distributed by: Record Merchandisers Distribution, Taylors, Terry Blood Distribution, Wynd-Up Distribution, Relay Distribution, Pickwick Distribution, Solomon & Peres Distribution, Polygram

Double cassette: released on K-Tel in Sep'82 by K-Tel Records. Distributed by: Record Merchandisers Distribution, Taylors, Terry Blood Distribution, Wynd-Up Distribution, Relay Distribution, Pickwick Distribution, Solomon & Peres Distribution, Polygram

Chartbusters

CHARTBUSTERS (Various Artists).
Album: released on Cambra in Aug'86 by Cambra Records. Distributed by: IDS, Conifer

Album: released on Here & Now in Jan'86. Distributed by: Spartan

Cassette: released on Here & Now in Jan'86. Distributed by: Spartan

CHARTBUSTERS VOL. 1 Various artists (Various Artists).
Double Album: released on Cambra in Dec'81 by Cambra Records. Distributed by: IDS, Conifer

Double cassette: released on Cambra in Dec'81 by Cambra Records. Distributed by: IDS, Conifer

CHARTBUSTERS - VOL.2 (Various Artists).
Album: released on Here & Now in Apr'86. Distributed by: Spartan

Cassette: released on Here & Now in Apr'86. Distributed by: Spartan

Chart Encounters...

CHART ENCOUNTERS OF THE HIT KIND Various original artists (Various Artists).
Album: released on Ronco in May'83

Cassette: released on Ronco in May'83

Charters, Ann

SCOTT JOPLIN & HIS FRIENDS.
Album: released on Sonet in '76 by Sonet Records. Distributed by: PRT

Chart Explosion

CHART EXPLOSION Various original artists (Various Artists).
Album: released on K-Tel in Oct'80 by K-Tel Records. Distributed by: Record Merchandisers Distribution, Taylors, Terry Blood Distribution, Wynd-Up Distribution, Relay Distribution, Pickwick Distribution, Solomon & Peres Distribution, Polygram

Chart Hits

CHART HITS 81 VOL.1&2 Various original artists (Various Artists).
Double Album: released on K-Tel in Nov'81 by K-Tel Records. Distributed by: Record Merchandisers Distribution, Taylors, Terry Blood Distribution, Wynd-Up Distribution, Relay Distribution, Pickwick Distribution, Solomon & Peres Distribution, Polygram

Double cassette: released on K-Tel in Nov'81 by K-Tel Records. Distributed by: Record Merchandisers Distribution, Taylors, Terry Blood Distribution, Wynd-Up Distribution, Relay Distribution, Pickwick Distribution, Solomon & Peres Distribution, Polygram

CHART HITS 82 Various original artists (Various Artists).
Double Album: released on K-Tel in Nov'82 by K-Tel Records. Distributed by: Record Merchandisers Distribution, Taylors, Terry Blood Distribution, Wynd-Up Distribution, Relay Distribution, Pickwick Distribution, Solomon & Peres Distribution, Polygram

CHART HITS 83 Various original artists (Various Artists).
Double Album: released on K-Tel in Nov'83 by K-Tel Records. Distributed by: Record Merchandisers Distribution, Taylors, Terry Blood Distribution, Wynd-Up Distribution, Relay Distribution, Pickwick Distribution, Solomon & Peres Distribution, Polygram

Double cassette: released on K-Tel in Nov'83 by K-Tel Records. Distributed by: Record Merchandisers Distribution, Taylors, Terry Blood Distribution, Wynd-Up Distribution, Relay Distribution, Pickwick Distribution, Solomon & Peres Distribution, Polygram

Chart Runners

CHART RUNNERS Various original artists (Various Artists).
Album: released on Ronco in Mar'83

Cassette: released on Ronco in Mar'83

Chart Stars

CHART STARS Various original artists (Various Artists).
Album: released on K-Tel in Jun'83 by K-Tel Records. Distributed by: Record Merchandisers Distribution, Taylors, Terry Blood Distribution, Wynd-Up Distribution, Relay Distribution, Pickwick Distribution, Solomon & Peres Distribution, Polygram

Cassette: released on K-Tel in Jun'83 by K-Tel Records. Distributed by: Record Merchandisers Distribution, Taylors, Terry Blood Distribution, Wynd-Up Distribution, Relay Distribution, Pickwick Distribution, Solomon & Peres Distribution, Polygram

Chart, The

CHART, THE.
Double Album: released on Telstar in Oct'86 by Telstar Records. Distributed by: RCA Distribution

Double cassette: released on Telstar in Oct'86 by Telstar Records. Distributed by: RCA Distribution

Chart Tracking

CHART TRACKING-THE HIT SQUAD Various original artists (Various Artists).
Album: released on Ronco in Sep'83

Cassette: released on Ronco in Sep'83

Chart Wars

CHART WARS Various original artists (Various Artists).
Album: released on Ronco in Nov'82

Cassette: released on Ronco in Nov'82

Chas

FOR YOUR LOVE.
Tracks: / For your love / Just say you will.
Single (12"): released on Expansion in Oct'86. Distributed by: PRT

Chasar

CHASAR.
Album: released on APK in Mar'85. Distributed by: Pinnacle

Chas & Dave

AIN'T NO PLEASING YOU.
Single (7"): released on Rockney in Feb'82 by Rockney Records. Distributed by: EMI

BEER BARREL BANJOS(ROLL OUT THE BARRELS).
Single (7"): released on Rockney in Jul'83 by Rockney Records. Distributed by: EMI

BUDDY (Chas & Dave/Mike Berry).
Cassette: released on Autograph in Apr'85. Distributed by: Record Services Distribution (Ireland)

CHAS AND DAVE'S CHRISTMAS CAROL ALBUM.
Album: released on Telstar in Nov'86 by Telstar Records. Distributed by: RCA Distribution

Cassette: released on Telstar in Nov'86 by Telstar Records. Distributed by: RCA Distribution

CHAS & DAVE.
Tracks: / Ponders end allotments club / Better get your shoes on / Dry Party / Ballad of the rich / Deceived / One fing'n'anuvver / It's so very hard / Woortcha / I am a rocker / Old time song / Old dog and me / Gertcha / Rabbit / Banging in your head, the / Got my beer in the sideboard here / What a miserable Saturday night / Pay up and look big / Lunatic asylum / Who d'ya think you're talking to? / I am a rocker (live version) / Scruffy old !"?!!"? / I go ape.
Notes: (P) Original sound recordings made by EMI Records Ltd.
Double Album: released on Music For Pleasure in Sep'86 by EMI Records. Distributed by: EMI

Double cassette: released on Music For Pleasure in Sep'86 by EMI Records. Distributed by: EMI

CHAS & DAVES CHRISTMAS JAMBOREE BAG NUMBER 1.
Album: released on Rockney in Nov'84 by Rockney Records. Distributed by: EMI

Cassette: released on Rockney in Nov'84 by Rockney Records. Distributed by: EMI

CHAS & DAVE'S KNEES UP.
Album: released on Rockney in Sep'83 by Rockney Records. Distributed by: EMI

Cassette: released on Rockney in Sep'83 by Rockney Records. Distributed by: EMI

CHRISTMAS JAMBOREE BAG.
Tracks: / Stars over 45 / Rabbit / Laughing policeman / Somebody stole my gal / Fall in and follow me / Are you from Dixie? / Margie / Where did you get that hat / Who were you with last night? / Swanee / Sideboard song, The / Baby face.
Album: released on Warwick in Nov'84. Distributed by: Multiple Sound Distributors

Cassette: released on Warwick in Nov'84. Distributed by: Multiple Sound Distributors

GERTCHA.
Album: released on Music For Pleasure (Holland) in Nov'83 by EMI Records. Distributed by: EMI

Cassette: released on Music For Pleasure (Holland) in Nov'83 by EMI Records. Distributed by: EMI

GREATEST HITS:CHAS & DAVE.
Album: released on Rockney in Nov'84 by Rockney Records. Distributed by: EMI

Cassette: released on Rockney in Nov'84 by Rockney Records. Distributed by: EMI

HALLEY'S COMET.
Tracks: / Halley's comet / Brother-in-law.
Single (7"): released on Rockney in Jul'86 by Rockney Records. Distributed by: EMI

HARRY WAS A CHAMPION.
Single (7"): released on Rockney in Nov'84 by Rockney Records. Distributed by: EMI

IN SICKNESS & IN HEALTH.
Single (7"): released on BBC in Sep'85 by BBC Records & Tapes. Distributed by: EMI, PRT,

I WONDER IN WHOSE ARMS.
Single (7"): released on Rockney in Sep'84 by Rockney Records. Distributed by: EMI

JAMBOREE BAG NUMBER 3.
Album: released on Rockney in Oct'85 by Rockney Records. Distributed by: EMI

Cassette: released on Rockney in Oct'85 by Rockney Records. Distributed by: EMI

JOB LOT.
Album: released on Rockney in Oct'82 by Rockney Records. Distributed by: EMI

Cassette: released on Rockney in Oct'82 by Rockney Records. Distributed by: EMI

LONDON GIRLS.
Single (7"): released on Rockney in Feb'83 by Rockney Records. Distributed by: EMI

LONG LONG AGO.
Tracks: / Silent night.
Single (7"): released on Hodgecock Productions in Nov'86. Distributed by: DMS, RCA

LOVE SONG.
Single (7"): released on Rockney in Oct'82 by Rockney Records. Distributed by: EMI

MARGATE.
Single (7"): released on Rockney in Jun'82 by Rockney Records. Distributed by: EMI

MY MELANCHOLY BABY.
Single (7"): released on Rockney in Nov'83 by Rockney Records. Distributed by: EMI

OILY RAGS.
Tracks: / Come up and see me anytime / Boiled beef and carrots / Time to kill / Baby doll / Holy cow / Silver dollar / Mailman bring me no more blues / Barefoot days / Jody and the kid / Country boy picker.
Album: released on Signature in Oct'85 by PRT Records. Distributed by: PRT

Cassette: released on Signature in Oct'85 by PRT Records. Distributed by: PRT

ON THE ROAD (LIVE).
Album: released on Rockney in Oct'86 by Rockney Records. Distributed by: EMI

Cassette: released on Rockney in Oct'86 by Rockney Records. Distributed by: EMI

POOR OLD MR.WOOGIE.
Single (7"): released on Rockney in Feb'81 by Rockney Records. Distributed by: EMI

RABBIT.
Single (7"): released on Rockney in Nov'80 by Rockney Records. Distributed by: EMI

ROCKNEY.
Cassette: released on EMI in '78 by EMI Records. Distributed by: EMI

ROCK'N'ROLL JAMBOREE MEDLEY.
Single (7"): released on Rockney in Nov'85 by Rockney Records. Distributed by: EMI

Single (12"): released on Rockney in Nov'85 by Rockney Records. Distributed by: EMI

ROMFORD RAP (Chas & Dave With The Matchroom Mob).
Tracks: / Romford Rap, The / Crackerjack theme.
Single (7"): released on Rainbow in Mar'87. Distributed by: I & B, CBS

STARS OVER 45.
Single (7"): released on Rockney in Nov'81 by Rockney Records. Distributed by: EMI

THERE IN YOUR EYES.
Single (7"): released on Rockney in Aug'84 by Rockney Records. Distributed by: EMI

TURN THAT NOISE DOWN.
Single (7"): released on Rockney in Aug'81 by Rockney Records. Distributed by: EMI

Single (12"): released on Rockney in Aug'81 by Rockney Records. Distributed by: EMI

WELL PLEASED.
Album: released on Rockney in Jul'84 by Rockney Records. Distributed by: EMI

Cassette: released on Rockney in Jul'84 by Rockney Records. Distributed by: EMI

YOU'RE JUST IN LOVE.
Tracks: / You're just in love / That's what I like.
Single (7"): released on Rockney in Jan'86 by Rockney Records. Distributed by: EMI

Chase

EVENSONG.
Single (7"): released on Corduroy Mouse Wax Co. in Mar'84. Distributed by: Pinnacle

Chase, Tommy

DRIVE.
Album: released on Palladin in May'85 by Palladin Records. Distributed by: Cartel

GROOVE MERCHANT.
Notes: Hard driving bop drummer, as seen on Channel 4. Extra track on cassette.
Compact disc: released on Stiff in Jun'87 by Stiff Records. Distributed by: EMI, Record Services Distribution (Ireland)

Album: released on Stiff in Jun'87 by Stiff Records. Distributed by: EMI, Record Services Distribution (Ireland)

Cassette: released on Stiff in Jun'87 by Stiff Records. Distributed by: EMI, Record Services Distribution (Ireland)

HARD (Chase, Tommy Quartet).
Tracks: / Minority / Blue sunset / Message, The / Del Sasser / No problem / Ladybirds.
Album: released on Boplicity in 3 Feb'84 by Boplicity Records. Distributed by: Ace Records, Pinnacle

KILLER JOE (RIGHT CROSS).
Tracks: / Killer Joe (right cross) / Double street.
Single (7"): released on Stiff in Feb'87 by Stiff Records. Distributed by: EMI, Record Services Distribution (Ireland)

Single (12"): released on Stiff in Feb'87 by Stiff Records. Distributed by: EMI, Record Services Distribution (Ireland)

ONE WAY (Chase, Tommy & Ray Warleigh 4(feat.Jon Eardley)).
Tracks: / I remember you / Stars fell on Alabama / Speak low / Like someone in love / Chasin' the Bimpt / What's new?.
Album: released on Spotlite in '83 by Spotlite Records. Distributed by: Cadillac, Jazz Music, Spotlite

TOMMY CHASE & RAY WARLEIGH QUARTET (Chase, Tommy & Ray Warleigh Quartet).
Tracks: / I remember you / Stars fell on Alabama / Speak low / Chasin' the Bimpt / Like someone in love / What's new?.
Album: released on Spotlite in Mar'79 by Spotlite Records. Distributed by: Cadillac, Jazz Music, Spotlite

Chastain

7TH OF NEVER, THE.
Album: released on Black Dragon in Jul'87 by Black Dragon Records. Distributed by: Rough Trade

MYSTERY OF ILLUSION.
Album: released on Roadrunner (Dutch) in Oct'85. Distributed by: Pinnacle

RULER OF THE WASTELAND.
Album: released on Roadrunner (Dutch) in Oct'86. Distributed by: Pinnacle

WORLD GONE MAD (Chastain's, David T 'CJSS').
Album: released on Black Dragon in Feb'86 by Black Dragon Records. Distributed by: Rough Trade

Chateau Vallon

CHATEAU VALLON (Various Artists).
Album: released on Carrere in Feb'87 by Carrere Records. Distributed by: PRT, Spartan

Cassette: released on Carrere in Feb'87 by Carrere Records. Distributed by: PRT, Spartan

Chateaux

CHAINED & DESPERATE.
Album: released on Ebony in Nov'83 by Ebony Records. Distributed by: Pinnacle, Ebony

FIRE POWER.
Album: released on Ebony in Jun'84 by Ebony Records. Distributed by: Pinnacle, Ebony

HIGHLY STRUNG.
Album: released on Ebony in Jul'85 by Ebony Records. Distributed by: Pinnacle, Ebony

Chatmon, Sam

SAM CHATMON.
Album: released on Rounder in Sep'79. Distributed by: Roots Distribution

Chat Show

KINGS OF CONFUSION.
Tracks: / Kings of Confusion / Reach.
Single (7"): released on Federation in Jun'87 by Federation Records. Distributed by: Red Rhino, Cartel

Single (12"): released on Federation in Jun'87 by Federation Records. Distributed by: Red Rhino, Cartel

RED SKIES.
Single (12"): released on Tanz in Apr'86. Distributed by: Red Rhino Distribution, Cartel Distribution

SHAKE IT DOWN.
Single (12"): released on Federation in Dec'86 by Federation Records. Distributed by: Red Rhino, Cartel

Chatton

PLAYING FOR TIME.
Album: released on RCA in Sep'81 by RCA Records. Distributed by: RCA, Roots, Swift, Wellard, Chris, I & B, Solomon & Peres Distribution

Cassette: released on RCA in Sep'81 by RCA Records. Distributed by: RCA, Roots, Swift, Wellard, Chris, I & B, Solomon & Peres Distribution

Chaucer, Geoffrey

WIFE OF BATH'S TALE (read by Prunella Scales & Richard Bebb).
Double cassette: released on Argo (Spokenword) in Jul'82 by Decca Records. Distributed by: Polygram

Chavis, Boozoo

BOOZOO ZYDECO.
Album: . Distributed by: Swift

PAPER IN MY SHOE.
Album: released on Ace in Apr'87 by Ace Records. Distributed by: Pinnacle, Swift, Hotshot, Cadillac

Chazer

PRACTISE MAKES PERFECT.
Single (7"): released on Polo in Jan'84 by Polo Records. Distributed by: PRT

Single (12"): released on Polo in Jan'84 by Polo Records. Distributed by: PRT

Che

WHAT YOU'VE BEEN THROUGH IS LOVE(SCREAM LIKE A SWIFT).
Single (7"): released on Desire in Jan'84 by Desire Records. Distributed by: Pinnacle

Single (12"): released on Desire in Jan'84 by Desire Records. Distributed by: Pinnacle

Cheap Frills

ALMOST AWAKE.
Single (7"): released on Mongrel in Aug'84 by Mongrel Records. Distributed by: ILA Distribution

Cheap In August

CHEAP IN AUGUST Greene,Graham (Burden, Hugh).
Cassette: released on Talking Tape in '84

Cheap Trick

AT THE BUDOKAN.
Tracks: / Hello there / Come on, come on / Lookout / Big eyes / Need your love / Ain't that a shame / I want you to want me / Surrender / Goodnight now / Clock strikes ten.
Notes: Recorded live at the Budokan.
Album: released on Epic in Feb'79 by CBS Records. Distributed by: CBS

CHEAP TRICK.
Album: released on Epic in Nov'81 by CBS Records. Distributed by: CBS Deleted '83.

Cassette: released on Epic in Nov'81 by CBS Records. Distributed by: CBS

DOCTOR (THE).
Tracks: / It's up to you / Rearview mirror romance / Doctor, The / Are you lonely tonight / Name of the game / Kiss me red / Good girls go to heaven (bad girls go everywhere) / Man-u-lip-u-lator / It's only love.
Compact disc: released on Epic in May'87 by CBS Records. Distributed by: CBS

IN COLOR.
Cassette: released on Epic in Nov'77 by CBS Records. Distributed by: CBS

NEXT POSITION.
Album: released on Epic in Oct'83 by CBS Records. Distributed by: CBS

Cassette: released on Epic in Oct'83 by CBS Records. Distributed by: CBS

STANDING ON THE EDGE.
Album: released on Epic in Nov'85 by CBS Records. Distributed by: CBS

Cassette: released on Epic in Nov'85 by CBS Records. Distributed by: CBS

TONIGHT IT'S YOU.
Single (7"): released on Epic in Feb'86 by CBS Records. Distributed by: CBS

Single (12"): released on Epic in Feb'86 by CBS Records. Distributed by: CBS

Cheaters

CONFIDANTE.
Single (7"): released on Holyrood in Aug'83 by Holyrood Records. Distributed by: Pinnacle

GROOVIN' WITH MR. BLOE.
Single (7"): released on Holyrood in Dec'83 by Holyrood Records. Distributed by: Pinnacle

Single (12"): released on Holyrood in Dec'83 by Holyrood Records. Distributed by: Pinnacle

HIT ME I'M HAPPY.
Album: released on Holyrood in Oct'83 by Holyrood Records. Distributed by: Pinnacle

Cassette: released on Holyrood in Oct'83 by Holyrood Records. Distributed by: Pinnacle

SPIRIT IN THE SKY.
Single (7"): released on Revelation in Jan'82

Cheatham, Doc

BLACK BEAUTY.
Tracks: / Travellin' all alone / Some of these days / Love will find a way / After you've gone / Someday you'll be sorry / Old fashioned love / I'm coming Virginia / Squeeze me / Memphis blues / I've got a feeling I'm falling / Louisiana.
Album: released on Sackville in Nov'83. Distributed by: Jazz Music, Jazz Horizons, Cadillac Music, Celtic Music, Swift

DOC & SAMMY (Cheatham, Doc & Sammy Price).
Tracks: / Honeysuckle rose / Sam & Doc's blues / Summertime / Tishomingo blues / Sheik of Araby / I can't give you anything but love / You can depend on me / Ain't misbehavin' / Dear old Southland.
Album: released on Sackville in Jul'86. Distributed by: Jazz Music, Jazz Horizons, Cadillac Music, Celtic Music, Swift

Cheatham, Jeannie

HOMEWARD BOUND (Cheatham, Jeannie & Jimmy).
Tracks: / Permanent solution / Goin' down slow / Daddy-O / Trouble in mind / You don't have to go / Hello, little boy / Detour ahead / Sometimes it be that way.
Notes: Personnel: Jeannie Cheatham - piano & vocals / Jimmy Cheatham - bass trombone / Red Callender - bass/ John 'Ironman' Harris - drums / Dinky Morris - Tenor & Baritone sax / Jimmie Noone - tenor saxophone & clarinet / Curtis Peagler - alto & tenor saxophone / Snooky Young - trumpet / Eddie "Cleanhead" Vinson - also sax &vocal (special guest).
Album: released on Concord Jazz in Jul'87 by Concord Jazz Records (USA). Distributed by: IMS, Polygram

Cassette: released on Concord Jazz (USA) in Jul'87 by Concord Jazz Records (USA). Distributed by: IMS, Polygram

Compact disc: released on Concord Jazz (USA) in Jul'87 by Concord Jazz Records (USA). Distributed by: IMS, Polygram

MIDNIGHT MAMA (Cheatham, Jeannie & Jimmy).
Tracks: / Wrong direction blues / C.C.Rider / Worried life blues / Big fat daddy blues / Midnight mama / Piney Brown / Finanace company / How long blues / Reel ya' deel ya dee dee dee..
Notes: This lively set of blues from singer/pianist Jeanie Cheatham and trombonist/arranger Jimmy Cheatham follows their overwhelmingly successful debut release 'Sweet baby blues' (CJ 258). Personnel: Jeannie Cheatham - piano & vocals/Jimmy Cheatham - bass trombone/Red Callender - bass/John'Ironman'Harris - drums/Dinky Morris - tenor, soprano & baritone sax/Jimmie Noone - tenor sax & clarinet/Curtis Peagler - alto sax/Snooky Young - trumpet. Special guest - Eddie 'Lockjaw' Davis - tenor sax.
Album: released on Concord Jazz (USA) in Apr'86 by Concord Jazz Records (USA). Distributed by: IMS, Polygram

Cassette: released on Concord Jazz (USA) in Apr'86 by Concord Jazz Records (USA). Distributed by: IMS, Polygram

SWEET BABY BLUES (Cheatham, Jeannie & Jimmy).
Album: released on Concord Jazz (USA) in Feb'85 by Concord Jazz Records (USA). Distributed by: IMS, Polygram

Cheatham, Oliver

CELEBRATE.
Single (7"): released on Champion in Nov'86 by Champion Records. Distributed by: RCA

Single (12"): released on Champion in Nov'86 by Champion Records. Distributed by: RCA

MAMA SAID.
Single (7"): released on Move in Aug'85 by Charly Records. Distributed by: Charly Distribution, Fast Forward Distribution, Cartel Distribution

Single (12"): released on Move in Aug'85 by Charly Records. Distributed by: Charly Distribution, Fast Forward Distribution, Cartel Distribution

S.O.S..
Tracks: / S.O.S. (Dub mix).
Single (7"): released on Champion in May'86 by Champion Records. Distributed by: RCA

Single (12"): released on Champion in May'86 by Champion Records. Distributed by: RCA

TURNING POINT.
Single (7"): released on PRT in Nov'85 by PRT Records. Distributed by: PRT

WISH ON A STAR.
Tracks: / Wish on a star / Wish on a star (acca dub).
Single (7"): released on Champion in Jun'87 by Champion Records. Distributed by: RCA

Single (12"): released on Champion in Jun'87 by Champion Records. Distributed by: RCA

Cheatham, Robert

GO FOR IT.
Album: released on Champion in Jul'87 by Champion Records. Distributed by: RCA

Cassette: released on Champion in Jul'87 by Champion Records. Distributed by: RCA

Compact disc: released on Champion in Jul'87 by Champion Records. Distributed by: RCA

Cheba, Eddie

LOOKING GOOD.
Single (7"): released on Destiny in Mar'80 by Destiny Records. Distributed by: Red Rhino, Cartel

Checker, Chubby

16 GREATEST HITS.
Compact disc: released on Bescol in Aug'87. Distributed by: Target

16 GREATEST HITS, THE.
Tracks: / Twist,The / Limbo rock / Slow twistin' / Fly,The / Let's twist again / Popeye the hitchiker / Loddy lo / Dancin' party / Dancin' party / Birdland / Hucklebuck,The / Twenty miles / Hooka tooka / Let's limbo some more / Hey,bobba needle / Dance the mess around.
Compact disc: released on Bescol in May'87. Distributed by: Target

BEST OF CHUBBY CHECKER.
Cassette: released on Creole (Everest-Europa) in Jul'84 by Creole Records. Distributed by: PRT, Rhino

Cassette: released on K-Tel Goldmasters in Aug'84 by K-Tel Records. Distributed by: K-Tel

CHUBBY CHECKER-GREATEST HITS.
Tracks: / Twist, The / Limbo rock / Dancin' party / Hey bobba needle / Loddy lo / Slow twistin' / Fly, The / Pony time / Let's twist again / Let's limbo some more / Birdland / Dance the mess around / Popeye (the hitchiker) / Twenty miles / Twist it up / Huckle buck.
Notes: This compilation (P) & (C) 1987 K-Tel International Ltd.
Compact disc: released on K-Tel in May'87 by K-Tel Records. Distributed by: Record Merchandisers Distribution, Taylors, Terry Blood Distribution, Wynd-Up Distribution, Relay Distribution, Pickwick Distribution, Solomon & Peres Distribution, Polygram

GARY US BONDS MEETS CHUBBY CHECKER (Checker, Chubby & Gary US Bonds).

LET'S TWIST AGAIN.
Album: released on K-Tel (Era) in Jun'83 by K-Tel Records. Distributed by: K-Tel

Cassette: released on K-Tel (Era) in Jun'83 by K-Tel Records. Distributed by: K-Tel

Compact disc: released on Creole in Aug'82 by Creole Records. Distributed by: Rhino PRT

LETS TWIST AGAIN.
Tracks: / Twist, The / Lets twist again / Dancin' party / Pony Time.
Single (7"): released on Creole Classics in Apr'87 by Creole Records. Distributed by: PRT, Rhino

Single (12"): released on Creole Classics in Apr'87 by Creole Records. Distributed by: PRT, Rhino

PONY TIME.
Single (7"): released on Creole in Aug'82 by Creole Records. Distributed by: Rhino, PRT

STILL TWISTIN.
Tracks: / Let's twist again / Twist, The / Slow twistin / Pony time / Fly, The / Birdland / Limbo rock / Let's limbo some more / Dancin' party / Hucklebuck / Dance the mess around / Twist it up.
Album: released on Charly in Oct'86 by Charly Records. Distributed by: Charly, Cadillac

Cassette: released on Charly in Oct'86 by Charly Records. Distributed by: Charly, Cadillac

STILL TWISTIN'.
Album: released on Topline in Dec'86 by Charly Records. Distributed by: Charly Distribution

TWIST, THE.
Single (7"): released on Creole in Aug'82 by Creole Records. Distributed by: Rhino, PRT

Check It Out

CHECK IT OUT VOL.1 (Various Artists).
Album: released on Greyhound in Jul'87 by Greyhound Records. Distributed by: Greyhound

Cassette: released on Greyhound in Jul'87 by Greyhound Records. Distributed by: Greyhound

Check Out The Groove

CHECK OUT THE GROOVE Various artists (Various Artists).
Tracks: / Can you handle it / I like (what you're doing to me) / Love rescue / Do it (till you're satisfied) / Check out the groove / Body talk / Love is gonna be on your side / I wanna do it / Breakaway / Hit and run lover.
Album: released on Creole in Nov'81 by Creole Records. Distributed by: Rhino, PRT

Cassette: released on Creole in Nov'81 by Creole Records. Distributed by: Rhino, PRT

Cheech & Chong

LET'S MAKE A NEW DOPE DEAL.
Album: released on Warner Bros. in Apr'81 by Warner Bros Records. Distributed by: WEA

Chee Chee

CHEE CHEE/TREASURE GIRL Comden, Betty - Richard Lewine (Chee Chee/Treasure Girl).
Album: released on That's Entertainment in Apr'83 by That's Entertainment Records. Distributed by: Pinnacle, PRT

Cheeky

DON'T MESS AROUND.
Single (7"): released on Woodbine in Jul'80

Cheeky Bee

GASGOW'S MILES BETTER.

SWEET DREAMS.
Tracks: / I'm nearly famous now / I'll get over you / Everything old is new again / How great thou art / Operator / Walkin' talkin' dolly / I could be so good for you / Could I have this dance / Miss Glasgow 1952 / Ain't no pleasin' you / Your good girl's gonna go bad / Sweet dreams.
Album: released on Emerald (Ireland) in Feb'82 by Emerald Records. Distributed by: I & B, Ross, PRT

Cheeky Chaps

GET YOUR LAUGHING GEAR ROUND THIS.
Tracks: / Things she wouldn't do / Bent bobby / Vegan's revenge / Wouldn't it be nice / Angel delight / My oh my / Knees up mother Brown / Swiss maid.
Notes: Cheeky chaps are Dave Arnold (Stark) and Dave Kent (The Cast). Dave Arnold: Voice, Synths, percussion. Dave Kent: Violin, voice and keyboards.
Cassette: released on Dead Happy in '86 by Dead Happy Records. Distributed by: Mason's Music Distributors/Wholesalers, Rough Trade

Cheepskates

RUN BETTER RUN.
Album: released on Midnight in Nov'84

Cheers...

CHEERS (...THE ESSENTIAL PARTY ALBUM) Various artists (Various Artists).
Album:

Cassette:

Cheetah Chrome Mother

PERMANENT SCAR.
Album: released on Children Of The Revolution in Jun'85 by Revolver Records. Distributed by: Revolver, Cartel

Cheetham, Doc

FESSORS NIGHTHAWKS (Cheetham, Doc with John Williams & Herb Hall).
Album: released on Metronome (Denmark) in Jun'81. Distributed by: Jazz Music Distribution

Cheever, John

SWIMMER & DEATH OF JUSTINA.
Cassette: released on Caedmon(USA) in Oct'81 by Caedmon (USA) Records. Distributed by: Taylors, Discovery

Chefs

24 HOURS.
Single (7"): by Graduate Records. Distributed by: Nine Mile, Cartel

SWEETIE.
Single (7"): released on Attrix in Sep'80. Distributed by: Pinnacle, Rough Trade

Chegwin, Keith

GONNA BE A FOOL NO MORE.
Single (7"): released on Moon in Jun'83 by Moon Records. Distributed by: PRT Distribution

Chekasin, Vladimir

EXERCISES.
Album: released on Leo in Sep'84. Distributed by: Recommended

NEW VITALITY.
Album: released on Leo Records in Jan'87 by Leo Records. Distributed by: Leo, Impetus

NOSTALGIA.
Album: released on Leo in Sep'84. Distributed by: Recommended

Chelsea

CHELSEA.
Tracks: / I'm on fire / Decide / Free the fighters / Your toy / Fools and soldiers / All the downs / Government / Twelve men / Many rivers / Trouble is the day.
Album: released on Step Forward in Jul'79 by Faulty Products Records. Distributed by: Faulty Products Distribution, Pinnacle

EVACUATE.
Tracks: / Evacuate / War across the nations / 40 people / Running free / Last drink / Only thinking / Tribal song / How do you know / Cover up / Bodies.
Album: released on Step Forward in Apr'82 by Faulty Products Records. Distributed by: Faulty Products Distribution, Pinnacle

Single (7"): released on Faulty Products in Nov'81 by Faulty Products Records. Distributed by: Faulty Products, Pinnacle

FREEMANS.
Single (7"): released on Step Forward in Sep'81 by Faulty Products Records. Distributed by: Faulty Products Distribution, Pinnacle

JUST FOR THE RECORD.
Album: released on Step Forward in Jan'85 by Faulty Products Records. Distributed by: Faulty Products Distribution, Pinnacle

ROCKIN' HORSE.
Single (7"): released on Faulty Products in Apr'81 by Faulty Products Records. Distributed by: Faulty Products, Pinnacle

ROCKS OFF.
Album: released on Jungle in Nov'86 by Jungle Records. Distributed by: Jungle, Cartel

STAND OUT.
Picture disc single: released on Step Forward in Oct'82 by Faulty Products Records. Distributed by: Faulty Products Distribution, Pinnacle

WAR ACROSS THE NATION.
Single (7"): released on Step Forward in Mar'82 by Faulty Products Records. Distributed by: Faulty Products Distribution, Pinnacle

Chelsea F.C....

BACK ON THE BALL (Chelsea F.C. Championship Squad).
Single (7"): released on WEA in Sep'84 by WEA Records. Distributed by: WEA

Cheltenham Ladies...

CANTIQUE.
Tracks: / All my trials / Donna Donna / Jamaica farewell / Lady Mary / Annie's song / Windmills of your mind / Lord's prayer, The / Give ear unto me / All people that on Earth do dwell / Cantique de Jean Racine / Come my way / Star carol / Away in a manger / In dulci jubilo / When Jesus Christ was born / Sussex carol / White blue and gold / Shepherd's cradle song, The / Christmas bell song.
Album: released on Alpha in Oct'81 by Alpha Records. Distributed by: H.R. Taylor

Cassette: released on Alpha in Oct'81 by Alpha Records. Distributed by: H.R. Taylor

Chemical Alice

GOODNIGHT VIENNA.
Single (7"): released on Acidic in May'82. Distributed by: Indies, Rough Trade

Chemist

DUB MIXTURE.
Tracks: / Dub mixture / Mellow dub / Crazy lady dub / Spirit dub / Suzanne dub / Damnation dub / Mean woman dub / Judgement dub / Leaving home dub / Milk and honey dub.
Album: released on Kingdom in '84 by Kingdom Records. Distributed by: Kingdom

DUB PRESCRIPTION.
Tracks: / Ital juice dub / Jah dub / Spliff dub / Rice & peas dub / Level vibes dub / Red stripe

dub / Ackee & saltfish dub / Rum & cla dub / Good woman dub / Roots dub.
Album: released on Kingdom in '84 by Kingdom Records. Distributed by: Kingdom

Cheng

TWO MASTERS PLAY THE CHINESE ZITHER.
Album: released on Lyrichord (USA) in Oct'81 by Lyrichord Records (USA). Distributed by: Flexitron Distributors Ltd

Chenier, Clifton

BAGALOUSA BOOGIE.
Album: released on Zydeco in '84. Distributed by: Accordion Record Club

BAYOU BLUES.
Tracks: / Bopping the rock / Things I did for you, The / Yesterday / Clifton's squeeze box / I'm on my way (Part 1) / Eh, petite fille / All night long / Opelousas hop / I'm on my way (Part 2) / Think it over / Zydico stomp / Cat's dreaming, The.
Album: by Sonet Records. Distributed by: PRT

BAYOU SOUL.
Album: released on Maison de Soul in Mar'79. Distributed by: Swift

BLACK SNAKE BLUES.
Album: released on Arhoolie in May'81 by Arhoolie Records. Distributed by: Projection, Topic, Jazz Music, Swift, Roots

Album: released on Zydeco in '84. Distributed by: Accordion Record Club

BOGALUSA BOOGIE Zydeco accordion dance music.
Album: released on Arhoolie in Jul'87 by Arhoolie Records. Distributed by: Projection, Topic, Jazz Music, Swift, Roots

BON TON ROULET.
Album: released on Arhoolie in May'81 by Arhoolie Records. Distributed by: Projection, Topic, Jazz Music, Swift, Roots

Album: released on Zydeco in '84. Distributed by: Accordion Record Club

BOOGALUSA BOOGIE.
Album: released on Arhoolie in May'81 by Arhoolie Records. Distributed by: Projection, Topic, Jazz Music, Swift, Roots

Boogie In black & white

BOOGIE'N'ZYDECO.
Tracks: / Shake it don't break it / Oh my Lucille / Choo choo ch-boogie / Nonc helaire / You can't sit down / Road runner / You used to call me / Je me fu pas mal.
Album: released on Sonet in Jan'80 by Sonet Records. Distributed by: PRT

CAJUN SWAMP MUSIC LIVE.
Album: released on Tomato in Mar'79

CLASSIC CHENIER.
Album: released on Arhoolie in May'81 by Arhoolie Records. Distributed by: Projection, Topic, Jazz Music, Swift, Roots

CLASSIC CLIFTON.
Album: released on Zydeco in '84. Distributed by: Accordion Record Club

CLIFTON CHENIER AND HIS RED HOT LOUISIANA BAND.
Album: released on Zydeco in '84. Distributed by: Accordion Record Club

CLIFTON CHENIER LIVE.
Album: released on Zydeco in '84. Distributed by: Accordion Record Club

COUNTRY BOY NOW Grammy award winner 1984.
Album: . Distributed by: Swift

FRENCHIN' THE BOOGIE.
Tracks: / Caldonia / Laissez les bons temps rouler (Let the good times roll) / Tu peux cogner mais tu peux pas rentrer (Keep-a-knockin'...) / Blues de la vache a lait, Le (Milkcow blues) / Moi, j'ai une petite femme (I got a woman) / Tous les jours mon coeur est blue (Everyday I have the blues / Je veux faire l'amour a toi (I just wanna make love to you) / Choo choo ch'boogie / Valse de Paris, La / Shake rattle and roll / Going down slow (in Paris) / Aye, aye mama / Don't you lie to me.
Album: released on Barclay (Import) in Nov'79

I'M HERE (Chenier, Clifton & His Red Hot Louisiana Band).
Album: released on Sonet in May'82 by Sonet Records. Distributed by: PRT

IN NEW ORLEANS.
Album: released on GNP Crescendo (USA) in Mar'79 by GNP Crescendo Records (USA). Distributed by: Swift

KING OF THE BAYOU.
Album: released on Arhoolie in May'81 by Arhoolie Records. Distributed by: Projection, Topic, Jazz Music, Swift, Roots

Album: released on Zydeco in '84. Distributed by: Accordion Record Club

LIVE AT A FRENCH DANCE.
Album: released on Arhoolie in May'81 by Arhoolie Records. Distributed by: Projection, Topic, Jazz Music, Swift, Roots

LIVE AT MONTREUX.
Double Album: released on Charly in Apr'84 by Charly Records. Distributed by: Charly, Cadillac

LIVE AT THE SAN FRANCISCO BLUES FESTIVAL.
Album: released on Arhoolie in Aug'85 by Arhoolie Records. Distributed by: Projection, Topic, Jazz Music, Swift, Roots

LOUISIANA BLUES AND ZYDECO.
Album: released on Arhoolie in Apr'81 by Arhoolie Records. Distributed by: Projection, Topic, Jazz Music, Swift, Roots

Album: released on Zydeco in '84. Distributed by: Accordion Record Club

OUT WEST.
Album: released on Arhoolie in '81 by Arhoolie Records. Distributed by: Projection, Topic, Jazz Music, Swift, Roots

Album: released on Zydeco in '84. Distributed by: Accordion Record Club

RED HOT LOUISIANA BAND.
Album: released on Arhoolie in '81 by Arhoolie Records. Distributed by: Projection, Topic, Jazz Music, Swift, Roots

SIXTY MINUTES WITH THE KING OF ZYDECO.
Compact disc: released on Arhoolie in Dec'86 by Arhoolie Records. Distributed by: Projection, Topic, Jazz Music, Swift, Roots

Chequered Past

CHEQUERED PAST.
Album: released on Heavy Metal America in Nov'85 by FM-Revolver Records. Distributed by: EMI

Cassette: released on Heavy Metal America in Nov'85 by FM-Revolver Records. Distributed by: EMI

Chequers

CHECK US OUT.
Album: released on Creole in '79 by Creole Records. Distributed by: Rhino, PRT

HARD TIMES.
Single (7"): released on M in Mar'83. Distributed by: M

Cher

BANG BANG My baby shot me down.
Single (7"): released on EMI Golden 45's in Jul'84 by EMI Records. Distributed by: EMI

BEST OF CHER, THE.
Tracks: / Bang bang (my baby shot me down) / All I really want to do / Where do you go / Hey Joe / Mama (when my dollies have babies) / I feel like something in the air (Magic in the air) / Like a rolling stone / Come to your window / Gypsies, tramps and thieves / You'd better sit down kids / Pied piper / I want you / Young girl, A / Come and stay with me / Dark lady / Half breed.
Album: released on Liberty in Sep'85 by Liberty-United. Distributed by: EMI

Cassette: released on Liberty in Sep'85 by Liberty-United. Distributed by: EMI

GOLDEN GREATS: CHER.
Album: released on MCA in Oct'85 by MCA Records. Distributed by: Polygram, MCA

Cassette: released on MCA in Oct'85 by MCA Records. Distributed by: Polygram, MCA

GYPSIES, TRAMPS AND THIEVES (SINGLE).
Single (7"): released on Old Gold in Jul'82 by Old Gold Records. Distributed by: Lightning, Jazz Music, Spartan, Counterpoint

GYPSIES, TRAMPS AND THIEVES.
Album: released on MFP in Aug'81 by EMI Records. Distributed by: EMI

Cassette: released on MFP in Aug'81 by EMI Records. Distributed by: EMI

PRISONER.
Album: released on Casablanca in Mar'80. Distributed by: Polygram, Phonogram

TAKE ME HOME.
Album: released on Casablanca in Apr'79. Distributed by: Polygram, Phonogram

TAKE ME HOME.
Album: released on Casablanca in Apr'79. Distributed by: Polygram, Phonogram

TWO THE HARD WAY (Cher & Gregg Allman).
Album: released on Warner Bros. in '77 by Warner Bros Records. Distributed by: WEA

Che & Ray

CALIFORNIA.
Album: released on EMI in May'80 by EMI Records. Distributed by: EMI

CHE & RAY & THE BOOGIE BAND (Che & Ray & The Boogie Band).
Album: released on Columbia in '78 by EMI Records. Distributed by: EMI

Cheri

WORKING GIRL.
Single (7"): released on 21 Records in Feb'83 by Polydor Records. Distributed by: Polydor

Single (12"): released on 21 Records in Feb'83 by Polydor Records. Distributed by: Polydor

Cherish

CHERISH (Various Artists).
Album: released on K-Tel (Era) in Jun'83 by K-Tel Records. Distributed by: K-Tel

Cassette: released on K-Tel (Era) in Jun'83 by K-Tel Records. Distributed by: K-Tel

Chernobal, S

RUSSIA:KUBAN COSSAKS CHORUS.
Album: released on Melodiya (USSR) in May'78. Distributed by: T.B.C Distribution

Cherrelle

ARTIFICIAL HEART.
Tracks: / Oh no it's U again.
Single (7"): released on Tabu in May'86 by CBS Records. Distributed by: CBS Distribution

FRAGILE.
Tracks: / Fragile...Handle with care / I didn't mean to turn you on / Like I will / I will wait for you / Who's it gonna be / Stay with me / When you look in my eyes / I need you now.
Album: released on Tabu in Sep'84 by CBS Records. Distributed by: CBS Distribution

Cassette: released on Tabu in Sep'84 by CBS Records. Distributed by: CBS Distribution Deleted '86.

HIGH PRIORITY.
Tracks: / Opening, The / You look so good to me / Artificial heart / Nw love / Oh no it's U again / Saturday love / Will you satisfy / Where do I run to / High priority / New love (Reprise).
Album: released on Tabu in Jan'86 by CBS Records. Distributed by: CBS Distribution

Cassette: released on Tabu in Jan'86 by CBS Records. Distributed by: CBS Distribution

I DIDN'T MEAN TO TURN YOU ON.
Single (7"): released on Tabu in Aug'84 by CBS Records. Distributed by: CBS Distribution

Single (12"): released on Tabu in Aug'84 by CBS Records. Distributed by: CBS Distribution

SATURDAY LOVE (Cherrelle & Alexandra O'Neal).
Tracks: / Saturday love / I didn't mean to turn you on / Saturday love (remix)*.
Single (7"): released on Tabu in Jan'86 by CBS Records. Distributed by: CBS Distribution

Single (12"): released on Tabu in Jan'86 by CBS Records. Distributed by: CBS Distribution

Single (12"): released on Tabu in Jan'86 by CBS Records. Distributed by: CBS Distribution

WILL YOU SATISFY?.
Tracks: / When you look in my eyes / Will you satisfy* / Saturday love* / Saturday love (remix)+.
Single (7"): released on Tabu in Feb'86 by CBS Records. Distributed by: CBS Distribution

Double-pack single: released on Tabu in Feb'86 by CBS Records. Distributed by: CBS Distribution

Single (12"): released on Tabu in Feb'86 by CBS Records. Distributed by: CBS Distribution

Double-pack single: released on Tabu in Feb'86 by CBS Records. Distributed by: CBS Distribution

Cherry Ann

ME AND YOU.
Single (7"): released on BB in Mar'82. Distributed by: Jetstar

Cherry Black Dawn

BLUE BABY BLUE.
Single (7"): released on Cherry Black in Jun'84 by Cherry Black Records. Distributed by: ILA

Cherry Bombz

COMING DOWN SLOW.
Notes: Featuring Nasty Suicide & Andy McCoy (Hanoi Rocks), Dave Tregunna (Sham 69), Terry Chimes (The Clash), and Anita. Recorded live at the Marquee, London 3.9.86.
Album: released on High Dragon in Mar'87. Distributed by: Pinnacle

Compact disc: released on High Dragon in Jun'87. Distributed by: Pinnacle

COMING DOWN SLOW.
Notes: Cassette version of the 'Live At The Marquee' album.
Cassette: released on High Dragon in Jun'87. Distributed by: Pinnacle

HOT GIRLS IN LOVE.
Tracks: / Feeline feeling / 4 track EP*.
Single (7"): released on Lick in Feb'86 by Cherry Bombz. Distributed by: Pinnacle

Single (12"): released on Lick in Feb'86 by Cherry Bombz. Distributed by: Pinnacle

HOUSE OF ECSTASY.
Tracks: / Declaration / Running* / Countryfield inner city blues*.
Single (7"): released on Lick in May'86 by Cherry Bombz. Distributed by: Pinnacle

Single (12"): released on Lick in May'86 by Cherry Bombz. Distributed by: Pinnacle

Cherry Boys

KARDOMAH CAFE/AIRS AND GRACES.
Single (7"): released on Crash in Jul'83 by Satril Records. Distributed by: PRT

ONLY FOOLS DIE/COME THE DAY.
Single (7"): released on Cherryosa in Nov'82. Distributed by: Probe, Cartel

SHOOT THE BIG SHOT/FALLING.
Single (7"): released on Crash in Nov'83 by Satril Records. Distributed by: PRT

Single (12"): released on Crash in Nov'83 by Satril Records. Distributed by: PRT

Cherry, Don

AVANTE-GARDE (Cherry, Don & John Coltrane).
Album: released on Atlantic in Jan'79 by WEA Records. Distributed by: WEA

COMPLETE COMMUNION.
Album: released on Blue Note (USA Import) in Sep'84

DON CHERRY.
Album:

EL CORAZON (Cherry, Don & Ed Blackwell).
Album: released on ECM (Germany) in Oct'82 by ECM Records. Distributed by: IMS, Polygram, Virgin through EMI

EL CORAZON (Cherry, Don & Ed Blackwell).

ETERNAL NOW, THE.
Album: by Sonet Records. Distributed by: PRT Deleted '74.

ETERNAL RHYTHM.
Album: released on Polygram in Dec'74 by Polygram Records. Distributed by: Polygram

HOME BOY, SISTER OUT.
Tracks: / Butterfly friend / I walk / Rappin' recipe / Reggae to the high tower / Art deco / Call me / Treat your lady right / Alphabet city / Bamako love.
Notes: Don Cherry first became known while playing his "pocket trumpet" with Ornette Coleman Quartet in the late fifties. He has been described as the "Universal WorldMusician". This new album on Barclay takes Cherry away from the the avante-garde. The theme here is contemporary black music and features the sounds of reggae, funk and rappin'.Cherry also sings as well as playing trumpet, piano and synthesizer. Personnel: Don Cherry/Ramuntoho Matta/Jannick Top/Claude Salmieri/Negrito Trasante/Elli Medieros/Abdoulaye Prosper Niang/Jean-Pierre Coco/Fil Mong.
Album: released on Barclay in Dec'85 by Decca Records. Distributed by: Polygram, Discovery, Conifer, IMS, Swift

Cassette: released on Barclay in Dec'85 by Decca Records. Distributed by: Polygram, Discovery, Conifer, IMS, Swift

Compact disc: by Decca Records. Distributed by: Polygram, Discovery, Conifer, IMS, Swift

IN ANKARA.
Album: released on Sonet in Aug'78 by Sonet Records. Distributed by: PRT

MU-FIRST PART.
Album: by Charly Records. Distributed by: Charly, Cadillac

MU-SECOND PART.
Album: released on Affinity in '78 by Charly Records. Distributed by: Charly, Cadillac

OLD AND NEW DREAMS (Cherry, Don/Dewey Redman/Charlie Haden/Eddie Blackwell).
Compact disc: released on Black Saint (Italy) in Jan'86. Distributed by: Target, Jazz Music, Harmonia Mundi

OLD AND NEW DREAMS.
Album: released on Black Saint in Jul'78. Distributed by: Projection, IMS, Polygram, Chris Wellard, Harmonia Mundi, Swift

ORIENT.
Album: released on Affinity in Mar'83 by Charly Records. Distributed by: Charly, Cadillac

Cheryl

IN YOUR SHADOW.
Tracks: / In your shadow again.
Single (7"): released on Creole in Jun'86 by Creole Records. Distributed by: Rhino, PRT

Single (12"): released on Creole in Jun'86 by Creole Records. Distributed by: Rhino, PRT

Chesapeke Minstrels

CREOLE BELLES.
Tracks: / Plantation medley / Jeannie with the light brown hair / Some folks / Creole medley / Pasquinade / Gentle Annie / Dixie's land / Hiawatha / Bethena / Creole belles / Maple leaf rag / My old Kentucky home / Waiting for the Robert E. Lee.
Album: released on Hyperion in Apr'83 by Hyperion Records. Distributed by: Taylors, PRT

Chess

CHESS Original recording (Various Artists).
Compact disc: by RCA Records. Distributed by: RCA, Roots, Swift, Wellard, Chris, I & B, Solomon & Peres Distribution

Album: released on RCA in Nov'84 by RCA Records. Distributed by: RCA, Roots, Swift, Wellard, Chris, I & B, Solomon & Peres Distribution

Cassette: released on RCA in Nov'84 by RCA Records. Distributed by: RCA, Roots, Swift, Wellard, Chris, I & B, Solomon & Peres Distribution

Compact disc: released on RCA in Nov'84 by RCA Records. Distributed by: RCA, Roots, Swift, Wellard, Chris, I & B, Solomon & Peres Distribution

ROCKABILIES Original Chess artists.
Album: released on Chess in Apr'78 by Charly Records. Distributed by: Charly, Swift, PRT, Discovery, IMS, Polygram

Chess Blues Rarities

CHESS - BLUES RARITIES Various artists (Various Artists).
Tracks: / Recession blues / Don't keep me waiting / Tickle britches / Don't break your promise / You can't put me out / Gettin' late / Rockin daddy / I didn't know / I better go now / New crawlin' king snake / My mind is ramblin' / Tail dragger / Poor wind that never changes / Stick around / Gully hully / That's it / American bandstand / Untitled instrumental / My love is real / Moanin' / Down home special / Watch out / Scrappin' / Sittin' here alone / Hound dog / Little village / Unseen eye.
Notes: Five great blues artists on one double album - BB King, Howlin' Wolf, Buddy Guy, Hound Dog Taylor and Sonny Boy Williamson perform some of their rarest sides. A must for blues fans.
Album: released on Chess in May'85 by Charly Records. Distributed by: Charly, Swift, PRT, Discovery, IMS, Polygram

Chess Doo Wop

CHESS DOO WOP (Various Artists).
Album: released on Chess in Jul'87 by Charly Records. Distributed by: Charly, Swift, PRT, Discovery, IMS, Polygram

Chess Masters

CHESS MASTERS Various artists (Various Artists).
Album: released on Chess(USA) in Apr'82 by Sugar Hill (USA). Distributed by: PRT, Swift

Chess Pieces

CHESS PIECES Various artists (Various Artists).
Tracks: / Merano / Arbiter, The / Nobody's side - heaven help my heart / Chess / Mountain duet / Embassy lament / Anthem / One night in Bangkok - pity the child / I know him so well / You and I - the story of chess.
Album: released on Telstar in Oct'85 by Telstar Records. Distributed by: RCA Distribution

Cassette: released on Telstar in Oct'85 by Telstar Records. Distributed by: RCA Distribution

Chess Sampler

CHESS SAMPLER Various artists (Various Artists).

Tracks: / My babe / Help me / Smokestack lightning / Mannis boy / Sugar mama / Dust my broom / Walking by myself / Road runner / Brown eyed hansome man / Wang dang doodle / We're gonna make it / High heeled sneakers / Soulful dress / Security.
Album: released on Chess in Oct'84 by Charly Records. Distributed by: Charly, Swift, PRT, Discovery, IMS, Polygram

Cassette: released on Chess in Oct'84 by Charly Records. Distributed by: Charly, Swift, PRT, Discovery, IMS, Polygram

Chess Sisters Of Soul

CHESS SISTERS OF SOUL Various artists (Various Artists).
Tracks: / Wang dang doodle / Selfish one / Mama didn't lie / Two sides (to every story) / Take me for a little while / Rescue me / Sally, go 'round the roses / Only time will tell / I had a talk with my man / Lovin' you more every day / Yield not to temptation.
Notes: Some of the greatest soul records of all time on one album. All performed by girls. A great package which is a must for all 60's soul freaks.
Album: released on Chess in Jun'84 by Charly Records. Distributed by: Charly, Swift, PRT, Discovery, IMS, Polygram

Cassette: released on Chess in Jun'84 by Charly Records. Distributed by: Charly, Swift, PRT, Discovery, IMS, Polygram

Chester

FOR THE TRUCKS SAKE.
Single (7"): released on Roxon in Sep'81 by Roxon Records. Distributed by: Pinnacle

Chester, Bob

EASY DOES IT.
Album: released on Golden Era in Jul'82 by Import Records. Distributed by: Wellard, Chris, Swift

Chesterfield Choir

IN QUIRES & PLACES, NO.23.
Album: released on Abbey in Jan'78 by Abbey. Distributed by: PRT, Taylors, Gamut

Chesterfield Kings

HERE ARE THE CHESTERFIELDS KINGS.
Album: released on Mirror in Sep'86 by Priority Records. Distributed by: Priority Distribution

STOP.
Album: released on Mirror in Sep'86 by Priority Records. Distributed by: Priority Distribution

Chesterfields

ASK JOHNNY DEE.
Tracks: / Ask Johnny Dee.
Single (7"): released on Subway in Mar'87. Distributed by: Revolver Distribution, Spartan Distribution

COMPLETELY AND UTTERLY.
Single (7"): released on Subway in Nov'86. Distributed by: Revolver Distribution, Spartan Distribution

GUITAR IN YOUR BATH, A.
Single (7"): released on Subway in Apr'86. Distributed by: Revolver Distribution, Spartan Distribution

KETTLE.
Album: released on Subway in Jun'87. Distributed by: Revolver Distribution, Spartan Distribution

Chester & Lester

GUITAR MONSTERS.
Notes: Artists: Chet Atkins/Les Paul.
Cassette: released on RCA in Aug'78 by RCA Records. Distributed by: RCA, Roots, Swift, Wellard, Chris, I & B, Solomon & Peres Distribution

Cassette: released on RCA in Aug'78 by RCA Records. Distributed by: RCA, Roots, Swift, Wellard, Chris, I & B, Solomon & Peres Distribution

Chester Recordings

CHESTER RECORDERS, THE.
Album: released on Plant Life in Nov'81. Distributed by: Roots

Chesworth, David

NO PARTICULAR PLACE.
Album: released on Rampant in Nov'86

Single (7"): released on Creepy In July, 1982 in Jul'82

Chevalier Brothers

BABY.
Tracks: / You're something else.

Single (7"): released on Disques Cheval in Mar'86. Distributed by: Rough Trade, Cartel

Single (12"): released on Disques Cheval in Mar'86. Distributed by: Rough Trade, Cartel

BARTENDER.
Single (12"): released on Waterfront in Feb'84 by Waterfront Records. Distributed by: Rough Trade, Cartel, Projection, Roots

I LIVE 'EM.
Single (7"): released on Mean in Aug'84 by Mean Records. Distributed by: Spartan

LIVE AND JUMPING.
Album: released on Disques Cheval in Oct'85. Distributed by: Rough Trade, Cartel

Chevalier, Maurice

Bing Crosby with Maurice Chevalier and Frankie Laine

BONJOUR D'AMOUR.
Album: released on Karussell (Germany) in Oct'82

Cassette: released on Karussell (Germany) in Oct'82

BRAVA MAURICE.
Tracks: / Quand on R'vient / Moonlight saving time / Oh, that Mitzi / You took the words right out of my mouth / Balance la / Poor Apache, The / Mon p'tit tom / Louise / Prosper / My love parade / Rhythm of the rain / I was lucky / Je ne dis pas non / My ideal / Mimi / Oh, Maurice / Mon p'tit Tom.
Album: released on Living Era in Jun'86 by ASV. Distributed by: PRT

Cassette: released on Living Era in Jun'86 by ASV. Distributed by: PRT

ENCORE MAURICE.
Compact disc: released on ASV in Feb'87 by Academy Sound & Vision Records. Distributed by: Pinnacle

: released on ASV Living Era in Sep'82 by ASV Records. Distributed by: PRT

Cassette: released on ASV Living Era in Sep'82 by ASV Records. Distributed by: PRT

GOLDEN AGE OF MAURICE CHEVALIER, THE.
Album: released on Golden Age in Jul'84 by Music For Pleasure Records. Distributed by: EMI

Cassette: released on Golden Age in Jul'84 by Music For Pleasure Records. Distributed by: EMI

MA POMME.
Album: released on EMI (France) in '83 by EMI Records. Distributed by: Conifer

MAURICE CHEVALIER.
Album: released on Deja Vu in Jan'87 by Deja Vu Records. Distributed by: Counterpoint Distribution, Record Services Distribution (Ireland)

Cassette: released on Deja Vu in Jan'87 by Deja Vu Records. Distributed by: Counterpoint Distribution, Record Services Distribution (Ireland)

...SINGS.
Album: released on World in '69. Distributed by: Jetstar

Album: released on World in '71. Distributed by: Jetstar

YOU BROUGH A NEW KIND OF LOVE TO ME.
Album: released on Monmouth in May'79

Chevi

GE ME MORE.
Single (7"): released on Fourth & Broadway in Aug'84 by Island Records. Distributed by: Polygram, EMI

Single (12"): released on Fourth & Broadway in Aug'84 by Island Records. Distributed by: Polygram, EMI Deleted '87.

MR. D.J.
Single (12"): released on Subversive in Jan'84. Distributed by: Backs, Cartel Distribution

ROSALIE, 2 PARTS.
Single (12"): released on Sunburn in Apr'83 by Orbitone Records. Distributed by: Jetstar Distribution

Cheviot Ranters

CHEVIOT BARN DANCE.
Album: released on Topic in '81. Distributed by: Roots Distribution

CHEVIOT HILLS.
Album: released on Topic in '81. Distributed by: Roots Distribution

SOUND OF THE CHEVIOTS.
Album: released on Topic in '81. Distributed by: Roots Distribution

Chevis, Wilfred & the Texas

FOOT STOMPIN' ZYDECO.
Album:

Chevron, Philip

CAPTAINS AND THE KINGS.
Single (7"): released on Imp in Oct'83 by Demon. Distributed by: Pinnacle

SONGS FROM BILL'S DANCEHALL.
Single (12"): released on Mosa in Nov'81. Distributed by: Pinnacle

Chevvy

OUT ON THE STREET.
Album: released on Champ in Oct'79 by Champ Records. Distributed by: Champ

TOO MUCH LOVING.
Single (7"): released on Avatar in Aug'81 by Avatar Communications. Distributed by: CBS

Chevy

TAKER.
Single (7"): released on Avatar in May'81 by Avatar Communications. Distributed by: CBS

Album: released on Avatar in Oct'80 by Avatar Communications. Distributed by: CBS

Cheyenne, Quinn

FEELS LIKE FLYING.
Single (7"): released on Crazy Viking in Jul'83 by Crazy Vikings Records. Distributed by: Pinnacle

Cheyne

CALL ME MR. TELEPHONE.
Single (12"): released on MCA in Jun'85 by MCA Records. Distributed by: Polygram, MCA

Chiasson, Warren

GOOD VIBES FOR KURT WEILL.
Album: released on Retrospect in Jan'87 by World Records

Chic

C'EST CHIC.
Album: released on Atlantic in Jan'79 by WEA Records. Distributed by: WEA

Cassette: released on Atlantic in Jan'79 by WEA Records. Distributed by: WEA Deleted '86.

GREATEST HITS:CHIC.
Album: released on WEA in Dec'79 by WEA Records. Distributed by: WEA

Cassette: released on WEA in Dec'79 by WEA Records. Distributed by: WEA

HANGIN.
Single (7"): released on Atlantic in Jan'83 by WEA Records. Distributed by: WEA

Single (12"): by WEA Records. Distributed by: WEA

LE FREAK.
Tracks: / Savoir faire / Chic (everybody say).
Single (12"): released on Atlantic in Aug'86 by WEA Records. Distributed by: WEA

LE FREAK.
Single (7"): released on Atlantic in '78 by WEA Records. Distributed by: WEA

Chicago

16.
Album: released on Full Moon in Jun'82 by Epic. Distributed by: CBS

Cassette: released on Full Moon in Jun'82 by Epic. Distributed by: CBS

Compact disc: released on Full Moon in '83 by Epic. Distributed by: CBS

17.
Album: released on Warner Bros. in Apr'84 by Warner Bros Records. Distributed by: WEA

Cassette: released on Warner Bros. in Apr'84 by Warner Bros Records. Distributed by: WEA

Compact disc: released on Full Moon in Jul'84 by Epic. Distributed by: CBS

18.
Tracks: / Niagra falls / Forever / If she would have been faithful.... / 25 or 6 to 4 / Will you still love me? / Over and over / It's alright / Nothin's gonna stop us now / I believe / One more day.
Album: released on Warner Brothers in Oct'86

by Warner Bros Records. Distributed by: WEA

Cassette: released on Warner Brothers in Oct'86 by Warner Bros Records. Distributed by: WEA

Compact disc: released on Warner Brothers in Oct'86 by Warner Bros Records. Distributed by: WEA

25 OR 624.
Single (12"): released on Warner Brothers in Oct'86 by Warner Bros Records. Distributed by: WEA

ALONG COMES A WOMAN.
Single (12"): released on Full Moon in Apr'85 by Epic. Distributed by: CBS

BEGINNINGS.
Album: released on Meteor in Dec'83 by Magnum Music Group Ltd. Distributed by: Magnum Music Group Ltd, PRT Distribution, Spartan Distribution

BEGINNINGS (CHARLY).
Album: released on Topline in Jan'85 by Charly Records. Distributed by: Charly Distribution

Cassette: released on Topline in Jan'85 by Charly Records. Distributed by: Charly Distribution

CHICAGO (Various Artists).
Notes: Jazz artists from Chicago.
Album: released on RCA (France) in '83 by RCA Records. Distributed by: Discovery

CHICAGO 16.
Compact disc: by Epic. Distributed by: CBS

CHICAGO 17.
Compact disc: by Epic. Distributed by: CBS

CHICAGO 18.
Compact disc: by Warner Bros Records. Distributed by: WEA

CHICAGO TRANSIT AUTHORITY, THE.
Tracks: / Does anybody really know what time it is / Beginnings / Questions 67 and 68 / Listen / Poem 58 / Free form guitar / South California purple / I'm a man / Prologue, August 29 / Someday (August 29 1968) / Liberation / Introduction.
Album: released on CBS in Sep'87 by CBS Records. Distributed by: CBS

Cassette: released on CBS in Sep'87 by CBS Records. Distributed by: CBS

GREATEST HITS: CHICAGO VOL.2.
Album: released on CBS in Jan'82 by CBS Records. Distributed by: CBS

Cassette: released on CBS in Jan'82 by CBS Records. Distributed by: CBS

GREATEST HITS:CHICAGO IX.
Album: released on CBS in Nov'84 by CBS Records. Distributed by: CBS

Cassette: released on CBS in Nov'84 by CBS Records. Distributed by: CBS

GREATEST ORIGINAL HITS.
Cassette: released on CBS in Jan'83 by CBS Records. Distributed by: CBS

HARD HABIT TO BREAK.
Single (7"): released on Full Moon in Aug'84 by Epic. Distributed by: CBS

Single (12"): released on Full Moon in Nov'84 by Epic. Distributed by: CBS

HARD TO SAY I'M SORRY/THINK.
Single (7"): released on Full Moon in Jul'82 by Epic. Distributed by: CBS

IF YOU LEAVE ME NOW.
Tracks: / If you leave me now / Saturday in the park / Feelin' stronger everyday / (I've been) searchin' so long / 25 or 6 to 4 / Baby what a big surprise / Wishing you were here / No tell lover / Another rainy day in New York City / Does anybody really know what time it is? / Song for you.
Album: released on CBS in Apr'86 by CBS Records. Distributed by: CBS

Cassette: released on CBS in Apr'86 by CBS Records. Distributed by: CBS

IF YOU LEAVE ME NOW/25 OR 6 TO 4.
Single (7"): released on CBS in Nov'82 by CBS Records. Distributed by: CBS

LIVE.
Tracks: / Beggininngs / Purples / I'm a man / 25 or 6 to 4 / Questions 67 / 68 / Liberation / Does anybody know what time it is?.
Album: released on Showcase in Apr'86. Distributed by: Counterpoint

Cassette: released on Showcase in Apr'86. Distributed by: Counterpoint

LOVE ME TOMORROW/BAD ADVICE.
Single (7"): released on Full Moon in Nov'82 by Epic. Distributed by: CBS

LOVE SONGS.
Album: released on TV in Nov'82

Cassette: released on TV in Nov'82

STAY THE NIGHT.
Single (7"): released on Warner Bros. in Jun'84 by Warner Bros Records. Distributed by: WEA

STREET PLAYER.
Album: released on CBS in Sep'79 by CBS Records. Distributed by: CBS

TORONTO ROCK 'N' ROLL REVIVAL 1969.
Album: released on Design in Jul'84 by Breakaway Records. Distributed by: PRT, Stage One

V.
Album: released on Hallmark in Apr'84 by Pickwick Records. Distributed by: Pickwick Distribution, PRT, Taylors

Cassette: released on Hallmark in Apr'84 by Pickwick Records. Distributed by: Pickwick Distribution, PRT, Taylors

WILL YOU STILL LOVE ME.
Tracks: / Will you still love me / Forever / Hard habit to break.
Notes: Hard habit to break is available on 12" version only.
Single (7"): released on Warner Bros. in Feb'87 by Warner Bros Records. Distributed by: WEA

Single (12"): released on Warner Bros. in Feb'87 by Warner Bros Records. Distributed by: WEA

YOU'RE THE INSPIRATION.
Single (7"): released on Full Moon in Feb'85 by Epic. Distributed by: CBS

Single (12"): released on Full Moon in Feb'85 by Epic. Distributed by: CBS

Chicago Bears

SUPERBOWL SHUFFLE.
Tracks: / Superbowl (Inst. mix).
Single (7"): released on Phonogram in Jun'86 by Phonogram Records. Distributed by: Polygram

Single (12"): released on Phonogram in Jun'86 by Phonogram Records. Distributed by: Polygram

Cassette single: released on Phonogram in Jun'86 by Phonogram Records. Distributed by: Polygram

Chicago Blues

CHICAGO BLUES Various artists (Various Artists).
Album: released on RCA in Feb'86 by RCA Records. Distributed by: RCA, Roots, Swift, Wellard, Chris, I & B, Solomon & Peres Distribution

Cassette: released on RCA in Feb'86 by RCA Records. Distributed by: RCA, Roots, Swift, Wellard, Chris, I & B, Solomon & Peres Distribution

CHICAGO BLUES ANTHOLOGY (Various Artists).
Album: released on Chess in Jul'84 by Charly Records. Distributed by: Charly, Swift, PRT, Discovery, IMS, Polygram

CHICAGO BLUES AT HOME (Various Artists).
Album: released on Advent in Apr'79. Distributed by: Celtic Music, Projection, Swift

CHICAGO BLUES (CHESS) (Various Artists).
Album: released on Chess(USA) in May'83 by Sugar Hill (USA). Distributed by: PRT, Swift

CHICAGO BLUES (RED LIGHTNIN') (Various Artists).
Album: released on Red Lightnin' in Jun'85 by Red Lightnin' Records. Distributed by: Roots, Swift, Jazz Music, Pinnacle, Cartel, Wynd-Up Distribution

CHICAGO BLUES VOL.1 (Various Artists).
Album: released on Wolf (Austria) in Aug'85

Chicago Bluesmasters

CHICAGO BLUESMASTER VOL.4 "CHILLS AND FEVER" Various artists (Various Artists).
Notes: 15 tracks from Vee Jay Records: featuring: L.C.McKinley/Jimmy Eager (Tampa Red)/Birmingham Jones/Hubert Sumlin/Willie Cobbs. Our fourth and final volume of this series, which, like CRB's 1042,1047 & 1067,presents some of the rarest, most collectable blues masters from the vaults of VJ Records. This volume contrasts differing styles of blues: Side One: Features downhome blues, with harmonica and guitar in rural style. Side Two: offers more sophisticated city guitars stylings. As with the three volumes the principal market for this release will of course be among hardcore blues collectors but the reputation of this series created by the previous volumes should ensure fairly broad interest and sales.
Album: released on Charly in Apr'85 by Charly Records. Distributed by: Charly, Cadillac

CHICAGO BLUESMASTERS VOL.1 (Various Artists).
Album: released on Charly in Mar'83 by Charly Records. Distributed by: Charly, Cadillac

CHICAGO BLUESMASTERS VOL.2: AIN'T TIMES HARD (Various Artists).

Chicago Boogie Piano

HEAVY TIMBRE Chicago boogie piano (Various Artists).
Album: released on Sirens in Apr'79. Distributed by: Swift

Chicago Breakdown

CHICAGO BREAKDOWN (Various Artists).
Album: released on Takoma (USA) in Jul'81. Distributed by: Allegiance Distribution

Chicago Calling

CHICAGO CALLING (Various Artists).
Tracks: / How long can this go on / Oh Mama / Mean cop / Win the dance / Remember the time / Off the hook / Lotta lovin / My man is a lover / Apache war dance / That ain't right / Bright sound, The / Early in the morning / That man / Will my man be home tonight / I stay mad / Cut you a loose.
Album: released on Charly in May'86 by Charly Records. Distributed by: Charly, Cadillac

Chicago Connection

CHICAGO CONNECTION Various artists (Various Artists).
Album: released on Affinity in Mar'87 by Charly Records. Distributed by: Charly, Cadillac

Chicago Hot Six

STOMPING AT THE GOOD TIME.
Album: released on GHB in Jun'86. Distributed by: Jazz Music, Swift

Chicago House Hustlers

SHOW ME HOW TO JACK.
Tracks: / Show me how to jack (dub version).
Single (12"): released on Spin-Off in Nov'86. Distributed by: DRC

Chicago In The Twenties

CHICAGO IN THE TWENTIES 1926-28 (Various Artists).
Album: released on Arcadia in Apr'79. Distributed by: Cartel

Chicago Jazz

CHICAGO JAZZ 1928-33 (Various Artists).
Album: released on Swaggie (Australia) in Jan'83

CHICAGO JAZZ VOL.2 Russell's Hot Six (Various Artists).
Album: released on Classic Jazz Masters in Jul'81 by Mainline Record Company. Distributed by: Mainline, Swift, Jazz Music

Chicago Jump

CHICAGO JUMP (Various Artists).
Album: released on JSP in Jan'82 by JSP Records. Distributed by: Swift, Projection

Chicago Rhythm

CHICAGO RHYTHM (Various Artists).
Notes: Frank Powers, John Otto, Ted Des Plantes etc.
Album: released on Jazzology in Feb'87. Distributed by: Jazz Music, Swift

ROUND EVENING.
Album: released on Jazzology in Jun'86. Distributed by: Jazz Music, Swift

Chicago Slickers

CHICAGO SLICKERS - 1948-1953 (Various Artists).
Notes: This album is released in mono. Featuring: Little Walter, Floyd Jones, John Brim, Robert Nighthawk etc.
Album: released on Nighthawk in Dec'86 by Faulty Products Records. Distributed by: Pinnacle, Swift

CHICAGO SLICKERS 1948-1953 (Various Artists).
Album: released on Nighthawk in Apr'79 by Faulty Products Records. Distributed by: Pinnacle, Swift

CHICAGO SLICKERS,VOLUME 2 - 1948-1955 (Various Artists).
Notes: This album is released in mono. Featuring: Little Walter, Floyd Jones, John Brim, Robert Nighthawk etc.
Album: released on Nighthawk in Jan'87 by Faulty Products Records. Distributed by: Pinnacle, Swift

Chicago Soul Uprising

CHICAGO SOUL UPRISING The real sound of Chicago 1967-1975 (Various Artists).
Tracks: / Since you showed me how to be happy / I love you / Give it away / Girl don't care / Am I the same girl / Sly slick and wicked / I'll be right there / Funky chicken / Follow the leader / Love uprising / Let me be the man my daddy was / Could I forget you / Got to find me a lover / Girl I need you / Wait a minute / Don't burn no bridges.
Album: released on Charly in Jul'87 by Charly Records. Distributed by: Charly, Cadillac

Cassette: released on Charly in Jul'87 by Charly Records. Distributed by: Charly, Cadillac

Chicago String Band

CHICAGO STRING BAND.
Album: released on Testament in May'86. Distributed by: Swift Distribution,

Chicago Transit Authority

LIVE.
Album: released on Barclay (France) in May'83 by Decca Records. Distributed by: IMS, Discovery, Conifer, Swift, Polygram

Cassette: released on Barclay (France) in May'83 by Decca Records. Distributed by: IMS, Discovery, Conifer, Swift, Polygram

Chicaynes

FURTHER THOUGHTS.
Single (7"): released on Bam Caruso in Aug'85 by Bam Caruso Records. Distributed by: Rough Trade, Revolver, Cartel

Pharoah's land/Second thoughts

Chichester...

CAROLS FROM CHICHESTER (Chichester Cathedral Choir).
Album: released on Alpha in '82 by Alpha Records. Distributed by: H.R. Taylor

Cassette: released on Alpha in '82 by Alpha Records. Distributed by: H.R. Taylor

ROBERT AND ELIZABETH (Chichester Festival Cast).
Album: released on First Night in Jun'87 by Safari Records. Distributed by: Pinnacle

Cassette: released on First Night in Jun'87 by Safari Records. Distributed by: Pinnacle

Chicken Ranch

HUSH.
Single (7"): released on Cannon Fodder in Sep'85. Distributed by: Red Rhino. Cartel

Chicken Rock

CHICKEN ROCK (Various Artists).
Album: released on Eagle (West Germany) in Jan'82 by Bear Family Records. Distributed by: Stage One

CHICKEN ROCK VOL.3 (Various Artists).
Album: released on Eagle (West Germany) in Jan'82 by Bear Family Records. Distributed by: Stage One

CHICKEN ROCK VOL.4 (Various Artists).
Album: released on Eagle (West Germany) in Jan'82 by Bear Family Records. Distributed by: Stage One

Chicken Shack

CHICKEN SHACK.
Album: released on Gull in Sep'79 by Gull Records. Distributed by: Pinnacle

CREEPER, THE.
Album: released on WEA in Feb'79 by WEA Records. Distributed by: WEA

I'D RATHER GO BLIND/TEARS IN THE WIND.
Single (7"): released on Old Gold in Jul'82 by Old Gold Records. Distributed by: Lightning, Jazz Music, Spartan, Counterpoint

IN THE CAN Featuring Chrisitine Perfect.
Album: released on CBS in '84 by CBS Records. Distributed by: CBS

Cassette: released on CBS in '84 by CBS Records. Distributed by: CBS

Chicory Tip

SON OF MY FATHER/WHAT'S YOUR NAME.
Single (7"): released on Old Gold in Jul'82 by Old Gold Records. Distributed by: Lightning, Jazz Music, Spartan, Counterpoint

Chico & The Chile Sisters

NO NEWS IS BETTER THAN BAD NEWS.
Single (7"): released on Creole in Oct'82 by Creole Records. Distributed by: Rhino, PRT

Single (12"): by Creole Records. Distributed by: Rhino, PRT

Chief Crazy

CHIEF CRAZY Various artists (Various Artists).
Album: released on Clay in Jul'87. Distributed by: Pinnacle

Chief John

CHIEF JOHN & HIS MAHOGANY HALL STOMPERS (Chief John & His Mahogany Hall Stompers).
Cassette: released on 504 in Feb'87 by 504 Records. Distributed by: Chris Wellard, Jazz Music

Chiefs of Relief

FREEDOM TO ROCK.
Single (7"): released on War in Oct'85 by War Records. Distributed by: PRT

Single (12"): released on War in Oct'85 by War Records. Distributed by: PRT

HOLIDAY.
Single (7"): released on MCA in Aug'84 by MCA Records. Distributed by: Polygram, MCA

Single (12"): released on MCA in Aug'84 by MCA Records. Distributed by: Polygram, MCA

WEEKENDS.
Tracks: / Weekends / Kiss of life.
Single (7"): released on WEA in Feb'87 by WEA Records. Distributed by: WEA

Single (12"): released on WEA in Feb'87 by WEA Records. Distributed by: WEA

Chieftains

BALLAD OF THE IRISH HORSE.
Album: released on Shanachie in Jun'85. Distributed by: Sterns/Triple Earth Distribution, Roots

BOIL THE BREAKFAST EARLY.
Album: released on CBS in Feb'80 by CBS Records. Distributed by: CBS Deleted '87.

Cassette: released on CBS in Feb'80 by CBS Records. Distributed by: CBS

BONAPARTE'S RETREAT.
Album: released on CBS in Aug'78 by CBS Records. Distributed by: CBS

CHIEFTAINS 3.
Album: released on CBS in Aug'78 by CBS Records. Distributed by: CBS

CHIEFTAINS 4.
Album: released on CBS in Aug'78 by CBS Records. Distributed by: CBS

CHIEFTAINS 5.
Album: released on CBS in Aug'78 by CBS Records. Distributed by: CBS

CHIEFTAINS 8.
Album: released on CBS in Jan'78 by CBS Records. Distributed by: CBS

CHIEFTAINS NO 1, THE.
Cassette: released on Claddagh in Jan'74 by Claddagh Records. Distributed by: I & B, Record Services Distribution (Ireland), Roots, Topic, Impetus, Projection,

CHIEFTAINS NO 2, THE.
Cassette: released on Claddagh in Jan'74 by Claddagh Records. Distributed by: I & B, Record Services Distribution (Ireland), Roots, Topic, Impetus, Projection,

CHIEFTAINS NO 3, THE.
Cassette: released on Claddagh in Jan'74 by Claddagh Records. Distributed by: I & B, Record Services Distribution (Ireland), Roots, Topic, Impetus, Projection

CHIEFTAINS NO 4, THE.
Cassette: released on Claddagh in Jan'74 by Claddagh Records. Distributed by: I & B, Record Services Distribution (Ireland), Roots, Topic, Impetus, Projection

CHIEFTANS LIVE.

LIVE IN CHINA.
Album: released on Claddagh in Aug'85 by Claddagh Records. Distributed by: I & B, Record Services Distribution (Ireland), Roots, Topic, Impetus, Projection,

Cassette: released on Claddagh in Aug'85 by Claddagh Records. Distributed by: I & B, Record Services Distribution (Ireland), Roots, Topic, Impetus, Projection

VOLUME 1.
Album: released on Claddagh in Jan'79 by Claddagh Records. Distributed by: I & B, Record Services Distribution (Ireland), Roots, Topic, Impetus, Projection,

VOLUME 2.
Album: released on Claddagh in Jan'79 by Claddagh Records. Distributed by: I & B, Record Services Distribution (Ireland), Roots, Topic, Impetus, Projection.

VOLUME 3.
Album: released on Claddagh in Jan'79 by Claddagh Records. Distributed by: I & B, Record Services Distribution (Ireland), Roots, Topic, Impetus, Projection,

VOLUME 4.
Album: released on Claddagh in Jan'79 by Claddagh Records. Distributed by: I & B, Record Services Distribution (Ireland), Roots, Topic, Impetus, Projection

VOLUME 5.
Album: released on Claddagh in Jan'79 by Claddagh Records. Distributed by: I & B, Record Services Distribution (Ireland), Roots, Topic, Impetus, Projection,

VOLUME 6.
Album: released on Claddagh in Jan'79 by Claddagh Records. Distributed by: I & B, Record Services Distribution (Ireland), Roots, Topic, Impetus, Projection,

VOLUME 7.
Album: released on Claddagh in Jan'79 by Claddagh Records. Distributed by: I & B, Record Services Distribution (Ireland), Roots, Topic, Impetus, Projection

VOLUME 8.
Album: released on Claddagh in Jan'79 by Claddagh Records. Distributed by: I & B, Record Services Distribution (Ireland), Roots, Topic, Impetus, Projection,

VOLUME 9.
Album: released on Claddagh in Jan'79 by Claddagh Records. Distributed by: I & B, Record Services Distribution (Ireland), Roots, Topic, Impetus, Projection.

WOMEN OF IRELAND.
Album: released on Island in Jan'76 by Island Records. Distributed by: Polygram

Chieftains,The

CELTIC WEDDING.
Album: released on RCA in Aug'87 by RCA Records. Distributed by: RCA, Roots, Swift, Wellard, Chris, I & B, Solomon & Peres Distribution

Cassette: released on RCA in Aug'87 by RCA Records. Distributed by: RCA, Roots, Swift, Wellard, Chris, I & B, Solomon & Peres Distribution

Chiesel

SALLY GARDENS.
Single (7"): released on Homespun(Ireland) in Sep'84 by Outlet Records. Distributed by: Outlet

Chiffons

DOO-LANG DOO-LANG DOO-LANG.
Album: released on Impact in Mar'85 by Ace Records. Distributed by: Rough Trade, Pinnacle, Swift, Backs, Counterpoint, Jungle, Hotshot, Cartel

EVERYTHING YOU WANTED TO HEAR BUT COULDN'T GET.
Album: released on Laurie in Jan'84 by RCA Records. Distributed by: RCA

Cassette: released on Laurie in Jan'84 by RCA Records. Distributed by: RCA

FLIPS, FLOPS AND RARITIES.
Tracks: / He's a bad one / Lucky me / What am I gonna do with you / Dream dream dream / Heavenly place / March / Tonight I'm gonna dream / Just for tonight / Up on the bridge / Real thing / Love me like you're gonna lose me / Easy to love / Teach me how / When I go to sleep at night / Open your eyes / If I knew then.
Album: released on Impact in Jan'86 by Ace Records. Distributed by: Rough Trade, Pinnacle, Swift, Backs, Counterpoint, Jungle, Hotshot, Cartel

HE'S SO FINE/ ONE FINE DAY.
Single (7"): released on RCA in May'82 by RCA Records. Distributed by: RCA, Roots, Swift, Wellard, Chris, I & B, Solomon & Peres Distribution

HE'S SO FINE/ SWEET TALKING GUY.

Single (7"): released on Creole in Aug'82 by Creole Records. Distributed by: Rhino, PRT

ONE FINE DAY/ A LOVE SO FINE.
Single (7"): released on RCA in Aug'81 by RCA Records. Distributed by: RCA, Roots, Swift, Wellard, Chris, I & B, Solomon & Peres Distribution

ONE FINE DAY/ HE'S SO FINE.
Single (7"): released on Creole in Aug'82 by Creole Records. Distributed by: Rhino, PRT

PICK HITS OF THE RADIO GOOD GUYS.
Album: . Distributed by: IMS-Polygram

SWEET TALKING GUY/ ONE FINE DAY.
Single (7"): released on Creole in Aug'82 by Creole Records. Distributed by: Rhino, PRT

SWEET TALKING GUYS/ HE'S SO FINE.

SWEET TALKING/ HE'S SO FINE.
Single (7"): released on J.B. in Jun'80. Distributed by: Warren, Mojo Distribution, Jetstar, Lightning, Arawak, Soundoff

SWEET TALKIN GUY.
Single (7"): released on Old Gold in Jun'84 by Old Gold Records. Distributed by: Lightning, Jazz Music, Spartan, Counterpoint

Chilcott, Steve

PLANXTY IRWIN (Chilcott, Steve & Les).
Single (7"): released on Gypsy Folk in Dec'82 by Gypsy Folk Records. Distributed by: Pinnacle

Childers, Buddy Big Band

JUST BUDDY'S.
Tracks: / Nica's dream / Try a little tenderness / Arriving soon / Underdog has arizen / Looking up old friends / Crimp cut / Just Buddy's / What the hell / Pretty / Off broadway.
Compact disc: by Discovery Records. Distributed by: Flexitron Distributors Ltd. Swift

Child In The Forest

CHILD IN THE FOREST Foley, W (Phillips, Sian).
Cassette: released on Chivers Audio Books in Jan'81 by Chivers Sound & Vision. Distributed by: Chivers Sound & Vision

Childish, Billy

WHICH DEAD DONKEY DADDY? (Childish, Billy & Sexton Ming).
Album: released on Hangman in Oct'87. Distributed by: Revolver, Cartel

Childish, Wild Billy

I'VE GOT EVERYTHING I NEED.
Album: released on Hangman in Jul'87. Distributed by: Revolver, Cartel

LAUGHING GRAVY.
Album: released on Empire in Apr'87 by Empire Records. Distributed by: Backs, Cartel, Jetstar

TOPIC.
Album: released on Ring in Jul'78. Distributed by: Cadillac

Childre, Lew

OLD TIME GET TOGETHER.
Album: released on Starday, Apr'87 by Gusto Records. Dist: Crusader, Midland Records, Swift, Lightning
Cat. no: **SLP 153**

Cassette: released on Starday, Apr'87 by Gusto Records. Dist: Crusader, Midland Records, Swift, Lightning

Children

FREEDOM.
Single 12": released on DJ Int.(USA), Nov'87 Dist: Westside, Pinnacle

Children Kinder Enfants

CHILDREN KINDER ENFANTS Various artists (Various artists).
Single 7": released on Sonet, May'85 by Sonet Records. Dist: Jazz Music, Swift, Celtic Music, Roots, PRT, Sonet

Children Of Tane

NEW ZEALAND BIRDS OF THE FOREST.
Album: released on Viking(New Zealand), Nov'79 by Viking Records. Dist: Flexitron Ltd., Harmonia Mundi

Children's...

CHILDREN'S ANIMAL FARMYARD (Various artists).
Cassette: released on Bibi(Budget Cassettes), Sep'83 Dist: Pinnacle

CHILDREN'S CLASSIC (Various artists).
Album: released on Super Tempo, May'84 by Multiple Sounds Records. Dist: Multiple Sound Distributors

Cassette: released on Super Tempo, May'84 by Multiple Sounds Records. Dist: Multiple Sound Distributors

CHILDREN,S NUMBER SONGS AND STORIES 19 favourite songs and stories (Various artists).
Cassette: released on Bibi(Budget Cassettes), Sep'83 Dist: Pinnacle

CHILDREN'S PARTY SONG'S AND GAMES (Various artists).
Album: released on Kiddicraft, Jun'80 Dist: Taylors

Cassette: released on Kiddicraft, Jun'80 Dist: Taylors

CHILDREN'S PARTY TIME 24 favourite party games, songs and stories (Various artists).
Cassette: released on Bibi(Budget Cassettes), Sep'83 Dist: Pinnacle

CHILDRENS PLAY ALBUM, THE (Various artists).
Album: released on Cherry Lane, May'85 by Cherry Lane Productions. Dist: PRT

Cassette: released on Cherry Lane, May'85 by Cherry Lane Productions. Dist: PRT

CHILDREN'S SINGING GAMES (Various artists).
Recording Notes: Singing games/ Skipping/ Clapping/ Dipping/ Ball Bouncing games collected in England, S.Ireland, Scotland and Wales.
Album: released on Saydisc, Nov'83 by Saydisc Records. Dist: Taylors, Jazz Music, Swift, Projection, Essex, Harmonia Mundi, Celtic Music

Cassette: released on Saydisc, Nov'83 by Saydisc Records. Dist: Taylors, Jazz Music, Swift, Projection, Essex, Harmonia Mundi, Celtic Music

CHILDREN'S TALES FROM AROUND THE WORLD (James, Sally).
Album: released on Super Tempo, May'84 by Multiple Sounds Records. Dist: Multiple Sound Distributors

Cassette: released on Super Tempo, May'84 by Multiple Sounds Records. Dist: Multiple Sound Distributors

GOLDEN HOUR OF CHILDREN'S TV FAVOURITES (Various artists).
Tracks: / Sesame street / Tra la la Song, (The) / Medley - Play school, Magic roundabout / Rupert the bear / Cuckoo clock, (The) / Joe / Hatty town / Felix the cat / Lollipopo loves Mrs. Mole / Sir Prancealot / Old McDonald / Parsley / Jackanory / Oh Susannah / Shaun the leprechaun / Andy Pandy / Dr Who / Scooby Doo / Thunder birds / Bonanza / Aqua Marina / Captain Scarlet / Virginian,(The) / Lidsville / Pink panther / Song of the diddymen / Maverick
Album: by PRT Records.

Children's Bible Choir

BIBLE STORIES IN SONG (Children's Bible Hour Choir).
Tracks: / I'm acquainted with the author / Only a boy named David / Gideon had the Lord / Jonah and the whale / Keep walking with the Lord / Wise man and the foolish man, The / Hornets / Count your blessings / Something more than gold / In the same wonderful way / Bible chorus medley / Fourth man / Battle belongs to God, The / Daniel prayed / Daniel was a man of prayer / I believe what the bible says / Standing on the promises / I see Jesus / Jesus gave her water / Then Jesus came / Ten thousand angels / I thank the Lord I am saved
Album: by Pilgrim Records. Dist: Rough Trade, Cartel

SING ALONG SONGS FOR CHILDREN VOL 1 (Children's Bible Hour Choir).
Tracks: / Boys and girls for Jesus / Mile after mile / Behold, behold / Jesus loves me / That's the way to find happiness / Boys and girls assurance march / He owns the cattles on a thousand hills / Happy all the time / All through the week / Grumblers / Heaven came down and glory filled the soul / Christian cowboy, A / Only a boy named David / How did Moses cross the Red Sea / Ot's new heart that you need / I'm a soldier / I'm not growing old / Mansion over hilltop / Saved every day of the week / Onward Christian soldiers / If I were only bigger / In the same wonderful way / B.I.B.L.E., The / Sunday go to meetin' Christian / I have the joy / I'm on the rock / I am the door / One door / This little light of mine / Isn't he wonderful / My sins are gone / Why worry when you can pray / I'm in the Lord's army / Clap your hands / Do you know that you've been born again / Lord is watching over me, The / Why should I care if the sun doesn't shine / Happiness is the Lord
Album: by Pilgrim Records. Dist: Rough Trade, Cartel

SINGALONG SONGS FOR CHILDREN VOL 2 (Children's Bible Hour Choir).
Tracks: / Jesus loves even me / Jewels / Oh how I love Jesus / Do you wonder why / I'll be a sunbeam / Jesus bids us shine / Birds upon the treetop, The / Gospel train, The / Do Lord / Trust in the Lord / Jesus is coming / Mighty army of the young / Give me oil in my lamp / I just keep trusting my Lord / Amen, brother, amen / Windows of Heaven, The / Labourers together with God / He's able / I'll do it all for Jesus / I love him better every day / Like a melody / I am determined / Jesus, the wonderful friend / Which way are you travelling / Along the road / Jesus said that whosoever will / Brighten up your pathway / Let's talk about Jesus / It's all different now / O say, but I'm glad
Album: by Pilgrim Records. Dist: Rough Trade, Cartel

Children's Day

MESSAGE TO PRETTY, A.
Album: released on Poshboy, Mar'87 Dist: Jungle, Cartel **Media Note:** Mini LP.

Children's Land Of Make believe

CHILDREN'S LAND OF MAKE BELIEVE various artists (Various artists).
Cassette: released on Bibi(Budget Cassettes), Sep'83 Dist: Pinnacle

Children's Musical

I WANT YOU.
Album: released on Light, Mar'75 by Word Records(UK)Ltd.. Dist: Word, CBS

Children's Songs

FROG HE WOULD A WOO'ING GO,A (Various artists).
Tracks: / Frog he would a woo'ing go, A / Dame get up and bake your pies / Hush a bye baby / I have four sister's / I love little pussy / Jack and Jill / John Cook had a little grey mare / Lavenders blue / Little Bo-Peep / Mary had a little lamb / Polly, put the kettle on / Simple Simon / Sing a song of sixpence / Derby Ram,(The) / Lion and the unicorn,(The) / There was a lady loved a swine / There was a little man and he woo'd a little maid / Where was a monkey / Three blind mice / Three little kittens / Where are you going to my pretty maid / Who killed cock Robin
Album: by BBC Records & Tapes. Dist: EMI

Children's Stories..

3 HOURS OF FAVOURITE CHILDREN'S STORIES various artists (Various artists).
Cassette: released on Trio, Nov'84 by Music For Pleasure Records. Dist: EMI

3 LITTLE PIGS & OTHER FAVOURITE STORIES (for children aged 3-7) (Various artists).
Cassette: released on VFM Cassettes, Jul'85 by VFM Cassettes., Wynd-Up

Child's Play

CHILD'S PLAY (Various artists).
Tracks: / Getting dressed - PLAY SCHOOL / Heigh ho- WATCH / House at Pooh corner,(The) / Orville's song / Willo the wisp- HOLIDAYS / Dr who / Clapping song,(The)-PLAY SCHOOL / Henry's cat- THE DISCO DOODLE / Mr Greedy's song / If your happy and you know it / Mr Happy, / Train song,(The)- PLAY SCHOOL / inkle the Zoo cat is lost and found / Polly put the kettle on
Album: released on BBC, Mar'84 by BBC Records & Tapes. Dist: EMI

Cassette: released on BBC, Mar'84 by BBC Records & Tapes. Dist: EMI

Chi-lites

20 GOLDEN PIECES: CHI-LITES.
Tracks: / I'm ready (if I don't get to go) / Love uprising / Love uprising / Coldest day of my life / Oh girl / I wanna pay you back / I like your lovin' / Have you seen her? / For God's sake give more power to the people / Are you my woman? / We are neighbours / Letter to myself, A / Homely girl / Too good to be forgotten / I found sunshine / Stoned out of my mind / Toby / Give it away / Lonely man, A / Living in the footsteps of another man / Devil's doing his work, The
Album: released on Bulldog Records, Aug'84 Dist: President, Jazz Music, Taylors, Spartan

BEST OF THE CHI-LITES.
Compact disc: released on Kent, Jun'87 by Kent Records. Dist: Pinnacle, Cadillac, Jazz Music

CHANGING FOR YOU.
Tracks: / Bad motor scooter / Changing for you / Touch me / Making love / Bottoms up / I just wanna hold you / You take the cake / I love
Album: released on R & B, Aug'83 by Red Bus Records. Dist: PRT

Cassette: released on R & B, Aug'83 by Red Bus Records. Dist: PRT
Cat. no: **ZCRB 1003**
Single 7": released on R & B, Jul'83 by Red Bus Records. Dist: PRT

Single 12": released on R & B, Jul'83 by Red Bus Records. Dist: PRT

CHI-LITES CLASSICS.
Tracks: / Have you seen her? / Give it away / I want to pay you back / Love uprising / I never had it so good / Too good to be forgotten / Toby / Coldest day of my life / Homely girl / Lonely man, A / I found sunshine / Stoned out of my mind / Oh girl / For God's sake give more power to the people
Album: released on SMP, Sep'83 Dist: Jetstar

Cassette: released on SMP, Sep'83 Dist: Jetstar

Single 7": released on Certain, Oct'85 by Certain Records. Dist: Pinnacle, EMI

Single 12": released on Certain, Oct'85 by Certain Records. Dist: Pinnacle, EMI

HAVE YOU SEEN HER ?.
Single 7": released on SKM, Jun'84 Dist: PRT
Cat. no: **SKM 2**
Single 12": released on SKM, Jun'84 Dist: PRT

HEAVENLY BODY.
Tracks: / Heavenly body / Strung out / Round and round / Love shock / Have you seen her? / All I wanna do is make love to you / Give me a dream / Super mad (about you, baby)
Album: released on 20th Century, Dec'80 by 20th Century Records. Dist: BMG, IMS, Polygram

MAKING LOVE.
Single 7": released on R & B, Sep'83 by Red Bus Records. Dist: PRT

Single 12": released on R & B, Sep'83 by Red Bus Records. Dist: PRT

ME AND YOU.
Tracks: / Me and you / Tell me where it hurts / Whole lot of good good lovin' / Oh girl / Get down with me / Try my side (of love) / Hot on a thing (called love) / Never speak to a stranger
Album: released on 20th Century, Dec'81 by 20th Century Records. Dist: BMG, IMS, Polygram

Chill Fac-torr

CHILL FAC-TORR.
Tracks: / Shout / Fox hunting / Twist (round 'n' round) / I'll satisfy your desire / Burning desires / It's been a long time / Let's get closer
Album: released on Philly World(USA), Nov'83 by Philly World(USA). Dist: Polygram

Cassette: released on Philly World(USA), Nov'83 by Philly World(USA). Dist: Polygram

SHOUT (THE EXOTIC).
Single 7": released on Philly World(USA), Oct'83 by Philly World(USA). Dist: Polygram

Single 12": released on Philly World(USA), Oct'83 by Philly World(USA). Dist: Polygram

TWIST.
Single 7": released on Philly World(USA), Mar'83 by Philly World(USA). Dist: Polygram
Cat. no: **PWS 109**
Single 12": released on Philly World(USA), Mar'83 by Philly World(USA). Dist: Polygram

Chilliwack

WANNA BE A STAR.
Tracks: / Sign here / So you wanna be a star? / Tell it to the telephone / Too many enemies / Living in stereo / Mr Rock / My girl / Don't wanna live for a living / Walk on / I believe
Album: released on RCA, Mar'82 by RCA Records. Dist: BMG

Chills

BLACK LEATHER JACKET.
Tracks: / Black leather jacket
Single 12": released on Flying Nun, Feb'87 Dist: Rough Trade, Cartel

HOUSE WITH 100 ROOMS.
Single 12": released on Flying Nun, Aug'87 Dist: Rough Trade, Cartel

KALEIDOSCOPE WORLD.
Album: released on Creation, Feb'86 Dist: Rough Trade, Cartel

LOST EP.
Single 12": released on Flying Nun, Mar'86 Dist: Rough Trade, Cartel

Chilton, Alex

BACH'S BOTTOM.
Compact disc: released on Line(W.Germany), Nov'87 Dist: Pinnacle

DOCUMENT.
Tracks: / Kizza me / Downs / Holocaust / Kangaroo / Big black car / Dream lover / Hey little child / My rival / Hook or crook / Like flies on sherbert / Bangkok / September gurls / In the street
Album: released on Aura, Jan'86 by Aura Records & Tapes. Dist: Pinnacle

Cassette: released on Aura, Jan'86 by Aura Records & Tapes. Dist: Pinnacle

HIGH PRIEST.
Compact disc: released on New Rose, Oct'87 Dist: Pinnacle. Estim retail price in Oct'87 was £13.11.

Album: released on New Rose, 7 Nov'87 Dist: Pinnacle

Cassette: released on New Rose, 7 Nov'87 Dist: Pinnacle

LIKE FLIES ON SHERBERT.
Album: released on Aura, Feb'80 by Aura Records & Tapes. Dist: Pinnacle

LOST DECADE.
Album: released on Fan Club, Mar'86 by New Rose Records. Dist: Rough Trade, Cartel, Pinnacle

MAKE A LITTLE MOVE.
Tracks: / Make a little move
Single 7": released on New Rose, Dec'87 Dist: Pinnacle

NO SEX.
Single 12": released on New Rose, May'86 Dist: Pinnacle

STUFF.
Compact disc: released on New Rose, '86 Dist: Pinnacle

Chilton, John Feetwarmers

RUNNING WILD.
Recording Notes: For full information see under MELLY, George & John Chilton's Feetwarmers.

Chimes

ONCE IN A WHILE.
Album: released on Chimes, Aug'87

Chimurenga

AFRICAN DAWN.
Album: released on AD, Sep'87 Dist: Jetstar

Chin, Junior & The Offbeat Posse

POSSE MOVE.
Tracks: / Posse move
Single 12": released on Y & D, Nov'87 Dist: Jetstar

Chin, Leonard

GROOVIN'.
Single 7": released on Cassia Music, Dec'83 by Solid Gold Records. Dist: Jetstar

HOW COULD I LEAVE YOU NOW.
Single 12": released on Cassia Music, Jul'85 by Solid Gold Records. Dist: Jetstar

VISIONS.
Single 12": released on Adelphi, Aug'84 by Adelphi Records. Dist: Jetstar

WHAT MORE CAN I SAY.
Single 12": released on Sanity, Feb'83 by Sanity Records. Dist: Pinnacle, Jetstar

China

ANCIENT CHINESE MELODIES.
Album: released on Lyrichord(USA), Oct'81 by Lyrichord Records(USA). Dist: Flexitron Ltd., Roots

CHINA.
Tracks: / On the slide / Meet me halfway / Broken woman / Hametheme / Savage / Dear you / One way ticket / For a while / Shameful disgrace / This time it's for you
Album: released on Rocket, Oct'77 by Phonogram Records. Dist: Polygram

CHINA INSTRUMENTAL HERITAGE.
Tracks: / Wild geese alighting on the sandy shore / Old monk sweeping the Buddhist temple / Ascending to the top of a tower / Hundred birds courting the phoenix, The / Farewell, The / Freedom march / Flowers on brocade / Remembering an old old friend / Relieving my heart / Winter ravens sporting over the water / Spring river in the flowery moonlight, The
Album: released on Lyrichord(USA), Oct'81 by Lyrichord Records(USA). Dist: Flexitron Ltd., Roots

Cassette: released on Lyrichord(USA), Oct'81 by Lyrichord Records(USA). Dist: Flexitron Ltd., Roots

CHINA'S TREASURES.
Album: released on Lyrichord(USA), Oct'81 by Lyrichord Records(USA). Dist: Flexitron Ltd., Roots

CHINESE BUDDHIST MUSIC.
Album: released on Lyrichord(USA), Oct'81 by Lyrichord Records(USA). Dist: Flexitron Ltd., Roots

CHINESE CLASSICAL MASTERPIECES FOR THE PI-PA & CH'IN.
Album: released on Lyrichord(USA), Oct'81 by Lyrichord Records(USA). Dist: Flexitron Ltd., Roots

CHINESE CLASSICAL MUSIC.
Album: released on Lyrichord(USA), Oct'81 by Lyrichord Records(USA). Dist: Flexitron Ltd., Roots

CHINESE DRUMS & GONGS.
Album: released on Lyrichord(USA), Oct'81 by Lyrichord Records(USA). Dist: Flexitron Ltd., Roots

CHINESE MASTERPIECES FOR THE CHENG.
Album: released on Lyrichord(USA), Oct'81 by Lyrichord Records(USA). Dist: Flexitron Ltd., Roots

CHINESE MASTERPIECES FOR THE CH'IN-ANCIENT & MODERN.
Album: released on Lyrichord(USA), Oct'81 by Lyrichord Records(USA). Dist: Flexitron Ltd., Roots

CHINESE MASTERPIECES FOR THE ERH-HU.
Album: released on Lyrichord(USA), Oct'81 by Lyrichord Records(USA). Dist: Flexitron Ltd., Roots

CHINESE OPERA.
Album: released on Lyrichord(USA), Oct'81 by Lyrichord Records(USA). Dist: Flexitron Ltd., Roots

CLASSICAL MUSIC OF CHINA.
Tracks: / Ti-tse / Ti-tse et p'i-p'a / P'i-p'a / P'i-p'a / Corbeaux de l'hiver / Glissant sur l'eau gelee / Plainte de la blanchisseuse / En soulageant mon coeur / Clair de lune sur une riviere au printemps / Wu hu you / Ta pa pan
Recording Notes: Traditional classical music of China.
Compact disc: released on Sunset (France), Jan'87 Dist: IMS-Polygram Distribution

EXOTIC MUSIC OF ANCIENT CHINA.
Tracks: / Four tokens of happiness / Spring thoughts at Han Palace / Bird's song, The / Sound of the temple / Great ambuscade, The / Yearning on River Shiang / Flowering streams, The / In remembrance of an old friend / Elegant orchid, The
Album: released on Lyrichord(USA), Oct'81 by Lyrichord Records(USA). Dist: Flexitron Ltd., Roots

PHASES OF THE MOON (TRADITIONAL CHINESE MUSIC).
Album: released on CBS(Masterworks), Jul'82 by CBS Records. Dist: CBS

Cassette: released on CBS(Masterworks), Jul'82 by CBS Records. Dist: CBS

SHANTUNG FOLK MUSIC & TRADITIONAL INSTRUMENTAL PIECES.
Album: by Nonesuch Records. Dist: Transatlantic Records

China Crisis

ARIZONA SKY.
Tracks: / Trading in gold / No more blue horizons / Red sails / African and white / Are we a worker / You never see it / Jean walks in fresh fields / Some people I know do lead fantastic lives / Christian / Seven sports of all / Feel to be driven away / Temptation's big blue eyes / Highest high / Strength of character / You did cut me / Black man Ray / Wall of god / Gift of freedom / King in a catholic style / Bigger the punch I'm feeling / World spins, The / I'm part of it / Blue sea
Single 7": released on Virgin, Oct'86 by Virgin Records. Dist: Virgin, EMI

Single 12": released on Virgin, Oct'86 by Virgin Records. Dist: Virgin, EMI

BEST KEPT SECRET.
Tracks: / Instigator, The / Black man Ray / You did cut me / Arizona sky / Little Italy
Compact disc single: released on Virgin, Jan'87 by Virgin Records. Dist: Virgin, EMI

Single 7": released on Virgin, Jan'87 by Virgin Records. Dist: Virgin, EMI
Cat. no: **VS 926**
Single 12": released on Virgin, Jan'87 by Virgin Records. Dist: Virgin, EMI

CHRISTIAN.
Single 7": released on Virgin, Jan'83 by Virgin Records. Dist: Virgin, EMI

Single 12": released on Virgin, Jan'83 by Virgin Records. Dist: Virgin, EMI

DIFFICULT SHAPES & PASSIVE RHYTHMS.
Tracks: / Seven sports for all* / No more blues horizons / Feel to be driven away* / Some people I know lead fantastic lives / Christian / African and white* / Are we a worker / Red sails / You never see it / Temptations big blue eyes / Jean walks in fresh fields
Recording Notes: (Side 1) All titles composed by Daly/Lundon/Reilly - All tracks produced and engineered by Peter Walsh except *produced and engineered by Steve Levine for Do Not Erase Productions. All published by Virgin Music (Publishers) Limited. (Side 2) All tracks produced by China Crisis and Gil Norton except *produced by Jeremy Lewis. All titles composed by Daly/Lundon/Reilly - All published by Virgin Music (Publishers) Limited.
Compact disc: released on Virgin, Jul'87 by Virgin Records. Dist: Virgin, EMI **Media Note:** Re-issue.Originally released April '86

Album: released on Virgin, Nov'82 by Virgin Records. Dist: Virgin, EMI

Cassette: released on Virgin, Nov'82 by Virgin Records. Dist: Virgin, EMI

FLAUNT THE IMPERFECTION.
Tracks: / Highest high, The / Strength of character / You did cut me / Black man ray / Wall of god / Gift of freedom / King in a catholic style / Bigger the punch I'm feeling / ...The world spins / I'm part of it / Blue sea
Album: released on Virgin, Apr'85 by Virgin Records. Dist: Virgin, EMI

Cassette: released on Virgin, Apr'85 by Virgin Records. Dist: Virgin, EMI

Compact disc: released on Virgin, Apr'85 by Virgin Records. Dist: Virgin, EMI

HANNA HANNA.
Single 7": released on Virgin, Mar'84 by Virgin Records. Dist: Virgin, EMI Deleted '86.
Cat. no: **VS 665**
Single 12": released on Virgin, Mar'84 by Virgin Records. Dist: Virgin, EMI

KING IN A CATHOLIC STYLE.
Single 7": released on Virgin, May'85 by Virgin Records. Dist: Virgin, EMI

Single 12": released on Virgin, May'85 by Virgin Records. Dist: Virgin, EMI

MAN RAY.

Single 7": released on Virgin, Mar'85 by Virgin Records. Dist: Virgin, EMI

Single 12": released on Virgin, Mar'85 by Virgin Records. Dist: Virgin, EMI

WHAT PRICE PARADISE?.
Tracks: / It's everything / Arizona sky / Safe as houses / Worlds apart / Hampton beach / Understudy (The) / Best kept secret / We do the same / June bride / Day's work for the dayo's done, A / Trading in gold / Day's work for the dayo's done, A
Cassette: released on Virgin, Nov'86 by Virgin Records. Dist: Virgin, EMI

Compact disc: released on Virgin, Nov'86 by Virgin Records. Dist: Virgin, EMI

WISHFUL THINKING.
Single 7": released on Virgin, Jan'84 by Virgin Records. Dist: Virgin, EMI

Single 12": released on Virgin, Jan'84 by Virgin Records. Dist: Virgin, EMI

WORKING WITH FIRE AND STEEL.
Tracks: / Working with fire and steel / When the piper calls / Hanna Hanna / Animals in jungles / Here comes a raincloud / Wishful thinking / Tragedy and mystery / Papua / Gates of door to door, The / Soul awakening, The
Album: released on Virgin, Oct'83 by Virgin Records. Dist: Virgin, EMI

Cassette: released on Virgin, Oct'83 by Virgin Records. Dist: Virgin, EMI

Compact disc: released on Virgin, Sep'84 by Virgin Records. Dist: Virgin, EMI

Single 7": released on Virgin, Sep'83 by Virgin Records. Dist: Virgin, EMI Deleted '86.

Single 12": released on Virgin, Sep'83 by Virgin Records. Dist: Virgin, EMI

China Doll

CHINA DOLL.
Single 7": by Graduate Records. Dist: Cartel

TURKISH DELIGHT.
Single 7": released on Parlophone, Jun'83 by EMI Records(UK). Dist: EMI

China Dolls

AIN'T LOVE AIN'T BAD.
Single 7": released on Speed, Nov'82 Dist: Spartan

Chinawhite

BLOOD ON THE STREETS.
Single 7": released on Future Earth, Apr'83 by Future Earth Records. Dist: Red Rhino, Cartel Deleted '87.

Chinese

SEE LANGUAGE COURSES.

Chinese Classical Orchestra

LOTUS LANTERN.
Album: released on Lyrichord(USA), Oct'81 by Lyrichord Records(USA). Dist: Flexitron Ltd., Roots

Chinese Gangster Element

EP.
Recording Notes: EP (4 track)
Single 7": released on Ted Rum, Feb'87 Dist: Red Rhino, Cartel

Chinese Orchestra

CHINESE FOLK SONGS.
Tracks: / Picnic in spring / Choice of a lover, The / Sorrow of Lady Wang Chao-Sun, The / Sweet memory of repose / West lake under autumn moonlight / Heavenly song / Swallows return when willows are green / Warning of autumn / Love in three stages / Agony in autumn, The
Recording Notes: Sung in Cantonese by the "Song Bird of South China", Lui Hung with Chinese Orchestra.
Album: released on Lyrichord(USA), Oct'81 by Lyrichord Records(USA). Dist: Flexitron Ltd., Roots

CHINESE OPERA AND FOLK THEMES.
Album: released on Lyrichord(USA), May'82 by Lyrichord Records(USA). Dist: Flexitron Ltd., Roots

Chinese Sheng

SONG OF THE PHOENIX.
Tracks: / North East: Chinese folk melody / Thinking about the world / Red flower of Tachai blossoms everywhere, The / Beautiful spring / Bai Yuan kills his wife / Golden phoenix / Spring morning on Hainan Island / Mother of clouds / Love song of the Hmong / Spring on South Mountain
Album: released on Lyrichord(USA), Mar'83 by Lyrichord Records(USA). Dist: Flexitron Ltd., Roots

Chinese Zither Music

CHINESE ZITHER MUSIC Various artists (Various artists).
Album: released on Nonesuch (USA), May'84 by Elektra/Asylum/Nonesuch Records. Dist: Conifer, WEA

Chingas, Johnny

PHONE HOME.

Single 7": released on CBS, Feb'83 by CBS Records. Dist: CBS

Single 12": released on CBS, Feb'83 by CBS Records. Dist: CBS

Chinv

TELL ME.
Single 12": released on H.R.Productions, Oct'87 Dist: Jetstar

Chiodini, John

WEIGHTLESS.
Tracks: / Ginger / Tahitian dude / Spacescape / Weightless / Famous amos / Joe's place / Gardens, The / Memory of a tree / Smiles
Album: released on MCA, May'87 by MCA Records. Dist: Polygram

Cassette: released on MCA, May'87 by MCA Records. Dist: Polygram

Compact disc: released on MCA, Jul'87 by MCA Records. Dist: Polygram

Chip, Kool

JAZZ IT UP (REMIX).
Single 12": released on Fourth & Broadway, Jul'87 by Island Records. Dist: Polygram

JAZZ IT UP - VOCAL.
Tracks: / Jazz it up - vocal / Jazz it up (dub) / Keep it mellow
Single 7": released on Fourth & Broadway, 20 Jun'87 by Island Records. Dist: Polygram

Single 12": released on Fourth & Broadway, 20 Jun'87 by Island Records. Dist: Polygram

Chipmunks

CHIPMUNK PUNK.
Tracks: / Let's go / Good girls don't / How do I make you? / Refugee / Frustrated / Call me / You may be right / Crazy little thing called love / My Sharona
Album: released on Mercury, Nov'80 by Phonogram Records. Dist: Polygram

MERRY CHRISTMAS FROM THE HAPPY CHIPMUNKS.
Album: released on Audio Fidelity(USA), Oct'84 by Audio Fidelity(USA). Dist: PRT

Cassette: released on Audio Fidelity(USA), Oct'84 by Audio Fidelity(USA). Dist: PRT

MERRY CHRISTMAS FUN WITH THE HAPPY CHIPMUNKS.
Album: released on Audio Fidelity(USA), Oct'84 by Audio Fidelity(USA). Dist: PRT

Cassette: released on Audio Fidelity(USA), Oct'84 by Audio Fidelity(USA). Dist: PRT

URBAN CHIPMUNK.
Tracks: / Gambler, The / I love a rainy night / Mamas, don't let your babies grow up to be cowboys / Chipmunks / Luckenbach, Texas (back to the basics of Love) / Lunchbox / On the road again / Coward of the county / Another somebody's done somebody wrong song / Made for each other / Thank God I'm a country boy
Album: released on RCA International (USA), Oct'81 by RCA Records. Dist: BMG

Cassette: released on RCA International (USA), Oct'81 by RCA Records. Dist: BMG

Chipperfield, Norma

NORMA CHIPPERFIELD.
Album: released on SRT, Oct'77 by SRT Records. Dist: Projection, Solomon & Peres, SRT, Pinnacle

Chippington, Ted

MAN IN A SUITCASE.
Album: released on Vindaloo, Mar'86 by Vindaloo Records. Dist: WEA, Cartel

NON-STOP PARTY HITS OF THE 50'S,60'S AND 70'S.
Single 7": released on Vindaloo, Jan'85 by Vindaloo Records. Dist: WEA, Cartel

SHE LOVES YOU.
Tracks: / Rockin' with Rita / Wierdness oh no *
Single 7": released on WEA, Apr'86 by WEA Records. Dist: WEA

Single 12": released on WEA, Apr'86 by WEA Records. Dist: WEA

WANDERER, THE.
Single 7": released on Vindaloo, Aug'87 by Vindaloo Records. Dist: WEA, Cartel

Single 12": released on Vindaloo, Aug'87 by Vindaloo Records. Dist: WEA, Cartel

Chiquitas

DANCE THE RHUMBA.
Single 7": released on Banana, Mar'84 Dist: Pinnacle, Fresh

Chirag Pegcgan

RAIL GADDI.
Album: released on Multitone/Savera, 21 Nov'87 by Multitone Records/Savera. Dist: Backs, Cartel

Cassette: released on Multitone/Savera, 21 Nov'87 by Multitone Records/Savera. Dist: Backs, Cartel

Chisel

HONEST WORK.
Album: released on WEA(Ireland), Mar'87 by WEA Records. Dist: WEA, Celtic Music, Projection, Roots, Solomon & Peres

Cassette: released on WEA(Ireland), Mar'87 by WEA Records. Dist: WEA, Celtic Music, Projection, Roots, Solomon & Peres

Chish & Fips

CHISH & FIPS Original Television Cast (Original Television Soundtrack).
Album: released on First Night, 7 Nov'87 by Safari Records. Dist: Pinnacle

Cassette: released on First Night, 7 Nov'87 by Safari Records. Dist: Pinnacle

Chisholm, Angus

EARLY RECORDINGS OF.....,THE.
Album: released on Shanachie(USA), Sep'79 Dist: Roots, Projection, Sterns, Celtic Music, Cadillac, Ross, Duncans, Impetus

Chisholm, George

GEORGE CHISHOLM,KEITH SMITH AND HEFTY JAZZ (Chisholm, George/Keith Smith/Hefty Jazz).
Album: released on Flutegrove, Jul'82, Wellard

SWINGING MR.C.
Tracks: / Swinging Mr.C / Tin roof blues / Sophisticated lady / One for monk / Flip-flop / You've changed / Don't worry 'bout me / Old feeling, The / Dear bix / I'm begining to see the lights
Album: released on Zodiac, Oct'86 Dist: Jazz Music

Chiswick Chartbusters

CHISWICK CHARTBUSTERS VOL.1 Various artists (Various artists).
Album: released on Chiswick, Aug'77 by Chiswick Records. Dist: Pinnacle

CHISWICK CHARTBUSTERS VOL.2 Various artists (Various artists).
Album: released on Chiswick, Mar'78 by Chiswick Records. Dist: Pinnacle

Chittison, Herman

AT THE PIANO.
Cassette: released on Holmia Cassettes, Jun'86 Dist: Jazz Music, Wellard

MELODY LINGERS ON.
Album: released on Audiophile, Jun'86 by Jazzology Records (USA). Dist: Jazz Music, Swift

Chloe

HE IS ELECTRIC.
Single 7": released on Sirocco, Feb'84 by Sirocco Records. Dist: Pinnacle

Choates, Harry

JOLE BLON.
Album: released on D/D (US), Mar'79 Dist: Swift

TRIBUTE TO....
Album: released on Flyright, Oct'86 by Flyright Records. Dist: Swift, Jazz Music, Wellard, Cadillac

Choc Stars

AWA ET BEN.
Tracks: / Nocha / Lascar pa kapi / Miyo motema
Album: released on Globestyle, Feb'86 by Ace Records. Dist: Projection, Celtic Music, Pinnacle, Cadillac, Jazz Music, Wellard

CHOC=SHOCK=CHOC.
Album: released on Globestyle, Mar'86 by Ace Records. Dist: Projection, Celtic Music, Pinnacle, Cadillac, Jazz Music, Wellard

Chocolate Dandies

CHOCOLATE DANDIES (1928-1933).
Album: released on Swaggie(Australia), Jan'83 Dist: Jazz Music

JAZZ BANDS 1926/30.
Album: , Swift, VJM, Wellard **Media Note:** Mono LP.

Chocolate Dream

DISCO SUNSET.
Cassette: released on Orchild Music, Feb'82

Chocolate Milk

BLUE JEANS.
Tracks: / Blue jeans / Like my lady's love / Running on empty / Honey bun / Let's go all the way / I've been loving you too long / Video queen
Album: released on RCA, Mar'82 by RCA Records. Dist: BMG

COMIN'.
Tracks: / Comin' / Something new / Do unto others / Feel the need / With all our love / Starbright / I refuse / Island love
Album: released on RCA, Jan'77 by RCA Records. Dist: BMG

Chocolate Watch Band

44.
Tracks: / Don't need your lovin' / No way out / It's all over now, baby blue / I'm not like everybody else / Misty lane / Loose lip sync ship / Are you gonna be there (at the love-in)? / Gone and passes by / Sitting there standing / She weaves a tender trap / Sweet young thing / I ain't no miracle worker / Blues theme
Album: released on Big Beat, Oct'84 by Ace Records. Dist: Celtic Music, Pinnacle, Jazz Music, Projection

Chocolateland Singers

SQUEAKALONG CHRISTMAS.
Cassette: released on PRT, Nov'87 by PRT Records. Dist: PRT

Choice

AN OLD FASHIONED CHRISTMAS.
Single 7": released on Weasel, Dec'82 by Weasel Records. Dist: Spart

SWEET LITTLE INDIANS.
Tracks: / After you're gone
Single 12": released on Climax, Jun'86 Dist: PRT, EMI, M.I.S.*

Choice Treats

LOVE ON THE REBOUND.
Single 7": released on Passion, Jan'84 by Passion Records. Dist: PRT

Single 12": released on Passion, Jan'84 by Passion Records. Dist: PRT

Choices Of The Heart

CHOICES OF THE HEART Various artists (Various artists).
Album: released on Stylus, Dec'85 Dist: Pinnacle, Terry Blood, Stylus Distribution

Cassette: released on Stylus, Dec'85 Dist: Pinnacle, Terry Blood, Stylus Distribution

Choir

TO THE CITY TOMORROW.
Single 7": released on A&M, Feb'83 by A&M Records. Dist: Polygram

Choir Militia

SHARPEN THE KNIFE.
Tracks: / Nothing that would
Single 7": released on War, Jun'86 by War Records.

Single 12": released on War, Jun'86 by War Records.

Choir Of...

20 FAVOURITE HYMNS OF CHARLES WESLEY (Choir Of Central Hall).
Compact disc: released on Abbey, Mar'85 by Abbey Records. Dist: PRT, Taylors,

BEHOLD THE MAN (Choir of St Micheal-le-Belfry).
Album: released on Word(UK), Nov'84 by Word Records(UK)Ltd.., CBS

Cassette: released on Word(UK), Nov'84 by Word Records(UK)Ltd.., CBS

CAROLS FROM CHRIST CHURCH (Choir of Christ Church Cathedral, Oxford).
Tracks: / Tomorrow shall be my dancing day / Remember thou, oh man / I sing of a maiden / Sing lullaby / Bethlehem down / Here is the little door / Sir Christmas / In Dulce Jubilo / Jesu, Thou are our Saviour / O sweet little one / Crown of roses, The / Spotless rose, A / Alleluya, a new work is come on hand
Recording Notes: Mostly less well-known carols.
Album: released on ASV(Academy Sound & Vision), Oct'83 by Academy Sound & Vision Records. Dist: Pinnacle

Cassette: released on ASV(Academy Sound & Vision), Oct'83 by Academy Sound & Vision Records. Dist: Pinnacle

Choirboys

CHOIRBOYS Original Soundtrack.
Album: released on MCA(USA), Mar'78 by MCA Records(USA). Dist: Pinnacle, Swift

Choirgirls

I COULD HAVE KISSED HIM THEN.
Single 7": released on BK, Sep'82

Chokers & Files

OLD TIME MUSIC.
Album: released on Rounder(USA), Sep'85 Dist: Jazz Music, Projection, Swift, Celtic Music, Cadillac, Ross, Duncans, Impetus

Chopin, Henri

AUDIOPOEMS.
Album: released on Tangent, Apr'81 by Tangent Records. Dist: Jazz Music, Projection, Swift, Celtic Music, Cadillac, Ross, Duncans, Impetus

Choral Classics

CHORAL CLASSICS - GOLDEN HOUR OF (Various artists).
Album: released on Golden Hour, Apr'78 by PRT Records.

Choral Guild Of America

CHRISTMAS MUSIC.
Album: released on Press Avant, Nov'85 by Compendium Int.Records. Dist: Pinnacle

Cassette: released on Press Avant, Nov'85 by Compendium Int Records. Dist: Pinnacle

Chorale
MOUNTAIN MEN.
Single 7": released on Telebell, Jun'85 by Towerbell Records. Dist: EMI

NATIONWIDE CAROL COMPETITION.
Album: by Decca Records. Dist: Polygram

SAFE AND SOUND.
Single 7": released on RCA, Jan'84 by RCA Records. Dist: BMG

Choralerna
BORNE ON WINGS.
Album: released on Myrrh, May'82 by Word Records(UK)Ltd.. Dist: Word, CBS

Cassette: released on Myrrh, May'82 by Word Records(UK)Ltd.. Dist: Word, CBS

LET THERE BE LIGHT.
Album: released on Myrrh, May'82 by Word Records(UK)Ltd.. Dist: Word, CBS

Cassette: released on Myrrh, May'82 by Word Records(UK)Ltd.. Dist: Word, CBS

Chorchazade
MADE TO BE DEVOURED.
Album: released on Get Ahead, Oct'86 by Revolver

Chord Of Love
CHORD OF LOVE.
Album: by Pilgrim Records. Dist: Rough Trade, Cartel

OUR GOD REIGNS.
Album: by Pilgrim Records. Dist: Rough Trade, Cartel

Chordettes
CHORDETTES, THE.
Album: released on Ace, Sep'83 by Ace Records. Dist: PRT, Pinnacle, Celtic Music, Cadillac, Jazz Music, Wellard

LOLLIPOP.
Single 7": released on Old Gold, Jul'82 by Old Gold Records. Dist: PRT, Counterpoint, Lightning, Jazz Music, Taylors

MR SANDMAN.
Single 7": released on Old Gold, Jul'82 by Old Gold Records. Dist: PRT, Counterpoint, Lightning, Jazz Music, Taylors

Chords
CHORDS, THE.
Album: released on Polydor, Apr'80 by Polydor Records. Dist: Polygram

Choristers
TELL US.
Single 7": released on Aul Reekie, Oct'84 Dist: EMI

Chorus
THESE STONES.
Single 7": released on AAZ, Jun'85 by AAZ Records. Dist: Red Rhino, Cartel

Chorus Line
CHORUS LINE, A Original cast recording (Various artists).
Cassette: released on CBS, Dec'76 by CBS Records. Dist: CBS

CHORUS LINE-FILM Original soundtrack (Various artists).
Album: released on Casablanca, Jan'86 by Polygram

Cassette: released on Casablanca, Jan'86 Dist: Polygram

Compact disc: Dist: Polygram

CHORUS LINE-NEW YORK Original cast:New York Shakespeare Festival (Various artists).
Tracks: / I hope I get it / I can do that / At the ballet / Sing / Hello twelve, hello thirteen, hello love / Nothing / Music and the mirror, The / Dance / Ten looks / Three / One / What I did for love / One, reprise / Finale
Album: by CBS Records. Dist: CBS

Chosen 3
NEVER AGAIN.
Single 7": released on Plezure, Oct'84 by Plezure Records. Dist: Pinnacle

---

Single 12": released on Plezure, Oct'84 by Plezure Records. Dist: Pinnacle

Chosen Brothers
SING AND SHOUT.
Album: released on Wackies, Jun'85 by Wackies Records. Dist: Jetstar

THERE YOU ARE.
Single 12": released on Wackies, Nov'84 by Wackies Records. Dist: Jetstar

Chosen Few
25-30 YEARS OF LOVE.
Tracks: / 25-30 years of love (Inst)
Single 12": released on Kufe, Apr'86 by Kufe Records. Dist: Pinnacle

DON'T KEEP ME WAITING.
Single 12": released on Kufe, Aug'85 by Kufe Records. Dist: Pinnacle

IN THE RAIN.
Single 12": released on Kufe, May'87 by Kufe Records. Dist: Pinnacle

LA LA MEANS I LOVE YOU.
Tracks: / Club mix
Single 12": released on Love & Unity, Aug'86 Dist: Jetstar

LOVE BETWEEN A BOY AND GIRL.
Single 12": released on Tree Roots, Feb'83 by Tree Roots Records. Dist: Jetstar

MY SWEET BABY.
Single 12":

ON THE RIGHT TRACK.
Single 12": released on Kufe, Jan'84 by Kufe Records. Dist: Pinnacle

SUNDAY MORNING.
Tracks: / Sunday morning (club mix)
Single 12": released on New Generation, Nov'86 Dist: Jetstar

TRYING TO MAKE A FOOL OF ME.
Single 12": released on Regal, Oct'82 by Regal Records. Dist: Jetstar

Chou Pahrot
CHOU PAHROT LIVE.
Album: released on Klub, Nov'79 by Klub Records. Dist: Celtic Music, Musac(Scotland)Ltd., Ross

Cassette: released on Klub, Nov'79 by Klub Records. Dist: Celtic Music, Musac(Scotland)Ltd., Ross

Chris & Cosey
ACTION.
Album: released on Licensed, Mar'87 Dist: Red Rhino, Cartel

CONSPIRACY.
Single 7": released on International One, Sep'84 by International One. Dist: Rough Trade

EUROPEAN RENDEZVOUS.
Album: released on Double Vision, Oct'84 by Double Vision Records. Dist: Rough Trade, Cartel

EXOTICA.
Compact disc: released on Pias, Oct'87 Dist: Cartel, Red Rhino

HEARTBEAT.
Album: released on Rough Trade, Nov'81 by Rough Trade Records. Dist: Rough Trade, Cartel

OCTOBER LOVE SONG.
Single 7": released on Rough Trade, May'83 by Rough Trade Records. Dist: Rough Trade, Cartel

Single 12": released on Rough Trade, May'83 by Rough Trade Records. Dist: Rough Trade, Cartel

SONGS OF LOVE & LUST.
Album: released on Rough Trade, '84 by Rough Trade Records. Dist: Rough Trade, Cartel

SWEET SURPRISE.
Album: released on Rough Trade, Nov'85 by Rough Trade Records. Dist: Rough Trade, Cartel

Album: released on Dragon, Jul'87 by Trojan Records. Dist: Jazz Music, Projection, Rollercoaster, Celtic Music, Cadillac, Ross, Duncans, Impetus

TAKE FIVE.
Recording Notes: Take five ia an ep.
Single 7": released on Licensed, Feb'87 Dist: Red Rhino, Cartel

---

TECHNO PRIMITIV.
Album: released on Rough Trade, Jan'86 by Rough Trade Records. Dist: Rough Trade, Cartel

TRANCE.
Album:

Chris, D
TIME STAND STILL (Chris, D/Divine Horseman).
Album: released on New Rose, Dec'84 Dist: Pinnacle

Christ On Parade
IS'NT LIFE A DREAM?.
Single 7": released on Mind Matter, Nov'86 Dist: Rough Trade, Cartel, Southern Record

Christendom Rock
CHRISTENDOM ROCK Various artists (Various artists).
Cassette: released on Vision, Mar'85 Dist: Vision

Christian
I'M STILL DANCING.
Single 7": released on Gypsy, Nov'82 by Gypsy Records. Dist: Spartan

Single 12": released on Gypsy, Nov'82 by Gypsy Records. Dist: Spartan

OH LITTLE MAMA.
Single 7": released on Gypsy, '81 by Gypsy Records. Dist: Spartan

Christian, Charlie
CHARLIE CHRISTIAN.
Recording Notes: Featuring Benny Goodman, Lester Young, Count Basie, Fletcher Henderson, etc.
Album: released on Giants of Jazz, Sep'87 by Hasmick Promotions Ltd.. Dist: Counterpoint, Taylors, Wellard, Swift, Crusader, Jazz Music

CHARLIE CHRISTIAN WITH BENNY GOODMAN SEXTET & ORCHESTRA.
Album: by Realm. Dist: CBS

Christian, Colin
COLIN CHRISTIAN.
Album: released on Tank, Jun'79 by Tank Records. Dist: Jazz Music

Christian Death
BELIEVERS OF THE UNPURE EP.
Single 12": released on Jungle, Feb'86 by Jungle Records. Dist: Jungle, Cartel

CATASTROPHE BALLET.
Recording Notes: (Cat.no. CONTE 105) 10 track studio Christian Death album, not available on U.K. release.
Album: released on Invitation Au Suicide, May'84 Dist: Rough Trade, Cartel

Album: released on Contempo(Italy), Nov'87 Dist: Pinnacle **Media Note:** 10 track studio Christian Death album, Not available on U.K. release.

CHRISTIAN DEATH - 7" BOX SET.
Single 7": released on Normal, Sep'87 by Jungle Records. Dist: Red Lightnin', Rough Trade, Cartel, Jungle

DEATHWISH.
Album: released on Invitation Au Suicide, Feb'84 Dist: Rough Trade, Cartel

DECOMPOSITION OF VIOLETS, THE.
Cassette: released on Roir, Aug'85 by Reach Out Int. Records. Dist: Red Rhino, Cartel

ONLY THEATRE OF PAIN.
Album: released on Invitation Au Suicide, Feb'85 Dist: Rough Trade, Cartel

SCRIPTURES.
Album: released on Normal, Dec'87 by Jungle Records. Dist: Red Lightnin', Rough Trade, Cartel, Jungle

Compact disc: released on Normal, Dec'87 by Jungle Records. Dist: Red Lightnin', Rough Trade, Cartel, Jungle

SICK OF LOVE.
Tracks: / Sick of love
Single 7": released on Jungle, Sep'87 by Jungle Records. Dist: Jungle, Cartel

Single 12": released on Jungle, Sep'87 by Jungle Records. Dist: Jungle, Cartel

THEATRE OF PAIN.
Album: released on Future, Aug'83 Dist: Pinnacle

WIND KISSED PICTURES.
Album: released on Supporti Fonograph(Italy), Nov'87 Dist: Pinnacle **Media Note:** Mini LP.

Christian, Emile
EMILE CHRISTIAN & HIS NEW ORLEANS JAZZ BAND (Christian, Emile & His New Orleans jazz band).
Album: released on Southland, Mar'87 Dist: Zodiac, Jazz Music

Christian, Michael
BOY FROM NEW YORK CITY.
Album: released on Pye International, Sep'79

Christiana F.
FINAL CHURCH (EP).
Single 12": released on Supermax(Germany), Aug'83 Dist: Cartel, Rough Trade

Christianhound
BUDGERIGAR.
Album: released on Deadman's Curve, Nov'86 Dist: Red Rhino, Cartel

NOT GUILTY.
Tracks: / Not guilty
Single 12": released on Constrictor, Jul'87 by Constrictor Records. Dist: Fast Forward, Cartel

Christians
CHRISTIANS, THE.
Tracks: / Forgotten town / When the fingers point / Born again / Ideal world / Save a soul in a million / And that's why / Hooverville / One in a million / Sad songs
Album: released on Island, Oct'87 by Island Records. Dist: Polygram. Estim retail price in Oct'87 was £6.29.

Cassette: released on Island, 7 Nov'87 by Island Records. Dist: Polygram

FORGOTTEN TOWN.
Tracks: / Why waltz / Heading for a hard time
Single 7": released on Island, Jan'87 by Island Records. Dist: Polygram

Single 12": released on Island, Jan'87 by Island Records. Dist: Polygram

FORGOTTEN TOWN.
Tracks: / Forgotten town / Why waltz / One in a million / Man oh man / Look around
Compact disc single: released on Art & Soul, Feb'87 by Island Records. Dist: Polygram

FORGOTTEN TOWN (REMIX).
Tracks: / Forgotten town (remix) / Why waltz / Heading for a hardtime
Single 12": released on Island, Feb'87 by Island Records. Dist: Polygram

HOOVERVILLE And they promised us the world.
Tracks: / Hooverville / No reason / Losing game, The / Born again / Drip drop
Single 7": released on Island, 30 May'87 by Island Records. Dist: Polygram

Single 12": released on Island, 30 May'87 by Island Records. Dist: Polygram **Media Note:** 'Extra track on 12'

Cassette single: released on Island, 13 Jun'87 by Island Records. Dist: Polygram

IDEAL WORLD.
Tracks: / Ideal world / Rocking chair blues / Say it ain't so
Single 7": released on Island, Nov'87 by Island Records. Dist: Polygram

Single 12": released on Island, Nov'87 by Island Records. Dist: Polygram

WHEN FINGERS POINT.
Tracks: / When fingers point / Rebecca
Single 7": released on Island, Sep'87 by Island Records. Dist: Polygram

Single 12": released on Island, Sep'87 by Island Records. Dist: Polygram

Christie
YELLOW RIVER.
Single 7": released on Old Gold, Apr'83 by Old Gold Records. Dist: PRT, Counterpoint, Lightning, Jazz Music, Taylors

Christie, Agatha
THIRTEEN PROBLEMS, THE (Hickson, Joan).
Cassette: released on Listen For Pleasure, Oct'87 Dist: EMI

Christie, David
OUR TIME HAS COME.
Single 7": released on KR, Nov'82 by KR Recordings Ltd.. Dist: BMG, Revolver, Cartel

Single 12": released on KR, Nov'82 by KR Recordings Ltd. Dist: BMG, Revolver, Cartel

SADDLE UP.
Single 7": released on KR, Jun'82 by KR Recordings Ltd. Dist: BMG, Revolver, Cartel

Single 12": released on KR, Jun'82 by KR Recordings Ltd. Dist: BMG, Revolver, Cartel

Christie, Janice
HEATSTROKE.
Tracks: Heatstroke (dub)
Single 7": released on London, Jan'87 by London Records. Dist: Polygram

Single 12": released on London, Jan'87 by London Records. Dist: Polygram

I'M HUNGRY FOR YOUR LOVE.
Single 12": released on Affair, Aug'86 by DMS, Spartan

Christie, Keith
HOMAGE TO THE DUKE See also under Johnny Dankworth/Ray Nance/Johnny Hodges.
Album: released on Esquire, Dec'87 by Titan International Productions Ltd.. Dist: Jazz Music, Cadillac Music, Swift, Wellard, Taylors

Christie, Lou
I'M GONNA MAKE YOU MINE.
Single 7": released on Flashback, Jan'83 by Flashback Records/PRT Records. Dist: Mainline

LIGHTNING STRIKES.
Single 7": released on Creole, Aug'82 by Creole Records. Dist: PRT

Single 7": released on Old Gold, Jul'84 by Old Gold Records. Dist: PRT, Counterpoint, Lightning, Jazz Music, Taylors

Christie, Pete
GOOD MORNING.
Single 7": released on PRT, Jan'83 by PRT Records. Dist: PRT

Christie, P.T
IF YOU'RE NOT THERE.
Tracks: Once a day / Carry me back / Four walls / Gambler, The / Little folks, The / Running bear / If you're not there / Geisha girl / Amanda / Here I am in Dallas / Crossroads, The / Take good care of her
Album: released on Neptune, Nov'80 by Lismor Records. Dist: Spartan

Cassette: released on Neptune, Nov'80 by Lismor Records. Dist: Spartan

Christie, Tony
AT HIS BEST.
Album: released on MFP, Sep'83 by Music For Pleasure Records. Dist: EMI

Cassette: released on MFP, Sep'83 by Music For Pleasure Records. Dist: EMI

BABY I'M A WANT YOU.
Tracks: Solitaire / Way we were, The / Happy birthday baby / Bewitched / Here's that rainy day / House is not a home, A / Feelings / Sittin' on the dock of a bay / Didn't we? / Drive safely darlin' / Easy to love / Daddy don't you walk so fast / My sweet lord / I'm gonna make you love me / Baby I'm a want you / You and I / Part time love / Drift away / Have you ever been to Georgia / Like sister and brother / On this night of a thousand stars / I did what I did for Maria / Las Vegas / Is this the way to Amarillo / Avenues and alleyways / Love hurts / Most beautiful girl, The / On broadway
Album: released on Cambra, Sep'86 by Cambra Records. Dist: Celtic Music

Cassette: released on Cambra, Sep'86 by Cambra Records. Dist: Celtic Music

GOLDEN GREATS: TONY CHRISTIE.
Album: released on MCA, Oct'85 by MCA Records. Dist: Polygram

Cassette: released on MCA, Oct'85 by MCA Records. Dist: Polygram

I DID WHAT I DID FOR MARIA.
Single 7": released on Old Gold, Jul'82 by Old Gold Records. Dist: PRT, Counterpoint, Lightning, Jazz Music, Taylors

LADIES MAN.
Album: released on RCA(Germany), Apr'83 by RCA Records. Dist: Conifer, Target

Cassette: released on RCA(Germany), Apr'83 by RCA Records. Dist: Conifer, Target

TONY CHRISTIE LIVE.
Tracks: You've lost that lovin' feelin' / Ol' man river / If it feels good do it / Las Vegas / Don't go down to Reno / I did what I did for Maria / MacArthur Park / Didn't we / (Is this the way to) Amarillo / West side story / Something's coming / Maria / Somewhere / Tonight / (Your love keeps lifting me) Higher and higher / Help me make it through the night / So deep is the night / Hey Jude / Solitaire
Album: released on MFP, Oct'80 by Music For Pleasure Records. Dist: EMI

WIND BENEATH MY WINGS.
Single 7": released on A.1, Jul'85 by A.1 Records. Dist: PRT

Christine
CHRISTINE Original soundtrack.
Tracks: Bad to the bone / Not fade away / Pledging my love / We belong together / Keep a-knockin' / I wonder why / Harlem nocturne / Little bitty pretty one / Rock 'n' roll is here to stay / Christine attacks / Bony Moronie
Album: released on Motown, Jul'84 by Motown Records. Dist: BMG

Cassette: released on Motown, Jul'84 by Motown Records. Dist: BMG

Christmann, Gunter
SOLOMUSIKEN FUR POSAUNE ETC.
Album: released on Ring, Jul'78 Dist: Cadillac

Christmann Schoenenberg
LIVE - MOERS FESTIVAL 76.
Album: released on Ring, Jul'78 Dist: Cadillac

TOPIC.
Album: released on Ring, Jul'78 Dist: Cadillac

Christmas....
CHRISTMAS ALBUM, THE Various artists (Various artists).
Recording Notes: See under: "Now - The Christmas Album".
Album: released on Deja Vu, Aug'86 by Deja Vu Records. Dist: Counterpoint, Jazz Music

Cassette: released on Deja Vu, Aug'86 by Deja Vu Records. Dist: Counterpoint, Jazz Music

CHRISTMAS ALBUM, THE - NOW THAT'S WHAT I CALL MUSIC Various artists (Various artists).
Tracks: Do they know it's Christmas / I wish it could be Christmas everyday / Merry Xmas everybody / Last Christmas / Step into Christmas / Il Dulce jubilo / Another Rock 'n' Roll Christmas / Wonderful Christmas time / Blue Christmas / Happy Xmas (war is over) / I believe in Father Christmas / Spaceman came travelling, A / Stop the cavalry / Little Saint Nick / Thank God it's Christmas / Lonely this Christmas / When a child is born / White Christmas
Recording Notes: * Not available on CD.
Album: released on Virgin, Nov'86 by Virgin Records. Dist: Virgin, EMI

Cassette: released on Virgin, Nov'86 by Virgin Records. Dist: Virgin, EMI

Compact discs: released on Virgin, Nov'86 by Virgin Records. Dist: Virgin, EMI

CHRISTMAS CAROL Dickens, Charles (Christmas Carol).
Cassette: released on Tellastory, Oct'79 by Bartlett Bliss Productions Ltd.. Dist: PRT, Taylors, Conifer

CHRISTMAS CAROL, A (Various artists).
Cassette: released on Tell-A-Tale, Oct'84 by Pickwick Records.

CHRISTMAS COLLECTION, THE Various artists (Various artists).
Album: released on Deja Vu, Oct'86 by Deja Vu Records. Dist: Counterpoint, Jazz Music

CHRISTMAS CRACKERS A selection of the most famous Christmas tunes (Various artists).
Album: released on RIM, Nov'79 by Rediffusion. Dist: Jazz Music, Pinnacle

CHRISTMAS MUSIC BOX Original music box medley of Christmas songs (Various artists).
Album: released on Bornand Music Box(USA), Nov'80 by Bornand Music Box Co.(USA). Dist: Bornand Music Box Co.(USA)

Cassette: released on Bornand Music Box(USA), Nov'80 by Bornand Music Box Co.(USA). Dist: Bornand Music Box Co.(USA)

PHIL SPECTOR CHRISTMAS ALBUM (Various artists).
Tracks: White christmas / Frosty the snowman / Bells of St. Mary, The / Santa Claus is comin' to town / Sleigh ride / (It's a) Marshmallow world / I saw mommy kissing Santa Claus / Rudolph the red-nose reindeer / Winter wonderland / Parade of the wooden soldiers / Christmas (baby please come home) / Here comes Santa Claus / Silent night
Album: released on Chrysalis, Oct'87 by Chrysalis Records. Dist: CBS

Cassette: released on Chrysalis, Oct'87 by Chrysalis Records. Dist: CBS

Compact disc: released on Chrysalis, Nov'87 by Chrysalis Records. Dist: CBS

Christmas bonanza
CHRISTMAS BONANZA Various artists (Various artists).
Album: released on Striker Lee, Dec'87 by Striker Lee Records. Dist: Jetstar

Christmas At Home
CHRISTMAS AT HOME various artists (Various artists).
Tracks: God rest ye merry, gentlemen / Sussex carol / Ding dong merrily on high / Angels from the realms of glory / First nowell, The / Away in a manger / We wish you a merry christmas
Cassette: released on Pickwick(Ditto series), '83 by Pickwick Records. Dist: PRT, Clyde Factors

Christmas Carols
CHRISTMAS CAROLS FROM CANTERBURY various artists (Various artists).
Tracks: O come all ye faithful / Gabriel's message / How far is it to Bethlehem / O come O come Emmanuel / Silent night / Unto us a boy is born / Infant king, The / In dulci jubilo / Personent hodie / Ding dong merrily on high / Angeles from the realms of glory / Tomorrow shall be my dancing day / Holly and the ivy, The / Masters in this hall / Kings of Orient / God rest ye merry gentlemen / Seven joys of Mary, The / Hark the herald angels sing / Chorale prelude / In dulci jubilo / Bells of Canterbury Cathedral
Album: released on BBC, Oct'81 by BBC Records & Tapes. Dist: EMI

Cassette: released on BBC, Oct'81 by BBC Records & Tapes. Dist: EMI

Christmas Country
CHRISTMAS COUNTRY Various artists (Various artists).
Tracks: Please come home for Christmas / Little drummer boy / Silver bells / Blue Christmas / Christmas song, The / Silent night / Rudolph the red-nosed reindeer / O holy night / White Christmas
Album: released on Planet, Nov'81 Dist: WEA

Christmas From St.Paul's
CHRISTMAS FROM ST.PAUL'S CATHEDRAL Various artists (Various artists).
Album: released on Prelude, 7 Nov'87 Dist: CBS, IMS

Cassette: released on Prelude, 7 Nov'87 Dist: CBS, IMS

Christmas Music...
JOY TO THE WORLD See Joy To The World.
Recording Notes: For full details see under: "Joy To The World (Christmas Music For Pan Pipes & Organ)"

Christmas New Orleans Style
CHRISTMAS NEW ORLEANS STYLE various artists (Various artists).
Album: released on Dawn Club, May'79 Dist: Cadillac, Swift, Jazz Music

Christmas Night in Bethlehem
CHRISTMAS NIGHT IN BETHLEHEM various artists (Various artists).
Album: released on Ariola, Dec'82 Dist: BMG, Ariola, Discovery, Target

Christmas Rap
CHRISTMAS RAP (Various artists).
Tracks: Christmas in Hollis / Let the jingle bells rock / Dana Dane is coming to town / Ghetto santa / Christmas in the city / Chillin' with Santa / He's Santa Claus / That's what I want for Christmas / Surf M.C. New Year, A
Album: released on London, Dec'87 by London Records. Dist: Polygram. Estim retail price in Dec'87 was £6.29.

Christmas
Cassette: released on London, Dec'87 by London Records. Dist: Polygram. Estim retail price in Dec'87 was £6.29.

CHRISTMAS RAP (IMPORT) Various artists (Various artists).
Recording Notes: (Rap compilation) Features unreleased tracks by Run DMC, Derek B, etc..
Album: released on Profile(USA), Nov'87 Dist: Pinnacle

Christmas Soul Special
CHRISTMAS SOUL SPECIAL Various artists (Various artists).
Album: released on Blue Moon, Nov'87 by Magnum Music Group Ltd. Dist: PRT

Christmas sting
CHRISTMAS STING Various artists (Various artists).
Album: released on Thunderbolt, Dec'87 by Thunderbolt Records. Dist: Jetstar

Christmas Teen
CHRISTMAS TEEN various artists (Various artists).
Album: released on K-Tel, Nov'82 by K-Tel Records. Dist: K-Tel, Celtic Music, Terry Blood, Wynd-Up, Taylors, Pickwick, Solomon & Peres, Polygram

Cassette: released on K-Tel, Nov'82 by K-Tel Records. Dist: K-Tel, Celtic Music, Terry Blood, Wynd-Up, Taylors, Pickwick, Solomon & Peres, Polygram

Christmas With...
CHRISTMAS WITH THE STARS various artists (Various artists).
Album: released on MGM, Dec'82 by Polydor Records. Dist: Polygram, Swift

Cassette: released on MGM, Dec'82 by Polydor Records. Dist: Polygram, Swift

Christopher Columbus
CHRISTOPHER COLUMBUS Original Soundtrack (Various artists).
Album: released on Colosseum(West Germany), Feb'86 Dist: Silva Screen Records

Christopher, Gavin
GAVIN CHRISTOPHER.
Tracks: Feelin' the love / Talkin' your love away / What can I say what can I do / Dancin' up a storm / We're in love / This side of heaven / Lady mysterious / We'll always be together / Be your own best friend
Album: released on RSO(USA), Aug'79 by Polydor Records. Dist: Polygram

ONE STEP CLOSER TO YOU.
Tracks: One step closer to you (inst) / One step closer to you (club mix) * / Accapella plus * / Short version *
Album: released on Manhattan, May'86 by EMI Records(UK). Dist: EMI

Cassette: released on Manhattan, May'86 by EMI Records(UK). Dist: EMI

Single 7": released on Manhattan, May'86 by EMI Records(UK). Dist: EMI

Single (12"): released on Manhattan in May'86 by President Records. Distributed by: Jazz Music, Swift, Taylors, Chris Wellard

Christ's College

MUSIC FOR CHRISTMAS (Christ's College Choir Cambridge).
: by Grosvenor Records. Distributed by: Taylors

Christy

CRY.
Single (7"): released on Le Cam in Jul'83

Christy, David

DAVID CHRISTY MEDLEY.
Single (7"): released on Record Shack in Apr'85 by Record Shack Records. Distributed by: PRT

Single (12"): released on Record Shack in Apr'85 by Record Shack Records. Distributed by: PRT

Christy, June

BEST THING FOR YOU.
Tracks: / When lights are low / My one and only love / How high the moon / Easy street / Kissin' bug / My heart belongs to you only / Something cool / Midnight sun / I'll take romance / This time the dream's on me / Dearly beloved / Until the real thing comes along / This year's kisses / When sunny gets blue / Best thing for you / Give me the simple life / Give me the simple life / My one and only love.
Album: released on Affinity in '86 by Charly Records. Distributed by: Charly, Cadillac

HOLLYWOOD BOWL PT.1 (Christy, June & Stan Kenton).
Album: released on First Heard in '84 by Submarine Records. Distributed by: Conifer, Taylors

Cassette: released on First Heard in '84 by Submarine Records. Distributed by: Conifer, Taylors

IMPROMPTU.
Album: released on Interplay in Sep'79 by Interplay Records. Distributed by: Jazz Music, Swift

INTERLUDE.
Album: released on Discovery (USA) in Apr'85 by Discovery Records (USA). Distributed by: Swift, Flexitron-Audio, Jazz Music

JUNE TIME (Christy, June & Friends).
Album: released on Swinghouse in Jun'85. Distributed by: Jazz Music Distribution, Swift Distribution, Chris Wellard Distribution

Cassette: released on Swinghouse in Jun'85. Distributed by: Jazz Music Distribution, Swift Distribution, Chris Wellard Distribution

MISTY MISS CHRISTY.
Tracks: / That's all / I didn't know about you / Day-dream / Sing something simple / Maybe you'll be there / Dearly beloved / Round midnight / Lovely way to spend an evening, A / Wind, The / This years' kisses / For all we know / There's no you.
Notes: Quite a rare album of late, this record was a best seller when it was first released in the 50's. This is one of Miss Cristy's most successful albums of late night listening also featuring the great writing talents of Berlin, Kern and Ellington.
Album: released on Capitol in Jan'86 by Capitol Records. Distributed by: EMI

Cassette: released on Capitol in Jan'86 by Capitol Records. Distributed by: EMI

THIS IS JUNE CHRISTY.
Album: released on Capitol in Apr'84 by Capitol Records. Distributed by: EMI

Cassette: released on Capitol in Apr'84 by Capitol Records. Distributed by: EMI

TOGETHER AGAIN (Christy, June & Stan Kenton).
Cassette: released on First Heard in Oct'84 by Submarine Records. Distributed by: Conifer, Taylors

Chromatics

99.
Tracks: / 99 / Noise annoys.
Single (7"): released on PVK in Aug'84

CHROMATICS, THE.
Tracks: / 99 / Do it again / I'm a rep / Doctor please / Drinkin' beer and playin' pool / You're late / Do you love me / Eat 'em up / Who's that man / Noise annoys / Woman like a limousine / Ain't gonna be your dog / Summertime romance / De-vo-t.
Album: released on Grenouille in Jan'87. Distributed by: Le Matt Music

FIRST.
Album: released on Grey Gull Records in May'83 by Future Earth Records. Distributed by: Red Rhino, Cartel

HOT STUFF.
Tracks: / Hot stuff / Jukin' at the joint.
Single (7"): released on Swoop in May'83. Distributed by: Le Matt Music Distribution

I'M A REP.
Tracks: / Eat em' up / I'm a rep.
Single (7"): released on Grenouille in Sep'86. Distributed by: Le Matt Music

LIVE MUSIC.
Tracks: / Correction / I love to ride on the choo choo / Live music / Right legs but the wrong dress, The / Miss teacher / T'tongue tied on the telephone line / Mean trucker / I wanna be a spaceman / Working at the bar / You never know / Playin' in the band / They'd never believe me.
Album: released on PVK in Apr'87

Chrome

3RD FROM THE SUN.
Album: released on Don't Fall Off The Mountain in Apr'82 by Don't Fall Off The Mountain Records. Distributed by: Pinnacle, Rough Trade, Nine Mile, Indies

BLOOD ON THE MOON.
Single (7"): released on Don't Fall Off The Mountain in Jun'81 by Don't Fall Off The Mountain Records. Distributed by: Pinnacle, Rough Trade, Nine Mile, Indies

DREAMING SEQUENCE.
Album: released on Dossier in Feb'87. Distributed by: Red Rhino, Cartel

FIREBOMB.
Single (7"): released on Don't Fall Off The Mountain in Apr'82 by Don't Fall Off The Mountain Records. Distributed by: Pinnacle, Rough Trade, Nine Mile, Indies

INWORLDS.
Single (12"): released on Don't Fall Off The Mountain in Jan'81 by Don't Fall Off The Mountain Records. Distributed by: Pinnacle, Rough Trade, Nine Mile, Indies

RED EXPOSURE.
Album: released on Beggars Banquet in Mar'80 by Beggars Banquet Records. Distributed by: WEA

Chrome Molly

I WANT TO FIND OUT.
Single (7"): released on Powerstation Records in Mar'86 by Powerstation Records. Distributed by: Pinnacle

Single (7"): released on Powerstation Records in Mar'86 by Powerstation Records. Distributed by: Pinnacle

STICK IT OUT.
Album: released on Powerstation Records in May'87 by Powerstation Records. Distributed by: Pinnacle

Compact disc: released on Powerstation Records in May'87 by Powerstation Records. Distributed by: Pinnacle

TAKE IT OR LEAVE IT.
Single (12"): released on Powerstation Records in Aug'85 by Powerstation Records. Distributed by: Pinnacle

WHEN THE LIGHTS.
Single (12"): released on Bulleon in May'84. Distributed by: Pinnacle

Single (12"): released on Bulleon in May'84. Distributed by: Pinnacle

YOU CAN'T HAVE IT ALL.
Album: released on Powerstation Records in Sep'85 by Powerstation Records. Distributed by: Pinnacle

Chron Gen

APOCALYPSE LIVE TOUR JUNE'81.
Album: released on Chaos in Apr'84 by Backs Records. Distributed by: Nine Mile, Cartel

CHRONIC GENERATION.
Album: released on Razor in Jul'86 by Razor. Distributed by: Pinnacle

Album: released on Secret in Jun'82 by Secret Records. Distributed by: EMI

JET BOY JET GIRL.
Single (7"): released on Secret in Jul'82 by Secret Records. Distributed by: EMI

NOWHERE TO RUN.
Album: released on Picasso in Sep'85 by Picasso Records. Distributed by: Pinnacle

OUTLAW/BEHIND CLOSED DOORS-DISCO.
Single (7"): released on Secret in Oct'82 by Secret Records. Distributed by: EMI

REALITY/SUBWAY SADIST.
Single (7"): released on Step Forward in Sep'81 by Faulty Products Records. Distributed by: Faulty Products Distribution, Pinnacle

Chronicle Of A Death...

CHRONICLE OF A DEATH FORETOLD Original soundtrack.
Album: released on Virgin in Jul'87 by Virgin Records. Distributed by: EMI, Virgin Distribution

Cassette: released on Virgin in Jul'87 by Virgin Records. Distributed by: EMI, Virgin Distribution

Chronicles of Narnia

HORSE AND HIS BOY, THE.
Notes: Michael Horden with music composed and played by Marsia Robles (Harp).
Cassette: released on ASV in Sep'81 by Academy Sound & Vision Records. Distributed by: Pinnacle

LAST BATTLE, THE.
Album: released on ASV in Dec'82 by Academy Sound & Vision Records. Distributed by: Pinnacle

Cassette: released on ASV in Dec'82 by Academy Sound & Vision Records. Distributed by: Pinnacle

LION, THE WITCH AND THE WARDROBE, THE.
Notes: Written by C.S.Lewis- read by Michael Horden with music composed and played by Marisa Robles (Harp).
Album: released on ASV in Sep'81 by Academy Sound & Vision Records. Distributed by: Pinnacle

Cassette: released on ASV in Sep'81 by Academy Sound & Vision Records. Distributed by: Pinnacle

Album: released on ASV in Sep'81 by Academy Sound & Vision Records. Distributed by: Pinnacle

MAGICIAN'S NEPHEW, THE.
Notes: Written by C.S.Lewis- Read by Michael Hordern with music composed and played by Marisa Robles (Harp).
Album: released on ASV in Sep'81 by Academy Sound & Vision Records. Distributed by: Pinnacle

Cassette: released on ASV in Sep'81 by Academy Sound & Vision Records. Distributed by: Pinnacle

PRINCE CASPIAN.
Album: released on ASV in Sep'81 by Academy Sound & Vision Records. Distributed by: Pinnacle

Cassette: released on ASV in Sep'81 by Academy Sound & Vision Records. Distributed by: Pinnacle

SILVER CHAIR, THE.
Notes: Written by C.S.Lewis, Read by Michael Hordern with music composed and played by Marisa Robles (Harp).
Album: released on ASV in Dec'81 by Academy Sound & Vision Records. Distributed by: Pinnacle

Cassette: released on ASV in Dec'81 by Academy Sound & Vision Records. Distributed by: Pinnacle

VOYAGE OF THE DAWN TREADER.
Notes: Written by C.S.Lewis, Read by Michael Hordern with music composed and played by Marisa Robles (Harp).
Album: released on ASV in Nov'81 by Academy Sound & Vision Records. Distributed by: Pinnacle

Cassette: released on ASV in Nov'81 by Academy Sound & Vision Records. Distributed by: Pinnacle

Chronos

CHRONOS Original Soundtrack (Stern, Michael).
Compact disc: released on Sonic Atmospheres in '86. Distributed by: Target

Chrysanthemum Ragtime...

CHRYSANTHEMUM RAGTIME BAND.
Album: released on Stomp Off in Jun'86 by Stomp Off Records. Distributed by: Jazz Music Distribution

PRESERVES.
Album: released on Stomp Off in Mar'87 by Stomp Off Records. Distributed by: Jazz Music Distribution

Chrysanthemums

IS THAT A FISH ON YOUR SHOULDER OR ARE YOU JUST PLEASED....
Notes: Full title : Is that a fish on your shoulder or are you just pleased to see me?
Album: released on Egg Plant in May'87 by Egg Plant Records. Distributed by: Nine Mile, Cartel

Chrystijo

FEY A VOLONTE.
Tracks: / La pergre / Feu a volonte / Rue des polyanthas / Accordeon de nuit / Waltz and boogie / Indifference / Vivre sans toi / Nouba / Ce que tu m'avais dit / Maldonne / Mon ami le boulanger / Regine / Les chevaux de bois.
Album: released on Accordion Record Club in Jul'86 by Accordion Record Club Records. Distributed by: Accordion Record Club

Cassette: released on Accordion Record Club in Jul'86 by Accordion Record Club Records. Distributed by: Accordion Record Club

Chuck, Raymond

BEST OF BOTH WORLDS.
Tracks: / We are the world.
Cassette: released on Accordion Record Club in Jul'86 by Accordion Record Club Records. Distributed by: Accordion Record Club

Single (7"): released on Agit Matter in Mar'86. Distributed by: Red Rhino, Cartel

Chulas Fronteras

CHULAS FRONTERAS Film soundtrack.
Album: released on Arhoolie in May'81 by Arhoolie Records. Distributed by: Projection, Topic, Jazz Music, Swift, Roots

Chumba Wumba

NEVER MIND THE BALLOT: HERE'S THE REST OF YOUR LIFE.
Album: released on Agit Pop in Jun'87. Distributed by: Red Rhino, Cartel

PICTURES OF STARVING CHILDREN.
Album: released on Agit Pop in Nov'86. Distributed by: Red Rhino, Cartel

REVOLUTION.
Single (7"): released on Agit Pop in Aug'85. Distributed by: Red Rhino, Cartel

STATE OF MIND.
Single (7"): released on Agit Matter in Mar'86. Distributed by: Red Rhino, Cartel

Church

BLURRED CRUSADE, THE.
Album: released on Carrere in Apr'85 by Carrere Records. Distributed by: PRT, Spartan

CHUCH, THE.
Album: released on Carrere in Apr'85 by Carrere Records. Distributed by: PRT, Spartan

DIFFERENT MAN 5 track EP.
Single (7"): released on Carrere in Apr'83 by Carrere Records. Distributed by: PRT, Spartan

DISENCHANTED.
Tracks: / Trance ending / You've got to go *.
Single (7"): released on Parlophone in Sep'86 by EMI Records. Distributed by: EMI

Single (12"): released on Parlophone in Sep'86 by EMI Records. Distributed by: EMI

HEYDAY.
Tracks: / Myrrh / Tristesse / Already yesterday / Columbus / Happy hunting ground / Tantalized / Disenchanted / Night of light / Youth worshipper / Roman / As you will * / View, The *.
Notes: The Church are an Australian 4-piece who up to 1985 had recorded 4 albums for Carrerre through WEA. EMI Australian signed them 9 months ago and this new Pete Walsh produced album which is already out in America and Australia has received some phenominal reviews.
Album: released on EMI in May'86 by EMI Records. Distributed by: EMI

Cassette: released on EMI in May'86 by EMI Records. Distributed by: EMI

IT'S NO REASON.
Single (7"): released on Carrere in Jun'84 by Carrere Records. Distributed by: PRT, Spartan

Single (12"): released on Carrere in Jun'84 by Carrere Records. Distributed by: PRT, Spartan

REMOTE LUXURY.
Cassette: released on Carrere in Apr'85 by Carrere Records. Distributed by: PRT, Spartan

SEANCE, THE.
Album: released on Carrere in May'85 by Carrere Records. Distributed by: PRT, Spartan

TANTALIZED.
Tracks: / View, The / As you will *
Single (7"): released on EMI in Apr'86 by EMI Records. Distributed by: EMI

Single (12"): released on EMI in Apr'86 by EMI Records. Distributed by: EMI

UNGUARDED MOMENT 4 track EP.
Extended-play record: released on Metropolis (France) in Nov'82 by Island Records. Distributed by: EMI

Church Bells

CHURCH BELLS OF KENT Canter-

bury Cathedral & 13 others (Church Bells of Kent).
Cassette: released on Saydisc in Jan'81 by Saydisc Records. Distributed by: Essex, Harmonia Mundi, Roots, H.R. Taylor, Jazz Music, Swift, Projection, Gamut

Churchical Chants
CHURCHICAL CHANTS OF THE NYABINGI Live field recordings.
Album: released on Rounder (USA) in Jan'84. Distributed by: Mike's Country Music Room Distribution, Jazz Music Distribution, Swift Distribution, Roots Records Distribution, Projection Distribution, Topic Distribution

Churchill, Savannah
MAE CARLISLE & SAVANNAH CHURCHILL, UNA.
Album: released on Harlequin in Jul'82 by Harlequin Records. Distributed by: Swift, Jazz Music, Wellard, Chris, IRS, Taylor, H.R.

TIME OUT FOR TEARS.
Album: released on Juke Box Lil (Sweden) in Jun'85

Churchill, Winston
CHURCHILL, SIR WINSTON.
Album: released on Decca in Feb'65 by Decca Records. Distributed by: Polygram

VOICE OF WINSTON CHURCHILL, THE.
Album: released on Decca in '65 by Decca Records. Distributed by: Polygram

Church mice
CHURCH MICE Oakley, Graham (Baker, Tom).
Cassette: released on Delyse in Oct'80 by Delyse Records. Distributed by: H.R. Taylor

CHURCH MICE, THE Oakley, Graham (Baker, Tom).
Cassette: released on Delyse in Oct'80 by Delyse Records. Distributed by: H.R. Taylor

Church Mouse
CHURCH MOUSE & CHURCH CAT Oakley, Graham (Church Mouse & Church Cat).
Cassette: released on MacMillan in Oct'81

C.I.A.
DISTANT LANDS.
Single (7"): released on Round, Apr'84 Dist: PRT, Red Rhino, Cartel

Ciarl, Claude
PLAYA, LA (Ciari, Claude & His Guitars).
Single (7"): released on EMI, Apr'83 by EMI Records. Dist: EMI

Ciccone Youth
INTO THE GROOVY.
Tracks: Burnin' up.
Single (12"): released on Blast First, Nov'86 by Sonic Youth Records. Dist: Rough Trade, Nine Mile, Red Rhino, Cartel

Cicero, Eugene
CLASSICS IN RHYTHM.
Compact disc: by Polydor Records. Dist: Polygram, Polydor

SPRING SONG.
Album: released on Timeless (Holland), Nov'85 Dist: JSU Distribution, Jazz Music Distribution, Jazz Horizons Distribution, Cadillac, Celtic Music Distribution

SPRING SONG (Cicero, Eugene Trio).
Tracks: Prelude No.2 / Caprice No.24 / Spinning son / Moldau, The / Spring song / Largo from preludes / Air from orchestral suite No.3 / Paraphrase in G flat.
Cassette: released on Timeless, Oct'86

Cider with Rosie
CIDER WITH ROSIE Lee, Laurie (Lee, Laurie).
Cassette: released on Argo (Spokenword), '82 by Decca Records. Dist: Polygram

Cijay
LOVE IS LIKE AN ITCHING IN MY HEART.
Single (12"): released on Eden, May'85 by Eden Records. Dist: Pinnacle

Cilmeri
CILMERI.
Album: released on Sain, Mar'86 by Roots

HANFFYNCH WELL.
Album: released on Sain, Mar'86 by Roots

Compact disc: released on Telarc (Import), Aug'84

Cimarons
BIG GIRLS DON'T CRY.
Single (7"): released on Safari, Aug'82 by Safari Records. Dist: Pinnacle

Single (12"): released on Safari, Aug'82 by Safari Records. Dist: Pinnacle

Picture disc single: released on Safari, Sep'82 by Safari Records. Dist: Pinnacle

IN TIME.
Album: released on Trojan, '83 by Trojan Records. Dist: PRT, Jetstar

LOVE AND AFFECTION.
Single (7"): released on Cimarons, Apr'83 Dist: Spartan

Single (12"): released on Cimarons, Apr'83 Dist: Spartan

ON DE ROCK part 2.
Album: released on Butt, Sep'83 by Butt Records. Dist: Counterpoint

REGGAEBILITY.
Album: released on Hallmark, Feb'82 by Pickwick Records. Dist: Pickwick Distribution, PRT, Taylors

Cassette: released on Hallmark, Feb'82 by Pickwick Records. Dist: Pickwick Distribution, PRT, Taylors

WITH A LITTLE LUCK.
Single (7"): released on Imp, Feb'82 by Demon. Dist: Pinnacle

Cincinnati Pops
STAR TRACKS.
Compact disc: released on Telarc (Import), Aug'84

STAR TRACKS (Cincinnati Pops Orchestra).
Compact disc: by H.R. Taylor

TIME WARP (Cincinnati Pops Orchestra).
Tracks: Star Trek / Battlestar Gallactica / 2001 / Space odyssey / Star Trek / Superman / Star wars / Alien / Night songs / Shake me / Nobody's fool / Nothin' for nothin' / Once around the ride / Hell on wheels / Somebody save me / In from the outside / Push, push / Back home again.
Compact disc: by H.R. Taylor. Dist: Unknown

Cincinnati Rock'n'Roll
CINCINNATI ROCK & ROLL various artists (Various Artists).
Album: released on Lee, Apr'79 by Lee Music Records. Dist: Stage One, Swoop

Cinderella
CINDERELLA various artists (Various Artists).
Cassette: released on Tellastory, Oct'79 by Bartlett Bliss Productions. Dist: PRT Distribution, Hayward Promotions Distribution, H.R. Taylor Distribution

Extended-play record: released on Disneyland, Dec'82 by Disneyland-Vista Records (USA). Dist: BBC Records & Tapes, Rainbow Communications Ltd(Distribution)

Cassette: released on Disneyland, Dec'82 by Disneyland-Vista Records (USA). Dist: BBC Records & Tapes, Rainbow Communications Ltd(Distribution)

CINDERELLA various artists (Various Artists).
Single (12"): released on Disneyland, Dec'82 by Disneyland-Vista Records (USA). Dist: BBC Records & Tapes, Rainbow Communications Ltd(Distribution)

Picture disc single: released on Disneyland, Dec'82 by Disneyland-Vista Records (USA). Dist: BBC Records & Tapes, Rainbow Communications Ltd(Distribution)

Cassette: released on Pickwick (Ladybird), '83

CINDERELLA (Crowther, Leslie).
Cassette: released on Listen Productions, Nov'84 Dist: H.R. Taylor, Hayward Promotions Distribution

CINDERELLA Original London cast.
Album: released on That's Entertainment, Apr'83 by That's Entertainment Records. Dist: Pinnacle, PRT

Cassette: released on That's Entertainment, Apr'83 by That's Entertainment Records. Dist: Pinnacle, PRT

CINDERELLA (Hampshire, Susan).
Cassette: released on Storytime Cassettes,

Aug'83

NIGHT SONGS.
Tracks: Night songs / Shake me / Nobody's fool / Nothin' for nothin' / Once around the ride / Hell on wheels / Somebody save me / In from the outside / In from the outside / Push push / Back home again.
Album: released on Vertigo, Aug'86 by Phonogram Records. Dist: Polygram

Compact disc: released on Vertigo, Jan'87 by Phonogram Records. Dist: Polygram

NOBODY'S FOOL.
Tracks: Nobody's fool / Shake me (live) / Galaxy blues, The*.
Single (7"): released on Vertigo, 23 May'87 by Phonogram Records. Dist: Polygram

Single (12"): released on Vertigo, 23 May'87 by Phonogram Records. Dist: Polygram

SHAKE ME.
Tracks: Shake me / Nightsongs / Hell on wheels.
Notes: Hell on wheels is only available on 12" version.
Single (7"): released on Vertigo, Feb'87 by Phonogram Records. Dist: Polygram

Single (12"): released on Vertigo, Feb'87 by Phonogram Records. Dist: Polygram

Cinderford Band
FOREST FESTIVAL BRASS.
Album: released on Grosvenor, Jan'79 by Grosvenor Records. Dist: Taylors

Cindy
HAPPY TO BE.
Single (7"): released on Unit 7, Aug'84 by Greensleeves Records. Dist: RCA

Single (12"): released on Unit 7, Aug'84 by Greensleeves Records. Dist: RCA

MOVE OVER DARLING (Cindy & Action Men).
Single (7"): released on Big Boy, Apr'83 by Big Boy Records. Dist: Pinnacle

PAST PRESENT FUTURE (Cindy & the Saffrons).
Single (7"): released on Disques Blue, Feb'83 by Disques Bleu.

TERRY (Cindy & the Saffrons).
Single (7"): released on Stiletto, Apr'83 by Fast Records. Dist: Cartel Distribution

Single (12"): released on Stiletto, Apr'83 by Fast Records. Dist: Cartel Distribution

Cindytalk
CAMOUFLAGE HEART.
Album: released on Midnight Music, Sep'84 by Midnight Music Records. Dist: Rough Trade Distribution, Cartel Distribution

Cinema Hits Album
CINEMA HITS ALBUM, THE Various artists (Various Artists).
Notes: Artists include: Duran Duran/Irene Cara/Eurythmics
Album: released on Towerbell, Mar'86 by Towerbell Records. Dist: EMI

Cassette: released on Towerbell, Mar'86 by Towerbell Records. Dist: EMI

Cinema Organ
BBC PRESENTS AT THE CINEMA ORGAN, THE.
Album: by BBC Records & Tapes. Dist: EMI, PRT,

Cinematics
FAREWELL TO THE PLAYGROUND.
Single (7"): released on Cinema Features, Nov'82 Dist: VCL

Cine Movie - The Album
CINE MOVIE- THE ALBUM Various artists (Various Artists).
Tracks: Prelude / Ending, The / Elephant man theme, The / Enchantment At Tugu / Russian Christmas Theme / Vivement Dimanche / La Notte / Days Of Heaven / Main Titles / Von Kern's Attack / Suite Pour Choeur Et Orchestre / Le Reve I / Timetable To Brooklyn / Garcon! / Folie Douce / Main Title.
Album: released on Milan France, Nov'86

Cassette: released on Milan France. Nov'86

Cinnamon
I NEED YOU NOW.
Single (7"): released on Jive, Mar'86 by Zomba Records. Dist: RCA, PRT

Single (12"): released on Jive, Mar'86 by

Zomba Records. Dist: RCA, PRT,

Cinnamond, Robert
YOUR RAMBLING BOYS OF PLEASURE.
Album: released on Topic, '81 Dist: Roots Distribution

Cinquette, Gigiola
SUPER DISC OF GIGIOLA CINQUETTI.
Album: released on A&M, Apr'79 by A&M Records. Dist: Polygram

Cintron
GET AWAY.
Single (7"): released on In Rock, Jan'83 Dist: Pinnacle

Cipolina, John
MONKEY MEDICINE (Cipolina, John & Nick Gravenites).
Album: released on Big Beat, Feb'83 by Ace Records. Dist: Projection, Pinnacle

Cipolla, Rudy
WORLD OF RUDY CIPOLLA, THE.
Album: released on Rounder (USA), Jan'84 by Mike's Country Music Room Distribution, Jazz Music Distribution, Swift Distribution, Roots Records Distribution, Projection Distribution, Topic Distribution

Circle Jerks
WILD IN THE STREETS.
Album: released on Steppers, Jul'82

Circles
CIRCLES.
Single (7"): released on Graduate, Jul'86 by Graduate Records. Dist: Nine Mile, Cartel

OPENING UP.
Single (7"): by Graduate Records. Dist: Nine Mile, Cartel

Circuit II
CAN'T TEMPT FATE.
Album: released on Elektra (USA), Nov'85 by Elektra/Asylum/Nonesuch Records. Dist: WEA

Circuit 7
MODERN STORY.
Single (7"): released on Micro, Sep'84 by Micro Records. Dist: Micro

Circuit Seven
VIDEO BOYS.
Single (7"): released on Rapp, Mar'84 by Rapp. Dist: Cartel

Circus Circus Circus
BUTCHER BITCHES.
Tracks: Butcher bitches / (Chop chop chop) / Six gears to heaven / Wooden man *.
Single (7"): released on Three, Mar'86 Dist: Priority Distribution, EMI

Single (12"): released on Three, Mar'86 Dist: Priority Distribution, EMI

INSIDE THE INSIDE OUT MAN.
Single (7"):

Single (12"):

MAGIC GIRL.
Single (7"): released on Sweatbox, Aug'87 by Sweatbox Records. Dist: Rough Trade, Cartel

Single (12"): released on Sweatbox, Aug'87 by Sweatbox Records. Dist: Rough Trade, Cartel

Circus Comes To Town
CIRCUS COMES TO TOWN various artists (Various Artists).
Album: released on Circus, Sep'81 Dist: Circus, Recommended

Circus Of Poets
NOW THEN DAVOS.
Single (7"):

Cirith Ungol
KING OF THE DEAD.
Album: released on Music For Nations, Aug'84 by Music For Nations Records. Dist: Pinnacle

ONE FOOT IN HELL.
Album: released on Metal Blade, Aug'86 Dist: Enigma Distribution

Cirkus
ONE.
Album: released on One Big Guitar, Aug'86 by

One Big Guitar Records. Dist: Revolver Distribution, Cartel Distribution, Pinnacle

Citizens Of Rome

SAINT MALO.
Single (7"): released on Someone Else's Music, Sep'82 by Someone Else's Music Records. Dist: Stage One

City Boy

DAY THE EARTH CAUGHT FIRE.
Album: released on Vertigo, Aug'79 by Phonogram Records. Dist: Polygram

HEADS ARE ROLLING.
Album: released on Vertigo, Nov'80 by Phonogram Records. Dist: Polygram

IN LOVE.
Single (12"): released on City Boy, Feb'82 by City Boy Records. Dist: Jetstar

City Centre

TO LOVE SOMEBODY.
Single (7"): released on Dingles, Aug'83 by Dingles Records. Dist: Projection

City Girl

DO YOU THINK I'M SEXY.
Single (12"): released on Touch, Jun'85 by Touch Records. Dist: Rough Trade, Cartel

City Limits Crew

FRESHER THAN EVER.
Single (7"): released on Survival, Apr'85 by Survival Records. Dist: Backs, Cartel Distribution

Single (12"): released on Survival, Apr'85 by Survival Records. Dist: Backs, Cartel Distribution

City Of Glasgow Police...

CITY OF GLASGOW POLICE PIPE BAND.
Tracks: / Scotland the brave / Nut Brown maiden / Jenny's Bawbee / 6/8 Marches / Midlothian pipe beaton / MacDonald's awa'tae the war / Muckin' O'Geordie's byre / Heilan' whisky / Hot punch / Raven's rock / Invernate house / Dark island / Caberfeidh / 5-(Quicksteps): / Man's a man for a'that, A / My love she's but a Lassie yet / Corn riggs / Gaelic Airs, Hornpipe & Jig / Waters of Kylesku / Mull of the bens / Mary with the witching eyes / Boys of blue hill / Paddy's leather breeches / 1-(2/4 Marches) / Highland Laddie / Corriechoillie / Teribus / Bonnie Galloway / Rowan tree / 6/8 Marches: / Kenmure's up and awa' / March of the cameron men / Because he was a bonnie lad / Louden's bonnie woods and braes / Tail toddle / Fairy dance / 5-(Slow march, Retreat Air & Quicksteps): / Road to the isles / Battle is O'er / Earl of Mansfield / Drum fanfare / 7-Pubroch variation 1: / Hail to my contry thomason / 8-(Scottish Air & Quickstep): / We're no awa' tae bide awa' / Happy we've been a'thegither.
Notes: Pipe Major: R.Lawrie (MCPS)
Album: released on Emerald (Ireland), Nov'84 by Emerald Records. Dist: I & B, Ross, PRT

City Of York, The

CITY OF YORK, THE various artists (Various Artists).
Cassette: released on Audiocord Cassettes, May'83

City Talk

TRICK OF THE LIGHT.
Single (7"): released on Pad, Jan'83 Dist: Pad

City, The

FOUNDATION.
Album: released on Chrysalis, Jan'87 by Chrysalis Records. Dist: CBS

City Waites, The

SOCIAL MUSIC FOR A 17TH CENTURY ENGLISHMAN.
Album: released on Hyperion, Jun'81 by Hyperion Records. Dist: Taylors, PRT, Gamut

Civil, Alan Band

SALUTE TO AMERICA, A.
Album: released on Phase 4, Nov'76

Civilised Society

SCRAP METAL.
Album: released on Manic Ears, Jan'87

VIOLENCE SUCKS.
Album: released on Manic Ears, Aug'87

Cj & Co

DEADEYE DICK.
Album: released on Westbound, Aug'78 Dist: WEA

DEVIL'S GUN.
Album: released on Westbound, Jul'77 Dist: WEA

CLADDAGH'S CHOICE Various artists (Various Artists).
Album: released on Claddagh, Nov'84 by Claddagh Records. Dist: I & B, Record Services Distribution (Ireland), Roots, Topic, Impetus, Projection,

Clail, Gary & Totp

HALF CUT FOR CONFIDENCE.
Single (12"): released on On-U-Sound, Oct'85 Dist: Rough Trade Distribution, Lightning

Claim

ARMSTRONGS REVENGE.
Album: released on Trickbag, Jan'86 Dist: Red Rhino, Cartel

Album: released on Tambourine, Sep'87 by Tambourine. Dist: Backs, Cartel. Estim retail price in Sep'87 was £5.67.

THIS PENCIL WAS OBVIOUSLY....
Notes: Full title: This Pencil Was Obviously Sharpened By A Left-Handed Indian Knife Thrower.
Single (12"): released on Tambourine, Sep'87 by Tambourine. Dist: Backs, Cartel

Single (7"): released on Tambourine, Aug'87 by The Dentists. Dist: Pinnacle

Claire And Friends

IT'S 'ORRIBLE BEING IN LOVE (WHEN YOU'RE 8 AND A HALF).
Single (7"): released on BBC, Jun'86 by BBC Records & Tapes. Dist: EMI, PRT

SUPERMAN.
Tracks: / Rainbow.

Single (7"): released on BBC, Sep'86 by BBC Records & Tapes. Dist: EMI, PRT, Pye

Single (12"): released on BBC, Sep'86 by BBC Records & Tapes. Dist: EMI, PRT, Pye

Claire, Valerie

I'M A MODEL.
Single (7"): released on Record Shack, Jun'85 by Record Shack Records. Dist: PRT

Single (12"): released on Record Shack, Jun'85 by Record Shack Records. Dist: PRT

SHOOT ME GINO.
Single (7"): released on Carrere, Nov'85 by Carrere Records. Dist: PRT, Spartan

Single (12"): released on Carrere, Nov'85 by Carrere Records. Dist: PRT, Spartan

Clair Obscur

PILGRIM'S PROGRESS.
Album: released on All The Madmen, May'86 by All The Madmen Records. Dist: Rough Trade, Cartel

Clamber

CHOOSE THE WAY.
Single (7"): released on Clamber, Mar'85 by Clamber Records. Dist: M.I.S.

Clan Campbell

CAMPBELLS ARE COMING, (THE) (Clan Campbell Scotch Whisky Pipes & Drums Band).
Album: released on Lochshore, Jul'82 by Klub Records. Dist: PRT

Cassette: released on Lochshore, Jul'82 by Klub Records. Dist: PRT

SCOTS BY TRADITION (Clan Campbell Pipes & Drums).
Album: released on Lochshore, Jun'83 by Klub Records. Dist: PRT

Cassette: released on Lochshore, Jun'83 by Klub Records. Dist: PRT

SEVEN TEARS (Clan Campbell Pipes & Drums).
Single (7"): released on Lochshore, Nov'82 by Klub Records. Dist: PRT

Clancy Brothers

BEST OF THE CLANCY BROTHERS, VOL 2 (Clancy Brothers & Tommy Makem).
Album: released on Harp(Ireland), Jul'80 by Pickwick Records. Dist: Taylors

Cassette: released on Harp(Ireland), Jul'80 by Pickwick Records. Dist: Taylors

BEST OF THE CLANCY BROTHERS, VOL 1 (Clancy Brothers & Tommy Makem).
Album: released on Harp(Ireland), Jul'80 by Pickwick Records. Dist: Taylors

Cassette: released on Harp(Ireland), Jul'80 by Pickwick Records. Dist: Taylors

COME FILL YOUR GLASS WITH US.
Album: released on Tradition, Nov'74 Dist: JSU, Cassion Distribution, Celtic Music, Jazz Music, Projection, Roots Records

RISING OF THE MOON.
Album: released on Tradition, Nov'74 Dist: JSU, Cassion Distribution, Celtic Music, Jazz Music, Projection, Roots Records

Clancy, Dennis

BONNIE SCOTLAND SHOW.
Cassette: released on Lismor, May'77 by Lismor Records. Dist: Lismor, Roots, Celtic Music

Clancy, Robert

SO EARLY IN THE MORNING.
Album: released on Tradition, Nov'74 Dist: JSU, Cassion Distribution, Celtic Music, Jazz Music, Projection, Roots Records

Clancy, Willie

MINSTREL FROM CLARE, (THE).
Album: released on Topic, '81 Dist: Roots Distribution

WEST WIND.
Cassette: released on Folktracks, Nov'79 by Folktracks Cassettes. Dist: Folktracks

Clannad

ALMOST SEEN (TOO LATE TO TURN).
Single (7"): released on RCA, Nov'85 by RCA Records. Dist: RCA, Roots, Swift, Wellard, Chris, I & B, Solomon & Peres Distribution

Single (12"): released on RCA, Nov'85 by RCA Records. Dist: RCA, Roots, Swift, Wellard, Chris, I & B, Solomon & Peres Distribution

CLANNAD IN CONCERT.
Album: released on Ogham, Sep'79 Dist: Celtic Music, Roots Records, Jazz Music, JSU, Projection

CLANNAD: VOLUME 2.
Album: released on Gael-Linn (Ireland), May'79 by Gael Linn Records. Dist: Roots, Projection, Celtic Music, Jazz Music

CLOSER TO YOUR HEART.
Tracks: / Closer to your heart / Buachaill on eirne / Theme from Harry's game / Robin (the hooded man).
Single (7"): released on RCA, Feb'86 by RCA Records. Dist: RCA, Roots, Swift, Wellard, Chris, I & B, Solomon & Peres Distribution

Single (12"): released on RCA, Feb'86 by RCA Records. Dist: RCA, Roots, Swift, Wellard, Chris, I & B, Solomon & Peres Distribution

Single (7"): released on RCA, Sep'75 by RCA Records. Dist: RCA, Roots, Swift, Wellard, Chris, I & B, Solomon & Peres Distribution

Single (12"): released on RCA, Sep'75 by RCA Records. Dist: RCA, Roots, Swift, Wellard, Chris, I & B, Solomon & Peres Distribution

CRANNULL.
Album: released on Philips, Nov'82 Dist: IMS-Polygram

Cassette: released on Philips, Nov'82 Dist: IMS-Polygram

Album: released on Tara (Ireland), '82 by Tara Records. Dist: I & B Records Distribution, Record Services Distribution (Ireland), Roots Distribution

Cassette: released on Tara (Ireland), '82 by Tara Records. Dist: I & B Records Distribution, Record Services Distribution (Ireland), Roots Distribution

DULAMAN.
Album: released on Gael-Linn (Ireland), May'79 by Gael Linn Records. Dist: Roots, Projection, Celtic Music, Jazz Music

FUAIN.
Album: released on Tara (Ireland), '82 by Tara Records. Dist: I & B Records Distribution, Record Services Distribution (Ireland), Roots Distribution

Cassette: released on Tara (Ireland), '82 by Tara Records. Dist: I & B Records Distribution, Record Services Distribution (Ireland), Roots Distribution

HARRY'S GAME THEME.
Single (7"): released on RCA, Oct'82 by RCA Records. Dist: RCA, Roots, Swift, Wellard, Chris, I & B, Solomon & Peres Distribution

Single (12"): released on RCA, Jan'86 by RCA Records. Dist: RCA, Roots, Swift, Wellard, Chris, I & B, Solomon & Peres Distribution

I SEE RED.
Single (7"): released on RCA, Mar'83 by RCA Records. Dist: RCA, Roots, Swift, Wellard, Chris, I & B, Solomon & Peres Distribution

LEGEND, (THE).
Album: released on RCA, Mar'84 by RCA Records. Dist: RCA, Roots, Swift, Wellard, Chris, I & B, Solomon & Peres Distribution

Cassette: released on RCA, Mar'84 by RCA Records. Dist: RCA, Roots, Swift, Wellard, Chris, I & B, Solomon & Peres Distribution

Compact disc: released on RCA, Mar'84 by RCA Records. Dist: RCA, Roots, Swift, Wellard, Chris, I & B, Solomon & Peres Distribution

MACALLA.
Compact disc: by RCA Records. Dist: RCA, Roots, Swift, Wellard, Chris, I & B, Solomon & Peres Distribution

Album: released on RCA, Oct'85 by RCA Records. Dist: RCA, Roots, Swift, Wellard, Chris, I & B, Solomon & Peres Distribution

Cassette: released on RCA, Oct'85 by RCA Records. Dist: RCA, Roots, Swift, Wellard, Chris, I & B, Solomon & Peres Distribution

Compact disc: released on RCA, Oct'85 by RCA Records. Dist: RCA, Roots, Swift, Wellard, Chris, I & B, Solomon & Peres Distribution

MAGICAL RING.
Compact disc: released on RCA, Jan'87 by RCA Records. Dist: RCA, Roots, Swift, Wellard, Chris, I & B, Solomon & Peres Distribution

Album: released on RCA, '84 by RCA Records. Dist: RCA, Roots, Swift, Wellard, Chris, I & B, Solomon & Peres Distribution

Cassette: released on RCA, '84 by RCA Records. Dist: RCA, Roots, Swift, Wellard, Chris, I & B, Solomon & Peres Distribution

MAGICAL RING.
Tracks: / Harry's game / Tower hill / Searchran chann tsail / I see red / Passing time / Coinleach glas an fhomair / Ta 'me mo shui / New grange / Fairy queen / Thios fa'n chosta.

NEW GRANGE.
Single (7"): released on RCA, May'83 by RCA Records. Dist: RCA, Roots, Swift, Wellard, Chris, I & B, Solomon & Peres Distribution

NOW IS HERE.
Single (7"): released on RCA, Jun'84 by RCA Records. Dist: RCA, Roots, Swift, Wellard, Chris, I & B, Solomon & Peres Distribution

PRETTY MAID, (THE).
Album: released on Philips, '82 Dist: IMS-Polygram

ROBIN OF SHERWOOD.
Tracks: / Robin of Sherwood / Robin (The hooded man) / Caislean oir / Now is here / Herne / I shot the sheriff / Knockin' on heaven's door / Swing low sweet chariot / Wonderful tonight / Sunshine of your love / Badge / Little wing / Layla / Cocaine / Presence of the lord / She's waiting / See what love can do / Same old blues / Knock on wood / Something's happening / Forever man / It all depends / Tangled in love / Never make you cry / Just like a prisoner / Behind the sun.
Single (7"): released on RCA, May'86 by RCA Records. Dist: RCA, Roots, Swift, Wellard, Chris, I & B, Solomon & Peres Distribution

Album: released on Starblend, Jul'86 by Starblend Records. Dist: PRT Distribution

Cassette: released on Starblend, Jul'86 by Starblend Records. Dist: PRT Distribution

Compact disc: released on RCA, Jun'84 by RCA Records. Dist: RCA, Roots, Swift, Wellard, Chris, I & B, Solomon & Peres Distribution

SCARLET INSIDE.
Single (7"): released on RCA, Mar'85 by RCA Records. Dist: RCA, Roots, Swift, Wellard, Chris, I & B, Solomon & Peres Distribution

Clan Of The Cave Bear

CLAN OF THE CAVE BEAR Original soundtrack by Alan Silvestri.
Album: released on Colosseum(West Germany), Sep'86 Dist: Silva Screen

Clanton, Jimmy

JUST A DREAM.
Album: released on Ace, Mar'84 by Ace Records. Dist: Pinnacle, Swift, Hotshot, Cadillac

Clapham Daredevils

CHER LOUISE.
Single (7"): released on Beach House Recorders, Mar'83 Dist: Beach House Recorders

Clapham South Escalators

GET ME TO THE WORLD ON TIME.
Single (7"): released on Upright, Dec'82 by Upright Records. Dist: Cartel, Rough Trade

Clapton, Eric

461 OCEAN BOULEVARD.

Album: released on RSO, '83

Cassette: released on RSO, '83

Compact disc: released on RSO. '83

461 OCEAN BOULEVARD/ANOTHER TICKET.
Cassette: released on RSO, '83

AFTER MIDNIGHT.
Album: released on RSO (Holland), Jun'84

Cassette: released on RSO (Holland), Jun'84

ANOTHER TICKET.
Tracks: / Something special / Black rose / Another ticket / I can't stand it / Hold me lord / Floating bridge / Catch me if you can / Rita Mae.
Compact disc: released on Polydor, Feb'87 by Polydor Records. Dist: Polygram, Polvdor

Album: released on RSO, Anr'84

Cassette: released on RSO, Apr'84

AUGUST.
Tracks: It's In The Way That You Use It / Run / Tearing Us Apart (Duet with Tina Turner) / Bad Influence / Hung Up On Your Love / I Take A Chance / Hold One / Miss You / Holy Mother / Behind The Mask.
Album: released on Warner Bros., Nov'86 by Warner Bros Records. Dist: WEA

Cassette: released on Warner Bros., Nov'86 by Warner Bros Records. Dist: WEA

Compact disc: released on Duck, Nov'86 by Duck Records. Dist: WEA

BACKLESS.
Album: released on RSO, Jul'83

Cassette: released on RSO. 'ul'83

BACKLESS/461 OCEAN BOULEVARD/SLOWHAND.
Triple album / cassette: released on RSO, Nov'82

BACKTRACKIN'.
Double compact disc: by Polydor Records. Dist: Polygram Distribution

Album: released on Starblend, Feb'85 by Starblend Records. Dist: PRT Distribution

Cassette: released on Starblend, Feb'85 by Starblend Records. Dist: PRT Distribution

Compact disc: released on RSO, Jun'84

BEHIND THE MASK.
Tracks: / Grand Illusion.
Single (7"): released on Duck, Jan'87 by Duck Records. Dist: WEA

Single (12"): released on Duck, Jan'87 by Duck Records. Dist: WEA

BEHIND THE SUN.
Compact disc: by Duck Records. Dist: WEA

Album: released un Warner Bros., Apr'85 by Warner Bros Records. Dist: WEA

Cassette: released on Warner Bros., Apr'85 by Warner Bros Records. Dist: WEA

Compact disc: released on Warner Bros., Apr'85 by Warner Bros Records. Dist: WEA

BIG BOSS MAN.
Album: released on Masters (Holland), Jan'87

Cassette: released on Masters (Holland),

Jan'87

BLUEBREAKER (Clapton, Eric & John Mayall).
Tracks: / All your love / Hideaway / Little girl / Another man / Double crossing time / What'd I say? / Key to love / Parchman farm / Have you heard? / Ramblin' on my mind / Steppin' out / It ain't right.
Compact disc: released on Decca, '83 by Decca Records. Dist: Polygram

BLUESBREAKERS (Clapton, Eric & John Mayall).
Compact disc: released on Decca, '83 by Decca Records. Dist: Polygram

BLUES WORLD OF, THE.
Album: released on World of Learning, Apr'75 by World Of Learning Records. Dist: World Of Learning

Cassette: released on Decca, '74 by Decca Records. Dist: Polygram

DON'T CARE NO MORE.
Album: released on Platinum (W.Germany), Oct'85 Dist: Mainline

Cassette: released on Platinum (W.Germany), Oct'85 Dist: Mainline

E.C. WAS HERE.
Tracks: / Have you ever loved a woman / Presence of the lord / Drifting blues / Can't find my way home / Rambling on my mind / Further on up the road.
Album: released on RSO, Aug'83

Cassette: released on RSO, Aug'83

EDGE OF DARKNESS (Clapton, Eric & Michael Kamen).
Tracks: / Shoot out.
Single (7"): released on BBC, Jan'86 by BBC Records & Tapes. Dist: EMI, PRT.

EDGE OF DARKNESS (Clapton, Eric with Michael Kamen).
Tracks: / Escape from Northmore.
Single (12"): released on BBC, Nov'85 by BBC Records & Tapes. Dist: EMI PRT

Cassette: released on BBC, Nov'85 by BBC Records & Tapes. Dist: EMI PRT

ERIC CLAPTON.
Tracks: / Slunky / Bad boy / Lonesome and a long way from home / After midnight / Easy now / Blues power / Bottle of red wine / Lovin' you loving me / I've told you for the last time / I don't know why / Let it rain / Bell bottom blues / Slunky / Have you ever loved a woman / Let it rain / Anyday / Key to the highway / Peaches and diesel / Watch out for Lucy / I shot the sheriff / Promises / Knockin' on heaven's door / Wonderful tonight / Cocaine / Lay down Sally / Willie and the hand jive / After midnight / Swing low sweet chariot / Let it grow / Blues power.
Album: released on RSO, Nov'83

Cassette: released on RSO, Nov'83

ERIC CLAPTON CONCERT, THE (VIDEO).
Notes: Released on Channel 5 Video in March 87. 58 minutes.

ERIC CLAPTON & THE YARDBIRDS (Clapton, Eric & The Yardbirds).
Album: released on Charly, Aug'77 by Charly Records. Dist: Charly, Cadillac

GOT LOVE IF YOU WANT IT (Clapton, Eric & The Yardbirds).
Tracks: / Too much monkey business / Got love if you want it / Smoke stack lightning / Good morning little school girl / I don't care anymore / Five long years / Here 'tis / Bye bye bird / Mister downchild / I wish you would / For your love / Certain night, A / Twenty / Three hours too long / Got to hurry.
Album: released on Showdown, Apr'86

Cassette: released on Showdown, Apr'86

GREATEST HITS:ERIC CLAPTON.
Album: released on Arcade Music Gala, Apr'86 Dist: Stage One

Cassette: released on Arcade Music Gala, Apr'86 Dist: Stage One

Album: released on Telefunken, Apr'78

HISTORY OF ERIC CLAPTON.
Album: released on RSO, Nov'77

Cassette: released on RSO, Oct'84

IN CONCERT Video.
Notes: Released on Video Gems

I SHOT THE SHERIFF.
Tracks: / Knockin' on heaven's door.
Single (7"): released on Old Gold, Mar'86 by Old Gold Records. Dist: Lightning, Jazz Music, Spartan, Counterpoint

Double compact disc: released on RSO, '83

IT'S IN THE WAY THAT YOU USE IT.
Tracks: / It's in the way that you use it / Bad influence / Old ways / Pretty girl.
Single (7"): released on Duck, Mar'87 by Duck Records. Dist: WEA

Single (12"): released on Duck, Mar'87 by Duck Records. Dist: WEA

I'VE GOT A ROCK & ROLL HEART.
Single (7"): released on Duck, Jan'83 by Duck Records. Dist: WEA

Single (12"): released on Duck, Jan'83 by Duck Records. Dist: WEA

JUST ONE NIGHT.
Double compact disc: by Polydor Records. Dist: Polygram Distribution

Double Album: released on RSO, May'80

LAYLA.
Compact disc: released on Polydor. Dist: Polygram, Polydor

Album: released on RSO (Import), Mar'83

Cassette: released on RSO (Import), Mar'83

Single (7"): released on RSO, Jan'82

Single (12"): released on RSO, Jan'82

LIVE 85.
Video-cassette (VHS): released on Polygram, Jan'86 by Polygram Records. Dist: Polygram

Compact disc: released on Duck, '83 by Duck Records. Dist: WEA

MONEY AND CIGARETTES.
Album: released on Duck, Feb'83 by Duck Records. Dist: WEA

Cassette: released on Duck, Feb'83 by Duck Records. Dist: WEA

Compact disc: released on Duck, '83 by Duck Records. Dist: WEA

MUSIC FOR THE MILLIONS.
Album: released on Polydor (Holland), Aug'83

Cassette: released on Polydor (Holland), Aug'83

NO REASON TO CRY.
Tracks: / Beautiful things / Carnival / All our past times / Hungry / County jail / Sign language / Hello old friend / Innocent times / Black summer rain / Double trouble.
Compact disc: released on Polydor, Dec'86 by Polydor Records. Dist: Polygram, Polydor

Album: released on RSO, Aug'83

Cassette: released on RSO, Aug'83

ON THE WHISTLE TEST.
Video-cassette (VHS): released on BBC, Oct'84 by BBC Records & Tapes. Dist: EMI, PRT,

RAINBOW CONCERT.
Compact disc: by Polydor Records. Dist: Polygram, Polydor

Album: released on RSO, Aug'83

Cassette: released on RSO, Aug'83

SHAPE YOU'RE IN.
Single (7"): released on Duck, Apr'83 by Duck Records. Dist: WEA

Single (12"): released on Duck, Apr'83 by Duck Records. Dist: WEA

SLOW DOWN LINDA.
Single (7"): released on Duck, May'83 by Duck Records. Dist: WEA

Single (12"): released on Duck, May'83 by Duck Records. Dist: WEA

SLOWHAND.
Compact disc: by Polydor Records. Dist: Polygram Distribution

Album: released on RSO, Aug'83

Cassette: released on RSO, Aug'83

Compact disc: released on RSO, Aug'83

Cassette: released on RSO, Aug'82

STEPPIN' OUT.
Album: released on Decca (Rock Echoes), Feb'82 by Decca Records. Dist' Polygram, IMS

Album: released on Decca (Rock Echoes), Feb'82 by Decca Records. Dist: Polygram, IMS

Cassette: released on Decca, Jun'81 by Decca Records. Dist: Polygram

SURVIVOR.
Album: released on Thunderbolt, Mar'86 by Magnum Music Group Ltd. Dist: Magnum Music Group Ltd, PRT Distribution, Spartan Distribution

Compact disc: released on Polydor, Nov'86 by Polydor Records. Dist: Polygram, Polydor

Album: released on RSO, Apr'75

Album: released on RSO, '85

Cassette: released on RSO, '85

TIMEPIECES.
Compact disc: by Polydor Records. Dist: Polygram Distribution

Compact disc: released on RSO, '83

TIME PIECES.
Album: released on RSO, '82

Cassette: released on RSO, '82

Compact disc: released on RSO, '83

TIMEPIECES 2.
Compact disc: by Polydor Records. Dist: Polygram Distribution

TIME PIECES VOL.11 'Live' in the seventies.

Album: released on RSO, '85

Cassette: released on RSO. '85

Compact disc: released on RSO, '85

TOO MUCH MONKEY BUSINESS.
Album: released on Astan, '84 by Astan Records. Dist: Counterpoint

Compact disc: released on Astan, '84 by Astan Records. Dist: Counterpoint

WONDERFUL TONIGHT.
Single (7"): released on RSO, '84

WONDERFUL TONIGHT.
Single (7"): released on Polydor, Aug'87 by Polydor Records. Dist: Polygram, Polydor

Single (12"): released on Polydor, Aug'87 by Polydor Records. Dist: Polygram, Polvdor

Single (12"): released on Chrysalis, Aug'87 by Chrysalis Records. Dist: CBS

Clare, Alan
Thou swell

Clare, Carl St
GREETINGS TO YOU.
Album: released on Trans Universal. '84

WONDERFUL ENGLISH FOOTBALL.
Single (12"): released on Trans Universal, '82

Clare's New Baby Brother
CLARE'S NEW BABY BROTHER (Snell, Nigel).
Cassette: released on Look & Listen, '84 by Listen For Pleasure. Dist: EMI

Clarinet...
CLARINET JAZZ GIANTS Golden hour of various original artists (Various Artists).
Album: released on Golden Hour, '78 by PRT Records. Dist: PRT

CLARINET PLAYING LEADERS Various artists (Various Artists).
Album: released on Golden Era, '79 by Import Records. Dist: Wellard, Chris, Swift

Clarinet Summit-Live
YOU BETTER FLY AWAY (Various Artists).
Album: released on MPS Jazz, '81

Clarity
WAY U MAKE ME FEEL, THE.
Single (7"): released on BPOP, '85

Single (12"): released on BPOP, '85

Clark, Anne
CHANGING PLACES.
Album: released on Red Flame, '83 by Red Flame Records. Dist: Nine Mile, Cartel

HOPELESS CASES.
Album: released on 10, Feb'87 by 10 Records. Dist: Virgin, EMI

Cassette: released on 10, Feb'87 by 10 Records. Dist: Virgin, EMI

Compact disc: released on 10, Feb'87 by 10 Records. Dist: Virgin, EMI

JOINED UP WRITING.
Album: released on Ink, '84 by Red Flame. Dist: Rough Trade, Cartel, Pinnacle

OUR DARKNESS.
Single (12"): released on Ink, '84 by Red Flame. Dist: Rough Trade, Cartel, Pinnacle

PRESSURE POINTS.
Album: released on Ten, Nov'85

Cassette: released on Ten, Nov'85

Compact disc: released on 10, Aug'86 by 10 Records. Dist: Virgin, EMI

SLEEPER IN METROPOLIS(EXT).
Compact disc: released on Ink, '85 by Red Flame. Dist: Rough Trade, Cartel, Pinnacle

TRUE LOVE TALKS.
Single (12"): released on Ink, Mar'86 by Red Flame. Dist: Rough Trade, Cartel, Pinnacle

WALLIES.
Single (12"): released on Ink, Sep'85 by Red Flame. Dist: Rough Trade, Cartel, Pinnacle

Clark, Dave
25 THUMPING GREAT HITS (Clark, Dave Five).

Tracks: / Glad all over / Do you love me? / Bits and pieces / Can't you see? / Catch us if you can / Because / Over and over / Reelin' and a-rockin' / You got what it takes / Everybody knows / Good old rock 'n' roll / Sweet little sixteen / Long tall Sally / Chantilly lace / Whole lotta shakin' goin' on / Blue suede shoes / Wild weekend / Here comes summer / Live in the sky / Red balloon, The / Come home / Sweet city woman / Sha-na-na / Put a little love in your heart / Everybody get together.
Album: released on Polydor, Feb'78 by Polydor Records. Dist: Polygram, Polydor

Clark, Dee

DEE CLARK.
Tracks: / Seven nights / Just like a fool / 24 Boyfriends / Why don't you come home / Blues get off my shoulder / Just can't help myself / Because I love you / Honey (that's what I want) / Dance on little girl / Drums in my heart / You are like the wind / Fever / Old man river / Little boy blue / How is he treating you / I'm going back to school.
Album: released on Charly, Apr'86 by Charly Records. Dist: Charly, Cadillac

RAINDROPS.
Tracks: / I'm a soldier boy / Shook up over you / I just can't help myself / When I call on you / Just like a fool / Seven nights / Why don't you come home / 24 Boyfriends / Oh little girl / Wondering / Nobody but you / Blues get off my shoulder / Just keep it up / Hey little girl / Your friends / Raindrops / You're telling our secrets / Walk away from me (Don't) / You are like the wind / Drums in my heart / Bring back my heart / Fever.
Notes: Original Vee Jay recording. Licensed from Charly Records International APS. This CD P 1987 Charly Holdings Inc. This CD C 1987 Charly Records Ltd.
Compact disc: released on Charly, Apr'87 by Charly Records. Dist: Charly, Cadillac

Single (7"): released on Creole, Aug'82 by Creole Records. Dist: Rhino, PRT

Clarke, Allan

BEST OF....
Album: released on Aura, Nov'81 by Hollywood Nites Distribution. Dist: Pinnacle

BORN TO RUN.
Single (7"): released on Aura, Nov'81 by Hollywood Nites Distribution. Dist: Pinnacle

I WASN'T BORN YESTERDAY.
Album: released on Aura, May'78 by Hollywood Nites Distribution. Dist: Pinnacle

ONLY ONE.
Single (7"): released on Aura, Oct'80 by Hollywood Nites Distribution. Dist: Pinnacle

ONLY ONE, THE.
Album: released on Aura, Nov'80 by Hollywood Nites Distribution. Dist: Pinnacle

SHADOW IN THE STREET.
Single (7"): released on Aura, Mar'82 by Hollywood Nites Distribution. Dist: Pinnacle

SOMEONE ELSE WILL.
Single (7"): released on Forever, Aug'82 by Forever Records. Dist: Pinnacle

WALLS.
Single (7"): released on Aura, Jan'81 by Hollywood Nites Distribution. Dist: Pinnacle

Clarke, Arthur

CHILDHOOD'S END.
Cassette: released on Caedmon(USA), May'80 by Caedmon (USA) Records. Dist: Taylors, Discovery

Clarke, Christopher

BELIEVE ME.
Tracks: / Believe me / Believe me (inst).
Single (12"): released on TER, Mar'87 Dist: Pinnacle

Clarke, Don

YOUNG REBEL.
Single 10": released on Top Notch, May'82

Clarke, Freddie

ARE WE GOING TO MAKE IT UP.
Single (12"): released on Live & Love, May'82 by Third World Records. Dist: Jetstar

Clarke, Grainne

SONGS OF ROGUES & HONEST MEN.
Album: released on Outlet, Apr'80 by Outlet Records. Dist: Outlet Distribution

Cassette: released on Outlet, Apr'80 by Outlet Records. Dist: Outlet Distribution

Clarke, Guy

BEST OF..., THE.
Album: released on RCA International, May'82

Cassette: released on RCA International, May'82

GUY CLARKE.
Album: released on WB, May'78

Clarke, John Cooper

ME AND MY BIG MOUTH.
Album: released on Epic, May'81 by CBS Records. Dist: CBS

OU EST LA MAISON DE FROMAGE?.
Album: released on Rabid, Jul'80 by Rabid Records. Dist: Pinnacle, Rough Trade

PSYCLE SLUTS.
Single (7"): released on Rabid, Sep'82 by Rabid Records. Dist: Pinnacle, Rough Trade

Clarke, Johnny

20 MASSIVE HITS.
Album: released on Striker Lee, Jun'85 by Striker Lee Records. Dist: Jetstar Distribution

APPLE OF MY EYE.
Single (12"): released on Hi Power, Nov'84 Dist: Jetstar

DO I DO I.
Single (12"): released on Ariwa, Feb'83 by Ariwa Records. Dist: Revolver, Cartel, Jetstar, Rough Trade

GIVE ME LOVE.
Single (12"): released on Cha-Cha, Jul'82 by Cha Cha. Dist: Jetstar

GIVE THANKS.
Album: released on Ariwa, Aug'85 by Ariwa Records. Dist: Revolver, Cartel, Jetstar, Rough Trade

GOT TO BE STRONG.
Single (12"): released on Jah Shaka, Mar'84 by Jah Shaka Records. Dist: Jetstar

GUIDANCE.
Single (12"): released on Red Nails, Jul'82

HE'S A WALLY.
Single (7"): released on President, Sep'82 by President Records. Dist: Taylors, Spartan

JOHNNY CLARKE MEETS CORNELL CAMPBELL IN NEW STYLE.
Album: released on Vista Sounds, '83 by Vista Sounds Records. Dist: Jetstar

LOVE WILL FIND A WAY.
Single (12"): released on Fashion, Dec'83 by Fashion Records. Dist: PRT, Jetstar

REGGAE PARTY.
Album: released on Vista Sounds, Jul'84 by Vista Sounds Records. Dist: Jetstar

Single (12"): released on L.E.D., Jul'84 by L.E.D. Records. Dist: Roots, Cartel, Jetstar

ROCKERS' TIME NOW.
Album: released on Virgin, Jul'76 by Virgin Records. Dist: EMI, Virgin Distribution

ROCKING TO THE A CLASS CHAMPIONS.
Single (12"): released on Fashion, Nov'82 by Fashion Records. Dist: PRT, Jetstar

Cassette single: released on Subway Organisation, Oct'83 Dist: Revolver, Cartel

RUDE BOY.
Single (12"): released on Art & Craft, Feb'82 Dist: Jetstar

SLY & ROBBIE PRESENT.
Album: released on Vista Sounds, Mar'85 by Vista Sounds Records. Dist: Jetstar

SWEET SENSATION.
Single (12"): released on Top Rank, Aug'85

TAKE HEED.
Single (12"): released on Black Joy, Aug'82 Dist: Jetstar

TOO MUCH WAR.
Single (12"): released on Black Joy, Jul'82 Dist: Jetstar

YOU BETTER TRY.
Single (12"): released on Art & Craft, Apr'82 Dist: Jetstar

YOU BRING ME JOY.
Single (12"): released on Success, May'85 Dist: Counterpoint Distribution

Clarke, Kenny

ALL BLUES.
Album: released on MPS Jazz, May'81

AT HER MAJESTY'S PLEASURE (Clarke, Kenny & Francy Boland's Big Band).
Album: released on Code D, Feb'75 by Black Lion Records. Dist: C.R.D.

DOIN' TIME (Clarke, Kenny & Francy Boland).
Album: released on Black Lion, Jan'85 by Black Lion Records. Dist: Jazz Music, Chris Wellard, Taylor, H.R., Counterpoint, Cadillac

KENNY CLARKE MEETS THE DETROIT JAZZMEN.
Album: released on Savoy (France), Feb'85

LIVE IN PARIS.
Album: released on EMI (France), Mar'84 by EMI Records. Dist: Conifer

Cassette: released on EMI (France), Mar'84 by EMI Records. Dist: Conifer

PARIS/COLOGNE 1957 AND 1960.
Album: released on Ace, Oct'86 by Ace Records. Dist: Pinnacle, Swift, Hotshot, Cadillac

Clarke, Louis

STILL LIFE.
Single (7"): released on Ratpack, Nov'84 by Ratpack. Dist: Spartan

Clarke, Phil Jnr

THAT'S LIFE.
Album: released on Lismor, Nov'76 by Lismor Records. Dist: Lismor, Roots, Celtic Music

Clarke, Rick

LOOKING OUT FOR YOU.
Single (7"): released on RCA, Aug'87 by RCA Records. Dist: RCA, Roots, Swift, Wellard, Chris, I & B, Solomon & Peres Distribution

Single (12"): released on RCA, Aug'87 by RCA Records. Dist: RCA, Roots, Swift, Wellard, Chris, I & B, Solomon & Peres Distribution

LOVE WITH A STRANGER.
Single (12"): released on Local, Oct'85 by Local Records. Dist: Pinnacle

Clarke, Rick & Emma

I REALLY WANT TO BE WITH YOU.
Tracks: / I really wnat to be with you / I've been watching you.
Single (7"): released on RCA, 13 Jun'87 by RCA Records. Dist: RCA, Roots, Swift, Wellard, Chris, I & B, Solomon & Peres Distribution

Single (12"): released on RCA, 13 Jun'87 by RCA Records. Dist: RCA, Roots, Swift, Wellard, Chris, I & B, Solomon & Peres Distribution

Clarke, Robin

YOU PULL ME AROUND.
Single (7"): released on Blue Train, Jun'84 by Checkmount Distribution. Dist: Spartan

Clarke, Sharon Dee

DANCE YOUR WAY OUT OF THE DOOR.
Tracks: / Dance your way...(Dub mix).
Single (7"): released on Arista, Oct'86 by Arista Records. Dist: RCA

Single (12"): released on Arista, Oct'86 by Arista Records. Dist: RCA

HE'S COMING BACK.
Tracks: / He's coming back (inst. mix) / He's coming back (7" mix) / He's coming back / 7 and museums / Water / Jiggs Casey / Cross country / Book store / Winny / Apt. / Babies and skiing / Introduction / Ants / Hitchhiking / Ice / Dog stay / Rachel.
Single (12"): released on Debut, Mar'87 by Skratch Music. Dist: PRT

Clarke Sisters

CHANNEL FOLK (Clarke Sisters (Stephanie & Leonie)).
Tracks: / Devoted to you / You've got a friend / Pack up your sorrows / Be bye love / This will be our last song together / Streets of London / Jet Plane / Find out / What if I should fall in love / Born in the USA / Sky's the limit, The / Don't turn the lights out / Cmpo Americano / Stero typica / Psychedelic / My life.
Notes: Popular songs in the folk idiom sung in sweet girlish voices with guitar accompaniment including the above songs and some arguably better songs. Eron Records, 27 Balmoral road, Kingsdown, Deal, Kent CT14 8BX.
Cassette: released on Eron, Sep'85 by Eron Records. Dist: Eron Records

Compact disc: released on CBS, Apr'86 by CBS Records. Dist: CBS

Clarke Soundbook

CLARKE SOUNDBOOK Clarke, A.C. (Various Artists).
Boxed set: released on Caedmon(USA), '81 by Caedmon (USA) Records. Dist: Gower, Taylors, Discovery

Clarke, Stanley

CLARKE/DUKE PROJECT 11, (THE) (Clarke, Stanley & George Duke).
Album: released on Epic, Dec'83 by CBS Records. Dist: CBS

Cassette: released on Epic, Dec'83 by CBS Records. Dist: CBS Deleted '85.

FIND OUT (Clarke, Stanley Band).
Compact disc: by CBS Records. Dist: CBS Cat. no: **CDCBS 26521**
Album: released on Epic, Jul'85 by CBS Records. Dist: CBS

Cassette: released on Epic, Jul'85 by CBS Records. Dist: CBS

FUSE ONE (Clarke, Stanley/Larry Coryell/John McLaughlin).
Album: released on Import Music Service (IMS), Mar'81 Dist: Concord Jazz Distributions, Pablo, Polygram

HEAVEN SENT YOU.
Single (7"): released on Epic, Jun'84 by CBS Records. Dist: CBS

HIDEAWAY.
Tracks: / Overjoyed / My love, her inspiration / Where do we go / Boys of Johnson street / Old friends / When it's cold outside / Listen to the beat of your heart / Basketball / I'm here to stay.
Album: released on Epic, Nov'86 by CBS Records. Dist: CBS

Cassette: released on Epic, Nov'86 by CBS Records. Dist: CBS

Compact disc: by CBS Records. Dist: CBS

I WANNA PLAY FOR YOU.
Cassette: released on Epic, Aug'79 by CBS Records. Dist: CBS

JOURNEY TO LOVE.
Album: released on Epic, Nov'81 by CBS Records. Dist: CBS Deleted '86.

Single 10": released on Epic, Nov'81 by CBS Records. Dist: CBS

MODERN MAN.
Compact disc: released on CBS, May'87 by CBS Records. Dist: CBS

Album: released on CBS, Feb'84 by CBS Records. Dist: CBS Deleted '86.

Cassette: released on CBS, Feb'84 by CBS Records. Dist: CBS

ROCKS, PEBBLES & SAND.
Album: released on Epic, Mar'83 by CBS Records. Dist: CBS Deleted '86.

Cassette: released on Epic, Mar'83 by CBS Records. Dist: CBS

SCHOOL DAYS.
Tracks: / School days / Quiet afternoon / Danger, the / Desert song / Hot fun / Life is just a game.
Compact disc: released on Epic, May'87 by CBS Records. Dist: CBS

SCHOOLDAYS.
Album: released on Epic, Mar'82 by CBS Records. Dist: CBS

Cassette: released on Epic, Mar'82 by CBS Records. Dist: CBS Deleted '86.

TIME EXPOSURE.
Album: released on Epic, May'84 by CBS Records. Dist: CBS

Cassette: released on Epic, May'84 by CBS Records. Dist: CBS Deleted '86.

Clarke, Vince

ONE DAY (Clarke, Vince & Paul Quinn).
Single (7"): released on Mute, Jun'85 Dist: Spartan Distribution, Rough Trade Distribution, Cartel Distribution

Single (12"): released on Mute, Jun'85 Dist: Spartan Distribution, Rough Trade Distribution, Cartel Distribution

ONLY YOU.
Single (7"): released on Mute, Apr'82 Dist: Spartan Distribution, Rough Trade Distribution, Cartel Distribution

WHO NEEDS LOVE LIKE THAT? (Clarke, Vince & Andy Bell).
Single (7"): released on Mute, Aug'85 Dist: Spartan Distribution, Rough Trade Distribution, Cartel Distribution

Single (12"): released on Mute, Aug'85 Dist: Spartan Distribution, Rough Trade Distribution, Cartel Distribution

Clarke, William

TIP OF THE TOP.
Album: released on Double Trouble, Jul'87

Clarke, Winston

LADY YOU ARE.
Single (12"): released on Sir George, Sep'84 by Sir George Records. Dist: Jetstar, Pinnacle

Clark, Gene

NO OTHER.
Tracks: / Life's greatest fool / Silver raven / No other / Strength of strings / From a silver phial / Some misunderstanding / True one, The / Lady of the north.
Album: by WEA Records. Dist: WEA

SO REBELLIOUS A LOVER (Clark, Gene & Carla Olsen).
Notes: Features: Gene Clark (The Byrds), Carla Olsen (Textones), Chris Hillman (Byrds) and Steve McCarthy (Long Ryders).
Album: released on Demon, Apr'87 by Demon Records. Dist: Pinnacle

Compact disc: released on Demon, Aug'87 by Demon Records. Dist: Pinnacle

TWO SIDES TO EVERY STORY.
Tracks: / Home run king / Lonely Saturday / In the pines / Kansas City southern / Give my love to Marie / Sister Moon / Marylou / Hear the wind / Past address / Silent crusade.
Album: released on Polydor, Mar'77 by Polydor Records. Dist: Polygram, Polydor

Clark,Guy

OLD NUMBER ONE.
Tracks: / Rita Ballou / L.A. freeway / She ain't goin' nowhere / Nickel for the fiddler, A / That old-time feeling / Texas, 1947 / Desperados waiting for the train / Like a coat from the cold / Instant coffee blues / Let him roll.
Album: released on RCA, Aug'76 by RCA Records. Dist: RCA, Roots, Swift, Wellard, Chris, I & B, Solomon & Peres Distribution

Single (12"): released on Cornerstone, Sep'84 Dist: Jetstar

Clark, Hutchison

GESTALT.
Tracks: / Man's best friend / Love is the light / Light burns on, The / Come up here / Disorientated, Part 1 / Boat in the mist, A / Orientated / First reminder / Mix elixir / Poison / Disorientated, Part 2.
Album: released on Deram, May'71 by Decca Records. Dist: Polygram

Clark, John

FACES.
Album: released on ECM (Import), May'81 by ECM Records. Dist: IMS, Polygram, Virgin through EMI

Clark, LaRena

CAMADOAM GARLAND, A.
Album: released on Topic, May'81 Dist: Roots Distribution

Clark, Louis

BEST OF HOOKED ON CLASSICS (Clark, Louis & Royal Philharmonic Orchestra).
Compact disc: by K-Tel Records. Dist: Record Merchandisers Distribution, Taylors, Terry Blood Distribution, Wynd-Up Distribution, Relay Distribution, Pickwick Distribution, Solomon & Peres Distribution, Polygram

FAVOURITE CLASSICS (Clark, Louis & Royal Philharmonic Orchestra).
Album: released on Ratpack, Dec'86 by Ratpack. Dist: Spartan

Cassette: released on Ratpack, Dec'86 by Ratpack. Dist: Spartan

GHANDI THEME (Clark, Louis & R.P Orchestra).
Single (7"): released on RCA, Dec'82 by RCA Records. Dist: RCA, Roots, Swift, Wellard, Chris, I & B, Solomon & Peres Distribution

HOOKED ON CHRISTMAS.
Tracks: / Viva Vivaldi.
Single (7"): released on Ratpack, Nov'86 by Ratpack. Dist: Spartan

HOOKED ON CHRISTMAS (Clark, Louis & R.P.O).
Single (7"): released on K-Tel, Dec'83 by K-Tel Records. Dist: Record Merchandisers Distribution, Taylors, Terry Blood Distribution, Wynd-Up Distribution, Relay Distribution, Pickwick Distribution, Solomon & Peres Distribution, Polygram

Single (7"): released on Jet, Dec'82 by Jet Records. Dist: CBS

HOOKED ON CLASSICS (Clark, Louis & Royal Philharmonic Orchestra).
Compact disc: by RCA Records. Dist: RCA, Roots, Swift, Wellard, Chris, I & B, Solomon & Peres Distribution

ONE DAY (Clark, Louis & Royal Philharmonic Orchestra).
Single (7"): released on Ratpack, Aug'85 by Ratpack. Dist: Spartan

PER-SPEK-TIV.
Album: released on Jet, Mar'79 by Jet Records. Dist: CBS

QUEEN MEDLEY (Clark, Louis & R.P.O).
Single (7"): released on EMI, Jun'82 by EMI Records. Dist: EMI

STILL LIFE (Clark, Louis & Royal Philharmonic Orchestra).
Album: released on Ratpack, Jun'85 by Ratpack. Dist: Spartan

Cassette: released on Ratpack, Jun'85 by Ratpack. Dist: Spartan

Clark, Mary Louise

SOMETHING HERE IN MY HEART.
Single (7"): released on Mr. Sam, Jun'85

Clark, Paul

NEW HORIZON, A.
Album: released on Myrrh, May'82 by Word Records. Dist: Word Distribution

Cassette: released on Myrrh, May'82 by Word Records. Dist: Word Distribution

Clark, Petula

100 MINUTES.
Cassette: released on PRT (100 Minute Series), Jun'82

AN HOUR IN CONCERT.
Album: released on Music For Pleasure, Nov'83 by EMI Records. Dist: EMI

Cassette: released on Music For Pleasure, Nov'83 by EMI Records. Dist: EMI

DOWNTOWN.
Tracks: / Downtown / I know a place.
Single (7"): released on PRT, Jul'87 by PRT Records. Dist: PRT

DOWNTOWN.
Single (7"): released on Old Gold, Jul'82 by Old Gold Records. Dist: Lightning, Jazz Music, Spartan, Counterpoint

EARLY YEARS.
Tracks: / Teasin' / Card, The / Boy in love, A / Who-is-it- song (The) / Million stars above, A / Pendulum song (The) / Tuna puna Trinidad / Fascinating rhythm / Majorca / Suddenly there's a valley / Another door opens / Million stars above, A / Fortune teller / Fibbin' / Band of gold / Alone / Long before I knew you / Gonna find me a blue bird / Memories are made of this / With all my heart / Who needs you? / Love me again / In a little moment / Baby lover / Ever been in love / Devotion / I've grown accustomed to his face / My favourite things / Little blue man / Boy in love, A / To you my love / Lucky day / Suddenly / Watch your heart / Long way to go, A / Made in heaven / Little shoemaker / Christmas cards / Little Johnny Rainbow / Romance in Rome / Chee chee oo chee.
Notes: Double album
Cassette: released on PRT, Oct'86 by PRT Records. Dist: PRT

Album: released on PRT, Oct'86 by PRT Records. Dist: PRT

GREATEST HITS:PETULA CLARK.
Double cassette: released on Pickwick (Ditto series), Jul'82

MR ORWELL.
Single (7"): released on PRT, Feb'85 by PRT Records. Dist: PRT

PETULA CLARK.
Double cassette: released on Cambra, Jan'82 by Cambra Records. Dist: IDS, Conifer

SAILOR.
Single (7"): released on Old Gold, Mar'86 by Old Gold Records. Dist: Lightning, Jazz Music, Spartan, Counterpoint

SPOTLIGHT ON PETULA CLARK.
Double Album: released on PRT, May'80 by PRT Records. Dist: PRT

Double Album: released on PRT, May'80 by PRT Records. Dist: PRT

THIS IS MY SONG.
Album: released on Flashback, Oct'85 by Flashback Records/PRT Records. Dist: Mainline, PRT

Cassette: released on Flashback, Oct'85 by Flashback Records/PRT Records. Dist: Mainline, PRT

Single (7"): released on Old Gold, Apr'83 by Old Gold Records. Dist: Lightning, Jazz Music, Spartan, Counterpoint

Clark, Roy

20 GOLDEN PIECES OF ROY CLARK.
Album: released on Bulldog, Feb'84 by Bulldog Records. Dist: President Distribution, Spartan, Swift, Taylor, H.R.

BEST OF ROY CLARK.
Tracks: / Simple thing as love, A / Then she's a lover / Do you believe this town / September song / I never picked cotton / Tips of my fingers / Yesterday when I was in love / Right or left at Oak street / Love is just a state of mind / Thank god and greyhounds / Malaguena.
Album: released on MCA Import, Mar'86 by MCA Records. Dist: Polygram, IMS

Clark, Sanford

FOOL, THE.
Album: released on Ace(MCA), Nov'83 by Ace Records. Dist: Pinnacle, Swift, Hotshot

ROCKIN' ROLLIN' VOL.1.
Tracks: / Modern romance / That' the way I feel / Man who made an angel cry / Ooo baby / Cross eyed alley cat, A / Till my baby comes back / Lou be doo / Travellin' man / Lonesome for a letter / Fool, The / Love charms / Every minute of the day / Ain't nobody here but us chickens / Don't care / Cheat, A / Usta be my baby / Nine pound hammer / Swannee river rock.
Album: released on Bear Family, Apr'86 by Bear Family Records. Dist: Rollercoaster Distribution, Swift

ROCKIN' ROLLIN' VOL.2.
Tracks: / Darling dear / Don't cry / Why did I choose you / Come what may / Fool's blues / Juice / Guitar man / Run boy run / I can't help it / Son of a gun / New kind of fool / Sing 'em some blues / Bad luck / Go on home / Pledging my love / Still as the night / My jealousy / Promise me baby / Glory of love.
Album: released on Bear Family, Apr'86 by Bear Family Records. Dist: Rollercoaster Distribution, Swift

Clark Sisters

HEART AND SOUL.
Album: released on Word, Mar'87 by Word Records. Dist: Word Distribution, CBS

Cassette: released on Word, Mar'87 by Word Records. Dist: Word Distribution, CBS

SALUTE TO THE GREAT SINGING GROUPS, A.
Album: released on Jasmine, May'83 by Jasmine Records. Dist: Counterpoint, Taylor, H.R., Wellard, Chris, Swift, Cadillac

SING SING SING.
Album: released on Jasmine, Mar'84 by Jasmine Records. Dist: Counterpoint, Taylor, H.R., Wellard, Chris, Swift, Cadillac

YOU BROUGHT THE SUNSHINE INTO MY LIFE.
Single (7"): released on Westbound, Aug'83 Dist: WEA

Single (12"): released on Westbound, Aug'83 Dist: WEA

Clark, Sonny

COOL STRUTTIN'.
Album: released on Blue Note (USA Import), Sep'84

LEAPIN' AND LOAPIN'.
Album: released on Blue Note, Oct'84 by EMI Records. Dist: EMI

SONNY CLARK TRIO (Clark, Sonny Trio).
Tracks: / I didn't know what time it was / I didn't know what time it was (alternate take) / I didn't know what time it was (alternate take) / I didn't know what time it was / Two bass hit (alternate take) / Be-bop / Tadd's delight (alternate take) / Tadd's delight / Softly as in a morning sunrise / I'll remember April.
Compact disc: released on Blue Note, Sep'87 by EMI Records. Dist: EMI. Estim retail price in Sep'87 was £11.99.

SONNY'S CRIB.
Tracks: / With a song in my heart / With a song in my heart (alternate take) / Speak low / Speak low (Alternate take) / Come rain or come shine / Sonny's crib / Sonny's crib (Alternate take) / News for Lulu.
Compact disc: released on Manhattan-Blue Note, Aug'87 by EMI America Records (USA). Dist: EMI

Compact disc: released on Blue Note, Aug'87 by EMI Records. Dist: EMI

Clark, Spencer

PLAY SWEET & HOT (Clark, Spencer & His Bass Sax).
Album: released on Audiophile, Jun'86 by Jazzology Records (USA). Dist: Jazz Music, Swift

Clark, Vivienne

IVE GOT THE BLUES.
Single (12"): released on God Sent, May'82 by Third World Records. Dist: Jetstar

Clark, Winston

YOUR LOVE.
Single (12"): released on Sir George, Apr'84 by Sir George Records. Dist: Jetstar, Pinnacle

Clash

12" TAPE, THE.
Tracks: / London calling / Magnificent dance This is radio clash / Rock the Casbah / This is England / Last chance.
Cassette: released on CBS, Sep'86 by CBS Records. Dist: CBS

Single (7"): released on Infrared, May'86 by Infrared Records. Dist: M.I.S., EMI

CLASH: INTERVIEW PICTURE DISC.
Picture disc album: released on Baktabak, May'87 by Baktabak Records. Dist: Arabesque

CLASH, (THE).
Album: released on CBS, Nov'82 by CBS Records. Dist: CBS
Cat. no: **CBS 32232**
Cassette: released on CBS, Nov'82 by CBS Records. Dist: CBS

COMBAT ROCK.
Tracks: / Know your rights / Car jamming / Should I stay or should I go / Rock the Casbah / Red angel dragnet / Straight to hell / Overpowered by funk / Atom tan / Sean Flynn / Ghetto defendant / Inoculated city.
Album: released on CBS, Nov'86 by CBS Records. Dist: CBS

Cassette: released on CBS, Nov'86 by CBS Records. Dist: CBS

Album: released on CBS, May'82 by CBS Records. Dist: CBS

Cassette: released on CBS, May'82 by CBS Records. Dist: CBS

CUT THE CRAP.
Album: released on CBS, Nov'85 by CBS Records. Dist: CBS

Cassette: released on CBS, Nov'85 by CBS Records. Dist: CBS

GIVE 'EM ENOUGH ROPE.
Cassette: released on CBS, '78 by CBS Records. Dist: CBS

Album: released on CBS, '84 by CBS Records. Dist: CBS

Cassette: released on CBS, '84 by CBS Records. Dist: CBS

I FOUGHT THE LAW.
Single (7"): released on CBS, May'79 by CBS Records. Dist: CBS

LONDON CALLING.
Album: released on CBS, Dec'79 by CBS Records. Dist: CBS

Cassette: released on CBS, Dec'79 by CBS Records. Dist: CBS

SANDINISTA.
Album: released on CBS, Dec'80 by CBS Records. Dist: CBS

Cassette: released on CBS, Dec'80 by CBS Records. Dist: CBS

THIS IS VIDEO CLASH.
Video-cassette (VHS): released on CBS-Fox, '85 by CBS Records. Dist: CBS, Fox

Class

WINNER, (THE).
Single (12"): released on CS, Jul'82

Class 50

OH, WHAT A LIFE.
Single (7"): released on Infrared, Oct'84 by Infrared Records. Dist: M.I.S., EMI

WRITING'S ON THE WALL.
Single (7"): released on Infrared, Jul'85 by Infrared Records. Dist: M.I.S., EMI

Class Action

WEEKEND.
Single (7"): released on Jive, Aug'85 by Zomba Records. Dist: RCA, PRT

Single (12"): released on Jive, Aug'85 by Zomba Records. Dist: RCA, PRT

Class Fifty

LIVING APART (UNDER THE SAME ROOF).
Tracks: / Living apart (under the same roof) / Last chance.
Single (7"): released on Infrared, Mar'87 by Infrared Records. Dist: M.I.S., EMI

Classic

ARMAGEDDON ROCK.
Single (12"): released on Sound Off, Aug'80

CLASSIC ALBERTA HUNTER Various Artists (Various Artists).
Album: released on Stash, Apr'81 Dist: Swift Distribution, Jazz Music Distribution, Jazz Hori-

zons Distribution, Celtic Music Distribution, Cadillac, .

CLASSIC BRITISH FILM THEMES OF THE 40S & 50S Various Artists (Various Artists).
Album: released on World (Retrospect Series), Feb'84

Cassette: released on World (Retrospect Series), Feb'84

CLASSIC COMMERCIALS Various Artists (Various Artists).
Album: released on Decca, May'79 by Decca Records. Dist: Polygram

Cassette: released on Decca, May'79 by Decca Records. Dist: Polygram

CLASSIC COUNTRY DUETS Various artists (Various Artists).
Album: released on MCA Import, Mar'86 by MCA Records. Dist: Polygram, IMS

CLASSIC COUNTRY ROCK Various Artists (Various Artists).
Album: released on RCA International, Jul'80

Cassette: released on RCA International, Jul'80

CLASSIC DANCE HITS Various artists (Various Artists).
Album: released on Towerbell, Sep'86 by Towerbell Records. Dist: EMI

Cassette: released on Towerbell, Sep'86 by Towerbell Records. Dist: EMI

CLASSIC HITS OF '84 Various Artists (Various Artists).
Triple album / cassette: released on Telstar, Nov'84 by Telstar Records. Dist: RCA Distribution

Triple album / cassette: released on Telstar, Nov'84 by Telstar Records. Dist: RCA Distribution

CLASSIC MOTORCYCLES (motorcycles).
Notes: Recordings of motorcycles built in the period when Britain led the world.
Cassette: released on Audiocord Cassettes, May'83

CLASSIC RAGS AND NOSTALGIA (VOLUME 16) Various Artists (Various Artists).
: released on Euphonic, Apr'79 by Euphonic Records. Dist: Jazz Music, Swift

CLASSICS GO SOLAR! Various Artists (Various Artists).
Double Album: released on Cambra, Apr'85 by Cambra Records. Dist: IDS, Conifer

Double cassette: released on Cambra, Apr'85 by Cambra Records. Dist: IDS, Conifer

CLASSICS ON PARADE (Classics On Parade Orchestra).
Album: released on Manhattan, Apr'81 by President Records. Dist: Jazz Music, Swift, Taylors, Chris Wellard

CLASSIC TENORS VOLUME 2 Various Artists (Various Artists).
Tracks: / Lover come back to me / Blues changes / Hello babe (alternate take) / I'm fer it too (alternate take) / Creamin' / My silent love / Long moan / Goin' along / Lockjaw / Afternoon in a doghouse / Surgery / Athlete's foot.
Album: released on Doctor Jazz (USA), Mar'85 by Doctor Jazz Records. Dist: CBS

CLASSIC TV THEMES Various Artists (Various Artists).
Album: released on Decca, Oct'80 by Decca Records. Dist: Polygram

Classical...

CLASSICAL CLASSICS Various Artists (Various Artists).
Triple album / cassette: released on Telstar, Nov'84 by Telstar Records. Dist: RCA Distribution

Triple album / cassette: released on Telstar, Nov'84 by Telstar Records. Dist: RCA Distribution

CLASSICAL ROMANTIC CLASSICS Various Artists (Various Artists).
Triple album / cassette: released on Telstar, Nov'84 by Telstar Records. Dist: RCA Distribution

Triple album / cassette: released on Telstar, Nov'84 by Telstar Records. Dist: RCA Distribution

Classical Two

NEW GENERATION.
Tracks: / New generation / Freak dog (She's a).
Single (12"): released on Jive, 20 Jun'87 by Zomba Records. Dist: RCA, PRT,

Classic Black

END OF THE LINE.
Single (7"): released on Classic Roots, Jun'82 Dist: Jetstar

SUNSHINE STREET.
Single (12"): released on Classic Roots, Sep'82 Dist: Jetstar

WHAT IS LIFE.
Single (12"): released on Classic Black, Jan'83 by Classic Black. Dist: Jetstar

Classic Jazz Quartet

CLASSIC JAZZ QUARTET, THE.
Notes: with Marty Grosz/Dick Sudhalter/Dick Wellstood.
Album: released on Jazzology, Jun'86 Dist: Jazz Music, Swift

Album: released on Stomp Off, Mar'87 by Stomp Off Records. Dist: Jazz Music Distribution

Classic Pop Hits

CLASSIC POP HITS MID 60'S (Various Artists).
Tracks: / Barbara Ann / Hi ho silver lining / Have I the right / Stop stop stop / Legend of Xanadu / If you gotta go go now / I'm a believer / 1-2-3 / Baby now that I've found you / Black is black / Yesterday man / Concrete and clay / You've got your troubles / Elusive butterfly.
Notes: They reflect the excitement and exhuberance of Mid 60's music as Britain moved from Mercury mania towards flower power, disco and rock.
Album: released on Old Gold, Nov'86 by Old Gold Records. Dist: Lightning, Jazz Music, Spartan, Counterpoint

Cassette: released on Old Gold, Nov'86 by Old Gold Records. Dist: Lightning, Jazz Music, Spartan, Counterpoint

CLASSIC POP HITS OF THE LATE 50'S (Various Artists).
Tracks: / Living doll / Sea of love / Teenager in love / Lipstick on your collar / Oh, Carol / C'mon everybody / Red river rock / What do you wanna make those eyes at me for? / Here comes summer / 'Til I kissed you / Come softly to me / Susie Darlin / Three bells / It doesn't matter anymore.
Notes: The late 50's provided a seemingly endless stream of pop hit songs that with thepassing of time have established themselves as oldies favourites for subsequent generations - here is just a selection.
Album: released on Old Gold, Nov'86 by Old Gold Records. Dist: Lightning, Jazz Music, Spartan, Counterpoint

Classic Rock

CLASSIC ROCK 1 Various artists (Various Artists).
Compact disc: released on Telstar, Nov'86 by Telstar Records. Dist: RCA Distribution

CLASSIC ROCK 3 Rhapsody in black (Various Artists).
Compact disc: released on Telstar, Nov'86 by Telstar Records. Dist: RCA Distribution

Classics By Candlelight

CLASSICS BY CANDLELIGHT Various artists (Various Artists).
Album: released on Stylus, Oct'86 Dist: Pinnacle, Terry Blood Distribution, Stylus Distribution

Cassette: released on Stylus, Oct'86 Dist: Pinnacle, Terry Blood Distribution, Stylus Distribution

Compact disc: released on Stylus, Jan'86 Dist: Pinnacle, Terry Blood Distribution, Stylus Distribution

Classic Song

CLASSIC SONG I love country (Various Artists).
Tracks: / Please help me, I'm falling in love with you / Jambalaya (on the bayou) / Goodnight Irene / Tumbling tumbleweeds / I'm just here to get my baby out of jail.
Album: released on CBS, Mar'87 by CBS Records. Dist: CBS

Cassette: released on CBS, Mar'87 by CBS Records. Dist: CBS

Classification of...

CLASSIFICATION OF FISHES AND GOATS Various Artists (Various Artists).
Cassette: released on Falling A, Nov'84 by Falling A Records. Dist: Falling A Distribution

CLASSIFICATION OF VEGETABLES Various Artists (Various Artists).
Cassette: released on Falling A, Nov'84 by Falling A Records. Dist: Falling A Distribution

Classified Info

DRUG CALLED LOVE.
Single (7"): released on Dead Dog, Jul'84 by Dead Dog Records. Dist: PRT

Classix Nouveaux

END OR THE BEGINNING.
Single (7"): released on Liberty, Oct'82 by Liberty-United. Dist: EMI

Picture disc single: released on Liberty, Oct'82 by Liberty-United. Dist: EMI

Single (12"): released on Liberty, Oct'82 by Liberty-United. Dist: EMI

FOREVER AND A DAY.
Single (7"): released on Liberty, Aug'83 by Liberty-United. Dist: EMI

Single (12"): released on Liberty, Aug'83 by Liberty-United. Dist: EMI

NEVER NEVER COMES.
Single (7"): released on Liberty, Nov'83 by Liberty-United. Dist: EMI

Single (12"): released on Liberty, Nov'83 by Liberty-United. Dist: EMI

Class of '55

BIRTH OF ROCK'N'ROLL.
Tracks: / Rock'n'roll fairs-do-do.
Single (7"): released on Smash (USA), Jun'86 Dist: IMS, Polygram

Single (12"): released on Smash (USA), Jun'86 Dist: IMS, Polygram

CLASS OF '55 Various artists (Various Artists).
Tracks: / Birth of rock and roll / Sixteen candles / Class of '55 / Waymore's blues / We remember the king / Coming home / Rock and roll (Fais-DO-DO) / Keep my motor running / I will rock an roll with you / Big train (from Memphis).
Notes: Together for the first time, four of the greats of Rock'n Roll:Jerry Lee Lewis, Carl Perkins, Johnny Cash and Roy Orbison. Recorded in the of Rock'n roll-Sun studios, in Memphis. Produced with the assistance of the legendary Sam Phillips, and with guest appearances by Dave Edmunds, John Fogerty, The Judds and more.
Album: released on Smash (USA), Jul'86 Dist: IMS, Polygram

Cassette: released on Smash (USA), Jul'86 Dist: IMS, Polygram

Compact disc: released on Smash (USA), Jul'86 Dist: IMS, Polygram

Class of 81

CLASS OF '81 Various Artists (Various Artists).
Album: released on Upper Class, Jan'81 by Chinless Productions. Dist: Spartan, Music Galore

Class War

BETTER DEAD THAN WED.
Single (7"): released on Mortarhate, Jul'86 by Dorane Ltd.

Claudette

MINOR ON.
Tracks: / That's what I like.
Single (7"): released on Play, Oct'86 by Play Records. Dist: Spartan

Claudia

DON'T GIVE UP YOUR LOVE.
Single (7"): released on Rhythmic, Nov'84 by Rhythmic Records. Dist: Havoc Distribution

Single (12"): released on Rhythmic, Nov'84 by Rhythmic Records. Dist: Havoc Distribution

HOLD ON.
Single (7"): released on Rhythmic, Jul'85 by Rhythmic Records. Dist: Havoc Distribution

Single (12"): released on Rhythmic, Jul'85 by Rhythmic Records. Dist: Havoc Distribution

Claudius the god

CLAUDIUS THE GOD Graves, Robert (Jacobi, Derek).
Double cassette: released on Argo (Spokenword), Mar'83 by Decca Records. Dist: Polygram

Cassette: released on Argo, Jan'80 by Decca Records. Dist: Polygram

Clausen, Thomas

THOMAS CLAUSEN 3.
Album: released on Matrix (Import), '81 Dist: Jazz Horizons, Jazz Music, J...

Clay

BREAKOUT.
Album: released on Clay, Jun'87 by Clay Records. Dist: Pinnacle

Clayborn, Rev. Edward W

GUITAR EVANGELIST - 1926-1929, THE.
Notes: Released in mono.
Album: released on Earl Archives, Jan'87 Dist: Swift, Jazz Music

Clayderman, Richard

A COMME AMOUR.
Album: released on Teldec (Germany), Nov'82 by Import Records. Dist: IMS Distribution, Polygram Distribution

Cassette: released on Teldec (Germany), Nov'82 by Import Records. Dist: IMS Distribution, Polygram Distribution

A PLEYEL.
Notes: Nicolas de Angelis - guitar
Double Album: released on Delphine, Nov'83 by Decca Records. Dist: Polygram

Cassette: released on Delphine, Nov'83 by Decca Records. Dist: Polygram

BALLADE POUR ADELINE (LIMITED EDITION).
Notes: This appears to be one of at least three different albums with identical names. This is the EEC Imports version subtitled Limited Edition.
Album: released on EEC Imports, Dec'82 Dist: IMS, Polygram

Cassette: released on EEC Imports, Dec'82 Dist: IMS, Polygram

BALLADE POUR ADELINE.
Tracks: / Secret of my life / L'enfant et la mer / Lys river / Black deal / Lyphard melodie / La miliere / Ballade pour adeline / Old fashion / Romantica serenade.
Notes: This appears to be one of at least three different albums with identical names. This is the Teldec(Germany)/Delphine version without a sub title.
Compact disc: by Decca Records. Dist: Polygram

Album: released on Teldec (Germany), Nov'82 by Import Records. Dist: IMS Distribution, Polygram Distribution

Cassette: released on Teldec (Germany), Nov'82 by Import Records. Dist: IMS Distribution, Polygram Distribution

BALLADE POUR ADELINE (THE LOVE SONG).
Notes: This appears to be one of at least three different albums with identical names. This is the Sonet offering, subtitled The love song.
Album: released on Sonet, Jan'81 by Sonet Records. Dist: PRT

Cassette: released on Sonet, Jan'81 by Sonet Records. Dist: PRT

BALLADE POUR ADELINE (SINGLE).
Notes: This is the Safari/Sonet single, not to be confused with the Delphine (Christmas1982) single (called Ballad for Adeline) or any of the eponymous albums.
Single (7"): released on Safari, '79 by Safari Records. Dist: Pinnacle

Single (7"): released on Sonet, Jan'81 by Sonet Records. Dist: PRT

BALLAD FOR ADELINE.
Notes: This is the Christmas 1982 single, not to be confused with the other recordings (At least three albums and one single with the same title in French).
Single (7"): released on Delphine, Nov'82 by Decca Records. Dist: Polygram

CHRISTMAS.
Tracks: / White christmas / Handel's largo / Jesu joy of man's desiring / On Christmas night the lights are burning / Silver bells / Christmas concerto / He was born the holy child / Moonlight sonata / Leise rieselt der schnee / Romance / Candles twinkle, The / On the christmas tree.
Compact disc: released on Delphine, Nov'86 by Decca Records. Dist: Polygram

Album: released on Delphine, Nov'85 by Decca Records. Dist: Polygram

Cassette: released on Delphine, Nov'85 by Decca Records. Dist: Polygram

CLASSIC TOUCH.
Tracks: / Piano concerto No. 1 in B flat minor / Piano concerto No. 21 in C major / Dream of Olwen, The / Variation of a theme of Paganini / Pathetique / Liebestraum / Warsaw concerto / Piano concerto in A minor / Cornish rhapsody / Piano concerto No. 2 / Rhapsody in blue / Clair de lune.
Notes: With the Royal Philharmonic Orchestra
Album: released on Delphine, '86 by Decca Records. Dist: Polygram

Cassette: released on Delphine, '86 by Decca Records. Dist: Polygram

Compact disc: released on Delphine, '86 by Decca Records. Dist: Polygram

COEUR FRAGILE.
Tracks: / Quand les enfants s'aiment / Les nuages / Solitude / L'Italienne / Vivre sans toi / L'Amour-tendresse / Tes yeux dans mes yeux / Une si jolie petite valse / Souviens toi de moi / Comme un rayon de lune / Dis dame / L'Asiatique / Coeur fragile.
Compact disc: released on Delphine (France), '85 by Decca Records. Dist: IMS, Polygram

Album: released on Delphine (France), Mar'85 by Decca Records. Dist: IMS, Polygram

Cassette: released on Delphine (France), Mar'85 by Decca Records. Dist: IMS, Polygram

DREAMING.
Album: released on Import Music Service (IMS), Mar'81 Dist: Concord Jazz Distributions, Pablo, Polygram

DREAMING 2.
Album: released on Teldec (Germany), Dec'81 by Import Records. Dist: IMS Distribution, Polygram Distribution

Cassette: released on Teldec (Germany), Dec'81 by Import Records. Dist: IMS Distribution, Polygram Distribution

DREAMING 3.
Notes: See also Traumereien 3
Album: released on Teldec (Germany), Dec'81 by Import Records. Dist: IMS Distribution, Polygram Distribution

Cassette: released on Teldec (Germany), Dec'81 by Import Records. Dist: IMS Distribution, Polygram Distribution

FEELINGS.
Single (7"): released on Delphine, Sep'83 by Decca Records. Dist: Polygram

FRANCE - MON AMOUR.
Album: released on Delphine (France), Aug'87 by Decca Records. Dist: IMS, Polygram

Cassette: released on Delphine (France), Aug'87 by Decca Records. Dist: IMS. Polygram

Compact disc: released on Delphine (France), Aug'87 by Decca Records. Dist: IMS, Polygram

HOLLYWOOD AND BROADWAY.
Tracks: / Night and day / Bewitched / Embraceable you / Long ago and far away / Way you look tonight (The) / Smoke gets in you eyes / People / All the things you are / I've grown accustomed to her face / On the street where you live / If I loved you / You'll never walk alone.
Album: released on Delphine, Nov'86 by Decca Records. Dist: Polygram

Cassette: released on Delphine, Nov'86 by Decca Records. Dist: Polygram

Compact disc: released on Delphine, Nov'86 by Decca Records. Dist: Polygram

ICH LIEBE DICH.
Album: released on Teldec (Germany), Jul'83 by Import Records. Dist: IMS Distribution, Polygram Distribution

Cassette: released on Teldec (Germany), Jul'83 by Import Records. Dist: IMS Distribution, Polygram Distribution

IN CONCERT.
Double Album: released on Teldec (Germany), Mar'82 by Import Records. Dist: IMS Distribution, Polygram Distribution

Double cassette: released on Teldec (Germany), Mar'82 by Import Records. Dist: IMS Distribution, Polygram Distribution

INTRODUCING RICHARD CLAYDERMAN.
Tracks: / Comme amour, A / A comme amour / La mer / My way / Lyphard melody / Tristesse / Fur Elise / Ballad pour Adeline / Bach gammon / Sentimental melody / Liebestraum / Moonlight sonata / Romeo & Juliet / Liebeslied.
Compact disc: released on Decca, Sep'86 by Decca Records. Dist: Polygram

LADY DI.
Single (7"): released on Delphine, Nov'83 by Decca Records. Dist: Polygram

LETTRE A MA MERE.
Tracks: / Souvenirs d'enfance / Nostalgia / Histoire d'un reve / Melodie des souvenirs / Tendresses / Lettre a ma mere / Les elans de coeur / Marriage d'amour / Premiers chagrins.
Compact disc: released on Delphine, Jul'86 by Decca Records. Dist: Polygram

Album: released on Teldec (Germany), Oct'82 by Import Records. Dist: IMS Distribution, Polygram Distribution

Cassette: released on Teldec (Germany), Oct'82 by Import Records. Dist: IMS Distribution, Polygram Distribution

MARIAGE D'AMOUR.
Double Album: released on Delphine (France), May'84 by Decca Records. Dist: IMS, Polygram

Cassette: released on Delphine (France), May'84 by Decca Records. Dist: IMS, Polygram

MELODY CONCERTO.
Album: released on Teldec (Germany), Oct'82 by Import Records. Dist: IMS Distribution, Polygram Distribution

Cassette: released on Teldec (Germany), Oct'82 by Import Records. Dist: IMS Distribution, Polygram Distribution

MUSIC OF LOVE, (THE).
Notes: CD title is Musiques de l'amour, (Les)
Album: released on Delphine, Nov'84 by Decca Records. Dist: Polygram

Cassette: released on Delphine, Nov'84 by Decca Records. Dist: Polygram

MUSIC OF RICHARD CLAYDERMAN, (THE).
Album: released on Delphine, Apr'84 by Decca Records. Dist: Polygram

Cassette: released on Delphine, Apr'84 by Decca Records. Dist: Polygram

MUSIQUES DE L'AMOUR, (LES).
Tracks: / Man and a woman, A / My way / La vraie musique de l'amour / Feelings / Lar's theme / Tristesse / Parlez-moi d'amour / When a man loves a woman / Strangers in the night / Voyage a Venise / Ave Maria / Aline / Man and a woman, A / Love me tender / Jardin secret / Plaisir d'amour / Michelle.
Album: released on Delphine (France), '86 by Decca Records. Dist: IMS, Polygram

Cassette: released on Delphine (France), '86 by Decca Records. Dist: IMS, Polygram

Compact disc: released on Delphine (France), '86 by Decca Records. Dist: IMS, Polygram

MUSIQUES DE L'AMOUR, (LES).
Album: released on Delphine (France), Dec'82 by Decca Records. Dist: IMS, Polygram

Cassette: released on Delphine (France), Dec'82 by Decca Records. Dist: IMS, Polygram

Compact disc: released on Delphine (France), Dec'82 by Decca Records. Dist: IMS, Polygram

MUSIQUES DE L'AMOUR, (LES).
Notes: Album/cassette title is Music of love, (The).
Compact disc: released on Delphine, Nov'84 by Decca Records. Dist: Polygram

PLAYS THE ROMANTIC MELODIES OF ROBERT STOLZ.
Album: released on Teldec (Germany), Jul'84 by Import Records. Dist: IMS Distribution, Polygram Distribution

Cassette: released on Teldec (Germany), Jul'84 by Import Records. Dist: IMS Distribution, Polygram Distribution

PROFILE.
Double Album: released on Teldec (Germany), Mar'84 by Import Records. Dist: IMS Distribution, Polygram Distribution

Double cassette: released on Teldec (Germany), Mar'84 by Import Records. Dist: IMS Distribution, Polygram Distribution

PROFILE VOLUME 1.
Album: released on Teldec (Germany), Aug'81 by Import Records. Dist: IMS Distribution, Polygram Distribution

Cassette: released on Teldec (Germany), Aug'81 by Import Records. Dist: IMS Distribution, Polygram Distribution

PROFILE VOLUME 2.
Album: released on Teldec (Germany), Dec'81 by Import Records. Dist: IMS Distribution, Polygram Distribution

Cassette: released on Teldec (Germany), Dec'81 by Import Records. Dist: IMS Distribution, Polygram Distribution

REVERIES.
Compact disc: released on Delphine, Jun'84 by Decca Records. Dist: Polygram

Compact disc: by Decca Records. Dist: Polygram

Album: released on Delphine (France), Dec'82 by Decca Records. Dist: IMS, Polygram

Cassette: released on Delphine (France), Dec'82 by Decca Records. Dist: IMS, Polygram

REVERIES/LETTRE A MA MERE/LES MUSIQUES DE L'AMOUR.
Boxed set: released on Teldec (Germany), Nov'82 by Import Records. Dist: IMS Distribution, Polygram Distribution

RICHARD CLAYDERMAN COLLECTION.
Boxed set: released on Delphine, Nov'86 by Decca Records. Dist: Polygram

Boxed set: released on Delphine, Nov'86 by Decca Records. Dist: Polygram

RICHARD CLAYDERMAN.
Notes: Another Clayderman title adorning more than one recording-you have been warned.
Cassette: released on Arcade Music Gala, Apr'86 Dist: Stage One

Compact disc: released on Delphine, '86 by Decca Records. Dist: Polygram

Album: released on Delphine (France), Sep'85 by Decca Records. Dist: IMS, Polygram

Cassette: released on Delphine (France), Sep'85 by Decca Records. Dist: IMS, Polygram

Album: released on Decca (Delphine), Sep'82 by Decca Records. Dist: Polygram, IMS

Cassette: released on Decca (Delphine), Sep'82 by Decca Records. Dist: Polygram, IMS

ROMANTIC.
Album: released on Delphine (France), Oct'86 by Decca Records. Dist: IMS, Polygram

Cassette: released on Delphine (France), Oct'86 by Decca Records. Dist: IMS, Polygram

RONDO POUR UN TOUT PETIT ENFANT.
Tracks: / Les chagrins oublies / L'ocean / L'heure bleue / Berceuse / Murmures / Les premiers sourires de Vanessa / L'espair / Triste coeur / Un fuite du temps / Concerto pour une juene fille nommee - je t'aime.
Album: released on Delphine, '86 by Decca Records. Dist: Polygram

Cassette: released on Delphine, '86 by Decca Records. Dist: Polygram

Album: released on Delphine (France), Dec'82 by Decca Records. Dist: IMS, Polygram

Cassette: released on Delphine (France), Dec'82 by Decca Records. Dist: IMS, Polygram

SONATES, (LES).
Tracks: / Diva / Mon pere / Les jours heureux / Pastorale / Les premiers pas / La fete / Angelica devina / L'amour heureux / La petite etoile / La mort d'un oiseau / L'offrandee / Les adieux.
Album: released on Delphine (France), Feb'86 by Decca Records. Dist: IMS, Polygram

Cassette: released on Delphine (France), Feb'86 by Decca Records. Dist: IMS, Polygram

Album: released on Arcade Music Gala, Apr'86 Dist: Stage One

Compact disc: by Decca Records. Dist: Polygram

SOUVENIRS.
Album: released on Sonet, Feb'82 by Sonet Records. Dist: PRT

Cassette: released on Sonet, Feb'82 by Sonet Records. Dist: PRT

TRAUMEREI 3.
Notes: See also Dreaming 3.
Album: released on Teldec (Germany), Jul'83 by Import Records. Dist: IMS Distribution, Polygram Distribution

Cassette: released on Teldec (Germany), Jul'83 by Import Records. Dist: IMS Distribution, Polygram Distribution

Clay, James

WIDE OPEN SPACES (Clay, James & David 'Fathead' Newman).
Notes: For full details see under NEWMAN, David Fathead/James Clay

Clay, Joe

DUCKTAIL.
Tracks: / Ducktail / Get on the right track / You look good to me / Did you mean jelly bean (what you said cabbage head) / Cracker Jack / Goodbye goodbye / Sixteen chicks / Slipping out and sneaking in / Doggon it / Get on the right track / You look good to me.
Album: released on Bear Family, Aug'86 by Bear Family Records. Dist: Rollercoaster Distribution, Swift

Clay, Judy

PRIVATE NUMBER (Clay, Judy & William Bell).
Tracks: / Private number / Love-eye-tis.
Single (7"): released on Stax, 13 Jun'87 by Ace Records. Dist: Pinnacle, Chris Wellard, IMS-Polygram

Single (7"): released on Old Gold, Sep'85 by Old Gold Records. Dist: Lightning, Jazz Music, Spartan, Counterpoint

Clay, Otis

LIVE IN JAPAN.
Album: released on Blue Sting, Nov'86 Dist: Swift

LOVE BANDIT.
Single (12"): released on Pinnacle, Jul'84 by Pinnacle Records. Dist: Pinnacle

TRYING TO LIVE MY LIFE WITHOUT YOU.
Album: released on Hi, May'87 by Demon Records. Dist: Pinnacle

Clay, Sonny

SONNY CLAY 1922-1960.
Album: released on Harlequin, Nov'85 by Harlequin Records. Dist: Swift, Jazz Music, Wellard, Chris, IRS, Taylor, H.R.

Clayson & The Argonauts

LAST RESPECTS.
Single (7"): released on Racket, Dec'82 Dist: Rough Trade

WHAT A DIFFERENCE A DECADE MADE.
Album: released on Butt, Nov'85 by Butt Records. Dist: Counterpoint

Clay, Tiggi

TIGGI CLAY.
Album: released on Morocco, Apr'84

WINNER GETS THE HEART.
Single (7"): by Motown Records. Dist: BMG Distribution

Clay, Tom

WHAT THE WORLD NEEDS NOW.
Single (7"): released on Mowest, Oct'81

Clayton, Buck

1966

BUCK CLAYTON, HOT LIPS PAGE & BUD FREEMAN (Clayton, Buck, B. Freeman & Hot Lips Page).

BUCK CLAYTON WITH HUMPHREY LYTTLETON VOL.2 (Clayton, Buck & Humphrey Lyttleton).
Album: released on Harlequin, Jan'86 by Harlequin Records. Dist: Swift, Jazz Music, Wellard, Chris, IRS, Taylor, H.R.

FEEL SO FINE (Clayton, Buck & Joe Turner).
Album: released on Black Lion, Jul'87 by Black Lion Records. Dist: Jazz Music, Chris Wellard, Taylor, H.R., Counterpoint, Cadillac

HUCKLE-BUCK AND ROBIN'S NEST 1953, (THE).
Album: released on Japanese Import, May'79

JAZZ FESTIVAL JAZZ (Clayton, Buck & Duke Ellington).
Album: released on Queen-Disc, Apr'81 Dist: Celtic Music, Jazz Horizons, Jazz Music

LIVE IN PARIS (Clayton, Buck & Jimmy Witherspoon).
Double Album: released on Vogue, Jan'77 Dist: Discovery, Jazz Music, PRT, Swift

TRUMPET SUMMIT (Clayton, Buck & Roy Eldridge).
Album: released on Pumpkin, Jun'78 Dist: Jazz Music, Wellard, Chris, Cadillac

Album: released on Pumpkin, Jun'78 Dist: Jazz Music, Wellard, Chris, Cadillac

Clayton, Kid

FIRST SESSION 1952, (THE).
Album: released on Folkways (USA), Mar'84 by Folkways (USA) Records. Dist: Swift, Projection, Recommended

Clayton, Lee

BORDER AFFAIR.
Album: released on Capitol, Apr'78 by Capitol Records. Dist: EMI

Clayton, Paul

Bluegrass session, 1952

DAYS OF MOBY DICK.
Album: released on Traditn, Nov'74

Clean

CLEAN COMPILATION.
Album: released on Flying Nun, May'87 Dist: Rough Trade, Cartel

Cleaners From Venus

GOING TO ENGLAND.
Album: released on Ammunition, Feb'87 Dist: Pinnacle

ILLYA KURYAKIN LOOKED AT ME.
Tracks: / Illya Kuryakin looked at me.
Single (12"): released on Ammunition, Mar'87 Dist: Pinnacle

LIVING WITH VICTORIA GREY.
Single (12"): released on Ammunition, 13 Jun'87 Dist: Pinnacle

UNDER WARTIME CONDITIONS.
Cassette: released on TAO, Jul'84

Clean Looking Boys

SENT TO COVENTRY.
Single (7"): released on DJM, Oct'83 by DJM Records. Dist: CBS, Polygram

Clean Tape

CLEAN TAPE Various Artists (Various Artists).
Album: released on Chapel Lane, Nov'83 Dist: RCA

Clearwater, Eddy

CHIEF, (THE).
Album: released on Rooster, Mar'84 by Rooster Records. Dist: PRT Distribution

FLIM DOOZIE.
Album: released on Rooster, Jul'87 by Rooster Records. Dist: PRT Distribution

TWO TIMES NINE.
Album: released on Charly, Jul'81 by Charly Records. Dist: Charly, Cadillac

Cleaver, Emrys

SONGS IN WELSH (& others).
Cassette: released on Folktracks, Nov'79 by Folktracks Cassettes. Dist: Folktracks

Cleaver, H. Robinson

ROBINSON CLEAVER IN CONCERT.
Album: released on Amberlee, Apr'79 by Amberlee Records. Dist: Amberlee Records, H.R. Taylor

Cleaver, Robinson

LET'S BREAK THE GOOD NEWS.
Notes: For full information see under Thorburn, Billy

ORGAN, THE DANCE AND ME, THE See Thorburn, Billy (Cleaver, Robinson & Billy Thorburn).
Album: released on President, Aug'84 by President Records. Dist: Taylors, Spartan

Clegg, Johnny

GREAT HEART (Clegg, Johnny & Savuka).
Tracks: / Great heart / African sky blue / Unfazi ondali.
Single (7"): released on EMI, Jul'87 by EMI Records. Dist: EMI

Single (12"): released on EMI, Jul'87 by EMI Records. Dist: EMI

GREAT HEART (EXT) (Clegg, Johnny & Savuka).
Tracks: / Great heart (ext) / African sky blue (live) / Umfazi undah (live) / Africa (live).
Cassette single: released on EMI, Jul'87 by EMI Records. Dist: EMI

SCATTERLINGS OF AFRICA (Clegg, Johnny & Savuka).
Tracks: / Third world child / Scatterlings of Africa / Don't walk away.
Single (7"): released on EMI, Apr'87 by EMI Records. Dist: EMI

Single (12"): released on EMI, Apr'87 by EMI Records. Dist: EMI

Compact disc single: released on EMI, May'87 by EMI Records. Dist: EMI

THIRD WORLD CHILD (Clegg, Johnny & Savuka).
Tracks: / Are you ready / Asimbonanga (Mandela) / Giyana / Scatterlings of Africa / Great heart / Missing / Ring on her finger / Third world child / Berlin wall / Don't walk away.
Notes: Composer: Johnny Clegg except 3 - Clegg/V. Mavuso. Publishers: Sweet 'n' Sour Songs Ltd. Producer/arranger: Hilton Rosenthal. Johnny Clegg is without doubt one of the most important artists to emerge anywhere and particularly South Africa in recent years. An honoury zulu, Clegg has lived in South Africa since early childhood picking up the realities of African music yet adding a unique influence of his own. Clegg was heavily involved with Paul Simon in the making of the Graceland album and in fact Clegg's producer Hilton Rosenthal has been credited by Simon as the man who put Graceland together. [EMI release sheet, May 1987]
Compact disc: released on EMI, May'87 by EMI Records. Dist: EMI

Album: released on EMI, Jan'87 by EMI Records. Dist: EMI

Cassette: released on EMI, Jan'87 by EMI Records. Dist: EMI

Compact disc: released on EMI, May'87 by EMI Records. Dist: EMI

Clements, Roberta

CHANNEL OF PEACE.
Album: by Pilgrim Records. Dist: Rough Trade, Cartel

Clements, Vassar

BLUEGRASS JAM (Clements, Vassar/Doug Jernigan/J. McReynolds).
Album: released on Flying Fish (USA), May'79 by Flying Fish Records (USA). Dist: Roots, Projection

CLEMENTS, HARTFORD & HOLLAND (Clements, Vassar/John Hartford/Dave Holland).
Album: released on Rounder (USA), Jul'85 Dist: Mike's Country Music Room Distribution, Jazz Music Distribution, Swift Distribution, Roots Records Distribution, Projection Distribution, Topic Distribution

CROSSING THE CATSKILLS.
Album: released on Rounder, Jan'87 Dist: Roots Distribution

HILLBILLY JAZZ RIDES AGAIN.
Album: released on Flying Fish (USA), Feb'87 by Flying Fish Records (USA). Dist: Roots, Projection

Cassette: released on Flying Fish (USA), Feb'87 by Flying Fish Records (USA). Dist: Roots, Projection

Clemons, Clarence

HERO (Clemons, Clarence & The Red Bank Rockers).
Tracks: / You're a friend of mine / Temptation / It's alright with me girl / Liberation fire (Mokshagun) / Sun ain't gonna shine anymore / I wanna be your hero / Cross the line / Kissin' on U / Christina.
Compact disc: released on CBS, '86 by CBS Records. Dist: CBS

Album: released on CBS, Dec'85 by CBS Records. Dist: CBS

Cassette: released on CBS, Dec'85 by CBS Records. Dist: CBS Deleted '87.

RESCUE (Clemons, Clarence & The Red Bank Rockers).
Album: released on CBS, Nov'83 by CBS Records. Dist: CBS Deleted '87.

Cassette: released on CBS, Nov'83 by CBS Records. Dist: CBS

YOU'RE A FRIEND OF MINE (Clemons, Clarence & Jackson Browne).
Tracks: / Let the music say it.
Single (7"): released on CBS, Feb'86 by CBS Records. Dist: CBS

Single (12"): released on CBS, Feb'86 by CBS Records. Dist: CBS

Clennell, Claire

ENCHANTED ISLE - MELODIES FOR A MILLENIUM, (THE).
Album: released on Emerald Gem, Jul'79 Dist: Spartan, MK

Cleobury, Stephen

MUSIC IN ROYAL WESTMINSTER.
Album: released on CJMO, Aug'77 Dist: Jazz Music, Spartan, Taylors

WEDDING FAVOURITES.
Album: released on Decca, Nov'79 by Decca Records. Dist: Polygram

Cassette: released on Decca, Nov'79 by Decca Records. Dist: Polygram

Clerc, Julien

DISQUE D'OR VOLUME 2.
Album: released on EMI (France), '83 by EMI Records. Dist: Conifer

JULIEN CLERC.
Album: released on Virgin, Oct'84 by Virgin Records. Dist: EMI, Virgin Distribution

Cassette: released on Virgin, Oct'84 by Virgin Records. Dist: EMI, Virgin Distribution

THERE IS NO DISTANCE.
Tracks: / There is no distance / Wine of words.
Single (7"): released on 10, Jun'87 by 10 Records. Dist: Virgin, EMI

THERE IS NO DISTANCE (LP).
Album: released on 10, Jun'87 by 10 Records. Dist: Virgin, EMI

Clermont, Rene

BONJOUR CHRISTIANE.
Album: released on Mercury (Import), Feb'82

Cassette: released on Mercury (Import), Feb'82

Cleveland, Barry

MYTHOS.
Compact disc: by Pacific Records (USA). Dist: Atlantic

Cleveland Crochet

CLEVELAND CROCHET AND ALL THE SUGAR BEES.
Album: released on Goldband, Feb'79 by Charly Records. Dist: Charly

Clever Polly and...

CLEVER POLLY AND THE STUPID WOLF Storr, Catherine (Griffiths, Derek).
Notes: Read by Derek Griffith.
Cassette: released on Cover to Cover, Sep'86 by Cover to Cover Cassettes. Dist: Conifer

Click

DIZZY SPINNIN' ROUND.
Single (7"): released on New World, Aug'83 by President Records. Dist: Swift, Spartan

JUST ANOTHER MONDAY.
Single (7"): released on New World, Nov'83 by President Records. Dist: Swift, Spartan

Single (12"): released on New World, Nov'83 by President Records. Dist: Swift, Spartan

Click Click

PARTY HATE.
Album: released on Roarschach Testing, Oct'86

RUN ME DOWN (EP).
Single (7"): released on Lung Function, '82

SKRIPGLOW.
Tracks: / Skripglow / Sack (The) / Rotor babe.
Single (12"): released on Rorschach Testing, Feb'87 by Rorschach Testing Records. Dist: Rough Trade Distribution

SWEET STUFF.
Single (12"): released on Rorschach Testing, Jul'86 by Rorschach Testing Records. Dist: Rough Trade Distribution

Single (12"): released on Rorschach Testing, '85 by Rorschach Testing Records. Dist: Rough Trade Distribution

Cliff Adams Singers

SING SOMETHING SIMPLE 100 Golden greats-featuring cliff Adams Singers.
Double Album: released on Ronco, Dec'82

Double cassette: released on Ronco, Dec'82

Cliff, Jimmy

ANOTHER CYCLE.
Album: by Island Records. Dist: Polygram

CLIFF HANGER.
Album: released on CBS, '85 by CBS Records. Dist: CBS

Cassette: released on CBS, '85 by CBS Records. Dist: CBS

CLIFF HANGER.
Tracks: / Hitting with music / American sweet / Arrival / Brown eyes / Reggae street / Hot shot / Sunrise / Dead and awake / Now and forever / Nuclear war.
Compact disc: released on CBS, Apr'86 by CBS Records. Dist: CBS

CLIFF, JIMMY Best of.
Album: released on Island, '76 by Island Records. Dist: Polygram

COLLECTION: JIMMY CLIFF.
Album: released on EMI (Germany), '83 by EMI Records. Dist: Conifer

FUNDAMENTAL REGGAY.
Tracks: / Fundamental reggay / Under the sun, moon and stars / Ripp off / On my life / Commercialization / You can't be wrong and get right / Oh Jamaica / No 1 ripp off man / Brother / House of exile / Long time no see / My love is as solid as rock / My people / Actions speak louder than words / Brave warrior.
Album: released on See For Miles, Feb'87 by See For Miles Records. Dist: Pinnacle

GIVE THANKS.
Album: released on WB, '78

HARDER THEY COME.
Tracks: / You can get it if you really want / Many rivers to cross / Harder they come, The / Sitting in limbo / Draw your brakes / Rivers of Babylon / Sweet and Dandy / Pressure drop / Johnny too bad / Shanty town.
Album: released on Island, Sep'86 by Island Records. Dist: Polygram

Cassette: released on Island, Sep'86 by Island Records. Dist: Polygram

I AM THE LIVING.
Cassette: released on WEA, '80 by WEA Records. Dist: WEA

Album: released on WEA, '80 by WEA Records. Dist: WEA

JIMMY CLIFF.
Album: released on Trojan, '83 by Trojan Records. Dist: PRT, Jetstar

Cassette: released on Trojan, '83 by Trojan Records. Dist: PRT, Jetstar

LOVE IS ALL/ORIGINATOR/ROOTS.
Single (7"): released on CBS, '83 by CBS Records. Dist: CBS

Single (12"): released on CBS, '83 by CBS Records. Dist: CBS

MANY RIVERS TO CROSS.
Single (12"): released on Trojan, '83 by Trojan Records. Dist: PRT, Jetstar

MIDNIGHT ROCKERS True Lovers.
Single (7"): released on Oneness, '82

Single (12"): released on Oneness, '82

OH JAMAICA.
Album: released on Nut, '76 by EMI Records. Dist: EMI

REGGAE GREATS.
Album: released on Island, '85 by Island Records. Dist: Polygram

Cassette: released on Island, '85 by Island Records. Dist: Polygram

REGGAE MOVEMENT.
Single (7"): released on CBS, '84 by CBS Records. Dist: CBS

Single (12"): released on CBS, '84 by CBS Records. Dist: CBS

REGGAE NIGHTS.
Single (7"): released on CBS, '84 by CBS Records. Dist: CBS

Single (12"): released on CBS, '84 by CBS Records. Dist: CBS

RUB A DUB PARTNER.
Single (12"): released on Oneness, '82

SPECIAL.
Album: released on CBS, '82 by CBS Records. Dist: CBS

Cassette: released on CBS, '82 by CBS Records. Dist: CBS

UNLIMITED.
Album: released on EMI, '73 by EMI Records. Dist: EMI

WE ARE ALL ONE/NO APOLOGY/PIECE OF THE PIE.
Single (7"): released on CBS, '84 by CBS Records. Dist: CBS

Single (12"): released on CBS, '84 by CBS Records. Dist: CBS

WONDERFUL WORLD BEAUTIFUL PEOPLE.
Single (7"): released on Old Gold, '83 by Old Gold Records. Dist: Lightning, Jazz Music, Spartan, Counterpoint

Cliff, Les

DEPENDING ON YOU.
Single (12"): released on Sea View, '84 by Sea View Records. Dist: Jetstar

Clifford, Billy

TRADITIONAL FLUTE SOLOS & BAND MUSIC....
Album: released on Topic, '81 Dist: Roots Distribution

Clifford, Bob

HOT ROCK (Clifford, Bob & The Hep Cats).
Album: released on Honeymoon, Jun'79 by Honeymoon Records. Dist: Lightning, Superdisc Distribution, Swift

Clifford, Buzz

BABY SITTIN' BOOGIE.
Single (7"): released on Old Gold, Jul'82 by Old Gold Records. Dist: Lightning, Jazz Music, Spartan, Counterpoint

Clifford, John

HUMOURS OF LISHEEN, (THE) (Clifford, John & Julia).
Album: released on Topic, Feb'77 Dist: Roots Distribution

STAR OF MUNSTER TRIO (Clifford, John, Julia & Billy).
Album: released on Topic, Feb'77 Dist: Roots Distribution

Clifford, Linda

I'M YOURS.
Cassette: released on RSO, Nov'80

LET ME BE YOUR WOMAN.
Album: released on RSO, May'79

RED LIGHT.
Single (7"): released on RSO, Jul'82

Cassette: released on RSO, Jul'82

RUNAWAY LOVE.
Single (7"): released on Cambra, Oct'84 by Cambra Records. Dist: IDS, Conifer

Cassette: released on Cambra, Oct'84 by Cambra Records. Dist: IDS, Conifer

Clifford, Mataya

IT'S GETTING HOT.
Single (7"): released on Batbeat, Aug'80

Clifton, Bill

Another happy day

ARE YOU FROM DIXIE? (Clifton, Bill & Red Rector).
Album: released on Bear Family, Sep'84 by Bear Family Records. Dist: Rollercoaster Distribution, Swift

BEATLE CRAZY.
Picture disc album: released on Bear Family, Oct'83 by Bear Family Records. Dist: Rollercoaster Distribution, Swift

BLUEGRASS SESSION, 1952 (Clifton, Bill & Paul Clayton).
Album: released on Bear Family, Sep'84 by Bear Family Records. Dist: Rollercoaster Distribution, Swift

BLUE RIDGE MOUNTAIN BLUEGRASS (Clifton, Bill & the Dixie Mountain Boys).
Album: released on Westwood, '82 by Westwood Records. Dist: Jazz Music, H.R. Taylor, Pinnacle, Ross Records

GETTING FOLK OUT OF THE COUNTRY (see West, Hedy) (Clifton, Bill/Hedy West).

GOING BACK TO DIXIE.
Double Album: released on Starday (USA), Sep'84

MOUNTAIN FOLK SONGS.
Album: released on Starday, Apr'87
Cat. no: **SLP 111**
Cassette: released on Starday, Apr'87

Clifton, Chris

MEMORIES OF A FRIEND (Clifton, Chris & His New Orleans All Stars).
Album: released on GHB, Feb'87 Dist: Jazz Music, Swift

Climax Blues Band

BEST OF CLIMAX BLUES BAND.
Album: released on RCA (Germany), '83

COULDN'T GET IT RIGHT.
Tracks: / Year of the cat.
Single (7"): released on Old Gold, Nov'86 by Old Gold Records. Dist: Lightning, Jazz Music, Spartan, Counterpoint

FLYING THE FLAG.
Album: released on Warner Brothers, Nov'80 by Warner Bros Records. Dist: WEA

LISTEN TO THE NIGHT.
Single (7"): released on Virgin, Feb'83 by Virgin Records. Dist: EMI, Virgin Distribution

LOOSEN UP (1974-76).
Album: released on See For Miles, Mar'84 by See For Miles Records. Dist: Pinnacle

LUCKY FOR SOME.
Album: released on Warner Bros., Oct'81 by Warner Bros Records. Dist: WEA

Cassette: released on Warner Bros., Oct'81 by Warner Bros Records. Dist: WEA

SHINE ON.
Album: released on Warner Bros., May'78 by Warner Bros Records. Dist: WEA

Cassette: released on Warner Bros., May'78 by Warner Bros Records. Dist: WEA

STAMP ALBUM.
Album: released on BTM, Sep'75 Dist: BMG Distribution

Climax Orchestra

INTERACTION.
Single (12"): released on Challenge, Nov'84 by Elite Records. Dist: Pinnacle

Climb

I CAN'T FORGET.
Single (7"): released on Rialto, Oct'82 by Rialto Records. Dist: Pinnacle

POACHER (IS AS POACHER DOES).
Single (7"): released on Second Vision, Aug'84 by Second Vision Records. Dist: Pinnacle

TOUCH ME (HEAVEN).
Single (7"): released on Camden(RCA), Mar'82 by RCA Records. Dist: Pickwick Distribution, Taylors, Swift

Clime

ALL OUR LIVES.
Single (7"): released on Tapir, Jul'84 by Tapir Records. Dist: Pinnacle

Climie Fisher

KEEPING THE MYSTERY ALIVE.
Tracks: / Keeping the mystery alive / Nothing but a feeling.
Single (7"): released on EMI, Mar'87 by EMI Records. Dist: EMI

Single (12"): released on EMI, Mar'87 by EMI Records. Dist: EMI

LOVE CHANGES EVERYTHING.
Tracks: / Never close the show.
Single (7"): released on EMI, Aug'87 by EMI Records. Dist: EMI

Single (12"): released on EMI, Aug'87 by EMI Records. Dist: EMI

Single (7"): released on EMI, Aug'87 by EMI Records. Dist: EMI

THIS IS ME.
Tracks: / Far across the water / This is me (remix).
Single (7"): released on EMI, Aug'86 by EMI Records. Dist: EMI

Single (12"): released on EMI, Aug'86 by EMI Records. Dist: EMI

Clinch

SWEETHEARTS.
Single (7"): released on Jigsaw, Jan'81 Dist: Roots, Pinnacle, Projection

Clinch, Matt

POSITIVE VIBRATIONS (A GOOD BUS TO RIDE).
Single (7"): released on Strange, Oct'85 by Strange Records. Dist: Pinnacle

Single (12"): released on Strange, Oct'85 by Strange Records. Dist: Pinnacle

Cline, Charlie

COUNTRY DOBRO.
Album: released on Adelphi, May'81 by Adelphi Records. Dist: Jetstar

MORE DOBRO (Cline, Charlie with the Marakesh Express).
Album: released on Adelphi, May'81 by Adelphi Records. Dist: Jetstar

Cline, Patsy

20 CLASSIC SONGS.
Album: released on Meteor, Jun'86 by Magnum Music Group Ltd. Dist: Magnum Music Group Ltd, PRT Distribution, Spartan Distribution

20 GOLDEN GREATS.
Album: released on Astan, Nov'84 by Astan Records. Dist: Counterpoint

Cassette: released on Astan, Nov'84 by Astan Records. Dist: Counterpoint

20 GOLDEN PIECES OF PATSY CLINE.
Album: released on Bulldog Records, Jul'82

ALWAYS.
Album: released on Hallmark, Oct'87 by Pickwick Records. Dist: Pickwick Distribution, PRT, Taylors

Cassette: released on Hallmark, Oct'87 by Pickwick Records. Dist: Pickwick Distribution, PRT, Taylors

BEST OF PATSY CLINE.
Album: released on Hallmark, Sep'86 by Pickwick Records. Dist: Pickwick Distribution, PRT, Taylors

Cassette: released on Hallmark, Sep'86 by Pickwick Records. Dist: Pickwick Distribution, PRT, Taylors

COUNTRY MUSIC HALL OF FAME, (THE).
Album: released on MCA, '83 by MCA Records. Dist: Polygram, MCA

Cassette: released on MCA, '83 by MCA Records. Dist: Polygram, MCA

CRAZY.
Tracks: / Crazy / Walking after midnight.
Single (7"): released on MCA, Mar'87 by MCA Records. Dist: Polygram, MCA

GOLDEN GREATS: PATSY CLINE.
Album: released on MCA, Jul'85 by MCA Records. Dist: Polygram, MCA

Cassette: released on MCA, Jul'85 by MCA Records. Dist: Polygram, MCA

GREATEST HITS:PATSY CLINE & JIM REEVES (Cline, Patsy & Jim Reeves).
Album: released on RCA, Mar'82 by RCA Records. Dist: RCA, Roots, Swift, Wellard, Chris, I & B, Solomon & Peres Distribution

HAVE YOU EVER BEEN LONELY?.
Album: released on MCA, '75 by MCA Records. Dist: Polygram, MCA

LOT OF RHYTHM IN MY SOUL.
Compact disc: released on Pickwick, Oct'86 by Pickwick Records. Dist: Pickwick Distribution, Prism Leisure Distribution, Lugtons

OFF THE RECORD WITH....
Double Album: released on Sierra, Aug'87 by Sierra Records. Dist: WEA. Estim retail price in Sep'87 was £4.99.

Double cassette: released on Sierra, Aug'87 by Sierra Records. Dist: WEA. Estim retail price in Sep'87 was £4.99.

PATSY CLINE.
Double cassette: released on Pickwick (Ditto series), Jul'82

Cassette: released on Audio Fidelity, Oct'84 Dist: PRT

PATSY CLINE STORY.
Tracks: / Heartaches / She's got you / Walking after midnight / Strange / Leavin' on your mind / South of the border / Foolin' round / I fall to pieces / Poor man's roses, A / Tra le la le la triangle / True love / Imagine that / Back in baby's arms / Crazy / You're stronger than me / Seven lonely days / Sweet dreams / Your cheatin' heart / San Antonio rose / Why can't he be you / Wayward way, The / So wrong / I love you so much it hurts / You belong to me.
Double Album: released on MCA Import, Mar'86 by MCA Records. Dist: Polygram, IMS

PORTRAIT OF PATSY CLINE, A.
Tracks: / Who can I count on / You took him off my hands / Your kinda love / Does your heart beat for me / Faded love / I'll sail my ship alone / When you need a laugh / Crazy arms / Always / When I'm through with you (you'll love me too) / Blue moon of Kentucky / Someday you'll want me to want you.
Album: released on MCA Import, Mar'86 by MCA Records. Dist: Polygram, IMS

REMEMBERING (Cline, Patsy & Jim Reeves).
Tracks: / Fall to pieces / So wrong / Misty moonlight / Back in baby's arms / Missing you / Walking after midnight / Blizzard / Why can't he be you / Distant drums / Leavin' on your mind.
Album: released on MCA Import, Mar'86 by MCA Records. Dist: Polygram, IMS

REPLAY ON.
Album: released on Sierra, Apr'86 by Sierra Records. Dist: WEA

Cassette: released on Sierra, Apr'86 by Sierra Records. Dist: WEA

SHOWCASE.
Album: released on Stetson, Apr'87 by Hasmick Promotions Ltd.. Dist: Counterpoint Distribution, H.R. Taylor Distribution, Swift Distribution, Chris Wellard Distribution

Cassette: released on Stetson, Apr'87 by Hasmick Promotions Ltd.. Dist: Counterpoint Distribution, H.R. Taylor Distribution, Swift Distribution, Chris Wellard Distribution

SONGWRITER'S TRIBUTE.
Album: released on MCA, Mar'87 by MCA Records. Dist: Polygram, MCA

Cassette: released on MCA, Mar'87 by MCA Records. Dist: Polygram, MCA

TRIBUTE TO PATSY CLINE, A.
Album: released on Stetson, Feb'86 by Hasmick Promotions Ltd.. Dist: Counterpoint Distribution, H.R. Taylor Distribution, Swift Distribution, Chris Wellard Distribution

Cassette: released on Stretson, Feb'86

UNFORGETTABLE PATSY CLINE (Lot of rhythm...).
Compact disc: released on Imp, Nov'86 by Demon. Dist: Pinnacle

Cline, Tammy

I WISH I'D WROTE THAT SONG.
Single (7"): released on President, Sep'83 by President Records. Dist: Taylors, Spartan

SINGS THE COUNTRY GREATS WITH THE SOUTHERN.
Tracks: / Here you come again / Help me make it through the night / Rose garden / Hurt / Harper Valley PTA / Carolina Moon / Stand by your man / Don't it make my brown eyes blue / Coalminers daughter / Love letters / Sweet dreams / I fell in love again last night.
Notes: Produced by Gordon Lorenz, Engineer Phil Ault, (P) 1987 Original Sound Recordings made by Gordon Lorenz Productions Ltd. Full title: Sings the country greats with the Southern Comfort Band.
Album: released on MFP, Mar'87 by EMI Records. Dist: EMI

Cassette: released on MFP, Mar'87 by EMI Records. Dist: EMI

SINGS THE COUNTRY GREATS.
Album: released on MFP, May'87 by EMI Records. Dist: EMI

Cassette: released on MFP, May'87 by EMI Records. Dist: EMI

TAMMY CLINE'S COUNTRY GOSPEL ALBUM.
Tracks: / Our god reigns / One day at a time / It is no secret / I saw the light / I believe / Old rugged cross (The) / It's good to be home / This little light of mine / He is my everything / Heaven's gonna be a blast / Softly and tenderly / How great thou art.
Album: released on Word, Mar'87 by Word Records. Dist: Word Distribution, CBS

Cassette: released on Word, Mar'87 by Word Records. Dist: Word Distribution, CBS

TAMMY CLINE & THE SOUTHERN COMFORT BAND (Cline, Tammy & The Southern Comfort Band).
Album: released on President, Sep'83 by President Records. Dist: Taylors, Spartan

Clinkscale, Jimmy

ACCORDION BONANZA NO 1.
Album: released on ARC (Accordion Records), '84 Dist: Accordion Record Club

ACCORDION BONANZA NO 2.
Album: released on ARC (Accordion Records), '84 Dist: Accordion Record Club

ACCORDION BONANZA NO 3.
Album: released on ARC (Accordion Records), '84 Dist: Accordion Record Club

Clinton, George

COMPUTER GAMES.
Album: released on Capitol, Nov'82 by Capitol Records. Dist: EMI

Cassette: released on Capitol, Nov'82 by Capitol Records. Dist: EMI Deleted '86.

DO FRIES GO WITH THAT SHAKE.
Tracks: / Do fries go with that shake / Pleasures of exhaustion (Do it till you drop) / Scratch medley.
Single (7"): released on Capitol, Apr'86 by Capitol Records. Dist: EMI

DOUBLE OH-OH.
Single (7"): released on Capitol, Jul'85 by Capitol Records. Dist: EMI

Single (12"): released on Capitol, Jul'85 by Capitol Records. Dist: EMI

LIVE FROM HOUSTON (VIDEO).
Notes: Released on Virgin Music Video in March 87. 30 minutes

SOME OF MY BEST JOKES ARE FRIENDS.
Album: released on Capitol, Sep'85 by Capitol Records. Dist: EMI

Cassette: released on Capitol, Sep'85 by Capitol Records. Dist: EMI

YOU SHOULDN'T NUF BIT FISH.
Album: released on Capitol, Jan'84 by Capitol Records. Dist: EMI Deleted '86.

Cassette: released on Capitol, Jan'84 by Capitol Records. Dist: EMI

Clinton, Larry

1941 & 1949 (Clinton, Larry & His Orchestra).
Album: released on Circle(USA), Jun'84 by Jazzology Records (USA). Dist: Jazz Music, Swift, Chris Wellard

FROM THE GLEN ISLAND CASINO 1938/9 (Clinton, Larry & His Orchestra).
Album: released on Kaydee, Jan'87 Dist: Jazz Music, Swift

Clock Dva

4 HOURS.
Single (7"): released on Fetish, May'81 by Fetish Records. Dist: Cartel, Pinnacle

ADVANTAGE.
Album: released on Polydor, May'83 by Polydor Records. Dist: Polygram, Polydor

Cassette: released on Polydor, May'83 by Polydor Records. Dist: Polygram, Polydor

FOUR HOURS.
Single (12"): released on Double Vision, Nov'85 by Double Vision Records. Dist: Rough Trade, Cartel

RESISTANCE.
Single (7"): released on Polydor, Apr'83 by Polydor Records. Dist: Polygram, Polydor

Single (12"): released on Polydor, Apr'83 by Polydor Records. Dist: Polygram, Polydor

THIRST.
Album: released on Fetish, '81 by Fetish Records. Dist: Cartel, Pinnacle

Album: released on Double Vision, Oct'85 by Double Vision Records. Dist: Rough Trade, Cartel

Clockhouse

VANISHING POINT.
Single (7"): released on Picturesque, Sep'83 by Picturesque Records. Dist: Rough Trade, Cartel, Independant

Clockwork Criminals

YOUNG AND BOLD.
Single (7"): released on Ace, Jul'83 by Ace Records. Dist: Pinnacle, Swift, Hotshot, Cadillac

Clockwork Orange

CLOCKWORK ORANGE Various artists (Various Artists).
Album: released on Warner Bros., Jul'84 by Warner Bros Records. Dist: WEA

Cassette: released on Warner Bros., Jul'84 by Warner Bros Records. Dist: WEA

CLOCKWORK ORANGE, A Original Film Soundtrack.
Compact disc: released on Warner Bros., Apr'84 by Warner Bros Records. Dist: WEA

Clockwork Soldiers

WET DREAMS.
Single (7"): released on Red Rhino, Mar'84 by Red Rhino Records. Dist: Red Rhino, Cartel

Clooney, Rosemary

BEST OF ROSEMARY CLOONEY.
Cassette: released on Creole (Everest-Europa), Jul'84 by Creole Records. Dist: PRT, Rhino

CLAP HANDS.
Album: released on RCA, Oct'84 by RCA Records. Dist: RCA, Roots, Swift, Wellard, Chris, I & B, Solomon & Peres Distribution

Cassette: released on RCA, Oct'84 by RCA Records. Dist: RCA, Roots, Swift, Wellard, Chris, I & B, Solomon & Peres Distribution

FANCY MEETING YOU HERE (Clooney, Rosemary & Bing Crosby).
Album: released on RCA International (USA), Jul'82 by RCA Records. Dist: RCA

Cassette: released on RCA International (USA), Jul'82 by RCA Records. Dist: RCA

Album: released on RCA International (USA), Jul'82 by RCA Records. Dist: RCA

Cassette: released on RCA International (USA), Jul'82 by RCA Records. Dist: RCA

GREATEST HITS:ROSEMARY CLOONEY.
Album: released on CBS Cameo, Mar'83 by CBS Records. Dist: CBS

Cassette: released on CBS Cameo, Mar'83 by CBS Records. Dist: CBS

HERE'S TO MY LADY.
Double Album: released on Concord, Mar'79 by Import Records. Dist: IMS, Polygram

MIXED EMOTIONS.
Tracks: / Bless this house / Beautiful brown eyes / Lady is a tramp, The / Be my life's companion / Why don't you haul off and love me / Too young / While we're young / I laughed until I cried / Close your eyes / Mixed emotions.
Album: released on CBS, Mar'86 by CBS Records. Dist: CBS

MY BUDDY (Clooney, Rosemary & Woody Herman Big Band).
Album: released on Concord Jazz(USA), Nov'83 by Concord Jazz Records (USA). Dist: IMS, Polygram

OUR FAVOURITE THINGS (Clooney, Rosemary with Les Brown & His Band).
Album: released on Dance Band Days, Jun'86 Dist: Geoff's Records International

Cassette: released on Dance Band Days, Jun'86 Dist: Geoff's Records International

RING AROUND ROSIE (Clooney, Rosemary & The Hi-Lo's).
Tracks: / Doncha go 'way mad / Moonlight becomes you / Love letters / I could write a book / I'm in the mood for love / Coquette / Together / Everything happens to me / What is there to say / I'm glad there is you / How about you.
Album: released on Memoir, Dec'85 by Memoir Records. Dist: PRT Distribution

Cassette: released on Memoir, Dec'85 by Memoir Records. Dist: PRT Distribution

ROSEMARY CLOONEY SINGS THE MUSIC OF IRVING BERLIN.
Album: released on Concord Jazz(USA), Nov'84 by Concord Jazz Records (USA). Dist: IMS, Polygram

Cassette: released on Concord Jazz(USA), Nov'84 by Concord Jazz Records (USA). Dist: IMS, Polygram

ROSEMARY CLOONEY SINGS HAROLD ARLEN.
Album: released on Concord Jazz, Apr'83 by Concord Jazz Records (USA). Dist: IMS, Polygram

Cassette: released on Concord Jazz, Apr'83 by Concord Jazz Records (USA). Dist: IMS, Polygram

ROSEMARY CLOONEY SONGBOOK (THE).
Notes: 2 LP set.
Double Album: released on CBS(Holland), Jun'84 by CBS Records. Dist: Discovery

Double cassette: released on CBS(Holland), Jun'84 by CBS Records. Dist: Discovery

ROSEMARY CLOONEY SINGS COLE PORTER.
Album: released on Concord Jazz, Apr'82 by Concord Jazz Records (USA). Dist: IMS, Polygram

Cassette: released on Concord Jazz, Apr'82 by Concord Jazz Records (USA). Dist: IMS, Polygram

ROSIE SOLVES THE SWINGIN' RIDDLE.
Album: released on RCA International, Nov'80

Cassette: released on RCA International, Nov'80

SINGS BALLADS.
Album: released on Concord Jazz(USA), Nov'85 by Concord Jazz Records (USA). Dist: IMS, Polygram

Cassette: released on Concord Jazz(USA), Nov'85 by Concord Jazz Records (USA). Dist: IMS, Polygram

SINGS THE MUSIC OF JIMMY VAN HEUSEN.
Tracks: / Love won't let you get away / I thought about you / My heart is a hobo / Second time around, The / It could happen to you / Imagination / Like someone in love / Call me irresponsible / Walking happy / Last dance, The.
Notes: Rosemary Clooney's eleventh album for Concord is an exquisite collection of popular Jimmy Van Heusen songs. She is backed by her usual stellar group of All Stars led by saxophonist Scott Hamilton and cornetist Warren Vache. Liner notes by Sammy Cahn. Personnel: Rosemary Clooney-vocals/Ed Bickert-guitar/Joe Cocuzzo-drums/ Scott Hamilton-tenor saxophone/Michael Moore-bass/John Oddo-piano/Emily Remier-guitar/Warren Vache-cornet.
Compact disc: released on Concord Jazz(USA), Mar'87 by Concord Jazz Records (USA). Dist: IMS, Polygram

Album: released on Concord Jazz(USA), Jan'87 by Concord Jazz Records (USA). Dist: IMS, Polygram

Cassette: released on Concord Jazz(USA), Jan'87 by Concord Jazz Records (USA). Dist: IMS, Polygram

SWING AROUND ROSIE (Clooney, Rosemary & The Buddy Cole Trio).
Tracks: / 'Deed I do / You took advantage of me / Blue moon / Sing you sinners / Touch of the blues, A / Goody, goody / Too close for comfort / Do nothin' till you hear from me / Moonlight Mississippi / I wish I were in love again / Sunday in Savanna / This can't be love.
Album: released on Jasmine, '83 by Jasmine Records. Dist: Counterpoint, Lugtons, Taylor, H.R., Wellard, Chris, Swift, Cadillac

THAT TRAVELIN' TWO-BEAT (Clooney, Rosemary & Bing Crosby).
Tracks: / Vienna woods / Mother Brown / Roamin' in the gloamin' / Adios senorita / Come to the Mardi Gras / Hear that band / Daughter of Molly Malone (The0 / Poor people of Paris, The / I get ideas / Ciao, ciao bambina.
Album: released on Capitol, Jan'78 by Capitol Records. Dist: EMI

WITH LOVE.
Tracks: / Just the way you are / Way we were (the) / Alone at last / Come in from the rain / Meditation / Hello young lovers / Just in time / Tenderly / Will you still be mine.
Notes: We have a limited quantity of this available on CD from Japan. Consisting of 9 beautiful standards from such writers as Billy Joel, Neil Sedaka and Richard Rogers, this compact disc is sure to please the many Rosemary Clooney fans and all lovers of popular standards delivered with style. Personnel: Scott Hamilton - tenor sax, Warren Vache - cornet and flugelhorn, Cal Collins - guitar, Nat Pierce - piano, Cal Tjader - vibes, Bob Maize - bass.
Compact disc: released on Capitol, Sep'84 by Capitol Records. Dist: EMI

Album: released on Concord, May'81 by Import Records. Dist: IMS, Polygram

Compact disc: released on Capitol (Japan), Sep'84 by Capitol Records. Dist: IMS, Polygram

Closed For Filming

PREJUDICE.
Single (7"): released on G.A.P., Mar'84 by G.A.P. Records. Dist: Revolver, Cartel

Close Encounters...

CLOSE ENCOUNTERS... (National Philharmonic Orchestra).
Tracks: / Five tones (The) / Experience begins (The) / Mountain visions / John Williams symphonic suite of 'Close Encounters...' / Conversation (the) / Appearance of the vistors (The) / Restoration / First light / Sky ride / Aeromancy.
Compact disc: by RCA Records. Dist: RCA, Roots, Swift, Wellard, Chris, I & B, Solomon & Peres Distribution

Album: released on Damont, Apr'78 by WEA Records. Dist: WEA

CLOSE ENCOUNTERS OF THE THIRD KIND Original film soundtrack (Various Artists).
Tracks: / Close encounters of the third kind-mountain visions / Nocturnal pursuit / Abduction of Barry (The) / I can't believe it's real / Climbing devil's tower / Arrival of sky harbor (The).
Album: released on Arista, Mar'78 by Arista Records. Dist: RCA

Cassette: released on Arista, Mar'78 by Arista Records. Dist: RCA

CLOSE ENCOUNTERS OF THE THIRD KIND/STAR WARS Various artists (Close Encounters Of The Third Kind/Star Wars).
Album: released on Red Seal, Mar'78 by RCA Records. Dist: RCA

CLOSE ENCOUNTERS/STAR WARS (National Philharmonic Orchestra).

Close Lobsters

GOING TO HEAVEN TO SEE IF IT RAINS.
Tracks: / Pathetic trivia.
Single (7"): released on Fire, Oct'86 by Twist and Shout Music. Dist: Nine Mile, Rough Trade, Cartel

Single (12"): released on Fire, Oct'86 by Twist and Shout Music. Dist: Nine Mile, Rough Trade, Cartel

NEVER SEEN BEFORE.
Tracks: / Never seen before.
Single (7"): released on Fire, Mar'87 by Twist and Shout Music. Dist: Nine Mile, Rough Trade, Cartel

Single (12"): released on Fire, Mar'87 by Twist and Shout Music. Dist: Nine Mile, Rough Trade, Cartel

Close Rivals

SHORT SHARP KICK IN THE TEETH.
Single (7"): released on Hyped, Apr'81 Dist: Spartan

Cloud

ALL NIGHT LONG.
Single (7"): released on Flashback, Oct'80 by Flashback Records/PRT Records. Dist: Mainline, PRT

RESTING PLACE, THE.
Album: released on Dove, May'79 by Dove Records. Dist: Jetstar

STEPPIN OUT WITH YOU.
Single (7"): released on Rygel, Jan'83 by Alan Osborne. Dist: Pinnacle

Single (12"): released on Rygel, Jan'83 by Alan Osborne. Dist: Pinnacle

WATERED GARDEN.
Album: released on Dove, May'79 by Dove Records. Dist: Jetstar

Clouds Have Groovy Faces

CLOUDS HAVE GROOVY FACES (THE) Various artists (Various Artists).
Album: released on Bam Caruso, Jan'87 by Bam Caruso Records. Dist: Rough Trade, Revolver, Cartel

Clout

Biographical Details: This South African all-girl group consisted of Cindi Alter, Bones Brettell, Jennie Garson, Inge Herbst, Sandie Robbie and Lee Tomlinson. One of the top bands in their native country, Clout achieved a one-off smash in Britain with 'Substitute'. This extremely catchy 1978 version of a **Righteous Brothers** LP track reached No.2 in the UK chart. It was a perfect pop single and, like the bulk of Clout's output, occupied the middle ground between sing-along pop and hard rock. By being South African and by being an all-female band, Clout were quite a novelty in the UK charts. This fact probably did them more harm than good, and their subsequent British releases failed to make an impact: their version of Eric Clapton's 'Let It Grow' flopped, and **Russ Ballard's** 'Since You've Been Gone' became a hit for **Rainbow** but not for Clout. They remained stars in their home country early into the eighties, before splitting up. [Bob Macdonald, 30.1.85]

CLOUT.
Tracks: / Substitute / Without love / Let it grow / You've got all of me / Ms. America / Since you've been gone / Feel my need / You make my world so colourful / Don't stop / Save me.
Album: released on EMI, '78 by EMI Records. Dist: EMI

Cassette: released on EMI, '78 by EMI Records. Dist: EMI

THREAT AND A PROMISE, A.
Tracks: / Threat and a promise, A / Best of me (The) / Wish I were loving you / Dead telephone / You / Portable radio / Hot shot / Lovers on the sidewalk / Gonna get it to you / Can't we talk it over.
Album: released on EMI, Apr'81 by EMI Records. Dist: EMI

Cloven Hoof

CLOVEN HOOF.
Tracks: / Nightstalker / March of the damned / Gates of Gehenna / Crack the whip / Laying down the law / Return of the passover.
Album: released on Neat, '85 by Neat Records. Dist: Pinnacle, Neat

Cassette: released on Neat, '85 by Neat Records. Dist: Pinnacle, Neat

Cassette: released on Neat, Jul'84 by Neat Records. Dist: Pinnacle, Neat

FIGHTING BACK.
Album: released on Receiver, Feb'87 by Receiver Records. Dist: Pinnacle

OPENING RITUAL.
Notes: 4 track EP.
Single (7"): released on Cloven H', Oct'82 by Indies Records. Dist: Neon

Clover

BEST OF CLOVER, THE.
Tracks: / Love love / Oh senorita / Streets of London / Chicken funk / Travellin' man / Keep on rollin' / Southern belles / Chain gang / California kid / I lie awake (and dream of you) / Still alive / Route '66.
Notes: Clover included in their members Huey Lewis and Sean Hopper (of The News) and John McFee (guitar player for The Doobie Brothers, Van Morrison and more). The best of their two Phonogram albums, plus two tracks previously available as singles only, and their previously unreleased version of 'Route 66' from the 1977 Levi's Jeans ad.
Album: released on Mercury, Nov'86 by Phonogram Records. Dist: Polygram Distribution

Clovers

FIVE COOL CATS.
Album: released on Edsel, Mar'86 by Demon Records. Dist: Pinnacle, Jazz Music, Projection

Cassette: released on Edsel, Mar'86 by Demon Records. Dist: Pinnacle, Jazz Music, Projection

Clovis Sessions

CLOVIS SESSIONS Volume 1 (Various Artists).
Tracks: / Starlight / Cast iron arm / Little ditty baby / Leave them cats alone / Lookie, lookie, lookie / That'll be alright / School is out / No minors allowed / Believe me / Fireball / Beacause I love you / My Suzanne / You've got love / Right now / Tiny kiss, A / I don't know / Since you went away to school / Jitterbuggin'.
Album: released on Charly, Sep'84 by Charly Records. Dist: Charly, Cadillac

Clower, Jerry

JERRY CLOWER'S GREATEST HITS.
Album: released on MCA Import, Mar'86 by MCA Records. Dist: Polygram, IMS

RUNAWAY TRACK.
Album: released on MCA, Apr'87 by MCA Records. Dist: Polygram, MCA

Cassette: released on MCA, Apr'87 by MCA Records. Dist: Polygram, MCA

Clox

ANIMALS CAME (THE).
Tracks: / Animals came (The) / Mountain to Mohammed.
Single (7"): released on B Flat, Oct'85 by Nine Mile Records. Dist: Cartel

FOLLOW ME.
Tracks: / Follow me / Into the water / This.
Single (7"): released on B Flat, Jun'85 by Nine Mile Records. Dist: Cartel

Clox Italia

AGEING AGENT/YOU BELONG TO ME.
Single (7"): released on B Flat, Jan'84 by Nine Mile Records. Dist: Cartel

Clubb Shott

STEPPIN' OUT WITH MANIAC.

Single (7"): released on Street Level, Apr'85

Single (12"): released on Street Level, Apr'85

Club Classics

CLUB CLASSICS Various artists (Various Artists).
Tracks: / Soul city walk (The) / Love is lost (The) / I don't love you anymore / It ain't reggae (but its funky) / Life on Mars / I'll always love my mamma / Do it any way you wanna / You'll never find another love like mine / If you wanna go back / Come go with me.
Album: released on CBS, Nov'84 by CBS Records. Dist: CBS

Cassette: released on CBS, Nov'84 by CBS Records. Dist: CBS

CLUB CLASSICS II Various artists (Various Artists).
Tracks: / Family affair / Let's groove / Harvest for the world / Jam, jam, jam (all night long) / Let's clean up the ghetto / Always there / Barbara Ann / Was that all it was / Sweetest pain.
Album: released on CBS, Apr'85 by CBS Records. Dist: CBS

Cassette: released on CBS, Apr'85 by CBS Records. Dist: CBS

Club Nouveau

JEALOUSY.
Tracks: / Lust / Jealousy (instrumental).
Single (7"): released on Warner Bros., Nov'86 by Warner Bros Records. Dist: WEA

Single (12"): released on Warner Bros., Nov'86 by Warner Bros Records. Dist: WEA

LEAN ON ME.
Tracks: / Lean on me / Pump it up / Lean on me (pump it up).
Single (7"): released on Warner Brothers, Feb'87 by Warner Bros Records. Dist: WEA

Single (12"): released on Warner Brothers, Feb'87 by Warner Bros Records. Dist: WEA

LIFE LOVE AND PAIN.
Tracks: / Jealousy / Why you treat me so bad / Lean on me / Promises promises / Situation number / Heavy on my mind / Let me go / Lean on me (pump it up).
Album: released on WEA, Nov'86 by WEA Records. Dist: WEA

Compact disc: released on Warner Brothers, Nov'86 by Warner Bros Records. Dist: WEA

Cassette: released on WEA, Nov'86 by WEA Records. Dist: WEA

Club Ska 67

CLUB SKA 67 Various artists (Various Artists).
Cassette: released on Island, Mar'80 by Island Records. Dist: Polygram

Club Soul

CLUB SOUL various artists (Various Artists).
Album: released on Kent, Aug'84 by Ace Records. Dist: Pinnacle

Clubsound

AND GOD CREATED WOMAN.
Single (7"):

AUNTY SADIE SAYS.
Tracks: / Aunty Sadie says (aerobics version).
Single (7"):

WAY OLD FRIENDS DO, THE.
Single (7"):

Club Sounds

CLUB SOUNDS various artists (Various Artists).
Album: released on Electricity, Dec'84 by Electricity Records. Dist: PRT

Cassette: released on Electricity, Dec'84 by Electricity Records. Dist: PRT

Club Tango

F.T.N.
Single (7"): released on Dining Out, Nov'81 by Dining Out Records. Dist: IKF, Independent

PERFORMANCE.
Single (7"): released on Dining Out, Jun'81 by Dining Out Records. Dist: IKF, Independent

Club Tracks

CLUB TRACKS VOLUME 3 Various artists (Various Artists).
Tracks: / She's strange / Let me run it / Don't give me up / I wanna make you feel good / Give me tonight / Weigh all the facts / Baby doll / Someday / Live wire (I want a girl that sweats).
Album: released on Club, Jul'84 by Phonogram Records. Dist: Polygram

Cassette: released on Club, Jul'84 by Phonogram Records. Dist: Polygram

COME WITH CLUB -CLUB TRACKS VOL.2 various artists (Various Artists).
Album: released on Club, Aug'83 by Phonogram Records. Dist: Polygram

Cassette: released on Club, Aug'83 by Phonogram Records. Dist: Polygram

Cluster

CLUSTER 11.
Album: released on Logo, '79 by Logo Records. Dist: Roots, BMG

STIMMUNGEN.
Album: released on Sky (Germany), Sep'84

Cluster & End

OLD LAND.
Album: released on Sky (Germany), Jan'86

Cluster of Nuts Band

FRIDGE IN THE FAST LAND.
Album: released on Poke, Oct'83 Dist: Roots

Clutha

BONNIE MILLE DAMS.
Album: released on Topic, '81 Dist: Roots Distribution

CLUTHA, THE.
Album: released on Topic, '81 Dist: Roots Distribution

Clyde, Alan

ANYTHING CAN HAPPEN.
Tracks: / I wish it was you.
Single (7"): released on Carrere, Jun'86 by Carrere Records. Dist: PRT, Spartan

Single (12"): released on Carrere, Jun'86 by Carrere Records. Dist: PRT, Spartan

Clydesiders

CLYDESIDERS ALBUM (79).
Album: released on Lismor, May'79 by Lismor Records. Dist: Lismor, Roots, Celtic Music

CLYDESIDERS ALBUM.
Album: released on Lismor, '79 by Lismor Records. Dist: Lismor, Roots, Celtic Music

Cassette: released on Lismor, '79 by Lismor Records. Dist: Lismor, Roots, Celtic Music

IT'S GOOD TO SEE YOU.
Album: released on Klub, Nov'85

Cassette: released on Klub, Nov'85

LEGENDS OF SCOTLAND, THE.
Cassette: released on Lochshore, Mar'87 by Klub Records. Dist: PRT

MAYBE SOME DAY.
Single (7"): released on Klub, Nov'85

MY LOVE IS LIKE A RED RED ROSE.
Single (7"): released on Klub, May'83

SAILING HOME.
Album: released on Lochshore, Jul'82 by Klub Records. Dist: PRT

Cassette: released on Lochshore, Jul'82 by Klub Records. Dist: PRT

SAILING HOME/LAND I HAVE LEFT.
Single (7"): released on Lochshore, Jul'82 by Klub Records. Dist: PRT

SCOTLAND'S JIM WATT.
Single (7"): released on Lochshore, Apr'81 by Klub Records. Dist: PRT

THINKING OF HOME.
Album: released on Klub, Oct'84

Cassette: released on Klub, Oct'84

TOUCH OF THE CLYDESIDERS.
Album: released on Lochshore, Apr'81 by Klub Records. Dist: PRT

Cassette: released on Lochshore, Apr'81 by Klub Records. Dist: PRT

WE'VE LIVED IN A DREAM.
Single (7"): released on Klub, Sep'84

WILD MOUNTAIN THYME.
Album: released on Klub, Nov'83

Cassette: released on Klub, Nov'83

WILD MOUNTAIN THYME/HOME TO THE KYLES.
Single (7"): released on Klub, Nov'83

Clyde Valley Stompers

FIDGETY FEET.
Album: released on Country House, Jul'85 by BGS Productions Ltd. Dist: Taylor, H.R., Record Merchandisers Distribution, Pinnacle, Sounds of Scotland Records

Album: released on Country House, Jul'85 by BGS Productions Ltd. Dist: Taylor, H.R., Record Merchandisers Distribution, Pinnacle, Sounds of Scotland Records

RENUNION '81.
Album: released on Country House, Dec'81 by BGS Productions Ltd. Dist: Taylor, H.R., Record Merchandisers Distribution, Pinnacle, Sounds of Scotland Records

Cassette: released on Country House, Dec'81 by BGS Productions Ltd. Dist: Taylor, H.R., Record Merchandisers Distribution, Pinnacle, Sounds of Scotland Records

CO2

SEX IN THE MOVIES/OH JACKIE.
Single (7"): released on Galaxy, Apr'82 by Galaxy Records. Dist: RCA, Red Lightnin' Distribution, Discovery, Swift

Coal Miner's Daughter

COAL MINER'S DAUGHTER Film soundtrack (Various Artists).
Album: released on MCA, Mar'87 by MCA Records. Dist: Polygram, MCA

Cassette: released on MCA, Mar'87 by MCA Records. Dist: Polygram, MCA

Coasters

20 GREAT ORIGINALS.
Album: released on Atlantic, May'78 by WEA Records. Dist: WEA

JUKE BOX GIANTS.
Album: released on Audio Fidelity, May'82 Dist: PRT

POISON IVY/CHARLIE BROWN.
Single (7"): released on Old Gold, Jul'82 by Old Gold Records. Dist: Lightning, Jazz Music, Spartan, Counterpoint

THUMBING A RIDE.
Album: released on Edsel, Sep'85 by Demon Records. Dist: Pinnacle, Jazz Music, Projection

Cassette: released on Edsel, Sep'85 by Demon Records. Dist: Pinnacle, Jazz Music, Projection

YAKETY YAK/ALONG CAME JONES.
Single (7"): released on Old Gold, Jul'82 by Old Gold Records. Dist: Lightning, Jazz Music, Spartan, Counterpoint

YAKETY YAK/CHARLIE BROWN.
Single (7"): released on Creole, Aug'82 by Creole Records. Dist: Rhino, PRT

Coast To Coast

BIM BAM.
Single (7"): released on Barry Collins, Mar'85 Dist: PRT

COASTING.
Album: released on Polydor, Aug'81 by Polydor Records. Dist: Polygram, Polydor

Cassette: released on Polydor, Aug'81 by Polydor Records. Dist: Polygram, Polydor

COAST TO COAST Various artists (Various Artists).
Tracks: / Voice of America / American fool / Better late than never / How far Jerusalem / Call of the wild / Hold back the night / Stand me up / Dancin' on midnight / Shoot for the heart / Surrender.
Album: released on FM, Jul'87 by FM-Revolver Records. Dist: EMI

Cassette: released on FM, Jul'87 by FM-Revolver Records. Dist: EMI

Compact disc: released on FM, Jul'87 by FM-Revolver Records. Dist: EMI

Coates, Ann

PLEASE DON'T CUT THE ROSES.
Album: released on Westwood, '78 by Westwood Records. Dist: Jazz Music, H.R. Taylor, Pinnacle, Ross Records

Coates, Eric

GOLDEN AGE OF ERIC COATES, THE.
Tracks: / Oxford Street - march from 'London again' suite / Knightsbridge - March (from 'London' suite) / In the country - rustic dance / Calling all worker - march / By the sleepy lagoon - valse serendade / Merrymakers, The - A miniature overture / Three bears, The - Phantasy / Television march / At the dance - from 'Summer days' suite / London calling - march / Saxo-rhapsody / Wood nymphs - valsette.
Notes: Tracks 1 - 5, 7, 9, 11 & 12 recorded at No.1 studio, Abbey Road London. Track 6 recorded in Kinsway Hall, London. Tracks 8 & 10- no details of venue available - probably recorded at Abbey Road. Publisher details taken from 78 rpm record labels. (P) Original Sound Recordings made by EMI Records Ltd.
Album: released on Golden Age, May'86 by Music For Pleasure Records. Dist: EMI

Cassette: released on Golden Age, May'86 by Music For Pleasure Records. Dist: EMI

Cobb, Arnett

AND HIS MOB (Cobb, Arnett & Dinah Washington).
Album: released on Phoenix, Apr'81 by Audio Fidelity Enterprises. Dist: Stage One

ARNETT COBB IS BACK.
Album: released on Progressive, Apr'81 by Progressive Records. Dist: Jetstar

COMPLETE APOLLO SESSIONS.
Album: released on Vogue (France), Mar'84 Dist: Discovery, Jazz Music, PRT, Swift

FUNKY BUTT.
Album: released on Progressive (Import). '81

LIVE AT SANDY'S.
Album: released on Muse, May'83 by Peerless Records.

PARTY TIME.
Album:

Cobham, Billy

FLIGHT TIME.
Album: released on Sandra, Apr'81

FUNKY SIDE OF THINGS.
Album: released on Atlantic, Oct'75 by WEA Records. Dist: WEA

LIFE AND TIMES.
Album: released on Atlantic, Mar'76 by WEA Records. Dist: WEA

POWER PLAY.
Tracks: / Times of my life / Zanzibar breeze / Radioactive / Light shines in your eyes, A / Summit Afrique / Foundation, The - Isisekelo Zulu / Dance of the blue men / Nomads, The / Debate, The (Indaba) / Little one, The (omncane) / Dessicated coconuts / Tinsel town.
Notes: Following on from the successful album 'Warning' (GRP 91020), Billy's debut recording for GRP, 'Power Play' is a dazzling display of the legendary drummer'stotal mastery of his power, style and technique. Cobham uses his skills as a writer to project a wide range of moods, rhythms and melodic ideas - a complete programme of contemporary sounds.

Album: released on GRP (USA), Jun'86 by GRP Records (USA). Dist: IMS, Polygram

Cassette: released on GRP (USA), Jun'86 by GRP Records (USA). Dist: IMS, Polygram

Compact disc: released on GRP (USA), Jun'86 by GRP Records (USA). Dist: IMS, Polygram

SMOKIN'.
Album: released on Elektra(Musician), Jun'83 by WEA Records. Dist: WEA

TOTAL ECLIPSE.
Album: released on Atlantic, Nov'74 by WEA Records. Dist: WEA

WARNING.
Tracks: / Moziak / Red and yellow cabriolet / Slow body poppin' / Unknown jeromes / Dancer, The / Stratus / Come join me / Go for it.
Compact disc: released on GRP (USA), Sep'85 by GRP Records (USA). Dist: IMS, Polygram

Album: released on GRP (USA), Sep'85 by GRP Records (USA). Dist: IMS, Polygram

Cobos, Luis

MEXICANO.
Album: released on CBS(Spain), Jun'84 by CBS Records. Dist: Conifer, Discovery, Swift

Cassette: released on CBS(Spain), Jun'84 by CBS Records. Dist: Conifer, Discovery, Swift

SOL Y SOMBRA.
Album: released on CBS(Spain), Jan'84 by CBS Records. Dist: Conifer, Discovery, Swift

Cassette: released on CBS(Spain), Jan'84 by CBS Records. Dist: Conifer, Discovery, Swift

Cobra

COBRA Original soundtrack (Various Artists).
Tracks: / Voice of America's sons / Feel the heat / Loving on borrowed time / Skyline / Hold on to your vision / Suave / Cobra / Angel of the city / Chase / Two into one.
Album: released on Scotti Brothers, Aug'86 by Scotti Brothers Records. Dist: CBS

Cassette: released on Scotti Brothers, Aug'86 by Scotti Brothers Records. Dist: CBS

Compact disc: released on CBS, Oct'86 by CBS Records. Dist: CBS

Cobras

THIS STUFF'S GONNA BUST YOUR BRAINS OUT (Cobras/Shakers).
Notes: For full information see under: SHAKERS, The/The COBRAS.

Cocciante, Richard

SINCERITY.
Album: released on Virgin, Apr'84 by Virgin Records. Dist: EMI, Virgin Distribution

Cochereau, Pierre

60 MINUTES OF MUSIC.
Tracks: / Toccata et fugue / En re mineur / Toccato / Andante en fa majeur / Choral-prelude op.122 no.10 / Toccata de la 5 symphonie / Chorale no.2 / Toccata pour l'elevation / Berceuse / Toccata / Toccata - marche des rois.
Notes: Popular organ works.
Cassette: released on Philips (France), Jul'86

Cochran, Eddie

20TH ANNIVERSARY ALBUM.
Album: released on Liberty-UA, Mar'80

25TH ANNIVERSARY ALBUM.
Album: released on Liberty, Apr'85 by Liberty-United. Dist: EMI

Cassette: released on Liberty, Apr'85 by Liberty-United. Dist: EMI

BEST OF ....
Tracks: / C'mon everybody / Twenty flight rock / Three steps to heaven / Summertime blues / Drive-in show / Nervous breakdown / Jeanie Jeanie Jeanie / Weekend / Somethin' else / Skinny Jim / Pink Peg slacks / Cut across Shorty / Sittin' in the balcony / Hellelujah, I love her so / My way.
Compact disc: released on EMI America, Apr'87 by EMI Records. Dist: EMI

BEST OF EDDIE COCHRAN.
Album: released on Liberty, Oct'85 by Liberty-United. Dist: EMI

Cassette: released on Liberty, Oct'85 by Liberty-United. Dist: EMI

CHERISHED MEMORIES.
Album: released on Liberty, Sep'83 by Liberty-United. Dist: EMI

Cassette: released on Liberty, Sep'83 by Liberty-United. Dist: EMI

CHERISHED MEMORIES (LIBERTY FRANCE).
Album: released on Liberty (France), '83

C'MON EVERYBODY.
Album: released on Sun Set, '70 by Sun Set Records. Dist: Jetstar Distribution

C'MON EVERYBODY (7").
Single (7"): released on EMI, Apr'83 by EMI Records. Dist: EMI

C'MON EVERYBODY/DON'T EVER LET ME GO.
Single (7"): released on United Artists, Mar'84

EDDIE.
Album: released on Pathe MarconiFrance), Jan'85

EDDIE COCHRAN.
Album: released on EMI (France), '83 by EMI Records. Dist: Conifer

EDDIE COCHRAN & GENE VINCENT Limited edition picture disc (Cochran, Eddie & Gene Vincent).
Album: released on Pathe MarconiEMI Europe), Jun'84

EDDIE COCHRAN LEGEND.
Album: released on Charly, Apr'80 by Charly Records. Dist: Charly, Cadillac

EDDIE COCHRAN SINGLES ALBUM.
Album: released on United Artists, Jul'79

Cassette: released on United Artists, Jul'79

HOLLYWOOD SESSIONS, THE.
Album: released on Rock Star, Jan'86 Dist: Lightning, Swift Distribution, Superdisc Distribution

INEDITS.
Album: released on Emerald (Ireland), '83 by Emerald Records. Dist: I & B, Ross, PRT

LEGENDARY MASTERS.
Album: released on United Artists, '72

LEGEND IN OUR TIME.
Album: released on Union Pacific, Apr'79 Dist: Swift, Jazz Music, Red Lightnin' Distribution

LEGEND IN OUR TIME (CHARLY).
Album: by Charly Records. Dist: Charly, Cadillac

LEGEND LIVES ON, A.
Compact disc: released on Card/Grand Prix, Jun'86 Dist: Target

MANY SIDES OF EDDIE COCHRAN.
Album: released on Rollercoaster, May'79 by Rollercoaster Records. Dist: Swift Distribution, Rollercoaster Distribution

MANY STYLES OF..., THE.
Tracks: / Pink-peg slacks / Fool's paradise / Skinny Jim / Instrumental blues / Half loved / Slow down / If I were dying / Country jam / Don't bye, bye baby me / Heart of a fool / My love to remember / Latch on / Chicken shot blues / Mr. Fiddle / Dark lonely street.
Notes: Licensed from Rockstar Records (whose Tony Barrett is a Cochran freak), this is a real collector's gem, featuring not only Eddie Cochran sessions with rare alternate takes giving us a few pleasant surprises but there are the Hank and Eddie Cochran sessions also included here, as well as a couple of fantastic instrumentals. The sleeve features rare photos of Eddie with Billy Fury, Joe Brown and Gene Vincent, contemporary rockers of the period. An album to delightEddie's fans especial in this his 25th Anniversary year of his tragic death, when his name will be on many lips.
Album: released on Conifer, Dec'85 by Conifer Records. Dist: Conifer

Cassette: released on Conifer, Dec'85 by Conifer Records. Dist: Conifer

MEMORIAL.
Album: released on EMI (France), '83 by EMI Records. Dist: Conifer

MEMORIAL ALBUM.
Album: by Liberty-United. Dist: EMI

MY WAY.
Album: released on Liberty (France), May'83

ON THE AIR.
Album: released on EMI (France), '83 by EMI Records. Dist: Conifer

PORTRAIT OF A LEGEND.
Album: released on Rockstar, Apr'85

REMEMBER ME.
Album: released on EMI (France), '83 by EMI Records. Dist: Conifer

ROCK'N'ROLL GREATS.
Tracks: / Summertime blues / My way / I remember / Three steps to heaven / Skinny Jim / Completely sweet / Lonely / Long tall sally / C'mon everybody / Teenage heaven / Boll weevil song / Pretty girl / Cherished memories / I'm ready / Sweetie pie / Eddie's blues.
Notes: Eddie Cochran - A rock'n'roll great! A unique compilation of 16 of the very bestrockin' classics by this surely-missed rock superstar. Not only the huge monster hits like "Summertime Blues", "C'mon Everybody" and "Three Steps To Heaven" but also "Skinny Jim", "Lonely" and the instrumental"Eddie's Blues". More than a quarter of a century has passed since Eddie's death but his music is still a part of today. An excellent sleeve with sleeve note by Roger St. Pierre.
Album: released on Music For Pleasure, Apr'86 by EMI Records. Dist: EMI

Cassette: released on Music For Pleasure, Apr'86 by EMI Records. Dist: EMI

ROCK'N'ROLL HEROES (Cochran, Eddie & Gene Vincent).
Album: released on Rockstar, May'85

ROCK'N'ROLL LEGEND.
Compact disc: released on Rockstar, Apr'87

SINGIN' TO MY BABY.
Album: released on EMI (France), '83 by EMI Records. Dist: Conifer

SKINNY JIM/HALF LOVED.
Single (7"): released on Rockstar, Dec'79

SOMETHIN' ELSE.
Album: released on Capehart, Jul'87

SUMMERTIME BLUES.
Single (7"): released on EMI Golden 45's, May'84 by EMI Records. Dist: EMI

THEIR FINEST YEARS (Cochran, Eddie & Gene Vincent).
Album: released on EMI (Germany), '83 by EMI Records. Dist: Conifer

THEIR FINEST YEARS 1958 & 1956 (Cochran, Eddie & Gene Vincent).
Album: released on Capitol, Nov'81 by Capitol Records. Dist: EMI

Cassette: released on Capitol, Nov'81 by Capitol Records. Dist: EMI

THREE STEPS TO HEAVEN/CUT ACROSS SHORTY.
Single (7"): released on United Artists, Oct'89

TWENTY FLIGHT ROCK.
Single (7"): released on United Artists, Mar'80

VERY BEST OF EDDIE COCHRAN 15th anniversary album.
Album: released on Fame, May'82 by Music For Pleasure Records. Dist: EMI

Cassette: released on Fame, May'82 by Music For Pleasure Records. Dist: EMI

WHAT'D I SAY/MILK COW BLUES.
Single (7"): released on Rock Star, Sep'79 Dist: Lightning, Swift Distribution, Superdisc Distribution

WORDS AND MUSIC.
Album: released on Rock Star, Mar'85 Dist: Lightning, Swift Distribution, Superdisc Distribution

YOUNG EDDIE COCHRAN.
Album: released on Rockstar, Sep'82

Cochrane, Nigel

DON'T TURN YOUR BACK ON THE ONE YOU LOVE.
Single (7"): released on Telebell, May'85 by Towerbell Records. Dist: EMI

Cochran, Jackie

BOP TOWN/MYSTERY TRAIN (Cochran, Jackie & Lee Wauken).
Single (7"): released on Rollin' Rock, Jun'80

FIDDLE FIT MAN.
Album: released on Off-Beat, Nov'85 by Off-Beat Records. Dist: Jetstar Distribution

ROCKABILLY LEGEND (Cochran, Jackie & Lee Wauken).
Album: released on Magnum Force, Nov'86 by Magnum Music Group Ltd. Dist: Magnum Music Group Ltd, PRT, Spartan

Album: released on Rollin' Rock, Jun'80

SWAMP FOX (Cochran, Jackie & Lee Wauken).
Album: released on Rollin' Rock, Jun'80

Cochran, Jack Waukeen

LONESOME DRIFTER.
Album: released on Rondelet, Nov'81 Dist: Spartan Distribution

MAMA DON'T YOU THINK I KNOW.
Single (7"): released on Rondelet, Oct'81 Dist: Spartan Distribution

Cochran, Tom

BOY INSIDE THE MAN (Cochran, Tom & Red Rider).
Single (7"): released on Capitol, Jan'87 by Capitol Records. Dist: EMI

Single (12"): released on Capitol, Jan'87 by Capitol Records. Dist: EMI

Cock and Bull Band

EYES CLOSED AND ROCKING.
Album: released on Topic, Nov'86 Dist: Roots Distribution

Cockatoos

BROKEN HEART.
Single (7"): released on Page One, Oct'83 by Page, Larry. Dist: PRT, Spartan

Cockburn, Bruce

BRUCE COCKBURN.
Album: released on True North (USA), Feb'85

Cassette: released on True North (USA), Feb'85

CIRCLES IN THE STREAM.
Album: released on True North (USA), Feb'85

DANCING IN THE DRAGON'S JAWS.
Album: released on True North (USA), Feb'85

FURTHER ADVENTURES OF....
Album: released on True North (USA), Feb'85

HIGH WINDS, WHITE SKY.
Album: released on True North (USA), Feb'85

Compact disc single: released on True North (USA), Feb'85

HUMANS.
Album: released on RCA, Nov'80 by RCA Records. Dist: RCA, Roots, Swift, Wellard, Chris, I & B, Solomon & Peres Distribution

Album: released on True North (USA), Feb'85

Cassette:

IF I HAD A ROCKET LAUNCHER.
Single (7"): released on Spindrift, Jun'85 Dist: Roots

INNER CITY FRONT.
Album: released on Planer (Germany), Aug'86

Album: released on True North (USA), Feb'85

Cassette: released on True North (USA), Feb'85

IN THE FALLING DARK.
Tracks: / Lord of the starfields / Vagabondage / In the falling dark / Little seahorse / Water into wine / Silver wheels / Giftbearer / Gavin's woodpile / I'm gonna fly someday / Festival of friends.
Notes: All composed by Bruce Cockburn except 'Vagabondage' - words by Cockburn and Moussette after Blaise Cendrars. Published by Golden Mountain Music Inc.(BMI) Produced by Eugene Martynec.
Album: released on True North (USA), Feb'85

JOY WILL FIND A WAY.
Album: released on True North (USA), Feb'85

Cassette: released on True North (USA), Feb'85

NIGHT VISION.
Album: released on True North (USA), Feb'85
TN 11
Cassette: released on True North (USA), Feb'85

RUMOURS OF GLORY.
Compact disc: released on Plane, '86 Dist: Projection, Celtic Music, Cadillac

SALT, SUN & TIME.
Cassette: released on True North (USA), Feb'85

Album: released on True North (USA) Feb'85

STEALING FIRE.
Compact disc: released on Plane, '86 Dist: Projection, Celtic Music, Cadillac

Album: released on Spindrift, Nov'84 Dist: Roots

SUNWHEEL DANCE.
Album: released on True North (USA), Feb'85

Cassette: released on True North (USA), Feb'85

Album: released on Capitol, Nov'83 by Capitol Records. Dist: EMI

TROUBLE WITH NORMAL.
Album: released on True North (USA), Feb'85

Cassette: released on True North (USA), Feb'85

WAITING FOR A MIRACLE The singles 1970-1987.
Tracks: / Mama just wants to barrelhouse all night long / All the diamonds in the world / Burn / Silver wheels / Laughter / Wondering where the lions are / Tokyo / Fascist architecture / Trouble with normal (The) / Rumours of glory / Coldest night of the year, The / You pay your money and take your chance / Lovers in a dangerous time / If I had a rocket launcher / Peggy's kitchen wall / People see through you / Call it democracy / Stolen land / Waiting for a miracle / One day I walk / It's going down slow.
Notes: A Revolver Records release. Revolver is a division of FM-Revolver Records. All songs written by Bruce Cockburn except "Stolen Land" - words by Bruce Cockburn, music by Bruce Cockburn and Hugh Marsh. (P) 1987 Original Sound recordings made by High Romance Music Ltd.
Double Album: released on Revolver, May'87 by Revolver Records. Dist: Revolver, Cartel

Cassette: released on Revolver, May'87 by Revolver Records. Dist: Revolver, Cartel

Compact disc: released on Revolver, May'87 by Revolver Records. Dist: Revolver, Cartel

WORLD OF WONDERS.
Tracks: / They call it democracy / Lily of the midnight sky / World of wonder / Berlin tonight / People see through you / See how I miss you / Santiago dawn / Dancing in paradise / Down here tonight.
Notes: Matrix numbers REVLP 73(a), REVMC 73(b). All songs written by Bruce Cockburn (Golden Mountain Music Corp/Rocksong Music Publishing Ltd). Produced by John Goldsmith and Kerry Crawford. (P) 1985 OSR made by High Romance Music Ltd. 1986 A Revolver Records Release. Revolver Records is a division of FM-Revolver Records Ltd.
Album: released on Revolver, Mar'87 by Revolver Records. Dist: Revolver, Cartel

Cassette: released on Revolver, Mar'87 by Revolver Records. Dist: Revolver, Cartel

Cocker, Joe

CIVILIZED MAN.
Tracks: / Civilized man / There goes my baby / Come on in / Tempted / Long drag off a cigarette / I love the night / Crazy in love / Girl like you, A / Hold on - I feel our love is changing / Even a fool would let go.
Compact disc: released on Capitol, Sep'84 by Capitol Records. Dist: EMI

Album: released on Capitol, Jun'84 by Capitol Records. Dist: EMI Deleted '86.

Cassette: released on Capitol, Jun'84 by Capitol Records. Dist: EMI Deleted '86.

COCKER.
Tracks: / You can leave your hat on / Heart of the matter / Inner city blues / Love is on a fade / Heaven / Shelter me / A to Z / Don't you love me anymore / Living without your love / Don't drink the water.
Notes: One of Britain's most respected and influential singers, Joe Cocker has completed his second album for the Capitol label. It features a total of ten songs, five of which are produced by Terry Manning who is noted for his recent work with ZZ Top. Also included is one song produced by Bernard Edwards, the other half of Chic, and two songs produced by Ron Nevison who has had phenomenal success recently in America with another Capitol act, Heart.
Album: released on Capitol, Apr'86 by Capitol Records. Dist: EMI

Cassette: released on Capitol, Apr'86 by Capitol Records. Dist: EMI

Compact disc: released on Capitol, Jul'86 by Capitol Records. Dist: EMI

COCKER HAPPY.
Album: released on Sierra, May'85 by Sierra Records. Dist: WEA

Cassette: released on Sierra, May'85 by Sierra Records. Dist: WEA

DELTA LADY.
Single (7"): released on Cube, Aug'82 by Dakota Records. Dist: PRT

DON'T YOU LOVE ME ANYMORE.
Tracks: / Don't you love me anymore / Tell me there's a way.
Single (7"): released on Capitol, Apr'86 by Capitol Records. Dist: EMI

Single (12"): released on Capitol, Apr'86 by Capitol Records. Dist: EMI

GREATEST HITS: JOE COCKER VOL.1.
Album: released on Hallmark, May'78 by Pickwick Records. Dist: Pickwick Distribution, PRT, Taylors

GREATEST HITS:JOE COCKER.
Album: released on Platinum (W.Germany), Oct'85 Dist: Mainline

Cassette: released on Platinum (W.Germany), Oct'85 Dist: Mainline

I CAN'T STAND A LITTLE RAIN.
Album: released on Cube, Oct'81 by Dakota Records. Dist: PRT

Cassette: released on Cube, Oct'81 by Dakota Records. Dist: PRT

I'M SO GLAD I'M STANDING HERE TODAY (Cocker, Joe & Crusaders).
Single (7"): released on MCA, Apr'83 by MCA Records. Dist: Polygram, MCA

JOE COCKER.
Album: released on Dakota (Countdown series), Oct'82 by Dakota Records. Dist: PRT

Cassette: released on Dakota (Countdown series), Oct'82 by Dakota Records. Dist: PRT

JOE COCKER COLLECTION, THE.
Tracks: / I can stand a little rain / It's a sin when you love somebody / Jamaica say you will / High time we went / Just like a woman / Do I still figure in your life / With a little help from my friends / Lawdy Miss Clawdy / Darling be home soon / Hello little friend / Pardon me sir / Marjorine / Midnight rider - live in L.A. / Love the one you're with - Live in L.A. / Bird on a wire / Feelin' alright / Let's go get stoned / Girl from the north country / Give peace a chance / She came in through the bathroom window / Space captain / Letter, The / Delta lady / Honky tonk women / Cry me a river.
Notes: Over 100 minutes of classic Cocker. All tracks licenced from Cube Records, C-Era Records: (c) 1985, Castle Communication PLC. Unit 7, 271 Merton Road, London SW18 5JS. Design: Shoot That Tiger!. Bar code 5 013428 131268:
Double cassette: released on Castle Classics, Apr'86 by Castle Communications. Dist: BMG

Compact disc: released on Castle Classics, '86 by Castle Communications. Dist: BMG

Album: released on Castle Classics, Apr'86 by Castle Communications. Dist: BMG

MAD DOGS AND ENGLISHMEN.
Notes: Starr Marketing Services Ltd, 90 Queens Road, Twickenham, Middx. TW1 4ET Tel: 01 891 6487.
Double compact disc: released on Mobile Fidelity, Jan'86 by Mobile Fidelity Records.

Double Album: by A&M Records. Dist: Polygram

Double cassette: by A&M Records. Dist: Polygram

OFF THE RECORD WITH JOE COCKER.
Album: released on Sierra, Nov'84 by Sierra Records. Dist: WEA

Cassette: released on Sierra, Nov'84 by Sierra Records. Dist: WEA

PLATINUM COLLECTION.
Album: released on Cube (Platinum coll), Oct'81

Cassette: released on Cube (Platinum coll), Oct'81

REPLAY ON.
Album: released on Sierra, May'86 by Sierra Records. Dist: WEA

Cassette: released on Sierra, May'86 by Sierra Records. Dist: WEA

SHEFFIELD STEEL.
Album: released on Island, May'82 by Island Records. Dist: Polygram

Cassette: released on Island, May'82 by Island Records. Dist: Polygram

SHELTER ME.
Tracks: / Shelter me / One more time / If you have love, give me some.

Single (7"): released on Capitol, Mar'86 by Capitol Records. Dist: EMI

Single (12"): released on Capitol, Mar'86 by Capitol Records. Dist: EMI

SPACE CAPTAIN.
Album: released on Cube, Apr'82 by Dakota Records. Dist: PRT

Cassette: released on Cube, Apr'82 by Dakota Records. Dist: PRT

SWEET LITTLE WOMAN.
Single (7"): released on Island, Jun'82 by Island Records. Dist: Polygram

UP WHERE WE BELONG (Cocker, Joe & Jennifer Warnes).

VERY BEST OF JOE COCKER, THE The Voice.
Tracks: / With a little help from my friends / Honky tonk women / Delta lady / Marjorine / Don't let me be misunderstood / Something / Pardon me sir / Talking back to the night / Up where we belong / She came in through the bathroom window / Letter (The) / Just like a woman / Jamaica say you will / Cry me a river / Midnight rider / Let it be.
Album: released on Telstar, May'86 by Telstar Records. Dist: RCA Distribution

Cassette: released on Telstar, May'86 by Telstar Records. Dist: RCA Distribution

Compact disc: released on Telstar, Jul'87 by Telstar Records. Dist: RCA Distribution

WITH A LITTLE HELP FROM MY FRIENDS.
Tracks: / With a little help from my friends / Marjorine / Delta lady / Letter, The.
Notes: All tracks licensed from C-Era Records.
Single (12"): released on Archive 4, Sep'86 by Castle Communications Records. Dist: Nine Mile, Cartel

Album: released on Cube, Oct'81 by Dakota Records. Dist: PRT

Cassette: released on Cube, Oct'81 by Dakota Records. Dist: PRT

Single (7"): released on Cube, Aug'82 by Dakota Records. Dist: PRT

YOU CAN LEAVE YOUR HAT ON.
Tracks: / You can leave your hat on - single version / You can leave your hat on - instrumental uncut strip mix.
Single (7"): released on Capitol, Jun'86 by Capitol Records. Dist: EMI

Single (12"): released on Capitol, Jun'86 by Capitol Records. Dist: EMI

Cock 'n' Bull Band

EYES CLOSED AND ROCKING.
Album: released on Topic, May'85 Dist: Roots Distribution

Cockney Rebel

HUMAN MENAGERIE, THE.
Album: released on EMI (Germany), May'83 by EMI Records. Dist: Conifer

PSYCHOMODO, THE.
Album: released on Fame, Sep'85 by Music For Pleasure Records. Dist: EMI

Cassette: released on Fame, Sep'85 by Music For Pleasure Records. Dist: EMI

Cockney Rejects

FLARES N SLIPPERS.
Single (7"): released on Small Wonder, Jan'79 by Small Wonder Records. Dist: Cartel, Indies

GREATEST COCKNEY RIP OFF.
Single (7"): released on Zonophone, May'80 by EMI Records. Dist: EMI

GREATEST HITS: COCKNEY REJECTS VOL.1.
Album: released on EMI, Mar'80 by EMI Records. Dist: EMI

GREATEST HITS: COCKNEY REJECTS VOL.2.
Album: released on Zonophone, Oct'80 by EMI Records. Dist: EMI

GREATEST HITS: COCKNEY REJECTS VOL 3.
Album: released on Zonophone, Apr'81 by EMI Records. Dist: EMI

Cassette: released on Zonophone, Apr'81 by EMI Records. Dist: EMI

TILL THE END OF THE DAY.
Single (7"): released on AKA, Nov'82 Dist: Stage One, IDS, Indies, Cartel

UNHEARD REJECTS.
Album: released on Wonderful World, Aug'85 Dist: M.I.S., EMI, Stage One

WE ARE THE FIRM.
Tracks: / I'm forever blowing bubbles / War on the terraces / On the water front / East end / Where the hell is Babylon / Headbanger / Oi, oi, oi / Greatest cockney rip off / Bad man / Power and the glory / Join the Rejects / I'm not a fool / Police car / Motorhead / We are the firm.
Notes: All tracks licensed from EMI Records Ltd.
Album: released on Dojo, Aug'86 by Castle Communications Records. Dist: Cartel

Cock Robin

AFTER HERE THROUGH MIDLAND.
Tracks: / Just around the corner / Biggest fool of all, The / El Norte / I'll send them your way / Another story / Coward's courage / Every moment / Precious dreams / After here through midland.
Album: released on CBS, Jul'87 by CBS Records. Dist: CBS

Cassette: released on CBS, Jul'87 by CBS Records. Dist: CBS

COCK ROBIN.
Tracks: / Thought you were on my side / Just when you're having fun / Promise you made, The / Because it keeps on working / Born with teeth / Once we might have known / More than willing / Little innocence, A / When your heart is weak.
Compact disc: released on CBS, Sep'86 by CBS Records. Dist: CBS

Album: released on CBS, Sep'86 by CBS Records. Dist: CBS

Cassette: released on CBS, Sep'86 by CBS Records. Dist: CBS

JUST AROUND THE CORNER.
Tracks: / Just around the corner / Open book.
Single (7"): released on CBS, May'87 by CBS Records. Dist: CBS

Single (12"): released on CBS, 23 May'87 by CBS Records. Dist: CBS

PROMISE YOU MADE, THE.
Tracks: / Promise you made, The / Have you any sympathy.
Single (7"): released on CBS, May'86 by CBS Records. Dist: CBS

Single (12"): released on CBS, May'86 by CBS Records. Dist: CBS

THAT'S WHEN YOUR HEART IS WEAK.
Tracks: / That's when your heart is weak / Peace on earth.
Single (7"): released on CBS, Aug'86 by CBS Records. Dist: CBS

Single (12"): released on CBS, Aug'86 by CBS Records. Dist: CBS

Cock Sparrer

ENGLAND BELONGS TO ME.
Single (7"): released on Carrere, Nov'82 by Carrere Records. Dist: PRT, Spartan

RUNNING RIOT IN '84.
Album: released on Syndicate, Oct'84

SHOCK TROOPS.
Album: released on Razor, Nov'83 by Razor. Dist: Pinnacle

TRUE GRIT.
Album: released on Razor, Mar'87 by Razor. Dist: Pinnacle

Cocoa Tea

COME AGAIN.
Album: released on Super Power, 30 May'87 by Super Power Records. Dist: Jetstar Distribution

I WANT TO LOVE YOU GIRL.
Tracks: / I want to love you girl / Love me true.
Single (12"): released on Gold Disc, Jan'86 Dist: Jetstar

JAMAICA SWEET.
Tracks: / Jamaica Sweet / Jamaica Sweet (version).
Single (12"): released on Skengdom, Jun'87 by Skengdom Records. Dist: Jetstar

PRESIDENT BOTHA.
Tracks: / President Botha (dub).
Single (12"): released on Rambo, Nov'86

Coconuts

TICKET TO THE TROPICS.
Single (7"): released on EMI America, Aug'83 by EMI Records. Dist: EMI

Single (12"): released on EMI America, Aug'83 by EMI Records. Dist: EMI

Cocoon

COCOON Original soundtrack (Various Artists).
Tracks: / Through the window / Lovemaking, The / Chase, The / Rose's death / Boys are out, The / Returning to the sea / Gravity / Discovered in the poolhouse / First tears / First tears / Sad goodbyes / Ascension, The / Theme from cocoon.
Notes: Composed by James Horner, the album is an instrumental expression of the film's varying moods. There is one vocal track by Michael Sembello (of Flashdance fame) entitled Gravity.
Compact disc: released on Polydor (Germany), Dec'85 Dist: IMS-Polygram

Album: released on Polydor, Sep'85 by Polydor Records. Dist: Polygram, Polydor

Cassette: released on Polydor, Sep'85 by Polydor Records. Dist: Polygram, Polydor

Coco Tea

COME AGAIN.
Single (12"): released on Live & Love, Feb'87 by Third World Records. Dist: Jetstar

MR COCO TEA.
Album: released on Corner Store, Oct'85

SWEET COCO TEA.
Single (12"): released on Crystal, Sep'85 by Crystal Records. Dist: Jetstar, Revolver, Cartel

TUNE IN.
Tracks: / Tune in / Ram up every corner.
Single (12"): released on Jammy's, Jul'86 by Jammy's Records. Dist: Jetstar

Cocteau Twins

AIKEA-GUINEA (EP).
Single (7"): released on 4AD, Mar'85 by 4AD Records. Dist: Rough Trade

Single (12"): released on 4AD, Mar'85 by 4AD Records. Dist: Rough Trade

COCTEAU TWINS: INTERVIEW PICTURE DISC.
Picture disc album: released on Baktabak, May'87 by Baktabak Records. Dist: Arabesque

ECHOES IN A SHALLOW BAY.
Single (12"): released on 4AD, Nov'85 by 4AD Records. Dist: Rough Trade

Album: released on 4AD, Jul'82 by 4AD Records. Dist: Rough Trade

Cassette: released on 4AD, Apr'84 by 4AD Records. Dist: Rough Trade

Album: released on 4AD, Oct'83 by 4AD Records. Dist: Rough Trade

GARLANDS.
Tracks: / Blood bitch / Wax and wane / But I'm not / Blind dum deaf / Gail overfloweth / Shallow than hallow / Hollow men, The / Garlands.
Compact disc: released on 4AD, '86 by 4AD Records. Dist: Rough Trade

HEAD OVER HEELS.
Tracks: / When mama was moth / 5-10-50 fold / Sugar hiccup / In our angelhood / Glass candle grenades / Multifoiled / In the gold dust rush / Tinderbox, The (of a heart) / My love paramour / Musette and drums + sunburst and snowblind EP.
Compact disc: released on 4AD, '86 by 4AD Records. Dist: Rough Trade

Cassette: released on 4AD, Apr'84 by 4AD Records. Dist: Rough Trade

IN OUR ANGEL HOOD.
Single (7"): released on 4AD, Oct'83 by 4AD Records. Dist: Rough Trade

Single (12"): released on 4AD, Oct'83 by 4AD Records. Dist: Rough Trade

LOVE'S EASY TEARS.
Tracks: / Love's easy tears / Those eyes, that mouth / Sigh's smell of farewell.
Single (7"): released on 4AD, Oct'86 by 4AD Records. Dist: Rough Trade

Single (12"): released on 4AD, Oct'86 by 4AD Records. Dist: Rough Trade

LULLABIES (EP).
Single (7"): released on 4AD, Sep'82 by 4AD Records. Dist: Rough Trade

PEARLY DEWDROPS DROPS.
Single (7"): released on 4AD, Apr'84 by 4AD Records. Dist: Rough Trade

Single (12"): released on 4AD, Apr'84 by 4AD Records. Dist: Rough Trade

PEPPERMINT PIG.
Single (7"): released on 4AD, Mar'83 by 4AD Records. Dist: Rough Trade

Single (12"): released on 4AD, Mar'83 by 4AD Records. Dist: Rough Trade

PINK OPAQUE.
Compact disc: released on 4AD, Jan'86 by 4AD Records. Dist: Rough Trade

PINK OPAQUE, THE.
Album: released on Relativity (USA), Sep'85 Dist: Pinnacle, Rough Trade, Cartel

SUNBURST AND SNOWBLIND (4 TRACK EP).
Single (12"): released on 4AD, Nov'83 by 4AD Records. Dist: Rough Trade

TINY DYNAMITE.
Single (12"): released on 4AD, Nov'85 by 4AD Records. Dist: Rough Trade

TINY DYNAMITE/ECHOES IN A SHALLOW BAY.
Compact disc: released on 4AD, Oct'86 by 4AD Records. Dist: Rough Trade

TREASURE.
Tracks: / Ivo / Lorelei / Beatrix / Persephone / Pandora - for Cindy / Amelia / Aloysius / Cicely / Otterley / Donimo.
Compact disc: released on 4AD, '86 by 4AD Records. Dist: Rough Trade

Album: released on 4AD, Nov'84 by 4AD Records. Dist: Rough Trade

Cassette: released on 4AD, Nov'84 by 4AD Records. Dist: Rough Trade

VICTORIA LAND.
Tracks: / Lazy calm / Fluffy tufts / Throughout the dark months of April and May / Whales tales / Oomingmac / Little spacey / Feet-like fins / How to bring a blush to the snow / Thinner the air, The.
Album: released on 4AD, Apr'86 by 4AD Records. Dist: Rough Trade

Cassette: released on 4AD, Apr'86 by 4AD Records. Dist: Rough Trade

Compact disc: released on 4AD, '86 by 4AD Records. Dist: Rough Trade

Codjoe, Ann

LONELY NIGHTS.
Single (12"): released on Hitbound, May'85 by Hitbound Records. Dist: Jetstar

Codling, Barbara

SWEETEST LOVE.
Single (7"): released on Cartridge, Jun'82 by Cartridge. Dist: Jetstar

Codona

CODONA 3.
Tracks: / Goshakabuch / Hey da ba doom / Travel by night (lullaby) / Trayra boia / Clicky clacky / Inner organs.
Notes: Personnel: Collin Walcott - sitar, hammered dulcimer, sanza, tabla, voice. Don Cherry - trumpet, organ, doussn'gouni, voice. Nana Vasconcelos - berimbau, percussion, voice.
Compact disc: released on ECM (Germany), Feb'86 by ECM Records. Dist: IMS, Polygram, Virgin through EMI

Cody, Tim

CIRCLE ONCE AGAIN.
Tracks: / Circle once again / War goes on.
Single (7"): released on Towerbell, Mar'86 by Towerbell Records. Dist: EMI

DAVEY.
Tracks: / Davey / Shallow land.
Single (7"): released on Towerbell, Aug'86 by Towerbell Records. Dist: EMI

Coe, David Allan

D.A.C.
Album: released on CBS, Jan'83 by CBS Records. Dist: CBS

Cassette: released on CBS, Jan'83 by CBS Records. Dist: CBS

DAVID ALLAN COE I love country.
Album: released on CBS, Mar'87 by CBS Records. Dist: CBS

Cassette: released on CBS, Mar'87 by CBS Records. Dist: CBS

FOR THE RECORD - THE FIRST 10 YEARS.
Album: released on CBS, Mar'85 by CBS Records. Dist: CBS

Cassette: released on CBS, Mar'85 by CBS Records. Dist: CBS

MATTER OF LIFE AND DEATH, A.
Tracks: / Ten commandments of love / Jody like a melody / Tanya Montana / If only your eyes could lie / Need a little time off for bad behaviour / Southern star / Actions speak louder than words / Child of God / Wild Irish rose / It's a matter of life and death.
Album: released on CBS, Apr'87 by CBS Records. Dist: CBS

Cassette: released on CBS, Apr'87 by CBS Records. Dist: CBS

TEXAS MOON.
Album: released on Charly, Nov'77 by Charly Records. Dist: Charly, Cadillac

UNCHAINED.
Album: released on CBS, Sep'86 by CBS Records. Dist: CBS

Cassette: released on CBS, Sep'86 by CBS Records. Dist: CBS

Coen, Jack

BRANCH LINE, THE Irish traditional music from Galway to New York (Coen, Jack & Charlie).
Album: released on Topic, '81 Dist: Roots Distribution

Coe, Pete

GAME OF ALL FOURS (Coe, Pete & Chris).
Album: released on Highway, '81 by Highway Records. Dist: Roots, Projection, Ross

GREATEST PUB BAND IN THE LAND (Coe, Pete Big Band).
Album: released on Jam Apr'79 Dist: Jazz Music

IT'S A MEAN OLD SCENE.
Album: released on Backshift, Oct'85 Dist: Roots, Projection

LIVE AT LEATHER BOTTLE (Coe, Pete Big Band).
Album: released on Jam, Mar'87 Dist: Jazz Music

OPEN THE DOOR AND LET US IN (Coe, Pete & Chris).
Tracks: / Acting song / Banks of red roses / Cheshire May day carol / Lady diamond / False knight / Joseph Baker / Wizard of Alderley Edge, The / Wife of ushers well, The / Eglos hayle ringers, The / Plains of Waterloo, The / High of Lincoln / Gay Fusiliers, The.
Album: released on Leader, '81 Dist: Jazz Music, Projection

OUT OF SEASON OUT OF RHYME (Coe, Pete & Chris).
Album: released on Leader, '81 Dist: Jazz Music, Projection

Coe, Tony

CHAT SE RETOURNE, (LE).
Tracks: / Marche funebre d'une marionnette - gounod / Paul / Petite suite en Avion I / Three for thee / Petite suite en Avion II / Les yeux prasins I / Les yeux prasins II / An-og mhadainn.
Album: released on Nato (France), Sep'86 by Disques Nato. Dist: Essex Record Distributors Ltd.

COE-EXISTENCE.
Album: released on Lee Lambert, May'80 by Lee Lambert Records. Dist: Cadillac

MAINLY MANCINI.
Tracks: / Pink panther, The / Crazy world / Hank neuf / Mister lucky / Mancinissimo / Days of wine and roses / Charade.
Notes: With Tony Hymas and Chris Laurence.
Album: released on Chabada(France), Sep'86 Dist: Essex

TOURNEE DU CHAT.
Tracks: / Jolly corner, The / Makoko / Vive la chantenay / Iberiana / Debussy.
Album: released on Nato (France), Jun'99 by Disques Nato. Dist: Essex Record Distributors Ltd.

Coffee

SHARON.
Tracks: / Sharon / Day-oh.
Single (12"): released on M & R Music, Aug'86 Dist: Jetstar Distribution

BACK HOME.
Album: released on Westbound, Jun'77 Dist: WEA

Cofi & The Lovetones

COUNTDOWN(HERE I COME).
Single (12"): released on Electricity, Feb'84 by Electricity Records. Dist: PRT

Cogan, Alma

ALMA COGAN.
Album: released on EMI (Germany), '83 by EMI Records. Dist: Conifer

SECOND COLLECTION.
Album: released on One Up, '78 by EMI Records.

VERY BEST OF ALMA COGAN 16 Favourites of the 50's.
Album: released on Music For Pleasure, Feb'84 by EMI Records. Dist: EMI

Cassette: released on Music For Pleasure, Feb'84 by EMI Records. Dist: EMI

WITH LOVE IN MIND.
Tracks: / Somebody loves me / Can't help falling in love / Hello young lovers / Our love affair / Love me as though there were no tomorrow / Love is just around the corner / Let me love you / If love were all / With you in mind / I dream of you more than you dream of me / Let's fall in love / In other words / My heart stood still / But beautiful / You'll never know / All I do is dream of you / What is there to say / Don't blame me / Falling in love with love / More see you, The / Can't give you anything but love / I've never been in love before / Lady's in love with you, The / I'm in the mood for love.
Notes: Two famous recordings of Alma Cogan's not available for more than 20 years. 'With You In Mind' (1961) and 'How About Love' (1962), coupled together to make a unique double album. Since the untimely death of Alma Cogan, there is still a great deal of interest in this truly professional artist. This is proved by the fact that Radio 2's David Jacobs has said "I have received more letters about Alma than any other artist featured on my show". With this being the 20thanniversary of her death, and the Alma Cogan convention which was held in LondonMay of this year, plus a very eye catching sleeve and extensive sleeve note by Chris White (Music Week), this album will be a very popular seller indeed.
Double Album: released on MFP, Jun'86 by EMI Records. Dist: EMI

Double cassette: released on MFP, Jun'86 by EMI Records. Dist: EMI

Coghill, Bobby

FAR FAE HAME.
Album: released on Ross, Jan'86 by Ross Records. Dist: Ross Distribution, Roots Distribution

Cassette: released on Ross, Jan'86 by Ross Records. Dist: Ross Distribution, Roots Distribution

FROM SCOTLAND TO CANADA WITH BOBBY COGHILL'S BAND SHOW (Coghill, Bobby Band Show).
Cassette: released on Ross, Dec'86 by Ross Records. Dist: Ross Distribution, Roots Distribution

HIGHLAND DANCE ALBUM.
Notes: Music for Highland and Scottish national dances. Bobby Coghill (Accordion)
Album: released on Ross, Jan'86 by Ross Records. Dist: Ross Distribution, Roots Distribution

Cassette: released on Ross, Jan'86 by Ross Records. Dist: Ross Distribution, Roots Distribution

HIGHLAND GATHERING (Coghill, Bobby Scottish Dance Band).
Album: released on Ross, Jan'86 by Ross Records. Dist: Ross Distribution, Roots Distribution

Cassette: released on Ross, Jan'86 by Ross Records. Dist: Ross Distribution, Roots Distribution

PIPING HOT ACCORDION.
Cassette: released on Ross, Jan'86 by Ross Records. Dist: Ross Distribution, Roots Distribution

SCOTTISH BAND SHOW VOL.1.
Album: released on Ross, Jan'86 by Ross Records. Dist: Ross Distribution, Roots Distribution

Cassette: released on Ross, Jan'86 by Ross Records. Dist: Ross Distribution, Roots Distribution

Coghill, Bryan

BY NORTHERN SHORES.
Cassette: released on Ross, Jan'86 by Ross Records. Dist: Ross Distribution, Roots Distribution

CHEORDAG SITHERLAND AT'E LETHERAN SHOW.
Cassette: released on Ross, Jan'86 by Ross Records. Dist: Ross Distribution, Roots Distribution

Coghill, Sandy

JUST FOR THE CRACK.
Tracks: / Seamus McNeil / Piper Major Sam Scott / Apple tree, The / CTS Empress / Agnes Ritchie / Inverness gathering, The / Agnes waltz, The / Jig of slurs / Lochhaber gathering, The / Madame Bonaparte / McNeil of Ugadale / Glens of Angus, the / Teetotaller, The / Arthur Bignold of Loch Rosque / Livingstone accordion club, The / Duke of Fife's welcome to Dundee.
Notes: Personnel: Sandy Coghill - button key accordian, drums/Derek Lawrence - piano, electric piano, piano accordion.
Album: released on REL, '77 Dist: Roots

Cassette: released on REL, '77 Dist: Roots

Cogic Choir

HE'S GOT THE WHOLE WORLD IN HIS HANDS.
Notes: This is more than just a re-release. True, it does feature some of the tracks from the previous album, 'Forgiven', but in addition it has the brand new singlewhich has been taken from the album and also gives the album it's title - 'He's got the whole world in his hands'. Because the choir are essentially liveperformers, two songs - 'Forgiven' and 'Only you' have been left exactly as theywere recorded during a live performance in 1985. This album has an overall feelof excitement which certainly matches up to the title track.
Album: released on Myrrh, Nov'86 by Word Records. Dist: Word Distribution

Cassette: released on Myrrh, Nov'86 by Word Records. Dist: Word Distribution

HE'S GOT THE WHOLE WORLD IN HIS HANDS (S).
Tracks: / He's got the whole world in his hands / You can't run from god.
Single (7"): released on Word, Nov'86 by Word Records. Dist: Word Distribution, CBS

Single (12"): released on Word, Nov'86 by Word Records. Dist: Word Distribution, CBS

Cogic(UK)

FORGIVEN.
Album: released on Myrrh, Aug'85 by Word Records. Dist: Word Distribution

Cassette: released on Myrrh, Aug'85 by Word Records. Dist: Word Distribution

Cognac

DON'T BOTHER TO KNOCK.
Single (7"): released on Rise, Apr'86 by Steve O'Donnell/Colin Jennings. Dist: Pinnacle

Single (12"): released on Rise, Apr'86 by Steve O'Donnell/Colin Jennings. Dist: Pinnacle

Cohan, George M.

YANKEE DOODLE DANDY.
Album: released on Olympic, Nov'74 Dist: Cassion (Melandy) Distribution, Celtic Music Distribution

Cohen, David

HOW TO PLAY FOLK GUITAR.
Album: released on Kicking Mule, Oct'76 by Sonet. Dist: Roots, PRT-Pye Distribution

Cohen, David Bennett

ROCK'N'ROLL GUITAR.
Album: by Sonet. Dist: Roots, PRT-Pye Distribution

Cohen, Izhar

OLE OLE.
Single (7"): released on PRT, May'85 by PRT Records. Dist: PRT

Cohen, Leonard

6 TRACK HITS.
Extended-play record: released on Scoop 33, Aug'83 by Pickwick Records. Dist: H.R. Taylor

Cassette: released on Scoop 33, Aug'83 by Pickwick Records. Dist: H.R. Taylor

DANCE ME TO THE END OF LOVE.
Single (7"): released on CBS, Feb'85 by CBS Records. Dist: CBS

DEATH OF A LADIES MAN.
Tracks: / True love leaves no traces / Iodine / Paper thin hotel / Memories / I left a woman waiting / Don't go home with your hard-on / Fingerprints / Death of a ladies man.
Album: released on Prix D'Ami (France), Sep'86

Cassette: released on Prix D'Ami (France), Sep'86

GREATEST HITS:LEONARD COHEN.
Album: released on CBS, Apr'85 by CBS Records. Dist: CBS

Cassette: released on CBS, Apr'85 by CBS Records. Dist: CBS

NEW SKIN FOR THE OLD CEREMONY.
Cassette: released on CBS, Jun'86 by CBS Records. Dist: CBS

SONG OF....
Album: by CBS Records. Dist: CBS

SONGS FROM A ROOM.
Album: released on CBS, Nov'81 by CBS Records. Dist: CBS

Cassette: released on CBS, Nov'81 by CBS Records. Dist: CBS

SONGS OF LOVE & HATE.
Album: released on CBS, Aug'84 by CBS Records. Dist: CBS

Cassette: released on CBS, Aug'84 by CBS Records. Dist: CBS

Album: released on CBS, Feb'85 by CBS Records. Dist: CBS

Cassette: released on CBS, Feb'85 by CBS Records. Dist: CBS

SONGS OF.....,THE.
Cassette: released on CBS, '74 by CBS Records. Dist: CBS

VARIOUS POSITIONS.
Compact disc: by CBS Records. Dist: CBS

Cohn, Al

AL & ZOOT (Cohn, Al Quintet feat. Zoot Sims).
Album: released on Jasmine, Jun'83 by Jasmine Records. Dist: Counterpoint, Lugtons, Taylor, H.R., Wellard, Chris, Swift, Cadillac

BODY AND SOUL (see Sims, Zoot) (Cohn, Al & Zoot Sims).

BODY & SOUL (Cohn, Al & Zoot Sims).
Album: released on Muse, Apr'81 by Peerless Records. Dist: Lugtons Distributors

BROTHERS, THE (Cohn, Al/Bill Perkins/Richie Kamuca).
Album: released on RCA (France), '83 by RCA Records. Dist: Discovery

EITHER WAY (Cohn, Al & Zoot Sims).
Album: released on Zim, Apr'81 Dist: JSU, Jazz Horizons, Jazz Music, Swift

FOUR BRASS, ONE TENOR.
Album: released on RCA (France), '83 by RCA Records. Dist: Discovery

FROM A TO Z (Cohn, Al & Zoot Sims Sextet).
Album: released on RCA, Feb'79 by RCA Records. Dist: RCA, Roots, Swift, Wellard, Chris, I & B, Solomon & Peres Distribution

Album: released on RCA (France), Oct'85 by RCA Records. Dist: Discovery

MOTORING ALONG (Cohn, Al & Zoot Sims).
Album: released on Sonet, '76 by Sonet Records. Dist: PRT

MPS JAZZ TIME,VOLUME 10 (Cohn, Al & James Moody).
Album: released on MPS, Jun'79

NATURAL SEVEN, THE.
Album: released on RCA (France), Aug'84 by RCA Records. Dist: Discovery

NIGHT FLIGHT TO DAKAR (Cohn/Billy Mitchell/Dolo Coker/Leroy Vinnegar/Frank Butler).
Album: released on Xanadu, Jan'83 Dist: Discovery, Jazz Horizons, Jazz Music, Swift

NON PAREIL.
Album: released on Concord, Aug'81 by Import Records. Dist: IMS, Polygram

OVERTONES.
Album: released on Concord Jazz(USA), Nov'82 by Concord Jazz Records (USA). Dist: IMS, Polygram

PROGRESSIVE AL COHN, THE.
Notes: Artists include: Al Cohn/tenor sax, George Wallington/piano, Tommy Potter/bass, Tony Kahn/drums - Recorded New York 1950. Nick Travis/trumpet, Al Cohn/tenor sax, Horace Silver/piano, Curley Russell/bassMax Roach/drums - Recorded New York 1953. Produced by Gus Statiras (then called Gus Grant after film star Cary) for his progressive label, Gus sold these masters to Savoy Records when his own financial mess became untenable, and so, here we are, thirty years later, with a fine album.
Album: released on Savoy Jazz, Dec'85 by RCA Records (Germany). Dist: Conifer

STANDARDS OF EXCELLENCE.
Album: released on Concord Jazz(USA), Jun'84 by Concord Jazz Records (USA). Dist: IMS, Polygram

Cassette: released on Concord Jazz(USA), Jun'84 by Concord Jazz Records (USA). Dist: IMS, Polygram

SUITABLY ZOOT.
Album: released on Pumpkin, Sep'79 Dist: Jazz Music, Wellard, Chris, Cadillac

TOUR DE FORCE (Cohn, Al/Scott Hamilton/Buddy Tate).
Double Album: released on Concord Jazz(USA), Mar'82 by Concord Jazz Records (USA). Dist: IMS, Polygram

Coil

ANAL STAIRCASE.
Tracks: / Blood from the air / Ravenous.
Single (12"): released on K 422, Dec'86 by K 422 Records. Dist: Rough Trade, Cartel

HORSE ROTAVATOR.
Album: released on K 422, Jan'87 by K 422 Records. Dist: Rough Trade, Cartel

HOW TO DESTROY ANGELS.
Single (12"): released on Himalaya, Jun'84 by Himalaya Records. Dist: Rough Trade, Cartel

PANIC.
Single (12"): released on K 422, Jun'85 by K 422 Records. Dist: Rough Trade, Cartel

SCATOLOGY.
Album: released on Some Bizarre, Feb'85 by Virgin Records. Dist: EMI, CBS, Polygram

Coll, Peter

SELFISH.
Single (12"): released on Prism, Aug'86 by Prism Records.

Coker, Jerry

MODERN MUSIC FROM INDIANA UNIVERSITY.
Album: by Fantasy Inc USA Records. Dist: IMS, Polygram

Cola, Kid Sheik

KID SHEIK COLA (Cola, Kid Sheik/Sadie Goodson Cola/Frank Fields/M. Dolliole).
Album: released on 504, Sep'86 by 504 Records. Dist: Chris Wellard, Jazz Music

N.O. - THE LEGENDS LIVE (Cola, Kid Sheik - Sheik's Swingers).
Notes: Recorded in mono.
Album: released on Jazzology, Jun'86 Dist: Jazz Music, Swift

Colby

MAKE A JOYFUL NOISE.
Album: released on Maranatha, Dec'84

Cassette: released on Maranatha, Dec'84

Colchester...

COLCHESTER SEARCHLIGHT TATOO 1980 Various bands (Various bands).
Album: released on Major Richards, Sep'80 by Major Richards Records. Dist: Taylors

INTERNATIONAL COLLECTION (Colchester Accordian Orchestra).
Album: released on ARC (Accordion Records), '84 Dist: Accordion Record Club

Cold Chisel

EAST.
Album: released on WEA, Mar'81 by WEA Records. Dist: WEA

Cold Comfort Farm

COLD COMFORT FARM Gibbons, Stella (Scales, Prunella).
Double cassette: released on Argo (Spokenword), Jul'82 by Decca Records. Dist: Polygram

Cold Danse

CHOICE.
Single (7"): released on Xcentric Noise, Apr'84 by Xcentric Noise Records & Tapes Records. Dist: Cartel

Colder, Ben

GOLDEN HITS: BEN COLDER.
Album: released on Gusto (USA), Oct'79 by Gusto Records (USA). Dist: Crusader

Cold Hand Band

TROPICANA.
Single (7"): released on BK, Jul'82

Single (7"): released on DJM, Jun'83 by DJM Records. Dist: CBS, Polygram

Single (12"): released on DJM, Jun'83 by DJM Records. Dist: CBS, Polygram

Colditz Story, The

COLDITZ STORY, THE (Allen, Patrick).
Cassette: released on Pinnacle, '79 by Pinnacle Records. Dist: Pinnacle

Coldman, Richard

HOME COOKING (Coldman, Richard & John Russell).
Album: released on Incus, Nov'79 Dist: Jazz Music, Cadillac

Coldstream Guards Band

CHANGING THE GUARDS AT BUCKINGHAM PALACE.
Album: released on Major Richards, Jul'83 by Major Richards Records. Dist: Taylors

CROWN IMPERIAL H.
Album: released on Bandleader, Jun'82 by Bandleader Records. Dist: PRT

FOCUS ON JOHN PHILIP SOUSA.
Cassette: released on Kingfisher Cassettes, Nov'81 by Fraser-Peacock Associates Ltd. Dist: PRT

GOLDEN HOUR PRESENTS COLDSTREAM GUARDS BAND.
Album: by PRT Records. Dist: PRT

MASTERPIECES FOR BAND.
Tracks: / Two Irish tone sketches / Folk song suite / Toccata marziale / Gaelic fantasy / Suites for military band / Three humouresques / Theme & variations.
Compact disc: released on Bandleader, Nov'86 by Bandleader Records. Dist: PRT

Album: released on Bandleader, Aug'85 by Bandleader Records. Dist: PRT

Cassette: released on Bandleader, Aug'85 by Bandleader Records. Dist: PRT

QUEEN'S SILVER JUBILEE.
Double Album: released on AJP Productions, Oct'76

Cold Tap

EVIL PRINCE, THE.
Cassette: released on Dining Out, Jun'81 by Dining Out Records. Dist: IKF, Independent

Cold War

MACHINIST.
Single (7"): released on Namedrop Records, Jun'83 by Namedrop Records. Dist: Rough Trade

Cold Water Problems

IT'S NEARLY TOO LATE.
Single (7"): released on Tat-R, Apr'83 by Tat-R Records. Dist: Tat-R Distribution

Cole, Ann

GOT MY MOJO WORKING.
Album: released on Krazy Kat (USA), Apr'84

Cole, Bobby

CHANGE PARTNERS.
Tracks: / Viyos con dios - waltz / I live for you / Stranger on the shore / Aria - saunter / Let this great big world keep turning / My buddy / What a swell party this is - swing / I'll never smile again / So what's new - quickstep / For once in my life / Change partners - rumba / Dream is a wish your heart makes, A / Again - cha-cha-cha / Watch what happens - samba / Caravan / It must be him - tango / Eye level / Rendezvous - gavotte.
Notes: Another dance music album featuring the organ and pianos of Bobby Cole.
Album: released on Sounds Ultimate, Jun'86 Dist: PRT, H.R. Taylor

DANCE & BE HAPPY.
Album: released on Sounds Ultimate, Jul'84 Dist: PRT, H.R. Taylor

DANCE-DANCE-DANCE.
Album: released on Sounds Ultimate, Apr'84 Dist: PRT, H.R. Taylor

DANCE MY WAY.
Album: released on Sounds Ultimate, Feb'85 Dist: PRT, H.R. Taylor

DANCING BY NIGHT.
Album: released on Sounds Ultimate, Jul'85 Dist: PRT, H.R. Taylor

DANCING IS MAGIC.
Album: released on Sounds Ultimate, Oct'84 Dist: PRT, H.R. Taylor

I BELIEVE IN DANCING.
Tracks: / I believe in music - swing / Happy days are here again - quickstep / Lover come back to me - quickstep / Days of wine and roses - rumba / Things we did last summer, The - rumba / Sway - cha-cha-cha / Sometimes when we touch - cha-cha-cha / Green cockatoo, The - samba / Fools rush in - samba / My own true love - Tara's theme - tango / Juliet bravo - theme from TV series - tango / Vienna city of my dreams - waltz / Charade - waltz / Autumn leaves - saunter / Never-the-less - saunter.
Album: released on Sounds Ultimate, Sep'86 Dist: PRT, H.R. Taylor

JUST LOVE DANCING.
Album: released on Sounds Ultimate, Oct'84 Dist: PRT, H.R. Taylor

JUST ONE MORE DANCE.
Album: released on Sounds Ultimate, Nov'85 Dist: PRT, H.R. Taylor

Cassette: released on Sounds Ultimate, Nov'85 Dist: PRT, H.R. Taylor

WITH YOU IN MY ARMS.
Tracks: / Tennessee waltz, The - waltz / Are you lonesome tonight - waltz / Do, do, do-I'm bidin' my time - saunter / Time on my hands - saunter / Falling in love again - foxtrot / One - foxtrot / Dance little lady - quickstep / This ol' house - quickstep / Somewhere - rumba / Just the way you are - rumba / It's a heartache - cha-cha-cha / Isn't this a lovely day - cha-cha-cha / Phantom of the opera - tango / Allure tango, The - tango / Easter Parade, The - saunter.
Notes: Vol.7 (Club series). Another dance music album featuring the organ and pianos of Bobby Cole. Musical arrangements: Bobby Cole. Produced and engineered by Jimmy Smith.
Album: released on Sounds Ultimate, Mar'86 Dist: PRT, H.R. Taylor

Cole, Buddy

BUDDY COLE REMEMBERED.
Album: released on Doric, Oct'80 by Amberlee Records. Dist: H.R. Taylor

CINEMA ORGAN ENCORES.
Album: released on Deroy, Jun'81 by Deroy Records. Dist: Jazz Music, Swift

Cole, Caren

I NEED A LOVER TONIGHT.
Tracks: / I need a lover tonight-dance version / I need a lover tonight-Instrumental version / I need a lover tonight-Single version.
Single (12"): released on Passion, Aug'86 by Skratch Records. Dist: PRT

Cole, Cozy

EARL'S BACKROOM & COZY'S CARAVAN (Cole, Cozy Septet/Hines, Earl Quartet).
Notes: For full details see under Earl Hines Quartet.

Cole, George

WHAT ARE WE GONNA GET 'ER INDOORS? (Cole, George & Dennis Waterman).
Single (7"): released on EMI, Dec'83 by EMI Records. Dist: EMI

Cole, Gordon

DRIVING TEST, THE.
Album: released on Spartan, Sep'78 by Spartan Records. Dist: Spartan

Colegrove, Jim

PANTHER CITY BLUES.
Album: released on Charly, Feb'82 by Charly Records. Dist: Charly, Cadillac

Cole, James

TOMMIE BRADLEY - JAMES COLE GROUP (Cole, James Group/Tommie Bradley).
Album: released on Matchbox, Aug'83 by Saydisc Records. Dist: Roots, Projection, Jazz Music, Celtic Music

Cole, Jordan

LET'S MAKE THIS A VERY MERRY CHRISTMAS.
Single (7"): released on Deluxe, Dec'83 by Deluxe Records. Dist: Pinnacle

Cole, Jude

JUDE COLE.
Tracks: / Like lovers do / Walls that bend / You were in my heart / Something that you want / Life of luxury / Hurt, The / Eeryone's in love / Better days / Walk on water / Crying Mary.

Album: released on Warner Bros., Jul'87 by Warner Bros Records. Dist: WEA

Cassette: released on Warner Bros., Jul'87 by Warner Bros Records. Dist: WEA

LIKE LOVERS DO.
Tracks: / Like lovers do / Crying Mary.
Single (7"): released on Warner Bros., Jul'87 by Warner Bros Records. Dist: WEA

Cole, Les

BE BOPPIN' DADDY (Cole, Les & The Echoes).
Tracks: / Be boppin' daddy / You've gotta pay.
Notes: Double A side
Single (7"): released on Detour, Jul'87 by Detour Records. Dist: Swift, RCA, Jazz Music, Projection

Cole, Lloyd

CUT ME DOWN - REMIX (Cole, Lloyd & The Commotions).
Tracks: / Cut me down - remix / Are you ready to be heartbroken - live / Are you ready to be heartbroken / Forest fire / Perfect blue - instrumental / Forest fire - live.
Single (7"): released on Polydor, Jan'86 by Polydor Records. Dist: Polygram, Polydor

Single (12"): released on Polydor, Jan'86 by Polydor Records. Dist: Polygram, Polydor

Double-pack single: released on Polydor, Jan'86 by Polydor Records. Dist: Polygram, Polydor

EASY PIECES (Cole, Lloyd & The Commotions).
Tracks: / Rich / Why I love country music / Pretty gone / Grace / Cut me down / Brand new friend / Lost weekend / James / Minor character / Perfect blue.
Compact disc: released on Polydor, Nov'85 by Polydor Records. Dist: Polygram, Polydor

Album: released on Polydor, Nov'85 by Polydor Records. Dist: Polygram, Polydor

Cassette: released on Polydor, Nov'85 by Polydor Records. Dist: Polygram, Polydor

LLOYD COLE & THE COMMOTIONS (Cole, Lloyd & The Commotions).
Video-cassette (VHS): released on Channel 5, Jun'86 Dist: W.H. Smiths

LOST WEEKEND (Cole, Lloyd & The Commotions).
Single 10": released on Polydor, Oct'85 by Polydor Records. Dist: Polygram, Polydor

RATTLESNAKES. (Cole, Lloyd & The Commotions).
Single (7"): released on Polydor, Oct'84 by Polydor Records. Dist: Polygram, Polydor

RATTLESNAKES (Cole, Lloyd & The Commotions).
Compact disc: by Polydor Records. Dist: Polygram, Polydor

Album: released on Polydor, Oct'84 by Polydor Records. Dist: Polygram, Polydor

Cassette: released on Polydor, Oct'84 by Polydor Records. Dist: Polygram, Polydor

Cole, Maggie

ON HISTORIC HARPSICHORDS.
Album: released on Amon Ra, Sep'86 by Saydisc Records. Dist: H.R. Taylor, PRT, Jazz Music, Essex Record Distributors Ltd., Projection, Swift

Coleman, Bill

1935-37.
Album: released on Pathe MarconiFrance), Sep'84

...IN PARIS Vol 2 (1936-38).
Album: released on Swaggie (Australia), Jan'83

...IN PARIS Vol 1 (1935-38).
Album: released on Swaggie (Australia), Jan'83

MAINSTREAM AT MONTREUX (Coleman, Bill & George Lafitte).
Album: released on Black Lion, Jul'87 by Black Lion Records. Dist: Jazz Music, Chris Wellard, Taylor, H.R., Counterpoint, Cadillac

SWINGIN' IN LONDON (Coleman, Bill & Ben Webster).
Album: released on Black Lion, Apr'85 by Black Lion Records. Dist: Jazz Music, Chris Wellard, Taylor, H.R., Counterpoint, Cadillac

Coleman Country...

MUSIC FROM THE COLEMAN COUNTRY (Coleman Country Trad Music Society).
Album: released on Leader, '81 Dist: Jazz Music, Projection

Coleman, Cy

BARNUM (Coleman, Cy Trio).
Album: released on Rhapsody, Aug'81 by President Records. Dist: Taylors, Swift, Jazz Music, Wellard, Chris

Coleman, Durrell

SOMEBODY TOOK MY LOVE.
Tracks: / Somebody took my love / When a man loves a woman.
Single (7"): released on Fourth & Broadway, Apr'86 by Island Records. Dist: Polygram, EMI

Single (12"): released on Fourth & Broadway, Apr'86 by Island Records. Dist: Polygram, EMI

Coleman, Earl

COOL WHALIN'.
Album: released on Spotlite, Sep'79 by Spotlite Records. Dist: Cadillac, Jazz Music, Spotlite

Coleman, Gary B. B.

NOTHIN' BUT THE BLUES.
Album: released on Krazy Kat (USA), 11 Apr'87

Coleman, George

AMSTERDAM AFTER DARK.
Album: released on Timeless, Apr'81

BONGO JOE.
Album: released on Arhoolie, May'81 by Arhoolie Records. Dist: Projection, Topic, Jazz Music, Swift, Roots

DUO (Coleman, George & Tete Montoliu).
Album: released on Timeless, '79

GEORGE COLEMAN OCTET.
Album: released on Affinity, Jan'81 by Charly Records. Dist: Charly, Cadillac

IN CONCERT (Coleman, George & Wynton Kelly).

MAMA ROOTS (Coleman, George & Charlie Earland).
Album: released on Muse (Import), Apr'81

MEDITATION (Coleman, George & Tete Montoliu).
Album: released on Timeless, Apr'81

Coleman Jacoby

MATHILDE MOUSE AND THE STORY OF SILENT NIGHT.
Cassette: released on Caedmon(USA), '82 by Caedmon (USA) Records. Dist: Taylors, Discovery

Coleman, Mick

MATCHSTALK MAN, THE Billy the snake.
Album: released on Picadilly, Oct'80

Coleman, Ornette

AT THE GOLDEN CICLE VOL.1.
Album: released on Blue Note (USA Import), Sep'84

AT THE GOLDEN CIRCLE VOL.2.
Album: released on Blue Note (USA Import), Sep'84

BODY META.
Album: released on Artists House, May'81 Dist: Swift

DANCING IN YOUR HEAD.
Album: released on Horizon, Aug'77 by A&M Records. Dist: CBS

EUROPEAN CONCERT (Coleman, Ornette Quartet).
Album: released on Unique Jazz, Nov'86 Dist: Swift, Jazz Music, Jazz Horizons

IN ALL LANGUAGES.
Album: released on Caravan Of Dreams (USA), Jul'87 by Caravan Of Dreams Records (USA). Dist: IMS, Polygram

Cassette: released on Caravan Of Dreams (USA), Jul'87 by Caravan Of Dreams Records (USA). Dist: IMS, Polygram

Compact disc: released on Caravan Of Dreams (USA), Jul'87 by Caravan Of Dreams Records (USA). Dist: IMS, Polygram

OF HUMAN FEELINGS.
Compact disc: released on Polystar (Japan), Jan'86 Dist: Target, Polygram
Cat. no: **J33D 20002**
Album: released on Antilles, Apr'82 by Island Records. Dist: Polygram

OPENING THE CARAVAN OF DREAMS (Coleman, Ornette & Prime Time).
Notes: Personnel: Bern Nix/Charles Ellerbee/Jamaaladeen Tacuma/Albert MacDowell/DenardoColeman/Sabir Kamal.
Album: released on Caravan Of Dreams (USA), Apr'87 by Caravan Of Dreams Records (USA). Dist: IMS, Polygram

ORNETTE LIVE AT PRINCE STREET.
Album: released on RCA (France), '83 by RCA Records. Dist: Discovery

SHAPE OF JAZZ TO COME, THE.
Compact disc: released on Atlantic Jazz, Jul'87 by WEA Records. Dist: WEA

SOAPSUDS SOAPSUDS (Coleman, Ornette & Charlie Haden).
Album: released on Artists House, May'81 Dist: Swift

SOMETHING ELSE.
Album: released on Contemporary, May'86 by Contemporary Records. Dist: Pinnacle

THAT'S JAZZ SERIES.
Album: released on Atlantic, Jul'76 by WEA Records. Dist: WEA

TOMORROW IS THE QUESTION.
Album: released on Boplicity, Jun'85 by Boplicity Records. Dist: Ace Records, Pinnacle

UNPRECEDENTED MUSIC OF ORNETTE COLEMAN, THE.
Album: released on Lotus, Apr'81 Dist: Counterpoint

WHO'S CRAZY?.
Album: released on Affinity, '83 by Charly Records. Dist: Charly, Cadillac

Coleman, Ray

JUKEBOX ROCK 'N' ROLL (Coleman, Ray & His Skyrockets).
Single (7"): released on Rollercoaster, '77 by Rollercoaster Records. Dist: Swift Distribution, Rollercoaster Distribution

Coleman, Steve

WORLD EXPANSION (Coleman, Steve & Five Elements).
Tracks: / Desperate move / Stone bone Jr / Mad monkey / Dream state / Tang lung / Yo ho / And they parted ... / In the park / Just a funky old song / Urilai Thrane / To perpetuate the funk / Koshine Koji / Tlydor's bane.
Notes: Personnel: Steve Coleman - alto saxophone, vocals / D.K. Dyson - vocals / Cassandra Wilson - vocals / Graham Haynes - trumpet / Robin Eubanks - trombone, background vocals / Geri Allen - keyboards, piano / Kelvyn Bell - electric guitar / Kevin Bruce Harris - electric bass, background vocals / Mark Johnson - drums.
Album: released on JMT (Germany), Jul'87

Compact disc: released on JMT (Germany), Jul'87

Cole, Natalie

EVERLASTING.
Tracks: / Everlasting / Jump start / Urge to merge, The / Split decision / When I fall in love / Pink cadillac / I live for your love / In my reality / I'm the one / More than the stars / What I must do / Everlasting / Jump start / Urge to merge, The / Split decision / When I fall in love / Pink cadillac / I live for your love / In my reality / I'm the one / More than the stars.
Album: released on Manhattan, Aug'87 by President Records. Dist: Jazz Music, Swift, Taylors, Chris Wellard

Cassette: released on Manhattan, Aug'87 by President Records. Dist: Jazz Music, Swift, Taylors, Chris Wellard

Compact disc: released on Manhattan, Aug'87 by President Records. Dist: Jazz Music, Swift, Taylors, Chris Wellard

I'M READY.
Album: released on Epic, Sep'83 by CBS Records. Dist: CBS

Cassette: released on Epic, Sep'83 by CBS Records. Dist: CBS

JUMP START.
Single (12"): released on Manhattan, Aug'87 by President Records. Dist: Jazz Music, Swift, Taylors, Chris Wellard

JUMP START (RADIO EDIT).
Tracks: / Jump start (radio edit) / More than the stars.
Single (7"): released on Manhattan, Jul'87 by President Records. Dist: Jazz Music, Swift, Taylors, Chris Wellard

Single (12"): released on Manhattan, Jul'87 by President Records. Dist: Jazz Music, Swift, Taylors, Chris Wellard

NATALIE LIVE.
Double Album: released on Capitol, Jul'78 by Capitol Records. Dist: EMI

THANKFUL.
Album: released on Capitol, Feb'78 by Capitol Records. Dist: EMI

UNFORGETTABLE - A TRIBUTE TO NAT 'KING' COLE (Cole, Natalie & Johnny Mathis).
Album: released on CBS, Sep'83 by CBS Records. Dist: CBS

Cassette: released on CBS, Sep'83 by CBS Records. Dist: CBS

Cole, Nat 'King'

16 GOLDEN CLASSICS.
Tracks: / Don't cry, cry baby / Last but not least / On the sunny side of the street / Yes sir that's my baby / Frim fram sauce / If you can't smile and say yes / Satchel mouth baby / Sweet Lorraine / Trouble with you is (The) / Old piano plays the blues / It's only a paper moon / Greatest invention, The / Bugle call rag / I'm lost / Nat meets June / Tea for two.
Notes: All tracks Licenced from the San Juan Music Group: Design: Shoot that tiger! (c)1986/Castle Communications Place, Unit 7, 271 Merton Road,London SW18 5JS: Bar code 5/013428/920022.
Album: released on Unforgettable, Dec'86 by Castle Communications Records. Dist: Counterpoint

Cassette: released on Unforgettable, Dec'86 by Castle Communications Records. Dist: Counterpoint

Compact disc: released on Unforgettable, '86 by Castle Communications Records. Dist: Counterpoint

1943-49 VOCAL SIDES, THE (Cole, Nat 'King' Trio).
Compact disc: released on Delta, Jun'86 by Delta Records. Dist: Target

20 GOLDEN GREATS.
Album: released on Capitol, Mar'79 by Capitol Records. Dist: EMI

Cassette: released on Capitol, Mar'78 by Capitol Records. Dist: EMI

AFTER MIDNIGHT.
Tracks: / Just you, just me / Sweet Lorraine / Sometimes I'm happy / Caravan / It's only a paper moon / You're lookin' at me / What is there to say / I was a little too lonely / Two loves have I / Lonely one / Don't let it go to your head / I know that you know / Blame it on my youth / When I grow too old to dream / Route 66 - get your kicks on / You can depend on me / Candy.

Notes: This excellent album heralds the second phase in our digitally re-mastered Nat King Cole re-issues. Contains 5 previously unreleased tracks from the original sessions, added to the 12-track version. Original sleeve design, plus new, informative sleeve note from broadcaster Alan Dell. This, Nat's last major piano album, will be enjoyed by Capitol and King Cole fans, but appeal will be broader still by the inclusion of a strong jazz flavour.
Album: released on Capitol, Feb'86 by Capitol Records. Dist: EMI. Estim retail price in Jul'87 was £3.99.

Cassette: released on Capitol, Feb'86 by Capitol Records. Dist: EMI

ANATOMY OF A JAM SESSION.
Album: released on Black Lion, Jan'85 by Black Lion Records. Dist: Jazz Music, Chris Wellard, Taylor, H.R., Counterpoint, Cadillac

ANY OLD TIME (Cole, Nat 'King' Trio).
Album: released on Giants of Jazz, Oct'86 by Hasmick Promotions Ltd.. Dist: Counterpoint, Jazz Music, Taylors, Swift, Mainline, Wellard, Chris

Cassette: released on Giants of Jazz, Oct'86 by Hasmick Promotions Ltd.. Dist: Counterpoint, Jazz Music, Taylors, Swift, Mainline, Wellard, Chris

AT HIS RARE OF ALL RAREST PERFORMANCES VOL.1.
Album: released on Kings Of Jazz, Jul'82 Dist: Jazz Horizons, Jazz Music, Celtic Music

BALLADS OF THE DAY.
Tracks: / Blossom fell, A / Unbelievable / Blue gardenia / Angel eyes / It happens to be me / Smile / Darling, je vous aime beaucoup / Alone too long / My one sin (in life) / Return to paradise / If love is good to me / Sand and the sea, The.
Notes: This album was originally released as a compilation album as a sequel to the 1955 album 'Unforgettable'. Arranged by Nelson Riddle, the songs contained on this album are stamped through with Nat's magical style and comprised of hit singles from between 1953 and 1954.
Album: released on Capitol, Dec'85 by Capitol Records. Dist: EMI

Cassette: released on Capitol, Dec'85 by Capitol Records. Dist: EMI

BEST OF NAT KING COLE, THE.
Compact disc: released on Card/Grand Prix, Jun'86 Dist: Target

BEST OF NAT KING COLE VOL.3.
Album: by Capitol Records. Dist: EMI

BEST OF NAT KING COLE.
Album: released on EMI (Holland), '83 by EMI Records. Dist: Conifer

BEST OF NAT KING COLE, VOL.2.
Album: released on Capitol, '70 by Capitol Records. Dist: EMI

BODY AND SOUL.
Tracks: / It's only a paper moon / Don't cry, cry baby / Cole's bop blues / Frim fram sauce / If you can't smile and say yes / On the sunny side of the street / Miss thing / Sweet Lorraine / Satchelmouth baby / Body and soul / Trouble with me is you / Sweet Georgia Brown / Yes sir, that's my baby / Last but not least.
Notes: Licensed from Charly International APS. This CD (P) 1987 Charly Holdings Ltd. (C) Charly Records Ltd
Compact disc: released on Topline, Apr'87 by Charly Records. Dist: Charly Distribution

BODY & SOUL.
Album: released on Ropline, Nov'84

CHRISTMAS SONG.
Album: released on MFP (Capitol), Dec'82 by EMI Records. Dist: EMI

CHRISTMAS SONG, THE.
Album: released on Capitol, Nov'84 by Capitol Records. Dist: EMI
Cat. no: **EG 2603221**
Cassette: released on Capitol, Nov'84 by Capitol Records. Dist: EMI

CLASSICS.
Double Album: released on Capitol, Jan'85 by Capitol Records. Dist: EMI

COLE ESPANOL.
Album: released on EMI (Holland), Aug'84 by EMI Records. Dist: Conifer

COLE ESPANOL AND MORE, VOL. 1.
Tracks: / Cachito / Maria Elena / Quizas quizas quizas (perhaps perhaps perhaps) / Las Mananitas (with Mariachis) / Acercate Mas (come close to me) / El Bodeguero (Grocer's cha cha) / Noche de Ronda / Te Quiero, Dijiste (magic is the moonlight) / Adelita (with Mariachis) / Ay, Cosita Linda / Aguellos ojus verdes / Saus Maos / Capullito de aleli / Fantastico / Nadie me ama.
Compact disc: released on Capitol, Apr'87 by Capitol Records. Dist: EMI

COLE ESPANOL AND MORE VOL. 2.
Tracks: / La Feria de Las Flores / Tres Palabras (without you) / Las Chiapanecas (while there's music there's romance) / Adios Mariquita Linda (adios and farewell my lover) / Vaya con Dios / La golondrina (the swallow) / No me platiques / Guadelajara / Solamente una verez (you belong to my heart) / Piel Canela / Yo vendo unos ojos negros / Perfidia / El Choclo / Ansiedad / No tenho lagrimas.
Compact disc: released on Capitol, Apr'87 by Capitol Records. Dist: EMI

COLLECTION: NAT 'KING' COLE.
Tracks: / Don't cry, cry baby / Last but not least / On the sunny side of the street / Sweet Georgia Brown / Yes sir that's my baby / Body and soul / Cole's bop blues / Frim fram Sauce / If you can't smile and say yes / Miss thing / Satchelmouth baby / Sweet Lorraine / Trouble with me is you, The / Old piano plays the blues / It's only a paper moon / Greatest invention, The / Bugle call rag / Blues / I'm lost / Nat meets June / Rosetta / Tea for two / Man on the little white keys, The.
Notes: Contains early recordings which can reveal quality limitations of the tape source.
Double Album: released on Castle Collectors, Jul'86 by Castle Communications Records. Dist: Pinnacle

Double cassette: released on Castle Collectors, Jul'86 by Castle Communications Records. Dist: Pinnacle

DISQUE D'OR(COLLECTION).
Tracks: / Love / Those lazy, hazy, crazy days of summer / Stardust / St. Louis blues / Blue gardenia / Girl from Ipanema, The / Unforgettable / Brazilian love song / Ramblin' rose / Three little words / Darling, je vous aime beaucoup / All over the world / Miss you / Les feuilles mortes.
Album: released on EMI (France), '83 by EMI Records. Dist: Conifer

ESPAGNOL.
Album: released on EMI (Holland), '83 by EMI Records. Dist: Conifer

ESPAGNOLE VOLUME 1.
Compact disc: released on Capitol, Mar'87 by Capitol Records. Dist: EMI

ESPAGNOLE VOLUME 2.
Compact disc: released on Capitol, Mar'87 by Capitol Records. Dist: EMI

FORGOTTEN YEARS (Cole, Nat 'King' Trio).
Tracks: / On the sunny side of the street / Man on the little white keys / Frim fram sauce / If you can't smile say yes / Trouble with me is you / Sweet Georgia Brown / Satchel mouth baby / Miss thing / Sweet Lorraine / Paper moon.
Album: released on Giants of Jazz, Jan'85 by Hasmick Promotions Ltd.. Dist: Counterpoint, Jazz Music, Taylors, Swift, Mainline, Wellard, Chris

FORGOTTEN YEARS, THE (Cole, Nat 'King' Trio).
Album: released on Giants of Jazz, Jan'85 by Hasmick Promotions Ltd.. Dist: Counterpoint, Jazz Music, Taylors, Swift, Mainline, Wellard, Chris

FROM THE VERY BEGINNING.
Album: released on MCA Coral, Apr'82 by MCA Records. Dist: Polygram

Cassette: released on MCA Coral, Apr'82 by MCA Records. Dist: Polygram

GREAT CAPITOL MASTERS.
Tracks: / I'm an errand boy for rhythm / Kee mo ky mo / I used to love you / These foolish things / Dream a little dream of me / Love nest, The / But all I've got is me / I've got a way with women / When I take my sugar to tea / I miss you so / You're the cream in my coffee / But she's my buddy's chick / Naughty Angeline / Best man, The / I think you get what I mean / That's what.
Notes: A new compilation of the Nat Cole Trio's earlier recordings for Capitol Records.This swinging collection of well known tracks combined with Nat's inimitable voice which provides a good blend of jazz and nostalgia.
Album: released on Capitol, Dec'85 by Capitol Records. Dist: EMI

Cassette: released on Capitol, Dec'85 by Capitol Records. Dist: EMI

GREATEST HITS:NAT 'KING' COLE.
Tracks: / Nature boy / Mona Lisa / Too young / When I fall in love / Quizas quizas quizas / Unforgettable / Fly me to the moon / Let there be love / Love / Darling je vous aime beaucoup / Ramblin' rose / Those lazy hazy crazy days of summer / Lost April / Answer me my love / Sweet Lorraine / I don't want to hurt anymore / Route 66 / Dear lonely hearts / Ay cosita Linda / Perfidia / Blue gardenia / It's only a paper moon / Acerta te mast / Smile / Blossom fell, A / Stardust / Love is the thing.
Album: released on Capitol (Holland), '83 by Capitol Records. Dist: Conifer

GREATEST LOVE SONGS.
Tracks: / Stardust / Answer me / Autumn leaves / Walkin' my baby back home / These foolish things remind me of you / There goes my heart / Nightingale sang in Berkeley Square, A / You made me love you / Blossom fell, A / More / Love letters / Oh, how I miss you tonight / Brazilian love song / You're my everything / Love is a many splendored thing / You'll never know / He'll have to go / Stay as sweet as you are / More I see you, The / Party's over, The.
Album: released on EMI, Nov'82 by EMI Records. Dist: EMI

Cassette: released on EMI, Nov'82 by EMI Records. Dist: EMI

HIS GREATEST SUCCESS.
Tracks: / Darling je vous aime beaucoup / Crazy but I'm in love / Sand and the sea, The / Stompin' down Broadway / Somebody loves me / I've grown accustomed to her face / Tea for two / Unforgettable / This can't be love / Beautiful friendship, A / Cuba Mona Lisa / Thou well / Two different worlds / It's only a paper moon / Early American / Till the end of the years / Sweet Sue, just you / I'm shooting high / Autumn leaves, The / Just one of those things / Little girl / When you're smiling / Night lights / Take me back in Toyland / Just in time / House with love in it, A / Mr. Santa Claus / You stepped out of a dream / Pick yourself up / Jingle bells / Christmas song, The.
Double Album: released on Musidisc (France), Oct'83 Dist: Discovery Distribution, Swift Distribution

INCOMPARABLE.
Album: released on Meteor, Sep'85 by Magnum Music Group Ltd. Dist: Magnum Music Group Ltd, PRT Distribution, Spartan Distribution

JUST ONE OF THOSE THINGS.
Tracks: / When your lover has gone / Cottage for sale, A / Who's sorry now / Once in a while / These foolish things remind me of you / Just for the fun of it / Don't get around much anymore / I understand / I understand / Just one of those things / Song is ended (The) (but the melody lingers on) / I should care / Party's over (The) / Day in - day out / I'm gonna sit right down (and write myself a letter) / Something makes me want to dance with you.
Notes: A full 12-track stereo, digitally re-mastered album containing songs of ended romance and unrequited love, by one of the great love song singers of all time. Billy May heads the orchestra, adding his own musical ideas, while Nat croons the message of the song in his intimate style, showing their compatible view of each number. Includes late night listening such as "Don't get around much anymore", "A cottage for sale" and "These foolish things", as well as more up- tempo easy listening in "Who's sorry now" and the title track "Just one of thosethings".
Compact disc: released on Capitol, Apr'87 by Capitol Records. Dist: EMI

Album: released on Capitol, Feb'86 by Capitol Records. Dist: EMI

Cassette: released on Capitol, Feb'86 by Capitol Records. Dist: EMI

LET'S FACE THE MUSIC.
Tracks: / Ebony Rhapsody / Too little, too late / Let's face the music and dance / Day in- day out / Bidin' my time / When my sugar walks down the street / Warm and willing / I'm gonna sit right down - and write myself a letter / Cold, cold heart / Something makes me want to dance with you / Moon love / Rules of the road, The.
Notes: (P) 1962 Original Sound Recordings made by Capitol Records Inc.
Album: released on Capitol, Aug'86 by Capitol Records. Dist: EMI

Cassette: released on Capitol, Aug'86 by Capitol Records. Dist: EMI

LET THERE BE LOVE (Cole, Nat 'King'/ George Shearing).
Tracks: / September song / Pick yourself up / I got it bad & that ain't good / Let there be love / Azure - te / Lost April / Beautiful friendship, A / Fly me to the moon / Serenata / I'm lost / There's a lull in my life / Don't go.
Album: released on Music For Pleasure, Apr'83 by EMI Records. Dist: EMI

Cassette: released on Music For Pleasure, Apr'83 by EMI Records. Dist: EMI

LET THERE BE LOVE (see Shearing, George) (Cole, Nat King & George Shearing).

LIVE - KONGRESSHAUS, ZURICH Oct. 19th 1950 (Cole, Nat 'King' Trio).
Album: released on Duke, Jul'87 by Melodisc Records. Dist: Jazz Horizons, Jazz Music, Celtic Music, Swift

L.O.V.E..
Tracks: / L.O.V.E. / Girl from Ipanema, The / Three little words / There's love / My kind of girl / Thanks to you / Your love / More / Coquette / How I'd love to love you / Swiss retreat.
Notes: (P) Original Sound Recordings made by Capitol Records Inc. Music conducted by Ralph Carmichael. Trumpet solos by Bobby Bryant.
Album: released on Capitol, Sep'86 by Capitol Records. Dist: EMI

Cassette: released on Capitol, Sep'86 by Capitol Records. Dist: EMI

LOVE IS THE THING.
Notes: A romantic collection of favourite love songs including "When I fall in love", "Stay as sweet as you are" and "It's all in the game", delivered in Nat Cole's unmistakable warm style. This predominantly stereo, digitally re-mastered album is the full 12-track original version. Until now, the only available album was the abridged 10-track U.S. release. Contains one of Nat's most popular songs, "Stardust", as well as a string of popular classics from the great composers of the day, with orchestra conducted by Gordon Jenkins.
Album: released on Capitol, Feb'86 by Capitol Records. Dist: EMI

Cassette: released on Capitol, Feb'86 by Capitol Records. Dist: EMI

Cassette: released on Capitol, Jun'78 by Capitol Records. Dist: EMI

Compact disc: released on Capitol, Apr'87 by Capitol Records. Dist: EMI

MEETS THE MASTER SAXES.
Tracks: / Heads / Pro-sky / It had to be you / I can't give you anything but love / Indiana / I can't get started / Tea for two / Body and soul / I found a new baby / Rosetta / Sweet Lorraine / I blowed and gone.
Album: released on Spotlite, '83 by Spotlite Records. Dist: Cadillac, Jazz Music, Spotlite

MONA LISA.
Tracks: / Mona Lisa / Kings Cross-follow Anderson.
Single (7"): released on Capitol, Aug'86 by Capitol Records. Dist: EMI

MORE COLE ESPANOL.
Album: released on EMI (Holland), Jan'85 by EMI Records. Dist: Conifer

MY KIND OF GIRL.
Tracks: / Ramblin' rose / Goodnight Irene / My kind of girl / Portrait of Jennie / Ballerina / Miss Otis regrets / Here's to my lady / Adelita / Sweet Lorraine / On a bicycle built for two / Girl from Ipanema, The / I thought about Marie / Marnie / Mona Lisa / Maria Elena / Annabelle.
Album: by Capitol Records. Dist: EMI

NAT COLE SINGS, GEORGE SHEARING PLAYS (see Shearing, George) (Cole, Nat King & George Shearing).

NAT COLE TRIO (Cole, Nat 'King' Trio).
Tracks: / Honeysuckle / Sweet Lorraine / This side up / Gone with the draft / Call the Police / That ain't right / Are you fer it? / Hit that jive Jack / Early morning blues / Babs / Scotchin' with soda / Slow Down / I like to Riff / This will make you laugh / Hit the Ramp / Stop, the red light's on.
Notes: MCPS Chappell Group Control
Cassette: released on Affinity, Sep'86 by Charly Records. Dist: Charly Cadillac

NAT KING COLE.
Tracks: / Non dimenticar / Too young / Smile, A / When I fall in love / Quizas quizas quizas / Tenderly / Darling Il vous aime beaucoup / Love is a many splendored thing / Blue gardenia / Tres palabras / Unforgettable / It's only a paper moon / Mona Lisa / Acerate mas / Autumn leaves / Stardust / Unforgettable / Mona Lisa / Those lazy hazy crazy days of summer / Ramblin' rose.
Album: released on Capitol, Apr'87 by Capitol Records. Dist: EMI

Digital audio tape: released on Capitol, Apr'87 by Capitol Records. Dist: EMI

Boxed set: released on World Records, Dec'81 Dist: Polygram

Double cassette: released on World Records, Dec'81 Dist: Polygram

Compact disc: released on Intertape, Jul'87 Dist: Target

NAT KING COLE AT THE SANDS.
Tracks: / Ballerina / Funny - not much / Continental, The / I wish you love / You leave me breathless / Thou swell / My kind of love / Surrey with the fringe on top, The / Where or when / Miss Otis regrets (she's unable to lunch today) / Joe Turner's blues.
Notes: A collection of popular classics recorded live at The Sands club in January 1960but not released until after his death in 1966. This unique album - Nat's only official onstage recording is being re-issued in its original gatefold packaging as part of our Nat king Cole re-issue programme. in keeping with this-series, an informative sleeve note is provided by renoned broadcaster, Alan Dell
Album: released on Capitol, May'86 by Capitol Records. Dist: EMI

Cassette: released on Capitol, May'86 by Capitol Records. Dist: EMI

NAT 'KING' COLE COLLECTION, THE.
Album: released on Deja Vu, Aug'85 by Deja Vu Records. Dist: Counterpoint Distribution, Record Services Distribution (Ireland)

Cassette: released on Deja Vu, Aug'85 by Deja Vu Records. Dist: Counterpoint Distribution, Record Services Distribution (Ireland)

Compact disc: released on Deja Vu, Jul'87 by Deja Vu Records. Dist: Counterpoint Distribution, Record Services Distribution (Ireland)

NAT KING COLE SINGS, THE GEORGE SHEARING QUINTET PLAYS.
Tracks: / September song / Pick yourself up / I got it bad and that ain't good / Let there be love / Azure te / Lost April / Everything happens to me / Beautiful friendship, A / Fly me to the moon - in other words / Serenata / I'm lost / There's a lull in my life / Don't go / Guess I'll go back home.
Album: released on Capitol, Aug'86 by Capitol Records. Dist: EMI

Cassette: released on Capitol, Aug'86 by Capitol Records. Dist: EMI

NAT KING COLE TRIO (Cole, Nat 'King' Trio).
Album: released on Deja Vu, Nov'85 by Deja Vu Records. Dist: Counterpoint Distribution, Record Services Distribution (Ireland)

Cassette: released on Deja Vu, Nov'85 by Deja Vu Records. Dist: Counterpoint Distribution, Record Services Distribution (Ireland)

NAT KING COLE TRIO CLASSICS (Cole, Nat 'King' Trio).
Album: released on Pathe MarconiFrance), Dec'84

NAT KING COLE WITH GEORGE SHEARING (Cole, Nat 'King'/ George Shearing).
Cassette: released on Capitol, May'78 by Capitol Records. Dist: EMI

NATURE BOY.
Album: released on Astan, Nov'84 by Astan Records. Dist: Counterpoint

PIECES OF COLE.
Album: released on Swinghouse, Oct'84 Dist: Jazz Music Distribution, Swift Distribution, Chris Wellard Distribution

Cassette: released on Swinghouse, Oct'84 Dist: Jazz Music Distribution, Swift Distribution, Chris Wellard Distribution

RAMBLING ROSE.
Single (7"): released on Capitol, Mar'78 by Capitol Records. Dist: EMI

RAMBLIN' ROSE.
Tracks: / Ramblin' Rose / Wolverton mountain / Twilight on the trail / I don't want it that way / He'll have to go / When you're smiling / Dear lonely hearts / All over the world / All by myself / Goodnight, Irene, goodnight / Your cheatin' heart / One has my name the other has my heart / Skip to my Lou / Good times (The) / Sing another song (and we'll all go home).
Notes: Orchestra and chorus conducted by Balford Hendricks. (P) 1962 Original Sound Recordings made by Capitol Records Inc.
Compact disc: released on Capitol, Apr'87 by Capitol Records. Dist: EMI

Album: released on Capitol, Sep'86 by Capitol Records. Dist: EMI

Cassette: released on Capitol, Sep'86 by Capitol Records. Dist: EMI

REPLAY ON NAT KING COLE.
Album: released on Sierra, Feb'85 by Sierra Records. Dist: WEA

Cassette: released on Sierra, Feb'85 by Sierra Records. Dist: WEA

SINGS FOR TWO IN LOVE.
Tracks: / Love is here to stay / Handful of stars, A / This can't be love / Little street where old friends meet, A / Autumn leaves / Let's fall in love / There goes my heart / Dinner for one please James / Almost like being in love / Tenderly / You stepped out of a dream / Too much / Thousand thoughts of you, A / If you said no.
Notes: On this album, Nat emerges as one of the world's most sensitive and artistic ballad singers. Originally an 8 song 10" album, the project was extended by 4 tracks to a 12" LP format.
Compact disc: released on Capitol, Apr'87 by Capitol Records. Dist: EMI

Album: released on Capitol, Dec'85 by Capitol Records. Dist: EMI

Cassette: released on Capitol, Dec'85 by Capitol Records. Dist: EMI

SINGS & PLAYS.
Album: released on Joker, Apr'81 Dist: Counterpoint, Mainline, Record Services Distribution (Ireland)

SOMETIMES.
Picture disc album: released on Lotus, Aug'86 Dist: Counterpoint

SONGS FOR 2 IN LOVE (& MORE).
Compact disc: by Capitol Records. Dist: EMI

SPECIAL YEARS.
Album: released on Arena, Feb'87 by Arena Records. Dist: Spartan

Cassette: released on Arena, Feb'87 by Arena Records. Dist: Spartan

TELL ME ALL ABOUT YOURSELF.
Tracks: / Tell me all about yourself / Until the real thing comes along / Best thing for you, The / When you walked by / Crazy she calls me / You've got the Indian sign on me / For you / Dedicated to you / You are my love / This is always / My life / I would do - anything for you.
Notes: This album, heralding the next batch of Nat King Cole re-issues in our ongoing series, was one of 7 recorded in 1958 - the busiest year of his career. Contains some colourful additions to his usual repertoire and is backed by the conventional brass and reed big band conducted by Dave Cavanaugh - a change from his usual string background. Tracks comprise of a good mixture of familiarstandards plus the new songs of the day.
Album: released on Capitol, May'86 by Capitol Records. Dist: EMI

Cassette: released on Capitol, May'86 by Capitol Records. Dist: EMI

THIS IS NAT 'KING' COLE.
Album: released on Capitol, Jul'85 by Capitol Records. Dist: EMI

Cassette: released on Capitol, Jul'85 by Capitol Records. Dist: EMI

Album: released on Capitol, Oct'84 by Capitol Records. Dist: EMI

Cassette: released on Capitol, Oct'84 by Capitol Records. Dist: EMI

THOSE LAZY-HAZY-CRAZY DAYS OF SUMMER.
Tracks: / Those lazy-hazy-crazy days of summer / Get out and get under the moon / There is a tavern in the town / On a bicycle built for two / That Sunday, that summer / On the sidewalks of New York / Our old home team / After the ball is over / You tell me your dream / That's what they meant-by the good old summertime / Don't forget / In the good old summertime / Those lazy-hazy-crazy days of summer.
Notes: Music conducted by Ralph Carmichael.
Album: released on Capitol, Sep'86 by Capitol Records. Dist: EMI

Cassette: released on Capitol, Sep'86 by Capitol Records. Dist: EMI

TOP POPS.
Tracks: / Somewhere along the way / If I give my heart to you / Faith can move mountains.
Notes: Originally released in 1956 and a welcome re-issue 30 years later.
Album: released on Capitol T (USA), Dec'85 Dist: Conifer

TOUCH OF YOUR LIPS, THE.
Tracks: / Touch of your lips, The / I remember you / Illusion / You're mine you / Funny / Poinciana / Sunday, Monday or always / Not so long ago / Nightingale sang in Berkley Square, A / Only forever / My need for you / Lights out.
Notes: A new conductor joins Nat on his album - Ralph Carmichael - a man of great versatility and ability who made a highly successful harmonious companion for the voice of Nat King Cole. As the title suggests, the tracks contained are easy listening material with a fair degree of smooch! As with all the albums in this series, we have digitally re-mastered the recordings and used the directmetal mastering technique for LP and high XDR tape for cassette to bing you the best sound quality ever.
Album: released on Capitol, May'86 by Capitol Records. Dist: EMI

Album: released on Capitol, May'86 by Capitol Records. Dist: EMI

TO WHOM IT MAY CONCERN.
Tracks: / Thousand thoughts of you, A / You're bringing out the dreamer in me / My heart's treasure / If you said no / Can't help it / Lovesville / Unfair / This morning it was summer / To whom it may concern / Love-wise / Too much / In the heart of Jane Doe.
Notes: In this collection of tracks, Nat is once again joined by the late, great NelsonRiddle and his Orchestra - one of the most successful partnerships in Nat's career. As always in this series, this genuine stereo album is both digitally re-mastered and direct metal mastered to bring you the best sound quality ever of this original recording.
Album: released on Capitol, Apr'86 by Capitol Records. Dist: EMI

Cassette: released on Capitol, Apr'86 by Capitol Records. Dist: EMI

TRIO DAYS.
Album: released on Affinity, Nov'84 by Charly Records. Dist: Charly, Cadillac

UNFORGETTABLE.
Tracks: / Unforgettable / Too young / Mona Lisa / I love you - for sentimental reasons / Pretend / Answer me / My love / Portrait of Jennie / What'll I do / Lost April / Red sails in the sunset / Make her mine / Hajji baba.
Notes: The first of our series of digitally recorded re-mastered albums of the unforgettable Nat King Cole. This album contains material recorded for Capitol between 1946 and 1954, and reflects the transition in Nat's career between the Nat King Cole Trio and the movement towards orchestral arrangements.
Album: released on Capitol, Dec'85 by Capitol Records. Dist: EMI. Estim retail price in Jul'87 was £3.99.

Cassette: released on Capitol, Dec'85 by Capitol Records. Dist: EMI

Album: released on Capitol(USA), Mar'84 by Capitol (USA) Records. Dist: EMI

UNFORGETTABLE (Cole, Nat 'King' Trio).
Album: released on Spot, May'86 by Pickwick Records. Dist: H.R. Taylor, Luctons

Cassette: released on Spot, May'86 by Pickwick Records. Dist: H.R. Taylor, Luctons

UNFORGETTABLE - IMPORT.
Tracks: / Too young / Party's over, The / More I see you, The / Love is here to stay / Quzas, quzas, quzas / Angel eyes / Portrait of Jennie / Teach me tonight / Ballerina / Very thought, The / She's funny that way / I wish I knew the way to your heart / You made me love you / Ramblin' rose / Love letter / Fascination / Unforgettable / Piel Canela / These foolish things / Around the world.
Album: released on EMI (Italy), Sep'86 by EMI Records. Dist: Conifer

Cassette: released on EMI (Italy), Sep'86 by EMI Records. Dist: Conifer

VERY BEST OF NAT 'KING' COLE.
Cassette: released on Capitol, '74 by Capitol Records. Dist: EMI

Album: released on Capitol, '73 by Capitol Records. Dist: EMI

VERY THOUGHT OF YOU, THE.
Tracks: / Very thought of you, The / But beautiful / Impossible / I wish I knew the way to your heart / I found a million dollar baby-in a five and ten cent store / Magnificent obsession / My heart tells me-should I believe my heart / Paradise / This is all I ask / Cherie, I love you / Making believe you're here / Cherchez la femme / For all we know / More I see you, the.
Notes: This album has as its title track on of Nat's all time favourite classics. Recorded in 1958 at Capitol's Hollywood studios with Gordon Jenkins, these tracks contain the rich string arrangements so evident in the previous re-issue of 'Love is the thing' which featured the same acclaimed vocalist/conductor collaboration.
Album: released on Capitol, Apr'86 by Capitol Records. Dist: EMI

Cassette: released on Capitol, Apr'86 by Capitol Records. Dist: EMI

Album: released on Capitol, '59 by Capitol Records. Dist: EMI

Cassette: released on Capitol, Jun'78 by Capitol Records. Dist: EMI

WELCOME TO THE CLUB.
Tracks: / Welcome to the club / Anytime, anyday, anywhere / Blues don't care - who's got them, The / Mood indigo / Baby, won't you please come home / Late, late show, the / Avalon / She's funny that way / I want a little girl / Wee baby blues / Look out for love.
Notes: This album will please both Nat Cole's 50's fans and those who followed the Nat King Cole Trio in earlier days. Accompanied by Dave Cavanaugh and orchestra, this collection of tracks have a decidedly jazz-orientated flavour so typical ofthe 'Trio' days while still retaining the Bat Cole style of the late 50's. The orchestra used on this recording was usually headed by Count Basie (who himself was signed to another company) - another, like Nat, whose roots were in jazz.
Album: released on Capitol, Apr'86 by Capitol Records. Dist: EMI

Cassette: released on Capitol, Apr'86 by Capitol Records. Dist: EMI

Album: released on Capitol(USA), Mar'84 by Capitol (USA) Records. Dist: EMI

Cassette: released on Capitol(USA), Mar'84 by Capitol (USA) Records. Dist: EMI

WHERE DID EVERYONE GO.
Tracks: / Where did everone go? / Say it isn't so / If love ain't there / Ah, the apple trees - when the world was young / Am I blue / Someone to tell it to / End of a love affair, the / I keep goin' back to Joe's / Laughing on the outside - crying on the inside / No, I don't want her / Spring is here / That's all there is there isn't any more.
Notes: Orchestra conducted by Gordon Jenkins.
Cassette: released on Capitol, Aug'86 by Capitol Records. Dist: EMI

Album: released on Capitol, Aug'86 by Capitol Records. Dist: EMI

WHITE CHRISTMAS (Cole, Nat 'King' & Dean Martin).
Album: released on MFP (Capitol), Dec'82 by EMI Records. Dist: EMI

Colenso Parade

DOWN BY THE BORDER.
Single (12"): released on Goliath, Apr'85 Dist: Nine Mile, Cartel

FONTANA EYES.
Tracks: / Fontana eyes / Here comes the night.
Single (7"): released on Fire, Oct'86 by Twist and Shout Music. Dist: Nine Mile, Rough Trade, Cartel

Single (12"): released on Fire, Oct'86 by Twist and Shout Music. Dist: Nine Mile, Rough Trade, Cartel

HALLELUJAH CHORUS.
Tracks: / Hallelujah chorus / Too late for anything sacred lover.
Single (12"): released on Fire, Dec'85 by Twist and Shout Music. Dist: Nine Mile, Rough Trade, Cartel

STANDING UP.
Single (7"): Dist: Nine Mile, Cartel Deleted Sep'84.

Cole Porter Collection

COLE PORTER COLLECTION (A) Various artists (Various Artists).
Album: released on Stash, Jun'86 Dist: Swift Distribution, Jazz Music Distribution, Jazz Horizons Distribution, Celtic Music Distribution, Cadillac, Zodiac Distribution

Cole, Richie

ALTO ANNIE'S THEME.
Album: released on Imported, Jun'84 Dist: Conifer

ALTO MADNESS.
Album: released on Muse (Import), Apr'81

HOLLYWOOD MADNESS.
Compact disc: released on Muse (USA), Feb'86 by Muse Records (USA). Dist: Conifer Distribution, Jazz Music Distribution

Album: released on Muse (Import), Apr'81

KEEPER OF THE FLAME.
Album: released on Muse (Import), Apr'81

LIVE AT THE VILLAGE VANGUARD.
Album: released on Muse (Import), Jul'82

NEW YORK AFTERNOON.
Album: released on Muse (Import), Apr'81

PURE IMAGINATION.
Tracks: / There'll be Bluebirds over the white cliffs of Dover / Dreamy / Come fly with me / Concord blues / Tin Palace shuffle / Flying down to Rio / Pure Imagination / Blue room / Starburst.
Notes: Personnel : Richie Cole-alto saxophone/Vic Jurusz-guitar/Ed Howard-bass/Victor "Yahya" Jones-drums/Ray Mantilla-percussion.
Album: released on Concord Jazz(USA), Jul'87 by Concord Jazz Records (USA). Dist: IMS, Polygram

Cassette: released on Concord Jazz(USA), Jul'87 by Concord Jazz Records (USA). Dist: IMS, Polygram

RETURN TO ALTO ACRES.
Cassette: released on Palo Alto (USA), Jul'86 by Palo Alto Records. Dist: Conifer

Album: released on Palo Alto (Italy), Jan'84

SIDE BY SIDE.
Tracks: / Save your love for me / Naughayde reality / Scrapple from the apple / Donna Lee / Polka dots and moonbeams / Eddie's mood/side by side.
Notes: Recorded live at The Historic Paramount Theatre - Denver.
Album: released on Muse (USA), Sep'86 by Muse Records (USA). Dist: Conifer Distribution, Jazz Music Distribution

STILL ON THE PLANET (Cole, Richie & E. Jefferson).
Album: released on Muse, Jun'77 by Peerless Records.

YAKETY MADNESS! (Cole, Richie & Boots Randolph).
Album: released on Palo Alto (Italy), Jan'84

Cassette: released on Palo Alto (Italy), Jan'84

Coles, Johnny

TWO AT THE TOP (Coles, Johnny/Frank Wess).
Notes: For full information see under: WESS *Frank/Johnny Coles.*

Coles, Maury

MAURY COLES.
Album: released on Onari (Canada), Jan'87 Dist: Jazz Music Distribution, Jazz Horizons Distribution

SOLO SAXOPHONE RECORD.
Album: released on Onari, Apr'81

Cole, Sonny

ROBINSON CRUSOE BOP.
Single (7"): released on Rollin' Rock, Jun'80

Cole, Stranger

PRETTY COTTAGE.
Single (7"): released on Pama Oldies, Jul'82

Colette

COLETTE A story with music by Johnny Dankworth.
Album: released on Evolution Sep'80 Dist: RCA, Folksound

Cassette: released on Evolution, Sep'80 Dist: RCA, Folksound

Colianni, John

JOHN COLIANNI.
Tracks: / Raincheck / Soft shoe / Pick yourself up / Home grown / Slow blues / I am in love / Get happy / All of you / Jitterbug waltz / Long ago and far away.
Notes: Twenty-three year old pianist John Colianni's debut performance for Concord. A former pianist for Lionel Hampton, his style hints of Art Tatum and Oscar Peterson. John is featured here in solo, trio, quartet and quintet settings. Personnel: John Colianni-piano/Bob Field-bass/Connie Kay-drums/Emily Remler-guitar/Joe Wilder trumpet.
Album: released on Concord Jazz(USA), Jan'87 by Concord Jazz Records (USA). Dist: IMS, Polygram

Cassette: released on Concord Jazz(USA) Jan'87 by Concord Jazz Records (USA). Dis IMS, Polygram

Collage

GET IN TOUCH WITH ME.
Tracks: / Get in touch with me / Winners and losers / Love is for everyone" / Romeo where's Juliet.
Single (7"): released on MCA, 20 Jun'87 by MCA Records. Dist: Polygram, MCA

Single (12"): released on MCA, 20 Jun'87 by MCA Records. Dist: Polygram, MCA

ROMEO WHERE'S JULIET.
Tracks: / Romeo where's Juliet / Let's rock and roll.
Single (7"): released on MCA, Oct'86 by MCA Records. Dist: Polygram, MCA

Single (12"): released on MCA, Oct'86 by MCA Records. Dist: Polygram, MCA

SHINE THE LIGHT.
Album: released on MCA, Nov'85 by MCA Records. Dist: Polygram, MCA

Collapsable Deckchairs

WILLIAM SHAKESPEARE.
Single (7"): released on Mordent, Aug'84 Dist: Red Rhino Distribution, Cartel Distribution

Coll, Brian

BEST OF BRIAN COLL.
Cassette: released on Homespun(Ireland), Dec'84 by Outlet Records. Dist: Outlet

COUNTRY CALLING.
Album: released on Homespun(Ireland), '82 by Outlet Records. Dist: Outlet

Cassette: released on Homespun(Ireland), '82 by Outlet Records. Dist: Outlet

COVER MAMAS FLOWERS.
Album: released on Harp(Ireland), May'80 by Pickwick Records. Dist: Taylors

SILVER HAIRED DADDY OF MINE.
Album: released on Homespun(Ireland), '82 by Outlet Records. Dist: Outlet

Cassette: released on Homespun(Ireland), '82 by Outlet Records. Dist: Outlet

THESE ARE MY MOUNTAINS.
Album: released on Harp(Ireland), Jul'81 by Pickwick Records. Dist: Taylors

Collection of...

COLLECTION OF CLASSIC MUTANTS
Hybrid Kids (Various Artists).
Album: released on Cherry Red, '82 by Cherry Red Records. Dist: Pinnacle

COLLECTION OF GOLD CHAPTER 1
Various artists (Various Artists).
Album: released on Bushranger, Jan'85 Dist: Jetstar

Collective Nox

COLLECTIVE NOX.
Album: released on Dossier, Feb'87 Dist: Red Rhino, Cartel

Collectors

SEVENTEENTH SUMMER.
Album: released on Edsel, Jun'87 by Demon Records. Dist: Pinnacle, Jazz Music, Projection

SEVENTH SUMMER.
Album: released on Edsel, Jul'87 by Demon Records. Dist: Pinnacle, Jazz Music, Projection

Collector's Items

COLLECTOR'S ITEMS Various artists (Various Artists).
Tracks: / I feel like I'm fixing to die rag / Super bird / Thing called love / Bass strings / Section 43 / Fire in the city / Johnny's gone to war / Kiss my ass / Tricky dicky / Free some day.
Notes: (P) tracks 1,2,6,7.(1965) Rag Baby Records): Tracks 3,4,5.(1966) Rag Baby Records): Tracks 8,9,10.(1971) Rag Baby Records (P) Charly Records Ltd (1987).
Album: released on Decal, Jan'87 by Charly Records. Dist: Charly

Collectors Jackpot

COLLECTORS JACKPOT (Various Artists).
Notes: Recorded in mono.
Album: released on Jazz Archives, Jul'86 by Jazz Archives Records. Dist: Jazz Music

COLLECTORS JACKPOT 2 (Various Artists).
Notes: Recorded in mono.
Album: released on Jazz Archives, Jul'86 by Jazz Archives Records. Dist: Jazz Music

COLLECTORS JACKPOT VOLUME 2
Various artists (Various Artists).
Album: released on Jazz Archives, Oct'79 by Jazz Archives Records. Dist: Jazz Music

College Hop

COLLEGE HOP (Various Artists).
Album: released on White, Apr'87

Collegiate Church

18 POPULAR HYMNS.
Album: by Abbey. Dist: PRT, Taylors, Gamut

POPULAR XMAS CAROLS.
Album: by Abbey. Dist: PRT, Taylors, Gamut

Collett, Dave

BACK TO BOOGIE WOOGIE (see Williams, G.O.) (Collett, Dave & G.O. Williams).

Collie, Max

20 YEARS JUBILEE (Collie, Max & his Rhythm Aces).
Album: released on Timeless(import), Sep'86 Dist: Cadillac

AT THE BEIDERBECKE FESTIVAL 1975.
Album: released on BBMS, Apr'79 Dist: Swift

BACK LINE VOL.2, THE (Collie, Max & His Rhythm Aces).
Album: released on Timeless (Holland), Apr'84 Dist: JSU Distribution, Jazz Music Distribution, Jazz Horizons Distribution, Cadillac, Celtic Music Distribution

BATTLE OF TRAFALGAR (Collie, Max & his Rhythm Aces).
Double Album: released on Reality, Mar'87

BY POPULAR DEMAND (Collie, Max & His Rhythm Aces).
Album: released on Black Lion, Mar'79 by Black Lion Records. Dist: Jazz Music, Chris Wellard, Taylor, H.R., Counterpoint, Cadillac

FRONT-LINE VOLUME 1 (Collie, Max & his Rhythm Aces).
Album: released on Timeless(import), Nov'85 Dist: Cadillac

GOSPEL TRAIN.
Album: released on Black Lion, Nov'77 by Black Lion Records. Dist: Jazz Music, Chris Wellard, Taylor, H.R., Counterpoint, Cadillac

JAZZ ROOLS OK.
Album: released on Black Lion, Jun'78 by Black Lion Records. Dist: Jazz Music, Chris Wellard, Taylor, H.R., Counterpoint, Cadillac

LIVE (Collie, Max & His Rhythm Aces).
Album: released on Happy Bird (Germany), Jul'83 Dist: Polygram, IMS

Cassette: released on Happy Bird (Germany), Jul'83 Dist: Polygram, IMS

LIVE IN SWEEDEN (Collie, Max & His Rhythm Aces).
Double Album: released on Sweet Folk All, May'81 by Sweet Folk All Records. Dist: Sweet Folk All, Roots, Celtic Music, Dragon, Impetus, Projection, Chris Wellard, Festival Records

MAX COLLIE'S RHYTHM ACES VOL 1 (Collie, Max & his Rhythm Aces).
Album: released on Wam, May'87

MAX COLLIE'S RHYTHM ACES VOL 2 H (Collie, Max & his Rhythm Aces).
Album: released on Wam, May'87

TEN YEARS TOGETHER (Collie, Max & His Rhythm Aces).
Double Album: released on Sweet Folk All, May'81 by Sweet Folk All Records. Dist: Sweet Folk All, Roots, Celtic Music, Dragon, Impetus, Projection, Chris Wellard, Festival Records

WORLD CHAMPIONS OF JAZZ (Collie, Max & His Rhythm Aces).
Double Album: released on Black Lion, Aug'76 by Black Lion Records. Dist: Jazz Music, Chris Wellard, Taylor, H.R., Counterpoint, Cadillac

Collier, Graham

DARIUS (Collier, Graham & Various artists).
Album: released on Mosaic, Jan'77 by Mosaic Records. Dist: Jazz Music Distribution, Impetus Distribution, JSU Distribution, Cadillac

DAY OF THE DEAD.
Double Album: released on Mosaic, Jun'78 by Mosaic Records. Dist: Jazz Music Distribution, Impetus Distribution, JSU Distribution, Cadillac

MIDNIGHT BLUE.
Album: released on Mosaic, Jan'77 by Mosaic Records. Dist: Jazz Music Distribution, Impetus Distribution, JSU Distribution, Cadillac

NEW CONDITIONS.
Album: released on Mosaic, Jan'77 by Mosaic Records. Dist: Jazz Music Distribution, Impetus Distribution, JSU Distribution, Cadillac

SYMPHONY OF SCORPIONS.
Album: released on Mosaic, Aug'77 by Mosaic Records. Dist: Jazz Music Distribution, Impetus Distribution, JSU Distribution, Cadillac

Collier, Norman

SPACE CHICKEN.
Tracks: / Smile.
Single (7"): released on Crystal, Dec'86 by Crystal Records. Dist: Jetstar, Revolver, Cartel

Collier, Sheila

CHANGE IS GONNA COME, A.
Album: released on Plant Life Jazz, Nov'81

Collins, Albert

ALIVE AND COOL.
Album: released on Red Lightnin', Sep'82 by Red Lightnin' Records. Dist: Roots, Swift, Jazz Music, JSU, Pinnacle, Cartel, Wynd-Up Distribution

ALLIGATOR SHOES.
Album: released on Sonet, Mar'85 by Sonet Records. Dist: PRT

COLD SNAP.
Tracks: / Cash talkin' / Bending like a willow tree / Good fool is hard to find, A / Lights are on but nobody's home / I ain't drunk / Hooked on you / Too many dirty dishes / Snatchin' it back / Fake ID / Good fool is hard to find, A.
Album: released on Sonet, Jan'87 by Sonet Records. Dist: PRT

COOL SOUND OF ALBERT COLLINS, THE.
Album: released on Crosscut, Jun'85 by IMS-Polygram Records. Dist: IMS, Polygram, Rollercoaster Distribution

FROSTBITE.
Album: released on Sonet, Jun'80 by Sonet Records. Dist: PRT

FROZEN ALIVE.
Album: released on Sonet, Nov'81 by Sonet Records. Dist: PRT

ICE COLD BLUES.
Tracks: / Harris county line / Conversation with Collins / Jawing / Grapeland gossip / Chatterbox / Trash talkin' / Leftovers / Got a good thing goin' / Lip service / Talking slim blues / Backyard backtalk / Tongue lashing / And it started raining / Stump poker.
Album: released on Charly, '86 by Charly Records. Dist: Charly, Cadillac

Cassette: released on Charly, '86 by Charly Records. Dist: Charly, Cadillac

ICE PICKIN'.
Tracks: / Talking woman blues / When the welfare turns its back on you / Ice pick / Cold, cold feeling / Too tired / Master charge / Conversation with Collins / Avalanche.
Compact disc: released on Sonet, Oct'86 by Sonet Records. Dist: PRT

ICE PICKING.
Album: released on Sonet, Jan'79 by Sonet Records. Dist: PRT

LIVE IN JAPAN.
Album: released on Sonet, Mar'85 by Sonet Records. Dist: PRT

SHOWDOWN (Collins, Albert/Johnny Copeland/Robert Cray).
Tracks: / T-bone shuffle / Moon is full, The / Lion's den / She's into something / Bring your fine self home / Black cat bone / Dream, The / Albert's alley / Blackjack.
Notes: See also under **Copeland,** Johnny and **Cray,** Robert.
Album: released on Sonet, Nov'85 by Sonet Records. Dist: PRT

Collins, Ansel

MAKING LOVE.
Single (12"): released on Londisc, Jun'83 by Londisc Records.

Collins, Ansell

RIDING HIGH.
Album: released on Oneness, May'87

Collins, Bootsy

BODY SLAM.
Single (12"): released on Bluebird, Aug'86 by Bluebird Records. Dist: EMI, Jetstar

Collins, Cal

CAL COLLINS.
Album: released on Concord, Apr'79 by Import Records. Dist: IMS, Polygram

CROSS COUNTRY.
Album: released on Concord, Dec'81 by Import Records. Dist: IMS, Polygram

OHIO BOSS GUITAR.
Album: released on Famous Door, Aug'79 Dist: Swift

Collins, Dave

DOUBLE BARREL (Collins, Dave & Ansel).
Single (7"): released on Old Gold, Apr'83 by Old Gold Records. Dist: Lightning, Jazz Music, Spartan, Counterpoint

Collins, Earl

BLUEGRASS CARDINALS.
Album: released on Sierra Briar, Mar'79

THAT'S EARL.
Album: released on Sierra Briar (USA), Apr'79 Dist: Mike's Country Music Room Distribution, Projection

Collins, Edwin

DON'T SHILLY SHALLY.
Tracks: / Don't shilly shally / If ever you're ready / Queer fish".
Single (7"): released on WEA, Jul'87 by WEA Records. Dist: WEA

Single (12"): released on WEA, Jul'87 by WEA Records. Dist: WEA

Collins/Ellis

INTERPLAY.
Album: released on Concord, Mar'81 by Import Records. Dist: IMS, Polygram

Collins, Johnny

JOHNNY'S PRIVATE ARMY (Collins, Johnny & Co.).
Album: released on Tradition, Aug'76 Dist: JSU, Cassion Distribution, Celtic Music, Jazz Music, Projection, Roots Records

TRAVELLER'S REST (Collins, Johnny & Friends).
Album: released on Tradition, Aug'76 Dist: JSU, Cassion Distribution, Celtic Music, Jazz Music, Projection, Roots Records

Collins, Judy

AMAZING GRACE Best of Judy Collins.
Album: released on Elektra (USA), '72 by Elektra/Asylum/Nonesuch Records. Dist: WEA

Cassette: released on Elektra (USA), '72 by Elektra/Asylum/Nonesuch Records. Dist: WEA

Album: released on Telstar, Nov'85 by Telstar Records. Dist: RCA Distribution

Cassette: released on Telstar, Nov'85 by Telstar Records. Dist: RCA Distribution

Compact disc: released on Telstar, Jul'87 by Telstar Records. Dist: RCA Distribution

AMAZING GRACE.
Single (7"): released on Elektra Asylum, Jul'81 by Elektra/Asylum/Nonesuch Records. Dist: WEA

Single (7"): released on Old Gold, Sep'85 by Old Gold Records. Dist: Lightning, Jazz Music, Spartan, Counterpoint

BOTH SIDES NOW.
Album: released on Hallmark, Oct'82 by Pickwick Records. Dist: Pickwick Distribution, PRT, Taylors

Cassette: released on Hallmark, Oct'82 by Pickwick Records. Dist: Pickwick Distribution, PRT, Taylors

JUDITH.
Compact disc: released on Elektra (USA), '83 by Elektra/Asylum/Nonesuch Records. Dist: WEA

RUNNING FOR MY LIFE.
Album: released on Elektra (USA), '80 by Elektra/Asylum/Nonesuch Records. Dist: WEA

Cassette: released on Elektra (USA), '80 by Elektra/Asylum/Nonesuch Records. Dist: WEA Deleted '83.

SEND IN THE CLOWNS.
Single (7"): released on Elektra (USA), Aug'77 by Elektra/Asylum/Nonesuch Records. Dist: WEA

WILD FLOWERS.
Compact disc: by Elektra/Asylum/Nonesuch Records. Dist: WEA

Collins, Kathleen

TRADITIONAL MUSIC OF IRELAND.
Album: released on Shanachie, Sep'79 Dist: Sterns/Triple Earth Distribution, Roots

Collins Kids

ROCKIN' ROLLIN' COLLINS KIDS.
Album: released on Bear Family, Sep'84 by Bear Family Records. Dist: Rollercoaster Distribution, Swift

ROCKIN' ROLLIN' COLLINS KIDS VOL.2.
Album: released on Bear Family, Oct'83 by Bear Family Records. Dist: Rollercoaster Distribution, Swift

Collins, Larry

ROCKIN' ROLLIN' (Collins, Larry & Joe Maphis).
Album: released on Bear Family, Oct'83 by Bear Family Records. Dist: Rollercoaster Distribution, Swift

Collins, Lee

IN THE 30'S.
Album: released on Collectors Items, Jul'86 Dist: Jazz Music, Swift, Chris Wellard

NIGHT AT THE VICTORY CLUB, A.
Album: released on New Orleans, Apr'79 Dist: Swift, Zodiac Distribution, Jazz Music,

RALPH SUTTON'S JAZZOLA SIX-VOL.1.
Album: released on Rarities, Apr'81

RALPH SUTTON'S JAZZOLA SIX-VOL.2.
Album: released on Rarities, Apr'81

Collins, Lewis

WHEN YOU COME HOME AGAIN.
Single (7"): released on Sour Grape, Sep'82 by Sour Grape Records. Dist: PRT

Collins, Phil

DON'T LET HIM STEAL YOUR HEART AWAY.
Single (7"): released on Virgin, Mar'83 by Virgin Records. Dist: EMI, Virgin

Single (12"): released on Virgin, Mar'83 by Virgin Records. Dist: EMI, Virgin

Page 230

FACE VALUE.
Album: released on Virgin, Feb'81 by Virgin Records. Dist: EMI, Virgin Distribution

Compact disc: by Virgin Records. Dist: EMI, Virgin Distribution

Cassette: released on Virgin, Feb'81 by Virgin Records. Dist: EMI, Virgin Distribution

HELLO I MUST BE GOING.
Compact disc: released on Virgin, '83 by Virgin Records. Dist: EMI, Virgin Distribution

Album: released on Virgin, Nov'82 by Virgin Records. Dist: EMI, Virgin Distribution

Cassette: released on Virgin, Nov'82 by Virgin Records. Dist: EMI, Virgin Distribution

INTERVIEW PICTURE DISC.
Album: released on Baktabak, May'87 by Baktabak Records. Dist: Arabesque

LIVE.
Video-cassette (VHS): released on Thorn-Emi, Jan'84

LIVE AT PERKIN'S PALACE.
Video-cassette (VHS): released on PMI, Jun'86 by PMI Records. Dist: EMI

Video-cassette [Betamax]: released on PMI, Jun'86 by PMI Records. Dist: EMI

NO JACKET REQUIRED.
Tracks: / Sussudio / Only you know and I know / Long long way to go / I don't wanna know / One more night / Don't lose my number / Who said I would / Doesn't anybody stay together anymore / Inside out / Take me home.
Compact disc: released on Virgin, Feb'85 by Virgin Records. Dist: EMI, Virgin Distribution

Video-cassette (VHS): released on Virgin, Jan'86 by Virgin Records. Dist: EMI, Virgin Distribution

Cassette: released on Virgin, Feb'85 by Virgin Records. Dist: EMI, Virgin Distribution

Album: released on Virgin, Feb'85 by Virgin Records. Dist: EMI, Virgin Distribution

NO TICKET REQUIRED.
Tracks: / Only you and I know / Against all odds / Who said I would / Sussudio / Behind the lines / Westside / One more night / In the air tonight / Like china / You can't hurry love / It don't matter to me / Hand in hand / Take me home / It's alright / Droned.
Video-cassette (VHS): released on WEA(Music), May'86

Video-cassette [Betamax]: released on WEA(Music), May'86

ONE MORE NIGHT.
Single (7"): released on Virgin, Mar'85 by Virgin Records. Dist: EMI, Virgin Distribution

Single (12"): released on Virgin, Mar'85 by Virgin Records. Dist: EMI, Virgin Distribution

SEPARATE LIVES (Collins, Phil & Marilyn Martin).
Single (7"): released on Virgin, Nov'85 by Virgin Records. Dist: EMI, Virgin Distribution

Single (12"): released on Virgin, Nov'85 by Virgin Records. Dist: EMI, Virgin Distribution

SUSSUDIO.
Single (7"): released on Virgin, Jan'85 by Virgin Records. Dist: EMI, Virgin Distribution

Single (12"): released on Virgin, Jan'85 by Virgin Records. Dist: EMI, Virgin Distribution

TAKE ME HOME.
Single (7"): released on Virgin, Jul'85 by Virgin Records. Dist: EMI, Virgin Distribution

Single (12"): released on Virgin, Jul'85 by Virgin Records. Dist: EMI, Virgin Distribution

VIDEO EP.
Video-cassette (VHS): released on PMI, Jun'86 by PMI Records. Dist: EMI

Video-cassette [Betamax]: released on PMI, Jun'86 by PMI Records. Dist: EMI

YOU CAN'T HURRY LOVE (VIDEO).
Tracks: / You can't hurry love / One more night.
Video-cassette (VHS): released on Gold Rushes, Mar'87 by Video Collection Records. Dist: Counterpoint

YOU CAN'T HURRY LOVE.
Single (7"): released on Virgin, Nov'82 by Virgin Records. Dist: EMI, Virgin Distribution

Single (12"): released on Virgin, Nov'82 by Virgin Records. Dist: EMI, Virgin Distribution

Picture disc single: released on Virgin, Nov'82 by Virgin Records. Dist: EMI, Virgin Distribution

Collins, Ronan

GAMES PEOPLE PLAY.
Cassette: released on Music City, Jul'87 Dist: Ross Distribution

Collins, Shirley

ADIEU TO OLD ENGLAND.
Album: released on Topic, '81 Dist: Roots Distribution

ANTHEMS IN EDEN (Collins, Shirley & Dolly).
Tracks: / Meeting, A - searching for lambs / Courtship, A - the wedding song / Denying, A - the blacksmith / Foresaking, A - our captain cried / Dream, A - lowlands / Leavetaking, A - pleasant and delightful / An awakening - whitsun dance / New beginning, A - the staines morris / Rembleaway / C'the yowes / God dog / Bonny cuckoo / Nellie / Gathering rushes in the month of May / Gower Wassall, The / Beginning, A.
Album: released on See For Miles, Jun'86 by See For Miles Records. Dist: Pinnacle

ANTHEMS IN EDEN SUITE.
Album: released on Harvest, Aug'76 by EMI Records. Dist: Roots, EMI

FOLK ROOTS NEW ROUTES (Collins, Shirley & Davey Graham).
Album: released on Righteous, Feb'81 Dist: Jazz Music, .

FOR AS MANY AS WILL (Collins, Shirley & Dolly).
Album: released on Topic, '81 Dist: Roots Distribution

Cassette: released on Topic, Jun'78 Dist: Roots Distribution

LOVE DEATH & THE LADY (Collins, Shirley & Dolly).
Notes: Sussex UK. Based folk singers. Active during the late sixties/early seventies. This album of traditional folk songs was originally released by EMI Harvest. Original fold sleeve.
Album: released on Beat Goes On, Mar'87 Dist: Pinnacle

NO ROSES (Collins, Shirley & The Albion Country Band).
Tracks: / Claudy banks / Little gypsy girl, The / Banks of the bann / Murder of Maria Martin / Van dieman's land / Just as the tide was a flowing / White hare, The / Hal-an-tow / Poor murdered woman.
Cassette: released on Mooncrest, Aug'86 by Mooncrest Records. Dist: PRT Distribution

NO ROSES.
Album: released on Mooncrest, '83 by Mooncrest Records. Dist: PRT Distribution

POWER OF THE TRUE LOVE KNOT.
Album: released on Hannibal, Jul'87 by Hannibal Records. Dist: Charly, Harmonia Mundi, Projection, Celtic Music, Roots

SWEET PRIMEROSES, THE.
Album: released on Topic, '81 Dist: Roots Distribution

Collins, Tom

FIDGETY FEET (Collins, Tom Jazz Band).
Album: released on Sweet Folk All, May'81 by Sweet Folk All Records. Dist: Sweet Folk All, Roots, Celtic Music, Dragon, Impetus, Projection, Chris Wellard, Festival Records

SATURDAY NIGHT FUNCTION (Collins, Tom Jazz Band).
Album: released on Sweet Folk All, May'81 by Sweet Folk All Records. Dist: Sweet Folk All, Roots, Celtic Music, Dragon, Impetus, Projection, Chris Wellard, Festival Records

Collins, Tommy

THIS IS....
Album: released on Pathe MarconiEMI Europe), Jun'84

Collins, Wilkie

WOMAN IN WHITE, THE.
Special: released on Cover to Cover, Jun'85 by Cover to Cover Cassettes. Dist: Conifer

Collins, William 'Bootsy'

ONE GIVETH, THE COUNT TAKETH AWAY, THE.
Album: released on Warner Brothers, Apr'82 by Warner Bros Records. Dist: WEA

Collins, Willie

WHERE YOU GONNA BE TONIGHT.
Tracks: / Ain't no woman / Determination / First time making love / Let's get started / Girl in the corner / Where you gonna be tonight / Restless / Sticky situation.
Notes: Executive producer: Beau Huggins. A debut album for Capitol Records from a new artist with a very promising pedigree. Willie Collins joins Capitol through his association with the same management group who guides the careers of Freddie Jackson, Melisa Morgan and Paul Laurence, and who collectively have had a very successful past year with their particularly high quality soul music.
Album: released on Capitol, May'86 by Capitol Records. Dist: EMI

Cassette: released on Capitol, May'86 by Capitol Records. Dist: EMI

WHERE YOU GONNA BE TONIGHT - EDIT.
Tracks: / Where you gonna be tonight - edit / Sticky situation.
Single (7"): released on Capitol, Jun'86 by Capitol Records. Dist: EMI

Single (12"): released on Capitol, Jun'86 by Capitol Records. Dist: EMI

Collister, Christine

MARKSMAN, THE (Music from BBC TV series).
Album: released on BBC, Aug'87 by BBC Records & Tapes. Dist: EMI, PRT, Pye

Cassette: released on BBC, Aug'87 by BBC Records & Tapes. Dist: EMI, PRT,

WARM LOVE GONE COLD.
Tracks: / Warm love gone cold / Cavatina / Warm love gone cold - extended version / For Lucille*.
Notes: Theme from the BBC-TV series "The Life And Loves Of A She Devil".
Single (7"): released on BBC, Sep'86 by BBC Records & Tapes. Dist: EMI, PRT,

Single (12"): released on BBC, Sep'86 by BBC Records & Tapes. Dist: EMI, PRT,

Collodi, C

PINOCCHIO.
Cassette: released on Tellastory, Dec'86 by Bartlett Bliss Productions. Dist: PRT Distribution, Hayward Promotions Distribution, H.R. Taylor Distribution

Cassette: released on Argo (Spokenword), Jul'82 by Decca Records. Dist: Polygram

Collodi, Carlo

PINOCCHIO.
Double cassette: released on Listen For Pleasure, Oct'85 by MFP Records. Dist: EMI

Colm III

TAKE ME HIGH.
Tracks: / You take me high.
Single (7"): released on Ruby Red, Aug'87

Colm & Sundowners

COUNTRY IS MY STYLE.
Album: released on Homespun(Ireland), '82 by Outlet Records. Dist: Outlet

Cassette: released on Homespun(Ireland), '82 by Outlet Records. Dist: Outlet

Cololur Supplement

MICHAELANGELO.
Single (7"): released on Headline, Jul'82 by Creole Records. Dist: PRT

Colombier, Michel

MICHAEL COLOMBIER.
Album: released on Chrysalis, Apr'79 by Chrysalis Records. Dist: CBS

Colonel Abrams

ALBUM, THE.
Tracks: / Truth, The / Specualtion / Never change / Picture me in love with you / Trapped / I'm not gonna let / Over and over / Margaux / Table for two.
Album: released on MCA, Mar'86 by MCA Records. Dist: Polygram, MCA

Cassette: released on MCA, Mar'86 by MCA Records. Dist: Polygram, MCA

MUSIC IS THE ANSWER.
Single (7"): released on PRT, Nov'85 by PRT Records. Dist: PRT

Single (12"): released on PRT, Nov'85 by PRT Records. Dist: PRT

OVER AND OVER.
Tracks: / Over and over / Speculation.
Single (7"): released on MCA, Aug'86 by MCA Records. Dist: Polygram, MCA

Single (12"): released on MCA, Aug'86 by MCA Records. Dist: Polygram, MCA

TRAPPED.
Single (7"): released on MCA, Aug'85 by MCA Records. Dist: Polygram, MCA

Single (12"): released on MCA, Aug'85 by MCA Records. Dist: Polygram, MCA

Single (12"): released on MCA, Sep'85 by MCA Records. Dist: Polygram, MCA

Colonel, Daddy

TAKE A TRIP.
Single (7"): released on UK Bubblers, Sep'85 by Greensleeves Records. Dist: RCA, Jetstar

Colonel Kilgore's...

COLONEL KILGORE'S VIETNAMESE FORMATION SURF TEAM (Colonel Kilgore's Vietnamese Formation Surf Team).
Album: released on Hang-Ten, Nov'86 Dist: Revolver

Colonel Redl

COLONEL REDL-ZDENKO TAMASSI
Original soundtrack (Colonel Kilgore's Vietnamese Formation Surf Team).
Album: released on Milan France, Dec'85

Colonel's lady

COLONEL'S LADY (Somerset Maugham).
Cassette: released on Talking Tape Company, '84 by Talking Tape Company Records.

Colon, Willie

CONTRABANDO.
Tracks: / Bailando asi / Manana amor / Contrabando / Che che cole / Barrunto / Te conozco / Calle luna calle sol / Lo que es de juan / Pregunta por ahi / Especial nr 5 / Soltera / Quien eres.
Notes: Brand new album from New Yorker and Salsa musician Willie Colon (recorded 1987) Currently in the Record Mirror Disco Dance chart with the 12" on A & M "She Don't Know I'm Alive". Willie Colon looks on course to repeating his previous chart success "Set Fire To Me" which got to number 1 in the same chart last year
Album: released on Messidor (Germany), Apr'87 Dist: IMS Distribution Polygram

SET FIRE TO ME - LATIN JAZZBO VERSION.
Tracks: / Set fire to me - latin jazzbo version / Inferno dub.
Single (7"): released on A&M, Jun'86 by A&M Records. Dist: Polygram

Single (12"): released on A&M, Jun'86 by A&M Records. Dist: Polygram

SHE DON'T KNOW I'M ALIVE.
Tracks: / She don't know I'm alive / She don't know I"m alive (dub) / Set fire to me.
Notes: Set fire to me on 12" version only.
Single (7"): released on A&M, Feb'87 by A&M Records. Dist: Polygram

Single (12"): released on A&M, Feb'87 by A&M Records. Dist: Polygram

TIEMPO PA'MATAR.
Tracks: / El diablo / Tiempo pa'matar / Noche de lose enmascarados / Callejon sin salido / Volo / Falta de consideracion / Gitana / Serenata.
Notes: New York born singer/trombonist and multi instrumentalist, Willie Colon is one of the leading figures of Salsa. With over twenty albums to his credt, many of which have reached gold status, Willie Colon is constantly in the American latinLP and singles charts. "Tiempo Pa'Matar was high in the US latin chart last year and also entered the UK latin chart as a direct American import.
Album: released on Messidor (Germany), Jan'87 Dist: IMS Distribution, Polygram

Colorado

BERWICK SPEEDWAY PRESENT.
Cassette: released on Trimtop, Mar'87

BOOGIE GRASS SATURDAY NIGHT.
Single (7"): released on Big R, Aug'81 by Big R Records. Dist: Pinnacle, Wynd-Up Distribution, Solomon & Peres Distribution, I & B, Swift, Record Merchandisers Distribution, Spartan

GREEN FIELDS OF FRANCE PARTS 1 & 2.
Single (7"): released on Big R, May'82 by Big R Records. Dist: Pinnacle, Wynd-Up Distribution, Solomon & Peres Distribution, I & B, Swift, Record Merchandisers Distribution, Spartan

SING COUNTRY MUSIC.
Cassette: released on Big R, Nov'80 by Big R Records. Dist: Pinnacle, Wynd-Up Distribution, Solomon & Peres Distribution, I & B, Swift, Record Merchandisers Distribution, Spartan

SINGS COUNTRY MUSIC.
Compact disc: released on Big R, Nov'80 by Big R Records. Dist: Pinnacle, Wynd-Up Distribution, Solomon & Peres Distribution, I & B, Swift, Record Merchandisers Distribution, Spartan

STILL BURNING.
Album: released on Trimtop, Jan'87
Cat. no: **TT104**
Cassette: released on Trimtop, Jan'87

TENNESEE WHISKY AND TEXAS WOMEN.
Single (7"): released on Big R, Dec'81 by Big R Records. Dist: Pinnacle, Wynd-Up Distribution, Solomon & Peres Distribution, I & B, Swift, Record Merchandisers Distribution, Spartan

Cat. no: **BR 07**

TENNESSEE INSPIRATION.
Album: released on Big R, Oct'81 by Big R Records. Dist: Pinnacle, Wynd-Up Distribution, Solomon & Peres Distribution, I & L . Swift, Record Merchandisers Distribution, Spartan

Album: released on Big R, Oct'81 by Big R Records. Dist: Pinnacle, Wynd-Up Distribution, Solomon & Peres Distribution, I & B, , Swift, Record Merchandisers Distribution, Soartan

Color Of Money

COLOR OF MONEY, THE Original soundtrack (Various Artists).
Tracks: / Who owns this place / It's in the way you use it / Let yourself in for it / Don't tell me nothin' / Two brothers and a stranger / Standing on the edge of love / Modern blues / Werewolves of London / My baby's in love with another guy / Main title, The.
Album: released on MCA, Feb'87 by MCA Records. Dist: Polygram, MCA

Cassette: released on MCA, Feb'87 by MCA Records. Dist: Polygram, MCA

Compact disc: released on MCA, May'87 by MCA Records. Dist: Polygram, MCA

Color Purple

COLOR PURPLE, THE Original soundtrack (Various Artists).
Notes: Music produced by Quincy Jones.
Double Album: released on Qwest, Aug'86 by WEA Records. Dist: WEA

Double cassette: released on Qwest, Aug'86 by WEA Records. Dist: WEA

Colors

L.O.S.(LOVE ON SIGHT).
Single (12"): released on Fourth & Broadway, Aug'85 by Island Records. Dist: Polygram, EMI

PAY ME BACK MY LOVE.
Tracks: / Pay me back my love / Pay me back my love-edited dub mix.
Single (7"): released on Prelude, Jul'86 Dist: CBS

Single (12"): released on Prelude, Jul'86 Dist: CBS

Colosseum

COLLECTORS COLOSSEUM, THE.
Album: by Island Records. Dist: Polvoram

EPITAPH.
Tracks: / Walking in the park / Bring out your dead / Those about to die / Beware the Ides of March / Daughter of time / Valentine suite.
Notes: Bar Code: 5 013428 140147. All tracks licensed from Bronze Records. Design: Shoot That Tiger! (C) Castle Communications PLC, Unit 7, 271 Merton Road, London SW18 5JS.
Album: released on Ray Power, Apr'86

Cassette: released on Ray Power, Apr'86

Compact disc: released on Raw Power, Apr'86 Dist: Pinnacle

LIVE.
Tracks: / Rope ladder to the moon / Walking in the park / Skelington / Tanglewood '63 / Encore...stormy monday blues / Lost angeles.
Notes: Double album. Recorded at Manchester University and Big Apple, Brighton, March 1971.
Album: released on Castle Classics, Mar'87 by Castle Communications. Dist: BMG

Colosseum II

STRANGE NEW FLESH.
Tracks: / Dark side of the moog / Down to you / Gemini and leo / Secret places / On second thoughts / Winds.
Album: released on Castle Classics, Apr'86 by Castle Communications. Dist: BMG

Compact disc: released on Castle Classics, '86 by Castle Communications. Dist: BMG

Colourbox

BABY I LOVE YOU.
Tracks: / Baby I love you / Looks like we're shy one horse / Shoot out*.
Single (7"): released on 4AD, May'86 by 4AD Records. Dist: Rough Trade

Single (12"): released on 4AD, May'86 by 4AD Records. Dist: Rough Trade

BREAKDOWN.
Single (7"): released on 4AD, Apr'83 by 4AD Records. Dist: Rough Trade

Single (12"): released on 4AD, Apr'83 by 4AD Records. Dist: Rough Trade

Single (7"): by Infrared Records. Dist: M.I.S., EMI

COLOURBOX.
Tracks: / Suspicion / Arena / Say you / Just give 'em whiskey / You keep me hanging on / Moon is blue, The / Manic / Sleepwalker / Inside informer / Punch.
Compact disc: released on 4AD, '86 by 4AD Records. Dist: Rough Trade

Album: released on 4AD, Aug'85 by 4AD Records. Dist: Rough Trade

COLOURBOX MINI LP.
Compact disc: released on 4AD, Nov'86 by 4AD Records. Dist: Rough Trade

MIXED UP MURDER.
Album: released on 4AD, Oct'83 by 4AD Records. Dist: Rough Trade

OFFICIAL COLOURBOX WORLD CUP THEME.
Single (7"): released on 4AD, Apr'86 by 4AD Records. Dist: Rough Trade

Single (12"): released on 4AD, Apr'86 by 4AD Records. Dist: Rough Trade

PUNCH.
Single (7"): released on 4AD, Apr'84 by 4AD Records. Dist: Rough Trade

Single (12"): released on 4AD, Apr'84 by 4AD Records. Dist: Rough Trade

SAY YOU.
Single (12"): released on 4AD, Mar'84 by 4AD Records. Dist: Rough Trade

Single (7"): released on 4AD, Jul'85 by 4AD Records. Dist: Rough Trade

Colour Code

DANCE WITH THE TIMES.
Single (7"): released on Ryker, Feb'85 by Ryker Records. Dist: CBS Distribution

Single (12"): released on Ryker, Feb'85 by Ryker Records. Dist: CBS Distribution

Single (7"): released on Ryker, Mar'85 by Ryker Records. Dist: CBS Distribution

Single (12"): released on Ryker, Mar'85 by Ryker Records. Dist: CBS Distribution

I'VE HAD ENOUGH.
Tracks: / I've had enough / I've had enough (7" mix) / It takes two.
Notes: (Self-061 485 6702)
Single (12"): released on Zebra Int., Apr'87

Colour Dreams

COLOUR DREAMS 14 Gonzoid wig lifters from the mid-sixties (Various Artists).
Album: released on Antar, Feb'86 by Bam Caruso Records. Dist: Rough Trade, Revolver

Coloured Stone

BLACK ROCK FROM THE RED CENTRE.
Album: released on Hot, Sep'86 by Hot Records. Dist: Rough Trade, Cartel

Colourfield

DECEPTION.
Tracks: / Badlands / Running away / From dawn to distraction / Confession / Miss Texas 1967 / She / Heart of America / Digging it deep / Monkey in winter / Goodbye Sun Valley.
Compact disc: released on Chrysalis, Mar'87 by Chrysalis Records. Dist: CBS

Album: released on Chrysalis, Mar'87 by Chrysalis Records. Dist: CBS

Cassette: released on Chrysalis, Mar'87 by Chrysalis Records. Dist: CBS

RUNNING AWAY.
Tracks: / Running away / Digging it deep.
Single (7"): released on Chrysalis, Feb'87 by Chrysalis Records. Dist: CBS

Single (12"): released on Chrysalis, Feb'87 by Chrysalis Records. Dist: CBS

SHE.
Tracks: / She / Monkey in winter.
Single (7"): released on Chrysalis, Jul'87 by Chrysalis Records. Dist: CBS

THINGS COULD BE BEAUTIFUL.
Tracks: / Things could be beautiful / Frosty morning.
Single (7"): released on Chrysalis, Jan'86 by Chrysalis Records. Dist: CBS

Single (12"): released on Chrysalis, Jan'86 by Chrysalis Records. Dist: CBS

THINKING OF YOU.
Single (7"): released on Chrysalis, Jan'85 by Chrysalis Records. Dist: CBS Deleted '87.

Single (12"): released on Chrysalis, Jan'85 by Chrysalis Records. Dist: CBS

VIRGINS AND PHILISTINES.
Album: released on Chrysalis, Apr'85 by Chrysalis Records. Dist: CBS

Cassette: released on Chrysalis, Apr'85 by Chrysalis Records. Dist: CBS

Colourman

KICK UP RUMPUS.
Album: released on Creation, Jun'86 Dist: Rough Trade, Cartel

Colour Me Pop

DON'T STOP.
Single (7"): released on Waterfall, Aug'84 by Waterfall Records. Dist: Revolver, Cartel

GIRL WHO SHARES MY SHIRT.
Single (12"): released on American Phonogram, Nov'83 by PRT Records. Dist: PRT

Single (7"): released on American Phonogram, Feb'84 by PRT Records. Dist: PRT

Single (12"): released on American Phonograph International, Feb'84 Dist: Pinnacle

Colour of money

COLOUR OF MONEY, THE Original Soundtrack.
Compact disc: released on MCA, Jul'87 by MCA Records. Dist: Polygram, MCA

Colour Out Of Time

SHE SPINS.
Single (7"): released on Monsters In Orbit, Nov'82 Dist: Rough Trade Distribution

Colours Of The...

COLOURS OF THE BASTARD ART Various artists (Various Artists).
Album: released on Lost Moments, Jan'87 Dist: Backs, Cartel

Colour Vision

UNTIL TOMORROW.
Single (7"): released on Alien, Jan'80

Colt & Colby

SAVE YOUR LOVE.
Single (7"): released on Hollywood, Aug'84 by Hollywood Records. Dist: Pinnacle

Single (12"): released on Hollywood, Aug'84 by Hollywood Records. Dist: Pinnacle

Colter, Jessi

COUNTRY STAR IS BORN, A.
Cassette: released on RCA International, Feb'81

Coltrane, John

See also under Burrell, Kenny

AFRICA (Coltrane, John & Wilbur Harden).
Compact disc: released on RCA, Nov'86 by RCA Records. Dist: RCA, Roots, Swift, Wellard, Chris, I & B, Solomon & Peres Distribution

AFRICA AND INDIA.
Notes: N.Y.C. 1961 - 1963
Album: released on Crusader Jazz Masterworks, Jun'86 Dist: Jazz Music

AFRICA BASS.
Album: released on Impulse, Oct'85 by Impulse Records. Dist: MCA, Polygram

AFRICA BRASS (Coltrane,John Quartet).
Album: released on Jasmine, Jun'82 by Jasmine Records. Dist: PRT

Cassette: released on Jasmine, Jun'82 by Jasmine Records. Dist: PRT

AFRICA BRASS VOL.2.
Album: released on Jasmine, Sep'82 by Jasmine Records. Dist: PRT

Cassette: released on Jasmine, Sep'82 by Jasmine Records. Dist: PRT

AFRO BLUE IMPRESSIONS.
Double Album: released on Pablo (USA), May'82 by Pablo Records (USA). Dist: Wellard, Chris, IMS-Polygram, BMG

Double cassette: released on Pablo (USA), May'82 by Pablo Records (USA). Dist: Wellard, Chris, IMS-Polygram, BMG

AND THE JAZZ GIANTS.
Compact disc: released on London, Apr'87 by London Records. Dist: Polygram

ARTISTRY IN JAZZ Greatest hits.
Compact disc: released on JVC Fantasy (Japan), May'87

ART OF JOHN COLTRANE.
Album: by WEA Records. Dist: WEA

ASCENSION (Coltrane, John Orchestra).
Album: released on Jasmine, Aug'82 by Jasmine Records. Dist: PRT

Cassette: released on Jasmine, Aug'82 by Jasmine Records. Dist: PRT

BAGS AND TRANE (see Jackson, Milt) (Coltrane, John & Milt Jackson).

BALLADS (Coltrane,John Quartet).
Album: released on Jasmine, Aug'82 by Jasmine Records. Dist: PRT

Cassette: released on Jasmine, Aug'82 by Jasmine Records. Dist: PRT

BEST OF JOHN COLTRANE, THE.
Notes: From live concerts.
Compact disc: released on Pablo (USA), May'86 by Pablo Records (USA). Dist: Wellard, Chris, IMS-Polygram, BMG

BLUE TRAIN.
Tracks: / Blue train / Moments notice / Lcomotion / I'm old fashioned / Lazy bird / Blue train / Moment's notice / Locomotion / I'm old fashioned / Lazy bird.
Album: released on Blue Note, Apr'85 by EMI Records. Dist: EMI

Cassette: released on Blue Note, Apr'85 by EMI Records. Dist: EMI

Compact disc: released on Blue Note, Sep'87 by EMI Records. Dist: EMI. Estim retail price in Sep'87 was £11.99.

BRAZILIA (Coltrane,John Quartet).
Album: released on Blue Parrot, Jan'80 Dist: Cadillac, Swift, JSU

BYE BYE BLACKBIRD.
Album: released on Pablo Jazz (USA), Oct'84 by United Artists. Dist: Swift

BYE BYE BLACKBIRD.
Tracks: / Bye bye blackbird / Traneing in.
Compact disc: released on Pablo (USA), Apr'87 by Pablo Records (USA). Dist: Wellard, Chris, IMS-Polygram, BMG

Album: released on Crusader, Nov'85 by Crusader Records. Dist: Spartan

COLETRANE QUARTET AND QUINTET.
Album: released on Jazz Connoisseur, Apr'79 Dist: Jazz Horizons, Jazz Music, Swift, Wellard,

COLTRANE (Coltrane,John Quartet).
Album: released on Jasmine, Jun'82 by Jasmine Records. Dist: PRT

Cassette: released on Jasmine, Jun'82 by Jasmine Records. Dist: PRT

COLTRANE.
Compact disc: released on Vanguard (USA), Apr'86

COLTRANE TIME.
Album: released on Boplicity, Sep'83 by Boplicity Records. Dist: Ace Records, Pinnacle

COLTRANOLOGY VOLUME 1.
Album: released on Affinity, May'78 by Charly Records. Dist: Charly, Cadillac

COLTRANOLOGY VOLUME 2.
Album: by Charly Records. Dist: Charly, Cadillac

COPENHAGEN CONCERTS, THE (Coltrane,John Quartet).
Album: released on Ingo, May'81 Dist: Jazz Horizons, Jazz Music, Celtic Music

COUNTDOWN (Coltrane, John & Wilbur Harden).
Tracks: / Wells Fargo - take 1 / Wells Fargo - take 2 / E.F.F.P.H. / Countdown - take 1 / Countdown - take 2 / Rhodomagnetics - take 1 / Rhodomagnetics - take 2 / Snuffy / West 42nd street.
Notes: See also under **Harden,** Wilbur.
Compact disc: released on RCA, Mar'86 by RCA Records. Dist: RCA, Roots, Swift, Wellard, Chris, I & B, Solomon & Peres Distribution

Album: released on RCA, Mar'86 by RCA Records. Dist: RCA, Roots, Swift, Wellard, Chris, I & B, Solomon & Peres Distribution

Cassette: released on RCA, Mar'86 by RCA Records. Dist: RCA, Roots, Swift, Wellard, Chris, I & B, Solomon & Peres Distribution

COUNTDOWN: THE SAVOY SESSIONS.
Double Album: released on Savoy (USA), Mar'85 by Arista Records. Dist: Polygram, Swift

CREATION (Coltrane,John Quartet).
Album: released on Blue Parrot, Feb'77 Dist: Cadillac, Swift,

CRESCENT (Coltrane,John Quartet).
Album: released on Jasmine, Aug'82 by Jasmine Records. Dist: PRT

Cassette: released on Jasmine, Aug'82 by Jasmine Records. Dist: PRT

DAKAR.

Album: released on Prestige, Mar'82 by Prestige Records (USA). Dist: RCA, JSU, Swift

EUROPEAN TOUR, THE.
Album: released on Pablo, May'82 by Pablo Records. Dist: Wellard, Chris, IMS-Polygram, BMG

Cassette: released on Pablo, May'82 by Pablo Records. Dist: Wellard, Chris, IMS-Polygram, BMG

EXOTIC.
Notes: OCI - Oliver Crombie Imports
Compact disc: released on Dunhill Compact Classics (USA), Jan'86

EXPRESSIONS.
Album: released on Jasmine, Feb'84 by Jasmine Records. Dist: PRT

FIRST STEPS 1951/54/56.
Notes: Recorded in mono.
Album: released on Jazz Live, Oct'86

GIANT STEPS.
Album: released on Atlantic, Apr'87 by WEA Records. Dist: WEA

GOLD COAST.
Tracks: / Tanganyika strut / Dial Africa / Gold coast / B.J.
Album: released on RCA, Oct'85 by RCA Records. Dist: RCA, Roots, Swift, Wellard, Chris, I & B, Solomon & Peres Distribution

Cassette: released on RCA, Oct'85 by RCA Records. Dist: RCA, Roots, Swift, Wellard, Chris, I & B, Solomon & Peres Distribution

IMPRESSIONS.
Notes: N.Y.C. 1961-1962
Album: released on Crusader Jazz Masterworks, Jun'86 Dist: Jazz Music

Album: released on Jasmine, Aug'82 by Jasmine Records. Dist: PRT

Cassette: released on Jasmine, Aug'82 by Jasmine Records. Dist: PRT

IMPRESSIONS OF EUROPE.
Album: released on Ingo, Nov'82 Dist: Jazz Horizons, Jazz Music, Celtic Music

IMPULSE (Coltrane, John & John Hartman).
Tracks: / They say it's wonderful / Dedicated to you / My one and only love / Lush life / You are too beautiful / Autumn serenade.
Notes: See also under John Hartman.
Compact disc: released on MCA, Apr'87 by MCA Records. Dist: Polygram, MCA

JOHN COLTRANE COLLECTION, THE.
Cassette: released on Deja Vu, Aug'85 by Deja Vu Records. Dist: Counterpoint Distribution, Record Services Distribution (Ireland)

JOHN COLTRANE & DUKE ELLINGTON (Coltrane, John & Duke Ellington).
Album: released on Jasmine, Jun'82 by Jasmine Records. Dist: Counterpoint, Taylor, H.R., Wellard, Chris, Swift, Cadillac

Cassette: released on Jasmine, Jun'82 by Jasmine Records. Dist: Counterpoint, Taylor, H.R., Wellard, Chris, Swift, Cadillac

JOHN COLTRANE LIVE AT THE VILLAGE VANGUARD.
Album: released on Jasmine, Jun'82 by Jasmine Records. Dist: PRT

Cassette: released on Jasmine, Jun'82 by Jasmine Records. Dist: PRT

JOHN COLTRANE/RAY DRAPER (Coltrane, John/Ray Draper).
Album: released on Jazz Reactivation, Jul'82 Dist: PRT

JOHN COLTRANE VOLUME 2.
Album: released on Charly, May'79 by Charly Records. Dist: Charly, Cadillac

KULA SE' MAMA.
Album: released on Jasmine, Sep'82 by Jasmine Records. Dist: PRT

Cassette: released on Jasmine, Sep'82 by Jasmine Records. Dist: PRT

LIVE (Coltrane & Miles Quintet).
Notes: For full information see under: MILES & COLTRANE QUINTET.

LIVE 1962.
Double Album: released on Musidisc (France), Aug'83 Dist: Discovery Distribution, Swift Distribution

LIVE AT BIRDLAND.
Tracks: / My favourite things / Body and soul / Mr. P.C. / Miles mode.
Notes: Featuring Eric Dolphy. A Vee Jay recording. An Affinity release from Charly Records International APS
Compact disc: released on Charly, Feb'87 by Charly Records. Dist: Charly, Cadillac

---

LIVE AT BIRDLAND.
Album: released on Affinity, Feb'82 by Charly Records. Dist: Charly, Cadillac

Album: released on Jasmine, Jun'82 by Jasmine Records. Dist: PRT

LIVE AT THE VILLAGE VANGUARD AGAIN.
Album: released on Jasmine, Jun'82 by Jasmine Records. Dist: PRT

Cassette: released on Jasmine, Jun'82 by Jasmine Records. Dist: PRT

LIVE IN STOCKHOLM - 1963.
Tracks: / Mr. P.C. / Traneing in / Spiritual / I want to talk about you.
Compact disc: released on Charly, Dec'86 by Charly Records. Dist: Charly, Cadillac

LOVE SUPREME, A.
Album: released on Impulse, Feb'82 by Impulse Records. Dist: MCA, Polygram

Cassette: released on Impulse, Feb'82 by Impulse Records. Dist: MCA, Polygram

Album: released on Jul'82 Dist: Jazz Horizons, Jazz Music, Celtic Music

Album: released on Impulse, Oct'85 by Impulse Records. Dist: MCA, Polygram

Notes: Live in Europe 1965.
Album: released on Crusader Jazz Masterworks, Jun'86 Dist: Jazz Music

Compact disc: released on Impulse, Feb'87 by Impulse Records. Dist: MCA, Polygram

LUSH LIFE.
Compact disc: released on JVC Fantasy (Japan), Nov'86

Compact disc: released on Carrere, Apr'87 by Carrere Records. Dist: PRT, Spartan

MEDITATIONS.
Album: released on Jasmine, Jan'85 by Jasmine Records. Dist: Counterpoint, Taylor, H.R., Wellard, Chris, Swift, Cadillac

MORE LASTING THAN BRONZE.
Double Album: released on Prestige, Feb'81 by Prestige Records (USA). Dist: RCA, Swift

Album: released on Prestige (USA), May'84

MY FAVOURITE THINGS.
Notes: N.J.F. 1963 and Europe 1962.
Compact disc: released on Atlantic Jazz, Jul'87 by WEA Records. Dist: WEA

NEW THING AT NEWPORT.
Album: released on Jasmine, Jun'82 by Jasmine Records. Dist: PRT

Cassette: released on Jasmine, Jun'82 by Jasmine Records. Dist: PRT

NEW THING AT NEWPORT (see Shepp, Archie) (Coltrane, John & Archie Shepp).

ONE, TWO & FOUR.
Double Album: released on Vogue Jazz (France), May'83

PARIS CONCERT, THE.
Album: released on Pablo, May'82 by Pablo Records. Dist: Wellard, Chris, IMS-Polygram, BMG

Cassette: released on Pablo, May'82 by Pablo Records. Dist: Wellard, Chris, IMS-Polygram, BMG

RARE.
Album: released on Duke, Jun'86 by Melodisc Records. Dist: Jazz Horizons, Jazz Music, Celtic Music, J3U, Swift

RARE JOHN COLTRANE QUARTET (Coltrane, John Quartet).
Album: released on Duke, Oct'82 by Melodisc Records. Dist: Jazz Horizons, Jazz Music, Celtic Music, JSU, Swift

REFLECTIONS.
Album: released on Audio Fidelity, Oct'82 Dist: PRT

SAVOY SESSIONS (Coltrane, John & Wilbur Harden).
Double Album: released on Savoy, Sep'78

SETTIN' THE PACE.
Album: released on Prestive (USA), Feb'84

SOULTRANE.
Compact disc: released on JVC Fantasy (Japan), Apr'86

Compact disc: released on Carrere, Apr'87 by Carrere Records. Dist: PRT, Spartan

STANDARD COLTRANE.

Album:

UNISSUED CONCERT IN GERMANY 1963 PART 1 (Coltrane, John Quartet).
Cassette: released on Jazz Galore, Sep'81 Dist: Jazz Music, Cadillac.

Columbia Brothers
YOU'RE LEAVING.
Single (7"): released on Hotel, May'80 Dist: Pinnacle

Columbia Orchestra
BEST OF SCREEN MUSIC.
Album: released on Denon, Mar'82 by Denon Records. Dist: Harmonia Mundi

LET'S DANCE VOL.1.
Compact disc: released on Denon, Apr'85 by Denon Records. Dist: Harmonia Mundi

LET'S DANCE VOLUME 1.
Compact disc: by Denon Records. Dist: Harmonia Mundi

LET'S DANCE VOLUME 2.
Compact disc: by Denon Records. Dist: Harmonia Mundi

Columbo, Russ
ON THE AIR 1933-4.
Album: released on Totem, May'79 Dist: Jazz Music, Projection, Swift

RUSS COLUMBO.
Album: released on Sandy Hook, Jan'79

RUSS COLUMBO 1931/1 & 1934.
Album: released on Sandy Hook, Apr'79

Colyer, Ken
CONCERT VOL.1.
Album: released on Wam, May'87

DECCA YEARS, VOL.2 (1955-59) (THE) (Colyer, Ken Jazzmen).
Tracks: / Perdido street blues / Dippermouth Blues / Heliotrope bouquet / Beale Street blues / Fig leaf rag / Gravier street blues / Canal street blues / World is waiting for the sunrise (The) / Girls go crazy, The / Entertainer, The / If I ever cease to love / Sensation / Kinklets / Maryland, my Maryland.
Album: released on Lake, Dec'86 by Fellside Recordings. Dist: Jazz Music, Fellside

GREAT REVIVAL, THE.
Album: released on Esquire, May'81 by Titan International Productions. Dist: Jazz Music, Cadillac Music, Swift, Wellard, Chris, Backs, Rough Trade, Revolver, Nine Mile

IN NEW ORLEANS 1953.
Album: released on Dawn Club, May'79 Dist: Cadillac, Swift,

KEN COLYER IN NEW ORLEANS - THE 1953 RECORDINGS.
Album: released on Dawn Club, Dec'86 Dist: Cadillac, Swift,

KEN COLYER & WHITE EAGLE NEW ORLEANS BAND VOL 2 (Colyer, Ken & White Eagle New Orleans Band).
Album: Deleted May'87.

KEN COYLER AT THE THAMES HOTEL (Colyer, Ken Jazzmen).
Album: by President Records. Dist: Jazz Music, Swift, President Distribution

LIVE AT THE 100 CLUB (Colyer, Ken Jazzmen).
Notes: Recorded in mono.
Album: released on GHB, Jun'86 Dist: Jazz Music, Swift

LIVE AT THE DANCING SLIPPER (Colyer, Ken Jazzmen).
Album: released on VJM, Dec'84 by Wellard. Dist: Wellard, Chris Distribution

ONE FOR MY BABY (Colyer, Ken Jazzmen).
Album: released on Joy, May'74 by President Records. Dist: Jazz Music, Swift, President Distribution

RAGTIME REVISITED (Colyer, Ken Jazzmen).
Album: released on Joy, May'82 by President Records. Dist: Jazz Music, Swift, President Distribution

RAREST KEN COYLER, THE.
Album: released on Nola, Apr'79 Dist: JSU, Jazz Music, Cadillac, Chris Wellard

SENSATION (Colyer, Ken Jazzmen).
Album: released on Lake, May'85 by Fellside Recordings. Dist: Jazz Music, Fellside

SPIRITUALS VOL.1 (Colyer, Ken Jazzmen).

Album: released on Joy, May'74 by President Records. Dist: Jazz Music, Swift, President Distribution

SPIRITUALS VOL.2 (Colyer, Ken Jazzmen).
Album: released on Joy, May'74 by President Records. Dist: Jazz Music, Swift, President Distribution

SWINGING AND SINGING.
Album: released on Happy Bird (Germany), Jul'83 Dist: Polygram, IMS

Cassette: released on Happy Bird (Germany), Jul'83 Dist: Polygram, IMS

WATCH THAT DIRTY TONE OF YOURS
There are ladies present (Colyer, Ken Jazzmen).
Album: released on Joy, May'74 by President Records. Dist: Jazz Music, Swift, President Distribution

Colyer, Kevin
OUT OF NOWHERE (Colyer, Kevin Jazzmen).
Album: released on Ken Colyer, Jul'87

Comateens
DEAL WITH IT.
Album: released on Virgin, Sep'84 by Virgin Records. Dist: EMI, Virgin Distribution

Cassette: released on Virgin, Sep'84 by Virgin Records. Dist: EMI, Virgin

RESIST HER.
Single (7"): released on Virgin, Jul'84 by Virgin Records. Dist: EMI, Virgin .

Combat 84
ORDERS OF THE DAY.
Single (7"): released on Victory, Dec'82

RAPIST.
Single (7"): released on Victory, Aug'83

SEND IN THE MARINES.
Album: released on Victory, Oct'83

Combelle, Alix
1937-40.
Album: released on Pathe Marconi(France), Sep'84

Combe Passe
MAMA TOLD HER.
Single (7"): released on Crazy Viking, Feb'83 by Crazy Vikings Records. Dist: Pinnacle

Single (12"): released on Crazy Viking, Feb'83 by Crazy Vikings Records. Dist: Pinnacle

Comber Quintette
COMING HOME.
Album: by Pilgrim Records. Dist: Rough Trade, Cartel

Combined Calvary
OLD COMRADES.
Album: released on Parade, Jan'81 Dist: MSD

Comboland
COMBOLAND (Various Artists).
Album: released on Spindrift, Apr'86 Dist: Roots

Come Alive
ON MY WAY.
Single (7"): released on Stinkfoot, Dec'84 by Stinkfoot Records. Dist: Pinnacle

Come all you bold miners
COME ALL YOU BOLD MINERS Various artists (Various Artists).
Cassette: released on Folktracks, Nov'79 by Folktracks Cassettes. Dist: Folktracks

Comedian Harmonists
COMEDIAN HARMONISTS various artists (Various Artists).
Album: released on EMI (Germany), '83 by EMI Records. Dist: Conifer

COMEDIAN HARMONISTS VOL.2 (Various Artists).
Album: released on EMI (Germany), '83 by EMI Records. Dist: Conifer

Comedians.,
COMEDIANS SING, THE various artists (Various original artists).
Album: released on BBC, Oct'76 by BBC Records & Tapes. Dist: EMI, PRT,

Comedy Spectacular

COMEDY SPECTACULAR various artists (Various original artists).
Album: released on BBC, Oct'76 by BBC Records & Tapes. Dist: EMI, PRT.

Come Josephine...

COME JOSEPHINE IN MY FLYING MACHINE (Various Artists).
Tracks: / Oceana Roll / Girl on the magazine cover / Hello, Frisco / On the 5.15 / He'd have to get under, get out and get under... / Come, Josephine, in my flying machine / Take your girlie to the movies / Everybody wants a key to my cellar / Argentines, the Portugese and the Greeks, The / Mr Radio man (tell my mammy to come back home) / Alabamy bound / All alone / Little white house (at the end of Honeymoon Lane) (The) / Lindbergh (the eagle of the USA) / Henry's made a lady out of Lizzie / If I had a talking picture of you.
Album: released on New World (USA), Feb'87 by New World Records (USA). Dist: Conifer

Come On

GUITAR PARTY.
Single (7"): released on Albion, May'84 by Albion Records. Dist: Spartan, Pinnacle

HOUSEWIVES PLAY TENNIS.
Single (7"): released on Aura, Mar'81 by Hollywood Nites Distribution. Dist: Pinnacle

Come Sunday

COME SUNDAY Various artists (Various Artists).
Cassette: released on Ampro Cassettes, Sep'81

Come To The Highlands

COME TO THE HIGHLANDS - VOL 1 (Various Artists).
Notes: Argo Cameron, Bobby Coghill, Ina Miller, Tommy Darky etc.
Cassette: released on Ross, Jan'87 by Ross Records. Dist: Ross Distribution, Roots Distribution

COME TO THE HIGHLANDS - VOL 2 (Various Artists).
Notes: The Moray Players, Turriff & District Pipe Band, Ina Miller etc.
Cassette: released on Ross, Jan'86 by Ross Records. Dist: Ross Distribution, Roots Distribution

COME TO THE HIGHLANDS - VOL 3 (Various Artists).
Cassette: released on Ross, Jan'86 by Ross Records. Dist: Ross Distribution, Roots Distribution

Comfort & Joy

JINGLE BELLE RAP.
Tracks: / Jingle belle rap / It's xmas.
Single (7"): released on DMC-Arista, Dec'86 by Ariola Records. Dist: RCA, Ariola

Single (12"): released on DMC-Arista, Dec'86 by Ariola Records. Dist: RCA, Ariola

Comhaltas Champions

COMHALTAS CHAMPIONS ON TOUR various artists (Various Artists).
Album: released on Comhaltas, Jun'79 Dist: Celtic Music, Jazz Music

Comic Cuts

COMIC CUTS various artists (Various Artists).
Album: released on Lamborghini, Nov'84 by Lamborghini Records. Dist: PRT

Cassette: released on Lamborghini, Nov'84 by Lamborghini Records. Dist: PRT

Album: released on Old Bean, May'85 Dist: Jazz Music

Cassette: released on Old Bean, May'85 Dist: Jazz Music

Comic Relief

UTTERLY UTTERLY LIVE.
Album: released on WEA, May'86 by WEA Records. Dist: WEA

Cassette: released on WEA, May'86 by WEA Records. Dist: WEA

Comic Strip

COMIC STRIP various artists (Various Artists).
Album: released on Springtime, Nov'81 by Springtime Records. Dist: Island Distribution, Polygram Distribution

Cassette: released on Springtime, Nov'81 by Springtime Records. Dist: Island Distribution, Polygram Distribution

Coming Of Arthur

COMING OF ARTHUR various artists (Various Artists).

Cassette: released on Anvil, Jan'81 Dist: Anvil

Coming Of The Grail

COMING OF THE GRAIL various artists (Various Artists).
Cassette: released on Anvil, Jan'81 Dist: Anvil

Commander Cody

CODY RETURNS FROM OUTER SPACE (Commander Cody & His Lost Planet Airmen).
Album: released on Edsel, Mar'87 by Demon Records. Dist: Pinnacle, Jazz Music, Projection

LET'S ROCK.
Tracks: / Let's rock / Rockin' over China / Midnight on the strand / Do you mind? / Angel got married / Truckstop at the end of the world / One more ride / Your cash ain't nothing but trash / Rockabilly funeral / Transfusion / Home of rock'n'roll.
Album: released on Special Delivery, May'87 Dist: Nine Mile, Cartel

Cassette: released on Special Delivery, May'87 Dist: Nine Mile, Cartel

Album: released on Special Delivery, Aug'87 Dist: Nine Mile, Cartel

VERY BEST OF COMMANDER CODY AND HIS LOST PLANET AIRMEN, THE (Commander Cody & His Lost Planet Airmen).
Tracks: / Back to Tennessee / Wine do yer stuff / Seeds and stems (again) / Daddy's gonna treat you right / Family Bible / Lost in the ozone / Hot rod Lincoln / Beat me daddy eight to the bar / Truckstop rock / Truck drivin' man / It should've been me / Watch my .38 / Everybody's doin' it / Rock that boogie / Smoke! smoke! smoke!(that cigarette) / Honeysuckle Honey / Sunset on the sage (live) / Cryin' time (live).
Album: released on See For Miles, Apr'86 by See For Miles Records. Dist: Pinnacle

Command Performance

COMMAND PERFORMANCE various artists (Various original artists).
Album: released on Hallmark, Feb'77 by Pickwick Records. Dist: Pickwick Distribution, PRT, Taylors

Cassette: released on Hallmark, Feb'77 by Pickwick Records. Dist: Pickwick Distribution, PRT, Taylors

NIGHT ON THE TOWN Command performance, Vol.2 (Various Artists).
Album: released on Hallmark, Apr'81 by Pickwick Records. Dist: Pickwick Distribution, PRT, Taylors

Cassette: released on RCA/Camden, Apr'81

Commentators

N-N-NINETEEN NOT OUT.
Single (7"): released on WEA, Jun'85 by WEA Records. Dist: WEA

Single (12"): released on WEA, Jun'85 by WEA Records. Dist: WEA

Commercial Break

COMMERCIAL BREAK(TV ADVERTS) various orchestras (Various Orchestras).
Cassette: released on CBS, Jun'78 by CBS Records. Dist: CBS

COMMERCIAL BREAK VOL.2 various artists (Various Artists).
Album: released on CBS, Oct'81 by CBS Records. Dist: CBS

Cassette: released on CBS, Oct'81 by CBS Records. Dist: CBS

Commercial Classics

COMMERCIAL CLASSICS various artists (Various Artists).
Album: released on Decca, Oct'80 by Decca Records. Dist: Polygram

Cassette: released on Decca, Oct'80 by Decca Records. Dist: Polygram

Committee

OPEN YOUR EYES.
Single (12"): released on Fire, Aug'85 by Twist and Shout Music. Dist: Nine Mile, Rough Trade, Cartel

Commodores

13.
Album: released on Motown, Sep'83 by Motown Records. Dist: BMG Distribution

Cassette: released on Motown, Sep'83 by Motown Records. Dist: BMG Distribution

14 GREATEST HITS.
Compact disc: released on Motown, May'84 by Motown Records. Dist: BMG Distribution

2 CLASSIC ALBUMS Natural high/Midnight magic.
Tracks: / Fire girl / X-rated movie / Flying high / Three times a lady / Such a woman / Say yeah / I like what you do / Visions / Gettin' it / Midnight magic / You're special / Still / Wonderland / Sexy lady / Lovin' you / Sail on / 12.01 A.M. - reprise.
Compact disc: released on Motown, Oct'86 by Motown Records. Dist: BMG Distribution

ALL THE GREAT LOVE SONGS.
Compact disc: by Motown Records. Dist: BMG Distribution

ANIMAL INSTINCT.
Single (7"): released on Motown, Apr'84 by Motown Records. Dist: BMG Distribution

Single (12"): released on Motown, Apr'84 by Motown Records. Dist: BMG Distribution

BEST OF THE COMMODORES, THE.
Album: released on Telstar, Nov'85 by Telstar Records. Dist: RCA Distribution

Cassette: released on Telstar, Nov'85 by Telstar Records. Dist: RCA Distribution

BRICK HOUSE.
Single (7"): released on Motown, Oct'81 by Motown Records. Dist: BMG Distribution

CAUGHT IN THE ACT.
Album: released on Motown, Apr'82 by Motown Records. Dist: BMG Distribution

Cassette: released on Motown, Apr'82 by Motown Records. Dist: BMG Distribution

COMPACT COMMAND PERFORMANCES 14 greatest hits.
Compact disc: released on Motown, '86 by Motown Records. Dist: BMG Distribution

EASY.
Single (7"): released on Motown, Oct'81 by Motown Records. Dist: BMG Distribution

FLIPHITS 4 track cassettes ep.
Cassette: released on Motown, Jul'83 by Motown Records. Dist: BMG Distribution

GOIN' TO THE BANK.
Tracks: / Goin' to the bank / Serious love.
Single (7"): released on Polydor, Oct'86 by Polydor Records. Dist: Polygram, Polydor

Single (12"): released on Polydor, Oct'86 by Polydor Records. Dist: Polygram, Polydor
Cat. no: **POSPX 826**

GREATISTS HITS.
Album: released on Motown, Oct'81 by Motown Records. Dist: BMG Distribution

Cassette: released on Motown, Oct'81 by Motown Records. Dist: BMG Distribution

HOT ON THE TRACKS/IN THE POCKET 2 Classic albums.
Tracks: / Let's get started / Girl I think the world about you / High on sunshine / Just to be close to you / Fancy dancer / Come inside / Thumpin' music / Captain Quickdraw / Can't let you tease me / Lady (you bring me up) / Saturday night / Keep on taking me higher / Oh no / Why you wanna try me / This love / Been lovin' you / Lucy.
Compact disc: released on Motown, Jul'87 by Motown Records. Dist: BMG Distribution

IN THE POCKET.
Album: released on Motown, Oct'81 by Motown Records. Dist: BMG Distribution

Cassette: released on Motown, Oct'81 by Motown Records. Dist: BMG Distribution

JANET.
Single (7"): released on Motown, Aug'85 by Motown Records. Dist: BMG Distribution

Single (12"): released on Motown, Aug'85 by Motown Records. Dist: BMG Distribution

JESUS IS LOVE.
Single (7"): released on Motown, Oct'81 by Motown Records. Dist: BMG Distribution

LADY (YOU BRING ME UP).
Single (7"): released on Motown, Oct'81 by Motown Records. Dist: BMG Distribution

Single (12"): released on Motown, Oct'81 by Motown Records. Dist: BMG Distribution

LIVE.
Tracks: / Won't you come dance with me / Slippery when wet / Come inside / Come inside / Just to be close to you / Zoom / Easy / Funny feelings / Fancy dancer / Sweet love / I feel sanctified / Brick house / Too hot ta trot.
Double Album: released on Motown, Jun'86 by Motown Records. Dist: BMG Distribution

Cassette: released on Motown, Jun'86 by Motown Records. Dist: BMG Distribution

Album: released on Motown, Oct'81 by Motown Records. Dist: BMG Distribution

Cassette: released on Motown, Oct'81 by Motown Records. Dist: BMG Distribution

LOVE SONGS.
Album: released on K-Tel, Jul'82 by K-Tel Records. Dist: Record Merchandisers Distribution, Taylors, Terry Blood Distribution, Wynd-Up Distribution, Relay Distribution, Pickwick Distribution, Solomon & Peres Distribution, Polygram

Cassette: released on K-Tel, Jul'82 by K-Tel Records. Dist: Record Merchandisers Distribution, Taylors, Terry Blood Distribution, Wynd-Up Distribution, Relay Distribution, Pickwick Distribution, Solomon & Peres Distribution, Polygram

LUCY.
Single (7"): released on Motown, Oct'82 by Motown Records. Dist: BMG Distribution

Single (12"): released on Motown, Oct'82 by Motown Records. Dist: BMG Distribution

MACHINE GUN.
Album: released on Motown, Oct'81 by Motown Records. Dist: BMG Distribution

Cassette: released on Motown, Oct'81 by Motown Records. Dist: BMG Distribution

MIDNIGHT MAGIC.
Album: released on Motown, Oct'81 by Motown Records. Dist: BMG Distribution

Cassette: released on Motown, Oct'81 by Motown Records. Dist: BMG Distribution

Album: released on Motown, May'85 by Motown Records. Dist: BMG Distribution

Cassette: released on Motown, May'85 by Motown Records. Dist: BMG Distribution

MOVIN' ON.
Album: released on Motown, Oct'81 by Motown Records. Dist: BMG Distribution

Cassette: released on Motown, Oct'81 by Motown Records. Dist: BMG Distribution

NATURAL HIGH.
Album: released on Motown, Nov'82 by Motown Records. Dist: BMG Distribution

Cassette: released on Motown, Nov'82 by Motown Records. Dist: BMG Distribution

Album: released on Motown, Feb'85 by Motown Records. Dist: BMG Distribution

Cassette: released on Motown, Feb'85 by Motown Records. Dist: BMG Distribution

GREAT LOVE SONGS BY LIONEL RICHIE.
Tracks: / Just to be close to you / Sweet love / Easy / Three times a lady / Still / Endless love / Sail on / Oh no / Lucy / Girl I think the world about you.
Album: released on Motown, Jun'86 by Motown Records. Dist: BMG Distribution

Cassette: released on Motown, Jun'86 by Motown Records. Dist: BMG Distribution

HEROES.
Album: released on Motown, Oct'81 by Motown Records. Dist: BMG Distribution

Cassette: released on Motown, Oct'81 by Motown Records. Dist: BMG Distribution

Single (7"): released on Motown, Oct'86 by Motown Records. Dist: BMG Distribution

HOT ON THE TRACKS.
Album: released on Motown, Oct'82 by Motown Records. Dist: BMG Distribution

Cassette: released on Motown, Oct'82 by Motown Records. Dist: BMG Distribution

Compact disc: released on Motown, Feb'85 by Motown Records. Dist: BMG Distribution

NIGHTSHIFT.
Compact disc: by Motown Records. Dist: BMG Distribution

Single (7"): released on Motown, Jan'85 by Motown Records. Dist: BMG Distribution

Single (12"): released on Motown, Jan'85 by Motown Records. Dist: BMG Distribution

OH NO.
Single (7"): released on Motown, Oct'81 by Motown Records. Dist: BMG Distribution

OLD FASHIONED LOVE.
Single (7"): released on Motown, Oct'81 by Motown Records. Dist: BMG Distribution

ONLY YOU.
Single (7"): released on Motown, Sep'83 by Motown Records. Dist: BMG Distribution

REACH HIGH.
Single (7"): released on Motown, Feb'83 by Motown Records. Dist: BMG Distribution

Single (12"): released on Motown, Feb'83 by Motown Records. Dist: BMG Distribution

RISE UP.
Compact disc: released on Blue Moon, May'87

Dist: Magnum Music Group Ltd, PRT, Spartan

Album: released on Blue Moon, Apr'87 Dist: Magnum Music Group Ltd, PRT, Spartan

Cassette: released on Blue Moon, Apr'87 Dist: Magnum Music Group Ltd, PRT, Spartan

Album: released on Perfect, Aug'87

Cassette: released on Perfect, Aug'87

SAIL ON.
Single (7"): released on Motown, Oct'81 by Motown Records. Dist: BMG Distribution

STILL.
Single (7"): released on Motown, Oct'81 by Motown Records. Dist: BMG Distribution

THERE'S A SONG IN MY HEART.
Album: released on Platinum (W.Germany), Oct'85 Dist: Mainline

Cassette: released on Platinum (W.Germany), Oct'85 Dist: Mainline

THREE TIMES A LADY.
Single (7"): released on Motown, Apr'83 by Motown Records. Dist: BMG Distribution

TURN OFF THE LIGHTS.
Single (7"): released on Motown, Nov'83 by Motown Records. Dist: BMG Distribution

Single (12"): released on Motown, Nov'83 by Motown Records. Dist: BMG Distribution

UNITED.
Tracks: / Goin' to the bank / Take it from me / United:love / Can't dance all night / You're the only woman I need / Land of the dreamer / Talk to me / I wanna rock you / Let's apologise / Serious love.
Notes: Executive producer: Dennis Lambert (Nightshift). Contains the singles 'going to the bank' and 'United love'. Supported by music press advertising and point of sale.
Album: released on Polydor, Nov'86 by Polydor Records. Dist: Polygram, Polydor

Cassette: released on Polydor, Nov'86 by Polydor Records. Dist: Polygram, Polydor

Compact disc: by Polydor Records. Dist: Polygram, Polydor

UNITED IN LOVE.
Tracks: / United in love / Talk to me / Going to the bank (credit card mix).
Single (7"): released on Polydor, May'87 by Polydor Records. Dist: Polygram, Polydor

Single (12"): released on Polydor, May'87 by Polydor Records. Dist: Polygram, Polydor

WHY YOU WANNA TRY ME.
Single (7"): released on Motown, Apr'82 by Motown Records. Dist: BMG Distribution

Single (12"): released on Motown, Apr'82 by Motown Records. Dist: BMG Distribution

WONDERLAND.
Single (7"): released on Motown, Oct'81 by Motown Records. Dist: BMG Distribution

ZOOM.
Album: released on Motown, May'84 by Motown Records. Dist: BMG Distribution

Cassette: released on Motown, May'84 by Motown Records. Dist: BMG Distribution

Single (7"): released on Motown, Oct'81 by Motown Records. Dist: BMG Distribution

Common Knowledge

VICTORIA.
Single (7"): released on Mercury, Jan'85 by Phonogram Records. Dist: Polygram Distribution

Communal Drop

FANATICS.
Single (12"): released on WRTR, May'85 Dist: Red Rhino, Cartel

Communards

COMMUNARDS.
Tracks: / Don't leave me this way / La dolarosa / Disenchanted / Reprise / So cold the night / You are my world / Lover man / Don't slip away / Heaven's above / Forbidden love / Breadline Britain* / Disenchanted - dance mix*.
Notes: Deluxe gatefold sleeve and inner lyric bag on all initial shipments. This LP has been direct metal cut from the finest sound quality. This is the Communards(Jimmy Somerville and Richard Coles) debut LP. Featuring the hits "Disenchanted"You are my world" and the single "Don't leave me this way.
Compact disc: released on London, Jul'86 by London Records. Dist: Polygram

Album: released on London, Jul'86 by London Records. Dist: Polygram

Cassette: released on London, Jul'86 by London Records. Dist: Polygram

DISENCHANTED.
Tracks: / Disenchanted / Johnny verso / Annie*.
Single (7"): released on London, May'86 by London Records. Dist: Polygram

Single (12"): released on London, May'86 by London Records. Dist: Polygram

DON'T LEAVE ME THIS WAY.
Tracks: / Don't leave me this way / Sanctified.
Single (7"): released on London, Aug'86 by London Records. Dist: Polygram

Single (12"): released on London, Aug'86 by London Records. Dist: Polygram

NIGHT, THE.
Single (7"): released on London, Nov'86 by London Records. Dist: Polygram

Single (12"): released on London, Nov'86 by London Records. Dist: Polygram

SO COLD THE NIGHT Remix.
Tracks: / Multimix featuring don't leave me this way (The) / So cold the night / Disenchanted.
Single (12"): released on London, Dec'86 by London Records. Dist: Polygram

TOMMORROW.
Tracks: / I just want let you know.
Single (7"): released on London, Aug'87 by London Records. Dist: Polygram

Single (12"): released on London, Aug'87 by London Records. Dist: Polygram

VIDEO SINGLES, THE.
Video-cassette (VHS): released on Polygram, Jan'87 by Polygram Records. Dist: Polygram

YOU ARE MY WORLD.
Tracks: / You are my world / Judgement day / Czardaz.
Notes: Czardaz is only available on 12" version.
Single (7"): released on London, Feb'87 by London Records. Dist: Polygram

Single (12"): released on London, Feb'87 by London Records. Dist: Polygram

Single (7"): released on London, Sep'85 by London Records. Dist: Polygram

Single (12"): released on London, Sep'85 by London Records. Dist: Polygram

Communion

COMMUNION various artists (Various Artists).
Album: released on Birdwing, May'82 by Word Records. Dist: Word Distribution

Cassette: released on Birdwing, May'82 by Word Records. Dist: Word Distribution

Communion Continued

COMMUNION CONTINUED.
Album: released on Birdwing, May'82 by Word Records. Dist: Word Distribution

Cassette: released on Birdwing, May'82 by Word Records. Dist: Word Distribution

Como, Perry

16 MILLION HITS.
Album: released on RCA (Germany), Jul'83

Cassette: released on RCA (Germany), Jul'83

1931-45.
Album: released on MCA, Dec'84 by MCA Records. Dist: Polygram, MCA

Cassette: released on MCA, Dec'84 by MCA Records. Dist: Polygram, MCA

20 GREATEST HITS vol.11.
Album: released on RCA International, '84

Cassette: released on RCA International, '84

20 GREATEST HITS vol 1.
Album: released on RCA International, '84

Cassette: released on RCA International, '84

AND I LOVE YOU SO.
Single (7"): released on RCA Golden Grooves, Jul'81 by RCA Records. Dist: RCA

AND I LOVE YOU SO.
Album: released on RCA, '84 by RCA Records. Dist: RCA, Roots, Swift, Wellard, Chris, I & B, Solomon & Peres Distribution

Cassette: released on RCA, '84 by RCA Records. Dist: RCA, Roots, Swift, Wellard, Chris, I & B, Solomon & Peres Distribution

AND I LOVE YOU SO.
Tracks: / And I love you so / Killing me softly with her song / For the good times / Aubrey / Sing / I want to give (ahora que soy libro) / Tie a yellow ribbon / I thought about you / It all seems to fall into line / I believe in music.
Album: released on RCA/Camden, Sep'86

Cassette: released on RCA/Camden, Sep'86

BEST OF PERRY COMO, THE.
Album: released on RCA/Brazil, Jan'84

Cassette: released on RCA/Brazil, Jan'84

BEST OF TIMES (THE).
Tracks: / All I do is dream of you / Gigi / Way you look tonight, The / What kind of fool am I? / They can't take that away from me / Red sails in the sunset / Hello, young lovers / I had the craziest dream / Try to remember / Father of girls, The / Moon river / Begin the beguine / Song on the sand (La da da da) / It's easy to remember / Best of times, The / Best of times, The (s) / Song on the sand - la da da da / How to handle a woman / Days of wine and roses / It had to be you.
Compact disc: released on RCA, '86 by RCA Records. Dist: RCA, Roots, Swift, Wellard, Chris, I & B, Solomon & Peres Distribution

Album: released on RCA, Nov'86 by RCA Records. Dist: RCA, Roots, Swift, Wellard, Chris, I & B, Solomon & Peres Distribution

Cassette: released on RCA, Nov'86 by RCA Records. Dist: RCA, Roots, Swift, Wellard, Chris, I & B, Solomon & Peres Distribution

Single (7"): released on RCA, Jun'86 by RCA Records. Dist: RCA, Roots, Swift, Wellard, Chris, I & B, Solomon & Peres Distribution

Single (12"): released on RCA, Jun'86 by RCA Records. Dist: RCA, Roots, Swift, Wellard, Chris, I & B, Solomon & Peres Distribution

CHRISTMAS DREAM.
Single (7"): released on RCA, Nov'84 by RCA Records. Dist: RCA, Roots, Swift, Wellard, Chris, I & B, Solomon & Peres Distribution

CHRISTMAS GREETINGS FROM PERRY COMO.
Cassette: released on Pickwick, Oct'79 by Pickwick Records. Dist: Pickwick Distribution, Prism Leisure

CHRISTMAS GREETINGS FROM.
Album: released on Pickwick, Oct'79 by Pickwick Records. Dist: Pickwick Distribution, Prism Leisure Distribution,

COMO'S GOLDEN HITS.
Album:

Cassette: released on RCA/Camden, '74

ESPECIALLY FOR YOU.
Album: released on RCA International (USA), Apr'80 by RCA Records. Dist: RCA

Cassette: released on RCA International (USA), Apr'80 by RCA Records. Dist: RCA

FLY ME TO THE MOON.
Album: released on RCA/Camden, Aug'75

FOR THE GOOD TIMES.
Album: released on Telstar, Nov'83 by Telstar Records. Dist: RCA Distribution

Cassette: released on Telstar, Nov'83 by Telstar Records. Dist: RCA Distribution

HERE IS....
Double Album:

HERE IS... vol.2.
: released on Victor, '73

IT'S IMPOSSIBLE.
Tracks: / El condor pasa / Close to you - they long to be / I think I love you / We've only just begun / It's impossible (single) / It's impossible / And I love you so (single) / Raindrops keep fallin' on my head / Something / Snowbird / House is not a home, A / Everybody is looking for an answer.
Notes: (P) 1971 & (C) Original Sound Recordings owned by RCA Records Ltd.
Single (7"): released on Old Gold, Oct'86 by Old Gold Records. Dist: Lightning, Jazz Music, Spartan, Counterpoint

Album: released on MFP, Sep'86 by EMI Records. Dist: EMI

Cassette: released on MFP, Sep'86 by EMI Records. Dist: EMI

Single (7"): released on RCA, Sep'75 by RCA Records. Dist: RCA, Roots, Swift, Wellard, Chris, I & B, Solomon & Peres Distribution

I WISH IT COULD BE CHRISTMAS FOREVER.
Album: released on RCA, Nov'84 by RCA Records. Dist: RCA, Roots, Swift, Wellard, Chris, I & B, Solomon & Peres Distribution

Cassette: released on RCA, Nov'84 by RCA Records. Dist: RCA, Roots, Swift, Wellard, Chris, I & B, Solomon & Peres Distribution

MAGIC MOMENTS.
Tracks: / Magic moments / Catch a falling star.
Single (7"): released on Old Gold, Oct'86 by Old Gold Records. Dist: Lightning, Jazz Music, Spartan, Counterpoint

Cassette: released on RCA, Jun'84 by RCA Records. Dist: RCA, Roots, Swift, Wellard, Chris, I & B, Solomon & Peres Distribution

Single (7"): released on RCA Golden Grooves, Oct'81 by RCA Records Dist: RCA

MEMORIES ARD MADE OF HITS.
Album: released on RCA International (USA), Sep'81 by RCA Records. Dist: RCA

Cassette: released on RCA International (USA), Sep'81 by RCA Records. Dist: RCA

PERRY COMO CHRISTMAS COLLECTION, THE.
Album: released on Pickwick, Oct'79 by Pickwick Records. Dist: Pickwick Distribution, Prism Leisure Distribution,

PERRY COMO COLLECTION.
Double Album: released on Pickwick, '76 by Pickwick Records. Dist: Pickwick Distribution, Prism Leisure Distribution

Cassette: released on Pickwick, Jul'80 by Pickwick Records. Dist: Pickwick Distribution, Prism Leisure Distribution,

PURE GOLD.
Compact disc: by RCA Records. Dist: RCA, Roots, Swift, Wellard, Chris, I & B, Solomon & Peres Distribution

RELAX WITH....
Album: by Pickwick Records. Dist: Pickwick Distribution, Prism Leisure Distribution, Lugtons

...SINGS.
Album: released on RCA/Camden, '71

...SINGS JUST FOR YOU.
Album: released on RCA/Camden, Aug'74

SO IT GOES.
Album: released on RCA, Jun'83 by RCA Records. Dist: RCA, Roots, Swift, Wellard, Chris, I & B, Solomon & Peres Distribution

Cassette: released on RCA, Jun'83 by RCA Records. Dist: RCA, Roots, Swift, Wellard, Chris, I & B, Solomon & Peres Distribution

SOMEBODY LOVES ME.
Album: released on RCA/Camden, '72

THIS IS PERRY COMO.
Album: released on RCA (Germany), '83

WARM AND MELLOW.
Double Album: released on RCA, Oct'79 by RCA Records. Dist: RCA, Roots, Swift, Wellard, Chris, I & B, Solomon & Peres Distribution

Compact d'Afrique

COMPACT D'AFRIQUE Various artists (Various Artists).
Compact disc: released on Globestyle, Aug'86 by Ace Records. Dist: Projection

Compact Disco

COMPACT DISCO Various artists (Various Artists).
Compact disc: by Phonogram Records. Dist: Polygram Distribution

COMPACT DISCO VOL.2 (Various Artists).
Compact disc: released on Mercury, Jul'87 by Phonogram Records. Dist: Polygram Distribution

Compact Rock

COMPACT ROCK Various artists (Various Artists).
Compact disc: by Polydor Records. Dist: Polygram, Polydor
Cat. no: **823 552-2**

Compact Soul

COMPACT SOUL Various artists (Various Artists).
Tracks: / It's alright / Hey girl don't bother me / Picking wild mountain barries / He made a woman out of me / He will break your heart / Neighbour, neighbour / You're gonna make me cry / Giving up / Pity the fool / You threw a lucky punch / Cry, cry, cry / Shell of a woman, A / Either way I lose / Eight men, four women / I stand accused / Reconsider me / Just be true / Stay in my corner / You can make it if you try / People get ready / Steal away / Lover's holiday.
Compact disc: released on Charly, Apr'86 by Charly Records. Dist: Charly, Cadillac

Compact Sounds

COMPACT SOUNDS Various artists (Various Artists).
Compact disc: by Polydor Records. Dist: Polygram, Polydor

Companion

ON THE LINE.
Album: released on Strawberry, Dec'83 Dist: Pinnacle

Company

COMPANY VOL.1 various artists (Various Artists).
Album: released on Incus, Nov'76 Dist: Jazz Music, Cadillac

COMPANY VOL.2 various artists (Various Artists).
Album: released on Incus, Nov'76 Dist: Jazz Music, Cadillac

COMPANY VOL.5 various artists (Various Artists).
Album: released on Incus, '78 Dist: Jazz Music, Cadillac

COMPANY VOL.6 various artists (Various Artists).
Notes: Featuring: Lol Coxhill, Derek Bailey, Steve Beresford, M. Mengelberg, Evan Parker, Steve Lacey, Leo Smith.
Album: released on Incus, Oct'86 Dist: Jazz Music, Cadillac

COMPANY VOL.7 various artists (Various Artists).
Notes: Featuring: Lol Coxhill, Tristan Honsinger, Martin V.R. Altena, Han Bennink.
Album: released on Incus, Oct'86 Dist: Jazz Music, Cadillac

FICTIONS.
Notes: Featuring: Lol Coxhill, Derek Bailey, Steve Beresford, M. Mengelberg.
Album: released on Incus, Oct'86 Dist: Jazz Music, Cadillac

Company B

COMPANY B.
Tracks: / Fascinated / Spin me around / Signed in your book of love / I'm satisfied / Perfect lover / Jam on me / Full circle / Infatuate me.
Album: released on Bluebird, Jul'87 by Bluebird Records. Dist: EMI, Jetstar

Album: released on Bluebird, Aug'87 by Bluebird Records. Dist: EMI, Jetstar

Cassette: released on Bluebird, Aug'87 by Bluebird Records. Dist: EMI, Jetstar

FASCINATED.
Tracks: / Fascinated / Sascidubbed.
Single (7"): released on Bluebird, Apr'87 by Bluebird Records. Dist: EMI, Jetstar

Single (12"): released on Bluebird, Apr'87 by Bluebird Records. Dist: EMI, Jetstar

JAM ON ME.
Tracks: / Jam on me (dub).
Single (12"): released on Bluebird, Nov'86 by Bluebird Records. Dist: EMI, Jetstar

PRIVATE LOVER.
Single (7"): released on Bluebird, Aug'87 by Bluebird Records. Dist: EMI, Jetstar

Single (12"): released on Bluebird, Aug'87 by Bluebird Records. Dist: EMI, Jetstar

Company of Wolves

COMPANY OF WOLVES original soundtrack.
Album: released on That's Entertainment, Dec'84 by That's Entertainment Records. Dist: Pinnacle, PRT

Company She Keeps

WHAT A GIRL WANTS.
Tracks: / What a girl wants / Little madness, A / Touch on my emotions" / Express interest".
Single (7"): released on Cold Harbour, 13 Jun'87 Dist: Pinnacle, Probe Plus Distribution, Cartel, M.I.S., EMI, DMS, RCA, Ariola

Single (12"): released on Cold Harbour, 13 Jun'87 Dist: Pinnacle, Probe Plus Distribution, Cartel, M.I.S., EMI, DMS, RCA, Ariola

Complaints

THERE WERE RAYS COMING OUT OF THEIR EYES.
Single (7"): released on Dog Breath, Feb'85 by Dog Breath Records. Dist: Cartel

Compleat Rugby Songs

COMPLEAT RUGBY SONGS various artists (Various Artists).
Album: released on Sportsdisc, Nov'82 by Sportsdisc Records. Dist: H.R. Taylor, MIS-EMI Distribution

Complete control

BRICKS,BLOOD AND GUTS (IN 1985).
Album: released on Oil, '85 Dist: Revolver Distribution

Complete Fitness

COMPLETE FITNESS COURSE, THE With Simon Ward & Al Murray (Complete Fitness Course, The).
Album: released on Lifestyle, '83 by Zomba Records. Dist: PRT, RCA

Video-cassette [Betamax]: released on Lifestyle, '83 by Zomba Records. Dist: CBS, PRT,

Complete swamp blues

COMPLETE SWAMP BLUES VOL.1 various artists (Various original artists).
Album: released on Sonet, Jun'78 by Sonet Records. Dist: PRT

Album: released on Sonet, '78 by Sonet Records. Dist: PRT

Composers,The

COMPOSERS,THE Best of Beethoven,Mozart,Strauss & Tchaikovsky (Various Artists).
Album: released on Ronco, '83

Cassette: released on Ronco, '83

Compton swing collection

SWITCH IN TIME.
Album: released on Alamo, '79 Dist: Jazz Music

Compton, Tony

TONY COMPTON.
Tracks: / One note samba/Brazil / Girl from Ipenema / Windmills of your mind (medley) / Jealousy/Blue tango etc. / Walk in the black forest / Sid goes west / When sunny gets blue (jazz) / Elephant walk.
Notes: Mail order distribution address: Accordion Record Club, 146 Birmingham Road, Kidderminster, Worcs DY10 2SL. Tel: 0562 746105.
Album: released on Accordion Record Club, Jul'86 by Accordion Record Club Records. Dist: Accordion Record Club

Computer Corn

COMPUTER CORN (Various Artists).
Album: released on Black Solidarity, Jun'87 by Black Solidarity Records. Dist: Jetstar

Comsat Angels

7 DAY WEEKEND.
Tracks: / Forever young / Day one / You move me / I'm falling / Believe it / New heart and hand / Close your eyes / You're the heroine / High tide / Still it's not enough.
Album: released on Jive, Nov'85 by Zomba Records. Dist: RCA, PRT,

Album: released on Jive, '85 by Zomba Records. Dist: RCA, PRT,

Cassette: released on Jive, '85 by Zomba Records. Dist: RCA, PRT,

CHASING SHADOWS.
Tracks: / Thought that counts, The / Cutting edge, The / Under the influence / Carried away / You'll never know / Lost continent / Flying dreams / Pray for rain.
Notes: Produced by the Comsat Angels and Kevin Moloney. Executive Producer - Robert Palmer.
Album: released on Island, Jan'87 by Island Records. Dist: Polygram

Compact disc: released on Island, Jan'87 by Island Records. Dist: Polygram

CUTTING EDGE, THE.
Tracks: / Cutting Edge, The / Something's got to give / Our secret.
Notes: Our Secret available on 12" version only.
Single (7"): released on Island, Feb'87 by Island Records. Dist: Polygram

Single (12"): released on Island, Feb'87 by Island Records. Dist: Polygram

DAY ONE.
Single (7"): released on Jive, '84 by Zomba Records. Dist: RCA, PRT,

Single (12"): released on Jive, '84 by Zomba Records. Dist: RCA, PRT,

ENZ.
Album: released on Polydor (Holland), '84

FOREVER YOUNG.
Single (7"): released on Jive, '85 by Zomba Records. Dist: RCA, PRT

Single (12"): released on Jive, '85 by Zomba Records. Dist: RCA, PRT

I'M FALLING.
Single (7"): released on Jive, '85 by Zomba Records. Dist: RCA, PRT,

Single (12"): released on Jive, '85 by Zomba Records. Dist: RCA, PRT,

INDEPENDANCE DAY/INTELLIGENCE....
Notes: Full title: Independance day/Intelligence/Mister Memory/Total war/After the rain
Single (7"): released on Jive, '84 by Zomba Records. Dist: RCA, PRT,

Single (12"): released on Jive, '84 by Zomba Records. Dist: RCA, PRT,

ISLAND HEART/SCISSORS & STONE.
Single (7"): released on Jive, '83 by Zomba Records. Dist: RCA, PRT,

Single (12"): released on Jive, '83 by Zomba Records. Dist: RCA, PRT,

LAND.
Album: released on Jive, '83 by Zomba Records. Dist: RCA, PRT,

Cassette: released on Jive, '83 by Zomba Records. Dist: RCA, PRT,

WILL YOU STAY TONIGHT Shining hour.
Single (7"): released on Jive, '83 by Zomba Records. Dist: RCA, PRT,

Single (12"): released on Jive, '83 by Zomba Records. Dist: RCA, PRT,

YOU MOVE ME.
Single (7"): released on Jive, '84 by Zomba Records. Dist: RCA, PRT,

Single (12"): released on Jive, '84 by Zomba Records. Dist: RCA, PRT,

Conan Doyle, Sir Arthur

MEMOIRS OF SHERLOCK HOLMES (Hardy, Robert).
Tracks: / Yellow face, The / Stockbroker's clerk, The / "Gloria Scott", The / Final problem, The.

Conan the barbarian

CONAN THE BARBARIAN Original picture soundtrack.
Album: released on MCA, '82 by MCA Records. Dist: Polygram, MCA

Concept

MR D.J..
Single (7"): released on Fourth & Broadway, '85 by Island Records. Dist: Polygram, EMI

Single (12"): released on Fourth & Broadway, '85 by Island Records. Dist: Polygram, EMI

Concert Arban

RAGTIME FROM SCOTT JOPLIN TO CLAUDE BOLLING.
Album: released on Arion (France), '85 Dist: Conifer, Discovery

Cassette: released on Arion (France), '85 Dist: Conifer, Discovery

Concert at Carnegie Hall

CONCERT AT CARNEGIE HALL Various artists (Various Artists).
Tracks: / Lullaby of birdland / Hawk talks, The / Tattooed Bride, The / Medley / I'm beginning to see the light / Night in Tunisia / Strike up the band / Just friends / Easy to love / Repetition / Sentimental mood, A.
Album: released on Charly, Dec'86 by Charly Records. Dist: Charly, Cadillac

Cassette: released on Charly, Dec'86 by Charly Records. Dist: Charly, Cadillac

Cassette: released on Charly, Dec'86 by Charly Records. Dist: Charly, Cadillac

Concert Royal

MUSIC AT BOWES.
Album: released on Plant Life, '81 Dist: Roots

Concord Jazz

CONCORD JAZZ ALL STARS Northsea Festival (Various Artists).
Album: released on Concord, '82 by Import Records. Dist: IMS, Polygram

Album: released on Concord Jazz, '83 by Concord Jazz Records (USA). Dist: IMS, Polygram

Cassette: released on Concord Jazz, '83 by Concord Jazz Records (USA). Dist: IMS, Polygram

CONCORD JAZZ GUITAR COLLECTION (Various Artists).
Album: released on Concord Jazz, '81 by Concord Jazz Records (USA). Dist: IMS, Polygram

Concord Sound

CONCORD SOUND, THE (Various Artists).
Album: released on Concord Jazz(USA), Nov'85 by Concord Jazz Records (USA). Dist: IMS, Polygram

Concord Super Band

CONCORD SUPER BAND IN TOKYO.
Album: released on Concord, '79 by Import Records. Dist: IMS, Polygram

Concrete Blonde

CONCRETE BLONDE.
Tracks: / True / Your haunted head / Dance along the edge / Still in Hollywood / Song for Kim (she said) / Beware of darkness / Over your shoulder / Little sister / (You're the only one) can make me cry / Cold (part of town) / True (Instrumental).
Album: released on I.R.S.(Independent Record Syndicate), Feb'87 by I.R.S.. Dist: MCA

Cassette: released on I.R.S.(Independent Record Syndicate), Feb'87 by I.R.S.. Dist: MCA

TRUE.
Tracks: / True / True 11.
Single (7"): released on IRS, 30 May'87 Dist: Polygram

Single (12"): released on IRS, 30 May'87 Dist: Polygram

Concrete God

FLOOR.
Tracks: / Floor.
Single (12"): released on Phlox, Mar'87 Dist: Pinnacle

TOYTOWN STAR.
Single (12"): released on Phlox, Aug'87 Dist: Pinnacle

Concrete Sox

YOUR TURN NEXT.
Album: released on Children Of The Revolution, Apr'86 by Revolver Records. Dist: Revolver, Cartel

Condemned 84

BATTLE SCARRED.
Album: released on Oil, Jan'86 Dist: Revolver Distribution

IN SEARCH OF THE NEW BREEN.
Tracks: / In search of the new breen.
Single (12"): released on RFB, Apr'87

OI AIN'T DEAD.
Single (7"): released on RFB, Jul'86

Single (12"): released on RFB, Jul'86

Condona 3

CONDONA 3.
Album: released on ECM (Germany), Mar'83 by ECM Records. Dist: IMS, Polygram, Virgin through EMI

Condon, Eddie

1938 (Condon, Eddie & His Windy City Seven).
Album: released on Commodore Class, Aug'82 by Teldec Records (Germany). Dist: Conifer, IMS, Polygram

AT THE JAZZ BAND BALL.
Tracks: / At the jazz band ball / Aunt Hagar's blues / There'll be some changes made / Somebody loves me / Improvisation for march of time / We called it music / She's funny that way / Impromptu ensemble no.1 / Nobody's sweetheart / Farewell blues / Down among the sheltering palms / Stars fell on Alabama / Nobody knows / Grace and beauty / Sheik of Araby, The / Friars point shuffle.
Notes: Licensed from MCA Records. This compilation (P) 1986 Charly Records Ltd. (C) 1986 Charly Records Ltd.
Album: released on Affinity, May'86 by Charly Records. Dist: Charly, Cadillac

CHICAGO STYLE.
Album: released on VJM, '85 by Wellard, Chris Distribution.

CHICAGO STYLED.
Album: released on Swaggie (Australia), '83

CHICAGO STYLE RHYTHMAKERS.
Album: released on Jazz Archives, '74 by Jazz Archives Records. Dist: Jazz Music

COMMODORE CLASSICS (Condon, Eddie & Fats Waller).
Album: released on Commodore, '83 Dist: Swift

CONDON CONCERT (Condon, Eddie & His All Stars).
Notes: All Stars include: Wild Bill/Cutty Cuttshall/Bob Wilber/Leonard Gaskin/George Wettling etc.
Album: released on Jazzology, Jun'86 Dist: Jazz Music, Swift

EDDIE CONDON.
Album: released on Kings Of Jazz, '81 Dist: Jazz Horizons, Jazz Music, Celtic Music

EDDIE CONDON BAND (Condon, Eddie Band).
Album: released on Rarities, '81

EDDIE CONDON & HIS JAZZ ORCHESTRA (Condon, Eddie & His Orchestra).
Album: released on Jazz Bird, '82 Dist: Cassion (Melandy)

Cassette: released on Jazz Bird, '82 Dist: Cassion (Melandy)

EDDIE CONDON - VOLUME ONE (1938).

Notes: Condon's Windy Seven and jam sessions.
Album: released on Commodore Classics, May'87 by Teldec Records (Germany). Dist: Conifer, IMS, Polygram

Compact disc: released on Commodore Classics, May'87 by Teldec Records (Germany). Dist: Conifer, IMS, Polygram

...FLOORSHOW.
Album: released on Queen-Disc, '81 Dist: Celtic Music, JSU, Jazz Horizons, Jazz Music

FLOORSHOW VOL. 2.
Album: released on Queen-Disc, Apr'81 Dist: Celtic Music, JSU, Jazz Horizons, Jazz Music

GOOD BAND IS HARD TO FIND, A (Condon, Eddie & His Orchestra).
Album: released on Commodore Class, '84 by Teldec Records (Germany). Dist: Conifer, IMS, Polygram

GOOD BAND IS HARD TO FIND, (A).
Album: released on Commodore Classics May'87 by Teldec Records (Germany). Dis Conifer, IMS, Polygram

HIS WINDY CITY 7 JAM SESSION AT COMMODORE (1935).
Album: released on Commodore Classics, Jan'85 by Teldec Records (Germany). Dist: Conifer, IMS, Polygram

INTOXICATING DIXIELAND (1944/45) (Condon, Eddie & The Dorsey Brothers).
Album: released on Rarities, Apr'81

JAM SESSION (Condon, Eddie & Bobby Hackett).
Album: released on Aircheck (USA), Oct'86 Dist: Swift, Jazz Music

LIEDERKRANZ SESSIONS, THE (Condon, Eddie & His Band).
Album: released on Commodore Classics, May'87 by Teldec Records (Germany). Dist: Conifer, IMS, Polygram

SIDNEY BECHET WITH THE EDDIE CONDON ALL STARS See Bechet,Sidney.

SPIRIT OF CONDON,THE.
Album: released on Jazzology, Aug'79 Dist: Jazz Music, Swift

TOWN HALL BROADCASTS (VOLUME 2 1944-45).
Notes: Rcorded in mono.
Album: released on Rhapsody, Jun'86 by President Records. Dist: Taylors, Swift, Jazz Music, Wellard, Chris

TOWN HALL (VOLUME 1) (Condon, Eddie & His All Stars).
Notes: Recorded in mono.
Album: released on Rhapsody, Jun'86 by President Records. Dist: Taylors, Swift, Jazz Music, Wellard, Chris

Condon Gang

JACK TEAGARDEN & THE CONDON GANG 1944 (see Teagarden,Jack) (Condon Gang/Jack Teagarden).

Conen, Marcia

OB-LA-DI, OB-LA-DA.
Tracks: / Ob-la-di, ob-la-da (Version).
Single (12"): released on Diamond C, Dec'86 by Diamond C Records. Dist: Jetstar

Conexion Latina

CALORCITO.
Album: released on Enja (Germany), Nov'84 by Enja Records (W.Germany). Dist: Cadillac Music

Coney Hatch

CONEY HATCH.
Album: released on Mercury, Apr'83 by Phonogram Records. Dist: Polygram Distribution

Cassette: released on Mercury, Apr'83 by Phonogram Records. Dist: Polygram Distribution

HEY OPERATOR.
Single (7"): released on Mercury, Mar'83 by Phonogram Records. Dist: Polygram Distribution

Single (12"): released on Mercury, Mar'83 by Phonogram Records. Dist: Polygram Distribution

OUTA HAND.
Album: released on Vertigo, Aug'83 by Phonogram Records. Dist: Polygram

VIDEO SINGLE, THE.
Video-cassette (VHS): released on Polygram, Jun'86 by Polygram Records. Dist: Polygram

Video-cassette [Betamax]: released on Polygram, Jun'86 by Polygram Records. Dist: Polygram

Conflict

BATTLE CONTINUES, (THE).
Single (7"): released on Mortarhate, Sep'85 by Dorane Ltd.

HOUSE THAT MAN BUILT.
Single (7"): released on Crass, Jun'82 by Exitstencil Music. Dist: Rough Trade, Cartel

INCREASE THE PRESSURE.
Album: released on Mortarhate, Jun'84 by Dorane Ltd.

IT'S TIME TO SEE WHO'S WHO.
Album: released on Corpus Christi, '81 by Exitstencil Music. Dist: Cartel

LIVE AT THE CENTRE IBERICO.
Single (7"): released on Xntrix, Oct'82

LOVE AT THE CENTRE IBERICO.
Single (7"): released on Mortarhate, Oct'84 by Dorane Ltd.

SERENADE IS DEAD.
Single (7"): released on Mortarhate, Oct'83 by Dorane Ltd.

THIS IS NOT ENOUGH.
Single (7"): released on Mortarhate, Feb'85 by Dorane Ltd.

TURNING REBELLION INTO MONEY.
Album: released on Mortarhate, Jun'87 by Dorane Ltd.

Cassette: released on Mortarhate, Jun'87 by Dorane Ltd.

UNGOVERNABLE FORCE, THE.
Album: released on Mortarhate, Aug'86 by Dorane Ltd.

Con Funk Shun

BURNIN' LOVE.
Tracks: / Do ya / Burnin' love / How long / Jo Jo / She's sweet / She's a star / It's time girl / You make me wanna love again / Burnin' love (single) / Burnin' love (dub edit).
Notes: A great album of soulful dance music from one of America's longest-running and most respected funk acts. Features Mark Berry mixes on 3 tracks, plus guest appearance by Jeff Lorber on 'You make me wanna love again' by Leon Ware and Billy Valentine - a beautiful soul ballad.
Album: released on Club, Aug'86 by Phonogram Records. Dist: Polygram

Cassette: released on Club, Aug'86 by Phonogram Records. Dist: Polygram

Single (7"): released on Club, Jun'86 by Phonogram Records. Dist: Polygram

Single (12"): released on Club, Jun'86 by Phonogram Records. Dist: Polygram

ELECTRIC LADY.
Album: released on Mercury (Holland), Aug'85 by Phonogram Records. Dist: Polygram Distribution

FEVER.
Album: released on Mercury (Holland), Feb'84 by Phonogram Records. Dist: Polygram Distribution

TO THE MAX.
Album: released on Mercury (Import), Feb'83

Congas, John

HE'S GONNA STEP ON YOU AGAIN.
Single (7"): released on Old Gold, Jul'82 by Old Gold Records. Dist: Lightning, Jazz Music, Spartan, Counterpoint

Congo

AT THE FEAST.
Single (12"): released on 99, Jun'82

Congo Ashanti Roy

AFRICAN BLOOD.
Single 10": released on LNU Sounds, Jun'83 by LNU Sounds. Dist: Jetstar

LEVEL VIBES.
Album: released on Sonic Boom, Mar'85 Dist: Jetstar

Congos

HEART OF THE CONGOS.
Album: released on Go Feet, Jan'81 by Arista Records. Dist: RCA

Congregation

SOFTLY WHISPERING I LOVE YOU.
Single (7"): released on Old Gold, Oct'83 by Old Gold Records. Dist: Lightning, Jazz Music, Spartan, Counterpoint

Congress

CONTRACT OF FAITH.
Tracks: / Contract of faith / Don't think love is to blame.
Single (7"): released on EMI, Mar'87 by EMI Records. Dist: EMI

Single (12"): released on EMI, Mar'87 by EMI Records. Dist: EMI

GIVE IT TO ME.
Single (7"): released on PRT, May'84 by PRT Records. Dist: PRT

Single (12"): released on PRT, May'84 by PRT Records. Dist: PRT

NEPTUNE.
Single (7"): released on PRT, Nov'83 by PRT Records. Dist: PRT

Single (12"): released on PRT, Nov'83 by PRT Records. Dist: PRT

THAT'S JAZZ (YOU SEXY THING).
Single (7"): released on Dancefloor, Sep'83 by Dancefloor Records. Dist: Vista Sounds Records, Jetstar

Single (12"): released on Dancefloor, Sep'83 by Dancefloor Records. Dist: Vista Sounds Records, Jetstar

Conjunto, Andes

SNOW MUSIC Flutes of Andes Conjunto.
Album: released on Sonet, '73 by Sonet Records. Dist: PRT

Conjunto Trio

SAN ANTONIO.
Album: released on Arhoolie, May'81 by Arhoolie Records. Dist: Projection, Topic, Jazz Music, Swift, Roots

Conlee, John

BUSTED.
Tracks: / Busted / Shame / Guilty / Two hearts / Little of you, A / Nothing behind you, nothing in sight / Common man / I don't remember loving you / Ain't no way to make a bad love grow / Woman's touch, A.
Album: released on MCA Import, Mar'86 by MCA Records. Dist: Polygram, IMS

GOT MY HEART SET ON YOU.
Tracks: / You've got a right.
Single (7"): released on CBS, Nov'86 by CBS Records. Dist: CBS

JOHN CONLEE GREATEST HITS.
Tracks: / Baby, you're something / Backside of thirty / Miss Emily's picture / Busted / Common man / I don't remember loving you / Rose colored glasses / Friday night blues / Lady lay down / She can't say that anymore.
Album: released on MCA Import, Mar'86 by MCA Records. Dist: Polygram, IMS

JOHN CONLEE GREATEST HITS VOLUME 2.
Tracks: / Lifetime guarantee / Years after you / In my eyes / As long as I'm rockin' with you / I'm only in it for love / Old school, The / Way back / Before my time / Working man / Blue highway.
Album: released on MCA Import, Mar'86 by MCA Records. Dist: Polygram, IMS

SONGS FOR THE WORKING MAN.
Tracks: / Common man / Busted / Arthur & Alice / Nothing behind you, nothing in sight / She loves my troubles away / Friday night blues / Working man / But she loves me / In crowd, The / An American trilogy.
Album: released on MCA Import, Mar'86 by MCA Records. Dist: Polygram, IMS

Conley, Arthur

SWEET SOUL MUSIC.
Tracks: / Sweet soul music / Down on Funky Street / Shake rattle and roll*.
Single (7"): released on WEA, May'87 by WEA Records. Dist: WEA

Single (12"): released on WEA, May'87 by WEA Records. Dist: WEA

Single (7"): released on Atlantic, Jul'81 by WEA Records. Dist: WEA

Single (12"): released on Atlantic, Apr'80 by WEA Records. Dist: WEA

Single (7"): released on Old Gold, Jan'85 by Old Gold Records. Dist: Lightning, Jazz Music, Spartan, Counterpoint

Connection

THIRD EYE.
Album: released on Ring, Jul'78 Dist: Cadillac

Connell, Brian

WATCHING TELEVISION.
Single (7"): released on Mr. Sam, Aug'85

Connells

DARKER DAYS.
Album: released on Demon, Nov'85 by Demon Records. Dist: Pinnacle

Conners, Gene

COPENHAGEN STEW (Conners, Gene 'Mighty Flea" (with Fessors session boys)).
Album: released on Storyville, Jun'86 by Storyville Records. Dist: Jazz Music Distribution, Swift Distribution, Chris Wellard Distribution, Counterpoint Distribution

Conners, Shag

LITTLE HOUSE UPON THE HILL, (THE).
Single (7"): released on Play, Jun'85 by Play Records. Dist: Spartan

Conniff, Ray

AMOR, AMOR (Conniff, Ray & His Orchestra).
Album: released on CBS(Spain), Jan'84 by CBS Records. Dist: Conifer, Discovery, Swift

Cassette: released on CBS(Spain), Jan'84 by CBS Records. Dist: Conifer, Discovery, Swift

EXCLUSIVAMENTE LATINO (Conniff, Ray & His Orchestra).
Album: released on CBS(Spain), Jan'84 by CBS Records. Dist: Conifer, Discovery, Swift

Cassette: released on CBS(Spain), Jan'84 by CBS Records. Dist: Conifer, Discovery, Swift

FANTASTICO (Conniff, Ray & His Orchestra).
Album: released on CBS(Spain), Jan'84 by CBS Records. Dist: Conifer, Discovery, Swift

Cassette: released on CBS(Spain), Jan'84 by CBS Records. Dist: Conifer, Discovery, Swift

HELLO YOUNG LOVERS (Conniff, Ray & His Orchestra & Chorus).
Album: released on Hallmark, Sep'85 by Pickwick Records. Dist: Pickwick Distribution, PRT, Taylors

Cassette: released on Hallmark, Sep'85 by Pickwick Records. Dist: Pickwick Distribution, PRT, Taylors

RAY CONNIFF SONGBOOK, (THE).
Double Album: released on CBS(Holland), Jun'84 by CBS Records. Dist: Discovery

Cassette: released on CBS(Holland), Jun'84 by CBS Records. Dist: Discovery

SMOKE GETS IN YOUR EYES.
Album: released on CBS Cameo, Jul'84 by CBS Records. Dist: CBS Deleted '87.

Cassette: released on CBS Cameo, Jul'84 by CBS Records. Dist: CBS

Connolly, Billy

BIG YIN DOUBLE HELPING, (A).
Album: released on Cambra, Apr'84 by Cambra Records. Dist: IDS, Conifer

Cassette: released on Cambra, Apr'84 by Cambra Records. Dist: IDS, Conifer

BILLY CONNOLLY IN CONCERT.
Album: released on Spot, Feb'83 by Pickwick Records. Dist: H.R. Taylor, Lugtons

Cassette: released on Spot, Feb'83 by Pickwick Records. Dist: H.R. Taylor, Lugtons

BILLY CONNOLLY LIVE.
Album: released on Transatlantic, Feb'81 by Logo Records. Dist: Roots Distribution, RCA Distribution

Cassette: released on Transatlantic, Feb'81 by Logo Records. Dist: Roots Distribution, RCA Distribution

CHANGE IS AS GOOD AS A REST, (A).
Album: released on Polydor, Jul'83 by Polydor Records. Dist: Polygram, Polydor

Cassette: released on Polydor, Jul'83 by Polydor Records. Dist: Polygram, Polydor

Album: released on Polydor, Feb'85 by Polydor Records. Dist: Polygram, Polydor Deleted '87.

Cassette: released on Polydor, Feb'85 by Polydor Records. Dist: Polygram, Polydor

DOUBLE HELPING.
Double Album: released on Cambra, Feb'85 by Cambra Records. Dist: IDS, Conifer

Double cassette: released on Cambra, Feb'85 by Cambra Records. Dist: IDS, Conifer

FREEDOM (Connolly, Billy & Chris Tummings).
Single (7"): released on Audiotrax, Jun'85 by Audiotrax. Dist: PRT

HUMBLEBUMS, THE (Connolly, Billy & Gerry Rafferty).
Album: released on Cambra, Apr'84 by Cambra Records. Dist: IDS, Conifer

PICK OF BILLY CONNOLLY, (THE).
Album: released on Polydor, Nov'83 by Polydor Records. Dist: Polygram, Polydor

Cassette: released on Polydor, Nov'83 by Polydor Records. Dist: Polygram, Polydor

RIOTOUS ASSEMBLY.
Album: released on Polydor, Oct'79 by Polydor Records. Dist: Polygram, Polydor

Cassette: released on Polydor, Oct'79 by Polydor Records. Dist: Polygram, Polydor

SOLO CONCERT.
Album: released on Transatlantic, May'74 by Logo Records. Dist: Roots Distribution, RCA Distribution

SUPER GRAN.
Single (7"): released on Stiff, Feb'85 by Stiff Records. Dist: EMI, Record Services Distribution (Ireland)

WRECK ON TOUR.
Album: released on Philips, Dec'85 Dist: IMS-Polygram

Cassette: released on Philips, Dec'85 Dist: IMS-Polygram

Connor, Bob
BOB CONNOR'S NEW YANKEE RHYTHM KINGS (Connor, Bob New Yankee Rhythm Kings).
Album: released on Stomp Off, Mar'87 by Stomp Off Records. Dist: Jazz Music Distribution

Connor, Chris
I HEAR MUSIC (Connor, Chris & Carmen McRae).
Album: released on Affinity, '83 by Charly Records. Dist: Charly, Cadillac

OUT OF THIS WORLD.
Album: released on Affinity, Jun'84 by Charly Records. Dist: Charly, Cadillac

SWEET AND SWINGING.
Album: released on Progressive, Apr'81 by Progressive Records. Dist: Jetstar

Connors, Farmer Shag
CLEANEST LITTLE PIGGY IN THE MARKET.
Single (7"): released on Play, Dec'85 by Play Records. Dist: Spartan

I'M JEALOUS OF THE FARMYARD COCKEREL.
Tracks: / I'm jealous of the farmyard cockerel / Put your shoulder to the wheel.
Single (7"): released on Play, Aug'86 by Play Records. Dist: Spartan

Connors, Gene
SANCTIFIED.
Album: released on JSP Records, Dec'81 by JSP Records. Dist: Jazz Music, Pinnacle

Connors, Norman
BEST OF NORMAN CONNORS AND FRIENDS, (THE).
Album: released on Buddah, May'79 Dist: Swift, Jazz Music, PRT

INVITATION.
Album: released on Pye, Nov'79
Cassette: released on Buddah, Nov'79 Dist: Swift, Jazz Music, PRT

ROMANTIC JOURNEY.
Album: released on Buddah, May'77 Dist: Swift, Jazz Music, PRT

THIS IS YOUR LIFE.
Album: released on Buddah, Jul'78 Dist: Swift, Jazz Music, PRT

YOU ARE MY STARSHIP.
Album: released on Buddah, Jan'77 Dist: Swift, Jazz Music, PRT

Connors, Shag
COTSWOLDS.
Single (7"): released on Play, Nov'84 by Play Records. Dist: Spartan

COUNTRY CAPERS (Connors, Shag & The Carrot Crunchers).
Album: released on Sweet Folk All, May'81 by Sweet Folk All Records. Dist: Sweet Folk All, Roots, Celtic Music, Dragon, Impetus, Projection, Chris Wellard, Festival Records

SING COUNTRY STYLE (Connors, Shag & The Carrot Crunchers).

Album: released on Sweet Folk All, May'81 by Sweet Folk All Records. Dist: Sweet Folk All, Roots, Celtic Music, Dragon, Impetus, Projection, Chris Wellard, Festival Records

WATCH IT.
Single (7"): released on A & R, Dec'82 Dist: Spartan

Conn, Tony
LIKE WOW.
Single (7"): released on Rollin, Jun'80

ROCKIN' W JACKIE LEE.
Single (7"): released on Rollin, Jun'80

Conny
ROCKT.
Album: released on Electrola, Oct'80 by Bear Family Records. Dist: Rollercoaster Distribution, Swift

Conover, Willis
WILLIS CONOVER'S HOUSE OF SOUND.
Album: released on Jasmine, Jun'83 by Jasmine Records. Dist: Counterpoint, Lugtons, Taylor, H.R., Wellard, Chris, Swift, Cadillac

Conqueroo
FROM THE VULCAN GAS CO.
Album: released on Five Hours Back, Aug'87 by One Big Guitar / Zippo Records. Dist: Pinnacle, Revolver, Cartel. Estim retail price in Sep'87 was £5.99.

Consort
BY THE SWORD DIVIDED.
Single (7"): released on BBC, Nov'83 by BBC Records & Tapes. Dist: EMI, PRT, Pye

MISS MARPLE THEME.
Single (7"): released on BBC, Dec'84 by BBC Records & Tapes. Dist: EMI, PRT, Pye

Consort of Musicke
MADRIGALS AND WEDDING SONGS FOR DIANA.
Album: released on Hyperion, Jun'81 by Hyperion Records. Dist: Taylors, PRT, Gamut

Conspiracy International
CONSPIRACY INTERNATIONAL TWO.
Single (12"): released on CTI, Feb'85 by Polydor Records. Dist: IMS, Polygram

Conspiracy Of Hope
CONSPIRACY OF HOPE (Various Artists).
Tracks: / Higher love / Biko / Passengers / I believe / No one is to blame / Pipes of peace / Strange fruit / Brothers in arms / Pink Houses / Ghost dancing / Tonight.
Notes: Released to coincide with Amnesty International's 25th Anniversary. All royalties are being given direct to Amnesty.
Album: released on Mercury, Nov'86 by Phonogram Records. Dist: Polygram Distribution

Cassette: released on Mercury, Nov'86 by Phonogram Records. Dist: Polygram Distribution

Compact disc: released on Mercury, Nov'86 by Phonogram Records. Dist: Polygram Distribution

Constantin
CONSTANTIN.
Album: released on Jungle, May'83 by Jungle Records. Dist: Jungle, Cartel

Constructive Anger
CONSTRUCTIVE ANGER Bach, George.
Cassette: released on Psychology Today, Oct'81

Contact-U
DANCING INNER SPACE.
Single (12"): released on Challenge, Mar'83 by Elite Records. Dist: Pinnacle

ECUADOR.
Single (12"): released on Challenge, Aug'83 by Elite Records. Dist: Pinnacle

Contemporaries
HE IS LORD.
Album: by Pilgrim Records. Dist: Rough Trade, Cartel

Contemporary guitar
CONTEMPORARY FOLK GUITAR Various artists (Various Artists).
Double Album: released on Cambra, '83 by Cambra Records. Dist: IDS, Conifer

Double cassette: released on Cambra, '83 by Cambra Records. Dist: IDS, Conifer

Album: released on Transatlantic, Apr'82 by Logo Records. Dist: Roots Distribution, RCA Distribution

Cassette: released on Transatlantic, Apr'82 by Logo Records. Dist: Roots Distribution, RCA Distribution

Album: released on Kicking Mule, '78 by Sonet. Dist: Roots, PRT-Pye Distribution

Album: released on Cambra, '83 by Cambra Records. Dist: IDS, Conifer

Double cassette: released on Cambra, '83 by Cambra Records. Dist: IDS, Conifer

CONTEMPORARY GUITAR WORKSHOP Various artists (Various Artists).
Album: released on Kicking Mule, '78 by Sonet. Dist: Roots, PRT-Pye Distribution

CONTEMPORARY RAGTIME GUITAR Various artists (Various Artists).
Album: released on Kicking Mule, '73 by Sonet. Dist: Roots, PRT-Pye Distribution

Contenders
CONTEMPORARY GUITAR ALBUM Various artists (Various Artists).
Album: released on Transatlantic, Apr'82 by Logo Records. Dist: Roots Distribution, RCA Distribution

Cassette: released on Transatlantic, Apr'82 by Logo Records. Dist: Roots Distribution, RCA Distribution

Album: released on Transatlantic, Apr'82 by Logo Records. Dist: Roots Distribution, RCA Distribution

Cassette: released on Transatlantic, Apr'82 by Logo Records. Dist: Roots Distribution, RCA Distribution

WHERE'S HARRY.
Tracks: / Where's Harry / Where's Harry instrumental.
Single (7"): released on Columbia, Jun'86 by EMI Records. Dist: EMI

Single (12"): released on Columbia, Jun'86 by EMI Records. Dist: EMI

Conti, Bill
DYNASTY.
Single (7"): released on Arista, Feb'83 by Arista Records. Dist: RCA

Continentals
COME TRUST THE LORD.
Album: released on Word, May'82 by Word Records. Dist: Word Distribution, CBS

Cassette: released on Word, May'82 by Word Records. Dist: Word Distribution, CBS

FOR YOU BABY.
Album: released on Rockhouse, Oct'86 by Rockhouse Records. Dist: Swift Distribution, Charly Distribution

TOGETHER WE WILL STAND.
Album: released on Word, Jul'85 by Word Records. Dist: Word Distribution, CBS

Cassette: released on Word, Jul'85 by Word Records. Dist: Word Distribution, CBS

Continentals '87
ELIJAH.
Notes: "Elijah" is a youth musical about the power of prayer'. The Musical was written by Cam Floria and is produced by Cam Floria and Ken Medema. Featured artists: Cindy Hotopp as "Storyteller", Ken Medema as 'Elijah', Luke Garrett as "Elisha", Dennis Kenn as "Jezebel" and Melodie Tunney solos on "Wings of an Eagle".
Album: released on Word, Jun'87 by Word Records. Dist: Word Distribution, CBS

Cassette: released on Word, Jun'87 by Word Records. Dist: Word Distribution, CBS

Continental Singers
AND THERE WAS LIGHT.
Album: released on Word, May'82 by Word Records. Dist: Word Distribution, CBS

Continuum
MAD ABOUT TADD.
Album: released on Palo Alto (Italy), May'84

Conti, Robert
LATIN LOVE AFFAIR (Conti, Robert Jazz Quintet).
Album: released on Verydisc (Import), Jun'83

LAURA.
Tracks: / Softly as I leave you / You are the sunshine of my life / People / My favorite things / I love you/easy to love / Like someone in love / Laura / His eyes, her eyes / Tenderly / When we met again / Hello young lovers / Stella by star-

light / Little girl blue / Nuages / My romance.
Compact disc: released on Trend (USA), Sep'86 by Discovery Records. Dist: Flexitron Distributors Ltd, Swift

Contortions
BUY.
Album: released on Island, Mar'80 by Island Records. Dist: Polygram

Contours
BABY HIT AND RUN.
Single (7"): released on Motown, Oct'81 by Motown Records. Dist: BMG Distribution

JUST A LITTLE MISUNDERSTANDING.
Single (7"): released on Motown, Oct'81 by Motown Records. Dist: BMG Distribution

Controlled Bleeding
HEADCRACK.
Album: released on Sterile, Jun'86 Dist: Red Rhino Distribution, Cartel Distribution

Controllers
CONTROLLERS, THE.
Album: released on Timeless, Jun'87

CONTROLLERS, (THE).
Album: released on MCA, Nov'84 by MCA Records. Dist: Polygram, MCA

Cassette: released on MCA, Nov'84 by MCA Records. Dist: Polygram, MCA

CRUSHED.
Single (7"): released on MCA, Oct'84 by MCA Records. Dist: Polygram, MCA Deleted '85.

Single (12"): released on MCA, Oct'84 by MCA Records. Dist: Polygram, MCA

Single (7"): released on Survival, Jun'84 by Survival Records. Dist: Backs, Cartel Distribution

MY LOVE IS REAL.
Album: released on Timeless, Aug'87

STAY.
Tracks: / Stay (single) / Undercover lover (single) / Distant lover / Stay / So glad / Bad bad jama / My secret fantasy / Break out the love / Deep in love / Got a thang.
Album: released on MCA, Jun'86 by MCA Records. Dist: Polygram, MCA

Cassette: released on MCA, Jun'86 by MCA Records. Dist: Polygram, MCA

Single (7"): released on MCA, '86 by MCA Records. Dist: Polygram, MCA

Single (12"): released on MCA, '86 by MCA Records. Dist: Polygram, MCA

Controls
DON'T ADJUST THE CONTROLS.
Cassette: released on Stupid Rabbit Tapes, '80 Dist: Stupid Rabbit Tapes

DRESS, DANCE, DEMAND AND DESIRE.
Single 10": released on Stupid Rabbit Tapes, '84 Dist: Stupid Rabbit Tapes

GOOD THING, (THE).
Cassette: released on Stupid Rabbit Tapes, '84 Dist: Stupid Rabbit Tapes

I DIDN'T KNOW YOU WERE LEAVING.
Cassette: released on Stupid Rabbit Tapes, '84 Dist: Stupid Rabbit Tapes

KEEP ME HERE.
Cassette: released on Stupid Rabbit Tapes, Aug'84 Dist: Stupid Rabbit Tapes

LATE NIGHT LOVE SONGS.
Cassette: released on Stupid Rabbit Tapes, '81 Dist: Stupid Rabbit Tapes

SEARCHING FOR THE PERFECT PARTNER.
Cassette: released on Stupid Rabbit Tapes, '84 Dist: Stupid Rabbit Tapes

SOCK IT TO 'EM DAVE.
Cassette: released on Stupid Rabbit Tapes, '80 Dist: Stupid Rabbit Tapes

Convertion
SWEET THING.
Single (7"): released on Wax, Nov'86 by Wax Records. Dist: Pinnacle

Single (12"): released on Wax, Nov'86 by Wax Records. Dist: Pinnacle

Convict
GO AHEAD...MAKE MY DAY.
Album: released on Roadrunner (Dutch).

Sep'85 Dist: Pinnacle

Convoy

CONVOY Various artists (Various Artists).
Album: released on EMI (Germany), '83 by EMI Records. Dist: Conifer

KEEP ON TRUCKIN'.
Notes: Starr Marketing Services Ltd., 90 Queens Road, Twickenham, Middlesex TW1 4ET. Tel: 01 891 6487.
Compact disc: released on Delta, Jun'86 by Delta Records. Dist: Target

Convoy, Billy

ROTHBURY HILLS.
Cassette: released on Folktracks, Nov'79 by Folktracks Cassettes. Dist: Folktracks

Convoy, Dave

FREEDOM (Convoy, Dave & Tony Sales).
Single (7"): released on Shibui, Jul'83 by Stage One Records. Dist: Pinnacle

Conway Brothers

RAISE THE ROOF.
Single (7"): released on 10, Dec'85 by 10 Records. Dist: Virgin, EMI

Single (12"): released on 10, Dec'85 by 10 Records. Dist: Virgin, EMI

TURN IT UP.
Album: released on 10, Feb'86 by 10 Records. Dist: Virgin, EMI

Cassette: released on 10, Feb'86 by 10 Records. Dist: Virgin, EMI

Single (7"): released on 10, Jun'85 by 10 Records. Dist: Virgin, EMI

Single (12"): released on 10, Jun'85 by 10 Records. Dist: Virgin, EMI

Conway, Francie

TO THE EDGE OF TIME.
Single (7"): released on Lamborghini, Aug'84 by Lamborghini Records. Dist: PRT

Conway, Lee

LOVE STILL MAKES THE WORLD GO ROUND.
Album: released on Emerald (Ireland), Jun'78 by Emerald Records. Dist: I & B, Ross, PRT

Conway, Mario

CONWAY.
Notes: Accordion Record Club, 146 Birmingham Road, Kidderminster, Worcs DY10 2SL. Tel: 0562 746105
Album: released on Accordion Record Club, Jul'86 by Accordion Record Club Records. Dist: Accordion Record Club

Conway, Russ

ALWAYS YOU AND ME.
Double Album: released on MFP, Oct'81 by EMI Records. Dist: EMI

Double cassette: released on MFP, Oct'81 by EMI Records. Dist: EMI

HIS GREATEST HITS.
Tracks: / Sidesaddle / Mack the knife / Westminster waltz / Snow coach / Pixilated penguin / Sam's song / Always / Wedding of the painted doll, The / World outside, The / China tea / Lesson one / Party pops / Roulette / Toy balloons / Pepe / Royal event / Lucky five / Passing breeze / Got a match / Always you and me / Pablo / Polka dots / Forgotten dreams / More party pops.
Cassette: released on Hour Of Pleasure, '86 by Music For Pleasure Records. Dist: EMI

LONG TIME AGO, A.
Album: released on Churchill, Oct'86 Dist: Spartan, Pinnacle

Cassette: released on Churchill, Oct'86 Dist: Spartan, Pinnacle

ONE AND ONLY, (THE).
Album: released on MFP, Apr'79 by EMI Records. Dist: EMI

SIDESADDLE.
Single (7"): released on Old Gold, Jul'82 by Old Gold Records. Dist: Lightning, Jazz Music, Spartan, Counterpoint

SONGS FROM STAGE AND SCREEN.
Tracks: / Cabaret / Man and a woman / Love story / I want to be happy / Born free / Everything's coming up roses / Days of wine and roses / Hello Dolly / Good old bad old days / I will wait for you / Charly girl / Charade / Raindrops keep falling on my head / Moon river / Put on a happy face / Thoroughly modern Millie.
Album: released on PRT Flashback, Jul'86

Cassette: released on PRT Flashback, Jul'86

TERRY FOX THEME.
Single (7"): released on Music Media, Jun'84 Dist: PRT Distribution

TWO SIDES OF RUSS CONWAY, THE.
Album: released on Platinum, Mar'86 by Geoffs Records.

Cassette: released on Platinum, Mar'86 by Geoffs Records.

VERY BEST OF RUSS CONWAY, (THE).
Album: released on EMI, May'76 by EMI Records. Dist: EMI

Conway, Steve

MEMORIES OF STEVEN CONWAY.
Album: released on MWM, Nov'81 by Mawson & Wareham. Dist: Spartan Distribution, Jazz Music Distribution, JSU Distribution

Cassette: released on MWM, Nov'81 by Mawson & Wareham. Dist: Spartan Distribution, Jazz Music Distribution, JSU Distribution

UNFORGETTABLE, (THE).
Album: released on Encore, '63 by EMI Records. Dist: EMI

Conway & Temple

YOU CAN LAY YOUR HEAD ON MY SHOULDER.
Single (7"): released on Jive, Jul'85 by Zomba Records. Dist: RCA, PRT, CBS

Single (12"): released on Jive, Jul'85 by Zomba Records. Dist: RCA, PRT, CBS

Cooder, Ry

BLUE CITY Motion picture soundtrack.
Tracks: / Blue city down / Elevation 13 foot / True believers/Marianne / Nice bike / Greenhouse / Billy and Annie / Pops & timer/tell me something slick / Blue city / Don't take your guns to town / Leader of men, A / Not even key west.
Album: released on Warner Bros., Jul'86 by Warner Bros Records. Dist: WEA

Cassette: released on Warner Bros., Jul'86 by Warner Bros Records. Dist: WEA

BOOMER'S STORY.
Album: by WEA Records. Dist: WEA

BOP TILL YOU DROP.
Tracks: / Little sister / Go home girl / Very thing that makes you rich makes me poor / I think it's going to work out fine / Down in Hollywood / Look at granny run run / Trouble / Don't mess up a good thing / I can't win.
Compact disc: released on Warner Brothers, '83 by Warner Bros Records. Dist: WEA

Album: released on Warner Bros., Aug'79 by Warner Bros Records. Dist: WEA

Cassette: released on Warner Bros., Aug'79 by Warner Bros Records. Dist: WEA

Compact disc: released on Warner Bros., '83 by Warner Bros Records. Dist: WEA

BORDERLINE.
Compact disc: by Warner Bros Records. Dist: WEA

Album: released on Warner Brothers, '80 by Warner Bros Records. Dist: WEA

Cassette: released on Warner Brothers, '80 by Warner Bros Records. Dist: WEA

CHICKEN SKIN MUSIC.
Album: released on Reprise, '76 by WEA Records. Dist: WEA

CROSSROADS Original motion picture soundtrack.
Tracks: / See you in hell, blind boy / Nitty gritty Mississippi / He made a woman out of me / Feelin' bad blues / Somebody's callin my name / Willie Brown blues / Walkin' away blues / Crossroads / Down in Mississippi / Cotton needs pickin' / Viola lee blues.
Album: released on Warner Bros., Jul'86 by Warner Bros Records. Dist: WEA

Cassette: released on Warner Bros., Jul'86 by Warner Bros Records. Dist: WEA

GYPSY WOMAN Alimony.
Single (7"): released on Warner Bros., '82 by Warner Bros Records. Dist: WEA

INTO THE PURPLE VALLEY.
Album: by WEA Records. Dist: WEA

JAZZ.
Album: released on Warner Brothers, '78 by Warner Bros Records. Dist: WEA

MUSIC FROM THE MOTION PICTURE ALAMO BAY.
Album: released on Slash, '85 by London Records. Dist: Polygram

Cassette: released on Slash, '85 by London Records. Dist: Polygram

PARADISE & LUNCH.
Album: released on Reprise, '74 by WEA Records. Dist: WEA

Cassette: released on Reprise, '82 by WEA Records. Dist: WEA

PARIS,TEXAS.
Album: released on Warner Bros., '85 by Warner Bros Records. Dist: WEA

Cassette: released on Warner Bros., '85 by Warner Bros Records. Dist: WEA

RY COODER.
Album: by WEA Records. Dist: WEA

SLIDE AREA,THE.
Album: released on Warner Brothers, '82 by Warner Bros Records. Dist: WEA

Cassette: released on Warner Brothers, '82 by Warner Bros Records. Dist: WEA

WHICH CAME FIRST How can a....
Single (7"): released on Warner Bros., '82 by Warner Bros Records. Dist: WEA

Single (12"): released on Fetish, Nov'81 by Fetish Records. Dist: Cartel, Pinnacle

WHY DON'T YOU TRY ME TONIGHT.
Tracks: / How can a poor man stand such times and live / Available space / Money honey / Tattler / He'll have to go / Smack dab in the middle / Dark end of the street / Down in Hollywood / Little sister / I think it's gonna work out fine / Crazy 'bout an automobile / 634-5789 / Why don't you try me.
Compact disc: released on Warner Brothers, '86 by Warner Bros Records. Dist: WEA

Album: released on Warner Brothers, Mar'86 by Warner Bros Records. Dist: WEA

Cassette: released on Warner Brothers, Mar'86 by Warner Bros Records. Dist: WEA

Cook, Barbara

IT'S BETTER WITH A BAND.
Tracks: / Come in from the rain / Sing a song with me / I never knew that men cried / It's better with a band / Remember / I love a piano / Chant la vie / Marianne / Them there eyes / Bernstein medley / I never meant to hurt you / Inside / Lullaby in ragtime / Ingenue, The / If love were all / Another Mr. Right left / Sweet Georgia Brown.
Notes: Recorded live in concert. Includes four extra tracks not on LP. Personnel: Michael Spivakowsky - violin / Leo Kahn - second violin / Sue Pray - viola / Gene Moye - cello / John Beal - double bass and fender bass / Sally Foster - harp / John Frosk - trumpet / Morty Bullman - trombone / Sam Pilafian - tuba / Sid Weinberg - oboe, English horn, tenor sax / Red Press - alto sax, flute, alto flute, piccolo, clarinet, bass clarinet / Brooks Tillotson - French horn / Hank Jaramillo - drums / Steve Little - percussion / Jim Mitchell - guitar, banjo / Wally Harper - piano. Orchestrations by Bill Brohn, Mark Schlefer and Luther henderson. Special thanks to: Marvin Saines, Arthur Cantor, Harvey Elliott, Marty Grupp, Fred Miller and George Otterson.
Compact disc: released on Moss (USA), Mar'87

Album: released on Moss Music Group (USA), Sep'86 Dist: Conifer Distribution

Cook Da Books

CARESS ME LIKE A FLOWER.
Single (7"): released on Virgin, '84 by Virgin Records. Dist: EMI, Virgin Distribution

LOW PROFILE Rich men don't.
Single (7"): released on Kiteland, '83 by Kiteland Records. Dist: Pinnacle

PIGGIE IN THE MIDDLE EIGHT.
Single (7"): released on Probe Plus, '82 by Probe Plus Records. Dist: Probe Plus Distribution

Single (12"): released on Probe Plus, '82 by Probe Plus Records. Dist: Probe Plus Distribution

RICH MEN DON'T Low profile.
Single (7"): released on Kite, '82 by Kite Records. Dist: Pinnacle

WOULDN'T WANNA KNOCK IT Up in smoke.
Single (7"): released on Kiteland, '83 by Kiteland Records. Dist: Pinnacle

YOUR EYES Rockin' at the hop.
Single (7"): released on Carrere, '83 by Carrere Records. Dist: PRT, Spartan

Cook, Doc

BROWN SUGAR (Cook, Doc & His Dreamland Orchestra).
Album: released on Joker, '81 Dist: Counterpoint, Mainline, Record Services Distribution (Ireland)

DOC COOK DREAMLAND ORCHESTRA (Cook, Doc & His Dreamland Orchestra).
Album: released on VJM, '79 by Wellard, Chris Distribution. Dist: Wellard, Chris Distribution

Cook,Drummond

TAE GAR YER LOUP (Cook,Drummond Scottish Country Dance Band).
Album: released on Beechwood, '85 by Beechwood Records. Dist: Ross

Cooke, Alastair

LETTERS FROM AMERICA.
Cassette: released on Listen For Pleasure, '79 by MFP Records. Dist: EMI

Cooke, Brandon

EYES OF A STRANGER.
Tracks: / Eyes of a stranger / Mission
Single (7"): released on Mercury, Sep'86 by Phonogram Records. Dist: Polygram Distribution

Single (12"): released on Mercury, Sep'86 by Phonogram Records. Dist: Polygram Distribution

SHARPE AS A KNIFE.
Tracks: / Sharpe as a knife / Voices calling.
Single (7"): released on Mercury, May'86 by Phonogram Records. Dist: Polygram Distribution

Single (12"): released on Mercury, May'86 by Phonogram Records. Dist: Polygram Distribution

Cooke, Derek

INSIDE INFORMATION.
Album: by Pilgrim Records. Dist: Rough Trade, Cartel

Cooke, Sam

20 GREATEST HITS.
Compact disc: released on The Compact Collection, Sep'87 by Conifer Records. Dist: Conifer Distribution

Compact disc: released on The Compact Collection, Sep'87 by Conifer Records. Dist: Conifer Distribution

ANOTHER SATURDAY NIGHT.
Tracks: / You send me / Little Red Rooster / Frankie & Johnny.
Single (7"): released on RCA, Apr'86 by RCA Records. Dist: RCA, Roots, Swift, Wellard, Chris, I & B, Solomon & Peres Distribution

Single (12"): released on RCA, Apr'86 by RCA Records. Dist: RCA, Roots, Swift, Wellard, Chris, I & B, Solomon & Peres Distribution

BEST OF SAM COOKE,THE.
Album: released on RCA (Germany), '83

FABULOUS,THE.
Album: released on Cambra, '85 by Cambra Records. Dist: IDS, Conifer

Cassette: released on Cambra, '85 by Cambra Records. Dist: IDS, Conifer

GOLDEN AGE OF SAM COOKE.
Album: released on RCA, '76 by RCA Records. Dist: RCA, Roots, Swift, Wellard, Chris, I & B, Solomon & Peres Distribution

HIS GREATEST HITS.
Album: released on RCA (Germany), '83

MAN & HIS MUSIC, THE.
Tracks: / Meet me at Mary's place / Good times / Shake / Sad mood / Bring it on home to me / That's where it's at / That's heaven to me / Touch the hem of his garment / You send me / I'll come running back to you / Win your love for me / Wonderful world / Cupid / Just for you / Chain gang / Only sixteen / When a boy falls in love / Rome wasn't built in a day / Everybody loves to cha cha cha / Nothing can change this love / Love will find a way / Another Saturday night / Having a party / Twistin' the night away / Smebody have mercy / Ain't that good news / Soothe me / Change is gonna come, A.
Double Album: released on RCA, Apr'86 by RCA Records. Dist: RCA, Roots, Swift, Wellard, Chris, I & B, Solomon & Peres Distribution

Double cassette: released on RCA, Apr'86 by RCA Records. Dist: RCA, Roots, Swift, Wellard, Chris, I & B, Solomon & Peres Distribution

Double compact disc: released on RCA, '86 by RCA Records. Dist: RCA, Roots, Swift, Wellard, Chris, I & B, Solomon & Peres Distribution

MR SOUL.
Album: released on RCA International, '80

Cassette: released on RCA International, '80

SAM COOKE.
Album: released on Deja Vu, Jan'87 by Deja Vu Records. Dist: Counterpoint Distribution, Record Services Distribution (Ireland)

Cassette: released on Deja Vu, Jan'87 by Deja Vu Records. Dist: Counterpoint Distribution, Record Services Distribution (Ireland)

Album: released on Dakota (Countdown series), '82 by Dakota Records. Dist: PRT

Cassette: released on Dakota (Countdown series), '82 by Dakota Records. Dist: PRT

Cassette: released on Audio Fidelity, '84 Dist: PRT

SOLITUDE.
Album: released on Cambra, '85 by Cambra Records. Dist: IDS, Conifer

Cassette: released on Cambra, '85 by Cambra Records. Dist: IDS, Conifer

---

SWING OUT BROTHER.
Tracks: / Solitude / Talk of the town / Crazy in love with you / I've got a right to sing the blues / Good morning heartaches / Ain't nobody's bizness if I do / Lover come back to me / That lucky old sun / They can't take that away from me / Moonlight in Vermont / When I fall in love.
Album: released on Topline, Apr'87 by Charly Records. Dist: Charly Distribution

Cassette: released on Topline, Apr'87 by Charly Records. Dist: Charly Distribution

---

TWISTIN' THE NIGHT AWAY.
Album: released on Premier, '84 by Premier Records. Dist: CBS

Cassette: released on Premier, '84 by Premier Records. Dist: CBS

WHEN I FALL IN LOVE.
Album: released on Arena, Feb'87 by Arena Records. Dist: Spartan

Cassette: released on Arena, Feb'87 by Arena Records. Dist: Spartan

Album: released on EMI, '79 by EMI Records. Dist: EMI

Cassette: released on Nut, '79 by EMI Records. Dist: EMI

WONDERFUL WORLD.
Compact disc: released on Card/Grand Prix, Apr'87 Dist: Target

---

WONDERFUL WORLD.
Tracks: / Chain gang / Cupid / Change is gonna come, A.
Single (12"): released on RCA, Mar'86 by RCA Records. Dist: RCA, Roots, Swift, Wellard, Chris, I & B, Solomon & Peres Distribution

---

YOU SEND ME.
Tracks: / You send me / Stealing kisses / There I've said it again / Ol' man river / All of my life / Steal away / Little things you do, The / Everybody loves to cha cha cha / Only sixteen / Win your love for me / I love you most of all / God bless this child / When I fall in love / Good morning heartaches.
Compact disc single: released on Topline, Apr'87 by Charly Records. Dist: Charly Distribution

Album: by Charly Records. Dist: Charly Distribution

Cassette: released on Topline, '86 by Charly Records. Dist: Charly Distribution

Single (12"): released on Perfect, May'87

Single (7"): released on EMI Golden 45's, '85 by EMI Records. Dist: EMI

Cooke, Tony

ON THE FLOOR (ROCK IT) H (Cooke, Tony & Party people).
Single (7"): released on Half Moon, '84 by Rondelet Music And Records. Dist: Spartan

Single (12"): released on Half Moon, '84 by Rondelet Music And Records. Dist: Spartan

Cookey Monster

SPACE AGE NIGGER Sniffer's dub.
Single (12"): released on Twinkle, '83 by Twinkle Records. Dist: Jetstar

Cookie & The Cupcakes

BY REQUEST-COOKIE & THE CUPCAKES.
Album: released on Jin, '79 by Priority Records. Dist: EMI

COOKIE AND THE CUPCAKES - VOL. 2.
Album: Dist: Swift

FEATURING SHELTON DUNAWAY & LITTLE ALFRED.
Album: released on Ace, '85 by Ace Records. Dist: Pinnacle, Swift, Hotshot, Cadillac

---

LEGENDARY COOKIE & THE CUPCAKES.
Album: released on Goldband, '79 by Charly Records. Dist: Charly

---

THREE GREAT ROCKERS.
Album: released on Jin, '79 by Priority Records. Dist: EMI

Cookin' with Kent

COOKIN' WITH KENT Various artists (Various Artists).
Tracks: / Three lonely guys / I've been hurt so many times / New breed, The / Baby take me back / I can't stand it (I can't take it no more) / I'm lonely for you / I've gotta get back / No more tears / S'been so long / All that shines is not gold / One more chance / New lease of life / It's crazy baby.
Album: released on Kent, Apr'86 by Ace Records. Dist: Pinnacle

Cook Island Spectacular

COOK ISLAND SPECTACULAR Various artists (Various Artists).
Album: released on Viking, '77 Dist: Harmonia Mundi Distributors

Cook, Junior

GOOD COOKIN'.
Album: released on Muse, '81 by Peerless Records. Dist: Lugtons Distributors

---

PRESSURE COOKER.
Album: released on Affinity, '81 by Charly Records. Dist: Charly, Cadillac

---

SOMETHIN'S COOKIN'.
Album: released on Muse, '82 by Peerless Records. Dist: Lugtons Distributors

Cookman, Brian

GRINNIN'.
Tracks: / Grinnin.
Album: released on Dambuster, Dec'85 by Dambuster Records. Dist: Projection, Celtic Music, Roots

---

MAN OVERBOARD Everyone.
Single (7"): released on Mummer, '83 by Mummer Records. Dist: Polygram Distribution

Cook, Peter

CLEAN TAPES (Cook, Peter & Dudley Moore).
Album: released on Cube, '81 by Dakota Records. Dist: PRT

Cassette: released on Cube, '81 by Dakota Records. Dist: PRT

DEREK & CLIVE COME AGAIN (Cook, Peter & Dudley Moore).
: released on Virgin, '77 by Virgin Records. Dist: EMI, Virgin Distribution

Cassette: released on Virgin, '77 by Virgin Records. Dist: EMI, Virgin Distribution

---

DEREK & CLIVE LIVE (Cook, Peter & Dudley Moore).
Album: released on Island, '78 by Island Records. Dist: Polygram

Cassette: released on Island, '81 by Island Records. Dist: Polygram

Cassette: released on Island, Aug'76 by Island Records. Dist: Polygram

---

HERE COMES THE JUDGE Live in concert.
Album: released on Virgin, '79 by Virgin Records. Dist: EMI, Virgin Distribution

---

THERE AIN'T NO MORNING Himazas.
Single (7"): released on Paramount, '83 by Paramount Records. Dist: PRT

WORLD OF PETE & DUD.
Album: released on World of Learning, '74 by World Of Learning Records. Dist: World Of Learning

Cook, Tony

DO WHAT YOU WANNA DO.
Single (7"): released on Half Moon, '83 by Rondelet Music And Records. Dist: Spartan

Coolah

JAH IS FOR EVERYONE.
Single (12"): released on Pops, Jul'82

Cool baby cool

COOL BABY COOL Various Artists (Various Artists).
Album: released on Eagle (West Germany), '82 by Bear Family Records. Dist: Stage One

Cool California

COOL CALIFORNIA Various artists (Various Artists).
Album: released on Savoy (France), '84

Album:

Cooley, Pat

DOUBLE TALK.
Album: released on Ichiban, Aug'87 by Ichiban Records. Dist: PRT

Cassette: released on Ichiban, Aug'87 by Ichiban Records. Dist: PRT

Cooley, Spade

ROMPIN', STOMPIN', SINGIN', SWINGIN' (Cooley, Spade & Tex Williams).
Album: released on Bear Family, Jun'83 by Bear Family Records. Dist: Rollercoaster Distribution, Swift

---

SWINGING THE DEVIL'S DREAM.
Album: released on Charly, '84 by Charly Records. Dist: Charly, Cadillac

Cool Heat

COOL HEAT Various artists (Various Artists).
Album: released on K-Tel, '83 by K-Tel Records. Dist: Record Merchandisers Distribution, Taylors, Terry Blood Distribution, Wynd-Up Distribution, Relay Distribution, Pickwick Distribution, Solomon & Peres Distribution, Polygram

Cassette: released on K-Tel, '83 by K-Tel Records. Dist: Record Merchandisers Distribution, Taylors, Terry Blood Distribution, Wynd-Up Distribution, Relay Distribution, Pickwick Distribution, Solomon & Peres Distribution, Polygram

Coolidge, Rita

ANYTIME...ANYWHERE.
Album: released on A&M, May'78 by A&M Records. Dist: Polygram

Cassette: released on A&M, May'78 by A&M Records. Dist: Polygram

---

BREAKAWAY (Coolidge, Rita & Kris Kristofferson).
Notes: For full information see under: KRISTOFFERSON,Kris & Rita Coolidge
Cassette: released on Monument, Mar'86 by CBS Records. Dist: CBS Distribution

Album: released on Monument, Mar'86 by CBS Records. Dist: CBS Distribution

---

FULL MOON (Coolidge, Rita & Kris Kristofferson).
Album: released on A&M, '73 by A&M Records. Dist: Polygram

LADY'S NOT FOR SALE, THE.
Album: released on Spot, Sep'85 by Pickwick Records. Dist: H.R. Taylor, Lugtons

Cassette: released on Spot, Sep'85 by Pickwick Records. Dist: H.R. Taylor, Lugtons

Album: released on MFP, Mar'81 by EMI Records. Dist: EMI

NATURAL ACT (Coolidge, Rita & Kris Kristofferson).
Notes: For full information see under KRISTOFFERSON, Kris & Rita Coolidge
Album: released on Hallmark, Feb'86 by Pickwick Records. Dist: Pickwick Distribution, PRT, Taylors

Cassette: released on Hallmark, Feb'86 by Pickwick Records. Dist: Pickwick Distribution, PRT, Taylors

Album: released on A&M, Mar'82 by A&M Records. Dist: Polygram

Cassette: released on A&M, Mar'82 by A&M Records. Dist: Polygram

---

WE'RE ALL ALONE.
Album: released on Pickwick (A&M), May'84

Cassette: released on Pickwick (A&M), May'84

Coolies

DIG.
Album: released on Fundamental, Aug'87 by Fundamental Records. Dist: Red Rhino, Cartel. Estim retail price in Sep'87 was £5.67.

Cool It Reba

MONEY FALL OUT OF THE SKY.
Single (12"): released on Hannibal, '83 by Hannibal Records. Dist: Charly, Harmonia Mundi, Projection, Celtic Music, Roots

Cool notes

BILLY THE KID - Kidnap my baby.
Single (12"): released on Jama, '80 by Jama Records.

DOWN TO EARTH.
Album: released on Mass media, '82

HAVE A GOOD FOREVER.
Tracks: / Look what you've done to me / My love is hot / Why not / Come on back to me / Have a good forever / Spend the night / You're never too young / I don't wanna stop / All I wanna do / I love you / In your car.
Album: released on Abstract Dance, '85 Dist: Priority, RCA

Cassette: released on Abstract Dance, '85 Dist: Priority, RCA

Single (7"): released on Abstract Dance, '85 Dist: Priority, RCA

Single (12"): released on Abstract Dance, '85 Dist: Priority, RCA

I FORGOT.
Single (7"): released on Abstract, '84 by Abstract. Dist: Pinnacle

Single (12"): released on Abstract, '84 by Abstract. Dist: Pinnacle

---

I FORGOT HOW TO LOVE YOU.
Single (7"): released on Mass media, '82

Single (12"): released on Mass media, '82
Cat. no: **MMM 12 1008**

INTO THE MOTION.
Tracks: / Into the motion / Come on back / Look what you've done to me (Remix).
Single (7"): released on Abstract Dance, May'86 Dist: Priority, RCA

Single (12"): released on Abstract Dance, May'85 Dist: Priority, RCA

IN YOUR CAR.
Single (7"): released on Abstract Dance, '85 Dist: Priority, RCA

Single (12"): released on Abstract Dance, '85 Dist: Priority, RCA

Single (12"): released on Abstract Dance, '85 Dist: Priority, RCA

I WANNA DANCE Blown it.
Single (7"): released on Sour Grape, '84 by Sour Grape Records. Dist: PRT

Single (12"): released on Sour Grape, '84 by Sour Grape Records. Dist: PRT

JUST GIRLS Sweet vibes.
Single (12"): released on Jama, '82 by Jama Records.

MOMENTARY VISION.
Tracks: / Momentary Vision / Girls night out / Your love is taking over.
Single (7"): released on Abstract Dance, Oct'86 Dist: Priority, RCA

Single (12"): released on Abstract Dance, Oct'86 Dist: Priority, RCA

MORNING CHILD.
Single (12"): released on Mass media, '82

MY TUNE.
Single (12"): released on Jama, '84 by Jama Records.

SPEND THE NIGHT.
Single (7"): released on Abstract Dance, '85 Dist: Priority, RCA

Single (12"): released on Abstract Dance, '85 Dist: Priority, RCA

Single (12"): released on Abstract Dance, '85 Dist: Priority, RCA

YOU'RE NEVER TO YOUNG.
Single (12"): released on Abstract Dance, '84 Dist: Priority, RCA

Cool, Phil

BRIDGE OVER TROUBLED WATER.
Tracks: / Australians / Pope (The) / Rolf Harris.
Single (7"): released on Virgin, Nov'86 by Virgin Records. Dist: EMI, Virgin Distribution

Single (12"): released on Virgin, Nov'86 by Virgin Records. Dist: EMI, Virgin Distribution

---

IT'S HARD BEING A STONE.
Single (7"): released on Castle, Feb'83 by Castle Records. Dist: Pinnacle

---

NOT JUST A PRETTY FACE.
Album: released on Virgin, Nov'86 by Virgin Records. Dist: EMI, Virgin Distribution

Cassette: released on Virgin, Nov'86 by Virgin Records. Dist: EMI, Virgin Distribution

Cool Runners

I SHOULD HAVE LOVED YOU.
Tracks: / I should have loved you / Satellite music.
Single (7"): released on Streetwave, Mar'86 by Streetwave Records. Dist: PRT Distribution

Single (12"): released on Streetwave, Mar'86 by Streetwave Records. Dist: PRT Distribution

Cool Running

ROBIN HOOD OF THE GHETTO.
Single (12"): released on Raka, Aug'83

Cool whalin'

COOL WHALIN' Various artists (Various Artists).
Album: released on Spotlite, Sep'79 by Spotlite Records. Dist: Cadillac, Jazz Music, Spotlite

Cooper, Al

JUMP STEADY (Cooper, Al & His Savoy Sultans).
Album: released on Affinity (MCA), Sep'83

Cooper, Alice

ALIVE COOPER SHOW, THE.
Cassette: released on Warner Brothers, Jan'78 by Warner Bros Records. Dist: WEA

BILLION DOLLAR BABIES.
Album: by Warner Bros Records. Dist: WEA

CONSTRICTOR.
Album: released on MCA, Oct'86 by MCA Records. Dist: Polygram, MCA

Cassette: released on MCA, Oct'86 by MCA Records. Dist: Polygram, MCA

DA DA.
Album: released on Warner Brothers, Nov'83 by Warner Bros Records. Dist: WEA

FOR BRITAIN ONLY.
Single (7"): released on Warner Brothers, May'82 by Warner Bros Records. Dist: WEA

Picture disc single: released on Warner Brothers, May'82 by Warner Bros Records. Dist: WEA

FREAK OUT SONG.
Tracks: / Freak out song / Ain't that just like a woman / Painting a picture / I've written home to mother / Science fiction / Goin' to the river / A.C. Instrumental / Nobody likes me.

Album: released on Showcase, Apr'86 Dist: Counterpoint

Cassette: released on Showcase, Apr'86 Dist: Counterpoint

...GOES TO HELL.
Album: released on Warner Brothers, Jun'76 by Warner Bros Records. Dist: WEA

GREATEST HITS:ALICE COOPER.
Cassette: released on Warner Brothers, '74 by Warner Bros Records. Dist: WEA

Album: released on Warner Brothers, Aug'74 by Warner Bros Records. Dist: WEA

HE'S BACK (THE MAN BEHIND THE MASK).
Tracks: / Billion Dollar rabies.
Single (7"): released on MCA, Oct'86 by MCA Records. Dist: Polygram, MCA

Single (12"): released on MCA, Oct'86 by MCA Records. Dist: Polygram, MCA

KILLER.
Album: by Warner Bros Records. Dist: WEA

LACE & WHISKEY.
Album: released on Warner Brothers, May'77 by Warner Bros Records. Dist: WEA

LADIES MAN.
Album: released on Thunderbolt, Apr'87 by Magnum Music Group Ltd. Dist: Magnum Music Group Ltd, PRT Distribution, Spartan Distribution

LOVE AT YOUR CONVENIENCE.
Single (7"): released on Warner Brothers Feb'82 by Warner Bros Records. Dist: WEA

LOVE IT TO DEATH.
Album: by Warner Bros Records. Dist: WEA

SCHOOL'S OUT.
Single (7"): released on Old Gold, Sep'85 by Old Gold Records. Dist: Lightning, Jazz Music, Spartan, Counterpoint

Single (7"): released on Warner Brothers Nov'76 by Warner Bros Records. Dist: WEA

Album: by Warner Bros Records. Dist: WEA

TEENAGE FRANKENSTEIN.
Tracks: / Teenage Frankenstein (live) / Schools out (live) / Oly women bleed.
Single (7"): released on MCA, Mar'87 by MCA Records. Dist: Polygram, MCA

Single (12"): released on MCA, Mar'87 by MCA Records. Dist: Polygram, MCA

TORONTO ROCK 'N' ROLL REVIVAL.
Album: released on Design, Jul'84 by Breakaway Records. Dist: PRT, Stage One

WELCOME NIGHHTMARE.
Video-cassette (VHS): released on Select-A-Tape, Jan'84 Dist: Gold & Sons

WELCOME TO MY NIGHTMARE.
Album: released on ABC, Feb'75 Dist: CBS, Pinnacle

Cooper, Anthony

COCAINE.
Single (12"): released on Keyman, Aug'85 by Keyman Records. Dist: Keyman, Revolver

Cooper, Bob

GROUP ACTIVITY (Cooper, Bob Sextet & Bill Holman Octet).
Album: released on Affinity, Jul'81 by Charly Records. Dist: Charly, Cadillac

SHIFTING WINDS.
Album: released on Affinity, Apr'81 by Charly Records. Dist: Charly, Cadillac

Cooper Brothers

DREAM NEVER DIES, THE.
Album: released on Capricorn, Mar'79 by Polydor Records. Dist: Polygram

Cooper, Giles

UNDER THE LOOFAH TREE/THE DISAGREEABLE OYSTER.
Cassette: released on BBC, May'84 by BBC Records & Tapes. Dist: EMI, PRT,

Cooper, Harry

HARRY COOPER, R.Q. DICKERSON & THE COTTON CLUB ORCHESTRA.
Album: released on Collectors Items, Apr'79 Dist: Jazz Music, Swift, Chris Wellard

Cooper, Lindsay

MUSIC FOR OTHER OCCASIONS.
Album: released on Recommended, Jun'86 by Recommended Records. Dist: Recommended, Impetus, Rough Trade

Co-optimists

CO-OPTIMISTS, THE Highlights by original artists.
Album: released on WRC, Aug'76

Coorse & Fine Songs...

COORSE AND FINE SONGS AND BALLADS OF DUNDEE Various artists (Various Artists).
Album: released on Springthyme, Feb'86 by Springthyme Records. Dist: Jazz Music Distribution, Projection Distribution, Roots Distribution

Cassette: released on Springthyme, Feb'86 by Springthyme Records. Dist: Jazz Music Distribution, Projection Distribution, Roots Distribution

Cope, Julian

EVE'S VOLCANO (COVERED IN SIN).
Tracks: / Eve's volcano / Almost beautiful child (1&2) / Spacehopper-annexe.
Single (12"): released on Island, Apr'87 by Island Records. Dist: Polygram

Compact disc single: released on Island, Apr'87 by Island Records. Dist: Polygram

EVE'S VOLCANO 'COVERED IN SIN'.
Tracks: / Eve's volcano 'covered in sin'. / Almost beautiful child (I & II) / Pulsar NX (Live) / Shot down (live).
Single (7"): released on Island, Mar'87 by Island Records. Dist: Polygram

FRIED.
Tracks: / Reynard the fox / Bill Drummond said / Laughing boy / Me singing / Sunspots / Bloody assizes,The / Search party / O, King of chaos / Holy love / Torpedo.
Compact disc: released on Mercury, Nov'84 by Phonogram Records. Dist: Polygram Distribution

GREATNESS AND PERFECTION OF LOVE.
Single (7"): released on Mercury, Mar'84 by Phonogram Records. Dist: Polygram Distribution

Single (12"): released on Mercury, Mar'84 by Phonogram Records. Dist: Polygram Distribution

INTERVIEW PICTURE DISC.
Album: released on Baktabak, Oct'87 by Baktabak Records. Dist: Arabesque. Estim retail price in Sep'87 was £4.91.

SAINT JULIAN.
Tracks: / Crack in the clouds, A / Trampolene / Shot down / Eve's volcano / Space hopper / Planet ride / World shut your mouth / Saint Julian / Pulsar / Screaming secrets / Crack in the clouds, A.
Notes: All songs composed by Julian Cope. Produced by Warne Livesey, Ed Stasium. Featuring: Julian Cope-vocals, guitar/Donald Ross Skinner-slide & electric guitar/Chris Whitten-drums/James Eller-bass/Double De Harrison-organ,clarinet.
Album: released on Island, Mar'87 by Island Records. Dist: Polygram

Cassette: released on Island, Mar'87 by Island Records. Dist: Polygram

Compact disc: released on Island, Mar'87 by Island Records. Dist: Polygram

SUNSHINE PLAYROOM.
Single (7"): released on Mercury, Nov'83 by Phonogram Records. Dist: Polygram Distribution

Single (12"): released on Mercury, Nov'83 by Phonogram Records. Dist: Polygram Distribution

SUN SPOTS.
Single (12"): released on Mercury, Feb'85 by Phonogram Records. Dist: Polygram Distribution

TRAMPOLENE.
Tracks: / Disaster / Mock Turtle / Warwick the king.
Single (7"): released on Island, Jan'87 by Island Records. Dist: Polygram

TROMPOLINE.
Single (12"): released on Island, Jan'87 by Island Records. Dist: Polygram

WORLD SHUT YOUR MOUTH.
Tracks: / World shut your mouth / Umpteenth unnatural blues / I've got levitation / Non-Alignment pact / Transporting / Umpteenth unnatural blues / World shut your mouth.
Compact disc: by Phonogram Records. Dist: Polygram Distribution

Single (7"): released on Island, Sep'86 by Island Records. Dist: Polygram

Single (12"): released on Island, Sep'86 by Island Records. Dist: Polygram

Single (7"): released on Island, Oct'86 by Island Records. Dist: Polygram

Single (12"): released on Island, Sep'86 by Island Records. Dist: Polygram

Album: released on Mercury, Feb'84 by Phonogram Records. Dist: Polygram Distribution

Cassette: released on Mercury, Feb'84 by Phonogram Records. Dist: Polygram Distribution

Copeland, Johnny

BRINGING IT ALL BACK HOME.
Album: released on Demon, Feb'86 by Demon Records. Dist: Pinnacle

COPELAND SPECIAL.
Album: released on Demon, May'82 by Demon Records. Dist: Pinnacle

DEDICATED TO THE GREATEST.
Album: released on Kent, Apr'87 by Ace Records. Dist: Pinnacle

DOWN ON BENDING KNEE.
Album: released on Mr. R&B (Sweden), Feb'85

I'LL BE AROUND.
Album: released on Mr. R&B (Sweden), Oct'84

MAKE MY HOME WHERE I HANG MY HAT.
Album: released on Rounder, Jan'87 Dist: Roots Distribution

Album: released on Demon, Nov'82 by Demon Records. Dist: Pinnacle

SHOWDOWN (Copeland, Johnny/Robert Cray/Albert Collins).
Notes: For full details see under **Collins, Albert.**

TEXAS TWISTER.
Album: released on Demon, '84 by Demon Records. Dist: Pinnacle

Copeland, Stewart

KOTEJA (Copeland, Stewart & Ray Lema).
Single (7"): released on A&M, Mar'85 by A&M Records. Dist: Polygram

LOVE LESSONS (Copeland, Stewart & Derek Holt).
Tracks: / Love lessons / Amy (silent movies).
Single (7"): released on I.R.S.(Independent Record Syndicate), Aug'86 by I.R.S.. Dist: MCA

Single (12"): released on I.R.S.(Independent Record Syndicate), Aug'86 by I.R.S.. Dist: MCA

RHYTHMATIST, THE.
Album: released on A&M, May'85 by A&M Records. Dist: Polygram

Cassette: released on A&M, May'85 by A&M Records. Dist: Polygram

RUMBLE FISH.
Album: released on A&M, Jan'84 by A&M Records. Dist: Polygram

Cassette: released on A&M, Jan'84 by A&M Records. Dist: Polygram

Copernicus

FROM BACTERIA.
Album: released on DMC, Jul'87 Dist: Red Rhino, Cartel

Copland's Greatest Hits

COPLAND'S GREATEST HITS Various artists (Various Artists).
Cassette: released on CBS, Jul'83 by CBS Records. Dist: CBS

Copley, Al

HANDFUL OF KEY,A.
Album: released on Off-Beat, Oct'86 by Off-Beat Records. Dist: Jetstar Distribution

Copper, Bob

BOB COPPER Countryside songs from the south.
Album: released on Topic, '81 Dist: Roots Distribution

TWANKYDILLO 2 generations country singers.
Cassette: released on Folktracks, Nov'79 by Folktracks Cassettes. Dist: Folktracks

TWO BRETHREN, THE.
Cassette: released on Folktracks, Nov'79 by Folktracks Cassettes. Dist: Folktracks

Copper Family

SONG FOR EVERY SEASON, A.
Double Album: released on Leader, '81 Dist: Jazz Music, Projection

Double Album: released on Leader, '81 Dist: Jazz Music, Projection

Copperfield, David

DAVID COPPERFIELD Dickens, Charles (Rees, Roger).
Cassette: released on Caedmon(USA), Apr'83 by Caedmon (USA) Records. Dist: Taylors, Discovery

Copperhead

COPPERHEAD.
Album: released on Edsel, Jun'84 by Demon Records. Dist: Pinnacle, Jazz Music, Projection

Copper, Mike

CONTINUOUS PREACHING BLUES, THE (Copper, Mike & Ian Anderson).
Album: released on Appaloosa, Jul'85 Dist: Roots, Folksound, Projection, Celtic Music, Chris Wellard

Coppin, Johnny

BELIEVE IN YOU.
Tracks: / Believe in you / Run to her.
Single (7"): released on Red Sky, Jan'80 by Red Sky Records. Dist: Red Sky, Projection, Celtic Music, Roots

ENGLISH MORNING Songs of Gloucestershire and beyond.
Tracks: / English morning / Everlasting mercy / Dover's hill / Hill,The / Tom Long's post / High hills,The / Holy brook,The / East wind / Nailsworth hill / Hill and vale / Cotswold tiles / Christmas eve / Winter / Forest carol / Under Robinswood.
Album: released on Red Sky, Jan'87 by Red Sky Records. Dist: Red Sky, Projection, Celtic Music, Roots

Cassette: released on Red Sky, Jan'87 by Red Sky Records. Dist: Red Sky, Projection, Celtic Music, Roots

EVERYBODY KNOWS.
Tracks: / Everybody knows / No going back.
Single (7"): released on Starward, Jan'80 Dist: Roots Distribution, Red Sky Distribution, Celtic Music Distribution, Projection Distribution

FOREST AND VALE AND HIGH BLUE HILL.
Tracks: / In flanders / Song of Gloucestershire,A / Piper's Wood / Fisherman of Newnham / Cotswold love / Briar roses / Legacy / Warning / High-Road,The / Field of Autumn / Cotswold lad / Song of Minsterworth Perry / Have wandered / Ctswold Farmers,The / This night the stars.
Album: released on Red Sky, Jul'86 by Red Sky Records. Dist: Red Sky, Projection, Celtic Music, Roots

Cassette: released on Red Sky, Jul'86 by Red Sky Records. Dist: Red Sky, Projection, Celtic Music, Roots

GET LUCKY.
Tracks: / New day / Get lucky / First time love / Contrary / Celebrate my life / Heaven knows / Never fly you way / Catherine / For you / Everybody knows.
Album: released on Starward, Jul'86 Dist: Roots Distribution, Red Sky Distribution, Celtic Music Distribution, Projection Distribution

LINE OF BLUE.
Tracks: / It's your life / Hurricane of '15, The / Everything to me / Keep a little light / Lost in love with you / Changing life / Rydal / Every roll of thunder / Hallelujah / Pride of all the ocean / Shine silently.
Album: released on Red Sky, Jul'86 by Red Sky Records. Dist: Red Sky, Projection, Celtic Music, Roots

Cassette: released on Red Sky, Jul'86 by Red Sky Records. Dist: Red Sky, Projection, Celtic Music, Roots

NO GOING BACK.
Tracks: / No going back / Can you feel it / Young girl town / Falling for you / Run to her / Part in my heart / Believe in you / Birmingham / He will let you know / We shall not pass.
Album: released on Rola, Jul'86 by Rola Records. Dist: Roots Distribution, Spartan Distribution

ROLL ON DREAMER.
Tracks: / Liberty / Never lost for love / Angelus / If that's the way you feel / Roll on dreamer / Worm forgives the plough / Archangel / Roads go down,The / Midwinter / Warm love.
Notes: Johnny Coppin, Red Sky Records, 57 Essex Street, Oxford. OX4 3AW. Tel: 0865-724408.
Album: released on Red Sky, Jul'86 by Red Sky Records. Dist: Red Sky, Projection, Celtic Music, Roots

WE SHALL NOT PASS.
Tracks: / We shall not pass / Can you feel it.
Single (7"): released on Red Sky, Jan'79 by Red Sky Records. Dist: Red Sky, Projection, Celtic Music, Roots

Cops

BABY IT'S YOU.
Single (7"): released on Logo, Apr'82 by Logo Records. Dist: Roots, BMG

Coptic Roots

ROOTS AND CULTURE.
Single (12"): released on Axumite, Nov'85 Dist: Jetstar

Copulatin' Blues

COPULATIN' BLUES 16 original blues vocals.
Album: released on Stash, Apr'81 Dist: Swift Distribution, Jazz Music Distribution, Jazz Horizons Distribution, Celtic Music Distribution, Cadillac, Zodiac Distribution

COPULATIN' BLUES VOL.1 Various artists (Various Artists).
Cassette: released on Stash (USA), Mar'85 Dist: Swift Distribution, Jazz Music Distribution, Jazz Horizons Distribution, Celtic Music Distribution, Cadillac, Zodiac Distribution

COPULATIN' BLUES VOL.2 Various artists (Various Artists).
Album: released on Stash (USA), May'84 Dist: Swift Distribution, Jazz Music Distribution, Jazz Horizons Distribution, Celtic Music Distribution, Cadillac, Zodiac Distribution

Copy Cats

TELL THE CAPTAIN.
Single (7"): released on Out To Lunch, Jan'84 by Out To Lunch Records. Dist: PRT Distribution

Single (12"): released on Out To Lunch, Jan'84 by Out To Lunch Records. Dist: PRT Distribution

Copykiller

COPYKILLER Original Soundtrack.
Album: released on General Music (France), Mar'86 by General Music Records (France). Dist: Studio Import & Export Distribution, Silva Screen

Cassette: released on General Music (France), Mar'86 by General Music Records (France). Dist: Studio Import & Export Distribution, Silva Screen

Coral Island

CORAL ISLAND By R.M. Ballantyne; read by M. Heller.
Double cassette: released on Colophone, Sep'81 by Audio-Visual Library Services. Dist: Audio-Visual Library Services

Corbett, Harry H.

OLD FASHIONED CHRISTMAS.
Single (7"): released on Pel Dec'80

STEPTOE & SON.
Album: released on Hallmark, '72 by Pickwick Records. Dist: Pickwick Distribution, PRT, Taylors

Corchia, Louis

TEMPO GRANDE VITESSE.
Tracks: / Rancho Grande / El Matinos / Roses De Picardie / Tempo Grande Vitesse / Bal De La Marine / Lettre A Evelyn / Tango Des Jours Heureux / J'Attendrai / Nationale / Rue De Charenton / Ave Maria / La Banboula.
Album: released on Accordion Record Club, Jul'86 by Accordion Record Club Records. Dist: Accordion Record Club

Cordell, Frank

BRITISH FILM MUSIC (Cordell, Frank & The Phoenix Orchestra).
Album: released on Phoenix Digital, Jan'83

Cordells

IN A MELLOW MOOD.
Album: released on Headphones, Nov'85 Dist: Jetstar

Cordner, Rodney

DON'T LOOK AWAY.
Album: by Pilgrim Records. Dist: Rough Trade, Cartel

Corea, Chick

AGAIN & AGAIN.
Compact disc: by Elektra/Asylum/Nonesuch Records. Dist: WEA

AGAIN AND AGAIN.
Compact disc: released on Elektra (USA), Jun'84 by Elektra/Asylum/Nonesuch Records. Dist: WEA

AGAIN AND AGAIN (JO BURG SESSION,THE).
Tracks: / No.3 / Waltze / Again and again / 1 - 2 - 1234 / Diddle diddle / Twang.
Album: released on Elektra(Musician), Feb'83 by WEA Records. Dist: WEA

ARC (Corea, Chick & Holland & Altschul).
Album: by ECM Records. Dist: IMS, Polygram, Virgin through EMI

BLISS.
Album: released on Muse, Apr'81 by Peerless Records. Dist: Lugtons Distributors

CHICK COREA ELEKTRIC BAND,THE.
Tracks: / Rumble / Side walk / Cool Weasel boogie / Got a match / Elektric city / No zone / King Cockroach / India town.
Album: released on GRP (USA), Apr'86 by GRP Records (USA). Dist: IMS, Polygram

Compact disc: released on GRP (USA), Apr'86 by GRP Records (USA). Dist: IMS, Polygram

CHILDREN'S SONGS.
Album: released on ECM (Germany), Apr'84 by ECM Records. Dist: IMS, Polygram, Virgin through EMI

Compact disc: released on ECM (Germany), Apr'84 by ECM Records. Dist: IMS, Polygram, Virgin through EMI

COMPACT JAZZ.
Compact disc: released on Polydor, Jul'87 by Polydor Records. Dist: Polygram, Polydor

FIESTA, (LA).
Album: released on IMS(Import), Oct'82 by Polydor Records. Dist: IMS, Polygram

IN CONCERT (Corea, Chick & Gary Burton).
Compact disc: released on ECM (Germany), '84 by ECM Records. Dist: IMS, Polygram, Virgin through EMI

INNER SPACE.
Album: released on Atlantic, Sep'74 by WEA Records. Dist: WEA

LIGHT AS A FEATHER.
Tracks: / You're everything / Light as a feather / Captain Marvel / 500 miles high / Children's song / Spain.
Compact disc: by ECM Records. Dist: IMS, Polygram, Virgin through EMI

LIGHT YEARS (Corea, Chick Elektric Band).
Notes: The jazz world's leading keyboardist and renowned innovator of the jazz fusion movement,Chick Corea & his newly formed Elektric Band present their second GRP album.
Album: released on GRP (USA), May'87 by GRP Records (USA). Dist: IMS, Polygram

Cassette: released on GRP (USA), May'87 by GRP Records (USA). Dist: IMS, Polygram

Compact disc: released on GRP (USA), May'87 by GRP Records (USA). Dist: IMS, Polygram

LIVE AT MIDEM, 1978 (Corea, Chick & Lionel Hampton).
Album: released on Gateway (USA), Sep'83 by Gemcom Inc.(USA) Records.

LYRIC SUITE FOR SEXTET (Corea, Chick & Gary Burton).
Album: released on ECM (Germany), Oct'83 by ECM Records. Dist: IMS, Polygram, Virgin through EMI

Album: released on ECM (Germany), Oct'83 by ECM Records. Dist: IMS, Polygram, Virgin through EMI

MEETING, THE (Corea, Chick & Friedrich Gulda).
Compact disc: Dist: IMS-Polygram

Compact disc: released on Philips, Aug'84 Dist: IMS-Polygram

MIRROR MIRROR (Corea, Chick/Joe Henderson).
Album: released on MPS Jazz, May'81

MY SPANISH HEART.
Compact disc: by ECM Records. Dist: IMS, Polygram, Virgin through EMI

Album: released on Polydor, Feb'77 by Polydor Records. Dist: Polygram, Polydor

Compact disc: released on Polydor, Feb'77 by Polydor Records. Dist: Polygram, Polydor

NO MYSTERY.
Compact disc: by Polydor Records. Dist: Polygram, Polydor

PIANO IMPROVISATION VOLUME 2.
Compact disc: by ECM Records. Dist: IMS, Polygram, Virgin through EMI

PIANO IMPROVISATIONS.
Tracks: / Noon Song / Song for Sally / Ballad for Anna / Song of the wind / Sometime ago / Where are you now ? - A suite of eight pictures.
Compact disc: by ECM Records. Dist: IMS, Polygram, Virgin through EMI

RETURN TO FOREVER.
Cassette: released on ECM (Germany), Jun'84 by ECM Records. Dist: IMS, Polygram, Virgin through EMI

SEA JOURNEY.
Album: released on Platinum (W.Germany), Oct'85 Dist: Mainline

Cassette: released on Platinum (W.Germany), Oct'85 Dist: Mainline

SECRET AGENT.
Album: released on Polydor, Jan'79 by Polydor Records. Dist: Polygram, Polydor

SEPTET.
Tracks: / 1st Movement / 2nd Movement / 3rd Movement / 4th Movement / 5th Movement / Temple of Isfahan,The.
Compact disc: by ECM Records. Dist: IMS, Polygram, Virgin through EMI

Album: released on ECM (Germany), Dec'85 by ECM Records. Dist: IMS, Polygram, Virgin through EMI

SONG OF SINGING.
Tracks: / Toy room / Ballad I. / Rhymes / Flesh / Ballad III / Neffertiti.
Compact disc: released on EMI, Mar'87 by EMI Records. Dist: EMI

SONG OF SINGING, (THE).
Album: released on Blue Note, Apr'85 by EMI Records. Dist: EMI

TRIO MUSIC.
Tracks: / Trio improvisation 1,2,3. / Duet improvisation 1,2,4,5 / Slippery when wet / Rhythm-a-ning / Round midnight / Eronel / Think of one / Little Rootie Tootie. / Reflections / Hackensack.
Double compact disc: by ECM Records. Dist: IMS, Polygram, Virgin through EMI

Double Album: released on ECM (Germany), Oct'82 by ECM Records. Dist: IMS, Polygram, Virgin through EMI

TRIO MUSIC LIVE IN EUROPE (Corea, Chick, Trio).
Notes: Recorded during their 1984 European tour. The compact disc contains an extra track which is a bass solo by Miroslav Vitous. Recorded in September 1984. Personnel: Chick Corea-piano, Miroslav Vitous-bass,Roy Haynes-drums.

TRIO MUSIC LIVE IN EUROPE.
Album: released on ECM (Germany), Dec'86 by ECM Records. Dist: IMS, Polygram, Virgin through EMI

Compact disc: released on ECM (Germany), Dec'86 by ECM Records. Dist: IMS, Polygram, Virgin through EMI

VOYAGE.
Tracks: / Mallorca / Diversions / Star Island / Free fall / Hong Kong.
Compact disc: by ECM Records. Dist: IMS, Polygram, Virgin through EMI

Album: released on ECM (Germany), Mar'85 by ECM Records. Dist: IMS, Polygram, Virgin through EMI

Compact disc: released on ECM (Germany), Mar'85 by ECM Records. Dist: IMS, Polygram, Virgin through EMI

WALKMAN JAZZ.
Album: released on Polydor, Jun'76 by Polydor Records. Dist: Polygram, .

WHERE HAVE I KNOWN YOU BEFORE?.
Album: released on Polydor, Jun'81 by Polydor Records. Dist: Polygram, Polydor

Compact disc: released on Polydor, Jun'81 by Polydor Records. Dist: Polygram, Polydor

WITH UNDERSTANDING (Corea, Chick & R. Davis).
Album: released on Muse, Jun'77 by Peerless Records.

WORKS.
Tracks: / Addendum / Where are you now / Noon song / Children's song / Brasilia / Slippery when wet / Duet improvisation / New place(Scenery).A / La Fiesta / Return to forever / Where are you now / Song of the wind / Round midnight / Rhythm-a-ning / Senor mouse / Sometime ago / La fiesta.
Compact disc: by ECM Records. Dist: IMS, Polygram, Virgin through EMI

Cassette: released on ECM (Germany), Nov'83 by ECM Records. Dist: IMS, Polygram, Virgin through EMI

Album: released on ECM/Works (Germany), May'85 by ECM Records. Dist: IMS, Polygram, Virgin through EMI

ZURICH CONCERT (Corea, Chick & Gary Burton).
Double Album: released on ECM, Nov'80 by ECM Records. Dist: IMS, Polygram, Virgin through EMI

Coren, Alan

ARTHUR AND THE BELLYBUTTON DIAMOND.
Notes: One of Alan Coren's many "Arthur Stories", read delightfully by Tom Baker.
Cassette: released on Talking Tape Company, Sep'84 by Talking Tape Company Records.

Corfield, Gemma

MAD FOR IT.
Tracks: / Mad for it / Laid in the USA.
Single (12"): released on Virgin, Aug'85 by Virgin Records. Dist: EMI, Virgin Distribution

Cori Jorsals

TAKIN' IT STRAIGHT Mirror of your....
Single (7"): released on Metropolis, Jan'83 by Carrere Records. Dist: RCA Distribution

Single (12"): released on Metropolis, Jan'83 by Carrere Records. Dist: RCA Distribution

Corkscrew

FOR OPENERS.
Album: released on Highway, '81 by Highway Records. Dist: Roots, Projection, Ross

HARD ROAD TO CALVARY.
Tracks: / Square rooms / Don't play with me.
Single (12"): released on Glim Bim, Jul'82 by Glim Bim Records. Dist: Jetstar

Corley, Al

SQUARE ROOMS.
Compact disc: by Polydor Records. Dist: Polygram, Polydor

Single (7"): released on Polydor, Jun'85 by Polydor Records. Dist: Polygram, Polydor

Single (12"): released on Polydor, Jun'85 by Polydor Records. Dist: Polygram, Polydor

Cormack, Arthur

NUAIR BHA MI OG.
Album: released on Temple, Jan'85 by Temple Records. Dist: Roots Distribution, Folksound Distribution, Celtic Music Distribution, Projection Distribution

Cormier, Clarence

HEE HAW BREAKDOWN Cajun waltz.
Single (7"): released on Swallow, Dec'82

Corn Bread

IT'S HOT.
Album: released on Sierra, Mar'79 by Sierra Records. Dist: WEA

LEROY MAC.
Album: released on Sierra, Mar'79 by Sierra Records. Dist: WEA

Corn Dollies

FOREVER STEVEN.
Tracks: / Forever Steven / About to believe.
Single (7"): released on Farm, Jul'87 by Farm Records. Dist: Nine Mile, Cartel

Cornelius, Eddie

HURRY UP.
Tracks: / Hurry up / That's love making in your eyes.
Single (7"): released on G&B, May'86 Dist: Gold & Sons

Cornelius, Helen

HELEN CORNELIUS.
Album: released on MCA, Mar'87 by MCA Records. Dist: Polygram, MCA

Cassette: released on MCA, Mar'87 by MCA Records. Dist: Polygram, MCA

Cornelius, Kay

AEROBIC WORKOUT EXERCISE PROGRAMME FOR MEN & WOMEN.
Album: released on K-Tel, May'83 by K-Tel Records. Dist: Record Merchandisers Distribution, Taylors, Terry Blood Distribution, Wynd-Up Distribution, Relay Distribution, Pickwick Distribution, Solomon & Peres Distribution, Polygram

Cassette: released on K-Tel, May'83 by K-Tel Records. Dist: Record Merchandisers Distribution, Taylors, Terry Blood Distribution, Wynd-Up Distribution, Relay Distribution, Pickwick Distribution, Solomon & Peres Distribution, Polygram

Corner, Amen

AMEN CORNER'S GREATEST HITS.
Notes: Featuring Andy Fairweather-Low
Album: released on Immediate, Jan'78 by Castle Communications. Dist: Cartel

BEND ME SHAPE ME.
Single (7"): released on Old Gold, Oct'83 by Old Gold Records. Dist: Lightning, Jazz Music, Spartan, Counterpoint

Single (7"): released on Decca, Oct'80 by Decca Records. Dist: Polygram

HALF AS NICE (IF PARADISE IS).
Single (7"): released on Old Gold, Jan'85 by Old Gold Records. Dist: Lightning, Jazz Music, Spartan, Counterpoint

RETURN OF THE MAGNIFICENT SEVEN.
Album: released on Immediate, Mar'76 by Castle Communications. Dist: Cartel

Cornwall, Hugh

FACTS & FIGURES.
Tracks: / Facts and figures (Version).
Single (7"): released on Virgin, Jan'87 by Virgin Records. Dist: EMI, Virgin Distribution

Single (12"): released on Virgin, Jan'87 by Virgin Records. Dist: EMI, Virgin Distribution

Cornwell, Charlotte

NEVER GOING HOME Ain't happened yet.
Single (7"): released on CBS, Apr'83 by CBS Records. Dist: CBS

Cornwell, Hugh

ONE IN A MILLION.
Tracks: / One in a million / Siren song.
Single (7"): released on Portrait, Aug'85 by CBS Records. Dist: CBS

Single (12"): released on Portrait, Aug'85 by CBS Records. Dist: CBS

Coronation Music

CORONATION MUSIC Various artists (Various Artists).
Compact disc: by PRT Records. Dist: PRT

Coroner

R.I.P..
Album: released on Noise, Jun'87 by Dorane. Dist: Revolver, Cartel

Corpse Grinders

VALLEY OF FEAR.
Album: released on New Rose, Nov'84 Dist: Rough Trade, Cartel

Corpses As Bedmates

VENUS HANDCUFFS.
Album: by Dave Henderson.

Correll, Denny

STANDIN' IN THE LIGHT.
Tracks: / Wings of the wind / Lead me home / Paradise / Witness (The) / Glory road / Living water / Faith / Standin' in the light / Noah / Redeemer / He's comin' again.
Album: released on Marantha Music, May'82

Cassette: released on Marantha Music, May'82

Corrib

CAREFREE.
Notes: A band of Irish origin - extremely popular throughout the U.K. and Eire.
Album: released on Dingles, '83 by Dingles Records. Dist: Projection

Corrie Folk Trio

In retrospect

Corries

Biographical Details: This British band, which comprises just two men, twice took their humour-laden Scottish music-making into the lower regions of the Uk album charts. The first occassion was May 1970, when they reached No. 46 with "Scottish Love Songs", "Sound Of Pibroch" took them to no.39 in September 1972. With their dialect laid on as thick as possible, the Corries style is to traditionally Scottish to appeal to audiences and record buyers outside that territory.

16 SCOTTISH FAVOURITES.
Tracks: / Collier laddie (The) / Where two hawks fly / Castle of Dromore (The) / Jack o' Hazeldean / Man's a man, A / Helen of Kirkconnel / Sherrifmuir / Scots wha hae / News from Moidart (The) / Kate Dalrumple / Petronella / Heidless cross (The) / I know my love / Lark in the morning (The) / Heiland Harry / Bluebells of Scotland (The).
Album: released on Glen, Apr'79 Dist: EMI, Outlet

BONNETT, BELT AND SWORD.
Tracks: / Hot asphalt / Cam ye o'er frae France / Joy of my heart / Jolly beggar (The) / Bring back my granny to me / My brother Bill's a fireman / Glenlyon lament / Johnny Cope / Gaberlunzie King / Haughs O'Cromdale / Banks of Newfoundland / Parcel o' rogues / North sea holes / Katie Bairdie / Oor wee school / I once loved a lass / Blow ye winds.
Notes: An entertaining, rousing and moving collection of traditional and contemporary songs from one of Scotland's and the world's, best-loved folk groups.
Album: released on Fontana, Jul'84 by Phonogram Records. Dist: Polygram

Cassette: released on Fontana, Jul'84 by Phonogram Records. Dist: Polygram

CORRIES, THE.
Album: released on Dara, Feb'86 by CML Distributors. Dist: MK, Projection

Cassette: released on Dara, Feb'86 by CML Distributors. Dist: MK, Projection

Cassette: released on Ideal(Tapes), Apr'80 Dist: EMI

LEGENDS OF SCOTLAND.
Tracks: / Black Douglas,The / Wha wadna fecht for Charlie / Isle of Skye,The / I will go / Sound the Pibroch / Derwentwater's farewell / Flood Garry / Bonnie Dundee / Peggy Gordon / Boy's of Bluehill and Derry Hornpipe,The / Abigail / Gartan mothers lullaby / Maids when you're young / Rose of Allandale,The / Kiss the children for me, Mary / Westering home.
Cassette: released on Lochshore, Jun'86 by Klub Records. Dist: PRT

LIVE AT THE ROYAL LYCEUM THEATRE EDINBURGH.
Tracks: / Wha wadna fecht for Charlie / Liberty / Side by side / Tramps and hawkers / Great silkie (The) / Lyceum blues / Ye Jacobites by name / Lowlands away / Abigail / Old triangle (The) / Dream Angus / Maids, when your young, never wed an old man / Bonnie Dundee.
Album: released on Note, Oct'76 by EMI Records. Dist: EMI

SPOTLIGHT ON....
Tracks: / Fond kiss, A / Bonnie lass of Fyvie (The) / Bring back my granny to me / Ca' the ewes / Cruel brother / Flower of Scotland / Gallus bloke / Glenlyon lament / Haughs O'Cromdale / Highland lament / Hills of Ardmorn / Johnny lad / Katie Bairdie / Kishmul's galley / Lewis bridal song / Lowlands of Holland (The) / My brother Bill's a fireman / Oor wee school / Parcel o' rogues / Road to Dundee / Roving journeyman / Sally free and easy / Toon o'Kelso / Twa corbies / Wild rover / Will ye go lassie go.
Album: released on Philips, Oct'77 Dist: IMS-Polygram

Corrigan, Ian

IRISH COUNTRY.
Cassette: released on Homespun(Ireland), Sep'79 by Outlet Records. Dist: Outlet

Corrosion Of Conformity

ANIMOSITY.
Album: released on Roadrunner (Dutch), Aug'85 Dist: Pinnacle

TECHNOCRACY.
Single (12"): released on Metal Blade, May'87 Dist: Enigma Distribution

TECHNOCRACY (LP).
Album: released on Metal Blade, Jun'87 Dist: Enigma Distribution

Cortez, Dave

HAPPY ORGAN (Cortez, Dave 'Baby').
Single (7"): released on Creole, Aug'82 by Creole Records. Dist: Rhino, PRT

RINKY DINK (Cortez, Dave 'Baby').
Single (7"): released on Creole, Aug'82 by Creole Records. Dist: Rhino, PRT

Corvettes

GIRLS CARS GIRLS SUN GIRLS SURF FUN GIRLS.
Tracks: / Girls cars girls sun girls surf fun girls / Beach is not enough (The).
Single (7"): released on Bitchen, Jul'84 by Bitchen Records. Dist: Pinnacle

SURF DON'T WALK.
Single (7"): released on Bitchen, Jun'86 by Bitchen Records. Dist: Pinnacle

Cory Band

CORY BAND.
Tracks: / Skyrider / Hungarian dance / Country scene / Nocturne & interlude / Girl I left behind me / Blue rondo a la Turk / Lullaby for Lisa / Lucky for some / Scarborough Fair / First shoot.
Album: released on Polyphonic Digital, Aug'86

Cassette: released on Polyphonic Digital, Aug'86

Album: released on Polyphonic, Apr'84 by Polyphonic Records. Dist: Taylors

Cassette: released on Polyphonic, Apr'84 by Polyphonic Records. Dist: Taylors

Single (7"): released on MGM, '80 Dist: Polygram Distribution, Swift Distribution

DANCES & ARIAS.
Album: released on Polyphonic, Jun'85 by Polyphonic Records. Dist: Taylors

Cassette: released on Polyphonic, Jun'85 by Polyphonic Records. Dist: Taylors

PRIDE OF THE RHONDAA.
Tracks: / Maple leaf rag / Land of the mountain and the flood (The) / Concert overture / Albertie / Les girls / Sweet gingerbread man / Magnificent seven (The) / La domino noir / Overture / Il silenzio / Prince of Denmark's march (The) / Virginian theme (The) / Miller magic.
Album: released on One Up, Feb'77 by EMI Records.

SALUTE TO THE NEW WORLD.
Tracks: / Salute to the new world overture / Rule Britannia / Chorale and rock out / Elegy from an epic symphony / Dashing away with a smoothing iron / March / Manhattan beach / Jeannie / Marche des Bouffons / Largo from the new world symphony / Fantasia on the dargason / Fanfare for Rocky / Procession of the sidar / Land of the long white cloud-aotearoa / Castleway / Blow the wind southerly / Variations on a ninth.
Album: released on Grosvenor, Jun'77 by Grosvenor Records. Dist: Taylors

Coryell, Larry

ASPECTS.
Tracks: / Kowloon jag / Titus / Pyramids / Rodrigo reflections / Yin-yang / Woman of truth and future.
Album: released on Arista, Jul'76 by Arista Records. Dist: RCA

AT VILLAGE GATE.
Album: by PRT Records. Dist: PRT

BACK TOGETHER (Coryell, Larry & A. Mouzon).
Tracks: / Beneath the earth / Phonse (The) / Transvested / Express / Crystallization / Rock'n'roll lovers / Get on up / Reconciliation / Back together again / Mr. C / High love.

BAREFOOT BOY.
Album: released on RCA (Germany), Dec'84

BOLERO (Coryell, Larry & Brian Keane).
Compact disc: released on Black & Blue (France), Jan'86 Dist: Swift, Target, Discovery

BOLERO & SCHEHERAZADE.
Compact disc: Dist: IMS-Polygram

COMING HOME.
Tracks: / Good citizen swallow / Glorielle / Twelve and twelve / Confirmation / It never entered my mind.
Compact disc: by Peerless Records. Dist: Lugtons Distributors

Album: released on Muse Jazz (USA), Jan'86

EQUIPOISE.
Album: released on Muse (USA), Feb'87 by Muse Records (USA). Dist: Conifer Distribution, Jazz Music Distribution

Compact disc: released on Muse (USA), Feb'87 by Muse Records (USA). Dist: Conifer Distribution, Jazz Music Distribution

FIREBIRD & PETROUCHKA,THE.
Album:

Compact disc:

INTRODUCING 11TH HOUSE.
Album: released on Vanguard, Jun'74 by PRT Records. Dist: PRT

LEVEL ONE.
Album: released on Arista, '76 by Arista Records. Dist: RCA

L'OISEAU DE FEU (THE FIREBIRD)/PETROUCHKA.
Compact disc: Dist: IMS-Polygram

PLANET END.
Album: released on Vanguard, '76 by PRT Records. Dist: PRT

RESTFUL MIND,THE.
Album: released on Vanguard, '75 by PRT Records. Dist: PRT

SACRE DU PRINTEMPS, (LE).
Compact disc: Dist: IMS-Polygram

SPACES.
Album: released on Vanguard, '74 by PRT Records. Dist: PRT

SPLENDID (Coryell, Larry & Philip Catherine).
Album: released on Elektra (USA), '78 by Elektra/Asylum/Nonesuch Records. Dist: WEA

TOGETHER (Coryell, Larry & Emily Remler).
Tracks: / Arabian nights / Joy spring / Ill wind / How my heart sings / Six beats, six strings / Gerri's blues / First things first.
Compact disc: released on Concord Jazz(USA), Nov'86 by Concord Jazz Records (USA). Dist: IMS, Polygram

TWIN HOUSE (Coryell, Larry & Philip Catherine).

Cosmat Angels

CUTTING EDGE (LIVE).
Tracks: / Cutting edge (live), (The) / Flying dream (live).
Single (12"): released on Island, Mar'87 by Island Records. Dist: Polygram

Cosma, Vladimir

KIDNAPPED (Cosma, Vladimir Orchestra).
Album: released on Decca, May'79 by Decca Records. Dist: Polygram

SENTIMENTAL PROMENADE La wally.
Single (7"): released on Palace, '83 Dist: PVG

Cosmetic

SO TRANQUILIZIN.
Tracks: / So Tranquilizin / Jet set,The / About the money / All things must change / Be my girl / Take it to the top / All my love / N-er-gize me.

SO TRANQUILIZIN.
Tracks: / So Tranquilizin.
Single (12"): released on Gramavision (USA), Dec'85 by Gramavison Records (USA). Dist: PRT, IMS, Polygram

SO TRANQUILIZIN.
Album: released on Gramavision (USA), '85 by Gramavison Records (USA). Dist: PRT, IMS, Polygram

Cassette: released on Gramavision (USA), '85 by Gramavison Records (USA). Dist: PRT, IMS, Polygram

Compact disc: released on Gramavision (USA), '85 by Gramavison Records (USA). Dist: PRT, IMS, Polygram

Cosmetics

CHAIN Closures.
Single (7"): released on Secret, '82 by Secret Records. Dist: EMI

COSMETIC New complexion.
Single (7"): released on Rough Trade, '82 by Rough Trade Records. Dist: Rough Trade Distribution, Cartel Distribution

CRACK,THE Caligraphy.
Single (12"): released on Illegal, '82 by Faulty Products Records. Dist: Pinnacle, Lightning, Cartel

GET READY Put it on.
Single (7"): released on Rough Trade, '82 by Rough Trade Records. Dist: Rough Trade Distribution, Cartel Distribution

Single (12"): released on Rough Trade, '82 by Rough Trade Records. Dist: Rough Trade Distribution, Cartel Distribution

Cosmic Circle

MAGIC.
Single (12"): released on C & E, Nov'86 Dist: Jetstar

Cosmos

COSMOS Various artists (Various Artists).
Album: released on RCA, '84 by RCA Records. Dist: RCA, Roots, Swift, Wellard, Chris, I & B, Solomon & Peres Distribution

Cassette: released on RCA, '84 by RCA Records. Dist: RCA, Roots, Swift, Wellard, Chris, I & B, Solomon & Peres Distribution

Cosmotheka

COSMOTHEKA.
Album: released on Dambuster, Dec'85 by Dambuster Records. Dist: Projection, Celtic Music, Roots

GOOD TURN OUT,A.
Album: released on Highway, Mar'86 by Highway Records. Dist: Roots, Projection, Ross

LITTLE BIT OFF THE TOP,A.
Album: released on Highway, Jan'85 by Highway Records. Dist: Roots, Projection, Ross

WINES AND SPIRITS.
Album: released on Highway, '81 by Highway Records. Dist: Roots, Projection, Ross

Cossu, Scott

ISLANDS.
Compact disc: Dist: AM

Album: released on Windham Hill, Nov'85 Dist: AM

Cassette: released on Windham Hill, Nov'85 Dist: AM

Compact disc: released on Windham Hill, Nov'85 Dist: AM

Album: released on Windham Hill (Germany), '85

WIND DANCE.
Album: released on Windham Hill (Germany), '84

Costa, Gal

FANTASIA.
Album:

Costa, Nikka

NIKKA COSTA.
Album: released on RCA, '82 by RCA Records. Dist: RCA, Roots, Swift, Wellard, Chris, I & B, Solomon & Peres Distribution

Co-stars

KISS ME AND MAKE UP.
Single (7"): released on Individual, '85 by Individual Records. Dist: Pinnacle

Single (12"): released on Individual, '85 by Individual Records. Dist: Pinnacle

Costello, Cecilia

SONGS FROM SHAKESPEARE'S COUNTRY.
Cassette: released on Folktracks, '79 by Folktracks Cassettes. Dist: Folktracks

Costello, Elvis

10 BLOODY MARYS.... And 10 how's your father's (Costello, Elvis & The Attractions).
Notes: Originally issued as a US only album; the UK counterpart being a cassette featuring slightly different tracks. This recording contains alternative takes and out-takes from other albums, along with B-sides from Elvis's singles.
Compact disc: released on Demon, '86 by Demon Records. Dist: Pinnacle

Album: released on Demon, '84 by Demon Records. Dist: Pinnacle

Cassette: released on Demon, '84 by Demon Records. Dist: Pinnacle

ALMOST BLUE.
Tracks: / Why don't you love me (like you used to) / Sweet dreams / I'm your toy / Tonight the bottle let me down / Brown to blue / Good year for the roses / Sittin' and thinkin / Colour of the blues / Too far gone / Honey hush / How much i lied.
Compact disc: by Demon Records. Dist: Pinnacle

ALMOST BLUE (Costello, Elvis & The Attractions).
Album: released on Demon, '84 by Demon Records. Dist: Pinnacle

Cassette: released on Demon, '84 by Demon Records. Dist: Pinnacle

ARMED FORCES (Costello, Elvis & The Attractions).
Album: released on Demon, '84 by Demon Records. Dist: Pinnacle

Cassette: released on Demon, '84 by Demon Records. Dist: Pinnacle

ARMED FORCES.
Tracks: / Accidents will happen / senior service / Oliver's army / big boys / green shirt / party girl / goon squad / busy bodies / Sunday's best / moods for moderns / chemistry class / two little Hitlers.
Compact disc: released on Demon, Jan'86 by Demon Records. Dist: Pinnacle

BEST OF ELVIS COSTELLO.
Album: released on Telstar, '85 by Telstar Records. Dist: RCA Distribution

Cassette: released on Telstar, '85 by Telstar Records. Dist: RCA Distribution

BLOOD AND CHOCOLATE.
Compact disc: released on Imp, '86 by Demon. Dist: Pinnacle

EVERYDAY I WRITE THE BOOK.
Single (7"): released on F-Beat, '83 by F-Beat Records. Dist: RCA, Pinnacle

Single (12"): released on F-Beat, '83 by F-Beat Records. Dist: RCA, Pinnacle

FROM HEAD TO TOE World of broken....
Single (7"): released on F-Beat, '82 by F-Beat Records. Dist: RCA, Pinnacle

GET HAPPY (Costello, Elvis & The Attractions).
Tracks: / Love for tender / Opportunity / Imposter (The) / Secondary modern / King horse / Possession / Man called uncle / Clowntime is over / New Amsterdam / High fidelity / I can't stand up for falling down / Black and white world / Five gears in reverse / B-movie / Motel matches / Human touch / Beaten to the punch / Temptation / I stand accused.
Compact disc: released on Demon, '86 by Demon Records. Dist: Pinnacle

Album: released on Demon, '84 by Demon Records. Dist: Pinnacle

Cassette: released on Demon, '84 by Demon Records. Dist: Pinnacle

Album: released on F-Beat, '84 by F-Beat Records. Dist: RCA, Pinnacle

Cassette: released on F-Beat, '84 by F-Beat Records. Dist: RCA, Pinnacle

GOODBYE CRUEL WORLD (Costello, Elvis & The Attractions).
Album: released on Demon, Jan'87 by Demon Records. Dist: Pinnacle

Cassette: released on Demon, Jan'87 by Demon Records. Dist: Pinnacle

GOODBYE CRUEL WORLD.
Tracks: / Only flame in town (The) / Home truth / Room with no number / Inch by inch / Worthless thing / Love field / I wanna be loved / Comedians (The) / Joe Powerhouse / Sour milk-cow blues / Great unknown (The) / Deportees club (The) / Peace in our time.
Compact disc: released on F-Beat, Mar'86 by F-Beat Records. Dist: RCA, Pinnacle

GREEN SHIRT.
Single (7"): released on F-Beat, '85 by F-Beat Records. Dist: RCA, Pinnacle

Single (12"): released on F-Beat, '85 by F-Beat Records. Dist: RCA, Pinnacle

IMPERIAL BEDROOM (Costello, Elvis & The Attractions).
Album: released on Demon, '84 by Demon Records. Dist: Pinnacle

Cassette: released on Demon, '84 by Demon Records. Dist: Pinnacle

IMPERIAL BEDROOM.
Compact disc: released on Demon, Jan'86 by Demon Records. Dist: Pinnacle

I'M YOUR TOY Cry cry cry.
Single (7"): released on F-Beat, '82 by F-Beat Records. Dist: RCA, Pinnacle

Single (12"): released on F-Beat, '82 by F-Beat Records. Dist: RCA, Pinnacle

INTERVIEW PICTURE DISC.
Album: released on Baktabak, 11 Apr'87 by Baktabak Records. Dist: Arabesque

I WANNA BE LOVED.
Single (7"): released on F-Beat, '84 by F-Beat Records. Dist: RCA, Pinnacle

Single (12"): released on F-Beat, '84 by F-Beat Records. Dist: RCA, Pinnacle

I WANT YOU.
Single (7"): released on Imp, Oct'86 by Demon. Dist: Pinnacle

Single 10": released on Imp, Oct'86 by Demon. Dist: Pinnacle

KING OF AMERICA.
Tracks: / Brilliant mistake / Loveable / Our little angel / Don't let me be misunderstood / Glitter gulch & I'll wear it proudly / Indoor fireworks / Little palaces / American without tears / Big light / Eisenhower Blues / Poisoned rose / Jack of all parades / Suit of lights / Sleep of the just.
Compact disc: released on F-Beat, Mar'86 by F-Beat Records. Dist: RCA, Pinnacle

LET THEM TALK Keep it confidential.
Single (7"): released on F-Beat, '83 by F-Beat Records. Dist: RCA, Pinnacle

Single (12"): released on F-Beat, '83 by F-Beat Records. Dist: RCA, Pinnacle

MAD ABOUT THE WRONG BOY (Costello, Elvis & The Attractions).
Album: released on Demon, '84 by Demon Records. Dist: Pinnacle

MAN.
Album: released on Demon, Jan'87 by Demon Records. Dist: Pinnacle

Cassette: released on Demon, Jan'87 by Demon Records. Dist: Pinnacle

MAN OUT OF TIME Town crier (Costello, Elvis & The Attractions).
Single (7"): released on F-Beat, '82 by F-Beat Records. Dist: RCA, Pinnacle

Single (12"): released on F-Beat, '82 by F-Beat Records. Dist: RCA, Pinnacle

MAN, THE.
Notes: Number of tracks: 22. Type of recording: Compilation. Total playing time: 65 minutes.
Video-cassette (VHS): released on Palace, Jan'86 Dist: PVG

MAN, THE.
Compact disc: by Demon Records. Dist: Pinnacle

Album: released on A&M, Jan'78 by A&M Records. Dist: Polygram

MY AIM IS TRUE.
Compact disc: by Demon Records. Dist: Pinnacle

Album: released on Demon, Jul'86 by Demon Records. Dist: Pinnacle

Cassette: released on Demon, Jul'86 by Demon Records. Dist: Pinnacle

Album: released on Stiff, '77 by Stiff Records. Dist: EMI, Record Services Distribution (Ireland)

Cassette: released on Stiff, '77 by Stiff Records. Dist: EMI, Record Services Distribution (Ireland)

OLIVERS ARMY My funny valentine.
Single (7"): released on Radar, '82 by WEA Music Ltd. Dist: WEA, PRT

ONLY FLAME IN TOWN,THE (Costello, Elvis & The Attractions).
Single (7"): released on F-Beat, '84 by F-Beat Records. Dist: RCA, Pinnacle

Single (12"): released on F-Beat, '84 by F-Beat Records. Dist: RCA, Pinnacle

PUNCH THE CLOCK.
Tracks: / Everyday I write the book / pills and soap / shipbuilding / let them all talk / Boxing day / Love went mad / greatest thing (The) / element within (The) / charm school / invisible man (The) / Mouth almighty / King of thieves / world and his wife (The).
Notes: Digital Stereo.
Compact disc: released on F-Beat, Sep'84 by F-Beat Records. Dist: RCA, Pinnacle

PUNCH THE CLOCK (Costello, Elvis & The Attractions).
Album: released on Demon, Jan'87 by Demon Records. Dist: Pinnacle

Album: released on F-Beat, '84 by F-Beat Records. Dist: RCA, Pinnacle

Cassette: released on F-Beat, '84 by F-Beat Records. Dist: RCA, Pinnacle

SWEET DREAMS/PSYCHO.
Single (7"): released on F-Beat, '81 by F-Beat Records. Dist: RCA, Pinnacle

THIS YEARS MODEL (Costello, Elvis & The Attractions).
Album: released on Demon, '84 by Demon Records. Dist: Pinnacle

Cassette: released on Demon, '84 by Demon Records. Dist: Pinnacle

THIS YEAR'S MODEL.
Tracks: / Beyond belief / Tears before bedtime / Shabby doll / Long honeymoon, The / Man out of time / Almost blue / And in every home / Loved ones (The) / Human hands / Kid about it / Little savage / Boy with a problem / Pidgin english / You little fool / Town cryer.
Compact disc: by Demon Records. Dist: Pinnacle

TOKYO STORM WARNING (PART 1) (Costello, Elvis & The Attractions).
Tracks: / Tokyo strom warning (Part 1) / Tokyo strom warning (Part 11) / Black sails in the sunset.
Single (7"): released on Imp, Aug'86 by Demon. Dist: Pinnacle

Single (12"): released on Imp, Aug'86 by Demon. Dist: Pinnacle

TRUST (Costello, Elvis & The Attractions).
Album: released on Demon, '84 by Demon Records. Dist: Pinnacle

Cassette: released on Demon, '84 by Demon Records. Dist: Pinnacle

TRUST.
Tracks: / Clubland / Lovers walk / You'll never be a man / Pretty words / Strict time / Luxembourg / Watch your step / New lace sleeve / From a whisper to a scream / Different finger / White knuckles / Shot with his own gun / Fish 'n' chip paper / Big sister clothes.
Compact disc: released on Demon, '86 by Demon Records. Dist: Pinnacle

WATCHING THE DETECTIVE.
Single (12"): released on Stiff, '85 by Stiff Records. Dist: EMI, Record Services Distribution (Ireland)

YOU LITTLE FOOL Big sister.
Single (7"): released on F-Beat, '82 by F-Beat Records. Dist: RCA, Pinnacle

Costello Show

BLUE CHAIR.
Tracks: / American without tears No. 2 (twilight version) / Shoes without heels.
Single (7"): released on Demon, Jan'87 by Demon Records. Dist: Pinnacle

Single (12"): released on Demon, Jan'87 by Demon Records. Dist: Pinnacle

DON'T LET ME BE MISUNDERSTOOD.
Tracks: / Don't let me be misunderstood / Babys got a brand new hair do / Get yourself another girl.
Single (7"): released on RCA, Jan'86 by RCA Records. Dist: RCA, Roots, Swift, Wellard, Chris, I & B, Solomon & Peres Distribution

Single (12"): released on RCA, Jan'86 by RCA Records. Dist: RCA, Roots, Swift, Wellard, Chris, I & B, Solomon & Peres Distribution

KING OF AMERICA.
Album: released on Demon, Jan'87 by Demon Records. Dist: Pinnacle

Cassette: released on Demon, Jan'87 by Demon Records. Dist: Pinnacle

Costello, Terry

PERFECT HUMAN FACE.
Single (7"): released on World Of Leisure, Aug'83 Dist: World Of Leisure

Cotswold

STORIES & REMINISCENCES OF COUNTRY LIFE.
Cassette: released on Saydisc, Apr'81 by Saydisc Records. Dist: Essex, Harmonia Mundi, Roots, H.R. Taylor, Jazz Music, Swift, Projection, Gamut

Cotswold Craftsman

COTSWOLD CRAFTSMEN Various artists (Various Artists).
Album: released on Saydisc, Apr'81 by Saydisc Records. Dist: Essex, Harmonia Mundi, Roots, H.R. Taylor, Jazz Music, Swift, Projection, Gamut

Cotswold Voices

COTSWOLD VOICES Various artists (Various Artists).
Cassette: released on Saydisc, Apr'81 by Saydisc Records. Dist: Essex, Harmonia Mundi, Roots, H.R. Taylor, Jazz Music, Swift, Projection, Gamut

Cottam, Geoff

JUBILEE STREET Contemporary blues & love songs.
Cassette: released on Folktracks, '79 by Folktracks Cassettes. Dist: Folktracks

Cottee, Jo

ARE THE PEOPLE CRAZY.
Single (7"): released on RCA, Feb'85 by RCA Records. Dist: RCA, Roots, Swift, Wellard, Chris, I & B, Solomon & Peres Distribution

Single (12"): released on RCA, Feb'85 by RCA Records. Dist: RCA, Roots, Swift, Wellard, Chris, I & B, Solomon & Peres Distribution

TURN AWAY.
Single (7"): released on Reluctant, Oct'85 Dist: MIS-EMI Distribution

Cotten, Elizabeth

ELIZABETH COTTEN LIVE.
Album: released on Arhoolie, Jul'84 by Arhoolie Records. Dist: Projection, Topic, Jazz Music, Swift, Roots

Cott, Gerry

BALLAD OF THE LONE RANGER.
Single (7"): released on Epic, Jan'83 by CBS Records. Dist: CBS

PIONEERS.
Single (7"): released on Epic, Apr'83 by CBS Records. Dist: CBS

Cottle, Richard

BARWICK GREEN Old bird (The).
Single (7"): released on WEA, Oct'82 by WEA Records. Dist: WEA

Cotton, Billy

BILLY COTTON (Cotton, Billy & His Band).
Album: released on World, '71 Dist: Jetstar

CRAZY WEATHER (Cotton, Billy & His Band).
Tracks: / Crazy weather / Isle of Capri / Why am I blue? / Margie / Lazybones / Annie doesn't live here any more / St. Louis blues / Two cigarettes in the dark / Judy / Hold me / I was in the mood / Man from Harlem (The) / Ole faithful / Oh! Mother, Mother (please speak to Willie) / Third tiger (tiger rag no. 3), The / Hand in hand (we go together) / Down a long, long road / Who made little boy blue?.
Album: released on Saville, Jan'86 by Conifer Records. Dist: Conifer

Cassette: released on Happy Days, Jul'86 by Conifer Records. Dist: Conifer

GOLDEN AGE OF BILLY COTTON (THE).
Album: released on Golden Age, Jul'84 by Music For Pleasure Records. Dist: EMI

Cassette: released on Golden Age, Jul'84 by Music For Pleasure Records. Dist: EMI

LET'S ALL JOIN IN (Cotton, Billy & His Orchestra).
Album: released on Bulldog, Nov'83 by Bulldog Records. Dist: President Distribution, Spartan, Swift, Taylor, H.R.

RHYTHM MAN, THE (Cotton, Billy & His Band).
Tracks: / from Monday on / My southern home / puttin' on the ritz / rhythm man (The) / You brought a new kind of love to me / new tiger rag (The) / Bessie couldn't help it / You're lucky to me / Memories of you / That Lindy Hop / It looks like love / Were you sincere? / Why shouldn't I? / You wouldn't / Parkin' in the moonlight / It's the girl / You call it madness(but I call it love) / Yes-yes (my baby said yes-yes) / Nobody's sweetheart / Sleepy time down south.
Album: released on Saville, '86 by Conifer Records. Dist: Conifer

Cassette: released on Saville, '86 by Conifer Records. Dist: Conifer

ROCK YOUR CARES AWAY (Cotton, Billy & His Band).
Album: released on Joy, Aug'83 by President Records. Dist: Jazz Music, Swift, President Distribution

SING A NEW SONG (Cotton, Billy & His Band).
Album: released on Saville, Jul'83 by Conifer Records. Dist: Conifer

SOMEBODY STOLE MY GAL (Cotton, Billy & His Band).
Tracks: / Diggin' my potatoes / Ying yang / 23 hours too long / No more doggin' / No cuttin' loose / Ain't doing too bad / sunny road / super-harp / easy loving / high compression.
Album: released on Old Bean, Jul'86 Dist: Jazz Music

WAKEE WAKEE (Cotton, Billy & His Band).
Album: released on ASV Living Era, Nov'85 by ASV Records. Dist: PRT

Cassette: released on ASV Living Era, Nov'85 by ASV Records. Dist: PRT

Cotton Club

COTTON CLUB Original soundtrack (Various Artists).
Album: released on Geffen, May'85 by Geffen Records. Dist: WEA, CBS

Cassette: released on Geffen, May'85 by Geffen Records. Dist: WEA, CBS

COTTON CLUB - THE ORIGINAL STARS Various artists (Various Artists).
Album: released on ASV Living Era, Jun'85 by ASV Records. Dist: PRT

Cassette: released on ASV Living Era, Jun'85 by ASV Records. Dist: PRT

Album: released on Sonet, Dec'84 by Sonet Records. Dist: PRT

Cotton Club Legend

COTTON CLUB LEGEND Various artists (Various Artists).
Album: released on RCA (France), May'85 by RCA Records. Dist: Discovery

Cotton Club Stars

RARE PERFORMANCES.
Album: released on SPI Milan (France), Apr'85 Dist: Silva Screen

Cassette: released on SPI Milan (France), Apr'85 Dist: Silva Screen

Cotton, James

FROM COTTON WITH VERVE.
Album: released on Black Magic, May'86 Dist: Swift

HIGH COMPRESSION.
Compact disc: released on Sonet, Oct'86 by Sonet Records. Dist: PRT

LIVE FROM CHICAGO.
Tracks: / Here I am / Part time love / Just to be with you / Hard headed / When it rains it pours / Cross your heart / Come back baby / Born in Chicago / Creeper, The.
Album: released on Aeroplane-Sonet, Apr'86 by Sonet Records. Dist: Sonet Records PRT

Cotton, James Band

LIVE AND ON THE MOVE VOLUME 1.
Album: released on Buddah, Oct'86 Dist: Swift, Jazz Music, PRT

LIVE AND ON THE MOVE - VOLUME 11.
Album: released on Buddah, Oct'86 Dist: Swift, Jazz Music, PRT

Cotton, Joseph

HALF SLIM.
Tracks: / Half slim / Half slim (version).
Single (12"): released on Body Music, Jul'87 by Body Music Records. Dist: Jetstar

NO TOUCH THE STYLE.
Tracks: / No touch the style / Cotton comes to Harlesden.
Single (7"): released on Fashion, 20 Jun'87 by Fashion Records. Dist: PRT, Jetstar

Single (12"): released on Fashion, 20 Jun'87 by Fashion Records. Dist: PRT, Jetstar

YUHA MI LOVER.
Tracks: / Yuha mi lover (Version).
Single (12"): released on CSA, Nov'86 by CSA Records. Dist: PRT, Jetstar

Cotton, Josie

JIMMY LOVES MARY ANN.
Tracks: / Jimmy loves Mary Ann / No pictures of Dad.
Single (7"): released on Elektra (USA), Apr'84 by Elektra/Asylum/Nonesuch Records. Dist: WEA

JOHNNY ARE YOU QUEER.
Single (7"): released on Bomp International, Jan'82

Cotton Mill Boys

BEST OF THE COTTON MILL BOYS Volume 1.
Album: released on Harp(Ireland), Jul'80 by Pickwick Records. Dist: Taylors

Cassette: released on Harp(Ireland), Jul'80 by Pickwick Records. Dist: Taylors

GOLD WATCH AND CHAIN Devil went....
Single (7"): released on Homespun(Ireland), May'83 by Outlet Records. Dist: Outlet

ORANGE BLOSSOM SPECIAL.
Cassette: released on Hawk, Mar'77 by Dolphin Records. Dist: I & B, Celtic Music, Solomon & Peres Distribution

Cotton, Sylvester

DETROIT BLUES VOL.1.
Album: released on Krazy Kat (USA), Aug'84

Cottrell, Louis

CLARINET LEGENDS (Cottrell, Louis & Herb).
Album: released on GBH, Mar'84 by GBH Records. Dist: Jazz Music, Swift

Cougar, John

AMERICAN FOOL.
Album: released on Mercury, Sep'85 by Phonogram Records. Dist: Polygram Distribution

Cassette: released on Mercury, Sep'85 by Phonogram Records. Dist: Polygram Distribution

Compact disc: released on Mercury, Sep'85 by Phonogram Records. Dist: Polygram Distribution

CHESTNUT STREET INCIDENT.
Tracks: / American dream / Oh, pretty woman / Jailhouse rock / Dream killin' town / Supergirl.
Notes: Guitar: Mike Boyer, Richard Kelly, David Parman, Mick Ronson,Mike Wanchic. Keyboards: Michael Karmen, Steve Linderman, Tom Wince. Bass: David Parmen. Percussion: Billy Bergman, Kirk Butler, David Parman. Steel Guitar, Mandolin, Violins: David Mansfield. Chimes: Tom Wince. Drums: Billy Berman, Jerry Deupree, Hilly J. Michaels. Saxophone: Wayne Hill. Moog Synthesizer: Kirk Butler. Small Talk: Skatelands Girls. Vocals: Johnny Cougar. Back up Vocals: Johnny Cougar & Parman save 'Chestnut Street'arranged by Tony Delfries and 'Chestnut Street Revisited' arranged by Johnny Cougar. Engineered by Kirk Butler & Bruce Targesen. Recorded at Gilloy Sound, Bloomington, Ind. Hit Factory NYC Record Plant, NYC. Mastered at MCA Recording Studios. Producer Tony Delfries. Co-Producer James C.A.Andrews, Licensed from Mainman S.A.A.G.
Album: released on Castle, May'86 by Castle Records. Dist: Pinnacle

Cassette: released on Castle, May'86 by Castle Records. Dist: Pinnacle

Compact disc: released on Castle Classics, '86 by Castle Communications. Dist: BMG

HAND TO HOLD ON TO.
Single (7"): released on Riva, Jan'83 Dist: PRT

Single (12"): released on Riva, Jan'83 Dist: PRT

HURT SO GOOD / CLOSE ENOUGH.
Single (7"): released on Riva, May'82 Dist: PRT

JACK AND DIANE/DANGER LIST.
Single (7"): released on Riva, Sep'82 Dist: PRT

Single (12"): released on Riva, Sep'82 Dist: PRT

JOHN COUGAR COLLECTION.
Tracks: / American dream / Oh, pretty woman / Jailhouse rock / Dream killin' town / Supergirl / Chestnut street / Kid inside / Take what you want / cheap shot / side walks and street lights / R. Gang / Good girls / Do you believe in magic / Twentieth Century Fox / Chestnut street revisited / Sad Lady / American son / Gearhead / Young genocides / Too young to live / Survive / Good girls / Do you believe in magic / Twentieth Century Fox / Chestnut Street Revisited / Sad Lady.
Notes: All tracks Licensed from Mainman Sagg' Design: Shoot That Tiger: This compilation (c) 1985: Castle Communications Ltd: Unit 7, 271 Merton Road, London SW18 5SJ Bar Code: 5 013428 131244: Double Album - Double Cassette:
Album: released on Collectors, Apr'86 by Castle Communications Records. Dist: PRT, Pinnacle, Jazz Music

Cassette: released on Collectors, Apr'86 by Castle Communications Records. Dist: PRT, Pinnacle, Jazz Music

Compact disc: released on Collectors, Apr'86 by Castle Communications Records. Dist: PRT, Pinnacle, Jazz Music

KID INSIDE (THE).
Tracks: / kid inside / Take what you want / cheap shot / Sidewalks and streetlights / R. Gang / American son / Gearhead / Young genocides / Too young to live / Survive.
Notes: Vocals - Cougar. Tiger Force: Larry Crane - Electric guitars, 11 & 6 String Guitars; David Parman - Bass guitar, Stratocaster, Violin, Percussion, Acoustic; Terrance Sala - Drums, Percussion; Wayne Hall - Sax, Flute, Percussion; Tom Wince -keyboards; Cougar - Acoustic Guitar, Percussion, Telecaster. All words and music by John Cougar. Published by Mainman SAAG. Produced by John Cougar/Mainman. Arranged by John Cougar/David Parman. Engineered by Ed Sprigg. Assistant Engineers Dave Prentice/Ted Spencer. Recorded at the HIT Factory mastered by Sterling Sound.
Album: released on Castle, May'86 by Castle Records. Dist: Pinnacle

Cassette: released on Castle, May'86 by Castle Records. Dist: Pinnacle

Coughing Up Fire

COUGHING UP FIRE Saxon studio international (Various Artists).
Album: released on UK Bubblers, Dec'84 by Greensleeves Records. Dist: RCA, Jetstar

Cassette: released on UK Bubblers, Dec'84 by Greensleeves Records. Dist: RCA, Jetstar

Coughlan, Mary

TIRED AND EMOTIONAL.
Tracks: / Double cross / Beach, The / Meet me where they play the blues / Delaney's gone back on the wind / Sense of silence (S.O.S) / Noody's business - the tango / Mamma just wants to barrelhouse all night long / Country fair dance (The cowboy song) / Lady in green / Seduced.
Notes: Produced by: Erik Visser - Featuring: Mary Coughlan - vocals/Erik Visser - Gerrad Coffey - Declan Gibbons - Guitars/Pat Macnamara, Tony Maher - Accordions/Carl Hession - piano & synth/Curly Keranen - bass/Micky Belton - drums/Keith Donald, Tony Chambers, - Saxophones/Jimmy Higgins - trumpet/John Dring - Morse/Erik Visser -Gerald O'Donoghue - Percussion/Johnny (Ringo) McDonagh - Bones: Mixed by Erik Visser & Sylvia Houtzanger.
Album: released on WEA, Mar'87 by WEA Records. Dist: WEA

Album: released on WEA, Mar'87 by WEA Records. Dist: WEA

UNDER THE INFLUENCE.
Tracks: / Laziest girl / Ice cream man / Ice cream van / Parade of clowns / My land is too green / Ride on / Ride on / Good morning heartache / Fifteen only / Awol / Dice, The / Don't smoke in bed / Blue surrender / Sunday morning / Copa.
Album: released on WEA, Aug'87 by WEA Records. Dist: WEA

Cassette: released on WEA, Aug'87 by WEA Records. Dist: WEA

Compact disc: released on WEA, Aug'87 by WEA Records. Dist: WEA

Could this be magic

COULD THIS BE MAGIC (Various Artists).
Album: released on PRT, Dec'81 by PRT Records. Dist: PRT

Could you walk...

COULD YOU WALK ON THE WATERS (Various Artists).
Album: released on Third Mind, Mar'85 by Third Mind Records. Dist: Backs, Cartel Distribution

Coulson, Julie

BIG TIME OPERATOR.
Single (7"): released on Ecstasy, Oct'85 by Creole Records. Dist: CBS

Coulter, Phil

GOOD THING GOING/RUNAWAY BUNION.
Single (7"): released on Neil Rushton, Mar'83

PHIL COULTER'S IRELAND.
Album: released on K-Tel, May'85 by K-Tel Records. Dist: Record Merchandisers Distribution, Taylors, Terry Blood Distribution, Wynd-Up Distribution, Relay Distribution, Pickwick Distribution, Solomon & Peres Distribution, Polygram

Cassette: released on K-Tel, May'85 by K-Tel Records. Dist: Record Merchandisers Distribution, Taylors, Terry Blood Distribution, Wynd-Up Distribution, Relay Distribution, Pickwick Distribution, Solomon & Peres Distribution, Polygram

SEA OF TRANQUILITY.
Album: released on K-Tel, Nov'84 by K-Tel Records. Dist: Record Merchandisers Distribution, Taylors, Terry Blood Distribution, Wynd-Up Distribution, Relay Distribution, Pickwick Distribution, Solomon & Peres Distribution, Polygram

Cassette: released on K-Tel, Nov'84 by K-Tel Records. Dist: Record Merchandisers Distribution, Taylors, Terry Blood Distribution, Wynd-Up Distribution, Relay Distribution, Pickwick Distribution, Solomon & Peres Distribution, Polygram

TRANQUILITY.
Single (7"): released on Panther, Oct'84 by MCA Records. Dist: CBS

Counce, Curtis

CARL'S BLUES.
Notes: 1960 release recorded shortly before the death of pianist Carl Perkins.
Album: released on Contemporary, May'87 by Contemporary Records. Dist: Pinnacle

COUNCELTATION.
Album: released on Contemporary, Dec'81 by Contemporary Records. Dist: Pinnacle

CURTIS BLUES.
Album: released on Contemporary, May'83 by Contemporary Records. Dist: Pinnacle

EXPLORING THE FUTURE.
Album: released on Boplicity, Jul'84 by Boplicity Records. Dist: Ace Records, Pinnacle

Council Collective

SOUL DEEP.

Single (7"): released on Polydor, Dec'84 by Polydor Records. Dist: Polygram, Polydor

Single (12"): released on Polydor, Dec'84 by Polydor Records. Dist: Polygram, Polydor

Count

INTUITION ELEMENT.
Album: released on New Rose, Feb'84 Dist: Rough Trade, Cartel

Count Bishops

GOOD GEAR.
Album: released on Lolita, May'84 by Lolita Records. Dist: Rough Trade, Cartel

Countdown compilation

COUNTDOWN COMPILATION (Various Artists).
Album: released on Countdown, Jul'85 by Stiff Records. Dist: EMI, Swift

Countess Maritza

COUNTESS MARITZA Original Sadler's Wells cast (Various Artists).
Album: released on That's Entertainment, Apr'83 by That's Entertainment Records. Dist: Pinnacle, PRT

Cassette: released on That's Entertainment, Apr'83 by That's Entertainment Records. Dist: Pinnacle, PRT

Compact disc: released on That's Entertainment, Apr'83 by That's Entertainment Records. Dist: Pinnacle, PRT

Count Five

PSYCHOTIC REACTION.
Album: released on Line (West Germany), Feb'84

Count Lorenzo

WHAT ARE YOU LOOKING AT CECIL.
Single (7"): released on Shades, Sep'84 Dist: Pinnacle

Count Offie

MAN FROM HIGHER HEIGHTS.
Album: released on Vista Sounds, May'84 by Vista Sounds Records. Dist: Jetstar

Count Of Luxembourg

COUNT OF LUXEMBOURG Original Sadler's Wells Cast (Sadler's Wells Cast).
Album: released on That's Entertainment, Apr'83 by That's Entertainment Records. Dist: Pinnacle, PRT

Cassette: released on That's Entertainment, Apr'83 by That's Entertainment Records. Dist: Pinnacle, PRT

Compact disc: released on That's Entertainment, Apr'83 by That's Entertainment Records. Dist: Pinnacle, PRT

Count Prince Miller

COME TO ME SOFTLY.
Tracks: / It ain't no big thing.
Single (12"): released on Hot Vinyl, Dec'86 by Hot Vinyl Records. Dist: Jetst--

Country...

20 COUNTRY GREATS various artists (Various Artists).
Album: released on Warwick Reflections, Jun'86 by Warwick Records.

Cassette: released on Warwick Reflections, Jun'86 by Warwick Records.

"COUNTRY" 50 GREAT NASHVILLE HITS (Various Artists).
Album: released on Ronco, Nov'83

Cassette: released on Ronco, Nov'83

COUNTRY ALL STARS (Various Artists).
Album: released on Sundown, Apr'84 by Magnum Music Group Ltd. Dist: Magnum Music Group Ltd, PRT Distribution, Spartan Distribution

COUNTRY BLUES-THE FIRST GENERATION 1927 (Various Artists).
Album: released on Matchbox (Bluesmaster), Nov'82

COUNTRY CAVALCADE (Various Artists).
Cassette: released on VFM, Jan'85 by VFM Records. Dist: Taylors, Wynd-Up Distribution

COUNTRY CHART BUSTERS Various artists (Various Artists).
Album: released on Hallmark, Jul'86 by Pickwick Records. Dist: Pickwick Distribution, PRT, Taylors

Cassette: released on Hallmark, Jul'86 by Pickwick Records. Dist: Pickwick Distribution, PRT, Taylors

COUNTRY COMMENT (Various Artists).
Album: released on Charly, Mar'77 by Charly Records. Dist: Charly, Cadillac

COUNTRY CRYIN' (Various Artists).
Cassette: released on Cambra, Aug'83 by Cambra Records. Dist: IDS, Conifer

COUNTRY FEELIN' 16 great classics (Various Artists).
Album: released on Everest (Premier), '83 by Everest Records. Dist: Pinnacle

Cassette: released on Everest (Premier), '83 by Everest Records. Dist: Pinnacle

COUNTRY GENTLEMEN (Various Artists).
Cassette: released on K-Tel Goldmasters, Aug'84 by K-Tel Records. Dist: K-Tel

COUNTRY HEARTBREAK (Various Artists).
Album: released on K-Tel (Era), Jun'83 by K-Tel Records. Dist: K-Tel

Cassette: released on K-Tel (Era), Jun'83 by K-Tel Records. Dist: K-Tel

COUNTRY IN CONCERT (Various Artists).
Album: released on RCA (S.I.S.), Aug'84

Cassette: released on RCA (S.I.S.), Aug'84

COUNTRY LINE SPECIAL (Various Artists).
Album: released on MFP, Apr'79 by EMI Records. Dist: EMI

COUNTRY NEGRO JAM SESSIONS Various artists (Various Artists).
Album: released on Arhoolie, May'81 by Arhoolie Records. Dist: Projection, Topic, Jazz Music, Swift, Roots

COUNTRY PEOPLE,VOL.2 Live at the British Country Music Festival (Various Artists).
Cassette: released on Bi Bi(Budget Cassettes), Jan'83

COUNTRY PIE Various session artists (Various Artists).
Cassette: released on AIM (Budget Cassettes), Feb'83

COUNTRY PORTRAITS Various original artists (Various original artists).
Album: released on Warwick, Jan'79 Dist: Multiple Sound Distributors

COUNTRY RAINBOW (Various Artists).
Special: released on Warwick, Nov'85 Dist: Multiple Sound Distributors

Double cassette: released on Warwick, Nov'85 Dist: Multiple Sound Distributors

COUNTRY SCENE Various original artists (Various original artists).
Album: released on MFP, Sep'82 by EMI Records. Dist: EMI

Cassette: released on MFP, Sep'82 by EMI Records. Dist: EMI

COUNTRY STARDUST Various artists (Various Artists).
Double Album: released on Mercury (USA), Nov'81 by Import Records. Dist: IMS Distribution, Polygram Distribution

Double cassette: released on Mercury (USA), Nov'81 by Import Records. Dist: IMS Distribution, Polygram Distribution

COUNTRY STORYTELLERS I love country (Various Artists).
Tracks: / Poncho & Lefty / Let him roll / He stopped loving her today / 16th Avenue / Weevils in the flour / Engineers don't wave from the trains anymore, The / Baron, The / Seven Spanish Angels / She used to sing on Sunday / Country Comfort / Music man / Ride, The / El Paso City / Red headed stranger.
Album: released on CBS, Mar'87 by CBS Records. Dist: CBS

Cassette: released on CBS, Mar'87 by CBS Records. Dist: CBS

COUNTRY WAY, THE (Various Artists).
Tracks: / Too hard to say I'm sorry / Little folks, The / Crystal chandelier / Act naturally / Does my ring hurt your finger / Mama don't cry for me / Day the world stood still, The / Gone, on the other hand / You can tell the world / I'll wander back to you / Life turned her that way / I threw away the rose.
Album: released on RCA, Jan'87 by RCA Records. Dist: RCA, Roots, Swift, Wellard, Chris, I & B, Solomon & Peres Distribution

Cassette: released on RCA, Jan'87 by RCA Records. Dist: RCA, Roots, Swift, Wellard, Chris, I & B, Solomon & Peres Distribution

Country Breeze

ALWAY'S.
Album: released on Igus, Oct'81 by Klub. Dist: PRT, Musac Distribution Ltd (Scotland)

BEAUTIFUL THINGS.
Album: released on Neptune, Jul'80 by Lismor. Dist: Spartan

Cassette: released on Neptune, Jul'80 by Lismor. Dist: Spartan

CENTRE SOUND OF COUNTRY BREEZE, THE.
Album: released on Nevis, May'79 Dist: H.R. Taylor

COUNTRY BREEZE.
Album: released on Lismor, Jul'77 by Lismor Records. Dist: Lismor, Roots, Celtic Music

Cassette: released on Lismor, Jul'77 by Lismor Records. Dist: Lismor, Roots, Celtic Music

Country Christmas

COUNTRY CHRISTMAS (Various Artists).
Album: released on RCA, Nov'83 by RCA Records. Dist: RCA, Roots, Swift, Wellard, Chris, I & B, Solomon & Peres Distribution

Cassette: released on RCA, Nov'83 by RCA Records. Dist: RCA, Roots, Swift, Wellard, Chris, I & B, Solomon & Peres Distribution

COUNTRY CHRISTMAS (Various original artists).
Album: released on Embassy, Nov'77 by CBS Records. Dist: CBS

Country Classics

COUNTRY CLASSICS Various artists (Various Artists).
Tracks: / Diggy diggy lo / Harper Valley PTA / Please help me I'm falling / Auctioneer, The / Me and ole CB / Honky tonk song / What a way to live / Angel of the morning / Rockin' Cajun / Big river / Why you been gone so long / Big boss man.
Album: released on Topline, '86 by Charly Records. Dist: Charly Distribution

Cassette: released on Topline, '86 by Charly Records. Dist: Charly Distribution

Compact disc: released on K-Tel, Aug'87 by K-Tel Records. Dist: Record Merchandisers Distribution, Taylors, Terry Blood Distribution, Wynd-Up Distribution, Relay Distribution, Pickwick Distribution, Solomon & Peres Distribution, Polygram

COUNTRY CLASSICS (Various Artists).
Album: released on K-Tel (Era), Jun'83 by K-Tel Records. Dist: K-Tel

Cassette: released on K-Tel (Era), Jun'83 by K-Tel Records. Dist: K-Tel

COUNTRY CLASSICS (3 LP SET) (Various Artists).
Album: released on Telstar, Nov'84 by Telstar Records. Dist: RCA Distribution

Cassette: released on Telstar, Nov'84 by Telstar Records. Dist: RCA Distribution

Country Collection

COUNTRY COLLECTION VOLUME 1 Various artists (Various Artists).
Tracks: / Folsom prison blues / Hey porter / Blue is the way I feel / You make me what I am / Home is where you're happy / I'm building heartaches / I've loved and lost again / Just out of reach / Hello walls / Ican't help it / Where do we go from here / Take my hand for a while / World's worst loser / I can't change overnight / I don't need to know that right now / Georgia in a jug / Release me / It wasn't God who made honky tonk angels / How do I hide from a memory / We're together again.
Compact disc: by Object Enterprises Ltd. Dist: Counterpoint Distribution

COUNTRY COLLECTION VOLUME 2 Various artists (Various Artists).
Tracks: / It's four in the morning / Harper Valley PTA / Luckenback Texas / Blue eyes cryin' in the rain / Take this job and shove it / No charge / From a jack to a king / Please help me I'm falling / Wolverton mountain / I love you because / Big bad John / Rose garden / Everything is beautiful / Good hearted woman.
Compact disc: by Object Enterprises Ltd. Dist: Counterpoint Distribution

COUNTRY COLLECTION VOL.1 Various artists (Various Artists).
Album: released on Pickwick, Mar'87 by Pickwick Records. Dist: Pickwick Distribution, Prism Leisure Distribution, Lugtons

Cassette: released on Pickwick, Mar'87 by Pickwick Records. Dist: Pickwick Distribution, Prism Leisure Distribution, Lugtons

COUNTRY COLLECTION (Various Artists).
Album: released on Neptune, Nov'80 by Lismor. Dist: Spartan

Cassette: released on Neptune, Nov'80 by Lismor. Dist: Spartan

Country Dance...

COUNTRY DANCE BAND English folk dances for young people.
Album: by EMI Records. Dist: EMI

COUNTRY DANCES (Various Artists).
Album: released on Unidisc (France), May'85 Dist: Discovery

Country Diary Of...

COUNTRY DIARY OF AN EDWARDIAN LADY Read by Francesca Annis (Annis, Francesca).
Boxed set: released on Warwick, Nov'79 Dist: Multiple Sound Distributors

Cassette: released on Warwick, Nov'81 Dist: Multiple Sound Distributors

Country Duets

COUNTRY DUETS Various artist (Various Artists).
Tracks: / Vision of mother, A / Candy man / Sometimes when we touch / Rock and Roll shoes / It's a dirty job / Golden ring / Get a little dirt on your hands / No memories hangin' around / All the soft places to fall / On my knees / It's only make believe / Where's the dress / There ain't no country music on this juke box / Making believe.
Album: released on CBS, Sep'86 by CBS Records. Dist: CBS

Cassette: released on CBS, Sep'86 by CBS Records. Dist: CBS

COUNTRY DUETS (SPOT) (Various Artists).
Album: released on Spot, Mar'85 by Pickwick Records. Dist: H.R. Taylor, Lugtons

Cassette: released on Spot, Mar'85 by Pickwick Records. Dist: H.R. Taylor, Lugtons

Country Friends

COUNTRY FRIENDS I love country (Various Artists).
Tracks: / Yesterday's wine / Slow Movin' Outlaw / Chet's country / I still hold her body (but I think I've lost her mind) / You can lead a heart to love (but you can't make it fall) / Country side / Big river / Ridin' High / This bottle (in my hand) / Beer drinkin' christian / Don't sing me no songs about Texas / Mammas don't let your babies grow up to be cowboys / Indian Summer / Friendship.
Album: released on CBS, Mar'87 by CBS Records. Dist: CBS

Cassette: released on CBS, Mar'87 by CBS Records. Dist: CBS

COUNTRY FRIENDS OF PAT & ROGER JOHNS VOL.3 (Various Artists).
Album: released on Future Earth, May'83 by Future Earth Records. Dist: Red Rhino, Cartel

Country Gazette

FROM THE BEGINNING.
Album: released on Sun Set, Apr'78 by Sun Set Records. Dist: Jetstar Distribution

Country Giants

COUNTRY GIANTS.
Album: released on Manhattan, Apr'81 by President Records. Dist: Jazz Music, Swift, Taylors, Chris Wellard

COUNTRY GIANTS (Various Artists).
Album: released on Pickwick, Jul'76 by Pickwick Records. Dist: Pickwick Distribution, Prism Leisure Distribution, Lugtons

Cassette: released on Pickwick, Apr'79 by Pickwick Records. Dist: Pickwick Distribution, Prism Leisure Distribution, Lugtons

COUNTRY GIANTS COLLECTION VOL.2 (Various Artists).
Album: released on Pickwick, Feb'78 by Pickwick Records. Dist: Pickwick Distribution, Prism Leisure Distribution, Lugtons

COUNTRY GIANTS USA (Various Artists).
Album: released on Pickwick, Feb'80 by Pickwick Records. Dist: Pickwick Distribution, Prism Leisure Distribution, Lugtons

COUNTRY GIANTS VOL.3 (Various Artists).
Album: released on Pickwick, Jul'79 by Pickwick Records. Dist: Pickwick Distribution, Prism Leisure Distribution, Lugtons

COUNTRY GIANTS VOL.1 (Various Artists).
Cassette: released on Pickwick, Jul'80 by Pickwick Records. Dist: Pickwick Distribution, Prism Leisure Distribution, Lugtons

Country Girls

COUNTRY GIRLS (O'Brien, Edna).
Cassette: released on Argo (Spokenword), Jul'82 by Decca Records. Dist: Polygram

COUNTRY GIRLS (Various Artists).
Cassette: released on Liberty, Mar'80 by Liberty-United. Dist: EMI

COUNTRY GIRLS 1926-29 (Various Artists).
Album: released on Matchbox, Apr'84 by Saydisc Records. Dist: Roots, Projection, Jazz Music, JSU, Celtic Music

Country Gold

COUNTRY GOLD (Various Artists).
Cassette: released on Cambra, '83 by Cambra Records. Dist: IDS, Conifer

COUNTRY GOLD - 30 ALL TIME COUNTRY & WESTERN HITS Various artists (Various Artists).
Tracks: / I'm so lonesome I could cry / So fine / I need a thing called love / Back home again / Can't you see / Blue train / I'm gonna feed them now / Who's been here since I've been gone / When I stop leaving / Look who I'm cheating on tonight / I can't belive that's it all over / Loving arms / Shadows of my mind / It don't hurt to dream / If I keep on going crazy / Fair and tender ladies / Let's take the long way round the world / If you gotta make a fool of somebody / Hurtin's all over, The / Then you can tell me goodbye / Whiskey trip / On the road again / That's the way love should be / Far far away / Light of a clear blue morning / I'm a trucker / Shine on / It should have been easy / True life country music / Loving you / Soldier of fortune.
Notes: Now to the Wild West with the likes of Willie Nelson, Dotti West and Bobby Bare. Every track a Country gem, every artists featured a Country star. (Double album)
Album: released on RCA (Germany), Nov'85

Cassette: released on RCA (Germany), Nov'85

COUNTRY GOLD (4 LP SET) (Various Artists).
Album: released on Effects Gold, Nov'80 by Ronco Records. Dist: Ronco Records

Cassette: released on Effects Gold, Nov'80 by Ronco Records. Dist: Ronco Records

COUNTRY GOLD (6 TRACK 7" LP) (Various Artists).
Album: released on Scoop 33, Sep'83 by Pickwick Records. Dist: H.R. Taylor

Cassette: released on Scoop 33, Sep'83 by Pickwick Records. Dist: H.R. Taylor

COUNTRY GOLD VOL.III (Various Artists).
Album: released on RCA/Camden, Mar'85

Cassette: released on RCA/Camden, Mar'85

COUNTRY GOLD VOL.IV (Various Artists).
Album: released on RCA/Camden, Mar'85

Cassette: released on RCA/Camden, Mar'85

Country Gospel

COUNTRY GOSPEL (Various Artists).
Album: released on Homespun(Ireland), Jan'79 by Outlet Records. Dist: Outlet

COUNTRY GOSPEL GUITAR CLASSICS (Various Artists).
Album: released on Wolf (Austria), Apr'85

Country Greats

COUNTRY GREATS 76 (Various Artists).
Cassette: released on VFM Cassettes, Jan'85

COUNTRY GREATS USA (Various Artists).
Cassette: released on Hallmark, Apr'80 by Pickwick Records. Dist: Pickwick Distribution, PRT, Taylors

Country Harvest

COUNTRY HARVEST (Various Artists).
Album: released on Pickwick, Sep'80 by Pickwick Records. Dist: Pickwick Distribution, Prism Leisure Distribution, Lugtons

Cassette: released on Pickwick, Sep'80 by Pickwick Records. Dist: Pickwick Distribution, Prism Leisure Distribution, Lugtons

COUNTRY HARVEST 16 GOLDEN COUNTRY HITS Various artists (Various Artists).
Tracks: / Behind closed doors / Big City / Gambler, The / Just started livin' today / Take this job and shove it / 'Til I gain control again / Key Largo / Stand by your man / Thing called love, A / Very special love song, A / Rose garden / He stopped loving her today / Sleeping with your memory / Delta dawn / If you ever change your mind / El Paso.
Notes: Licensed from CBS Records. (P) & (C) Warwick Records - A Warwick Leisure Product. Made & printed in the U.K. Bar Code 5 012106 220089.
Album: released on Warwick Reflections, Jun'86 by Warwick Records.

Cassette: released on Warwick Reflections, Jun'86 by Warwick Records.

Country Hits

16 NUMBER ONE COUNTRY HITS (Various Artists).
Album: by CBS Records. Dist: CBS

COUNTRY HITS (Various Artists).
Cassette: released on RCA, May'85 by RCA Records. Dist: RCA, Roots, Swift, Wellard, Chris, I & B, Solomon & Peres Distribution

COUNTRY HITS VOL.1 (Various Artists).
Album: released on Cambra, Aug'83 by Cambra Records. Dist: IDS, Conifer

Cassette: released on Cambra, Aug'83 by Cambra Records. Dist: IDS, Conifer

COUNTRY HITS VOL.2 (Various Artists).
Album: released on Cambra, '83 by Cambra Records. Dist: IDS, Conifer

Cassette: released on Cambra, '83 by Cambra Records. Dist: IDS, Conifer

Country Jays

SILVER MEDALS AND SWEET MEMORIES.
Album: released on Country House, Feb'83 by BGS Productions Ltd. Dist: Taylor, H.R., Record Merchandisers Distribution, Pinnacle, Sounds of Scotland Records

Cassette: released on Country House, Feb'83 by BGS Productions Ltd. Dist: Taylor, H.R., Record Merchandisers Distribution, Pinnacle, Sounds of Scotland Records

Country Joe

COLLECTORS ITEMS First three EP's, The (Country Joe & The Fish).
Album: released on Decal, Mar'87 by Charly Records. Dist: Charly

Album: released on New Rose, Mar'87 Dist: Rough Trade, Cartel

ELECTRIC MUSIC FOR THE MIND AND BODY (Country Joe & the Fish).
Album: by PRT Records. Dist: PRT

I FEEL LIKE I'M FIXIN' TO DIE (Country Joe & The Fish).
Album: by PRT Records. Dist: PRT

LIFE AND TIMES OF HAIGHT ASHBURY TO WOODSTOOK, THE (Country Joe & The Fish).
Album: released on Vanguard, Nov'83 by PRT Records. Dist: PRT

Country Ladies

COUNTRY LADIES I love country (Various Artists).
Tracks: / Little bit of rain, A / Tell me a lie / If you ever change your mind / Livin' in these troubled times.
Cassette: released on CBS, Mar'87 by CBS Records. Dist: CBS

Album: released on CBS, Mar'87 by CBS Records. Dist: CBS

Country Legends

COUNTRY LEGENDS (Various Artists).
Album: released on Hallmark, Feb'86 by Pickwick Records. Dist: Pickwick Distribution, PRT, Taylors

Cassette: released on Hallmark, Feb'86 by Pickwick Records. Dist: Pickwick Distribution, PRT, Taylors

Compact disc: released on Pickwick, Apr'86 by Pickwick Records. Dist: Pickwick Distribution, Prism Leisure Distribution, Lugtons

COUNTRY LEGENDS (RONCO) (Various Artists).
Album: released on Ronco, Oct'80

Country Life Posse

FREE HORIZONS.
Single (12"): released on Pitch, Sep'85 Dist: Backs, Cartel

Country Love

COUNTRY LOVE (Various Artists).
Album: released on K-Tel (Era), Jan'80 by K-Tel Records. Dist: K-Tel

COUNTRY LOVE AND COUNTRY HEARTACHE (Various Artists).
Cassette: released on Ditto, May'86 by Pickwick Records. Dist: H.R. Taylor

Country Lovin'

COUNTRY LOVIN' (Various Artists).
Album: released on Cambra, Aug'83 by Cambra Records. Dist: IDS, Conifer

COUNTRY LOVIN', VOL.2 Various artists (Various Artists).
Album: released on Cambra, May'85 by Cambra Records. Dist: IDS, Conifer

Cassette: released on Cambra, May'85 by Cambra Records. Dist: IDS, Conifer

Countryman

COUNTRYMAN Original soundtrack.
Album: released on Island, May'82 by Island Records. Dist: Polygram

Cassette: released on Island, May'82 by Island Records. Dist: Polygram

Countrymen

CONFRONTATION.
Single (12"): released on Jaydee, Aug'82 by Jaydee Records. Dist: Jetstar

Country Music

COUNTRY MUSIC South & West (Various Artists).
Tracks: / There'll come a time / Wanna be a cowboy's sweetheart / Rescue from moose river gold mine, The / Railroad boomer / Born to lose / It won't be long / Chant of the wanderer / Dark as a dungeon / Cotton eyed Joe / Georgia wildcat breakdown / Blue yodel no.11 / Sweet fern / Dreaming with tears in my eyes / Gospel ship / Fais pas ca (don't do that) / Last round up / Forgotten soldier boy / Ida, sweet as apple cider.
Album: released on New World (USA), Aug'86 by New World Records (USA). Dist: Conifer

COUNTRY MUSIC COUNTRY STYLE Various session artists.
Cassette: released on AIM (Budget Cassettes), Feb'83

COUNTRY MUSIC EXPRESS VOL.1 (Various Artists).
Double Album: released on Success, Oct'85 Dist: Counterpoint Distribution

Double cassette: released on Success, Oct'85 Dist: Counterpoint Distribution

COUNTRY MUSIC HITS, VOL.1 Various original artists (Various Artists).
Album: released on Mercury (Italy), Jun'83

Cassette: released on Mercury (Italy), Jun'83

COUNTRY MUSIC IN THE MODERN ERA (Various Artists).
Tracks: / Bouquet of roses / Never no more blues / Much too young to die / Squid jiggin' ground / There's poison in your heart / Try me one more time / Love letters in the sand / Jean's song / Mystery train / Little ole you / Jimmy Martinez / I'm a honky-tonk girl / Lorena / Don't let her know / All I love is you / Sing a sad song / Coat of many colors / Help me make it through the night.
Notes: Recorded in mono and stereo. (1940's - 1970's)
Album: released on New World (USA), Aug'86 by New World Records (USA). Dist: Conifer

COUNTRY MUSIC LEGENDS Various artists (Various Artists).
Cassette: released on Orchid Cassettes, Feb'82 Dist: H.R. Taylor Distribution

COUNTRY MUSIC PEOPLE,VOL.2 Various artists (Various Artists).
Album: released on Sonet, Oct'79 by Sonet Records. Dist: PRT

COUNTRY MUSIC SAMPLER Various artists (Various Artists).
Album: released on Sweet Folk All, May'81 by Sweet Folk All Records. Dist: Sweet Folk All, Roots, Celtic Music, Dragon, Impetus, Projection, Chris Wellard, Festival Records

COUNTRY MUSIC STANDARDS, VOL.2 Various artists (Various Artists).
Cassette: released on Bibi, Jan'82

COUNTRY MUSIC, VOL.2 Various artists (Various Artists).
Cassette: released on VFM, Apr'79 by VFM Records. Dist: Taylors, Wynd-Up Distribution

COUNTRY MUSIC,VOL.3 Various artists (Various Artists).
Cassette: released on VFM, May'79 by VFM Records. Dist: Taylors, Wynd-Up Distribution

COUNTRY MUSIC,VOL.4 Take me home country roads (Various Artists).
Cassette: released on VFM Cassettes, Jan'85

Country Rock

COUNTRY ROCK Various original artists (Various original artists).
Album: released on Warwick, Sep'82 Dist: Multiple Sound Distributors

Cassette: released on Warwick, Sep'82 Dist: Multiple Sound Distributors

COUNTRY ROCK SIDES Various artists (Various Artists).
Album: released on Sun, May'85 by Charly Records. Dist: Charly Distribution

Country Roundup

COUNTRY ROUNDUP Various original artists (Various original artists).
Double cassette: released on Pickwick (Ditto series), Jul'82

COUNTRY ROUNDUP,VOL.2 Various session artists (Various original artists).
Cassette: released on AIM (Budget Cassettes), Feb'83

Country Sailor

HEARTACHES ARE KNOCKING.
Album: released on SRT, Sep'78 by SRT Records. Dist: Pinnacle, Solomon & Peres Distribution, SRT Distribution, H.R. Taylor Distribution, PRT Distribution

Country's Greatest Hits

COUNTRY'S GREATEST HITS various artists (Various Artists).
Album: released on Island, Nov'85 by Island Records. Dist: Polygram

Cassette: released on Island, Nov'85 by Island Records. Dist: Polygram

Country Shack

PORTAIT, A.
Album: released on Sweet Folk All, May'81 by Sweet Folk All Records. Dist: Sweet Folk All, Roots, Celtic Music, Dragon, Impetus, Projection, Chris Wellard, Festival Records

WHICH WAY IS GONE?.
Album: released on JSU-Projection-Chris Wellard, May'81

Country Singers

FAVOURITE SONGS OF IRELAND.
Cassette: released on Polydor, Feb'85 by Polydor Records. Dist: Polygram, Polydor

Country Smash Hits

COUNTRY SMASH HITS VOL. 1 Various artists (Various Artists).
Notes: Featuring Lynn Anderson, Ned Miller, Hank Locklin, Skeeter Davis, Kitty Wells, Don Williams etc.
Compact disc: released on Bridge, '86 Dist: CD Centre Distribution, Pinnacle, Target

COUNTRY SMASH HITS VOL. 2 Various artists (Various Artists).
Notes: Featuring Barbara Fairchild, Leroy van Dyke, Faron Young, Bobby Bare, Stonewall Jackson, Dave Dudley etc.
Compact disc: released on Bridge, '86 Dist: CD Centre Distribution, Pinnacle, Target

Country Special

COUNTRY SPECIAL Various original artists (Various original artists).
Album: released on Bulldog Records, Jul'82

COUNTRY SPECIAL,VOL.1 Various artists (Various Artists).
Cassette: released on Homespun(Ireland), Feb'83 by Outlet Records. Dist: Outlet

COUNTRY SPECIAL,VOL.2 Various artists (Various Artists).
Cassette: released on Homespun(Ireland), Feb'83 by Outlet Records. Dist: Outlet

COUNTRY SPECIAL,VOL.3 Various artists (Various Artists).
Cassette: released on Homespun(Ireland), Feb'83 by Outlet Records. Dist: Outlet

Country Stars

COUNTRY STARS Various artists (Various Artists).
Album: released on Cambra, Aug'85 by Cambra Records. Dist: IDS, Conifer

Cassette: released on Cambra, Aug'85 by Cambra Records. Dist: IDS, Conifer

COUNTRY STARS & HITS Various artists (Various Artists).
Notes: 20 tracks by Jeannie C.Riley,Johnny Cash,Kingston Trio,Jimmy Dean,Lynn Anderson etc.
Compact disc: released on Delta, May'87 by Delta Records. Dist: Target

Country Sunrise

COUNTRY SUNRISE Various artists (Various Artists).
Album: released on Word Twenty, May'85

Cassette: released on Word Twenty, May'85

COUNTRY SUNRISE & COUNTRY SUNSET Various artists (Various Artists).
Double Album: released on Ronco, Sep'81

Double cassette: released on Ronco, Sep'81

Country Superstars

COUNTRY SUPERSTARS (Various Artists).
Cassette: released on Ditto, Sep'86 by Pickwick Records. Dist: H.R. Taylor

COUNTRY SUPERSTARS,VOL.1-11 Various artists (Various Artists).

Double Album: released on Pickwick, Mar'85 by Pickwick Records. Dist: Pickwick Distribution, Prism Leisure Distribution, Lugtons

Double cassette: released on Pickwick, Mar'85 by Pickwick Records. Dist: Pickwick Distribution, Prism Leisure Distribution

COUNTRY SUPERSTARS Various original artists (Various original artists).
Album: released on Lotus, Apr'79 Dist: Counterpoint

Country Trail

COUNTRY TRAIL various country artists (Various Artists).
Cassette: released on Pickwick, Apr'83 by Pickwick Records. Dist: Pickwick Distribution, Prism Leisure Distribution,

Country Truck Festival

COUNTRY TRUCK FESTIVAL VOL.1 (Various Artists).
Cassette: released on Success, Oct'86 Dist: Counterpoint Distribution

COUNTRY TRUCK FESTIVAL VOL.2 (Various Artists).
Cassette: released on Success, Oct'85 Dist: Counterpoint Distribution

Country & Western

COUNTRY AND WESTERN HITS VOLUME 1 1950-59 Various artists (Various Artists).
Notes: Tele: 01 891 6487

COUNTRY AND WESTERN HITS VOLUME 2 1960-69 Various artists (Various Artists).
Notes: Tele: 01 891 6487
Compact disc: released on Delta, Feb'86 by Delta Records. Dist: Target

COUNTRY & WESTERN FESTIVAL VOL. 3 Various artists (Various Artists).
Cassette: released on Success, Oct'85 Dist: Counterpoint Distribution

COUNTRY & WESTERN FESTIVAL VOL. 1 Various artists (Various Artists).
Cassette: released on Success, Oct'85 Dist: Counterpoint Distribution

COUNTRY & WESTERN FESTIVAL VOL. 2 Various artists (Various Artists).
Cassette: released on Success, Oct'85 Dist: Counterpoint Distribution

COUNTRY & WESTERN HITS VOL.3/1970-1979 Various artists (Various Artists).
Notes: Featuring Lynn Anderson, David Houston, Lacosta Tucker, Melba Montgomery, Faron young etc.
Compact disc: released on Delta, '86 by Delta Records. Dist: Target

COUNTRY & WESTERN HITS 1970-1979 Various artists (Various Artists).
Notes: Lynn Anderson, David Houston, Lacosta Tucker, Melba Montgomery, Faron Young etc.
Compact disc: released on Delta, Apr'87 by Delta Records. Dist: Target

COUNTRY & WESTERN HITS 1950-1959 Various artists (Various Artists).
Notes: Featuring the Kingston Trio, Porter Wagoner, Wanda Jackson, Stonewall Jackson etc.
Compact disc: released on Delta, Apr'87 by Delta Records. Dist: Target

COUNTRY & WESTERN HITS 1960-1969 Harious artists (Various Artists).
Notes: Jeanie C.Riley, Del Reeves, Johnny Russell, Billy Walker, Wanda Jackson, Jimmy Dean etc.
Compact disc: released on Delta, Apr'87 by Delta Records. Dist: Target

COUNTRY & WESTERN HITS VOL.1/1950-1959 Various artists (Various Artists).
Notes: Featuring the Kingston Trio, Porter Wagoner, Wanda Jackson, Stonewall Jackson etc.
Compact disc: released on Delta, '86 by Delta Records. Dist: Target

COUNTRY & WESTERN HITS VOL.2/1960-1969 Various artists (Various Artists).
Notes: Featuring Jeannie C. Riley, Del Reeves, Johnny Russell, Billy Walker, Wanda Jackson, Jimmy Dean etc.

COUNTRY & WESTERN MUSIC Various artists (Various Artists).
Notes: Featuring Mel McBrown, Earl Ricker etc.
Compact disc: released on Delta, '86 by Delta Records. Dist: Target

COUNTRY & WESTERN MUSIC FESTIVAL Various artists (Various Artists).
Notes: Featuring Judy Miller, Denis Olson, Faron Young, Skeeter Davis, Frankie Miller, JC Riley etc.
Compact disc: released on Delta, '86 by Delta Records. Dist: Target

MUSIC FOR THE MILLIONS H (Various Artists).
Album: released on Mercury (Italy), Jun'84
Cat. no: **8125 841**
Cassette: released on Mercury (Italy), Jun'84

SINGALONG.
Album: by Pilgrim Records. Dist: Rough Trade, Cartel

Country & Western Hymnal

COUNTRY & WESTERN HYMNAL, NO.2 various artists (Various Artists).
Album: by Pilgrim Records. Dist: Rough Trade, Cartel

County, Jayne

AMERIKAN CLEOPATRA.
Album: released on Konnexion, Feb'87 Dist: Roots, Pinnacle

PRIVATE OYSTER.
Tracks: / Private Oyster / Man enough to be a woman / Fun in America / I fell in love with a Russian soldier / Bad in bed / Are you a boy or are you a girl / When queens collide (part 1) / Double shot / Xerox that man / That lady dye twist / Love lives on lies.
Notes: Produced by Jayne County for "Sweet Jane Productions" Copyright Control. (P) 1986 Original Sound Recordings made by Heighway Robbery Wreckords. 1986 A Revolver Records release. Revolver Records is a division of FM-Revolver Records Ltd.
Album: released on Revolver, Mar'87 by Revolver Records. Dist: Revolver, Cartel

ROCK'N'ROLL.
Album: released on Safari, '81 by Safari Records. Dist: Pinnacle

WHEN QUEENS COLLIDE.
Single (7"): released on Heighway, May'86 Dist: Pinnacle

County Line

HEROES.
Tracks: / Heroes / Long way to go, A.
Single (7"): released on BBC, Apr'86 by BBC Records & Tapes. Dist: EMI, PRT

County Singers

FAVOURITE SONGS OF IRELAND.
Tracks: / Boys from the county Armagh, The / McNamara's band / Spinning wheel, The / I'll tell ma' / Danny boy / Jig medley * / March medley * / Galway bay / Irish rover, The / Slattery's mounted fut / Molly Malone / March medley 2 *.
Cassette: released on Philips (Ireland), Aug'86 Dist: IMS-Polygram

County, Wayne

BERLIN (County, Wayne & the Electric Chairs).
Single (7"): released on Safari, '79 by Safari Records. Dist: Pinnacle

Single (12"): released on Safari, '79 by Safari Records. Dist: Pinnacle

BLANTANTLY OFFENSIVE ep (County, Wayne & the Electric Chairs).
Single (7"): released on Safari, '80 by Safari Records. Dist: Pinnacle

EDDIE AND SHEENA (County, Wayne & The Electric Chairs).
Single (7"): released on Safari, '79 by Safari Records. Dist: Pinnacle

FUCK OFF (County, Wayne & the Electric Chairs).
Single (7"): released on Safari, Jun'83 by Safari Records. Dist: Pinnacle

STORM GATES OF HEAVEN (County, Wayne & The Electric Chairs).
Tracks: / Storm gates of heaven / Cry of angels / Speed demon / Mr Norman / Man enough to be a woman / Trying to get on the radio / I had too much to dream last night / Tomorrow is another day.
Album: released on Safari, Jun'79 by Safari Records. Dist: Pinnacle

TRYING TO GET ON THE RADIO (County, Wayne & the Electric Chairs).
Single (7"): released on Safari, '79 by Safari Records. Dist: Pinnacle

WHAT YOUR MOTHER NEVER TOLD YOU.
Album: released on Safari, May'79 by Safari Records. Dist: Pinnacle

Coup De Villes

BIG TROUBLE IN LITTLE CHINA (THEME).
Tracks: / Big trouble in little China / Pork chop express.
Single (7"): released on Silva Screen, Nov'86 by Silva Screen Records. Dist: Silva Screen

Courage the Guard Dog

COURAGE THE GUARD DOG sound effect.
Cassette: released on West 4 Tapes & Records, Aug'82

Court Martial

GOTTA GET OUT ep.
Single (7"): released on Riot City, Feb'82 by Riot City Records. Dist: Revolver

NO SOLUTION ep.
Single (7"): released on Riot City, Jul'82 by Riot City Records. Dist: Revolver

Courtneidge, Cicely

GOLDEN AGE OF..., THE.
Album: released on Golden Age, Jun'84 by Music For Pleasure Records. Dist: EMI

Cassette: released on Golden Age, Jun'84 by Music For Pleasure Records. Dist: EMI

...& JACK HULBERT.
Album: released on World, '68 Dist: Jetstar

Courtney-King, Barbara

PASTOURELLE.
Single (7"): released on RCA, Feb'83 by RCA Records. Dist: RCA, Roots, Swift, Wellard, Chris, I & B, Solomon & Peres Distribution

Courtney, Terry

COURT IN THE ACT.
Album: released on Tank, Nov'79 by Tank Records.

Courville, Sady

VIELLE MUSIQUE ACADIENNE, (LA) (Courville, Sady/Dennis McGhee).

Courville, S.D

TRADITIONAL CAJUN FIDDLING.
Album: released on Morning Star, Apr'79 Dist: Projection Distribution

Cousin Joe

GOSPEL-WAILING-JAZZ PLAYING.
Album: released on Big Bear, '82 by Big Bear Records. Dist: Big Bear, Swift

IN HIS PRIME (Cousin Joe from New Orleans).
Album: released on Oldie Blues Holland, Dec'84

Cousin Phyllis

GASKELL, ELIZABETH.
Notes: For full details see under Gaskell, Elizabeth "Cousin Phyllis"

Cousins, Dave

OLD SCHOOL SONGS.
Album: released on Sly, Sep'79 by Sly Records. Dist: Revolver, Cartel

Couture,Charlelie

CHARLELIE COUTURE.
Album: released on Island, Jun'84 by Island Records. Dist: Polygram

Cassette: released on Island, Jun'84 by Island Records. Dist: Polygram Deleted '87.

Couza, Jim

ENCHANTED VALLEY, THE (Couza, Jim with Eileen Monger).
Album: released on Saydisc, Aug'83 by Saydisc Records. Dist: Essex, Harmonia Mundi, Roots, H.R. Taylor, Jazz Music, Swift, Projection, Gamut

Cassette: released on Saydisc, Aug'83 by Saydisc Records. Dist: Essex, Harmonia Mundi, Roots, H.R. Taylor, Jazz Music, Swift, Projection,

FRIENDS AND NEIGHBOURS.
Album: released on Greenwich Village, May'84 by Sweet Folk All Records. Dist: Roots, Projection, Lightning, Celtic Music, Wellard, Chris

Album: released on Folk Freak, Nov'84 Dist: Projection

Covay, Don

HOUSE OF... (Covay, Don/Lemon Jefferson Blues Band).
Album: released on Atlantic, Mar'76 by WEA Records. Dist: WEA

MERCY (Covay, Don & the Goodtimers).
Album: released on Edsel, May'84 by Demon Records. Dist: Pinnacle, Jazz Music, Projection

SWEET THANG.
Tracks: / Sweet thang / Daddy please don't go tonight / Why did you put your shoes under my bed / Stop by / Bad luck / Hitching a ride / Standing in the grits line / In the sweet bye & bye / Ain't nothing a young girl can do / If there's a will there's a way / What's in the headlines.
Notes: Licensed from Charly Records International APS This compilation: P 1985 Charly Holdings Inc C 1985 Charly Records Ltd.
Album: released on Topline, May'87 by Charly Records. Dist: Charly Distribution

Cassette: released on Topline, May'87 by Charly Records. Dist: Charly Distribution

Coventry City...

IN CONCERT (Coventry City Band).
Album: released on Grosvenor, Jun'77 by Grosvenor Records. Dist: Taylors

SKY BLUES GO FOR IT (Coventry City Cup Final Squad).
Single (7"): released on Stether Music, May'87

SOUNDS OF BRASS SERIES vol.7 (Coventry City Band).
Album: by Decca Records. Dist: Polygram

Coverdale, David

NORTHWINDS.
Album: released on Fame (Liberty), Apr'84 by Music For Pleasure Records. Dist: EMI

Cassette: released on Fame (Liberty), Apr'84 by Music For Pleasure Records. Dist: EMI

Album: released on EMI (Germany), Feb'84 by EMI Records. Dist: Conifer

WHITESNAKE.
Album: released on Purple, May'77 by Purple Records. Dist: EMI

Cover girl

I'M A WINNER.
Tracks: / I'm a winner.
Single (7"): released on Space Station, May'86 Dist: PRT

Cover Girls

L.O.V.E.
Single (7"): released on Nectar, Nov'83 by Nectar Records. Dist: Pinnacle

SHOW ME.
Tracks: / Show me / Drumapella / Show me (nest mix) / Show me (heart-throb mix) / Show me (Florida mix).
Notes: Produced by Andy "Panda" Tripoli and The Latin Rascals. Edited by The Latin Ras cals for Latin Rascal Productions and Little Louie Vega for Small Wonders Productions Inc.
Single (7"): released on Magnet, May'87 by Magnet Records. Dist: BMG

Single (12"): released on Magnet, May'87 by Magnet Records. Dist: BMG

Cover up

LOVE THE ONE YOU'RE WITH.
Tracks: / Feel the fire / Without an aim.
Notes: Extra tracks on 12" version only
Single (7"): released on Venom, Jan'86 Dist: Pinnacle

Single (12"): released on Venom, Jan'86 Dist: Pinnacle

Covington, Julie

DON'T CRY FOR ME ARGENTINA.
Single (7"): released on Old Gold, Jul'84 by Old Gold Records. Dist: Lightning, Jazz Music, Spartan, Counterpoint

HOUSEWIVES CHOICE.
Single (7"): released on BBC, Nov'82 by BBC Records & Tapes. Dist: EMI, PRT

Coward Brothers

PEOPLE'S LIMOUSINE.
Single (7"): released on Imp, Jun'85 by Demon. Dist: Pinnacle

Coward, Noel

AT LAS VEGAS.
Album: released on CBS Cameo, Aug'85 by CBS Records. Dist: CBS

Cassette: released on CBS Cameo, Aug'85 by CBS Records. Dist: CBS

GREAT SHOWS.
Tracks: / Bitter sweet / I'll see you again / If love were all / Dear little cafe' / Zigeuner / Cavalcade / Lover of my dreams / Twentieth century blues / Toast to England / Conversation piece / I'll follow my secret heart / Regency rakes / Charming, charming / Dear little soldiers / There's always something fishy about the French / English lessons / Melanie's nevermore / Operette / Countless Mitzi / Dearest love / Gypsy melody / Stately homes of England (The) / Where are the songs we sung / Ace of clubs / Nothing can last forever / I'd never know / Something about a sailor / My kind of man / This could be true / Josephine / Sail away / Why does love get in the way / In a boat on a lake with my darling / Chase me Charlie / Evening in summer / I like America / Three juvenile delinquents.

Notes: A third re-issued from the series of Noel Coward double album packages originally released on World Records. Features a selection from some of the favourite shows written by Coward - the songwriter, director, actor, novelist, playwriter and singer popularies through theatre, readiom film, record and televison. Sleeve notes give a breif history on each of the five piece shows paid tribute on this collection: *Bitter sweet Cavalcade Conversation piece Operette* and *Ace of clubs* along with scenes from the shows shown on the gatefold inner spread. (Double album...)
Album: released on Retrospect Series, Nov'86

Cassette: released on Retrospect Series, Nov'86

GREAT SHOWS, THE.
Double Album: released on Retrospect, Jan'87 by World Records.

GREAT SHOWS, THE (Various Artists).
Album: Dist: Polygram

MASTER, THE (Various Artists).
Double Album: released on EMI, '78 by EMI Records. Dist: EMI

NOEL COWARD & GERTRUDE LAWRENCE.
Album: released on Monmouth, Mar'79

NOEL COWARD SINGS HIS SCORE Girl who came to supper (The).
Album: released on DRG (USA), Jul'79 by DRG Records. Dist: Conifer, RCA

REVUES, THE (Various Artists).
Album: released on World (Retrospect Series), Feb'84

Cassette: released on World (Retrospect Series), Feb'84

TALENT TO AMUSE, A.
Album: released on Parlophone, '73 by EMI Records. Dist: EMI

Cowardy Custard

COWARDY CUSTARD original London cast.
Double Album: by RCA Records. Dist: RCA

Cowboy Copas

16 GREATEST HITS.
Album: released on Starday, Apr'87

Cassette: released on Starday, Apr'87

BEST OF..., THE.
Album: released on Starday, Jan'80

NOT FORGOTTEN (Cowboy Copas, Patsy Cline, Hawkshaw Hawkins).
Album: released on Starday, Apr'87

Cassette: released on Starday, Apr'87

Cowboys International

ORIGINAL SIN, THE.
Album: released on Virgin, Oct'79 by Virgin Records. Dist: EMI, Virgin Distribution

Cowell, Stanley

BLUES FOR THE VIET CONG.
Album: released on Freedom, May'79 by Logo Records. Dist: RCA, Discovery, Wellard, Chris

NEW WORLD.
Album: released on Galaxy, Sep'81 by Galaxy Records. Dist: RCA, Red Lightnin' Distribution, Discovery, Swift

Cow, Henry

CONCERTS.
Album: by Virgin Records. Dist: EMI, Virgin Distribution

HENRY COW LEGEND, THE.
Album: released on Virgin, May'73 by Virgin Records. Dist: EMI, Virgin Distribution

IN PRAISE OF LEARNING.
Album: released on Recommended, Mar'86 by Recommended Records. Dist: Recommended, Impetus, Rough Trade

Album: released on Virgin, May'75 by Virgin Records. Dist: EMI, Virgin Distribution

UNREST.
Album: released on Virgin, May'74 by Virgin Records. Dist: EMI, Virgin Distribution

WESTERN CULTURE.
Album: released on Recommended, Oct'79 by Recommended Records. Dist: Recommended, Impetus, Rough Trade

Cowie, Charlie

FIDDLE FROLIC.
Album: released on Lismor, Jan'78 by Lismor [illegible] Lismor, Roots, Celtic Music

Cowles, Barry

SHADOW OF YOUR SMILE, THE (Cowles, Barry & the Riha Orchestra).
Cassette: released on VFM, May'85 by VFM Records. Dist: Taylors, Wynd-Up Distribution

Cox, Harry

SEVENTEEN COME SUNDAY.
Cassette: released on Folktracks, Nov'79 by Folktracks Cassettes. Dist: Folktracks

Coxhill, Lol

10:02 (Coxhill, Lol & Daniel Deshays).
Tracks: / On golden flaque / Fromage a varese incl. Regardez Edgar / Solitudinette / Ceux qu ils aiment inc. Keep it on the island / Cleito incl. Tape dancing / Un homme au plafond incl. Practice makes / Amies Americaines / Choral a tchang / Sergent De Ville tres occupe / Tea for two incl: Fortitude.
Album: released on Nato (France), Sep'86 by Disques Nato. Dist: Essex Record Distributors Ltd.

CHANTENAY 80 (Coxhill, Lol/Raymond Boni/Maurice Horsthuis).

C/M/M/C (Coxhill, Lol & Steve Miller).
Album: released on Caroline, '73 Dist: Virgin, Island, Polygram, CBS

COUSCOUS.
Tracks: / West lawn dirige/just a closer walk with thee / West lawn dirige/Just a closer walk with thee/Diversions / Hotlavaband extensions / Variations pour violoncelle, Contrebasse, Sopranino et piano / And lo, the chapel walls trembled at the voice of the M.C.
Notes: With: Buck Funk/Reverend Anthony W.Reves/Alan Tomlinson/Phil Minton/Steve Bere- sford/Jac BerrocaL/Sylvia Hallett/Georgie Born/Susan Ferrar/Mike Cooper/Peter Bennink/Fred Van Hove/Joelle Leandre/Roger Turner/Veryan Weston.
Album: released on Nato (France), Sep'86 by Disques Nato. Dist: Essex Record Distributors Ltd.

DIVERSE.
Album: released on Ogun, Oct'86 Dist: Jazz Music, JSU, Cadillac

DUNOIS SOLOS, THE.
Tracks: / Dunois sols, The / Distorted reminiscences / Further developments.
Album: released on Nato (France), Sep'86 by Disques Nato. Dist: Essex Record Distributors Ltd.

FLEAS IN CUSTARD.
Album: released on Caroline, Feb'76 Dist: Virgin, Island, Polygram, CBS

FRENCH GIGS (Coxhill, Lol/Fred Frith).
Tracks: / French gigs.
Album: released on AAA (France), Oct'86 by AAA (France) Records.

INIMITABLE, THE.
Tracks: / Moon was yellow, The / Spring is here / Folks who lives on the hill, The / It never entered my mind / Little froggies / Certain smile, A / Time after time / Change partners / Requiem major / Cocktail for two / Two sleepy people.
Album: released on Chabada(France), Sep'86 Dist: Essex

INSTANT REPLAY.
Tracks: / Le bagad de kemperle / La Chantenay / Sienne A1-A2-A3-B1-B2 / Embraceable you -B3-C1 / Pot pourri / Caravan-C2-C3-D1-D2.
Album: released on Nato (France), Sep'86 by Disques Nato. Dist: Essex Record Distributors Ltd.

JOHNNY RONDO DUO PLUS (Coxhill, Lol/ David G.Holland/Mike Cooper).
Tracks: / Johnny Rondo duo plus.
Album: released on SAJ (W.Germany), Oct'86

JOY OF PARANOIA, THE.
Album: released on Ogun, '78 Dist: Jazz Music, JSU, Cadillac

LOL COXHILL WITH TOTSUZEN DANBALL (Coxhill, Lol with Totsuzen Danball).

SOON (Coxhill, Lol with Astronauts).
Notes: see under ATRONAUTS with Lol Coxhill

STORY SO FAR-OH REALLY (Coxhill, Lol & Steve Miller).
Album: released on Caroline, Oct'74 Dist: Virgin, Island, Polygram, CBS

Cox, Ida

IDA COX (Cox, Ida/Hill, Bertha Chippie).
Album: released on Queen-Disc, Apr'81 Dist: Celtic Music, JSU, Jazz Horizons, Jazz Music

IDA COX 1923 vol.1.
Album: released on Fountain, Apr'79 by Retrieval Records. Dist: Jazz Music, Swift, VJM, Wellard, Chris, Retrieval

IDA COX 1923-4 vol.2.
Album: released on Fountain, Apr'79 by Retrieval Records. Dist: Jazz Music, Swift, VJM, Wellard, Chris, Retrieval

Cox, Jess

BRIDGES.
Single (7"): released on Neat, May'83 by Neat Records. Dist: Pinnacle, Neat

Single (7"): released on Neat, May'83 by Neat Records. Dist: Pinnacle, Neat

ONE IN A MILLION.
Single (7"): released on Neat, Jan'84 by Neat Records. Dist: Pinnacle, Neat

PIECE OF THE ACTION.
Album: released on Neat, Sep'83 by Neat Records. Dist: Pinnacle, Neat

THIRD STEP (Cox, Jess Band).
Tracks: / One in a million / Fallen hero / Two time loser / Ghosts / Danger signs / Bridges / Living your love (off the wall) / Tunnel, The.
Album: released on Neat, '85 by Neat Records. Dist: Pinnacle, Neat

Coyne, Kevin

BEAUTIFUL EXTREMES ET CETERA.
Album: released on Cherry Red, Feb'83 by Cherry Red Records. Dist: Pinnacle

BLAME IT ON THE NIGHT.
Album: released on Virgin, '74 by Virgin Records. Dist: EMI, Virgin Distribution

DANDELION YEARS.
Album: released on Butt, Mar'82 by Butt Records. Dist: Counterpoint

HEARTBURN.
Album: released on Virgin, Feb'76 by Virgin Records. Dist: EMI, Virgin Distribution

IN LIVING BLACK & WHITE.
Album: released on Virgin, Jan'77 by Virgin Records. Dist: EMI, Virgin Distribution

LEGLESS IN MANILA.
Album: released on Collapse, Feb'84 Dist: Rough Trade

MARJORY RAZORBLADE.
Album: released on Virgin, '74 by Virgin Records. Dist: EMI, Virgin Distribution

MATCHING HEAD AND FEET.
Album: released on Virgin, Apr'75 by Virgin Records. Dist: EMI, Virgin Distribution

POINTING THE FINGER.
Album: released on Cherry Red, Oct'81 by Cherry Red Records. Dist: Pinnacle

POLITICZ.
Album: released on Cherry Red, '82 by Cherry Red Records. Dist: Pinnacle

SO STRANGE/FATHER DEAR FATHER.
Single (7"): released on Cherry Red, Oct'82 by Cherry Red Records. Dist: Pinnacle

Coyote Sisters

COYOTE SISTERS.
Album: released on Motown, Oct'84 by Motown Records. Dist: BMG Distribution

Cassette: released on Motown, Oct'84 by Motown Records. Dist: BMG Distribution

I'VE GOT A RADIO.
Single (7"): released on Morocco, Oct'84
Cat. no: **TMG 1362**

STRAIGHT FROM THE HEART.
Single (7"): released on Morocco, Aug'84

Single (12"): released on Morocco, Aug'84

CPO Disco Strings

DISCO ROUND THE MOON.
Album: released on CJMO, Jun'78 Dist: Jazz Music, Spartan, Taylors

Craaft

CRAAFT.
Tracks: / I wanna look in your eyes / Breakin' walls ain't easy / Hold me / You're the best thing in my life / I guess you are the number one / Stranger / Don't wanna wait no more / Now that you're gone / Wasted years / Cool town lovers.
Album: released on CBS, Jul'86 by CBS Records. Dist: CBS

Cassette: released on CBS, Jul'86 by CBS Records. Dist: CBS

I WANNA LOOK IN YOUR EYES.
Tracks: / I wanna look in your eyes / I guess you are the number one.
Single (7"): released on Epic, Jun'86 by CBS Records. Dist: CBS

Crab That Played

CRAB THAT PLAYED/HOW THE RHINO (Ogilvy, Ian).
Cassette: released on Listen Productions, Nov'84 Dist: H.R. Taylor, Hayward Promotions Distribution

Crack

ALL OR NOTHING/I CAUGHT YOU OUT.
Single (7"): released on RCA, Feb'83 by RCA Records. Dist: RCA, Roots, Swift, Wellard, Chris, I & B, Solomon & Peres Distribution

Cracked Mirror

CRACKED MIRROR.
Album: released on Cracked Mirror, Jul'83 by Cracked Mirror Records. Dist: Mason's Music Distributors/Wholesalers

Crack The Sky

ANIMAL NOTES.
Album: released on Lifesong, Jul'77

SAFETY IN NUMBERS.
Album: released on Lifesong, Jun'78

Single (7"): released on Human, Jan'80 Dist: Roots, Stage One

Craddock, Billy Crash

BEST OF BILLY CRASH CRADDOCK.
Tracks: / Rub it in / Broken down in tiny pieces / You better move on / First time, The / Sweet magnolia blossom / Easy as pie / Still thinkin' bout you / Ain't nothing shakin' / Don't be angry / Slippin' and slidin' / Knock three times / Dream lover / I'm gonna knock on your wall / Walk softly / I love the blues / Ruby baby / Tear fell, A / Till the water stops runnin' / Afraid I'll want to love her one more time / You rubbed it in all wrong.
Double Album: released on MCA Import, Mar'86 by MCA Records. Dist: Polygram, IMS

BILLY 'CRASH' CRADDOCK.
Album: released on Capitol, May'78 by Capitol Records. Dist: EMI

CRASH CRADDOCK.
Notes: Track details not advised
Album: released on MCA Import, Mar'86 by MCA Records. Dist: Polygram, IMS

Cradle

IT'S TOO HIGH.
Single (7"): released on Rough Trade, Apr'87 by Rough Trade Records. Dist: Rough Trade Distribution, Cartel Distribution

Single (12"): released on Rough Trade, Apr'87 by Rough Trade Records. Dist: Rough Trade Distribution, Cartel Distribution

Cradle Will Rock

CRADLE WILL ROCK Original cast album (Various Artists).
Compact disc: Dist: Pinnacle

Album: released on TER, Oct'85 Dist: Pinnacle

Cassette: released on TER, Oct'85 Dist: Pinnacle

Craft

CRAFT.
Tracks: / Aries / Taurus / Gemini / Cancer / Leo / Virgo.
Album: released on Shanghai, Aug'86

Craft Village Buskers

NO CHANCE TO DREAM.
Single (7"): released on ESO, Aug'83 by ESO Records. Dist: ESO, Wynd-Up Distribution

Craig, Gary

BLUE RIDGE MOUNTAIN.
Album: Dist: Jazz Music, Projection

NORTH CAROLINA BOYS.
Album: Dist: Jazz Music, Projection

Craig, Gerry

ELVIS PRESLEY'S LOVE SONGS.
Cassette: released on Kingfisher Cassettes, Nov'81 by Fraser-Peacock Associates Ltd. Dist: PRT

Craig, Wendy

CHILDREN'S HOUR.
Album: released on Multi-Media, Jul'81 by Multi Media Tapes Records. Dist: Pinnacle, Conifer Distribution, H.R. Taylor Distribution, Stage One Distribution

CHILDREN'S HOUR (1983).
Album: released on Multi-Media, Feb'83 by Multi Media Tapes Records. Dist: Pinnacle, Conifer Distribution, H.R. Taylor Distribution, Stage One Distribution

Cassette: released on Multi-Media, Feb'83 by Multi Media Tapes Records. Dist: Pinnacle, Conifer Distribution, H.R. Taylor Distribution, Stage One Distribution

TREASURY OF FAIRY TALES CHAPTER ONE.
Album: released on Polydor, Dec'80 by Polydor Records. Dist: Polygram, Polydor

YOUR FAVOURITE FAIRY STORIES.
Album: released on Spot, Feb'84 by Pickwick Records. Dist: H.R. Taylor, Lugtons

Cassette: released on Spot, Feb'84 by Pickwick Records. Dist: H.R. Taylor, Lugtons

Cramer, Floyd

20 OF THE BEST.
Tracks: / On the rebound / Java / Flip flop and bop / Lovesick blues / Corn crib symphony / Dream baby (how long must i dream?) / Honky tonk (part 2) / Maple leaf rag / Sugarfoot rag / Boogie, boogie, boogie / What'd i say / Boogie woogie / Proud Mary / In' crowd, The / Work song / Work song / (Himmo a la Alegria) / My melody of love / Games people play / Smile / Last date.
Album: released on RCA, Mar'86 by RCA Records. Dist: RCA, Roots, Swift, Wellard, Chris, I & B, Solomon & Peres Distribution

BEST OF FLOYD CRAMER (1980).
Album: released on RCA International (USA), Apr'80 by RCA Records. Dist: RCA

Cassette: released on RCA International (USA), Apr'80 by RCA Records. Dist: RCA

BEST OF FLOYD CRAMER.
Album: released on RCA/Brazil, Jan'84

Cassette: released on RCA/Brazil, Jan'84

DALLAS.
Album: released on RCA International (USA), Sep'81 by RCA Records. Dist: RCA

Cassette: released on RCA International (USA), Sep'81 by RCA Records. Dist: RCA

ON THE REBOUND/BOOGIE WOOGIE.
Single (7"): released on RCA, Jul'81 by RCA Records. Dist: RCA, Roots, Swift, Wellard, Chris, I & B, Solomon & Peres Distribution

Cramps

CAN YOUR PUSSY DO THE DOG.
Single (7"): released on Big Beat, Oct'85 by Ace Records. Dist: Projection, Pinnacle

Cassette: released on Big Beat, Oct'85 by Ace Records. Dist: Projection, Pinnacle

DATE WITH ELVIS, A.
Tracks: / How far can too far go / Hot pearl snatch / People ain't no good / What's inside a girl? / Can your pussy do the dog / Kizmiaz / Cornfed dames / Chicken / Womanneed / Aloha from hell / It's just that song.
Album: released on Big Beat, Feb'86 by Ace Records. Dist: Projection, Pinnacle

Cassette: released on Big Beat, Feb'86 by Ace Records. Dist: Projection, Pinnacle

Compact disc: released on Big Beat, Apr'86 by Ace Records. Dist: Projection, Pinnacle

DATE WITH ELVIS, A.
Compact disc: by Ace Records. Dist: Projection, Pinnacle

GOREHOUND.
Single (7"): released on New Rose, Mar'84 Dist: Rough Trade, Cartel

GRAVEST HITS.
Album: released on Illegal, Jul'79 by Faulty Products Records. Dist: Pinnacle, Lightning, Cartel

KISMIAZ.
Tracks: / Kismiax.
Single (7"): released on Ace, Jun'86 by Ace Records. Dist: Pinnacle, Swift, Hotshot, Cadillac

Single (12"): released on Ace, Jun'86 by Ace Records. Dist: Pinnacle, Swift, Hotshot, Cadillac

OFF THE BONE.
Compact disc: released on Illegal, Jan'87 by Faulty Products Records. Dist: Pinnacle, Lightning, Cartel

Album: released on Illegal, May'83 by Faulty Products Records. Dist: Pinnacle, Lightning, Cartel

PSYCHEDELIC JUNGLE.
Album: released on A&M, May'81 by A&M Records. Dist: Polygram

SMELL OF FEMALE.
Tracks: / Most exalted potentate of love, The / You got good taste / Call of the wig hat / Faster pussycat / I ain't nothin' but a gorehound / Psychotic reaction.

Compact disc: Dist: Rough Trade, Cartel

Album: released on Big Beat, Nov'83 by Ace Records. Dist: Projection, Pinnacle

Picture disc album: released on Big Beat, Jun'84 by Ace Records. Dist: Projection, Pinnacle

SONGS THE LORD TAUGHT US.
Album: released on Illegal, Mar'80 by Faulty Products Records. Dist: Pinnacle, Lightning, Cartel

WHAT'S INSIDE A GIRL.
Tracks: / What's inside a girl.
Single (7"): released on Big Beat, Apr'86 by Ace Records. Dist: Projection, Pinnacle

Single (12"): released on Big Beat, Apr'86 by Ace Records. Dist: Projection, Pinnacle

WHAT'S INSIDE A GIRL (EP).
Tracks: / What's a girl inside (EP).
Cassette single: released on Big Beat, Mar'87 by Ace Records. Dist: Projection, Pinnacle

YOU'VE GOT GOOD TASTE.
Picture disc single: released on New Rose, Mar'84 Dist: Rough Trade, Cartel

Cranitch, Matt

EISTIGH SEAL.
Album: released on Gael-Linn (Ireland), Feb'85 by Gael Linn Records. Dist: Roots, Projection, Celtic Music, Jazz Music
Cat. no: **CEF 104**
Cassette: released on Gael-Linn (Ireland), Feb'85 by Gael Linn Records. Dist: Roots, Projection, Celtic Music, Jazz Music

Crap Stops Here

CRAP STOPS HERE, THE (Various Artists).
Album: released on Rabid, Jul'80 by Rabid Records. Dist: Pinnacle, Rough Trade

Crash

ALMOST.
Tracks: / Almost / My Machine / On and on.
Single (12"): released on Remorse, Nov'86 by Remorse Records. Dist: Revolver, Cartel

BRIGHT COLOURED LIGHTS.
Single (7"): released on Remorse, Aug'87 by Remorse Records. Dist: Revolver, Cartel

DON'T LOOK NOW (NOW!).
Tracks: / Don't look now (now!).
Single (12"): released on Remorse, Nov'86 by Remorse Records. Dist: Revolver, Cartel

I FEEL FINE.
Album: released on Remorse, Feb'87 by Remorse Records. Dist: Revolver, Cartel

Crash Course In Hari Kari

SPY, THE.
Tracks: / Spy, The / Theme from a video nasty.
Single (7"): released on AWA, Jun'86 by AWA Records. Dist: Pinnacle

Crash Crew

2468 HERE WE ARE.
Single (7"): released on Sugar Hill USA, Nov'85 by MCA Records. Dist: Roots Distribution, Mike's Country Music Room Distribution, Projection Distribution, PRT Distribution

Crass

10 NOTES ON A SUMMER'S DAY.
Tracks: / 10 Notes on a Summer's Day.
Single (7"): released on Crass, Nov'86 by Exitstencil Music. Dist: Rough Trade, Cartel

BLOODY REVOLUTIONS/PERSONS UNKNOWN (Crass/Poison Girls).
Single (7"): released on Crass, Dec'80 by Exitstencil Music. Dist: Rough Trade, Cartel

FEEDING OF 5,000.
Single (12"): released on Crass, Oct'81 by Exitstencil Music. Dist: Rough Trade, Cartel

NAGASAKI NIGHTMARE.
Single (7"): released on Crass, Oct'81 by Exitstencil Music. Dist: Rough Trade, Cartel

PENIS ENVY.
Album: released on Crass, Oct'81 by Exitstencil Music. Dist: Rough Trade, Cartel

PENIS ENVY (12").
Single (12"): released on Crass, May'81 by Exitstencil Music. Dist: Rough Trade, Cartel

PERSONS UNKNOWN (Crass/Poison Girls).
Single (7"): released on Crass, May'81 by Exitstencil Music. Dist: Rough Trade, Cartel

REALITY ASYLUM.
Single (7"): released on Crass, Dec'80 by Exitstencil Music. Dist: Rough Trade, Cartel

SHEEP FARMING IN THE FALKLANDS.
Single (7"): released on Crass, May'83 by Exitstencil Music. Dist: Rough Trade, Cartel

STATIONS OF THE CRASS.
Single (12"): released on Crass, Oct'81 by Exitstencil Music. Dist: Rough Trade, Cartel

YES SIR I WILL.
Album: released on Crass, Jun'83 by Exitstencil Music. Dist: Rough Trade, Cartel

Cravats

CRAVATS IN TOYTOWN.
Album: released on Small Wonder, Oct'80 by Small Wonder Records. Dist: Cartel, Indies

CRAVATS SING NERMINUS AND OTHER HITS.
Single (12"): released on Glass, Aug'82 by Glass Records. Dist: Nine Mile, Rough Trade, Red Rhino, Play It Again Sam

LAND OF THE GIANTS.
Tracks: / Land of the giants.
Single (12"): released on Ref.ax, Feb'86

OFF THE BEACH/AND THE SUN SHONE.
Single (7"): released on Small Wonder, Nov'81 by Small Wonder Records. Dist: Cartel, Indies

RUB ME OUT.
Single (7"): released on Crass, Jul'82 by Exitstencil Music. Dist: Rough Trade, Cartel

TERMINUS/LITTLE YELLOW FROGGY.
Single (7"): released on Glass, Feb'82 by Glass Records. Dist: Nine Mile, Rough Trade, Red Rhino, Play It Again Sam

Crawford, Hank

HANK CRAWFORD'S BACK.
Album: released on Kudu, Apr'77 Dist: IMS-Polygram

INDIGO BLUE.
Compact disc: released on Fantasy (USA), Nov'86 by Fantasy Inc USA Records. Dist: IMS, Polygram

ROADHOUSE SYMPHONY (Crawford, Hank & Doctor John).
Tracks: / Roadhouse symphony / Track Magick / Jubilee / Say it isn't so / Time is on our side / Precious Lord / Sugar ditch.
Notes: Some fine blues playing here from alto sax player Hank Crawford who first came to prominence as a key soloist with the Ray Charles orchestra during the late fifties and early sixties. Since those early years he has made countless albums, mainly int the jazz funk mold, for Atlantic and more recently CTI's Kuda label. Throughout the album Doctor John plays keyboards and sings on the track 'Tragick Magick'. Recommended tracks: 'Tragick Magick', 'Precious Lord' and 'Sugar Ditch'. Personnel: Hank Crawford-alto sax/Doctor John- piano, organ, vocal/Melvin Spark- guitar/Wilbur Bascombe,Jnr-bass/Bernard Purdie - drums/Randy Brecker, Alan Rubin - trumpets/ Howard Johnson-baritone sax/ Houston Person - tenor sax/ David Fathead Newman - tenor and alto sax.

SOUL SURVIVORS (Crawford, Hank & Jimmy McGriff).
Tracks: / Can't stand the pain / Actual emotional love / World of fools / Betcha / Higher than anyone can count / Gettin' away with murder / Desire / Overnight / Almaz / Don't wanna be normal.
Notes: For full information see under "McGriff, Jimmy & Hank Crawford

TICO RICO.
Album: released on Kudu, Sep'77 Dist: IMS-Polygram

Crawford, Jesse

CINEMA ORGAN ENCORES.
Album: released on Deroy, Jun'81 by Deroy Records. Dist: Jazz Music, Swift

Crawford, Jimmy

JIMMY THE JOKER.
Single (7"): released on Response, Sep'82 by Priority Records. Dist: BMG

Crawford, Johnny

BEST OF....
Album: released on Rhino (USA), Feb'85 by Rhino Records (USA).

Crawford, Michael

BILLY.
Cassette: released on CBS, May'74 by CBS Records. Dist: CBS

MUSIC OF THE NIGHT (Crawford, Michael & Sarah Brightman).
Tracks: / Wishing you were somehow here again.
Single (7"): released on Polydor, Jan'87 by Polydor Records. Dist: Polygram, Polydor

Crawford, Randy

ABSTRACT EMOTIONS.
Compact disc: by Warner Bros Records. Dist: WEA

Cassette: released on Warner Bros., Jul'86 by Warner Bros Records. Dist: WEA

Cassette: released on Warner Bros., Jul'86 by Warner Bros Records. Dist: WEA

ALMAZ.
Tracks: / Almaz / Desire.
Single (7"): released on Warner Bros., Oct'86 by Warner Bros Records. Dist: WEA

Single (12"): released on Warner Bros., Oct'86 by Warner Bros Records. Dist: WEA

EVERYTHING MUST CHANGE.
Album: released on Warner Brothers, Nov'80 by Warner Bros Records. Dist: WEA

Cassette: released on Warner Brothers, Nov'80 by Warner Bros Records. Dist: WEA

GETTING AWAY WITH MURDER.
Tracks: / Getting away with murder / Overnight / Don't wanna be normal.
Single (7"): released on Warner Brothers, Jul'86 by Warner Bros Records. Dist: WEA

Single (12"): released on Warner Brothers, Jul'86 by Warner Bros Records. Dist: WEA

GREATEST HITS: RANDY CRAWFORD.
Album: released on K-Tel, Sep'84 by K-Tel Records. Dist: Record Merchandisers Distribution, Taylors, Terry Blood Distribution, Wynd-Up Distribution, Relay Distribution, Pickwick Distribution, Solomon & Peres Distribution, Polygram

Cassette: released on K-Tel, Sep'84 by K-Tel Records. Dist: Record Merchandisers Distribution, Taylors, Terry Blood Distribution, Wynd-Up Distribution, Relay Distribution, Pickwick Distribution, Solomon & Peres Distribution, Polygram

HE REMINDS ME.
Single (7"): released on Warner Bros., Jan'83 by Warner Bros Records. Dist: WEA

Single (12"): released on Warner Bros., Jan'83 by Warner Bros Records. Dist: WEA

HIGHER THAN ANYONE CAN COUNT.
Tracks: / Higher than anyone can count / Tender falls the rain.
Single (7"): released on Warner Brothers, Mar'87 by Warner Bros Records. Dist: WEA

Single (12"): released on Warner Brothers, Mar'87 by Warner Bros Records. Dist: WEA

IMAGINE.
Single (7"): released on Warner Brothers, Jan'82 by Warner Bros Records. Dist: WEA

LOVE THEME-THE COMPETITION.
Single (7"): released on MCA, Mar'81 by MCA Records. Dist: Polygram, MCA

NIGHTLINE.
Compact disc: by Warner Bros Records. Dist: WEA

Album: released on Warner Bros., Nov'83 by Warner Bros Records. Dist: WEA

Cassette: released on Warner Bros., Nov'83 by Warner Bros Records. Dist: WEA

NOW WE MAY BEGIN.
Album: released on Warner Brothers, May'80 by Warner Bros Records. Dist: WEA

Cassette: released on Warner Brothers, May'80 by Warner Bros Records. Dist: WEA

ONE DAY I'LL FLY AWAY.
Tracks: / One day I'll fly away / You might need somebody.
Single (7"): released on Old Gold, Mar'86 by Old Gold Records. Dist: Lightning, Jazz Music, Spartan, Counterpoint

ONE DAY I WILL FLY AWAY.
Single (7"): released on Warner Brothers, Aug'80 by Warner Bros Records. Dist: WEA

Cassette: released on Warner Brothers, Aug'80 by Warner Bros Records. Dist: WEA

RAW SILK.
Cassette: released on Warner Brothers, Oct'82 by Warner Bros Records. Dist: WEA

SECRET COMBINATION.
Album: released on Warner Brothers, May'81 by Warner Bros Records. Dist: WEA

Cassette: released on Warner Brothers, May'81 by Warner Bros Records. Dist: WEA

Compact disc: released on Warner Bros., Mar'87 by Warner Bros Records. Dist: WEA

WHY.
Single (7"): released on Warner Bros, Jan'84 by Warner Bros Records. Dist: WEA

Single (12"): released on Warner Bros, Jan'84 by Warner Bros Records. Dist: WEA

WINDSONG.
Album: released on Warner Brothers, Jun'82 by Warner Bros Records. Dist: WEA

Cassette: released on Warner Brothers, Jun'82 by Warner Bros Records. Dist: WEA

Crawford, Sandra
CAN'T BE YOUR PART-TIME LOVER.
Tracks: / Can't be your part-time lover (inst).
Single (12"): released on Star Records, Dec'86

Crawford, Sugar Boy
SUGAR BOY CRAWFORD.
Album: released on Pathe Marconi(France), Apr'85

Crawley, Wilton
CRAWLEY CLARINET MOAN 1927-28.
Album: released on Harlequin, Sep'85 by Harlequin Records. Dist: Swift, Jazz Music, Wellard, Chris, IRS, Taylor, H.R.

Crawling Chaos
C.
Album: released on Foetus, Mar'84 by Foetus Productions. Dist: Red Rhino, Cartel

SEX MACHINE.
Single (7"): released on Factory, Mar'81 by Factory Records. Dist: Cartel, Pinnacle

WAQQUZZ.
Tracks: / Waqquzz.
Album: released on Foetus, Apr'86 by Foetus Productions. Dist: Red Rhino, Cartel

Crawling Walls
INER SECRETS.
Album: released on Eva-Lolita, Nov'86 Dist: Pinnacle

Craxton, Janet
ART OF JANET CRAXTON, THE.
Album: released on BBC, Apr'87 by BBC Records & Tapes. Dist: EMI, PRT, Pye

Cassette: released on BBC, Apr'87 by BBC Records & Tapes. Dist: EMI, PRT, Pye

Compact disc: released on BBC, Apr'87 by BBC Records & Tapes. Dist: EMI, PRT, Pye

Album: released on BBC, Jun'87 by BBC Records & Tapes. Dist: EMI, PRT, Pye

Cassette: released on BBC, Jun'87 by BBC Records & Tapes. Dist: EMI, PRT, Pye

Compact disc: released on BBC, Jun'87 by BBC Records & Tapes. Dist: EMI, PRT, Pye

Cray, Robert
BAD INFLUENCE (Cray, Robert Band).
Tracks: / Phone booth / Grinder, The / Got to make a comeback / So many women, so little time / Where do I go from here? / Waiting for a train / March on / Don't touch me / No big deal / Bad influence.
Compact disc: released on Sound Product, '86 Dist: Pinnacle

Compact disc: released on Demon, Jun'87 by Demon Records. Dist: Pinnacle

Album: by Demon Records. Dist: Pinnacle

Cassette: by Demon Records. Dist: Pinnacle

CHANGE OF HEART CHANGE OF MIND (Cray, Robert Band).
Single (12"): released on Demon, Nov'85 by Demon Records. Dist: Pinnacle

FALSE ACCUSATION (Cray, Robert Band).
Tracks: / Porch light, Change of heart, change of mind (S O F T,) / She's gone / Playin' in the dirt / I've slipped her mind / False accusations / Last time, The (I got burned like this) / Payin' for it now - Sonny
Compact disc: released on Sound, '86 by Sound Target

Album: released on Demon, '86 by Demon Records. Dist: Pinnacle

Compact disc: released on Demon, '86 by Demon Records. Dist: Pinnacle

I GUESS I SHOWED HER.
Tracks: / I guess I showed her / It slipped her mind / Got to make a comeback * / Share what you've got, keep what you need*
Single (7"): released on Mercury, Oct'86 by Phonogram Records. Dist: Polygram Distribution

Single (12"): released on Mercury, Oct'86 by Phonogram Records. Dist: Polygram Distribution

NOTHIN' BUT A WOMAN.
Single (7"): released on Mercury, Aug'87 by Phonogram Records. Dist: Polygram Distribution

Single (12"): released on Mercury, Aug'87 by Phonogram Records. Dist: Polygram Distribution

Single (10"): released on Mercury, Aug'87 by Phonogram Records. Dist: Polygram Distribution

RIGHT NEXT DOOR (Cray, Robert Band).
Tracks: / Right next door / New blood / Show what you got, keep what you need*
Single (7"): released on Mercury, 30 May'87 by Phonogram Records. Dist: Polygram Distribution

Single (12"): released on Mercury, 30 May'87 by Phonogram Records. Dist: Polygram Distribution

SHOWDOWN (Cray, Robert/Albert Collins/Johnny Copeland).
Notes: For full details see under Collins, Albert.

SMOKING GUN.
Tracks: / Smoking gun / Fantasised / I guess I showed her / Divided heart.
Notes: I guess I showed her/Divided heart available on 12" version only.
Single (7"): released on Mercury, Feb'87 by Phonogram Records. Dist: Polygram Distribution

Single (12"): released on Mercury, Feb'87 by Phonogram Records. Dist: Polygram Distribution

STRONG PERSUADER (Cray, Robert Band).
Tracks: / Smoking gun / I guessed I showed her / Right next door (because of me) / Nothin' but a woman / Still around / More than I can stand / Foul play / I wonder / Fantasized / New blood.
Album: released on Mercury, Nov'86 by Phonogram Records. Dist: Polygram Distribution

Cassette: released on Mercury, nov'86 by Phonogram Records. Dist: Polygram Distribution

Compact disc: released on Mercury, Nov'86 by Phonogram Records. Dist: Polygram Distribution

WHO'S BEEN TALKIN' (Cray, Robert Band).
Tracks: / Too many cooks / Score (The) / Welfare (The) (turns its back on you) / That's what I'll do / I'd rather be a wino / Who's been talkin' / Sleeping in the ground / I'm gonna forget about you / Nice as a fool can be / If you're thinkin' what I'm thinkin'.
Notes: Licensed from Kevin Eggers Ltd.
Compact disc: released on Charly, Oct'86 by Charly Records. Dist: Charly, Cadillac

WHO'S BEEN TALKING (Cray, Robert Band).
Tracks: / Who's been talking / Sleeping in the ground / I'm gonna forget about you / Nice as a fool can be / If you're thinking what I'm thinking / Too many cooks / Score, The / Welfare (turns its back on you), The / That's what I'll do / I'd rather be a wino.
Notes: Licensed from Kevin Eggers Ltd This compilation: P 1986 Charly Records Ltd C 1986 Charly Records Ltd
Album: released on Charly, Oct'87 by Charly Records. Dist: Charly, Cadillac

Cassette: released on Charly, Oct'87 by Charly Records. Dist: Charly, Cadillac

Crayton, Pee Wee
EVERY DAY I HAVE THE BLUES.
Album: released on Pablo (USA), May'82 by Pablo Records (USA). Dist: Wellard, Chris, IMS-Polygram, BMG

Cassette: released on Pablo (USA), May'82 by Pablo Records (USA). Dist: Wellard, Chris, IMS-Polygram, BMG

GREAT RHYTHM AND BLUES VOL.5.
Album: released on Bulldog Records, Jul'82

MEMORIAL ALBUM.
Double Album: released on Ace, May'86 by Ace Records. Dist: Pinnacle, Swift, Hotshot, Cadillac

PEACE OF MIND.
Album: released on Charly, May'82 by Charly Records. Dist: Charly, Cadillac

ROCKING DOWN ON CENTRAL AVENUE.

Album: released on Ace, Nov'82 by Ace Records. Dist: Pinnacle, Swift, Hotshot, Cadillac

Crazy Albert
YIPPEE-I-AY.
Single (7"): released on WMWOCD, Nov'85

Single (12"): released on WMWOCD, Nov'85

Crazy Alligator
CRAZY ALLIGATOR Various artists (Various Artists).
Album: released on White Label (Holland), Feb'85 Dist: CSA, PRT

Crazy Backward...
CRAZY BACKWARD ALPHABET (Crazy Backward Alphabet).
Album: released on SST, Oct'87 by SST Records. Dist: Pinnacle, Cadillac. Estim retail price in Sep'87 was £6.49.

Crazy Blaze
BROKEN DREAM.
Tracks: / Broken dreams / No peace for the wicked.
Single (7"): released on Short, Aug'86 Dist: Short

Crazy Cats
CRAZY ROCKIN'.
Single (7"): released on Magnum Force, Dec'81 by Magnum Music Group Ltd. Dist: Magnum Music Group Ltd, PRT, Spartan

Crazy Cavan
COOL AND CRAZY (Crazy Cavan & The Rhythm Rockers).
Album: released on Rockstar, Oct'82

COOL AND CRAZY ROCK-A-BILLY.
Album: released on Magnum Force, Jul'82 by Magnum Music Group Ltd. Dist: Magnum Music Group Ltd, PRT, Spartan

CRAZY RHYTHM (Crazy Cavan & The Rhythm Rockers).
Album: released on Charly, May'78 by Charly Records. Dist: Charly, Cadillac

LIVE AT PICKETTS LOCK (Crazy Cavan N' the Rhythm Rockers).
Album: released on See For Miles, Sep'83 by See For Miles Records. Dist: Pinnacle

LIVE AT THE RAINBOW (Crazy Cavan 'N' the Rhythm Rockers).
Album: released on Charly, Apr'78 by Charly Records. Dist: Charly, Cadillac

Cassette: released on Charly, Jan'82 by Charly Records. Dist: Charly, Cadillac

MR COOL (Crazy Cavan & The Rhythm Rockers).
Album: released on Charly, Jan'81 by Charly Records. Dist: Charly, Cadillac

OUR OWN WAY OF ROCKIN' (Crazy Cavan & The Rhythm Rockers).
Album: released on Charly, May'77 by Charly Records. Dist: Charly, Cadillac

RED HOT N' ROCKABILLY.
Album: released on Charly, Aug'79 by Charly Records. Dist: Charly, Cadillac

Cassette: released on Charly, Aug'79 by Charly Records. Dist: Charly, Cadillac

ROCKABILITY (Crazy Cavan 'N' the Rhythm Rockers).
Album: released on Charly, Aug'76 by Charly Records. Dist: Charly, Cadillac

ROCKABILLY IN PARIS (Crazy Cavan & The Rhythm Rockers).
Album: released on Magnum Force, Jul'82 by Magnum Music Group Ltd. Dist: Magnum Music Group Ltd, PRT, Spartan

Single (7"): released on Magnum Force, Oct'81 by Magnum Music Group Ltd. Dist: Magnum Music Group Ltd, PRT, Spartan

STILL CRAZY (Crazy Cavan & The Rhythm Rockers).
Album: released on Crazy Rhythm, Jan'80

TEDDY JIVE (Crazy Cavan & The Rhythm Rockers).
Album: released on Charly, Mar'82 by Charly Records. Dist: Charly, Cadillac

Crazy English
CRAZY ENGLISH.
Single (7"): released on Cherry Hinton, Jul'82 by Cherry Hinton Records. Dist: Cartel

Crazyhead
BABY TURPENTINE.
Tracks: / Baby Turpentine / That kind of love / Bang bang* / That stinking feeling*.
Single (7"): released on Food, Jul'87 by Food Records. Dist: Rough Trade, Cartel, WEA

Single (12"): released on Food, Jul'87 by Food Records. Dist: Rough Trade, Cartel, WEA

WHAT GIVES YOU THE THE IDEA THAT YOUR SO AMAZING BABY?
Tracks: / What gives you the idea your so amazing baby? / Out on a limb / Snake eyes.
Single (12"): released on Food, Mar'87 by Food Records. Dist: Rough Trade, Cartel, WEA

Crazy Horse
CRAZY HORSE.
Album: released on Edsel, Mar'86 by Demon Records. Dist: Pinnacle, Jazz Music, Projection

CRAZY MOON.
Album: released on RCA (Germany), Jan'83

Crazy House
FIRST TIME.
Single (7"): released on T.W., Jun'82 by T.W. Records. Dist: Cartel

THEY DANCED LIKE THIS FROM AS FAR OFF AS THE CRAZY HOUSE.
Album: released on T.W., Jul'82 by T.W. Records. Dist: Cartel

WE EMPHATICALLY DENY THAT PIGS CAN FLY.
Album: released on T.W., Jun'83 by T.W. Records. Dist: Cartel

Crazy Pink Revolvers
FIRST DOWN.
Album: released on Chainsaw, May'87 by Chainsaw Records. Dist: Red Rhino, Cartel

Crazy Trains
BETTER OFF WITHOUT YOU.
Single (7"): released on Spellbound, Aug'84 by Spellbound Records. Dist: CBS

TAXI DRIVER.
Single (7"): released on Spellbound, Aug'84 by Spellbound Records. Dist: CBS

Cream
BEST OF CREAM.
Album: released on Arcade Music Gala, Apr'86 Dist: Stage One

BEST OF CREAM.
Cassette: released on RSO, Nov'77

CREAM.
Album: released on Polydor, Jan'79 by Polydor Records. Dist: Polygram, Polydor

CREAM 2.
Cassette: released on RSO, Apr'78

CREAM BOXSET.
Boxed set: released on Polydor, Oct'80 by Polydor Records. Dist: Polygram, Polydor

DISRAELI GEARS.
Compact disc: released on Polydor Records. Dist: Polygram

Album: released on RSO, Nov'77

Compact disc: released on RSO, Nov'77

FAREWELL CONCERT.
Notes: The farewell performance at the Royal Albert half by the original rock super- group - Eric Clapton, Jack Bruce and Ginger baker. 1968 production.
Video-cassette (VHS): released on Polygram Records. Dist: Polygram

FRESH CREAM.
Compact disc: Dist: Polygram

FRESH CREAM.
Album: released on Reaction, Sep'83 Dist: Polygram

GOODBYE.
Compact disc: by Polydor Records. Dist: Polygram, Polydor

GOODBYE CREAM.
Album: released on RSO, Aug'84

Cassette: released on RSO, Aug'84

GREATEST HITS:CREAM.
Double Album: released on Polydor, Nov'80 by Polydor Records. Dist: Polygram, Polydor

Cassette: released on Polydor, Nov'80 by Polydor Records. Dist: Polygram, Polydor

HEAVY CREAM.
Double Album: by Polydor Records. Dist: Polygram, Polydor

Album: released on Karussell (Import), Mar'82

Cassette: released on Karussell (Import), Mar'82

I FEEL FREE.
Tracks: / I feel free / Badge.
Single (7"): released on RSO, Jul'86

Single (7"): released on Old Gold, Jul'84 by Old Gold Records. Dist: Lightning, Jazz Music, Spartan, Counterpoint

LIVE CREAM.
Album: released on RSO, Mar'85

LIVE CREAM - VOLUME 1.
Compact disc: released on Polydor, Feb'87 by Polydor Records. Dist: Polygram, Polydor

LIVE CREAM - VOLUME 2.
Compact disc: released on Polydor, Feb'87 by Polydor Records. Dist: Polygram, Polydor

STORY OF CREAM VOL.1.
Album: released on Polydor, Oct'83 by Polydor Records. Dist: Polygram, Polydor

Cassette: released on Polydor, Oct'83 by Polydor Records. Dist: Polygram, Polydor

STORY OF CREAM VOL.2.
Album: released on Polydor, Oct'83 by Polydor Records. Dist: Polygram, Polydor

Cassette: released on Polydor, Oct'83 by Polydor Records. Dist: Polygram, Polydor

STRANGE BREW.
Single (7"): released on Old Gold, Jul'84 by Old Gold Records. Dist: Lightning, Jazz Music, Spartan, Counterpoint

STRANGE BREW - THE VERY BEST OF CREAM.
Album: released on RSO, Feb'83

Cassette: released on RSO, Feb'83

SUNSHINE OF YOUR LOVE.
Single (7"): released on Old Gold, Jul'84 by Old Gold Records. Dist: Lightning, Jazz Music, Spartan, Counterpoint

VERY BEST OF CREAM, THE.
Album: released on RSO (Holland), Jul'84

Cassette: released on RSO (Holland), Jul'84

WHEELS OF FIRE.
Tracks: / White room / Sitting on top of the world / Passing the time / As you said / Pressed rat and warthog / Politician / Those were the days / Born under a bad sign / Deserted cities of the heart / Crossroads / Spoonful / Train time / Toad.

WHEELS OF FIRE (IN THE STUDIO).
Album: released on RSO, Nov'77

Cassette: released on RSO, Nov'77

Compact disc: released on RSO, Nov'77

WHEELS OF FIRE (IN THE STUDIO) LIVE AT FILLMORE.
Double Album: released on RSO, Jan'84

Double cassette: released on RSO, Jan'84

WHEELS OF FIRE (LIVE VERSION).
Double compact disc:

WHEELS OF FIRE - LIVE AT FILLMORE.
Album: released on RSO, Nov'77

WHITE ROOM.
Single (7"): released on Old Gold, Jul'84 by Old Gold Records. Dist: Lightning, Jazz Music, Spartan, Counterpoint

Creamies

CHERRY ON THE TOP.
Single (7"): released on Creamies Intl. Assoc., Mar'84 Dist: ILA

Cream of Country

CREAM OF COUNTRY various artists (Various Artists).
Album: released on Big R, Nov'81 by Big R Records. Dist: Pinnacle, Wynd-Up Distribution, Solomon & Peres Distribution, I & B, JSU, Swift, Record Merchandisers Distribution, Spartan

Creation

HOW DOES IT FEEL.
Album: released on Edsel, Sep'82 by Demon Records. Dist: Pinnacle, Jazz Music, Projection

MAKING TIME.
Single (7"): released on Edsel, May'84 by Demon Records. Dist: Pinnacle, Jazz Music, Projection

RECREATION.
Album: released on Line (Germany), Feb'84

SPIRIT CALLED LOVE, A.
Tracks: / Spirit called love, A / Making time / Mumbo jumbo.
Single (7"): released on Jet, Apr'87 by Jet Records. Dist: CBS

Single (12"): released on Jet, Apr'87 by Jet Records. Dist: CBS

WE ARE PAINTERMEN.
Album: released on Line (Germany), Feb'84

Creation Rebel

BUBBLES (Creation Rebel(Undivided Roots)).
Single (12"): released on Echo, Jun'82 by Vista Sounds. Dist: Jazz Music

INDEPENDANT MAN.
Single (7"): released on On-U-Sound, Mar'82 Dist: Rough Trade Distribution, Lightning

LOVE I CAN FEEL.
Single (7"): released on Cherry Red, Jul'82 by Cherry Red Records. Dist: Pinnacle

LOWS & HIGHS.
Album: released on Cherry Red, Jul'82 by Cherry Red Records. Dist: Pinnacle

THREAT TO CREATION (Creation Rebel/New Age Steppers).
Album: released on Cherry Red, Nov'81 by Cherry Red Records. Dist: Pinnacle

Creation Rockers

CREATION ROCKERS, VOL.1 Various artists (Various Artists).
Album: released on Trojan, '83 by Trojan Records. Dist: PRT, Jetstar

CREATION ROCKERS, VOL.2 Various artists (Various Artists).
Album: released on Trojan, '83 by Trojan Records. Dist: PRT, Jetstar

CREATION ROCKERS,VOL.3 Various artists (Various Artists).
Album: released on Trojan, '83 by Trojan Records. Dist: PRT, Jetstar

CREATION ROCKERS, VOL.5 Various artists (Various Artists).
Album: released on Trojan, '83 by Trojan Records. Dist: PRT, Jetstar

CREATION ROCKERS, VOL.6 Various artists (Various Artists).
Album: released on Trojan, '83 by Trojan Records. Dist: PRT, Jetstar

CREATION ROCKERS, VOL.6 Various artists (Various Artists).
Album: released on Trojan, '83 by Trojan Records. Dist: PRT, Jetstar

Creativ

CREATIV Various artists (Various Artists).
Album: released on Leo, Sep'84 Dist: Recommended

Creative Connection

SCRATCH MY NAME.
Tracks: / Scratch my name / Baby I'm on my way / Full power remix * / Normal power remix * / Reeperbahn mix ** / Love call mix **.
Single (7"): released on Conifer, Mar'86 by Conifer Records. Dist: Conifer

Single (12"): released on Conifer, Mar'86 by Conifer Records. Dist: Conifer

Single (12"): released on Conifer, Mar'86 by Conifer Records. Dist: Conifer

SCRATCH MY NAME (IMPORT).
Tracks: / Scratch my name / Baby I'm on my way.
Single (12"): released on Teldec (Import), Mar'86

Creative Construction Co.

CREATIVE CONSTRUCTION COMPANY,VOL.2 Various artists (Various Artists).
Album: released on Muse, '79 by Peerless Records. Dist: Lugtons Distributors

Creature Comfort

KAMIKAZE.
Single (7"): released on Eye to Eye, Jun'84 by Eye to Eye Records. Dist: Eye to Eye Records

Creatures

FEAST.
Album: released on Wonderland, May'83 by Polydor Records. Dist: Polygram

Cassette: released on Wonderland, May'83 by Polydor Records. Dist: Polygram

Creatures Of Habit

DOUBLE VISION.
Single (7"): released on Underground Music, Mar'82 Dist: Pinnacle

Creedence Clearwater

BAD MOON RISING.
Single (7"): released on Fantasy, Oct'81 by RCA Records. Dist: RCA, Jetstar

Single (7"): released on Old Gold, Sep'85 by Old Gold Records. Dist: Lightning, Jazz Music, Spartan, Counterpoint

BAYOU COUNTRY.
Album: released on Fantasy, Jul'84 by RCA Records. Dist: RCA, Jetstar

Cassette: released on Fantasy, Jul'84 by RCA Records. Dist: RCA, Jetstar

BAYOU COUNTRY.
Compact disc: released on Fantasy, Aug'87 by Ace Records. Dist: Pinnacle. Estim retail price in Sep'87 was £10.68.

Cassette: released on Fantasy, Aug'87 by Ace Records. Dist: Pinnacle. Estim retail price in Sep'87 was £4.90.

Album: released on Fantasy, Aug'87 by Ace Records. Dist: Pinnacle. Estim retail price in Sep'87 was £4.90.

CHRONICLE 20 Greatest hits.
Tracks: / Suzie Q / I put a spell on you / Proud Mary / Bad moon rising / Lodi / Green river / Commotion / Down on the corner / Fortunate son / Travelin' band / Who'll stop the rain / Up aound the bend / Run through the jungle / Lookin' out my back door / Long as I can see the light / I heard it through the grapevine / Have you ever seen the rain / Hey tonight / Sweet hitch hiker / Someday never comes.
Notes: Between 1969 and 1970 Creedence Clearwater Revival were without question the most successful and exhilarating band in America. All their singles went gold and their seven albums achieved platinum status. This double album contains alltheir American and UK hit singles.
Compact disc: released on Polydor, Jun'87 by Polydor Records. Dist: Polygram, Polydor

Double Album: released on Fantasy (USA), Apr'86 by Fantasy Inc USA Records. Dist: IMS, Polygram

Double cassette: released on Fantasy (USA), Apr'86 by Fantasy Inc USA Records. Dist: IMS, Polygram

Compact disc: released on Big Beat, Jun'87 by Ace Records. Dist: Projection, Pinnacle

CHRONICLE VOL. 2.
Compact disc: released on Big Beat, Jun'87 by Ace Records. Dist: Projection, Pinnacle

COSMO'S FACTORY.
Tracks: / Ramble tamble / Before you accuse me / Travellin' band / Ooby dooby / Looking out my back door / Run through the jungle / Up around the bend / My baby left me / Who'll stop the rain / I heard it through the grapevine / Long as I can see the light.
Compact disc: released on Fantasy (USA), Dec'86 by Fantasy Inc USA Records. Dist: IMS, Polygram

Album: released on Fantasy, Jul'84 by RCA Records. Dist: RCA, Jetstar

Cassette: released on Fantasy, Jul'84 by RCA Records. Dist: RCA, Jetstar

Album: released on EMI (Holland), '83 by EMI Records. Dist: Conifer

Compact disc: released on Fantasy, Aug'87 by Ace Records. Dist: Pinnacle. Estim retail price in Sep'87 was £10.68.

CREEDENCE CLEARWATER REVIVAL HITS ALBUM.
Album: released on Fantasy, Mar'82 by RCA Records. Dist: RCA, Jetstar

Cassette: released on Fantasy, Mar'82 by RCA Records. Dist: RCA, Jetstar

CREEDENCE CLEARWATER REVIVAL.
Cassette: released on Fantasy, Aug'87 by Ace Records. Dist: Pinnacle

Album: released on Fantasy, Aug'87 by Ace Records. Dist: Pinnacle

Compact disc: released on Fantasy, Aug'87 by Ace Records. Dist: Pinnacle

CREEDENCE CLEARWATER REVIVAL.
Album: released on Fantasy, Jul'84 by RCA Records. Dist: RCA, Jetstar

Cassette: released on Fantasy, Jul'84 by RCA Records. Dist: RCA, Jetstar

CREEDENCE COLLECTION, THE.
Album: released on Impression, Oct'85 Dist: CBS

Cassette: released on Impression, Oct'85 Dist: CBS

GOLD.
Album: released on EMI (Holland), '83 by EMI Records. Dist: Conifer

GREEN RIVER.
Cassette: released on Fantasy, Aug'87 by Ace Records. Dist: Pinnacle. Estim retail price in Sep'87 was £4.90.

Album: released on Fantasy, Aug'87 by Ace Records. Dist: Pinnacle. Estim retail price in Sep'87 was £4.90.

Compact disc: released on Fantasy, Aug'87 by Ace Records. Dist: Pinnacle

GREEN RIVER.
Compact disc: released on Fantasy (USA), Nov'86 by Fantasy Inc USA Records. Dist: IMS, Polygram

Album: released on Fantasy, Jul'84 by RCA Records. Dist: RCA, Jetstar

Cassette: released on Fantasy, Jul'84 by RCA Records. Dist: RCA, Jetstar

MARDI GRAS.
Album: released on Fantasy, Jul'84 by RCA Records. Dist: RCA, Jetstar

Cassette: released on Fantasy, Jul'84 by RCA Records. Dist: RCA, Jetstar

MUSIC FOR MILLIONS.
Album: released on Polydor (Holland), Jul'84

Cassette: released on Polydor (Holland), Jul'84

PENDULUM.
Album: released on Fantasy, Jul'84 by RCA Records. Dist: RCA, Jetstar

Cassette: released on Fantasy, Jul'84 by RCA Records. Dist: RCA, Jetstar

PROUD MARY.
Single (7"): released on Fantasy, Aug'81 by RCA Records. Dist: RCA, Jetstar

Single (7"): released on Old Gold, Sep'85 by Old Gold Records. Dist: Lightning, Jazz Music, Spartan, Counterpoint

ROYAL ALBERT HALL CONCERT, THE.
Album: released on Fantasy, Feb'81 by RCA Records. Dist: RCA, Jetstar

Cassette: released on Fantasy, Feb'81 by RCA Records. Dist: RCA, Jetstar

SINGLES 1968-72.
Album: released on EMI (Holland), '83 by EMI Records. Dist: Conifer

WILLY & THE POORBOYS.
Album: released on Fantasy, Aug'87 by Ace Records. Dist: Pinnacle. Estim retail price in Sep'87 was £4.90.

Cassette: released on Fantasy, Aug'87 by Ace Records. Dist: Pinnacle. Estim retail price in Sep'87 was £4.90.

WILLY & THE POORBOYS.
Compact disc: released on Fantasy (USA), Nov'86 by Fantasy Inc USA Records. Dist: IMS, Polygram

Album: released on Fantasy, Jul'84 by RCA Records. Dist: RCA, Jetstar

Cassette: released on Fantasy, Jul'84 by RCA Records. Dist: RCA, Jetstar

Compact disc: released on Fantasy, Aug'87 by Ace Records. Dist: Pinnacle. Estim retail price in Sep'87 was £10.68.

Creed, Kyle

KYLE CREED WITH BOBBY PATTERSON & THE CAMP CREEK BOYS (Creed, Kyle/Bobby Patterson/Camp Creek Boys).
Album: released on Leader, '73 Dist: Jazz Music, Projection

Creek

CREEK.
Tracks: / Love found me / Reach and touch / Arthur Whiteside / You don't owe me / Institute of rock 'n' roll / Six days to sunday / Dialing numbers / Love will stay / Just another fool / Lead me down that road.
Album: released on Music For Nations, Oct'86 by Music For Nations Records. Dist: Pinnacle

Creepers

BABY'S ON FIRE.
Tracks: / Baby's on fire / Another song about motor bikes.
Single (7"): released on Tape, May'86

Single (12"): released on Tape, May'86

Page 252

CREEPERS Original Soundtrack.
Album: released on Heavy Metal, Feb'86 by FM-Revolver Records. Dist: EMI

MISERABLE SINNERS.
Album: released on In Tape, Nov'86 by In Tape Records. Dist: Red Rhino, Cartel

Cassette: released on In Tape, Nov'86 by In Tape Records. Dist: Red Rhino, Cartel

Creeps
ENJOY THE CREEPS.
Album: released on Re-Elect The President, Mar'87 Dist: Backs, Cartel

Creepshow
FU MAN CHU (EP).
Single (12"): released on Criminal Damage, Aug'84 by Criminal Damage Records. Dist: Backs, Cartel

Cree, Wounded John Scott
WIVABANDON ONEZONE.
Album: released on Pye, Feb'79

Cassette: released on PRT, Feb'79 by PRT Records. Dist: PRT

Cregagh Choir
WORLD'S 100 BEST LOVED HYMNS VOL.1.
Album: released on Emerald (Ireland), Oct'81 by Emerald Records. Dist: I & B, Ross, PRT

Cassette: released on Emerald (Ireland), Oct'81 by Emerald Records. Dist: I & B, Ross, PRT

Crelier, Louis
33 DETOURS.
Album: released on Jungle, May'83 by Jungle Records. Dist: Jungle, Cartel

Crenshaw, Marshall
CYNICAL GIRL.
Single (7"): released on Warner Bros., Jul'82 by Warner Bros Records. Dist: WEA

DISTANCE BETWEEN.
Tracks: / Distance between / Someday someway / There she goes again * / Little wild one (no 5).
Single (7"): released on Warner Bros., Feb'86 by Warner Bros Records. Dist: WEA

Single (12"): released on Warner Bros., Feb'86 by Warner Bros Records. Dist: WEA

DOWNTOWN.
Album: released on Warner Bros., Nov'85 by Warner Bros Records. Dist: WEA

Cassette: released on Warner Bros., Nov'85 by Warner Bros Records. Dist: WEA

MARY JEAN AND 9 OTHERS.
Tracks: / This is easy / Hundred dollars, A / Calling out for love (at crying time) / Wild abandon / This street / Somebody crying / Mary Jean / Steel strings / Til that moment / They never will know.
Album: released on WEA, Jun'87 by WEA Records. Dist: WEA

Cassette: released on WEA, Jun'87 by WEA Records. Dist: WEA

SOME DAY SOME WAY.
Single (7"): released on Warner Bros., Nov'82 by Warner Bros Records. Dist: WEA

SOMETHINGS GONNA HAPPEN.
Single (7"): released on Albion, May'83 by Albion Records. Dist: Spartan, Pinnacle

Single (12"): released on Albion, May'83 by Albion Records. Dist: Spartan, Pinnacle

WHENEVER YOU'RE ON MY MIND.
Single (7"): released on Warner Bros., Jun'83 by Warner Bros Records. Dist: WEA

Single (12"): released on Warner Bros., Jun'83 by Warner Bros Records. Dist: WEA

Crentsil, A.B.
TANTE ALABA.
Album: released on Earthworks, Aug'84 by Earthworks Records. Dist: Earthworks Distribution, Rough Trade, Cartel, Projection

Creole, Kid
DANCIN' AT THE BAINS DOUCHES
(Creole, Kid & The Coconuts).
Tracks: / Dancin' at the bains douches / Midsummer madness (The refrain).
Single (7"): released on Sire, Jul'87

Single (12"): released on Sire, Jul'87

Crèque, Neal
BLACK VELVET ROSE.

Album: released on Muse (Import), '81

Crescent City Bounce
CRESCENT CITY BOUNCE New orleans Vol.2 (Various Artists).
Album: released on Ace, Oct'86 by Ace Records. Dist: Pinnacle, Swift, Hotshot, Cadillac

Crest Of The Wave
CREST OF THE WAVE Novello, Ivor (Various Artists).
Album: released on World, Nov'74 Dist: Jetstar

Cretu, Michael
INVISIBLE MAN, THE.
Album: released on Virgin, Jul'85 by Virgin Records. Dist: EMI, Virgin Distribution

Cassette: released on Virgin, Jul'85 by Virgin Records. Dist: EMI, Virgin Distribution

SILVER WATER.
Single (7"): released on Virgin, Jul'85 by Virgin Records. Dist: EMI, Virgin Distribution

Single (12"): released on Virgin, Jul'85 by Virgin Records. Dist: EMI, Virgin Distribution Deleted '86.

Crew Cuts
CREW CUTS Various artists (Various Artists).
Album: released on Island, Jun'84 by Island Records. Dist: Polygram

Cassette: released on Island, Jun'84 by Island Records. Dist: Polygram

CREW CUTS- LESSON 2 Various artists (Various Artists).
Album: released on Island, Oct'84 by Island Records. Dist: Polygram

Cassette: released on Island, Oct'84 by Island Records. Dist: Polygram

ROCK AND ROLL BASH.
Tracks: / Party night / Music drives me crazy / Crazy 'bout ya baby / Don't be angry / Honey hair, sugar lips, eyes of blue / Ring a rosie eula / Two hearts, two kisses / Gum drop / Susie Q / Slam bam / Sh boom (life could be a dream) / Ko ko mo / Story untold, A / Oop shoop / Tell me why / Earth angel.
Album: released on Bear Family, Feb'86 by Bear Family Records. Dist: Rollercoaster Distribution, Swift

SH-BOOM.
Single (7"): released on Creole, Aug'82 by Creole Records. Dist: Rhino, PRT

TWO HEARTS.
Single (7"): released on Pinner, Aug'84 by Pinner Records. Dist: Rough Trade, Cartel, Backs

Cribbins, Bernard
ARABEL'S RAVEN.
Album: released on BBC, Oct'77 by BBC Records & Tapes. Dist: EMI, PRT, Pye

GIGGLING GERTIE.
Cassette: released on One Up, Feb'81 by EMI Records.

MORE ABOUT PADDINGTON BEAR.
Cassette: released on Pinnacle, '79 by Pinnacle Records. Dist: Pinnacle

MR. SHIFTER & THE REMOVAL MEN
(Cribbins, Bernard/John Junkin).
Album: released on Seasharp, Oct'78

PADDINGTON BEAR, VOL.1.
Album: released on Pinnacle, Jan'75 by Pinnacle Records. Dist: Pinnacle

SNOWMAN, THE Briggs, Raymond.
Album: released on CBS, Dec'83 by CBS Records. Dist: CBS

Cassette: released on CBS, Dec'83 by CBS Records. Dist: CBS

WOMBLE STORIES.
Album: released on BBC, Oct'76 by BBC Records & Tapes. Dist: EMI, PRT, Pye

Cricket, Jimminy
WHEN YOU WISH UPON A STAR.
Tracks: / When you wish upon a star / I've got no strings.
Single (7"): released on BBC, Aug'86 by BBC Records & Tapes. Dist: EMI, PRT, Pye

Crickets
COMPLETE CRICKETS, THE.
Album: released on Charly, Feb'84 by Charly Records. Dist: Charly, Cadillac

CRUISE IN IT.
Single (7"): released on Rollercoaster, Jul'79 by Rollercoaster Records. Dist: Swift Distribution, Rollercoaster Distribution

FILE 1961 - 1965.
Tracks: / He's old enough to kinow better / I'm feeling better / I'm not a bad guy / Parisian girl / My little girl / Don't try to change me / Lost and alone / April avenue / Don't say you love me / You can't be in between / Right or wrong / Money / Fool never learns, A / From me to you / California sun / All over you / I pledge my love to you / Now hear this / We gotta get together / Everybody's got a little problem / Fool never learns, A.
Album: released on See For Miles, Feb'87 by See For Miles Records. Dist: Pinnacle

MAYBE BABY.
Single (7"): released on Old Gold, Jul'82 by Old Gold Records. Dist: Lightning, Jazz Music, Spartan, Counterpoint

MILLION DOLLAR MOVIE.
Single (7"): released on Rollercoaster, Mar'80 by Rollercoaster Records. Dist: Swift Distribution, Rollercoaster Distribution

OH BOY.
Single (7"): released on Old Gold, Jul'82 by Old Gold Records. Dist: Lightning, Jazz Music, Spartan, Counterpoint

SOMETHING OLD, SOMETHING NEW.
Album: released on Pathe MarconiEMI Europe, Jun'84

THAT'LL BE THE DAY.
Single (7"): released on Old Gold, Jul'82 by Old Gold Records. Dist: Lightning, Jazz Music, Spartan, Counterpoint

Crimeless Criminals
SOUL INSPIRING.
Cassette: released on Plankton, Nov'85 by Plankton Records. Dist: Cantio (Sweden)

Crimes of the heart
CRIMES OF THE HEART Original soundtrack.

Crime & The City Solution
DANGLING MAN.
Single (12"): released on Mute, Jun'85 Dist: Spartan Distribution, Rough Trade Distribution, Cartel Distribution

JUST SOUTH OF HEAVEN.
Album: released on Mute, Aug'85 Dist: Spartan Distribution, Rough Trade Distribution, Cartel Distribution

KENTUCKY CLICK.
Tracks: / Kentucky click / Adventure / It takes two to burn.
Single (12"): released on Mute, May'86 Dist: Spartan Distribution, Rough Trade Distribution, Cartel Distribution

ROOM OF LIGHTS.
Album: released on Mute, Oct'86 Dist: Spartan Distribution, Rough Trade Distribution, Cartel Distribution

Criminal Class
FIGHTING THE SYSTEM.
Single (7"): released on Inferno, Nov'82 by Inferno Records. Dist: Inferno, Cartel, Pinnacle

Criminal Element Orchestra
PUT THE NEEDLE TO THE RECORD.
Single (7"): released on Cool Tempo, Aug'87 by Chrysalis Records. Dist: CBS

Single (12"): released on Cool Tempo, Aug'87 by Chrysalis Records. Dist: CBS

Single (12"): released on Criminal (USA), Aug'87 by Criminal Records (USA). Dist: Pinnacle

Criminals
CRIMINALS.
Album: released on Fan Club, Jan'85 by New Rose. Dist: Rough Trade, Cartel

Crimson Glory
CRIMSON GLORY.
Album: released on Roadrunner (Dutch), Nov'86 Dist: Pinnacle

Crimson Tide
CRIMSON TIDE.
Album: released on Capitol, '78 by Capitol Records. Dist: EMI

Crippled Pilgrims
UNDERWATER.
Album: released on Fountain Of Youth, Feb'86 Dist: Rough Trade, Cartel

Cripps, Geoff
ICARUS (Cripps, Geoff/Louisa Rugg).
Album: released on Steam Pie, Jun'85

Crishan, Horea
PAN FLUTE MAGIC VOLUME 2.
Album: released on Polydor (Germany), Oct'84 Dist: IMS-Polygram

Cassette: released on Polydor (Germany), Oct'84 Dist: IMS-Polygram

Compact disc: released on Polydor (Germany), Oct'84 Dist: IMS-Polygram

Crisis
ALIENATION.
Single (7"): released on Ardkore, Nov'81 Dist: Rough Trade

ARMED TO THE TEETH.
Album: released on Bulleon, Aug'84 Dist: Pinnacle

HOLOCAUST UK (EP).
Single (12"): released on Dead Russian, Aug'82

Crispell, Marilyn
AND YOUR IVORY VOICE SINGS (Crispell, Marilyn and Doug James).
Album: released on Leo, Oct'85 Dist: Recommended

RHYTHMS HUNG IN UNDRAWN SKY.
Album: released on Leo, Sep'84 Dist: Recommended

Crisp, John
FARMER ON A BIKE.
Single (7"): released on Ampersand, Sep'82

LOVELY NORFOLK DUMPLINGS.
Single (7"): released on Ampersand, Nov'82

WEEKEND IN EAST ANGLIA, THE.
Album: released on Ampersand, '83

Crisp, Quentin
AN EVENING WITH QUENTIN CRISP.
Double Album: released on Cherry Red, Jun'81 by Cherry Red Records. Dist: Pinnacle

Crispy Ambulance
BLUE & YELLOW OF THE YACHT CLUB.
Cassette: released on CSBT Tapes, Nov'83

LIVE.
Album: released on Les Temps Modernes, Jul'85 Dist: Fast Forward, Cartel

NOT WHAT I EXPECTED.
Single (7"): released on Factory, Jun'81 by Factory Records. Dist: Cartel, Pinnacle

OPEN GATES OF FIRE.
Cassette: released on CSBT Tapes, Nov'83

SEXUS.
Single (12"): released on Factory Benelux, Mar'84 by Rough Trade Records. Dist: Cartel

Crispy & Co.
CRISPY & CO..
Album: released on Creole, '79 by Creole Records. Dist: Rhino, PRT

Criss, Peter
KISS.
Compact disc: released on Casablanca, '78 Dist: Polygram, Phonogram

Criss, Sonny
CINCH, THE (Criss, Sonny & Buddy Rich Quintet).
Album: released on Spotlite, Jan'80 by Spotlite Records. Dist: Cadillac, Jazz Music, Spotlite

CRISSCRAFT.
Album: released on Muse, Apr'81 by Peerless Records. Dist: Lugtons Distributors

OUT OF NOWHERE.
Album: released on Muse, Apr'81 by Peerless Records. Dist: Lugtons Distributors

Cristian, Babette
QUESTIONS.
Single (12"): released on Jenieves, Dec'82

Cristian, Chris
OH LITTLE MAMA.
Single (7"): released on Gipsy, Oct'81 by Gipsy Records. Dist: PRT

Cristina
SLEEP IT OFF.
Album: released on Ze-Mercury, Aug'84

Album: released on Coda, Sep'84 by Coda Records. Dist: Pinnacle, Cartel, WEA, Roots

Cassette: released on Coda, Sep'84 by Coda Records. Dist: Pinnacle, Cartel, WEA, Roots

Critchinson, John

NEW NIGHT.
Compact disc: by Coda Records. Dist: Pinnacle, Cartel, WEA, Roots

SUMMER AFTERNOON.
Tracks: / Summer afternoon / 5 for 3 / Doing it right / Another fine mess / Yet another yesterday / Love lies bleeding / Eype down / La pigalle.
Compact disc: by Coda Records. Dist: Pinnacle, Cartel, WEA, Roots

Album: released on Coda, Oct'84 by Coda Records. Dist: Pinnacle, Cartel, WEA, Roots

ULYSSES & THE CYCLOPS.
Album: released on Coda, Sep'84 by Coda Records. Dist: Pinnacle, Cartel, WEA, Roots

Cassette: released on Coda, Sep'84 by Coda Records. Dist: Pinnacle, Cartel, WEA, Roots

Critchlow, Slim

COWBOY SONGS.
Album: released on Arhoolie, May'81 by Arhoolie Records. Dist: Projection, Topic, Jazz Music, Swift, Roots

Critical Mass

OPERATION:DREAMING OF BABYLON (EP).
Tracks: / Numbercruncher / Brainyard / Use them or lose them / Whirr.
Single (12"): released on Timebox, 20 Jun'87 by Timebox records. Dist: Pinnacle

Croad, Terry Orchestra

JOHN WILLIAMS WORKS (Croad, Terry Grand Orchestra).
Album: released on Denon, Mar'82 by Denon Records. Dist: Harmonia Mundi

SCREEN REPORT (Croad, Terry Grand Orchestra).
Album: released on Denon, Mar'82 by Denon Records. Dist: Harmonia Mundi

Croatia

MEMORIES OF CROATIA (Croatia : Croatian Folkel Re Group Koleda).
Album: released on Viking, Nov'79 Dist: Harmonia Mundi Distributors

Croce, Jim

DOWN THE HIGHWAY.
Tracks: / I got a name / Mississippi lady / New York's not my home / Chain gang medley / Chain gang / He don't love you / Searchin' / You don't mess around with Jim / Old man river / Which way are you goin' / Bad, bad Leroy Brown / Walkin' back to Georgia / Box no.10 / Speedball Tucker / Alabama rain.
Compact disc: by Castle Records. Dist: Pinnacle

Album: released on Castle, Sep'86 by Castle Records. Dist: Pinnacle

Cassette: released on Castle, Sep'86 by Castle Records. Dist: Pinnacle

FACES I'VE BEEN, THE.
Double Album: released on Lifesong, Jul'77

FIRST ALBUM (Croce, Jim & Ingrid).
Album: released on EMI (Holland), Jan'83 by EMI Records. Dist: Conifer

GREATEST HITS: JIM CROCE.
Compact disc: released on The Compact Collection, Sep'87 by Conifer Records. Dist: Conifer Distribution

GREATEST HITS:JIM CROCE.
Album: released on Platinum (W.Germany), Oct'85 Dist: Mainline

Cassette: released on Platinum (W.Germany), Oct'85 Dist: Mainline

HIS GREATEST HITS.
Album: released on Lifesong, Jul'77

JIM CROCE COLLECTION, THE.
Tracks: / Time in a bottle / Operator(that's no the way it feels) / Salon Saloon / Alabama rain / Dreamin' again / It doesn't have to be that way / I'll have to say I love you in a song / Lover's cross / Thursday / These dreams / Long time ago, A / Photographs and memories / Long time ago, A.
Notes: Design: Shoot That Tiger!, The recordings are licenced from Saja Music Co. (c) 1986/Castle Communications Place, Unit 7, 271 Merton Road, London SW18 5JS. Bar code: 5/013428/131541.
Double Album: released on Collectors, Dec'86 by Castle Communications Records. Dist: PRT, Pinnacle, Jazz Music

Cassette: released on Collectors, Dec'86 by Castle Communications Records. Dist: PRT, Pinnacle, Jazz Music

TIME IN A BOTTLE.
Tracks: / Time in a bottle / Operator (that's not the way it feels) / Salon and saloon / Alabama rain / Dreamin' again / It doesn't have to be that way / I'll have to say I love you in a song / Lovers cross / Thursday / These dreams / Long time ago, A / Photographs and memories.
Compact disc: released on Castle, Nov'86 by Castle Records. Dist: Pinnacle

Album: released on Castle, Sep'86 by Castle Records. Dist: Pinnacle

Cassette: released on Castle, Sep'86 by Castle Records. Dist: Pinnacle

Crock

SILLY FELLOW.
Single (7"): released on Bridgehouse, Apr'80 Dist: Pinnacle

Crocker, Barry

NEIGHBOURS.
Tracks: / Neighbours / Neighbours (inst) / Chase*.
Single (7"): released on BBC, 23 May'87 by BBC Records & Tapes. Dist: EMI, PRT, Pye

Single (12"): released on BBC, 23 May'87 by BBC Records & Tapes. Dist: EMI, PRT, Pye

Crocker, John

FINE AND DANDY (Crocker, John Quartet).
Album: released on Just Jazz, Jan'83

Crockett, Tony

QUEEN OF HEARTS.
Single (12"): released on Alternative, Jul'82 Dist: PRT

Crocodile Dundee

CROCODILE DUNDEE Original soundtrack.
Compact disc: released on Silva Productions, Dec'86

Album: released on Silva Screen, Dec'86 by Silva Screen Records. Dist: Silva Screen

Cassette: released on Silva Screen, Dec'86 by Silva Screen Records. Dist: Silva Screen

Crocodile Harris

GIVE ME THE GOOD NEWS.
Single (7"): released on WEA, Nov'82 by WEA Records. Dist: WEA

Crocodiles

NEW WAVE GOODBYE.
Album: released on Aura, Nov'81 by Hollywood Nites Distribution. Dist: Pinnacle

Single (7"): released on Aura, Aug'81 by Hollywood Nites Distribution. Dist: Pinnacle

Crocodile Tears

CROCODILE TEARS.
Album: released on Dodgy Ticket, Feb'86 Dist: Sonar

Croft, Rachel

I KNOW SHE CARES FOR ME.
Single (7"): released on Tempo, Mar'82 by Warwick Records. Dist: Multiple Sound Distributors

Croisette

LANDSLIDE.
Tracks: / Landslide / Landslide instrumental.
Single (7"): released on Passion, Jul'86 by Skratch Records. Dist: PRT

Single (12"): released on Passion, Jul'86 by Skratch Records. Dist: PRT

Croker, Brendan

CLOSE SHAVE, A (Croker, Brendan & The 5 O'Clock Shadows).
Album: released on Unamerican Activities, Jan'86 by Hotshot Records. Dist: Cartel, Projection, Red Rhino, Hotshot

DARLIN' (Croker, Brendan & The 5 O'Clock Shadows).
Single (7"): released on Red Rhino, Jul'87 by Red Rhino Records. Dist: Red Rhino, Cartel

THAT'S THE WAY ALL MY MONEY GOES (Croker, Brendan & The 5 O'Clock Shadows).
Tracks: / That's the way all my money goes.
Single (7"): released on Unamerican Activities, Mar'87 by Hotshot Records. Dist: Cartel, Projection, Red Rhino, Hotshot

Cromags

AGE OF QUARREL.
Album: released on GWR, May'87 by GWR Records. Dist: RCA

Cassette: released on GWR, May'87 by GWR Records. Dist: RCA

Crombie, Tony

RE'LAUNCH (Crombie, Tony and his Rockets).
Tracks: / We're gonna rock tonight / Big heat, The / Rock, rock, rock / Let's you and I rock / Sham rock / Brighton rock / London rock / Teach you to rock / Shornin' bread rock, rock / Shuffle boogie / Forgive me baby / Dumplin's / Twon special / Ungaug / Plakukauugcung / Rock-cha-cha / Lonesome train (on a lonesome track) / Red for danger / Sticks and stones / Stop it (I like it) / Rock'n'roll coaster / Rex rocks.
Album: released on See For Miles, Dec'86 by See For Miles Records. Dist: Pinnacle

RELAUNCH (Crombie, Tony and his Rockets).
Album: released on See For Miles, Jan'83 by See For Miles Records. Dist: Pinnacle

Crompton, Barry

HARBINGER.
Album: released on Dove, May'79 by Dove Records. Dist: Jetstar

Cronin, A.J

SPANISH GARDENER, THE.
Cassette: released on Soundings, Feb'85 Dist: Soundings

Cronshaw, Andrew

'A' IS FOR ANDREW - 'Z' IS FOR ZITHER.
Album: released on Xtra, Jul'74 by Relic Records. Dist: Swift

EARTHED IN CLOUD VALLEY.
Album: released on Leader, May'77 Dist: Jazz Music, Projection

GREAT DARK WATER, (THE).
Notes: Features June Tabor, Ric Sanders, Martin Simpson.
Album: released on Waterfront, Mar'84 by Waterfront Records. Dist: Rough Trade, Cartel, Projection, Roots

WADE IN THE FLOOR.
Album: released on Trailer, '81 Dist: Jazz Music, Celtic Music, JSU

Crook Brothers

OPRY OLD TIMERS (Crook Brothers with Sam & Kirk McGee).
Album: released on Starday, Apr'87

Cassette: released on Starday, Apr'87

Crooked Oak

FOOT O'WOR STAIRS, THE.
Tracks: / Bonny Woodall / Band o'shearers / Low lands of Holland / A U (me) / Hinny Bird / Will Jobling.
Notes: Traditional songs and fabulous instrumentals on Northumbrian and irish pipes, cittern, fiddle and guitars, whistles etc. Eron Records., 27 Balmoral Road, Kingsdown, Deal, Kent CT 14 8BX.
Album: released on Eron, Sep'85 by Eron Records. Dist: Eron Records

Cassette: released on Eron, Sep'85 by Eron Records. Dist: Eron Records

Crookfinger Jack

Beggar boy of the north, (The) and other northern tunes

BEGGAR BOY OF THE NORTH AND OTHER,THE (Crookfinger Jack/Greg Stephens).
Album: released on Fellside (Cumbria), '83 by Fellside Records. Dist: Roots, Projection, CM, Jazz Music

Crosby, Bill

THOSE OF YOU WITH OR WITHOUT CHILDREN.
Tracks: / Genesis / Great quote,The / Window of life,The.
Notes: Full title of album: Those of you with or without children, you'll understand
Album: released on Geffen, Jul'86 by Geffen Records. Dist: WEA, CBS

Crosby, Bing

16 GOLDEN CLASSICS.
Tracks: / As time goes by / Way we were (The) / Hey Jude / Little green apples / Both sides now / It's all in the game / Those were the days / Carolina in the morning / Way down yonder in New Orleans / Georgia on my mind / Besame mucho / Spanish eyes / If you should ever need me / Swanne / Night is young and you're so beautiful (The) / Breeze and I, The.
Notes: All tracks licenced from the Decca Records Co. Ltd/Design: Shoot that tiger! (c) 1986/Castle Communications Place,Unit 7, 271 Merton Road, London SW18 5JS: Bar code 5/013428/920169.
Album: released on Unforgettable, Dec'86 by Castle Communications Records. Dist: Counterpoint

Cassette: released on Unforgettable, Dec'86 by Castle Communications Records. Dist: Counterpoint

20 GOLDEN GREATS VOL.2.
Cassette: released on Nostalgia (USA), Dec'85 by Sonic Arts Corporation.

ALL THE WAY.
Album: released on Blue & Gold (USA), Oct'86 Dist: Jazz Music

BEST OF BING.
Album: released on MCA, Aug'81 by MCA Records. Dist: Polygram, MCA

Cassette: released on MCA, Aug'81 by MCA Records. Dist: Polygram, MCA

BING AND AL VOLUME 1 (Crosby, Bing & Al Jolson).
Album: released on Totem, Jun'79 Dist: Jazz Music, Projection, Swift

BING AND AL VOLUME 2 (Crosby, Bing & Al Jolson).
Album: released on Totem, Jun'79 Dist: Jazz Music, Projection, Swift

BING AND AL VOLUME 3 (Crosby, Bing & Al Jolson).
Album: released on Totem, Jun'79 Dist: Jazz Music, Projection, Swift

BING AND AL VOLUME 4 (Crosby, Bing & Al Jolson).
Album: released on Totem, Jun'79 Dist: Jazz Music, Projection, Swift

BING AND AL VOLUME 5 (Crosby, Bing & Al Jolson).
Album: released on Totem, Jun'79 Dist: Jazz Music, Projection, Swift

BING AND AL VOLUME 6 (Crosby, Bing & Al Jolson).
Album: released on Totem, Jun'79 Dist: Jazz Music, Projection, Swift

BING CROSBY.
Double Album: released on RCA, Jul'86 by RCA Records. Dist: RCA, Roots, Swift, Wellard, Chris, I & B, Solomon & Peres Distribution

Double cassette: released on RCA, Jul'86 by RCA Records. Dist: RCA, Roots, Swift, Wellard, Chris, I & B, Solomon & Peres Distribution

Compact disc: released on Intertape, Jul'87 Dist: Target

BING CROSBY AND JOAN BLONDELL (Crosby, Bing/Joan Blondell).
Album: released on Totem, Jun'79 Dist: Jazz Music, Projection, Swift

BING CROSBY COLLECTION, (A) VOLUME 3 (14 sides never released on LPs).
Album: released on CBS, '84 by CBS Records. Dist: CBS

Cassette: released on CBS, '84 by CBS Records. Dist: CBS

BING CROSBY COLLECTION.
Album: released on Deja Vu, Dec'85 by Deja Vu Records. Dist: Counterpoint Distribution, Record Services Distribution (Ireland)

Cassette: released on Deja Vu, Dec'85 by Deja Vu Records. Dist: Counterpoint Distribution, Record Services Distribution (Ireland)

BING CROSBY COLLECTION, (A) VOLUME 2 (14 sides never released on LPs).
Album: released on CBS, '84 by CBS Records. Dist: CBS

Cassette: released on CBS, '84 by CBS Records. Dist: CBS

BING CROSBY COLLECTION, (A) (14 sides never released on LPs).
Album: released on CBS, '84 by CBS Records. Dist: CBS

Cassette: released on CBS, '84 by CBS Records. Dist: CBS Deleted '85.

BING CROSBY & FRIENDS VOLUME 2.
Album: released on Magic, '84 Dist: Jazz Music, Submarine, Swift, Chris Wellard, Conifer

Cassette: released on Magic, '84 Dist: Jazz Music, Submarine, Swift, Chris Wellard, Conifer

BING CROSBY & FRIENDS VOLUME 1.
Album: released on Magic(UK), Apr'85

Cassette: released on Magic(UK), Apr'85

BING CROSBY, JUDY GARLAND & THE ANDREWS SISTERS (Crosby, Bing/Judy Garland/Andrews Sisters).
Album: released on Black Lion, Oct'82 by Black Lion Records. Dist: Jazz Music, Chris Wellard, Taylor, H.R., Counterpoint, Cadillac

BING CROSBY ON THE AIR.
Album: released on Sandy Hook, Jan'79

BING CROSBY'S CHRISTMAS CLASSICS.
Album: released on Capitol, Dec'85 by Capitol Records. Dist: EMI

Cassette: released on Capitol, Dec'85 by Capitol Records. Dist: EMI

BING CROSBY WITH AL JOLSON (Crosby, Bing & Al Jolson).
Album: released on Black Lion, Jan'87 by Black Lion Records. Dist: Jazz Music, Chris Wellard, Taylor, H.R., Counterpoint, Cadillac

BING CROSBY WITH MAURICE CHEVALIER AND FRANKIE LAINE (Crosby, Bing/Maurice Chevalier/Frankie Laine).
Album: released on Black Lion, Jul'84 by Black Lion Records. Dist: Jazz Music, Chris Wellard, Taylor, H.R., Counterpoint, Cadillac

BING CROSBY WITH SPIKE JONES & JIMMY DURANTE (Crosby, Bing/Spike Jones/Jimmy Durante).
Album: released on Black Lion, Jan'87 by Black Lion Records. Dist: Jazz Music, Chris Wellard, Taylor, H.R., Counterpoint, Cadillac

BING - FINAL CHAPTER.
Cassette: released on BBC, Nov'80 by BBC Records & Tapes. Dist: EMI, PRT

BING IN THE THIRTIES VOLUME 3 (On the air from Kraft Music Hall).
Album: released on Spokane (USA), Jun'84 by Spokane Records. Dist: Jazz Music, Swift, Zodiac Distribution

BING IN THE THIRTIES VOLUME 1.
Album: released on Spokane, May'79 by Spokane Records. Dist: Jazz Music, Swift, Zodiac Distribution

Album: released on JSP, Aug'84 by JSP Records. Dist: Swift, Projection

BING IN THE THIRTIES VOL.3.
Album: released on JSP, Sep'86 by JSP Records. Dist: Swift, Projection

BING IN THE THIRTIES VOLUME 5 (On the air from Kraft Music Hall).
Album: released on Spokane (USA), Jun'84 by Spokane Records. Dist: Jazz Music, Swift, Zodiac Distribution

BING IN THE THIRTIES VOLUME 2.
Album: released on JSP, Jan'85 by JSP Records. Dist: Swift, Projection

BING IN THE THIRTIES VOLUME 4 (On the air from Kraft Music Hall).
Album: released on Spokane (USA), Jun'84 by Spokane Records. Dist: Jazz Music, Swift, Zodiac Distribution

BING 'N' BASIE (Crosby, Bing & Count Basie).
Tracks: / Gentle on my mind / Everything is beautiful / Gonna build a mountain / Sunrise, sunset / Hangin' loose / All his children / Put your hand in the hand / Snowbird / Little green apples / Sugar don't you know / Have a nice day.
Compact disc: by Phonogram Records. Dist: Polygram

BING SINGS BROADWAY.
Album: released on MCA, '82 by MCA Records. Dist: Polygram, MCA

Cassette: released on MCA, '82 by MCA Records. Dist: Polygram, MCA

BINGS MAGIC.
Album: released on Magic, '84 Dist: Jazz Music, Submarine, Swift, Chris Wellard, Conifer

Cassette: released on Magic, Aug'85 Dist: Jazz Music, Submarine, Swift, Chris Wellard, Conifer

BING'S MUSIC HALL HIGHLIGHTS.
Album: released on Spokane, Oct'86 by Spokane Records. Dist: Jazz Music, Swift, Zodiac Distribution

BING'S PARTY.
Album: released on Artistry, Nov'79 Dist: Jazz Music

Cassette: released on Artistic, Oct'84 by Submarine Records. Dist: JSU, Chris Wellard, Jazz Music, Swift, Clyde Factors Distributors

BING - THE FINAL CHAPTER.
Album: released on BBC, Nov'80 by BBC Records & Tapes. Dist: EMI, PRT,

BING & TRUDY ON THE AIR (Crosby, Bing & Trudy Erwin).
Album: released on Spokane, Oct'86 by Spokane Records. Dist: Jazz Music, Swift, Zodiac Distribution

BLACK MOONLIGHT.
Tracks: / Once in a blue moon / Snuggled on your shoulder / If you should ever need me / Home on the range / Where the blue of the night / Black moonlight / Just one more chance / ow deep is the ocean / Song of the islands / Our big love scene / May I / Out of nowhere / Brother can you spare a dime / Lazy day / Goodnight sweetheart / Star dust / Try a little tenderness / Sweet Georgia Brown.
Album: released on Joy, May'87 by President Records. Dist: Jazz Music, Swift, President Distribution

CHRISTMAS ALBUM (Crosby, Bing & Rosemary Clooney).
Album: released on Meteor, Nov'86 by Magnum Music Group Ltd. Dist: Magnum Music Group Ltd, PRT Distribution, Spartan Distribution

Cassette: released on Meteor, Nov'86 by Magnum Music Group Ltd. Dist: Magnum Music Group Ltd, PRT Distribution, Spartan Distribution

CHRISTMAS ALBUM, THE.
Album: released on Deja Vu, Aug'86 by Deja Vu Records. Dist: Counterpoint Distribution, Record Services Distribution (Ireland)

Cassette: released on Deja Vu, Aug'86 by Deja Vu Records. Dist: Counterpoint Distribution, Record Services Distribution (Ireland)

CHRONOLOGICAL BING CROSBY VOL.6, THE.
Album: released on Jonzo, Jun'86 by Jonzo Records. Dist: IRS, Jazz Music, Swift

CHRONOLOGICAL BING CROSBY VOL.1, THE.
Album: released on Jonzo, Jun'85 by Jonzo Records. Dist: IRS, Jazz Music, Swift

CHRONOLOGICAL BING CROSBY VOL.7 - 1928-29, THE.
Album: released on Jonzo, Oct'86 by Jonzo Records. Dist: IRS, Jazz Music, Swift

CHRONOLOGICAL BING CROSBY VOL.2, THE.
Album: released on Jonzo, Jun'85 by Jonzo Records. Dist: IRS, Jazz Music, Swift

CHRONOLOGICAL BING CROSBY VOL.8 1929.
Album: released on Jonzo, Jul'87 by Jonzo Records. Dist: IRS, Jazz Music, Swift

CHRONOLOGICAL, THE - VOLUME 4 - 1928.
Album: released on Jonzo, Dec'86 by Jonzo Records. Dist: IRS, Jazz Music, Swift

CHRONOLOGICAL, THE - VOLUME 5 - 1928.
Album: released on Jonzo, Dec'86 by Jonzo Records. Dist: IRS, Jazz Music, Swift

CHRONOLOGICAL, THE - VOLUME 3 - 1928.
Album: released on Jonzo, Dec'86 by Jonzo Records. Dist: IRS, Jazz Music, Swift

COME RAIN OR COME SHINE.
Album: released on Philips, May'80 Dist: IMS-Polygram

COME SHARE THE WINE.
Album: released on Liberty-United, Apr'80 by EMI Records. Dist: EMI

DARK MOON.
Tracks: / Blacksmith blues / Come what may / Pittsberg Pennsylvania / Please wait Mr Sun / Everything I have is yours / Thousand violins, A / Dark moon / Blues my naughty sweetie gave to me / Down yonder / Feet up / Glow worm / Mr. Moon / Cockeyed optimist / Now that I need you / Lady play your mandolin / Blame it on my youth / Chi chi o chi / Maybe it's because.
Notes: Mono recording.
Album: released on Magic, Jul'86 Dist: Jazz Music, Submarine, Swift, Chris Wellard, Conifer

Cassette: released on Magic, Jul'86 Dist: Jazz Music, Submarine, Swift, Chris Wellard, Conifer

DER BINGLE Great World War 2 songs.
Album: released on Spokane, Oct'86 by Spokane Records. Dist: Jazz Music, Swift, Zodiac Distribution

FOREVER (30 evergreens).
Tracks: / Whispering / Some sunny day / Exactly like you / Mack the knife / Them there eyes / I's a good day / Mary / Muddy water / Loveable / Brazil / Ol' man river / How about you / Isle of Capri / High water / Just a gigolo / I'm thru with love / Just one more chance / Mama loves papa.
Double Album: released on RCA, Aug'86 by RCA Records. Dist: RCA, Roots, Swift, Wellard, Chris, I & B, Solomon & Peres Distribution

Double cassette: released on RCA, Aug'86 by RCA Records. Dist: RCA, Roots, Swift, Wellard, Chris, I & B, Solomon & Peres Distribution

Double Album: released on RCA (Germany), May'83

Double cassette: released on RCA (Germany), May'83

FRANK SINATRA & BING CROSBY (see Sinatra, Frank) (Crosby, Bing & Frank Sinatra).

GIVE ME THE SIMPLE LIFE.
Tracks: / Give me the simple life / Any town in Paris when you're young / Dance ballerina dance / Kiss in your eyes, The / Pretty baby / Marrying for love / Watermelon weather / Love thy neighbour / Sunshine cake / When the world was young (le chevalier de Paris) / But beautiful / I love Paris / It's more fun than a picnic / Some enchanted evening / When you're in love / Laroo, laroo Lilli Bolero.
Album: released on MCA, May'87 by MCA Records. Dist: Polygram, MCA

Cassette: released on MCA, May'87 by MCA Records. Dist: Polygram, MCA

GOLDEN AGE OF AMERICAN RADIO.
Album: released on United Artists, '78

HAVIN' FUN (Crosby, Bing & Louis Armstrong).
Album: released on Jasmine, 11 Apr'87 by Jasmine Records. Dist: Counterpoint, Lugtons, Taylor, H.R., Wellard, Chris, Swift, Cadillac

Cassette: released on Jasmine, 11 Apr'87 by Jasmine Records. Dist: Counterpoint, Lugtons, Taylor, H.R., Wellard, Chris, Swift, Cadillac

HOLIDAY INN AND THE BELLS OF ST. MARY'S (Radio adaptations).
Album: released on Spokane, May'79 by Spokane Records. Dist: Jazz Music, Swift, Zodiac Distribution

IN DEMAND.
Tracks: / Getting to know you / Love walked in / Isle of Innesfree / Waltz you saved for me, The / Dearly beloved / Golden earings / Out of this world / Rosalie / Vaya con dios / La vie en rose / Beautiful love / Indian summer / It had to be you / Rose of Tralee, the / Story of Sorrento, The / I'll remember April / One rose, The (that's left my heart) / Yours in my heart alone / Granada.
Notes: The first album from the Crosby catalogue in some time finds twenty memorable performances coming to light. The selection has ben especially chosen by the Bing Crosby Appreciation Society and endorsed by Radio 2's David Jacobs.
Album: released on MCA, May'86 by MCA Records. Dist: Polygram, MCA

JAZZIN' BING CROSBY, THE.
Album: released on Joker, Apr'81 Dist: Cadillac, Zodiac Distribution, Jazz Horizons, Jazz Music, JSU, Celtic Music

KRAFT MUSIC HALL DECEMBER 24, 1942.
Album: released on Spokane, May'79 by Spokane Records. Dist: Jazz Music, Swift, Zodiac Distribution

MANY HAPPY RETURNS.
Album: released on Vocalion, Jan'76 Dist: Swift

MUSIC HALL HIGHLIGHTS (Crosby, Bing & John Scott Trotter Orchestra).
Album: released on Spokane, Oct'86 by Spokane Records. Dist: Jazz Music, Swift, Zodiac Distribution

MUSIC, MUSIC, MUSIC.
Album: released on Grappenhauser, '81 by Grappenhauser Records. Dist: Wellard, Chris

ON THE AIR.
Notes: Kraft Music Hall. May 27, 1937.
Album: released on Spokane, Oct'86 by Spokane Records. Dist: Jazz Music, Swift, Zodiac Distribution

PEACE ON EARTH (Crosby, Bing & David Bowie).
Single (7"): released on RCA, Nov'82 by RCA Records. Dist: RCA, Roots, Swift, Wellard, Chris, I & B, Solomon & Peres Distribution

Single (12"): released on RCA, Dec'82 by RCA Records. Dist: RCA, Roots, Swift, Wellard, Chris, I & B, Solomon & Peres Distribution

RADIO YEARS, THE - VOLUME 4.
Album: released on PRT, Jan'87 by PRT Records. Dist: PRT

Cassette: released on PRT, Jan'87 by PRT Records. Dist: PRT

RADIO YEARS, THE - VOLUME 3.
Album: released on PRT, Jan'87 by PRT Records. Dist: PRT

Cassette: released on PRT, Jan'87 by PRT Records. Dist: PRT

RADIO YEARS VOL.1.
Album: released on PRT, Nov'85 by PRT Records. Dist: PRT

Cassette: released on PRT, Nov'85 by PRT Records. Dist: PRT

RADIO YEARS VOL.2, THE.
Album: released on PRT, Jun'86 by PRT Records. Dist: PRT

Cassette: released on PRT, Jun'86 by PRT Records. Dist: PRT

REMEMBERING.
Tracks: / Please / Did you ever see a dream walking / I've got the world on a string / Sweet Georgia Brown / I don't stand - a ghost of a chance with you / My honey's lovin' arms / Down the old ox road / How deep is the ocean / Temptation / St Louis blues / Dinah / Somebody stole Gabriels horn / Stay on the right side of the road / Someday sweetheart / Some of these days / Shine / I'm coming Virginia / There's a cabin in the pines.
Album: released on Conifer, Jan'86 by Conifer Records. Dist: Conifer

Album: released on Conifer, Jan'86 by Conifer Records. Dist: Conifer

REPLAY ON.
Album: released on Sierra, May'86 by Sierra Records. Dist: WEA

Cassette: released on Sierra, May'86 by Sierra Records. Dist: WEA

SHHH VOL.4.
Album: released on Crosbyana, Oct'86 Dist: Jazz Music

SINGS AGAIN.
Compact disc: released on MCA, Apr'87 by MCA Records. Dist: Polygram, MCA

SONGS OF A LIFETIME.
Double Album: released on Philips, Apr'79 Dist: IMS-Polygram

SPECIAL MAGIC OF BING CROSBY, THE.
Album: released on Polydor, Dec'79 by Polydor Records. Dist: Polygram, Polydor

SPECIAL MAGIC OF BING & SATCHMO, THE (Crosby, Bing & Louis Armstrong).
Album: by Polydor Records. Dist: Polygram, Polydor

THAT OLD FEELING (Crosby, Bing & Louis Armstrong).
Album: released on Polydor (Import), Feb'82

Cassette: released on Polydor (Import), Feb'82

THAT TRAVELIN' TWO-BEAT (Crosby, Bing & Rosemary Clooney).
Album: released on Capitol, Jan'78 by Capitol Records. Dist: EMI

THIS IS....
Double Album: released on RCA, Sep'75 by RCA Records. Dist: RCA, Roots, Swift, Wellard, Chris, I & B, Solomon & Peres Distribution

TRIBUTE TO....
Album: released on SRT, May'80 by SRT Records. Dist: Pinnacle, Solomon & Peres Distribution, SRT Distribution, H.R. Taylor Distribution, PRT Distribution

TRUE LOVE.
Album:

Cassette:

Single (7"): released on Capitol, Nov'83 by Capitol Records. Dist: EMI

TWENTY GOLDEN GREATS.
Cassette: released on MCA, Dec'79 by MCA Records. Dist: Polygram, MCA

WELL DID YOU EVAH (see Sinatra, Frank) (Crosby, Bing & Frank Sinatra).

WHEN THE BLUE OF THE NIGHT.
Album: released on Meteor, 11 Apr'87 by Magnum Music Group Ltd. Dist: Magnum Music Group Ltd, PRT Distribution, Spartan Distribution

WHITE CHRISTMAS.
Tracks: / God rest ye merry gentlemen.
Single (7"): released on MCA, Nov'86 by MCA Records. Dist: Polygram, MCA

Album: released on MFP (MCA), Dec'82 by EMI Records. Dist: EMI

Cassette: released on MFP (MCA), Dec'82 by EMI Records. Dist: EMI

WRAP YOUR TROUBLES IN DREAMS.
Album:

Crosby, Bob

20 GOLDEN PIECES OF BOB CROSBY (Crosby, Bob & His Ochestra).
Album: released on Bulldog, Nov'81 by Bulldog Records. Dist: President Distribution, Spartan, Swift, Taylor, H.R.

Cassette: released on Bulldog, Nov'81 by Bulldog Records. Dist: President Distribution, Spartan, Swift, Taylor, H.R.

ACCENT ON SWING (Crosby, Bob & His Ochestra).
Notes: Quig Quigley/J Hopkins.
Album: released on Giants of Jazz, Jun'86 by Hasmick Promotions Ltd.. Dist: Counterpoint, Jazz Music, Taylors, Swift, Mainline, Wellard, Chris

AT THE RAINBOW GRILL (Crosby, Bob & The Bop Cats).
Album: released on Monmouth, Mar'79

BOB CROSBY 1940.
Album: released on Aircheck, Apr'79

BOB CROSBY & HIS BOBCATS Vol.2 (1938-42).
Album: released on Swaggie (Australia), Jan'83

BOB CROSBY & HIS ORCHESTRA 1935-36.
Album: released on Rarities, Apr'81

BOB CROSBY'S CARAVAN VOLUME 2 The summer of '39.
Album: released on Giants of Jazz, Oct'85 by Hasmick Promotions Ltd.. Dist: Counterpoint, Jazz Music, Taylors, Swift, Mainline, Wellard, Chris

BOB CROSBY VOL.1.
Album: released on Kings Of Jazz, Aug'81 Dist: Jazz Horizons, Jazz Music, Celtic Music

BOB CROSBY VOL.1 (1935).
Album: released on Ajax, Apr'79

BOB CROSBY VOL.2 (1935).
Album: released on Ajax, Apr'79

BOB CROSBY VOL.3 (1936/7).
Album: released on Ajax, Apr'79

CAMEL CARAVANS THE SUMMER OF 39.
Album: released on Giants of Jazz, Oct'85 by Hasmick Promotions Ltd.. Dist: Counterpoint, Jazz Music, Taylors, Swift, Mainline, Wellard, Chris

DIXIELAND BAND, THE.
Album: released on Halcyon (USA), Dec'86 by Halcyon Records (USA). Dist: Jazz Music, Conifer, Taylors

Cassette: released on Halcyon (USA), Dec'86 by Halcyon Records (USA). Dist: Jazz Music, Conifer, Taylors

MARDI GRAS PARADE (Crosby, Bob & The Bop Cats).
Album: released on Monmouth, Mar'79

MORE 1938 (Crosby, Bob & His Ochestra).
Album: released on Circle(USA), Jun'86 by Jazzology Records (USA). Dist: Jazz Music, Swift, Chris Wellard

MOURNIN' BLUES (Crosby, Bob & The Bop Cats).
Tracks:/ Mournin' blues / South rampart street parade/ Washington and Lee swing / Love nest, The / Squeeze me/ Spain / Call me a taxi / Yancey special / Gin mill blues / Who's sorry now / I hear you talking / All by myself / Jazz me blues / Till we meet again / Tin roof blues / I'm prayin' humble.
Album: released on Affinity, Nov'85 by Charly Records. Dist: Charly, Cadillac

Cassette: released on Affinity, Nov'85 by Charly Records. Dist: Charly, Cadillac

PLAYS (Crosby, Bob & His Ochestra).
Album: released on Circle, Aug'79 Dist: Jazz Music

SUDDENLY IT'S 1939.
Album: released on Giants of Jazz, Jan'85 by Hasmick Promotions Ltd.. Dist: Counterpoint, Jazz Music, Taylors, Swift, Mainline, Chris

SUDDENLY ITS 1939.
Cassette: released on Giants of Jazz, Oct'86 by Hasmick Promotions Ltd.. Dist: Counterpoint, Jazz Music, Taylors, Swift, Mainline, Wellard, Chris

THAT DA DA STRAIN (Crosby, Bob & His Ochestra).
Album: released on Joker (Import), Apr'81

THESE FOOLISH THINGS (Crosby, Bob, Bunny Berigan, J. Lunceford).
Notes: 1936.
Album: released on Nostalgia, Mar'87 Dist: Jazz Music, Counterpoint

VOLUME 2 - 1952-53.
Album: released on Hindsight(UK), Jun'86 Dist: Jazz Music

Crosby, David
GRAHAM NASH & DAVID CROSBY.
Album: by WEA Records. Dist: WEA

IF I COULD ONLY REMEMBER MY NAME.
Album: by WEA Records. Dist: WEA

WIND ON THE WATER.
Album: released on Polydor, Dec'75 by Polydor Records. Dist: Polygram, Polydor

Crosby, Hope
TWO COMPLETE PROGRAMS (Crosby, Hope & Garland).
Album: released on Totem, Jun'79 Dist: Jazz Music, Projection, Swift

Crosby & Nash
BEST OF CROSBY & NASH, THE.
Album: released on Polydor, Nov'80 by Polydor Records. Dist: Polygram, Polydor

Cassette: released on Polydor, Nov'80 by Polydor Records. Dist: Polygram, Polydor

Crosby, Stills & Nash
4 WAY STREET.
Album: by WEA Records. Dist: WEA

Cassette: by WEA Records. Dist: WEA

ALLIES.
Tracks:/ War games / Raise a voice / Turn your back on love / He played real good for free / Barrel of gain / Shadow captain / Dark star / Blackbird / For what it's worth / Wasted on the way.
Compact disc: by WEA Records. Dist: WEA

CROSBY, STILLS & NASH.
Album: by WEA Records. Dist: WEA

Compact disc: released on Atlantic, Jul'87 by WEA Records. Dist: WEA

CSN.
Album: released on Atlantic, Jun'77 by WEA Records. Dist: WEA

Cassette: released on Atlantic, Jun'77 by WEA Records. Dist: WEA

DEJA VU.
Tracks:/ Carry on / Teach your children / Almost cut my hair / Helpless / Woodstock / Deja vu / Our house / 4 + 20 / Country girl / Everybody I love you.
Compact disc: by WEA Records. Dist: WEA

Album: by WEA Records. Dist: WEA

Cassette: by WEA Records. Dist: WEA

FOUR WAY STREET.
Compact disc: released on Atlantic, Mar'87 by WEA Records. Dist: WEA

REPLAY.
Cassette: released on Atlantic, Nov'80 by WEA Records. Dist: WEA

SO FAR.
Album: released on Atlantic, Aug'74 by WEA Records. Dist: WEA

Cassette: released on Atlantic, Aug'74 by WEA Records. Dist: WEA

Compact disc: released on Atlantic, Jan'87 by WEA Records. Dist: WEA

SOUTHERN CROSS.
Single (7"): released on Atlantic, Nov'82 by WEA Records. Dist: WEA

WAR GAMES.
Single (7"): released on Atlantic, Jul'83 by WEA Records. Dist: WEA

Single (12"): released on Atlantic, Jul'83 by WEA Records. Dist: WEA

WASTED ON THE WAY.
Single (7"): released on Atlantic, Jun'82 by WEA Records. Dist: WEA

Cross, Christopher
ALL RIGHT.
Single (7"): released on Warner Brothers, Jan'83 by Warner Bros Records. Dist: WEA

Single (12"): released on Warner Brothers, Jan'83 by Warner Bros Records. Dist: WEA

Single (7"): released on Warner Brothers, Sep'83 by Warner Bros Records. Dist: WEA

ANOTHER PAGE.
Tracks:/ No time for talk / Baby says no / What am I supposed to believe? / Deal 'em again / Think of Laura / All right / Talking in my sleep / Nature of the game / Long weird / Words of wisdom.
Compact disc: by Warner Bros Records. Dist: WEA

Album: released on Warner Brothers, Feb'83 by Warner Bros Records. Dist: WEA

Cassette: released on Warner Brothers, Feb'83 by Warner Bros Records. Dist: WEA

ARTHUR'S THEME.
Single (7"): released on Warner Brothers, Sep'81 by Warner Bros Records. Dist: WEA

CHANCE AT HEAVEN.
Single (7"): released on CBS, Jun'84 by CBS Records. Dist: CBS

CHRISTOPHER CROSS.
Tracks:/ Say you'll be mine / I really don't know anymore / Spinning / Never be the same / Poor Shirley / Ride like the wind / Light is on, The / Sailing / Minstrel 616010.
Compact disc: by Warner Bros Records. Dist: WEA

Album: released on Warner Brothers, '80 by Warner Bros Records. Dist: WEA

Cassette: released on Warner Brothers, '80 by Warner Bros Records. Dist: WEA

DEAL 'EM AGAIN.
Single (7"): released on Warner Brothers, Jun'83 by Warner Bros Records. Dist: WEA

Single (12"): released on Warner Brothers, Jun'83 by Warner Bros Records. Dist: WEA

EVERY TURN OF THE WORLD.
Tracks:/ Every turn of the world / Charm the snake / I hear you call / Don't say goodbye / It's you that really matters / Love is love / Swing street / Love found a home / That girl / Open your heart.
Compact disc: released on Warner Bros Records. Dist: WEA

Album: released on Warner Brothers, Oct'85 by Warner Bros Records. Dist: WEA

Cassette: released on Warner Brothers, Oct'85 by Warner Bros Records. Dist: WEA

NO TIME FOR TALK.
Single (7"): released on Warner Brothers, Apr'83 by Warner Bros Records. Dist: WEA

Single (12"): released on Warner Brothers, Apr'83 by Warner Bros Records. Dist: WEA

THAT GIRL.
Tracks:/ That girl / Open your heart / I really don't know anymore *
Single (7"): released on Warner Bros., Feb'86 by Warner Bros Records. Dist: WEA

Single (12"): released on Warner Bros., Feb'86 by Warner Bros Records. Dist: WEA

THINK OF LAURA.
Single (7"): released on WEA, Mar'84 by WEA Records. Dist: WEA

Crossfire
ALIAS LOVE.
Single (7"): released on Good Foot, Jun'81 by Good Foot Records (USA). Dist: Pinnacle

SECOND ATTACK.
Album: released on Mausoleum, Apr'85 by Mausoleum Records. Dist: Pinnacle

Cassette: released on Mausoleum, Apr'85 by Mausoleum Records. Dist: Pinnacle

SEE YOU IN HELL.
Album: released on Mausoleum, Mar'84 by Mausoleum Records. Dist: Pinnacle

Cassette: released on Mausoleum, May'84 by Mausoleum Records. Dist: Pinnacle

Crossfire Choir
CROSSFIRE CHOIR.
Compact disc: by Pacific Records (USA). Dist: Atlantic

Cross, Jimmy
I WANT MY BABY BACK.
Single (7"): released on Rollercoaster, Mar'79 by Rollercoaster Records. Dist: Swift Distribution, Rollercoaster Distribution

Cross, Kris
SINGING BINGO (Cross, Kris & Billy Pearce).
Single (7"): released on Direct, Dec'80 by Phonogram Records. Dist: Polygram

Cross of Iron
CROSS OF IRON Original soundtrack.
Album: released on EMI, Jan'77 by EMI Records. Dist: EMI

Crossover Dreams
CROSSOVER DREAMS Original soundtrack (Various Artists).
Tracks:/ Elegua / Good for baby / Rudy's theme / Todos vuelven / Liz's theme / Goodbye el barrio / Liza timbero / Sin fe / Zonga-o / Ban-con-tin / Otra dia, otra amore / El down / Todos vuelven reprise / Rudy's theme reprise.
Album: released on Elektra (USA), Apr'86 by Elektra/Asylum/Nonesuch Records. Dist: WEA

Cassette: released on Elektra (USA), Apr'86 by Elektra/Asylum/Nonesuch Records. Dist: WEA

Cross, Sandra
COUNTRY DUB (Cross, Sandra, Mad Professor & Friends).

Album: released on Ariwa, Dec'86 by Ariwa Records. Dist: Revolver, Cartel, Jetstar, Rough Trade

COUNTRY LIFE.
Album: released on Ariwa, Jul'87 by Ariwa Records. Dist: Revolver, Cartel, Jetstar, Rough Trade

CROSSING OVER.
Album: released on Firm, Dec'85 by Firm Records. Dist: Jetstar

GLUE ON THE PAPER.
Single (12"): released on Student, Apr'82

HARD UP BATCHELOR.
Tracks:/ Hard up batchelor / Hard up batchelor (version).
Single (12"): released on Ariwa, Jul'87 by Ariwa Records. Dist: Revolver, Cartel, Jetstar, Rough Trade

IT'S YOU.
Single (7"): released on Ariwa, Apr'86 by Ariwa Records. Dist: Revolver, Cartel, Jetstar, Rough Trade

Single (12"): released on Ariwa, Apr'86 by Ariwa Records. Dist: Revolver, Cartel, Jetstar, Rough Trade

MY GUY.
Single (12"): released on Ariwa, May'87 by Ariwa Records. Dist: Revolver, Cartel, Jetstar, Rough Trade

YOU'RE LYING.
Single (7"): released on Ariwa, Dec'85 by Ariwa Records. Dist: Revolver, Cartel, Jetstar, Rough Trade

Single (12"): released on Ariwa, Dec'85 by Ariwa Records. Dist: Revolver, Cartel, Jetstar, Rough Trade

Cross Section
WAKE UP IN THE MORNING.
Single (7"): released on Warehouse, Aug'82 by Warehouse Records. Dist: PRT

Crosstalk AV
QUEUE, THE.
Single (7"): released on Tufty Club, Nov'82

Cross, Tim
CLASSIC LANDSCAPE.
Compact disc: by Coda Records. Dist: WEA

Album: released on Coda Landscape, Jan'86 by Coda Records. Dist: WEA

Cassette: released on Coda Landscape, Jan'86 by Coda Records. Dist: WEA

Crouch, Andrae
BEST OF ANDRAE CROUCH & THE DISCIPLES, THE (Crouch, Andrae & The Disciples).
Double Album: released on Light, May'82 by Mainline Record Company. Dist: Mainline

Double cassette: released on Light, May'82 by Mainline Record Company. Dist: Mainline

I'LL BE THINKING OF YOU (Crouch, Andrae & Stevie Wonder).
Single (7"): released on Light, Jun'81 by Mainline Record Company. Dist: Mainline

LIVE AT CARNEGIE HALL (Crouch, Andrae & The Disciples).
Album: released on Light, May'82 by Mainline Record Company. Dist: Mainline

Cassette: released on Light, May'82 by Mainline Record Company. Dist: Mainline

LIVE IN LONDON (Crouch, Andrae & The Disciples).
Double Album: released on Light, May'82 by Mainline Record Company. Dist: Mainline

Double cassette: released on Light, May'82 by Mainline Record Company. Dist: Mainline

MORE OF THE BEST....
Album: released on Light, May'82 by Mainline Record Company. Dist: Mainline

Cassette: released on Light, May'82 by Mainline Record Company. Dist: Mainline

NO TIME TO LOSE.
Album: released on Myrrh, Jan'85 by Word Records. Dist: Word Distribution

Cassette: released on Myrrh, Jan'85 by Word Records. Dist: Word Distribution

TAKE ME BACK (Crouch, Andrae & The Disciples).
Album: released on Light, May'82 by Mainline Record Company. Dist: Mainline

Cassette: released on Light, May'82 by Mainline Record Company. Dist: Mainline

THIS IS ANOTHER DAY (Crouch, Andrae & The Disciples).
Album: released on Light, May'82 by Mainline Record Company. Dist: Mainline

Cassette: released on Light, May'82 by Mainline Record Company. Dist: Mainline

Crouch, Sandra
WE'RE WAITING.
Notes: Brother Andrae featured on the title track and his presence is in evidence as co-producer and occasional instrumentalist. Like many of the best recordings ofblack gospel music this was recorded live and then enhanced in the recording studio. Thus the freshness and infectious joy of the live sound is retained butwith the rough edges taken off and a first-rate sound mix given to bring out thepunch in the rhythms.
Album: released on Light, Apr'86 by Mainline Record Company. Dist: Mainline

Cassette: released on Light, Apr'86 by Mainline Record Company. Dist: Mainline

Croudson, Henry
PARAMOUNT PERFORMANCE, A.
Album: released on Acorn, Jul'77 Dist: Folksound, Jazz Music

Crow
GERONIMO.
Single (7"): released on WEA, Nov'85 by WEA Records. Dist: WEA

YOUR AUTUMN OF TOMORROW.
Single (7"): released on Inferno, Jul'80 by Inferno Records. Dist: Inferno, Cartel, Pinnacle

Crow, Alvin
WELCOME TO TEXAS.
Album: released on TRP, Nov'85 Dist: Charly

Crow Bar
HIPPIE PUNKS.
Single (7"): released on Skinhead, Jan'84 by Skinhead Records. Dist: Cartel Distribution

Crowd
ENGLAND.
Single (7"): released on JSO, May'82

REAL THING.
Single (7"): released on New Age, Sep'84 by New Age Records. Dist: Cartel

YOU'LL NEVER WALK ALONE.
Single (7"): released on A.1, Jun'85 by A.1 Records. Dist: Spartan

Single (12"): released on Spartan, Jun'85 by Spartan Records. Dist: Spartan

Crowded House
CROWDED HOUSE.
Tracks: / World where you live / Now we're getting somewhere / Don't dream it's over / Mean to me / Love you 'til the day I die / Something so strong / Hole in the river / I walk away / Tombstone / That's what I call love.
Compact disc: released on Capitol, Apr'87 by Capitol Records. Dist: EMI

Album: released on Capitol, Aug'86 by Capitol Records. Dist: EMI

Cassette: released on Capitol, Aug'86 by Capitol Records. Dist: EMI

DON'T DREAM IT'S OVER.
Tracks: / Don't dream it's over / That's what I call love.
Single (7"): released on Capitol, Mar'87 by Capitol Records. Dist: EMI

Single (12"): released on Capitol, Mar'87 by Capitol Records. Dist: EMI

Cassette single: released on Capitol, 20 Jun'87 by Capitol Records. Dist: EMI

SOMETHING SO STRONG.
Single (7"): released on Capitol, Aug'87 by Capitol Records. Dist: EMI

Single (12"): released on Capitol, Aug'87 by Capitol Records. Dist: EMI

WORLD WHERE YOU LIVE.
Tracks: / World where you live / That's what I call love / Can't carry on ".
Single (7"): released on Capitol, Aug'86 by Capitol Records. Dist: EMI

Single (12"): released on Capitol, Aug'86 by Capitol Records. Dist: EMI

Crowe, J.D.
BLACKJACK.
Album: released on Sundown, Jun'87 by Magnum Music Group Ltd. Dist: Magnum Music Group Ltd, PRT Distribution, Spartan Distribution

MODEL CHURCH, THE.
Album: released on Sundown, Jan'87 by Magnum Music Group Ltd. Dist: Magnum Music Group Ltd, PRT Distribution, Spartan Distribution

STRAIGHT AHEAD.
Compact disc: released on Rounder, Jun'87 Dist: Roots Distribution

Crowell, Rodney
SHAME ON THE MOON.
Single (7"): released on Warner Brothers, Mar'82 by Warner Bros Records. Dist: WEA

STREET LANGUAGE.
Tracks: / Let freedom ring / Ballad of fat Eddi / When I'm free again / She loves the jerk / Whe the blue hour comes / Oh king Richard / Look ing for you / Stay (don't be cruel) / Best I can. The / Past like a mast.
Album: released on CBS, Sep'86 by CBS Records. Dist: CBS

Cassette: released on CBS, Sep'86 by CBS Records. Dist: CBS

Crow, Joe
COMPULSION.
Single (7"): released on Cherry Red, Oct'82 by Cherry Red Records. Dist: Pinnacle

Crowley
CROWLEY TWO STEP.
Album: released on Flyright, Oct'86 by Flyright Records. Dist: Krazy Kat, Swift, Jazz Music

Crowley, Jim
BOYS OF FAIR HILL, THE.
Album: released on Mulligan, Nov'79 by Topic Records. Dist: Roots Distribution, Jazz Music Distribution, JSU Distribution, I & B Distribution Projection Distribution, Wynd-Up Distribution, Celtic Distributions

CAMP HOUSE BALLADS (Crowley, Jim & Stokers Lodge).
Album: released on Mulligan, Nov'79 by Topic Records. Dist: Roots Distribution, Jazz Music Distribution, JSU Distribution, I & B Distribution Projection Distribution, Wynd-Up Distribution Celtic Distributions

Crowley, Jimmy
JIMMY MO MHILE STOR.
Album: released on Gael-Linn (Ireland), May'67 by Gael Linn Records. Dist: Roots, Projection, Celtic Music, Jazz Music

Crowley, Jimmy & Greg Smith
UP LIKE THE SWALLOW also see Stewart, Bob with Jacky Daly.
Album: released on Broadside, Jun'81 by Broadside Records. Dist: Celtic Distributions, H.R. Taylor, Jazz Music, Projection, Jazz Services Unlimited Dist. (JSU)

Cassette: released on Broadside, Jun'81 by Broadside Records. Dist: Celtic Distributions, H.R. Taylor, Jazz Music, Projection, Jazz Services Unlimited Dist. (JSU)

Crowley two-step
CROWLEY TWO-STEP - 1960'S CAJUN AT IT'S BEST Various artists (Various Artists).
Album: released on Flyright, Sep'85 by Flyright Records. Dist: Krazy Kat, Swift, Jazz Music

CroWifeh
DON'T BELIEVE.
Single (12"): released on Ultimate, Nov'86 by Ultimate Records. Dist: Spartan

Crown
ALL THAT ROCK AND ROLL.
Album: released on Thunderbolt, Dec'84 by Magnum Music Group Ltd. Dist: Magnum Music Group Ltd, PRT Distribution, Spartan Distribution

RED ZONE.
Album: released on Thunderbolt, Apr'85 by Magnum Music Group Ltd. Dist: Magnum Music Group Ltd, PRT Distribution, Spartan Distribution

Crown Heights Affair
MAKE ME THE ONE.
Tracks: / Make me the one / Make me the one instrumental.
Single (7"): released on Citybeat, May'86 Dist: WEA

ROCK THE WORLD.
Single (7"): released on De-Lite, Sep'83 by Phonogram Records. Dist: Polygram

Single (12"): released on De-Lite, Sep'83 by Phonogram Records. Dist: Polygram

Crown Of Thorns
KINGDOM COME.
Single (7"): released on Illegal, Jan'83 by Faulty Products Records. Dist: Pinnacle, Lightning, Cartel

Single (12"): released on Illegal, Jan'83 by Faulty Products Records. Dist: Pinnacle, Lightning, Cartel

Crow People
CLOUD SONGS.
Single (12"): released on Meantime, Aug'87 Dist: Red Rhino, Cartel

Crows
CROWS.
Album: released on Dingles, '83 by Dingles Records. Dist: Projection

REDMAN.
Single (12"): released on Ravin', Mar'87 Dist: Fast Forward

SUN WENT IN, THE.
Tracks: / Sun went in, The / Round and round.
Single (7"): released on Ravin', Apr'86 Dist: Fast Forward

Single (12"): released on Ravin', Apr'86 Dist: Fast Forward

Crowther, Leslie
WORLD I'D LIKE TO SEE (Crowther, Leslie & Bernie Winters).
Single (7"): released on Monarch, May'83 by Chart Records. Dist: Pinnacle

Crow & Wodwo
CROW & WODWO Read by Ted Hughes.
Cassette: released on Caedmon(USA), May'80 by Caedmon (USA) Records. Dist: Gower, Taylors, Discovery

Croydon High School...
FERGIE.
Single (7"): released on D-Sharp, Jul'86 by D Sharp Records. Dist: D Sharp, Pinnacle

Crozier, Trevor
TROUBLE OVER BRIDGWATER.
Album: released on One Up, Aug'77 by EMI Records.

Crucial Collection
CRUCIAL COLLECTION Reggae Superstars.
Album: released on Vista Sounds, '83 by Vista Sounds Records. Dist: Jetstar

Crucial Electro
CRUCIAL ELECTRO Various artsits (Various Artists).
Album: released on Streetsounds, Jan'84

Cassette: released on Streetsounds, Jan'84

CRUCIAL ELECTRO 2 Various artists (Various Artists).
Album: released on Streetsounds, Jul'84

Cassette: released on Streetsounds, Jul'84

CRUCIAL ELECTRO - VOLUME 3 (Various Artists).
Album: released on Streetsounds, Dec'86

Cassette: released on Streetsounds, Dec'86

Crucial Reggae
CRUCIAL REGGAE Various artists (Various Artists).
Album: released on Island, Oct'80 by Island Records. Dist: Polygram

Crucif...
CRUCIF....
Album: released on Alternative Tentacles, Dec'84 by Alternative Tentacles Records. Dist: Rough Trade, Pinnacle

Crucifixion
FOX, THE.
Single (7"): released on Miramar, Sep'80 by Miramar Records. Dist: Miramar

MOON RISING.
Single (7"): released on Neat, Jan'84 by Neat Records. Dist: Pinnacle, Neat

TAKE IT OR LEAVE IT.
Single (7"): released on Neat, Sep'82 by Neat Records. Dist: Pinnacle, Neat

Crudup, Arthur
BIG BOY CRUDUP & LIGHTNING HOPKINS (Crudup, Big Boy & Lightning Hopkins).
Album: released on Krazy Kat (USA), Nov'83

CRUDUP'S MOOD.
Album: Dist: Projection, Swift, Cadillac

CRUDUP'S ROCKIN'** (Crudup, Arthur 'Big Boy').
Album: released on RCA, Oct'85 by RCA Records. Dist: RCA, Roots, Swift, Wellard, Chris, I & B, Solomon & Peres Distribution

Cassette: released on RCA, Oct'85 by RCA Records. Dist: RCA, Roots, Swift, Wellard, Chris, I & B, Solomon & Peres Distribution

I'M IN THE MOOD.
Album: released on Krazy Kat (USA Import), Jul'83

LOOK ON YONDERS WALL.
Album: Dist: Projection, Swift, Cadillac

Cruella DeVille
GYPSY GIRL.
Single (7"): released on EMI, Oct'83 by EMI Records. Dist: EMI

Single (12"): released on EMI, Oct'83 by EMI Records. Dist: EMI

HONG KONG SWING.
Single (7"): released on Parlophone, Aug'84 by EMI Records. Dist: EMI

Single (12"): released on Parlophone, Aug'84 by EMI Records. Dist: EMI Deleted '87.

I'LL DO THE TALKING.
Single (7"): released on CPL, Dec'84 Dist: Pinnacle

Cruel Sea
CRUEL SEA, THE Read by Nicholas Monsarrat.
Cassette: released on Caedmon(USA), Oct'79 by Caedmon (USA) Records. Dist: Gower, Taylors, Discovery

Cruickshank, Ian
HIGHLAND SPIRIT.
Cassette: released on Deefay, Jan'87 by Deefay Music. Dist: Ross

Cruikshank, Andrew
STORIES GRANDAD TELLS.
Cassette: released on VFM Cassettes, Jan'85

Cruisers
GET A JOB.
Single (7"): released on Harbour, Jan'81 by Harbour Records. Dist: Wellard, Chris

REBEL ED'S REBEL BOP.
Single (7"): released on Badge, Jul'80 by Carlin Music Corporation Records. Dist: RCA

SWINGIN' ROCKIN & ROLLIN.
Album: released on Charly, Jan'81 by Charly Records. Dist: Charly, Cadillac

Cruisin'
CRUISIN' various artists (Various Artists).
Album: released on Hallmark, Jun'81 by Pickwick Records. Dist: Pickwick Distribution, PRT, Taylors

Cassette: released on Hallmark, Jun'81 by Pickwick Records. Dist: Pickwick Distribution, PRT, Taylors

Cruisin' Gang
AMERICA.
Tracks: / America / Radio / America instrumental.
Single (12"): released on ZYX (Germany), Mar'86 by ZYX Records. Dist: Greyhound

Cruising Collection
CRUISING COLLECTION, THE (Various Artists).
Tracks: / Rumble / Batman - theme / Sea cruise / Go Jimmy go / Goodnight my love pleasant dreams / Great maker's here / High blood pressure / Good rockin' daddy / Dance with me Henry / Snake eyes / Leave my woman alone / When will I be loved / Eddie my love / Tossin' & Turnin' / Mr Sandman / Tramp / Poetry in motion / Teenager in love, A / Mary Lou / Stranded in the jungle / White lightening / Wanderer, The / Runaround Sue.
Double Album: released on Castle Collectors, May'86 by Castle Communications Records. Dist: Pinnacle

Double cassette: released on Castle Collectors, May'86 by Castle Communications Records. Dist: Pinnacle

Cruisin' Years
CRUISIN' YEARS 1955-63, THE (Various Artists).
Album: released on Increase(USA), Jun'87 by Quicksilver Records (USA).

Crumb, R

ELEPHANT SONGS AND COW COW CLUBS (Crumb, R & the Cheap Suit Serenaders).
Album: released on Blue Goose, Jan'79 Dist: Projection, Swift

R. CRUMB & HIS CHEAPSUIT SERENADERS (Crumb, R & the Cheap Suit Serenaders).
Album: released on Blue Goose, Oct'76 Dist: Projection, Swift

Crumit, Frank

MOUNTAIN GREENERY.
Album: released on ASV, Apr'81 by Academy Sound & Vision Records. Dist: Pinnacle

Cassette: released on ASV, Apr'81 by Academy Sound & Vision Records. Dist: Pinnacle

RETURN OF THE GAY CABALLERO.
Album: released on Living Era, Apr'82 by ASV. Dist: PRT

Album: released on Living Era, Apr'82 by ASV. Dist: PRT

Cassette: released on Living Era, Apr'82 by ASV. Dist: PRT

Crumsuckers

LIFE OF DREAMS.
Album: released on Rough Justice, Jul'86 by MFN Records. Dist: Pinnacle

Album: released on MCA, May'86 by MCA Records. Dist: Polygram, MCA

Crusaders

BEST OF THE CRUSADERS.
Album: released on ABC, Oct'81 Dist: CBS, Pinnacle

Cassette: released on ABC, Dec'76 Dist: CBS, Pinnacle

CHAIN REACTION.
Album: released on ABC, Apr'77 Dist: CBS, Pinnacle

Album: released on Mobile Fidelity SD Lab, Jun'79 by Mobile Fidelity Records.

FREE AS THE WIND.
Album: released on MCA (ABC), '83 by MCA Records. Dist: Polygram, MCA

Cassette: released on MCA (ABC), '83 by MCA Records. Dist: Polygram, MCA

GOOD AND BAD TIMES, THE.
Notes: The first Crusader album in two years is also released to coincide with the thirtieth anniversary of the formation of the Jazz Crusaders by Joe Sample and Wilton Felder at the beginning of 1957. Joe and Wilton are joined by L.A. session players, as well as special guest vocalist Nancy Wilson, and guitarist (and former Crusader) Larry Carlton.
Album: released on MCA, Dec'86 by MCA Records. Dist: Polygram, MCA

Cassette: released on MCA, Dec'86 by MCA Records. Dist: Polygram, MCA

GOOD & THE BAD TIMES, THE.
Compact disc: by MCA Records. Dist: Polygram, MCA

Album: released on Music For Nations, May'85 by Music For Nations Records. Dist: Pinnacle

Cassette: released on Music For Nations, May'85 by Music For Nations Records. Dist: Pinnacle

IMAGES.
Album: released on ABC, Aug'81 Dist: CBS, Pinnacle

Cassette: released on ABC, Aug'81 Dist: CBS, Pinnacle

I'M SO GLAD I'M STANDING HERE TODAY.
Single (12"): released on MCA, Sep'81 by MCA Records. Dist: Polygram, MCA

NEW MOVES.
Single (7"): released on MCA, Jul'84 by MCA Records. Dist: Polygram, MCA

NIGHT LADIES.
Single (7"): released on MCA, Apr'84 by MCA Records. Dist: Polygram, MCA

Single (12"): released on MCA, Apr'84 by MCA Records. Dist: Polygram, MCA Deleted '85.

ONGAKU DAI-LIVE IN JAPAN.
Album: released on Crusaders (Audiophile series), Apr'82

RHAPSODY IN BLUE.
Compact disc: released on MCA (Twinpax Cassettes), Sep'84

ROYAL JAM.
Tracks: / Overture (I'm so glad I'm standing here today) / One day I'll fly away / Fly with wings of love / Burnin' up the carnival / Last call / Thrill is gone (The) / Better not look down / Hold on / Street life / I just can't leave your love alone / Never make a move to soon.
Notes: With B.B King & The Royal Philharmonic Orchestra
Compact disc: released on MCA, Jul'87 by MCA Records. Dist: Polygram, MCA

ROYAL JAM.
Album: released on MCA, Jun'82 by MCA Records. Dist: Polygram, MCA

Cassette: released on MCA, Jun'82 by MCA Records. Dist: Polygram, MCA

SCRATCH.
Album: released on MCA (Blue Thumb-ABC), Sep'82 by MCA Records. Dist: Polygram

Cassette: released on MCA (Blue Thumb-ABC), Sep'82 by MCA Records. Dist: Polygram

Single (7"): released on MCA, Jul'82 by MCA Records. Dist: Polygram, MCA

Single (12"): released on MCA, Jul'82 by MCA Records. Dist: Polygram MCA

STREET LIFE.
Tracks: / Street life / My lady / Rodeo drive (high steppin') / Carnival of the night / Hustler, The / Night faces.
Compact disc: by MCA Records. Dist: Polygram, MCA

THOSE SOUTHERN NIGHTS.
Album: released on Bluetime, Feb'82 by Charly Records. Dist: Charly

Cassette: released on Bluetime, Feb'82 by Charly Records. Dist: Charly

VOCAL TAPE, THE.
Album: released on MCA, Aug'83 by MCA Records. Dist: Polygram, MCA

Cassette: released on MCA, Aug'83 by MCA Records. Dist: Polygram, MCA

Crush, Bobby

BOBBY CRUSH SINGALONG ALBUM, THE.
Album: released on Warwick, Nov'84 Dist: Multiple Sound Distributors

Cassette: released on Warwick, Nov'84 Dist: Multiple Sound Distributors

FIRST LOVE.
Album: released on President, Apr'84 by President Records. Dist: Taylors, Spartan

INCREDIBLE DOUBLE DECKER PARTY, THE.
Album: released on Warwick, Nov'83 Dist: Multiple Sound Distributors

Cassette: released on Warwick, Nov'83 Dist: Multiple Sound Distributors

LONELY BALLERINA.
Single (7"): released on President, Jun'84 by President Records. Dist: Taylors, Spartan

PEPE.
Tracks: / Pepe / Brendan's theme.
Single (7"): released on President, Nov'86 by President Records. Dist: Taylors, Spartan

Crutchfield, James

ORIGINAL BARREL-HOUSE BLUES.
Album: released on Swingmaster, Jul'85 Dist: Jazz Music Distribution

Crux

CRUX/CRASH 8 track two bad ep (Crux/crash).
Single (12"): released on No Future, Nov'82 by No Future Records. Dist: Pinnacle, Rough Trade, Cartel

Cruzados

CRUZADOS.
Album: released on Arista, Mar'86 by Arista Records. Dist: RCA

Cassette: released on Arista, Mar'86 by Arista Records. Dist: RCA

HANGING OUT IN CALIFORNIA.
Tracks: / Hanging out in California / Motorcycle girl / 1,000 miles.
Single (7"): released on Arista, Jul'86 by Arista Records. Dist: RCA

Single (12"): released on Arista, Jul'86 by Arista Records. Dist: RCA

MOTOR CYCLE GIRL.
Single (12"): released on Arista, Nov'86 by Arista Records. Dist: RCA

Cruz, Celia

CELIA & WULLIE.
Album: released on Salsa, '81

Cry

QUICK, QUICK, SLOW.
Album: released on Arista, Jun'84 by Arista Records. Dist: RCA

Cassette: released on Arista, Jun'84 by Arista Records. Dist: RCA

TAKE IT ROUND AGAIN.
Single (7"): released on Arista, May'84 by Arista Records. Dist: RCA

Single (12"): released on Arista, May'84 by Arista Records. Dist: RCA

Cryar, Morgan

FUEL ON THE FIRE.
Notes: Morgan Cryar, with his debut album "Keep No Secrets", has chiseled a significant groove in the main stream of contemporary Christian music. His second album "Fuel On The Fire" hosts as a hardworking roster of songs with a strong lyrical message. The album has a guitar base and an interesting mix of styles. For example, 'Underneath Your Feet' has an African feel whereas 'Pray In The USA' is driving rock'n'roll and 'Hideaway" is a whispered prayer. His passionate and energetic vocals communicate clearly the messages within his lyrics.
Album: released on Solid Rock, Sep'86 Dist: Word Distribution

Cassette: released on Solid Rock, Sep'86 Dist: Word Distribution

Cry Before Dawn

CRIMES OF CONSCIENCE.
Tracks: / Seed that's been sown, The / Girl in the ghetto / Tender years / Flags / Second sight / Gone forever / White strand / Nobody knows / Stateside Europe.
Album: released on Epic, Jul'87 by CBS Records. Dist: CBS

Cassette: released on Epic, Jul'87 by CBS Records. Dist: CBS

Compact disc: released on Epic, Jul'87 by CBS Records. Dist: CBS

GONE FOREVER.
Tracks: / Darkest night / Sentimental / Gone forever.
Single (7"): released on Epic, Mar'87 by CBS Records. Dist: CBS

Single (12"): released on Epic, Mar'87 by CBS Records. Dist: CBS

SEED THAT'S BEEN SOWN, THE.
Tracks: / Seed that's been sown, The / Back to basics.
Single (7"): released on Epic, Jul'87 by CBS Records. Dist: CBS

Single (7"): released on Epic, Jul'87 by CBS Records. Dist: CBS

Single (12"): released on Epic, Jul'87 by CBS Records. Dist: CBS

Single 10": released on Epic, Aug'87 by CBS Records. Dist: CBS

Cry Cry Crying

CRY CRY CRYING various artists (Various Artists).
Album: released on Kent, Nov'84 by Ace Records. Dist: Pinnacle

Cryin' Shames

PLEASE STAY.
Single (7"): released on Decca, Feb'82 by Decca Records. Dist: Polygram

Cry No More

CRY NO MORE.
Tracks: / Cry no more / You don't hurt / Tears on the ballroom floor / Recipe for romance / Oh Bessie / Real love / Every single time / Marion Jones / Hit the big drum / Don't leave me here.
Album: released on Parlophone, Sep'87 by EMI Records. Dist: EMI. Estim retail price in Sep'87 was £5.99.

Cassette: released on Parlophone, Sep'87 by EMI Records. Dist: EMI. Estim retail price in Sep'87 was £5.99.

DANCING IN THE DANGER ZONE (THE SOUTH AFRICAN SUITE).
Tracks: / Dancing in the danger zone (the South African suite) / Dancing in the danger zone (single version) / Oh Bessie.
Single (12"): released on Parlophone, Aug'86 by EMI Records. Dist: EMI

DANCING IN THE DANGER ZONE.
Tracks: / Dancing in the danger zone / South Africa Suite.
Single (7"): released on Parlophone, Sep'86 by EMI Records. Dist: EMI

REAL LOVE.
Tracks: / Cry no more / Don't leave me here.
Single (7"): released on Parlophone, Nov'86 by EMI Records. Dist: EMI

Single (12"): released on Parlophone, Nov'86 by EMI Records. Dist: EMI

RECIPE FOR ROMANCE.
Single (7"): released on Parlophone, Aug'87 by EMI Records. Dist: EMI

Single (12"): released on Parlophone, Aug'87 by EMI Records. Dist: EMI

SMILE.
Album: released on Cold Harbour, Dec'86 Dist: Pinnacle, Probe Plus Distribution, Cartel, M.I.S., EMI, DMS, RCA, Ariola

Cry of the Innocent

SUSANS STORY ep.
Single (12"): released on Wild Music, Jul'85 Dist: Nine Mile, Cartel

Cryptadia

CRYPTADIA (Various Artists).
Notes: Artists include: Musica Antigua, Anderson Singers, DerekHyde and Jenny Jubb. Non-religious (but inoffensive) Elizabethan songs and madrigals cleverly arranged plus superb dance tunes played on ancient instruments. Dowland, Byrd, Rosseter, Morley, Phalese, Susato, Praetorius, Dalza, etc.
Album: released on Eron, Sep'85 by Eron Records. Dist: Eron Records

Cassette: released on Eron, Sep'85 by Eron Records. Dist: Eron Records

Cryptic Slaughter

CONVICTED.
Album: released on Metal Blade, Aug'86 Dist: Enigma Distribution

MONEY TALKS.
Album: released on Metal Blade, Jun'87 Dist: Enigma Distribution

Crystal

CLEAR.
Album: released on Blackhawk, Aug'86 by Blackhawk Records (USA). Dist: IMS-Polygram

Crystal, Billy

YOU LOOK MARVELLOUS.
Tracks: / You look marvellous (instrumental).
Single (7"): released on A&M, Nov'86 by A&M Records. Dist: Polygram

Single (12"): released on A&M, Nov'86 by A&M Records. Dist: Polygram

Crystallized Movements

MIND DISATER.
Album: released on Psycho, Aug'84 Dist: Funhouse, Rough Trade

Crystal Remedy

CRYSTAL REMEDY.
Album: released on SRT, Oct'77 by SRT Records. Dist: Pinnacle, Solomon & Peres Distribution, SRT Distribution, H.R. Taylor Distribution, PRT Distribution

Crystals

DA DO RON RON.
Tracks: / And then he kissed me.
Single (7"): released on Creole, Aug'82 by Creole Records. Dist: Rhino, PRT

Single (7"): released on Creole Classics, Aug'87 by Creole Records. Dist: PRT, Rhino

Single (12"): released on Creole Classics, Aug'87 by Creole Records. Dist: PRT Rhino

PHILSPECTOR WALL OF SOUND.
Album: released on Phil Spector Int., Oct'75

Cry, The Beloved Country

CRY THE BELOVED COUNTRY (Paton, Alan).
Cassette: released on Caedmon(USA), Oct'79 by Caedmon (USA) Records. Dist: Gower, Taylors, Discovery

C.S.A

STOCKADE.
Album: released on Billy Goat, Jan'79 by Chick-A-Boom Records. Dist: PRT

CSA Collection

CSA COLLECTION VOL.3 Chant rub-a-dub (Various Artists).
Tracks: / Metric system / Walk with jah love / Sammy dead / If you break the curfew / Gwan go do it / My love / Betcha by golly wow / You move me / Chant rub-a-dub / Give me / Without love / How can I / Carrot & onion / Picture on the wall.

Notes: Artists include Errold Dunkley, John Holt, Natural Ites.
Album: released on CSA, Nov'85 by CSA Records. Dist: PRT, Jetstar

CSA COLLECTION VOL.1 Reggae music all night (Various Artists).
Tracks: / Tu sheng pang / Unity is strength / Rich man poor man / Automatic Boom / Out a hand / Saturday night at the movies / Water Jelly / Ain't nobody love nobody; Girl it's over / True love / Picture on the wall / Burning sun / Nice time (Late night blues)
Album: released on CSA, Oct'83 by CSA Records. Dist: PRT, Jetstar

CSA COLLECTION VOL.2 (Various Artists).
Album: released on CSA, Sep'84 by CSA Records. Dist: PRT, Jetstar

C/Slam
NIGHT AIR.
Single (7"): released on Summerhouse, Jun'83 Dist: Red Rhino Distribution, Cartel

CTI
ELEMENTAL 7 (CTI(Creative Technology Institute)).

Cua, Rick
WEAR YOUR COLOURS.
Album: released on Birdwing, Mar'87 by Word Records. Dist: Word Distribution
    Cat. no: **BIRD R 182**
Cassette: released on Birdwing, Mar'87 by Word Records. Dist: Word Distribution

Cuban Heels
WORK OUR WAY TO HEAVEN.
Album: released on Virgin, Oct'81 by Virgin Records. Dist: EMI, Virgin Distribution

Cuban Soldiers
DANCE TO THE RHYTHM.
Single (7"): released on Radial Choice, Feb'82

Cube
DUEL OF THE HEART.
Single (7"): released on Volume, May'85 by Volume Records. Dist: Pinnacle
    Cat. no: **VOL 14**
Single (12"): released on Volume, May'85 by Volume Records. Dist: Pinnacle

Cuber, Ronnie
NEW YORK JAZZ (Cuber, Ronnie/Tom Harrell/Rein deGraff/Sam Jones/Louis Hayes).
Album: released on Timeless, Apr'81

PASSION FRUIT.
Tracks: / Passion fruit / You promised to be true / What it is / Love notes / Come dance with me / It's only in your mind.
Notes: Ronnie Cuber, baritone sax, is best known for his work with George Benson. Also-worked in the bands of Lionel Hampton and Woody Herman and spent a year on the road with Kay Curtis and Aretha Franklin. George Benson is featured on "Passion Fruit" and "You Promised To Be True".
Personnel: Ronnie Cuber - baritone sax/George Benson - guitar/George Wadenius - guitar/Richard Tee - electric piano/Rob Mounsey - synthesiser/Will Lee - bass/ Dave Weckl - bass/Sammy Figueroa - percussion/Manolo Badrena - percussion.
Album: released on King (Japan), Jul'86 Dist: IMS, Polygram

PIN POINT.
Album: released on King (USA), Nov'86 by Gusto Records. Dist: Gusto Distribution, IMS, Swift

Cuca Records Story
CUCA RECORDS STORY VOLUME 1 Various artists (Various Artists).
Album: released on White, Jul'87

CUCA RECORDS STORY VOL.2 Various artists (Various Artists).
Album: released on White, Jul'87

CUCA RECORDS STORY VOL.3 Various artists (Various Artists).
Album: released on White, Jul'87

Cuchulainn the hero
CUCHULAINN THE HERO Various Artists (Various Artists).
Cassette: released on Anvil, Jan'81 Dist: Anvil

Cuddly Toys
GUILLOTINE THEATRE.
Album: released on Fresh, Apr'81 Dist: Jetstar

IT'S A SHAME.
Single (7"): released on Fresh, Jan'82 Dist: Jetstar

MADMAN.

Single (7"): released on Fresh, Apr'81 Dist: Jetstar

SOMEONES CRYING.
Single (7"): released on Fresh, Feb'81 Dist: Jetstar

Single (12"): released on Fresh, Feb'81 Dist: Jetstar

TRIALS AND CROSSES.
Album: released on Fresh, Apr'82 Dist: Jetstar

Cudy & Bink Band
HOME BOY (Home girls too).
Single (7"): released on Sound Of New York, Apr'83 by Sound Of New York Records. Dist: PRT

Single (12"): released on Sound Of New York, Apr'83 by Sound Of New York Records. Dist: PRT

Cuff Links
TRACY.
Single (7"): released on Old Gold, Jul'82 by Old Gold Records. Dist: Lightning, Jazz Music, Spartan, Counterpoint

Cuffy, Claudia
DON'T GIVE UP (your love).
Single (7"): released on Rhythmic, Oct'84 by Rhythmic Records. Dist: Havoc Distribution

Cugat, Xavier
1944/5 (Cugat, Xavier & his orchestra).
Album: released on Circle(USA), Jun'84 by Jazzology Records (USA). Dist: Jazz Music, Swift, Chris Wellard

TO ALL MY FRIENDS (Cugat, Xavier & his orchestra).
Album: released on Intersound, Jul'79 by Intersound Records. Dist: Jazz Music

Culbert, Hugh
UNTIL THEN.
Notes: John McIlwaine - organ
Cassette: released on Outlet (Praise), Jul'84

Culbertson, Clive
BELFAST ROCK.
Album: released on Brain Trans., 79

I CAN'T FIGHT IT.
Single (7"):

JUST A LITTLE BIT.
Single (7"):

KISS ME.
Single (7"):

Cull, Bob
WELCOME TO THE FAMILY.
Album: released on Maranatha, May'79

Culpepper County
AT HOME.
Album: released on Sweet Folk, May'77 Dist: Roots Distribution

YOUR REQUEST OUR PLEASURE.
Album:

Album: released on Beggars Banquet, Sep'84 by Beggars Banquet Records. Dist: WEA
    Cat. no: **BEGA 57**
Cassette: released on Beggars Banquet, Sep'84 by Beggars Banquet Records. Dist: WEA

Picture disc album: released on Beggars Banquet, Sep'84 by Beggars Banquet Records. Dist: WEA

Cult
DREAMTIME.
Tracks: / Horse nation / Spiritwalker / 83rd dream / Butterflies / Go west / Gimmick / Flower in the desert / Dreamtime / Rider in the snow / Bad medicine waltz.
Compact disc: by Beggars Banquet Records. Dist: WEA

DREAMTIME AT THE LYCEUM.
Notes: Formerly Southern Death Cult, and still a band very popular on the punk orientated indie circuit, here in strong form on stage at London's Lyceum.
Video-cassette (VHS): released on Beggars Banquet, Sep'84 by Beggars Banquet Records. Dist: WEA

GO WEST Crazy spinning circles.
Single (7"): released on Beggars Banquet, Jul'84 by Beggars Banquet Records. Dist: WEA

Single (12"): released on Beggars Banquet, Jul'84 by Beggars Banquet Records. Dist: WEA

Album: released on Beggars Banquet, Oct'85 by Beggars Banquet Records. Dist: WEA

Cassette: released on Beggars Banquet, Oct'85 by Beggars Banquet Records. Dist: WEA

LIL' DEVIL.
Tracks: / Lil' devil / Zap city / She sells sanctuary (live)* / Bone bag (live)* / Wild thing+ / Louie louie+ / Phoenix+.
Notes: + + Extra track on Cassette only * + Extra track on 12" only
Single (7"): released on Beggars Banquet, Apr'87 by Beggars Banquet Records. Dist: WEA

Single (12"): released on Beggars Banquet, Apr'87 by Beggars Banquet Records. Dist: WEA

Cassette single: released on Beggars Banquet, Apr'87 by Beggars Banquet Records. Dist: WEA

LOVE.
Tracks: / She sells sanctuary / Rain / Nirvana / Big neon glitter / Brother wolf, sister moon / Phoenix / Hollow man / Revolution / Black Angel / Love.
Compact disc: by Beggars Banquet Records. Dist: WEA

LOVE REMOVAL MACHINE.
Notes: Also available in double pack with CON-QUISTADOR/GROOVE CO. D.
Single (7"): released on Beggars Banquet, Feb'87 by Beggars Banquet Records. Dist: WEA

Single (12"): released on Beggars Banquet, Feb'87 by Beggars Banquet Records. Dist: WEA

LOVE REMOVAL MACHINE (VIDEO).
RAIN.
Single (7"): released on Beggars Banquet, Sep'85 by Beggars Banquet Records. Dist: WEA

Single (12"): released on Beggars Banquet, Sep'85 by Beggars Banquet Records. Dist: WEA

RESURRECTION JOE.
Single (7"): released on Beggars Banquet, Dec'84 by Beggars Banquet Records. Dist: WEA

Single (12"): released on Beggars Banquet, Dec'84 by Beggars Banquet Records. Dist: WEA

REVOLUTION.
Single (7"): released on Beggars Banquet, Nov'85 by Beggars Banquet Records. Dist: WEA

Single (12"): released on Beggars Banquet, Nov'85 by Beggars Banquet Records. Dist: WEA

Gatefold sleeve: released on Beggars Banquet, Nov'85 by Beggars Banquet Records. Dist: WEA

SHE SELLS SANCTUARY.
Single (7"): released on Beggars Banquet, May'85 by Beggars Banquet Records. Dist: WEA

Single (12"): released on Beggars Banquet, May'85 by Beggars Banquet Records. Dist: WEA

SPIRIT WALKER.
Single (7"): released on Situation 2, Apr'84 Dist: Cartel, Pinnacle

Single (12"): released on Situation 2, Apr'84 Dist: Cartel, Pinnacle

WILD FLOWER.
Double-pack single: released on Beggars Banquet, Aug'87 by Beggars Banquet Records. Dist: WEA

WILDFLOWER, THE.
Single (7"): released on Beggars Banquet, Aug'87 by Beggars Banquet Records. Dist: WEA

Picture disc single: released on Beggars Banquet, Aug'87 by Beggars Banquet Records. Dist: WEA

Single (12"): released on Beggars Banquet, Aug'87 by Beggars Banquet Records. Dist: WEA

Cassette single: released on Beggars Banquet, Aug'87 by Beggars Banquet Records. Dist: WEA

Single (12"): released on Beggars Banquet, Aug'87 by Beggars Banquet Records. Dist: WEA

Cult Figures
I REMEMBER.
Single (7"): released on Rather, Jun'81 Dist: Rough Trade

ZIP NOLAN.
Single (7"): released on Rather, Jun'81 Dist: Rough Trade

Cult Mania
AMERICAN DREAM Black mass.
Single (7"): released on Elephant Rock, Feb'83 by Plastic Head Records Limited. Dist: Pinnacle

BLITZ.
Single (7"): released on Elephant Rock, Nov'82 by Plastic Head Records Limited. Dist: Pinnacle

Cult Maniax
AMAZING ADVENTURES OF JOHNNY THE DUCK.
Single (7"): released on Xcentric Noise, Nov'84 by Xcentric Noise Records & Tapes Records. Dist: Cartel

Single (12"): released on Xcentric Noise, Nov'84 by Xcentric Noise Records & Tapes Records. Dist: Cartel

COOL CATS DANCING.
Single (7"): released on Xcentric Noise, Jul'84 by Xcentric Noise Records & Tapes Records. Dist: Cartel

WHERE DO WE ALL GO.
Single (12"): released on Xcentric Noise, May'85 by Xcentric Noise Records & Tapes Records. Dist: Cartel

Cultural Roots
GHETTO RUNNING.
Single (12"): released on Reggae, Apr'83 by Reggae Records. Dist: Jetstar, Morpheus Distribution

HELL A GO POP.
Album: released on Greensleeves, Feb'84 by Greensleeves Records. Dist: BMG, Jetstar, Spartan

Single (12"): released on Greensleeves, Jan'84 by Greensleeves Records. Dist: BMG, Jetstar, Spartan

MR. LION MAN People come a dancing.
Single (12"): released on Cultural Roots, Oct'82

REALITY.
Single (12"): released on Cultural Roots Up Front, Oct'82

WHO IS THE BOSS.
Single (12"): released on Chris's, May'86 Dist: Jetstar

Cultural Vibe
MA FOOM BAY.
Tracks: / Ma foom bay / Ma foom bay-dub version.
Single (7"): released on Crossover-Serious, Sep'86 by Serious Records. Dist: PRT

POWER.
Tracks: / Power / Mind games.
Single (12"): released on Hardcore, 30 May'87 by Hardcore Records. Dist: PRT

Cultural Youth
PEACE AND LOVE.
Single (12"): released on Joe Gibbs, Nov'83 by Joe Gibbs Records. Dist: Jetstar

Culture
BALD HEAD BRIDGE.
Album: released on Blue Moon, Nov'83 Dist: Magnum Music Group Ltd, PRT, Spartan

CULTURE AT WORK.
Album: released on Blue Mountain, Jul'86 Dist: Jetstar

Cassette: released on Blue Mountain, Jul'86 Dist: Jetstar

DISOBEDIENT CHILDREN.
Single (12"): released on Kingdom, Sep'81 by Kingdom Records. Dist: Kingdom

FORWARD TO AFRICA.
Single (12"): released on Kingdom, May'83 by Kingdom Records. Dist: Kingdom

LION ROCK.
Album: released on Heartbeat, Jun'85 Dist: Revolver, Pinnacle

MONEY GIRL.
Tracks: / Money girl / Dance hall style.
Single (12"): released on Blue Mountain, Jun'86 Dist: Jetstar

TWO SEVENS CLASH.
Tracks: / Calling Rasta for I / I'm alone in the wilderness / Pirate days / Two sevens clash / I'm not ashamed / Get ready to ride the lion to Zion / Black starliner must come / Jah pretty face / See them a come / Natty dread taking over.
Album: released on Blue Moon, Apr'87 Dist: Magnum Music Group Ltd, PRT, Spartan

Album: released on Magnum Force, Apr'83 by Magnum Music Group Ltd. Dist: Magnum Music Group Ltd, PRT, Spartan

Compact disc: released on The CD Label, Jul'87

VITAL SELECTION.
Album: released on Virgin, Jul'81 by Virgin Records. Dist: EMI, Virgin Distribution

Culture, Bobby

HEALTH AND STRENGTH Buenos dias.
Single (12"): released on Leggo, Jul'82

Culture Club

CHURCH OF THE POISON MIND Man shake.
Single (7"): released on Virgin, Apr'83 by Virgin Records. Dist: EMI, Virgin Distribution

Single (7"): released on Virgin, Apr'83 by Virgin Records. Dist: EMI, Virgin Distribution

COLOUR BY NUMBERS.
Compact disc: by Virgin Records. Dist: EMI, Virgin Distribution

Album: released on Virgin, Oct'83 by Virgin Records. Dist: EMI, Virgin Distribution

Cassette: released on Virgin, Oct'83 by Virgin Records. Dist: EMI, Virgin Distribution

DO YOU REALLY WANT TO HURT ME.
Single (7"): released on Virgin, Sep'82 by Virgin Records. Dist: EMI, Virgin Distribution

Single (12"): released on Virgin, Sep'82 by Virgin Records. Dist: EMI, Virgin Distribution

FROM LUXURY TO HEARTACHE.
Tracks: / Move away / I pray / Work on me baby / Gusto blusto / Heaven's children / God thank you woman / Reasons / Too bad / Come clean / Sexuality.
Compact disc: by Virgin Records. Dist: EMI, Virgin Distribution

Album: released on Virgin, '86 by Virgin Records. Dist: EMI, Virgin Distribution

Cassette: released on Virgin, '86 by Virgin Records. Dist: EMI, Virgin Distribution

GOD THANK YOU WOMAN.
Tracks: / God thank you woman / From luxury to heartache.
Single (7"): released on Virgin, May'86 by Virgin Records. Dist: EMI, Virgin Distribution

Single (7"): released on Virgin, May'86 by Virgin Records. Dist: EMI, Virgin Distribution

I'M AFRAID OF ME Murder rap track.
Single (7"): released on Virgin, Jun'82 by Virgin Records. Dist: EMI, Virgin Distribution

Single (12"): released on Virgin, Jun'82 by Virgin Records. Dist: EMI, Virgin Distribution

IT'S A MIRACLE.
Single (7"): released on Virgin, Mar'84 by Virgin Records. Dist: EMI, Virgin Distribution

Single (12"): released on Virgin, Mar'84 by Virgin Records. Dist: EMI, Virgin Distribution

KARMA CHAMELEON.
Single (7"): released on Virgin, Aug'83 by Virgin Records. Dist: EMI, Virgin Distribution

Single (12"): released on Virgin, Aug'83 by Virgin Records. Dist: EMI, Virgin Distribution

KISS ACROSS THE OCEAN, A.
Video-cassette (VHS): released on Virgin, Oct'84 by Virgin Records. Dist: EMI, Virgin Distribution

KISSING TO BE CLEVER.
Compact disc: released on Virgin, Jul'87 by Virgin Records. Dist: EMI, Virgin Distribution

Album: released on Virgin, Oct'82 by Virgin Records. Dist: EMI, Virgin Distribution

Cassette: released on Virgin, Oct'82 by Virgin Records. Dist: EMI, Virgin Distribution

MEDAL SONG.
Single (7"): released on Virgin, Nov'84 by Virgin Records. Dist: EMI, Virgin Distribution

Single (12"): released on Virgin, Nov'84 by Virgin Records. Dist: EMI, Virgin Distribution

MOVE AWAY.
Tracks: / Move away / Sexuality.
Single (7"): released on Virgin, Mar'86 by Virgin Records. Dist: EMI, Virgin Distribution

Single (12"): released on Virgin, Mar'86 by Virgin Records. Dist: EMI, Virgin Distribution

Picture disc single: released on Virgin, Mar'86 by Virgin Records. Dist: EMI, Virgin Distribution

THIS TIME.
Compact disc: released on Virgin, Apr'87 by Virgin Records. Dist: EMI, Virgin Distribution

TIME Clock of the heart.
Single (7"): released on Virgin, Nov'82 by Virgin Records. Dist: EMI, Virgin Distribution

Single (12"): released on Virgin, Nov'82 by Virgin Records. Dist: EMI, Virgin Distribution

Picture disc single: released on Virgin, Nov'82 by Virgin Records. Dist: EMI, Virgin Distribution

VICTIMS.
Single (7"): released on Virgin, Nov'83 by Virgin Records. Dist: EMI, Virgin Distribution

Single (12"): released on Virgin, Nov'83 by Virgin Records. Dist: EMI, Virgin Distribution

WAKING UP WITH THE HOUSE ON FIRE.
Tracks: / Dangerous man / War song, The / Unfortunate thing / Crimetime / Mistake no.3 / Dive, The / Medal song, The / Don't talk about it / Mannequin / Hello goodbye.
Compact disc: released on Virgin, Jul'87 by Virgin Records. Dist: EMI, Virgin Distribution

Album: released on Virgin, Oct'84 by Virgin Records. Dist: EMI, Virgin Distribution

Cassette: released on Virgin, Oct'84 by Virgin Records. Dist: EMI, Virgin Distribution

Picture disc single: released on Virgin, Oct'84 by Virgin Records. Dist: EMI, Virgin Distribution

WAR SONG.
Single (7"): released on Virgin, Sep'84 by Virgin Records. Dist: EMI, Virgin Distribution

Single (12"): released on Virgin, Sep'84 by Virgin Records. Dist: EMI, Virgin Distribution

WHITE BOY DANCE.
Single (7"): released on Virgin, Apr'82 by Virgin Records. Dist: EMI, Virgin Distribution

Single (12"): released on Virgin, Apr'82 by Virgin Records. Dist: EMI, Virgin Distribution

Culture, Jahfa

COMMANDER COMMANDO.
Tracks: / Commander commando / Fatty boy.
Single (12"): released on Roots Connection, Sep'86 Dist: Jetstar

Culture, Peter

PRESSURE MAN.
Album: released on Kingdom Records, Oct'86 by Kingdom Records. Dist: Kingdom Records

Culverwell, Andrew

TAKE ANOTHER LOOK.
Album: by Word Records. Dist: Word Distribution, CBS

Cumbrian

CANNY CUMBERLAND.
Album: released on Fellside, Jan'79 by Fellside Records. Dist: Roots, Jazz Music, Celtic Music, Projection

Culture, Smiley

COCKNEY TRANSLATION.
Single (7"): released on Fashion, Aug'84 by Fashion Records. Dist: PRT, Jetstar

Single (12"): released on Fashion, Aug'84 by Fashion Records. Dist: PRT, Jetstar

Single (7"): released on Fashion, Dec'84 by Fashion Records. Dist: PRT, Jetstar

Single (12"): released on Fashion, Dec'84 by Fashion Records. Dist: PRT, Jetstar

Single (7"): released on Fashion, Mar'85 by Fashion Records. Dist: PRT, Jetstar

Single (12"): released on Fashion, Mar'85 by Fashion Records. Dist: PRT, Jetstar

MR KIDNAPPER.
Tracks: / Mr Kidnapper / Supa supe.
Single (7"): released on Polydor, Oct'86 by Polydor Records. Dist: Polygram, Polydor

Single (12"): released on Polydor, Oct'86 by Polydor Records. Dist: Polygram, Polydor

NOFF PERSONALITY.
Single (7"): released on Culture, Nov'85

Single (12"): released on Culture, Nov'85

POLICE OFFICER.
Single (7"): released on Fashion, Nov'84 by Fashion Records. Dist: PRT, Jetstar

Single (12"): released on Fashion, Nov'84 by Fashion Records. Dist: PRT, Jetstar

TONGUE IN CHEEK.
Tracks: / School time chronicle / Mr Kidnapper / Customs officer / Here comes the style / Sling ting / Police officer / Cockney translator / Westland helicopter / Nuclear weapon / I've got the time / Nuff personality *.
Album: released on Polydor, Oct'86 by Polydor Records. Dist: Polygram, Polydor

Cassette: released on Polydor, Oct'86 by Polydor Records. Dist: Polygram, Polydor

Cunliffe, John

MORE POSTMAN PAT STORIES.
Tracks: / Postman Pat's rainy day / Postman Pat's secret / Postman Pat's tractor express / Postman Pat's foggy day / Postman Pat to the rescue / Postman Pat's thirsty day..
Cassette: released on Tellastory, Dec'86 by Bartlett Bliss Productions. Dist: PRT Distribution, Hayward Promotions Distribution, H.R. Taylor Distribution

POSTMAN PAT STORIES, THE.
Cassette: released on Tellastory, Dec'86 by Bartlett Bliss Productions. Dist: PRT Distribution, Hayward Promotions Distribution, H.R. Taylor Distribution

Cunliffe, Roger

REBECCA.
Single (7"): released on Voix, Sep'83

Cunningham, David

COME AND SEE SCOTLAND.
Album: released on Beltona, '71 by Decca Records. Dist: Polygram

Cunningham, Earl

AFRICAN MAN.
Single (12"): released on Jah Shaka, Jan'83 by Jah Shaka Records. Dist: Jetstar

BAD BOY.
Single (12"): released on Struggle, Jul'83 by Struggle Records. Dist: Jetstar Distribution

EARL CUNNINGHAM.
Album: released on Vista Sounds, May'83 by Vista Sounds Records. Dist: Jetstar

FOOLS FALL IN LOVE.
Single (12"): released on Midnight Rock, Dec'83 Dist: Jetstar Distribution, Kingdom Distribution

JAILHOUSE/JAILHOUSE ROCK.
Single (12"): released on Art & Craft, Feb'82 Dist: Jetstar

JOHN TOM.
Album: released on Time, Nov'84 Dist: Jetstar Distribution

SHOW CASE.
Album: released on Vista Sounds, '83 by Vista Sounds Records. Dist: Jetstar

SOCA PART 1 (Cunningham, Earl & Papa Bruce).
Single (12"): released on Roots, Oct'84 by Topic Records. Dist: Swift Distribution

Single (7"): released on Hobo, Feb'85 by Hobo Records. Dist: Hobo

Cunningham, Joan

HELLO AGAIN AND GOODBYE.
Tracks: / Petit Fleur.
Single (7"): released on Hobo, Nov'86 by Hobo Records. Dist: Hobo

Cunningham, John

AGAINST THE STORM (Cunningham, John & Phil (of Silly Wizard)).
Album: released on Highway, '81 by Highway Records. Dist: Roots, Projection, Ross

THOUGHTS FROM ANOTHER WORLD.
Album: released on Highway, '85 by Highway Records. Dist: Roots, Projection, Ross

Cunningham, Larry

BEST OF COUNTRY & IRISH.
Album: released on Harp(Ireland), May'80 by Pickwick Records. Dist: Taylors

COME BACK TO ERIN.
Album: released on Harp(Ireland), Jul'80 by Pickwick Records. Dist: Taylors

Cassette: released on Harp(Ireland), Jul'80 by Pickwick Records. Dist: Taylors

SHARE OUR WORLD (Cunningham, Larry & Margo).
Album: released on Sonus, Mar'84 by Sonus Records. Dist: Spartan

Cassette: released on Sonus, Mar'84 by Sonus Records. Dist: Spartan

THIS IS LARRY CUNNINGHAM.
Album: released on Homespun(Ireland), '82 by Outlet Records. Dist: Outlet

Cassette: released on Homespun(Ireland), '82 by Outlet Records. Dist: Outlet

WHERE THE GRASS GROWS THE GREENEST.
Album: released on Stoic, Mar'84 by Stoic Records. Dist: Spartan Distribution

Cassette: released on Stoic, Mar'84 by Stoic Records. Dist: Spartan Distribution

Cunningham, Matt

GREEN HILLS OF ERIN, THE.
Tracks: / Reels / Jigs / Waltzs / Whistle solo / Fiddle reels / Green hills of Erin / Jigs / Hornpipes / Tin whistle / Reels / Vocals / Band selection.
Album: released on Accordion Record Club, Jul'86 by Accordion Record Club Records. Dist: Accordion Record Club

Cassette: released on Accordion Record Club, Jul'86 by Accordion Record Club Records. Dist: Accordion Record Club

Cunningham, Phil

AIRS AND GRACES.
Album: released on Radio Edinburgh, Dec'84

Cassette: released on Radio Edinburgh, Dec'84

FIRE IN THE GLEN (Cunningham, Phil, Andy M.Stewart, Manus Lunny).
Notes: For full information see under: STEWART, Andy M./Phil Cunningham/Manus Lunny.

RELATIVITY (Cunningham, Phil & Johnny/O Domhnaill,M/Ni Dhomhnail,T).
Album: released on WEA Ireland, Mar'87 by WEA Records. Dist: Celtic Distributions, Projection, I & B

Cassette: released on WEA Ireland, Mar'87 by WEA Records. Dist: Celtic Distributions, Projection, I & B

Cupar & District...

CUPAR & DISTRICT PIPE BAND (Cupar & District Pipe Band).
Cassette: released on Springthyme, '83 by Springthyme Records. Dist: Jazz Music Distribution, Projection Distribution, Roots Distribution

Cupid's Inspiration

YESTERDAY HAS GONE.
Tracks: / Yesterday has gone / My world.
Single (7"): released on NB, May'87 by NB.

Single (7"): released on NB, May'87 by NB.

Single (7"): released on MBS, May'87 Dist: PRT

Cupol

LIKE THIS FOR AGES.
Single (12"): released on 4AD, Jul'80 by 4AD Records. Dist: Rough Trade

Cupp, Pat

DO ME NO WRONG.
Single (7"): released on Rollin' Rock, Jun'80

I GUESS ITS MEANT THIS WAY.
Single (7"): released on Rollin' Rock, Jun'80

LONG GONE DADDY.
Single (7"): released on Rollin' Rock, Jun'80

MODERN ROCKABILITY (Cupp, Pat & His Flying Saucers).
78 rpm record: released on Ace(Cadet), May'81 by Ace Records. Dist: Pinnacle, Swift, Hotshot

Curb In the sky

CURB IN THE SKY, (THE) & OTHER THURBER STORIES Thurber, James (Ustinov, Peter).
Album: released on Caedmon(USA), Sep'80 by Caedmon (USA) Records. Dist: Gower, Taylors, Discovery

Cassette: released on Caedmon(USA), Feb'81 by Caedmon (USA) Records. Dist: Gower, Taylors, Discovery

Cure

ALL THE HITS/UNAVAILABLE 'B' SIDES.
Tracks: / Killing an arab / Boys don't cry / Jumping someone elses train / Forest, A / Primary / Charlotte sometimes / Hanging garden, The / Let's go to bed / Walk, The / Love cats, The / Caterpillar, The / In between days / Close to me / I'm cold / Another journey by train / Descent / Splintered in her head / Mr Pink eyes / Happy the man / Throw your foot / Exploding body, The

/ Few hours after this, A / Man inside my mouth, A / Stop dead / New day.
Cassette: released on Fiction, May'86 by Fiction Records. Dist: Polygram

BOYS DON'T CRY.
Tracks: / Boys don't cry / Plastic passion / 10.15 Saturday night / Accuracy / Object / Jumping someone else's train / Subway song / Killing an arab / Fire in Cairo / Another day / Grinding halt / World war / Three imaginary boys / Boys don't cry (new voice, new mix) / Pill box tails / Do the hansa *.
Compact disc: released on Fiction, '86 by Fiction Records. Dist: Polygram

Single (7"): released on Fiction, Apr'86 by Fiction Records. Dist: Polygram

Single (12"): released on Fiction, Apr'86 by Fiction Records. Dist: Polygram

BOY'S DON'T CRY.
Album: released on Fiction, Aug'83 by Fiction Records. Dist: Polygram

Cassette: released on Fiction, Aug'83 by Fiction Records. Dist: Polygram

CATCH.
Tracks: / Catch / Breathe / Chain of flowers / Kyoto song (live) / Night like this (live).
Single (7"): released on Polydor, Jul'87 by Polydor Records. Dist: Polygram, Polydor

Single (12"): released on Polydor, Jul'87 by Polydor Records. Dist: Polygram, Polydor

Extended-play record: released on Polydor, Jul'87 by Polydor Records. Dist: Polygram, Polydor

CLOSE TO ME.
Single (7"): released on Fiction, Sep'85 by Fiction Records. Dist: Polygram

Single (12"): released on Fiction, Sep'85 by Fiction Records. Dist: Polygram

Single 10": released on Fiction, Sep'85 by Fiction Records. Dist: Polygram

CONCERT - THE CURE LIVE.
Tracks: / Shake dog shake / Primary / Charlotte sometimes / Hanging garden, The / Give me it / Walk, The / One hundred years / Forest, A / 10.15 Saturday night / Killing an arab.
Compact disc: released on Fiction, Oct'84 by Fiction Records. Dist: Polygram

Album: released on Fiction, Oct'84 by Fiction Records. Dist: Polygram

Cassette: released on Fiction, Oct'84 by Fiction Records. Dist: Polygram

CURE - THREE IMAGINARY BOYS.
Album: released on Fiction, May'79 by Fiction Records. Dist: Polygram

Cassette: released on Fiction, May'79 by Fiction Records. Dist: Polygram

FAITH.
Tracks: / All the cats are grey / Carnage visors / Doubt / Drowning man, The / Faith / Funeral party / Holy hour, The / Other voices / Primary.
Compact disc: released on Fiction, Jan'86 by Fiction Records. Dist: Polygram

Album: released on Fiction, '80 by Fiction Records. Dist: Polygram

FAITH/CARNAGE VISORS.
Double cassette: released on Fiction, '80 by Fiction Records. Dist: Polygram

HANGING GARDEN, THE.
Double-pack single: released on Fiction, Jun'82 by Fiction Records. Dist: Polygram

Album: released on Fiction, Aug'85 by Fiction Records. Dist: Polygram

Cassette: released on Fiction, Aug'85 by Fiction Records. Dist: Polygram

HEAD ON THE DOOR, THE.
Tracks: / Inbetween days / Kyoto song / Blood, The / Six different ways / Push / Baby screams, The / Close to me / Night like this, A / Screw / Sinking.
Compact disc: released on Fiction, Aug'85 by Fiction Records. Dist: Polygram

INBETWEEN DAYS.
Single (7"): released on Fiction, Jul'85 by Fiction Records. Dist: Polygram

Single (12"): by Fiction Records. Dist: Polygram

INTERVIEW PICTURE DISC.

SEVENTEEN SECONDS.
Compact disc: by Fiction Records. Dist: Polygram

STANDING ON A BEACH - THE SINGLES.
Tracks: / Killing an arab / Boys don't cry / Jumping someone elses train / Forest, A / Primary / Charlotte sometimes / Hanging gardens, The / Let's go to bed / Walk, The / Love cats, The / Caterpillar, The / In between days / Close to me.
Album: released on Fiction, May'86 by Fiction Records. Dist: Polygram

STARING AT THE SEA.
Compact disc: released on Fiction, '86 by Fiction Records. Dist: Polygram

STARING AT THE SEA-THE IMAGES.
Video-cassette (VHS): released on Palace, May'86 Dist: PVG

TOP, THE.
Tracks: / Caterpillar, The / Piggy in the mirror / Empty world, The / Bananafish bones / Top, The / Shake dog shake / Bird mad girl / Wailing wall / Give me it / Dressing up.
Compact disc: released on Fiction, Mar'84 by Fiction Records. Dist: Polygram

Album: released on Fiction, Apr'84 by Fiction Records. Dist: Polygram

Cassette: released on Fiction, Apr'84 by Fiction Records. Dist: Polygram
Album: released on Baktabak, May'87 by Baktabak Records. Dist: Arabesque

JAPANESE WHISPERS.
Album: released on Fiction, Dec'83 by Fiction Records. Dist: Polygram

Cassette: released on Fiction, Dec'83 by Fiction Records. Dist: Polygram

Album: released on Fiction, Apr'80 by Fiction Records. Dist: Polygram

Cassette: released on Fiction, Apr'80 by Fiction Records. Dist: Polygram

KISS ME, KISS ME, KISS ME.
Double Album: released on Fiction, Jun'87 by Fiction Records. Dist: Polygram

Double cassette: released on Fiction, Jun'87 by Fiction Records. Dist: Polygram

Compact disc: released on Polydor, Jun'87 by Polydor Records. Dist: Polygram, Polydor

PORNOGRAPHY.
Tracks: / Pornography / Hanging gardens / One hundred years / Siamese twins / Figurehead / Strange day, A / Cold / Short term effect, A.
Compact disc: released on Fiction, Jan'86 by Fiction Records. Dist: Polygram

Album: released on Fiction, Apr'82 by Fiction Records. Dist: Polygram

Cassette: released on Fiction, Apr'82 by Fiction Records. Dist: Polygram

Curfew

MAKE IT UP.
Single (12"): released on TNT, Jan'84 by TNT Records. Dist: Jetstar Distribution

MERRY GO ROUND.
Single (12"): released on Street Beat, Jul'85 by Pinnacle Records. Dist: Pinnacle

YOU KNOW.
Single (12"): released on TNT, Oct'82 by TNT Records. Dist: Jetstar Distribution

Curing depression

CURING DEPRESSION Kline, Nathan S. (Kline, Nathan S.).
Cassette: released on Psychology Today, Oct'81

Curiosity Killed the Cat

DOWN TO EARTH.
Tracks: / Down to earth / Down to earth instrumental / Shallow memory *.
Single (7"): released on Mercury, Nov'86 by Phonogram Records. Dist: Polygram Distribution

Single (12"): released on Mercury, Nov'86 by Phonogram Records. Dist: Polygram Distribution

KEEP YOUR DISTANCE.
Album: released on Mercury, May'87 by Phonogram Records. Dist: Polygram Distribution

Cassette: released on Mercury, May'87 by Phonogram Records. Dist: Polygram Distribution

Compact disc: released on Mercury, May'87 by Phonogram Records. Dist: Polygram Distribution

MISFIT.
Tracks: / Misfit / Man / Corruption *.
Single (7"): released on Mercury, 30 May'87 by Phonogram Records. Dist: Polygram Distribution

Single (12"): released on Mercury, 30 May'87 by Phonogram Records. Dist: Polygram Distribution

ORDINARY DAYS.
Tracks: / Bullet.
Single (7"): released on Mercury, Mar'87 by Phonogram Records. Dist: Polygram Distribution

Single (12"): released on Mercury, Mar'87 by Phonogram Records. Dist: Polygram Distribution

Curious collection

CURIOUS COLLECTION Various artists (Various Artists).
Album: released on Street Tunes, Sep'83 by Street Tunes Records. Dist: Pinnacle

Curless, Dick

20 GREAT TRUCK HITS.
Album: released on EMI (Sweden), '83 by EMI Records. Dist: Conifer

Curlew

CURLEW.
Notes: Re-issue. Featuring Bill Laswell.
Album: released on Landslide (USA), Mar'85 Dist: Compendium, Rough Trade, Cartel

FIDDLE MUSIC FROM SHETLAND AND BEYOND.
Album: released on Topic, Mar'85 Dist: Roots Distribution

MUSIC FROM SHETLAND AND BEYOND.
Album: released on Topic, Nov'86 Dist: Roots Distribution

Curran, Eamonn

FAREWELL TO EIRINN (Curran, Eamonn & Dolores Kleane & John Faulkner).

Current 93

IMPERIUM.
Album: released on Maldoror, Aug'87 by Maldoror Records. Dist: Rough Trade, Cartel

IN MENSTRUAL NIGHT.
Picture disc album: released on Maldoror, May'86 by Maldoror Records. Dist: Rough Trade, Cartel

LASHTAL.
Single (12"): released on Layla, Apr'86 by Layla Records. Dist: Rough Trade, Cartel

LIVE AT BAR MALDOROR.
Album: released on None, Jan'85

NATURE UNVEILED.
Album: released on Layla, Apr'86 by Layla Records. Dist: Rough Trade, Cartel

Currie Brothers

BY SPECIAL REQUEST.
Album: released on ARC (Accordion Records), '84 Dist: Accordion Record Club

HOT STUFF.
Album: released on Lismor, Jul'77 by Lismor Records. Dist: Lismor, Roots, Celtic Music

Cassette: released on Lismor, Jul'77 by Lismor Records. Dist: Lismor, Roots, Celtic Music

TAKE THREE.
Album: released on Lismor, Jul'80 by Lismor Records. Dist: Lismor, Roots, Celtic Music

Cassette: released on Lismor, Jul'80 by Lismor Records. Dist: Lismor, Roots, Celtic Music

TAKE TWO.
Album: released on Lismor, May'79 by Lismor Records. Dist: Lismor, Roots, Celtic Music

Curson, Ted

TED CURSON & CO.
Album: released on India Navigation, May'84 by India Navigation Records. Dist: Cadillac, Projection, Swift

TRIO, (THE).
Album: released on Interplay, Aug'79 by Interplay Records. Dist: Jazz Music, Swift

Curtess, Buddy

BRIDGE OVER TROUBLED WATER (Curtess, Buddy & The Grasshoppers).
Tracks: / Bridge over troubled water / Load up.
Single (7"): released on Mercury, Jul'87 by Phonogram Records. Dist: Polygram Distribution

HELLO SUZIE (Curtess, Buddy & The Grasshoppers).
Tracks: / Hot shot / Main Line.
Single (7"): released on Mercury, Nov'86 by Phonogram Records. Dist: Polygram Distribution

Single (12"): released on Mercury, Nov'86 by Phonogram Records. Dist: Polygram Distribution. Estim retail price in Aug'87 was £11.99.

SHOOBEE BABY (Curtess, Buddy & The Grasshoppers).
Tracks: / Shoobee baby / Hypnotise me / Better be sure / Scoobeedoo *.
Single (7"): released on Gyrate, Feb'86 by Gyrate Records. Dist: Jungle, Cartel

Single (12"): released on Gyrate, Feb'86 by Gyrate Records. Dist: Jungle, Cartel

SHOUT (Curtess, Buddy & The Grasshoppers).
Tracks: / Shout / Heart and soul.
Single (7"): released on Mercury, Jul'86 by Phonogram Records. Dist: Polygram Distribution

Curtie & The Boom Box

BLACK KISSES NEVER MAKE YOU BLUE.
Single (7"): released on RCA, Aug'85 by RCA Records. Dist: RCA, Roots, Swift, Wellard, Chris, I & B, Solomon & Peres Distribution

Single (12"): released on RCA, Aug'85 by RCA Records. Dist: RCA, Roots, Swift, Wellard, Chris, I & B, Solomon & Peres Distribution

Curtin, D.J.

ALMOST PERSUADED.
Album: released on Harp(Ireland), Oct'81 by Pickwick Records. Dist: Taylors

Curtin, Glen

WE WILL MAKE LOVE.
Single (7"):

Curtis, Clem

BABY, NOW THAT I'VE FOUND YOU (Curtis, Clem & The Foundations).
Tracks: / Baby, now that I've found you / Baby, now that I've found you (inst).
Single (7"): released on Opium, May'87

Single (12"): released on Opium, May'87

BROADWAY H (Curtis, Clem & The Foundations).
Single (7"): released on IDM, Aug'84 by IDM Records. Dist: PRT

Single (12"): released on IDM, Aug'84 by IDM Records. Dist: PRT

Curtis, Dave

BROKEN HILL.
Album: released on Tank, Jun'79 by Tank Records.

TAKIN' THE ROUGH WITH THE SMOOTH.
Album: released on Tank, Nov'79 by Tank Records.

Curtis, Debbie

CHARLIE SO GOOD.
Tracks: / Charlie so good / Anything can shake your tree.
Single (7"): released on 42nd Street, May'86 by 42nd Street Records. Dist: EMI

Curtis, Joe

WHAT PEOPLE SAY.
Single (7"): released on PRT, Aug'83 by PRT Records. Dist: PRT

Single (12"): released on PRT, Aug'83 by PRT Records. Dist: PRT

Curtis, King

20 GOLDEN PIECES OF KING CURTIS.
Album: released on Bulldog Records, Jul'82

JAZZ GROOVE.
Double Album: released on Prestige, Sep'80 by Prestige Records (USA). Dist: RCA, JSU, Swift

KING CURTIS.
Album: released on Red Lightnin', May'83 by Red Lightnin' Records. Dist: Roots, Swift, Jazz Music, JSU, Pinnacle, Cartel, Wynd-Up Distribution

LIVE IN NEW YORK.
Album: released on JSP, Aug'85 by JSP Records. Dist: Swift, Projection

MEMPHIS SOUL STEW.
Single (12"): released on Atlantic, Apr'80 by WEA Records. Dist: WEA

Curtis, Mac

GOOD ROCKIN' TOMORROW.
Album: released on Rollin, Jun'80

GRANDADDY'S ROCKIN' YOU.
Album: released on Rollin, Jun'80

HOT ROCK BOOGIE.
Single (7"): released on Hot, Jun'80 by Hot Records. Dist: Rough Trade, Cartel

HOW COME IT.
Single (7"): released on Rollin, Jun'80

HOW LOW DO YOU FEEL?.
Single (7"): released on Rollin, Jun'80

PISTOL PACKIN' MAMA.
Single (7"): released on Rollin, Jun'80

ROCK (Curtis, Mac/Johnny Carrou).
Single (7"): released on Rollin, Jun'80

ROCKIN' MOTHER.
Album: released on Radar, May'79 by WEA Music Ltd. Dist: WEA, PRT

ROCK ME.
Album: released on Rollin, Jun'80

RUFFABILLY.
Album: released on Rollin, Jun'80

Curtis, Ron
RON CURTIS PLAYS THE MIGHTY COMPTON ORGAN.
Album: released on Amberlee, '82 by Amberlee Records. Dist: Amberlee Records, H.R. Taylor

Curtis, Ronald
BYE BYE BLUES.
Album: released on Saydisc, Sep'81 by Saydisc Records. Dist: Essex, Harmonia Mundi, Roots, H.R. Taylor, Jazz Music, Swift, Projection, Gamut

YES I REMEMBER IT WELL.
Album: released on Saydisc, Sep'81 by Saydisc Records. Dist: Essex, Harmonia Mundi, Roots, H.R. Taylor, Jazz Music, Swift, Projection, Gamut

YES I REMEMBER IT WELL.
Album: released on Saydisc, Sep'81 by Saydisc Records. Dist: Essex, Harmonia Mundi, Roots, H.R. Taylor, Jazz Music, Swift, Projection, Gamut

Curtis, Sonny
I THINK I'M IN LOVE.
Single (7"): released on Songworks, Jun'85 Dist: MIS-EMI Distribution

NOW I'VE GOT A HEART OF GOLD.
Single (7"): released on Songworks, Oct'85 Dist: MIS-EMI Distribution

ROCK'N'ROLL.
Single (7"): released on Rollercoaster, Mar'80 by Rollercoaster Records. Dist: Swift Distribution, Rollercoaster Distribution

SPECTRUM.
Album: released on Nightflite, Aug'87 by Adrian Owlett. Dist: Charly, Spartan

Curtis, T.C
BODYSHAKE.
Single (12"): released on Groove PR, Dec'81 by Beggars Banquet Records. Dist: WEA, PRT

DANCE TO THE BEAT.
Single (12"): released on Hot Melt, Mar'84 by Hot Melt Records. Dist: Pinnacle, Spartan

LET'S MAKE LOVE.
Tracks: / Step by step / Dance to the beat (remix).
Single (7"): released on Hot Melt, Apr'86 by Hot Melt Records. Dist: Pinnacle, Spartan

Single (7"): released on Hot Melt, Apr'86 by Hot Melt Records. Dist: Pinnacle, Spartan

Single (7"): released on Hot Melt, Jul'86 by Hot Melt Records. Dist: Pinnacle, Spartan

Single (12"): released on Hot Melt, Jul'86 by Hot Melt Records. Dist: Pinnacle, Spartan

LOVE GOT ME ON A MERRY GO ROUND.
Tracks: / Love got me on a merry go round / What's your problem / Reunited.
Single (12"): released on Hot Melt, May'87 by Hot Melt Records. Dist: Pinnacle, Spartan

PARTY DOWN.
Single (7"): released on Romantic, Nov'82 Dist: MCA Distribution

SLAVE OF LOVE.
Tracks: / Slave of love / Slave of love - dub mix.
Single (7"): released on Hot Melt, Sep'86 by Hot Melt Records. Dist: Pinnacle, Spartan

Single (12"): released on Hot Melt, Sep'86 by Hot Melt Records. Dist: Pinnacle, Spartan

SLAVE OF LOVE-FINAL COUNTDOWN MIX.
Page 262

Tracks: / Let's make love.
Single (12"): released on Hot Melt, Jan'87 by Hot Melt Records. Dist: Pinnacle, Soartan

SLAVE OF LOVE REMIX.
Tracks: / Slave of love remix / Let's make love remix / Body shake remix.
Single (12"): released on Hot Melt, Nov'86 by Hot Melt Records. Dist: Pinnacle, Spartan

YOU SHOULD HAVE KNOWN BETTER.
Single (7"): released on Hot Melt, Feb'85 by Hot Melt Records. Dist: Pinnacle, Spartan Deleted '85.

Single (12"): released on Hot Melt, Feb'85 by Hot Melt Records. Dist: Pinnacle, Spartan

Curtis, T.C. & T. Jam
JACKO.
Notes: Remix.
Single (12"): released on Hot Melt, Sep'87 by Hot Melt Records. Dist: Pinnacle, Spartan

Single (7"): released on Hot Melt, Aug'87 by Hot Melt Records. Dist: Pinnacle, Spartan

Single (12"): released on Hot Melt, Aug'87 by Hot Melt Records. Dist: Pinnacle, Spartan

Curtis, Tony
CIRCUMSPECT.
Album: released on Wire, Dec'85 Dist: Nine Mile, Cartel

Curtis, Winston
BE THANKFUL.
Single (12"): released on World Entertainment, Jul'84

Curve
LOVE GOES BY.
Single (7"): released on Bright, Sep'83

Single (12"): released on Bright, Sep'83

Curved Air
AIR CONDITIONING.
Album: by Warner Bros Records. Dist: WEA

BACK STREET LOVE.
Single (7"): released on Decca, Mar'82 by Decca Records. Dist: Polygram

BEST OF CURVED AIR, THE.
Album: released on Warner Brothers, Apr'76 by Warner Bros Records. Dist: WEA

MIDNIGHT WIRE.
Album: released on BTM, Oct'75 Dist: BMG Distribution

PHANTASMAGORIA.
Cassette: released on Warner Brothers, '74 by Warner Bros Records. Dist: WEA

RENEGADE.
Single (7"): released on Pearl Key, Jul'84 by Pearl Key Records. Dist: Pinnacle

Cusack, Peter
AFTER BEING IN HOLLAND.
Album: released on Bead, Feb'78 Dist: Cadillac

Cussick, Ian
DANGER IN THE AIR.
Album: released on A&M, Jan'84 by A&M Records. Dist: Polygram

Cut & Dry Band
CUT AND DRY.
Album: released on Topic, '81 Dist: Roots Distribution

Cut & Dry Dolly
CUT & DRY DOLLY Collection of Northumbrian pipe tunes.
Album: released on Topic, '81 Dist: Roots Distribution

Cuthbertson, Iain
I'M DEFINATELY BACK.
Single (7"): released on Thumbs Up, Jan'81 Dist: Spartan Distribution

Cutler, Adge
ADGE CUTLER'S CIDER DRINKING FAVOURITES (Cutler, Adge & The Wurzels).
Album: released on Note, Jun'80 by EMI Records. Dist: EMI

ADGE CUTLER & THE WURZELS (Cutler, Adge & The Wurzels).
Album: released on Columbia, Aug'76 by EMI Records. Dist: EMI

DON'T TELL I, TELL 'EE (Cutler, Adge & The Wurzels).

Album: released on EMI, '84 by EMI Records. Dist: EMI

VERY BEST OF ADGE CUTLER, THE.
Tracks: / When I need you.
Album: released on EMI, '84 by EMI Records. Dist: EMI

Cutler, Ivor
DANDRUFF.
Cassette: released on Virgin, Mar'84 by Virgin Records. Dist: EMI, Virgin Distribution

Album: released on Virgin, Mar'84 by Virgin Records. Dist: EMI, Virgin Distribution

GRUTS.
Album: released on Rough Trade, Apr'86 by Rough Trade Records. Dist: Rough Trade Distribution, Cartel Distribution

JAMMY SMEARS.
Album: released on Virgin, Jul'83 by Virgin Records. Dist: EMI, Virgin Distribution

Cassette: released on Virgin, Jul'83 by Virgin Records. Dist: EMI, Virgin Distribution

LIFE IN A SCOTCH SITING ROOM VOL.2.
Album: released on Harvest, Mar'78 by EMI Records. Dist: Roots, EMI

PRINCE IVOR.
Double Album: released on Rough Trade, Nov'86 by Rough Trade Records. Dist: Rough Trade Distribution, Cartel Distribution

PRIVILEGE (Cutler, Ivor & Linda Hirst).
Album: released on Rough Trade, '84 by Rough Trade Records. Dist: Rough Trade Distribution, Cartel Distribution

VELVET DONKEY.
Album: released on Virgin, Mar'84 by Virgin Records. Dist: EMI, Virgin Distribution

Cassette: release: on Virgin, Mar'84 by Virgin Records. Dist: EMI, Virgin Distribution

WOMAN OF THE WORLD.
Single (7"): released on Rough Trade, Aug'83 by Rough Trade Records. Dist: Rough Trade Distribution, Cartel Distribution

Cut Loose
HARD WAY TO LIVE.
Single (7"): released on Western, Jun'84 by Western Records. Dist: Chris Wellard, Red Rhino

Cutmaster DC
BROOKLYN'S IN MY HOUSE.
Single (7"): released on Cherry Red, Jun'86 by Cherry Red Records. Dist: Pinnacle

Single (12"): released on Cherry Red, May'86 by Cherry Red Records. Dist: Pinnacle

Cuttin' A Groove
CUTTIN' A GROOVE (Various Artists).
Album: released on Vinyl, Dec'86

Cutting Crew
ANY COLOUR.
Tracks: / Any colour / Fear of falling, A.
Notes: Pic bag
Single (7"): released on Siren, Apr'87 by Virgin Records. Dist: EMI

Single (12"): released on Siren, Apr'87 by Virgin Records. Dist: EMI

BROADCAST.
Tracks: / Any colour / One for the mocking bird / I've been in love before / Life in a dangerous time / Fear of falling / (I just) died in your arms tonight / Don't look back / Sahara / It shouldn't take too long / Broadcast, The.
Notes: Czardaz is available on 12" version only.
Album: released on Siren, Nov'86 by Virgin Records. Dist: EMI

Cassette: released on Siren, Nov'86 by Virgin Records. Dist: EMI

Compact disc: released on Siren, Nov'86 by Virgin Records. Dist: EMI

Single (7"): released on London, Feb'87 by London Records. Dist: Polygram

Single (12"): released on London, Feb'87 by London Records. Dist: Polygram

I JUST DIED IN YOUR ARMS.
Tracks: / I just died in your arms / For the longest time / I just died in your arms (remix).
Single (7"): released on Siren, Jul'86 by Virgin Records. Dist: EMI

Single (12"): released on Siren, Jul'86 by Virgin Records. Dist: EMI

I'VE BEEN IN LOVE BEFORE.
Single (7"): released on Siren, Nov'86 by Virgin Records. Dist: EMI

Picture disc single: released on Siren, Nov'86 by Virgin Records. Dist: EMI

Single (12"): released on Siren, Nov'86 by Virgin Records. Dist: EMI

ONE FOR THE MOCKINGBIRD.
Tracks: / Mirror & a blade (live).
Single (7"): released on Siren, Feb'87 by Virgin Records. Dist: EMI

Single (12"): released on Siren, Feb'87 by Virgin Records. Dist: EMI

Compact disc single: released on Siren, Mar'87 by Virgin Records. Dist: EMI

Cutting Edge
CUTTING EDGE (Various Artists).
Album: released on Razor, Nov'85 by Razor. Dist: Pinnacle

CUTTING EDGE.
Album: released on Odin, Oct'84 by Odin Records. Dist: Pinnacle, Cadillac

Cassette: released on Odin, Oct'84 by Odin Records. Dist: Pinnacle, Cadillac

CUTTING EDGE (COOKING VINYL) (Various Artists).
Notes: A selection of contemporary British Roots music including The Oyster Band and The Mekons.
Album: released on Cooking Vinyl, May'87 Dist: Nine Mile, Cartel, Red Rhino

Cassette: released on Cooking Vinyl, May'87 Dist: Nine Mile, Cartel, Red Rhino

OUR MAN IN PARADISE.
Album: released on Odin, Oct'84 by Odin Records. Dist: Pinnacle, Cadillac

Cassette: released on Odin, Oct'84 by Odin Records. Dist: Pinnacle, Cadillac

Cuttin' The Boogie
CUTTIN' THE BOOGIE (Various Artists).
Tracks: / Chicago stomp / Mr. Freddie blues / Suitcase blues / Pinetop's boogie woogie / Jump steady blues / Honky tonk train / Yancey special / Mr. Freddie blues / Boogie woogie stomp / Bass goin' crazy / Mellow blues, The / Tell 'em about me/ Climin' and screamin' /Blues on the downbeat / Kaycee on my mind / Cuttin' the boogie.
Notes: Recorded in mono. Piano blues and boogie-woogie 1926-1941.
Album: released on New World (USA), Mar'87 by New World Records (USA). Dist: Conifer

Cutty, Gordon
GRAND OLD FASHIONED DANCE, A.
Album: released on Free Reed, Sep'79 by Free Reed Records. Dist: Roots, Projection, Hobgoblin Records, Oblivion

Cutty Sark
DIE TONIGHT.
Album: released on Mausoleum, Jun'84 by Mausoleum Records. Dist: Pinnacle

Cassette: released on Mausoleum, Jun'84 by Mausoleum Records. Dist: Pinnacle

HARD ROCK POWER.
Album: released on Mausoleum, Jun'84 by Mausoleum Records. Dist: Pinnacle

HEROES.
Album: released on Mausoleum, Apr'85 by Mausoleum Records. Dist: Pinnacle

Cutty's, Gordon, Band
GRAND OLD FASHIONED DANCE, A.
Album: released on Free Reed, Jan'87 by Free Reed Records. Dist: Roots, Projection, Hobgoblin Records, Oblivion

Cuzacq, Gilles
FUNK DANS MON ACCORDEON.
Tracks: / Femmes ne changez pas / Fleur de caves ou de paves / Winner / Y du funk dans mon accordeon / One two three / Accordeon disco march / Ivre l'auvergne et les auvernats / Sensibilty inspiration / Genius twist / Toros el paso / Marche armoriaine.
Album: released on Accordion Record Club, Jul'86 by Accordion Record Club. Dist: Accordion Record Club

Album: released on Accordion Record Club, Jul'86 by Accordion Record Club Records. Dist: Accordion Record Club

Cwmbran...
CWMBRAN MALE CHOIR, THE Conducted by Huw Davis.
Album: released on Top Brass, Nov'79 by PRT Records. Dist: PRT Distribution

CWR Singers
O MAGNIFY THE LORD WITH US.
Notes: CWR and Word have been at work once

again to bring together the very best in praise and worship. 'O Magnify The Lord' soans many musical tastes and containssome musical suprises! (Warning) This is not just another praise recording.
Album: released on Word, Oct'86 by Word Records. Dist: Word Distribution, CBS

Cassette: released on Word, Oct'86 by Word Records. Dist: Word Distribution, CBS

Cwrt-Y-Gollen
STAND AND FIGHT (Cwrt-Y-Gollen Junior Band & Choir).
Album: released on Music Masters, Sep'81 b Music Masters Records. Dist: Taylors

C.W.S. (Manchester) Band
FESTIVAL OF MARCHES FOR BRASS BAND, A.
Album: released on Bandleader, Apr'83 by Bandleader Records. Dist: PRT

Cassette: released on Bandleader, Apr'83 by Bandleader Records. Dist: PRT

Cyan
REMEMBER THE BEACH GIRL.
Single (7"): released on Rialto, Sep'83 by Rialto Records. Dist: Pinnacle

Cycle Of The West
CYCLE OF THE WEST Read by John Neilhardt.
Cassette: released on Caedmon(USA), Oct'81 by Caedmon (USA) Records. Dist: Gower, Taylors, Discovery

Cylinder Jazz
CYLINDER JAZZ Various artists (Various Artists).

Album: released on Saydisc, '82 by Saydisc Records. Dist: Essex, Harmonia Mundi, Roots, H.R. Taylor, Jazz Music, Swift, Projection, Gamut

Cassette: released on Saydisc, '82 by Saydisc Records. Dist: Essex, Harmonia Mundi, Roots, H.R. Taylor, Jazz Music, Swift, Projection, Gamut

Cymbal, Johnny
MR BASSMAN.
Single (7"): released on Creole, '82 by Creole Records. Dist: Rhino, PRT

Single (7"): released on Old Gold, '82 by Old Gold Records. Dist: Lightning, Jazz Music, Spartan, Counterpoint

Cymone, Andre
A.C..
Album: released on CBS, '85 by CBS Records. Dist: CBS

Cassette: released on CBS, '85 by CBS Records. Dist: CBS

SURVIVIN' IN THE 80'S.
Album: released on CBS, '83 by CBS Records. Dist: CBS

Cassette: released on CBS, '83 by CBS Records. Dist: CBS

Single (7"): by CBS Records. Dist: CBS

Single (12"): by CBS Records. Dist: CBS

Cyncis
ROCK APOCALYPSE.
Single (7"): released on Stinkfoot, '84 by Stink-

---

foot Records. Dist: Pinnacle

Cyrille, Andrew
CELEBRATION.
Album: released on IPS, '80 Dist: JSU

JUNCTION.
Album: released on IPS, '80 Dist: JSU

NUBA.
Album: released on Black Saint, '79 Dist: Projection, IMS, Polygram, Chris Wellard, Harmonia Mundi, Swift

WHAT ABOUT.
Album: released on Affinity, '82 by Charly Records. Dist: Charly, Cadillac

Cyril Trotts to Bogna
TWO TRIPES Yu rats.
Single (7"): released on Yowsa Yowsa, '84 by Cyril Trotts to Bogna. Dist: Pinnacle

Single (12"): released on Yowsa Yowsa, '84 by Cyril Trotts to Bogna. Dist: Pinnacle

Czechoslovak Brass
MILITARY MASTERPIECES.
Notes: 3 albums of Military band recordings including many favourite marches and an LP of famous pieces by John Philip Sousa. Conducted by Rudolph urbanec.
Album: released on Avon, Nov'85 by Avon Records. Dist: Counterpoint

Cassette: released on Avon, Nov'85 by Avon Records. Dist: Counterpoint

---

Czukay, Holger
COOL IN THE POOL Oh Lord.
Single (7"): released on EMI, '83 by EMI Records. Dist: EMI

DER ESTEN IST ROT.
Album: released on Virgin, '84 by Virgin Records. Dist: EMI, Virgin Distribution

Cassette: released on Virgin, '84 by Virgin Records. Dist: EMI, Virgin Distribution

DER OSTEN IST ROT.
Album: released on Virgin, Apr'86 by Virgin Records. Dist: EMI, Virgin Distribution

Cassette: released on Virgin, Apr'86 by Virgin Records. Dist: EMI, Virgin Distribution

MOVIES.
Tracks: / Cool in the pool / Oh lord give us more money / Persian love / Hollywood symphony.
Album: released on EMI, Jan'80 by EMI Records. Dist: EMI

ROME REMAINS ROME.
Album: released on Virgin, Jan'87 by Virgin Records. Dist: EMI, Virgin Distribution

Cassette: released on Virgin, Jan'87 by Virgin Records. Dist: EMI, Virgin Distribution

Compact disc: by Virgin Records. Dist: EMI, Virgin Distribution

SNAKE CHARMER.
Album: released on Island, '83 by Island Records. Dist: Polygram

Cassette: released on Island, '83 by Island Records. Dist: Polygram

D

Dab Hand
HIGH ROCK AND LOW GLEN.
Album: released on Celtic Music, Aug'85 by Celtic Music Distribution. Dist: Celtic Music, Jazz Music, Projection, Roots

D'abo, Mike
INDESTRUCTABLE.
Tracks: / Loving on a shoestring / Love instructable / Horns of Memphis / Nobody else but you / Easy street / Time warp / Thank you / Wonder of a woman / Slow burning love / Whose heart / Ships / Revival / There's a lovely lake in London / Isle of Capri / South American Joe / Mocking bird went cuckoo / Keeping up with the Joneses / Cherie / In my little bottom drawer / I'm ninety nine today / Sally / Sing as we go / Roll along prairie moon / One of the little orphans of the storm / Just one more chance / Winter draws on / Red sails in the sunset / What can you give a nudist on his birthday / Love, life and laughter / I took my harp to a party.
Album: released on President, May'87 by President Records. Dist: Taylors, Spartan

Cassette: released on President, May'87 by President Records. Dist: Taylors, Spartan

LOVING ON A SHOESTRING.
Tracks: / Loving on a shoestring / Thank you.
Single (7"): released on President, May'87 by President Records. Dist: Taylors, Spartan

Da Costa, Glen
SERENADE OF LOVE (Da Costa, Glen & The Wailers).
Album: released on Vista Sounds, Mar'85 by Vista Sounds Records. Dist: Jetstar

Da Costa, Paulino
AGORA.
Album: released on Pablo, '82 by Pablo Records. Dist: Wellard, Chris, IMS-Polygram, BMG

Cassette: released on Pablo, '82 by Pablo Records. Dist: Wellard, Chris, IMS-Polygram, BMG

SUNRISE.
Compact disc: released on Pablo (USA), Apr'87 by Pablo Records (USA). Dist: Wellard, Chris, IMS-Polygram, BMG

Album: released on Verve (USA), Sep'84 by Polydor. Dist: Polygram

Cassette: released on Verve (USA), Sep'84 by Polydor. Dist: Polygram

TAJ MAHAL.
Single (12"): released on Pablo, Sep'84 by Pablo Records. Dist: Wellard, Chris, IMS-Polygram, BMG

TUDO BEM (Da Costa, Paulino & Joe Pass).
Album: released on Pablo (USA), '82 by Pablo Records (USA). Dist: Wellard, Chris, IMS-Polygram, BMG

Cassette: released on Pablo (USA), '82 by Pablo Records (USA). Dist: Wellard, Chris, IMS-Polygram, BMG

Dada
PEARL.
Single (12"): released on Dadisk, Jan'87 Dist: Revolver, Cartel

Daddy Sandy
RIDDLE BUBBLE.
Single (12"): released on UK Bubblers, Dec'84 by Greensleeves Records. Dist: RCA, Jetstar

D'a Dev
DON'T PUSH.
Album:

Daemion
DIZZY.
Single (7"): released on Si Jenn, Feb'83 by Si Jenn Records. Dist: Si Jenn Distribution

DAF
ABSOLUTELY BODY CONTROL.
Single (12"): released on Illuminated, Aug'85 by IKF Records. Dist: Pinnacle, Cartel, Jetstar

ALLES IST GUT.
Album: released on Virgin, Mar'84 by Virgin Records. Dist: EMI, Virgin Distribution

BROTHERS.
Single (7"): released on Illuminated, Oct'85 by IKF Records. Dist: Pinnacle, Cartel, Jetstar

Single (12"): released on Illuminated, Oct'85 by IKF Records. Dist: Pinnacle, Cartel, Jetstar

DER RAUBER UND DER PRINZ.
Single (7"): released on Mute, Oct'80 Dist: Spartan Distribution, Rough Trade Distribution, Cartel Distribution

Single (12"): released on Mute, Oct'80 Dist: Spartan Distribution, Rough Trade Distribution, Cartel Distribution

DIE KLEINEN UN DIE BOSEN (Deutsch Amerikanische Freundschaft).
Album: released on Mute, '81 Dist: Spartan Distribution, Rough Trade Distribution, Cartel Distribution

KEBAB TRAUME (Deutsch Amerikanische Freundschaft).
Single (7"): released on Mute, Mar'80 Dist: Spartan Distribution, Rough Trade Distribution, Cartel Distribution

LIVE IN BERLIN 1980.
Cassette: released on Music For Midgets, May'84 Dist: Backs, Cartel Distribution

Daffodils To The...
DAFFODILS TO THE DAFFODILS HERE'S THE DAFFODILS Various Artists (Various Artists).
Album: released on Pax, Aug'84 by Pax Records. Dist: Red Rhino, Cartel

Dagaband
SECOND TIME AROUND.
Single (7"): released on MHM, Mar'83

Daggermen
DAGGERS IN MY MIND.
Album: released on Own-Up, Nov'86 Dist: Rough Trade Distribution, Cartel Distribution

INTRODUCING THE DAGGERMEN.
Extended-play record: released on Empire, Feb'86 by Empire Records. Dist: Backs, Cartel, Jetstar

Dagradi, Tony
LUNAR ECLIPSE.
Album: released on Gramavision (USA), Jul'83

PAUL DAIGLE AND... (Daigle, Paul, Robert Elkins & Cajun Gold).
Album: released on Swallow (USA), Nov'86 Dist: Swift Distribution

Daigrepont, Bruce
STIR UP THE ROUX.
Album: released on Rounder Europa, Jun'87

Album: released on Ebony, Jul'84 by Ebony Records. Dist: Pinnacle, Ebony

Daily, E.G.
MIND OVER MATTER.
Single (7"): released on A&M (USA), Aug'87 Dist: Pinnacle

SAY IT, SAY IT.
Single (7"): released on A&M, Jun'86 by A&M Records. Dist: Polygram

Single (12"): released on A&M, Jun'86 by A&M Records. Dist: Polygram

by Gramavision Records (USA). Dist: PRT, IMS, Polygram

OASIS.
Album: released on Gramavision (USA), Jul'83 by Gramavision Records (USA). Dist: PRT, IMS, Polygram

Dahl, Roald
FANTASTIC MR.FOX.
Notes: Read by Lionel Jefferies
Cassette: released on Cover to Cover, Nov'86 by Cover to Cover Cassettes. Dist: Conifer

Daily Flash
I FLASH DAILY.
Album: released on Psycho, Nov'84 Dist: Funhouse, Rough Trade

Daintees
ROLL ON SUMMERTIME.
Single (7"): released on Kitchenware, Jun'84 by Kitchenware Records. Dist: Cartel, CBS, Polygram, RCA-Ariola Distribution

RUNNING WATER (Daintees & Martin Stephenson).
Single (7"): released on Kitchenware, May'86 by Kitchenware Records. Dist: Cartel, CBS, Polygram, RCA-Ariola Distribution

Dalbello
GONNA GET CLOSER TO YOU.
Single (7"): released on Capitol, May'84 by Capitol Records. Dist: EMI

Single (12"): released on Capitol, May'84 by Capitol Records. Dist: EMI

Dale & Grace
I'M LEAVING IT UP TO YOU.
Album: released on Michelle, Apr'79

Dale, Jackie
OH WHY.
Single (12"): released on Freedom Sounds, Jun'82 by Freedom Sounds Records. Dist: Jetstar

SWEET AND MELLOW (Dale, Jackie & Friends).
Album: released on Virgo Stomach, Dec'86 by Virgo Stomach Records. Dist: Jetstar

Dale, Just
UNTIL YOU COME BACK TO ME.
Tracks: / Until you come back to me / Duke, the.
Single (12"): released on Ariwa, Feb'86 by Ariwa Records. Dist: Revolver, Cartel, Jetstar, Rough Trade

Dalek I Love You
AMBITION.
Single (7"): released on Korova, Sep'83 Dist: WEA

Single (12"): released on Korova, Sep'83 Dist: WEA

DALEK I LOVE YOU.
Album: released on Korova, Nov'83 Dist: WEA Deleted '86.

Cassette: released on Korova, Nov'83 Dist: WEA

HOLIDAY IN DISNEYLAND.
Single (7"): released on Korova, Jul'82 Dist: WEA

Single (12"): released on Korova, Jul'82 Dist: WEA

Dale, Ronnie
GREAT SCOTII'S RONNIE DALE.
Album: released on Lismor, '75 by Lismor Records. Dist: Lismor, Roots, Celtic Music

YIELD NOT TO TEMPTATION.
Single (7"): released on Coochly St., Jan'82 by MK Records. Dist: MK

Dales & Wales 1984
ENTER HIS GATES.
Album: released on Solid Rock, Nov'84 Dist: Word Distribution

Cassette: released on Solid Rock, Nov'84 Dist: Word Distribution

Dale, Syd
SYD DALE & HIS ORCHESTRA (Dale, Syd & His Orchestra).
Album: released on Response, Apr'82 by Priority Records. Dist: BMG

Daley, Derek
YOUR LOVE.
Tracks: / Your love / Kingston town.
Single (12"): released on Viking, Jul'86 Dist: Harmonia Mundi Distributors

Daley, Larry
CHICKEN ON A RAFT Plymouth folk sounds.
Cassette: released on Folktracks, Nov'79 by

Folktracks Cassettes. Dist: Folktracks

Dalqez, Claudio
WATER GARDEN (THE).
Tracks: / Water garden (The) / Water garden (The)(dub mix).
Single (12"): released on Production House, Apr'87 Dist: Bluebird, Revolver, Cartel

Dalglish, Kenny
JUST LIKE KENNY.
Single (7"): released on Zuma, Apr'85 by Zuma Records. Dist: CBS, PRT

Single (12"): released on Zuma, Apr'85 by Zuma Records. Dist: CBS, PRT

Dalida
BORN TO SING.
Album: released on VIP, Dec'84 Dist: Jetstar Distribution

DALIDA VOL.1.
Album: released on Decca Records. Dist: IMS, Discovery, Conifer, Swift, Polygram

DALIDA VOL.2.
Album: released on Decca Records. Dist: IMS, Discovery, Conifer, Swift, Polygram

GREATEST HITS:DALIDA.
Double Album: by Decca Records. Dist: IMS, Discovery, Conifer, Swift, Polygram

Dali's Car
JUDGEMENT IS THE MIRROR, THE.
Single (7"): released on DOX, Oct'84 by DOX Records. Dist: Neon

Single (12"): released on DOX, Oct'84 by DOX Records. Dist: Neon

WAKING HOUR.
Tracks: / Dali's car / His box / Cornwall stone / Artemis / Create and melt / Moonlife / Judgement is the mirror.
Compact disc: by Virgin Records. Dist: EMI

Album: released on 10, Nov'84 by 10 Records. Dist: Virgin, EMI

Cassette: released on 10, Nov'84 by 10 Records. Dist: Virgin, EMI

Dalla, Lucio
1983.
Compact disc: by RCA Records. Dist: RCA, Roots, Swift, Wellard, Chris, I & B, Solomon & 'eres Distribution

BEST OF LUCIO DALLA.
Compact disc: by RCA Records. Dist: RCA,
Roots, Swift, Wellard, Chris, I & B, Solomon &
Peres Distribution

Dallas

DALLAS (Various Artists).
Tracks: / I wanna reach out and touch (Jock &
Miss Ellie's song) / Makin' up for lost time (the
Dallas lover's song) / Few good men, A (Pam &
Jenna's song for Bobby) / J.R.Who do you think
you are? / Working mans song (the Ewing/Bar-
nes legacy) / Lonliness in Lucy's eyes, the (the
life Sue Ellen is living) / I'm a survivor (from the
women of Dallas) / I'll know then what I know
now / Theme from Dallas (Dallas dreams) / Who
killed Jock Ewing.
Album: released on Warner Bros., Jul'86 by
Warner Bros Records. Dist: WEA

Cassette: released on Warner Bros., Jul'86 by
Warner Bros Records. Dist: WEA

Dallas, Rex
REX DALLAS SINGS.
Album: released on Westwood, '82 by West-
wood Records. Dist: Jazz Music, H.R. Taylor,
JSU, Pinnacle, Ross Records

Dallas Symphony Orchestra
**GERSHWIN - AMERICAN IN
PARIS/PORGY & BESS.**
Compact disc: by RCA Records. Dist: RCA,
Roots, Swift, Wellard, Chris, I & B, Solomon &
Peres Distribution

Dallas T.R.
HARD TO BE HUMBLE.
Album: released on Release, May'81 by Release Records. Dist: I & B, Wynd-Up Distribution, Taylors, Solomon & Peres Distribution

Dalls, Leroy
BLUES ALL AROUND MY BED Blues
Roots Vol.2.
Notes: See under Blues Roots Vo.2

Dallwitz, Dave
**DAVE DALLWITZ EUPHONIC RAGTIME
ENSEMBLE** (Dallwitz, Dave Euphonic Rag-
time Ensemble).
Album: released on Stomp Off, Jun'86 by
Stomp Off Records. Dist: Jazz Music Distribu-
tion

**DAVE DALLWITZ & SCHAMPUS ALL
STARS** (Dallwitz, Dave & The Schampus All
Stars).
Album: released on Dawn Club, May'79 Dist:
Cadillac, Swift, JSU

ELEPHANT STOMP (Dallwitz, Dave Jazz
Band).
Album: released on Stomp Off, Mar'87 by
Stomp Off Records. Dist: Jazz Music Distribu-
tion

FLOATING PALAIS (Dallwitz, Dave Jazz
Band).
Album: released on Swaggie, Mar'87 Dist: Jazz
Music Distribution

GOLD FEVER (1977) (Dallwitz, Dave Jazz
Band).
Album: released on Swaggie (Australia),
Jan'83

GULGONG SHUFFLE (1977) (Dallwitz,
Dave Jazz Band).
Album: released on Swaggie, Jan'83 Dist: Jazz
Music Distribution

ILLAWARRA FLAME(1974) (Dallwitz,
Dave Jazz Band).
Album: released on Swaggie (Australia),
Jan'83

MELBOURNE SUITE(1973) (Dallwitz,
Dave Jazz Band).
Album: released on Swaggie (Australia),
Jan'83

RAGTIME (Dallwitz, Dave Euphonic Ragtime
Ensemble).
Album: released on Swaggie (Australia),
Jan'83

SUNDAY MORNING RAG (Dallwitz, Dave
& The Schampus All Stars).
Album: released on Dawn Club, Dec'86 Dist:
Cadillac, Swift, JSU

D'Almaine, Michael
LOVE FOR LOVE.
Single (7"): released on Monarch, Jul'83 by
Chart Records. Dist: Pinnacle

Dalmations
**DALMATIONS WITH VARIOUS AR-
TISTS(EP)** (Dalmations/Various Artists).
Single (12"): released on Dog Rock, Dec'82 by
Dog Rock Records. Dist: Backs, Cartel

Dalmellington Band
DOON VALLEY BRASS.
Album: released on Neptune, Oct'77 by Lis-
mor. Dist: Spartan

Dalto, Jorge
URBAN OASIS.
Album: released on Concord Jazz(USA),
Sep'85 by Concord Jazz Records (USA). Dist:
IMS, Polygram

Cassette: released on Concord Jazz(USA),
Sep'85 by Concord Jazz Records (USA). Dist:
IMS, Polygram

Dalton, Guy
NIGHT PEOPLE.
Single (12"): released on Magic, Aug'83 Dist:
Jazz Music, Submarine, Swift, Chris Wellard,
Conifer

YOU CAN DO MAGIC.
Single (7"): released on Magic, Feb'84 Dist:
Jazz Music, Submarine, Swift, Chris Wellard,
Conifer

Dalton, Lacy J
BLUE EYED BLUES.
Tracks: / That's good-that's bad / Gotta serve
somebody / I'll love them whatever they are /
Hillybilly girl with the blues / 16th Avenue / My
old yellow car / Love gone cold / Have I got a
heart for you / It's a dirty job / Blue eyed blues.
Album: released on CBS, Jun'87 by CBS Records. Dist: CBS

Cassette: released on CBS, Jun'87 by CBS
Records. Dist: CBS

**CAN'T RUN AWAY FROM YOUR
HEART.**
Album: released on CBS, Aug'85 by CBS Rec-
ords. Dist: CBS

Cassette: released on CBS, Aug'85 by CBS
Records. Dist: CBS

HARD TIMES.
Tracks: / Hard times / Hillbilly girl with the blues
/ China doll / Oldsoldier / Ain't nobody who could
do it like my Daddy could / You can't fool lona /
Wide eyed and willing / Girls from Santa Cruz,
the / Whisper / Me'n'you.
Album: released on CBS, Apr'86 by CBS Rec-
ords. Dist: CBS

Cassette: released on CBS, Apr'86 by CBS
Records. Dist: CBS

HIGHWAY DINER.
Tracks: / Working class man / 12:05 / Changing all the time / Taking it all in stride / Can't see
me without you / This ol' town / Up with the wind
/ Boomtown / Gone again / Closing time.
Album: released on CBS, Aug'86 by CBS Records. Dist: CBS

Cassette: released on CBS, Aug'86 by CBS
Records. Dist: CBS

LACY J DALTON I love country.
Album: released on CBS, Mar'87 by CBS Records. Dist: CBS

Cassette: released on CBS, Mar'87 by CBS
Records. Dist: CBS

Dalton, Mike
**COUNTRY SIDE OF MIKE DALTON,
THE.**
Album: released on Tank, Dec'77 by Tank Rec-
ords.

Daltrey, Roger
AFTER THE FIRE.
Single (7"): released on 10, Sep'85 by 10 Rec-
ords. Dist: Virgin, EMI

Single (12"): released on 10, Sep'85 by 10
Records. Dist: Virgin, EMI

CAN'T WAIT TO SEE THE MOVIE.
Compact disc: released on 10, Jul'87 by 10
Records. Dist: Virgin, EMI

Album: released on 10, Jul'87 by 10 Records.
Dist: Virgin, EMI

Cassette: released on 10, Jul'87 by 10 Records. Dist: Virgin, EMI

DALTREY.
Album: released on Polydor (Import), Aug'82

Cassette: released on Polydor (Import), Aug'82

HEARTS ON FIRE.
Tracks: / Hearts on fire / Lovers storm / Quick
silver lightning*.
Single (7"): released on 10, 20 Jun'87 by 10
Records. Dist: Virgin, EMI

Single (12"): released on 10, 20 Jun'87 by 10
Records. Dist: Virgin, EMI

ONE OF THE BOYS.
Album: released on Polydor, May'77 by Polydor Records. Dist: Polygram, Polydor

PRIDE YOU HIDE, THE.
Tracks: / Pride you hide, The / Break out / Don't
talk to strangers* / Don't talk to strangers (live)**
/ Pictures of Lilly (live)**
Notes: 86
Single (7"): released on 10, May'86 by 10 Rec-
ords. Dist: Virgin, EMI

Single (12"): released on 10, May'86 by 10
Records. Dist: Virgin, EMI

Double-pack single: released on 10, May'86
by 10 Records. Dist: Virgin, EMI

RIDE A ROCK HORSE.
Album: released on Polydor, Jul'75 by Polydor
Records. Dist: Polygram, Polydor

UNDER A RAGING MOON.
Tracks: / Under a raging moon / Move better in
the night / Behind blue eyes / 5:15 / Won't get
fooled again.
Compact disc: by 10 Records. Dist: Virgin,
EMI

MCVICAR.
Album: released on Polydor, '80 by Polydor
Records. Dist: Polygram, Polydor

Single (7"): released on 10, Feb'86 by 10 Records. Dist: Virgin, EMI

Single (12"): by 10 Records. Dist: Virgin, EMI

Double-pack single: released on 10, Feb'86
by 10 Records. Dist: Virgin, EMI

Album: released on 10, Oct'85 by 10 Records.
Dist: Virgin, EMI

Cassette: released on 10, Oct'85 by 10 Records. Dist: Virgin, EMI

WALKING IN MY SLEEP.
Single (7"): released on WEA, Feb'84 by WEA
Records. Dist: WEA

Single (12"): released on WEA, Feb'84 by
WEA Records. Dist: WEA

Daly, Bryan
VELVET GUITAR OF BRYAN DALY.
Album: released on Gold Crown, Mar'80 by
Decca Records. Dist: Polygram

Daly, Glen
CABARET TIME.
Album: released on Pye Special, Jan'78

Cassette: released on PRT, Jan'78 by PRT
Records. Dist: PRT

GLASGOW NIGHT OUT, A.
Album: released on Marble Arch, Apr'74 Dist:
Taylors

GLEN'S BIRTHDAY PARTY.
Album: released on Pye Special, Jul'76

Cassette: released on PRT, Jul'76 by PRT
Records. Dist: PRT

**HUNDRED THOUSAND WELCOMES,
A.**
Tracks: / Hundred thousand welcomes, A /
Scotland medley / Tipperary medley / Misty is-
lands of the highlands / For me and my gal /
Show me the way to go home / Suvla bay /
Green oak tree / Auld land syne.
Cassette: released on Highlander, Jun'86 Dist:
PRT

LEGENDS OF SCOTLAND.
Tracks: / Scotland the brave / Dacent Irish boy,
The / Northern lights of old Aberdeen / Road
and the miles to Dundee / China doll / Wild colonial boy / Auld Scots mither o' mine / You need
hands / Gordon for me, A / When I leave this
world behind / When I leave old Glasgow behind / Come in, come in / Bonnie Scotland I
adore thee / McNamara's band / Granny's highland hame / In dear old Glasgow toon / Little
grey home in the West / On mother Kelly's doorstep / Lovely stornaway / Why did you make me
care / The day that I was born in Glasgow / I belong to Glasgow.
Cassette: released on Lochshore, Jun'86 by
Klub Records. Dist: PRT

LIVE AT THE ASHFIELD,GLASGOW.
Album: by PRT Records. Dist: PRT
Cat. no: GGL 0434
Cassette: released on Marble Arch, Oct'71
Dist: Taylors

**LIVE AT THE PAVILLION THEATRE,
GLASGOW.**
Tracks: / Wedding of Sandy Mac, The / Pal of
my cradle days / I love a lassie / Bonnie wells o'
weri / Paddy McGinty's goat / Amazing grace /
Oh boy what joy we had in barefoot days / Dear
little boy of mine / Just a wee doch and doris /
Now is the hour.
Cassette: released on Highlander, Oct'86 Dist:
PRT

MEMORIES.
Album: released on Pye, Dec'76

Cassette: released on PRT, Dec'76 by PRT
Records. Dist: PRT

Daly, Jackie
BUTTONS AND BOWS (Daly, Jackie &
McGuire, Seamus & Manus).
Album: released on WEA Ireland, Mar'87 by
WEA Records. Dist: Celtic Distributions, Projec-
tion, I & B

Cassette: released on WEA Ireland, Mar'87 by
WEA Records. Dist: Celtic Distributions, Projection, I & B

Eavesdropper,The
JACKIE DALY & SEAMUS CREAGH
(Daly, Jackie & Seamus Creagh).
Album: released on Gael-Linn (Ireland),
May'77 by Gael Linn Records. Dist: Roots, Pro-
jection, Celtic Music, Jazz Music

**MUSIC FROM SLIABH LUACHRA
VOL.6.**
Album: released on Topic, '81 Dist: Roots Dis-
tribution

Damage
CROWDED COMPANY.
Single (7"): released on Danger, Jan'83 by
Danger Records. Dist: ILA

Damaris
WHAT ABOUT MY LOVE.
Single (7"): released on CBS, Mar'84 by CBS
Records. Dist: CBS

Single (12"): released on CBS, Mar'84 by CBS
Records. Dist: CBS

Damascus
OPEN YOUR EYES.
Single (12"): released on Damascus, Apr'85 by
Probe Records. Dist: Cartel

Dambert No Bacon
UNFAIRYTALE, THE.
Album: released on Flowmotion, Mar'85 Dist:
Red Rhino, Cartel

D'Ambrosia, Meredith
IT'S YOUR DANCE.
Tracks: / Some upon a tempo /
Listen little girl / Devil may care / August moon
/ Nobody else but me / Humpty dumpty heart /
It's your dance / Underdog, The / It isn't so good-
it couldn't be better / Off again on again / No one
remembers but me / Miss Harper goes bizarre /
Strange meadowlark.
Notes: Meredith D'Ambrosio - Vocals &
piano/Harold Danko - Piano/Kevin Eubanks
Electric guitar
Album: released on Sunnyside (USA), Jan'86

Compact disc: released on Sunnyside (USA),
Feb'86 Dist: Mole Jazz Distribution, Conifer Distribution

LITTLE JAZZ BIRD.
Album: released on Palo Alto (Italy), Jan'84

MEREDITH....ANOTHER TIME.
Tracks: / All of us in it together / Aren't you glad
you're you / It's so peaceful in the country / Rain
rain (don't go away) / Dear Bix / Lazy afternoon
/ Where's the child I used to hold / Love is a
simple thing / You are there / While we're young
/ Small day tomorrow / Child is born, A / Piano
player, The (a thousand and one saloons) /
Some day my prince will come / Such a lonely
girl am I / Wheelers and dealers / I was doin' all
right / Skylark / Child is born, A.
Album: released on Sunnyside (USA), Feb'87
Dist: Mole Jazz Distribution, Conifer Distribution

Dameronia
LOOK STOP LISTEN (Dameronia & Philly
Joe Jones).
Notes: For full information see under: JONES,
Philly Joe/Dameronia.

Dameron, Tadd
BIG 10/ROYAL ROOST JAM.
Album: released on Beppo, Jun'76

CROSS CURRENTS (Dameron, Tadd &
Lennie Tristano).

KEYBOP (Dameron, Tadd & Dodo Marmaro-
sa).
Album: released on Jazz Live, Apr'81

MATING CALL.
Album:

Damian
TIME WARP, THE.
Single (7"): released on Sedition, Mar'86 Dist:
PRT

Single (12"): released on Sedition, Mar'86 Dist: PRT

Damien

DAMIEN:OMEN 2 Original Soundtrack (Damien:Omen 2).
Album: released on Silva Screen, Jun'87 by Silva Screen Records. Dist: Silva Screen

Cassette: released on Silva Screen, Jun'87 by Silva Screen Records. Dist: Silva Screen

Damien Thorne

SIGN OF THE JACKAL, THE.
Album: released on Roadrunner (Dutch), Aug'86 Dist: Pinnacle

Dammaj

MUTINY.
Album: released on Roadrunner (Dutch), Jan'87 Dist: Pinnacle

Damned

ALONE AGAIN OR.
Tracks: / Psychomania / Eloise / Alone again or / In dulce decorum.
Single (7"): released on MCA, Apr'87 by MCA Records. Dist: Polygram, MCA

Single (12"): released on MCA, Apr'87 by MCA Records. Dist: Polygram, MCA

Double-pack single: released on MCA, Apr'87 by MCA Records. Dist: Polygram, MCA

ANYTHING.
Tracks: / Alone again or / Portrait / Restless / In dulce decorum / Girl goes down / Gigolo / Anything / Tightrope walk / Psychomania / Anything / Year of the jackal, The / Thanks for the night.

Album: released on MCA, Nov'86 by MCA Records. Dist: Polygram, MCA

Cassette: released on MCA, Nov'86 by MCA Records. Dist: Polygram, MCA

Compact disc: released on MCA, Nov'86 by MCA Records. Dist: Polygram, MCA

Single (7"): released on MCA, Nov'86 by MCA Records. Dist: Polygram, MCA

Single (12"): released on MCA, Nov'86 by MCA Records. Dist: Polygram, MCA

ANYTHING (10").
Tracks: / Year of the jackal (The).
Single 10": released on MCA, Nov'86 by MCA Records. Dist: Polygram, MCA

BEST OF THE DAMNED, THE.
Album: released on Ace, Nov'81 by Ace Records. Dist: Pinnacle, Swift, Hotshot, Cadillac

Cassette: released on Ace, Jan'82 by Ace Records. Dist: Pinnacle, Swift, Hotshot, Cadillac

Compact disc: released on Big Beat, Oct'87 by Ace Records. Dist: Projection, Pinnacle

BLACK ALBUM, THE.
Double Album: released on Big Beat, Sep'82 by Ace Records. Dist: Projection, Pinnacle

Double cassette: released on Big Beat, Sep'82 by Ace Records. Dist: Projection, Pinnacle

Cassette: released on Big Beat, Jun'85 by Ace Records. Dist: Projection, Pinnacle

BLACK ALBUM, THE.
Tracks: / Wait for the blackout / Lively arts / Silly kids games / Drinking about my baby / Twisted nerve / Hit or miss / Dr.Jeckyll & Mr.Hyde / Sick of this and that / History of the world part 1 / 13th floor vendetta / Therapy / Curtain call.
Compact disc: by Ace Records. Dist: Projection, Pinnacle

CAPTAIN'S BIRTHDAY PARTY, THE.
Notes: Live at the Roundhouse
Album: released on Stiff, Jun'86 by Stiff Records. Dist: EMI, Record Services Distribution (Ireland)

DAMNED BUT NOT FORGOTTEN.
Tracks: / Dozen girls / Lovely money / I think I'm wonderful / Disguise / Take that / Torture me / Disco man / Tanks for the night / Take me away / Some girls are ugly / Nice cup of tea / Billy bad breaks.
Album: released on Dojo, May'86 by Castle Communications Records. Dist: Cartel

Cassette: released on Dojo, May'86 by Castle Communications Records. Dist: Cartel

Compact disc: released on Dojo, '86 by Castle Communications Records. Dist: Cartel

DAMNED, DAMNED, DAMNED.
Notes: Re-issue of the Damned's debut album originally on the Stiff label in 1977. The first ever punk album is now also available on CD for those of you who never want to 'smash it up'.Includes such brilliant songs as "New Rose", "Neat, neat, neat', "Fan club" and "Feel the pain"

Album: released on Demon, Apr'87 by Demon Records. Dist: Pinnacle

Cassette: released on Demon, Apr'87 by Demon Records. Dist: Pinnacle

Compact disc: released on Demon, Apr'87 by Demon Records. Dist: Pinnacle

Album: released on Stiff, Feb'77 by Stiff Records. Dist: EMI, Record Services Distribution (Ireland)

ELOISE.
Tracks: / Eloise / Temptation / Beat girl.
Single (7"): released on MCA, Jan'86 by MCA Records. Dist: Polygram, MCA

Single (12"): released on MCA, Jan'86 by MCA Records. Dist: Polygram, MCA

Single (7"): released on PRT, Jan'86 by PRT Records. Dist: PRT

Single (7"): released on PRT, Jan'86 by PRT Records. Dist: PRT

FRIDAY 13TH (EP).
Tracks: / Disco man / Limit club, The / Billy bad breaks / Citadel.
Extended-play record: released on Nems, Nov'86 Dist: Castle Communications Records, Pinnacle Records

GIGOLO.
Tracks: / Portrait.
Single (7"): released on MCA, Jan'87 by MCA Records. Dist: Polygram, MCA

Single (12"): released on MCA, Jan'87 by MCA Records. Dist: Polygram, MCA

GRIMLY FIENDISH.
Single (7"): released on MCA, Mar'85 by MCA Records. Dist: Polygram, MCA

Single (12"): released on MCA, Mar'85 by MCA Records. Dist: Polygram, MCA

Single (12"): released on MCA, Mar'85 by MCA Records. Dist: Polygram, MCA

HISTORY OF THE WORLD.
Single (12"): released on Chiswick, May'82 by Chiswick Records. Dist: Pinnacle

INTERVIEW.
Notes: Interview with band members.
Double-pack single: released on Vlad, May'86 Dist: Revolver

Album: released on Society, Sep'86 by Arista Records. Dist: Polygram

INTERVIEW PICTURE DISC.
Album: released on Arabesque, Jun'87 Dist: D Sharp Records, Pinnacle

IS IT A DREAM.
Single (7"): released on MCA, Sep'85 by MCA Records. Dist: Polygram, MCA

Single (12"): released on MCA, Sep'85 by MCA Records. Dist: Polygram, MCA

LIVE AT SHEPPERTON.
Album: released on Ace, Nov'82 by Ace Records. Dist: Pinnacle, Swift, Hotshot, Cadillac

Cassette: released on Big Beat, Jun'85 by Ace Records. Dist: Projection, Pinnacle

LIVE IN NEWCASTLE.
Album: released on Damned, Nov'83 by Damned Records. Dist: Pinnacle

LIVELY ARTS.
Single (7"): released on Big Beat, Oct'82 by Ace Records. Dist: Projection, Pinnacle

Single 10": released on Big Beat, Oct'82 by Ace Records. Dist: Projection, Pinnacle

LOVE SONG.
Single (7"): released on Big Beat, Feb'82 by Ace Records. Dist: Projection, Pinnacle

MACHINE GUN ETIQUETTE.
Tracks: / Plan 9 channel 7 / Liar / Noise, noise, noise / Smash it up / Anti-pope / Looking at you / Love song / Melody Lee / I just can't be happy today / These hands / Machine gun etiquette.
Compact disc: by Ace Records. Dist: Projection, Pinnacle

Album: released on Big Beat, May'82 by Ace Records. Dist: Projection, Pinnacle

Cassette: released on Big Beat, May'82 by Ace Records. Dist: Projection, Pinnacle

Cassette: released on Big Beat, Jun'85 by Ace Records. Dist: Projection, Pinnacle

MUSIC FOR PLEASURE.
Album: released on Stiff, Nov'77 by Stiff Records. Dist: EMI, Record Services Distribution (Ireland)

NEW ROSE.
Single (12"): released on Stiff, Nov'85 by Stiff Records. Dist: EMI, Record Services Distribution (Ireland)

NOT THE CAPTAIN'S BIRTHDAY PARTY.
Album: released on Demon, Oct'86 by Demon Records. Dist: Pinnacle

PEEL SESSION 10.5.77.
Tracks: / Sick of being sick / Stretcher case / Fan club / Feel the pain.
Cassette single: released on Strange Fruit, 13 Jun'87 by Clive Selwood. Dist: Pinnacle

PHANTASMAGORIA.
Compact disc: by MCA Records. Dist: Polygram, MCA

Album: released on MCA, Jul'85 by MCA Records. Dist: Polygram, MCA

Cassette: released on MCA, Jul'85 by MCA Records. Dist: Polygram, MCA

Picture disc album: released on MCA, Jul'85 by MCA Records. Dist: Polygram, MCA

SHADOW OF LOVE.
Single (7"): released on MCA, Jun'85 by MCA Records. Dist: Polygram, MCA

Single 10": released on MCA, Jun'85 by MCA Records. Dist: Polygram, MCA

Single 10": released on MCA, Jun'85 by MCA Records. Dist: Polygram, MCA

SMASH IT UP.
Single (7"): released on Big Beat, Feb'82 by Ace Records. Dist: Projection, Pinnacle

STRAWBERRIES.
Tracks: / Ignite / Generals / Stranger on the town / Dozen girls / Dog, The / Gun fury / Pleasure and the pain / Life goes on / Bad time for Bonzo / Under the floor again / Don't bother me.
Notes: Rat Scabies-drums, Dave Banian-vocals, Captain Sensible-Guitars/Keyboards (vocals on 'Life goes on' and 'Don't bother me'),Paul Gray (draught)Bass, Roman Jugg-Keyboard solos.
Album: released on Legacy, Mar'86 Dist: PRT

Cassette: released on Legacy, Mar'86 Dist: PRT

Album: released on Dojo, Dec'86 by Castle Communications Records. Dist: Cartel

Compact disc: released on Dojo, '86 by Castle Communications Records. Dist: Cartel

THANKS FOR THE NIGHT.
Picture disc single: released on Damned, Apr'86 by Damned Records. Dist: Pinnacle

Single (7"): released on Damned, May'84 by Damned Records. Dist: Pinnacle

Single (12"): released on Damned, May'84 by Damned Records. Dist: Pinnacle

THERE AIN'T NO SANITY CLAUSE.
Tracks: / There ain't no sanity clause / Looking at you (live) / Anti-pope.
Single (12"): released on Big Beat, May'86 by Ace Records. Dist: Projection, Pinnacle

Single (7"): released on Big Beat, Dec'83 by Ace Records. Dist: Projection, Pinnacle

WAIT FOR THE BLACKOUT.
Single (7"): released on Big Beat, May'82 by Ace Records. Dist: Projection, Pinnacle

Picture disc single: released on Big Beat, May'82 by Ace Records. Dist: Projection, Pinnacle

WHITE RABBIT.
Single (7"): released on Big Beat, Mar'83 by Ace Records. Dist: Projection, Pinnacle

Single (12"): released on Big Beat, Mar'83 by Ace Records. Dist: Projection, Pinnacle

Damon Edge

SURREAL ROCK, THE.
Album: released on Dossier, Jun'87 Dist: Red Rhino, Cartel

Damone, Vic

16 GOLDEN CLASSICS.
Tracks: / Feelings / If / Ghost riders in the sky / Softly / Windmills of your mind / People / Top of the world / Over the rainbow / Song is you (The) / All I need is a girl / By the time I get to Phoenix / Little green apples / Moment of truth (The) / Didn't we / Look of love (The) / Can't take my eyes off you.
Notes: All tracks licenced from Interworld Communications; Design: Shoot That Tiger! (c) 1986: Castle Communications Place, Unit 7, 271 Merton road, London SW18 5JS. Bar code: 5/013428/920060.
Album: released on Unforgettable, Dec'86 by Castle Communications Records. Dist: Counterpoint

Cassette: released on Unforgettable, Dec'86 by Castle Communications Records. Dist: Counterpoint

20 GOLDEN PIECES OF VIC DAMONE.
Album: released on Bulldog Records, Jan'82

CHRISTMAS WITH VIC DAMONE.
Album: released on Audio Fidelity, Oct'84 Dist: PRT

Cassette: released on Audio Fidelity, Oct'84 Dist: PRT

CLOSER THAN A KISS.
Tracks: / Closer than a kiss / I kiss your hand / Madam / We kiss in a shadow / Cuddle up a little closer / Cuddle up a little closer / A toujours / You and the night and the music / Prelude to a kiss / How deep is the ocean? / Day by day / As time goes by / Close as pages in a book / Out of nowhere / Night has a thousand eyes, The / Ooh my love / You stepped out of a dream / I cried for you / Spring is here / Deep purple / Toot toot tootsie / Swingin' down the lane / I got it bad and that ain't good.
Album: released on CBS(Blue Diamond), Jun'85 by CBS Records. Dist: CBS

Cassette: released on CBS(Blue Diamond), Jun'85 by CBS Records. Dist: CBS

DAMONE'S FEELINGS 1978.
Album: released on Rebecca, Apr'79 by Rebecca Records. Dist: Pinnacle

DAMONE TYPE OF THING, THE.
Album: released on RCA, Feb'84 by RCA Records. Dist: RCA, Roots, Swift, Wellard, Chris, I & B, Solomon & Peres Distribution

Cassette: released on RCA, Feb'84 by RCA Records. Dist: RCA, Roots, Swift, Wellard, Chris, I & B, Solomon & Peres Distribution

DIAMONE'S FEELINGS 1978.

DIDN'T WE.
Tracks: / Song is you, The / All I need is a girl / By the time I get to Phoenix / Little green apples / Moment of truth, The / Didn't we / Look of love, The / Can't take my eyes of you / Feelings / If / Ghost riders in the sky / Windmills of your mind / People / Top of the world / Over the rainbow.
Album: released on Showcase, Apr'86 Dist: Counterpoint

Cassette: released on Showcase, Apr'86 Dist: Counterpoint

FEELINGS.
Tracks: / Feelings / Lazy afternoon / Ghost riders in the sky / Softly / Windmills of your mind / People / Top of the world / Farewell to paradise / Over the rainbow.
Album: released on President, Mar'85 by President Records. Dist: Taylors, Spartan

Cassette: released on President, Mar'85 by President Records. Dist: Taylors, Spartan

LINGER AWHILE.
Tracks: / Linger awhile / Soft lights and sweet music / Close your eyes / Deep night / Stella by starlight / One love / Let's face the music and dance / After the lights go down low / Change partners / There, I've said it again / In the still of the night / When lights are low.
Album: released on Capitol, Feb'84 by Capitol Records. Dist: EMI

LIVELY ONES, THE.
Album: released on Capitol, Apr'85 by Capitol Records. Dist: EMI

Cassette: released on Capitol, Apr'85 by Capitol Records. Dist: EMI

LOVE LETTERS.
Album: released on Bulldog, May'85 by Bulldog Records. Dist: President Distribution, Spartan, Swift, Taylor, H.R.

Cassette: released on Bulldog, May'85 by Bulldog Records. Dist: President Distribution, Spartan, Swift, Taylor, H.R.

Cassette: released on Memoir, Oct'85 by Memoir Records. Dist: PRT Distribution

MAGIC MOMENTS WITH VIC DAMONE.
Cassette: released on RCA, May'85 by RCA Records. Dist: RCA, Roots, Swift, Wellard, Chris, I & B, Solomon & Peres Distribution

MAGIC OF VIC DAMONE (THE).
Album: released on Arena, Feb'87 by Arena Records. Dist: Spartan

Cassette: released on Arena, Feb'87 by Arena Records. Dist: Spartan

MAKE SOMEONE HAPPY.
Album: released on RCA International (USA), Dec'81 by RCA Records. Dist: RCA

Cassette: released on RCA International (USA), Dec'81 by RCA Records. Dist: RCA

MY BABY LOVES TO SWING.
Tracks: / I'm nobody's baby / Everybody loves my baby(but my baby don't love nobody but me / You must have been a beautiful baby / Alright,

okay, you win / My melancholy baby / Let's sit this one out / My baby loves to swing / My baby just cares for me / Is you is, or is you ain't (ma baby) / Baby, baby all the time / Baby won't you please come home / Make this a slow goodbye.
Notes: A selection of popular standards from one of the great 'ladies men' of the 50's. This album, bouncing full of 'baby' songs, swings it's way through 'Everybody Loves My Baby', 'My Baby Loves To Swing', 'My Melancholy Baby', 'Baby Won't You Please Come Home', and many more. Accompanied by Jack Marshall's Music withy his spritely arrangements - a must for 50's enthusiasts.
Album: released on Capitol, May'86 by Capitol Records. Dist: EMI

Cassette: released on Capitol, May'86 by Capitol Records. Dist: EMI

NOW.
Album: released on RCA, Apr'81 by RCA Records. Dist: RCA, Roots, Swift, Wellard, Chris, I & B, Solomon & Peres Distribution

Cassette: released on RCA, Jan'84 by RCA Records. Dist: RCA, Roots, Swift, Wellard, Chris, I & B, Solomon & Peres Distribution

NOW AND FOREVER.
Album: released on RCA International, Dec'82

Cassette: released on RCA International, Dec'82

ON THE SOUTH SIDE OF CHICAGO.
Album: released on RCA, Feb'84 by RCA Records. Dist: RCA, Roots, Swift, Wellard, Chris, I & B, Solomon & Peres Distribution

Cassette: released on RCA, Feb'84 by RCA Records. Dist: RCA, Roots, Swift, Wellard, Chris, I & B, Solomon & Peres Distribution

PLEASURE OF HER COMPANY.
Single (7"): released on CBS, May'83 by CBS Records. Dist: CBS

SINGS THE GREAT SONGS.
Album: released on CBS Cameo, Mar'83 by CBS Records. Dist: CBS

Cassette: released on CBS Cameo, Mar'83 by CBS Records. Dist: CBS

STAY WITH ME.
Album: released on RCA, Feb'84 by RCA Records. Dist: RCA, Roots, Swift, Wellard, Chris, I & B, Solomon & Peres Distribution

Cassette: released on RCA, Feb'84 by RCA Records. Dist: RCA, Roots, Swift, Wellard, Chris, I & B, Solomon & Peres Distribution

STRANGE ENCHANTMENT.
Album: released on Capitol, Feb'84 by Capitol Records. Dist: EMI

TIME FOR LOVE,A.
Album: released on Cambra, Mar'85 by Cambra Records. Dist: IDS, Conifer

Cassette: released on Cambra, Mar'85 by Cambra Records. Dist: IDS, Conifer

VIC DAMONE & DICK HAYMES (see Haymes, Dick & Vic Damone) (Damone, Vic & Dick Haymes).

VIC DAMONE/ DICK HAYMES Great performers series.
Album: released on Jazz Greats, Jan'79 Dist: Swift

VIC DAMONE'S BEST.
Album: released on RCA, Jan'84 by RCA Records. Dist: RCA, Roots, Swift, Wellard, Chris, I & B, Solomon & Peres Distribution

Cassette: released on RCA, Jan'84 by RCA Records. Dist: RCA, Roots, Swift, Wellard, Chris, I & B, Solomon & Peres Distribution

WHY CAN'T I WALK AWAY.
Album: released on RCA, Feb'84 by RCA Records. Dist: RCA, Roots, Swift, Wellard, Chris, I & B, Solomon & Peres Distribution

Cassette: released on RCA, Feb'84 by RCA Records. Dist: RCA, Roots, Swift, Wellard, Chris, I & B, Solomon & Peres Distribution

Damon Silver

PUT YOUR HEAD ON MY SHOULDER.
Single (7"): released on AWA, Jun'84 by AWA Records. Dist: Pinnacle

Damron, Dick

LOST IN THE MUSIC.
Album: released on RCA, Jun'78 by RCA Records. Dist: RCA, Roots, Swift, Wellard, Chris, I & B, Solomon & Peres Distribution

NORTHWEST REBELLION (Damron, Dick/ Roy Warhurst).
Album: released on Westwood, Nov'76 by Westwood Records. Dist: Jazz Music, H.R. Taylor, JSU, Pinnacle, Ross Records

THOUSAND SONGS OF GLORY, A.
Album: released on Westwood, May'78 by Westwood Records. Dist: Jazz Music, H.R. Taylor, JSU, Pinnacle, Ross Records

Dan

CAN YOU DIG IT.
Single (7"): released on Meantime, Dec'86 Dist: Red Rhino, Cartel

Dana

ALL KINDS OF EVERTHING.
Single (7"): released on Decca, May'82 by Decca Records. Dist: Polygram

Single (7"): released on Old Gold, Sep'85 by Old Gold Records. Dist: Lightning, Jazz Music, Spartan, Counterpoint

BABY COME BACK TO ME.
Tracks: / Baby come back to me / Lipstick on your collar.
Single (7"): released on Ritz, Mar'87 by Outlet Records. Dist: Outlet, Prism Leisure Distribution, Record Services Distribution (Ireland), Roots

DARIO CAN YOU GET ME INTO STUDIO 54 (Dana & Gene).

Single (7"): released on Pinnacle, Nov'79 by Pinnacle Records. Dist: Pinnacle

DREAM LOVER.
Single (7"): released on Creole, Nov'81 by Creole Records. Dist: Rhino, PRT

I FEEL LOVE COMIN' ON.
Single (7"): released on Creole, Mar'82 by Creole Records. Dist: Rhino, PRT

IF I GIVE MY HEART TO YOU.
Single (7"): released on Ritz, Oct'85 by Outlet Records. Dist: Outlet, Prism Leisure Distribution, Record Services Distribution (Ireland), Roots

IF YOU REALLY LOVE ME.
Single (7"): released on Creole, Jan'83 by Creole Records. Dist: Rhino, PRT

I GIVE MY HEART TO YOU.
Album: released on Ritz, Nov'85 by Outlet Records. Dist: Outlet, Prism Leisure Distribution, Record Services Distribution (Ireland), Roots

Cassette: released on Ritz, Nov'85 by Outlet Records. Dist: Outlet, Prism Leisure Distribution, Record Services Distribution (Ireland), Roots

I WANT TO STAY HERE.
Tracks: / I want to stay here / Baby come back to me.
Single (7"): released on Ritz, Mar'86 by Outlet Records. Dist: Outlet, Prism Leisure Distribution, Record Services Distribution (Ireland), Roots

LET THERE BE LOVE.
Album: released on Word, May'85 by Word Records. Dist: Word Distribution, CBS

Cassette: released on Word, May'85 by Word Records. Dist: Word Distribution, CBS

LIPSTICK ON YOUR COLLAR.
Tracks: / Lipstick on your collar / Baby come back to me.
Single (7"): released on Ritz, Nov'86 by Outlet Records. Dist: Outlet, Prism Leisure Distribution, Record Services Distribution (Ireland), Roots

LITTLE THINGS MEAN A LOT.
Single (7"): released on Ritz, Jun'85 by Outlet Records. Dist: Outlet, Prism Leisure Distribution, Record Services Distribution (Ireland), Roots

PLEASE TELL HIM THAT I SAID HELLO.
Album: released on Spot, Feb'84 by Pickwick Records. Dist: H.R. Taylor, Lugtons

Cassette: released on Spot, Feb'84 by Pickwick Records. Dist: H.R. Taylor, Lugtons

TOTALLY YOURS.
Album: released on Word, May'85 by Word Records. Dist: Word Distribution, CBS

Cassette: released on Word, May'85 by Word Records. Dist: Word Distribution, CBS

WORLD OF DANA, THE.
Album: released on World of Learning, Apr'75 by World Of Learning Records. Dist: World Of Learning

Cassette: released on Decca, '74 by Decca Records. Dist: Polygram

YER MAN (Dana & N.Ireland World Cup Squad 82).

Single (7"): released on Towerbell, May'82 by Towerbell Records. Dist: EMI

YOU NEVER GAVE ME YOUR LOVE.
Single (7"): released on Creole, Aug'82 by Creole Records. Dist: Rhino, PRT

Dana Dane

CINDERFELLA DANNA DANE.
Single (12"): released on Profile (USA), Aug'87 Dist: Pinnacle

Danball, Totsuzen

LOL COXHILL WITH TOTSUZEN DANBALL (Danball, Totsuzen & Lol Coxhill).
Tracks: / Lol Coxhill with Totsuzen Danball.
Album: released on Floor (Japan), Oct'86 by Floor (Japan) Records. Dist: Essex Record Distributors Ltd.

Dance...

DANCE BOX Various artists (Various Artists).
Album: released on Impact, Sep'84 by Ace Records. Dist: Rough Trade, Pinnacle, Swift, Backs, Counterpoint, Jungle, Hotshot, Cartel

Cassette: released on Impact, Sep'84 by Ace Records. Dist: Rough Trade, Pinnacle, Swift, Backs, Counterpoint, Jungle, Hotshot, Cartel

DANCE CAN'T LAST NICE WITHOUT WE (Various Artists).
Album: released on O.T.Teys, Jul'87

DANCE CHART H (Various Artists).
Notes: Inc. Jackie Wilson, Taffy, Mel & Kim.
Album: released on Telstar, Mar'87 by Telstar Records. Dist: RCA Distribution

Cassette: released on Telstar, Mar'87 by Telstar Records. Dist: RCA Distribution

DANCE COMPILATION Harious artists (Various Artists).
Album: released on Survival, Sep'84 by Survival Records. Dist: Backs, Cartel Distribution

DANCE CRAZE Original film soundtrack (Various Artists).
Album: released on Two-Tone, Feb'81 by Chrysalis Records. Dist: H.R. Taylor

Cassette: released on Two-Tone, Feb'81 by Chrysalis Records. Dist: H.R. Taylor

DANCE DANCE DANCE Various artists (Various Artists).
Album: released on Starblend, Jan'86 by Starblend Records. Dist: PRT Distribution

Cassette: released on Starblend, Jan'86 by Starblend Records. Dist: PRT Distribution

Album: released on K-Tel, Sep'81 by K-Tel Records. Dist: Record Merchandisers Distribution, Taylors, Terry Blood Distribution, Wynd-Up Distribution, Relay Distribution, Pickwick Distribution, Solomon & Peres Distribution, Polygram

Cassette: released on K-Tel, Sep'81 by K-Tel Records. Dist: Record Merchandisers Distribution, Taylors, Terry Blood Distribution, Wynd-Up Distribution, Relay Distribution, Pickwick Distribution, Solomon & Peres Distribution, Polygram

DANCE FOREVER Various artists (Various Artists).
Album: released on EMI (France), Aug'83 by EMI Records. Dist: Conifer

Boxed set: released on EMI (France), Aug'83 by EMI Records. Dist: Conifer

Double Album: released on EMI (France), Aug'83 by EMI Records. Dist: Conifer

DANCE MACHINE Carious original artists (Various Artists).
Album: released on Motown, '82 by Motown Records. Dist: BMG Distribution

Cassette: released on Motown, '82 by Motown Records. Dist: BMG Distribution

DANCE MANIA VOL.1 (Various Artists).
Album: released on Needle, Jun'87 Dist: Pinnacle

Cassette: released on Needle, Jun'87 Dist: Pinnacle

DANCEMASTER - VOLUME 1 Various artists (Various Artists).
Album: released on Decca, Dec'83 by Decca Records. Dist: Polygram

Cassette: released on Decca, Dec'83 by Decca Records. Dist: Polygram

DANCE PARTY Various artists (Various Artists).
Album: released on PRT, Dec'83 by PRT Records. Dist: PRT

Cassette: released on PRT, Dec'83 by PRT Records. Dist: PRT

DANCE TO IT Various artists (Various Artists).
Album: released on Lost Moments, Mar'85 Dist: Backs, Cartel

IN LUST.
Single (12"): released on Statik, Aug'81 Dist: Rough Trade Distribution, Stage One Distribution

SHE LIKES TO BEAT.
Single (12"): released on Gogoroo, Jul'80 by Gogoroo Records. Dist: Rough Trade

Dance Band

NO SOUL.
Single (7"): released on Cool King, Nov'81 Dist: Pinnacle

Dance Band Days

DANCE BAND DAYS - BEST OF VOL.1 (Various Artists).
Compact disc: released on Dance Band Days, Jul'87 Dist: Geoff's Records International

Compact disc: released on Dance Band Days, Jul'87 Dist: Geoff's Records International

Dance Bands

DANCE BANDS ON THE AIR - VOLUME 1 Various original bands (Various bands).
Album: released on BBC, Nov'76 by BBC Records & Tapes. Dist: EMI, PRT, Pye

DANCE BANDS ON THE AIR - VOLUME 2 Various original bands (Various bands).
Album: released on BBC, Nov'76 by BBC Records & Tapes. Dist: EMI, PRT, Pye

Dance, Cadence

DANCE, CADENCE Various artists (Various Artists).
Album: released on Globestyle, Mar'85 by Ace Records. Dist: Projection

Dance Chapter

ANONYMITY.
Single (7"): released on Armageddon, Dec'80 by Armageddon Records. Dist: Revolver, Cartel, Pinnacle

CHAPTER II.
Single (7"): released on 4AD, Nov'81 by 4AD Records. Dist: Rough Trade

Dance Floor Hits

DANCE DECADE 1973-1983 Various artists (Various Artists).
Boxed set: released on Streetsounds, Nov'85

Boxed set: released on Streetsounds, Nov'85

DANCE FLOOR HITS (Various Artists).
Notes: Artists include Billy Ocean/Samantha Fox
Album: released on Jive, Sep'86 by Zomba Records. Dist: RCA, PRT, CBS

Cassette: released on Jive, Sep'86 by Zomba Records. Dist: RCA, PRT, CBS

Dance Hall...

DANCE HALL COMBINATION Various artists (Various Artists).
Single (12"): released on Striker Lee, Nov'84 by Striker Lee Records. Dist: Jetstar Distribution

DANCE HALL LIFE (Various Artists).
Double Album: released on Street Corner, Dec'85

DANCE HALL SESSION (Various Artists).
Album: released on R.A.S, Jul'87 by Greensleeves Records. Dist: RCA

Dance Hits

DANCE HITS '86 (Various Artists).
Album: released on K-Tel, Sep'86 by K-Tel Records. Dist: Record Merchandisers Distribution, Taylors, Terry Blood Distribution, Wynd-Up Distribution, Relay Distribution, Pickwick Distribution, Solomon & Peres Distribution, Polygram

Cassette: released on K-Tel, Sep'86 by K-Tel Records. Dist: Record Merchandisers Distribution, Taylors, Terry Blood Distribution, Wynd-Up Distribution, Relay Distribution, Pickwick Distribution, Solomon & Peres Distribution, Polygram

DANCE HITS ALBUM (Various Artists).
Tracks: / Say I'm your number one / Caribbean queen / Frankie / All fall down / Treat her like a lady / Rhythm of the night / Body and soul / Knock on wood / Automatic / Nightshift / Yah mo b there / Your personal touch / Turn it up / Let it all blow / Mated.
Album: released on Towerbell, Jan'86 by Towerbell Records. Dist: EMI

DANCE HITS VOL.II (Various Artists).
Album: released on Towerbell, Jul'86 by Towerbell Records. Dist: EMI

Cassette: released on Towerbell, Jul'86 by Towerbell Records. Dist: EMI

Dance I.D.
DANCE I.D.NO.1 (Various Artists).
Tracks: / Love bizarre, A / Let my people go / Heat of heat, The / Loves gonna get you / Color

of success / It doesn't really matter / My magic man / Funky sensation / Don't cha go nowhere.
Album: released on WEA, Apr'86 by WEA Records. Dist: WEA

Cassette: released on WEA, Apr'86 by WEA Records. Dist: WEA

DANCE I.D.NO.2 (Various Artists).
Tracks: / Sex machine / Stop and think / Doo wa ditty / Shante / Bambaataa's theme / Two of hearts / Cool / You're a star.
Album: released on I.D., Oct'86 by I.D. Records. Dist: Revolver, Cartel

Cassette: released on I.D., Oct'86 by I.D. Records. Dist: Revolver, Cartel

Dance In Reverse
DANCE ME TO THE FLOOR.
Single (7"): released on Atlantic, Nov'86 by WEA Records. Dist: WEA

Single (12"): released on Atlantic, Sep'86 by WEA Records. Dist: WEA

Dance Like A Mother
PRIVATE NUMBER.
Tracks: / Private number / Physical love.
Single (7"): released on Virgin, Jul'87 by Virgin Records. Dist: EMI, Virgin Distribution

Single (12"): released on Virgin, Jul'87 by Virgin Records. Dist: EMI, Virgin Distribution

YOU AIN'T SO TOUGH.
Tracks: / You ain't so tough / Love or Lust.
Single (7"): released on Virgin, Feb'87 by Virgin Records. Dist: EMI, Virgin Distribution

Single (12"): released on Virgin, Feb'87 by Virgin Records. Dist: EMI, Virgin Distribution

Dance Mix
DANCE MIX - DANCE HITS Various artists (Various Artists).
Album: released on Epic, Jun'83 by CBS Records. Dist: CBS

Cassette: released on Epic, Jun'83 by CBS Records. Dist: CBS

DANCE MIX - DANCE HITS VOULUME 2 Various artists (Various Artists).
Album: released on Epic, Sep'83 by CBS Records. Dist: CBS

Cassette: released on Epic, Sep'83 by CBS Records. Dist: CBS

DANCE MIX - DANCE HITS VOLUME 3 Various artists (Various Artists).
Album: released on Epic, '84 by CBS Records. Dist: CBS

Cassette: released on Epic, '84 by CBS Records. Dist: CBS

DANCE MIX - DANCE HITS VOLUME 4 Various artists (Various Artists).
Album: released on Epic, Jun'84 by CBS Records. Dist: CBS

Cassette: released on Epic, Jun'84 by CBS Records. Dist: CBS

Dance Motto
TELL JACK.
Single (7"): released on Rhythm King, Jun'87 Dist: Rough Trade, Cartel

Single (12"): released on Rhythm King, Jun'87

Dist: Rough Trade, Cartel

Dance Reaction
DISCO TRAIN.
Single (7"): released on Carrere, May'82 by Carrere Records. Dist: PRT, Spartan

Single (12"): released on Carrere, May'82 by Carrere Records. Dist: PRT, Spartan

Dance The...
DANCE THE PASO DOBLE Various artists (Various Artists).
Album: released on Polygram, Sep'85 by Polygram Records. Dist: Polygram

Cassette: released on Polygram, Sep'85 by Polygram Records. Dist: Polygram

DANCE THE TANGO Various artists (Various Artists).
Album: released on Polygram, Sep'85 by Polygram Records. Dist: Polygram

Cassette: released on Polygram, Sep'85 by Polygram Records. Dist: Polygram

Dancetime Orchestra
DANCETIME YEARS VOL.2.
Album: released on Savoy, May'86

LANCERS & QUADRILLES.
Album: released on Savoy, May'86

TIME FOR OLD TIME.
Album: released on Savoy, May'86

Dance Trance
DO THE DANCE.
Tracks: / Do the dance / Sail away.
Single (7"): released on CBS, Jul'86 by CBS Records. Dist: CBS

Single (12"): released on CBS, Jul'86 by CBS Records. Dist: CBS

IT TAKES TWO.
Single (7"): released on Rollerball, Feb'85 Dist: EMI through Priority

Single (12"): released on Rollerball, Feb'85 Dist: EMI through Priority

Dancette
GOING GREEN.
Single (7"): released on Bel, Oct'82

Dance With A Stranger
DANCE WITH A STRANGER Original soundtrack.
Album: released on Compact Organisation, Feb'85 Dist: PRT

D'Ancey, Graham Philip
ALLUMA.
Album: released on Stage One, Jul'83 by Stage One Records. Dist: Stage One Distribution

LISTEN.
Single (7"): released on Blue September, Jun'82 Dist: Pinnacle

SACRED HEART.
Single (7"): released on Blue September, Apr'82 Dist: Pinnacle

Dancin'
DANCIN' (Various Artists).
Album: released on In Recordings, Dec'86 Dist: RCA, DMS

Cassette: released on In Recordings, Dec'86 Dist: RCA, DMS

Album: released on Telstar, Nov'82 by Telstar Records. Dist: RCA Distribution

Cassette: released on Telstar, Nov'82 by Telstar Records. Dist: RCA Distribution

DANCIN' AND ROMANCIN' (Various Artists).
Tracks: / Up on the mountain / Down off the mountain / You ain't ready / Crazy over you / Feeling alright / Stop / Get lost / Tears on my pillow / Caddy bo / Blues in the letter / Secret love / For all we know / Ozeta / Hurry home baby / Lonely one, The / Now that it's over / I was wrong / Hellow dear.
Album: released on Charly, Jan'86 by Charly Records. Dist: Charly, Cadillac

Dancing Did
AND DID THOSE FEET.
Album: released on Kamera, Nov'82

BADGER BOYS.
Single (7"): released on Kamera, Feb'83

DANCING DID (THE).
Single (7"): released on Fruit And Veg, Oct'79 by Fruit And Veg Records. Dist: Rough Trade, Cartel

GREEN MAN & THE MARCH OF THE BUNGALOWS.
Single (7"): released on Kamera, May'82

LOST PLATOON.
Single (7"): released on Stiff, Nov'81 by Stiff Records. Dist: EMI, Record Services Distribution (Ireland)

Dancing Hoods
12 JEALOUS ROSES.
Tracks: / Peasure / Impossible years / Build a house / Blue letter / Girls problems / Surfing all over the world / Bye bye Jim / Watching you sleep / (Take my) chances / She may call you up tonight / Wild and the lonely.
Album: released on Fun After All, Jul'86 Dist: Pinnacle

BLUE LETTER.
Tracks: / Blue letter / Antenna's up / Pleasure.
Single (7"): released on Fun After All, Jun'86 Dist: Pinnacle

Single (12"): released on Fun After All, Jun'86

Dist: Pinnacle

Dancing In Exile
LIKE A TRAIN.
Single (7"): released on Lambs To The Slaughter, Feb'86 by Prism Records. Dist: Pinnacle, Red Rhino, Cartel

Single (12"): released on Lambs To The Slaughter, Feb'86 by Prism Records. Dist: Pinnacle, Red Rhino, Cartel

Dancing Princess
DANCING PRINCESS Various artists (Various Artists).
Cassette: released on Anvil, Jul'82 Dist: Anvil

Dancing The Night Away
DANCING THE NIGHT AWAY (Various Artists).
Tracks: / On the sunny side of the street / I was true / Ya got love / There's a ring around the moon / Lazybones / In a little rocky valley / What more can I ask? / Dancing time / I never had a chance / Stardust / You're looking for romance, I'm looking for love / Supposin' / Moon over Miami / You're telling me / My heart's to let / La-di-da-di-da / Old man of the mountain, The / Crying my heart out for you / I'm keeping company / Ridin' high / Beat me daddy, eight to a bar / Waves of the ocean are whisp'ring goodnight / Will you remember (sweetheart) / One meatball / Rehearsing a lullaby / Snakehips swing / New swing alphabet, The / I'll buy that dream / Sweetheart of all my dreams / Sambi-na / I got rhythm / All through the day / Gnat jump / Nathering around / I'll dance at your wedding / Dark town strutters' ball, The / Get happy / My wubba dolly / What do I have to do (to make you love me) / Quien no lorra no mama.
Notes: This is a double album and a double cassette.
Double Album: released on Decca (London), Mar'87 by Decca Records. Dist: Polygram, IMS

Cassette: released on Decca (London), Mar'87 by Decca Records. Dist: Polygram, IMS

Dancing 'Til Dawn
DANCING 'TIL DAWN Various artists (Various Artists).
Album: released on Kent, Oct'84 by Ace Records. Dist: Pinnacle

Dancin' Party
DANCIN' PARTY Various artists (Various Artists).
Cassette: released on Pickwick (Ditto series), Jul'82

DOWN STREET.
Single (7"): released on Magnet, Jul'83 by Magnet Records. Dist: BMG

Single (12"): released on Magnet, Jul'83 by Magnet Records. Dist: BMG

Dando Shaft
KINGDOM.
Album: released on Rubber, Jun'82 by Rubber Records. Dist: Roots Distribution, Projection Distribution, Jazz Music Distribution, Celtic Music Distribution, JSU Distribution, Spartan Distribution

D'Andrea, Franco
MADE IN ITALY.
Album: released on Red, Apr'83 Dist: Projection, Jazz Horizons

Dandridge, Putney
CHRONOLOGICAL STUDY, A Volume 1.
Album: released on Rarities, Apr'81

CHRONOLOGICAL STUDY, A - VOLUME 2.
Album: released on Rarities, Apr'81

CHRONOLOGICAL STUDY, A - VOLUME 3.
Album: released on Rarities, Apr'81

Dandy Flash
MUSIC FOR DANCING.
Single (7"): released on Page One, Mar'83 by Page, Larry. Dist: PRT, Spartan

Dandy, Jim
READY AS HELL.
Album: released on Heavy Metal America, Nov'84 by FM-Revolver Records. Dist: EMI

Picture disc album: released on Heavy Metal, Aug'85 by FM-Revolver Records. Dist: EMI

Single (7"): released on Heavy Metal, Aug'85 by FM-Revolver Records. Dist: EMI

Dane, Clem
GREAT DANE (THE).
Album: released on Klub, Sep'80

Dist: Pinnacle

Cassette: released on Klub, Sep'80

Dane, Glen
GLEN DANE'S GREATEST HITS.
Album: released on Klub, Apr'78

Daneman, Paul
COUNT OF MONTE CRISTO Read by Paul Daneman.
Cassette: released on Kiddy Kassettes, Aug'77

Dan & Farmers
COUNTRY BOY.
Album: released on Homespun(Ireland), Nov'76 by Outlet Records. Dist: Outlet

DOWN ON THE FARM.
Album: released on Homespun(Ireland), '75 by Outlet Records. Dist: Outlet

Danger
DANGER.
Album: released on Mausoleum, Oct'84 by Mausoleum Records. Dist: Pinnacle

Dangermouse
DANGERMOUSE & PUBLIC ENEMY NO.1 Various artists (Various Artists).
Cassette: released on Tempo, Aug'84 by Warwick Records. Dist: Multiple Sound Distributors

DANGERMOUSE - THE GREAT BONE IDOL Various artists (Various Artists).
Cassette: released on Tempo, Aug'84 by Warwick Records. Dist: Multiple Sound Distributors

DANGERMOUSE & THE PLANET OF THE CATS Various artists (Various Artists).
Cassette: released on Tempo, Aug'84 by Warwick Records. Dist: Multiple Sound Distributors

TAKE IT EASY.
Single (7"): released on Hot Rod, Mar'84 by Hot Rod Records. Dist: Jetstar

Dangerous Girls
MAN IN THE GLASS.
Single (7"): released on Human, Nov'80 Dist: Roots, Stage One

STEP OUT.
Single (7"): released on Human, Apr'81 Dist: Roots, Stage One

Dangerously close
DANGEROUSLY CLOSE (Various Artists).
Album: released on Enigma, Nov'86 by Enigma Records. Dist: Rough Trade, Cartel, EMI

Danger Youth
SIXTEEN.
Tracks: / Sixteen / Sixteen (version).
Single (12"): released on Trouble Music, May'86 by Ragin' Lion. Dist: Jetstar

Dang, Ken
KEN DANG.
Album: released on Strawberry-Uniton, Dec'83

D'Ango, Pino
MA QUALE IDEA.
Single (7"): released on System, May'82 Dist: ERC Records

Single (12"): released on System, May'82 Dist: ERC Records

Daniel Goleman
MEDITATION.
Cassette: released on Psychology Today, Oct'81

Daniel, Jeffrey
AC-DC.
Single (7"): released on Polydor, Mar'84 by Polydor Records. Dist: Polygram, Polydor

Single (12"): released on Polydor, Mar'84 by Polydor Records. Dist: Polygram, Polydor

Daniel Kamua Orchestra
DENYAFRICA (VOL.1).

KENYAFRICA (VOL.1).
Album: released on Playasound, Mar'79 Dist: Conifer, Discovery

Danlelle, Suzanne
CHRISTMAS STOCKINGS.
Single (7"): released on Grab, Dec'82 by Grab Records. Dist: Pinnacle

Daniels, Bebe

NOSTALGIA TRIP TO THE STARS 1920-50 (Daniels, Bebe & others).
Album: released on Monmouth, Apr'79

Daniels, Billy

AT THE CRESCENDO.
Album: released on Pye, May'78

Daniels, Charlie

NIGHT RIDER (Daniels, Charlie Band).
Album:

POWDER KEG (Daniels, Charlie Band).
Tracks: / Bogged down in love with you / Bottom line / Love pouring out of me / Saturday night USA / Dance with me / Powder keg / What she do to me / Trapped in the city / Stay with me / Juanita.
Album: released on Epic, Sep'87 by CBS Records. Dist: CBS

Cassette: released on Epic, Sep'87 by CBS Records. Dist: CBS

Daniels, Charlie Band

ME AND THE BOYS.
Tracks: / Me and the boys / Still hurtin' me / Talking to the moon / Class of 63 / American farmer / M.I.A. / American rock and roll / Ever changing lady / Louisiana fai dodo / Drinkin' my baby goodbye.
Album: released on Epic, Jan'86 by CBS Records. Dist: CBS

Cassette: released on Epic, Jan'86 by CBS Records. Dist: CBS

Daniels, Dennis

SOMETHING BIG.
Album: released on MBC Jazz, May'77

Daniels, Eddie

BREAKTHROUGH.
Tracks: / Solfeggietto / Metamorphosis.
Album: released on GRP (USA), Apr'86 by GRP Records (USA). Dist: IMS, Polygram

Compact disc: released on GRP (USA), Apr'86 by GRP Records (USA). Dist: IMS, Polygram

BRIEF ENCOUNTER.
Album: released on Muse, Apr'81 by Peerless Records.

TO BIRD WITH LOVE.
Notes: A beautiful tribute to Charlie Parker from the master clarinettist Eddie Daniels who received rave reviews for his debut GRP album 'Break-through'. Supported by: Fred Hersch-piano/Al Foster-drums/John Patitucci-bass. CD contains an extra track featuring Roger Kellaway on piano.
Album: released on GRP (USA), May'87 by GRP Records (USA). Dist: IMS, Polygram
Cat. no: **GRP 91034**
Cassette: released on GRP (USA), May'87 by GRP Records (USA). Dist: IMS, Polygram
Cat. no: **GRPM 91034**
Compact disc: released on GRP (USA), May'87 by GRP Records (USA). Dist: IMS, Polygram

Daniels, Jill

RASTAFARIAN DELIGHT.
Single (7"): released on Jade, Aug'82 by Jade Records. Dist: Jade

Daniels, Joe

STEPPIN' OUT TO SWING (Daniels, Joe & his Hotshots).
Album: released on Saville, Sep'84 by Conifer Records. Dist: Conifer

Daniels, Julius

ATLANTA BLUES 1927-30 (Daniels, Julius & Lil McClintock).
Tracks: / My mama was a sailor / Ninety nine year blues / I'm gonna tell God how you doin' / Slippin' and slidin' up the golden street / Can't put the bridle on that mule this mornin' / Richmond blues / Crow jane blues / Furniture man / Don't think I'm santa calus / Sow good seeds / Mother called her child to her dying bed.
Notes: The repertoires of Julius Daniels and Lil McClintock were more in older and previously little researched area of 'Songsters'. Paul Oliver has now carefully studied this area and published his revealing book 'Songsters & Saints' and Matchbox has issued two accompanying sets to this (MSEX 2001/2, 2003/4). The current album explores the output of these two obscure performers by including their complete recorded works. Alot more interst is being shown in the non-blues, and blues-fringe elements of the Race records catalogues and this issue is a valuable addition of the material available.
Album: released on Matchbox, Feb'86 by Saydisc Records. Dist: Roots, Projection, Jazz Music, Celtic Music

Daniels, Maxine

EVERY NIGHT ABOUT THIS TIME.
Album: released on Calligraph, Mar'86 by Calligraph Records. Dist: PRT

Daniels, Mike

1957-1959 (Daniels, Mike Delta Jazzmen).
Tracks: / Milenberg joys / You're just my type / At a Georgia camp meeting / Riverboat shuffle / Weather bird rag / Baby doll / Aunt Hagars blues / I'm confessin' / You made me love you / Blues are brewing / When you and I were young Maggie / That's my weakness now / Don't forget to mess around.
Album: released on Harlequin, Jun'86 by Harlequin Records. Dist: Swift, Jazz Music, Wellard, Chris, Taylor, H.R.

Danielson

WIDE POINT, THE (Danielson/Mangelsdorff/Jones).

Danielson, Palle

TRILOGUE-LIVE (Danielson, Palle/Mangelsdorff/Pastorius).

Daniels, Paul

MAGIC CIRCLE RECORD, THE.
Album: released on Technical, Dec'80 Dist: Stage One Distribution

Daniels, Philip

ALIBI OF GUILT.
Cassette: released on Soundings, Apr'85 Dist: Soundings

GOLDMINE LONDON W1.
Cassette: released on Soundings, Apr'85 Dist: Soundings

Daniels, Roly

ALMOST SOMEONE.
Single (7"):

BECAUSE I LOVE YOU.
Tracks: / Because I love you.
Single (7"): released on Mint, Sep'86 by Emerald Records. Dist: Ross Distribution, PRT Distribution, Solomon & Peres Distribution

BEST OF..., THE.
Album: released on Harp(Ireland), Oct'81 by Pickwick Records. Dist: Taylors

HELLO DARLIN.
Single (7"): released on Homespun(Ireland), Jun'84 by Outlet Records. Dist: Outlet
Cat. no: **HS 081**
Single (7"):

HE STOPPED LOVIN' HER TODAY.
Single (7"): released on Emerald (Ireland), Apr'84 by Emerald Records. Dist: I & B, Ross, PRT

I CAN FLY HIGHER.
Tracks: / Wind beneath my wings (The) / She's gonna win your heart / Part of me / Hey Lord it's me / More of you / Touch me / Only a lonely heart knows / If all the magic is gone / I'm the one who's breaking up / Seven spanish angels / Let's leave the lights on tonight / Womans touch, A.
Album:

I FEEL LIKE LOVING YOU AGAIN.
Single (7"):

IT'S ALL IN THE GAME.
Tracks: / It's all in the game / Sometimes when we touch.
Single (7"):

I WISH YOU LOVE.
Tracks: / Sometimes when we touch / Someone I ain't / I will love you all my life / You've lost that lovin' feelin' / Hello Darlin' / Rest your love on me / Stand by me / What's forever for / I will always love you / Together again / He stopped lovin' her today / Happy the clown.
Notes: All MCPS/produced by:George doherty and John Anderson at Hydepark studios.
Album:

Cassette:

LAST CHEATERS WALTZ.
Single (7"):

LET'S FALL IN LOVE.
Tracks: / Ain't no california / If you've got ten minutes-lets fall in love / Friend,Lover,Wife / Almost Someone / Your Eyes / Normal Crazy Person / Do you ever fool around / Mr. Jones / Heart on fire / Devil went down to Georgia, The / I'm comin' home mama / Sweet love.
Notes: Side 1/2 =MCPS (p) 1980
Album: released on Emerald (Ireland), Nov'84 by Emerald Records. Dist: I & B, Ross, PRT

Album: released on Emerald (Ireland), Nov'84 by Emerald Records. Dist: I & B, Ross, PRT

LET'S LEAVE THE LIGHTS ON TONIGHT.
Tracks: / Let's leave the lights on tonight.
Single (7"):

LIKE STRANGERS (Daniels, Roly & Ann Williamson).
Single (7"): released on Mint, Feb'83 by Emerald Records. Dist: Ross Distribution, PRT Distribution, Solomon & Peres Distribution
Cat. no: **CHEW 74**

ROLY DANIELS.
Album: released on Emerald (Ireland), Apr'84 by Emerald Records. Dist: I & B, Ross, PRT
Cat. no: **GES 1229**
Cassette: released on Emerald (Ireland), Apr'84 by Emerald Records. Dist: I & B, Ross, PRT

SOMEONE I AIN'T.
Single (7"):

Daniels, Rory

I WILL LOVE YOU ALL MY LIFE.
Single (7"):

Daniels, Trevor

TIME WAS....
Album: released on Grosvenor, Feb'82 by Grosvenor Records. Dist: Taylors

Danish Accordion Ensemble

DET DANSKE HARMONIKA ENSEMBLE.

MARCHENFARBEN.
Album: released on ARC (Accordion Records), '84 Dist: Accordion Record Club

Danish Radio Big Band

BY JONES, I THINK WE'VE GOT IT.
Album: released on Metronome (Denmark), Jun'81 Dist: Jazz Music Distribution

GOOD TIME WAS HAD BY ALL, A.
Album: released on Metronome (Denmark), Jun'81 Dist: Jazz Music Distribution

LIVE AT MONTMARTRE.
Album: Dist: Jazz Music Distribution, Jazz Horizons

Danko, Harold

INK AND WATER.
Tracks: / Snow blossoms / Sand storms / Dew and petals / High mountains pines / High mountain pines / Children's walking song / Footbridge over the rushing stream / Animals on a four screen landscape / Leaves in a rock garden / Play song / Across the cliffs / Sunrise watch / Walk at dawn / Willow,wind and water / Roots and Vines / Icicles in the cave / Reflections in a pond / Snow Blossoms.
Album: released on Sunnyside (USA), Feb'86 Dist: Mole Jazz Distribution, Conifer Distribution

Dankworth, Johnny

1953-58 FEATURING CLEO LANE.
Album: released on EMI Retrospect, Aug'84 by EMI Records. Dist: EMI
Cat. no: **EG 260 187 1**
Cassette: released on EMI Retrospect, Aug'84 by EMI Records. Dist: EMI

BOP AT CLUB 11 (Dankworth, John Quartet/Ronnie Scott boptet).
Notes: The complete 1949 concert.
Album: released on Esquire, Jun'86 by Titan International Productions. Dist: Jazz Music, Cadillac Music, Swift, Wellard, Chris, Backs, Rough Trade, Revolver, Nine Mile

FAIR OAK FUSIONS (Dankworth, Johnny & Julian Lloyd Webber).
Album: released on Sepia, Jan'83 by Sepia Records. Dist: PRT

Cassette: released on Sepia, Jan'83 by Sepia Records. Dist: PRT

GET HAPPY (Dankworth, John Seven & Cleo Lane).
Album: released on Esquire, May'86 by Titan International Productions. Dist: Jazz Music, Cadillac Music, Swift, Wellard, Chris, Backs, Rough Trade, Revolver, Nine Mile

GONE HITCHIN (Dankworth, Johnny Quintet).
Album: released on Sepia, May'83 by Sepia Records. Dist: PRT

Cassette: released on Sepia, May'83 by Sepia Records. Dist: PRT

In retrospect

LOVER & HIS LASS, A (Dankworth, Johnny & Cleo Laine).
Album: released on Esquire, Dec'76 by Titan International Productions. Dist: Jazz Music, Cadillac Music, Swift, Wellard, Chris, Backs, Rough Trade, Revolver, Nine Mile

METRO.
Album: released on Repertoire, Nov'83

OCTAVIUS (Dankworth, Johnny/Paul Hart Octet).
Album: released on Sepia, Apr'83 by Sepia Records. Dist: PRT

SYMPHONIC FUSIONS (Dankworth, Johnny & The London Symphony Orchestra).
Tracks: / Paganini in perpetuo / Ev'ry time we say goodbye / Decline and fall of a bridge / Afterglow / Sing, sing, sing / Further experiments with mice / Shadow of your smile / African waltz / Fantasia enigma / Paganini in perpetuo / Decline and fall of a bridge / Fantasia enigma / Further experiments with mice / Shadow off your smile.
Compact disc: released on Pickwick International inc, Jan'86 by Pickwick International Inc.Records (USA). Dist: Pickwick Distribution, Taylor, H.R., PRT

Album: released on Pickwick, Aug'86 by Pickwick Records. Dist: Pickwick Distribution, Prism Leisure Distribution,

Cassette: released on Pickwick, Aug'86 by Pickwick Records. Dist: Pickwick Distribution, Prism Leisure Distribution,

WHAT THE DICKENS (Dankworth, Johnny & his Orchestra).

ZODIAC VARIATIONS (Dankworth, Johnny & his Orchestra).
Album: released on Sepia, Jul'83 by Sepia Records. Dist: PRT

DannIebelle

LET ME HAVE A DREAM.
Album: released on Sparrow, May'82 by Word Records. Dist: Spartan
Cat. no: **BIRD 113**
Cassette: released on Sparrow, May'82 by Word Records. Dist: Spartan

Danny Boys

DAYS OF THE WEEK.
Tracks: / Days of the week.
Single (12"): released on Ugly Man, Feb'87 Dist: Cartel

LIVE IN SWEDEN WITH CHORALERNA.
Album: released on Sparrow, May'82 by Word Records. Dist: Spartan

Cassette: released on Sparrow, May'82 by Word Records. Dist: Spartan

Danny-D-Collision

PARTY PEOPLE.
Single (7"): released on Elite, Jun'85 Dist: PRT

Single (12"): released on Elite, Jun'85 Dist: PRT

Danny & Dusty

LOST WEEKEND(THE).
Album: released on Zippo, Nov'85

Danny & Shirley

HEY PAULA.
Single (12"): released on Black Jack, Jul'82 Dist: Jetstar, Spartan

Single (7"): released on Old Gold, Jul'82 by Old Gold Records. Dist: Lightning, Jazz Music, Spartan, Counterpoint

Danny & The Juniors

AT THE HOP.
Tracks: / At the hop / Rock and roll is here to stay.
Single (7"): released on MCA, Jul'87 by MCA Records. Dist: Polygram, MCA

Danny & the Mongoose Team

BMX BOYS.
Single (7"): released on Gipsy, Nov'83 by Gipsy Records. Dist: PRT

Danny & the Nogoodniks

BIKE.
Single (7"): released on Chrysalis, Dec'82 by Chrysalis Records. Dist: CBS

Danny Wilson

DAVY.
Tracks: / Davy / I won't forget / Pleasure to pleasure.
Single (7"): released on Virgin, May'87 by Virgin Records. Dist: EMI, Virgin Distribution
Cat. no: **VS 965**
Single (12"): released on Virgin, May'87 by Virgin Records. Dist: EMI, Virgin Distribution

Danovak

CARAMBA (LET'S DO THE RUMBA).
Single (7"): released on Plaza, Jan'84 by Plaza Records. Dist: Spartan

Single (12"): released on Plaza, Jan'84 by Plaza Records. Dist: Spartan

Danovak & Co.

MAGDALENA.
Single (7"): released on Plaza, Jun'85 by Plaza

Records. Dist: Spartan

QUEEN OF ILLUSIONS
Tracks: / Queen of illusions / Queen of illusions (hot rock).
Single (7"): released on Plaza, Jul'87 by Plaza

Records. Dist: Spartan

WHAT HAVE YOU DONE TO MY HEART.
Single (7"): released on Plaza, Nov'82 by Plaza Records. Dist: Spartan
Cat. no: PLAZA 2
Single (12"): by Plaza Records. Dist: Spartan Deleted Nov'82.

Dansan Orchestra
DREAM LOVER.
Album: released on Dansan, May'83 by Spartan Records. Dist: Spartan

Danse Macabre
OH NO NOT I.
Single (7"): released on Hexagon, Jul'83 Dist: Hexagon

Danse Society
CLOCK.
Single (7"): released on Society, Jul'83 by Arista Records. Dist: Polygram

DOLPHINS.
Single (12"): released on KSV, Aug'81 by Kingsley Sound & Vision. Dist: Kingsley Sound & Vision Distribution

HEAVEN IS WAITING.
Album: released on Society, Feb'84 by Arista Records. Dist: Polygram

Cassette: released on Society, Feb'84 by Arista Records. Dist: Polygram

HOLD ON To what you've got.
Tracks: / Hold on / Danse mood / Heaven is waiting / Dance mix.
Single (7"): released on Society, Feb'86 by Arista Records. Dist: Polygram

Single (12"): released on Arista, Feb'86 by Arista Records. Dist: RCA

LOOKING THROUGH.
Album: released on Society, Aug'86 by Arista Records. Dist: Polygram

NO SHAME IN DEATH.
Single (12"): released on Society, Jul'83 by Arista Records. Dist: Polygram

SAY IT AGAIN.
Single (7"): released on Society, Jun'85 by Arista Records. Dist: Polygram

Single (12"): released on Society, Jun'85 by Arista Records. Dist: Polygram

SEDUCTION.
Album: released on Society, Oct'82 by Arista Records. Dist: Polygram

SOMEWHERE.
Single (7"): released on Society, Mar'83 by Arista Records. Dist: Polygram

Single (12"): released on Society, Mar'83 by Arista Records. Dist: Polygram

WE'RE SO HAPPY.
Single (12"): released on Society, Jul'83 by Arista Records. Dist: Polygram

WOMAN'S OWN.
Single (7"): released on Pax, Mar'82 by Pax Records. Dist: Red Rhino, Cartel

Single (12"): released on Pax, Mar'82 by Pax Records. Dist: Red Rhino, Cartel

Dansworks
SAY WHAT YOU MEAN.
Tracks: / Makes you happy (do something).
Single (7"): released on FM-Revolver, Nov'86 by FM-Revolver Records. Dist: BMG (RCA/Ariola), Pathe Marconi, Polygram

Single (12"): released on FM-Revolver, Nov'86 by FM-Revolver Records. Dist: BMG (RCA/Ariola), Pathe Marconi, Polygram

Dante
DIVINE COMEDY, THE Inferno cantos 1-6.
Cassette: released on Caedmon(USA), Sep'80 by Caedmon (USA) Records. Dist: Gower, Taylors, Discovery

FREAK IN ME.
Tracks: / Freak in me / Edit / One more time.
Single (12"): released on Bluebird, Mar'86 by Bluebird Records. Dist: EMI, Jetstar

Dany
LONDON JO.
Single (7"): released on Waterfront, Sep'85 by Waterfront Records. Dist: Rough Trade, Cartel, Projection, Roots

Daouda
SENTIMENTAL, (LE) (IVORY COAST).
Tracks: / Mon coeur balance / Bouquet de fleurs / Maimouna / Je suis fatigue / Yafa nema / Le sentimental.
Notes: A light, lively selection which launched the Ivorian singer in his home country. A big hit in West Africa. "A great creator of lyrics. Daouda shot to fame with this revamped "Mon Coeur Balance" album. (Backbeat International)
Album: released on Sterns, Sep'86 by Sterns Records. Dist: Sterns/Triple Earth Distribution

Dapogny, Jim
CHICAGO JAZZ BAND (Dapogny, Jim Chicago Jazz Band).
Album: released on Jazzology, Feb'87 Dist: Jazz Music, Swift

JIM DAPOGNY'S CHICAGO JAZZ BAND (Dapogny, Jim Chicago Jazz Band).
Album: released on Jazzology, Jun'86 by Jazz Music, Swift

Darby, Alan
CHARGE YOU UP.
Tracks: / Charge you up.
Single (7"): released on Siren, Mar'87 by Virgin Records. Dist: EMI
Cat. no: SIREN 17
Single (12"): released on Siren, Mar'87 by Virgin Records. Dist: EMI

Darby, Blind Terry
1929-37.
Album: released on Earl Archives, Jan'85 Dist: Swift, Jazz Music

SAINT LOUIS COUNTRY BLUES 1929-1937.
Album: released on Earl Archives, Jun'85 Dist: Swift, Jazz Music

Darbyshire, Richard
AIRWAVES.
Single (7"): released on Arcadian Research Authority, Jan'82 Dist: Independant

D'arby, Terence Trent
IF YOU LET ME STAY
Tracks: / If you let me stay / Loving you is another word for lonely.
Single (7"): released on CBS, Feb'87 by CBS Records. Dist: CBS

Single (12"): released on CBS, Feb'87 by CBS Records. Dist: CBS

INTRODUCING THE HARDLINE ACCORDING TO TERENCE TRENT D'ARBY.
Tracks: / If you all get to heaven / If you let me stay / Wishing well / I'll never turn my back on you (fathers words) / Dance little sister / Seven more days / Let's go forward / Rain / Sign your name / As yet untitled / Who's loving you.
Album: released on CBS, Jul'87 by CBS Records. Dist: CBS

Cassette: released on CBS, Jul'87 by CBS Records. Dist: CBS

Compact disc: released on CBS, Jul'87 by CBS Records. Dist: CBS

WISHING WELL.
Tracks: / Wishing Well / Elevators and hearts.
Single (7"): released on CBS, Jun'87 by CBS Records. Dist: CBS

Single (12"): released on CBS, Jun'87 by CBS Records. Dist: CBS

Single (7"): released on CBS, Jun'87 by CBS Records. Dist: CBS

Gatefold sleeve: released on CBS, Jun'87 by CBS Records. Dist: CBS

WISHING WELL (THE COOL IN THE SHADE MIX).
Tracks: / Wishing well / Wonderful world / Elevators and hearts.
Single (7"): released on CBS, Jun'87 by CBS Records. Dist: CBS

D'arc
LETTER, THE.
Single (7"): released on Flying, Jul'82 by Flying Records. Dist: DMS

Dardanelle
DOWN HOME.
Album: released on Audiophile, Jun'86 by Jazzology Records (USA). Dist: Jazz Music, Swift

ECHOES SINGING LADIES.
Notes: With: George Duvivier/J. Basile
Album: released on Audiophile, Jun'86 by Jazzology Records (USA). Dist: Jazz Music, Swift

SONGS FOR NEW LOVERS.
: released on Stash, Apr'81 Dist: Swift Distribution, Jazz Music Distribution, Jazz Horizons Distribution, Celtic Music Distribution, Cadillac, Zodiac Distribution

Dardanelle Trio
GOLD BRAID.
Notes: Artists inclued: Paul Edenfield/Tal Farrow
Album: released on Audiophile, Jun'86 by Jazzology Records (USA). Dist: Jazz Music, Swift

Dardis, Paul
BYE BYE LOVE (EVERLY BROTHERS HITS).
Cassette: released on VFM, May'81 by VFM Records. Dist: Taylors, Wynd-Up Distribution

Darin, Bobby
BOBBY DARIN.
Album: released on Deja Vu, Jan'87 by Deja Vu Records. Dist: Counterpoint Distribution, Record Services Distribution (Ireland)

Cassette: released on Deja Vu, Jan'87 by Deja Vu Records. Dist: Counterpoint Distribution, Record Services Distribution (Ireland)

BOBBY DARIN'S GREATEST.
Album: released on Atlantic, '70 by WEA Records. Dist: WEA

DARIN 1936-1973.
Album: released on Motown, Aug'82 by Motown Records. Dist: BMG Distribution

Cassette: released on Motown, Aug'82 by Motown Records. Dist: BMG Distribution

DREAM LOVER.
Single (7"): released on Old Gold, Jul'82 by Old Gold Records. Dist: Lightning, Jazz Music, Spartan, Counterpoint

FROM HELLO DOLLY TO GOODBYE CHARLIE.
Tracks: / Hello, Dolly / Call me irresponsible / Day of wine and roses (The) / More / End of never (The) / Charade / Once in a lifetime / Sunday in New York / Where love has gone / Look at me / Goodbye, Charlie.
Album: released on Capitol (USA), Nov'85 Dist: Conifer

LEGEND OF BOBBY DARIN, THE.
Album: released on Stylus, Oct'85 Dist: Pinnacle, Terry Blood Distribution, Stylus Distribution

Cassette: released on Stylus, Oct'85 Dist: Pinnacle, Terry Blood Distribution, Stylus Distribution

OH LOOK AT ME NOW.
Tracks: / All by myself / My buddy / There's a rainbow around my shoulder / Roses of Picardy / You'll never know / Blue skies / Always / You made me love you / Nightingale sang in Berkely Square, A / I'm beginning to see the light / Oh look at me now / Party's over (The).
Notes: Tracks 1-6 total time (15.56) - Tracks 7-12 total time (15.54) Produced by Tom Morgan, arranged and conducted by Billy May
Album: released on Capitol, Jun'86 by Capitol Records. Dist: EMI

Cassette: released on Capitol, Jun'86 by Capitol Records. Dist: EMI

SPLISH SPLASH.
Single (7"): released on Old Gold, Jul'82 by Old Gold Records. Dist: Lightning, Jazz Music, Spartan, Counterpoint

THINGS.
Single (7"): released on Old Gold, Jan'85 by Old Gold Records. Dist: Lightning, Jazz Music, Spartan, Counterpoint

VERSATILE BOBBY DARIN, THE.
Album: released on Capitol, Aug'85 by Capitol Records. Dist: EMI

Cassette: released on Capitol, Aug'85 by Capitol Records. Dist: EMI

Darius Recorded live
DARIUS RECORDED LIVE Various artists (Various Artists).
Album: released on Mosaic, Sep'76 by Mosaic Records. Dist: Jazz Music Distribution, Impetus Distribution, JSU Distribution, Cadillac

Dark
CHEMICAL WARFARE.

Album: released on Fresh, Mar'82 Dist: Jetstar

EINSTEIN'S BRAIN.
Single (7"): released on Fresh, Apr'81 Dist: Jetstar

HAWAII FIVE-0.
Single (7"): released on Fresh, Apr'81 Dist: Jetstar

LIVING END, THE Live.
Single (7"): released on Fall Out, Aug'82 by Swift, Red Rhino, Cartel

MASQUE.
Single (7"): released on Fresh, Jan'82 Dist: Jetstar

MY FRIENDS.
Single (7"): released on Fresh, Apr'81 Dist: Jetstar

ON THE WIRES.
Single (7"): released on Fresh, Aug'81 Dist: Jetstar

Dark Angel
DARKNESS DESCENDS.
Tracks: / Darkness descends / Burning of Sodom, The / Hunger of the undead / Merciless death / Death is certain (life is not) / Black prophesies / Perish in flames.
Album: released on Under One Flag, Nov'86 Dist: Pinnacle

Dark City
COME ON OVER.
Tracks: / Come on over.
Single (7"): released on Virgin, Sep'86 by Virgin Records. Dist: EMI, Virgin Distribution
Cat. no: VS 891
Single (12"): released on Virgin, Sep'86 by Virgin Records. Dist: EMI, Virgin Distribution

DARK CITY.
Compact disc: released on Virgin, Jul'87 by Virgin Records. Dist: EMI, Virgin Distribution

RESCUE ME.
Tracks: / Rescue me.
Single (7"): released on Virgin, Jun'86 by Virgin Records. Dist: EMI, Virgin Distribution
Cat. no: VS 869
Single (12"): released on Virgin, Jun'86 by Virgin Records. Dist: EMI, Virgin Distribution

Dark Crystal
DARK CRYSTAL, THE Original Soundtrack.
Album: released on CBS, Apr'83 by CBS Records. Dist: CBS

Darken
STORMY WEATHER.
Single (7"): released on Vinyl Cuts, Jun'84 by Vinyl Cuts Records. Dist: Jetstar

Dark Heart
SHADOWS OF THE NIGHT.
Album: released on Music For Nations, Aug'84 by Music For Nations Records. Dist: Pinnacle

Dark, John
OUTLAW.
Single (7"): released on JD, Jun'84

OUTSIDE LOOKING IN.
Single (12"): released on Outlaw, Jul'84

SILHOUETTE.
Single (7"): released on Zonophone, Jan'83 by EMI Records. Dist: EMI

Darkness and Jive
FURNACE.
Single (7"): released on Red Rhino, May'83 by Red Rhino Records. Dist: Red Rhino, Cartel

HOOKED ON YOU.
Single (7"): released on Red Rhino, Nov'82 by Red Rhino Records. Dist: Red Rhino, Cartel

JIGSAW.
Single (7"): released on Floating World, Jul'85 by Indiet Records. Dist: Pinnacle

Darko, George
HIGH LIFE TIME.
Album: released on Oval, Aug'84 Dist: Projection

Single (7"): released on Oval, Jun'84 Dist: Projection

Single (12"): released on Oval, Jun'84 Dist: Projection

MONI PALAVA.
Album: released on A & B, Jan'87 by A & B

Dark Secret
WHERE ARE YOU.
Tracks: / Where are you.
Single (7"): released on MCA, Aug'86 by MCA Records. Dist: Polygram, MCA

Dark Side Of The Sun
DARK SIDE OF THE SUN Original soundtrack.
Album: released on BBC, Sep'83 by BBC Records & Tapes. Dist: EMI, PRT, Pye

Cassette: released on BBC, Sep'83 by BBC Records & Tapes. Dist: EMI, PRT, Pye

Dark Star
LADY OF MARS.
Single (7"): released on Avatar, Aug'81 by Avatar Communications. Dist: CBS

ON TOUR.
Album: released on Avatar, Nov'81 by Avatar Communications. Dist: CBS

Cassette: released on Avatar, Nov'81 by Avatar Communications. Dist: CBS

REAL TO REEL.
Tracks: / Voice of America / Rock'n'roll heroes / Only time will tell / Spy zone / Homocide on first and last / Stadium of tears / Sad day in London town / One way love / Goin' nowhere / Two songs don't make a right.
Notes: (P) 1987 Original sound recordings made by FM-Revolver Records Ltd.
Album: released on FM, Jul'87 by FM-Revolver Records. Dist: EMI

Cassette: released on FM, Jul'87 by FM-Revolver Records. Dist: EMI

Album: released on EMI, Nov'84 by EMI Records. Dist: EMI

Cassette: released on EMI, Nov'84 by EMI Records. Dist: EMI

Album: released on FM-Revolver, Aug'87 by FM-Revolver Records. Dist: BMG (RCA/Ariola), Pathe Marconi, Polygram

Darktown Strutters
JAZZ THE WAY IT USED TO BE.
Album: released on Kiwi-Pacific (New Zealand), May'84 Dist: Flexitron Distributors Ltd

Cassette: released on Kiwi-Pacific (New Zealand), May'84 Dist: Flexitron Distributors Ltd

Dark Wizard
DEVIL'S VICTIM.
Album: released on Mausoleum, Jun'84 by Mausoleum Records. Dist: Pinnacle

REIGN OF EVIL.
Album: released on Mausoleum, Jul'85 by Mausoleum Records. Dist: Pinnacle

Darky, Tommy
FROM STORNAWAY TO BOTANY BAY.
Album: released on Ross, Jan'86 by Ross Records. Dist: Ross Distribution, Roots Distribution

Cassette: released on Ross, Jan'86 by Ross Records. Dist: Ross Distribution, Roots Distribution

HAPPY WANDERER, THE.
Cassette: released on Ross, Jan'87 by Ross Records. Dist: Ross Distribution, Roots Distribution

Album: released on Ross, Aug'84 by Ross Records. Dist: Ross Distribution, Roots Distribution

Cassette: released on Ross, Aug'84 by Ross Records. Dist: Ross Distribution, Roots Distribution

HOMECOMING.
Album: released on Lochshore, Jun'85 by Klub Records. Dist: PRT

Cassette: released on Lochshore, Jun'85 by Klub Records. Dist: PRT

UNIQUE ACCORDION SOUND OF....., THE.
Album: released on Ross, Jan'86 by Ross Records. Dist: Ross Distribution, Roots Distribution

Cassette: released on Ross, Jan'86 by Ross Records. Dist: Ross Distribution, Roots Distribution

UNIQUE SOUND OF (THE).
Notes: Retail price given by ARC excluding P&P (via Mail Order) is 4.99. Mail order distribution address: Accordion Record Club, 146 Birmingham Road, Lugtons, Worcs. DY10 2SL. Tel: 0562 - 746105.

Darlinda
DARLINDA REVEALS THE TAROT.
Album: released on Klub, May'83

Cassette: released on Klub, May'83

Darling Buds
IF I SAID.
Tracks: / If I said.
Single (7"): released on Darling Buds, Feb'87 by Revolver Records. Dist: Cartel

Darling, David
CYCLES.
Album: released on ECM (Germany), Jul'82 by ECM Records. Dist: IMS, Polygram, Virgin through EMI

JOURNAL OCTOBER.
Tracks: / Slow return / Bells and gongs / Far away lights / Solo cello / Minor blue / Clouds / Solo cello and voice / Journal October / Stuttgart.
Compact disc: by ECM Records. Dist: IMS, Polygram, Virgin through EMI

Darling, Gloria
GLORIA DARLING.
Album: released on Release, Jun'77 by Release Records. Dist: I & B, Wynd-Up Distribution, Taylors, Solomon & Peres Distribution

Darling Happy Anniversary
DARLING HAPPY ANNIVERSARY Various artists (Various Artists).
Album: released on Homespun(Ireland), May'83 by Outlet Records. Dist: Outlet

Cassette: released on Homespun(Ireland), May'83 by Outlet Records. Dist: Outlet

Da Rock
ROCK PARTY.
Single (7"): released on DMC, Aug'87 Dist: Red Rhino, Cartel

Single (12"): released on DMC, Aug'87 Dist: Red Rhino, Cartel

Daron, Mal
LADIES MAN.
Album: released on Folk Heritage, Jul'82 by Folk Heritage Records. Dist: Roots, Wynd-Up Distribution, Jazz Music, Folk Heritage

Darrell, Johnny
GREATEST HITS:JOHNNY DARRELL.
Album: released on Gusto (USA), Oct'79 by Gusto Records (USA). Dist: Crusader

Darren, Jenny
QUEEN OF FOOLS.
Album: released on DJM, May'78 by DJM Records. Dist: CBS, Polygram

D-Art
PRISENCCLINENSINAINC.
Tracks: / Prisencclinensinainc / Mystic Warrior.
Single (7"): released on WEA Int, Mar'87

Single (12"): released on WEA Int, Mar'87

Darts
6 TRACK HITS.
Single (7"): released on Scoop 33, Aug'84 by Pickwick Records. Dist: H.R. Taylor

Cassette: released on Scoop 33, Aug'84 by Pickwick Records. Dist: H.R. Taylor

BLOW AWAY.
Single (7"): released on Choice Cuts, May'85 by Choice Cuts Records. Dist: PRT

Cassette: released on Choice Cuts, May'85 by Choice Cuts Records. Dist: PRT

CAN'T TEACH A FOOL.
Single (7"): released on Choice Cuts, Oct'83 by Choice Cuts Records. Dist: PRT

DART ATTACK.
Album: released on Magnet, Sep'79 by Magnet Records. Dist: BMG

Cassette: released on Magnet, Sep'79 by Magnet Records. Dist: BMG

DARTS GREATEST HITS.
Album: released on Magnet, May'83 by Magnet Records. Dist: BMG

Cassette: released on Magnet, May'83 by Magnet Records. Dist: BMG

Album: released on Spot, Feb'84 by Pickwick Records. Dist: H.R. Taylor, Lugtons

Cassette: released on Spot, Feb'84 by Pickwick Records. Dist: H.R. Taylor, Lugtons

DOUBLE TOP.
Album: released on Hallmark, Sep'81 by Pickwick Records. Dist: Pickwick Distribution, PRT,

---

Taylors

Cassette: released on Hallmark, Sep'81 by Pickwick Records. Dist: Pickwick Distribution, PRT, Taylors

GROOVIN'.
Single (7"): released on Choice Cuts, Jun'84 by Choice Cuts Records. Dist: PRT

LORRAINE.
Single (7"): released on Choice Cuts, Jul'83 by Choice Cuts Records. Dist: PRT

Single (7"): released on Sunburst, Aug'82 Dist: Sunburst Records

MYSTERY RAGOULA.
Single (7"): released on Choice Cuts, Apr'83 by Choice Cuts Records. Dist: PRT

Single (12"): released on Choice Cuts, Apr'83 by Choice Cuts Records. Dist: PRT

Darwen ladies choir
DARWEN LADIES CHOIR.
Album: released on Castle Studio, May'81 by Castle Studio Records.

Darxon
KILLED IN ACTION.
Album: released on Wishbone/Earthshaker, Aug'84

D. Asher
RAGAMUFFIN HIP-HOP.
Single (12"): released on Music Of Life, Aug'87 Dist: Streetwave

Das Psych-Oh Rangers
HOMAGE TO THE BLESSED.
Tracks: / Homage to the blessed / Essential art of communication (The) / He he radical / Medea tearorah.
Single (7"): released on ZTT, Oct'86 by Island Records. Dist: Polygram

Single (12"): released on ZTT, Oct'86 by Island Records. Dist: Polygram

Data
2 TIME.
Album: released on Illuminated, Feb'85 by IKF Records. Dist: Pinnacle, Cartel, Jetstar

BLOW.
Single (12"): released on Illuminated, Feb'85 by IKF Records. Dist: Pinnacle, Cartel, Jetstar

ELEGANT MACHINERY.
Album: released on Proto, Nov'85 by Proto Records. Dist: WEA

Cassette: released on Proto, Nov'85 by Proto Records. Dist: WEA

LIVING INSIDE ME.
Single (12"): released on Illuminated, Apr'85 by IKF Records. Dist: Pinnacle, Cartel, Jetstar

OPERA ELECTRONICA.
Album: released on Illuminated, Jun'82 by IKF Records. Dist: Pinnacle, Cartel, Jetstar

RICHOCHETED LOVE.
Tracks: / Richocheted love / In love....DJ.
Single (7"): released on Sire, Jan'86

Single (12"): released on Sire, Jan'86

STOP.
Single (7"): released on Proto-Sire, Sep'85

Single (12"): released on Proto-Sire, Sep'85

Data-Bank, A
CONTINENTAL DRIFT.
Album: released on New Rose, Aug'87 Dist: Rough Trade, Cartel. Estim retail price in Sep'87 was £6.29.

Datblygu
HUGR-GRAWTH-OG.
Single (7"): released on Anhrefn, Feb'87 by Revolver, Cartel

Datcher, Clarke
YOU FOOLED HIM ONCE AGAIN.
Single (7"): released on Blue Knight, Oct'81 Dist: Swift

Single (12"): released on Blue Knight, Oct'81 Dist: Swift

Datchler, Clark
THINGS CAN'T GET ANY WORSE.
Single (7"): released on RAK, Nov'84 by RAK Dist: EMI

Datc Orchestra
JUNGLE SIGNAL.
Single (12"): released on DATC, Sep'82 by DATC Records. Dist: Rough Trade

Daughter of Darkness
DAUGHTER OF DARKNESS various artists (Various Artists).
Cassette: released on VFM, May'85 by VFM Records. Dist: Taylors, Wynd-Up Distribution

Dave & Bobby
REGGAE SEGGAE vol. 1.
Album: released on Vista Sounds, '83 by Vista Sounds Records. Dist: Jetstar

REGGAE SEGGAE, VOL. 1.
Album: released on Vista Sounds, '83 by Vista Sounds Records. Dist: Jetstar

Dave & Dana
MORNING STAR.
Album: by Pilgrim Records. Dist: Rough Trade, Cartel

Dave Dee, Dozy...
BEND IT (Dave Dee, Dozy, Beaky, Mick & Titch).
Album: released on Polydor (Import), Apr'82

Cassette: released on Polydor (Import), Apr'82

GREATEST HITS:DAVE DEE, DOZY, BEAKY, MICK & TITCH (Dave Dee, Dozy, Beaky, Mick & Titch).
Album: released on Fontana, Aug'81 by Phonogram Records. Dist: Polygram

Cassette: released on Fontana, Aug'81 by Phonogram Records. Dist: Polygram

Cassette: released on Autogram, Apr'85 Dist: Projection

Album: released on Philips, May'84 Dist: IMS-Polygram

Cassette: released on Philips, May'84 Dist: IMS-Polygram

HOLD TIGHT (Dave Dee, Dozy, Beaky, Mick & Titch).
Single (7"): released on Old Gold, Jan'85 by Old Gold Records. Dist: Lightning, Jazz Music, Spartan, Counterpoint

LEGEND OF XANADU (Dave Dee, Dozy, Beaky, Mick & Titch).
Single (7"): released on Old Gold, Jan'82 by Old Gold Records. Dist: Lightning, Jazz Music, Spartan, Counterpoint

Davenport, Bob
BEES ON HORSEBACK (Davenport, Bob & June Tabor).
Album: released on Free Reed, Nov'77 by Free Reed Records. Dist: Roots, Projection, Hobgoblin Records, Oblivion

BOB DAVENPORT.
Album: released on Leader, '81 Dist: Jazz Music, Projection

BOB DAVENPORT & THE RAKES 1977.
Album: released on Topic, '81 Dist: Roots Distribution

DOWN THE LONG ROAD.
Album: released on Topic, Apr'75 Dist: Roots Distribution

PAL OF MY CRADLE DAYS.
Album: released on Leader, '81 Dist: Jazz Music, Projection

POSTCARDS HOME.
Album: released on Topic, '81 Dist: Roots Distribution

Davenport, Cow Cow
COW COW DAVENPORT 1925-30.
Album: released on Magpie, Apr'79 Dist: Projection

Davern, Kenny
CHALUMEAU BLUE (Davern, Kenny & Bob Wilder).
Album: released on Pye International, Apr'77

EL RADO SCHUFFLE-A TRIBUTE TO JIMMY NOONE.
Album: released on Kenneth, Jul'82 Dist: Chris Wellard

EL RADO SCUFFLE Tribute to Jimmie Noone.
Album: released on Kenneth, Mar'87 Dist: Chris Wellard

LIVE HOT JAZZ (Davern, Kenny, Dick Wellstood, Chuck Riggs).
Album: released on Statiras, May'86 by Statiras Records. Dist: Jazz Music Distribution

SOPRANO SUMMIT.
Album: released on World Jazz, '75 by World Jazz Records. Dist: World Jazz, JSU, Jazz Music

THIS OLD GANG OF OURS (Davern, Kenny & Humphrey Littleton).
Album: released on Calligraph, Nov'86 by Calligraph Records. Dist: PRT

Dave & Sugar

DAVE & SUGAR.
Tracks: / How about us / Two broken hearts / Got my heart set on you / No secret anymore / My angel baby / Signal for help / Feel good with me / Take it from the heart / Don't walk away / Queen of the silver dollar.
Album: released on MCA Import, Mar'86 by MCA Records. Dist: Polygram, IMS

GREATEST HITS:DAVE & SUGAR.
Album: released on RCA International (USA), May'82 by RCA Records. Dist: RCA

Cassette: released on RCA International (USA), May'82 by RCA Records. Dist: RCA

Davey, Damien

I'M A MAN.
Tracks: / I'm a man / Sounds so fine.
Single (7"): released on Passion, May'87 by Skratch Records. Dist: PRT

Single (12"): released on Passion, May'87 by Skratch Records. Dist: PRT

Davey, Shaun

GRANUAILE.
Tracks: / Dubhdarra / Ripples in the rockpools / Defence of hens castle (The) / Free and easy / Rescue of Hugh de Lacy (The) / Dismissal (The) / Hens march (The) / Death of Richard-an-Irainn / Sir Richard Bingham / Spanish Armada (The) / New age (The).
Notes: Granuaile is a new work by Irish composer Shaun Davey, featuring Dublin singer Rita Connolly who, with Liam O'Flynn (Uilean Pipes) and a 25 piece orchestra and band, tells the life of Grace O'Malley, the 16th century 'pirate queen'. The music brings together both traditional and classical elements and should appeal to folk and classical outlets alike.
Album: released on Tara (Ireland), Feb'86 by Tara Records. Dist: I & B Records Distribution, Record Services Distribution (Ireland), Roots Distribution

Cassette: released on Tara (Ireland), Feb'86 by Tara Records. Dist: I & B Records Distribution, Record Services Distribution (Ireland), Roots Distribution

SAMSON.
Single (7"): released on CMS, Dec'84 by CMS Records. Dist: Celtic Music

David

AM I NORMAL.
Single (7"): released on Stiletto, Jan'83 by Fast Records. Dist: Cartel Distribution

Single (12"): released on Stiletto, Jan'83 by Fast Records. Dist: Cartel Distribution

David and Jonathan

LOVERS OF THE WORLD UNITE.
Album: released on See For Miles, Apr'84 by See For Miles Records. Dist: Pinnacle

Single (7"): released on Old Gold, Oct'83 by Old Gold Records. Dist: Lightning, Jazz Music, Spartan, Counterpoint

David and the Giants

INHABITANTS OF THE ROCK.
Album: released on Myrrh, Feb'85 by Word Records. Dist: Word Distribution

Cassette: released on Myrrh, Feb'85 by Word Records. Dist: Word Distribution

David & David

AIN'T SO EASY.
Tracks: / Ain't so easy / Let's just be friends / Swiming in the ocaen.
Single (7"): released on A&M, May'87 by A&M Records. Dist: Polygram

Single (12"): released on A&M, May'87 by A&M Records. Dist: Polygram

BOOMTOWN.
Tracks: / Boomtown / Rock for the forgotten, A.
Compact disc: by A&M Records. Dist: Polygram

Single (7"): released on A&M, Oct'86 by A&M Records. Dist: Polygram

Single (12"): released on A&M, Oct'86 by A&M Records. Dist: Polygram

SWALLOWED BY THE CRACKS.
Tracks: / Alone in the big city / Swimming in the Ocean.
Single (7"): released on A&M, Jan'87 by A&M Records. Dist: Polygram

Single (12"): released on A&M, Jan'87 by A&M Records. Dist: Polygram

David Disco Dance

DON'T WALK GO Go to a disco (David Disco Dance Orchestra).
Album: released on David Disco, Jan'86 Dist: PRT

David, F.R.

I NEED YOU.
Single (7"): released on Carrere, Sep'83 by Carrere Records. Dist: PRT, Spartan

LONG DISTANCE FLIGHT.
Album: released on Carrere, May'85 by Carrere Records. Dist: PRT, Spartan

MUSIC.
Single (7"): released on Carrere, Jun'83 by Carrere Records. Dist: PRT, Spartan

PICK UP THE PHONE.
Single (7"): released on Carrere, Feb'83 by Carrere Records. Dist: PRT, Spartan

SAHARA NIGHTS.
Single (7"): released on Epic, Aug'86 by CBS Records. Dist: CBS

Single (12"): released on Epic, Aug'86 by CBS Records. Dist: CBS

THIS TIME I HAVE TO WIN.
Single (7"): released on Carrere, Apr'85 by Carrere Records. Dist: PRT, Spartan

Single (12"): released on Carrere, Jul'85 by Carrere Records. Dist: PRT, Spartan

WORDS.
Album: released on Carrere, Apr'85 by Carrere Records. Dist: PRT, Spartan

Single (7"): released on Carrere, Jul'85 by Carrere Records. Dist: PRT, Spartan

David, J

BLUE MOODS.
Single (7"): released on Glass, Jul'85 by Glass Records. Dist: Nine Mile, Rough Trade, Red Rhino, Play It Again Sam

CROCODILE TEARS AND THE VELVET COSH.
Album: released on Glass, Apr'85 by Glass Records. Dist: Nine Mile, Rough Trade, Red Rhino, Play It Again Sam

Single (7"): released on Glass, Apr'85 by Glass Records. Dist: Nine Mile, Rough Trade, Red Rhino, Play It Again Sam

Single (12"): released on Glass, Apr'85 by Glass Records. Dist: Nine Mile, Rough Trade, Red Rhino, Play It Again Sam

I CAN'T SHAKE THIS SHADOW OF FEAR.
Single (7"): released on Glass, Sep'84 by Glass Records. Dist: Nine Mile, Rough Trade, Red Rhino, Play It Again Sam

Single (12"): released on Glass, Sep'84 by Glass Records. Dist: Nine Mile, Rough Trade, Red Rhino, Play It Again Sam

JOE ORTON'S WEDDING ep.
Single (7"): released on Situation 2, Aug'83 Dist: Cartel, Pinnacle

Single (12"): released on Situation 2, Aug'83 Dist: Cartel, Pinnacle

David, John

I COULDN'T SAY NO.
Single (7"): released on Albion, Apr'84 by Albion Records. Dist: Spartan, Pinnacle

ON THE MOUNTAIN.
Single (7"): released on Albion, Jul'83 by Albion Records. Dist: Spartan, Pinnacle

David, Matthew

DON'T LET LOVE GET YOU DOWN.
Tracks: / Don't let love get you down.
Single (12"): released on Bluebird, May'86 by Bluebird Records. Dist: EMI, Jetstar

David & Michael

CAMBRIDGE BUSKERS-ZWISCHEN PINTE UND PODIUM.
Album: released on Polydor, Jan'79 by Polydor Records. Dist: Polygram, Polydor

David's First Day...

DAVID'S FIRST DAY AT SCHOOL Snell, Nigel (Snell, Nigel).

Cassette: released on Look Back In Anger, Nov'84 Dist: Menace Breaker Distributors

Davidson, Billy

ON THE ROAD.
Album: released on Lismor, Nov'76 by Lismor Records. Dist: Lismor, Roots, Celtic Music

STAR WARS OF DARKNESS & LIGHT.
Album: by Pilgrim Records. Dist: Rough Trade, Cartel

Davidson, Harry Orchestra

THOSE WERE THE DAYS VOL.1.
Album: released on Savoy, May'86

THOSE WERE THE DAYS VOL.2.
Album: released on Savoy, May'86

Davidson, Howard

VOYAGE OF THE HEROES.
Single (7"): released on BBC, Oct'85 by BBC Records & Tapes. Dist: EMI, PRT, Pye

Davidson, Jim

ENGLAND.
Tracks: / I love the sun.
Single (7"): released on Sierra, Dec'86 by Sierra Records. Dist: WEA

JIM DAVIDSON ALBUM, THE.
Album: released on West Five, Nov'85 Dist: PRT

Cassette: released on West Five, Nov'85 Dist: PRT

JIM DAVIDSON LIVE...TOO RISKY.
Album: released on Rock City, Apr'85 by Brian Adams. Dist: Pinnacle

MAGGIE.
Single (7"): released on Relax, Aug'85 Dist: CBS

Double-pack single: released on Relax, Sep'85 Dist: CBS

SILVER THREADS.
Single (7"): released on Relax, Jan'85 Dist: CBS

SUPERSTAR AND THE ROADIE.
Single (7"): released on Rock City, Dec'81 by Brian Adams. Dist: Pinnacle

TOO RISKY.
Album: released on Scratch, May'81

Cassette: released on Scratch, May'81

WHITE CHRISTMAS.
Single (7"): released on Scratch, Nov'80

YOU WON'T BE BLUE WILL YOU.
Album: released on PRT, Nov'81 by PRT Records. Dist: PRT

Cassette: released on PRT, Nov'81 by PRT Records. Dist: PRT

Davidsons

MUSCLE JERKS (EP).
Extended-play record: released on Cake, Jul'87 by Cake Records. Dist: Nine Mile, Cartel

Davidson, 'Wild' Bill

WILD BILL DAVISON'S 75TH ANNIVERSARY JAZZ BAND.
Album: released on Jazzology, Jul'87 Dist: Jazz Music, Swift

David & Sylvain

TOKYO DOLLS LIVE.
Album: released on Fan Club, Sep'86 by New Rose. Dist: Rough Trade, Cartel

Davies, Allun

YOU'LL NEVER WALK ALONE.
Album: released on Grosvenor, Feb'82 by Grosvenor Records. Dist: Taylors

Davies, Bobby

SING SONGS FROM THE TWO OF US - (Davies, Bobby & Annette Hawes).
Album: released on Street Value, Nov'85 Dist: Jetstar Distribution

Davies, Carol

BUNNY AND THE BUBBLE.
Single (7"): released on EKL, Oct'84 by EKL Records. Dist: Pinnacle

Davies, Cyril

COUNTRY LINE SPECIAL.
Single (7"): released on PRT, Jun'84 by PRT Records. Dist: PRT

Single (12"): released on PRT, Jun'84 by PRT Records. Dist: PRT

Davies, Dave

CHOSEN PEOPLE.
Album: released on Warner Bros., Sep'83 by Warner Bros Records. Dist: WEA

Cassette: released on Warner Bros., Sep'83 by Warner Bros Records. Dist: WEA

DAVE DAVIES.
Album: released on RCA, Apr'83 by RCA Records. Dist: RCA, Roots, Swift, Wellard, Chris, I & B, Solomon & Peres Distribution

Cassette: released on RCA, Sep'80 by RCA Records. Dist: RCA, Roots, Swift, Wellard, Chris, I & B, Solomon & Peres Distribution

DEATH OF A CLOWN.
Single (7"): released on Old Gold, Aug'82 by Old Gold Records. Dist: Lightning, Jazz Music, Spartan, Counterpoint

GLAMOUR.
Album: released on RCA, Oct'81 by RCA Records. Dist: RCA, Roots, Swift, Wellard, Chris, I & B, Solomon & Peres Distribution

Cassette: released on RCA, Oct'81 by RCA Records. Dist: RCA, Roots, Swift, Wellard, Chris, I & B, Solomon & Peres Distribution

Davies, Gail

JAGGED EDGE OF A BROKEN HEART.
Single (7"): released on RCA, Apr'85 by RCA Records. Dist: RCA, Roots, Swift, Wellard, Chris, I & B, Solomon & Peres Distribution

WHERE IS A WOMAN TO GO.
Album: released on RCA, Apr'85 by RCA Records. Dist: RCA, Roots, Swift, Wellard, Chris, I & B, Solomon & Peres Distribution

Cassette: released on RCA, Apr'85 by RCA Records. Dist: RCA, Roots, Swift, Wellard, Chris, I & B, Solomon & Peres Distribution

Davies, H.G.

ALL IN THE GAME (Davies, H.G. & Paulette Miller).

Davies, Lesley A.

IF I TOLD YOU A LIE I'M SORRY.
Single (12"): released on Sea View, Dec'83 by Sea View Records. Dist: Jetstar

Davies, Ray

HOLLYWOOD HITS vol. 1 (Davies, Ray Orchestra).
Album: released on Dansan, Feb'85 by Spartan Records. Dist: Spartan

I LOVE LATIN (Davies, Ray & Button Down Brass).
Album: released on Dansan, Oct'84 by Spartan Records. Dist: Spartan

QUIET LIFE.
Tracks: / Quiet life / Voices in the dark.
Notes: From the soundtrack of the film "Absolute Beginners"
Single (7"): released on Virgin, May'86 by Virgin Records. Dist: EMI, Virgin Distribution

Single (12"): released on Virgin, May'86 by Virgin Records. Dist: EMI, Virgin Distribution

Davies, Ryan

CWMANFA GANU.
Album: released on Black Mountain, Aug'80 by Black Mountain Records.

FO A FE welsh record.
Album: released on Black Mountain, Aug'79 by Black Mountain Records.

RYAN AT THE RANK, VOL.1.
Album: released on Black Mountain, Oct'75 by Black Mountain Records.

Album: released on Black Mountain, Aug'80 by Black Mountain Records.

Davies, Walter

1949-1952.
Album: released on Krazy Kat, Sep'86 Dist: Jazz Music, Swift, Chris Wellard, H.R. Taylor, Charly, Hotshot, IRS Distribution

Davies, William

AT THE ORGAN OF TATTON HALL, KNUTSFORD, CHESHIRE.
Album: released on Lancastrian Organ Trust, Sep'86 Dist: Jazz Music

EVERY NIGHT IS MUSIC NIGHT.
Album: released on Acorn, Jun'79 Dist: Folksound, Jazz Music

MUSIC FROM THE MOVIES.
Tracks: / Diane / Spitfire prelude / Charade /

Wedding processional / Tara's theme / Exodus / Somebody loves me / I didn't know what time / I could write a book / Warsaw concerto / Thoroughly modern Millie / Summer place / Summer of '42.
Cassette: released on Audicord, '87 Dist: H.R. Taylor

TROCADERO CINEMA ORGAN, THE.
Album: released on BBC, Apr'79 by BBC Records & Tapes. Dist: EMI, PRT, Pye

Cassette: released on BBC, Apr'79 by BBC Records & Tapes. Dist: EMI, PRT, Pye

Davis, Anthony

EPISTEME.
Album: released on Gramavision (USA), Jul'83 by Gramavision Records (USA). Dist: PRT, IMS, Polygram

Album: released on Gramavision (USA), Jul'83 by Gramavision Records (USA). Dist: PRT, IMS, Polygram

I'VE KNOWN RIVERS (Davis, Anthony & James Newton and Abdul Wadud).
Album: released on Gramavision (USA), Jul'83 by Gramavision Records (USA). Dist: PRT, IMS, Polygram

MIDDLE PASSAGE.
Tracks: / Behind the rock / Middle passage / Particle W / Proposition for life.
Compact disc: by Gramavision Records (USA). Dist: PRT, IMS, Polygram

Album: released on Gramavision (USA), Feb'85 by Gramavision Records (USA). Dist: PRT, IMS, Polygram

Cassette: released on Gramavision (USA), Feb'85 by Gramavision Records (USA). Dist: PRT, IMS, Polygram

Compact disc: released on Gramavision (USA), Feb'85 by Gramavision Records (USA). Dist: PRT, IMS, Polygram

OF BLUES & DREAMS.
Album: released on Sackville, Apr'81 Dist: JSU, Jazz Music, Jazz Horizons, Cadillac Music, Celtic Music, Swift

PAST LIVES.
Album: released on Red Rhino, May'79 by Red Rhino Records. Dist: Red Rhino, Cartel

SONGS FOR A NEW WORLD.
Album: released on Indiana, May'79 Dist: PRT

Davis, Bette

MISS BETTE DAVIS.
Album: released on Platinum, Feb'83 by Geoffs Records.

Davis, Billie

KISS, THE.
Single (7"): released on Alternative, Dec'84 Dist: PRT

Single (12"): released on Alternative, Dec'84 Dist: PRT

TELL HIM.
Single (7"): released on Old Gold, Aug'85 by Old Gold Records. Dist: Lightning, Jazz Music, Spartan, Counterpoint

Davis, Blind John

IN MEMORIAM 1938.
Album: released on Document, Jul'87

Davis, Brother

CAN I CHANGE MY MIND (Davis, Brother Tyronne).
Album: released on Manhattan, Sep'80 by President Records. Dist: Jazz Music, Swift, Taylors, Chris Wellard

Davis, Carl

CHAMPIONS THEME (Davis, Carl & Philharmonia Orch.).
Single (7"): released on Island, Apr'84 by Island Records. Dist: Polygram

COMMANDING SEA, THE.
Album: released on EMI, Apr'81 by EMI Records. Dist: EMI

Cassette: released on EMI, Apr'81 by EMI Records. Dist: EMI

NAPOLEON soundtrack album.
Album: released on Chrysalis, May'83 by Chrysalis Records. Dist: CBS

Cassette: released on Chrysalis, May'83 by Chrysalis Records. Dist: CBS Deleted '87.

Davis, Carlene

BABY BUNNY.
Tracks: / Baby bunny / Baby bunny (instrumental).

Single (12"): released on Vanessa, Jul'86 by Vanessa Records. Dist: Vanessa

FIRST WORD, THE.
Single (12"): released on Revue, Jun'85 by Revue Records. Dist: Creole

LOVE A WOMAN SHOULD GIVE TO A MAN, A.
Single (12"): released on Moby Dick, May'84 by ERC Records. Dist: PRT Distribution

PARADISE.
Album: released on Range, Sep'84 Dist: PRT, Jetstar

SANTA CLAUS.
Single (12"): released on Creole, Dec'84 by Creole Records. Dist: Rhino, PRT

WINNIE MANDELA.
Tracks: / Winnie Mandela / One by one.
Single (12"): released on Greensleeves, 23 May'87 by Greensleeves Records. Dist: BMG, Jetstar, Spartan

WITH YOU.
Single (12"): released on Nicole, Dec'84 by Nicole Records. Dist: Jetstar

YESTERDAY, FOREVER, TODAY.
Album: released on Nicole, Sep'85 by Nicole Records. Dist: Jetstar

Davis, Carl/LPO

FEELING LOVE ON THE SIDE.
Single (12"):

FIRE AND ICE.
Album: released on First Night, Dec'86 by Safari Records. Dist: Pinnacle

Cassette: released on First Night, Dec'86 by Safari Records. Dist: Pinnacle

FIRE AND ICE.
Notes: For full information see under: Davis, Carl/LPO

Davis, Darlene

I FOUND LOVE (The Belated '87 Valentine).
Tracks: / I found love / I Found Love(premature '88 mix).
Single (7"): released on Serious, Mar'87 by Serious Records. Dist: PRT

I FOUND LOVE (RADIO MIX).
Tracks: / I found love (radio mix) / I found love (inst mix) / Dare to dance.
Notes: Dare to dance available on 12" version only.
Single (7"): released on Serious, Feb'87 by Serious Records. Dist: PRT

Single (12"): released on Serious, Feb'87 by Serious Records. Dist: PRT

Davis, Desmond

WENT DOWNTOWN.
Single (12"): released on Real Wax, Oct'82

Davis, Eddie

BEST OF EDDIE 'LOCKJAW' DAVIS, THE (Davis, Eddie 'Lockjaw').
Album: released on Pablo, '82 by Pablo Records. Dist: Wellard, Chris, IMS-Polygram, BMG

Cassette: released on Pablo, '82 by Pablo Records. Dist: Wellard, Chris, IMS-Polygram, BMG

COUNTIN' WITH BASIE.
Album: released on Vogue (France), Apr'84 Dist: Discovery, Jazz Music, PRT, Swift

HEAVY HITTER, THE (Davis, Eddie 'Lockjaw').
Album: released on Muse, Apr'81 by Peerless Records. Dist: Lugtons Distributors

HEY LOCK! (Davis, Eddie 'Lockjaw').
Album: released on Vogue Jazz (France), May'83

JAWS BLUES (Davis, Eddie 'Lockjaw').
Album: released on Enja (Germany), Jan'82 by Enja Records (W.Germany). Dist: Cadillac Music

JAZZ AT THE PHILHARMONIC 1983 (Davis, Eddie 'Lockjaw').
Album: released on Pablo, May'83 by Pablo Records. Dist: Wellard, Chris, IMS-Polygram, BMG

Cassette: released on Pablo, May'83 by Pablo Records. Dist: Wellard, Chris, IMS-Polygram, BMG

MPS JAZZ TIME (Davis, Eddie 'Lockjaw').
Album: released on MPS, Jun'79

RAREST SESSIONS OF THE '40'S, THE (Davis, Eddie 'Lockjaw').
Album: released on Pinnacle, Jul'82 by Pinnacle Records. Dist: Pinnacle

SIMPLY SWEETS (Davis, Eddie 'Lockjaw').
Album: released on Pablo, '82 by Pablo Records. Dist: Wellard, Chris, IMS-Polygram, BMG

Cassette: released on Pablo, '82 by Pablo Records. Dist: Wellard, Chris, IMS-Polygram, BMG

SONNY, SWEETS & JAWS (Davis, Eddie 'Lockjaw'/Sonny Stitt/Harry 'sweets' Edison).
Album: released on Gateway (USA), Jun'82 by Gemcom Inc.(USA) Records.

Album: released on Gateway (USA), Jun'82 by Gemcom Inc.(USA) Records.

STRAIGHT AHEAD (Davis, Eddie 'Lockjaw').
Album: released on Pablo, '82 by Pablo Records. Dist: Wellard, Chris, IMS-Polygram, BMG

Cassette: released on Pablo, '82 by Pablo Records. Dist: Wellard, Chris, IMS-Polygram, BMG

SWINGIN' TIL GIRLS (Davis, Eddie 'Lockjaw').
Album: released on Steeplechase, Feb'77

Davis, Eddie 'Lockjaw'

EDDIE 'LOCKJAW' DAVIS FOUR.
Album: released on Pablo, '82 by Pablo Records. Dist: Wellard, Chris, IMS-Polygram, BMG

Cassette: released on Pablo, '82 by Pablo Records. Dist: Wellard, Chris, IMS-Polygram, BMG

EDDIE'S FUNCTION.
Tracks: / People will say we're in love / You are too beautiful / All the things you are / Lady bird / Scotty boo / Tiajuana / I wished on the moon / Ebb tide / Eddie's function / Out of nowhere.
Album: released on Affinity, Jul'86 by Charly Records. Dist: Charly, Cadillac

JAWS.
Album:

OPUS FUNK VOL.2.
Notes: For full details see under EDISON, Harry Sweets

TENOR OF EDDIE 'LOCKJAW' DAVIS, THE.
Compact disc: released on Vogue, Dec'86 Dist: Discovery, Jazz Music, PRT, Swift

THAT'S ALL.
Tracks: / Exactly like you / L'amour est une drole / Pitch-tree thing / Out of nowhere / That's all / Chef.
Album: released on Kingdom Records, Jun'86 by Kingdom Records. Dist: Kingdom Records

Cassette: released on Kingdom Records, Jun'86 by Kingdom Records. Dist: Kingdom Records

Album: released on Pathe Marconi, Feb'87 Dist: Swift

TOUGH TENORS.
Tracks: / Again'n'again / Tin tin deo / If I had you / Jim dawg / When we were one / Gigi.
Notes: Count Basie veteran Eddie ' Lockjaw' Davis and hard-bop extraordinaire Johnny Griffin formed their 'Tough Tenors Quintet' during the '60's when jazz was going through it's 'soul' stage and swinging 'get down and boogie' playing was the order of the day. Recorded 24 April 1970 with Kenny Clarke-Francy Boland Big Band rhythm section of Kenny Clarke, drums, Francy Boland, piano and Jimmy Woode, bass.
Compact disc: released on Milestone, Jun'86 by Ace Records. Dist: PRT

Davis, Eddy

EDDY DAVIS & THE HOT JAZZ ORCHESTRA (Davis, Eddy & The Hot Jazz Orchestra).
Album: released on Jazzology, Jul'87 Dist: Jazz Music, Swift

Davis, Jackie

JACKIE DAVIS.
Album: released on EMI (Holland), '83 by EMI Records. Dist: Conifer

JUMPIN' JACKIE.
Album: released on Capitol (Holland), '83 by Capitol Records. Dist: Conifer

Davis, Jimmie

ROCKIN' BLUES.
Cassette single: released on Bear Family, Apr'84 by Bear Family Records. Dist: Rollercoaster Distribution, Swift

Davis Jnr., Sammy

CLOSEST OF FRIENDS.
Compact disc: released on Vogue (France), Jun'84 Dist: Discovery, Jazz Music, PRT. Swift

WHAT I'VE GOT IN MIND.
Album: released on President, Mar'85 by President Records. Dist: Taylors, Spartan

Cassette: released on President, Mar'85 by President Records. Dist: Taylors, Spartan

Davis, Joe

BIG BAND JAZZ 1940-1952.
Album: released on Harlequin, Jun'86 by Harlequin Records. Dist: Swift, Jazz Music, Wellard, Chris, IRS, Taylor, H.R.

R'N'B VOL.2 1955-56.
Notes: Mono
Album: released on Krazy Kat, May'86 Dist: Jazz Music, Swift, Chris Wellard, H.R. Taylor, Charly, Hotshot, IRS Distribution

Davis, John

AIN'T THAT ENOUGH FOR YOU (Davis, John & the Monster Orchestra).
Album: by Gull Records. Dist: PRT Distribution

Davis, Johnny

EXPAND YOUR MIND.
Single (7"): released on Creole, Mar'85 by Creole Records. Dist: Rhino, PRT

Davis Jr., Walter

URANUS.
Album: released on Palcoscenico (Italy), '81 Dist: Jazz Music

Davis, Leslie

I WON'T LET YOU DOWN.
Tracks: / I won't let you down / Dry your eyes.
Single (12"): released on Union, Feb'87 Dist: Jetstar

Davis, Lockjaw

CHEWIN' THE FAT.
Album: released on Spotline, '83

Davis, Mac

20 GOLDEN SONGS.
Album: released on Astan, Nov'84 by Astan Records. Dist: Counterpoint

Cassette: released on Astan, Nov'84 by Astan Records. Dist: Counterpoint

CAROLINE'S STILL IN GEORGIA.
Single (7"): released on Casablanca, Apr'84 Dist: Polygram, Phonogram

MIDNIGHT CRAZY.
Album: released on Casablanca, Nov'81 Dist: Polygram, Phonogram

Cassette: released on Casablanca, Nov'81 Dist: Polygram, Phonogram

SOFT TALK.
Album: released on Casablanca, Apr'84 Dist: Polygram, Phonogram

Cassette: released on Casablanca, Apr'84 Dist: Polygram, Phonogram

TILL I MADE IT WITH YOU.
Tracks: / I never made love (till I made it with you) / Too big for words / Shake, Ruby, shake / Rainy day lovin' / Regrets / Special place in heaven, A / Save that dress / I think I'm gonna rain / I feel the country callin' me / Sexy young girl.
Album: released on MCA Import, Mar'86 by MCA Records. Dist: Polygram, IMS

Davis, Miles

1958 MILES.
Album: released on Japanese Import, May'79

AGHARTA.
Notes: Double album.
Album: released on CBS, Jan'87 by CBS Records. Dist: CBS

ARTISTRY IN JAZZ Greatest hits.
Compact disc: released on JVC Fantasy (Japan), May'87

ASCENSEUR POUR L'ECHAFAUD.
Compact disc: by Phonogram Records. Dist: Polygram

ASCENSEUR PUR L'ECHAFAUD (Davis, Miles/Art Blakey Jazz Messengers).
Compact disc: released on Phonogram Import, Jul'85

AT BIRDLAND (Davis, Miles Sextet).
Album: released on Jazz Live, Apr'81

AT BIRDLAND, 1951.
Album: released on Beppo, Jun'76

AT HIS RAREST OF ALL RARE PERFORMANCES: VOL 1.
Album: Dist: Jazz Horizons, Jazz Music, Celtic Music

AT LAST (Davis, Miles & The Lighthouse All Stars).
Album: released on Boplicity, May'85 by Bo-

Page 273

plicity Records. Dist: Ace Records, Pinnacle

BAG'S GROOVE.
Album:

Compact disc: released on JVC Fantasy (Japan), Nov'86

BIRTH OF THE COOL.
Cassette: released on Capitol, Jul'78 by Capitol Records. Dist: EMI

BITCHES BREW.
Tracks: / Pharoah's dance / Bitches brew / Spanish key / John McLaughlin / Miles runs the voodoo down / Sanctuary.
Album: released on CBS, Sep'87 by CBS Records. Dist: CBS

Album: released on CBS, Sep'87 by CBS Records. Dist: CBS

Cassette: released on CBS, Sep'87 by CBS Records. Dist: CBS

BITCH'S BREW.
Double Album: by CBS Records. Dist: CBS

BLUE CHRISTMAS.
Album: released on CBS, May'83 by CBS Records. Dist: CBS

Cassette: released on CBS, May'83 by CBS Records. Dist: CBS

BLUE HAZE.
Album: released on Original Jazz Classics (USA), Jun'86 Dist: Fantasy (USA) Distribution, Chris Wellard Distribution, IMS-Polygram Distribution

Album: released on Prestige (USA), Aug'84

CHRONICLE: THE COMPLETE PRESTIGE RECORDINGS.
Boxed set: released on Prestige, Dec'80 by Prestige Records (USA). Dist: RCA, JSU, Swift

CLASSICS.
Double Album: released on CBS(Holland), Aug'84 by CBS Records. Dist: Discovery

COLLECTOR'S ITEMS.
Compact disc: released on Carrere, Apr'87 by CBS Records. Dist: PRT, Spartan

Album: released on Prestige (USA). Feb'84

COMPLETE AMSTERDAM CONCERT, THE.
Album: released on Celluloid (France), Jul'85 by Island. Dist: Polygram

Cassette: released on Celluloid (France), Jul'85 by Island. Dist: Polygram

COOKIN' WITH THE MILES DAVIS QUINTET.
Compact disc:

DECOY.
Compact disc: by CBS Records. Dist: CBS

Album: released on CBS, Jun'84 by CBS Records. Dist: CBS

Cassette: released on CBS, Jun'84 by CBS Records. Dist: CBS

Compact disc: released on CBS, Jun'84 by CBS Records. Dist: CBS

EARLY YEARS, (THE).
Album: released on Saar Giants Of Jazz (Italy), Sep'85 Dist: Mainline

Cassette: released on Saar Giants Of Jazz (Italy), Sep'85 Dist: Mainline

EZZ-THETIC (Davis, Miles & Lee Konitz).
Album: released on Fantasy (USA), Feb'86 by Fantasy Inc USA Records. Dist: IMS, Polygram

FOUR & MORE.
Notes: Recorded live in concert
Album: released on CBS, Jan'87 by CBS Records. Dist: CBS

GET UP WITH IT.
Album: by CBS Records. Dist: CBS

GETZ/DAVIS (Davis, Miles & Stan Getz).
Album: released on Kings Of Jazz, Aug'81 Dist: Jazz Horizons, Jazz Music, Celtic Music

GOLDEN HIGHLIGHTS OF MILES DAVIS.
Album: released on CBS(Import), Jun'86 by CBS Records. Dist: Conifer, Discovery, Swift

Cassette: released on CBS(Import), Jun'86 by CBS Records. Dist: Conifer, Discovery, Swift

IN A SILENT WAY.
Album: by CBS Records. Dist: CBS

MAN WITH THE HORN.
Tracks: / Fat time / Back seat Betty / Shout aida / Man with the horn, the / Ursula.
Cassette: released on Prix D'Ami, Sep'86

Compact disc: by CBS Records. Dist: CBS

MILES AHEAD.
Album: released on CBS(Import), Jun'86 by CBS Records. Dist: Conifer, Discovery, Swift

MILES DAVIS.
Album: released on Prestige (USA), May'84

MILES DAVIS ALL STARS & GIL EVANS
(Davis, Miles & Gil Evans).
Album: released on Beppo, Jun'76

MILES DAVIS COLLECTION, (THE).
Cassette: released on Deja Vu, Aug'85 by Deja Vu Records. Dist: Counterpoint Distribution, Record Services Distribution (Ireland)

MILES DAVIS, DIZZY GILLESPIE & CHARLIE PARKER (Davis, Miles/Dizzy Gillespie/Charlie Parker).
Double Album: released on Vogue, Nov'76 Dist: Discovery, Jazz Music, PRT, Swift

MILES DAVIS' GREATEST HITS.
Album: by CBS Records. Dist: CBS

MILES DAVIS IN L.A., 1946.
Album: released on Joker, '79 Dist: Cadillac, Zodiac Distribution, Jazz Horizons, Jazz Music, JSU, Celtic Music

MILES DAVIS & JOHN COLTRANE LIVE
(Davis, Miles & John Coltrane).
Album: released on Unique Jazz, Apr'81 Dist: Swift, Jazz Music, Jazz Horizons

Compact disc: released on CBS, '83 by CBS Records. Dist: CBS

IN EUROPE Antibes 1964.
Album: released on CBS(Import), Jun'86 by CBS Records. Dist: Conifer, Discovery, Swift

Album: released on CBS(Import), Jun'75 by CBS Records. Dist: Conifer, Discovery, Swift

KIND OF BLUE.
Tracks: / So what? / Freddie Freeloader / Blue in green / All blues / Flamenco sketches.
Compact disc: released on CBS, Mar'87 by CBS Records. Dist: CBS

KIND OF BLUE.
Album: released on CBS, '83 by CBS Records. Dist: CBS

Compact disc: released on CBS, '83 by CBS Records. Dist: CBS

LIVE IN STOCKHOLM - 1960 (Davis, Miles & John Coltrane).
Compact disc: released on AVI (USA), Jan'86 by A.V.I. Records. Dist: Target, PRT

Double Album: released on Dragon, Jun'86 by Dragon Records. Dist: Jazz Music, Projection, Cadillac

MILES DAVIS & THE LIGHTHOUSE ALLSTARS (Davis, Miles & Lighthouse Allstars).
Compact disc: released on Carrere, Apr'87 by Carrere Records. Dist: PRT, Spartan

MILES DAVIS VOL.2.
Cassette: released on Blue Note, Apr'87 by EMI Records. Dist: EMI

Album: released on Blue Note, Apr'87 by EMI Records. Dist: EMI

MILES DAVIS: VOLUME 2.
Album: released on Blue Note, Jul'85 by EMI Records. Dist: EMI

MILES IN BERLIN.
Compact disc: released on CBS, May'87 by CBS Records. Dist: CBS

MILES IN ST LOUIS (Davis, Miles Quintet).
Album: released on VGM, Apr'81 Dist: Jazz Horizons, JSU

MILES OF FUN.
Album: released on Manhattan, Jul'80 by President Records. Dist: Jazz Music, Swift, Taylors, Chris Wellard

MILES OF JAZZ (Davis, Miles & Charlie Parker).

MUSINGS OF MILES, (THE).
Album: released on Prestige, Jun'84 by Prestige Records (USA). Dist: RCA, JSU, Swift

MY FUNNY VALENTINE.
Compact disc: released on CBS, May'87 by CBS Records. Dist: CBS

NIGHT IN TUNISIA, A.
Album: released on Star Jazz USA, Apr'86 by Charly Records. Dist: Charly Distribution

Cassette: released on Star Jazz USA, Apr'86 by Charly Records. Dist: Charly Distribution

Album: released on Joker Import, Apr'81

Album: released on Chase Music, Nov'84 by Chase Records. Dist: PRT

ON THE CORNER.
Album: released on CBS, Jan'87 by CBS Records. Dist: CBS

PORGY AND BESS (Davis, Miles & Gil Evans Orchestra).
Album: released on CBS, Sep'82 by CBS Records. Dist: CBS

Cassette: released on CBS, Sep'82 by CBS Records. Dist: CBS

PRE-BIRTH OF THE COOL (Davis, Miles & His Tuba Band).
Album: released on Jazz Live Apr'81

RELAXIN' WITH MILES (Davis, Miles Quintet).
Compact disc: released on Vanguard (USA), Apr'86

ROUND ABOUT MIDNIGHT.
Album: released on CBS(Import), Jun'86 by CBS Records. Dist: Conifer, Discovery, Swift

Compact disc: released on CBS, May'87 by CBS Records. Dist: CBS

SEVEN STEPS TO HEAVEN.
Album: released on CBS(Import), Jun'86 by CBS Records. Dist: Conifer, Discovery, Swift

SKETCHES OF SPAIN.
Tracks: / Concierto de aranjuez / El amor brujo / Pan piper / Saeta / Solea.
Compact disc: by CBS Records. Dist: CBS

Album: released on CBS, Mar'81 by CBS Records. Dist: CBS

Cassette: released on CBS, Mar'81 by CBS Records. Dist: CBS

Cassette: released on CBS, Feb'83 by CBS Records. Dist: CBS

SOMEDAY MY PRINCE WILL COME.
Album: released on CBS(Import), Jun'86 by CBS Records. Dist: Conifer, Discovery, Swift

SOME DAY MY PRINCE WILL COME.
Compact disc: released on Mobile Fidelity, Jan'86 by Mobile Fidelity Records.

SOMETHING ELSE (Davis, Miles & Cannonball Adderley).
Album: released on Blue Note, May'79 by EMI Records. Dist: EMI

SORCERER.
Tracks: / Prince of darkness / Vonetta / Limbo / Masqualero / Pee Wee / Sorcerer, The.
Album: released on CBS, Jul'87 by CBS Records. Dist: CBS

Cassette: released on CBS, Jul'87 by CBS Records. Dist: CBS

STAR PEOPLE.
Compact disc: by CBS Records. Dist: CBS

STEAMIN' WITH THE MILES DAVIS QUINTET.
Compact disc:

TALLEST TREES.
Double Album: released on Prestige, '73 by Prestige Records (USA). Dist: RCA, JSU, Swift

TUTU.
Tracks: / Tutu / Tomaas / Portia / Splatch / Backyard ritual / Perfect way / Don't lose your mind / Full nelson.
Compact disc: by Warner Bros Records. Dist: WEA

Album: released on Warner Bros., Oct'86 by Warner Bros Records. Dist: WEA

Cassette: released on Warner Bros., Oct'86 by Warner Bros Records. Dist: WEA

VOLUME 2.
Cassette: released on Blue Note, May'87 by EMI Records. Dist: EMI

VOLUME ONE.
Tracks: / Tempus fugit / Kelo / Enigma / Rya's idea / How deep is the ocean / C.T.A. / Dear old Stockholm / Chance it / Yesterdays / Donna / CTA / Wouldn't you.
Album: released on Blue Note, May'85 by EMI Records. Dist: EMI

Cassette: released on Blue Note, May'85 by EMI Records. Dist: EMI

WALKIN' (Davis, Miles All Stars).
Notes: All Stars include: Jay Jay Johnson etc.
Compact disc: released on JVC Fantasy (Japan), Apr'87

WALKIN'.
Album:

Compact disc: released on Carrere, Apr'87 by Carrere Records. Dist: PRT, Spartan

WATER BABIES.
Tracks: / Water babies / Sweet pea / Duel Mr.Tillman Anthony / Two faced / Capricorn.
Album: released on CBS, Jul'86 by CBS Records. Dist: CBS

Cassette: released on CBS, Jul'86 by CBS Records. Dist: CBS

WORKIN' WITH THE MILES DAVIS QUINTET.
Compact disc:

Compact disc: released on Vanguard (USA), Apr'86

WORLD OF JAZZ.
Album: released on Manhattan, Jul'80 by President Records. Dist: Jazz Music, Swift, Taylors, Chris Wellard

YOU'RE UNDER ARREST.
Compact disc: by CBS Records. Dist: CBS

Album: released on CBS, Jun'85 by CBS Records. Dist: CBS

Cassette: released on CBS, Jun'85 by CBS Records. Dist: CBS

Davis, Nathan.
RULES OF FREEDOM (Davis, Nathan Quartet).
Notes: With Hampton Hawes/A. Taylor
Album: released on Hot House, Dec'86 Dist: Jazz Music

Davison, Peter
STORY OF CHRISTMAS (THE).
Tracks: / Away in a manger / In the bleak mid winter / Silent night.
Notes: Original music composed by Robert Howes and performed by Robert Howes and Rod Argent. Original Sound Recordings made by W.H.Smith & Son Ltd. Producer Robert Howes.
Cassette: released on Fame, Oct'86 by Music For Pleasure Records. Dist: EMI

Davison, Wild Bill
ALL AMERICAN BAND.
Album: released on Sonet, May'82 by Sonet Records. Dist: PRT

BUT BEAUTIFUL.
Album: released on Storyville, Sep'86 by Storyville Records. Dist: Jazz Music Distribution, Swift Distribution, Chris Wellard Distribution, Counterpoint Distribution

CHICAGO JAZZ.

Cassette:

INDIVIDUALISM OF WILD BILL DAVISON.
Double Album:

JOHNNY HODGES, WILD BILL DAVISON (Davison, Wild Bill & Johnny Hodges).
Album: released on RCA (France), '83 by RCA Records. Dist: Discovery

LADY OF THE EVENING.
Album: released on Jazzology, Jun'86 Dist: Jazz Music, Swift

LIVE AT THE MEMPHIS FESTIVAL.
Notes: Mono
Album: released on Jazzology, Jun'86 Dist: Jazz Music, Swift

RUNNING WILD.
Album: released on JSP, Jul'82 by JSP Records. Dist: Swift, Projection

THAT'S A PLENTY.
Album: released on Commodore Classics, Mar'83 by Teldec Records (Germany). Dist: Conifer, IMS, Polygram

THAT'S A PLENTY - VOLUME ONE (1943) (Davison, Wild Bill & His Commodores).
Album: released on Commodore Classics, May'87 by Teldec Records (Germany). Dist: Conifer, IMS, Polygram

THIS IS JAZZ Volume 1.
Notes: Mono production
Album: released on Storyville, Jun'86 by Storyville Records. Dist: Jazz Music Distribution, Swift Distribution, Chris Wellard Distribution, Counterpoint Distribution

TOGETHER AGAIN (Davison, Wild Bill & Ralph Sutton).
Notes: Mono production
Album: released on Storyville, Jun'86 by Storyville Records. Dist: Jazz Music Distribution, Swift Distribution, Chris Wellard Distribution,

Counterpoint Distribution

WILD BILL DAVISON.
Notes: Mono production: with Eddie Condon's All Stars
Album: released on Storyville, May'86 by Storyville Records. Dist: Jazz Music Distribution, Swift Distribution, Chris Wellard Distribution, Counterpoint Distribution

WILD BILL DAVISON & THE JAZZ GIANTS (Davison, Wild Bill & The Jazz Giants).
Album: released on Sackville, Jul'96 Dist: JSU, Jazz Music, Jazz Horizons, Cadillac Music, Celtic Music, Swift

WILD TRUMPETS (Davison, Wild Bill & Valdemars Orchestra).
Album: released on CSA, Jan'87 by CSA Records. Dist: PRT, Jetstar

Davis, Ossie

TSHINDAO (Davis, Ossie & Ruby Dee).
Album: released on Caedmon(USA), Nov'76 by Caedmon (USA) Records. Dist: Gower, Taylors, Discovery

UP FROM SLAVERY.
Double Album: released on Caedmon(USA), Aug'77 by Caedmon (USA) Records. Dist: Gower, Taylors, Discovery

Davis, Paul

COOL NIGHT.
Album: released on Arista, Mar'82 by Arista Records. Dist: RCA

SONG OF CHANTER (Davis, Paul & Brian Vallely).
Album: released on Outlet (Ireland), Jul76

Davis, Rev. Gary

BEST OF GARY DAVIS IN CONCERT, (THE).
Album: released on Kicking Mule, Sep'79 by Sonet. Dist: Roots, PRT-Pye Distribution

CHILDREN OF ZION (IN CONCERT).
Album: released on Heritage, Jul'85 by Heritage Records. Dist: Chart

I AM A TRUE VINE (1962-63).
Album: released on Heritage, Mar'85 by Heritage Records. Dist: Chart

LET US GET TOGETHER.
Album: released on Kicking Mule, '74 by Sonet. Dist: Roots, PRT-Pye Distribution

LO I BE WITH YOU ALWAYS.
Album: released on Kicking Mule, '73 by Sonet. Dist: Roots, PRT-Pye Distribution

O GLORY.
Album: released on Adelphi, May'81 by Adelphi Records. Dist: Jetstar

RAGTIME GUITAR.
Album: released on Heritage, Oct'85 by Heritage Records. Dist: Chart

Davis, Richard

EPISTROPHY.
Cassette: released on Muse (Import), Mar'81

WAY OUT WEST.
Album: released on Muse (Import), Apr'81

WITH UNDERSTANDING.
Album: released on Muse (Import), Apr'81

Davis, Ronnie

LOVE I CAN FEEL.
Single (12"): released on GG'S, Sep'84 by GG'S Records. Dist: Jetstar

PLAY ME.
Single (12"): released on Top Rank, Jun'85

RONNIE DAVIES SINGS FOR YOU AND I.
Album: released on Vista Sounds, Mar'85 by Vista Sounds Records. Dist: Jetstar

Davis, Sammy Jnr.

BEST OF SAMMY DAVIS JNR, (THE).
Album: released on MCA, Aug'82 by MCA Records. Dist: Polygram, MCA

Cassette: released on MCA, Aug'82 by MCA Records. Dist: Polygram, MCA

CLOSEST OF FRIENDS.
Compact disc: Dist: Discovery, Jazz Music, PRT, Swift

Compact disc: released on Vogue (France), Jun'84 Dist: Discovery, Jazz Music, PRT, Swift

HELLO DETRIOT.
Single (7"): released on Motown, Sep'84 by

Motown Records. Dist: BMG Distribution

Single (12"): released on Motown, Sep'84 by Motown Records. Dist: BMG Distribution

SAMMY DAVIS JNR.IN PERSON, 1977.
Album: released on RCA (Germany), Aug'83

Cassette: released on RCA (Germany), Aug'83

SONG AND DANCE MAN, (THE).
Album: released on 20th Century Fox, Jan'77

Davis, Skeeter

20 OF THE BEST.
Album: released on RCA International (USA), Apr'85 by RCA Records. Dist: RCA

Cassette: released on RCA International, Apr'85

BEST OF SKEETER DAVIS, THE.
Album: released on RCA, '84 by RCA Records. Dist: RCA, Roots, Swift, Wellard, Chris, I & B, Solomon & Peres Distribution

Cassette: released on RCA, '84 by RCA Records. Dist: RCA, Roots, Swift, Wellard, Chris, I & B, Solomon & Peres Distribution

BEST OF, THE.
Tracks: / End of the world / I can't help you / I'm falling too / I will / Something precious / Now I lay me down too sleep / Gonna get along without you now / He says the same things to me / I can't stay mad at you / I ever known more than you'll ever know / My last date with you / Am I that easy to forget.
Album: released on RCA/Camden, Jul'86

Cassette: released on RCA/Camden, Jul'86

END OF THE WORLD.
Tracks: / End of the world, The / Silver threads and golden needles / Mine is a lonely life / Once upon a time / Why I'm walkin' / Don't let me cross over / My coloring book / Where nobody wants me (I want to go) / Keep your hands off my kid / Something precious / Longing to hold you again / He called my baby.
Album: released on RCA, Jan'87 by RCA Records. Dist: RCA, Roots, Swift, Wellard, Chris, I & B, Solomon & Peres Distribution

Cassette: released on RCA, Jan'87 by RCA Records. Dist: RCA, Roots, Swift, Wellard, Chris, I & B, Solomon & Peres Distribution

END OF WORLD (SINGLE).
Single (7"): released on Old Gold, Oct'86 by Old Gold Records. Dist: Lightning, Jazz Music, Spartan, Counterpoint

HOMEBREAKER.
Tracks: / End of the world (The) / Gonna get along without you now / What does it take / Goin' down the road feelin' bad / I forgot more than you'll ever know / Set him free / Homebreaker / My last date with you / Am I that easy to forget / I can't help you / I'm falling too / I can't believe it's over.
Notes: Licensed from Kilo Music Ltd
Album: released on Topline, Dec'86 by Charly Records. Dist: Charly Distribution

Cassette: released on Topline, Dec'86 by Charly Records. Dist: Charly Distribution

SHE SINGS THEY PLAY (Davis, Skeeter & NRBQ).
Album: released on Rounder (USA), Dec'85 Dist: Mike's Country Music Room Distribution, Jazz Music Distribution, Swift Distribution, Roots Records Distribution, Projection Distribution, Topic Distribution

Album: released on Demon, Nov'86 by Demon Records. Dist: Pinnacle

SINGS BUDDY HOLLY.
Album: released on Detour, Dec'86 by Detour Records. Dist: Swift, RCA, Jazz Music, Projection

YOU'VE GOT A FRIEND.
Album: released on Pickwick, Feb'80 by Pickwick Records. Dist: Pickwick Distribution, Prism Leisure Distribution, Lugtons

Cassette: released on RCA, Apr'80 by RCA Records. Dist: RCA, Roots, Swift, Wellard, Chris, I & B, Solomon & Peres Distribution

Davis, Spencer

BEST OF (Davis, Spencer Group).
Tracks: / Back into my life again / Waltz from Lumumba / Together til the end of time / Keep on running / Trampoline / When I come home / Strong love / Somebody help me / She put the hurt on me / Goodbye Stevie / I'm a man / Gimme some lovin' / Every little bit hurts / This hammer.
Album: released on Island, Oct'86 by Island Records. Dist: Polygram

Cassette: released on Island, Oct'86 by Island Records. Dist: Polygram

CROSSFIRE.
Album: released on Allegiance, Apr'84 by PRT Records. Dist: PRT

Cassette: released on Allegiance, Apr'84 by PRT Records. Dist: PRT

KEEP ON RUNNING (Davis, Spencer Group).
Extended-play record: released on Island, May'78 by Island Records. Dist: Polygram

PRIVATE NUMBER (Davis, Spencer & Dusty Springfield).
Cassette: released on Allegiance, Mar'84 by PRT Records. Dist: PRT

Davis, Steve

GET 'EM OUT.
Single (7"): released on Animus, Mar'84 Dist: Rough Trade, Cartel

Davis, Teddy

NO, NO SIN, NO SIN AT ALL.
Tracks: / Candice- my heart.
Single (12"): released on TR, Nov'86

TABANKA.
Tracks: / Tabanka / Bobby beat.
Single (12"): released on BB, Feb'86 Dist: Jetstar

Davis, Terry

OCEANS AWAY.
Tracks: / Oceans away / Davis cup theme / Oceans away.
Single (12"): released on Tedious, Sep'86 Dist: M.I.S. Distribution, EMI

Single (7"): released on Tedious, Oct'86 Dist: M.I.S. Distribution, EMI

WAITING IN THE WINGS.
Tracks: / Waiting in the wings.
Single (7"): released on Tedious, Sep'86 Dist: M.I.S. Distribution, EMI

Davis, Tyrone

MAN OF STONE.
Album: released on Timeless, Aug'87

TYRONE DAVIS STORY, THE.
Cassette: released on Kent, Mar'85 by Ace Records. Dist: Pinnacle

Davis, Walter

ABIDE WITH ME.
Album: released on Denon, Mar'82 by Denon Records. Dist: Harmonia Mundi

BULLET SIDES 1949-52 (THE).
Album: released on Krazy Kat (USA), Oct'86

NIGHT SONG.
Album: released on Denon, Mar'82 by Denon Records. Dist: Harmonia Mundi

Davis, William

BEST OF BRITISH BRASS (Davis, William Construction Band).
Album: released on ASV, Oct'81 by Academy Sound & Vision Records. Dist: Pinnacle

Cassette: released on ASV, Oct'81 by Academy Sound & Vision Records. Dist: Pinnacle

CONSTRUCTIVE BRASS (Davis, William Construction Band).
Album: released on Grosvenor, Nov'76 by Grosvenor Records. Dist: Taylors

Davy D

DAVY'S RIDE.
Tracks: / Davy's ride / Get busy (we ain't new to this) / Keep your distance / Feel for you / Bustin' loose / Your love is like money in the bank / Live on hollis day / Oh girl / Have you seen Davy / Do ya do / Bring it / Let's rock.
Album: released on Def Jam (USA), Jun'87 by CBS Records. Dist: CBS

Cassette: released on Def Jam (USA), Jun'87 by CBS Records. Dist: CBS

Daw, All

I'M JUST A BABY.
Single (7"): released on Tristar, Oct'83 by Tristar Records. Dist: Pinnacle

Dawa, Mwendo

FOUR VOICES.
Album: released on Dragon, Jun'86 by Dragon Records. Dist: Jazz Music, Projection, Cadillac

NEW YORK LINES.
Album: released on Dragon, Jun'86 by Dragon Records. Dist: Jazz Music, Projection, Cadillac

Dawkins, Jimmy

ALL BLUES.
Notes: With Phil Guy and Professor Eddie Lusks.

Album: released on JSP, Jun'86 by JSP Records. Dist: Swift, Projection

ALL FOR BUSINESS.
Album: Dist: Projection, Swift, Cadillac

FAST FINGERS.
Album: Dist: Projection, Swift, Cadillac

FEEL THE BLUES.
Album: released on JSP, Oct'85 by JSP Records. Dist: Swift, Projection

TRANSATLANTIC 770.
Album: released on Sonet, Aug'78 by Sonet Records. Dist: PRT

Dawkins, Paul

COME, MY BABY (Dawkins, Paul & The Heptics).
Tracks: / Baby blues.
Single (12"): released on Starlight, Dec'86 by Starlight Records. Dist: Jetstar Distribution

Dawn

CANDIDA.
Single (7"): released on Old Gold, Jul'82 by Old Gold Records. Dist: Lightning, Jazz Music, Spartan, Counterpoint

DAWN.
Cassette: released on Pickwick, Sep'80 by Pickwick Records. Dist: Pickwick Distribution, Prism Leisure Distribution, Lugtons

KNOCK THREE TIMES.
Single (7"): released on Old Gold, Jul'82 by Old Gold Records. Dist: Lightning, Jazz Music, Spartan, Counterpoint

SWEET GYPSY ROSE.
Single (7"): released on Old Gold, Jul'82 by Old Gold Records. Dist: Lightning, Jazz Music, Spartan, Counterpoint

TIE A YELLOW RIBBON.
Single (7"): released on Old Gold, Jul'82 by Old Gold Records. Dist: Lightning, Jazz Music, Spartan, Counterpoint

Dawn Chorus

I'M GOING DOWN.
Single (7"): released on WWOCD, Oct'85 Dist: Red Rhino, Cartel

TEENAGE KICKS (Dawn Chorus & The Bluetits).
Single (7"): released on WWOCD, Apr'85 Dist: Red Rhino, Cartel

WHEN YOU WALK IN THE ROOM.
Tracks: / When you walk in the room / Lonely lips.
Single (7"): released on Magnet, Mar'87 by Magnet Records. Dist: BMG

Single (12"): released on Magnet, Mar'87 by Magnet Records. Dist: BMG

Dawn, Elizabeth

WORLD OF SMILES.
Album: released on Bowler Music, Feb'82

Dawn of Love

DAWN OF LOVE, (THE) Cartland, Barbara (Carson, John).
Cassette: released on Pickwick Talking Books, '83

Dawn Patrol

ALL OUR YESTERDAYS.
Single (7"): released on Dinosaur, Nov'81 by Dinosaur Records. Dist: Pinnacle

Dawson, Cliff

SOMEHOW.
Single (7"): released on Half Moon, Sep'82 by Rondelet Music And Records. Dist: Spartan

Single (12"): released on Half Moon, Sep'82 by Rondelet Music And Records. Dist: Spartan

Dawson, Dan

NO TEA PARTY (Dawson, Dan & Teddy Johnson).
Album: released on Nola, May'80 by JSU, Jazz Music, Cadillac, Chris Wellard

Dawson, Julian

AS REAL AS DISNEYLAND (Dawson, Julian & The Flood).
Album: released on Polydor (Germany), Oct'87 Dist: IMS-Polygram

Cassette: released on Polydor Int., Aug'87

Compact disc: released on Polydor Int., Aug'87

Dawson, Les
LAUGH WITH LES DAWSON.
Album: by BBC Records & Tapes. Dist: EMI, PRT, Pye

Cassette: released on BBC, '79 by BBC Records & Tapes. Dist: EMI, PRT, Pye

Dawson, Peter
FLORAL DANCE, (THE).
Album: released on Encore, Jun'78 by EMI Records. Dist: EMI

GOLDEN AGE OF PETER DAWSON, (THE).
Album: released on Golden Age, Jul'83 by Music For Pleasure. Dist: EMI

GOLDEN ALBUM, (THE).
Album: released on EMI Retrospect, May'84 by EMI Records. Dist: EMI

Cassette: released on EMI Retrospect, May'84 by EMI Records. Dist: EMI

SONGS OF THE SEA.
Album: released on World, '70 Dist: Jetstar

VERY BEST OF PETER DAWSON, (THE).
Album: released on Encore, Jun'78 by EMI Records. Dist: EMI

Dawson, Sandy
GOING TO SANDY'S CEILIDH.
Notes: With the Lomond Cornkisters Songs, dance music, pipes.
Cassette: released on Ross, Jan'86 by Ross Records. Dist: Ross Distribution, Roots Distribution

Dax, Danielle
BIG HOLLOW MAN.
Single (7"): released on Awesome, Jul'87 by Awesome Records. Dist: Rough Trade, Cartel

Single (12"): released on Awesome, Jul'87 by Awesome Records. Dist: Rough Trade, Cartel

INKY BLOATERS.
Compact disc: released on Awesome, Jun'87 by Awesome Records. Dist: Rough Trade, Cartel

Album: released on Awesome, Jun'87 by Awesome Records. Dist: Rough Trade, Cartel

JESUS, THE EGG THAT WEPT.
Album: released on Awesome, Oct'84 by Awesome Records. Dist: Rough Trade, Cartel

POP EYES.
Album: released on Initial, Jun'83 by Initial Records. Dist: Pinnacle

Album: released on Awesome, Apr'85 by Awesome Records. Dist: Rough Trade, Cartel

WHERE THE FLIES ARE.
Tracks: / Where the flies are.
Single (7"): released on Awesome, Oct'86 by Awesome Records. Dist: Rough Trade, Cartel

Single (12"): released on Awesome, Oct'86 by Awesome Records. Dist: Rough Trade, Cartel

YUMMER YUMMER MAN.
Single (7"): released on Awesome, Oct'85 by Awesome Records. Dist: Rough Trade, Cartel

Single (12"): released on Awesome, Oct'85 by Awesome Records. Dist: Rough Trade, Cartel

Day, Bobby
LITTLE BITTY PRETTY ONE.
Single (7"): released on Creole, Aug'82 by Creole Records. Dist: Rhino, PRT

ROCKIN' ROBIN.
Album: released on Ace, Feb'87 by Ace Records. Dist: Pinnacle, Swift, Hotshot, Cadillac

Single (7"): released on Creole, Aug'82 by Creole Records. Dist: Rhino, PRT

Day, Doris
BEST OF DORIS DAY, THE.
Tracks: / Secret love / Tacher's pet / Bewitched / Everybody loves a loser / It's magic / Bushel and a pock, a / Again / Again / Sentimental journey / Whatever will be, will be (Que sera sera) / Black hills of Dakota, the / Hernando's hideaway / If I give my heart to you / Deadwood stage, the (whip crack-away) / Tunnel of love / Move over darling / Love me or leave me.
Album: released on CBS, May'87 by CBS Records. Dist: CBS

Cassette: released on CBS, May'87 by CBS Records. Dist: CBS

BEST OF DORIS DAY, (THE).
Cassette: released on Creole (Everest-Europa) Jul'84 by Creole Records. Dist: PRT, Rhino

Album: released on Spot, Aug'83 by Pickwick Records. Dist: H.R. Taylor, Lugtons

Cassette: released on Spot, Aug'83 by Pickwick Records. Dist: H.R. Taylor, Lugtons

Album: released on CBS, Jul'80 by CBS Records. Dist: CBS

CALAMITY JANE/PYJAMA GAME.
Album: released on CBS, Sep'82 by CBS Records. Dist: CBS

Cassette: released on CBS, Sep'82 by CBS Records. Dist: CBS

DORIS DAY.
Album: released on Deja Vu, Jan'87 by Deja Vu Records. Dist: Counterpoint Distribution, Record Service Distribution (Ireland)

Cassette: released on Deja Vu, Jan'87 by Deja Vu Records. Dist: Counterpoint Distribution, Record Service Distribution (Ireland)

DORIS DAY'S GREATEST HITS.
Album: released on CBS Cameo, Jul'84 by CBS Records. Dist: CBS

Cassette: released on CBS Cameo, Jul'84 by CBS Records. Dist: CBS

DORIS DAY SONGBOOK,(THE).
Album: released on CBS(Holland), Jun'84 by CBS Records. Dist: Discovery

Cassette: released on CBS(Holland), Jun'84 by CBS Records. Dist: Discovery

DUET (Day, Doris & Andre Previn).
Album: released on Polydor (Germany), Jun'83 Dist: IMS-Polygram

GREATEST HITS:DORIS DAY.
Album: by CBS Records. Dist: CBS

GREAT MOVIE HITS.
Album: released on CBS(Blue Diamond), Jun'85 by CBS Records. Dist: CBS

Cassette: released on CBS(Blue Diamond), Jun'85 by CBS Records. Dist: CBS

MOVE OVER DARLING.
Tracks: / Deadwood stage / Move over darling / Teachers pet.
Notes: * = Extra track on 12" only
Single (12"): released on CBS, Apr'87 by CBS Records. Dist: CBS

Single (7"): released on CBS, Apr'87 by CBS Records. Dist: CBS

SECRET LOVE.
Single (7"): released on Old Gold, Jul'82 by Old Gold Records. Dist: Lightning, Jazz Music, Spartan, Counterpoint

SENTIMENTAL JOURNEY.
Album: released on CBS Cameo, Mar'83 by CBS Records. Dist: CBS

Cassette: released on CBS Cameo, Mar'83 by CBS Records. Dist: CBS

UNCOLLECTED (THE).
Album: released on Hindsight(UK), Apr'86 Dist: Jazz Music

WHATEVER WILL BE WILL BE.
Tracks: / Singin' in the rain / Close your eyes / I's easy to remember / If I give my heart to you / That old feeling / Whatever will be will be / Time to say goodnight / Moonglow / Lamp is low (The).
Album: released on CBS, Mar'86 by CBS Records. Dist: CBS

Cassette: released on CBS, Mar'86 by CBS Records. Dist: CBS

WHAT EVER WILL BE WILL BE.
Single (7"): released on Old Gold, Jul'82 by Old Gold Records. Dist: Lightning, Jazz Music, Spartan, Counterpoint

Day, Edith
EDITH DAY.
Album: released on World, '70 Dist: Jetstar

EDITH DAY IN RIO RITA, ROSE MARIE & SHOWBOAT.
Album: released on Monmouth, Mar'79

IRENE.
Album: released on Monmouth, Mar'70

Day, Margie
I'LL GET A DEAL (Day, Margie & The Griffin Brothers Orchestra).
Album: released on Mr. R & B, May'86 Dist: Jazz Music Distribution, Swift Distribution

---

Day, Morris
COLOR OF SUCCESS.
Tracks: / Color of success.

Single (7"): released on Warner Bros., Feb'86 by Warner Bros Records. Dist: WEA

Single (12"): released on Warner Bros., Feb'86 by Warner Bros Records. Dist: WEA

Album: released on Warner Bros., Nov'85 by Warner Bros Records. Dist: WEA

Cassette: released on Warner Bros., Nov'85 by Warner Bros Records. Dist: WEA

OAK TREE (THE).
Tracks: / Oak tree-dance inst. (The) / OAak tree-acapella (The).
Single (7"): released on Warner Bros., Jan'86 by Warner Bros Records. Dist: WEA

Single (12"): released on Warner Bros., Jan'86 by Warner Bros Records. Dist: WEA

Day, Muriel
NINE TIMES OUT OF TEN.
Single (7"): released on Soul Stop, Aug'82 by Soul Stop Record 3. Dist: Spartan

Day Of...
DAY OF THE SARDINE (Chaplin, Sid).
Cassette: released on Soundings, Mar'85 Dist: Soundings

DAY OF THE TRIFFIDS Wyndham, John (Powell, Robert).
Notes: This is John Wyndham's famous story of a world dominated by monstrous stinging plants, capable of walking and of some form of communication. Plants which had previously been considered curiosities to be handled with care, but not to be feared. Then the balance of power is unexpectedly shifted and the monstrous plants begin to take overs. Running time: 2 hours approx.

Day, Ricky
WELCOME TO THE ISLE OF WIGHT.
Single (7"): released on Round, Jul'85 Dist: PRT, Red Rhino, Cartel

WE'LL MEET AGAIN.
Single (7"): released on Heart, Jun'83 Dist: Pinnacle

Day's, Helen Wild Affair
FACE THAT BROKE A THOUSAND HEARTS.
Single (7"): released on Buzz, Sep'83

Days of 29
DESTINATION D-DAY.
Single (12"): released on Braw Products, Jul'85 Dist: Fast Forward, Cartel

Dayton
FEEL THE MUSIC.
Album: released on Capitol, Nov'93 by Capitol Records. Dist: EMI Deleted '86.

Cassette: released on Capitol, Nov'93 by Capitol Records. Dist: EMI

Daze
DEEP SOUTH.
Single (7"): released on Mynah, Jan'84 by Mynah Records. Dist: Mynah, ILA

Dazz
DEAR AUNTIE AGATHA.
Single (7"): released on Polo, Mar'81 by Polo Records. Dist: PRT

EVERYTHING'S ELECTRIC.
Single (7"): released on Polo, Mar'80 by Polo Records. Dist: PRT

Dazz Band
GREATEST HITS:DAZZ BAND.
Tracks: / Let it whip / Joystick / Invitation to love / Party right here / Swoop-I'm your's / Keep it live / Cheek to cheek / Knock knock / On the one for fun / Let it all blow.
Album: released on Motown, Jul'86 by Motown Records. Dist: BMG Distribution

Cassette: released on Motown, Jul'86 by Motown Records. Dist: BMG Distribution

HEARTBEAT.
Single (7"): released on Motown, Jan'85 by Motown Records. Dist: BMG Distribution

Single (12"): released on Motown, Jan'85 by Motown Records. Dist: BMG Distribution

HOT SPOT.
Single (7"): released on Motown, Jul'85 by Motown Records. Dist: BMG Distribution

Single (12"): released on Motown, Jul'85 by Motown Records. Dist: BMG Distribution

---

INVITATION TO LOVE.
Album: released on Motown, Oct'81 by Motown Records. Dist: BMG Distribution

JOYSTICK.
Cassette: released on Motown, Apr'84 by Motown Records. Dist: BMG Distribution

Album: released on Motown, Apr'84 by Motown Records. Dist: BMG Distribution

Single (12"): released on Motown, Jan'84 by Motown Records. Dist: BMG Distribution

JUKEBOX.
Album: released on Motown, Nov'84 by Motown Records. Dist: BMG Distribution

Cassette: released on Motown, Nov'84 by Motown Records. Dist: BMG Distribution

KEEP IT LIVE.
Album: released on Motown, Sep'82 by Motown Records. Dist: BMG Distribution

Single (7"): released on Motown, Feb'83 by Motown Records. Dist: BMG Distribution

Single (12"): released on Motown, Feb'83 by Motown Records. Dist: BMG Distribution

LET IT ALL BLOW.
Single (7"): released on Motown, Oct'84 by Motown Records. Dist: BMG Distribution

Single (12"): released on Motown, Oct'84 by Motown Records. Dist: BMG Distribution

LET IT WHIP.
Single (7"): released on Motown, Oct'82 by Motown Records. Dist: BMG Distribution

LOVE M.I.A..
Tracks: / Love M.I.A / Place in my heart.
Single (7"): released on Geffen, Sep'86 by Geffen Records. Dist: WEA, CBS

Single (12"): released on Geffen, Sep'86 by Geffen Records. Dist: WEA, CBS

ON THE ONE.
Album: released on Motown, Mar'83 by Motown Records. Dist: BMG Distribution

Single (7"): released on Motown, Mar'83 by Motown Records. Dist: BMG Distribution

Single (12"): released on Motown, Mar'83 by Motown Records. Dist: BMG Distribution

SHAKE IT UP.
Single (7"): released on Motown, Oct'81 by Motown Records. Dist: BMG Distribution

Single (12"): released on Motown, Oct'81 by Motown Records. Dist: BMG Distribution

SWOOP I'M YOURS.
Single (7"): released on Motown, '84 by Motown Records. Dist: BMG Distribution

Single (12"): released on Motown, '84 by Motown Records. Dist: BMG Distribution

WILD AND FREE.
Tracks: / Wild & free / Body and mind / Time / Beat that's right (The) / All I need / Love M.I.A / Hooks in me / Sunglasses / It's alright / Something you said.
Album: released on Geffen, Aug'86 by Geffen Records. Dist: WEA, CBS

Cassette: released on Geffen, Aug'86 by Geffen Records. Dist: WEA, CBS

Compact disc: released on Geffen, Mar'87 by Geffen Records. Dist: WEA, CBS

Dazzlers
DAZZLERS,THE.
Album: released on Rockhouse, '83 by Rockhouse Records. Dist: Swift Distribution, Charly Distribution

DBL Crew
BUST IT.
Tracks: / Bust it.
Single (7"): released on Affair, Jul'86 Dist: DMS, RCA

DB's
AMPLIFIER.
Tracks: / Nothing is wrong / Neverland / In Spain / Happenstance / Living a lie / From a window to a scream / Ask for Jill / Amplifier / Bad reputation / Big brown eyes / Moving in your sleep / Black and white / I feel good toady / Ups and downs.
Album: released on Dojo, Aug'86 by Castle Communications Records. Dist: Cartel

AMPLIFIER/ASK FOR JILL.
Single (7"): released on Albion, '82 by Albion Records. Dist: Spartan, Pinnacle

BIG BROWN EYES Baby talk.
Single (7"): released on Albion, '81 by Albion Records. Dist: Spartan, Pinnacle

DYNAMITE.
Single (7"): released on Albion, '81 by Albion Records. Dist: Spartan, Pinnacle

LIVING A LIE In Spain.
Single (7"): released on Albion, '82 by Albion Records. Dist: Spartan, Pinnacle

NEVERLAND Ph Factor.
Single (7"): released on Albion, '82 by Albion Records. Dist: Spartan, Pinnacle

REPERCUSSION.
Album: released on Albion, '82 by Albion Records. Dist: Spartan, Pinnacle

Cassette: released on Albion, '82 by Albion Records. Dist: Spartan, Pinnacle

D.C.L. Locomotive
KING MIDAS IN REVERSE.
Single (12"): released on Reflex, Jun'84

D.C.Nighthawks
NIGHTHAWKS.
Album: released on Mercury, Sep'80 by Phonogram Records. Dist: Polygram Distribution

D.C.S.
FROM EAST TO WEST (D.C.S.with Runa Laila).
Album: released on H.M.V., Nov'83 by EMI Records. Dist: EMI

D.C. & The T.B.'s
TEDDY BEAR'S PICNIC.
Single (7"): released on Bear, Nov'82

D, Davy
DAVY'S RIDE.
Album: released on Def Jam (USA), Jul'87 by CBS Records. Dist: CBS

Cassette: released on Def Jam (USA), Jul'87 by CBS Records. Dist: CBS

HAVE YOU SEEN DAVY.
Tracks: / Have you seen Davy / Keep your distance.
Single (7"): released on Def Jam (USA), Jul'87 by CBS Records. Dist: CBS

Single (12"): released on Def Jam (USA), Jul'87 by CBS Records. Dist: CBS

D-Day Despatches
D-DAY DESPATCHES (War correspondents reports).
Album: released on BBC, '84 by BBC Records & Tapes. Dist: EMI, PRT, Pye

Cassette: released on BBC, '84 by BBC Records & Tapes. Dist: EMI, PRT, Pye

DDHE
DET DANSKE HARMONIKA ENSEMBLE.
Tracks: / Donna Diana / Bach goes to town / Champagne gallop / Florentine march / Russian & Ljudmilla overture / Koncert suite for accordion / Sabeldans fra balletten gayaneh.
Notes: Retail price given by ARC excluding P&P (via Mail Order) is 5.49. Mail Order distribution address: Accordion Record Club, 146 Birmingham Road, Kidderminster, Worcs. DY10 2SL. Tel: 0562 - 746105
Album: released on Accordion Record Club, Jul'86 by Accordion Record Club Records. Dist: Accordion Record Club

Album: released on ARC (Accordion Records), '84 Dist: Accordion Record Club

MARCHENFARBER.
Tracks: / Abenlied & marchenfarben / Introduktion & toccata / Dansk rapsodi / Anno & Mikko.
Notes: Retail price given by ARC excluding P & P (via Mail Order) is 6.00. Mail order distribution address: Accordion Record Club, 146 Birmingham Road, Kidderminster, Worcs. DY10 2SL. Tel: 0562 - 746105.
Album: released on Accordion Record Club, Jul'86 by Accordion Record Club Records. Dist: Accordion Record Club

VIVA (DDHE, Jeanette Dyremose).
Notes: Retail price given by ARC excluding P & P (Via Mail Order) is 5.49. Mail order distribution address: Accordion Record Club, 146 Birmingham Road, Kidderminster, Worcs. DY10 2SL. Tel: 0562 - 746105.
Album: released on Accordion Record Club, Jun'86 by Accordion Record Club Records. Dist: Accordion Record Club

DDK
SOMETHING FOR THE WEEKEND.
Notes: DDK are: Dave Arnold (Stark) with Dave Kent and Keith Rodway (The Cast).Tracks include "Bog dub" which boasts a moving vocal performance recorded in a lavatory.
Cassette: released on Dead Happy, '86 by Dead Happy Records. Dist: Mason's Music Distributors/Wholesalers, Rough Trade

Deacon Blue
DIGNITY.
Tracks: / Dignity / Riches / Ribbons & bows **.
Notes: Extra track Ribbons & Bows on 12" only **
Single (7"): released on CBS, Mar'87 by CBS Records. Dist: CBS

Single (12"): released on CBS, Mar'87 by CBS Records. Dist: CBS

LOADED.
Tracks: / Loaded / Long distance from just across the road / Which side are you on* / Kings of the western world*.
Single (7"): released on CBS, Jun'87 by CBS Records. Dist: CBS

Single (12"): released on CBS, Jun'87 by CBS Records. Dist: CBS

Cassette single: released on CBS, Jun'87 by CBS Records. Dist: CBS

RAINTOWN.
Tracks: / Born in a storm / Raintown / Ragman / He looks like Spencer Tracy now / Loaded / When will you (make my telepone ring) / Chocolate girl / Dignity / Very thing, The / Love's great fears / Town to be blamed.
Compact disc: released on CBS, Jun'87 by CBS Records. Dist: CBS

Album: released on CBS, May'87 by CBS Records. Dist: CBS

Cassette: released on CBS, May'87 by CBS Records. Dist: CBS

YOU MAKE MY PHONE RING.
Single (7"): released on CBS, Aug'87 by CBS Records. Dist: CBS

Single (12"): released on CBS, Aug'87 by CBS Records. Dist: CBS

Dead Beats
CRAZY HOUND DOG.
Single (7"): released on Sheet, Jun'82 Dist: Rough Trade

ON A TAR BEACH.
Album: released on New Rose, May'85 Dist: Rough Trade, Cartel

Dead Boys
ALL THE WAY DOWN.
Single (12"): released on Relativity (USA), Aug'87 Dist: Pinnacle, Rough Trade, Cartel

NIGHT OF THE LIVING DEAD BOYS.
Album: released on Lolita, May'84 by Lolita Records. Dist: Rough Trade, Cartel

YOUNG LOUD AND SNOTTY.
Album: released on Sire, Sep'78

Dead Can Dance
DEAD CAN DANCE.
Tracks: / Passage in time, A / Fatal Impact, The / Trial, The / Frontier / Fortune / Ocean / East of Eden / Threshold / Passage in time, A / Wild in the woods / Musica eternal.
Compact disc: released on 4AD, Feb'87 by 4AD Records. Dist: Rough Trade

Album: released on 4AD, Feb'84 by 4AD Records. Dist: Rough Trade

GARDEN OF THE ARCANE.
Single (12"): released on 4AD, Sep'84 by 4AD Records. Dist: Rough Trade

SPLEEN AND IDEAL.
Tracks: / This tide / De profundis / out of the depth of sorrow / Ascension / Circumradiant dawn / Cardinal sin, The / Mesmerism / Enigma of the absolute / Advent / Abatar / Indoctrination / a design for living.
Compact disc: by 4AD Records. Dist: Rough Trade

Album: released on 4AD, Nov'85 by 4AD Records. Dist: Rough Trade

Cassette: released on 4AD, Nov'85 by 4AD Records. Dist: Rough Trade

Compact disc: released on 4AD, Jan'86 by 4AD Records. Dist: Rough Trade

WITHIN THE REALM OF THE DYING SUN.
Compact disc: released on 4AD, Jul'87 by 4AD Records. Dist: Rough Trade

WITHIN THE REALM OF A DYING SUN.
Album: released on 4AD, Jul'87 by 4AD Records. Dist: Rough Trade

Cassette: released on 4AD, Jul'87 by 4AD Records. Dist: Rough Trade

Dead Dog Limited
DEVIOUS WOMAN.
Tracks: / Devious woman.
Single (7"): released on Island, Oct'86 by Island Records. Dist: Polygram

Single (12"): released on Island, Oct'86 by Island Records. Dist: Polygram

Dead Fingers Talk
STORM THE REALITY STUDIOS.
Album: released on Pye, Jun'78

Dead Goldfish Ensemble
MUSIC FOR BOWLS.
Tracks: / Intro / Grey earls / All the hands / Dazzle one / Little bit of nonsense, (A) / Openings / Eric / Cool walls.
Cassette: released on Peerless, Jan'87

STRUCTURES AND STRICTURES.
Tracks: / Dead goldfish / Don't fight back / Modes of thought / Important haircuts / No static at all.
Cassette: released on Peerless, Jun'85

Dead Kennedys
BEDTIME FOR DEMOCRACY.
Album: released on Alternative Tentacles, Dec'86 by Alternative Tentacles Records. Dist: Rough Trade, Pinnacle

Cassette: released on Alternative Tentacles, Dec'86 by Alternative Tentacles Records. Dist: Rough Trade, Pinnacle

Compact disc: by Pacific Records (USA). Dist: Atlantic

BLEED FOR ME.
Single (7"): released on Statik, Jul'82 Dist: Rough Trade Distribution, Stage One Distribution

Single (12"): released on Statik, Jul'82 Dist: Rough Trade Distribution, Stage One Distribution

CALIFORNIA UBER ALLES.
Single (7"): released on Fast, Dec'80 by Fast Forward Communications (Scotland). Dist: Cartel

FRANKENCHRIST.
Album: released on Alternative Tentacles, Dec'85 by Alternative Tentacles Records. Dist: Rough Trade, Pinnacle

Compact disc: released on Alternative Tentacles, Jan'86 by Alternative Tentacles Records. Dist: Rough Trade, Pinnacle

FRESH FRUIT FOR ROTTING VEGETABLES.
Compact disc: by Cherry Red Records. Dist: Pinnacle

Album: released on Cherry Red, '82 by Cherry Red Records. Dist: Pinnacle

GIVE ME CONVENIENCE OR GIVE ME DEATH.
Album: released on Alternative Tentacles, Jun'87 by Alternative Tentacles Records. Dist: Rough Trade, Pinnacle

HALLOWEEN.
Single (7"): released on Alternative, Dec'82 Dist: PRT

Single (12"): released on Alternative, Dec'82 Dist: PRT Deleted '85.

HOLIDAY IN CAMBODIA.
Single (7"): released on Cherry Red, Sep'81 by Cherry Red Records. Dist: Pinnacle

Single (12"): released on Cherry Red, Sep'81 by Cherry Red Records. Dist: Pinnacle

IN GOD WE TRUST.
Single (7"): released on Statik, Dec'81 Dist: Rough Trade Distribution, Stage One Distribution

KILL THE POOR.
Single (7"): released on Cherry Red, Aug'81 by Cherry Red Records. Dist: Pinnacle

PLASTIC SURGERY DISASTERS.
Tracks: / Government flu / Terminal preppie / Trust your mechanic / Well paid scientist / Buzzbomb / Forest fire / Halloween / Winnebago warrior / Riot / Bleed for me / I am the owl / Dead end / Moon over marin.
Notes: CD also includes *In God we trust.*
Compact disc: released on Statik, Nov'86 Dist: Rough Trade Distribution, Stage One Distribution

Album: released on Statik, Oct'85 Dist: Rough Trade Distribution, Stage One Distribution

TOO DRUNK TO **.**
Single (7"): released on Cherry Red, Jun'81 by Cherry Red Records. Dist: Pinnacle

Single (12"): released on Cherry Red, Jun'81 by Cherry Red Records. Dist: Pinnacle

Dead Mans Shadow
ANOTHER YEAR.
Single (7"): released on Criminal Damage, Nov'83 by Criminal Damage Records. Dist: Backs, Cartel

BOMB SCARE.
Single (7"): released on Rondelet, Mar'82 Dist: Spartan Distribution

FLOWER IN THE GUN.
Single (7"): released on Rondelet, Nov'82 Dist: Spartan Distribution

IN MY DREAMS.
Single (7"): released on Expulsion, Jun'83 by Expulsion Records. Dist: Stage One

TO MOHAMMED....A MOUNTAIN.
Album: released on Criminal Damage, Mar'84 by Criminal Damage Records. Dist: Backs, Cartel

Dead Milkmen
EAT YOUR PAISLEY.
Album: released on Enigma (Europe), Nov'86 by Enigma Records. Dist: Rough Trade, Cartel, EMI

Dead Neighbors
HARMONY IN HELL.
Album: released on Sharko 2, Aug'84 Dist: Rough Trade, Cartel

STRANGE DAYS, STRANGE WAYS.
Album: released on Sharko 2, Mar'85 Dist: Rough Trade, Cartel

Dead Or Alive
BRAND NEW LOVER.
Tracks: / Brand new lover / In too deep/live.
Single (7"): released on Epic, Sep'86 by CBS Records. Dist: CBS

Single (12"): released on Epic, Sep'86 by CBS Records. Dist: CBS

HOOKED ON LOVE.
Tracks: / Hooked on love / You spin me round.
Single (7"): released on Epic, Mar'87 by CBS Records. Dist: CBS

I'D DO ANYTHING.
Single (7"): released on Epic, Jan'84 by CBS Records. Dist: CBS

Single (12"): released on Epic, Jan'84 by CBS Records. Dist: CBS

I'M FALLING.
Single (7"): released on Inevitable, Mar'81 by Inevitable Records. Dist: Rough Trade

IN TOO DEEP.
Single (7"): released on Epic, Jun'85 by CBS Records. Dist: CBS

Gatefold sleeve: released on Epic, Jun'85 by CBS Records. Dist: CBS

Single (12"): released on Epic, Jun'85 by CBS Records. Dist: CBS Deleted '86.

Single (12"): released on Epic, Jun'85 by CBS Records. Dist: CBS

MAD, BAD AND DANGEROUS TO KNOW.
Tracks: / Brand new lover / I'll save you all my kisses / Son of a gun / Then there was you / Come inside / Something in my house / Hooked on love / I want you / I want you / Special star.
Album: released on Epic, Feb'87 by CBS Records. Dist: CBS

Cassette: released on Epic, Feb'87 by CBS Records. Dist: CBS

MISTY CIRCLES.
Single (7"): released on Epic, May'83 by CBS Records. Dist: CBS

Single (12"): released on Epic, May'83 by CBS Records. Dist: CBS

Picture disc single: released on Epic, Jun'83 by CBS Records. Dist: CBS

SOMETHING IN MY HOUSE.
Tracks: / DJ hit that button / DJ hit that button.
Single (7"): released on Epic, Dec'86 by CBS Records. Dist: CBS

Single (12"): released on Epic, Dec'86 by CBS Records. Dist: CBS

Single (7"): released on Epic, Jan'87 by CBS Records. Dist: CBS

SOPHISTICATED BOOM BOOM.
Tracks: / I'd do anything / That's the way (I like it) / Absolutely nothing / What I want / Far too hard / You make me wanna / Sit on it / Wish you were here / Misty circles / Do.
Album: released on Epic, Nov'86 by CBS Records. Dist: CBS

Cassette: released on Epic, Nov'86 by CBS Records. Dist: CBS

Cassette: released on Epic, Apr'84 by CBS Records. Dist: CBS

Album: released on Epic, Apr'84 by CBS Records. Dist: CBS Deleted '87.

STRANGER, (THE).
Single (7"): released on Black Eyes, Sep'82 Dist: Rough Trade

THAT'S THE WAY I LIKE IT.
Single (7"): released on Epic, Mar'84 by CBS Records. Dist: CBS

Single (12"): released on Epic, Mar'84 by CBS Records. Dist: CBS

WHAT I WANT.
Single (7"): released on Epic, Jun'84 by CBS Records. Dist: CBS

Single (12"): released on Epic, Jun'84 by CBS Records. Dist: CBS

YOUTHQUAKE.
Album: released on Epic, May'85 by CBS Records. Dist: CBS

Cassette: released on Epic, May'85 by CBS Records. Dist: CBS

Dead Pan Tractor
GRUMBLE.
Single (12"): released on Black Lagoon, Sep'85 by Black Lagoon Records. Dist: Red Rhino, Cartel

Dead Sea Surfers
DON'T SING ALOHA.
Album: released on Plant Life, May'83 Dist: Roots

Dead Veins
GTF.
Album: released on Batfish, Nov'85 Dist: Red Rhino, Cartel

Dead Wretched
CONVICTED.
Single (7"): released on Inferno, Sep'82 by Inferno Records. Dist: Inferno, Cartel, Pinnacle

NO HOPE FOR ANYONE.
Single (7"): released on Inferno, Feb'82 by Inferno Records. Dist: Inferno, Cartel, Pinnacle

Deaf Comet Crew
AT THE MARBLE BOY.
Single (12"): released on Beggars Banquet, Mar'85 by Beggars Banquet Records. Dist: WEA

Deal, Bill
BILL DEAL & THE RHONDELLS (Deal, Bill & The Rhondells).
Album: released on Rhino (USA), May'86 by Rhino Records (USA).

Dealer
FIRST STRIKE.
Album: released on Ebony, Feb'87 by Ebony Records. Dist: Pinnacle, Ebony

Dean, Chris
MY FIRST CHOICE.
Album: released on Major Richards, Sep'80 by Major Richards Records. Dist: Taylors

Deane, Geoff
HOLIDAY IN (Deane, Geoff/Tropical Fish, (The)).
Single (7"): released on Record Shack, Jul'85 by Record Shack Records. Dist: PRT

Single (12"): released on Record Shack, Jul'85 by Record Shack Records. Dist: PRT

NAVY LARK (Deane, Geoff/Valley Girls).
Single (7"): released on WEA, Apr'83 by WEA Records. Dist: WEA

Single (12"): released on WEA, Apr'83 by WEA Records. Dist: WEA

Deane, Geoffrey
WHAT ABOUT ROMANCE.
Single (7"): released on Plastic Palm Trees, Oct'83

Single (12"): released on Plastic Palm Trees, Oct'83

Dean, Elton
CHEQUE IS IN THE MAIL, (THE).
Album: released on Ogun, Aug'77 by Ogun Dist: Jazz Music, JSU, Cadillac

MERCY DASH (Dean, Elton/Hopper, Hugh/Gallivan, Joe/Tippet, Keith).

Notes: For full information see under: Tippet, Keith etc.

Deane, Uel
EVERGREEN.
Album: released on Valentine, Nov'84 by Valentine Records. Dist: PRT

Cassette: released on Valentine, Nov'84 by Valentine Records. Dist: PRT

De Angelis, Nicolas
GOA.
Album: released on Polydor (France), '85 Dist: Polygram

Cassette: released on Polydor (France), '85 Dist: Polygram

GUITAR GUITAR.
Tracks: / El condor pasa / Island in the sun / Girl of Impanema / Cuando calienta el sol / L'espagnole / Guantanamera / Maria Helena / Girl from Ipanema / L'amour amor / La paloma / Begin the beguine / Cuando calienta / Mas que nada / brazil / Amor amor / Les jardins d'Alcantara / Vaya con dios / Cuando calienta el sol / Sola mente una vez / La Nina paloma / O'cangaceiro / L'espagnole / Ave Maria no moro / Guantanamera / Maria Helena / L'amour amor / La paloma / Begin the beguine / Mas que nada / Brazil / Amor amor / Les jardins d'alcantara / Vaya con dios / Solamente una vez / La nina paloma / O'cangaceiro / Ave Maria no moro.
Notes: Popular guitarist Nicholas De Angelis performing well-known & original compositions with orchestral backing. 19 titles & 57 minutes of music
Album: released on Polydor, Mar'87 by Polydor Records. Dist: Polygram, Polydor

GUITAR GUITAR.
Compact disc: released on Delphine, Nov'86 by Decca Records. Dist: Polygram

NICOLAS DE ANGELIS.
Album: released on London, Nov'85 by London Records. Dist: Polygram

Cassette: released on London, Nov'85 by London Records. Dist: Polygram

QUELQUES NOTES POUR ANNA.
Album: released on Delphine (France), '85 by Decca Records. Dist: IMS, Polygram

Cassette: released on Delphine (France), '85 by Decca Records. Dist: IMS, Polygram

SONG FOR ANNA.
Tracks: / Song for Anna / Guantanamera / Evidence of the heart.
Single (7"): released on London, Feb'87 by London Records. Dist: Polygram

De Angelo, Nino
GUARDIAN ANGEL.
Single (7"): released on Carrere, '85 by Carrere Records. Dist: PRT, Spartan

Single (12"): released on Carrere, '85 by Carrere Records. Dist: PRT, Spartan

NINO DE ANGELO.
Cassette: released on Carrere, '84 by Carrere Records. Dist: PRT, Spartan

Album: released on Carrere, '84 by Carrere Records. Dist: PRT, Spartan

Dean, Hazell
ALWAYS DOESN'T MEAN FOREVER.
Tracks: / Always doesn't mean forever / Always doesn't mean forever (inst).
Single (7"): released on EMI, Jun'87 by EMI Records. Dist: EMI

Single (12"): released on EMI, Jun'87 by EMI Records. Dist: EMI

BACK IN MY ARMS (once again).
Single (7"): released on Proto, Oct'84 by Proto Records. Dist: WEA

Single (12"): released on Proto, Oct'84 by Proto Records. Dist: WEA

E.S.P.
Tracks: / E.S.P. / Image in the mirror.
Single (7"): released on EMI, Apr'86 by EMI Records. Dist: EMI

Single (12"): released on EMI, Apr'86 by EMI Records. Dist: EMI

HEART FIRST.
Compact disc: released on Bellaphon, '86 by Bellaphon Records. Dist: IMS-Polygram

Album: released on Proto, Nov'84 by Proto Records. Dist: WEA

Cassette: released on Proto, Nov'84 by Proto Records. Dist: WEA

JEALOUS LOVE.
Single (7"): released on Proto, Jan'84 by Proto Records. Dist: WEA

Single (12"): released on Proto, Jan'84 by

Proto Records. Dist: WEA

Picture disc single: released on Proto, Jan'84 by Proto Records. Dist: WEA

NO FOOL.
Single (7"): released on Proto, Feb'85 by Proto Records. Dist: WEA

Single (12"): released on Proto, Feb'85 by Proto Records. Dist: WEA

Picture disc single: released on Proto, Feb'85 by Proto Records. Dist: WEA

SEARCHIN.
Tracks: / Searchin / Whatever i do / Stand up/High a a kite megamix / Stand up/Love ends Love.
Single (12"): released on EMI, Oct'86 by EMI Records. Dist: EMI

SEARCHIN'.
Single (7"): released on Proto, Apr'84 by Proto Records. Dist: WEA

Single (12"): released on Proto, Apr'84 by Proto Records. Dist: WEA

STAND UP.
Tracks: / Love ends, love parts / Whatever i do/ extended play / Searching/ extended play / Stand up.
Notes: Extra tracks in double pack
Single (7"): released on EMI, Aug'86 by EMI Records. Dist: EMI

Single (12"): released on EMI, Aug'86 by EMI Records. Dist: EMI

Double-pack single: released on EMI, Aug'86 by EMI Records. Dist: EMI

THEY SAY IT'S GONNA RAIN.
Single (7"): released on Parlophone, Sep'85 by EMI Records. Dist: EMI

Single (12"): released on Parlophone, Sep'85 by EMI Records. Dist: EMI

WHATEVER I DO (wherever I go).
Single (7"): released on Proto, Aug'84 by Proto Records. Dist: WEA

Single (12"): released on Proto, Aug'84 by Proto Records. Dist: WEA

Dean, James
TRIBUTE TO.
Notes: Realeased on picture disc.
Album: released on Astan, Dec'85 by Astan Records. Dist: Counterpoint

Dean & Jean
HEY JEAN, HEY DEAN.
Album: released on Impact, Oct'86 by Ace Records. Dist: Rough Trade, Pinnacle, Swift, Backs, Counterpoint, Jungle, Hotshot, Cartel

Dean, Jimmy
BIG BAD JOHN.
Tracks: / Steelman.
Single (7"): released on Old Gold, Jan'87 by Old Gold Records. Dist: Lightning, Jazz Music, Spartan, Counterpoint

HIS TOP HITS.
Cassette: released on Timeless Treasures, Jul'86 Dist: Counterpoint Distribution

Dean, Johnny
SITTING AROUND MY TABLE.
Single (12"): released on Move, Oct'85 by Charly Records. Dist: Charly Distribution, Fast Forward Distribution, Cartel Distribution

Dean, Letitia
SOMETHING OUTA NOTHING (Dean, Letitia & Paul Medford).
Tracks: / Something outa nothing / Time square/ Instrumental.
Single (7"): released on BBC, Oct'86 by BBC Records & Tapes. Dist: EMI, PRT, Pve

Single (12"): released on BBC, Oct'86 by BBC Records & Tapes. Dist: EMI, PRT, Pve

Dean, Mel
ZOLA ZOLA.
Single (7"): released on Rubber Trumpet, Jun'85 by Rubber Trumpet Records. Dist: M.I.S. Distribution

Dean, Peter
I CAN'T GET A TICKET FOR THE WORLD CUP.
Tracks: / I can't get a ticket for the world cup / Right here, don't panic.
Single (7"): released on Portrait, May'86 by CBS Records. Dist: CBS

WHERE DID THE MAGIC GO?.
Album: released on Retrospect, Jan'87 by World Records.

Dean, Raddie
PARTY NIGHT.
Single (12"): released on Sapphire, Jan'84 by Sapphire Records. Dist: Jetstar

Dean, Rick
ALLEY OOP.
Single (12"): released on Monarch, Sep'82 by Chart Records. Dist: Pinnacle

Dean, Roger Lysis
CYCLES.
Album: released on Mosaic, Aug'77 by Mosaic Records. Dist: Jazz Music Distribution, Impetus Distribution, JSU Distribution, Cadillac

LYSIS LIVE.
Album: released on Mosaic, Jan'77 by Mosaic Records. Dist: Jazz Music Distribution, Impetus Distribution, JSU Distribution, Cadillac

Dean, Sparky
YIP YAP RABBIT.
Single (12"): released on UK Bubblers, Nov'85 by Greensleeves Records. Dist: RCA, Jetstar

Dean, Terry
TERRY DEAN'S APACHE BAND.
Album: released on Zero, Apr'79 by Zero Records. Dist: Zero Distribution

Dear Anyone
DEAR ANYONE Various Artists (Various Artists).
Album: released on DJM, Jun'78 by DJM Records. Dist: CBS, Polygram

Cassette: released on DJM, Jun'78 by DJM Records. Dist: CBS, Polygram

Dearie, Blossom
BLOSSOM DEARIE.
Album: released on Verve (USA), May'83 by Polydor. Dist: Polygram

BLOSSOM DEARIE SINGS 1973.
Album: released on Daffodil, Apr'79 by Swift

MAY I COME IN.
Album: released on Capitol, Apr'81 by Capitol Records. Dist: EMI

MY NEW CELEBRITY IS YOU.
Double Album: released on Daffodil, Apr'79 Dist: Swift

WINCHESTER IN APPLE BLOSSOM TIME.
Double Album: released on Daffodil, Apr'79 Dist: Swift

Dear old Donegal
DEAR OLD DONEGAL Various Artists (Various Artists).
Album: released on Harp(Ireland), Aug'83 by Pickwick Records. Dist: Taylors

Cassette: released on Harp(Ireland), Aug'83 by Pickwick Records. Dist: Taylors

Deasy, Pat
YOU OUGHT TO PUT IT TO MUSIC.
Single (7"): released on Play, Jul'85 by Play Records. Dist: Spartan

Death
SCREAM BLOODY GORE.
Album: released on Under One Flag, Jun'87 Dist: Pinnacle

Compact disc: released on Under One Flag, Jun'87 Dist: Pinnacle

Death Angel
ULTRA-VIOLENCE.
Album: released on Under One Flag, May'87 Dist: Pinnacle

Death Cult
BROTHERS GRIMM.
Single (12"): released on Situation 2, Jul'83 Dist: Cartel, Pinnacle

GOD'S ZOO.
Single (7"): released on Situation 2, Nov'83 Dist: Cartel, Pinnacle

Single (12"): released on Situation 2, Nov'83 Dist: Cartel, Pinnacle

Death, Glory &...
DEATH, GLORY & RETRIBUTION Various Artists (Various Artists).
Album: released on Capitol, Sep'85 by Capitol Records. Dist: EMI

Cassette: released on Capitol, Sep'85 by Capitol Records. Dist: EMI

Death In June

.....AND MURDER LOVE.
Single (7"): released on Ner, Dec'85 by New European Records/Death in June. Dist: Rough Trade, Cartel

Single (12"): released on Ner, Dec'85 by New European Records/Death in June. Dist: Rough Trade, Cartel

BORN AGAIN.
Single (12"): released on Ner, Mar'85 by New European Records/Death in June. Dist: Rough Trade, Cartel

HEAVEN STREET.
Single (12"): released on New European, Jan'84 by New European Records/Death in June. Dist: Rough Trade, Cartel

MDISNATHROPY.
Album: released on Ner, Sep'86 by New European Records/Death in June. Dist: Rough Trade, Cartel

NADA.
Album: released on Ner Bad, Feb'85 by New European Records/Death in June. Dist: Rough Trade, Cartel

S..E SAID DESTROY.
Single (7"): released on New European, Aug'84 by New European Records/Death in June. Dist: Rough Trade, Cartel

Single (12"): released on New European, Aug'84 by New European Records/Death in June. Dist: Rough Trade, Cartel

STATE LAUGHTER.
Single (7"): released on New European, Nov'82 by New European Records/Death in June. Dist: Rough Trade, Cartel

TO DROWN A ROSE.
Single 10": released on Ner, 30 May'87 by New European Records/Death in June. Dist: Rough Trade, Cartel

WORLD THAT SUMMER, THE.
Album: released on Ner, Sep'86 by New European Records/Death in June. Dist: Rough Trade, Cartel

Death In Venice

DEATH IN VENICE Original Soundtrack.
Album: released on RCA (Germany), '83

Death Leaves An Echo

DEATH LEAVES AN ECHO (Various Artists).
Notes: Compilation featuring tracks from :Paul Haigh,Idabelle Antena,Wim Mertens,Pale Fountains,Piscine & Charles,French Impressionists,Border Boys,Winston Tong, 52nd.Street,Stanton Miranda & Ludus.
Album: released on Les Disques Du Crepuscule, Mar'87 Dist: Rough Trade, Pinnacle, Island, Polygram

Death Mask

SPLIT THE ATOM.
Album: released on Killerwatt, Oct'86 Dist: Kingdom Records, Pinnacle

Death of a soldier

DEATH OF A SOLDIER Original Soundtrack (Original Soundtrack).
Tracks: / Boys from the USA / Annie's Jive / In the mood / Dinah Might / Sentimental dreams / Boogie woogie bugle boy / Jersey Trott / Sweetie pie / When Johnny comes marching home / Swanston Street Parade / Overture / Mud murder / Shoot-out / Pauline's murder.
Notes: Music from the film "Death of a Soldier" composed by Allen Zavod, and capturing the musical spirit of the 40s and the golden era of the big bands. Sleeve notesby Woody Herman and Cab Calloway.
Album: released on DRG (USA), Jul'87 by DRG Records. Dist: Conifer, RCA

Death Of Samantha

LAUGHING IN THE FACE OF.
Album: released on Homestead, Dec'86 Dist: Rough Trade, Cartel, Shigaku

Death Pop

ROGER'S GONE MAD.
Single (7"): released on Twinkle, Sep'84 by Twinkle Records. Dist: Jetstar

Deathrow

RAGING STEEL.
Album: released on Noise International, Aug'87 Dist: Revolver, Cartel. Estim retail price in Sep'87 was £6.99.

Death Sentence

DEATH AND PURE DESTRUCTION.
Single (7"): released on Beat-The-System, Aug'82 by Lightbeat Records. Dist: Pinnacle

Deathwish

EDGE OF DAMNATION.
Album: released on Metalworks, May'87

DeBarge

ALL THIS LOVE.
Single (7"): released on Motown, Jul'83 by Motown Records. Dist: BMG Distribution

Single (12"): released on Motown, Jul'83 by Motown Records. Dist: BMG Distribution

DANCE ALL NIGHT.
Tracks: / Dance all night / Dance all night (inst).
Single (7"): released on Striped Horse, Jun'87 by Striped Horse Records. Dist: Pinnacle, Spartan Distribution

Single (12"): released on Striped Horse, Jul'87 by Striped Horse Records. Dist: Pinnacle, Spartan Distribution

EL DEBARGE.
Tracks: / Who's Johnny / Secrets of the night / I wanna hear it from my heart / Someone / When love has gone away / Private line / Love always / Lost without her love / Thrill of the chase / Don't say it's over.
Album: released on Gordy (USA), Jul'86 by Motown Records. Dist: RCA

Cassette: released on Gordy (USA), Jul'86 by Motown Records. Dist: RCA

Compact disc: released on Motown, Mar'87 by Motown Records. Dist: BMG Distribution

GREATEST HITS:DEBARGE.
Compact disc: released on Motown, Dec'86 by Motown Records. Dist: BMG Distribution

I LIKE IT.
Single (7"): released on Motown, Mar'83 by Motown Records. Dist: BMG Distribution

Single (12"): released on Motown, Mar'83 by Motown Records. Dist: BMG Distribution

IN A SPECIAL WAY.
Album: released on Gordy (USA), Apr'84 by Motown Records. Dist: RCA

Cassette: released on Gordy (USA), Apr'84 by Motown Records. Dist: RCA

LOVE ALWAYS.
Tracks: / Love always / Walls (come tumbling down) / You wear it well.
Single (7"): released on Motown, Aug'86 by Motown Records. Dist: BMG Distribution

Single (12"): released on Motown, Aug'86 by Motown Records. Dist: BMG Distribution

RHYTHM OF THE NIGHT (SINGLE).
Single (7"): released on Gordy (USA), Mar'85 by Motown Records. Dist: RCA

Single (12"): released on Gordy (USA), Mar'85 by Motown Records. Dist: RCA

RHYTHM OF THE NIGHT.
Tracks: / Prime time / Heart is not so smart / Who's holding Donna now / Give it up / Single heart / You wear it well / Walls came tumbling down / Share my world / Rhythm of the night.
Compact disc: released on Gordy (USA), May'85 by Motown Records. Dist: RCA

Album: released on Gordy (USA), May'85 by Motown Records. Dist: RCA

Cassette: released on Gordy (USA), May'85 by Motown Records. Dist: RCA

STOP DON'T TEASE ME.
Single (12"): released on Gordy (USA), Sep'82 by Motown Records. Dist: RCA

TIME WILL REVEAL.
Single (7"): released on Motown, Mar'84 by Motown Records. Dist: BMG Distribution

Single (12"): released on Motown, Mar'84 by Motown Records. Dist: BMG Distribution

WHO'S HOLDING DONNA NOW.
Single (7"): released on Gordy (USA), Jun'85 by Motown Records. Dist: RCA

Single (12"): released on Gordy (USA), Jun'85 by Motown Records. Dist: RCA

WHO'S JOHNNY.
Tracks: / Who's Johnny (short circuit theme) / Love me in a special way / Rhythm.
Single (7"): released on Motown, May'86 by Motown Records. Dist: BMG Distribution

Single (12"): released on Motown, May'86 by Motown Records. Dist: BMG Distribution

Debarge, Chico

CHICO DEBARGE.
Tracks: / Talk to me / Who are you kidding / You can make it better / I'll love you for now / I like my body / Girl next door / Cross that line / You're much too fast / If it takes all night.

Album: released on Motown, Nov'86 by Motown Records. Dist: BMG Distribution

Cassette: released on Motown, Nov'86 by Motown Records. Dist: BMG Distribution

GIRL NEXT DOOR, THE.
Tracks: / Girl next door, The / You're much too fast.
Single (7"): released on Motown, Mar'87 by Motown Records. Dist: BMG Distribution

TALK TO ME.
Tracks: / Talk to me / If it takes all night.
Single (7"): released on Motown, Oct'86 by Motown Records. Dist: BMG Distribution

Single (12"): released on Motown, Oct'86 by Motown Records. Dist: BMG Distribution

Debbie, D.J. & Pins

HULA HOOP.
Single (7"): released on Straight 8, Aug'83

Deb, Debbie

WHEN I HEAR THE MUSIC.
Single (12"): released on Sunny View, Aug'84 by Sunny View Records. Dist: PRT Distribution

De Blanc

MON AMOUR.
Tracks: / Mon amour / Mon amour (inst) / Mon amour (Instrumental).
Single (7"): released on Diamond, Jul'87 by Diamond Records. Dist: Spartan

Single (12"): released on Diamond, Aug'87 by Diamond Records. Dist: Spartan

TEMPTATION Lady is a fool,The.
Single (7"): released on Avatar, '82 by Avatar Communications. Dist: CBS

Single (12"): released on Avatar, '82 by Avatar Communications. Dist: CBS

WAYS OF THE WORLD.
Single (7"): released on Avatar, '83 by Avatar Communications. Dist: CBS

Deblanc, Ralph

WAYS OF THE WORLD.
Single (7"): released on Avatar, Jan'84 by Avatar Communications. Dist: CBS

Deborah

DANGER FOR LOVE.
Tracks: / Danger for love /Remix instrumental.
Single (12"): released on ZYX (Germany), Mar'86 by ZYX Records. Dist: Greyhound

De Brunhoff, Jean

STORY OF BARBAR.
Tracks: / Babar's travels / Babar the king.
Notes: Read by John Nettleton.
Cassette: released on Tellastory, Dec'86 by Bartlett Bliss Productions. Dist: PRT Distribution, Hayward Promotions Distribution, H.R. Taylor Distribution

De Burgh, Chris

AT THE END OF A PERFECT DAY.
Tracks: / Broken wings / Round and around / I will / Summer rain / Discovery / Brazil / In a country churchyard / Rainy night in Paris, A / If you really love her let her go / Perfect day.
Album: released on A&M, Aug'77 by A&M Records. Dist: Polygram

Cassette: released on A&M, Aug'77 by A&M Records. Dist: Polygram

BEST MOVES.
Tracks: / Every drop of rain / In a country churchyard / Patricia the stripper / Satin green shutters / Spanish train / Waiting for the hurricane / Broken wings (live version) / Lonely sky / Spaceman came travelling, A / Crusader.
Notes: Essentially a best of compliation featuring Chris's best loved songs thus far from his five album career. These recordings were produced by Glyn Johns.
Album: released on A&M, Aug'81 by A&M Records. Dist: Polygram

Cassette: released on A&M, Aug'81 by A&M Records. Dist: Polygram

CRUSADER.
Tracks: / Carry on / I had the love in my eyes / Something else again / Girl with April in her eyes, The / Just in time / Devil's eyes, The / It's such a long way home / Old fashioned people / Quiet moments / Crusader / You and me.
Album: released on A&M, Sep'86 by A&M Records. Dist: Polygram

Cassette: released on A&M, Sep'86 by A&M Records. Dist: Polygram

EASTERN WIND.
Tracks: / Traveler, The / Record company bash, The / Tonight / Wall of silence / Flying home / Shadows and lights / Some things never change / Tourist attraction / Eastern wind.
Album: released on A&M, Aug'80 by A&M Records. Dist: Polygram

FAR BEYOND THESE CASTLE WALLS.
Tracks: / Hold on / Key, The / Windy night / Sin city / New moon / Watching the world / Lonesome cowboy / Satin green shutters / Turning around / Goodnight.
Album: released on A&M, Sep'84 by A&M Records. Dist: Polygram

FATAL HESITATION.
Tracks: / Fatal hesitation / Ecstasy of flight, I love the night, The.
Single (7"): released on A&M, Sep'86 by A&M Records. Dist: Polygram

Single (12"): released on A&M, Sep'86 by A&M Records. Dist: Polygram

FIRE ON THE WATER.
Tracks: / Fire on the water / Vision, The / Leader, The / What about me.
Single (7"): released on A&M, Apr'86 by A&M Records. Dist: Polygram

Single (12"): released on A&M, Apr'86 by A&M Records. Dist: Polygram

GETAWAY, THE.
Tracks: / Don't pay the ferryman / Living on the island / Crying and laughing / I'm counting on you / Getaway, The / Ship to shore / Borderline / Where peaceful waters flow / Revolution, The / Light a fire / Liberty.
Compact disc: released on A&M, Apr'84 by A&M Records. Dist: Polygram

Album: released on A&M, Oct'82 by A&M Records. Dist: Polygram

Cassette: released on A&M, Oct'82 by A&M Records. Dist: Polygram

GETAWAY, THE/LIVING ON THE ISLAND.
Tracks: / Getaway, The / Living on the island.
Single (7"): released on A&M, Nov'82 by A&M Records. Dist: Polygram

INTO THE LIGHT.
Tracks: / One word straight to the heart / For rosanna / Leader, The / Vision, The / What about me / Last night / Fire on the water / Ballroom of romance, The / Lady in red, The / Say goodbye to it all / Spirit of man,The / Fatal hesitation.
Album: released on A&M, May'86 by A&M Records. Dist: Polygram

Cassette: released on A&M, May'86 by A&M Records. Dist: Polygram

Compact disc: released on A&M, May'86 by A&M Records. Dist: Polygram

LADY IN RED, THE.
Tracks: / Lady in red, The.
Single (7"): released on A&M, Jun'86 by A&M Records. Dist: Polygram

Single (12"): released on A&M, Jun'86 by A&M Records. Dist: Polygram

MAN ON THE LINE.
Tracks: / Ecstasy of flight (I love the night) / Sight & touch / Taking it to the top / Head & the heart, The / Sound of a gun, The / High on emotion / Much more than this / Man on the line / Moonlight & vodka / Transmission ends.
Album: released on A&M, May'84 by A&M Records. Dist: Polygram

Cassette: released on A&M, May'84 by A&M Records. Dist: Polygram

Compact disc: released on A&M, May'84 by A&M Records. Dist: Polygram

MUNICH CONCERTS.
Video-cassette (VHS): released on A&M, Nov'86 by A&M Records. Dist: Polygram

SIGHT AND TOUCH.
Tracks: / Sight and touch / Taking it to the top.
Single (7"): released on A&M, Feb'85 by A&M Records. Dist: Polygram

SPACEMAN CAME TRAVELLING.
Tracks: / Spaceman came travelling, A / Border line / Ballroom of romance (remix) (double A) / Getaway.
Single (7"): released on A&M, Nov'86 by A&M Records. Dist: Polygram

Single (7"): released on A&M, Dec'84 by A&M Records. Dist: Polygram

SPANISH TRAIN.
Tracks: / Spanish train / Lonely sky / This song for you / Patricia the stripper / Spaceman came travelling, A / I'm going home / Painter, The / Old friend / Tower,The / Just another poor boy.
Compact disc: released on A&M, Apr'86 by A&M Records. Dist: Polygram

VERY BEST OF CHRIS DE BURGH, THE.

Tracks: / Don't pay the ferryman / Ecstasy of flight (I love the night) / Traveller, The / The Ship to shore / Flying home / Satin green shutters / Spaceman came travelling, A / Spanish train / High on emotion / Borderline / Lonely sky / In a country churchyard / Patricia the stripper / Waiting for the hurricane / Don't pay the ferryman / Ecstasy of flight I love the night, The / Ship to shore / Flying home / Satin green shutters / Spaceman came travelling, A / Spanish train / High on emotion / Borderline / Lonely sky / In a country churchyard / Waiting for the hurricane / Traveller, The / Patricia the stripper.
Notes: Produced by Rupert Hine. Produced by David Anderle. Produced by Robin Geoffrey Cable. Produced by Samwell Smith. Produced by Glyn Johns.
Album: released on Telstar, Dec'84 by Telstar Records. Dist: RCA Distribution

Cassette: released on Telstar, Dec'84 by Telstar Records. Dist: RCA Distribution

Compact disc: released on Telstar, '86 by Telstar Records. Dist: RCA Distribution

VERY BEST OF CHRIS DE BURGH.
Compact disc: by Telstar Records. Dist: RCA Distribution

Debussy's greatest hits
DEBUSSY'S GREATEST HITS Various Artists (Various Artists).
Cassette: released on CBS, Jul'83 by CBS Records. Dist: CBS

Debut
DEBUT 01 Various Artists (Various Artists).
Special: released on Debut Magazines, May'84

DEBUT 02 Various Artists (Various Artists).
Special: released on Debut Magazines, Jun'84

DEBUT 03 Various Artists (Various Artists).
Special: released on Debut Magazines, Jul'84

DEBUT 04 Various Artists (Various Artists).
Special: released on Debut Magazines, Aug'84

DEBUT 05 Various Artists (Various Artists).
Special: released on Debut Magazines, Sep'84

DEBUT 06 Various Artists (Various Artists).
Tracks: / Deeper and deeper / Ball and chain / Don't take it all away / Mist / Flesh and steel / Sweet thing / Killy me you're killing me / Can't cloud my view / You are on my side / Within these walls of without you / Pretty girls make graves.
Special: released on Debut Magazines, Oct'84

Decameron
DECAMERON Boccaccio, G. (McCallum, D.).
Cassette: released on Caedmon(USA), Oct'81 by Caedmon (USA) Records. Dist: Gower, Taylors, Discovery

De Cap Organ
BEERSE.
Album: by President Records. Dist: Jazz Music, Swift, President Distribution Cat. no: JOYS 213
ENGLAND'S PRIDE (121 KEY BAND ORGAN).
Album: released on Joy, '82 by President Records. Dist: Jazz Music, Swift, President Distribution

Decca originals
DECCA ORIGINALS VOLUME 1 (1960-4) Various Artists (Various Artists).
Tracks: / Wimowh / Memphis Tennessee / Just like Eddie / Money / Crying game, The / Theme from the man with the golden arm / Halfway to paradise / Hold me / Do you love me / Well I ask you / Tell him / Telstar / Loco-motion, The / Tell me when / It might as well rain until September / Diamonds.
Album: released on Decca (Rock Echoes), Aug'82 by Decca Records. Dist: Polygram, IMS Deleted '85.

Cassette: released on Decca (Rock Echoes), Aug'82 by Decca Records. Dist: Polygram, IMS

December Band
DECEMBER BAND VOL. 1 (Various Artists).
Notes: Kid Thomas, Big Jim Robinson, S. Rimmington, Capt. John Handy, Bill Sinclair, D. Griffith, "Mouldy Dick" McCarthy.
Album: released on GHB, Feb'87 by Jazz Music, Swift

DECEMBER BAND - VOL 2 (Various Artists).
Notes: Various Artists include: Kid Thomas, Jim Robinson, John Handy, S. Rimmington, Sammy Penn, Bill Sinclair, D. McCarthy and D. Griffith.
Album: released on GHB, Jan'87 by Jazz Music, Swift

Deckchairs Overboard
DECKCHAIRS OVERBOARD.
Tracks: / Fight for love / Can't stop the motor / It's all in the game / I need you more / Love takes over / Every other day / Teach me to cry / I get hungry / Overboard / Walking in the dark.
Album: released on WEA, Oct'85 by WEA Records. Dist: WEA

FIGHT FOR LOVE.
Tracks: / Fight for love / Love takes over.
Single (7"): released on WEA, Jan'86 by WEA Records. Dist: WEA

Single (12"): released on WEA, Jan'86 by WEA Records. Dist: WEA

Declaration of...
DECLARATION OF INDEPENDENTS Various Artists (Various Artists).
Album: released on Stiff, Apr'81 by Stiff Records. Dist: EMI, Record Services Distribution (Ireland)

Decorators
REBEL SONGS.
Single (12"): released on Red Flame, Dec'83 by Red Flame Records. Dist: Nine Mile, Cartel

STRANGE ONE.
Single (7"): released on Red Flame, Jun'82 by Red Flame Records. Dist: Nine Mile, Cartel

Single (12"): released on Red Flame, Jun'82 by Red Flame Records. Dist: Nine Mile, Cartel

TABLETS.
Tracks: / Curious / Strange one / We know it / Red sky over Wembley / American ways.
Album: released on Red Flame, Jul'82 by Red Flame Records. Dist: Nine Mile, Cartel

TWILIGHT VIEW.
Single (7"): released on New Hormones, Jul'81 by New Hormones Records.

Decoupage
PUERTO RICO.
Single (7"): released on Red Bus, Jan'82 by Red Bus Records. Dist: PRT

Single (12"): released on Red Bus, Jan'82 by Red Bus Records. Dist: PRT

Decoy
NO LOOKING BACK.
Single (7"): released on Springsong, May'83 by Springsong Records. Dist: Unknown

De Creed, Jacquie
232 (AND A LITTLE BIT MORE).
Single (7"): released on Polydor, '85 by Polydor Records. Dist: Polygram, Polydor

De Danann
ANTHEM.
Notes: Track details not advised
Album: released on Dara, '85 by CML Distributors. Dist: MK, Projection

Cassette: released on Dara, '85 by CML Distributors. Dist: MK, Projection

ARRIVAL OF THE QUEEN OF SHEBA.
Single (7"): released on Cara, '83 Dist: Spartan, Roots, Folksound

BALLROOM.
Album: released on De Dannan, Jul'87 by De Dannan Records. Dist: WEA

Cassette: released on De Dannan, Jul'87 by De Dannan Records. Dist: WEA

BANKS OF THE NILE.
Single (7"): released on Decca, '80 by Decca Records. Dist: Polygram

BEST OF.
Album: released on Shanachie, '85 Dist: Sterns/Triple Earth Distribution, Roots

DE DANANN.
Tracks: / Tripping up the stairs / A trip to Athlone / Sunny banks, The - Farewell to Erin / Mountain streams, The / Cathleen Hehir's / Eighteen years old / Green fields of Rossbeigh, The / Toss the feathers / Duke of Leinster - Tarbolton / Blackbird, The - The jolly clamdiggers / Rambling Irishman / Gold ring, The / Shores of Lough Bran, The / Sleighbid hornpipe - Mountain lark - The musical priest.
Notes: 86
Album: released on Polydor (Ireland), Aug'86 by Polydor Records. Dist: Polygram, I & B

Cassette: released on Polydor (Ireland), Aug'86 by Polydor Records. Dist: Polygram, I & B

Compact disc: released on Polydor (Ireland), Jul'87 by Polydor Records. Dist: Polygram, I & B

MIST COVERED MOUNTAIN, THE.
Album: released on Gael-Linn (Ireland), '81 by Gael Linn Records. Dist: Roots, Projection, Celtic Music, Jazz Music

SONG FOR IRELAND.
Album: released on Cara, '85 Dist: Spartan, Roots, Folksound

STAR SPANGLED MOLLY, THE.
Album: released on Ogham, '82 Dist: Celtic Music, Roots Records, Jazz Music, JSU, Projection

STARSPANGLED MOLLY Boys of Malin.
Single (7"): released on Cara, '82 Dist: Spartan, Roots, Folksound

Dedrick, Rusty
ISHAM JONES EVERGREENS (Dedrick, Rusty, Orchestra).
Album: released on Monmouth, Mar'79

Dedringer
HOT LADY (Deadringer).
Single (7"): released on Neat, Nov'82 by Neat Records. Dist: Pinnacle, Neat

SECOND ARISING.
Tracks: / Rock night / Going to the movies / Sold me lonely / I'm on the outside / Donna / Comin out fightin / Throw me the line / Never gonna loes it / Never gonna loes it / Eagle never fails, The.
Album: released on Neat, Jan'85 by Neat Records. Dist: Pinnacle, Neat

Dee
BACK TO BACK (Dee & Colin).
Single (7"): released on Thunderbay, Feb'83 Dist: Spartan Distribution

MOON RIVER.
Tracks: / Moon river / Some girls.
Single (7"): released on Pow, May'86 Dist: Spartan

Single (12"): released on Pow, May'86 Dist: Spartan

Deebank, Maurice
INNER THOUGHT ZONE.
Album: released on Cherry Red, Jul'84 by Cherry Red Records. Dist: Pinnacle

Dee, Brian
SIDE BY SIDE WITH TWO BRYANS (sic) (Dee, Brian/Bryan Smith).
Album: released on Dansan, Oct'81 by Spartan Records. Dist: Spartan

SWING DOODLE (Dee, Brian, quintet).
Tracks: / Shady lane / Nova bossa nova / Everyday affair / Talk my way / Swing Doodle / Cos I'm in love / Toe tapper / Minor degrees / Brightly shining / Angelique / Anytime at all / Burt's back.
Album: released on Raphaele, Oct'82 by Mozart Edition (Music Publishers). Dist: Wellard, Chris, Jazz Music, Swift

Dee, Carolyn
MASQUERADE.
Tracks: / Masquerade.
Notes: Limited edition
Single (7"): released on Bam Caruso, Mar'87 by Bam Caruso Records. Dist: Rough Trade, Revolver, Cartel

Dee-jay Superclash!
DEE-JAY SUPERCLASH! Various artists (Various Artists).
Album: released on CSA, Aug'84 by CSA Records. Dist: PRT, Jetstar

Dee, Jazzy
GET ON UP.
Single (7"): released on Laurie, Feb'83 by RCA Records. Dist: RCA

Single (12"): released on Laurie, Feb'83 by RCA Records. Dist: RCA

Dee, Jeannie
INTRODUCING JEANNIE.
Tracks: / Your good girl's gonna go bad / You and me / I fall to pieces / Peaceful easy feeling / Standing tall / What I've got in mind / Blue eyes crying in the rain / How many lovers / Crazy arms / Fight and scratch / Stand by your man.
Album: released on Sylvatone (Ireland), Aug'84

Cassette: released on Sylvatone (Ireland), Aug'84

Dee, Joni
HERE COMES THE HOLIDAYS (Dee, Joni/The Times).
Single (7"): released on Twist & Shout, Jul'82

Dee, Kiki
ANGEL EYES.

STAR SPANGLED MOLLY, THE.
Album: released on Columbia, Apr'87 by EMI Records. Dist: EMI

Cassette: released on Columbia, Apr'87 by EMI Records. Dist: EMI

Compact disc: released on Columbia, Apr'87 by EMI Records. Dist: EMI

ANOTHER DAY COMES /ANOTHER DAY GOES.
Tracks: / Another day comes / another day goes / Nightmare mix / Nightmare Dub mix.
Single (7"): released on Columbia, Feb'86 by EMI Records. Dist: EMI

Single (12"): released on Columbia, Feb'86 by EMI Records. Dist: EMI

Single (12"): released on Columbia, May'86 by EMI Records. Dist: EMI

I FALL IN LOVE TOO EASILY.
Tracks: / I fall in love too easily / Don't cry / Beyond Control **.
Single (7"): released on Columbia, Mar'87 by EMI Records. Dist: EMI

Single (12"): released on Columbia, Mar'87 by EMI Records. Dist: EMI

KIKI DEE.
Album: released on Rocket, Feb'77 by Phonogram Records. Dist: Polygram Distribution

LOSER GETS TO WIN.
Single (7"): released on EMI, Oct'83 by EMI Records. Dist: EMI

LOVING AND FREE.
Album: released on Rocket, Jun'76 by Phonogram Records. Dist: Polygram Distribution

PERFECT TIMING.
Tracks: / Star / Loving you is sweeter than ever / Wild eyes / 24 hours / Perfect timing /it will be precise / Midnight flyer / There's a need / Another break / Love is just a moment away / You are my hope in this world.
Album: released on Music For Pleasure, Jul'86 by EMI Records. Dist: EMI

STAY CLOSE TO YOU.
Tracks: / Stay close to you / Africa / We cry on / Star.
Single (7"): released on Columbia, Apr'87 by EMI Records. Dist: EMI

Single (12"): released on Columbia, Apr'87 by EMI Records. Dist: EMI

Single (12"): released on Columbia, 13 Jun'87 by EMI Records. Dist: EMI

Dee, Michael
PORTRAITS.
Album: released on Ediesta, Oct'86 by Ediesta Records. Dist: Red Rhino, Cartel

Deene, Carol
NATIVITY SONG.
Single (7"): released on Koala, Nov'80

Deep Freeze Mice
SAW A RANCH HOUSE BURNING LAST NIGHT.
Album: released on Mole Embalming, Oct'83

Deep Lancashire
DEEP LANCASHIRE Songs and ballads of the industrial northwest.
Album: released on Topic, '81 Dist: Roots Distribution

Deep Purple
24 CARAT PURPLE.
Album: released on Purple, May'75 by Purple Records. Dist: EMI

Cassette: released on Purple, May'79 by Purple Records. Dist: EMI

Album: released on Fame, Sep'85 by Music For Pleasure Records. Dist: EMI

Cassette: released on Fame, Sep'85 by Music For Pleasure Records. Dist: EMI

ANTHOLOGY, THE.
Album: released on Harvest, Jun'85 by EMI Records. Dist: Roots, EMI

Cassette: released on Harvest, Jun'85 by EMI Records. Dist: Roots, EMI

BLACKNIGHT.
Single (12"): released on Harvest, Jun'85 by EMI Records. Dist: Roots, EMI

BLACK NIGHT/PAINTED HORSE.
Single (7"): released on Purple, Oct'77 by Purple Records. Dist: EMI

BLACK NIGHT/STRANGE KIND OF WOMAN.
Single (7"): released on Harvest, Mar'79 by EMI Records. Dist: Roots, EMI

BOOK OF TALIESYN, THE.
Album: released on Harvest, Jun'85 by EMI Records. Dist: Roots, EMI

Cassette: released on Harvest, Jun'85 by EMI Records. Dist: Roots, EMI

BURN.
Album: released on Purple, '85 by Purple Records. Dist: EMI

Cassette: released on Purple, '85 by Purple Records. Dist: EMI

CALIFORNIA JAM.
Video-cassette (VHS): released on BBC, Sep'84 by BBC Records & Tapes. Dist: EMI, PRT, Pye

CALL OF THE WILD.
Single (7"): released on Polydor, Feb'87 by Polydor Records. Dist: Polygram, Polydor

Single (12"): released on Polydor, Feb'87 by Polydor Records. Dist: Polygram, Polydor

CHILD IN TIME.
Single (7"): released on Purple-Harvest (Holland), Jul'84

COME TASTE THE BAND.
Album: released on Purple, Jun'85 by Purple Records. Dist: EMI

Cassette: released on Purple, Jun'85 by Purple Records. Dist: EMI

DEEPEST PURPLE.
Compact disc: by EMI Records. Dist: Roots, EMI

Album: released on EMI, Jul'80 by EMI Records. Dist: EMI

Cassette: released on EMI, Jul'80 by EMI Records. Dist: EMI

DEEP PURPLE.
Album: released on Harvest, Jun'85 by EMI Records. Dist: Roots, EMI

Cassette: released on Harvest, Jun'85 by EMI Records. Dist: Roots, EMI

DEEP PURPLE IN CONCERT.
Double Album: released on Harvest, Nov'80 by EMI Records. Dist: Roots, EMI

Cassette: released on Harvest, Nov'80 by EMI Records. Dist: Roots, EMI

DEEP PURPLE SINGLES - A'S/B'S.
Album: released on Harvest, '78 by EMI Records. Dist: Roots, EMI

FIREBALL.
Tracks: / Fireball / No,no,no / Demon's eye / Anyone's daughter / Mule (The) / Fools / No one came / Fireball / No, no, no / Demon's eye / Anyone's daughter / Mule, The / Fools / No one came.
Compact disc: released on EMI, Mar'87 by EMI Records. Dist: EMI

Album: released on Harvest, Apr'87 by EMI Records. Dist: Roots, EMI

Cassette: released on Harvest, Apr'87 by EMI Records. Dist: Roots, EMI

Album: released on Fame (Harvest), Mar'84 by Music For Pleasure Records. Dist: EMI

Cassette: released on Fame (Harvest), Mar'84 by Music For Pleasure Records. Dist: EMI

Picture disc album: released on EMI, Jan'85 by EMI Records. Dist: EMI

Single (12"): released on Harvest, Jun'85 by EMI Records. Dist: Roots, EMI

HARD ROCK HEROES.
Tracks: / Highway star / Hush / Stormbringer / Lady double dealer / Strange kind of woman / Mandrake root / Woman from Tokyo / Black night / Demons eye / Lay down,stay down / Hold on / Burn / Why didn't Rosemary / Mistreated / Emeretta / Smoke on the water / Help / Hey Joe / Speed king / Into the fire / Child in time.
Notes: 3 record set
Album: released on EMI (France), Apr'87 by EMI Records. Dist: Conifer

HOUSE OF BLUE LIGHT.
Tracks: / Bad attitude / Unwritten law / Call of the wild / Mad dog / Black & white / Hard lovin' woman / Spanish archer / Strange-ways / Mitzi dupree / Dead or alive.
Album: released on Polydor, Jan'87 by Polydor Records. Dist: Polygram, Polydor

Cassette: released on Polydor, Jan'87 by Polydor Records. Dist: Polygram, Polydor

Compact disc: released on Polydor, Jan'87 by Polydor Records. Dist: Polygram, Polydor

IN LIVE CONCERT.
Album: released on Harvest, '70 by EMI Records. Dist: Roots, EMI

IN ROCK.
Tracks: / Speed king / Blood sucker / Child in time / Flight of the rat / Into the fire / Living wreck / Hard lovin' man.
Compact disc: released on EMI, Mar'87 by EMI Records. Dist: EMI

IN ROCK.
Picture disc album: released on EMI, Jan'85 by EMI Records. Dist: EMI

INTERVIEW PICTURE DISC.
Album: released on Baktabak, Jun'87 by Baktabak Records. Dist: Arabesque

KNOCKING ON YOUR BACK DOOR.
Single (7"): released on Polydor, Jun'85 by Polydor Records. Dist: Polygram, Polydor

Single (12"): released on Polydor, Jun'85 by Polydor Records. Dist: Polygram, Polydor

LAST CONCERT IN JAPAN.
Album: released on EMI (France), '83 by EMI Records. Dist: Conifer

LIVE IN LONDON.
Album: released on Harvest, Aug'82 by EMI Records. Dist: Roots, EMI

Cassette: released on Harvest, Aug'82 by EMI Records. Dist: Roots, EMI

MACHINE HEAD.
Tracks: / Highway star / Maybe I'm a Leo / Pictures of home / Never before / Smoke on the water / Lazy / Space Truckin'.
Album: released on Fame, Oct'86 by Music For Pleasure Records. Dist: EMI

Compact disc: released on EMI, Mar'87 by EMI Records. Dist: EMI

MACHINE HEAD.
Album: released on Purple, '85 by Purple Records. Dist: EMI

Cassette: released on Purple, '85 by Purple Records. Dist: EMI

MADE IN EUROPE.
Album: released on Purple, Oct'76 by Purple Records. Dist: EMI

Cassette: released on Purple, Oct'76 by Purple Records. Dist: EMI

MADE IN JAPAN.
Double Album: released on Purple, '72 by Purple Records. Dist: EMI

Double cassette: released on Purple, '72 by Purple Records. Dist: EMI

MARK 1 AND MARK 2.
Double Album: released on EMI (Germany), '83 by EMI Records. Dist: Conifer

MARK 2 SINGLES.
Album: released on EMI (Holland), Nov'83 by EMI Records. Dist: Conifer

NEW LIVE AND RARE - VOL.3.
Single (7"): released on Harvest, Oct'80 by EMI Records. Dist: Roots, EMI

PERFECT STRANGERS.
Tracks: / Knocking at your back door / Under the gun / Nobody's home / Mean streak / Perfect strangers / Gypsy's kiss, A / Wasted sunsets / Hungry daze.
Compact disc: by Polydor Records. Dist: Polygram, Polydor

Album: released on Polydor, Nov'84 by Polydor Records. Dist: Polygram, Polydor

Cassette: released on Polydor, Nov'84 by Polydor Records. Dist: Polygram, Polydor

Picture disc album: released on Polydor, Jun'85 by Polydor Records. Dist: Polygram, Polydor

Single (7"): released on Polydor, Jan'85 by Polydor Records. Dist: Polygram, Polydor

Single (12"): released on Polydor, Jan'85 by Polydor Records. Dist: Polygram, Polydor

POWERHOUSE.
Album: released on Purple, Jun'85 by Purple Records. Dist: EMI

Cassette: released on Purple, Jun'85 by Purple Records. Dist: EMI

SHADES OF DEEP PURPLE.
Album: released on Harvest, Feb'77 by EMI Records. Dist: Roots, EMI

SMOKE ON THE WATER.
Single (7"): released on Purple, Apr'77 by Purple Records. Dist: EMI

Single (12"): released on Purple, Jun'85 by Purple Records. Dist: EMI

STORMBRINGER.
Tracks: / Stormbringer / Love don't mean a thing / Holy man / Hold on / Lady double dealer / You can't do it right / High ball shooter / Gypsy, The / Soldier of fortune.
Notes: Original catalogue number: TPS 3508/album;TCTPS 3508/cassette;
Album: released on Purple, Jun'85 by Purple Records. Dist: EMI

Cassette: released on Purple, Jun'85 by Purple Records. Dist: EMI

STRANGE KIND OF WOMAN.
Single (12"): released on Harvest, Jun'85 by EMI Records. Dist: Roots, EMI

WHO DO WE THINK WE ARE!.
Album: released on Purple, Jun'85 by Purple Records. Dist: EMI

Cassette: released on Purple, Jun'85 by Purple Records. Dist: EMI

Deep River Boys

ROCK A BEATIN BOOGIE.
Tracks: / Not too old to rock and roll / That's right / Shake rattle and roll / Rock-a-beatin boogie / Just a little bit more / Adam never had no mammy / Settle down / Itchy twitchy feeling / I shall not be moved / Slow train to nowhere / Ashes of roses / St. Louis blues / Honey Honey / Whole lotta shakin goin on / Smack dab in the middle / Rock around the clock.
Album: released on See For Miles, Sep'86 by See For Miles Records. Dist: Pinnacle

Deep Sea Jivers

DANCING AND DINING WITH THE DEEP SEA JIVERS.
Single (12"): released on Mermaid, Feb'85 by Mermaid Records. Dist: Making Waves

DEEP SEA JIVING.
Single (7"): released on Mermaid, Nov'86 by Mermaid Records. Dist: Making Waves

RAPTURES OF THE DEEP.
Album: released on Mermaid, Jan'86 by Mermaid Records. Dist: Making Waves

Deep Switch

NINE INCHES OF GOD.
Album: released on Switch, Sep'86 Dist: Backs, Cartel Distribution

Deep Throat

DEEP THROAT Original soundtrack.
Album: released on Sandy Hook (USA Import), Jul'81

Deep Voices

SOUNDS OF WHALES, THE.
Album: by Capitol Records. Dist: EMI

Deering, Richard

BEATLES CONCERTO, THE.
Album: released on Denon, Mar'82 by Denon Records.

Dee, Ruby

TSHINDAO (see Davis, Ossie).

Dee, Sandra

TEARS FALL FROM MY EYES.
Single (12"): released on Ital, Jul'82 Dist: Pinnacle

Deeside Ladies Pipe Band

WHITE BALMORALS, THE.
Album: released on Lochshore, Jul'87 by Klub Records. Dist: PRT

Cassette: released on Lochshore, Jul'87 by Klub Records. Dist: PRT

Dees, Sam

SURVIVE.
Tracks: / Survive / Fly angel fly / Survive /long version.
Single (12"): released on Move, Sep'86 by Charly Records. Dist: Charly Distribution, Fast Forward Distribution, Cartel Distribution

Dee Tees

SHAKIN' ALL OVER.
Single (7"): released on Shibui, Sep'83 by Stage One Records. Dist: Pinnacle

Single (7"): released on Shibui, Jan'85 by Stage One Records. Dist: Pinnacle
Cat. no: **SHS 002**

Dee, Tony

BELONG TO THE WILD.
Single (12"): released on Sunburn, Mar'83 by Orbitone Records. Dist: Jetstar Distribution
Cat. no: **SBD 22**

BREAK LOOSE RUN FREE.
Tracks: / Break loose, run free / Move over.
Notes: Side B. Move over /Pete Watkinson.
Single (12"): released on Amanda, Jul'86 Dist: Jetstar
Cat. no: **AMD 003**

DANCE TO THE MUSIC.
Single (12"): released on Sunburn, Jul'83 by Orbitone Records. Dist: Jetstar Distribution
Cat. no: **SBD 33**

DON'T MESS.
Tracks: / Don't mess / No chance.
Single (12"): released on Whiplash, Jul'86 by Whiplash Records. Dist: Amanda Records Distribution
Cat. no: **WLD 004**

SOCA MELODY (Dee, Tony & Belinda Parker).
Single (12"): released on Sunburst, Nov'82 Dist: Sunburst Records
Cat. no: **SBD 15**

Dee, Trevor

CRY BABY CRY.
Single (12"): released on Ruff Cut, Nov'83 by Ruff Cut Records. Dist: Jetstar Distribution
Cat. no: **RC 006**

Dee, Wanda

BLUE EYES.
Tracks: / Blue eyes / Blue eyes (Instrumental).
Single (7"): released on Lisson, May'86 Dist: PRT
Cat. no: **DOLE 1**

Single (12"): released on Lisson, May'86 Dist: PRT
Cat. no: **DOLEQ 1**

De Falla Trio

DE FALLA TRIO, THE.
Tracks: / Symphony no.1 / Aragon (Fantasia) / Fandango / Suite from el amor brujo / Spain.
Notes: De Falla Trio are: Terry Graves, Susan Bogdanovic and Kenton Youngstrom.
Album: released on Concord Jazz(USA), Jan'87 by Concord Jazz Records (USA). Dist: IMS, Polygram
Cat. no: **CC 2011**

Def Beats

DEF BEATS 1 Compilation recordings (Defilm).
Album: released on Music Of Life, Mar'87 Dist: Streetwave
Cat. no: **MODEF 1**

Cassette: released on Music Of Life, Mar'87 Dist: Streetwave
Cat. no: **MODEF 1C**

Defective Turtles

FANNING FIRES.
Single (7"): released on Barbel, Feb'84 by Barbel Records. Dist: Barbel
Cat. no: **GS 1**

Defects

DEFECTIVE BREAKDOWN.
Album: released on WXYZ, Nov'82
Cat. no: **LMNOP 2**

SURVIVAL.
Single (7"): released on WXYZ, Apr'82
Cat. no: **ABCD 3**

SUSPICIOUS MINDS.
Single (7"): released on I.D., Jan'84 by I.D. Records. Dist: Revolver, Cartel
Cat. no: **EYE 2**

Defferary, John

Nicholas, Albert/John Defferary Jazztet

Defiante pose

DEFIANTE POSE, THE Various groups (Various Artists).
Tracks: / Fall / Models / Cramps / Wall of voodoo / Alarm / Business / Circle jerks.
Album: released on Illegal, Oct'83 by Faulty Products Records. Dist: Pinnacle, Lightning, Cartel
Cat. no: **ILP 013**

Defilm

BITTER SURPRISE.
Tracks: / Btter surprise / Telegram.
Single (7"): released on Portrait, Apr'86 by CBS Records. Dist: CBS
Cat. no: **A 7091**

Single (12"): released on Portrait, Apr'86 by CBS Records. Dist: CBS
Cat. no: **TA 7091**

DEFILM.
Tracks: / I saw your dream / Bitter surprise / Yellow / Julia / Here we are / 747 / Telegram / Turkish delight / Love is over / Cuba libra.
Album: released on Portrait, May'86 by CBS Records. Dist: CBS
Cat. no: **PRT 26849**

I SAW YOUR DREAM.
Tracks: / I saw your dream / Julia.
Single (7"): released on Portrait, Jan'86 by CBS Records. Dist: CBS
Cat. no: **A 6643**

Single (12"): released on Portrait, Jan'86 by

CBS Records. Dist: CBS

Def Jam Sampler

DEF JAM SAMPLER (Various Artists).
Tracks: / Rock hard / Def jam / Word, The / Sardines / Pump that bass / Live / Finer things in life, The / I'm bad / Read my mind / Can you feel it / You're gonna get yours / Here I go again.
Album: released on Def Jam (USA), Jul'87 by CBS Records. Dist: CBS

Cassette: released on Def Jam (USA), Jul'87 by CBS Records. Dist: CBS

Def Leppard

ANIMAL.
Tracks: / Animal / Tear it down.
Single (7"): released on Bludgeon-Riffola, Jul'87 Dist: Pinnacle

Single (12"): released on Bludgeon-Riffola, Jul'87 Dist: Pinnacle

BRINGING ON THE HEARTBREAK.
Single (7"): released on Vertigo, Jan'82 by Phonogram Records. Dist: Polygram

Single (12"): released on Vertigo, Jan'82 by Phonogram Records. Dist: Polygram

HIGH AND DRY.
Album: released on Vertigo, Sep'83 by Phonogram Records. Dist: Polygram

Cassette: released on Vertigo, Sep'83 by Phonogram Records. Dist: Polygram

ON THROUGH THE NIGHT.
Album: released on Vertigo, Mar'80 by Phonogram Records. Dist: Polygram

Cassette: released on Vertigo, Mar'80 by Phonogram Records. Dist: Polygram

PHOTOGRAPH.
Single (7"): released on Vertigo, Jan'83 by Phonogram Records. Dist: Polygram

Single (12"): released on Vertigo, Jan'83 by Phonogram Records. Dist: Polygram

PYROMANIA.
Compact disc: by Phonogram Records. Dist: Polygram Distribution

Album: released on Vertigo, Mar'83 by Phonogram Records. Dist: Polygram

Cassette: released on Vertigo, Mar'83 by Phonogram Records. Dist: Polygram

De Florette, Jean

JEAN DE FLORETTE Original Soundtrack.
Compact disc: released on Milan France, Aug'87

JEAN DE FLORETTE Original soundtrack (Original Soundtrack).
Album: released on SPI Milan (France), Aug'87 Dist: Silva Screen

Cassette: released on SPI Milan (France), Aug'87 Dist: Silva Screen

Defoe, Daniel

ROBINSON CRUSOE.
Double cassette: released on Argo (Spokenword), Oct'85 by Decca Records. Dist: Polygram

De Forest, Carmaig

I SHALL BE RELEASED.
Notes: Produced by Alex Chilton, who produced the first Cramps records.
Album: released on New Rose, May'87 Dist: Rough Trade, Cartel

Cassette: released on MFN, May'87 by Music For Nations Records. Dist: Pinnacle

De Franco, Buddy

BLACK MAGIC (De Franco, Buddy & Helen Forest).
Album: released on Shamrock (Ireland), '78 Dist: I & B, EMI (Ireland), Swift, Chris Wellard, Solomon & Peres Distribution, Jazz Music

BLUES BAG (see Blakey, Art).

HARK (De Franco, Buddy & Oscar Peterson Quartet).
Notes: See also under Oscar Peterson.
Compact disc: released on Pablo (USA), Apr'87 by Pablo Records (USA). Dist: Wellard, Chris, IMS-Polygram, BMG

LIKE SOMEONE I LOVE (De Franco, Buddy Quintet).
Album: released on Progressive, '79 by Progressive Records. Dist: Jetstar

LIVELIEST, THE.
Album: released on Hep, '82 by H.R. Taylor Records. Dist: Jazz Music, Cadillac Music, JSU, Taylors, Wellard, Chris, Zodiac, Swift, Fast Forward

Defries, David

SECRET CITY, THE.
Album: released on MMC, Jul'85 by MMC Records. Dist: PRT Distribution, Pinnacle

Defunkt

DEFUNKT.
Album: released on Hannibal, Jan'84 by Hannibal Records. Dist: Charly, Projection, Celtic Music, Roots

RAZORS EDGE.
Single (7"): released on Hannibal, Oct'81 by Hannibal Records. Dist: Charly, Projection, Celtic Music, Roots

Single (12"): released on Hannibal, Oct'81 by Hannibal Records. Dist: Charly, Harmonia Mundi, Projection, Celtic Music, Roots

THERMONUCLEAR SWEAT.
Album: released on Hannibal, Jan'84 by Hannibal Records. Dist: Charly, Harmonia Mundi, Projection, Celtic Music, Roots

De Gaetani, Jan

CLASSIC COLE (De Gaetani, Jan/Smit, Leo).
Notes: Jan DeGaetani - mezzo soprano Leo Smit - piano
Album: released on CBS, Sep'80 by CBS Records. Dist: CBS

Degen, Bob

CHARTREUSE.
Album: released on Enja (Germany), Jan'82 by Enja Records (W.Germany). Dist: Cadillac Music

CHILDREN OF THE NIGHT.
Album: released on Enja (Germany), Jan'82 by Enja Records (W.Germany). Dist: Cadillac Music

SEQUOIA SONG.
Album: released on Enja (Germany), Jan'82 by Enja Records (W.Germany). Dist: Cadillac Music

Dego

DANCING TIME.
Single (12"): released on A.1, Mar'82 by A.1 Records. Dist: PRT

Dego Ranking

OPERATION COUNTRY.
Single (12"): released on Disco Rockers, Nov'82

De Graaff, Rein

MODAL SOUL (De Graaff, Rein & Dick Vennick Quartet).
Album: released on Timeless(import), Sep'86 Dist: Cadillac

Album: released on Timeless, Apr'81

DeGrassi, Alex

CLOCKWORK.
Album: released on Windham Hill (Germany), Sep'84

SOUTHERN EXPOSURE.
Album: released on Windham Hill, Nov'85 Dist: AM

Cassette: released on Windham Hill, Nov'85 Dist: AM

Compact disc: released on Windham Hill, Nov'85 Dist: AM

De Havilland, Peter

BOIS DU BOULOGNE.
Album: released on Venture, Jul'87 Dist: Revolver, Cartel

Cassette: released on Venture, Jul'87 Dist: Revolver, Cartel

Dehumanizers

END OF TIME.
Album: released on Neg Effects, Jul'87

Deighton Family

ACOUSTIC MUSIC TO SUIT MOST OCCASIONS.
Album: released on Rogue, Jul'87 by Fast Forward Records. Dist: Nine Mile Distribution, Cartel Distribution

Deisel Smoke &...

DEISEL SMOKE & DANGEROUS CURVES (Various Artists).
Album: released on Starday, Apr'87

Cassette: released on Starday, Apr'87

Deja

SERIOUS.
Tracks: / You and me tonight.
Single (7"): released on 10, Aug'87 by 10 Records. Dist: Virgin, EMI

Single (12"): released on 10, Aug'87 by 10 Records. Dist: Virgin, EMI

Dejan, Joseph

DUO (Dejan, Joseph and Gerrard Maurais).
Album: released on Open, Aug'77 Dist: Cadillac

Dejan's Brass Band

DEJAN'S OLYMPIA BRASS BAND 1968
(Dejan's Olympia Brass Band).
Album: released on Nola, Apr'79 Dist: JSU, Jazz Music, Cadillac, Chris Wellard

Dejan's Olympia Brass Band

JAZZLY YOURS.
Album: Dist: Swift

Deja View

DEJA VIEW The Ultimate 60's Party Video (Various Artists).
Notes: Inc. Procul Harem - 'Whiter shade of pale', Rascals - 'Good lovin', Lesley Gore - 'It's my party'
Video-cassette (VHS): released on Video Collection, May'87 by Video Collection Records. Dist: Counterpoint

Deja Vu

TV.
Tracks: / TV / China doll.
Single (7"): released on TVR, Aug'86 by TVR Records. Dist: TVR

Dejohnette, Jack

ALBUM ALBUM.
Tracks: / Ahmad the terrible / Monk's mood / Festival / New Orleans strut / Third world anthem / Zoot suite.
Notes: Personnel: John Purcell - alto and soprano sax/David Murray- tenor sax/Howard Johnson - tuba, baritone sax/Rufus Reid - acoustic and electric bass/Jack De Johnette - drums and keyboards.
Compact disc: released on ECM (Germany), Feb'86 by ECM Records. Dist: IMS, Polygram, Virgin through EMI

Album: released on ECM (Germany), '84 by ECM Records. Dist: IMS, Polygram, Virgin through EMI

DE JOHNETTE,JACK/WENER PIRCHER/HARRY PEPL (De Johnette,Jack/Wener Pircher/Harry Pepl).
Album: released on ECM (Germany), '83 by ECM Records. Dist: IMS, Polygram, Virgin through EMI

DE JOHNETTE'S,JACK SPECIAL EDITION.
Album: released on ECM (Germany), '83 by ECM Records. Dist: IMS, Polygram, Virgin through EMI

NEW DIRECTIONS IN EUROPE.
Tracks: / Salsa for eddie / Bayou Fever / Where or Wayne / Multo spillagio.
Notes: Personnel: Jack De Johnette - drumsmpiano/Lester Bowie - trumpet/John Abercrom- bie - guitar, mandolin guitar/Eddie Gomez - Bass.
Compact disc: by ECM Records. Dist: IMS, Polygram, Virgin through EMI

SPECIAL EDITION (Dejohnette, Jack's Special Edition).
Tracks: / One for Eric / Zoot suite / Central park west / India / Journey to the twin planet.
Notes: Personnel: Jack De Johnette - drums, piano, melodica/David Murrray - tenor sax, bass clarinet/Arthur Blythe - alto sax,/Peter Warren - bass.
Compact disc: by ECM Records. Dist: IMS, Polygram, Virgin through EMI

TIN CAN ALLEY (Dejohnette, Jack's Special Edition).
Album: released on ECM (France), '81 by ECM Records. Dist: IMS, Polygram, Virgin through EMI

WORKS.
Tracks: / Bayou fever / Gri gri man, The / To be continued / One for Eric / Ushielded desire / Blue.
Compact disc: by ECM Records. Dist: IMS, Polygram, Virgin through EMI

Album: released on ECM/Works (Germany), '85 by ECM Records. Dist: IMS, Polygram, Virgin through EMI

Compact disc: released on ECM/Works (Germany), '85 by ECM Records. Dist: IMS, Polygram, Virgin through EMI

Dejoney, Zena

I'VE GOT TO FIND A WAY.
Single (7"): by Calibre Records. Dist: PRT

Single (12"): by Calibre Records. Dist: PRT

De Jongh, Richard

SO EASY.
Single (12"): released on Challenge, Aug'83 by Elite Records. Dist: Pinnacle

Dekka Danse

IMMAGNETIZED.
Single (7"): released on CBS, Feb'84 by CBS Records. Dist: CBS

Single (12"): released on CBS, Feb'84 by CBS Records. Dist: CBS

SOUL SEPARATION.
Single (7"): released on CBS, Jun'84 by CBS Records. Dist: CBS

Single (12"): released on CBS, Jun'84 by CBS Records. Dist: CBS

Dekker, Desmond

20 GOLDEN PIECES OF DESMOND DEKKER.
Tracks: / You can get it if you really want / I believe / Perseverance / Get up little Suzie / Pickney gal / Rudy got soul / That's the way life goes / Peace of mind / Man, The / Ah it mek / Israelites / It's not easy / Intensified / Tips of my fingers / Too much too soon / Nincompoop / Problems / For once in my life / Rude boy train / My precious love.
Album: released on Bulldog, Apr'87 by Bulldog Records. Dist: President Distribution, Spartan, Swift, Taylor

Cassette: released on Bulldog, Apr'87 by Bulldog Records. Dist: President Distribution, Spartan, Swift, Taylor,

BLACK & DEKKER.
Tracks: / Israelites / Lickin' stick / It mek / Please don't bend / Many rivers to cross / Hippo / 007 / Workout / Problems / Rude boy train / Pickney girl / Why fight?.
Album: released on Stiff, Jul'80 by Stiff Records. Dist: EMI, Record Services Distribution (Ireland)

BOOK OF RULES.
Single (7"): released on Stiff, Mar'82 by Stiff Records. Dist: EMI, Record Services Distribution (Ireland)

COMPASS POINT.
Tracks: / I'll get by / Moving on / We can and shall / Hurts so bad / Isabella / Come back to me / Cindy / I do believe / My destiny / Big headed / That's my woman / Allamanna.
Album: released on Stiff, Jul'81 by Stiff Records. Dist: EMI, Record Services Distribution (Ireland)

HIPPOPTAMUS (Dekker, Desmond & The Aces).
Single (7"): released on Trojan, Sep'84 by Trojan Records. Dist: PRT, Jetstar

Single (12"): released on Trojan, Sep'84 by Trojan Records. Dist: PRT, Jetstar

HOT CITY.
Single (7"): released on Stiff, Aug'83 by Stiff Records. Dist: EMI, Record Services Distribution (Ireland)

Single (12"): released on Stiff, Sep'83 by Stiff Records. Dist: EMI, Record Services Distribution (Ireland)

ISRAELITES.
Tracks: / Israelites / Beware / Everybody join hands / It mek / Sing a little song / Busted lad / My world is blue / Mother nature / Money and friends / No place like home.
Album: released on Cactus, Nov'80 by Creole Records. Dist: CBS

Single (7"): released on Creole Replay, Aug'84 by Creole Records. Dist: PRT, Rhino

Single (7"): released on Scoop, Jun'84

Cassette: released on Scoop, Jun'84

ISRAELITES/ SUGAR DUMPLING.
Single (7"): released on Creole, Feb'80 by Creole Records. Dist: Rhino, PRT

ISRAELITES/ WHY FIGHT.
Single (7"): released on Stiff, Apr'80 by Stiff Records. Dist: EMI, Record Services Distribution (Ireland)

Single (12"): released on Stiff, Apr'80 by Stiff Records. Dist: EMI, Record Services Distribution (Ireland)

ISRAELITES/ YOU CAN GET IT (Dekker, Desmond & The Aces).
Single (7"): released on Old Gold, Apr'83 by Old Gold Records. Dist: Lightning, Jazz Music, Spartan, Counterpoint

MANY RIVERS TO CROSS.
Single (7"): released on Stiff, Nov'80 by Stiff Records. Dist: EMI, Record Services Distribution (Ireland)

ORIGINAL REGGAE HITSOUND, THE (Dekker, Desmond & The Aces).
Tracks: / 007 / Get up, Edina / Beautiful and dangerous / Shing a ling / Pretty Africa / Wise man / Sabotage / Unity / It pays / Israelites / It mek / Warlock / Archie wah wah / Pickney girl / Reggae recipe / You can get it if you really want / Hippopotamus / Lickin' stick / More you live, The.
Album: released on Trojan, Mar'85 by Trojan Records. Dist: PRT, Jetstar

Cassette: released on Trojan, Mar'85 by Trojan Records. Dist: PRT, Jetstar

PROFILE.
Cassette: released on Teldec (Germany), Jun'81 by Import Records. Dist: IMS Distribution, Polygram Distribution

PROFILE OF DESMOND DEKKER.
Album: released on Teldec (Germany), May'81 by Import Records. Dist: IMS Distribution, Polygram Distribution

SWEET 16 HITS.
Tracks: / Reggae recipe / Lickin' stick / Pickney girl / It mek / Life of opportunity / I believe / My reward / 007 / You can get it / Archie wah wah / Mother nature / Where did it go? / More you live, The / What will you gain? / Look what they're doing to me / Israelites.
Album: released on Trojan, Jul'84 by Trojan Records. Dist: PRT, Jetstar

Cassette: released on Trojan, Jul'84 by Trojan Records. Dist: PRT, Jetstar

TWENTY GOLDEN PIECES OF DESMOND DEKKER.
Album: released on Bulldog, Feb'87 by Bulldog Records. Dist: President Distribution, Spartan, Swift, Taylor, H.R.

WE CAN AND SHALL.
Single (7"): released on Stiff, Jun'81 by Stiff Records. Dist: EMI, Record Services Distribution (Ireland)

YOU CAN GET IT IF YOU REALLY WANT.
Tracks: / You can get it if you really want / Israelites.
Single (7"): released on Bulldog, Feb'87 by Bulldog Records. Dist: President Distribution, Spartan, Swift, Taylor, H.R.

Dekker, George

ATLANTIC ROAD.
Single (7"): released on Safari, May'85 by Safari Records. Dist: Pinnacle

REGGAE MAN.
Tracks: / Raggae man.
Single (7"): released on Trojan, Sep'86 by Trojan Records. Dist: PRT, Jetstar

Single (12"): by Trojan Records. Dist: PRT, Jetstar

Delafose, John

UNCLE BUD ZYDECO.
Album: released on Arhoolie, Mar'84 by Arhoolie Records. Dist: Projection, Topic, Jazz Music, Swift, Roots

ZYDECO EXCITEMENT.
Album: Dist: Swift

De Lago, Franco

ACCORDION HITS.
Compact disc: released on Bridge, Jan'86 Dist: CD Centre Distribution, Pinnacle, Target

Delahaye, Junior

LOVE.
Single (12"): released on Solid Groove, Jul'82 Dist: Jetstar, Pinnacle

Delaney & Bonnie

BEST OF....
Album: by WEA Records. Dist: WEA

ON TOUR (Delaney & Bonnie & E.Clapton).
Album: by WEA Records. Dist: WEA

Delano, Stewart

ETERNAL LOVE.
Single (12"): released on Hawkeye, '85 by Hawkeye Records. Dist: Hawkeye, Lightning (WEA) Distribution, Jetstar, PRT

De La Paz, Gil

CASA.

Tracks: / Three different mixer.
Single (12"): released on Kool Kat, Aug'87 by Kool Kat Records. Dist: PRT

Delaware Water Gap

STRING BAND MUSIC.
Album: released on Adelphi, '81 by Adelphi Records. Dist: Jetstar

Delayed Action

NEW LOVE Fire in the streets.
Single (7"): released on Cricket International, '82 by Cricket International Records. Dist: Stage One

Single (12"): released on Cricket International, '82 by Cricket International Records. Dist: Stage One

THEY SAID I've got to get you off.
Single (7"): released on Zilch, '82 by Zilch Records. Dist: Stage One

Single (12"): released on Zilch, '82 by Zilch Records. Dist: Stage One

Delayline

KEEP THAT SMILE.
Tracks: / Keep that smile / Summer soul mix.
Single (7"): released on ISR, Oct'86 by ISR Records. Dist: DMS, RCA

Single (12"): released on ISR, Oct'86 by ISR Records. Dist: DMS, RCA

Single (7"): released on Big Top, '85 Dist: Cartel

Single (12"): released on Big Top, '85 Dist: Cartel

WE CAN MAKE IT.
Single (12"): released on Gas, '85 by Gas Records. Dist: Pinnacle

Del-Byzanteens

DRAFT RIOT Sally go round the roses.
Single (7"): released on Don't Fall Off The Mountain, '82 by Don't Fall Off The Mountain Records. Dist: Pinnacle, Rough Trade, Nine Mile, Indies

LIES TO LIVE BY.
Album: released on Don't Fall Off The Mountain, '82 by Don't Fall Off The Mountain Records. Dist: Pinnacle, Rough Trade, Nine Mile, Indies

MY WORLD.
Single (12"): released on Don't Fall Off The Mountain, '81 by Don't Fall Off The Mountain Records. Dist: Pinnacle, Rough Trade, Nine Mile, Indies

Delegation

EAU DE VIE.
Cassette: released on Ariola-Hansa, '79 by Hansa Records. Dist: Polygram

IF YOU WERE A SONG.
Single (7"): released on Dude, '82 by Dude Records.

PROMISE OF LOVE,THE.
Album: released on State, '77 by State Records.

Deleru, Georges

SILKWOOD.
Single (7"): released on PRT, '84 by PRT Records. Dist: PRT

THEME FROM THE BORGIAS (Deleru, Georges Orchestra).
Single (7"): released on BBC, '81 by BBC Records & Tapes. Dist: EMI, PRT, Pye

Delfonics

LA LA MEANS I LOVE YOU.
Single (7"): released on Old Gold, '82 by Old Gold Records. Dist: Lightning, Jazz Music, Spartan, Counterpoint

SUPER HITS.
Album: released on Bell, '72 by Arista Records. Dist: Polygram

Del Fuegos

BOSTON, MASSACHUSSETTS.
Album: released on Slash, Oct'85 by London Records. Dist: Polygram

Cassette: released on Slash, Oct'85 by London Records. Dist: Polygram

I STILL WANT YOU.
Tracks: / I still want you / Don't run wild / Missing you.
Notes: Missing you only on 12" single.
Single (7"): released on Slash, Jan'86 by London Records. Dist: Polygram

Single (12"): released on Slash, Jan'86 by London Records. Dist: Polygram

LONGEST DAY, THE.
Album: released on Slash, Jan'87 by London Records. Dist: Polygram

Cassette: released on Slash, Jan'87 by London Records. Dist: Polygram

Cassette: released on Slash, Jan'87 by London Records. Dist: Polygram

Album: released on Rough Trade, Dec'84 by Rough Trade Records. Dist: Rough Trade Distribution, Cartel Distribution

STAND UP.
Tracks: / Wear it like a cape / New old world / Names names / Lonf slide (for an out) / He had a lot to drink today / Town called love, A / I can't take this place / News from nowhere / Scratching at your door / I'll sleep with you.
Notes: Produced by Mitchall Froom, this is the third LP from the Del Fuegos.
Album: released on Slash, Mar'87 by London Records. Dist: Polygram

Cassette: released on Slash, Mar'87 by London Records. Dist: Polygram

Delgado, Junior

BUSHMASTER.
Album: released on Incredible Jux, '85 by Incredible Jux Records. Dist: Jetstar

CLASSICS.
Album: released on Macabeen, '85 by Macabeen Records. Dist: Jetstar

COME FOLLOW ME.
Tracks: / Come follow me / Come follow me (Version).
Single (12"): released on Jammy's, Nov'86 by Jammy's Records. Dist: Jetstar

HOT STUFF.
Tracks: / Hot stuff / It takes two to tango.

Single (12"): released on Fashion, Feb'86 by Fashion Records. Dist: PRT, Jetstar

HOW DO YOU FEEL.
Single (12"): released on Sweetcorn, '85 by Sweetcorn Records. Dist: Jetstar

IF THIS WORLD WERE MINE For love.
Single (12"): released on Prestige, '82 by Prestige Records (USA). Dist: RCA, JSU, Swift

IN GRIECHENLAND.
Album: released on Arcade Music Gala, Apr'86 Dist: Stage One

Cassette: released on Arcade Music Gala, Apr'86 Dist: Stage One

IT TAKES TWO TO TANGO (12").
Tracks: / It takes two to tango.
Single (12"): released on Fashion, Mar'86 by Fashion Records. Dist: PRT, Jetstar

IT TAKES TWO TO TANGO (LP).
Album: released on Fashion, Apr'87 by Fashion Records. Dist: PRT, Jetstar

Cassette: released on Fashion, Apr'87 by Fashion Records. Dist: PRT, Jetstar

LIVESTOCK.
Single (12"): released on Incredible Music, '85 Dist: Jetstar

MOVIN' DOWN THE ROAD.
Album: released on World Enterprise, Dec'86 Dist: Jetstar

NICE AND SWEET.
Tracks: / Nice and sweet / Melody.
Notes: Melody /Michael Bani Rose.
Single (12"): released on Incredible Music, Nov'86 Dist: Jetstar

PART TIME LOVER.
Single (12"): released on Art & Craft, '82 Dist: Jetstar

PERSONALITY Rock it baby.
Single (12"): released on Art & Craft, '82 Dist: Jetstar

RAGAMUFFIN YEAR.
Tracks: / Ragamuffin year / Closer & closer.
Notes: Closer & closer/ Junior Delgado & Johnny osbourne.
Single (12"): released on Greensleeves, Sep'86 by Greensleeves Records. Dist: BMG, Jetstar, Spartan

RAGGAMUFFIN YEAR.
Tracks: / Chilly / I'm tipping / Love you tonight / Prisoner of love / King of kings / Hope that is for real / Closer & closer / Promised land / Call me.
Notes: Produced and arranged by: Augustus Pablo & Junior Delgado for Rockers Productions, Records at Creative Sounds & Tuff Gong Studios: Kingston, Jamaica & H.C.F Studios. USA
Album: released on Island, Nov'86 by Island Records. Dist: Polygram

Cassette: released on Island, Nov'86 by Island Records. Dist: Polygram

READY OR NOT.
Single (12"): released on Incredible Jux, '84 by Incredible Jux Records. Dist: Jetstar

REGGA-MUFFIN YEAR.
Tracks: / Ragga-Muffin year / Ragga-Muffin year dub / Closer & closer.
Notes: Extra tracks on 12" version only.
Single (12"): released on Island, Nov'86 by Island Records. Dist: Polygram

RICH MAN POOR MAN First on Sunday.
Single (12"): released on Live & Love, '82 by Third World Records. Dist: Jetstar

RON COME.
Single (12"): released on Crystal, '85 by Crystal Records. Dist: Jetstar, Revolver, Cartel

SISTERS AND BROTHERS.
Album: released on Blue Moon, '85 Dist: Magnum Music Group Ltd, PRT, Spartan

SWEET DARLING.
Single (12"): released on Macabeen, '85 by Macabeen Records. Dist: Jetstar

TICHEN.
Single (12"): released on Revue, '84 by Revue Records. Dist: Creole

TIME TO WORK.
Tracks: / Time to work / Let of mass.
Single (12"): released on Saxon Studio, May'86 by Saxon Studio Records. Dist: Jetstar

TROUBLE.
Single (12"): released on Incredible Music, '84 Dist: Jetstar

TWICE NICE.
Tracks: / Twice nice / original.
Single (12"): released on Legal Light, Mar'86 Dist: Jetstar

WHAT A HEART.
Single (12"): released on Toughest, '85 Dist: Jetstar

YOU REALLY DON'T LOVE ME (Delgado, Junior & Ranking Dread).
Single (12"): released on Sound Off, '80

Delgado, Roberto

BLUE TROPICAL.
Album: released on Polydor (Germany), '81 Dist: IMS-Polygram

Cassette: released on Polydor (Germany), '81 Dist: IMS-Polygram

BOUZOUKI MAGIC.
Album: released on Polydor, '75 by Polydor Records. Dist: Polygram, Polydor

EVIVA ROBERTO.
Album: released on Karussell (Import), '82

Cassette: released on Karussell (Import), '82

ROBERTO DELGADO MEETS KALINKA (Delgado, Roberto & His Orchestra).
Album: released on Memoir, '85 by Memoir Records. Dist: PRT Distribution

Cassette: released on Memoir, '85 by Memoir Records. Dist: PRT Distribution

Delharmonics

DELHARMONICS,THE.
Album: released on SRT, '76 by SRT Records. Dist: Pinnacle, Solomon & Peres Distribution, SRT Distribution, H.R. Taylor Distribution, PRT Distribution

Delius, Kerry

SLIPPING AWAY.
Single (7"): released on Arrival, '85 by Arrival. Dist: Revolver, Cartel

Single (12"): released on Arrival, '85 by Arrival. Dist: Revolver, Cartel

THEY SAY IT'S GONNA RAIN.
Single (7"): released on Arrival, '85 by Arrival. Dist: Revolver, Cartel

Single (12"): released on Arrival, '85 by Arrival. Dist: Revolver, Cartel

Single (12"): released on Arrival, Aug'87 by Arrival. Dist: Revolver, Cartel

Deliverance

DEVIL'S MEAT.
Notes: Distribution C/O 01-947 8004
Album: released on Metalworks, Apr'87

Delixx

UPRISING IN DUB.
Cassette: released on Micron, Sep'86 by Micron Records. Dist: Jetstar Distribution

Album: released on Kinck, '85 by Kinck Records. Dist: Jetstar

Delkass, Christine

MY MAN.
Single (12"): released on PMS, Apr'82

Del Lords

FRONTIER DAYS.
Album: released on Demon, Jul'85 by Demon Records. Dist: Pinnacle

JOHNNY COMES MARCHING HOME.
Tracks: / Heaven / love lies dying / Drug deal / Soldier's home / Saint jake / Dream come true / True love / Everlovin / Against my will / No waitress no more.
Notes: producer Neil Geraldo. Publishers Prince of the Bronx.
Album: released on EMI America, May'86 by EMI Records. Dist: EMI

Cassette: released on EMI America, May'86 by EMI Records. Dist: EMI

SOLDIER'S HOME.
Tracks: / Soldier's home / No waitress no more.
Single (7"): released on EMI America, May'86 by EMI Records. Dist: EMI

Dells

BREEZY BALLADS & TENDER TUNES.
Album: released on Solid Smoke (USA), Feb'85 Dist: Rhino

FROM STREETCORNER TO SOUL.
Album: released on Charly(R&B), Dec'84 by Charly Records. Dist: Charly, Cadillac

ROCKIN' ON BANDSTAND.
Album: released on Charly, Aug'83 by Charly Records. Dist: Charly, Cadillac

STAY IN MY CORNER.
Single (7"): released on Charly, Jul'80 by Charly Records. Dist: Charly, Cadillac

Single (7"): released on Chess, Jul'85 by Charly Records. Dist: Charly, Swift, PRT, Discovery, IMS, Polygram

WHATEVER TURNS YOU ON.
Album: released on 20th Century, Dec'81 Dist: RCA, IMS-Polygram

Delmar, Elaine

I'VE GOT THE WORLD ON A STRING.
Tracks: / When the world was young / I've got the world on a string / My funny valentine / Honeysuckle rose / I've got it bad and that ain't good / September song / Basin street blues / Mountain greenery / More than you know / Don't get around much anymore / Stardust / I gotta right to sing the blues.
Album: released on World, Aug'77 Dist: Jetstar

Del Mero Corazon

DEL MERO CORAZON film soundtrack.
Album: released on Arhoolie, May'81 by Arhoolie Records. Dist: Projection, Topic, Jazz Music, Swift, Roots

Delmonas

COMIN' HOME BABY.
Single (7"): released on Big Beat, Dec'84 by Ace Records. Dist: Projection, Pinnacle

DANGEROUS CHARMS.
Tracks: / Peter Gunn locomotion / You did him wrong / Hello I love you / Comin' home baby / Lies / C.C. Rider / He tells me he loves me / Hidden charms / Twist and shout / I'm the one for you / Fever / Chains / Please don't tell my baby / I want you / Take me home tonight / Woa now.
Album: released on Big Beat, Jun'85 by Ace Records. Dist: Projection, Pinnacle

DELMONAS FIVE.
Album: released on Empire, Aug'86 by Empire Records. Dist: Backs, Cartel, Jetstar

HELLO WE LOVE YOU.
Single (7"): released on Big Beat, Dec'84 by Ace Records. Dist: Projection, Pinnacle

SALLY-SHE-BROWN.
Single (7"): released on Empire, Aug'85 by Empire Records. Dist: Backs, Cartel, Jetstar

Delmondi

CAFE CONTINENTALE.
Tracks: / Norwegian polka / My Florence waltz / Temperamental tango / Rue de bal / Havana by night / Zingarella / Leger papillon / Triolets / Valise des as / Bandoneon infranto / Geraldine / Gilou.
Album: released on ARC (Accordion Records), '84 Dist: Accordion Record Club

Delmore Brothers

BEST OF....
Notes: 10 tracks
Album: released on Starday, Apr'87

Cassette: released on Starday, Apr'87

WHEN THEY LET THE HAMMER FALL (Delmore Brothers & Wayne Raney).
Tracks: / Red ball to nather / Jack and Jill boogie / Lost John boogie / Beale street boogie / Peach tree boogie / Boogie woogie baby / When they let the hammer down / Barnyard boogie / Hillbilly boogie / Freight train boogie / Down home boogie / Stop that boogie / Del Rio boogie / Pan American boogie / Real hot boogie / Used car blues.
Album: released on Bear Family, Nov'84 by Bear Family Records. Dist: Rollercoaster Distribution, Swift

Delnell, Mike

BLUEPRINT REFLECTIONS.
Album: released on Silberklang, Jun'79

LISTEN CAREFULLY.
Tracks: / Listen carefully (instrumental).
Cassette: released on Silberkla, Jan'86

OPUS 21.
Tracks: / Opus 21 theme mix.
Notes: Brilliant re-working of the original "However can I tell her" song given a new instrumental version by the master of the Bentley CPO, Mike Delnell.
Cassette: released on Silberkla, Jun'87

REFLECTIONS.
Tracks: / Reflections / Caro / Without reason / Without reason (instrumental).
Cassette: released on Silberkla, Jan'83

Single (7"): released on Silberkla, Jun'79

Deloria, Vine

GREAT AMERICAN INDIAN SPEECHES.
Double Album: released on Caedmon(USA), Nov'76 by Caedmon (USA) Records. Dist: Gower, Taylors, Discovery

Delta

TOUCH THE HEART.
Tracks: / Touch the heart (Inst).
Single (7"): released on Siren, Nov'86 by Virgin Records. Dist: EMI

Single (12"): released on Siren, Nov'86 by Virgin Records. Dist: EMI

Delta 5

MIND YOUR OWN BUSINESS.
Single (7"): released on Rough Trade, Oct'79 by Rough Trade Records. Dist: Rough Trade Distribution, Cartel Distribution

SEE THE WHIRL....
Album: released on Pre, Jul'81 by Charisma. Dist: Polygram

Cassette: released on Pre, Jul'81 by Charisma. Dist: Polygram

TRY.
Single (7"): released on Rough Trade, Nov'80 by Rough Trade Records. Dist: Rough Trade Distribution, Cartel Distribution

YOU.
Single (7"): released on Rough Trade, May'80 by Rough Trade Records. Dist: Rough Trade Distribution, Cartel Distribution

Delta Blues Band

SUNNYLAND SLIM'S BLUES JAM.
Album: released on Storyville, May'77 by Storyville Records. Dist: Jazz Music Distribution, Swift Distribution, Chris Wellard Distribution, Counterpoint Distribution

Delta Force

DELTA FORCE Original Sound Track.
Album: released on Milan France, Jun'86

Cassette: released on Milan France, Jun'86

Deltas

BOOGIE DISEASE.
Album: released on Nervous, Jul'84 by Nervous Records. Dist: Nervous, Rough Trade

HEART ATTACK.
Single (7"): released on Nervous, Jun'81 by Nervous Records. Dist: Nervous, Rough Trade

De Lucia, Paco

ENTRE DOS AGUAS.
Tracks: / Entre dos aguas / Zorongo gitano / Rio ancho / En la caleta / Convite / Monasterio de sal / Panaderos flamencos / Punta umbria / Chanela / La nina de puerta oscura / Castro marin / Gua'iras de lucia / Mantilla de feria / El vito.
Compact disc: released on Philps (Holland), Dec'86

ONE SUMMER NIGHT.
Tracks: / Altamar / Solo quero caminar / Chiquito / Gitanos andaluces / Palenque.
Notes: Paco de Lucia is simply, the greatest flamenco guitarist in the world. This is alive recording of Paco's sextet on their 1984 world tour. The music is an electric blend of flamenco and jazz fusion: a logical progression for Paco. Following the success of his collaboratcion with John McLaughin and Al DiMeola, both live and on record, interest in Paco is increasing steadily among connois- seurs of technique and passion. This album is digitally recorded mixed and mastered, and released simutaneously on Compact Disc: the ideal format to appreciate the artistry of a true musical genius- Paco de Lucia.
Compact disc: Dist: IMS-Polygram

Album: released on Mercury, Oct'84 by Phonogram Records. Dist: Polygram Distribution

Cassette: released on Mercury, Oct'84 by Phonogram Records. Dist: Polygram Distribution

SOLO QUIERO CAMINAR.
Tracks: / Solo quiero caminar / La tumbona / Convite / Montino / Chanela / Monosterio de sal / Pinonate / Palenrue.
Compact disc: Dist: IMS-Polygram

Deluxe A

BOYS ON TV.
Single (7"): released on EMI, Jan'83 by EMI Records. Dist: EMI

Single (12"): released on EMI, Jan'83 by EMI Records. Dist: EMI

Deluxe Blues Band

LIVE.
Single (7"): released on Hot Box, Jul'81 by Armageddon. Dist: Pinnacle

STREET CAR NAMED DELUXE, A.
Album: released on Appaloosa (Import), Dec'83

DeLys, Helaine

DELOVELY DELYS.
Album: released on Audiophile, Jan'87 by Jazzology Records (USA). Dist: Jazz Music, Swift

Delysia, Alice

ALICE DELYSIA.
Album: released on World, '71 Dist: Jetstar

De Marchi, Suze

BIG WEDNESDAY.
Tracks: / Big wednesday / Don't go away.
Single (7"): released on EMI, Jul'87 by EMI Records. Dist: EMI

Single (12"): released on EMI, Jul'87 by EMI Records. Dist: EMI

YOUNG HEARTS.
Tracks: / Young hearts / Biara.
Single (7"): released on EMI, Apr'86 by EMI Records. Dist: EMI

Single (12"): released on EMI, Apr'86 by EMI Records. Dist: EMI

Demenga, Thomas

CELLORGANICA (Demenga, Thomas & Heinz Reber).
Notes: Original music for cello and pipe organ composed by Heinz Reber and Thomas Demenga. Contemporary Classical. Digital recording. Thomas Demenga-cello/Heinz Reber-pipe organ.
Compact disc: released on ECM (Germany), Jan'87 by ECM Records. Dist: IMS, Polygram, Virgin through EMI

Album: released on ECM (Germany), Jul'81 by ECM Records. Dist: IMS, Polygram, Virgin through EMI

Demented Are Go

HOLY HACK JACK.
Tracks: / Holy hack jack / Rubber buccaneer / Don't go in the woods.
Single (12"): released on I.D., Jul'86 by I.D. Records. Dist: Revolver, Cartel

IN SICKNESS & IN HEALTH.
Album: released on I.D., Jul'86 by I.D. Records. Dist: Revolver, Cartel

Dementia

DEMENTIA.
Album: released on Skysaw, Apr'85 by Skysaw Records. Dist: Red Rhino, Cartel

DeMerle, Les

ON FIRE.
Album: released on Palo Alto (Italy), Jan'84

Demestos, Johnny

LEAVE MY JELLYBABIES ALONE.
Single (7"): released on Button, Nov'82 by Musical Characters Records. Dist: Spartan

Demob

NO ROOM FOR YOU.
Single (7"): released on Round Ear, Nov'81 Dist: Rough Trade Distribution

Demolished Men

GHOST TRAIN.
Single (7"): released on Anthem, May'84 by Anthem. Dist: ILA

Demon

BRITISH STANDARD APPROVED.
Album: released on Clay, Mar'85 by Clay Records. Dist: Pinnacle

DEMON.
Tracks: / Demon.
Single (12"): released on Clay, Mar'86 by Clay Records. Dist: Pinnacle

HAVE WE BEEN HERE BEFORE.
Single (7"): released on Carrere, Jul'82 by Carrere Records. Dist: PRT, Spartan

HEARTS OF OUR TIME.
Album: released on Clay, Nov'85 by Clay Records. Dist: Pinnacle

Cassette: released on Clay, Nov'85 by Clay Records. Dist: Pinnacle

NIGHT OF THE DEMON.
Album: released on Carrere, Jul'81 by Carrere Records. Dist: PRT, Spartan

ONE HELLUVA NIGHT.
Single (7"): released on Carrere, Mar'82 by Carrere Records. Dist: PRT, Spartan

PLAGUE, THE.
Single (7"): released on Clay, Aug'83 by Clay Records. Dist: Pinnacle

Album: released on Clay, Jun'83 by Clay Records. Dist: Pinnacle

Cassette: released on Clay, Jun'83 by Clay Records. Dist: Pinnacle

UNEXPECTED GUEST, THE.
Tracks: / Observation / Don't break the circle / Spell / Sign of a mad man / Total possession / Victim of fortune / Have we been here before? / Strange institution / Grand illusion / Beyond the gates / Deliver us from evil.
Album: released on Clay, Jan'87 by Clay Records. Dist: Pinnacle

Album: released on Carrere, Jul'82 by Carrere Records. Dist: PRT, Spartan

Cassette: released on Carrere, Jul'82 by Carrere Records. Dist: PRT, Spartan

WONDERLAND.
Single (7"): released on Clay, Nov'84 by Clay Records. Dist: Pinnacle

Single (12"): released on Clay, Nov'84 by Clay Records. Dist: Pinnacle

Demon Eyes

RITES OF CHAOS.
Album: released on Ebony, Jul'84 by Ebony Records. Dist: Pinnacle, Ebony

Demon Rockers

IRON LADY.
Single (12"): released on Unity, Mar'85 by Unity Records. Dist: Jetstar

Demons In Brentford

DEMONS IN BRENTFORD Various artists (Various Artists).
Album: released on Demon, Sep'84 by Demon Records. Dist: Pinnacle

Dempsey, Tommy

GREEN GROW THE LAUREL.
Album: released on Leader, '81 Dist: Jazz Music, Projection

Dendy, John

SECRET LOVER.
Tracks: / Secret lover / Secret lover (Instrumental).
Single (7"): released on Mainfeature, May'86 Dist: Gold & Sons, Cartel, O.I.D, Backs

Single (12"): released on Mainfeature, May'86 Dist: Gold & Sons, Cartel, O.I.D, Backs

Deneb, Lenny

MUSTIQUE GIRL.
Single (12"): released on L.E.D., Dec'84 by L.E.D. Records. Dist: Roots, Cartel, Jetstar

SOLDIERS.
Single (12"): released on L.E.D., Feb'85 by L.E.D. Records. Dist: Roots, Cartel, Jetstar

Dene, Terry

LEARNING HOW TO ROCK AND ROLL.
Single (7"): released on Logo, May'82 by Logo Records. Dist: Roots, BMG

Single 10": released on Logo, May'82 by Logo Records. Dist: Roots, BMG

WHITE SPORTS COAT.
Single (7"): released on Decca, Mar'82 by

Decca Records. Dist: Polygram

De Nijs, Rob

LET LOVE BE THE ANSWER.
Tracks: / Let love be the answer / Love of my life.
Single (7"): released on Columbia, Oct'86 by EMI Records. Dist: EMI

Denke, Frank

FABULOUS FRANK AT THE PIANO.
Album: released on Doric, Jan'76 by Amberlee Records. Dist: H.R. Taylor

SALUTES GREAT JAZZ PIANISTS.
Album: released on Doric, Jan'77 by Amberlee Records. Dist: H.R. Taylor

Denko, Harold

MIRTH SONG (Denko, Harold & Rufus Reid).
Album: released on Sunnyside (USA), Apr'84 Dist: Mole Jazz Distribution, Conifer Distribution

Dennerlein, Barbara

BEBAB.
Compact disc: released on Polystar (Japan), Jan'86 Dist: Target, Polygram

Dennis, B

REGGAE MUSIC.
Tracks: / Reggae music / Dub music.
Single (12"): released on Blakarmix, Jul'86 by Blakarmix Records. Dist: Jetstar

Dennis D D

WHAT AM I LIVING FOR.
Single (12"): released on Pioneer International, Jul'85 by Pioneer International Records. Dist: Jetstar

Dennis, Denny

DENNY DENNIS & LES ALLEN.
Album: released on World, Jul'79 Dist: Jetstar

Cassette: released on World, Jul'79 Dist: Jetstar

STARLIGHT SERENADES.
Notes: For full information see undeer "starlight serenades".

THIS IS ROMANCE (Dennis, Denny with Roy Fox & His Band).
Album: released on Joy, Jul'85 by President Records. Dist: Jazz Music, Swift, President Distribution

Dennis, Denzel

ENTERTAINER.
Single (12"): released on Rock'n'Groove, Mar'85 by Rock'n'Groove Records. Dist: Jetstar Distribution

Dennis, Jackie

ROCK YOUR LOVER.
Single (12"): released on Special Request, Apr'82

Dennis, Julie

DRAINED (Dennis, Julie & Certain Elements).
Single (7"): released on Indiscreet, Nov'84 Dist: Red Rhino, Cartel

Denny & Dunipace...

PLAY SCOTLANDS BEST (Denny & Dunipace Pipe Band).
Tracks: / Scotland the Brave / Rowan Tree / Bonnie Galloway / Old rustic bridge,The / Black Watch Polka,The / Mull of Kintyre / Green Hills,The / When the battle's o'er / Lynn Shannon's Wedding / Dunipace / Danish knife grinders spring song,The / Crossing the Minch / A. Cameron's strathspey / Miller of drone,The / Donald's Wedding / McFarlane's reel / Wilson,John / Wilson,John / Denny & Dunipace pipe band,The / Muckin' o'Georgie's byre,The / Glendurel Highlander,The / Bonnie Dundee / Amazing Grace / Day Thou gavest,The / Flower of Scotland / Mackays Farewell to the 71st / Rose amoung the heather,The / Fiddlers joy / Deil amang the tailors,The / Pigeon on the gate / Kate Dalrymple / Going home / Mist covered mountains / Morag of Dunvegan / Skye boat song,The / Dark island,The / Highland Wedding / Susan Macleod / Kate Robertson / Barron rocks of Aden,The / Highland Laddie / Mhairi's wedding / Black bear,The / Flowers of the forest / Drum salute.
Compact disc: released on Scotdisc, May'87 Dist: Clyde Factors Distributors

Denny, Sandy

BEST OF SANDY DENNY, THE.
Compact disc: released on Island, Aug'87 by Island Records. Dist: Polygram

Album: released on Island, Aug'87 by Island Records. Dist: Polygram

NORTH STAR GRASSMAN AND THE RAVENS.
Tracks: / Later November / Blackwaterside / Sea Captain / Down in the flood / John the gun / Next time around / Optimist / Let's jump the broomstick / Wretched Wilbur / North star grassman and the ravens / Crazy lady blues.
Album: released on Island, Nov'86 by Island Records. Dist: Polygram

ORIGINAL SANDY DENNY, THE.
Album: released on Mooncrest, Mar'84 by Mooncrest Records. Dist: PRT Distribution

Cassette: released on Mooncrest, '85 by Mooncrest Records. Dist: PRT Distribution

RENDEZVOUS.
Album: released on Hannibal, Jan'87 by Hannibal Records. Dist: Charly, Harmonia Mundi, Projection, Celtic Music, Roots

WHO KNOWS WHERE THE TIME GOES?.
Tracks: / Lady, The / Nothing more / Memphis Tennessee. / Solo / John the gun / Knockin on heaven's door / Who knows where the time goes / Music weaver, The / Take away the load / Sweet rosemary / Now and then / By the time it gets dark / What is true / Sail away to the sea / Farewell Farewell / Quiet joys of brotherhood / Tam lin / You never wanted me / Autopsy / One more chance / Stranger to himself / Pond and the stream, The / Banks of the nile, The / Two weeks last summer / Late November / Gypsy Davey / Winter winds / Sea, The / When will I be loved / Listen listen / Next time around / Tomorrow is a long time / One way donkey ride / Burton Town / Blackwaterside / It'll take a long time / Walking the floor over you / Friends / For Shame of doing wrong / I'm a dreamer / Full moon.
Notes: A 4 record set including her greatest released and unreleased recordings, live performances, outtakes and demos 1967-77.
Album: released on Hannibal, Jun'86 by Hannibal Records. Dist: Charly, Harmonia Mundi, Projection, Celtic Music, Roots

Dental Mechanics Daughter

LOVE ME NOW.
Tracks: / love me now / Dental Mechanics Daughter, The.
Single (7"): released on Gold Rush, May'86 Dist: Backs, Cartel

Dent, Ian

IAN DENT.
Notes: Daylight Records, The Daylight Co./Distribution\ ltd.,2 Dorset Place, New StreetHoniton, Devon EX14 8AB:
Cassette: released on Daylight, Jan'86 by Daylight Records. Dist: Daylight

Dentists

DOWN AND OUT IN PARIS AND CHATHAM.
Tracks: / Down and out in Paris and Chatham.
Single (7"): released on Tambourine, Jun'86 by The Dentists. Dist: Pinnacle

STRAWBERRIES ARE GROWING IN MY GARDEN (AND IT'S WINTER TIME).
Single (7"): released on Spruck, Nov'86 Dist: Backs, Cartel Distribution

WRITHING ON THE SHAGPILE.
Single (12"): released on Tambourine, 13 Jun'87 by The Dentists. Dist: Pinnacle

YOU AND YOUR BLOODY ORANGES.
Album: released on Spruck, Nov'85 Dist: Backs, Cartel Distribution

Denver, Jeannie

LIVE - SPUR & SADDLE.
Album: released on Westwood, Nov'76 by Westwood Records. Dist: Jazz Music, H.R. Taylor, JSU, Pinnacle, Ross Records

QUEEN OF THE SILVER DOLLAR.
Album: released on Westwood, '76 by Westwood Records. Dist: Jazz Music, H.R. Taylor, JSU, Pinnacle, Ross Records

WITH LOVE.
Album: released on Westwood, '82 by Westwood Records. Dist: Jazz Music, H.R. Taylor, JSU, Pinnacle, Ross Records

YORSHIRE ROSE.
Album: released on Westwood, '76 by Westwood Records. Dist: Jazz Music, H.R. Taylor, JSU, Pinnacle, Ross Records

Denver, John

ANNIES SONG.
Tracks: / Annie's song / Take me home county roads.
Single (7"): released on Old Gold, Nov'86 by Old Gold Records. Dist: Lightning, Jazz Music, Spartan, Counterpoint

BACK HOME AGAIN.
Album: released on RCA, Nov'84 by RCA Records. Dist: RCA, Roots, Swift, Wellard, Chris, I & B, Solomon & Peres Distribution

Cassette: released on RCA, Nov'84 by RCA Records. Dist: RCA, Roots, Swift, Wellard, Chris, I & B, Solomon & Peres Distribution

BEST OF... VOL.2.
Album: released on RCA, Sep'81 by RCA Records. Dist: RCA, Roots, Swift, Wellard, Chris, I & B, Solomon & Peres Distribution

Cassette: released on RCA, Sep'81 by RCA Records. Dist: RCA, Roots, Swift, Wellard, Chris, I & B, Solomon & Peres Distribution

COLLECTION: JOHN DENVER.
Album: released on Telstar, Dec'84 by Telstar Records. Dist: RCA Distribution

Cassette: released on Telstar, Dec'84 by Telstar Records. Dist: RCA Distribution

DON'T CLOSE YOUR EYES TONIGHT.
Single (7"): released on RCA, '85 by RCA Records. Dist: RCA, Roots, Swift, Wellard, Chris, I & B, Solomon & Peres Distribution

DON'T CLOSE YOUR EYES.
Tracks: / Don't close your eyes / Wild heart looking.
Single (7"): released on RCA, Apr'86 by RCA Records. Dist: RCA, Roots, Swift, Wellard, Chris, I & B, Solomon & Peres Distribution

DREAMLAND EXPRESS.
Tracks: / Dreamland express / Claudette / Gimme your love / Got my heart set on you / Harder they fall / Don't close your eyes tonight / Wild heart looking for home / Desired / Trail of tears / African sunrise.
Compact disc: by RCA Records. Dist: RCA, Roots, Swift, Wellard, Chris, I & B, Solomon & Peres Distribution

FAREWELL ANDROMEDA.
Album: released on RCA, Nov'84 by RCA Records. Dist: RCA, Roots, Swift, Wellard, Chris, I & B, Solomon & Peres Distribution

Cassette: released on RCA, Nov'84 by RCA Records. Dist: RCA, Roots, Swift, Wellard, Chris, I & B, Solomon & Peres Distribution

GREATEST HITS: JOHN DENVER VOL.2.
Compact disc: by RCA Records. Dist: RCA, Roots, Swift, Wellard, Chris, I & B, Solomon & Peres Distribution

Album: released on RCA, '84 by RCA Records. Dist: RCA, Roots, Swift, Wellard, Chris, I & B, Solomon & Peres Distribution

Cassette: released on RCA, '84 by RCA Records. Dist: RCA, Roots, Swift, Wellard, Chris, I & B, Solomon & Peres Distribution

GREATEST HITS: JOHN DENVER VOL.3.
Tracks: / Dancing with the mountains / Wild Montana skies / I want to live / Gold & beyond / Autograph / How can I leave you again / Some days are Diamonds / Shanghai breezes / Seasons of the heart / Perhaps love / Love again.
Album: released on RCA, Mar'85 by RCA Records. Dist: RCA, Roots, Swift, Wellard, Chris, I & B, Solomon & Peres Distribution

Cassette: released on RCA, Mar'85 by RCA Records. Dist: RCA, Roots, Swift, Wellard, Chris, I & B, Solomon & Peres Distribution

Compact disc: released on RCA, Oct'86 by RCA Records. Dist: RCA, Roots, Swift, Wellard, Chris, I & B, Solomon & Peres Distribution

GREATEST HITS:JOHN DENVER.
Compact disc: by RCA Records. Dist: RCA, Roots, Swift, Wellard, Chris, I & B, Solomon & Peres Distribution

Album: released on RCA, '84 by RCA Records. Dist: RCA, Roots, Swift, Wellard, Chris, I & B, Solomon & Peres Distribution

Cassette: released on RCA, '84 by RCA Records. Dist: RCA, Roots, Swift, Wellard, Chris, I & B, Solomon & Peres Distribution

Cassette: released on Autograph, '85 Dist: Record Services Distribution (Ireland)

HOLD ME TIGHTLY.
Single (7"): released on RCA, Oct'83 by RCA Records. Dist: RCA, Roots, Swift, Wellard, Chris, I & B, Solomon & Peres Distribution

IT'S ABOUT TIME.
Compact disc: released on RCA, Apr'84 by RCA Records. Dist: RCA, Roots, Swift, Wellard, Chris, I & B, Solomon & Peres Distribution

Compact disc: by RCA Records. Dist: RCA, Roots, Swift, Wellard, Chris, I & B, Solomon & Peres Distribution

Album: released on RCA, Nov'84 by RCA Records. Dist: RCA, Roots, Swift, Wellard, Chris, I & B, Solomon & Peres Distribution

Cassette: released on RCA, Nov'84 by RCA Records. Dist: RCA, Roots, Swift, Wellard, Chris, I & B, Solomon & Peres Distribution

JOHN DENVER COLLECTION.
Tracks: / Annie's song / Take me home country roads / Rocky mountain high / Starwood in aspen / Follow me / I'd rather be a cowboy /Lady's chains / Rhymes and reasons / Perhaps love / Calypso / Country love / Leaving on a jet plane / Thank God I'm a country boy / Dancing with the mountains / Baby you look good to me tonight / Wild montana skies / Love again.
Compact disc: by Telstar Records. Dist: RCA Distribution

LIVE IN LONDON.
Album: released on RCA, May'76 by RCA Records. Dist: RCA, Roots, Swift, Wellard, Chris, I & B, Solomon & Peres Distribution

Cassette: released on RCA, '84 by RCA Records. Dist: RCA, Roots, Swift, Wellard, Chris, I & B, Solomon & Peres Distribution

ONE WORLD.
Tracks: / Along for the ride / I can't escape / True love takes time / One world / It's a possibilty / Love is the master / Love again / Let us begin / I remember you / Hey there Mr. Lonely-Heart / Flying for me / Love is the master / Love again / I remember you / Hey there lonely heart / Let us begin / Flying for me / Along for the ride / True love takes time.
Album: released on RCA, Aug'86 by RCA Records. Dist: RCA, Roots, Swift, Wellard, Chris, I & B, Solomon & Peres Distribution

Cassette: released on RCA, Aug'86 by RCA Records. Dist: RCA, Roots, Swift, Wellard, Chris, I & B, Solomon & Peres Distribution

Compact disc: released on RCA, Jan'86 by RCA Records. Dist: RCA, Roots, Swift, Wellard, Chris, I & B, Solomon & Peres Distribution

PERHAPS LOVE (see Domingo, Placido) (Denver, John & Placido Domingo).
Album: released on CBS, Oct'81 by CBS Records. Dist: CBS

Cassette: released on CBS, Oct'81 by CBS Records. Dist: CBS

POEMS, PRAYERS & PROMISES.
Album: released on RCA, Nov'84 by RCA Records. Dist: RCA, Roots, Swift, Wellard, Chris, I & B, Solomon & Peres Distribution

Cassette: released on RCA, Nov'84 by RCA Records. Dist: RCA, Roots, Swift, Wellard, Chris, I & B, Solomon & Peres Distribution

ROCKY MOUNTAIN HIGH.
Album: released on RCA, Nov'84 by RCA Records. Dist: RCA, Roots, Swift, Wellard, Chris, I & B, Solomon & Peres Distribution

Cassette: released on RCA, Nov'84 by RCA Records. Dist: RCA, Roots, Swift, Wellard, Chris, I & B, Solomon & Peres Distribution

SEASONS OF THE HEART.
Tracks: / Seasons of the heart / Opposite tables / Relatively speaking / Dreeams / Nothing but a breeze / What one man can do / Shanghai breeze / islands / Heart to heart / Perhaps love / Childen of the Universe.
Compact disc: released on RCA, Jan'84 by RCA Records. Dist: RCA, Roots, Swift, Wellard, Chris, I & B, Solomon & Peres Distribution

Album: released on RCA, '84 by RCA Records. Dist: RCA, Roots, Swift, Wellard, Chris, I & B, Solomon & Peres Distribution

Cassette: released on RCA, '84 by RCA Records. Dist: RCA, Roots, Swift, Wellard, Chris, I & B, Solomon & Peres Distribution

SOME DAYS ARE DIAMONDS.
Album: released on RCA, '84 by RCA Records. Dist: RCA, Roots, Swift, Wellard, Chris, I & B, Solomon & Peres Distribution

Cassette: released on RCA, '84 by RCA Records. Dist: RCA, Roots, Swift, Wellard, Chris, I & B, Solomon & Peres Distribution

SPIRIT.
Album: released on RCA, Nov'84 by RCA Records. Dist: RCA, Roots, Swift, Wellard, Chris, I & B, Solomon & Peres Distribution

Cassette: released on RCA, Nov'84 by RCA Records. Dist: RCA, Roots, Swift, Wellard, Chris, I & B, Solomon & Peres Distribution

WINDSONG.
Album: released on RCA, Nov'84 by RCA Records. Dist: RCA, Roots, Swift, Wellard, Chris, I & B, Solomon & Peres Distribution

Cassette: released on RCA, Nov'84 by RCA Records. Dist: RCA, Roots, Swift, Wellard, Chris, I & B, Solomon & Peres Distribution

Denver, Karl

WIMOWEH Gypsy Davy.
Single (7"): released on Old Gold, '85 by Old Gold Records. Dist: Lightning, Jazz Music, Spartan, Counterpoint

WIMOWEH/GYPSY DAVY.
Single (7"): released on Decca, '82 by Decca Records. Dist: Polygram

Denver Spur

FIRST TIME OUT.
Album: released on Sweet Folk All, '81 by Sweet Folk All Records. Dist: Sweet Folk All, Roots, Celtic Music, Dragon, Impetus, Projection, Chris Wellard, Festival Records

Denyer, Frank

WHEAT.
Album: released on Orchid, '85 Dist: Impetus Distribution, Orchid

Denym

BABY IT'S LOVE.
Single (12"): released on Real Wax, '82

Deodato

DEODATO.
Album: released on Proto, '84 by Proto Records. Dist: WEA

Cassette: released on Proto, '84 by Proto Records. Dist: WEA

HAPPY HOUR.
Album: released on Warner Brothers, '82 by Warner Bros Records. Dist: WEA

HAPPY HOUR/NIGHT CRUISER/WHISTLE BUMP.
Single (12"): released on Warner Bros., '82 by Warner Bros Records. Dist: WEA

HAPPY HOUR/SWEET MAGIC.
Single (7"): released on Warner Bros., '82 by Warner Bros Records. Dist: WEA

JOAO DONATO.
Album: released on Muse, '77 by Peerless Records. Dist: Lugtons Distributors

KEEP ON MOVING/WHISTLE BUMP.
Single (7"): released on Warner Bros., '82 by Warner Bros Records. Dist: WEA

Single (12"): released on Warner Bros., '82 by Warner Bros Records. Dist: WEA

LOVE ISLAND.
Album: released on Warner Brothers, '78 by Warner Bros Records. Dist: WEA

PRELUDE.
Album: released on CTI, '76 by Polydor Records. Dist: IMS, Polygram

VERY TOGETHER.
Album: released on MCA, '76 by MCA Records. Dist: Polygram, MCA

WHIRLWINDS.
Album: released on MCA, '74 by MCA Records. Dist: Polygram, MCA

Deodato, Eumir

BEST OF DEODATO.
Compact disc: by Phonogram Records. Dist: Polygram Distribution

DEODATO,THE BEST OF.
Compact disc: released on Mercury (USA), '84 by Import Records. Dist: IMS Distribution, Polygram Distribution

Deparis Brothers

Jimmy Ryans & The Uptown Cafe Society...

Department S

IS VIC THERE/SOLID GOLD EASY ACTION.
Single (7"): released on Demon, '81 by Demon Records. Dist: Pinnacle

Album: released on Mute, '82 Dist: Spartan Distribution, Rough Trade Distribution, Cartel Distribution

Cassette: released on Mute, '82 Dist: Spartan Distribution, Rough Trade Distribution, Cartel Distribution

I WANT MORE/MONTE CARLO.
Single (7"): released on Stiff, '81 by Stiff Records. Dist: EMI, Record Services Distribution (Ireland)

Single (12"): released on Stiff, '81 by Stiff Records. Dist: EMI, Record Services Distribution (Ireland)

De Paul, Lynsey

LYNSEY SINGS.
Album: by M.A.M. Records. Dist: T.B.C

Depeche Mode

BLACK CELEBRATION.
Tracks: / Black celebration / Fly on the windscreen - Final / Question of lust / Sometimes / It doesn't matter two / Question of time, A / Stripped / Here is the house / World full of nothing / Dressed in black / New dress / Pipeline / Everything counts / Two minute warning.
Compact disc: released on Mute, Jan'86 Dist: Spartan Distribution, Rough Trade Distribution, Cartel Distribution

Cassette: released on Mute, Mar'86 Dist: Spartan Distribution, Rough Trade Distribution, Cartel Distribution

BROKEN FRAME, A.
Compact disc: Dist: Spartan Distribution, Rough Trade Distribution. Cartel Distribution

CONSTRUCTION TIME AGAIN.
Compact disc: released on Mute, Jan'86 Dist: Spartan Distribution, Rough Trade Distribution, Cartel Distribution

Album: released on Mute, '83 Dist: Spartan Distribution, Rough Trade Distribution, Cartel Distribution

Cassette: released on Mute, '83 Dist: Spartan Distribution, Rough Trade Distribution, Cartel Distribution

DREAMING OF ME/ICE MACHINE.
Single (7"): released on Mute, '81 Dist: Spartan Distribution, Rough Trade Distribution, Cartel Distribution

EVERYTHING COUNTS/WORK HARD.
Single (7"): released on Mute, '83 Dist: Spartan Distribution, Rough Trade Distribution, Cartel Distribution

Single (12"): released on Mute, '83 Dist: Spartan Distribution, Rough Trade Distribution, Cartel Distribution

IT'S CALLED A HEART.
Single (7"): released on Mute, '85 Dist: Spartan Distribution, Rough Trade Distribution, Cartel Distribution

Single (12"): released on Mute, '85 Dist: Spartan Distribution, Rough Trade Distribution, Cartel Distribution

Single (12"): released on Mute, '85 Dist: Spartan Distribution, Rough Trade Distribution, Cartel Distribution

JUST CAN'T GET ENOUGH.
Single (7"): released on Mute, '81 Dist: Spartan Distribution, Rough Trade Distribution, Cartel Distribution

LEAVE IN SILENCE/MY SECRET GARDEN.
Single (7"): released on Mute, '82 Dist: Spartan Distribution, Rough Trade Distribution, Cartel Distribution

Single (12"): released on Mute, '82 Dist: Spartan Distribution, Rough Trade Distribution, Cartel Distribution

Single (12"): released on Mute, '82 Dist: Spartan Distribution, Rough Trade Distribution, Cartel Distribution

MASTER AND SERVANT.
Single (7"): released on Mute, '84 Dist: Spartan Distribution, Rough Trade Distribution, Cartel Distribution

Single (12"): released on Mute, '84 Dist: Spartan Distribution, Rough Trade Distribution, Cartel Distribution

MEANING OF LOVE/OBERKURN.
Single (7"): released on Mute, '82 Dist: Spartan Distribution, Rough Trade Distribution, Cartel Distribution

Single (12"): released on Mute, '82 Dist: Spartan Distribution, Rough Trade Distribution, Cartel Distribution

NEVER LET ME DOWN AGAIN.
Tracks: / Pleasure, little treasure.
Single (7"): released on Mute, Aug'87 Dist: Spartan Distribution, Rough Trade Distribution, Cartel Distribution

Single (12"): released on Mute, Aug'87 Dist: Spartan Distribution, Rough Trade Distribution, Cartel Distribution

NEW LIFE/SHOUT.
Single (7"): released on Mute, '81 Dist: Spartan Distribution, Rough Trade Distribution, Cartel Distribution

PEOPLE ARE PEOPLE.
Single (7"): released on Mute, '84 Dist: Spartan Distribution, Rough Trade Distribution, Cartel Distribution

Single (12"): released on Mute, '84 Dist: Spartan Distribution, Rough Trade Distribution, Cartel Distribution

QUESTION OF LUST, A.
Tracks: / Question of lust, A / Christmas Island / People are people/live / It doesn't matter / two / Question of lust, A /minimal.
Single (7"): released on Mute, Apr'86 Dist: Spartan Distribution, Rough Trade Distribution, Cartel Distribution

Single (12"): released on Mute, Apr'86 Dist: Spartan Distribution, Rough Trade Distribution, Cartel Distribution

QUESTION OF TIME.
Tracks: / Question of time.
Notes: Limited edition side A. Remix.
Single (12"): released on Mute, Sep'86 Dist: Spartan Distribution, Rough Trade Distribution, Cartel Distribution

QUESTION OF TIME, A.
Tracks: / Question of time, A / Black celebration/live / Something to do/live / Stripped/live.
Notes: Extra track on 12" version only.
Single (7"): released on Mute, Aug'86 Dist: Spartan Distribution, Rough Trade Distribution, Cartel Distribution

SEE YOU NOW/THIS IS FUN.
Single (7"): released on Mute, '82 Dist: Spartan Distribution, Rough Trade Distribution, Cartel Distribution

Single (12"): released on Mute, '82 Dist: Spartan Distribution, Rough Trade Distribution, Cartel Distribution

SHAKE THE DISEASE.
Single (7"): released on Mute, '85 Dist: Spartan Distribution, Rough Trade Distribution, Cartel Distribution

Single (12"): released on Mute, '85 Dist: Spartan Distribution, Rough Trade Distribution, Cartel Distribution

SINGLES '81-'85.
Tracks: / People are people / Master and servant / It's called a heart / Just can't get enough / See you / Shake the disease / Everything counts / New life / Blasphemous rumours / Leave in silence / Get the balance right / Love in itself / Dreaming of me.

SINGLES '81-'85, THE.
Compact disc: Dist: Spartan Distribution, Rough Trade Distribution. Cartel Distribution

Album: released on Mute, '85 Dist: Spartan Distribution, Rough Trade Distribution, Cartel Distribution

Cassette: released on Mute, '85 Dist: Spartan Distribution, Rough Trade Distribution, Cartel Distribution

Compact disc: released on Mute, '85 Dist: Spartan Distribution, Rough Trade Distribution, Cartel Distribution

SOMEBODY.
Extended-play record: released on Mute, '84 Dist: Spartan Distribution, Rough Trade Distribution, Cartel Distribution

Single (12"): released on Mute, '84 Dist: Spartan Distribution, Rough Trade Distribution, Cartel Distribution

SOME GREAT REWARD.
Tracks: / If you want to / Master and servant / Lie to me / Something to do / Blasphemous rumours / Somebody / People are people / It don't matter / Stories of old / Pipeline / Everything counts / Two minute warning.
Album: released on Mute, '84 Dist: Spartan Distribution, Rough Trade Distribution, Cartel Distribution

Cassette: released on Mute, '84 Dist: Spartan Distribution, Rough Trade Distribution, Cartel Distribution

Compact disc: released on Mute, '84 Dist: Spartan Distribution, Rough Trade Distribution, Cartel Distribution

SOME GREAT VIDEOS.
Notes: Number of tracks: 10. Type of recording: Compilation. Total playing time: 46 minutes. Retail price: 19.99.
Video-cassette (VHS): released on Virgin, Jan'86 by Virgin Records. Dist: EMI, Virgin Distribution

SPEAK & SPELL.
Tracks: / New life / Just can't get enough / I sometimes wish I was dead / Puppets / Boys say go / No disco / What's your name / Photographic / Tora tora tora / Big muff / Any second now.
Album: released on Mute, '81 Dist: Spartan Distribution, Rough Trade Distribution, Cartel Distribution

Album: released on Mute, '81 Dist: Spartan Distribution, Rough Trade Distribution, Cartel Distribution

STRANGELOVE.
Tracks: / Strangelove / Pimp.
Single (12"): released on Mute, 30 May'87 Dist: Spartan Distribution, Rough Trade Distribution, Cartel Distribution

STRANGE LOVE.
Tracks: / Strange love / Pimps.
Single (7"): released on Mute, Apr'87 Dist: Spartan Distribution, Rough Trade Distribution, Cartel Distribution

Single (12"): released on Mute, Apr'87 Dist: Spartan Distribution, Rough Trade Distribution, Cartel Distribution

STRIPPED.
Tracks: / Stripped / But not tonight / Breathing in fumes / Fly on the windscreen (Quiet Mix) / Black day.
Single (7"): released on Mute, Feb'86 Dist: Spartan Distribution, Rough Trade Distribution, Cartel Distribution

De Plata, Manitas

GUITARS EN FETE.
Album: released on CBS(Import), Sep'86 by CBS Records. Dist: Conifer, Discovery, Swift

Cassette: released on CBS, Sep'86 by CBS Records. Dist: CBS

De Pra, Sylvio

SOUVENIRS FOR YOU.
Tracks: / Marina / Quando quando / Old fashioned way / I love you so / Mlody of love / Turkish march / Can't help falling / Buon natale / Top of the world / Snowbird / Guantanamera / Marilena / Who pays the ferryman / Beautiful song / Sole mio / Danza / Viva espana / Roma.
Notes: Retail price given by ARC ecluding P&P via mail order is 4.95. Mail order distribution address: Accordion Record Club, 146 Birmingham Road, Kidderminster, Worc. DY10 2SL. Tel. 0562 - 746105.
Album: released on Accordion Record Club, Jul'86 by Accordion Record Club Records. Dist: Accordion Record Club

Depraved

COME ON DOWN.
Album: released on Cor, Jan'86 Dist: Revolver, Cartel

SOME GREAT REWARD.
Compact disc: Dist: Spartan Distribution, Rough Trade Distribution, Cartel Distribution

STUPIDITY MAKETH THE MAN.
Album: released on Children Of The Revolution, Oct'86 by Revolver Records. Dist: Revolver, Cartel

Depress

ON THE OTHER SIDE.
Album: released on Uniton Records, Sep'84 Dist: Cartel

Cassette: released on Uniton Records, Sep'84 Dist: Cartel

Derek, B

GET DOWN.
Single (12"): released on Music Of Life, Aug'87 Dist: Streetwave

ROCK THE BEAT.
Single (12"): released on Music Of Life, May'87 Dist: Streetwave

Derek & Clive

AD NAUSEAM.
Tracks: / Endangered species / Racing / T.V. / Bruce / Records / Soul time / Russia / Sir / Celebrity suicide / Politics / Labels / Street music / Horn (The) / Mona / Critics (The).
Album: released on Virgin, Apr'86 by Virgin Records. Dist: EMI, Virgin Distribution

Cassette: released on Virgin, Apr'86 by Virgin Records. Dist: EMI, Virgin Distribution

Album: released on Virgin, '78 by Virgin Records. Dist: EMI, Virgin Distribution

LIVE.
Album: released on Island, Aug'76 by Island Records. Dist: Polygram

Derek & Dominoes

IN CONCERT.
Double Album: by Polydor Records. Dist: Polygram, Polydor

LAYLA.
Single (7"): released on RSO-Polydor Jul'72

Single (7"): released on Old Gold, Jul'84 by Old Gold Records. Dist: Lightning, Jazz Music, Spartan, Counterpoint

LAYLA & OTHER ASSORTED LOVE SONGS.
Album: released on RSO, Jan'84

Double compact disc: by Polydor Records. Dist: Polygram Distribution

Derek, Jon

WITH A LITTLE HELP FROM MY FRIENDS.
Album: released on Westwood, Nov'76 by Westwood Records. Dist: Jazz Music, H.R. Taylor, JSU, Pinnacle, Ross Records

Der Plan

FETTE JAHRE.
Album: released on Atatak, Apr'86 by Atatak Records. Dist: Rough Trade, Cartel

Derri Airs

DERRI AIRS Nazareth house, Derry.
Album: released on Outlet (Ireland), Aug'82

Cassette: released on Outlet (Ireland), Aug'82

Derrick & Sounds.
SHAKE ME I RATTLE.
Single (7"):

Derry, Pat
FISTFUL OF COUNTRY.
Album: released on Homespun(Ireland), '82 by Outlet Records. Dist: Outlet

Cassette: released on Homespun(Ireland), '82 by Outlet Records. Dist: Outlet

GHOST RIDERS IN THE SKY.
Album: released on Homespun(Ireland), May'83 by Outlet Records. Dist: Outlet

Cassette: released on Homespun(Ireland), May'83 by Outlet Records. Dist: Outlet

Desair
LOVELY LADY OF THE ROSES.
Single (7"): released on Crammed Discs (Belgium), Jun'82 Dist: Rough Trade, Nine Mile, Cartel

Des Airs
LUNGA NOTTE.
Album: released on Crammed UK, Sep'84 Dist: Rough Trade, Nine Mile, Cartel

De Santo, Dan
IN SOUTH AFRICA.
Tracks: / In south Africa.
Single (7"):

IN SOUTH AFRICA.
Tracks: / In South Africa / Sun city.
Single (7"):

Desanto, Sugar Pie
LOVIN' TOUCH.
Album: released on Diving Duck, Jul'87

Desarlo, Teri
OVERNIGHT SUCCESS.
Single (7"): released on Epic, Feb'85 by CBS Records. Dist: CBS

Desborough School Choir
WHY NOT BUY AN EXTRA PRESENT.
Single (7"): released on Jira, Nov'83 Dist: Spartan

Descendents
ALL.
Album: released on SST, Jun'87 by SST Records. Dist: Pinnacle

Cassette: released on SST, Jun'87 by SST Records. Dist: Pinnacle

BONUS FAT.
Single (7"): released on SST, Aug'87 by SST Records. Dist: Pinnacle

Descloux, Lizzy Mercier
ONE FOR THE SOUL.
Tracks: / One for the soul / Simply beautiful / Fog horn blues / Women don't like me / My funny valentine / Sound of Leblon beach / Garden of Alas / God-spell me wrong / Off all pleasure / Long voodoo ago / Love streams.
Notes: French cult artist Lizzy Mercier Descloux's three previous albums have been praised by the English music press. Recorded in Brazil, 'One For The Soul' is a collection of ten songs all in English. Special guest artist, American trumpeter Chet Baker plays on five songs. The CD has three extra songs, 'Queen Of Overdub Kisses', 'A Word Is A Whah' and 'Scala Saga Scamba'.
Album: released on Polydor (France), Jul'86 Dist: Polygram

Cassette: released on Polydor (France), Jul'86 Dist: Polygram

Compact disc: released on Polydor (France), Jul'86 Dist: Polygram

ZULU ROCK.
Single (7"): released on CBS, Apr'84 by CBS Records. Dist: CBS

Single (12"): released on CBS, Apr'84 by CBS Records. Dist: CBS

Desert Song
DESERT SONG   Original London cast (1920's).
Album: released on World, Oct'77 Dist: Jetstar

DESERT SONG (Romberg, Sigmund).
Album: released on Monmouth, '73

DESERT SONG   Various artists (Various Artists).
Album: released on Starline, '71 by EMI Records. Dist: EMI

Desert String Band
DESERT STRING BAND, THE.
Album: released on Shanachie (USA), Jan'85

Desford Colliery Band
CELEBRATION.
Album: released on Polyphonic, Jul'81 by Polyphonic Records. Dist: Taylors

Cassette: released on Polyphonic, Jul'81 by Polyphonic Records. Dist: Taylors

ENGLISH HERITAGE SERIES VOL.1.
Album: released on Polyphonic, Oct'84 by Polyphonic Records. Dist: Taylors

Cassette: released on Polyphonic, Oct'84 by Polyphonic Records. Dist: Taylors

ENGLISH HERITAGE SERIES-ELGAR VOL.2.
Album: released on Polyphonic, Oct'84 by Polyphonic Records. Dist: Taylors

Cassette: released on Polyphonic, Oct'84 by Polyphonic Records. Dist: Taylors

JINGLE BELLS.
Tracks: / Jingle bells / Merry tijuana, A.
Single (7"): released on Hallamshire, Dec'86 Dist: Pinnacle

SHOWCASE.
Tracks: / Duet for two cats / Polovtsian dances / Czardas / Poeme / President, The / Sailing by / Clock and the dresden china figures, The / Apres un reve / Dances from West Side Story / Perpetuum mobile / Folk festival / Girl with the flaxen hair.
Notes: A brand new album especially recorded for MFP featuring one of this country's foremost Brass Bands. A fascinating programme of 15 classic bands of pure brassband craftsmanship recorded at Abbey Road Studios, packaged in a superb sleeve. Highlights include 'Duet for two cats' by Rossini, Saint-Saens 'The swan', Bach's 'Air on the G-String' and a 10 minute medley of music from 'West Side Story'.
Cassette: released on Music For Pleasure, Feb'87 by EMI Records. Dist: EMI

SHOWCASE.
Tracks: / Air on the G string / Swan / Golliwog's cake-walk.
Album: released on MFP, Feb'87 by EMI Records. Dist: EMI

Deshotel, Ed & Bee
CAJUN TROUBADOURS.
Album: released on Swallow, Feb'79

VIE DES CAJUNS, (LA).
Album: released on Swallow, Feb'79

Desi
I WANT TO BE WITH YOU.
Tracks: / I want to be with you / I'm much too shy / I want to be with you (Ext.).
Single (7"): released on Certain, Jan'86 Dist: Priority, EMI, Pinnacle

Single (12"): released on Certain, Jan'86 Dist: Priority, EMI, Pinnacle

Single (7"): released on Decca, Aug'72 Dist: Decca Records. Dist: Polygram

Desi, Dirty
BIG BATTY BETTY.
Single (12"): released on D.A.D., Dec'84 by D.A.D. Records. Dist: Jetstar

Design 9
ROULETTE.
Single (7"): released on Quickstep, Jun'84 by Quickstep Records. Dist: Pinnacle

Designed For...
DESIGNED FOR DANCING - VOL. 1 (Various Artists).
Album: released on GC, Nov'86 by GC Recordings. Dist: DMS, RCA

DESIGNED FOR DANCING (Various Artists).
Album: released on Design Communications, Feb'84

Cassette: released on Design Communications, Feb'84

DESIGNED FOR LIVING (Various Artists).
Album: released on GC, Oct'86 by GC Recordings. Dist: DMS, RCA

Designer
FEELING NICE.
Single (7"): released on Trindisc, Nov'83 by Trindisc Records. Dist: Jetstar, Pinnacle, Rough Trade, Cartel

Single (12"): released on Trindisc, Nov'83 by Trindisc Records. Dist: Jetstar, Pinnacle, Rough Trade, Cartel

Single (12"): released on Trindisc, Mar'84 by Trindisc Records. Dist: Jetstar, Pinnacle, Rough Trade, Cartel

Design For Living
DESIGN FOR LIVING.
Single (7"): released on Anthem, May'84 by Anthem. Dist: ILA

SLOWLY SHOUTING.
Album: released on Music For Living, Aug'83 by Music For Living Records. Dist: Stage One Distribution

Desmond, Andy
ANDY DESMOND.
Album: released on Ariola, Apr'78 Dist: RCA, Ariola

Desmond, Johnny
MEMORIAL ALBUM.
Album: released on Magic, Dec'85 Dist: Jazz Music, Submarine, Swift, Chris Wellard, Conifer

Cassette: released on Magic, Dec'85 Dist: Jazz Music, Submarine, Swift, Chris Wellard, Conifer

Desmond, Paul
BLUES IN TIME (Desmond, Paul & Gerry Mulligan).
Album: released on Verve (USA), Mar'84 by Polydor. Dist: Polygram

EAST OF THE SUN.
Compact disc: released on Discovery (USA), Dec'86 by Discovery Records (USA). Dist: Swift, Flexitron-Audio, Jazz Music

GREATEST HITS:PAUL DESMOND.
Tracks: / Take ten / I've grown accustomed to her face / Black orpheus / Hi-lili, hi-lo / Desmond blue / Embarcadero / All the things you are / El prince / Alone together / Taste of honey / O Gato.
Album: released on RCA, Jun'86 by RCA Records. Dist: RCA, Roots, Swift, Wellard, Chris, I & B, Solomon & Peres Distribution

Cassette: released on RCA, Jun'86 by RCA Records. Dist: RCA, Roots, Swift, Wellard, Chris, I & B, Solomon & Peres Distribution

MASTER OF JAZZ.
Album: released on RCA (Germany), Aug'83   Cat. no: CL 42790

ONLY RECORDED PERFORMANCE, THE (Desmond, Paul Quartet).
Album: released on Finesse, Nov'84 by PRT Records. Dist: PRT

Cassette: released on Finesse, Nov'84 by PRT Records. Dist: PRT

PAUL DESMOND.
Album: released on Artists House, May'81 by JSU, Swift

PAUL DESMOND QUARTET LIVE (Desmond, Paul Quartet).
Double Album: released on Horizon, Jul'76 by A&M Records. Dist: CBS

PURE DESMOND.
Album: released on CTI (Musidisc France), Feb'84 by Polydor Records. Dist: IMS, Polygram

SKYLARK.
Compact disc: released on CTI (Musidisc France), Feb'84 by Polydor Records. Dist: IMS, Polygram

Desmond, Tommy
APRIL WON'T BE HERE UNTIL SEPTEMBER.
Single (7"): released on Sin, Aug'80 Dist: Red Rhino, Cartel

Desolation Angels
DESOLATION ANGELS.
Tracks: / Rock 'n' roll / Crazy circles / Gone gone gone / Evil wind / Early in the morning / Oh Atlanta / Take the time / Rhythm machine / She brings me love.
Album: released on Thameside, Jun'86 Dist: Red Rhino, Cartel

De Souza, Paul
DON'T ASK MY NEIGHBORS.
Album: by Capitol Records. Dist: EMI

Desperadoes
DESPERADOES, THE.
Album: released on Charisma, Jul'81 by Virgin Records. Dist: EMI

Album: released on Charisma, Jul'81 by Virgin Records. Dist: EMI

Desperate rock 'n roll vol.2
DESPERATE ROCK 'N ROLL VOL.2
Various artists (Various Artists).
Notes: Featuring Danny Ross, Jimmy Johnson, Eddie Kirkland, Chavis Brothers etc.
Album: released on Flame, Aug'87 by Nimbus Records. Dist: Nimbus, Swift

Dessau, Joanna
AMAZING GRACE.
Cassette: released on Soundings, Mar'85 Dist: Soundings

Dessus
GHETTO CHILDREN.
Single (7"): released on LEJ, Jan'82 Dist: Jetstar

De Stijl
ANATOMY   Do the deal.
Single (7"): released on Small Run, '83 by Small Run Records. Dist: Pinnacle

Destiny
MARATHON (THE).
Single (7"): released on Windmill Music, Apr'84

Destiny Orchestra
SPRING RAIN.
Single (7"): released on Destiny, Oct'79 by Destiny Records. Dist: Red Rhino, Cartel

Destri, Jimmy
HEART ON A WALL.
Album: released on Chrysalis, Feb'82 by Chrysalis Records. Dist: CBS

Cassette: released on Chrysalis, Feb'82 by Chrysalis Records. Dist: CBS

Destroy All Monsters
BORED.
Single (7"): released on Cherry Red, Feb'79 by Cherry Red Records. Dist: Pinnacle

NOBODY KNOWS.
Single (7"): released on Cherry Red, Oct'79 by Cherry Red Records. Dist: Pinnacle

Destruction
ETERNAL DEVASTATION.
Album: released on Steamhammer, Jul'86

INFERNAL OVERKILL.
Album: released on Steamhammer (Germany), Nov'85 Dist: Greyhound, Revolver Distribution

Destructors
BOMB HANOI, BOMB SAIGON, BOMB DISNEYLAND.
Album: released on Carnage Benelux, Aug'84 Dist: Cartel, Jetstar

CRY HAVOC AND UNLEASH THE DOGS OF...
Single (12"): released on Criminal, Aug'83 by Criminal Records. Dist: Jetstar

FORCES OF LAW.
Single (7"): released on Illuminated, Apr'83 IKF Records. Dist: Pinnacle, Cartel, Jetstar

JAILBAIT.
Single (7"): released on Illuminated, Oct'82 by IKF Records. Dist: Pinnacle, Cartel, Jetstar

MEANINGLESS NAMES.
Single (7"): released on Carnage, Jun'82 Dist: Cartel, Pinnacle

RELIGION THERE IS NO RELIGION.
Single (7"): released on Carnage, Jun'82 Dist: Cartel, Pinnacle

SENSELESS VIOLENCE.
Single (7"): released on Paperback, Apr'82

WILD THING.
Single (12"): released on Illuminated, Jul'83 by IKF Records. Dist: Pinnacle, Cartel, Jetstar

Destructors V
TV EYE.
Single (7"): released on Criminal Damage, Feb'84 by Criminal Damage Records. Dist: Backs, Cartel

Destry Rides Again
DESTRY RIDES AGAIN   Original London cast (Various Artists).
Album: released on That's Entertainment, Apr'83 by That's Entertainment Records. Dist:

Pinnacle, PRT

Cassette: released on That's Entertainment, Apr'83 by That's Entertainment Records. Dist: Pinnacle, PRT

Desvarieux, J

CHWAZI.
Compact disc: by Sterns. Dist: Sterns, Triple Earth

GOREE.
Compact disc: by Sterns. Dist: Sterns, Triple Earth

Desylvia,Brown

DESYLVA,BROWN & HENDERSON Songs by (Desylvia,Brown & Henderson).
Album: released on Monmouth, '79

Detail

OKHELA To make a fire.
Album: released on Affinity, Jun'84 by Charly Records. Dist: Charly, Cadillac

Detective

BAG BUSINESS.
Tracks: / Hong kong calls me / Rampage / As young as you feel / Green dream / Reagan is a moron / Green eyes / Reluctant hero / Can I please you / As young as you feel (slurry mix) / Red / End bag.
Cassette: released on Peerless, Feb'87

DETECTIVE.
Album: released on Swansong, Jun'77

IT TAKES ONE TO KNOW ONE.
Album: released on Swansong, May'78

Detente

RECOGNIZE NO AUTHORITY.
Album: released on Roadrunner (Dutch), Aug'86 Dist: Pinnacle

Determination

HOT HOT HOT.
Album: released on Determination, Apr'85 by Determination Records. Dist: Jetstar

SHOW CASE Volume 1.
Album: released on Determination, Apr'85 by Determination Records. Dist: Jetstar

Detonators

GANGSTER.
Album: released on Burning Sounds, Sep'79 by Ross, Bill/Burning Sounds Records. Dist: PRT

Detroit...

DETROIT A-GO-GO Various artists (Various Artists).
Album: released on Inferno Soul Club, Jun'84 by Inferno Records. Dist: Inferno, Cartel, Pinnacle

DETROIT GHETTO BLUES 1948-54 recordings (Various Artists).
Album: released on Nighthawk, Apr'79 by Faulty Products Records. Dist: Pinnacle, Swift

DETROIT GIRL GROUPS Various artists (Various Artists).
Album: released on Relic (US), Mar'85

DETROIT GOSPEL (Various Artists).
Album: released on Heritage, Sep'86 by Heritage Records. Dist: Chart

Detroit Emeralds

DANCE SCHOOL.
Single (7"): released on Orbit, Nov'83 by Orbit Records. Dist: PRT Distribution

Single (12"): released on Orbit, Nov'83 by Orbit Records. Dist: PRT Distribution

FEEL THE NEED.
Single (7"): released on Atlantic, Jun'77 by WEA Records. Dist: WEA

LET'S GET TOGETHER.
Album: released on Atlantic, May'78 by WEA Records. Dist: WEA

Detroit Gold

DETROIT GOLD VOLUME 1 Various artists.
Album: released on Solid Smoke (USA), Jul'84 Dist: Rhino

DETROIT GOLD VOLUME 2 Various artists.
Album: released on Solid Smoke (USA), Jul'84 Dist: Rhino

Detroit House Party

PIANO BLUES.
Album: released on JSP, Jul'82 by JSP Records. Dist: Swift, Projection

Detroit Spinners

20 GOLDEN CLASSICS.
Album: released on Motown, Jun'80 by Motown Records. Dist: BMG Distribution

Cassette: released on Motown, Jun'80 by Motown Records. Dist: BMG Distribution

CAN'T SHAKE THIS FEELING.
Album: released on Atlantic, Nov'81 by WEA Records. Dist: WEA

DANCIN' AND LOVIN'.
Cassette: released on Atlantic, Mar'80 by WEA Records. Dist: WEA

DETROIT SPINNERS.
Album: released on Atlantic, Feb'78 by WEA Records. Dist: WEA

GOLDEN GREATS: DETROIT SPINNERS.
Album: released on Atlantic, Aug'85 by WEA Records. Dist: WEA

Cassette: released on Atlantic, Aug'85 by WEA Records. Dist: WEA

GRAND SLAM.
Album: released on Atlantic, Nov'82 by WEA Records. Dist: WEA

Cassette: released on Atlantic, Nov'82 by WEA Records. Dist: WEA

I'LL BE AROUND.
Single (7"): released on Atlantic, Jan'83 by WEA Records. Dist: WEA

Single (12"): released on Atlantic, Jan'83 by WEA Records. Dist: WEA

IT'S A SHAME.
Single (7"): released on Motown, Oct'80 by Motown Records. Dist: BMG Distribution

LABOR OF LUST.
Album: released on Atlantic, Mar'81 by WEA Records. Dist: WEA

LOVE IS IN SEASON.
Single (7"): released on Atlantic, Aug'85 by WEA Records. Dist: WEA

Single (12"): released on Atlantic, Aug'85 by WEA Records. Dist: WEA

LOVIN' FEELING.
Album: released on Atco, Oct'85 by Atlantic Records. Dist: WEA

Cassette: released on Atco, Oct'85 by Atlantic Records. Dist: WEA

MAGIC IN THE MOONLIGHT.
Single (7"): released on Atlantic, Nov'82 by WEA Records. Dist: WEA

Single (12"): released on Atlantic, Nov'82 by WEA Records. Dist: WEA

PUT US TOGETHER AGAIN.
Tracks: / Put us together again / Show me your magic / Right or wrong.
Single (7"): released on Atlantic, Jan'86 by WEA Records. Dist: WEA

Single (12"):

Single (12"): released on Atlantic, Jan'86 by WEA Records. Dist: WEA

SMASH HITS.
Album: released on Atlantic, Apr'77 by WEA Records. Dist: WEA

Deuchar, Jimmy

SCOTS CONNECTION (THE) (Deuchar, Jimmy Quintet).
Album: released on Jazz Music, Apr'81 Dist: Jazz Music

THOU SWELL (Deuchar, Jimmy, Alan Clare, Victor Feldman & Tony Kinsey).
Tracks: / They can't take that away from me / Close as pages in a book / Folks who live on the hill, The / Thou swell / Why do I love you / Things we did last summer, The / This can't be love / Just one of those things.
Album: released on Esquire, Jul'87 by Titan International Productions. Dist: Jazz Music, Cadillac Music, Swift, Wellard, Chris, Backs, Rough Trade, Revolver, Nine Mile

Album: released on Esquire, Jul'87 by Titan International Productions. Dist: Jazz Music, Cadillac Music, Swift, Wellard, Chris, Backs, Rough Trade, Revolver, Nine Mile

Deuringer, H.

SWING AND HAPPY (see Wunderlich, Klaus) (Deuringer, H. & Klaus Wunderlich).

Deuter

CALL OF THE UNKNOWN-SELECTED PIECES 1972-1986.
Album: released on Kuckuck (USA), Feb'87 Dist: Celestial Harmonies Distribution

Cassette:

CICADA.
Compact disc: released on Kuckuck (Germany), Jan'86

Album: released on Kuckuck, Feb'87 Dist: PRT

Cassette: released on Kuckuck, Feb'87 Dist: PRT

Compact disc: released on Kuckuck, Feb'87 Dist: PRT

NIRVANA ROAD.
Compact disc: Dist: PRT

NIRVANA ROAD.
Album: released on Kuckuck (Germany), Jul'84

Deuter-D

DEUTER-D.
Album: released on Kuckuck (Germany), Aug'85

Deutscher, Drafi

TEENY.
Album: released on Telefunken-Hansa, '80

Deux Filles

DAY FOR NIGHT.
Cassette: released on Touch, Mar'84 by Touch Records. Dist: Rough Trade, Cartel

DOUBLE HAPPINESS.
Album: released on Papier Mache, Oct'84 by Papier Mache Records. Dist: Rough Trade, Cartel

SILENCE AND WISDOM.
Album: released on Papier Mache, Mar'83 by Papier Mache Records. Dist: Rough Trade, Cartel

Devastate To Liberate

DEVASTATE TO LIBERATE (Various Artists).
Album: released on Tangki, Nov'85

Devastation

DRAG YOU DOWN.
Single (7"): released on Creative Reality, Nov'84 Dist: Cartel

VIOLENT TERMINATION.
Album: released on Zombo (USA), Aug'87

Devaughan, William

CREME DE CREME.
Single (7"): released on Excaliber, Dec'82 by Red Bus Records. Dist: PRT

Single (12"): released on Excaliber, Dec'82 by Red Bus Records. Dist: PRT

Deviants

HUMAN GARBAGE Live at Dingwalls '84.
Album: released on Psycho, May'84 Dist: Funhouse, Rough Trade

PTOOFF.
Album: released on Psycho, Dec'83 Dist: Funhouse, Rough Trade

Device

22B3.
Tracks: / Hanging on a heart attack / Who says / Pieces on the ground / Tough and tender / When love is good / Didn't i read you right / Fall apart,golden heart / I've got no room for your love / Who's on the line / Sand,stone,cobwebs and dust.
Notes: Produced by mike chapman.The band fronted by holly knight,one of the most unsuccessful songwriters of the last five years.
Album: released on Chrysalis, Aug'86 by Chrysalis Records. Dist: CBS

Cassette: released on Chrysalis, Aug'86 by Chrysalis Records. Dist: CBS

HANGING ON A HEART ATTACK.
Tracks: / Hanging on a heart attack.
Single (7"): released on Chrysalis, Jul'86 by Chrysalis Records. Dist: CBS

Single (12"): released on Chrysalis, Jul'86 by Chrysalis Records. Dist: CBS

Devil And Daniel Webster

DEVIL AND DANIEL WEBSTER (THE) Benet, Stephen Vincent (Hingle, Pat).
Cassette: released on Caedmon(USA), Apr'83 by Caedmon (USA) Records. Dist: Gower, Taylors, Discovery

Deville

SQUEEZE YOU HOLD YOU.
Single (7"):

Single (12"):

Devil & Mary Ann

DEVIL & MARY ANN Cookson, Catherine (Jameson, Susan).
Cassette: released on Chivers Audio Books, '81 by Chivers Sound & Vision. Dist: Chivers Sound & Vision

Devil Rides Out

DEVIL RIDES OUT (THE) Wheatley, Dennis (Rodgers, Anton).
Cassette: released on Listen For Pleasure, '83 by MFP Records. Dist: EMI

Devils Music

DEVILS MUSIC (THE) Various original artists (Various Artists).
Album: released on Red Lightnin', Sep'82 by Red Lightnin' Records. Dist: Roots, Swift, Jazz Music, JSU, Pinnacle, Cartel, Wynd-Up Distribution

MORE DEVIL MUSIC Various artists (Various Artists).
Album: released on Red Lightnin', Jun'83 by Red Lightnin' Records. Dist: Roots, Swift, Jazz Music, JSU, Pinnacle, Cartel, Wynd-Up Distribution

Devil With The Devil

DEVIL WITH THE DEVIL Various artists (Various Artists).
Album: released on Rambler, Jul'81 Dist: Swift

Devine, Eddie

STOP CHILDREN ADULTS ONLY.
Album: released on Igus, Oct'81 by Klub. Dist: PRT, Musac Distribution Ltd (Scotland)

Devine, Mike

PART OF ME, A.
Album: released on Ross, Jan'86 by Ross Records. Dist: Ross Distribution, Roots Distribution

Cassette: released on Ross, Jan'86 by Ross Records. Dist: Ross Distribution, Roots Distribution

Devine, Sidney

ENCORES.
Tracks: / Nobody's child / Singing the blues / Down the trail of aching hearts / Tiny bubbles / Church, a courtroom and then goodbye, A / China doll / Have a drink on me / Mocking bird hill / Am i that easy to forget / Forty shades of green / There's nothing there / Jealous heart / Things / When Mexico gave up the rumba.
Album: released on Emerald (Ireland), Jan'86 by Emerald Records. Dist: I & B, Ross, PRT

FAVOURITE MEMORY OF MINE.
Tracks: / Almost persuaded.
Single (7"): released on Country House, Nov'86 by BGS Productions Ltd. Dist: Taylor, H.R., Record Merchandisers Distribution, Pinnacle, Sounds of Scotland Records

SINGS YOUR FAVOURITE COUNTRY SONGS.
Tracks: / This songs just for you / Ten guitars / Tennesse waltz / Only the heart aches / Married by the bible,divorced by the law / Do what you do,do well / Wild side of life (The) / Act naturally / When you and i were young maggie / Your cheatin' heart / I love you because / Little arrows.
Album: released on Emerald (Ireland), May'85 by Emerald Records. Dist: I & B, Ross, PRT

SYD'S SING SONG COUNTRY ALBUM.
Tracks: / Country roads / Early morning rain / Gentle on my mind / Hello Mary Lou / Gypsy woman / You're my best friend / 'Till the rivers all run dry / Four walls / He'll have to go / You're free to go / Tiny bubbles / Pearly shells / Stand beside me / Sweet dreams / Send me the pillow / Satin sheets / Eighteen yellow roses / Room full of roses / Ramblin' rose / Red roses for a blue lady / Dear god / Where could I go but to the lord / House of gold / You'll never walk alone / Oh lonesome me / Sea of heartbreak / Lonesome / Blue blue day / Blanket on the ground / Old flames / Blowing in the wind / Sing me / Irene / Lucille / Amanda / Please help me I'm falling / Fraulein / I fall to pieces / It keeps right on a-hurting / Lovesick blues / Singing the blues / Knee deep in the blues / Long gone lonesome blues / Wild side of life / This song is just for you / Blackboard of my heart / Married by the bible / Cryin' time / Together again / I can't stop loving you / Take the chains from my heart.
Album: released on Country House, Dec'86 by BGS Productions Ltd. Dist: Taylor, H.R., Record Merchandisers Distribution, Pinnacle, Sounds of Scotland Records

Cassette: released on Country House, Dec'86 by BGS Productions Ltd. Dist: Taylor, H.R., Record Merchandisers Distribution, Pinnacle, Sounds of Scotland Records

TAKE MY HANDS PRECIOUS LORD.
Tracks: / Old rugged cross / They'll be peace in the valley / Midnight special-i'd like to see jesus / What a friend we have in jesus / Only believe / Take my hand precious lord / Precious memories / We call on him / Family Bible / It Is

Page 288

No Secret / Who Am I / Only If You Praise The Lord.
Album: released on Emerald (Ireland), May'82 by Emerald Records. Dist: I & B, Ross, PRT

Devine, Sydney

25TH ANNIVERSARY ALBUM.
Album: released on Philips, Apr'80 Dist: IMS-Polygram

Cassette: released on Philips, Apr'80 Dist: IMS-Polygram

BY REQUEST.
Album: released on Country House, Dec'83 by BGS Productions Ltd. Dist: Taylor, H.R., Record Merchandisers Distribution, Pinnacle, Sounds of Scotland Records

Cassette: released on Country House, Dec'83 by BGS Productions Ltd. Dist: Taylor, H.R., Record Merchandisers Distribution, Pinnacle, Sounds of Scotland Records

CRYING TIME.
Album: released on Emerald (Ireland), Oct'81 by Emerald Records. Dist: I & B, Ross, PRT

Cassette: released on Emerald (Ireland), Oct'81 by Emerald Records. Dist: I & B, Ross, PRT

FAVOURITE MEMORIES OF MINE.
Album: released on Country House, Sep'83 by BGS Productions Ltd. Dist: Taylor, H.R., Record Merchandisers Distribution, Pinnacle, Sounds of Scotland Records

Cassette: released on Country House, Sep'83 by BGS Productions Ltd. Dist: Taylor, H.R., Record Merchandisers Distribution, Pinnacle, Sounds of Scotland Records

FAVOURITE MEMORY OF MINE.
Single (7"): released on Country House, Dec'83 by BGS Productions Ltd. Dist: Taylor, H.R., Record Merchandisers Distribution, Pinnacle, Sounds of Scotland Records

FROM SCOTLAND WITH LOVE.
Album: released on Scotdisc, Sep'84 Dist: Clyde Factors Distributors

Cassette: released on Scotdisc, Sep'84 Dist: Clyde Factors Distributors

GREATEST HITS:SYDNEY DEVINE.
Album: released on Emerald (Ireland), Oct'81 by Emerald Records. Dist: I & B, Ross, PRT

Cassette: released on Emerald (Ireland), Oct'81 by Emerald Records. Dist: I & B, Ross, PRT

HEARTACHES.
Cassette: released on Philips, Feb'81 Dist: IMS-Polygram

HOW GREAT THOU ART.
Single (7"): released on Time, Mar'82 Dist: Jetstar Distribution

LIKE STRANGERS.
Single (7"):

LIVE FROM THE CITY HALL,GLASGOW.
Album: released on Hallmark, Apr'78 by Pickwick Records. Dist: Pickwick Distribution, PRT, Taylors

PEARLY SHELLS.
Single (7"): released on Country House, Nov'83 by BGS Productions Ltd. Dist: Taylor, H.R., Record Merchandisers Distribution, Pinnacle, Sounds of Scotland Records

SCOTLAND FOREVER.
Single (7"): released on Time, Mar'82 Dist: Jetstar Distribution

SCOTLAND WE LOVE.
Single (7"): released on Scotdisc, Sep'84 Dist: Clyde Factors Distributors

SYDNEY DEVINE COLLECTION, THE.
Double Album: released on Pickwick, Jul'79 by Pickwick Records. Dist: Pickwick Distribution, Prism Leisure Distribution, Lugtons

Cassette: released on Pickwick, Jul'80 by Pickwick Records. Dist: Pickwick Distribution, Prism Leisure Distribution, Lugtons

SYDNEY DEVINE COUNTRY.
Album: released on Emerald (Ireland), Oct'81 by Emerald Records. Dist: I & B, Ross, PRT

Cassette: released on Emerald (Ireland), Oct'81 by Emerald Records. Dist: I & B, Ross, PRT

SYDNEY DEVINE SINGS YOUR FAVOURITE COUNTRY SONGS.
Album: released on Emerald Gem, Aug'85 Dist: Spartan, MK
Cat. no: **BER 012**
Album: released on Emerald Gem, Aug'85 Dist: Spartan, MK

SYDNEY DIVINE SING-SONG COUNTRY.
Single (7"): released on August (USA), Nov'85 Dist: Taylors

VERY BEST OF SYDNEY DEVINE.
Album: released on Emerald (Ireland), Oct'81 by Emerald Records. Dist: I & B, Ross, PRT

Cassette: released on Emerald (Ireland), Oct'81 by Emerald Records. Dist: I & B, Ross, PRT

Devlin, Johnny

REAL NERVOUS (Devlin, Johnny & The Devils).
Album: released on Rebel (Australia), Feb'84 Dist: Swift

Devlin, Pat

BREAK THE ICE.
Single (7"): released on Head To Head, Jul'85 by Head To Head Records. Dist: Pinnacle

Devlin, Sheila

COUNTRY GIRL.
Cassette: released on Homespun(Ireland), Jun'83 by Outlet Records. Dist: Outlet

Devo

BE STIFF.
Album: released on Stiff, Jan'79 by Stiff Records. Dist: EMI, Record Services Distribution (Ireland)

COME BACK JONEE (EP).
Single (12"): released on Virgin, Apr'83 by Virgin Records. Dist: EMI, Virgin Distribution

DEVO- LIVE.
Album: released on Virgin, Jun'81 by Virgin Records. Dist: EMI, Virgin Distribution

DUTY FOR THE FUTURE NOW.
Album: released on Virgin, Mar'84 by Virgin Records. Dist: EMI, Virgin Distribution

FREEDOM OF CHOICE.
Album: released on Virgin, Mar'84 by Virgin Records. Dist: EMI, Virgin Distribution

Q:ARE WE NOT MEN?.A:WE ARE DEVO.
Album: released on Virgin, Mar'84 by Virgin Records. Dist: EMI, Virgin Distribution

Cassette: released on Virgin, Mar'84 by Virgin Records. Dist: EMI, Virgin Distribution

THEME FROM DR. DETROIT.
Single (7"): released on MCA, Jun'83 by MCA Records. Dist: Polygram, MCA

Single (12"): released on MCA, Jun'83 by MCA Records. Dist: Polygram, MCA

Devon...

BRASS IN BLUE.
Album: released on Black Mountain, May'79 by Black Mountain Records.

DEVON MUSEUM OF MECHANICAL MUSIC Various (Various Artists).
Album: released on Saydisc, Jul'81 by Saydisc Records. Dist: Essex, Harmonia Mundi, Roots, H.R. Taylor, Jazz Music, Swift, Projection, Gamut

Cassette: released on Saydisc, Jul'81 by Saydisc Records. Dist: Essex, Harmonia Mundi, Roots, H.R. Taylor, Jazz Music, Swift, Projection, Gamut

Devonne

THIEF IN THE NIGHT.
Tracks: / Thief In The Night.
Single (7"): released on Unit, Apr'86 by Unit Records. Dist: PRT

Single (12"): released on Unit, Apr'86 by Unit Records. Dist: PRT

Devonport Field Gun Crew

COME ON YE GUNNERS.
Single (7"): released on Monarch, Jun'82 by Chart Records. Dist: Pinnacle

Devonshire & Dorset...

DEVONSHIRE & DORSET BRASS BAND Military band series.
Cassette: released on VFM Cassettes, Jan'85

JANNERS IN CONCERT.
Album: released on Music Masters, Mar'81 by Music Masters Records. Dist: Taylors

Devonshire Haymakers

SONG & DANCES.
Cassette: released on Folktracks, Nov'79 by Folktracks Cassettes. Dist: Folktracks

Devon Tradition

DEVON TRADITION Various artists (Various Artists).
Album: released on Topic, '81 Dist: Roots Distribution

Devotion, Sheila B

SPACER.
Single (7"): released on Carrere, Jul'85 by Carrere Records. Dist: PRT, Spartan

Single (12"): released on Carrere, Jul'85 by Carrere Records. Dist: PRT, Spartan

Devoto, Howard

JERKY VERSIONS OF THE DREAM.
Album: released on Virgin, Aug'83 by Virgin Records. Dist: EMI, Virgin Distribution Deleted '85.

Album: released on Virgin, Aug'83 by Virgin Records. Dist: EMI, Virgin Distribution

Dewar, Colin

PRESENTING COLIN DEWAR'S SCOTTISH DANCE BAND.
Album: released on Lapwing, Jul'87 by Lapwing Records Ltd. Dist: Celtic Music, Projection, Roots Records, Ross, Gordon Duncan Distribution, Graham Tosh Distribution, Chans Records

Dewhurst, Brian

FOLLOW THAT WITH YOUR SEA-LIONS.
Album: released on Fellside, '83 by Fellside Records. Dist: Roots, Jazz Music, Celtic Music, Projection

HUNTER & THE HUNTED, THE.
Album: released on Folk Heritage, Jul'82 by Folk Heritage Records. Dist: Roots, Wynd-Up Distribution, Jazz Music, Folk Heritage

De Wilde, Graham

FLYIN' SO FREE (De Wilde, Graham, Wind Sand & Stars).
Single (7"): released on TPL, Aug'87 Dist: PRT

THRESHOLD.
Single (7"): released on BBC, '84 by BBC Records & Tapes. Dist: EMI, PRT, Pye

Dex

BACKS AGAINST THE WALL.
Tracks: / Backs against the wall.
Album: released on A-Side, Aug'86 by Sonet Records. Dist: PRT

Dexter, Ray

SOUND SHOW.
Album: released on Sweet Folk, Nov'76 Dist: Roots Distribution

UP COUNTRY.
Cassette: released on AIM (Budget Cassettes), Feb'83

Dexy's Midnight Runners

BECAUSE OF YOU.
Tracks: / Because of you / Kathleen / Mavoureen / Somtimes theme.
Single (7"): released on Mercury, Oct'86 by Phonogram Records. Dist: Polygram Distribution

Single (12"): released on Mercury, Oct'86 by Phonogram Records. Dist: Polygram Distribution

BREAKING DOWN THE WALLS OF HEARTACHE.
Single (7"): released on Parlophone, Mar'80 by EMI Records. Dist: EMI

COME ON EILEEN.
Single (7"): released on Mercury, Oct'84 by Phonogram Records. Dist: Polygram Distribution

Single (12"): released on Mercury, Oct'84 by Phonogram Records. Dist: Polygram Distribution Deleted '86.

DANCE STANCE.
Single (7"): released on EMI Golden 45's, Mar'84 by EMI Records. Dist: EMI

DON'T STAND ME DOWN.
Tracks: / Occasional flicker / This is what she's like / Knowledge of beauty / Reminisce part two / Listen this to this / Waltz.
Compact disc: by Phonogram Records. Dist: Polygram Distribution

GENO.
Tracks: / Geno / Plan B / Breakin'down the walls of heartache / Dance stance / Horse, The / There there my dear / Keep it / One way love / I'm just looking / Soul finger.
Album: released on EMI, Mar'83 by EMI Records. Dist: EMI

Cassette: released on EMI, Mar'83 by EMI Records. Dist: EMI

GENO (7").
Single (7"): released on Parlophone, Feb'83 by EMI Records. Dist: EMI

SEARCHING FOR THE YOUNG SOUL REBELS.
Tracks: / Burn it down / Tell me when my light turns to green / Teams that meet in the caffs / I'm just looking / Geno / Seven day's to long / I couldn't help it if I tried / Thankfully not living in Yorkshire,it doesn't apply / Keep it / Love part 1 / There,there my dear.
Compact disc: released on EMI, Mar'87 by EMI Records. Dist: EMI

THIS IS WHAT SHE'S LIKE.
Single (7"): released on Mercury, Nov'85 by Phonogram Records. Dist: Polygram Distribution Deleted '86.

Single (12"): released on Mercury, Nov'85 by Phonogram Records. Dist: Polygram Distribution

Double-pack single: released on Mercury, Nov'85 by Phonogram Records. Dist: Polygram Distribution Deleted '86.

TOO-RYE-AY.
Tracks: / Celtic soul brothers / Let's make this precious / All in all / Old / Plan B / Jackie Wilson said / I'll show you / Liars to be / Until / Come on Eileen.
Album: released on Mercury, Jul'86 by Phonogram Records. Dist: Polygram Distribution

Cassette: released on Mercury, Jul'86 by Phonogram Records. Dist: Polygram Distribution

Compact disc: released on Mercury, Jan'83 by Phonogram Records. Dist: Polygram Distribution

Album: released on Mercury, Jul'82 by Phonogram Records. Dist: Polygram Distribution

Cassette: released on Mercury, Jul'82 by Phonogram Records. Dist: Polygram Distribution

Dey, Charley

TIME ON MY HANDS.
Tracks: / Bed of Roses / Saginaw Michigan / Green fields of France.
Cassette: released on Ross, May'86 by Ross Records. Dist: Ross Distribution, Roots Distribution

Dey, Joy

CAN I TOUCH YOU.
Single (7"): released on Gipsy, May'83 by Gipsy Records. Dist: PRT

D, Heavy

CHUNKY BUT FUNKY (D, Heavy & The Boyz).
Tracks: / Chunky but funky / Chunky but funky (inst).
Single (7"): released on MCA, Jul'87 by MCA Records. Dist: Polygram, MCA

Single (12"): released on MCA, Jul'87 by MCA Records. Dist: Polygram, MCA

D.I.

ANCIENT ARTIFACTS.
Album: released on Triple XXX (USA), Aug'87 Dist: Pinnacle

HORSE BITES DOG CRIES.
Album: released on Triple XXX (USA), Aug'87 Dist: Pinnacle

TEAM GOON.
Album: released on Triple XXX (USA), Aug'87 Dist: Pinnacle

Diamanda Galas

DIVINE PUNISHMENT (THE).
Album: released on Mute, Jul'86 Dist: Spartan Distribution, Rough Trade Distribution, Cartel Distribution

Diamond

DIAMOND MISTRESS.
Album: released on Roadrunner (Dutch), Aug'85 Dist: Pinnacle

Diamond Accordion Band

25 GREAT COUNTRY HITS.
Tracks: / Stand by your man / Banks of the Oio / Jealous heart / I walk the line / Love you because / He'll have to go / Crystal chandeliers / I'm fallin' / Yellow ribbon / Right on / China doll / Nobody's child / Cheatin' heart / Pillow you dream on.
Album: released on Accordion Record Club, Jul'86 by Accordion Record Club Records. Dist: Accordion Record Club

Cassette: released on Accordion Record Club, Jul'86 by Accordion Record Club Records. Dist: Accordion Record Club

D.A.B. PLAY JOLSON. •
Tracks: / Robert E Lee / Baby face / Carolina/Mammy / Tootsie/Chinatown / Ma/Dixie melody / Swanee / Blackbird/Broadway melody

/ Bobbin along / Sonny boy / Lullaby of broadway / Melancholy baby / Top of the world.
Album: released on Accordion Record Club, Jul'86 by Accordion Record Club Records. Dist: Accordion Record Club

Cassette: released on Accordion Record Club, Jul'86 by Accordion Record Club Records. Dist: Accordion Record Club

GO COUNTRY.
Tracks: / Make it through the night / Old shep / Rhinestone cowboy / My best friend / One day at a time / Love was / Cold cold heart/Take these chains / Blue and the lonely, The / River road / Release me / Wrong road/Year for Mexico / Door is always open.
Album: released on Accordion Record Club, Jul'86 by Accordion Record Club Records. Dist: Accordion Record Club

Cassette: released on Accordion Record Club, Jul'86 by Accordion Record Club Records. Dist: Accordion Record Club

JUST A CLOSER WALK WITH THEE.
Tracks: / When the saints / Marching on / Fight the good fight / Love lifted me / Praise my soul / Lord is my shepherd, The / How great thou art / Rivers of Babylon / Closer walk with thee / Precious Lord / Plough the fields / Whispering hope.
Album: released on Accordion Record Club, Jul'86 by Accordion Record Club Records. Dist: Accordion Record Club

Cassette: released on Accordion Record Club, Jul'86 by Accordion Record Club Records. Dist: Accordion Record Club

MARCHING WITH JESUS.
Tracks: / Old old story, The / Friend in Jesus / Christian soldiers/Abide with me / It is no secret / Nearer my God / Amazing grace / In ages past / Wondrous cross / Green hill / I need thee every hour / Old rugged cross / Be though my vision / Rock of ages.
Album: released on Accordion Record Club, Jul'86 by Accordion Record Club Records. Dist: Accordion Record Club

Cassette: released on Accordion Record Club, Jul'86 by Accordion Record Club Records. Dist: Accordion Record Club

WALTZING AROUND THE WORLD.
Tracks: / Four in the morning / Morning has broken / Oh what a beautiful morning / Three o' clock in the morning / Softly softly / Good luck, good health, God bless you / Old rockin' chair / There goes my everything / Annie's song / Tulips from Amsterdam / By the side of the Zuyder Zee / Reine de musette / Last waltz / Adios, amigo / Funny, familiar forgotten feelings / Moon river / Plaisir d'amour (fleeting love) / Edelweiss / We will make love / Delilah / Lady of Spain / Twelfth of never / Are you lonesome tonight / Eternally / Gordon for me, A / Northern lights of old Aberdeen / These are my mountains / Bourrasque / Anna Marie / When the girl in your arms / You're the only good thing that's happened to me / I wonder who's kissing her now / Far away places / Ramona.
Notes: Recorded and mixed at Hydepark Studios. Produced by: George Doherty.
Album: released on Emerald (Ireland), May'86 by Emerald Records. Dist: I & B, Ross, PRT

YOUR FAVOURITE SINGALONGS.
Tracks: / My guys come back / Little brown jug / American patrol / In the mood / Lobby song, The / Snow waltz / Blacksmith, The / Old flames (can't hold a candle to you) / Yellow submarine / Lily the pink / Match of the day / Bunch of thyme / Catch me / Shine on harvest moon / Birdie song, The / I love a lassie / Roamin' in the gloamin' / Little peace, A / Portsmouth / Scotch on the rocks / When you were sweet sixteen / Le yenka / Hucklebuck / Pal of my cradle days / Could I have this dance.
Album: released on Emerald (Ireland), Mar'83 by Emerald Records. Dist: I & B, Ross, PRT

Cassette: released on Accordion Record Club, Jul'86 by Accordion Record Club Records. Dist: Accordion Record Club

YOUR FAVOURITE SINGALONGS VOLUME II.
Tracks: / Here we are again / Ship ahoy / If I had my way / Man on the flying trapeze / Bless 'em all / In the shade of the old apple tree / I'm forever blowing bubbles / I've got a lovely bunch of coconuts / I do like to be beside the seaside / Man who broke the bank at Monte Carlo, The / Blaydon races / Side by side / White cliffs of Dover, The / We'll meet again / She's a lassie from Lancashire / Down at the old Bull & Bush / Don't dilly dally on the way / Goodbye Dolly Gray / Run, rabbit, run / Wish me luck / You made me love you / Maybe it's because I'm a Londoner / Underneath the arches / Whatever will be will be (Que sera sera) / Liverpool Lou / How much is that doggie in the window / After the ball is over / Happy wanderer, The / Roll out the barrel / It's a long way to Tipperary / Pack up your troubles in your old kit bag / By the light of the silvery moon / Lily of Laguna / Mockingbird hill / Oh dear what can the matter be / Two lovely black eyes / Two little girls in blue / I'll be your sweetheart / Oh, oh, Antonio / Take me back to dear old blighty.
Album: released on Emerald (Ireland), Oct'84 by Emerald Records. Dist: I & B, Ross, PRT

Cassette: released on Emerald (Ireland), Oct'84 by Emerald Records. Dist: I & B, Ross, PRT

YOUR FAVOURITE WALTZES.
Tracks: / Carnival of Venice / Anniversary waltz/Beautiful dreamer / Somewhere my love / Springtime in the rockies / Florence / Home on the range / Too old to dream / Cruisin' the river / Blue of night / Irene / Blossom time / Liebestraume.
Album: released on Accordion Record Club, Jul'86 by Accordion Record Club Records. Dist: Accordion Record Club

Cassette: released on Accordion Record Club, Jul'86 by Accordion Record Club Records. Dist: Accordion Record Club

Diamond Head

AM I EVIL.
Tracks: / Am I evil? / Heat of the night / Don't you ever leave me / Borrowed time / To Heaven from Hell / Dead reckoning / Lightning to the nations / Sucking my love.
Album: released on FM, May'87 by FM-Revolver Records. Dist: EMI

Cassette: released on FM, May'87 by FM-Revolver Records. Dist: EMI

Compact disc: released on FM, Aug'87 by FM-Revolver Records. Dist: EMI

BEHOLD THE BEGINNING.
Album: released on Metal Masters, Apr'86 by Razor Records. Dist: Pinnacle

DIAMOND HEAD.
Album: released on Heavy Metal, May'87 by FM-Revolver Records. Dist: EMI

Cassette: released on Heavy Metal, May'87 by FM-Revolver Records. Dist: EMI

Compact disc: released on Heavy Metal, May'87 by FM-Revolver Records. Dist: EMI

Diamond Hidden...

DIAMOND HIDDEN IN THE MOUTH OF A CORPSE, A (Various Artists).
Notes: Includes Cabaret Voltaire, Husker Du etc.
Album: released on Giorno Poetry System, Jan'86 Dist: Rough Trade, Cartel

Cassette: released on Giorno Poetry System, Jan'86 Dist: Rough Trade, Cartel

Diamond, Jim

DESIRE.
Tracks: / Desire / Together.
Single (7"): released on A&M, Apr'86 by A&M Records. Dist: Polygram

Single (12"): released on A&M, Apr'86 by A&M Records. Dist: Polygram

DESIRE FOR FREEDOM.
Album: released on A&M, Sep'86 by A&M Records. Dist: Polygram

Cassette: released on A&M, Sep'86 by A&M Records. Dist: Polygram

Compact disc: released on A&M, Sep'86 by A&M Records. Dist: Polygram

DOUBLE CROSSED.
Compact disc: by A&M Records. Dist: Polygram

HI HO SILVER.
Single (7"): released on A&M, Jan'86 by A&M Records. Dist: Polygram

Single (12"): released on A&M, Jan'86 by A&M Records. Dist: Polygram

SHOUT IT OUT.
Tracks: / Shout it out / Message of chidwatch, The.
Single (7"): released on Tembo, 20 Jun'87 by Tembo (Canada). Dist: IMS Distribution, Polygram Distribution

Single (12"): released on Tembo, 20 Jun'87 by Tembo (Canada). Dist: IMS Distribution, Polygram Distribution

TONY BANKS (EP) (see Banks, Tony).

YOUNG LOVE (carry me away).
Tracks: / Young love (carry me away) / Blue songs / Young love / I should have known better / Remember I love you / Hi ho silver.
Single (7"): released on A&M, Jul'86 by A&M Records. Dist: Polygram

Special: released on A&M, Jul'86 by A&M Records. Dist: Polygram

Diamond, King

FATAL PORTRAIT.
Compact disc: released on Roadrunner (Dutch), Feb'87 Dist: Pinnacle

Diamond, Neil

12 GREATEST HITS.
Compact disc: by MCA Records. Dist: Polygram, MCA

12 GREATEST HITS VOL.2.
Compact disc: by CBS Records. Dist: CBS

BEAUTIFUL NOISE.
Compact disc: by CBS Records. Dist: CBS

Album: released on CBS, 11 Apr'87 by CBS Records. Dist: CBS

Cassette: released on CBS, 11 Apr'87 by CBS Records. Dist: CBS

BEST OF NEIL DIAMOND, THE.
Album: released on Hallmark, Sep'86 by Pickwick Records. Dist: Pickwick Distribution, PRT, Taylors

Cassette: released on Hallmark, Sep'86 by Pickwick Records. Dist: Pickwick Distribution, PRT, Taylors

CLASSICS.
Compact disc: released on CBS, May'87 by CBS Records. Dist: CBS

Compact disc: released on Polydor, Jan'83 by Polydor Records. Dist: Polygram, Polydor

HEADED FOR THE FUTURE.
Tracks: / Headed for the future / Man you need, The / I'll see you on the radio (Laura) / Stand up for love / It should have been me / Lost in Hollywood / Story of my life, The / Angel / Me beside you / Love doesn't live here anymore.
Album: released on CBS, May'86 by CBS Records. Dist: CBS

Cassette: released on CBS, May'86 by CBS Records. Dist: CBS

Compact disc: by CBS Records. Dist: CBS

HEARTLIGHT.
Compact disc: released on CBS, May'87 by CBS Records. Dist: CBS

HIS 12 GREATEST HITS.
Compact disc: by MCA Records. Dist: Polygram, MCA

HOT AUGUST NIGHTS.
Double compact disc: by MCA Records. Dist: Polygram, MCA

I'M GLAD YOU'RE HERE WITH ME TONIGHT.
Tracks: / God only knows / Let me take you in my arms / Once in a while / Let the little boy sing / I'm glad you're here with me tonight / Lament in D minor / Dance of the sabres / Desiree / You don't bring me flowers / Free man in Paris.
Compact disc: by CBS Records. Dist: CBS

I'M GLAD YOU'RE HERE WITH ME TONIGHT (VIDEO).
Notes: 53 minutes. Released on Vestron Video

JAZZ SINGER, THE.
Compact disc: by Capitol Records. Dist: EMI

LOVE AT THE GREEK.
Tracks: / Street life / Kentucky woman / Sweet Caroline / Last Picasso / Longfellow serenade / Beautiful noise / Lady-oh / Stargazer / If you know what I mean / Surviving the life / Glory road / Song sung blue / Holly Holy / Brother love's travelling salvation show / Johnathan Livingstone Seagull / I've been this way before.
Compact disc: released on CBS, Mar'87 by CBS Records. Dist: CBS

Video-cassette (VHS): released on Vestron, Oct'86

MOODS.
Compact disc: by MCA Records. Dist: Polygram, MCA

NEIL DIAMOND.
Tracks: / Song sung blue / Morning side / Play me / Cracklin' rosie / Brother louis / Salvation show.
Album: released on Music For Pleasure (Holland), '86 by EMI Records. Dist: EMI

Cassette: released on Music For Pleasure (Holland), '86 by EMI Records. Dist: EMI

ON THE WAY TO THE SKY.
Compact disc: released on CBS, May'87 by CBS Records. Dist: CBS

PRIMITIVE.
Compact disc: by CBS Records. Dist: CBS

SEPTEMBER MORN.
Compact disc: released on CBS, May'87 by CBS Records. Dist: CBS

SERENADE.
Tracks: / I've been this way before / Rosemary's wine / Lady Magdelene / Last Picasso / Longfellow serenade / Yes I will / Reggae strut / Gift of song, The.
Compact disc: released on CBS, Mar'87 by CBS Records. Dist: CBS

STAND UP FOR LOVE.
Tracks: / Stand up for love / Story of my life, The.
Single (7"): released on CBS, Jul'86 by CBS Records. Dist: CBS

Single (12"): released on CBS, Jul'86 by CBS Records. Dist: CBS

SWEET CAROLINE.
Tracks: / Brother Love's travelling salvation show / River runs, new grown plums / Juliet / Glory road / If I never knew your name / Hurtin' you don't come easy / Dig in / Long gone / Deep in the morning / Memphis streets / You're so sweet horseflies keep hangin' round your face / And the grass won't pay no mind / Sweet Caroline.
Compact disc: released on MCA, Jul'87 by MCA Records. Dist: Polygram, MCA

SWEET CAROLINE II.
Tracks: / Brother love's traveling salvation show / Dig in / River runs, new grown plums / Juliet / Long gone / And the grass won't pay no mind / Glory road / Deep in the morning / If I never knew your name / Memphis streets / You're so sweet / Horseflies keep hangin' round your face / Hurtin' you don't come easy / Sweet Caroline (good times never seemed so good).
Compact disc: released on MCA, Sep'87 by MCA Records. Dist: Polygram, MCA

TAP ROOT MANUSCRIPT.
Compact disc: by MCA Records. Dist: Polygram, MCA

YOU DON'T BRING ME FLOWERS.
Compact disc: released on CBS, May'87 by CBS Records. Dist: CBS

Diamonds

JUST CAN'T FIGURE IT OUT.
Tracks: / Just can't figure it out / Keep it like it is.
Single (7"): released on Classy, Apr'86 Dist: PRT

Di'Anno, Paul

CHILDREN OF MADNESS (Di'Anno, Paul Battlezone).
Album: released on Powerstation Records, Jun'87 by Powerstation Records. Dist: Pinnacle

FIGHTING BACK (Di'Anno, Paul Battlezone).
Tracks: / Fighting back (Forever) / Welcome to the battlezone / Warchild / In the darkness / Land God gave to Cain, The / Running blind / Too much to heart / Voice on the radio / Voice on the radio / Welfare warriors / Feel the rock.
Album: released on Raw Power, Jul'86 Dist: Pinnacle

Cassette: released on Raw Power, Jul'86 Dist: Pinnacle

Di'anno's Battlezone

CHILDREN OF MADNESS.
Album: released on Powerstation Records, Aug'87 by Powerstation Records. Dist: Pinnacle

Diaz, Joanne

WORDS (Diaz, Joanne & Kirk ST. James).
Tracks: / Dream Bermuda.
Single (7"): released on Heartbreak, Nov'86 Dist: Essex

Dibango, Manu

AFRIJAZZY.
Notes: Features contributions from Sly & Robbie, Hugh Masekela, D.ST, Herbie Hancock, Bernie Worrell & Bootsy Collins amongst others, and is produced by Bill Laswell.
Album: released on Polydor, Jun'87 by Polydor Records. Dist: Polygram, Polydor

Cassette: released on Polydor, Jun'87 by Polydor Records. Dist: Polygram, Polydor

Compact disc: released on Polydor, Jun'87 by Polydor Records. Dist: Polygram, Polydor

MAKOSSA.
Tracks: / Makossa / Gombo sauce.
Single (7"): released on Urban, May'87 by Polydor Records. Dist: Polygram

Single (12"): released on Urban, May'87 by Polydor Records. Dist: Polygram

Dice

I CAN'T TAKE IT.
Tracks: / I can't take it / I can't take it (inst).
Notes: Bluebird, Tel: 01 723 9090
Single (12"): released on Production House, Jan'87 Dist: Bluebird, Revolver, Cartel

YOU GOT ME RUNNING.
Tracks: / You got me running / You got me running (inst dub mix).
Single (12"): released on Production House, 13 Jun'87 Dist: Bluebird, Revolver, Cartel

SOUL MAKOSSA.
Compact disc: released on Dusidisc, Dec'86 Dist: Swift

Dicken

SOLID GOLD.
Tracks: / Solid gold / Beat speaks, The.

Single (7"): released on Mercury, Jul'86 by Phonogram Records. Dist: Polygram Distribution

Dickens, Charles

CHRISTMAS CAROL, A.
Cassette: released on Listen For Pleasure, Oct'84 by MFP Records. Dist: EMI

Cassette: released on Tellastory, Dec'86 by Bartlett Bliss Productions. Dist: PRT Distribution, Hayward Promotions Distribution, H.R. Taylor Distribution

Dickenson, Peter

RAGS, BLUES & PARODIES.
Notes: Featuring *Stevie's Tunes*
Album: released on Conifer, Dec'86 by Conifer Records. Dist: Conifer

Dickenson, Vic

ESSENTIAL VIC DICKENSON.
Album: released on Vogue Jazz, May'83

JUST FRIENDS.
Notes: Featuring Red Richards/John Williams
Album: released on Sackville, Jun'86 Dist: Jazz Music, Jazz Horizons, Cadillac Music, Celtic Music, Swift

NICE '78'.
Album: released on Hefty Jazz, Apr'79 Dist: Swift, Wellard, Chris, Jazz Music, Cadillac Music

...PLAYS BESSIE SMITH (TROMBONE CHOLLY).
Album: released on Sonet, Aug'87 by Sonet Records. Dist: PRT

VIC DICKENSON QUINTET.
Album: released on Storyville, Aug'81 by Storyville Records. Dist: Jazz Music Distribution, Swift Distribution, Chris Wellard Distribution, Counterpoint Distribution

VIC DICKENSON'S QUARTET (Dickenson, Vic Quintet).
Notes: Mono production. Featuring Buddy Tate/G.Duvivier/O.Jackson
Album: released on Storyville, Jun'86 by Storyville Records. Dist: Jazz Music Distribution, Swift Distribution, Chris Wellard Distribution, Counterpoint Distribution

YACHT CLUB SWING 1964-1965 (Dickenson, Vic All Stars).
Notes: Mono
Album: released on Harlequin, May'86 by Harlequin Records. Dist: Swift, Jazz Music, Wellard, Chris, Taylor, H.R.

Dickerson, Walt

I HEAR YOU JOHN (Dickerson, Walt & Jimmi Johnson).
Album: released on Steeplechase, Jun'81

SHADES OF LOVE.
Album: released on Steeplechase Feb'79

VISIONS (Dickerson, Walt & Sun Ra).
Album: released on Steeplechase, Sep'79

Dickie, James F

DICKIE STYLE, THE.
Notes: With Ivory Duncan, Jim Duncan and Maureen Rutherford.
Cassette: released on Ross, Jan'86 by Ross Records. Dist: Ross Distribution, Roots Distribution

JAMES F DICKIE'S DELIGHTS.
Album: released on Topic, '81 Dist: Roots Distribution

Cassette: released on Ross, Oct'84 by Ross Records. Dist: Ross Distribution, Roots Distribution

Dickies

GIGANTOR/BOWLING WITH BEDROCK BARNEY.
Single (7"): released on A&M, Jun'80 by A&M Records. Dist: Polygram

INCREDIBLE SHRINKING DICKIES.
Album: released on A&M, Feb'79 by A&M Records. Dist: Polygram

WE AREN'T THE WORLD.
Album: released on Roir, Apr'86 by Reach Out International Records. Dist: Red Rhino Distribution, Cartel Distribution

Dickinson, John

...PLAYS BALDWIN STUDIO II ORGAN.
Album: released on Grosvenor, '75 by Grosvenor Records. Dist: Taylors

Dicks

KILL FROM THE HEART.
Album: released on SST, Oct'83 by SST Records. Dist: Pinnacle

THESE PEOPLE.
Album: released on Alternative Tentacles, Jul'85 by Alternative Tentacles Records. Dist: Rough Trade, Pinnacle

Dickson, Barbara

ALL FOR A SONG.
Album: released on Epic, Feb'82 by CBS Records. Dist: CBS

Cassette: released on Epic, Feb'82 by CBS Records. Dist: CBS
Cat. no: **40 10030**
Album: released on Epic, Aug'87 by CBS Records. Dist: CBS

ALL FOR A SONG/ HEARTBEATS.
Album: released on Epic, Aug'87 by CBS Records. Dist: CBS

ANOTHER SUITCASE ANOTHER HALL.
Single (7"): released on Old Gold, Jul'84 by Old Gold Records. Dist: Lightning, Jazz Music, Spartan, Counterpoint

ANSWER ME.
Album: released on RSO, Aug'83

Cassette: released on RSO, Aug'83

BARBARA DICKSON ALBUM.
Album: released on Epic, Apr'85 by CBS Records. Dist: CBS

Cassette: released on Epic, Apr'85 by CBS Records. Dist: CBS

BARBARA DICKSON (FOUR TRACK CASSETTE EP).
Cassette: released on Epic, Aug'82 by CBS Records. Dist: CBS

BARBARA DICKSON SONGBOOK, THE.
Compact disc: by K-Tel Records. Dist: Record Merchandisers Distribution, Taylors, Terry Blood Distribution, Wynd-Up Distribution, Relay Distribution, Pickwick Distribution, Solomon & Peres Distribution, Polygram

Album: released on K-Tel, Dec'84 by K-Tel Records. Dist: Record Merchandisers Distribution, Taylors, Terry Blood Distribution, Wynd-Up Distribution, Relay Distribution, Pickwick Distribution, Solomon & Peres Distribution, Polygram

Cassette: released on K-Tel, Dec'84 by K-Tel Records. Dist: Record Merchandisers Distribution, Taylors, Terry Blood Distribution, Wynd-Up Distribution, Relay Distribution, Pickwick Distribution, Solomon & Peres Distribution, Polygram

BLOOD BROTHERS.
Album: released on Legacy, 30 May'87 Dist: PRT

Cassette: released on Legacy, 30 May'87 Dist: PRT

BLOOD BROTHERS (MINI LP).
Album: released on Legacy, Jul'83 Dist: PRT

CARAVAN SONG.
Single (7"): released on Portrait, May'85 by CBS Records. Dist: CBS

COLLECTION, THE.
Tracks: / Drift away / Dancing in the street / Stardust / Come rain or come shine / Crying game, The / As time goes by / Fallen angels / Think it over.
Notes: Tracks include those listed above.
Double Album: released on Collector Series, Sep'87 by Castle Communications Records. Dist: PRT, Pinnacle, RCA, Ariola

Cassette: released on Collector Series, Sep'87 by Castle Communications Records. Dist: PRT, Pinnacle, RCA, Ariola

FATE O' CHARLIE.
Album: Dist: Jazz Music, Celtic Music, JSU

FATE O' CHARLIE, (THE) (see Fisher, Archie).

FOR I KNOW HIM SO WELL (Dickson, Barbara & Elaine Paige).
Single (7"): released on RCA, Dec'84 by RCA Records. Dist: RCA, Roots, Swift, Wellard, Chris, I & B, Solomon & Peres Distribution

Single (12"): released on RCA, Dec'84 by RCA Records. Dist: RCA, Roots, Swift, Wellard, Chris, I & B, Solomon & Peres Distribution

GOLD.
Compact disc: by K-Tel Records. Dist: Record Merchandisers Distribution, Taylors, Terry Blood Distribution, Wynd-Up Distribution, Relay Distribution, Pickwick Distribution, Solomon & Peres Distribution, Polygram

Album: released on K-Tel, Nov'85 by K-Tel Records. Dist: Record Merchandisers Distribution, Taylors, Terry Blood Distribution, Wynd-Up Distribution, Relay Distribution, Pickwick Distribution, Solomon & Peres Distribution, Polygram

Cassette: released on K-Tel, Nov'85 by K-Tel Records. Dist: Record Merchandisers Distribution, Taylors, Terry Blood Distribution, Wynd-Up Distribution, Relay Distribution, Pickwick Distribution, Solomon & Peres Distribution, Polygram

Compact disc: released on K-Tel, Nov'86 by K-Tel Records. Dist: Record Merchandisers Distribution, Taylors, Terry Blood Distribution, Wynd-Up Distribution, Relay Distribution, Pickwick Distribution, Solomon & Peres Distribution, Polygram

GREATEST ORIGINAL HITS (FOUR TRACK EP).
Single (7"): released on Epic, Mar'83 by CBS Records. Dist: CBS

HERE WE GO (LIVE ON TOUR).
Album: released on Epic, Nov'82 by CBS Records. Dist: CBS

Cassette: released on Epic, Nov'82 by CBS Records. Dist: CBS

I DON'T BELIEVE IN MIRACLES.
Single (7"): released on Epic, May'84 by CBS Records. Dist: CBS

IF YOU'RE RIGHT.
Tracks: / If you're right / Rivals.
Single (7"): released on K-Tel, Apr'86 by K-Tel Records. Dist: Record Merchandisers Distribution, Taylors, Terry Blood Distribution, Wynd-Up Distribution, Relay Distribution, Pickwick Distribution, Solomon & Peres Distribution, Polygram

JANUARY FEBRUARY/ISLAND IN THE SNOW.
: released on Epic, May'82 by CBS Records. Dist: CBS

JANUARY FEBURARY.
Tracks: / Caravan song.
Single (7"): released on Old Gold, Jan'87 by Old Gold Records. Dist: Lightning, Jazz Music, Spartan, Counterpoint

KEEPING MY LOVE.
Single (7"): released on Epic, Mar'84 by CBS Records. Dist: CBS

MORNING COMES QUICKLY.
Album: released on RSO, Mar'85

Cassette: released on RSO, Mar'85

RIGHT MOMENT (THE).
Tracks: / Right moment(The) / Tenderley / She move thro' the fair / Time after time / Follow you,Follow me / Time After Time / It's Raining again today / Wouldn't it be good / Boulder to Birmingham / Who are you anyway / Vanishing days of love (The) / Angie baby / Making history / Fine partly cloudy / If you go away.
Album: released on K-Tel, Oct'86 by K-Tel Records. Dist: Record Merchandisers Distribution, Taylors, Terry Blood Distribution, Wynd-Up Distribution, Relay Distribution, Pickwick Distribution, Solomon & Peres Distribution, Polygram

SONGBOOK.
Compact disc: released on K-Tel, Nov'86 by K-Tel Records. Dist: Record Merchandisers Distribution, Taylors, Terry Blood Distribution, Wynd-Up Distribution, Relay Distribution, Pickwick Distribution, Solomon & Peres Distribution, Polygram

STILL IN THE GAME.
Single (7"): released on MCA, Mar'85 by MCA Records. Dist: Polygram, MCA

STOP IN THE NAME OF LOVE/FIND......
Single (7"): released on Epic, Jan'83 by CBS Records. Dist: CBS

SWEET OASIS/YOU KNOW IT'S ME.
Cassette: released on Epic, Aug'83 by CBS Records. Dist: CBS

TIME AFTER TIME.
Tracks: / Time after time / She moves thro' the fair.
Single (7"): released on K-Tel, Sep'86 by K-Tel Records. Dist: Record Merchandisers Distribution, Taylors, Terry Blood Distribution, Wynd-Up Distribution, Relay Distribution, Pickwick Distribution, Solomon & Peres Distribution, Polygram

VERY BEST OF BARBARA DICKSON.
Album: released on Telstar, Oct'86 by Telstar Records. Dist: RCA Distribution

Cassette: released on Telstar, Oct'86 by Telstar Records. Dist: RCA Distribution

YOU KNOW IT'S ME.
Album: released on Epic, May'81 by CBS Records. Dist: CBS

Cassette: released on Epic, May'81 by CBS Records. Dist: CBS

Dickson, Don

PRAYING MANTIS.
Tracks: / Praying mantis / Wake Up / When a man loves a woman / Andy.
Single (12"): released on Demon, Mar'86 by Demon Records. Dist: Pinnacle

Dictators

BLOOD BROTHERS.
Album: released on Asylum, Aug'78 by WEA Records. Dist: WEA

FUCK 'EM IF THEY CAN'T TAKE A JOKE.
Album: released on Reach Out Int, '83

Diddle Daddle

DIDDLE DADDLE Mouth music of Britain (Various Artists).
Cassette: released on Folktracks, Nov'79 by Folktracks Cassettes. Dist: Folktracks

Diddley, Bo

AIN'T IT GOOD TO BE FREE.
Album: released on New Rose, Jun'84 Dist: Rough Trade, Cartel

BO DIDDLEY.
Compact disc: released on Vogue, Dec'86 Dist: Discovery, Jazz Music, PRT, Swift

Album: released on Chess, Apr'87 by Charly Records. Dist: Charly, Swift, PRT, Discovery, IMS, Polygram

Cassette: released on Chess, Apr'87 by Charly Records. Dist: Charly, Swift, PRT, Discovery, IMS, Polygram

BO DIDDLEY (7").
Single (7"): released on Chess, Jul'85 by Charly Records. Dist: Charly, Swift, PRT, Discovery, IMS, Polygram

CHESS MASTERS.
Album: released on Chess, Apr'81 by Charly Records. Dist: Charly, Swift, PRT, Discovery, IMS, Polygram

GO BO DIDDLEY.
Album: released on Chess, Apr'87 by Charly Records. Dist: Charly, Swift, PRT, Discovery, IMS, Polygram
Cat. no: **GCH 8021**
Cassette: released on Chess, Apr'87 by Charly Records. Dist: Charly, Swift, PRT, Discovery, IMS, Polygram

HAVE GIUTAR,WILL TRAVEL.
Album: released on Charly, Aug'86 by Charly Records. Dist: Charly, Cadillac

Cassette: released on Charly, Aug'86 by Charly Records. Dist: Charly, Cadillac

HEY.
Tracks: / Intro/Bo Diddley vamp / Doctor Jeckyll / Everleen / I don't know where i've been / You can't judge a book / Roadrunner / I'm a man / Mona.
Album: released on Conifer, Apr'86 by Conifer Records. Dist: Conifer

Cassette: released on Conifer, Apr'86 by Conifer Records. Dist: Conifer

HEY,BO DIDDLEY.
Album: released on Magnum Force, Aug'86 by Magnum Music Group Ltd. Dist: Magnum Music Group Ltd, PRT, Spartan

HIS GREATEST SIDES VOL.1.
Album: released on Chess, Aug'86 by Charly Records. Dist: Charly, Swift, PRT, Discovery, IMS, Polygram

Cassette: released on Chess, Aug'86 by Charly Records. Dist: Charly, Swift, PRT, Discovery, IMS, Polygram

I'M A MAN.
Album: released on Black Lion, Oct'82 by Black Lion Records. Dist: Jazz Music, Chris Wellard, Taylor, H.R., Counterpoint, Cadillac

IN THE SPOTLIGHT.
Album: released on Chess, Oct'87 by Charly Records. Dist: Charly, Swift, PRT, Discovery, IMS, Polygram

Cassette: released on Chess, Oct'87 by Charly Records. Dist: Charly, Swift, PRT, Discovery, IMS, Polygram

IT'S GREAT TO BE RICH (EP) (Diddley, Bo & Billy Boy).
Single (12"): released on Red Lightnin', Jun'83 by Red Lightnin' Records. Dist: Roots, Swift, Jazz Music, Pinnacle, Cartel, Wynd-Up Distribution

ROAD RUNNER.
Album: released on Black Lion, Jul'84 by Black Lion Records. Dist: Jazz Music, Chris Wellard, Taylor, H.R., Counterpoint, Cadillac

Did ee ever yur tell

DID EE EVER YUR TELL Recitations (Various Artists).
Cassette: released on Folktracks, Nov'79 by Folktracks Cassettes. Dist: Folktracks

Die Doraus & Die Marinas

FRED FROM JUPITER.
Single (7"): Deleted Mar'82.

Died Pretty

BLUE SKY DAY.
Single (7"): released on What Goes On, Dec'86 Dist: Rough Trade, Cartel,

FREE DIRT.
Album: released on What Goes On, Oct'86 Dist: Rough Trade, Cartel,

NEXT TO NOTHING.
Single (12"): released on What Goes On, Nov'85 Dist: Rough Trade, Cartel

OUT OF THE UNKNOWN.
Single (12"): released on What Goes On, Feb'85 Dist: Rough Trade, Cartel,

Dieghton Family

ACOUSTIC MUSIC FOR MOST OCCASIONS.
Single (7"): released on Rogue, Aug'87 by Fast Forward Records. Dist: Nine Mile Distribution, Cartel Distribution

Die grossen marsche

DIE GROSSEN MARSCHE Various Artists (Various Artists).
Tracks: / Alte kameraden / Weidmannsheil / Tolzer Schutzenmarsch / Radetzky-marsch / Konig Ludwig II marsch / In die weite welt / Preussens Gloria / Gamsgebirgsmarsch-so leb'denn wohl.../ Waldlemarsch-ja, mir sab vom wald,juchhee / Konig Karl marsch / Gruss an Kiel / Egerlandermarsch.
Album: Dist: IMS-Polygram Deleted Sep'86.

Cassette: released on Polydor (Germany), Sep'86 Dist: IMS-Polygram

Die Haut

BURNING THE ICE (Die Haut/Nick Cave).
Album: released on Illuminated, Feb'85 by IKF Records. Dist: Pinnacle, Cartel, Jetstar

KARIBISCHER WESTERN (Die Haut/Lydia Lunch).
Single (12"): released on Zensor, Aug'83 by Zensor Records. Dist: Rough Trade

Dieheim, Susan

DESERT EQUATIONS (Dieheim, Susan & Richard Horowitz).
Album: released on Made To Measure, Feb'87 by Made To Measure Records. Dist: Pinnacle

Die Hoch-Und...

UNTER DEM DOPPELADLER (Die Hoch-Und Duetschmeister).
Notes: A Military extravaganza "direkt aus Deutchland".Superb brass band performances with the precision we have come to expect from our German neighbours. "unter Dem Doppeladler (Under The Double Eagle)"
Album: released on Teldec (Germany), Dec'85 by Import Records. Dist: IMS Distribution, Polygram Distribution

Cassette: released on Teldec (Germany), Dec'85 by Import Records. Dist: IMS Distribution, Polygram Distribution

Die Krupps

GOLDFINGER.
Single (12"): released on Quiet, Jun'84 by Quiet Records. Dist: Nine Mile, Cartel

GOLDFINGER/ZUEI HERZEN.
Single (7"): released on WEA, Jun'82 by WEA Records. Dist: WEA

Die neue deutsche

DIE NEUE DEUTSCHE WELLE IST DA DA DA Various german artists (Various Artists).
Album: released on Phonogram (Germany), Aug'82

Cassette: released on Phonogram (Germany), Aug'82

Diesel

WATTS IN A TANK.
Album: released on Mercury, Nov'81 by Phonogram Records. Dist: Polygram Distribution

Diesel Park West

WHEN THE HOODOO COMES.
Tracks: / When the hoodoo comes / Above these things / Girl with the name, The*.
Single (7"): released on Food, Jul'87 by Food Records. Dist: Rough Trade, Cartel, WEA

Single (12"): released on Food, Jul'87 by Food Records. Dist: Rough Trade, Cartel, WEA

Diesel trains

DELTIC DUTIES.
Cassette: released on Audiocord Cassettes, May'83

DIESELS ON DAINTON.
Cassette: released on Audiocord Cassettes, May'83

DIESELS ON THE LICKEY INCLINE.
Cassette: released on Audiocord Cassettes, May'83

DYNAMIC DIESELS.
Cassette: released on Audiocord Cassettes, May'83

FAREWELL TO THE DELTICS.
Cassette: released on Audiocord Cassettes, May'83

HST 125 & DMU.
Cassette: released on Audiocord Cassettes, May'83

WESTERN WAYS.
Cassette: released on Audiocord Cassettes, May'83

Die Todliche Doris

WIE GEHT ES DIR JETZ.
Album: released on Atatak, Apr'86 by Atatak Records. Dist: Rough Trade, Cartel

Die Toten Hosen

SCHOENE BESCHERUNG/KNEGHT RUPRECAT.
Single (7"): released on Totenkopf (Import), Feb'84

Dietrich, Marlene

AN EVENING WITH.
Video-cassette (VHS): released on PMI, Jun'86 by PMI Records. Dist: EMI

Video-cassette [Betamax]: released on PMI, Jun'86 by PMI Records. Dist: EMI

AN EVENING WITH... (VIDEO).
Notes: Filmed in 1972 at the New London Theatre.
Video-cassette (VHS): released on Video Collection, May'87 by Video Collection Records. Dist: Counterpoint

BEST OF MARLENE DIETRICH.
Album: released on EMI, Aug'85 by EMI Records. Dist: EMI

Cassette: released on EMI, Aug'85 by EMI Records. Dist: EMI

DIETRICH IN RIO.
Tracks: / Look me over closely / You're the cream in my coffee / My blue heaven / Boys in the backroom (The) / Das lied ist aus / Je tire ma reverance / Alright,Okay,Yeu win / Makin' Whoopee! / I've grown accustomed to her face / One for my baby / Maybe I'll come back / Luar do sertao.
Album: released on CBS, Mar'86 by CBS Records. Dist: CBS

Cassette: released on CBS, Mar'86 by CBS Records. Dist: CBS

IN LONDON.
Tracks: / I can't give you anything but love / Laziest gal in town / Shirc hatan / La vie en rose / Johnny / Go away from my windo / Lili marlene / Allein / Lola / I wish you love / Marie Marie / Honeysuckle rose / Falling in love again.
Album: released on PRT Flashback, Jul'86

Cassette: released on PRT Flashback, Jul'86

LEGENDARY, LOVELY MARLENE.
Album: released on MCA, May'82 by MCA Records. Dist: Polygram, MCA

Cassette: released on MCA, May'82 by MCA Records. Dist: Polygram, MCA

LILI MARLENE (CBS).
Album: released on CBS Cameo, Nov'83 by CBS Records. Dist: CBS

Album: released on CBS Cameo, Nov'83 by CBS Records. Dist: CBS Deleted '87.

LILI MARLENE (EMI).
Tracks: / Lili Marleen / Wer wird den weinen / In das kasernen / Me in blondes baby / Peter / Allien / Wenn ich mir'was wunschen durfte / Iche bin die fesche lola / Ich bin von kopf bis fub auf liebe eingestellt / Wenn die soldaten / Johnny wenn du geburtstag / Ich weib nicht,zu wem ich gehore / Ich hab' noch einen koffer in Berlin / Kinder,heut'abend / Marie-Marie.
Album: released on EMI (Italy), Dec'86 by EMI Records. Dist: Conifer

Cassette: released on EMI (Italy), Dec'86 by EMI Records. Dist: Conifer

LILI MARLENE (NOSTALGIA).
Album: released on Nostalgia, Apr'85 Dist: Jazz Music, Counterpoint

MAGIC OF MARLENE DIETRICH, THE.
Tracks: / Ich bin von kopf bis fuss auf liebe eingestellt / Wenn die soldaten / Mein blondes baby / Paff, der zauberdrachen / Allein in einer grossen stadt (alone) / Der trommelmann (Little drummer boy) / Cherche la rose / Where have all the flowers gone / Ich bin die fesch Lola (Lola) / Die antwort weiss ganz allein der wind / Jonny, wenn du geburtstag hast (Johnny) / In den kasernen / Ich weiss nicht zu wem ich gehore / Lili Marlen / Peter / Sag mir wo die blumen sind.
Notes: (*) With orchestra conducted by Burt Bacharach. (P) Original sound recordings made by EMI Electrola GMBH
Album: released on Music For Pleasure, Jun'87 by EMI Records. Dist: EMI

MAGIC OF..., THE.
Tracks: / Ich bin von kopf bis fuss auf liebe eingestellt / Wenn die soldaten / Mein blondes baby / Paff, der zauberdrachen (Puff the magic dragon) / Allein in einer grossen stadt (Alone) / Der Trommelmann (The little drummer boy) / Cherche la rose / Where have all the flowers gone / Ich bin die fesch Lola (Lola) / Die antwort weiss ganz allein der wind / Jonny, wenn du geburtstag hast (Johnny) / In den kasernen / Ich weiss nicht zu wem ich gehore / Lili Marlen (Lili Marlene) / Peter / Sag Mir wo die blumen sind (Where have all the flowers gone.
Notes: The most distinctive female voice ever is that of Marlene Dietrich and here on this album she is heard singing her most popular songs. Recorded in the early 60's when she was at the height of her cabaret career, the peak of which was probably a Royal Variety Performance in 1964 - The Beatles were on the sam bill. 16classic performances are featured here.
Album: released on MFP, Jun'87 by EMI Records. Dist: EMI

Cassette: released on MFP, Jun'87 by EMI Records. Dist: EMI

MARLENE.
Tracks: / Kinder, heute abend, da such ich mir was aus / Leben ohne kannst du nicht / Falling in love again / Ich bin di fesche lola / Quand l'amour meurt / Johnny / Mein blondes baby / Wenn die beste freundin / wenn ich mir was wunschen durfte / Allein in einer grossen stadt / Ich bin von fuss auf liebe eingestellt / Es lieght in der luft-potpourri / Nimm dich in acht vor blonden frauen / Give me the man.
Notes: What more is there to be said about this 'Legend-in-her-lifetime', truly one of the outstanding entertainers of the twentieth century.The voice,as the beautifulface,is quite unmistakable,even ageless.She was one of the few artists of her generation able to hold an audience in the palm of her hand from the moment she walked on the stage.She had a charisma that was almost unique,and was a perfect-ionist.This disc,with a stunning sleeve,is a collectors item.
Album: released on ASV Living Era, Feb'86 by ASV Records. Dist: PRT

Cassette: released on ASV Living Era, Feb'86 by ASV Records. Dist: PRT

MARLENE DIETRICH.
Album: released on Deja Vu, Jan'87 by Deja Vu Records. Dist: Counterpoint Distribution, Record Services Distribution (Ireland)

Cassette: released on Deja Vu, Jan'87 by Deja Vu Records. Dist: Counterpoint Distribution, Record Services Distribution (Ireland)

MARLENE DIETRICH LEGEND (MYTHOS).
Album: released on EMI (Germany), '83 by EMI Records. Dist: Conifer

Dieval, Jack

ALL THE THINGS YOU ARE.
Album: released on Velvet, Jul'77 by Peerless Records.

Die Zimmermanner

ANJA/GERMAN VERSION.
Single (7"): released on Cherry Red, Jan'84 by Cherry Red Records. Dist: Pinnacle

Single (12"): released on Cherry Red, Jan'84 by Cherry Red Records. Dist: Pinnacle

GOETHE.
Album: released on Atatak, Jun'84 by Atatak Records. Dist: Rough Trade, Cartel

Diez, Stephan

MIRRORS.
Album: released on Ego Sep'79 by Ego Records. Dist: Cadillac Music

Die Zwei

COUNTRY BOY.
Single (12"): released on Zensor, Mar'85 by Zensor Records. Dist: Rough Trade

GRAPSCH.
Single (12"): released on Cherry Red, Apr'84 by Cherry Red Records. Dist: Pinnacle

Different For Domeheads

DIFFERENT FOR DOMEHEADS (Various Artists).
Album: released on Creation, Sep'85 Dist: Rough Trade, Cartel

Different Kind Of Tension

DIFFERENT KIND OF TENSION Various artists (Various Artists).
Tracks: / Like an angel / I know everything / Like one thousand violins / Cut the cake / Every conversation / Hundred words, A / Romance is over(The) / Kitchen Table / Once more / Happy days.
Album: released on Pressures Of The Real World, Sep'86 Dist: EMI

Differents

CAROLINE/BE HARD AND BOOGIE.
Single (7"): released on City, Sep'82 by City Records. Dist: Pinnacle

Difford & Tillbrook

DIFFORD & TILLBROOK.
Album: released on A&M, Jul'84 by A&M Records. Dist: Polygram

Cassette: released on A&M, Jul'84 by A&M Records. Dist: Polygram

Dif Juz

EXTRACTIONS.
Tracks: / Crosswinds / Starting point, A / Love insane / Twin and earth / Starting point, A.
Compact disc: released on 4AD, Feb'87 by 4AD Records. Dist: Rough Trade

Album: released on 4AD, Aug'85 by 4AD Records. Dist: Rough Trade

OUT OF THE STREETS.
Album: released on 4AD, Nov'86 by 4AD Records. Dist: Rough Trade

VIBRATING AIR.
Single (7"): released on 4AD, Nov'81 by 4AD Records. Dist: Rough Trade

WHO SAYS SO.
Album: released on Red Flame, Aug'83 by Red Flame Records. Dist: Nine Mile, Cartel

Di Franco, Linda

MY BOXX.
Tracks: / My boxx / Dance it up.
Single (7"): released on WEA, May'86 by WEA Records. Dist: WEA

Single (12"): released on WEA, May'86 by WEA Records. Dist: WEA

RISE OF THE HEART (THE).
Tracks: / T.V Scene / Look of love, The / Yankee / Stay / Dance it up / My boss / Bless my soul / Fran / Blame it on rio / Rise of the heart, The.
Album: released on WEA, May'86 by WEA Records. Dist: WEA

Cassette: released on WEA, May'86 by WEA Records. Dist: WEA

Digance, Richard

COMMERCIAL ROAD.
Album: released on Chrysalis, Nov'79 by Chrysalis Records. Dist: CBS

DIGANCE INDULGENCE.
Album: released on Dambuster, Feb'85 by Dambuster Records. Dist: Projection, Celtic Music, Roots

DRAG QUEEN BLUES.
Tracks: / Drag queen blues / Red lights of antwerp(The) / How the west was lost / Englands green and pleasant land / I hear the press gang / Beaver the believer / Teddy bears picnic / Christopher Robin / Runaway train / Working class millionaire / Migration memoirs / Final bow / Rosemary Mclaren of the Strand.
Album: released on Conifer, Aug'86 by Conifer Records. Dist: Conifer

DRINKING WITH ROSIE/HERBERT THE TURBOT.
Single (7"): released on Coast, Feb'82 by Coast Records. Dist: Phonogram, Polygram

...& FRIENDS LIVE AT Q.E. HALL.
Album: released on Chrysalis, Jun'78 by Chrysalis Records. Dist: CBS

Cassette: released on Chrysalis, Jun'78 by Chrysalis Records. Dist: CBS

HOW THE WEST WAS LOST.
Album: released on Transatlantic, Apr'75 by Logo Records. Dist: Roots Distribution, RCA Distribution

IN CONCERT.
Album: released on Transatlantic, Oct'80 by Logo Records. Dist: Roots Distribution, RCA Distribution

LIVE AT FAIRFIELD HALLS.
Album: released on Dambuster, Dec'85 by Dambuster Records. Dist: Projection, Celtic Music, Roots

Digging The Water

DIGGING THE WATER (Various Artists).
Album: released on Children Of The Revolution, Apr'87 by Revolver Records. Dist: Revolver, Cartel

Diggs, David

REAL WORLD.
Cassette: released on Palo Alto (USA), Jul'86 by Palo Alto Records. Dist: Conifer

Album: released on Palo Alto (Italy), Jan'84

Digital...

DIGITAL MASSED CHOIRS SPECTACULAR Various artists (Various Artists).
Compact disc: released on Bandleader, '86 by Bandleader Records. Dist: PRT

DIGITAL SHOWCASE Various artists (Various Artists).
Compact disc: released on Bandleader, Nov'86 by Bandleader Records. Dist: PRT

Digital Emotion

GET UP ACTION.
Single (12"): released on Carrere, May'84 by Carrere Records. Dist: PRT, Spartan

Digital pressure

GRIP OF THE GLOVE.
Single (7"): released on Fragile, Aug'85 by Fragile Records. Dist: Cartel

Digital Sex

ESSENCE & CHARM.
Tracks: / Dervish dance / How many more times / Romance isn't over, The / Whisper words / Steps toward freedom / In her smile / Oceans of space / Second wind / Sex in the spring / Roses on Wednesday / Within these walls / I can't wait / Sun in my eyes / When feelings change / Without hesitation / Look for outstretched arms / Essence / Tortured beauty / Tingler, The.
Compact disc: released on Sordide Sentimental (France), Jun'87 Dist: Cartel

Dignum, Keith & Simon

BY CHANCE IT WAS.
Album: released on Dingles, '83 by Dingles Records. Dist: Projection

Dig This

DIG THIS A tribute to the great strike (Various Artists).
Album: released on Forward Sounds, Oct'85 by Forward Sounds Records. Dist: Rough Trade, Cartel

Dig This Drill

CRANKING UP RELIGION.
Tracks: / Cranking up religion.
Single (12"): released on Native, Feb'86 by Native Records. Dist: Red Rhino, Cartel

Digvisdrill

SPELL SURVIVAL.
Single (12"): released on Native, Feb'87 by Native Records. Dist: Red Rhino, Cartel

Dikker, Loek

SUMMER SUITE.
Tracks: / Overture / First rain in August / Susan loves the sea / Summer suite / Banana song / Dark tango / Aknathon.
Album: released on Daybreak, Oct'82 Dist: Jazz Horizons, Jazz Music

Dillard & Clark

AINT IT GOOD TO BE FREE (7").
Single (7"): released on New Rose, Aug'84 Dist: Rough Trade, Cartel

THROUGH THE MORNING & THROUGH THE NIGHT.
Album: released on Demon, Jul'86 by Demon Records. Dist: Pinnacle

Dillard, Doug Band

JACKRABBIT.
Notes: Top US Country artist. Top session musicians. Original American colour sleeve.
Album: released on Sundown, Mar'86 by Magnum Music Group Ltd. Dist: Magnum Music Group Ltd, PRT Distribution, Spartan Distribution

Dillard Hartford Dillard

DILLARD HARTFORD DILLARD.
Album: released on Sonet, Jul'77 by Sonet Records. Dist: PRT

Dillard, Rodney

AT SILVER DOLLAR CITY.
Album: released on Flying Fish (USA), Apr'86 by Flying Fish Records (USA). Dist: Roots, Projection

SILVER DOLLAR CITY.
Album: released on Flying Fish (USA), Apr'86 by Flying Fish Records (USA). Dist: Roots, Projection

Single (12"): released on Champagne, Jan'86 by DJM Records.

Dillards

DECADE WALTZ.
Album: released on Flying Fish (USA), May'79 by Flying Fish Records (USA). Dist: Roots, Projection

Dillard, Varetta

DOUBLE CROSSING DADDY.
Album: released on Mr. R&B (Sweden), Sep'84

Dillinger

BEST OF DILLINGER (LIVE).
Album: released on Vista Sounds, Feb'84 by Vista Sounds Records. Dist: Jetstar

BIONIC DREAD.
Album: released on Island, Jan'78 by Island Records. Dist: Polygram

BLACKBOARD JUNGLE.
Album: released on Culture Press, Sep'84 by Vista Sounds Records. Dist: Jetstar, Rough Trade

CB 200.
Album: released on Island, Jan'78 by Island Records. Dist: Polygram

385

COCAINE.
Tracks: / Cocaine in my brain / In my brain / Jah love / Funkey punk / Mickey mouse crab louse / I thirst / Loving pauper / Flat foot hustlin' / Crabs in my pants / Marijuana in my brain / Cocaine (Remix).
Album: released on New Cross, Nov'84 by Charly Records. Dist: Charly

003

Cassette: released on New Cross, Nov'84 by Charly Records. Dist: Charly

Compact disc: by Charly Records. Dist: Charly, Cadillac

Compact disc: by Charly Records. Dist: Charly, Cadillac

COCAINE (12").
Single (12"): released on Champagne, Sep'85 by DJM Records.

COCAINE IN MY BRAIN/BUCKIN'HAM.
Single (7"): released on Island, Jul'81 by Island Records. Dist: Polygram

CORN BREAD.
Album: released on Vista Sounds, '83 by Vista Sounds Records. Dist: Jetstar

FIVE MAN ARMY/FIVE MAN DUB.
Single (7"): released on Oak Sound, Feb'82

Single (12"): released on Oak Sound, Feb'82

KING PHARAOH.
Album: released on Blue Moon, May'84 Dist: Magnum Music Group Ltd, PRT, Spartan

Cassette: released on Blue Moon, May'84 Dist: Magnum Music Group Ltd, PRT, Spartan

LIVE AT LONDON (Dillinger/Clint Eastwood).
Album: released on Vista Sounds, '83 by Vista Sounds Records. Dist: Jetstar

LIVE AT THE MUSIC MACHINE.
Album: released on Vista Sounds, Mar'84 by Vista Sounds Records. Dist: Jetstar

MARIJUANA IN MY BRAIN.
Album: released on Vista Sounds, '83 by Vista Sounds Records. Dist: Jetstar

TALKIN' BLUES.
Album: released on Magnum, Dec'77 by Bulldog Records. Dist: Spartan

TOP RANKING DILLINGER.
Album: released on Third World, Dec'77 Dist: Jetstar Distribution

TRIBAL WAR.
Tracks: / Rock to the music / Get on the good side / Super cock / Sex me baby / Soul food / Tribal war / Tallowah / Mr Flint / Rockers.
Notes: Produced by Larry Sevitt and Webster Shrowder for Vaidene Productions.
Album: released on New Cross, May'86 by Charly Records. Dist: Charly

Cassette: released on Charly, May'86 by Charly Records. Dist: Charly, Cadillac

TRIBAL WAR/WAR DUBBING.
Single (12"): released on 10, Nov'83 by 10 Records. Dist: Virgin, EMI

VERSES TRINITY CLASH.
Album: released on Burning Sounds, May'78 by Ross, Bill/Burning Sounds Records. Dist: PRT

Dillon, Sandy

FLOWERS.
Single (7"): released on Mainman, Aug'85 by Mainman Records.

Dils

LIVE.
Album: released on Triple XXX (USA), Aug'87 Dist: Pinnacle

Dimaccio, Christian

CHRISTIAN DIMACCIO.
Album: released on Accordion Record Club, '84 by Accordion Record Club Records. Dist: Accordion Record Club

Dimentia 13

DIMENTIA 13.
Album: released on Midnight (USA), Mar'86

Di Meola, Al

CASINO.
Tracks: / Egyptian danza / Chasin' the voodoo / Dark eye tango / Senor mouse / Fantasia suite for two guitars / Viva la danzarina / Guitars of the exotic isle / Rhapsody Italia / Bravoto fantasia / Casino.
Compact disc: by CBS Records. Dist: CBS

Album: released on CBS, Mar'82 by CBS Records. Dist: CBS Deleted '87.

Cassette: released on CBS, Mar'82 by CBS Records. Dist: CBS Deleted '87.

CIELO E TERRA.
Tracks: / Traces of a tear / Vertigo shadow / Cielo e Terra / Enigma of desire / Atavism of twilight / Coral / When your gone / Etude / Solace.
Notes: Debut album for the Manhatten label from guitar virtuoso Al Di Meola. He produces the album and composes all tunes with the exception of one, written by Keith Jarrett. Underlining Manhatten Records comitment to the more specialist areas of the market, the addition of Di Meola to the roster will undoubtedly serve to broaden further the appeal of this already well established artist.
Album: released on Manhattan, May'85 by President Records. Dist: Jazz Music, Swift, Taylors, Chris Wellard

Cassette: released on Manhattan, May'85 by President Records. Dist: Jazz Music, Swift, Taylors, Chris Wellard

ELECTRIC RENDEZVOUS.
Tracks: / God bird / Change / Electric rendezvous / Passion, grace and fire / Cruisin' / Black cat shuffle / Ritmo de la noche / Somalia / Jewel inside a dream.
Notes: Al Dimeola is a unique craftsman-he can turn his talents to any style of guitar playing from classical to heavy electric, "Electric Rendezvous" is a celebrationof these two very distinct musical styles. Steve Gaad, Paco de Lucia and Jan Hammer join Al on this LP.
Compact disc: released on CBS, May'87 by CBS Records. Dist: CBS

Album: released on CBS, Mar'82 by CBS Records. Dist: CBS Deleted '85.

Cassette: released on CBS, Mar'82 by CBS Records. Dist: CBS Deleted '85.

ELEGANT GYPSY.
Tracks: / Flight over Rio / Midnight tango / Mediterranan sundance / Race with devil on the Spanish highway / Lady of Rome / Sister of Brazil / Elegant gypsy suite.
Album: released on CBS, May'77 by CBS Records. Dist: CBS Deleted '85.

Cassette: released on CBS, '79 by CBS Records. Dist: CBS

FRIDAY NIGHT IN SAN FRANCISCO.
Tracks: / Mediterranean sundance / Rio ancho / Short tales of the black forest / Frevo resgado / Fantasia suite for two guitars / Guardian angel.
Album: released on CBS, Jun'81 by CBS Records. Dist: CBS

Cassette: released on CBS, Jun'81 by CBS Records. Dist: CBS

SOARING THROUGH A DREAM.
Tracks: / Capoeira / Traces (of a tear) / Ballad / July / Marina / Soaring through a dream.
Notes: Acclaimed guitarist Al Di Meola releases a second album for Manhatten records this being an electric project in contrast to his last accoustic work on Cielo E Terra. Joining Di Meola on this new project is noted Brazillian percussionistAirto moreira who also assists and compoitions on the three of the albums six cuts. the group performed live in Britain, at the appolo Manchester on September28th and the Odeon Hammersmith on September 29th as part of a European tour.
Album: released on Manhattan, Oct'85 by President Records. Dist: Jazz Music, Swift, Taylors, Chris Wellard

Cassette: released on Manhattan, Oct'85 by President Records. Dist: Jazz Music, Swift, Taylors, Chris Wellard

Dimples

BEAUTIFUL FEELING/EXPERIMENTAL.
Single (12"): released on Sunburst, May'82 Dist: Sunburst Records

CONFIDENTIAL/PIANO VERSION.
Single (12"): released on Orbitone, May'82 by Orbitone Records. Dist: Jetstar Distribution

Dinah Rod & The Drains

SOMEBODY'S IN MY DRAINS (2 PARTS).
Single (7"): released on Secret, '83 by Secret Records. Dist: EMI

Single (12"): released on Secret, '83 by Secret Records. Dist: EMI

Din A Test Bild

PROGRAMME 3.
Album: released on Innovative Communication, '85 by Innovative Communication Records. Dist: Pickwick Distribution

Dindiscs 1980

DINDISCS 1980 (Various Artists).
Tracks: / Waiting for the man / Messages / Electricity.
Notes: Artists include: Martha & The Muffins;Orchestral Manoeuvres In The Dark;Revillos;Monochrome Set;Dedringer Tracks as above aswell as others
Album: released on Dindisc, '80 by Virgin Records. Dist: Virgin, EMI

Cassette: released on Dindisc, '80 by Virgin Records. Dist: Virgin, EMI

Dinger

AIR OF MYSTERY.
Single (7"): released on Face Value, '85 by Face Value Records. Dist: M.I.S.

Dingle's Regatta

DINGLE'S REGATTA (Various Artists).
Album: released on Dingles, '79 by Dingles Records. Dist: Projection

Dingo

HOUSE WITHOUT A NAME (THE).
Tracks: / House without a name (The) / Tell me now.
Single (7"): released on Sonet, May'86 by Sonet Records. Dist: PRT

Single (12"): released on Sonet, Sep'86 by Sonet Records. Dist: PRT

Dinning, Judy

WAITING FOR THE CHANGE (Dinning, Judy & Dave Smith).
Album: released on Rubber, '83 by Rubber Records. Dist: Roots Distribution, Projection Distribution, Jazz Music Distribution, Celtic Music Distribution, JSU Distribution, Spartan Distribution

Dinning Sisters

DINNING SISTERS.
Tracks: / Sentimental gentleman / Where or when / You're a character, baby / Once in a while / Buttons and bows / Harlem sandman / Beg your pardon / Way you look tonight, The / Aunt Hagar's blues / Please don't talk about me / Brazil / I love my love / Love on a greyhound bus / San Antonio rose.
Album: released on Capitol(USA), '84 by Capitol (USA) Records. Dist: EMI

VOLUME II.
Tracks: / Lolita Lopaz / My adobe hacienda / Do you love me / I wonder who's kissing her now / Iggedy song (The) / Last thing I want is your pity (The) / Bride and groom polka (The) / I get blue when it rains / Years and years ago / Fun and fancy free / Melancholy / Wave to me my lady / If I had to live my life over / Oh Monah.
Notes: Obviously akin to the Andrew Sisters, this trio, employing a familiar style of close harmony, enjoyed a string of hits during the 40's and 50's. The album comprises a good selection of tempo's from slow to swinging.
Album: released on Capitol, Jan'86 by Capitol Records. Dist: EMI

Cassette: released on Capitol, Jan'86 by Capitol Records. Dist: EMI

Dinosaur

DINOSAUR.
Album: released on Homestead, '85 Dist: Rough Trade, Cartel, Shigaku

REPULSION.
Tracks: / Repulsion.
Single (7"): released on Homestead, Mar'86 Dist: Rough Trade, Cartel, Shigaku

YOU'RE LIVING ALL OVER ME.
Album: released on SST, Jul'87 by SST Records. Dist: Pinnacle

Cassette: released on SST, Jul'87 by SST Records. Dist: Pinnacle

Dinosaur L

GO BANG.
Tracks: / Go bang.
Single (12"): released on Citybeat, Jun'86 Dist: WEA

Dinosaur Record

DINOSAUR RECORD (Croft, Mike).
Album: released on Super Tempo, '84 by Multiple Sounds Records. Dist: Multiple Sound Distributors

Cassette: released on Super Tempo, '84 by Multiple Sounds Records. Dist: Multiple Sound Distributors

Dinosaur rock

DINOSAUR ROCK (Michele Valeri & Michael Stein).
Cassette: released on Caedmon(USA), '84 by Caedmon (USA) Records. Dist: Gower, Taylors, Discovery

Dinzee, Pietro

WHEN YOU GET WHAT YOU WANTED.
Single (7"): released on Priority, '83 by Priority Records. Dist: RCA

Single (12"): released on Priority, '83 by Priority Records. Dist: RCA

Dio

DREAM EVIL.
Compact disc: released on Vertigo, Aug'87 by Phonogram Records. Dist: Polygram

Album: released on Vertigo, Aug'87 by Phonogram Records. Dist: Polygram

Cassette: released on Vertigo, Aug'87 by Phonogram Records. Dist: Polygram

HIDING THE RAINBOW.
Tracks: / Hiding the rainbow / Living for heaven / Shame on the night / Egypt-the chains are on / Stand up and shout / Holy diver / Gypsy / Caught in the middle / Don't talk to strangers / Straight through the heart / Invisible / Rainbow in the dark / Shame on the night.
Single (12"): released on Vertigo, May'86 by Phonogram Records. Dist: Polygram

HOLY DIVER.
Tracks: / Stand up and shout / Holy diver / Gypsy / Caught in the middle / Don't talk to strangers / Straight through the heart / Invisible / Rainbow in the dark / Shame on the night.
Compact disc: by Phonogram Records. Dist: Polygram

Album: released on Vertigo, '83 by Phonogram Records. Dist: Polygram

Cassette: released on Vertigo, '83 by Phonogram Records. Dist: Polygram

HOLY DIVER/EVIL EYES/DON'T TALK.
Single (7"): released on Vertigo, '83 by Phonogram Records. Dist: Polygram

HUNGRY FOR HEAVEN.
Tracks: / Hungry for heaven / Hide in the rainbow / Shine on the night / Egypt-the chains on.
Single (7"): released on Vertigo, May'86 by Phonogram Records. Dist: Polygram

Single (12"): released on Vertigo, May'86 by Phonogram Records. Dist: Polygram

Double-pack single: released on Vertigo, May'86 by Phonogram Records. Dist: Polygram

I COULD HAVE BEEN A DREAMER.
Tracks: / I could have been a dreamer / Night People / Sunset Superman.
Single (7"): released on Vertigo, Jul'87 by Phonogram Records. Dist: Polygram

Single (12"): released on Vertigo, Jul'87 by Phonogram Records. Dist: Polygram

INTERMISSION.
Tracks: / King of rock and roll / Rainbow in the dark / Sacred heart / Time to burn / Rock 'n' roll children / We rock.
Notes: 5 tracks recorded live from the 'Sacred Geart' tour. 'Time To Burn' a brand new studio track featuring new Dio guitarist Craig Goldie. 34 minutes of metal magic from the world's most spectacular live heavy metal band. Mini-album.
Album: released on Vertigo, Jun'86 by Phonogram Records. Dist: Polygram

Cassette: released on Vertigo, Jun'86 by Phonogram Records. Dist: Polygram

LAST IN LINE.
Tracks: / We rock / Last in line, The / Breathless / I speed at night / One night in the city / Evil eyes / Mystery / Eat your heart out / Egypt (the chains are on).
Compact disc: by Phonogram Records. Dist: Polygram

Album: released on Vertigo, '84 by Phonogram Records. Dist: Polygram

Cassette: released on Vertigo, '84 by Phonogram Records. Dist: Polygram

Compact disc: released on Vertigo, '84 by Phonogram Records. Dist: Polygram

LIVE IN CONCERT.
Notes: Number of tracks: 8. Type of recording: Live. Total playing time: 60 minutes.
Video-cassette (VHS): released on Channel 5, Apr'86 Dist: W.H. Smiths

MYSTERY.
Single (7"): released on Vertigo, '84 by Phonogram Records. Dist: Polygram

Picture disc single: released on Vertigo, '84 by Phonogram Records. Dist: Polygram

RAINBOW IN THE DARK.
Single (7"): released on Vertigo, '83 by Phonogram Records. Dist: Polygram

SACRED HEART.
Tracks: / King of rock and roll / Sacred heart / Another lie / Rock 'N' roll children / Hungry for heaven / Like the beat of a heart / Just another day / Fallen angels / Shoot shoot.
Notes: Produced by Ronnie James Dio
Album: released on Vertigo, '85 by Phonogram Records. Dist: Polygram

Cassette: released on Vertigo, '85 by Phonogram Records. Dist: Polygram

Compact disc: released on Vertigo, '85 by Phonogram Records. Dist: Polygram

SPECIAL FROM THE SPECTRUM.
Notes: Heavy Metal vocalist Ronnie James Dio (formerly with Rainbow) and his eponymous band, recorded on stage in Philadelphia on nine hard-rocking tracks. 1986 production. Number of tracks: 9. Total playing time: 50 minutes.
Video-cassette (VHS): released on Polygram, Sep'86 by Polygram Records. Dist: Polygram

TRYING TO BURN THE SUN.
Album: released on Safari, '84 by Safari Records. Dist: Pinnacle

Cassette: released on Safari, '84 by Safari Records. Dist: Pinnacle

WE ROCK.
Single (7"): released on Vertigo, '84 by Phonogram Records. Dist: Polygram

Dion

ABRAHAM, MARTIN AND JOHN.
Album: released on Ace, Feb'87 by Ace Records. Dist: Pinnacle, Swift, Hotshot, Cadillac

ALONE WITH DION.
Album: released on Ace, '85 by Ace Records. Dist: Pinnacle, Swift, Hotshot, Cadillac

GREATEST HITS:DION & THE BELMONTS (Dion & The Belmonts).
Tracks: / I wonder why / Every little thing I do / No one knows / Funny feeling, A / Tag along / That's my desire / Don't pity me / Just you / That's how I need you / Teenager in love, A / Lovers prayer, A / My day / Where or when / My private joy / In the still of the night / I'm through with love / Will you love me still / When you wish upon a star.
Album: released on Laurie, '82 by RCA Records. Dist: RCA

Cassette: released on Laurie, Mar'82 by RCA Records. Dist: RCA

GREATEST HITS:DION.
Tracks: / Runaround Sue / Sandy / Lovers who wander / Lonely teenager / Runaway girl / Havin' fun / Little Miss Blue / Queen of the hop / Lonely world / Love came to me / King without a queen / Kissin' game, The / Tonight tonight.
Notes: Originally released in December 1981 on LRSLP 1002/LRSK 1002
Album: released on RCA, '84 by RCA Records. Dist: RCA, Roots, Swift, Wellard, Chris, I & B, Solomon & Peres Distribution

Cassette: released on RCA, '84 by RCA Records. Dist: RCA, Roots, Swift, Wellard, Chris, I & B, Solomon & Peres Distribution

GREATEST HITS: DION VOL.2.

HITS (Dion & The Belmonts).
Tracks: / Runaround Sue / Sandy / Teenager in love / Wanderer / Born to cry / Majestic / Don't pity me / Lonely teenager / Lover's prayer / Little Diane / I wonder why / Where or when.
Compact disc: by Ace Records. Dist: Pinnacle, Swift, Hotshot, Cadillac

Album: released on Ace, Aug'86 by Ace Records. Dist: Pinnacle, Swift, Hotshot, Cadillac

Cassette: released on Ace, Aug'86 by Ace Records. Dist: Pinnacle, Swift, Hotshot, Cadillac

INSIDE JOB.
Album: released on Day Spring, '82 by Word Records. Dist: Word Distribution, CBS

Cassette: released on Day Spring, '82 by Word Records. Dist: Word Distribution, CBS

I PUT AWAY MY IDOLS.
Album: released on Dyaspring, '85

Cassette: released on Dyaspring, '85
Cat. no: **TCDA 4016**

KINGDOM IN THE STREETS.
Album: released on Day Spring, '85 by Word Records. Dist: Word Distribution, CBS

Cassette: released on Day Spring, '85 by Word Records. Dist: Word Distribution, CBS

LOVERS WHO WANDER.
Tracks: / Lovers who wander / Come go with me / King without a queen / So long friend / Twist / Little Diane / Mi muchacha / Stagger Lee / Shout / Tonight, tonight / Born to cry / Queen of the hop / Candy man / Sandy / Lost for sure / Love came to me.
Album: released on Ace, Jan'86 by Ace Records. Dist: Pinnacle, Swift, Hotshot, Cadillac

PRESENTING DION & THE BELMONTS (Dion & The Belmonts).
Tracks: / I wonder why / I wonder why.
Album: released on Ace(Laurie), '84 by Ace Records. Dist: Pinnacle, Swift, Hotshot

RUNAROUND SUE.
Album: released on Ace, '85 by Ace Records. Dist: Pinnacle, Swift, Hotshot, Cadillac

Single (7"): released on Old Gold, '84 by Old Gold Records. Dist: Lightning, Jazz Music, Spartan, Counterpoint

RUNAROUND SUE (OLD GOLD).

RUNAROUND SUE/RUNAWAY GIRL.
Single (7"): released on RCA, '81 by RCA Records. Dist: RCA, Roots, Swift, Wellard, Chris, I & B, Solomon & Peres Distribution

SO WHY DIDN'T YOU DO THAT THE FIRST TIME (Dion & The Belmonts).
Tracks: / Wanderer / My private joy / Moon river / Ain't that better baby / Every little thing I do / We went away / Come take a walk with me / In a room / Lovers who wander / Tag along / Crying / It was never meant to be / Will you love me still / Teenager in love / That's how I need you / Baby what you want me to do.
Album: released on Ace, Nov'85 by Ace Records. Dist: Pinnacle, Swift, Hotshot, Cadillac

TEENAGER IN LOVE.
Single (7"): released on Laurie, '81 by RCA Records. Dist: RCA

Single (7"): released on Old Gold, '84 by Old Gold Records. Dist: Lightning, Jazz Music, Spartan, Counterpoint

WANDERER.
Single (7"): released on Old Gold, '84 by Old Gold Records. Dist: Lightning, Jazz Music, Spartan, Counterpoint

WANDERER/LOVE CAME TO ME.
Single (7"): released on Laurie, '81 by RCA Records. Dist: RCA

WAY YOU DO THE THINGS YOU DO.
Single (7"): by Hollywood Nites Distribution. Dist: Pinnacle

WE DON'T TALK ANYMORE.
Single (7"): released on Aura, '83 by Hollywood Nites Distribution. Dist: Pinnacle

WISH UPON A STAR.
Album: released on Ace, '85 by Ace Records. Dist: Pinnacle, Swift, Hotshot, Cadillac

Diorio, Joe etc

FEEDLES.
Album: released on Timeless, '80

Dio, Ronnie James

CAROLINA COUNTRY BALL.
Album: released on Safari, '84 by Safari Records. Dist: Pinnacle

Cassette: released on Safari, '84 by Safari Records. Dist: Pinnacle

Dip In The Pool

SILENCE.
Album: released on Rough Trade, Nov'86 by Rough Trade Records. Dist: Rough Trade Distribution, Cartel Distribution

Diplomats

I'LL KEEP HOLDING ON.
Single (7"): released on Exchange, Nov'82 Dist: ILA

Direct Drive

ABC (FALLING IN LOVES NOT EASY).
Single (7"): released on Boiling Point, Apr'85 by Polydor Records. Dist: Polygram

Single (12"): released on Boiling Point, Apr'85 by Polydor Records. Dist: Polygram

ANYTHING.
Single (7"): released on Direct Drive, Nov'84 by Direct Drive Records. Dist: PRT

Single (7"): released on Polydor, Jan'85 by Polydor Records. Dist: Polygram, Polydor

Single (12"): released on Polydor, Jan'85 by Polydor Records. Dist: Polygram, Polydor

DON'T DEPEND ON ME.
Single (12"): released on Oval, Jan'82 Dist: Projection

I'M THE ONE.
Single (7"): released on Oval, Apr'82 Dist: Projection

Single (12"): released on Oval, Apr'82 Dist: Projection

IN THE MIDDLE OF SPRING.
Cassette: released on Passion, Jul'83 by Skratch Records. Dist: PRT

Single (12"): released on Passion, Jul'83 by Skratch Records. Dist: PRT

NEED SOME SUNSHINE.
Single (7"): released on DDR, Nov'85 by Direct Drive Records. Dist: PRT

Single (12"): released on DDR, Nov'85 by Direct Drive Records. Dist: PRT

OH YEAH.
Tracks: / Oh yeah.
Notes: Featuring Stan Sultzman. Limited edition.
Single (12"): released on Direct Drive, Mar'86 by Direct Drive Records. Dist: PRT

OH YEAH (MIX 1).
Single (12"): released on DDR, Aug'87 by Direct Drive Records. Dist: PRT

PASS THE PAPER.
Single (7"): released on DDR, Aug'84 by Direct Drive Records. Dist: PRT

Direct Hit

SHE DIDN'T REALLY CARE.
Single (7"): released on Direct, Mar'85 by Phonogram Records. Dist: Polygram

Direct Hits

BLOW UP.
Album: released on Whaam, Jun'84 Dist: Pinnacle

DIRECT HITS (Various Artists).
Tracks: / Bull dance / Crude blues / Roots / Sarsaparilla / Song for the bearded lady / Suspension / Taste of sarsaparilla, A / Torso.
Album: released on Telstar, Nov'82 by Telstar Records. Dist: RCA Distribution

Cassette: released on Telstar, Nov'82 by Telstar Records. Dist: RCA Distribution

HOUSE OF SECRETS.
Album: released on Make, Mar'86 Dist: Nine Mile, Cartel

MODESTY BLAISE.
Single (7"): released on Whaam, Oct'82 Dist: Pinnacle

SNAKES AND LADDERS.
Single (12"): released on Forbidden, Jul'87 by Forbidden Records. Dist: Nine Mile, Cartel

Directions

DIRECTIONS (Various Artists).
Double Album: released on 101 International, Mar'84

Director

CHRISTMAS SOCA.
Tracks: / Christmas soca / Christmas soca-instrumental.
Single (7"): released on Bumble Bee, Dec'86 by CSA Records. Dist: PRT, Jetstar, CSA

Dire Straits

ALCHEMY - LIVE.
Tracks: / Once upon a time in the west / Romeo and Juliet / Expresso love / Pivate investigations / Sultans of swing / Two young lovers / Two young lovers / Telegraph road / Solid rock / Going home theme from local hero.
Double compact disc: by Phonogram Records. Dist: Polygram

Video-cassette (VHS): released on Channel 5, May'86 Dist: W.H. Smiths

ALCHEMY - LIVE.
Cassette: released on Vertigo, Mar'84 by Phonogram Records. Dist: Polygram

Album: released on Vertigo, Mar'84 by Phonogram Records. Dist: Polygram

Compact disc: released on Vertigo, Mar'84 by Phonogram Records. Dist: Polygram

BROTHERS IN ARMS.
Tracks: / So far away / Money for nothing / Walk of life / Your latest trick / Why worry? / Ride across the river / Man's too strong, The / One world / Brothers in arms.
Compact disc: released on Vertigo, May'85 by Phonogram Records. Dist: Polygram

Album: released on Vertigo, May'85 by Phonogram Records. Dist: Polygram

Album: released on Vertigo, May'85 by Phonogram Records. Dist: Polygram

BROTHERS IN ARMS (SINGLE).
Single (7"): released on Vertigo, Oct'85 by Phonogram Records. Dist: Polygram

Single 10": released on Vertigo, Oct'85 by Phonogram Records. Dist: Polygram Deleted '86.

Single (12"): released on Vertigo, Oct'85 by Phonogram Records. Dist: Polygram

Double-pack single: released on Vertigo, Nov'85 by Phonogram Records. Dist: Polygram Deleted '87.

BROTHERS IN ARMS - THE VIDEO SINGLES.
Notes: Number of tracks: 4. Type of recording: E.P. Total playing time: 15 minutes.
Video-cassette (VHS): released on Polygram, May'86 by Polygram Records. Dist: Polygram

COMMUNIQUE.
Compact disc: by Phonogram Records. Dist: Polygram

Album: released on Vertigo, Aug'79 by Phonogram Records. Dist: Polygram

Cassette: released on Vertigo, Jul'79 by Phonogram Records. Dist: Polygram

DIRE STRAITS.
Compact disc: by Phonogram Records. Dist: Polygram

Cassette: released on Vertigo, May'78 by Phonogram Records. Dist: Polygram

DIRE STRAITS (HALF SPEED MASTER EDITION).
Album: released on Mercury, Jun'82 by Phonogram Records. Dist: Polygram Distribution

INTERVIEW PICTURE DISC.
Album: released on Baktabak, Jun'87 by Baktabak Records. Dist: Arabesque

LOVE OVER GOLD.
Compact disc: by Phonogram Records. Dist: Polygram

Album: released on Vertigo, Sep'82 by Phonogram Records. Dist: Polygram

Cassette: released on Vertigo, Sep'82 by Phonogram Records. Dist: Polygram

MAKING MOVIES.
Compact disc: by Phonogram Records. Dist: Polygram

Cassette: released on Vertigo, Oct'80 by Phonogram Records. Dist: Polygram

MAKING MOVIES (HALF SPEED MASTER EDITION).
Album: released on Mercury(limited ed.), Apr'82

MONEY FOR NOTHING.
Single (7"): released on Vertigo, Jun'85 by Phonogram Records. Dist: Polygram

Single 10": released on Vertigo, Jun'85 by Phonogram Records. Dist: Polygram Deleted '87.

Single (12"): released on Vertigo, Jun'85 by Phonogram Records. Dist: Polygram

Picture disc single: released on Vertigo, Jul'85 by Phonogram Records. Dist: Polygram Deleted '86.

ROMEO & JULIET.
Single (7"): released on Vertigo, Oct'84 by Phonogram Records. Dist: Polygram

SO FAR AWAY.
Single (7"): released on Vertigo, Apr'85 by Phonogram Records. Dist: Polygram

Single 10": released on Vertigo, Apr'85 by Phonogram Records. Dist: Polygram Deleted '86.

Single (12"): released on Vertigo, Apr'85 by Phonogram Records. Dist: Polygram

SULTANS OF SWING.
Single (7"): released on Vertigo, Nov'82 by Phonogram Records. Dist: Polygram

Single (12"): released on Vertigo, Nov'82 by Phonogram Records. Dist: Polygram

TWISTING BY THE POOL.
Single (7"): released on Vertigo, Jan'83 by Phonogram Records. Dist: Polygram

Single (12"): released on Vertigo, Jan'83 by Phonogram Records. Dist: Polygram

WALK OF LIFE.
Tracks: / Walk of life / Two young lovers / Sultans of swing-live / Sultans of swing / Eastbound train.
Single (7"): released on Vertigo, Dec'85 by Phonogram Records. Dist: Polygram

Single (12"): released on Vertigo, Dec'85 by Phonogram Records. Dist: Polygram

Double-pack single: released on Vertigo, Dec'85 by Phonogram Records. Dist: Polygram

YOUR LATEST TRICK.
Tracks: / Your latest trick / Irish boy / Long road (The).
Single (7"): released on Vertigo, May'86 by Phonogram Records. Dist: Polygram

Single (12"): released on Vertigo, May'86 by Phonogram Records. Dist: Polygram

Dirt

NEVER MIND DIRT - HERE'S THE BOLLOCKS.
Album: released on Crass, Jan'83 by Exitstencil Music. Dist: Rough Trade, Cartel

OBJECT REFUSE REJECT ABUSE.
Single (7"): released on Crass, Feb'82 by Exitstencil Music. Dist: Rough Trade, Cartel

Dirt Band

DIRT, SILVER & GOLD.
Triple album / cassette:

MAKE A LITTLE MAGIC.
Album: released on Liberty, Mar'81 by Liberty-United. Dist: EMI

TONITE.
Video-cassette (VHS): released on PMI, Jun'86 by PMI Records. Dist: EMI

Video-cassette [Betamax]: released on PMI, Jun'86 by PMI Records. Dist: EMI

Dirty Desi

SEXY LIKE A BOTTLE OF PEPSI.
Single (7"): released on Ragin' Lion, Apr'84

Dirty Dozen

DIRTY DOZEN (Various Artists).
Tracks: / Main title / Building the barracks / Battle begins, The / Girls of the evening / Dirty dozen, The / Erinsam / Mission accomplished / Bramble bush / Col. Breed's folly / Sham Battle, The / Chateau, The / Switch-hitters / Finale and end title.
Album: released on CBS, Feb'87 by CBS Records. Dist: CBS

Cassette: released on CBS, Feb'87 by CBS Records. Dist: CBS

Dirty Dozen Brass Band

LIVE MARDI GRAS IN MONTREUX.
Album: released on Rounder Europa, Mar'87

MARDI GRAS IN MONTREUX - LIVE.
Album: released on Rounder Europa, Jun'86

MY FEET CAN'T FAIL ME NOW.
Album: released on George Wein Concord Jazz (USA), Oct'84 by Concord Jazz Records (USA). Dist: IMS, Polygram

Dirty Looks

TURN IT UP.
Album: released on Stiff, Jun'81 by Stiff Records. Dist: EMI, Record Services Distribution (Ireland)

Dirty Roseanna

DIRTY ROSEANNA.
Tracks: / Dirty Roseanne.
Single (12"): released on Deep, Mar'86 Dist: Rough Trade, Cartel

Dirty Tricks

HIT & RUN.
: released on Polydor, Sep'77 by Polydor Records. Dist: Polygram, Polydor

Dirty Work Work

LOVE YOU FEEL ME.
Tracks: / Love you feel me (remix) / Nothing can hurt me now.
Single (12"): released on Wire, 23 May'87 Dist: Nine Mile, Cartel

Single (7"): released on Wire, 23 May'87 Dist: Nine Mile, Cartel

Disc Bleu

I GOT YOUR NUMBER.
Single (7"): released on MCA, Mar'84 by MCA Records. Dist: Polygram, MCA

Single (12"): released on MCA, Mar'84 by MCA Records. Dist: Polygram, MCA

Disc Drive

DISC DRIVE (Various Artists).
Album: released on Jive, Oct'85 by Zomba Records. Dist: RCA, PRT, CBS

Cassette: released on Jive, Oct'85 by Zomba Records. Dist: RCA, PRT, CBS

Discharge

DECONTROL.
Single (7"): released on Clay, Jul'81 by Clay Records. Dist: Pinnacle

DISCHARGE 1980-1986.
Album: released on Clay, Jul'87 by Clay Records. Dist: Pinnacle

FIGHT BACK.

FOUR TRACK SINGLE.
Single (7"): released on Clay, Apr'80 by Clay Records. Dist: Pinnacle

GRAVE NEW WORLD.
Album: released on Clay, Jul'86 by Clay Records. Dist: Pinnacle

HEAR NOTHING SEE NOTHING SAY NOTHING.
Album: released on Clay, May'82 by Clay Records. Dist: Pinnacle

IGNORANCE.
Single (7"): released on Clay, May'85 by Clay Records. Dist: Pinnacle

Single (12"): released on Clay, May'85 by Clay Records. Dist: Pinnacle

MORE I SEE.
Single (7"): released on Clay, May'84 by Clay Records. Dist: Pinnacle

Single (12"): released on Clay, May'84 by Clay Records. Dist: Pinnacle

NEVER AGAIN.
Album: released on Clay, Jul'84 by Clay Records. Dist: Pinnacle

Single (7"): released on Clay, Oct'81 by Clay Records. Dist: Pinnacle

PRICE OF SILENCE.
Single (7"): released on Clay, Mar'83 by Clay Records. Dist: Pinnacle

REALITIES OF WAR.
Tracks: / Realities of war.
Single (7"): released on Clay, Feb'87 by Clay Records. Dist: Pinnacle

Single (7"): released on Clay, Jul'81 by Clay Records. Dist: Pinnacle

STATE VIOLENCE.
Single (7"): released on Clay, Oct'83 by Clay Records. Dist: Pinnacle

WARNING - H.M.GOVERNMENT.
Single (12"): released on Clay, Sep'83 by Clay Records. Dist: Pinnacle

WHY.
Single (12"): released on Clay, Jul'81 by Clay Records. Dist: Pinnacle

Dischord Singles

DISCHORD SINGLES COMPILATION (Various Artists).
Album: released on Dischord, Jan'85 Dist: Rough Trade, Cartel

Disco

DISCO 50 great dancing hits (Various Artists).
Album: released on Ronco, Nov'83

Cassette: released on Ronco, Nov'83

DISCO CLASSICS (Various Artists).
Triple album / cassette: released on Telstar, Nov'84 by Telstar Records. Dist: RCA Distribution

Cassette: released on Telstar, Nov'84 by Telstar Records. Dist: RCA Distribution

DISCO DANCE HITS (Various Artists).
Cassette: released on PRT, Jun'82 by PRT Records. Dist: PRT

DISCO DANCER (Various Artists).
Album: released on K-Tel, Oct'82 by K-Tel Records. Dist: Record Merchandisers Distribution, Taylors, Terry Blood Distribution, Wynd-Up Distribution, Relay Distribution, Pickwick Distribution, Solomon & Peres Distribution, Polygram

Cassette: released on K-Tel, Oct'82 by K-Tel Records. Dist: Record Merchandisers Distribution, Taylors, Terry Blood Distribution, Wynd-Up Distribution, Relay Distribution, Pickwick Distribution, Solomon & Peres Distribution, Polygram

DISCO DAZE - DISCO NITES (Various Artists).
Double Album: released on Ronco, Apr'81

Double cassette: released on Ronco, Apr'81

DISCO INFERNO (Various Artists).
Cassette: released on VFM, Jan'85 by VFM Records. Dist: Taylors, Wynd-Up Distribution

DISCO LADY (Various Artists).
Cassette: released on Aim, Feb'83 Dist: H.R. Taylor

DISCO LIGHTNING (Various Artists).
Cassette: released on Bravo, Feb'80 by Pickwick Records. Dist: Lugtons

DISCO MANIA (Various Artists).
Cassette: released on Pickwick, Feb'80 by Pickwick Records. Dist: Pickwick Distribution, Prism Leisure Distribution, Lugtons

DISCOMANIA/PARTY FEVER (Various Artists).
Album: released on TV, Nov'82

Cassette: released on TV, Nov'82

DISCONIGHTS (Various Artists).
Cassette: released on Pickwick, Feb'80 by Pickwick Records. Dist: Pickwick Distribution, Prism Leisure Distribution, Lugtons

DISCO NIGHTS Various artists (Various Artists).
Cassette: released on Bravo, Feb'85 by Pickwick Records. Dist: Lugtons

DISCO SATURDAY NIGHT (Various Artists).
Cassette: released on Pickwick, Sep'79 by Pickwick Records. Dist: Pickwick Distribution, Prism Leisure Distribution, Lugtons

DISCO UK/DISCO USA (Various Artists).
Album: released on Ronco, Mar'82

Disco Aid

GIVE GIVE GIVE.
Tracks: / Give give give.
Single (7"): released on Total Control, Oct'86

Single (12"): released on Total Control, Oct'86

Disco Beach Party

DISCO BEACH PARTY various artists (Various Artists).
Album: released on Stylus, May'86 Dist: Pinnacle, Terry Blood Distribution, Stylus Distribution

Cassette: released on Stylus, May'86 Dist: Pinnacle, Terry Blood Distribution, Stylus Distribution

Album: released on Stylus, Aug'85 Dist: Pinnacle, Terry Blood Distribution, Stylus Distribution

Album: released on Stylus, Aug'85 Dist: Pinnacle, Terry Blood Distribution, Stylus Distribution

Disco Connection

BORN TO BE ALIVE.
Single (7"): released on PRT, Nov'83 by PRT Records. Dist: PRT

Single (12"): released on PRT, Nov'83 by PRT Records. Dist: PRT

Single (12"): released on ZYX (Germany), Nov'85 by ZYX Records. Dist: Greyhound

ROCK YOUR BABY.
Tracks: / Rock your baby.
Single (12"): released on ZYX (Germany), Mar'87 by ZYX Records. Dist: Greyhound

Disco Dog

I'M GONNA BREAK YOUR BONES.
Single (12"): released on Malaco, Jan'84 by Malaco Records. Dist: Charly

Disconnection

BALI HAI.
Single (7"): released on Y, Nov'82

Single (12"): released on Y, Nov'82

Disconnections

DISCONNECTIONS Various artists (Various Artists).
Double Album: released on Calibre, Jun'81 by Calibre Records. Dist: PRT

Cassette: released on Calibre, Jun'81 by Calibre Records. Dist: PRT

Disco Scooters

FROM MUD TO THE MOON....
Tracks: / Questionably tortoisehead / Perfect murder (The) / Hey stowaway / Quicksilver / Arable land / From mud to the moon / Hummingbird / Rain rein reign supreme / Some tree talking / I couldn't sing / Rock 'n' roll.
Notes: Playground 37-39 Norman Road, St. Leonards-on-sea. TN38 0EG.
Cassette: released on Playground, Oct'86 by Playground Records. Dist: Playground

Discount Chiefs

TRUMPETS WILL BLOW.
Single (7"): released on Round Ear, Jul'81 Dist: Rough Trade Distribution

Discover Country

DISCOVER NEW COUNTRY Various Artist (Various Artists).
Notes: Artist include Dolly parton, kenny Rogers, Eagles, Judds, Roseanna Cash, Crystal-Gayle - Glen Campbell, Gary morris, Anne murray, Johnny Cash, Conway Twitty, Willie Nelson, Lee Greenwood. Double Album.
Album: released on Starblend, Jul'86 by Starblend Records. Dist: PRT Distribution

Cassette: released on Starblend, Jul'86 by Starblend Records. Dist: PRT Distribution

Discover Scotland

DISCOVER SCOTLAND Various artists (Various Artists).
Tracks: / Original / Kathleen's reel / Bauaria / Dixie / Do you think you could love me again / Skye boat song / Richmora / Pomander jig, The / Wee Sergeant, The / Rab Smillies J.G / Maggie / Silver darlin / Marie's wedding / Vist tramping song / Marquis of Huntly, The / Roxburgh castle / Scotland the brave / From Scotland with love / Wild mountain thyme / Marching through the heather / Johnny lad / Flower of Scotland / Jigtime / McFlannels / Para handy / Mans a man for a'that, A / Scots wha' hae / Auld lang syne / I love a lassie / Roaming in the gloaming / Wee Deoch & Doris / Stop your ticklin' Jock / Keep right on to the end of the road / Denny & Dunipace Pipe Band, The / Major Bobby / Muckin' o' Geordies byre, The / Glendurel highlander, The / Bonnie Dundee.
Cassette: released on Scotdisc, May'87 Dist: Clyde Factors Distributors

Disco Volante

NO MOTION.
Single (7"): released on Catalyst Box, Jul'84 by Catalyst Box. Dist: Pinnacle

Disco Zombies

HERE COMES THE BUTS.
Single (7"): released on Dining Out, Jun'81 by Dining Out Records. Dist: IKF, Independent

TOP OF THE POPS.
Single (7"): released on Uptown (USA), '79 by Uptown Records. Dist: Jazz Music

Discreet Campaigns

DISCREET CAMPAIGNS Various Artist (Various Artists).
Notes: Artist include: New order, Cocteau Twins, James, etc.
Album: released on Rorschach Testing, Jan'86 by Rorschach Testing Records. Dist: Rough Trade Distribution

Disirt Tola

DISIRT TOLA.
Album: released on LP, Mar'85 by LP Records. Dist: Pinnacle

Disley, Diz

VIOLINSPIRATION (Disley, Diz Trio & Stephane Grappelli).

ZING! WENT THE STRINGS (Disley, Diz & The Soho Quintette).
Album: released on Waterfront, Nov'86 by Waterfront Records. Dist: Rough Trade, Cartel, Projection, Roots

ZING WENT THE STRINGS.
Album: released on Waterfront, Sep'86 by Waterfront Records. Dist: Rough Trade, Cartel, Projection, Roots

Disley, Will

KEEP ON RUNNIN'.
Single (7"): released on Web, Aug'83 by Web Records. Dist: ILA, PRT, Web

Single (12"): released on Web, Aug'83 by Web Records. Dist: ILA, PRT, Web

Dislocation

DISLOCATION DANCE.
Single (7"): released on New Hormones, Jul'81 by New Hormones Records.

ROSEMARY.
Single (7"): released on New Hormones, Jun'82 by New Hormones Records.

SLIP THAT DISC.
Single (12"): released on New Hormones, Jun'81 by New Hormones Records.

Dislocation Dance

MIDNIGHT SHIFT.
Album: released on Rough Trade, Aug'84 by Rough Trade Records. Dist: Rough Trade Distribution, Cartel Distribution

SHOW ME.
Single (12"): released on Rough Trade, Oct'83 by Rough Trade Records. Dist: Rough Trade Distribution, Cartel Distribution

VIOLETTE.
Single (7"): released on The Music Label, Jun'83

WHAT'S GOING ON.
Single (12"): released on Slipped Discs, Dec'85 by Slipped Discs Records. Dist: PRT, Self Distribution

YOU'LL NEVER KNOW.
Single (7"): released on New Hormones, Oct'82 by New Hormones Records.

Disney

CHRISTMAS FAVOURITES (Various Artists).
Album: released on Pickwick, Oct'79 by Pickwick Records. Dist: Pickwick Distribution, Prism Leisure Distribution, Lugtons

DISNEY CLASSICS FOR CHILDREN Various artists (Various Artists).
Album: released on Golden Hour, Dec'76 by PRT Records. Dist: PRT

DISNEY FAVOURITES, MORE Various artists (Various Artists).
Album: released on Golden Hour, Dec'76 by PRT Records. Dist: PRT

DISNEY HITS (Various Artists).
Tracks: / When you wish upon a star / Thomas O'Malley cat / Give a little whistle / When I see an Elephant fly / Who's afraid of the big bad wolf. / Ugly bug ball, The / Whistle while you work / Winnie the pooh / Heigh ho / Siamese cat song / Bare necessities, The / Supercalifragilisticexpialidocious. / Colonel Hathi's march / Trust in me / That's what friends are for / I wanna be like you / Never smile at a crocodile / Feed the birds / Aristocats, The / Hi Diddle Dee Dee / Ev'rybody want to be a cat / My own home / I've got no strings.
Cassette: released on Hour Of Pleasure, Jan'86 by Music For Pleasure Records. Dist: EMI

DISNEY'S ORIGINAL SOUNDTRACK VOLUME 3.

DISNEY'S ORIGINAL SOUNDTRACK COLLECTION VOLUME 4.

DISNEY'S ORIGINAL SOUNDTRACK COLLECTION VOLUME 1.
Album: released on Hallmark, Nov'76 by Pickwick Records. Dist: Pickwick Distribution, PRT, Taylors

Album: released on Hallmark, Nov'76 by Pickwick Records. Dist: Pickwick Distribution, PRT, Taylors

Album: released on Hallmark, Nov'76 by Pickwick Records. Dist: Pickwick Distribution, PRT, Taylors

DISNEY'S ORIGINAL SOUNDTRACK COLLECTION VOLUME 2.
Album: released on Hallmark, Nov'76 by Pickwick Records. Dist: Pickwick Distribution, PRT, Taylors

DISNEY STORIES FOR CHILDREN Various artists (Various Artists).
Album: released on Golden Hour, Dec'76 by PRT Records. Dist: PRT

GOLDEN HOUR: DISNEY (Various Artists).
Album: released on Golden Hour, Oct'76 by PRT Records. Dist: PRT

GOLDEN HOUR PRESENTS DISNEY TODAY.
Album: by PRT Records. Dist: PRT

GREATEST HITS:WALT DISNEY (Various Artists).
Album: released on Disneyland, Dec'83 by Disneyland-Vista Records (USA). Dist: BBC Records & Tapes, Rainbow Communications Ltd(Distribution)

Cassette: released on Disneyland, Dec'83 by Disneyland-Vista Records (USA). Dist: BBC Records & Tapes, Rainbow Communications Ltd(Distribution)

ORIGINAL SOUNDTRACK PARADE VOLUME 1 (Various Artists).
Album: by Pickwick Records. Dist: Pickwick Distribution, Prism Leisure Distribution, Lugtons

Disorder

COMPLETE DISORDER.
Extended-play record: released on Disorder, Jun'81 by Heartbeat Records. Dist: Revolver

DISTORTION TO DEAFNESS.
Single (7"): released on Disorder, Dec'81 by Heartbeat Records. Dist: Revolver

LIVE IN OSLO.
Album: released on Disorder, Nov'85 by Heartbeat Records. Dist: Revolver

MENTAL DISORDER.
Extended-play record: released on Disorder, Mar'83 by Heartbeat Records. Dist: Revolver

ONE DAY SON, ALL THIS WILL BE YOURS (Disorder & Kaska Process).
Album: released on Disorder, Nov'86 by Heartbeat Records. Dist: Revolver

PERDITION.
Album: released on Disorder, Jun'84 by Heartbeat Records. Dist: Revolver

Single (12"): released on Riot City, Sep'82 by Riot City Records. Dist: Revolver

SINGLES COLLECTION, THE.
Album: released on Riot City, Jan'84 by Riot City Records. Dist: Revolver

UNDER THE SCALPEL BLADE.
Album: released on Disorder, Jun'84 by Heartbeat Records. Dist: Revolver

Disorderlies

DISORDERLIES Original soundtrack (Various Artists).
Tracks: / Don't treat me like this / Edge of a broken heart / Trying to dance / Roller one / Fat off my back / Work me down / Baby you're a rich man / I heard a rumour / Disorderly conduct / Big money.
Notes: This is the soundtrack album from the motion picture 'Disorderlies' which stars the Fat Boys.
Compact disc: released on London, Jul'87 by London Records. Dist: Polygram

Album: released on London, Aug'87 by London Records. Dist: Polygram

Cassette: released on London, Jul'87 by London Records. Dist: Polygram

Disruptors

ALIVE IN THE ELECTRIC CHAIR.
Single (12"): released on Radical Change, Aug'85 by Backs Records. Dist: Backs, Cartel

BOMB HEAVEN.
Single (7"): released on Radical Change, Apr'84 by Backs Records. Dist: Backs, Cartel

Single (7"): released on Radical Change, Apr'86 by Backs Records. Dist: Backs, Cartel

PLAYING WITH FIRE.
Album: released on Radical Change, Nov'84 by Backs Records. Dist: Backs, Cartel

SHELTERS FOR THE RICH.
Single (7"): released on Radical Change, Jul'82 by Backs Records. Dist: Backs, Cartel

YOUNG OFFENDER.
Single (7"): released on Radical Change, Nov'81 by Backs Records. Dist: Backs, Cartel

Dissidenten

SAHARA ELECTRIC.
Album: released on Globestyle, Sep'85 by Ace Records. Dist: Projection

Distance

JUST ONE MORE KISS.
Single (12"): released on Challenge, Mar'84 by Elite Records. Dist: Pinnacle

MOSHI MOSHI.
Album: released on Philips, May'81 Dist: IMS-Polygram

Distant Drums

PERFECT EYES.
Single (7"): released on Rhythmic, Aug'83 by Rhythmic Records. Dist: Havoc Distribution

Distel, Sacha

20 FAVOURITE LOVE SONGS.
Album: released on Mercury, Nov'79 by Phonogram Records. Dist: Polygram Distribution

GOLDEN HOUR OF SACHA DISTEL.
Album: released on Golden Hour, Sep'78 by PRT Records. Dist: PRT

IMAGINE.
Single (7"): released on Towerbell, Nov'85 by Towerbell Records. Dist: EMI

LOVE IS ALL.
Album: released on Pye, Oct'76

MORE AND MORE.
Album: by Warner Bros Records. Dist: WEA

MOVE CLOSER.
Album: released on Towerbell, Nov'85 by Towerbell Records. Dist: EMI

Cassette: released on Towerbell, Nov'85 by Towerbell Records. Dist: EMI

NIGHT AND MUSIC AND YOU, THE.
Album: released on Pye, Jun'79

SACHA DISTEL COLLECTION, THE.
Double Album: released on Pickwick, Jul'80 by Pickwick Records. Dist: Pickwick Distribution, Prism Leisure Distribution, Lugtons

Cassette: released on Pickwick, Jul'80 by Pickwick Records. Dist: Pickwick Distribution, Prism Leisure Distribution, Lugtons

STRONGER THAN BEFORE.
Single (7"): released on Towerbell, Dec'85 by Towerbell Records. Dist: EMI

THAT'S THE WAY I LIKE IT.
Single (7"): released on Hansa, Jul'82 by Hansa Records. Dist: Polygram

Single (12"): released on Hansa, Jul'82 by Hansa Records. Dist: Polygram

Distributors

GET RID OF THESE THINGS.
Single (7"): released on Red Rhino, Nov'81 by Red Rhino Records. Dist: Red Rhino, Cartel

District Singers

TWELFTH PARTY SING A LONG.
Album: released on Ulster, Jul'83 Dist: Outlet

Cassette: released on Ulster, Jul'83 Dist: Outlet

District Six

AKUZWAKALE (LET'S BE HEARD).
Album: released on District Six, Mar'85

Cassette: released on District Six, Mar'85

LEAVE MY NAME AT THE DOOR.
Tracks: / Leave my name at the door / Nameless one, The / In our hands / Ilanga / Koko / Drums for nelson / Mangwane.
Notes: Second album from District six whose inspiration is drawn from South African folk music, Contemporary Jazz and free expression. They have gained wide recogn ition in the jazz world since their jazz Service Tour, numerous appearances at the major festivals and a German tour with Annie Whitehead guesting. The group has slightly changed in the line-up with the departure of Russell herman and Ruthie Smith. 'Leaving My Name At The Door' is an exciting second album recordinga live performance at the Bass Clef Club London November 1985. Personnel; Jim Dvorak-trumpet, pocket trumpet, penny whistle, vocals and percussion/ harrison Smith-saxophones and flute/mervyn Africa - piano, vocals, cabassa and hand cymbals/Dill katz-/fretless bass guitar /Brian Abrahams-drums and vocals.
Album: released on Wave, Feb'86 by Charly Records. Dist: Charly

Diva

DIVA Original soundtrack (Various Artists).
Compact disc: by Pacific Records (USA). Dist: Atlantic

SENTIMENTAL PROMENADE.
Single (7"): released on Palace Video, Jan'83

Divine

BORN TO BE CHEAP.
Single (7"): released on Situation 2, Jul'81 Dist: Cartel, Pinnacle

HARD MAGIC.
Single (7"): released on Proto, Oct'85 by Proto Records. Dist: WEA

Single (12"): released on Proto, Oct'85 by Proto Records. Dist: WEA

I'M SO BEAUTIFUL.
Single (7"): released on Proto, Sep'84 by Proto Records. Dist: WEA

Single (12"): released on Proto, Sep'84 by Proto Records. Dist: WEA

JUNGLE JEZEBEL.
Album: released on O, Mar'83 by Vanguard

(USA). Dist: PRT Distribution

Album: released on Vanguard (USA). May'84

LITTLE BABY.
Tracks: / Little baby (Inst).
Single (7"): released on Recordings, Jan'87

Single (12"): released on Recordings, Jan'87

LITTLE BABY (DANCE REMIX).
Tracks: / Little baby(dance remix) / Little baby (Instrumental).
Single (12"): released on In Recordings, Feb'87 by RCA, DMS

LOVE REACTION.
Single (7"): released on Design Communications, Oct'83

Single (12"): released on Design Communications, Oct'83

MEDLEY.
Tracks: / Medley / Native love.
Single (12"): released on Proto, Feb'86 by Proto Records. Dist: WEA

MEDLEY,THE.
Tracks: / Medley, The.
Single (12"): released on Receiver, Nov'86 by Receiver Records. Dist: Pinnacle

NAME GAME.
Single (7"): released on Situation 2, Jan'84 Dist: Cartel, Pinnacle

NATIVE LOVE.
Tracks: / Native love / Love reaction/no.1.
Single (12"): released on Receiver, Sep'86 by Receiver Records. Dist: Pinnacle

NATIVE LOVE (STEP BY STEP).
Single (12"): released on O, Nov'82 by Vanguard (USA). Dist: PRT Distribution

SHAKE IT UP.
Single (7"): released on Design Communications, Nov'83

Single (12"): released on Design Communications, Nov'83

SHOOT YOUR SHOT.
Tracks: / Shoot your shot / Shake it up /No.2.
Single (12"): released on Receiver, Sep'86 by Receiver Records. Dist: Pinnacle

Single (12"): released on O, Feb'83 by Vanguard (USA). Dist: PRT Distribution

STORY SO FAR.
Compact disc: released on Bellaphon, '86 by Bellaphon Records. Dist: IMS-Polygram

STORY SO FAR (GREATEST HITS), THE.
Album: released on Proto, May'85 by Proto Records. Dist: WEA

Cassette: released on Proto, May'85 by Proto Records. Dist: WEA

STORY SO FAR, THE.
Single (12"): released on Receiver, Aug'87 by Receiver Records. Dist: Pinnacle

TWISTIN' THE NIGHT AWAY.
Single (7"): released on Proto, Jun'85 by Proto Records. Dist: WEA

Single (12"): released on Proto, Jun'85 by Proto Records. Dist: WEA

WALK LIKE A MAN.
Single (7"): released on Proto, Apr'85 by Proto Records. Dist: WEA

Picture disc single: released on Proto, Apr'85 by Proto Records. Dist: WEA

Single (12"): released on Proto, Apr'85 by Proto Records. Dist: WEA

WHAT'S INSIDE.
Album: released on Chainsaw, Aug'85 by Chainsaw Records. Dist: Red Rhino, Cartel

YOU THINK YOU'RE A MAN.
Tracks: / You think you're a man / Walk like a man/no. 3.
Single (12"): released on Receiver, Sep'86 by Receiver Records. Dist: Pinnacle

Single (7"): released on Proto, Jun'84 by Proto Records. Dist: WEA

Single (12"): released on Proto, Jun'84 by Proto Records. Dist: WEA

Divine Horsemen
DEVIL'S RIVER.
Album: released on New Rose, Dec'86 Dist: Rough Trade, Cartel

MIDDLE OF THE NIGHT.
Single (12"): released on New Rose, 13 Jun'87 Dist: Rough Trade, Cartel

Divine Sounds
WHAT PEOPLE DO FOR MONEY.
Tracks: / What people do for money.
Single (12"): released on Streetwave, Feb'86 by Streetwave Records. Dist: PRT Distribution

Divine Weeks
THROUGH AND THROUGH.
Album: released on Enigma, Jan'87 by Enigma Records. Dist: Rough Trade, Cartel, EMI

Divinyls
SCIENCE FICTION.
Single (7"): released on Chrysalis, May'83 by Chrysalis Records. Dist: CBS

Single (12"): released on Chrysalis, May'83 by Chrysalis Records. Dist: CBS

WHAT A LIFE.
Tracks: / Guillotine day / Pleasure and pain / Don't you go walking / Gooddie young / Sleeping beauty / Motion / In my life / Casual encounter / Heat telegraph / Gillotine day / Dear diary / Heart telegraph / Gillotine / Dear diary.
Album: released on Chrysalis, Jan'86 by Chrysalis Records. Dist: CBS

Cassette: released on Chrysalis, Jan'86 by Chrysalis Records. Dist: CBS

Divorce me darling
DIVORCE ME DARLING Original London Cast
Album: released on TER, Jan'85 Dist: Pinnacle Cat. no: **TER 1077**
Cassette: released on TER, Jan'85 Dist: Pinnacle

Dixie bop
DIXIE BOP Various artists (Various Artists).
Album: released on Charly, Feb'82 by Charly Records. Dist: Charly, Cadillac

Dixie Cups
CHAPEL OF LOVE.
Single (7"): released on Creole (Reissue), Aug'82 by Creole Records. Dist: PRT, Rhino

Single (7"): released on Old Gold, Jul'82 by Old Gold Records. Dist: Lightning, Jazz Music, Spartan, Counterpoint

DIXIE CUPS MEET THE SHANGRI-LAS (Dixie Cups/Shangri-las).
Tracks: / Chapel of love / I'm gonna get you yet / All grown up / Gee the moon is shining bright / Gee baby gee / Another boy like mine / Iko Iko / Wrong direction / Ain't that nice / Thank you mama, thank you papa / Little bell / People say / Remember (walking in the sand) / Train from Kansas City / Heaven only knows / Out in the streets / Leader of the pack / I can never go home anymore / Long live love / Give him a great big kiss / Give us your blessing / What is love / Sophisticated boom boom / Past, present and future.
Notes: See also under Shangri-las.
Compact disc: released on Charly, Dec'86 by Charly Records. Dist: Charly, Cadillac

TEEN ANGUISH VOL 1.
Album: released on Charly, Apr'80 by Charly Records. Dist: Charly, Cadillac

Dixie Dregs
FREE FALL.
Album: released on Capricorn, Oct'77 by Polydor Records. Dist: Polygram

NIGHT OF THE LIVING DREGS.
Album: released on Capricorn, Mar'79 by Polydor Records. Dist: Polygram

WHAT IF.
Album: released on Capricorn, Aug'79 by Polydor Records. Dist: Polygram

Dixie Four
CHICAGO SOUTH SIDE (Dixie Four/Midnight Rounders/State Street Ramblers).
Album: released on Collectors Items, Feb'87 Dist: Jazz Music, Swift, Chris Wellard

Dixie Hummingbirds
CHRISTIAN TESTIMONIAL, A.
Cassette: released on MCA (USA), Jun'84 Dist: Pinnacle

Dixieland Bands
JAZZ SOUNDS OF THE TWENTIES.
Album: released on Swaggie (Australia), Jan'83

Dixieland Jubilee
DIXIELAND JUBILEE VOL 1 Various artists (Various Artists).
Double Album: released on Black Lion, Oct'82 by Black Lion Records. Dist: Jazz Music, Chris Wellard, Taylor, H.R., Counterpoint, Cadillac

Double Album: released on Black Lion-Inter-

cord, May'82

Cassette: released on Black Lion-Intercord, May'82

DIXIELAND JUBILEE VOL 2 Various artists (Various Artists).
Album: released on Black Lion, Oct'82 by Black Lion Records. Dist: Jazz Music, Chris Wellard, Taylor, H.R., Counterpoint, Cadillac

Double Album: released on Black Lion-Intercord, May'82

Double cassette: released on Black Lion-Intercord, May'82

DIXIELAND JUBILEE VOL 3 Various artists (Various Artists).
Double Album: released on Black Lion-Intercord, May'82

Double cassette: released on Black Lion-Intercord, May'82

DIXIELAND JUBILEE VOL 4 Various artists (Various Artists).
Double Album: released on Black Lion-Intercord, May'82

Double cassette: released on Black Lion-Intercord, May'82

DIXIELAND JUBILEE VOL 5 Various artists (Various Artists).
Double Album: released on Black Lion-Intercord, May'82

Double cassette: released on Black Lion-Intercord, May'82

Dixieland Sound Spectacular
AT THE JAZZBAND BALL.
Album: released on Fantasy (USA), Feb'86 by Fantasy Inc USA Records. Dist: IMS, Polygram

Dixie Party
DIXIE PARTY Various artists (Various Artists).
Album: released on Fontana Import, May'83 by Phonogram Records. Dist: Polygram

Cassette: released on Fontana Import, May'83 by Phonogram Records. Dist: Polygram

Album: released on Black Lion-Intercord, May'82

Dixon, Don
MOST OF THE GIRLS LIKE TO DANCE.
Tracks: / Praying mantis / You're a big girl now / Swallowing pride / Wake up / Talk to me / Rocket / Fighting for my life / Eyes on fire.
Notes: Full title:- Most of the girls like to dance, but only some of the boys like to
Album: released on Demon, Nov'85 by Demon Records. Dist: Pinnacle

Cassette: released on Demon, Nov'85 by Demon Records. Dist: Pinnacle

Compact disc: released on Demon, Jan'86 by Demon Records. Dist: Pinnacle

Dixon, Floyd
EMPTY STOCKING BLUES.
Album: released on Route 66 (Sweden), Aug'85 by Mr. R&B Records. Dist: Swift Distribution, Cadillac, Jazz Music Distribution

HOUSTON JUMP.
Album: released on Route 66, Jun'80

OPPORTUNITY BLUES.
Album: released on Route 66, Jun'80

ROCKIN'THIS JOINT TONITE.
Album: released on JSP, Feb'79 by JSP Records. Dist: Swift, Projection

Dixon House Band
FIGHTING ALONE.
Album: released on Infinity, Dec'79 by MCA Records. Dist: EMI

Dixon, Jessy
IT'S ALL RIGHT NOW.
Album: released on Light USA, May'82 by Lexicon Music. Dist: Word Distribution

Cassette: released on Light USA, May'82 by Lexicon Music. Dist: Word Distribution

SATISFIED (LIVE).
Album: released on Light USA, May'82 by Lexicon Music. Dist: Word Distribution

Cassette: released on Light USA, May'82 by Lexicon Music. Dist: Word Distribution

Dixon, Karen
COS I LOVE YOU BABY.
Single (12"): released on Neville King, Apr'82 by Neville King Records. Dist: Jetstar

I LIKE YOUR MOVE.
Single (12"): released on Neville King, Oct'81 by Neville King Records. Dist: Jetstar

I WANT TO BE FREE.
Single (12"): released on Neville King, Sep'83 by Neville King Records. Dist: Jetstar

LOVE.
Single (12"): released on Neville King, Jan'85 by Neville King Records. Dist: Jetstar

TOUCH ME BABY.
Single (12"): released on NK, Apr'83

Dixon, Prince
IT'S A SAD SITUATION.
Album: released on Joliet, Apr'79 by Sonet Records. Dist: PRT

Dixon, Reginald
AT THE MOVIES.
Album: released on One Up, Jun'76 by EMI Records.

BLACKPOOL LIGHTS.
Album: released on EMI, Aug'85 by EMI Records. Dist: EMI

Cassette: released on EMI, Aug'85 by EMI Records. Dist: EMI

BLAZE AWAY.
Cassette: released on Encore, Jun'78 by EMI Records. Dist: EMI

FAREWELL MR BLACKPOOL.
Album: released on Columbia, '70 by EMI Records. Dist: EMI

GREAT ORGAN FAVOURITES.
Album: released on One Up, Apr'77 by EMI Records.

ISN'T THIS A LOVELY DAY.
Cassette: released on Note, Aug'80 by EMI Records. Dist: EMI

Album: released on Note, Aug'80 by EMI Records. Dist: EMI

MAGIC OF REGINALD DIXON,(THE).
Album: released on Music For Pleasure (Holland), Jun'85 by EMI Records. Dist: EMI

Cassette: released on Music For Pleasure (Holland), Jun'85 by EMI Records. Dist: EMI

OVER THE WAVES.
Album: released on Encore, Aug'81 by EMI Records. Dist: EMI

Cassette: released on Encore, Aug'81 by EMI Records. Dist: EMI

PLAY A SIMPLE MELODY.
Cassette: released on Note, Sep'79 by EMI Records. Dist: EMI

REGINALD DIXON AT THE WURLITZER ORGAN.
Cassette: released on Ideal(Tapes), '81 Dist: EMI

SENTIMENTAL JOURNEY.
Cassette: released on One Up, '78 by EMI Records.

SING ALONG AT THE TOWER.
Album: released on EMI, Jun'83 by EMI Records. Dist: EMI

Cassette: released on EMI, Jun'83 by EMI Records. Dist: EMI

TOWER BALLROOM FAVOURITES.
Tracks: / Tiger rag / Autum leaves / Dardanella / Elizabethan Serenade / La paloma / Russian rag / Peanut vendor / Wedding of the painted doll / These foolish things / Temptation rag / Sabre dance / Czardas / Sweet and lonely / Canadian capers / Moonlight serenade / Continental, The / Jealousy / 12th street rag / Deep purple / Cherokee / Toy trumpet / Stardust.
Cassette: released on Hour Of Pleasure, Jan'86 by Music For Pleasure Records. Dist: EMI

Dixon, Sharon
CANDY BLUES (TALKIN'82).
Single (7"): released on Red Rhino, Jul'82 by Red Rhino Records. Dist: Red Rhino, Cartel

HOW CAN I LOVE AGAIN.
Single (12"): released on Cartridge, May'82 by Cartridge. Dist: Jetstar

Dixon, Tyrone
PRISONER OF LOVE.
Single (12"): released on Hawkeye, Jul'80 by Hawkeye Records. Dist: Hawkeye, Lightning (WEA) Distribution, Jetstar, PRT

Dixon, Willie

ONE OF THESE MORNINGS.
Notes: For full information see under: Lenior, J.B/Willie Dixon.

WILLIE DIXON.
Album: released on Deja Vu, Jan'87 by Deja Vu Records. Dist: Counterpoint Distribution, Record Services Distribution (Ireland)

Cassette: released on Deja Vu, Jan'87 by Deja Vu Records. Dist: Counterpoint Distribution, Record Services Distribution (Ireland)

WILLIE'S BLUES (Dixon, Willie & Memphis Slim).
Album: released on Original Blues Classics (USA), May'84

Dixon/Winter/Homnick

WHOOPIN'.
Notes: see under Winter/Dixon/Homnick

Diz & the Doormen

BLUECOAT MAN.
Single (7"): released on Ace, Nov'82 by Ace Records. Dist: Pinnacle, Swift, Hotshot, Cadillac

CHALK FARM FIESTA.
Album: released on Ace, May'82 by Ace Records. Dist: Pinnacle, Swift, Hotshot, Cadillac

Dizzy Heights

TO THE SOUND OF THE DRUMS AND THE BASE.
Tracks: / To the sound of the drums and the bass/complete works. / DIY rap track.
Single (7"): released on Parlophone, Oct'86 by EMI Records. Dist: EMI

Single (12"): released on Parlophone, Sep'86 by EMI Records. Dist: EMI

WOULD I FIND LOVE.
Tracks: / Would I find/Dub / Gospel, The / Would I find love/Instrumental..
Notes: Tracks on 12" version only Would I find/Dub. The Gospel.
Single (7"): released on Parlophone, Mar'86 by EMI Records. Dist: EMI

Single (12"): released on Parlophone, Mar'86 by EMI Records. Dist: EMI

Dizzy Satellites

ORBIT DRIVE.
Album: released on Music Maniac, Oct'86 Dist: Rough Trade Distribution, Cartel Distribution

Django D.J

BUBBLING POT.
Single (12"): released on African Museum, Mar'83 Dist: Jetstar

Djavan

FLOR DE LIS.
Album: released on Sign (France), Apr'86 Dist: Greyhound

D-Jay, Richie

LOVE DON'T STRIKE TWICE.
Single (12"): released on Elite, Jun'82 Dist: PRT

D.J. Battle

D.J. BATTLE D.J. Battle (D.J. Battle/Trinity/Ranking Joe/Charlie Charlie).
Album: released on Kingdom, '84 by Kingdom Records. Dist: Kingdom

DJ Jazzy Jeff

MAGNIFICENT JAZZY JEFF (DJ Jazzy Jeff & Fresh Prince).
Tracks: / Magnificent jazzy jeff / Magnificent jazzy jeff (inst dub).
Single (7"): released on Champion, Feb'87 by Champion Records. Dist: RCA

Single (12"): released on Champion, Feb'87 by Champion Records. Dist: RCA

ROCK THE HOUSE (DJ Jazzy Jeff & Fresh Prince).
Album: released on Champion, Feb'87 by Champion Records. Dist: RCA

Cassette: released on Champion, Feb'87 by Champion Records. Dist: RCA

TOUCH OF JAZZ (DJ Jazzy Jeff & Fresh Prince).
Tracks: / Touch of jazz / Touch of jazz (street mix) / Touch of jazz (retouch mix).
Single (7"): released on Champion, May'87 by Champion Records. Dist: RCA

Single (12"): released on Champion, May'87 by Champion Records. Dist: RCA

D.J. Munch

PARTY ROCK.
Single (12"): released on FM Dance, Jul'87 by FM-Revolver Records. Dist: BMG, RCA, Ariola

D.J.'s

REGGAE GREATS various artists.
Album: released on Island, Mar'85 by Island Records. Dist: Polygram

Cassette: released on Island, Mar'85 by Island Records. Dist: Polygram

DJ's Factory

WORK.
Tracks: / Work / Work (Instrumental mix)/ Bass Mix.
Single (12"): released on Teldec (Import), Mar'86

D. Lenny & Tommy

EVERYTHING BAMBOO.
Tracks: / Everything bamboo / Everything bamboo (club music edit) / Everything bamboo (dub music edit).
Single (7"): released on Magnetic Dance, May'87 by Magnetic Dance Records. Dist: BMG

Single (12"): released on Magnetic Dance, May'87 by Magnetic Dance Records. Dist: BMG

D, Longsy

HIP HOP REGGAE (D, Longsy & Cutmaster M.C.).
Single (7"): released on Big One, Aug'87 Dist: Jetstar, Marcus Distribution, PRT

Single (12"): released on Big One, Aug'87 Dist: Jetstar, Marcus Distribution, PRT

Dmochowski, Jedrez

SHA-LA-LA-LA.
Single (7"): released on Whaam, Nov'83 Dist: Pinnacle

STALLIONS OF MY HEART.
Album: released on Whaam, Jul'82 Dist: Pinnacle

DNA

ATLANTIC FLYER.
Single (7"): released on DNA, Jul'82

PARTY TESTED.
Album: released on Polydor, Feb'84 by Polydor Records. Dist: Polygram, Polydor Deleted '85.

Cassette: released on Polydor, Feb'84 by Polydor Records. Dist: Polygram, Polydor

ROAD TO HONG KONG.
Single (7"): released on DNA, Nov'82

TASTE OF DNA, A ep.
Single (12"): released on Rough Trade, Aug'81 by Rough Trade Records. Dist: Rough Trade Distribution, Cartel Distribution

Do7 Shirati...

KENYAFRICA (VOL.4) (Do7 Shirati Luo Jazz Orchestra).
Album: released on Playasound, '74 Dist: Conifer, Discovery

Do'a

ANCIENT BEAUTY.
Compact disc: released on Philo (USA), Dec'86

BLOODIED BUT UNBOWED.
Album: released on Alternative Tentacles, Feb'84 by Alternative Tentacles Records. Dist: Rough Trade, Pinnacle

COMPANIONS OF THE CRIMSON COLOURED ARK.
Compact disc: released on Philo (USA), Dec'86

DON'T TURN YOUR BACK(ON DESPERATE TIMES).
Single (12"): released on Alternative Tentacles, Mar'85 by Alternative Tentacles Records. Dist: Rough Trade, Pinnacle

POSITIVELY D.O.A.(EP).
Single (7"): released on Alternative Tentacles, Feb'82 by Alternative Tentacles Records. Dist: Rough Trade, Pinnacle

WAR ON 45.
Album: released on Alternative Tentacles, May'84 by Alternative Tentacles Records. Dist: Rough Trade, Pinnacle

Dobson, Anita

ANYONE CAN FALL IN LOVE (Dobson, Anita & The Simon May Orchestra.).
Tracks: / Anyone can fall in love / Eastenders/Theme / Variation on the theme /Julia's theme.
Notes: Extra track on 12" version only:- Variation on the theme/Julia's theme.
Single (7"): released on BBC, Aug'86 by BBC Records & Tapes. Dist: EMI, PRT, Pye

Single (12"): released on BBC, Aug'86 by BBC Records & Tapes. Dist: EMI, PRT, Pye

ON MY OWN.

ON MY OWN.
Tracks: / All in the air.
Album: released on Telstar, Oct'86 by Telstar Records. Dist: RCA Distribution

Compact disc: released on Telstar, Jul'87 by Telstar Records. Dist: RCA Distribution

Cassette: released on Telstar, Oct'86 by Telstar Records. Dist: RCA Distribution

TALKING OF LOVE.
Tracks: / Talking of love / Sweet walkin'.
Single (7"): released on Parlophone, Jul'87 by EMI Records. Dist: EMI

Single (12"): released on Parlophone, Jul'87 by EMI Records. Dist: EMI

Picture disc single: released on Parlophone, Jul'87 by EMI Records. Dist: EMI

Dobson, Bonnie

ABSENCE OF ROMANCE.
Single (7"): released on Ritz, Feb'83 by Outlet Records. Dist: Outlet, Prism Leisure Distribution, Record Services Distribution (Ireland), Roots

WATER IS WIDE.
Single (7"): released on Cara, Dec'84 Dist: Spartan, Roots, Folksound

Dobson, Dobby

SEEMS TO ME.
Single (12"): released on Music Works, Jan'83 Dist: Jetstar Distribution

SWEET DREAMS.
Album: released on Sarge, Aug'84 by Sarge Records. Dist: Jetstar

SWEETHEART.
Single (7"): released on Top Ranking, Oct'82

TO ALL THE GIRLS I'VE LOVED BEFORE.
Single (12"): released on Capo, Sep'84 by Capo Records. Dist: Jetstar

Docherty, Con

CINEMA ORGAN ENCORES.
Album: released on Deroy, Jun'81 by Deroy Records. Dist: Jazz Music, Swift

CINEMA ORGAN FAVOURITES.
Album: released on Deroy, Jun'81 by Deroy Records. Dist: Jazz Music, Swift

CINEMA ORGAN FAVOURITES.

Docherty, Terry

TELLER OF TALES, THE.
Album: released on Follside, Jul'77 by Follside Records. Dist: Roots, Jazz Music, Celtic Music, Projection

TERRY DOCHERTY COLLECTION, THE.
Cassette: released on Lake, Oct'80 by Lake Recordings. Dist: Jazz Music, Follside

Doc, John

JOHN DOC AT THE CAROUSEL.
Album: released on Nevis, Jan'79 Dist: H.R. Taylor

Doctor

BABY WHEN THE NIGHT.
Single (7"):

Doctor Alimantado

BEST DRESSED CHICKEN IN TOWN, THE.
Tracks: / Gimme mi gun / Plead I cause / Poison flour / Ride on / Just the other day / Best dressed chicken in town / Unitone skank.
Compact disc: released on Keyman, Feb'87 by Keyman Records. Dist: Keyman, Revolver

BORN FOR A PURPOSE.
Single (7"): released on Greensleeves, May'78 by Greensleeves Records. Dist: BMG, Jetstar, Spartan

IN THE MIX.
Album: released on Keyman, May'85 by Keyman Records. Dist: Keyman, Revolver

IN THE MIX/PART 2.
Album: released on Keyman, May'86 by Keyman Records. Dist: Keyman, Revolver

JUDGEMENT DAY.
Single (12"): released on Keyman, Dec'84 by Keyman Records. Dist: Keyman, Revolver

KINGS BREAD.

Album: released on Ital Sounds, Jul'86 Dist: Revolver, Cartel

KINGS BREAD DUB.
Album: released on Keyman, Jun'87 by Keyman Records. Dist: Keyman, Revolver

KING'S DEAD.
Cassette: released on ISCA, Jun'87

LOVE IS.
Single (7"): released on Keynote, Nov'83 by Keynote Records. Dist: Cartel

NO MORE HEARTACHES.
Tracks: / No more heartaches / Zion gates.
Single (12"): released on Keyman, May'87 by Keyman Records. Dist: Keyman, Revolver

REGGAE REVIEW part 1.
Album: released on Keyman, Mar'85 by Keyman Records. Dist: Keyman, Revolver

SONS OF THUNDER.
Album: released on Greensleeves, Jul'81 by Greensleeves Records. Dist: BMG, Jetstar, Spartan

WONDERFUL TIME.
Tracks: / Wonderful time.
Single (12"): released on Keyman, Nov'86 by Keyman Records. Dist: Keyman, Revolver

Doctor at Large

DOCTOR AT LARGE Gordon, R (Nedweel, Robin).
Cassette: released on Chivers Audio Books, Oct'81 by Chivers Sound & Vision. Dist: Chivers Sound & Vision

Doctor Buzzards

DOCTOR BUZZARDS ORIGINAL SAVANNAH BAND.
Album: released on RCA (Special Imports Service), Jul'84

Doctor Calculus

DESIGNER BEATNIK.
Tracks: / Blasted with ecstasy / Programme 7. / Moments of being / Killed by poetry / Man / Dream machine/ Candyfloss pink/ Just another honey / Designer Beatnik / Perfume from spain..
Album: released on 10, Aug'86 by 10 Records. Dist: Virgin, EMI

Cassette: released on 10, Aug'86 by 10 Records. Dist: Virgin, EMI

PERFUME FROM SPAIN.
Tracks: / Perfume form Spain / Straight stereo..
Single (7"): released on 10, Jun'86 by 10 Records. Dist: Virgin, EMI

Single (12"):

PROGRAMME 7.
Single (7"): released on 10, Dec'84 by 10 Records. Dist: Virgin, EMI Deleted '86.

Single (12"): released on 10, Dec'84 by 10 Records. Dist: Virgin, EMI

Doctor Feelgood

BE SEEING YOU.
Album: released on United Artists, Sep'77

CASE HISTORY - THE BEST OF DR. FEELGOOD.
Tracks: / Going back home / Back in the night / Roxette / She does it right / Sneakin' suspicion / No Mo Do Yakomo / She's a windup / As long as the price is right / Down at the doctor's / Milk and alcohol / Violent love / Jumping from love to love / Best in the world / Rat race / Close but no cigar / Play dirty / Don't wait up / See you later alligator.
Notes: A brand new 18 track compilation featuring material throughout their career including tracks from their albums on Stiff and Demon. From their beginnings in the punk era, the Feelgoods have been a strong influential rock band churning out classics such as "Milk and Alcohol" and "Down at the Doctors". The band is still very much alive today, with a new album, backed by singles, being released on Stiff Records in the summer. Here for the first time, the best of Dr. Feelgood from over a decade of solid rock music (1975-86) - a must for their mass following and those just joining the ranks.
Compact disc: released on Emus, Apr'87 by Emus Records. Dist: Swift

CASE OF THE SHAKES, A.
Tracks: / Jumping from love to love / Going some place else / Beat in the world / Punch drunk / King for a day / Violent love / No Mo Do Yakamo / Love hound / Coming to you / Who's winning / Drives me wild / Case of the shakes.
Album: released on Demon, Jul'86 by Demon Records. Dist: Pinnacle

CASE OF THE SHAKES , A.
Album: released on United Artists, Sep'80

Cassette: released on United Artists, Sep'80

CRAZY ABOUT GIRLS.
Single (7"): released on Chiswick, Mar'83 by Chiswick Records. Dist: Pinnacle

DON'T WAIT UP.
Tracks: / Don't wait up / Something good.
Single (7"): released on Stiff, Aug'86 by Stiff Records. Dist: EMI, Record Services Distribution (Ireland)

Single (12"): released on Stiff, Aug'86 by Stiff Records. Dist: EMI, Record Services Distribution (Ireland)

DOWN BY THE JETTY.
Album: released on Familiar, May'82 by Familiar Records. Dist: Projection

Cassette: released on Fame (United Artists), May'82 by Music For Pleasure Records. Dist: EMI

Album: released on Fame (United Artists), May'82 by Music For Pleasure Records. Dist: EMI

Album: released on Edsel, Sep'85 by Demon Records. Dist: Pinnacle, Jazz Music, Projection

FAST WOMEN AND SLOW HORSES.
Album: released on Chiswick, Oct'82 by Chiswick Records. Dist: Pinnacle

HUNTING SHOOTING FISHING.
Tracks: / Hunting shooting fishing / Big enough / Don't underestimate your enemy.
Single (7"): released on Stiff, May'87 by Stiff Records. Dist: EMI, Record Services Distribution (Ireland)

Single (12"): released on Stiff, May'87 by Stiff Records. Dist: EMI, Record Services Distribution (Ireland)

LET IT ROLL.
Album: released on United Artists, Sep'79
             Cat. no: UAG 30269
Cassette: released on United Artists, Sep'79

MAD MAN BLUES.
Album: released on I.D., Oct'85 by I.D. Records. Dist: Revolver, Cartel

MALPRACTICE.

MY WAY.
Single (7"): released on Demon, Dec'84 by Demon Records. Dist: Pinnacle

PRIVATE PRACTICE.
Album: released on United Artists, Sep'78

SEE YOU LATER ALLIGATOR.
Tracks: / See you later alligator / I love you so you're mine.
Single (7"): released on Stiff, Nov'86 by Stiff Records. Dist: EMI, Record Services Distribution (Ireland)

Single (12"): released on Stiff, Nov'86 by Stiff Records. Dist: EMI, Record Services Distribution (Ireland)

SNEAKIN' SUSPICION.
Tracks: / Sneakin' suspicion / Paradise / Nothin' shakin' (but the leaves on the trees) / Time & the devil / Lights out / Lucky seven / All my love / You'll be mine / Walking on the edge / Hey mama keep your mouth shut.
Album: released on Fame, May'87 by Music For Pleasure Records. Dist: EMI

Cassette: released on Fame, May'87 by Music For Pleasure Records. Dist: EMI

STUPIDITY.
Album: released on United Artists, Sep'76
             Cat. no: UAS 29990
Album: released on Liberty, Aug'85 by Liberty-United. Dist: EMI

Cassette: released on Liberty, Aug'85 by Liberty-United. Dist: EMI

TRYING TO LIVE MY LIFE WITHOUT YOU.
Single (7"): released on Chiswick, Aug'82 by Chiswick Records. Dist: Pinnacle

WHAT'S UP DOC (Doctor Feelgood & the Interns).
Album: released on Edsel, Jan'84 by Demon Records. Dist: Pinnacle, Jazz Music, Projection

Doctor Filth
HORSE.
Single (7"): released on Monsters In Orbit, Mar'82 by Rough Trade Distribution

Doctor Heavy
DOCTOR HEAVY.
Single (7"): released on Swoop, Mar'83 Dist: Le Matt Music Distribution

Single (7"): released on Switch, Mar'83 Dist: Backs, Cartel Distribution

Doctor Hook
COLLECTION: DOCTOR HOOK.
Album: released on EMI (Germany), '83 by EMI Records. Dist: Conifer

DOCTOR HOOK'S GREATEST HITS.
Album: released on Capitol, Nov'80 by Capitol Records. Dist: EMI

Cassette: released on Capitol, Nov'80 by Capitol Records. Dist: EMI

GIRLS CAN GET IT.
Album: released on Karussell Gold (Germany), Aug'85

Cassette: released on Karussell Gold (Germany), Aug'85

GREATEST HITS:DOCTOR HOOK And more.
Tracks: / Sylvia's mother / Cover of the Rolling Stone (The) / Only sixteen / Little bit more / A Walk right in / Make love and music / I couldn't believe / Couple more years, A / Sharing the night together / When you're in love with a beautiful woman / Better love next time / Sexy eyes / Years from now / Radio (The) / Sweetest of all.
Compact disc: released on Capitol, Apr'87 by Capitol Records. Dist: EMI

LITTLE BIT MORE, A.
Tracks: Little bit more, A / When you're in love with a beautiful woman.
Notes: Also contains:"When you're in love with a beautiful woman" by Doctor Hook
Single (7"): released on Old Gold, Apr'87 by Old Gold Records. Dist: Lightning, Jazz Music, Spartan, Counterpoint

Album: released on Fame (Capitol), Sep'84 by Music For Pleasure Records. Dist: EMI

Cassette: released on Fame (Capitol), Sep'84 by Music For Pleasure Records. Dist: EMI

Single (7"): released on Capitol, May'76 by Capitol Records. Dist: EMI

LIVE IN THE U.K.
Album: released on Music For Pleasure, Jan'85 by EMI Records. Dist: EMI

Cassette: released on Music For Pleasure, Jan'85 by EMI Records. Dist: EMI

LOVELINE.
Single (7"): released on Mercury, May'82 by Phonogram Records. Dist: Polygram Distribution

MAKIN LOVE & MUSIC.
Cassette: released on Capitol, Oct'77 by Capitol Records. Dist: EMI

PLAYERS IN THE DARK.

PLAYING IN THE DARK.
Compact disc: by Phonogram Records. Dist: Polygram Distribution

PLEASURE & PAIN.
Album: released on Capitol, '85 by Capitol Records. Dist: EMI

Album: released on Capitol, '85 by Capitol Records. Dist: EMI

SOMETIMES YOU WIN.
Album: released on Fame (Capitol), May'82 by Music For Pleasure Records. Dist: EMI

Cassette: released on Fame (Capitol), May'82 by Music For Pleasure Records. Dist: EMI

SYLVIA'S MOTHER.
Album: released on CBS, Nov'81 by CBS Records. Dist: CBS

Cassette: released on CBS, Nov'81 by CBS Records. Dist: CBS

Album: released on Hallmark, Apr'84 by Pickwick Records. Dist: Pickwick Distribution, PRT, Taylors

Cassette: released on Hallmark, Apr'84 by Pickwick Records. Dist: Pickwick Distribution, PRT, Taylors

SYLVIAS MOTHER (Doctor Hook & the Medicine Show).
Single (7"): released on Old Gold, Apr'83 by Old Gold Records. Dist: Lightning, Jazz Music, Spartan, Counterpoint

WHEN YOU'RE IN LOVE WITH A BEAUTIFUL WOMAN.
Tracks: / When you're in love with a beautiful woman / Little bit more, A.
Notes: Also contains:"A little bit more" by Doctor Hook
Single (7"): released on Old Gold, Apr'87 by Old Gold Records. Dist: Lightning, Jazz Music, Spartan, Counterpoint

Single (7"): released on EMI Golden 45's, May'84 by EMI Records. Dist: EMI

Doctor Jekyll & Mr Hyde
DOCTOR JEKYLL & MR. HYDE Stevenson,Robert Louis (Baker, Tom).
Album: released on Argo, Apr'79 by Decca Records. Dist: Polygram

Cassette: released on Pickwick Talking Books, Oct'81

Doctor John
BRIGHTEST SMILE IN TOWN, THE.
Album: released on Demon, Nov'83 by Demon Records. Dist: Pinnacle

DR.JOHN PLAYS MAC REBENNACK.
Album: released on Demon, Sep'82 by Demon Records. Dist: Pinnacle

I BEEN HOODOOD.
Album: released on Edsel, Apr'84 by Demon Records. Dist: Pinnacle, Jazz Music, Projection

IN THE NIGHT.
Album: released on Topline, Jan'85 by Charly Records. Dist: Charly Distribution

Cassette: released on Topline, Jan'85 by Charly Records. Dist: Charly Distribution

LOSER FOR YOU BABY.
Album: released on Fontana Import, Oct'82 by Phonogram Records. Dist: Polygram

Cassette: released on Fontana Import, Oct'82 by Phonogram Records. Dist: Polygram

MACK REBENNACK/BRIGHTEST SMILE IN TOWN.
Cassette: released on Demon, Feb'86 by Demon Records. Dist: Pinnacle

NEARNESS OF YOU.
Single (7"): released on Demon, Sep'82 by Demon Records. Dist: Pinnacle

ROADHOUSE SYMPHONY (Doctor John & Hank Crawford).
Notes: For full information see under Crawford, Hank & Doctor John.
Album: released on Fantasy (USA), Feb'86 by Fantasy Inc USA Records. Dist: IMS, Polygram

ROADHOUSE SYMPHONY (Doctor John & Hank Crawford).

SUCH A NIGHT. LIVE IN LONDON.
Album: released on Spindrift, Jun'84 Dist: Roots

Cassette: released on Spindrift, Jun'84 Dist: Roots

TAKE ME BACK TO NEW ORLEANS (Doctor John & Chris Barber).
Album: released on Black Lion, Feb'83 by Black Lion Records. Dist: Jazz Music, Chris Wellard, Taylor, H.R., Counterpoint, Cadillac

ZU ZU MAN.
Tracks: / Cat and mouse game / She just a square / Bald headed / In the night / Helpin' hand / Zu zu man / Mean cheatin' woman / Woman's the root of all evil / Trader John / Shoo-ra / Tipatina / One night late.
Notes: Licensed from Charly International APS. This cd (P) 1987 Charly Holdings Ltd (C) Charly Records Ltd y
Compact disc: released on Topline, Apr'87 by Charly Records. Dist: Charly Distribution

Doctor J.R Cool
COMPLETE STORY OF... (Doctor J.R Cool & the other Roxannes).
Album: released on PRT, Aug'85 by PRT Records. Dist: PRT

Doctor Mix
I CAN'T CONTROL MYSELF.
Single (7"): released on Roke, '79 Dist: Roke Distribution

NO FUN.
Single (7"): released on Rough Trade, Jun'79 by Rough Trade Records. Dist: Rough Trade Distribution, Cartel Distribution

WALL OF NOISE.
Album: released on Rough Trade, '84 by Rough Trade Records. Dist: Rough Trade Distribution, Cartel Distribution

Doctor No
DOCTOR NO original soundtrack (Doctor No/Monty Norman).
Album: released on EMI Golden 45's, '83 by EMI Records. Dist: EMI

Doctor on approval
DOCTOR ON APPROVAL McConnell, Jean (McConnell, Jean).
Double cassette: released on Soundings, Mar'85 Dist: Soundings

Doctor Pablo
NORTH OF THE RIVER THAMES (Doctor Pablo & Dub Syndicate).
Album: released on On-U-Sound, Apr'84 Dist: Rough Trade Distribution, Lightning

Doctor Ross
CAT SQUIRREL.
Single (7"): released on Backs, Mar'84 by Backs Records. Dist: Backs, Cartel

Harmonica blues, The

HARMONICA BOSS.
Album: released on Big Bear, Oct'86 by Big Bear Records. Dist: Big Bear, Swift

HARMONICA MAN, THE.
Album: released on Big Bear, '82 by Big Bear Records. Dist: Big Bear, Swift

HIS FIRST RECORDING.
Compact disc single: released on Arhoolie, May'81 by Arhoolie Records. Dist: Projection, Topic, Jazz Music, Swift, Roots

JIVIN' THE BLUES.
Album: released on Bilabel, Sep'79

ONE MAN BAND.
Album: released on Sonet (Takoma USA), Jul'81 by Sonet Records. Dist: PRT

Doctors Children
GIRL WITH GREEN EYES.
Tracks: / Girl with green eyes / Harvest moon / Iam the son / Two fat men.
Single (12"): released on Buffalo (UK), Jun'87

KING BUFFALO.
Album: released on Upright, Mar'87 by Upright Records. Dist: Cartel, Rough Trade

ROSE COTTAGE EP.
Tracks: / Rose cottage, The / Me-Sept 24th 1983 / When I was young / Blessed is the man.
Single (12"): released on Upright, Jun'86 by Upright Records. Dist: Cartel, Rough Trade

Doctor's Mob
HEADACHE MACHINE.
Album: released on One Big Guitar, Jul'86 by One Big Guitar Records. Dist: Revolver Distribution, Cartel Distribution, Pinnacle

Doctor Sting
BREAKING UP LOVE (Doctor Sting & Thinnerone).
Single (12"): released on Lucky, Sep'82 by Lucky Records.

Doctor Strut
DOCTOR STRUT.
Album: released on Motown, Oct'81 by Motown Records. Dist: BMG Distribution

STRUTTIN.
Album: released on Motown, Oct'81 by Motown Records. Dist: BMG Distribution

Single (7"): released on Motown, Oct'81 by Motown Records. Dist: BMG Distribution

Doctor Sushine
SUNNY SONGS FOR CHILDREN.
Album: released on Kettle, Nov'83 Dist: Folksound, Celtic Music, MK

Doctor & the Medics
2 PIECES OF CLOTH CAREFULLY STICHED TOGETHER.
Single (12"): released on Illegal, May'87 by Faulty Products Records. Dist: Pinnacle, Lightning, Cartel

BURN.
Tracks: / Burn / Captain Freeze / Love, Peace and Bananas / Paranoid.
Single (7"): released on IRS, Jul'86 Dist: Polygram

Single (12"): released on IRS, Jul'86 Dist: Polygram

DRUIDS AR EHERE.
Single (7"): released on Whaam, Aug'82 Dist: Pinnacle

HAPPY BUT TWISTED.
Single (12"): released on I.R.S. (Independent Record Syndicate), May'85 by I.R.S.. Dist: MCA

LAUGHING AT THE PIECES.
Tracks: / No one loves you when you got no shoes / Kettle on a long chain / Come on call me / Watermelon runaway / Fried egg bad Monday / Spirit in the sky / Lucky Lord Jim / Moon song / Barbara can't dance / Smallness of the mustard pot.
Notes: Limited edition picture disc.
Compact disc: by I.R.S.. Dist: MCA

Album: released on IRS, Jul'86 Dist: Polygram

Cassette: released on IRS, Jul'86 Dist: Polygram

Picture disc album: released on IRS, Jul'86 Dist: Polygram

MIRACLE OF THE AGE, THE.
Single (7"): released on I.R.S.(Independent Record Syndicate), Oct'85 by I.R.S.. Dist: MCA

MORE.
Tracks: / Pretty little Henry.
Single (7"): released on I.R.S.(Independent Record Syndicate), Aug'87 by I.R.S.. Dist: MCA

SPIRIT IN THE SKY.
Tracks: / Spirit in the sky / Laughing at the pieces / Love, Peace and Bananas/Live. / Fried egg bad Monday/Live. / Good golly Miss Molly/Live.
Single (7"): released on IRS, Apr'86 Dist: Polygram

Single (12"): released on IRS, Apr'86 Dist: Polygram

WATERLOO.
Tracks: / Waterloo / Damaged Brains / Stare crazy / Nothing.
Single (7"): released on IRS, Nov'86 Dist: Polygram

Single (12"): released on IRS, Nov'86 Dist: Polygram

Doctor Who

DOCTOR WHO Music from the T.V series.
Album: released on BBC, Mar'83 by BBC Records & Tapes. Dist: EMI, PRT,

Cassette: released on BBC, Mar'83 by BBC Records & Tapes. Dist: EMI, PRT

DOCTOR WHO AND THE PESCATONS (Doctor Who and the Pescatons).
Album: released on Argo, Apr'85 by Decca Records. Dist: Polygram

Cassette: released on Argo, Apr'85 by Decca Records. Dist: Polygram

DOCTOR WHO (SOUND EFFECTS).
Album: released on BBC, '79 by BBC Records & Tapes. Dist: EMI, PRT

GENESIS OF THE DALEKS Doctor Who.
Album: released on BBC, '78 by BBC Records & Tapes. Dist: EMI, PRT,

Cassette: released on BBC, Sep'79 by BBC Records & Tapes. Dist: EMI, PRT,

Doctor York

NEW.
Album: released on Spartan, Nov'85 by Spartan Records. Dist: Spartan

Cassette: released on Spartan, Nov'85 by Spartan Records. Dist: Spartan

SHAKE 'N' SKATE.
Single (7"): released on Groove PR, Sep'81 by Beggars Banquet Records. Dist: WEA, PRT

Single (12"): released on Groove PR, Sep'81 by Beggars Banquet Records. Dist: WEA, PRT

Doctor Zhivago

DOCTOR ZHIVAGO (Schofield, Paul).
Cassette: released on Listen For Pleasure, Dec'79 by MFP Records. Dist: EMI

DOCTOR ZHIVAGO (Various Artists).
Tracks: / Overture from DR Zhivago / Main title / Lara leaves Yuri / At the student cafe / Komarovsky and Lara's Rendezvous / Revolution / Tonya arrives at Varykino / Yuri writes a poem for Lara.
Compact disc: released on CBS, Mar'87 by CBS Records. Dist: CBS

Album: released on CBS, Jul'86 by CBS Records. Dist: CBS

Cassette: released on CBS, Jul'86 by CBS Records. Dist: CBS

Dodd, Billy

DOCTOR BILLY DODD & FRIENDS.
Notes: Butterfield, J. Mince, Trummy Young, Lesberg.
Album: released on Jazzology, Feb'87 Dist: Jazz Music, Swift

Dodd, Doctor Billy

DODD, DOCTOR BILLY & HIS FRIENDS (Dodd, Doctor Billy & His Friends).
Notes: Friends include: Billy Buterfield/Johnny Mince/Trummy Young/Jack Lesberg/ Ed Graham.
Album: released on Jazzology, Jun'86 Dist: Jazz Music, Swift

Dodd, Jegsy

ALWAYS THE BRIDESMAID (Dodd, Jegsy & The Sons Of Harry Cross).
Tracks: / Always the bridesmaid / 8,000 miles away / Jewel in the flat cap, The.
Single (12"): released on Probe Plus, 20 Jun'87 by Probe Plus Records. Dist: Probe Plus Distribution

Dodd, Ken

20 GOLDEN GREATS OF KEN DODD.
Album: released on Warwick, Nov'80 Dist: Multiple Sound Distributors

GREATEST HITS:KEN DODD.
Tracks: / Happiness / Love is like a violin / Somewhere my love / River, The / Eight by ten / They didn't believe me / As time goes by / I wish you love / More than ever / So deep is the night / Tears / Still / Broken-Hearted / She / Old fashioned way, The / For all we know / What a wonderful world / Happy days and lonely nights / Just out of reach / Let me cry on your shoulder / Promises.
Album: released on Hour Of Pleasure, Oct'86 by Music For Pleasure Records. Dist: EMI

HAPPY MOTORING.
Cassette: released on Mobile Fidelity, '78 by Mobile Fidelity Records.

HOLD MY HAND.
Single (7"): released on Images, Nov'81 by MSD Records. Dist: PRT

IT'S NO SECRET (Dodd, Ken & Dana).
Single (7"): released on Warwick, Dec'80 Dist: Multiple Sound Distributors

KEN DODD.
Cassette: released on Ideal(Tapes), Jun'81 Dist: EMI

LITTLE WORDS.
Single (7"): released on Ritz, Nov'84 by Outlet Records. Dist: Outlet, Prism Leisure Distribution, Record Services Distribution (Ireland), Roots

MORE THAN EVER.
Album: released on MFP, Oct'81 by EMI Records. Dist: EMI. Estim retail price in Jul'87 was £2.25.

Cassette: released on MFP, Oct'81 by EMI Records. Dist: EMI

NOW AND FOREVER.
Album: released on VIP, Dec'83 Dist: Jetstar Distribution

Single (7"): released on PRT, Feb'84 by PRT Records. Dist: PRT

Single (7"): released on PRT, Feb'84 by PRT Records. Dist: PRT

TEARS.
Single (7"): released on Old Gold, Jul'82 by Old Gold Records. Dist: Lightning, Jazz Music, Spartan, Counterpoint

VERY BEST OF KEN DODD,THE.
Album: released on Music For Pleasure (Holland), Oct'83 by EMI Records. Dist: EMI

Cassette: released on Music For Pleasure, Oct'83 by EMI Records. Dist: EMI

Dodds, David

SPORTING DOGS.
Cassette: released on Folktracks, Nov'79 by Folktracks Cassettes. Dist: Folktracks

Dodds, Johnny

1926-28.
Album: released on Swaggie (Australia), Jan'83

1927 (Dodds, Johnny with his Trio).
Album: released on Swaggie (Australia), Jan'83

BLUE CLARINET STOMP 1926-1928.
Tracks: / Weary blues / New Orleans Stomp / Wild man blues / Melancholy / Come on & stomp,stomp,stomp / After you've gone / Joe Turner blues / When Erastus plays his old kazoo / Blue clarinet stomp / Blue piano stomp / Bucktown stomp / Weary city / Bull fiddle blues / Blue washboard stomp / Sweet Lorraine A / Pencil papa / My little Isabel-A / Heah' me talking / Goober dance / Too tight-A.
Notes: Johnny Dodds' Black Bottom Stompers,Trio,Washboard Band & Orchestra
Album: released on VJM, Mar'87 by Wellard, Chris Distribution. Dist: Wellard, Chris Distribution

GREAT ORIGINAL PERFORMANCES 1923-29.
Notes: Jazz Classics in Digial Sterio: What Australian Robert Parker has succeeded in achieving- with remarkable results is to give a whole new dimesion to some of the greatest music recorded.
Album: released on BBC, Oct'86 by BBC Records & Tapes. Dist: EMI, PRT,

Cassette: released on BBC, Oct'86 by BBC Records & Tapes. Dist: EMI, PRT,

IMMORTAL, THE.
Album: released on VJM, Mar'83 by Wellard, Chris Distribution. Dist: Wellard, Chris Distribution

STOMP TIME.
Album: released on Rhapsody, Apr'83 by President Records. Dist: Taylors, Swift, Jazz Music, Wellard, Chris

VOL 1.
Album: released on Classic Jazz Masters, Dec'86 by Mainline Record Company. Dist: Mainline, Swift, Jazz Music

Dodds, Pete

CARDBOARD CITY.
Single (7"): released on Button, Aug'83 by Musical Characters Records. Dist: Spartan

Dodge, Jim

F U P.
Cassette: released on Caedmon(USA), Apr'85 by Caedmon (USA) Records. Dist: Gower, Taylors, Discovery

Dodie, Smith

101 DALMATIONS, THE (read by Joanna Lumley).
Cassette: released on Listen For Pleasure, '83 by MFP Records. Dist: EMI

Dodo Wop

DODO WOP various artists (Various Artists).
Album: released on Special Agent, '73 Dist: Black Grape

Dog Crusoe

DOG CRUSOE (Boland, Arthur).
Cassette: released on Colophone, Nov'81 by Audio-Visual Library Services. Dist: Audio-Visual Library Services

Dog Faced Hermans

UNBEND.
Tracks: / Unbend.
Single (7"): released on Demon Radge, Mar'87 Dist: Fast Forward, Cartel

Doggett, Bill

16 BANDSTAND FAVOURITES.
Album: released on Starday, Apr'87

Cassette: released on Starday, Apr'87

GON' DOGGETT.
Album: released on Charly(R&B), Jul'85 by Charly Records. Dist: Charly, Cadillac

Cassette: released on Charly(R&B), Jul'85 by Charly Records. Dist: Charly, Cadillac

HONKY TONK part 1.
Single (7"): released on Creole, Aug'82 by Creole Records. Dist: Rhino, PRT

MR. HONKY TONK.
Notes: Mono.
Album: released on Black & Blue RCA (France), Nov'85 by RCA Records. Dist: Discovery

Doggy Style

LAST LAUGH.
Notes: Free condom, lyric sheet sheet included.
Album: released on National Trust (USA), Aug'87

Dog It Was That Died

DOG IT WAS THAT DIED/DISSOLUTION OF DOMINIC BOOT (see Stoppard, Tom) (Various Artists).

Dogmatic Element

STRANGE PASSIONS.
Single (7"): released on Castle Co, Aug'82 by Menace Music Records. Dist: Menace Breaker Distributors

Dogmatics

EVERYBODY DOES IT.
Album: released on Homestead, Jun'86 Dist: Rough Trade, Cartel,

THAYER STREET.
Album: released on Homestead, Feb'85 Dist: Rough Trade, Cartel, Shigaku

Dogs

RUBBISH.
Single (7"): released on Eagle (West Germany), Aug'81 by Bear Family Records. Dist: Stage One

TOO MUCH CLASS FOR THE NEIGHBOURHOOD.
Album: released on Epic, Nov'82 by CBS Records. Dist: CBS

Dogwatch

PENFRIEND.
Album: released on Bridgehouse, Sep'79 Dist: Pinnacle

Doherty, Al

SEEING THE COUNTRY.
Album: released on Folk Heritage, Jul'82 by Folk Heritage Records. Dist: Roots, Wynd-Up Distribution, Jazz Music, Folk Heritage

Doherty, John

BUNDLE AND GO.
Album: released on Topic, '81 Dist: Roots Distribution

STAR OF DONEGAL, THE.
Cassette: released on Folktracks, Nov'79 by Folktracks Cassettes. Dist: Folktracks

Doherty, Michael

FIDDLER AND THE FAIRY, THE (Doherty, Michael & John).
Cassette: released on Folktracks, Nov'79 by Folktracks Cassettes. Dist: Folktracks

Do It fluid...

DO IT FLUID: 6 RARE GROOVES (Various Artists).
Album: released on BGP, Oct'87 by Ace Records. Dist: PRT. Estim retail price in Oct'87 was £5.67.

Dojoji

DOJOJI (Dojoji/Lesley Woods).
Album: released on Plexus (Holland), Feb'85

Dokken

BREAKIN' THE CHAINS.
Album: released on Carrere, May'82 by Carrere Records. Dist: PRT, Spartan

IN MY DREAMS.
Tracks: / In my dreams / Tell the living end / Alone again.
Notes: Track on 12" version only:- Alone again
Single (7"): released on Elektra (USA), Mar'86 by Elektra/Asylum/Nonesuch Records. Dist: WEA

Single (12"): released on Elektra (USA), Mar'86 by Elektra/Asylum/Nonesuch Records. Dist: WEA

TOOTH AND NAIL.
Album: released on Elektra (USA), Oct'84 by Elektra/Asylum/Nonesuch Records. Dist: WEA

UNDER LOCK AND KEY.
Tracks: / Unchain the night / Hunter, The / In my dreams / Slippin away / Lightnin strikes again / It's not love / Jaded heart / Don't lie to me / Will the sun rise / Til the livin end.
Cassette: released on Elektra (USA), Mar'86 by Elektra/Asylum/Nonesuch Records. Dist: WEA

Compact disc: released on Elektra (USA), Mar'86 by Elektra/Asylum/Nonesuch Records. Dist: WEA

Compact disc: by Elektra/Asylum/Nonesuch Records. Dist: WEA

Album: released on Elektra (USA), Mar'86 by Elektra/Asylum/Nonesuch Records. Dist: WEA

Dolang & The Twisters

20 TOP 20 TWISTS.
Album: released on See For Miles, Dec'84 by See For Miles Records. Dist: Pinnacle

Dolan, Joe

COME BACK HOME.
Single (7"): released on Ritz, Oct'84 by Outlet Records. Dist: Outlet, Prism Leisure Distribution, Record Services Distribution (Ireland), Roots

Single (12"): released on Ritz, Oct'84 by Outlet Records. Dist: Outlet, Prism Leisure Distribution, Record Services Distribution (Ireland), Roots

CRAZY WOMAN.
Album: released on Pye, Jan'77

I NEED YOU.
Album: released on Pye, Nov'77

IT'S ONLY MAKE BELIEVE.
Single (7"): released on Ritz, May'82 by Outlet Records. Dist: Outlet, Prism Leisure Distribution, Record Services Distribution (Ireland), Roots

IT'S YOU,IT'S YOU.
Single (7"): released on Ritz, Feb'83 by Outlet Records. Dist: Outlet, Prism Leisure Distribution, Record Services Distribution (Ireland), Roots

IT'S YOU,IT'S YOU,IT'S YOU(REMIX 85).
Single (7"): released on Ritz, Sep'85 by Outlet Records. Dist: Outlet, Prism Leisure Distribution, Record Services Distribution (Ireland), Roots

IT'S YOU, IT'S YOU, IT'S YOU..
Album: released on Ritz, May'86 by Outlet Records. Dist: Outlet, Prism Leisure Distribution, Record Services Distribution (Ireland), Roots

Cassette: released on Ritz, May'86 by Outlet Records. Dist: Outlet, Prism Leisure Distribution, Record Services Distribution (Ireland), Roots

LADY IN BLUE.
Album: released on Pye, Sep'75

MAKE ME AN ISLAND.
Single (7"): released on Old Gold, Jul'82 by Old Gold Records. Dist: Lightning, Jazz Music, Spartan, Counterpoint

MORE & MORE.
Single (7"): released on Ritz, Jul'82 by Outlet Records. Dist: Outlet, Prism Leisure Distribution, Record Services Distribution (Ireland), Roots

TAKE ME I'M YOURS.
Tracks: / Take me I'm yours / Hang tough.
Single (7"): released on Ritz, May'86 by Outlet Records. Dist: Outlet, Prism Leisure Distribution, Record Services Distribution (Ireland), Roots

TURN OUT THE LIGHT.
Album: released on Pye, Feb'80

Dolby's Cube

GET OUT OF MY MIX.
Single (7"): released on Parlophone, Oct'83 by EMI Records. Dist: EMI

Single (12"): released on Parlophone, Oct'83 by EMI Records. Dist: EMI

HOWARD THE DUCK.
Tracks: / Howard the duck / Don't turn away.
Single (7"): released on MCA, Nov'86 by MCA Records. Dist: Polygram, MCA

Single (12"): released on MCA, Nov'86 by MCA Records. Dist: Polygram, MCA

MAY THE CUBE BE WITH YOU.
Single (7"): released on Parlophone, Jul'85 by EMI Records. Dist: EMI

Single (12"): released on Parlophone, Jul'85 by EMI Records. Dist: EMI

Single (12"): released on Parlophone Odeon, Aug'85 by EMI Records. Dist: EMI, EMI, YND

Dolby, Thomas

DEVIL IS AN ENGLISHMAN.
Tracks: / Devil is an Englishman, The / Fantasmagoria.
Single (7"): released on Virgin, Feb'87 by Virgin Records. Dist: EMI, Virgin Distribution

Single (12"): released on Virgin, Feb'87 by Virgin Records. Dist: EMI, Virgin Distribution

FLAT EARTH, THE.
Compact disc: by EMI Records. Dist: EMI

Album: released on Parlophone (Venice in Peril), Feb'84 by EMI. Dist: EMI

Cassette: released on Parlophone (Venice in Peril), Feb'84 by EMI. Dist: EMI

GOLDEN AGE OF WIRELESS, THE.
Tracks: / She blinded me with science / Radio silence / Airwaves / Flying North / Weightless / Europa and the pirate twins / Windpower / Commercial breakup / One of our submarines / Cloudburst at Shingle Street.
Notes: Thomas Dolby's first album recorede and released in 1982. Contains the hit single "She blinded me with science" which featured the T.V. science programme presenter Dr. Magnus Pike on Voiceovers.
Album: released on Fame, Jun'87 by Music For Pleasure Records. Dist: EMI

Cassette: released on Fame, Jun'87 by Music For Pleasure Records. Dist: EMI

Album: released on Venice In Peril, Aug'83 by Thomas Dolby. Dist: EMI

Cassette: released on Venice In Peril, Aug'83 by Thomas Dolby. Dist: EMI

LIVE WIRELESS.
Video-cassette (VHS): released on PMI, Jun'86 by PMI Records. Dist: EMI

Video-cassette [Betamax]: released on PMI, Jun'86 by PMI Records. Dist: EMI

RADIO SILENCE.
Single (7"): released on Venice In Peril, Apr'82 by Thomas Dolby. Dist: EMI

SHE BLINDED ME WITH SCIENCE.
Single (7"): released on Venice In Peril, Jun'83 by Thomas Dolby. Dist: EMI

Single (12"): released on Venice In Peril, Jun'83 by Thomas Dolby. Dist: EMI

URGES.
Single (7"): released on Armageddon, Feb'81 by Armageddon Records. Dist: Revolver, Cartel, Pinnacle

WINDPOWER.
Single (7"): released on Venice In Peril, Jul'82 by Thomas Dolby. Dist: EMI

Single (12"): released on Venice In Peril, Jul'82 by Thomas Dolby. Dist: EMI Deleted '85.

WINDPOWER.

Dolce, Joe

CHRISTMAS ALBUM, THE.
Album: released on Red Bus, Dec'82 by Red Bus Records. Dist: PRT Deleted '85.

Cassette: released on Red Bus, Dec'82 by Red Bus Records. Dist: PRT

CHRISTMAS AT OUR HOUSE.
Single (7"): released on Red Bus, Dec'81 by Red Bus Records. Dist: PRT

SHADDUP YOU FACE.
Album: released on Epic, Jun'81 by CBS Records. Dist: CBS

Cassette: released on Epic, Jun'81 by CBS Records. Dist: CBS

Doldinger, Klaus

BOAT.
Single (7"): released on WEA, May'82 by WEA Records. Dist: WEA

Dole

NEW WAVE LOVE.
Single (7"): released on Ultimate, Jun'81 by Ultimate Records. Dist: Spartan

RUMROAD.
Tracks: / Rumroad / Wreckaway, The.
Single (12"): released on Play It Again Sam, Nov'85 Dist: Red Rhino, Cartel

Single (7"): released on Play It Again Sam, Dec'85 Dist: Red Rhino, Cartel

SMALL TOWN.
Single (7"): Dist: Red Rhino, Cartel

SPEED OF HOPE.
Album: released on Play It Again Sam, Apr'86 Dist: Red Rhino, Cartel

Dollar

FLIPHITS (EP).
Cassette: released on Carrere, Jul'83 by Carrere Records. Dist: PRT, Spartan

GIVE ME BACK MY HEART.
Single (7"): released on WEA, Mar'82 by WEA Records. Dist: WEA

GIVE ME SOME KIND OF MAGIC.
Single (7"): released on WEA, Sep'82 by WEA Records. Dist: WEA

HAVEN'T WE SAID GOODBYE BEFORE.
Tracks: / Platinum.
Single (7"): released on Arista, Nov'86 by Arista Records. Dist: RCA

Single (12"): released on Arista, Nov'86 by Arista Records. Dist: RCA

LOVE'S GOT A HOLD ON ME.
Single (7"): released on Carrere, Jul'79 by Carrere Records. Dist: PRT, Spartan

OH, L'AMOUR.
Single (7"): released on London, Jul'87 by London Records. Dist: Polygram

Single (12"): released on London, Jul'87 by London Records. Dist: Polygram

RING RING.
Single (7"): released on Carrere, Feb'82 by Carrere Records. Dist: PRT, Spartan

SHOOTING STARS.
Album: released on Carrere, Jul'79 by Carrere Records. Dist: PRT, Spartan

Cassette: released on Carrere, Jul'79 by Carrere Records. Dist: PRT, Spartan

VERY BEST OF DOLLAR, THE.
Tracks: / Who were you with in the moonlight? / I need your love / Ring, ring / Love's gotta hold on me / Love street / Overture / Shooting star / Tokyo / Star control / I wanna hold your hand.
Album: released on Carrere, '82 by Carrere Records. Dist: PRT, Spartan

Cassette: released on Carrere, '82 by Carrere Records. Dist: PRT, Spartan

WALK IN LOVE.
Tracks: / Walk in love / Love tonight / If this is Love / Walk in love / Love tonight.
Notes: Extra tracks on 12" version only.

Single (7"): released on Arista, Jul'86 by Arista Records. Dist: RCA

Single (12"): released on Arista, Jul'86 by Arista Records. Dist: RCA

Single (7"): released on Arista, Jul'86 by Arista Records. Dist: RCA

Dollar Brand

AFRICAN DAWN.
Album: released on Enja (Germany), Sep'84 by Enja Records (W.Germany). Dist: Cadillac Music

ANTHEM FOR THE NEW NATIONS.
Tracks: / Anthem for the new nations / Biral / Liberation dance / Trial / Cape Town / Thabu nchu.
Compact disc: by Denon Records. Dist: Harmonia Mundi

CONFLUENCE (Dollar Brand & Gato Barbieri).

EKAYA (Dollar Brand(Abdullah Ibrahim)).
Tracks: / Ekaya / Sotho blue / Ntyilo, Ntyilo / Bra timing from Phomolong / Ek se ou windhoek toe nou / Cape Town.
Album: released on Ekapa (USA), Jul'84 by Ekapa Records. Dist: IMS, Polygram

LIVE AT MONTREUX.
Album: released on Enja (Germany), Sep'84 by Enja Records (W.Germany). Dist: Cadillac Music

LIVE AT SWEET BASIL (Dollar Brand(Abdullah Ibrahim)withCarlos Ward).
Tracks: / Dream, The / And find me a shelter in the storm / Mummy / For Coltrane II / New York City / Anthem for the new nations / Gwangwa / Theme from King Kong / Black lightning / Gwidza / Strides, The / Soweto.
Album: released on Ekapa (USA), Feb'85 by Ekapa Records. Dist: IMS, Polygram

This Is Dollar Brand

ZIMBABWE.
Album: released on Enja (Germany), Sep'84 by Enja Records (W.Germany). Dist: Cadillac Music

Doll By Doll

DOLL BY DOLL.
Album: released on Magnet, '83 by Magnet Records. Dist: BMG

Cassette: released on Magnet, '83 by Magnet Records. Dist: BMG

GRAND PASSION.
Album: released on Magnet, '83 by Magnet Records. Dist: BMG

Cassette: released on Magnet, '83 by Magnet Records. Dist: BMG

GYPSY BLOOD.
Album: released on Automatic, Oct'79 Dist: WEA, Independant

REMEMBER.
Album: released on Automatic, Mar'79 Dist: WEA, Independant

Cassette: released on Automatic, Mar'79 Dist: WEA, Independant

Dollie Deluxe

CARMEN.
Tracks: / Carmen / Gimme some lovin / Na.
Single (7"): released on Spartan, Mar'86 by Spartan Records. Dist: Spartan

Single (12"): released on Spartan, Mar'86 by Spartan Records. Dist: Spartan

ROCK V OPERA.
Album: released on Spartan, Dec'86 by Spartan Records. Dist: Spartan

Cassette: released on Spartan, Dec'86 by Spartan Records. Dist: Spartan

Compact disc: released on Nabo, Dec'86 Dist: MK

Cassette: released on Spartan, Dec'86 by Spartan Records. Dist: Spartan

Dollops

HERE COME THE DOLLOPS.
Single (7"): released on Peebly, Apr'80 Dist: Pinnacle

NOBODY LOVES YOU LIKE THE DOLLOPS DO.
Single (7"): released on Dollop, Feb'81 by Dollop Records. Dist: Pinnacle

Doll's House, A

DOLLS HOUSE, A Ibsen, Henrik (Bloom Claire).
Album: released on Caedmon(USA), '74 by Caedmon (USA) Records. Dist: Gower, Taylors, Discovery

Cassette: released on Caedmon(USA), '74 by Caedmon (USA) Records. Dist: Gower, Taylors, Discovery

Dolly Dots

DON'T GIVE UP.
Single (7"): released on WEA, Mar'84 by WEA Records. Dist: WEA

DO WAH DIDDY DIDDY.
Single (7"): released on WEA, Nov'82 by WEA Records. Dist: WEA

MONEY LOVER(BITE THE DUST).
Single (7"): released on WEA, Jul'83 by WEA Records. Dist: WEA

PS I LOVE YOU.
Single (7"): released on WEA, Jan'82 by WEA Records. Dist: WEA

Single (12"): released on WEA, Jan'82 by WEA Records. Dist: WEA

Dolly Mixtures

DEMONSTRATION TAPES-A DOUBLE ALBUM.
Double Album: released on Dead Good Dolly Platters, Dec'83

REMEMBER THIS.
Single (7"): released on Dead Good Dolly Platters, Jan'84

Dolmann

HIGH SEX DRIVE(REMIX).
Single (12"): released on Passion, Oct'84 by Skratch Records. Dist: PRT

Dolphin

HEY JOE.
Single (7"): released on Gale, Apr'80 by Gale Records. Dist: Spartan

Dolphin Brothers

CATCH THE FALL.
Album: released on Virgin, Jul'87 by Virgin Records. Dist: EMI, Virgin Distribution

Cassette: released on Virgin, Jul'87 by Virgin Records. Dist: EMI, Virgin Distribution

SECOND SIGHT.
Tracks: / Host to the holy.
Single (7"): released on Virgin, Aug'87 by Virgin Records. Dist: EMI, Virgin Distribution

Single (12"): released on Virgin, Aug'87 by Virgin Records. Dist: EMI, Virgin Distribution

SHINING.
Tracks: / Shining / My winter.
Single (7"): released on Virgin, Jun'87 by Virgin Records. Dist: EMI, Virgin Distribution

Single (12"): released on Virgin, Jun'87 by Virgin Records. Dist: EMI, Virgin Distribution

Dolphin Club

OUT OF THE BLUE.
Cassette: released on Move, Jun'86 by Charly Records. Dist: Charly Distribution, Fast Forward Distribution, Cartel Distribution

Dolphy, Eric

1961 (Dolphy, Eric Quartet).
Album:

3 DOLPHY GROUPS.
Notes: Previously unreleased including: Mel Lewis/Herbie Hancock.
Album: released on Unique Jazz, Nov'86 Dist: Swift, Jazz Music, Jazz Horizons

ARTISTRY IN JAZZ Greatest hits.
Compact disc: released on JVC Fantasy (Japan), May'87

AT THE FIVE SPOT, VOLUME 2..
Compact disc: released on Vanguard (USA), Apr'86

AT THE FIVE SPOT, VOLUME 1..
Compact disc: released on Vanguard (USA), Apr'86

BERLIN CONCERTS.
Album: released on Enja (Germany), Jan'82 by Enja Records (W.Germany). Dist: Cadillac Music

COLLECTION: ERIC DOLPHY.
Album: released on Deja Vu, Aug'86 by Deja Vu Records. Dist: Counterpoint Distribution, Record Services Distribution (Ireland)

Cassette: released on Deja Vu, Aug'86 by Deja Vu Records. Dist: Counterpoint Distribution, Record Services Distribution (Ireland)

ERIC DOLPHY QUARTET (1961) (with L.Schifrin/B.Cunningham/M.Lewis) (Dolphy, Eric Quartet).
Album: released on Jazz Connoisseur, Jun'81 Dist: Jazz Horizons, Jazz Music, Swift, Wellard, Chris

ESSENTIAL, THE.
Compact disc: released on Fantasy (USA), Apr'87 by Fantasy Inc USA Records. Dist: IMS, Polygram

LIVE AT GASLIGHT INN (Dolphy, Eric Quintet).
Album: released on Ingo, Jul'82 Dist: Jazz Horizons, Jazz Music, Celtic Music

LIVE AT THE FIVE SPOT II.
Album:

LOOKING AHEAD (Dolphy, Eric & Ken McIntyre).
Notes: For full information see under McIntyre, Ken & Eric Dolphy.

OTHER ASPECTS.
Tracks: / Jim Crow / Inner Flight I / Dolphy'n / Inner Flight II / Improvisations & Tukras.
Notes: Blue Note proudly announce the discovery & release of a variety of tapes from the private libary of the late,great Eric Dolphy.These recordings have been carefully remixed to digital tape for the best possible sound reproduction.This extraordinary find actually reveals three sides of the amazing reedman & composer. Jim Crow with a classical ensemble shows Dolphy's Previously unrecorded talents as a classical player & composer.'Improvisations & Tukras'is an authentic excursion into the music of India.His 2 unaccompanied flute solos"Inner Flight 1 & II"& his duet with bassist Ron Carter entitled "Dolphy'n"are masterful jazz improvisations.These diverse & exciting discoveries add a wealth to the legacy of an under-recorded genius who died all too young.This may be the FIND of the year.
Album: released on Blue Note, Mar'87 by EMI Records. Dist: EMI

OUT TO LUNCH.
Tracks: / Hat & bread / Something sweet,something tender / Gazzelloni / Out to lunch / Straight up and down / Hat and bread / Something sweet / Something tender / Gazzellioni.
Album: released on Blue Note, Nov'85 by EMI Records. Dist: EMI

Compact disc: released on Blue Note, Jun'87 by EMI Records. Dist: EMI

Cassette: released on Blue Note, Sep'87 by EMI Records. Dist: EMI. Estim retail price in Sep'87 was £5.99.

Quest, The

QUINTET U.S.A..
Tracks: / Miss Ann / Left alone / G.W. / 2.45.
Album: released on Unique Jazz, Apr'81 Dist: Swift, Jazz Music, Jazz Horizons

STOCKHOLM SESSIONS.
Album: released on Enja (Germany), Jan'82 by Enja Records (W.Germany). Dist: Cadillac Music

USA (Dolphy, Eric Quintet).
Album: released on Unique Jazz, Nov'86 Dist: Swift, Jazz Music, Jazz Horizons

Dome

WILL YOU SPEAK THIS WORD.
Album: released on Uniton Records, Sep'84 Dist: Cartel

Domestos

TEN COMMANDMENTS.
Single (7"): released on Button, Nov'84 by Musical Characters Records. Dist: Spartan

Domestos, Johnny

TEN COMMANDMENTS, THE.
Single (7"): released on Button, Jul'84 by Musical Characters Records. Dist: Spartan

Domingo, Belcanto

BELCANTO DOMINGO.
Tracks: / Calvalleria rusticana / Turandot / Lucia di Lammermoor / Un ballo in machera / Aida / Il travatore.
Notes: Nello Santi & German Opera Orchestra, Berlin. Grand Prix Du Disque winner. A collection of Arias from various operas.
Compact disc: released on Teldec, May'87

Cassette: released on Teldec, May'87

Album: released on Teldec, May'87

Domingo, Placido

ADORO.
Album: released on CBS(Masterworks), Jul'82 by CBS Records. Dist: CBS

Cassette: released on CBS(Masterworks), Jul'82 by CBS Records. Dist: CBS

CON AMORE.
Album: released on Red Seal, Jul'82 by RCA Records. Dist: RCA

Cassette: released on Red Seal, Jul'82 by RCA Records. Dist: RCA

HOSANNA/ FROM REQUIEM.
Tracks: / Hosanna/ From Requiem / Ingemisco.
Single (7"): released on H.M.V., Dec'85 by EMI Records. Dist: EMI

I COULDN'T LIVE WITHOUT YOU FOR A DAY.
Single (7"): released on CBS, Apr'83 by CBS Records. Dist: CBS

MAGIC OF PLACIDO DOMINGO, THE with the L.S.O.
Tracks: / Martha / L'elisir d'amore / La Boheme / Manon / L'Arlesiana / I Pagliacci / La Fanciulla del West / Rigoletto / Le Cid / L'Africana.
Album: released on RCA/Camden, Oct'82

Cassette: released on RCA/Camden, Oct'82

MY LIFE FOR A SONG.
Tracks: / I couldn't live with you for a day / Besame Mucho / I don't talk to strangers / Follow me / My life for a song / Remembering / Blue moon / Moon river / Autum leaves / There will be love / Songs of summer.
Compact disc: released on CBS, Jan'86 by CBS Records. Dist: CBS

MY LIFE FOR A SONG.
Tracks: / I couldn't live without you for a day / Besame mucho / I don't talk to strangers / Follow me / My life for a song / Remembering / Blue moon / Moon river / Autumn leaves / There will be love / Songs of summer, The.
Compact disc: by CBS Records. Dist: CBS

Album: released on CBS, May'83 by CBS Records. Dist: CBS

Cassette: released on CBS, May'83 by CBS Records. Dist: CBS

MY LIFE FOR A SONG (7").
Single (7"): released on CBS, Jun'83 by CBS Records. Dist: CBS

PIE JESU (Domingo, Placido & Others).
Single (7"): released on EMI, Mar'85 by EMI Records. Dist: EMI

Single (12"): released on EMI, Mar'85 by EMI Records. Dist: EMI

PLACIDO DOMINGO.
Compact disc: released on Stylus Music, Jan'86

PLACIDO DOMINGO COLLECTION.
Album: released on Stylus, Nov'86 Dist: Pinnacle, Terry Blood Distribution, Stylus Distribution

Cassette: released on Stylus, Nov'86 Dist: Pinnacle, Terry Blood Distribution, Stylus Distribution

PLACIDO DOMINGO SINGS TANGOS.
Tracks: / Caminito / Nostalgias / Volver / Vida mia / Mi buenos / Aires querido / Dia me quieras / Maria / Uno / Alma de Bohemio / Cuesta abajo.
Compact disc: by Polydor Records. Dist: Polygram

Album: released on DGG, Mar'85 by Polydor Records. Dist: Polygram

Cassette: released on DGG, Mar'85 by Polydor Records. Dist: Polygram

SONGS OF ERNESTO LECUONA.
Album: released on CBS, Dec'84 by CBS Records. Dist: CBS

Cassette: released on CBS, Dec'84 by CBS Records. Dist: CBS

Dominican Republic

MERENGUES.
Album: released on Lyrichord (USA), Oct'81 by Lyrichord Records (USA). Dist: Flexitron Distributors Ltd

Dominique

SONGS FROM AROUND THE WORLD.
Album: released on Lake, Oct'80 by Fellside Recordings. Dist: Jazz Music, Fellside

Dominko, Steve

ACCORDION MASTERWORKS.
Tracks: / Hungarian rhapsody no.2 / Traumerei / Sonata no.7 in D / Fantasia / Poet speaks / Prelude in G minor - English suite no.3 Allemande / Sun will never shine, The / Someone there you know / Little lapwing / Song for dying / Poet, The / After the day / Thank you / I'm over you / Harry's song / Ball and chain / Delph town morn / Blue John's blues.
Album: released on ARC (Accordion Records), '84 Dist: Accordion Record Club

Domino, Anna

ANNA DOMINO.
Album: released on Factory, Sep'86 by Factory Records. Dist: Cartel, Pinnacle

EAST AND WEST.
Album: released on Les Disques Du Crepuscule, Feb'84 Dist: Rough Trade, Pinnacle, Island, Polygram

RYTHM.
Single (7"): released on Operation Afterglow, Aug'85 Dist: Pinnacle

Single (7"): released on Operation Afterglow, Aug'85 Dist: Pinnacle

SUMMER.
Tracks: / Summer.
Single (7"): released on Factory, Aug'86 by Factory Records. Dist: Cartel, Pinnacle

Single (12"): released on Factory, Aug'86 by Factory Records. Dist: Cartel, Pinnacle

TAKE THAT.
Tracks: / Take that / Koo Koo / Take that /Sing it yourself mix..
Single (12"): released on Operation Afterglow, Dec'85 Dist: Pinnacle

TRUST IN LOVE.
Single (7"): released on Les Disques Du Crepuscule, Nov'83 Dist: Rough Trade, Pinnacle, Island, Polygram

Domino Band

FOOL IN LOVE.
Tracks: / Fool in love / Fool in love (Instrumental).
Single (12"): released on Carrere, Mar'86 by Carrere Records. Dist: PRT, Spartan

Domino Effect

DOLCE VITA, (LA).
Single (7"): released on Stiletto, Jun'81 by Fast Records. Dist: Cartel Distribution

GETTING SERIOUS.
Single (7"): released on Stiletto, Oct'81 by Fast Records. Dist: Cartel Distribution

MAN SHE WANTS.
Single (7"): released on Disques Blue, May'82 by Disques Bleu.

Dominoes

HAVE MERCY BABY.
Tracks: / Sixty minute man / Pedal pushin' Papa / Chicken blues / You can't keep a good man down / Bells / I'd be satisfied / Weeping willow blues / Do something for me / If I never get to heaven / My baby's 3-D / Pedal pushin' Papa / Don't leave me this way / I am with you / I'm gonna move to the outskirts of town / That's what you're doing to me.
Compact disc: released on Charly, Jan'87 by Charly Records. Dist: Charly, Cadillac

Album: released on Charly(R&B), Jul'85 by Charly Records. Dist: Charly, Cadillac

Cassette: released on Charly(R&B), Jul'85 by Charly Records. Dist: Charly, Cadillac

Domino, Fats

16 GREATEST HITS.
Compact disc: released on Bescol, Aug'87 Dist: Target

16 GREATEST HITS, THE.
Tracks: / Blueberry hill / I'm in love again / Ain't that a shame / I'm walking / Blue monday / Whole lotta loving / I want to walk you home / I'm ready / My blue heaven / I'm gonna be a wheel someday / Jambalaya / So long / When the saints go marching in / Heart break hill / Kansas city / Walking to new orleans.
Compact disc: released on Bescol, May'87 Dist: Target

20 ROCK'N'ROLL HITS.
Album: released on EMI (Germany), Jan'83 by EMI Records. Dist: Conifer

AIN'T THAT A SHAME.
Single (7"): released on EMI Golden 45's, May'84 by EMI Records. Dist: EMI

BE MY GUEST.
Tracks: / Blueberry hill / Whole lotta lovin / Im in love again / Blue Monday / I want to walk you home / Ain't that a shame / Be my guest / My girl Josephine / Let the four winds blow / I'm ready.
Notes: All tracks side 2 United partnership Music Ltd. except Franci,Day & Hunter Ltd. All selections courtesy of Jefferson Jazz Inc. under license from CBS Special Products. A service of CBS Records, a division of CBS Inc.
Album: released on Bulldog, May'86 by Bulldog Records. Dist: President Distribution, Spartan, Swift, Taylor, H.R.

Cassette: released on Bulldog, May'86 by Bulldog Records. Dist: President Distribution, Spartan, Swift, Taylor, H.R.

BEST OF.
Cassette: released on Creole (Everest-Europa), Jul'84 by Creole Records. Dist: PRT, Rhino

BEST OF FATS DOMINO (THE).
Tracks: / Blueberry hill / Wole lotta lovin' / Fat man / Blue monday / I'm walkin' / I'm in love again / Valley of tears / Be my guest / When my dream boat comes home / Let the four winds blow / I'm gonna be a wheel someday / Walking to New Orleans / Ain't that a shame / I want to walk you home / My blue heaven.
Compact disc: released on EMI America, Apr'87 by EMI Records. Dist: EMI

BEST OF FATS DOMINO, THE.
Album: released on Liberty, Oct'85 by Liberty-United. Dist: EMI

Cassette: released on Liberty, Oct'85 by Liberty-United. Dist: EMI

BLUEBERRY HILL.
Album: released on Preimer, '84

Cassette: released on Preimer, '84

Single (7"): released on SMP, Jun'84 Dist: Jetstar, PRT

Single (7"): released on EMI, Apr'83 by EMI Records. Dist: EMI

Single (7"): released on United Artists, Oct'80

BOOGIE WOOGIE BABY.
Album: released on Ace, Sep'85 by Ace Records. Dist: Pinnacle, Swift, Hotshot, Cadillac

COLLECTION: FATS DOMINO.
Compact disc: released on Spectrum, Jul'86 Dist: ACD

FABULOUS MR D, THE.
Album: released on Imperial(France), Jan'83 by K-Tel Records. Dist: K-Tel, Taylors, Polygram

FAT MAN-LIVE, THE.
Notes: Legendary Artist. Previously unreleased material.
Album: released on Magnum Force, Mar'86 by Magnum Music Group Ltd. Dist: Magnum Music Group Ltd, PRT, Spartan

FAT MAN, THE.
Album: released on Topline, Nov'84 by Charly Records. Dist: Charly Distribution

Cassette: released on Topline, Nov'84 by Charly Records. Dist: Charly Distribution

FATS DOMINO.
Tracks: / Introduction / Blueberry hill / Please don't leave me / Domino twist / Let the four winds blow / Whole lotta loving / Blue monday / You win again / I'm walking / I'm gonna be a wheel some day / I'm in the mood for love / Jambalaya / O, What a price / Ain't that a shame / So long / When the saints go marching in / Deep in the heart of Texas.
Notes: Live album containing 16 of Fats' best known songs including 'Blueberry hill', 'Blue Monday' and 'Ain't that a shame',
Picture disc album: released on Astan, Dec'85 by Astan Records. Dist: Counterpoint

Cassette: released on Audio Fidelity, Oct'84 Dist: PRT

Album: released on Mercury (Holland), Jul'85 by Phonogram Records. Dist: Polygram Distribution

Cassette: released on Mercury (Holland), Jul'85 by Phonogram Records. Dist: Polygram Distribution

FATS DOMINO COLLECTION, THE.
Cassette: released on Deja Vu, Aug'85 by Deja Vu Records. Dist: Counterpoint Distribution, Record Services Distribution (Ireland)

FATS DOMINO COLLECTION.
Album: released on Deja Vu, Nov'85 by Deja Vu Records. Dist: Counterpoint Distribution, Record Services Distribution (Ireland)

Cassette: released on Deja Vu, Nov'85 by Deja Vu Records. Dist: Counterpoint Distribution, Record Services Distribution (Ireland)

Compact disc: released on Deja Vu, Jul'87 by Deja Vu Records. Dist: Counterpoint Distribution, Record Services Distribution (Ireland)

FATS IS BACK.
Album: released on Mercury (USA), Nov'81 by Import Records. Dist: IMS Distribution, Polygram Distribution

Cassette: released on Mercury (USA), Nov'81 by Import Records. Dist: IMS Distribution, Polygram Distribution

GETAWAY WITH FATS.
Tracks: / When my dream boat comes home / Wigs / Trouble in mind / Man that's all / Kansas city / Reelin' and rockin' / On a slow boat to China / Monkey business / Heartbeat hill / Girl I'm gonna marry, The / Why don't you do right? / Ballin' the jack.
Notes: Originally published 1965.

GREATEST HITS:FATS DOMINO.
Tracks: / I'm walking / Blue Monday / Blueberry hill / When the saints go marching in.
Compact disc: released on Card/Grand Prix, Apr'87 Dist: Target

HERE STANDS FATS DOMINO.
Album: released on EMI (France), '83 by EMI Records. Dist: Conifer

I MISS YOU SO.
Album: released on Imperial(France), '83 by K-Tel Records. Dist: K-Tel, Taylors, Polygram

JAMBALAYA.
Album: released on Astan, Nov'84 by Astan Records. Dist: Counterpoint

Cassette: released on Astan, Nov'84 by Astan Records. Dist: Counterpoint

KINGS OF ROCK (Domino, Fats & Bill Haley).
Tracks: / See you later alligator / Shake rattle and roll / Rock around the clock / Blueberry hill / Jambalaya.
Album: released on Polydor (Import), Feb'82

Cassette· released on Polydor (Import), Feb'82

Double Album: released on EMI (France), Jun'83 by EMI Records. Dist: Conifer

LET'S DANCE WITH DOMINO.
Album: released on EMI (France), '81 by EMI Records. Dist: Conifer

LIVE IN CONCERT.
Tracks: / Fat man, The / Blueberry hill / Domino twist / What a price / Let the four winds blow / Jambalaya(on the bayou) / Medley: I'm in love again / Honey chile / Red sails in the sunset / Ain't that a shame / Medley: so long / Natural born lover / C.C rider / I'm in the mood for love / I want to walk you home.
Album: released on Charly, Jan'85 by Charly Records. Dist: Charly, Cadillac

LOT OF DOMINOS, A.
Album: released on EMI (France), '83 by EMI Records. Dist: Conifer

MILLION RECORDS HITS.
Album: released on Imperial(France), '83 by K-Tel Records. Dist: K-Tel, Taylors, Polvgram

MOTIVE SERIES.
Tracks: / My blue heaven / Blueberry hill / When the saints go marchin' in / Deep in the heart of Texas / Left my heart in San Francisco / Blue Monday / You win again / Walking to New Orleans / Mardi gras in New Orleans / I'm walking / I don't get over it.

MY BLUE HEAVEN.
Album: released on Astan, Nov'84 by Astan Records. Dist: Counterpoint

Cassette: released on Astan, Nov'84 by Astan Records. Dist: Counterpoint

MY TOOT TOOT (Domino, Fats/Doug Kershaw).
Single (7"): released on Magnum Force, Aug'85 by Magnum Music Group Ltd. Dist: Magnum Music Group Ltd, PRT, Spartan

NEW ORLEANS ROCK 'N' ROLL.
Album: released on Pathe MarconiFrance), '85

REELIN AND ROCKIN.
Album: released on Charly, Jun'83 by Charly Records. Dist: Charly, Cadillac

ROCK AND ROLLIN.
Album: released on EMI (France), Jan'83 by EMI Records. Dist: Conifer

Album: released on EMI (France), Jan'83 by EMI Records. Dist: Conifer

ROCK'N'ROLL GREATS.
Tracks: / Be my guest / Margie / Ain't that a shame / I hear you knockin / When my dreamboat comes home / All by myself / Honey chile / Jambalaya / I'm in love again / What a party / Blueberry hill / I've been around / My blue heaven / My girl Josephine / Natural born lover.
Notes: The 'Fats Man' himself - Fats Domino - A Rock 'n' Roll Great. Currently in this Country, and still hugely popular, Fars Domino's recording career spans almost 40 years. This new compilarion includes not only big hits like Blueberry hill, Ain't that a shame, and I hear you knockin, but also Margie, What a party, and an early B side Natural born lover, lasting over 4 minutes. A great moody sleeveand full sleeve note by Roger St,Pierre.
Album: released on Music For Pleasure, Apr'86 by EMI Records. Dist: EMI

Cassette: released on Music For Pleasure, Apr'86 by EMI Records. Dist: EMI

SLEEPING ON THE JOB.
Album: released on Sonet, May'79 by Sonet Records. Dist: PRT

THIS IS FATS.
Album: released on Imperial(France), Jan'83 by K-Tel Records. Dist: K-Tel, Taylors, Polygram

THIS IS FATS DOMINO.
Album: released on EMI (France), Jan'83 by EMI Records. Dist: Conifer

TWENTY GREATEST HITS.
Album: released on United Artists, Mar'77

VERY BEST OF FATS DOMINO, THE.
Album: released on Libertv (Germany), Jan'83

WALKING TO NEW ORLEANS/ THE FAT MAN.
Single (7"): released on United Artists, Oct'80

WALKIN TO NEW ORLEANS.
Album: released on Pathe Marconi, Sep'84 Dist: Swift

WHAT A PARTY.
Album: released on Pathe Marconi, Sep'84 Dist: Swift

Domnerus, Arne

A.D. 1980.
Album: released on Phontastic (Sweden), Jan'82 by Wellard, Chris Distribution. Dist: Wellard, Chris Distribution

Album: released on Phontastic (Sweden), '82 by Wellard, Chris Distribution. Dist: Wellard, Chris Distribution

ALLT UNDER HIMMELENS FASTE (Domnerus, Arne & Ola Hoglund).
Notes: Full details see under Hoglund,Ola/Arne Domnerus.

BLUE AND YELLOW - A SWEDISH RHAPSODY.
Album: released on Phontastic (Sweden), Jan'82 by Wellard, Chris Distribution. Dist: Wellard, Chris Distribution

DOWNTOWN MEETING.
Album: released on Phontastic (Sweden), Jan'82 by Wellard, Chris Distribution. Dist: Wellard, Chris Distribution

DUKE'S MELODY (Domnerus, Arne/Knud Jorgensen).
Album: released on Phontastic (Sweden), Jan'82 by Wellard, Chris Distribution. Dist: Wellard, Chris Distribution

FRAGMENT.
Album: released on Phontastic (Sweden), Jan'82 by Wellard, Chris Distribution. Dist: Wellard, Chris Distribution

RAPTUROUS REEDS.
Album: released on Phontastic (Sweden), Jan'82 by Wellard, Chris Distribution. Dist: Wellard, Chris Distribution

SWEDISH JINGLES.
Album: released on Phontastic (Sweden), Jan'82 by Wellard, Chris Distribution. Dist: Wellard, Chris Distribution

SWEDISH JINGLES (Domnerus, Arne/Bengt Hallberg/Svenska Truddelutter).

Domra, Sydney

MEMORIES OF RUSSIA (Domra, Sydney Ensemble).
Album: released on Viking, Jan'80 Dist: Harmonia Mundi Distributors

Donachue, Jerry

TELECASTING.
Album: released on Spindrift, Aug'86 Dist: Roots

Donaghadee School Choir

THANK YOU FOR THE MUSIC (Donaghadee Primary School Choir).
Album: released on Outlet, Nov'79 by Outlet Records. Dist: Outlet Distribution

Donaghy, Eileen

12 FAVOURITE IRISH SONGS.
Cassette: released on Homespun(Ireland), Mar'84 by Outlet Records. Dist: Outlet

EILEEN DONAGHY ENTERTAINS.
Album: released on Spin, Jul'76 by Symphola. Dist: Solomon & Peres Distribution

IRISH SINGALONG.
Cassette: released on Polydor (Eire), Feb'85

IRISH SING ALONG.
Tracks: / If you're Irish come into the parlour. / When Irish eyes are smiling. / With a shillelagh under my arm / Dear little shamrock / Mountains of Mourne, The / Hannigan's Hooley.' / Phil the Fluter's ball / Cockles and Mussels. / MacNamara's band / Believe me if all those endearing young charms. / Galway Bay / Danny boy / Mother Machree / It's a long, long way to Tipperary..
Cassette: released on Polydor (Ireland), Aug'86 by Polydor Records. Dist: Polygram, I & B

Donahue, Sam

CONVOY (Donahue, Sam Navy Band).
Album: released on Hep, Apr'81 by H.R. Taylor Records. Dist: Jazz Music, Cadillac Music, JSU, Taylors, Wellard, Chris, Zodiac, Swift, Fast Forward

DOUBLE DATE (Donahue, Sam and Les Brown).

HOLLYWOOD HOP.
Album: released on Hep, Apr'83 by H.R. Taylor Records. Dist: Jazz Music, Cadillac Music, JSU, Taylors, Wellard, Chris, Zodiac, Swift, Fast Forward

LST PARTY (Donahue, Sam Navy Band).
Album: released on Hep, Apr'81 by H.R. Taylor Records. Dist: Jazz Music, Cadillac Music, JSU, Taylors, Wellard, Chris, Zodiac, Swift, Fast Forward

Donald & Lulu

BEAUTIFUL GARDEN (Donald & Lulu with the Wailers).
Tracks: / Just cool runnin's / You'd better believe it / I know you're a child / Lulu, what we gonna do / Dream of me / Love one another / Marble stones / I never wrote a love song / Destiny / Beautiful garden.
Notes: Donald Davidson and Lulu Kevan are two reggae artists - getting the services of Bob Marley's Wailers they have to be good. Lulu Kevan and Donald Davidson - Lead vocals, Acoustic guitar. The Wailers: Aston 'Family-man' Barrett - bass guitar, percussion, organ/ Carlton 'Carly' Barrett - drums/ Julian 'Junior' Marvin - Lead guitar/ Alvin 'Seeco' Pattrson - percussion/ Earl 'Wire' Lindo - Keyboard, organ/ Leroy Hamilton - rhythm guitar/ Stephen Stewart - Keyboard, piano.
Album: released on Third World Sound (Germany), Jun'84 Dist: IMS Distribution, Polygram Distribution

Donald, Mike

YORKSHIRE SONGS OF THE BROAD ACRES.
Album: released on Folk Heritage, Jul'82 by Folk Heritage Records. Dist: Roots, Wynd-Up Distribution, Jazz Music, Folk Heritage

Donaldson Brothers

SCOTTISH WELCOME, A.
Album: released on Glen, May'81 Dist: EMI, Outlet

Donaldson, David

ENGLISH LANGUAGE, THE.
Album: released on Stag, Nov'83 by Creole. Dist: CBS Distribution

Cassette: released on Stag, Nov'83 by Creole. Dist: CBS Distribution

Donaldson, Eric

CHERRY OH BABY.
Single (7"): released on Trojan, Nov'83 by Trojan Records. Dist: PRT, Jetstar

Single (12"): released on Trojan, Nov'83 by Trojan Records. Dist: PRT, Jetstar

Single (7"): released on Dynamic, Apr'84 by Creole Records. Dist: CBS, Essex

Single (12"): released on Dynamic, Apr'84 by Creole Records. Dist: CBS, Essex

EASY SQUEEZE (Donaldson, Eric & Herbert Spliffy).
Single (12"): released on World Enterprise, Jul'84 Dist: Jetstar

FESTIVAL 84.
Single (12"): released on Stage, Oct'84 by Stage Records. Dist: Jetstar Distribution

HOW BOUT MAYBE.
Single (12"): released on Jah Congo, Dec'82 by Jah Congo Records. Dist: Jetstar

KEEP ON RIDING.
Album: released on Dynamic, Aug'76 by Creole Records. Dist: CBS, Essex

KENT VILLAGE.
Album: released on Dynamic, Jan'78 by Creole Records. Dist: CBS, Essex

MAYBE.
Single (12"): released on Yah Congo, Dec'82

PROUD TO BE JAMAICAN.
Single (12"): released on Stage, Oct'84 by Stage Records. Dist: Jetstar Distribution

RIGHT ON TIME.
Album: released on Dynamic Sound, Sep'85 by Arrowtabs Records.

Donaldson, Lou

BLUES WALK.
Tracks: / Blues Walk / Move / Masquerade is over,The / Play Ray / Autumn Nocturne / Callin' All Cats.
Compact disc: released on Manhattan-Blue Note, May'87 by EMI America Records (USA). Dist: EMI

Album: released on Blue Note, Jul'85 by EMI Records. Dist: EMI

HERE TIS.
Cassette: released on Blue Note (USA Import), Sep'84

LIVE IN BOLOGNA, VOLUME 2.
Notes: Quartet with Herman Foster.
Album: released on Timeless, Oct'86

LUSH LIFE.
Tracks: / Sweet slumber / You've changed / Good life,The / Stardust / What will I tell my heart / It might as well be spring. / Sweet and lovely.
Album: released on Manhattan-Blue Note, Jul'86 by EMI America Records (USA). Dist: EMI

NATURAL SOUL.
Tracks: / Funky Mama / Love walked in / Spaceman twist / Sow belly blues / That's all / Nice 'N' Greasy.
Notes: Produced by Alfred Lion.
Album: released on Manhattan, Nov'86 by President Records. Dist: Jazz Music, Swift, Taylors, Chris Wellard

SWEET POPPA LOU.
Album: released on Muse (Import), Jan'81

Donaldson, Stephen R.

WHITE GOLD WIELDER.
Cassette: released on Caedmon(USA), Aug'83 by Caedmon (USA) Records. Dist: Gower, Taylors, Discovery

Donaldson, Walter

GREATEST SONG HITS OF WALTER DONALDSON.
Album: released on Monmouth, Mar'79

Donal Ring Sound

WINDING BANKS OF THE LEE.
Tracks: / Polka reel selection / Where the river Shannon flows / Marches / Hornpipe / Plaxty O'Rourke / Reel Selection / Winding banks of the Lee / Selection of Jigs / March Selection / Selection of Waltzes / Selection of Reels / Selection of Jigs.
Cassette: released on Polydor (Ireland), Aug'86 by Polydor Records. Dist: Polygram, I & B

Don & Annie

QUEEN OF THE SILVER DOLLAR.
Cassette: released on Bi Bi(Budget Cassettes), Jan'83

Donat, Robert

ROBERT DONAT READS.
Double cassette: released on Argo (Spokenword), Jul'82 by Decca Records. Dist: Polygram

Dondadio, Atillio

CAPOLINEA CLUB (Dondadio, Atillio Big Band).
Album: released on Intersound, Dec'86 by Intersound Records. Dist: Jazz Music

Doneda, Michel

TERRA.
Tracks: / Le Passeur D'Etoiles / Vert et Jaune / Theatre / Ene Maetia / Rose Noir / Xorri Fourmy / When did you come / Lile D'Hanako.
Album: released on Nato (France), Sep'86 by Disques Nato. Dist: Essex Record Distributors Ltd.

Donegan, Dorothy

BROWN GAL 1946-50 (Donegan, Dorothy/Camille Howard/Lil Armstrong).
Notes: For ful information see under Howard, Camille/Dorothy Donegan etc..

Donegan, Lonnie

GAMBLIN' MAN.
Single (7"): released on Old Gold, Jul'82 by Old Gold Records. Dist: Lightning, Jazz Music, Spartan, Counterpoint

GOLDEN HOUR OF GOLDEN HITS,VOL.2.
Album: released on Golden Hour, '73 by PRT Records. Dist: PRT

GOLDEN HOUR OF GOLDEN HITS.
Cassette: released on PRT, '74 by PRT Records. Dist: PRT

GREATEST HITS:LONNIE DONEGAN.
Cassette: released on Pickwick (Ditto series), Mar'83

Cassette: released on Bravo, Feb'80 by Pickwick Records. Dist: Lugtons

JUBILEE CONCERT.
Album: released on Dakota, Dec'81 by Dakota Records. Dist: PRT

Cassette: released on Dakota, Dec'81 by Dakota Records. Dist: PRT

LONNIE DONEGAN FILE, THE.
Cassette: released on PRT, Nov'77 by PRT Records. Dist: PRT

MY OLD MAN'S A DUSTMAN.
Single (7"): released on Flashback, Apr'79 by Flashback Records/PRT Records. Dist: Mainline, PRT

PUTTIN' ON THE STYLE.
Album: released on Chrysalis, Feb'78 by Chrysalis Records. Dist: CBS

Cassette: released on Chrysalis, '79 by Chrysalis Records. Dist: CBS

RARE & UNISSUED GEMS.
Album: released on Bear Family, Jun'85 by Bear Family Records. Dist: Rollercoaster Distribution, Swift

ROCK ISLAND LINE.
Album: released on Flashback, Oct'85 by Flashback Records/PRT Records. Dist: Mainline, PRT

Cassette: released on Flashback, Oct'85 by Flashback Records/PRT Records. Dist: Mainline, PRT

ROCK ISLAND LINE (7").
Single (7"): released on Decca, Mar'82 by Decca Records. Dist: Polygram

Donegan, Martin

SHORT STORIES-EDGAR ALLAN POE,VOL.1.
Album: released on Peerless, Jan'75

Donegan's Dancing...

DONEGAN'S DANCING SUNSHINE BAND (Donegan's Dancing Sunshine Band).
Tracks: / Donegan's Dancing Sunshine Band / Leaving blues.
Single (7"): released on Rosie, Jul'87 by Rosie Records. Dist: PRT Distribution

Don Juans

LOVING YOU.
Album: released on Bullseye, Jul'79 Dist: Bullseye Music

MORE MONSTER HITS.
Album: released on Bullseye, Jul'79 Dist: Bullseye Music

SOLID GOLD.
Album: released on Bullseye, Jan'79 Dist: Bullseye Music

Donkey Cabbages

DONKEY CABBAGES various artists (Various Artists).
Cassette: released on Anvil, Jan'81 Dist: Anvil

Donley, Jimmy

GIVE ME MY FREEDOM.
Tracks: / Kickin' my hound around / Come along / Radio jukebox & TV / Please come home / Now I Know / I can't love you / My baby's gone / Shape you left me in (The) / Born to be a loser / Give me my freedom / Baby how long / I'm alone / What must I do / Our love / Child love.
Album: released on Charly, Feb'87 by Charly Records. Dist: Charly, Cadillac

Donnelly, Bill

MOVE OVER LITTLE DONKEY.
Tracks: / Move over little Donkey / Bill and Phil-Hush.
Single (7"): released on Splash, Nov'86 by Splash Records. Dist: CBS

Donner, Ral

1935-1977,I'VE BEEN AWAY FOR A WHILE.
Double Album: released on Picadilly, Aug'80

DAY THE BEAT STOPPED.
Single (7"): released on Thunder, May'83 Dist: Swift Distribution

DON'T LET IT SLIP AWAY.
Single (7"): released on Inferno, May'79 by Inferno Records. Dist: Inferno, Cartel, Pinnacle

YOU DON'T KNOW WHAT YOU GOT.
Album: released on Pye International, '78

Donoghue, Jim

JIM DONOGHUE.
Album: released on Mulligan, Sep'80 by Topic Records. Dist: Roots Distribution, Jazz Music Distribution, JSU Distribution, I & B Distribution, Projection Distribution, Wynd-Up Distribution, Celtic Distributions

Don & Oli

SUPERMAN.
Single (12"): released on Cartridge, May'82 by Cartridge. Dist: Jetstar

Donovan

CATCH THE WIND.
Tracks: / Universal / Soldier / Little tin soldier / Catch the wind / Candy man / Josie / Colours of Geraldine / War drags on,The / Remember the Alamo.
Album: released on Showcase, Apr'86 Dist: Counterpoint

Cassette: released on Showcase, Apr'86 Dist: Counterpoint

CATCH THE WIND (7").
Single (7"): released on PRT Flashback, Jul'80

Single (7"): released on Old Gold, Jul'82 by Old Gold Records. Dist: Lightning, Jazz Music, Spartan, Counterpoint

COLOURS.
Album: released on Flashback, Oct'85 by Flashback Records/PRT Records. Dist: Mainline, PRT

Cassette: released on Flashback, Oct'85 by Flashback Records/PRT Records. Dist: Mainline, PRT

DONOVAN FILE, THE.
Double Album: released on Pye, Nov'77

Cassette: released on Pye, Nov'77

LADY OF THE STARS.
Album: released on RCA (Import), Jan'84

Cassette: released on RCA (Import), Jan'84

LAY DOWN LASSIE.
Single (7"): released on Luggage, Oct'81 by Luggage. Dist: Multicord

LOVE IS ONLY FEELING.
Album: released on RCA (Germany), '83

MELLOW YELLOW.
Single (7"): released on EMI Golden 45's, Feb'85 by EMI Records. Dist: EMI

MINSTREL BOY.
Album: released on PRT, Jul'83 by PRT Records. Dist: PRT

Cassette: released on PRT, Jul'83 by PRT Records. Dist: PRT

NEUTRONICA.
Album: released on RCA (Germany), '83

Cassette: released on RCA (Germany), '83

SPOTLIGHT ON DONOVAN.
Double Album: released on PRT, Oct'81 by PRT Records. Dist: PRT

Double cassette: released on PRT, Oct'81 by PRT Records. Dist: PRT

UNIVERSAL SOLDIER.
Album: released on Spot, Feb'83 by Pickwick Records. Dist: H.R. Taylor, Lugtons
Cat. no: **SPR 8514**
Cassette: released on Spot, Feb'83 by Pickwick Records. Dist: H.R. Taylor, Lugtons

WORLD OF DONOVAN.
Double Album: released on CBS(Holland), Feb'85 by CBS Records. Dist: Discovery

Don Quixote

DON QUIXOTE various artists (Various Artists).
Cassette: released on Anvil, Jan'81 Dist: Anvil

Dons

GREEN ONIONS (Dons featuring Daphne).
Single (7"): released on Scratch, Apr'80

Don Slepian

REFLECTIONS.
Compact disc: by Pacific Records (USA). Dist: Atlantic

Don't...

DON'T CALL IT DIXIE Various artists (Various Artists).
Double Album: released on BAJC, Apr'79 Dist: Swift

DON'T LET THE HOPE CLOSE DOWN Various artists (Various Artists).
Album: released on Hope Springs Eternal, Nov'84 by Ace Records. Dist: Pinnacle

DON'T SHOOT (Various Artists).
Album: released on Zippo, Dec'86

DON'T STEP ON MY BLUE SUEDE SHOES Various artists (Various Artists).
Album: released on Charly, Aug'77 by Charly Records. Dist: Charly, Cadillac

DON'T STOP various artists (Various Artists).
Cassette: released on EMI, Jun'81 by EMI Records. Dist: EMI

DON'T STOP DANCING Various original artists (Various Artists).
Album: released on Telstar, May'84 by Telstar Records. Dist: RCA Distribution

Cassette: released on Telstar, May'84 by Telstar Records. Dist: RCA Distribution

DON'T WATCH THAT, WATCH THIS. Various Artists (Various Artists).
Tracks: / Soul train / You drag me down / Rough Justice / More you live,The more you love,The. / Small Town Boy / Mothers Talk / Young at heart / Everybody's Laughing / Down on the street / Perfect skin / Ten thousand voices / Blue Emotion / Day before you came, The / Wonderland / Closest thing to heaven / Hot water / Feel it / Cry and be free / Come back / You're the best thing / Caterpillar / We are Ninja / Love over gold.
Notes: A compilation of promo video's for no less tha 23 recent Polygram group hit singles, including Bronski Beat's Small Town Boy, Blancmange's The Day Before You Came ahd Tears For Fears Mother Talk.
Video-cassette (VHS): released on Polygram Music, Sep'84 by Polygram Records. Dist: Polygram

Video-cassette [Betamax]: released on Polygram Music, Sep'84 by Polygram Records. Dist: Polygram

DON'T YOU STEP ON MY BLUE SUEDE SHOES Suns greatest hits (Various original artists).
Album: released on Sun, Jul'81 by Charly Records. Dist: Charly Distribution

Cassette: released on Sun, Jul'81 by Charly Records. Dist: Charly Distribution

Don't Look Now

DON'T LOOK NOW Original soundtrack (Various Artists).
Album: released on That's Entertainment, Apr'83 by That's Entertainment Records. Dist: Pinnacle, PRT

Doobie Brothers

BEST OF.
Tracks: / China grove / Long train runnin / Takin it to the streets / Listen to the music / Black water / Rockin down the highway / Jesus is just alright / It keeps you runnin / South city midnight lady / Take me in your arms / Without you.
Compact disc: released on Warner Bros., Jan'86 by Warner Bros Records. Dist: WEA

BEST OF THE DOOBIE BROTHERS.
Compact disc: by Warner Bros Records. Dist: WEA

BEST OF THE DOOBIES, VOL.II.
Album: released on Warner Bros., Nov'81 by Warner Bros Records. Dist: WEA

Cassette: released on Warner Bros., Nov'81 by Warner Bros Records. Dist: WEA

BEST OF THE DOOBIES.
Album: released on Warner Bros., Jan'77 by Warner Bros Records. Dist: WEA

Cassette: released on Warner Bros., Jan'77 by Warner Bros Records. Dist: WEA

CAPTAIN & ME, THE.
Cassette: released on Warner Bros., '74 by Warner Bros Records. Dist: WEA

Album: released on Warner Bros., '74 by Warner Bros Records. Dist: WEA

DOOBIE BROTHERS.
Album: by Warner Bros Records. Dist: WEA

LISTEN TO THE MUSIC.
Tracks: / Listen to the music / What a fool believes.
Single (7"): released on Old Gold, Mar'86 by Old Gold Records. Dist: Lightning, Jazz Music, Spartan, Counterpoint

MINUTE BY MINUTE.
Compact disc: by Warner Bros Records. Dist: WEA

Compact disc: released on Warner Brothers, Jan'83 by Warner Bros Records. Dist: WEA

Cassette: released on Warner Bros., Jan'79 by Warner Bros Records. Dist: WEA

Album: released on Warner Bros., Jan'79 by Warner Bros Records. Dist: WEA

ONE STEP CLOSER.
Album: released on Warner Bros., Oct'80 by Warner Bros Records. Dist: WEA

TAKIN' IT TO THE STREETS.
Cassette: released on Warner Bros., Oct'82 by Warner Bros Records. Dist: WEA

TOULOUSE STREET.
Album: by Warner Bros Records. Dist: WEA

WHAT A FOOL BELIEVES.
Tracks: / Minute by minute / Real love.
Notes: Featuring Michael McDonald.
Single (7"): released on Warner Bros., Jan'87 by Warner Bros Records. Dist: WEA

Single (12"): released on Warner Bros., Jan'87 by Warner Bros Records. Dist: WEA

Dooleys

BEST OF THE DOOLEYS.
Album: released on GTO, Jun'79 by GTO Records. Dist: CBS

Cassette: released on GTO, Jun'79 by GTO Records. Dist: CBS

FLAVOUR OF THE MONTH.
Single (7"): released on R 'n' R, Aug'83

FULL HOUSE.
Album: released on GTO, Oct'80 by GTO Records. Dist: CBS

Cassette: released on GTO, Oct'80 by GTO Records. Dist: CBS

GREATEST HITS:DOOLEYS.
Album: released on Spot, Feb'83 by Pickwick Records. Dist: H.R. Taylor, Lugtons

Cassette: released on Spot, Feb'83 by Pickwick Records. Dist: H.R. Taylor, Lugtons

SIX TRACK HITS.
Single (7"): released on Scoop 33, Aug'84 by Pickwick Records. Dist: H.R. Taylor

Cassette: released on Scoop 33, Aug'84 by Pickwick Records. Dist: H.R. Taylor

Doonan, John

AT THE FEIS.
Album: released on Topic, '81 Dist: Roots Distribution

FLUTE FOR THE FEIS.
Album: Dist: Jazz Music, Projection

Doonicans

FISHERWOMAN'S WAY.
Tracks: / Fisherwoman's way / Chanter's song / Drunken pretender, The / Piper's song.
Single (12"): released on Probe Plus, Jun'87 by Probe Plus Records. Dist: Probe Plus Distribution

Doonican, Val

20 PERSONAL FAVOURITES FOR YOU.
Tracks: / Snowbird / I'm just a country boy / Little green apples / My cup runneth over / You and me against the world / Folk's who live on the hill,The / All I ever need is you / Try to remember / Mysterious people / Annie's song / Things / Walking in the sunshine / Morning of my life / He'll have to go / Sing a rainbow / Portrait of my love / Small world / Man chase a girl, A / King of the road / Scarlet ribbons.
Notes: Licensed from Valdo Enterprises Ltd./P/ & /C/ Warwick Records. A warwick LeisureProduct. Made & printed in the U.K. Bar code: 5 012106 220010.
Album: released on Warwick Reflections, Jun'86 by Warwick Records.

Cassette: released on Warwick Reflections, Jun'86 by Warwick Records.

BY REQUEST.
Tracks: / Umbrella man (Flanagan & Allen medley) / Hometown (Flanagan & Allen medley) / Underneath the arches (Flanagan & Allen medley) / You'll never know / More I see you, The / As time goes by / Very thought of you, The / You are my sunshine (singalong medley) / I'll be with you in Apple Blossom time (singalong medley) / Whispering (singalong medley) / Moonlight and roses (singalong medley) / Bye bye blues (singalong medley) / My resistance is low (Hoagy Carmichael medley) / Ole buttermilk sky (Hoagy Carmichael medley) / Old music master (Hoagy Carmichael medley) / What a difference a day made / But beautiful / When I fall in love / Smilin' through / When you and I were young Maggie (Irish medley) / I'll take you home again Kathleen (Irish medley) / Galway bay.
Notes: Orchestrated conducted by Ronnie Hazlehurst.
Album: released on MFP, Sep'87 by EMI Records. Dist: EMI

Cassette: released on MFP, Sep'87 by EMI Records. Dist: EMI

FOCUS ON VAL DOONICAN.
Album: released on Decca, Mar'76 by Decca Records. Dist: Polygram

Cassette: released on Decca, Feb'76 by Decca Records. Dist: Polygram

FORTY SHADES OF GREEN.
Album: released on Music For Pleasure, Nov'83 by EMI Records. Dist: EMI

Cassette: released on Music For Pleasure, Nov'83 by EMI Records. Dist: EMI

IMAGES.
Tracks: / Welcome to my world / Songs sung blue / Spanish eyes / Everybody's talkin / Amazing Grace.
Album: released on West Five, Nov'85 Dist: PRT

Cassette: released on West Five, Nov'85 Dist: PRT

MEMORIES ARE MADE OF THIS.
Album: released on Decca (Elite), Sep'81 by Decca Records. Dist: Polygram. IMS

Cassette: released on Decca (Elite), Sep'81 by Decca Records. Dist: Polygram, IMS Deleted '86.

MR MUSIC MAN.
Album: released on Hallmark, Jun'81 by Pickwick Records. Dist: Pickwick Distribution, PRT, Taylors

Cassette: released on Hallmark, Jun'81 by Pickwick Records. Dist: Pickwick Distribution, PRT, Taylors

QUIET MOMENTS.
Album: released on RCA, Apr'81 by RCA Records. Dist: RCA, Roots, Swift, Wellard, Chris, I & B, Solomon & Peres Distribution

Cassette: released on RCA, Apr'81 by RCA Records. Dist: RCA, Roots, Swift, Wellard, Chris, I & B, Solomon & Peres Distribution

RELAX WITH VAL DOONICAN.
Album: released on MFP, Sep'82 by EMI Records. Dist: EMI

Cassette: released on MFP, Sep'82 by EMI Records. Dist: EMI

SIX TRACK HITS.
Extended-play record: released on Scoop 33, Sep'83 by Pickwick Records. Dist: H.R. Taylor

Cassette: released on Scoop 33, Sep'83 by Pickwick Records. Dist: H.R. Taylor

SONGBOOK, (THE).
Album: released on Spot, Feb'83 by Pickwick Records. Dist: H.R. Taylor, Lugtons

Cassette: released on Spot, Feb'83 by Pickwick Records. Dist: H.R. Taylor,

VAL DOONICAN MUSIC SHOW.
Album: released on BBC, May'84 by BBC Records & Tapes. Dist: EMI, PRT,

Cassette: released on BBC, May'84 by BBC Records & Tapes. Dist: EMI, PRT,

VAL SINGS BING.
Album: released on RCA International, Mar'82

Cassette: released on RCA International, Mar'82

VERY BEST OF VAL DOONICAN, (THE).
Album: released on Music For Pleasure, Oct'84 by EMI Records. Dist: EMI

Cassette: released on Music For Pleasure, Oct'84 by EMI Records. Dist: EMI

WALK TALL.
Single (7"): released on Decca, Feb'82 by Decca Records. Dist: Polygram

WORLD OF VAL DOONICAN: VOL 3.
Cassette: released on Decca, '79 by Decca Records. Dist: Polygram

WORLD OF VAL DOONICAN.
Album: released on World of Learning, '68 by World Of Learning Records. Dist: World Of Learning

Doors

13.
Album: released on Elektra (USA), '71 by Elektra/Asylum/Nonesuch Records. Dist: WEA

Cassette: released on Elektra (USA), '71 by Elektra/Asylum/Nonesuch Records. Dist: WEA

ABSOLUTELY LIVE.
Double Album: released on Elektra (USA), '71 by Elektra/Asylum/Nonesuch Records. Dist: WEA

Compact disc: released on Elektra (USA), Mar'87 by Elektra/Asylum/Nonesuch Records. Dist: WEA

ALIVE SHE CRIED.
Compact disc: released on Elektra (USA), Jul'84 by Elektra/Asylum/Nonesuch Records. Dist: WEA

Compact disc: by Elektra/Asylum/Nonesuch Records. Dist: WEA

Compact disc: released on Elektra (USA), Jul'84 by Elektra/Asylum/Nonesuch Records. Dist: WEA

AMERICAN PRAYER, (AN).
Album: released on Elektra (USA), '78 by Elektra/Asylum/Nonesuch Records. Dist: WEA

Cassette: released on Elektra (USA), '78 by Elektra/Asylum/Nonesuch Records. Dist: WEA

BEST OF.
Tracks: / Break on through / Light my fire / Crystal ship, The / People are strange / Strange days / Love me two times / Five to one / Waiting for the sun / Spanish caravan / When the music's over / Hello I love you / Roadhouse blues / L.A.Woman / Riders on the storm / Touch me / Love her madly/Been so long / Unknown soldier, The / End, The.
Double compact disc: released on Elektra (USA), Nov'85 by Elektra/Asylum/Nonesuch Records. Dist: WEA

BEST OF DOORS.
Album: released on Elektra (USA), Oct'76 by Elektra/Asylum/Nonesuch Records. Dist: WEA

Cassette: released on Elektra (USA), Oct'76 by Elektra/Asylum/Nonesuch Records. Dist: WEA

BEST OF THE DOORS.
Double compact disc: by Elektra/Asylum/Nonesuch Records. Dist: WEA

Album: released on Elektra (USA), Nov'85 by Elektra/Asylum/Nonesuch Records. Dist: WEA

Cassette: released on Elektra (USA), Nov'85 by Elektra/Asylum/Nonesuch Records. Dist: WEA

Compact disc: released on Elektra (USA), Nov'85 by Elektra/Asylum/Nonesuch Records. Dist: WEA

CLASSICS.
Album: released on Elektra (USA), Jun'85 by Elektra/Asylum/Nonesuch Records. Dist: WEA

Cassette: released on Elektra (USA), Jun'85 by Elektra/Asylum/Nonesuch Records. Dist: WEA

DANCE ON FIRE.
Notes: Number of tracks 16. Type of recording:Compilation. Total playing time 65 minute
Video-cassette (VHS): released on CIC Video, Jan'85 by CBS Records. Dist: CBS, Pickwick Distribution

DOORS.
Album: released on Elektra (USA), '71 by Elektra/Asylum/Nonesuch Records. Dist: WEA

Cassette: released on Elektra (USA), '71 by Elektra/Asylum/Nonesuch Records. Dist: WEA

Compact disc: released on Elektra (USA), '71 by Elektra/Asylum/Nonesuch Records. Dist: WEA

Compact disc: released on Elektra (USA), '83 by Elektra/Asylum/Nonesuch Records. Dist: WEA

DOORS, THE.
Compact disc: by Elektra/Asylum/Nonesuch Records. Dist: WEA

DOORS: VOL 2.
Album: released on Elektra (USA), '75 by Elektra/Asylum/Nonesuch Records. Dist: WEA

Cassette: released on Elektra (USA), '75 by Elektra/Asylum/Nonesuch Records. Dist: WEA

GREATEST HITS:DOORS.
Album: released on Elektra (USA), Oct'80 by Elektra/Asylum/Nonesuch Records. Dist: WEA

Cassette: released on Elektra (USA), Oct'80 by Elektra/Asylum/Nonesuch Records. Dist: WEA

L.A. WOMAN.
Compact disc: by Elektra/Asylum/Nonesuch Records. Dist: WEA

L.A WOMAN.
Tracks: / Changeling / Love her madly / Cars hiss by my window / L.A.Woman / L'America / Hyacinth house / Crawling king snake / Wasp,The/Texas radio and the big beat. / Riders on the storm.
Compact disc: released on Elektra (USA), Jun'85 by Elektra/Asylum/Nonesuch Records. Dist: WEA

L.A. WOMAN.
Album: released on Elektra (USA), '71 by Elektra/Asylum/Nonesuch Records. Dist: WEA

Cassette: released on Elektra (USA), '71 by Elektra/Asylum/Nonesuch Records. Dist: WEA

Compact disc: released on Elektra (USA), '71 by Elektra/Asylum/Nonesuch Records. Dist: WEA

LIGHT MY FIRE.
Single (7"): released on Elektra (USA), Sep'76 by Elektra/Asylum/Nonesuch Records. Dist: WEA

LIVE AT THE HOLLYWOOD BOWL.
Tracks: / Wake up / Light my fire / Unknown soldier, The / Little game, A / Hill dwellers, The / Spanish caravan.
Album: released on Elektra (USA), Jul'87 by Elektra/Asylum/Nonesuch Records. Dist: WEA

Cassette: released on Elektra (USA), Jul'87 by Elektra/Asylum/Nonesuch Records. Dist: WEA

Compact disc: released on Elektra (USA), Jul'87 by Elektra/Asylum/Nonesuch Records. Dist: WEA

MORRISON HOTEL.
Tracks: / Roadhouse blues / Waiting for the sun / You make me real / Peace frog / Blue sunday / Ship of fools / Land Ho! / Spy, The / Queen of the highway / Indian summer / Maggie M'gill.
Compact disc: released on Elektra (USA), Apr'86 by Elektra/Asylum/Nonesuch Records. Dist: WEA

Compact disc: by Elektra/Asylum/Nonesuch Records. Dist: WEA

Cassette: released on Elektra (USA), Oct'82 by Elektra/Asylum/Nonesuch Records. Dist: WEA

Album: released on Elektra (USA), '71 by Elektra/Asylum/Nonesuch Records. Dist: WEA

Compact disc: released on Elektra (USA), '71 by Elektra/Asylum/Nonesuch Records. Dist: WEA

RIDERS ON THE STORM.
Single (7"): released on Elektra (USA), Jul'81 by Elektra/Asylum/Nonesuch Records. Dist: WEA

Single (7"): released on Elektra (USA), Feb'76 by Elektra/Asylum/Nonesuch Records. Dist: WEA

Single (7"): released on Old Gold, Sep'85 by Old Gold Records. Dist: Lightning, Jazz Music, Spartan, Counterpoint

SOFT PARADE.
Cassette: released on Elektra (USA), Oct'82 by Elektra/Asylum/Nonesuch Records. Dist: WEA

Album: released on Elektra (USA), '71 by Elektra/Asylum/Nonesuch Records. Dist: WEA

Cassette: released on Elektra (USA), '71 by Elektra/Asylum/Nonesuch Records. Dist: WEA

STRANGE DAYS.
Compact disc: by Elektra/Asylum/Nonesuch Records. Dist: WEA

Album: released on Elektra (USA), '71 by Elektra/Asylum/Nonesuch Records. Dist: WEA

Compact disc: released on Elektra (USA), '71 by Elektra/Asylum/Nonesuch Records. Dist: WEA

WAITING FOR THE SUN.
Compact disc: released on Elektra (USA), Jan'86 by Elektra/Asylum/Nonesuch Records. Dist: WEA

Compact disc: by Elektra/Asylum/Nonesuch Records. Dist: WEA

Album: released on Elektra (USA), '71 by Elektra/Asylum/Nonesuch Records. Dist: WEA

WEIRD SCENES INSIDE THE GOLD-MINE.
Double Album: released on Elektra (USA), '71 by Elektra/Asylum/Nonesuch Records. Dist: WEA

Double cassette: released on Elektra (USA), '71 by Elektra/Asylum/Nonesuch Records. Dist: WEA

Door To Door

DOOR TO DOOR (Various Artists).
Compact disc: released on Vogue, Jul'87 Dist: Discovery, Jazz Music, PRT, Swift

Doo Wop

DOO WOP Best of Chess/Checker/Cadet (Various Artists).
Album: released on Chess, Jun'81 by Charly Records. Dist: Charly, Swift, PRT, Discovery, IMS, Polygram

DOO WOP DREAMS Various artists (Various Artists).
Tracks: / Stay in my corner / Oh what a nite / At my front door / B'm bam boom / Glitter in your eyes / Come to me / You gave me peace of mind / Goodnight sweetheart goodnight / Up the mountain / Give me back my heart / Golden teardrops / Blues in the letter / 219 train / Live it up / There is something on your mind / Secret love / Walkin in the rain / Come back my love / Don't say tomorrow / For all we know.
Compact disc: released on Charly, Jan'87 by Charly Records. Dist: Charly, Cadillac

DOO-WOP OLDTOWN various artists (Various Artists).
Album: released on Sonet, Jun'80 by Sonet Records. Dist: PRT

DOO-WOP/ROCK,ROCK,ROCK'N'ROLL various artists (Various Artists).
Album: released on Mercury (USA), Jul'83 by Import Records. Dist: IMS Distribution, Polygram Distribution

Do Piano

AGAIN.
Tracks: / Again.
Single (7"): released on Record Shack, Jul'86 by Record Shack Records. Dist: PRT

Single (12"): released on Record Shack, Jul'86 by Record Shack Records. Dist: PRT

Doppelganger

COMMUNICATION BREAKDOWN.
Single (7"): released on Manhattan, Apr'85 by President Records. Dist: Jazz Music, Swift, Taylors, Chris Wellard

Single (12"): released on Manhattan, Apr'85 by President Records. Dist: Jazz Music, Swift, Taylors, Chris Wellard

MISTY EYED 33.
Single (7"): released on Holyrood, Nov'82 by Holyrood Records. Dist: Pinnacle

Dorane Parade

YOU ARE MY FRIEND.
Single (7"): released on Zippo, Feb'85

Doran, Felix

FOX CHASE.
Cassette: released on Folktracks, Nov'79 by Folktracks Cassettes. Dist: Folktracks

LAST OF THE TRAVELLING PIPERS, (THE).
Album: released on Topic, '81 Dist: Roots Distribution

Dorchester, Des

POOR LITTLE ANGELINE (Dorchester, Des & His Orchestra).
Single (7"): released on Dingles, Aug'83 by Dingles Records. Dist: Projection

Dore, Charlie

LISTEN.
Album: released on Chrysalis, Aug'81 by Chrysalis Records. Dist: CBS

Cassette: released on Chrysalis, Aug'81 by Chrysalis Records. Dist: CBS

Do Re Mi

DOMESTIC HARMONY.
Tracks: / Theme from Uncle Jim / After the volcano / Idiot grin / Cuttlefish beach / Warnings moving clockwise / Black crocodiles / Man overboard / Big accident / Racing to zero / New taboos / 1000 Mouths.
Compact disc: released on Virgin, Jul'87 by Virgin Records. Dist: EMI, Virgin Distribution

Album: released on Virgin, Feb'86 by Virgin Records. Dist: EMI, Virgin Distribution

Cassette: released on Virgin, Feb'86 by Virgin Records. Dist: EMI, Virgin Distribution

DO-RE-MI original London cast.
Album: released on That's Entertainment, Sep'84 by That's Entertainment Records. Dist: Pinnacle, PRT

Cassette: released on That's Entertainment, Sep'84 by That's Entertainment Records. Dist: Pinnacle, PRT

MAN OVERBOARD.
Tracks: / Man overboard / Warning moving clockwise / Idiot grin / Fish tank.
Notes: Tracks on 12" version only:- Idiot grin, Fish tank.
Single (7"): released on Virgin, May'86 by Virgin Records. Dist: EMI, Virgin Distribution

Single (12"): released on Virgin, May'86 by Virgin Records. Dist: EMI, Virgin Distribution

Single (12"): released on Virgin, Jul'85 by Virgin Records. Dist: EMI, Virgin Distribution

Dorham, Kenny

AFRO-CUBAN.
Tracks: / Afrodisia / Lotus flower / Minor's holiday / Minor's holiday (Alternate take) / Basheer's dream / K.D.'s motion / La villa / Venita's dance / K.D.'s cab ride.
Compact disc: released on Manhattan-Blue Note, Aug'87 by EMI America Records (USA). Dist: EMI

Compact disc: released on Blue Note, Aug'87 by EMI Records. Dist: EMI

BUT BEAUTIFUL.
Double Album: released on Milestone, Sep'76 by Ace Records. Dist: PRT

DEXTER GORDON/KENNY DORHAM (Dorham, Kenny & Dexter Gordon).
Album: released on Jazz Reactivation, Jul'82 Dist: PRT

EASE IT.
Album: released on Muse, Apr'81 by Peerless Records. Dist: Lugtons Distributors

MUSIC OF KENNY DORHAM.
Notes: With Cedar Walton/Ron Carter and B. Higgins etc.
Album: released on Uptown (USA), Nov'86 by Uptown Records. Dist: Jazz Music

NEW BLUE HORNS (Dorham, Kenny & Chet Baker).
Notes: For full information see: Baker, Chet/Kenny Dorham.

QUIET KENNY.
Album:

Compact disc: released on JVC Fantasy (Japan), Nov'86

Compact disc: released on Carrere, Apr'87 by Carrere Records. Dist: PRT, Spartan

ROUND ABOUT MIDNIGHT AT THE CAFE BOHEMIA Vol II.
Tracks: / Royal roost / My heart stood still / Prophet, The / K.D.'s Blues / Riffin' / Who cares / Monaco / N Y Theme.
Compact disc: released on Manhattan-Blue Note, Jun'87 by EMI America Records (USA). Dist: EMI

ROUND ABOUT MIDNIGHT AT THE CAFE BOHEMIA Vol. 1.
Tracks: / Monaco / 'Round midnight / Mexico City / Night in Tunisia / Autumn in New York / Hill's edge / K.D's blues / Who cares / Mexico City (alternate take).
Compact disc: released on Manhattan-Blue Note, Jul'87 by EMI America Records (USA). Dist: EMI

ROUND MIDNIGHT AT THE CAFE BOHEMIA.
Tracks: / Mexico City / Night in Tunisia / Autumn in New York / Hill's Edge / Monaco / Round Midnight.
Notes: Produced by Alfred Lyon.1986 Mahattan Records,a division of Capitol Records Inc.After leaving the Jazz Messengers,trumpeter Kenny Dorham decided to put togethera similar ensamble called Jazz Prophets with saxophinist J.R Montrose and pianist Bobby Timmons.Although the group was shortlived,we are fortunate that Blue Note was present one evening at The Cafe Bohemia to preserve this outstand-ing band with guest artist Kenny Burrell on several titles.Aside from the title tune,highlights such Dorham originals as'monaco''mexico city'and hill's edge'.
Album: released on Blue Note, May'86 by EMI Records. Dist. EMI

SCANDIA SKIES.
Album: released on Steeplechase, Apr'81

TROMPETA TOCCATA.
Album: released on Blue Note, Jul'85 by EMI Records. Dist: EMI Deleted '86.

UNA MAS.
Tracks: / Una mas (one more time) / Straight ahead / Sao Paulo / If ever I would leave you.
Notes: P 1987 Manhattan Records,a division of Capitol Records Inc.
Compact disc: released on Manhattan-Blue Note, May'87 by EMI America Records (USA). Dist: EMI

Dorian Gray

TOUCH.
Tracks: / Touch.
Single (12"): released on Leeds Independent, May'86 by Revolver Records. Dist: Cartel

Doris

LOVE IS FIRE.
Single (7"): released on Sonet, May'86 by Sonet Records. Dist: PRT

Dormannu

DEGENERATE.
Single (12"): released on Illuminated, Mar'85 by IKF Records. Dist: Pinnacle, Cartel, Jetstar

DREAD, (THE).
Single (12"): released on Illuminated, Feb'85 by IKF Records. Dist: Pinnacle. Cartel, Jetstar

POWDERED LOVER.
Single (7"): released on Illuminated, Mar'85 by IKF Records. Dist: Pinnacle, Cartel, Jetstar

RETURN OF QUEBEC.
Album: released on Illuminated, Feb'85 by IKF Records. Dist. Pinnacle, Cartel Jetstar

Dorper, Ralph

RAZORHEAD, (THE).
Single (12"): released on Operation Twilight, Jan'83

Dors, Diana

SWINGIN' DORS.
Tracks: / Point of no return(The) / That's how it is / Let there be love / Namely you / Imagination / Roller Coaster Blues / Gentleman is a dope(The) / April heart / In love for the first time / Crazy he calls me / Come by sunday / Tired of love.
Notes: When first released in 1960 on PYE Records,this album caused a sensation.firstlybecause it showed that,not only was Miss Dors stunning to behold (which everyoneknew anyway)but also has a terrific voice.Now 25 years later we are thrilled that Conifer has picked up the exclusive rights to this lovely album which has been unavailable for many years.We have packaged the delightful goods in a supernew,deliciously designed sleeve showing Diana at her sultry sexy best.With WallyScott Arrangements swingin' along Diana is obviously having a great time singingsuch goldies as 'Crazy He calls Me'and,'The Point Of No Return'and just listen to her sizzle on the sensual 'Roller Coaster Blues'Phew!
Album: released on Conifer, Dec'85 by Conifer Records. Dist: Conifer

Cassette: released on Conifer, Dec'85 by Conifer Records. Dist: Conifer

Album: released on Conifer, Dec'85 by Conifer Records. Dist: Conifer

WHERE DID THEY GO?.
Single (7"): released on Nomis, Dec'81 by Simon Napier-Bell. Dist: Pinnacle, PRT Distribution

Dorsey Brothers

HARLEM LULLABY.
Notes: Featuring Mildred Bailey/Bing Crosby/Ethel Waters
Album: released on Hep, Nov'86 by H.R. Taylor Records. Dist: Jazz Music, Cadillac Music, JSU, Taylors, Wellard, Chris, Zodiac, Swift, Fast Forward

YOUNG DORSEY BROTHERS, 1928-30, (THE) (Dorsey Brothers Orchestra).
Double Album: released on World Records, Oct'80 Dist: Polygram

Cassette: released on World Records, Oct'80 Dist: Polygram

Dorsey, Don

BACH BUSTERS.
Compact disc: by H.R. Taylor. Dist: Unknown

Dorsey, Jack

BIG BAND GOLD 50 years of swing (Dorsey, Jack Orchestra).

BIG BAND GOLD: 50 YEARS OF SWING (Dorsey, Jack Orchestra).
Triple album / cassette: released on Ronco, Nov'83

Triple album / cassette: released on Ronco, Nov'83

Triple album / cassette: released on Ronco, Nov'83

Triple album / cassette: released on Ronco, Nov'83

JACK DORSEY BIG BAND.
Compact disc: released on K-Tel, Jan'86 by K-Tel Records. Dist: Record Merchandisers Distribution, Taylors, Terry Blood Distribution, Wynd-Up Distribution, Relay Distribution, Pickwick Distribution, Solomon & Peres Distribution, Polygram

OF CARPENTERS AND KINGS (Dorsey, Jack Galaxy of Strings).
Album: by BBC Records & Tapes. Dist: EMI, PRT.

Dorsey, Jimmy

CAN ANYONE EXPLAIN?.
Album: released on Astan (USA), Mar'85

CONTRASTS 1945 (Dorsey, Jimmy Orchestra).
Album: released on Magic, Jul'87 Dist: Jazz Music, Submarine, Swift, Chris Wellard, Conifer

DORSEYLAND BAND.
Album: released on Hindsight(UK), Apr'85 Dist: Jazz Music

JIMMY DORSEY & HIS ORCHESTRA, 1944-47 (Dorsey, Jimmy & His Orchestra).
Album: released on First Heard, Apr'79 by Submarine Records. Dist: Conifer, Taylors

JIMMY DORSEY ORCHESTRA (Dorsey, Jimmy Orchestra).
Album: released on Queen-Disc, Apr'81 Dist: Celtic Music, JSU, Jazz Horizons, Jazz Music

JIMMY DORSEY, VOL 10, 1939.
Album: released on Ajax, Apr'79

JIMMY DORSEY, VOL 1, 1935-36.
Album: released on Ajax, Apr'79

JIMMY DORSEY, VOL 2, 1936.
Album: released on Ajax, Apr'79

JIMMY DORSEY, VOL 3, 1936-37.
Album: released on Ajax, Apr'79

JIMMY DORSEY, VOL 4, 1937-38.
Album: released on Ajax, Apr'79

JIMMY DORSEY, VOL 5, 1938.
Album: released on Ajax, Apr'79

JIMMY DORSEY, VOL 6, 1938.
Album: released on Ajax, Apr'79

JIMMY DORSEY, VOL 7, 1938.
Album: released on Ajax, Apr'79

JIMMY DORSEY, VOL 8, 1938-39.
Album: released on Ajax, Apr'79

JIMMY DORSEY, VOL 9, 1939.
Album: released on Ajax, Apr'79

MOSTLY 1940 (Dorsey, Jimmy Orchestra).
Album: released on Circle(USA), Mar'84 by Jazzology Records (USA). Dist: Jazz Music, Swift, Chris Wellard

MUSCAT RAMBLE (Dorsey, Jimmy & His Dorseylanders).
Tracks: / Muscat ramble / Royal garden blues / Sweet Lorraine / Charley my boy / Memphis blues / That's a-plenty / Johnson rag / Wolverine blues / Beale street blues / Panama / Jazz me blues.
Album: released on Swinghouse, Mar'87 Dist: Jazz Music Distribution, Swift Distribution, Chris Wellard Distribution

Cassette: released on Swinghouse, Mar'87 Dist: Jazz Music Distribution, Swift Distribution, Chris Wellard Distribution

MUSCRAT RAMBLE.
Album: released on Swinghouse, '84 Dist: Jazz Music Distribution, Swift Distribution, Chris Wellard Distribution

SPOTLIGHTING THE FABULOUS DORSEYS.
Album: released on Giants of Jazz, Oct'84 by Hasmick Promotions Ltd.. Dist: Counterpoint, Jazz Music, Taylors, Swift, Mainline, Wellard, Chris

Dorsey, Lee

ALL WAYS FUNKY.
Album: released on Charly(R&B), Feb'82 by Charly Records. Dist: Charly, Cadillac

CAN YOU HEAR ME?.
Tracks: / Mellow good time, A / Working in a coal mine / Can you hear me / Greatest love / Mellow good time, A / Mexico / Get out of my love woman / Ride your pony / Confusion / Holy cow / Don't you ever leave me / Neighbours daughter / Little dab a doya, A / Kitty cat song / Shor / Shortnin' bread / So long / People I wish you could see me / Work work work / Here comes the hurt again / Hello mama / Feelin' / My old car / Everthing I do gonh be funky / Little dab a doya, A.
Compact disc: released on Charly, Jan'87 by Charly Records. Dist: Charly, Cadillac

GET OUT OF MY LIFE WOMAN.
Single (7"): released on Charly, Mar'81 by Charly Records. Dist: Charly, Cadillac

GONH BE FUNK.
Album: released on Charly(R&B), '85 by Charly Records. Dist: Charly, Cadillac

WORKING IN THE COALMINE.
Album: released on Topline, Nov'84 by Charly Records. Dist: Charly Distribution

Single (7"): released on Charly, Jul'80 by Charly Records. Dist: Charly, Cadillac

Single (7"): released on Old Gold, Jul'82 by Old Gold Records. Dist: Lightning, Jazz Music, Spartan, Counterpoint

Single (7"): released on Creole, Aug'84 by Creole Records. Dist: Rhino, PRT

Single (7"): released on SMP, Jun'84 Dist: Jetstar, PRT

WORKIN' IN A COALMINE.
Single (7"): released on SMP, Jun'84 Dist: Jetstar, PRT

Single (7"): released on Creole Replay, Aug'84 by Creole Records. Dist: PRT, Rhino

Single (7"): released on Old Gold, Jul'82 by Old Gold Records. Dist: Lightning, Jazz Music, Spartan, Counterpoint

Single (7"): released on Charly, Jul'80 by Charly Records. Dist: Charly, Cadillac

Album: released on Topline, Nov'84 by Charly Records. Dist: Charly Distribution

Cassette: released on Topline, Nov'84 by Charly Records. Dist: Charly Distribution

Dorsey, Tommy

1935 SESSIONS.
Album: released on Halcyon (USA), Jun'86 by Halcyon Records (USA). Dist: Jazz Music, Conifer, Taylors

1950-1952 (Dorsey, Tommy & His Orchestra).
Tracks: / Picalily dilly / Let me love you tonight / Isn't it romantic (medley) / I kiss your hand Madame / This is romance / Sleepy lagoon / Wagon wheels / Non-drastic / Life is just a bowl of cherries / Sweet Georgie Brown / Bells of St.Mary's, The / I'm in the mood for love / Shaver's shivers / Maybe / Taking a chance on love / My sweetie went away.
Notes: Featuring Charlie Shavers, Sam Donahue, Boomie Richman, Walt Levinsky, Louis Bellson.
Album: released on Solid Sender, Apr'81 Dist: JSU, Jazz Music

AT THE FAT MANS.
Tracks: / Blue skies / Dawn on the desert / At the Fat mans / Bingo bango boffo / Marie / Chloe / Well git it / At sundown / Opus 1 / Candy / Continental / Call you sweetheart / Feels so good / Pussy Willow / Broadcasts from 1945-1948.
Album: released on Hep, '81 by H.R. Taylor Records. Dist: Jazz Music, Cadillac Music, JSU, Taylors, Wellard, Chris, Zodiac, Swift, Fast Forward

BEST OF FRANK SINATRA & TOMMY DORSEY (see Sinatra, Frank) (Dorsey, Tommy & Frank Sinatra).

BEST OF..., THE (Dorsey, Tommy & Frank Sinatra).
Tracks: / Stardust / I think of you / There are such things / How about you / I'll never smile again / I'll be seeing you / Without a song / Street of dreams / Poor you / April played the fiddle / This love of mine / The one I love / I guess I'll have to dream the rest / We three.
Album: released on RCA (Brazil), Jan'84

Cassette: released on RCA (Brazil), Jan'84

BEST OF TOMMY DORSEY, THE.
Tracks: / Maria / Star dust / Little white lies / I'll never smile again / Yes Indeed / Boogie woogie / Opus one / Song of India / Who / Royal garden blues / Once in a while / I'm getting sentimental over you.
Notes: Originally released in April 1980 on INTS 5017/INTK 5017
Album: released on RCA International, '84

Cassette: released on RCA International, '84

BIG REUNION PART 1.
Album: released on First Heard, '84 by Submarine Records. Dist: Conifer, Taylors

Cassette: released on First Heard, '84 by Submarine Records. Dist: Conifer, Taylors

FRANK SINATRA WITH... (Dorsey, Tommy & His Orchestra).
Tracks: / Sinner kissed an angel, A / Polka dots and moonbeams / Fools rush in (where angels fear to tread) / Imagination / I could make you care / This love of mine / Without a song / Everything happens to me / Violets for your furs / sky fell down, The / Be careful, it's my heart / In the blue of the evening.
Album: by RCA Records. Dist: RCA, Roots, Swift, Wellard, Chris, I & B, Solomon & Peres Distribution

IN CONCERT.
Album: released on RCA (Germany), May'84

Cassette: released on RCA (Germany), May'84

INDISPENSABLE TOMMY DORSEY VOL.1/2 1935-1937.
Tracks: / Weary blues / I'm getting sentimental over you / Music goes round and round, The / Rhythm in my nursery rhymes / I'm shooting high / Day I let you get away, The / Rhythm saved the world / Stardust / Royal garden blues / Jada / At the codfish ball / Mary had a little lamb / You've gotta eat your spinach baby / On the beach at Bali Bali / San Francisco / That's plenty / After you've gone / Head over heels in love / Sleep / Maple leaf tag / Keepin' out of mischief now / Melody in F / Song of India / Marie / Liebestraum / Mendelssohn's spring song / Jammin' / They can't take that away from me / Humoresque / Beale street blues.
Double Album: released on RCA (France), '83 by RCA Records. Dist: Discovery

INDISPENSABLE TOMMY DORSEY VOL.3/4.
Double Album: released on RCA (Germany), Aug'84

JAMBOREE 1935-6 (Dorsey, Tommy & His Orchestra).
Album: released on Halcyon (USA), Jul'87 by Halcyon Records (USA). Dist: Jazz Music, Conifer, Taylors

Cassette: released on Halcyon (USA), Jul'87 by Halcyon Records (USA). Dist: Jazz Music, Conifer, Taylors

LEGEND VOLUMES I-III, THE.
Tracks: / On the sunny side of the street / Cicago / Chloe (Song of the swamp) / Hucklebuck, The / It's delovely / I get a kick out of you / I'm getting sentimental over you / Star dust / That's a plenty / After you've gone / Keepin' out of mischief now / Liebestraum / Satan takes a holiday / Stop, look and listen / Stop, look and listen / Beale Stret blues / Night and day / Smoke gets in your eyes / Once in a while / Lady is a tramp, The / Who? / Little white lies / Shine on harvest moon / What'll I do / I hadn't anyone 'til you / A-tisket, a-tasket / Boogie woogie / You must have been a beautiful baby / Sweet Sue - just you / Hawaiian war chant / Milenberg joys / tea for two / Night in Sudan / March of the toys / I'll be seeing you / Say it / This is the beginning of the end / Devil may care / East of the sun (and west of the moon) / I'll never smile again / Whispering / One I love, The (belongs to somebody else) / Do you know why? / Song of India / Marie / For you / Whatcha know Joe? / Yes indeed / Will you still be mine / Swing low sweet chariot / This love of mine / I guess I'll have to dream the rest / Loose lid special / Blue skies / Hallelujah / What is this thing called love? / Snooty little cutie / Well, git it / Street of dreams / Sleepy lagoon / Opus one.
Compact disc: released on RCA, Jan'87 by RCA Records. Dist: RCA, Roots, Swift, Wellard, Chris, I & B, Solomon & Peres Distribution

LITTLE WHITE LIES.
Tracks: / I've got a note / Royal Garden blues / Ja-Da / Maple leaf rag / Who / Little white lies / Symphony in Riffs / Copenhagen / Old black Joe / Well alright / Back to back / Stomp off.
Album: released on Joker, Apr'81 Dist: Counterpoint, Mainline, Record Services Distribution (Ireland)

LIVE AT THE MEADOWBROOK - FEBRUARY 11 1941.
Album: released on Fanfare, Apr'79 by Ferroway/Fanfare Records. Dist: PRT

MAKING BIG BAND HISTORY (1944).
Album: released on First Heard, Feb'81 by Submarine Records. Dist: Conifer, Taylors

ONE NIGHT STAND 1940.
Album: released on Sandy Hook (USA), Apr'79 Dist: Swift, Jazz Music, IMS-Polygram

ON THE SUNNY SIDE OF THE STREET.
Album: released on Saar Giants Of Jazz (Italy), Sep'85 Dist: Mainline

Cassette: released on Saar Giants Of Jazz (Italy), Sep'85 Dist: Mainline

SENTIMENTAL JOURNEY.
Double Album: released on Cambra, Apr'85 by Cambra Records. Dist: IDS, Conifer

Double cassette: released on Cambra, Apr'85 by Cambra Records. Dist: IDS, Conifer

SINGS THE STANDARDS.
Tracks: / I'll be seeing you / Whispering somewhere a voice is calling blue skies / Stardust / Without a song / Hear my song Violetta / Yours is my heart alone / East of the sun / One I love (belongs to somebody else), The / Let's get away from it all / Fools rush in / I'll never smile again / Polka dots and moonbeams / Imagination / Daybreak / Violets for your furs / Everything happens to me / How about you / This love of mine.
Notes: Featuring vocal Frank Sinatra. Originally released in October 1981 on INTS 5098/INTK 5098
Album: released on RCA International, '84

Cassette: released on RCA International, '84

SOLID SWING.
Tracks: / Chez faire / Capital idea / Swanee River / Continental / Chloe / On the sunny side of the street / Puddle wump / Non drastic / Sweet Georgie Brown / Hollywood hat / Lullaby in boogie / Song of India / Swing ti me up in Harlem / Why begin again / Summertime / At the fat man's / Brotherly jump / Harlem Express / I'm beginning to see the light / Midriff / Swing high / Dry bones / Another one of them things / Coming through the Rye.
Notes: Featuring a super-band with supersound and super soloists: Louis Bellson/Tommy Dorsey/Irving Josephs/Walt Lovinsky/Boomie Richman/Doc Severinson/Charlie Shavers. Mono....
Album: released on First Heard, '84 by Submarine Records. Dist: Conifer, Taylors

Cassette: released on First Heard, '84 by Submarine Records. Dist: Conifer, Taylors

SONG OF INDIA.
Compact disc: released on Dance Band Days, Jul'87 Dist: Geoff's Records International

STORY.
Album: released on Big Band International, Oct'79 Dist: Swift

SWING HIGH.
Tracks: / Swing high / Always / Pussy Willow / That's it.
Album: released on Astan (USA), Mar'85

SWINGING BIG BANDS, THE 1937-46 (Dorsey, Tommy & His Orchestra).
Tracks: / Boogie woogie / Copenhagen / Lonesome road, The / Hawaiian War Chant / Sleepy lagoon / L.A. April 1946 / Then I'll be happy / Liebestraum / Song of India / Opus NR / I'm getting sentimental over you / Once in a while / Music, maestro please.
Album: released on Joker, Apr'81 Dist: Counterpoint, Mainline, Record Services Distribution (Ireland)

THIS IS TOMMY DORSEY.
Album: released on RCA (Germany), '83

THIS IS TOMMY DORSEY VOL.2.
Album: released on RCA (Germany), '83

TOMMY AND JIMMY DORSEY (Dorsey, Tommy & His Orchestra).
Album: released on Bright Orange, Apr'79 Dist: Swift

TOMMY DORSEY.
Album: released on Bright Orange, Apr'79 Dist: Swift

TOMMY DORSEY COLLECTION, THE.
Album: released on Deja Vu, Aug'85 by Deja Vu Records. Dist: Counterpoint Distribution, Record Services Distribution (Ireland)

Cassette: released on Deja Vu, Aug'85 by Deja Vu Records. Dist: Counterpoint Distribution, Record Services Distribution (Ireland)

TOMMY DORSEY & COMPANY (Dorsey, Tommy & Company).
Album: released on First Heard, '84 by Submarine Records. Dist: Conifer, Taylors

Cassette: released on First Heard, '84 by Submarine Records. Dist: Conifer, Taylors

TOMMY DORSEY & HIS ORCHESTRA.
Tracks: / I'm getting sentimental over you / Maple leaf rag / Melody in F / Marie / Twilight in Turkey / Song of India / Stop, look and listen / Liebestraum / Boogie woogie / Smoke gets in your eyes / Lady is a tramp, The / Who / Shine on harvest moon / Washboard blues / Chinatown / Davenport blues / Hawaiian war chart / Tin roof blues / Symphony in riffs / Milenberg joys / Stomp it off / Swanee River / Easy does it / On the sunny side of the street / Loose lid special / Minor goes a muggin', The / Blue blazes / At the fat man's / Well git it / Chloe / Opus No.1.
Double Album:

TOMMY DORSEY & HIS ORCHESTRA WITH FRANK SINATRA (Dorsey, Tommy & His Orchestra with Frank Sinatra).
Tracks: / Marie / Too romantic / Polka dots and moonbeams / This is the beginning of the end / Hear my song violetta / I haven't time to be a millionaire / Head on my pillow / I'll never smile again / One I love, The / Call of the canyon, The / Shadows on the sand / Do you know why / Yearning / Not so long ago / Star dust / How am I to know / Oh! Look at me now / You lucky people you / Without a song / Everything happens to me / Let's get away from it all / Love me as I am / This love of mine / Blue skies / How do you do without me? / Violets for your furs / How about you / My melancholy baby / Dig down deep / It started all over again / I'll take Tallulah / Song is you, The.
Double Album: released on RCA (France), '83 by RCA Records. Dist: Discovery

TOMMY DORSEY ORCHESTRA (Dorsey, Tommy & His Orchestra).
Tracks: / Jump time / Milenberg joys / Sweet potato / Hawaiian war chant / Song of India / Blues no more / Swing low sweet chariot / I say I'm sorry / Quiet please / Easy does it / March of the toy soldiers / I know that you know.
Album: released on Jazz Live, Apr'81

TOMMY & JIMMY DORSEY ORCHESTRA (Dorsey, Tommy & Jimmy Orchestra).
Tracks: / By heck / Stop,look and listen / Milenberg joys / St. Louis blues / Honeysuckle rose / Basin St. blues / Weary blues / Tailspin / That eccentric rag / Dese dem dose / Dippermouth blues.
Album: released on Kings Of Jazz, Apr'81 Dist: Jazz Horizons, Jazz Music, Celtic Music

D'Ossche, Albert

CROSSOVER (D'Ossche, Albert & Robert Force).
Tracks: / Salvador do bahia / Spring of '65 / In the fall / Pokerface smile / Workaday daddy / Tabac allegria / Paradise boy (hush your eyes) / Sing sailor / Krummi (the raven) / Like a ship.
Album: released on Kicking Mule, Aug'80 by Sonet. Dist: Roots, PRT-Pye Distribution

Doss, Tommy

OF THE SONGS OF THE PIONEERS.
Tracks: / Call (The) / So much to remember / If you would only be mine / I invented the word / Memory (The) / Trouble in mind / Rosa / King of the fools / Sing a sad song / I care no more / Every fool has a rainbow.
Album: released on Bear Family, Jun'87 by Bear Family Records. Dist: Rollercoaster Distribution, Swift

Do They Mean Us?

DO THEY MEAN US? various artists (Various Artists).

Dotrice Family

READ PETER PAN.
Double cassette: released on Conifer, Dec'85 by Conifer Records. Dist: Conifer

Dotrice, Roy

BARDELL & PICKWICK.
Double Album: released on Argo, '78 by Decca Records. Dist: Polygram

BRIEF LIVES.
Double Album: released on Argo, Nov'74 by Decca Records. Dist: Polygram

CHRISTMAS CAROL, A By Charles Dickens.
Double Album: released on Argo, Nov'77 by Decca Records. Dist: Polygram

PETER PAN AND HIS FAMILY.
Triple album / cassette: released on Argo, Nov'77 by Decca Records. Dist: Polygram

READS CHRISTMAS CAROLS.
Double cassette: released on Conifer, Dec'85 by Conifer Records. Dist: Conifer

SCENES FROM WATERSHIP DOWN.
Album: released on Argo, Sep'78 by Decca Records. Dist: Polygram

Double

BLUE.
Tracks: / Woman of the world / I know a place / Captain of her heart (The) / Your prayer takes me off / Rangoon moon / Urban nomad / Love is a plane / Tomorrow.
Album: released on Polydor, Feb'86 by Polydor Records. Dist: Polygram, Polydor

Cassette: released on Polydor, Feb'86 by Polydor Records. Dist: Polygram, Polydor

Compact disc: released on Polydor, Feb'86 by Polydor Records. Dist: Polygram, Polydor

Double Deckers

DOUBLE DECKERS Various artists (Various Artists).
Tracks: / Just an illusion / Never let you go / Just a little bit / Love you've been fakin', The / Ease your mind / Jingo / Feels like I'm in love / Love is gonna be on your side / Do it ('til your satisfied) / Lock it up / Take your time / Nice and slow / I like plastic / I can't turn away / Puerto Rico / I like what you're doing to me / You don't like my music / Nice and soft / It's just a groove / Dancin' and prancin'.
Double Album: released on Red Bus, Nov'82 by Red Bus Records. Dist: PRT

Double cassette: released on Red Bus, Nov'82 by Red Bus Records. Dist: PRT

Double Image

IN LANDS I NEVER SAW.
Album: released on Celestial Harmonies, Feb'87 by TM Records. Dist: PRT

Cassette: released on Celestial Harmonies, Feb'87 by TM Records. Dist: PRT

Compact disc: released on TM Records, Feb'87

Double Twinspin

DOUBLE TWINSPIN VOL.1 (Various Artists).
Album: released on Wild Enterprise, Apr'87

Double Vision

NEW DAY.
Single (7"): released on And, Aug'84 Dist: PRT

Douce France

DOUCE FRANCE Various artists (Various Artists).
Double Album: released on EMI (France), '83 by EMI Records. Dist: Conifer

Doucet, Camey

CAJUN GOODIES.
Album: released on Swallow (USA), Feb'79 Dist: Swift Distribution

CAJUN GOOD TIME MUSIC.
Album:

CAMEY DOUCET ET MUSIQUE.
Album: released on Swallow (USA), Feb'79 Dist: Swift Distribution

Doucet, Michael

CHRISTMAS BAYOU.
Album: released on Swallow, Jun'87

PARLEZ NOUS A BOINE (Doucet, Michael & Bea Soleil).
Album: released on Arhoolie, Mar'85 by Arhoolie Records. Dist: Projection, Topic, Jazz Music, Swift, Roots

Doug

DEBORAH.
Single (7"): released on Shattered, Oct'82 Dist: Pinnacle

Doughty, Johnny

ROUND RYE BAY FOR MORE Traditional songs from the Sussex coast.
Tracks: / Herrings' heads / Wreck of the Northfleet, The / When I was single / Golden vanity, The / Saucy sailor, The / Baltimore / While going round the Cape / Round Rye Bay for more / Spanish ladies / Sailor's alphabet, The / Mermaid marry me / I'm going to be mother today / Barbara Allen / My boy Billy / Dick Turpin / Let her go back / Rye Harbour girl / Streets of Port Arthur, The.
Album: released on Topic, '81 Dist: Roots Distribution

Douglas, Carl

GOLDEN HOUR OF CARL DOUGLAS.
Album: released on Golden Hour, Jun'79 by PRT Records. Dist: PRT

Cassette: released on Golden Hour, Jun'79 by PRT Records. Dist: PRT Deleted '81

KUNG FU FIGHTING.
Single (7"): released on PRT, Apr'79 by PRT Records. Dist: PRT

Single (12"): released on Old Gold, Jul'82 by Old Gold Records. Dist: Lightning, Jazz Music, Spartan, Counterpoint

STIR A LITTLE SWEETNESS IN ME.
Single (12"): released on Landslide, Dec'82 by Dorane Ltd.

Douglas, Carol

20 GOLDEN PIECES OF CAROL DOUGLAS.
Tracks: / Doctor's orders / Midnight love affair / Light my fire / Burnin' / Night fever / Baby don't let this good love die / We're gonna make it / Dancing queen / All night long / I fell in love with love / Take me (make me lose control) / Hurricane is coming tonight / We do it / I want to stay with you / I'll take a chance on love / Who what when where and why / I got you on my mind / Boy you know just what I'm after / Friend in need, A / Will we make it tonight.
Album: released on Bulldog, Oct'81 by Bulldog Records. Dist: President Distribution, Spartan, Swift, Taylor, H.R.

Album: released on Bulldog, '81 by Bulldog Records. Dist: President Distribution, Spartan, Swift, Taylor, H.R.

Douglas, Craig

LOVE IS A CAROUSEL.
Single (7"): released on Easy On The Ear, Aug'83 by Battersea. Dist: PRT

ONLY SIXTEEN.
Tracks: / Our favourite melodies / Time / Hundred pounds of clay, A / Another you / Change of heart, A / Rainbows / Riddle of love / When my little girl is smiling / Pretty blue eyes / No greater love / Girl next door, The / Wsh it were me / Sandy / Hello spring / Oh what a day / Dream lover / Ring-a-ding / Our favourite melodies / Time / Hundred pounds of clay / Another you / Change of heart / Rainbows / Riddle of love / When my little girl is smiling / Teenager in love, A / Only sixteen / Pretty blue eyes / No greater love / Girl next door, The / Wish it were me / Sandy / Hello spring / Oh what a day / Dream lover / Ring-a-ding.
Album: released on See For Miles, Nov'84 by See For Miles Records. Dist: Pinnacle

ONLY SIXTEEN.
Tracks: / Pretty Blue Eyes / Only sixteen.
Single (7"): released on Old Gold, Mar'87 by Old Gold Records. Dist: Lightning, Jazz Music, Spartan, Counterpoint

Douglas, Dev

GUITAR MAGIC.
Tracks: / San Marco / Leaving / Celso / Bendy / Turnip Green rag / Tell me / Lonesome / JW 3 / Sunshine in my eyes / Wiggle / Zapata / Toad's tune.
Album: released on Magnum Force, Apr'84 by Magnum Music Group Ltd. Dist: Magnum Music Group Ltd, PRT, Spartan

Douglas, Duncan

FREEDOM.
Tracks: / Freedom (Inst).
Single (12"): released on Live, Dec'86 Dist: Jetstar, PRT

Douglas, Jerry

FLUXOLOGY.
Album: released on Rounder, May'79 Dist: Roots Distribution

Page 307

UNDER THE WIRE.
Tracks: / T.O.B. / Dhaka rock / Time gone by / Monroe's hornpipe / Before the blues / Trip to Kilkerrin / Grant's corner / Redhill / Two friends / New day, A.
Notes: Jerry Douglas - who's played dobro and guitar on literally dozens of million sellers recorded in Nashville.
Album: released on MCA, Jun'86 by MCA Records. Dist: Polygram, MCA

Cassette: released on MCA, Jun'86 by MCA Records. Dist: Polygram, MCA

Compact disc: released on MCA, Apr'87 by MCA Records. Dist: Polygram, MCA

Douglas, Joe

VISAGE (Douglas, Joe Trio).
Tracks: / This girl / Promenade / Blue horizons / What do you do? / Visage / Silvana / Into living.
Album: released on Spotlite, '83 by Spotlite Records. Dist: Cadillac, Jazz Music, Spotlite

Douglas, John

SCOTTISH WELCOME, A.
Tracks: / Mary of Argyll / Tartan, The / Take me back / Lassie come and dance with me / Bonnie Gallaway / Will you walk? / Granny's highland hame / Dark island, The / Massacre of Glencoe / Fiona / Fond kiss, A / Roses of Prince Charles / Scotland the brave / Lochnagar / Dae ye mind? / Road and miles to Dundee.
Album: released on Lochshore, Nov'82 by Klub Records. Dist: PRT

Cassette: released on Lochshore, Nov'82 by Klub Records. Dist: PRT

Douglas, Johnny

MANY SIDES OF JOHNNY DOUGLAS AND HIS ORCHESTRA, THE (Douglas, Johnny & His Orchestra).
Tracks: / Feelings / What I did for love / Deep purple / You only live twice / I write the songs / Red roses for a blue lady / Nobody does it better / Shadow of your smile / Aquarius / Hello Dolly / Please / Pennies from Heaven / What are you doing the rest of your life? / Theme from Charlie's Angels / Theme from The Railway Children / Look of love, The / Calcutta / Too many rings around Rosie / I don't want to walk without you / Dancing queen / You light up my life / You'll never find another love like mine / Tea for two.
Album: released on Cambra, '83 by Cambra Records. Dist: IDS, Conifer

Cassette: released on Cambra, '83 by Cambra Records. Dist: IDS, Conifer

Douglas, Johnny & His Or-

MANY SIDES OF, THE.
Tracks: / Feelings / What I did for love / Deep purple / You only live twice / I write the songs / Red roses for a blue lady / Nobody does it better / Shadow of your smile / Aquarius / Hello Dolly / Please / Pennies from heaven / What are you doing for the rest of your life / Theme from Charlies Angels / Theme from the Railway Children / Look of love, The / Calcutta / Too many rings around Rosie / I don't want to walk without you / Dancing queen / You light up my life / You'll never find another love like mine / Tea for two.
Album: released on Cambra, Sep'86 by Cambra Records. Dist: IDS, Conifer

Cassette: released on Cambra, Sep'86 by Cambra Records. Dist: IDS, Conifer

Douglas, Johnny Strings,The

ROMANCE WITH THE CLASSICS.
Tracks: / Melody in F / Fantaisie impromptu / Piano concerto K 467 / Consolation No.3 / Lullaby / Clair de Lune / Romance / Nocturne Op.9 No.2 / Piano Concerto / Etude Op.10 No.3 / L'inverno (from "Four Seasons") Concerto No.4 Op.8 / Return to Mijas / Chant sans paroles / Ballade Op.23 / Romance (Spanish folk song) / Barcarolle (The Seasons - June).
Album: released on Dulcima, Sep'87 by Living Productions Records. Dist: H.R. Taylor

Cassette: released on Dulcima, Sep'87 by Living Productions Records. Dist: H.R. Taylor

Compact disc: released on Dulcima, Sep'87 by Living Productions Records. Dist: H.R. Taylor

Douglas, K.C.

COOL DOWN AMENA.
Single (12"): released on Fashion, Mar'82 by Fashion Records. Dist: PRT, Jetstar

COUNTRY BOY, THE.
Album: released on Arhoolie, '81 by Arhoolie Records. Dist: Projection, Topic, Jazz Music, Swift, Roots

Douglas, Keith

BOOM.
Single (12"): released on Natty Congo, Dec'83 by Natty Congo Records. Dist: Jetstar

CALL IT OFF.
Single (12"): released on Oak Sound, Oct'84

COME OVER.
Single (12"): released on Natty Congo, Jun'85 by Natty Congo Records. Dist: Jetstar

FRONT LINE.
Single (12"): released on Zip, Jun'84 by Zip Records. Dist: Zip Distribution, Graduate

LOVE WITH STYLE.
Album: released on Hot Pepper, Aug'86 Dist: Jetstar

SOMETHING IN MY EYES.
Single (12"): released on London Gemi, May'84 Dist: Pinnacle

TEACHER NEVER TAUGHT ME.
Single (12"): released on His Majesty, Oct'81 Dist: Pinnacle

TRY LOVE AGAIN.
Single (12"): released on Fashion, Dec'82 by Fashion Records. Dist: PRT, Jetstar

WE'VE GOT TO BELIEVE.
Tracks: / We've got to believe / Believe (dub).
Single (12"): released on Hot Pepper, Mar'86 Dist: Jetstar

WHAT THE WORLD NEEDS.
Album: released on Natty Congo, Dec'85 by Natty Congo Records. Dist: Jetstar

YOU MOVE ME.
Single (12"): released on CSA, May'85 by CSA Records. Dist: PRT, Jetstar

ZION CITY.
Single (12"): released on 24 Karat, Nov'84 by 24 Karat Records. Dist: Jetstar

Douglas, Mona

SONGS IN MANX GAELIC (& OTHERS).
Cassette: released on Folktracks, Nov'79 by Folktracks Cassettes. Dist: Folktracks

Douglas, Shirley

HEART ON THE LOOSE, A.
Tracks: / First time ever I saw your face, The / Snowbird / Greensleeves / Heart on the loose / Right thing to do / Big yellow taxi / You've got a friend / Amazing grace / Try to remember / I'm gonna be a country girl again / Jamie / Everything I own / Wishing and wanting / Nobody knows / If that's what it takes / Until it's time for you to go.
Album: released on President, Oct'80 by President Records. Dist: Taylors, Spartan

Douglas, Tony

HOLLY HOLY.
Single (12"): released on Natty Congo, Dec'83 by Natty Congo Records. Dist: Jetstar

IT'S NOT BECAUSE I DON'T LOVE YOU.
Tracks: / It's not because I don't love you / It's not because I don't love you (version).
Single (12"): released on Love & Unity, Jun'86 Dist: Jetstar

YOUR LOVE.
Single (12"): released on Body Music, Jun'83 by Body Music Records. Dist: Jetstar

Dowe, Brent

DOWN HERE IN BABYLON.
Single (12"):

Dowlais Choir

FAMOUS CHOIRS OF WALES VOL.2 (Dowlais Male Choir).
Album: by Decca Records. Dist: Polygram

Down...

DOWN AT THE OL' BULL AND BUSH Various artists (Various Artists).
Cassette: released on AIM (Budget Cassettes), Feb'83

DOWN AT THE OLD PEBBLE MILL Various artists (Various Artists).
Album: released on BBC, '78 by BBC Records & Tapes. Dist: EMI, PRT, Pye

DOWN BEHIND THE RISE, 1947-1953 Force (Various Artists).
Notes: FEATURING: Jesse Thomas, Frankie Lee Simms, Lighnin' Hopkins, etc.
Album: released on Nighthawk, Dec'86 by Faulty Products Records. Dist: Pinnacle, Swift

DOWNHOME BLUES Various artists (Various Artists).
Album: released on JSP, Jan'84 by JSP Records. Dist: Swift, Projection

DOWNHOME DELTA BLUES 1949-1952 (Various Artists).
Notes: Featuring: Little Sam Davis, Earl Hooker, Big Joe Williams, Luther Huff etc.
Album: released on Nighthawk, Jan'87 by Faulty Products Records. Dist: Pinnacle, Swift

DOWN IN THE GROOVY Various artists (Various Artists).
Album: released on Krazy Kat (USA Import), Jan'84

DOWN ON BROADWAY & MAIN Compilation Recording (Various Artists).
Tracks: / Peg leg woman / Mistreating me / Rock 'n' Roll deacon / Tell me pretty baby / East St.Louis / Teach me how / St.Louis sunset twist / My baby has gone / She's my baby / Don't quit me baby / Nona baby / Look out pretty baby.
Album: released on Red Lightnin', Mar'87 by Red Lightnin' Records. Dist: Roots, Swift, Jazz Music, JSU, Pinnacle, Cartel, Wynd-Up Distribution

DOWN THE CUT Canal Age In Song with Various artists (Various Artists).
Album: released on Saydisc, Jun'76 by Saydisc Records. Dist: Essex, Harmonia Mundi, Roots, H.R. Taylor, Jazz Music, Swift, Projection, Gamut

DOWN TO EARTH The life and times of Mrs Emily Elliot (Various Artists).
Album: released on Saydisc, Oct'79 by Saydisc Records. Dist: Essex, Harmonia Mundi, Roots, H.R. Taylor, Jazz Music, Swift, Projection, Gamut

Down All The Days

JUST ONE WORD.
Single (7"): released on Outrider, Aug'83 by Outrider Records. Dist: Outrider Distribution

Downchild

BLOODRUN HOT.
Album: released on Attic, Apr'82 Dist: Pinnacle

Down County Boys

BETTER TIMES A' COMING.
Album: released on Tank, Dec'77 by Tank Records.

Downes, Julia

LET SLEEPING DOGS LIE.
Album: released on Naive, Mar'83 by Naive. Dist: Spartan

Single (7"): released on Naive, Nov'82 by Naive. Dist: Spartan

MISSION TONITE.
Single (7"): released on Naive, Jul'83 by Naive. Dist: Spartan

PLAYING FOR TIME.
Single (7"): released on Naive, Aug'82 by Naive. Dist: Spartan

Downes, Paul

DANCE WITHOUT MUSIC (Downes, Paul & Phil Beer).
Tracks: / Dance without music / Song, The / Let me play / Somewhere in green / Sunday supplement / Five-poster bed / Take back your pictures / Flower girl / Born again / Friends.
Album: released on Sweet Folk All, '81 by Sweet Folk All Records. Dist: Sweet Folk All, Roots, Celtic Music, Dragon, Impetus, Projection, Chris Wellard, Festival Records

STILL LIFE.
Tracks: / Same old friends / I could not take my eyes off her / Some words / Did you like the battle? / First time ever, The / Still life / Puss in boots / Changeless story, The / You'll be next / Sweet air season / Across the hills.
Album: released on Sweet Folk All, '81 by Sweet Folk All Records. Dist: Sweet Folk All, Roots, Celtic Music, Dragon, Impetus, Projection, Chris Wellard, Festival Records

Downes, Wray

DOWNES, WRAY/AU PRIVAVE/DAVE YOUNG/ED BICKERT (Downes, Wray/Au Privave/Dave Young/Ed Bickert).
Album: released on Sackville, Jul'86 Dist: JSU, Jazz Music, Jazz Horizons, Cadillac Music, Celtic Music, Swift

Down Home

DOWN HOME VOL. 1 Various artists (Various Artists).
Album: released on Lismor Folk, Jul'87

DOWN HOME VOL.1 (FIDDLE MUSIC) (Various Artists).
Notes: Artists include: Aly Bain/Lerwick Lounge Ensemble/Peter Rowan Band/Buddy MacMaster/Jean Carignan/Bill Neely/Tommy Jarrell/Bill Monroe & Bluegrass Boys/Mike Seegar etc.
The absolute cream of the worlds fiddle players from the traditional and country music fields. One of two great albums for folkies, fiddlers or country music fans; 39 tracks, over 60 artists on 2 beauties!
Album: released on Lismor, May'86 by Lismor Records. Dist: Lismor, Roots, Celtic Music

Cassette: released on Lismor, May'86 by Lismor Records. Dist: Lismor, Roots, Celtic Music

DOWN HOME VOL.2 Fiddle music (Various Artists).
Notes: Artists include: Boys Of The Lough/Jean Ritchie/Cape Breton Fiddlers/Lee Creme/Alvin Crow & Pleasant Valley Boys/Junior Dougherty/J.P. & Annadeene Fraley/Tom Anderson etc.
The absolute cream of the worlds fiddle players from the traditional and country music fields. One of two great albums for folkies, fiddlers or country music fans, 39 tracks, over 60 artists on 2 beauties!
Album: released on Lismor, May'86 by Lismor Records. Dist: Lismor, Roots, Celtic Music

Cassette: released on Lismor, May'86 by Lismor Records. Dist: Lismor, Roots, Celtic Music

DOWN HOME VOL. 2 Various artists (Various Artists).
Album: released on Lismor Folk, Jul'87

Dow, Nick

BURD MARGARET.
Album: released on Dingles, Mar'79 by Dingles Records. Dist: Projection

Downliners

SHOWBIZ.
Album: released on Sky International, Feb'80

Downliners Sect

COUNTRY SECT, THE.
Album: released on Charly, Nov'77 by Charly Records. Dist: Charly, Cadillac

CROSS SECTION.
Tracks: / Little Egypt / One ugly child / Our little rendezvous / Sect appeal / Baby what's on your mind / Cops and robbers / Blood hound / Ballad of the hounds / Rocks in my bed / I got mine / Bad storm coming / I want my baby back again / Now she's dead / Everything I've got to give / Comin' home baby / Why don't you smile now / Outside.
Notes: Produced by Mike Collier.
Album: released on Charly, May'87 by Charly Records. Dist: Charly, Cadillac

ROCK SECTS IN, THE.
Album: by Charly Records. Dist: Charly, Cadillac

SECT, THE.
Album: released on Charly, Apr'77 by Charly Records. Dist: Charly, Cadillac

Down & Out In...

DOWN AND OUT IN BEVERLEY HILLS Original Soundtrack (Force).
Album: released on MCA, May'86 by MCA Records. Dist: Polygram, MCA

Cassette: released on MCA, May'86 by MCA Records. Dist: Polygram, MCA

Downtown Girls

DOWNTOWN GIRLS.
Tracks: / Downtown Girls / Downtown Girls (remix).
Single (12"): released on Hardcore, 30 May'87 by Hardcore Records. Dist: PRT

Downtown Strutz

PRETTY FLAMINGO.
Single (7"): released on Underworld, Dec'81 Dist: Pinnacle

Downy Mildew

BROOMTREE.
Album: released on Glass, 30 May'87 by Glass Records. Dist: Nine Mile, Rough Trade, Red Rhino, Play It Again Sam

Doyle, Danny

BORN A RAMBLIN' MAN.
Album: released on Solo, Jan'76 by Solo Records. Dist: PRT

DAISY A DAY, A.
Album: released on Harp(Ireland), Jul'81 by Pickwick Records. Dist: Taylors

DANNY DOYLE VOL.1.
Album: released on Music Box, Jul'76

DANNY DOYLE VOL.2.
Album: released on Music Box, Jul'76

GRAND OLE IRISH OPREY.
Album: by Release Records. Dist: I & B, Wynd-Up Distribution, Taylors, Solomon & Peres Distribution

VERY SPECIAL LOVE SONG, A.
Album: released on Release (Ireland), Nov'76

WEST'S AWAKE, THE.
Album: released on Music Box, Mar'77

Cassette: released on Music Box (Ireland), Mar'77

Doyle, Jimmy

KINGDOM OF KERRY.
Album: released on Shanachie, Sep'79 Dist: Sterns/Triple Earth Distribution, Roots

Doyle, Peter

DO YOU WANT TO MAKE LOVE.
Single (7"): released on Limelight, Jun'80

THIS AND THAT.

Doyle, Sir Arthur Conan

HOUND OF THE BASKERVILLES, THE.
Cassette: released on Caedmon(USA), '84 by Caedmon (USA) Records. Dist: Gower, Taylors, Discovery

Cassette: released on Caedmon(USA), '84 by Caedmon (USA) Records. Dist: Gower, Taylors, Discovery

STUDY IN SCARLET, A.
Cassette: released on BBC, May'84 by BBC Records & Tapes. Dist: EMI, PRT, Pye

D'Oyly Carte

COX & BOX/GONDOLIERS (D'Oyly Carte Opera Company).
Triple album / cassette: released on Decca, '61 by Decca Records. Dist: Polygram

GILBERT & SULLIVAN GALA, A (D'Oyly Carte Opera Company).
Album: released on Decca (Elite), May'82 by Decca Records. Dist: Polygram, IMS

Cassette: released on Decca (Elite), May'82 by Decca Records. Dist: Polygram, IMS

GONDOLIERS/COX & BOX (D'Oyly Carte Opera Company).
Triple album / cassette: released on Decca, '61 by Decca Records. Dist: Polygram

GONDOLIERS, THE (D'Oyly Carte Opera Company).
Double Album: released on Decca, Jul'77 by Decca Records. Dist: Polygram

HMS PINAFORE (D'Oyly Carte Opera Company).
Album: released on Decca, Oct'84 by Decca Records. Dist: Polygram

Cassette: released on Decca, Oct'84 by Decca Records. Dist: Polygram

HMS PINAFORE.
Album: released on Decca, '71 by Decca Records. Dist: Polygram

HMSPINAFORE (D'Oyly Carte Opera Company).
Album: released on Decca, Oct'84 by Decca Records. Dist: Polygram

Cassette: released on Decca, Oct'84 by Decca Records. Dist: Polygram

IF PATRIOTIC SENTIMENT (D'Oyly Carte Opera Company).
Cassette: released on Decca, Aug'77 by Decca Records. Dist: Polygram

IOLANTHE (D'Oyly Carte Opera Company).
Double Album: released on Decca, '60 by Decca Records. Dist: Polygram

MIKADO (D'Oyly Carte Opera Company).
Double Album: released on Decca, '58 by Decca Records. Dist: Polygram

PATIENCE (D'Oyly Carte Opera Company).
Double Album: released on Decca, '61 by Decca Records. Dist: Polygram

PIRATES OF PENZANCE, THE (D'Oyly Carte Opera Company).
Album: released on Decca, Oct'84 by Decca Records. Dist: Polygram

Cassette: released on Decca, Oct'84 by Decca Records. Dist: Polygram

RUDDIGORE.
Double Album: released on Decca, '62 by Decca Records. Dist: Polygram

RUDDIGORE (D'Oyly Carte Opera Company).
Double Album: released on Decca, Nov'79 by Decca Records. Dist: Polygram

SORCERER (D'Oyly Carte Opera Company).
Double Album: released on Decca, '59 by Decca Records. Dist: Polygram

WORLD OF GILBERT & SULLIVAN VOL.1 (D'Oyly Carte Opera Company).
Album: released on World of Learning, '69 by World Of Learning Records. Dist: World Of Learning

WORLD OF GILBERT & SULLIVAN VOL.2 (D'Oyly Carte Opera Company).
Album: released on World of Learning, '69 by World Of Learning Records. Dist: World Of Learning

YEOMAN OF GUARD (D'Oyly Carte Opera Company).
Double Album: by Decca Records. Dist: Polygram

Album: released on Decca, '66 by Decca Records. Dist: Polygram

Do You Remember

DO YOU REMEMBER VOL.2 various artists (Various Artists).
Album: released on Music For Pleasure (Holland), Apr'83 by EMI Records. Dist: EMI

Cassette: released on Music For Pleasure (Holland), Apr'83 by EMI Records. Dist: EMI

Do You Wanna Dance

DO YOU WANNA DANCE Various Artist (Various Artists).
Tracks: / 40 Miles of bad road / Tallahassee Lassie / Haunted House / By the light of the silvery moon / Rebel rouser / Way down younder in new orleans / Tossin and turnin / Baby face / Because they're young / Do you wanna dance / Little darling / La Bamba.
Notes: Licensed from Kilo Music Ltd.
Album: released on Topline, Sep'86 by Charly Records. Dist: Charly Distribution

Cassette: released on Topline, Sep'86 by Charly Records. Dist: Charly Distribution

Album: released on PRT, Dec'81 by PRT Records. Dist: PRT

Dozier Boys & Others

DOO WOPPIN' THE BLUES.
Album: released on Rarin', Jan'79 Dist: Swift
Cat. no: **777**

Dozier, Lamond

MOTOR CITY (PARTS 1 & 2).
Single (7"): released on Demon, Feb'84 by Demon Records. Dist: Pinnacle

Single (12"): released on Demon, Feb'84 by Demon Records. Dist: Pinnacle

Dozier, Lamont

BIGGER THE LIFE.
Album: released on Demon, Nov'83 by Demon Records. Dist: Pinnacle

DON'T LEAVE ME.
Single (7"): released on HDH(Holland/Dozier/Holland), Aug'84 by Demon Records. Dist: Pinnacle

Single (12"): released on HDH(Holland/Dozier/Holland), Aug'84 by Demon Records. Dist: Pinnacle

SCARLETT O'HARA.
Single (7"): released on Demon, Oct'83 by Demon Records. Dist: Pinnacle

Single (12"): released on Demon, Oct'83 by Demon Records. Dist: Pinnacle

Dracula

DRACULA Original soundtrack.
Album: released on MCA, Sep'79 by MCA Records. Dist: Polygram, MCA

DRACULA See Stoker, Bram (Spoken Word).

Dragees

SHOOT TO KILL.
Single (7"): released on Sohoho, Nov'84 Dist: Cartel

Dragon

BODY AND THE BEAT.
Cassette: released on Polydor, Sep'84 by Polydor Records. Dist: Polygram, Polydor

Album: released on Polydor, Sep'84 by Polydor Records. Dist: Polygram, Polydor Deleted '85.

Dragonette, Jessica

WITH LOVE.
Album: released on Totem, May'78 Dist: Jazz Music, Projection, Swift

Dragoni Brothers

AN EVENING WITH THE DRAGONI BROTHERS.
Album: released on Rubber, Jun'82 by Rubber Records. Dist: Roots Distribution, Projection Distribution, Jazz Music Distribution, Celtic Music Distribution, JSU Distribution, Spartan Distribution

Cassette: released on Rubber, Jun'82 by Rubber Records. Dist: Roots Distribution, Projection Distribution, Jazz Music Distribution, Celtic Music Distribution, JSU Distribution, Spartan Distribution

DANCE LITTLE BIRDIE.
Single (7"): released on Picador, Sep'81

DISCO VIVA.
Single (7"): released on Picador, Dec'81

Dragons

PARFUMS DE LA REVOLUTION.
Album: released on Polydor, May'82 by Polydor Records. Dist: Polygram, Polydor

Drag's Half Fast Jazz...

DRAG'S HALF FAST JAZZ BAND.
Album: released on GHB, Jul'87 Dist: Jazz Music, Swift

Dragsters

I'M NOT AN AMERICAN.
Tracks: / I'm not an American / Land of the giants.
Single (7"): released on Union City, Jul'87 Dist: Fast Forward

WHERE IS THE HAMBURGER RELISH.
Tracks: / Where is the hamburger relish / I wanna be an albino.
Single (7"): released on Union City, Nov'86 Dist: Fast Forward

Drake, Nick

BEST OF NICK DRAKE Heaven in a wild flower.
Tracks: / Fruit tree / Cello song / Thoughts of Mary Jane / Northern sky / River man / At the chime of the city clock / Intro / Hazey Jane 1 / Hazy Jane 2 / Pink moon / Road / Which will / Things behind the sun / Time has told me.
Album: released on Island, Sep'86 by Island Records. Dist: Polygram

Cassette: released on Island, Sep'86 by Island Records. Dist: Polygram

BRYTER LAYTER.
Compact disc: released on Island, May'87 by Island Records. Dist: Polygram

Album: by Island Records. Dist: Polygram

FIVE LEAVES LEFT.
Tracks: / Time has told me / River man / Three hours / Day is done / Way to blue / 'Cello song / Thoughts of Mary Jane, The / Man in a shed / Fruit tree / Saturday sun.
Compact disc: released on Island, Feb'87 by Island Records. Dist: Polygram

FRUIT TREE.
Notes: 4 L.P. Set includes: *Time of no reply*, as well as the tree original Drake albums, *Five leaves left*, *Bryter Layter* and *Pink moon* in their original four colour sleeves. Re-issue.
Album: released on Hannibal, Jan'87 by Hannibal Records. Dist: Charly, Harmonia Mundi, Projection, Celtic Music, Roots

Special: released on Hannibal, Aug'86 by Hannibal Records. Dist: Charly, Harmonia Mundi, Projection, Celtic Music, Roots

PINK MOON.
Album: by Polygram Records. Dist: Polydor

TIME OF NO REPLY.
Tracks: / Joey / Clothes of sand / May fair / I was made to love magic / Strange meetings II / Been smoking too long.
Notes: Also includes the four songs from the 'latest session' included on the *Pink moon* disc in the previous addition of *Fruit tree* as well as alternate takes of *Fly*, *Man in a shed* and *Thoughts of Mary Jane*. Re-issue.
Album: released on Hannibal, Jan'87 by Hannibal Records. Dist: Charly, Harmonia Mundi, Projection, Celtic Music, Roots

Drake, Pete

PETE DRAKE SHOW, (THE).
Album: released on Stop, Jun'76

STEEL AWAY.
Album: by Word Records. Dist: Word Distribution

Drake's dream

DRAKE'S DREAM Various Artists (Various Artists).
Album: released on President, '77 by President Records. Dist: Taylors, Spartan

Dramarama

CINEMA VERITE.
Album: released on New Rose, Nov'85 Dist: Rough Trade, Cartel

Dramatics

BEST OF, THE.
Compact disc: released on London, Apr'87 by London Records. Dist: Polygram

IN THE RAIN.
Single (7"): released on Stax, Aug'87 by Ace Records. Dist: Pinnacle, Chris Wellard, IMS-Polygram

SOMEWHERE IN TIME.
Notes: This is the Dramatics reuninion album after an absence from the scene of some five years. As a successful group on the legendary Stax label during the late Sicties and early Seventies they had several major hits in the States, the most memorable of which were "Whatcha See Is What You Get" and "In The Rain". Both of these went top 10.
Album: released on Arhoolie, Jun'86 by Arhoolie Records. Dist: Projection, Topic, Jazz Music, Swift, Roots

Drame, Adama

AFRICAN PERCUSSION.
Tracks: / B Mondet / Dougouba dya / Barra / Abounaye / Solo sania / Sabouyouma / Badina / Elodia / Layana.

Dransfield, Barry

BLOWIN' AND SCRAPIN'.
Tracks: / Rattling roaring Willie / Metal man / Fiddler's progress / Who's knows where the time goes / My pagan love / Sheffield hornpipe / Pet of the pipers / Up the aisle (Swedish wedding march) / Wedding song / Bridie's Wedding / Norwegian wedding march / Wedding Morris / Sandy Bell's / obliged to fiddle / Planxty Oavy / Spanish cloak / Bushes and briars / Swedish air / O'Carolan's concerto / Recitation upon a gentleman sitting on a Cremona violin / Sally gardens / Conmel races.
Album: released on Topic, '81 Dist: Roots Distribution

Dransfield, Robin

LORD OF ALL I BEHOLD (Dransfield, Robin & Barry).
Tracks: / Faithful Johnny / Bold Nelson's favourite / Who liveth so merry / Adam & the beasts / Lord of all I behold / Paddy Ryan's dream / Still he sings / Bold William Taylor / Just as the tide was flowing / Wild rose, The.
Album: released on Leader, '81 Dist: Jazz Music, Projection

POPULAR TO CONTRARY BELIEF (Dransfield, Robin & Barry).
Album: by Free Reed Records. Dist: Roots, Projection, Hobgoblin Records, Oblivion Deleted Jan'87.

Album: released on Free Reed, Nov'77 by Free Reed Records. Dist: Roots, Projection, Hobgoblin Records, Oblivion

ROUT OF THE BLUES (Dransfield, Robin & Barry).
Tracks: / Rout of the blues, The / Scarborough fair / St. Clements jig / Huntsman's chorus, The / Nancy / Waters of Tyne, The / Earl of Totnes, The / Tapestry / Trees they do grow high, The / Week before Easter, A / Fair maid walking all in her garden, A / Who's the fool now.
Album: released on Leader, '81 Dist: Jazz Music, Projection

Draper, Rusty

SEVEN COME ELEVEN.
Single (7"): released on Pinner, Jul'84 by Pinner Records. Dist: Rough Trade, Cartel, Backs

Draughtsman's contract

DRAUGHTSMAN'S CONTRACT Original Soundtrack (Hyman, Michael).
Album: released on Charisma, Feb'83 by Virgin Records. Dist: EMI

Drayton, Leslie

LOVE IS A FOUR LETTER WORD (Drayton, Leslie Orchestra).
Tracks: / Greasy brown paper sack, A / Love is a four letter word / When will you be mine / You ain't gonna keep me blue / Greasy brown paper sack, A / Stormy Monday / What if? / I need your love so bad / Love is a four letter word (instrumental).
Notes: A fusion album featuring soul, blues and jazz from singer Barbara Harrison.
Album: released on Bellaphon (Germany), Jan'87 by Bellaphon Records. Dist: Target, JSU

WHAT IT IS IS WHAT IT IS (Drayton, Leslie & Fun).
Tracks: / What it is is what it is / Sausalito Ferry / I'll take it easy / I'll take it easy / Comin' at ya / Pershing Square / Brownie points / I'm really gonna miss you.
Notes: Straight out of the American jazz chart an album of contemporary R&B fused with soul & jazz. Led by trumpeter Leslie drayton, Fun take us through 7 great compositions, the highlight of which is "I'll take it easy" featuring vocals by Barbara Morrison.

Dread, Alvin

GIRL OF MINE.
Single (12"): released on Hot Line, Oct'83 by Hotline Records. Dist: Jetstar

PICTURE ON THE WALL.
Single (12"): released on Hot Line, Feb'83 by Hotline Records. Dist: Jetstar

Dreadful snakes
DREADFUL SNAKES Various Artists (Various Artists).
Album: released on Rounder (USA), Apr'84 Dist: Mike's Country Music Room Distribution, Jazz Music Distribution, Swift Distribution, Roots Records Distribution, Projection Distribution, Topic Distribution

Dread, Judge
40 BIG ONES.
Double Album: released on Creole, Nov'83 by Creole Records. Dist: Rhino, PRT

BEDTIME STORIES.
Album: released on Cactus, Nov'75 by Creole Records. Dist: CBS

BEST WORST OF JUDGE D, (THE).
Album: released on Cactus, '76 by Creole Records. Dist: CBS

BIG ONE, (THE).
Extended-play record: released on Trojan, '83 by Trojan Records. Dist: PRT, Jetstar

BIG SEVEN '85.
Single (7"): released on Creole, Sep'85 by Creole Records. Dist: Rhino, PRT

Single (12"): released on Creole, Sep'85 by Creole Records. Dist: Rhino, PRT

DREADMANIA.
Album: released on Trojan, Sep'81 by Trojan Records. Dist: PRT, Jetstar

HELLO BABY.
Compact disc: released on Creole, May'81 by Creole Records. Dist: Rhino, PRT

Single (12"): released on Creole, May'81 by Creole Records. Dist: Rhino, PRT

JERK YOUR BODY.
Tracks: / Jerk your body / Bring back the skins.
Single (7"): released on Rhino, Jul'87 by Creole Records. Dist: PRT, Rhino

Single (12"): released on Rhino, Jul'87 by Creole Records. Dist: PRT, Rhino

LAST OF THE SKINHEADS.
Album: released on Cactus, Sep'76 by Creole Records. Dist: CBS

MY NAME'S DICK.
Single (7"): released on Dreamworks, Nov'82

NOT GUILTY.
Album: released on Creole, Nov'84 by Creole Records. Dist: Rhino, PRT

Single (12"): released on Creole, Nov'84 by Creole Records. Dist: Rhino, PRT

NOT GUILTY (SINGLE).
Single (7"): released on Kingdom, Dec'83 by Kingdom Records. Dist: Kingdom

RELAX.
Single (7"): released on Creole, Sep'84 by Creole Records. Dist: Rhino, PRT

Single (12"): released on Creole, Sep'84 by Creole Records. Dist: Rhino, PRT

RUB-A-DUB.
Album: released on Creole, Oct'81 by Creole Records. Dist: Rhino, PRT

RUB-A-DUB (SINGLE).
Single (7"): released on Creole, Oct'81 by Creole Records. Dist: Rhino, PRT

Single (12"): released on Creole, Oct'81 by Creole Records. Dist: Rhino, PRT

WILL I WHAT.
Single (7"): released on Creole, Nov'80 by Creole Records. Dist: Rhino, PRT

WORKING CLASS 'ERO.
Album: released on Trojan, Sep'81 by Trojan Records. Dist: PRT, Jetstar

Dread, Mikey
BREAK DOWN THE WALLS.
Single (7"): released on Dread, Oct'80

Single (12"): released on Dread, Oct'80

BREAKING DOWN THE PRESSURE
(Dread, Mikey/Congo Ashanti Roy).
Single 10": released on On-U-Sound, Dec'83 Dist: Rough Trade Distribution, Lightning

DREAD AT THE CONTROLS.
Tracks: / Everybody needs a proper education / Dream combination / Love the dread / Voice of Jah / Dthey go mad / Walk rastafari way / King in the ring / Barber saloon.

Album: released on Trojan, Feb'86 by Trojan Records. Dist: PRT, Jetstar

Cassette: released on Trojan, Feb'86 by Trojan Records. Dist: PRT, Jetstar

PAVE THE WAY.
Album: released on Heartbeat, Oct'84 Dist: Revolver, Pinnacle

PAVE THE WAY PARTS 1 & 2.
Album: released on DEP International, Apr'85 by DEP International Records. Dist: Virgin Records, EMI

Cassette: released on DEP International, Apr'85 by DEP International Records. Dist: Virgin Records, EMI

ROCKERS DELIGHT.
Single (7"): released on DATC, Jul'80 by DATC Records. Dist: Rough Trade

ROOTS AND CULTURE.
Single (12"): released on Dread At The Controls, Mar'82 Dist: Dub Vendor, Virgin Records, EMI

RUDE LITTLE DREAD.
Single (12"): released on Dread At The Controls, Mar'86 Dist: Dub Vendor, Virgin Records, EMI

SUNDAY SCHOOL.
Single (12"): released on DATC, Mar'83 by DATC Records. Dist: Rough Trade

S.W.A.L.K..
Album: released on Do-It, '82 by Do-It Records. Dist: Virgin, EMI

WARNING.
Single (12"): released on Dread At The Controls, Jun'82 Dist: Dub Vendor, Virgin Records, EMI

WORLD WAR III.
Album: released on Dread At The Controls, Apr'86 Dist: Dub Vendor, Virgin Records, EMI

Dread, Sammy
AFRICA.
Single (12"): released on Love Lite, Mar'82

BE MINE.
Single (12"): released on Love Light, Jul'82

DREADLOCKS GIRL.
Single (12"): released on Ethnic, Sep'82 Dist: Kingdom

LABOUR WARD (Dread, Sammy/Lui Lepke).
Single (12"): released on Echo, Feb'82 by Vista Sounds. Dist: Jazz Music

METAL DETECTOR.
Single (12"): released on Life Music, Apr'85 by Life Music Records. Dist: Jetstar

ONE COMBINATION.
Single (12"): released on Capri, Nov'82 Dist: Jetstar

RAP UP A DRAW.
Album: released on Seven Seas, Mar'85

SALLY.
Single (12"): released on Sonic Sounds, Oct'83 by Sonic Sound Records. Dist: Jetstar

TOP OF THE TOPS (Dread, Sammy & Lui Lepke).
Single (12"): released on Jah Life, Mar'82 by Jah Life Records. Dist: Jetstar

YOU MEAN SO MUCH TO ME.
Single (12"): released on Seven Leaves, Oct'84 by Seven Leaves Records. Dist: Jetstar

Dream
DESIRES (AT HER CLOSEST).
Single (12"): released on Black, Aug'87 by FM-Revolver Records. Dist: Revolver, Probe Plus Distribution, Cartel

DREAM Various artists (Various Artists).
Notes: With Toshiyuki Honda, Chick Corea, Miroslav Vitous, Roy Haynes.

DREAM BABIES Various Artists (Various Artists).
Album: released on Capitol, Sep'85 by Capitol Records. Dist: EMI

Cassette: released on Capitol, Sep'85 by Capitol Records. Dist: EMI

DREAM DAYZE (Various Artists).
Tracks: / Happy new year / Breaking down / Renaissance fair / She's not there / Halo in my hair / Portobello Road / Nite is a comin' / Michael Angelo / Some good advice / Catherines wheel / Mythological Sunday / Supermarket full of cans / Say you don't mind / Summer of last year / Bird has flown / Sycamore Sid / Summer evening / Doo dah.

Album: released on Decal, Jan'87 by Charly Records. Dist: Charly

DREAM GIRLS Original cast (Various Artists).
Album: released on Geffen, Jul'82 by Geffen Records. Dist: WEA, CBS

Cassette: released on Geffen, Jul'82 by Geffen Records. Dist: WEA, CBS

DREAM HORSES Various Artists (Various Artists).
Cassette: released on Bibi, Feb'82

DREAM MELODIES Various Artists (Various Artists).
Triple album / cassette: released on Nouveau, Mar'85

Triple album / cassette: released on Nouveau, Mar'85

DREAM SEQUENCE Various Artists (Various Artists).
Double Album: released on 101 International, '84

Dream Academy
DREAM ACADEMY.
Album: released on Blanco Y Negro, Oct'85 by WEA Records. Dist: WEA

Cassette: released on Blanco Y Negro, Oct'85 by WEA Records. Dist: WEA

LIFE IN A NORTHERN TOWN.
Single (7"): released on Blanco Y Negro, Mar'85 by WEA Records. Dist: WEA

Single (12"): released on Blanco Y Negro, Mar'85 by WEA Records. Dist: WEA

LOVE PARADE.
Single (7"): released on Blanco Y Negro, Aug'85 by WEA Records. Dist: WEA

Single (12"): released on Blanco Y Negro, Aug'85 by WEA Records. Dist: WEA Deleted '86.

PLEASE PLEASE LET ME GET WHAT I WANT.
Single (7"): released on Blanco Y Negro, Nov'85 by WEA Records. Dist: WEA

Single (12"): released on Blanco Y Negro, Nov'85 by WEA Records. Dist: WEA

Dream Baby Scream
IS THERE A REASON.
Tracks: / Is there a reason / Alone with you / Love somebody.
Single (7"): released on So Romantik, Jun'87 by So Romantik Records. Dist: So Romantik

Dream Factory
FASHION TOYS.
Single (7"): released on Inferno, Mar'85 by Inferno Records. Dist: Inferno, Cartel, Pinnacle

Single (12"): released on Inferno, Mar'85 by Inferno Records. Dist: Inferno, Cartel, Pinnacle

Dreaming.....
DREAMING ON THE RIVER TO NEW ORLEANS (Various Artists).
Notes: Featuring Thomas Jefferson
Album: released on Southland. Jan'87

Dream Merchants
AS THE WORLD TURNS.
Single (7"): released on Legacy, Aug'83 Dist: PRT

Single (12"): released on Legacy, Aug'83 Dist: PRT

Dream of a strange land
DREAM OF A STRANGE LAND Greene, Graham (Burden, Hugh).
Cassette: released on Talking Tape Company, '84 by Talking Tape Company Records.

Dreamscape
DREAMSCAPE various artists (Various Artists).
Album: released on Sonic Atmospheres, Dec'84 Dist: Target

Dreams & Desires
DREAMS & DESIRES various artists (Various Artists).
Cassette: released on Pleasantly Surprised Tapes, Dec'84 Dist: Fast Forward, Spartan

Dream Sequence
FUNKIN' REBELS.
Single (7"): released on Red Bus, Aug'82 by Red Bus Records. Dist: PRT

Single (12"): released on Red Bus, Aug'82 by Red Bus Records. Dist: PRT

OUTSIDE LOOKING IN.
Single (7"): released on Red Bus, Apr'82 by Red Bus Records. Dist: PRT

Single (12"): released on Red Bus, Apr'82 by Red Bus Records. Dist: PRT

Dreams & Themes
DREAMS & THEMES various artists (Various Artists).
Album: released on Ronco, Feb'84

Cassette: released on Ronco, Feb'84

Dream Syndicate
50 IN A 25 ZONE.
Tracks: / 50 in a 25 zone / Drinking problem / Blood money / Lonely bull, The.
Single (12"): released on Big Time, Aug'87 by Mainline Record Company. Dist: Mainline

DAYS OF WINE AND ROSES, (THE).
Album: released on Rough Trade, '84 by Rough Trade Records. Dist: Rough Trade Distribution, Cartel Distribution

DAYS OF WINE AND ROSES.
Album: released on Slash, Jan'87 by London Records. Dist: Polygram

Cassette: released on Slash, Jan'87 by London Records. Dist: Polygram

DREAM SYNDICATE.
Album: released on Demon, Jun'85 by Demon Records. Dist: Pinnacle

MEDECINE SHOW.
Album: released on A&M, Jun'84 by A&M Records. Dist: Polygram

Cassette: released on A&M, Jun'84 by A&M Records. Dist: Polygram

OUT OF THE GREY.
Tracks: / Out of the grey / Forest for the trees / 50 in a 25 zone / Boston / Slide away / Dying embers / Now I ride alone / Dancing blind / You can't forget / Blood money / Drinking problem.
Notes: Produced by: Paul B.Cutler
Album: released on Chrysalis, Jun'86 by Chrysalis Records. Dist: CBS

Cassette: released on Chrysalis, Jun'86 by Chrysalis Records. Dist: CBS

TELL ME WHEN IT'S OVER.
Single (12"): released on Rough Trade, Dec'83 by Rough Trade Records. Dist: Rough Trade Distribution, Cartel Distribution

THIS IS NOT THE NEW DREAM SYNDICATE ALBUM.
Album: released on A&M (Holland), Feb'85

Dream Team
BOY GEORGE.
Single (7"): released on Hollywood, Oct'84 by Hollywood Records. Dist: Pinnacle

Dreamtime
BUNNY UP.
Album: released on Charly, Feb'84 by Charly Records. Dist: Charly, Cadillac

Dream Unit
FOUR WAVES ep.
Single (7"): released on Northeast Music, Jul'83 by Northeast Music Records. Dist: Northeast Music Distribution, Pinnacle

Dredd Foole & The Din
EAT MY DUST.
Album: released on Homestead, Dec'85 Dist: Rough Trade, Cartel, Shigaku

Dregs
INDUSTRY STANDARD.
Album: released on Aristocrat, Jun'82 by Lithon Recording & Music Publishing.

UNSUNG HEROES.
Tracks: / Cruise control / Divided we stand / I'll just pick / Day 444 / Rock 'n' roll park / Attila the Hun / Kat food / Go for baroque.
Album: released on Arista, Jul'81 by Arista Records. Dist: RCA

Drew, Kenny
AFTERNOON IN EUROPE (Drew, Kenny Trio).
Tracks: / Golden striker / midnight sun / Jeg gik mig ud en sommerdag at hore / Tivoli strool / Ach varmeland,du skona / Afternoon in Paris / The quiet cathedral.
Album: released on RCA (Import), '83

AND FAR AWAY (Drew, Kenny Quartet).
Compact disc: released on Soul Note (Italy), Jan'86 Dist: Harmonia Mundi Distributors

BY REQUEST.
Notes: With Neils-Henninining Orsted Pederson.
Compact disc: released on RCA Jazz (Japan), Jan'86

KENNY DREW TRIO (Drew, Kenny Trio).
Compact disc:

Compact disc: released on Vanguard (USA), Apr'86

PRIZE WINNERS (Drew, Kenny/Henning/Pedersen/Asmussen/Thigden).
Tracks: / Django / A pretty girl / Golgatha / Bridgetown Baby / Hush-a-bye / Donna Lee / You are the sunshine of my life / Evening in the park / Careless love.
Album: released on Matrix (Denmark), Apr'81 Dist: Jazz Horizons, Jazz Music, JSU

YOUR SOFT EYES (Drew, Kenny Trio).
Compact disc: released on Soul Note (Italy), Jan'86 Dist: Harmonia Mundi Distributors

Drew, Martin

BRITISH JAZZ ARTISTS vol.3 (Drew, Martin, Band).
Album: released on Lee Lambert, May'80 by Lee Lambert Records. Dist: Cadillac

Drewo, Carl

SAX MESSAGE.
Album: released on Intersound, Dec'86 by Intersound Records. Dist: Jazz Music

Drew, Ronnie

IT'S GUARANTEED RONNIE DREW.
Album: released on Dolphin, Aug'78 Dist: I & B Records Distribution, Prism Leisure Corporation Records, Record Services Distribution (Ireland)

RONNIE DREW.
Album: released on Ram, Jan'76 by Ram. Dist: PRT

Dr. Feelgood

SNEAKIN' SUSPICION.
Album: released on Fame, May'87 by Music For Pleasure Records. Dist: EMI

Cassette: released on Fame, May'87 by Music For Pleasure Records. Dist: EMI

Dr.Hook

DR.HOOK Greatest Hits.
Compact disc: released on Capitol, '87 by Capitol Records. Dist: EMI

D.R.I.

22 SONGS.
Album: released on Radical (USA), Aug'87

DEALING WITH IT.
Album: released on Armageddon, Sep'86 by Armageddon Records. Dist: Revolver, Cartel, Pinnacle

Drifterfolk

ALL KINDS OF FOLK.
Tracks: / Coat of many colours / Rambling boy / Evermore the biplane / Ballad of Glencoe / Gallowa' hills / The land I love so well / Cotton fields / Jinkin' geordie / Bringing in the sheaves / Highland queen / Goodbye again / Fiddler's green.
Album: released on Lismor, Nov'76 by Lismor Records. Dist: Lismor, Roots, Celtic Music

REFLECTIONS.
Tracks: / The piper o'Dundee / Tiree love song / Spanish lady / Sheriffmuir / Mursheen Durkin / Streets of London / Reflections / Cam' ye O'er Frae France / Mingulay boat songs / The fiery cross / Johnnie Cope / The bonnie lass O'Fyvie.
Album: by Lismor Records. Dist: Lismor, Roots, Celtic Music

Drifters

20 GREATEST HITS.
Compact disc: Dist: ACD

24 ORIGINAL HITS.
Tracks: / Saturday night at the movies / Dance with me / Some kind of wonderful / When my little girl is smiling / Come on over to my place / Save the last dance for me / At the club / Up on the roof / On Broadway / There goes my baby / I'll take you where the music's playing / Under the boardwalk / Sweet Caroline (Good times never seemed so good) / I'm free (for the rest of your life) / Kissing in the back row of the movies / Every night / Like sister like brother / Songs we used to sing, The / There goes my first love / Love games / Love me love the life I lead / If it feels good do it / Blessing in disguise / Down on the beach tonight.
Album: released on Atlantic, Nov'75 by WEA Records. Dist: WEA

Cassette: released on Atlantic, Nov'75 by WEA Records. Dist: WEA

6 TRACK HITS y.
Extended-play record: released on Scoop 33, Sep'83 by Pickwick Records. Dist: H.R. Taylor

COLLECTION: DRIFTERS.
Compact disc: by Object Enterprises Ltd. Dist: Counterpoint Distribution

COME ON OVER TO MY PLACE.
Tracks: / Come on over to my place / Up on the roof / I don't want to go on without you.
Single (7"): released on Atlantic, Sep'86 by WEA Records. Dist: WEA

DANCE WITH ME.
Single (7"): released on Creole, Aug'82 by Creole Records. Dist: Rhino, PRT

DRIFTERS, THE.
Tracks: / Up on the roof / Saturday night at the movies / Save the last dance for me / There goes my baby / This magic moment / Dance with me / On Broadway / Sweets for my sweet / Please stay / Under the boardwalk.
Compact disc: released on The Collection, Apr'87 by Object Enterprises Ltd. Dist: Counterpoint Distribution

GOLDEN HITS: DRIFTERS.
Tracks: / There goes my baby / True love,true love (If you cry) / Dance with me / This magic moment / Save the last dance for me / I count the tears / Some kind of wonderful / Up on the roof / Up on the roof / On Broadway / Under the boardwalk / I've got sand in my shoes / Saturday night at the movies.
Compact disc: released on Atlantic, Jan'87 by WEA Records. Dist: WEA

Album: by WEA Records. Dist: WEA

Cassette: released on Atlantic, '74 by WEA Records. Dist: WEA

GREATEST.
Tracks: / Hello happiness / Kissing in the back row of the movies / Always something there to remind me (There's) / Every night / Sweet Caroline / If it feels good / Save the last dance for me / There goes my first love / Like sister & brother / I can't live without you / Harlem child / You've got your troubles / Love games / Down on the beach tonight.
Album: released on MFP, Oct'85 by EMI Records. Dist: EMI

Cassette: released on MFP, Oct'85 by EMI Records. Dist: EMI

GREATEST HITS LIVE: DRIFTERS.
Album: released on Astan, Nov'84 by Astan Records. Dist: Counterpoint

Cassette: released on Astan, Nov'84 by Astan Records. Dist: Counterpoint

JUKE BOX GIANTS.
Tracks: / There goes my baby / This magic moment / Some kind of wonderful / Dance with me / Save the last dance for me / Sweets for my sweet / Saturday night at the movies / I'll take you home / Under the broadwalk / I count the tears / Up on the roof / Please stay / On Broadway / When my little girl is smiling / White christmas / (If you cry)True love ,True love.
Album: released on Audio Fidelity, May'82 Dist: PRT

KISSING IN THE BACK ROW.
Single (7"): released on Old Gold, Jul'84 by Old Gold Records. Dist: Lightning, Jazz Music, Spartan, Counterpoint

LITTLE SISTER AND BROTHER.
Single (7"): released on Old Gold, Jul'82 by Old Gold Records. Dist: Lightning, Jazz Music, Spartan, Counterpoint

LIVE AT HARVARD UNIVERSITY.
Tracks: / White christmas / Lonely winds / Bells of St.Mary / True love / This magic moment / Up on the roof / Up on the roof / Honey love / Under the boardwalk / There goes my baby / Saturday night at the movies / When my little girl is smiling / On broadway / Save the last dance for me / Money honey.
Album: released on Showcase, Apr'86 Dist: Counterpoint

Cassette: released on Showcase, Apr'86 Dist: Counterpoint

SATURDAY NIGHT AT THE MOVIES.
Tracks: / Saturday night at the movies / Under the boardwalk / Up on the roof / Save the last dance for me.
Single (7"): released on Creole Classics, Mar'87 by Creole Records. Dist: PRT, Rhino

Single (12"): released on Creole Classics, Mar'87 by Creole Records. Dist: PRT, Rhino

Single (7"): released on Atlantic, '74 by WEA Records. Dist: WEA

Single (7"): released on Creole, Aug'82 by Creole Records. Dist: Rhino, PRT

Single (7"): released on Old Gold, Jul'82 by Old Gold Records. Dist: Lightning, Jazz Music, Spartan, Counterpoint

SAVE THE LAST DANCE FOR ME The definitive collection.
Tracks: / Saturday night at the movies / Come on over to my place / Save the last dance for me / At the club / I count the tears / When my little girl is smiling / Up on the roof / Dance with me / Under the boardwalk / I've got sand in my shoes / There goes my baby / On broadway / I'll take you home / This magic moment / Some kind of wonderful / I'll take you where the music's playing / If you cry-true love / True love / Sweets for my sweet / Please stay / Drip drop.
Album: released on Atlantic, 30 May'87 by WEA Records. Dist: WEA

Cassette: released on Atlantic, 30 May'87 by WEA Records. Dist: WEA

Compact disc: released on Atlantic, Jul'87 by WEA Records. Dist: WEA

Cassette: released on Orchild Music, Feb'82

Single (7"): released on Atlantic, '74 by WEA Records. Dist: WEA

Single (7"): released on Old Gold, Jul'82 by Old Gold Records. Dist: Lightning, Jazz Music, Spartan, Counterpoint

Compact disc: released on Atlantic, Jul'87 by WEA Records. Dist: WEA

SOME KIND OF WONDERFUL.
Album: released on Meteor, Apr'87 by Magnum Music Group Ltd. Dist: Magnum Music Group Ltd, PRT Distribution, Spartan Distribution

STAND BY ME Ultimate Collection (The) (Drifters & Ben E. King).
Notes: Full details see under King,Ben E.

THEIR TOP HITS.
Cassette: released on Timeless Treasures, Jul'86 Dist: Counterpoint Distribution

THIS MAGIC MOMENT.
Album: released on Astan, Nov'84 by Astan Records. Dist: Counterpoint

Cassette: released on Astan, Nov'84 by Astan Records. Dist: Counterpoint

UNDER THE BOARDWALK.
Single (12"): released on Atlantic, Apr'80 by WEA Records. Dist: WEA

VERY BEST OF THE DRIFTERS.
Album: released on Telstar, Oct'86 by Telstar Records. Dist: RCA Distribution

Cassette: released on Telstar, Oct'86 by Telstar Records. Dist: RCA Distribution

Compact disc: released on Intersound, Nov'86 by Intersound Records. Dist: Jazz Music

Compact disc: released on Telstar, Nov'86 by Telstar Records. Dist: RCA Distribution

YOU BETTER MOVE ON.
Single (7"): released on Atlantic, Aug'82 by WEA Records. Dist: WEA

Driftwood

RAINBOW WATERS.
Single (7"): released on Jigsaw, Jan'80 Dist: Roots, Pinnacle, Projection

Driftwood, Jimmie

SONGS OF BILLIE YANK AND JOHNNY REB.
Tracks: / Won't you come along and go / Billy Yank and Johnny Reb / How do youlike the army / On top of Shiloh's hill / I'm a pome rebel soldier / Giant on the thunderhead, The / Rock of Chickamauga / My black bird has gone / Oh Florie / When I swim the golden river / Git along little yearlings / Goodbye Reb, you'all come.
Album: released on RCA, Jan'87 by RCA Records. Dist: RCA, Roots, Swift, Wellard, Chris, I & B, Solomon & Peres Distribution

Cassette: released on RCA, Jan'87 by RCA Records. Dist: RCA, Roots, Swift, Wellard, Chris, I & B, Solomon & Peres Distribution

Drinking Electricity

CRUISING MISSILES.
Single (7"): released on Pop Aural, Nov'80 Dist: Fresh, Rough Trade, Swift, Spartan, Virgin

GOOD TIMES.
Single (7"): released on Survival, Mar'82 by Survival Records. Dist: Backs, Cartel Distribution

Single (7"): released on Survival, Mar'82 by Survival Records. Dist: Backs, Cartel Distribution

OVERLOAD.
Album: released on Survival, Mar'82 by Survival Records. Dist: Backs, Cartel Distribution

SUBLIMINAL.
Single (7"): released on Survival, Jun'82 by Survival Records. Dist: Backs, Cartel Distribution

Single (12"): released on Survival, Jun'82 by Survival Records. Dist: Backs, Cartel Distribution

Driscoll, Julie

BEST OF JULIE DRISCOLL, THE.
Album: released on Polydor (Import), Nov'82

Cassette: released on Polydor (Import), Nov'82

GREATEST HITS:JULIE DRISCOLL & BRIAN AUGER (Driscoll, Julie & Brian Auger).
Double Album: released on Polydor, Nov'80 by Polydor Records. Dist: Polygram, Polydor

Cassette: released on Polydor Int., Nov'80

JULIE DRISCOLL & BRIAN AUGER (Driscoll, Julie & Brian Auger).
Album: released on Charly, Feb'81 by Charly Records. Dist: Charly, Cadillac

LONDON 1964/1967 (see Auger, Brian).
Tracks: / I know you love me not / I don't to have to do it / If you should ever leave me / I don't know where you are / Shadows of you / Kiko / Foolkiller / Let's do it tiger / Come back to Croydon / Own up Lady Astor.
Album: released on Charly, Jan'77 by Charly Records. Dist: Charly, Cadillac

THIS WHEEL'S ON FIRE (Driscoll, Julie & the Brian Auger Trinity).
Single (7"): released on Old Gold, Jul'84 by Old Gold Records. Dist: Lightning, Jazz Music, Spartan, Counterpoint

Driscoll, Phil

POWER OF PRAISE.
Album: released on Sparrow, Sep'85 by Word Records. Dist: Spartan

Cassette: released on Sparrow, Sep'85 by Word Records. Dist: Spartan

D'Rivera, Paquito

LIVE AT KEYSTONE CORNER.
Album: released on CBS(France), Jan'84 by CBS Records. Dist: Conifer, Discovery, Swift

WHY NOT.
Album: released on CBS(France), May'85 by CBS Records. Dist: Conifer, Discovery, Swift

Cassette: released on CBS(France), May'85 by CBS Records. Dist: Conifer, Discovery, Swift

Drivers

SHORT CUTS.
Album: released on Greyhound, Jul'83 by Greyhound Records. Dist: PRT, Greyhound

TALK ALL NIGHT.
Single (7"): released on Greyhound, Jul'83 by Greyhound Records. Dist: PRT, Greyhound

Drive Time USA

DRIVE TIME USA.
Tracks: / Drive / You can do magic / After the fire / I can dream about you / Chuck E's in love / Heat is on, The / Secrets in the street / Rock and roll dreams come through / Rocky mountain way / Jack and Diane / Hotel California / Cocaine / Willin' / Roll on down the highway / Well all right / Joker, The / Little sister / Ride like the wind / Sweet home Alabama / Ramblin' man / What a fool believes.
Double Album: released on K-Tel, Jul'86 by K-Tel Records. Dist: Record Merchandisers Distribution, Taylors, Terry Blood Distribution, Wynd-Up Distribution, Relay Distribution, Pickwick Distribution, Solomon & Peres Distribution, Polygram

Cassette: released on K-Tel, Jul'86 by K-Tel Records. Dist: Record Merchandisers Distribution, Taylors, Terry Blood Distribution, Wynd-Up Distribution, Relay Distribution, Pickwick Distribution, Solomon & Peres Distribution, Polygram

Special: released on K-Tel, Jul'86 by K-Tel Records. Dist: Record Merchandisers Distribution, Taylors, Terry Blood Distribution, Wynd-Up Distribution, Relay Distribution, Pickwick Distribution, Solomon & Peres Distribution, Polygram

Drivin'

DRIVIN' IN THE VALLEYS various artists (Various Artists).
Cassette: released on EMI, May'79 by EMI Records. Dist: EMI

DRIVIN' MOVIE THEMES various artists (Various Artists).
Cassette: released on Mobile Music, May'79

Dr John & Chris Barber

CHRIS BARBER & DR JOHN (VOL 2) (see Barber, Chris).

CHRIS BARMER & DR JOHN (VOL 1) (see Barber, Chris).

TAKE ME BACK TO NEW ORLEANS (see Barber, Chris).
Tracks: / Take me back to New Orleans / Ti-pi-ti-na / Perdido Street blues / New Orleans, Louisiana / Decatur Drive / New Orleans / Meet me on the Levee / Harlem rag / Ride on / The big

bass drum / At the cemetery / Concert on Canal Street / Bourbon Street scene / Basin Street / Just a little while to stay here / Oration by Dr. John / Wha a friend we have in Jesus / When the Saints go Marching In / Concert in Canal Street / When the Saints / Buddy Bolden Blues / South Rampart Street Parade / Burgandy Street Blues / Canal Street Blues / Bourbon Street Parade / Do you know what it means to miss New Orleans / Professor Longhair's Tip / Brass Band Blues / Basin Street Blues.
Notes: Personnel: Special guests Freddie Kohlman and the New Orleans Brass Band. 2 LP Set.

Dr. No
DR. NO James Bond Original Soundtrack.
Tracks: / James Bond theme / Kingston calypso / Jamaican rock / Jump up / Audio bongo / Under the mango tree / Twisting with James / Jamaica jazz / Under the mango tree / Jump up / Dr. No's fantasy / Kingston calypso / Island speaks, The / Under the mango tree / Boy chase / Dr. No's fantasy / James Bond theme / Love at last.
Notes: Composed and conducted by Monty Norman. Produced by Harry Saltzman and Cubby Broccoli. Published by Eon Productions Ltd. partnership. Eon Productions Ltd.
Album: released on Liberty, Jul'87 by Liberty-United. Dist: EMI

Cassette: released on Liberty, Jul'87 by Liberty-United. Dist: EMI

Drohar, Tox
NO KIDDING (Drohar, Tox & Charlie Burchell).
Album: released on Wave, Apr'79 by Charly Records. Dist: Charly

Droid World
DROID WORLD various artists (Various Artists).
Album: released on Disneyland, Jul'83 by Disneyland-Vista Records (USA). Dist: BBC Records & Tapes, Rainbow Communications Ltd(Distribution)

Cassette: released on Disneyland, Jul'83 by Disneyland-Vista Records (USA). Dist: BBC Records & Tapes, Rainbow Communications Ltd(Distribution)

Drones
FURTHER TEMPTATIONS.
Album: released on Valer, Dec'77

Droney, Chris
FLOWING TIDE, THE.
Album: released on Topic, Oct'75 Dist: Roots Distribution

Drongos for Europe
DEATH'S A CAREER ep.
Single (7"): released on Inferno, Feb'82 by Inferno Records. Dist: Inferno, Cartel, Pinnacle

ETERNITY.
Single (7"): released on Inferno, Nov'82 by Inferno Records. Dist: Inferno, Cartel, Pinnacle

PEACE.
Single (7"): released on Drongos For Europe, Oct'81

Droogs
STONE COLD WORLD.
Album: released on Spindrift, May'86 Dist: Roots

Drowning Craze
HEAT.
Single (7"): released on Situation 2, Feb'82 Dist: Cartel, Pinnacle

STORAGE CASE.
Single (7"): released on Situation 2, Jul'81 Dist: Cartel, Pinnacle

TRANCE.
Single (7"): released on Situation 2, Nov'81 Dist: Cartel, Pinnacle

Drowsy Maggie
SING AN IRISH SONG.
Tracks: / Molly Malone / Sing an Irish song.
Single (7"): released on Starbind, Mar'87 by Starbind Records. Dist: PRT Distribution

Dru
CAN'T LIVE WITHOUT YOU, I.
Single (7"): by Creole Records. Dist: PRT

Single (12"): by Creole Records. Dist: PRT

Drummer, John
OWN UP IF YOU'RE OVER 25 (Drummer, John & Helen April).
Single (7"): released on Red Sky, Jan'81 by Red Sky Records. Dist: Red Sky, Projection, Celtic Music, Roots

Drummond, Bill
KING OF JOY, THE.
Tracks: / King of joy, The.
Single (12"): released on Creation, Mar'87 Dist: Rough Trade, Cartel

MAN.
Album: released on Creation, Nov'86 Dist: Rough Trade, Cartel

Drummond, Daniel
BLUE HOUR, THE.
Album: released on DTS, Aug'87 by Record & Tape Sales. Dist: Revolver, Cartel. Estim retail price in Sep'87 was £5.99.

PROGRAM, THE.
Single (12"): released on DTS, Aug'87 by Record & Tape Sales. Dist: Revolver, Cartel

Drummond, Don
CLASH & SPECIALS GO TO JAIL. (Drummond, Don Jnr & the Ska Stars).
Single (12"): released on Russ, Jul'80 Dist: Spartan Distribution

Drummond, Keith
PEOPLE OF THE WORLD.
Single (12"): released on Carousel, Mar'83 by Carousel Records. Dist: Spartan, Rough Trade

Drum night at Birdland
DRUM NIGHT AT BIRDLAND (Various Artists).
Notes: With Art Blakey, Philly Joe Jones, Charlie Persip & Elvin Jones.
Compact disc: released on Vogue (France), '86 Dist: Discovery, Jazz Music, PRT, Swift

Drum Theatre
EL DORADO.
Tracks: / Jungle of people / El Dorado.
Single (7"): released on Epic, Dec'86 by CBS Records. Dist: CBS

Single (12"): released on Epic, Dec'86 by CBS Records. Dist: CBS

Single (12"): released on Epic, Dec'86 by CBS Records. Dist: CBS

EVERYMAN.
Tracks: / Home (is where the heart is) / Eldorado / Reunion / Wide Sargasso Sea / Rhythm of your heart / Living in the past / Children of tomorrow / Moving targets / Once in your lifetime / Once in your lifetime / Runners.
Album: released on Epic, Apr'87 by CBS Records. Dist: CBS

Cassette: released on Epic, Apr'87 by CBS Records. Dist: CBS

Compact disc: released on Epic, Apr'87 by CBS Records. Dist: CBS

HOME IS WHERE THE HEART IS.
Single (12"): released on Epic, Jun'86 by CBS Records. Dist: CBS

Single (7"): released on Epic, Jun'86 by CBS Records. Dist: CBS

LIVING IN THE PAST.
Tracks: / Living in the past / Seventh sin / Living in the past (remix).
Single (7"): released on Epic, Dec'85 by CBS Records. Dist: CBS

Single (12"): released on Epic, Dec'85 by CBS Records. Dist: CBS

Single (12"): released on Epic, Jan'86 by CBS Records. Dist: CBS

MOVING TARGETS.
Tracks: / Moving targets(instrumental) / 7th fine.
Single (7"): released on Epic, Mar'87 by CBS Records. Dist: CBS

Single (12"): released on Epic, Mar'87 by CBS Records. Dist: CBS

Drupi
VADO VIA.
Single (7"): released on Old Gold, Jul'82 by Old Gold Records. Dist: Lightning, Jazz Music, Spartan, Counterpoint

Drusky, Roy
ANYMORE.
Album: released on Stetson, 11 Apr'87 by Hasmick Promotions Ltd.. Dist: Counterpoint Distribution, H.R. Taylor Distribution, Swift Distribution, Chris Wellard Distribution

Cassette: released on Stetson, 11 Apr'87 by Hasmick Promotions Ltd.. Dist: Counterpoint Distribution, H.R. Taylor Distribution, Swift Distribution, Chris Wellard Distribution

COUNTRY ROSE.
Album: released on Colorado, Dec'85 Dist: Counterpoint

Cassette: released on Colorado, Dec'85 Dist: Counterpoint

NIGHT FLYING.
Album: released on Big R, Oct'81 by Big R Records. Dist: Pinnacle, Wynd-Up Distribution, Solomon & Peres Distribution, I & B, JSU, Swift, Record Merchandisers Distribution, Spartan

Cassette: released on Big R, Oct'81 by Big R Records. Dist: Pinnacle, Wynd-Up Distribution, Solomon & Peres Distribution, I & B, JSU, Swift, Record Merchandisers Distribution, Spartan

Single (7"): released on Big R, Aug'81 by Big R Records. Dist: Pinnacle, Wynd-Up Distribution, Solomon & Peres Distribution, I & B, JSU, Swift, Record Merchandisers Distribution, Spartan

ROY.
Album: released on Big R, Feb'81 by Big R Records. Dist: Pinnacle, Wynd-Up Distribution, Solomon & Peres Distribution, I & B, JSU, Swift, Record Merchandisers Distribution, Spartan

Dry Branch Fire Squad
GOOD NEIGHBOURS AND FRIENDS.
Album: released on Rounder (USA), Sep'85 Dist: Mike's Country Music Room Distribution, Jazz Music Distribution, Swift Distribution, Roots Records Distribution, Projection Distribution, Topic Distribution

Dry Cane
WITH COUNTRY IN MIND.
Album: released on Country House, Dec'81 by BGS Productions Ltd. Dist: Taylor, H.R., Record Merchandisers Distribution, Pinnacle, Sounds of Scotland Records

Cassette: released on Country House, Dec'81 by BGS Productions Ltd. Dist: Taylor, H.R., Record Merchandisers Distribution, Pinnacle, Sounds of Scotland Records

Dry Ice
HARRY THE HIPPIE.
Single (7"): released on Simple, Oct'84 by Simple Records. Dist: EMI

Dr. York
RE-NEW.
Album: released on Preset, Jul'87 Dist: Pinnacle

Cassette: released on Preset, Jul'87 Dist: Pinnacle

Dry Throat Five
WHO'S BLUE.
Album: released on Stomp Off, Oct'86 by Stomp Off Records. Dist: Jazz Music Distribution

Dr.Zhivago
DR.ZHIVAGO Original soundtrack (Various Artists).
Compact disc: released on CBS, Apr'87 by CBS Records. Dist: CBS

Compact disc: released on CBS, Apr'87 by CBS Records. Dist: CBS

D.S.M.
DESTINY.
Single (7"): released on Elite, May'86 Dist: PRT

Single (12"): released on Elite, May'86 Dist: PRT

D.S.T.
HOME OF HIP HOP.
Single (7"): released on Celluloid, Aug'85 by Charly Records. Dist: Charly

MEAN MACHINE (D.S.T. & Jalal).
Single (12"): released on Celluloid-Carrere, Sep'84 by Celluloid. Dist: PRT, Spartan

MEGAMIX 11,WHY IS IT FRESH.
Single (12"): released on Celluloid-Carrere, Sep'84 by Celluloid. Dist: PRT, Spartan

D & The Rockets
PURE ROCK'N'ROLL.
Single (7"): released on Deb, Oct'81 by Deb Records. Dist: Spartan

D-Train
D-TRAIN.
Album: released on Prelude, Apr'82 by CBS

Cassette: released on Prelude, Apr'82 Dist: CBS

D-TRAIN(EP).
Cassette: released on Epic, Aug'82 by CBS Records. Dist: CBS

MUSIC.
Single (7"): released on Prelude, Sep'85 Dist: CBS

Single (12"): released on Prelude, Sep'85 Dist: CBS

MUSIC(PART 1).
Single (7"): released on Prelude, Apr'83 Dist: CBS

Single (12"): released on Prelude, Apr'83 Dist: CBS

SOMETHING'S ON YOUR MIND.
Album: released on Prelude, Apr'84 Dist: CBS

Cassette: released on Prelude, Apr'84 Dist: CBS

THANK YOU.
Single (12"): released on Prelude, Jul'84 Dist: CBS

YOU'RE THE ONE FOR ME.
Album: released on Prelude, Sep'85 Dist: CBS

Cassette: released on Prelude, Sep'85 Dist: CBS

YOU'RE THE ONE FOR ME(1).
Single (7"): released on Prelude, Jul'85 Dist: CBS

Single (12"): released on Prelude, Jul'85 Dist: CBS

DTS
TRIBUTE TO MARC Medley-2 parts.
Single (7"): released on HME (USA), Oct'82 Dist: CBS

Duadi Kabaka
KENYAFRICA (VOL.3) (Duadi Kabaka & The T B Eagles).

Duane & Co
J.B. ON THE ONE.
Single (7"): released on Serious, Aug'87 by Serious Records. Dist: PRT

Single (12"): released on Serious, Aug'87 by Serious Records. Dist: PRT

Duart, John
MOTORBIKE.
Single (7"): released on Dreyfus, Apr'80

Dubious Brothers
DON'T LAUGH AT ME.
Tracks: / Don't laugh at me / Sugar daddy / Don't laugh at me (cementmix).
Single (7"): released on Fend For Yourself, Oct'86 by Fend For Yourself Records. Dist: Probe Plus Distribution, Cartel

Single (7"): released on Fend For Yourself, Sep'86 by Fend For Yourself Records. Dist: Probe Plus Distribution, Cartel

EGG.
Tracks: / Egg / Save me / Protest song (cakemix) / Dance of the undertaker.
Single (7"): released on Fend For Yourself, Sep'86 by Fend For Yourself Records. Dist: Probe Plus Distribution, Cartel

LIKES OF YOU.
Tracks: / Likes of you / Protest song / Stay awake my little emperor / Bible stories.
Single (7"): released on Fend For Yourself, Sep'86 by Fend For Yourself Records. Dist: Probe Plus Distribution, Cartel

SOUTH AMERICA WELCOMES THE NAZIS.
Tracks: / South America welcomes the Nazis / Lord of the flies / Bible stories / They're coming to take me away.
Single (12"): released on Fend For Yourself, Feb'87 by Fend For Yourself Records. Dist: Probe Plus Distribution, Cartel

Dublane Organ
GREAT ORGAN MUSIC (Dublane Cathedral Organ).
Album: released on Lismor, Jul'77 by Lismor Records. Dist: Lismor, Roots, Celtic Music

Dublin City Ramblers
BOYS OF THE OLD BRIGADE.
Tracks: / Boys of the old brigade / Three flowers / Over the wall / Broad black brimmer / Lord Inchiquinn / Cliffs on Dooneen / Wrap the green flag round / Reluctant patriot / Gypsy, The / Tricolour ribbon / James Larkin / Lark in the morning, The.
Cassette: released on Polydor (Eire), Feb'85

DUBLIN CITY RAMBLERS.
Album: released on Harp(Ireland), May'80 by Pickwick Records. Dist: Taylors

Dubliners

AT THEIR BEST.
Tracks: / Wild rover, The / Easy and slow / Home, boys, home / Chief O'Neill's favourite / Rocky road to Dublin / Leaving of Liverpool / I'll tell my ma / Mason's apron, The / Foggy dew, The / Old orange flute / Roisin dubh / Holy ground, The / Nelson's farewell / Twang man, The / Jar of porter / Bonlavogue / Glendalough saint, The / Air fa la la la / Off to Dublin in the green / Sunshine hornpipe / Mountain road, The / Peggy Lettermore / Donegal reel / Longfore collector, The / Roddy McCorley.
Album: released on Cambra, Feb'85 by Cambra Records. Dist: IDS, Conifer

Cassette: released on Cambra, Feb'85 by Cambra Records. Dist: IDS, Conifer

BEST OF..., THE.
Album: released on Harp(Ireland), Feb'82 by Pickwick Records. Dist: Taylors

Cassette: released on Harp(Ireland), Feb'82 by Pickwick Records. Dist: Taylors

BEST OF, THE.
Album: released on Polydor (Holland), Feb'85

Cassette: released on Polydor (Holland), Feb'85

BEST OF THE DUBLINERS, THE.
Tracks: / Whiskey in the jar / Fiddler's Green / Town I loved so well, The / Old triangle, The / Dirty old town / Wild rover, The / Wonder horn, The / Farewell to Carlingford / Lord of the dance / Killieburne Brae / Rebellion: wrap the green flag round me, boys / West's awake, The / Nation once again, A.
Album: released on Spot, Feb'83 by Pickwick Records. Dist: H.R. Taylor,

Cassette: released on Spot, Feb'83 by Pickwick Records. Dist: H.R. Taylor,

Album: released on Transatlantic, May'81 by Logo Records. Dist: Roots Distribution, RCA Distribution

Cassette: released on Transatlantic, May'81 by Logo Records. Dist: Roots Distribution, RCA Distribution

BEST OF THE DUBLINERS.
Tracks: / Off to Dublin in the green / Will you come to the bower? / I'll tell me ma / Home, boys, home / Foggy dew, The / Wild rover, The / Easy and slow / Mason's apron, The / Nelson's farewell / Glendalough saint, The / Jar of porter / Seven drunken nights / Whiskey in the jar / Leaving of Liverpool / Seven deadly sins / Sunshine hornpipe / Mountain road, The.
Album: released on Music for Pleasure (Holland), Apr'83 Dist: Conifer Distribution

Cassette: released on Music for Pleasure (Holland), Apr'83 Dist: Conifer Distribution

COLLECTION: DUBLINERS.
Compact disc: released on Castle Collectors, Jul'87 by Castle Communications Records. Dist: Pinnacle

DUBLINERS 25 YEARS CELEBRATION.
Notes: Double album.
Double Album: released on Stylus, Apr'87 Dist: Pinnacle, Terry Blood Distribution, Stylus Distribution

Double cassette: released on Stylus, Apr'87 Dist: Pinnacle, Terry Blood Distribution, Stylus Distribution

Double compact disc: released on Stylus, Apr'87 Dist: Pinnacle, Terry Blood Distribution, Stylus Distribution

DUBLINERS LIVE.
Tracks: / Finnegan's Wake / Fiddle solo / Monto / Dublin fusiliers / Chief O'Neill's favourite / Sea around us / McAlpine's fusiliers / Hot asphalt / Glendlock saint / Air fa la la la lo / Peggy Lettermore / Easy and slow / My love is in America / One morning in March / Old orange flute / Leaving of Liverpool.
Album: released on Polydor, Mar'84 by Polydor Records. Dist: Polygram, Polydor

Cassette: released on Polydor, Mar'84 by Polydor Records. Dist: Polygram, Polydor

DUBLINERS NOW.
Album: released on Polydor, Feb'82 by Polydor Records. Dist: Polygram, Polydor

DUBLINERS, THE.
Cassette: released on Ideal(Tapes), Apr'80 Dist: EMI

GOLDEN FOLK SONGS.
Tracks: / Wild rover, The / Fiddler's Green / Johnston's motor car / Town I loved so well, The / Skibereen / Finnegan's Wake / Donegal Danny / Seven drunken nights / Dirty old town / Holy ground, The / Whiskey in the jar / Ballad of Ronnie's mare.
Album: released on Polydor (Germany), Feb'84 Dist: IMS-Polygram

Cassette: released on Polydor (Germany), Feb'84 Dist: IMS-Polygram

GREATEST HITS:DUBLINERS.
Cassette: released on Note, Feb'80 by EMI Records. Dist: EMI

HERE'S THE DUBLINERS.
Tracks: / Maid of the sweet brown knowe / Old alarm clock, The / Colonel Fraser and O'Rourke's reel / Rising of the moon / McCafferty / I'm a rover / Maloney wants a drink / Travelling people / Limerick rake / Zoological gardens / Fairmoye lasses and sporting Paddy / Poor Paddy on the railway / Net-hauling song / Nancy Whiskey / Many young men of twenty / Paddy's gone to France / Molly Bawn / Dundee weaver, The / Tibby Dunbar / Inniskellen dragoons / Piper's chair, The / Bill Hart's jig / Nights of St Patrick / I wish I were back in Liverpool / Carby O'Leary / Go to sea no more.
Album: released on Music For Pleasure, Jun'84

Cassette: released on Music For Pleasure, Jun'84

HOME BOYS HOME.
Album: released on Harp(Ireland), May'80 by Pickwick Records. Dist: Taylors

IN CONCERT.
Album: released on Harp(Ireland), Feb'82 by Pickwick Records. Dist: Taylors

Cassette: released on Harp(Ireland), Feb'82 by Pickwick Records. Dist: Taylors

LIVE.
Album: released on Cambra, Jun'85 by Cambra Records. Dist: IDS, Conifer

Cassette: released on Cambra, Jun'85 by Cambra Records. Dist: IDS, Conifer

LIVE IN CARRE.
Tracks: / Sweets of May / Dicey Reil[illegible] Song for Ireland / Building up and tearir[illegible]ngland down / Dunphy's hornpipe / Leitrim fancy / Down the broom / Dirty old town / Old triangle, The / Whiskey in the jar / Humours of Scarin / Flannel jacket, The / Galway races / Prodigal son / Sick note, The / Wild rover, The / Seven drunken nights.
Album: released on Polydor (Ireland), Sep'85 by Polydor Records. Dist: Polygram, I & B

Cassette: released on Polydor (Ireland), Sep'85 by Polydor Records. Dist: Polygram, I & B

SEVEN DEADLY SINS.
Album: by EMI Records. Dist: EMI

SEVEN DRUNKEN NIGHTS.
Album: by EMI Records. Dist: EMI

Cassette: released on Encore, Jun'78 by EMI Records. Dist: EMI

VERY BEST OF THE DUBLINERS.
Album: by EMI Records. Dist: EMI

Dubliners, The

COLLECTION, THE.
Tracks: / Wild rover / Chief O'Neill's favourite / Glendalough saint, The / Off to Dublin in the green / Love is pleasing / Nelson's farewell / Monto / Dublin fusiliers.
Notes: Tracks include those listed above.
Double Album: released on Collector Series, Sep'86 by Castle Communications Records. Dist: PRT, Pinnacle, RCA, Ariola

Double cassette: released on Collector Series, Sep'87 by Castle Communications Records. Dist: PRT, Pinnacle, RCA, Ariola

Compact disc: released on Collector Series, Sep'87 by Castle Communications Records. Dist: PRT, Pinnacle, RCA, Ariola

Dub Poets Dub

DUB POETS DUB various artists (Various Artists).
Album: released on Heartbeat (USA), Apr'84 Dist: Mike's Country Music Room Distribution, Swift, Projection, Topic, Jetstar, Ruff Lion Distribution

Dub Set

FLESH BEAT FEVER.
Single (7"): released on Elektra (USA), Jun'84 by Elektra/Asylum/Nonesuch Records. Dist: WEA

Single (12"): released on Elektra (USA), Jun'84 by Elektra/Asylum/Nonesuch Records. Dist: WEA Deleted '85.

NAMELESS DREAD.
Single (7"): released on Elektra (USA), Sep'84 by Elektra/Asylum/Nonesuch Records. Dist: WEA

Dub Syndicate

ONE WAY SYSTEM.
Cassette: released on Reach Out Int, Jul'83

TUNES FROM THE MISSING CHANNEL.
Album: released on On-U-Sound, Jun'85 Dist: Rough Trade Distribution, Lightning

Dub War

DUB WAR VOL.1 various artists (Various Artists).
Album: released on Vista Sounds, Mar'85 by Vista Sounds Records. Dist: Jetstar

Duccia, Ron

MUSIC FROM THE BIG TOMATO.
Album: released on Armageddon, Jul'81 by Armageddon Records. Dist: Revolver, Cartel, Pinnacle

Duchess & High School

FRIDAYS, SATURDAY & SUNDAY.
Single (7"): released on RPS, Oct'84

Duchess of Duke Street

DUCHESS OF DUKE STREET (Hardwick, Mollie).
Cassette: released on Chivers Audio Books, '81 by Chivers Sound & Vision. Dist: Chivers Sound & Vision

Duck Food

DUCK FOOD.
Album: released on Earthworks, May'86 by Earthworks Records. Dist: Earthworks Distributors, Rough Trade, Cartel, Projection

Duck, Jay

JAY DUCK'S THEME (Duck, Jay & J.D. Revolution).
Single (7"): released on Magnet, Jul'83 by Magnet Records. Dist: BMG

Ducks Deluxe

DON'T MIND ROCKIN' TONIGHT.
Tracks: / Coast to coast / Fireball / Saratoga Suzie / Don't mind rockin' tonight / Daddy put the bomp / Please, please, please / It's all over now / Love's melody / Two time twister / I fought the law / Paris 9 / My music / Somethings going on / Here comes the night.
Album: released on RCA, Oct'86 by RCA Records. Dist: RCA, Roots, Swift, Wellard, Chris, I & B, Solomon & Peres Distribution

Cassette: released on RCA, Oct'86 by RCA Records. Dist: RCA, Roots, Swift, Wellard, Chris, I & B, Solomon & Peres Distribution

LAST NIGHT OF A PUB ROCK BAND.
Album: released on Blue Moon, Dec'82 Dist: Magnum Music Group Ltd, PRT, Spartan

Ducktail

ROCKIN' DADDY.
Single (7"): released on Ducktail, Jul'80

Duck You Sucker

LOVE IS CRIMINAL.
Single (7"): released on Magnet, Dec'84 by Magnet Records. Dist: BMG

Dudley, Dave

20 GREAT TRUCK HITS.
Album: released on EMI (Sweden), '83 by EMI Records. Dist: Conifer

COLLECTION: DAVE DUDLEY.
Album: released on EMI (Germany), '83 by EMI Records. Dist: Conifer

HERE HE IS!.
Notes: Starr Marketing Services, 90 Queens Road, Twickenham, Middlesex TW1 4ET.

HERE HE IS.
Compact disc: released on Delta, '86 by Delta Records. Dist: Target

ON THE ROAD.
Cassette: released on Import Music Service (IMS), Apr'81 Dist: Concord Jazz Distributions, Pablo, Polygram

TRUCK SONGS.
Album: released on Mercury (Import), Mar'84
Cat. no: 9279 147
Cassette: released on Mercury (Import), Mar'84

Duelling banjos

DUELLING BANJOS Various artists (Various Artists).
Cassette: released on Aim (Budget Cassettes), Sep'83

Duet Emmo

OR SO IT SEEMS.
Album: released on Mute, Aug'83 Dist: Spartan Distribution, Rough Trade Distribution, Cartel Distribution

Single (12"): released on Mute, Mar'83 Dist: Spartan Distribution, Rough Trade Distribution, Cartel Distribution

Duffo

BOB THE BIRDMAN.
Album: released on PVK, Jul'81

DISAPPEARING BOY.
Album: released on PVK, Jun'80

GONNA SEND THE BOYS AROUND.
Single (12"): released on Yowza, Aug'85

I WANT TO BE THE PILOT.
Single (7"): released on PVK, Jun'82

WALK ON THE WILD SIDE.
Single (7"): released on PVK, Oct'82

Duffus D

IS IT JUST A DREAM?.
Single (12"): released on Jay Dee, Dec'82 by Jaydee Records. Dist: Jetstar

Duffus, George

STANDING ROOM ONLY.
Album: released on Lismor, Nov'82 by Lismor Records. Dist: Lismor, Roots, Celtic Music

Cassette: released on Lismor, Nov'82 by Lismor Records. Dist: Lismor, Roots, Celtic Music

Duffy Brothers

COUNTRY MUSIC, VOL 14.
Cassette: released on VFM, May'79 by VFM Records. Dist: Taylors, Wynd-Up Distribution

HILLBILLY COUNTRY.
Album: released on Value for Money, Aug'78

IF I NEEDED YOU.
Single (7"): released on Marina, Dec'82

NASSINGTON FLYER (Duffy Brothers & Ron Ryan).
Album: released on Buffalo (UK), Mar'79

WILD OVER US.
Album: released on Folk Heritage, Jul'82 by Folk Heritage Records. Dist: Roots, Wynd-Up Distribution, Jazz Music, Folk Heritage

Duffy, Johnny

LIVE FROM LONDON.
Album: released on Nevis, May'77 Dist: H.R. Taylor

Duffy, Patrick

TOGETHER WE ARE STRONG (Duffy, Patrick & Mireille Matthieu).
Single (7"): released on Arista, Apr'83 by Arista Records. Dist: RCA

Duffy, Stephen A.J.

UNKISS THAT KISS.
Single (7"): released on 10, Aug'85 by 10 Records. Dist: Virgin, EMI

Cassette: released on 10, Aug'85 by 10 Records. Dist: Virgin, EMI

Duffy, Stephen 'Tintin'

BECAUSE WE LOVE YOU.
Tracks: / Something special / Lot of ink, A / Sunday supplement / Why shouldn't I / Unkiss that kiss / I love you / When you go to bed / Love station / We'll never argue / Julie Christie.
Album: released on 10, '86 by 10 Records. Dist: Virgin, EMI

Cassette: released on 10, '86 by 10 Records. Dist: Virgin, EMI

Compact disc: released on 10, '86 by 10 Records. Dist: Virgin, EMI

ICING ON THE CAKE.
Single (7"): released on 10, May'85 by 10 Records. Dist: Virgin, EMI

Single (12"): released on 10, May'85 by 10 Records. Dist: Virgin, EMI

I LOVE YOU.
Tracks: / I love you / Love is driving me insane / I love you (the inversion) / I love you / Wednesday Jones / Icing on the cake / Kiss me.
Single (7"): released on 10, Aug'86 by 10 Records. Dist: Virgin, EMI

Single 10": released on 10, Aug'86 by 10 Records. Dist: Virgin, EMI

Single (12"): released on 10, Aug'86 by 10 Records. Dist: Virgin, EMI

Single (7"): released on 10, Feb'86 by 10 Records. Dist: Virgin, EMI

Single (12"): released on 10, Feb'86 by 10 Records. Dist: Virgin, EMI

KISS ME.
Single (7"): released on 10, Feb'85 by 10 Records. Dist: Virgin, EMI

Single (12"): released on 10, Feb'85 by 10 Records. Dist: Virgin, EMI

SOMETHING SPECIAL.
Tracks: / Something special / Disenchanted, The / Cocksure.
Single (7"): released on 10, Apr'86 by 10 Records. Dist: Virgin, EMI

Single (12"): released on 10, Apr'86 by 10 Records. Dist: Virgin, EMI

UPS AND DOWNS, (THE).
Album: released on 10, Apr'85 by 10 Records. Dist: Virgin, EMI

Cassette: released on 10, Apr'85 by 10 Records. Dist: Virgin, EMI

Compact disc: released on 10, Apr'85 by 10 Records. Dist: Virgin, EMI

Duffy, Steve

SHE MAKES ME QUIVER.
Single (7"): released on 10, Sep'84 by 10 Records. Dist: Virgin, EMI

Single (12"): released on 10, Sep'84 by 10 Records. Dist: Virgin, EMI

Dugmore, Barry & John

IT'S GOOD WITH YOU.
Single (7"): released on JSO, May'82

Duhaney, Rick

ON BROADWAY.
Cassette: released on Chevron, Aug'85 Dist: Multiple Sound Distributors

Duignan, Packie

MUSIC FROM COUNTY LEITRIM.
Album: released on Topic, Feb'78 Dist: Roots Distribution

Duke

HE'S THUNDER.
Single (12"): released on Hot Vinyl, Jul'87 by Hot Vinyl Records. Dist: Jetstar

PARTY TIME.
Album: released on Ebony, Jul'86 by Ebony Records. Dist: Pinnacle, Ebony

Duke, George

CLARKE/DUKE PROJECT 11, (THE) (see Clarke, Stanley).
Album: released on Epic, Dec'83 by CBS Records. Dist: CBS

Cassette: released on Epic, Dec'83 by CBS Records. Dist: CBS

GEORGE DUKE.
Tracks: / Broken glass / I just want to be in your life / Good friend / So mean to me / Stand with your man / Island girl / King for a day / Morning, you and love / I can make it better / African violet.
Album: released on Elektra (USA), Oct'86 by Elektra/Asylum/Nonesuch Records. Dist: WEA

Cassette: released on Elektra (USA), Oct'86 by Elektra/Asylum/Nonesuch Records. Dist: WEA

GUARDIAN OF THE LIGHT.
Album: released on Epic, May'83 by CBS Records. Dist: CBS Deleted '85.

Cassette: released on Epic, May'83 by CBS Records. Dist: CBS

I LOVE THE BLUES.
Compact disc: released on Polydor, May'84 by Polydor Records. Dist: Polygram, Polydor

I LOVE THE BLUES, SHE HEARD MY CRY.
Album: released on MPS (Germany), Sep'84 Dist: IMS-Polygram Distribution, Parnote Distribution (Formerly MDC)

Compact disc: released on Polydor, Sep'84 by Polydor Records. Dist: Polygram, Polydor

REACH OUT.
Single (7"): released on Epic, Apr'83 by CBS Records. Dist: CBS

Single (12"): released on Epic, Apr'83 by CBS Records. Dist: CBS

THIEF IN THE NIGHT.
Compact disc: by Elektra/Asylum/Nonesuch Records. Dist: WEA

Album: released on Elektra, May'85 by WEA Records. Dist: WEA

Cassette: released on Elektra, May'85 by WEA Records. Dist: WEA

Compact disc: released on Elektra, May'85 by WEA Records. Dist: WEA

Duke, James

HOLD ON.
Tracks: / Hold on / Zyzafon.
Single (7"): released on Creole, Aug'86 by Creole Records. Dist: Rhino, PRT

Compact disc: released on Creole, Aug'86 by Creole Records. Dist: Rhino, PRT

Dukeless Gang

DUKELESS GANG (Dukeless Gang/Sonny Greer Sextet).
Tracks: / Sleepy baboon / Kansas city caboose (2 takes) / Ration stomp / Helena's dream (2 takes) / Triple play / Why was I born / You're drivin' me crazy / Key largo / Design for jivin' / Life with fatha / I love my lovin' lover / Blues on my weary mind / Trouble, trouble / I'll get by.
Album: released on Queen-Disc, Apr'81 Dist: Celtic Music, JSU, Jazz Horizons, Jazz Music

Duke of Edinburgh

DUKE OF EDINBURGH'S ROYAL REGIMENT (Duke of Edinburgh's Royal Regiment).
Album: released on Grosvenor, Jul'77 by Grosvenor Records. Dist: Taylors

QUESTION OF BALANCE, A (Duke of Edinburgh, HRH).
Cassette: released on Listen For Pleasure, Jul'84 by MFP Records. Dist: EMI

Duke of Wellington

DUKES ON PARADE, THE.
Album: released on Music Masters, Apr'81 by Music Masters Records. Dist: Taylors

DUKES ON THE ROCK, THE.
Tracks: / Gibraltar story / Trumpet filigree / Jada / Victory beatings / Misty / Sousarama / Chariots of Fire / Selection from Grease / Drummer's delight / Theme from 'The Proffesionals' / Concert rock / Regimental march the wellesley.
Album: released on Music Masters, May'83 by Music Masters Records. Dist: Taylors

Cassette: released on Music Masters, May'83 by Music Masters Records. Dist: Taylors

Dukes

I'M A SURVIVOR (Dukes (Bugatti & Musker)).
Single (7"): released on WEA, Aug'82 by WEA Records. Dist: WEA

Duke, Sister Doris

FUNKY FOX.
Album: released on Manhattan, Mar'81 by President Records. Dist: Jazz Music, Swift, Taylors, Chris Wellard

Dukes Of Dixieland

DUKES OF DIXIELAND various artists (Various Artists).
Cassette: released on Audio Fidelity, Oct'84 Dist: PRT

Dukes of Stratosphear

25 O'CLOCK.
Album: released on Virgin, Mar'85 by Virgin Records. Dist: EMI, Virgin Distribution

Cassette: released on Virgin, Mar'85 by Virgin Records. Dist: EMI, Virgin Distribution

CHIPS FROM THE CHOCOLATE FIREBALL.
Compact disc: released on Virgin, Aug'87 by Virgin Records. Dist: EMI, Virgin Distribution

PSONIC PSUNSPOT.
Album: released on Virgin, Aug'87 by Virgin Records. Dist: EMI, Virgin Distribution

Cassette: released on Virgin, Aug'87 by Virgin Records. Dist: EMI, Virgin Distribution

YOU'RE A GOOD MAN, ALBERT BROWN.
Tracks: / You're a good man, Albert Brown / Vanishing girl / Mole from the ministry* / My love explodes*.
Single (7"): released on Virgin, Jul'87 by Virgin Records. Dist: EMI, Virgin Distribution

Single (7"): released on Virgin, Jul'87 by Virgin Records. Dist: EMI, Virgin Distribution

Single (12"): released on Virgin, Jul'87 by Virgin Records. Dist: EMI, Virgin Distribution

Dukov, Bruce

DEPARTURES.
Tracks: / Viva Vivaldi / Sad song rondo / Sleepy shores / Unaccompanied cello suite No 1 / Bailero / For Kreisler's sake / Heart-throb romance / Could it be magic? / Meow ski / Variegated Maria, A.
Album: released on CBS, Apr'83 by CBS Records. Dist: CBS

Cassette: released on CBS, Apr'83 by CBS Records. Dist: CBS

FOR KRIESLER'S SAKE.
Single (7"): released on Epic, Apr'83 by CBS Records. Dist: CBS

Dumb Blondes

STRANGE LOVE.
Single (7"): released on Fresh, Apr'81 Dist: Jetstar

Dumbells

GIDDY UP.
Single (7"): released on Polydor, Nov'81 by Polydor Records. Dist: Polygram, Polydor

Dumbo

DUMBO various artists (Various Artists).
Album: released on Disneyland, Dec'82 by Disneyland-Vista Records (USA). Dist: BBC Records & Tapes, Rainbow Communications Ltd(Distribution)

Cassette: released on Disneyland, Dec'82 by Disneyland-Vista Records (USA). Dist: BBC Records & Tapes, Rainbow Communications Ltd(Distribution)

DUMBO original film soundtrack.
Tracks: / Look out for Mr. Stork-(Main Title) / Casey Jr- / It's a circus day again / Dumbo theme / Pink elephants on parade / Dumbo and Timothy / Pyramid of Elephants / Dumbo disgraced / When I see an elephant fly / Dumbo's triumph / Finale / Song of the roustabouts.
Album: released on Disney, Oct'84 by BBC Records & Tapes. Dist: BBC Records & Tapes, PRT

Cassette: released on Disney, Oct'84 by BBC Records & Tapes. Dist: BBC Records & Tapes, PRT

Dummies

DUMMIES, THE.
Album: released on Conquest, May'85 Dist: Red Rhino, Cartel

Dumptruck

POSITIVELY.
Tracks: / Back where I belong / Secrets / Nine people / Autumn lights / Winter / Alone / 7 steps / Change / Walk into mirrors / Ethics.
Album: released on Big Time, Jun'87 by Mainline Record Company. Dist: Mainline

Cassette: released on Big Time, Jun'87 by Mainline Record Company. Dist: Mainline

Dumpy's Rusty Bolts

JUST FOR KICKS.
Single (7"): released on Cool King, Aug'82 Dist: Pinnacle

Dumpy's Rusty Nuts

HOT LOVER.
Album: released on Gas, Sep'85 by Gas Records. Dist: Pinnacle

SOMEWHERE IN ENGLAND Live.
Album: released on Gas, Jan'86 by Gas Records. Dist: Pinnacle

Album: released on Landslide, Sep'84 by Dorane Ltd.

Dunbar, Aynsley

BLUE WHALE.
Tracks: / Willing to fight / Willie the pimp / It's your turn / Days / Going home.
Album: released on Charly, '78 by Charly Records. Dist: Charly, Cadillac

Dunbar, Sly

SLY-GO-VILLE.
Tracks: / Slippin into darkness / Gonna love you / Battle of Jericho / Inner city blues / If you want it / River Niger / Hot you're hot / Un metred taxi.
Album: released on Island, Aug'82 by Island Records. Dist: Polygram

Cassette: released on Island, Aug'82 by Island Records. Dist: Polygram Deleted '85.

Dunbar, Ted

JAZZ GUITARIST.
Tracks: / Winding blues / Total conversation / Trees and grass and nice things / Nica's dream / Hi-fly / Bougie / Epistrophy.
Album: released on Xanadu, Jan'83 Dist: Discovery, Jazz Horizons, Jazz Music, Swift

OPENING REMARKS.
Album: released on Xanadu, Mar'79 Dist: Discovery, Jazz Horizons, Jazz Music, Swift

Dunbar, Valerie

BLUE EYES.
Tracks: / Blue eyes crying in the rain / Old Rugged cross, The / Amazing grace / Bless this house / If I had my way / Twelfth of never, The / True love / Beautiful dreamer / Pal of my cradle days / Silver threads among the gold / Somewhere my love / Another year passes(Aniversary song) / I'd rather die young / Morning has broken / When I grow too old to dream / Loves old sweet song / Now is the hour.
Notes: Valerie's sucess in the UK charts with 'Pal of my cradle days'won her many new fans and it's for them and her existing fans that this Album is aimed.This also features her new single 'Blue eyes crying in the rain'
Cassette: released on Klub, Jun'83

Cassette: released on Klub, Jun'83

BLUE EYES CRYING IN THE RAIN.
Single (7"): released on Klub, Jun'83

FLOWER OF SCOTLAND.
Tracks: / How great thou art / Flower of Scotland / Loch Lomond / Thistle of Scotland / Bluebells of Scotland / Uist tramping song / Scotland forever / There was a man / Bonnie Scotland I adore thee / Where were you, Lord / Down in the glen / David / Eternally / Till the boys come home / Roses of Picardy / Goodbye.
Album: released on Klub, Oct'84

Cassette: released on Klub, Oct'84

FOR MY AIN FOLK.
Album: released on Klub, Sep'80

Cassette: released on Klub, Sep'80

I'LL SAY FAREWELL.
Album: released on Klub, Oct'82

Cassette: released on Klub, Oct'82

Single (7"): released on Klub, Oct'82

LEGENDS OF SCOTLAND.
Cassette: released on Lochshore, Mar'87 by Klub Records. Dist: PRT

PAL OF MY CRADLE DAYS.
Single (7"): released on Klub, Feb'82

PORTRAIT OF VALERIE DUNBAR, A.
Album: released on Klub, Oct'79

Cassette: released on Klub, Oct'79

RELAX WITH.
Album: released on Klub, Nov'85

Cassette: released on Klub, Nov'85

ROSE.
Album: released on Klub, Nov'86

Cassette: released on Klub, Nov'86

ROWAN TREE.
Single (7"): released on Klub, Jun'79

THERE WAS A MAN.
Single (7"): released on Klub, Nov'83

Duncan, Alex

IT'S A VET'S LIFE.
Cassette: released on Soundings, Mar'85 Dist: Soundings

TO BE A COUNTRY DOCTOR.
Cassette: released on Soundings, Mar'85 Dist: Soundings

VET HAS NINE LIVES, THE.
Cassette: released on Soundings, Feb'85 Dist: Soundings

Duncan, Anne Marie

NO TIME FOR LOVE.
Tracks: / No time for love / No time for love (version).
Single (12"): released on Diamond, Feb'86 by Revolver Records. Dist: Cartel

Duncan, Arlene

WANNA GROOVE, I.
Single (12"): released on Proto, Jan'83 by Proto Records. Dist: WEA

Duncan, Carey

ALL I HAVE TO DO IS DREAM.
Single (7"): released on Decibel, Jul'81

I'M YOUR WOMAN.
Single (7"): released on DB, Nov'80 by DB Records. Dist: Pinnacle

NOBODY'S CHILD.
Single (7"): released on Double B, Apr'82 Dist: Spartan

RAINING IN MY HEART.
Single (7"): released on Ritz, Jun'84 by Outlet Records. Dist: Outlet, Prism Leisure Distribution, Record Services Distribution (Ireland), Roots

TURNING AWAY.
Single (7"): released on Ritz, Jan'85 by Outlet Records. Dist: Outlet, Prism Leisure Distribution, Record Services Distribution (Ireland), Roots

Duncan,Carrie

I CAN HEAR KENTUCKY CALLING ME (Duncan,Carrie & Billie Jo Spears).
Single (7"): released on Ritz, Apr'83 by Ritz Records. Dist: Spartan

Duncan, Celena

FASTER THAN THE EYE CAN SEE.
Tracks: / Faster than the eye can see (instrumental) / Faster than the eye can see.
Single (7"): released on Nightmare, Mar'87 by Nightmare Records. Dist: PRT

Single (12"): released on Nightmare, Mar'87 by Nightmare Records. Dist: PRT

WANT YOUR LOVE BACK, I 2 Parts.
Single (7"): released on RCA, Feb'83 by RCA Records. Dist: RCA, Roots, Swift, Wellard, Chris, I & B, Solomon & Peres Distribution

Single (12"): released on RCA, Feb'83 by RCA Records. Dist: RCA, Roots, Swift, Wellard, Chris, I & B, Solomon & Peres Distribution

Duncan, Daryll

ROCK THE HOUSE.
Tracks: / Rock the house / Rock the house (inst).
Single (7"): released on Motown, May'87 by Motown Records. Dist: BMG Distribution

Single (12"): released on Motown, May'87 by Motown Records. Dist: BMG Distribution

Duncan, Frank

WIND IN THE WILLOWS Spoken Word.
Cassette: released on Pinnacle, '79 by Windsong. Dist: Pinnacle

Duncan, Hugo

BRADY FROM STRABANE.
Tracks: / Brady from Strabane / Misty rollin' Midlands.
Single (7"): released on Homespun(Ireland), Aug'86 by Outlet Records. Dist: Outlet

COME DOWN THE MOUNTAIN KATIE DALY.
Tracks: / Come down the mountain Katie Daly / Heart you break may be your own, (The) / Sun in the morning, (The) / My Kathleen / Band of gold / Sweetest of all / O'Hara from Tara / We're gonna go fishin' / Fields of Athenry / Fairy reel, (The) / Home to Mayo / If I didn't have a dime / I'll forgive and try to forget / I wonder could I live there anymore.
Album: released on Homespun(Ireland), Jul'87 by Outlet Records. Dist: Outlet

Cassette: released on Homespun(Ireland), Jul'87 by Outlet Records. Dist: Outlet

DEAR OLD GALWAY TOWN.
Single (7"): released on Homespun(Ireland), Jul'83 by Outlet Records. Dist: Outlet

HITS OF HUGO DUNCAN, THE.
Tracks: / Dear God / Cry cry again / Almost persuaded / Old Bog Road / Angel Judy / Pain of loving you / Heartaches by the number / Cinderella / Three-leaf shamrock / Tall men / Two of the usual / Eileen O'Grady.
Album: released on Homespun(Ireland), '82 by Outlet Records. Dist: Outlet

Cassette: released on Homespun(Ireland), '82 by Outlet Records. Dist: Outlet

IF WE ONLY HAD OLD IRELAND OVER HERE.
Album: released on Homespun(Ireland), Jul'83 by Outlet Records. Dist: Outlet

Cassette: released on Homespun(Ireland), Jul'83 by Outlet Records. Dist: Outlet

IRELANDS FAVOURITE SINGER.
Tracks: / Brady of Strabane / After all these years.
Album: released on Homespun(Ireland), Sep'86 by Outlet Records. Dist: Outlet

Cassette: released on Homespun(Ireland), Sep'86 by Outlet Records. Dist: Outlet

IRISH REQUESTS.
Tracks: / Village where I went to school / Dear old Galway town / Stone outside Dan Murphy's door / Eileen O'Grady / Old bog road / Misty rollin' midlands / Take me back to the castlebar / Pretty girl from Omagh / Long before your time / Slievenamon / Do you want yer aul lobby washed down / Hometown of the foyle / My Eileen is waiting for me / Catch me if you can.
Cassette: released on Homespun(Ireland), Feb'87 by Outlet Records. Dist: Outlet

ISLE OF INISFREE.
Tracks: / Isle of Inisfree / Pretty Kitty Kelly / Talk back tremblin' lips / Stone outside Dan Murphy's door / Long before your time / Nora Malone (call me by 'phone) / I love you more and more every day / Patsy McCann / Jody and the kids / Me and Bobby Magee / If I had my life to live over / Daddy Frank.
Album: released on Homespun(Ireland), Apr'84 by Outlet Records. Dist: Outlet

Cassette: released on Homespun(Ireland), Apr'84 by Outlet Records. Dist: Outlet

IT'S MY MOTHERS BIRTHDAY TODAY.
Tracks: / It's my mother's birthday today / If those lips could only speak.
Single (7"): released on Homespun(Ireland), Mar'85 by Outlet Records. Dist: Outlet

MOST REQUESTED SONGS.
Tracks: / Mary Ann regrets / Boston burglar / My own peculiar way / Do you want your aul lobby washed down? / Town I loved so well / Kentucky in the morning / Take me back to Castlebar / Village where I went to school / I'll take you home again, Kathleen / Galway shawl / Cottage on the borderline / Dear old Donegal.
Album: released on Homespun(Ireland), Mar'85 by Outlet Records. Dist: Outlet

Cassette: released on Homespun(Ireland), Mar'85 by Outlet Records. Dist: Outlet

WEDDING SONG, THE.
Tracks: / Ring your mother wore / Hometown on the Foyle / My wild Irish rose / Rose of Castlerea / Blacksmith / Pretty little girl from Omagh / Limerick you're a lady / Wedding song, The / Take good care of her / Old flames can't hold a candle to you / Keeps right on ahurtin' / Old house / 40 miles from Poplar Bluff / Answer to everything.
Cassette: released on Homespun(Ireland), Dec'85 by Outlet Records. Dist: Outlet

Cassette: released on Homespun(Ireland), Dec'85 by Outlet Records. Dist: Outlet

Single (7"): released on Homespun(Ireland), Nov'85 by Outlet Records. Dist: Outlet

YOU'RE AS WELCOME AS THE FLOWERS IN MAY.
Tracks: / I love you the best of all.
Single (7"): released on Homespun(Ireland), Nov'86 by Outlet Records. Dist: Outlet

Duncan, Johnny

LAST TRAIN TO SAN FERNANDO.
Tracks: / Last train to San Fernando / Itching for my baby / Geisha girl / Jig along home / Railroad, steamboat, river and canal / I heard the bluebirds sing / Git along home Cindy / Raise a ruckus tonight / Rock-a-billy baby / Detour / Dang me / Which way did he go / Blue, blue heartache / Footprints in the snow / My little baby / Yellow moon / Pan American / I'm movin' on.
Album: released on Bear Family, Jun'85 by Bear Family Records. Dist: Rollercoaster Distribution, Swift

WORLD OF COUNTRY MUSIC VOL 2.
Tracks: / Mustang prang / Life can be beautiful / Hello heartache / If it feels good, do it / Wild side of life, The / Just for what I am / Salty dog blues / Just a little lovin' / Footprints in the snow / Blue, blue heartaches / Someone to give my love to / Hey good lookin' / I can't help it / Jambalaya / Smoke, smoke, smoke / Tom Dooley / Last train to San Fernando / Mustang prang (revisited).
Album: released on World of Learning, '73 by World Of Learning Records. Dist: World Of Learning

Duncan, Kenny

DANCING THROUGH SCOTLAND.
Album: released on Dansan, Jun'81 by Spartan Records. Dist: Spartan

Duncan, Peter

COLD AS ICE.
Single (7"): released on Deb, May'83 by Deb Records. Dist: Spartan

Duncans

GONNA STAY IN LOVE.
Album: released on Malaco, May'82 by Malaco Records. Dist: Charly

Single (7"): released on Proto, Feb'83 by Proto Records. Dist: WEA

Single (12"): released on Proto, Feb'83 by Proto Records. Dist: WEA

Duncan, Sammy

SWINGIN' JAZZ (Duncan, Sammy & His All-Stars).

Duncan Sisters

DUNCAN SISTERS, THE.
Album: released on Casablanca, Feb'80 Dist: Polygram, Phonogram

Dundas, David

JEANS ON.
Single (7"): released on Air, Jul'76 by Chrysalis Records. Dist: Polygram

VERTICAL HOLD.
Tracks: / It ain't so easy / Doing the best I can / Guy the gorilla / Lady you are my only worry / Gimme a little bit / When I saw you today / Radio fun / Never surrender / 12 bar blues / America.
Album: by Cynic Records. Dist: Stage One

Dundee Strathspey...

BOWS & STRINGS, BUTTONS & KEYS.
Album: released on Ross, Jan'87 by Ross Records. Dist: Ross Distribution, Roots Distribution

Cassette: released on Ross, Jan'86 by Ross Records. Dist: Ross Distribution, Roots Distribution

Dune

DANCIN' HEATWAVES.
Single (7"): released on Ultra, Jul'82 by Ultra Records. Dist: PRT

DUNE original soundtrack.
Album: released on CTI, Nov'77 by Polydor Records. Dist: IMS, Polygram

DUNE Original Soundtrack (Various Artists).
Tracks: / Dune / Prologue / Main title / Robot fight / Leto's theme / Box (The) / Floating fat man(The) / Trip to Arrakis / First attack / Phrophecy theme / Dune(Desert home) / Paul meets Chani / Prelude(Take my hand) / Paul takes the water of life / Big battle / Paul kills Feyd / Final dream / Take my hand.
Compact disc: released on Polydor, Dec'84 by Polydor Records. Dist: Polygram, Polydor

Album: released on Polydor, Dec'84 by Polydor Records. Dist: Polygram, Polydor

Cassette: released on Polydor, Dec'84 by Polydor Records. Dist: Polygram, Polydor

Compact disc: released on Polydor, Dec'84 by Polydor Records. Dist: Polygram, Polydor

Dune: Heretics Of

HERETICS OF DUNE (CHAPTERS 1 & 2) Written & read by Frank Herbert (Herbert, Frank).
Cassette: released on Caedmon(USA), '84 by Caedmon (USA) Records. Dist: Gower, Taylors, Discovery

Dune Trilogy Songbook

DUNE TRILOGY SOUNDBOOK various artists (Various Artists).
Cassette: released on Caedmon(USA), '81 by Caedmon (USA) Records. Dist: Gower, Taylors, Discovery

Dunham, Andrew

DETROIT BLUES vol.2-1948-9 (Dunham, Andrew & Friends).
Album: released on Krazy Kat, Dec'84 Dist: Jazz Music, Swift, Chris Wellard, H.R. Taylor, Charly, Hotshot, IRS Distribution

Dunham, Sonny

1943-1944 (Dunham, Sonny & His Orchestra).
Notes: Mono.
Album: released on Circle(USA), Jan'87 by Jazzology Records (USA). Dist: Jazz Music, Swift, Chris Wellard

Dunkley, Errol

AUTOGRAPH (Dunkley, Errol & the Chosen Few).
Single (12"): released on Scom, Oct'85 by Scom Records. Dist: Jetstar

BETCHA BY GOLLY WOW.
Single (7"): released on CSA, Sep'82 by CSA Records. Dist: PRT, Jetstar

78 rpm record: released on CSA, Sep'82 by CSA Records. Dist: PRT, Jetstar

CHILDREN OF THE NIGHT.
Single (12"): released on Music Hawk, Oct'82 by Music Hawk Records. Dist: Jetstar Distribution

DARLING OOH.
Tracks: / You never know / Movie star / Created by the father / Little way different, A / Like to be boosted / Darling ooh / Baby I love you / You're gonna need me / I'm not the man for you / It was nice while it lasted.
Album: released on Trojan, Sep'81 by Trojan Records. Dist: PRT, Jetstar

Single (12"): released on Londisc, Aug'84 by Londisc Records.

DOWN BELOW (Dunkley, Errol & Johnny Clarke).
Single (12"): released on Success, Jul'8 Dist: Counterpoint Distribution

HAVE YOU EVER BEEN BAD.
Single (12"): released on PD Music, Jun'82

HOW COULD I LET YOU GET AWAY.
Single (12"): released on Music Hawk, Dec'82 by Music Hawk Records. Dist: Jetstar Distribution

LITTLE BIT OF LOVING.
Single (12"): released on King Jam, Dec'82 by King Jam Records. Dist: Jetstar

LOVE IN THE HOUSE.
Single (12"): released on Londisc, Aug'83 by Londisc Records.

LOVE IN TIME.
Single (12"): released on Judah, May'82

LOVE LIKE THIS.
Single (12"): released on King Jam, Feb'83 by King Jam Records. Dist: Jetstar

MY EYES.
Single (12"): released on Easy Street, Nov'83 by Easy Street Records. Dist: Jetstar

OK FRED.
Single (7"): released on Scope, Sep'79 by Lightning Records. Dist: WEA

ONLY A SMILE.
Single (12"): released on Natty Congo, Nov'82 by Natty Congo Records. Dist: Jetstar

PROFILE OF ERROL DUNKLEY.
Album: released on Third World, Nov'79 Dist: Jetstar Distribution

RAGAMUFFIN GONE TO JAIL.
Single (12"): released on Value Gold, Aug'87 Dist: Jetstar

SPECIAL GIRL.
Single (12"): released on Mobiliser, Oct'83 by Jetstar Records. Dist: Jetstar Distribution

TOUCH ME IN THE MORNING.
Single (12"): released on Music Hawk, Jul'83 by Music Hawk Records. Dist: Jetstar Distribution

YOU HAVE BEEN BAD.
Single (12"): released on PC, Feb'82 Dist: Jetstar

Dunloy Accordian Band

MARCHING TO CHURCH.
Cassette: released on Outlet (Praise), Jul'84

Dunn, Bill

THANK GOD I AM FREE.
Album: by Pilgrim Records. Dist: Rough Trade, Cartel

Dunn & Bruce Street

IF YOU COME WITH ME.
Single (7"): released on Satril, May'83 by Satril Records. Dist: PRT

SHOUT FOR JOY.
Single (7"): released on Satril, Aug'82 by Satril Records. Dist: PRT

Single (12"): released on Satril, Aug'82 by Satril Records. Dist: PRT

Dunn, Clive

GRANDAD.
Single (7"): released on Columbia, Sep'70 by EMI Records. Dist: EMI

Single (7"): released on Old Gold, Oct'83 by Old Gold Records. Dist: Lightning, Jazz Music, Spartan, Counterpoint

NOT MUCH CHANGE (Dunn, Clive & John Le Mesurier).
Single (7"): released on KA, Sep'82

Dunn, George

DUNN,GEORGE.
Album: released on Leader, Jun'86 Dist: Jazz Music, Projection

GEORGE DUNN.
Album: released on Leader, '81 Dist: Jazz Music, Projection

Dunn, Johnny

JOHNNY DUNN'S ORIGINAL JAZZ HOUNDS 1923-27 (Dunn, Johnny Original Jazz Hounds).
Album: released on VJM, Apr'79 by Wellard, Chris Distribution. Dist: Wellard, Chris Distribution

Dunn, Kevin

C'EST TOUJOURS LA....
Notes: mini
Album: released on Press, Jul'86 by Press Records.

C'EST TOUJOURS LA MEME GUITAR.
Album: released on Press (USA), Mar'85

JUDGEMENT OF PARIS, THE (Dunn, Kevin & Regiment of Women).
Album: released on Armageddon, Jul'81 by Armageddon Records. Dist: Revolver, Cartel, Pinnacle

OKTYABRINA (Dunn, Kevin & Regiment of Women).
Single (7"): released on Armageddon, Jul'81 by Armageddon Records. Dist: Revolver, Cartel, Pinnacle

TANZFELD.
Tracks: / Nam / Clear title / You better move / Burnig love '81 / 5.9148 / Louie,Louie / Giovinezza / Nadine / Something new to get upset about.
Album: released on Press, Jul'86 by Press Records.

Dunn Thing

STICKING TO MY GUNS.
Single (7"): released on GC, Dec'84 by GC Recordings. Dist: DMS, RCA

Single (12"): released on GC, Dec'84 by GC Recordings. Dist: DMS, RCA

Dunphy, Sean

20 IRISH GREATS.
Album: released on Dolphin, May'81 Dist: I & B Records Distribution, Prism Leisure Corporation Records, Record Services Distribution (Ireland)

THRU OLD IRELAND WITH...
Album: released on Dolphin, Jan'78 Dist: I & B Records Distribution, Prism Leisure Corporation Records, Record Services Distribution (Ireland)

Dunphy, Tom

VERY BESTOF TOM DUNPHY.
Album: released on Talisman, Oct'76 by EMI (Ireland) Records. Dist: EMI (Ireland) Distribution, I & B Distribution

Dunsany, Baron

BOOK OF WONDER (THE).
Cassette: released on Caedmon(USA), Sep'82 by Caedmon (USA) Records. Dist: Gower, Taylors, Discovery

Dunvant Male Choir

POWER AND GLORY (THE).
Tracks: / Soldiers'chorus from Faust / Sarah / Lord's prayer (The) / Amazing Grace / My old Kentucky Home / Close thine eyes / Soldiers'Farewell / Bandits chorus from 'Ernani.
Notes: Formerly recording for EMI,we welcome yet another top-flight Welsh male choir with superb guest soloists to the Grassmere label with a delightful and commercial programme.
Album: released on Grasmere, Apr'86 by Grasmere Records. Dist: EMI

Cassette: released on Grasmere, Apr'86 by Grasmere Records. Dist: EMI

Duo Greco

BOUZOUKI AT THE BRIDGE.
Cassette: released on Plato Tapes, Sep'83 by Plato Tapes. Dist: Plato Tapes

Duo, Joanne

TOGETHER.
Album: released on Eron, May'80 by Eron Records. Dist: Eron Records

Dupe, Mo

GRATITUDE (see Ade, King Sunny) (Dupe, Mo/King Sunny Ade).

Dupree, Champion Jack

1944-1945 THE OTHER TAKES.
Tracks: / She makes good jelly / Rum cola blues / Lover's lane / Black wolf / Outside man / Forget it mama / You've been drunk / G.R Boogie / Santa Claus blues / Love strike blues / Wet deck Mama / Big legged Mama / I'm a doctor for waman.
Notes: Mono Recording
Album: released on Krazy Kat (USA), Jun'86

BEST OF THE BLUES(THE).
Notes: Mono production.
Album: released on Storyville, May'86 by Storyville Records. Dist: Jazz Music Distribution, Swift Distribution, Chris Wellard Distribution, Counterpoint Distribution

CHAMPION JACK DUPREE 1944-1945.
Album: released on Red Pepper, Jul'82 Dist: Jazz Music, Wellard, Chris

DEATH OF LOUIS ARMSTRONG.
Compact disc: released on Vogue, Dec'86 Dist: Discovery, Jazz Music, PRT, Swift

FROM NEW ORLEANS TO CHICAGO.
Album: released on Crosscut, Jul'85 by IMS-Polygram Records. Dist: IMS, Polygram, Rollercoaster Distribution

I'M GROWING OLDER EVERY DAY
Blues Roots Volume 6.
Notes: See under Blues Roots Volume 6

INCREDIBLE, THE.
Album: by Sonet Records. Dist: PRT

JUNKER BLUES 1940-41.
Album: released on Travellin' Man, Oct'85 Dist: Jazz Music

LEGACY OF THE BLUES,VOL.3.
Album: by Sonet Records. Dist: PRT

SHAKE BABY SHAKE.
Tracks: / The ups / Lonely road blues / Story of my life / Wen I get married / Dirty woman / Old time rock 'n' roll / Down the lane / Rocky Mountain / Just like a woman / Shake baby shake / The wrong woman / You're always cryin' the blues / Woman trouble again / My baby's like a clock / Hello darlin' / Lollipop baby / Shake baby shake.
Notes: A complete anthology of Dupree's recordings from RCA's VIK and Groove subsidiary labels 1956-57, including many unissued titles.
Album: released on Detour, Jul'87 by Detour Records. Dist: Swift, RCA, Jazz Music, Projection

WON'T BE A FOOL NO MORE.
Tracks: / Third degree / TV mama / He knows the rules / Ain't it a shame / Ooh-la-la / Big leg Emma's (going down to) / Won't be a fool no more / Calcutta blues / Take it slow and easy / She's all my life / Poor poor me / 24 Hours / Pigfoot and a bottle of beer / Down in the valley / Too early in the morning / Shim-sham-shimmy.
Album: released on See For Miles, Jan'86 by See For Miles Records. Dist: Pinnacle

Dupree, Cornell

GUITAR GROOVE.
Tracks: / Staying alive I & II / Boogie nights / Shake it well / How deep is your love / Lovely day / Slip sliding away / It's so easy.
Album: released on Topline, Feb'87 by Charly Records. Dist: Charly Distribution

Cassette: released on Topline, Apr'87 by Charly Records. Dist: Charly Distribution

Cassette: released on Topline, Apr'87 by Charly Records. Dist: Charly Distribution

Dupree, Jack

BLUES FOR EVERYONE.
Double Album: released on Gusto (USA), Oct'79 by Gusto Records (USA). Dist: Crusader

Dupree, Robbie

ROBBIE DUPREE.
Album: released on Elektra Asylum, Sep'80 by Elektra/Asylum/Nonesuch Records. Dist: WEA

STREET CORNER HEROES.
Album: released on Elektra, Aug'81 by WEA Records. Dist: WEA

Dupree, Simon

AMEN (Dupree, Simon & The Big Sound).
Album: released on See For Miles, Mar'82 by See For Miles Records. Dist: Pinnacle

Cassette: released on See For Miles, Mar'82 by See For Miles Records. Dist: Pinnacle

KITES (Dupree, Simon & The Big Sound).
Tracks: / Kites / Like the sun like the fire / Sleep / For whom the bells toll / Broken hearted pirates / Minutes of your love / Lot of love / Love / Get off my bach / There's a little picture playhouse / Day time / Night time / I see the light / What is soul / Amen / Who cares / She gave me the sun / Thinking about my life / It is finished / I've seen it all before / You need a man / Reservations.
Album: released on See For Miles, Dec'86 by See For Miles Records. Dist: Pinnacle

Single (7"): released on Old Gold, Mar'87 by Old Gold Records. Dist: Lightning, Jazz Music, Spartan, Counterpoint

Single (7"): released on EMI, '78 by EMI Records. Dist: EMI

Duprez, John

OH MY PAPA.
Single (7"): released on Impression, Nov'83 Dist: CBS

Single (12"): released on Impression, Nov'83 Dist: CBS

Duran Duran

ARENA.
Tracks: / Is there something I should know / Hungry like a wolf / New religion / Save a prayer / Wild boys(The) / Seventh stranger(The) / Chauffeur(The) / Union of the snake / Planet earth / Careless memories.
Video-cassette (VHS): released on PMI, Jun'86 by PMI Records. Dist: EMI

Video-cassette [Betamax]: released on PMI, Jun'86 by PMI Records. Dist: EMI

Compact disc: by EMI Records. Dist: EMI

Album: released on Parlophone, Nov'84 by EMI Records. Dist: EMI

Cassette: released on Parlophone, Nov'84 by EMI Records. Dist: EMI

CARELESS MEMORIES.
Single (7"): released on EMI, Aug'83 by EMI Records. Dist: EMI

Single (12"): released on EMI, Aug'83 by EMI Records. Dist: EMI

DANCING ON THE VALENTINE.
Tracks: / Reflex, The / Union of the snake / New moon on Monday.
Notes: Video EP of the promo videos fro three Duran Duran hits-'THE REFLEX','NEW MOON ON MONDAY'and 'UNION OF THE SNAKE',plus linking footage.
Video-cassette (VHS): released on PMI, Oct'84 by PMI Records. Dist: EMI

Video-cassette [Betamax]: released on PMI, Oct'84 by PMI Records. Dist: EMI

Video-cassette (VHS): released on Video Collection, May'87 by Video Collection Records. Dist: Counterpoint

DURAN DURAN.
Tracks: / Girls on film / Planet earth / Anyone out there / To the shore / Careless memories / Night boat / Sound of thunder / Friends of mine / Tel aviv.
Compact disc: by EMI Records. Dist: EMI

Album: released on EMI, Aug'83 by EMI Records. Dist: EMI

Cassette: released on EMI, Aug'83 by EMI Records. Dist: EMI

Album: released on Fame, Sep'87 by Music For Pleasure Records. Dist: EMI. Estim retail price in Sep'87 was £3.49.

Cassette: released on Fame, Sep'87 by Music For Pleasure Records. Dist: EMI. Estim retail price in Sep'87 was £3.49

GIRLS ON FILM.
Single (7"): released on EMI, Aug'83 by EMI Records. Dist: EMI

Single (12"): released on EMI, Aug'83 by EMI Records. Dist: EMI

GIRLS ON FILM (VIDEO).
Tracks: / Girls on film / Hungry like the wolf.
Video-cassette (VHS): released on Gold Rushes, Mar'87 by Video Collection Records. Dist: Counterpoint

HUNGRY LIKE THE WOLF.
Tracks: / Hungry like the wolf / Girls on film.
Video-cassette (VHS): released on Gold Rushes, Mar'87 by Video Collection Records. Dist: Counterpoint

Single (7"): released on EMI, Aug'83 by EMI Records. Dist: EMI

Single (12"): released on EMI, Aug'83 by EMI Records. Dist: EMI

INTERVIEW PICTURE DISC.
Picture disc album: released on Baktabak, 11 Apr'87 by Baktabak Records. Dist: Arabesque

IS THERE SOMETHING I SHOULD KNOW?.
Single (7"): released on EMI, Aug'83 by EMI Records. Dist: EMI

Single (12"): released on EMI, Aug'83 by EMI Records. Dist: EMI

MAKING OF ARENA(THE).
Notes: Behind the scenes video of arena.
Video-cassette (VHS): released on PMI, Jun'86 by PMI Records. Dist: EMI

Video-cassette [Betamax]: released on PMI, Jun'86 by PMI Records. Dist: EMI

MEET EL PRESIDENTE.
Tracks: / Meet El Beat* / Meet El Presidente / Vertigo (Do the demolition).
Notes: * = Extra track on CD only
Single (7"): released on EMI, Apr'87 by EMI Records. Dist: EMI

Compact disc single: released on EMI, Apr'87 by EMI Records. Dist: EMI

Single (7"): released on EMI, Apr'87 by EMI Records. Dist: EMI

Single (12"): released on EMI, Apr'87 by EMI Records. Dist: EMI

MY OWN WAY.
Single (7"): released on EMI, Aug'83 by EMI Records. Dist: EMI

Single (12"): released on EMI, Aug'83 by EMI Records. Dist: EMI

NEW MOON ON MONDAY.
Single (7"): released on EMI, Jan'84 by EMI Records. Dist: EMI

Single (12"): released on EMI, Jan'84 by EMI Records. Dist: EMI

NOTORIOUS.
Tracks: / Notorious / American science / Skin trade / Hold me / Vertigo (do the demolition) / So misled / Meet el Presidente' / Winter marches on / Proposition / Matter of feeling, A.
Album: released on EMI, Dec'86 by EMI Records. Dist: EMI

Cassette: released on EMI, Dec'86 by EMI Records. Dist: EMI

Compact disc: released on EMI, Jan'86 by EMI Records. Dist: EMI

Single (7"): released on EMI, Oct'86 by EMI Records. Dist: EMI

Single (12"): released on EMI, Oct'86 by EMI Records. Dist: EMI

NOTORIOUS (LATIN RASCALS MIX).
Tracks: / Winter marches / Notorious (Latin rascals mix).
Single (7"): released on EMI, Nov'86 by EMI Records. Dist: EMI

Cassette: released on EMI, Nov'86 by EMI Records. Dist: EMI

PLANET EARTH.
Single (7"): released on EMI, Aug'83 by EMI Records. Dist: EMI

Single (12"): released on EMI, Aug'83 by EMI Records. Dist: EMI

REFLEX.
Single (7"): released on EMI, Apr'84 by EMI Records. Dist: EMI

Single (12"): released on EMI, Apr'84 by EMI Records. Dist: EMI

Picture disc single: released on EMI, May'84 by EMI Records. Dist: EMI

RIO.
Tracks: / Rio / My own way / Lonely in your nightmare / Hungry like the wolf / Hold back the rain / New religion / Last chance on the stairway / Save a prayer / Chaffeur.
Compact disc: by EMI Records. Dist: EMI

Album: released on EMI, Aug'83 by EMI Records. Dist: EMI

Cassette: released on EMI, Aug'83 by EMI Records. Dist: EMI

Single (7"): released on EMI, Aug'83 by EMI Records. Dist: EMI

Single (12"): released on EMI, Aug'83 by EMI Records. Dist: EMI

SAVE A PRAYER.
Single (7"): released on EMI, Aug'83 by EMI Records. Dist: EMI

Single (12"): released on EMI, Aug'83 by EMI Records. Dist: EMI

SEVEN AND THE RAGGED TIGER.
Notes: Digital stereo
Compact disc: released on EMI, Mar'84 by EMI Records. Dist: EMI

Album: released on EMI, Nov'83 by EMI Records. Dist: EMI

Cassette: released on EMI, Nov'83 by EMI Records. Dist: EMI

SEVEN & THE RAGGED TIGER.
Compact disc: by EMI Records. Dist: EMI

SING BLUE SILVER.
Notes: Includes music taken from four Duran Duran albums:'Duran Duran','Rio','Seven and the Ragged Tiger'and 'Arena'. 'Sing Blue Silver'is a new concept in music video.It is a video programme running 85 minutes that records Duran Duran's sensational North America Tour during the spring of 1984. Thrilling in concert footage is intercut with a candid behind the scenes cover- age of the band's lifestyle on the road.'Sing Blue Silver'is a phrase from DuranDuran's song,'The Chaffeur'which features in the video along with a number of special new versions of classic hits such as 'The Reflex','Planet Earth','Rio' and many more.Released to coincide with the band's best selling album,'Arena' 'Sing Blue Silver' is bound to reaffirm Duran Duran's status as one of the true blockbuster acts on music video.
Video-cassette (VHS): released on PMI, Nov'84 by PMI Records. Dist: EMI

Video-cassette [Betamax]: by PMI Records. Dist: EMI

SKINTRADE.
Tracks: / Skintrade (Radio cut) / Wee need you.
Cassette single: released on EMI, Mar'87 by EMI Records. Dist: EMI

SKIN TRADE (RADIO CUT).
Tracks: / Skin trade (radio cut) / We need you.
Single (7"): released on EMI, Feb'87 by EMI Records. Dist: EMI

Single (12"): released on EMI, Feb'87 by EMI Records. Dist: EMI

UNION OF THE SNAKE.
Single (7"): released on EMI, Oct'83 by EMI Records. Dist: EMI

Single (12"): released on EMI, Oct'83 by EMI Records. Dist: EMI

VIDEO ALBUM (THE).
Notes: Number of tracks: 11. Type of recirding: Compilation. Total playing time: 55 minutes.
Video-cassette (VHS): released on PMI, Jun'86 by PMI Records. Dist: EMI

Video-cassette [Betamax]: released on PMI, Jun'86 by PMI Records. Dist: EMI

VIDEO (THE).
Video-cassette (VHS): released on Thorn-Emi, Jan'84

VIEW TO A KILL, (A).
Single (7"): released on Parlophone, May'85 by EMI Records. Dist: EMI

Special: released on Parlophone, May'85 by EMI Records. Dist: EMI Deleted '86.

WILD BOYS, (THE).
Single (7"): released on EMI, Oct'84 by EMI Records. Dist: EMI

Single (12"): released on EMI, Oct'84 by EMI Records. Dist: EMI

WILD BOYS(THE WILDER THAN WILD BOYS EXT MIX).
Single (12"): released on EMI, Oct'84 by EMI Records. Dist: EMI

Duran, Eddie

ONE BY ONE (see Bell, Dee) (Duran, Eddie & Dee Bell).

Duran, Elena

BRANDENBURG BOOGIE (Duran, Elena with Grappelli, Holloway, Walley & Ganley).
Album: released on EMI, Nov'80 by EMI Records. Dist: EMI

Cassette: released on EMI, Nov'80 by EMI Records. Dist: EMI

MARY ROSE.
Single (7"): released on RCA, Jun'82 by RCA Records. Dist: RCA, Roots, Swift, Wellard, Chris, I & B, Solomon & Peres Distribution

NORWEGIAN WOOD (Duran, Elena & Stephane Grappelli).
Album: released on RCA, Oct'81 by RCA Records. Dist: RCA, Roots, Swift, Wellard, Chris, I & B, Solomon & Peres Distribution

Cassette: released on RCA, Oct'81 by RCA Records. Dist: RCA, Roots, Swift, Wellard, Chris, I & B, Solomon & Peres Distribution

VIVA ELENA.
Album: released on RCA, Jun'82 by RCA Records. Dist: RCA, Roots, Swift, Wellard, Chris, I & B, Solomon & Peres Distribution

Cassette: released on RCA, Jun'82 by RCA Records. Dist: RCA, Roots, Swift, Wellard, Chris, I & B, Solomon & Peres Distribution

Durante, Jimmy

Bing Crosby with Spike Jones & Jimmy Durante

Durbin, Deanna

BEST OF DEANNA DURBIN, VOL 2. (THE).
Album: released on MCA, Jan'83 by MCA Records. Dist: Polygram, MCA

Cassette: released on MCA, Jan'83 by MCA Records. Dist: Polygram, MCA

BEST OF DEANNA DURBIN, THE.
Album: released on MCA, Dec'81 by MCA Records. Dist: Polygram, MCA

Cassette: released on MCA, Dec'81 by MCA Records. Dist: Polygram, MCA

CAN'T HELP SINGING.
Album: released on MFP, Apr'82 by EMI Records. Dist: EMI

Cassette: released on MFP, Apr'82 by EMI Records. Dist: EMI

DEANNA DURBIN.
Album: released on Deja Vu, Jan'87 by Deja Vu Records. Dist: Counterpoint Distribution, Record Services Distribution (Ireland)

Cassette: released on Deja Vu, Jan'87 by Deja Vu Records. Dist: Counterpoint Distribution, Record Services Distribution (Ireland)

MOVIE SONGS.
Album: released on MCA Coral, Apr'82 by MCA Records. Dist: Polygram

Cassette: released on MCA Coral, Apr'82 by MCA Records. Dist: Polygram

SONGS OF THE SILVER SCREEN.
Tracks: / One night of love / My heart is singing / You're as pretty as a picture / Mighty like a rose / Give me a little kiss / Granada / Carousel in the park / Waltz song from Romeo and Juliet / La capinera / Good-bye / I love to whistle / Going home / With a heart that's free / Largo al factotum / Seguidilla / Serenade to the stars, A / Chapel bells / When I sing / Viennese waltz.
Notes: The continual demand for Deanna Durbin records prompts this brand new compilation of twenty much sought after tracks. Beautifully packaged, this album will delight her many admirers. Mono
Album: released on MCA, May'86 by MCA Records. Dist: Polygram, MCA

Durham Brothers

BLUE WATER.
Single (7"): released on Pastafont, Jun'83 by Pastafont Records.

Durham Cathedral Choir

CHRISTMAS CAROLS from Durham Cathedral.
Album: released on Abbey, Nov'83 by Abbey. Dist: PRT, Taylors, Gamut

Cassette: released on Abbey, Nov'83 by Abbey. Dist: PRT, Taylors, Gamut

CHRISTMAS CAROLS FROM DURHAM CATHEDRAL.
Album: released on Abbey, Nov'83 by Abbey. Dist: PRT, Taylors, Gamut

Cassette: released on Abbey, Nov'83 by Abbey. Dist: PRT, Taylors, Gamut

Durham, Sonny

ON THE AIR (Durham, Sonny & His Orchestra).
Album: released on Aircheck, May'79

Durle, Jo

WIMBLEDON LAWNS.
Single (7"): released on Blue Hat, Jun'83 by Blue Hat Records. Dist: Blue Hat

Durno, Duncan

HILLS OF CULDRAIN.
Tracks: / Buchan Ploorman, The / Waddin' o' McPhee / Drumdelgie / Livetside / Gartley.
Notes: There are 18 tracks altogether on this cassette.
Cassette: released on Ross, Dec'86 by Ross Records. Dist: Ross Distribution, Roots Distribution

Durrant, Buggs

BABY COME BACK.
Single (7"): released on Shoc-Wave, Feb'84 by Uniton Records. Dist: Pinnacle

Single (12"): released on Shoc-Wave, Feb'84 by Uniton Records. Dist: Pinnacle

DISCO JUMP.
Single (7"): released on Shoc-Wave, Jul'80 by Uniton Records. Dist: Pinnacle

GONNA MAKE YOUR BODY GIVE UP.
Single (7"): released on Shoc-Wave, Jun'82 by Uniton Records. Dist: Pinnacle

Single (12"): released on Shoc-Wave, Jun'82 by Uniton Records. Dist: Pinnacle

YOU ARE GONE.
Single (7"): released on Shoc-Wave, Jul'82 by Uniton Records. Dist: Pinnacle

Durutti Column

ANOTHER SETTING.
Album: released on Factory, Aug'83 by Factory Records. Dist: Cartel, Pinnacle

CIRCUS & BREAD.
Tracks: / Pauline / Tomorrow / Dance II / For Hilary / Street fight / Royal infirmary / Black horses / Dance I / Blind elevator girl / Osaka.
Album: released on Factory, '86 by Factory Records. Dist: Cartel, Pinnacle

Cassette: released on Factory, '86 by Factory Records. Dist: Cartel, Pinnacle

Compact disc: released on Factory, '86 by Factory Records. Dist: Cartel, Pinnacle

DEUX TRIANGLES.
Single (12"): released on Les Disques Du Crepuscule, Aug'87 Dist: Rough Trade, Pinnacle, Island, Polygram

DOMO ARIGATO.
Compact disc: by Factory Records. Dist: Cartel, Pinnacle

Video-cassette (VHS): released on Factory, Jul'86 by Factory Records. Dist: Cartel, Pinnacle

Compact disc: released on Factory, Nov'85 by Factory Records. Dist: Cartel, Pinnacle

L.C..
Album: released on Factory, Nov'81 by Factory Records. Dist: Cartel, Pinnacle

Cassette: released on Factory, Nov'84 by Factory Records. Dist: Cartel, Pinnacle

RETURN OF THE DURUTTI COLUMN.
Album: released on Factory, Jul'80 by Factory Records. Dist: Cartel, Pinnacle

Cassette: released on Factory, Nov'84 by Factory Records. Dist: Cartel, Pinnacle

SAY WHAT YOU MEAN, MEAN WHAT YOU SAY.
Single (7"): released on Factory, Mar'85 by Factory Records. Dist: Cartel, Pinnacle

TOMORROW.
Single (7"): released on Factory Benelux, Feb'86 by Rough Trade Records. Dist: Cartel

Single (12"): released on Factory Benelux, Feb'86 by Rough Trade Records. Dist: Cartel

TWO TRIANGLES (EP).
Single (12"): released on Factory, Mar'82 by Factory Records. Dist: Cartel, Pinnacle

VALUABLE PASSAGES.
Tracks: / Sketch for summer / Conduct / Sketch for winter / Lips that would kiss / Belgium friends / Danny / Piece for out of tune piano / Never know / Jacqueline / Missing boy / Prayer / Spent time / Without mercy stanzas 2-8 12-15 / Room / Blinf elevator girl / Tomorrow / LFO MOD.
Cassette: released on Factory, Dec'86 by Factory Records. Dist: Cartel, Pinnacle

Compact disc: released on Factory, Dec'86 by Factory Records. Dist: Cartel, Pinnacle

WITHOUT MERCY.
Album: released on Factory, Nov'86 by Factory Records. Dist: Cartel, Pinnacle

Cassette: released on Factory, Nov'86 by Factory Records. Dist: Cartel, Pinnacle

Dury, Ian

DO IT YOURSELF.
Album: released on Stiff, Aug'79 by Stiff Records. Dist: EMI, Record Services Distribution (Ireland)

GREATEST HITS:IAN DURY.
Album: released on Fame (Stiff), Sep'82 by Music For Pleasure Records. Dist: EMI

Cassette: released on Fame (Stiff), Sep'82 by Music For Pleasure Records. Dist: EMI

HOLD ON TO YOUR STRUCTURE.
Notes: Dury and his re-formed backing group recorded live at Hammersmith Odeon. The nine songs include 'What A Waste', 'Rhythm Stick' and all his other major hits. Number of tracks: 9. Type of recording: Live. Total playing time: 65 minutes.
Video-cassette (VHS): released on PMI, Jun'86 by PMI Records. Dist: EMI

Video-cassette [Betamax]: released on PMI, Jun'86 by PMI Records. Dist: EMI

HOLD ON TO YOUR STRUCTURE (VIDEO) (Dury, Ian & The Blockheads).
Notes: At The Hammersmith Odeon, 24/6/85.
Video-cassette (VHS): released on Video Collection, May'87 by Video Collection Records. Dist: Counterpoint

I WANT TO BE STRAIGHT.
Single (7"): released on Stiff, Aug'80 by Stiff Records. Dist: EMI, Record Services Distribution (Ireland)

JUKE BOX DURY.
Album: released on Stiff, Nov'81 by Stiff Records. Dist: EMI, Record Services Distribution (Ireland)

Cassette: released on Stiff, Nov'81 by Stiff Records. Dist: EMI, Record Services Distribution (Ireland)

LAUGHTER (Dury, Ian & The Blockheads).
Album: released on Stiff, Nov'80 by Stiff Records. Dist: EMI, Record Services Distribution (Ireland)

Cassette: released on Stiff, Nov'80 by Stiff Records. Dist: EMI, Record Services Distribution (Ireland)

NEW BOOTS AND PANTIES (Dury, Ian & The Blockheads).
Tracks: / Sweet Gene Vincent.
Compact disc: by Demon Records. Dist: Pinnacle

Album: released on Demon, Sep'86 by Demon Records. Dist: Pinnacle

Cassette: released on Demon, Sep'86 by Demon Records. Dist: Pinnacle

Cassette: by Stiff Records. Dist: EMI, Record Services Distribution (Ireland)

PROFOUNDLY IN LOVE WITH PANDORA.
Single (7"): released on EMI, Nov'85 by EMI Records. Dist: EMI

Picture disc single: released on EMI, Nov'85 by EMI Records. Dist: EMI

SEX'N'DRUGS'N'ROCK'N'ROLL (Dury, Ian & The Blockheads).
Notes: Compilation featuring the best of Ian Dury's days at Stiff Records.Features manyhit singles & "Best of.." tracks.
Compact disc: released on Demon, Apr'87 by Demon Records. Dist: Pinnacle

Album: released on Demon, Apr'87 by Demon Records. Dist: Pinnacle

Cassette: released on Demon, Apr'87 by Demon Records. Dist: Pinnacle

SPECIAL PAUL HARDCASTLE 12" MIXES (Dury, Ian & The Blockheads).
Single (12"): released on Stiff, May'85 by Stiff Records. Dist: EMI, Record Services Distribution (Ireland)

SUEPERMANS BIG SISTER.
Single (7"): released on Stiff, Oct'80 by Stiff Records. Dist: EMI, Record Services Distribution (Ireland)

Single (12"): released on Stiff, Oct'80 by Stiff Records. Dist: EMI, Record Services Distribution (Ireland)

WHAT A WASTE.
Single (7"): released on Stiff, Nov'81 by Stiff Records. Dist: EMI, Record Services Distribution (Ireland)

Duskin, Big Joe

CINCINNATI STOMP.
Album: released on Arhoolie, May'81 by Arhoolie Records. Dist: Projection, Topic, Jazz Music, Swift, Roots

Dusseldorf, La

TINTARELLA DI.
Single (7"): released on Albion, Dec'81 by Albion Records. Dist: Spartan, Pinnacle

VIVA.
Album: released on Radar, Feb'79 by WEA Music Ltd. Dist: WEA, PRT

Dust

DUST.
Album: released on Wishbone, Sep'83 by Wishbone Records. Dist: Pinnacle

Dust Devils

DUST DEVILS various artists (Various Artists).
Single 10": released on Prophane 9, Sep'86 Dist: Red Rhino, Cartel

SEEDS OF THE SPOIL.
Tracks: / Seeds of the spoil.
Single (12"): released on Rouska, Jul'86 Dist: Red Rhino Distribution, Cartel Distribution

Dusty, Slim

PUB WITH NO BEER.
Tracks: / Pub with no beer.
Single (7"): released on Old Gold, Mar'87 by Old Gold Records. Dist: Lightning, Jazz Music, Spartan, Counterpoint

Single (7"): released on Old Gold, Jul'82 by Old Gold Records. Dist: Lightning, Jazz Music, Spartan, Counterpoint

Dutch Swing College Band

40 YEARS, 1945-1985, AT ITS BEST.
Album: released on Timeless, Sep'86

BAND'S BEST, THE.
Album: released on Verve (USA), Oct'84 by Polydor. Dist: Polygram

Cassette: released on Verve (USA), Oct'84 by Polydor. Dist: Polygram

DIGITAL ANNIVERSARY.
Tracks: / Bourbon Street parade / Wabash blues / Caribbean parade / Is it true what they say about Dixie? / Clarinet games / Saturday night is the lonliest night of the week / Coal black shine / Third Street blues / Gladiolus rag / Columbus stockade blues / Devil in the moon / Original Dixieland one step.
Compact disc: by Phonogram Records. Dist: Polygram

Album: released on Phonogram Import, Apr'86

Cassette: released on Phonogram Import, Apr'86

DIGITAL DIXIE.
Compact disc: Dist: IMS-Polygram

Album: released on Philips (Import), Feb'82

Cassette: released on Philips (Import), Feb'82

DIGITAL DUTCH.
Compact disc: Dist: IMS-Polygram

JUBILEE CONCERT.
Cassette: released on Pablo, Nov'80 by Pablo Records. Dist: Wellard, Chris, IMS-Polygram, BMG

MUSIC FOR THE MILLIONS.
Album: released on Philips (Import), Apr'83

Cassette: released on Philips (import), Apr'83

ON TOUR.
Album: released on Philips (Import), Aug'81

Cassette: released on Philips (Import), Aug'81

SWINGING STUDIO SESSIONS.
Compact disc: Dist: IMS-Polygram

WHEN THE SWING COMES MARCHING IN.
Album:

Cassette:

Duteil, Yves

YVES DUTEIL.
Album: released on EMI (France), '83 by EMI Records. Dist: Conifer

Duul, Amon

AIRS ON A SHOESTRING.
Compact disc: released on Thunderbolt, Aug'87 by Magnum Music Group Ltd. Dist: Magnum Music Group Ltd, PRT Distribution, Spartan Distribution

HAWK MEETS PENGUIN Volume 1.
Album: released on Demi Monde, Mar'86 Dist: Charly

Duvall, Huelyn

CHALLENGE MASTERS, THE.
Tracks: / Comin' or goin' / Boom boom baby / Pucker paint / Juliet / Friday night on a dollar bill / You knock me out / Danny Wolfe: Fool's hall of fame / Teen Queen (take 11) / Teen Queen (Take 12) / Three months to kill / Hum-m-m-dinger / Fool's hall of fame (take 11) / Little boy blue.
Album: released on Bear Family, Sep'87 by Bear Family Records. Dist: Rollercoaster Distribution, Swift

HUELYN DUVALL (Duvall, Huelyn & The Tight Strings).
Album: released on White, Feb'87

MORE HUELYN DUVAL.
Album: released on White Label (Holland), Feb'85 Dist: CSA, PRT

Du-val, Ray

BOPPIN' WITH A BAD GIRL (Du-val, Raye & the Rockmates).
Cassette: released on Quiff, Aug'85 Dist: Ray-Du-Val

VIVE ROCK'N'ROLL.
Album: released on Lorraine-Soho, '85 Dist: Ray-Du-Val

Cassette: released on Lorraine-Soho, '85 Dist: Ray-Du-Val

Special: released on Lorraine-Soho, '85 Dist: Ray-Du-Val

Duvant Male Choir

WITH A VOICE OF SINGING.
Album: released on Note, Jun'79 by EMI Records. Dist: EMI

D & V

SNARE.
Single (12"): released on One Little Indian, Feb'87 by One Little Indian Records. Dist: Nine Mile Distribution, Cartel Distribution

DVA

HIGH HOLY DISCO MASS.
Single (7"): released on Polydor, Nov'82 by Polydor Records. Dist: Polygram, Polydor

Single (12"): released on Polydor, Nov'82 by Polydor Records. Dist: Polygram, Polydor

Dvorin, Miriam

YIDDISH SONGS.
Album: released on Arhoolie, Jul'84 by Arhoolie Records. Dist: Projection, Topic, Jazz Music, Swift, Roots

Dwyer, Finbarr

BEST OF FINBARR DWYER (THE).
Cassette: released on Accordion Record Club, Jul'86 by Accordion Record Club Records. Dist: Accordion Record Club

IRELAND'S OWN TRADITIONAL ACCORDIONIST.
Cassette: released on Accordion Record Club, Jul'86 by Accordion Record Club Records. Dist: Accordion Record Club

Dyall, Valentine

ECHOES FROM THE MACABRE (Echoes from the macabre).
Cassette: released on Chivers Audio Books, May'81 by Chivers Sound & Vision. Dist: Chivers Sound & Vision

House of the seven flies

TALES OF TERROR Spoken Word.
Cassette: released on Storyteller, '79

Dyani, John

JOHN DYANI WITH JOHN TCHICAI & DUDU PUKWANA.
Album: released on Steeplechase, '78

Dyani, Johnny

BORN UNDER THE HEAT (Dyani, Johnny Mbizo).
Album: released on Dragon, Jul'87 by Dragon Records. Dist: Jazz Music, Projection, Cadillac

Dyani, Temiz, Feza

MUSIC FOR XABA.
Album: released on Sonet, '74 by Sonet Records. Dist: PRT

Dyer, Johnny

JOHNNY DYER AND THE L.A.JUKES (Dyer, Johnny & the L.A. Jukes).
Album: released on Murray Brothers (USA), May'84 Dist: Swift Distribution

Dying Inside

DYING INSIDE (Silverberg, Robert).
Cassette: released on Caedmon(USA), May'80 by Caedmon (USA) Records. Dist: Gower, Taylors, Discovery

Dyke, Leroy Van

AUCTIONEER, THE.
Tracks: / Auctioneer / Pocketbook song / My good mind went bad on me / Honky tonk song / Leather jacket / I fell in love with a pony tail / One heart / Heartbreak cannonball / I'm moving on / Chicken shack.
Album: released on Ace, Apr'84 by Ace Records. Dist: Pinnacle, Swift, Hotshot, Cadillac

AUCTIONEER, THE (4 TRACK EP).
Single (7"): released on MCA, '78 by MCA Records. Dist: Polygram, MCA

Dyke & the Blazers

SO SHARP.
Album: released on Kent, Sep'83 by Ace Records. Dist: Pinnacle

Dylan, Bob

ANOTHER SIDE OF BOB DYLAN.
Tracks: / All I really want to do / Black crow blues / Spanish Harlem incident / Chimes of freedom / I shall be free, No 10 / To Ramona / Motorpsycho nightmare / My back pages / I don't believe you / Ballads in plain D / It ain't me babe.
Album: released on CBS, Mar'81 by CBS Records. Dist: CBS

Cassette: released on CBS, Mar'81 by CBS Records. Dist: CBS

AT BUDOKAN.
Album: released on CBS, May'79 by CBS Records. Dist: CBS

Cassette: released on CBS, May'79 by CBS Records. Dist: CBS

BAND OF THE HAND (Dylan, Bob & The Heartbreakers).
Tracks: / Band of the hand / Theme from Joe's death.
Single (7"): released on MCA, Aug'86 by MCA Records. Dist: Polygram, MCA

Single (12"): released on MCA, Aug'86 by MCA Records. Dist: Polygram, MCA

BASEMENT TAPES.
Tracks: / Odds and ends / Orange juice blues (blues for breakfast) / Million dollar bash / Yaroo Street scandal / Goin' to Acapulco / Kate's been gone / You ain't goin' nowhere / Don't ya tell Henry / Nothing was delivered / Open the door, Homer / Long distance operator / This wheel's on fire / Lo and behold / Bessie Smith / Clothes line saga / Apple suckling tree / Mrs Henry / Tears of rage / Too much of nothing / Yea, heavy and a bottle of bread / Ain't no more cane / Crash on the levee (down in the flood) / Ruben Remus / Tiny Montgomery.
Cassette: released on CBS, Aug'75 by CBS Records. Dist: CBS

BEFORE THE FLOOD.
Tracks: / Most likely you'll go your way and I'll go mine / Lay lady lay / Rainy day women Nos 12 & 35 / Knocking on Heaven's door / It ain't me babe / Ballad of a thin man / Up on Cripple Creek / I shall be released / Endless highway / Night they drove old Dixie down / Stagefright / Don't think twice it's alright / Just like a woman / It's alright, ma (I'm only bleeding) / Shape I'm in, The / When you awake / Weight, The / All along the watchtower / Highway '61 revisited / Like a rolling stone / Blowin' in the wind.
Double compact disc: released on CBS, Jul'87 by CBS Records. Dist: CBS

Album: released on CBS, Sep'82 by CBS Records. Dist: CBS

Cassette: released on CBS, Sep'82 by CBS Records. Dist: CBS

BIOGRAPH.
Tracks: / Lay lady lay / If not for you / Times they are a-changing (The) / Blowin' in the wind / Masters of war / Percy's song / Like a rolling stone / Subterranean homesick blues / Mr. tambourine man / It ain't me babe / Million dollar bash / It's all over now baby blue / Positively 4th street / I wanna be your lover / Heart of mine / I believe in you / Time passes slowly / Forever young / Lay lady lay / Baby let me follow you down / If not for you / I'll be your baby tonight / I'll keep it with mine / Times they are a-changin' / Blowin' in the wind / Masters of war / Lonesome death of Hattie Carroll / Percy's song / Mixed-up confusion / Tombstone blues / Groom's still waiting at the altar / Most likely you'll go your way and I'll go mine / Like a rolling stone / Jet pilot / Lay down your weary tune / Subterranean homesick blues / I don't believe you (she acts like we never have met) / Visions of Johanna / Every grain of sand / Quinn the Eskimo / Mr Tambourine Man / Dear landlord / It ain't me babe / You angel you / Million dollar bash / To Ramona / You're a big girl now / Abandoned love / Tangled up in blue / It's all over now, baby blue / Can you please crawl out your window? / Positively 4th Street / Isis / Caribbean wind / Up to me / Baby I'm in the mood for you / I wanna be your lover / I want you / Heart of mine / On a night like this / Just like a woman / Romance in Durango / Senor (tales of Yankee power) / Gotta serve somebody / I believe in you / Time passes slowly / I shall be released / Knocking on Heaven's door / All along the watchtower / Solid rock / Forever young.
Notes: 3 CD Records
Compact disc: released on CBS, Jan'86 by CBS Records. Dist: CBS

Album: released on CBS, Nov'85 by CBS Records. Dist: CBS

Cassette: released on CBS, Nov'85 by CBS Records. Dist: CBS

BLONDE ON BLONDE.
Tracks: / Rainy day women Nos 12 & 35 / Pledging my time / Visions of Johanna / One of us must know / I want you / Stuck inside a mobile with the Memphis blues again / Leopardskin pillbox hat / Just like a woman / Most likely you'll go your way and I'll go mine / Temporarily like Achilles / Absolutely sweet Marie / Fourth time around / Obviously five believers / Sad-eyed lady of the lowlands.
Compact disc: released on CBS, Jul'87 by CBS Records. Dist: CBS

Album: released on CBS, May'82 by CBS Records. Dist: CBS

Cassette: released on CBS, May'82 by CBS Records. Dist: CBS

BLOOD ON THE TRACKS.
Tracks: / Tangled up in blue / Simple twist of fate / You're a big girl now / Idiot wind / You're gonna make me lonesome when you go / Meet me in the morning / Lily Rosemary and the jack of hearts / If you see her / Say hello / Shelter from the storm / Buckets of rain / Tangled up in blue / Simple twist of fate / You're a big girl now / Idiot wind / You're gonna make me lonesome when you go / Meet me in the morning / Lily Rosemary and the Jack of Hearts / If you see her say hello / Shelter from the storm / Buckets of rain.
Compact disc: released on CBS, Dec'85 by CBS Records. Dist: CBS

Album: released on CBS, Nov'74 by CBS Records. Dist: CBS

Cassette: released on CBS, Nov'74 by CBS Records. Dist: CBS

BLOWIN' IN THE WIND.
Album: released on Platinum (W.Germany), Oct'85 Dist: Mainline

Cassette: released on Platinum (W.Germany), Oct'85 Dist: Mainline

BOB DYLAN.
Tracks: / She's no good / Talkin' New York blues / In my time of dyin' / Man of constant sorrow / Fixing to die blues / Pretty Peggy-O / Highway 51 blues / Gospel plow / Baby let me follow you down / House of the Rising Sun / Freight train blues / Song to Woody / See that my grave is kept clean.
Album: released on CBS, '84 by CBS Records. Dist: CBS

Cassette: released on CBS, '84 by CBS Records. Dist: CBS

BRINGING IT ALL BACK HOME.
Tracks: / Subterranean homesick blues / She belongs to me / Maggie's farm / Love minus zero - no limit / Outlaw blues / On the road again / Bob Dylan's 15th dream / Mr tambourine man / Gates of Eden / It's alright, ma (I'm only bleeding) / It's all over now, baby blue.
Compact disc: released on CBS, Jul'87 by CBS Records. Dist: CBS

Album: released on CBS, Jul'83 by CBS Records. Dist: CBS

Cassette: released on CBS, Jul'83 by CBS Records. Dist: CBS

DESIRE.
Tracks: / Hurricane / Isis / Mozambique / One more cup of coffee / Oh sister / Joey / Romance in Durango / Black Diamond Bay / Sara.
Album: released on CBS, Apr'85 by CBS Records. Dist: CBS

Cassette: released on CBS, Apr'85 by CBS Records. Dist: CBS

DYLAN.
Tracks: / Lily of the west / Can't help falling in love / Sarah Jane / Ballad of Ira Hayes, The / Mr Bojangles / Mary Ann / Big yellow taxi / Fool such as I / Spanish is the loving tongue.
Album: released on CBS, Mar'83 by CBS Records. Dist: CBS

Cassette: released on CBS, Mar'83 by CBS Records. Dist: CBS

EMPIRE BURLESQUE.
Tracks: / Tight connection to my heart (has anybody seen my love?) / Seeing the real you at last / I'll remember you / Clean cut kid / Never gonna be the same again / When the night comes falling from the sky / Trust yourself / Emotionally yours / Dark eyes / Something's burning baby / Seeing the real you at last / I'll remember you / Clean-cut kid / Never gonna be the same again / Trust yourself / Emotionally yours / When the night comes / Falling from the sky / Something burning / Baby / Dark eyes.
Compact disc: released on CBS, Dec'85 by CBS Records. Dist: CBS

Album: released on CBS, Jun'85 by CBS Records. Dist: CBS

Cassette: released on CBS, Jun'85 by CBS Records. Dist: CBS

FREEWHEELIN' BOB DYLAN.
Tracks: / Blowin' in the wind / Girl from the North Country / Masters of war / Down the highway / Bob Dylan's blues / Hard rain's gonna fall / Don't think twice it's alright / Bob Dylan's dream / Oxford Town / Talking World War III blues / Corrina Corrina / Honey, just allow me one more chance / I shall be free.
Album: released on CBS, '66 by CBS Records. Dist: CBS

Cassette: released on CBS, '66 by CBS Records. Dist: CBS

GASLIGHT TAPES.
Compact disc: released on The Compact Collection, Sep'87 by Conifer Records. Dist: Conifer Distribution

GREATEST HITS:BOB DYLAN.
Tracks: / Blowin' in the wind / It ain't me babe / Times they are a-changin' / Mr tambourine man / She belongs to me / It's all over now, baby blue / Subterranean homesick blues / One of us must know / Like a rolling stone / Just like a woman / Rainy day women Nos 12 & 35 / I want you.
Album: released on CBS, '70 by CBS Records. Dist: CBS

Cassette: released on CBS, '70 by CBS Records. Dist: CBS

HARD RAIN.
Tracks: / Maggie's farm / One too many mornings / Stuck inside a mobile with the Memphis blues again / Oh sister / Lay lady lay / Shelter from the storm / You're a big girl now / I threw it all away / Idiot wind.
Album: released on CBS, Apr'83 by CBS Records. Dist: CBS

Cassette: released on CBS, Apr'83 by CBS Records. Dist: CBS

HARD TO HANDLE (Dylan, Bob, Tom Petty & The Heartbreakers).
Notes: Total playing time : 56mins.
Video-cassette (VHS): released on Virgin, Feb'87 by Virgin Records. Dist: EMI, Virgin Distribution

HE WAS A FRIEND OF MINE.
Album: released on Platinum (W.Germany), Oct'85 Dist: Mainline

Cassette: released on Platinum (W.Germany), Oct'85 Dist: Mainline

HIGHWAY '61 REVISITED (LIVE).
Single (7"): released on CBS, Jan'85 by CBS Records. Dist: CBS

HIGHWAY '61 REVISITED.
Tracks: / Like a rolling stone / Tombstone blues / It takes a lot to laugh, it takes a train to cry /

Page 318

From a buick / Ballad of a thin man / Queen Jane approximately / Highway 61 revisited / Just like Tom Thumb's blues / Desolation row / Like a rolling stone / Tombstone blues / It takes a lot to laugh, it takes a train to cry / From a Buick 6 / Ballad of a thin man / Queen Jane approximately / Highway 61 revisited / Just like Tom Thumb's blues / Desolation Row.
Compact disc: released on CBS, Dec'85 by CBS Records. Dist: CBS

Album: released on CBS, '68 by CBS Records. Dist: CBS

Cassette: released on CBS, '68 by CBS Records. Dist: CBS

HISTORICAL ARCHIVES VOL.2.

Album: released on Go International (Germany), Oct'83 by Go International Records (Germany). Dist: IMS, Polygram

Cassette: released on Go International (Germany), Oct'83 by Go International Records (Germany). Dist: IMS, Polygram

HISTORICAL ARCHIVES VOL.1.
Tracks: / Man on the street / He was a friend of mine / Talkin' Bear Mountain picnic massacre blues / Song to Woody / Car car / Pretty Polly / two trains runnin' / Ramblin' on my mind.
Album: released on Go International (Germany), Oct'83 by Go International Records (Germany). Dist: IMS, Polygram

Cassette: released on Go International (Germany), Oct'83 by Go International Records (Germany). Dist: IMS, Polygram

INFIDELS.
Tracks: / Jokerman / Sweetheart like you / Neighbourhood bully / License to kill / Man of peace / Union sundown / I and I / Don't fall apart on me tonight.
Compact disc: by CBS Records. Dist: CBS

Album: released on CBS, Nov'83 by CBS Records. Dist: CBS

Cassette: released on CBS, Nov'83 by CBS Records. Dist: CBS

JOHN WESLEY HARDING.
Tracks: / John Wesley Harding / As I went out one morning / I dreamed I saw St Augustine / Drifter's escape / All along the watchtower / I am a lonesome hobo / Ballad of Frankie Lee and Judas Priest / Dear landlord / I pity the poor immigrant / Wicked messenger, The / Down along cove / I'll be your baby tonight.
Album: released on CBS, '69 by CBS Records. Dist: CBS

Cassette: released on CBS, '69 by CBS Records. Dist: CBS

JOKERMAN.
Single (7"): released on CBS, Jun'84 by CBS Records. Dist: CBS

JUST LIKE A WOMAN/I WANT YOU.
Single (7"): released on CBS, May'82 by CBS Records. Dist: CBS

KNOCKED OUT LOADED.
Tracks: / You wanna ramble / They killed him / Driftin' too far from shore / Precious memories / Maybe someday / Brownsville girl / Got my mind made up / Under your spell.
Album: released on CBS, Jul'86 by CBS Records. Dist: CBS

Cassette: released on CBS, Jul'86 by CBS Records. Dist: CBS

LIKE A ROLLING STONE/GATES OF EDEN.
Single (7"): released on CBS, May'82 by CBS Records. Dist: CBS

LIVE AT THE BUDOKAN.
Compact disc: released on CBS, Jul'87 by CBS Records. Dist: CBS

MORE BOB DYLAN'S GREATEST HITS.
Tracks: / Watching the river flow / Don't think twice / It's alright / Lay lady lay / Stuck inside a

---

mobile with the Memphis blues again / I'll be your baby tonight / All I really want to do / My back pages / Maggie's farm / Tonight I'll be staying here with you / Positively 4th Street / All along the watchtower / Mighty Quinn, The / Just like Tom Thumb's blues / Hard rain's gonna fall / If not for you / New morning / Tomorrow is a long time / When I paint my masterpiece / I shall be released / You ain't goin' nowhere / Down in the flood.
Album: released on CBS, '72 by CBS Records. Dist: CBS

Cassette: released on CBS, '72 by CBS Records. Dist: CBS

NASHVILLE SKYLINE.
Tracks: / Girl of the North country / Nashville skyline rag / To be alone with you / I threw it all away / Peggy day / Lay lady lay / One more night / Tell me that it isn't true / Country pie / Tonight I'll be stayinh here with you / Girl of the North Country / Nashville skyline rag / To be alone with you / I threw it all away / Peggy Day / Lay lady lay / One more night / Tell me that it isn't true / Country pie / Tonight I'll be staying here with you.
Compact disc: released on CBS, Jan'86 by CBS Records. Dist: CBS

Album: released on CBS, May'87 by CBS Records. Dist: CBS

Cassette: released on CBS, May'87 by CBS Records. Dist: CBS

NEW MORNING.
Tracks: / If not for you / Day of the locusts / Time passes slowly / Went to see the gypsy / Winterlude / If dogs run free / New morning / Sign in the window / One more weekend / Man in me, The / Three angels / Father of night.
Album: released on CBS, Sep'83 by CBS Records. Dist: CBS

Cassette: released on CBS, Sep'83 by CBS Records. Dist: CBS

PAT GARRET & BILLY THE KID Original soundtrack.
Tracks: / Main title theme (Billy) / Cantina theme (Workin' for the law) / Billy 1 / Bunkhouse theme / River theme / Turkey chase / Knocking on Heaven's door / Final theme / Billy 4 / Billy 7.
Album: released on CBS, Apr'82 by CBS Records. Dist: CBS

Cassette: released on CBS, Apr'82 by CBS Records. Dist: CBS

PLANET WAVES.
Tracks: / On a night like this / Going going gone / Tough mama / Hazel / Something there is about you / Forever young / Dirge / You angel you / Never say goodbye / Wedding song.
Album: released on CBS, Sep'82 by CBS Records. Dist: CBS

Cassette: released on CBS, Sep'82 by CBS Records. Dist: CBS

REAL LIVE.
Tracks: / Highway '61 revisited / Maggie's farm / I and I / License to kill / It ain't me babe / Tangled up in blue / Masters of war / Ballad of a thin man / Girl from the North Country / Tombstone blues.

Compact disc: by CBS Records. Dist: CBS

Album: released on CBS, Dec'84 by CBS Records. Dist: CBS

Cassette: released on CBS, Dec'84 by CBS Records. Dist: CBS

SAVED.
Album: released on CBS, Sep'86 by CBS Records. Dist: CBS

Cassette: released on CBS, Sep'86 by CBS Records. Dist: CBS

SELF PORTRAIT.
Tracks: / All the tired horses / Alberta 1 / I've forgotten more than you'll ever know / Days of '49 / Early morning rain / In search of little Sadie / Let it be me / Woogie boogie / Belle Isle / Living the blues / Like a rolling stone / Copper kettle / Gotta travel on / Blue moon / Boxer, The / Mighty Quinn, The / Take me as I am / It hurts me too / Minstrel boy / She belongs to me / Wigwam / Alberta no.2.

Album: released on CBS, Sep'87 by CBS Records. Dist: CBS

Cassette: released on CBS, Sep'87 by CBS Records. Dist: CBS

SLOW TRAIN COMING.
Tracks: / Gotta serve somebody / Precious angel when you gonna wake me up / I believe in you / Slow train / Gonna change my way of thinkin' / Do right to me baby / When he returns / Man gave names to all his animals / Changing of the guards / New pony / No time to think / Baby stop crying / Is your love in vain / Senor / True love tends to forget / We better talk this over / Where are you tonight / Journey through dark heat / Gotta serve somebody / Precious angel / I believe in you / Slow train / Gonna change my way of thinking / Do right to me, baby (do unto others) / When you gonna wake up? / Man gave names to all the animals / When he returns.
Compact disc: released on CBS, Mar'86 by CBS Records. Dist: CBS

Album: released on CBS, Nov'85 by CBS Records. Dist: CBS

Cassette: released on CBS, Nov'85 by CBS Records. Dist: CBS

STREET LEGAL.
Tracks: / Changing of the guards / New pony / No time to think / Baby stop crying / Is your love in vain? / Senor (tales of Yankee power) / True love tends to forget / We better talk this over / Where are you tonight? / Journey through dark heat.
Compact disc: released on CBS, Mar'86 by CBS Records. Dist: CBS

Album: released on CBS, Jun'78 by CBS Records. Dist: CBS

Cassette: released on CBS, Jun'78 by CBS Records. Dist: CBS

TIMES THEY ARE A-CHANGIN'.
Tracks: / Times they are a-changin' / Ballad of Hollis Brown / With God on our side / One too many mornings / North Country blues / Only a pawn in their game / Boots of Spanish leather / When the ship comes in / Lonesome death of Hattie Carroll / Restless farewell.
Album: released on CBS, '84 by CBS Records. Dist: CBS

Cassette: released on CBS, '84 by CBS Records. Dist: CBS

TIMES THEY ARE A-CHANGIN'/BOB DYLAN.
Cassette: released on CBS, Feb'83 by CBS Records. Dist: CBS

TIMES THEY ARE A-CHANGIN'/HONEY.
Single (7"): released on CBS, May'82 by CBS Records. Dist: CBS

WHEN THE NIGHT COMES FALLING FROM THE SKY.
Single (7"): released on CBS, Aug'85 by CBS Records. Dist: CBS Deleted '86.

Single (12"): released on CBS, Aug'85 by CBS Records. Dist: CBS

Dynamite band
ROCKIN' IS OUR BUSINESS.
Album: released on Ace, Jul'82 by Ace Records. Dist: Pinnacle, Swift, Hotshot, Cadillac

Dynamix II
JUST GIVE THE D.J. A BREAK.
Tracks: / Just give the D.J. a break / Straight from the jungle.
Single (7"): released on Cool Tempo, Jul'87 by Chrysalis Records. Dist: CBS

Single (12"): released on Cool Tempo, Jul'87 by Chrysalis Records. Dist: CBS

Dynasty
ADVENTURES IN THE LAND OF MUSIC.
Album: released on Solar, Aug'80 by MCA Records. Dist: Polygram Distribution

---

DOES THAT RING A BELL.
Single (7"): released on Elektra, Apr'83 by WEA Records. Dist: WEA

Single (12"): released on Elektra, Apr'83 by WEA Records. Dist: WEA

ONLY ONE/CHECK IT OUT.
Single (7"): released on Solar, Jul'83 by MCA Records. Dist: Polygram Distribution

Single (12"): released on Solar, Jul'83 by MCA Records. Dist: Polygram Distribution

RIGHT BACK AT CHA.
Album: released on Solar, Nov'82 by MCA Records. Dist: Polygram Distribution

Dynasty & Mimi
DYNASTY RAP.
Tracks: / Dynasty rap / Story of the Carrington crew (The) / Bugging animal farm (The) / Story of the Carrington crew / Blake beat boy mix / Dynasty rap / Alexis acapella.
Single (7"): released on Jive, Feb'86 by Zomba Records. Dist: RCA, PRT, CBS

Single (12"): released on Jive, Feb'86 by Zomba Records. Dist: RCA, PRT, CBS

Dyna Tones
LIVE IT UP.
Album: released on Rounder (USA), Apr'86 Dist: Mike's Country Music Room Distribution, Jazz Music Distribution, Swift Distribution, Roots Records Distribution, Projection Distribution, Topic Distribution

TOUGH TO SHAKE.
Album: released on Rounder (USA), Jul'85 Dist: Mike's Country Music Room Distribution, Jazz Music Distribution, Swift Distribution, Roots Records Distribution, Projection Distribution, Topic Distribution

Dynell, Johnny
JAM HOT (RUMBA ROCK).
Single (7"): released on Epic, Jun'83 by CBS Records. Dist: CBS

Single (12"): released on Epic, Jun'83 by CBS Records. Dist: CBS

Dynes, Sean
PADDY'S GREEN SHAMROCK SHORE.
Album: released on Homespun(Ireland), Jul'76 by Outlet Records. Dist: Outlet

Dysart & Dundonald
SKIRL O' THE PIPES (Dysart & Dundonald Pipe Band).
Album: released on Lismor, Nov'76 by Lismor Records. Dist: Lismor, Roots, Celtic Music

SUPREME CHAMPIONS (Dysart & Dundonald Pipe Band).
Album: released on Lismor, Jun'75 by Lismor Records. Dist: Lismor, Roots, Celtic Music

WORLD CHAMPIONS (Dysart & Dundonald Pipe Band).
Album: released on Lismor, Apr'79 by Lismor Records. Dist: Lismor, Roots, Celtic Music

Dyson, Ronnie
ALL OVER YOUR FACE/DON'T NEED YOU NOW.
Single (12"): released on Cotillion (Import), Sep'83 by Atlantic Records. Dist: WEA

Dzata
UNDERGROUND.
Album: released on Deo, Nov'84 by DEO Records. Dist: Jetstar

E

Eade, Colin
KILLER, THE.
Tracks: / Killer, The / Aids-the-killer / If in doubt leave it out / Love your life / Cry for the last time.
Notes: Available from First Time Records, 12 Trewartha Road, Praa Sands, Penzance, Cornwall TR20 9ST. Tel: 0736 762826.
Single (7"): released on First Time/Fugore, Mar'87 by First Time Records. Dist: First Time Records

Eager, Allen
RENAISSANCE.
Album: released on Uptown (USA), Nov'86 by Uptown Records. Dist: Jazz Music

Eager, Vince
20 YEARS ON.
Album: released on Nevis, Jul'78 Dist: H.R. Taylor

Eagles
BEST OF THE EAGLES.
Compact disc: by Elektra/Asylum/Nonesuch Records. Dist: WEA

Album: released on Asylum, May'85 by WEA Records. Dist: WEA

Cassette: released on Asylum, May'85 by WEA Records. Dist: WEA

DESPERADO.
Tracks: / Doolin Dalton / 21 / Out of control / Tequila sunrise / Desperado / Certain kind of fool / Outlaw man / Saturday night / Bitter Creek.
Compact disc: released on Asylum, Feb'87 by WEA Records. Dist: WEA

Album: released on Asylum, Jun'76 by WEA Records. Dist: WEA

Cassette: released on Asylum, Jun'76 by WEA Records. Dist: WEA

DESPERADO/ONE OF THESE NIGHTS.
Tracks: / Doolin Dalton / Twenty one / Out of control / Tequila sunrise / Desperado / Certain kind of fool / Doolin Dalton (instrumental) / Outlaw man / Saturday night / Bitter creek / Desperado (reprise) / One of these nights / Too many hands / Hollywood waltz / Journey to the sorcerer / Lying eyes / Take it to the limit / Visions / After the thrill is gone / I wish you peace.
Cassette: released on Asylum, '83 by WEA Records. Dist: WEA

EAGLES.
Tracks: / Take it easy / Witchy woman / Chug all night / Most of us are sad / Nightingale / Train leaves here this morning / Take the devil / Earlybird / Peaceful easy feeling / Tryin' / Take it easy / Witchy woman / Chug all night / Most of us are sad / Nightingale / Train leave here this morning / Take the devil / Earlybird / Peaceful easy feeling / Tryin' / Doolin Dalton / Twenty one / Out of control / Tequila sunrise / Desperado / Certain kind of fool / Outlaw man / Saturday night / Bitter creek.
Compact disc: released on Asylum, Feb'87 by WEA Records. Dist: WEA

Album: released on Asylum, Jun'76 by WEA Records. Dist: WEA

EAGLES LIVE.
Tracks: / Hotel California / Heartache tonight / I can't tell you why / Long run, The / New kid in town / Life's been good / Seven bridges road / Wasted time / Take it to the limit / Doolin Dalton / Desperado / Saturday night / All night long / Life in the fast lane / Take it easy.
Album: released on Asylum, Nov'80 by WEA Records. Dist: WEA

Cassette: released on Asylum, Nov'80 by WEA Records. Dist: WEA

GREATEST HITS: EAGLES VOL.2.
Tracks: / Hotel California / Heartache tonight / Seven bridges road / Victim of love / Sad cafe, The / Life in the fast lane / I can't tell you why / New kid in town / Long run, The / After the thrill is gone.

Album: released on Asylum, Oct'82 by WEA Records. Dist: WEA

Cassette: released on Asylum, Oct'82 by WEA Records. Dist: WEA

Compact disc: released on Asylum, Oct'82 by WEA Records. Dist: WEA

HOTEL CALIFORNIA.
Tracks: / Hotel California / New kid in town / Life in the fast lane / Wasted time (reprise) / Victim of love / Pretty maids all in a row / Try and love again / Last resort, The / Hotel California / New kid in town / Life in the fast lane / Wasted time / Hotel California (reprise) / Victim of love / Pretty maids all in a row / Try and love again / Last resort, The.
Compact disc: by WEA Records. Dist: WEA

Album: released on Asylum, Jan'77 by WEA Records. Dist: WEA

Cassette: released on Asylum, Jan'77 by WEA Records. Dist: WEA

HOTEL CALIFORNIA (7").
Single (7"): released on Asylum, Jun'85 by WEA Records. Dist: WEA

HOTEL CALIFORNIA (OLD GOLD).
Single (7"): released on Old Gold, Sep'85 by Old Gold Records. Dist: Lightning, Jazz Music, Spartan, Counterpoint

HOTEL CALIFORNIA/PRETTY MAIDS ALL.

HOTEL CALIFORNIA/THE LONG RUN.
Cassette: released on Asylum, Nov'83 by WEA Records. Dist: WEA

Single (7"): released on Elektra, Jul'81 by WEA Records. Dist: WEA

LONG RUN, THE.
Tracks: / Long run, The / I can't tell you why / In the city / Disco strangler, The / King of Hollywood / Heartache tonight / Those shoes / Teenage jail / Greeks don't want no freaks, The / Sad cafe, The.
Compact disc: by WEA Records. Dist: WEA

Album: released on Asylum, Sep'79 by WEA Records. Dist: WEA

Cassette: released on Asylum, Sep'79 by WEA Records. Dist: WEA

Compact disc: released on Asylum, Sep'79 by WEA Records. Dist: WEA

LYIN' EYES.
Single (7"): released on Old Gold, Sep'85 by Old Gold Records. Dist: Lightning, Jazz Music, Spartan, Counterpoint

ONE OF THESE NIGHTS.
Tracks: / One of these nights / Too many hands / Hollywood waltz / Journey of the sorcerer / Lying eyes / Take it to the limit / Visions / After the thrill is gone / I wish you peace.
Compact disc: by Elektra/Asylum/Nonesuch Records. Dist: WEA

Album: released on Asylum, Jun'76 by WEA Records. Dist: WEA

Cassette: released on Asylum, Jun'76 by WEA Records. Dist: WEA

ON THE BORDER.
Tracks: / Already gone / You never cry like a lover / Midnight flyer / My man / On the border / James Dean / 01 55 / Is it true / Good day in hell / Best of my love.
Compact disc: by Elektra/Asylum/Nonesuch Records. Dist: WEA

Album: released on Asylum, Jun'76 by WEA Records. Dist: WEA

Cassette: released on Asylum, Jun'76 by WEA Records. Dist: WEA

TAKE IT TO THE LIMIT.
Single (7"): released on Old Gold, Sep'85 by Old Gold Records. Dist: Lightning, Jazz Music, Spartan, Counterpoint

---

TAKE IT TO THE LIMIT/SEVEN BRIDGES.
Single (7"): released on Elektra, Feb'81 by WEA Records. Dist: WEA

THEIR GREATEST HITS 1971-1975.
Tracks: / Take it easy / Witchy woman / Lying eyes / Already gone / Desperado / One of these nights / Tequila sunrise / Take it to the limit / Peaceful easy feeling / Best of my love.
Compact disc: by WEA Records. Dist: WEA

Album: released on Asylum, Feb'76 by WEA Records. Dist: WEA

Cassette: released on Asylum, Feb'76 by WEA Records. Dist: WEA

Eaglesham, Bobby
WEATHER THE STORM.
Tracks: / Weather the storm / Helen of Kirconnel / Tramps and hawkers / Bonnie George Campbell / Rowan tree * / Planxty irwin * / Cock o' the north * / Atholl highlanders* / Shearing, The / She moved through the fair / Redundant Mr. Brown, The / Soor milk cairt / Curwen jig / Without me just with you.
Album: released on Fellside, '83 by Fellside Records. Dist: Roots, Jazz Music, Celtic Music, Projection

Eaglin, Snooks
BABY YOU CAN GET YOUR GUN.
Album: released on Demon, Jan'87 by Demon Records. Dist: Pinnacle

DOWN YONDER.
Tracks: / Down yonder / No more doggin' / Talk to your daughter / Going to the river / Oh red / Yours truly / Travelling mood / St. Pete Florida blues / Teeny bit of your love, A / Mustang Sally / Let the four winds blow / San Jose.
Album: released on Sonet, Aug'78 by Sonet Records. Dist: PRT

LEGACY OF BLUES VOL.2.
Tracks: / Boogie children / Who's loving you / Lucille / Drive it home / Good news / Funky Malaguena / Pine top's boogie-woogie / That same old train / I get the blues / Young boy blues / Tomorrow night / Little girl of mine.
Album: released on Sonet Records. Dist: PRT

POSSUM UP A SIMMON TREE.
Album: released on Arhoolie, May'81 by Arhoolie Records. Dist: Projection, Topic, Jazz Music, Swift, Roots

Earby Band
EARBY BAND.
Tracks: / Nibelungen / Cavatina / Nightingale / All creatures great and small / We've only just begun / Dominique / Amazing grace / In Dublin's fair city / Don't know how to love love / Copacabana / Feelings / Cowshed capers.
Album: released on Castle Studio, '81 by Castle Studio Records.

Eardley, Jon
JON EARDLEY-MICK PYNE (Eardley, Jon/Mick Pyne).
Tracks: / Crazy rhythm / Basin Street blues / Emily / My funny valentine / You don't know what love is / My old flame / You'd be so nice to come home to / Nightingale sang... A.
Album: released on Spotlite, '83 by Spotlite Records. Dist: Cadillac, Jazz Music Spotlite

NAMELY ME.
Tracks: / Andrea / Namely me / Sabam / Laugh little boy / Konigawenz / Bell and bugle / Horseshoe curve.
Album: released on Spotlite, '83 by Spotlite Records. Dist: Cadillac, Jazz Music, Spotlite

STABLEMATES (Eardley, Jon/Al Haig).
Album: released on Spotlite, '83 by Spotlite Records. Dist: Cadillac, Jazz Music, Spotlite

Eareckson, Joni
JONI'S SONG.
Album: released on Word, May'85 by Word Records. Dist: Word Distribution, CBS

Cassette: released on Word, May'85 by Word Records. Dist: Word Distribution, CBS

Eargasm
THIS IS LOVERS ROCK TOO.
Tracks: / Lovers medley.
Single (12"): released on G Spot, Dec'86 by G Spot Records. Dist: Jetstar

Earland, Charles
DOGGIE BOOGIE BABY.
Single (7"): by MCA Records. Dist: Polygram, MCA

Single (12"): by MCA Records. Dist: Polygram, MCA

INFANT EYES.
Album: released on Muse, Apr'81 by Peerless Records. Dist: Lugtons Distributors

IN THE POCKET.
Album: released on Muse, Aug'82 by Peerless Records. Dist: Lugtons Distributors

PLEASANT AFTERNOON.
Album: released on Muse, '81 by Peerless Records. Dist: Lugtons Distributors

Earle, Steve
EARLY TRACKS.
Tracks: / Nothin' but you / If you need a fool / Continental trailways blues / Open up your door / Breakdown lane / Squeeze me in / Annie, is tonight the night / My baby worships me / Cadillac / Devil's right hand.
Album: released on Epic, Jul'87 by CBS Records. Dist: CBS

Cassette: released on Epic, Jul'87 by CBS Records. Dist: CBS

EXIT O.
Tracks: / Nowhere road / Sweet little '66 / No. 29 / Angry young man / San Antonio Girl / Rain came down. (The) / I ain't ever satisfied / Week of living dangerously, (The) / I love you too much / It's all up to you.
Album: released on MCA, Apr'87 by MCA records. Dist: Polygram, MCA

Cassette: released on MCA, Apr'87 by MCA Records. Dist: Polygram, MCA

Compact disc: released on MCA, Apr'87 by MCA Records. Dist: Polygram, MCA

FEARLESS HEART.
Tracks: / Fearless heart / Little Rock & Roller.
Single (7"): released on MCA, Mar'87 by MCA Records. Dist: Polygram, MCA

Single (12"): released on MCA, Mar'87 by MCA Records. Dist: Polygram, MCA

GUITAR TOWN.
Tracks: / Guitar town / Goodbye's all we've got left / Hillbilly highway / Good ol' boy (gettin' tough) / My old friend the blues / Someday / Think it over / Fearless heart / Little rock'n'roller / Down the road / Good ol' boy (getting tough).
Compact disc: released on MCA, Apr'87 by MCA Records. Dist: Polygram, MCA

Album: released on MCA, Aug'86 by MCA Records. Dist: Polygram, MCA

Cassette: released on MCA, Aug'86 by MCA Records. Dist: Polygram, MCA

I AIN'T NEVER SATISFIED.
Tracks: / I ain't never satisfied / Nowhere Road.
Single (7"): released on MCA, 23 May'87 by MCA Records. Dist: Polygram, MCA

Single (12"): released on MCA, 23 May'87 by MCA Records. Dist: Polygram, MCA

SOMEDAY.
Tracks: / Someday / Guitar town / Good ol' boy (live) / Goodbye's all we got left.
Notes: Goodbye's all we got left,is an extra track available on the 12" version only.
Single (7"): released on MCA, Feb'87 by MCA Records. Dist: Polygram, MCA

Single (12"): released on MCA, Feb'87 by MCA Records. Dist: Polygram, MCA

SOMEDAY (1).
Tracks: / Someday / Guitar man.
Single (7"): released on MCA, Oct'86 by MCA Records. Dist: Polygram, MCA

Earl, Ronnie

RONNIE EARL & THE BROADCASTERS (Earl, Ronnie & the Broadcasters).
Album: released on Black Top (USA), Feb'85

SMOKING (Earl, Ronnie & the Broadcasters).
Album: released on Making Waves, Sep'85 by Making Waves Records.

THEY CALL ME MR EARL.
Album: released on Spindrift, May'86 Dist: Roots

Earls

REMEMBER THEN.
Single (7"): released on Old Gold, Jul'82 by Old Gold Records. Dist: Lightning, Jazz Music, Spartan, Counterpoint

Earl Soham Slog

EARL SOHAM SLOG (Various Artists).
Album: released on Topic, '81 Dist: Roots Distribution

Early...

EARLY AMERICAN MINSTREL SHOW (THE) (Various Artists).
Tracks: / De boatman's dance / Old Joe / Fine old color'd gentleman (The) / Dr. Hekog jig / Stop dat knocking / Mary Blane / Instrumental medley / Miss Lucy Long / Old uncle Ned / De ole jawbone / Pea patch jig / Lucy Neal / Hard times.
Notes: Blackface minstrelsy had its beginnings in the 1830's when minstrel musical acts appeared as interludes in an evening's theatrical entertainment or as one act in a circus. In 1843 four performers banded together in New York and put on the first full-scale minstrel show. There were a big hit, spawning many imitators and initiating what was to be the most popular of popular entertainments for the next forty years. One of the most important factors in this popularity was the music, for the minstrel show was primarily a musical event. This recording attempts to re-create the music of a typical minstrel show of the late 1840's, when this music struck the nations fancy most forcefully and before the minstrel show gradually became indistinguishable from other forms of variety entertainment. THE PERFORMERS: Vincent Turo - fiddle, Percy Danforth - bones, Matthew Heuman - tambourine, Robert Winans - banjo, David Van Kersblick - tenor, Peter DiSante - lead, Brian Mark - baritone, Roger Smith - bass. [New World release sheet, May '87]
Album: released on New World (USA), May'87 by New World Records (USA). Dist: Conifer

EARLY SESSIONS (Various Artists).
Album: released on Ariwa, Sep'84 by Ariwa Records. Dist: Revolver, Cartel, Jetstar, Rough Trade

EARLY VIPER JIVE Rare scat vocals (Various Artists).
Album: released on Stash, Apr'81 Dist: Swift Distribution, Jazz Music Distribution, Jazz Horizons Distribution, Celtic Music Distribution, Cadillac, JSU Distribution, Zodiac Distribution

Early B

FOUR WHEEL NO REAL.
Album: released on Midnight Rock, Jun'85 Dist: Jetstar Distribution, Kingdom Distribution

GHOSTBUSTERS.
Album: released on Black Solidarity, Jun'85 by Black Solidarity Records. Dist: Jetstar

HISTORY OF JAMAICA.
Single (12"): released on Musical Ambassador, Oct'82

Josey Wales meets Early B

REALLY REALLY.
Album: released on Sunset, Dec'85 Dist: EMI

RIGHTEOUS RASTA.
Single 10": released on King Jam, Dec'82 by King Jam Records. Dist: Jetstar

Single (12"): released on King Jam, Feb'83 by King Jam Records. Dist: Jetstar

SUNDAY DISH.
Album: released on Sunset, Mar'85 Dist: EMI

Early Cante Flamenco

CLASSIC RECORDINGS OF THE 1930'S & 40'S-VOL.2.
Album: released on Folklyric (USA), Dec'86 by Arhoolie Records. Dist: Topic, Projection

EARLY CANTE FLAMENCO VOL.2 (Various Artists).
Cassette:

Album: released on Folklyric (USA), Mar'85 by Arhoolie Records. Dist: Topic, Projection

Earons

LAND OF HUNGER.
Single (12"): released on Island, May'84 by Island Records. Dist: Polygram

Earth And Fire

EARTH AND FIRE.
Album: released on Polydor (Import), May'83

Cassette: released on Polydor (Import), May'83

Earthly Delights

EARTHLY DELIGHTS (Various Artists).
Notes: Artists include: Whores of Babylon, Nocturnal emissions.
Album: released on Sterile Sep'86 Dist: Red Rhino Distribution, Cartel Distribution

Earth Opera

GREAT AMERICAN EAGLE TRAGEDY, THE.
Album: released on Edsel, Feb'87 by Demon Records. Dist: Pinnacle, Jazz Music, Projection

Earth Shaker

BLONDIE GIRL.
Single (12"): released on Music For Nations, Nov'83 by Music For Nations Records. Dist: Pinnacle

EARTH SHAKER.
Album: released on Music For Nations, Nov'83 by Music For Nations Records. Dist: Pinnacle

FUGITIVE.
Album: released on Music For Nations, Apr'84 by Music For Nations Records. Dist: Pinnacle

Cassette: released on MFN, Jan'85 by Music For Nations Records. Dist: Pinnacle

MIDNIGHT FLIGHT.
Album: released on Music For Nations, Feb'86 by Music For Nations Records. Dist: Pinnacle

Earth, Wind & Fire

ALL IN ALL.
Compact disc: released on CBS, May'87 by CBS Records. Dist: CBS

ALL'N'ALL.
Album: released on CBS, Mar'83 by CBS Records. Dist: CBS

Cassette: released on CBS, Mar'83 by CBS Records. Dist: CBS

BEST OF...VOLUME 1.
Tracks: / Got to get you into my life / Fantasy / Saturday night / Love music / Getaway / That's the way of the world / September / Shining star / Reasons / Singasong.
Compact disc: released on CBS, Mar'87 by CBS Records. Dist: CBS

Album: released on CBS, Nov'84 by CBS Records. Dist: CBS

Cassette: released on CBS, Nov'84 by CBS Records. Dist: CBS

BOOGIE WONDERLAND.
Tracks: / Boogie wonderland / Let's groove.
Single (7"): released on CBS, Jun'86 by CBS Records. Dist: CBS

Single (12"): released on CBS, Jun'86 by CBS Records. Dist: CBS

Single (7"): released on Old Gold, Sep'85 by Old Gold Records. Dist: Lightning, Jazz Music, Spartan, Counterpoint

COLLECTION: EARTH, WIND & FIRE.
Album: released on K-Tel, May'86 by K-Tel Records. Dist: Record Merchandisers Distribution, Taylors, Terry Blood Distribution, Wynd-Up Distribution, Relay Distribution, Pickwick Distribution, Solomon & Peres Distribution, Polygram

Cassette: released on K-Tel, May'86 by K-Tel Records. Dist: Record Merchandisers Distribution, Taylors, Terry Blood Distribution, Wynd-Up Distribution, Relay Distribution, Pickwick Distribution, Solomon & Peres Distribution, Polygram

Compact disc: released on K-Tel, Nov'86 by K-Tel Records. Dist: Record Merchandisers Distribution, Taylors, Terry Blood Distribution, Wynd-Up Distribution, Relay Distribution, Pickwick Distribution, Solomon & Peres Distribution, Polygram

EARTH, WIND & FIRE.
Triple album / cassette: released on CBS, Oct'79 by CBS Records. Dist: CBS

FACES.
Double Album: released on CBS, Oct'80 by CBS Records. Dist: CBS

Cassette: released on CBS, Oct'80 by CBS Records. Dist: CBS

FALL IN LOVE WITH ME.
Single (7"): released on CBS, Jan'83 by CBS Records. Dist: CBS

Single (12"): released on CBS, Jan'83 by CBS Records. Dist: CBS

FANTASY.
Single (7"): released on Old Gold, Sep'85 by Old Gold Records. Dist: Lightning, Jazz Music, Spartan, Counterpoint

GRATITUDE.
Tracks: / Introduction medley / Africano/power / Yearnin' learnin' / Devotion / Sun goddess / Reasons / Sing a message to you / Shining star / New world symphony / Sunshine / Sunshine / Sing a song / Gratitude / Celebrate / You can't hide love.
Compact disc: released on CBS, May'87 by CBS Records. Dist: CBS

Compact disc: released on CBS, May'87 by CBS Records. Dist: CBS

HEAD TO THE SKY.
Album: released on CBS, Mar'81 by CBS Records. Dist: CBS Deleted '83.

Cassette: released on CBS, Mar'81 by CBS Records. Dist: CBS

I AM.
Compact disc: released on CBS, May'87 by CBS Records. Dist: CBS

Album: released on CBS, Jun'85 by CBS Records. Dist: CBS

Album: released on CBS, Jun'85 by CBS Records. Dist: CBS

LAST DAYS AND TIME.
Album: released on CBS, Oct'79 by CBS Records. Dist: CBS

Cassette: released on CBS, Oct'79 by CBS Records. Dist: CBS

RAISE.
Tracks: / Let's groove / Lady sun / You are a winner / My love / Evolution orange / Kalimba tree / I've had enough / Wanna be with you / Changing times.
Cassette: released on CBS, Aug'86 by CBS Records. Dist: CBS

Compact disc: released on CBS, '83 by CBS Records. Dist: CBS

Album: released on CBS, Aug'86 by CBS Records. Dist: CBS

SEPTEMBER.
Single (7"): released on CBS, Apr'82 by CBS Records. Dist: CBS

SPIRIT.
Album: released on Hallmark, Apr'84 by Pickwick Records. Dist: Pickwick Distribution, PRT, Taylors

Album: released on CBS, Nov'76 by CBS Records. Dist: CBS

SPREAD YOUR LOVE.
Single (7"): released on CBS, Mar'83 by CBS Records. Dist: CBS

STAR.
Tracks: / Star / Saturday nite / After the love is gone / I've had enough.
Single (12"): released on Old Gold, Feb'86 by Old Gold Records. Dist: Lightning, Jazz Music, Spartan, Counterpoint

THAT'S THE WAY OF THE WORLD.
Compact disc: released on CBS, May'87 by CBS Records. Dist: CBS

Ear to the ground

EAR TO THE GROUND (Various Artists).
Cassette: released on Banana, Apr'85 Dist: Pinnacle, Fresh

Ear Trumpet

BRING ON THE DIRT.
Album: released on DTS, Aug'87 by Record & Tape Sales. Dist: Revolver, Cartel

Easin' In

EASIN' IN: WOMEN SING THE BLUES 1924/41 (Various Artists).
Album: released on Muskadine (USA), Mar'84

East

EAST (Various Artists).
Album: released on Dead Good, Feb'80

East Bay Ray

TROUBLE IN TOWN.
Single (7"): released on Alternative Tentacles, Jun'84 by Alternative Tentacles Records. Dist:

Eastbound Expressway

FRANTIC LOVE.
Single (7"): released on Record Shack, May'84 by Record Shack Records. Dist: PRT

Single (12"): released on Record Shack, May'84 by Record Shack Records. Dist: PRT

KNOCK ME SENSELESS.
Tracks: / Knock me senseless / Knock me senseless (Inst).
Single (7"): released on Passion, Oct'86 by Skratch Records. Dist: PRT

Single (12"): released on Passion, Oct'86 by Skratch Records. Dist: PRT

PRIMITIVE DESIRE.
Single (12"): released on Record Shack, Nov'83 by Record Shack Records. Dist: PRT

RAINSTORM.
Tracks: / Rainstorm / Rainstorm (Nightmare dub mix).
Single (12"): released on Passion, Apr'87 by Skratch Records. Dist: PRT

YOU'RE A BEAT.
Tracks: / You've a beat / You're a beat(Dub version).
Single (7"): released on Passion, Mar'86 by Skratch Records. Dist: PRT

Single (12"): released on Passion, Mar'86 by Skratch Records. Dist: PRT

East Coast Offering

DON'T YOU EVER TAKE YOUR LOVE AWAY.
Single (7"): released on MCA, Aug'84 by MCA Records. Dist: Polygram, MCA

Single (12"): released on MCA, Aug'84 by MCA Records. Dist: Polygram, MCA Deleted '85.

EAST COAST OFFERING.
Album: released on MCA, Aug'84 by MCA Records. Dist: Polygram, MCA

Cassette: released on MCA, Aug'84 by MCA Records. Dist: Polygram, MCA

Eastenders

EASTENDERS (Various Artists).
Tracks: / Hello, hello, who's your lady friend / Man who broke the bank at Monte Carlo / Ship ahoy (all the nice girls love a sailor) / It's a long way to Tipperary / I do like to be beside the seaside / Pack up your troubles in your old kit bag / Goodbye Dolly Gray / Don't dilly dally on the way / Run rabbit run / Wot'cher (knocked 'em in the Old Kent Road) / Waitin' at the church (my wife won't let me) / Strollin' / Underneath the arches / Hometown / Lily of Laguna / On mother Kelly's doorstep / I'm forever blowing bubbles / Barrow boy song, The / Lambeth walk / Nice cup of tea, A / Daddy wouldn't buy me a bow-wow / I'm Henery the eighth I am / Boiled beef and carrots / Any old iron / My old man's a dustman / I've got a lovely bunch of coconuts / Knees up mother brown / Give my regards to Broadway / Are you from Dixie / If you knew Susie (like I know Susie) / Maybe it's because I'm a londoner / Hold your hand out, naughty boy / Who were you with last night.
Album: released on MFP, Oct'86 by EMI Records. Dist: EMI

Cassette: released on MFP, Oct'86 by EMI Records. Dist: EMI

Cassette: released on BBC, Nov'85 by BBC Records & Tapes. Dist: EMI, PRT, Pye

Album: released on BBC, Nov'85 by BBC Records & Tapes. Dist: EMI, PRT, Pye

EASTENDERS SING-ALONG Original BBC-TV cast recording (Various Artists).
Tracks: / How ya gonna keep 'em down on the farm / Baby face / Four leaf clover (I'm looking over a0 / Toot, Toot, Tootsie (goo'bye) / Somebody stole my girl / Put your arms around me honey / Oh Johnny, oh Johnny, oh Johnny oh / Yes sir, that's my baby / For me and my gal / Shine on Harvest moon / Who's sorry now / You made me love you / It had to be you / Some of these days / Alabamy bound / Waiting for the Robert E. Lee / When you're smiling (the whole world smiles with you) / California here I come / Swanee / Roll out the barrell / Row row row / She'll be coming round the mountain.

Easterhouse

COMING UP FOR AIR.
Single (7"): released on Easterhouse, Mar'85 by Easterhouse. Dist: Rough Trade, Cartel

CONTENDERS.
Album: released on Rough Trade, Jun'86 by Rough Trade Records. Dist: Rough Trade Distribution, Cartel Distribution

Cassette: released on Rough Trade, Jun'86 by Rough Trade Records. Dist: Rough Trade Distribution, Cartel Distribution

Compact disc: released on Rough Trade, May'87 by Rough Trade Records. Dist: Rough

Trade Distribution, Cartel Distribution

INSPIRATION.
Tracks: / Inspiration / Johnny I hardly knew you / Easter rising 1969.
Single (7"): released on Rough Trade, Apr'86 by Rough Trade Records. Dist: Rough Trade Distribution, Cartel Distribution

Single (12"): released on Rough Trade, Apr'86 by Rough Trade Records. Dist: Rough Trade Distribution, Cartel Distribution

WHISTLING IN THE DARK.
Tracks: / Whistling in the dark / Ain't that always the way / Confrontation.
Single (7"): released on Rough Trade, Jan'86 by Rough Trade Records. Dist: Rough Trade Distribution, Cartel Distribution

Single (12"): by Rough Trade Records. Dist: Rough Trade Distribution, Cartel Distribution

Eastern Alliance

KEYS TO THE HOUSE.
Single (7"): released on Bronze, Jun'84 by Polygram Records. Dist: Polydor

LOVE YOU YOU BANANA.
Single (7"): released on Bronze, Aug'84 by Polygram Records. Dist: Polydor

Eastern Dark

LONG LIVE THE NEW FLASH.
Album: released on What Goes On, Dec'86 Dist: Rough Trade, Cartel, Shigaku

Eastern Variation

BABY I LOVE YOU.
Tracks: / Baby I love you / Baby I love you (Version).
Single (12"): released on Cartridge, Aug'86 by Cartridge. Dist: Jetstar

Easter Parade

EASTER PARADE Original soundtrack (Various Artists).
Compact disc: released on CBS, Jun'87 by CBS Records. Dist: CBS

East European Folk Group

EAST EUROPEAN FOLK MUSIC.
Cassette: released on Goat Bag, Mar'85 by Goat Bag Records. Dist: E.F.D.S.S., London, Sterns, Collet's Records, Int. Bookshop Record Dept., Triple Earth

East India Company

MOVE YOUR BODY.
Tracks: / Move your body / Night sky.
Single (12"): released on Nine O Nine, Apr'87 by Creole Records. Dist: Rhino, PRT

Eastley, Max

NEW & REDISCOVERED INSTRUMENTS (Eastley, Max/David Toop).
Album: released on Obscure, Apr'78 by Polydor Records. Dist: Polygram Distribution

Eastman-Dryden Orchestra

VICTOR HERBERT SOUVENIR.
Compact disc: released on Arabesque, Nov'85 Dist: D Sharp Records, Pinnacle

Eastman Marimba Band

EASTMAN MARIMBA BAND.
Notes: Virtuoso pieces for marimbas.
Album: released on Mercury, Jun'86 by Phonogram Records. Dist: Polygram Distribution

Eastman-Rochester Pops

MALAGUENA.
Notes: Spanish and Latin American favourites including 'Malaguena' and Jamaican Rumba.
Album: released on Mercury (USA), Jun'86 by Import Records. Dist: IMS Distribution, Polygram Distribution

Eastman Symphonic Wind...

MARCHING ALONG.
Album: released on Mercury, Jul'83 by Phonogram Records. Dist: Polygram Distribution

East Of Croydon

EAST OF CROYDON (Various Artists).
Album: released on Nothing Shaking, Jul'81

East Of Eden

JIG A JIG.
Single (7"): released on Decca, May'70 by Decca Records. Dist: Polygram

SNAFU.
Album: by Decca Records. Dist: Polygram

WORLD OF EAST OF EDEN.
Album: released on Decca, '71 by Decca Records. Dist: Polygram

East Of Java

BURNING SUN.
Single (7"): released on RCA, Jul'84 by RCA Records. Dist: RCA, Roots, Swift, Wellard, Chris, I & B, Solomon & Peres Distribution

Single (12"): released on RCA, Jul'84 by RCA Records. Dist: RCA, Roots, Swift, Wellard, Chris, I & B, Solomon & Peres Distribution

DIFFERENT WORLD.
Single (7"): released on RCA, Aug'85 by RCA Records. Dist: RCA, Roots, Swift, Wellard, Chris, I & B, Solomon & Peres Distribution

Single (12"): released on RCA, Aug'85 by RCA Records. Dist: RCA, Roots, Swift, Wellard, Chris, I & B, Solomon & Peres Distribution

SOME PEOPLE (SAY WAR).
Single (7"): released on RCA, Oct'84 by RCA Records. Dist: RCA, Roots, Swift, Wellard, Chris, I & B, Solomon & Peres Distribution

Single (12"): released on RCA, Oct'84 by RCA Records. Dist: RCA, Roots, Swift, Wellard, Chris, I & B, Solomon & Peres Distribution

(TAIPO SAY) DRUM.
Single (7"): released on RCA, Jan'85 by RCA Records. Dist: RCA, Roots, Swift, Wellard, Chris, I & B, Solomon & Peres Distribution

Single (12"): released on RCA, Jan'85 by RCA Records. Dist: RCA, Roots, Swift, Wellard, Chris, I & B, Solomon & Peres Distribution

Easton, Sheena

DO IT FOR LOVE.
Single (7"): released on EMI, Nov'85 by EMI Records. Dist: EMI

Single (12"): released on EMI, Nov'85 by EMI Records. Dist: EMI

DO YOU.
Compact disc: by EMI Records. Dist: EMI

FOR YOUR EYES ONLY.
Single (7"): released on EMI, Jun'81 by EMI Records. Dist: EMI

IT'S CHRISTMAS ALL OVER THE WORLD.
Tracks: / It's christmas all over the world / Thank you santa.
Single (7"): released on EMI America, Nov'86 by EMI Records. Dist: EMI

LIVE AT THE PALACE, HOLLYWOOD.
Tracks: / Prisoner / Help is on its way / I wouldn't beg for water / Are you man enough / Fooled around and fell in love / When he shines / Modern girl / Madness, money and music / In the winter / Weekend in Paris / Morning train (9 to 5) / You could have been with me / Raised on robbery / Wind beneath my wings / For your eyes only.
Notes: Sheena in sensational form-and voice-captured live this year on a sixty minute video. All her big hit songs are here including '9 to 5', 'Modern girl', 'when heshines', 'you could have been with me' and 'For your eyes only'.The new single, 'Are you man enough?' and tracks from the new album 'madness, money and music' are performed along with songs from her successful tour. Fifteen tracks in all. Live recording in stereo. total playing time is 60 minutes.
Video-cassette (VHS): released on EMI, Nov'82 by EMI Records. Dist: EMI

Video-cassette [Betamax]: released on EMI, Nov'82 by EMI Records. Dist: EMI

MADNESS,MONEY & MUSIC.
Album: released on EMI, Sep'82 by EMI Records. Dist: EMI

Cassette: released on EMI, Sep'82 by EMI Records. Dist: EMI

MAGIC OF LOVE.
Tracks: / Magic of love / Money back guarantee.
Single (7"): released on EMI, Feb'86 by EMI Records. Dist: EMI

Single (12"): released on EMI, Feb'86 by EMI Records. Dist: EMI

MODERN GIRL.
Single (7"): released on EMI Golden 45's, Mar'84 by EMI Records. Dist: EMI

NO SOUND BUT A HEART.
Tracks: / Eternity / Still willing to try / Still in love / Wanna give my love / Last to know, The / No sound but a heart / What if we fall in love / No ordinary love / Floating hearts.
Compact disc: released on EMI, Jun'87 by EMI Records. Dist: EMI

Album: released on EMI, Jun'87 by EMI Records. Dist: EMI

Cassette: released on EMI, Jun'87 by EMI Records. Dist: EMI

PRIVATE HEAVEN, A.
Compact disc: by EMI Records. Dist: EMI

Album: released on EMI, Oct'84 by EMI Records. Dist: EMI

Cassette: released on EMI, Oct'84 by EMI Records. Dist: EMI

TAKE MY TIME.
Tracks: / Don't send flowers / Cry / Take my time / When he shines / One man woman / Prisoner / 9 to 5 / So much in love / Voice on the radio / Calm before the storm / Modern girl / No-one ever knows.
Notes: Original catalogue No. EMC 3354 (album); TCEMC 3354 (cassette).
Album: released on EMI, Feb'81 by EMI Records. Dist: EMI

Cassette: released on EMI, Feb'81 by EMI Records. Dist: EMI

WE'VE GOT TONIGHT (Easton, Sheena & Kenny Rogers).
Single (7"): released on United Artists, Jan'83

YOU COULD HAVE BEEN WITH ME.
Album: released on Music For Pleasure (Holland), Oct'84 by EMI Records. Dist: EMI

Cassette: released on Music For Pleasure (Holland), Oct'84 by EMI Records. Dist: EMI

Easton, Ted & His Friends

SALUTE TO SATCHMO.
Album: released on Circle(USA), Jun'86 by Jazzology Records (USA). Dist: Jazz Music, Swift, Chris Wellard

East Seventeen

GOOD OLD JUMBLE SALE.
Single (7"): released on Goldliner, May'83 Dist: Spartan, Stage One

Eastside

MEMORIES.
Tracks: / (No.2 The sequel).
Single (7"): released on Rime, Dec'86 Dist: DMS-RCA

Single (12"): released on Rime, Dec'86 Dist: DMS-RCA

East Side Band

WON'T YOU BE MINE.
Single (7"): released on Black Label (USA), May'81 by HSE Of America Records (USA).

East Side Stompers

ALGIERS STRUT 1985.
Album: released on VJM, Jul'86 by Wellard, Chris Distribution. Dist: Wellard, Chris Distribution

ORIGINAL EAST SIDE STOMPERS, THE.
Album: released on VJM, Apr'79 by VJM (UK) Records. Dist: Swift

East Side Torpedoes

COAST TO COAST.
Album: released on Valium, May'83 by Mawson & Wareham Records. Dist: Spartan

HIGHER AND HIGHER.
Single (7"): released on Volume, Sep'85 by Volume Records. Dist: Pinnacle

East Wall

APPEARING IN PERSONS.
Tracks: / Appearing in persons / Selfish heart (a hard time).
Single (7"): released on Regent, Apr'86 Dist: MIS-EMI Distribution

East-West Trading

EAST-WEST TRADING various artists.
Album: released on East-West Trading Company, Mar'84 by Cherry Red Records. Dist: Pinnacle

Eastwood, Clint

AFRICAN YOUTH.
Album: released on Third World, Jun'78 Dist: Jetstar Distribution

BEST OF CLINT EASTWOOD, THE.
Album: released on Culture Press, Sep'84 by Vista Sounds Records. Dist: Jetstar, Rough Trade

DEATH IN THE ARENA.
Album: released on Cha-Cha, Jul'78 by Cha Cha. Dist: Jetstar

JAH LIGHTS SHINING.
Album: released on Vista Sounds, Feb'84 by Vista Sounds Records. Dist: Jetstar

KOOL & DEAD (Eastwood, Clint & General Saint).
Tracks: / Kool & dead / Kool and dead (Inst).
Single (12"): released on Rhino, Jun'86 by Creole Records. Dist: PRT, Rhino

LOST PLANE(ONE WAY TICKET).
Single (7"): released on MCA, Sep'84 by MCA Records. Dist: Polygram, MCA

Single (12"): released on MCA, Sep'84 by MCA Records. Dist: Polygram, MCA

LOVE & HAPPINESS.
Album: released on Burning Sounds, Sep'79 by Ross, Bill/Burning Sounds Records. Dist: PRT

MAKE MY DAY (see Sheppard, T.G.) (Eastwood, Clint & T.G. Sheppard).

MATTY GUNGA WALK (Eastwood, Clint & General Saint).
Single (12"): released on Greensleeves, Jul'82 by Greensleeves Records. Dist: BMG, Jetstar, Spartan

ROCK WITH ME (Eastwood, Clint & General Saint).
Single (7"): released on Greensleeves, Sep'83 by Greensleeves Records. Dist: BMG, Jetstar, Spartan

Single (12"): released on Greensleeves, Sep'83 by Greensleeves Records. Dist: BMG, Jetstar, Spartan

SEX EDUCATION.
Album: released on Greensleeves, Feb'80 by Greensleeves Records. Dist: BMG, Jetstar, Spartan

SHAME & SCANDAL (Eastwood, Clint & General Saint).
Single (7"): released on Greensleeves, Sep'82 by Greensleeves Records. Dist: BMG, Jetstar, Spartan

Single (12"): released on Greensleeves, Sep'82 by Greensleeves Records. Dist: BMG, Jetstar, Spartan

STOP THAT TRAIN (Eastwood, Clint & General Saint).
Tracks: / Stop Jack / True vegetarian / Everything crash / Monkey man / H.A.P.P.Y. / Stop that train / Vote for me / Nuclear crisis / Rock with me / Shame and scandal.
Compact disc: released on Greensleeves, Feb'87 by Greensleeves Records. Dist: BMG, Jetstar, Spartan

Album: released on Greensleeves, Apr'83 by Greensleeves Records. Dist: BMG, Jetstar, Spartan

STOP THAT TRAIN(SINGLE) (Eastwood, Clint & General Saint).
Single (7"): released on Greensleeves, Apr'83 by Greensleeves Records. Dist: BMG, Jetstar, Spartan

Single (12"): released on Greensleeves, Apr'83 by Greensleeves Records. Dist: BMG, Jetstar, Spartan

TALK ABOUT RUN (Eastwood, Clint & General Saint).
Single (7"): released on Greensleeves, Dec'81 by Greensleeves Records. Dist: BMG, Jetstar, Spartan

Single (12"): released on Greensleeves, Dec'81 by Greensleeves Records. Dist: BMG, Jetstar, Spartan

TWO BAD DJ'S (Eastwood, Clint & General Saint).
Album: released on Greensleeves, Dec'81 by Greensleeves Records. Dist: BMG, Jetstar, Spartan

Easwaran, Eknath

MEDITATION.
Album: released on Arhoolie, May'81 by Arhoolie Records. Dist: Projection, Topic, Jazz Music, Swift, Roots

Easy Action

WE GO RACING.
Single (7"): released on Sire, Apr'84

Single (12"): released on Sire, Apr'84

Easybeats

BEST OF THE EASYBEATS, THE.
Album: released on Rhino (USA), Jan'86 by Rhino Records (USA).

FRIDAY ON MY MIND.
Tracks: / Hllo how are you / Friday on my mind.
Single (7"): released on Old Gold, Apr'87 by Old Gold Records. Dist: Lightning, Jazz Music, Spartan, Counterpoint

FRIDAY ON MY MIND (LP).
Album: released on Fan Club, Nov'85 by New Rose. Dist: Rough Trade, Cartel

Easy Club

EASY CLUB, THE.
Album: released on Abby Hill, Jul'85 Dist: Roots

SKIRLIE BEAT.
Album: released on R.E.L, May'87 by REL Records. Dist: Gordon Duncan Distribution, Celtic Music, Record Merchandisers Distribution, Projection, Graeme Tosh music

Easy Listening Beatles
EASY LISTENING BEATLES various artists (Various Artists).
Album: released on CBS Cameo, Aug'85 by CBS Records. Dist: CBS

Cassette: released on CBS Cameo, Aug'85 by CBS Records. Dist: CBS

Easy Rider
EASY RIDER Original Soundtrack (Various Artists).
Album: released on ABC, Feb'82 Dist: CBS, Pinnacle

Cassette: released on ABC, Feb'82 Dist: CBS, Pinnacle

Easy Riders Jazz Band
RED WING.
Notes: Mono.
Album: released on GHB, Jun'86 Dist: Jazz Music, Swift

Eat At Joe's
DON'T RUN AWAY.
Single (7"): released on Goldiner, Nov'81 by Spartan, Stage One

Eater
HISTORY OF EATER VOL.1.
Album: released on De Lauren, Feb'85 by Backs Records. Dist: Cartel

Eaton, Cleveland
BAMA BOOGIE WOOGIE.
Album: released on Miracle, Jan'79 by Gull Records. Dist: PRT Distribution

KEEP LOVE ALIVE.
Album: released on Miracle, Mar'80 by Gull Records. Dist: PRT Distribution

E.A.V.
BA-BA-BANK ROBBERY.
Tracks: / Ba-ba-bank robbery / Ba-ba-bank ubersall.
Single (7"): released on Columbia, Aug'86 by EMI Records. Dist: EMI

Eavesdropper
MARCH HARE, THE.
Album: released on Greenwich Village, Sep'84 by Sweet Folk All Records. Dist: Roots, Projection, Lightning, Celtic Music, Wellard, Chris

Eazle Ryder
MOTORBIKIN'.
Single (7"): by Graduate Records. Dist: Nine Mile, Cartel

Ebb,Nitzer
ISN'T IT FUNNY HOW YOUR BODY WORKS?.
Single (12"): released on Power Of Voice Communications, Jan'85 Dist: Backs, Cartel

Extended-play record: released on NEP, Jan'85

Ebeneezer
AFRICA SAYS THANK YOU.
Single (12"): released on Nadiya, Dec'85

EBN-OZN
A E I O U (SOMETIMES Y).
Single (7"): released on Arista, Sep'84 by Arista Records. Dist: RCA

Single (12"): released on Arista, Sep'84 by Arista Records. Dist: RCA

Ebony
EBONY (Solitaire collection) (Various original artists).
Double Album: released on Starblend, '83 by Starblend Records. Dist: PRT Distribution

Double cassette: released on Starblend, '83 by Starblend Records. Dist: PRT Distribution

Ebony Brothers
BRIGHTEN UP YOUR NIGHT.
Single (7"): released on RCA, Nov'83 by RCA Records. Dist: RCA, Roots, Swift, Wellard, Chris, I & B, Solomon & Peres Distribution

Ebony Eyes
DON'T CALL ME, I'LL CALL YOU.
Tracks: / Don't call me (I'll call you) / Don't call me (I'll call you) (dub).
Single (12"): released on Independent Soul Recordings, May'87 Dist: PRT

Ebony Quartet
FLYING HOME.
Notes: Telephone no. : 05086-4274.
Album: released on Merlin, Nov'85 by Merlin Distribution

Ebony Sisters
I MUST BE DREAMING.
Single (12"): released on Jama, Sep'85 by Jama Records.

Ebor Brass
CHINESE JUNK.
Single (7"): released on Superville, Jun'82 Dist: Pinnacle

Eccleton & Jarrett
GREEDY GIRL.
Single (7"): released on CF, Apr'84 by CF Records. Dist: Jetstar

Echo Base
BUY ME.
Album: released on DEP International, May'85 by DEP International Records. Dist: Virgin Records, EMI

Cassette: released on DEP International, May'85 by DEP International Records. Dist: Virgin Records, EMI Deleted May'86.

Echoes of The Duke
ECHOES OF THE DUKE (Various Artists).
Cassette: released on Calligraph, Jun'86 by Calligraph Records. Dist: PRT

Echo & The Bunnymen
BACK OF LOVE.
Single (7"): released on Korova, May'82 Dist: WEA

Single (12"): released on Korova, May'82 Dist: WEA

BRING ON THE DANCING HORSES.
Single (7"): released on Korova, Oct'85 Dist: WEA

Single (12"): released on Korova, Oct'85 Dist: WEA

CROCODILES.
Album: released on Korova, Jul'80 Dist: WEA

CUTTER, THE.
Single (7"): released on Korova, Jan'83 Dist: WEA

Single (12"): released on Korova, Jan'83 Dist: WEA

ECHO AND THE BUNNYMEN.
Tracks: / Game, The / Over you / Bedbugs and ballyhoo / All in your mind / Bombers bay / Lips like sugar / Lost and found / New direction / Bue blue ocean / Satellite / All my life.
Album: released on WEA, Jul'87 by WEA Records. Dist: WEA

Cassette: released on WEA, Jul'87 by WEA Records. Dist: WEA

Compact disc: released on WEA, Jul'87 by WEA Records. Dist: WEA

GAME, THE.
Tracks: / Game, The / Lost and found / Ship of fools*.
Single (7"): released on WEA, 30 May'87 by WEA Records. Dist: WEA

Single (12"): released on WEA, 30 May'87 by WEA Records. Dist: WEA

Album: released on Rola, Oct'81 by Rola Records. Dist: Roots Distribution, JSU Distribution, Spartan Distribution

HEAVEN UP HERE.
Album: released on Korova, May'81 Dist: WEA
Cat. no: KODE 3
Cassette: released on Korova, May'81 Dist: WEA

INTERVIEW PICTURE DISC.
Album: released on Baktabak, Jul'87 by Baktabak Records. Dist: Arabesque

KILLING MOON.
Single (7"): released on Korova, Jan'84 Dist: WEA

Single (12"): released on Korova, Jan'84 Dist: WEA

LIPS LIKE SUGAR.
Tracks: / Lips like sugar / Rollercoaster / People are strange*.
Single (7"): released on WEA, Jul'87 by WEA Records. Dist: WEA

Single (12"): released on WEA, Jul'87 by WEA Records. Dist: WEA

NEVER STOP.
Single (7"): released on Korova, Jul'83 Dist: WEA

Single (12"): released on Korova, Jul'83 Dist: WEA

OCEAN RAIN.
Compact disc: Dist: WEA

Album: released on Korova, Apr'84 Dist: WEA

Cassette: released on Korova, Apr'84 Dist: WEA

Compact disc: released on Korova, Apr'84 Dist: WEA

PORCUPINE.
Album: released on Korova, Jan'83 Dist: WEA

Cassette: released on Korova, Jan'83 Dist: WEA

PROMISE, A.
Single (7"): released on Korova, Jul'81 Dist: WEA

Single (12"): released on Korova, Jul'81 Dist: WEA

PUPPET.
Single (7"): released on Korova, Sep'80 Dist: WEA

RESCUE.
Single (7"): released on Korova, Apr'80 Dist: WEA

Single (12"): released on Korova, Apr'80 Dist: WEA

SEVEN SEAS.
Single (7"): released on Korova, Jun'84 Dist: WEA

Single (12"): released on Korova, Jun'84 Dist: WEA

SILVER.
Single (12"): released on Korova, May'84 Dist: WEA

SONGS TO LEARN AND SING The singles.
Tracks: / Rescue / Puppet, The / Do it clean / Promise, A / Back of love, The / Cutter, The / Never stop / Killing moon, The / Silver / Seven seas / Bring on the dancing horses.
Compact disc: released on Korova, Nov'85 Dist: WEA

Album: released on Korova, Nov'85 Dist: WEA

Cassette: released on Korova, Nov'85 Dist: WEA

Echo Valley Boys
WASH MACHINE BOOGIE.
Single (7"): released on Rollercoaster, Jul'79 by Rollercoaster Records. Dist: Swift Distribution, Rollercoaster Distribution

Eckstine, Billy
BACK TO BACK.
Double Album: released on Mercury, May'78 by Phonogram Records. Dist: Polygram Distribution

Cassette: released on Mercury, May'78 by Phonogram Records. Dist: Polygram Distribution

GOLDEN HOUR: BILLY ECKSTINE.
Album: released on Golden Hour, Oct'75 by PRT Records. Dist: PRT

GREATEST HITS:BILLY ECKSTINE.
Album: released on Polydor, Mar'84 by Polydor Records. Dist: Polygram, Polydor

Cassette: released on Polydor, Mar'84 by Polydor Records. Dist: Polygram, Polydor

I AM A SINGER.
Album: released on Kimbo, Nov'86 Dist: Jazz Music

Album: released on Kim, Mar'87

IRVING BERLIN SONGBOOK, (THE) (see Vaughan, Sarah) (Eckstine, Billy & Sarah Vaughan).

PASSING STRANGERS (see Vaughan, Sarah) (Eckstine, Billy & Sarah Vaughan).

SAVOY SESSIONS, THE (Eckstine, Billy/Mr B & The Band).
Double Album:

SOMETHING MORE.
Album: released on Stax, Oct'81 by Ace Records. Dist: Pinnacle, Chris Wellard, IMS-Poly-

gram

Cassette: released on Stax, Oct'81 by Ace Records. Dist: Pinnacle, Chris Wellard, IMS-Polygram

TOGETHER (Eckstine, Billy Big Band).
Album: released on Spotlite, May'83 by Spotlite Records. Dist: Cadillac, Jazz Music, Spotlite

Eclipse
MESSIAH.
Single (7"): released on Clubland, Oct'82 by Clubland Records. Dist: EMI, Pinnacle

MICHAEL ROW THE BOAT ASHORE.
Single (7"): released on Mellowdance, Jul'83

ECM Spectrum
ECM SPECTRUM VOL.1 (Various Artists).
Notes: Unique compilation available only on CD. 13 tracks presented in their entirety from 1974-1984. Over 67 minutes of music from Pat Metheny, Keith Jarrett, Oregan, John Surman, Charlie Haden, Terje Rypdal, Shankar, Egberto Gismonti, Nana Vascocelos, John Abercrombie, Don Cherry, Ed Blackwell.

Eddi
I DON'T WANT TO LOSE YOU.
Single (12"): released on PC, Mar'82 Dist: Jetstar

Eddie and the Cruisers
EDDIE AND THE CRUISERS Original Soundtrack.
Album: released on Scotti Bros, Jan'85

Cassette: released on Scotti Bros, Jan'85

Eddie and The Tide
GO OUT AND GET IT.
Album: released on Atco, Oct'85 by Atlantic Records. Dist: WEA

Eddie Condon
EDDIE CONDON-CHICAGO STYLE (Various Artists).
Notes: artists include: Chicago Rhythm Kings, Eddie's Hot Shots.
Album: released on VJM, Jan'86 by Wellard, Chris Distribution. Dist: Wellard, Chris Distribution

Eddie, John
JOHN EDDIE.
Tracks: / Dream house / Pretty little rebel / Hide out / Just some guy / Please Jodi / Cool walk / Jungle boy / Stranded / Waste me / Romance / Buster / Living doll.
Album: released on CBS, Sep'86 by CBS Records. Dist: CBS

Cassette: released on CBS, Sep'86 by CBS Records. Dist: CBS

JUNGLE BOY.
Tracks: / Jungle boy / Gay's ghost.
Single (7"): released on CBS, Jul'86 by CBS Records. Dist: CBS

Single (12"): released on CBS, Aug'86 by CBS Records. Dist: CBS

Eddie & Sugar Lou
EDDIE & SUGAR LOU'S HOTEL TYLER ORCHESTRA 1929-31 (Eddie & Sugar Lou's Hotel Tyler Orchestra).
Album: released on Everybody's, Jul'87 by Everybody's Records. Dist: Jazz Music, Swift

Eddie & Sunshine
ALL I SEE IS YOU.
Single (7"): released on Survival, Feb'83 by Survival Records. Dist: Backs, Cartel Distribution

Single (12"): released on Survival, Feb'83 by Survival Records. Dist: Backs, Cartel Distribution

PERFECT STRANGER.
Single (7"): released on Survival, Jun'83 by Survival Records. Dist: Backs, Cartel Distribution

Single (12"): released on Survival, Jun'83 by Survival Records. Dist: Backs, Cartel Distribution

PERFECT STRANGERS.
Album: released on Survival, May'83 by Survival Records. Dist: Backs, Cartel Distribution

THERE'S SOMEONE FOLLOWING ME.
Single (7"): released on Survival, Mar'83 by Survival Records. Dist: Backs, Cartel Distribution

Single (12"): released on Survival, Mar'83 by Survival Records. Dist: Backs, Cartel Distribution

Eddie & The Hot rods

FOUGHT FOR YOU.
Single (7"): released on Waterfront, Feb'85 by Waterfront Records. Dist: Rough Trade, Cartel, Projection, Roots

ONE STORY TOWN.
Album: released on Waterfront, Sep'85 by Waterfront Records. Dist: Rough Trade, Cartel, Projection, Roots

Eddy, Duane

BECAUSE THEY'RE YOUNG.
Single (7"): released on London, Jul'60 by London Records. Dist: Polygram

BEST OF DUANE EDDY, THE.
Album:

Album: released on Nouveau Music, Sep'84 Dist: PRT Distribution

Cassette: released on Nouveau Music, Sep'84 Dist: PRT Distribution

DANCE WITH THE GUITAR MAN.
Album: released on Arena, Feb'87 by Arena Records. Dist: Spartan

Cassette: released on Arena, Feb'87 by Arena Records. Dist: Spartan

DUANE EDDY.
Tracks: / Kickin' ashphalt / Rockestra theme / Theme for something really important / Spies / Blue city / Trembler,The / Los Campaneros / Lost innocence / Rockabilly holiday / Last look back.
Album: released on Capitol, Jun'87 by Capitol Records. Dist: EMI

Cassette: released on Capitol, Jun'87 by Capitol Records. Dist: EMI

DUANE EDDY COLLECTION, THE.
Album: released on RCA (Germany), May'83

DUANE EDDY COLLECTION.
Double Album: released on Pickwick, Aug'78 by Pickwick Records. Dist: Pickwick Distribution, Prism Leisure Distribution, Lugtons

Cassette: released on Pickwick, Jul'80 by Pickwick Records. Dist: Pickwick Distribution, Prism Leisure Distribution, Lugtons

FABULOUS DUANE EDDY, THE.
Album: released on Cambra, May'83 by Cambra Records. Dist: IDS, Conifer

Cassette: released on Cambra, May'83 by Cambra Records. Dist: IDS, Conifer

FOREVER.
Tracks: / Guitar man (Dance with the) / Peppermint twist, The / Raunchy / Moanin' 'n' twistin' / Wild Watusi / Summer place, A / Water skiing / Sugar foot rag / Twangsville / Let's twist again / Bali ha'i / He's so fine / Deep in the heart of Texas / Wake ballet, The / Boss guitar / Rumble / Scrape, The / Walk right in / Lonely boy, lonely guitar / New hully gully / Moon river / Guitar'd and feathered / Rebel rouser / Rebel rouser / Your baby's gone surfin' / Mr guitar man / Ballad of Paladin / Shindig / Secret love / Walkin' 'n' twistin' / Twist, The.
Notes: Double album
Album: released on RCA, Jul'86 by RCA Records. Dist: RCA, Roots, Swift, Wellard, Chris, I & B, Solomon & Peres Distribution

Cassette: released on RCA, Jul'86 by RCA Records. Dist: RCA, Roots, Swift, Wellard, Chris, I & B, Solomon & Peres Distribution

FORTY MILES OF BAD WORLD.
Single (7"): released on Creole, Aug'82 by Creole Records. Dist: Rhino, PRT

GUITAR MAN.
Tracks: / Guitar man (Dance with the) / Fireball mail / Lonely boy, lonely guitar / Your baby's gone surfin' / Wildwood flower / Boss guitar / Rebel rouser / Ballad of Paladin / Deep in the heart of Texas / Tequila / Stranger on the shore / Swingin' shepherd blues.
Notes: This compilation (P) 1986 & (C) RCA Records Ltd. issued under exclusive license to Music For Pleasure.
Album: released on MFP, Sep'86 by EMI Records. Dist: EMI

Cassette: released on MFP, Sep'86 by EMI Records. Dist: EMI

LEGEND OF ROCK.
Double Album: released on Deram, May'75 by Decca Records. Dist: Polygram

MOVIN' 'N' GROOVIN'.
Album: released on London, May'70 by London Records. Dist: Polygram

REBEL ROUSER.
Single (7"): released on Creole, Aug'82 by Creole Records. Dist: Rhino, PRT

REBEL ROUSIN'.
Album: released on Magnum Force, Nov'84 by Magnum Music Group Ltd. Dist: Magnum Music Group Ltd, PRT, Spartan

TWANGIN THE GOLDEN HITS.
Album: released on RCA (Germany), Aug'83

Cassette: released on RCA (Germany), Aug'83

TWENTY TERRIFIC TWANGIES.
Album: released on RCA, Oct'84 by RCA Records. Dist: RCA, Roots, Swift, Wellard, Chris, I & B, Solomon & Peres Distribution

Cassette: released on RCA, Oct'84 by RCA Records. Dist: RCA, Roots, Swift, Wellard, Chris, I & B, Solomon & Peres Distribution

Eddy Duchin Story

EDDY DUCHIN STORY Original sountrack.
Album: released on MCA Coral, Apr'82 by MCA Records. Dist: Polygram

Cassette: released on MCA Coral, Apr'82 by MCA Records. Dist: Polygram

Eddy, Nelson

20 GOLDEN HITS (Eddy, Nelson/Jeanette MacDonald).
Album: released on Nostalgia, Apr'85 Dist: Jazz Music, Counterpoint

Cassette: released on Nostalgia, Apr'85 Dist: Jazz Music, Counterpoint

20 GREATEST HITS (Eddy, Nelson/Jeanette MacDonald).

Jeanette MacDonald & Nelson Eddy

LEGENDARY (Eddy, Nelson/Jeanette MacDonald).
Album: released on RCA, Jul'78 by RCA Records. Dist: RCA, Roots, Swift, Wellard, Chris, I & B, Solomon & Peres Distribution

Cassette: released on RCA, Jul'78 by RCA Records. Dist: RCA, Roots, Swift, Wellard, Chris, I & B, Solomon & Peres Distribution

Edelhagen, Kurt

BIG BAND HITS.
Album: released on Polydor (Germany), Jun'82 Dist: IMS-Polygram

Cassette: released on Polydor (Germany), Jun'82 Dist: IMS-Polygram

KURT EDELHAGEN AND HIS ORCHESTRA.
Album: released on Golden Era, May'82 by Import Records. Dist: Wellard, Chris, Swift

PORTRAIT.
Double Album: released on Polydor (Germany), Jun'82 Dist: IMS-Polygram

SWINGTIME.
Album: released on Polydor (Germany), Oct'82 Dist: IMS-Polygram

Cassette: released on Polydor (Germany), Oct'82 Dist: IMS-Polygram

Edelman, Randy

BEST OF....(UPTOWN UPTEMPO).
Cassette: released on 20th Century, Feb'80 Dist: RCA, IMS-Polygram

CARE-A-LOT.
Single (7"): released on Cherry Lane, Oct'85 by Cherry Lane Productions. Dist: PRT

CARE BEARS TO THE RESCUE.
Album: released on Cherry Lane, Mar'85 by Cherry Lane Productions. Dist: PRT

Cassette: released on Cherry Lane, Mar'85 by Cherry Lane Productions. Dist: PRT

GROWING OLDER.
Single (7"): released on Elecstar, Aug'85 by Elecstar Records. Dist: PRT

NOBODY MADE ME.

Single (7"): released on Rocket, Jun'82 by Phonogram Records. Dist: Polygram Distribution

ON TIME.
Album: released on Rocket, Aug'82 by Phonogram Records. Dist: Polygram Distribution

Cassette: released on Rocket, Aug'82 by Phonogram Records. Dist: Polygram Distribution

PRETTY GIRLS.
Single (7"): released on Rocket, Nov'82 by Phonogram Records. Dist: Polygram Distribution

RANDY EDELMAN AND HIS PIANO.
Album: released on Elecstar, May'84 by Elecstar Records. Dist: PRT

Cassette: released on Elecstar, May'84 by Elecstar Records. Dist: PRT

SWITCH OF THE SEASONS.
Notes: Recorded at ABBA's studio in Sweden. Randy's latest songs add to his timeless hits such as 'Concrete and clay', Uptown uptempo woman and Weekend in New England. These tracks are included on this album.
Album: released on Elecstar, Dec'85 by Elecstar Records. Dist: PRT

SWITCH OF THE SEASON.
Album: released on Elecstar, Aug'85 by Elecstar Records. Dist: PRT

Cassette: released on Elecstar, Aug'85 by Elecstar Records. Dist: PRT

UPTOWN,UPTEMPO-THE BEST OF RANDY EDELMAN.
Cassette: released on 20th Century, Nov'79 Dist: RCA, IMS-Polygram

UPTOWN,UPTEMPO WOMAN.
Single (7"): released on Old Gold, Jan'85 by Old Gold Records. Dist: Lightning, Jazz Music, Spartan, Counterpoint

YOU'RE THE ONE.
Album: released on 20th Century, Apr'79 Dist: RCA, IMS-Polygram

Eden

FREE.
Single (7"): released on Polydor, Jun'85 by Polydor Records. Dist: Polygram, Polydor

Single (12"): released on Polydor, Jun'85 by Polydor Records. Dist: Polygram, Polydor

Edge

CAPTIVES Original soundtrack.
Album: released on Virgin, Sep'86 by Virgin Records. Dist: EMI, Virgin Distribution

Cassette: released on Virgin, Sep'86 by Virgin Records. Dist: EMI, Virgin Distribution

EDGE, THE.
Notes: Features John Moss of Culture Club and Heartbeat UK. Produced by Liam Sternbergof Bangles fame.
Album: released on Preset, Aug'87 Dist: Pinnacle

HEROINE.
Tracks: / Heroine / Heroine(Inst).
Single (7"): released on Virgin, Sep'86 by Virgin Records. Dist: EMI, Virgin Distribution

Single (12"): released on Virgin, Sep'86 by Virgin Records. Dist: EMI, Virgin Distribution

LITTLE GIRL BLUE.
Single (7"): released on Volume, Mar'86 by Volume Records. Dist: Pinnacle

Single (12"): released on Volume, Mar'86 by Volume Records. Dist: Pinnacle

SNAKE CHARMER (Edge/Jah Wobble/Holger Czukay).
Album: released on Island, Oct'83 by Island Records. Dist: Polygram

Cassette: released on Island, Oct'83 by Island Records. Dist: Polygram

TAKE A WALK.
Single (7"): released on Volume, Sep'85 by Volume Records. Dist: Pinnacle

UNEASY PEACE.
Album: released on Chiltern Sound, Apr'79 by Chiltern Sound Records. Dist: JSU, Lightning, Pinnacle

Edge Brothers

COCONUT GIRL.
Single (7"): released on Code, Aug'83 by Code Records. Dist: Jetstar, EMI

Single (12"): released on Code, Aug'83 by Code Records. Dist: Jetstar, EMI

VIDEO.
Single (7"): released on Edge, Nov'82 Dist: WEA

Edge, Damon

ALLIANCE.
Album: released on New Rose, Mar'85 Dist: Rough Trade, Cartel

GRAND VISIONS.
Album: released on New Rose, Jun'86 Dist: Rough Trade, Cartel

WIND IS TALKING, (THE).
Album: released on New Rose, Jun'85 Dist: Rough Trade, Cartel

Edge, Dave

NEW WORLD.
Single (7"): released on Clay, Nov'81 by Clay Records. Dist: Pinnacle

Edgerton, Andy

COUNTRY WORLD OF...,(THE).
Cassette: released on Viking, Apr'80 Dist: Harmonia Mundi Distributors

Edifanko

EDIFANKO-THE PACESETTERS (Edifanko African Super Band).
Album: released on Editions EG, Sep'81 by Virgin Records. Dist: EMI

Edinburgh...

6DINBURGH MILITARY TATTOO 1977
Various artists (Various Artists).
Album: released on Waverley, Sep'77 by EMI Records. Dist: EMI

EDINBURGH FESTIVAL FRINGE 1976
Various artists (Various Artists).
Album: released on Sweet Folk and Country, Dec'77 Dist: Chris Wellard Distribution

Album: released on Waverley, Sep'76 by EMI Records. Dist: EMI

EDINBURGH MILITARY TATTOO 1978
Various bands (Various bands).
Album: released on Waverley, Aug'78 by EMI Records. Dist: EMI

EDINBURGH MILITARY TATTOO - 1982
(Various bands).
Album: released on Ross, Dec'86 by Ross Records. Dist: Ross Distribution, Roots Distribution

Cassette: released on Ross, Dec'86 by Ross Records. Dist: Ross Distribution, Roots Distribution

EDINBURGH MILITARY TATTOO 1975
Various artists (Various Artists).
Album: released on Waverley, Sep'75 by EMI Records. Dist: EMI

EDINBURGH MILITARY TATTOO 1976
Various artists (Various Artists).

EDINBURGH MILITARY TATTOO 1953
(Various bands).
Album: released on Ross, Dec'86 by Ross Records. Dist: Ross Distribution, Roots Distribution

Cassette: released on Ross, Dec'86 by Ross Records. Dist: Ross Distribution, Roots Distribution

Album: released on Ross, Oct'83 by Ross Records. Dist: Ross Distribution, Roots Distribution

EDINBURGH MILITARY TATTOO 1979
Various bands (Various bands).
Album: released on Waverley, Aug'79 by EMI Records. Dist: EMI

Cassette: released on Waverley, Aug'79 by EMI Records. Dist: EMI

EDINBURGH MILITARY TATTOO 1980
Various Bands (Various bands).
Cassette: released on Glen, Aug'80 Dist: EMI, Outlet

Edinburgh Choristers

TELL US 13th Commonwealth games.
Tracks: / Tell us / Tell us (Inst).
Single (7"): released on PRT, Jul'86 by PRT Records. Dist: PRT

Edinburgh, Eddie

EDDIE EDINBURGH & HIS NEW ORLEANS WILD CATS.
Album: released on VJM, Apr'79 by Wellard, Chris Distribution. Dist: Wellard, Chris Distribution

Edison, Harry

BEST OF HARRY EDISON, THE.
Tracks: / Edison's lights / Ain't misbehavin' / Avalon / "E" / Miz Kitty's blues / Feelings / My ideal / Simply sweets / Edison's lights / Ain't misbehavin' / Avalon / "E" / Miz Kitty's blues / Feelings / My ideal / Simply sweets.
Album: released on Pablo (USA), '82 by Pablo Records (USA). Dist: Wellard, Chris, IMS-Polygram, BMG

Cassette: released on Pablo (USA), '82 by Pablo Records (USA). Dist: Wellard, Chris, IMS-Polygram, BMG

BLUES FOR BASIE.
Tracks: / Blues for Piney Brown / Blues for the blues / Blues for Bill Basie / Gee, baby ain't I good to you / You're getting to be a habit with me / Taste on the place / Moonlight in Vermont.
Album: released on Verve, Jun'77 by Phonogram Records. Dist: Polygram

EDISON'S LIGHTS.
Tracks: / Edison's lights / Ain't misbehavin' / Avalon / E / Helena's theme / Homegrown / Spring is here / On the trail.
Album: released on Pablo, '82 by Pablo Records. Dist: Wellard, Chris, IMS-Polygram, BMG

Cassette: released on Pablo, '82 by Pablo Records. Dist: Wellard, Chris, IMS-Polygram, BMG

JAZZ AT THE PHILHARMONIC 1983 (Edison, Harry/Eddie "Lockjaw" Davis/Al Grey).
Album: released on Pablo, May'83 by Pablo Records. Dist: Wellard, Chris, IMS-Polygram, BMG

Cassette: released on Pablo, May'83 by Pablo Records. Dist: Wellard, Chris, IMS-Polygram, BMG

JUST FRIENDS (Edison, Harry Sweets and John Haley Sims).
Album: released on Pablo (USA), '82 by Pablo Records (USA). Dist: Wellard, Chris, IMS-Polygram, BMG

Cassette: released on Pablo (USA), '82 by Pablo Records (USA). Dist: Wellard, Chris, IMS-Polygram, BMG

OSCAR PETERSON AND HARRY EDISON (Edison, Harry and Oscar Peterson).
Notes: For full details see under Peterson, Oscar.
Album: released on Pablo (USA), '82 by Pablo Records (USA). Dist: Wellard, Chris, IMS-Polygram, BMG

Cassette: released on Pablo (USA), '82 by Pablo Records (USA). Dist: Wellard, Chris, IMS-Polygram, BMG

Album: by Pablo Records (USA). Dist: Wellard, Chris, IMS-Polygram, BMG

Cassette: by Pablo Records (USA). Dist: Wellard, Chris, IMS-Polygram, BMG

SIMPLY SWEETS (Edison, Harry Sweets & Eddie 'Lockjaw' Davis).
Tracks: / Dirty butt blues / Feelings / One for the Count / My ideal / Simply sweets / Opus funk / Lax / Miz Kitty's blues / Dirty butt blues / Feelings / One for the Count / My ideal / Simply sweets / Opus funk / Lax.
Album: released on Pablo (USA), '82 by Pablo Records (USA). Dist: Wellard, Chris, IMS-Polygram, BMG

Cassette: released on Pablo (USA), '82 by Pablo Records (USA). Dist: Wellard, Chris, IMS-Polygram, BMG

SWEET TRACKS (Edison, Harry & Jimmy Forrest).
Tracks: / Pussy Willow / Centerpiece / Indiana / If I had you / Jive at five / Imagination / Louisiana / Candy / Harriet / Sweetnings / Paradise / I happened in Monerey / Angel eyes / Sweet cakes / It's easy to remember (so hard to forget) / Twenty-forty / There is no greater love / Tea for two / They can't take that away from me / Candid sweets / Ain't misbehavin' / I'm confessin' that I love you / Blue skies / Witchcraft.
Album: released on Vogue, Jul'78 Dist: Discovery, Jazz Music, PRT, Swift

SWINGER, THE.
Tracks: / Pussy Willow / Nasty / Thought of you, The / Stroller, The / Sunday / Fairground / Pussy Willow / Nasty / The thought of you / Stroller, The / Sunday / Fairground.
Notes: Recorded 1958 with Jimmy Forrest/Jimmy Jones/Freddie Green/Joe Benjamin.
Album: released on Verve, May'82 by Phonogram Records. Dist: Polygram

Edison, Harry Sweets

OPUS FUNK VOL. 2.
Album: released on Storyville, May'86 by Storyville Records. Dist: Jazz Music Distribution, Swift Distribution, Chris Wellard Distribution, Counterpoint Distribution

SONNY, SWEETS & JAWS (Edison, Harry/Eddie "Lockjaw" Davis/Sonny Stitt).

Edison Lighthouse

ENDEARING YOUNG CHARMS.
Single (7"): released on Greenstone, Jun'81 by Greenstone Records. Dist: Pinnacle

LOVE GROWS.
Tracks: / It's gonna be a lonely.
Single (7"): released on Old Gold, Apr'83 by Old Gold Records. Dist: Lightning, Jazz Music, Spartan, Counterpoint

Edith et Marcel

EDITH ET MARCEL Original motion picture soundtrack (Various Artists).
Tracks: / Avante toi / Le fanion de la legion / La Marseillaise / Qu'est ce qu'on attend / Pour etre heureux / Insensiblement / C'set un gars / La priere / Viens au creux de mon epaule / Avant toi (Versailles) / La chant d'amour / Bal dans la rue / Le diable de la bastille / Margot coeur gros / Comme moi / C'est Merveilleux (du film) "Etoile sans lumiere" / La fould / L'homme que j'aimerai / Je n'attendais que toi / La mer / Le club des cinq / La Marseillaise / La mort de Cerdan / Combat de boxe / Avec toi / La vie en rose (in English) / Un homme comme les autres / C'est un gars / L'effet qu'tu m'fais / C'est peut etre ca / Je t'ai dans la peau (du film "Boum sur Paris") / Medley d'Edith et Marcel.
Notes: "Edith et Marcel"-A major new film about the life of Edith Piaf. Edith Piaf recordings and new music specially written by Francis Lai and performed by Charles Aznavour who also stars in the film. "Edith et Marcel" has been made by the world famous French director Claude Lelouch.
Album: released on EMI, May'83 by EMI Records. Dist: EMI

Cassette: released on EMI, May'83 by EMI Records. Dist: EMI

Editors

THOUGHT POLICE.
Single (7"): released on Devil, May'81 by Devil Records. Dist: Spartan

Edit Point

BRIGHT SIDE.
Single (7"): released on PVK, Jul'81

Single (12"): released on PVK, Jul'81

Edmed, John

CRO 55Q.
Single (12"): released on Illuminated, Apr'86 by IKF Records. Dist: Pinnacle, Cartel, Jetstar

Edmonds, John

NON STOP NURSERY RHYMES.
Album: released on Cherry Lane, Mar'84 by Cherry Lane Productions. Dist: PRT

Cassette: released on Cherry Lane, Mar'84 by Cherry Lane Productions. Dist: PRT

Edmonds, Noel

CROQUE MONSIEUR (Edmonds, Noel radio orchestra).
Single (7"): released on BBC, Dec'81 by BBC Records & Tapes. Dist: EMI, PRT,

NOEL'S FUNNY PHONE CALLS VOL.2.
Tracks: / Ceiling, The / Washing machine, The / Impressionist, The / Lady rowers / Molecatcher / Registration plates / Cosmetic surgery / Shocking telephone, The / Crutches / Netball knickers / Mrs.Cockshot / DIY traffic lights / Siamese cat meeting, The.
Album: released on BBC, Oct'82 by BBC Records & Tapes. Dist: EMI, PRT,

Cassette: released on BBC, Oct'82 by BBC Records & Tapes. Dist: EMI, PRT,

NOEL'S FUNNY PHONE CALLS VOL.3.
Tracks: / Streaker / Nude choir, The / Polish cooker / Arab and the oranges, The / Water hoarding / Lost teeth / Vocalist required for "pelvic thrust" / Flying nuns, The / Bubble car / Thai beatle, The / R.A.F. pass / Pigeon fancier, The / Malcolm the puffin / Birth film, The.
Album: released on BBC, Oct'83 by BBC Records & Tapes. Dist: EMI, PRT,

Cassette: released on BBC, Oct'83 by BBC Records & Tapes. Dist: EMI, PRT,

NOEL'S FUNNY PHONE CALLS.
Tracks: / Telephone engineer, The / Telephone consumer service / Mickey mouse phone / Spanish holiday, The / Pony trekking in Wales / New driving test with 'extra', The / Emergency stop, The / Wrong highway code, The / American parking ticket / Going into hospital / Playing cricket in prison / Booking a band to play in the nude / Laundrette, The / Unusual gift, The / Robin cousins fit it / Haggis shooting.
Album: released on BBC, Nov'81 by BBC Records & Tapes. Dist: EMI, PRT,

Cassette: released on BBC, Nov'81 by BBC Records & Tapes. Dist: EMI, PRT

Edmunds, Dave

BABY I LOVE YOU.
Single (7"): released on RCA, May'82 by RCA Records. Dist: RCA, Roots, Swift, Wellard, Chris, I & B, Solomon & Peres Distribution

BEST OF DAVE EDMUNDS.
Tracks: / Deborah / Girls talk / I knew the bride / A1 on the jukebox / Race is on, The / I hear you knocking / Almost saturday night / Sabre dance / Queen of hearts / Crawling from the wreckage / Here comes the weekend / Trouble boys / Ju ju man / Singing the blues / Born to be with you.
Album: released on Swansong, Nov'81

Cassette: released on Swansong, Nov'81

CLASSIC TRACKS 1968/1972 Love sculpure.
Tracks: / I hear you knocking / You can't catch me / In the land of the few / Farandole (from L'Arlesienne) / Summertime (from "Porgy and Bess") / Blues helping / Stumble, The / Down down down / Seagull / Sabre dance / Outlaw blues / Promised land, The.
Album: released on EMI, Sep'74 by EMI Records. Dist: EMI

CLASSIC TRACKS (1968-72).
Album: released on Fame, Mar'86 by Music For Pleasure Records. Dist: EMI

Cassette: released on Fame, Mar'86 by Music For Pleasure Records. Dist: EMI

D.E.7..
Tracks: / From small things, big things come / Me and the boys / Bail you out / Generation rumber / Other guy's girls / Warmed over kisses (left over love) / Deep in the heart of Texas / Louisiana man / Paula meet Jeanne / Oe more night / Dear dad.
Album: released on Fame (Arista), Mar'84 by Music For Pleasure Records. Dist: EMI

Cassette: released on Fame (Arista), Mar'84 by Music For Pleasure Records. Dist: EMI

EARLY WORKS 1968/72.
Tracks: / Sabre dance / Think of love / River to another day / Brand new woman / Farandole / You can't catch me / In the land of the few / Stumble / Wang-dang-doodle / I believe to my soul / So unkind / On the road again / Shake your hips / Blues helping / Down down down / I hear you knocking / Hell of pain / It ain't easy / Promised land, The / Black Bill / I'm coming home / Country roll / Dance dance dance / Lover not a fighter / Egg or the hen / Sweet little rock and roller / Outlaw blues / Blue Monday / I'll get along.
Album: released on EMI (France), '83 by EMI Records. Dist: Conifer

HIGH SCHOOL NIGHTS.
Tracks: / Porky's revenge.
Single (7"): released on CBS, Jul'85 by CBS Records. Dist: CBS

I HEAR YOU KNOCKING.
Tracks: / I hear you knocking / She's about a mover / Sabre dance (love sculpture).
Notes: Double 'A' side
Single (7"): released on Old Gold, Apr'87 by Old Gold Records. Dist: Lightning, Jazz Music, Spartan, Counterpoint

Single (7"): released on EMI Golden 45's, Mar'84 by EMI Records. Dist: EMI

I HEAR YOU ROCKIN'.
Compact disc: released on Arista, Apr'87 by Arista Records. Dist: RCA

LIVE.
Compact disc: released on Arista, Jun'87 by Arista Records. Dist: RCA

Album: released on Arista, Jun'87 by Arista Records. Dist: RCA

Cassette: released on Arista, Jun'87 by Arista Records. Dist: RCA

ORIGINAL ROCKPILE, THE Volume II.
Tracks: / I hear you knocking / Down down down / Hell of a pain / It ain't easy / Country roll / Dance dance dance / Lover not a fighter / Egg or the hen / Sweet little rock and roller / Outlaw blues / Blue Monday / Black Bill / I'll get along / Promised land, The / I'm comin' home / Sabre dance.
Album: released on Harvest, Aug'87 by EMI Records. Dist: Roots, EMI

Cassette: released on Harvest, Aug'87 by EMI Records. Dist: Roots, EMI

ROCKPILE.
Album: released on EMI (France), Apr'83 by EMI Records. Dist: Conifer

SINGLES A'S & B'S (Edmunds, Dave & Love Sculpture).
Cassette: released on Harvest, Aug'80 by EMI Records. Dist: Roots, EMI

Album: released on Harvest, Aug'80 by EMI Records. Dist: Roots, EMI

SLIPPING AWAY.
Single (7"): released on Arista, Mar'83 by Arista Records. Dist: RCA

Single (12"): released on Arista, Mar'83 by Arista Records. Dist: RCA

SOMETHING ABOUT YOU.
Single (7"): released on Arista, Jul'84 by Arista Records. Dist: RCA

Single (12"): released on Arista, Jul'84 by Arista Records. Dist: RCA

SUBTLE AS A FLYING MALLET.
Album: released on RCA International (USA), Sep'81 by RCA Records. Dist: RCA

Cassette: released on RCA International (USA), Sep'81 by RCA Records. Dist: RCA

VOLUME 2-THE ORIGINAL ROCKPILE.
Album: released on Harvest, Aug'87 by EMI Records. Dist: Roots, EMI

Cassette: released on Harvest, Aug'87 by EMI Records. Dist: Roots, EMI

Edward II

EDWARD II Christopher Marlowe (Various Artists).
Double cassette: released on Argo (Spokenword), Oct'83 by Decca Records. Dist: Polygram

Edward, John

BLUE RIDGE (Edward, John & The Seldom Scene).
Album: released on Sugarhill (USA), May'86 by PRT Records. Dist: PRT Distribution

Cassette: released on Sugarhill (USA), May'86 by PRT Records. Dist: PRT Distribution

Edwards, Alf Concertina

FIRST PERSON.
Album: released on Topic, '81 Dist: Roots Distribution

Edwards, Alton

TAKE ME.
Single (7"): released on CBS, Feb'83 by CBS Records. Dist: CBS

Single (12"): released on CBS, Feb'83 by CBS Records. Dist: CBS

Edward, Sandra

ENDLESSLY.
Single (12"): released on Sir George, Nov'84 by Sir George Records. Dist: Jetstar, Pinnacle

Edwards, Charles

GOOD ROCKIN' CHARLES.
Album: released on Mr Blues, Apr'79 Dist: Swift Distribution

Edwards, Cliff

CLIFF EDWARDS & HIS HOT COMBINATION (Edwards, Cliff & His Hot Combination).
Album: released on Fountain, Oct'79 by Retrieval Records. Dist: Jazz Music, Swift, VJM, Wellard, Chris, Retrieval

HOTTEST MAN IN TOWN, THE.
Album: released on Living Era, Dec'81 by ASV. Dist: PRT

Cassette: released on Living Era, Dec'81 by ASV. Dist: PRT

I WANT A GIRL (Edwards, Cliff (Ukelele Ike)).
Album: released on Totem, May'78 Dist: Jazz Music, Projection, Swift

Edwards, Devon

LAY DOWN FLAT.
Single (12"): released on CF, Oct'84 by CF Records. Dist: Jetstar

Edwards, Eddie

EDDIE EDWARDS ORIGINAL DIXELAND JAZZ BAND.
Notes: With Tony Sbarbaro
Album: released on Commodore Classics, '87 by Teldec Records (Germany). Dist: Conifer, IMS, Polygram

Edwards, Idlater

LOVING SWEET DEVOTION.
Single (12"): released on Pressure, Nov'85 Dist: Priority

Edwards, Jackie

BABY COME BACK TO ME (Edwards, Jackie & Doreen).
Single (12"): released on Shuttle, Apr'83 Dist: RCA

BEFORE THE NEXT TEARDROP.
Album: released on Third World, Dec'77 Dist: Jetstar Distribution

BEFORE THE NEXT TEARDROP FALLS.
Single (12"): released on Tim, Aug'84 Dist: Backs, Cartel Distribution

CARRY ON HENRY.
Single (12"): released on Starlight, Jul'82 by Starlight Records. Dist: Jetstar Distribution

Music, Projection, Swift

Edwards, David

DAVID EDWARDS.
Album: released on Myrrh, May'82 by Word Records. Dist: Word Distribution

Cassette: released on Myrrh, May'82 by Word Records. Dist: Word Distribution

Edwards, Dennis

COOLIN' OUT.
Album: released on Gordy (USA), Aug'85 by Motown Records. Dist: RCA

Cassette: released on Gordy (USA), Aug'85 by Motown Records. Dist: RCA

DON'T LOOK ANY FURTHER.
Tracks: / Don't look any further / I thought I could handle it.

Single (7"): released on Motown, Jun'87 by
Motown Records. Dist: BMG Distribution

Single (12"): released on Motown, Jun'87 by
Motown Records. Dist: BMG Distribution

DON'T LOOK ANY FURTHER (LP).
Album: released on Gordy (USA), Apr'84 by
Motown Records. Dist: RCA

Cassette: released on Gordy (USA), Apr'84 by
Motown Records. Dist: RCA

YOU'RE MY APHRODISIAC.
Single (7"): released on Gordy (USA), May'84
by Motown Records. Dist: RCA

Single (12"): released on Gordy (USA), May'84
by Motown Records. Dist: RCA

Edwards, Devon
LAY DOWN FLAT.
Single (12"): released on CF, Oct'84 by CF
Records. Dist: Jetstar

Edwards, Eddie
EDDIE EDWARDS ORIGINAL DIXE-
LAND JAZZ BAND.
Notes: With Tony Sbarbaro.
Album: released on Commodore Classics, '87
by Teldec Records (Germany). Dist: Conifer,
IMS, Polygram

Edwards, Idiater
LOVING SWEET DEVOTION.
Single (12"): released on Pressure, Nov'85
Dist: Priority

Edwards, Jackie
BABY COME BACK TO ME (Edwards,
Jackie & Doreen).
Single (12"): released on Shuttle, Apr'83 Dist:
RCA

BEFORE THE NEXT TEARDROP.
Album: released on Third World, Dec'77 Dist:
Jetstar Distribution

BEFORE THE NEXT TEARDROP
FALLS.
Single (12"): released on Tim, Aug'84 Dist:
Backs, Cartel Distribution

CARRY ON HENRY.
Single (12"): released on Starlight, Jul'82 Dist:
Jetstar Distribution

COME TO ME SOFTLY.
Album: released on Third World, Feb'79 Dist:
Jetstar Distribution

LET'S FALL IN LOVE.
Album: released on Third World, Sep'78 Dist:
Jetstar Distribution

ORIGINAL MR.COOL RULER, THE.
Album: released on Vista Sounds, '83 by Vista
Sounds Records. Dist: Jetstar

PEEPING JUKEBOX.
Single (12"): released on Time, Jan'85 Dist:
Jetstar Distribution

Edwards, Jayne
HARMONY.
Single (7"): released on RCA, Oct'83 by RCA
Records. Dist: RCA, Roots, Swift, Wellard,
Chris, I & B, Solomon & Peres Distribution

Single (12"): released on RCA, Oct'83 by RCA
Records. Dist: RCA, Roots, Swift, Wellard,
Chris, I & B, Solomon & Peres Distribution

IT SHOULD HAVE BEEN ME.
Single (7"): released on Profile, Jun'84 by
Profile Records (USA).

Single (12"): released on Profile, Jun'84 by
Profile Records (USA).

Edwards, Jonathan
SING ALONG WITH... (Edwards, Jonathan
& Darlene).
Album: released on RCA International, May'82

Cassette: released on RCA International,
May'82

Edwards, Rupie
HIT PICK VOL.1.
Album: released on Success, Mar'84 Dist:
Counterpoint Distribution

IRE FEELINGS.
Album: released on Cactus, Apr'75 by Creole
Records. Dist: CBS

YOU LEFT ME IN TEARS.
Single (12"): released on Success, Mar'85
Dist: Counterpoint Distribution

Edwards, Sandra
GIVE ME SOME EMOTION.
Tracks: / Give me some emotion / I love you.
Single (12"): released on Soultown, Jul'86 Dist:

Pinnacle

Edwards, Sharon
ON & OFF.
Single (12"): released on Sir George, Apr'84 by
Sir George Records. Dist: Jetstar, Pinnacle

Edwards, Steve
ROCK WITH ME.
Tracks: / Rock with me / Club.
Single (7"): released on Do-It, Oct'86 by Do-It
Records. Dist: Virgin, EMI

Edwards, Teddy
GOOD GRAVY (Edwards, Teddy Quartet).
Album: released on Timeless (Holland), Apr'84
Dist: JSU Distribution, Jazz Music Distribution,
Jazz Horizons Distribution, Cadillac, Celtic
Music Distribution

OUT OF THIS WORLD (Edwards, Teddy
Quartet).
Album: released on Steeplechase(USA),
Jun'81

TEDDY'S READY!
Album: released on Contemporary, Sep'81 by
Contemporary Records. Dist: Pinnacle

Album: released on Boplicity, Jun'85 by Boplicity Records. Dist: Ace Records. Pinnacle

WISE IN TIME (Edwards, Teddy & Howard
McGhee).
Notes: For full information see under: McGhee,
Howard/Teddy Edwards.

Edwards, Terry
MARTY ROBBIN'S SONGBOOK.
Cassette: released on AIM (Budget Cassettes), Sep'83

SLIM WHITMAN SONGBOOK(VOL.2),
THE.
Cassette: released on AIM (Budget Casset-
tes), Sep'83

Edwards, Tibby
TIBBY EDWARDS.
Album: released on Bear Family, Jun'85 by
Bear Family Records. Dist: Rollercoaster Dis-
tribution, Swift

Edwards, Tommy
IT'S ALL IN THE GAME.
Single (12"): released on Old Gold, Jul'84 by Old
Gold Records. Dist: Lightning, Jazz Music,
Spartan, Counterpoint

Edwards, Vince
WHERE DOES THE LOVE GO?.
Single (7"): released on Free The Spirit, Aug'85
Dist: PRT

Single (12"): released on Free The Spirit,
Aug'85 Dist: PRT

Edward's Voice
FALLING FROM ANOTHER HIGH
BUILDING.
Single (7"): released on Edward's Voice,
Oct'82 by Edward's Voice Records. Dist: Red
Rhino

Eek-A-Mouse
ANAREXOL.
Album: released on Greensleeves,
Sep'83 by Greensleeves Records. Dist: BMG,
Jetstar, Spartan

ASSASSINATOR.
Album: released on Ras, Mar'84 by Real Auth-
entic Sound. Dist: Greensleeves Records,
RCA, Jetstar

Album: released on Greensleeves, Aug'8b by
Greensleeves Records. Dist: BMG, Jetstar,
Spartan

CHRISTMAS A COME.
Single (12"): released on Greensleeves,
Dec'81 by Greensleeves Records. Dist: BMG,
Jetstar, Spartan

DEE-DI-DOO.
Tracks: / Dee-di-doo / Dee-di-do (dub mix).
Single (7"): released on Original Sounds,
May'87 Dist: Jetstar Distribution

DO YOU REMEMBER.
Single (12"): released on Greensleeves,
May'82 by Greensleeves Records. Dist: BMG,
Jetstar, Spartan

GEORGIE PORGIE.
Single (12"): released on Echo, Feb'82 by Vista
Sounds. Dist: Jazz Music

I WANT TO KNOW.
Single (12"): released on D-Music, Nov'83 by
D-Music Records. Dist: Jetstar

KING AND I.
Album: released on Original Sounds, May'87
Dist: Jetstar Distribution

Album: released on RAS, Mar'87

MICHIGAN & SMILEY LIVE AT REGGAE
SUNSPLASH.
Album: released on Sunsplash, Mar'84 by Sun-
splash Records. Dist: Jetstar Distribution

MICHIGAN & SMILEY LIVE FROM REG-
GAE SUNSPLASH.
Album: released on Vista Sounds, May'84 by
Vista Sounds Records. Dist: Jetstar

MODEL SHE A MODEL.
Single (7"): released on Creole, Apr'85 by Creole Records. Dist: Rhino, PRT

Single (12"): released on Creole, Apr'85 by
Creole Records. Dist: Rhino, PRT

MOUSE AND THE MAN, (THE).
Album: released on Greensleeves, May'83 by
Greensleeves Records. Dist: BMG, Jetstar,
Spartan

MOUSEKETEER.
Album: released on Greensleeves, Mar'84 by
Greensleeves Records. Dist: BMG, Jetstar,
Spartan

SKIDIP.
Album: released on Greensleeves, Jul'82 by
Greensleeves Records. Dist: BMG, Jetstar,
Spartan

TERRORISTS IN THE CITY.
Single (12"): released on Greensleeves,
Apr'83 by Greensleeves Records. Dist: BMG,
Jetstar, Spartan

VERY BEST OF EEK-A-MOUSE, THE.
Compact disc: released on Greensleeves,
Aug'87 by Greensleeves Records. Dist: BMG,
Jetstar, Spartan

Album: released on Greensleeves, Aug'87 by
Greensleeves Records. Dist: BMG, Jetstar,
Spartan

Cassette: released on Greensleeves, Aug'87
by Greensleeves Records. Dist: BMG, Jetstar,
Spartan

VIRGIN GIRL.
Single (7"): released on Joe Gibbs, Feb'82 by
Joe Gibbs Records. Dist: Jetstar

Single (12"): released on Joe Gibbs, Feb'82 by
Joe Gibbs Records. Dist: Jetstar

WA-DO-DEM.
Single (7"): released on Greensleeves, Sep'83
by Greensleeves Records. Dist: BMG, Jetstar,
Spartan

WA DO DEM.
Compact disc: released on Greensleeves,
May'87 by Greensleeves Records. Dist: BMG,
Jetstar, Spartan

WILD LIKE A TIGER.
Single (12"): released on Greensleeves,
Nov'82 by Greensleeves Records. Dist: BMG,
Jetstar, Spartan

Eezi Eezi
SAYO SAYO.
Single (12"): released on Shaka Productions,
Nov'83 Dist: Pinnacle

E.F. Band
DEEP CUT.
Album: released on Bullet, Oct'83 Dist: Bullet
Distribution

DEVIL'S EYE, (THE).
Single (7"): released on Red Ball, Oct'80 Dist:
Red Rhino, Bullet Distribution, Rough Trade,
JSU

LAST LAUGH IS ON YOU.
Album: released on Mercury, Aug'81 by Phonogram Records. Dist: Polygram Distribution

NIGHT ANGEL.
Single (7"): released on E.F. Band, Apr'80 Dist:
Pinnacle

SELF MADE SUICIDE.
Single (7"): released on Red Ball, Feb'80 Dist:
Red Rhino, Bullet Distribution, Rough Trade,
JSU

Effect
ABUSING MYSELF.
Single (7"): released on Initial, Nov'81 by Initial
Records. Dist: Pinnacle

Egan, Joe
STUCK IN THE MIDDLE (see Rafferty,
Gerry) (Egan, Joe & Gerry Rafferty).
Album: released on A&M, Sep'78 by A&M Rec-

ords. Dist: Polygram

Egan, Walter
FULL MOON FIRE.
Single (7"): released on MCA, May'83 by MCA
Records. Dist: Polygram, MCA

Egan, Willie
GOING BACK TO LOUISIANA.
Album: released on Ace, Mar'84 by Ace Records. Dist: Pinnacle, Swift, Hotshot, Cadillac

WILLIE EGAN & HIS FRIENDS.
Album: released on Relic (US), Mar'85

Eger, Lucinda
SUNSET RED.
Single (12"): released on Pure Trash, Apr'87
Dist: Swift

Egg
SEVEN IS A JOLLY GOOD TIME.
Single (12"): released on See For Miles, Apr'85 by
See For Miles Records. Dist: Pinnacle

E(gg)clectic 1
FRIED EGG COLLECTION, (A).
Album: released on Fried Egg, Jul'81 by Fried
Egg Records. Dist: Rough Trade, Cartel

Egg Hunt
ME AND YOU.
Tracks: / All fall down.
Single (7"): released on Dischord, Nov'86 Dist:
Rough Trade, Cartel

Eggs Over Easy
GOOD 'N' CHEAP.
Album: released on Demon, Jul'86 by Demon
Records. Dist: Pinnacle

Ehmig, Michael Dan
FOR ALL THE CHILDREN.
Single (7"): released on Open Space, May'84
by Open Space Records. Dist: Pinnacle

Ehrlich, John
SPILL THE WINE.
Single (7"): released on Polo, Aug'87 by Polo
Records. Dist: PRT

Single (12"): released on Polo, Aug'87 by Polo
Records. Dist: PRT

Ehrlinger, Hans
TAKE THE CHANCE FOR A DANCE
(Ehrlinger, Hans & His Orchestra).
Album: released on Intersound, Dec'86 by In-
tersound Records. Dist: Jazz Music

TROMBONE TALK (Ehrlinger, Hans & His
Orchestra).
Album: released on Intersound, Dec'86 by In-
tersound Records. Dist: Jazz Music

Elder, Max
BEST KISSER IN THE WORLD, THE.
Tracks: / My other life / Sensitive touch / Bel Air
home / Rosemary / It has to be you / Quiet lives
/ Raking up leaves / Sense of motion / Let
somebody down / Perfect companion.
Notes: All tracks produced by John A. Rivers
and Max Elder.
Album: released on Big Time, Sep'87 by Mainline Record Company. Dist: Mainline. Estim retail price in Sep'87 was £6.29.

Cassette: released on Big Time, Sep'87 by
Mainline Record Company. Dist: Mainline.
Estim retail price in Sep'87 was £6.29.

CONSPIRACY (Elder, Max Versus Jazz
Butcher).
Single (12"): released on Glass, May'86 by
Glass Records. Dist: Nine Mile, Rough Trade,
Red Rhino, Play It Again Sam

Elelo
LAND OF OPPORTUNITIES.
Cassette: released on Demon, Feb'86 by
Demon Records. Dist: Pinnacle

LAND OF OPPORTUNITY.
Album: released on Demon, Sep'85 by Demon
Records. Dist: Pinnacle

Eight-0-One
801 LIVE.
Album: released on Polydor, Feb'77 by Polydor Records. Dist: Polygram, Polydor

Eighteen...
18 IRISH REBEL SONGS various artists
(Various Artists).
Album: released on Derry, Jul'76 by Outlet
Records. Dist: Outlet Records

18 SMASH HITS various artists (Various Artists).
Album: released on Pye International, Mar'77

EIGHTEEN TV/FILM THEMES (Various Artists).
Album: released on Sierra, Dec'86 by Sierra Records. Dist: WEA

Cassette: released on Sierra, Dec'86 by Sierra Records. Dist: WEA

Eighteen Twelve
TRUTH IMAGE OF 1812, THE.
Album: released on Sweet Folk, May'81 Dist: Roots Distribution

Eight Eyed Spy
DIDDY WAH DIDDY.
Single (7"): released on Fetus Productions, May'82 by Red Rhino Records. Dist: Red Rhino, Cartel

EIGHT EYED SPY.
Album: released on Fetish, '81 by Fetish Records. Dist: Cartel, Pinnacle

LIVE With Lydia Lunch.
Cassette: released on Reach Out International, '83 Dist: Red Rhino, Cartel

Eighth Day
CALL ME UP.
Single (7"): released on Funk America, Apr'83 by A&M Records. Dist: CBS

Single (12"): released on Funk America, Apr'83 by A&M Records. Dist: CBS

EIGHTH DAY.
Album: released on A&M, Apr'83 by A&M Records. Dist: Polygram

TOO MANY COOKS (SPOIL THE BROTH).
Single (7"): released on HDH(Holland/Dozier/Holland), Jun'84 by Demon Records. Dist: Pinnacle

TOO MANY CROOKS.
Single (7"): released on HDH(Holland/Dozier/Holland), Sep'84 by Demon Records. Dist: Pinnacle

Eighth Wonder
WILL YOU REMEMBER.
Tracks: / Having it all.
Single (7"): released on CBS, Jan'87 by CBS Records. Dist: CBS

Single (12"): released on CBS, Jan'87 by CBS Records. Dist: CBS

Eightie's Band
WE WANT A GOAL.
Single (7"): released on JSO. Jul'81

Eighties Ladies
TURNED ON TO YOU.
Tracks: / Turned on to you / Turned on to you (alternative mix).
Single (7"): released on Music Of Life, Aug'86 Dist: Streetwave

Single (12"): released on Music Of Life, Aug'86 Dist: Streetwave

Eight Point Five
MARY.
Tracks: / I can't get you out of my head.
Single (7"): released on Epic, Feb'87 by CBS Records. Dist: CBS

Single (12"): released on Epic, Feb'87 by CBS Records. Dist: CBS

Eighty four...
84 CHARING CROSS ROAD Original Soundtrack (Various Artists).
Notes: Starring Anne Bancroft & Anthony Hopkins. The story of an American authoress' postal relationship with an antiquarian bookshop at 84...
Album: released on TER, Apr'87 Dist: Pinnacle

Cassette: released on TER, Apr'87 Dist: Pinnacle

Eighty Six...
'86 POPULAR HITS NOW Various artists (Various Artists).
Compact disc: released on Denon, May'86 by Denon Records. Dist: Harmonia Mundi

Einsturzende Neubauten
1/2 MENSCH.
Compact disc: released on Some Bizzare, Jan'87 by Charisma Records. Dist: EMI, CBS, Polygram

DURSTIGES TIER (EP).
Single (12"): released on Zick Zack (Germany), Aug'83 by Zick Zack Records. Dist: Rough Trade

FUNF AUF DER NACHT OBEN OFFENEN RICHTERSKALA.
Album: released on Some Bizzare, Jul'87 by Virgin Records. Dist: EMI, CBS, Polygram

Cassette: released on Some Bizzare, Jul'87 by Virgin Records. Dist: EMI, CBS, Polygram

PORTRAIT OF PATIENT O.T..
Album: released on Some Bizzare, Nov'83 by Virgin Records. Dist: EMI, CBS, Polygram

SEUNS AUF DER NACH OBEN OFFENEN RICHTERS KALA.
Album: released on Some Bizzare, Jan'87 by Charisma Records. Dist: EMI CBS, Polygram

Compact disc: released on Some Bizzare, Jul87 by Charisma Records. Dist: EMI, CBS, Polygram

STRATEGIES AGAINST ARCHITECTURE.
Album: released on Mute, Jan'84 Dist: Spartan Distribution, Rough Trade Distribution, Cartel Distribution

YU GUNG.
Single (12"): released on Some Bizzare, Mar'85 by Virgin Records. Dist: EMI, CBS, Polygram

Ejected
HAVE YOU GOT 10P?.
Single (7"): released on Riot City, Sep'72 by Riot City Records. Dist: Revolver

NOISE FOR THE BOYS (EP).
Single (7"): released on Riot City, Feb'83 by Riot City Records. Dist: Revolver

SPIRIT OF REBELLION.
Album: released on Riot City, Aug'84 by Riot City Records. Dist: Revolver

TOUCH OF CLASS, A.
Album: released on Riot City, May'83 by Riot City Records. Dist: Revolver

EK.1
AS ONE.
Tracks: / As one / Summers end / As one (Inst.).
Notes: Distributed by Be There, 2, Cherry gardens, Broadstairs, Kent CT10 2NE.
Single (7"): released on Be There, Mar'86 by Be There Records. Dist: Be There

Ekland, Britt
TRUE BRITT Britt Ekland reads from her autobiography.
Cassette: released on Argo (Spokenword), Jul'82 by Decca Records. Dist: Polygram

Ek, Lars
DIZZY ACCORDION.
Tracks: / Vision of love / Mariposita / Thoughts of love / Dizzy accordion / Coquette polka / Jolly caballero / Atacka Marschen / Yodelling accordion / Jularboglade / Dansar shottis / Sambo hambo / Waltz grundstrom.
Album: released on Accordion Record Club, Jul'86 by Accordion Record Club Records. Dist: Accordion Record Club

Compact disc: released on Accordion Record Club, Jul'86 by Accordion Record Club Records. Dist: Accordion Record Club

EK, LARS X 2 Various artists (Various Artists).
Album: released on ARC (Accordion Records), '84 Dist: Accordion Record Club

LARS EK IN DISNEYLAND.
Album: released on Accordion Record Club, Jul'86 by Accordion Record Club Records. Dist: Accordion Record Club

Cassette: released on Accordion Record Club, Jul'86 by Accordion Record Club Records. Dist: Accordion Record Club

LARS EK PLAYS FROSINI.
Tracks: / Dizzy fingers / Vieni amore / Bel fiore / Varserenade / Bel viso / La mariposita / Hot fingers / Olive blossom / Jolly caballero / Musette masuka / Love smiles / Through the park.
Album: released on Accordion Record Club, Jul'86 by Accordion Record Club Records. Dist: Accordion Record Club

LARS EK'S HOT TRIO.
Tracks: / Raggin' the scale / Echo mazurka / Voss on the rocks / Fors majeur.
Album: released on Accordion Record Club, Jul'86 by Accordion Record Club Records. Dist: Accordion Record Club

Cassette: released on Accordion Record Club, Jul'86 by Accordion Record Club Records. Dist: Accordion Record Club

Eko Eko
I CAN'T TAKE THE HURT AGAIN.
Single (7"): released on Red Bus, Jun'84 by Red Bus Records. Dist: PRT

Single (12"): released on Red Bus, Jun'84 by Red Bus Records. Dist: PRT

Elaine & Derick
HOW MANY TIMES CAN WE SAY?.
Single (7"): released on BB, Nov'85 Dist: Jetstar

Elbert, Donnie
YOU DON'T HAVE TO BE A STAR.
Single (7"): released on Sugar Hill USA, Jul'81 by MCA Records. Dist: Roots Distribution, Mike's Country Music Room Distribution, Projection Distribution, PRT Distribution

Single (12"): released on Sugar Hill USA, Jul'81 by MCA Records. Dist: Roots Distribution, Mike's Country Music Room Distribution, Projection Distribution, PRT Distribution

El Chicano
LET ME DANCE WITH YOU.
Single (7"): released on Streetwave, Aug'84 by Streetwave Records. Dist: PRT Distribution

Single (12"): released on Streetwave, Aug'84 by Streetwave Records. Dist: PRT Distribution

El Debarge
HEART IS NOT SO SMART, (THE).
Single (7"): released on Motown, Nov'85 by Motown Records. Dist: BMG Distribution

Single (12"): released on Motown, Nov'85 by Motown Records. Dist: BMG Distribution

YOU WEAR IT WELL (El Debarge with Debarge).
Single (7"): released on Motown, Aug'85 by Motown Records. Dist: BMG Distribution

Single (12"): released on Motown, Aug'85 by Motown Records. Dist: BMG Distribution

Eldorados
BIM BAM BOOM.
Album: released on Charly, Jul'81 by Charly Records. Dist: Charly, Cadillac

Eldridge & Hawkins
EUROPEAN CONCERT (Eldridge & Hawkins Quintet).
Notes: For full information see under: HAWKINS & ELDRIDGE QUINTET.
Album: released on Unique Jazz (Import), '81

Eldridge, Roy
ARCADIA BALLROOM 39.
Notes: Mono.
Album: released on Jazz Archives, Jul'86 by Jazz Archives Records. Dist: Jazz Music

BEST OF ROY ELDRIDGE, THE.
Album: released on Pablo (USA), '82 by Pablo Records (USA). Dist: Wellard, Chris, IMS-Polygram, BMG

Cassette: released on Pablo (USA), '82 by Pablo Records (USA). Dist: Wellard, Chris, IMS-Polygram, BMG

BODY & SOULD AT THE BAYOU CLUB: VOL 2 (see Hawkins, Coleman) (Eldridge, Roy & Coleman Hawkins).

EUROPEAN CONCERT (see Hawkins, Coleman) (Eldridge, Roy & Coleman Hawkins).

GREAT ENGLISH CONCERT, THE (Eldridge, Roy & Tiny Grimes).
Album: released on Jazz Groove, Jul'82 Dist: Jazz Music

GREAT ENGLISH CONCERT, (THE) (see Hawkins, Coleman) (Eldridge, Roy/Coleman Hawkins/Stan Getz).

HAPPY TIME.
Album: released on Pablo (USA), '82 by Pablo Records (USA). Dist: Wellard, Chris, IMS-Polygram, BMG

Cassette: released on Pablo (USA), '82 by Pablo Records (USA). Dist: Wellard, Chris, IMS-Polygram, BMG

HAWK AND ROY (see Hawkins, Coleman) (Eldridge, Roy & Coleman Hawkins).

HEAT'S ON, THE (Eldridge, Roy/Howard McGhee).
Album: released on Esquire, Apr'79 by Titan International Productions. Dist: Jazz Music, Cadillac Music, Swift, Wellard, Chris, Backs, Rough Trade, Revolver, Nine Mile

JAM SESSION (1944-46) Roy meets Horn/Old Rob Roy.
Album: released on Joker, Apr'81 by Counterpoint, Mainline, Record Services Distribution (Ireland)

JAZZ MATURITY...WHERE IT'S COMING FROM (Eldridge, Roy & Dizzy Gillespie).
Album: released on Pablo (USA), '82 by Pablo Records (USA). Dist: Wellard, Chris, IMS-Polygram, BMG

Cassette: released on Pablo (USA), '82 by Pablo Records (USA). Dist: Wellard, Chris, IMS-Polygram, BMG

LITTLE JAZZ.
Double Album: released on Vogue Jazz, May'83

LITTLE JAZZ PARIS SESSIONS.
Double Album: released on Vogue, Apr'77 Dist: Discovery, Jazz Music, PRT, Swift

LITTLE JAZZ SPECIAL.
Album: released on Queen, Jun'86 Dist: Jazz Music

NEVER TOO OLD (Eldridge, Roy & Tiny Grimes).
Album: released on Sonet, Jan'78 by Sonet Records. Dist: PRT

NIFTY CAT, THE.
Tracks: / Jolly Hollis / Cotton / 5400 North / Ball of fire / Wineola / Nifty cat (The).
Notes: Roy Eldridge, trumpet (vocal on Wineola); Budd Johnson, tenor and soprano saxophones; Benny Morton, trombone; Nat Pierce, piano; Tommy Bryant, bass; Oliver Jackson, drums.
Produced by Bill Weilbacher. Recording engineer: Roger Rhodes. Recorded nov 24th1970 in New York.
Compact disc: released on New World (USA), Dec'86 by New World Records (USA). Dist: Conifer

OSCAR PETERSON AND ROY ELDRIDGE (Eldridge, Roy and Oscar Peterson).
Album: released on Pablo (USA), '82 by Pablo Records (USA). Dist: Wellard, Chris, IMS-Polygram, BMG

Cassette: released on Pablo (USA), '82 by Pablo Records (USA). Dist: Wellard, Chris, IMS-Polygram, BMG

PORTRAITS IN JAZZ (Eldridge, Roy/Richie Kamuca).
Album: released on Pumpkin, Apr'79 Dist: Jazz Music, Wellard, Chris, Cadillac

RARE BROADCASTS.
Album: released on Duke, Jun'86 by Melodisc Records. Dist: Jazz Horizons, Jazz Music, Celtic Music, JSU, Swift

ROY ELDRIDGE AT JERRY NEWMAN'S.
Album: released on Xanadu, Jan'83 Dist: Discovery, Jazz Horizons, Jazz Music, Swift

ROY ELDRIDGE FOUR.
Album: released on Pablo (USA), '82 by Pablo Records (USA). Dist: Wellard, Chris, IMS-Polygram, BMG

Cassette: released on Pablo (USA), '82 by Pablo Records (USA). Dist: Wellard, Chris, IMS-Polygram, BMG

TIPPIN' OUT.
Album: released on Affinity, Oct'85 by Charly Records. Dist: Charly, Cadillac

UNE PETITE LAITUE.
Album: released on Jazz Legacy (France), Sep'79 Dist: Discovery, Jazz Music, Swift

WHAT'S IT ALL ABOUT.
Album: released on Pablo (USA), '82 by Pablo Records (USA). Dist: Wellard, Chris, IMS-Polygram, BMG

Cassette: released on Pablo (USA), '82 by Pablo Records (USA). Dist: Wellard, Chris, IMS-Polygram, BMG

Eleanor Rigby
CENSORSHIP.
Album: released on Waterloo Sunset, Jul'87 by Waterloo Sunset Records. Dist: MIS-EMI Distribution, Backs

Elected
PRESS THE BUTTON.
Single (7"): released on Riot City, Dec'83 by Riot City Records. Dist: Revolver

Electric Arc
HONKY TONK RAP.
Single (7"): released on Red Bus, Sep'83 by Red Bus Records. Dist: PRT

Electric Banana
SEVENTIES, THE.
Album: released on Butt, Nov'85 by Butt Records. Dist: Counterpoint

SIXTIES, THE.
Album: released on Butt, Mar'82 by Butt Records. Dist: Counterpoint

Electric Bluebirds

BACK ON THE TRAIN.
Tracks: / Stranger's just a friend, A / Back on the train.
Single (7"): released on Making Waves, Sep'86 by Making Waves Records.

ELECTRIC BLUEBIRDS, THE.
Album: released on Making Waves, Jul'86 by Making Waves Records.

Cassette: released on Making Waves, Jul'86 by Making Waves Records.

MONEY'S ALL GONE, THE.
Single (7"): released on Making Waves, Oct'86 by Making Waves Records.

TELL IT LIKE IT IS.
Tracks: / Tell it like it is / Wake me, shake me.
Single (7"): released on Making Waves, Jun'86 by Making Waves Records.

Electric Ceilidh Band

CEANN TRAIGH GHRUINHEARD.
Single (12"): released on Raucous, Mar'84 by MK Records. Dist: MK

Electric Chairs

ELECTRIC CHAIRS.
Album: by Safari Records. Dist: Pinnacle

SO MANY WAYS.
Single (7"): released on Safari, '79 by Safari Records. Dist: Pinnacle

Electric Crayon Set

ELECTRIC CRAYON SET (Various Artists).
Album: released on Bam Caruso, Dec'86 by Bam Caruso Records. Dist: Rough Trade, Revolver, Cartel

Electric Dance

ELECTRIC DANCE Various artists (Various Artists).
Album: released on Telstar, May'84 by Telstar Records. Dist: RCA Distribution

Cassette: released on Telstar, May'84 by Telstar Records. Dist: RCA Distribution

Electric Dreams

ELECTRIC DREAMS Various artists (Various Artists).
Notes: Artists include: **Jeff Lynne, Culture Club, Giorgio Moroder, Helen terry, heaven 17, P.P. Arnold.** Digital stereo.
Compact disc: released on Virgin, Oct'84 by Virgin Records. Dist: EMI, Virgin Distribution

Album: released on Virgin, Sep'84 by Virgin Records. Dist: EMI, Virgin Distribution

Cassette: released on Virgin, Sep'84 by Virgin Records. Dist: EMI, Virgin Distribution

Electric Eels

AGITATED.
Single (7"): released on Rough Trade, Jan'79 by Rough Trade Records. Dist: Rough Trade Distribution, Cartel Distribution

Electric Flag

GROOVIN' IS EASY.
Album: released on Thunderbolt, Nov'83 by Magnum Music Group Ltd. Dist: Magnum Music Group Ltd, PRT Distribution, Spartan Distribution

TRIP.
Album: released on Edsel, Mar'87 by Demon Records. Dist: Pinnacle, Jazz Music, Projection

Electric Guitars

GENGHIS KHAN.
Single (12"): released on Stiff, Oct'82 by Stiff Records. Dist: EMI, Record Services Distribution (Ireland)

HEALTH.
Single (7"): released on Fried Egg, Jul'81 by Fried Egg Records. Dist: Rough Trade, Cartel

LANGUAGE PROBLEMS.
Single (7"): released on Stiff, May'82 by Stiff Records. Dist: EMI, Record Services Distribution (Ireland)

Single (12"): released on Stiff, May'82 by Stiff Records. Dist: EMI, Record Services Distribution (Ireland)

WOLFMAN TAP.
Single (7"): released on Naive, May'83 by Naive. Dist: Spartan

Single (12"): released on Naive, May'83 by Naive. Dist: Spartan

WORK.
Single (7"): released on Recreational, Oct'81 by Revolver Records. Dist: Rough Trade

Electricity All Stars

ELECTRICITY MEDLEY various artists.
Single (12"): released on Passion, Mar'85 by Skratch Records. Dist: PRT

Electric Light Orchestra

10538 OVERTURE.
Single (7"): released on EMI Golden 45's, May'84 by EMI Records. Dist: EMI

BALANCE OF POWER.
Tracks: / Heaven only knows / So serious / Getting to the point / Secret lives / Is it alright / Sorrow about to fall / Without someone / Calling America / Endless lies / Send it.
Compact disc: by CBS Records Dist: CBS

Album: released on Epic, Mar'86 by CBS Records. Dist: CBS

Cassette: released on Epic, Mar'86 by CBS Records. Dist: CBS

CALLING AMERICA.
Tracks: / Calling America / Caught in a trap.
Single (7"): released on Epic, Feb'86 by CBS Records. Dist: CBS

Single (12"): released on Epic, Feb'86 by CBS Records. Dist: CBS

COLLECTION: ELECTRIC LIGHT ORCH..
Album: released on EMI (Germany), '83 by EMI Records. Dist: Conifer

DISCOVERY.
Tracks: / Shine a little love / Confusion / Need her love / Diary of Horace Wimp, The / Last train to London / Midnight blue / On the run / Wishing / Don't bring me down.
Compact disc: by Jet Records. Dist: CBS

Album: released on Epic, Nov'86 by CBS Records. Dist: CBS

Cassette: released on Epic, Nov'86 by CBS Records. Dist: CBS

ELECTRIC LIGHT ORCHESTRA VOL.2.
Album: released on Fame (Harvest), May'82 by Music For Pleasure Records. Dist: EMI

Cassette: released on Fame (Harvest), May'82 by Music For Pleasure Records. Dist: EMI

FACE THE MUSIC.
Album: released on Epic, Jun'85 by CBS Records. Dist: CBS

Cassette: released on Epic, Jun'85 by CBS Records. Dist: CBS

FIRST MOVEMENT.
Tracks: / First movement / Look at me now / 10538 Overture / Queen of the hours / Battle of Marston Moor, The (July 2nd, 1644) / Mr. Radio / Kuiama / Roll over Beethoven / From the sun to the world / Momma / In Old England town / Showdown.
Notes: ELO emerged in 1971 as a development of **The Move**, which included Roy Wood, Bev Bevan (drums), and the newest member Jeff Lynne from **The Move's** original line-up This new compilation includes the complete version of '10538 overture, released in June 1972, which became their first top ten hit- hot on the heels of'California man', the final single by **The Move.** Also included are their other two hit singles from their time on the **Harvest** label: 'Roll over Beethoven' and 'showdown'.
Album: released on Harvest, Apr'86 by EMI Records. Dist: Roots, EMI

Cassette: released on Harvest, Apr'86 by EMI Records. Dist: Roots, EMI

Compact disc: released on EMI, Jul'87 by EMI Records. Dist: EMI

GETTING TO THE POINT.
Tracks: / Getting to the point / Secret lives.
Single (7"): released on Epic, Jul'86 by CBS Records. Dist: CBS

Single (12"): released on Epic, Jul'86 by CBS Records. Dist: CBS

GREATEST HITS:ELECTRIC LIGHT ORCHESTRA.
Tracks: / Telephone line / Evil woman / Livin' thing / Can't get it out of my head / Showdown / Turn to stone / Rockaria / Sweet talkin' woman / Ma ma ma belle / Strange magic / Mr Blue sky.
Compact disc: released on Jet, '86 by Jet Records. Dist: CBS

Album: released on Epic, Jan'87 by CBS Records. Dist: CBS

Cassette: released on Epic, Jan'87 by CBS Records. Dist: CBS

Album: released on Jet, Nov'79 by Jet Records. Dist: CBS

Cassette: released on Jet, Nov'79 by Jet Records. Dist: CBS

LIGHT SHINES ON, THE.
Album: released on Harvest, Apr'77 by EMI Records. Dist: Roots, EMI

Cassette: released on Harvest, Apr'77 by EMI Records. Dist: Roots, EMI

MILESTONES.
Double Album: released on EMI (Holland), '83 by EMI Records. Dist: Conifer

NEW WORLD RECORD, A.
Tracks: / Tightrope / Telephone line / Rockaria / Mission (A new world record) / So fine / Livin' thing / Above the clouds / Do ya / Shangri-la.
Compact disc: released on Epic, Mar'87 by CBS Records. Dist: CBS

Album: released on Jet, Nov'84 by Jet Records. Dist: CBS

Cassette: released on Jet, Nov'84 by Jet Records. Dist: CBS

NIGHT THE LIGHT WENT OUT, THE.
Album: released on Epic, Nov'85 by CBS Records. Dist: CBS

Cassette: released on Epic, Nov'85 by CBS Records. Dist: CBS

ON THE THIRD DAY.
Album: released on Jet, Jun'77 by Jet Records. Dist: CBS

Cassette: released on Jet, Jun'77 by Jet Records. Dist: CBS

OUT OF THE BLUE.
Tracks: / Turn to stone / It's over / Sweet talkin' woman / Across the border / Night in the city / Starlight / Jungle / Believe me now / Steppin' out / Standin' in the rain / Big wheels / Summer and lightning / Mr.Blue Sky / Sweet is the night / Whale, the / Birmingham blues / Wild West hero.
Double compact disc: by Jet Records. Dist: CBS

Album: released on Epic, May'87 by CBS Records. Dist: CBS

Cassette: released on Epic, May'87 by CBS Records. Dist: CBS

Double Album: released on Jet, Oct'77 by Jet Records. Dist: CBS

Double cassette: released on Jet, Oct'77 by Jet Records. Dist: CBS

ROCK'N'ROLL IS KING.
Single (7"): released on Jet, Jun'83 by Jet Records. Dist: CBS

Single (12"): released on Jet, Jun'83 by Jet Records. Dist: CBS

SECRET MESSAGES.
Compact disc: by Jet Records. Dist: CBS

SHOWDOWN.
Single (7"): released on Harvest, Mar'79 by EMI Records. Dist: Roots, EMI

SO SERIOUS.
Tracks: / So serious / Matter of fact, a / Matter of fact, A (alternative lyrics).
Single (7"): released on Epic, Apr'86 by CBS Records. Dist: CBS

Single (12"): released on Epic, Apr'86 by CBS Records. Dist: CBS

THREE LIGHT YEARS.
Triple album / cassette: released on Jet, '78 by Jet Records. Dist: CBS

TIME.
Tracks: / Prologue / Twilight / Yours truly 2095 / Ticket to the moon / Way life's meant to be, The / Another heart breaks / Rain is falling / From the end of the world / Lights go down, The / Here is the news / 21st century man / Hold on tight / Epilogue.
Notes: All music and lyrics by Jeff Lynne. (C) 1981 Jet Music\April Music Ltd. Produced by Jeff Lynne.
Album: released on Jet, Jul'81 by Jet Records. Dist: CBS

Cassette: released on Jet, Jul'81 by Jet Records. Dist: CBS

TWILIGHT.
Single (7"): released on Jet, Oct'81 by Jet Records. Dist: CBS

WAY LIFE'S MEANT TO BE.
Single (7"): released on Jet, Mar'82 by Jet Records. Dist: CBS

Electric Mind

PICK ME UP (CAN WE GO).
Single (7"): released on Passion, Jul'83 by Skratch Records. Dist: PRT

Single (12"): released on Passion, Jul'83 by Skratch Records. Dist: PRT

Electric Moods

ELECTRIC MOODS Various Artists (Various Artists).
Compact disc: released on K-Tel, Aug'87 by K-Tel Records. Dist: Record Merchandisers Distribution, Taylors, Terry Blood Distribution, Wynd-Up Distribution, Relay Distribution, Pickwick Distribution, Solomon & Peres Distribution, Polygram

Electric Prunes

I HAD TOO MUCH TO DREAM LAST NIGHT.
Album: released on WEA (Germany), Oct'84

Single (7"): released on Radar, Mar'79 by WEA Music Ltd. Dist: WEA, PRT

LONG DAY'S FLIGHT.
Album: released on Edsel, Mar'86 by Demon Records. Dist: Pinnacle, Jazz Music, Projection

Cassette: released on Edsel, Mar'86 by Demon Records. Dist: Pinnacle, Jazz Music, Projection

Electric Sixties

ELECTRIC SIXTIES (Various Artists).
Notes: Artists include Canned Heat, Cream.
Album: released on Trax Baby Boomer Classics, Apr'87

Cassette: released on Trax Baby Boomer Classics, Apr'87

Electric Slacks

ELECTRIC BLUES.
Single (7"): released on Fundamental, Jun'85 by Fundamental Records. Dist: Red Rhino, Cartel

Electric Smoke

FREAK IT OUT.
Single (7"): released on Nite Life, May'83

Electric Sugar Cube..

ELECTRIC SUGAR CUBE FLASHBACKS various artists (Various Artists).
Album: released on Archive Int. Productions (USA Import), Dec'83

ELECTRIC SUGAR CUBE FLASHBACKS VOL.2 Various artists (Various Artists).
Album: released on Archive Int. Productions (USA Import), Dec'83

Electric Sun

EARTHQUAKE.
Album: released on Brain, Dec'79

FIRE WIND.
Album: released on Brain, Mar'82

Electric Toilet

IN THE HANDS OF KARMA.
Album: released on Psycho, Sep'83 Dist: Funhouse, Rough Trade

Electronic Art Ensemble

INQUIETUDE.
Album: released on Gramavision (USA), Jul'83 by Gramavison Records (USA). Dist: PRT, IMS, Polygram

Electronic Ensemble

IT HAPPENED THEN.
Single (7"): released on Superstition, Oct'80

Electronics

BIRD DANCE, THE.
Album: released on Polydor (Germany), Dec'81 Dist: IMS-Polygram

Cassette: released on Polydor (Germany), Dec'81 Dist: IMS-Polygram

Electronic Sylvia Plath

ELECTRONIC SYLVIA PLATH Various artists (Various Artists).
Cassette: released on Brokenskull, Nov'84 by Carrere Records-Broken Hill (USA).

Electronic Synthesizer...

SYNTHESIS VOL. 1.
Cassette: released on E.S.S.P., Dec'79 by E.S.S.P. Records. Dist: E.S.S.P.

SYNTHESIS VOL.2.
Cassette: released on E.S.S.P., Dec'80 by E.S.S.P. Records. Dist: E.S.S.P.

SYNTHESIS VOL.3.
Cassette: released on E.S.S.P., Dec'81 by E.S.S.P. Records. Dist: E.S.S.P.

Electropop Trax
SUBTLE HINTS.
Album: released on Sane, Sep'83 Dist: E.S.S.P. Distributors

Electro Reggae
ELECTRO REGGAE VOLUME 1 (Various Artists).
Notes: Produced by Sly Dunbar & Robbie Shakespeare except 'Twilight Zone'(A.Tucker), Sly dunbar & N Robinson for Taxi Promotions. Compiled by Michael Roots.
Album: released on Mango, Jul'86 by Inferno Records. Dist: Inferno

Cassette: released on Mango, Jul'86 by Inferno Records. Dist: Inferno

Electroshock
ELECTROSHOCK-THE SIXTIES (Various Artists).
Tracks: / Please let me love you / Don't be long / Been burnt / March of the mad duke's circus / Black roses / Mr Blue / Red sox are winning / Home to you / Nevertheless / I like Marijuana / In a Gadda-da-Vida / Rock and roll circus / Go back / Apricot brandy / I need love / Christing / Right on be free / Someday / Get ourselves together / Arthur comics / Frozen warnings / East-West / Way back in the 1960's / My little red book / Hey Joe / Signed D.C. / Seven and seven is / She comes in colours / Alone again or / Andmoreagain / Singing cowboy / Aren't you the girl / Strange street / Affair under blue / I can't see you / No man can find the war / Pleasant Street / Dream letter / Morning glory / Kick out the jams / Come together / Motor City is burning / Ramblin' rose / Starship / 1969 / I wanna be your dog / No fun / TV eye / 1970 / Bird song.
Triple album / cassette: released on Elektra (USA), Mar'86 by Elektra/Asylum/Nonesuch Records. Dist: WEA

Electro Shock Voltage
ELECTRO SHOCK VOLTAGE ONE various artists (Various Artists).
Album: released on Epic, Feb'84 by CBS Records. Dist: CBS

Cassette: released on Epic, Feb'84 by CBS Records. Dist: CBS

Elektro Robotik Dub...
STRIKTY AUTOMATIK.
Album: released on Ariwa, Nov'84 by Ariwa Records. Dist: Revolver, Cartel, Jetstar, Rough Trade

Element Of Crime
TRY TO BE MENSCH.
Album: released on Polydor (Germany), Aug'87 Dist: IMS-Polygram

Cassette: released on Polydor (Germany), Aug'87 Dist: IMS-Polygram

Compact disc: released on Polydor (Germany), Aug'87 Dist: IMS-Polygram

Element Of Light
ELEMENT OF LIGHT (Hitchcock, Robyn & The Egyptians).
Album: released on Glass Fish, Oct'86 Dist: Rough Trade

Elements
ELEMENTS.
Notes: A bona-fide oddball from the Wooleys Mini.
Album: released on Press, Jul'86 by Press Records.

Elements Band
I WANNA DANCE.
Tracks: / I wanna dance / Get up stand up.
Single (12"): released on ADA, Feb'86 Dist: Jetstar

Elen, Gus
YOU HAVE MADE A NICE OLD MESS OF IT.
Album: released on Topic, Jan'81 Dist: Roots Distribution

Elephant Table Album
ELEPHANT TABLE ALBUM Various artists (Various Artists).
Album: released on Xtract, Oct'83 by Xtract Records. Dist: Cartel

Elephant Talk
ASK.
Single (7"): released on Fragile, Mar'84 by Fragile Records. Dist: Cartel

Elevation
TRAITOR.
Single (7"): released on Illuminated, Oct'85 by IKF Records. Dist: Pinnacle, Cartel, Jetstar

Single (12"): released on Illuminated, Oct'85 by IKF Records. Dist: Pinnacle, Cartel, Jetstar

Eleven Go Mad In Lewisham
11 GO MAD IN LEWISHAM On yer bike album, The (Various Artists).
Tracks: / Golden lady / Pray for the fallen angels / Breaking up my heart / Hillbilly jump / Got some love / America / 24 hours / Ain't gonna trap / Fish song, The / Lets move / Party.
Notes: Address: 8 Hatcham Park Road, London, SE14 5QD. Tel: 01 635 8985.
Album: released on Hummingbird, Mar'86 by Hummingbird. Dist: Hummingbird

Eleventh Hour
GOING STRONG.
Single (7"): released on Loppylugs, Jan'82 by Loppylugs Records. Dist: Pinnacle, Loppylugs

Elf
CAROLINA COUNTRY BALL.
Album: released on Safari, Aug'84 by Safari Records. Dist: Pinnacle

Cassette: released on Safari, Aug'84 by Safari Records. Dist: Pinnacle

ELF.
Album: released on CBS, Sep'86 by CBS Records. Dist: CBS

Cassette: released on CBS, Sep'86 by CBS Records. Dist: CBS

GARGANTUAN ELF ALBUM.
Compact disc: released on Safari, '86 by Safari Records. Dist: Pinnacle

TRYING TO BURN THE SUN (Elf & Ronnie James Dio).
Album: released on Safari, Aug'84 by Safari Records. Dist: Pinnacle

Cassette: released on Safari, Aug'84 by Safari Records. Dist: Pinnacle

Elfman, Danny
GRATITUDE.
Single (7"): released on MCA, May'85 by MCA Records. Dist: Polygram, MCA

Single (12"): released on MCA, May'85 by MCA Records. Dist: Polygram, MCA

Elgart, Larry
HOOKED ON SWING (Elgart, Larry & His Manhatten Swing Orchestra).
Album: released on RCA, Oct'82 by RCA Records. Dist: RCA, Roots, Swift, Wellard, Chris, I & B, Solomon & Peres Distribution

Cassette: released on RCA, Oct'82 by RCA Records. Dist: RCA, Roots, Swift, Wellard, Chris, I & B, Solomon & Peres Distribution

Single (7"): released on RCA, Oct'82 by RCA Records. Dist: RCA, Roots, Swift, Wellard, Chris, I & B, Solomon & Peres Distribution

Single (12"): released on RCA, Oct'82 by RCA Records. Dist: RCA, Roots, Swift, Wellard, Chris, I & B, Solomon & Peres Distribution

Elgins
HEAVEN MUST HAVE SENT YOU.
Single (7"): released on Motown, Oct'81 by Motown Records. Dist: BMG Distribution

Elgin Strathspey
STRINGS O'MORAY (Elgin Strathspey & Reel Society).
Tracks: / March/Strathspey & Reel / Highland Scottishes / Weaving set / Andy Ross two-step, The / Slow air / Pipe marchse / Waltzes / Reels (a trip to Bavaria) / Marches / Tom Burns Polka (The) / Slow air (2) / March/Strathspey & Reel (2) / John Huband's dancing fingers / Moray jigs / Bothy ballads / Reels.
Album: released on Scotdisc, Dec'86 Dist: Clyde Factors Distributors

Cassette: released on Scotdisc, Dec'86 Dist: Clyde Factors Distributors

Elias
TOM HARK (Elias & His Zig Zag Flutes).
Single (7"): released on Old Gold, Jul'82 by Old Gold Records. Dist: Lightning, Jazz Music, Spartan, Counterpoint

Eliot, George
MILL ON THE FLOSS, THE.
Cassette: released on Cover to Cover, Jun'85 by Cover to Cover Cassettes. Dist: Conifer

SILAS MARNER read by Judi Dench.
Cassette: released on Argo (Spokenword), Jul'82 by Decca Records. Dist: Polygram

Ellovson, Steve
DAWN DANCE.
Album: released on ECM, Nov'81 by ECM Records. Dist: IMS, Polygram, Virgin through EMI

Elite
YOU DON'T CARE ABOUT I.
Single (7"): released on State, Jan'83 by State Records.

Single (12"): released on State, Jan'83 by State Records.

Elite Syncopation
ELITE SYNCOPATION Various artists (Various Artists).
Album: by Sonet. Dist: Roots, PRT-Pye Distribution

Elixia
SOHO PHAZE.
Single (7"): released on Record Shack, May'83 by Record Shack Records. Dist: PRT

Single (12"): released on Record Shack, May'83 by Record Shack Records. Dist: PRT

Elizabeth 1
ELIZABETH 1- 1533/1603 Various artists (Vahey, Robert).
Cassette: released on History Makers, Jun'82 by Ivan Berg. Dist: Pinnacle

Elkin, Gilly
JUST ANOTHER NIGHT.
Single (7"): released on Hit, Jan'83 by Hit Records. Dist: Pinnacle, Backs, Cartel

LOVING ON THE RUN.
Single (7"): released on Mantabridge, Jul'83 Dist: Pinnacle

Ellboj, Lulle Och Hans
MODERN DANSMUSIK.
Album: released on Dragon, Jun'86 by Dragon Records. Dist: Jazz Music, Projection, Cadillac

Ellegaard, Mogens
ELEGANT ELLEGAARD.
Tracks: / Partita piccola / In the zoo / Toccata & fugue in D min. / Toccata No.1 / Italian concerto, 1st movement / Histoires (La marchant d'eau, le meneuse de tortues d'or).
Album: released on Accordion Record Club, Jul'86 by Accordion Record Club Records. Dist: Accordion Record Club

MADE IN DENMARK.
Album: released on ARC (Accordion Records), Jan'84 Dist: Accordion Record Club

PLASTICITY.
Album: released on ARC (Accordion Records), Jan'84 Dist: Accordion Record Club

Ellery Bop
FIRE IN REFLECTION.
Single (12"): released on Desire, May'85 by Desire Records. Dist: Pinnacle

HIT THE MOON.
Single (7"): released on Base Ideas, Apr'82 by Base Ideas Records. Dist: Independent

RINGING.
Single (7"): released on Base Ideas, Apr'82 by Base Ideas Records. Dist: Independent

WE DENY.
Single 10": released on Base Ideas, Jul'82 by Base Ideas Records. Dist: Independent

Ellington & Armstrong
REUNION CONCERT.
Notes: Starr marketing services Ltd, 90, Queens Road, Twickenham, Middlesex. TW1 4ET. Tel. 01 891 6487.
Compact disc: released on Mobile Fidelity, Oct'86 by Mobile Fidelity Records.

REUNION CONCERT.
Notes: Double Album.

Ellington, DeLange
NEWPORT 1958.
Album: released on CBS(Import), Jun'86 by CBS Records. Dist: Conifer, Discovery, Swift

Cassette:

NUTCRACKER SUITE.
Album: released on CBS(Import), Jun'86 by CBS Records. Dist: Conifer, Discovery, Swift

Ellington, Duke
1927-1928 (Ellington, Duke & His Orchestra).
Album: released on VJM, Apr'85 by Wellard, Chris Distribution. Dist: Wellard, Chris Distribution

1928-1933 (Ellington, Duke & His Orchestra).
Album: released on Joker (Import), Apr'81

1943 VOL. 1 (Ellington, Duke & His Orchestra).
Notes: Mono
Album: released on Jazzology, Jan'87 Dist: Jazz Music, Swift

1943 VOL. 2.
Notes: Mono
Album: released on Jazzology, Jan'87 Dist: Jazz Music, Swift

1943 VOL. 3 (Ellington, Duke & His Orchestra).
Album: released on Jazzology, Jan'87 Dist: Jazz Music, Swift

1946-47.
Album: released on Queen-Disc (Import), Apr'81

1953 PASADENA CONCERT, THE.
Album: released on PRT, May'86 by PRT Records. Dist: PRT

Cassette: released on PRT, May'86 by PRT Records. Dist: PRT

Compact disc: Dist: Discovery, Jazz Music, PRT, Swift

1954 LOS ANGELES CONCERT.
Compact disc: released on Vogue, Jul'87 Dist: Discovery, Jazz Music, PRT, Swift

AFRO-BOSSA (Ellington, Duke & His Orchestra).
Album: released on Discovery, Jun'83 Dist: PRT

ALLSTAR ROAD BAND.
Album: released on Dr Jazz, Mar'86 by Doctor Jazz Records. Dist: CBS, PRT

Album: released on Doctor Jazz (USA), Mar'84 by Doctor Jazz Records. Dist: CBS

Cassette: released on Doctor Jazz (USA), Mar'84 by Doctor Jazz Records. Dist: CBS

ANATOMY OF A MURDER.
Album: released on CBS(Import), Jun'86 by CBS Records. Dist: Conifer, Discovery, Swift

AND HIS MOTHER CALLED HIM BILL.
Album: released on RCA (France), Feb'84 by RCA Records. Dist: Discovery

AND THE ELLINGTONIANS.
Tracks: / Cat walk / Moonlight fiesta / She / Happening, The / Swamp drums / Sultry serenade / Indian summer / Britt and butter blues / Caravan / Alternate / Hoppin' John / Jumpin' with symphony Sid / Caravan / Alternate / Hoppin' John / New piano roll blues, The / Perdido / Take the 'A' train / Oscalypso / Blues for Blanton / Thing ain't what they used to be / Make no mistake / In a blue summer garden / Cotton tail / Flamingo / Bang up blues / "C" Jam blues / Johnny come lately / Great times.
Double Album: released on Vogue Jazz (France), May'83

AN EVENING WITH THE DUKE, JAN 17TH 1945 (Ellington, Duke & His Orchestra).
Album: released on Giants of Jazz, Jun'86 by Hasmick Promotions Ltd.. Dist: Counterpoint, Jazz Music, Taylors, Swift, Mainline, Wellard, Chris

AT CARNEGIE HALL NOV. 23 1946 (Ellington, Duke Orchestra).
Tracks: / Eighth veil, The / Golden feather / Flippant flurry / Golden cress / Unbooted character, The / Sultry sunset / Deep south suite.
Album: released on Queen-Disc, Apr'81 Dist: Celtic Music, JSU, Jazz Horizons, Jazz Music

AT HIS VERY BEST.
Tracks: / Jack the Bear / Concerto for Cootie(Do nothin' till you hear from me) / Harlem air shaft / Across the track blues / Chloe (song of the swamp) / Royal Garden blues / Warm valley / Koko / Black, brown and beige / Creole love call / Transbluecency (a blue fog that you can almost see through).
Album: released on RCA, Jan'73 by RCA Records. Dist: RCA, Roots, Swift, Wellard, Chris, I & B, Solomon & Peres Distribution

AT NEWPORT.
Album: released on CBS(Import), Jun'86 by CBS Records. Dist: Conifer, Discovery, Swift

AT NEWPORT (II).
Album: released on CBS(Import), Jun'86 by CBS Records. Dist: Conifer, Discovery, Swift

AT TANGLEWOOD - JULY 15, 1956 VOL.1 (Ellington, Duke Orchestra).
Tracks: / Newport Jazz Festival Suite / Festival junction / Blues to be there / Newport up / Hawk talks, The / Prelude to a kiss / I got it bad / La Virgen de la Macarena.
Album: released on Queen-Disc, Apr'81 Dist: Celtic Music, JSU, Jazz Horizons, Jazz Music

AT TANGLEWOOD - JULY 15, 1956 VOL.2 (Ellington, Duke Orchestra).
Album: released on Queen-Disc, Apr'81 Dist: Celtic Music, JSU, Jazz Horizons, Jazz Music

AT THE BAL MASQUE.
Tracks: / Satin doll / Lady in red / Indian love call / Donkey serenade, The / Gypsy love song / Laugh, clown, laugh / Alice blue gown / Who's afraid of the big bad wolf? / Got a date with an angel / Poor butterfly / Satan takes a holiday / Peanut vendor.

Album: released on CBS, Jul'87 by CBS Records. Dist: CBS

Cassette: released on CBS, Jul'87 by CBS Records. Dist: CBS

AT THE BAL MASQUE.
Album: released on CBS(Import), Jun'86 by CBS Records. Dist: Conifer, Discovery, Swift

AT THE BLUE NOTE, CHICAGO.
Compact disc: Dist: Discovery, Jazz Music, PRT, Swift

AT THE COTTON CLUB.
Tracks: / I've got to be a rug cutter / Every day / Azure / Carnival in Caroline / Dinah's in a jam / Oh babe, maybe someday / East St. Louis toodle-oo / In a sentimental mood / I'm slappin' Seventh Avenue / Alabamy home / If you were in my place / Frolic Sam / List in meditation.
Album: released on Joker, Apr'81 Dist: Counterpoint, Mainline, Record Services Distribution (Ireland)

BACK TO BACK (Ellington, Duke & Johnny Hodges).
Tracks: / Weary blues / Saint Louis Blues / Loveless love / Royal Garden blues / Wabash Blues / Basin street blues / Beale street blues.
Cassette: released on Verve (USA), Jun'84 by Polydor. Dist: Polygram

Album: released on Verve, Jun'81

BERNE LEIGHTON PLAYS DUKE ELLINGTON AT JIMMY WESTON'S.
Album: released on Monmouth, Mar'79

BEST OF DUKE ELLINGTON.
Tracks: / Star spangled banner / East St. Louis toodle-oo / Black and tan fantasy / Creole love call / Mooche, The / Mood Indigo / Rockin' in rhythm / Echoes of the jungle / Harlem speaks / Caravan / Conga Prava / Cottontail / Take the 'A' train.
Album: released on Joker, Apr'81 Dist: Counterpoint, Mainline, Record Services Distribution (Ireland)

BEST OF DUKE ELLINGTON, THE.
Album: released on Pablo (USA), '82 by Pablo Records (USA). Dist: Wellard, Chris, IMS-Polygram, BMG

Cassette: released on Pablo (USA), '82 by Pablo Records (USA). Dist: Wellard, Chris, IMS-Polygram, BMG

BEST OF, THE.
Album: released on Music Disc (France), Apr'84 Dist: IMS-Polygram Distribution

BEST OF..., THE.
Album: released on Joker (Import), Apr'81

BIG BAND BOUNCE AND BOOGIE (Ellington, Duke & His Orchestra).
Tracks: / Summertime / Laura / I can't get started / My funny Valentine / Everything but you / Fustration / Cotton tail / Daydream / Deep Purple / Indian Summer / Blues.
Album: released on Affinity, Apr'85 by Charly Records. Dist: Charly, Cadillac

BLACK, BROWN AND BEIGE.
Album: released on CBS(Import), Jun'86 by CBS Records. Dist: Conifer, Discovery, Swift

BLACK BROWN AND BEIGE.
Album: released on Monmouth, Mar'79

BLANTON-WEBSTER YEARS, THE.
Tracks: / You, you darlin' / Jack the bear / Koko / Morning glory / So far, so good / Conga brava / Concerto for Cootie / Me and you / Cottontail / Never no lament / Dusk / Bojangles (A portrait of Bill Robinson) / Portrait of Bert Williams, A / Blue goose / Harlem air shaft / At a Dixie roadside diner / All too soon / Rumpus in Richmond / My greatest mistake / Sepia panorama / There shall be no night / In a mellotone / Five o'clock whistle / Warm valley / Flaming sword, The / Jumpin' punkins / Across the track blues / John Hardy's wife / Blue serge / Across the track blues / After all / After all / Chloe (Song of the swamp) / Bakiff / Are you sticking? / I never feltthis way before / Just a settin' and a rockin' / Giddybug gallop,The / Sidewalks of New York,The / Chocolate shake / Flamingo / I got it bad (and that ain't good) / Clementine / Brown-skin gal (in the calico gown) / Girl in my dreams tries to look like you, The / Jump for joy / Moon over Cuba / Take the A train / Five o'clock drag / Rocks in my bed / Bli-blip / Chelsea Bridge / Raincheck / What good would it do? / I don't know what kind of blues I got / I don't know what kind of blues I got / Perdido / C jam blues / Moon mist / Moon mist / What am I here for? / I don't mind / Someone / My little brown book / Main stem / Johnny come lately / Hayfoot strawfoot / Sentimental lady / Sip of the lip, A (can sink a ship) / Sherman shuffle.
Special: released on RCA, Jan'87 by RCA Records. Dist: RCA, Roots, Swift, Wellard, Chris, I & B, Solomon & Peres Distribution

BLUE ROSE.
Album: released on CBS(Import), Jun'86 by CBS Records. Dist: Conifer, Discovery, Swift

BLUES IN ORBIT.
Album: released on CBS(Import), Jun'86 by CBS Records. Dist: Conifer, Discovery, Swift

CARNEGIE HALL CONCERT (Ellington, Duke & His Orchestra).
Album: released on Musicraft (USA), Nov'84 by Discovery Records (USA). Dist: Flexitron Distributors Ltd, Swift Distribution

COMPLETE 1947/52.
Notes: 6 LP set.
Album: released on CBS(Import), Jun'86 by CBS Records. Dist: Conifer, Discovery, Swift

CONCERT IN THE VIRGIN ISLANDS (Ellington, Duke & His Orchestra).
Album: released on Discovery (USA), Jan'84 by Discovery Records (USA). Dist: Swift, Flexitron-Audio, Jazz Music

Cassette: released on Discovery (USA), Jan'84 by Discovery Records (USA). Dist: Swift, Flexitron-Audio, Jazz Music

CONCERT OF SACRED MUSIC.
Album: released on RCA (France), Jan'83 by RCA Records. Dist: Discovery

CONCERTS IN CANADA 1956 Stratford - 1973 Winnipeg (Ellington, Duke & His Orchestra).

COSMIC SCENE, THE.
Album: released on CBS(Import), Jun'86 by CBS Records. Dist: Conifer, Discovery, Swift

COTTON CLUB DAYS (Ellington, Duke & His Orchestra).
Tracks: / Creole love call / Blues I love to sing / Black and tan fantasy / East St Louis toodle-oo / Black beauty / Mooche / Cotton Club stomp / Misty morning / Duke steps out / Shout 'em aunt Tillie / Mood indigo / Old man blues.
Notes: Mono.
Album: released on RCA, Jul'86 by RCA Records. Dist: RCA, Roots, Swift, Wellard, Chris, I & B, Solomon & Peres Distribution

DANCE DATE (Ellington, Duke & His Orchestra).

DANCE DATE.
Album: released on Unique Jazz, Nov'86 Dist: Swift, Jazz Music, Jazz Horizons

DANCE DATE (2) Air Force 1960.
Album: released on Unique Jazz, Nov'86 Dist: Swift, Jazz Music, Jazz Horizons

DIGITAL DUKE (Ellington, Duke & His Orchestra).
Notes: An authentic recreation of original classic Ellington material.Conducted by Mercer Ellington, the album features original band members Louis Bellson,drums;Norris Turney,saxophone;Clark Terry,trumpet;Chuck Connors & Bruce Woodman, trombones,Eddie Daniels, clarinet & special guest Branford Marsalis.
Album: released on GRP (USA), May'87 by GRP Records (USA). Dist: IMS, Polygram

Cassette: released on GRP (USA), May'87 by GRP Records (USA). Dist: IMS, Polygram

Compact disc: released on GRP (USA), May'87 by GRP Records (USA). Dist: IMS, Polygram

DRUM IS A WOMAN, A.
Album: released on CBS(Import), Jun'86 by CBS Records. Dist: Conifer, Discovery, Swift

DUKE.
Album: released on Varese Sarabande (USA), Mar'79 by Varese Sarabande Records (USA). Dist: PRT

DUKE 1940, THE.
Notes: live from the Crystal Ballroom in Fargo, N.D. Mono.

DUKE 56/62 vol.1.
Album: released on CBS(France), May'85 by CBS Records. Dist: Conifer, Discovery, Swift

Cassette: released on CBS(France), May'85 by CBS Records. Dist: Conifer, Discovery, Swift Deleted '87.

DUKE 56/62 (VOL.2).
Album: released on CBS(France), May'85 by CBS Records. Dist: Conifer, Discovery, Swift

Cassette: released on CBS(France), May'85 by CBS Records. Dist: Conifer, Discovery, Swift

DUKE 56/62 (VOL.3).
Album: released on CBS(France), May'85 by CBS Records. Dist: Conifer, Discovery, Swift

Cassette: released on CBS(France), May'85 by CBS Records. Dist: Conifer, Discovery, Swift

DUKE-CLASSIC TRANSCRIPTIONS.
Tracks: / West Indian pancake / Love and I / John Hardy's wife / Clementine / Love like this can't last / After all / Girl of my dreams, the / Jumpin' punkins / Frankie and Johnny / Flamingo / It's sad but true / Mooch, The / Ring dem bells / Frustration / Coloratura / Rose of the Rio Grande / Love you madly / Take the 'A' train / Tone parallel to Harlem / Duet / Take the 'A' train / bounce / I hear a rhapsody / Madame will drop her shawl / Frenesi / Until tonight.
Notes: Double album, double cassette. Mono.A Vee Jay recording. Licensed from Charly Records APS. This compilation (P) 1986 Charly Holdings Ltd. (C) 1986 Charly Records Ltd. Double LP.
Album: released on Affinity, May'86 by Charly Records. Dist: Charly, Cadillac

DUKE ELLINGTON On various discs 1945-46.
Album: released on Jazz Live, Apr'81

Album: released on Kings Of Jazz, Apr'81 Dist: Jazz Horizons, Jazz Music, Celtic Music

Cassette: released on Audio Fidelity, Oct'84 Dist: PRT

DUKE ELLINGTON 1927-30.
Album: released on Swaggie (Australia), Jan'83

DUKE ELLINGTON AND HIS ORCHESTRA (Ellington, Duke & His Orchestra).
Notes: Featuring Paul Gonsalves.
Compact disc: released on Carrere(France), Dec'86 by Carrere Records (France). Dist: PRT

DUKE ELLINGTON COLLECTION, THE.
Album: released on Deja Vu, Aug'85 by Deja Vu Records. Dist: Counterpoint Distribution, Record Services Distribution (Ireland)

Cassette: released on Deja Vu, Aug'85 by Deja Vu Records. Dist: Counterpoint Distribution, Record Services Distribution (Ireland)

DUKE ELLINGTON DANCE 1958.
Album: released on Unique Jazz, Apr'81 Dist: Swift, Jazz Music, Jazz Horizons

Album: released on Jazz Connoisseur, Apr'79 Dist: Jazz Horizons, Jazz Music, Swift, Wellard, Chris

DUKE ELLINGTON & HIS ORCHESTRA : 1943 VOL.4 (Ellington, Duke & His Orchestra).
Album: released on Circle, Jul'87 Dist: Jazz Music

DUKE ELLINGTON & HIS ORCHESTRA 1940-41 (Ellington, Duke & His Orchestra).
Album: released on Joker (Import), Apr'81

DUKE ELLINGTON & HIS FAMOUS ORCHESTRA (Ellington, Duke & Johnny Hodges & His Famous Orchestra).
Album: released on Rarities, Apr'81

DUKE ELLINGTON & JOHN COLTRANE (Ellington, Duke & John Coltrane).
Album: released on Jasmine, Jun'82 by Jasmine Records. Dist: Counterpoint, Lugtons, Taylor, H.R., Wellard, Chris, Swift, Cadillac

Cassette: released on Jasmine, Jun'82 by Jasmine Records. Dist: Counterpoint, Lugtons, Taylor, H.R., Wellard, Chris, Swift, Cadillac

DUKE ELLINGTON MEETS COLEMAN HAWKINS.
Tracks: / Limbo jazz / Mood indigo / Ray Charles's place / Wanderlust / You dirty dog / Self portrait(of the bean) / Jeep is jumpin' (the) / Recitative (The).
Compact disc: released on Impulse, Feb'87 by Impulse Records. Dist: MCA, Polygram

Album: released on Jasmine, Jun'82 by Jasmine Records. Dist: Counterpoint, Lugtons, Taylor, H.R., Wellard, Chris, Swift, Cadillac

Cassette: released on Jasmine, Jun'82 by Jasmine Records. Dist: Counterpoint, Lugtons, Taylor, H.R., Wellard, Chris, Swift, Cadillac

DUKE ELLINGTON ORCHESTRA (Ellington, Duke & His Orchestra).
Album: released on Queen-Disc, Apr'81 Dist: Celtic Music, JSU, Jazz Horizons, Jazz Music

Album: released on Gramercy 5, Mar'79 by Gramercy 5 Records. Dist: Swift

Album: released on Queen-Disc, Apr'73 Dist: Celtic Music, JSU, Jazz Horizons, Jazz Music

DUKE ELLINGTON & PAUL GONSALVES (Ellington, Duke & Paul Gonsalves).
Compact disc: released on Carrere, Apr'87 by Carrere Records. Dist: PRT, Spartan

DUKE ELLINGTON PRESENTS.
Tracks: / Summertime / Laura / I can't get started / My funny valentine / Everything but you / Frustration / Cotton tail / Daydream / Deep purple / Indian summer / Blues.
Notes: A Bethlehem recording.
Cassette: released on Affinity, Sep'86 by Charly Records. Dist: Charly, Cadillac

DUKE ELLINGTON WITH ALICE BABS & NILS LINDBERG (Ellington, Duke & Alice Babs).
Album: released on Phontastic, May'79 Dist: Wellard, Chris

DUKE FEATURES HODGES (Ellington, Duke & His Orchestra).
Album: released on Unique Jazz, Jul'83 Dist: Swift, Jazz Music, Jazz Horizons

DUKE IS ON THE AIR 1952, THE.
Album: released on Aircheck, Apr'79

DUKE'S BIG 4.
Compact disc: by Pablo Records. Dist: Wellard, Chris, IMS-Polygram BMG

DUKE'S BIG FOUR (Ellington, Duke, Quartet).
Album: released on Pablo, '82 by Pablo Records. Dist: Wellard, Chris, IMS-Polygram, BMG

Cassette: released on Pablo, '82 by Pablo Records. Dist: Wellard, Chris, IMS-Polygram, BMG

DUKE,THE 1940.
Notes: Live from the Crystal Ballroom in Fargo, N.D. Mono.
Double Album: released on Jazz Society, Mar'87 Dist: Jazz Music, Swift

EARLY CLASSICS VOL.III, THE 1926-28.
Cassette: released on Neovox, Jan'82 by Neovox Records. Dist: VJM Records, Jazz Music, JSU, Chris Wellard

EARLY CLASSICS VOL.2, THE.
Album: released on Nevox, Oct'79

EARLY CLASSICS VOL.1, THE.
Album: released on Nevox, Oct'79

ELEGANT MR ELLINGTON, THE.
Album: released on Swinghouse, '84 Dist: Jazz Music Distribution, Swift Distribution, Chris Wellard Distribution

Cassette: released on Swinghouse, '84 Dist: Jazz Music Distribution, Swift Distribution, Chris Wellard Distribution

ELLINGTON '56.
Compact disc: by Charly Records. Dist: Charly, Cadillac

Tracks: / East St Louis toddle-oo / Creole love call / Stompy Jones / Jeep is jumpin' / Jack the bear / In a mellow tone / Ko-ko / Midriff / Stomp, look and listen / Unbooted character / Lonesome lullaby / Upper Manhattan medical group / Cottontail / Daydream / Deep purple / Indian summer / Laura / Blues.
(Ellington, Duke & His Orchestra).
Notes: Mono production. With Johnny Hodges & His Orch.
Album: released on Storyville, May'86 by Storyville Records. Dist: Jazz Music Distribution, Swift Distribution, Chris Wellard Distribution, Counterpoint Distribution

ELLINGTON INDIGOES.
Album: released on CBS(Import), Jun'86 by CBS Records. Dist: Conifer, Discovery, Swift

ELLINGTON MEETS COLEMAN HAWKINS.
Tracks: / You dirty dog / Self portrait (of the bean) / Jeep is jumpin', The / Recitative / Limbo jazz / Mood indigo / Ray Charles's place / Wanderlust.
Album: released on MCA, Aug'86 by MCA Records. Dist: Polygram, MCA

Album: released on Impulse, Oct'85 by Impulse Records. Dist: MCA, Polygram

ELLINGTON ON THE AIR (Ellington, Duke & His Orchestra).
Album: released on Bulldog, Sep'82 by Bulldog Records. Dist: President Distribution, Spartan, Swift, Taylor, H.R.

Cassette: released on Bulldog, Sep'82 by Bulldog Records. Dist: President Distribution, Spartan, Swift, Taylor, H.R.

ELLINGTON SUITES, THE.
Album: released on Pablo (USA), '82 by Pablo Records (USA). Dist: Wellard, Chris, IMS-Polygram, BMG

Cassette: released on Pablo (USA), '82 by Pablo Records (USA). Dist: Wellard, Chris, IMS-Polygram, BMG

ELLINGTON UPTOWN.
Album: released on CBS(Import), Jun'86 by CBS Records. Dist: Conifer, Discovery, Swift

ESSENTIAL DUKE ELLINGTON VOL.1, THE 1924-27.
Album: released on VJM, Apr'79 by Wellard, Chris Distribution. Dist: Wellard, Chris Distribution

FABULOUS FORTIES, THE (Ellington, Duke & His Orchestra).
Album: released on Rarities, Apr'81

FABULOUS FORTIES VOL.2, THE (Ellington, Duke & His Orchestra).
Album: released on Rarities, Apr'81

FANTASTIC.
Album: released on RCA (Special Imports Service), Jul'84

FAR AWAY STAR.
Album: released on Phontastic (Sweden), '82 by Wellard, Chris Distribution. Dist: Wellard, Chris Distribution

Cassette: released on Phontastic (Sweden), '82 by Wellard, Chris Distribution. Dist: Wellard, Chris Distribution

FESTIVAL SESSION.
Tracks: / Idiom '59. Pt.1, Vapor / Idiom 59 Pt.2 / Idiom 59-Pt III / Things ain't what they used to be / Launching pad / Perdido / Copout estension / Duael fuel-Pt.1 / Duael fuel-Pt.2 / Duael fuel-Pt.3.
Album: released on CBS, Jul'86 by CBS Records. Dist: CBS

GOIN' UP (Ellington, Duke Orchestra).
Album: released on Duke (Import), '81

Album: released on Duke, Jul'87 by Melodisc Records. Dist: Jazz Horizons, Jazz Music, Celtic Music, JSU, Swift

GOLDEN DUKE.
Double Album: released on Prestige, Oct'80 by Prestige Records (USA). Dist: RCA, JSU, Swift

GREATEST HITS:DUKE ELLINGTON.
Album: released on CBS, May'83 by CBS Records. Dist: CBS

Cassette: released on CBS, May'83 by CBS Records. Dist: CBS

GREAT, THE (Ellington, Duke & His Orchestra).
Album: released on Premier, May'85 by Premier Records. Dist: CBS

Cassette: released on Premier, May'85 by Premier Records. Dist: CBS

GREAT TIMES (Ellington, Duke & Billy Strayhorn).
Album: released on Riverside (USA), Aug'84 Dist: Fantasy (USA) Distribution

HAND SHORTS.
Album: released on Meteor, Jan'87 by Magnum Music Group Ltd. Dist: Magnum Music Group Ltd, PRT Distribution, Spartan Distribution

HARLEM.
Tracks: / Blow by blow / Caravanytutti for Cootie / Satin doll / Harlem / Things ain't what they used to be / All of me / Prowling cat, the / Opera, The / Happy reunion, A.
Compact disc: released on Pablo Jazz (USA), Apr'86 by United Artists. Dist: Swift

Album: released on Pablo (USA), Aug'85 by Pablo Records (USA). Dist: Wellard, Chris, IMS-Polygram, BMG

Cassette: released on Pablo (USA), Aug'85 by Pablo Records (USA). Dist: Wellard, Chris, IMS-Polygram, BMG

HOLLYWOOD BOWL CONCERT VOL.2 (Ellington, Duke & His Orchestra).
Album: released on Unique Jazz, Apr'81 Dist: Swift, Jazz Music, Jazz Horizons

HOLLYWOOD BOWL CONCERT, THE (Ellington, Duke & His Orchestra).
Album: released on Unique Jazz, Apr'81 Dist: Swift, Jazz Music, Jazz Horizons

HOT FROM THE COTTON CLUB (Ellington, Duke & His Orchestra).
Tracks: / Mooch, The / Harlem twist (East St St Louis toodle-oo) / Hot & bothered / Diga diga doo / Black beauty / Mood indigo / Ring dem bells / Doin' the new low down / Black and tan fantasy / Jungle jamboree / Big house blues / Old man blues / Rockin' in rhythm / Blues with a feeling, The / Misty mornin' / Goin' to town / Black and tan fantasy.
Album: released on EMI Retrospect, May'85 by EMI Records. Dist: EMI

Cassette: released on EMI Retrospect, May'85 by EMI Records. Dist: EMI

Compact disc: released on Retrospect, Oct'87 by World Records.. Estim retail price in Sep'87 was £11.99.

INDISPENSABLE DUKE ELLINGTON, VOLS.1\2.
Tracks: / Creole love call / Blues I love to sing, the / Black and tan fantasy / Washington wobble / Harlem river quiver / East St Louis toodle-oo / Blue bubbles / Black beauty / Jubilee stomp / Got everything but you / Mooche, The / Flaming youth / Saturday night function / High life / Doin' the voom voom / Harlemania / Dicty glide, The / Hot feet / Sloppy Joe / Stevedore stomp / Cotton Club stomp / Misty mornin' / Saratoga swing / Mississippi dry / Duke stops out, The / Haunted nights / Swanee shuffle / Breakfast dance / Jazz lips.
Notes: Double album. Double cassette. Mono.

INDISPENSABLE DUKE ELLINGTON VOLS. 3\4.
Tracks: / Stompy Jones / Solitude / Blue feeling / Ebony rhapsody / Live and love tonight / I met my Waterloo / My old flame / Troubled waters / My old flame / Double check stomp / Sweet dreams of love / Jungle nights in Harlem / Sweet jazz o' mine / Shout 'em / Aunt Tillie / Ring dem bells / Old man blues / Nine little miles from ten Ten Tennessee / When a black man's blue / Mood indigo / Rockin' in rhythm / Creole rhapsody Parts 1&2 / Limehouse blues / Echoes of the jungle / It's glory / Mystery song, The / Dinah / Bugle call rag / Rude interlude / Dallas doings / Dear old Southland / Daybreak express / Delta serenade.
Notes: Double album. Double cassette. Mono.
Album: released on Jazz Tribune (USA), Sep'86 Dist: Discovery

INDISPENSABLE DUKE ELLINGTON VOL.5/6, THE 1940.
Double Album: released on RCA (France), '83 by RCA Records. Dist: Discovery

INDISPENSABLE DUKE ELLINGTON VOL3/4, THE 1930-1934.
Double Album: released on RCA (France), '83 by RCA Records. Dist: Discovery

INDISPENSABLE DUKE ELLINGTON VOL.7/8, THE.
Double Album: released on RCA (France), Feb'85 by RCA Records. Dist: Discovery

INDISPENSABLE DUKE ELLINGTON VOLS. 5\6.
Tracks: / Jack the bear / Ko-ko / Ko-ko (II) / Morning glory / Conga brava / Concerto for Cootie / Bojangles / Cotton tail / Never no lament / Dusk / Bojangles (II) / Portrait of Bert Williams / Blue goose / Harlem air shaft / At a dixie roadside diner / All too soon / Rumpus in Richmond / Sepia panorama / In a mellotone / Five o'clock whistle / Warm valley / Across the track blues / Chloe / Sidewalks of New York / Pitter panther patter / Pitter panther patter (II) / Body and soul / Body and soul (II) / Sophisticated / Sophisticated lady (II) / Mr J.B. blues.
Notes: Double album. Double cassette. Mono.
Album: released on Jazz Tribune (USA), Sep'86 Dist: Discovery

Double cassette: released on Jazz Tribune (USA), Sep'86 Dist: Discovery

INDISPENSABLE DUKE ELLINGTON VOL 1/2, THE 1927-1929.
Double Album: released on RCA (France), '83 by RCA Records. Dist: Discovery

IN SWEDEN (6TH NOVEMBER 1958).
Album: released on Route 66, Oct'86

IN THE SIXTIES.
Compact disc: by RCA Records. Dist: RCA, Roots, Swift, Wellard, Chris, I & B, Solomon & Peres Distribution

IN THE UNCOMMON MARKET.
Tracks: / Bula / Silk Lace / Asphalt jungle / Starcrossed lovers / Getting sentimental over you / E.S.P. (extra sensory perception) / Paris blues / Shepherd, The (first concept) / Kinda Dukish.
Notes: Previously unreleased recordings from European concerts during the 60's. With the exception of Getting Sentimental Over You all the titles are Ellington compositions. Personnel: Cootie Williams/Cat Anderson/Roy Burrowes/Ray Nance/Lawrence Brown/ Buster Cooper/Chuck Connors/Johnny Hodges/Russell Procope/Jimmy Hamilton/ Paul Gonsalves/Harry Carney/Ernie Shepard/Sam Woodyard.
Album: released on Pablo (USA), Jan'87 by Pablo Records (USA). Dist: Wellard, Chris, IMS-Polygram, BMG

Cassette: released on Pablo (USA), Jan'87 by Pablo Records (USA). Dist: Wellard, Chris, IMS-Polygram, BMG

INTIMACY (Ellington, Duke-Small Bands).
Tracks: / Combo suite / Intimacy of the blues, The / Out south / Tell me 'bout my baby / Kentucky Avenue A.C. / Near North / Soul country / Noon morning / Rockochet / Tippy-toeing through the jungle garden / Just a-sittin' and a-rockin' / All too soon.
Notes: The material on this excellent album was recorded between March 1967 and June 1970 and features small group sessions using regular salaried musicians from the Ellington Orchestra. All these sessions were made were made during the orchestra's brief lay-offs and much of the material here was recorded almost as a rehearsal for later full orchestral versions. Personnel includes: Duke Ellington-piano\Cat Anderson-trumpet\Lawrence brown- trombone\Johnny Hodges-alto saxophone\John Lamb-Bass\Rufus Jones-Drums\Paul Consalves-tenor saxophone\Harry Carney-baritone-saxophone\Wild bill Davis- organ\Willie cook-trumpet\Victor Kaskin, Paul Kondziela-basses\Norris Turney- flute\Joe Benjamin-Bass\Harold Ashby-tenor saxophone.
Album: released on Arhoolie, Aug'86 by Arhoolie Records. Dist: Projection, Topic, Jazz Music, Swift, Roots

INTIMATE DUKE ELLINGTON, THE.
Album: released on Pablo (USA), '82 by Pablo Records (USA). Dist: Wellard, Chris, IMS-Polygram, BMG

Cassette: released on Pablo (USA), '82 by Pablo Records (USA). Dist: Wellard, Chris, IMS-Polygram, BMG

JAZZ COCKTAIL (Ellington, Duke & His Orchestra).
Album: released on ASV Living Era, Oct'83 by ASV Records. Dist: PRT

Cassette: released on ASV Living Era, Oct'83 by ASV Records. Dist: PRT

JAZZ PARTY IN STEREO.
Album: released on CBS(Import), Jun'86 by CBS Records. Dist: Conifer, Discovery, Swift

JEEP IS JUMPIN', THE (Ellington, Duke & His Orchestra).
Album: released on Affinity, May'82 by Charly Records. Dist: Charly, Cadillac

JIMMY BLANTON YEARS.
Album: released on Queen-Disc (Import), Apr'81

JOHN COLTRANE & DUKE ELLINGTON (see under Coltrane,John) (Ellington, Duke & John Coltrane).

JUMP FOR JOY.
Compact disc: released on The Compact Collection, Sep'87 by Conifer Records. Dist: Conifer Distribution

LIVE.
Double Album: released on Affinity, Aug'79 by Charly Records. Dist: Charly, Cadillac

LIVE FROM HOTEL SHERMAN, CHICAGO-VOL.1 (Ellington, Duke & His Orchestra).
Album: released on Jazz Supreme, Dec'86 Dist: Jazz Music

LIVE IN PARIS (Ellington, Duke & His Orchestra).
Tracks: / Deep purple / All of me / What else can you do with a drum / Harlem air shaft / Such sweet thunder / Stompy Jones / Things ain't what they used to be / Hi fi fo fum / El gato.
Album: released on Magic, Apr'86 Dist: Jazz Music, Submarine, Swift, Chris Wellard. Conifer

Cassette: released on Magic, Apr'86 Dist: Jazz Music, Submarine, Swift, Chris Wellard. Conifer

LOUIS ARMSTRONG & DUKE ELLINGTON VOL.1 (Ellington, Duke & Louis Armstrong).
Tracks: / Duke's place / I'm just a lucky so and so / Cotton tail / Mood indigo / Drop me off in Harlem / Do nothing till you hear from me / Beautiful American / Black and tan fantasy / Mooch / In a mellow time.
Album: released on Jazz Reactivation, Jan'82 Dist: PRT

LOUIS ARMSTRONG & DUKE ELLINGTON VOL.2 (Ellington, Duke & Louis Armstrong).
Album: released on Jazz Reactivation, May'83 Dist: PRT

MARCH 27TH, 1959 (Ellington, Duke & His Orchestra).
Album: released on From The Jazz Vault, Oct'80 by Damont Records. Dist: Swift, Taylor, H.R.

MASTERPIECES BY....
Album: released on CBS(Import), Jun'86 by CBS Records. Dist: Conifer, Discovery, Swift

Cassette:

MASTERS OF JAZZ.
Album: released on RCA (Germany), '83

MASTERS OF JAZZ VOL.6.
Album: released on Storyville, May'86 by Storyville Records. Dist: Jazz Music Distribution, Swift Distribution, Chris Wellard Distribution, Counterpoint Distribution

MIDNIGHT IN PARIS.
Album: released on CBS(Import), Jun'86 by CBS Records. Dist: Conifer, Discovery, Swift

MONEY JUNGLE.
Tracks: / Money jungle / Fleurette Africaine (The African flower) / Very special / Warm valley / REM blues / Little Max (Parfait), A / Wig wise / Switchblade / Caravan / Backward country boy blues / Solitude.
Compact disc: released on EMI, Mar'87 by EMI Records. Dist: EMI

MONEY JUNGLE*.
Notes: Original session produced by Alan Douglas. Produced for release by Michael Cuscuna.
Album: released on Manhattan, Nov'86 by President Records. Dist: Jazz Music, Swift, Taylors, Chris Wellard

MONKEY JUNGLE.
Album: released on Blue Note (USA), Sep'84

MY PEOPLE.
Album: released on Joker (Import), Apr'81

NEW ORLEANS SUITE.
Compact disc: released on Atlantic Jazz, Jul'87 by WEA Records. Dist: WEA

ONE NIGHT STAND.
Album: released on Joyce, Jul'82

PARIS JAZZ PARTY (Ellington, Duke & His Orchestra).
Album: released on Affinity, Mar'81 by Charly Records. Dist: Charly, Cadillac

PIANO IN THE BACKGROUND.
Album: released on CBS(Import), Jun'86 by CBS Records. Dist: Conifer, Discovery, Swift

PIANO IN THE FOREGROUND.
Album: released on CBS(Import), Jun'86 by CBS Records. Dist: Conifer, Discovery, Swift

PIANO REFLECTIONS (Ellington, Duke & Coleman Hawkins).
Album: released on MFP (France), May'84 by EMI Records. Dist: EMI

Cassette: released on MFP (France), May'84 by EMI Records. Dist: EMI

PIANO REFLECTIONS 1953 (Ellington, Duke Trio).
Album: released on Swaggie (Australia), Jan'83

POPULAR DUKE ELLINGTON, THE.
Album: released on RCA International, Nov'84

RAINBOW ROOM BROADCASTS 1967 (Ellington, Duke Octet).
Album: released on Unique Jazz, Apr'81 Dist: Swift, Jazz Music, Jazz Horizons

RARE LIVE PERFCORMANCES (Ellington, Duke & His Orchestra).
Album: released on Swinghouse, Apr'86 Dist: Jazz Music Distribution, Swift Distribution, Chris Wellard Distribution

Cassette: released on Swinghouse, Apr'86 Dist: Jazz Music Distribution, Swift Distribution, Chris Wellard Distribution

RARE OF ALL RAREST PERFORMANCES VOL.2.
Album: released on Kings Of Jazz, Jul'82 Dist: Jazz Horizons, Jazz Music, Celtic Music

ROCKIN' IN RHYTHM.
Tracks: / Rockin' in rhythm / Mood indigo / Double check stomp / Awful Sad / Yellow dog blues / Louisiana / Black and tan fantasy / Creole rhapsody (parts 1 & 2) / Immigration blues / East St. Louis toodle-oo / Mooche, The / New Orleans Low Down / Rent Party Blues / Cotton club stomp No. 1 / Home Again Blus / Sweet Mama / Harlem Flat Blues / Jungle Jamboree.
Album: released on Affinity, Mar'87 by Charly Records. Dist: Charly, Cadillac

ROYALTY.
Album: released on Allegiance, Jul'84 by PRT Records. Dist: PRT

Cassette: released on Allegiance, Jul'84 by PRT Records. Dist: PRT

SERENADE TO SWEEDEN.
Album: released on Black Lion, Oct'82 by Black Lion Records. Dist: Jazz Music, Chris Wellard, Taylor, H.R., Counterpoint, Cadillac

Cassette: released on Black Lion, '83 by Black Lion Records. Dist: Jazz Music, Chris Wellard, Taylor, H.R., Counterpoint, Cadillac

SHOWCASE.
Triple album / cassette: released on Pathe MarconiFrance), Dec'84

SIDE BY SIDE (Ellington, Duke & Johnny Hodges).
Tracks: / Stompy Jones / Squeeze me / Big shoe / Going up / Just a memory / Let's fall in love / Ruin / Bend one / You need go rock.
Album: released on Polydor, Feb'86 by Polydor Records. Dist: Polygram, Polydor

Cassette: released on Polydor, Feb'86 by Polydor Records. Dist: Polygram, Polydor

Compact disc: released on Polydor, Feb'86 by Polydor Records. Dist: Polygram, Polydor

SIDE BY SIDE.
Compact disc: by Polydor Records. Dist: Polygram, Polydor

SONGBOOK 2 (see Vaughan, Sarah) (Ellington, Duke & Sarah Vaughan).

SOPHISTICATED LADY.
Tracks: / Take the 'A' train / Perdido / In a mellow tone / Happy go lucky local / Sophisticated lady / I got it bad and that ain't good / Mood indigo / It don't mean a thing / Things ain't what they used to be / I let a song go out of my heart / Something to live for / Black beauty / Caravan / Dancers in love / Solitude / Black and tan fantasy.
Album: released on CBS, Jul'86 by CBS Records. Dist: CBS

Cassette: released on CBS, Jul'86 by CBS Records. Dist: CBS

Album: released on CBS(France), Jan'84 by CBS Records. Dist: Conifer, Discovery, Swift

Cassette: released on CBS(France), Jan'84 by CBS Records. Dist: Conifer, Discovery, Swift

STOCKHOLM CONCERT 1966, THE (see Fitzgerald, Ella & Duke Ellington) (Ellington, Duke & Ella Fitzgerald).

STUDIO SERIES, THE, VOL.8 - 1933-1967.
Album: released on Up To Date (USA), Jan'87 Dist: Jazz Music

STUDIO SERIES, VOLUME 6 1930\58.
Album: released on Up To Date, May'86

STUDIO SERIES, VOLUME 7-1929-62.
Album: released on Up To Date, May'86

SYMPHONIC ELLINGTON (Ellington, Duke & His Orchestra).
Album: released on Trend (USA), Jun'83 by Discovery Records. Dist: Flexitron Distributors Ltd, Swift

TAKE THE A TRAIN.
Album: released on Astan, Nov'84 by Astan Records. Dist: Counterpoint

Cassette: released on Astan, Nov'84 by Astan Records. Dist: Counterpoint

TENDERLY.
Tracks: / Overture from Nutcracker Suite / Such sweet thunder / Black and tan fantasy / Creole love call / Mooch, The / Tulip or turnip / Tenderly / All of me / Jeeps blues.
Album: released on Showcase, Apr'86 Dist: Counterpoint

Cassette: released on Showcase, Apr'86 Dist: Counterpoint

THIS ONE'S FOR BLANTON (Ellington, Duke & Ray Brown).
Album: released on Pablo (USA), '82 by Pablo Records (USA). Dist: Wellard, Chris, IMS-Polygram, BMG

Cassette: released on Pablo (USA), '82 by Pablo Records (USA). Dist: Wellard, Chris, IMS-Polygram, BMG

TRANSCRIPTIONS YEARS, THE (Ellington, Duke & His Orchestra).
Album: released on Swaggie (Australia), Jan'83

TREASURY SHOW VOL.1.
Album: released on Nostalgia (Sweden), '82 by Wellard, Chris Distribution. Dist: Wellard, Chris Distribution

TREASURY SHOW VOL.2.
Album: released on Nostalgia (Sweden), '82 by Wellard, Chris Distribution. Dist: Wellard, Chris Distribution

TREASURY SHOW VOL.3.
Album: released on Nostalgia (Sweden), '82 by Wellard, Chris Distribution. Dist: Wellard, Chris Distribution

TREASURY SHOW VOL.4.
Album: released on Nostalgia (Sweden), '82 by Wellard, Chris Distribution. Dist: Wellard, Chris Distribution

TREASURY SHOW VOL.5.
Album: released on Nostalgia (Sweden), '82 by Wellard, Chris Distribution. Dist: Wellard, Chris Distribution

TREASURY SHOW VOL.6.
Album: released on Nostalgia (USA), '82 by Sonic Arts Corporation.

TREASURY SHOW VOL.7.
Album: released on Nostalgia (Sweden), '82 by Wellard, Chris Distribution. Dist: Wellard, Chris Distribution

TREASURY SHOW VOL.8.
Album: released on Nostalgia (Sweden), '82 by Wellard, Chris Distribution. Dist: Wellard, Chris Distribution

UNCOMMON MARKET, (THE).
Compact disc: released on Pablo (USA), Apr'87 by Pablo Records (USA). Dist: Wellard, Chris, IMS-Polygram, BMG

UNFORGETTABLE DUKE ELLINGTON, THE.
Double cassette: released on Pickwick (Ditto series), Jan'83

UNUSUAL ELLINGTON, THE (Ellington, Duke & His Orchestra).
Album: released on Nostalgia (Sweden), '82 by Wellard, Chris Distribution. Dist: Wellard, Chris Distribution

UP IN DUKE'S WORKSHOP.
Album: released on Pablo (USA), '82 by Pablo Records (USA). Dist: Wellard, Chris, IMS-Polygram, BMG

Cassette: released on Pablo (USA), '82 by Pablo Records (USA). Dist: Wellard, Chris, IMS-Polygram, BMG

VIP.
Album: released on Swinghouse, '84 Dist: Jazz Music Distribution, Swift Distribution, Chris Wellard Distribution

VOL.1 - DUKE 56\62.
Tracks: / Black and tan fantasy / A-flat minor / Suburban beauty / Cafe au lait / West Indian dance / Cop out / Allah-bye / Piano improvisations Pt.1, Pt.2, Pt.3, Pt.4 / Commercial time / Mood indigo / Willow weep for me / Mood indigo (II) / Where or when / All the things you are / Night and day / Slamar in D flat / Track / Jones / Lullaby of birdland / Feet bone / Red carpet / Satin doll / When I trilly with my filly / Anatomy of a murder.
Album: released on CBS, Jul'86 by CBS Records. Dist: CBS

Cassette: released on CBS, Jul'86 by CBS Records. Dist: CBS

VOL II - DUKE 56\62.
Tracks: / Brown penny / Pie eyes blues / Sentimental lady / Sweet and pungent / Swinger's jump / Lullaby of birdland / Dreamy sort of thing / Wailer, The / Asphalt jungle suite- wild car, cops and robbers / Lotus blossom / Matume / Just a-sittin' and a-rockin' / Tulip or turnip / Jingle bells / One more once / Blues in hoss flat / Asphalt jungle theme-Pt 1, Pt 3 / Bon amour (guitar amour) / Paris blues- Pt.I, Pt.II, Pt.III / Turkish coffee / Jingle bells.
Notes: Double album.
Album: released on CBS, Jul'86 by CBS Records. Dist: CBS

Cassette: released on CBS, Jul'86 by CBS Records. Dist: CBS

VOLUME III - DUKE 56-62.
Tracks: / If you were in my place / Just a-sittin' and a-rockin' / Pomegranate / Rock city rock / Your love has faded / My heart, my mind, my everything / Together / Duke's place / Hand me down love / Walkin' and singin' the blues / I can't give you anything but love / To know you is to love you / Lonely ones, / Lost in loveliness / I'm just a lucky so and so / One more once / Day in, day out / Why was I born / Love you madly / Where in the world / Song from 'Moulin Rouge'.
Album: released on CBS, Jul'86 by CBS Records. Dist: CBS

Cassette: released on CBS, Jul'86 by CBS Records. Dist: CBS

WASHINGTON D.C. ARMORY CONCERT, THE.
Album: released on Nostalgia (Sweden), '82 by Wellard, Chris Distribution. Dist: Wellard, Chris Distribution

WAY LOW - LANGLEY FIELDS BROADCAST 8/12/43 - 19/11/42 - 5/43 (Ellington, Duke Orchestra).
Album: released on Duke, Jul'87 by Melodisc Records. Dist: Jazz Horizons, Jazz Music, Celtic Music, JSU, Swift

WEST COAST TOUR.
Album: released on Jazz Bird, '82 Dist: Cassion (Melandy)

Cassette: released on Jazz Bird, '82 Dist: Cassion (Melandy)

Ellington, Ray

GOON SHOW HITS (Ellington, Ray & Quartet).
Album: released on BBC, '74 by BBC Records & Tapes. Dist: EMI, PRT, Pye

LONG BLACK NYLONS.
Single (7"): by Northwood Records. Dist: Backs-Cartel

Elliot, Derek

YORKSHIRE RELISH (Elliot, Derek & Dorothy & Nadine).
Album: released on Tradition, Aug'76 Dist: JSU, Cassion Distribution, Celtic Music, Jazz Music, Projection, Roots Records

Elliot, Ian

FAKE ALL YOUR DREAMS.
Single (7"): released on Office Box, Dec'82 by Office Box Records. Dist: Red Rhino Distribution, Cartel Distribution

Single (12"): released on Office Box, Dec'83 by Office Box Records. Dist: Red Rhino Distribution, Cartel Distribution

Elliott, Jack

JACK ELLIOTT OF BIRTLEY.
Album: released on Leader, '81 Dist: Jazz Music, Projection

MAKIN' ME HAPPY.
Single (7"): released on Rubber, May'83 by Rubber Records. Dist: Roots Distribution, Projection Distribution, Jazz Music Distribution, Celtic Music Distribution, JSU Distribution, Spartan Distribution

MULESKINNER.
Album: released on Topic, '81 Dist: Roots Distribution

OUT OF THE BROWN.
Album: released on Rubber, Jun'82 by Rubber Records. Dist: Roots Distribution, Projection Distribution, Jazz Music Distribution, Celtic Music Distribution, JSU Distribution, Spartan Distribution

ROLL ON BUDDY.
Album: released on Topic, '81 Dist: Roots Distribution

TALKING WOODY GUTHRIE.
Album: released on Topic, '81 Dist: Roots Distribution

Elliott, Mike

AT LAST IT'S MIKE ELLIOTT.
Album: released on Rubber, Jul'83 by Rubber Records. Dist: Roots Distribution, Projection Distribution, Jazz Music Distribution, Celtic Music Distribution, JSU Distribution, Spartan Distribution

Cassette: released on Rubber, Jul'83 by Rubber Records. Dist: Roots Distribution, Projection Distribution, Jazz Music Distribution, Celtic Music Distribution, JSU Distribution, Spartan Distribution

Ellis, Alton

25TH SILVER JUBILEE.
Album: released on Skynote, May'84 Dist: Sidewalk Records

Cassette: released on Skynote, Sep'84 Dist: Sidewalk Records

BABY I LOVE YOU (Ellis, Alton & Ranking Trevor).
Single (12"): released on Treasure Isle, Oct'83 by Treasure Isle Records. Dist: Jetstar

BAMMY IN MY TIME.
Single (12"): released on All Tone, Jul'85 Dist: Jetstar

CONTINUATION.
Album: released on All Tone, Dec'85 Dist: Jetstar

DAY DREAMING.
Album: released on Silver Camel, Feb'83 Dist: Jetstar, Rough Trade

FOREVER AND EVER.
Single (12"): released on Skynote, Mar'84 Dist: Sidewalk Records

GIMME YOUR LOVE.
Single (12"): released on Jah Life, Oct'85 by Jah Life Records. Dist: Jetstar

I CAN'T STAND IT.
Single (12"): released on Treasure Isle, Dec'83 by Treasure Isle Records. Dist: Jetstar

I DON'T KNOW WHY.
Tracks: / I don't know why / Iron rock special.
Single (12"): released on All Tone, Apr'86 Dist: Jetstar

JUBILEE VOL.2.
Cassette: released on Skynote, Sep'86 Dist: Sidewalk Records

JUBILEE VOLUME 2.
Album: released on Skynote, Jul'85 Dist. Sidewalk Records

LIVE AND LOVE (Ellis, Alton & John Holt).
Tracks: / live and love / Live and love (Version).
Single (12"): released on Magnificent Master Blaster, Sep'86 Dist: Jetstar

LOVE IS TOPS.
Single (7"): released on Body Music, Apr'83 by Body Music Records. Dist: Jetstar

LOVE TO SHARE.
Album: released on Third World, Apr'79 Dist: Jetstar Distribution

STILL IN LOVE.
Album: released on Horse, Feb'85 by Trojan Records. Dist: Pinnacle

SUNDAY MORNING.
Album: released on Studio One, Aug'87 Dist: Jetstar

TELEPHONE LINE (Ellis, Alton & Tony J.).
Single (12"): released on Cypron, Aug'83

TOO LATE TO TURN BACK NOW.
Single (12"): released on Fashion, Nov'82 by Fashion Records. Dist: PRT, Jetstar

WISE BIRD.
Single (7"): released on Bluebird, May'83 by Bluebird Records. Dist: EMI, Jetstar

Ellis, Bobbie

UNDER BEACON'S BROW.
Album: released on Fellside, '83 by Fellside Records. Dist: Roots, Jazz Music, Celtic Music, Projection

Album: released on Fellside, Apr'81 by Fellside Records. Dist: Roots, Jazz Music, Celtic Music, Projection

Ellis, Don

HOW TIME PASSES.
Album: released on Candid, Dec'85 Dist: Counterpoint, Cadillac

Ellis, Ellie

BREATH OF FRESH AIR, A (Ellis, Ellie & Sara Grey).
Album: released on Fellside, '83 by Fellside Records. Dist: Roots, Jazz Music, Celtic Music, Projection

Ellis, Herb

GREAT GUITARS AT THE WINERY (Ellis, Herb, Charlie Byrd & Barney Kessel).

HERB MIX.
Album: released on Concord Jazz(USA), Apr'82 by Concord Jazz Records (USA). Dist: IMS, Polygram

SOFT AND MELLOW.
Album: released on Concord Jazz(USA), Mar'79 by Concord Jazz Records (USA). Dist: IMS, Polygram

TWO FOR THE ROAD (Ellis, Herb & Joe Pass).
Compact disc: released on Pablo (USA), May'86 by Pablo Records (USA). Dist: Wellard, Chris, IMS-Polygram, BMG

Album: released on Pablo (USA), '82 by Pablo Records (USA). Dist: Wellard, Chris, IMS-Polygram, BMG

Cassette: released on Pablo (USA), '82 by Pablo Records (USA). Dist: Wellard, Chris, IMS-Polygram, BMG

Ellis, Hortense

JAMAICAS FIRST LADY OF SONG.
Album: released on Third World, Dec'77 Dist: Jetstar Distribution

UNEXPECTED PLACES.
Single (12"): released on Burning Sounds, Jun'82 by Ross, Bill/Burning Sounds Records. Dist: PRT

Ellis, John

FIRE IN THE KILT (Ellis, John & His Highland Country Band).
Album: released on Lismor, Jul'87 by Lismor Records. Dist: Lismor, Roots, Celtic Music

JOHN ELLIS & HIS HIGHLAND COUNTRY BAND (Ellis, John & His Highland Country Band).
Album: released on Lismor, Nov'80 by Lismor Records. Dist: Lismor, Roots, Celtic Music

JOHN ELLIS & HIS HIGHLAND COUNTRY BAND (Ellis, John & His Highland Country Band).
Album: released on Ross, Dec'86 by Ross Records. Dist: Ross Distribution, Roots Distribution

Cassette: released on Ross, Dec'86 by Ross Records. Dist: Ross Distribution, Roots Distribution

REEL KICK, A (Ellis, John & His Highland Country Band).
Album: released on Lismor, Nov'82 by Lismor Records. Dist: Lismor, Roots, Celtic Music

Cassette: released on Lismor, Nov'82 by Lismor Records. Dist: Lismor, Roots, Celtic Music

Ellis, John Fury

MICROGROOVE.
Tracks: / Babies in jars / Curve of the earth / Amazaface / Hit man / Hollow Graham.
Single (12"): released on Shanghai, Jan'87

Ellis, Mark

CRAZY LOVE.
Single (12"): released on EAB, Mar'83 by EAB Records. Dist: Jetstar

Ellis, Michael

ALL MY LOVE FOR YOU.
Tracks: / All my love for you.
Single 10": released on Big One, Feb'87 Dist: Jetstar, Marcus Distribution, PRT

Single (12"): released on Big One, Feb'87 Dist: Jetstar, Marcus Distribution, PRT

SUPER LOVE.
Single (12"): released on Big One, Aug'87 Dist: Jetstar, Marcus Distribution, PRT

Ellis, Noel

DANCING PARTNER.
Tracks: / Dancing partner / Dreadlocks time.
Single (12"): released on VIP, Aug'86 Dist: Jetstar Distribution

Single (12"): released on Jam Can, Dec'83 by Jam Can Records. Dist: Jetstar

GENESIS TO REVELATIONS.
Single (12"): released on All Tone, Jun'84 Dist: Jetstar

Single (12"): released on All Tone, Jun'84 Dist: Jetstar

Ellison, Lorraine
STAY WITH ME.
Album: released on Blue Moon, Aug'85 Dist: Magnum Music Group Ltd, PRT, Spartan

Single (7"): released on Warner Brothers, Jul'81 by Warner Bros Records. Dist: WEA

Ellis, Ron
HERE COMES SUMMER.
Single (7"): released on Rox, Jun'81 by Rox Records. Dist: Spartan Distribution

Ellis, Shirley
CLAPPING SONG.
Single (7"): released on Old Gold, Jul'82 by Old Gold Records. Dist: Lightning, Jazz Music, Spartan, Counterpoint

Ellis & The Crew
SHAKA.
Album: released on Dublar, Aug'85 by Dublar Records. Dist: Jetstar

Ellis, Tony
BABA TUNDE.
Album: released on Polydor, Apr'82 by Polydor Records. Dist: Polygram, Polydor

Elman, Ziggy
1947 (Elman, Ziggy & His Orchestra).
Notes: With Virginia Maxey, Bob Manning.
Album: released on Circle(USA), Jun'86 by Jazzology Records (USA). Dist: Jazz Music, Swift, Chris Wellard

El Mubarak, Abdel Aziz
ABEL AZIZ EL MUBARAK.
Album: released on Globestyle, 7 Sep'87 by Ace Records. Dist: Projection

Eloy
CODENAME WILDGEESE.
Album: released on IMS, Mar'85 by Polydor Records. Dist: IMS, Polygram

COLOURS.
Album: released on EMI (Germany), '83 by EMI Records. Dist: Conifer

FOOLS.
Single (7"): released on Heavy Metal Worldwide, Nov'83 by FM-Revolver Records. Dist: EMI

Picture disc single: released on Heavy Metal Worldwide, Nov'83 by FM-Revolver Records. Dist: EMI

INSIDE.
Album: released on EMI (Germany), Jun'83 by EMI Records. Dist: Conifer

LIVE.
Album: released on EMI (Germany), '83 by EMI Records. Dist: Conifer

METROMANIA.
Compact disc: by FM-Revolver Records. Dist: EMI

Album: released on Heavy Metal Worldwide, Sep'84 by FM-Revolver Records. Dist: EMI

Special: released on Heavy Metal Worldwide, Sep'84 by FM-Revolver Records. Dist: EM'

Cassette: released on Heavy Metal Worldwi 1e, Sep'84 by FM-Revolver Records. Dist: EMI

PERFORMANCE.
Album: released on Heavy Metal, Apr'83 by FM-Revolver Records. Dist: EMI

Cassette: released on Heavy Metal, Apr'83 by FM-Revolver Records. Dist: EMI

Picture disc single: released on Heavy Metal, Apr'83 by FM-Revolver Records. Dist: EMI

PLANETS.
Album: released on Heavy Metal, Jul'82 by FM-Revolver Records. Dist: EMI

Picture disc album: released on Heavy Metal, Jul'82 by FM-Revolver Records. Dist: EMI

Cassette: released on Heavy Metal, Jul'82 by FM-Revolver Records. Dist: EMI

Album: released on EMI (Germany), '83 by EMI Records. Dist: Conifer

TIME TO TURN.
Album: released on Heavy Metal, Jan'83 by FM-Revolver Records. Dist: EMI

Cassette: released on Heavy Metal, Jan'83 by FM-Revolver Records. Dist: EMI

Album: released on EMI (Germany), '83 by EMI Records. Dist: Conifer

Elphick, Kenny
RAINBOW.
Single (7"): released on Flamingo, Sep'84 by Carlin Music Corp. Dist: RCA

SATURDAY.
Single (7"): released on Flamingo, Mar'84 by Carlin Music Corp. Dist: RCA

Elsdon, Alan
JAZZ JOURNEYMEN.
Album: released on Black Lion, Aug'77 by Black Lion Records. Dist: Jazz Music, Chris Wellard, Taylor, H.R., Counterpoint, Cadillac

El Seven
ENDLESS SEA.
Single (7"): released on Pop Records International, Mar'81 Dist: Pinnacle

RADIO TOKYO.
Single (7"): released on Pop Records International, Jun'80 Dist: Pinnacle

El Sonido
OYE COLUMBIA.
Tracks: / Oye Columbia / Mi Melodia.
Single (12"): released on Banana, Mar'87 Dist: Pinnacle, Fresh

Elstar, Jon
I SEE YOU COMING I want to run away.

I SEE YOU COMIN' (I WANT TO RUN AWAY).
Tracks: / I see you comin' (I want to run away) / I see you comin' (Inst).
Single (7"): released on Trojan, Aug'86 by Trojan Records. Dist: PRT, Jetstar

Single (7"): released on Trojan, Sep'85 by Trojan Records. Dist: PRT, Jetstar

El Train
ACTION STYLE.
Single (7"): released on War, Jul'85 by War Records. Dist: PRT

Single (12"): released on War, Jul'85 by War Records. Dist: PRT

Elves..
ELVES AND THE SHOEMAKER, THE various artists (Various Artists).
Cassette: released on Pickwick, '83 by Pickwick Records. Dist: Pickwick Distribution, Prism Leisure Distribution, Lugtons

Elvin, Simon
SOMEWHERE IN TIME.
Tracks: / Another land / Caught in the clouds / His love / Lifetime / Somewhere in time / King for a day / Stepping in time with you / Need in me, The / Eye for an eye / This one love / Love will take me home.
Album: released on Myrrh, Jul'87 by Word Records. Dist: Word Distribution

Cassette: released on Myrrh, Jul'87 by Word Records. Dist: Word Distribution

Elvis Brothers
FIRE IN THE CITY.
Single (7"): released on Portrait, Feb'84 by CBS Records. Dist: CBS

Elvis Connection
ELVIS CONNECTION various artists (Various Artists).
Album: released on RCA International (USA), Mar'81 by RCA Records. Dist: RCA

Cassette: released on RCA International (USA), Mar'81 by RCA Records. Dist: RCA

Elvis Hits In Deutch
ELVIS HITS IN DEUTCH (Various Artists).
Tracks: / Du liebst nicht heisse rhythmen (Baby I don't care) / Ohne dich (Loving you) / O baby, mach dich schon (Treat me nice) / Ich brauch keinen ring (Wear my ring around your neck) / Wunderbar wie du huet' wieder kuss (I got stung) / Dixieland rock / Unser haus / Hotel zur einsamkeit (Heartbreak hotel) / Tuuti Fruiti / O, wie gut (Don't be cruel) / Teddybar (teddy bear) / Immer wieder lieb' ich dich (Love me tender) / Total veruckt (All shook up).
Album: released on Bear Family, Mar'86 by Bear Family Records. Dist: Rollercoaster Distribution, Swift

Elvis hits In German
ELVIS HITS IN GERMAN VOL.3 (Various Artists).
Tracks: / Hotel zur einsamkeit / Heute geh ich nicht nach haus (Hound dog) / Blaue wildlederschuh' / Einsamer cowboy / Ich such dich, Ich brauch dich, Ich lieb dich / Immer wieder lieb 'ich dich (Love me tender) / Mach dich schon (Treat me nice) / Komm' (Don't) / King creole / Ja,so 'ne party (Party) / Wer weiss warum (Don't ask me why) / Hey baby (A big hunk of love) / Lach' nicht so (Stuck on you) / Leibe kalter als eis (Devil in disguise) / Bossa nova baby / Wer heisst hier Johnny (witchcraft).
Album: released on Bear Family, Jun'86 by Bear Family Records. Dist: Rollercoaster Distribution, Swift

ELVIS HITS IN GERMAN VOL.4 (Various Artists).
Tracks: / Manitou (Flaming star) / Das lied von der liebe (Wild in the country) / Die junge liebe ist suss (Just tell her Jim said hello) / Weit, so weit (Can't help falling in love) / Rock a hula baby / Was ist schon dabei (Moonlight swim) / Du gehorst auf's titelbuild (Good luck charm) / Der King (King of the whole wide world) / Und mit blumen im haar (The fair is moving on) / Das ist Rock and Roll (Hound dog) / Ich brauche dich dazu (I need your love tonight) / Ich komme wieder (It's now or never) / Adieu, lebewohl, goodbye (Tonight's so right for love) / Ich such dich auf allen wegen (Surrender) / Du schaust mich an (She's not you) / Bist du einsam heut' nacht (Are you lonesome tonight).
Notes: De-luxe gatefold cover.
Album: released on Bear Family, Sep'86 by Bear Family Records. Dist: Rollercoaster Distribution, Swift

ELVIS HITS IN GERMAN VOL.2 (Various Artists).
Tracks: / Bist du einsam heut nacht (Are you lonesome tonight) / Ein fremder mann (Lonely man) / Ich find kein bett (I feel so bad) / Ich suche dich (His latest flame) / Mach dich schon (Treat me nice) / Ich brauche dich dazu (I need your love tonight) / Ab und zu (A fool such as I) / Wooden heart / Hey baby (A big hunk of love) / Herz ohne gluck (Wild in the country) / Little Linda (Little sister) / Sie war all sein gluck (His latest flame) / Mein wunsch wird wahr (My wish came true) / Tut mir lied (Stuck on you) / Ich komme wieder (It's now or never) / Adieu lebewohl (Goodbye) (Tonight is so right for love).
Album: released on Bear Family, Apr'86 by Bear Family Records. Dist: Rollercoaster Distribution, Swift

Elvis, Scotty & Bill
IN THE BEGINNING.
Tracks: / Biff Collie interview / There's good rockin' tonight / Baby let's play house / Blue moon of Kentucky / I got a woman / That's all right mama / Elvis Presley interview / Tweedlee dee / Baby let's play house / Maybelline.
Compact disc: released on Topline, Apr'87 by Charly Records. Dist: Charly Distribution

Album: released on Topline, Nov'84 by Charly Records. Dist: Charly Distribution

Cassette: released on Topline, Nov'84 by Charly Records. Dist: Charly Distribution

Elvis, The Movie
ELVIS, THE MOVIE (Various Artists).
Notes: Starring kurt Russell and shelley Winters. Directed by John carpenter. The name Elvis Presley is a legend. His records have sold in excess of 500,000,000 copies. He had 32 gold albums, made 32 feature films. Elvis, themovie recreates events that actually happened. Now, for the fist time, the truthis told. This film will appeal not only to Elvis fans but to anyone interested in the life of the worlds most famous and beloved star. Total playing time: 120 minutes.
Video-cassette (VHS): released on Picture Time Video, Sep'86 Dist: VCL

Ely, Joe
HI-RES.
Album: released on MCA, Apr'84 by MCA Records. Dist: Polygram, MCA

Cassette: released on MCA, Apr'84 by MCA Records. Dist: Polygram, MCA

JOE ELY.
Album: released on MCA, Aug'81 by MCA Records. Dist: Polygram, MCA

Cassette: released on MCA, Aug'81 by MCA Records. Dist: Polygram, MCA

LORD OF THE HIGHWAY.
Notes: Brand new LP by cult Texan country rocker. Only LP on UK release, band features ex-Rolling Stones sax player Bobby Keyes.
Album: released on Demon, Sep'87 by Demon Records. Dist: Pinnacle. Estim retail price in Sep'87 was £5.99.

Album: released on Demon, Sep'87 by Demon Records. Dist: Pinnacle. Estim retail price in Sep'87 was £5.99.

Compact disc: released on Demon, Sep'87 by Demon Records. Dist: Pinnacle. Estim retail price in Sep'87 was £11.99.

Ely, Pat
COUNTRY TRACKING.
Album: released on Homespun(Ireland), '82 by Outlet Records. Dist: Outlet

Cassette: released on Homespun(Ireland), '82 by Outlet Records. Dist: Outlet

Emanon
FRESH BEATS.
Single (7"): released on Urban, Aug'87 by Polydor Records. Dist: Polygram

Single (12"): released on Urban, Aug'87 by Polydor Records. Dist: Polygram

Emblow, Jack
ALABAMY BOUND (Emblow, Jack & His Riverboat Collection).
Album: released on Maestro, Mar'87 by Maestro Records.

AROUND THE WORLD (Emblow, Jack & The French Collection).
Album: released on Dansan, Dec'83 by Spartan Records. Dist: Spartan

BEST OF (Emblow, Jack & The French Collection).
Compact disc: released on Maestro, Jul'86 by Maestro Records.

ENJOY YOURSELF VOL.2.
Tracks: / J'attendrai / Tango musette / Tango of the bells / Canadian capers / Five foot two / Good morning / Irish medley / Singing piano / Call you sweetheart / Summer holiday / Spread a little happiness / Rumba cassis / Tonight / Sleepy time gal.
Notes: Mail order address: Accordion Record Club, 146, Birmingham Road, kidderminster, Worcs. DY10 2SL. Tel: 0562 746105.
Album: released on Accordion Record Club, Jul'86 by Accordion Record Club Records. Dist: Accordion Record Club

ENJOY YOURSELF VOL.1.
Tracks: / Whistle medley / Happy talk / Smile / Under the roofs of Paris / Blowin' bubbles / Sophie's choice / Enjoy yourself / Frenesi / Numero / Nola / Bring me sunshine.
Notes: Mail order distribution address: Accordion Record Club, 146, Birmingham Road, Kidderminster, Worcs. DY10 2SL. Tel: 0562 746105.
Album: released on Accordion Record Club, Jul'86 by Accordion Record Club Records. Dist: Accordion Record Club

Cassette: released on Accordion Record Club, Jul'86 by Accordion Record Club Records. Dist: Accordion Record Club

I LOVE PARIS.
Tracks: / I love Paris / Milord\People of Paris / April in Paris / C'est si bon / La Ronde / I wish you love / 'Allo 'allo / Chanson d'amour / Mam'selle\Autumn leaves / Umbrellas of Cherbourg / Boom / Louise / My prayer.
Notes: Mail order address: 146, Birmingham Road, Kidderminster, Worcs. DY10 2SL. Tel: 0562 746105.
Album: released on Accordion Record Club, Jul'86 by Accordion Record Club Records. Dist: Accordion Record Club

VOLUME 2 (Emblow, Jack & The French Collection).
Album: released on Maestro, Jul'86 by Maestro Records.

Embryo
AFRICA.
Album: released on Materiali Sonori Maso, Mar'87

ROCK SESSIONS.
Album: released on Logo, '79 by Logo Records. Dist: Roots, BMG

Emcee 5
BEBOP FROM THE EAST COAST 1961-62.
Tracks: / One that got away, The / Stephenson rocket / Grooving at the downbeat / Mike's delema / Cox's pippin / Bridge, The / Preludes / Leftie's tune / Bell's blues / Dobsons choice.
Album: released on Birdland Records, Jun'87 by Birdland Records. Dist: RCA

HARD BOP 1960-62.
Album: released on Birdland Records, Jul'87 by Birdland Records. Dist: RCA

Emerald
DOWN TOWN.
Album: released on Megaton, Jul'86 by Megaton Records. Dist: Rough Trade Distribution, Cartel Distribution

Album: released on Megaton, Sep'85 by Megaton Records. Dist: Rough Trade Distribution, Cartel Distribution

Emerald Classics
EMERALD CLASSICS various artists (Various Artists).
Album: released on Stoic (Ireland), Jun'84

Cassette: released on Stoic (Ireland), Jun'84

Emerald Forest
EMERALD FOREST Original soundtrack (Various Artists).
Notes: Artists include; Junior Homrich, brian Gascoigne.
Album: released on Colosseum(West Germany), Jan'86 Dist: Silva Screen

Emeralds
AIN'T EASY.
Single (12"): released on Bad Gong, Oct'84 by Bad Gong Records. Dist: Jetstar

Emerald, Steve
LEARN'T ABOUT WOMAN FROM HER, I.
Single (7"): released on The Alien, Feb'83 by Alien Records. Dist: PRT Distribution

MICHAEL CARMICHAEL OF CLARE.
Single (7"): released on The Alien, Dec'82 by Alien Records. Dist: PRT Distribution

Emerald Web
CATSPAW.
Compact disc: by Pacific Records (USA). Dist: Atlantic

Emergency
POINTS OF VIEW ep.
Single (7"): released on Riot City, Mar'83 by Riot City Records. Dist: Revolver

Emerson
SOMETHING SPECIAL.
Single (7"): released on Neat, Dec'83 by Neat Records. Dist: Pinnacle, Neat

Emerson, Billy 'The Kid'
CRAZY 'BOUT AUTOMOBILES.
Special: released on Charly, '82 by Charly Records. Dist: Charly, Cadillac

LITTLE FINE HEALTHY THING.
Album: released on Charly, May'80 by Charly Records. Dist: Charly, Cadillac

Emerson, Keith
BEST OF KEITH EMERSON, (THE).
Album: released on Chord, Apr'85 by Chord Records. Dist: Charly

BEST REVENGE.
Album: released on Chord, Oct'86 by Chord Records. Dist: Charly

EMERSON COLLECTION, THE.
Tracks: / Inferno / Mater Tenebrarun / Starship / Chic Charni / Dreamer, The / Playing for keeps / Orchestral suite from Best revenge / Bach before the mast/Hello sailor / Salt cay / Prelude to Candice / Candice / Nighthawks.
Compact disc: released on Chord, Dec'86 by Chord Records. Dist: Charly

EMERSON SAMPLER.
Album: released on Chord, Oct'86 by Chord Records. Dist: Charly

HARMAGEDDON.
Album: released on Chord, Feb'87 by Chord Records. Dist: Charly

HONKY.
Album: released on Chord, May'86 by Chord Records. Dist: Charly

Album: released on Chord, Apr'85 by Chord Records. Dist: Charly

MURDEROCK.
Album: released on Chord, May'86 by Chord Records. Dist: Charly

UP THE ELEPHANT AND ROUND THE CASTLE.
Single (7"): released on Red Bus, Dec'83 by Red Bus Records. Dist: PRT

Emerson Lake & Palmer
BEST OF.
Compact disc: released on Manticore, '83 by Atlantic Records. Dist: WEA

Album: released on Atlantic, '80 by WEA Records. Dist: WEA

Cassette: released on Atlantic, '80 by WEA Records. Dist: WEA

BRAIN SALAD SURGERY.
Album: released on Manticore, '73 by Atlantic Records. Dist: WEA

Cassette: released on Manticore, '73 by Atlantic Records. Dist: WEA Deleted '86.

EMERSON, LAKE & PALMER.
Album: released on Manticore, '70 by Atlantic Records. Dist: WEA

FANFARE FOR THE COMMON MAN.
Single (7"): released on Atlantic, Jun'77 by WEA Records. Dist: WEA

IN CONCERT.
Album: released on Atlantic, Oct'79 by WEA Records. Dist: WEA Deleted '86.

Cassette: released on Atlantic, Oct'79 by WEA Records. Dist: WEA

LOVE BEACH.
Album: released on Atlantic, '78 by WEA Records. Dist: WEA

Cassette: released on Atlantic, '78 by WEA Records. Dist: WEA

PICTURES AT AN EXHIBITION.
Album: released on Manticore, '70 by Atlantic Records. Dist: WEA

Cassette: released on Manticore, '70 by Atlantic Records. Dist: WEA

TARKUS.
Album: released on Manticore, '70 by Atlantic Records. Dist: WEA

Cassette: released on Manticore, '70 by Atlantic Records. Dist: WEA Deleted '86.

TRILOGY.
Album: released on Manticore, '72 by Atlantic Records. Dist: WEA

Cassette: released on Manticore, '72 by Atlantic Records. Dist: WEA

WELCOME BACK.
Album: released on Manticore, Aug'74 by Atlantic Records. Dist: WEA

Cassette: released on Manticore, Aug'74 by Atlantic Records. Dist: WEA

WORKS.
Double Album: released on Atlantic, Dec'74 by WEA Records. Dist: WEA

Double cassette: released on Atlantic, Dec'74 by WEA Records. Dist: WEA Deleted '86.

WORKS VOLUME 2.
Tracks: / Tiger in the spotlight / When the apple blossoms bloom in the windmills of your mind / I'll be your valentine / Bullfrogs / Brain salad surgery / Barrelhouse shake down / Watching over you / So far to fall / Maple leaf rag / I believe in Father Christmas / Close but not touching.
Album: released on Atlantic, Dec'77 by WEA Records. Dist: WEA

Cassette: released on Atlantic, Dec'77 by WEA Records. Dist: WEA

Emerson Lake & Powell
EMERSON LAKE & POWELL.
Tracks: / Mars the bringer of war / Score / Learning to fly / Miracle / Touch & go / Love blind / Step aside / Lay down your guns.
Album: released on Polydor, '86 by Polydor Records. Dist: Polygram, Polydor

Cassette: released on Polydor, '86 by Polydor Records. Dist: Polygram, Polydor

Compact disc: by Polydor Records. Dist: Polygram, Polydor

TOUCH AND GO.
Tracks: / Touch and go / Learning to fly / Locomotion, The.
Single (7"): released on Polydor, Jun'86 by Polydor Records. Dist: Polygram, Polydor

Single (12"): released on Polydor, Jun'86 by Polydor Records. Dist: Polygram, Polydor

Emily
TO THE GLORY OF GOD.
Album: released on Key, May'79 by Key Records. Dist: Spartan

Emma
DON'T MAKE ME CHOOSE.
Tracks: / Only love.
Single (7"): released on RCA, Aug'87 by RCA Records. Dist: RCA, Roots, Swift, Wellard, Chris, I & B, Solomon & Peres Distribution

Single (12"): released on RCA, Aug'87 by RCA Records. Dist: RCA, Roots, Swift, Wellard, Chris, I & B, Solomon & Peres Distribution

EMMA Austen, Jane (Scales, Prunella).
Double cassette: released on Argo (Spokenword), Jul'82 by Decca Records. Dist: Polygram

FIND A WAY.
Tracks: / Find a way / Find a way (Inst.).
Single (7"): released on RCA, Sep'86 by RCA Records. Dist: RCA, Roots, Swift, Wellard, Chris, I & B, Solomon & Peres Distribution

Single (12"): released on RCA, Sep'86 by RCA Records. Dist: RCA, Roots, Swift, Wellard, Chris, I & B, Solomon & Peres Distribution

Emmanuel
EMMANUEL Various Artists (Various Artists).
Album: released on Maranatha Music, May'82

Cassette: released on Maranatha Music, May'82

Emmanuel, David
GIVING IT UP FOR LOVE.
Single (7"): released on White Lodge, Jul'83 by White Lodge Records. Dist: Unknown

WAR CRY.
Single (7"): released on In Recordings, Feb'87 Dist: RCA, DMS

Single (12"): released on In Recordings, Feb'87 Dist: RCA, DMS

WHEN I FALL IN LOVE.
Single (7"): released on White Lodge, Dec'83 by White Lodge Records. Dist: Unknown

Emmanuel, Eli
TURNING POINT.
Single (12"): released on Silver Camel, Dec'82 Dist: Jetstar, Rough Trade

Emmanuelle
EMMANUELLE 2 Original Soundtrack.
Album: by Warner Bros Records. Dist: WEA

EMMANUELLE 4 Original Soundtrack (Magna, Michael).
Album: released on Carrere(France), May'84 by Carrere Records (France). Dist: PRT

Cassette: released on Carrere(France), May'84 by Carrere Records (France). Dist: PRT

Emmanuel, Marie-Anne
MERRY CHRISTMAS AND HAPPY NEW YEAR.
Single (7"): released on Button, Nov'84 by Musical Characters Records. Dist: Spartan

Emmanuel, Robert
DON'T GET WEARY.
Single (12"): released on Black Roots, Jul'82 by Black Roots Records. Dist: Jetstar

GOT TO GET YOUR LOVE.
Single (12"): released on Black Roots, Mar'84 by Black Roots Records. Dist: Jetstar

Emma's boogie band
CROSSROADS.
Single (7"): released on Gutta (Sweden), Apr'84 Dist: Plankton Distribution

Emma's War
EMMA'S WAR Original soundtrack.
Album: released on Filmtrax, Jul'87 by Filmtrax Records. Dist: EMI

Cassette: released on Filmtrax, Jul'87 by Filmtrax Records. Dist: EMI

Emmerdale Farm
EMERDALE FARM CHURCH ALBUM (Emmerdale Farm Church Choir).
Notes: Proceeds to Save the Children.
Album: released on Spartan, Nov'85 by Spartan Records. Dist: Spartan

Cassette: released on Spartan, Nov'85 by Spartan Records. Dist: Spartan

Emmons, Buddy
BUDDY EMMONS SINGS BOB WILLS.
Album: released on Sundown, Jun'86 by Magnum Music Group Ltd. Dist: Magnum Music Group Ltd, PRT Distribution, Spartan Distribution

MINORS ALOUD.
Album: released on Flying Fish (USA), May'79 by Flying Fish Records (USA). Dist: Roots, Projection

Emotional Play
STRANGER IN MY HOME.
Single (12"): released on Edible Music, May'83

Emotion Pictures
THEY SAY SPACE IS COLD.
Single (7"): released on Cherry Red, '81 by Cherry Red Records. Dist: Pinnacle

Emotions
BEST OF MY LOVE.
Tracks: / Best of my love / Lady Marmalade / Disco lady / Indian summer (Africa).
Single (12"): released on Old Gold, Feb'86 by Old Gold Records. Dist: Lightning, Jazz Music, Spartan, Counterpoint

EMOTIONS Various artists (Various Artists).
Notes: Romantic melodies played by Roger Williams, Ronnie Aldrich, Laurindo Almeida, Chet Atkins, Nelson Riddle etc.
Compact disc: released on Bridge, Apr'87 Dist: CD Centre Distribution, Pinnacle, Target

EMOTIONS Various Session Artists (Various session artists).
Cassette: released on AIM (Budget Cassettes), Feb'83

FLOWERS.
Tracks: / Flowers / Best of my love.
Single (12"): released on Streetwave, Jul'86 by Streetwave Records. Dist: PRT Distribution

IF I ONLY KNEW.
Album: released on Motown, Jun'85 by Motown Records. Dist: BMG Distribution

Cassette: released on Motown, Jun'85 by Motown Records. Dist: BMG Distribution

MISS YOUR LOVE.
Single (7"): released on Motown, May'85 by Motown Records. Dist: BMG Distribution

Single (12"): released on Motown, May'85 by Motown Records. Dist: BMG Distribution

Emotions & Cancer
EMOTIONS & CANCER Leshan, Lawrence.
Cassette: released on Psychology, Oct'81

Emperor's new clothes
EMPEROR'S NEW CLOTHES Various Artists (Various Artists).
Special: released on Pickwick (Ladybird), Feb'83

EMPEROR'S NEW CLOTHES, (THE) Various Artists (Various Artists).
Cassette: released on Anvil, Jul'82 Dist: Anvil

EMPEROR'S NEW CLOTHES (Asher, Jane).
Cassette: released on Listen Productions, Nov'84 Dist: H.R. Taylor, Hayward Promotions Distribution

Emperor & the nightingale
EMPEROR & THE NIGHTINGALE, (THE) Various Artists (Various Artists).
Cassette: released on Anvil, Jul'82 Dist: Anvil

Empire
EXPENSIVE SOUND.
Album: released on White Line, Sep'81 by White Line Records. Dist: Pinnacle

HOT SEAT.
Single (7"): released on White Line, Sep'81 by White Line Records. Dist: Pinnacle

Empire Brass Quintet
BROADWAY BRASS.
Compact disc:

Compact disc: released on Sine Qua Non (USA), May'85 by Sine Qua Non Records (USA). Dist: Conifer

Empire State
EMPIRE STATE Original soundtrack.
Compact disc: released on Priority, '87 by Priority Records. Dist: RCA

Album: released on Priority, Jun'87 by Priority Records. Dist: RCA

Cassette: released on Priority, Jun'87 by Priority Records. Dist: RCA

Empire Strikes Back
EMPIRE STRIKES BACK Original soundtrack (Various Artists).
Compact disc: Dist: Pinnacle

Album: released on RSO, May'80

Cassette: released on RSO, May'80 Deleted '83.

Compact disc: released on RSO, May'80

Album: released on Disneyland, Dec'82 by Disneyland-Vista Records (USA). Dist: BBC Records & Tapes, Rainbow Communications Ltd(Distribution)

Cassette: released on Disneyland, Dec'82 by Disneyland-Vista Records (USA). Dist: BBC Records & Tapes, Rainbow Communications Ltd(Distribution)

Empty Quarter

DELIRIUM.
Album: released on Illuminated, May'86 by IKF Records. Dist: Pinnacle, Cartel, Jetstar

Enchanted Carols

ENCHANTED CAROLS Various artists (Various Artists).
Compact disc: by Saydisc Records. Dist: Essex, Harmonia Mundi, Roots, H.R. Taylor, Jazz Music, Swift, Projection, Gamut

FEAST OF CHRISTMAS MUSIC WITH ENCHANTED CAROLS, (A) Various Artists (Various Artists).
Album: released on Saydisc, Nov'81 by Saydisc Records. Dist: Essex, Harmonia Mundi, Roots, H.R. Taylor, Jazz Music, Swift, Projection, Gamut

Cassette: released on Saydisc, Nov'81 by Saydisc Records. Dist: Essex, Harmonia Mundi, Roots, H.R. Taylor, Jazz Music, Swift, Projection, Gamut

Compact disc: released on Saydisc, Nov'81 by Saydisc Records. Dist: Essex, Harmonia Mundi, Roots, H.R. Taylor, Jazz Music, Swift, Projection, Gamut

Enchanted valley

ENCHANTED VALLEY Various Artists (Various Artists).
Album: released on Saydisc, Sep'83 by Saydisc Records. Dist: Essex, Harmonia Mundi, Roots, H.R. Taylor, Jazz Music, Swift, Projection, Gamut

Cassette: released on Saydisc, Sep'83 by Saydisc Records. Dist: Essex, Harmonia Mundi, Roots, H.R. Taylor, Jazz Music, Swift, Projection, Gamut

Enchanting...

ENCHANTING WORLD OF COUNTRY MUSIC Various Session Artists (Various session artists).
Cassette: released on AIM (Budget Cassettes), Feb'83

Enchantment

FEEL LIKE DANCIN'.
Single (7"): released on Prelude, Apr'85 Dist: CBS

Encore Encore

ENCORE ENCORE Hits from the West End stage (London Theatre Orchestra & Singers).
Tracks: / Educating Rita / Memory / Maria / Another suitcase another hall / I know him so well / Aquarius / Edelweis / One night in Bangkok / She's so beautiful / Tomorrow / Grease / Hey there / Prepare the way of the lord / People / Don't cry for me Argentina / I don't know how to love him / Impossible dream, The / Day by day / Sound of music, The / Till there was you.
Compact disc: released on The Collection, Apr'87 by Object Enterprises Ltd. Dist: Counterpoint Distribution

Endgames

BUILDING BEAUTY.
Album: released on Virgin, Oct'83 by Virgin Records. Dist: EMI, Virgin Distribution

Cassette: released on Virgin, Oct'83 by Virgin Records. Dist: EMI, Virgin Distribution

Endless journey

ENDLESS JOURNEY PHASE 1 Various Artists (Various Artists).
Album: released on Psycho, Sep'83 Dist: Funhouse, Rough Trade

Album: released on Psycho, Sep'83 Dist: Funhouse, Rough Trade

ENDLESS JOURNEY PHASE 2 Various Artists (Various Artists).

ENDLESS JOURNEY PHASE 3 Various Artists (Various Artists).
Album: released on Psycho, Dec'83 Dist: Funhouse, Rough Trade

Endless Love

ENDLESS LOVE 15 of Motown's greatest love songs (Various Artists).
Tracks: / Endless love / With you I'm born again / Touch me in the morning / Being with you / Cruisin' / Do you know where you're going to / It's my turn / I've never been to me / Love child / Tears of a clown / All this love / Three times a lady / Someday we'll be together / I was made to love her / You're all I need to get by.
Compact disc: released on Motown, Dec'86 by Motown Records. Dist: BMG Distribution

ENDLESS LOVE Various Artists (Various Artists).
Album: released on TV, Sep'82

Cassette: released on TV, Sep'82

Endless waves

WHO PUT THE BOMP.
Single (7"): released on Meteor, Sep'84 by Magnum Music Group Ltd. Dist: Magnum Music Group Ltd, PRT Distribution, Spartan Distribution

Single (12"): released on Meteor, Sep'84 by Magnum Music Group Ltd. Dist: Magnum Music Group Ltd, PRT Distribution, Spartan Distribution

Enemies of the state

ENEMIES OF THE STATE Various Artists.
Album: released on 1 In 12, Jul'84 by Backs Records. Dist: Cartel

Enemy

FALLEN HERO.
Single (7"): released on Fall Out, Mar'82 Dist: Swift, Red Rhino, Cartel

GATEWAY TO HELL, THE.
Album: released on Fall Out, Oct'83 Dist: Swift, Red Rhino, Cartel

LAST BUT NOT LEAST.
Album: released on Rot, May'84 by Rot Records. Dist: Red Rhino Through Cartel Distributions

LAST BUT NOT LEAST (SINGLE).
Single (7"): released on Rot, May'84 by Rot Records. Dist: Red Rhino Through Cartel Distributions

LAST RITES.
Single (7"): released on Fall Out, Jul'83 Dist: Swift, Red Rhino, Cartel

PUNK'S ALIVE.
Single (7"): released on Fall Out, Aug'82 Dist: Swift, Red Rhino, Cartel

STRIKE.
Single (7"): released on Rough Trade, Nov'84 by Rough Trade Records. Dist: Rough Trade Distribution, Cartel Distribution

Single (12"): released on Rough Trade, Nov'84 by Rough Trade Records. Dist: Rough Trade Distribution, Cartel Distribution

Enemy Mine

ENEMY MINE Original soundtrack (Various Artists).
Album: released on Colosseum(West Germany), Feb'86 Dist: Silva Screen

Cassette: released on Colosseum(West Germany), Feb'86 Dist: Silva Screen

Enemy Within

TOUCH OF SUNBURN.
Tracks: / All quiet / Chinese white boy / Rock and roll feeling / Doctor / Four minute melody / Post modern blues / Eprom song / Intesity of vision / Camel's eye blues / Way you dance / End zone / Nietzche's ass.
Notes: Musicians: The Raven- Voice, guitar, programming, kalimba, saxophone. Mick Green: guitar. Ed Deane: Slide guitar, guitar synth. Peter Green: Bass, guitar. Gypie mayo: guitar, bass. Gary Peters: guitar (atonal). Lawrence Garman:harmonica.
Album: released on Red Lightnin', Jul'86 by Red Lightnin' Records. Dist: Roots, Swift, Jazz Music, JSU, Pinnacle, Cartel, Wynd-Up Distribution

Energhighs

ENERGHIGHS Various Artists (Various Artists).
Album: released on Epic, Aug'84 by CBS Records. Dist: CBS

Cassette: released on Epic, Aug'84 by CBS Records. Dist: CBS

Energy

ENERGY Various Artists.
Album: released on Electricity, Dec'84 by Electricity Records. Dist: PRT

Cassette: released on Electricity, Dec'84 by Electricity Records. Dist: PRT

ENERGY VOLUME 1 Various Artists (Various Artists).
Album: released on Electricity, Jun'85 by Electricity Records. Dist: PRT

RADIO RADIO-O.
Tracks: / Radio radio-o / Rebel with a cause.
Single (7"): released on Aros, Aug'86 by Priority. Dist: RCA

Engel, Detlef

MISTER BLUE.
Album: released on Telefunken, '80

Engelhardt, Toulouse

TOULOUSIONS.
Album: released on Briar (USA), Apr'79 by Sierra Records. Dist: Mike's Country Music Room Distribution, Projection

Engineers

POMEII LOVERS.
Single (12"): released on Waterfront, Aug'87 by Waterfront Records. Dist: Rough Trade, Cartel, Projection, Roots

Engine Room

WILD TIMES.
Single (7"): released on Arista, Sep'84 by Arista Records. Dist: RCA

Single (12"): released on Arista, Sep'84 by Arista Records. Dist: RCA

YOUR KISS IS A WEAPON.
Single (7"): released on Arista, Feb'85 by Arista Records. Dist: RCA

Single (12"): released on Arista, Feb'85 by Arista Records. Dist: RCA

Special: released on Arista, Feb'85 by Arista Records. Dist: RCA

England

LONDON STORY.
Single (7"): released on Jet, Jun'84 by Jet Records. Dist: CBS

VICTORIANA.
Single (7"): released on Jet, Nov'83 by Jet Records. Dist: CBS

WORLD OF ENGLAND, (THE) Various Artists (Various Artists).
Album: by Decca Records. Dist: Polygram

England Dan

DOWDY FERRY ROAD (England Dan/John Ford Coley).
Album: released on Big Tree, Apr'77

DR. HECKLE & MR. JIVE (England Dan/John Ford Coley).
Album: released on Atlantic, Jul'79 by WEA Records. Dist: WEA

I HEAR THE MUSIC (England Dan/John Ford Coley).
Album: released on A&M, Nov'76 by A&M Records. Dist: Polygram

NIGHTS ARE FOREVER (England Dan/John Ford Coley).
Album: released on Big Tree, Aug'76
Cat. no: **K 50297**

SOME THINGS DON'T COME EASY (England Dan/John Ford Coley).
Album: released on Big Tree, May'78

England, Natasha

DON'T WALK AWAY.
Album: released on Towerbell, Mar'85 by Towerbell Records. Dist: EMI

Cassette: released on Towerbell, Mar'85 by Towerbell Records. Dist: EMI

STAY WITH ME.
Single (7"): released on Towerbell, Nov'85 by Towerbell Records. Dist: EMI

Englands Glory

LEGENDARY LOST RECORDINGS.
Album: released on Five Hours Back, May'87 by One Big Guitar / Zippo Records. Dist: Pinnacle, Revolver, Cartel

England Supporters

OH SWEET ENGLAND.
Notes: Picture disc: plus package incl. badge, rosette etc.
Single (7"): released on Peak Records, Apr'86 by Peak Records. Dist: MIS-EMI Distribution

OH SWEET ENGLAND (1982 RELEASE).
Single (7"): released on Peak Records, Apr'82 by Peak Records. Dist: MIS-EMI Distribution

England Under Snow

CONVERSATIONS.
Tracks: / First / Strawberry / Paris / Meadow / Mersey / Petula / Ride / Five / Ice / Arthur / Edward / Jacqueline / Seaside / Waltz / Castles / Tango / Turkey / Sewing / Hornpipe / Polonaise / Barn / Goodbye.
Album: released on Snow Company, The, Aug'84 Dist: Probe Plus Distribution, Cartel

CONVERSATIONS PART 2.
Tracks: / Forget / Home / Relax / Banana / Hate / Gardening / Seven / Proud / Spain / Funk / Sad / Mirror / Umbrella / E. / Boogie / Rock / Chocolates / China / Passion / Lawn / Swing / Swing / Pain / Gold / Class / Woman / Woman (II) / Horses / Psycho / Last.
Notes: the full 'Conversations' project is now available on disc.
Album: released on Snow Company, The, Sep'86 Dist: Probe Plus Distribution, Cartel

INVITATIONS.
Tracks: / Invitations / Portrait / Use them to feel / Boys in the backroom, The / Misty blue.
Album: released on Snow Company, The, Apr'85 Dist: Probe Plus Distribution, Cartel

STUPID SEPTEMBER.
Tracks: / Stupid September / Elephant ride, The / Only for ourselves / And the problem / Stanley.
Notes: 5 - tracks: 12" lasts 20 minutes. 7" and 12" have complementary sleeves.
Single (7"): released on Snow Company, The, Sep'87 Dist: Probe Plus Distribution, Cartel

Single (12"): released on Snow Company, The, Sep'87 Dist: Probe Plus Distribution, Cartel

England World Cup Squad

THIS TIME (we'll get it right).
Single (7"): released on Englander, Mar'82 Dist: Spartan

Picture disc single: released on Englander, Mar'82 Dist: Spartan

THIS TIME.
Album: released on K-Tel, Apr'82 by K-Tel Records. Dist: Record Merchandisers Distribution, Taylors, Terry Blood Distribution, Wynd-Up Distribution, Relay Distribution, Pickwick Distribution, Solomon & Peres Distribution, Polygram

Cassette: released on K-Tel, Apr'82 by K-Tel Records. Dist: Record Merchandisers Distribution, Taylors, Terry Blood Distribution, Wynd-Up Distribution, Relay Distribution, Pickwick Distribution, Solomon & Peres Distribution, Polygram

WE'VE GOT THE WORLD AT OUR FEET.
Tracks: / When we are far from home / We've got the whole world at our feet.
Single (7"): released on Liberty, Mar'86 by Liberty-United. Dist: EMI

Single (12"): released on Columbia, May'86 by EMI Records. Dist: EMI

WORLD CUP PARTY.
Tracks: / Rule Britannia (medley) / When we are far from home / Whatever will be will be (medley) / Yellow rose of Texas (medley) / Barbados (medley) / Chicago (medley) / We've got the whole world at our feet / Happy wanderer (medley) / South of the border (medley) / On a slow boat to China (medley).
Cassette: released on Columbia, Apr'86 by EMI Records. Dist: EMI

Album: released on Columbia, Apr'86 by EMI Records. Dist: EMI

Engleman, Harry

TANGO TIME (Engleman, Harry & His Tango Orchestra).
Album: released on Savoy, Mar'87

English...

ENGLISH CANALS Various Artists (Various Artists).
Album: released on Broadside, Jun'81 by Broadside Records. Dist: Celtic Distributions, H.R. Taylor, Jazz Music, Projection, Jazz Services Unlimited Dist. (JSU)

Cassette: released on Broadside, Jun'81 by Broadside Records. Dist: Celtic Distributions, H.R. Taylor, Jazz Music, Projection, Jazz Services Unlimited Dist. (JSU)

ENGLISH GARLAND - TOPIC SAMPLER NUMBER 8 Various Artists (Various Artists).
Album: released on Topic, '81 Dist: Roots Distribution

ENGLISH MELODION PLAYERS (Various Artists).
Album: released on Plant Life, Sep'86 Dist: Roots

ENGLISH MONARCHS (line of succession).
Cassette: released on Sound Fact, Jul'81 by H.R. Taylor. Dist: Essex

ENGLISH MUSIC HERITAGE Various Artists (Various Artists).
Cassette: released on Ampro Cassettes, Sep'81

ENGLISH SPORTING BALLADS Various Artists (Various Artists).
Album: released on Broadside, Jun'81 by Broadside Records. Dist: Celtic Distributions, H.R. Taylor, Jazz Music, Projection, Jazz Services Unlimited Dist. (JSU)

Cassette: released on Broadside, Jun'81 by Broadside Records. Dist: Celtic Distributions, H.R. Taylor, Jazz Music, Projection, Jazz Services Unlimited Dist. (JSU)

Album: released on Broadside, Jun'81 by Broadside Records. Dist: Celtic Distributions, H.R. Taylor, Jazz Music, Projection, Jazz Services Unlimited Dist. (JSU)

English Air

HEY HEY(SUCH IS LIFE).
Single (7"): released on Wye, '85 Dist: Roots

JULY MARCH/ENGLISH AIR.
Single (7"): released on Paradise, '83 Dist: Jetstar, JSU, WEA

SPACE IN BETWEEN, THE.
Album: released on Wye, Jun'86 Dist: Roots

English Chamber Orchestra

MONSIGNOR QUIXOTE SUITE.
Notes: Conducted by Anton Garcia Abril.
Album: released on Red Bus, Dec'85 by Red Bus Records. Dist: PRT

Cassette: released on Red Bus, Dec'85 by Red Bus Records. Dist: PRT

MONSIGNOR QUIXOTE.
Tracks: / Monsignor Quixote / Windmills or giants.
Notes: Conducted by Anton Garcia Abril.
Single (7"): by Red Bus Records. Dist: PRT

English Chorale

CAROLS FOR CHRISTMAS.
Tracks: / O come all ye faithful / While shepherds watched / We three kings / God rest you merry gentlemen / Il dulce jubilo / Silent night / Good King Wenceslas / O little town of Bethlehem / In the bleak midwinter / First Nowell, The / Once in royal David's city / Away in a manger / Hark the herald angels sing.
Notes: All titles published (C) 1986 Chorale Music (MCPS). (P) 1986 original Sound recordings made by W.H.Smith & son Ltd.
Album: released on Fame, Oct'86 by Music For Pleasure Records. Dist: EMI

Cassette: released on Fame, Oct'86 by Music For Pleasure Records. Dist: EMI

GOLDEN GOSPEL.
Double Album: released on Warwick, Nov'83 Dist: Multiple Sound Distributors

Double cassette: released on Warwick, Nov'83 Dist: Multiple Sound Distributors

NATIONWIDE CAROLS.
Album: released on Word, Nov'79 by Word Records. Dist: Word Distribution, CBS
Cat. no: **WRD 3001**

English Country Blues

DON'T TAKE LOVE/PUT....
Single (7"): released on Rogue, '83 by Fast Forward Records. Dist: Nine Mile Distribution, Cartel Distribution

HOME AND DERANGED.
Album: released on Rogue, '83 by Fast Forward Records. Dist: Nine Mile Distribution, Cartel Distribution

Cassette: released on Rogue, '83 by Fast Forward Records. Dist: Nine Mile Distribution, Cartel Distribution

NO RULES.
Album: released on Dingles, '82 by Dingles Records. Dist: Projection

English Country Music

ENGLISH COUNTRY MUSIC Various Artists (Various Artists).
Notes: Walter Bulwer - fiddle, mandolin-banjo
Daisy Bulwer - piano
Billy Cooper - hammer dulcimer
Reg Hall - melodeon, fiddle
Mervyn Plunkett - drums
Russell Wortley - pipe, tabor
Album: released on Topic, '81 Dist: Roots Distribution

ENGLISH COUNTRY MUSIC FROM EAST ANGLIA Various artists (Various Artists).
Album: released on Topic, '81 Dist: Roots Distribution

English Dogs

FORWARD INTO BATTLE.
Album: released on Rot, '85 by Rot Records. Dist: Red Rhino Through Cartel Distributions

INVASION OF THE PORKY MEN.
Album: released on Clay, '84 by Clay Records. Dist: Pinnacle

MAD PUNX & ENGLISH DOGS.
Single (12"): released on Clay, '83 by Clay Records. Dist: Pinnacle

METALMORPHOSIS (EP).
Tracks: / Nightmare of reality / Absolution / Let the killing begin.
Single (12"): released on Under One Flag, May'86 Dist: Pinnacle

TO THE END OF THE EARTH.
Single (12"): released on Rot, '84 by Rot Records. Dist: Red Rhino Through Cartel Distributions

WHERE LEGEND BEGAN.
Album: released on Under One Flag, Nov'86 Dist: Pinnacle

English Evenings

AFTER DARK.
Album: released on Safari, '85 by Safari Records. Dist: Pinnacle

Cassette: released on Safari, '85 by Safari Records. Dist: Pinnacle

I WILL RETURN.
Single (7"): released on Safari, '85 by Safari Records. Dist: Pinnacle

Single (12"): released on Safari, '85 by Safari Records. Dist: Pinnacle

TEAR YOU DOWN.
Single (7"): released on Safari, '84 by Safari Records. Dist: Pinnacle

Single (12"): released on Safari, '84 by Safari Records. Dist: Pinnacle

THOSE BRILLIANT TEENS.
Single (7"): released on GFM, Jan'87 by GFM Records. Dist: Fast Forward, Cartel, PRT, Projection

Single (12"): released on GFM, Jan'87 by GFM Records. Dist: Fast Forward, Cartel, PRT, Projection

TOUCH/THE FINAL SUPPER.
Single (7"): released on Safari, '84 by Safari Records. Dist: Pinnacle

Single (12"): released on Safari, '84 by Safari Records. Dist: Pinnacle

WHAT'S THE MATTER WITH HELEN
English evenings.
Single (7"): released on Safari, '83 by Safari Records. Dist: Pinnacle

English folk...

ENGLISH FOLK DANCES Various Artists (Various Artists).
Album: released on H.M.V., Oct'74 by EMI Records. Dist: EMI

ENGLISH FOLK DANCES FOR YOUNG PEOPLE Various Artists (Various Artists).
Album: by EMI Records. Dist: EMI

ENGLISH FOLK SONGS A selection from the Penguin book (Various Artists).
Tracks: / When I was young / Gaol song, The / Whale catchers / Young and single sailor / False bride, The / Ratcliffe highway / Grey cock, The / Basket of eggs / One night as I lay on my bed / Banks of green willow / All things are quite silent.
Notes: Recorded and produced by Paul Adams, April 1985. Artists: Linda Adams-Vocals & english concertina\John Bowden-Vocals & anglo concertina\Martin Carthy-Vocals & guitar\Roy Harris-Vocals\Jez Lowe-vocals, guitar, Appalachian Dulcimer, cittern,harmonica & keyboards.
Album: released on Fellside, '85 by Fellside Records. Dist: Roots, Jazz Music, Celtic Music, Projection

English, Joe Band

WHAT YOU NEED.
Notes: Joe English is hard to miss. For three years he was Paul McCartney's drummer in Wings, during which time the group sold 22 million records. His conversion followed the miraculous healing of his wife who had been crippled in a road accident. Since then, he has released several christian albums and provided expertise on numerous other projects, such as Adrian Snell's 'The Virgin'. This album is punchy, rocky and direct. The songs are first class as, naturally,the playing.
Album: released on Myrrh, Mar'86 by Word Records. Dist: Word Distribution

Cassette: released on Myrrh, Mar'86 by Word Records. Dist: Word Distribution

English, Junior

BETWEEN YOU AN ME.
Single (12"): released on International English, '84 by International English Records. Dist: Jetstar

DADDY'S HOME/THE WAY WE WERE.
Single (12"): released on Exclusive, '82 Dist: Jetstar

EQUAL LOVE/WEEPING KNIGHT.
Single (12"): released on Sunsplash, '83 by Sunsplash Records. Dist: Jetstar Distribution

JACK THE RIPPER.
Album: released on Form, '81 by Form Records. Dist: Pinnacle

ONLY SIXTEEN.
Single (7"): by PRT Records. Dist: PRT

Single (12"): by PRT Records. Dist: PRT

SHE DON'T LET NOBODY.
Tracks: / She don't let nobody / She don't let nobody (version).
Single (12"): released on International English, 23 May'87 by International English Records. Dist: Jetstar

TEARS OF A CLOWN.
Single (12"): released on Ruff Cut, '84 by Ruff Cut Records. Dist: Jetstar Distribution

YOU ARE MY EVERYTHING.
Single (12"): released on International English, '84 by International English Records. Dist: Jetstar

English & Scottish

ENGLISH & SCOTTISH FOLK BALLADS Various Artists (Various Artists).
Album: released on Topic, '81 Dist: Roots Distribution

English Sub-titles

ORIGINAL DIALOGUE.
Album: released on Illuminated, '81 by IKF Records. Dist: Pinnacle, Cartel, Jetstar

TANNOY/CARS ON FIRE.
Single (7"): released on Glass, '81 by Glass Records. Dist: Nine Mile, Rough Trade, Red Rhino, Play It Again Sam

English With A Dialect

ENGLISH WITH A DIALECT.
Album: released on BBC, '74 by BBC Records & Tapes. Dist: EMI, PRT, Pye

Cassette: released on BBC, Jan'79 by BBC Records & Tapes. Dist: EMI, PRT, Pye

English With An Accent

ENGLISH WITH AN ACCENT Various Artists (Various Artists).
Album: released on BBC, '74 by BBC Records & Tapes. Dist: EMI, PRT, Pye

Cassette: released on BBC, Jan'79 by BBC Records & Tapes. Dist: EMI, PRT, Pye

Englund, Ernie

ENGLUND, ERNIE, HIS TRUMPET & THE VISBY BIG BAND (Englund, Ernie, His Trumpet & The Visby Big Band).
Album: released on Phontastic, May'86 Dist: Wellard, Chris

Enid

AERIE FAERIE NONSENSE.
Album: released on Enid, '84 by Hyperion Records. Dist: Pinnacle

Album: released on EMI, '84 by EMI Records. Dist: EMI

FAND SYMPHONIC TONE POEM.
Album: released on Enid, '85 by Hyperion Records. Dist: Pinnacle

IN THE REGION OF THE SUMMER STARS.
Album: released on Hyperion, '84 by Hyperion Records. Dist: Taylors, PRT, Gamut

Album: released on EMI, '84 by EMI Records. Dist: EMI

ITCHYCOO PARK.
Single (7"): released on Sedition, Sep'86 Dist: PRT

Single (12"): released on Sedition, Sep'86 Dist: PRT

LIVE AT HAMMERSMITH.
Album: released on Enid, '84 by Hyperion Records. Dist: Pinnacle

Album: released on Enid, '84 by Hyperion Records. Dist: Pinnacle

LOVER AND FOOLS.
Tracks: / Hall of mirrors / Sheets of blue / Lovers, The / Evensong / Bright star / Flames of power, The / Fool / Falling tower, The / Something wicked this way comes / Summer / Flood, The / In the region of the summer stars / Fantasy on Scarborough fair.
Album: released on Dojo, Aug'86 by Castle Communications Records. Dist: Cartel

Cassette: released on Dojo, Aug'86 by Castle Communications Records. Dist: Cartel

RHAPSODY IN ROCK.
Album: released on Pye, '80

SALOME.
Album: released on Enid, Mar'86 by Hyperion Records. Dist: Pinnacle

SIX PIECES.
Album: released on Hyperion, '84 by Hyperion Records. Dist: Taylors, PRT, Gamut

Cassette: released on PRT, '79 by PRT Records. Dist: PRT

SOMETHING WICKED THIS WAY COMES.
Compact disc: released on Standz-Caroline, Jan'87 Dist: Pinnacle

Album: released on Enid, '83 by Hyperion Records. Dist: Pinnacle

SPELL, THE.
Compact disc: released on Standz-Caroline, Jan'87 Dist: Pinnacle

Album: released on Hyperion, '84 by Hyperion Records. Dist: Taylors, PRT, Gamut

THEN THERE WERE NONE/LETTER....
Single (7"): released on RAK, '82 by RAK. Dist: EMI

TOUCH ME.
Album: released on Pye, '79
Cat. no: **NSPH 18593**
Cassette: released on PRT, '79 by PRT Records. Dist: PRT

Album: released on Enid, '84 by Hyperion Records. Dist: Pinnacle

Enigma

AIN'T NO STOPPIN'.
Album: released on Creole, '81 by Creole Records. Dist: Rhino, PRT

AIN'T NO STOPPING-DISCO MIX 81.
Single (7"): released on Creole, '81 by Creole Records. Dist: Rhino, PRT

Single (12"): released on Creole, '81 by Creole Records. Dist: Rhino, PRT

ENIGMA Original soundtrack (Various Artists).
Album: released on That's Entertainment, '83 by That's Entertainment Records. Dist: Pinnacle, PRT

I LOVE THE MUSIC.
Single (7"): released on Creole, '81 by Creole Records. Dist: Rhino, PRT

Single (12"): released on Creole, '81 by Creole Records. Dist: Rhino, PRT

WHICH WAY IS UP.
Tracks: / Which way is up / Car wash / Pull up to the bumper / Shake your body / Space ride.
Single (12"): released on Debut, Mar'87 by Skratch Music. Dist: PRT

Enjoy enjoy enjoy

ENJOY ENJOY ENJOY Various artists (Various Artists).
Album: released on New York Connexion, '83 by New York Connexion Records.

Ennis, Ethel

MOON WAS YELLOW, THE.
Tracks: / Moon was yellow, The / Night club.
Single (7"): released on RCA, Jul'87 by RCA Records. Dist: RCA, Roots, Swift, Wellard, Chris, I & B, Solomon & Peres Distribution

THIS IS ETHEL ENNIS.
Tracks: / He loves me / An occasional man / Dear friend / Nobody told me / A you desire me / Joey,Joey,Joey / Moon was yellow(and the night was young),The / Who will buy? / Night club / Love don't turn away / Starry eyed and breathless / When did I fall in love.
Album: released on RCA, Jun'87 by RCA Records. Dist: RCA, Roots, Swift, Wellard, Chris, I & B, Solomon & Peres Distribution

Cassette: released on RCA, Jun'87 by RCA Records. Dist: RCA, Roots, Swift, Wellard, Chris, I & B, Solomon & Peres Distribution

Ennis, Seamus

40 YEARS OF IRISH PIPING.
Album: released on Free Reed, '79 by Free Reed Records. Dist: Roots, Projection, Hobgoblin Records, Oblivion

FOX CHASE,THE.
Album: released on Tara, '79
Cat. no: **TARA 1009**
Album: released on Tara (Ireland), '82 by Tara Records. Dist: I & B Records Distribution, Record Services Distribution (Ireland), Roots Distribution

Cassette: released on Tara (Ireland), '82 by Tara Records. Dist: I & B Records Distribution, Record Services Distribution (Ireland), Roots Distribution

MUSIC AT THE GATE.
Cassette: released on Folktracks, '79 by Folktracks Cassettes. Dist: Folktracks

PURE DROP,THE.
Album: released on Tara (Ireland), '82 by Tara Records. Dist: I & B Records Distribution, Record Services Distribution (Ireland), Roots Distribution

Cassette: released on Tara (Ireland), '82 by Tara Records. Dist: I & B Records Distribution, Record Services Distribution (Ireland), Roots Distribution

SEAMUS ENNIS.
Album: released on Leader, '81 Dist: Jazz Music, Projection

UILEAN PIPES.
Album: released on Tara, '80

Album: released on Tara, '80

WANDERING MINSTREL,THE.
Album: released on Topic, '81 Dist: Roots Distribution

Ennis, Tom

James Morrison & Tom Ennis

Eno

AFTER THE HEAT (Eno/Mobius/Rodelius).
Album: released on Sky, Mar'79 by President Records.

BEGEGNUNGEN (Eno/Mobius/Rodelius/Plank).
Album: released on Sky (Germany), Aug'85

MORE BLANK THAN FRANK*.
Cassette: released on E.G., Mar'86 by Virgin Records. Dist: Virgin, EMI

Eno, Brian

AMBIENT 4 ON LAND.
Album: released on Editions EG, Apr'82 by Virgin Records. Dist: EMI

Cassette: released on Editions EG, Apr'82 by Virgin Records. Dist: EMI

ANOTHER GREEN WORLD.
Tracks: / Sky saw / Over fire island / St Elmo's fire / In dark trees / Big ship / I'll come running / Another green world / Sombre reptiles / Little fishes / Golden hours / Becalmed / Zawinul / Lava / Everything merges with the night / Spirits drifting.
Album: released on E.G., Jan'87 by Virgin Records. Dist: Virgin, EMI

Cassette: released on E.G., Jan'87 by Virgin Records. Dist: Virgin, EMI

Compact disc: released on E.G., May'87 by Virgin Records. Dist: Virgin. EMI

Album: released on Polydor, Mar'77 by Polydor Records. Dist: Polygram, Polydor

APOLLO.
Tracks: / Under stars / Secret place / Matta / Signals / Ending ascent / Under stars II / Drift / Silver morning / Deep blue day / Weightless / Always returning / Stars.
Album: released on E.G., Jan'87 by Virgin Records. Dist: Virgin, EMI

Cassette: released on E.G., Jan'87 by Virgin Records. Dist: Virgin, EMI

Compact disc: released on E.G., Jan'87 by Virgin Records. Dist: Virgin, EMI

Album: released on E.G., Jul'83 by Virgin Records. Dist: Virgin, EMI

Cassette: released on E.G., Jul'83 by Virgin Records. Dist: Virgin, EMI

BEFORE & AFTER SCIENCE.
Tracks: / No one receiving / Backwater / Kurt's rejoinder / Energy fools the magician / King's lead hat / Here he comes / Julie with ... / By this river / Through hollow lands / Spider and I.
Album: released on E.G., Jan'87 by Virgin Records. Dist: Virgin, EMI

Cassette: released on E.G., Jan'87 by Virgin Records. Dist: Virgin, EMI

Compact disc: released on E.G., Jan'87 by Virgin Records. Dist: Virgin, EMI

BEFORE AND AFTER SCIENCE.
Album: released on Polydor, Jan'78 by Polydor Records. Dist: Polygram, Polydor

DESERT ISLAND SELECTION More blank than Frank.
Tracks: / Here he comes / Everything merges with the night / I'll come running to tie your shoe / On some faraway beach / Spirits drifting / Back in Judy's jungle / St. Elmo's fire / No one recieving / Julie with... / Talking tiger mountain / 1/1.
Compact disc: by Virgin Records. Dist: Virgin, EMI

Compact disc: released on E.G., Jun'87 by Virgin Records. Dist: Virgin, EMI

DISCREET MUSIC.
Album: released on Editions EG, Jan'87 by Virgin Records. Dist: EMI

HERE COME THE WARM JETS.
Tracks: / Needles in the camel's eye / Paw paw negro blowtorch (The) / Baby's on fire / Cindy tells me / Driving me backwards / On some faraway beach / Black Frank / Dead finks don't talk / Some of them are old / Here come the warm jets.
Cassette: released on E.G., Jan'87 by Virgin Records. Dist: Virgin, EMI

Album: released on E.G., Jan'87 by Virgin Records. Dist: Virgin, EMI

Album: released on Polydor, Apr'77 by Polydor Records. Dist: Polygram, Polydor

MORE BLANK THAN FRANK.
Tracks: / Here he comes / Everything merges with the night / On some faraway beach / I'll come running / Taking tiger mountain / Backwater / St. Elmo's fire / No one receiving / Great pretender / King's lead hat.
Album: released on E.G., Apr'86 by Virgin Records. Dist: Virgin, EMI

MUSIC FOR AIRPORTS.
Tracks: / One / Side one / Two / Side two / Side two Eno.
Album: released on Editions EG, Jan'87 by Virgin Records. Dist: EMI

Cassette: released on Editions EG, Jan'87 by Virgin Records. Dist: EMI

Compact disc: released on Editions EG, Jan'87 by Virgin Records. Dist: EMI

Album: released on Ambient, Mar'79 by Polydor Records. Dist: Polygram

Cassette: released on Ambient, Mar'79 by Polydor Records. Dist: Polygram

MUSIC FOR FILMS.
Tracks: / M386 / Aragon / From the same hill / Inland sea / Two rapid formations / Show water / Sparrowfall, Part 1 / Sparrowfall, Part 2 / Sparrow fall, Part 3 / Quartz / Events in dense fog / There is nobody / Measured room, A / Patrolling wire borders / Task force / Alternative 3 / Strange light / Final sunset / Measured room, A.
Album: released on Editions EG, Jan'87 by Virgin Records. Dist: EMI

Cassette: released on Editions EG, Jan'87 by Virgin Records. Dist: EMI

Album: released on Polydor, Feb'79 by Polydor Records. Dist: Polygram, Polydor

MUSIC FOR FILMS VOL.2.
Album: released on Editions EG, Jan'87 by Virgin Records. Dist: EMI

Cassette: released on Editions EG, Jan'87 by Virgin Records. Dist: EMI

MY LIFE IN THE BUSH OF GHOSTS (Eno, Brian & David Byrne).
Tracks: / America is waiting / Mea culpa / Help me somebody / Regiment / Jezebel spirit / Qu'ran / Moonlight in glory / Come with us / Carrier / My secret life / Mountain of needles.
Album: released on E.G., Jan'87 by Virgin Records. Dist: Virgin, EMI

Cassette: released on E.G., Jan'87 by Virgin Records. Dist: Virgin, EMI

ON LAND.
Tracks: / Lizard Point / Lost day / Tal Coat / Shadow / Latern Marsh / Unfamiliar wind / Clearing / Dunwich Beach / Autumn 1960.
Album: released on Editions EG, Jan'87 by Virgin Records. Dist: EMI

Cassette: released on Editions EG, Jan'87 by Virgin Records. Dist: EMI

Compact disc: released on Editions EG, Jan'87 by Virgin Records. Dist: EMI

PEARL (THE) (Eno, Brian & Harold Budd).
Notes: For full information see under: BUDD, Harold & BRIAN ENO

TAKING TIGER MOUNTAIN By strategy.
Tracks: / Burning airlines give you so much more / Back in Judy's jungle / Fat lady of Limbourg, The / Mother whale eyeless / Great pretender / Third uncle / Put a straw under baby / True wheel, The / China my china / Taking tiger mountain.
Album: released on E.G., Jan'87 by Virgin Records. Dist: Virgin, EMI

Cassette: released on E.G., Jan'87 by Virgin Records. Dist: Virgin, EMI

Album: released on Polydor, Mar'77 by Polydor Records. Dist: Polygram, Polydor

THURSDAY AFTERNOON.
Compact disc: released on E.G., Jan'87 by Virgin Records. Dist: Virgin, EMI

Compact disc: released on E.G., Oct'85 by Virgin Records. Dist: Virgin, EMI

Enormous Crocodile...

ENORMOUS CROCODILE & THE MAGIC FINGER,THE Dahl, Roald (Dahl, Roald).
Album: released on Caedmon(USA), Sep'80 by Caedmon (USA) Records. Dis' Taylors, Discovery

Enormous Room

100 DIFFERENT WORDS.
Single (12"): released on Sharp, Sep'86 by Sharp Records. Dist: Red Rhino, Cartel

I DON'T NEED YOU.
Tracks: / I don't need you / Melanie and Martin.
Single (7"): released on Medium, Jul'86 Dist: Red Rhino Distribution, Cartel Distribution

Eno, Roger

VOICES.
Tracks: / Place in the wilderness, A / Day after, The / At the water's edge / Grey promenade / Paler sky, A / Place in the wilderness, A / Through the blue / Paler sky, A / Evening tango / Recalling winter / Voices / Old dance (The) / Reflections on IKB.
Album: released on Editions EG, Jan'87 by Virgin Records. Dist: EMI

Cassette: released on Editions EG, Jan'87 by Virgin Records. Dist: EMI

VOICES (Eno, Roger/Brian Eno).
Album: released on E.G., Aug'85 by Virgin Records. Dist: Virgin, EMI

Cassette: released on E.G., Aug'85 by Virgin Records. Dist: Virgin, EMI

Enriquez, Bobby

ESPANA.
Album: released on PRT, Dec'83 by PRT Records. Dist: PRT

Cassette: released on PRT, Dec'83 by PRT Records. Dist: PRT

LIVE IN TOKYO.
Album: released on PRT, Oct'84 by PRT Records. Dist: PRT

WILD MAN, (THE).
Album: released on PRT, May'82 by PRT Records. Dist: PRT

Ensemble Tzigane...

SERENADE (Ensemble Tzigane Chiokerly).
Compact disc:

Entertainer

ENTERTAINER, (THE) Various Artists (Various Artists).
Album: by Sonet. Dist: Roots, PRT-Pye Distribution

Entertainers...

ENTERTAINERS OF THE JAZZ AGE SERIES 5 (Various Artists).
Notes: Artists include; Charles Hamp, Eddie Walters.
Cassette: released on Emporium Cassettes, Jul'86 by Emporium Cassettes Records. Dist: Jazz Music

Entertainment From...

ENTERTAINMENT FROM THE USA (Various Artists).
Album: released on Stylus, Feb'86 Dist: Pinnacle, Terry Blood Distribution, Stylus Distribution

Cassette: released on Stylus, Feb'86 Dist: Pinnacle, Terry Blood Distribution, Stylus Distribution

Enthusiasts

COLUMN BRIGADE.
Single (7"): released on Out Of Town, Aug'82

Entwistle, John

TOO LATE THE HERO.
Album: released on WEA, Nov'81 by WEA Records. Dist: WEA

Cassette: released on WEA, Nov'81 by WEA Records. Dist: WEA

TOO LATE THE HERO (SINGLE).
Single (7"): released on WEA, Sep'81 by WEA Records. Dist: WEA

Envy

AIN'T IT A SIN.
Tracks: / Ain't it a sin? / I believe in you / Heartache / Lie here waiting / Wait on you / You're so hot / All the reasons / I see the light / I'm not your lover / Hurt me.
Album: released on Atlantic, Jul'87 by WEA Records. Dist: WEA

Cassette: released on Atlantic, Jul'87 by WEA Records. Dist: WEA

Enya

ENYA.
Album: released on BBC, Feb'87 by BBC Records & Tapes. Dist: EMI, PRT.

Cassette: released on BBC, Feb'87 by BBC Records & Tapes. Dist: EMI, PRT

Compact disc: released on BBC, Feb'87 by BBC Records & Tapes. Dist: EMI, PRT.

I WANT TOMORROW.
Tracks: / I want tomorrow / Celts, The.
Single (7"): released on BBC, Feb'87 by BBC Records & Tapes. Dist: EMI. PRT.

Epic Soundtracks

JELLY BABIES.
Single (7"): released on Rough Trade, Sep'81 by Rough Trade Records. Dist: Rough Trade Distribution, Cartel Distribution

RAIN RAIN RAIN (Epic Soundtracks/Jowe Head).
Single (7"): released on Rough Trade, Jul'82 by Rough Trade Records. Dist: Rough Trade Distribution, Cartel Distribution

Epidemics

EPIDEMICS, THE.
Tracks: / Never take no for an answer / What would I do without you / Situations / You don't love me anymore / Love is alright / You can be anything / No cure / Don't I know you / Give an inch / Full moon.
Notes: The Epidemics are a group led by Indian violinist Shankar and as you will see from the personnel this is very much a rock album. Shankar is well known for hisinterpretations of classical Indian music and his improvisational skills with musicians such as Jan Garbarek. Having always been interested in and influenced by western pop music, the formation of the Epidemics is a natural development. He has already worked with many famous rock artists including Frank Zappa, Phil Collins, Peter Gabriel, Echo and The Bunnymen, and Talking Heads to name but a few. Personnel: Caroline - vocals, keyboards and tamours. Caroline has been collaborating with shankar for the past four years, together they co-wrote all the marerial for The Epidemics. Steve Vai - guitar. Steve formerly played Frank Zappa and Alcatrazz. He is currently working with David Lee Roth. Percy Jones - bass. Percy is a former member of Brand X and Soft machine, he has also worked with artists such as Brian Eno, Peter Gabriel and many others.
Compact disc: by ECM Records. Dist: IMS, Polygram, Virgin through EMI

Album: released on ECM (Germany), Feb'86 by ECM Records. Dist: IMS, Polygram, Virgin through EMI

Epigram

MARIONS FLIGHT.
Single (7"): released on Epigram, Mar'84 by Epigram Records. Dist: Rough Trade

Epileptics

1970S.
Single (7"): released on Spiderleg, Jan'82 Dist: Rough Trade

LAST BUS TO DEBDEN.
Single (7"): released on Spiderleg, Oct'81 Dist: Rough Trade

EQ

GOODBYE LOVE.
Single (7"): released on Atlantic, Sep'85 by WEA Records. Dist: WEA Deleted '86.
Cat. no: **A 9577**
Single (12"): released on Atlantic, Sep'85 by WEA Records. Dist: WEA

Equa

IN THE RED.
Single (12"): released on Fox, Dec'83 by Fox Records. Dist: Jazz Music

Equals

20 GREATEST HITS.
Album: released on Astan, Nov'84 by Astan Records. Dist: Counterpoint

Cassette: released on Astan, Nov'84 by Astan Records. Dist: Counterpoint

6 TRACK HITS.
Special: released on Scoop 33, Sep'83 by Pickwick Records. Dist: H.R. Taylor

Cassette: released on Scoop 33, Sep'83 by Pickwick Records. Dist: H.R. Taylor

BABY COME BACK.
Album: released on Platinum (W.Germany), Oct'85 Dist: Mainline

Cassette: released on Platinum (W.Germany), Oct'85 Dist: Mainline

BABY COME BACK (SINGLE).
Single (7"): released on Old Gold, Jul'82 by Old Gold Records. Dist: Lightning, Jazz Music, Spartan, Counterpoint

BEST OF THE EQUALS, (THE).
Album: released on Joy, '73 by President Records. Dist: Jazz Music, Swift, President Distribution

Album: released on Astan, Nov'84 by Astan Records. Dist: Counterpoint

Cassette: released on Astan, Nov'84 by Astan Records. Dist: Counterpoint

BLACK SKINNED BLUE-EYED BOY.
Single (7"): released on Old Gold, Jul'82 by Old Gold Records. Dist: Lightning, Jazz Music, Spartan, Counterpoint

DOIN THE 45S.
Album: released on Astan, Nov'84 by Astan Records. Dist: Counterpoint

Cassette: released on Astan, Nov'84 by Astan Records. Dist: Counterpoint

Album: released on Rhapsody, '74 by President Records. Dist: Taylors, Swift, Jazz Music, Wellard, Chris

NO PLACE TO GO.
Single (7"): released on Moggie, Jul'83 by Moggie Records. Dist: PRT Distribution

Single (12"): released on Moggie, Jul'83 by Moggie Records. Dist: PRT Distribution

PROFILE.
Album: released on Teldec (Germany), Mar'83 by Import Records. Dist: IMS Distribution, Polygram Distribution

Cassette: released on Teldec (Germany), Mar'83 by Import Records. Dist: IMS Distribution, Polygram Distribution

VIVA BOBBY JOE.
Single (7"): released on Old Gold, Jul'82 by Old Gold Records. Dist: Lightning, Jazz Music, Spartan, Counterpoint

Equators
BABY COME BACK.
Single (7"): released on Stiff, Oct'80 by Stiff Records. Dist: EMI, Record Services Distribution (Ireland)

Single (12"): released on Stiff, Oct'80 by Stiff Records. Dist: EMI, Record Services Distribution (Ireland)

DREAMING.
Single (7"): released on Philharmonics, Mar'85 by The Equators. Dist: Creole

HOT.
Album: released on Stiff, Jul'81 by Stiff Records. Dist: EMI, Record Services Distribution (Ireland)

IF YOU NEED ME.
Single (7"): released on Stiff, May'81 by Stiff Records. Dist: EMI, Record Services Distribution (Ireland)

Single (12"): released on Stiff, May'81 by Stiff Records. Dist: EMI, Record Services Distribution (Ireland)

Equin, Inch
CITY ON THE LAG.
Tracks: / City on the lag / Clove rock.
Single (7"):

Eraserhead
ERASERHEAD original film soundtrack.
Album: released on Alternative Tentacles, Jan'84 by Alternative Tentacles Records. Dist: Rough Trade, Pinnacle

Erasure
HEAVENLY ACTION.
Single (7"): released on Mute, Nov'85 Dist: Spartan Distribution, Rough Trade Distribution, Cartel Distribution

Single (12"): released on Mute, Nov'85 Dist: Spartan Distribution, Rough Trade Distribution, Cartel Distribution

Special: released on Mute, Nov'85 Dist: Spartan Distribution, Rough Trade Distribution, Cartel Distribution

IT DOESN'T HAVE TO BE.
Tracks: / It doesn't have to be.
Compact disc single: released on Mute, Mar'87 Dist: Spartan Distribution, Rough Trade Distribution, Cartel Distribution

IT DOESN'T HAVE TO BE.
Tracks: / It doesn't have to be / In the hall of the mountain king / Who needs love like that (remix).
Notes: Who needs love like that (remix) is only available on 12" version.
Single (7"): released on Mute, Feb'87 Dist: Spartan Distribution, Rough Trade Distribution, Cartel Distribution

Single (12"): released on Mute, Feb'87 Dist: Spartan Distribution, Rough Trade Distribution, Cartel Distribution

IT DOESN'T HAVE TO BE.
Tracks: / It doesn't have to be.
Single (12"): released on Mute, Mar'87 Dist: Spartan Distribution, Rough Trade Distribution, Cartel Distribution

OH L'AMOUR.
Tracks: / Oh l'amour / March on down the line / Gimme! Gimme! Gimme!.
Single (7"): released on Mute, Apr'86 Dist: Spartan Distribution, Rough Trade Distribution, Cartel Distribution

SOMETIMES.
Tracks: / Sexuality / Sometimes.
Single (7"): released on Mute, Nov'86 Dist: Spartan Distribution, Rough Trade Distribution, Cartel Distribution

SOMETIMES (12").
Tracks: / Sometimes / Sexuality / Say what (remix).
Single (12"): released on Mute, Oct'86 Dist: Spartan Distribution, Rough Trade Distribution, Cartel Distribution

VICTIM OF LOVE.
Tracks: / Victim of love / Soldiers of return, The.
Single (7"): released on Mute, May'87 Dist: Spartan Distribution, Rough Trade Distribution, Cartel Distribution

Single (12"): released on Mute, May'87 Dist: Spartan Distribution, Rough Trade Distribution, Cartel Distribution

Picture disc single: released on Mute, Jun'87 Dist: Spartan Distribution, Rough Trade Distribution, Cartel Distribution

WHO NEEDS LOVE LIKE THAT.
Single (7"): released on Mute, Aug'85 Dist: Spartan Distribution, Rough Trade Distribution, Cartel Distribution

Single (12"): released on Mute, Aug'85 Dist: Spartan Distribution, Rough Trade Distribution, Cartel Distribution

WONDERLAND.
Compact disc: Dist: Spartan Distribution, Rough Trade Distribution, Cartel Distribution

Album: released on Mute, Jun'86 Dist: Spartan Distribution, Rough Trade Distribution, Cartel Distribution

Cassette: released on Mute, Jun'86 Dist: Spartan Distribution, Rough Trade Distribution, Cartel Distribution

Erazerhead
APE MAN.
Single (7"): released on Test Pressing, Jul'81 by Test Pressing Records. Dist: Indies Distribution

LIVE AT KLUB FOOT 4 track ep.
Single (7"): released on Flicknife, Jan'83 by Flicknife Records. Dist: Spartan

RUMBLE OF THE EAST, THE.
Album: released on Flicknife, Nov'82 by Flicknife Records. Dist: Spartan

SHELL SHOCK.
Single (7"): released on Flicknife, May'82 by Flicknife Records. Dist: Spartan

SHELLSHOCKED 1980-4.
Album: released on Flicknife, Mar'85 by Flicknife Records. Dist: Spartan

SUMMERTIME.
Single (7"): released on Flicknife, Apr'84 by Flicknife Records. Dist: Spartan

TAKE ME TO YOUR LEADER.
Album: released on Flicknife, Sep'84 by Flicknife Records. Dist: Spartan

Single (12"): released on Cafe Associates, Sep'84 Dist: Backs, Cartel

TEENAGER IN LOVE.
Double compact disc: released on Flicknife, Aug'82 by Flicknife Records. Dist: Spartan

WEREWOLF.
Single (7"): released on Flicknife, Apr'83 by Flicknife Records. Dist: Spartan

Erfolg, Rudolf Wurther
RUDOLF WURTHER ERFOLG various artists (Various Artists).
Album: released on ARC (Accordion Records), '84 Dist: Accordion Record Club

Erica
TONIGHT TONIGHT Instrumental.
Single (12"): released on Sanity, Nov'82 by Sanity Records. Dist: Pinnacle, Jetstar

Eric B
ERIC B FOR PRESIDENT.
Single (12"): released on Cool Tempo, Aug'86 by Chrysalis Records. Dist: CBS

Ericksen, Joe
HIGH SCHOOL SWEETHEARTS (Erick-

sen, Big Joe).
Single (7"): released on Joy Kick, Jul'83

Single (12"): released on Joy Kick, Jul'83

Erickson, Roky
HOLIDAY INN TAPES.
Album: released on Fan Club, Sep'87 by New Rose. Dist: Rough Trade, Cartel. Estim retail price in Sep'87 was £6.29.

Ericson, Joe
TAKE YOUR TIME.
Single (7"): released on Steinar, Jul'83

Single (12"): released on Steinar, Jul'83

Ericsson, Lena
BARNDOMSJUL.
Single (7"): released on Phontastic, Nov'82 Dist: Wellard, Chris

CHRISTMAS TREE.
Single (7"): released on Phontastic, Nov'82 Dist: Wellard, Chris

Erikson, Roky
BEAST, THE.
Tracks: / Beast, The / Heroin.
Single (12"): released on O.B.G., Apr'86 Dist: Pinnacle

CASTING THE RUNES.
Album: released on Five Hours Back, Aug'87 by One Big Guitar / Zippo Records. Dist: Pinnacle, Revolver, Cartel. Estim retail price in Sep'87 was £5.99.

DON'T SLANDER ME.
Album: released on Demon, Jun'87 by Demon Records. Dist: Pinnacle

GREMLINS HAVE PICTURES.
Album: released on Demon, Jan'87 by Demon Records. Dist: Pinnacle

I THINK OF DEMONS (Erikson, Roky & The Aliens).
Album: released on Edsel, Jan'87 by Demon Records. Dist: Pinnacle, Jazz Music. Projection

Eritrea
MUSIC OF ERITREA.
Album: released on Tangent, Apr'81 Dist: Roots Distribution, Lugtons Distributors, Taylors, Spartan Distribution

Erogenous Zones
SAY IT'S NOT SO.
Single (7"): released on Safari, May'81 by Safari Records. Dist: Pinnacle

Erotic dreams
EROTIC DREAMS Various artists (Various Artists).
Album: released on Hallmark, Dec'81 by Pickwick Records. Dist: Pickwick Distribution, PRT, Taylors

Cassette: released on Hallmark, Dec'81 by Pickwick Records. Dist: Pickwick Distribution, PRT, Taylors

Erotic Drum Band
CREAM DREAM.
Single (12"): released on Street Level, Mar'85

Ersatz
SMILE IN SHADOW.
Single (7"): released on Leisure Sounds, Jan'81 by Leisure Sounds Records. Dist: Red Rhino, Rough Trade, Small Wonder, Virgin, Backs

Erskine-Hill, Mark
BLOODSHED.
Single (12"): released on EHI, Oct'87 by EHI Records. Dist: PRT

FLY AWAY.
Single (7"): released on EHI, Jun'85 by EHI Records. Dist: PRT

MONDAY.
Tracks: / Monday / No one stops.
Single (7"): released on EHI, Feb'86 by EHI Records. Dist: PRT

SHE'S A VERY LONELY GIRL.
Tracks: / She's a very lonely girl / Through the trees.
Single (7"): released on EHI, May'86 by EHI Records. Dist: PRT

Erskine, Peter
PETER ERSKINE.
Tracks: / Leroy street / E.S.P. / All's well that ends / Coyote blues / In statu nascendi / Change of mind / My ship.

Notes: Peter Erskine-drums/Michael Brecker-tenor sax/Randy Bracker-trumpet/Eddie Gomez-bass/Mike Mainieri-vibes/Don Grolnick-electric piano/Bob Mintzer-tenor sax/Don Alias-congas/Kenny Kirkland-piano.
Album: released on Polydor (Import) Mar'83

Eruption
ERUPTION.
Tracks: / I can't stand the rain / Movin' / I'll take you there / Computor love / Way we were, The / Do you know what it feels like / Be yourself / I can't carry on / Wayward love / Party party.
Album: released on Atlantic, Apr'78 by WEA Records. Dist: WEA

JOY TO THE WORLD.
Single (7"): released on Red Bus, Dec'82 by Red Bus Records. Dist: PRT

WHERE DO I BEGIN.
Tracks: / Where do I begin / Broke away / Snap.
Single (12"): released on FM-Revolver, Oct'86 by FM-Revolver Records. Dist: BMG, Pathe Marconi, Polygram

Ervin, Booker
BOOK COOKS, THE.
Album: released on Affinity, May'82 by Charly Records. Dist: Charly, Cadillac

LAMENT FOR BOOKER ERVIN.
Album: released on Enja (Germany), Jan'82 by Enja Records (W.Germany). Dist: Cadillac Music

SONG BOOK, THE.
Album: released on Prestige, Apr'76 by Prestige Records (USA). Dist: RCA, Swift

THAT'S IT.
Album: released on Candid/Black Lion, Jun'86 Dist: Jazz Music, Swift

Erwin, Randy
TILL THE COWS COME HOME.
Album: released on Heartland, Jun'87

Escalator
LET'S MAKE SOME NOISE (EVERYBODY IN THE HOUSE).
Tracks: / Let's make some noise / Ride the escalator.
Single (12"): released on Elite, Oct'86 Dist: PRT

Escalators
BEACH BOYS.
Single (7"): released on Rococo, Aug'85 Dist: Fast Forward Distribution, Cartel Distribution

MONDAY.
Single (7"): released on Big Beat, Jul'83 by Ace Records. Dist: Projection, Pinnacle

MOVING STAIRCASES.
Album: released on Big Beat, Jul'83 by Ace Records. Dist: Projection, Pinnacle

SOMETHING'S MISSING.
Single (7"): released on Big Beat, Mar'83 by Ace Records. Dist: Projection, Pinnacle

Escape
AMSTERDAM.
Single (7"): released on Mercury, Sep'83 by Phonogram Records. Dist: Polygram Distribution

Single (12"): released on Mercury, Sep'83 by Phonogram Records. Dist: Polygram Distribution

NO GO.
Single (7"): released on Volatile, Sep'82 by Volitile Records. Dist: Revolver, Cartel

RUSSIAN LADY.
Single (12"): released on Mercury, Jun'84 by Phonogram Records. Dist: Polygram Distribution

Escape Club
BREATHING.
Single (7"): released on Bright, Jul'83

HARD WAY, THE.
Tracks: / Hard way, The / I will be there / Push, The * / 100 years *.
Single (7"): released on Parlophone, Oct'86 by EMI Records. Dist: EMI

Single (12"): released on Parlophone, Oct'86 by EMI Records. Dist: EMI

Double-pack single: released on Parlophone, Oct'86 by EMI Records. Dist: EMI

I WILL BE THERE.
Tracks: / I will be there / Money and guns.
Single (7"): released on EMI, Mar'86 by EMI Records. Dist: EMI

Single (12"): released on EMI, Mar'86 by EMI

Records. Dist: EMI

RESCUE ME.
Tracks: / Rescue me / In my town.
Single (7"): released on EMI, Sep'85 by EMI Records. Dist: EMI

Single (12"): released on EMI, Sep'86 by EMI Records. Dist: EMI

WHERE ANGELS CRY.
Tracks: / Where angels cry / Tonight (for the poor boy).
Single (7"): released on Parlophone, Jun'86 by EMI Records. Dist: EMI

Single (12"): released on Parlophone, Jun'86 by EMI Records. Dist: EMI

WHITE FIELDS.
Tracks: / Push, The / Sound of the city / Fall / Where angels cry / I will be there / Blood and water / Hard way, The / White fields / Rescue me / Slow train.
Notes: The Escape Club are a London based 4-piece who havesupported China Crisis and The Alarm on tour in the last six months as well as regularly playing on their own dates around the country and are regular headliners at The Marquee. All tracks composed by Holliday, Steel, Christo, Zekevica.
Album: released on EMI, May'86 by EMI Records. Dist: EMI

Cassette: released on EMI, May'86 by EMI Records. Dist: EMI

Escape from New York

ESCAPE FROM NEW YORK Original soundtrack.
Album: released on That's Entertainment, Dec'81 by That's Entertainment Records. Dist: Pinnacle, PRT

Escorts

FROM THE BLUE ANGEL.
Album: released on Edsel, Oct'82 by Demon Records. Dist: Pinnacle, Jazz Music, Projection

Escovedo, Pete

YESTERDAY'S MEMORIES - TOMORROW'S DREAMS.
Tracks: / Charango sunrise / Moving pictures / Azteca Mozambique / Ah ah / Cueros / Modern dance / Zina's Zamba / Yesterday's memories, tomorrow's dreams / Revolt.
Notes: Pete Escovedo and his 12 piece Latin / Fusion Band.
Album: released on Concord Jazz(USA), Jul'87 by Concord Jazz Records (USA). Dist: IMS, Polygram

Cassette: released on Concord Jazz(USA), Jul'87 by Concord Jazz Records (USA). Dist: IMS, Polygram

Compact disc: released on Concord Jazz, Jul'87 by Concord Jazz Records (USA). Dist: IMS, Polygram

E.S.G.

YOU'RE NO GOOD.
Single (7"):

E, Sheila

KOO KOO.
Tracks: / Koo koo / Paradise garden.
Single (7"): released on Warner Bros., Jun'87 by Warner Bros Records. Dist: WEA

Single (12"): released on Warner Bros., Jun'87 by Warner Bros Records. Dist: WEA

ESP

TELL ME.
Tracks: / Tell me / Illusion confusion.
Single (7"): released on WDTC, Mar'86 Dist: M.I.S., EMI

Espionage

SOUND OF BREAKING HEARTS.
Single (7"): released on A&M, Apr'83 by A&M Records. Dist: Polygram

Compact disc: released on A&M, Apr'83 by A&M Records. Dist: Polygram

ESP Is Alive & Well

ESP IS ALIVE & WELL Stanley Krippner (Krippner, Stanley).
Cassette: released on Psychology Today, Oct'81

Esplin, Joss

SCOTLAND PAST AND PRESENT.
Cassette: released on Beechwood, Feb'87 by Beechwood Records. Dist: Ross

Esposito, Joe 'Bean'

DOWN IN YOUR SOUL.
Tracks: / Down in your soul / Down in your soul (Instr. Mix) / Down in your soul (Dub mix).
Single (12"): released on Teldec (Import), Mar'86

SOLITARY MEN (Esposito, Joe & Giorgio Moroder).
Album: released on Teldec (Germany), Nov'83 by Import Records. Dist: IMS Distribution, Polygram Distribution

Cassette: released on Teldec (Germany), Nov'83 by Import Records. Dist: IMS Distribution, Polygram Distribution

Esposito, Tony

KALIMBA DE LUNA.
Single (7"): released on Red Bus, Nov'84 by Red Bus Records. Dist: PRT

Single (12"): released on Red Bus, Nov'84 by Red Bus Records. Dist: PRT

Compact disc: released on Carrere, Oct'84 by Carrere Records. Dist: PRT, Spartan

Esquerita

ESQUERITA.
Album: released on Pathe MarconiEMI Europe), Jun'84

Esquire

ESQUIRE.
Tracks: / To the rescue / Sunshine / Knock twice for heaven / Up down turnaround / Blossomtime / Hourglass / Moving together / Silent future / Special greeting / What you've been saying.
Album: released on Geffen, Apr'87 by Geffen Records. Dist: WEA, CBS

Cassette: released on Geffen, Apr'87 by Geffen Records. Dist: WEA, CBS

Esquire Jazz All Stars

ON THE AIR 1944.
Album: released on Aircheck, May'79

Essence

CAT, THE.
Tracks: / Cat, The (remix) / Confusion / Happiness, The / Cat, The (extended version).
Single (12"): released on Midnight Music, Jun'86 by Midnight Music Records. Dist: Rough Trade Distribution, Cartel Distribution

ENDLESS LAKES.
Single (12"): released on Midnight Music, Jul'85 by Midnight Music Records. Dist: Rough Trade Distribution, Cartel Distribution

OIL IN MY LAMP.
Single (7"): released on North Of Watford, Sep'80 by North Of Watford Records. Dist: Wynd-Up Distribution

PURITY.
Album: released on Midnight Music, Sep'85 by Midnight Music Records. Dist: Rough Trade Distribution, Cartel Distribution

Essential Bop

ELOQUENT SOUNDS.
Single (7"): released on Monopause, Nov'80

FLICK WAS BOSS, THE.
Album: released on Tsar, Jan'85 by Essential Bop. Dist: Revolver

Essential electro

ESSENTIAL ELECTRO The business (box set) (Various Artists).
Album: released on Streetsounds, Dec'84

Essential Firmament

ESSENTIAL FIRMAMENT, THE.
Notes: A bona-fide oddball from the Woolleys: Mini.
Album: released on Press, Jul'86 by Press Records.

ESSENTIAL FIRMAMENT & THE ELEMENTS.
Album: released on Music Galore, Aug'85 by Shanghai records. Dist: Counterpoint Distribution

Essential Logic

AEROSOL BURNS.
Single (7"): released on Cells, Jun'78 by Cells Records. Dist: Rough Trade

BEAT RHYTHM NEWS.
Album: released on Rough Trade, '84 by Rough Trade Records. Dist: Rough Trade Distribution, Cartel Distribution

EUGENE/TAME THE NEIGHBOURS.
Single (7"): released on Rough Trade, Nov'80 by Rough Trade Records. Dist: Rough Trade Distribution, Cartel Distribution

FANFARE IN THE GARDEN.
Single (7"): released on Rough Trade, Jun'81 by Rough Trade Records. Dist: Rough Trade Distribution, Cartel Distribution

MUSIC IS A BETTER NOISE.
Single (7"): released on Rough Trade, Feb'81 by Rough Trade Records. Dist: Rough Trade Distribution, Cartel Distribution

Essential Sound Effects

ESSENTIAL SOUND EFFECTS (Various Artists).
Album: released on BBC, Aug'82 by BBC Records & Tapes. Dist: EMI, PRT Pye

Essex, David

6 TRACK HITS.
Extended-play record: released on Scoop 33, Sep'83 by Pickwick Records. Dist: H.R. Taylor

Cassette: released on Scoop 33, Sep'83 by Pickwick Records. Dist: H.R. Taylor

BACK IN ENGLAND FOR CHRISTMAS.
Single (7"): released on Lamplight, Nov'86 Dist: Priority, RCA/DMS/Distribution

Single (12"): released on Lamplight, Nov'86 Dist: Priority, RCA/DMS/Distribution

CENTRE STAGE.
Tracks: / 42nd Street\Lullaby of Broadway / Summertime / Corner of the sky / Tahiti / Bright eyes / Pinball wizard / Ghost buster / I wanna be like you / Phantom of the opera, The / Save the people / I dreamed a dream / Out here on my own.
Compact disc: released on K-Tel, May'87 by K-Tel Records. Dist: Record Merchandisers Distribution, Taylors, Terry Blood Distribution, Wynd-Up Distribution, Relay Distribution, Pickwick Distribution, Solomon & Peres Distribution, Polygram

Album: released on K-Tel, Oct'86 by K-Tel Records. Dist: Record Merchandisers Distribution, Taylors, Terry Blood Distribution, Wynd-Up Distribution, Relay Distribution, Pickwick Distribution, Solomon & Peres Distribution, Polygram

Cassette: released on K-Tel, Oct'86 by K-Tel Records. Dist: Record Merchandisers Distribution, Taylors, Terry Blood Distribution, Wynd-Up Distribution, Relay Distribution, Pickwick Distribution, Solomon & Peres Distribution, Polygram

DAVID ESSEX 4 TRACK CASSETTE EP.
Cassette: released on CBS, Dec'82 by CBS Records. Dist: CBS

FALLING ANGELS.
Single (7"): released on Mercury, Jan'85 by Phonogram Records. Dist: Polygram Distribution

FISHING FOR THE MOON.
Single (7"): released on Phonogram, Mar'84 by Phonogram Records. Dist: Polygram

FREEDOM (Essex, David/Frank Finlay etc).
Single (7"): released on Lamplight, Oct'85 Dist: Priority, RCA/DMS/Distribution

FRIENDS.
Single (7"): released on Lamplight, May'85 Dist: Priority, RCA/DMS/Distribution

GONNA MAKE YOU A STAR.
Single (7"): released on Old Gold, Sep'85 by Old Gold Records. Dist: Lightning, Jazz Music, Spartan, Counterpoint

HOT LOVE.
Tracks: / Hot love / I luv ya / Talking with your body / Zebra kid / Heart on my sleeve / Reality / Rock 'n' roll me / Cold as ice / Swim against the flow / On my bike.
Album: released on Mercury (Germany), Apr'85 by Phonogram Records. Dist: Polygram Distribution

LIVE AT THE ROYAL ALBERT HALL.
Notes: Mike mansfield-directed live show featuring versions of many of Essex' greatest hits. Packaged with a free audio cassette of the soundtrack.
Video-cassette (VHS): released on Polygram Music, Dec'84 by Polygram Records. Dist: Polygram

MYFANWY.
Tracks: / Myfanwy / Love theme.
Single (7"): released on Arista, Mar'87 by Arista Records. Dist: RCA

Compact disc single: released on Arista, May'87 by Arista Records. Dist: RCA

SILVER DREAM RACER.
Tracks: / Dunes, The / Silver dream machine / Looking for something / Bike, The / Where is love? / When I'm dancing / Suzuki warlord / Sea of love / I think I'll always love you / Race, The.
Album: released on Mercury, Jun'82 by Phonogram Records. Dist: Polygram Distribution

Cassette: released on Mercury, Jun'82 by Phonogram Records. Dist: Polygram Distribution

SIX TRACK HITS.
Tracks: / Rollin' stone / Ooh darling / America / Cool out tonight / Turn me loose / Stay with me, baby.

SMILE, THE/SLAVE.
Single (7"): released on Mercury, May'83 by Phonogram Records. Dist: Polygram Distribution

Single (12"): released on Mercury, May'83 by Phonogram Records. Dist: Polygram Distribution

Picture disc single: released on Mercury, May'83 by Phonogram Records. Dist: Polygram Distribution

STAGE STRUCK.
Tracks: / No substitute / Oh la baby blonde / You're so fierce / Me and my girl (night clubbing) / You don't know like I know / Call me your lover / Sweethearts / Romance / Verity / Secondhand love / Sleeping with the director / Stage struck.
Album: released on Mercury, Jun'82 by Phonogram Records. Dist: Polygram Distribution

Cassette: released on Mercury, Jun'82 by Phonogram Records. Dist: Polygram Distribution

VERY BEST OF DAVID ESSEX.
Tracks: / Gonna make you a star / Rock on / Oh what a circus / Heart on my sleeve / No substitute / Silver dream machine / Rollin' stone / Hold me close / Me and my girl (night clubbing) / Brave new world / Hot love / Lamplight / If I could / Imperial wizard / Ships that pass in the night / Stardust.
Album: released on TV, Nov'82

Cassette: released on TV, Nov'82

YOU'RE IN MY HEART/COME ON LITTLE DARLIN'.
Single (7"): released on Mercury, Nov'83 by Phonogram Records. Dist: Polygram Distribution

Essex, Mike

THANKS.
Tracks: / Thanks / Theme from thanks.
Notes: First Time Music, 12 Trewartha Rd, Praa Sands, Penzance, Cornwall, TR20 9ST. Telephone: 762826 (Penzance).
Single (7"): released on First Time/Fugore, Mar'87 by First Time Records. Dist: First Time Records

Esson, Aston

I'LL GET OVER IT.
Tracks: / I'll get over it / I'll get over it (II).
Single (12"): released on Fine Style, Oct'86 by Fine Style Records. Dist: Revolver, Jetstar, PRT, Cartel

Estefan, Gloria

LET IT LOOSE (Estefan, Gloria & Miami Sound Machine).
Tracks: / Betcha say that / Let it loose / Can't stay away from you / Give it up / Surrender / Rhythm is gonna get you / Love toy / I want you so bad / 1-2-3 / Anything for you.
Album: released on Epic, Aug'87 by CBS Records. Dist: CBS

Cassette: released on Epic, Aug'87 by CBS Records. Dist: CBS

Compact disc: released on Epic, Aug'87 by CBS Records. Dist: CBS

RHYTHM'S GONNA GET YOU (Estefan, Gloria & Miami Sound Machine).
Tracks: / Rhythm's gonna get you / Give it up.
Single (7"): released on Epic, Jun'87 by CBS Records. Dist: CBS

Single (12"): released on Epic, Jun'87 by CBS Records. Dist: CBS

Estelle, Don

ECOUTEZ MA CHANSON.
Single (7"): released on Lofty, Oct'83 by Monarch Records. Dist: PRT

GOODBYE/RULE BRITANNIA (Estelle, Don/Jack Douglas).
Single (7"): released on Lofty, Mar'82 by Monarch Records. Dist: PRT

LITTLE DONKEY/AULD LANG SYNE.
Single (7"): released on Lofty, Nov'82 by Monarch Records. Dist: PRT

ROSE MARIE.
Single (7"): released on Lofty, Apr'81 by Monarch Records. Dist: PRT

WITH A SONG IN MY HEART.
Album: released on Lofty, Mar'82 by Monarch Records. Dist: PRT

Cassette: released on Lofty, Mar'82 by Monarch Records. Dist: PRT

Estes, Simon

SPIRITUALS.
Tracks: / Swing low / Ride on King Jesus / Ezekiel / City called Heaven / Plenty good room / Let us break bread together / Witness / Go down Moses / No hiding place / Nobody knows the trouble I've seen / Every time I feel the spirit /

Steal away to Jesus / Sometimes I feel like a motherless child / Standin' in the need of prayer / He's got the whole world in his hands.
Compact disc: Dist: IMS-Polygram

Estes, Sleepy John
1929-30 SESSIONS.
Album: released on Roots, May'86 by Topic Records. Dist: Swift Distribution

BLUES OF SLEEPY JOHN ESTES.
Album: released on Swaggie (Australia), Jan'82

BLUES OF SLEEPY JOHN ESTES VOL.II.
Album: released on Swaggie (Australia), Jan'83

BROKE AND HUNGRY.
Album: Dist: Projection, Swift, Cadillac

BROWNSVILLE BLUES.
Album: Dist: Projection, Swift, Cadillac

ELECTRIC SLEEP.
Album: Dist: Projection, Swift, Cadillac

LEGEND OF....
Album: Dist: Projection, Swift, Cadillac

SLEEPY JOHN ESTES.
Notes: with Furry Lewis/Gus Cannon/Charlie Burse etc.
Album: released on Southland, Mar'87

Estonian Singers And Orch
BEST LOVED ESTONIAN SONGS.
Album: released on Accordion Record Club, '84 by Accordion Record Club Records. Dist: Accordion Record Club

Estus, Dean
LOVE HURTS.
Single (7"): released on Legacy, Mar'84 by PRT

Single (12"): released on Legacy, Mar'84 Dist: PRT

SPELL.
Single (7"): released on Geffen, Jul'86 by Geffen Records. Dist: WEA, CBS

Single (12"): released on Geffen, Jul'86 by Geffen Records. Dist: WEA, CBS

Estus, Deon
1-2-3.
Single (7"): released on Geffen, Aug'87 by Geffen Records. Dist: WEA, CBS

Single (12"): released on Geffen, Aug'87 by Geffen Records. Dist: WEA. CBS

My guy, my guy

E.T.
E.T. - THE EXTRATERRESTRIAL. Narrated by Michael Jackson (Jackson, Michael).
Album: released on MCA, Jan'83 by MCA Records. Dist: Polygram, MCA

Cassette: released on MCA, Jan'83 by MCA Records. Dist: Polygram, MCA

Etc Etc
SCANNING THE CROWDS (CASS 45).
Single (7"): released on Blue Rhythm, Aug'82 Dist: Swift

Eternal Triangle
NOTHING BUT A FRIEND.
Single (7"): released on Situation 2, May'84 Dist: Cartel, Pinnacle

Single (12"): released on Situation 2, May'84 Dist: Cartel, Pinnacle

ONLY IN THE NIGHT.
Single (7"): released on Situation 2, Apr'84 Dist: Cartel, Pinnacle

Single (12"): released on Situation 2, Apr'84 Dist: Cartel, Pinnacle

TOUCH & LET GO.
Album: released on Situation 2, Apr'84 Dist: Cartel, Pinnacle

Ethiopia
ETHIOPIAN URBAN AND TRIBAL MUSIC VOLUME 1 Mindanao mistiru.
Album: released on Lyrichord (USA), Oct'81 by Lyrichord Records (USA). Dist: Flexitron Distributors Ltd

ETHIOPIAN URBAN AND TRIBAL MUSIC VOLUME 2 Gold from wax.
Album: released on Lyrichord (USA), Oct'81 by Lyrichord Records (USA). Dist: Flexitron Distributors Ltd

MUSIC OF THE CENTRAL HIGHLANDS VOLUME 1.
Album: Dist: Roots Distribution, Lugtons Distributors, Taylors, JSU Distribution, Spartan Distribution

MUSIC OF THE DESERT NOMADS VOLUME 2.
Album: released on Tangent, Apr'81 Dist: Roots Distribution, Lugtons Distributors, Taylors, JSU Distribution, Spartan Distribution

Ethiopian
OPEN THE GATE OF ZION.
Album: released on GG'S, Jul'84 by GG'S Records. Dist: Jetstar

Ethiopians
ORIGINAL REGGAE HIT SOUNDS.
Album: released on Trojan, Jul'86 by Trojan Records. Dist: PRT, Jetstar

Cassette: released on Trojan, Jul'86 by Trojan Records. Dist: PRT, Jetstar

PIRATE.
Single (12"): released on Trojan, Oct'86 by Trojan Records. Dist: PRT, Jetstar

SLAVE CALL.
Album: released on Third World, Dec'77 Dist: Jetstar Distribution

SOLID AS A ROCK.
Single (12"): released on Success, Mar'84 Dist: Counterpoint Distribution

WHIP, (THE).
Single (12"): released on Treasure Isle, Nov'83 by Treasure Isle Records. Dist: Jetstar

Etkind, Annabel
NEW ROMANCE, (A).
Album: released on Lifestyle, Nov'83 by Zomba Records. Dist: CBS, PRT, RCA

Cassette: released on Lifestyle, Nov'83 by Zomba Records. Dist: CBS, PRT, RCA

OXYGENE PART 4.
Single (7"): released on Lifestyle, Nov'83 by Zomba Records. Dist: CBS, PRT, RCA

Eton Crop
GAY BOYS ON THE BATTLEFIELD (EP).
Single (12"): released on Bigger Bank Balance, May'84 Dist: Cartel

IT'S MY DOG, MAESTRO.
Album: released on Grunt Grunt A Go-Go, Jan'86 Dist: Backs, Cartel

YES PLEASE, BOB.
Album: released on Ediesta, Nov'86 by Ediesta Records. Dist: Red Rhino, Cartel

YES PLEASE, BOB (7").
Single (7"): released on Ediesta, Nov'86 by Ediesta Records. Dist: Red Rhino, Cartel

Ettaswell Brass Band
SOUNDING BRASS.
Album: released on Pye, Nov'79

Etting, Ruth
KEEP SWEEPING THE COBWEB.
Notes: Mono. With Ted Lewis and his band.
Cassette: released on Emporium Cassettes, Jul'86 by Emporium Cassettes Records. Dist: Jazz Music

ON THE AIR.
Album: released on Totem, May'79 Dist: Jazz Music, Projection, Swift

TEN CENTS A DANCE.
Album: released on ASV, Oct'81 by Academy Sound & Vision Records. Dist: Pinnacle

Cassette: released on ASV, Oct'81 by Academy Sound & Vision Records. Dist: Pinnacle

E-Types
E-TYPES VS MYSTIC TIDE (E-Types/Mystic Tide).
Album: released on Eva-Lolita, Mar'84 Dist: Pinnacle

E.U.
E.U.FREEZE.
Single (7"): released on Fourth & Broadway, Apr'85 by Island Records. Dist: Polygram, EMI

Single (12"): released on Fourth & Broadway, Apr'85 by Island Records. Dist: Polygram, EMI Deleted '87.

Eubanks, Kevin
FACE TO FACE.
Notes: For his third album on GRP, Kevin Eubanks takes another major step as one of the leading guitarists performing today. Framed in a setting of lush strings that bring still another poetic dimension to his warm and sensitive guitar, "Face to face" is a highly expressive and masterful recording. Produced by Dave Grusin, Larry Rosen and Kevin Eubanks, with strings arranged and conducted by dave Grusin, "Face to face" boasts the faces of such world class musicians as Marcus Miller - electric bass; Ralph McDonald - percussion; Ron Carter - acoustic bass; Buddy Williams - drums and dave grusin on keyboards.
Compact disc: released on GRP (USA), Oct'86 by GRP Records (USA). Dist: IMS, Polygram

Album: released on GRP (USA), Oct'86 by GRP Records (USA). Dist: IMS, Polygram

Cassette: released on GRP (USA), Oct'86 by GRP Records (USA). Dist: IMS, Polygram

GUITARIST.
Album: released on Elektra(Musician), Feb'83 by WEA Records. Dist: WEA

OPENING NIGHT.
Album: released on GRP (USA), Jul'85 by GRP Records (USA). Dist: IMS, Polygram

Cassette: released on GRP (USA), Jul'85 by GRP Records (USA). Dist: IMS, Polygram

Compact disc: released on GRP (USA), Jul'85 by GRP Records (USA). Dist: IMS, Polygram

OPENING NIGHTS.
Tracks: / Opening nights / Shades of black / Navigator, the / Thought about thinking / In flight from omelas / Place before you've been, A / Vera's isle / To be continued.
Compact disc: released on GRP (USA), Jul'85 by GRP Records (USA). Dist: IMS, Polygram

Eugene, Wendell
WENDELL EUGENE\TEDDY RILEY\MICHAEL WHITE\KID SHEIK COLA (Eugene, Wendell, Teddy Riley, Michael White, Kid Sheik Cola).
Album: released on 504, Sep'86 by 504 Records. Dist: Chris Wellard, Jazz Music

Cassette: released on 504, Sep'86 by 504 Records. Dist: Chris Wellard, Jazz Music

WEST INDIAN BLUES (Eugene, Wendell/ New Orleans Band 1968).
Album: released on Nola, Apr'79 Dist: JSU, Jazz Music, Cadillac, Chris Wellard

Euraslantea
LIBERTY(DANCE WITH ME).
Single (7"):

Eurobeat
EUROBEAT (Various Artists).
Album: released on Streetsounds, Apr'86

Cassette: released on Streetsounds, Apr'86

Eurogliders
ABSOLUTELY.
Tracks: / Can't wait to see you / City of soul, The / What kind of fool / So tough / We will together / Absolutely / Jesse / Moving away / Enough love / We will together *.
Album: released on CBS, Feb'86 by CBS Records. Dist: CBS

Cassette: released on CBS, Feb'86 by CBS Records. Dist: CBS

CAN'T WAIT TO SEE YOU.
Tracks: / Can't wait to see you / I like to hear it.
Single (7"): released on CBS, Jun'86 by CBS Records. Dist: CBS

CITY OF SOUL.
Tracks: / City of soul / When the stars come out.
Single (7"): released on CBS, Jan'86 by CBS Records. Dist: CBS

Single (12"): released on CBS, Jan'86 by CBS Records. Dist: CBS

HEAVEN.
Single (7"): released on CBS, Dec'84 by CBS Records. Dist: CBS

Single (12"): released on CBS, Dec'84 by CBS Records. Dist: CBS

Euro-Hits
EURO-HITS various artists.
Album: released on Carrere, Oct'85 by Carrere Records. Dist: PRT, Spartan

Cassette: released on Carrere, Oct'85 by Carrere Records. Dist: PRT, Spartan

Eurok
ACTION MAN.
Single (7"): released on Dork, Sep'84 by Dork Records. Dist: Probe, Cartel

Europe
EUROPE.

Europe
Album: released on Chord, Jan'87 by Chord Records. Dist: Charly

FINAL COUNTDOWN, THE.
Tracks: / Final countdown / On broken wings.
Single (7"): released on Epic, Oct'86 by CBS Records. Dist: CBS

Single (12"): released on Epic, Oct'86 by CBS Records. Dist: CBS

FINAL COUNTDOWN (THE).
Tracks: / Love chaser / On the loose / Heart of stone / Time has come / Final countdown, The / Cherokee / Ninja / Danger on the track / Rock the night / Carrie.
Compact disc: released on Epic, Jan'87 by CBS Records. Dist: CBS

Video-cassette (VHS): released on CBS, Apr'87 by CBS Records. Dist: CBS

INTERVIEW PICTURE DISC.
Album: released on Baktabak, May'87 by Baktabak Records. Dist: Arabesque

ROCK THE NIGHT.
Tracks: / Rock the night / Seven doors hotel / Storm wind / Wings of tomorrow.
Notes: Extra tracks on 12" version only.
Single (7"): released on Epic, Feb'87 by CBS Records. Dist: CBS

European...
EUROPEAN BRASS BAND CHAMPIONSHIP 1981 featuring the winning bands (Various bands).
Album: released on Polyphonic, Mar'82 by Polyphonic Records. Dist: Taylors

EUROPEAN BRASS BAND CHAMPIONSHIP 1984 Various Brass Bands (Various bands).
Double Album: released on Chandos, Jul'84 by Chandos Records. Dist: Harmonia Mundi, Taylors

Double cassette: released on Chandos, Jul'84 by Chandos Records. Dist: Harmonia Mundi, Taylors

European Brass Orchestra
NATIONAL ANTHEMS.
Compact disc: released on Delta, Apr'87 by Delta Records. Dist: Target

European Jazz
EUROPEAN JAZZ QUINTET (European Jazz Quintet).
Album: released on Ego, Sep'79 by Ego Records. Dist: Jazz Services Unlimited Dist. (JSU), Cadillac Music

LIVE AT MOERS FESTIVAL '77 (European Jazz Quartet).
Album: released on Ring, Jul'78 Dist: Cadillac

Europeans
EUROPEANS/VOICES.
Single (7"): released on Heartbeat, Jul'79 Dist: Revolver, Pinnacle

RECURRING DREAMS.
Tracks: / 1,001 arguments / Home town / Burning inside you / You don't want me (in your life) / Writing for survival / Love has let me down / Don't give your heart to anybody / Acid rain.
Album: released on A&M, Oct'84 by A&M Records. Dist: Polygram

Cassette: released on A&M, Oct'84 by A&M Records. Dist: Polygram

European Sun
ANSWER ME.
Single (7"): released on Iguana, Sep'84 by Iguana Records. Dist: ILA, Grapevine

European Tales
FAVOURITE EUROPEAN TALES (Hepburn, Katharine).
Cassette: released on Listen For Pleasure, Oct'84 by MFP Records. Dist: EMI

European Toys
I AM CREATOR.
Single (7"): released on Subversive, Jul'83 Dist: Backs, Cartel Distribution

KOREA.
Single (12"): by Backs Records. Dist: Backs, Cartel

Single (12"): released on JKO, Jun'84 by JKO Records. Dist: Pinnacle

NINE MEN APPLAUDING.
Album: released on Backs, Feb'85 by Backs Records. Dist: Backs, Cartel

Europe, Jim
1907-1919 (Europe, Jim & Arthur Pryor Bands).

Album: released on Saydisc, Apr'81 by Saydisc Records. Dist: Essex, Harmonia Mundi, Roots, H.R. Taylor, Jazz Music, Swift, Projection, Gamut

Eurovision Song Contest

EUROVISION SONG CONTEST WINNERS 1956-81 (Various Artists).
Album: released on Polydor, Aug'81 by Polydor Records. Dist: Polygram, Polydor

Cassette: released on Polydor, Aug'81 by Polydor Records. Dist: Polygram, Polydor

Eurythmics

1984.
Compact disc: by Virgin Records. Dist: EMI, Virgin Distribution

Album: released on Virgin, Nov'84 by Virgin Records. Dist: EMI, Virgin Distribution

Cassette: released on Virgin, Nov'84 by Virgin Records. Dist: EMI, Virgin Distribution

BE YOURSELF TONIGHT.
Tracks: / Would I lie to you? / There must be an angel (Playing with my heart) / Love you like a ball and chain / Sisters are doin' it for themselves / Conditioned soul / Adrian / It's alright (Baby's coming back) / Here comes that sinking feeling / Better to have lost in love, than to have never loved at all.
Compact disc: released on RCA, Jun'85 by RCA Records. Dist: RCA, Roots, Swift, Wellard, Chris, I & B, Solomon & Peres Distribution

Album: released on RCA, Apr'85 by RCA Records. Dist: RCA, Roots, Swift, Wellard, Chris, I & B, Solomon & Peres Distribution

Cassette: released on RCA, Apr'85 by RCA Records. Dist: RCA, Roots, Swift, Wellard, Chris, I & B, Solomon & Peres Distribution

HERE COMES THE RAIN AGAIN.
Single (7"): released on D & A, Jan'84 by RCA Records. Dist: RCA

Single (12"): released on D & A, Jan'84 by RCA Records. Dist: RCA

Picture disc single: released on D & A, Jan'84 by RCA Records. Dist: RCA

IN THE GARDEN.
Tracks: / English summer / Belinda / Take me to your heart / She's invisible now / Your time will come / Caveman head / Never gonna cry again / All the young people / Sing sing / Revenge.
Compact disc: released on RCA, Jan'87 by RCA Records. Dist: RCA, Roots, Swift, Wellard, Chris, I & B, Solomon & Peres Distribution

Album: released on RCA, '84 by RCA Records. Dist: RCA, Roots, Swift, Wellard, Chris, I & B, Solomon & Peres Distribution

Cassette: released on RCA, '84 by RCA Records. Dist: RCA, Roots, Swift, Wellard, Chris, I & B, Solomon & Peres Distribution

IT'S ALRIGHT (BABY'S COMING BACK).
Tracks: / It's alright (baby's coming back) / Conditioned soul / Late notification.
Single (7"): released on RCA, Jan'86 by RCA Records. Dist: RCA, Roots, Swift, Wellard, Chris, I & B, Solomon & Peres Distribution

Single (12"): released on RCA, Jan'86 by RCA Records. Dist: RCA, Roots, Swift, Wellard, Chris, I & B, Solomon & Peres Distribution

JULIA.
Single (7"): released on Virgin, Jan'85 by Virgin Records. Dist: EMI, Virgin Distribution

Single (12"): released on Virgin, Jan'85 by Virgin Records. Dist: EMI, Virgin Distribution

LOVE IS A STRANGER/MONKEY MONKEY.
Single (7"): released on D & A, Sep'82 by RCA Records. Dist: RCA

Single (12"): released on D & A, Sep'82 by RCA Records. Dist: RCA

Picture disc single: released on D & A, Sep'82 by RCA Records. Dist: RCA

MIRACLE OF LOVE.
Tracks: / When tomorrow comes (live) / Who's that girl (live)*.
Single (7"): released on D & A, Nov'86 by RCA Records. Dist: RCA

Single (12"): released on D & A, Nov'86 by RCA Records. Dist: RCA

MISSIONARY MAN.
Tracks: / Missionary man / Last time, The (live).
Single (7"): released on D & A, Feb'87 by RCA Records. Dist: RCA

Single (12"): released on D & A, Feb'87 by RCA Records. Dist: RCA

REVENGE.
Tracks: / Let's go / Take your pain away / Little of you, A / Thorn in my side / In this town / I remember you / Missionary man / Last time, The / When tomorrow comes / My last lost melody.
Compact disc: released on RCA, Jul'86 by RCA Records. Dist: RCA, Roots, Swift, Wellard, Chris, I & B, Solomon & Peres Distribution

Album: released on RCA, Jul'86 by RCA Records. Dist: RCA, Roots, Swift, Wellard, Chris, I & B, Solomon & Peres Distribution

Cassette: released on RCA, Jul'86 by RCA Records. Dist: RCA, Roots, Swift, Wellard, Chris, I & B, Solomon & Peres Distribution

RIGHT BY YOUR SIDE.
Single (7"): released on D & A, Oct'83 by RCA Records. Dist: RCA

Single (12"): released on D & A, Oct'83 by RCA Records. Dist: RCA

SEXCRIME (1984).
Single (7"): released on Virgin, Oct'84 by Virgin Records. Dist: EMI, Virgin Distribution
Cat. no: **VS 728**
Single (12"): released on Virgin, Oct'84 by Virgin Records. Dist: EMI, Virgin Distribution
Cat. no: **VS 728-12**

SISTERS ARE DOIN' IT FOR THEMSELVES (see also Aretha Franklin) (Eurythmics & Aretha Franklin).
Single (7"): released on RCA, Oct'85 by RCA Records. Dist: RCA, Roots, Swift, Wellard, Chris, I & B, Solomon & Peres Distribution

Single (12"): released on RCA, Oct'85 by RCA Records. Dist: RCA, Roots, Swift, Wellard, Chris, I & B, Solomon & Peres Distribution

SWEET DREAMS (ARE MADE OF THIS).
Single (7"): released on RCA, Jan'83 by RCA Records. Dist: RCA, Roots, Swift, Wellard, Chris, I & B, Solomon & Peres Distribution

Single (12"): released on RCA, Jan'83 by RCA Records. Dist: RCA, Roots, Swift, Wellard, Chris, I & B, Solomon & Peres Distribution

SWEET DREAMS (ARE MADE OF THIS).
Compact disc: released on RCA, '83 by RCA Records. Dist: RCA, Roots, Swift, Wellard, Chris, I & B, Solomon & Peres Distribution

Album: released on RCA, '84 by RCA Records. Dist: RCA, Roots, Swift, Wellard, Chris, I & B, Solomon & Peres Distribution

Cassette: released on RCA, '84 by RCA Records. Dist: RCA, Roots, Swift, Wellard, Chris, I & B, Solomon & Peres Distribution

THERE MUST BE AN ANGEL (PLAYING WITH MY HEART).
Single (7"): released on RCA, Jun'85 by RCA Records. Dist: RCA, Roots, Swift, Wellard, Chris, I & B, Solomon & Peres Distribution

Single (12"): released on RCA, Jun'85 by RCA Records. Dist: RCA, Roots, Swift, Wellard, Chris, I & B, Solomon & Peres Distribution

THIS IS THE HOUSE/YOUR TIME WILL...
Single (12"): released on RCA, Apr'82 by RCA Records. Dist: RCA, Roots, Swift, Wellard, Chris, I & B, Solomon & Peres Distribution

THORN IN MY SIDE.
Tracks: / Thorn in my side / In this town.
Notes: Extra track on 12" version not known
Single (7"): released on D & A, Aug'86 by RCA Records. Dist: RCA

Single (12"): released on D & A, Aug'86 by RCA Records. Dist: RCA

TOUCH.
Tracks: / Here comes the rain again / Regrets / Right by your side / Cool blue / Who's that girl? / First cut, The / Aqua / No fear, no hate, no pain (no broken hearts) / Paint a rumour.
Notes: Tracks include: First cut, Paint a rumour and Cool blue etc. Digital stereo.
Compact disc: released on RCA, Sep'84 by RCA Records. Dist: RCA, Roots, Swift, Wellard, Chris, I & B, Solomon & Peres Distribution

Album: released on D & A, Nov'83 by RCA Records. Dist: RCA

Cassette: released on D & A, Nov'83 by RCA Records. Dist: RCA

TOUCH DANCE 7 track mini album.
Album: released on D & A, Jun'84 by RCA Records. Dist: RCA

Cassette: released on RCA, Jun'84 by RCA Records. Dist: RCA, Roots, Swift, Wellard, Chris, I & B, Solomon & Peres Distribution

WALK, THE/MORNING/INVISIBLE HANDS.
Single (7"): released on RCA, Jul'82 by RCA Records. Dist: RCA, Roots, Swift, Wellard, Chris, I & B, Solomon & Peres Distribution

WALK, THE/STEP ON THE BEAST.
Single (7"): released on RCA, Jun'82 by RCA Records. Dist: RCA, Roots, Swift, Wellard, Chris, I & B, Solomon & Peres Distribution

WHEN TOMORROW COMES.
Tracks: / When tomorrow comes / Take your pain away.
Single (7"): released on D & A, May'86 by RCA Records. Dist: RCA

Single (12"): released on D & A, May'86 by RCA Records. Dist: RCA

WHO'S THAT GIRL/YOU TAKE SOME LENTILS.
Single (7"): released on D & A, Jul'83 by RCA Records. Dist: RCA

Single (12"): released on D & A, Jul'83 by RCA Records. Dist: RCA

WOULD I LIE TO YOU.
Single (7"): released on RCA, Apr'85 by RCA Records. Dist: RCA, Roots, Swift, Wellard, Chris, I & B, Solomon & Peres Distribution

Single (12"): released on RCA, Apr'85 by RCA Records. Dist: RCA, Roots, Swift, Wellard, Chris, I & B, Solomon & Peres Distribution

Evan, Lurie

HAPPY HERE.
Album: released on Crepescule, Nov'85 by Island Records. Dist: Polygram, Pinnacle

Evans, A

MARCHING ON.
Single (12"): released on Yardbeat, Oct'85 Dist: Jetstar

Evans, Bill

ALTERNATIVE MAN.
Tracks: / Alternative man, The / Path of least resistance / Let the juice loose / Gardiners garden / Survival of the fittest / Jo Jo / Cry in her eyes, The / Miles away / Flight of the falcon / Alternative man, The / Path of least resistance, The / Let the juice loose / Gardiners garden / Survival of the fittest / Jojo / Cry in her eyes, The / Miles away / Flight of the falcon.
Notes: Bill Evans is one of a new breed of jazz-orientated musicians whose music, builton a solid jazz basis, appeals to an ever-widening audience, examples being Wynton Marsalis and Stanley Jordan. A multi-talented reed player, Evans played with Miles Davis' band during miles' comeback. He has also played on albums by David Sanborn, Ron Carter and Michael Franks as well as a spell as a member of The Mahavishnu Orchestra. Personnel on "The Alternative Man" encapsulates most of the Mahavishnu Orchestra together with special guest John McLaughlin. The rhythm section of danny Gottlieb and Mark Egan are ex-members of the Pat MethenyGroup and Gottlieb just finished a european tour with Al DiMeola while Mark Eganappeared on the new Duran Duran project- Arcadia. Chuck Loeb and Mitchell Formanhave both played with Stan Getz at different times. Hiram Bullock and Lew Soloffare top flight session musicians with credits too numerous to list. Al Foster and Marcus Miller both played with Bill Evans in the Miles Davis band and milleris fast becoming a very well known name through his work with Luther Vandross. Altogether a first class line-up of talent on an album with a very wide rangeof appeal.
Album: released on Blue Note, Dec'85 by EMI Records. Dist: EMI

Cassette: released on Blue Note, Dec'85 by EMI Records. Dist: EMI

Compact disc: released on Blue Note, Sep'87 by EMI Records. Dist: EMI. Estim retail price in Sep'87 was £11.99.

ARTISTRY IN JAZZ Greatest hits.
Compact disc: released on JVC Fantasy (Japan), May'87

AT MONTREUX JAZZ FESTIVAL.
Album: released on Verve, Mar'81 by Phonogram Records. Dist: Polygram
Cat. no: **2304 152**
Tracks: / One for Helen / Sleeping bee, A / Mother of pearl / Nardis / O loves you Porgy / Touch of your lips / Embraceable you / Someday my prince will come / Walkin' up / Quiet now.
Notes: Personnel: Bill Evans - piano\Eddie Gomez - bass\Jack DeJohnette - drums. Recorded in 1968, two years before Bill Evans' death, this is one of the great jazz performances- winning a Grammy award for best instrumental jazz performance(small group). With a generous 58 minutes playing time, the CD benefits from twoadditional tracks which were never available on the original album. These are: Bill Evans playing solo piano on "I loves you Porgy" and "Quiet now".
Compact disc: by Phonogram Records. Dist: Polygram

AT THE VILLAGE VANGUARD (Evans, Bill Trio).
Compact disc: released on London, Apr'87 by London Records. Dist: Polygram

AUTUMN LEAVES.
Notes: Recorded New York City 1961.
Album: released on Crusader Jazz Masterworks, Jun'86 Dist: Jazz Music

AUTUMN LEAVES (LOTUS).
Album: released on Lotus, Apr'81 Dist: Counterpoint

BILL EVANS.
Cassette: released on Deja Vu, Nov'85 by Deja Vu Records. Dist: Counterpoint Distribution, Record Services Distribution (Ireland)

BILL EVANS TRIO AT SHELLEY'S MANNEHOLE (Evans, Bill Trio).
Album:

CALIFORNIA HERE I COME.
Album: released on Verve, Apr'83 by Phonogram Records. Dist: Polygram

COMPACT JAZZ.
Compact disc: released on Verve, Jul'87 by Phonogram Records. Dist: Polygram

CONVERSATION WITH MYSELF.
Compact disc: by Phonogram Records. Dist: Polygram

ELOQUENCE (Evans, Bill & Eddie Gomez).
Compact disc: released on JVC Fantasy (Japan), May'87

EVERYBODY DIGS BILL EVANS.
Compact disc: released on Vanguard (USA), Apr'86

Compact disc: released on Carrere, Apr'87 by Carrere Records. Dist: PRT, Spartan

EXPLORATIONS.
Compact disc: released on JVC Fantasy (Japan), May'87

GREEN DOLPHIN STREET (Evans, Bill & Philly Joe Jones).
Compact disc: released on JVC Fantasy (Japan), May'87

IN YOUR OWN SWEET WAY.
Album: released on Affinity, Mar'81 by Charly Records. Dist: Charly, Cadillac

LIVE IN EUROPE.
Album: released on Unique Jazz, Apr'81 Dist: Swift, Jazz Music, Jazz Horizons

MONTREUX 2.
Cassette: released on CTI (Musidisc France), Feb'84 by Polydor Records. Dist: IMS, Polygram

NEW JAZZ CONCEPTIONS.
Album: released on Original Jazz Classics (USA), Jun'86 Dist: Fantasy (USA) Distribution, Chris Wellard Distribution, IMS-Polygram Distribution

PORTRAIT IN JAZZ.
Compact disc: released on JVC Fantasy (Japan), May'87

Album: released on Riverside (USA), Feb'84 Dist: Fantasy (USA) Distribution

QUIET NOW.
Tracks: / Very airy / Sleeping bee / Quiet now / Turn out the stars / Autumn leaves.
Compact disc: by Charly Records. Dist: Charly, Cadillac

Album: released on Affinity, Dec'81 by Charly Records. Dist: Charly, Cadillac

QUINTESSENCE.
Compact disc: released on Fantasy (USA), Nov'86 by Fantasy Inc USA Records. Dist: IMS, Polygram

Compact disc: released on Carrere, Apr'87 by Carrere Records. Dist: PRT, Spartan

RE: PERSON I KNEW.
: released on Fantasy, Sep'81 by RCA Records. Dist: RCA, Jetstar

SUNDAY AT THE VILLAGE VANGUARD.
Compact disc: released on Carrere(France), Dec'86 by Carrere Records (France). Dist: PRT

SUNDAY NIGHT AT THE VILLAGE VANGUARD (Evans, Bill Trio).
Compact disc: released on JVC Fantasy (Japan), May'87

SYMBIOSIS.
Album: released on MPS Jazz, Apr'81

TIME REMEMBERED.
Album: released on Carrere(France), Apr'84 by Carrere Records (France). Dist: PRT

TOWN HALL.
Compact disc: released on Polydor, Feb'87 by Polydor Records. Dist: Polygram, Polydor

TRIO 64.
Compact disc: by Phonogram Records. Dist: Polygram

Album: released on Verve (France), Jul'84

TRIO 65.
Compact disc: released on Verve, Apr'84 by Phonogram Records. Dist: Polygram

Cassette: released on MWM, May'86 by Mawson & Wareham. Dist: Spartan Distribution, Jazz Music Distribution, JSU Distribution

Album: released on Verve (France), Jun'83

TRIO/DUO.
Album: by Polydor Records. Dist: Polygram, Polydor

TWO SUPPER (Evans, Bill Trio).
Album: released on Unique Jazz, Nov'86 Dist: Swift, Jazz Music, Jazz Horizons

UNDERCURRENT.
Notes: with Jim Hall - guitar. Recd. 1959 for United Artists, never before on a U.K. label.
Album: released on Memoir, Mar'87 by Memoir Records. Dist: PRT Distribution

Cassette: released on Memoir, Mar'87 by Memoir Records. Dist: PRT Distribution

WALKMAN JAZZ.
Cassette: released on Polydor, Jun'87 by Polydor Records. Dist: Polygram, Polydor

WALTZ FOR DEBBY (Evans, Bill Trio).
Compact disc: released on JVC Fantasy (Japan), Dec'86

Compact disc: released on Carrere, Apr'87 by Carrere Records. Dist: PRT, Spartan

WE WILL MEET AGAIN.
Album: released on WEA (France), Jul'85 Dist: Celtic Music Distribution, Swift

WHAT'S NEW (Evans, Bill & Jeremy Steig).
Album: released on Import Music Service (IMS), Apr'81 Dist: Concord Jazz Distributions, Pablo, Polygram

WITH SYMPHONY ORCHESTRA.
Album: released on Verve (USA), Sep'84 by Polydor. Dist: Polygram

Cassette: released on Verve (USA), Sep'84 by Polydor. Dist: Polygram

Compact disc: released on Verve (USA), Sep'84 by Polydor. Dist: Polygram

Evans, Dave

SAD PIG DANCE.
Album: by Sonet. Dist: Roots, PRT-Pye Distribution

TAKE A BITE OUT OF LIFE.
Album: released on Kicking Mule, Jan'78 by Sonet. Dist: Roots, PRT-Pye Distribution

Evans, Don

GONNA CARE FOR YOU.
Single (12"): released on Move, Jul'85 by Charly Records. Dist: Charly Distribution, Fast Forward Distribution, Cartel Distribution

Evans, Dr. Christopher

DREAMS & DREAMING.
Cassette: released on Semp, Oct'81 Dist: Mojo Distribution, Lightning

Evans, Frank

FRANK EVANS.
Album: Dist: Jazz Music, Chris Wellard

NOCTUARY.
Album: Dist: Jazz Music, Chris Wellard

Evans, George

GREAT FOR DANCING (Evans, George & His Symphony of Saxes).
Album: released on MWM (UK), Jan'87

Evans, Gil

2 DEGREES EAST/3 DEGREES WEST (Evans, Gil Orchestra).
Tracks: / Love me or leave me / I can't get started / Easy living / 2 degrees east - 3 degrees west / Skylark / Almost like being in love.
Boxed set: released on Blue Note, Aug'87 by EMI Records. Dist: EMI

Cassette: released on Blue Note, Aug'87 by EMI Records. Dist: EMI

BLUES IN ORBIT.
Album: released on Enja (Germany), Jan'82 by Enja Records (W.Germany). Dist: Cadillac Music

BRITISH ORCHESTRA, THE.
Notes: Featuring Stan Sulzmann/John Surman (solos)/Ray Russell
Compact disc: released on Mole, May'87 by Mole Records. Dist: Mole Music Co., Spartan Distribution

BRITISH ORCHESTRA (THE).
Notes: Re-issue to coincide with Gil evans Tour. Gil evans "The British Orchestra" received rave reviews when first released on LP.
Compact disc: released on Mole Jazz, Apr'87 by Mole Jazz Records. Dist: Mole Jazz Distributors

Album: released on Mole, May'83 by Mole Records. Dist: Mole Music Co., Spartan Distribution

Compact disc: released on Mole, May'83 by Mole Records. Dist: Mole Music Co., Spartan Distribution

CHET BAKER AND CREW (Evans, Gil Orchestra).
Tracks: / To Micky's memory / Slightly above moderate / Halema / Revelation / Something for Liza / Luscious Lu / Worrying the life out of me / Medium rock.
Boxed set: released on Blue Note, Aug'87 by EMI Records. Dist: EMI

Cassette: released on Blue Note, Aug'87 by EMI Records. Dist: EMI

GREAT JAZZ STANDARDS (Evans, Gil Orchestra).
Tracks: / Davenport blues / Straight no chaser / Ballad of the sad young men / Joy spring / Django / Chant of the weed / Theme.
Boxed set: released on Blue Note, Aug'87 by EMI Records. Dist: EMI

Cassette: released on Blue Note, Aug'87 by EMI Records. Dist: EMI

GUITAR FORMS (Evans, Gil & Kenny Burrell).
Album: released on Verve, Aug'81 by Phonogram Records. Dist: Polygram

JAZZ GUITAR (Evans, Gil Orchestra).
Tracks: / Stompin' at the Savoy / Things ain't what they used to be / Thanks for the memory / Tangerine / Stella by starlight / 9.20 special / Deep in a dream / Look for the silver lining / Seven come eleven / Things ain't what they used to be (alternative take) / Too close for comfort.
Boxed set: released on Blue Note, Aug'87 by EMI Records. Dist: EMI

Cassette: released on Blue Note, Aug'87 by EMI Records. Dist: EMI

KONITZ MEETS MULLIGAN (Evans, Gil Orchestra).
Tracks: / I can't believe that you're in love with me / Broadway / Almost like being in love / Sextet I / Lady be good / Too marvelous for words / Lover man / I'll remember April / These foolish things / All the things you are.
Boxed set: released on Blue Note, Aug'87 by EMI Records. Dist: EMI

Cassette: released on Blue Note, Aug'87 by EMI Records. Dist: EMI

LITTLE WING.
Album: released on Circle, May'79 Dist: Jazz Music

LIVE AT SWEET BASIL. VOL.2 (Evans, Gil & The Monday Night Orchestra).
Notes: Gil Evans will be bringing his New York Orchestra to the UK in May 1987 to celebrate his 75th birthday. Interest around this great jazz arranger and composer will be high. Recorded August 1984.
Double Album: released on King (USA), Apr'87 Dist: Gusto Distribution

LIVE AT SWEET BASIL (Evans, Gil & The Monday Night Orchestra).
Tracks: / Parabola / Voodoo chile / Orange was the colour of her dress, then silk blue / Prince of darkness / Blues in 'C' (John's memory) / Cheryl / Bird feathers / Relaxin' at Camarillo / Goodbye pork pie hat / Up from the skies.
Notes: Legendary composer, arranger and orchestra leader Gil Evans recorded live at Sweet Basil with 14 piece orchestra. Compositions by Jimi Hendrix, Herbie Hancock and Charles Mingus. Gil Evans is probably best known for his work with Miles Davis between 1957-60 and was associated with the nine piece Miles had during this period that was dubbed the 'Birth of The Cool'. Personnel: Gil Evans-acoustic and electric pianos\Lew Soloff - trumpet\Hannibal Marvin Peterson - trumpet\Shunzo Ohno - trumpet\Miles Evans - trumpet\George Adams - tenor sax\ Chris Hunter - alto sax\Howard Johnson - tuba, baritone sax, bass clarinet\Tom Malone - trombone\Hiram Bullock-Pete Levin - synthesizer\Mark Egan - bass\Adam Nussbaum - drums\Mino Cinelu - percussion. Double album.
Album: released on King (Japan), Jul'86 Dist: IMS, Polygram

LONG HELLO, THE VOL 4.
Album: released on Shanghai, Sep'84

MILES DAVIS ALL STARS & GIL EVANS (see Davis, Miles) (Evans, Gil & Miles Davis).

NEW BOTTLE, OLD WINE (Evans, Gil Orchestra).
Tracks: / St Louis blues / King Porter stomp / Willow tree / Struttin' with some barbecue / Lester leaps in / Round midnight / Manteca / Bird feathers.
Boxed set: released on Blue Note, Aug'87 by EMI Records. Dist: EMI

Cassette: released on Blue Note, Aug'87 by EMI Records. Dist: EMI

OUT OF THE COOL.
Tracks: / La nevada / Where flamingos fly / Bilbao song / Stratosphunk / Sunken treasure.
Compact disc: released on MCA, May'87 by MCA Records. Dist: Polygram, MCA

Album: released on Jasmine, Sep'82 by Jasmine Records. Dist: Counterpoint, Lugtons, Taylor, H.R., Wellard, Chris, Swift, Cadillac

Cassette: released on Jasmine, Sep'82 by Jasmine Records. Dist: Counterpoint, Lugtons, Taylor, H.R., Wellard, Chris, Swift, Cadillac

OUT OF THE COOL (IMPULSE).
Album: released on Impulse, Oct'85 by Impulse Records. Dist: MCA, Polygram

PARABOLA.
Album: released on Horo, Oct'79 Dist: Cadillac Music

PRIESTESS (Evans, Gil Orchestra).
Compact disc: released on Polystar (Japan), '86 Dist: Target, Polygram

PRIESTESS.
Album: released on Antilles, May'87 by Island Records. Dist: Polygram

Cassette: released on Antilles, May'87 by Island Records. Dist: Polygram

REST OF GIL EVANS LIVE AT THE RFH 1978.
Album: released on Mole, Feb'81 by Mole Records. Dist: Mole Music Co., Spartan Distribution

Evans, Joe

TWO POOR BOYS (Evans, Joe & Arthur McClain).
Notes: The complete recordings of Joe Evans & Arthur McClain. Recorded in mono.
Album: released on Earl Archives, Jan'87 Dist: Swift, Jazz Music

Evans, John

BOY NAMED BEN, A.
Single (7"): released on City, Dec'85 by City Records. Dist: Pinnacle

Evans, Junior

GIMME LITTLE LOVING.
Single (12"): released on Must Dance, Nov'85 by Must Dance Records. Dist: Jetstar Distribution

Evans, Paul

SEVEN LITTLE GIRLS.
Single (7"): released on Creole, Aug'82 by Creole Records. Dist: Rhino, PRT

Evans, Tony

10 DANCE CHAMPIONSHIPS (Evans, Tony & His Orchestra).
Tracks: / Cheek to cheek / Dancing with you in my arms / Dearly beloved / In dreams a memory / Adios muchachos / Cavatina / Who's taking you home / Very thought of you, The / Kiss me honey / And I love you so / Spanish eyes / Sucu sucu / Spanish matador / Johnson rag.
Album: released on Tema, Jun'86 by Tema Records. Dist: EMI

ARTISTRY IN SWING (Evans, Tony & His Orchestra).
Album: released on Tema, Jun'86 by Tema Records. Dist: EMI

Cassette: released on Tema, Nov'80 by Tema Records. Dist: EMI

BALLROOM DANCING CHAMPION STYLE (Evans, Tony & His Orchestra).
Album: released on Rediffusion, Nov'79

DANCE IN THE OLD FASHIONED WAY (Evans, Tony & His Orchestra).
Album: released on Tema, Jun'86 by Tema Records. Dist: EMI

DANCE WITH ME (Evans, Tony & His Orchestra).
Album: released on Tema, Jun'86 by Tema Records. Dist: EMI

Cassette: released on Tema, '84 by Tema Records. Dist: EMI

GENTLE ON MY MIND (Evans, Tony & His Orchestra).
Tracks: / Look of love / Here there and everywhere / Dancing with a dream / Witchita lineman / By the time I get to Phoenix / Hey Jude / Gentle on my mind / For once in my life / Once more / Ob la di ob la da / Impossible dream, The / Last waltz, The.
Album: released on Tema, Jun'86 by Tema Records. Dist: EMI

Cassette: released on VFM, May'85 by VFM Records. Dist: Taylors, Wynd-Up Distribution

I'M IN THE MOOD FOR DANCING (Evans, Tony & His Orchestra).
Album: released on Tema, Jun'86 by Tema Records. Dist: EMI

IN TIJUANA (Evans, Tony & His Orchestra).
Album: released on Elite, Apr'83 Dist: PRT

IT'S MY PARTY (Evans, Tony & His Orchestra).
Album: released on Tema, Nov'84 by Tema Records. Dist: EMI

Cassette: released on Tema, Nov'84 by Tema Records. Dist: EMI

JIVE ALIVE (Evans, Tony & His Orchestra).
Single (12"): released on Tema, Nov'82 by Tema Records. Dist: EMI

KEEP ON DANCING (Evans, Tony & His Orchestra).
Tracks: / Love grows where my Rosemary goes (medley) / Go go (medley) / Simon says (medley) / Back off boogaloo / Leader of the gang (medley) / You came you saw you conquered (medley).
Album: released on Tema, Jun'86 by Tema Records. Dist: EMI

MAY I HAVE THE NEXT DREAM (Evans, Tony & His Orchestra).
Tracks: / Mr Sandman / Pretend / Every dream / Roses of Picardy / I dont want to walk without you / May I have the next dream / Hasta luego / I wonder who's kissing her now / Song of my life / Mexican hat dance / Ole guapa / Golden tango.
Album: released on Tema, Jun'86 by Tema Records. Dist: EMI

Cassette: released on Tema, Apr'82 by Tema Records. Dist: EMI

MERRY CHRISTMAS (Evans, Tony & His Orchestra).
Album: released on Tema, Jun'86 by Tema Records. Dist: EMI

Cassette: released on Tema, Nov'84 by Tema Records. Dist: EMI

NO TIME LIKE OLD TIME (Evans, Tony & His Orchestra).
Album: released on Tema, Jun'86 by Tema Records. Dist: EMI

Cassette: released on Tema, Feb'81 by Tema Records. Dist: EMI

PLAYS THE DANCE CLUB (Evans, Tony & His Orchestra).
Album: released on Tema, Jun'86 by Tema Records. Dist: EMI

ROARIN' RAGTIME (Evans, Tony & His Orchestra).
Tracks: / Bugle call rag / Mississippi rag / Tiger rag / Barnsley chop rag / Johnson rag / Alexander's rag / Cincinnatti rag / 12th Street rag / Greengate rag / Russian rag / Maple leaf rag.
Album: released on Tema, Jun'86 by Tema Records. Dist: EMI

Cassette: released on Tema, Sep'81 by Tema Records. Dist: EMI

ROMANTIC LATIN BY ROMANA (Evans, Tony & His Orchestra).
Album: released on Tema, Dec'82 by Tema Records. Dist: EMI

SHALL WE DANCE (Evans, Tony & His Orchestra).
Tracks: / Shall we dance / You do something to me / Stay as sweet as you are / For you are beautiful / First day of spring / Answer me (oh my love) / Mardi gras cha cha / Wheels cha cha / Forever and ever / So near to you / Moonlight serenade / Sol-y-mar samba.
Album: released on Tema, Jun'86 by Tema Records. Dist: EMI

SIMPLY BEAUTIFUL (Evans, Tony & His Orchestra).
Album: released on Tema, Jun'86 by Tema Records. Dist: EMI

SPANISH FIRE-WONDERFUL WORLD OF TANGOS (Evans, Tony & His Orchestra).
Album: released on Tema, Jun'86 by Tema Records. Dist: EMI

Cassette: released on Tema, Sep'84 by Tema Records. Dist: EMI

TOUCH OF CLASS FOR YOUR DANCING OR LISTENING PLEASURE (Evans, Tony & His Orchestra).
Album: released on Tema, Oct'81 by Tema Records. Dist: EMI

UK MODERN BALLROOM CHAMPIONSHIPS IN SEQUENCE (Evans, Tony & His Orchestra).
Album: released on Tema, Jun'86 by Tema Records. Dist: EMI

WONDERFUL WORLD OF FOXTROTS (Evans, Tony & His Orchestra).
Album: released on Tema, Jun'86 by Tema Records. Dist: EMI

WONDERFUL WORLD OF QUICKSTEPS (Evans, Tony & His Orchestra).
Album: released on Tema, Jun'86 by Tema Records. Dist: EMI

WONDERFUL WORLD OF WALTZES (Evans, Tony & His Orchestra).
Notes: Tracks include; "The first day of spring", "Wonderful one", "My autumn love", "Cavatina" etc.
Album: released on Tema, Jun'86 by Tema Records. Dist: EMI

Cassette: released on Tema, Apr'85 by Tema Records. Dist: EMI

WORLD LATIN CHAMPIONSHIPS (Evans, Tony & His Orchestra).
Album: released on Tema, Jun'86 by Tema Records. Dist: EMI

WORLD MODERN BALLROOM CHAMPIONSHIPS (Evans, Tony & His Orchestra).
Album: released on Tema, Jun'86 by Tema Records. Dist: EMI

Evans, Tyrone

LONESOME LAD.
Single (12"): released on Black Music, Feb'83 by Black Music Records. Dist: Jetstar

WAR INTERNATIONAL (Evans, Tyrone & John Wayne).
Single (12"): released on Shuttle, Apr'83 Dist: RCA

Evans, Victor Romero

ONE FOR MY BABY.
Single (12"): released on Special Agent, Aug'83 Dist: Black Grape

SPECIAL REQUEST.
Single (12"): released on Special Request, Sep'82

Evan & The MBT Band

SOMEDAY WE'LL BE TOGETHER.
Single (7"): released on MBT, Jul'85 by MBT Records. Dist: Pinnacle

Single (12"): released on MBT, Jul'85 by MBT Records. Dist: Pinnacle

Evasions

JOCK'S RAP (THE PASSAGE).
Single (7"): released on Groove PR, Dec'82 by Beggars Banquet Records. Dist: WEA, PRT

Single (12"): released on Groove PR, Dec'82 by Beggars Banquet Records. Dist: WEA, PRT

WIKKA WRAP.
Single (7"): released on Groove PR, Jul'81 by Beggars Banquet Records. Dist: WEA, PRT

Single (12"): released on Groove PR, Jul'81 by Beggars Banquet Records. Dist: WEA, PRT

Evening With...

EVENING WITH THE ORIGINAL BLACK COUNTRY NIGHT OUT SHOW Various artists (Various Artists).
Album: released on Broadside, Jun'81 by Broadside Records. Dist: Celtic Distributions, H.R. Taylor, Jazz Music, Projection, Jazz Services Unlimited Dist. (JSU)

Cassette: released on Broadside, Jun'81 by Broadside Records. Dist: Celtic Distributions, H.R. Taylor, Jazz Music, Projection, Jazz Services Unlimited Dist. (JSU)

EVENING WITH WINDHAM HILL-LIVE Various artists (Various Artists).
Album: released on Windham Hill (Germany), Sep'84

Compact disc: released on Windham Hill, Feb'85 Dist: AM

Evening Without

EVENING WITHOUT Various artists (Various Artists).
Album: released on Original, Oct'81 Dist: RCA Distribution, Jazz Music Distribution, PRT Distribution

Cassette: released on Original, Oct'81 Dist: RCA Distribution, Jazz Music Distribution, PRT Distribution

Evens, Don

TELLING ME.
Single (12"): released on Technic, May'85

Event Band

WHAT'S MY LINE.
Single (7"): released on Mayhem, Jul'82 by International Records & Tapes. Dist: Pinnacle

Eventually

CULTURE MUSIC EP.
Single (12"): released on Friendly Musicians, Aug'85 Dist: Jetstar

Everett, Betty

1957 - 1961 (Everett, Betty & Lillian Offitt).
Tracks: / Tell me darling / I'll weep no more / Killer diller / My life depends on you / My love / Ain't gonna cry / Oh mama / Will my man be home tonight / Man don't work / My man is a lover / Troubles / Shine on.
Album: released on Flyright, Oct'86 by Flyright Records. Dist: Krazy Kat, Swift, Jazz Music

GETTING MIGHTY CROWDED/SHOOP.
Single (7"): released on Charly, Jul'80 by Charly Records. Dist: Charly, Cadillac

JERRY & BETTY (Everett, Betty & Jerry Butler).
Album: released on Charly, Nov'81 by Charly Records. Dist: Charly, Cadillac

REAL THING, THE.
Compact disc: released on Charly, Jan'87 by Charly Records. Dist: Charly, Cadillac

Everette, Leon

LEON EVERETTE'S GREATEST HITS.
Tracks: / Giving up easy / Don't feel like the lone ranger / I love that woman (like the devil loves sin) / I don't want to lose / Over / If I keep on going crazy / Hurricane / Midnight rodeo / Don't be angry / Just give me what you think is fair / Soul searchin' / Shadows of my mind / My lady loves me (just as I am) / Lady she's right / I could'a had you / Shot in the dark.
Album: released on RCA, Jan'87 by RCA Records. Dist: RCA, Roots, Swift, Wellard, Chris, I & B, Solomon & Peres Distribution

Cassette: released on RCA, Jan'87 by RCA Records. Dist: RCA, Roots, Swift, Wellard, Chris, I & B, Solomon & Peres Distribution

Everett, Kenny

KENNY EVERETT NAUGHTY JOKE BOX.
Album: released on Relax, Oct'84 Dist: CBS

Cassette: released on Relax, Oct'84 Dist: CBS

SNOT RAP 2.
Single (7"): released on RCA, Feb'85 by RCA Records. Dist: RCA, Roots, Swift, Wellard, Chris, I & B, Solomon & Peres Distribution

Single (12"): released on RCA, Feb'85 by RCA Records. Dist: RCA, Roots, Swift, Wellard, Chris, I & B, Solomon & Peres Distribution

SNOT RAP (2 PARTS).
Single (7"): released on RCA, Mar'83 by RCA Records. Dist: RCA, Roots, Swift, Wellard, Chris, I & B, Solomon & Peres Distribution

Single (12"): released on RCA, Mar'83 by RCA Records. Dist: RCA, Roots, Swift, Wellard, Chris, I & B, Solomon & Peres Distribution

Everett, Rupert

GENERATION OF LONLINESS.
Tracks: / Generation of lonliness / Blood under the bridge.
Single (7"): released on Chrysalis, May'87 by Chrysalis Records. Dist: CBS

Single (12"): released on Chrysalis, May'87 by Chrysalis Records. Dist: CBS

Evergreens A Go Go

EVERGREENS A GO GO (Various Artists).
Compact disc: released on Bellaphon, '86 by Bellaphon Records. Dist: IMS-Polygram

Everhart, Bob

COUNTRY.
Album: released on Westwood, Nov'81 by Westwood Records. Dist: Jazz Music, H.R. Taylor, JSU, Pinnacle, Ross Records

Everlasting love

EVERLASTING LOVE Various artists (Various Artists).
Cassette: released on Autograph, Apr'85 Dist: Record Services Distribution (Ireland)

Everly Brothers

20 GOLDEN LOVE SONGS.
Compact disc: released on Spectrum, Jul'86 Dist: ACD

20 GREATEST HITS.
Compact disc: released on Spectrum (Holland), Jul'86

ALBUM FLASH.
Notes: Cameras follow the duo recording in London and Nashville. Includes songs by PaulMcCartney and Jeff Lynne. Video EP highlighting four tracks from the brothers new comeback studio album (including the hit "On the wings of a nightingale", plus interviews. Number of tracks: 4. Total playing time: 30 minutes.
Video-cassette (VHS): released on Polygram Music, Oct'84 by Polygram Records. Dist: Polygram

Video-cassette [Betamax]: released on Polygram Music, Oct'84 by Polygram Records. Dist: Polygram

ALL I HAVE TO DO IS DREAM.
Single (7"): released on Old Gold, Jul'82 by Old Gold Records. Dist: Lightning, Jazz Music, Spartan, Counterpoint

ALL THEY HAD TO DO WAS DREAM.
Album: released on Rhino (USA), Jan'86 by Rhino Records (USA).

BEAT AND SOUL.
Album: released on WB, Dec'85

BEST OF THE EVERLY BROTHERS.
Cassette: released on Creole (Everest-Europa), Jul'84 by Creole Records. Dist: PRT, Rhino

BEST OF THE EVERLY BROTHERS, (THE).
Album: released on Warner Bros., Nov'83 by Warner Bros Records. Dist: WEA

Cassette: released on Warner Bros., Nov'83 by Warner Bros Records. Dist: WEA

BORN YESTERDAY.
Tracks: / Amanda Ruth / I know love / Born yesterday / These shoes / Arms of Mary / That uncertain feeling / Thinking 'bout you / Why worry / Abandoned love / Don't say goodnight / Always drive a Cadillac / You send me.
Notes: Produced by Dave Edmunds. Songs by Bob Dylan, Sam Cooke, Mark Knopfler, The Sutherland Brothers and Don and Phil Everly.
Compact disc: released on Mercury, Nov'85 by Phonogram Records. Dist: Polygram Distribution

Album: released on Mercury, Nov'85 by Phonogram Records. Dist: Polygram Distribution

Cassette: released on Mercury, Nov'85 by Phonogram Records. Dist: Polygram Distribution

BOTH SIDES OF AN EVENING.
Album: released on Warner Bros., May'85 by Warner Bros Records. Dist: WEA

BYE BYE LOVE.
Cassette: released on VFM Cassettes, Jan'85 Cat. no: **VCA 110**
Single (7"): released on Old Gold, Jul'82 by Old Gold Records. Dist: Lightning, Jazz Music, Spartan, Counterpoint

CADENCE CLASSICS 20 greatest hits.
Compact disc: released on Rhino, '86 by Creole Records. Dist: PRT, Rhino

CATHY'S CLOWN.
Single (7"): released on Warner Bros., Dec'83 by Warner Bros Records. Dist: WEA

Single (7"): released on Old Gold, Jul'82 by Old Gold Records. Dist: Lightning, Jazz Music, Spartan, Counterpoint

COLLECTION: EVERLY BROTHERS.
Tracks: / Problems / When will I be loved / This little girl of mine / Be bop a lula / Leave my woman alone / Roving gambler / Lightning express / Rockin' alone (in an old rockin' chair) / Like strangers / Wake up little susie / Devoted to you / Bird dog / Rip it up / Brand new heartache / Should we tell him / Keep a knockin' / Put my little shoes away / Kentucky / Long time gone / Down in the willow garden / Take a message to Mary / Maybe tomorrow / Since you broke my heart / Let it be me.
Notes: Double album, double cassette.
Album: released on Castle Collectors, May'86 by Castle Communications Records. Dist: Pinnacle

Cassette: released on Castle Collectors, May'86 by Castle Communications Records. Dist: Pinnacle

DATE WITH THE EVERLY BROTHERS, (A).
Album: released on Warner Bros., May'85 by Warner Bros Records. Dist: WEA

DEVOTED TO YOU.
Single (7"): released on Impression, Nov'83 Dist: CBS

Single (12"): released on Impression, Nov'83 Dist: CBS

EVERLY BROTHERS Nashville, Tennessee, November 1955.
Tracks: / Keep a' lovin' me / Sun keeps shining, The / If her love isn't true / That's the life I have to live.
Album: released on Bear Family, Sep'91 by Bear Family Records. Dist: Rollercoaster Distribution, Swift

EVERLY BROTHERS.
Album: released on Rhino (USA), Jan'86 by Rhino Records (USA).

EVERLY BROTHERS (EP) Nashville, Tennessee.
Single (7"): released on Bear Family, Sep'82 by Bear Family Records. Dist: Rollercoaster Distribution, Swift

EVERLY BROTHERS' GREATEST HITS: VOL 2.
Tracks: / Take a message to Mary / Poor Jenny / 'Til I kissed you / Oh what a feeling / Let it be me / I'm here to get my baby out of jail / When will I be loved? / Be bop a lula / Like strangers / Brand new heartache / Since you broke my heart / Lightning express.
Album: released on Pickwick, May'85 by Pickwick Records. Dist: Pickwick Distribution, Prism Leisure Distribution, Lugtons

Cassette: released on Pickwick, May'85 by Pickwick Records. Dist: Pickwick Distribution, Prism Leisure Distribution, Lugtons

EVERLY BROTHERS GREATEST HITS: VOL 1.
Album: released on Hallmark, Feb'85 by Pickwick Records. Dist: Pickwick Distribution, PRT, Taylors

Cassette: released on Hallmark, Feb'85 by Pickwick Records. Dist: Pickwick Distribution, PRT, Taylors

EVERLY BROTHERS' GREATEST HITS.
Tracks: / All I have to do is dream / Wake up little Susie / When will I be loved? / Be bop a lula.
Double cassette: released on Pickwick, Mar'83 by Pickwick Records. Dist: Pickwick Distribution, Prism Leisure Distribution, Lugtons

EVERLY BROTHERS REUNION ALBUM.
Album: released on Impression, Nov'83 Dist: CBS

Cassette: released on Impression, Nov'83 Dist: CBS

EVERLY BROTHERS SING GREAT COUNTRY HITS.
Tracks: / Oh lonesome me / Born to lose / Just one time / Send me the pillow you dream on / Release me / Please help me, I'm falling / I walk the line / Lonely street / Silver threads and golden needles / I'm so lonesome I could cry / Sweet dreams / This is the last song I'm ever going to sing.
Album: released on WB, Dec'85

EVERLY BROTHERS, (THE).
Tracks: / On the wings of a nightingale / Danger danger / Story of me, The / I'm taking my time / First in line, The / Lay lady lay / Following the sun / You make it seem so easy / More than I can handle / Asleep.
Album: released on Mercury, Oct'84 by Phonogram Records. Dist: Polygram Distribution

Cassette: released on Mercury, Oct'84 by Phonogram Records. Dist: Polygram Distribution

Compact disc: released on Mercury, Oct'84 by Phonogram Records. Dist: Polygram Distribution

FABULOUS STYLE OF THE EVERLY BROTHERS.
Album: released on Rhino (USA), Jan'86 by Rhino Records (USA).

GOLDEN HITS: EVERLY BROTHERS.
Tracks: / That's old fashioned (that's the way love should be) / How can I meet her? / Crying in the rain / I'm not angry / Don't blame me / Ebony eyes / Cathy's clown / Walk right back / Lucille / So sad to watch good love go bad / Muskrat / Temptation.
Album: by Warner Bros Records. Dist: WEA

GONE GONE GONE.
Tracks: / Lonely island / Facts of life / Ain't that loving you, baby / Love is all I need / Torture / Drop out, The / Radio and TV / Honolulu / It's been a long dry spell / Ferris wheel / Gone gone gone.
Album: released on Warner Bros., May'85 by Warner Bros Records. Dist: WEA

GREATEST HITS:EVERLY BROTHERS.
Picture disc album: released on Astan, Dec'85 by Astan Records. Dist: Counterpoint

GREATEST RECORDINGS.
Album: released on Ace, Nov'86 by Ace Records. Dist: Pinnacle, Swift, Hotshot, Cadillac

Cassette: released on Ace, Nov'86 by Ace Records. Dist: Pinnacle, Swift, Hotshot, Cadillac

GREAT RECORDINGS.
Compact disc: released on Ace, May'86 by Ace Records. Dist: Pinnacle, Swift, Hotshot, Cadillac

HEARTACHES AND HARMONIES.
Picture disc album: released on Rhino (USA), Jan'86 by Rhino Records (USA).

IN GERMANY & ITALY.
Album: released on Musketeer, Jan'87

IN OUR IMAGE.
Tracks: / Leave my girl alone / Chained to a memory / I'll never get over you / Doll house is empty, The / Glitter and gold / Power of love, The / Price of love, The / It's all over / I used to love you / Lovely Kravezit / June is as cold as December / It only cost a dime.
Album: released on Warner Bros., May'85 by Warner Bros Records. Dist: WEA

INSTANT PARTY.
Tracks: / Jezebel / Oh my papa / Step it up and go / True love / Bye bye blackbird / Trouble in mind / Love makes the world go round / Long lost John / Autumn leaves / Party's over / Ground hawg / When it's night time in Italy.
Album: released on Warner Bros., Oct'86 by Warner Bros Records. Dist: WEA

IN THE STUDIO.
Album: released on Ace, Nov'85 by Ace Records. Dist: Pinnacle, Swift, Hotshot, Cadillac

IT'S EVERLY TIME.
Tracks: / So sad / Just in case / Memories are made of this / That's what you do to me / Sleepless nights / What kind of girl are you / Oh true love / Carol Jane / Some sweet day / Nashville blues / You thrill me / I want you to know.
Album: released on Warner Bros., May'85 by Warner Bros Records. Dist: WEA

LET IT BE ME.
Single (7"): released on Old Gold, Jul'82 by Old Gold Records. Dist: Lightning, Jazz Music, Spartan, Counterpoint

LIKE STRANGERS.
Single (7"): released on Old Gold, Jul'82 by Old Gold Records. Dist: Lightning, Jazz Music, Spartan, Counterpoint

LOVE HURTS.
Tracks: / All I have to do is dream / 'Til I kissed you / So sad / Let it be me / Problems / Love of my life / No one can make my sunshine smile / Devoted to you / Take a message to Mary / When will I be loved? / Love hurts / Walk right back / Memories are made of this / Like strangers / Brand new heartache / Since you broke my heart / Love is strange / Crying in the rain / Donna Donna / Cathy's clown.
Album: released on K-Tel, Dec'84 by K-Tel Records. Dist: Record Merchandisers Distribution, Taylors, Terry Blood Distribution, Wynd-Up Distribution, Relay Distribution, Pickwick Distribution, Solomon & Peres Distribution, Polygram

Cassette: released on K-Tel, Dec'84 by K-Tel Records. Dist: Record Merchandisers Distribution, Taylors, Terry Blood Distribution, Wynd-Up Distribution, Relay Distribution, Pickwick Distribution, Solomon & Peres Distribution, Polygram

NEW ALBUM, (THE).
Tracks: / Silent treatment / Dancing on my feet / Gran Mamou / Burma shave / Nancy's minuet / He's got my sympathy / Little Hollywood girl / Omaha / Empty boxes / I can't say goodbye to you / Nothing matters but you / When snowflakes fall in the summer / I'll see your light / Why not?.
Album: released on Warner Brothers, Oct'77 by Warner Bros Records. Dist: WEA

NICE GUYS.
Album: released on Magnum Force, Sep'84 by Magnum Music Group Ltd. Dist: Magnum Music Group Ltd, PRT, Spartan

POOR JENNY.
Single (7"): released on Old Gold, Jul'82 by Old Gold Records. Dist: Lightning, Jazz Music, Spartan, Counterpoint

PRICE OF LOVE, (THE).
Single (7"): released on Old Gold, Jul'82 by Old Gold Records. Dist: Lightning, Jazz Music, Spartan, Counterpoint

PROBLEMS.
Single (7"): released on Old Gold, Jul'82 by Old Gold Records. Dist: Lightning, Jazz Music, Spartan, Counterpoint

PROFILE.
Album: released on Teldec (Germany), Jun'81 by Import Records. Dist: IMS Distribution, Polygram Distribution

Cassette: released on Teldec (Germany), Jun'81 by Import Records. Dist: IMS Distribution, Polygram Distribution

PURE HARMONY.
Tracks: / Bye bye love / Like strangers / Oh what a feeling / Bird dog / I wonder if I care as much / Take a message to Mary / All I have to do is dream / Wake up little Susie / Devoted to you / Maybe tomorrow / Love of my life / 'Til I kissed you / Since you broke my heart / Let it be me.
Album: released on Ace(Barnaby USA), Oct'84 by Ace Records. Dist: Pinnacle, Swift, Hotshot

REUNION ALBUM.
Album: released on Impression, Oct'84 Dist: CBS

Cassette: released on Impression, Oct'84 Dist: CBS

REUNION CONCERT.
Compact disc: released on Mercury, Feb'86 by Phonogram Records. Dist: Polygram Distribution

REUNION CONCERT.
Video-cassette (VHS): released on MGM, Dec'84 Dist: Polygram Distribution, Swift Distribution

RIP IT UP.
Tracks: / Rip it up / Leave my woman alone / Hey doll baby / Brand new heartache / Problems / Be bop a lula / Poor Jenny / This little girl of mine / Claudette / Should we tell him? / When will I be loved? / Keep a knockin'.
Album: released on Ace(Barnaby USA), Feb'83 by Ace Records. Dist: Pinnacle, Swift, Hotshot

Double cassette: released on Ace, Feb'85 by Ace Records. Dist: Pinnacle, Swift, Hotshot, Cadillac

ROCKING IN HARMONY.
Tracks: / Wake up little Susie / Devoted to you / This little girl of mine / Like strangers / Roving gambler / Leave my woman alone / Bird dog / Long time gone / Problems / When will I be loved / I'm here to get my baby out of jail / Be-bop-a-lula.
Album: released on Crown, Feb'86 by Ace Records. Dist: Pinnacle, Swift

Cassette: released on Crown, Feb'86 by Ace Records. Dist: Pinnacle, Swift

ROCK 'N' SOUL.
Tracks: / That'll be the day / So fine / Maybelline / Dancing in the street / Kansas City / I got a woman / Love hurts / Slippin' and slidin' / Susie Q / Hound dog / I'm gonna move to the outskirts of town / Lonely weekends.
Album: released on Warner Bros., May'85 by Warner Bros Records. Dist: WEA

ROCK & ROLL ODYSSEY.
Notes: A documentary of the superstar duo from childhood to their current performing reunion, including interviews and musical archive footage covering nearly thirtyyears.
Video-cassette (VHS): released on MGM, Oct'84 Dist: Polygram Distribution, Swift Distribution

ROOTS.
Tracks: / Everly family (1952) / Mama tried / Less of me / T for Texas / I wonder if I care as much / Ventura Boulevard / Shady grove / Illinois / Living too close to the ground / You done me wrong / Turn around / Sing me back home / Everly family (1952) Shady grove, Kentucky.
Album: released on Warner Bros., Oct'86 by Warner Bros Records. Dist: WEA

ROOTS (EDSEL).
Album: released on Edsel, Sep'86 by Demon Records. Dist: Pinnacle, Jazz Music, Projection

SINGLES SET.
Boxed set: released on Old Gold, Jul'80 by Old Gold Records. Dist: Lightning, Jazz Music, Spartan, Counterpoint

SIX TRACK HITS.
Tracks: / All I have to do is dream / Wake up little Susie / Bye bye love / Bird dog / Problems / 'Til I kissed you.
Extended-play record: released on Scoop 33, Sep'83 by Pickwick Records. Dist: H.R. Taylor

Cassette: released on Scoop 33, Sep'83 by Pickwick Records. Dist: H.R. Taylor

SONGS OUR DADDY TAUGHT US.
Tracks: / Roving gambler / Down in the willow garden / Long time gone / Lightning express / That silver-haired daddy of mine / Who's gonna shoe your pretty little feet? / Barbara Allen / Oh so many years / I'm here to get my baby out of jail / Rockin' alone (in an old rocking chair) / Kentucky / Put my little shoes away.
Album: released on Ace(Barnaby USA), Aug'83 by Ace Records. Dist: Pinnacle, Swift, Hotshot

SO SAD.
Single (7"): released on Old Gold, Jul'82 by Old Gold Records. Dist: Lightning, Jazz Music, Spartan, Counterpoint

STORY OF ME.
Single (7"): released on Mercury, Nov'84 by Phonogram Records. Dist: Polygram Distribution

SUSIE Q.
Album: released on Magnum Force, Jun'87 by Magnum Music Group Ltd. Dist: Magnum Music Group Ltd, PRT, Spartan

Cassette: released on Magnum Force, Jun'87 by Magnum Music Group Ltd. Dist: Magnum Music Group Ltd, PRT, Spartan

TILL I KISSED YOU.
Single (7"): released on Old Gold, Jul'82 by Old Gold Records. Dist: Lightning, Jazz Music, Spartan, Counterpoint

VERY BEST OF THE EVERLY BROTHERS, (THE).
Tracks: / Bye bye love / 'Til I kissed you / Wake up little Susie / Crying in the rain / Walk right back / Cathy's clown / Bird dog / All I have to do is dream / Devoted to you / Lucille / So sad to watch good love go bad / Ebony eyes.
Album: released on Warner Bros., '74 by Warner Bros Records. Dist: WEA

Cassette: released on Warner Bros., '74 by Warner Bros Records. Dist: WEA

WAKE UP LITTLE SUSIE.
Single (7"): released on Old Gold, Jul'82 by Old Gold Records. Dist: Lightning, Jazz Music, Spartan, Counterpoint

WALK RIGHT BACK.
Compact disc: released on Warner Bros., Jan'87 by Warner Bros Records. Dist: WEA

Single (7"): released on Old Gold, Jul'82 by Old Gold Records. Dist: Lightning, Jazz Music, Spartan, Counterpoint

WALK RIGHT BACK WITH THE EVERLYS.
Tracks: / Walk right back / Crying in the rain / Wake up little Susie / Love hurts / 'Til I kissed you / Love is strange / How can I meet her? / Temptation / Don't blame me / Cathy's clown / So sad to watch good love go bad / Bird dog / No one can make my sunshine smile / Ferris wheel / Price of love / Muskrat / Ebony eyes / Bye bye love.
Album: released on Warner Bros., Oct'75 by Warner Bros Records. Dist: WEA

WHEN WILL I BE LOVED?.
Single (7"): released on Old Gold, Jul'82 by Old Gold Records. Dist: Lightning, Jazz Music, Spartan, Counterpoint

YOU'RE JUST WHAT I WAS LOOKING FOR.
Single (7"): released on Revival, Jul'82 Dist: Lightning, Swift

Everly, Don

BROTHER JUKE BOX.
Tracks: / Brother juke box / Love at last sight / So sad to watch good love go bad / Lettin' go / Since you broke my heart / Never like this / Deep water / Yesterday just passed my way again / Oh I'd like to go away / Oh what a feeling / Turn the memories loose again.
Album: released on Sundown, '83 by Magnum Music Group Ltd. Dist: Magnum Music Group Ltd, PRT Distribution, Spartan Distribution

Single (7"): released on Sundown, Nov'85 by Magnum Music Group Ltd. Dist: Magnum Music Group Ltd, PRT Distribution, Spartan Distribution

Everly, Phil

OH BABY OH.
Single (7"): released on Capitol, Jun'83 by Capitol Records. Dist: EMI

PHIL EVERLY.
Tracks: / She means nothing to me / I'll mend your broken heart / God bless older ladies / Sweet pretender / Never gonna dream again / Better than now / Woman and a man / Louise / When I'm dead and gone / Sweet Suzanne / Oh baby oh (you're the star).
Album: released on Capitol, Apr'83 by Capitol Records. Dist: EMI

Cassette: released on Capitol, Apr'83 by Capitol Records. Dist: EMI

SHE MEANS NOTHING TO ME (Everly, Phil & Cliff Richard).
Single (7"): released on Capitol, Jan'83 by Capitol Records. Dist: EMI

SWEET PRETENDER.
Single (7"): released on Capitol, Apr'83 by Capitol Records. Dist: EMI

Ever Ready Band

EVER READY BAND PLAYS PATRICK MOORE.
Album: released on Pye Top Brass, Nov'79

Everton...

BOYS IN BLUE (Everton Cup Squad '84).
Single (7"): released on PRT, Jun'84 by PRT Records. Dist: PRT

EVERYBODY'S CHEERING THE BLUES (Everton Football Team 1986).
Tracks: / Everybody's cheering the blues / Only 90 minutes away.
Single (7"): released on Columbia, Apr'86 by EMI Records. Dist: EMI

Picture disc single: released on Columbia, Apr'86 by EMI Records. Dist: EMI

HEAVEN (Everton & Tracy King).
Single (7"): released on Legacy, Oct'84 Dist: PRT

HERE WE GO Offical Everton F.C. record, 1985 (Everton Football Club).
Single (7"): released on Columbia, May'85 by EMI Records. Dist: EMI

Album: released on Sterile, Feb'85 Dist: Red Rhino Distribution, Cartel Distribution

SOUVENIR ALBUM (Everton Football Club).
Album: released on Columbia, Aug'85 by EMI Records. Dist: EMI

Cassette: released on Columbia, Aug'85 by EMI Records. Dist: EMI

SPIRIT OF THE BLUES (Everton Football Club).
Single (7"): released on Direct, Apr'84 by Phonogram Records. Dist: Polygram

Everybody...

EVERYBODY IN THE WHOLE CELL BLOCK Various artists (Various Artists).
Album: released on Hybrid, Jul'85 by Statik Records. Dist: Pinnacle

EVERYBODY'S MOVIN' AGAIN Various artists (Various Artists).
Album: released on Ace, Jul'84 by Ace Records. Dist: Pinnacle, Swift, Hotshot, Cadillac

Everybody Loves Somebody

EVERYBODY LOVES SOMEBODY Original Artists (Original artists).
Compact disc: released on The Compact Collection, Sep'87 by Conifer Records. Dist: Conifer Distribution

Everyday Stories

EVERYDAY STORIES NO.1 various artists (Various Artists).
Cassette: released on Audiocord Cassettes, May'83

Cassette: released on Audiocord Cassettes, May'83

EVERYDAY STORIES NO.2 various artists (Various Artists).

Every Great Motown Song

EVERY GREAT MOTOWN SONG VOLS. 1 & 2 The first 25 years as originally recorded (Various Artists).
Tracks: / Where did our love go / Shop around / Dancing in the street / Reach out, I'll be there / Take me in your arms (rock me a little while) / I heard it through the grapevine / Baby love / How sweet it is to be loved by you / Heat wave / My girl / You keep me hangin' on / Ooh baby / Please Mr Postman / Standing in the shadows of love / Ain't no mountain high enough / If i were your woman / Never can say goodbye / Just my imagination / Touch me in the morning / Three times a lady / Got to give it up / Sail on.
Compact disc: released on Motown, Oct'86 by Motown Records. Dist: BMG Distribution

Everyman

EVERYMAN-VISIONS FROM PIERS PLOWMAN William Langland (Various Artists).
Double cassette: released on Argo (Spokenword), Mar'84 by Decca Records. Dist: Polygram

Everyman Band

EVERYMAN BAND.
Album: released on ECM (Germany), Sep'82 by ECM Records. Dist: IMS, Polygram, Virgin through EMI

WITHOUT WARNING.
Compact disc: by ECM Records. Dist: IMS, Polygram, Virgin through EMI

Album: released on ECM (Germany), Jul'85 by ECM Records. Dist: IMS, Polygram, Virgin through EMI

Every Man Needs A Woman

EVERY MAN NEEDS A WOMAN Various artists (Various Artists).
Tracks: / Every man has a woman who loves him / Silver horse / I'm moving on / Nobody sees me like you do / Dogtown / Goodbye sadness / Walking on thin ice / Wake up / Dream love / Now or never / It's alright / Every man has a woman who loves him / Silver horse / I'm moving on / Nobody sees me like you do / Dogtown / Goodbye sadness / Walking on thin ice / Wake up / Dream love / Now or never / It's alright.
Notes: Digital stereo
Compact disc: released on Polydor, Sep'84 by Polydor Records. Dist: Polygram, Polydor

Album: released on Polydor, Sep'84 by Polydor Records. Dist: Polygram, Polydor

Cassette: released on Polydor, Sep'84 by Polydor Records. Dist: Polygram, Polydor

Everything But The Girl

ANGEL.
Single (7"): released on Blanco Y Negro, May'85 by WEA Records. Dist: WEA Deleted '86.

Single (12"): released on Blanco Y Negro, May'85 by WEA Records. Dist: WEA

BABY THE STARS SHINE BRIGHT.
Tracks: / Come on home / Don't leave me behind / Country mile, A / Cross my heart / Don't let the teardrops rust your shining heart / Careless / Sugar Finney / Come hell or high water / Fighting talk / Little Hitler.
Album: released on Blanco Y Negro, Aug'86 by WEA Records. Dist: WEA

Compact disc: released on Blanco Y Negro, Aug'86 by WEA Records. Dist: WEA

COME ON HOME.
Tracks: / Come on home / Draining the bar / I

fall to pieces *.
Single (7"): released on Blanco Y Negro, Jul'86 by WEA Records. Dist: WEA

Single (12"): released on Blanco Y Negro, Jul'86 by WEA Records. Dist: WEA

DON'T LEAVE ME BEHIND.
Tracks: / Don't leave me behind / Alfie / Where's the playground *.
Single (7"): released on Blanco Y Negro, Sep'86 by WEA Records. Dist: WEA

Single (12"): released on Blanco Y Negro, Sep'86 by WEA Records. Dist: WEA

EACH & EVERYONE.
Single (7"): released on Blanco Y Negro, May'84 by WEA Records. Dist: WEA

Single (12"): released on Blanco Y Negro, May'84 by WEA Records. Dist: WEA

EDEN.
Tracks: / Each and every one / Bittersweet / Tender blue / Another bridge / Spice of life / Dust bowl / Crabwalk / Even so / Frost and fire / Fascination / I must confess / Soft touch.
Compact disc: by WEA Records. Dist: WEA

Album: released on Blanco Y Negro, Jun'84 by WEA Records. Dist: WEA

Cassette: released on Blanco Y Negro, Jun'84 by WEA Records. Dist: WEA

LOVE NOT MONEY.
Compact disc: by WEA Records. Dist: WEA

Album: released on Blanco Y Negro, May'85 by WEA Records. Dist: WEA

Cassette: released on Blanco Y Negro, May'85 by WEA Records. Dist: WEA

NATIVE LAND.
Single (7"): released on Blanco Y Negro, Sep'84 by WEA Records. Dist: WEA Deleted '85.

Single (12"): released on Blanco Y Negro, Sep'84 by WEA Records. Dist: WEA

NIGHT AND DAY.
Tracks: / Night and day / Feeling dizzy / On my mind.
Single (7"): released on Cherry Red, Jul'83 by Cherry Red Records. Dist: Pinnacle

Single (12"): released on Cherry Red, Jul'83 by Cherry Red Records. Dist: Pinnacle

Every which way but loose

EVERY WHICH WAY BUT LOOSE Original film soundtrack.
Album: released on Elektra, Feb'79 by WEA Records. Dist: WEA

Evie

COME ON RING THOSE BELLS.
Tracks: / Come on ring those bells / Away in a manger / No room / Have you any room? / Mary's boy child / Silent night / O holy night / What child is this? / Some children see Him / One small child.
Album: released on Word, May'82 by Word Records. Dist: Word Distribution, CBS

EVIE.
Tracks: / My tribute / Sweet, sweet song of salvation / Blood will never lose its power, The / Movin' in the spirit / Would you? / Praise the Lord, He never changes / One more day / Say "I do" / On the wings of a snow white dove / I surrender all / I need Thee every hour.
Album: released on Word, May'82 by Word Records. Dist: Word Distribution, CBS

Cassette: released on Word, May'82 by Word Records. Dist: Word Distribution, CBS

EVIE AGAIN.
Tracks: / Sunday morning / Clean before my Lord / Give yourself to Jesus / Someone who can / Have Thine own way / Welcome back to Jesus / Stop, look and listen / That day is coming closer / All the time in the world / Jesus loves me / And oh how He loves you and me.
Album: released on Word, May'82 by Word Records. Dist: Word Distribution, CBS

Cassette: released on Word, May'82 by Word Records. Dist: Word Distribution, CBS

FAVOURITES (VOL.1).
Tracks: / My tribute / Praise the Lord, He never changes / Say "I do" / Clean before my Lord / Jesus loves me / And oh how He loves you and me / Name of Jesus, The / Give them all to Jesus / Part the waters / Broken up people / Born again / Mirror.
Album: released on Word, May'82 by Word Records. Dist: Word Distribution, CBS

Cassette: released on Word, May'82 by Word Records. Dist: Word Distribution, CBS

GENTLE MOMENTS.
Tracks: / Give them all / Part the waters / You got the power / I don't have to worry / Meet me here / Pass it on / Broken up people / Waiting / For baby (for Bobbie) / Shepherd of love.
Album: released on Word, May'82 by Word Records. Dist: Word Distribution, CBS

Cassette: released on Word, May'82 by Word Records. Dist: Word Distribution, CBS

LITTLE SONG OF JOY FOR MY LITTLE FRIENDS, A.
Tracks: / Step into the sunshine / Why complain? / Tree song / His will / All day song / I am safe / Jesus, I believe what You said / It's not just a story / Will the circle be unbroken? / This little light of mine / Creature praise / Into my heart.
Album: released on Word, May'82 by Word Records. Dist: Word Distribution, CBS

Cassette: released on Word, May'82 by Word Records. Dist: Word Distribution, CBS

MIRROR.
Tracks: / Mirror / Lord, send that morning / If Heaven never was promised to me / Jesus was there all the time / Now is the time / He loves me / Four feet eleven / Praise You just the same / Born again / Just because I asked.
Album: released on Word, May'82 by Word Records. Dist: Word Distribution, CBS

NEVER THE SAME.
Tracks: / Live for Jesus / Hold on / Special delivery / Never the same again / This life / Shine / At the River of Jordan / Don't run from reality / Home / You have everything in your hands / Jesus, I love You.
Album: released on Word, May'82 by Word Records. Dist: Word Distribution, CBS

Cassette: released on Word, May'82 by Word Records. Dist: Word Distribution, CBS

UNFAILING LOVE.
Tracks: / How I love you, Lord / Bind us together / Cross where Jesus gave His life, The / Be still / I love my Jesus / Unfailing love / Picture of you, A / All the glory / You gave a song / Lord's prayer, The.
Album: released on Word, May'82 by Word Records. Dist: Word Distribution, CBS

Cassette: released on Word, May'82 by Word Records. Dist: Word Distribution, CBS

WHEN ALL IS SAID AND DONE.
Notes: The songs on this album hold the same type of message that Evie has always sung,but there is some fresh vitality in some of the thoughts as well as in the musical expression. A new freshness has come to Evie, and an eagerness to share that message with the people who have supported her in years gone by. Altogether, this collection should confirm the fact that Evie is very much interested in continuing to express the things she feels strongly about. Nostalgia may be a great part of this album as it will recall some of the great songs Evie has sung in the past. With all these new songs, you will recall the styles that have been a trademark of Evie.
Album: released on Word, Feb'87 by Word Records. Dist: Word Distribution, CBS

Cassette: released on Word, Feb'87 by Word Records. Dist: Word Distribution, CBS

Evil Dead

EVIL DEAD II Original Soundtrack.
Album: released on That's Entertainment, Jul'87 by That's Entertainment Records. Dist: Pinnacle, PRT

Cassette: released on That's Entertainment, Jul'87 by That's Entertainment Records. Dist: Pinnacle, PRT

Evil Under The Sun

EVIL UNDER THE SUN featuring the music of Cole Porter (Various Artists).
Album: released on RCA International, May'82

Cassette: released on RCA International, May'82

Evita

EVITA Original London cast recording (Various Artists).
Compact disc: by MCA Records. Dist: Polygram, MCA

Album: released on MCA, Jul'85 by MCA Records. Dist: Polygram, MCA

Cassette: released on MCA, Jul'85 by MCA Records. Dist: Polygram, MCA

EVITA Original Cast.
Album: released on MCA, May'80 by MCA Records. Dist: Polygram, MCA

Cassette: released on MCA, Nov'76 by MCA Records. Dist: Polygram, MCA

Double Album: released on MCA, Nov'76 by MCA Records. Dist: Polygram, MCA

EVITA SELECTION FROM THE MUSICAL Various artists (Various Artists).
Album: released on Polydor, Jul'77 by Polydor Records. Dist: Polygram, Polydor

Ewans, Kai

DANISH JAZZ VOL 1.
Album: released on Storyville, Jul'82 by Storyville Records. Dist: Jazz Music Distribution, Swift Distribution, Chris Wellard Distribution, Counterpoint Distribution

Ewell, Don

DON EWELL QUINTET (Ewell, Don Quintet).
Album: released on Jazzology, Jun'86 Dist: Jazz Music, Swift

IN NEW ORLEANS.
Album: released on GHB, Oct'86 Dist: Jazz Music, Swift

IN NEW ORLEANS (Ewell, Don & Herb Hall Quartet).
Album: released on New Orleans, Sep'86 Dist: Swift, Zodiac Distribution, Jazz Music. JSU

TOGETHER (Ewell, Don/Bob Green).
Album: released on Jazzology, Aug'79 Dist: Jazz Music, Swift

Ex

1936.
Single (7"): released on Ron Johnson, Aug'86 by Ron Johnson Records. Dist: Nine Mile Distribution, Cartel Distribution

STOP.
Album: released on Shanghai, Nov'83

Ex, Alerta

RED DANCE PACKAGE.
Single (12"): released on CNT, Jan'84 Dist: Rough Trade, Cartel

Excalibur

BITTER END, THE.
Album: released on Conquest, Sep'85 Dist: Red Rhino, Cartel

EXCALIBUR Music inspired by the film.
Album: released on Island, Jul'81 by Island Records. Dist: Polygram

Cassette: released on Island, Jul'81 by Island Records. Dist: Polygram

ONLY TIME WILL TELL.
Album: released on Conquest, May'85 Dist: Red Rhino, Cartel

Ex Cathedra

CHRISTMAS MUSIC BY CANDLELIGHT.
Album: released on Alpha, Oct'81 by Alpha Records. Dist: H.R. Taylor, Gamut

Excelsior Brass Band

EXCELSIOR BRASS BAND.
Album: released on Wizard, Apr'79 Dist: Jazz Music, Swift, Chris Wellard

Excelsius

DING DONG DISCO.
Single (7"): released on SRT, Jan'82 by SRT Records. Dist: Pinnacle, Solomon & Peres Distribution, SRT Distribution, H.R. Taylor Distribution, PRT Distribution

Exception

JUMP WITH IT.
Tracks: / Jump with it / Jump with it (Dub mix).
Single (12"): released on Supreme, Oct'86 by Supreme Records. Dist: PRT Distribution

SLAP YOU BACK.
Tracks: / Slap you back / Slap you back (dub mix).
Single (7"): released on Citybeat, Feb'86 Dist: WEA

Single (12"): released on Citybeat, Feb'86 Dist: WEA

Exchange

AND NOW SHE'S GONE.
Tracks: / And now she's gone / Alien.
Single (7"): released on Yellow Brick Road, Feb'87 Dist: DMS-RCA, O.I.D

GIVE ME THE MUSIC.
Single (7"): released on PRT, Oct'85 by PRT Records. Dist: PRT

Single (12"): released on PRT, Oct'85 by PRT Records. Dist: PRT

Exciter

FEEL THE KNIFE.
Single (12"): released on Music For Nations, Jun'85 by Music For Nations Records. Dist: Pinnacle

HEAVY METAL MANIAC.
Album: released on Roadrunner (Dutch), Apr'86 Dist: Pinnacle

LONG LIVE THE LOUD.
Album: released on Music For Pleasure (Holland), May'85 by EMI Records. Dist: EMI

VIOLENCE AND FORCE.
Album: released on Music For Nations, Feb'84 by Music For Nations Records. Dist: Pinnacle

E-X-E

STRICKEN BY MIGHT.
Album: released on Axis, Jul'87 by Red Rhino Records. Dist: Cartel

Executioner

BREAK THE SILENCE.
Album: released on Positive Force (USA), Aug'87

Executive

CELEBRATE YOUR LOVE.
Single (7"): released on Personal, May'84 by Personal Records. Dist: PRT

Single (12"): released on Personal, May'84 by Personal Records. Dist: PRT
Cat. no: **12 PERS 102**

Executives

DIANA.
Single (7"): released on Creole, Apr'82 by Creole Records. Dist: Rhino, PRT

Executive Slacks

FIRE AND ICE.
Album: released on Fundamental, Apr'86 by Fundamental Records. Dist: Red Rhino, Cartel

NAUSEA.
Album: released on Fundamental, Aug'85 by Fundamental Records. Dist: Red Rhino, Cartel

ROCK'N'ROLL.
Single (12"): released on Play It Again Sam, Aug'86 Dist: Red Rhino, Cartel

YOU CAN'T HUM WHEN YOU'RE DEAD.
Album: released on Fundamental, May'85 by Fundamental Records. Dist: Red Rhino, Cartel

Exhibit 4

HIGH TECHNOLOGY.
Single (7"): released on Underground Music, Mar'82 Dist: Pinnacle

Exhibit B

IT'S HYPOTHETICAL.
Tracks: / It's hypothetical / Who killed the smile / Nobody's business * / Other side, The *.
Single (7"): released on Grove Street, Sep'86 Dist: Probe Plus Distribution, Cartel

Single (12"): released on Grove Street, Sep'86 Dist: Probe Plus Distribution, Cartel

WHO KILLED THE SMILE.
Tracks: / Who killed the smile / It's hypothetical / Nobody's business.
Single (12"): released on Exhibit, May'86 Dist: Probe, Cartel

Exile

EXILE.
Album: released on Epic, Sep'84 by CBS Records. Dist: CBS

Cassette: released on Epic, Sep'84 by CBS Records. Dist: CBS Deleted May'86.

GIVE ME ONE MORE CHANCE.
Single (7"): released on Epic, Jan'85 by CBS Records. Dist: CBS

GREATEST HITS:EXILE.
Tracks: / Woke up in love / I don't want to be a memory / Give me one more chance / She's a miracle / Hang on to your heart / Girl can't help it, The / I could get used to you / Crazy for your love / Super love / Kiss you all over.
Album: released on Epic, Sep'86 by CBS Records. Dist: CBS

Cassette: released on Epic, Sep'86 by CBS Records. Dist: CBS

HANG ON TO YOUR HEART.
Tracks: / Promises promises / I could get used to you / Hang on to your heart / She likes her lovin' / Music / I got love (super duper love) / It'll be me / Practice makes perfect / She's too good to be true / Proud to be her man.
Album: released on Epic, Mar'86 by CBS Records. Dist: CBS

Cassette: released on Epic, Mar'86 by CBS Records. Dist: CBS

HANG ON TO YOUR HEART (7").
Tracks: / Hang on to your heart / She likes her lovin'.
Single (7"): released on Epic, Dec'85 by CBS

Records. Dist: CBS

I COULD GET USED TO YOU.
Single (7"): released on Epic, Apr'86 by CBS Records. Dist: CBS

WOKE UP IN LOVE.
Single (7"): released on Epic, Jun'84 by CBS Records. Dist: CBS

Exile in the kingdom
FREEDOM.
Single (7"): released on Prophet, Jan'85 by Prophet Records. Dist: Pinnacle

Exiles
FREEDOM COME ALL YE.
Album: released on Topic, May'81 Dist: Roots Distribution

HALE AND THE HANGED, THE.
Album: released on Topic, May'81 Dist: Roots Distribution

Exises
EXISES.
Album: released on Megaton, Jul'86 by Megaton Records. Dist: Rough Trade Distribution, Cartel Distribution

Exit
MONEY TO BURN.
Notes: Daylight Records, The Daylight co. (Distribution) Ltd, 2, Dorset place, New St. Honiton, Devon EX 14 8AB.
Album: released on Daylight, '86 by Daylight Records. Dist: Daylight

Cassette: released on Daylight, '86 by Daylight Records. Dist: Daylight

PLANETOID PASSION.
Single (7"): released on Red Beret, Sep'83

Exit 13
FIELDS OF JOY.
Single (7"): released on Squad, Nov'85 by Exit 13. Dist: Revolver Distribution, Cartel Distribution

OVER THE BRIDGE.
Tracks: / Over the bridge.
Single (7"): released on Squad, Oct'86 by Exit 13. Dist: Revolver Distribution, Cartel Distribution

Exit-Stance
CRIME AGAINST HUMANITY.
Single (12"): released on Fight Back, Jun'84 by Fight Back Records. Dist: Jungle, Cartel

ESTHETICS.
Single (7"): by Exit Stance Records. Dist: Revolver, Cartel

Exit Visa
FOOLS IN THE NIGHT.
Single (7"): released on Infrared, Jun'83 by Infrared Records. Dist: M.I.S., EMI

Ex 'n' Dans
EX 'N' DANS Various artists (Various Artists).
Cassette: released on Dansan, Jul'82 by Spartan Records. Dist: Spartan

Exodus
BONDED BY BLOOD.
Album: released on Music For Nations, Apr'85 by Music For Nations Records. Dist: Pinnacle

ENGLISH BLACK BOYS.
Single (12"): released on Factory, Apr'80 by Factory Records. Dist: Cartel, Pinnacle

EXODUS Original Motion Picture Soundtrack.
Tracks: / Theme of Exodus / Summin Cyprus/Escape / Ari / Karen / Valley of Jezreel / Fight for survival / In Jerusalem / Brothers, The / Conspiracy / Prison Break / Dawn / Fight for peace / Hatikvah.
Album: released on CBS, Feb'87 by CBS Records. Dist: CBS

Picture disc single: released on Cherry Red, Jan'85 by Cherry Red Records. Dist: Pinnacle

Explained Emma
UNECESSARY STRAIN.
Single (7"): released on Pig Posse, Mar'85 Cat. no: POSSE 101

Explainer
HIS HORSE.
Tracks: / His horse / His horse (version).
Single (12"): released on Charlie's, Jun'87 by Charlie's Records. Dist: Jetstar

POSITIVE VIBRATIONS.
Album: released on Vista Sounds, May'83 by Vista Sounds Records. Dist: Jetstar

Cassette: released on Vista Sounds, May'83 by Vista Sounds Records. Dist: Jetstar

Explaires
SYMPATHY.
Single (7"): released on Rockburgh, Mar'80

TO SEE YOU.
Single (7"): released on Zoo, Feb'82

Exploding Seagulls
JOHNNY RUNS.
Single (7"): released on Fried Egg, Jul'81 by Fried Egg Records. Dist: Rough Trade, Cartel

Exploding White Mice
IN A NEST OF VIPERS.
Album: released on Big Time, May'86 by Mainline Record Company. Dist: Mainline

Exploited
ARMY LIFE.
Single (7"): released on Exploited, Oct'80 Dist: Red Rhino, Cartel

Single (7"): released on Secret, Apr'81 by Secret Records. Dist: EMI

ATTACK.
Single (7"): released on Secret, Jul'82 by Secret Records. Dist: EMI

COMPUTERS DON'T BLUNDER.
Single (7"): released on Secret, Oct'82 by Secret Records. Dist: EMI

DEAD CITIES.
Tracks: / Dead cities / Punk's not dead / Army life / Barmy army.
Notes: Written by Wattie\Buchan and published by Panache\Sara Music Ltd except track 1 Duncan\Campbell\McCormack Published by Secret Music. Licensed from Panache MusicLtd. Limited edition.
Single (12"): released on Archive 4, Aug'86 by Castle Communications Records. Dist: Nine Mile, Cartel

Single (7"): released on Secret, Jul'82 by Secret Records. Dist: EMI

DOGS OF WAR.
Single (7"): released on Virgin, Apr'81 by Virgin Records. Dist: EMI, Virgin Distribution

DON'T LET 'EM GRIND YOU DOWN (EP) (Exploited & Anti Pasti).
Single (7"): released on Superville, Oct'81 Dist: Pinnacle

Cassette: released on CBS, Feb'87 by CBS Records. Dist: CBS

Exodus Supreme
STEPPIN' IN THE FUTURE.
Album: released on 52 West, Apr'85 by 52 West Records. Dist: Jetstar

Exon Singers
EXON SINGERS.
Album: released on Alpha, Jul'80 by Alpha Records. Dist: H.R. Taylor, Gamut

Exorcist
NIGHTMARE THEATRE.
Album: released on Roadrunner (Dutch), Sep'86 Dist: Pinnacle

Exotica Maximus
PAINT IT BLACK.
Single (7"): released on MVM, Aug'83

Single (12"): released on MVM, Aug'83

YOUNGER NOW.
Single (7"): released on Flux, Jan'83 by Flux Records. Dist: Cartel

Expandis
MYSTIC MAN.
Single (7"): released on Rocket, Aug'83 by Phonogram Records. Dist: Polygram Distribution

Single (12"): released on Rocket, Aug'83 by Phonogram Records. Dist: Polygram Distribution

Expelled
DREAMING.
Single (7"): released on Riot City, Apr'82 by Riot City Records. Dist: Revolver

GOVERMENT CITY.
Extended-play record: released on Riot City, Dec'82 by Riot City Records. Dist: Revolver

MAKE IT ALONE.
Single (7"): released on Riot City, Oct'82 by Riot City Records. Dist: Revolver

SINGLES, THE (EP).
Single (12"): released on Riot City, Sep'84 by Riot City Records. Dist: Revolver

Experience
EXPERIENCE (SOUNDTRACK FEATURING JIMI HENDRIX) Original Soundtrack (Experience (Soundtrack featuring Jimi Hendrix)).
Album: released on Bulldog Records, Jul'82

Experiments with Ice
EXPERIMENTS WITH ICE.
Album: released on Experimental, Oct'81 by United Dairies Records. Dist: Indies

Ex Pistols
LAND OF HOPE AND GLORY.
Single (7"): released on Cherry Red, Jan'85 by Cherry Red Records. Dist: Pinnacle

Single (12"): released on Cherry Red, Jan'85 by Cherry Red Records. Dist: Pinnacle

EXPLOITED BARMY ARMY.
Single (7"): released on Secret, Apr'81 by Secret Records. Dist: EMI

EXPLOITED ON STAGE.
Album: released on Superville, Oct'81 Dist: Pinnacle

HORROR EPICS.
Tracks: / Horror epics / Don't forget the chaos / Law and order / I hate you / No more idols / Maggie / Dangerous vision / Down below / Treat you like shit / Forty odd years ago / My life.
Notes: Produced by Phil Chilton and Wattie Buchan (and a crate of Fosters); Engineered by Phil Chilton and John Ravenhall; recorded at The Yard Studios, London. Personnel: Wattie - vocals; Wayne - bass; karl - guitar; Willie - Drums & guitar. Special thanks to: Dee - backing vocals; captain Scarlet - guitar.
Album: released on Dojo, Aug'86 by Castle Communications Records. Dist: Cartel

Album: released on Konexion, Mar'85 by Konexion Records. Dist: Pinnacle

Cassette: released on Konexion, Mar'85 by Konexion Records. Dist: Pinnacle

INNER CITY DECAY.
Album: released on Snow, Mar'87

JESUS IS DEAD.
Tracks: / Jesus is dead (EP) / Drug squad man / Privacy invasion / Jesus is dead / Politicians.
Single (12"): released on Rough Justice, Aug'86 by MFN Records. Dist: Pinnacle

LET'S START A WAR (SAID MAGGIE ONE DAY).
Album: released on Pax, Dec'83 by Pax Records. Dist: Red Rhino, Cartel

LIVE AT THE WHITEHOUSE.
Album: released on Suck, Feb'86 Dist: Rough Trade Distribution, Cartel Distribution

LIVE ON THE APOCALYPSE NOW TOUR 1981.
Album: released on Chaos, Feb'87 by Backs Records. Dist: Nine Mile, Cartel

ON STAGE.
Tracks: / Cop cars / Crashed out / Dole q / Dogs of war / Army life / Out of control / Ripper / Mod song / Exploited / Barmy army / Royalty / Sex & violence / Punk's not dead / I believe in anarchy.
Album: released on Dojo, Apr'86 by Castle Communications Records. Dist: Cartel

PUNKS NOT DEAD.
Album: released on Secret, Jun'82 by Secret Records. Dist: EMI

RIVAL LEADER.
Single (7"): released on Pax, Oct'83 by Pax Records. Dist: Red Rhino, Cartel

TOTALLY EXPLOITED.
Tracks: / Punk's not dead / Army life / Fuck a mod / Barmy army / Dogs of war / Dead cities / Sex & violence / Yops / Daily news / Dole Q / Believe in anarchy / God save the queen / Psycho / Blown to bits / Insanity / SPG / Jimmy Boyle / USA / Attack / Rival leaders.
Album: released on Dojo, Apr'86 by Castle Communications Records. Dist: Cartel

Compact disc: released on Dojo, Jun'86 by Castle Communications Records. Dist: Cartel

TROOPS OF TOMORROW.
Album: released on Secret, Jun'82 by Secret Records. Dist: EMI

Cassette: released on Major Richards, Jun'78 by Major Richards Records. Dist: Taylors

Explorers
EXPLORERS.
Compact disc: released on Virgin, Jul'87 by Virgin Records. Dist: EMI, Virgin Distribution

EXPLORERS, THE.
Album: released on Virgin, May'85 by Virgin Records. Dist: EMI, Virgin Distribution

Cassette: released on Virgin, May'85 by Virgin Records. Dist: EMI, Virgin Distribution

Compact disc: released on Virgin, May'85 by Virgin Records. Dist: EMI, Virgin Distribution

Album: released on Tartar (New Zealand), '84

Cassette: released on Tartar (New Zealand), '84

VENUE DE MILO.
Single (7"): released on Virgin, Jun'85 by Virgin Records. Dist: EMI, Virgin Distribution

Single (12"): released on Virgin, Jun'85 by Virgin Records. Dist: EMI, Virgin Distribution

Expose
COME GO WITH ME.
Tracks: / Come go with me / December.
Single (7"): released on Arista, Mar'87 by Arista Records. Dist: RCA

Single (12"): released on Arista, Mar'87 by Arista Records. Dist: RCA

EXPOSED TO LOVE.
Tracks: / Exposed to love / Exposed to love (dub).
Single (12"): released on Arista, Apr'86 by Arista Records. Dist: RCA

EXPOSURE.
Tracks: / Come go with me / Let me be the one / Exposed to love / Seasons change / Extra extra / Point of no return / Love is our destiny / I know you know / You're the one I need / December.
Album: released on Arista, Jan'87 by Arista Records. Dist: RCA

Cassette: released on Arista, Jan'87 by Arista Records. Dist: RCA

Compact disc: released on Arista, Jan'87 by Arista Records. Dist: RCA

POINT OF NO RETURN.
Tracks: / Point of no return / Extra extra.
Single (7"): released on Arista, Jul'87 by Arista Records. Dist: RCA

Single (12"): released on Arista, Jul'87 by Arista Records. Dist: RCA

Ex-Post-Facto
DANCING CHILD.
Single (7"): released on Prose Plus, Nov'83

Single (12"): released on Prose Plus, Nov'83

OCEANIC EXPLORERS (EP).
Single (12"): released on Probe Plus, Nov'82 by Probe Plus Records. Dist: Probe Plus Distribution

SHE'LL RAPE THE WORLD.
Album: released on Skysaw, Nov'84 by Skysaw Records. Dist: Red Rhino, Cartel

Exposure
EXPERIENCE (EP).
Single (12"): released on Abstract, Apr'83 by Abstract. Dist: Pinnacle

INSTITUTION.
Single (7"): released on Statik, Jun'84 Dist: Rough Trade Distribution, Stage One Distribution

Single (12"): released on Statik, Jun'84 Dist: Rough Trade Distribution, Stage One Distribution

LIEF DES LIED.
Single (7"): released on Statik, Sep'84 Dist: Rough Trade Distribution, Stage One Distribution

Single (12"): released on Statik, Sep'84 Dist: Rough Trade Distribution, Stage One Distribution

LOVERS ROCK.
Single (7"): released on Abstract, Jul'82 by Abstract. Dist: Pinnacle

OUT OF THE DARK INTO THE LIGHT.
Album: released on Abstract, Nov'82 by Abstract. Dist: Pinnacle

SOUND SYSTEM.
Single (7"): released on Abstract, Mar'82 by Abstract. Dist: Pinnacle

STILL THE WIND BLOWS STILL.
Single (7"): released on Statik, May'85 Dist: Rough Trade Distribution, Stage One Distribution

Single (12"): released on Statik, May'85 Dist:

Rough Trade Distribution, Stage One Distribution

WILD.
Album: released on Statik, Nov'84 Dist: Rough Trade Distribution, Stage One Distribution

Cassette: released on Statik, Nov'84 Dist: Rough Trade Distribution, Stage One Distribution

Expressions
EXPRESSIONS various artists (Various Artists).
Album: released on K-Tel, Sep'85 by K-Tel Records. Dist: Record Merchandisers Distribution, Taylors, Terry Blood Distribution, Wynd-Up Distribution, Relay Distribution, Pickwick Distribution, Solomon & Peres Distribution, Polygram

Cassette: released on K-Tel, Sep'85 by K-Tel Records. Dist: Record Merchandisers Distribution, Taylors, Terry Blood Distribution, Wynd-Up Distribution, Relay Distribution, Pickwick Distribution, Solomon & Peres Distribution, Polygram

External Menace
YOUTH OF TODAY (EP).
Single (7"): released on Beat-The-System, Feb'83 by Lightbeat Records. Dist: Pinnacle

Extras
BOOMERANG, THE.
Single (7"): released on Dancefloor, Oct'83 by Dancefloor Records. Dist: Vista Sounds Records, Jetstar

Single (12"): released on Dancefloor, Oct'83 by Dancefloor Records. Dist: Vista Sounds Records, Jetstar

HAVEN'T BEEN FUNKED ENOUGH.
Single (12"): released on T.M.T., Jan'83 by T.M.T. Records. Dist: Unknown

I CAN'T KEEP STILL.
Single (7"): released on Dancefloor, Mar'83 by Dancefloor Records. Dist: Vista Sounds Records, Jetstar

Single (12"): released on Dancefloor, Mar'83 by Dancefloor Records. Dist: Vista Sounds Records, Jetstar

WATCHER, THE.
Single (7"): released on Audiotrax, Jun'84 by Audiotrax. Dist: PRT

Extra T's
FLASH BOOGIE.
Single (12"): released on Sunny View, Jan'84 by Sunny View Records. Dist: PRT Distribution

Extremes
EAST MY DUST.
Single (7"): released on Destiny, Aug'87 by Destiny Records. Dist: Red Rhino, Cartel

Extrol
E.S.P..
Single (12"): released on Red Rooster, Dec'83 by Red Rooster Records. Dist: Pinnacle

Eye Do It
I LOST MY MIND.
Single (7"): released on No Rip Off, Mar'84 by No Rip Off Records. Dist: Cartel Distribution

Eyeless In Gaza
BACK FROM THE RAINS.
Tracks: / Between these dreams / Twilight / Back from the rains / Lie still, sleep long / Catch me / Evening music / She moves through the fair / Sweet life longer / New love here / Welcome now / Your rich sky / Flight of swallows / My last lost melody.
Album: released on Cherry Red, Jun'86 by Cherry Red Records. Dist: Pinnacle

Cassette: released on Cherry Red, Jun'86 by Cherry Red Records. Dist: Pinnacle

CAUGHT IN A FLUX.
Album: released on Cherry Red, Sep'81 by Cherry Red Records. Dist: Pinnacle

DRUMMING THE BEATING HEART.
Album: released on Cherry Red, Sep'82 by Cherry Red Records. Dist: Pinnacle

INVISIBILITY.
Single (7"): released on Cherry Red, Apr'81 by Cherry Red Records. Dist: Pinnacle

KISS THE RAIN GOODBYE.
Single (12"): released on Cherry Red, Jun'86 by Cherry Red Records. Dist: Pinnacle

KODAK GHOSTS RUN AMOK - 1980-1986.
Tracks: / Kodak ghosts run amok / Invisibility / No noise / Others / Pencil sketch / Veil like calm / Bright play of eyes / New risen / No perfect stranger / Sunbursts in / Welcome now / New love here / Back from the rains.
Album: released on Cherry Red, Feb'87 by Cherry Red Records. Dist: Pinnacle

Cassette: released on Cherry Red, Feb'87 by Cherry Red Records. Dist: Pinnacle

NEW RISEN.
Single (7"): released on Cherry Red, May'83 by Cherry Red Records. Dist: Pinnacle

Single (12"): released on Cherry Red, May'83 by Cherry Red Records. Dist: Pinnacle

OTHERS.
Single (7"): released on Cherry Red, Nov'81 by Cherry Red Records. Dist: Pinnacle

PALE HANDS I LOVE SO WELL.
Album: released on Uniton (Norway), Apr'85 Dist: Cartel

PHOTOGRAPHS AS MEMORIES.
Tracks: / Seven years / Fixation / Looking daggers / From ATO B / Clear cut apparently /

Speech rapid fire / John of Patmos / Knives replace air / Faceless / In your painting / Keepsake, A / Whitewash / No noise.
Album: released on Cherry Red, '82 by Cherry Red Records. Dist: Pinnacle

RUST RED SEPTEMBER.
Album: released on Cherry Red, Jun'83 by Cherry Red Records. Dist: Pinnacle

Cassette: released on Cherry Red, Jun'83 by Cherry Red Records. Dist: Pinnacle

SUNBURSTS IN.
Single (7"): released on Cherry Red, Jan'84 by Cherry Red Records. Dist: Pinnacle

Single (12"): released on Cherry Red, Jan'84 by Cherry Red Records. Dist: Pinnacle

WELCOME NOW.
Single (7"): released on Cherry Red, Oct'85 by Cherry Red Records. Dist: Pinnacle

Single (12"): released on Cherry Red, Oct'85 by Cherry Red Records. Dist: Pinnacle

Eyelids
PASSAGE FROM JUDEA.
Single (7"): released on Idyllic, Jan'82 Dist: Idyllic

Eye Of The Needle
EYE OF THE NEEDLE Original soundtrack.
Album: released on That's Entertainment, Dec'81 by That's Entertainment Records. Dist: Pinnacle, PRT

Eyermann, Tim
ALOHA (Eyermann, Tim & East Coast Offering).
Album: released on Inner City, Sep'80 Dist: Jetstar

Eyes
BLINK.
Album: released on Bam Caruso, Jun'84 by Bam Caruso Records. Dist: Rough Trade, Revolver, Cartel

Album: released on Bam Caruso, Jun'84 by Bam Caruso Records. Dist: Rough Trade, Revolver, Cartel

SCENE BUT NOT HEARD.
Album: released on Bam Caruso, Feb'87 by Bam Caruso Records. Dist: Rough Trade, Revolver, Cartel

SCENE NOT HEARD.
Album: released on Bam Caruso, Nov'85 by Bam Caruso Records. Dist: Rough Trade, Revolver, Cartel

Eyes On You
RECEIVED WITH THANKS.
Album: released on Children Of The Revolution, Mar'87 by Revolver Records. Dist: Revolver, Cartel

Eyk, Tonny
DIGITAL DANCE DATE (Eyk, Tonny And His Trio).
Tracks: Cocktails for two / Hello Dolly / I've got a crush on you / Always / Make believe / Here's that rainy day / So in love / Woman in love, A / I'll see you again / Please / Out of my dreams / Mona Lisa.
Notes: Dutch pianist Tonny Eyk playing a popular selection of melodies from the great songbooks of Sam coslow, Jerry Herman, George Gershwin, Irving Berlin, Jerome Kern, Cole Porter, Noel Coward, Richard Rodgers and others.
Compact disc: released on Phillips Holland, Jun'86

Ezeke
CHRISTMAS BLUES.
Tracks: / Christmas blues (version).
Single (7"): released on Orbitone, Dec'86 by Orbitone Records. Dist: Jetstar Distribution

Single (12"): released on Orbitone, Dec'86 by Orbitone Records. Dist: Jetstar Distribution

Ezell & Others
PIANO RAGTIME OF THE 20'S & 30'S, VOL.3.
Album: released on Herwin, Feb'79 Dist: Jazz Music

Ezell, Will
PITCHIN' BOOGIE 1927-29.
Album: released on Oldie Blues Holland, Apr'86

Ezintabeni
AMASWAZI EMVELO.
Album: released on Earthworks, Mar'84 by Earthworks Records. Dist: Earthworks Distributors, Rough Trade, Cartel, Projection

EZO
EZO.
Tracks: / House of 1,000 pleasures / Fashback heart attack / Mr.Midnight / Here it comes / I walk alone / Destroyer / Big changes / Kiss of fire / Desiree.
Album: released on Geffen, Jun'87 by Geffen Records. Dist: WEA, CBS

Cassette: released on Geffen, Jun'87 by Geffen Records. Dist: WEA, CBS

EZO.
Album: released on Geffen, Jun'87 by Geffen Records. Dist: WEA, CBS

Cassette: released on Geffen, Jun'87 by Geffen Records. Dist: WEA, CBS

Cassette: released on Old Gold, Jun'87 by Old Gold Records. Dist: Lightning, Jazz Music, Spartan, Counterpoint

F

Fab Five Freddy
UNE SAL HISTOIRE.
Single (12"): released on Celluloid, May'83 by Charly Records. Dist: Charly

Fab Food
NEVER ALONE.
Single (7"): released on Smile, Jun'81 by Smile Records. Dist: Spartan

Fabian
TEEN KINGS (Fabian & Frankie Avalon).
Tracks: / String along / About this thing called love / Got the feeling / Long before / Kissin' and twistin' / Tiger (Fabian) / Just ask your heart / Gingerbread / Why / Venus / Teacher's pet / Boy without a girl (Frankie Avalon).
Album: released on Crown, Feb'86 by Ace Records. Dist: Pinnacle, Swift

Cassette: released on Crown, Feb'86 by Ace Records. Dist: Pinnacle, Swift

TIGER.
Single (7"): released on Revival, Jul'82 Dist: Lightning, Swift

Fables Of Aesop
FABLES OF AESOP, THE Various artists (Various Artists).
Cassette: released on Audiocord Cassettes, May'83

Fabrique, Tina
ALIVE WITH LOVE.
Single (7"): released on Electricity, Apr'84 by Electricity Records. Dist: PRT

Single (12"): released on Electricity, Apr'84 by Electricity Records. Dist: PRT

Fabulous Fifties
FABULOUS FIFTIES, THE Various artists (Various Artists).
Cassette: released on Ditto, Sep'86 by Pickwick Records. Dist: H.R. Taylor

Fabulous Five
MILES AND MILES OF MUSIC.
Album: released on Stage, Mar'85 by Stage Records. Dist: Jetstar Distribution

YOU SAFE.
Single (12"): released on Sunburn, Apr'85 by Orbitone Records. Dist: Jetstar Distribution

YU SAFE.

Fabulous Pop Tarts
NEW YORK CITY BEAT.
Single (7"): released on PRT, Oct'85 by PRT Records. Dist: PRT

Single (12"): released on PRT, Oct'85 by PRT Records. Dist: PRT

Fabulous Pythons
RICO LAMENTE/JOHNNY ROCKER.
Single (7"): released on Chiswick, Jul'82 by Chiswick Records. Dist: none

Fabulous Thunderbirds
BUTT ROCKIN'.
Album: released on Chrysalis, Mar'81 by Chrysalis Records. Dist: CBS

FABULOUS THUNDERBIRDS, THE.
Album: released on Chrysalis, Oct'79 by Chrysalis Records. Dist: CBS

HOT NUMBER.
Tracks: / Stand back / Hot number / Wasted tears / It comes to me naturally / Love in common / How do you spell love / Streets of gold / Sofa circuit / Don't bother tryin' to steal her love / It takes a big man to cry.
Album: released on Epic, Aug'87 by CBS Rec-

---

ords. Dist: CBS

Cassette: released on Epic, Aug'87 by CBS Records. Dist: CBS

PORTFOLIO.
Tracks: / Crawl, The / She's tuff / Scratch my back / Tip on in.
Compact disc: released on Chrysalis, Jul'87 by Chrysalis Records. Dist: CBS

Album: released on Chrysalis, Jul'87 by Chrysalis Records. Dist: CBS

Cassette: released on Chrysalis, Jul'8 / by Chrysalis Records. Dist: CBS

STAND BACK.
Tracks: / Stand back / It takes a big man to cry.
Single (7"): released on Epic, Jul'87 by CBS Records. Dist: CBS

T-BIRD RHYTHM.
Album: released on Chrysalis, Oct'82 by Chrysalis Records. Dist: CBS

Cassette: released on Chrysalis, Oct'82 by Chrysalis Records. Dist: CBS

TUFF ENUFF.
Tracks: / Tuff enuff / Look at that.
Single (7"): released on Epic, Oct'86 by CBS Records. Dist: CBS

Single (12"): released on Epic, Oct'86 by CBS Records. Dist: CBS

TUFF ENUFF.
Tracks: / Tuff enuff / Tell me / Look at that, look at that / Two time my lovin' / Amnesia / Wrap it up / True love / Why get up / I don't care / Down at Antones.
Album: released on Epic, Jun'86 by CBS Records. Dist: CBS

Cassette: released on Epic, Jun'86 by CBS Records. Dist: CBS

WHAT'S THE WORD.
Album: released on Chrysalis, May'80 by Chrysalis Records. Dist: CBS

Fabulous Wonderfuls
BEING IN LOVE.
Single (7"): released on Eagle (London), Nov'81 by Eagle Records (London). Dist: Stage One

Face
PARADISE.
Single (7"): released on Wimp, Nov'83 by Wimp Records. Dist: Backs, Cartel

WHERE'S THE SENSE IN LOVING YOU.
Single (7"): released on Wimp, May'84 by Wimp Records. Dist: Backs, Cartel

WHO ARE WE.
Tracks: / Who are we (instrumental).
Picture disc single: released on Face, Dec'86 by Face Records & Music. Dist: T.One Records

Single (7"): released on Face, Dec'86 by Face Records & Music. Dist: T.One Records

Face, George
SINCE I MET YOU BABY.
Single (12"): released on Dancebeat, Jan'84 by Dancebeat Records. Dist: Jetstar
Cat. no: DBD 1320

Face of Concern
RIGHT.
Tracks: / Right.
Single (12"): released on Press, Jul'86 by Press Records.

Single (12"): released on Press, Feb'85 by Press Records.

SAFE.
Single (12"): released on Press, Jun'85 by Press Records.

Faces
2 ORIGINALS OF....
Double Album: released on Warner Brothers, Jan'76 by Warner Bros Records. Dist: WEA

FACES FEATURING ROD STEWART (Faces & Rod Stewart).
Album: released on Pickwick, Sep'80 by Pickwick Records. Dist: Pickwick Distribution, Prism Leisure Distribution,

FEATURING ROD STEWART.
Cassette: released on Pickwick, Sep'80 by Pickwick Records. Dist: Pickwick Distribution, Prism Leisure Distribution,

FIRST STEP.
Album: released on Edsel, Jul'87 by Demon Records. Dist: Pinnacle, Jazz Music, Projection

FIRST STEP / LONG PLAYER.
Double Album: released on Warner Brothers, Oct'75 by Warner Bros Records. Dist: WEA

I HAVEN'T STOPPED DANCING YET.
Single (12"): released on Long Island Sound, Oct'85 by Long Island Sound. Dist: Pinnacle

Long player / First step
NOD'S AS GOOD AS A WINK TO A BLIND HORSE, A.
Album: by Warner Bros Records. Dist: WEA

SEARCHING.
Tracks: / Searching.
Single (12"): released on L.I.S., Aug'86 Dist: Pinnacle

Face To Face
10-9-8.
Single (7"): released on Epic, Jun'84 by CBS Records. Dist: CBS

Single (12"): released on Epic, Jun'84 by CBS Records. Dist: CBS

CONFRONTATION.
Tracks: / Tell me why / confess / Why do I say / too late / 4th watch, The / Walk into the fire / When time stands still / Shake the world / Boy like you, A / America's Dream.
Album: released on Epic, Apr'86 by CBS Records. Dist: CBS

Cassette: released on Epic, Apr'86 by CBS Records. Dist: CBS

Album: released on Epic, Apr'86 by CBS Records. Dist: CBS

TELL ME WHY.
Tracks: / Tell me why / Shake the world.
Single (7"): released on Epic, Mar'86 by CBS Records. Dist: CBS

Single (12"): released on Epic, Mar'86 by CBS Records. Dist: CBS

Facey, Sonia
TOGETHER.
Single (12"): released on Ethnic, Jun'84 by Kingdom

Fact
ALWAYS THERE.
Single (12"): released on Tollhouse, Nov'86

AS A MATTER OF.......FACT.
Album: released on Mausoleum, Mar'85 by Mausoleum Records. Dist: Pinnacle

Factor 33
NO PAIN NO GAIN.
Single (7"): released on Stage One, Apr'84 by Stage One Records. Dist: Stage One Distribution

Factory
BLACK STAMP.
Album: released on Cobra, Sep'79 by Cobra

Records. Dist: Projection, EMI

HOLD OUT.
Tracks: / Hold out.
Single (7"):

Single (12"):

YOU ARE THE MUSIC / HISTORY OF THE....
Single (7"): released on F. Earth, Mar'83 by F. Earth Records. Dist: Pinnacle

Factory Benelux
FACTORY BENELUX GREATEST HITS (1983) Various artists (Various Artists).
Album: released on Factory, Jan'84 by Factory Records. Dist: Cartel, Pinnacle

Factory Quartet
FACTORY QUARTET Various Artists (Various Artists).
Cassette: released on Factory, Nov'85 by Factory Records. Dist: Cartel, Pinnacle

Facts Of Life
FACTS OF LIFE Somerset Maugham.
Cassette: released on Talking Tape Company, '84 by Talking Tape Company Records.

FACTS OF LIFE, (THE) Maugham, Somerset (Burden, Hugh).
Cassette: released on Talking Tape, '84

Facts Of Love
FACTS OF LOVE (Various Artists).
Tracks: / Facts of love.
Single (7"): released on Club, Mar'87 by Phonogram Records. Dist: Polygram

Single (12"): released on Club, Mar'87 by Phonogram Records. Dist: Polygram

Faddis, Jon
GOOD AND PLENTY.
Compact disc: released on Dunhill Compact Classics (USA), '86

LEGACY.
Tracks: / West end blues / Little jazz / Night in Tunisia / Instigator / Things to come / Child is born, A / Li'l darlin' / Whisper not.
Album: released on Concord Jazz(USA), Feb'86 by Concord Jazz Records (USA). Dist: IMS, Polygram

Cassette: released on Concord Jazz(USA), Feb'86 by Concord Jazz Records (USA). Dist: IMS, Polygram

Compact disc: released on Concord Jazz(USA), Dec'86 by Concord Jazz Records (USA). Dist: IMS, Polygram

OSCAR PETERSON AND JON FADDIS (Faddis, Jon & Oscar Peterson).
Album: released on Pablo (USA), '82 by Pablo Records (USA). Dist: Wellard, Chris, IMS-Polygram, BMG

Cassette: released on Pablo (USA), '82 by Pablo Records (USA). Dist: Wellard, Chris, IMS-Polygram, BMG

Album: released on Pablo (USA), '82 by Pablo Records (USA). Dist: Wellard, Chris, IMS-Polygram, BMG

Cassette: released on Pablo (USA), '82 by Pablo Records (USA). Dist: Wellard, Chris, IMS-Polygram, BMG

YOUNG BLOOD.
Album: released on Pablo (USA), '82 by Pablo Records (USA). Dist: Wellard, Chris, IMS-Polygram, BMG

Cassette: released on Pablo (USA), '82 by Pablo Records (USA). Dist: Wellard, Chris,

Fad Gadget
BACK TO NATURE / THE BOX.

Single (7"): released on Mute, Oct'79 Dist: Spartan Distribution, Rough Trade Distribution, Cartel Distribution

Box, The / Back to nature

COLLAPSING NEW PEOPLE / SPOIL THE CHILD.
Single (7"): released on Mute, Jan'84 Dist: Spartan Distribution, Rough Trade Distribution, Cartel Distribution

Single (12"): released on Mute, Jan'84 Dist: Spartan Distribution, Rough Trade Distribution, Cartel Distribution

FIRESIDE FAVOURITES.
Album: released on Mute, '81 Dist: Spartan Distribution, Rough Trade Distribution, Cartel Distribution

FIRESIDE FAVOURITES / INSECTICIDE.
Single (7"): released on Mute, Sep'80 Dist: Spartan Distribution, Rough Trade Distribution, Cartel Distribution

FOR WHOM THE BELL TOLLS.
Single (7"): released on Mute, Jan'83 Dist: Spartan Distribution, Rough Trade Distribution, Cartel Distribution

Single (12"): released on Mute, Jan'83 Dist: Spartan Distribution, Rough Trade Distribution, Cartel Distribution

GAG.
Album: released on Mute, Feb'84 Dist: Spartan Distribution, Rough Trade Distribution, Cartel Distribution

Cassette: released on Mute, Feb'84 Dist: Spartan Distribution, Rough Trade Distribution, Cartel Distribution

Hand shake / Rickey's hand

I DISCOVER LOVE / LEMMINGS ON LOVERS ROCK.
Single (7"): released on Mute, Oct'83 Dist: Spartan Distribution, Rough Trade Distribution, Cartel Distribution

Single (12"): released on Mute, Oct'83 Dist: Spartan Distribution, Rough Trade Distribution, Cartel Distribution

INCONTINENT.
Album: released on Mute, '81 Dist: Spartan Distribution, Rough Trade Distribution, Cartel Distribution

INSECTICIDE / FIRESIDE FAVOURITES
(see Fireside favourites / Insecticide).

KING OF THE FLIES / PLAIN CLOTHES.
Single (7"): released on Mute, Apr'82 Dist: Spartan Distribution, Rough Trade Distribution, Cartel Distribution

Lady shave / Make room

Lemmings on lovers rock / I discover rock

LIFE ON THE LINE / 4M.
Single (7"): released on Mute, Sep'82 Dist: Spartan Distribution, Rough Trade Distribution, Cartel Distribution

Single (12"): released on Mute, Sep'82 Dist: Spartan Distribution, Rough Trade Distribution, Cartel Distribution

MAKE ROOM / LADY SHAVE.
Single (7"): released on Mute, Mar'81 Dist: Spartan Distribution, Rough Trade Distribution, Cartel Distribution

ONE MAN'S MEAT.
Single (7"): released on Mute, May'84 Dist: Spartan Distribution, Rough Trade Distribution, Cartel Distribution

Single (12"): released on Mute, May'84 Dist: Spartan Distribution, Rough Trade Distribution, Cartel Distribution

Plain clothes / King of the flies

RICKEY'S HAND / HAND SHAKE.
Single (7"): released on Mute, Mar'80 Dist: Spartan Distribution, Rough Trade Distribution, Cartel Distribution

SATURDAY NIGHT SPECIAL.
Single (7"): released on Mute, Jan'82 Dist: Spartan Distribution, Rough Trade Distribution, Cartel Distribution

Spoil the child / Collapsing new people

UNDER THE FLAG.
Album: released on Mute, Sep'82 Dist: Spartan Distribution, Rough Trade Distribution, Cartel Distribution

Cassette: released on Mute, Sep'82 Dist: Spartan Distribution, Rough Trade Distribution, Cartel Distribution

Fagan, Donald

STEELY DAN - THE EARLY YEARS
(Fagan, Donald & Walter Becker).
Album: released on Teldec (Germany), May'84 by Import Records. Dist: IMS Distribution, Polygram Distribution

Fagan, Michael

GOD SAVE THE QUEEN.
Single (7"): released on Charly, May'83 by Charly Records. Dist: Charly, Cadillac

Fagen, Donald

I.G.Y. / WALK BETWEEN RAINDROPS.
Single (7"): released on Warner Brothers, Nov'82 by Warner Bros Records. Dist: WEA

Maxine / New frontier

NEW FRONTIER / MAXINE.
Single (7"): released on Warner Brothers, Jan'83 by Warner Bros Records. Dist: WEA

Single (12"): released on Warner Brothers, Jan'83 by Warner Bros Records. Dist: WEA

NIGHTFLY.
Compact disc: released on Warner Bros., Jan'83 by Warner Bros Records. Dist: WEA

NIGHTFLY, THE.
Album: released on Warner Brothers, Oct'82 by Warner Bros Records. Dist: WEA

Cassette: released on Warner Brothers, Oct'82 by Warner Bros Records. Dist: WEA

RUBY BABY / WALK BETWEEN RAINDROPS.
Single (7"): released on Warner Brothers, Apr'83 by Warner Bros Records. Dist: WEA

Steely Dan-the early years

Walk between raindrops / I.G.Y.

Walk between raindrops / Ruby baby

Fagin, Joe

BACK WITH THE BOYS.
Tracks: / Back with the boys / Get it right / That's livin' alright / That's livin' alright / Breakin' away.
Single (7"): released on Towerbell, Mar'86 by Towerbell Records. Dist: EMI

Single (12"): released on Towerbell, Mar'86 by Towerbell Records. Dist: EMI

BEST OF AUFWIEDERSEHEN PET
(Fagin, Joe & Dave Mackay).
Cassette: released on Towerbell, Apr'86 by Towerbell Records. Dist: EMI

Album: released on Towerbell, Apr'86 by Towerbell Records. Dist: EMI

BREAKIN' AWAY / THAT'S LIVING ALRIGHT.
Single (7"): released on Towerbell, Jan'84 by Towerbell Records. Dist: EMI

LOVE HANGS BY A THREAD.
Album: released on Towerbell, May'85 by Towerbell Records. Dist: EMI

Cassette: released on Towerbell, May'85 by Towerbell Records. Dist: EMI

Single (7"): released on Towerbell, Sep'85 by Towerbell Records. Dist: EMI

MONEY MONEY.
Single (7"): released on Towerbell, Jun'84 by Towerbell Records. Dist: EMI

NUMBER ONE (SAVIN' FACE).
Single (7"): released on Towerbell, Apr'85 by Towerbell Records. Dist: EMI

Single (12"): released on Towerbell, Apr'85 by Towerbell Records. Dist: EMI

PRIDE OF MERSEYSIDE.
Single (7"): released on GFM, Mar'87 by GFM Records. Dist: Fast Forward, Cartel, PRT, Projection

Single (12"): released on GFM, Mar'87 by GFM Records. Dist: Fast Forward, Cartel, PRT, Projection

PRIDE OF MERSEYSIDE (PIC. DISC).
Single (7"): released on GFM, Mar'87 by GFM Records. Dist: Fast Forward, Cartel, PRT, Projection

Single (12"): released on GFM, Mar'87 by GFM Records. Dist: Fast Forward, Cartel, PRT, Projection

That's living alright / Breakin' away

TIDE OF MERSEYSIDE.
Tracks: / Tide of Merseyside / Don't care much anymore.

WHY DON'T WE SPEND THE NIGHT.
Single (7"): released on Towerbell, Mar'84 by Towerbell Records. Dist: EMI

Fahey, John

AMERICA.
Album: by Sonet Records. Dist: PRT

BEST OF JOHN FAHEY 1959-1977.
Album: released on Sonet, Sep'77 by Sonet Records. Dist: PRT

BEST OF JOHN FAHEY 1959-1977, THE.
Album: released on Takoma, Nov'84 by PRT Records. Dist: PRT Distribution

Cassette: released on Takoma, Nov'84 by PRT Records. Dist: PRT Distribution

BLIND JOE DEATH VOL.1.
Album: by Sonet Records. Dist: PRT

CHRISTMAS ALBUM.
Album: released on Sonet, '76 by Sonet Records. Dist: PRT

DEATH CHANTS.
Album: by Sonet Records. Dist: PRT

FARE FORWARD VOYAGERS.
Album: released on Sonet, '74 by Sonet Records. Dist: PRT

LEO KOTTKE WITH PETER LANG & JOHN FAHEY
(see Kottke, Leo with Peter Lang & John Fahey).

LET GO.
Album: released on Varrick (USA), Sep'84 Dist: Mike's Country Music Room Distribution, Swift, Projection, Topic, Jetstar, Ruff Lion Distribution

LIVE IN TASMANIA.
Album: released on Sonet, Jun'81 by Sonet Records. Dist: PRT

OF RIVERS AND RELIGION (Fahey, John & His Orchestra).
Album: released on Edsel, Mar'87 by Demon Records. Dist: Pinnacle, Jazz Music, Projection

OLD FASHIONED LOVE.
Album: released on Sonet, '76 by Sonet Records. Dist: PRT

POPULAR SONGS OF CHRISTMAS AND NEW YEAR.
Album: released on Rounder (USA), Jan'84 Dist: Mike's Country Music Room Distribution, Jazz Music Distribution, Swift Distribution, Roots Records Distribution, Projection Distribution, Topic Distribution

RAILROADS 1.
Tracks: / Frisco leaving Birmingham / Oneonta / Summer cat by my door / Steve Talbot on the keddie wye / Afternoon espee through salem / Enigmas and perplexities of the Norfolk and Western / Charlie Becker's meditation / Imitation train whistles / Life is like a mountain railroad / Delta dog through the book of revelation.
Album: released on Takoma (USA), Apr'84 Dist: Allegiance Distribution

Cassette: released on Takoma (USA), Apr'84 Dist: Allegiance Distribution

RAIN FORESTS, OCEANS AND OTHER THEMES.
Album: released on Varrick (USA), Dec'85 Dist: Mike's Country Music Room Distribution, Swift, Projection, Topic, Jetstar, Ruff Lion Distribution

Cassette: released on Varrick (USA), Dec'85 Dist: Mike's Country Music Room Distribution, Swift, Projection, Topic, Jetstar, Ruff Lion Distribution

Compact disc: released on Rounder (USA), Dec'86 Dist: Mike's Country Music Room Distribution, Jazz Music Distribution, Swift Distribution, Roots Records Distribution, Projection Distribution, Topic Distribution

REQUIA / THE YELLOW PRINCESS.
Double Album: released on Vanguard, Jun'78 by PRT Records. Dist: PRT

TRANSFIGURATION OF BLIND JOE DEATH, THE.
Album: released on Takoma (USA), Apr'84 Dist: Allegiance Distribution

Cassette: released on Takoma (USA), Apr'84 Dist: Allegiance Distribution

Album: released on Sonet, Aug'79 by Sonet Records. Dist: PRT

TRIBUTE TO... Various artists (Various Artists).
Album: released on Kicking Mule, Mar'80 by Sonet. Dist: Roots, PRT-Pye Distribution

Yellow Princess, The / Requia

Faine Jade

INTROSPECTION: A FAINE JADE RECITAL.
Album: released on Psycho, '83 Dist: Funhouse, Rough Trade

Fairchild, Barbara

ANSWER GAME/BYE BYE LOVE.
Single (7"): released on RCA, '82 by RCA Records. Dist: RCA, Roots, Swift, Wellard, Chris, I & B, Solomon & Peres Distribution

ANSWER GAME,THE.
Album: released on RCA International, '82

Cassette: released on RCA International, '82

JUST OUT RIDING AROUND.
Tracks: / Just out riding around / You burned me so bad.
Single (7"): released on Capitol, Jun'86 by Capitol Records. Dist: EMI

MISSISSIPPI.
Album: released on CBS, '77 by CBS Records. Dist: CBS

Fair Deal

ALBION MARKET THEME.
Single (7"): released on Columbia, '85 by EMI Records. Dist: EMI

Fairey Band

BEST OF THE FAIREY BAND.
Album: released on RCA, '76 by RCA Records. Dist: RCA, Roots, Swift, Wellard, Chris, I & B, Solomon & Peres Distribution

Fairey Engineering

CHAMPION BRASS.
Album: released on BBC, '78 by BBC Records & Tapes. Dist: EMI, PRT, Pye

Cassette: released on BBC, '78 by BBC Records & Tapes. Dist: EMI, PRT, Pye

Fairport Convention

ANGEL DELIGHT.
Album: by Island Records. Dist: Polygram

A.T.2..
Cassette: released on Woodworm, '84 by Charly Records. Dist: Charly

BONNY BUNCH OF ROSES,THE.
Album: released on Vertigo, '77 by Phonogram Records. Dist: Polygram

FAIRPORT CONVENTION.
Album: released on Polydor, '75 by Polydor Records. Dist: Polygram, Polydor

FAIRPORT CONVENTION 9.
Album: by Island Records. Dist: Polygram

FAIRWELL FAIRWELL.
Album: released on Simon, '79 by Supertunes Records. Dist: Pinnacle

FULL HOUSE.
Album: by Island Records. Dist: Polygram

FULL HOUSE.
Album: released on Hannibal, Jul'87 by Hannibal Records. Dist: Charly, Harmonia Mundi, Projection, Celtic Music, Roots

GLADYS LEAP.
Album: released on Woodworm, '85 by Charly Records. Dist: Charly

HEYDAY BBC Radio sessions.
Album: released on Hannibal, Oct'87 by Hannibal Records. Dist: Charly, Harmonia Mundi, Projection, Celtic Music, Roots. Estim retail price in Sep'87 was £5.99.

Cassette: released on Hannibal, Oct'87 by Hannibal Records. Dist: Charly, Harmonia Mundi, Projection, Celtic Music, Roots. Estim retail price in Sep'87 was £5.99.

HISTORY OF...,THE.
Album: by Island Records. Dist: Polygram

HOUSE FULL (Live in L.A.).
Notes: This version of the album differs from the original mid-70's release, with an alternative take of "Sloth", and the addition of "Battle of the Somme", "Sir Patrick Spens" and the deleted "Yellow Bird".
Album: released on Hannibal, Jan'87 by Hannibal Records. Dist: Charly, Harmonia Mundi, Projection, Celtic Music, Roots

Album: released on Hannibal, Apr'87 by Hannibal Records. Dist: Charly, Harmonia Mundi, Projection, Celtic Music, Roots

JOHN BARBBACOME LEE.
Double Album: by Island Records. Dist: Polygram

LIEGE & LIEF.
Tracks: / Come all ye / Reynardine / Matty groves / Farewell farewell / Deserter (The) / Lark in the morning medley / Tam lin / Crazy man Michael.
Album: released on Island, Sep'86 by Island Records. Dist: Polygram

Cassette: released on Island, Sep'86 by Island Records. Dist: Polygram

Compact disc: released on Island, Sep'86 by

Island Records. Dist: Polygram

LIVE.
Album: by Island Records. Dist: Polygram

MEET ON THE LEDGE.
Tracks: / Meet on the ledge / Sigh beg sigh more / John Barleycorn*.
Single (7"): released on Island, 23 May'87 by Island Records. Dist: Polygram

Single (12"): released on Island, 23 May'87 by Island Records. Dist: Polygram

MOAT ON THE LEDGE.
Album: released on Woodworm, '84 by Charly Records. Dist: Charly

MOAT ON THE LEDGE: LIVE AT BROUGHTON CASTLE.
Cassette: released on Stoney Plain, '85

RISING FOR THE MOON.
Album: released on Island, '75 by Island Records. Dist: Polygram

ROSIE.
Album: by Island Records. Dist: Polygram

UNHALFBRICKING.
Tracks: / Genesis hall / Si tu dois partir / Autopsy / Sailor's life, A / Cajun woman / Who knows where the time goes / Percy's song / Million dollar bash / Sailor's life, A.
Compact disc: released on Island, Feb'87 by Island Records. Dist: Polygram

WHAT WE DID ON OUR HOLIDAYS.
Album: by Island Records. Dist: Polygram

Fairweather, Digby

SONGS FOR SANDY.
Album: released on Hep, '83 by H.R. Taylor Records. Dist: Jazz Music, Cadillac Music, JSU, Taylors, Wellard, Chris, Zodiac, Swift, Fast Forward

Fairweather-Low, Andy

BOSSA NOVA.
Tracks: / Bossa Nova / House of blue.
Single (7"): released on Stiff, Aug'86 by Stiff Records. Dist: EMI, Record Services Distribution (Ireland)

Single (12"): released on Stiff, Aug'86 by Stiff Records. Dist: EMI, Record Services Distribution (Ireland)

MEGA-SHEBANG.
Album: released on WEA, '80 by WEA Records. Dist: WEA

Cassette: released on Warner Bros., '80 by Warner Bros Records. Dist: WEA

WIDE EYED AND LEGLESS.
Single (7"): released on Scoop, '84

Cassette: released on Scoop, '84

Fairy Engineering Band

LISTEN WITH MOTHER THEME.
Single (7"): released on Mont, '83 by Mont Records. Dist: Spartan Distribution

Fairy stories

FAIRY STORIES (Lancaster, Ann).
Cassette: released on Pickwick (Ditto series), '82

FAIRY STORIES (Grimm).
Cassette: released on Argo, '84 by Decca Records. Dist: Polygram

MORE WELL LOVE FAIRY STORIES.
Cassette: released on Listen For Pleasure, '79 by MFP Records. Dist: EMI

MY FAVOURITE FAIRY STORIES Read by Nanette Newman,Richard Norman,Judi Dench,Pete Murray (Various Artists).
Cassette: released on Listen For Pleasure, Nov'77 by MFP Records. Dist: EMI

Fair, Yvonne

I SHOULD HAVE BEEN ME/YOU CAN'T....
Single (7"): released on Motown, '81 by Motown Records. Dist: BMG Distribution

Faith

LIVE FAITH.
Album: released on Dove, '79 by Dove Records. Dist: Jetstar

Faith, Adam

BEST OF ADAM FAITH.
Album: released on MFP, '85 by EMI Records. Dist: EMI

Cassette: released on MFP, '85 by EMI Records. Dist: EMI

NOT JUST A MEMORY.
Album: released on See For Miles, '83 by See For Miles Records. Dist: Pinnacle

WHAT DO YOU WANT/HOW ABOUT THAT.
Single (7"): released on Old Gold, '83 by Old Gold Records. Dist: Lightning, Jazz Music, Spartan, Counterpoint

WHAT DO YOU WANT/POOR ME.
Single (7"): released on EMI, '77 by EMI Records. Dist: EMI

Faith Brothers

COUNTRY OF THE BLIND.
Single (7"): released on Siren, '85 by Virgin Records. Dist: EMI

Single (12"): released on Siren, '85 by Virgin Records. Dist: EMI

EVENTIDE.
Album: released on Siren, Nov'85 by Virgin Records. Dist: EMI

Cassette: released on Siren, Nov'85 by Virgin Records. Dist: EMI

EVENTIDE(A HYMN FOR CHANGE).
Single (7"): released on Siren, '85 by Virgin Records. Dist: EMI

Single (12"): released on Siren, '85 by Virgin Records. Dist: EMI

HUMAN SOUND, A.
Compact disc: released on Siren, May'87 by Virgin Records. Dist: EMI

STRANGER ON HOME GROUND.
Single (7"): released on Siren, '85 by Virgin Records. Dist: EMI

Single (12"): released on Siren, '85 by Virgin Records. Dist: EMI

THAT'S JUST THE WAY IT IS WITH ME.
Tracks: / That's just the way it is with me / Different kind of wonderful, A / Letter to the times, A.
Single (7"): released on Siren, Mar'87 by Virgin Records. Dist: EMI

Single (12"): released on Siren, Mar'87 by Virgin Records. Dist: EMI

WHISTLING IN THE DARK.
Tracks: / Whistling in the dark / Easter Parade.
Single (7"): released on Siren, Mar'86 by Virgin Records. Dist: EMI

Single (12"): released on Siren, Mar'86 by Virgin Records. Dist: EMI

Faithful Breath

GOLD 'N' GLORY.
Album: released on Mausoleum, '84 by Mausoleum Records. Dist: Pinnacle

Cassette: released on Mausoleum, '84 by Mausoleum Records. Dist: Pinnacle

Faithfull, Marianne

AS TEARS GO BY.
Tracks: / As tears go by / Trouble in mind (The return) / This hawk El Gavian*.
Single (7"): released on Island, 20 Jun'87 by Island Records. Dist: Polygram

Single (12"): released on Island, 20 Jun'87 by Island Records. Dist: Polygram

Album: released on Decca, '81 by Decca Records. Dist: Polygram

AS TEARS GO BY/COME AND STAY WITH ME.
Single (7"): released on Decca, '80 by Decca Records. Dist: Polygram

Single (7"): released on Old Gold, '83 by Old Gold Records. Dist: Lightning, Jazz Music, Spartan, Counterpoint

BROKEN ENGLISH.
Tracks: / Working class hero / What's the hurry / Ballad of Lucy Jordan / Why d'ya do it / Broken English / Witches' song / Guilt / Brain drain.
Album: released on Island, Sep'86 by Island Records. Dist: Polygram

Cassette: released on Island, Sep'86 by Island Records. Dist: Polygram

Compact disc: released on Island, Feb'87 by Island Records. Dist: Polygram

CHILD'S ADVENTURE,A.
Album: released on Island, '83 by Island Records. Dist: Polygram

CHILDS ADVENTURE, A.
Notes: "A Child's Adventure" is Marianne Faithfull's third album for Island Records and illustrates her continuing maturity as a writer and artist. Recorded in NewYork it features all new songs, mostly written by Marianne Faithfull and augmented by the work of her long-time guitarist Barry Reynolds, who also shares writing credits on several tracks. The album is produced by Barry Reynolds, Harvey Goldberg and Islands own keyboard artist/composer, Wally Badarou.
Album: released on Island, Apr'87 by Island Records. Dist: Polygram

Cassette: released on Island, Apr'87 by Island Records. Dist: Polygram

DANGEROUS ACQUAINTANCES.
Album: released on Island, '81 by Island Records. Dist: Polygram

Cassette: released on Island, '81 by Island Records. Dist: Polygram

DREAMIN' MY DREAMS.
Album: released on Nems, '77 Dist: Castle Communications Records, Pinnacle Records

MARIANNE FAITHFULL.
Album: Dist: Castle Communications Records, Pinnacle Records

Album: released on Decca, '84 by Decca Records. Dist: Polygram

MUSIC FOR THE MILLIONS.
Tracks: / Yesterday / Sunny Goodge street / Coquillages / Blowin' in the wind / Counting / Come and stay with me / Monday Monday / Summer nights / What have I done wrong / Go away from my world / Sister morphine.
Album: released on Decca (Germany), Dec'85 by Decca Records. Dist: Polygram, IMS

Cassette: released on Decca (Germany), Dec'85 by Decca Records. Dist: Polygram, IMS

RICH KID BLUES.
Tracks: / Rich kid blues / Long black veil / Sad Lisa / It's all over now baby blue / Southern butterfly / Chords of fame / Visions of Johannah / It takes a lot to laugh, it takes a train to cry / Beware of darkness / Corrina, Corrina / Mud slide slim / Crazy lady blues / All I want to do in life / I'll be your baby tonight / Wait for me down by the river / That was the day (Nashville) / This time / Way you want me to be, The / Dreamin' my dreams / Wrong road again / Fairytale hero / Vanilla o'lay / Lady Madelaine / Honky Tonk Angels.
Compact disc: released on Collector Series, '86 by Castle Communications Records. Dist: PRT, Pinnacle, RCA, Ariola

Album: released on Castle Communications, '85 by Castle Communications. Dist: Cartel, Pinnacle, Counterpoint

Cassette: released on Castle Communications, '85 by Castle Communications. Dist: Cartel, Pinnacle, Counterpoint

STRANGE WEATHER.
Tracks: / Stranger intro / Boulevard of broken dreams / I ain't goin' down to the well no more / Yesterdays / Sing of judgement / Strange weather / Love life and money / I'll keep it with mine / Hello stranger / Penthouse serenade / As tears go by / Stranger on earth, A.
Compact disc: released on Island, Aug'87 by Island Records. Dist: Polygram

WORLD OF MARIANNE FAITHFULL.
Album: by Decca Records. Dist: Polygram

Faith, George

FIRST CLASS.

HAPPY ANNIVERSARY.
Album: released on Music Track, Sep'86 Dist: Jetstar Distribution

OLD FASHIONED LOVE.
Single (12"): released on Londisc, '84 by Londisc Records.

SAY YOU,SAY ME.
Tracks: / Say You,Say Me / Say you, say me (Version).
Single (12"): released on Top Rank, Jan'86

SINGS FOR LOVERS ONLY.
Album: released on Hawkeye, May'87 by Hawkeye Records. Dist: Hawkeye, Lightning (WEA) Distribution, Jetstar, PRT

STRAIGHT TO THE HEART.
Album: released on EAD, Feb'86 by EAD Records. Dist: Jetstar

TO LOVE SOMEBODY.
Single (12"): released on Foundation, '83 by Foundation Records, The. Dist: Jetstar

Faith Global

EARTH REPORT.
Single (12"): released on Survival, '83 by Survival Records. Dist: Backs, Cartel Distribution

SAME MISTAKES,THE.
Album: released on Survival, '83 by Survival Records. Dist: Backs, Cartel Distribution

Faith No More

INTRODUCE YOURSELF.
Album: released on Slash, Apr'87 by London Records. Dist: Polygram

Cassette: released on Slash, Apr'87 by London Records. Dist: Polygram

Faith, Percy

MOODS.
Album: released on Pickwick (Ditto series), '83

SUMMER PLACE.
Single (7"): released on Old Gold, '82 by Old Gold Records. Dist: Lightning, Jazz Music, Spartan, Counterpoint

VIA MEXICO.
Album: released on CBS, Sep'86 by CBS Records. Dist: CBS

Cassette: released on CBS, Sep'86 by CBS Records. Dist: CBS

Falay, Maffy

WE SIX.
Notes: Bernt Resengren, Elvan Araci, Ake Johansson.
Album: released on Phontastic, Mar'87 Dist: Wellard, Chris

Falco

EMOTIONAL.
Tracks: / Der Komissar* / Kiss of Kathleen Turner (The)* / Emotional / Kamikaza Cappa / Crime time / Cowboyz and indianz / Coming Home / Star of moon and sun (The) / Les nouveaux riches / Sound of Musik (The) / Kiss of Kathleen Turner, The / Emotional (New York mix English version) / Emotional (Continental version).
Notes: * = Extra track on 12" only
Compact disc: released on WEA, Oct'86 by WEA Records. Dist: WEA

Album: released on WEA, Nov'86 by WEA Records. Dist: WEA

Cassette: released on WEA, Nov'86 by WEA Records. Dist: WEA

Compact disc: released on WEA, Nov'86 by WEA Records. Dist: WEA

Single (7"): released on WEA Int, Apr'87

Single (12"): released on WEA Int, Apr'87

FALCO 3.
Tracks: / Rock me Amadeus / America / Tango the night / Munich girls(looking for love) / Jeanny / Vienna calling / Manner des westens / It's all over now baby blue / Jeannny(German version).
Album: released on A&M, Apr'86 by A&M Records. Dist: Polygram

Cassette: released on A&M, Apr'86 by A&M Records. Dist: Polygram

JEANNY.
Tracks: / Rock me Amadeus/Extended '86 edit / Girl is missing (German language version).
Single (7"): released on A&M, Jul'86 by A&M Records. Dist: Polygram

Single (12"): released on A&M, Jul'86 by A&M Records. Dist: Polygram

JUNGE ROEMER.
Single (7"): released on A&M, '84 by A&M Records. Dist: Polygram

Single (12"): released on A&M, '84 by A&M Records. Dist: Polygram

ROCK ME AMADEUS US Version.
Tracks: / Rock me Amadeus / Urban Tropical / Rock me amadeus/Salieri mix.
Single (7"): released on A&M, Mar'86 by A&M Records. Dist: Polygram

Single (12"): released on A&M, Mar'86 by A&M Records. Dist: Polygram

SOUND OF MUSIK(THE).
Tracks: / Sound of musik(The)/Single edit / Sound of musik(The)/Rock 'n' Roll soul edit.
Single (7"): released on WEA, Sep'86 by WEA Records. Dist: WEA

Single (12"): released on WEA, Sep'86 by WEA Records. Dist: WEA

VIENNA CALLING.
Tracks: / Vienna calling / Americas.
Single (7"): released on A&M, May'86 by A&M Records. Dist: Polygram

Single (12"): released on A&M, May'86 by A&M Records. Dist: Polygram

Falcon and the Snowman

FALCON AND THE SNOWMAN Original motion picture soundtrack (Various Artists).
Album: released on EMI, '85 by EMI Records. Dist: EMI

Cassette: released on EMI, '85 by EMI Records. Dist: EMI

Falcon, Joseph
LOUISIANNA CAJUN MUSIC.
Album: released on Arhoolie, '81 by Arhoolie Records. Dist: Projection, Topic, Jazz Music, Swift, Roots

Falcons
I FOUND LOVE.
Album: released on Relic (US), '85

YOU'RE SO FINE.
Album: released on Relic (US), '85

Falco's Panther Burns, Tav
BEHIND THE MAGNOLIA CURTAIN.
Album: released on Fan Club, Aug'87 by New Rose. Dist: Rough Trade, Cartel

Falco, Tav
DROP YOUR MASK.
Tracks: / Drop your mask.
Single (7"): released on New Rose, Mar'87 Dist: Rough Trade, Cartel

NOW (Falco, Tav Panther Burns).
Cassette: released on Frenzi, Aug'86 Dist: Fast Forward, Cartel

WORLD WE KNEW, THE (Falco, Tav Panther Burns).
Album: released on New Rose, Jun'87 Dist: Rough Trade, Cartel

Falem Foundation
TURBO REGGAE.
Single (12"): released on Solid Music, '85 by Solid Music Records. Dist: Jetstar

Falkirk Childrens Theatre
IT'S CHRISTMAS.
Single (7"): released on Klub, '83

Falklands Task Force
ABIDE WITH US.
Tracks: / Last post / Prayer for all those who serve our country in Armed Forces / Reveille / Guide me, O thou great redeemer / Lord's my shepherd, The / Praise my soul, The king of heaven / Immortal, invisible / God only wise / Eternal father, strong to save / Dear lord and father of mankind / All people that on earth do dwell / And did those feet in ancient time / Walk upon England's mountain green ? / He who would valient be / Lord of all hopefulness / Lead us, heavenly father / Abide with me, fast falls the eventide / Thy hand, O god, has guided / God be in my head and in my understanding / Day thou gavest, Lord is ended, The.
Album: released on ASV, '83 by Academy Sound & Vision Records. Dist: Pinnacle

Cassette: released on ASV, '83 by Academy Sound & Vision Records. Dist: Pinnacle

Fall
BAND SINISTER.
Album: released on Beggars Banquet, Sep'86 by Beggars Banquet Records. Dist: WEA
Cat. no: BEGA 75
Cassette: released on Beggars Banquet, Sep'86 by Beggars Banquet Records. Dist: WEA

BEND SINISTER.
Tracks: / R.O.D. / Dktr Faustus / Shoulder pads / Mr Pharmacist / Gross chapel - British Grenadiers / U.S. 80's - 90's / Terry Waite sez / Bournemouth Runner / Riddler! / Shoulder pads 2.
Album: released on Beggars Banquet, Nov'86 by Beggars Banquet Records. Dist: WEA

Cassette: released on Beggars Banquet, Nov'86 by Beggars Banquet Records. Dist: WEA

COULDN'T GET AHEAD.
Single (7"): by Beggars Banquet Records. Dist: WEA

Single (12"): by Beggars Banquet Records. Dist: WEA

CREEP.
Single (7"): by Beggars Banquet Records. Dist: WEA

Single (12"): by Beggars Banquet Records. Dist: WEA

CRUISERS CREEK.
Single (7"): released on Beggars Banquet, '85 by Beggars Banquet Records. Dist: WEA

Single (12"): released on Beggars Banquet, '85 by Beggars Banquet Records. Dist: WEA

DRAYGO'S GUILT.
Single (12"): released on Beggars Banquet, '84 by Beggars Banquet Records. Dist: WEA

FALL LIVE,THE.
Album: released on Rough Trade, '80 by Rough Trade Records. Dist: Rough Trade Distribution, Cartel Distribution

GROTESQUE.
Album: released on Rough Trade, Nov'80 by Rough Trade Records. Dist: Rough Trade Distribution, Cartel Distribution

HEY, LUCIANI.
Tracks: / Shoulder pads.
Single (7"): released on Beggars Banquet, Nov'86 by Beggars Banquet Records. Dist: WEA

Single (12"): released on Beggars Banquet, Nov'86 by Beggars Banquet Records. Dist: WEA

HIP PRIESTS AND KAMERADS.
Album: released on Situation 2, '85 Dist: Cartel, Pinnacle

Cassette: released on Situation 2, '85 Dist: Cartel, Pinnacle

LIVE AT THE WITCH TRIALS.
Album: released on Step Forward, Jan'79 by Faulty Products Records. Dist: Faulty Products Distribution, Pinnacle

LIVING TOO LATE.
Tracks: / Living too late / Hot after shave bop / Living too long.
Single (12"): released on Beggars Banquet, Jul'86 by Beggars Banquet Records. Dist: WEA

MR. PHARMACIST.
Tracks: / Mr. Pharmacist / Lucifer over Lancashire / Auto tech pilot.
Single (7"): released on Beggars Banquet, Aug'86 by Beggars Banquet Records. Dist: WEA

Single (12"): released on Beggars Banquet, Aug'86 by Beggars Banquet Records. Dist: WEA

OH BROTHER.
Single (7"): released on Beggars Banquet, '84 by Beggars Banquet Records. Dist: WEA

Single (12"): released on Beggars Banquet, '84 by Beggars Banquet Records. Dist: WEA

PEEL SESSION 27.11.78.
Single (7"): released on Strange Fruit, 13 Jun'87 by Clive Selwood. Dist: Pinnacle

PERVETED BY LANGUAGE.
Album: released on Rough Trade, Feb'84 by Rough Trade Records. Dist: Rough Trade Distribution, Cartel Distribution

Cassette: released on Rough Trade, Feb'84 by Rough Trade Records. Dist: Rough Trade Distribution, Cartel Distribution

ROLLIN' DANNY.
Single (7"): released on Beggars Banquet, '85 by Beggars Banquet Records. Dist: WEA

Single (12"): released on Beggars Banquet, '85 by Beggars Banquet Records. Dist: WEA

THERE'S A GHOST IN MY HOUSE.
Tracks: / There's a ghost in my house / Sleep debt / Snatches / Haf found Bormann / Mark'll sink us all.
Single (12"): released on Beggars Banquet, May'87 by Beggars Banquet Records. Dist: WEA

Single (7"): released on Beggars Banquet, Apr'87 by Beggars Banquet Records. Dist: WEA

THIS NATION'S SAVING GRACE.
Album: released on Beggars Banquet, '85 by Beggars Banquet Records. Dist: WEA

Cassette: released on Beggars Banquet, '85 by Beggars Banquet Records. Dist: WEA

TOTAL'S TURNS.
Album: released on Rough Trade, '84 by Rough Trade Records. Dist: Rough Trade Distribution, Cartel Distribution

WONDERFUL AND FRIGHTENING WORLD OF THE FALL,THE.
Album: released on Beggars Banquet, '84 by Beggars Banquet Records. Dist: WEA

Cassette: released on Beggars Banquet, '84 by Beggars Banquet Records. Dist: WEA

Falla Trio
VIRTUOSO MUSIC FOR 3 GUITARS.
Album: released on Concord Jazz(USA), Feb'84 by Concord Jazz Records (USA). Dist: IMS, Polygram

Fallen Angels
AMPHETAMINE BLUES.
Single (7"): released on Fall Out, Feb'84 by Swift, Red Rhino Cartel

FALLEN ANGELS.
Album: released on Fall Out, Feb'84 by Swift, Red Rhino

HEY SUSIE.
Single (7"): released on Jungle, Nov'86 by Jungle Records. Dist: Jungle, Cartel

IN LOVING MEMORY.
Album: released on Jungle, Nov'86 by Jungle Records. Dist: Jungle, Cartel

INNER PLANET LOVE.
Single (7"): released on Fall Out, Jun'84 Dist: Swift, Red Rhino, Cartel

Single (12"): released on Fall Out, Jun'84 Dist: Swift, Red Rhino, Cartel

SIX POINT SIX.
Album: released on Wishbone, Oct'84 by Wishbone Records. Dist: Pinnacle

Fallout
BUTCHERY.
Album: released on I Records, Feb'84 Dist: Backs, Cartel

SALAMI TACTICS.
Single (7"): released on Mouth Too Small To Fight, Jan'83

Fallout Club
WONDERLUST.
Single (7"): released on Happy Birthday, Oct'81 by Stage One

Single (12"): released on Happy Birthday, Oct'81 by Stage One

False Prophets
FALSE PROPHETS.
Album: released on Alternative Tentacles, Jul'86 by Alternative Tentacles Records. Dist: Rough Trade, Pinnacle

Faltermeyer, Harold
AXEL F SHOOTOUT.
Single (7"): released on MCA, Mar'85 by MCA Records. Dist: Polygram, MCA

Single (12"): released on MCA, Mar'85 by MCA Records. Dist: Polygram, MCA

Cassette single: released on MCA, Mar'85 by MCA Records. Dist: Polygram, MCA

'TOP GUN' ANTHEM.
Tracks: / Memories.
Single (7"): released on CBS, Nov'86 by CBS Records. Dist: CBS

Faltskog, Agnetha
CAN'T SHAKE LOOSE.
Single (7"): released on Epic, Oct'83 by Epic Records. Dist: CBS

Picture disc single: released on Epic, Oct'83 by CBS Records. Dist: CBS

EYES OF A WOMAN.
Compact disc: by CBS Records. Dist: CBS

HEAT IS ON.
Single (7"): released on Epic, May'83 by Epic Records. Dist: CBS

Picture disc single: released on Epic, May'83 by CBS Records. Dist: CBS

WAY YOU ARE (THE) (Faltskog, Agnetha & Olga Hakansson).
Tracks: / Way you are (The) / Fly like the eagle.
Single (7"): released on Sonet, Nov'86 by Sonet Records. Dist: PRT

WRAP YOUR ARMS AROUND ME.
Single (7"): released on Epic, Jul'83 by Epic Records. Dist: CBS

Single (12"): released on Epic, Jul'83 by CBS Records. Dist: CBS

Album: released on Epic, Jun'83 by CBS Records. Dist: CBS

Cassette: released on Epic, Jun'83 by CBS Records. Dist: CBS

Compact disc: released on Epic, Jun'83 by CBS Records. Dist: CBS

Fame
FAME Motion picture soundtrack (Various Artists).
Tracks: / Fame / Out here on my own / Hot lunch jam / Dogs in the yard / Red light / Is it okay if I call you mine? / Never alone / Ralph and Monty / I sing the body electric / Fame / Never alone.
Notes: Digital stereo
Compact disc: released on RSO, Nov'84

Album: released on RSO, Nov'84

Cassette: released on RSO, Nov'84

Fame, Georgie
20 BEAT CLASSICS.
Album: released on RSO, Sep'83

Cassette: released on RSO, Sep'83

BALLAD OF BONNIE & CLYDE.
Single (7"): released on Old Gold, Sep'85 by Old Gold Records. Dist: Lightning, Jazz Music, Spartan, Counterpoint

CLOSING THE GAP.
Cassette: released on Piccadilly, Sep'80 by PRT Records. Dist: PRT

FAME GEORGIE/LENA ERICSON/LASSE SAMUELSON (Fame, Georgie, Lena Ericson, Lasse Samuelson).
Album: released on Four Leaf Clover, Jul'86 Dist: Jazz Music, Swift

GEORGIE FAME AND THE BLUE FLAMES (Fame, Georgie & The Blue Flames).
Compact disc: released on Delta, '86 by Delta Records. Dist: Target

GEORGIE FAME WITH ALAN PRICE (Fame, Georgie & Alan Price).
Cassette: released on Pickwick (Ditto series) May'84

IN GOODMAN'S LAND (Fame, Georgie & Sylvia Vrethammar).
Album: released on Sonet, Nov'83 by Sonet Records. Dist: PRT

IN HOAGLAND 81 (Fame, Georgie & Annie Ross).
Album: released on Bald Eagle, Sep'81 Dist: Pinnacle

Live at Montreux
MY FAVOURITE SONGS (Fame, Georgie & The Blue Flames).
Album: released on Teldec (Germany), Feb'84 by Import Records. Dist: IMS Distribution, Polygram Distribution

Cassette: released on Teldec (Germany), Feb'84 by Import Records. Dist: IMS Distribution, Polygram Distribution

RHYTHM AND BLUES AT THE FLAMINGO.
Album: released on RSO, Nov'84

Cassette: released on RSO, Nov'84 Deleted '86.

ROSETTA (Fame, Georgie & Alan Price).
Single (7"): released on CBS, Jul'84 by CBS Records. Dist: CBS

Single (12"): released on Old Gold, Sep'85 by Old Gold Records. Dist: Lightning, Jazz Music, Spartan, Counterpoint

SAMBA.
Tracks: / Samba / Willow King.
Single (7"): released on Ensign, Oct'86 by Ensign Records. Dist: CBS Distribution

Single (12"): released on Ensign, Oct'86 by Ensign Records. Dist: CBS Distribution

THAT'S WHAT FRIENDS ARE FOR.
Cassette: released on PRT, Oct'79 by PRT Records. Dist: PRT

YEH YEH.
Tracks: / Get away.
Single (7"): released on Old Gold, Mar'86 by Old Gold Records. Dist: Lightning, Jazz Music, Spartan, Counterpoint

Fame-Music & Songs From
FAME-MUSIC & SONGS FROM Famous D.dance school choir & orchestra.
Album: released on Music For Pleasure, Nov'83 by EMI Records. Dist: EMI

Cassette: released on Music For Pleasure, Nov'83 by EMI Records. Dist: EMI

Famille, (La)
DANCER.
Single (12"): released on Chequers, Nov'82 Dist: Chequers

LOST IN PARADISE.
Single (7"): released on BPOP, Feb'85

Single (12"): released on BPOP, Feb'85

Family
ANYWAY.
Album: by WEA Records. Dist: WEA

BANDSTAND.
Album: by WEA Records. Dist: WEA

BEST OF....
Album: released on Reprise, Jul'74 by WEA Records. Dist: WEA

BURLESQUE.
Single (7"): released on Rebecca, Jan'82 by Rebecca Records. Dist: Pinnacle

FAMILY ENTERTAINMENT.
Album: by WEA Records. Dist: WEA

Album: released on See For Miles, Sep'87 by See For Miles Records. Dist: Pinnacle. Estim retail price in Sep'87 was £5.67.

Compact disc: released on See For Miles, Aug'87 by See For Miles Records. Dist: Pinnacle. Estim retail price in Sep'87 was £11.89.

FAMILY, THE.
Album: released on Warner Brothers, Aug'85 by Warner Bros Records. Dist: WEA

FEARLESS.
Album: by WEA Records. Dist: WEA

MUSIC IN A DOLL'S HOUSE.
Tracks: / Chase, The / Mellowing grey / Never like this / Me my friend / Variation on a theme of Hey Mr. Policeman / Winter / Old songs new songs / Variation on a theme of the breeze / Hey Mr. Policeman / See through windows / Variations on a theme of me my friend / Peace of mind / Voyage / Breeze, The / 3 X time.
Album: by WEA Records. Dist: WEA

Album: released on See For Miles, Aug'87 by See For Miles Records. Dist: Pinnacle. Estim retail price in Sep'87 was £5.67.

Compact disc: released on See For Miles, Aug'87 by See For Miles Records. Dist: Pinnacle. Estim retail price in Sep'87 was £11.89

OLD SONGS, NEW SONGS.
Album: by WEA Records. Dist: WEA

RISE - VERY BEST OF FAMILY.
Album: released on Rebecca, Nov'81 by Rebecca Records. Dist: Pinnacle

SCREAM OF PASSION, THE.
Single (7"): released on Warner Brothers, Nov'85 by Warner Bros Records. Dist: WEA

Family Brown

I'M GONNA GETCHA.
Single (12"): released on Buzz Int., Apr'84

Family Favourites

FAMILY FAVOURITES Various artists (Various Artists).
Tracks: / Who were you thinking of / Blacksmith, The / Pal of my cradle days / Behind the footlights / Could I have this dance / My Jones / Tears on the telephone / Last cheater's waltz / I wanna hold you in my dreams tonight.
Album: released on Emerald (Ireland), Nov'82 by Emerald Records. Dist: I & B, Ross, PRT

FAMILY FAVOURITES-VOL.II Various artists (Various Artists).
Tracks: / I will love you all my life / Sweet dreams / Baby blue / Birdie song / When I grow too old to dream / You ought to be in pictures / Way old friends do, The / Like strangers / Hey / Tyrolean vagabond / Maggie / It didn't have to be a diamond / My lagan softly flowing / We will make love.
Album: released on Emerald (Ireland), Dec'83 by Emerald Records. Dist: I & B, Ross, PRT

Cassette: released on Emerald (Ireland), Dec'83 by Emerald Records. Dist: I & B, Ross, PRT

Family Fodder

ALL STYLES.
Album: released on Jungle, Jun'83 by Jungle Records. Dist: Jungle, Cartel

BIG DIG.
Single (7"): released on Fresh, May'82 Dist: Jetstar

COAL.
Single (7"): released on Jungle, Nov'82 by Jungle Records. Dist: Jungle, Cartel

DEBBIE HARRY.
Single (7"): released on Fresh, Apr'81 Dist: Jetstar

GREATEST HITS:FAMILY FODDER.
Album: released on Crammed UK, Sep'84 Dist: Rough Trade, Nine Mile, Cartel

MONKEY BANANA KITCHEN.
Album: released on Fresh, Apr'81 Dist: Jetstar

PLAYING GOLF.
Single (7"): released on Fresh, Apr'81 Dist: Jetstar

SAVOIR-FAIRE.
Single (7"): released on Crammed, May'83 Dist: Rough Trade, Nine Mile, Cartel

Single (7"): released on Fresh, Apr'81 Dist: Jetstar

SCHIZOPHRENIA PARTY.
Single (12"): released on Fresh, Sep'81 Dist: Jetstar

SUNDAY GIRLS.
Single (12"): released on Fresh, Apr'81 Dist: Jetstar

WARM.
Single (7"): released on Fresh, Apr'81 Dist: Jetstar

Family love

DECISION.
Single (12"): released on Inner City, Feb'82 Dist: Jetstar

HOOKED ON YOU.
Single (12"): released on Firehouse, Jun'83 Dist: Jetstar

RELUCTANT LOVER.
Single (12"): released on Rock'n'Groove, Apr'85 by Rock'n'Groove Records. Dist: Jetstar Distribution

STAY WITH ME.
Single (12"): released on Firehouse, Nov'82 Dist: Jetstar

TEAZER.
Single (12"): released on Firehouse, Mar'84 Dist: Jetstar

Family Ness

FAMILY NESS: ELSPETH & ANGUS BUY A PUPPY.
Cassette: released on Tempo, Aug'84 by Warwick Records. Dist: Multiple Sound Distributors

FAMILY NESS: ELSPETH & ANGUS MEET THE NESSIES.
Special: released on Tempo, Aug'84 by Warwick Records. Dist: Multiple Sound Distributors

FAMILY NESS: ELSPETH & ANGUS MEET THE PROFESSOR.
Special: released on Tempo, Aug'84 by Warwick Records. Dist: Multiple Sound Distributors

FAMILY NESS, (THE) Various Artists (Various Artists).
Album: released on BBC, Oct'84 by BBC Records & Tapes. Dist: EMI, PRT, Pye

Cassette: released on BBC, Oct'84 by BBC Records & Tapes. Dist: EMI, PRT, Pye

FAMILY NESS: THE NESSIES HELP WITH HOMEWORK.
Cassette: released on Tempo, Aug'84 by Warwick Records. Dist: Multiple Sound Distributors

YOU'LL NEVER FIND A NESSIE IN THE ZOO.
Single (7"): released on BBC, Oct'84 by BBC Records & Tapes. Dist: EMI, PRT, Pye

Family requests

FAMILY REQUESTS Various Artists (Various Artists).

Album: released on Homespun(Ireland), Dec'83 by Outlet Records. Dist: Outlet

Cassette: released on Homespun(Ireland), Dec'83 by Outlet Records. Dist: Outlet

Family Reunion

AULD LANG SYNE.
Single (7"): released on Romantic, Dec'82 Dist: MCA Distribution

Famous...

FAMOUS FAIRY TALES (Reid, Beryl).
Cassette: released on Pinnacle, '79 by Pinnacle Records. Dist: Pinnacle

FAMOUS FIVE Various Artists (Various Artists).
Album: released on Warwick (Super Tempo), Sep'83

FAMOUS GUITARS - ACOUSTIC COLOURS Various Artists (Various Artists).
Album:

Cassette:

FAMOUS LEGENDS BOOK 2 Various Artists (Various Artists).
Special: released on Tell-a-tale (Cassettes), Oct'84

FAMOUS OVERTURES Various Artists (Various Artists).
Double cassette: released on Pickwick (Ditto series), Jul'82

FAMOUS THEMES: REMEMBER THESE? Various artists (Various Artists).
Tracks: / Portrait of a flirt/Will o'the wisp/Jumping bean / Journey into melody / Sapphires and sables / Invitation waltz (Ring round the moon) / By the sleepy lagoon (Desert island discs) / Puffin' Billy (Children's favourites) / Coronation Scot (Paul Temple) / Rhythm on rails (Morning music) / Music everywhere (Rediffusion's call sign) / Gorse guards, Whitehall (Down your way) / Devil's galop (Dick Barton Special Agent) / Destruction by fire (Pathe news) / On a spring note (Pathe Gazzette) / All sports march (Pathe News) / Cavalcade of youth (Barlows of Beddington) / Drum majorette (Ertswhile match of the day) / Girls in grey (BBC TV News) / Elizebethan serenade (Music in miniature) / Melody on the move / Alpine pastures (my word) / Young ballerina (Potters wheel interlude) / Horse feathers (Meet the Huggets).
Notes: A unique nostalgic selection of radio, TV and newsreel themes from the late 1940's and early '50's. Over 64 minutes of music which will ring a bell with all who"listened in" during that exciting post-war era.
Album: released on Grasmere, May'86 by Grasmere Records. Dist: EMI

Cassette: released on Grasmere, '86 by Grasmere Records. Dist: EMI

Famous Imposter

WOULD ANYTHING CHANGE.
Single (12"): released on Children Of The Revolution, Jul'86 by Revolver Records. Dist: Revolver, Cartel

Famous Potatoes

I LIKE CHICKEN PIE.
Single (7"): released on Waterfront, Aug'84 by Waterfront Records. Dist: Rough Trade, Cartel, Projection, Roots

IT WAS GOOD FOR MY OLD MA.
Cassette: released on Waterfront, Jun'86 by Waterfront Records. Dist: Rough Trade, Cartel, Projection, Roots

Album: released on Waterfront, Sep'85 by Waterfront Records. Dist: Rough Trade, Cartel, Projection, Roots

SOUND OF THE GROUND, THE.
Album: released on Waterfront, Sep'86 by Waterfront Records. Dist: Rough Trade, Cartel, Projection, Roots

Cassette: released on Waterfront, Sep'86 by Waterfront Records. Dist: Rough Trade, Cartel, Projection, Roots

Famous Themes

MORE FAMOUS THEMES (Various Artists).
Tracks: / Voice of London / Calling all workers / Champagne March / Out of tune march / Miss World / Skippy / Westminster waltz / Star is born, A / Holiday spirit / High adventure / Quiet stroll, A / Looking around / Country canter / Moomin / Shooting star / Muse in Mayfair / Old clockmaker, The / Melody fair / Sporting occasion.
Album: released on Grasmere, Jun'87 by Grasmere Records. Dist: EMI

Cassette: released on Grasmere, Jun'87 by Grasmere Records. Dist: EMI

Fanchette, Sterge

RUSSIAN SONGS AND ROMANCES.
Album: released on Vox Mundi (France), Feb'85 Dist: Discovery

Cassette: released on Vox Mundi (France), Feb'85 Dist: Discovery

Fancy

CHINESE EYES.
Single (7"): released on Personal, Jun'85 by Personal Records. Dist: PRT

Single (12"): released on Personal, Jun'85 by Personal Records. Dist: PRT

FANCIES & GOODNIGHTS Collier, J. (Price, Vincent).
Cassette: released on Caedmon(USA), '81 by Caedmon (USA) Records. Dist: Gower, Taylors, Discovery

SLICE ME NICE.
Single (7"): released on Greyhound, Apr'87 by Greyhound Records. Dist: PRT, Greyhound

Fane, Little Billy

GEORDIE'S HEAR.
Album: released on MWM, Dec'85 by Mawson & Wareham. Dist: Spartan Distribution, Jazz Music Distribution, JSU Distribution

Fanhauser, Merrell

FAPARDOKLY.
Album: released on O.B.G., Dec'86 Dist: Pinnacle

MESSAGE TO THE UNIVERSE.
Album: released on O.B.G., Dec'86 Dist: Pinnacle

Fania Allstars

LIVE.

Album: released on Salsa, Jan'82

Fanny & Danny

SECOND HAND RAG.
Single (7"): released on Aggro, Jul'81 by Chantel Records.

Fans

COME ON THE FOREST.
Single (7"): released on Soccer, Jan'80 Dist: Gamut

GIVING ME THAT LOOK.
Single (7"): released on Fried Egg, Jul'81 by Fried Egg Records. Dist: Rough Trade, Cartel

I'M A FAN NOT A MORON.
Tracks: / Net fever.
Single (7"): released on Persuasion, Jan'86 Dist: MIS-EMI Distribution

TRUE.
Single (7"): released on Albion, Jan'81 by Albion Records. Dist: Spartan, Pinnacle

YOU DON'T LIVE HERE.
Single (7"): released on Fried Egg, Jul'81 by Fried Egg Records. Dist: Rough Trade, Cartel

Fanshawe, David

AFRICAN SANCTUS.
Album: released on Philips, Jul'77 Dist: IMS-Polygram

Fantasia

EVERGREEN.
Single (12"): released on Passion, Jan'84 by Skratch Records. Dist: PRT

FANTASIA Original soundtrack (Philadelphia Orchestra/Leopold Stokowski).
Double Album: released on Disneyland, Aug'82 by Disneyland-Vista Records (USA). Dist: BBC Records & Tapes, Rainbow Communications Ltd(Distribution)

Double cassette: released on Disneyland, Aug'82 by Disneyland-Vista Records (USA). Dist: BBC Records & Tapes, Rainbow Communications Ltd(Distribution)

Double Album: released on Disney, Oct'84 by BBC Records & Tapes. Dist: BBC Records & Tapes, PRT

Double cassette: released on Disney, Oct'84 by BBC Records & Tapes. Dist: BBC Records & Tapes, PRT

Fantasist, The

FANTASIST Original Film Soundtrack (Various Artists).
Tracks: / More passionate than we are / Up on the roof / Another day come another day goes / Living in a world upside down / I'll do it all again / Fantasist, The / Fantasist, The / Temple of Venus / Childhood story / Clocks / Rooftops / Discovery.
Album: released on President, Apr'87 by President Records. Dist: Taylors, Spartan

Fantastic Baggys

SURFIN' CRAZE.
Album: released on Edsel, May'83 by Demon Records. Dist: Pinnacle, Jazz Music, Projection

Fantasticks

FANTASTICKS Original Cast (Various Artists).
Album: released on TER, Apr'85 Dist: Pinnacle

Cassette: released on TER, Apr'85 Dist: Pinnacle

Fantastic Mr.Fox

FANTASTIC MR. FOX Dahl, Roald (Jeffries, Lionel).
Cassette: released on Cover to Cover, Jun'85 by Cover to Cover Cassettes. Dist: Conifer

FANTASTIC MR. FOX (Dahl, Roald).
Album: released on Caedmon(USA), '79 by Caedmon (USA) Records. Dist: Gower, Taylors, Discovery

ROALD DAHL.
Notes: For full information see under "Dahl, Roald"

Fantastics

SOMETHING OLD SOMETHING NEW.
Single (7"): released on Stagecoach, Jun'81

Single (7"): released on Creole, Aug'82 by Creole Records. Dist: Rhino, PRT

Fantastic Something

FANTASTIC SOMETHING.

Page 352

Album: released on Blanco Y Negro, Jun'85 by WEA Records. Dist: WEA

Cassette: released on Blanco Y Negro, Jun'85 by WEA Records. Dist: WEA Deleted '86.

IF SHE DOESN'T SMILE (it'll rain).
Single (7"): released on Cherry Red, May'83 by Cherry Red Records. Dist: Pinnacle

Fantastique
MAMA TOLD ME.
Single (12"): released on Carrere, Jun'84 by Carrere Records. Dist: PRT, Spartan

Fantasy
I WANT WHAT I WANT.
Single (12"): released on Affair, Sep'86 Dist: DMS, RCA

Fantasy 10
BIG BANG, THE.
Single (7"): released on Greyhound, Jun'87 by Greyhound Records. Dist: PRT, Greyhound

Fantasy Of The Seventies
FANTASY OF THE SEVENTIES - VOLUME 1 (Various Artists).
Album: released on Band Of Gold, Jan'87 by Stylus Records. Dist: Stylus

Cassette: released on Band Of Gold, Jan'87 by Stylus Records. Dist: Stylus

Fantasy Strings
FANTASY STRINGS.
Compact disc: released on Delta, Apr'87 by Delta Records. Dist: Targe

IN LOVE.
Compact disc: released on Delta, Apr'87 by Delta Records. Dist: Target

Fantoms
HEARTS OF STONE.
Single (7"): released on Ear To Ear, Apr'83 by Oakwood Records. Dist: Pinnacle

Faraway stars
DISHONEST.
Single (7"): released on Runaway, May'83

UNDER THE SUN.
Album: released on Runaway, '82

Farber, Mitch
STARCLIMBER.
Album: released on Muse, May'83 by Peerless Records.

Far Canadian Fields
FAR CANADIAN FIELDS Various artists (Various Artists).
Album: released on Leader, Jun'86 Dist: Jazz Music, Projection

Far Corporation
DIVISION ONE.
Tracks: / Stairway to heaven / You are the woman / One of your lovers / Live inside your dreams / Johnny don't go the distance / Fire and water / If you could see you through my eyes / Rock'n'roll connection.
Compact disc: released on Arista, Jan'86 by Arista Records. Dist: RCA

Album: released on Arista, Dec'85 by Arista Records. Dist: RCA

Cassette: released on Arista, Dec'85 by Arista Records. Dist: RCA

FIRE AND WATER.
Tracks: / Life on the inside.
Single (7"): released on Arista, May'86 by Arista Records. Dist: RCA

Single (12"): released on Arista, May'86 by Arista Records. Dist: RCA

SEBASTAIN.
Single (7"): released on Arista, Aug'87 by Arista Records. Dist: RCA

Single (12"): released on Arista, Aug'87 by Arista Records. Dist: RCA

STAIRWAY TO HEAVEN.
Single (7"): released on Arista, Oct'85 by Arista Records. Dist: RCA

Single (12"): released on Arista, Oct'85 by Arista Records. Dist: RCA

YOU ARE THE WOMAN.
Tracks: / No one else will do.
Single (7"): released on Arista, Feb'86 by Arista Records. Dist: RCA

Single (12"): released on Arista, Feb'86 by

Arista Records. Dist: RCA

Fardon, Don
INDIAN RESERVATION.
Single (7"): released on Old Gold, Jul'82 by Old Gold Records. Dist: Lightning, Jazz Music, Spartan, Counterpoint

Single (7"): released on Young Blood, Aug'84 by Young Blood Records. Dist: Pinnacle

Fardon, Lee
BEAT SINCERE.
Tracks: / Straight to the heart.
Single (7"): released on Chord, May'86 by Chord Records. Dist: Charly

GAMES PEOPLE PLAY.
Album: released on Chord, Oct'86 by Chord Records. Dist: Charly

GAMES PEOPLE PLAY (SINGLE 7").
Tracks: / Treason in the heart.
Single (7"): released on Chord, Dec'86 by Chord Records. Dist: Charly

GOD GIVEN RIGHT, (THE).
Album: released on Aura, May'82 by Hollywood Nites Distribution. Dist: Pinnacle

SAVAGE ART OF LOVE.
Tracks: / Thousand shoes, A / Straight to the heart / Magical dance / No wonder / Anger and the rest (36 rooms) / Treason in the heart / Maria and the writer / Bear me away / Beat sincere, The / Thousand shoes, A / Jugband blues.
Compact disc: released on Chord, Dec'86 by Chord Records. Dist: Charly

STORIES OF ADVENTURE.
Album: released on Aura, Jun'81 by Hollywood Nites Distribution. Dist: Pinnacle

Single (7"): released on Aura, Aug'81 by Hollywood Nites Distribution. Dist: Pinnacle

TOGETHER IN THE HEAT.
Single (7"): released on Aura, Jun'82 by Hollywood Nites Distribution. Dist: Pinnacle

Far east
FAR EAST, (THE), VOLUME 1 Various Artists (Various Artists).
Album: released on Lyrichord (USA), Oct'81 by Lyrichord Records (USA). Dist: Flexitron Distributors Ltd

Farenholtz, Peter
RAGTIME SOLO.
Album: released on Wam, May'87

Farewell...
FAREWELL NANCY Various Artists (Various Artists).
Album: released on Topic, '81 Dist: Roots Distribution

FAREWELL TO MAX'S Various Artists (Various Artists).
Album: released on Max's Kansas City, May'85 by President Records. Dist: President Distribution, Jazz Music, Taylors, Spartan

Far From The Madding Crowd
FAR FROM THE MADDING CROWD Hardy, Thomas (Thorne, Stephen).
Cassette: released on Cover to Cover, Jun'85 by Cover to Cover Cassettes. Dist: Conifer

Fargo, Donna
QUEENS OF COUNTRY (Fargo, Donna/Dolly Parton).
Album: released on Sundown, Jul'83 by Magnum Music Group Ltd. Dist: Magnum Music Group Ltd, PRT Distribution, Spartan Distribution

Cassette: released on Sundown, Jul'83 by Magnum Music Group Ltd. Dist: Magnum Music Group Ltd, PRT Distribution, Spartan Distribution

Fargo, Wells
WHO'S BUYING.
Album: released on Tank, Jun'79 by Tank Records.

Farina, Mimi
SOLO.
Compact disc: released on Philo (USA), Dec'86

Album: released on Philo, Jul'86 Dist: Roots

Farley 'Jackmaster' Funk
LOVE CAN'T TURN AROUND.
Tracks: / Dub can't turn around.
Single (7"): released on London, Jul'86 by London Records. Dist: Polygram

Single (12"): released on London, Jul'86 by

London Records. Dist: Polygram

Farlow
ON STAGE (Farlow/Norvo/Jones/Brown/Hanna).
Album: released on Concord, Mar'81 by Import Records. Dist: IMS, Polygram

Farlowe, Chris
BORN AGAIN (Farlowe, Chris & The Thunderbirds).
Album: released on Brand New, Oct'86 by Brand New Records. Dist: Ace Records, Chiswick Records, Pinnacle

Cassette: released on Brand New, Oct'86 by Brand New Records. Dist: Ace Records, Chiswick Records, Pinnacle

BUZZ WITH FUZZ (Farlowe, Chris & The Thunderbirds).
Album: released on Decal, Aug'87 by Charly Records. Dist: Charly. Estim retail price in Sep'87 was £5.99.

CHRIS FARLOWE & THE THUNDERBIRDS (Farlowe, Chris & The Thunderbirds).
Album: released on Charly, Nov'77 by Charly Records. Dist: Charly, Cadillac

GREATEST HITS:CHRIS FARLOWE.
Album: released on Immediate, Jan'78 by Castle Communications. Dist: Cartel

LET THE HEARTACHES BEGIN.
Single (7"): released on CBS, Oct'82 by CBS Records. Dist: CBS

LIVING AIN'T EASY WITHOUT YOU.
Single (7"): released on Taurus, Oct'83 Dist: Jetstar

MR.SOULFUL.
Tracks: / Think / It was easier to hurt her / Fool, The / I'm free / Handbags and gladrags / In the midnight hour / I've been lovin' you too long / Reach out I'll be there / Mr.Pitiful / Pint it black.
Album: released on Showcase, Sep'86 Dist: Counterpoint

Cassette: released on Showcase, Sep'86 Dist: Counterpoint

OUT OF THE BLUE.
Album: released on Thunderbolt, Jan'86 by Magnum Music Group Ltd. Dist: Magnum Music Group Ltd, PRT Distribution, Spartan Distribution

OUT OF THE BLUE (Farlowe, Chris & The Thunderbirds).
Album: released on Polydor (Germany), Jul'85 Dist: IMS-Polygram

OUT OF TIME.
Single (7"): released on Virgin, Jun'80 by Virgin Records. Dist: EMI, Virgin Distribution
       Cat. no: SV 102
Single (7"): released on Castle Communications, Oct'82 by Castle Communications. Dist: Cartel
       Cat. no: IMS 201
Single (7"): released on Old Gold, Jan'85 by Old Gold Records. Dist: Lightning, Jazz Music, Spartan, Counterpoint

OUT OF TIME.
Album: released on Immediate, Dec'75 by Castle Communications. Dist: Cartel

OUT OF TIME - PAINT IT BLACK.
Album: released on Charly, Aug'78 by Charly Records. Dist: Charly, Cadillac

Farlow, Tal
AUTUMN IN NEW YORK.
   Notes: Tal Farlow - guitar
  Jerry Wiggins - piano
  Ray   Brown - bass
Chico Hamilton - drums
Album: released on Verve (USA), May'83 by Polydor. Dist: Polygram

CHROMATIC PALETTE.
Album: released on Concord, Aug'81 by Import Records. Dist: IMS, Polygram
       Cat. no: CJ 154
COOKIN ON ALL BURNERS.
   Notes: Tal Farlow - guitar
James Williams - piano
Gary Mazzaropi - bass
Vinnie Johnson - drums
Album: released on Concord Jazz(USA), Mar'83 by Concord Jazz Records (USA). Dist: IMS, Polygram

LEGENDARY, (THE).
   Notes: Tal Farlow - guitar
Sam Most - flute, tenor saxophone
Frank Strazzeri - piano
Bob   Maize - bass
Al 'Tootle' Heath - drums
Album: released on Concord Jazz(USA), Apr'86 by Concord Jazz Records (USA). Dist: IMS, Polygram

SWINGING GUITAR OF TAL FARLOW, (THE).
   Notes: Tal Farlow - guitar

Eddie Costa - piano
Vinnie Burke - bass
Album: released on Verve (USA), Aug'82 by Polydor. Dist: Polygram

Farm
HEARTS AND MINDS.
Single (12"): released on Skysaw, Nov'84 by Skysaw Records. Dist: Red Rhino, Cartel

PASTURES OLD AND NEW.
Album: released on Fire, Sep'86 by Twist and Shout Music. Dist: Nine Mile, Rough Trade, Cartel

SOME PEOPLE.
Tracks: / Standing together / Sign of the times / Moroccan.
Single (7"): released on Blaze, Sep'86 by Blaze Records. Dist: Nine Mile, Cartel

Single (12"): released on Blaze, Sep'86 by Blaze Records. Dist: Nine Mile, Cartel

STEPS OF EMOTION.
Single (7"): released on Admiralty, Nov'85 by Probe Records. Dist: Cartel

Single (12"): released on Admiralty, Nov'85 by Probe Records. Dist: Cartel

Farm Blues Bossmen
FARM BLUES BOSSMEN & BOLL WEEVILS.
Album: released on Arhoolie, May'81 by Arhoolie Records. Dist: Projection, Topic, Jazz Music, Swift, Roots

Farmer, Art
ART FARMER QUINTET (Farmer, Art Quintet).
Album: released on Original Jazz Classics (USA), Jan'87 Dist: Fantasy (USA) Distribution, Chris Wellard Distribution, IMS-Polygram Distribution

ART SEPTET FARMER (Farmer, Art Septet).
Album: released on Original Jazz Classics (USA), Jun'86 Dist: Fantasy (USA) Distribution, Chris Wellard Distribution, IMS-Polygram Distribution

ARTWORKER.
   Notes: Art Farmer - trumpet
Ernie Royal - trumpet
Jimmy Cleveland - trombone
Oscar Estelle - 'alt;ten;bar'
Harold Mabern - piano
Jimmy Woode - bass
Roy McCurdy - drums
Album: released on Lotus, Apr'81 Dist: Counterpoint

CRAWL SPACE.
Album: released on CTI (Musidisc France), Feb'84 by Polydor Records. Dist: IMS, Polygram

INTERACTION (Farmer, Art Quartet).
Album: released on Atlantic, Nov'80 by WEA Records. Dist: WEA

MANHATTAN (Farmer, Art Quintet).
Notes: With Sahib Shihab, Kenny Drew, Mads Vinding, Ed Thigpen.
Compact disc: released on Soul Note (Italy), '86 Dist: Harmonia Mundi Distributors

Album: released on Soul Note, Jul'82 Dist: Harmonia Mundi Distributors

MIRAGE (Farmer, Art Quintet).
Notes: With Clifford Jordan.
Compact disc: released on Soul Note (Italy), '86 Dist: Harmonia Mundi Distributors

ON THE ROAD.
Album: released on Contemporary (Boplicity), Oct'85 Dist: Pinnacle

PORTRAIT OF.
Tracks: / Back in the cage / Stable mates / Very thought of you / And now..... / Nita / By myself / Too late noe / Earth.
Album: released on Contemporary, Aug'86 by Contemporary Records. Dist: Pinnacle

PORTRAIT OF ART FARMER.
Album: released on Contemporary, Mar'79 by Contemporary Records. Dist: Pinnacle

SING ME SOFTLY OF THE BLUES (Farmer, Art Quartet).
Album: released on Atlantic, Aug'80 by WEA Records. Dist: WEA

SLEEPING BEE, (THE).
Album: released on Sonet, '76 by Sonet Records. Dist: PRT

SOMETHING YOU GOT.
Album: released on CTI (Musidisc France), Feb'84 by Polydor Records. Dist: IMS, Polygram

TWO TRUMPETS (Farmer, Art & Donald

Byrd).
Album: released on Original Jazz Classics (USA), Jan'86 Dist: Fantasy (USA) Distribution, Chris Wellard Distribution, IMS-Polygram Distribution

WARM VALLEY.
Album: released on Concord Jazz, May'83 by Concord Jazz Records (USA). Dist: IMS, Polygram

Cassette: released on Concord Jazz, May'83 by Concord Jazz Records (USA). Dist: IMS, Polygram

WHEN FARMER MET GRYCE (Farmer, Art/Gigi Gryce).
Album: released on Prestige (USA), Feb'84

WORK OF ART, (A).
Album: released on Concord, Apr'82 by Import Records. Dist: IMS, Polygram

YAMA (Farmer, Art/Joe Henderson).
Album: released on CTI (Musidisc France), Feb'84 by Polydor Records. Dist: IMS, Polygram

YOU MAKE ME SMILE (Farmer, Art Quintet).
Notes: With Clifford Jordan.
Compact disc: released on Soul Note (Italy), '86 Dist: Harmonia Mundi Distributors

Farmers Boys
IN THE COUNTRY.
Special: released on EMI, Aug'84 by EMI Records. Dist: EMI

Single (12"): released on EMI, Aug'84 by EMI Records. Dist: EMI

I THINK WE NEED HELP.
Single (7"): released on Waap, Apr'82 by Waap Records. Dist: Cartel

MORE THAN A DREAM.
Single (7"): released on EMI, Jan'83 by EMI Records. Dist: EMI

MUCK IT OUT (Demo).
Double-pack single: released on EMI, Jul'83 by EMI Records. Dist: EMI

MUCK IT OUT.
Picture disc single: released on EMI, Jun'83 by EMI Records. Dist: EMI

PHEW WOW.
Single (7"): released on EMI, Oct'84 by EMI Records. Dist: EMI

Single (12"): released on EMI, Oct'84 by EMI Records. Dist: EMI Deleted '86.

WHATEVER IS HE LIKE.
Single (7"): released on Backs, Jul'82 by Backs Records. Dist: Backs, Cartel

WITH THESE HANDS.
Album: released on EMI, Mar'85 by EMI Records. Dist: EMI

Cassette: released on EMI, Mar'85 by EMI Records. Dist: EMI

Farm Life
SUSIE'S PARTY.
Single (7"): released on Dining Out, Feb'82 by Dining Out Records. Dist: IKF, Independent

Farmstead
SHEEP AND THE HAY, (THE).
Album: released on Fellside, '83 by Fellside Records. Dist: Roots, Jazz Music, Celtic Music, Projection

Farnham, John
PRESSURE DOWN.
Tracks: / Let me out.
Single (7"): released on Wheatley, Aug'87 by RCA Records. Dist: BMG

Single (12"): released on Wheatley, Aug'87 by RCA Records. Dist: BMG

WHISPERING JACK.
Tracks: / Pressure down / You're the voice / One step away / Reasons / Going, going, gone / No one comes close / Love to shine / Trouble / Touch of paradise / Let me out.
Album: released on RCA, Jan'87 by RCA Records. Dist: RCA, Roots, Swift, Wellard, Chris, I & B, Solomon & Peres Distribution

Cassette: released on RCA, Jan'87 by RCA Records. Dist: RCA, Roots, Swift, Wellard, Chris, I & B, Solomon & Peres Distribution

Compact disc: released on RCA, Jan'87 by RCA Records. Dist: RCA, Roots, Swift, Wellard, Chris, I & B, Solomon & Peres Distribution

YOU'RE THE VOICE.
Tracks: / You're the voice / Going going gone / Help (live version) / Reasons'
Single (7"): released on RCA, Feb'87 by RCA

Page 354

Records. Dist: RCA, Roots, Swift, Wellard, Chris, I & B, Solomon & Peres Distribution

Single (12"): released on RCA, Feb'87 by RCA Records. Dist: RCA, Roots, Swift, Wellard, Chris, I & B, Solomon & Peres Distribution

Cassette single: released on RCA, Jun'87 by RCA Records. Dist: RCA, Roots, Swift, Wellard, Chris, I & B, Solomon & Peres Distribution

Farnon, Robert
ROBERT FARNON AND L.S.O..
Album: released on Citadel, Dec'79 Dist: Swift

ROBERT FARNON & LONDON PHILHARMONIC ORCHESTRA.
Tracks: / Colditz march / My fair lady medley / Laura / Porgy & Bess suite / Farnon Fantasy.
Notes: Robert Farnon at the Royal Festival Hall.
Compact disc: released on Nouveau Music, '86 Dist: PRT Distribution

Far pavillions
FAR PAVILLIONS TV soundtrack (Various Artists).
Album: released on Chrysalis, Jan'84 by Chrysalis Records. Dist: CBS

Cassette: released on Chrysalis, Jan'84 by Chrysalis Records. Dist: CBS

Farrell, Bobby
HAPPY SONG (Farrell, Bobby/The School Rebels).
Single (7"): released on Carrere, Jan'85 by Carrere Records. Dist: PRT, Spartan

Single (12"): released on Carrere, Jan'85 by Carrere Records. Dist: PRT, Spartan

Farrell, John
RIDING ON AN ANGELS WING.
Single (7"): released on Press colour. Dec'83

Farren, Mick
MONA.
Album: released on Psycho (USA), Mar'84

Farr, Gary
DEM BONES.
Album: released on EVA, Jun'84

LONDON 1964-1965 (Farr, Gary & The T-Bones).
Album: released on Charly, Jan'77 by Charly Records. Dist: Charly, Cadillac

ONE MORE CHANCE (Farr, Gary & The T-Bones).
Tracks: / I'm a lover not a fighter / Won't you give him one more chance / Bony maronie / In deed I do / Louisiana red / You don't love me / Quit teasing me baby / Oh baby baby / Feel alright / C.C. rider / Dearest darling / How many more times / Hamish's express relief / Give all she's got / Don't stop & stare / Jump back / Got love if you want it.
Notes: licensed from charly International APS. (P) 1987 Charly Holdings Ltd. (C) 1987 Charly Records Ltd.
Album: released on Decal, May'87 by Charly Records. Dist: Charly

Album: released on Decal, Aug'87 by Charly Records. Dist: Charly

Farriers
BRUMMAGEM BALLADS (Farriers/Kempion).
Cassette: released on Broadside, Jan'81 by Broadside Records. Dist: Celtic Distributions, H.R. Taylor, Jazz Music, Projection, Jazz Services Unlimited Dist. (JSU)

Cassette: released on Broadside, Jan'81 by Broadside Records. Dist: Celtic Distributions, H.R. Taylor, Jazz Music, Projection,

Farrow, Gene
MOVE YOUR BODY.
Cassette: released on Magnet, Dec'78 by Magnet Records. Dist: BMG

MOVE YOUR BODY.
Single (7"): released on Magnet, Jan'78 by Magnet Records. Dist: BMG

UNIQUE MYSTIQUE.
Single (7"): released on Rialto, Jan'82 by Rialto Records. Dist: Pinnacle

Single (12"): released on Rialto, Nov'81 by Rialto Records. Dist: Pinnacle

Farr, Richard
FARR COUNTRY.
Album: released on Igus, Apr'81 by Klub. Dist: PRT, Musac Distribution Ltd (Scotland)

Cassette: released on Igus, Apr'81 by Klub.

Dist: PRT, Musac Distribution Ltd (Scotland)

Farthest shore
FARTHEST SHORE Le Guin, Ursula (Hood, Morag).
Cassette: released on Colophone, Nov'81 by Audio-Visual Library Services. Dist: Audio-Visual Library Services

Fascinating Alda
BUNCH OF OLD SEQUINS, A.
Album: released on First Night, Aug'87 by Safari Records. Dist: Pinnacle. Estim retail price in Sep'87 was £6.29.

Cassette: released on First Night, Aug'87 by Safari Records. Dist: Pinnacle. Estim retail price in Sep'87 was £6.29.

GET KNOTTED.
Single (7"): released on BBC, Jan'85 by BBC Records & Tapes. Dist: EMI, PRT,

SWEET F.A.
Album: released on BBC, Sep'85 by BBC Records & Tapes. Dist: EMI, PRT,

Compact disc: released on BBC, Sep'85 by BBC Records & Tapes. Dist: EMI, PRT.

Fascination
OUT TO GET YOU.
Single (7"): released on Banana, Mar'84 Dist: Pinnacle, Fresh

Single (12"): released on Banana, Mar'84 Dist: Pinnacle, Fresh

SHINE MY LOVE.
Single (7"): released on Banana, Dec'84 Dist: Pinnacle, Fresh

Fashanu, Justin
DO IT COS' YOU LIKE IT.
Single (7"): released on Rondelet, Dec'81 by Spartan Distribution

Single (12"): released on Rondelet, Dec'81 Dist: Spartan Distribution

Fashion
DREAMING.
Single (7"): released on Epic, Apr'84 by CBS Records. Dist: CBS

Single (12"): released on Epic, Apr'84 by CBS Records. Dist: CBS

FABRIQUE.
Album: released on Arista, Jun'82 by Arista Records. Dist: RCA

Cassette: released on Arista, Jun'82 by Arista Records. Dist: RCA

I TALK.
Single (7"): released on Epic, Jan'84 by CBS Records. Dist: CBS

Single (12"): released on Epic, Jan'84 by CBS Records. Dist: CBS

PRODUCT PERFECT.
Album: released on Fashion, Jan'79 by Fashion Records. Dist: PRT, Jetstar

YOU IN THE NIGHT.
Single (7"): released on De Stijl, Jun'84 by Epic Records. Dist: CBS

Cassette: released on De Stijl, Jun'84 by Epic Records. Dist: CBS

Single (7"): released on Epic, Jun'84 by Epic Records. Dist: CBS

Fashion, Chris
EETEE WE LOVE YOU.
Single (7"): released on State, Dec'82 by State Records.

Fasoli, Claudio
LIDO.
Album: released on Soul Note, Nov'83 Dist: Harmonia Mundi Distributors

Fastaway
ALL FIRED UP.
Single (7"): released on CBS, Jun'84 by CBS Records. Dist: CBS

Single (12"): released on CBS, Jun'84 by CBS Records. Dist: CBS

Faster Pussycat
FASTER PUSSYCAT.
Tracks: / Don't change that song / Bathroom wall / No room for emotion / Cathouse / Babylon on and on / Smash alley / Shooting you down / City has no heart / Ship rolls in / Bottle in front of me.

Album: released on Elektra (USA), Jul'87 by Elektra/Asylum/Nonesuch Records. Dist: WEA

Cassette: released on Elektra (USA), Jul'87 by Elektra/Asylum/Nonesuch Records. Dist: WEA

Fast Forward
FAST FORWARD Original soundtrack.
Album: released on Warner Bros., Jun'85 by Warner Bros Records. Dist: WEA

Fast Product
FAST PRODUCT - THE FIRST YEAR Various artists (Various Artists).
Album: released on EMI, Apr'82 by EMI Records. Dist: EMI

Cassette: released on EMI, Apr'82 by EMI Records. Dist: EMI

Fast Radio
UNDER MY THUMB.
Single (7"): released on Excaliber, Apr'83 by Red Bus Records. Dist: PRT

Fastway
EASY LIVIN.
Single (7"): released on CBS, Mar'83 by CBS Records. Dist: CBS

Single (12"): released on CBS, Mar'83 by CBS Records. Dist: CBS

FAST FORWARD TO HELL Various artists
Notes: Compilation featuring the best of british thrash metal/artists include:Deliverance,Deathwish,Virus).
Album: released on Metalworks, Jun'87

Cassette: released on Metalworks, Jun'87

STRANGER, THE.
Single (7"): released on CBS, May'84 by CBS Records. Dist: CBS

TRICK OR TREAT.
Tracks: / Trick or treat / After midnight / Don't stop the fight / Stand up / Tear down the wall / Get tough / Hold on to the night / Heft / If you could see.
Album: released on CBS, Mar'87 by CBS Records. Dist: CBS

Cassette: released on CBS, Mar'87 by CBS Records. Dist: CBS

Records. Dist: CBS

Compact disc: released on CBS, May'87 by CBS Records. Dist: CBS

WAITING FOR THE ROAR.
Compact disc: released on CBS, May'87 by CBS Records. Dist: CBS

WE BECOME ONE.
Single (7"): released on CBS, Jun'83 by CBS Records. Dist: CBS

Single (12"): released on CBS, Jun'83 by CBS Records. Dist: CBS

WORLD WAITS FOR YOU, THE.
Tracks: / Waiting for the roar / Girl / Back door man / Doin' just fine / World waits for you, The / Kill me with your heart / Tired of your love / Change / Move over / Little by little / Rock on.
Single (7"): released on CBS, Jan'86 by CBS Records. Dist: CBS

Single (12"): released on CBS, Jan'86 by CBS Records. Dist: CBS

Album: released on CBS, Feb'86 by CBS Records. Dist: CBS

Cassette: released on CBS, Feb'86 by CBS Records. Dist: CBS

Fatal Charm
ENDANGERED SPECIES.
Single (7"): released on Carrere, Nov'85 by Carrere Records. Dist: PRT, Spartan

IMAGES OF FIRE.
Tracks: / I'm sure not in tune with it / City of dreams.
Single (7"): released on Native, Aug'86 by Native Records. Dist: Red Rhino, Cartel

Single (12"): released on Native, Aug'86 by Native Records. Dist: Red Rhino, Cartel

KING OF COMEDY.
Single (7"): released on Carrere, Apr'85 by Carrere Records. Dist: PRT, Spartan

Single (12"): released on Carrere, Apr'85 by Carrere Records. Dist: PRT, Spartan

LUCILLE.
Single (7"): released on Native, Feb'87 by Native Records. Dist: Red Rhino, Cartel

Single (12"): released on Native, Feb'87 by Native Records. Dist: Red Rhino, Cartel

SUMMER SPIES.
Tracks: / Summer spies / Final Door, The.
Single (7"): released on Carrere, Feb'87 by Carrere Records. Dist: PRT, Spartan

Single (12"): released on Carrere, Dec'84 by Carrere Records. Dist: PRT, Spartan

YOU KNOW (YOU'LL NEVER BELIEVE).
Single (7"): released on Carrere, Sep'85 by Carrere Records. Dist: PRT, Spartan

Single (12"): released on Carrere, Sep'85 by Carrere Records. Dist: PRT, Spartan

Fatal Flowers
FATAL FLOWERS.
Album: released on WEA, Oct'85 by WEA Records. Dist: WEA

Fatal Gift
WATCH, THE.
Single (7"): released on Yucca Ur, Oct'84 by Revolver Records. Dist: Cartel

Fatal Microbes
VIOLENCE GROWS.
Single (7"): released on Small Wonder, '79 by Small Wonder Records. Dist: Cartel, Indies

Fatback
14 KARAT.
Album: released on Polydor, Nov'80 by Polydor Records. Dist: Polygram, Polydor

GIRL IS FINE(SO FINE).
Single (7"): released on Spring, Apr'83 by Polydor Inc.. Dist: Polygram Distribution

Single (12"): released on Spring, Apr'83 by Polydor Inc.. Dist: Polygram

GREATEST HITS:FATBACK.
Album: released on Important, Sep'85 Dist: EMI

Cassette: released on Important, Sep'85 Dist: EMI

IS THIS THE FUTURE?.
Album: released on Polydor, Jul'83 by Polydor Records. Dist: Polygram, Polydor

IS THIS THE FUTURE.
Single (7"): released on Important, Oct'85 Dist EMI

Single (12"): released on Important, Oct'85 Dist: EMI

LOVER UNDER COVER.
Single (7"): released on Atlantic, Jun'85 by WEA Records. Dist: WEA Deleted '86.

Single (12"): released on Atlantic, Jun'85 by WEA Records. Dist: WEA

ON THE FLOOR.
Album: released on Spring, Jul'82 by Polydor Inc.. Dist: Polygram

SO DELICIOUS.
Album: released on Cotillion, Apr'85 by WEA Records. Dist: WEA

Cassette: released on Cotillion, Apr'85 by WEA Records. Dist: WEA

Fatback Band
BEST OF THE FATBACK BAND, THE.
Album: released on Spring, Dec'76 by Polydor Inc.. Dist: Polygram

FATBACK BAND "LIVE".
Compact disc: released on Old Gold, Jun'87 by Old Gold Records. Dist: Lightning, Jazz Music, Spartan, Counterpoint

Album: released on Old Gold, Jun'87 by Old Gold Records. Dist: Lightning, Jazz Music, Spartan, Counterpoint

I FOUND LOVIN'.
Single (7"): released on Master Mix, Jun'84 by PRT Records. Dist: PRT

Single (12"): released on Master Mix, Jun'84 by PRT Records. Dist: PRT

I FOUND LOVING.
Tracks: / Is this the future.
Single (7"): released on Important, Jun'86 Dist: EMI

Single (12"): released on Important, Jun'86 Dist: EMI

I FOUND LOVIN'(THE LONDON BOYS MIX).
Tracks: / Anthem (Live), The.

Single (12"): released on important, Aug'86 Dist: EMI

RHYTHM OF THE NIGHT.
Tracks: / Rhythm of the night / Naughty dancer.
Single (7"): released on Groove & Move, 20 Jun'87 by G&M Records. Dist: G&M Records, PRT

Single (12"): released on Groove & Move, 20 Jun'87 by G&M Records. Dist: G&M Records, PRT

Fat Boys
BIG AND BEAUTIFUL.
Tracks: / Sex machine / Go for it / Breakdown / Double-O Fat Boys / Big and beautiful / Rapp symphony (In C minor) / Beatbox part 3 / In the house / Beatbox is rockin'.
Album: released on Sutra-Atlantic, Jun'86

Cassette: released on Sutra-Atlantic, Jun'86

FAT BOY'S.
Album: released on WEA, May'85 by WEA Records. Dist: WEA

Cassette: released on WEA, May'85 by WEA Records. Dist: WEA

FAT BOYS ARE BACK, THE.
Tracks: / Fat boys are back, The / Don't be stupid / Human beatbox +2 / Yes, yes, y'all / Hard core reggae / Pump it up / Fat boys scratch / Rock'n'roll.
Album: released on WEA, Oct'85 by WEA Records. Dist: WEA

Cassette: released on WEA, Oct'85 by WEA Records. Dist: WEA

JAIL HOUSE RAP.
Tracks: / Stick em.
Single (7"): released on WEA, Apr'85 by WEA Records. Dist: WEA

Single (12"): released on WEA, Apr'85 by WEA Records. Dist: WEA

SEX MACHINE.
Tracks: / Beatbox is rocking.
Single (7"): released on Atlantic, May'86 by WEA Records. Dist: WEA

Single (12"): released on Atlantic, May'86 by WEA Records. Dist: WEA

Fat Boys & The Beach Boys
WIPE OUT.
Single (7"): released on Polydor, Aug'87 by Polydor Records. Dist: Polygram, Polydor

Single (12"): released on Polydor, Aug'87 by Polydor Records. Dist: Polygram, Polydor

Fates
FURIA.
Album: released on Hag, Nov'84 Dist: Rough Trade, Cartel

Fates Warning
AWAKEN THE GUARDIAN.
Album: released on Roadrunner (Dutch), Jan'87 Dist: Pinnacle

SPECTRE WITHIN, THE.
Album: released on Road Runner, Nov'85

Fat & Frantic
BIG HATS & SMALL HEADS.
Cassette: released on I'll Call You (Icy) Records, Oct'85 by I'll-Call-You (Icy) Records. Dist: I'll Call You

WAXING A HOTTIE.
Cassette: released on I'll Call You (Icy) Records, May'86 by I'll-Call-You (Icy) Records. Dist: I'll Call You

Fathead
BAD BOY SKANKING (see Yellowman) (Fathead/Yellowman).

CHAMPION.
Album: released on Greensleeves, Apr'83 by Greensleeves Records. Dist: BMG, Jetstar, Spartan

IT'S ME.
Single (12"): released on Greensleeves, Jan'83 by Greensleeves Records. Dist: BMG, Jetstar, Spartan

RAT TRAP.
Single (12"): released on Greensleeves, Oct'82 by Greensleeves Records. Dist: BMG, Jetstar, Spartan

Father Christmas
LAST CHRISTMAS.
Single (7"): released on Go For It, Dec'84 by Go For It Records. Dist: ILA

Father Xmas & Tuffty
READ & LISTEN & LEARN.
Cassette: released on Bi-Bi Magnetics, Jan'82 Dist: Taylor.

Fat Lady Sings
FEAR AND FAVOUR.
Single (7"): released on Good Vibration, Dec'86 by Good Vibrations Records. Dist: Pinnacle, Rough Trade

Fat Larry's Band
NICE.
Tracks: / Which one should I choose.
Single (7"): released on Omni, May'86 Dist: Pinnacle

Single (12"): released on Omni, May'86 Dist: Pinnacle

STRAIGHT FROM THE HEART.
Tracks: / Straight from the heart / Imagination / Stubborn kind of fellow / Always / Kilowatt / Tune me up / In my song / Don't let it go to your head / Hitman.
Album: released on Virgin, Nov'83 by Virgin Records. Dist: EMI, Virgin Distribution

Cassette: released on Virgin, Nov'83 by Virgin Records. Dist: EMI, Virgin Distribution

Fat Man Ridim Section
KING OF LOVE.
Album: released on Circle, May'84 Dist: Jazz Music

Fats Comet
DON'T FORGET THAT BEAT.
Single (12"): released on Rough Trade, May'85 by Rough Trade Records. Dist: Rough Trade Distribution, Cartel Distribution

ROCHESTER.
Single (12"): released on World, Jan'87 Dist: Jetstar

STORMY WEATHER.
Single (12"): released on Rough Trade, Jun'85 by Rough Trade Records. Dist: Rough Trade Distribution, Cartel Distribution

Fats, Happy
CAJUN & COUNTRY SONGS (Fats, Happy & Alex Broussard).
Album: released on Swallow, Feb'79

Fattburger
ONE OF A KIND.
Tracks: / 59th Street / Park Lane / Yum yum / Auto bahn / Fattburger / One of a kind / I knew that.
Notes: Fattburger are a highly talented quintet from America's West Coast, playing sophisticated jazz-orientated dance music. This album was high in the American "BlackMusic" and "Jazz" charts last year. Recommended tracks: 'Yum, Yum', 'One Of A Kind', 'I Knew That'. Special guest: Tommy Aros - percussion.
Album: released on Optimism (Germany), Apr'87

Faulkner, John
FAREWELL TO EIRINN (Faulkner, John & Dolores Kleane & Eamonn Curran).

Faust
EXTRACTS FROM FAUST PARTY 3.
Single (7"): released on Recommended, Mar'80 by Recommended Records. Dist: Recommended, Impetus, Rough Trade

FAUST.
Album: released on Recommended, Sep'86 by Recommended Records. Dist: Recommended, Impetus, Rough Trade

MUNIC AND ELSEWHERE.
Album: released on Recommended, Sep'86 by Recommended Records. Dist: Recommended, Impetus, Rough Trade

ONE.
Album: released on Recommended, Oct'79 by Recommended Records. Dist: Recommended, Impetus, Rough Trade

SO FAR.
Album: released on Recommended, Sep'86 by Recommended Records. Dist: Recommended, Impetus, Rough Trade

Album: released on Recommended, Oct'79 by Recommended Records. Dist: Recommended, Impetus, Rough Trade

Favourite
FAVOURITE BRASS Various artists (Various Artists).
Double Album: released on Music For Pleasure, Jun'84 by EMI Records. Dist: EMI

Cassette: released on Music For Pleasure, Jun'84 by EMI Records. Dist: EMI

FAVOURITE EUROPEAN TALES Katharine Hepburn (Favourite European Tales).
Cassette: released on Listen For Pleasure, Oct'84 by MFP Records. Dist: EMI

FAVOURITE FAIRY STORIES Read by Sally James (Favourite Fairy Stories).
Album: released on Super Tempo, May'84 by Multiple Sounds Records. Dist: Multiple Sound Distributors

Cassette: released on Super Tempo, May'84 by Multiple Sounds Records. Dist: Multiple Sound Distributors

Cassette: released on Tempo Storytime, May'84

FAVOURITE FAIRY STORIES Various artists (Various Artists).
Album: released on Spot, Feb'83 by Pickwick Records. Dist: H.R. Taylo

Cassette: released on Spot, Feb'83 by Pickwick Records. Dist: H.R. Taylor,

Cassette: released on VFM Cassettes, Jan'85

Favourites of the...
FAVOURITES OF THE FORTIES Various original artists (Various original artists).
Album: released on MFP, Apr'82 by EMI Records. Dist: EMI

Cassette: released on MFP, Apr'82 by EMI Records. Dist: EMI

Album: released on Music for Pleasure, Oct'84 by EMI Records. Dist: MFP Distribution

Cassette: released on Music for Pleasure, Oct'84 by EMI Records. Dist: MFP Distribution

FAVOURITES OF THE PHILHARMONIC: VOL 2 Various orchestras (Various Orchestras).
Album: released on Music For Pleasure, Oct'83 by EMI Records. Dist: EMI

Cassette: released on Music For Pleasure, Oct'83 by EMI Records. Dist: EMI

Favre, Pierre
DRUM CONVERSATION.
Album: released on Calig, Oct'79

SINGLE DRUMS (Favre, Pierre Ensemble).
Album: released on ECM (Germany), Jan'85 by ECM Records. Dist: IMS, Polygram, Virgin through EMI

Fawcett & Kazakov
VIRTUOSISSIMI.
Tracks: / Thieving magpie overture / La cumparsita / Carnival of Venice / Dringo's serenade / Spic and spam / Toccatta and fugue in DMI musical box / Ukranian folk variations / Russian comic dancing songs.
Album: released on Accordion Record Club, Jul'86 by Accordion Record Club Records. Dist: Accordion Record Club

Fawcett, Pearl
ACCORDION TAPESTRY.
Album: released on ARC (Accordion Records), '84 Dist: Accordion Record Club

MUSETTE PARISIENNE.
Album: released on ARC (Accordion Records), '84 Dist: Accordion Record Club

MUSIC ON THE MOVE.
Tracks: / Italian tarantella/Hospalisa etc / Edelweiss/Plaisir / D'amour/poem / Cumpasita/El choclo / September song/Gondolira etc / Muzurka / Mack the knife/king of the road etc / Sleepy blues / Carnival of Venice etc / Boogie etc.
Cassette: released on Accordion Record Club, Jul'86 by Accordion Record Club Records. Dist: Accordion Record Club

Fawkes, Wally
OCTOBER SONG (Fawkes, Wally & Friends).
Album: released on Calligraph, Sep'86 by Calligraph Records. Dist: PRT

WALLY FAWKES NEO-TROGLODYKES (Fawkes, Wally & The Neo-Troglodykes).
Album: released on Dawn Club, May'79 Dist: Cadillac, Swift,

Fawlty Towers
FAWLTY TOWERS: A LA CARTE (Various Artists).
Album: released on BBC, Oct'83 by BBC Records & Tapes. Dist: EMI, PRT,

Cassette: released on BBC, Oct'83 by BBC Records & Tapes. Dist: EMI, PRT,

FAWLTY TOWERS: AT YOUR SERVICE Original cast (Various Artists).
Album: released on BBC, Oct'82 by BBC Records & Tapes. Dist: EMI, PRT,

Cassette: released on BBC, Oct'82 by BBC Records & Tapes. Dist: EMI, PRT,

FAWLTY TOWERS: EXTRACTS, VOL 1 Original cast (Various Artists).
Album: released on BBC, Nov'79 by BBC Records & Tapes. Dist: EMI, PRT,

Cassette: released on BBC, Nov'79 by BBC Records & Tapes. Dist: EMI, PRT.

FAWLTY TOWERS: SECOND SITTING Original cast (Various Artists).
Album: released on BBC, Jan'81 by BBC Records & Tapes. Dist: EMI, PRT,

Cassette: released on BBC, Jan'81 by BBC Records & Tapes. Dist: EMI, PRT,

Faye, Alice

ALICE FAYE & THE SONGS OF HARRY WARREN.
Album: released on Citadel, Mar'79 Dist: Swift

ALICE FAY & PHIL HARRIS: TWO COMPLETE RADIO BROADCASTS (Faye, Alice & Phil Harris).
Album: released on Radio Archives, Aug'77 Dist: Jazz Music, Swift

IN HOLLYWOOD.
Album: released on CBS Cameo, Jul'83 by CBS Records. Dist: CBS

Cassette: released on CBS Cameo, Jul'83 by CBS Records. Dist: CBS Deleted '85.

ON THE AIR: VOL 1.
Album: released on Totem, Jun'79 Dist: Jazz Music, Projection, Swift

ON THE AIR: VOL 2.
Album: released on Totem, May'79 Dist: Jazz Music, Projection, Swift

Fayte, Kevin

RIDIN' IN ROCKET (Fayte, Kevin & Rocket 8).
Album: released on Nervous, Oct'86 by Nervous Records. Dist: Nervous, Rough Trade

Fazarro, Susan

FINE AND MELLOW (Fazarro, Susan & Richard Stoker).
Album: released on JSO, Nov'81

Faze One

GOOD FRIENDS.
Tracks: / Good friends / Pleasure seekers.
Single (7"): released on Westside, 30 May'87 by Streetsounds Records. Dist: BMG

Single (12"): released on Westside, 30 May'87 by Streetsounds Records. Dist: BMG

LAYIN' DOWN A BEAT.
Tracks: / Stronger than strong.
Single (7"): released on Streetwave, Sep'86 by Streetwave Records. Dist: PRT Distribution

Single (12"): released on Streetwave, Sep'86 by Streetwave Records. Dist: PRT Distribution

Fazzini, Tom

NECK TO NECK.
Album: released on Omission, Sep'84 Dist: Red Rhino Distribution

Fearless Four

PROBLEMS OF THE WORLD.
Single (7"): released on WEA, Apr'84 by WEA Records. Dist: WEA

ROCKIN'IT.
Single (12"): released on Y, Jun'83

Single (12"): released on NYC, Sep'83

Fear of Darkness

FEAR OF DARKNESS.
Single (12"): released on Heartbeat, Aug'84 Dist: Revolver, Pinnacle

LAY ME DOWN.
Single (12"): released on Sugar Shack, 20 Jun'87

VIRGIN LAND, THE.
Album: released on Embryo, Jan'86 by Embryo Records. Dist: Revolver, Cartel, WEA

Fear of Falling

LIKE A LION.
Single (12"): released on Excellent, May'83 by Survival Records. Dist: Pinnacle

Fear Of The Dark

THIS IS THE BLUES.
Single (7"): released on Lambs To The Slaughter, Feb'86 by Prism Records. Dist: Pinnacle, Red Rhino, Cartel

Single (12"): released on Lambs To The Slaughter, Feb'86 by Prism Records. Dist: Pinnacle, Red Rhino, Cartel

Fearon, Phil

AIN'T NOTHING BUT A HOUSE PARTY.
Tracks: / Burning all my bridges.
Single (7"): released on Ensign, Nov'86 by Ensign Records. Dist: CBS Distribution

Single (12"): released on Ensign, Nov'86 by Ensign Records. Dist: CBS Distribution

EVERYBODY'S LAUGHING (Fearon, Phil & Galaxy.).
Single (7"): released on Ensign, Jun'84 by Ensign Records. Dist: CBS Distribution Deleted '87.

Single (12"): released on Ensign, Jun'84 by Ensign Records. Dist: CBS Distribution Deleted '87.

Picture disc single: released on Ensign, Jun'84 by Ensign Records. Dist: CBS Distribution

FANTASY REAL (Fearon, Phil & Galaxy.).
Single (7"): released on Ensign, Oct'83 by Ensign Records. Dist: CBS Distribution

Single (12"): released on Ensign, Oct'83 by Ensign Records. Dist: CBS Distribution

NOTHING IS TOO GOOD FOR YOU.
Tracks: / Nothing is too good for you / You've still got my love.
Single (7"): released on Ensign, Jul'87 by Ensign Records. Dist: CBS Distribution

Single (12"): released on Ensign, Jul'87 by Ensign Records. Dist: CBS Distribution

THIS KIND OF LOVE (Fearon, Phil & Galaxy.).
Single (7"): released on Ensign, Jul'85 by Ensign Records. Dist: CBS Distribution

Single (12"): released on Ensign, Jul'85 by Ensign Records. Dist: CBS Distribution Deleted '87.

THIS KIND OF LOVE (Fearon, Phil & Galaxy, featuring Dee Galdes).
Single (12"): released on Ensign, Aug'85 by Ensign Records. Dist: CBS Distribution

WHAT DO I DO? (Fearon, Phil & Galaxy.).
Single (7"): released on Ensign, Mar'84 by Ensign Records. Dist: CBS Distribution

Single (12"): released on Ensign, Mar'84 by Ensign Records. Dist: CBS Distribution

Feast of...

FEAST OF BRASS AND VOICES Various artists (Various Artists).
Double Album: Dist: R. Smith & Co. Records,

FEAST OF BRITISH FOLK Various artists (Various Artists).
Album: released on Broadside, Jun'81 by Broadside Records. Dist: Celtic Distributions, H.R. Taylor, Jazz Music, Projection,

Cassette: released on Broadside, Jun'81 by Broadside Records. Dist: Celtic Distributions, H.R. Taylor, Jazz Music, Projection,

FEAST OF IRISH FOLK Various artists (Various Artists).
Tracks: / Cliffs of Nooneen / Wind in the willows / Nancy Spain / Clare to here / Town I loved so well / Tebhair dom de lamh / Only our rivers / Rambling Irishman / Lonesome boatman / Yarmouth town / Silver in the stubble / Fiddlers green / Bunch of thyme / Shores of Lough Bran / Gently Annie / Banks of Claudy.
Album: released on Polydor (Ireland), Aug'86 by Polydor Records. Dist: Polygram, I & B

Cassette: released on Polydor (Ireland), Aug'86 by Polydor Records. Dist: Polygram, I & B

Feather

CHEN YOU LIPS.
Album: released on Discovery, Jun'83 Dist: PRT

ZANZIBAR.
Album: released on Discovery (USA), Apr'85 by Discovery Records (USA). Dist: Swift, Flexitron-Audio, Jazz Music

Feather, Leonard

PRESENTS 'JAZZ FROM 2 SIDES'.
Album: released on Concept, Jun'87 Dist: Jazz Music, Swift, Chris Wellard, Polygram

Feather, Lorraine

SWEET LORRAINE.
Album: released on Concord, Mar'79 by Import Records. Dist: IMS, Polygram

Feathers, Charlie

LEGENDARY 1956 DEMO SESSION, THE.
Album: released on Zu Jazz, Oct'86 Dist: Charly

NEW JUNGLE FEVER.
Album: released on New Rose, Jun'87 Dist: Rough Trade, Cartel

ROCKABILLY'S MAIN MAN.
Album: by Charly Records. Dist: Charly, Cadillac

THAT CERTAIN FEMALE.
Single (7"): released on Rollin' Rock, Jun'80

Federal Music Society

COME AND RIP IT UP (Hyman, Dick & Schwarz, Gerard & Their Orchestra's).
Tracks: / Prima donna waltz / Jenny Lind Polka / Minuet and gavotte / Country fiddle music / Natilie polka-mazurka / Flying cloud Schottische / Victoria gallop / Flirt polka (The) / La sonnambula / Eliza Jane McCue / Blaze-away / Hiawatha / Sweet man.
Notes: MEMBERS OF THE FEDERAL MUSIC SOCIETY: Conductor - John Baldon, Soloists - Ellen Farren - pianoforte, Rodney Miller - fiddle, Allen Moore - pianoforte, Judith Plant - keyed bugle

PRIMARY ENSEMBLE PLAYERS: Mary Barto - flute, Joanne Tanner - principal violin, Richard Wagner - clarinet. THE ENSEMBLE: Kathy Seplow, Diane Volpe, Carol Zeavin, Nancy Diggs - violons, Julie Tanner - cello, Frederick Selch - contrabass. GERARD SCHWARZ AND HIS DANCE ORCHESTRA: Gerard Schwarz - cornet and conductor, Miles Anderson - trombone, John Beal - bass, Harvey Estrin - flute and piccolo, Mark Gould - cornet, Herb Harris - drums and percussion, John Moses - clarinet, Tony Mottola - guitar, Eugene Moye - cello, Max Pollikoff - violin, Charles Russo - clarinet. DICK HYMAN AND HIS DANCE BAND: Dick Hyman - pioao and conductor, John Beal - bass, Phil Bodner - piccolo, flute, clarinet and saxophone, Ray Crisara - cornet, Jack Gale - trombone, Al Gallodoro - clarinet and saxophone, Phil Kaus - drums and percussion, Tony Mottola - guitar and banjo, Max Pollikoff - violin, Richard Sudhalter - cornet. [New World release sheet, April '87]
Album: released on New World (USA), Apr'87 by New World Records (USA). Dist: Conifer

Feedback

SIMPLY MAGIC.
Tracks: / Simply magic / Simply magic (magic mix).
Single (7"): released on Production House, Jul'87 Dist: Bluebird, Revolver, Cartel

Single (12"): released on Production House, Jul'87 Dist: Bluebird, Revolver, Cartel

SO FINE.
Tracks: / So fine / Feedback of the mind.
Single (12"): released on Production House, Mar'87 Dist: Bluebird, Revolver, Cartel

Single (7"): released on Production House, May'87 Dist: Bluebird, Revolver, Cartel

Feed The Folk

FEED THE FOLK Various artists (Various Artists).
Notes: A charity album with tracks by Richard Thompson/Loudon Wainwright III/Steeleye span/Roches/Kate & Anna McGarrigle/Billy Conolly/Fairport Convention/Lindisfarne/Chieftains/Martin Carthy/Paul Brady/Battlefield Band. All proceeds going to charities in the Third World.
Album: released on Feed The Folk, Jul'86 Dist: Projection

Album: released on Temple, Sep'85 by Temple Records. Dist: Roots Distribution, Folksound Distribution, Celtic Music Distribution, Projection Distribution

Cassette: released on Temple, Sep'85 by Temple Records. Dist: Roots Distribution, Folksound Distribution, Celtic Music Distribution, Projection Distribution

Feehan, Tim

WHERE'S THE FIRE.
Single (7"): released on Scotti Brothers, Jan'87 by Scotti Brothers Records. Dist: CBS

Feel

I'D LIKE TO.
Single (7"): released on Buddah, Jan'83 Dist: Swift, Jazz Music, PRT

Cassette: released on Buddah, Jan'83 Dist: Swift, Jazz Music, PRT

Feelabeella

FEEL IT.
Single (7"): released on Interdisc, Sep'84 by Interdisc Records. Dist: Island, EMI

Feelies

CRAZY RHYTHMS.
Album: released on Stiff, Jan'80 by Stiff Records. Dist: EMI, Record Services Distribution (Ireland)

Cassette: released on Stiff, Jan'80 by Stiff Records. Dist: EMI, Record Services Distribution (Ireland)

EVERYBODY'S GOT SOMETHING TO HIDE.
Single (7"): released on Stiff, Jan'80 by Stiff Records. Dist: EMI, Record Services Distribution (Ireland)

GOOD EARTH, THE.
Album: released on Rough Trade, Sep'86 by Rough Trade Records. Dist: Rough Trade Distribution, Cartel Distribution

NO ONE KNOWS.
Single (12"): released on Rough Trade, Dec'86 by Rough Trade Records. Dist: Rough Trade Distribution, Cartel Distribution

RAISED EYEBROWS.
Single (7"): released on Rough Trade, Sep'79 by Rough Trade Records. Dist: Rough Trade Distribution, Cartel Distribution

Feelin' country

FEELIN' COUNTRY: VOL 1 Various artists (Various Artists).
Album: released on Premier, Jun'85 by Premier Records. Dist: CBS

Cassette: released on Premier, Jun'85 by Premier Records. Dist: CBS

FEELIN' COUNTRY: VOL 2 Various artists (Various Artists).
Album: released on Premier, Jun'85 by Premier Records. Dist: CBS

Cassette: released on Premier, Jun'85 by Premier Records. Dist: CBS

Feelin' fine

FEELIN' FINE Various artists (Various Artists).
Cassette: released on K-Tel Goldmasters, Aug'84 by K-Tel Records. Dist: K-Tel

Feelings

FEELINGS Various artists (Various Artists).
Cassette: released on K-Tel Goldmasters, Aug'84 by K-Tel Records. Dist: K-Tel

FEELINGS: THE GOLDEN LOVE SONGS Various artists (Various Artists).
Album: released on Decca (Elite), Sep'82 by Decca Records. Dist: Polygram, IMS

Cassette: released on Decca (Elite), Sep'82 by Decca Records. Dist: Polygram, IMS

Feel Like Rockin'

FEEL LIKE ROCKIN' (Various Artists).
Tracks: / Rockin' love / Some enchanted evening / Take these chains from my heart / Hey baby doll / No more cryin' the blues / Tied to your apron string / I fell in love / Love crazy baby / Walkin' with my best friend / Apron string / Crazy baby / I feel in love / Lordy hoody / Feel like rockin' / Tennessee zip / Love crazy baby / You call everybody darlin' / Treat me right.
Album: released on Sun, Mar'87 by Charly Records. Dist: Charly Distribution

Feezey, John

JOHN FEEZEY.
Album: released on Gael-Linn (Ireland), Feb'86 by Gael Linn Records. Dist: Roots, Projection, Celtic Music, Jazz Music

Fehlmann, Thomas

READY MADE.
Single (7"): released on Transglobal Rhythm King, Feb'87 by Mute Records. Dist: Rough Trade, Cartel

Single (12"): released on Transglobal Rhythm King, Feb'87 by Mute Records. Dist: Rough Trade, Cartel

Fehlmans Readymade

READY MADE.
Tracks: / Ready made (remixed).
Single (7"): released on Rhythm King, Mar'87 Dist: Rough Trade, Cartel

Single (12"): released on Rhythm King, Mar'87 Dist: Rough Trade, Cartel

Felder, Wilton

GENTLE FIRE.

Album: released on MCA, Apr'83 by MCA Records. Dist: Polygram, MCA

Cassette: released on MCA, Apr'83 by MCA Records. Dist: Polygram, MCA

I WILL STILL BE LOOKING UP TO YOU.
Single (7"): released on MCA, Jan'85 by MCA Records. Dist: Polygram, MCA

Single (12"): released on MCA, Jan'85 by MCA Records. Dist: Polygram, MCA

SECRETS.
Album: released on MCA, Feb'85 by MCA Records. Dist: Polygram, MCA

Cassette: released on MCA, Feb'85 by MCA Records. Dist: Polygram, MCA

WE ALL HAVE A STAR.
Album: released on ABC, Feb'82 Dist: CBS, Pinnacle

Cassette: released on ABC, Feb'82 Dist: CBS, Pinnacle

Feldman, Victor

BIG BANDS,THE VOL.2 Ninetet & Quintet.
Album: released on Jasmine, Feb'83 by Jasmine Records. Dist: Counterpoint, Lugtons, Taylor, H.R., Wellard, Chris, Swift, Cadillac

IN LONDON VOL.1.
Album: released on Jasmine, Dec'83 by Jasmine Records. Dist: Counterpoint, Lugtons, Taylor, H.R., Wellard, Chris, Swift, Cadillac

SECRET OF THE ANDES.
Album: released on Palo Alto (Italy), Jan'85

Spike Robinson/Tommy Pollard's Downbeat Five/Victor Feldman

SUITE SIXTEEN.
Album: released on Contemporary, May'87 by Contemporary Records. Dist: Pinnacle

THOU SWELL See under Deucher, Jimmy.
Notes: See under: Deuchar, Jimmy with Alan Clare, Victor Feldman & Tony Kinsey.

TO CHOPIN WITH LOVE (Feldman, Victor Trio).
Album: released on Palo Alto (Italy), Jun'84

TRANSATLANTIC ALLIANCE with Dizzy Reece/Tubby Hayes/Jimmy Deuchar.
Album: released on Jasmine, Feb'83 by Jasmine Records. Dist: Counterpoint, Lugtons, Taylor, H.R., Wellard, Chris, Swift, Cadillac

YOUNG VIC, THE.
Tracks: / Mop mop / Lady bird / Quaternity / Moonlight in Vermont / Gone with the wind / Ego / Jolly Rogers / Evening in Paris / Kashmir / Pakistan / Harem scarem / Monkey business / Serenade in blue / For you alone / Body and soul.
Notes: A tribute to the late victor Feldman.
Album: released on Esquire, Jul'87 by Titan International Productions. Dist: Jazz Music, Cadillac Music, Swift, Wellard, Chris, Backs, Rough Trade, Revolver, Nine Mile

Feldon, Barbara

99.
Single (7"): released on Au-Go-Go (Australia), Oct'83 by Au-Go-Go Records (Australia). Dist: Rough Trade, Cartel

Feliciano, Jose

ALIVE,ALIVE O.
Album: released on RCA (Germany), '83

BAG FULL OF SOUL, A.
Album: released on RCA (Germany), Apr'83

BEST OF.
Tracks: / Light my fire / California dreamin' / And the sun will shine / Windmills of your mind, The / Miss Otis regrets / Rain / Frst of May / Guantanamera / Che sara / Destiny / Susie-Q / Hi-heel sneakers / Cico and the man (Main theme) / Hitchcock railway / Malaguena / No dogs allowed.
Notes: Often,"Best of...." collections are just one or two hits and ten or twelve fillers. This time, RCA have put together one heck of an album, 16 tracks, everyone a winner, all from Feliciano's peak years 1968-1974.
Album: released on RCA (Germany), Nov'85

Cassette: released on RCA (Germany), Nov'85

BY DESIGN (Feliciano, Jose & Diane Schuur).
Notes: For full information see under "Schuur, Diane & Jose Feliciano"

ENCORE.
Double Album: released on RCA (Germany), Jul'83

ESCENAS DE AMOR.
Album: released on Latino, Oct'82 by Motown Records. Dist: RCA

Cassette: released on Latino, Oct'82 by Motown Records. Dist: RCA

FANTASTIC FELICIANO.
Album: released on RCA (Germany), '83

FELICIANO.
Tracks: / California dreamin' / Light my fire / Don't let the sun catch you crying / In my life / And I love her / Nena, Nana / There's always something there to remind me / Just a little bit of rain / Sunny / Here, there and everywhere / Last thing on my mind.
Album: released on RCA, Oct'86 by RCA Records. Dist: RCA, Roots, Swift, Wellard, Chris, I & B, Solomon & Peres Distribution
Cat. no: **NL 89845**
Cassette: released on RCA, Oct'86 by RCA Records. Dist: RCA, Roots, Swift, Wellard, Chris, I & B, Solomon & Peres Distribution

Album: released on RCA, Sep'81 by RCA Records. Dist: RCA, Roots, Swift, Wellard, Chris, I & B, Solomon & Peres Distribution

Cassette: released on RCA, Sep'81 by RCA Records. Dist: RCA, Roots, Swift, Wellard, Chris, I & B, Solomon & Peres Distribution

JOSE FELICIANO.
Album: released on Motown, Dec'81 by Motown Records. Dist: BMG Distribution

Cassette: released on Motown, Dec'81 by Motown Records. Dist: BMG Distribution

LIGHT MY FIRE.
Album: released on RCA (Germany), '83

LONELY TEARDROPS.
Single (7"): released on Motown, May'83 by Motown Records. Dist: BMG Distribution

LOS EXITOS DE.
Album: released on Latino, Nov'84 by Motown Records. Dist: RCA

Cassette: released on Latino, Nov'84 by Motown Records. Dist: RCA

PORTRAIT.
Album: released on Telstar, Jul'85 by Telstar Records. Dist: RCA Distribution

Cassette: released on Telstar, Jul'85 by Telstar Records. Dist: RCA Distribution

ROMANCE IN THE NIGHT.
Album: released on Latino, May'83 by Motown Records. Dist: RCA

Cassette: released on Latino, May'83 by Motown Records. Dist: RCA

SAMBA PATI.
Single (7"): released on Latino, Oct'82 by Motown Records. Dist: RCA

SINGS & PLAYS THE BEATLES.
Album: released on RCA, Oct'85 by RCA Records. Dist: RCA, Roots, Swift, Wellard, Chris, I & B, Solomon & Peres Distribution

Cassette: released on RCA, Oct'85 by RCA Records. Dist: RCA, Roots, Swift, Wellard, Chris, I & B, Solomon & Peres Distribution

SPANISH PORTRAIT, A.
Album: released on RCA (France), Oct'85 by RCA Records. Dist: Discovery

Cassette: released on RCA (France), Oct'85 by RCA Records. Dist: Discovery

Feline Jive

KISS'N'TELL.
Single (7"): released on Massive, Feb'87 Dist: Revolver, Cartel

Felix, Julie

AMAZING GRACE Twenty classic tracks.
Tracks: / Man gave names to all the animals / Soldier from the sixties / El condor pasa / Amazing grace / Mr. Tambourine man / Early morning rain / Blowin' in the wind / Vincent / Going to the zoo / Where have all the flowers gone / Let it be / Last thing on my mind / Scarborough fair / San Francisco / I miss you / Mr preservation kit / Where are you / We better talk this over / Colours in the rain / Changing / In vitro bread.
Album: released on Starburst, Jul'87 by Starburst Records. Dist: CBS Distribution. Estim retail price in Sep'87 was £5.49.

Album: released on Starburst, Aug'87 by Starburst Records. Dist: CBS Distribution

Cassette: released on Starburst, Aug'87 by Starburst Records. Dist: CBS Distribution

BLOWIN' IN THE WIND.
Album: released on Dingles, '83 by Dingles Records. Dist: Projection

DANCE WITH ME.
Single (7"): released on Gipsy, Oct'83 by Gipsy Records. Dist: PRT

HOTA CHOCOLATE.
Album: released on Gull, Jun'79 by Gull Records. Dist: Pinnacle

YOKO.
Single (7"): released on Gipsy, Jan'84 by Gipsy Records. Dist: PRT

Felling Male Voice Choir

VOICES OF THE TYNE.
Album: released on Mawson & Wareham, Sep'83 by Mawson & Wareham Records. Dist: Roots, Celtic Music, Spartan, Jazz Music, Projection

Fellini

FELLINI Original Soundtrack.
Album: released on Silva Screen, Jun'87 by Silva Screen Records. Dist: Silva Screen

Cassette: released on Silva Screen, Jun'87 by Silva Screen Records. Dist: Silva Screen

Fellside...

FELLSIDE'S FOLK FAVOURITES (Various Artists).
Cassette: released on Fellside, Jul'87 by Fellside Records. Dist: Roots, Jazz Music, Celtic Music, Projection

FELLSIDE SONG SAMPLER VOL.1 (Various Artists).
Cassette: released on Fellside, Jul'87 by Fellside Records. Dist: Roots, Jazz Music, Celtic Music, Projection

FELLSIDE SONG SAMPLER VOL.2 (Various Artists).
Cassette: released on Fellside, Jul'87 by Fellside Records. Dist: Roots, Jazz Music, Celtic Music, Projection

Felony

FANATIC.
Single (7"): released on Scotti Bros, Apr'83

Felt

BALLAD OF THE BAND.
Tracks: / Ballad of the band / I didn't mean to hurt you / Candles in a church / Ferdinand magellan.
Single (7"): released on Creation, May'86 Dist: Rough Trade, Cartel

Single (12"): released on Creation, May'86 Dist: Rough Trade, Cartel

CRUMBLING THE ANTISEPTIC BEAUTY/SPLENDOUR OF FEAR, THE.
Tracks: / Evergreen dazed / Fortune / Birdmen / Cathedral / I worship the sun / Templeroy / Red Indians / World is as soft as lace, The / Optimist and the poet, The / Mexican bandits / Stagnant pool / Preacher in new England.
Compact disc: released on Cherry Red, Sep'86 by Cherry Red Records. Dist: Pinnacle

CRUMBLING THE ANTISEPTIC BEAUTY.
Album: released on Cherry Red, Mar'82 by Cherry Red Records. Dist: Pinnacle

FINAL RESTING OF THE ARK, THE.
Single (7"): released on Creation, Jul'87 Dist: Rough Trade, Cartel

FOREVER BREATHES THE LONELY WORD.
Album: released on Creation, Oct'86 Dist: Rough Trade, Cartel

Cassette: released on Creation, Oct'86 Dist: Rough Trade, Cartel

GOLDMINE TRASH.
Compact disc: released on Cherry Red, Sep'87 by Cherry Red Records. Dist: Pinnacle. Estim retail price in Sep'87 was £9.62.

Album: released on Cherry Red, Oct'79 by Cherry Red Records. Dist: Pinnacle. Estim retail price in Sep'87 was £5.99.

Cassette: released on Cherry Red, Oct'79 by Cherry Red Records. Dist: Pinnacle. Estim retail price in Sep'87 was £5.99.

IGNITE THE SEVEN CANNONS.
Album: released on Cherry Red, Sep'85 by Cherry Red Records. Dist: Pinnacle

LET THE SNAKES CRINKLE THEIR HEADS TO DEATH.
Album: released on Creation, Sep'86 Dist: Rough Trade, Cartel

MEXICAN BANDITS.
Single (7"): released on Cherry Red, Mar'84 by Cherry Red Records. Dist: Pinnacle

PENELOPE TREE.
Tracks: / Preacher in New England, A.
Single (7"): released on Cherry Red, Jul'86 by Cherry Red Records. Dist: Pinnacle

Single (12"): released on Cherry Red, Jun'83 by Cherry Red Records. Dist: Pinnacle

PRIMITIVE PAINTERS.
Single (12"): released on Cherry Red, Aug'85 by Cherry Red Records. Dist: Pinnacle

RAIN OF CRYSTAL SPIRES.
Tracks: / Rain of crystal spires / I will die with my head / Gather up your wings and fly / I will die with my head in flames / Sandmans on the rise again.
Single (7"): released on Creation, Sep'86 Dist: Rough Trade, Cartel

Single (12"): released on Creation, Sep'86 Dist: Rough Trade, Cartel

SOMETHING SENDS ME TO SLEEP.
Single (7"): released on Cherry Red, '81 by Cherry Red Records. Dist: Pinnacle

SPLENDOUR OF FEAR, THE.
Tracks: / Rosses are red / I'm not a fool anymore / Please don't tell me how the story ends / You can't get here from there / I love my rancho grande / Wasted days and wasted nights / I almost called your name / Before the next teardrop falls / Wildside of life / After the fire is gone / Then you can tell me goodbye.
Album: released on Cherry Red, Nov'83 by Cherry Red Records. Dist: Pinnacle

Single (12"): released on Cherry Red, Nov'83 by Cherry Red Records. Dist: Pinnacle

Album: released on MCA Import, Mar'86 by MCA Records. Dist: Polygram, IMS

STRANGE IDOLS PATTERN & OTHER SHORT STORIES.
Album: released on Cherry Red, Oct'84 by Cherry Red Records. Dist: Pinnacle

SUNLIGHT BATHED THE GOLDEN GLOW.
Single (7"): released on Cherry Red, Jul'84 by Cherry Red Records. Dist: Pinnacle

Single (12"): released on Cherry Red, Jul'84 by Cherry Red Records. Dist: Pinnacle

TRAILS OF COLOURS DISSOLVE.
Single (7"): released on Cherry Red, Sep'82 by Cherry Red Records. Dist: Pinnacle

Felts, Narvel

TEEN'S WAY, A (Felts, Narvel & The Rockets).
Tracks: / I'm headin' home / Foolish thoughts / Cry, baby, cry / Vada Lou / Little girl step this way / Rocket ride / Why don't you love (like you used to do) / Remember me / Come back baby / Fool in Paradise, A / Lonely river / Kiss a me baby / Your touch / Your first broken heart / Teen's way, A / Dream world / Lonesome feeling.
Album: released on Bear Family, May'87 by Bear Family Records. Dist: Rollercoaster Distribution, Swift

Feminine Touch

I GAVE YOU MY HEART.
Single (12"): released on King & City, Sep'82 Dist: Jetstar

Fender, Freddy

20 GREATEST HITS.
Album: released on Astan, Nov'84 by Astan Records. Dist: Counterpoint

Cassette: released on Astan, Nov'84 by Astan Records. Dist: Counterpoint

BEFORE THE NEXT TEARDROP FALLS(7").
Single (7"): released on Old Gold, Jul'82 by Old Gold Records. Dist: Lightning, Jazz Music, Spartan, Counterpoint

BEFORE THE NEXT TEARDROP FALLS.
Tracks: / Coming home soon / Mean woman blues / Just because / Something on your mind / Only one / Since I met you baby / Before the next teardrop falls / Wasted days and wasted nights / La Bamba / Oh poo pah doo / Rains came, The / Wild side of life, the.
Album: released on Topline, Mar'87 by Charly Records. Dist: Charly Distribution

Cassette: released on Topline, Mar'87 by Charly Records. Dist: Charly Distribution

Album: released on Sundown, Mar'85 by Magnum Music Group Ltd. Dist: Magnum Music Group Ltd, PRT Distribution, Spartan Distribution

BEST OF.
Album: released on CBS, Apr'85 by CBS Records. Dist: CBS

Cassette: released on CBS, Apr'85 by CBS Records. Dist: CBS

EARLY YEARS 1959-1963.
Album: released on Krazy Kat, May'86 Dist: Jazz Music, Swift, Chris Wellard, H.R. Taylor, Charly, Hotshot,

Fender, Jack

GOLDEN GUITAR POP.
Compact disc: released on Delta, Feb'86 by Delta Records. Dist: Target

Fendermen

MULE SKINNER BLUES.
Single (7"): released on Revival, Jul'82 Dist: Lightning, Swift

Fenhoulet, Paul

STAIRWAY TO THE STARS (Fenhoulet, Paul & Skyrockets Dance Orchestra).
Album: released on Saville, Jul'83 by Conifer Records. Dist: Conifer

Fenix Jazz Band

GRANDPA'S SPELLS.
Notes: Buenos Aires, Argentina.
Album: released on Stomp Off, Mar'87 by Stomp Off Records. Dist: Jazz Music Distribution

Fenner

FENNER various artists (Various Artists).
Cassette: released on Bibi, Feb'82

Fenton, David

FRESH AIR.
Single (7"): released on Razor, Aug'83 by Razor. Dist: Pinnacle

Fenton, George

BERGERAC THEME.
Single (7"): released on Food For Thought, Oct'85 by Food For Thought Records. Dist: Pinnacle

OUT (Fenton, George Orchestra).
Single (7"): released on EMI, Aug'83 by EMI Records. Dist: EMI

Fenton, Shane

I'M A MOODY GUY (Fenton, Shane & The Fentones).
Tracks: / I'm a moody guy / Five foot two / Eyes of blue / Why little girl / It's all over now / It's gonna take magic / Cindy's birthday / Too young for sad memories / Fallen leaves on the ground / You're telling me / Walk away / Don't do that / I'll know / Fool's paradise, A / You need love / Somebody else not me / I ain't got nobody / Hey miss Ruby / Hey Lulu / I do do you / Breeze and I, The / Fool's paradise, A.
Album: released on See For Miles, Dec'86 by See For Miles Records. Dist: Pinnacle

Cassette: released on See For Miles, Aug'82 by See For Miles Records. Dist: Pinnacle

Ferez, Earl

ARTISTRY IN HAMMOND.
Album: released on President, Sep'77 by President Records. Dist: Taylors, Spartan

Fergus

BROKEN WINGS.
Single (7"): released on Climber, Apr'85 by Climber Records. Dist: PRT

CAVAN BEGGARMAN.
Single (7"): released on Rondercrest, Oct'80 by Rondercrest Records. Dist: M.I.S. Distribution

GOOD CLEAN FUN.
Single (7"): released on Rondercrest, '78 by Rondercrest Records. Dist: M.I.S. Distribution

LET'S GO DANCE IN THE MOONLIGHT.
Single (7"): released on Loopy, Sep'81 by Loopy Records. Dist: Loopy

ROMANY HEARTS.
Single (7"): released on Loopy, May'82 by Loopy Records. Dist: Loopy

ROUNDABOUT.
Single (7"): released on Climber, Jul'85 by Climber Records. Dist: PRT

Ferguson, Dave

SOMEWHERE OVER THE RAINBOW.
Album: released on Breakdown, Mar'77

Ferguson, Horace

SINCE THE ADDICT.
Album: released on Ujama, Aug'87 by Ujama Records. Dist: Spartan, Jetstar

Ferguson, Maynard

BEST OF MAYNARD FERGUSON.
Album: released on CBS, Jul'80 by CBS Records. Dist: CBS

BLUES ROAR, THE.
Compact disc: released on Mobile Fidelity, '86 by Mobile Fidelity Records.

BODY AND SOUL.
Tracks: / Expresso / Body & soul / M.O.T. / Mira Mira / Last dive / Beautiful hearts / Central park.
Notes: Super trumpet star Maynard Ferguson's brand new album "Body and Soul" is the first recording of his reorganized young band that has turned on large audiences in the US and abroad during the past year. It introduces a hot 11-piece road band with a powerful sound. Personnel:Maynard Ferguson-MF Horn Trumpets, Flugelhorn/Wayne Bergeron-Lead Trumpet, Flugelhorn/Alan Wise-Trumpet-Flugelhorn/Alex Iles-Trombones/Tim Ries-Alto, Tenor & Soprano Saxophones, Flute/Rick Margitza-Tenor,Soprano,Saxophones/Todd Carlon-Keyboards/Dave Miller-Drums/Dave Carpenter-Bass/Staeve Fisher-Percussion/Michael Higgins-Guitar.

Album: released on Blackhawk, Sep'86 by Blackhawk Records (USA). Dist: IMS-Polygram

Cassette: released on Blackhawk, Sep'86 by Blackhawk Records (USA). Dist: IMS-Polygram

BODY & SOUL.
Tracks: / Expresso / Body & soul / M.O.T. / Mira Mira / Last drive / Beautiful hearts / Central Park.
Compact disc: released on Blackhawk, Mar'87 by Blackhawk Records (USA). Dist: IMS-Polygram

CONDUCTS THE BIRDLAND DREAMBAND VOL.1/2.
Double Album: released on RCA (France), '83 by RCA Records. Dist: Discovery

MAYNARD FERGUSON & HIS ORIGINAL DREAMBAND (Ferguson, Maynard & His Original Dreamband).
Album: released on Artistry, Sep'86 Dist: Jazz Music

THREE KENTON'S BE BOPPERS GROUPS 1947-50 (Ferguson, Maynard / Vido Musso / Eddie Safranski).
Album: released on Unique Jazz, Jul'83 Dist: Swift, Jazz Music, Jazz Horizons

TRUMPETS OUT FRONT (Ferguson, Maynard & Herb Pomeroy).
Double Album: released on Vogue Jazz (France), May'83

Double cassette: released on Vogue Jazz (France), May'83

Ferguson S

DO IT AGAIN.
Single (12"): released on White Label, Feb'85 by White Label Records. Dist: Jetstar

Ferguson, Sonia

ONE NIGHT STAND.
Single (12"): released on Cha-Cha, May'83 by Cha Cha. Dist: Jetstar

Fergus, Winston

I WILL SING.
Album: released on John Dread Production, Nov'85 Dist: Jetstar

KEEP DANCING.
Single (12"): released on Burning Sounds, Mar'83 by Ross, Bill/Burning Sounds Records. Dist: PRT

ROCKERS ROCK.
Single (12"): released on Three Kings, Nov'83 by Three Kings Records. Dist: Jetstar Distribution

TOWN CALLED ALICE, A.
Tracks: / Town called Alice, A (Version).
Single (12"): released on Hands & Hearts, Jul'86 Dist: Jetstar

Fernandel

FELICIE AUSSI.
Double Album: released on EMI (France), '83 by EMI Records. Dist: Conifer

Fernandez, Bianco

TOMORROW DOESN'T MATTER TONIGHT.
Single (12"):

Fernest & Thunders

FERNEST & THE THUNDERS.
Album: released on Blues Unlimited, Sep'79 Dist: Swift

Ferns, Peter

STREETS OF BELFAST.
Cassette: released on Eron, Sep'85 by Eron Records. Dist: Eron Records

Ferrante & Teicher

TWIN PIANOS OF FERRANTE & TEICHER.
Cassette: released on Ideal(Tapes), Jul'84 Dist: EMI

Ferrat, Jean

CHANSON FRANCAISE, (LA).
Album: released on Barclay, Nov'79 by Decca Records. Dist: Polygram, Discovery, Conifer, IMS, Swift

CHANTE'ARAGON.
Compact disc: released on EMI (France), May'86 by EMI Records. Dist: Conifer

JE NE SUIS QU'UN CRI.
Compact disc: released on EMI (France), May'86 by EMI Records. Dist: Conifer

Ferre, Boulou & Elois

GYPSY DREAMS.
Album: released on Steeplechase, May'81

Ferrer, Violeta

FEDERICO GARCIA LORCA II.
Tracks: / Son de Negros en Cuba / Asesinato / Oda al rey de harlem / Oda a Walt Whitman / Omega / Hida de Nueva York / Cafe Cantante / Romance somnambulo / Postal a Luis Bunuel / Luna Y Panorama de los insectos / Romance de la pena negra / Pequeno poema infinito / Romance de la luna / Luna / Cometa / LLuvia.
Album: released on Nato (France), Sep'86 by Disques Nato. Dist: Essex Record Distributors Ltd.

POEMAS DE FEDERICO GARCIA LORCA.
Tracks: / Zorongo / Romance de la guardia civil Espaniola / Danza (en el huerto de la petenera) / Prendimiento de Antonio el Cambrio en el Camino de Sevilla / Muerte de Antonio el Cambrio / El Grito / Reyerta / La Guitarra / LLanto por Ignacio Sanchez Mejias / El Silencio.
Album: released on Nato (France), Sep'86 by Disques Nato. Dist: Essex Record Distributors Ltd.

Ferrie, Glen

GLENFERRIE TRAM.
Single (7"): released on Glen Ferrie, Feb'83 by Glen Ferrie Records. Dist: Glen Ferrie

Ferrier, Al

BOPPIN' TONIGHT (see Storm,Warren/Al Ferrier) (Ferrier, Al/Warren Storm).

FROM 1955-1975 -THE SOUND OF ROCKABILLY.
Album: released on Showtime, Feb'79 by Relic. Dist: Swift

LET'S GO BOPPIN' TONIGHT.
Tracks: / Blues stop knocking / She left me / Honey baby / I'm the man / Love me baby / Indian rock and roll / You win again / Hey baby / Send her back / Gunsmoke / Chrisholm trail rock.
Album: released on Flyright, Oct'86 by Flyright Records. Dist: Krazy Kat, Swift, Jazz Music

Ferrier, Kathleen

KATHLEEN FERRIER.
Album: released on BBC, '79 by BBC Records & Tapes. Dist: EMI, PRT,

SINGER, THE PERSON,(THE).
Cassette: released on BBC, Oct'79 by BBC Records & Tapes. Dist: EMI, PRT

WORLD OF KATHLEEN FERRIER.
Album: released on World of Learning, '71 by World Of Learning Records. Dist: World Of Learning

Ferron, Friddy

TRIBUTE.
Single (12"): released on High Music, Sep'84 by High Music Records. Dist: Jetstar

Ferry Aid

LET IT BE.
Tracks: / Let it be / Let it be (Gospel version).
Notes: All proceeds to Zeebrugge Disaster Fund
Single (7"): released on Sun-Zeebrugge Disaster Fund, Mar'87

Ferry, Bryan

ANOTHER TIME ANOTHER PLACE.
Compact disc: by Polydor Records. Dist: Polygram, Polydor

Album: released on Polydor, Feb'77 by Polydor Records. Dist: Polygram, Polydor

Cassette: released on Polydor, Feb'77 by Polydor Records. Dist: Polygram, Polydor

Compact disc: released on Polydor, Feb'77 by Polydor Records. Dist: Polygram, Polydor

BOYS AND GIRLS.
Tracks: / Sensation / Slave to love / Don't stop the dance / Wasteland / Windswept / Chosen one, The / Great unknown, The / Stone woman / Boys and girls.
Album: released on E.G., Jan'87 by Virgin Records. Dist: Virgin, EMI

Cassette: released on E.G., Jan'87 by Virgin Records. Dist: Virgin, EMI

Compact disc: released on E.G., Jan'87 by Virgin Records. Dist: Virgin, EMI

BOYS & GIRLS.
Tracks: / Sensation / Slave to love / Don't stop the dance / Wasreland, A / Windswept / Chosen one, The / Valentine / Stone woman / Boys and girls.
Compact disc: released on E.G., Jul'85 by Virgin Records. Dist: Virgin, EMI

BRIDE STRIPPED BARE (THE).
Tracks: / Sign of the times / Can't let go / Hold on / I'm coming / Same old blues / When she walks in the room / Take me to the river / What goes on / Carrickfergus / That's how strong my love is / This island Earth.
Compact disc: released on E.G., Jan'87 by Virgin Records. Dist: Virgin, EMI

Album: released on E.G., Jan'87 by Virgin Records. Dist: Virgin, EMI

Cassette: released on E.G., Jan'87 by Virgin Records. Dist: Virgin, EMI

BRIDE STRIPPED BARE, (THE).
Album: released on Polydor, Apr'78 by Polydor Records. Dist: Polygram, Polydor

Cassette: released on Polydor, Apr'78 by Polydor Records. Dist: Polygram, Polydor

Compact disc: released on Polydor, Apr'78 by Polydor Records. Dist: Polygram, Polydor

DON'T STOP THE DANCE.
Single (7"): released on E.G., Aug'85 by Virgin Records. Dist: Virgin, EMI

Single (12"): released on E.G., Aug'85 by Virgin Records. Dist: Virgin. EMI

INTERVIEW PICTURE DISC.
Album: released on Baktabak, May'87 by Baktabak Records. Dist: Arabesque

IN YOUR MIND.
Tracks: / This is tomorrow / All night operator / One kiss / Love me madly again / Tokyo Joe / Party doll / Rock of ages / In your mind.
Album: released on E.G., Jan'87 by Virgin Records. Dist: Virgin, EMI

Cassette: released on E.G., Jan'87 by Virgin Records. Dist: Virgin, EMI

Compact disc: released on E.G., Jan'87 by Virgin Records. Dist: Virgin, EMI

Album: released on Polydor, Feb'77 by Polydor Records. Dist: Polygram, Polydor

Cassette: released on Polydor, Feb'77 by Polydor Records. Dist: Polygram, Polydor

Compact disc: released on Polydor, Feb'77 by Polydor Records. Dist: Polygram, Polydor

IS YOUR LOVE STRONG ENOUGH?.
Tracks: / Windswept (Inst).
Single (7"): released on E.G., Mar'86 by Virgin Records. Dist: Virgin, EMI

Single (12"): released on E.G., Mar'86 by Virgin Records. Dist: Virgin, EMI

Compact disc: released on Polydor, Jun'84 by Polydor Records. Dist: Polygram, Polydor

LET'S STICK TOGETHER.
Tracks: / Let's stick together / Casanova / Sea Breezes / Shame, shame, shame. / 2HB / Price of love (The) / Chance meeting / It's only love / You go to my head / Re-make re-model / Heart on my sleeve.
Album: released on E.G., Jan'87 by Virgin Records. Dist: Virgin, EMI

Cassette: released on E.G., Jan'87 by Virgin Records. Dist: Virgin, EMI

Compact disc: released on E.G., Jan'87 by Virgin Records. Dist: Virgin, EMI

Album: released on Polydor, Feb'77 by Polydor Records. Dist: Polygram Polydor

Cassette: released on Polydor, Feb'77 by Polydor Records. Dist: Polygram, Polydor

Compact disc: released on Polydor, Jul'84 by Polydor Records. Dist: Polygram, Polydor

SLAVE TO LOVE.
Single (7"): released on E.G., Apr'85 by Virgin Records. Dist: Virgin, EMI

Single (12"): released on E.G., Apr'85 by Virgin Records. Dist: Virgin, EMI

STREETLIFE (Ferry, Bryan & Roxy Music).
Tracks: / Virginia Plain / Hard rain's a-gonna fall / Pyamarama / Do the Strand / These foolish things / Street life / Let's stick together / Smoke gets in your eyes / Love is the drug / Sign of the times / Dance away / Angel eyes / Oh yeah / Over you / Same old scene / In the midnight hour / More than this / Avalon / Slave to love / Jealous guy.
Album: released on E.G., Apr'86 by Virgin Records. Dist: Virgin, EMI

Cassette: released on E.G., Apr'86 by Virgin Records. Dist: Virgin, EMI

Compact disc: released on E.G., Apr'86 by Virgin Records. Dist: Virgin, EMI

Compact disc: released on Polydor, Jul'84 by Polydor Records. Dist: Polygram, Polydor

THESE FOOLISH THINGS.
Tracks: /Hard rain's a-gonna fall, A / Hard rain's a-gonna fall, A / River of salt / Don't ever change / Piece of my heart / Baby I don't care / It's my party / Don't worry baby / Sympathy for the devil / Tracks of my tears / You won't see me / I love how you love me / Loving you is sweeter than ever / These foolish things.
Compact disc: released on E.G., Jan'87 by Virgin Records. Dist: Virgin, EMI

Album: released on E.G., Jan'87 by Virgin Records. Dist: Virgin, EMI

Cassette: released on E.G., Jan'87 by Virgin Records. Dist: Virgin, EMI

Album: released on Polydor, Feb'77 by Polydor Records. Dist: Polygram, Polydor

Cassette: released on Polydor, Feb'77 by Polydor Records. Dist: Polygram, Polydor

Compact disc: released on Polydor, Jul'84 by Polydor Records. Dist: Polygram, Polydor

WINDSWEPT.
Single (7"): released on E.G., Nov'85 by Virgin Records. Dist: Virgin, EMI

Single (7"): released on E.G., Nov'85 by Virgin Records. Dist: Virgin, EMI

Single (12"): released on E.G., Nov'85 by Virgin Records. Dist: Virgin, EMI

Feso Trombone
FREEDOM TRAIN.
Album: released on Africagram, Apr'84 by Cherry Red Records. Dist: Pinnacle

Fessor's Big City Band
HOT BISCUITS.
Album: released on Storyville, Jul'81 by Storyville Records. Dist: Jazz Music Distribution, Swift Distribution, Chris Wellard Distribution, Counterpoint Distribution

Fessors Session Boys
George Kelly & Al Vasey/Fessors Session Boys

Festa New Orleans
FESTA NEW ORLEANS MUSIC ASCONA (Various Artists).
Notes: Featuring: The King Oliver Centennial band, Lillian Boutte & Her Music Friends, Storyville Shakers, Louis Nelson N.O. Band, Al Rapone & The Zydeco Express, Jambalaya Four & Freddie Kohlman, S.Rimmington Band, Thomas Jefferson, Papa Toms Lamentation Jazz Band, New Orleans Blue Serenade.
Album: released on Festa New Orleans, Nov'86 Dist: Jazz Music

Festival
EVITA.
Album: released on RSO, Jan'80

Festival '84
FESTIVAL '84 Various artists (Various Artists).
Cassette: released on Sonic Sounds, Sep'84 by Sonic Sound Records. Dist: Jetstar

Festival at Blairgowrie
FESTIVAL AT BLAIRGOWRIE Various artists (Various Artists).
Album: released on Topic, '81 Dist: Roots Distribution

Festival de musique Aca-
FESTIVAL DE MUSIQUE ACADIENNE '81 LIVE Various artists (Various Artists).
Album:

Festival flamenco gitano
FESTIVAL FLAMENCO GITANO - LIVE VOL.1 (Various Artists).
Compact disc: released on L & R, Dec'86 Dist: Swift

FESTIVAL FLAMENCO GITANO - VOL.2 (Various Artists).
Compact disc: released on L & R, Dec'86 Dist: Swift

Festival for Latin America
FESTIVAL FOR LATIN AMERICA (Various Artists).
Notes: Inc. Pete Seeger, Capri.
Album: released on Waterfront, May'87 by

Waterfront Records. Dist: Rough Trade, Cartel, Projection, Roots

Festival of...
FESTIVAL OF CAROLS Various choirs (Various Artists).
Album: released on MFP, Oct'80 by EMI Records. Dist: EMI

FESTIVAL OF LESSONS AND CAROLS (King's College).
Album: released on Argo, '78 by Decca Records. Dist: Polygram

FESTIVAL OF MASSED ENGLISH MALE CHOIRS Various choirs (Various Artists).
Album: released on Grosvenor, Jan'79 by Grosvenor Records. Dist: Taylors

FESTIVAL OF PRAISE Various artists (Various Artists).
Album: released on Abbey, Mar'80 by Abbey. Dist: PRT, Taylors.

Festival Singers
HAPPY BIRTHDAY TO YOU.
Single (7"): released on EMI, Dec'77 by EMI Records. Dist: EMI

Fest, Manfredo
SEND IN THE CLOWNS.
Single (7"): released on Bluebird, May'83 by Bluebird Records. Dist: EMI, Jetstar

Single (12"): released on Bluebird, May'83 by Bluebird Records. Dist: EMI, Jetstar

Fetchin' Bones
CABIN FLOUNDER.
Album: released on DB-Stiff, Nov'85 by Stiff Records. Dist: Stiff Records, EMI

Fete de la biere, (La)
FETE DE LA BIERE, (LA) Various Artists (Various Artists).
Album: released on Deesse (France). May'85

Fettig, Mary
IN GOOD COMPANY.
Album: released on Concord Jazz(USA), Sep'85 by Concord Jazz Records (USA). Dist: IMS, Polygram

Fetus Production
ENVIRONMENTAL.
Album: released on Fetus Productions, Nov'84 by Red Rhino Records. Dist: Red Rhino, Cartel

Feud
TO LOAD BUT ONCE.
Album: released on Feud, Nov'84 by Feud Records. Dist: Jetstar

Fever Tree
PIXIE SHOP, (THE).
Single (7"): released on Plan B, Sep'85 by Plan B Records. Dist: Cartel

Single (12"): released on Plan B, Sep'85 by Plan B Records. Dist: Cartel

SAN FRANCISCO GIRLS.
Tracks: / Imitation situation / Where do you go? / San Francisco girls / 99 and one half / Man who paints the picture (Parts 1 & 2) / Filigree and the shadow / Sun also rises, The / Day tripper/We can work it out / Nowaday's Clancey can't even sing / Unlock my door / Come with me / Peace of mind / Death is the dancer.
Album: released on See For Miles, Jun'86 by See For Miles Records. Dist: Pinnacle

Few Shells
SOUND SENSE.
Single (7"): released on Loose, Oct'84 by Loose Records. Dist: Nine Mile, Cartel

Single (12"): released on Loose, Oct'84 by Loose Records. Dist: Nine Mile, Cartel

Feyer, George
ESSENTIAL COLE PORTER, THE.
Album: released on Vanguard (France), Jun'84

Ffrench, Robert
GIRL NOWADAYS.
Single (12"): released on Joe Gibbs, Sep'83 by Joe Gibbs Records. Dist: Jetstar

MR BABYLON.
Single (12"): released on EAD, Apr'84 by EAD Records. Dist: Jetstar

MY BABY.
Single (12"): released on Londisc, Sep'84 by Londisc Records.

ON THE DANCE FLOOR.

Single (12"): released on Joe Gibbs, Nov'83 by Joe Gibbs Records. Dist: Jetstar

PUMPEE SWEETIE.
Single (12"): released on Reggae Sound, Nov'83 by Reggae Sound Records. Dist: Jetstar

SECRET LOVER.
Single (12"): by Lightning Records. Dist: Jetstar

Single (12"): by Lightning Records. Dist: Jetstar

Fialka, Karel
EAT, DRINK, DANCE, RELAX.
Single (7"): released on Carrere, May'83 by Carrere Records. Dist: PRT, Spartan

STILL LIFE.
Album: released on Blue Print, Jun'80 Dist: PRT

Album: released on Blue Print, '80 Dist: PRT

HEY MATTHEW.
Single (7"): released on I.R.S.(Independent Record Syndicate), Aug'87 by I.R.S.. Dist: MCA

Single (12"): released on I.R.S.(Independent Record Syndicate), Aug'87 by I.R.S.. Dist: MCA

Flat Lux
BLUE EMOTION.
Single (7"): released on Polydor, Mar'84 by Polydor Records. Dist: Polygram, Polydor Deleted '84.

Single (12"): released on Polydor, Mar'84 by Polydor Records. Dist: Polygram, Polydor

Single (7"): released on Polydor, Mar'84 by Polydor Records. Dist: Polygram, Polydor Deleted '84.

FEELS LIKE WINTER AGAIN.
Single (7"): released on Cocteau, Mar'85 by Cocteau Records. Dist: Pinnacle.

HIRED HISTORY.
Album: released on Polydor, Aug'84 by Polydor Records. Dist: Polygram, Polydor

Cassette: released on Polydor, Aug'84 by Polydor Records. Dist: Polygram, Polydor Deleted '87.

SOLITARY LOVERS.
Single (7"): released on Polydor, Jan'85 by Polydor Records. Dist: Polygram, Polydor

Single (12"): released on Polydor, Jan'85 by Polydor Records. Dist: Polygram, Polydor

Fiction, Eddie
U.F.O.
Single (7"): released on Absurd, Sep'82 by Absurd. Dist: Pinnacle, Rough Trade

Fiction Factory
ALL OR NOTHING.
Single (7"): released on CBS, May'84 by CBS Records. Dist: CBS

Single (12"): released on CBS, May'84 by CBS Records. Dist: CBS

FEELS LIKE HEAVEN.

Single (7"): released on CBS, Jan'84 by CBS Records. Dist: CBS

Single (12"): released on CBS, Jan'84 by CBS Records. Dist: CBS

GHOST OF LOVE.
Single (7"): released on CBS, Mar'84 by CBS Records. Dist: CBS

Single (12"): released on CBS, Mar'84 by CBS Records. Dist: CBS

NO TIME.
Single (7"): released on Foundry, Jun'85 by Foundry Records. Dist: Virgin, EMI

Single (12"): released on Foundry, Jun'85 by Foundry Records. Dist: Virgin, EMI

NOT THE ONLY ONE.
Single (7"): released on Foundry, Mar'85 by Foundry Records. Dist: Virgin, EMI

Single (12"): released on Foundry, Mar'85 by Foundry Records. Dist: Virgin, EMI

THROW THE WARPED WHEEL OUT.
Tracks: / Feels like heaven / Heart and mind / Hanging gardens / All or nothing / Hit the mark / Ghost of love / Tears of tears / First step, The / Warped wheel, The.
Album: released on CBS, Apr'86 by CBS Records. Dist: CBS

Cassette: released on CBS, Apr'86 by CBS Records. Dist: CBS

Fiddle & banjo Bluegrass
FIDDLE & BANJO BLUEGRASS Various artists (Various Artists).
Album: released on Arlon (France), Aug'83 Dist: Conifer, Discovery

Fiddler of the Reels
FIDDLER OF THE REELS Hardy, Thomas (Morant, Richard).
Cassette: released on Talking Tape Company, '84 by Talking Tape Company Records.

Cassette: released on Talking Tape, '84

Fiddler On The Roof
FIDDLER ON THE ROOF Original Soundtrack (Various Artists).
Tracks: / Prologue and "Tradition" & Main title / If I were a rich man / Sabbath prayer / To life / Miracle of miracles / Tevye's dream / Sunrise sunset / Wedding celebration and the bottle dance / Do you love me? / Far from the home I love / Chava ballet sequence / Anatevka / Finale.
Compact disc: released on EMI, Jul'87 by EMI Records. Dist: EMI

FIDDLER ON THE ROOF Original London cast.
Album: released on Embassy, Jul'77 by CBS Records. Dist: CBS

FIDDLER ON THE ROOF Original film soundtrack.
Album: released on RCA (Germany), '83

Double Album: released on United Artists, '71

Fiddlers Dram
BEERCART LANE.
Single (7"): released on Dingles, Mar'80 by Dingles Records. Dist: Projection

BLACK HOLE.
Single (7"): released on Dingles, Jul'81 by Dingles Records. Dist: Projection

DANCING IN THE MOONLIGHT.
Single (7"): released on Dingles, Aug'83 by Dingles Records. Dist: Projection

DAY TRIP TO BANGOR.
Single (7"): released on Dingles, Dec'79 by Dingles Records. Dist: Projection

FIDDLERS DRAM.
Album: released on Dingles, Feb'80 by Dingles Records. Dist: Projection

Cassette: released on Dingles, Feb'80 by Dingles Records. Dist: Projection

LITTLE RAY OF SUNSHINE.
Single (7"): released on Dingles, Dec'81 by Dingles Records. Dist: Projection

Fiddlers Hall Of Fame
FIDDLERS HALL OF FAME (Various Artists).
Album: released on Starday, Apr'87

Cassette: released on Starday, Apr'87

Fiddlers Three Plus Two
FIDDLERS THREE PLUS TWO.
Tracks: / Isle of Skye, The / Scottish legacy (The) / Dean Brig Reel, The / Green shades of gask / Loch of the rising mist / Cutty Sark / Sarah Graces of Oban / Fairy dance, The / Mason's apron (The) / Kilt is me delight, The / Thistle hornpipe / Dancing feet / Galley watch / Morning fair / Kildare fancy, The / Hamilton house.
Album: released on Lochshore, Nov'86 by Klub Records. Dist: PRT

Cassette: released on Lochshore, Nov'86 by Klub Records. Dist: PRT

Fidel
SNOWBLINDE.
Single (12"): released on Leeds Independent, Jul'86 by Revolver Records. Dist: Cartel

Fidelio Quartet
TIPPETT.
Album: released on PRT, Jan'85 by PRT Records. Dist: PRT

Cassette: released on PRT, Jan'85 by PRT Records. Dist: PRT

Fiedler, Arthur
ARTHUR FIEDLER & THE BOSTON POPS ORCHESTRA.
Double Album: released on Cambra, '83 by Cambra Records. Dist: IDS, Conifer

Double cassette: released on Cambra, '83 by Cambra Records. Dist: Conifer

SATURDAY NIGHT FIEDLER (Fiedler,

Arthur & The Boston Pops Orchestra).
Album: released on Bulldog Records. Jul'82

Field, Billy

TRUE LOVE.
Single (7"): released on CBS, Dec'82 by CBS Records. Dist: CBS

Field guide to...

FIELD GUIDE TO THE MAMMAL VOICES OF EUROPE.
Double Album: released on Swedish Broadcasting Corp., Jul'82 Dist: Conifer

Fielding, Jerry

SWINGIN' IN HI-FI (Fielding, Jerry & His Orchestra).
Album: released on Jasmine, Sep'83 by Jasmine Records. Dist: PRT

Field, Paul

DIFFERENT YET THE SAME.
Notes: Paul has worked with Roy Martin to produce his third solo album. Roy first worked with Paul in the days of Nutshell when he played piano at concerts from about 1975/77. Since Paul started doing solo concerts in 1982, Roy has become increasingly involved, not only as a piano player but as a songwriter. The new album is designed to relate strongly to their concerts.
Album: released on Myrrh, Jan'86 by Word Records. Dist: Word Distribution

Cassette: released on Myrrh, Jan'86 by Word Records. Dist: Word Distribution

RESTLESS HEART.
Album: released on Myrrh, May'82 by Word Records. Dist: Word Distribution

Cassette: released on Myrrh, May'82 by Word Records. Dist: Word Distribution

VISIONS.
Album: released on Myrrh, Jul'85 by Word Records. Dist: Word Distribution

Cassette: released on Myrrh, Jul'85 by Word Records. Dist: Word Distribution

Field, Richard

TELLIN IT LIKE IT IS (Field, Richard Dimples).
Tracks: / Tell it like it is / You're everything I want in a woman / Hooked on your lovin' / Stand up on it / Never gonna let the sweet get sour / Dor or hog / I won't rush you / I can't live with or without you / Do you belong to the dope man.
Album: released on CBS, Sep'87 by CBS Records. Dist: CBS

Cassette: released on CBS, Sep'87 by CBS Records. Dist: CBS

Fields, Gracie

AMAZING GRACIE FIELDS.
Album: released on Monmouth, May'79

BEST OF HER BBC BROADCASTS.
Album: released on BBC, May'80 by BBC Records & Tapes. Dist: EMI, PRT,

FOCUS ON GRACIE FIELDS.
Cassette: released on Decca, '81 by Decca Records. Dist: Polygram

GOLDEN AGE OF..., THE.
Album: released on Golden Age, Apr'85 by Music For Pleasure Records. Dist: EMI

Cassette: released on Golden Age, Apr'85 by Music For Pleasure Records. Dist: EMI

GRACIE FIELDS STORY, THE.
Double Album: released on EMI, Oct'79 by EMI Records. Dist: EMI

INCOMPARABLE.
Tracks: / Reviens / Punch and Judy show, The / Gracie's christmas party / My Ohio home / Our avenue / When the fields are white with daises, I'll return / Would a Manx cat wag it's tail? / Home sweet home / Looking on the bright side of life / They all make love but me / Clatter of clogs / Life's desire / I took my harp to a party / Just one more chance / In my little bottom drawer / Isle of Capri / Mocking bird went cuckoo / Sing as we go / My blue heaven / We're living at the cloisters / Take a look at mine / Like the big pots do / Serenade / Singin' in the bathtub.
Album: released on Saville, Dec'85 by Conifer Records. Dist: Conifer

Cassette: released on Saville, Dec'85 by Conifer Records. Dist: Conifer

ISLE OF CAPRI.
Album: released on Joy, May'87 by President Records. Dist: Jazz Music, Swift, President Distribution

LAUGHTER AND SONG.
Tracks: / Charmaine / Because I love you / My blue heaven / House is haunted, The / Dancing with tears in my eyes / Home / I'm playing with fire / Take a good look at mine / How deep is the ocean / Play to me gypsy / Say it isn't so / You're driving me crazy / I lift up my finger and I say tweet tweet / One little hair on his head, The / Fred Fannakapan / Heaven will protect an honest girl / Little pudden basin / Photograph of mother's wedding group / Sitting on a five bar gate / He forgot to come back / Will you love me when I'm Mutton.
Notes: All tracks with orchestra conducted by Ray Noble except tracks 1 & 10. Track 10 accompanied by Herbie Dawson at the organ. Engineered by Peter Bown. Produced, compiled and transferred by Chris Ellis.
Album: released on Retrospect Series, Jun'87
Cat. no: **SH 510**
Cassette: released on Retrospect Series, Jun'87

THIS IS.
Album: released on EMI, Jun'80 by EMI Records. Dist: EMI

WORLD OF GRACIE FIELDS.
Album: released on World of Learning, '70 by World Of Learning Records. Dist: World Of Learning

WORLD OF VOL.1.
Cassette: released on Decca, '74 by Decca Records. Dist: Polygram

Fields, Judy

HALFWAY TO PARADISE.
Album: released on Victory (USA), Oct'86 by

Fields, Kim

HE LOVES ME, HE LOVES ME NOT.
Single (7"): released on Arista, Nov'84 by Arista Records. Dist: RCA

Single (12"): released on Arista, Nov'84 by Arista Records. Dist: RCA

Fields Of Plastic

LOVE I LOVE, THE.
Tracks: / What love can do for you.
Single (7"): released on WEA, Aug'87 by WEA Records. Dist: WEA

Single (12"): released on WEA, Aug'87 by WEA Records. Dist: WEA

Fields Of The Nephilim

BURNING THE FIELDS.
Single (7"): released on Tower, Feb'86 by Tower Records. Dist: Jungle, Cartel

Single (12"): released on Tower, Jun'86 by Tower Records. Dist: Jungle, Cartel

Single (12"): released on Tower, Aug'85 by Tower Records. Dist: Jungle, Cartel

BURNING THE FIELDS (MINI LP).
Album: released on Tower, Jun'87 by Tower Records. Dist: Jungle, Cartel

DAWNRAZOR.
Album: released on Situation 2, May'87 Dist: Cartel, Pinnacle

Cassette: released on Situation 2, May'87 Dist: Cartel, Pinnacle

DAWN RAZOR.
Compact disc: released on Situation 2, May'87 Dist: Cartel, Pinnacle

POWER.
Tracks: / Power / Secrets / Tower.
Single (12"): released on Situation 2, Aug'86 Dist: Cartel, Pinnacle

PREACHER MAN.
Tracks: / Preacher man / Laura 11.
Single (7"): released on Situation 2, Mar'87 Dist: Cartel, Pinnacle

Single (12"): released on Situation 2, Mar'87 Dist: Cartel, Pinnacle

Fields, Richard

DARK GABLE.
Album: released on RCA, Sep'85 by RCA Records. Dist: RCA, Roots, Swift, Wellard, Chris, I & B, Solomon & Peres Distribution

Cassette: released on RCA, Sep'85 by RCA Records. Dist: RCA, Roots, Swift, Wellard, Chris, I & B, Solomon & Peres Distribution

MMM....
Compact disc: by RCA Records. Dist: RCA, Roots, Swift, Wellard, Chris, I & B, Solomon & Peres Distribution

Album: released on RCA, Aug'84 by RCA Records. Dist: RCA, Roots, Swift, Wellard, Chris, I & B, Solomon & Peres Distribution

Cassette: released on RCA, Aug'84 by RCA Records. Dist: RCA, Roots, Swift, Wellard, Chris, I & B, Solomon & Peres Distribution

YOUR WIFE IS CHEATIN ON US (Fields, Richard Dimples).
Single (7"): released on RCA, Jun'84 by RCA Records. Dist: RCA, Roots, Swift, Wellard, Chris, I & B, Solomon & Peres Distribution

Cassette: released on RCA, Jun'84 by RCA Records. Dist: RCA, Roots, Swift, Wellard, Chris, I & B, Solomon & Peres Distribution Deleted '85.

Fierce

FIERCE Dance cuts number one (Various Artists).
Tracks: / Do it properly / Let's get brutal / Living in a box / Show you how to jack / I know you got soul / I ain't into that / Put the needle to the record / Heartbeat / Last night.
Notes: Inc. Living In A Box, Kid 'N Play.
Album: released on Cool Tempo, Jul'87 by Chrysalis Records. Dist: CBS

Cassette: released on Cool Tempo, Jul'87 by Chrysalis Records. Dist: CBS

Fierce Heart

FIERCE HEART.
Album: released on Polydor, Nov'85 by Polydor Records. Dist: Polygram, Polydor

Cassette: released on Polydor, Nov'85 by Polydor Records. Dist: Polygram, Polydor

Fiestas

OH SO FINE.
Album: released on Ace, May'86 by Ace Records. Dist: Pinnacle, Swift, Hotshot, Cadillac

Fifo

KLEESHAY.
Single (7"): released on 1159, May'82

Fifteen Big Ones

15 BIG ONES Various artists (Various Artists).
Album: released on Vista Sounds, Dec'84 by Vista Sounds Records. Dist: Jetstar

Fifteen Heart Breakers

15 HEART BREAKERS Various Original artists (Various Artists).
Album: released on Hallmark, Mar'79 by Pickwick Records. Dist: Pickwick Distribution, PRT, Taylors

Cassette: released on Hallmark, Mar'79 by Pickwick Records. Dist: Pickwick Distribution, PRT, Taylors

Fifteen Mersey hits

15 MERSEY HITS Various artists (Various Artists).
Album: released on Hallmark, Mar'79 by Pickwick Records. Dist: Pickwick Distribution, PRT, Taylors

Cassette: released on Hallmark, Mar'79 by Pickwick Records. Dist: Pickwick Distribution, PRT, Taylors

Fifteen Monster Hits

15 MONSTER HITS (VOL 1) various original artists (Various original artists).
Album: released on Hallmark, Mar'79 by Pickwick Records. Dist: Pickwick Distribution, PRT, Taylors

Cassette: released on Hallmark, Mar'79 by Pickwick Records. Dist: Pickwick Distribution, PRT, Taylors

15 MONSTER HITS (VOL 2) Various Original Artists (Various original artists).
Album: released on Hallmark, Mar'79 by Pickwick Records. Dist: Pickwick Distribution, PRT, Taylors

Cassette: released on Hallmark, Mar'79 by Pickwick Records. Dist: Pickwick Distribution, PRT, Taylors

Fifteen Rabbits

FIFTEEN RABBITS (Felix Salten -Celebration of life).
Cassette: released on Caedmon(USA), Sep'80 by Caedmon (USA) Records. Dist: Gower, Taylors, Discovery

Fifteen Tear Jerkers

15 TEAR JERKERS various original artists (Various original artists).
Album: released on Hallmark, Mar'79 by Pickwick Records. Dist: Pickwick Distribution, PRT, Taylors

Cassette: released on Hallmark, Mar'79 by Pickwick Records. Dist: Pickwick Distribution, PRT, Taylors

Fifteenth

ANDELINE.
Single (12"): released on Tanz, Apr'86 Dist: Red Rhino Distribution, Cartel Distribution

Fifteen Years Of...

15 YEARS OF THE TOP OF THE POPS Various artists (Various Artists).
Album: released on BBC, '79 by BBC Records & Tapes. Dist: EMI, PRT,

Cassette: released on BBC, '79 by BBC Records & Tapes. Dist: EMI, PRT

Fifth Angel

FIFTH ANGEL.
Album: released on Roadrunner (Dutch), Aug'86 Dist: Pinnacle

Fifth Dimension

6 TRACK HITS.
Extended-play record: released on Scoop 33, Sep'83 by Pickwick Records. Dist: H.R. Taylor

Cassette: released on Scoop 33, Sep'83 by Pickwick Records. Dist: H.R. Taylor

SURRENDER.
Single (7"): released on Buddah, Jul'83 Dist: Swift, Jazz Music, PRT

Single (12"): released on Buddah, Jul'83 Dist: Swift, Jazz Music, PRT

Fifties...

50'S: JUKE JOINT BLUES (Various Artists).
Album: released on Ace, Jun'87 by Ace Records. Dist: Pinnacle, Swift, Hotshot, Cadillac

Cassette: released on Ace, Jun'87 by Ace Records. Dist: Pinnacle, Swift, Hotshot, Cadillac

Compact disc: released on Ace, Jul'87 by Ace Records. Dist: Pinnacle, Swift, Hotshot, Cadillac

50'S MILLION SELLERS VOL 2 Various artists (Various Artists).
Cassette: released on Cambra, Aug'86 by Cambra Records. Dist: IDS, Conifer

50'S MILLION SELLERS VOL.1 Various artists (Various Artists).
Cassette: released on Cambra, Aug'86 by Cambra Records. Dist: IDS, Conifer

50'S: R & B VOCAL GROUPS (Various Artists).
Album: released on Ace, Jun'87 by Ace Records. Dist: Pinnacle, Swift, Hotshot, Cadillac

Cassette: released on Ace, Jun'87 by Ace Records. Dist: Pinnacle, Swift, Hotshot, Cadillac

Compact disc: released on Ace, Jul'87 by Ace Records. Dist: Pinnacle, Swift, Hotshot, Cadillac

50'S: ROCKABILLY FEVER (Various Artists).
Album: released on Ace, Jun'87 by Ace Records. Dist: Pinnacle, Swift, Hotshot, Cadillac

Cassette: released on Ace, Jun'87 by Ace Records. Dist: Pinnacle, Swift, Hotshot, Cadillac

Compact disc: released on Ace, Jul'87 by Ace Records. Dist: Pinnacle, Swift, Hotshot, Cadillac

FIFTIES,THE: JUKE JOINT BLUES (Various Artists).
Cassette: released on Ace, Jul'87 by Ace Records. Dist: Pinnacle, Swift, Hotshot, Cadillac

Album: released on Ace, Jun'87 by Ace Records. Dist: Pinnacle, Swift, Hotshot, Cadillac

Compact disc: released on Ace, Jun'87 by Ace Records. Dist: Pinnacle, Swift, Hotshot, Cadillac

FIFTIES VOLUME 1, (THE) Various artists (Various Artists).
Tracks: / To know him is to love him / Born too late / It's all in the game / Great pretender, (The) / Tammy / All I have to do is dream / Day the rains came, (The) / Only sixteen / Story of my life, (The) / Remember you're mine / Young love / It's only make believe / Who's sorry now? / Donna.
Album: released on Old Gold, Nov'85 by Old Gold Records. Dist: Lightning, Jazz Music, Spartan, Counterpoint

Cassette: released on Old Gold, Nov'85 by Old Gold Records. Dist: Lightning, Jazz Music, Spartan, Counterpoint

FIFTIES VOLUME 2, (THE) Various artists (Various Artists).
Tracks: / Bye bye love / Singing the blues / Yes tonight Josephine / Ninety-nine ways / Butterfly / Don't forbid me / Garden of Eden / That'll be the day / Diana / At the hop / Little darlin' / When / Whole lotta woman / Ma, he's making eyes at me.
Album: released on Old Gold, Nov'85 by Old Gold Records. Dist: Lightning, Jazz Music, Spartan, Counterpoint

Cassette: released on Old Gold, Nov'85 by Old Gold Records. Dist: Lightning, Jazz Music,

Page 360

Spartan, Counterpoint

Fifty...

50 ALL TIME COUNTRY HITS Various artists (Various Artists).
Double Album: released on Pickwick, May'77 by Pickwick Records. Dist: Pickwick Distribution, Prism Leisure Distribution, Lugtons

Double cassette: released on Pickwick, May'77 by Pickwick Records. Dist: Pickwick Distribution, Prism Leisure Distribution, Lugtons

50 CLASSIC PUB SONGS Various artists (Various Artists).
Album: released on A & R, '84 Dist: Spartan

Cassette: released on A & R, '84 Dist: Spartan

50 DJ JINGLES Various artists (Various Artists).
Cassette: released on Roger Squires, Jun'78

50 EASY LISTENING FAVOURITES Various artists (Various Artists).
Cassette: released on MFP (Trio), Oct'85

50 FABULOUS MILLION SELLERS Various artists (Various Artists).
Notes: Three LP boxed set, two double-play cassettes
Album: released on Warwick, Nov'85 Dist: Multiple Sound Distributors

Cassette: released on Warwick, Nov'85 Dist: Multiple Sound Distributors

50 FAVOURITE BALLADS Various artists (Various Artists).
Cassette: released on MFP (Trio), Oct'85

50 FAVOURITE NURSERY RHYMES (Bisco, Patsy).
Album: released on Children's Favourites, Aug'82 Dist: Taylors

50 FAVOURITES OF THE 70'S Various artists (Various Artists).
Cassette: released on MFP (Trio), Oct'85

50 HAMMOND ORGAN FAVOURITES Various artists (Various Artists).
Triple album / cassette: released on Trio, Nov'84 by MFP. Dist: EMI

50 INSTRUMENTAL GREATS Various artists (Various Artists).
Double Album: released on Polydor, Aug'80 by Polydor Records. Dist: Polygram, Polydor

Double cassette: released on Polydor, Aug'80 by Polydor Records. Dist: Polygram, Polydor

50 PIANO FAVOURITES Various artists (Various Artists).
Triple album / cassette: released on Trio, Nov'84 by MFP. Dist: EMI

50'S BOPPERS Various artists (Various Artists).
Album: released on Collector (White Label Holland), Jan'85 Dist: Swift

50 YEARS OF COUNTRY MUSIC - VOL.1 Various artists (Various Artists).
Album: released on RCA Camden, Feb'80 by RCA Records. Dist: Pickwick Distribution, Taylor, H.R.

Cassette: released on RCA Camden, Feb'80 by RCA Records. Dist: Pickwick Distribution, Taylor, H.R.

50 YEARS OF ROYAL BROADCASTS Various artists (Various Artists).
Double Album: released on BBC, '74 by BBC Records & Tapes. Dist: EMI, PRT, Pye

Cassette: released on BBC, '74 by BBC Records & Tapes. Dist: EMI, PRT, Pye

Fifty Fantastics

GOD'S GOT RELIGION.
Single (7"): released on Dining Out, Jun'81 by Dining Out Records. Dist: IKF, Independent

Fifty favourite...

50 FAVOURITE BALLADS Various artists (Various Artists).
Cassette: released on Trid, Nov'85

50 FAVOURITE SHOWSTOPPERS Various artists (Various Artists).
Cassette: released on Trid, Nov'85

Fifty Favourites...

50 FAVOURITES OF THE 60'S Various artists (Various Artists).
Tracks: / I like it / Our favourite melodies / Guitar tango / James Bond theme / I'm the urban spaceman / First time, (The) / Hello little girl / Yes I will / I've been a bad bad boy / Stand by me / Pretty flamingo / World without love / Good golly Miss Lolly / Walkin' back to happiness / I'll keep you satisfied / Hungry for love / House of the rising sun / Pretty blue eyes / Don't make my baby blue / Walk don't run / I'll take you home / You're sixteen, you're beautiful and you're mine / How can I tell her? / If you've gotta make a fool of somebody / Sabre dance / High time / Here I go again / Surfin' USA / There's a kind of hush (all over the world) / Little children / Shot of rhythm and blues, (A) / Supergirl / Wonderful land / One way love / Love of the loved / Kites / Message to Martha / I'm telling you now / I'm the one / Searchin' / I remember you / If you gotta go, go now / I'm into something good / Don't make me over / Boom bang-a-bang / Lily the pink / I'm a moody guy / Tribute to Buddy Holly / Rubber ball.
Cassette: released on Trio, Sep'86 by MFP. Dist: EMI

50 FAVOURITES OF THE 70'S Various artists (Various Artists).
Cassette: released on Trid, Nov'85

50 MORE COUNTRY FAVOURITES Various artists (Various Artists).
Tracks: / Folsom Prison blues / Treat me mean, treat me cruel / I'm building heartaches / I'm blue again / Time has made a change in me / Love's gonna live here / Daddy sang bass / Promises and hearts / I fall to pieces / Lost and I'll never find the way / Where do we go from here? / Little jewels / All that's keepin' me alive / Livin' in the sunshine of your love / Baby I want to love you / That's all it took / Blue is the way I feel / Will you remember mine? / Girl I used to know, A / Just out of reach / Take my hand for a while / Sticks and stones / Home is where you're happy / Wild and windy night / You made me what I am / Say, won't you be mine? / Hey porter / Release me / World's worst loser / Your cheatin' heart / I've loved and lost again / What am I living for? / Forgive and forget / We're together again / I don't need to know that right now / Two different worlds / I can't help it / And so will you, my love / Where I stand / It wasn't God who made honky tonk angels / Lighthouse bar / Silver wings / Love hurts / Tonight, ain't gonna fight again / It's so easy / Is there something on your mind? / Sugartime / I can't change overnight / You still want to go / You'll never walk alone.
Cassette: released on MFP, Sep'86 by EMI Records. Dist: EMI

50 ORCHESTRAL FAVOURITES Various artists (Various Artists).
Tracks: / What the world needs now is love / Theme from "Love Story" / She / Girl from Ipanema / Aces high / Sunrise, sunset / Snowbird / Laura / 633 Squadron / Spanish eyes / El'Condor Pasa / Shadow of your smile, (The) / Theme from "Where Eagles Dare" / Autumn leaves / Forever and ever (and ever) / "Chariots of Fire" theme / Legend of the glass mountain / Somewhere my love / Let it be / Tonight / Do you know the way to San Jose? / Spanish Harlem / Leaving on a jet plane / Portrait of my love / Raindrops keep fallin' on my head / Moon River / Bridge over troubled water / Misty / Tara theme / Ebb tide / Make it easy on yourself / Love letters / This guy's in love with you / Fools rush in (where angels fear to tread) / White rose of Athens, (The) / Love theme from "The Godfather" / When I fall in love / Theme from "Limelight" / Sardust / On a clear day you can see forever / A time for us / Bali Ha'i / Around the world / Magnificent Seven, (The) / Girl with the misty eyes / Desafinado / Elizabethan serenade / Walk on by.
Cassette: released on Trio, Nov'86 by MFP. Dist: EMI

Fifty/Fifty

MEMORIES LINGER.
Single (7"): released on PRT, Nov'82 by PRT Records. Dist: PRT

Single (12"): released on PRT, Nov'82 by PRT Records. Dist: PRT

TALK TOO MUCH.
Single (7"): released on PRT, Apr'83 by PRT Records. Dist: PRT

Single (12"): released on PRT, Apr'83 by PRT Records. Dist: PRT

Fifty Hertz...

THIS RADIO STATION (Fifty Hertz One Hundred Kils).
Single (7"): released on Prairie, May'83

Fifty Second Street

ARE YOU RECEIVING ME.
Tracks: / Make up your mind.
Single (7"): released on 10, Aug'87 by 10 Records. Dist: Virgin, EMI

Single (7"): released on 10, Aug'87 by 10 Records. Dist: Virgin, EMI

CAN'T AFFORD.
Single (12"): released on Factory, Nov'84 by Factory Records. Dist: Cartel, Pinnacle

CHILDREN OF THE NIGHT.
Tracks: / Tell me (how it feels) / Never give up on you / You're my last chance / Abandon love / Children of the night / Look I've heard / I can't let you go / Smiling eyes / I'm available / Let's celebrate.
Album: released on 10, Jul'86 by 10 Records. Dist: Virgin, EMI

Cassette: released on 10, Jul'86 by 10 Records. Dist: Virgin, EMI

Compact disc: released on 10, Jul'86 by 10 Records. Dist: Virgin, EMI

COOL AS ICE.
Single (7"): released on Factory, Mar'83 by Factory Records. Dist: Cartel, Pinnacle

I CAN'T LET YOU GO.
Tracks: / I can't let you go / I can't let you go (jazz style) / I can't let you go (M & M style) / I can't let you go (Timmy Regisford mix) / Tell me how it feels.
Single (7"): released on 10, Feb'86 by 10 Records. Dist: Virgin, EMI

Single (12"): released on 10, Feb'86 by 10 Records. Dist: Virgin, EMI

I'LL RETURN.
Tracks: / I'll return / Jamaica boy.
Single (7"): released on 10, Jun'87 by 10 Records. Dist: Virgin, EMI

Single (12"): released on 10, Jun'87 by 10 Records. Dist: Virgin, EMI

LOOK INTO MY EYES.
Single (7"): released on Factory, Aug'82 by Factory Records. Dist: Cartel, Pinnacle

TELL ME HOW IT FEELS.
Single (7"): released on 10, Oct'85 by 10 Records. Dist: Virgin, EMI

Single (12"): released on 10, Oct'85 by 10 Records. Dist: Virgin, EMI

YOU'RE MY LAST CHANCE.
Tracks: / You're my last chance / I'm available.
Single (7"): released on 10, Jan'86 by 10 Records. Dist: Virgin, EMI

Single (12"): released on 10, Jan'86 by 10 Records. Dist: Virgin, EMI

Single (12"): released on 10, Jan'86 by 10 Records. Dist: Virgin, EMI

Fifty Thousand...

FIFTY THOUSAND GLASS FANS CAN'T BE WRONG (Various Artists).
Notes: Clear vinyl.
Album: released on Glass, Dec'86 by Glass Records. Dist: Nine Mile, Rough Trade, Red Rhino, Play It Again Sam

Fifty Three Bus

HORIZONTAL DANCING.
Single (7"): released on Custom Car, Jun'84 by Custom Car Records. Dist: Pinnacle

Figgy Duff

AFTER THE TEMPEST.
Album: released on Celtic Music, Jun'85 by Celtic Music Distribution. Dist: Celtic Music, Jazz Music, Projection, Roots

FIGGY DUFF.
Album: released on Dingles, Aug'82 by Dingles Records. Dist: Projection

Fight

FIGHT (Various Artists).
Notes: Inc. Hula, In The Nursery.
Album: released on Cathexis, Feb'87 Dist: Fast Forward, Cartel

Fight Back

FIGHT BACK (Various Artists).
Single (7"): released on Endangered Musik, Jan'87 by Endangered Musik Records. Dist: Revolver

Single (7"): released on Clay, Jul'81 by Clay Records. Dist: Pinnacle

Fightin'...

FIGHTIN' SIDE OF THINGS various artists (Various Artists).
Album: released on Sonus, May'84 by Sonus Records. Dist: Spartan

Figures On A Beach

STANDING ON CEREMONY.
Tracks: / No stars / Glamour of motion, The / Feel the mood / Angels working overtime / Rhythm / Elvis' house / Pagan gift, A / Paris / State of emergency / Delirium / Big top, The.
Album: released on Sire, Jul'87

Cassette: released on Sire, Jul'87

Filarfolket

LIVE.
Album: released on Temple, May'86 by Temple Records. Dist: Roots Distribution, Folksound Distribution, Celtic Music Distribution, Projection Distribution

Album: released on Amalthea (Sweden), Jul'86 Dist: Projection

File Under Pop

HEATHROW.
Single (7"): released on Rough Trade, Jan'79 by Rough Trade Records. Dist: Rough Trade Distribution, Cartel Distribution

Fillipponio

ALL ARREMBAGGIO Lets go for it.
Single (12"): released on Eden, May'84 by Eden Records. Dist: Pinnacle

Fillmore

LAST DAYS, THE.
Double Album: by Warner Bros Records. Dist: WEA

Film 81

FILM 81 various artists (Various Artists).
Album: released on CBS, Oct'81 by CBS Records. Dist: CBS

Cassette: released on CBS, Oct'81 by CBS Records. Dist: CBS

Films Concert

FILMS CONCERT Original soundtracks (Various Artists).
Tracks: / Diva / Kramer versus Kramer / Apocalypse now / Clockwork orange, A / Runaway train / 2001 A space odyssey / Death in Venice / E la nave va.
Notes: Compilation of popular film themes.
Compact disc: released on Milan France, May'87

Film Star Parade

FILM STAR PARADE various artists (Various Artists).
Album: released on ASV Living Era, Feb'83 by ASV Records. Dist: PRT

Cassette: released on ASV Living Era, Feb'83 by ASV Records. Dist: PRT

Filmtracks

FILMTRACKS various artists (Various Artists).
Album: released on London, May'85 by London Records. Dist: Polygram

Cassette: released on London, May'85 by London Records. Dist: Polygram

Compact disc: released on London, May'85 by London Records. Dist: Polygram

Final Academy

NIGHT CAFE.
Single (7"): released on Spectrum, Oct'83 Dist: ACD

Final Conflict

FINAL CONFLICT-OMEN III Original Soundtrack.
Album: released on Colosseum(West Germany), Sep'86 Dist: Silva Screen

Final Eclipse

BIRDSONG.
Single (7"): released on Heartbeat, '81 Dist: Revolver, Pinnacle

Final Frame

MASK, THE Falls away.
Single (7"): released on Skeleton, Jun'84 by Skeleton Records. Dist: Cartel, Probe

Final Takes

FINAL TAKES various artists (Various Artists).
Album: released on Flyright, May'84 by Flyright Records. Dist: Krazy Kat, Swift, Jazz Music

Finch, Horace

CINEMA ORGAN ENCORES.
Album: released on Deroy, Jun'81 by Deroy Records. Dist: Jazz Music, Swift

Album: released on Deroy, Jun'81 by Deroy Records. Dist: Jazz Music, Swift

Album: released on Deroy, Jun'81 by Deroy Records. Dist: Jazz Music, Swift

WURLITZER ORGAN ENCORES.
Album: released on Deroy, May'86 by Deroy Records. Dist: Jazz Music, Swift

Finchley Boys

PRACTIC SESSIONS.
Album: released on Eva-Lolita, Feb'84 Dist: Pinnacle

Findask

BETWEEN THE WHITE LINES.
Album: released on Temple, May'84 by Temple Records. Dist: Roots Distribution, Folksound Distribution, Celtic Music Distribution, Projection Distribution

Fine Hunting Day

FINE HUNTING DAY various artists (Various Artists).
Album: released on Leader, '81 Dist: Jazz

Fine Mess, A
FINE MESS, A Original soundtrack (Various Artists).
Tracks: / Fine mess, A / Walk like a man / Easier said than done / Can't help falling in love / Slow down / Love's closing in / Wishful thinking / Moving so close / I'm gonna be a wheel someday / Stan & Ollie.
Album: released on Motown, Sep'86 by Motown Records. Dist: BMG Distribution

Cassette: released on Motown, Sep'86 by Motown Records. Dist: BMG Distribution

Fine Next Time
BENEATH THE HOUSES.
Single (7"): released on Stiff, Mar'86 by Stiff Records. Dist: EMI, Record Services Distribution (Ireland)

Finesse
TOGETHER 2 parts.
Single (7"): released on Intense, Aug'83 by Intense Records. Dist: PRT, Kingdom

TONIGHT WILL LAST FOREVER.
Single (7"): released on Tudor, Sep'84 Dist: Parnote Distribution (Formerly MDC), Wynd-Up Distribution

Single (12"): released on Tudor, Sep'84 Dist: Parnote Distribution (Formerly MDC), Wynd-Up Distribution

Finest Hour Of Sixties Punk
FINEST HOURS OF SIXTIES PUNK various artists (Various Artists).
Album: released on Eva-Lolita, May'84 Dist: Pinnacle

Fine Young Cannibals
BLUE.
Single (7"): released on London, Oct'85 by London Records. Dist: Polygram

Single (12"): released on London, Oct'85 by London Records. Dist: Polygram

Double-pack single: released on London, Oct'85 by London Records. Dist: Polygram

EVER FALLEN IN LOVE.
Tracks: / Ever fallen in love / Couldn't care more.
Single (7"): released on London, Mar'87 by London Records. Dist: Polygram

Single (12"): released on London, Mar'87 by London Records. Dist: Polygram

Compact disc single: released on London, Apr'87 by London Records. Dist: Polygram

Compact disc single: by London Records. Dist: Polygram

FINE YOUNG CANNIBALS (VIDEO).
Video-cassette (VHS): released on Polygram, Jun'86 by Polygram Records. Dist: Polygram

FINE YOUNG CANNIBALS.
Album: released on London, Dec'85 by London Records. Dist: Polygram

Cassette: released on London, Dec'85 by London Records. Dist: Polygram

Compact disc: released on London, Jan'86 by London Records. Dist: Polygram

FUNNY HOW LOVE IS.
Tracks: / Motherless girl.
Single (7"): released on London, Mar'86 by London Records. Dist: Polygram

Single (12"): released on London, Mar'86 by London Records. Dist: Polygram

JOHNNIE COME HOME.
Single (7"): released on London, May'85 by London Records. Dist: Polygram

Single (12"): released on London, May'85 by London Records. Dist: Polygram

SUSPICIOUS MINDS.
Tracks: / Don't ask me to choose / Time isn't kind (Live) / Pick up your ears.
Single (7"): released on London, Jan'86 by London Records. Dist: Polygram

Single (12"): released on London, Jan'86 by London Records. Dist: Polygram

Fine Young Things
CANDY MAN.
Album: released on ISR, Dec'86 by ISR Records. Dist: DMS, RCA

Cassette: released on ISR, Dec'86 by ISR Records. Dist: DMS, RCA

CANDY MAN (SINGLE).
Tracks: / Money talks.
Single (7"): released on ISR, Nov'86 by ISR

Records. Dist: DMS, RCA
Cat. no: KEV 2 (s)
Single (12"): released on ISR, Nov'86 by ISR Records. Dist: DMS, RCA

IT SHOULD HAVE BEEN ME.
Tracks: / It should have been me / Candy man (remix).
Notes: Featuring Mervlyn.
Single (7"): released on Electricity, Feb'87 by Electricity Records. Dist: PRT

Finger, Peter
ACOUSTIC ROCK GUITAR.
Album: released on Kicking Mule, '78 by Sonet. Dist: Roots, PRT-Pye Distribution

BOTTLENECK GUITAR SOLOS.
Album: by Sonet. Dist: Roots, PRT-Pye Distribution

Fingerprintz
BEAT NOIR.
Album: released on Virgin, Jun'81 by Virgin Records. Dist: EMI, Virgin Distribution

VERY DAB, THE.
Album: released on Virgin, Oct'79 by Virgin Records. Dist: EMI, Virgin Distribution

Fingers
REMEMBER MINGUS.
Album: released on Spotlite, '83 by Spotlite Records. Dist: Cadillac, Jazz Music, Spotlite

Finger Snappers
FINGER SNAPPERS Various artists (Various Artists).
Tracks: / Never fail to amaze me / Be that way sometime / I'm gonna love you / Give in to the power of love / Say something nice to me / Couldn't last a day without your love / It takes love / Permanent vacation / I need a love / Feel good all over / I'm doing the best I can / Shame, shame, shame / Can't live without you / You're gone.
Album: released on Soul Supply, Jan'87 by High Energy Records. Dist: Charly

Fingertips
BE YOUNG, BE FOOLISH, BE HAPPY.
Tracks: / Be young, be foolish, be happy / Geronimo / Love is a serious business.
Single (7"): released on Priority, May'87 by Priority Records. Dist: RCA

Single (12"): released on Priority, May'87 by Priority Records. Dist: RCA

BILLY.
Tracks: / Party.
Single (7"): released on Absolute, Aug'86 by Absolute. Dist: Spartan

Fings Ain't What...
FINGS AIN'T WOT THEY USED T'BE Original London cast.
Album: released on That's Entertainment, Apr'83 by That's Entertainment Records. Dist: Pinnacle, PRT

Cassette: released on That's Entertainment, Apr'83 by That's Entertainment Records. Dist: Pinnacle, PRT

Finians Rainbow
FINIANS RAINBOW Reprise Repertory Theatre.
Album: released on Reprise, Aug'81 by WEA Records. Dist: WEA

Fini Tribe
CURLING & STRETCHING ep.
Single (12"): released on Fire, Aug'84 by Twist and Shout Music. Dist: Nine Mile, Rough Trade, Cartel

I WANT MORE (ROW, ROW, ROW THE MIX).
Tracks: / Idiot strength.
Single (12"): released on Waxtrax, Aug'87 by Jungle Records. Dist: PRT

LET THE TRIBE GROW.
Tracks: / De Testimony.
Single (12"): released on Cathexis, Oct'86 Dist: Fast Forward, Cartel

Fink Brothers
MUTANTS IN MEGACITY 1.
Single (7"): released on Zarjazz, Jan'85 by Virgin. Dist: EMI

Single (12"): released on Zarjazz, Jan'85 by Virgin. Dist: EMI

Fink, Cathy
GRANDMA SLID DOWN THE MOUNTAIN (Fink, Cathy & Friends).
Album: released on Rounder (USA), Jan'85 Dist: Mike's Country Music Room Distribution,

---

Jazz Music Distribution, Swift Distribution, Roots Records Distribution, Projection Distribution, Topic Distribution

LEADING ROLE.
Album: released on Rounder (USA), Jun'86 Dist: Mike's Country Music Room Distribution, Jazz Music Distribution, Swift Distribution, Roots Records Distribution, Projection Distribution, Topic Distribution

Finlayson, Willy
ON THE AIR TONIGHT.
Tracks: / After the fall.
Single (7"): released on PRT, Sep'86 by PRT Records. Dist: PRT

Single (12"): released on PRT, Sep'86 by PRT Records. Dist: PRT

SKYE BOAT SONG, THE.
Single (7"): released on PRT, Nov'85 by PRT Records. Dist: PRT

Finley, Karin
TALES OF TABOO.
Single (12"): released on Les Disques Du Crespuscle, Nov'86 Dist: Rough Trade, Pinnacle, Island, Polygram

Finnegan
EASY WE EASY (Finnegan & Junior Rankin).
Tracks: / What a Gwan / Tell me why / Dem a draw card / Easy we easy / News headlines / Do what you doing / Stop study evil / Trodding the biscayne.
Album: released on CSA, Jun'86 by CSA Records. Dist: PRT, Jetstar

Finn, Fred
FRED FINN & PETER HORAN.
Album: released on Mulligan, Sep'80 by Topic Records. Dist: Roots Distribution, Jazz Music Distribution, JSU Distribution, I & B Distribution, Projection Distribution, Wynd-Up Distribution, Celtic Distributions

Finn, Lee
CAT ALL NIGHT.
Single (7"): released on Rollin' Rock, Jun'80

Finn, Tim
BIG CANOE.
Tracks: / Are we one or are we two? / Searching the streets / Hole in my heart / Spiritual hung / Don't bury my heart / Timmy / So into wine / Hyacinth / Big canoe.
Album: released on Virgin, '86 by Virgin Records. Dist: EMI, Virgin Distribution

Cassette: released on Virgin, '86 by Virgin Records. Dist: EMI, Virgin Distribution

Compact disc: released on Virgin, Jul'87 by Virgin Records. Dist: EMI, Virgin Distribution

CARVE YOU IN MARBLE.
Tracks: / Hole in my heart.
Single (7"): released on Virgin, Jul'86 by Virgin Records. Dist: EMI, Virgin Distribution

Single (12"): released on Virgin, Jul'86 by Virgin Records. Dist: EMI, Virgin Distribution

FRACTION TOO MUCH FRICTION.
Single (7"): released on Epic, Apr'84 by CBS Records. Dist: CBS

NO THUNDER NO FIRE NO CAR.
Tracks: / Searching for the streets.
Single (7"): released on Virgin, Mar'86 by Virgin Records. Dist: EMI, Virgin Distribution

Fintry Style
PUTTING ON THE STYLE.
Cassette: released on Klub, Nov'85

Fiona
BEYOND THE PALE.
Tracks: / Tragedy / Hopelessly love you / Living in a boy's world / Thunder and lightning / Tender is the heart / Running out of night / In my blood / He's on my side / You better wait / Keper of the flame.
Album: released on Atlantic, May'86 by WEA Records. Dist: WEA

Cassette: released on Atlantic, May'86 by WEA Records. Dist: WEA

FIONA.
Album:

Cassette: released on Atlantic, Jun'85 by WEA Records. Dist: WEA Deleted '86.

LIVING IN A BOYS WORLD.
Tracks: / Keeper of the flame.
Single (7"): released on Atlantic, May'86 by WEA Records. Dist: WEA

TALK TO ME.
Tracks: / June.

Single (7"): released on Atlantic, May'85 by WEA Records. Dist: WEA

Fireball XL5
GO FOR IT.
Album: released on Northwood, Aug'85 by Northwood Records. Dist: Backs-Cartel

MAN WITH NO NAME.
Single (7"): released on Northwood, May'85 by Northwood Records. Dist: Backs-Cartel

ROCKIN SHOES.
Single (7"): by Northwood Records. Dist: Backs-Cartel

Firebrand
NEVER FELT THIS WAY BEFORE.
Single (7"): released on What Goes On, May'85 Dist: Rough Trade, Cartel, Shigaku

Single (12"): released on What Goes On, May'85 Dist: Rough Trade, Cartel, Shigaku

Fire Brigade
OLD SOAKS AND NEW FLAMES.
Album: released on Bullseye, '79 Dist: Bullseye Music

SHANGALI.
Single (7"): released on Fox Hole, May'84 by Fox Hole Records. Dist: Revolver, Cartel

Fire & Desire
AIN'T NOTHING.
Single (7"): released on Hot Melt, Oct'86 by Hot Melt Records. Dist: Pinnacle, Spartan

Single (12"): released on Hot Melt, Oct'86 by Hot Melt Records. Dist: Pinnacle, Spartan

Fire Engines
BIG GOLD DREAM.
Single (7"): released on Pop Aural, Nov'81 Dist: Fresh, Rough Trade, Swift, Spartan, Virgin

Single (12"): released on Pop Aural, Nov'81 Dist: Fresh, Rough Trade, Swift, Spartan, Virgin

CANDY SKIN.
Single (7"): released on Pop Aural, May'81 Dist: Fresh, Rough Trade, Swift, Spartan, Virgin

GET UP AND USE ME.
Single (7"): released on Codex, 1 Feb'80 by Codex Records. Dist: Spartan

Firefly
STAY No time.
Single (7"): released on Break, May'85 by Greyhound

Firefox
FIRE.
Tracks: / Stand up (for what you believe in).
Single (7"): released on Atlantic, Jan'86 by WEA Records. Dist: WEA

Single (12"): released on Atlantic, Jan'86 by WEA Records. Dist: WEA

FIRE FOX.
Tracks: / We just wanna dance / Come and teke my lovin' / Action speaks louder than words / Stand up (for what you believe in) / Fire / Round trip ticket / You make me feel brand new / Fire down below.
Album: released on Atlantic, Jan'86 by WEA Records. Dist: WEA

Cassette: released on Atlantic, Jan'86 by WEA Records. Dist: WEA

IF YOU GOTTA GO GO NOW.
Single (7"): released on Shell, Nov'82 by Shell Records.

Firehose
RAGIN' FULL ON.
Album: released on SST, Jun'87 by SST Records. Dist: Pinnacle

RAGIN' ON FULL.
Cassette: released on SST, Aug'87 by SST Records. Dist: Pinnacle

Firehouse Five
DIXIELAND (Firehouse Five Plus Two).
Compact disc: released on Carrere, Apr'87 by Carrere Records. Dist: PRT, Spartan

DIXIELAND FAVOURITES.
Compact disc: released on London, Apr'87 by London Records. Dist: Polygram

GOOD TIME JAZZ (Firehouse Five Plus Two).
Album: released on MFP, Feb'82 by EMI Rec-

ords. Dist: EMI

Cassette: released on MFP, Feb'82 by EMI Records. Dist: EMI

Fire Hydrant Men

MISSED IT BY THAT MUCH.
Album: released on Backs, Feb'85 by Backs Records. Dist: Backs, Cartel

Fire In Harmony

FIRE IN HARMONY various artists (Various Artists).
Album: released on Elusive, Jun'85 by All Round Productions Company Records. Dist: EMI

Fire Next Time

BENEATH THE HAMMERS.
Tracks: / Beneath the Hammers / Chains.
Single (7"): released on Stiff, Apr'86 by Stiff Records. Dist: EMI, Record Services Distribution (Ireland)

I CAN'T GO BACK.
Tracks: / I can't go back / Tumbling walls / Picket line*.
Notes: * = Extra track on 12" only
Single (7"): released on Flying Nun, Apr'87 Dist: Rough Trade, Cartel

Single (12"): released on Flying Nun, Apr'87 Dist: Rough Trade, Cartel

Fire On Blonde

STOP AND THINK.
Tracks: / Stop and think (Instrumental).
Single (7"): released on Atlantic, Aug'86 by WEA Records. Dist: WEA

Single (12"): released on Atlantic, Aug'86 by WEA Records. Dist: WEA

Firewater

BRAND NEW VINTAGE.
Tracks: / Crazy / Almost Saturday night / Sea of heartbreak / Lonely road cafe / Whisky drinking man / Driving my life away etc..
Notes: Top UK country act.
Album: released on Sundown, Apr'86 by Magnum Music Group Ltd. Dist: Magnum Music Group Ltd, PRT Distribution, Spartan Distribution

CRAZY.
Tracks: / Crazy / Saving up my nights.
Single (7"): released on Sundown, Apr'86 by Magnum Music Group Ltd. Dist: Magnum Music Group Ltd, PRT Distribution, Spartan Distribution

Firing Squad

NIGHT MANOEUVRES.
Single (7"): released on Shattered, Aug'81 Dist: Pinnacle

Firm

ARTHUR DALEY 'E'S ALRIGHT.
Single (7"): released on Bark, Jun'82 by Stiff Records. Dist: CBS

BRAVO COSTA BRAVA.
Single (7"): released on Bark, Aug'85 by Stiff Records. Dist: CBS

CASH IN HAND.
Single (7"): released on Bark, Nov'82 by Stiff Records. Dist: CBS

FIRM.
Compact disc: by WEA Records. Dist: WEA

Album: released on Atlantic, Feb'85 by WEA Records. Dist: WEA

Cassette: released on Atlantic, Feb'85 by WEA Records. Dist: WEA

LONG LIVE THE NATIONAL.
Single (7"): released on Bark, May'83 by Stiff Records. Dist: CBS

MEAN BUSINESS.
Tracks: / Fortune hunter / Cadillac / All the kings horses / Live in peace / Tear down the walls / Dreaming / Free to live / Spirit of love.
Album: released on Atlantic, Apr'86 by WEA Records. Dist: WEA

Cassette: released on Atlantic, Apr'86 by WEA Records. Dist: WEA

Compact disc: released on Atlantic, Apr'86 by WEA Records. Dist: WEA

STAR TREKKIN'.
Tracks: / Star Trekkin' / Dub trek.
Single (7"): released on Bark, 23 May'87 by Stiff Records. Dist: CBS

Firmament

FESTIVAL OF FROTHY MUGGAMENT (Firmament & The Elements).
Single (7"): released on Armageddon, Jul'81 by Armageddon Records. Dist: Revolver, Cartel, Pinnacle

Firm, The

ALL THE KINGS HORSES.
Tracks: / All the kings horses / Fortune hunter.
Single (7"): released on Atlantic, Apr'86 by WEA Records. Dist: WEA

First Blood

FIRST BLOOD Original Soundtrack.
Album: released on That's Entertainment, Apr'83 by That's Entertainment Records. Dist: Pinnacle, PRT

First British Corps...

ALLIANCE PARADE.
Album: released on Major Richards, Jul'79 by Major Richards Records. Dist: Taylors

First Call

AN EVENING IN DECEMBER.
Album: released on Day, Nov'86

Cassette: released on Day, Nov'86

UNDIVIDED.
Notes: First Call is an amzingly precise harmony group, comprising of three singers and songwriters - Bonnie Keen, Delodie Tunney and Marty McCall. The album - which boasts no less than four producers - features a wide variety of musical styles and drwas attention to the impressive versatility of the singers. While the groups vocal approach borrows from the Manhattan Transfer and The Second Chapter Of Acts, the compositional concepts and aggresive arrangements bring this album into the 80's. An impressive 'debut' from atruly contemporary Christian vocal band.
Album: released on Word, Sep'86 by Word Records. Dist: Word Distribution, CBS

Cassette: released on Word, Sep'86 by Word Records. Dist: Word Distribution, CBS

First Choice

LET NO MAN PUT US UNDER.
Single (7"): released on Serious, Jun'87 by Serious Records. Dist: PRT

Single (12"): released on Serious, Jun'87 by Serious Records. Dist: PRT

First Church

DEBBYDID (First Church of Napoleon Solo).
Single (7"): released on Off-Beat, Jun'85 by Off-Beat Records. Dist: Jetstar Distribution

First Circle

BOYS NIGHT OUT.
Tracks: / Working up a sweat / Miracle worker / In the name of love / Dream you came back / Get off it / Can't find a love / You're on my mind / Boy's night out.
Notes: First Circle are a New York-based quintet newly-signed to the EMI America label. *Boys night out* is their debut album and includes the current dance smash *Workin' up a sweat.* The album is already gaining much interest as an import, as it features at least three other strong cuts and potential singles - *In the name of love, Miracle worker* and *Can't find love.* The album is produced by Randy Muller known for his work with Brass Construction and New York Skyy. [EMI release sheet, April 87]

Album: released on EMI America, Apr'87 by EMI Records. Dist: EMI

Album: released on EMI America, Apr'87 by EMI Records. Dist: EMI

MIRACLE WORKER.
Tracks: / Miracle worker / Miracle worker (Hocus Pocus mix) / Miracle worker (inst. remix) / Miracle worker (dub remix).
Single (12"): released on EMI America, 23 May'87 by EMI Records. Dist: EMI

MIRACLE WORKERS.
Tracks: / Miracle worker (radio edit) / Miracle worker (dub version) / Can't find a love.
Single (7"): released on EMI America, May'87 by EMI Records. Dist: EMI

Single (12"): released on EMI America, May'87 by EMI Records. Dist: EMI

First Class

BEACH BABY.
Single (7"): released on Sunny, May'82 by Sunny Records. Dist: PRT Distribution
Cat. no: **EON 102**
Single (7"): released on Old Gold, Jul'82 by Old Gold Records. Dist: Lightning, Jazz Music, Spartan, Counterpoint

GIMME LITTLE SIGN.
Single (7"): released on Sunny, Jul'83 by Sunny Records. Dist: PRT Distribution

First Cut

FIRST CUT- THE OXFORD SOUND various artists (Various Artists).
Album: released on Waterfall, Nov'83 by Waterfall Records. Dist: Revolver, Cartel

GOT TO GET CLOSE TO YOU.
Single (12"): released on Hot Rod, Aug'84 by Hot Rod Records. Dist: Jetstar

First Cuts Are..

FIRST CUTS ARE THE DEEPEST, THE (Various Artists).
Notes: Incl. Yr Anrefn/Elfyn Presli
Extended-play record: released on Words Of Warning, Mar'87 Dist: Revolver, Cartel

First Division

WHERE THE ACTION IS.
Single (7"): released on Panther, Apr'84 by MCA Records. Dist: CBS

First Fragile Sampler

FIRST FRAGILE SAMPLER, THE various artists (Various Artists).
Cassette: released on Fragile, Jun'85 by Fragile Records. Dist: Cartel

First House

ERINDIRA.
Tracks: / Day away, A / Innocent erendira / Journeyers to the East, The / Bracondale / Grammenos / Stranger than paradise / Bridge call / Doubt / Further away.
Notes: Debut album from an adventurous young British group who hail from the Manchester area. Founded in January 1984, First house won the 'European' Young Jazz Artistsaward of the International Jazz Federation in October of the same year. They toured extensively throughout the UK, played at Ronnie Scott's, recorded for the BBC, appeared at European festivals and recorded this their first album - all in the summer of 1985. First House prove to be an amazingly mature configuration, presenting a set of unconventionally structured tunes with abrupt tempo changes, free passages and extended harmonies. First House's music is complex and highly individual, reflecting a wide range of contemporary influences (Jazz Forum). Personnel: Ken Stubbs - alto and soprano saxophones/Django Bates - piano (also with Loose Tubes)/Mick Hutton - bass/Martin France - drums and percussion.
Album: released on ECM (Germany), Apr'86 by ECM Records. Dist: IMS, Polygram, Virgin through EMI

Compact disc: released on ECM (Germany), Apr'86 by ECM Records. Dist: IMS, Polygram, Virgin through EMI

First Ladies

FIRST LADIES OF COUNTRY various artists (Various Artists).
Album: released on CBS, '84 by CBS Records. Dist: CBS

Cassette: released on CBS, '84 by CBS Records. Dist: CBS

Album: released on Music For Pleasure (Holland), Jan'85 by EMI Records. Dist: EMI

Cassette: released on Music For Pleasure (Holland), Jan'85 by EMI Records. Dist: EMI

FIRST LADIES OF COUNTRY, VOL.11 various artists (Various Artists).
Cassette: released on CBS, Dec'81 by CBS Records. Dist: CBS

Cassette: released on CBS, Dec'81 by CBS Records. Dist: CBS

FIRST LADIES OF COUNTRY MUSIC various artists (Various Session Artists).
Cassette: released on Aim, Feb'83 Dist: H.R. Taylor

First Light

1ST LIGHT.
Album: released on Metronome (Germany), Aug'83 Dist: Jazz Music Distribution

A.M.
Single (7"): released on Oval, Nov'82 Dist: Projection

Single (12"): released on Oval, Nov'82 Dist: Projection

EXPLAIN THE REASON.
Single (7"): released on London, May'83 by London Records. Dist: Polygram

Single (12"): released on London, May'83 by London Records. Dist: Polygram

HORSE WITH NO NAME.
Single (7"): released on Oval, Jun'82 Dist: Projection

Single (12"): released on Oval, Jun'82 Dist: Projection

WISH YOU WERE HERE.
Single (7"): released on London, Jan'84 by London Records. Dist: Polygram

Single (12"): released on London, Jan'84 by London Records. Dist: Polygram

First Love

FIRST LOVE various artists (Various Artists).
Album: released on Arcade, Jan'80 Dist: Prism Leisure Corporation Records

First Offence

NIGHT THE PUNKS TURNED UGLY.
Single (7"): released on Chaos, Sep'83 by Backs Records. Dist: Nine Mile, Cartel

First Queen

FIRST QUEEN ELIZABETH (First Queen Elizabeth).
Cassette: released on Pickwick, May'84 by Pickwick Records. Dist: Pickwick Distribution, Prism Leisure Distribution, Lugtons

First Quest

FIRST QUEST (Various Artists).
Double Album: released on Filmtrax, Nov'85 by Filmtrax Records. Dist: EMI

Cassette: by Filmtrax Records. Dist: EMI

First Sunday Singalong

FIRST SUNDAY SINGALONG Various artists (Various Artists).
Notes: Features 34 Sunday School songs sung by children.

First Travelling...

FIRST TRAVELLING SALESLADY, THE Musical (Various Artists).
Notes: Srars Ginger Rogers & Carol Channing
Video-cassette (VHS): released on Video Collection, May'87 by Video Collection Records. Dist: Counterpoint

Fisc

TRACKER y.
Album: released on Mausoleum, Oct'84 by Mausoleum Records. Dist: Pinnacle

Fischer Choir

40 YEARS OF THE FISCHER CHOIR.
Tracks: / Radetzy-marsch / Adieu mein kleiner gardeoffizier / Gefangenchor aus "nabucco" / Triumph marsch / Matrosenchor aus "der fliegende Hollander" / Grob is dien name / Madonna aus peru / Frieden / Das wandern ist des mullers lust / Wem gott will rechte gunst erweisen / Alle vogel sind schon da / Heimatmelodie / Finkensalzer / Im schosten weisengrunde / Andulka.
Notes: To celbrate their 40th anniversary, Polydor Germany have issued this compilation of the Choir's most popular and requested repertoire.
Album: released on Polydor (Germany), Apr'86 Dist: IMS-Polygram

Cassette: released on Polydor (Germany), Apr'86 Dist: IMS-Polygram

GLORY HALLELUJA.
Album: released on Polydor (Import), Nov'82

Cassette: released on Polydor (Import), Nov'82
Cat. no: **3472 136**

MELODIEN FUR MILLIONEN.
Album: released on Polydor (Import), Nov'81

Cassette: released on Polydor (Import), Nov'81

MUSIC FOR THE MILLIONS.
Album: released on Polydor (Holland), Dec'83
Cat. no: **8153 211**
Cassette: released on Polydor (Holland), Dec'83

SENSATIONAL FISCHER CHOIR.
Album: released on Polydor, Mar'77 by Polydor Records. Dist: Polygram, Polydor

Fischer, Clare

Biographical Details: See under Rich, Lisa with...

AND SOMETIMES VOICES (Fischer, Clare & Salsa Picante).
Album: released on Discovery (USA), Jan'84

CRAZY BIRD (Fischer, Clare & Salsa Picante).
Tracks: / Bernie's tune / Where are the children? / Serenidade / La mucura / Pajaro loco / Solar patrol / Canto Africano / Pavillion.
Notes: Featuring Bill Watrous and Jeff Berlin
Compact disc: released on Discovery (USA), Sep'86 by Discovery Records (USA). Dist: Swift, Flexitron-Audio, Jazz Music

EASY LIVIN'.
Album: released on Revelation, Apr'81

EXTENSION (Fischer, Clare Orchestra, featuring Jerry Coker).
Album: released on Discovery (USA), Apr'84

GREAT WHITE HOPE.
Album: released on Revelation, Apr'81

JAZZ SONG.
Notes: Unaccompanied piano.
Album: released on Revelation, Mar'87

Album: released on Revelation, Apr'84

MACHACA.
Album: released on MPS Jazz Parnote May'81

ONE TO GET READY.
Album: released on Revelation. Apr'81

RECLAMATION ACT OF 1972.
Album: released on Revelation, Apr'81

STARBRIGHT (Fischer, Clare & Gary Foster).
Album: released on Discovery (USA), Jan'84

Cassette: released on Discovery (USA), Jan'84

STATE OF HIS ART, (THE).
Album: released on Revelation, Apr'81

T' DA-A-A-A-A (Fischer, Clare & Yamaha Quartet).
Album: released on Revelation. Apr'81

WHOSE WOODS ARE THESE?.
Album: released on Discovery (USA), Feb'84

Fischer-Z
GOING DEAF FOR A LIVING.
Album: released on EMI (Holland), Mar'84 by EMI Records. Dist: Conifer

Cassette: released on EMI (Holland), Mar'84 by EMI Records. Dist: Conifer

Fish
COCKS.
Single (7"): released on Communication, Sep'82 Dist: Menace Breakers

Fish, Bob
FIRST SNOW.
Single (7"): released on Stiff, Nov'83 by Stiff Records. Dist: EMI, Record Services Distribution (Ireland)

Fish Co
BENEATH THE LAUGHTER.
Album: by Pilgrim Records. Dist: Rough Trade, Cartel

Fisher, Archie
FATE O' CHARLIE, (THE) (Fisher, Archie & Barbara Dickson).
Album: released on Leader, '81 Dist: Jazz Music, Projection

WILL YE GANG, LOVE.
Album: released on Topic, '81 Dist: Roots Distribution

Fisher, Cilla
BALCANQUHAL (Fisher, Cilla & Artie Tresize).
Album: released on Leader, '81 Dist: Jazz Music, Projection

CILLA & ARTIE (Fisher, Cilla & Artie Tresize).
Album: released on Topic, '81 Dist: Roots Distribution

FOR FOUL DAY AND FAIR (Fisher, Cilla & Artie Tresize).
Album: released on Kettle, Nov'79 Dist: JSU, Folksound, Celtic Music, MK

SONGS OF THE FISHING.
Album: released on Kettle, Oct'83 Dist: JSU, Folksound, Celtic Music, MK

Fisher, Danny
TAKIN' MA LAGER TAE MALAGA.
Single (7"): released on Heavenly Sound Productions, Apr'82 Dist: MK

Fisher, Eddie
AS LONG AS THERE'S MUSIC.
Album: released on RCA, Aug'87 by RCA Records. Dist: RCA, Roots, Swift, Wellard, Chris, I & B, Solomon & Peres Distribution

Cassette: released on RCA, Aug'87 by RCA Records. Dist: RCA, Roots, Swift, Wellard, Chris, I & B, Solomon & Peres Distribution

EDDIE FISHER'S GREATEST HITS.
Album: released on RCA International, Oct'81

Cassette: released on RCA International, Oct'81 Deleted May'85.

Fisher Family
FISHER FAMILY, (THE).
Album: released on Topic, May'81 Dist: Roots

Page 364

Distribution

Fisherfolk
BE LIKE YOUR FATHER.
Album: released on Celebration, '83 by Celebration Services(Int.)Ltd.. Dist: Kingsway Music

Cassette: released on Celebration, '83 by Celebration Services(Int.)Ltd.. Dist: Kingsway Music

CELEBRATE THE WHOLE OF IT.
Album: released on Celebration, '83 by Celebration Services(Int.)Ltd.. Dist: Kingsway Music

Cassette: released on Celebration, '83 by Celebration Services(Int.)Ltd.. Dist: Kingsway Music

COME & WORSHIP.
Album: released on Celebration, '83 by Celebration Services(Int.)Ltd.. Dist: Kingsway Music

Cassette: released on Celebration, '83 by Celebration Services(Int.)Ltd.. Dist: Kingsway Music

CRY HOSANNA.
Album: released on Celebration, '83 by Celebration Services(Int.)Ltd.. Dist: Kingsway Music

Cassette: released on Celebration, '83 by Celebration Services(Int.)Ltd.. Dist: Kingsway Music

GOD MAKE US YOUR FAMILY.
Cassette: released on Celebration, '83 by Celebration Services(Int.)Ltd.. Dist: Kingsway Music

Album: released on Celebration, '83 by Celebration Services(Int.)Ltd.. Dist: Kingsway Music

IN THE PRESENCE OF YOUR PEOPLE.
Album: released on Celebration, '83 by Celebration Services(Int.)Ltd.. Dist: Kingsway Music

Cassette: released on Celebration, '83 by Celebration Services(Int.)Ltd.. Dist: Kingsway Music

JOY IN THE MORNING.
Cassette: released on Celebration, '83 by Celebration Services(Int.)Ltd.. Dist: Kingsway Music

Album: released on Celebration, '83 by Celebration Services(Int.)Ltd.. Dist: Kingsway Music

JOY OF CHRISTMAS, (THE).
Album: released on Celebration, Nov'83 by Celebration Services(Int.)Ltd.. Dist: Kingsway Music

Cassette: released on Celebration, Nov'83 by Celebration Services(Int.)Ltd.. Dist: Kingsway Music

LOVE DIVINE.
Album: released on Celebration, '83 by Celebration Services(Int.)Ltd.. Dist: Kingsway Music

Cassette: released on Celebration, '83 by Celebration Services(Int.)Ltd.. Dist: Kingsway Music

MORE SONGS FROM SOUND OF LIVING WATERS/FRESH SOUNDS.
Cassette: released on Celebration, '83 by Celebration Services(Int.)Ltd.. Dist: Kingsway Music

Album: released on Celebration, '83 by Celebration Services(Int.)Ltd.. Dist: Kingsway Music

O FOR A THOUSAND TONGUES.
Album: released on Celebration, '83 by Celebration Services(Int.)Ltd.. Dist: Kingsway Music

ON TIPTOE.
Album: released on Celebration, '83 by Celebration Services(Int.)Ltd.. Dist: Kingsway Music

Cassette: released on Celebration, '83 by Celebration Services(Int.)Ltd.. Dist: Kingsway Music

PEACE WITH THE FATHER.
Album: released on Celebration, '83 by Celebration Services(Int.)Ltd.. Dist: Kingsway Music

Cassette: released on Celebration, '83 by Celebration Services(Int.)Ltd.. Dist: Kingsway Music

REJOICE WITH THE FISHERFOLK.
Cassette: released on Celebration, '83 by Celebration Services(Int.)Ltd.. Dist: Kingsway Music

---

SING PRAISE WITH THE FISHERFOLK.
Album: released on Celebration, '83 by Celebration Services(Int.)Ltd.. Dist: Kingsway Music

Cassette: released on Celebration, '83 by Celebration Services(Int.)Ltd.. Dist: Kingsway Music

SING THE WORD WITH THE FISHERFOLK.
Cassette: released on Celebration, '83 by Celebration Services(Int.)Ltd.. Dist: Kingsway Music

Album: released on Celebration, '83 by Celebration Services(Int.)Ltd.. Dist: Kingsway Music

SONGS FROM FRESH SOUNDS.
Album: released on Celebration, '83 by Celebration Services(Int.)Ltd.. Dist: Kingsway Music

Cassette: released on Celebration, '83 by Celebration Services(Int.)Ltd.. Dist: Kingsway Music

SONGS FROM SOUND OF LIVING WATERS.
Cassette: released on Celebration, '83 by Celebration Services(Int.)Ltd.. Dist: Kingsway Music

Album: released on Celebration, '83 by Celebration Services(Int.)Ltd.. Dist: Kingsway Music

SPECTRUM.
Album: released on Celebration, '83 by Celebration Services(Int.)Ltd.. Dist: Kingsway Music

Cassette: released on Celebration, '83 by Celebration Services(Int.)Ltd.. Dist: Kingsway Music

SUN'S GONNA SHINE, (THE).
Album: released on Celebration, Nov'83 by Celebration Services(Int.)Ltd.. Dist: Kingsway Music

Cassette: released on Celebration, Nov'83 by Celebration Services(Int.)Ltd.. Dist: Kingsway Music

SWEET WATER.
Album: released on Celebration, Nov'83 by Celebration Services(Int.)Ltd.. Dist: Kingsway Music

Cassette: released on Celebration, Nov'83 by Celebration Services(Int.)Ltd.. Dist: Kingsway Music

THIS IS THE DAY.
Album: released on Celebration, Nov'83 by Celebration Services(Int.)Ltd.. Dist: Kingsway Music

Cassette: released on Celebration, May'83 by Celebration Services(Int.)Ltd.. Dist: Kingsway Music

WAKE UP TO SING THE PRAISE OF JESUS.
Album: released on Celebration, May'83 by Celebration Services(Int.)Ltd.. Dist: Kingsway Music

Cassette: released on Celebration, May'83 by Celebration Services(Int.)Ltd.. Dist: Kingsway Music

WILLING TO ROW.
Album: released on Celebration, May'83 by Celebration Services(Int.)Ltd.. Dist: Kingsway Music

Cassette: released on Celebration, May'83 by Celebration Services(Int.)Ltd.. Dist: Kingsway Music

WITH THANKGIVING.
Album: released on Celebration, May'83 by Celebration Services(Int.)Ltd.. Dist: Kingsway Music

Cassette: released on Celebration, May'83 by Celebration Services(Int.)Ltd.. Dist: Kingsway Music

WORSHIP WITH THE FISHERFOLK.
Album: released on Celebration, May'83 by Celebration Services(Int.)Ltd.. Dist: Kingsway Music

Cassette: released on Celebration, May'83 by Celebration Services(Int.)Ltd.. Dist: Kingsway Music

Fisher, Morgan
IVORIES.
Album:

LOOK AT LIFE.
Album: released on Cherry Red, Nov'84 by Cherry Red Records. Dist: Pinnacle

---

Cassette: released on Cherry Red, Nov'84 by Cherry Red Records. Dist: Pinnacle

SEASONS.
Album: released on Cherry Red, Sep'83 by Cherry Red Records. Dist: Pinnacle

UN HOMME ET UNE FILLE.
Single (7"): released on Cherry Red, Sep'83 by Cherry Red Records. Dist: Pinnacle

Fisher, Ray
BONNIE BRIDE, (THE).
Album: released on Leader, May'81 Dist: Jazz Music, Projection

Fisher, Sonny
TEXAS ROCKABILLY TEAR UP.
Album: released on Magnum Force, Jul'82 by Magnum Music Group Ltd. Dist: Magnum Music Group Ltd, PRT, Spartan

Fisher, Sue
CHRISTENING, (THE).
Single (7"): released on Wembley, Jul'82 by International Records & Tapes. Dist: Pinnacle

Fisher, Tony
EXTRACTING THE DIGITAL (Fisher, Tony & John Fiddy Enterprise).
Album: released on Intersound, Nov'86 by Intersound Records. Dist: Jazz Music

Fishin' In My Pond
FISHIN' IN MY POND (Various Artists).
Album: released on Flyright, Oct'86 by Flyright Records. Dist: Krazy Kat, Swift, Jazz Music

Fish Turned Human
ANIMAL MAGNETISM.
Single (7"): released on Detour, Sep'81 by Detour Records. Dist: Swift, RCA, Jazz Music, Projection

Fission
MILLER LITE.
Tracks: / Private Dick.
Single (7"): released on Streetwave, Nov'86 by Streetwave Records. Dist: PRT Distribution

Single (12"): released on Streetwave, Nov'86 by Streetwave Records. Dist: PRT Distribution

PRIVATE DICK.
Tracks: / Private dick / Miller light.
Single (7"): released on Spacematic, Oct'86

Single (12"): released on Spacematic, Oct'86

Fist
BACK WITH A VENGEANCE.
Tracks: / Feeling's right,The / Dog soldier / All I can do / Turn the hell on / Devil rise / S.S.Giro / Going wild tonight / Too hot / Lost and found / Feelings alright, The / Dog soldier / All I can do / Devil rise / Going wild tonight.
Album: released on Neat, '85 by Neat Records. Dist: Pinnacle, Neat

NAME RANK AND NUMBER.
Single (7"): released on Neat, Apr'80 by Neat Records. Dist: Pinnacle, Neat

WANDERER.
Single (7"): released on Neat, Nov'82 by Neat Records. Dist: Pinnacle, Neat

Fistful of Dollars
FISTFUL OF DOLLARS/FOR A FEW DOLLARS MORE Original soundtrack.
Album: released on RCA, May'70 by RCA Records. Dist: RCA, Roots, Swift, Wellard, Chris, I & B, Solomon & Peres Distribution

Cassette: released on RCA Camden, May'74

Fitchet, Angus
LEGENDARY ANGUS FITCHET,(THE).
Album: released on Lochshore, Oct'83 by Klub Records. Dist: PRT

Cassette: released on Lochshore, Oct'83 by Klub Records. Dist: PRT

Fits
ACHILLES HEEL.
Single (7"): released on Masterchord, Apr'84 by Masterchord Records & Tapes. Dist: PRT

FACT OR FICTION.
Single (12"): released on Trapper, Nov'85 Dist: Pinnacle, Rough Trade

Album: released on Trapper, Oct'85 Dist: Pinnacle, Rough Trade

Single (7"): released on Trapper, Oct'85 Dist: Pinnacle, Rough Trade

LAST LAUGH.
Single (7"): released on Rondelet, Dec'82 Dist: Spartan Distribution

THINK FOR YOUSELF BURIAL.
Single (7"): released on Rondelet, Dec'81 Dist: Spartan Distribution

YOU'RE NOTHING YOU'RE NOWHERE.
Album: released on Rondelet Music & Records, Jun'82

Cassette: released on Rondelet Music & Records, Jun'82

YOU SAID WE'D NEVER MAKE IT.
Single (7"): released on Lightbeat, Jan'82 by Lightbeat Records. Dist: Pinnacle

Fitzbooth, Ella

DOWN IN POVERTY.
Single (12"): released on Natty Congo, Nov'82 by Natty Congo Records. Dist: Jetstar

Fitzgerald, Ella

ANTONIO CARLOS JOBIM SONGBOOK,(THE).
Double Album: released on Pablo (USA), May'82 by Pablo Records (USA). Dist: Wellard, Chris, IMS-Polygram, BMG

Double cassette: released on Pablo (USA), May'82 by Pablo Records (USA). Dist: Wellard, Chris, IMS-Polygram, BMG

AT THE MONTREUX JAZZ FESTIVAL 1975.
Album: released on Pablo, '82 by Pablo Records. Dist: Wellard, Chris, IMS-Polygram, BMG

Cassette: released on Pablo, '82 by Pablo Records. Dist: Wellard, Chris, IMS-Polygram, BMG

AT THE OPERA HOUSE.
Tracks: / It's all right with me / Don'cha go 'way mad / Bewitched, bothered and bewildered / Stompin' at the Savoy / These foolish things / Ill wind / Goody goody / Moonlight in Vermont / Lady be good.
Compact disc: released on Polydor, Jun'87 by Polydor Records. Dist: Polygram, Polydor

Album: released on Verve (USA), Oct'84 by Polydor. Dist: Polygram

AT THE SOUTHLAND OF BOSTON (Fitzgerald, Ella & Chick Webb).
Album: released on Jazz Live, Apr'81

BEST IS YET TO COME (THE) (Fitzgerald, Ella & Nelson Riddle).
Notes: See also under Nelson Riddle.

Compact disc: released on Pablo (USA), Apr'87 by Pablo Records (USA). Dist: Wellard, Chris, IMS-Polygram, BMG

BEST OF ELLA FITZGERALD.
Album: released on MCA, Aug'81 by MCA Records. Dist: Polygram, MCA

Cassette: released on MCA, Aug'81 by MCA Records. Dist: Polygram, MCA

BEST YEARS, (THE).
Album: released on Joker (Import), Apr'81

BEWITCHED.
Cassette: released on Polydor, Jun'82 by Polydor Records. Dist: Polygram, Polydor

Album: released on Polydor, Jun'82 by Polydor Records. Dist: Polygram, Polydor

CLASSY PAIR, A (Fitzgerald, Ella & Count Basie).
Tracks: / I'm getting sentimental over you / Organ grinder's swing / Just a sittin' and a rockin' / My kind of trouble is you / Ain't misbehavin' / Some other spring / Teach me tonight / Don't worry 'bout me / Honeysuckle rose / Sweet Lorraine / Please don't talk about me when I'm gone.
Compact disc: released on Pablo Jazz (USA), Apr'86 by United Artists. Dist: Swift

Album: released on Pablo, '82 by Pablo Records. Dist: Wellard, Chris, IMS-Polygram, BMG

Cassette: released on Pablo, '82 by Pablo Records. Dist: Wellard, Chris, IMS-Polygram, BMG

COLE PORTER SONG BOOK VOLUME 1.
Compact disc: by Phonogram Records. Dist: Polygram

COLE PORTER SONG BOOK VOLUME 2.
Compact disc: by Phonogram Records. Dist: Polygram

COMPACT JAZZ.
Compact disc: released on Verve, Jul'87 by Phonogram Records. Dist: Polygram

COMPILATION.
Compact disc: by Phonogram Records. Dist: Polygram

DIGITAL 111 AT MONTREUX (Fitzgerald, Ella/Joe Pass/Count Basie).
Album: released on Pablo, '82 by Pablo Records. Dist: Wellard, Chris, IMS-Polygram, BMG

Cassette: released on Pablo, '82 by Pablo Records. Dist: Wellard, Chris, IMS-Polygram, BMG

DO GERSHWIN 'NICE WORK IF YOU CAN GET IT (Fitzgerald, Ella & Andre Previn).
Compact disc: released on Pablo (USA), May'86 by Pablo Records (USA). Dist: Wellard, Chris, IMS-Polygram, BMG

DREAM DANCING (Fitzgerald, Ella & Cole Porter).
Album: released on Pablo, '82 by Pablo Records. Dist: Wellard, Chris, IMS-Polygram, BMG

Cassette: released on Pablo, '82 by Pablo Records. Dist: Wellard, Chris, IMS-Polygram, BMG

ELLA.
Notes: Montreaux, July 1975
Compact disc: released on Pablo (USA), May'86 by Pablo Records (USA). Dist: Wellard Chris, IMS-Polygram, BMG

ELLA AND HER FELLAS.
Album: released on MCA, Aug'82 by MCA Records. Dist: Polygram, MCA

Cassette: released on MCA, Aug'82 by MCA Records. Dist: Polygram, MCA

ELLA A NICE.
Album: released on Pablo, Mar'84 by Pablo Records. Dist: Wellard, Chris, IMS-Polygram, BMG

Cassette: released on Pablo, Mar'84 by Pablo Records. Dist: Wellard, Chris, IMS-Polygram, BMG

ELLA AT MONTREAUX 1975.
Tracks: / Caravan / Satin doll / Teach me tonight / Wave / It's all right with me / Let's do it / ow high the moon.
Notes: Personnel: Ella Fitzgerald/Tommy Flanagan/Keter Betts/Bobby Durham
Compact disc: released on Pablo (USA), Jul'86 by Pablo Records (USA). Dist: Wellard, Chris, IMS-Polygram, BMG

ELLA AT MONTREUX 1975..
Tracks: / How high the moon / Girl form Ipanema,The / T'aint nobody's bizness.
Notes: Personnel: Ella Fitzgerald/Tommy Flanagan/Keter Betts/Bobby Durham.

ELLA & BASIE (Fitzgerald, Ella & Count Basie).

ELLA & ELLIS (Fitzgerald, Ella & Ellis Larkin).
Album: released on MCA, Feb'84 by MCA Records. Dist: Polygram, MCA

Cassette: released on MCA, Feb'84 by MCA Records. Dist: Polygram, MCA Deleted

ELLA FITZGERALD COLLECTION, (THE).
Album: released on Deja Vu, Aug'85 by Deja Vu Records. Dist: Counterpoint Distribution, Record Services Distribution (Ireland)

Cassette: released on Deja Vu, Aug'85 by Deja Vu Records. Dist: Counterpoint Distribution, Record Services Distribution (Ireland)

ELLA FITZGERALD SINGS THE JOHNNY MERCER SONGBOOK.
Cassette: released on Verve, Oct'84 by Phonogram Records. Dist: Polygram

ELLA FITZGERALD SONGBOOK,(THE).
Special: released on World Records, Dec'81 Dist: Polygram

Special: released on World Records, Dec'81 Dist: Polygram

ELLA FITZGERALD & THE CHICK WEBB ORCHESTRA (Fitzgerald, Ella/Chick Webb Orchestra).
Album: released on Joker, Apr'81 Dist: Counterpoint, Mainline, Record Services Distribution (Ireland)

ELLA IN BERLIN.
Compact disc: released on Verve, Apr'87 by Phonogram Records. Dist: Polygram

ELLA IN LONDON.
Tracks: / Sweet Georgie Brown / happy blues.
Notes: Personnel:Ella Fitzgerald/Tommy Flanagan/Joe pass Keeter Betts/Bobby Durham.

Album: released on Pablo, '82 by Pablo Records. Dist: Wellard, Chris, IMS-Polygram, BMG

Cassette: released on Pablo, '82 by Pablo Records. Dist: Wellard, Chris, IMS-Polygram, BMG

ELLA IN LONDON.
Tracks: / Sweet Georgia Brown / They can't take that away / Everytime we say goodbye / Man I love, The / It don't mean a thing / You've got a friend / Lemon drop / Very though of you, The / Happy blues.
Notes: Ella Fitzgerald/Tommy Flanagan/Joe Pass/Keeter Betts/Bobby Durham
Compact disc: released on Pablo (USA), Jul'86 by Pablo Records (USA). Dist: Wellard, Chris, IMS-Polygram, BMG

ELLA & LOUIS (Fitzgerald, Ella & Louis Armstrong).
Compact disc: by Phonogram Records. Dist: Polygram

Triple album / cassette: released on Verve, Mar'81 by Phonogram Records. Dist: Polygram

Compact disc: released on Verve, Sep'85 by Phonogram Records. Dist: Polygram

ELLA & LOUIS AGAIN (Fitzgerald, Ella & Louis Armstrong).
Compact disc: released on Polygram/Verve (W.Germany), '86 by Polygram Records. Dist: Polygram

ELLA & OSCAR (Fitzgerald, Ella & Oscar Peterson).
Tracks: / Mean to me / How long has this been going on / When your lover has gone / More than you ever know / There's a lull in my life / Midnight sun / I hear music / Street of dreams / April in Paris / Hear music.
Notes: Personnel: Ella Fitzgerald/Oscar Peterson/Ray Brown
Compact disc: released on Pablo (USA), Jul'86 by Pablo Records (USA). Dist: Wellard, Chris, IMS-Polygram, BMG

Album: released on Pablo, '82 by Pablo Records. Dist: Wellard, Chris, IMS-Polygram, BMG

Cassette: released on Pablo, '82 by Pablo Records. Dist: Wellard, Chris, IMS-Polygram, BMG

ELLA & RAY (Fitzgerald, Ella & Ray Brown).
Album: released on Jazz Live, Apr'81

ELLA SINGS GERSHWIN.
Tracks: / Someone to watch over me / My one and only (what am I gonna do) / But not for me / Looking for a boy / Nice work if you can get it / Oh lady be good / I've got a crush on you / How long has this been going on / Maybe / Soon / I'm just a lucky so and so / I didn't mean a word I said.
Notes: A welcome rerelease of a classic album. Ella Fitzgerald singing Gershwin will prove to be immensely popular with many people.
Album: released on MCA, May'86 by MCA Records. Dist: Polygram, MCA

ELLA SWINGS LIGHTLY.
Album: released on Verve, Dec'79 by Phonogram Records. Dist: Polygram

EV'RY TIME WE SAY GOODBYE.
Single (7"): released on Old Gold, Jul'84 by Old Gold Records. Dist: Lightning, Jazz Music, Spartan, Counterpoint

FINE AND MELLOW.
Album: released on Pablo, '82 by Pablo Records. Dist: Wellard, Chris, IMS-Polygram, BMG

Cassette: released on Pablo, '82 by Pablo Records. Dist: Wellard, Chris, IMS-Polygram, BMG

FITZGERALD AND PASS....AGAIN.
Album: released on Pablo (USA), May'82 by Pablo Records (USA). Dist: Wellard, Chris, IMS-Polygram, BMG

Cassette: released on Pablo (USA), May'82 by Pablo Records (USA). Dist: Wellard, Chris, IMS-Polygram, BMG

FOREVER YOUNG VOL.1.
Album: released on Swingtime, Jun'86 Dist: Jazz Music Distribution

FOREVER YOUNG VOL.2.
Album: released on Swingtime, Jun'86 Dist: Jazz Music Distribution

Album: released on Swingtime, Sep'86 Dist: Jazz Music Distribution

GEORGE GERSHWIN SONG BOOK, THE.
Compact disc: by Phonogram Records. Dist: Polygram

Album: released on Verve, Aug'85 by Phonogram Records. Dist: Polygram

Cassette: released on Verve, Aug'85 by Phonogram Records. Dist: Polygram

GERSHWIN SONGBOOK 1.
Double Album: by Polydor Records. Dist: Polygram, Polydor

GET HAPPY.
Album: released on Polydor (France), Oct'83 Dist: Polygram

GOLDEN GREATS: ELLA FITZGERALD.
Album: released on MCA, Jul'85 by MCA Records. Dist: Polygram, MCA

Cassette: released on MCA, Jul'85 by MCA Records. Dist: Polygram, MCA

HELLO LOVE.
Album: released on Memoir, Aug'87 by Memoir Records. Dist: PRT Distribution

Cassette: released on Memoir, Aug'87 by Memoir Records. Dist: PRT Distribution

INCOMPARABLE, (THE).
Album: released on Polydor, Apr'80 by Polydor Records. Dist: Polygram, Polydor

Cassette: released on Polydor, Apr'80 by Polydor Records. Dist: Polygram, Polydor

IRVING BERLIN SONGBOOK VOLUME 1.
Tracks: / Reaching for the moon / Slumming on Park Avenue / Song is ended (The) / I'm putting all my eggs in one basket / Now it can be told / Always / It's a lovely day today / Change partners / No strings / I've got my love to keep me warm / Let's face the music and dance / Your laughing at me / Let yourself go / You can have him / Russian lullaby / Putting on the Ritz / Get thee behind me satan / Alexander's ragtime band / Top hat, white tie and tails / How about me / Cheek to cheek / I used to be colour blind / Lazy / How deep is the ocean / All by myself / (You forgot to) remember / Suppertime / How's chances / Heat wave / Isn't this a lovely day / You keep coming back like a song.
Compact disc: released on Polydor, Nov'86 by Polydor Records. Dist: Polygram, Polydor

IRVING BERLIN SONGBOOK VOLUME 2.
Compact disc: released on Polydor, Nov'86 by Polydor Records. Dist: Polygram, Polydor

IT HAPPENED ONE NIGHT (Fitzgerald, Ella/Dizzie Gellespie/Charlie Parker).

JEROME KERN SONG BOOK.
Compact disc: by Polydor Records. Dist: Polygram, Polydor

JOHNNY MERCER SONG BOOK.
Compact disc: by Phonogram Records. Dist: Polygram

LADY TIME.
Album: released on Pablo (USA), May'82 by Pablo Records (USA). Dist: Wellard, Chris, IMS-Polygram, BMG

Cassette: released on Pablo (USA), May'82 by Pablo Records (USA). Dist: Wellard, Chris, IMS-Polygram, BMG

LIKE SOMEONE IN LOVE.
Album: released on Verve, Oct'75 by Phonogram Records. Dist: Polygram

LIVE AT CARNEGIE HALL (5/7/73).
Album: released on CBS(France), Apr'84 by CBS Records. Dist: Conifer, Discovery, Swift

LOVER COME BACK TO ME.
Album: released on MFP (France), Mar'84 by EMI Records. Dist: EMI

Cassette: released on MFP (France), Mar'84 by EMI Records. Dist: EMI

LOVE SONGS.
Tracks: / You'll never know / Some one to watch over me / I had'nt anymore till you / My one and only love.
Notes: Mono.

LOVE SONGS.
Tracks: / I can't get started / It might as well be spring / You'll never know / I wished on the moon / Please be kind / Someone to watch over me / M one and only love / I'm glad there is you / Angel eyes / Walking by the river / How long has this been going on / Old devil moon / Baby doll.
Album: released on Memoir, Dec'85 by Memoir Records. Dist: PRT Distribution

Cassette: released on Memoir, Dec'85 by Memoir Records. Dist: PRT Distribution

LULLABIES OF BIRDLAND.
Album: released on Jasmine, Aug'83 by Jasmine Records. Dist: Counterpoint, Taylor, H.R., Wellard, Chris, Swift, Cadillac

NICE WORK IF YOU CAN GET IT (Fitzgerald, Ella & Andre Previn).
Tracks: / Let's call the whole thing off / Let's call the whole thing off / How long has this been going on / Who care / I got a crush on you / Someone to watch over me / I got a crush on you / Embraceable you / They can't take that away from me / Foggy day, A / Nice work if you can get it / But not for me.
Compact disc: released on Verve (USA), Sep'86 by Polydor. Dist: Polygram

ON THE SUNNY SIDE OF THE STREET.
Compact disc: by Phonogram Records. Dist: Polygram

PERFECT MATCH, A (Fitzgerald, Ella & Count Basie).

PETE KELLY'S BLUES.
Album: released on Jasmine, Sep'83 by Jasmine Records. Dist: PRT

PORGY AND BESS (Fitzgerald, Ella & Louis Armstrong).
Album: released on Verve (France), May'85

Cassette: released on Verve (France), Mav'85

Compact disc: released on Verve, '83 by Phonogram Records. Dist: Polygram

PORGY & BESS.
Compact disc: by Polydor Records. Dist: Polygram, Polydor

RARE OF ALL RAREST PERFORMANCES VOL 1.
Album: released on Kings Of Jazz, May'82 Dist: Jazz Horizons, Jazz Music, Celtic Music

RAREST, (THE).
Album: released on Joker (Import), Apr'81

RHYTHM IS MY BUSINESS.
Album: released on Verve (USA), Nov'82 by Polydor. Dist: Polygram

RODGERS & HART SONG BOOK 1.
Compact disc: by Phonogram Records. Dist: Polygram

ROGERS AND HART SONGBOOK.
Double Album: released on Verve, Feb'75 by Phonogram Records. Dist: Polygram

Compact disc: released on Verve, Feb'75 by Phonogram Records. Dist: Polygram

Compact disc: released on Verve, Feb'75 by Phonogram Records. Dist: Polygram

ROGERS AND HART SONGBOOK II.
Compact disc: released on Verve, Jul'85 by Phonogram Records. Dist: Polygram

SINGS CHRISTMAS.
Album: released on MFP (Capitol), Dec'82 by EMI Records. Dist: EMI

Cassette: released on MFP (Capitol), Dec'82 by EMI Records. Dist: EMI

SINGS COLE PORTER SONGBOOK.
Double Album: released on Verve, Jul'84 by Phonogram Records. Dist: Polygram

Compact disc: released on Verve, Jul'74 by Phonogram Records. Dist: Polygram

Compact disc: released on Verve, Jul'74 by Phonogram Records. Dist: Polygram

SINGS IRVING BERLIN SONGBOOK.
Double Album: by Polydor Records. Dist: Polygram, Polydor

SINGS THE GEORGE AND IRA GERSHWIN SONGBOOK.
Special: released on Verve (USA), Mar'83 by Polydor. Dist: Polygram

SINGS THE JOHNNY MERCER SONGBOOK.
Double Album: released on Verve, Oct'76 by Phonogram Records. Dist: Polygram

Compact disc: released on Verve, Oct'76 by Phonogram Records. Dist: Polygram

SONGBOOKS, (THE).
Compact disc: released on Verve, Nov'84 by Phonogram Records. Dist: Polygram

SPEAK LOVE.
Album: released on Pablo Jazz (USA), Oct'84 by United Artists. Dist: Swift

SPECIAL MAGIC OF ELLA FITZGERALD.
Album: released on Verve, Aug'77

STOCKHOLM CONCERT 1966, (THE).
Album: released on Pablo (USA), Feb'85 by Pablo Records (USA). Dist: Wellard, Chris, IMS-Polygram, BMG

Cassette: released on Pablo (USA), Feb'85 by Pablo Records (USA). Dist: Wellard, Chris, IMS-Polygram, BMG

STOCKHOLM CONCERT (Fitzgerald, Ella & Duke Ellington).
Compact disc: released on Pablo, Aug'86 by Pablo Records. Dist: Wellard, Chris, IMS-Polygram, BMG

SUNSHINE OF YOUR LOVE.
Album: released on MPS (Germany), Sep'84 Dist: IMS-Polygram Distribution, Parnote Distribution (Formerly MDC)

SWEET & HOT.
Album: released on Jasmine, Oct'84 by Jasmine Records. Dist: Counterpoint, Taylor, H.R., Wellard, Chris, Swift, Cadillac

SWINGING CHRISTMAS.
Album: released on Verve, Dec'81 by Phonogram Records. Dist: Polygram

TAKE LOVE EASY (Fitzgerald, Ella & Joe Pass).
Tracks: / Take love easy / Once I loved / Don't be that way / You're blase / Lush life / Foggy day, A / Gee baby ain't good to you / You got to my head / I want to talk about you.
Compact disc: released on Pablo (USA), Jul'86 by Pablo Records (USA). Dist: Wellard, Chris, IMS-Polygram, BMG

Album: released on Pablo (USA), May'82 by Pablo Records (USA). Dist: Wellard, Chris, IMS-Polygram, BMG

Cassette: released on Pablo (USA), May'82 by Pablo Records (USA). Dist: Wellard, Chris, IMS-Polygram, BMG

THAT OLD ELLA MAGIC.
Album: released on Music for Pleasure, Sep'83 by EMI Records. Dist: MFP Distribution

Cassette: released on Music for Pleasure, Sep'83 by EMI Records. Dist: MFP Distribution

THESE ARE THE BLUES.
Compact disc: released on Polydor, Nov'86 by Polydor Records. Dist: Polygram, Polydor

VERY THOUGHT OF YOU.
Album: released on Contour, May'87 by Pickwick Records. Dist: Pickwick Distribution, PRT

VOLUME 1.
Album: released on Swingtime, Jun'86 Dist: Jazz Music Distribution

WALKMAN JAZZ.
Cassette: released on Polydor, Jun'87 by Polydor Records. Dist: Polygram, Polydor

Album: released on I.D., Jun'87 by I.D. Records. Dist: Revolver, Cartel

WEBB ON THE AIR.
Album: released on Jazz Bird, May'82 Dist: Cassion (Melandy)

Cassette: released on Jazz Bird, May'82 Dist: Cassion (Melandy)

WHEN THE SAINTS GO MARCHING IN.
Album: released on Joker (Import), Apr'81

WHISPER NOT.
Album: released on Verve (USA), Jun'81 by Polydor. Dist: Polygram

WITH CHICK WEBB.
Album: released on Astan, Nov'84 by Astan Records. Dist: Counterpoint

Cassette: released on Astan, Nov'84 by Astan Records. Dist: Counterpoint

WITH DIZZY GILLESPIE ORCHESTRA.
Album: released on Natural Organic Import, Apr'81

WITH THE TOMMY FLANAGAN TRIO.
Album: released on Pablo (USA), May'82 by Pablo Records (USA). Dist: Wellard, Chris, IMS-Polygram, BMG

Cassette: released on Pablo (USA), May'82 by Pablo Records (USA). Dist: Wellard, Chris, IMS-Polygram, BMG

Fitzgerald, Kathleen

BEST OF.....
Cassette: released on Homespun(Ireland), May'79 by Outlet Records. Dist: Outlet

KATHLEEN FITZGERALD SINGS.
Tracks: / My lovely Irish rose / Meetings of the waters / Dan O'Hara / Spinning wheel / Lovely lough gil / Terry / Three lovely lasses from Bannion / Its heaven around Galway / Kitty of Coleraine / Moonlight in Mayo / Killarney / Beautiful Bundoran.
Cassette: released on Philips (Ireland), Aug'86 Dist: IMS-Polygram

Fitzgerald, Patrick

DRIFTING INTO SILENCE.
Album: released on Himalaya, Feb'84 by Himalaya Records. Dist: Rough Trade, Cartel

GIFTS AND TELEGRAMS.
Album: released on Red Flame, Nov'82 by Red Flame Records. Dist: Nine Mile, Cartel

PERSONAL LOSS.
Single (7"): released on Red Flame, Sep'82 by Red Flame Records. Dist: Nine Mile, Cartel

TONIGHT.
Single (7"): released on Red Flame, Apr'84 by Red Flame Records. Dist: Nine Mile, Cartel

Fitzgerald, Scott

IF I HAD WORDS.
Single (7"): released on EMI (Holland), Jul'84 by EMI Records. Dist: Conifer

LOVE IS LOVE IS LOVE.
Single (7"): released on Young Blood, Jan'85 by Young Blood Records. Dist: Pinnacle

MONTEGO BAY.
Single (7"): released on Creole, Jul'80 by Creole Records. Dist: Rhino, PRT

Fitzpatrick, Gene

EMERALD SMILE, (THE).
Album: released on Homespun(Ireland), Dec'84 by Outlet Records. Dist: Outlet

Cassette: released on Homespun(Ireland), Dec'84 by Outlet Records. Dist: Outlet

FITZ OF LAUGHTER.
Album: released on Homespun(Ireland), Aug'82 by Outlet Records. Dist: Outlet

Cassette: released on Homespun(Ireland), Aug'82 by Outlet Records. Dist: Outlet

KINGDOM I CALL HOME.
Single (7"): released on Homespun(Ireland), Sep'82 by Outlet Records. Dist: Outlet

LET THE REST OF THE WORLD GO BY.
Single (7"): released on Homespun(Ireland), Jan'83 by Outlet Records. Dist: Outlet

LIVE AT THE GROUP THEATRE.
Album: released on Homespun(Ireland), May'82 by Outlet Records. Dist: Outlet

Cassette: released on Homespun(Ireland), May'82 by Outlet Records. Dist: Outlet

VIVA IRELAND.
Single (7"): released on Lismor, Mar'82 by Lismor Records. Dist: Lismor, Roots, Celtic Music

Fitzroy, Eddie

COMING UP STRONG.
Album: released on Sunpower, Aug'87 Dist: Jetstar

PRETTY WOMAN.
Single (12"): released on Attack, Mar'81 by Trojan Records. Dist: Trojan, Pinnacle, Red Rhino

Fitzroy, Edi

CHANT IT TO THE RHYTHM.
Single (12"): released on Musical Ambassador, Jul'82

PRINCESS BLACK.
Single (12"): released on Pama, Oct'84 by Pama Records. Dist: Pama, Enterprise, Jetstar

Fitzsimmons, A.

: see under J. & A. Mageean.

Five ...

5,4,3,2,1 GO! Various artists (Various Artists).
Album: released on Countdown, May'85 by Stiff Records. Dist: EMI, Swift

Cassette: released on Countdown, May'85 by Stiff Records. Dist: EMI, Swift

FIVE BIRDS AND A MONK (Five Birds And A Monk).
Album: released on Galaxy, Sep'81 by Galaxy Records. Dist: RCA, Red Lightnin' Distribution, Discovery, Swift

FIVE CHILDREN AND IT By E. Nesbitt read by S Donald (Nesbitt, E).
Cassette: released on Colophone, Sep'81 by Audio-Visual Library Services. Dist: Audio-Visual Library Services

FIVE GO ADVENTURING AGAIN By Enid Blyton (Blyton, Enid).
Album: released on Super Tempo, May'84 by Multiple Sounds Records. Dist: Multiple Sound Distributors

Cassette: released on Super Tempo, May'84 by Multiple Sounds Records. Dist: Multiple Sound Distributors

FIVE GO DOWN TO THE SEA Enid Blyton read by Jane Asher (Blyton, Enid).
Double cassette: released on Listen For Pleasure, Oct'82 by MFP Records. Dist: EMI

FIVE LITTLE PEPPERS, THE By Margaret Sidney read by Julie Harris (Sidney, Margaret).
Album: released on Caedmon(USA), '79 by Caedmon (USA) Records. Dist: Gower, Taylors, Discovery

Cassette: released on Caedmon(USA), '79 by Caedmon (USA) Records. Dist: Taylors, Discovery

NEXT TIME.
Tracks: / Next time / Clean living.
Notes: Available by mail order for 3.29 plus 60p p&p from: 29 Bath Street, Edinburgh, EH15 1HB.
Single (12"): released on Five, Aug'87 by Five Records. Dist: Five Records

Five-0-One

LET THE NIGHT TAKE THE BLAME.
Single (7"): released on Fanfare, Jul'85 by Ferroway/Fanfare Records. Dist: PRT

Single (12"): released on Fanfare, Jul'85 by Ferroway/Fanfare Records. Dist: PRT

Five-0-One's

WE ARE INVINCIBLE.
Single (7"): released on ERC, Jun'84 by ERC Records. Dist: PRT

Five A Slide

FIVE A SLIDE Various artists (Various Artists).
Notes: Artists include: Roy Williams/Pete Strange/Jim Shepherd/John Beecham/ Campbell Burnap.
Album: released on Audiophile, Jun'86 by Jazzology Records (USA). Dist: Jazz Music, Swift

Five Blind Boys...

FIVE BLIND BOYS OF ALABAMA (Five Blind Boys Of Alabama).
Album: released on Heritage, 11 Apr'87 by Heritage Records. Dist: Chart

Five Go Down To The Sea

FIVE GO DOWN TO THE SEA.
Single (7"): released on Kabuki, Mar'83 by Gareth Ryan. Dist: Rough Trade

GLEE CLUB, THE.
Single (12"): released on Abstract, Sep'84 by Abstract. Dist: Pinnacle

HAWKING.
Single (12"): released on Creation, Aug'85 Dist: Rough Trade, Cartel

Five Go Mad In Europe

DEDACENCE.
Single (12"): released on Criminal Damage, Jul'84 by Criminal Damage Records. Dist: Backs, Cartel

Five Hand Reel

BUNCH OF FIVES, A.
Album: released on Topic, '81 by Topic Records. Dist Projection Distribution, Jazz Music Distribution

NOTHING BUT THE BEST.
Album: released on RCA, Sep'80 by RCA Records. Dist: RCA, Roots, Swift, Wellard, Chris, I & B, Solomon & Peres Distribution

Five Happy Fellas

IT'S ILLEGAL, IT'S IMMORAL OR IT MAKES YOU FAT.
Single (7"): released on Crash, Nov'82 by Satril Records. Dist: PRT

Five Harmaniacs

FIVE HARMANIACS.
Album: released on Puritan, Apr'79 Dist: Swift

Five Keys

IT'S A GROOVE.
Tracks: / Hucklebuck with Jimmy / How do you expect me to / Old MacDonald / Why oh why / Serve another round / I'm so high / Glory of love (The) / Rockin' & cryin' blues / She's the most / From the bottom of my heart / Close your eyes / Now don't that prove I love you / That's right / Out of sight, out of mind / My pigeon's gone.
Compact disc: released on Charly, Mar'87 by Charly Records. Dist: Charly, Cadillac

Five Letters

CRAZY MAN (Five O).
Single (7"): released on Earlobe, Mar'81 by Earlobe Records. Dist: Pinnacle

Five Miles To Midnight

CHOICES.
Single (12"): released on Pax, Aug'81 by Pax Records. Dist: Red Rhino, Cartel

Five Or Six

ANOTHER REASON.
Single (7"): released on Cherry Red, '81 by Cherry Red Records. Dist: Pinnacle

FOUR FROM FIVE OR SIX.
Single (12"): released on Cherry Red, Oct'82 by Cherry Red Records. Dist: Pinnacle

POLAR EXPLOSION.
Single (12"): released on Cherry Red, Oct'81 by Cherry Red Records. Dist: Pinnacle

THRIVING AND HAPPY LAND, A.
Album: released on Cherry Red, Sep'82 by Cherry Red Records. Dist: Pinnacle

Fivepenny Piece

THIS IS FIVEPENNY PIECE.
Album: released on EMI, '80 by EMI Records. Dist: EMI

Page 366

Five Red Caps

LENOX AVENUE JUMP.
Album: released on Krazy Kat, Oct'83 Dist: Jazz Music, Swift, Chris Wellard, H.R. Taylor, Charly, Hotshot,

VOL.2 1943-1946.
Album: released on Krazy Kat, May'86 Dist: Jazz Music, Swift, Chris Wellard, H.R. Taylor, Charly, Hotshot, IRS Distribution

Five Royales

ROOTS OF SOUL.
Tracks: / Tell the truth / Dont let it be in vain / Slummer the slum, The / I'm with you / I'm gonna run it down / Devil with the rest / You didn't learn it at home / Mohawk squaw / How I wonder / When I get like this / I ain't getting caught / Right around the corner / I could love you if you let me / Come on and save me / Get something out of it / Think.
Compact disc: released on Charly, Feb'87 by Charly Records. Dist: Charly, Cadillac

Five Sapphires

DUKE OF EARL.
Single (7"): released on Warner Brothers, Feb'79 by Warner Bros Records. Dist: WEA

ONCE IN A WHILE.
Single (7"): released on Warner Brothers, May'79 by Warner Bros Records. Dist: WEA

Five Smith Brothers

MR & MRS SMITH'S FIVE LITTLE BOYS.
Album: released on MWM, Jun'82 by Mawson & Wareham. Dist: Spartan Distribution, Jazz Music Distribution, JSU Distribution

Cassette: released on MWM, Jun'82 by Mawson & Wareham. Dist: Spartan Distribution, Jazz Music Distribution,

MR & MRS SMITH'S FIVE LITTLE BOYS-VOL 2.
Cassette: released on MWM, Jun'82 by Mawson & Wareham. Dist: Spartan Distribution, Jazz Music Distribution,

Five Special

JUST A FEELING.
Single (7"): released on Elektra, Jan'82 by WEA Records. Dist: WEA

Single (12"): released on Elektra, Jan'82 by WEA Records. Dist: WEA

Five Star

ALL FALL DOWN.
Single (7"): released on RCA, Apr'85 by RCA Records. Dist: RCA, Roots, Swift, Wellard, Chris, I & B, Solomon & Peres Distribution

Single (12"): released on RCA, Apr'85 by RCA Records. Dist: RCA, Roots, Swift, Wellard, Chris, I & B, Solomon & Peres Distribution

FIND THE TIME.
Tracks: / Find the time / Sky.
Single (7"): released on Tent, Jul'86 by RCA Records. Dist: BMG Distribution

Single (12"): released on Tent, Jul'86 by RCA Records. Dist: BMG Distribution

IF I SAY YES.
Tracks: / If I say yes / Let me down easy / Can't wait another minute / Say goodbye / Crazy / Winning.
Single (7"): released on RCA, Nov'86 by RCA Records. Dist: RCA, Roots, Swift, Wellard, Chris, I & B, Solomon & Peres Distribution

Single (12"): released on RCA, Nov'86 by RCA Records. Dist: RCA, Roots, Swift, Wellard, Chris, I & B, Solomon & Peres Distribution

LAST TAKEOVER.
Single (7"): released on RCA, Aug'85 by RCA Records. Dist: RCA, Roots, Swift, Wellard, Chris, I & B, Solomon & Peres Distribution

Single (12"): released on RCA, Aug'85 by RCA Records. Dist: RCA, Roots, Swift, Wellard, Chris, I & B, Solomon & Peres Distribution

LET ME BE THE ONE.
Single (7"): released on RCA, Jul'85 by RCA Records. Dist: RCA, Roots, Swift, Wellard, Chris, I & B, Solomon & Peres Distribution

Single (12"): released on RCA, Jul'85 by RCA Records. Dist: RCA, Roots, Swift, Wellard, Chris, I & B, Solomon & Peres Distribution

LUXURY OF LIFE.
Tracks: / Love take over / All fall down / Let me be the one / System addict / Hide and seek / R.S.V.P. / Now I'm in control.
Album: released on Tent, Aug'86 by RCA Records. Dist: BMG Distribution

Cassette: released on Tent, Aug'86 by RCA Records. Dist: BMG Distribution

Compact disc: released on Tent, Aug'86 by RCA Records. Dist: BMG Distribution

LUXURY OF LIFE VIDEO SELECTION.
Video-cassette (VHS): released on RCA, May'86 by RCA Records. Dist: RCA, Roots, Swift, Wellard, Chris, I & B, Solomon & Peres Distribution

PROBLEMATIC.
Single (7"): released on Tent, Oct'83 by RCA Records. Dist: BMG Distribution

Single (7"): released on Tent, Oct'83 by RCA Records. Dist: BMG Distribution

RAIN OR SHINE.
Tracks: / Rain or shine.
Single (7"): released on Tent, Aug'86 by RCA Records. Dist: BMG Distribution

Single (12"): released on Tent, Aug'86 by RCA Records. Dist: BMG Distribution

R.S.V.P..
Single (7"): released on Tent, Nov'85 by RCA Records. Dist: BMG Distribution

Single (12"): released on Tent, Nov'85 by RCA Records. Dist: BMG Distribution

SILK AND STEEL.
Tracks: / Can't wait another minute / Find the time / Rain or shine / If I say yes / Please don't say goodnight / Stay out of my life / Are you man enough / Show me what you've got for me / Slightest touch / Don't you know I love you.
Album: released on Tent, Aug'86 by RCA Records. Dist: BMG Distribution

Cassette: released on Tent, Aug'86 by RCA Records. Dist: BMG Distribution

Compact disc: released on Tent, Aug'86 by RCA Records. Dist: BMG Distribution

STAY OUT OF MY LIFE.
Tracks: / Stay out of my life / How dare you stay out of my life / If I say yes Lew hahn us dub mix*.
Single (7"): released on RCA, Jan'87 by RCA Records. Dist: RCA, Roots, Swift, Wellard, Chris, I & B, Solomon & Peres Distribution

Single (12"): released on Tent, Jan'87 by RCA Records. Dist: BMG Distribution

SYSTEM ADDICT.
Tracks: / System addict / Pure energy / Winning.
Single (7"): released on Tent, Jan'86 by RCA Records. Dist: BMG Distribution

Single (12"): released on Tent, Jan'86 by RCA Records. Dist: BMG Distribution

WHENEVER YOU'RE READY.
Single (7"): released on Tent, Aug'87 by RCA Records. Dist: BMG Distribution

Single (12"): released on Tent, Aug'87 by RCA Records. Dist: BMG Distribution

Five TA

ANGEL.
Single (7"): released on Torch Productions, May'84 by Torch Productions Records.

Single (12"): released on Torch Productions, May'84 by Torch Productions Records.

Album: released on Charly(R&B), Jul'85 by Charly Records. Dist: Charly, Cadillac

Cassette: released on Charly(R&B), Jul'85 by Charly Records. Dist: Charly, Cadillac

HEAVEN.
Tracks: / Heaven / Ting the bell.
Single (7"): released on Arista, Nov'86 by Arista Records. Dist: RCA

Single (12"): released on Arista, Nov'86 by Arista Records. Dist: RCA

KIND OF TRIUMPH, A.
Tracks: / Question of belief / Decadent and sexy / My brilliant career / We are the men / Heaven / Walking on the water / Fine day / Law of the jungle / Salt / Trinity / Laws of the jungle (Judge Allen mix) / Trinity (Highly strung mix).
Compact disc: released on Arista, Jan'87 by Arista Records. Dist: RCA

Album: released on Arista, Jan'87 by Arista Records. Dist: RCA

Cassette: released on Arista, Jan'87 by Arista Records. Dist: RCA

LOW RIDER.
Tracks: / Low rider (mezcal mix) / Law of the jungle.
Single (12"): released on Arista, Apr'87 by Arista Records. Dist: RCA

MY BRILLIANT CAREER.
Tracks: / My brilliant career / Ring the bell.
Single (7"): released on Arista, Jun'86 by Arista Records. Dist: RCA

Single (12"): released on Arista, Jun'86 by Arista Records. Dist: RCA

Five Thirty

CATCHER IN THE RYE.
Single (12"): released on Other, Oct'85 by Waterfall Records. Dist: Revolver Distribution

WEIGHT OF THE WORLD.
Single (12"): released on Other, Nov'85 by Waterfall Records. Dist: Revolver Distribution

Five Year Plan

NOTHING WILL GO WRONG.
Tracks: / Nothing will go wrong / Brand new car / Give me a lifetime / Something to make you laugh.
Single (12"): released on Breaking Down, May'86 Dist: Revolver

Fixed Up

VITAL HOURS.
Album: released on I.D., May'87 by I.D. Records. Dist: Revolver, Cartel

Fixx

ARE WE OURSELVES.
Single (7"): released on MCA, '84 by MCA Records. Dist: Polygram, MCA

I WILL.
Single (7"): released on MCA, '85 by MCA Records. Dist: Polygram, MCA

Single (12"): released on MCA, '85 by MCA Records. Dist: Polygram, MCA

LESS CITIES MORE MOVING PEOPLE.
Single (7"): released on MCA, '84 by MCA Records. Dist: Polygram, MCA

Single (12"): released on MCA, '84 by MCA Records. Dist: Polygram, MCA

PHANTOMS.
Compact disc: by MCA Records. Dist: Polygram, MCA

Album: released on MCA, '84 by MCA Records. Dist: Polygram, MCA

Cassette: released on MCA, '84 by MCA Records. Dist: Polygram, MCA

Compact disc: released on MCA, '84 by MCA Records. Dist: Polygram, MCA

REACH THE BEACH.
Tracks: / One things leads to another / Sign of fire, The / Running / Saved by zero / Opinions / Reach the beach / Changing / Liner / Privilege / Outside.
Compact disc: released on MCA, '86 by MCA Records. Dist: Polygram, MCA

Album: released on MCA, '83 by MCA Records. Dist: Polygram, MCA

Cassette: released on MCA, '83 by MCA Records. Dist: Polygram, MCA

SECRET SEPARATION.
Tracks: / Secret separation / Sense the adventure / Rediscover.
Single (7"): released on MCA, Jun'86 by MCA Records. Dist: Polygram, MCA

Single (12"): released on MCA, Jun'86 by MCA Records. Dist: Polygram, MCA

SHUTTERED ROOM.
Album: released on Fixx, '82 by MCA Records. Dist: Polygram, CBS

Cassette: released on Fixx, '82 by MCA Records. Dist: Polygram, CBS

WALKABOUT.
Tracks: / Built for the future / Treasure it / Chase the fire.
Notes: The Fixx play their own complex brand of rock music. All their previous albums have been best sellers in Europe and the United States. Their new album sees the Foxx poised to break in this country. "Walkabout" features the airplay hit "Secret Separartions". The Fixx features guitarist Jamie West-Oram who played on Tina Turner's "Private Dancer" album. Jamie West-Oram was a member of her touring band.
Album: released on MCA, Sep'86 by MCA Records. Dist: Polygram, MCA

Cassette: released on MCA, Sep'86 by MCA Records. Dist: Polygram, MCA

Compact disc: released on MCA, Sep'86 by MCA Records. Dist: Polygram, MCA

Fixx, The

WALKABOUT.
Tracks: / Secret seperation / Built for the future / Treasure it / Chase the fire / Can't finish / Walkabout / One look up / Read between the lines / Sense the adventure / Camphor.
Compact disc: released on MCA, '87 by MCA Records. Dist: Polygram, MCA

Fizzbombs

SIGN ON THE LINE.
Tracks: / Sign on the line / Lines that, The.
Single (7"): released on Narodnik, 30 May'87 Dist: Fast Forward, Cartel

Flacke, Nils

NILS FLACKE IN BREADTH.
Tracks: / United nations polka / Allevalsen springtime / Snickerpelles waltz / Jugansbohambo / Intermezzo / Stars and stripes / Waltz accordi / Hopsassa promenade rhythm / indo waltz / March gall rini / Internationalen.
Album: by Accordion Record Club Records. Dist: Accordion Record Club

Flack, Roberta

BACK TOGETHER AGAIN (Flack, Roberta & Donny Hathaway).
Single (7"): released on Atlantic, '80 by WEA Records. Dist: WEA

Single (12"): released on Atlantic, '80 by WEA Records. Dist: WEA

BEST OF ROBERTA FLACK,THE.
Album: released on Atlantic, '81 by WEA Records. Dist: WEA

Cassette: released on Atlantic, '81 by WEA Records. Dist: WEA

BEST OF ROBERTA FLACK (THE).
Tracks: / Killing me softly with his song / Closer I get to you (The) / You've got a friend / Feel like makin' love / Will you still love me tomorrow / Wrere is the love? / First time ever I saw your face (The) / Back together again / If I ever see you again / You are my heaven / Jesse.
Compact disc: released on Atlantic, Feb'87 by WEA Records. Dist: WEA

BLUE LIGHTS IN THE BASEMENTS.
Cassette: released on Atlantic, '78 by WEA Records. Dist: WEA

BORN TO LOVE (Flack, Roberta, Peabo Bryson).
Album: released on Capitol, '83 by Capitol Records. Dist: EMI

Cassette: released on Capitol, '83 by Capitol Records. Dist: EMI

FEATURING DONNY HATHAWAY.
Album: released on Atlantic, '80 by WEA Records. Dist: WEA

FIRST TAKE/CHAPTER TWO.
Double Album: released on Atlantic, '75 by WEA Records. Dist: WEA

FIRST TIME I EVER SAW YOUR FACE.
Single (7"): released on Atlantic, '72 by WEA Records. Dist: WEA

Single (7"): released on Atlantic, '84 by WEA Records. Dist: WEA

GREATEST HITS:ROBERTA FLACK.
Album: released on K-Tel, '84 by K-Tel Records. Dist: Record Merchandisers Distribution, Taylors, Terry Blood Distribution, Wynd-Up Distribution, Relay Distribution, Pickwick Distribution, Solomon & Peres Distribution, Polygram

Cassette: released on K-Tel, '84 by K-Tel Records. Dist: Record Merchandisers Distribution, Taylors, Terry Blood Distribution, Wynd-Up Distribution, Relay Distribution, Pickwick Distribution, Solomon & Peres Distribution, Polygram

KILLING ME SOFTLY.
Album: by WEA Records. Dist: WEA

Cassette: released on Atlantic, '74 by WEA Records. Dist: WEA

Single (7"): released on Atlantic, '81 by WEA Records. Dist: WEA

KILLING ME SOFTLY WITH HIS SONG.
Single (7"): released on Old Gold, '85 by Old Gold Records. Dist: Lightning, Jazz Music, Spartan, Counterpoint

LIVE-AND MORE (Flack, Roberta, Peabo Bryson).
Double Album: released on Atlantic, '81 by WEA Records. Dist: WEA

Cassette: released on Atlantic, '81 by WEA Records. Dist: WEA

LOVE IS A WAITING GAME (Flack, Roberta, Peabo Bryson).
Single (7"): released on Atlantic, '81 by WEA Records. Dist: WEA

Single (12"): released on Atlantic, '81 by WEA Records. Dist: WEA

MAKING LOVE/JESSE.
Single (7"): released on Atlantic, '82 by WEA Records. Dist: WEA

Single (12"): released on Atlantic, '82 by WEA Records. Dist: WEA

ROBERTA FLACK.
Album: released on Atlantic, '78 by WEA Records. Dist: WEA

Cassette: released on Atlantic, '78 by WEA Records. Dist: WEA

ROBERTA FLACKS GREATEST HITS.
Album: released on K-Tel, '84 by K-Tel Records. Dist: Record Merchandisers Distribution, Taylors, Terry Blood Distribution, Wynd-Up Distribution, Relay Distribution, Pickwick Distribution, Solomon & Peres Distribution, Polygram

Cassette: released on K-Tel, '84 by K-Tel Records. Dist: Record Merchandisers Distribution, Taylors, Terry Blood Distribution, Wynd-Up Distribution, Relay Distribution, Pickwick Distribution, Solomon & Peres Distribution, Polygram

WHERE IS THE LOVE (Flack, Roberta & Donny Hathaway).
Single (7"): released on Old Gold, Jan'85 by Old Gold Records. Dist: Lightning, Jazz Music, Spartan, Counterpoint

Flag of Convenience

LAST TRAIN TO SAFETY.
Tracks: / Last train to safety.
Notes: Feat. Steve Diggle (ex Buzzcocks)
Single (12"): released on Flag Of Convenience, Apr'87

LIFE ON THE TELEPHONE.
Single (7"): released on Sire, Sep'82

NEW HOUSE.
Single (7"): released on MCM, Apr'86 Dist: Harmonia Mundi Distributors, Pinnacle

Flags of Dublin

FLAGS OF DUBLIN Various artists (Various Artists).
Album: released on Topic, Jan'81 Dist: Roots Distribution

Flairck

EAST WEST EXPRESS.
Single (7"): released on Polydor, Mar'83 by Polydor Records. Dist: Polygram, Polydor

FLAIRCK LIVE.
Album: released on Polydor, Nov'83 by Polydor Records. Dist: Polygram, Polydor

Cassette: released on Polydor, Nov'83 by Polydor Records. Dist: Polygram, Polydor

SLEIGHT OF HAND.
Tracks: / At the blacksmith's hands / Sleight of hand / Behind the glass curtain / Trick of the night / Walk upon dreams / Seven card tango / Thin air / Lady shuffles, The / At the blacksmith's hands-part 2.
Album: released on Columbia, Feb'87 by EMI Records. Dist: EMI

Cassette: released on Columbia, Feb'87 by EMI Records. Dist: EMI

TRICK OF THE NIGHT.
Tracks: / Seven card tango.
Single (7"): released on Columbia, Jan'87 by EMI Records. Dist: EMI

VARIATIONS ON A LADY.
Album: released on Polydor, Aug'80 by Polydor Records. Dist: Polygram, Polydor

Flamenco Espanol

FLAMENCO ESPANOL Various artists (Various Artists).
Album: released on Polydor (Germany), Sep'84 Dist: IMS-Polygram

Flames

YOUR LOVE IS SLIPPIN AWAY.
Single (7"): released on Masquerade, Jan'83

Flamin Ember

WESTBOUND NO.9.
Single (7"): released on HDH(Holland/Dozier/Holland), Jan'85 by Demon Records. Dist: Pinnacle

Flaming Groovies

SHAKE SOME ACTION.
Single (7"): released on ABC, Aug'87 Dist: CBS, Pinnacle

Flaming Hands

BREAK DOWN AND CRY.
Tracks: / Break down and cry / Cross my heart.
Single (7"): released on Sierra, Feb'86 by Sierra Records. Dist: WEA

Single (12"): released on Sierra, Feb'86 by Sierra Records. Dist: WEA

Flaming Lips

HEAR IT IT.
Album: released on Enigma (Europe), Nov'86 by Enigma Records. Dist: Rough Trade, Cartel, EMI

Flaming Mussolinis

GIRL ON A TRAIN.
Single (7"): released on Epic, Aug'87 by CBS Records. Dist: CBS

Single (12"): released on Epic, Aug'87 by CBS Records. Dist: CBS

JANK MAMBA A.K.A.
Tracks: / Animal tactics (7" version) / Rumble (The) / Standing in your light / Time and Prize / Animal tactics (extended) / Way things are (The) / Show me something / Young hearts wear scarlet.
Notes: Sav - vocals & guitar, Jeff Fogarty - saxaphones, piano, keyboards & FX, Martin Alderdice - guitars, piano & percussion, Doug Maloney - bass guitars, Dave Palfreeman - drums, percussion & synthesiser, The Janket-tes - backing vocals. all tracks written by Jank Mamba. All tracks licenced from Rout Productions.
Album: released on Dojo, Dec'86 by Castle Communications Records. Dist: Cartel

MASUKA DAN.
Tracks: / Masuka Dan / Street garden.
Single (7"): released on Portrait, May'86 by CBS Records. Dist: CBS

Single (12"): released on Portrait, May'86 by CBS Records. Dist: CBS

MY CLEOPATRA.
Tracks: / My Cleopatra / Privilege.
Single (7"): released on Portrait, Jan'86 by CBS Records. Dist: CBS

Single (12"): released on Portrait, Jan'86 by CBS Records. Dist: CBS

SWALLOW GLASS.
Tracks: / Swallow glass / Movie girl.
Single (7"): released on Portrait, Jun'86 by CBS Records. Dist: CBS

WATCHING THE FILM.
Tracks: / My Cleopatra / Horror Show / Catholic Wedding / Ember Days / Dangerous Persuasion / Swallow Glass / Landslide / Holding Sand / Long Way To Fall-A / Masuka Dan.
Album: released on Portrait, Jul'86 by CBS Records. Dist: CBS

Cassette: released on Portrait, Jul'86 by CBS Records. Dist: CBS

Flamingoes

REQUESTFULLY YOURS.
Album: released on End, Apr'79 by End Records. Dist: Swift

SERENADE.
Album: released on End, Apr'79 by End Records. Dist: Swift

Flamingo Express

HONEYMOON IN SPAIN.
Single (7"): released on Monarch, Jul'83 by Chart Records. Dist: Pinnacle

Flamingo Kid

FLAMINGO KID Original soundtrack.
Album: released on Motown, Oct'85 by Motown Records. Dist: BMG Distribution

Cassette: released on Motown, Oct'85 by Motown Records. Dist: BMG Distribution

Flamingos

CHESS SESSIONS, THE.
Album: released on Chess, Jul'87 by Charly Records. Dist: Charly, Swift, PRT, Discovery, IMS, Polygram

IT'S GOTTA BE BAD.
Single (7"): released on Cambridge, May'82 Dist: PRT

THIS HEAT.
Single (12"): released on Rorschach Testing, Aug'85 by Rorschach Testing Records. Dist: Rough Trade Distribution

Flamin' Groovies

JUMPIN IN THE NIGHT.
Album: released on Sire, Jun'79

ONE NIGHT STAND.
Notes: Half the songs on this album are new, the others are re-recordings of their classic songs inc. "Shake some action, Teenage head, Slow death & Tallahassee Lassie
Album: released on ABC, Mar'87 Dist: CBS, Pinnacle

ROAD HOUSE.
Album: released on Edsel, Mar'86 by Demon Records. Dist: Pinnacle, Jazz Music, Projection

Cassette: released on Edsel, Mar'86 by Demon Records. Dist: Pinnacle, Jazz Music, Projection

STILL SHAKIN.
Album: released on Buddah, Jul'85 Dist: Swift, Jazz Music, PRT

Cassette: released on Buddah, Jul'85 Dist: Swift, Jazz Music, PRT

SUPERGREASE.
Album: released on Skydog, May'84 by Skydog Records.

SUPERSNAZZ.
Album: released on Edsel, Feb'86 by Demon Records. Dist: Pinnacle, Jazz Music, Projection

Flanagan & Allen

BEST OF FLANAGAN AND ALLEN.
Album: released on Encore, Jan'78 by EMI Records. Dist: EMI

Cassette: released on Encore, Jan'78 by EMI Records. Dist: EMI

UNDERNEATH THE ARCHES.
Album: released on Contour, Apr'82 by Pickwick Records. Dist: Pickwick Distribution, PRT

Cassette: released on Contour, Apr'82 by Pickwick Records. Dist: Pickwick Distribution, PRT

WE'LL SMILE AGAIN.
Album: released on Ace Of Clubs, Jan'65 by Decca Records. Dist: Polygram

Flanagan Brothers

AN IRISH DELIGHT.
Album: released on Topic, Jan'81 Dist: Roots Distribution

Flanagan, Tommy

3.
Notes: Montreux 1977
Compact disc: released on Pablo (USA), May'86 by Pablo Records (USA). Dist: Wellard, Chris, IMS-Polygram, BMG

ALONE TOO LONG Music for piano.
Album: released on Denon, Mar'82 by Denon Records. Dist: Harmonia Mundi

BALLADS AND BLUES.
Album: released on Enja (Germany), Jan'82 by Enja Records (W.Germany). Dist: Cadillac Music

BEST OF TOMMY FLANAGAN, THE.
Album: released on Pablo (USA), Jan'82 by Pablo Records (USA). Dist: Wellard, Chris, IMS-Polygram, BMG

Cassette: released on Pablo (USA), Jan'82 by Pablo Records (USA). Dist: Wellard, Chris, IMS-Polygram, BMG

CATS, THE (Flanagan, Tommy, John Coltrane, Kenny Burrell).
Album: released on Original Jazz Classics (USA), Jun'86 Dist: Fantasy (USA) Distribution, Chris Wellard Distribution, IMS-Polygram Distribution

CONFIRMATION.
Album: released on Enja (Germany), Jan'82 by Enja Records (W.Germany). Dist: Cadillac Music

ECLYPSO.
Album: released on Enja (Germany), Jan'82 by Enja Records (W.Germany). Dist: Cadillac Music

HOME COOKING.
Album: released on Phontastic (Sweden), Jan'82 by Wellard, Chris Distribution. Dist: Wellard, Chris Distribution

I'M ALL SMILES (Flanagan, Tommy & Hank Jones).
Album: released on MPS (Germany), Sep'84 Dist: IMS-Polygram Distribution, Parnote Distribution (Formerly MDC)

Cassette: released on MPS (Germany), Sep'84 Dist: IMS-Polygram Distribution, Parnote Distribution (Formerly MDC)

IN STOCKHOLM 1957.
Notes: With Wilbur Little and Elvin Jones.
Album: released on Dragon, Jun'86 by Dragon Records. Dist: Jazz Music, Projection, Cadillac

MAGNIFICENT TOMMY FLANAGAN, THE.
Album: released on Progressive, Jul'82 by Progressive Records. Dist: Jetstar

OUR DELIGHTS (Flanagan, Tommy & Hank Jones).
Tracks: / Our delight / Autumn leaves / Robbins nest / Jordu / Confirmation / Child is born, A / Lady bird / Child is born, A.
Notes: Tommy Flanagan and Hank Jones - pianos
Compact disc: released on Fantasy (USA), Jan'87 by Fantasy Inc USA Records. Dist: IMS, Polygram

SUPER JAZZ TRIO, THE (Flanagan, Tommy and Reggie Workman and Joe Chambers).
Album: released on RCA (France), Jan'83 by RCA Records. Dist: Discovery

SUPER SESSION.
Album: released on Enja (Germany), Jan'82 by Enja Records (W.Germany). Dist: Cadillac Music

TOGETHER.
Compact disc: by Denon Records. Dist: Harmonia Mundi

Album: released on Denon, Mar'82 by Denon Records. Dist: Harmonia Mundi

Cassette: released on Denon, Mar'82 by Denon Records. Dist: Harmonia Mundi

TOKYO RECITAL (Flanagan, Tommy Trio).
Album: released on Pablo (USA), Jan'82 by Pablo Records (USA). Dist: Wellard, Chris, IMS-Polygram, BMG

Cassette: released on Pablo (USA), Jan'82 by Pablo Records (USA). Dist: Wellard, Chris, IMS-Polygram, BMG

TOMMY FLANAGAN THREE.
Album: released on Pablo, Jan'82 by Pablo Records. Dist: Wellard, Chris, IMS-Polygram, BMG

Cassette: released on Pablo (USA), Jan'82 by Pablo Records (USA). Dist: Wellard, Chris, IMS-Polygram, BMG

YOU'RE ME.
Album: released on Phontastic (Sweden), Jan'82 by Wellard, Chris Distribution. Dist: Wellard, Chris Distribution

Flanders & Swann

AT THE DROP OF A HAT.
Album: released on Encore, '78 by EMI Records. Dist: EMI

Cassette: released on Encore, '78 by EMI Records. Dist: EMI

AT THE DROP OF ANOTHER HAT.
Album: released on Encore, '78 by EMI Records. Dist: EMI

Cassette: released on Encore, '78 by EMI Records. Dist: EMI

BESTIARY OF FLANDERS AND SWANN.
Album: by EMI Records. Dist: EMI

Flashback to the 60's

FLASHBACK TO THE 60'S Various artists (Various Artists).
Tracks: / I like it / World without love, A / Walkin' back to happiness / One way love / Kites / Anyone who had a heart / Bad to me / Look through any window / I'm telling you now / Kon-Tiki / You're driving me crazy / Pretty Flamingo / Little loving, A / I'm the urban spaceman / What do you want? / Surfin' USA / I remember you / House of the Rising Sun / I'm into something good / Up on the roof / Lily the pink / I'm a tiger / I'll never fall in love again / I've been a bad, bad boy.
Double Album: released on MFP, Oct'87 by EMI Records. Dist: EMI

Double cassette: released on MFP, Oct'87 by EMI Records. Dist: EMI

Flash Company

FLASH COMPANY (Various Artists).
Notes: A celebration of the first ten years of Fellside Records including:Martin CarthyJez Lowe,Peter Bellamy ETC.
Album: released on Fellside, Jul'86 by Fellside Records. Dist: Roots, Jazz Music, Celtic Music, Projection

Flashdance

FLASHDANCE Various artists (Various Artists).
Video-cassette (VHS): released on CIC Video, Sep'84 by CBS Records. Dist: CBS, Pickwick Distribution

FLASHDANCE Original film solundtrack.
Compact disc: released on Casablanca, Dec'83 Dist: Polygram, Phonogram

Flash, Diana

SAVING ON MY LOVE.
Tracks: / Saving on my love / My love(Version).
Single (12"): released on Hawkeye, May'86 by Hawkeye Records. Dist: Hawkeye, Lightning (WEA) Distribution, Jetstar, PRT

Flatmates

COULD BE IN HEAVEN(I).
Tracks: / Could be in heaven (I).
Single (7"): released on Subway, Sep'86 Dist: Revolver Distribution, Spartan Distribution

HAPPY ALL THE TIME.
Tracks: / Happy all the time.
Notes: 12" version includes 4 extra tracks
Single (7"): released on Subway, Mar'87 Dist: Revolver Distribution, Spartan Distribution

Single (12"): released on Subway, Mar 87 Dist: Revolver Distribution, Spartan Distribution

Flat Stanley
FLAT STANLEY.
Cassette: released on Cover to Cover, Sep'86 by Cover to Cover Cassettes. Dist: Conifer

Flatt, Lester
LIVE AT THE BLUEGRASS FESTIVAL.
Tracks: / Foggy mountain breakdown(Instrumental) / Lost all my money / Homestead on the farm / Rawhide(Instrumental) / Wabash cannon ball / Orange blossom social(Instrumental) / Nine pound hammer / Flint hill special (Instrumental) / Get in line brother / Blue moon of kentucky / Me you be lovin' another man / Little cabin home on the hill / Salty dog blues / Dig a hole in the meadow / Cumberland gap.
Album: released on RCA, Mar'86 by RCA Records. Dist: RCA, Roots, Swift, Wellard, Chris, I & B, Solomon & Peres Distribution

Cassette: released on RCA, Mar'86 by RCA Records. Dist: RCA, Roots, Swift, Wellard, Chris, I & B, Solomon & Peres Distribution

LIVE BROADCAST (Flatt, Lester & Earl Scruggs).
Album: released on Sandy Hook, Dec'86

Fleetwood Mac
BIG LOVE.
Tracks: / Big love / You & I (part1).
Single (7"): released on WEA, Mar'87 by WEA Records. Dist: WEA

COLLECTION: FLEETWOOD MAC.
Compact disc: released on Castle Collectors, Jul'87 by Castle Communications Records. Dist: Pinnacle

FLEETWOOD MAC.
Tracks: / Monday morning / Warm always / Blue letter / Rhiannon / Over my head / Crystal / Say you love me / Landslide / I'm so afraid / World turning / Sugar daddy.
Compact disc: released on Reprise, Dec'85 by WEA Records. Dist: WEA

IN CONCERT Mirage Tour.
Video-cassette (VHS): released on Channel 5, Mar'86 Dist: W.H. Smiths

LITTLE LIES.
Tracks: / Ricky.
Single (7"): released on Warner Brothers, Aug'87 by Warner Bros Records. Dist: WEA

Single (12"): released on Warner Brothers, Aug'87 by Warner Bros Records. Dist: WEA

LIVE.
Compact disc: released on The Compact Collection, Sep'87 by Conifer Records. Dist: Conifer Distribution

LONDON LIVE '68.
Album: released on Thunderbolt, Nov'86 by Magnum Music Group Ltd. Dist: Magnum Music Group Ltd, PRT Distribution, Spartan Distribution

Cassette: released on Thunderbolt, Nov'86 by Magnum Music Group Ltd. Dist: Magnum Music Group Ltd, PRT Distribution, Spartan Distribution

Compact disc: released on Thunderbolt, Apr'87 by Magnum Music Group Ltd. Dist: Magnum Music Group Ltd, PRT Distribution, Spartan Distribution

MIRAGE.
Compact disc: released on Warner Brothers, Dec'83 by Warner Bros Records. Dist: WEA
Cat. no: 256952

RATTLESNAKE SHAKE.
Compact disc:

RUMOURS.
Compact disc: released on Warner Brothers, Dec'83 by Warner Bros Records. Dist: WEA

SEVEN WONDERS.
Tracks: / Seven wonders / Book of miracles.
Single (7"): released on Warner Bros., Jun'87 by Warner Bros Records. Dist: WEA

Single (12"): released on Warner Bros., Jun'87 by Warner Bros Records. Dist: WEA

TANGO IN THE NIGHT.
Tracks: / Big love / Seven wonders / Everywhere / Caroline / Tango in the night / Mystified / Little lies / Family man / Welcome to the room...Sara / Isn't it midnight / When I see you again / You and I, part II.
Album: released on Warner Bros., Apr'87 by Warner Bros Records. Dist: WEA

Cassette: released on Warner Bros., Apr'87 by Warner Bros Records. Dist: WEA

Compact disc: released on Warner Bros., Apr'87 by Warner Bros Records. Dist: WEA

TUSK.
Compact disc: released on Warner Bros., Mar'87 by Warner Bros Records. Dist: WEA

Fleetwood, Mick
VISITOR, THE.
Album: released on RCA, Jun'81 by RCA Records. Dist: RCA, Roots, Swift, Wellard, Chris, I & B, Solomon & Peres Distribution

Cassette: released on RCA, Jun'81 by RCA Records. Dist: RCA, Roots, Swift, Wellard, Chris, I & B, Solomon & Peres Distribution

Fleetwoods
COME SOFTLY TO ME.
Single (7"): released on Creole, Aug'82 by Creole Records. Dist: Rhino, PRT

Fleetwood's Zoo
I WANT YOU BACK.
Single (7"): released on RCA, Oct'83 by RCA Records. Dist: RCA, Roots, Swift, Wellard, Chris, I & B, Solomon & Peres Distribution

Fleming, Chuck
SHAKE LOOSE THE BORDER (Fleming, Chuck & Gerry Kaley).
Album: released on Black Crow, Dec'85 by Mawson & Wareham Records. Dist: Projection

Fleming, George
I'M GONNA TELL.
Single (7"): released on Rollercoast, Sep'80

Fleming, Ian
DIAMONDS ARE FOREVER.
Cassette: released on Listen For Pleasure, Sep'84 by MFP Records. Dist: EMI

FROM RUSSIA WITH LOVE.
Cassette: released on LFP, May'85

GOLDFINGER.
Cassette: released on Listen For Pleasure, Oct'85 by MFP Records. Dist: EMI

LIVE AND LET DIE.
Cassette: released on Listen For Pleasure, Sep'84 by MFP Records. Dist: EMI

Fleming, Luther
OOH BABY.
Single (12"): released on Double L, Aug'81

Flemming, Rochelle
LOVE ITCH.
Tracks: / Love itch.
Single (7"): released on Streetnoise, Mar'86 by Streetnoise Records. Dist: PRT Distribution

Single (12"): released on Streetnoise, Mar'86 by Streetnoise Records. Dist: PRT Distribution

Flesh
2ND CHOICE, THE.
Tracks: / 2nd Choice(The) / Sell yourself.
Single (7"): released on London, Mar'86 by London Records. Dist: Polygram

Single (12"): released on London, Mar'86 by London Records. Dist: Polygram

FLESH.
Album: released on Illuminated, Feb'82 by IKF Records. Dist: Pinnacle, Cartel, Jetstar

MY BOY LOLLIPOP.
Single (7"): released on Dancing, Jul'80

YOU CAN'T HELP Sentimental sunday.
Single (7"): released on London, Sep'85 by London Records. Dist: Polygram

Single (12"): released on London, Sep'85 by London Records. Dist: Polygram

Flesh and blood
FLESH AND BLOOD Original soundtrack by Basil Poledouris.
Album: released on Vinilo Spain, May'86 by Vinilo Spain Records. Dist: Silva Screen

Flesh Eaters
GREATEST HITS: FLESH EATERS Destroyed by fire.
Album: released on Fan Club, May'87 by New Rose. Dist: Rough Trade, Cartel

MINUTE TO PRAY A SECOND TO DIE, A.
Album: released on Initial, Sep'81 by Initial Records. Dist: Pinnacle

Flesh & Fell
ANGER.
Single (12"): released on Scarface, Nov'85 by Scarface Records. Dist: Cartel

HUNGER.
Tracks: / Hunger.
Single (12"): released on Scarface, Jan'86 by Scarface Records. Dist: Cartel

Flesh for Lulu
BABY HURRICANE.
Single (7"): released on Statik, Oct'85 Dist: Rough Trade Distribution, Stage One Distribution

Single (12"): released on Statik, Oct'85 Dist: Rough Trade Distribution, Stage One Distribution

BIG FUN CITY.
Album: released on Statik, Nov'85 by Statik Trade Distribution, Stage One Distribution

Cassette: released on Statik, Nov'85 Dist: Rough Trade Distribution, Stage One Distribution

BIG FUN CITY/BLUE SISTERS SWING.
Tracks: / Baby hurricane / Cat burglar / Let go / vaguely human / Rent boy / Golden handshake girl / In your smile / Blue / Laundromat kat / Just one second / Seven hail Marys / Death shall come / I may have said you're beautiful / Who's in danger / Black tatoo.
Compact disc: released on Statik, Dec'86 Dist: Rough Trade Distribution, Stage One Distribution

BLUE SISTERS SWING.
Album: released on Hybrid, Apr'85 by Statik Records. Dist: Pinnacle

FLESH FOR LULU.
Album: released on Polydor, Oct'84 by Polydor Records. Dist: Polygram, Polydor

IDOL.
Tracks: / Sleeping dogs / Life of crime / Spaceball ricochet.
Single (7"): released on Beggars Banquet, Nov'86 by Beggars Banquet Records. Dist: WEA

Single (12"): released on Beggars Banquet, Nov'86 by Beggars Banquet Records. Dist: WEA

LONG LIVE THE NEW FLESH.
Tracks: / Lucky day / Postcards from paradise / Hammer of love / Slamese twist / Sooner or later / Good for you / Crash / Way to go / Sleeping dogs / Dream on cowboy.
Album: released on Beggars Banquet, Jul'87 by Beggars Banquet Records. Dist: WEA

Cassette: released on Beggars Banquet, Jul'87 by Beggars Banquet Records. Dist: WEA

Compact disc: released on Beggars Banquet, Jul'87 by Beggars Banquet Records. Dist: WEA

POSTCARDS FROM PARADISE.
Tracks: / Postcards from Paradise / Im not like everybody else / Sometimes good guys don't wear white?
Single (7"): released on Beggars Banquet, Jun'87 by Beggars Banquet Records. Dist: WEA

Single (12"): released on Beggars Banquet, Jun'87 by Beggars Banquet Records. Dist: WEA

SIAMESE TWIST.
Tracks: / Siamese twist / Dumbest thing / Blue sky / Idol.
Single (7"): released on Beggars Banquet, Mar'87 by Beggars Banquet Records. Dist: WEA

Cassette single: released on Beggars Banquet, May'87 by Beggars Banquet Records. Dist: WEA

SUBTERRANEANS.
Single (7"): released on Polydor, Jun'84 by Polydor Records. Dist: Polygram, Polydor

Fleshtones
BLAST OFF.
Cassette: released on Reach Out Int, Jan'83

FLESHTONES VS. REALITY.
Album: released on Emergo, Mar'87 by Roadrunner Records (Germany). Dist: Pinnacle

FLESHTONES VS.REALITY.
Compact disc: released on Emergo, Jun'87 by Roadrunner Records (Germany). Dist: Pinnacle

RIGHT SIDE OF A GOOD THING.
Single (7"): released on IRS, Jul'83 Dist: Polygram

Fletch
FLETCH Original soundtrack (Various Artists).
Compact disc: by MCA Records. Dist: Polygram, MCA

Album: released on MCA, Sep'85 by MCA Records. Dist: Polygram, MCA

Cassette: released on MCA, Sep'85 by MCA Records. Dist: Polygram, MCA

Compact disc: released on MCA, Sep'85 by MCA Records. Dist: Polygram, MCA

FLETCH Original soundtrack.

Fletcher, Cyril
ADVENTURES OF ALICE IN WONDERLAND, THE.
Album: released on Acorn, Sep'79 Dist: Folksound, Jazz Music

Fletcher, Guy
BERTHA.
Tracks: / Bertha / Mrs Tupp.
Single (7"): released on BBC, Sep'86 by BBC Records & Tapes. Dist: EMI, PRT, Pye

Fletcher, Lorna
JUST THE TWO OF US.
Single (12"): released on Virgo, Mar'83

Fletcher, Vo
ENGLISH AIR (Fletcher, Vo and Rachel).
Album: released on Paradise, Feb'84 Dist: Jetstar, JSU, WEA

Fleur, (La)
BOOGIE NIGHTS.
Single (7"): released on Proto, Jul'83 by Proto Records. Dist: WEA

Single (12"): released on Proto, Jul'83 by Proto Records. Dist: WEA

F.L.E.X.
WHY DID YOU DO IT.
Tracks: / Why did you do it / Move to the machine.
Single (12"): released on GC, Feb'87 by GC Recordings. Dist: DMS, RCA

YOU LOSE.
Tracks: / You lose / Believe it / Hate jazz / Chance, A.
Notes: Doublepack.
Double-pack single: released on Peart, Mar'87 by Peart Records. Dist: Peart

YOU LOSE.
Tracks: / You lose / Believe it / Hate Jazz / Chance, A.
Notes: Peart Records, 37b Bath Street, Abingdon, Oxon, OX14 3RB. Tel:0235 32155
Single (7"): released on Peart, Feb'87 by Peart Records. Dist: Peart

Flic
FUZZIN THE TRACKS MEDLEY.
Single (7"): released on Towerbell, Aug'84 by Towerbell Records. Dist: EMI

Flicks
LOOK, THE.
Single (7"): released on Flying, Sep'82 by Flying Records. Dist: DMS

Flies
GET BURNED.
Album: released on Homestead, May'86 Dist: Rough Trade, Cartel, Shigaku

GET WISE.
Album: released on Homestead, May'85 Dist: Rough Trade, Cartel, Shigaku

Flight Of The Condor
FLIGHT OF THE CONDOR Original soundtrack.
Album: released on BBC, Dec'83 by BBC Records & Tapes. Dist: EMI, PRT, Pye

Cassette: released on BBC, Dec'83 by BBC Records & Tapes. Dist: EMI, PRT, Pye

Flim & The BB's
BIG NOTES.
Notes: With Billy Barber, Bill Berg and Dick Oattes.
Compact disc: released on DMP, '86 by DMP Records. Dist: Venture

TRI CYCLE.
Notes: With Flim Johnson, Billy Barber, Bill Berg and Dick Oatts.
Compact disc: released on DMP, '86 by DMP Records. Dist: Venture

TUNNEL.
Notes: With Flim Johnson, Billy Barber, Bill Berg and Dick Oatts.
Compact disc: released on DMP, '86 by DMP Records. Dist: Venture

Single (7"): by Tycos Records. Dist: Tycos

Flindt, Lennart
ONLY LOVE IS THE WAY (Flindt, Lennart Trio).
Album: released on Metronome, Jan'81 Dist: Jazz Music Distribution, Jazz Horizons

Flint, Bernie

DAISY A DAY (Flint, Bernie & The Kids).
Single (7"): released on Sumatra, Nov'83 by Sumatra Records. Dist: Pinnacle

Flintlock

HOT FROM THE LOCK.
Album: released on Pinnacle, Nov'76 by Pinnacle Records. Dist: Pinnacle

ON THE WAY.
Album: released on Pinnacle, Dec'75 by Pinnacle Records. Dist: Pinnacle

TEARS N CHEERS.
Album: released on Pinnacle, Oct'77 by Pinnacle Records. Dist: Pinnacle

Flint, Michael

ROCKING DOLLY.
Tracks: / Rocking Dolly / Crowd awe.
Single (12"): released on Ranking Joe, Apr'86 by Ranking Joe Records. Dist: Jetstar

Flip

I'LL BE THERE.
Single (7"): released on Satril, Aug'85 by Satril Records. Dist: PRT

PLAGUE OF HEARTS.
Single (7"): released on Arista, Aug'84 by Arista Records. Dist: RCA

Cassette: released on Arista, Aug'84 by Arista Records. Dist: RCA

Flipper

BLOWING CHUNKS.
Cassette: released on Roir, Feb'84 by Reach Out International Records. Dist: Red Rhino Distribution, Cartel Distribution

HA HA HA.
Single (7"): released on Alternative, Jan'82 Dist: PRT

PUBLIC FLIPPER LIMITED.
Album: released on Fundamental, Feb'87 by Fundamental Records. Dist: Red Rhino, Cartel

Flips

LESS IS MORE.
Album: released on Midnight, May'85

Flirtations

EARTHQUAKE.
Single (7"): released on Siam, Oct'83 by Siam Records. Dist: PRT

Single (12"): released on Siam, Oct'83 by Siam Records. Dist: PRT

READ ALL ABOUT IT.
Tracks: / Read all about it / Nightmare dub mix.
Single (12"): released on Passion, Nov'86 by Skratch Records. Dist: PRT

Flirts

ALL YOU EVER THINK OF IS SEX.
Single (7"): released on Epic, Nov'86 by CBS Records. Dist: CBS

Single (12"): released on Epic, Jan'87 by CBS Records. Dist: CBS

FLIRTS.
Album: released on Vanguard, Mar'83 by PRT Records. Dist: PRT

JUKEBOX Don't put another dime.
Single (7"): released on O, Nov'82 by Vanguard (USA). Dist: PRT Distribution

Single (12"): released on O, Nov'82 by Vanguard (USA). Dist: PRT Distribution

MISS YOU.
Tracks: / Miss you / Voulez vouz.
Single (7"): released on Epic, Aug'86 by CBS Records. Dist: CBS

Single (12"): released on Epic, Aug'86 by CBS Records. Dist: CBS

PASSION.
Single (7"): released on O, Apr'83 by Vanguard (USA). Dist: PRT Distribution

Single (7"): released on O, Apr'83 by Vanguard (USA). Dist: PRT Distribution

QUESTIONS OF THE HEART.
Tracks: / All you ever think about is (sex) / Daddy I'm not a baby / Boys on the beach / My boyfriend is a marine / Just another kiss / Special angel / Motorama(turn up the radio) / Forgive / Like a thief in the night / After midnight.
Album: released on Epic, Feb'87 by CBS Records. Dist: CBS

Cassette: released on Epic, Feb'87 by CBS Records. Dist: CBS

YOU AND ME.

YOU AND ME.
Tracks: / You and me.
Single (7"): released on Epic, May'86 by CBS Records. Dist: CBS

Single (12"): released on Epic, May'86 by CBS Records. Dist: CBS

Floaters

FLOAT ON.
Single (7"): released on Old Gold, Jul'82 by Old Gold Records. Dist: Lightning, Jazz Music, Spartan, Counterpoint

Float Up CP

JOY'S ADDRESS.
Single (7"): released on Rough Trade, Jul'84 by Rough Trade Records. Dist: Rough Trade Distribution, Cartel Distribution

Single (12"): released on Rough Trade, Jul'84 by Rough Trade Records. Dist: Rough Trade Distribution, Cartel Distribution

KILL ME IN THE MORNING.
Album: released on Rough Trade, Nov'85 by Rough Trade Records. Dist: Rough Trade Distribution, Cartel Distribution

Flock Of Seagulls

BEST OF A FLOCK OF SEAGULLS.
Album: released on Jive, Oct'86 by Zomba Records. Dist: RCA, PRT, CBS

Cassette: released on Jive, Oct'86 by Zomba Records. Dist: RCA, PRT, CBS

COLLECTION OF TEN 12" SINGLE.
Single (12"): released on Jive, Jun'85 by Zomba Records. Dist: RCA, PRT, CBS

COLLECTION OF TEN 7" SINGLES.
Single (7"): released on Jive, Jun'85 by Zomba Records. Dist: RCA, PRT, CBS

DREAM COME TRUE.
Album: released on Jive, Mar'86 by Zomba Records. Dist: RCA, PRT, CBS

Cassette: released on Jive, Mar'86 by Zomba Records. Dist: RCA, PRT, CBS

FLOCK OF SEAGULLS, A.
Album: released on Jive, '83 by Zomba Records. Dist: RCA, PRT, CBS

Picture disc album: released on Jive, '83 by Zomba Records. Dist: RCA, PRT, CBS

HEARTBEAT LIKE A DRUM.
Tracks: / Heartbeat like a drum.
Single (7"): released on Jive, Feb'86 by Zomba Records. Dist: RCA, PRT, CBS

Single (12"): released on Jive, Feb'86 by Zomba Records. Dist: RCA, PRT, CBS

I RAN.
Single (7"): released on Jive, Mar'82 by Zomba Records. Dist: RCA, PRT, CBS

Single (12"): released on Jive, Mar'82 by Zomba Records. Dist: RCA, PRT, CBS

IT'S NOT ME TALKING.
Single (7"): released on Cocteau, Mar'83 by Cocteau Records. Dist: Pinnacle, IDS

Single (12"): released on Jive, Aug'83 by Zomba Records. Dist: RCA, PRT, CBS

Single (12"): released on Jive, Aug'83 by Zomba Records. Dist: RCA, PRT, CBS

LISTEN.
Picture disc album: released on Jive, May'83 by Zomba Records. Dist: RCA, PRT, CBS

MODERN LOVE IS AUTOMATIC.
Single (7"): released on Jive, Nov'81 by Zomba Records. Dist: RCA, PRT, CBS

Single (12"): released on Jive, Nov'81 by Zomba Records. Dist: RCA, PRT, CBS

MORE YOU LIVE THE MORE YOU LOVE.
Single (7"): released on Jive, Jun'84 by Zomba Records. Dist: RCA, PRT, CBS

Single (12"): released on Jive, Jun'84 by Zomba Records. Dist: RCA, PRT, CBS

Picture disc single: released on Jive, Jun'84 by Zomba Records. Dist: RCA, PRT, CBS

NEVER AGAIN (THE DANCER).
Single (7"): released on Jive, Sep'84 by Zomba Records. Dist: RCA, PRT, CBS

Single (12"): released on Jive, Sep'84 by Zomba Records. Dist: RCA, PRT, CBS

NIGHTMARES.
Single (7"): released on Jive, Apr'83 by Zomba

Records. Dist: RCA, PRT, CBS

Single (12"): released on Jive, Apr'83 by Zomba Records. Dist: RCA, PRT, CBS

Picture disc single: released on Jive, Apr'83 by Zomba Records. Dist: RCA, PRT, CBS

SPACE AGE LOVE SONG.
Single (7"): released on Jive, May'82 by Zomba Records. Dist: RCA, PRT, CBS

Picture disc single: released on Jive, May'82 by Zomba Records. Dist: RCA, PRT, CBS

Single (12"): released on Jive, May'82 by Zomba Records. Dist: RCA, PRT, CBS

STORY OF A YOUNG HEART, THE.
Compact disc: by Zomba Records. Dist: RCA, PRT, CBS

Compact disc: released on Jive, Aug'84 by Zomba Records. Dist: RCA, PRT, CBS

TALKING.
Single (7"): released on Cocteau, Jul'81 by Cocteau Records. Dist: Pinnacle, IDS

Single (12"): released on Cocteau, Jul'85 by Cocteau Records. Dist: Pinnacle, IDS

TELECOMMUNICATION.
Single (7"): released on Jive, Sep'81 by Zomba Records. Dist: RCA, PRT, CBS

Single (7"): released on Jive, Sep'81 by Zomba Records. Dist: RCA, PRT, CBS

Single (12"): released on Jive, Jan'82 by Zomba Records. Dist: RCA, PRT, CBS

Single (12"): released on Jive, Jan'82 by Zomba Records. Dist: RCA, PRT, CBS

TRANSFER AFFECTION.
Single (7"):

Single (12"): released on Jive, Jun'83 by Zomba Records. Dist: RCA, PRT, CBS

Picture disc single: released on Jive, Jul'83 by Zomba Records. Dist: RCA, PRT, CBS

WHO'S THAT GIRL (SHE'S GOT IT).
Single (7"): released on Jive, Oct'85 by Zomba Records. Dist: RCA, PRT, CBS

Single (12"): released on Jive, Oct'85 by Zomba Records. Dist: RCA, PRT, CBS

WISHING (IF I HAD A PHOTOGRAPH OF YOU).
Single (7"): released on Jive, Oct'82 by Zomba Records. Dist: RCA, PRT, CBS

Single (12"): released on Jive, Oct'82 by Zomba Records. Dist: RCA, PRT, CBS

Flood

COLD COLD WORLD.
Single (7"): released on Midnight Music, Dec'84 by Midnight Music Records. Dist: Rough Trade Distribution, Cartel Distribution

Floor Kiss

GOODNIGHT MOON.
Album: released on Lasuicide, Jun'85

Floorshakers

FLOORSHAKERS Various artists (Various Artists).
Album: released on Kent, Oct'83 by Ace Records. Dist: Pinnacle

Flora Purim & Airto

MAGICIANS, THE.
Compact disc: released on Concord Jazz(USA), Dec'86 by Concord Jazz Records (USA). Dist: IMS, Polygram

Florence, Bob

LIVE AT CONCERT BY THE SEA (Florence, Bob Big Band).
Compact disc: released on Trend, Jan'87 by Discovery Records. Dist: Flexitron Distributors Ltd, Swift

MAGIC TIME (Florence, Bob Limited Edition).
Tracks: / Magic time / Double barrel blues / Industrial strength stomp (The) / Rythum and blues / Bluephoria / Sailing.
Notes: Bob Florence - piano / Charly Davis, George Graham, Nelson Hatt, SteveHufstetter, Warren Luening - trumpets/ Chauncey Welsh, Charley Loper, Herbie Harper, Don Waldrop - trombones/ Bob Cooper, Bob Elford, John Lowe, Dick Mitchell, Lanny Morgan, Tim Richmond - woodwinds/ Joel DiBartolo - bass/ Nick Ceroli - drums.
Compact disc: released on Trend (USA), Sep'86 by Discovery Records. Dist: Flexitron Distributors Ltd, Swift

WESTLAKE (Florence, Bob Big Band).
Compact disc: released on Discovery (USA),

Jan'87 by Discovery Records (USA). Dist: Swift, Flexitron-Audio, Jazz Music

Florence, Bob Big Band

MAGIC TIME.
Album: released on Trend (USA), Sep'84 by Discovery Records. Dist: Flexitron Distributors Ltd, Swift

Cassette: released on Trend (USA), Aug'84 by Discovery Records. Dist: Flexitron Distributors Ltd, Swift

Floren, Myron

ACCORDION MAN.
Album: released on ARC (Accordion Records), '84 Dist: Accordion Record Club

Florentines

MAN OF MINE.
Tracks: / Man of mine / Lose that long face / Whisper not / Get out of town.
Single (12"): released on EL, Mar'87 by El Records. Dist: Rough Trade, Cartel, Pinnacle

Floria, Cam

COME BLESS THE LORD (Floria's, Cam Continentals).
Album: released on Word, May'82 by Word Records. Dist: Word Distribution, CBS

Cassette: released on Word, May'82 by Word Records. Dist: Word Distribution, CBS

COME PRAISE AND BLESS THE LORD (Floria's, Cam Continentals).
Album: released on Word, May'82 by Word Records. Dist: Word Distribution, CBS

Cassette: released on Word, May'82 by Word Records. Dist: Word Distribution, CBS

SING IT WITH LOVE (Floria's, Cam Continentals).
Album: released on Word, May'82 by Word Records. Dist: Word Distribution, CBS

Cassette: released on Word, May'82 by Word Records. Dist: Word Distribution, CBS

SKY SHALL UNFOLD, THE.
Album: released on Word, May'82 by Word Records. Dist: Word Distribution, CBS

Cassette: released on Word, May'82 by Word Records. Dist: Word Distribution, CBS

Florida

CITY RACES.
Single (7"): released on Musik, Jun'85 Dist: PRT Distribution, MIS-EMI Distribution

Florida Sun

DON'T WANNA LOVE ANYMORE.
Single (7"): released on Sparkle, Jul'85 Dist: Pinnacle

HURT Featuring Ronnie Harwood.
Tracks: / Hurt / Again.
Single (7"): released on Tembo, Jun'87 by Tembo (Canada). Dist: IMS Distribution, Polygram Distribution

IF DREAMS COME TRUE.
Single (7"):

I'M SORRY.
Tracks: / I'm sorry / Florida rock.
Single (7"): released on Sparkle, Mar'86 Dist: Pinnacle

Flory, Med

SUPERSAX (Flory, Med Five Saxophone Band).
Tracks: / Just friends / Night in Tunisia / Stareyes / Donna Lee / Tempus fugit / Around midnite / Scrapple from the apple.
Video-cassette (VHS): released on Chris Wellard, Sep'86 Dist: Independent Video Sales

WEST COAST SCENE VOL.3.
Double Album: released on Vogue Jazz, Apr'82

Flotsam & Jetsam

DOMESDAY FOR THE RECIEVER.
Album: released on Roadrunner (Dutch), Oct'86 Dist: Pinnacle

DOOMSDAY FOR THE DECEIVER.
Notes: Limited edition picture disc version of 'Doomsday for the deceiver'. Produced by Brain Slagel (prod. Slayer) and featuring Jason Newsted (Metallica).
Compact disc: released on Roadrunner (Dutch), Jun'87 Dist: Pinnacle

Picture disc album: released on Metal Blade (USA), Aug'87 Dist: Enigma Distribution

Flourgon

HOL A SPLIFF.

Single (12"): released on Techniques, Aug'87 Dist: Jetstar Distribution

Flouride, Klaus

SHORTNING BREAD.
Single (12"): released on Alternative, May'82 Dist: PRT

Flowchart

ASK THE BOSS (Flowchart (The New Harlem Funk)).
Single (7"): released on Greyhound, Nov'84 by Greyhound Records. Dist: PRT, Greyhound

Single (12"): released on Greyhound, Apr'83 by Greyhound Records. Dist: PRT, Greyhound

Flower Drum Song

FLOWER DRUM SONG Original London cast.
Album: released on That's Entertainment, Apr'83 by That's Entertainment Records. Dist: Pinnacle, PRT

Single (12"): released on That's Entertainment, Apr'83 by That's Entertainment Records. Dist: Pinnacle, PRT

Flower, E

ART OF MINSTREL (Flower, E & Martin Best).

Flowerpot Men

ALLIGATOR BAIT.
Single (12"): released on Aminita, Mar'87 by Aminita Records. Dist: Pinnacle

JO'S SO MEAN.
Single (12"): released on Compost, Nov'84 Dist: Cartel

LET'S GO TO SAN FRANCISCO.

Tracks: / Let's go to San Francisco / Let's go to San Francisco / Walk in the sky, A / Am I loosing you / You can never be wrong / Man without a woman / In a moment of madness / Young birds fly / Journeys end / Mythological Sunday / Blow away / Piccolo man / Let's go back to San Francisco / Silicon City.
Notes: For the first time on LP, this is a specially gathered together collection of tracks recorded at the height of Flowerpot, when 'love' and 'peace' were words on everyones' lips. Side one contains all the group's single releases, the most successful being, of course, the title track, at No 4 in 1967. Side two is made up of hitherto unreleased tracks. The album gives us great insight into Flowerpot and the imagery that went with it. But it also shows that here was a group with some great pop music, largely under-rated at the time of being recorded, mostly written or co-written by John Carter, who later gave us first class 'Beach Baby' and had in the mid-60's been a main member of The Ivy League.
Album: released on Teldec (Germany), Nov'86 by Import Records. Dist: IMS Distribution, Polygram Distribution

Cassette: released on Teldec (Germany), Nov'86 by Import Records. Dist: IMS Distribution, Polygram Distribution

SAN FRANCISCO.
Single (7"): released on Old Gold, Jul'82 by Old Gold Records. Dist: Lightning, Jazz Music, Spartan, Counterpoint

WALKING ON GILDED SPLINTERS.
Single (7"): released on Aminita, Nov'85 by Aminita Records. Dist: Pinnacle

Single (12"): released on Aminita, Nov'85 by Aminita Records. Dist: Pinnacle

Flower Power Hits

FLOWER POWER HITS OF THE 60'S (Various Artists).
Album: released on Old Gold, Jun'85 by Old Gold Records. Dist: Lightning, Jazz Music, Spartan, Counterpoint

Cassette: released on Old Gold, Jun'85 by Old Gold Records. Dist: Lightning, Jazz Music, Spartan, Counterpoint

Flowers And Frolics

SOLD OUT.
Album: released on E.F.D.S.S., Nov'84 by E.F.D.S.S. Records. Dist: Projection, Roots

Flowers For Agatha

FREEDOM CRUISE.
Tracks: / Freedom cruise.
Single (12"): released on Lil, Jan'86 Dist: Red Rhino, Cartel

YOUNG FOOLISH OLD AND STUPID.
Tracks: / Young foolish old and stupid.
Single (12"): released on Lil, Aug'86 Dist: Red Rhino, Cartel

Flowers From The Doctor

FLOWERS FROM THE DOCTOR Andrews.Lucilla (Clarke, Marie).

Double cassette: released on Soundings, Mar'85 Dist: Soundings

Flowers, Herbie

I LOVE 'ER.
Single (7"): released on Magic, Jan'83 Dist: Jazz Music, Submarine, Swift, Chris Wellard, Conifer

Flowers In The Dustbin

LICK MY CRAZY COLOURS.
Tracks: / Lick my crazy colours / Continuing tragedy of Mr Smith, The / Stranger in a strange land.
Single (7"): released on Cold Harbour, Apr'87 Dist: Pinnacle, Probe Plus Distribution, Cartel, M.I.S., EMI, DMS, RCA, Ariola

Single (12"): released on Cold Harbour, Nov'86 Dist: Pinnacle, Probe Plus Distribution, Cartel, M.I.S., EMI, DMS, RCA, Ariola

NAILS OF THE HEART.
Single (7"):

Flowers Of The Past

FUHRER, THE.
Single (7"): released on Memorial, Aug'83 by Memorial Records. Dist: Cartel Distribution

Flowmotion

FLOWMOTION (Various Artists).
Album: released on Flowmotion, '84 Dist: Red Rhino, Cartel

Floyd

LITTLE MAN, THE.
Album: released on Compact Organisation, Jun'85 Dist: PRT

MINUTE BY MINUTE.
Single (7"): released on Compact Organisation, Jun'85 Dist: PRT

Single (12"): released on Compact Organisation, Jun'85 Dist: PRT

SEAL SONG, THE.
Single (7"): released on Compact Organisation, Oct'85 Dist: PRT

Floyd, Bobby

OH NO.
Single (12"): released on Musical Ambassador, Oct'86

Floyd, Eddie

KNOCK ON WOOD.
Single (7"): released on Old Gold, Jan'85 by Old Gold Records. Dist: Lightning, Jazz Music, Spartan, Counterpoint

Single (7"): released on Creole, Aug'82 by Creole Records. Dist: Rhino, PRT

Single (7"): released on Stax, Aug'87 by Ace Records. Dist: Pinnacle, Chris Wellard, IMS-Polygram

Floy Joy

FRIDAY NIGHT.
Tracks: / Friday night / Friday night.
Single (7"): released on Virgin, Mar'86 by Virgin Records. Dist: EMI, Virgin Distribution

Single (12"): released on Virgin, Mar'86 by Virgin Records. Dist: EMI, Virgin Distribution

INTO THE HOT.
Album: released on Virgin, Sep'84 by Virgin Records. Dist: EMI, Virgin Distribution

UNTIL YOU COME BACK TO ME.
Single (12"): released on Virgin, Oct'84 by Virgin Records. Dist: EMI, Virgin Distribution Deleted '85.

WEAK IN THE PRESENCE OF BEAUTY.
Tracks: / Weak in the presence of beauty / You and me / Weak in the presence of beauty / Friday night / Penny in my pocket / Too drunk to funk / Ask the lonely / Chinese a go go / Crackdown / Walking in the night / This is my time / It makes no difference to me.
Single (12"): released on Virgin, Jun'86 by Virgin Records. Dist: EMI, Virgin Distribution

Album: released on Virgin, Mar'86 by Virgin Records. Dist: EMI, Virgin Distribution

Cassette: released on Virgin, Mar'86 by Virgin Records. Dist: EMI, Virgin Distribution

Compact disc: released on Virgin, Jul'87 by Virgin Records. Dist: EMI, Virgin Distribution

Single (7"): released on Virgin, Jun'86 by Virgin Records. Dist: EMI, Virgin Distribution

Flue

SOMETIMES.
Album: released on Torso, May'87 by Torso Records. Dist: Rough Trade, Cartel, EMI

Flute Indienne

EL CONDOR PASA.
Album: released on EMI (France), Mar'84 by EMI Records. Dist: Conifer

Cassette: released on EMI (France), Mar'84 by EMI Records. Dist: Conifer

Flux

NEW SMELL.
Tracks: / New smell / Taking a liberty.
Single (12"): released on One Little Indian, Mar'87 by One Little Indian Records. Dist: Nine Mile Distribution, Cartel Distribution

Single (7"): released on Crass, Oct'81 by Exitstencil Music. Dist: Rough Trade, Cartel

Single (12"): released on One Little Indian Aug'87 by One Little Indian Records. Dist: Nine Mile Distribution, Cartel Distribution

UNCARVED BLOCK.
Album: released on One Little Indian, Aug'87 by One Little Indian Records. Dist: Nine Mile Distribution, Cartel Distribution

VISION.
Single (12"): released on One Little Indian, 23 May'87 by One Little Indian Records. Dist: Nine Mile Distribution, Cartel Distribution

Flux Of Pink Indians

NEW SMELL.
Single (7"): released on One Little Indian, Aug'87 by One Little Indian Records. Dist: Nine Mile Distribution, Cartel Distribution

STRIVE.
Album: released on One Little Indian, Aug'87 by One Little Indian Records. Dist: Nine Mile Distribution, Cartel Distribution

STRIVE TO SURVIVE CAUSING THE LEAST SUFFERING POSSIBLE.
Album: Dist: Rough Trade

TAKING A LIBERTY.
Single (7"): released on Spiderleg, Mar'85 Dist: Rough Trade

TREAT.
Album: released on One Little Indian, Aug'87 by One Little Indian Records. Dist: Nine Mile Distribution, Cartel Distribution

Fly away

FLY AWAY (Various Artists).
Compact disc: by Phonogram Records. Dist: Polygram

Flyde Coast Jazzmen

RUNNING WILD.
Album: released on Folk Heritage, Jul'82 by Folk Heritage Records. Dist: Roots, Wynd-Up Distribution, Jazz Music, Folk Heritage

Flying Burrito Brothers

BURRITO DELUXE.
Album: released on Demon, Jul'86 by Demon Records. Dist: Pinnacle

DIM LIGHTS, THICK SMOKE & LOUD MUSIC.
Compact disc single: released on Edsel, Mar'87 by Demon Records. Dist: Pinnacle, Jazz Music, Projection

Single (7"): released on Edsel, Mar'87 by Demon Records. Dist: Pinnacle, Jazz Music, Projection

GILDED PALACE OF SIN, THE.
Album: released on Edsel, Jul'86 by Demon Records. Dist: Pinnacle, Jazz Music, Projection

Cassette: released on Edsel, Jul'86 by Demon Records. Dist: Pinnacle, Jazz Music, Projection

LAST OF THE RED HOT BURRITOS.
Album: by A&M Records. Dist: Polygram

LIVE FROM TOKYO.
Notes: Top country band - Unreleased material - Top country musicians.
Album: released on Sundown, Jan'86 by Magnum Music Group Ltd. Dist: Magnum Music Group Ltd, PRT Distribution, Spartan Distribution

Compact disc: released on Sundown, '86 by Magnum Music Group Ltd. Dist: Magnum Music Group Ltd, PRT Distribution, Spartan Distribution

SLEEPLESS NIGHTS.
Cassette: released on A&M, Jun'76 by A&M Records. Dist: Polygram

Flying Colour

DEAR FRIEND.
Tracks: / Dear Friend / Look my way.
Single (7"): released on Shigaku, Feb'87

Flying Colours

ABSTRACT ARTS.
Single (7"): released on No, Jul'81 Dist: Rough Trade

Flying Column

FOUR GREEN FIELDS.
Tracks: / An old main in a garrett / Castle of Dromore, The / Legion of the rearguard / Song of the dawn, The / Four Green Fields / Roisin Duph / Sam Hall / Dirty old Town / Sean South/Boys of Wexford/Bold Fenain Men / Mamdame Bonaparte / Johnston's motor car / Boolavogue / Golden Jubilee.
Album: released on Emerald (Ireland), Jun'85 by Emerald Records. Dist: I & B, Ross, PRT

FOUR GREEN FIELDS.
Album: released on Emerald (Ireland), Oct'81 by Emerald Records. Dist: I & B, Ross, PRT

Cassette: released on Emerald (Ireland), Oct'81 by Emerald Records. Dist: I & B, Ross, PRT

Flying Down To Rio

FLYING DOWN TO RIO Musical (Various Artists).
Notes: Fred and Ginger's first film together; features beautiful girls tap dancing on aeroplane wings.
Video-cassette (VHS): released on Video Collection, May'87 by Video Collection Records. Dist: Counterpoint

Flying Lizards

DIZZY MISS LIZZIE.
Single (7"): released on Statik, Oct'84 Dist: Rough Trade Distribution, Stage One Distribution

Single (12"): released on Statik, Oct'84 Dist: Rough Trade Distribution, Stage One Distribution

SEX MACHINE.
Single (7"): released on Statik, Aug'84 Dist: Rough Trade Distribution, Stage One Distribution

Single (12"): released on Statik, Aug'84 Dist: Rough Trade Distribution, Stage One Distribution

TOP TEN.
Tracks: / Tutti frutti / Sex machine / What's new pussycat / Whole lotta shaking going on / Purple haze / Great balls of fire / Dizzy Miss Lizzy / Suzanne / Then he kissed me / Tears.
Compact disc: released on Statik, Dec'86 Dist: Rough Trade Distribution, Stage One Distribution

Album: released on Statik, Nov'84 Dist: Rough Trade Distribution, Stage One Distribution

Cassette: released on Statik, Nov'84 Dist: Rough Trade Distribution, Stage One Distribution

Flying Padovanis

THEY CALL ME CRAZY.
Album: released on Razor, Feb'87 by Razor. Dist: Pinnacle

WESTERN PASTA.
Single (7"): released on Demon, Apr'81 by Demon Records. Dist: Pinnacle

Flying Pickets

FLYING PICKETS LIVE.
Album: released on 10, Nov'85 by 10 Records. Dist: Virgin, EMI

Cassette: released on 10, Nov'85 by 10 Records. Dist: Virgin, EMI

FLYING PICKETS LIVE AT THE ALBANY EMPIRE.
Album: released on AVM, Dec'82 Dist: PRT

Cassette: released on AVM, Dec'82 Dist: PRT

LOST BOYS.
Tracks: / Remember this / I heard it through the grapevine / Disco down / So close / Tears of a clown, The / When you're young and in love / You've lost that lovin' feelin' / Psycho killer / Wild boy / Factory / Monica engineer / Only you / Masters of war.
Compact disc: released on 10, Jul'87 by 10 Records. Dist: Virgin, EMI

Album: released on 10, May'84 by 10 Records. Dist: Virgin, EMI

Cassette: released on 10, May'84 by 10 Records. Dist: Virgin, EMI

SO CLOSE.
Single (7"): released on Virgin, Jun'84 by Virgin Records. Dist: EMI, Virgin Distribution

TAKE MY BREATH AWAY.
Tracks: / Rubies & dimes.
Single (7"): released on Creole, Nov'86 by Creole Records. Dist: Rhino, PRT

Flying Saucers

AT THE PICKETTS LOCK.
Album: released on Charly, Jun'83 by Charly Records. Dist: Charly, Cadillac

FLYING SAUCERS ROCK'N'ROLL (Various Artists).
Single 10": released on Charly, Sep'81 by Charly Records. Dist: Charly, Cadillac

GET A JOB.
Single (7"): released on Harbour, Jan'81 by Harbour Records. Dist: Wellard, Chris

KEEP ON COMIN'.
Album: released on Charly, Jul'81 by Charly Records. Dist: Charly, Cadillac

PLANET OF THE DRAPES.
Album: released on Nevis, Apr'81 Dist: H.R. Taylor

TEENAGE BOOGIE.
Single (7"): released on Harbour, Mar'81 by Harbour Records. Dist: Wellard, Chris

Flyin' Spiderz

CITY BOY.
Tracks: / City boy / I don't wanna go.
Single (7"): released on R2 Records, Jun'87 by R2 Records. Dist: R2

Flynn Brothers

TIME AND CHANCE.
Tracks: / Time and chance.
Notes: Available from N. J. Records James Flynn, 26 Southcroft Road, Tooting, London London SW17
Single (7"): released on N.J., May'86 Dist: N.J.

Flynn, Errol

ERROL FLYNN ALBUM, THE.
Album: released on Citadel, Mar'79 Dist: Swift

Flyright

LEGENDARY JAY MILLER SESSION 5.
Album: released on Flyright, Dec'76 by Flyright Records. Dist: Krazy Kat, Swift, Jazz Music

Fly, The

FLY (THE) (Various Artists).
Notes: Composed by Howard Shore and played by The London Philharmonic Orch.
Album: released on TER, Mar'87 Dist: Pinnacle

Cassette: released on TER, Mar'87 Dist: Pinnacle

FM

AMERICAN GIRLS.
Tracks: / American Girls / That girl / American girls (Remix) / That girl.
Single (7"): released on Portrait, Aug'86 by CBS Records. Dist: CBS

Single (12"): released on Portrait, Aug'86 by CBS Records. Dist: CBS

CITY OF FEAR.
Album: released on Logo, Sep'81 by Logo Records. Dist: Roots, BMG

FM Film Soundtrack (Various Artists).
Album: released on MCA, Mar'87 by MCA Records. Dist: Polygram, MCA

Cassette: released on MCA, Mar'87 by MCA Records. Dist: Polygram, MCA

FROZEN HEART.
Tracks: / Frozen heart / Love lasts forever / Otherside of midnight / Addicted to love / Hot legs.
Notes: Otherside of Midnight is only available on 12" version. DIDGE 1 - Gatefold sleeve in double pack with Addicted to Love/Hot legs.
Single (7"): released on Portrait, Feb'87 by CBS Records. Dist: CBS

Single (12"): released on Portrait, Feb'87 by CBS Records. Dist: CBS

INDISCREET.
Tracks: / That girl / Other side of midnight / Love lies dying / I belong to the night / American girls / Hot wired / Face to face / Frozen Heart / Heart of the matter / That girl / Other side of midnight / Love lies dying / I belong to the night / American girl / Hot wired / Face to face / Frozen heart / Heart of the matter.
Album: released on Portrait, Sep'86 by CBS Records. Dist: CBS

Compact disc: released on Portrait, '86 by CBS Records. Dist: CBS

LET LOVE BE THE LEADER.
Tracks: / Let love be the leader / Let love be the leader (live version) / I belong to the night (87 version).
Single (12"): released on Portrait, Jun'87 by CBS Records. Dist: CBS

Single (7"): released on Portrait, 20 Jun'87 by CBS Records. Dist: CBS

Single (12"): released on Portrait, 20 Jun'87 by CBS Records. Dist: CBS

Picture disc single: released on Portrait, 20 Jun'87 by CBS Records. Dist: CBS

LOVE WAS DYING.
Tracks: / Love was dying / Captured.
Single (7"): released on Portrait, Jun'86 by CBS Records. Dist: CBS

Single (12"): released on Portrait, Jun'86 by CBS Records. Dist: CBS

THAT GIRL.
Tracks: / That girl / American girls.
Single (7"): released on Portrait, Mar'86 by CBS Records. Dist: CBS

FN Guns

NIGHTMARE.
Album: released on Mausoleum, Apr'85 by Mausoleum Records. Dist: Pinnacle

Focus

FOCUS Various Dutch orchestras of 'Novam' (Various Artists).
Tracks: / Overture on a spiritual / Divertissment / Musikk for saxofon og accordeon / Ayres Danzas / Air for two / Modal music / Symphonietta voor acc orkest.
Notes: Retail price given by ARC excluding P & P (via Mail Order) is 6.00. Mail order distribution address: Accordion Record Club, 146 Birmingham Road, Kidderminster, Worcs. DY10 2SL. Tel: 0562-746105
Album: released on Accordion Record Club, Jul'86 by Accordion Record Club Records. Dist: Accordion Record Club

FOCUS 2.
Album: released on EMI (Holland), '83 by EMI Records. Dist: Conifer

FOCUS AT THE RAINBOW.
Album: released on EMI (Holland), '83 by EMI Records. Dist: Conifer

FOCUS - JAN AKKERMAN & THIJS VAN LEER.
Tracks: / Russian Roulette / King Kong / Le Tango / Indian Summer / Beethoven's Revenge / Old Judy / Who's calling.
Album: released on Vertigo (Holland), Jul'85

Cassette: released on Vertigo (Holland), Jul'85

FOCUS ON FOCUS.
Album: released on EMI (Holland), '83 by EMI Records. Dist: Conifer

GREATEST HITS:FOCUS Moving Waves.
Album: released on Fame, Sep'84 by Music For Pleasure Records. Dist: EMI

Cassette: released on Fame, Sep'84 by Music For Pleasure Records. Dist: EMI

HOCUS POCUS.
Single (7"): released on EMI (Holland), Jul'84 by EMI Records. Dist: Conifer

HOUSE OF THE KING.
Album: released on EMI (Holland), '83 by EMI Records. Dist: Conifer

MOVING WAVES.
Double Album: released on EMI (Holland), '83 by EMI Records. Dist: Conifer

SYLVIA.
Tracks: / Sylvia / Hocus pocus.
Single (7"): released on Old Gold, Mar'87 by Old Gold Records. Dist: Lightning, Jazz Music, Spartan, Counterpoint

Single (7"): released on EMI Golden 45's, Feb'85 by EMI Records. Dist: EMI

Foda Musa Suso

WATTA SITTA.
Compact disc: by Charly Records. Dist: Charly

Fodem

OBSESSED BY CRUELTY.
Album: released on Steamhammer, Jun'86

Foden Motor Works Band

FODEN MOTOR WORKS BAND.
Album: released on Grosvenor, Jun'81 by Grosvenor Records. Dist: Taylors

Fodens, Massed Bands Of

WORLD OF BRASS BANDS.
Cassette: released on Decca, '79 by Decca Records. Dist: Polygram

Foehner, Gale

RHYMS IN RAGTIME.
Album: released on Stomp Off, Jun'86 by Stomp Off Records. Dist: Jazz Music Distribution

Foetus

BEDROCK (Foetus All Nude Revue).
Tracks: / Bedrock / Diabolus in musica / Shut / Rattlesnake insurance / Bedrock strip.
Extended-play record: released on Some Bizzare, 13 Jun'87 by Charisma Records. Dist: EMI, CBS, Polygram

Foetus Art Terrorism

CALAMITY CRUSH.
Single (12"): released on Self Immolation, Oct'84 Dist: Rough Trade

Foetus On Your Breath

WASH IT ALL OFF.
Single (12"): released on Self Immolation, Jan'85 Dist: Rough Trade

Foetus Over Frisco

CUSTOM BUILT FOR CAPITALISM.
Single (12"): released on Self Immolation, Mar'82 Dist: Rough Trade

FINELY HONED MACHINE.
Single (12"): released on Self Immolation, Feb'85 Dist: Rough Trade

Foffo Spearjig

TIE YOUR LACES TIGHT.
Single (7"): released on Eccentric, Mar'83

Fogelberg, Dan

EXILES.
Tracks: / Exiles / What are you doing / Lonely in love / Seeing you again / She don't look back / Way it must be, The / Hearts in decline / It doesn't matter / Our last farewell.
Album: released on Epic, Aug'87 by CBS Records. Dist: CBS

Cassette: released on Epic, Aug'87 by CBS Records. Dist: CBS

GREATEST HITS:DAN FOGELBERG.
Album: released on Epic, Jun'85 by CBS Records. Dist: CBS

Cassette: released on Epic, Jun'85 by CBS Records. Dist: CBS

LANGUAGE OF LOVE.
Single (7"): released on Epic, Apr'84 by CBS Records. Dist: CBS

PHOENIX.
Album: released on Epic, Mar'80 by CBS Records. Dist: CBS

Cassette: released on Epic, Mar'80 by CBS Records. Dist: CBS

Fogerty, John

BLUE RIDGE RANGERS.
Album: released on Fantasy (Germany), Aug'86 by Fantasy Records. Dist: IMS, Polygram

CENTREFIELD.
Notes: Digital Stereo.
Compact disc: released on Warner Bros., Feb'85 by Warner Bros Records. Dist: WEA

Album: released on Warner Bros., Feb'85 by Warner Bros Records. Dist: WEA

Cassette: released on Warner Bros., Feb'85 by Warner Bros Records. Dist: WEA

EYE OF A ZOMBIE.
Album: released on Warner Bros., Oct'86 by Warner Bros Records. Dist: WEA

Cassette: released on Warner Bros., Oct'86 by Warner Bros Records. Dist: WEA

Compact disc: released on Warner Bros., Oct'86 by Warner Bros Records. Dist: WEA

EYE OF THE ZOMBIE.
Single (7"): released on Warner Bros., Oct'86 by Warner Bros Records. Dist: WEA

Single (12"): released on Warner Bros., Oct'86 by Warner Bros Records. Dist: WEA

JOHN FOGERTY.
Album: released on Fantasy, 7 Sep'87 by Ace Records. Dist: Pinnacle

Cassette: released on Fantasy, 7 Sep'87 by Ace Records. Dist: Pinnacle

Compact disc: released on Fantasy, 7 Sep'87 by Ace Records. Dist: Pinnacle

Foggy

IT'S FOGGY AGAIN.
Album: released on Look, Dec'79 Dist: R. Smith & Co. Records, H.R. Taylor

Foghat

GIRLS TO CHAT AND BOYS TO BOUNCE.
Album: released on Bearsville (USA), Jan'82 by Warner Bros Records. Dist: WEA

Cassette: released on Bearsville (USA), Jan'82 by Warner Bros Records. Dist: WEA

Fogle, Adeen

BAKED A CAKE.
Single (7"): released on Eureka, Dec'84 by Eureka Records. Dist: Pinnacle

Fogli, Riccardo

FOR LUCIA.
Single (7"): released on Ariola, Apr'83 Dist: RCA, Ariola

Fog, The

FOG, THE Original Soundtrack.
Notes: Artist: John Carpenter.
Album: released on Colosseum(West Germany), Jan'86 Dist: Silva Screen

Foley, Connie

ISLE OF INNISFREE.
Album: released on Outlet, Nov'76 by Outlet Records. Dist: Outlet Distribution

SING AN IRISH SONG.
Cassette: released on Homespun(Ireland), Mar'80 by Outlet Records. Dist: Outlet

Foley, Ellen

ANOTHER BREATH.
Album: released on Epic, Apr'83 by CBS Records. Dist: CBS

Cassette: released on Epic, Apr'83 by CBS Records. Dist: CBS

JOHNNY & MARY.
Single (7"): released on Epic, Mar'83 by CBS Records. Dist: CBS

NIGHT OUT.
Album: released on Epic, Sep'79 by CBS Records. Dist: CBS

Foley, Keith

MUSIC FOR CHRISTMAS.
Compact disc: released on DMP, '86 by DMP Records. Dist: Venture

Foley, Red

RED AND ERNIE (Foley, Red & Ernest Tubb).
Tracks: / Tennessee Border (No.2) / Goodnight / Irene / Hillbilly Fever (No. 2) / Don't be ashamed of your age / It's a mileage that's slowin' us down / Double datin' / No help wanted (No.2) / Too old to cut the mustard / Kentucky waltz / I'm in love with Molly / Strange little girl / You're a real good friend.
Album: released on Stetson, Nov'85 by Hasmick Promotions Ltd.. Dist: Counterpoint Distribution, H.R. Taylor Distribution, Swift Distribution, Chris Wellard Distribution

Cassette: released on Stetson, Nov'85 by Hasmick Promotions Ltd.. Dist: Counterpoint Distribution, H.R. Taylor Distribution, Swift Distribution, Chris Wellard Distribution

RED FOLEY SHOW, THE.
Album: released on Stetson, Sep'86 by Hasmick Promotions Ltd.. Dist: Counterpoint Distribution, H.R. Taylor Distribution, Swift Distribution, Chris Wellard Distribution

Cassette: released on Stetson, Sep'86 by Hasmick Promotions Ltd.. Dist: Counterpoint Distribution, H.R. Taylor Distribution, Swift Distribution, Chris Wellard Distribution

RED FOLEY STORY, THE.
Tracks: / Chattanoogie shoe shine boy / Blues in my heart / Salty dog rag / Old shep / Tennessee Saturday night / Hominy grits / Tennessee polka / Hearts of stone / Nobody / Tennessee Border / M-i-s-s-i-s-s-i-p-p-i / Steal away / Old Pappy's new banjo / Peace in the valley / Satisfied mind, A / I'll be a sunbeam / My god is real / Beyond the sunset / Should you go first / Take my hand, precious lord / Just a closer walk with thee / God walks these hills with me / Jesus loves me / He'll understand and say well done.
Notes: Double album
Album: released on MCA Import, Mar'86 by MCA Records. Dist: Polygram, IMS

TENNESSEE SATURDAY NIGHT.
Album: released on Charly, Feb'84 by Charly Records. Dist: Charly, Cadillac

Folk...

FOLK AT THE BLACK HORSE Various artists (Various Artists).
Tracks: / Stanton Drew / Jock Stewart / I like to rise / Carrickfergus / Doffin mistress / Arthur McBride.
Notes: Artists include: Plum Duff, Telham Tinkers, Brian Boru (residents at this famous Sussex folk club). Traditional songs including the above songs, plus Irish reels and jigs with uillean pipes, fiddle, whistle and guitar. Eron Records, 27 Balmoral Road, Kingsdown, Deal, Kent CT14 8BX.

Album: released on Eron, Sep'85 by Eron Records. Dist: Eron Records

Cassette: released on Eron, Sep'85 by Eron Records. Dist: Eron Records

FOLK FESTIVAL OF THE BLUES Various artists (Various Artists).
Album: released on Chess, Aug'86 by Charly Records. Dist: Charly, Swift, PRT, Discovery, IMS, Polygram

Cassette: released on Chess, Aug'86 by Charly Records. Dist: Charly, Swift, PRT, Discovery, IMS, Polygram

Album: released on Chess(USA), Apr'82 by Sugar Hill (USA). Dist: PRT, Swift

FOLK MUSIC OF NORWAY Various players & singers (Various Artists).
Album: released on Topic, May'81 by Topic Records. Dist: JSU Distribution, Projection Distribution, Jazz Music Distribution

Folk 77

TRY TO REMEMBER.
Album: released on Foldback, Oct'80 by Foldback Records. Dist: Lugtons

Folk Devils

BEAUTIFUL MONSTER.
Single (7"): released on Ganges, Aug'84 by Ganges Records. Dist: Rough Trade, Cartel

Single (12"): released on Ganges, Aug'84 by Ganges Records. Dist: Rough Trade, Cartel

BEST PROTECTION, THE.
Tracks: / Best protection, The / Your mistake / Third stroke, The.
Single (12"): released on Situation 2, 13 Jun'87 Dist: Cartel, Pinnacle

FIRE AND CHROME.
Single (12"): released on Karbon, Jul'85 by Karbon Records. Dist: Pinnacle, Red Rhino, Cartel

HANK TURNS BLUE.
Single (7"): released on Ganges, Mar'84 by Ganges Records. Dist: Rough Trade, Cartel

Folk Hymnal

SINGALONG.
Album: by Pilgrim Records. Dist: Rough Trade, Cartel

Folk Songs

FOLK SONGS Topic sampler No.1 (Various Artists).
Album: released on Topic, '81 Dist: Roots Distribution

FOLK SONGS (2) Topic sampler No.2 (Various Artists).
Album: released on Topic, '81 Dist: Roots Distribution

FOLK SONGS (6) Topic sampler No.6 (Various Artists).
Album: released on Topic, '81 Dist: Roots Distribution

SONGS OF COURTSHIP Folk Songs Of Great Britain Vol.1 (Various Artists).
Album: released on Topic, '81 Dist: Roots Distribution

SONGS OF SEDUCTION Folk songs of Great Britain Vol.2 (Various Artists).
Album: released on Topic, '81 Dist: Roots Distribution

Folk Synth Orchestra

FOLK SYNTH ORCHESTRA.
Album: released on Amigo, Jul'87 Dist: Red Rhino, Cartel

Follies

FOLLIES Original Broadway Cast (Various Artists).
Tracks: / Prologue - Beautiful girls / Don't look at me / Waiting for the girls upstairs / Ah Paris, Broadway baby / Road you didn't take, The / In Buddy's eyes / Who's that woman / I'm still here / Too many mornings / Right girl, The / Could I leave you? / You're gonna love tomorrow (love will see us through) / God-why-don't-you-love-me blues, The / Losing my mind / Story of Lucy and Jessie / Live, laugh, love.
Notes: Music and lyrics by Stephen Sondheim. Book by James Goldman. Orchestra and chorus conducted by Harold Hastings. Original sound recording madeby Capitol Records Inc. Produced by Dick Jones.
Album: released on Capitol, Jul'87 by Capitol Records. Dist: EMI

Cassette: released on Capitol, Jul'87 by Capitol Records. Dist: EMI

Follow The Fleet

FOLLOW THE FLEET Musical (Various Artists).
Notes: With Fred Astaire. Inc. 'Let's face the music and dance'

Video-cassette (VHS): released on Video Collection, May'87 by Video Collection Records. Dist: Counterpoint

Fontaine, Eddie

ROCK WITH ME.
Album: released on Charly, Aug'87 by Charly Records. Dist: Charly, Cadillac

Fontaine, Roy

ONE IS A LONELY NUMBER.
Tracks: / One is a lonely number / One is a lonely number (Inst).
Single (7"): released on Abstract Dance, Jul'86 Dist: Priority, RCA

Single (12"): released on Abstract Dance, Jul'86 Dist: Priority, RCA

Fontana, Wayne

GAME OF LOVE (Fontana, Wayne & the Mindbenders).
Single (7"): released on Old Gold, Jul'82 by Old Gold Records. Dist: Lightning, Jazz Music, Spartan, Counterpoint

PAMELA PAMELA.
Single (7"): released on Old Gold, Jan'85 by Old Gold Records. Dist: Lightning, Jazz Music, Spartan, Counterpoint

Fontane Sisters

ROCK AGAIN LOVE.
Tracks: / Rock love / Fool around / You're mine / Listen to your heart / Ragtime rock'n'roll / Old piano roll blues, The / Rollin' stone / Still / Chanson d'amour / Got you on my mind / You always hurt the one you love / Lonesome lover blues / I understand / If I could be with you.
Album: released on Charly, Sep'86 by Charly Records. Dist: Charly, Cadillac

ROCK LOVE.
Album: released on Charly, Feb'84 by Charly Records. Dist: Charly, Cadillac

Fonteyn, Margot

DAME MARGOT FONTEYN (Fonteyn, Dame Margot).
Cassette: released on Argo (Spokenword), Jul'82 by Decca Records. Dist: Polygram

Food For Millions

FOOD FOR MILLIONS China, USA, Third World, UK.
Cassette: released on International Report, Oct'81 by Seminar Cassettes. Dist: Audio-Visual Library Services, Davidson Distribution, Eastern Educational Products Distrib., Forlaget Systime Distribution, MacDougall Distribution, Talktapes Distribution, Watkins Books Ltd Distribution, Norton, Jeff Distribution

Fools Dance

FOOLS AND DANCE.
Tracks: / Fools dance.
Single (7"): released on Prism, Aug'86 by Prism Records.

FOOLS DANCE.
Tracks: / Sa'ha / Don Diddy song, The / Priest hole, The / Happy families / Waiting (at the sky lab landing bay) / I'm so many (talk talk).
Notes: This mini 5 track LP from Fools Dance is led by Simon Gallup, bass player with The Cure. The album was recorded recently during the period that Simon Gallup left The Cure - he is now back with them. The Cure have a huge following and this album will definitely become a collector's item. Personnel: Gary Biddles/Simon Gallup/Stuart Curran/Ron Howe/Pete Gardner.
Album: released on Turn, Dec'85 Dist: IMS-Polygram

Foort, Reginald

KEEP SMILING.
Album: released on World (Retrospect Series), Feb'84

Cassette: released on World (Retrospect Series), Feb'84

Football

CELTIC SOUVENIR Highlights 1965-1970.
Album: released on Quality, Oct'81

CUP WINNERS CUP-1971 Chelsea v Real Madrid.
Album: released on Quality, Oct'81

EUROPEAN CUP FINAL-1968 Manchester United v Benfica.
Album: released on Quality, Oct'81

EUROPEAN CUP FINAL-1977 Liverpool v Borrusia MGB.
Album: released on Quality, Oct'81

EUROPEAN CUP FINAL-1978 Liverpool v Bruges.
Album: released on Quality, Oct'81

EUROPEAN CUP FINALS-1979 & 1980 Nottingham forest's double.
Album: released on Quality, Oct'81

EUROPEAN CUP FINAL-1981 Liverpool v Real Madrid.
Album: released on Quality, Oct'81

EUROPEAN CUP FINAL-1982 Villa-The Champions of Europe.
Album: released on Quality, Oct'82

EUROPE CUP FINAL-1982 Villa-The Champions of Europe.

F.A. CUP FINAL-1970 Chelsea v Leeds.
Album: released on Quality, Oct'81

F.A. CUP FINAL-1971 Arsenal v Liverpool.
Album: released on Quality, Oct'81

F.A. CUP FINAL-1972 Arsenal v Leeds.
Album: released on BBC, Oct'81 by BBC Records & Tapes. Dist: EMI, PRT, Pye

F.A. CUP FINAL-1973 Sunderland v Leeds.

F.A. CUP FINAL-1974 Liverpool v Newcastle.
Album: released on Quality, Oct'81

F.A. CUP FINAL-1975 West Ham v Fulham.
Album: released on Quality, Oct'81

F.A. CUP FINAL-1976 Southampton v Manchester United.
Album: released on Quality, Oct'81

F.A. CUP FINAL-1977 Manchester United v Liverpool.
Album: released on Quality, Oct'81

F.A. CUP FINAL-1978 Ipswich v Arsenal.
Album: released on Quality, Oct'81

F.A. CUP FINAL-1979 Arsenal v Manchester.
Album: released on Quality, Oct'81

F.A. CUP FINAL-1980 West Ham v Arsenal.
Album: released on Quality. Oct'81

F.A. CUP FINAL-1981 (100th) Tottenham Hotspurs v Manchester City.

LEAGUE CHAMPIONSHIP 1979-80 SEASON Liverpool.
Album: released on Quality, Oct'81

LEAGUE CHAMPIONSHIP 1980-81 SEASON Aston Villa.
Album: released on Quality, Oct'81

LEAGUE CUP FINAL-1971 Tottenham Hotspurs v Aston Villa.
Album: released on Quality, Oct'81

LEAGUE CUP FINAL-1972 Stoke City v Chelsea.
Album: released on Quality, Oct'81

LEAGUE CUP FINAL-1973 Tottenham Hotspurs v Norwich.
Album: released on Quality, Oct'81

LEAGUE CUP FINAL-1974 Wolves v Manchester city.
Album: released on Quality, Oct'81

LEAGUE CUP FINAL-1975 Aston Villa v Norwich.
Album: released on Quality, Oct'81

LEAGUE CUP FINAL-1976 Manchester city v Newcastle.
Album: released on Quality, Oct'81

LEAGUE CUP FINAL-1977 Aston Villa v Everton.
Album: released on Quality, Oct'81

LEAGUE CUP FINAL-1978 Nottingham Forest v Liverpool.
Album: released on Quality, Oct'81

LEAGUE CUP FINAL-1979 Nottingham Forest v Southampton.
Album: released on Quality, Oct'81

LEAGUE CUP FINAL-1980 Wolves v Nottingham Forest.
Album: released on Quality, Oct'81

LEAGUE CUP FINAL-1981 Liverpool v West Ham.
Album: released on Quality, Oct'81

LEAGUE CUP FINAL-1982 Liverpool v Tottenham Hotspur.
Album: released on Quality, Jul'82

SCOTTISH CUP-1976 Rangers v Hearts.
Album: released on Quality, Oct'81

UEFA CUP-1976 Liverpool v Bruges.
Album: released on Quality, Oct'81

WORLD CUP FINALS-1966 & 1970 HIGHLIGHTS.
Album: released on Quality, Oct'81

Foote, Wayne

UNCOOL.
Tracks: / Uncool / Son of uncle.
Single (7"): released on Blanco Y Negro, Oct'86 by WEA Records. Dist: WEA

Single (12"): released on Blanco Y Negro, Oct'86 by WEA Records. Dist: WEA

Footloose

FOOTLOOSE Original Soundtrack (Various Artists).
Notes: Low-price musical feature film recently big in the cinemas, and including items like the title track by Kenny Loggins, and Deniece Williams "Let's hear it for the boy".
Video-cassette (VHS): released on CIC Video, Sep'84 by CBS Records. Dist: CBS, Pickwick Distribution

Compact disc: released on CBS, Aug'84 by CBS Records. Dist: CBS

FOOTLOOSE Original Soundtrack (Various Artists).
Album: released on CBS, Mar'84 by CBS Records. Dist: CBS

Cassette: released on CBS, Mar'84 by CBS Records. Dist: CBS

Footstompers

FOOTSTOMPERS Various artists (Various Artists).
Album: released on Kent, Mar'84 by Ace Records. Dist: Pinnacle

For A Few Dollars More

FOR A FEW DOLLARS MORE Ennio Morricone.
Album: released on RCA (Germany), '83

For A Few Pussies More

FOR A FEW PUSSIES MORE Various artists (Various Artists).
Tracks: / Surf City / Tiny minds / I get so excited / How can I find you / Rumble in the jungle / Big gun / Six brides for Jerry Lee / Holy hack Jack / Howard Hughes / 13 Lines / Extra flesh / Boneshaker baby / She's gone / Thee holy jukebox.
Notes: P: 1987 Original compilation made by Anagram Records-a division of Cherry Red Records Ltd.
Album: released on Anagram, Jul'87 by Cherry Red Records. Dist: Pinnacle

Forbert, Steve

ALIVE ON ARRIVAL.
Album: released on Epic, Nov'81 by CBS Records. Dist: CBS Deleted '87.
Cat. no: **EPC 32053**
Cassette: released on Epic, Nov'81 by CBS Records. Dist: CBS

Force

EYE TO EYE.
Tracks: / Tomorrow may never come / Amigo.
Single (7"): released on Valentino. Jan'87

Single (12"): released on Valentino, Jan'87

FORCE.
Tracks: / New frontiers / Eye to eye / No fixed emotion / Amigo / Change your heart / Tomorrow may never come / All too much / Turn to love / All alone / I hear the sound / Shout.
Album: released on Valentino, Jan'87

Cassette: released on Valentino, Jan'87

FORCE (THE).
Album: released on Valentine, Feb'87 by Valentine Records. Dist: PRT

Cassette: released on Valentine, Feb'87 by Valentine Records. Dist: PRT

FORCE, THE.
Tracks: / New frontiers / Eye to eye / No fixed emotion / Amigo / Change your heart / Tomorrow may never come / All too much / Turn to love / All alone / I hear the sound / Shout.
Album: released on Valentino, Jan'87

MUSIC.
Single (12"): released on Destiny, Mar'80 by Destiny Records. Dist: Red Rhino, Cartel

SET ME FREE.
Album: released on Heavy Metal, Apr'84 by FM-Revolver Records. Dist: EMI

Cassette: released on Heavy Metal, Apr'84 by FM-Revolver Records. Dist: EMI

TOMORROW MAY NEVER COME.
Tracks: / Tomorrow may never come / I heard the sound.
Single (7"): released on Valentino, Apr'87

Force 10

FORCE 10.
Album: released on Warner Brothers, Oct'81 by Warner Bros Records. Dist: WEA

ONE AND ONLY.
Single (7"): released on Monarch, Jul'83 by Chart Records. Dist: Pinnacle

Force 8

FIESTA.
Single (7"): released on New Merseysound, Aug'85 Dist: EMI

Single (12"): released on New Merseysound, Aug'85 Dist: EMI

Forcefield

SMOKE ON THE WATER.
Tracks: / Smoke on the water / Shine it on me.
Single (12"): released on President, Feb'87 by President Records. Dist: Taylors, Spartan

Force M.D.'s

FORGIVE ME GIRL.
Single (7"): released on Tommy Boy, Oct'84 by Warner Brothers. Dist: WEA Distribution

Single (12"): released on Tommy Boy, Oct'84 by Warner Brothers. Dist: WEA Distribution Deleted '87.

HERE I GO AGAIN.
Tracks: / Here I go again / Itchin' for a scratch.
Single (7"): released on Island, Jun'86 by Island Records. Dist: Polygram

Single (12"): released on Island, Jun'86 by Island Records. Dist: Polygram

LOVE IS A HOUSE.
Tracks: / Love is a house / Love is a house (inst).
Single (7"): released on Warner Bros., Jul'87 by Warner Bros Records. Dist: WEA

TEARS.
Single (7"): released on Tommy Boy, Feb'85 by Warner Brothers. Dist: WEA Distribution

Single (12"): released on Tommy Boy, Feb'85 by Warner Brothers. Dist: WEA Distribution Deleted '87.

TENDER LOVE.
Tracks: / One plus one / Tears / Uh oh! / Here I go again / Chillin' / Tender love / Will you be my girlfriend? / Walking on air / Force MD's meet The Fat Boys / Smoke on the water / Shine it on me.
Notes: Photography; Front, by Mike Prior. Back, by Lynn Goldsmith. Grooming: Jonathan Wallace. Stylist: Florie Birnes. Painted Backdrop: Angie Coquerane. Cover by Island Art.
Album: released on Tommy Boy, May'86 by Warner Brothers. Dist: WEA Distribution

Cassette: released on Tommy Boy, May'86 by Warner Brothers. Dist: WEA Distribution

Single (7"): released on President, Jan'86 by President Records. Dist: Taylors, Spartan

Single (12"): released on Tommy Boy, Mar'86 by Warner Brothers. Dist: WEA Distribution

TOUCH & GO.
Album: released on Tommy Boy, Aug'87 by Warner Brothers. Dist: WEA Distribution

Cassette: released on Tommy Boy, Aug'87 by Warner Brothers. Dist: WEA Distribution

For Collectors Only

FOR COLLECTORS ONLY (Various Artists).
Tracks: / Not me baby / Hey girl (where are you going) / Sweet magic / What a love this is (Oh, oh, oh) / Baby I dig you / I must love you / Too much of a good thing / Something is bad / Nothing can compare to you / I don't like to lose / Try my love / Meet me halfway / My life with you / You didn't have to leave.

Album: released on Soul Supply, Jan'87 by High Energy Records. Dist: Charly

Album: released on Soul Supply, Dec'84 by High Energy Records. Dist: Charly

Album: released on Soul Supply, Dec'84 by High Energy Records. Dist: Charly

For Dancers...

FOR DANCERS ALSO Various artists (Various Artists).
Album: released on Kent (Cadet, USA), Apr'83 by Ace Records. Dist: Pinnacle

FOR DANCERS ALWAYS Various artists (Various Artists).
Cassette: released on Kent, Feb'85 by Ace Records. Dist: Pinnacle

FOR DANCERS ONLY Various artists (Various Artists).
Album: released on Kent, Sep'82 by Ace Records. Dist: Pinnacle

Ford, Andy

GROOVY KIND OF LOVE.
Single (7"): released on Tabitha, Aug'84 by Tabitha Records. Dist: Tabitha Distribution

TEENAGE LOVE.
Single (7"): released on Tabitha, Jan'84 by Tabitha Records. Dist: Tabitha Distribution

Ford, Barry

I WANNA REACH OUT AND TOUCH YOU.
Single (12"): released on Albion, Apr'84 by Albion Records. Dist: Spartan, Pinnacle

RADIO ACTIVE.
Single (7"): released on Albion, Nov'82 by Albion Records. Dist: Spartan, Pinnacle

Single (12"): released on Albion, Nov'82 by Albion Records. Dist: Spartan, Pinnacle

Ford, Charles

REAL CHARLES FORD BAND, THE.
Album: released on Arhoolie, '81 by Arhoolie Records. Dist: Projection, Topic, Jazz Music, Swift, Roots

Forde, Ben

LIGHTS OF HOME, THE.
Album: by Pilgrim Records. Dist: Rough Trade, Cartel

SUPREME SACRIFICE, THE.
Album: by Pilgrim Records. Dist: Rough Trade, Cartel

Ford, Emile

WHAT DO YOU WANT TO MAKE THOSE EYES AT ME FOR.
Single (7"): released on Old Gold, Jul'82 by Old Gold Records. Dist: Lightning, Jazz Music, Spartan, Counterpoint

Forder, Timothy

BILL THE MINDER.
Tracks: / Old Crispin / King (The) / Navigator (The) / Aunt Galladia / Respectable gentleman (The) / Chloe / Doctor (The) / Sicilian cleaning lady (The) / Button crane of Bararoo (The) / Waiter (The) / Bosworth.
Cassette: released on Tellastory, Apr'87 by Bartlett Bliss Productions. Dist: PRT Distribution, Hayward Promotions Distribution, H.R. Taylor Distribution

Ford, Frankie

LET'S TAKE A SEA CRUISE WITH....
Album: released on Ace, Feb'83 by Ace Records. Dist: Pinnacle, Swift, Hotshot, Cadillac

NEW ORLEANS DYNAMO.
Album: released on Ace, Sep'84 by Ace Records. Dist: Pinnacle, Swift, Hotshot, Cadillac

SEA CRUISE.
Single (7"): released on Creole, Aug'82 by Creole Records. Dist: Rhino, PRT

Ford, Gerry

LET'S HEAR IT FOR THE WORKING MAN.
Album: released on Big R, Jan'82 by Big R Records. Dist: Pinnacle, Wynd-Up Distribution, Solomon & Peres Distribution, I & B, JSU, Swift, Record Merchandisers Distribution, Spartan

Cassette: released on Big R, Jan'82 by Big R Records. Dist: Pinnacle, Wynd-Up Distribution, Solomon & Peres Distribution, I & B, JSU, Swift, Record Merchandisers Distribution, Spartan

LORD I'D FORGOTTEN.
Single (7"): released on Big R, Jun'81 by Big R Records. Dist: Pinnacle, Wynd-Up Distribution, Solomon & Peres Distribution, I & B, JSU, Swift, Record Merchandisers Distribution, Spartan

ON THE ROAD.
Album: released on Big R, Mar'81 by Big R Records. Dist: Pinnacle, Wynd-Up Distribution, Solomon & Peres Distribution, I & B, JSU, Swift, Record Merchandisers Distribution, Spartan

Cassette: released on Big R, Mar'81 by Big R Records. Dist: Pinnacle, Wynd-Up Distribution, Solomon & Peres Distribution, I & B, JSU, Swift, Record Merchandisers Distribution, Spartan

THANK GOD FOR RADIO.
Album: released on Trimtop, Jan'87

Cassette: released on Trimtop, Jan'87

Ford, Jed

BOSS O' THE BLACK.
Tracks: / Boss o' the black / Willie Thorne, king of the maximum break.
Single (7"): released on BBC, May'86 by BBC Records & Tapes. Dist: EMI, PRT, Pye

IS ANYONE GOIN SAN ANTONE.
Album: released on SRT, May'75 by SRT Records. Dist: Pinnacle, Solomon & Peres Distribution, SRT Distribution, H.R. Taylor Distribution, PRT Distribution

I WONDER WHAT SHE'S DOING NOW.
Album: released on SRT, Jan'75 by SRT Records. Dist: Pinnacle, Solomon & Peres Distribution, SRT Distribution, H.R. Taylor Distribution, PRT Distribution

Ford, John T.

WHAT YOU GONNA DO.
Tracks: / What you gonna do / Tell me something new.
Notes: Pic bag
Single (7"): released on Splash, Apr'87 by Splash Records. Dist: CBS

Ford, Ken

CANADIAN PACIFIC (Ford, Ken/Billie).
Album: released on VFM, Mar'79 by VFM Records. Dist: Taylors, Wynd-Up Distribution

COUNTRY STARS (Ford, Ken/Billie).
Album: released on Outlet, Jun'77 by Outlet Records. Dist: Outlet Distribution

I DON'T WANT TO CRY (Ford, Ken/Billie).
Album: released on Look, Jul'79 Dist: R. Smith & Co. Records, H.R. Taylor

KEN & BILLIE FORD (Ford, Ken/Billie).
Cassette: released on VFM Cassettes, Jan'85

REMEMBER THE ALAMO (Ford, Ken/Billie).
Album: released on Silver Dollar, Mar'79 by VFM Records.

Cassette: released on Silver Dollar, Mar'79 by VFM Records.

Cassette: released on Silver Dollar, Mar'79 by VFM Records.

Ford, Lita

DANCIN ON THE EDGE.
Album: released on Vertigo, May'84 by Phonogram Records. Dist: Polygram

Cassette: released on Vertigo, May'84 by Phonogram Records. Dist: Polygram

GOTTA LET GO.
Single (7"): released on Vertigo, Apr'84 by Phonogram Records. Dist: Polygram

Single (12"): released on Vertigo, Apr'84 by Phonogram Records. Dist: Polygram

OUT FOR BLOOD (Ford, Lita Band).
Album: released on Mercury, Jul'83 by Phonogram Records. Dist: Polygram Distribution

Cassette: released on Mercury, Jul'83 by Phonogram Records. Dist: Polygram Distribution

Ford, Pennye

CHANGE YOUR WICKED WAYS.
Single (7"): released on Total Experience, Oct'84 by Phonogram. Dist: Polygram

DANGEROUS.
Single (7"): released on Total Experience, Apr'85 by Phonogram. Dist: Polygram

Single (12"): released on Total Experience, Apr'85 by Phonogram. Dist: Polygram

PENNYE.
Album: released on Total Experience, Jun'85 by Phonogram. Dist: Polygram

Cassette: released on Total Experience, Jun'85 by Phonogram. Dist: Polygram

Ford, Ricky

FLYING COLORS.
Album: released on Muse, Apr'81 by Peerless Records. Dist: Lugtons Distributors

INTERPRETATIONS.
Album: released on Muse, Nov'82 by Peerless Records. Dist: Lugtons Distributors

LOXODONTA AFRICANA The Jazz Sound.
Tracks: / Loxodonta Africana / UCIL / Blues Peru / Dexter / My romance / One up one down / Aerolinos.
Album: released on New World (USA), Jul'86 by New World Records (USA). Dist: Conifer

MANHATTAN PLAZA.
Album: released on Muse, Apr'81 by Peerless Records. Dist: Lugtons Distributors

SHORTER IDEAS.
Tracks: / Yes or no / Miyako / Dance cadaverous / Pinnochio / Tabloid blues / Wolf trap / Happy reunion.
Notes: Produced by Michael Cuscana. Arranged by Ricky Ford. Engineer: Rudy Van Gelder. Cover photo: Clarence Eastmond. Black liner photos: J. Flint. Art direction: Dick Smith. Recorded at the Van Gelder Studio, Englewood Cliffs, on 28.8.84. Mastered by Rudy Van Gelder.
Album: released on Muse (USA), May'86 by Muse Records (USA). Dist: Conifer Distribution, Jazz Music Distribution

Ford, Sugar Ray

EXOTIC HOTSHOTS (Ford, Sugar Ray & The Hotshots).
Album: released on Big Beat, Jun'85 by Ace Records. Dist: Projection, Pinnacle

Ford, Tennessee Ernie

HE TOUCHED ME.
Album: released on Word, May'82 by Word Records. Dist: Word Distribution, CBS

Cassette: released on Word, May'82 by Word Records. Dist: Word Distribution, CBS

OL' ROCKIN' ERN.
Album: released on Stetson, Jul'87 by Hasmick Promotions Ltd.. Dist: Counterpoint Distribution, H.R. Taylor Distribution, Swift Distribution, Chris Wellard Distribution

Cassette: released on Stetson, Jul'87 by Hasmick Promotions Ltd.. Dist: Counterpoint Distribution, H.R. Taylor Distribution, Swift Distribution, Chris Wellard Distribution

PRECIOUS MOMENTS.
Compact disc: released on Capitol, Apr'7 by Capitol Records. Dist: EMI

SIXTEEN TONS.
Tracks: / Sixteen tons / Zambesi.
Notes: Also contains:"Zambesi" by Lou Busch
Single (7"): released on Old Gold, Apr'87 by Old Gold Records. Dist: Lightning, Jazz Music, Spartan, Counterpoint

SUNDAY'S STILL A SPECIAL DAY.
Album: released on Word, May'85 by Word Records. Dist: Word Distribution, CBS

Cassette: released on Word, May'85 by Word Records. Dist: Word Distribution, CBS

SWING WIDE YOUR GOLDEN GATE.
Album: released on Word, May'82 by Word Records. Dist: Word Distribution, CBS

Cassette: released on Word, May'82 by Word Records. Dist: Word Distribution, CBS

TELL ME THE OLD, OLD STORY.
Album: released on Word, May'82 by Word Records. Dist: Word Distribution, CBS

Cassette: released on Word, May'82 by Word Records. Dist: Word Distribution, CBS

THERE'S A SONG IN MY HEART.
Album: released on Word, May'82 by Word Records. Dist: Word Distribution, CBS

Cassette: released on Word, May'82 by Word Records. Dist: Word Distribution, CBS

VERY BEST OF TENNESSEE ERNIE FORD.
Album: released on Music For Pleasure (Holland), Apr'83 by EMI Records. Dist: EMI

Ford, Tommy

MODEL T.
Album: released on Lismor, Jan'83 by Lismor Records. Dist: Lismor, Roots, Celtic Music

Cassette: released on Lismor, Jan'83 by Lismor Records. Dist: Lismor, Roots, Celtic Music

Foreign Bodies

GOING BANANAS.
Single (7"): released on GC, Feb'83 by GC Recordings. Dist: DMS, RCA

Foreigner

4.
Album: released on Atlantic, Jun'81 by WEA Records. Dist: WEA

Cassette: released on Atlantic, Jun'81 by WEA Records. Dist: WEA

Compact disc: released on Atlantic, Jun'81 by WEA Records. Dist: WEA

AGENT PROVOCATEUR.
Compact disc: released on Atlantic, Jan'85 by WEA Records. Dist: WEA

Album: released on Atlantic, Jan'85 by WEA Records. Dist: WEA

Cassette: released on Atlantic, Jan'85 by WEA Records. Dist: WEA

DON'T LET GO.
Single (7"): released on Atlantic, Mar'82 by WEA Records. Dist: WEA

DOUBLE VISION.
Album: released on Atlantic, Aug'78 by WEA Records. Dist: WEA

Cassette: released on Atlantic, Aug'78 by WEA Records. Dist: WEA

Compact disc: released on Atlantic, Aug'78 by WEA Records. Dist: WEA

FOREIGNER.
Compact disc: released on Atlantic, Apr'77 by WEA Records. Dist: WEA

Album: released on Atlantic, Apr'77 by WEA Records. Dist: WEA

HEAD GAMES.
Tracks: / Dirty white boy / Love on the telephone / Women I'll get even with you / Seventeen / Head games / Modern day / Blinded by science / Do what you like / Rev on the red line.
Compact disc: released on Atlantic, Nov'85 by WEA Records. Dist: WEA

Album: released on WEA, Sep'79 by WEA Records. Dist: WEA

Cassette: released on Atlantic, Nov'79 by WEA Records. Dist: WEA

I WANT TO KNOW WHAT LOVE IS.
Single (7"): released on Atco, Nov'84 by Atlantic Records. Dist: WEA

Single (12"): released on Atco, Nov'84 by Atlantic Records. Dist: WEA

RECORDS.
Album: released on Atlantic, Dec'82 by WEA Records. Dist: WEA

Cassette: released on Atlantic, Dec'82 by WEA Records. Dist: WEA

Compact disc: released on Atlantic, '83 by WEA Records. Dist: WEA

WAITING FOR A GIRL LIKE YOU.
Single (7"): released on Atlantic, Dec'81 by WEA Records. Dist: WEA

Foreign Legion

TRENCH LINE.
Single (7"): released on Rentaracket, Jul'86

Single (7"): released on Rentaracket, Jul'86

Foreign Press

CLIMBING.
Single (12"): released on Music International, Aug'82 by Music International Records. Dist: Pinnacle

Forest, Earl

EARL FOREST & THE BEALE STREETERS WITH BOBBY BLAND... various artists (Forest, Earl & The Beale Streeters With Bobby Bland...).
Notes: Also featuring on this LP is Johnny Ace.
Album: released on Ace, Jun'87 by Ace Records. Dist: Pinnacle, Swift, Hotshot, Cadillac

Forester, C.S.

HUNTING THE BISMARCK.
Cassette: released on Listen For Pleasure, Jul'84 by MFP Records. Dist: EMI

Cassette: released on Listen For Pleasure, Jul'84 by MFP Records. Dist: EMI

Forester Sisters

PERFUME, RIBBONS, AND PEARLS.
Album: released on Warner Bros., 11 Apr'87 by Warner Bros Records. Dist: WEA

Cassette: released on Warner Bros., 11 Apr'87 by Warner Bros Records. Dist: WEA

Forest, Jimmy

OUT OF THE FOREST.
Album: released on Prestige (USA), Aug'84

Forever

FOREVER Various artists (Various Artists).
Album: released on K-Tel, Oct'86 by K-Tel Records. Dist: Record Merchandisers Distribution, Taylors, Terry Blood Distribution, Wynd-Up Distribution, Relay Distribution, Pickwick Distribution, Solomon & Peres Distribution, Polygram

Cassette: released on K-Tel, Oct'86 by K-Tel Records. Dist: Record Merchandisers Distribution, Taylors, Terry Blood Distribution, Wynd-Up Distribution, Relay Distribution, Pickwick Distribution, Solomon & Peres Distribution, Polygram

FOREVER AND EVER.
Tracks: / Wicked bitch / D.B.L. / Sail on / Just to live / I'm lost / No chance / Cry for life / Enter eternity / Harsh reality.
Album: released on Heavy Metal America, Apr'86 by FM-Revolver Records. Dist: EMI

Forever Country

FOREVER COUNTRY Various artists (Various Artists).
Album: released on Pickwick, Jan'83 by Pickwick Records. Dist: Pickwick Distribution, Prism Leisure Distribution, Lugtons

Cassette:

Forever Gene Vincent

FOREVER GENE VINCENT (Various Artists).
Tracks: / Bring it on home / Rose of Love, The / Hey hey hey hey / Party doll / Say mama / Black leather rebel / Right now / Rocky road blues / Dance to the bop / Be bop boogie / Lotta lovin'.
Notes: Features four tracks by Gene Vincent and others by several artists includingJohnny Carroll.
Album: released on Magnum Force, Jul'87 by Magnum Music Group Ltd. Dist: Magnum Music Group Ltd, PRT, Spartan. Estim retail price in Aug'87 was £6.55.

Cassette: released on Magnum Force, Jul'87 by Magnum Music Group Ltd. Dist: Magnum Music Group Ltd, PRT, Spartan. Estim retail price in Aug'87 was £6.55.

Forever Gold

FOREVER GOLD Various artists (Various Artists).
Album:

Cassette:

Forever Reaction

B.E.D. '34.
Single (12"): released on Streetwave, Jun'84 by Streetwave Records. Dist: PRT Distribution

Forever Young

FOREVER YOUNG Various artists (Various Artists).
Compact disc: released on Bellaphon, '86 by Bellaphon Records. Dist: IMS-Polygram

Forgiven

VOILA.
Album: released on Lolita, Jun'86 by Lolita Records. Dist: Rough Trade, Cartel

Forgiving heart

FORGIVING HEART Various artists (Various Artists).
Cassette: released on Candlelight, Jun'81 by Audio-Visual Library Services. Dist: Audio-Visual Library Services

For Lovers Only

FOR LOVERS ONLY Various artists (Various Artists).
Album: released on Ronco, Jun'83

Cassette: released on Ronco, Jun'83

Forman, Bruce

DYNAMICS (Forman, Bruce & George Cables).
Album: released on Concord Jazz(USA), Nov'85 by Concord Jazz Records (USA). Dist: IMS, Polygram

FULL CIRCLE (Forman, Bruce Quintet).
Album: released on Concord Jazz(USA), Oct'84 by Concord Jazz Records (USA). Dist: IMS, Polygram

RIVER JOURNEY.
Album: released on Muse (Import), '81

Formby, George

CHIP OFF THE OLD BLOCK, THE (Formby, George, Senior & Junior).
Album: released on ASV, Mar'81 by Academy Sound & Vision Records. Dist: Pinnacle

GEORGE FORMBY.
Album: released on World, '70 Dist: Jetstar

LEANING ON A LAMP POST.
Tracks: / When I'm cleaning windows / Fanlight Fanny / Chinese laundry blues / My ukulele / Baby / I do do things I do / Sunbathing in the park / I went all hot and cold / Fiddler kept on fiddling (The) / Let's all go to Reno / Leaning on a lamp post / Auntie Maggie's remedy / I told my baby with the ukulele / Believe it or not / In a little Wigan garden / Levi's minkey Mike / She's never been seen since then / Wedding of Mr. Wu (The) / If you don't want the goods, don't maul 'em / There's nothing proud about me / Madam Moscovitch / As the hours... / Why don't women like me / Running round the fountains in Trafalger Square / Sitting on the ice in the ice rink / I could make a good living at that / John Willie at the license office / Part 1 & 2 / Come hither with your zither / Do de o do / John Willie's jazz band / Swimmin' with the wimmin' / You can't keep a growing lad down / Old kitcher kettle (The) / Best of schemes (The) / John Willie goes carolling / Parts 1 & 2.
Notes: 1986 marks the 25th anniversary of the lamented death of one of Britain's most original and enduring talents: George Formby. Star of music hall and 22 successful films, George travelled the world entertaining packed houses. Adored by almost everyone from the Royal Family to many foreign troops he visited on his global jaunts, Formby remained unspoilt by the millions he earned during his carreer. This small tribute package features almost all of his recorded Decca output from the Thirties and Fifties and contains many of his biggest hits. The LP particulary boasts a lengthy and detailed note in excess of 5 000 words!, and with several of the numbers never before having been available on anything other than the original 78 r.p.m. discs, this promoses to be a real winner. Double Album - Double Cassette: Mono.
Album: released on Recollection, Sep'86

Cassette: released on Recollection, Sep'86

Double Album: released on Music For Pleasure (Holland), Jul'83 by EMI Records. Dist: EMI

Double cassette: released on Music For Pleasure, Jul'83 by EMI Records. Dist: EMI

MAN WITH THE UKELELE.
Album: released on World, '70 Dist: Jetstar

WINDOW CLEANER.
Single (7"): released on Columbia, Dec'72 by EMI Records. Dist: EMI

WORLD OF GEORGE FORMBY, THE.
Album: released on World of Learning, '69 by World Of Learning Records. Dist: World Of Learning

WORLD OF GEORGE FORMBY & HIS UKELELE, THE.
Cassette: released on Decca, '75 by Decca Records. Dist: Polygram

Formula 30

FORMULA 30 Various artsits (Various Artists).
Double Album: released on Decca, Nov'83 by Decca Records. Dist: Polygram

Double cassette: released on Decca, Nov'83 by Decca Records. Dist: Polygram

Formula One

DREAMWORLD.
Single (7"): released on West Coast, May'83 Dist: Stage One

Formula Thirty 2

FORMULA THIRTY 2 various artists (Various Artists).
Tracks: / I want to break free / I'm still standing / All night long / Oliver's army / 2-4-6-8 motorway / Rollin' home / More than this / Vienna / Walk of life / In a big country / Who are you / Shout / I love the sound of breaking glass / Hit me with your rhythm stick / I don't like Mondays / Video killed the radio star.
Album: released on Mercury, Oct'86 by Phonogram Records. Dist: Polygram Distribution

Cassette: released on Mercury, Oct'86 by Phonogram Records. Dist: Polygram Distribution

Compact disc: released on Mercury, Oct'86 by Phonogram Records. Dist: Polygram Distribution

Forrest

FEEL THE NEED IN ME.
Single (7"): released on CBS, May'83 by CBS Records. Dist: CBS

Single (12"): released on CBS, May'83 by CBS Records. Dist: CBS

FORREST.
Album: released on CBS, Oct'83 by CBS Records. Dist: CBS Deleted '85.

Cassette: released on CBS, Oct'83 by CBS Records. Dist: CBS

ROCK THE BOAT.
Single (7"): released on CBS, Feb'83 by CBS Records. Dist: CBS

Single (12"): released on CBS, Feb'83 by CBS Records. Dist: CBS

SHE'S SO DIVINE.
Single (7"): released on CBS, Aug'84 by CBS Records. Dist: CBS

Single (12"): released on CBS, Aug'84 by CBS Records. Dist: CBS

Forrester, Helen

THREE WOMEN OF LIVERPOOL.
Cassette: released on Soundings, Feb'85 Dist: Soundings

Forrest, Helen

NOW & FOREVER.
Album: released on Stash, Mar'87 Dist: Swift Distribution, Jazz Music Distribution, Jazz Horizons Distribution, Celtic Music Distribution, Cadillac, JSU Distribution, Zodiac Distribution

Forrest, Jackie

SHOW ME HOW TO LOVE.
Single (7"): released on Neil Rushton (Import), Mar'83

Forrest, Jimmy

ALL THE GIN IS GONE.
Album: Dist: Projection, Swift, Cadillac

BLACK FOREST.
Album: Dist: Projection, Swift, Cadillac

HEART OF THE FORREST.
Album: released on Palo Alto (Italy), Jan'84

LIVE IN CHICAGO (Forrest, Jimmy & Al Grey).
Album: released on Aviva(USA), Apr'79 Dist: Jazz Music, Swift

SWEET TRACKS (Forrest, Jimmy & Harry Edison).
Double Album: released on Vogue, Jul'78 Dist: Discovery, Jazz Music, PRT, Swift

For Sentimental Reasons

FOR SENTIMENTAL REASONS.
Tracks: / Golden earring / Manana / I love you for sentimental reasons / Christmas song, The / Blue moon / Again / Tampico / Tree in the meadow / Long ago and far away / Dream / Hurry on down / Personality / On the Atchison, Topeka & The Santa Fe / Buttons and bows / Cow-Cow Boogie / Temptation.
Notes: From the hit parade 1942-49
Album: released on Memoir, Jan'87 by Memoir Records. Dist: PRT Distribution

Cassette: released on Memoir, Jan'87 by Memoir Records. Dist: PRT Distribution

Forsey, Keith

DYNAMITE.
Album: released on Carrere, Mar'82 by Carrere Records. Dist: PRT, Spartan

Forster, E.M.

PASSAGE TO INDIA (Various Artists).
Cassette: released on Argo (Cassettes), Sep'84 by Decca Records. Dist: Polygram

Forsyth, Frederick

FOURTH PROTOCOL, THE.
Cassette: released on Listen For Pleasure, May'85 by MFP Records. Dist: EMI

For The Good Times

FOR THE GOOD TIMES Various artists (Various Artists).
Album: released on Epic, Nov'82 by CBS Records. Dist: CBS

Cassette: released on Epic, Nov'82 by CBS Records. Dist: CBS Deleted '85.

For Those I Loved

FOR THOSE I LOVED Original soundtrack.
Album: released on BBC, Aug'84 by BBC Records & Tapes. Dist: EMI, PRT.

Cassette: released on BBC, Aug'84 by BBC Records & Tapes. Dist: EMI, PRT.

FOR THOSE I LOVED - VOL.2 Various artists (Various Artists).
Album: released on General Music (France), May'85 by General Music Records (France). Dist: Studio Import & Export Distribution, Silva Screen

Cassette: released on General Music (France), May'85 by General Music Records (France). Dist: Studio Import & Export Distribution, Silva Screen

Forth Worth Teen Scene

FORT WORTH TEEN SCENE The Major Bill tapes vol. 2.
Album: released on Big Beat, May'87 by Ace Records. Dist: Projection, Pinnacle

Fortress

HANDS IN THE TILL.
Album: released on Atlantic, May'81 by WEA Records. Dist: WEA

Cassette: released on Atlantic, May'81 by WEA Records. Dist: WEA

Fortunate Sons

HAMMERHEAD.
Single (12"): released on Bam Caruso, Jul'87 by Bam Caruso Records. Dist: Rough Trade, Revolver, Cartel

RISING.
Album: released on Bam Caruso, Jun'86 by Bam Caruso Records. Dist: Rough Trade, Revolver, Cartel

SOMETIMES YOU WIN.
Tracks: / Sometimes you win / Me and my uncle.
Single (7"): released on Bam Caruso, Jun'86 by Bam Caruso Records. Dist: Rough Trade, Revolver, Cartel

Single (7"): released on Bam Caruso, Jun'86 by Bam Caruso Records. Dist: Rough Trade, Revolver, Cartel

Fortunes

BEST OF THE FORTUNES, (THE).
Album: released on EMI (Holland), Aug'83 by EMI Records. Dist: Conifer

Cassette: released on EMI (Holland), Aug'83 by EMI Records. Dist: Conifer

GREATEST HITS:FORTUNES.
Cassette: released on Autograph, Apr'85 Dist: Record Services Distribution (Ireland)

HIT COLLECTION, (THE).
Album: released on Elecstar, Jun'84 by Elecstar Records. Dist: PRT

Cassette: released on Elecstar, Jun'84 by Elecstar Records. Dist: PRT

MUSIC FOR THE MILLIONS.
Album: released on Decca (Holland), Jun'84 by Decca Records. Dist: Polygram, IMS

Cassette: released on Decca (Holland), Jun'84 by Decca Records. Dist: Polygram. IMS

REMEMBERING.
Album: released on Decca, Sep'76 by Decca Records. Dist: Polygram

YOU'VE GOT YOUR TROUBLES.
Extended-play record: released on Decca, Jul'80 by Decca Records. Dist: Polygram

YOU'VE GOT YOUR TROUBLES.
Single (7"): released on Old Gold, Oct'83 by Old Gold Records. Dist: Lightning, Jazz Music, Spartan, Counterpoint

Fortune Tellers

MUSICK WITHOUT TEARS.
Album: released on New Rose, Jun'87 Dist: Rough Trade, Cartel

Forty...

40 BRASS BAND FAVOURITES Various artists (Various Artists).
Album: released on Pickwick, Sep'79 by Pickwick Records. Dist: Pickwick Distribution, Prism Leisure Distribution,

Cassette: released on Pickwick, Sep'79 by Pickwick Records. Dist: Pickwick Distribution, Prism Leisure Distribution

40 CHRISTMAS CAROLS (Forty Christmas Carols).
Double Album: released on Abbey, Nov'83 by Abbey. Dist: PRT, Taylors, Gamut

Double cassette: released on Abbey, Nov'83 by Abbey. Dist: PRT, Taylors, Gamut

40 COUNTRY CLASSICS Various artists (Various Artists).
Album: released on Pickwick, Sep'79 by Pickwick Records. Dist: Pickwick Distribution, Prism Leisure Distribution,

Cassette: released on Pickwick, Sep'79 by Pickwick Records. Dist: Pickwick Distribution, Prism Leisure Distribution,

40 COUNTRY MASTERPIECES Various artists (Various Artists).
Album: released on Pickwick, Sep'79 by Pickwick Records. Dist: Pickwick Distribution, Prism Leisure Distribution,

Cassette: released on Pickwick, Sep'79 by Pickwick Records. Dist: Pickwick Distribution, Prism Leisure Distribution,

40 FAVOURITE NURSERY RHYMES Various artists (Various Artists).
Album: released on Polydor, Nov'76 by Polydor Records. Dist: Polygram, Polydor

Album: released on Hawk, Jan'77 by Dolphin Records. Dist: I & B, Celtic Music, Solomon & Peres Distribution

Album: released on Kiddicraft, Oct'77 by MacDonald Educational Records. Dist: H.R. Taylor

Cassette: released on Kiddicraft, Oct'77 by MacDonald Educational Records. Dist: H.R. Taylor

40 GOLDEN COUNTRY HITS - VOL.2 Various artists (Various Artists).
Album: released on Teldec (Germany), Jun'81 by Import Records. Dist: IMS Distribution, Polygram Distribution

Cassette: released on Teldec (Germany), Jun'81 by Import Records. Dist: IMS Distribution, Polygram Distribution

40 NON STOP NUMBER ONES Various artists (Various Artists).
Album: released on Music for Pleasure, Nov'83 by EMI Records. Dist: MFP Distribution

Cassette: released on Music for Pleasure, Nov'83 by EMI Records. Dist: MFP Distribution

40 NON STOP ROCK 'N' ROLL SMASH HITS Various artists (Various Artists).
Album: released on Music for Pleasure, Nov'81 by EMI Records. Dist: MFP Distribution

Cassette: released on Music for Pleasure, Nov'81 by EMI Records. Dist: MFP Distribution

40 SHOW STOPPERS Various artists (Various Artists).
Album: released on MFP, Apr'81 by EMI Records. Dist: EMI

Cassette: released on MFP, Apr'81 by EMI Records. Dist: EMI

40 SMASH HITS COUNTRY STYLE Various artists (Various Artists).
Double Album: released on MFP, Sep'79 by EMI Records. Dist: EMI

Double cassette: released on MFP, Sep'79 by EMI Records. Dist: EMI

40 SOLID GOLD HITS Various artists (Various Artists).
Album: released on Pickwick, Sep'79 by Pickwick Records. Dist: Pickwick Distribution, Prism Leisure Distribution,

Cassette: released on Pickwick, Sep'79 by Pickwick Records. Dist: Pickwick Distribution, Prism Leisure Distribution,

40 UNFORGETTABLE MEMORIES Various artists (Various Artists).
Album: released on Pickwick, Sep'79 by Pickwick Records. Dist: Pickwick Distribution, Prism Leisure Distribution,

Cassette: released on Pickwick, Sep'79 by Pickwick Records. Dist: Pickwick Distribution, Prism Leisure Distribution

FORTY MINUTES OF DAYLIGHT Various artists (Various Artists).
Album: released on Daylight, '86 by Daylight Records. Dist: Daylight

FORTY YEARS OF WOMEN IN JAZZ (Forty Years Of Women In Jazz).
Album: released on Stash (Import), Jul'82 Dist: Swift Distribution, Jazz Music Distribution, Jazz Horizons Distribution, Celtic Music Distribution, Cadillac, JSU Distribution, Zodiac Distribution

FORTY YEARS ON (Bennett, Alan).
Cassette: released on BBC, May'84 by BBC Records & Tapes. Dist: EMI, PRT,

Forty Eight Cameras

B SIDES ARE FOR LOVERS.
Album: released on 139K, Jun'85 Dist: Red Rhino, Cartel

Forty Eight Chairs

70% PARANOID.
Album: released on Relentless, Nov'82 by Relentless Records. Dist: Cartel

LIVE IN COGNITO.
Album: released on Relentless, Oct'83 by Relentless Records. Dist: Cartel

SNAP IT AROUND.
Single (7"): released on Absurd, Sep'82 by Absurd. Dist: Pinnacle, Rough Trade

Forty Five's

SECRETS AND WHISPERS.
Single (7"): released on 45, Sep'81 Dist: Pinnacle

Forty Four Magnum

DANGER.
Album: released on Roadrunner, Jan'85 by Roadrunner Records (Germany). Dist: Pinnacle

STREET ROCK 'N' ROLLER.
Album: released on Road Runner, Nov'84

Forty Hour Week

AS RIGHT NOW.
Tracks: / As right now / If it ain't Dixie / Nobody but me / 40 hour week / Can't keep a good man down / There's no way / Down on Longboat Key / Louisianna moon / I want to know you before we make love / Fireworks.
Compact disc: released on RCA, Sep'85 by RCA Records. Dist: RCA, Roots, Swift, Wellard, Chris, I & B, Solomon & Peres Distribution

Forty Nine...

FORTY NINE MINUTE TECHNICOLOUR DREAM (Various Artists).
Album: released on Bam Caruso, Feb'87 by Bam Caruso Records. Dist: Rough Trade, Revolver, Cartel

Forty Nine Americans

WONDER EP.
Single (7"): released on No Bad, Mar'80 by No Bad Records. Dist: Pinnacle, Wynd-Up Distribution (Scotland)

Forty-One Degrees

OPEN HEART.
Album: released on 41 Degrees, Aug'83

Forward

FORWARD Various Artists (Various Artists).
Album: released on Greensleeves, Nov'83 by Greensleeves Records. Dist: BMG, Jetstar, Spartan

Forward Motion

PROGRESSIONS.
Album: released on Hep, Mar'87 by H.R. Taylor Records. Dist: Jazz Music, Cadillac Music, JSU, Taylors, Wellard, Chris, Zodiac, Swift, Fast Forward

For Your Eyes Only

FOR YOUR EYES ONLY Original soundtrack.
Album: released on Liberty-UA, Jun'81

Cassette: released on Liberty-UA, Jun'81

Foster & Allen

AFTER ALL THESE YEARS.
Album: released on Ritz, Sep'85 by Outlet Records. Dist: Outlet, Prism Leisure Distribution, Record Services Distribution (Ireland), Roots

Cassette: released on Ritz, Sep'85 by Outlet Records. Dist: Outlet, Prism Leisure Distribution, Record Services Distribution (Ireland), Roots

AFTER ALL THOSE YEARS.
Tracks: / After all those years / Rose of Allendale.
Single (7"): released on Ritz, Jan'86 by Outlet Records. Dist: Outlet, Prism Leisure Distribution, Record Services Distribution (Ireland), Roots

AT THE TOP.
Album: released on Ritz, Aug'85 by Outlet Records. Dist: Outlet, Prism Leisure Distribution, Record Services Distribution (Ireland), Roots

Cassette: released on Ritz, Aug'85 by Outlet Records. Dist: Outlet, Prism Leisure Distribution, Record Services Distribution (Ireland), Roots

AT THE TOP WITH FOSTER & ALLEN.
Album: released on Release, May'81 by Release Records. Dist: I & B, Wynd-Up Distribution, Taylors, Solomon & Peres Distribution

BUNCH OF THYME.
Single (7"): released on Ritz, Feb'82 by Outlet Records. Dist: Outlet, Prism Leisure Distribution, Record Services Distribution (Ireland), Roots

BUNCH OF THYME, (A).
Album: released on Ritz, Apr'82 by Outlet Records. Dist: Outlet, Prism Leisure Distribution, Record Services Distribution (Ireland), Roots

Cassette: released on Ritz, Apr'82 by Outlet Records. Dist: Outlet, Prism Leisure Distribution, Record Services Distribution (Ireland), Roots

FOSTER & ALLEN SELECTION, (THE).
Album: released on Ritz, Oct'82 by Outlet Records. Dist: Outlet, Prism Leisure Distribution, Record Services Distribution (Ireland), Roots

Cassette: released on Ritz, Oct'82 by Outlet Records. Dist: Outlet, Prism Leisure Distribution, Record Services Distribution (Ireland), Roots

I WILL LOVE YOU ALL MY LIFE.
Single (7"): released on Ritz, Oct'83 by Outlet Records. Dist: Outlet, Prism Leisure Distribution, Record Services Distribution (Ireland), Roots

I WILL LOVE YOU ALL OF MY LIFE.
Album: released on Ritz, Oct'83 by Outlet Records. Dist: Outlet, Prism Leisure Distribution, Record Services Distribution (Ireland), Roots

Cassette: released on Ritz, Oct'83 by Outlet Records. Dist: Outlet, Prism Leisure Distribution, Record Services Distribution (Ireland), Roots

JUST FOR OLD TIMES SAKE.
Single (7"): released on Ritz, Jun'84 by Outlet Records. Dist: Outlet, Prism Leisure Distribution, Record Services Distribution (Ireland), Roots

LOVE SONGS The very best of Foster & Allen Volume 2.
Compact disc: released on Ritz, Oct'86 by Outlet Records. Dist: Outlet, Prism Leisure Distribution, Record Services Distribution (Ireland), Roots

MAGGIE.
Single (7"): released on Ritz, Jan'83 by Outlet Records. Dist: Outlet, Prism Leisure Distribution, Record Services Distribution (Ireland), Roots

MAGGIE.
Album: released on Ritz, '82 by Outlet Records. Dist: Outlet, Prism Leisure Distribution, Record Services Distribution (Ireland), Roots

Cassette: released on Ritz, '82 by Outlet Records. Dist: Outlet, Prism Leisure Distribution, Record Services Distribution (Ireland), Roots

OLD FLAME.
Single (7"): released on Ritz, Aug'82 by Outlet Records. Dist: Outlet, Prism Leisure Distribution, Record Services Distribution (Ireland), Roots

REMINISCING.
Tracks: / Reminiscing.
Album: released on Stylus, Sep'86 Dist: Pinnacle, Terry Blood Distribution, Stylus Distribution

Cassette: released on Stylus, Sep'86 Dist: Pinnacle, Terry Blood Distribution, Stylus Distribution

Compact disc: released on Stylus, Sep'86 Dist: Pinnacle, Terry Blood Distribution, Stylus Distribution

Single (7"): released on Honey, Oct'86 Dist: MRC Distribution

VERY BEST OF FOSTER & ALLEN VOLUME 1(THE).
Compact disc: released on Ritz, Oct'86 by Outlet Records. Dist: Outlet, Prism Leisure Distribution, Record Services Distribution (Ireland), Roots

VERY BEST OF FOSTER & ALLEN, (THE).
Album: released on Ritz, Nov'84 by Outlet Records. Dist: Outlet, Prism Leisure Distribution, Record Services Distribution (Ireland), Roots

Cassette: released on Ritz, Nov'84 by Outlet Records. Dist: Outlet, Prism Leisure Distribution, Record Services Distribution (Ireland), Roots

WE WILL MAKE LOVE.
Single (7"): released on Ritz, Oct'84 by Outlet Records. Dist: Outlet, Prism Leisure Distribution, Record Services Distribution (Ireland), Roots

WHEN I DREAM.
Tracks: / When I Dream / Green Fields Round Ferbane(The) / Maggie / Will I love you all my life.
Single (7"): released on Ritz, May'86 by Outlet Records. Dist: Outlet, Prism Leisure Distribution, Record Services Distribution (Ireland), Roots

WHEN MY BLUE MOON TURNS GOLD.
Tracks: / When my blue moon... / Morning glory.
Single (7"): released on Ritz, 30 May'87 by Outlet Records. Dist: Outlet, Prism Leisure Distribution, Record Services Distribution (Ireland), Roots

Foster, Chris

ALL THINGS IN COMMON.
Album: released on Topic, '81 Dist: Roots Distribution

LAYERS.
Album: released on Topic, '81 Dist: Roots Distribution

Foster, Chuck

1945-1946 (Foster, Chuck & His Orchestra).
Album: released on Circle(USA), Jun'86 by Jazzology Records (USA). Dist: Jazz Music, Swift, Chris Wellard

CHUCK FOSTER 1945.
Album: released on Aircheck, Apr'79

MUSIC IN THE FOSTER FASHION (Foster, Chuck & His Orchestra).
Album: released on Aircheck, Feb'78

Foster, David

BEST OF ME, THE.
Tracks: / Best of Me(The) / Saje.
Compact disc: released on Mobile Fidelity, '86 by Mobile Fidelity Records.

BEST OF ME, THE (Foster, David & Olivia Newton-John).
Single (7"): released on Atlantic, Jul'86 by WEA Records. Dist: WEA

DAVID FOSTER.
Tracks: / Love theme from St.Elmo's Fire / Theme from The Colour Purple / Flight of the Snowbirds / All that my heart can hold / Bst of

Me (The) / Tap Dance / Who's gonna love you tonight / Elizabeth / Playing with fire / Saje.
Album: released on Atlantic, Jul'86 by WEA Records. Dist: WEA

Cassette: released on Atlantic, Jul'86 by WEA Records. Dist: WEA

Compact disc: released on Atlantic, Jul'86 by WEA Records. Dist: WEA

LOVE THEME FROM SAINT ELMO'S FIRE.
Single (7"): released on Atlantic, Oct'85 by WEA Records. Dist: WEA

SONGWRITERS FOR THE STARS 2 (Foster, David/Barry Mann/Cynthia Weil).
Album: released on Polydor, Oct'83 by Polydor Records. Dist: Polygram, Polydor

Foster, Frank

2 FRANKS PLEASE (Foster, Frank/Frank Wess).
Double Album:

FRANKLY SPEAKING (Foster, Frank & Frank Weiss).
Tracks: / When did you leave heaven? / Up and coming / One morning in may / Two Franks / This is all i ask / Blues backstage / An' all such stuff as'dat / Summer knows (The).
Compact disc: released on Concord Jazz(USA), Sep'86 by Concord Jazz Records (USA). Dist: IMS, Polygram

FRANKLY SPEAKING (Foster, Frank/Frank Wess).
Album: released on Concord Jazz(USA), Sep'85 by Concord Jazz Records (USA). Dist: IMS, Polygram

MANHATTAN FEVER (Foster, Frank/Loud Minority).
Album: released on Denon, Mar'82 by Denon Records. Dist: Harmonia Mundi

SHINY STOCKINGS (Foster, Frank/Loud Minority).
Album: released on Denon, Mar'82 by Denon Records. Dist: Harmonia Mundi

TWO FOR THE BLUES (Foster, Frank/Frank Wess).
Album: released on Pablo (USA), Sep'84 by Pablo Records (USA). Dist: Wellard, Chris, IMS-Polygram, BMG

Cassette: released on Pablo (USA), Sep'84 by Pablo Records (USA). Dist: Wellard, Chris, IMS-Polygram, BMG

Foster, Gary

GRAND CRU CLASSE.
Album: released on Revelation, Apr'81

STARBRIGHT (Foster, Gary & Clare Fischer).
Album: released on Discovery (USA), Jan'84

Cassette: released on Discovery (USA), Jan'84

STARBRIGHT (see Fischer, Clare) (Foster, Gary & Clare Fischer).

SUBCONSCIOUSLY.
Album: released on Revelation, Apr'81

Foster, Herman

LIVE IN BOLOGNA VOLUME 2 (Foster, Herman & Lou Donaldson Quartet).
Notes: See under Donaldson,Lou Quartet

ONE AND ONLY(THE) (Herman Foster Trio).
Album: released on Timeless, Oct'86

Foster, Ian

IAN FOSTER.
Notes: Soul album, featuring the singles 'Out for the count', 'This time' and 'We've lost this feeling'.
Album: released on MCA (USA), Aug'87

OUT FOR THE COUNT.
Single (7"): released on MCA, Aug'87 by MCA Records. Dist: Polygram, MCA

Single (12"): released on MCA, Aug'87 by MCA Records. Dist: Polygram, MCA

TELL ME IT'S TRUE.
Tracks: / Tell me it's true / Tell me it's true (instrumental).
Single (7"): released on MCA, May'86 by MCA Records. Dist: Polygram, MCA

Single (12"): released on MCA, May'86 by MCA Records. Dist: Polygram, MCA

Foster, Jerry

FOOL FOR YOU MAMA.
Single (7"): Dist: PRT, Jetstar

Foster, Michael

DANCING ACCORDION.
Tracks: / Showmans fancy etc - Hornpipes / Paddy the Dandy etc - Jigs / My Home - Waltzes / Sweets of May etc - Jigs / Irish polkas / Bridge Jig etc. / Oslo road Waltzes etc. / Beer barrel polka / Bag of Spuds - Reels / Sally Gardens etc - Reels.
Album: released on Accordion Record Club, Jul'86 by Accordion Record Club Records. Dist: Accordion Record Club

Fote

SHAKING THE HOUSE.
Single (7"): released on Le Rey, Nov'81

Fotheringay

FOTHERINGAY (Fotheringay with Sandy Denny).
Album: released on Hannibal, Jul'87 by Hannibal Records. Dist: Charly, Harmonia Mundi, Projection, Celtic Music, Roots

Foton

BAMBOO CURTAIN.
Single (7"): released on Feltwain, May'83 by Pinnacle Records. Dist: Pinnacle

Single (12"): released on Feltwain, May'83 by Pinnacle Records. Dist: Pinnacle

Fotostat

FOTOSTAT.
Single (7"): released on Sour Grape, Nov'82 by Sour Grape Records. Dist: PRT

Foundation

WISE UP.
Single (7"): released on Breakout, Sep'85 by A&M Records. Dist: Polygram

Single (12"): released on Breakout, Sep'85 by A&M Records. Dist: Polygram

Foundation Choir

TAKE A CHANCE.
Tracks: / Take a Chance / Happy in the Glory Way.
Single (7"): released on Millenium, Dec'85 Dist: RCA Distribution

Foundations

BABY, NOW THAT I FOUND YOU.
Tracks: / Baby, now that I found you / Build me up buttercup.
Notes: Pic bag
Single (7"): released on PRT, Apr'87 by PRT Records. Dist: PRT

Single (12"): released on PRT, Apr'87 by PRT Records. Dist: PRT

BABY NOW THAT I FOUND YOU.
Single (7"): released on PRT, Apr'79 by PRT Records. Dist: PRT

Single (7"): released on Old Gold, Jun'84 by Old Gold Records. Dist: Lightning, Jazz Music, Spartan, Counterpoint

BACK TO THE BEAT.
Album: released on PRT, Apr'83 by PRT Records. Dist: PRT

Cassette: released on PRT, Apr'83 by PRT Records. Dist: PRT

GOLDEN HOUR OF THE FOUNDATIONS GREATEST HITS.
Album: by PRT Records. Dist: PRT

Foundations Of...

FOUNDATIONS OF MODERN JAZZ (Various Artists).
Notes: O.C.I. = Oliver Crombie Imports.
Compact disc: released on Dunhill Compact Classics (USA), '86

Foundry Bar Band

FOUNDRY BAR BAND, THE.
Album: released on Springthyme, Oct'86 by Springthyme Records. Dist: Jazz Music Distribution, Projection Distribution, Roots Distribution

Cassette: by Springthyme Records. Dist: Jazz Music Distribution, Projection Distribution, Roots Distribution

Album: released on Springthyme, '83 by Springthyme Records. Dist: Folksound Distribution

ON THE ROAD WITH......
Album: released on Springthyme, Oct'86 by Springthyme Records. Dist: Folksound Distribution

Cassette: released on Springthyme, Oct'86 by Springthyme Records. Dist: Jazz Music Distribution, Projection Distribution, Roots Distribution

Fountainhead

BURNING TOUCH (THE).
Tracks: / Open up / Feel it now / So good now (with you) / When the lifeline begins / Rhythm / Sometimes / Seeing is believing / Faraway / Take my life.
Album: released on China, Jun'86 by Chrysalis Records. Dist: Chrysalis

Cassette: released on China, Jun'86 by Chrysalis Records. Dist: Chrysalis

FEEL IT NOW.
Tracks: / Feel it now / Open up China.
Single (7"): released on China, May'86 by Chrysalis Records. Dist: Chrysalis

Single (12"): released on China, May'86 by Chrysalis Records. Dist: Chrysalis

RHYTHM METHOD.
Tracks: / Rhythm Method / Far Away.
Single (7"): released on China, Jul'86 by Chrysalis Records. Dist: Chrysalis

Single (12"): released on China, Jul'86 by Chrysalis Records. Dist: Chrysalis

RHYTHM METHOD.
Single (12"): released on Fountain, Sep'85 by Retrieval Records. Dist: Jazz Music, Swift, VJM, Wellard, Chris, Retrieval

SO GOOD NOW.
Tracks: / Heart and soul.
Single (7"): released on China, Jan'87 by Chrysalis Records. Dist: Chrysalis

Single (12"): released on China, Jan'87 by Chrysalis Records. Dist: Chrysalis

Fountain, Pete

ALIVE IN NEW ORLEANS.
Album: released on First American, Apr'79 by First American (US) Records. Dist: Swift

SUPER JAZZ 1 (Fountain, Pete & Al Hirt).
Double Album: released on Monument, May'76 by CBS Records. Dist: CBS Distribution

Four...

FOUR DECADES OF JAZZ Various artists (Various Artists).
Double Album: released on Xanadu, Mar'79 Dist: Discovery, Jazz Horizons, Jazz Music, Swift

FOUR FROM THE MADDING CROWD... (Various Artists).
Album: released on Third Mind, Feb'87 by Third Mind Records. Dist: Backs, Cartel Distribution

FOUR GIRLS Soundtrack (North, Alex).
Album: released on Varese International, Mar'79

FOUR ON THE FLOOR EP Various artists (Various Artists).
Extended-play record: released on Big Beat, Feb'80 by Ace Records. Dist: Projection, Pinnacle

FOUR POETS OF THE TWENTIETH CENTURY Various artists (Various Artists).
Cassette: released on Argo (Spokenword), Oct'84 by Decca Records. Dist: Polygram

FOUR STAR COUNTRY various artists (Various Artists).
Album: released on K-Tel, Aug'85 by K-Tel Records. Dist: Record Merchandisers Distribution, Taylors, Terry Blood Distribution, Wynd-Up Distribution, Relay Distribution, Pickwick Distribution, Solomon & Peres Distribution, Polygram

Cassette: released on K-Tel, Aug'85 by K-Tel Records. Dist: Record Merchandisers Distribution, Taylors, Terry Blood Distribution, Wynd-Up Distribution, Relay Distribution, Pickwick Distribution, Solomon & Peres Distribution, Polygram

FOUR STAR SHOWCASE Various artists (Various Artists).
Album: released on RCAS, Mar'85 by RCAS Records. Dist: Jetstar

FOUR TRADITIONAL FAIRY TALES Various artists (Various Artists).
Album: released on Tempo, Nov'79 Dist: MSD Distribution

Cassette: released on Tempo, Nov'79 Dist: MSD Distribution

Four Aces

BEST OF.
Cassette: released on Creole (Everest-Europa), Jul'84 by Creole Records. Dist: PRT, Rhino

BEST OF THE FOUR ACES, THE.
Album: released on MCA, May'82 by MCA Records. Dist: Polygram, MCA

Cassette: released on MCA, May'82 by MCA Records. Dist: Polygram, MCA

GOLDEN GREATS: FOUR ACES.
Album: released on MCA, Jul'85 by MCA Records. Dist: CBS

Cassette: released on MCA, Jul'85 by MCA Records. Dist: CBS

THREE COINS IN THE FOUNTAIN.
Single (7"): released on Old Gold, Jul'84 by Old Gold Records. Dist: Lightning, Jazz Music, Spartan, Counterpoint

Four Away

WANDERER.
Tracks: / Wanderer / Leaving by the back door.
Single (7"): released on President, May'86 by President Records. Dist: Taylors, Spartan

Four Big Guitars...

THAT'S COOL,THAT'S TRASH (Four Big Guitars from Texas).
Album: released on Demon, May'86 by Demon Records. Dist: Pinnacle

Cassette: released on Demon, May'86 by Demon Records. Dist: Pinnacle

Four Brothers

MAKOROTO.
Single (7"): released on Earthworks, Jun'83 by Earthworks Records. Dist: Earthworks Distributors, Rough Trade, Cartel, Projection

Four Came Home

FOUR CAME HOME.
Tracks: / Four came home / Passion of ice.
Notes: Double 'A' side
Single (7"): released on Wounded Knee, May'87 by Endangered Musik Records. Dist: Revolver

Four Corners

MILLION TO ONE, A.
Single (12"): released on Jungle Rhythm, Jan'85

STANDING ON THE CORNER.
Single (7"): released on Red Bus, Nov'83 by Red Bus Records. Dist: PRT

Four Corners Of The World

CUT THE BEAT.
Single (12"): released on Jungle Rhythm, Aug'84

Four Design

TALL PEOPLE.
Single (7"): released on Official, Jun'85 by Official Records. Dist: Revolver Distribution, Cartel Distribution

Four Freshmen

LIVE AT BUTLER UNIVERSITY (Four Freshmen with Stan Kenton Orch.).
Album: released on Jasmine, May'85

STARS IN OUR EYES.
Tracks: / Shangri-la / Sentimental me / Standing on the corner / Lamplighter's serenade,The / Teach me tonight / Tom dooley / Opus one / I thought about you / Love is a many splendoured thing / Green fields / In apple blossom time / Imagination.
Notes: Following close on the heels of the imported album "Voices In Fun" which re-kindled the public interest in thr group,this album brings another fine selection ofsongs from The Four Freshmen.Again,the Freshmen salute outstanding vocal group as The Andrews Sisters,The Mills Brothers and The King Sisters.These unique interpretations of vocal classics are completmented perfectly by the orchestral arrangements directed by Dick Reynolds.
Album: released on Capitol, May'86 by Capitol Records. Dist: EMI

Cassette: released on Capitol, May'86 by Capitol Records. Dist: EMI

Cassette: released on Capitol, May'86 by Capitol Records. Dist: EMI

VOICES OF FUN.
Tracks: / I want to be happy / Ole buttermilk / I can't give you anything but love / You make me feel so young / Save the bones for henry Jones / Swinging on a star / On sunny side of the street / Manana / On the atchison topeka and santa fe / Aren't you glad you're you / Happy talk / Accent-tchu-ate the positive.
Notes: A fantastic album featuring the Four Freshmen singing all time favourites such as 'I want to be happy'and'On the sunny side of the street'.All the swinging and often humourous arrangements are by ever popular Billy May,who also conducts theorchestra.
Album: released on Capitol, Jan'86 by Capitol Records. Dist: EMI

Cassette: released on Capitol, Jan'86 by Capitol Records. Dist: EMI

Fourgiven

VIOLA.
Album: released on Eva-Lolita, Jul'86 Dist: Pinnacle

Four Hundred Blows

BEAT THE DEVIL.
Single (7"): released on Concrete Productions, Jul'82 Dist: Revolver, Cartel, Nine Mile, Red Rhino, Pinnacle

BREAKDOWN.
Single (12"): released on Illuminated, Mar'85 by IKF Records. Dist: Pinnacle, Cartel, Jetstar

BREAKDOWN, (A).
Tracks: / Breakdown, (A) / Run away.
Single (12"): released on Illuminated, Apr'86 by IKF Records. Dist: Pinnacle, Cartel, Jetstar

DECLARATION OF INTENT.
Single (12"): released on Illuminated, Feb'85 by IKF Records. Dist: Pinnacle, Cartel, Jetstar

G.I..
Single (12"): released on Saderal, Mar'86 Dist: Nine Mile, Cartel

GOOD CLEAN ENGLISH FIST, (THE).
Tracks: / Movin (extented remix 12" version) / Declaration of intent / Pressure / Jive 69 / Them thar hills / Goove jumping / Return of the dog / Breakdown / Conscience / For Jackie M..
Album: released on Dojo, Apr'86 by Castle Communications Records. Dist: Cartel

Cassette: released on Dojo, Apr'86 by Castle Communications Records. Dist: Cartel

GOOD CLEAN ENGLISH FIST THE.
Album: released on Dojo, Sep'85 by Castle Communications Records. Dist: Cartel

GROOVE JUMPING.
Single (12"): released on Illuminated, Feb'85 by IKF Records. Dist: Pinnacle, Cartel, Jetstar

IF I KISSED HER I'D HAVE TO KILL HER FIRST.
Album: released on Illuminated, Feb'85 by IKF Records. Dist: Pinnacle, Cartel, Jetstar

LET THE MUSIC PLAY.
Single (7"): released on KR, Jan'87 by KR Recordings Ltd. Dist: RCA, Revolver, Cartel

Single (12"): released on KR, Jan'87 by KR Recordings Ltd. Dist: RCA, Revolver, Cartel

LOOK.
Album: released on Illuminated, Nov'86 by IKF Records. Dist: Pinnacle, Cartel, Jetstar

MOVIN.
Single (7"): released on Illuminated, May'85 by IKF Records. Dist: Pinnacle, Cartel, Jetstar

Single (12"): released on Illuminated, May'85 by IKF Records. Dist: Pinnacle, Cartel. Jetstar

PRESSURE.
Single (12"): released on Illuminated, Mar'85 by IKF Records. Dist: Pinnacle, Cartel, Jetstar

RETURN OF THE DOG THE.
Single (12"): released on Illuminated, Feb'85 by IKF Records. Dist: Pinnacle, Cartel, Jetstar

RUNAWAY.
Single (7"): released on Illuminated, Sep'85 by IKF Records. Dist: Pinnacle, Cartel, Jetstar

Single (12"): released on Illuminated, Sep'85 by IKF Records. Dist: Pinnacle, Cartel, Jetstar

Four Kings

LOVING YOU IS NO DISGRACE.
Single (7"): released on Fresh, Apr'81 Dist: Jetstar

PRESENT FOR JESUS.
Single (7"): released on Tyger, Jan'81

ROCK'N'ROLL.
Single (7"): released on Fresh, '79 Dist: Jetstar

Four Lads & Four Aces

THEIR HITS.
Cassette: released on Timeless Treasures, Jul'86 Dist: Counterpoint Distribution

Four Lanes Male Choir

SING WE FOR PLEASURE.
Album: released on Burlington, Oct'86 by Plant Life Records. Dist: Jazz Music, Celtic Music, Clyde Factors Distributors, I.R.S., Projection, Wellard, Chris, Roots

Four Million Telephones

FRENCH GIRLS.
Tracks: / Ice box / Ice box / Same thing* / Mrs Brown*.

Single (7"): released on Summerhouse, Jan'87 Dist: Red Rhino Distribution Cartel

Single (12"): released on Summerhouse, Jan'87 Dist: Red Rhino Distribution, Cartel

Fourmost

FIRST AND FOURMOST.
Album: released on See For Miles, Mar'82 by Charly Records. Dist: Spartan

Cassette: released on See For Miles, Aug'82 by Charly Records. Dist: Spartan

Fourmost Guitars

FOURMOST GUITARS WITH RANEY WAINE (Fourmost Guitars/Raney Waine).
Album: released on Jasmine, Jun'84 by Jasmine Records. Dist: PRT

Four on Four

FOUR ON FOUR Various artists (Various Artists).
Single (7"): released on Big Beat, Oct'84 by Ace Records. Dist: Projection, Pinnacle

Four Pennies

JULIET.
Single (7"): released on Old Gold, Aug'82 by Old Gold Records. Dist: Lightning, Jazz Music, Spartan, Counterpoint

Four Perfections

I'M NOT STRONG ENOUGH.
Single (7"): released on Neil Rushton, Apr'83

Single (12"): released on Neil Rushton, Apr'83

Four Preps

BIG MAN.
Single (7"): released on Creole, Aug'82 by Creole Records. Dist: Rhino, PRT

Four Seasons

BIG GIRLS DON'T CRY.
Single (7"): released on Old Gold, Apr'83 by Old Gold Records. Dist: Lightning, Jazz Music, Spartan, Counterpoint

FRANKIE VALLI & THE FOUR SEASONS (Four Seasons & Frankie Valli).
Double Album: released on K-Tel, Aug'82 by K-Tel Records. Dist: Record Merchandisers Distribution, Taylors, Terry Blood Distribution, Wynd-Up Distribution, Relay Distribution, Pickwick Distribution, Solomon & Peres Distribution, Polygram

Double cassette: released on K-Tel, Aug'82 by K-Tel Records. Dist: Record Merchandisers Distribution, Taylors, Terry Blood Distribution, Wynd-Up Distribution, Relay Distribution, Pickwick Distribution, Solomon & Peres Distribution, Polygram

HARMONY.
Single (7"): released on WB, May'79

I'VE GOT YOU UNDER MY SKIN.
Single (7"): released on Old Gold, Apr'83 by Old Gold Records. Dist: Lightning, Jazz Music, Spartan, Counterpoint

LETS HANG ON.
Single (7"): released on Old Gold, Apr'83 by Old Gold Records. Dist: Lightning, Jazz Music, Spartan, Counterpoint

RAG DOLL.
Single (7"): released on Old Gold, Apr'83 by Old Gold Records. Dist: Lightning, Jazz Music, Spartan, Counterpoint

REUNITED LOVE (Four Seasons & Frankie Valli).
Double Album: released on Warner Brothers, Feb'81 by WEA Records. Dist: WEA

Cassette: released on Warner Brothers, Feb'81 by WEA Records Dist: WEA

SHERRY.
Single (7"): released on Old Gold, Apr'83 by Old Gold Records. Dist: Lightning, Jazz Music, Spartan, Counterpoint

DECEMBER '63(OH! WHAT A NIGHT) (Four Seasons & Frankie Valli).
Single (7"): released on Old Gold, Apr'83 by Old Gold Records. Dist: Lightning, Jazz Music, Spartan, Counterpoint

WHO LOVES YOU.
Single (7"): released on Old Gold, Apr'83 by Old Gold Records. Dist: Lightning, Jazz Music, Spartan, Counterpoint

Album: released on Warner Brothers, Dec'75 by WEA Records. Dist: WEA

Cassette: released on Warner Brothers, Dec'75 by WEA Records. Dist: WEA

Four Skins

FISTFUL OF....FOUR SKINS, A.
Album: released on Syndicate, Oct'83

FROM CHAOS TO 1984.
Album: released on Syndicate, Jun'84

GOOD THE BAD AND THE FOUR SKINS, THE.
Album: released on Secret, Jun'82 by Secret Records. Dist: EMI

LOW LIFE.
Single (7"): released on Secret, Oct'82 by Secret Records. Dist: EMI

ONE LAW FOR THEM.
Single (7"): released on Clockwork Fun, Jul'81 by Panache Records. Dist: Island, EMI

WONDERFUL WORLD OF THE 4 SKINS.
Album: released on Kink, Feb'87

YESTERDAYS HEROES.
Extended-play record: released on Secret, Dec'81 by Secret Records. Dist: EMI

Four Squares

GATES OF HELL.
Single (7"): released on New World, Aug'83 by President Records. Dist: Swift, Spartan

Four Stars

DANCE.
Album: released on Tangent (France), Aug'85

Fourteen...

14 COUNTRY FAVOURITES various artists (Various Artists).
Album: released on Emerald, '78 by Emerald Records. Dist: Ross, PRT, Solomon & Peres Distribution

Cassette: released on Emerald, '78 by Emerald Records. Dist: Ross, PRT, Solomon & Peres Distribution

Fourteen-Eighteen

GOOD-BYE-EE (20 great hits from the war years).
Album: released on Magnet, Dec'75 by Magnet Records. Dist: BMG

Fourteen Great Truck Hits

14 GREAT TRUCK HITS Various artists (Various Artists).
Tracks: / Movin' on / From a jack to a king / Six days on the road / Born to be a trucker / Trucker's paradise / Tombstone every mile.
Album: released on Music For Pleasure (Holland), '86 by EMI Records. Dist: EMI

Cassette: released on Music For Pleasure (Holland), '86 by EMI Records. Dist: EMI

Album: released on EMI (Holland), '83 by EMI Records. Dist: Conifer

Fourteen Iced Bears

INSIDE.
Tracks: / Bluesuit / Cut.
Single (7"): released on Frank, Nov'86 Dist: Backs, Cartel

INSIDE (EP), (THE).
Single (12"): released on Frank, Sep'86 Dist: Backs, Cartel

LIKE A DOLPHIN.
Tracks: / Balloon song / Train song / Lie to choose.
Single (12"): released on Frank, Feb'87 Dist: Backs, Cartel

Fourth Folly

FOURTH FOLLY Various artists (Various Artists).
Cassette: released on Candlelight, Jun'81 by Audio-Visual Library Services. Dist: Audio-Visual Library Services

Fourth Party

LIVING IN THE ZOO.
Single (7"): released on Pip Pip Pop, Oct'83 by Pip Pip Pop Records. Dist: Cartel

Fourth Protocol

FOURTH PROTOCOL Original soundtrack.
Album: released on Filmtrax, Apr'87 by Filmtrax Records. Dist: EMI

Fourth To Deal

FOURTH TO DEAL Various artists (Various Artists).
Album: released on Treasure, Feb'86 Dist: Jetstar

Four Tops

20 GOLDEN GREATS.
Album: released on Motown, Oct'81 by RCA Records. Dist: RCA Distribution

Cassette: released on Motown, Oct'81 by RCA Records. Dist: RCA Distribution

2 CLASSIC ALBUMS : REACH OUT/ STILL WATERS RUN DEEP.
Tracks: / Reach out / Walk away Renee / 7 rooms of gloom / If I were a carpenter / Last train to Clarksville / I'll turn to stone / Bernadette / Cherish / Wonderful baby / What else is there to do (but think about you) / Still water (love) / Reflections / It's all in the game / Everybody's talking / Love is the answer / I wish I were your mirror / Elusive butterfly / Bring me together / L.A (my town) / Still water (peace).
Compact disc: released on Motown, Oct'86 by Motown Records. Dist: BMG Distribution

7 ROOMS OF GLOOM.
Single (7"): released on Motown, Oct'81 by RCA Records. Dist: RCA Distribution

ANTHOLOGY.
Tracks: / Sad sourvenirs / Ask the lonely / Then / Helpless / Reach out / Macarthur park / Place in the sun / Hey man / You a woman / For once in my life / Reflections / Still water / Just seven numbers / I got a feeling / Everybody's talking / Walk away renee / Yesterday's dreams / Baby I need your loving / Without the one you love (life's not worthwhile) / Sad souveneirs / Ask the lonely / I can't help myself / Helpless / It's the same old song / Something about you / Shake me wake me (when it's over) / Loving you is sweeter than ever / Then / Reach out I'll be there / Standing in the shadows of love / I got a feeling / Bernadette / Seven rooms of gloom / I'll turn to stone / McArthur park / Climb ev'ry mountain / Everybody's talkin' / For once in my life / Place in the sun, A / Reflections / You keep running away / Walk away Renee / If I were a carpenter / Yesterdays dreams / I'm in a different world / Can't seem to get you out of my mind / Don't let him take your love from me / It's all in the game / Still water / River deep mountain high / Just seven numbers / In these changing times / I can't quit your love / (It's the way) nature planned it / You gotta have love in your heart / Hey man / We got to get you a woman / I just can't walk away / Don't tell me that it's over.
Double compact disc: released on Motown, Oct'86 by Motown Records. Dist: BMG Distribution

Double Album: released on Motown, Sep'82 by RCA Records. Dist: RCA Distribution

Double cassette: released on Motown, Sep'82 by RCA Records. Dist: RCA Distribution

BABY I NEED YOUR LOVING.
Single (7"): released on Motown, Apr'82 by RCA Records. Dist: RCA Distribution

Single (12"): released on Motown, Apr'82 by RCA Records. Dist: RCA Distribution

BACK WHERE I BELONG.
Album: released on Motown, Nov'83 by RCA Records. Dist: RCA Distribution

Cassette: released on Motown, Nov'83 by RCA Records. Dist: RCA Distribution

BERNADETTE.
Single (7"): released on Motown, Apr'85 by RCA Records. Dist: RCA Distribution

Single (12"): released on Motown, Apr'85 by RCA Records. Dist: RCA Distribution

BEST OF THE FOUR TOPS, THE.
Album: released on K-Tel, Jan'82 by K-Tel Records. Dist: Record Merchandisers Distribution, Taylors, Terry Blood Distribution, Wynd-Up Distribution, Relay Distribution, Pickwick Distribution, Solomon & Peres Distribution, Polygram

Cassette: released on K-Tel, Jan'82 by K-Tel Records. Dist: Record Merchandisers Distribution, Taylors, Terry Blood Distribution, Wynd-Up Distribution, Relay Distribution, Pickwick Distribution, Solomon & Peres Distribution, Polygram

COMPACT COMMAND PERFORMANCE.
Tracks: / Ask the lonely / It's the same / Shake me wake me / Reach out i'll be there / Bernadette / Walk away renee / Yesterday's dream's / It's all in the game / Still water / Just seven numbers / Macarthur park / Nature planned it.
Notes: Digital Stereo.Exclusive CD compilation.
Compact disc: released on Motown, Oct'84 by Motown Records. Dist: BMG Distribution

FABULOUS FOUR TOPS, THE.
Album: released on Motown, '82 by RCA Records. Dist: RCA Distribution

Cassette: released on Motown, '82 by RCA Records. Dist: RCA Distribution

FLIPHITS(4 TRACK CASSETTE EP).
Cassette: released on Motown, Jul'83 by RCA Records. Dist: RCA Distribution

FOUR TOPS (Four Tops & The Supremes).
Cassette: released on Motown, May'83 by RCA Records. Dist: RCA Distribution

FOUR TOPS.
Album: released on Motown, Mar'82 by RCA Records. Dist: RCA Distribution

Cassette: released on Motown, Mar'82 by RCA Records. Dist: RCA Distribution

FOUR TOPS SECOND ALBUM.
Tracks: / Baby I need your loving / Without the one you love / Where did you go / Ask the lonely / Your love is amazing / Sad souvenirs / Tea house in China / Left with a broken heart / Love has gone / Call on me / I can't help myself / Love feels like fire / Is there anything that I can do / Something about you / It's the same old song.
Compact disc: released on Motown, Nov'86 by Motown Records. Dist: BMG Distribution

FOUR TOPS STORY.
Double Album: released on Motown, Oct'81 by RCA Records. Dist: RCA Distribution

GREATEST HITS: FOUR TOPS.
Album: released on Motown, Apr'85 by RCA Records. Dist: RCA Distribution

Cassette: released on Motown, Apr'85 by RCA Records. Dist: RCA Distribution

HITS OF GOLD.
Album: released on Motown, Oct'82 by Motown Records. Dist: BMG Distribution

Cassette: released on Motown, Oct'82 by Motown Records. Dist: BMG Distribution

HOT NIGHTS.
Tracks: / Hot nights / Red hot love / I believe in you and me / Let's jam / We got bus'ness / This is love / So up for you / Livin it up too much / Four of us.
Album: released on Motown, Oct'86 by Motown Records. Dist: BMG Distribution

Compact disc: released on Motown, Oct'86 by Motown Records. Dist: BMG Distribution

I CAN'T HELP MYSELF.
Single (7"): released on Motown, Mar'83 by RCA Records. Dist: RCA Distribution

I JUST CAN'T WALK AWAY.
Single (7"): released on Motown, Oct'83 by RCA Records. Dist: RCA Distribution

Single (12"): released on Motown, Oct'83 by RCA Records. Dist: RCA Distribution

I'LL TURN TO STONE.
Single (7"): released on Motown, Oct'81 by RCA Records. Dist: RCA Distribution

IT'S ALL IN THE GAME.
Single (7"): released on Motown, Oct'81 by RCA Records. Dist: RCA Distribution

Cassette: released on MFP, Jan'79 by EMI Records. Dist: EMI

Album: released on MFP, Jan'79 by EMI Records. Dist: EMI

KEEPER OF THE CASTLE.
Album: released on ABC, '75 Dist: CBS, Pinnacle

LIVE.
Album: released on Motown, Feb'83 by RCA Records. Dist: RCA Distribution

Cassette: released on Motown, Feb'83 by RCA Records. Dist: RCA Distribution

MAGIC.
Album: released on Motown, Jul'85 by RCA Records. Dist: RCA Distribution

Cassette: released on Motown, Jul'85 by RCA Records. Dist: RCA Distribution

MAGNIFICENT 7, THE (Four Tops & The Supremes).
Album: released on Motown, Oct'81 by RCA Records. Dist: RCA Distribution

Cassette: released on Motown, Oct'81 by RCA Records. Dist: RCA Distribution

MAIN STREET PEOPLE.
Tracks: / Main street people (into) / I just can't get you out of my mind / It won't be the first time / Sweet understanding love / Am I my brothers keeper / Are you man enough / Whenever there's blue / Too little, too late / Peace of mind / One woman/man / Main street people.
Album: released on Charly, Jun'86 by Charly Records. Dist: Charly, Cadillac

ONE MORE MOUNTAIN.
Album: released on Casablanca, Aug'82 Dist: Polygram, Phonogram

Cassette: released on Casablanca, Aug'82 Dist: Polygram, Phonogram

REACH OUR, I'LL BE THERE.
Single (7"): released on Motown, Oct'81 by RCA Records. Dist: RCA Distribution

REACH OUT.
Album: released on Motown, Oct'81 by RCA Records. Dist: RCA Distribution

Cassette: released on Motown, Oct'81 by RCA Records. Dist: RCA Distribution

REACH OUT AND TOUCH (Four Tops & The Supremes).
Single (7"): released on Motown, Oct'81 by RCA Records. Dist: RCA Distribution

REACH OUT/STILL WATERS RUN DEEP.
Tracks: / What else is there to do but think about you? / If I were a carpenter / Reach out, I'll be there / Walk away Renee / Seven nights of gloom / Last train to Clarksville / I'll turn to stone / Still water (love and peace) / Reflections / It's all in the game / Everybody's talkin' / Love is the answer / I wish I were your mirror / Elusive butterfly / ring me together / LA (my town) / I'm a believer / Standing in the shadows of love / Cherish / Bernadette / Wonderful baby.
Compact disc: released on Motown, Feb'87 by Motown Records. Dist: BMG Distribution

SAD HEARTS.
Single (7"): released on Casablanca, Jul'82 Dist: Polygram, Phonogram

Single (12"): released on Casablanca, Jul'82 Dist: Polygram, Phonogram

SECOND ALBUM.
Album: released on Motown, Oct'82 by RCA Records. Dist: RCA Distribution

Cassette: released on Motown, Oct'82 by RCA Records. Dist: RCA Distribution

SIMPLE GAME.
Single (7"): released on Motown, Oct'81 by RCA Records. Dist: RCA Distribution

STILL WATERS RUN DEEP.
Album: released on Motown, Jun'82 by RCA Records. Dist: RCA Distribution

Cassette: released on Motown, Jun'82 by RCA Records. Dist: RCA Distribution

SUPER HITS.
Album: released on Motown, Oct'81 by RCA Records. Dist: RCA Distribution

Cassette: released on Motown, Oct'81 by RCA Records. Dist: RCA Distribution

TONIGHT.
Tracks: / When she was my girl / Don't walk away / Tonight / I'm gonna love you / Who's right, who's wrong / Let me set you free / Something to remember / From a distance / All I do / I'll never ever leave again.
Compact disc: released on Casablanca, Jan'83 Dist: Polygram, Phonogram

Album: released on Casablanca, Nov'81 Dist: Polygram, Phonogram

Cassette: released on Casablanca, Nov'81 Dist: Polygram, Phonogram

TONIGHT I'M GONNA LOVE YOU ALL OVER.
Single (7"): released on Casablanca, Feb'82 Dist: Polygram, Phonogram

Single (12"): released on Casablanca, Feb'82 Dist: Polygram, Phonogram

WALK AWAY RENEE.
Single (7"): released on Motown, Oct'81 by RCA Records. Dist: RCA Distribution

YOUR SONG.
Single (7"): released on Calibre, Jun'84 by Calibre Records. Dist: PRT

Single (12"): released on Calibre, Jun'84 by Calibre Records. Dist: PRT

Four & Twenty...

FOUR & TWENTY NURSERY RHYMES VOL.1 Various artists (Various Artists).
Album: released on White Dove, Nov'80 by White Dove Records. Dist: Pinnacle

Fourty-eight...

WE KNOW NONSENSE.
Album: released on Chug, Oct'86 Dist: Rough Trade, Cartel

Four x

BALLET DANCER.
Album: released on APK, Mar'85 Dist: Pinnacle

Four Yn Y Bar

BYTH ADRA.
Album: released on Sain, Jul'85 by Sain Records. Dist: Projection, Sain

Fowler, Barbara

COME AND GET MY LOVIN'.
Single (12"): released on Master Mix, Sep'84 by PRT Records. Dist: PRT

Fowler, Eileen

AS YOUNG AS YOU FEEL.
Album: released on BBC, Jun'78 by BBC Records & Tapes. Dist: EMI, PRT, Pye

Cassette: released on BBC, '79 by BBC Records & Tapes. Dist: EMI, PRT

DANCE KEEP FIT & SLIM TO MUSIC.
Album: released on BBC, May'80 by BBC Records & Tapes. Dist: EMI, PRT,

Cassette: released on BBC, May'80 by BBC Records & Tapes. Dist: EMI, PRT,

ENJOY YOUR SLIMMING.
Album: released on BBC, Oct'77 by BBC Records & Tapes. Dist: EMI, PRT

Cassette: released on BBC, Oct'77 by BBC Records & Tapes. Dist: EMI, PRT,

FAMILY KEEP FIT WITH EILEEN FOWLER.
Album: released on BBC, Jun'78 by BBC Records & Tapes. Dist: EMI, PRT,

SLIM TO RHYTHM.
Album: released on BBC, Jun'78 by BBC Records & Tapes. Dist: EMI, PRT.

Fowler, Kim

LIVING IN THE STREETS.
Single (7"): released on Sonet, Aug'78 by Sonet Records. Dist: PRT

Fowler, Pete

ONE HEART ONE SONG.
Single (7"): released on Oval, May'82 by Oval Records. Dist: Pinnacle

Fowley, Kim

SUNSET BOULEVARD.
Album: released on Illegal, Jan'79 by Faulty Products Records. Dist: Pinnacle, Lightning, Cartel

Fox

ELECTRO PEOPLE.
Single (7"): released on BBC, Feb'82 by BBC Records & Tapes. Dist: EMI, PRT,

SET ME FREE.
Tracks: / Set me free / Never / Where have all the boys gone.
Single (12"): released on Malaco, Mar'86 by Malaco Records. Dist: Charly

Fox, Bob

NOWT SO GOOD'LL PASS (Fox, Bob & Stu Luckley).
Album: released on Rubber, Jun'82 by Rubber Records. Dist: Roots Distribution, Projection Distribution, Jazz Music Distribution, Celtic Music Distribution, JSU Distribution, Spartan Distribution

WISH WE NEVER HAD PARTED (Fox, Bob & Stu Luckley).
Album: released on Black Crow, May'83 by Mawson & Wareham Records. Dist: Projection

Fox, Charles

SEASONS.
Album: released on RCA, Aug'81 by RCA Records. Dist: RCA, Roots, Swift, Wellard, Chris, I & B, Solomon & Peres Distribution

Cassette: released on RCA, Aug'81 by RCA Records. Dist: RCA, Roots, Swift, Wellard, Chris, I & B, Solomon & Peres Distribution

Foxes

FOXES Original motion picture soundtrack (Various Artists).
Album: released on IMS, May'81 by Polydor Records. Dist: IMS, Polygram

Cassette: released on IMS, May'81 by Polydor Records. Dist: IMS, Polygram

Fox In Socks

SOUND PATTERNS.
Single (7"): released on Gesticulation, Sep'82 by Gesticulation Records. Dist: Cartel

Fox, John

GERSHWIN'S GREATEST HITS (Fox, John & The Radio Orchestra).
Album: by BBC Records & Tapes. Dist: EMI, PRT, Pye

SAILING BY (Fox, John Orchestra).
Album: released on BBC, Jun'77 by BBC Records & Tapes. Dist: EMI, PRT,

Fox, John Singers

FAIREST ISLE.
Album: released on BBC, Oct'77 by BBC Records & Tapes. Dist: EMI, PRT, Pye

Fox, June

MEANT TO BE.
Single (12"): released on Clair, Nov'83 by Clair Records. Dist: Jetstar

Fox, Noosha

HOT AS SUN.
Single (7"): released on Earlobe, Jul'81 by Earlobe Records. Dist: Pinnacle

MORE THAN MOLECULES.

Fox, Roy

AT MONSEIGNEUR RESTAURANT, PICCADILLY (Fox, Roy & His Band).
Album: released on Ace Of Clubs, '64 by Decca Records. Dist: Polygram

BANDS THAT MATTER, THE.
Album: by Decca Records. Dist: Polygram

FOX FAVOURITES (Fox, Roy & His Orchestra).
Album: released on Jasmine, Mar'83 by Jasmine Records. Dist: Counterpoint, Lugtons, Taylor, H.R., Wellard, Chris, Swift, Cadillac

GOLDEN AGE OF ROY FOX.
Album: released on Golden Age, Apr'85 by Music For Pleasure Records. Dist: EMI

Album: released on Golden Age, Apr'85 by Music For Pleasure Records. Dist: EMI

Cassette: released on Golden Age, Apr'85 by Music For Pleasure Records. Dist: EMI

INVITATION TO DANCE.
Album: released on Saville, Sep'86 by Conifer Records. Dist: Conifer

ROY FOX AND HIS BAND VOLUME 2 (Fox, Roy & His Band).
Album: released on Joy, Jul'83 by President Records. Dist: Jazz Music, Swift, President Distribution

ROY FOX & HIS BAND (Fox, Roy & His Band featuring Al Bowlly).
Album: released on Joy, Nov'82 by President Records. Dist: Jazz Music, Swift, President Distribution

ROY FOX & HIS ORCHESTRA WITH VOCAL REFRAIN (Fox, Roy & His Orchestra).
Album: released on VJM, Mar'79 by Wellard, Chris Distribution. Dist: Wellard, Chris Distribution

ROY FOX & HIS ORCHESTRA 1936-1938 (Fox, Roy & His Orchestra).
Double Album: released on World, Oct'75 Dist: Jetstar

STRICTLY INSTRUMENTAL (Fox, Roy & His Orchestra).
Tracks: / I got rhythm / Black eyes / Way down yonder in New Orleans / You're the cream in my coffee / Lady be good / Birth of the blues, the / Happy feet / Mean to me / That's a plenty / Someday sweetheart / Everybody loves my baby / On the sunny side of the street / Tiger rag / Let's do it, let's fall in love / Impressions of Harlem / China boy / Chicago / Ain't she sweet / Congo / Mr Sweeney's learned to swing / Song of India.

Cassette: released on Halcyon (USA), May'87 by Halcyon Records (USA). Dist: Jazz Music, Conifer, Taylors

Album: released on Halcyon (USA), Dec'82 by Halcyon Records (USA). Dist: Jazz Music, Conifer, Taylors

THIS IS ROMANCE (Fox, Roy & His Band).
Album: released on Saville, Jan'84 by Conifer Records. Dist: Conifer

THIS IS ROY FOX.
Album: released on Halcyon (USA), Dec'82 by Halcyon Records (USA). Dist: Jazz Music, Conifer, Taylors

VOLUME 2 (Fox, Roy & His Band).
Album: released on Joy, Jul'86 by President Records. Dist: Jazz Music, Swift, President Distribution

WHISPERING (Fox, Roy & His Band).
Album: released on Decca, Sep'81 by Decca Records. Dist: Polygram

Fox, Samantha

AIM TO WIN.
Tracks: / Aim to win / Holiday / Aim To Win (extended) / Holding.
Single (7"): released on Genie, Apr'86 by Genie Records. Dist: Spartan, CBS

Picture disc single: released on Genie, May'86 by Genie Records. Dist: Spartan, CBS

Single (7"): released on Lamborghini, Apr'84 by Lamborghini Records. Dist: PRT

DO YA DO YA Wanna please me.
Tracks: / Do Ya Do Ya / Never Gonna Fall In Love Again / Do Ya Do Ya(vision mix)* / Do Ya Do Ya(dance mix)* / Never Never gonna fall in love again.
Single (7"): released on Jive, Jun'86 by Zomba Records. Dist: RCA, PRT, CBS

Single (12"): released on Jive, Jun'86 by Zomba Records. Dist: RCA, PRT, CBS

Single (12"): released on Jive, Jul'86 by Zomba Records. Dist: RCA, PRT, CBS

HOLDING.
Tracks: / Holding (dub mix) / Holding / Holding(Dub Mix).
Single (7"): released on Genie, Oct'86 by Genie Records. Dist: Spartan, CBS

Single (12"): released on Genie, Oct'86 by Genie Records. Dist: Spartan, CBS

Single (12"): released on Genie, Nov'86 by Genie Records. Dist: Spartan, CBS

HOLD ON TIGHT.
Tracks: / Hold on tight.
Single (7"): released on Jive, Aug'86 by Zomba Records. Dist: RCA, PRT, CBS

Single (12"): released on Jive, Aug'86 by Zomba Records. Dist: RCA, PRT, CBS

I'M ALL YOU NEED.
Tracks: / Want you to want me / Touch me (I want your body) / Do ya do ya wanna please me / Hold on tight.
Single (7"): released on Jive, Nov'86 by Zomba Records. Dist: RCA, PRT, CBS

Single (12"): released on Jive, Nov'86 by Zomba Records. Dist: RCA, PRT, CBS

INTERVIEW DISC 2.
Picture disc album: released on Baktabak, Oct'87 by Baktabak Records. Dist: Arabesque. Estim retail price in Sep'87 was £4.91.

INTERVIEW PICTURE DISC.
Album: released on Baktabak, Jul'87 by Baktabak Records. Dist: Arabesque

I SURRENDER To the spirit of the night.
Tracks: / I surrender / Best is yet to come, The.
Gatefold sleeve: released on Jive, Jul'87 by Zomba Records. Dist: RCA, PRT, CBS

Single (12"): released on Jive, Jul'87 by Zomba Records. Dist: RCA, PRT, CBS

NOTHING'S GONNA STOP ME NOW (CLUB MIX).
Tracks: / Nothing's gonna stop me now (club mix) / Dream city (want you to want me).
Single (12"): released on Jive, 20 Jun'87 by Zomba Records. Dist: RCA, PRT, CBS

NOTHING'S GONNA STOP ME NOW.
Tracks: / Nothing's gonna stop me now / Dream city / Want you to want me*.
Single (7"): released on Jive, May'87 by Zomba Records. Dist: RCA, PRT, CBS

Single (12"): released on Jive, May'87 by Zomba Records. Dist: RCA, PRT, CBS

Picture disc single: released on Jive, 30 May'87 by Zomba Records. Dist: RCA, PRT, CBS

SAMANTHA FOX.
Album: released on Jive, Jul'87 by Zomba Records. Dist: RCA, PRT, CBS

Cassette: released on Jive, Jul'87 by Zomba Records. Dist: RCA, PRT, CBS

Album: released on Jive, Aug'87 by Zomba Records. Dist: RCA, PRT, CBS

TOUCH ME... I want your body.
Tracks: / Touch me (I want your body) / I'm all you need / Suzie, don't leave me with your boyfriend / Wild kinda love / Hold on tight / Do ya do ya (wanna please me) / Baby I'm lost for words / It's only love / He's got sex / Drop me a line / Touch me... / Tonights the night.
Single (7"): released on Jive, Mar'86 by Zomba Records. Dist: RCA, PRT, CBS

Single (12"): released on Jive, Mar'86 by Zomba Records. Dist: RCA, PRT, CBS

Single (12"): released on Jive, Mar'86 by Zomba Records. Dist: RCA, PRT, CBS

Single (12"): released on Jive, Mar'86 by Zomba Records. Dist: RCA, PRT, CBS

Album: released on Jive, Jul'86 by Zomba Records. Dist: RCA, PRT, CBS

Cassette: released on Jive, Jul'86 by Zomba Records. Dist: RCA, PRT, CBS

Compact disc: released on Jive, Dec'86 by Zomba Records. Dist: RCA, PRT, CBS

TOUCH ME - THE ALBUM.
Notes: 3 LP Set.
Picture disc album: released on Jive, Aug'86 by Zomba Records. Dist: RCA, PRT, CBS

Fox The Fox

PRECIOUS LITTLE DIAMOND.
Tracks: / Precious little diamond / Man on the run.
Single (7"): released on Epic, Jun'86 by CBS Records. Dist: CBS

Single (12"): released on Epic, Jun'86 by CBS Records. Dist: CBS

Fox & The Hound

FOX & THE HOUND.
Album: released on Disneyland, Dec'82 by Disneyland-Vista Records (USA). Dist: BBC Records & Tapes, Rainbow Communications Ltd(Distribution)

Cassette: released on Disneyland, Dec'82 by Disneyland-Vista Records (USA). Dist: BBC Records & Tapes, Rainbow Communications Ltd(Distribution)

Single (12"): released on Disneyland, Dec'82 by Disneyland-Vista Records (USA). Dist: BBC Records & Tapes, Rainbow Communications Ltd(Distribution)

Special: released on Disneyland, Dec'82 by Disneyland-Vista Records (USA). Dist: BBC Records & Tapes, Rainbow Communications Ltd(Distribution)

Album: released on BBC, Oct'85 by BBC Records & Tapes. Dist: EMI, PRT, Pye

Cassette: released on BBC, Oct'85 by BBC Records & Tapes. Dist: EMI, PRT, Pye

Foxton, Bruce

PLAY THIS GAME TO WIN.
Tracks: / Play this game to win / Welcome to the hero / Living in a dreamworld / Living in a dreamworld.
Single (7"): released on Harvest, Nov'86 by EMI Records. Dist: Roots, EMI

Single (12"): released on Harvest, Nov'86 by EMI Records. Dist: Roots, EMI

S.O.S. (MY IMAGINATION).
Single (7"): released on Arista, Jul'84 by Arista Records. Dist: RCA

Single (12"): released on Arista, Jul'84 by Arista Records. Dist: RCA

Foxx, Charlie

MOCKINGBIRD Best of Charlie & Inez Foxx, The (Foxx, Charlie & Inez).
Tracks: / Mockingbird / Searching for my C.C. / Broken hearted fool / My Momma told me / Don't do it no more / I wanna see my baby / If I need anyone / Here we go round the mulberry bush / Hurt by love / Sitting hero / La de da I love you / I fancy you / Down by the seashore / Ask me / Confusion / Jaybirds.
Notes: A brand new compilation on Stateside label by a duo very much in the mould of their Sue labelmates Ike'n'Tina Turner. The best in danceable 60's soul music and two part harmony singing. Features their big hit 'Mockingbird' - covered in the 70's by James Taylor and Carly Simon.
Album: released on Stateside, Mar'86 Dist: EMI

Cassette: released on Stateside, Mar'86 Dist: EMI

Single (7"): released on EMI Golden 45's, Feb'85 by EMI Records. Dist: EMI

Foxx, John

GARDEN, THE.
Album: released on Metal Beat, Mar'84 Dist: Virgin Distribution, CBS Distribution

Cassette: released on Metal Beat, Mar'84 Dist: Virgin Distribution, CBS Distribution

GOLDEN SECTION, THE.
Album: released on Virgin, Oct'83 by Virgin Records. Dist: EMI, Virgin Distribution Deleted '85.

Cassette: released on Virgin, Oct'83 by Virgin Records. Dist: EMI, Virgin Distribution

IN MYSTERIOUS WAYS.
Tracks: / Stars on fire / Lose all sense of time / What kind of girl / Shine on / Shine on / Enter the angel / In mysterious ways / This side of paradise / Stepping softly / Morning glory.
Compact disc: released on Virgin, Jul'87 by Virgin Records. Dist: EMI, Virgin Distribution

Album: released on Virgin, Oct'85 by Virgin Records. Dist: EMI, Virgin Distribution

Cassette: released on Virgin, Oct'85 by Virgin Records. Dist: EMI, Virgin Distribution

METAMATIC.
Album: released on Metal Beat, Mar'84 Dist: Virgin Distribution, CBS Distribution

Cassette: released on Metal Beat, Mar'84 Dist: Virgin Distribution, CBS Distribution

Fracture

SIGN, A.
Single (7"): released on Shock, Aug'82

Fraggle Rock

FRAGGLE ROCK.
Album: released on RCA, Mar'84 by RCA Records. Dist: RCA, Roots, Swift, Wellard, Chris, I & B, Solomon & Peres Distribution

Cassette: released on RCA, Mar'84 by RCA Records. Dist: RCA, Roots, Swift, Wellard, Chris, I & B, Solomon & Peres Distribution

Single (7"): released on RCA, Jan'84 by RCA Records. Dist: RCA, Roots, Swift, Wellard, Chris, I & B, Solomon & Peres Distribution

Picture disc single: released on RCA, Jan'84 by RCA Records. Dist: RCA, Roots, Swift, Wellard, Chris, I & B, Solomon & Peres Distribution

IF I WERE KING OF THE UNIVERSE.
Cassette: released on Look & Listen, Nov'84 by Listen For Pleasure. Dist: EMI

TALE OF TRAVELLING MATT, THE.
Cassette: released on Look & Listen, Nov'84 by Listen For Pleasure. Dist: EMI

WHAT DO DOOZERS DO.
Cassette: released on Look & Listen, Nov'84 by Listen For Pleasure. Dist: EMI

WHAT'S A FRAGGLE.
Cassette: released on Look & Listen, Nov'84 by Listen For Pleasure. Dist: EMI

Fraggles

ALL AROUND THE WORLD.
Single (7"): released on RCA, May'85 by RCA Records. Dist: RCA, Roots, Swift, Wellard, Chris, I & B, Solomon & Peres Distribution

Fragile Friends

NOVELTY WEARS OFF, THE.
Single (7"): released on KC, Jul'85 by KC Records. Dist: Cartel

PAPER DOLL.
Single (7"): released on KC, Feb'85 by KC Records. Dist: Cartel

Fra Lippo Lippi

ANGEL.
Single (7"): released on Virgin, Aug'87 by Virgin Records. Dist: EMI, Virgin Distribution

Single (12"): released on Virgin, Aug'87 by Virgin Records. Dist: EMI, Virgin Distribution

COME SUMMER.
Single (7"): released on Virgin, Jul'86 by Virgin Records. Dist: EMI, Virgin Distribution

Single (12"): released on Virgin, Jul'86 by Virgin Records. Dist: EMI, Virgin Distribution

EVERYTIME I SEE YOU.
Tracks: / Everytime I see you / Heather on the hall, The / True story.
Single (7"): released on Virgin, Apr'86 by Virgin Records. Dist: EMI, Virgin Distribution

Single (12"): released on Virgin, Apr'86 by Virgin Records. Dist: EMI, Virgin Distribution

IN SILENCE.
Album: released on Uniton Records, Sep'84 Dist: Cartel

NOW AND FOREVER.
Cassette:

SAY SOMETHING.
Single (12"): released on Uniton Records, Jan'84 Dist: Cartel

SHOULDN'T HAVE TO BE LIKE THAT.
Tracks: / Shouldn't have to be like that / Distance between us, The / Say something.
Single (7"): released on Virgin, Jan'86 by Virgin Records. Dist: EMI, Virgin Distribution

Single (12"): released on Virgin, Jan'86 by Virgin Records. Dist: EMI, Virgin Distribution

SMALL MERCIES.
Album: released on Uniton (Norway), Apr'85 Dist: Cartel

SONGS.
Notes: Includes 'Shouldn't have to be like that' and 'Everytime I see you'.
Album: released on Virgin, '86 by Virgin Records. Dist: EMI, Virgin Distribution

Cassette: released on Virgin, '86 by Virgin Records. Dist: EMI, Virgin Distribution

Compact disc: released on Virgin, '86 by Virgin Records. Dist: EMI, Virgin Distribution

Frame By Frame

LIES.
Tracks: / Lies / Think of me / Your space / It's a miracle.
Single (7"): released on Skratch, Feb'86 by Skratch Records. Dist: PRT

Single (12"): released on Skratch, Feb'86 by Skratch Records. Dist: PRT

Framed

GONNA TAKE YOU INTO MY LIFE.
Picture disc single: released on Thunderbay, Dec'82 Dist: Spartan Distribution

INTO MY LIFE.
Single (7"): released on Thunderbay, Jul'83 Dist: Spartan Distribution

WONDERLAND.
Single (7"): released on Thunderbay, Apr'83 Dist: Spartan Distribution

Frampton, Peter

ALL EYES ON YOU.
Tracks: / All eyes on you / Into view.
Single (7"): released on Virgin, Apr'86 by Virgin Records. Dist: EMI, Virgin Distribution

Single (12"): released on Virgin, Apr'86 by Virgin Records. Dist: EMI, Virgin Distribution

BEST OF FRAMPTON COMES ALIVE.
Album: released on Hallmark, Feb'85 by Pickwick Records. Dist: Pickwick Distribution, PRT, Taylors

Cassette: released on Hallmark, Feb'85 by Pickwick Records. Dist: Pickwick Distribution, PRT, Taylors

CRYING.
Tracks: / Crying / You know so well.
Single (7"): released on Virgin, Dec'85 by Virgin Records. Dist: EMI, Virgin Distribution

Single (12"): released on Virgin, Dec'85 by Virgin Records. Dist: EMI, Virgin Distribution

FRAMPTON COMES ALIVE.
Album: released on A&M, Feb'76 by A&M Records. Dist: Polygram

Cassette: released on A&M, Feb'76 by A&M Records. Dist: Polygram

PREMONITION.
Album: released on Virgin, Jan'86 by Virgin Records. Dist: EMI, Virgin Distribution

Cassette: released on Virgin, Jan'86 by Virgin Records. Dist: EMI, Virgin Distribution

Compact disc: released on Virgin, Jul'87 by Virgin Records. Dist: EMI, Virgin Distribution

SHOW ME THE WAY.
Single (7"): released on Old Gold, Oct'83 by Old Gold Records. Dist: Lightning, Jazz Music, Spartan, Counterpoint

SHOW ME THE WAY(EP).
Single (7"): released on Scoop, Jun'84

Cassette single: released on Scoop, Jun'84

Fran & Anna

INCREDIBLE FRAN & ANNA, THE.
Album: released on Neptune, '78 by Lismor. Dist: Spartan

IT'S SCOTLAND FOREVER.
Single (7"): released on Big R, May'82 by Big R Records. Dist: Pinnacle, Wynd-Up Distribution, Solomon & Peres Distribution, I & B, JSU, Swift, Record Merchandisers Distribution, Spartan

LOVE FROM FRAN AND ANNA.
Album: by Lismor Records. Dist: Lismor, Roots, Celtic Music

SCOTTISH SINGALONG.
Single (7"): released on Neptune, May'77 by Lismor. Dist: Spartan

France

GIVE HIM A GREAT BIG KISS.
Single (7"): released on Satril, Oct'85 by Satril Records. Dist: PRT

Single (12"): released on Satril, Oct'85 by Satril Records. Dist: PRT

France Joli

FRANCE JOLI.
Album: released on Ariola, Jan'80 Dist: RCA, Ariola

Frances, Phil

LAUGH IT OFF.
Single (12"): released on Jama, Jan'84 by Jama Records.

Franchi, Sergio

LAUGH YOU SILLY CLOWN.
Single (7"): released on Bulldog, Jan'81 by Bulldog Records. Dist: President Distribution, Spartan, Swift, Taylor, H.R.

Francie & Josie

FRANCIE & JOSIE.
Album: released on Lochshore, Oct'81 by Klub Records. Dist: PRT

Francis, Bob
THIS IS MY LIFE.
Album: released on Pye, Feb'80

Francisco, Don
ONE HEART AT A TIME.
Album: released on Myrrh, May'85 by Word Records. Dist: Word Distribution

Cassette: released on Myrrh, May'85 by Word Records. Dist: Word Distribution

POWER, THE.
Album: released on Star Song, May'87 Dist: Word Distribution

Cassette: released on Star Song, May'87 Dist: Word Distribution

Francis, Connie
AMONG MY SOUVENIRS.
Album: released on Karussell Gold (Germany), Aug'85

Cassette: released on Karussell Gold (Germany), Aug'85

CONNIE FRANCIS The very best of.
Compact disc: released on Polydor, '87 by Polydor Records. Dist: Polygram, Polydor

Double Album: released on Polydor (MGM), Jan'83

CONNIE FRANCIS & PETER KRAUS - VOL.1 (Francis, Connie & Peter Kraus).
Album: released on Polydor (MGM), Sep'84

CONNIE FRANCIS & PETER KRAUS - VOL.2 (Francis, Connie & Peter Kraus).
Album: released on Polydor (MGM), Sep'84

GREATEST HITS: CONNIE FRANCIS VOL.1 & 2.
Double Album: released on Polydor (MGM), Jul'82

Double cassette: released on Polydor (MGM), Jul'82

ICH GEB"NE PARTY HEUT'NACHT.
Album: released on Bear Family, Jul'84 by Bear Family Records. Dist: Rollercoaster Distribution, Swift

LIPSTICK ON YOUR COLLAR.
Single (7"): released on Old Gold, Jul'84 by Old Gold Records. Dist: Lightning, Jazz Music, Spartan, Counterpoint

LOVE'N'COUNTRY.
Album: released on Contour, Sep'86 by Pickwick Records. Dist: Pickwick Distribution, PRT

Cassette: released on Contour, Sep'86 by Pickwick Records. Dist: Pickwick Distribution, PRT

MY SOUVENEIRS.
Album: released on Arcade Music Gala, Apr'86 Dist: Stage One

Cassette: released on Arcade Music Gala, Apr'86 Dist: Stage One

SINGS GREAT COUNTRY HITS.
Album: released on MGM, Mar'84 Dist: Polygram Distribution, Swift Distribution

Cassette: released on MGM, Mar'84 Dist: Polygram Distribution, Swift Distribution

SINGS R & R MILLION SELLERS.
Album: released on Musketeer, Jan'87

STUPID CUPID.
Single (7"): released on Old Gold, Jul'84 by Old Gold Records. Dist: Lightning, Jazz Music, Spartan, Counterpoint

TWENTY ALL TIME GREATS.
Album: released on Polydor, Jun'77 by Polydor Records. Dist: Polygram, Polydor

Cassette: released on Polydor, Jun'77 by Polydor Records. Dist: Polygram, Polydor

WHO'S SORRY NOW.
Single (7"): released on Old Gold, Jul'84 by Old Gold Records. Dist: Lightning, Jazz Music, Spartan, Counterpoint

Francis, Dick
BREAK IN.
Notes: Read by Nigel Havers. Running time: 2 hours approx. Double cassette 'Break In' concerns family relationships and the abuse of power by those in the gutter press who will go to any lengths to get the information they seek, and then use that information in any way they choose.
Special: released on Listen For Pleasure, Sep'86 by MFP Records. Dist: EMI

DANGER, THE.
Cassette: released on Listen For Pleasure, Mar'85 by MFP Records. Dist: EMI

ODDS AGAINST.
Notes: Read by Robert Powell. Champion steeplechase jockeySid Halley has to leave racing when he damages his hand beyond repair. His Father-in-law arranges for him to work at Radnors, an investigating agency with a racing section, but it is a poor substitute for racing. While convalescing at his Father-in-law's home he becomes involved in saving Seabury racecourse from the greedy clutches of Howard Kraye, high powered businessman and land grabber par excellence. Kray, deceived by Halley's low profile, does not think him an opponent worth bothering about. Halley's skill and success at entrapping the perverted Kraye helps him to regain his own well esteem. ODDS AGAINST is produced by Betty Davies.
Cassette: released on Cover to Cover, Sep'86 by Cover to Cover Cassettes. Dist: Conifer

Francis, Jan
BALLET SHOES.
Notes: This gay, amusing and good-humoured story for children, written by the late Noel Streatfeild, was said to be one of her best stories. She portrays a warm atmosphere of home, making the best of things, perseverance and success. Pauline, Petrova and Posy all became the wards of old Matthew Brown and were given the surname Fossil because the old man's absorbing hobby was collecting fossils. Although none of the children were related to him, or each other, or to anyone else in the story, strange beginnings, unconventional circumstances and an unusual family make a romantic background for this story.   Running time approx. 3 hrs.
Cassette: released on Listen For Pleasure, Apr'87 by MFP Records. Dist: EMI

Francis, Mike
FEATURES OF LOVE.
Tracks: / Features of love / Uside down / Prelude reprise.
Single (7"): released on Club, May'87 by Phonogram Records. Dist: Polygram

Single (12"): released on Club, May'87 by Phonogram Records. Dist: Polygram

Francis, Morris
FUN IN ARCADIANA.
Album: released on Maison De Soul (USA), Oct'86 Dist: Swift

Francis, N
POOR ME NATTY DREAD.
Tracks: / Countryman / Natty dread (version).
Single (12"): released on Mi Music, Jan'87 Dist: Jetstar Distribution

Francis, Stewart
LET'S HAVE A (ROCK 'N' ROLL) PARTY.
Single (12"): released on Debut, Mar'85 by Skratch Music. Dist: PRT

Francis, Stu
OOH I COULD CRUSH A GRAPE.
Single (7"): released on Tembo, Nov'83

Single (7"): released on Tembo, Jan'85 by Tembo (Canada). Dist: IMS Distribution, Polygram Distribution

Francis, Syd
SOMETHING SPECIAL.
Album: released on SRT, Aug'78 by SRT Records. Dist: Pinnacle, Solomon & Peres Distribution, SRT Distribution, H.R. Taylor Distribution, PRT Distribution

Francis, Winston
CALIFORNIA DREAMING.
Single (12"): released on Black Jack, Jan'81 Dist: Jetstar, Spartan

GROOVY KIND OF LOVE, A.
Tracks: / Groovy kind of love / Inna de groove.
Single (12"): released on Falcon, May'86 by Jetstar, M.I.S.

HOLDING YOU BACK.
Tracks: / Holding you back / Go find yourself a fool.
Single (12"): released on Wambesi, Feb'87 by Wambesi records. Dist: Jetstar

TONIGHT.
Single (12"): released on Red Nail, Feb'82 by B & C Music Ltd.. Dist: Jetstar

Francis X & The Bushmen
SOUL INCEST.
Album: released on Revolver, Mar'87 by Revolver Records. Dist: Revolver, Cartel

Franco, Buddy De
BORINQUIN.
Album: released on Sonet, Aug'77 by Sonet

Records. Dist: PRT

HARK (Franco, Buddy De & The Oscar Peterson Quartet).
Album: released on Pablo (USA), Sep'85 by Pablo Records (USA). Dist: Wellard, Chris, IMS-Polygram, BMG

Cassette: released on Pablo (USA), Sep'85 by Pablo Records (USA). Dist: Wellard, Chris, IMS-Polygram, BMG

LIKE SOMEONE IN LOVE (Franco, Buddy De Quintet).
Album: released on Progressive (Import), Apr'81

MR LUCKY.
Album: released on Pablo (USA), Sep'84 by Pablo Records (USA). Dist: Wellard, Chris, IMS-Polygram, BMG

Cassette: released on Pablo (USA), Sep'84 by Pablo Records (USA). Dist: Wellard, Chris, IMS-Polygram, BMG

Franco Et Le TPOK Jazz
CHEZ RHYTHMES ET MUSIC A PARIS.
Album: released on Deipop (France), Feb'85

Francois Rabelais
HISTORIES OF GARGANTUA AND PANTAGRUEL (James Mason).
Cassette: released on Caedmon(USA), Jan'82 by Caedmon (USA) Records. Dist: Gower, Taylors, Discovery Deleted '1.

Franco & Josky
CHOC, CHOC, CHOC 3.
Album: released on Choc(France), Jun'84

Franco : Rochereau
OM NA WAPI.
Album: released on Shanachie, Jun'85 Dist: Sterns/Triple Earth Distribution, Roots

Franc, Rene
BLACK STICK.
Album: released on Wam, May'87

Frank, Anne
DIARY OF ANNE FRANK, THE.
Cassette: released on Caedmon(USA), Aug'79 by Caedmon (USA) Records. Dist: Gower, Taylors, Discovery

Frank Chickens
BLUE CANARY.
Single (7"): released on Kaz, Oct'85 by Kaz Records. Dist: PRT

Single (12"): released on Kaz, Oct'85 by Kaz Records. Dist: PRT

WE ARE FRANK CHICKENS.
Album: released on Kaz, Oct'84 by Kaz Records. Dist: PRT

WE ARE NINJA.
Single (7"): released on Kaz, Jan'84 by Kaz Records. Dist: PRT

Single (12"): released on Kaz, Jan'84 by Kaz Records. Dist: PRT

YELLOW TOAST.
Single(7"): released on Flying Lecords, Aug'87

Single (12"): released on Flying Lecords, Aug'87

Franke & Knockouts
FRANKE & THE KNOCKOUTS.
Album: released on RCA, Jun'81 by RCA Records. Dist: RCA, Roots, Swift, Wellard, Chris, I & B, Solomon & Peres Distribution

Frankenstein
FRANKENSTEIN Mary Shelley (Read by James Mason).
Album: released on Caedmon(USA), '79 by Caedmon (USA) Records. Dist: Gower, Taylors, Discovery

Cassette: released on Caedmon(USA), '79 by Caedmon (USA) Records. Dist: Gower, Taylors, Discovery

FRANKENSTEIN (Powell, Robert).
Cassette: released on Squirrel, Nov'81

FRANKENSTEIN Various artists (Various Artists).
Cassette: released on Tell-A-tale (Cassettes), Aug'84

FRANKENSTEIN & MONSTER BAND (Frankenstein & All Star Monster Band).
Album: released on Sonet, Jul'84 by Sonet Records. Dist: PRT

Franke, Rennee
DING DONG BOOGIE.
Tracks: / Ding dong boogie / Bimmelbahn boogie (choo choo boogie) / Sailors boogie / Columbus boogie / Krahwinkel boogie / Der kuck-kuck swing / Botch a me (englisch) / Der teddy mit dem dudelsack / Musikverrucko (crazy man crazy) / Dreissig tassen kaffee / Mr.Patton aus Manhattan (see you later alligator) / Das ist der richt'ge rhythmus fur die jungen madchen schuhpu / Gerne mocht 'ich kussen (botch a me) / Mi no mel och.
Album: released on Bear Family, Dec'86 by Bear Family Records. Dist: Rollercoaster Distribution, Swift

Frankhauser, Merrell
THINGS.
Album: released on Time Stood Still, Apr'85

Frankie B
PRESSURE ME.
Single (12"): released on Ital Stuff, Aug'85 by Ital Stuff Records. Dist: Jetstar

Frankie B.'All Rounder'
FRUITY.
Tracks: / Fruity / Scratch me back.
Single (12"): released on Ital Stop, May'86 Dist: Jetstar

Frankie & Casuals
WHAT SHALL I DO.
Single (12"): released on Disco Demand, '74 Dist: PRT

Frankie Goes To Hollywood
CARNAGE Two tribes.
Single (12"): released on ZTT, Jul'84 by Island Records. Dist: Polygram

INTERVIEW PICTURE DISC.
Album: released on Baktabak, May'87 by Baktabak Records. Dist: Arabesque

LIVERPOOL.
Album: released on ZTT, Oct'86 by Island Records. Dist: Polygram

Cassette: released on ZTT, Oct'86 by Island Records. Dist: Polygram

Compact disc: released on ZTT, Oct'86 by Island Records. Dist: Polygram

POWER OF LOVE.
Single (7"): released on ZTT, Nov'84 by Island Records. Dist: Polygram

Single (12"): released on ZTT, Nov'84 by Island Records. Dist: Polygram

Cassette: released on ZTT, Nov'84 by Island Records. Dist: Polygram

Single (12"): released on ZTT, Dec'84 by Island Records. Dist: Polygram

RAGE HARD.
Tracks: / Rage hard / (Don't lose what's left of) your mind / Suffragette city.
Single (7"): released on ZTT, Aug'86 by Island Records. Dist: Polygram

Single (12"): released on ZTT, Aug'86 by Island Records. Dist: Polygram

Single (12"): released on ZTT, Aug'86 by Island Records. Dist: Polygram

Single (12"): released on ZTT, Aug'86 by Island Records. Dist: Polygram

RELAX.
Picture disc single: released on ZTT, Aug'84 by Island Records. Dist: Polygram

Cassette: released on ZTT, Aug'84 by Island Records. Dist: Polygram

RELAX (MOVE).
Single (7"): released on Zang Tumb Tuum, Nov'83

RELAX SEX MIX (FUCK).
Single (12"): released on Zang Tumb Tuum, Nov'83

TWO TRIBES.
Single (7"): released on ZTT, Jun'84 by Island Records. Dist: Polygram

Single (12"): released on ZTT, Jun'84 by Island Records. Dist: Polygram

Picture disc single: released on ZTT, Jun'84 by Island Records. Dist: Polygram

Single (12"): released on ZTT, Aug'84 by Island Records. Dist: Polygram

Cassette: released on ZTT, Aug'84 by Island Records. Dist: Polygram

WAR (HIDE YOURSELF).
Picture disc single: released on ZTT, Jul'84 by Island Records. Dist: Polygram

WARRIORS (of the wasteland).
Cassette single: released on ZTT, Nov'86 by Island Records. Dist: Polygram

WARRIORS (OF THE WASTELAND).
Single (7"): released on ZTT, Nov'86 by Island Records. Dist: Polygram

Single (12"): released on ZTT, Nov'86 by Island Records. Dist: Polygram

WARRIORS (TURN ON THE KNIFE).
Tracks: / Warriors (return) / Warriors (end).
Single (12"): released on ZTT, Dec'86 by Island Records. Dist: Polygram

WATCHING THE WILD LIFE.
Tracks: / Watching the wildlife / Waves, The.
Single (7"): released on ZTT, Feb'87 by Island Records. Dist: Polygram

Single (12"): released on ZTT, Feb'87 by Island Records. Dist: Polygram

WATCHING THE WILDLIFE (12").
Tracks: / Watching the wildlife / Die letzen tage der nesheit mix / Waves (The).
Single (12"): released on ZTT, Mar'87 by Island Records. Dist: Polygram

Single (12"): released on ZTT, Mar'87 by Island Records. Dist: Polygram

WATCHING THE WILDLIFE (CASSETTE).
Tracks: / Watching the wildlife / Orchestral wildlife / Hotter wildlife / Waves / One bit / 2 bit / Condom mix (The).
Cassette single: released on ZTT, Mar'87 by Island Records. Dist: Polygram

WELCOME TO THE HIPPODROME.
Compact disc: by Island Records. Dist: Polygram

WELCOME TO THE PLEASURE DOME.
Single (7"): released on ZTT, Mar'85 by Island Records. Dist: Polygram

Single (12"): released on ZTT, Mar'85 by Island Records. Dist: Polygram

Picture disc single: released on ZTT, Apr'85 by Island Records. Dist: Polygram

Single (12"): released on ZTT, Apr'85 by Island Records. Dist: Polygram

Album: released on ZTT, Nov'84 by Island Records. Dist: Polygram

Cassette: released on ZTT, Nov'84 by Island Records. Dist: Polygram

Compact disc: released on ZTT, Nov'84 by Island Records. Dist: Polygram. Estim retail price in Aug'87 was £11.99.

WELCOME TO THE PLEASURE DOME (REMIX).
Cassette single: released on ZTT, Mar'85 by Island Records. Dist: Polygram

Frankies

YO YO.
Single (7"): released on Human, Jan'81 Dist: Roots, Stage One

Frankie & the Hit Men

Single (7"): released on Neil Rushton, Mar'83

IT'S A GAME.
Single (7"): released on Debonaire, Jan'84 by Debonaire Records. Dist: EMI

Single (7"): released on Nouveau, Feb'84

Frank, Jackson C.

JACKSON AGAIN.
Album: released on B & C, '85 by B&C Records. Dist: PRT

Franklin, Alan

BLUES CLIMAX, THE (Franklin, Alan Explosion).
Album: released on Psycho, Dec'83 Dist: Funhouse, Rough Trade

Franklin, Aretha

20 GREATEST HITS.
Compact disc: released on Atlantic, Jul'87 by WEA Records. Dist: WEA

AIN'T NOBODY EVER LOVED YOU.
Tracks: / Ain't nobody ever loved you / Integrity / Ain't nobody ever loved you (dub mix) / (Percappella) integrity.
Single (7"): released on Arista, Jul'86 by Arista Records. Dist: RCA

Single (12"): released on Arista, Jul'86 by Arista Records. Dist: RCA

Single (12"): released on Arista, Aug'86 by Arista Records. Dist: RCA

ALMIGHTY FIRE.
Album: released on Atlantic, Jun'78 by WEA Records. Dist: WEA

ANOTHER NIGHT.
Tracks: / Love me forever / School days / Another night / Kind of man / Nightlife mix / Come to me / I can't turn you loose / United together / Take me with you / Whatever it is / What a fool believes / Together again.
Single (7"): released on Arista, Feb'86 by Arista Records. Dist: RCA

Single (7"): released on Arista, Feb'86 by Arista Records. Dist: RCA

Single (12"): released on Arista, Feb'86 by Arista Records. Dist: RCA

ARETHA.
Tracks: / Jimmy Lee / I knew you were waiting (for me) / Do you still remember? / Jumpin' Jack Flash / Rock-a-lott / An angel cries / He'll come along / If you need my love tonight / Look to the rainbow.
Album: released on Arista, Oct'86 by Arista Records. Dist: RCA

Cassette: released on Arista, Oct'86 by Arista Records. Dist: RCA

Compact disc: released on Arista, Nov'86 by Arista Records. Dist: RCA

Album: released on Fame, Jun'86 by Music For Pleasure Records. Dist: EMI

Cassette: released on Fame, Jun'86 by Music For Pleasure Records. Dist: EMI

Album: released on Arista, Oct'80 by Arista Records. Dist: RCA

Cassette: released on Arista, Oct'80 by Arista Records. Dist: RCA

Album: released on CBS Cameo, Jan'84 by CBS Records. Dist: CBS

Cassette: released on CBS Cameo, Jan'84 by CBS Records. Dist: CBS Deleted '87.

ARETHA FRANKLIN COLLECTION, THE.
Tracks: / Walk on by / It ain't necessarily so / What a difference a day made (live) / Once in a lifetime (live) / Over the rainbow / You made me love you / Say it isn't so / Unforgettable / Unforgettable / My guy.
Double Album: released on Castle Collectors, Jul'87 by Castle Communications Records. Dist: Pinnacle

Double cassette: released on Castle Collectors, Jul'87 by Castle Communications Records. Dist: Pinnacle

Compact disc: released on Castle Collectors, Jul'87 by Castle Communications Records. Dist: Pinnacle

ARETHA'S GREATEST HITS.
Album: by WEA Records. Dist: WEA

BEST OF ARETHA FRANKLIN, THE.
Album: released on Atlantic, Jul'84 by WEA Records. Dist: WEA

Cassette: released on Atlantic, Jul'84 by WEA Records. Dist: WEA

COLLECTION PARTS 1&2(THE).
Tracks: / Walk on by / It Ain't necessarily so / Exactly like you / Try a little tenderness / I'm Sitting On Top Of The World / Skylark / Solitude / Where Are You / What A Difference A Day Made(Live) / Once In A Lifetime(Live) / Love For Sale(Live) / Swanee / Over The Rainbow / You made Me Love You / I Surrender Dear / Look For The Silver Lining / Lover Come Back To Me / Make Someone Happy / Say It Isn't So / Unforgettable / My Guy / Misty / OL Man River / I apologise.
Notes: This compilation (P) CBS Records.Original sound recordings made by CBS INC. Matrix number:5 013428 131527.Double Album & Musicassette.
Album: released on Castle Collectors, Sep'86 by Castle Communications Records. Dist: Pinnacle

Cassette: released on Castle Collectors, Sep'86 by Castle Communications Records. Dist: Pinnacle

FIRST LADY OF SOUL.
Album: released on Stylus/Atlantic, Nov'85

Cassette: released on Stylus/Atlantic, Nov'85

FREEWAY OF LOVE.
Tracks: / Freeway Of Love / Until You Say You Love Me / Jump To It / Freeway Of Love(Pink Cadillac Mix) / Jump To It / Freeway Of Love(Rock Mix) / Freeway Of Love(7" Version) / Until You Say You Love Me.
Single (7"): released on Arista, Apr'86 by Arista Records. Dist: RCA

Single (12"): released on Arista, May'86 by Arista Records. Dist: RCA

Single (7"): released on Arista, Apr'86 by Arista Records. Dist: RCA

Single (12"): released on Arista, Apr'86 by Arista Records. Dist: RCA

GET IT RIGHT.
Album: released on Arista, Jul'83 by Arista Records. Dist: RCA

Cassette: released on Arista, Jul'83 by Arista Records. Dist: RCA

GREATEST HITS:ARETHA FRANKLIN.
Cassette: released on Atlantic, '75 by WEA Records. Dist: WEA

GREATEST HITS: ARETHA FRANKLIN 1960-65.
Tracks: / Soulville / Lee Cross / Skylark / Take it like you give it / Try a little tenderness / Take a look / Runnin' out of fools / Sweet bitter love / Rock-a-bye your baby with a dixie melody / Cry like a baby / God bless the child.
Album: released on CBS, 11 Apr'87 by CBS Records. Dist: CBS

Cassette: released on CBS, 11 Apr'87 by CBS Records. Dist: CBS

I KNEW YOU WERE WAITING (FOR ME) (Franklin, Aretha & George Michael).
Single (7"): released on Epic, Jan'87 by CBS Records. Dist: CBS

Single (12"): released on Epic, Jan'87 by CBS Records. Dist: CBS

JIMMY LEE.
Tracks: / Jimmy Lee / You need my love tonight / Aretha megamix / An angel cries / Jimmy Lee (dub).
Notes: Aretha megamix is only available on 12" version.
Single (7"): released on Arista, Feb'87 by Arista Records. Dist: RCA

Single (12"): released on Arista, Feb'87 by Arista Records. Dist: RCA

Compact disc single: released on Arista, Mar'87 by Arista Records. Dist: RCA

JUMPIN' JACK FLASH.
Tracks: / Jumpin' Jack Flash / Integrity.
Single (7"): released on Arista, Oct'86 by Arista Records. Dist: RCA

Single (12"): released on Arista, Oct'86 by Arista Records. Dist: RCA

JUMP TO IT.
Album: released on Arista, Mar'84 by Arista Records. Dist: RCA

Cassette: released on Arista, Mar'84 by Arista Records. Dist: RCA

LOVE ALL THE HURT AWAY.
Album: released on Arista, Sep'81 by Arista Records. Dist: RCA

Cassette: released on Arista, Sep'81 by Arista Records. Dist: RCA Deleted '85.

LOVE ME RIGHT.
Single (7"): released on Arista, Jan'83 by Arista Records. Dist: RCA

Single (12"): released on Arista, Jan'83 by Arista Records. Dist: RCA

NATURAL WOMAN You make me feel like a.
Tracks: / Natural woman(You make me feel like a) / Never loved a man(the way I love you) / Do right woman,Do right man.

Single (7"): released on Atlantic, May'86 by WEA Records. Dist: WEA

Single (12"): released on Atlantic, May'86 by WEA Records. Dist: WEA

NEVER GROW OLD (Franklin, Aretha & Reverend Franklin).
Album: released on Chess, Jan'87 by Charly Records. Dist: Charly, Swift, PRT, Discovery, IMS, Polygram

Cassette: released on Chess, Jan'87 by Charly Records. Dist: Charly, Swift, PRT, Discovery, IMS, Polygram

RESPECT.
Tracks: / Respect / Do right woman, do right man / Rock steady*.
Single (7"): released on Atlantic, Jun'87 by WEA Records. Dist: WEA

Single (12"): released on Atlantic, Jun'87 by WEA Records. Dist: WEA

ROCKALOTT.
Tracks: / Rockalott / Look at the rainbow.
Single (7"): released on Arista, Jun'87 by Arista Records. Dist: RCA

Single (12"): released on Arista, Jun'87 by Arista Records. Dist: RCA

SAY A LITTLE PRAYER, A.
Single (7"): released on Old Gold, Jul'82 by Old Gold Records. Dist: Lightning, Jazz Music, Spartan, Counterpoint

SOUL SURVIVOR.
Album: released on Blue Moon, Jun'86 Dist: Magnum Music Group Ltd, PRT, Spartan

TEN YEARS OF GOLD.
Cassette: released on Atlantic, Dec'76 by WEA Records. Dist: WEA

WHO'S ZOOMIN' WHO?.
Tracks: / Freeway of love / Another night / Sweet bitter love / Who's zoomin' who? / Sisters are doin' it for themselves / Until you say you love me / Push / Ain't nobody ever loved you / Integrity.
Compact disc: released on Arista, Jan'86 by Arista Records. Dist: RCA

Album: released on Arista, Dec'85 by Arista Records. Dist: RCA

Cassette: released on Arista, Dec'85 by Arista Records. Dist: RCA

Single (7"): released on Arista, Nov'85 by Arista Records. Dist: RCA

Single (12"): released on Arista, Nov'85 by Arista Records. Dist: RCA

YEAH.
Tracks: / This could be the start the something / Once in a lifetime / Misty / More / There is no greater love / Muddy water / If I had a hammer / Impossible / Today / Today I love ev'rybody / Without the one you love / Trouble in mind / Love for sale.
Album: released on CBS, Jul'86 by CBS Records. Dist: CBS

Cassette: released on CBS, Jul'86 by CBS Records. Dist: CBS

Franklin, Phil

PHIL FRANKLIN JAZZ BAND (Franklin, Phil Jazz Band).
Album: released on Timeless, Sep'86

Franklin, Rex

COUNTRY WORLD OF..., THE.
Cassette: released on Viking, Apr'80 Dist: Harmonia Mundi Distributors

Franklin, Rodney

GROOVE(THE).
Tracks: / Groove(The) / In the bush / Check out the groove / Strut your funky stuff.
Single (12"): released on Old Gold, Feb'86 by Old Gold Records. Dist: Lightning, Jazz Music, Spartan, Counterpoint

GROOVE, THE.
Single (7"): released on Old Gold, Sep'85 by Old Gold Records. Dist: Lightning, Jazz Music, Spartan, Counterpoint

IT TAKES TWO.
Tracks: / Motion / Look what's showing through / Broken wings / Eagle and the Condor(The) / It takes two / Rollin' in our love / My wish / Let there be piece.
Album: released on CBS, Aug'86 by CBS Records. Dist: CBS

Cassette: released on CBS, Aug'86 by CBS Records. Dist: CBS

SKYDANCE.
Album: released on CBS, Jun'85 by CBS Records. Dist: CBS

Cassette: released on CBS, Jun'85 by CBS Records. Dist: CBS Deleted '87.

Franklyn, Fiona

BUSTED UP ON LOVE.
Single (7"): released on Virgin, Jan'85 by Virgin Records. Dist: EMI, Virgin Distribution

Single (12"): released on Virgin, Jan'85 by Virgin Records. Dist: EMI, Virgin Distribution

Frank, Nanette

CAN'T BE YOUR PART TIME LOVER.
Single (7"): released on EMI, Apr'87 by EMI Records. Dist: EMI

Single (12"): released on EMI, Apr'87 by EMI Records. Dist: EMI

Franks, Michael

ART OF TEA.
Tracks: / Nightmoves / Egg plant / Monkey see, Monkey do / St.Elmo's fire / Don't know why i'm so happy i'm sad / Jive / Popsicle toes / Mr.Blue / Sometimes i just forget to smile.
Notes: Digital stereo.
Compact disc: released on Reprise, May'84 by WEA Records. Dist: WEA

OBJECTS OF DESIRE.
Album: released on Warner Brothers, Mar'82 by Warner Bros Records. Dist: WEA

Cassette: released on Warner Brothers, Mar'82 by Warner Bros Records. Dist: WEA

PASSION FRUIT.

Album: released on Warner Bros., Nov'83 by Warner Bros Records. Dist: WEA

SKIN DIVE.
Album: released on Warner Brothers, May'85 by Warner Bros Records. Dist: WEA

Franks, Preston
ZYDECO, VOL.2 (Franks, Preston/Sam Ambrose).
Album: released on Arhoolie, Aug'85 by Arhoolie Records. Dist: Projection, Topic, Jazz Music, Swift, Roots

Frank, Stanley
PLAY IT TILL IT HURTS.
Album: released on A&M, May'81 by A&M Records. Dist: Polygram

Frantic Elevators
HOLDING BACK THE YEARS.
Single (7"): released on No Waiting, Nov'82

Frantic Five
Don Lang gets the bug

Frantix
SO DAMNED UGLY.
Tracks: / In my town.
Single (7"): released on Payola, Nov'86

Fraser, Alasdair
PORTRAIT OF A SCOTTISH FIDDLER.
Album: released on Ross, '86 by Ross Records. Dist: Ross Distribution, Roots Distribution

Cassette: released on Ross, '86 by Ross Records. Dist: Ross Distribution, Roots Distribution

SKYEDANCE (Fraser, Alasdair & Paul Machlis).
Album: released on Culbirnie, Feb'87 Dist: Ross

Cassette: released on Culbirnie, Jul'87 Dist: Ross

Fraser, Dean
REDEMPTION SONG.
Single (7"): released on Island, Sep'84 by Island Records. Dist: Polygram Deleted '87.

Single (12"): released on Island, Sep'84 by Island Records. Dist: Polygram

Fraser, Simon
NOUS SOMMES PRETS (Fraser, Simon University Pipe Band).
Tracks: / Children / Cameronian Rant / MacAlisters dirk / All through the night / Willie Davie / Linen cap / Ms Joy Cairns / Kitchen piper / Muldron glen / Streaker / Arniston castle.
Notes: There are 37 titles altogether.
Album: released on Lismor, Nov'85 by Lismor Records. Dist: Lismor, Roots, Celtic Music

Cassette: by Lismor Records. Dist: Lismor, Roots, Celtic Music

Frawzles & Scrumpy
FOOD & DRINK.
Cassette: released on Folktracks, Nov'79 by Folktracks Cassettes. Dist: Folktracks

Frazer, Dean
NICE.
Single (7"): released on Beverly, Oct'84 by Beverly Records. Dist: Jetstar

YOU ARE.
Single (12"): released on Tads, Apr'84 by Tads Records. Dist: Jetstar Distribution

Frazer, Grant
MY LAND IS SCOTLAND.
Album: released on Nevis, Jul'81 Dist: H.R. Taylor

Cassette: released on Nevis, Jul'81 Dist: H.R. Taylor

ONE HUNDRED THOUSAND WELCOMES.
Album: released on Country House, Dec'83 by BGS Productions Ltd. Dist: Taylor, H.R., Record Merchandisers Distribution, Pinnacle, Sounds of Scotland Records

Cassette: released on Country House, Dec'83 by BGS Productions Ltd. Dist: Taylor, H.R., Record Merchandisers Distribution, Pinnacle, Sounds of Scotland Records

Frazer, Phillip
BLOOD OF THE SAINT.
Single (7"): released on Silver Camel, Oct'82 Dist: Jetstar, Rough Trade

DANCING TIME.
Single (12"): released on Saxon Studio, Nov'85 by Saxon Studio Records. Dist: Jetstar

REGGAE EXPLOSION.
Single (12"): released on Rockers Forever, Jul'85 Dist: Jetstar Distribution

RUNNING AROUND.
Single (12"): released on Negus Roots, Jan'85 by Negus Roots Records. Dist: Jetstar

SIREN, THE.
Single (12"): released on Rosie Solidarity, Sep'84 by Rosie Solidarity Records. Dist: Jetstar Distribution

TONIGHT.
Single (12"): released on Corner Store, Oct'84

Frazier, Bernice
WILL YOU BE THE ONE.
Single (12"): released on Streetwave, Jul'85 by Streetwave Records. Dist: PRT Distribution

Frazier, Rob
CUT IT AWAY.
Album: released on Light, Apr'85 by Mainline Record Company. Dist: Mainline

Cassette: released on Light, Apr'85 by Mainline Record Company. Dist: Mainline

Freake, Syd
BUM BITES.
Single (7"): released on Sparky Lapwing, Dec'82 Dist: Rough Trade

Fred
ALL RIGHTS RESERVED.
Single (7"): released on Tyger, Mar'82

Freddie Goes To...
RELAPSE Don't ban it (Freddie Goes To Cricklewood).
Single (7"): released on Yum Yum Tum, Jan'85 by Yum Yum Tum Records. Dist: Yum Yum Tum

Freddie & The Dreamers
BEST OF FREDDIE & THE DREAMERS.
Tracks: / I'm telling you now / Playboy / If you've got a minute, baby / Short shorts / Over you / I understand / If you gotta make a fool of somebody / Do the Freddie / What have I done to you / Don't make me cry / You were made for me / I don't love you anymore / Tell me when / Just for you / Little you, A / I just don't understand / I'm a hog for you / Johnny B Goode / I love you baby / It doesn't matter any more.
Album: released on C5, Jul'87 by See For Miles Records. Dist: Counterpoint

FREDDIE AND THE DREAMERS.
Album: released on EMI (Holland), '83 by EMI Records. Dist: Conifer

YOU WERE MADE FOR ME.
Single (7"): released on Juke Box, Mar'82

Freddy the Detective
FREDDY THE DETECTIVE Brooks, Walter R. (Carroll, Pat).
Cassette: released on Caedmon(USA), Sep'82 by Caedmon (USA) Records. Dist: Gower, Taylors, Discovery

Fredericks
CLOSER I GET TO YOU.
Tracks: / Closer I get to you, The / Closer I get to you, The (version).
Single (12"): released on People Like Us, 20 Jun'87

Fredericks, Bill
YOU'LL NEVER FIND ANOTHER LOVE LIKE MINE.
Tracks: / You'll never find... / Juke box girl.
Single (7"): released on Sedition, 20 Jun'87 Dist: PRT

Single (12"): released on Sedition, 20 Jun'87 Dist: PRT

Fredericks, Dee
LOOK BEFORE YOU LEAP (Fredericks, Dee & Cast).
Single (7"): released on Royal, Nov'82 by Royal Records. Dist: Stage One Distribution

Fred, John
JUDY IN DISGUISE (Fred, John & the Playboys).
Single (7"): released on Old Gold, Jul'82 by Old Gold Records. Dist: Lightning, Jazz Music, Spartan, Counterpoint

Single (7"): released on Creole, Aug'82 by Creole Records. Dist: Rhino, PRT

BEST OF JOHN FRED & THE PLAYBOYS.
Album: Dist: Swift

Fredlocks
FERTILE GROUND.
Tracks: / Fertile ground / Fertilse sound.
Single (12"): released on Rising Sun, Jul'86 Dist: Jetstar

Fredricks, Bill
JACK, (LEGS) DIAMOND, RACKATEER AND GANGSTER (Fredricks, Bill (Speakeasy)).
Single (7"): released on Touch, Nov'85 by Touch Records. Dist: Rough Trade, Cartel

Single (12"): released on Touch, Nov'85 by Touch Records. Dist: Rough Trade, Cartel

TOO BUSY THINKING 'BOUT MY BABY.
Single (7"): released on Unigram, Mar'83

Single (12"): released on Unigram, Mar'83

Free
COMPLETELY FREE.
Album: released on Island, Oct'82 by Island Records. Dist: Polygram

FIRE AND WATER.
Tracks: / Oh ! Wept / Remember / Heavy load / Fire and water / Mr.Big / Dont say you love me / All right now.
Album: released on Island, Sep'86 by Island Records. Dist: Polygram

Cassette: released on Island, Sep'86 by Island Records. Dist: Polygram

Compact disc: released on Island, Sep'86 by Island Records. Dist: Polygram

FREE AT LAST.
Album: by Island Records. Dist: Polygram

FREE LIVE.
Album: by Island Records. Dist: Polygram

FREE STORY, THE.
Cassette: released on Island, '75 by Island Records. Dist: Polygram

HEARTBREAKER.
Album: released on Island, Jan'78 by Island Records. Dist: Polygram

HIGHWAY.
Album: by Island Records. Dist: Polygram

I'LL BE CREEPIN'.
Album: by Island Records. Dist: Polygram

LIVE.
Album: released on Island, Jan'78 by Island Records. Dist: Polygram

Cassette: released on Island, Jan'78 by Island Records. Dist: Polygram

TONS OF SOBS.
Album: by Island Records. Dist: Polygram

WISHING WELL.
Single (7"): released on Island, May'85 by Island Records. Dist: Polygram

Single (12"): released on Island, May'85 by Island Records. Dist: Polygram Deleted '87

Freed, Alan
ALAN FREED'S ROCK & ROLL DANCE PARTY, VOL.5.
Album: released on Wins, Jul'79

ALAN FREED'S ROCK & ROLL DANCE PARTY, VOL.1.
Album: released on Wins, Apr'79

ALAN FREED'S ROCK & ROLL DANCE PARTY, VOL.2.
Album: released on Wins, Apr'79

ALAN FREED'S ROCK & ROLL DANCE PARTY, VOL 3.
Album: released on Wins, Apr'79

ALAN FREED'S ROCK & ROLL DANCE PARTY, VOL.4.
Album: released on Wins, Apr'79

ROCK & ROLL DANCE PARTY, VOL.1.
Album: released on Jasmine, Feb'84 by Jasmine Records. Dist: Counterpoint, Lugtons, Taylor, H.R., Wellard, Chris, Swift, Cadillac

Freedom Songs
FREEDOM SONGS A young choir from Uppsala (Various Artists).
Album: released on Phontastic (Sweden), '82 by Wellard, Chris Distribution. Dist: Wellard, Chris Distribution

Freeez
ALONE.
Single (7"): released on Beggars Banquet, Jan'82 by Beggars Banquet Records. Dist: WEA

Single (12"): released on Beggars Banquet, Jan'82 by Beggars Banquet Records. Dist: WEA

ANTI-FREEEZ.
Album: released on Beggars Banquet, Jul'84 by Beggars Banquet Records. Dist: WEA

Single (7"): released on Beggars Banquet, Oct'81 by Beggars Banquet Records. Dist: WEA

Single (12"): released on Beggars Banquet, Oct'81 by Beggars Banquet Records. Dist: WEA

FLYING HIGH.
Single (7"): released on Beggars Banquet, Apr'81 by Beggars Banquet Records. Dist: WEA

Single (12"): released on Beggars Banquet, Apr'81 by Beggars Banquet Records. Dist: WEA

GONNA GET YOU.
Album: released on Beggars Banquet, Nov'83 by Beggars Banquet Records. Dist: WEA

Cassette: released on Beggars Banquet, Nov'83 by Beggars Banquet Records. Dist: WEA

IDLE VICE.
Album: released on Beggars Banquet, Oct'85 by Beggars Banquet Records. Dist: WEA

Cassette: released on Beggars Banquet, Oct'85 by Beggars Banquet Records. Dist: WEA

I.O.U.
Single (7"): released on Beggars Banquet, Jun'83 by Beggars Banquet Records. Dist: WEA

Single (12"): released on Beggars Banquet, Jun'83 by Beggars Banquet Records. Dist: WEA

ONE TO ONE.
Single (7"): released on Beggars Banquet, Jun'82 by Beggars Banquet Records. Dist: WEA

Single (12"): released on Beggars Banquet, Jun'82 by Beggars Banquet Records. Dist: WEA

SOUTHERN FREEZ.
Album: released on Beggars Banquet, Feb'81 by Beggars Banquet Records. Dist: WEA

Cassette: released on Beggars Banquet, Feb'81 by Beggars Banquet Records. Dist: WEA

Single (7"): released on Beggars Banquet, Feb'81 by Beggars Banquet Records. Dist: WEA

Single (12"): released on Beggars Banquet, Feb'81 by Beggars Banquet Records. Dist: WEA

SOUTHERN FREEZ (7" RADIO MIX).
Tracks: / Southern Freeez / Southern Freeez (inst).
Single (7"): released on Total Control, May'87

Single (12"): released on Total Control, May'87

TRAIN OF THOUGHT.
Single (7"): released on Beggars Banquet, Jul'85 by Beggars Banquet Records. Dist: WEA Deleted '86.

Single (12"): released on Beggars Banquet, Jul'85 by Beggars Banquet Records. Dist: WEA
Cat. no: BEG 141T

Free Fair
FREE FAIR, VOL.2.
Album: released on Timeless, Apr'81

Freeflight
BEYOND THE CLOUDS.
Album: released on Palo Alto (Italy), Jan'85

JAZZ CLASSICAL UNION(THE).
Album: released on Palo Alto (Italy), Jul'86

Cassette: released on Palo Alto (Italy), Jul'86

JAZZ, THE Classical union.
Album: released on Palo Alto (Italy), Jan'84

Cassette: released on Palo Alto (Italy), Jan'84

SOARING.
Album: released on Imported, Jun'84 Dist: Conifer

Freeland Barbour

FIRE IN THE HEARTH.
Album: released on REL, '77 Dist: Roots

Cassette: released on REL, '77 Dist: Roots

Freel, Brian

TORC.
Album: released on BR Music Records, May'83

Freeman, Bobby

DO YOU WANNA DANCE?.
Single (7"): released on Revival, Jul'82 Dist: Lightning, Swift

Single (7"): released on Creole, Aug'82 by Creole Records. Dist: Rhino, PRT

Freeman, Bud

Buck Clayton, Hot Lips Page & Bud Freeman

BUD FREEMAN.
Album: released on Monmouth, Mar'79
Cat. no: **MES 7022**

BUD FREEMAN & HIS ALL STARS (Freeman, Bud & His All Stars).
Album: released on Swinghouse, '84 Dist: Jazz Music Distribution, Swift Distribution, Chris Wellard Distribution

BUD FREEMAN & SHORTY BAKER ALLSTARS (Freeman, Bud & The Shorty Baker Allstars).
Notes: Recording in MONO.
Album: released on Jazz Archives, Jul'86 by Jazz Archives Records. Dist: Jazz Music

BUD FREEMAN TAPES, (THE) (Freeman, Bud with the Cambridge City Jassband).
Album: released on Plant Life Jazz, Nov'81

BUD FREEMAN WITH THE BOB BARNARD JAZZBAND (Freeman, Bud with the Bob Barnard Jazzband).
Album: released on Swaggie (Australia), Jan'83

CHICAGO.
Album: released on Black Lion, Jan'85 by Black Lion Records. Dist: Jazz Music, Chris Wellard, Taylor, H.R., Counterpoint, Cadillac
Cat. no: **BLP 30108**

CHICAGOANS IN NEW YORK.
Album: released on Dawn Club, Jun'79 Dist: Cadillac, Swift, JSU

CHICAGO-STYLED, 1935-40, VOL 1.
Album: released on Swaggie (Australia), Jan'83

COMMODORE STYLE (Freeman, Bud & George Wettling).
Album: released on Commodore Classics, '87 by Teldec Records (Germany). Dist: Conifer, IMS, Polygram

FAMOUS CHICAGOANS (Freeman, Bud & His City Five).
Notes: Featuring: His Summa Cum Laude Orchestra.

KEEP SMILIN' AT TROUBLE.
Tracks: / Keep smilin' at trouble / Sail fish, The / What is there to say / Oh! baby / Big boy / That Da-Da strain / Wailing blues / Copenhagen / As long as I live / Sensation rag / Sunday / Satanic Blues / Buzzard, The / I need some pettin' / Fidgety feet / Tillie's downtown now / Tia juana / Susie.
Album: released on Affinity, Apr'87 by Charly Records. Dist: Charly, Cadillac

LAST NIGHT WHEN WE WERE YOUNG.
Album: released on Black Lion, '78 by Black Lion Records. Dist: Jazz Music, Chris Wellard, Taylor, H.R., Counterpoint, Cadillac

SWINGING TENORS (Freeman, Bud & Eddie Miller).
Album: released on Affinity, Apr'81 by Charly Records. Dist: Charly, Cadillac

THREE'S NO CROWD (Freeman, Bud Trio, The).
Notes: Personnel:Bud Freeman-Tenor Sax/Jess Stacy-Piano/George Wetting-Drums. All sessions from New York in 1938,MONO recording
Album: released on Commodore Classics, Nov'86 by Teldec Records (Germany). Dist: Conifer, IMS, Polygram

Album: released on Commodore Classics, Jul'82 by Teldec Records (Germany). Dist: Conifer, IMS, Polygram

TWO BEAUTIFUL (Freeman, Bud & Buddy Tate).
Album: released on Circle(USA), Jun'86 by Jazzology Records (USA). Dist: Jazz Music, Swift, Chris Wellard

Freeman, Chico

DESTINY'S DANCE.
Album: released on Contemporary, Apr'82 by Contemporary Records. Dist: Pinnacle

LIVE AT RONNIE SCOTT'S.
Compact disc: released on Hendring Video, Jan'87 by Charly Records. Dist: Charly, PVG

MORNING PRAYER.
Album: released on India Navigation, Oct'84 by India Navigation Records. Dist: Cadillac, Projection, Swift

NO TIME LEFT (Freeman, Chico Quartet).
Compact disc: released on Black Saint (Italy), '86 Dist: Target, Jazz Music, Harmonia Mundi
Cat. no: **BSR 0036**
Album: released on Black Saint, Jan'80 Dist: Projection, IMS, Polygram, Chris Wellard, Harmonia Mundi, Swift

PIED PIPER, THE.
Album: released on Blackhawk, Aug'86 by Blackhawk Records (USA). Dist: IMS-Polygram
Cat. no: **BKH 50801**
Cassette: released on Blackhawk, Aug'86 by Blackhawk Records (USA). Dist: IMS-Polygram

SEARCH, (THE).
Album: released on India Navigation, May'84 by India Navigation Records. Dist: Cadillac, Projection, Swift

SPIRIT SENSITIVE.
Album: released on India Navigation, Jan'80 by India Navigation Records. Dist: Cadillac, Projection, Swift

TANGENTS.
Album: released on Elektra, Sep'84 by WEA Records. Dist: WEA

Freeman, Evelyn

DIDN'T IT RAIN?.
Single (7"): released on EMI (France), Apr'83 by EMI Records. Dist: Conifer

Freeman, George

BIRTH SIGN.
: Dist: Projection, Swift, Cadillac

Freeman, Ken

TRIPODS - OPENING THEME.
Single (7"): released on BBC, Oct'85 by BBC Records & Tapes. Dist: EMI, PRT, Pye

Freeman, Von

HAVE NO FEAR.
Album: released on Nessa, Mar'79 Dist: Projection, Swift

VON FREEMAN.
Album: released on Daybreak (Import), '81
Cat. no: **D 002**

Free Russell

I'VE GOT A SONG FOR YOU.
Single (12"): released on Half Moon, Nov'83 by Rondelet Music And Records. Dist: Spartan

Free Style

I WANT YOU.
Single (7"): released on Swift, Jul'82 Dist: Swift Distribution

Freestyle Express

FREESTYLE.
Single (7"): released on Sunny View, May'84 by Sunny View Records. Dist: PRT Distribution

Single (12"): released on Sunny View, May'84 by Sunny View Records. Dist: PRT Distribution

Freez

IN ALL HONESTY.
Tracks: / In all honesty / Take a little time.
Single (7"): released on Siren, May'86 by Virgin Records. Dist: EMI

Single (12"): released on Siren, May'86 by Virgin Records. Dist: EMI

Freeze

I.O.U. Go-go club mix.
Single (7"): released on Citybeat, Dec'86 Dist: WEA

Single (12"): released on Citybeat, Dec'86 Dist: WEA

Freeze Frame

FOXHOLE.
Single (7"): released on Inevitable, Jan'84 by Inevitable Records. Dist: Rough Trade

Single (12"): released on Inevitable, Jan'84 by Inevitable Records. Dist: Rough Trade

TODAY TOMORROW.
Single (7"): released on Inevitable, Aug'85 by Inevitable Records. Dist: Rough Trade

Single (12"): released on Inevitable, Aug'85 by Inevitable Records. Dist: Rough Trade

TOUCH.
Single (7"): released on Crackin' Up, Aug'82 by Crackin' Up Records. Dist: Cartel

Single (7"): released on Inevitable, Feb'85 by Inevitable Records. Dist: Rough Trade

Single (12"): released on Inevitable, Feb'85 by Inevitable Records. Dist: Rough Trade

YOUR VOICE.
Single (7"): released on Inevitable, Jul'83 by Inevitable Records. Dist: Rough Trade

Frehley, Ace

FREHLEY'S COMET.
Tracks: / Rock soldiers / Breakout / Into the night / Something moved / We got your rock / Love me right / Calling to you / Dolls / Stranger in a strange land / Fractured too.
Album: released on Atlantic, Jun'87 by WEA Records. Dist: WEA

Cassette: released on Atlantic, Jun'87 by WEA Records. Dist: WEA

INTO THE NIGHT.
Tracks: / Into the night / Fracture too / Breakout.
Single (7"): released on WEA, 30 Jun'87 by WEA Records. Dist: WEA

Single (12"): released on WEA, 30 Jun'87 by WEA Records. Dist: WEA

Freight Train

MAN'S LAUGHTER.
Tracks: / Man's Laughter.
Single (7"): released on Bam Caruso, Feb'86 by Bam Caruso Records. Dist: Rough Trade, Revolver, Cartel

French

RIVER FLOWS EAST, (THE).
Single (7"): released on Sanguine, Sep'82

French accordion

FRENCH ACCORDION Various artists (Various Artists).
Tracks: / La java / C'es un mauvais garcon / Las plus bath de javas / Ca gaze / Aubade d'oiseaux / Le gros Lulu / La panse / La goualante du pauvre Jean / Suois le ciel de Paris / Fais gaffe / Java, te revoila - le p'tit bal du samedi soir / Rue de lappe / La mattchiche / La java des dockers / La marche le gosses / Le denicheur / Ca tourne rond / Padam padam / Accordeon / Passe musette.
Notes: A compilation of typical French accordion music. Issued by popular request.
Double Album: released on Polydor (France), Sep'84 Dist: Polygram

Double cassette: released on Polydor (France), Sep'84 Dist: Polygram

French Impression

BREAKING LOVE.
Single (7"): released on Steinar, Mar'85

Single (12"): released on Steinar, Mar'85

GET UP AND DANCE.
Single (7"): released on Steinar, Jul'85

Single (12"): released on Steinar, Jul'85

SANTA BABY.
Single (7"): released on Operation Twilight, Dec'82

French Lieutenant's Woman

FRENCH LIEUTENANT'S WOMAN Original soundtrack.
Album: released on DRG (USA), '83 by DRG Records. Dist: Conifer, RCA

Cassette: released on DRG (USA), '83 by DRG Records. Dist: Conifer, RCA

French, Paul

HALFWAY HOTEL.
Single (7"): released on Flying, Feb'85 by Flying Records. Dist: DMS

IT'S CHRISTMAS.
Single (7"): released on Flying, Dec'83 by Flying Records. Dist: DMS

French, Robert

FAVOURITE, (THE).
Album: released on Black Solidarity, Jun'85 by Black Solidarity Records. Dist: Jetstar

MEET ME BY THE RIVER.
Single (12"): released on Real Wax, May'85

NATURAL LADY.
Single (12"): released on Sweetcorn, Jan'85 by Sweetcorn Records. Dist: Jetstar

NICE TIME.
Single (12"): released on TG Productions, Jun'84 by TG Records. Dist: Jetstar Distribution

ROBERT FRENCH MEETS ANTHONY JOHNSON (French, Robert & Anthony Johnson).
Album: released on Midnight Rock, Nov'84 Dist: Jetstar Distribution, Kingdom Distribution

SATISFACTION GUARANTEED.
Single (12"): released on Top Rank, Aug'85

SETTLE DOWN GIRL.
Single (12"): released on White Label, Dec'84 by White Label Records. Dist: Jetstar

SHOWCASE.
Album: released on Progressive, Jun'85 by Progressive Records. Dist: Jetstar

SOMETHING ON MY MIND.
Single (12"): released on Uptempo, May'85 by Uptempo Records. Dist: Jetstar Distribution

WONDERING.
Album: released on Blue Mountain, Dec'85 Dist: Jetstar

French Toast

FRENCH TOAST.
Tracks: / Why not? / Joe Cool / Ion you / B A express / Butter (tribute to Quentin Jackson) / Calentado, man-part 2 of the 'suite sandrine'.
Notes: Acoustic fusion band playing original compositions and featuring all star musicians. Lew Soloff; worked with numerous jazz stars and was featured soloist with jazz rock bank Blood, Sweat and Tears.Jerry Dodgion: played in the bands of Gerald Wilson, Benny Carter and Thad Jones, Mel Lewis: Busy freelance, recording with Count Basie, Herbie Hancock and more.David Weckl: currently in Chick Corea's Elektric Band. Steve Gadd: probably the best and most widely known drummer in popmusic and studio work.Strong jazz roots, appeared on many CTI albums of the 70's.Personnel: Peter Gordon - french horn/Lew Soloff - trumpet/Jerry Dodgion - altosax/Michel Camilo - piano/Anthony Jackson - bass/David Weckl - drums/Sammy Figueroa - percussion/Gordon Gottlieb - percussion/Steve Gadd - drums.
Album: released on King (Japan), Jul'86 Dist: IMS, Polygram

Frenzy

CLOCKWORK TOY.
Album: released on I.D., Aug'86 by I.D. Records. Dist: Revolver, Cartel

HALL OF MIRRORS.
Album: released on Nervous, Mar'85 by Nervous Records. Dist: Nervous, Rough Trade

I SEE RED.
Tracks: / I see red / Whose life.
Single (7"): released on I.D., Jul'86 by I.D. Records. Dist: Revolver, Cartel

Single (12"): released on I.D., Jul'86 by I.D. Records. Dist: Revolver, Cartel

ROBOT RIOT.
Single (12"): released on Nervous, Nov'84 by Nervous Records. Dist: Nervous, Rough Trade

WHO'S LOVING YOU.
Tracks: / Who's loving you / Who's loving you (Inst.).
Single (12"): released on Debut, Feb'86 by Skratch Music. Dist: PRT

Frequency

BILLS.
Single (7"): released on Hard Times, Feb'83 by Hard Times Records. Dist: Stage One

Fresh

SUMMER IN THE CITY.
Tracks: / Love life (an invitation to).
Single (7"): released on Jive, Aug'87 by Zomba Records. Dist: RCA, PRT, CBS

Single (12"): released on Jive, Aug'87 by Zomba Records. Dist: RCA, PRT, CBS

Fresh, Doug E

ALL THE WAY TO HEAVEN.
Tracks: / All the way to heaven / Nuthin' / All the way to heaven (Inst) / Nuthin' (inst).
Single (7"): released on Cool Tempo, Jul'86 by Chrysalis Records. Dist: CBS

Single (12"): released on Cool Tempo, Jul'86 by Chrysalis Records. Dist: CBS

JUST HAVING FUN.
Tracks: / Just having fun.
Single (12"): released on Streetwave, Dec'85 by Streetwave Records. Dist: PRT Distribution

OH MY GOD.
Album: released on Cool Tempo, Jan'87 by Chrysalis Records. Dist: CBS

Cassette: released on Cool Tempo, Jan'87 by Chrysalis Records. Dist: CBS

Fresh Face

HUERO DANCING.

Freshies

DANCING DOCTORS.
Single (7"): released on Pinnacle, Oct'81 by Pinnacle Records. Dist: Pinnacle

FASTEN YOUR SAFETY BELTS.
Single (7"): released on Stiff, Aug'82 by Stiff Records. Dist: EMI, Record Services Distribution (Ireland)

OH GIRL.
Single (7"): released on Razz, Jul'80 by Razz. Dist: Pinnacle

WE'RE LIKE YOU.
Single (7"): released on Razz, Sep'82 by Razz. Dist: Pinnacle

YELLOW SPOT.
Single (7"): released on Razz, Aug'80 by Razz. Dist: Pinnacle

Freshman

YOU'VE NEVER HEARD ANYTHING.
Single (7"): released on Release (Ireland), Oct'79

Fresh New Beats

FRESH NEW BEATS Various artists (Various Artists).
Tracks: / Show, The / (Nothing serious) Just buggin' / Pee wee's dance (extended version) / Eric B. for President / All the way to heaven (Extended version) / Bassline / Bite this (extended version) / Who me? / We work hard (full version) / (Bang zoom) Let's go go. (Extended version).
Notes: Following the succession of Dance Classics from the Cooltempo Label this album will be a winner in the dance market.
Album: released on Cool Tempo, Aug'86 by Chrysalis Records. Dist: CBS

Cassette: released on Cool Tempo, Aug'86 by Chrysalis Records. Dist: CBS

Fresh 'n' up

FRESH 'N' UP Various artists (Various Artists).
Album: released on Jungle, Nov'84 by Jungle Records. Dist: Jungle, Cartel

Cassette: released on Jungle, Nov'84 by Jungle Records. Dist: Jungle, Cartel

Fresh selection

FRESH SELECTION Various artists (Various Artists).
Album: released on Fresh, Jan'82 Dist: Jetstar

Fretton, Matt

IT'S ALL OVER (DON'T SAY YOU'RE IN LOVE).
Single (7"): released on Chrysalis, Apr'84 by Chrysalis Records. Dist: CBS

Single (12"): released on Chrysalis, Apr'84 by Chrysalis Records. Dist: CBS

IT'S SO HIGH.
Single (7"): released on Chrysalis, May'83 by Chrysalis Records. Dist: CBS

Single (12"): released on Chrysalis, May'83 by Chrysalis Records. Dist: CBS

PALPITATING HEART.
Tracks: / Palpitating heart / Caution to the wind.
Single (7"): released on IDK, Sep'86 Dist: Rough Trade

Single (12"): released on IDK, Sep'86 Dist: Rough Trade

Freud

FREUD Film soundtrack: composed by Jerry Goldsmith.
Album: released on Citadel, Mar'79 Dist: Swift

Single (12"): released on CF, Jan'84 by CF Records. Dist: Jetstar

Freud, James

BREAKING SILENCE.
Tracks: / Modern girl / Television's hungry,The / Saviours,The / Enemy lines / Butane babies / Star to star / 19 again / No more telephone / Automatic crazy / Blue moon.
Album: released on Carrere, Mar'82 by Carrere Records. Dist: PRT, Cadillac

Freur

DOOT DOOT.
Tracks: / Doot doot / Runaway / Riders in the night / Theme from the film of the same name / Tender surrender / Matters of the heart / My room / Whispering steam machine / All too much.
Notes: Freur, who are also known by a logo for a name, have completed their debut album written and produced by the band with help from John Hudson, includes their best known single

---

"Doot doot".
Single (7"): released on CBS, Jan'84 by CBS Records. Dist: CBS

Single (12"): released on CBS, Jan'84 by CBS Records. Dist: CBS

LOOK IN THE BACK FOR ANSWERS.
Single (7"): released on CBS, Feb'85 by CBS Records. Dist: CBS

Single (12"): released on CBS, Feb'85 by CBS Records. Dist: CBS

MATTERS OF THE HEART.
Single (7"): released on CBS, Jun'83 by CBS Records. Dist: CBS

Single (12"): released on CBS, Jun'83 by CBS Records. Dist: CBS

RIDERS IN THE NIGHT.
Single (7"): released on CBS, Apr'84 by CBS Records. Dist: CBS

Single (12"): released on CBS, Apr'84 by CBS Records. Dist: CBS

Frey, Glenn

ALLNIGHTER, THE.
Album: released on MCA, Jul'85 by MCA Records. Dist: Polygram, MCA

Cassette: released on MCA, Jul'85 by MCA Records. Dist: Polygram, MCA

Compact disc: released on MCA, Jul'85 by MCA Records. Dist: Polygram, MCA

HEAT IS ON, THE.
Single (7"): released on MCA, Jan'85 by MCA Records. Dist: Polygram, MCA

Single (12"): released on MCA, Jan'85 by MCA Records. Dist: Polygram, MCA

NO FUN ALOUD.
Album: released on Elektra Asylum, Jun'82 by Elektra/Asylum/Nonesuch Records. Dist: WEA

Cassette: released on Elektra Asylum, Jun'82 by Elektra/Asylum/Nonesuch Records. Dist: WEA

SMUGGLERS BLUES.
Single (7"): released on BBC, Jun'85 by BBC Records & Tapes. Dist: EMI PRT Pye

Single (12"): released on BBC, Jun'85 by BBC Records & Tapes. Dist: EMI, PRT, Pye

YOU BELONG TO THE CITY.
Tracks: / You belong to the City / I got love.
Notes: 86
Single (7"): released on MCA, Mar'86 by MCA Records. Dist: Polygram, MCA

Single (12"): released on MCA, Mar'86 by MCA Records. Dist: Polygram, MCA

Fricke, Janie

AFTER MIDNIGHT.
Tracks: / Are you satisfied / I hurt / I don't like being lonely / Teach me how to forget / If I didn't care / Baby you're gone / My eternal flame / Nobody ever loved me so good / From time to time(it feels like love again) / I won't be easy.
Album: released on CBS, Jun'87 by CBS Records. Dist: CBS

Cassette: released on CBS, Jun'87 by CBS Records. Dist: CBS

Album: released on CBS, 30 May'87 by CBS Records. Dist: CBS

Cassette: released on CBS, 30 May'87 by CBS Records. Dist: CBS

ALWAYS HAS ALWAYS WILL.
Tracks: / Don't put it past my heart.
Single (7"): released on CBS, Nov'86 by CBS Records. Dist: CBS

AT THE COUNTRY STORE.
Album: released on Country Store, Dec'85 by Starblend Records. Dist: PRT, Prism Leisure Corporation Records

Cassette: released on Country Store, Dec'85 by Starblend Records. Dist: PRT, Prism Leisure Corporation Records

BLACK AND WHITE.
Tracks: / Till I can't take it anymore / He's breaking down my neck / Take me like a vacation / Nothing left to say / Comin' apart at the seams / Always have always will / Don't put it past my heart / When a woman cries / He's making a long short story / I'd take you back again.
Album: released on CBS, Aug'86 by CBS Records. Dist: CBS

Cassette: released on CBS, Aug'86 by CBS Records. Dist: CBS

FROM THE HEART.
Album: released on CBS, Apr'80 by CBS Records. Dist: CBS

JANIE FRICKE I love country.
Tracks: / I'll need someone to hold me (when I

---

cry) / Please help me, I'm falling (in love with you) / Pride / It ain't easy bein' easy / Let's stop talkin' about it / But love me / Down to my last broken heart / What're you doing tonight / He's a heartache (looking for a place to happen) / Homeward bound / Cry / Do me with love / Walkin' a broken heart / Always / Don't worry 'bout me baby / She's single again.
Album: released on CBS, Mar'87 by CBS Records. Dist: CBS

LOVE NOTES.
Tracks: / I'll love away your troubles for awhile / Somewhere to come when it rains / River blue / Let's try again / Let me love you good-bye / Love is worth it all / You're the one I love / Playin' hard to get / Stirrin' up feelin's / Got my mojo working.
Album: released on CBS, Mar'86 by CBS Records. Dist: CBS

Cassette: released on CBS, Mar'86 by CBS Records. Dist: CBS

Album: released on CBS, Jun'79 by CBS Records. Dist: CBS

TELL ME A LIE.
Single (7"): released on CBS, Mar'84 by CBS Records. Dist: CBS

VERY BEST OF JANIE FRICKE, THE.
Album: released on CBS, Sep'86 by CBS Records. Dist: CBS

Cassette: released on Epic, Sep'86 by CBS Records. Dist: CBS

Fricker, Thomas

SUMMER OF ROSES.
Album: released on Sweet Folk Country, Nov'76 Dist: Chris Wellard Distribution

Friction Groove

BLACK BOX, THE.
Album: released on Atlantic, Oct'85 by WEA Records. Dist: WEA

Frida

HERE WE'LL STAY.
Single (7"): released on Epic, Jun'83 by CBS Records. Dist: CBS

Friday

STRANGERS IN THE NIGHT.
Tracks: / Strangers in the night / End, the.
Single (7"): released on Riversmeet, Aug'86 Dist: Priority, RCA

Single (12"): released on Riversmeet, Aug'86 Dist: Priority, RCA

Friday, Gavin

YOU CAN'T ALWAYS GET WHAT YOU WANT (Friday, Gavin & Simon Carmody).

Friday Night...

FRIDAY NIGHT AT THE VILLAGE VANGUARD (Urbianak, Michael).
Album: released on Storyville, Nov'86 by Storyville Records. Dist: Jazz Music Distribution, Swift Distribution, Chris Wellard Distribution, Counterpoint Distribution

FRIDAY NIGHT IS MUSIC NIGHT Various artists (Various Artists).
Album: released on BBC, Nov'85 by BBC Records & Tapes. Dist: EMI, PRT, Pye

Cassette: released on BBC, Nov'85 by BBC Records & Tapes. Dist: EMI, PRT, Pye

Friday Rock Show

FRIDAY ROCK SHOW Various rock groups (Various Artists).
Album: released on BBC, Nov'81 by BBC Records & Tapes. Dist: EMI. PRT. Pye

Cassette: released on BBC, Nov'81 by BBC Records & Tapes. Dist: EMI, PRT, Pye

Friday the 13th

FRIDAY THE 13TH, PART 1,2,&3 original film soundtrack.
Album: released on Gramavision (USA), May'83 by Gramavision Records (USA). Dist: PRT, IMS, Polygram

Fridge

BRAND NEW REVOLUTION.
Single (7"): released on Young Blood, May'85 by Young Blood Records. Dist: Pinnacle

COME ON COME ON.
Single (7"): released on Young Blood, Nov'85 by Young Blood Records. Dist: Pinnacle

Friedhoffer, Hugo

THIS EARTH IS MINE Film soundtrack.
Album: released on Varese Sarabande (USA), May'79 by Varese Sarabande Records (USA).

Dist: PRT

Friedman, Dean

DEAN FRIEDMAN.
Album: released on Lifesong, May'78

I DIDN'T MEAN TO MAKE YOU CRY.
Single (7"): released on Hi Rise, Jun'85 Dist: PRT

LAKELANDS, THE.
Single (7"): released on Peach River, Dec'83 by Peach River Records. Dist: PRT

WELL WELL SAID THE ROCKING CHAIR.
Album: released on GTO, Feb'79 by GTO Records. Dist: CBS

Friedman, Don

FUTURES PASSED (Friedman, Don Quartet).
Album: released on Enja (Germany), Jan'82 by Enja Records (W.Germany). Dist: Cadillac Music

HOT KNEPPER AND PEPPER.
Album: released on Progressive (Import), '81

OF THE WIND'S EYE (Friedman, Don Quartet).
Album: released on Enja (Germany), Jan'82 by Enja Records (W.Germany). Dist: Cadillac Music

Frieman,David

DOUBLE IMAGE.
Album: released on JSU Germany, Jan'82

Friend

STAND ALONE.
Single (7"): released on Endangered Musik, Sep'85 by Endangered Musik Records. Dist: Revolver

Friendly Hopefuls

TRIBUTE TO THE PUNKS OF '76.
Single (7"): released on Abstract, Sep'81 by Abstract. Dist: Pinnacle

Friendly Persuasion

TRIBUTE TO KAREN CARPENTER, A.
Tracks: / Tribute to Karen Carpenter, a / Only yesterday.
Single (7"): released on Button, Jun'86 by Musical Characters Records. Dist: Spartan

Friends

FAR AND AWAY.
Tracks: / Burning bridges.
Single (12"): released on Summerhouse, Aug'87 Dist: Red Rhino Distribution, Cartel

FRIENDS original soundtrack (Various Artists).
Album: released on MCA (ABC), '83 by MCA Records. Dist: Polygram, MCA

Cassette: released on MCA (ABC), '83 by MCA Records. Dist: Polygram, MCA

IT'S GETTING LOUDER.
Single (7"): released on Summerhouse, Nov'86 Dist: Red Rhino Distribution, Cartel

MEDDLIN' WITH SHALAMAR.
Single (7"): released on Challenge, May'83 by Elite Records. Dist: Pinnacle

Single (12"): released on Challenge, May'83 by Elite Records. Dist: Pinnacle

NIGHT WALKER.
Single (7"): released on Rock Shop, Nov'83

Friends Again

FRIENDS AGAIN various artists (Various Artists).
Album: released on Impression, Nov'84 Dist: CBS

Cassette: released on Impression, Nov'84 Dist: CBS

HONEY AT THE CORE.
Single (7"): released on Moonboot, May'83 Dist: Polygram Distribution

Single (7"): released on Phonogram, May'84 by Phonogram Records. Dist: Polygram

Single (12"): released on Phonogram, May'84 by Phonogram Records. Dist: Polygram

SUNKISSED.
Single (7"): released on Moonboot, Aug'83 Dist: Polygram Distribution

Single (12"): released on Moonboot, Aug'83 Dist: Polygram Distribution

TRAPPED & UNWRAPPED.

Compact disc: by Phonogram Records. Dist: Polygram Distribution

Friends & Lovers

FRIENDS AND LOVERS (Various Artists).
Tracks: / Can't be with you tonight / On my own / All cried out / Always and forever / How 'bout us / When a man loves a woman / Heartbreaker / Greatest love of all, The / Every loser wins / Coming round again / Kiss and say goodbye / Stand by me / Right moment, The / Don't wanna go home alone / Always there / Nikita.
Album: released on K-Tel, Jun'87 by K-Tel Records. Dist: Record Merchandisers Distribution, Taylors, Terry Blood Distribution, Wynd-Up Distribution, Relay Distribution, Pickwick Distribution, Solomon & Peres Distribution, Polygram

Cassette: released on K-Tel, Jun'87 by K-Tel Records. Dist: Record Merchandisers Distribution, Taylors, Terry Blood Distribution, Wynd-Up Distribution, Relay Distribution, Pickwick Distribution, Solomon & Peres Distribution, Polygram

Compact disc: released on K-Tel, 30 May'87 by K-Tel Records. Dist: Record Merchandisers Distribution, Taylors, Terry Blood Distribution, Wynd-Up Distribution, Relay Distribution, Pickwick Distribution, Solomon & Peres Distribution, Polygram

FRIENDS AND LOVERS (Various Artists).
Album: released on K-Tel, 30 May'87 by K-Tel Records. Dist: Record Merchandisers Distribution, Taylors, Terry Blood Distribution, Wynd-Up Distribution, Relay Distribution, Pickwick Distribution, Solomon & Peres Distribution, Polygram

Cassette: released on K-Tel, 30 May'87 by K-Tel Records. Dist: Record Merchandisers Distribution, Taylors, Terry Blood Distribution, Wynd-Up Distribution, Relay Distribution, Pickwick Distribution, Solomon & Peres Distribution, Polygram

THAT'S WHAT FRIENDS ARE FOR.
Single (12"): released on S&G, Feb'82 Dist: Pinnacle

Friends Of Fats

"FRIENDS OF FATS" Various artists (Various Artists).
Notes: Artists include: Herman Autrey/Fred Robinson/Rudy Powell/Etc.
Album: released on Collectors Items, Jul'86 Dist: Jazz Music, Swift, Chris Wellard

Friends Of The Family

ROTTEN TO THE CORE.
Tracks: / Rotten to the core / Honey.
Single (7"): released on Ediesta, Feb'87 by Ediesta Records. Dist: Red Rhino, Cartel

Single (12"): released on Ediesta, Feb'87 by Ediesta Records. Dist: Red Rhino, Cartel

Frier, Tich

GOING STRAIGHT.
Album: released on Celtic Music, Dec'84 by Celtic Music Distribution. Dist: Celtic Music, Jazz Music, Projection, Roots

Friesen, David

AMBER SKIES (Friesen, David/Chic Corea/Paul Horn/Airto).
Album: released on Palo Alto (Italy), Jul'84

PATHS BEYOND TRACING.
Album: released on Steeplechase, Apr'81

Fright Night

"FRIGHT NIGHT" Original sound track.
Tracks: / Fright Night / You can't hide from the beast inside / Good man in a bad time / Rock myself to sleep / Let's talk / Armies of the night / Give it up / Save me tonight / Boppin' tonight / Come to me.
Album: released on Epic, May'86 by CBS Records. Dist: CBS

Cassette: released on Epic, May'86 by CBS Records. Dist: CBS

Frighty Gadman

FUNNY DREAMS (Frighty Gadman & The Offbeat Posse).
Single (12"): released o... Y & D, Jul'87

Frijid Pink

HOUSE OF THE RISING SUN.
Single (7"): released on Deram, Feb'70 by Decca Records. Dist: Polygram

Single (7"): released on Old Gold, Sep'85 by Old Gold Records. Dist: Lightning, Jazz Music, Spartan, Counterpoint

Fripp & Eno

EVENING STAR.
Tracks: / Wind on water / Evening star / Evensong / Wind on wind / An index of metals.
Album: released on E.G., Jan'87 by Virgin Records. Dist: Virgin, EMI

Album: released on Polydor, Oct'77 by Polydor Records. Dist: Polygram, Polydor

NO PUSSY FOOTING.
Tracks: / Heavenly music corporation, The / Swastika girls.
Album: released on E.G., Jan'87 by Virgin Records. Dist: Virgin, EMI

Compact disc: released on Editions EG, Jan'87 by Virgin Records. Dist: EMI

Album: released on Polydor, Oct'77 by Polydor Records. Dist: Polygram, Polydor

Fripp, Robert

BEWITCHED.
Album: released on A&M, Sep'84 by A&M Records. Dist: Polygram

Cassette: released on A&M, Sep'84 by A&M Records. Dist: Polygram

EXPOSURE.
Tracks: / Breathless / Chicago / Disengage / Exposure / First inaugural address to the I.A.C.E. / Sherbourne House / Haaden two / Here comes the flood / I may not have had enough of me but I've had enough of you / Mary / North star / NY3 / Postscript / Preface / Urban landscape / Water music / You burn me up / I'm a cigarette.
Album: released on E.G., Jan'87 by Virgin Records. Dist: Virgin, EMI

Compact disc: released on E.G., Jan'87 by Virgin Records. Dist: Virgin, EMI

Compact disc: released on E.G., Jan'87 by Virgin Records. Dist: Virgin, EMI

Album: released on E.G., Apr'79 by Virgin Records. Dist: Virgin, EMI

Cassette: released on E.G., Apr'79 by Virgin Records. Dist: Virgin, EMI

Album: released on E.G., Jul'85 by Virgin Records. Dist: Virgin, EMI

GOD SAVE THE KING League of gentlemen.
Tracks: / God save the King / Under heavy manners / Heptaparaparshinokh / Inductive resonance / Cognitive dissonance / Dislocated / H.G.Wells / Eye needles / Trap.
Album: released on Editions EG, Jan'87 by Virgin Records. Dist: EMI

Album: released on Editions EG, Jun'85 by Virgin Records. Dist: EMI

GOLD SAVE THE QUEEN.
Cassette: released on E.G., Mar'80 by Virgin Records. Dist: Virgin, EMI

I ADVANCE MASKED (Fripp, Robert & Andy Summers).
Album: released on A&M, Oct'82 by A&M Records. Dist: Polygram

Cassette: released on A&M, Oct'82 by A&M Records. Dist: Polygram

LET THE POWER FALL.
Tracks: / 1984 / 1985 / 1986 / 1987 / 1988 / 1989.
Album: released on Editions EG, Jan'87 by Virgin Records. Dist: EMI

NETWORK.
Tracks: / North Star / Water music/Here comes the flood / God save the King / Under heavy manners.
Album: released on E.G., Jan'87 by Virgin Records. Dist: Virgin, EMI

Cassette: released on E.G., Jan'87 by Virgin Records. Dist: Virgin, EMI

ROBERT FRIPP LIVE With the league of crafty guitarists (Fripp, Robert & The League Of Crafty Guitarists).
Compact disc: released on Editions EG, Nov'86 by Virgin Records. Dist: EMI

Album: released on Editions EG, Nov'86 by Virgin Records. Dist: EMI

Album: released on Editions EG, Nov'86 by Virgin Records. Dist: EMI

UNDER HEAVY MANNERS.
Album: released on E.G., Jan'87 by Virgin Records. Dist: Virgin, EMI

Cassette: released on E.G., Jan'87 by Virgin Records. Dist: Virgin, EMI

Frisco Jazz Band

GOOD MAN IS HARD TO FIND, A.
Album: released on Dawn Club, Dec'86 Dist: Cadillac, Swift, JSU

Frisell, Bill

IN LINE.
Album: released on ECM (Import), May'83 by ECM Records. Dist: IMS, Polygram, Virgin through EMI

RAMBLER.
Tracks: / Tone / Music I heard / Rambler / When we go / Resistor / Strange meeting / Wizard of odds.
Notes: American guitarist Bill Frisell has built up quite a lot of interest since "In Line" (ECM 1241) his first LP on ECM - which was released in 1983.His music is influenced by rock and folk music as well as jazz."Rambler" sees him teamed up with some superb musicians including Kenny Wheeler and Paul Motian. Personnel: Bill Frissell - guitar, guitar synthesizer/Kenny Wheeler - trumpet, cornet, flugelhorn/Bob Stewart - tuba/Jerome Harris - electric bass/ Paul Motian - drums.
Album: released on ECM (Germany), May'85 by ECM Records. Dist: IMS, Polygram, Virgin through EMI

Compact disc: released on ECM (Germany), May'85 by ECM Records. Dist: IMS, Polygram, Virgin through EMI

Frith, Fred

NOUS AUTRE (Frith, Fred & Rene Luiser).
Album: released on Recommended, Jun'87 by Recommended Records. Dist: Recommended, Impetus, Rough Trade

Frizzby Fox

PRETTY BOYS.
Tracks: / Pretty boys / Cut me loose.
Single (7"): released on Hippodrome, Jul'86 Dist: EMI

Single (12"): released on Hippodrome, Jul'86 Dist: EMI

Frizzell, David

I'M GONNA HIRE A WINO TO DECORATE....
Single (7"): released on Warner Brothers, Sep'82 by Warner Bros Records. Dist: WEA

Frizzel, Lefty

HONKY TONKIN'.
Album: released on Flyright, Oct'86 by Flyright Records. Dist: Krazy Kat, Swift, Jazz Music

Frizzell, Lefty

HIS LIFE HIS MUSIC.
Album: released on Bear Family, Nov'84 by Bear Family Records. Dist: Rollercoaster Distribution, Swift

LEGENDARY LAST SESSIONS, THE.
Tracks: / I can't get over you to save my life / I never go around mirrors / If I had half the sense (A fool was born with) / Somebody's words / Lucky arms / Thats the way love goes / If she just helps me to get over you / I buy the wine / Let me give her the flowers / Railroad lady / Lifes's like poetry / She's found the key / Fallin' / I'm not that good at goodbye / My house is your honky tonk / Yesterday just passed my way again / Sittin' and thinkin' / My wishing room / I love you a thousand ways.
Notes: Double album
Album: released on MCA Import, Mar'86 by MCA Records. Dist: Polygram, IMS

Froese, Edgar

AGES.
Tracks: / Metropolis / Era of the slaves / Tropic of Capricorn / Nights of Automaticwoman / Icarus / Children's deeper study / Ode to Granny A / Pizarro and Atahuallpa / Golgatha and the circle closes.
Double Album: released on Virgin, Jan'78 by Virgin Records. Dist: EMI, Virgin Distribution

AQUA.
Tracks: / Ngc 891 / Upland / qua / Panorphelia / NGC 891 / Upland / Aqua / Panorphelia.
Compact disc: released on Virgin, Jun'87 by Virgin Records. Dist: EMI, Virgin Distribution

Album: released on Virgin, Mar'84 by Virgin Records. Dist: EMI, Virgin Distribution

EPSILON IN MALAYSIAN PALE.
Tracks: / Epsilon in Malaysian pale / Maroubra bay.
Compact disc: released on Virgin, Jun'87 by Virgin Records. Dist: EMI, Virgin Distribution

Album: released on Virgin, Mar'84 by Virgin Records. Dist: EMI, Virgin Distribution

MACULA TRANSFER.
Tracks: / Os 452 / Af 765 / Pa 701 / Quantas 611 / If 810.
Album: released on Brain, Mar'82

STUNTMAN.
Tracks: / Drunken Mozart in the desert / If 810 / Tropic of Capricorn / Epsilon in Malaysian pale / Pa 701 / Stunman / OS 452 / Pizarro and Atahuallpa / NGC 891.
Album: released on Virgin, Mar'84 by Virgin Records. Dist: EMI, Virgin Distribution

Frog

FROG HE WOULD A WOOING GO, (A) (& 21 other favourite children's songs).
Album: released on BBC, Feb'76 by BBC Records & Tapes. Dist: EMI, PRT, Pye

Froggatt, Raymond

DON'T LET ME CRY AGAIN.
Single (7"): released on Astra, May'83 by Astra. Dist: Spartan

JETTIN'.
Tracks: / Don't let me cry again.
Single (7"): released on Lots More Music, Nov'86

STAY WITH ME.
Album: released on Merco, Jan'81 Dist: MSD Distribution

Froggits

DR. JAZZ.
Tracks: / Dr. Jazz / Cruising down the river.
Single (7"): released on Tembo, Jun'87 by Tembo (Canada). Dist: IMS Distribution, Polygram Distribution

Frog Prince

FROG PRINCE, (THE) Original Soundtrack (Enya).
Album: released on Island, Oct'85 by Island Records. Dist: Polygram

Cassette: released on Island, Oct'85 by Island Records. Dist: Polygram

Frogs

SUGAR CANE.
Single (12"): released on Sunburst, May'82 Dist: Sunburst Records

Frogs, Freddy

AT MY FRONT DOOR.
Album: released on Nervous, Jul'84 by Nervous Records. Dist: Nervous, Rough Trade

Frohliche Blasmusik

FROHLICHE BLASMUSIK German brass band.
Album: released on Polydor (Germany), Mar'83 Dist: IMS-Polygram

Cassette: released on Polydor (Germany), Mar'83 Dist: IMS-Polygram

From...

Various artists compilations

FROM BROMLEY WITH LOVE Various artists (Various Artists).
Album: released on Alternative, Nov'81 Dist: PRT

FROM BRUSSELS WITH LOVE (Various Artists).
Album: released on Himalaya, Oct'86 by Himalaya Records. Dist: Rough Trade, Cartel

FROM CANADA WITH LOVE Various artists (Various Artists).
Album: released on PM, Jan'80

FROM ERIN'S GREEN SHORE Various artists (Various Artists).
Album: released on Wynd-up, '81 Dist: Wynd-Up Distribution

FROM FINLAND WITH LOVE Various artists (Various Artists).
Album: released on ARC (Accordion Records), '84 Dist: Accordion Record Club

FROM KONGA TO ZION Various artists (Various Artists).
Album: released on Rounder (USA), Jan'84 Dist: Mike's Country Music Room Distribution, Jazz Music Distribution, Swift Distribution, Roots Records Distribution, Projection Distribution, Topic Distribution

FROM L A TO L A Various artists (Various Artists).
Album: released on JSP, Jan'84 by JSP Records. Dist: Swift, Projection

FROM MOTOR CITY TO CENTRAL PARK 1959-67 (Various Artists).
Album: released on Stateside, Jul'87 Dist: EMI

Cassette: released on Stateside, Jul'87 Dist: EMI

FROM SEWINGSHIELDS TO GLENDALE Various artists (Various Artists).
Album: released on MWM, Jul'86 by Mawson & Wareham. Dist: Spartan Distribution, Jazz Music Distribution, JSU Distribution

Cassette: released on MWM, Jun'86 by Mawson & Wareham. Dist: Spartan Distribution, Jazz Music Distribution, JSU Distribution

FROM SWING TO BE-BOP Various artists (Various Artists).
Boxed set: released on RCA (France), '83 by RCA Records. Dist: Discovery

FROM ZE TO ETERNITY Various artists (Various Artists).
Tracks: / Be bop kid / Sweetheart / Twist / Cry for love / Heatwave / Contort yourself / Disco

Clone / Baby you can drive my car / There but for the grace of God go I / Darrio.
Album: released on Island, Oct'80 by Island Records. Dist: Polygram

From 52nd Street

LOOK INTO MY EYES.
Single (12"): released on Factory, Aug'82 by Factory Records. Dist: Cartel, Pinnacle

From Russia With Love

FROM RUSSIA WITH LOVE James bond Original Soundtrack.
Tracks: / James Bond is back - opening titles / From Russia with love / James Bond theme / Tania meets Klebb / Meeting in St. Sophia / Golden horn, The / Girl trouble / Bond meets Tania / 007 / Gypsy camp / Death of Grant / From Russia with love / Spectre island / Guitar lament / Man overboard - Smersh in action / James Bond with bongos / Stalking / Leila dances / Death of Kerim / 007 takes the lektor.
Notes: Conducted by Jonh Barry. All titles published by SBK United Partnership
Album: released on Liberty, Jul'87 by Liberty-United. Dist: EMI

Cassette: released on Liberty, Jul'87 by Liberty-United. Dist: EMI

FROM RUSSIA WITH LOVE Original film soundtrack.
Album: by EMI Records. Dist: Conifer

From the...

Various artists compilations

FROM THE FIFTIES: VOL 2 Various artists (Various Artists).
Album: Dist: Jazz Horizons, Jazz Music, Celtic Music

FROM THE FIFTIES: VOL 1 Various artists (Various Artists).
Album: Dist: Jazz Horizons, Jazz Music, Celtic Music

FROM THE FORTIES: VOL 2 Various artists (Various Artists).
Album: Dist: Jazz Horizons, Jazz Music, Celtic Music

FROM THE FORTIES: VOL 1 Various artists (Various Artists).
Album: Dist: Jazz Horizons, Jazz Music, Celtic Music

FROM THE HOUSE OF LORDS (Various Artists).
Album: released on Bam Caruso, Jan'87 by Bam Caruso Records. Dist: Rough Trade, Revolver, Cartel

FROM THE IRISH TRADITION: VOL 1 Various artists (Various Artists).
Cassette: released on Gael-Linn (Ireland), Aug'85 by Gael Linn Records. Dist: Roots, Projection, Celtic Music, Jazz Music

FROM THE IRISH TRADITION: VOL 2 Various artists (Various Artists).
Cassette: released on Gael-Linn (Ireland), Aug'85 by Gael Linn Records. Dist: Roots, Projection, Celtic Music, Jazz Music

FROM THE IRISH TRADITION: VOL 3 Various artists (Various Artists).
Cassette: released on Gael-Linn (Ireland), Aug'85 by Gael Linn Records. Dist: Roots, Projection, Celtic Music, Jazz Music

FROM THE VAULTS Various Motown artists (Various Artists).
Album: released on Motown, Nov'82 by Motown Records. Dist: BMG Distribution

Cassette: released on Motown, Nov'82 by Motown Records. Dist: BMG Distribution

From The Time You Say Good-

FROM THE TIME YOU SAY GOODBYE Original artists (Original artists).
Compact disc: released on The Compact Collection, Sep'87 by Conifer Records. Dist: Conifer Distribution

Front 242

GEOGRAPHY.
Album: released on Mask, Nov'86 Dist: Rough Trade

INTERCEPTION.
Single (12"): released on Red Rhino (Europe), Nov'86

NO COMMENT.
Album: released on MK, Jan'87

NO SHUFFLE.
Tracks: / No shuffle / Body to body.
Single (7"): released on Himalaya, Feb'86 by Himalaya Records. Dist: Rough Trade, Cartel

Single (12"): released on Himalaya, Feb'86 by Himalaya Records. Dist: Rough Trade, Cartel

OFFICIAL VERSION.
Tracks: / What you have is what you get / Rerun / Television station / Agressive due / Masterhit pts 1 & 2 / Slaughter / Quite unusual / Red team / Agressive angst.
Notes: CD includes 2 extended tracks
Compact disc: released on Red Rhino, Jun'87 by Red Rhino Records. Dist: Red Rhino, Cartel

PRINCIPLES.
Single (7"): released on New Dance, May'82 Dist: Rough Trade, Red Rhino, Cartel

TWO IN ONE.
Tracks: / Two in one.
Single (12"): released on 242, Jan'86 Dist: Red Rhino, Cartel

U MEN.
Single (7"): released on New Dance, May'82 Dist: Rough Trade, Red Rhino. Cartel

Front line

FRONT LINE Various artists (Various Artists).
Tracks: / Right time / Natty rebel / Declaration of rights / Don't touch I man locks / Looks in deceiving / Great Psalms, The / Civilisation / Know your self mankind / Africa.
Album: released on Caroline, May'77 Dist: Virgin, Island, Polygram, CBS

FRONT LINE 11 Various artists (Various Artists).
Tracks: / Jah works / Natty dread upon a mountain top / I love you so / Foggy road / Mr. Brassie / Sister bella / Make a truce / Dread beat and blood / Rub a dub style / Holy mount zion / Tribute to Steve Biko / Love we a deal with / Jordan river / Cocaine.
Album: by Virgin Records. Dist: EMI, Virgin Distribution

FRONTLINE SAMPLER Various artists (Various Artists).
Album: released on Virgin, Sep'79 by Virgin Records. Dist: EMI, Virgin Distribution

Frost, Frank

FRANK FROST.
Album: released on Jewel, Sep'79
Cat. no: **JEWEL 5013**

HEY BOSS MAN (Frost, Frank with the Night Hawks).
Album: released on Charly, Feb'81 by Charly Records. Dist: Charly, Cadillac

RIDE WITH YOUR DADDY TONIGHT.
Tracks: / My back scratcher / Never leave me at home / Harpin' on it / Things you do / Feel good babe / Pocket full of money / Ride with your Daddy tonight / Got my Mojo working / Janie on my mind / Harp and soul / Didn't mean no harm / Pretty baby / Five long years.
Notes: Publishers: Jog Music - Hillsboro except 'Five years long' - Frederick Music. A Jewel Recording.
Album: released on Charly(R&B), May'85 by Charly Records. Dist: Charly, Cadillac

Frost, Kid

TERMINATOR.
Tracks: / Terminator (vocal mix) / Terminator (Inst.).
Single (12"): released on ZYX (Germany), Feb'86 by ZYX Records. Dist: Greyhound

Frozen Ghost

FROZEN GHOST.
Tracks: / Should Isee / Promises / Yum Bai Ya / Promises / Beware the Masque / Love like a fire / End of the line / Time is the answer / Love without lies / Soldiers cry / Truth in lies.
Album: released on WEA, Jul'87 by WEA Records. Dist: WEA

Cassette: released on WEA, Jul'87 by WEA Records. Dist: WEA

SHOULD I SEE.
Tracks: / Should I see / Suspended humanation.
Single (7"): released on WEA (Canada), Jul'87

Frugivores

MOTH INTO THE FLAME.
Tracks: / Moth into the flame / Scales.
Single (7"): released on Coda, 23 May'87 by Coda Records. Dist: Pinnacle, Cartel, WEA, Roots

NEW AGE SONGS.
Album: released on Coda, Aug'87 by Coda Records. Dist: Pinnacle, Cartel, WEA, Roots
Cat. no: **NAGE 13**
Cassette: released on Coda, Aug'87 by Coda Records. Dist: Pinnacle, Cartel, WEA. Roots

Fruit of the original sin

FRUIT OF THE ORIGINAL SIN Various artists (Various Artists).
Double Album: released on Les Disques Du Crepuscule, Sep'81 Dist: Rough Trade, Pinnacle, Island, Polygram

Fruits of Passion

ALL I EVER WANTED.
Single (7"): released on Siren, Mar'85 by Virgin Records. Dist: EMI

EVERYTHING I EVER WANTED.
Tracks: / Everything I ever wanted / Everything I had.
Single (7"): released on Siren, Aug'86 by Virgin Records. Dist: EMI

Single (12"): released on Siren, Aug'86 by Virgin Records. Dist: EMI

FRUITS OF PASSION, THE.
Album: released on Siren, Oct'86 by Virgin Records. Dist: EMI

Cassette: released on Siren, Oct'86 by Virgin Records. Dist: EMI

KISS ME NOW.
Tracks: / Kiss me now / Place in the heart,A.
Single (7"): released on Siren, May'86 by Virgin Records. Dist: EMI

Single (12"): released on Siren, May'86 by Virgin Records. Dist: EMI

LOVE'S GLORY.
Tracks: / Love's glory.
Single (7"): released on Siren-Virgin, Mar'86

Single (12"): released on Siren-Virgin, Mar'86

NO MORE TEARS.
Tracks: / Nothing but a prayer / Kissing me (ext).
Single (7"): released on Siren, Nov'86 by Virgin Records. Dist: EMI

Single (12"): released on Siren, Nov'86 by Virgin Records. Dist: EMI

Fruscella, Tony

FRU & BREW (Fruscella, Tony/Brew Moore).
Album: released on Spotlite, '83 by Spotlite Records. Dist: Cadillac, Jazz Music, Spotlite

Fudge, Mickie

IF WE STOP.
Single (7"): released on PRT, May'84 by PRT Records. Dist: PRT

Fugs

GOLDEN FILTH.
Album: released on Edsel, Feb'87 by Demon Records. Dist: Pinnacle, Jazz Music, Projection

IT CRAWLED INTO MY HAND, HONEST.
Album: released on Edsel, Mar'86 by Demon Records. Dist: Pinnacle, Jazz Music, Projection

Cassette: released on Edsel, Mar'86 by Demon Records. Dist: Pinnacle, Jazz Music, Projection

NO MORE SLAVERY.
Album: released on New Rose, Mar'86 Dist: Rough Trade, Cartel

Compact disc: released on New Rose, Jul'86 Dist: Rough Trade, Cartel

REFUSE TO BE BURNT-OUT.
Album: released on New Rose, Apr'85 Dist: Rough Trade, Cartel

STAR PEACE.
Double Album: released on New Rose, Jun'87 Dist: Rough Trade, Cartel

Fuhrs and Frohling

AMMERLAND.
Album: released on Logo, '79 by Logo Records. Dist: Roots, BMG

DIARY.
Album: released on Brah, May'81

Fukumura, Hiroshi

HUNT UP WIND.
Album: released on Inner City, Sep'80 Dist: Jetstar

Full Circle

FULL CIRCLE original film sound track (Towns, Colin).
Album: released on Virgin, Feb'78 by Virgin Records. Dist: EMI, Virgin Distribution

WORKIN' UP A SWEAT.
Tracks: / Workin' up a sweat / Workin' up a sweat dub version.
Single (7"): released on EMI America, Feb'87 by EMI Records. Dist: EMI

Single (12"): released on EMI America, Feb'87 by EMI Records. Dist: EMI

Fuller, Blind Boy

BLUE AND WORRIED MAN.
Album: released on Travelin' Man (USA), Jan'84

ON DOWN 1937-40.
Album: released on Magpie, Oct'79 Dist: Projection

SHAKE THAT SHIMMY (1935-8).
Album: released on Magpie, Apr'79 Dist: Projection

TRUCKIN' MY BLUES AWAY.
Album: released on Yazoo, May'79 Dist: Swift, Projection

Fuller, Bobby

BOBBY FULLER INSTRUMENTAL ALBUM.
Album: released on Rockhouse, Sep'85 Dist: Pinnacle

I FOUGHT THE LAW (Fuller, Bobby Four).
Single (7"): released on Revival, Jul'82 Dist: Lightning, Swift

INSTRUMENTAL ALBUM.
Album: released on Rockhouse, Nov'85 by Rockhouse Records. Dist: Swift Distribution, Charly Distribution

LIVE AGAIN.
Album: released on EVA, Dec'84

LOVE'S MADE A FOOL OF YOU.
Single (7"): released on Rockhouse, Sep'84 by Rockhouse Records. Dist: Swift Distribution, Charly Distribution

MEMORIES OF BUDDY HOLLY.
Album: released on Rockhouse, May'84 by Rockhouse Records. Dist: Swift Distribution, Charly Distribution

Fuller, Curtis

ALL STAR SEXTETS.
Double Album:

BLUESETTE.
Notes: Artists include:Curtis Fuller-Trombone/Benny Golson-Tenor Sax./Tommy Flanagan- Piano/Jimmy Garrison-Bass/Al Harewood-Drums. The excellent trombonist, Curtis Fuller, aged 24, followed success with LP's on Prestige and Blue Note, and musicans Kenny Burrell, Sonny Clarke and Lee Morgan to record this superb album as a leader for Savoy in 1959 and that year he was rewarded by winning the Trom-bone New Star Category' in the 'down beat' critics' poll. At the same time, Benny Golson - also featured in this album - won the 'down beat' Outstanding New Arranger Award. Recorded in New Jersey 1959.
Album: released on Savoy Jazz, Dec'85 by RCA Records (Germany). Dist: Conifer

Album: released on Savoy (France), Nov'84

FIRE & FILIGREE.
Album: released on Beehive (USA), Dec'79 by Cadillac Records. Dist: JSU

FOUR ON THE OUTSIDE.
Notes: With Pepper Adams/J.Williams/Etc.
Album: released on Timeless(import), Sep'86 Dist: Cadillac

NEW TROMBONE.
Album: released on Prestige (USA), Feb'84

WITH FRENCH HORNS.
Album: released on Fantasy Inc USA, Feb'86 by Fantasy Inc USA Records. Dist: IMS, Polygram

Fuller, Jesse

FRISCO BLUES.
Album: released on Arhoolie, May'81 by Arhoolie Records. Dist: Projection, Topic, Jazz Music, Swift, Roots

JAZZ FOLKSONGS,SPIRITUALS & BLUES.
Album: released on Good Time Jazz (USA), Sep'81 by Good Time Jazz Records (USA). Dist: Polygram

MOVE ON DOWN THE LINE.
Album: released on Topic, '81 Dist: Roots Distribution

SAN FRANCISCO BAY BLUES.
Album: released on Contemporary (USA), Sep'82 Dist: Fantasy (USA) Distribution

Album: released on Ace, 7 Sep'87 by Ace Records. Dist: Pinnacle, Swift, Hotshot, Cadillac

Fuller, Johnny

FOOLS PARADISE.
Album: released on Diving Duck (Holland)duckh, Sep'84

Fullerton College

PRIMARILY JAZZ.
Album: released on AM-PM USA, Apr'84 Dist: Swift

TIME TRIPPIN'.
Album: released on AM-PM USA, Apr'84 Dist: Swift

UNFORGETTABLE.
Tracks: / In the mood / But Beautiful / Sweet Georgie Brown / Easy livin / Someday my Prince will come / That's all and more.
Notes: Winner of the 1985 National Association of Jazz Educator's Disney-world-competition and opening band for the 1985 Playboy Jazz Festival: Tom Ranier/Jim Linahon/Jeff Tower/Doug Gregan/Tim Grindheim:
Compact disc: by A&M Records. Dist: Polygram

Full Faith

DEBUT (Full Faith & Credit Big Band).
Album: released on Palo Alto (Italy), Jan'84

JAZZFAIRE (Full Faith & Credit Big Band).
Album: released on Palo Alto (Italy), Jan'84

Full Force

ALICE I WANT YOU JUST FOR ME.
Tracks: / Alice I want you just for me / Alice /Erol's favourite.
Single (7"): released on CBS, Dec'85 by CBS Records. Dist: CBS

Single (12"): released on CBS, Dec'85 by CBS Records. Dist: CBS

FULL FORCE.
Album: released on CBS, Sep'85 by CBS Records. Dist: CBS

Cassette: released on CBS, Sep'85 by CBS Records. Dist: CBS

FULL FORCE GET READY 1 TIME.
Tracks: / Unfaithful / Never had another lover / Old flames never die / Child's play /part1 / So much / Chain me to the night / Body heavenly / Love scene / Child's play /partII.
Album: released on CBS, Aug'86 by CBS Records. Dist: CBS

Cassette: released on CBS, Aug'86 by CBS Records. Dist: CBS

TEMPORARY LOVE THING, THE.
Tracks: / Temporary love thing, The / Temporary bow legged theatre..
Single (7"): released on CBS, Sep'86 by CBS Records. Dist: CBS

Single (12"): released on CBS, Sep'86 by CBS Records. Dist: CBS

UNSELFISH LOVER.
Tracks: / Unselfish lover / Have you kissed your child lately.
Single (7"): released on CBS, Feb'86 by CBS Records. Dist: CBS

Full house

FULL HOUSE Various artists (Various Artists).
Album: released on Dansan, Feb'83 by Spartan Records. Dist: Spartan

Full Metal Jacket

FULL METAL JACKET Original soundtrack.
Album: released on Warner Brothers, Oct'87 by Warner Bros Records. Dist: WEA

Cassette: released on Warner Brothers, Oct'87 by Warner Bros Records. Dist: WEA

Full Time Men

FAST IS MY NAME.
Tracks: / Fast is my name/EP.
Single (12"): released on Homestead, Oct'86 Dist: Rough Trade, Cartel, Shigaku

Full Wood

STOP AND THINK ME OVER.
Single (12"): released on Freedom Sounds, Dec'84 by Freedom Sounds Records. Dist: Jetstar

Fulson, Lowell

BLUE DAYS, BLACK NIGHTS.
Tracks: / Talkin woman / Black nights / Sittin here thinkin / Little angel / Shattered dreams / I found love / Hustler's game / Get your game uptight / Tramp / Back to Chicago / Everyday / Funky broadway.
Notes: 12" LP.
Album: released on Ace, Aug'86 by Ace Records. Dist: Pinnacle, Swift, Hotshot, Cadillac

BLUES GOT ME DOWN, THE.
Album: released on Diving Duck (Holland)duckh, May'85

HUNG DOWN HEAD.
Album: released on Chess, Oct'86 by Charly Records. Dist: Charly, Swift, PRT, Discovery, IMS, Polygram

I DON'T KNOW MY MIND.
Tracks: / Kansas City / Drifting blues / I cried like a baby / I want affection not protection / Don't make promises you can't keep / Blood sweat and tears / You're gonna miss me / Let me ride in your automobile / Getting drunk / Walk on / Sweetest thing / Come back baby / Your woman / You don't know my mind.
Album: released on Bear Family, Sep'87 by Bear Family Records. Dist: Rollercoaster Distribution, Swift. Estim retail price in Aug'87 was £8.99.

IN A HEAVY BAG.
Album: released on Jewel, Sep'79

I'VE GOT THE BLUES.
Album: released on Topline, Aug'87 by Charly Records. Dist: Charly Distribution. Estim retail price in Sep'87 was £2.99.

Cassette: released on Topline, Aug'87 by Charly Records. Dist: Charly Distribution. Estim retail price in Sep'87 was £2.99.

LOWELL FULSON.
Album: released on Chess, Jun'84 by Charly Records. Dist: Charly, Swift, PRT, Discovery, IMS, Polygram

Cassette: released on Chess, Jun'84 by Charly Records. Dist: Charly, Swift, PRT, Discovery, IMS, Polygram

LOWELL FULSON & HIS GUITAR.
Album: released on Arhoolie, May'81 by Arhoolie Records. Dist: Projection, Topic, Jazz Music, Swift, Roots

MAN OF MOTION.
Album: released on Charly, Mar'81 by Charly Records. Dist: Charly, Cadillac

OL' BLUES SINGER, THE.
Album: released on Jet, Jan'76 by Jet Records. Dist: CBS

THINK TWICE BEFORE YOU SPEAK.
Album: released on JSP, Dec'84 by JSP Records. Dist: Swift, Projection

Fulton, Bill

BAKER'S DOZEN.
Album: released on REL, May'79 Dist: Roots

Fun At One

FUN AT ONE Comedy from Radio 1 (Various Artists).
Album: by BBC Records & Tapes. Dist: EMI, PRT, Pye

Cassette: released on BBC, Nov'79 by BBC Records & Tapes. Dist: EMI, PRT, Pye

MORE FUN AT ONE Various artists (Various Artists).
Album: released on BBC, Nov'80 by BBC Records & Tapes. Dist: EMI, PRT, Pye

Fun Boy Three

BEST OF FUN BOY THREE, THE.
Album: released on Chrysalis, Jun'84 by Chrysalis Records. Dist: CBS

Cassette: released on Chrysalis, Jun'84 by Chrysalis Records. Dist: CBS

BEST OF..., THE.
Notes: Inc:The lunatics have taken over the asylum/Our lips are sealed/T'aint what you do/Tunnel of love etc
Compact disc: released on Chrysalis, Jun'87 by Chrysalis Records. Dist: CBS

FUN BOY THREE.
Album: released on Chrysalis, Mar'82 by Chrysalis Records. Dist: CBS

Cassette: released on Chrysalis, Mar'82 by Chrysalis Records. Dist: CBS

Album: released on Fame, Nov'84 by Music For Pleasure Records. Dist: EMI

Cassette: released on Fame, Nov'84 by Music For Pleasure Records. Dist: EMI

OUR LIPS ARE SEALED.
Single (7"): released on Chrysalis, Apr'83 by Chrysalis Records. Dist: CBS

Single (12"): released on Chrysalis, Apr'83 by Chrysalis Records. Dist: CBS

WAITING.
Album: released on Chrysalis, Feb'83 by Chrysalis Records. Dist: CBS

Cassette: released on Chrysalis, Feb'83 by Chrysalis Records. Dist: CBS

Fundeburgh, Anson

TALK TO YOU BY HAND (Fundeburgh, Anson & The Rockets).
Album: released on Krazy Kat (USA), Jan'83

Funeral Directors

CORPSE GRINDER.
Single (7"): released on Hell Apostal, Oct'82 Dist: Rough Trade, Cartel

Funeral Parade

FUNERAL PARADE(EP).
Single (7"): released on Paraworm, Feb'83

Fun & Frenzy

FALLEN DOWN IN LOVE.
Single (7"): released on Broiler, May'84

Fun Fun

BAILA BOLERO.
Tracks: / Happy station.
Single (7"): released on Carrere, Aug'87 by Carrere Records. Dist: PRT, Spartan

Single (12"): released on Carrere, Aug'87 by Carrere Records. Dist: PRT, Spartan

Funhouse

BED OF NAILS.
Single (7"): released on Flux, May'84 by Flux Records. Dist: Cartel

Funkadelic

HARDCORE JOLLIES.
Album: released on Warner Bros., Feb'78 by Warner Bros Records. Dist: WEA

ONE NATION UNDER A GROOVE.
Single (7"): released on Warner Bros., '78 by Warner Bros Records. Dist: WEA

Funkcrew

BREAKING HEARTS.
Tracks: / Breaking hearts / Work hard work / Ghosts in the machinery.
Single (7"): released on Sophisticated Noise, Oct'86

Single (12"): released on Sophisticated Noise, Oct'86

Funk Deluex

THIS TIME.
Tracks: / This time / This time (Dub Version).
Single (12"): released on Streetwave, Jun'86 by Streetwave Records. Dist: PRT Distribution

Funk, Farley Jackmaster

LOVE CAN'T TURN AROUND.
Tracks: / Love can't turn around / Love can't turn around /Dub..
Single (7"): released on London, Aug'86 by London Records. Dist: Polygram

Single (12"): released on London, Aug'86 by London Records. Dist: Polygram

Funkin Marvellous

FUNKIN MARVELLOUS Various Artists (Various Artists).
Album: released on Steiner, Nov'85

Cassette: released on Steiner, Nov'85

Funk Masters

BOUWKOOL.
Single (12"): released on Master Funk, Nov'82 by Master Funk Records. Dist: PRT

HAVE YOU GOT THE TIME.
Tracks: / Have you got the time / Have you got the time (version).
Single (7"): released on Master Funk, Jul'87 by Master Funk Records. Dist: PRT

Single (12"): released on Master Funk, Jul'87 by Master Funk Records. Dist: PRT

IT'S OVER.
Single (7"): released on Master Funk, Oct'84 by Master Funk Records. Dist: PRT

Single (12"): released on Master Funk, Oct'84 by Master Funk Records. Dist: PRT

LOVE MONEY.
Single (12"): released on Tania Music, Oct'81

MERRY CHRISTMAS.
Single (7"): released on Master Funk, Nov'84 by Master Funk Records. Dist: PRT

Single (12"): released on Master Funk, Nov'84 by Master Funk Records. Dist: PRT

Funkmeister

DEBAUCH MIX, THE.
Picture disc single: released on Ryker, Jan'85 by Ryker Records. Dist: CBS Distribution

Single (12"): released on Ryker, Jan'85 by Ryker Records. Dist: CBS Distribution

WAR DANCE.
Single (7"): released on Ryker, Jan'85 by Ryker Records. Dist: CBS Distribution

Single (12"): released on Ryker, Jan'85 by Ryker Records. Dist: CBS Distribution

Funk 'n' Soul Revolution

FUNK 'N' SOUL REVOLUTION Various Artists. (Various Artists).
Notes: Artists include: Boobie Knight & Universal Lady/Alvin Cash/Eliminators/Chi Lites/B.W. & Next Edition/Hamilton Bohannon/Sidney Joe Qualis/Chuck Jones & Company/ Rare Pleasure/Sly & Family Stone/Ann Bailey/Tyrone Davis.
Album: released on Kent, Feb'86 by Ace Records. Dist: Pinnacle

Funkrew

GOTTA BE STRONG.
Tracks: / Gotta be strong / Gotta be strong (gospel version) / Ghost in the machine*.
Single (7"): released on Arista, 20 Jun'87 by Arista Records. Dist: RCA

Single (12"): released on Arista, 20 Jun'87 by Arista Records. Dist: RCA

Funky

FUNKY various artists.
Album: released on Mercury, Dec'81 by Phonogram Records. Dist: Polygram Distribution
Cat. no: **6498 141**

Cassette: released on Mercury, Dec'81 by Phonogram Records. Dist: Polygram Distribution

Funky Alternative

FUNKY ALTERNATIVES (VOL. 2) Various artists (Various Artists).
Notes: LP collection featuring Stump, The Dave Howard singers (Yon Yonson), Chakk,Caba ret-Voltaire, Quando Quango, The Original Unknown Deejays and New York Pig Fun kers.
Album: Dist: Revolver, Cartel, Nine Mile, Red Rhino, Pinnacle. Estim retail price in Sep'87 was £6.29.

Funky Christmas Band

FUNKY CHRISTMAS.
Single (12"): released on JJ, Nov'85 Dist: Stage One

Funky Party

FUNKY PARTY various artists (Various Artists).
Cassette: released on Mercury (France)_, Nov'84

Fun Lovers

JOYRIDE.
Album: released on Rebel (Australia), Feb'84 Dist: Swift

Funny Commercials...

FUNNY COMMERCIALS & OTHER RADIO FLUFFS various artists (Various Artists).
Album: released on Tandem, '78 Dist: Solomon & Peres Distribution

Funny Feeling

FUNNY FEELING various artists (Various Artists).
Album: released on Burning Sounds, '78 by Ross, Bill/Burning Sounds Records. Dist: PRT

Funny Feet

FUNNY FEET variousa (Various Artists).
Album: released on Invicta, Jul'84 by Audio-Visual Productions. Dist: Spartan

Funny Girl

FUNNY GIRL Original soundtrack(starring Barbara Streisand) (Various Artists).
Compact disc: released on CBS, May'87 by CBS Records. Dist: CBS

Album: by CBS Records. Dist: CBS

FUNNY GIRL - ORIGINAL BROADWAY CAST with Barbara Streisand & Sidney Chaplin (Various Artists).
Tracks: / Overture / If a girl isn't pretty / I'm the greatest star / Cornet man / Who taught her everything / His love makes me beautiful / I want to be seen with you tonight / Henry Street / People / You are woman / Don't rain on my parade / Sadie Sadie / Find yourself a man / Rat-tat-tat-tat / Who are you now / Music that makes me dance, The / Finale.
Notes: Inc. Barbra Streisand, Sydney Chaplin, Kay Medford, Danny Meehan, Jean Stapleton. Conducted by Milton Rosenstock. Songs by Jule Styne & Bob Merrill.
Compact disc: released on EMI, Jun'87 by EMI Records. Dist: EMI

Album: released on Capitol, May'85 by Capitol Records. Dist: EMI

Cassette: released on Capitol, May'85 by Capitol Records. Dist: EMI

Page 388

Funny Man

FUNNY MAN various artists from the 20's & 30's (Various Artists).
Album: released on World Records, Jun'81 Dist: Polygram

Cassette: released on World Records, Jun'81 Dist: Polygram

Funny thing happened...

FUNNY THING HAPPENED... ...on the way to the Forum (Various Artists).
Tracks: / Overture / Comedy tonight / Love, I hear / Lovely / Pretty little picture / Everybody ought to have a maid / I'm calm / Impossible / Bring me my bride / That dirty old man / That'll show him / Lovely (2) / Funeral sequence and dance / Comedy tonight (2).
Notes: Book by B.Shevelove & L.Gelbart: Music and Lyrics by S.Sondheim: Published by Chappell Music Ltd: (P) 1963:Original Sound recordings made by EMI Records Ltd.
Album: released on EMI, Feb'87 by EMI Records. Dist: EMI

Cassette: released on EMI, Feb'87 by EMI Records. Dist: EMI

Fun Patrol

RIGHT WAY TO BE WRONG, THE.
Single (12"): released on Thrush, 30 May'87 Dist: Pinnacle

Furay, Richie

I'VE GOT A REASON.
Album: released on Myrrh, May'82 by Word Records. Dist: Word Distribution

Cassette: released on Myrrh, May'82 by Word Records. Dist: Word Distribution

SEASONS OF CHANGE.
Album: released on Myrrh, May'82 by Word Records. Dist: Word Distribution

Cassette: released on Myrrh, May'82 by Word Records. Dist: Word Distribution

Fur Bible

PLUNDER THE TOMBS.
Single (12"): released on New Rose, Nov'85 Dist: Rough Trade, Cartel

Furey Brothers

EMIGRANT (Furey Brothers & Davey Arthur).
Album: released on Polydor (Eire), Jan'85

FUREYS IN CONCERT, THE (Furey Brothers & Davey Arthur).
Album: released on Ritz, Jul'84 by Outlet Records. Dist: Outlet, Prism Leisure Distribution, Record Services Distribution (Ireland), Roots

Cassette: released on Ritz, Jul'84 by Outlet Records. Dist: Outlet, Prism Leisure Distribution, Record Services Distribution (Ireland), Roots

MORNING ON A DISTANT SHORE (Furey Brothers & Davey Arthur).
Album: released on Polydor (Eire), Jan'85

Furey,Eddie & Finbar

COLLECTION: EDDIE & FINBAR FUREY.
Compact disc: released on Castle Collectors, Jul'87 by Castle Communications Records. Dist: Pinnacle

FINBAR & EDDIE FUREY.
Double Album: released on Cambra, Apr'85 by Cambra Records. Dist: IDS, Conifer

Double cassette: released on Cambra, Apr'85 by Cambra Records. Dist: IDS, Conifer

Album: released on Harp(Ireland), Feb'82 by Pickwick Records. Dist: Taylors

Cassette: released on Harp(Ireland), Feb'82 by Pickwick Records. Dist: Taylors

TOWN IS NOT THEIR OWN, THE.
Album: released on Harp(Ireland), May'80 by Pickwick Records. Dist: Taylors

Furey, Finbar

TRADITIONAL IRISH PIPE MUSIC.
Cassette: released on Autograph, Apr'85 Dist: Record Services Distribution (Ireland)

Fureys

ANNIVERSARY SONG.
Single (7"): released on Ritz, Sep'82 by Outlet Records. Dist: Outlet, Prism Leisure Distribution, Record Services Distribution (Ireland), Roots

AT THE END OF THE DAY (Fureys & Davey Arthur).
Album: released on K-Tel, Nov'85 by K-Tel Records. Dist: Record Merchandisers Distribution, Taylors, Terry Blood Distribution, Wynd-Up Distribution, Relay Distribution, Pickwick Distribution, Solomon & Peres Distribution, Polygram

Cassette: released on K-Tel, Nov'85 by K-Tel Records. Dist: Record Merchandisers Distribution, Taylors, Terry Blood Distribution, Wynd-Up Distribution, Relay Distribution, Pickwick Distribution, Solomon & Peres Distribution, Polygram

COLLECTION, THE (Furey, Finbar & Eddie).
Tracks: / Rakish Paddy / Hag with the money, The / Bill Hart's favourite / Dance around the spinning wheel / Fin's favourite / Spanish cloak, The / Young girl milking the cow, The / Set dance - piper in the meadow straying.
Notes: Tracks include those listed above.
Double Album: released on Collector Series, Sep'87 by Castle Communications Records. Dist: PRT, Pinnacle, RCA, Ariola

Cassette: released on Collector Series, Sep'87 by Castle Communications Records. Dist: PRT, Pinnacle, RCA, Ariola

Compact disc: released on Collector Series, Sep'87 by Castle Communications Records. Dist: PRT, Pinnacle, RCA, Ariola

DREAMING MY DREAMS.
Single (7"): released on Ritz, Jun'85 by Outlet Records. Dist: Outlet, Prism Leisure Distribution, Record Services Distribution (Ireland), Roots

FIRST LEAVES OF AUTUMN, THE (Fureys & Davey Arthur).
Tracks: / First leaves of Autumn / Sitting alone.
Single (7"): released on Ritz, Sep'86 by Outlet Records. Dist: Outlet, Prism Leisure Distribution, Record Services Distribution (Ireland), Roots

FUREYS & DAVEY ARTHUR,THE (Fureys & Davey Arthur).
Compact disc: released on K-Tel, Nov'86 by K-Tel Records. Dist: Record Merchandisers Distribution, Taylors, Terry Blood Distribution, Wynd-Up Distribution, Relay Distribution, Pickwick Distribution, Solomon & Peres Distribution, Polygram

GOLDEN DAYS (Fureys & Davey Arthur).
Album: released on K-Tel, Oct'84 by K-Tel Records. Dist: Record Merchandisers Distribution, Taylors, Terry Blood Distribution, Wynd-Up Distribution, Relay Distribution, Pickwick Distribution, Solomon & Peres Distribution, Polygram

Cassette: released on K-Tel, Oct'84 by K-Tel Records. Dist: Record Merchandisers Distribution, Taylors, Terry Blood Distribution, Wynd-Up Distribution, Relay Distribution, Pickwick Distribution, Solomon & Peres Distribution, Polygram

GREEN FIELDS OF FRANCE.
Single (7"): released on Ritz, Jul'82 by Outlet Records. Dist: Outlet, Prism Leisure Distribution, Record Services Distribution (Ireland), Roots

I WILL LOVE YOU EVERYTIME.
Single (7"): released on Ritz, Feb'82 by Outlet Records. Dist: Outlet, Prism Leisure Distribution, Record Services Distribution (Ireland), Roots

NOW IS THE HOUR (FAREWELL) (Fureys & Davey Arthur).
Single (7"): released on Ritz, May'83 by Outlet Records. Dist: Outlet, Prism Leisure Distribution, Record Services Distribution (Ireland), Roots

SCARLET RIBBONS (Fureys & Davey Arthur).
Single (7"): released on Ritz, Nov'84 by Outlet Records. Dist: Outlet, Prism Leisure Distribution, Record Services Distribution (Ireland), Roots

SOUND OF,THE (Fureys & Davey Arthur).
Tracks: / Green fields of France,The / Gypsy Davey / Reason I left Mullinger,The / Clare to here / Ask me father / Finbar Dwyers / Old oak tree,The / Lark on the strand / Her father didn't like me anyway. / Shipyard slips / Leaving of Nancy,The / O'Carolans tribute / Roster,The / Night ferry / Lament / Beer,beer,beer / Lonesome boatmam.
Album: released on Polydor (Ireland), Sep'86 by Polydor Records. Dist: Polygram, I & B

Cassette: released on Polydor (Ireland), Sep'86 by Polydor Records. Dist: Polygram, I & B

STEAL AWAY (Fureys & Davey Arthur).
Album: released on Ritz, Oct'83 by Outlet Records. Dist: Outlet, Prism Leisure Distribution, Record Services Distribution (Ireland), Roots

STEAL AWAY(7") (Fureys & Davey Arthur).
Single (7"): released on Ritz, Oct'83 by Outlet Records. Dist: Outlet, Prism Leisure Distribution, Record Services Distribution (Ireland), Roots

TOMORROW WE PART (Fureys & Bob Stewart).
Album: released on Broadside, May'85 by Broadside Records. Dist: Celtic Distributions, H.R. Taylor, Jazz Music, Projection, Jazz Services Unlimited Dist. (JSU)

WHEN YOU WERE SWEET SIXTEEN (Fureys & Davey Arthur).
Compact disc: released on Ritz, Oct'86 by Outlet Records. Dist: Outlet, Prism Leisure Distribution, Record Services Distribution (Ireland), Roots

Album: released on Ritz, Apr'82 by Outlet Records. Dist: Outlet, Prism Leisure Distribution, Record Services Distribution (Ireland), Roots

Cassette: released on Ritz, Apr'82 by Outlet Records. Dist: Outlet, Prism Leisure Distribution, Record Services Distribution (Ireland), Roots

WHEN YOU WERE SWEET 16 (Fureys & Davey Arthur).
Single (7"): released on Ritz, Aug'81 by Outlet Records. Dist: Outlet, Prism Leisure Distribution, Record Services Distribution (Ireland), Roots

Furies

DREAMING MY DREAMS.
Tracks: / Dreaming my dreams / Paddy in Paris.
Single (7"): released on Ritz, May'87 by Outlet Records. Dist: Outlet, Prism Leisure Distribution, Record Services Distribution (Ireland), Roots

FIRST LEAVES OF AUTUMN, THE.
Album: released on Ritz, Nov'86 by Outlet Records. Dist: Outlet, Prism Leisure Distribution, Record Services Distribution (Ireland), Roots

Cassette: released on Ritz, Nov'86 by Outlet Records. Dist: Outlet, Prism Leisure Distribution, Record Services Distribution (Ireland), Roots

Furious Apples

FURIOUS APPLES (EP).
Single (7"): released on Sonar, Nov'83 by Sonar Records. Dist: Sonar

Furious Pig

I DON'T LIKE YOUR FACE.
Single (7"): released on Rough Trade, Mar'81 by Rough Trade Records. Dist: Rough Trade Distribution, Cartel Distribution

Single (12"): released on Rough Trade, Feb'81 by Rough Trade Records. Dist: Rough Trade Distribution, Cartel Distribution

Furniss, Paul

VANITY FAIR with the Eclipse Valley Five-1974.
Album: released on Swaggie (Australia), Jan'83

Furniture

BRILLIANT MIND.
Tracks: / Brilliant mind / To Gus.
Single (7"): released on Stiff, Apr'86 by Stiff Records. Dist: EMI, Record Services Distribution (Ireland)

Single (12"): released on Stiff, Apr'86 by Stiff Records. Dist: EMI, Record Services Distribution (Ireland)

DANCING THE HARD BARGAIN.
Single (7"): released on Survival, Apr'84 by Survival Records. Dist: Backs, Cartel Distribution

Single (12"): released on Survival, Apr'84 by Survival Records. Dist: Backs, Cartel Distribution

I CAN'T CRACK.
Single (12"): released on Premonition, May'85 by Survival Records. Dist: Backs, Cartel

LOVE MONGERS,THE.
Tracks: / Love mongers,The / Talking Kittens / I can't crack.
Single (7"): released on Premonition, Feb'86 by Survival Records. Dist: Backs, Cartel

Single (12"): released on Premonition, Feb'86 by Survival Records. Dist: Backs, Cartel

LOVE YOUR SHOES.
Tracks: / Love your shoes / Turnuspeed / Me and you and the name.
Single (7"): released on Stiff, Oct'86 by Stiff Records. Dist: EMI, Record Services Distribution (Ireland)

Single (12"): released on Stiff, Oct'86 by Stiff Records. Dist: EMI, Record Services Distribution (Ireland)

WHEN THE BOOM WAS ON.
Album: released on Survival, Aug'83 by Survival Records. Dist: Backs, Cartel Distribution

WRONG PEOPLE,THE.
Album: released on Stiff, Aug'86 by Stiff Records. Dist: EMI, Record Services Distribution (Ireland)

Cassette: released on Stiff, Aug'86 by Stiff Records. Dist: EMI, Record Services Distribution (Ireland)

YOUR BRILLIANT MIND.
Single (7"): released on Survival, Sep'84 by Survival Records. Dist: Backs, Cartel Distribution

Single (12"): released on Survival, Sep'84 by Survival Records. Dist: Backs, Cartel Distribution

Furple

BURPLE.
Single (7"): released on Turning Purple, 24 May'84

Further Railway Stories

FURTHER RAILWAY STORIES Rev.W.Awdry (Rushton, Willie).
Cassette: released on Argo (Spokenword), Jun'84 by Decca Records. Dist: Polygram

FURTHER RAILWAY STORIES Read by William Rushton (Awdry, Rev. W.).

Fury

RIVER DEEP MOUNTAIN HIGH.
Single (12"): released on Jet, Mar'83 by Jet Records. Dist: CBS

Fury, Billy

BEST OF BILLY FURY, THE.
Tracks: / I will / Like I've never been gone / Last night was made for love / I'm lost without you / When will you say I love you / Run to my loving arms / It's only make believe / Maybe tomorrow / In thoughts of you / Give me your word / That's love / Once upon a dream / Colette / Wondrous place / One thousand stars / I'll never find another you / Fools errand (Do you really love me) / Jealousy / Somebody else's girl / Halfway to paradise.
Notes: (P) & (C) 1983 K-Tel International (UK) Ltd.
Compact disc: released on K-Tel, May'87 by K-Tel Records. Dist: Record Merchandisers Distribution, Taylors, Terry Blood Distribution, Wynd-Up Distribution, Relay Distribution, Pickwick Distribution, Solomon & Peres Distribution, Polygram

BILLY FURY.
Cassette: released on Spot, Apr'86 by Pickwick Records. Dist: H.R. Taylor, Lugtons

Album: released on See For Miles, Nov'84 by See For Miles Records. Dist: Pinnacle

BILLY FURY COLLECTION, THE.
Tracks: / Don't leave me this way / Margo / Collette / I love how you love me / Halfway to paradise / Nobody's child / Hippy hippy shake, The / Push push.
Double Album: released on Castle Collectors, Jul'87 by Castle Communications Records. Dist: Pinnacle

Double cassette: released on Castle Collectors, Jul'87 by Castle Communications Records. Dist: Pinnacle

BILLY FURY HIT PARADE, THE.
Album: released on Decca (Rock Echoes), Apr'82 by Decca Records. Dist: Polygram, IMS

Cassette: released on Decca (Rock Echoes), Apr'82 by Decca Records. Dist: Polygram, IMS

BILLY FURY STORY.
Double Album: released on Decca, Feb'77 by Decca Records. Dist: Polygram

Cassette: released on Decca, Feb'77 by Decca Records. Dist: Polygram

COLLECTION-PART ONE.
Notes: Bar code no. 5 013428 131602
Album: released on Collector Series, Mar'87 by Castle Communications Records. Dist: PRT, Pinnacle, RCA, Ariola

Cassette: released on Collector Series, Mar'87 by Castle Communications Records. Dist: PRT, Pinnacle, RCA, Ariola

COLLECTION-PART TWO.
Tracks: / Halfway to paradise / Nobody's child / Run to my lovin' arms / Cross my heart / That's love / Turn my back on you / Hippy hippy shake (The) / Push, push / Do you really love me too / Alright, goodbye / Twist kid (The) / Jealousy.
Album: released on Collector Series, Mar'87 by Castle Communications Records. Dist: PRT, Pinnacle, RCA, Ariola

Cassette: released on Collector Series, Mar'87 by Castle Communications Records. Dist: PRT, Pinnacle, RCA, Ariola

EP COLLECTION,THE.
Tracks: / Turn your lamp down low / Don't walk away / You're having the last dance with me / Wondrous place / What am I living for / That's enough / You got me dizzy / Saved / Keep away / My Christmas prayer / I can feel it / I love how you love me / Would you stand by me / Margo / Play it cool / Don't jump / Please don't go / What did I do / Ill never quite get out of you / Nobody's child.
Album: released on See For Miles, Jun'86 by

See For Miles Records. Dist: Pinnacle

E.P., THE.
Album: released on See For Miles, Sep'85 by Charly Records. Dist: Spartan

BILLY FURY EP COLLECTION.
Cassette: released on See For Miles, Sep'87 by See For Miles Records. Dist: Pinnacle. Estim retail price in Sep'87 was £5.67

HALFWAY TO PARADISE.
Single (7"): released on Decca-Originals, Feb'83 by Decca Records. Dist: Polygram, IMS

Single (7"): released on Old Gold, Oct'83 by Old Gold Records. Dist: Lightning, Jazz Music, Spartan, Counterpoint

LOVING YOU.
Album: released on Magnum Force, May'84 by Magnum Music Group Ltd. Dist: Magnum Music Group Ltd, PRT, Spartan

Cassette: released on Magnum Force, May'84 by Magnum Music Group Ltd. Dist: Magnum Music Group Ltd, PRT, Spartan

MEMORIES.
Album: released on K-Tel, Jun'83 by K-Tel Records. Dist: Record Merchandisers Distribution, Taylors, Terry Blood Distribution, Wynd-Up Distribution, Relay Distribution, Pickwick Distribution, Solomon & Peres Distribution, Polygram

Cassette: released on K-Tel, Jun'83 by K-Tel Records. Dist: Record Merchandisers Distribution, Taylors, Terry Blood Distribution, Wynd-Up Distribution, Relay Distribution, Pickwick Distribution, Solomon & Peres Distribution, Polygram

MISSING YEARS (1967-1980), THE.
Album: released on Red Bus, Nov'83 by Red Bus Records. Dist: PRT

Cassette: released on Red Bus, Nov'83 by Red Bus Records. Dist: PRT

ONLY ONE, THE.
Album: released on Polydor, Mar'83 by Polydor Records. Dist: Polygram, Polydor

Cassette: released on Polydor, Mar'83 by Poly-

dor Records. Dist: Polygram, Polydor Deleted '85.

STICKS'N'STONES.
Album: released on Magnum Force, Mar'85 by Magnum Music Group Ltd. Dist: Magnum Music Group Ltd, PRT, Spartan

SUZANNE IN THE MIRROR(EP).
Single (7"): released on Magnum, Jul'85 by Bulldog Records. Dist: Spartan

WE WANT BILLY! (Fury, Billy & The Tornados).
Album: released on Decca (Rock Echoes), Feb'83 by Decca Records. Dist: Polygram, IMS

Cassette: released on Decca (Rock Echoes), Feb'83 by Decca Records. Dist: Polygram, IMS

WORLD OF BILLY FURY, VOL.1.
Album: released on Decca, Mar'80 by Decca Records. Dist: Polygram Deleted '85.

Cassette: released on Decca, Mar'80 by Decca Records. Dist: Polygram

WORLD OF BILLY FURY, VOL.2.
Cassette: released on Decca, '72 by Decca Records. Dist: Polygram

Album: released on Decca, '72 by Decca Records. Dist: Polygram

Furyo

FURYO.
Album: released on Anagram, May'84 by Cherry Red Records. Dist: Pinnacle

LEGACY.
Single (12"): released on Anagram, Oct'84 by Cherry Red Records. Dist: Pinnacle

Futura

FEELIN' HOT.
Single (12"): released on Graffitti, Feb'83 by Rialto Records. Dist: Projection

Futura 2000
ESCAPADES OF FUTURA 2000 (Futura 2000 featuring The Clash).

Single (7"): released on Celluloid, May'83 by Charly Records. Dist: Charly

Single (7"): released on Celluloid, May'83 by Charly Records. Dist: Charly

Future

HOME TOWN GIRLS.
Single (7"): released on Paro, Oct'82 by Paro Records. Dist: Spartan

WAR OF THE ROSES.
Tracks: / War of the roses / Main attraction.
Single (7"): released on 10, Apr'86 by 10 Records. Dist: Virgin, EMI

Future Daze

VENUS.
Single (7"): released on Polydor, Oct'82 by Polydor Records. Dist: Polygram, Polydor

Future Primitives

RUNNING AWAY.
Single (7"): released on Illuminated, Jul'81 by IKF Records. Dist: Pinnacle, Cartel, Jetstar

Future Shock

FUTURE SHOCK Various artists (Various Artists).
Album: released on Thunderbolt, Mar'85 by Magnum Music Group Ltd. Dist: Magnum Music Group Ltd, PRT Distribution, Spartan Distribution

SANTA LEFT US MICHROCHIPS FOR CHRISTMAS.
Single (7"): released on Whisper, Nov'80 by Whisper Records. Dist: Spartan

Future Tense

FUTURE TENSE Various Artists (Various Artists).
Notes: Includes: Attrition/Legendary Pink Dots/Beautiful Pea Green Boat/Bill Pritchard.
Album: released on Third Mind, Aug'86 by Third Mind Records. Dist: Backs, Cartel Distribution

Future World Orchestra

MIRACLES.
Single (7"): released on Cambra, Jul'84 by Cambra Records. Dist: IDS, Conifer

Futurhythm

ANTI MATTER.
Tracks: / Anti matter.
Notes: Distributed by Esoteric 33 Barberry House, Shannon Road, Kings Norton. Birmingham, B38   9BX. Telephone.021-458-7503.
Single (7"): released on Exoteric, Jan'85 by Exoteric Records. Dist: Rough Trade

Fuze

FALKLAND SOUND.
Single (7"): released on Relentless, Sep'82 by Relentless Records. Dist: Cartel

Fuzztones

BAD NEWS TRAVELS FAST.
Tracks: / Bad news travels fast / Green slime / Strychine / As time's gone.
Single (12"): released on ABC, Jul'86 Dist: Pinnacle

LEAVE YOUR MIND AT HOME-LIVE.
Album: released on Midnight, Dec'84

LYSERGIC EMMANATIONS.
Album: released on ABC, Mar'85 Dist: CBS, Pinnacle

SHE'S WICKED.
Single (7"): released on ABC, Aug'85 Dist: CBS, Pinnacle

Single (12"): released on ABC, Aug'85 Dist: CBS, Pinnacle

FV's

MR TAMBOURINE MAN.
Single (7"): released on Smile, Sep'81 by Smile Records. Dist: Spartan

G

Gabby

BOOTS.
Single (7"): released on London, Jul'84 by London Records. Dist: Polygram

Single (12"): released on London, Jul'84 by London Records. Dist: Polygram

Gaberlunzie

FREEDOM'S SWORD.
Album: released on Lochshore, May'81 by Klub Records. Dist: PRT

Cassette: released on Lochshore, May'81 by Klub Records. Dist: PRT

LEGENDS OF SCOTLAND.
Cassette: released on Lochshore, Mar'87 by Klub Records. Dist: PRT

SAM THE SKULL/GLASGOW DAN.
Double cassette: released on Klub, Oct'81

SCOTLAND AGAIN.
Album: released on Klub, Oct'79

Cassette: released on Klub, Oct'79

SCOTS WA HEY.
Album: released on Lochshore, Jul'87 by Klub Records. Dist: PRT

SUPERSTITION.
Album: released on Klub, Nov'82

:

TRAVELLING MAN, THE.
Album: released on Klub, Nov'80

Cassette: released on Klub, Nov'80

WIND AND WATER, TIME & TIDE.
Album: released on Klub, Oct'84

Cassette: released on Klub, Oct'84

Gable, Nicci

I DON'T GIVE A DAMN.
Single (12"): released on Passion, Jun'84 by Skratch Records. Dist: PRT

STRANGE DESIRE.
Single (12"): released on Passion, May'84 by Skratch Records. Dist: PRT

Gabor, B.B.

B.B.GABOR.
Album: released on Blue Print, May'80 Dist: PRT

LASER LOVE.
Single (7"): released on Blue Print, Sep'79 Dist: PRT

METROPOLITAN LIFE.
Single (7"): released on Blue Print, May'80 Dist: PRT

NYET NYET SOVIET.
Single (7"): released on Blue Print, Mar'80 Dist: PRT

SOVIET JEWELRY.
Single (7"): released on Pye, May'79

Gabriell Brass

NEW FOREST/HILLS AND VALLEYS.
Single (7"): released on Cube, Sep'82 by Dakota Records. Dist: PRT

Gabriel, Peter

BIG TIME.
Tracks: / Big time / Curtains.
Single (7"): released on Virgin, Mar'87 by Virgin Records. Dist: EMI, Virgin Distribution

Single (12"): released on Virgin, Mar'87 by Virgin Records. Dist: EMI, Virgin Distribution

BIG TIME (CD).
Tracks: / Big time / Curtains / No self control / Big time(7").
Compact disc single: released on Virgin, Apr'87 by Virgin Records. Dist: EMI, Virgin Distribution

BIKO/JETZ KOMMT DIE FLUT.
Single (7"): released on Charisma, Sep'80 by Virgin Records. Dist: EMI Deleted '81.

BIRDY.
Album: released on Charisma, Mar'85 by Virgin Records. Dist: EMI

Cassette: released on Charisma, Mar'85 by Virgin Records. Dist: EMI

Compact disc: released on Charisma, Mar'85 by Virgin Records. Dist: EMI

BIRDY - MUSIC FROM THE FILM.
Tracks: / At night / Floating dogs / Quiet and alone / Close up / Slow water / Dressing the wound / Birdy's flight / Slow marimbas / Heat, The / Sketchpad with trumpet and voice / Under lock and key / Powerhouse at the foot of the mountain.
Compact disc: released on Charisma, Jun'85 by Virgin Records. Dist: EMI

DON'T GIVE UP.
Tracks: / Don't give up / In your eyes.
Single (7"): released on Virgin, Oct'86 by Virgin Records. Dist: EMI, Virgin Distribution

Single (12"): released on Virgin, Oct'86 by Virgin Records. Dist: EMI, Virgin Distribution

I DON'T REMEMBER/SOLSBURY HILL.
Single (7"): released on Charisma, Jul'83 by Virgin Records. Dist: EMI Deleted '84.

Single (12"): released on Charisma, Jul'83 by Virgin Records. Dist: EMI Deleted '84.

I HAVE THE TOUCH/ACROSS THE RIVER.
Single (7"): released on Charisma, Dec'82 by Virgin Records. Dist: EMI

INTERVIEW PICTURE DISC.
Album: released on Arabesque, Jun'87 Dist: D Sharp Records, Pinnacle

PETER GABRIEL.
Tracks: / Rhythm of the heart / San Jacinto / I have the touch / Family and the fishing net / Shock the monkey / Lay your hands on me / Wall flower / Kiss of life.
Notes: Digital Stereo
Compact disc: released on Virgin, May'87 by Virgin Records. Dist: EMI, Virgin Distribution

PETER GABRIEL 2.
Compact disc: released on Virgin, May'87 by Virgin Records. Dist: EMI, Virgin Distribution

Album: released on Charisma, Mar'84 by Virgin Records. Dist: EMI

Cassette: released on Charisma, Mar'84 by Virgin Records. Dist: EMI

PETER GABRIEL 3.
Compact disc: released on Virgin, May'87 by Virgin Records. Dist: EMI, Virgin Distribution

Album: released on Charisma, Sep'83 by Virgin Records. Dist: EMI

Cassette: released on Charisma, Sep'83 by Virgin Records. Dist: EMI

PETER GABRIEL 4.
Tracks: / Rhythm of the heart / San Jacinto / I have the touch / Family and the fishing net / Shock the monkey / Lay your hands on me / Wallflower / Kiss of life.
Compact disc: released on Charisma, '86 by Virgin Records. Dist: EMI

Album: released on Charisma, Sep'83 by Virgin Records. Dist: EMI

Cassette: released on Charisma, Sep'83 by Virgin Records. Dist: EMI

PETER GABRIEL (DOUBLE CASSETTE).
Cassette: released on Charisma, Mar'83 by Virgin Records. Dist: EMI

PETER GABRIEL PLAYS LIVE.
Tracks: / San Jacinto / Solsbury hill / No self control / Shock the monkey / I don't remember / Humdrum / On the air / Biko / Rhythm of the heat / I have the touch / Not one of us / Family snapshot / D.I.Y. / Family & the fishing net / Intruder / I go swimming.
Compact disc: released on Charisma, Jun'85 by Virgin Records. Dist: EMI

Album: released on Charisma, Jun'83 by Virgin Records. Dist: EMI

Cassette: released on Charisma, Jun'83 by Virgin Records. Dist: EMI

RED RAIN.
Tracks: / Red rain / Ga ga / Walk through the fire.
Single (7"): released on Virgin, Jun'87 by Virgin Records. Dist: EMI, Virgin Distribution

Single (12"): released on Virgin, Jun'87 by Virgin Records. Dist: EMI, Virgin Distribution

SHOCK THE MONKEY.
Picture disc single: released on Charisma, Oct'82 by Virgin Records. Dist: EMI

SHOCK THE MONKEY/SOFT DOG.
Single (12"): released on Charisma, Sep'82 by Virgin Records. Dist: EMI

SLEDGEHAMMER.
Tracks: / Sledgehammer / Don't break this rhythm.
Single (7"): released on Virgin, Apr'86 by Virgin Records. Dist: EMI, Virgin Distribution

Single (12"): released on Virgin, Apr'86 by Virgin Records. Dist: EMI, Virgin Distribution

SO.
Album: released on Charisma, May'86 by Virgin Records. Dist: EMI

Cassette: released on Charisma, May'86 by Virgin Records. Dist: EMI

Compact disc: released on Charisma, '86 by Virgin Records. Dist: EMI

SOLSBURY HILL.
Single (7"): released on Old Gold, Jul'82 by Old Gold Records. Dist: Lightning, Jazz Music, Spartan, Counterpoint

WALK THROUGH THE FIRE.
Single (7"): released on Virgin, Jun'84 by Virgin Records. Dist: EMI, Virgin Distribution

Gaddis, Mark

POINT OF REFUGE.
Album: released on Ovation, Mar'80 by Gull Records. Dist: PRT Distribution Deleted '83.

Gadd, Pablo

CRISIS TIME/SADDEST MISTAKE:
Single (12"): released on His Majesty, Oct'81 Dist: Pinnacle

GUN FEVER/FEVER DUB.
Single (12"): released on Form, Oct'81 by Form Records. Dist: Pinnacle

HARD TIMES.
Album: released on Form, Oct'81 by Form Records. Dist: Pinnacle

HARD TIMES/LIGHTER SHADE OF BLACK.
Single (12"): released on His Majesty, Oct'81 Dist: Pinnacle

KING OF KINGS.
Tracks: / King of kings / Lord of Lords.
Single (12"): released on Jah Shaka, Jun'86 by Jah Shaka Records. Dist: Jetstar

MEET ME ON THE CORNER.
Single (12"): released on CD Presents, Feb'83 Dist: IMS, Polygram

NURSERY RHYME/BUBBLING ANGELO.
Single (12"): released on Form, Oct'81 by Form Records. Dist: Pinnacle

PROPHET BOB MARLEY, THE/IN DUB.
Single (12"): released on CDJ, Aug'83 by CDJ Records. Dist: Jetstar

Gadd, Steve

GADDABOUT.
Tracks: / Gaddabout / My little brother / Montauk moon / Duke, The / Lucky 13 / Leavin' tomorrow.
Notes: Steve Gadd's first album as leader. Strong rhythmic fusion jazz with R & B/Soul undertones.Music to dance to.All compositions by Steve Gadd and David Matthews. Personnel: Steve Gadd/Richard Tee/Jeff Mironow/Neil Jason/George Young/Lew Soloff/Ronnie Cuber.
Album: released on King (Japan), Jul'86 Dist: IMS, Polygram

Gaddy, Bob

BICYCLE BOOGIE.
Album: released on Moonshine, Nov'86 Dist: Projection Distribution

RIPPING & RUNNING WITH.
Tracks: / Come on little children / Operator / I love my baby / Rip and run / Woe woe is me / What would I do / Paper lady / Out of my name / I'll go my way / Things that I used to do / What wrong did I do / Girl who promises / Forgive me / Take my advice / Stormy Monday blues / Till the day I die.
Album: released on Ace, Feb'86 by Ace Records. Dist: Pinnacle, Swift, Hotshot, Cadillac

Gadgets

FRUIT OF AKELDAMA.
Album: released on Plastic Head, Nov'86 Dist: Pinnacle, Rough Trade. Cartel

GADGETS BLUE ALBUM, THE.
Album: released on Glass, Jun'83 by Glass Records. Dist: Nine Mile, Rough Trade, Red Rhino, Play It Again Sam

Cassette: released on Glass, Jun'83 by Glass Records. Dist: Nine Mile, Rough Trade, Red Rhino, Play It Again Sam

WE HAD NO WAY OF KNOWING/ACID BATH.
Single (7"): released on Glass, Jun'83 by Glass Records. Dist: Nine Mile, Rough Trade, Red Rhino, Play It Again Sam

Single (12"): released on Glass, Jun'83 by Glass Records. Dist: Nine Mile, Rough Trade, Red Rhino, Play It Again Sam

Gad, Jennifer

NATTY NAH RUN.
Tracks: / Natty nah run / Babylon must fall.
Single (12"): released on Slag, Oct'86

Gadney, Reg

FAVOURITE COUNTRY LOVE SONGS.
Cassette: released on Bibi, Jan'82

Gad, Pablo

SPRING IN THE AIR.
Tracks: / Spring in the air / Spring in the air (Version).
Single (12"): released on Try A Ting, Feb'86 Dist: Jetstar

Gaelforce Orchestra

DUMBARTON DRUM.
Tracks: / Old rustic brig.
Single (7"): released on Lismor, Nov'86 by Lismor Records. Dist: Lismor, Roots, Celtic Music

MELODIES OF SCOTLAND.
Album: released on Lismor, Dec'86 by Lismor Records. Dist: Lismor, Roots, Celtic Music

Gaelic Folk Songs
SOUND OF MULL, (THE).
Album: released on Lismor, May'75 by Lismor Records. Dist: Lismor, Roots, Celtic Music

Gaelic psalms From Lewis
SCOTTISH TRADITION VOL.6.
Album: released on Tangent, Apr'81 Dist: Roots Distribution, Lugtons Distributors, Taylors, JSU Distribution, Spartan Distribution

Gaffa
MAN WITH MOTIVE.
Single (7"): released on Gaffa'n' Products, Aug'80 Dist: Pinnacle Deleted '80.

Gaffer
GAFFER, THE / WITHOUT SOMEONE TO LOVE.
Single (7"): released on Eagle (London), Mar'82 by Eagle Records (London). Dist: Stage One

Gage, Yvonne
DOIN' IT IN A HAUNTED HOUSE (Yoakam, Dwight).
Single (7"): released on Epic, Jun'84 by CBS

Records. Dist: CBS

Single (12"): released on Epic, Jun'84 by CBS Records. Dist: CBS

GARDEN OF EVE/TONIGHT I WANNA.
Single (7"): released on Atlantic, Jan'82 by WEA Records. Dist: WEA Deleted '84.

Single (12"): released on Atlantic, Jan'82 by WEA Records. Dist: WEA Deleted '84.

LOVER OF MY DREAMS.
Single (7"): released on Pinnacle, Apr'84 by Pinnacle Records. Dist: Pinnacle

Single (12"): released on Pinnacle, Apr'84 by Pinnacle Records. Dist: Pinnacle

Gaiety Orchestra
MAGIC OF VIENNA.
Album: released on Pye, Sep'75 Deleted '83.

Gaillard, Slim
ANYTIME ANYPLACE, ANYWHERE.
Album: released on Hep, May'83 by H.R. Taylor Records. Dist: Jazz Music, Cadillac Music, JSU, Taylors, Wellard, Chris, Zodiac, Swift, Fast Forward

AT BIRDLAND.
Album: released on Hep, Apr'81 by H.R. Taylor Records. Dist: Jazz Music, Cadillac Music, JSU, Taylors, Wellard, Chris, Zodiac, Swift, Fast Forward

CEMENT MIXER.
Album: released on Folklyric (USA), Jun'84 by Arhoolie Records. Dist: Topic Projection

CEMENT MIXER PUT-TI PUT-TI.
Album: released on Folklyric (USA), Dec'86 by Arhoolie Records. Dist: Topic Projection

OPERA IN VOUT.
Album: released on Verve, Jun'82 by Phonogram Records. Dist: Polygram

ROOTS OF VOUTY.
Album: released on Putti-Putti, Nov'83 Dist: Cadillac Music

SLIM GAILLARD, HELEN HUMES & WILD BILL MOORE (Gaillard, Slim/Helen Humes/Wild Bill Moore).
Album: released on Savoy (USA), May'85 by Arista Records. Dist: Polygram, Swift

VOUTEST, THE.
Album: released on Hep, Jan'83 by H.R. Taylor Records. Dist: Jazz Music, Cadillac Music, JSU, Taylors, Wellard, Chris, Zodiac, Swift, Fast Forward

Gainen, Maury
JAZZ SUNRISE.
Album: released on Discovery, Jun'83 Dist: PRT

Gaines, Earl
YEARNING AND BURNING.
Tracks: / Certain girl, A / I'll take care of you / If you want what i got / Been so long / Taking all the love I can / Trust in me / Keep your mind on me / Turn on your love light / Hymn No. 5 / Nine pound steel / It takes you / I can't face it / Thats how strong my love is / Since I lost you / Yearning and burning / You're the one.
Album: released on Charly, Oct'86 by Charly

Page 392

Records. Dist: Charly, Cadillac

Gaines, Roy
GAINELINING.
Album: released on Red Lightnin', May'86 by Red Lightnin' Records. Dist: Roots, Swift, Jazz Music, JSU, Pinnacle, Cartel, Wynd-Up Distribution

Gainsbourg, Serge
AUX ARMES ET CAETERA.
Album: released on Island, Aug'79 by Island Records. Dist: Polygram Deleted '83.

Gaither, Bill
1935-41 LEROY'S BUDDY.
Album: released on Document, Jul'87

20 BEST LOVED GOSPEL SONGS.
Album: by Pilgrim Records. Dist: Rough Trade, Cartel

BLESS THE LORD WHO REIGNS IN BEAUTY.
Album: released on Word, May'82 by Word Records. Dist: Word Distribution, CBS

Cassette: released on Word, May'82 by Word Records. Dist: Word Distribution, CBS

ESPECIALLY FOR CHILDREN.
Album: by Pilgrim Records. Dist: Rough Trade, Cartel

HE TOUCHED ME.
Album: by Pilgrim Records. Dist: Rough Trade, Cartel

LIVE ACROSS AMERICA.
Album: released on Word, May'82 by Word Records. Dist: Word Distribution, CBS

Cassette: released on Word, May'82 by Word Records. Dist: Word Distribution, CBS

VERY BEST OF THE VERY BEST.
Album: released on Word, May'82 by Word Records. Dist: Word Distribution, CBS

Cassette: released on Word, May'82 by Word Records. Dist: Word Distribution, CBS

WE ARE PERSUADED.
Album: released on Word, May'82 by Word Records. Dist: Word Distribution, CBS

Cassette: released on Word, May'82 by Word Records. Dist: Word Distribution, CBS

Gaizmauskas, Yurgis
RUSSIAN SONGS & DANCES (YURGIS GAIZMAUSKAS).
Cassette: released on Melodiya (USSR), Feb'79 Dist: T.B.C Distribution

Gala Performance
GALA PERFORMANCE Various Other Artists (Various Artists).
Album: released on Pickwick, '78 by Pickwick Records. Dist: Pickwick Distribution, Prism Leisure Distribution, Lugtons Deleted '83.

Galas, Diamanda
SAINT OF THE PIT.
Album: released on Mute, Nov'86 Dist: Spartan Distribution, Rough Trade Distribution, Cartel Distribution

Galaxy
BOOK OF RULES.
Single (7"): released on Sidewalk, Apr'79 by Sidewalk Records. Dist: Mojo Distribution, Jetstar

DANCING TIGHT.
Single (7"): released on Ensign, Apr'83 by Ensign Records. Dist: CBS Distribution Deleted '85.

Single (12"): released on Ensign, Apr'83 by Ensign Records. Dist: CBS Distribution Deleted '85.

HEAD OVER HEELS.
Single (7"): released on Ensign, Aug'82 by Ensign Records. Dist: CBS Distribution

Single (12"): released on Ensign, Aug'82 by Ensign Records. Dist: CBS Distribution

PRIVATE COLLECTION.
Single (7"): released on Galaxy, Nov'82 by Galaxy Records. Dist: RCA, Red Lightnin' Distribution, Discovery, Swift

WAIT UNTIL TONIGHT.
Single (7"): released on Ensign, Jul'83 by Ensign Records. Dist: CBS Distribution Deleted '85.

Single (12"): released on Ensign, Jul'84 by Ensign Records. Dist: CBS Distribution Deleted '85.

YOU DON'T NEED A REASON (Galaxy and Phil Fearon).
Single (7"): released on Ensign, Jun'85 by Ensign Records. Dist: CBS Distribution

Single (12"): released on Ensign, Jun'85 by Ensign Records. Dist: CBS Distribution Deleted '87.

Galbraith ,Charlie
PORTRAIT OF CHARLIE GALBRAITH.
Album: released on Plant Life, Nov'81 Dist: Roots

Galdez, Claudio
WATER GARDEN.
Tracks: / Water garden / Water garden (Dub. instr.).
Single (12"): released on Production House, Mar'87 Dist: Bluebird, Revolver, Cartel

Galdez, Dorothy
NEVER TOO LATE.
Tracks: / Never too late / Never too late.
Single (7"): released on A&M, Aug'86 by A&M Records. Dist: Polygram

Single (12"): released on A&M, Aug'86 by A&M Records. Dist: Polygram

Gale, Crystal
CLASSIC CRYSTAL.
Tracks: / Somebody loves you / Don't it make your brown eyes blue / Ready for the times to get better / You never miss a real good thing(until he says goodbye) / When I dream / I'll do it all over again / I'll get over you / Wrong road again / Talking in your sleep / Why have you left the one you left me for.
Compact disc: released on EMI, Mar'87 by EMI Records. Dist: EMI

Gale, Eric
BLUE HORIZON.
Album: released on Elektra(Musician), '82 by WEA Records. Dist: WEA Deleted '85.

PART OF YOU.
Album: released on CBS, Aug'79 by CBS Records. Dist: CBS Deleted '83.

Cassette: released on CBS, Jul'79 by CBS Records. Dist: CBS Deleted '81.

TOUCH OF SILK.
Album: released on CBS, Dec'80 by CBS Records. Dist: CBS

Cassette: released on CBS, Dec'80 by CBS Records. Dist: CBS

Gale, Erica
AIN'T GONNA LOSE MY HEAD.
Single (7"): released on Cassia Music, Dec'83 by Solid Gold Records. Dist: Jetstar

JUST FOR A MOMENT.
Single (12"): released on Ital, Jul'82 Dist: Pinnacle

WHERE ARE THEY NOW.
Single (12"): released on Ital, Feb'82 Dist: Pinnacle

Gale, Warren
BEBOP AND BEYOND.
Album: released on Concord Jazz(USA), Jul'84 by Concord Jazz Records (USA). Dist: IMS, Polygram

Gale, Wilson and Co
GIFT WRAPPED.
Cassette: released on Jet, May'80 by Jet Records. Dist: CBS Deleted '81.

Gallagher & Lyle
BREAKAWAY.
Album: released on A&M, Jan'76 by A&M Records. Dist: Polygram

Album: released on A&M, Jan'76 by A&M Records. Dist: Polygram

Album: released on Spot, May'84 by Pickwick Records. Dist: H.R. Taylor. Lugtons

Cassette: released on Spot, May'84 by Pickwick Records. Dist: H.R. Taylor. Lugtons

GALLAGHER & LYLE.
Album: by A&M Records. Dist: Polygram

I WANNA STAY WITH YOU.
Single (7"): released on Old Gold, Jul'82 by Old Gold Records. Dist: Lightning, Jazz Music, Spartan, Counterpoint

LAST COWBOY.
Album: released on A&M, '74 by A&M Records. Dist: Polygram

WILLIE & THE LAP DOG.
Album: released on A&M, '73 by A&M Records. Dist: Polygram

Gallagher, Rory
AGAINST THE GRAIN.
Album: released on Chrysalis, Oct'75 by Chrysalis Records. Dist: CBS

BLUEPRINT.
Album: by Chrysalis Records. Dist: CBS

Cassette: released on Chrysalis, '79 by Chrysalis Records. Dist: CBS

CALLING CARD.
Album: released on Chrysalis, Aug'76 by Chrysalis Records. Dist: CBS

Cassette: released on Chrysalis, Aug'76 by Chrysalis Records. Dist: CBS

DEFENDER.
Notes: Free 7" with first 10,000, Seems to me/ No peace for the wicked.
Album: released on Demon, Jul'87 by Demon Records. Dist: Pinnacle

Cassette: released on Demon, Jul'87 by Demon Records. Dist: Pinnacle

DEUCE.
Cassette: released on Chrysalis, '79 by Chrysalis Records. Dist: CBS

IN THE BEGINNING Vocal and guitar.
Album: released on Gem Emerald, '74 Dist: Accordion Record Club

IRISH TOUR '74....
Album: by Chrysalis Records. Dist: CBS

Cassette: released on Chrysalis, '79 by Chrysalis Records. Dist: CBS

LIVE IN EUROPE.
Album: by Chrysalis Records. Dist: CBS

PHOTO-FINISH.
Album: by Chrysalis Records. Dist: CBS

Cassette: released on Chrysalis, '79 by Chrysalis Records. Dist: CBS

RORY GALLAGHER.
Album: by Chrysalis Records. Dist: CBS

Cassette: released on Pickwick, May'80 by Pickwick Records. Dist: Pickwick Distribution, Prism Leisure Distribution, Lugtons

TATTOO.
Cassette: released on Chrysalis, '79 by Chrysalis Records. Dist: CBS

TOP PRIORITY.
Album: released on Chrysalis, Sep'79 by Chrysalis Records. Dist: CBS

Gallery
GALLERY.
Album: released on ECM, Dec'81 by ECM Records. Dist: IMS, Polygram, Virgin through EMI

Galliano, Richard
RICHARD GALLIANO Various artists (Various Artists).
Album: released on ARC (Accordion Records), '84 Dist: Accordion Record Club

Galliard Brass Ensemble
CAROLS FOR BRASS.
Compact disc: by Academy Sound & Vision Records. Dist: Pinnacle

Gallivan, Joe
EXPRESSION TO WINDS (Gallivan, Joe & Charles Austin).
Album: released on Spitball, May'78

MERCY DASH (Gallivan, Joe, Keith Tippett, Elton Dean, Hugh Hopper).
Notes: For full information see under: Tippett, Keith/Gallivan, Joe/Dean, Elton/Hopper, Hugh.

Galloway, Jim
BOJANGLES.
Album: released on Hep, Mar'81 by H.R. Taylor Records. Dist: Jazz Music, Cadillac Music, JSU, Taylors, Wellard, Chris, Zodiac, Swift, Fast Forward

JIM GALLOWAY/METRO STOMPERS/KEN DEAN/RUSS FEARON/DAN MASTRI.
Album: released on Sackville, Jul'86 Dist: JSU, Jazz Music, Jazz Horizons, Cadillac Music, Celtic Music, Swift

METRO STOMPERS, THE.
Album: released on Sackville (Import), Apr'81 Dist: Cadillac

THOU SWELL.
Album: released on Sackville (Import), May'83 Dist: Cadillac

THREE IS COMPANY (Galloway, Jim, Dick Wellstood & Pete Magadini).
Album: released on Sackville (Import), Apr'79 Dist: Cadillac

Gallowglass Ceili Band

GALLOWGLASS CEILI BAND.
Double cassette: released on Pickwick (Ditto series), Jul'82

WILD COLONIAL BOY.
Album: released on Stoic (Ireland), Jul'84

Cassette: released on Stoic (Ireland), Jul'84

Galper, Hal

IVORY FOREST.
Album: released on Enja (Germany), Jan'82 by Enja Records (W.Germany). Dist: Cadillac Music

NOW HEAR THIS.
Album: released on Enja (Germany), Jan'82 by Enja Records (W.Germany). Dist: Cadillac Music

SPEAK WITH A SINGLE VOICE (Galper, Hal Quintet).
Album: released on Enja (Germany), Jan'82 by Enja Records (W.Germany). Dist: Cadillac Music

WINDOWS (Galper, Hal & Lee Konitz).
Album: released on Steeplechase, Feb'77

Galsworthy, John

IN CHANCERY (FORSYTE SAGA).
Notes: Read by Sir Michaael Hordern. Double Cassette
Cassette: released on Listen For Pleasure, Aug'86 by MFP Records. Dist: EMI

MAN OF PROPERTY, THE.
Notes: Read by Sir Michael Hordern.The Man Of Property is the first of nine novels by John Galsworthy which make up the Forste Saga. The books cover fifty years of the decline of the Forsyte family from the 1880's to the 1930's. Beautifully read by Sir Michael Hordern this classic of our time lasts approximately 2.30 hours.
Cassette: released on Listen For Pleasure, Feb'86 by MFP Records. Dist: EMI

Galwad Ar Hol...

GALWAD AR HOL FILWYR BYFFOA CYMRU Various artists (Various Artists).
Tracks: / Galwad ar hol filwyr byffoa cymru (4 Track EP).
Single (7"): released on Anhrefn, Aug'86 Dist: Revolver, Cartel

Galway, James

BABY ELEPHANT WALK (Galway, James & Henry Mancini).
Single (7"): released on RCA, Nov'84 by RCA Records. Dist: RCA, Roots, Swift, Wellard, Chris, I & B, Solomon & Peres Distribution

EXCEPTIONAL TALENT OF..., THE.
Double Album: released on Pickwick, Feb'82 by Pickwick Records. Dist: Pickwick Distribution, Prism Leisure Distribution,

Double cassette: released on Pickwick, Feb'82 by Pickwick Records. Dist: Pickwick Distribution, Prism Leisure Distribution,

IN THE PINK (Galway, James & Henry Mancini).
Tracks: / Pink Panther / Thorn birds / Breakfast at Tiffiny's / Penny whistle jig / Crazy world / Pie in the face polka / Baby elephany walk / Two for the road / Speedy Gonzalez / Molly McGuires / Cameo for flute / Days of wine / Roses / Charade / Moon River.
Notes: Digital Stereo
Compact disc: released on RCA, Jan'85 by RCA Records. Dist: RCA, Roots, Swift, Wellard, Chris, I & B, Solomon & Peres Distribution

Album: released on RCA, Oct'84 by RCA Records. Dist: RCA, Roots, Swift, Wellard, Chris, I & B, Solomon & Peres Distribution

Cassette: released on RCA, Oct'84 by RCA Records. Dist: RCA, Roots, Swift, Wellard, Chris, I & B, Solomon & Peres Distribution

JAMES GALWAY COLLECTION - VOLS 1 & 2.
Double Album: released on Telstar, Nov'82 by Telstar Records. Dist: RCA Distribution

Double cassette: released on Telstar, Nov'82 by Telstar Records. Dist: RCA Distribution

JAMES GALWAY COLLECTION - VOL 2.
Compact disc: released on Telstar, '86 by Telstar Records. Dist: RCA Distribution

JAMES GALWAY COLLECTION - VOL 1.
Compact disc: released on Telstar, '86 by Telstar Records. Dist: RCA Distribution

MAGIC FLUTE OF JAMES GALWAY.
Album: released on Red Seal, Oct'76 by RCA Records. Dist: RCA

NOCTURNE.
Compact disc: released on RCA, Jan'83 by RCA Records. Dist: RCA, Roots, Swift, Wellard, Chris, I & B, Solomon & Peres Distribution

Album: released on Red Seal, Jul'83 by RCA Records. Dist: RCA

Cassette: released on Red Seal, Jul'83 by RCA Records. Dist: RCA

PACHELBEL CANON, THE.
Album: released on RCA, Oct'81 by RCA Records. Dist: RCA, Roots, Swift, Wellard, Chris, I & B, Solomon & Peres Distribution

Cassette: released on RCA, Oct'81 by RCA Records. Dist: RCA, Roots, Swift, Wellard, Chris, I & B, Solomon & Peres Distribution

PLAY SONGS FOR ANNIE.
Album: released on RCA, '84 by RCA Records. Dist: RCA, Roots, Swift, Wellard, Chris, I & B, Solomon & Peres Distribution

Compact disc: released on RCA, '83 by RCA Records. Dist: RCA, Roots, Swift, Wellard, Chris, I & B, Solomon & Peres Distribution

SOMETIMES WHEN WE TOUCH (Galway, James & Cleo Laine).
Album: released on RCA, '84 by RCA Records. Dist: RCA, Roots, Swift, Wellard, Chris, I & B, Solomon & Peres Distribution

Cassette: released on RCA, '84 by RCA Records. Dist: RCA, Roots, Swift, Wellard, Chris, I & B, Solomon & Peres Distribution

SONG OF THE SEASHORE.
Tracks: / Oboro Tsukiyo (misty moon night) / Hana (cherry blossom) / Komorebi - Introduction(Sun light shining through the trees) / Kojo No Tsuki (The moon on the ruined castle) / Hamabe No Ula (Song of the seashore) / Itsuki no komoriuta (Lullaby) / Komorebi - coda (sunlight shining through the trees) / Aka tombo (Red dragonfly) / Hana (Cherry Blossom time) / Yoi Mach Igusa (the evening primrose) / Sakura-gai no uta (Song of the seashore) / Farusato (My home land) / Hana - introduction (cherry blossoms) / Habu n minato (The port of Habu0 / Yashi No Mi (the coconut shell).
Notes: Digital Stereo
Compact disc: released on RCA International, Oct'84

Album: released on RCA International, Oct'84

Cassette: released on RCA International, Oct'84

WAYWARD WIND, THE.
Album: released on RCA, '84 by RCA Records. Dist: RCA, Roots, Swift, Wellard, Chris, I & B, Solomon & Peres Distribution

Cassette: released on RCA, '84 by RCA Records. Dist: RCA, Roots, Swift, Wellard, Chris, I & B, Solomon & Peres Distribution

Gama, Armando

WHEN LOVE HAS GONE.
Single (7"): released on WEA, Jun'83 by WEA Records. Dist: WEA

Gambaccini, Paul

AMERICA'S GREATEST HITS Various artists (Various Artists).
Album: by BBC Records & Tapes. Dist: EMI, PRT, Pye

Gambia:

SONGS OF THE GAMBIA various artists (Various Artists).
Album: released on Sonet, '77 by Sonet Records. Dist: PRT

Gambit Of Shame

NO BOUNDS.
Single (7"): released on Gambit Of Shame, Dec'82 by Gambit of Shame Records. Dist: Rough Trade, Cartel

Gamble, Dee Dee

WHAT COLOUR IS LOVE (Gamble, Dee Dee Sharp).
Album: released on Philadelphia International, Jan'78 by CBS Records. Dist: CBS

Gamble, Loni

COULD IT BE LOVE.
Single (7"): released on DJM, Jan'84 by DJM Records. Dist: CBS, Polygram

Single (12"): released on DJM, Jan'84 by DJM Records. Dist: CBS, Polygram

Gambler, The

GAMBLER,THE Various Artists (Various Artists).
Album: released on First Night, Sep'86 by Safari Records. Dist: Pinnacle

Cassette: released on First Night, Sep'86 by Safari Records. Dist: Pinnacle

Games To Avoid

NECKSPOTS.
Single (7"): released on Very Mouth, Feb'83 by Very Mouth Records. Dist: Cartel

Game Theory

BIG SHOT C IRONICLES.
Album: released on Enigma (Europe), Nov'86 by Enigma Records. Dist: Rough Trade, Cartel, EMI

Gamma

GAMMA II.
Cassette: released on Elektra Asylum, Mar'81 by Elektra/Asylum/Nonesuch Records. Dist: WEA

Gammer

ROCKET TICKET (Gammer & His Familiars).
Album: released on Gammer, Jul'82 by Gammer Records. Dist: Pinnacle

WILL THE NEW BABY (Gammer & His Familiars).
Single (7"): by Gammer Records. Dist: Pinnacle

Gamson, David

SUGAR SUGAR.
Single (7"): released on Rough Trade, Dec'81 by Rough Trade Records. Dist: Rough Trade Distribution, Cartel Distribution

Ganderton, Ron

GIGGLE AMIDST THE TEARS.
Single (7"): released on Centridge, Nov'82 by Centridge Records. Dist: PRT

Gandhi

GANDHI Original film soundtrack.
Album: released on RCA, Jan'83 by RCA Records. Dist: RCA, Roots, Swift, Wellard, Chris, I & B, Solomon & Peres Distribution

Cassette: released on RCA, Jan'83 by RCA Records. Dist: RCA, Roots, Swift, Wellard, Chris, I & B, Solomon & Peres Distribution

Ganelin Trio

ANCORA DA CAPO.
Album: released on Leo, Sep'84 Dist: Recommended

ANCORA DA CAPO (2).
Album: released on Leo, Sep'84 Dist: Recommended

CON AFFETTO.
Album: released on Leo, Oct'85 Dist: Recommended

CON FUOCO.
Album: released on Leo, Sep'84 Dist: Recommended

GREAT CONCERTS OF NEW JAZZ.
Double Album: released on Leo, Jan'87 Dist: Recommended

LIVE IN EAST GERMANY.
Album: released on Leo, Sep'84 Dist: Recommended

NEW WINE.
Album: released on Leo, Sep'84 Dist: Recommended

STRICTLY FOR OUR FRIENDS.
Album: released on Leo, Sep'84 Dist: Recommended

VIDE.
Album: released on Leo, Sep'84 Dist: Recommended

Gang Bang Band

GANG BANG BAND.
Single (12"): released on Quiet, Aug'87 by Quiet Records. Dist: Nine Mile, Cartel

Ganges Orchestra

DREAM/GANGA: MEDITASIAN.
Single (7"): released on Indipop, Mar'83 by Indipop Records. Dist: Independent

Gang Of Four

ENTERTAINMENT.
Album:

Cassette:

IS IT LOVE / MAN WITH A GOOD CAR.
Single (7"): released on EMI, Aug'83 by EMI Records. Dist: EMI

Single (12"): released on EMI, Aug'83 by EMI Records. Dist: EMI

LORD MAKE ME A COWBOY.
Single (7"): released on Vinyl, Aug'82

PEEL SESSION 18.1.79.
Cassette single: released on Strange Fruit, 13 Jun'87 by Clive Selwood. Dist: Pinnacle

SILVER LINING / INDEPENDENCE.
Single (7"): released on EMI, Nov'83 by EMI Records. Dist: EMI

Gangsters

GANGSTERS, THE.
Album: released on Stortbeat, Nov'79 by Stortbeat Records. Dist: Spartan Distribution

Gangsters and Good Guys

GANGSTERS AND GOOD GUYS Original Soundtrack (Various Artists).
Album: released on RCA, Dec'84 by RCA Records. Dist: RCA, Roots, Swift, Wellard, Chris, I & B, Solomon & Peres Distribution

Cassette: released on RCA, Dec'84 by RCA Records. Dist: RCA, Roots, Swift, Wellard, Chris, I & B, Solomon & Peres Distribution

Gangway

MY GIRL AND ME.
Tracks: / My girl and me / Do you remember.
Single (7"): released on Irmgardz, Nov'86 Dist: Nine Mile, Cartel

OUT ON THE REBOUND FROM LOVE.
Single (7"): released on Irmgardz, Nov'85 Dist: Nine Mile, Cartel

TWIST, THE.
Album: released on Irmgardz, Jul'85 Dist: Nine Mile, Cartel

Gannon, Mick

LADY DIANA.
Single (7"): released on Smile, Apr'81 by Smile Records. Dist: Spartan

Gannon, Oliver

I DIDN'T KNW ABOUT YOU (Gannon, Oliver & Fraser Macpherson).
Notes: For full details see under : Macpherson,Fraser/Oliver Gannon

Ganpot, David

GIVIN' IT UP FOR LOVE.
Single (7"): released on Osceola, Mar'83 by Osceola Records. Dist: Charly, Pinnacle

Gant, Cecil

CECIL BOOGIE.
Album: released on Flyright, Sep'76 by Flyright Records. Dist: Krazy Kat, Swift, Jazz Music

KILLER DILLER BOOGIE.
Album: released on Magpie, Jun'79 Dist: Projection

ROCK LITTLE BABY.
Album: released on Flyright, Oct'76 by Flyright Records. Dist: Krazy Kat, Swift, Jazz Music

ROCK THIS BOOGIE.
Tracks: / Cecil boogie / Hit that jive Jack / Hogan's alley / I gotta gal / Boogie blues / Little baby you're running wild / Long distance / Am I to blame / Rock the boogie / Blues in LA / Cecil boogie No. 2 / What's on your worried mind / Stuff you gotta watch / Syncopated boogie / Time will tell / Cecil's mop mop.
Album: released on Krazy Kat, May'83 Dist: Jazz Music, Swift, Chris Wellard, H.R. Taylor, Charly, Hotshot, IRS Distribution

Ganzheit

BRAINS TO THE WALL.
Single (12"): released on Ediesta, Nov'86 by Ediesta Records. Dist: Red Rhino, Cartel

Gap Band

BEST OF GAP BAND,THE.
Tracks: / Oops upside your head / Early in the morning / Yearning for your love / Outstanding / Burn rubber on me / Can't get over you / You dropped a bomb on me / Someday / Party train.
Notes: The definitive Gap Band album featuring all their big club tracks as well as the hit singles:
Album: released on Club, May'86 by Phono-

gram Records. Dist: Polygram

Cassette: released on Club, May'86 by Phonogram Records. Dist: Polygram

BEST OF THE GAP BAND, THE.
Tracks: / Oops upside your head / Early in the morning / Yearning for your love / Outstanding / Burn rubber on me / Can't get over you / You dropped a bomb on me / Someday / Party train.
Album: released on Club, Jan'87 by Phonogram Records. Dist: Polygram

Cassette: released on Club, Jan'87 by Phonogram Records. Dist: Polygram

Album: released on Mercury (USA), Aug'87 by Import Records. Dist: IMS Distribution, Polygram Distribution

Cassette: released on Mercury (USA), Aug'87 by Import Records. Dist: IMS Distribution, Polygram Distribution

BIG FUN.
Tracks: / (Serious dub mix).
Single (7"): released on Total Experience, Nov'86 by Phonogram. Dist: Polygram

Single (12"): released on Total Experience, Nov'86 by Phonogram. Dist: Polygram

GAP BAND 8.
Tracks: / Big fun / I can't live without your love / Get loose, get funky / Don't take it away / Going in circles / Keep holding on / I'll always love you / Bop B da B da da (How music came about) / I owe it to myself.
Album: released on RCA, Jan'87 by RCA Records. Dist: RCA, Roots, Swift, Wellard, Chris, I & B, Solomon & Peres Distribution

Cassette: released on RCA, Jan'87 by RCA Records. Dist: RCA, Roots, Swift, Wellard, Chris, I & B, Solomon & Peres Distribution

GAP BAND IV.
Tracks: / Early in the morning / Seasons no reason to change / Lonely like me / Outstanding / Stay with me / You dropped a bomb me / I can't get over you / Talkin' back.
Album: released on Mercury, Jun'82 by Phonogram Records. Dist: Polygram Distribution

Cassette: released on Mercury, Jun'82 by Phonogram Records. Dist: Polygram Distribution

Album: released on RCA, Nov'84 by RCA Records. Dist: RCA, Roots, Swift, Wellard, Chris, I & B, Solomon & Peres Distribution

Cassette: released on RCA, Nov'84 by RCA Records. Dist: RCA, Roots, Swift, Wellard, Chris, I & B, Solomon & Peres Distribution

GAP BAND VII.
Album: released on Total Experience, Jan'86 by Phonogram. Dist: Polygram

Cassette: released on Total Experience, Jan'86 by Phonogram. Dist: Polygram

GOING IN CIRCLES.
Tracks: / Going in circles / Keep holding on / Disrespect.
Single (7"): released on Total Experience, Apr'87 by Phonogram. Dist: Polygram

Single (12"): released on Total Experience, Apr'87 by Phonogram. Dist: Polygram

HOW MUSIC CAME ABOUT (BOP B DA B DA DA).
Tracks: / How music came about(bop b da b da da) / I owe it to myself.
Single (7"): released on Total Experience, Feb'87 by Phonogram. Dist: Polygram

Single (12"): released on Total Experience, Feb'87 by Phonogram. Dist: Polygram

I'M READY (IF YOU'RE READY).
Single (7"): released on Total Experience, Oct'83 by Phonogram. Dist: Polygram

Single (12"): released on Total Experience, Oct'83 by Phonogram. Dist: Polygram

OOPS UPSIDE YOUR HEAD ('87 MIX).
Tracks: / Oops upside your head / Oops uppercut.
Single (7"): released on Club, Jun'87 by Phonogram Records. Dist: Polygram

Single (12"): released on Club, Jun'87 by Phonogram Records. Dist: Polygram

OUTSTANDING.
Single (7"): released on Total Experience, Jan'83 by Phonogram. Dist: Polygram

Single (12"): released on Total Experience, Jan'83 by Phonogram. Dist: Polygram Deleted '86.

THAT'S HOW MUSIC CAME ABOUT.
Tracks: / That's how music came about / I owe it to myself / Bop-b-da-b-da da.
Notes: Bop-b-da-b-da da only available on 12" version.

Garage

SAVED BY THE BELL.
Single (12"): released on Drum, Sep'84 by Drum Records. Dist: Cartel

Garage goodies

GARAGE GOODIES Various artists (Various Artists).
Album: released on Hit, Feb'85 by Hit Records. Dist: Pinnacle, Backs, Cartel

Garbarek,J

WITCHI-TAI-TO (Garbarek,J/Bobo Stenson).
Album: released on ECM (Germany), Sep'74 by ECM Records. Dist: IMS, Polygram, Virgin through EMI

Album: released on Burlington, Nov'81 by Plant Life Records. Dist: Jazz Music, Celtic Music, Clyde Factors Distributors, I.R.S., Projection, Wellard, Chris, Roots

Garbarek, Jan

ALL THOSE BORN WITH WINGS.
Tracks: / Last clown, The / Yellow fever / Soulful Bill / La divetta / Cool train / Loop, The.
Notes: Saxophonist Jan Garbarek's first solo album and released on the eve of his first British tour.After years of experimenting with all sorts of electronic sounds in group formats,he has created an album that is hauntingly beautiful with a sound structure that has a strong visual component.
Compact disc: released on ECM (Germany), Mar'87 by ECM Records. Dist: IMS, Polygram, Virgin through EMI

Album: released on ECM (Germany), Feb'87 by ECM Records. Dist: IMS, Polygram, Virgin through EMI

DANSERE.
Compact disc: released on ECM (Germany), Oct'86 by ECM Records. Dist: IMS, Polygram, Virgin through EMI

DIS.
Tracks: / Vandrere / Krusning / Viddene / Skygger / YR / Dis.
Notes: Personnel: Jan Garbarek-tenor and soprano sax, wood flute/Ralph Towner-12 string and classical guitars.
Compact disc: released on ECM (Germany), Feb'86 by ECM Records. Dist: IMS, Polygram, Virgin through EMI

ESOTERIC CIRCLE.
Album: released on Freedom, Nov'77 by Logo Records. Dist: RCA, Discovery, Wellard, Chris

EVENTYR.
Album: released on ECM, Nov'81 by ECM Records. Dist: IMS, Polygram, Virgin through EMI

FOLK SONGS.
Tracks: / Folk songs / Bodas De Prata / Cego Aderaldo / Veien / Equilibrista / For Turiya.
Notes: Personnel: Charlie Haden - bass/Jan Garbarek - tenor and soprano sax/Egberto Gismonti - 8 string guitar, super 8 guitar, piano.
Compact disc: released on ECM (Germany), Jul'86 by ECM Records. Dist: IMS, Polygram, Virgin through EMI

LISTEN TO THE GRAY VOICE.
Album: released on ECM (Germany), Nov'85 by ECM Records. Dist: IMS, Polygram, Virgin through EMI

PATHS, PRINTS.
Album: released on ECM (Germany), Oct'82 by ECM Records. Dist: IMS, Polygram, Virgin through EMI

PLACES.
Compact disc: released on ECM (Germany), Oct'86 by ECM Records. Dist: IMS, Polygram, Virgin through EMI

WAYFARER.
Tracks: / Gesture / Wayfarer / Gentle / Pendulum / Spor / Singsong.
Notes: Personnel: Jan Garbarek - tenor and soprano sax/Bill Frisell - guitar/Eberhard Weber - bass/Michael DiPasqua - drums, percussion.
Compact disc: released on ECM (Germany), Aug'86 by ECM Records. Dist: IMS, Polygram, Virgin through EMI

Album: released on ECM (Germany), Sep'83 by ECM Records. Dist: IMS, Polygram, Virgin through EMI

WORKS.
Album: released on ECM (Germany), Nov'84 by ECM Records. Dist: IMS, Polygram, Virgin through EMI

Compact disc: released on ECM (Germany), Nov'84 by ECM Records. Dist: IMS, Polygram, Virgin through EMI

Garber, Jan

1944 (Garber, Jan & His Orchestra).
Notes: Liz Tilton. Bob Davis

JAN GARBER & ORCHESTRA PLAY 22 BIG BAND RECORDINGS (Garber, Jan & His Orchestra).
Album: released on Hindsight(USA), Jun'84 by Hindsight Records (USA). Dist: Swift, Charly

UNCOLLECTED JAN GARBER & HIS ORCHESTRA (Garber, Jan & His Orchestra).
Album: released on Hindsight(USA), Apr'85 by Hindsight Records (USA). Dist: Swift, Charly

UNCOLLECTED,THE.
Album: released on Hindsight(UK), Apr'86 Dist: Jazz Music

Garber, Lloyd

ENERGY PATTERNS.
Album: released on Onari (Canada), Jan'87 Dist: Jazz Music Distribution, Jazz Horizons Distribution

Album: released on Onari, Apr'81

Garbo

DANCING STRANGE.
Single (7"): released on Ram, Apr'83 by Ram. Dist: Greensleeves Records, RCA

Garbutt, Vin

ESTON CALIFORNIA.
Album: released on Topic, '81 Dist: Roots Distribution

KING GOODEN.
Album: released on Trailer, Feb'87 Dist: Jazz Music, Celtic Music, JSU

Album: released on Leader, '81 Dist: Jazz Music, Projection

LITTLE INNOCENTS.
Album: released on Topic, '83 Dist: Roots Distribution

SHY TOT AND COMPANY (LIVE).
Cassette: released on Celtic Music, Feb'85 by Celtic Music Distribution. Dist: Celtic Music, Jazz Music, Projection, Roots

SHY TOT POMMY.
Album: released on Celtic Music, Aug'85 by Celtic Music Distribution. Dist: Celtic Music, Jazz Music, Projection, Roots

VALLEY OF TEES, (THE).
Album: released on Leader, Jun'85 Dist: Jazz Music, Projection

VIN GARBUTT (UNTITLED).
Album: released on Topic, '81 Dist: Roots Distribution

YOUNG TIN WHISTLE PEST,THE.
Album: released on Leader, Jun'86 Dist: Jazz Music, Projection

YOUNG TIN WHISTLE PEST, (THE).
Album: released on Leader, '81 Dist: Jazz Music, Projection

Garcia, Jerry

OLD AND IN THE WAY (Garcia, Jerry/David Grisman/Peter Rowan).
Album: released on Sugarhill (USA), Feb'85 by PRT Records. Dist: PRT Distribution

RUN FOR THE ROSES.
Album: released on Arista, Nov'82 by Arista Records. Dist: RCA

Garden

NEGATIVE ALLEGORY (EP).
Extended-play record: released on Gogs House, Jul'87 by Gogs House Records. Dist: Revolver, Cartel

Garden, Bill

BILL GARDEN'S HIGHLAND FIDDLE ORCHESTRA (Garden, Bill & His Highland Fiddle Orchestra).
Tracks: / Real mysterieux, Le / Porteau Blanc / Snowshoers reel / Quintuplets reel / Masons apron / Fairy dance / Deil among the tailors / Blackthorn stick / Roaring jelly / Brumley brae / Bonnie Mary of Argyle / Highland whisky / Laird o' Drumblair / Kate Dalrymple / Jans dance / Mathematician, The / High level, The / Reel of Tulloch, The / Comin' through the rhy / Scots wha hae / Ye banks and braes / Maries wedding / Vist tramping songs / Marquis of Huntly, The / Scotland the brave / Phil the fluter's ball / Flannel jacket / March hare / Mrs McLeod / Speed the plough / Rollicking Irishman / Pet of the pipers / Irish washerwoman, The / Rowan tree, The / Jigtime / McFlannels (Glasgow Highlanders) / Para handy / Turkey in the straw / Arkansas traveller / Smiths reel / Orange blossom special / Road and the miles to Dundee, The / Northern lights of old Aberdeen, The / I belong to Glasgow / Lady Madeline Sinclair / Jelly bawbee / Lord Moira / Orange and blue / Drunken piper / Roamin' in the Gloamin' / I love a lassie / Stop your ticklin' Jock / Wee Deoch and Doris.
Compact disc: released on Scotdisc, May'87 Dist: Clyde Factors Distributors

DEALS COUNTRY GOLD HITS.
Album: released on Country House, Jun'81 by BGS Productions Ltd. Dist: Taylor, H.R., Record Merchandisers Distribution, Pinnacle, Sounds of Scotland Records

Cassette: released on Country House, Jun'81 by BGS Productions Ltd. Dist: Taylor, H.R., Record Merchandisers Distribution, Pinnacle, Sounds of Scotland Records

HIGHLAND FIDDLE ORCHESTRA (Garden, Bill & His Highland Fiddle Orchestra).
Tracks: / French Canadian Special, The / Strings to the bow (reels & jigs) / Slow air/Strathspey & reel / Hornpipes / Reel of Tulloch, The / Robert Burns waltz, The / March/Strathspey & reel / Scots & Irish, The (reel & jigs) / Rowan tree, The / Polkas / Country hoedown / Intercity waltz, The / Scottische/reel / Sir Harry Lauder selection.
Album: released on Scotdisc, Dec'86 Dist: Clyde Factors Distributors

Cassette: released on Scotdisc, Dec'86 Dist: Clyde Factors Distributors

Garden Gang

GERTRUDE GOOSEBERRY & BELINDA BLACKCURRENT.
Cassette: released on Pickwick (Tell-a-tale), Oct'84 by Pickwick Records. Dist: Pickwick Distribution

PATRICK PEAR & COLIN CUCUMBER.
Cassette: released on Pickwick (Tell-a-tale), Oct'84 by Pickwick Records. Dist: Pickwick Distribution

PEDRO PEPPER & THE CHERRY TWINS.
Cassette: released on Pickwick (Tell-a-tale), Oct'84 by Pickwick Records. Dist: Pickwick Distribution

PETER POTATO & ALICE APPLE.
Cassette: released on Pickwick (Tell-a-tale), Oct'84 by Pickwick Records. Dist: Pickwick Distribution

ROBERT RASPBERRY & GRACE GRAPE.
Cassette: released on Pickwick (Tell-a-tale), Oct'84 by Pickwick Records. Dist: Pickwick Distribution

Gardenia

CHIQUITA LINDA.
Single (7"): released on London, Oct'85 by London Records. Dist: Polygram

Single (12"): released on London, Oct'85 by London Records. Dist: Polygram

Gardening by Moonlight

METHOD IN THE MADNESS.
Album: released on Interdisc, Sep'83 by Interdisc Records. Dist: Island, EMI

Gardiner, Boris

ELIZABETHAN REGGAE.
Single (7"): released on Old Gold, Apr'83 by Old Gold Records. Dist: Lightning, Jazz Music, Spartan, Counterpoint

EVERYTHING TO ME.
Tracks: / Wrong end of the rainbow / All in my dreams / Last night / I'm falling in love / Next to you / Jean / Cara mia / I want to wake up with you / Let's make it tonight.
Album: released on Revue, Nov'86 by Revue Records. Dist: Creole

Cassette: released on Revue, Nov'86 by Revue Records. Dist: Creole

FRIENDS AND LOVERS (Gardiner, Boris & Gwen Guthrie).
Tracks: / She's everything a man could want.

IT'S NICE TO BE WITH YOU.
Album: released on K & K, Sep'86 by K & K. Dist: Jetstar

IT'S NICE TO WITH YOU.
Album: released on K & K, Jun'84 by K & K. Dist: Jetstar

I WANT TO WAKE UP WITH YOU (VIDEO).
Tracks: / I want to wake up with you / You're everything to me.
Video-cassette (VHS): released on Gold Rushes, Mar'87 by Video Collection Records. Dist: Counterpoint

I WANT TO WAKE UP WITH YOU.
Single (7"): released on Revue, Jul'86 by Revue Records. Dist: Creole

Single (12"): released on Revue, Jul'86 by Revue Records. Dist: Creole

LET'S KEEP IT THAT WAY.
Tracks: / Let's keep it that way / Let's keep it this way (Instrumental).
Single (7"): released on Londisc, Sep'86 by Londisc Records.

Single (12"): released on Londisc, Sep'86 by Londisc Records.

Page 394

Single (12"): released on Londis, Oct'85

MEANING OF CHRISTMAS.
Single (12"): released on Revue, Dec'84 by Revue Records. Dist: Creole

YOU MAKE ME FEEL BRAND NEW.
Tracks: / You make me feel brand new / Elizabethan reggae.
Single (7"): released on Trojan, Sep'86 by Trojan Records. Dist: PRT, Jetstar

Single (12"): released on Trojan, Sep'86 by Trojan Records. Dist: PRT, Jetstar

YOU'RE EVERYTHING TO ME.
Tracks: / You're everything to me / Last night.
Single (7"): released on Revue, Sep'86 by Revue Records. Dist: Creole

Single (12"): released on Revue, Sep'86 by Revue Records. Dist: Creole

Gardiner, Paul

STORMTROOPER IN DRAG (Gardiner, Paul with Gary Newman).
Single (7"): released on Beggars Banquet, Jul'81 by Beggars Banquet Records. Dist: WEA

VENUS IN FURS.
Single (7"): released on Numa, Jul'84 by Numa Records. Dist: PRT Distribution

Single (12"): released on Numa, Jul'84 by Numa Records. Dist: PRT Distribution

Gardner, Freddy

MUSIC MAESTRO PLEASE (Gardner, Freddy & His Swing Orchestra).
Album: released on Decca (Recollections), Aug'84 by Decca Recollections. Dist: Polygram, IMS

Gardner, Joanna

WATCHING YOU.
Single (7"): released on Polydor, May'85 by Polydor Records. Dist: Polygram, Polydor

Single (12"): released on Polydor, May'85 by Polydor Records. Dist: Polygram, Polydor

Gareth of Orkney

GARETH OF ORKNEY Various artists (Various Artists).
Cassette: released on Anvil, Jan'81 Dist: Anvil

Garfunkel, Art

ANIMALS CHRISTMAS,THE.
Tracks: / Annunciation,The / Creatures of the field,The / Just a simple little tune / Decree,The / Incredible phat / Friendly beasts,The / Song of the camels,The / Words from an old Spanish Carol / Carol of the birds / Frog,The / Herod / Wild geese.
Album: released on CBS, Dec'86 by CBS Records. Dist: CBS

Cassette: released on CBS, Dec'86 by CBS Records. Dist: CBS

ART GARFUNKEL.
Boxed set: released on CBS, Oct'79 by CBS Records. Dist: CBS

ART GARFUNKEL ALBUM, THE.
Tracks: / Bright eyes / Break away / Heart in New York,A / I shall sing / 99 Miles from L.A. / All I know / I only have eyes for you / Watermark / Sometimes when I'm dreaming / Travellin boy / Same old tears on a new background,The / (What a) wonderful world / I believe (When I fall in love it will be forever) / Scissors cut.
Album: released on CBS, Nov'85 by CBS Records. Dist: CBS

Cassette: released on CBS, Nov'85 by CBS Records. Dist: CBS

Compact disc: released on CBS, Nov'85 by CBS Records. Dist: CBS

BREAKAWAY.
Tracks: / I believe / Rag doll / Breakaway / Disney girls / My little town / Waters of March / I only have eyes for you / Looking for the right one / 99 Miles from L.A. / Same old tears on a new background.
Compact disc: released on CBS, Apr'86 by CBS Records. Dist: CBS

Album: released on CBS, Nov'85 by CBS Records. Dist: CBS

Cassette: released on CBS, Nov'85 by CBS Records. Dist: CBS

SCISSORS CUT.
Tracks: / Scissors cut / Heart in New York,A / Up in the world / Hang on in / So easy to begin / Can't turn my heart away / French waltz,The / Romance / In cars / That's all I've got to say (Theme from 'the last Unicorn').
Notes: The long wait since Art Garfunkel's last solo album has been well worth it. "Scissors Cut" is produced by Ray Hallee ("Bridge over troubled water") and features the finest songs (like the single "A heart in New York") from the finest writers around (Gallagher & Lyle/ Jimmy Webb) backed by some of the world's top musicians including Paul Simon.
Album: released on CBS, Sep'81 by CBS Records. Dist: CBS

Cassette: released on CBS, Sep'81 by CBS Records. Dist: CBS

WATERMARK.
Tracks: / Crying in my sleep / Marionette / Shine it on me / Watermark / Saturday suit / All my loves laughter / Wonderful world (what a) / Mr Shuck'n'jive / Paper chase / She moved through the fair / Someone else (1958) / Wooden planes / (What a) wonderful world.
Album: released on CBS, Jan'87 by CBS Records. Dist: CBS

Cassette: released on CBS, Jan'87 by CBS Records. Dist: CBS

Album: released on CBS, Feb'78 by CBS Records. Dist: CBS

Cassette: released on CBS, Feb'78 by CBS Records. Dist: CBS

Gargoyles

MRS TWO DINNERS.
Album: released on Reasonable, Jul'86 by Gargoyle. Dist: Red Rhino, Cartel

Garloch Blend

DANCERS DELIGHT.
Album: released on Donside, Jan'87 Dist: Roots

Garland, Judy

16 GOLDEN CLASSICS.
Tracks: / Medley / For me and my girl / Trolley song / Swanee / I'm nobody's baby / Alexanders ragtime band / Over the rainbow / I feel a song coming on / Rock a bye your baby / Medley (A) Almost like being in love / Medley (B) This can't be love / Fly me to the moon / That's entertainment / Chicago / Battle hymn of the republic / Come rain or come shine / Smile / I can't give you anything but love / Hey look me over.
Album: released on Unforgettable, Dec'86 by Castle Communications Records. Dist: Counterpoint

Cassette: released on Unforgettable, Dec'86 by Castle Communications Records. Dist: Counterpoint

Compact disc: released on Unforgettable, '86 by Castle Communications Records. Dist: Counterpoint

ALL ALONE.
Tracks: / Man that got away, The / For me and my gal / Trolley song / Swanee / I'm nobody's baby / After you've gone / Alexander's rag time band / Over the rainbow / I feel a song comin' on / Rock-a-bye your baby / I'm always chasing rainbows / All alone.
Album: released on Meteor, Jul'87 by Magnum Music Group Ltd. Dist: Magnum Music Group Ltd, PRT Distribution, Spartan Distribution

AMERICAS TREASURE.
Notes: O.C.I. = Oliver Crombie Imports.
Compact disc: released on Dunhill Compact Classics (USA), '86

CHASING RAINBOWS.
Tracks: / I never knew / Oceans apart / Love / But not for me / Embraceable you / Over the rainbow / Blues in the night / How about you / Poor little rich girl / No lover no nothing / For me and my gal / Trolley song / This heart of mine / You made me love you.
Cassette: released on Cambra, May'84 by Cambra Records. Dist: IDS, Conifer

FOR COLLECTORS ONLY: LIVE, 1962.
Album: released on Paragon (USA), May'84 Dist: Swift

GARLAND AT THE GROVE.
Tracks: / Trolley song,The / Over the rainbow / When you're smiling (the whole world smiles with you) / Zing went the strings of my heart / Purple people eater / You made me love you / For me and my gal / When the sun comes out / Rock-a-bye your baby with a Dixie melody / After you've gone / Pretty girl milking her cow,A / Swanee.
Notes: An on-the-spot recording of Judy Garland's opening night at the Cocoanut Grove in Los Angeles - which captures the excitement of this unique occasion. Judy Garland is now a legendary figure and this recording from one of the peaks of her career sees her in fine form with favourites like "Over the rainbow", "Zing went the strings of my heart", "The trolley song" and more.
Album: released on Capitol, Apr'84 by Capitol Records. Dist: EMI

Cassette: released on Capitol, Apr'84 by Capitol Records. Dist: EMI

GOLDEN GREATS: JUDY GARLAND.
Album: released on MCA, Oct'85 by MCA Records. Dist: Polygram, MCA

Cassette: released on MCA, Oct'85 by MCA Records. Dist: Polygram, MCA

GREAT GARLAND DUETS, THE.
Album: released on Paragon (USA), May'84 Dist: Swift

HITS OF JUDY GARLAND (THE).
Tracks: / Medley / Over the rainbow / Swanee / Come rain or come shine / Man that got away (The) / Chicago / I can't give you anything but love / Zing went the strings of my heart / April showers / Rock-a-bye your baby with a Dixie melody / When you're smiling.
Compact disc: released on Capitol, Apr'87 by Capitol Records. Dist: EMI

JUDY.
Tracks: / Come rain or come shine / Just imagine / I feel a song coming on / Last night when we were young / Life is just a bowl of cherries / April showers / Maybe I'll come back / Dirty hands, dirty face / Lucky day / Memories of you / Any place I hang my hat is home.
Album: released on Capitol, Mar'84 by Capitol Records. Dist: EMI

Cassette: released on Capitol, Mar'84 by Capitol Records. Dist: EMI

JUDY AT CARNEGIE HALL.
Tracks: / When you're smiling (the whole world smiles with you) / Medley / Who cares? (so long as you care for me) / Puttin' on the Ritz / How long has this been goin' on? / Just you, just me / Man that got away (The) / San Francisco / That's entertainment / Come rain or come shine / You're nearer / Foggy day, A / If love were all / Zing went the strings of my heart / Stormy weather / Medley / Rock-a-bye your baby with a Dixie melody / Over the rainbow / Swanee / After you're gone / Chicago / Trolley song,The / Over the rainbow / Man that got away,The / When you're smiling (the whole world smiles with you) / Almost like being in love / This can't be love / Do it again / You go to my head / Alone together / Who cares? (so long as you care for me) / Puttin' on the ritz / How long has this been going on / Just you, just me / Man that got away,The / San Francisco / I can't give you anything but love / That's entertainment / Come rain or come shine / You're nearer / Foggy day,A / If love where all / Zing went the strings of my heart / Stormy weather / You made me love you / For me and my gal / Rock-a-bye your baby with a Dixie melody / Swanee / After you've gone / Chicago.
Notes: Double album; Featuring "Come rain or come shine", "Stormy weather", "The trolley song", "Over the rainbow", "Chicago" and many more. One of the classic all-time live records and probably Judy Garland's finest album.
Compact disc: released on Capitol, Apr'87 by Capitol Records. Dist: EMI

Album: released on Capitol, May'85 by Capitol Records. Dist: EMI

Cassette: released on Capitol, May'85 by Capitol Records. Dist: EMI

JUDY GARLAND.
Album: released on Lotus, Aug'86 Dist: Counterpoint

Cassette: released on Lotus, Aug'86 Dist: Counterpoint

Album: released on Audio Fidelity, Oct'84 Dist: PRT

Cassette: released on Audio Fidelity, Oct'84 Dist: PRT

JUDY GARLAND COLLECTION,THE.
Tracks: / Man tha got away,The / For me and my girl / Trolley song / Swanee / I'm nobody's baby / After your gone / Alexander's rag time band / Over the rainbow / I feel a song coming on / Rock a bye your baby / I'm always chasing rainbows / From this moment on / Sweet little Alice blue gown / Sweet danger / When your lover has gone / Some people / Ohshenandoah / Free and easy / Almost like being in love / This can't be love / Never will I marry / I'm old fashioned / Old devil moon / Fly me to the moon / That's entertainment / More / Chicago / Come rain or come shine / Smile / I can't give you anything but love / Hey look me over.
Double Album: released on Collectors, Apr'86 by Castle Communications Records. Dist: PRT, Pinnacle, Jazz Music

Double cassette: released on Collectors, Apr'86 by Castle Communications Records. Dist: PRT, Pinnacle, Jazz Music

JUDY GARLAND COLLECTION, THE.
Album: released on Deja Vu, Aug'85 by Deja Vu Records. Dist: Counterpoint Distribution, Record Services Distribution (Ireland)

Cassette: released on Deja Vu, Aug'85 by Deja Vu Records. Dist: Counterpoint Distribution, Record Services Distribution (Ireland)

JUDY GARLAND: HER GREATEST HITS.
Double Album: released on Musidisc (France), Oct'83 Dist: Discovery Distribution, Swift Distribution

JUDY GARLAND: VOL 1.
Cassette: released on Audio Fidelity, Oct'84 Dist: PRT

JUDY GARLAND: VOL 2.
Cassette: released on Audio Fidelity, Oct'84 Dist: PRT

JUDY GARLAND: VOL 3.
Cassette: released on Audio Fidelity, Oct'84 Dist: PRT

JUDY GARLAND VOLUME IV.
Cassette: released on Audio Fidelity, Oct'84 Dist: PRT

JUDY IN LOVE.
Album: released on Pathe MarconiFrance), Mar'85

Album: released on Pathe MarconiFrance), Mar'85

LAST CONCERT 20-7-68.
Album: released on Paragon (USA), May'84 Dist: Swift

LAST LAST CONCERT 20-7-68.

LETTER, THE (Garland, Judy with John Ireland).
Album: released on Capitol, Jul'85 by Capitol Records. Dist: EMI Deleted '86.

Cassette: released on Capitol, Jul'85 by Capitol Records. Dist: EMI

LIVE AT THE LONDON PALLADIUM (Garland, Judy & Liza Minnelli).
Tracks: / Over the rainbow / What now, my love / Liza / Travellin' life, The / Smile / Man that got away, The / Gypsy in my soul / Hello Dolly / Together (Wherever we go) / We could make such beautiful music / Bob White (Whatcha gonna sing tonight?) / Hooray for love / After you've gone / By myself / 'S wonderful / How about you / Lover come back to me / You and the night and the music / It all depends on you / Who's sorry now / How could you believe me... / What now, my love / Take me along / If I could be with you one hour tonight / Tea for two / Who / They can't take that away from me / By myself / Take me along / My mammy / Make someone happy / Never will I marry / Smile / Music that makes me dance, The / When the saints go marching in / He's got the whole world in his hands / Swanee / Chicago / Over the rainbow / San Francisco.
Notes: A live recording of the legendary mother and daughter in their first-time-together performance that was completely sold out before it could be advertised! Unlike the previous UK abridged version, this deluxe double package contains the original, full tracklisting plus informative sleeve notes and photos from the occassion. A clasic performance from the now late Judy Garland with the then 'new' talent of Liza Minnelli - now established as a International Artiste. All the favourites including "Over The Rainbow", "Hello Dolly", "Smile", "How About Y o u " e t c .
[EMI release sheet, May 1987]
Double Album: released on Capitol, May'87 by Capitol Records. Dist: EMI

Double cassette: released on Capitol, May'87 by Capitol Records. Dist: EMI

MAGIC OF JUDY GARLAND,THE.
Tracks: / I never knew(I could love anybody like I'm loving you) / On the sunny side of the street / F.D.R. Jones / But not for me / I'm always chasing rainbows / Our love affair / Old black magic,The / Pretty girl milking her cow,A / On the Atchison,Topeka & the Santa Fe / Embraceable you / Zing went the strings of my heart / I'm nobody's baby.
Notes: A very worth addition to MCA's strong mid-line catalogue from an artist who still continues to sell exceptionally well.
Album: released on MCA, May'86 by MCA Records. Dist: Polygram, MCA

OVER THE RAINBOW.
Album: released on Phoenix, Oct'82 by Audio Fidelity Enterprises. Dist: Stage One, Lugtons

RECITAL.
Tracks: / April showers / Rock-a -bye your baby with a Dixie melody / Alone together / That's entertainment / Chicago / Zing! went the strings of my heart. / When you're smiling (the whole world smiles with you) / Come rain or come shine / Just you just me / Medley / Over the rainbow / Swanee.
Album: released on EMI (Italy), Dec'86 by EMI Records. Dist: Conifer

STAR IS BORN, (A).
Tracks: / Gotta have me go with you / Man that got away,The / Born in a trunk / I'll get by / You took advantage of me / Black bottom,The / Peanut vendor / My melancholy baby / Swanee / Here's what I'm here for / It's a new world / Someone at last / Lose that long face.
Album: released on CBS Cameo, Jul'84 by CBS Records. Dist: CBS

Cassette: released on CBS Cameo, Jul'84 by CBS Records. Dist: CBS Deleted '87.

YOUNG JUDY GARLAND, THE.
Album: released on MCA, Jan'83 by MCA Records. Dist: Polygram, MCA

Cassette: released on MCA, Jan'83 by MCA Records. Dist: Polygram, MCA

Garland, Red

BRIGHT AND BREEZY.
Album:

FEELIN' RED.

Album: released on Muse, Apr'81 by Peerless Records. Dist: Lugtons Distributors

GROOVY.
Compact disc: released on Carrere, Apr'87 by Carrere Records. Dist: PRT, Spartan

GROOVY (Garland, Red Trio).
Album: released on Original Jazz Classics (USA), Jun'86 Dist: Fantasy (USA) Distribution, Chris Wellard Distribution, IMS-Polygram Distribution

I LEFT MY HEART.
Tracks: / Will you still be mine / Please send me someone to love / Bye bye Blackbird / Body and soul / Bags' Groove / I left my heart in San Francisco.
Notes: Produced by: Todd Barkan/Assistant Producer-Michael Bloom/Recorded live at Keystone Korner/San Fransisco,Calif.May 1978. Red Garland -Piano/Leo Wright-Alto sax. (Side two only) Chris Amberger - Bass/ Eddie Moore-drums.
Album: released on Muse Jazz (USA), Jan'86

MISTY RED (Garland, Red Trio).
Compact disc: released on RCA Jazz (Japan), '86

MOODSVILLE 6 (Garland, Red Trio).
Album:

RED GARLAND.
Compact disc: released on JVC Fantasy, Jul'87 Dist: Target

RED GARLAND'S PIANO.
Album: released on Prestige (USA), Feb'84

SOUL JUNCTION (Garland, Red Quintet).
Compact disc: released on Vanguard (USA), Apr'86

Garlow, Clarence

BON TON ROOLA.
Tracks: / Cry cry baby / I'll never hold it against you / Foggy blues / If I keep on worrying / You gonna get old / New bon ton roola / I called you up daddy / Let me be your Santa Claus / Sound the Bell / Carry on / I'm just a cry cry baby.
Album: released on Flyright, Oct'86 by Flyright Records. Dist: Krazy Kat, Swift, Jazz Music

Album: released on Flyright, Mar'83 by Flyright Records. Dist: Krazy Kat, Swift, Jazz Music

BON TON ROULE.
Single (7"): released on Bally Hoo (USA), Dec'82 Dist: Swift

ROUTE 90.
Tracks: / Route 90 / Crawfishin'.
Notes: This just has to be one of the best black rock 'n' roll records ever made. Recorded in the same year as Elvis' first ('That's All Right' - 1954), these records couldn't be more different. However, both were seminal building blocks for the exploding new rock 'n' roll scene of the day. This legendary Texan guitarist/singer was a steady influence on the blues/R&B scene and this superb coupling was recorded on the West Coast and features the exciting and tightly cooking band ofMaxwell Davis. (Detour Records).
Single (7"): released on Detour, Jul'87 by Detour Records. Dist: Swift, RCA, Jazz Music, Projection

Garner, Erroll

AT THE PIANO.
Tracks: / Caravan / No greater love / Avalon / Lullaby of Birdland / Memories of you / Will you still be mine.
Album: released on Avan-Guard (CBS Recordings), Aug'86 Dist: Conifer, Discovery

Album: released on CBS(Import), Jun'86 by CBS Records. Dist: Conifer, Discovery, Swift

BEST OF, THE.
Album: released on Verve, May'87 by Phonogram Records. Dist: Polygram

CLASSIC PIANOS.
Cassette: released on Doctor Jazz (USA), Mar'84 by Doctor Jazz Records. Dist: CBS

CLOSEUP IN SWING.
Album: released on RCA (Octave)(France), Feb'85

COMPACT JAZZ.
Tracks: / Misty / Oh lady be good / Begin the beguine.
Compact disc: released on Phonogram, Jul'87 by Phonogram Records. Dist: Polygram

Cassette: released on Phonogram, Jul'87 by Phonogram Records. Dist: Polygram

Compact disc: released on Mercury, Jul'87 by Phonogram Records. Dist: Polygram Distribution

COMPLETE SAVOY SESSIONS VOL. 3.
Tracks: / This can't belove / Man I love, The / Moonglow / I want a little girl / She's funny that way / Until the real thing comes along / Confessin' / Stormy weather / On the sunny side of the street / Rosalie / Everything happens to me / Stairway to the stars.

COMPLETE SAVOY SESSIONS VOL. 1 (1945 - 49).
Tracks: / Play fiddle play / Dark eyesky / Laff slam laff / Jumpin' at the deuces / Laura / Stardust / Somebody loves me / Back home again in Indiana / I cover the waterfront / It's easy to remember / Penthouse serenade / Love walked in / September song / Body and soul.
Album: released on RCA, Jan'87 by RCA Records. Dist: RCA, Roots, Swift, Wellard, Chris, I & B, Solomon & Peres Distribution

Cassette: released on RCA, Nov'86 by RCA Records. Dist: RCA, Roots, Swift, Wellard, Chris, I & B, Solomon & Peres Distribution

COMPLETE SAVOY SESSION VOL.1., THE.
Album: released on Savoy (France), Oct'85

COMPLETE SAVOY VOLUME 3.
Album: released on RCA, Feb'87 by RCA Records. Dist: RCA, Roots, Swift, Wellard, Chris, I & B, Solomon & Peres Distribution

Cassette: released on RCA, Feb'87 by RCA Records. Dist: RCA, Roots, Swift, Wellard, Chris, I & B, Solomon & Peres Distribution

CONCERT BY THE SEA.
Cassette: released on CBS(Import), Jun'86 by CBS Records. Dist: Conifer, Discovery, Swift

CONCERT GARNER, THE.
Album: released on Jazz Groove, Jul'82 Dist: Jazz Music

DREAMY.
Album: released on CBS(Import), Jun'86 by CBS Records. Dist: Conifer, Discovery, Swift

EARLY ERROLL.
Album: released on Jazz Connoisseur, Apr'79 Dist: Jazz Horizons, Jazz Music, Swift, Wellard, Chris

EARLY ERROLL VOL.2.
Album: released on Jazz Connoisseur, Apr'79 Dist: Jazz Horizons, Jazz Music, Swift, Wellard, Chris

ELF, THE.
Album:

ENCORES IN HI FI.
Tracks: / Moonglow / Sophisticated Lady / Robbins' nest / Creme De Menthe / Humouresque / How high the moon / Fancy / Groovy day / Man I love,The.
Album: released on CBS, Jun'86 by CBS Records. Dist: CBS

Cassette: released on CBS, Jun'86 by CBS Records. Dist: CBS

ERROLL GARNER.
Album: released on Kings Of Jazz, '81 Dist: Jazz Horizons, Jazz Music, Celtic Music

ERROLL GARNER - A NIGHT AT THE MOVIES.
Album: released on Bulldog, Mar'84 by Bulldog Records. Dist: President Distribution, Spartan, Swift, Taylor, H.R.

ERROLL GARNER & ART TATUM, VOL 1 (Garner, Erroll & Art Tatum).
Album: released on Kings Of Jazz, Aug'81 Dist: Jazz Horizons, Jazz Music, Celtic Music

ERROLL GARNER COLLECTION, THE.
Album: released on Deja Vu, Aug'85 by Deja Vu Records. Dist: Counterpoint Distribution, Record Services Distribution (Ireland)

Cassette: released on Deja Vu, Aug'85 by Deja Vu Records. Dist: Counterpoint Distribution, Record Services Distribution (Ireland)

ERROLL GARNER PLAYS GERSHWIN AND KERN.
Album: released on Bulldog, Sep'83 by Bulldog Records. Dist: President Distribution, Spartan, Swift, Taylor, H.R.

ERROLL GARNER VOL 1.
Album: released on Joker, Apr'81 Dist: Counterpoint, Mainline, Record Services Distribution (Ireland)

ERROLL GARNER VOL 2.
Album: released on Joker, Apr'81 Dist: Counterpoint, Mainline, Record Services Distribution (Ireland)

ERROLL'S A GARNER.
Compact disc: released on Vogue, Dec'86 Dist: Discovery, Jazz Music, PRT, Swift

GEMS.
Tracks: / Laura / Indiana / I'm in the mood for love / Way you look tonight,The / Penthouse serenade(when we're alone) / Frenesi(cancion tropical) / Play, piano, play / Body and soul / I cover the waterfront / Oh, lady be good / Mean to me / Easy to love.
Album: released on CBS, Jul'86 by CBS Records. Dist: CBS

Cassette: released on CBS, Jul'86 by CBS Records. Dist: CBS

GREAT GARNER, THE.
Album: released on Atlantic, '79 by WEA Records. Dist: WEA

KING OF THE JAZZ PIANO.
Album: released on Meteor, May'85 by Magnum Music Group Ltd. Dist: Magnum Music Group Ltd, PRT Distribution, Spartan Distribution

MISTY.
Album: released on CBS Cameo, Mar'83 by CBS Records. Dist: CBS

Cassette: released on CBS Cameo, Mar'83 by CBS Records. Dist: CBS

MISTY/CONCERT BY THE SEA.
Album: released on CBS(Blue Diamond), Jun'85 by CBS Records. Dist: CBS

Cassette: released on CBS(Blue Diamond), Jun'85 by CBS Records. Dist: CBS

MOONGLOW.
Album: released on Pathe MarconiFrance), Dec'84

Album: released on Pathe MarconiFrance), Dec'84

MOST HAPPY PIANO.
Tracks: / But not for me / Alexander's ragtime band / Time on my hands / Time on my hands / Girl of my dreams / Mambo 207 / Way back blues, The / Ol' man river / Full moon and empty arms / Passing through.
Album: released on CBS, Jul'87 by CBS Records. Dist: CBS

Cassette: released on CBS, Jul'87 by CBS Records. Dist: CBS

OTHER VOICES.
Tracks: / Misty / Very thought of you,The / It might as well be spring / Dreamy / I didn't know what time it was / Moment's delight / On the street / Where you live / Other voices / This is always / Solitaire.
Album: released on CBS, Mar'86 by CBS Records. Dist: CBS

Cassette: released on CBS, Mar'86 by CBS Records. Dist: CBS

PLAY PIANO, PLAY.
Album: released on Spotlite, '83 by Spotlite Records. Dist: Cadillac, Jazz Music, Spotlite

PLAYS GERSHWIN & KERN.
Tracks: / Strike up the band / Love walked in / I got rhythm / Someone to watch over me / Foggy day / Nice work if you can get it / Lovely to look at / Can't help lovin dat man / Only make believe / Old man river / Dearly beloved / Why do I love you / Fine romance.
Notes: Personnel: Erroll Garner - Piano/Eddie Calhoun - Bass/Kelly Martin - Drums/ Charles Isaacs - Bass/Jimmy Smith - Drums/Jose Mangual - Congas. Recorded between 1964-1968 in New York. Erroll Garner's only recording dedicat-ed to the works of two great American song-writers and previously unreleased(he died in 1977 aged 55). Garner was one of the most popular jazz artists internat-ionally appearing in concerts and festivals around the world. His best known composition is Misty which he re-recorded for use in the film, Play Misty For MeStarring Clint Eastwood. Misty was also a major hit for Ray Stevens. These reco-rdings were made in one takes and completely ad lib. The tracks Nice work if you can get it and Why do I love you are previously unreleased.
Compact disc: released on Mercury (USA), Jun'86 by Import Records. Dist: IMS Distribution, Polygram Distribution

RELAXIN'.
Album: released on Vogue (France), Mar'84 Dist: Discovery, Jazz Music, PRT, Swift

ROMANTIC & SWINGING.
Album: released on Mercury (USA), Oct'83 by Import Records. Dist: IMS Distribution, Polygram Distribution

Cassette: released on Mercury (USA), Oct'83 by Import Records. Dist: IMS Distribution, Polygram Distribution

SAVOY COMPLETE VOLUME 2.
Album: released on RCA, Feb'86 by RCA Records. Dist: RCA, Roots, Swift, Wellard, Chris, I & B, Solomon & Peres Distribution

Cassette: released on RCA, Feb'86 by RCA Records. Dist: RCA, Roots, Swift, Wellard, Chris, I & B, Solomon & Peres Distribution

SHADOW OF YOUR SMILE, THE.
Album: released on Up International, Apr'81

STARDUST.
Album: released on Astan, Nov'84 by Astan Records. Dist: Counterpoint

Cassette: released on Astan, Nov'84 by Astan Records. Dist: Counterpoint

THAT'S MY KICK.
Album: released on RCA (France), Oct'85 by RCA Records. Dist: Discovery

Garner,Gigi

CITY BOY / SURRENDER.
Single (7"): released on Runaway, Aug'82

HEART BREAKER/ALL MY LOVE.
Single (7"): released on Runaway, Mar'82

LOVE HURTS/IF LOVIN' WAS EASY.
Single (7"): released on Runaway, Jul'82

REFLECTIONS OF MY LIFE.
Single (7"): released on Safari, Apr'83 by Safari Records. Dist: Pinnacle

Garner,Kate

LOVE ME LIKE A ROCKET.
Single (7"): released on Regard, Oct'83

Single (12"): released on Regard, Oct'83

Garnie & The Roosters

SHAKE IT DOWN.
Album: released on FM, Dec'85 by FM-Revolver Records. Dist: EMI

Garon, Jesse

BILLY WHIZZ, THE (5 TRACK EP) (Garon, Jesse & The Desperadoes).
Extended-play record: released on Narodnik, 30 May'87 Dist: Fast Forward, Cartel

RAIN FELL DOWN, THE (Garon, Jesse & The Desperadoes).
Tracks: / Rain fell down.
Notes: see also under Desperadoes/Jesse Garon
Single (7"): released on Narodnik, Mar'87 Dist: Fast Forward, Cartel

SPLASHING ALONG (Garon, Jesse & The Desperadoes).
Tracks: / Splashing along / Presence dear.
Single (7"): released on Narodnik, Nov'86 Dist: Fast Forward, Cartel

Garrett, Amos

AMOS BEHAVIN.
Album: released on Stony Plain (USA), Feb'84

GO CAT GO.
Album: released on Waterfront, Mar'86 by Waterfront Records. Dist: Rough Trade, Cartel, Projection, Roots

GO CAT GO.
Album: released on Waterfront, Mar'84 by Waterfront Records. Dist: Rough Trade, Cartel, Projection, Roots

Garrett,Leif

CAN'T EXPLAIN.
Album: released on Atlantic, Feb'81 by WEA Records. Dist: WEA

LEIF GARRETT.
Album: released on Atlantic, Mar'78 by WEA Records. Dist: WEA

Garrett,Tommy

FIFTY GUITARS OF TOMMY GARRETT, THE.
Cassette: released on Ideal(Tapes), Jul'84 Dist: EMI

Garrett,Winston

BIG BAD BOY.
Single (12"): released on Oak Sound, Dec'84

Garrick,Michael

YOU'VE CHANGED.
Album: released on Hep, May'81 by H.R. Taylor Records. Dist: Jazz Music, Cadillac Music, JSU, Taylors, Wellard, Chris, Zodiac, Swift, Fast Forward

Garry

BRAND NEW HAIRCUT/URBAN ROCKABILLY.
Single (7"): released on Sin City, Feb'83 by Sin City Records.

Garvey,Nick

BLUE SKIES.
Album: released on Virgin, Sep'83 by Virgin Records. Dist: EMI, Virgin Distribution

Garvin,Rex

SOCK IT TO 'EM JB.
Single (12"): released on Atlantic, Apr'80 by WEA Records. Dist: WEA

Garwood, Patrick

HURTING ME / REVOLUTIONARIES.
Single (12"): released on Cha-Cha, Nov'81 by Cha Cha. Dist: Jetstar

Gary Byrd...

GARY BYRD'S SWEET INSPIRATIONS various artists (Various Artists).
Album: released on BBC, Nov'84 by BBC Records & Tapes. Dist: EMI, PRT, Pye

Cassette: released on BBC, Nov'84 by BBC Records & Tapes. Dist: EMI, PRT, Pye

Gary,John

SINCERELY YOURS.
Album: released on RCA, Sep'84 by RCA Records. Dist: RCA, Roots, Swift, Wellard, Chris, I & B, Solomon & Peres Distribution

Cassette: released on RCA, Sep'84 by RCA Records. Dist: RCA, Roots, Swift, Wellard, Chris, I & B, Solomon & Peres Distribution

YOURS.
Single (7"):

Single (7"): released on RCA, Sep'84 by RCA Records. Dist: RCA, Roots, Swift, Wellard, Chris, I & B, Solomon & Peres Distribution

Gary O

WATCHING YOU.
Single (7"): released on Arista, Oct'85 by Arista Records. Dist: RCA

Single (12"): released on Arista, Oct'85 by Arista Records. Dist: RCA

Gary's Gang

KNOCK ME OUT/INSTRUMENTAL VERSION.
Single (12"): released on Arista, Oct'82 by Arista Records. Dist: RCA

Single (7"): released on Arista, Oct'82 by Arista Records. Dist: RCA

Gash

GASH.
Album: released on Cleopatra, Dec'86 by Musicland Records. Dist: Rough Trade, Cartel

Gaskell, Elizabeth

COUSIN PHYLLIS.
Notes: Read by:Kenneth Branagh. Against the background of new commercial ideas confronting traditional pastoral themes Mrs.Gaskell in one of her most mature and perf-ect works of fiction, tells a poignant story of unfulfilled love. A young stude-nt railway engineer Paul Manning becomes captivated y his distant cousin Phllis and her family. His older and more sophisticated colleague Holdsworth also come under the spell of Hope Farm Heathbridge and the scholarly charm of Phyllis's father Ebenezer Holman. But Holdsworths visits and subsequent departure for Canada have an effect on Phyllis that is almost more than she can bear and ensu-res that can never go back to the peace of the old days. 1 volume : 3 cassettes listening time 3 hours 55 minutes. Cousin Phyllis is produced by Jane Ervingham.Cover to cover cassettes limited, Dene house, Lockeridge, Marlborough,Wiltshire.
Cassette: released on Cover to Cover, Sep'86 by Cover to Cover Cassettes. Dist: Conifer

Gaskin

END OF THE WORLD.
Album: released on Rondelet, Jul'81 Dist: Spartan Distribution

I'M NO FOOL.
Single (7"): released on Rondelet, Apr'81 Dist: Spartan Distribution

MONY MONY.
Single (7"): released on Rondelet, Jun'82 Dist: Spartan Distribution

NO WAY OUT.
Album: released on Rondelet Music & Records, Jun'82

Cassette: released on Rondelet Music & Records, Jun'82

Gaslini, Giorgio

SCHUMANN REFLECTIONS.
Album: released on Soul Note, May'85 Dist: Harmonia Mundi Distributors

Gaston, Bill

WINTER AND THE WHITE WITCH.
Cassette: released on Soundings, Mar'85 Dist: Soundings

Gatecrashers

ALTOGETHER NOW.
Album: released on Royal, Jan'85 by Royal Records. Dist: Stage One Distribution

TOO SHORT FOR A QUIFF.
Album: released on Future Earth, Jun'83 by Future Earth Records. Dist: Red Rhino, Cartel

YOU CAN'T DO THAT TO ME.
Single (7"): released on Bluff Tunes, Sep'81

Gateley, Sid

PARTY DANCES 70'S STYLE (Gateley, Sid & His Music).
Album: released on Response, Feb'81 by Priority Records. Dist: BMG

Gatemouth

BOGALUSA BOOGIE MAN.
Album: released on Barclay, Nov'79 by Decca Records. Dist: Polygram, Discovery, Conifer, IMS, Swift

Gates, David

COME HOME FOR CHRISTMAS.
Single (7"): released on Arista, Nov'82 by Arista Records. Dist: RCA

DAVID GATES - FIRST.
Cassette: released on Elektra, '75 by WEA Records. Dist: WEA

FALLING IN LOVE AGAIN.
Cassette: released on Elektra, Jan'80 by WEA Records. Dist: WEA

FIRST.
Album: released on Elektra, Nov'76 by WEA Records. Dist: WEA

GOODBYE GIRL.
Cassette: released on Elektra, Jul'78 by WEA Records. Dist: WEA

NEVER LET HER GO.
Album: released on Elektra, Nov'76 by WEA Records. Dist: WEA

Gates, Pearly

ACTION.
Tracks: / Action(The Tony Atkins Mix) / Action(The original mix).
Single (7"): released on Funkin' Marvellous, Jun'86 Dist: Priority, RCA, Ariola

Single (12"): released on Funkin' Marvellous, Jun'86 Dist: Priority, RCA, Ariola

NO TWO WAYS ABOUT IT.
Single (12"): released on Nightmare Gold, Feb'87 Dist: PRT

Gateway Jazz Band

GATEWAY JAZZ BAND WITH GEORGE CHISHOLM (Gateway Jazz Band & George Chisholm).
Album: released on Fellside, Apr'81 by Fellside Records. Dist: Roots, Jazz Music, Celtic Music, Projection

LIVE JAZZ FROM THE SOLENT AREA.
Cassette: released on All That's Jazz, Jun'86 Dist: Jazz Music

Gathering

GATHERING.
Album: released on Damaged, Nov'86 Dist: Backs

Gathering Peascods

GATHERING PEASCODS Period dances.
Cassette: released on Folktracks, Nov'79 by Folktracks Cassettes. Dist: Folktracks

Gatlin Brothers

GREATEST HITS:GATLIN BROTHERS.
Cassette: released on Spot, Apr'86 by Pickwick Records. Dist: H.R. Taylor, Lugtons

Gatlin Brothers Band

Help yourself

Straight ahead

Gatlin, Larry

HELP YOURSELF (Gatlin, Larry & The Gatlin Brothers Band).
Album: released on CBS, Jan'81 by CBS Records. Dist: CBS

Cassette: released on CBS, Jan'81 by CBS Records. Dist: CBS

LARRY GATLIN I love country.
Tracks: / All the gold in California.
Album: released on CBS, Mar'87 by CBS Records. Dist: CBS

Cassette: released on CBS, Mar'87 by CBS Records. Dist: CBS

SMILE (Gatlin, Larry & The Gatlin Brothers).
Tracks: / Runaway go home / One on one / Say / I saved your place / Everytime freedom changes hands / Can't stay away from her fire / Get me into this love, Lord. / I'd throw it all away / Nothing but your love matters / Indian summer.
Album: released on CBS, Jan'86 by CBS Records. Dist: CBS

Cassette: released on CBS, Jan'86 by CBS Records. Dist: CBS

STRAIGHT AHEAD (Gatlin, Larry & The Gatlin Brothers Band).
Album: released on CBS, Jan'80 by CBS Records. Dist: CBS

Cassette: released on CBS, Jan'80 by CBS Records. Dist: CBS

Gaudin Fair Organ

ALL THE FUN OF THE FAIR.
Album: released on Joy, '70 by President Records. Dist: Jazz Music, Swift, President Distribution

ALL THE FUN OF THE FAIR - VOL.2.
Album: by President Records. Dist: Jazz Music, Swift, President Distribution

COME TO THE FAIR.
Album: released on Joy, '70 by President Records. Dist: Jazz Music, Swift, President Distribution

COME TO THE FAIR - VOL.2.
Album: by President Records. Dist: Jazz Music, Swift, President Distribution

Gaugers

BEWARE OF THE ABERDONIAN.
Album: released on Topic, '81 Dist: Roots Distribution

Gaughan, Dick

COPPERS & BRASS Scots & Irish dance music on guitar.
Album: released on Topic, '81 Dist: Roots Distribution

DIFFERENT KIND OF LOVE SONG, A.
Album: released on Celtic Music, Sep'84 by Celtic Music Distribution. Dist: Celtic Music, Jazz Music, Projection, Roots

Cassette: released on CMC, Feb'85 by CMC Records. Dist: Celtic Music

GAMES PEOPLE PLAY.
Single (7"):

GAUGHAN.
Album: released on Topic, '81 Dist: Roots Distribution

KIST OF GOLD.
Album: released on Leader, Sep'85 Dist: Jazz Music, Projection

NO MORE FOREVER.
Album: released on Leader, '81 Dist: Jazz Music, Projection

Songs of Ewan MacColl

SONGS OF EWAN MACCOLL (Gaughan, Dick, Dave Burland & Tony Capstick).
Album: released on Rubber, Jun'82 by Rubber Records. Dist: Roots Distribution, Projection Distribution, Jazz Music Distribution, Celtic Music Distribution, JSU Distribution, Spartan Distribution

Gavin, Eric

POVERTY LINE.
Single (7"): released on Trial, Dec'82 by Trial Records. Dist: Pinnacle

Single (7"): released on Towerbell, Jan'84 by Towerbell Records. Dist: EMI

Gavin, Frankie

TRADITIONAL MUSIC OF IRELAND.
Album: released on Shanachie, Sep'79 Dist: Sterns/Triple Earth Distribution, Roots

Gawain & Lancelot

GAWAIN & LANCELOT (Various Artists).
Cassette: released on Anvil, Jan'81 Dist: Anvil

Gay 90's

GAY 90'S Twelve beautiful old Victorian musical boxes & early pianola (Various Artists).
Album: released on Saydisc, Jan'81 by Saydisc Records. Dist: Essex, Harmonia Mundi, Roots, H.R. Taylor, Jazz Music, Swift, Projection, Gamut

Cassette: released on Saydisc, Jan'81 by Saydisc Records. Dist: Essex, Harmonia Mundi, Roots, H.R. Taylor, Jazz Music, Swift, Projection, Gamut

Gay Divorcee, The

GAY DIVORCEE, THE Musical (Various Artists).
Notes: Fred and Gingers best film, featuring the spectacular dance routine for 'The Continental'
Video-cassette (VHS): released on Video Collection, May'87 by Video Collection Records. Dist: Counterpoint

Gaye Bykers On Acid

EVERYTHING'S GROOVY.
Single (7"): released on In Tape, Nov'86 by In Tape Records. Dist: Red Rhino, Cartel

Single (12"): released on In Tape, Nov'86 by In Tape Records. Dist: Red Rhino, Cartel

NOSEDIVE KARMA.
Single 10": released on In Tape, May'87 by In Tape Records. Dist: Red Rhino, Cartel

Gaye, Marvin

15 GREATEST HITS.
Notes: Track detail see under compact disc section.
Compact disc: released on Motown, May'84 by Motown Records. Dist: BMG Distribution

20 GREATEST HITS-COMPACT COMMAND PERFORMANCES-VOL 2.
Compact disc: by Motown Records. Dist: BMG Distribution

2 CLASSIC ALBUMS : GREATEST HITS (Gaye, Marvin, Diana Ross, Tammi Terrell).

ABRAHAM, MARTIN & JOHN.
Single (7"): released on Motown, Oct'81 by Motown Records. Dist: BMG Distribution

ANTHOLOGY Volumes 1 & 2).
Tracks: / Chained / End of our road / Mercy me / Inner city blues / Trouble man / Distant lover / After the dance / Once upon a time / Forever / It takes two / I this world were mine.etc. / Stubborn kind of fellow / Hitch hike / Pride and joy / Can I get a witness / What's the matter with you baby / You're a wonderful one / Try it baby / Baby don't you do it / What good am I without you / How sweet it is (to be loved by you) / It takes two / I'll be doggone / Pretty little baby / Ain't that peculiar / Ain't no mountain high enough / One more heartache / Take this heart of mine / Your precious love / Little darling (I need you) / Your unchanging love / If this world were mine / You / If I could build my whole world around you / Ain't nothing like the real thing / How can I forget / Heaven sent you, I know / I heard it through the grapevine / Good lovin' ain't easy to come by / Too busy thinking about my baby / That's the way love is / You're all I need to get by / What's going on / Mercy, mercy me (the ecology) / Save the children / You're the man (part 1) / Let's get it on / Come get to this / I want you / Got to give it up (part 1).
Double compact disc: released on Motown, Oct'86 by Motown Records. Dist: BMG Distribution

Album: released on Motown, Oct'81 by Motown Records. Dist: BMG Distribution

BEST OF MARVIN GAYE.
Album: released on Motown, Oct'81 by Motown Records. Dist: BMG Distribution

Cassette: released on Motown, Oct'81 by Motown Records. Dist: BMG Distribution

COMPACT COMMAND PERFORMANCES - VOL. 2.
Tracks: / Stubborn kind of fellow / Hitch hike / Pride and joy / Can I get a witness? / You're a wonderful one / Try it baby / Baby don't you do it / I'll be doggone / Pretty little baby / One more heartache / Take this heart of mine / Little darling (I need you) / Your unchanging love / You / Chained / How can I forget? / End of our road, The / Come get to this / After the dance / Distant lover.
Compact disc: released on Motown, Mar'87 by Motown Records. Dist: BMG Distribution

DIANA & MARVIN (Gaye, Marvin & Diana Ross).
Album: released on Motown, Oct'81 by Motown Records. Dist: BMG Distribution

Cassette: released on Motown, Oct'81 by Motown Records. Dist: BMG Distribution

EARLY YEARS 1961-1964.
Album: released on Motown, Oct'81 by Motown Records. Dist: BMG Distribution

Cassette: released on Motown, Oct'81 by Motown Records. Dist: BMG Distribution

EGO TRIPPING OUT.
Single (7"): released on Motown, Oct'81 by Motown Records. Dist: BMG Distribution

GOT TO GIVE IT UP.
Single (7"): released on Motown, Apr'85 by Motown Records. Dist: BMG Distribution

Single (12"): released on Motown, Apr'85 by Motown Records. Dist: BMG Distribution

Single (7"): released on Motown, Oct'81 by Motown Records. Dist: BMG Distribution

GREATEST HITS LIVE: MARVIN GAYE.
Video-cassette (VHS): released on Videoform Music, Sep'84 Dist: EMI

GREATEST HITS:MARVIN GAYE & TAMMI TERRELL (Gaye, Marvin & Tammi Terrell).
Album: released on Motown, Jul'82 by Motown Records. Dist: BMG Distribution

Cassette: released on Motown, Jul'82 by Motown Records. Dist: BMG Distribution

Album: released on Motown, Oct'81 by Motown Records. Dist: BMG Distribution

Cassette: released on Motown, Oct'81 by Motown Records. Dist: BMG Distribution

GREATEST HITS:MARVIN GAYE.
Album: released on Telstar, Nov'83 by Telstar Records. Dist: RCA Distribution

Cassette: released on Telstar, Nov'83 by Telstar Records. Dist: RCA Distribution

GREATEST HITS VIDEO: MARVIN GAYE.
Notes: Released on Channel 5 Video in May 87

HEAVY LOVE AFFAIR.
Single (7"): released on Motown, Oct'81 by Motown Records. Dist: BMG Distribution

Single (12"): released on Motown, Oct'81 by Motown Records. Dist: BMG Distribution

HERE MY DEAR.
Double Album: released on Motown, Oct'81 by Motown Records. Dist: BMG Distribution

Double cassette: released on Motown, Oct'81 by Motown Records. Dist: BMG Distribution

HITS OF MARVIN GAYE.
Album: released on Motown, Oct'81 by Motown Records. Dist: BMG Distribution

I HEARD IT THROUGH THE GRAPEVINE/I WANT YOU.
Tracks: / You / Tear it down / Chained / I heard it through the grapevine / Some kind of wonderful / Loving you is sweeter than ever / Change what you can / It's love I need / Every now and then / You're whats happening (in the world now) / There goes my baby / I want you (plus into jam) / Come live with me angel / After the dance (plus instrumental) / Feel all my love inside / I wanna be where you are / All the way around / Since I had you / Soon I'll be loving you again / At last (I found a love).
Compact disc: released on Motown, Nov'86 by Motown Records. Dist: BMG Distribution

Album: released on Motown, Apr'85 by Motown Records. Dist: BMG Distribution

Cassette: released on Motown, Apr'85 by Motown Records. Dist: BMG Distribution

I HEARD IT THROUGH THE GRAPEVINE.
Tracks: / I heard it through the grapevine / Can I get a witness / That's the way love is / You're a wonderful one.
Single (7"): released on Motown, Apr'86 by Motown Records. Dist: BMG Distribution

Single (12"): released on Motown, Apr'86 by Motown Records. Dist: BMG Distribution

Cassette: released on Tamla Motown, May'86 by Motown Records. Dist: RCA Distribution

Single (7"): released on Motown, Oct'81 by Motown Records. Dist: BMG Distribution

IN OUR LIFETIME.
Album: released on Motown, Oct'81 by Motown Records. Dist: BMG Distribution

Cassette: released on Motown, Oct'81 by Motown Records. Dist: BMG Distribution

IT TAKES TWO (Gaye, Marvin & Kim Weston).
Single (7"): released on Motown, Oct'81 by Motown Records. Dist: BMG Distribution

I WANT YOU.
Album: released on Motown, Oct'81 by Motown Records. Dist: BMG Distribution

JOY (PART 1).
Single (7"): released on CBS, Mar'83 by CBS Records. Dist: CBS

Single (12"): released on CBS, Mar'83 by CBS Records. Dist: CBS

LET'S GET IT ON.
Album: released on Motown, Mar'82 by Motown Records. Dist: BMG Distribution

Cassette: released on Motown, Mar'82 by Motown Records. Dist: BMG Distribution

Album: released on Motown, Apr'84 by Motown Records. Dist: BMG Distribution

Cassette: released on Motown, Apr'84 by Motown Records. Dist: BMG Distribution

Single (7"): released on Motown, Mar'83 by Motown Records. Dist: BMG Distribution

LIVE AT THE LONDON PALLADIUM.
Tracks: / You're all I need to get by / Ain't nothing like the real thing / Your precious love / It takes two / Ain't no mountain high enough / Intro theme / All the way around / Since I had you / Come get to this / Let's get it on / Closing theme / Got to give it up / Ain't that peculiar / You're a wonderful one / Stubborn kind of fellow / Pride and joy / Little darling (I need you) / I heard it through the grapevine / Hitch hike / You / Too busy thinking about my baby / How sweet it is (to be loved by you) / Inner city blues / God is love / What's going on? / Save the children.
Compact disc: released on Motown, Mar'87 by Motown Records. Dist: BMG Distribution

LIVE AT THE LONDON PALLADIUM..
Tracks: / Let's get it on / Trouble man / Medleys / Distant lover.
Album: released on Motown, Aug'86 by Motown Records. Dist: BMG Distribution

Cassette: released on Motown, Aug'86 by Motown Records. Dist: BMG Distribution

MAGIC OF MARVIN GAYE, (THE).
Album: released on Motown, '82 by Motown Records. Dist: BMG Distribution

Cassette: released on Motown, '82 by Motown Records. Dist: BMG Distribution

MARVIN GAYE AND HIS GIRLS.
Album: released on Motown, Feb'83 by Motown Records. Dist: BMG Distribution

Cassette: released on Motown, Feb'83 by Motown Records. Dist: BMG Distribution

MARVIN GAYE AND HIS WOMEN.
Notes: Artists include: Marvin Gaye/Diana Ross/Marry Wells/Kim Weston/Tammi Terrell:
Compact disc: released on Motown, Jan'86 by Motown Records. Dist: BMG Distribution

MARVIN GAYE LIVE His Classic Live Album.

MARVIN GAYE LIVE! His classic live album.

MARVIN GAYE: LIVE.
Album: released on Motown, Mar'82 by Motown Records. Dist: BMG Distribution

Cassette: released on Motown, Mar'82 by Motown Records. Dist: BMG Distribution

MIDNIGHT LOVE.
Tracks: / Midnight Lady / Sexual Healing / Rockin after midnight / Til tomorrow / Turn on some music / Third world girl / Joy / My love is waiting.
Album: released on CBS, Apr'86 by CBS Records. Dist: CBS

Cassette: released on CBS, Apr'86 by CBS Records. Dist: CBS

Album: released on CBS, Nov'82 by CBS Records. Dist: CBS

Cassette: released on CBS, Nov'82 by CBS Records. Dist: CBS

MOTOWN REMEMBERS MARVIN GAYE.
Tracks: / Heard it through the grapevine / World is rated X / Lonely lover / Just like a man / I'm going home / No greater love / Dark side of the world / Loving and affection / I'm in love with you / That's the way it goes / Baby I'm glad that things worked out so well / Baby don't you leave me.
Album: released on Motown, Jun'86 by Motown Records. Dist: BMG Distribution

Cassette: released on Motown, Jun'86 by Motown Records. Dist: BMG Distribution

M.P.G..
Album: released on Motown, Aug'82 by Motown Records. Dist: BMG Distribution

Cassette: released on Motown, Aug'82 by Motown Records. Dist: BMG Distribution

MY LOVE IS WAITING.
Single (7"): released on CBS, Dec'83 by CBS Records. Dist: CBS

Single (12"): released on CBS, Dec'83 by CBS Records. Dist: CBS

ONION SONG (Gaye, Marvin & Tammi Terrell).
Single (7"): released on Motown, Apr'85 by Motown Records. Dist: BMG Distribution

Single (12"): released on Motown, Apr'85 by Motown Records. Dist: BMG Distribution

Single (7"): released on Motown, Oct'81 by Motown Records. Dist: BMG Distribution

PRAISE.
Single (7"): released on Motown, Oct'81 by Motown Records. Dist: BMG Distribution

Single (12"): released on Motown, Oct'81 by Motown Records. Dist: BMG Distribution

ROMANTICALLY YOURS.
Album: released on CBS, Dec'85 by CBS Records. Dist: CBS

Cassette: released on CBS, Dec'85 by CBS Records. Dist: CBS

Album: released on CBS, Aug'87 by CBS Records. Dist: CBS

SEXUAL HEALING.
Single (7"): released on CBS, Nov'85 by CBS Records. Dist: CBS

Single (12"): released on CBS, Nov'85 by CBS Records. Dist: CBS

STOP, LOOK,LISTEN TO YOUR HEART.
Single (7"): released on Motown, Oct'81 by Motown Records. Dist: BMG Distribution

THAT STUBBORN KINDA FELLOW/HOW SWEET IT IS 2 Classic albums.
Tracks: / Stubborn kind of fellow / Pride and joy / Hitch hike / Get my hands on some lovin' / Wherever I lay my hat (that's my home) / Soldier's plea / It hurt me too / Taking my time / Hello there angel / I'm yours, you're mine / You're a wonderful one / How sweet it is (to be loved by you) / Try it baby / Baby don't you do it / Need your lovin' (want you back) / One of these days / No good without you / Stepping closer to your heart / Need somebody / Me and my lonely room / Now that you've won me / Forever.
Compact disc: released on Motown, Jul'87 by Motown Records. Dist: BMG Distribution

TOO BUSY THINKING 'BOUT MY BABY.
Single (7"): released on Motown, Oct'81 by Motown Records. Dist: BMG Distribution

TROUBLE MAN.
Album: released on Motown, Jul'82 by Motown Records. Dist: BMG Distribution

Cassette: released on Motown, Jul'82 by Motown Records. Dist: BMG Distribution

TROUBLE MAN/M.P.G. 2 Classic albums.
Tracks: / Tere goes Mr.T / Too busy thinking about my baby / This magic moment / That's the way love is / End of our road / Seek & you shall find / Memories / Only a lonely man would know / It's a bitter pill to swallow / More than a heart can stand / Try my true love / It don't take much to keep me / I got to get to California / Trouble Man / T plays it cool / Poor Abbey Walsh / Break in / T stands for trouble / Cleo's apartment / Life is a gamble / Don't mess with Mr. T / Deep in it / Main theme from Trouble Man / Break in (Police shoot big),The / Theme from trouble man / There goes mister T/M.P.G.:.
Compact disc: released on Motown, Feb'87 by Motown Records. Dist: BMG Distribution

TWO CAN HAVE A PARTY (Gaye, Marvin & Tammi Terrell).
Single (7"): released on Motown, Oct'81 by Motown Records. Dist: BMG Distribution

UNITED (Gaye, Marvin & Tammi Terrell).
Album: released on Motown, Mar'82 by Motown Records. Dist: BMG Distribution

Cassette: released on Motown, Mar'82 by Motown Records. Dist: BMG Distribution

VERY BEST OF MARVIN GAYE,THE.
Tracks: / I heard it through the grapevine / Let's get it on / Too busy thinking about my baby / How sweet it is (to be loved by you) / Your all I need to get by / Got to give it up / You are everything / Midnight lady / Sexual healing / Whats going on / Abraham Martin and John / It takes two / Stop look and listen(to your heart) / It takes two / My love is waiting / Onion song,The / Wherever I lay my hat (that's my home).
Compact disc: released on Telstar, Jul'86 by Telstar Records. Dist: RCA Distribution

WHAT'S GOING ON?.
Album: released on Motown, Oct'81 by Motown Records. Dist: BMG Distribution

Cassette: released on Motown, Oct'81 by Motown Records. Dist: BMG Distribution

Single (7"): released on Motown, Mar'83 by Motown Records. Dist: BMG Distribution

Single (7"): released on Motown, Nov'83 by Motown Records. Dist: BMG Distribution

Single (12"): released on Motown, Nov'83 by Motown Records. Dist: BMG Distribution

WHAT'S GOING ON/LET'S GET IT ON.
Tracks: / What's going on / What's happening brother / Flying high (in the friendly sky) / Save the children / God is love / Mercy mercy me (the ecology) / Right on / Wholly holy / Inner city blues (make me wanna holler) / Let's get it on / Please don't stay (once you go away) / If I should die tonight / Keep gettin' it on / Come get to this / Distant lover / Sure love to ball / Just to keep you satisfied.
Compact disc: released on Motown, Nov'86 by Motown Records. Dist: BMG Distribution

WHEREVER I LAY MY HAT.
Single (7"): released on Motown, Jul'69 by Motown Records. Dist: BMG Distribution

WORLD IS RATED X,THE.
Tracks: / World is rated X,The / Lonely lover / World is rated X,The(instrumental).
Single (7"): released on Motown, Jun'86 by Motown Records. Dist: BMG Distribution

Single (12"): released on Motown, Jun'86 by Motown Records. Dist: BMG Distribution

YOU ARE EVERYTHING (Gaye, Marvin & Diana Ross).
Single (7"): released on Motown, May'82 by Motown Records. Dist: BMG Distribution

Single (7"): released on Motown, Oct'81 by Motown Records. Dist: BMG Distribution

YOU'RE ALL I NEED (Gaye, Marvin & Tammi Terrell).
Album: released on Motown, Oct'81 by Motown Records. Dist: BMG Distribution

Cassette: released on Motown, Oct'81 by Motown Records. Dist: BMG Distribution

Gayle, Crystal

20 LOVE SONGS.
Album: released on Music For Pleasure (Liberty-UA), Nov'83

Cassette: released on Music For Pleasure (Liberty-UA), Nov'83

6 TRACK HITS.
Special: released on Scoop 33, Aug'84 by Pickwick Records. Dist: H.R. Taylor

Cassette: released on Scoop 33, Aug'84 by Pickwick Records. Dist: H.R. Taylor

BABY WHAT ABOUT YOU.
Single (7"): released on Elektra, Apr'83 by WEA Records. Dist: WEA

Single (12"): released on Elektra, Apr'83 by WEA Records. Dist: WEA

Single (7"): released on Warner Bros., Sep'83 by Warner Bros Records. Dist: WEA

CAGE THE SONGBIRD.
Album: released on Warner Brothers, Oct'83 by Warner Bros Records. Dist: WEA

Cassette: released on Warner Brothers, Oct'83 by Warner Bros Records. Dist: WEA Deleted '87.

COUNTRY GIRL.
Album: released on Music For Pleasure, Jan'85 by EMI Records. Dist: EMI

Cassette: released on Music For Pleasure, Jan'85 by EMI Records. Dist: EMI

CRY.
Tracks: / Crazy in the heart.
Single (7"): released on Warner Bros., Nov'86 by Warner Bros Records. Dist: WEA

CRYSTAL CHRISTMAS,A.
Tracks: / White Christmas / Oh holy night / Winter wonderland / I'll be home for Christmas / Have yourself a merry little christmas / Rudolph the red nosed Reindeer / Little drummer boy,The / Christmas Songs,The / Jingle bells / Silver bells / Silent night.
Album: released on Warner Bros., Nov'86 by Warner Bros Records. Dist: WEA

CRYSTAL GAYLE COLLECTION.
Album: released on CBS, Dec'82 by CBS Records. Dist: CBS

Cassette: released on CBS, Dec'82 by CBS Records. Dist: CBS

DON'T IT MAKE MY BROWN EYES.
Single (7"): released on United Artists, Oct'77

DON'T IT MAKE MY BROWN EYES BLUE.
Single (7"): released on EMI Golden 45's, May'84 by EMI Records. Dist: EMI

EVERYTHING I OWN.
Single (7"): released on Elektra, Dec'82 by WEA Records. Dist: WEA

Single (12"): released on Elektra, Jan'83 by WEA Records. Dist: WEA

IN CONCERT (VIDEO) Hamilton Place, Canada.
Video-cassette (VHS): released on Video Collection, May'87 by Video Collection Records. Dist: Counterpoint

LOVE SONGS.
Album: released on Hallmark, Apr'83 by Pickwick Records. Dist: Pickwick Distribution, PRT, Taylors

Cassette: released on Hallmark, Apr'83 by Pickwick Records. Dist: Pickwick Distribution, PRT, Taylors

MISS THE MISSISSIPPI.
Tracks: Half the way / Other side for one

more,The / Room for one more / Don't go my love / Dancing the night away / It's like we never said goodbye / Blue side, The / Little bit of rain, A / Danger zone / Miss the Mississippi and you.
Album: released on CBS, Mar'86 by CBS Records. Dist: CBS

Cassette: released on CBS, Mar'86 by CBS Records. Dist: CBS

MOST BEAUTIFUL SONGS OF CRYSTAL GALE,THE.
Album: released on Music For Pleasure (Holland), Jan'86 by EMI Records. Dist: EMI

Cassette: released on Music For Pleasure (Holland), Jan'86 by EMI Records. Dist: EMI

NOBODY WANTS TO BE ALONE.
Album: released on Warner Brothers, May'85 by Warner Bros Records. Dist: WEA

Cassette: released on Warner Brothers, May'85 by Warner Bros Records. Dist: WEA
Cat. no: **925 154-4**

...SINGLES ALBUM.
Album: released on Liberty, '85 by Liberty-United. Dist: EMI

Cassette: released on Liberty, '85 by Liberty-United. Dist: EMI

STRAIGHT TO THE HEART.
Tracks: / Straight to the heart / Cry / Take this heart / Little bit closer, A / Do I have to say goodbye / Deep down / Crazy in the heart / Only love can save me now / Nobody should have to love this way / Lonely girl.
Cassette: released on Warner Bros., Oct'86 by Warner Bros Records. Dist: WEA

Compact disc: released on Warner Bros., Mar'87 by Warner Bros Records. Dist: WEA

TALKING IN YOUR SLEEP.
Single (7"): released on United Artists, Jun'78

TRUE LOVE.
Album: released on Elektra, Dec'82 by WEA Records. Dist: WEA Deleted '87.

Cassette: released on Elektra, Dec'82 by WEA Records. Dist: WEA

WE MUST BELIEVE IN MAGIC.
Cassette: released on United Artists, Aug'77

WOMAN IN ME, THE.
Album: released on Hallmark, Mar'85 by Pickwick Records. Dist: Pickwick Distribution, PRT, Taylors

Cassette: released on Hallmark, Mar'85 by Pickwick Records. Dist: Pickwick Distribution, PRT, Taylors

Gayle, Erica

IT'S ALRIGHT.
Single (12"): released on Ital, Oct'82 Dist: Pinnacle

Gayle, Roy

UP ALL NIGHT (DOING IT).
Single (7"): released on Musik UK, Feb'87 Dist: PRT Distribution

Single (12"): released on Musik UK, Feb'87 Dist: PRT Distribution

Gaylords

NA NA NA MARIE.
Single (7"): released on Pinner, Jan'87 by Pinner Records. Dist: Rough Trade, Cartel, Backs

Gaynair, Wilton

BLUE BOGEY (Gaynair, Wilton 'Bogey').
Album: released on Jasmine, Mar'83 by Jasmine Records. Dist: Counterpoint, Lugtons, Taylor, H.R., Wellard, Chris, Swift, Cadillac

Gay, Noel

GOLDEN AGE OF NOEL GAY.
Album: released on Music For Pleasure (Holland), May'84 by EMI Records. Dist: EMI

Cassette: released on Music For Pleasure (Holland), May'84 by EMI Records. Dist: EMI

Gaynor, Gloria

BE SOFT WITH ME TONIGHT.
Tracks: / Be soft with me tonight / Be soft with me tonight (club mix) / If only you'd believe it / If only you'd believe it (inst).
Compact disc single: released on Fanfare, Apr'87 by Ferroway/Fanfare Records. Dist: PRT

DON'T DARE CALL IT LOVE.
Tracks: / Don't dare call it love.
Single (7"): Dist: Pinnacle, Terry Blood Distribution, Stylus Distribution

Single (12"): Dist: Pinnacle, Terry Blood Distribution, Stylus Distribution

EVERY BREATH YOU TAKE.
Tracks: / Every breath you take.
Single (7"): released on Stylus, Jun'86 Dist: Pinnacle, Terry Blood Distribution, Stylus Distribution

Single (12"): released on Stylus, Jun'86 Dist: Pinnacle, Terry Blood Distribution, Stylus Distribution

GLORIA GAYNOR.
Album: released on Ecstasy, Nov'83 by Creole Records. Dist: CBS

Cassette: released on Ecstasy, Nov'83 by Creole Records. Dist: CBS

GLORIA GAYNOR'S GREATEST HITS.
Album: released on Polydor, Jun'82 by Polydor Records. Dist: Polygram, Polydor

Cassette: released on Polydor, Jun'82 by Polydor Records. Dist: Polygram, Polydor

I AM GLORIA GAYNOR.
Album: released on Chrysalis, Mar'84 by Chrysalis Records. Dist: CBS

Cassette: released on Chrysalis, Mar'84 by Chrysalis Records. Dist: CBS

I AM WHAT I AM.
Single (7"): released on Chrysalis, Dec'83 by Chrysalis Records. Dist: CBS

Single (12"): released on Chrysalis, Dec'83 by Chrysalis Records. Dist: CBS

I KINDA LIKE ME.
Album: released on Polydor, Jun'81 by Polydor Records. Dist: Polygram, Polydor

I WILL SURVIVE.
Single (12"): released on Polydor, Oct'82 by Polydor Records. Dist: Polygram, Polydor

LOVE ME REAL.
Single (7"): released on Ecstasy, Sep'83 by Creole Records. Dist: CBS

Single (12"): released on Ecstasy, Sep'83 by Creole Records. Dist: CBS

MY LOVE IS MUSIC.
Single (7"): released on Carrere, Mar'85 by Carrere Records. Dist: PRT, Spartan

Single (12"): released on Carrere, Mar'85 by Carrere Records. Dist: PRT, Spartan

NEVER CAN SAY GOODBYE.
Album: released on MGM, Mar'75 Dist: Polygram Distribution, Swift Distribution

Single (7"): released on MGM, '74 Dist: Polygram Distribution, Swift Distribution

POWER OF,THE.
Tracks: / Don't you dare call it love / Eye of the tiger / Heat is on / Every breath you take / Feel so real / Broken wings / Power of love.etc.
Album: released on Stylus, Jan'86 Dist: Pinnacle, Terry Blood Distribution, Stylus Distribution

Cassette: released on Stylus, Jan'86 Dist: Pinnacle, Terry Blood Distribution, Stylus Distribution

Compact disc: released on Stylus, Jan'86 Dist: Pinnacle, Terry Blood Distribution, Stylus Distribution

STRIVE.
Single (7"): released on Chrysalis, Mar'84 by Chrysalis Records. Dist: CBS

Single (12"): released on Chrysalis, Mar'84 by Chrysalis Records. Dist: CBS

Gayten, Paul

CREOLE GAL (Gayten, Paul & Annie Laurie).
Album: released on Route 66, Jun'80

Gazarian, Ani

AMAZING ANNO DAZUMAL, THE.
Album: released on Phontastic (Sweden), '82 by Wellard, Chris Distribution. Dist: Wellard, Chris Distribution

Gazebo

GAZEBO.
Album: released on Baby, Oct'83 by New Rose Records. Dist: Cartel

Cassette: released on Baby, '85 by New Rose Records. Dist: Cartel

I LIKE CHOPIN'.
Single (7"): released on Baby, Sep'83 by New Rose Records. Dist: Cartel

Single (12"): released on Baby, Sep'83 by New Rose Records. Dist: Cartel

MASTERPIECE.
Single (7"): released on Baby, Sep'82 by New Rose Records. Dist: Cartel

Single (12"): released on Baby, Sep'82 by New Rose Records. Dist: Cartel

Gaz & Groovers

MELLOW SAXOPHONE.
Single (7"): released on Fliptone, Feb'82 Dist: Spartan

Gaz's Rebel Blues...

TRIGGER HAPPY (Gaz's Rebel Blues Rockers).
Single (7"): released on Risk, Sep'83 by Rough Trade Records. Dist: Rough Trade

Gaz's Rockin' Blues

GAZ'S ROCKIN' BLUES Various artists (Various Artists).
Album: released on Ace(Cadet), Dec'81 by Ace Records. Dist: Pinnacle, Swift, Hotshot

Gazuzu

GO GO GORILLA.
Single (7"): released on Ecstasy, Jan'84 by Creole Records. Dist: CBS

Single (12"): released on Ecstasy, Jan'84 by Creole Records. Dist: CBS

GBH

CATCH 23.
Single (7"): released on Clay, Apr'83 by Clay Records. Dist: Pinnacle

CITY BABIES ATTACKED BY RATS/CITY BABIES REVENGE.
Compact disc: released on Road Runner, Mar'87

CITY BABIES REVENGE.
Album: released on Clay, Dec'83 by Clay Records. Dist: Pinnacle

Cassette: released on Clay, Dec'83 by Clay Records. Dist: Pinnacle

CITY BABY ATTACKED BY RATS.
Album: released on Clay, Jul'82 by Clay Records. Dist: Pinnacle

CLAY YEARS 81-84, THE.
Album: released on Clay, Jul'86 by Clay Records. Dist: Pinnacle

DO WHAT YOU DO.
Single (7"): released on Clay, Aug'84 by Clay Records. Dist: Pinnacle

Single (12"): released on Clay, Aug'84 by Clay Records. Dist: Pinnacle

GIVE ME FIRE.
Single (7"): released on Clay, Nov'82 by Clay Records. Dist: Pinnacle

Picture disc single: released on Clay, Nov'82 by Clay Records. Dist: Pinnacle

LEATHER BRISTLES STUDS ACNE.
Single (12"): released on Clay, Mar'84 by Clay Records. Dist: Pinnacle

MIDNIGHT MADNESS AND BEYOND.
Compact disc: released on Rough Justice, Aug'87 by MFN Records. Dist: Pinnacle

MIDNIGHT MADNESS & BEYOND.
Album: released on Rough Justice, Feb'86 by MFN Records. Dist: Pinnacle

Cassette: released on Rough Justice, Feb'86 by MFN Records. Dist: Pinnacle

NO SURVIVORS.
Single (7"): released on Clay, Jan'82 by Clay Records. Dist: Pinnacle

OH NO IT'S GBH AGAIN.
Tracks: / Oh no it's GBH again.
Single (12"): released on Rough Justice, Sep'86 by MFN Records. Dist: Pinnacle

Album: released on Raw, Jun'78 by Raw Records. Dist: Spartan

SICK BOY.
Single (7"): released on Clay, Jun'82 by Clay Records. Dist: Pinnacle

GB Rockers

SHEREE SHEREE.
Single (7"): released on Runaway, May'83

WHEN YOU'RE HOT YOU'RE HOT.
Album: released on Runaway, '82

G.C.E. O Level...

ENGLISH LANGUAGE.
Cassette: released on Real Revision, Jan'84

ENGLISH LITERATURE Midsummer night's dream, A.
Cassette: released on Real Revision, Jan'84

ENGLISH LITERATURE Henry IV part 1.
Cassette: released on Real Revision, Jan'84

ENGLISH LITERATURE Macbeth.
Cassette: released on Real Revision, Jan'84

ENGLISH LITERATURE Romeo and Juliet.
Cassette: released on Real Revision, Jan'84

FRENCH.
Cassette: released on Real Revision, Jan'84

MATHEMATICS.
Cassette: released on Real Revision, Jan'84

SPANISH.
Cassette: released on Real Revision, Jan'84

G-Clefs

I UNDERSTAND.
Single (7"): released on Old Gold, Oct'83 by Old Gold Records. Dist: Lightning, Jazz Music, Spartan, Counterpoint

Gebruder Enger

SKANDAL.
Album: released on Sky, May'79 by President Records.

Geddes Axe

ESCAPE FROM NEW YORK.
Single (12"): released on Bullet, Jun'83 Dist: Bullet Distribution

RETURN OF THE GODS.
Single (7"): released on ACS, May'81 Dist: Pinnacle

SHARPEN YOUR WITS.
Single (7"): released on Steel City, Aug'82

Geddes, Graham

AT HOME WITH (Geddes, Graham & His Scottish Dance Band).
Album: released on Ross, '86 by Ross Records. Dist: Ross Distribution, Roots Distribution

Cassette: released on Ross, '86 by Ross Records. Dist: Ross Distribution, Roots Distribution

AT HOME WITH GRAHAM GEDDES.
Album: released on Ross, Feb'85 by Ross Records. Dist: Ross Distribution, Roots Distribution

BLOOMS OF BON ACCORD,THE (Geddes, Graham & His Band).

BLOOMS OF BON-ACCORD, THE (Geddes, Graham & His Scottish Dance Band).
Cassette: released on Ross, '86 by Ross Records. Dist: Ross Distribution, Roots Distribution

SEVEN THISTLES (Geddes, Graham & His Scottish Dance Band).
Album: released on Ross, '86 by Ross Records. Dist: Ross Distribution, Roots Distribution

Cassette: released on Ross, '86 by Ross Records. Dist: Ross Distribution, Roots Distribution

STEP IN TIME, A (Geddes, Graham & His Band).
Cassette: released on Ross, '86 by Ross Records. Dist: Ross Distribution, Roots Distribution

Gee, Bobby

BIG DEAL.
Tracks: / Big deal / I Want to say.
Single (7"): released on Polydor, Sep'86 by Polydor Records. Dist: Polygram, Polydor

Single (12"): released on Polydor, Sep'86 by Polydor Records. Dist: Polygram, Polydor

Single (7"): released on BBC, Oct'84 by BBC Records & Tapes. Dist: EMI, PRT, Pye

Single (12"): released on BBC, Nov'84 by BBC Records & Tapes. Dist: EMI, PRT, Pye

Gee, Debbie

WILL I EVER DO.
Single (12"): released on TNT, Dec'82 by TNT Records. Dist: Jetstar Distribution

Gee, H

AFTER MIDNIGHT.
Album: released on Street Value, Nov'86 Dist: Jetstar Distribution

Gee, Junior

CAVEMAN ROCK.
Single (7"): released on PRT, Nov'84 by PRT Records. Dist: PRT

CHECK US OUT (Gee, Junior & Capitol Boys).
Single (12"): released on Taiwan, Sep'84 by Tania Music Records. Dist: Tania Music Distribution

TERMINATOR, THE (Gee, Junior & The "A" Team).
Tracks: / Terminator, The / Terminator, The (Dub Edit) / Terminator, The (Perfect madness mix) / Terminator (Remix)(7" Radio edit) / Terminator (Instrumental).
Notes: see also under A Team & Junior Gee
Single (7"): released on Fourth & Broadway, Feb'87 by Island Records. Dist: Polygram, EMI

Single (12"): released on Fourth & Broadway, Feb'87 by Island Records. Dist: Polygram, EMI

Single (12"): released on Fourth & Broadway, Mar'87 by Island Records. Dist: Polygram, EMI

Gee, Lorna

GOTTA FIND A WAY.
Single (12"):

SING-A-LONG.
Tracks: / Sing-a-long / Russian Roulette.
Single (12"): released on Ariwa, Sep'86 by Ariwa Records. Dist: Revolver, Cartel, Jetstar, Rough Trade

THREE WEEKS GONE.
Single (12"): released on Ariwa, Feb'85 by Ariwa Records. Dist: Revolver, Cartel, Jetstar, Rough Trade

Gee, MC Miker

DON'T LET THE MUSIC STOP.
Tracks: / Don't let the music stop / Don't let the music stop (inst).
Single (7"): released on Nine O Nine, Jul'87 by Creole Records. Dist: Rhino, PRT

Single (12"): released on Nine O Nine, Jul'87 by Creole Records. Dist: Rhino, PRT

Gee Mr Tracey

HARMONY'RAPSODY'DESTINY'..
Album: released on Backs, Aug'86 by Backs Records. Dist: Backs, Cartel

I WISH THE WHOLE DAMN WORLD WAS IN A BOTTLE.
Single (7"): released on Backs, Jul'85 by Backs Records. Dist: Backs, Cartel

LAVA MAN.
Tracks: / Lava man / Mr. Unlucky.
Single (7"): released on Backs, Jan'86 by Backs Records. Dist: Backs, Cartel

PERMANENT SWOON.
Tracks: / Permanent swoon / I fell through the floor.
Single (7"): released on Backs, Jun'86 by Backs Records. Dist: Backs, Cartel

SHOOTMETHATSHERBERT.
Album: released on Backs, Mar'85 by Backs Records. Dist: Backs, Cartel

YOU MAKE MY HOUSE SHINE.
Single (7"): released on Backs, Mar'85 by Backs Records. Dist: Backs, Cartel

Gee, Norman

ROLL THE DICE.
Tracks: / Roll the dice / It's a must(Stricker Banton).
Single (12"): released on Gentlesounds, Apr'86 Dist: Jetstar

Geesin, Ron

AS HE STANDS.
Album: released on Ron Geesin, May'79

ELECTROSOUND.
Album: released on Ron Geesin, May'79

Music from the body

PATRUNS.
Album: released on Ron Geesin, May'79

RIGHT THROUGH.
Album: released on Ron Geesin, May'79

Gee Sloley

I LIKE YOUR LOVING.
Single (12"): released on Red Man, Dec'82 by Red Man Records. Dist: Jetstar

Gee, Tony

ONE MINUTE MORE.
Single (7"): released on Mass Enterprise, Jun'85 Dist: M.I.S., EMI

Single (12"): released on Mass Enterprise, Jun'85 Dist: M.I.S., EMI

Gehmann

BMW.
Tracks: / BMW / Life in G Major.
Single (12"): released on BGI, Sep'86 Dist: Jetstar

Geils, J., Band

FLASHBACK.
Compact disc: released on EMI America, Apr'87 by EMI Records. Dist: EMI

FLASHBACK - THE BEST OF J. GEILS.
Tracks: / Love stinks / Freeze-frame / Flamethrower / Just can't wait / I do / Centrefold / Come back / Wild man / One last kiss / Land of a thousand dances.
Compact disc: released on EMI America, Apr'87 by EMI Records. Dist: EMI

FREEZE FRAME.
Compact disc: released on EMI America, Mar'84 by EMI Records. Dist: EMI

I DO.
Single (7"): released on EMI America, Jan'83 by EMI Records. Dist: EMI

LADIES INVITED.
Album: released on Atlantic, Jan'74 by WEA Records. Dist: WEA

LOVE STINKS.
Album: released on EMI (France), May'84 by EMI Records. Dist: Conifer

VIDEO EP.
Notes: The title says it all-promo videos included are Love Stinks, Angel in Blue, Freeze Frame, and Cntrefold.
Video-cassette (VHS): released on PMI, Jun'86 by PMI Records. Dist: EMI

Video-cassette [Betamax]: released on PMI, Jun'86 by PMI Records. Dist: EMI

Geiser

COMPILATION.
Album: released on Enigma, Jun'87 by Enigma Records. Dist: Rough Trade, Cartel, EMI

Geisha

PHANTASMAGORIA.
Tracks: / You got what it takes / Shock rock school / Gangland sector 21 / Alive and scratching / Claws of sin / Underworld (The) / S & M youth.
Notes: Produced by Geisha and Peter Mark. (P) 1987 Original Sound recordings made by The Geisha Brotherhood. 1987 A Heavy Metal Worldwide Release. Heavy Metal Worldwide is a division of FM-Revolver Records Ltd.
Album: released on Heavy Metal Worldwide, Apr'87 by FM-Revolver Records. Dist: EMI

Geisha Girls

I'M A TEAPOT.
Single (7"): released on Dog Breath, Sep'83 by Dog Breath Records. Dist: Cartel

SLAVE OF LOVE.
Single (7"): released on Dog Breath, Feb'85 by Dog Breath Records. Dist: Cartel

Single (12"): released on Dog Breath, Feb'85 by Dog Breath Records. Dist: Cartel

Geisterfaher

MADISH AHB'ELL.
Single (7"): released on Upright, Jul'82 by Upright Records. Dist: Cartel, Rough Trade

Geldof, Bob

DEEP IN THE HEART OF NOWHERE.
Tracks: / This is the world calling / In the pouring rain / Love like a rocket / Words from heaven / Deep in the heart of nowhere / Pulled apart by horses / When I was young / This heartless heart / Night turns to day / Beat of the night, The / Good boys in the wrong / I cry too / August was a heavy month / Truly truly blue.

Album: released on Mercury, Nov'86 by Phonogram Records. Dist: Polygram Distribution

Cassette: released on Mercury, Nov'86 by Phonogram Records. Dist: Polygram Distribution

Compact disc: released on Mercury, Nov'86 by Phonogram Records. Dist: Polygram Distribution

I CRY TOO.
Tracks: / I cry too / Let's go / Night turns to day* / Deep in the heart of nowhere*.
Single (7"): released on Mercury, Jun'87 by Phonogram Records. Dist: Polygram Distribution

Single (12"): released on Mercury, Jun'87 by Phonogram Records. Dist: Polygram Distribution

LOVE LIKE A ROCKET.
Tracks: / Love like a rocket / Tis is the world calling / Pulled apart by horses / Truly true blue / Love like a rocket (12" mix).
Compact disc single: released on Mercury, Feb'87 by Phonogram Records. Dist: Polygram Distribution

THIS IS THE WORLD CALLING.
Tracks: / This is the world calling / Talk me up.
Single (7"): released on Mercury, Oct'86 by Phonogram Records. Dist: Polygram Distribution

Single (12"): released on Mercury, Oct'86 by Phonogram Records. Dist: Polygram Distribution

Geller, Herb

RHYME AND REASON (Geller, Herb Octet).
Album: released on Discovery, Aug'83 Dist: PRT

WEST COAST SCENE.
Double Album: released on Vogue Jazz, Apr'82

Double Album: released on Vogue, Sep'77 Dist: Discovery, Jazz Music, PRT, Swift

Gemini

ANOTHER YOU ANOTHER ME.
Tracks: / Another you another me / Falling / Copy love.
Single (7"): released on Polydor, Oct'86 by Polydor Records. Dist: Polygram, Polydor

Single (12"): released on Polydor, Oct'86 by Polydor Records. Dist: Polygram, Polydor

GEMINI.
Album: released on Polydor, Oct'86 by Polydor Records. Dist: Polygram, Polydor

Cassette: released on Polydor, Oct'86 by Polydor Records. Dist: Polygram, Polydor

Compact disc: released on Polydor, Nov'86 by Polydor Records. Dist: Polygram, Polydor

Album: released on Bulldog, Jun'85 by Bulldog Records. Dist: President Distribution, Spartan, Swift, Taylor, H.R.

JUST LIKE THAT.
Tracks: / Just like that / Live on the love.
Single (7"): released on Polydor, Mar'86 by Polydor Records. Dist: Polygram, Polydor

Single (12"): released on Polydor, Mar'86 by Polydor Records. Dist: Polygram, Polydor

Gemini Sound...

GEMINI SOUND LIVE AT SKATELAND
Various artists (Various Artists).
Album: released on Vista Sounds, Jan'83 by Vista Sounds Records. Dist: Jetstar

Gem Lucky Jazz Orchestra

KENYAFRICA (VOL.2).
Album: released on Playasound, '74 Dist: Conifer, Discovery

Gem, Robert

NIGHTWALKER.
Single (7"): released on President, Jun'85 by President Records. Dist: Taylors, Spartan

Gems

GEMS Various artists (Various Artists).
Album: released on Kent, May'84 by Ace Records. Dist: Pinnacle

LEAVING.
Tracks: / Leaving / Forever.
Single (12"): released on Silent, Mar'87 Dist: Stiff

STAND UP SIT DOWN.
Tracks: / Stand up sit down / Here it comes again / Stand up sit down (instrumental).
Single (7"): released on Silent, Feb'86 Dist: Stiff

Single (12"): released on Silent, Feb'86 Dist: Stiff

WALK AWAY.
Tracks: / Walk away / Wasted land.
Single (7"): released on Silent, Mar'87 Dist: Stiff

Single (12"): released on Silent, Mar'87 Dist: Stiff

YOUNG MANS DREAM.
Tracks: / Young mans dream / Hand over fist.
Single (7"): released on Silent, May'86 Dist: Stiff

Single (12"): released on Silent, May'86 Dist: Stiff

Gems From Treasure Isle

GEMS FROM TREASURE ISLE Various artists (Various Artists).
Album: released on Trojan, Jan'83 by Trojan Records. Dist: PRT, Jetstar

Gendall, Richard

LUL-HA-LAY 26 SONGS IN CORNISH.
Cassette: released on Folktracks, Nov'79 by Folktracks Cassettes. Dist: Folktracks

SONGS IN CORNISH.
Cassette: released on Folktracks, Nov'79 by Folktracks Cassettes. Dist: Folktracks

Gene & Eunice

THIS IS MY STORY.
Album: released on Pathe MarconiFrance), Apr'85

Gene Loves Jezebel

BRUISES.
Single (7"): released on Situation 2, Jul'83 Dist: Cartel, Pinnacle

Single (12"): released on Situation 2, Jul'83 Dist: Cartel, Pinnacle

COW.
Single (7"): released on Situation 2, May'85 Dist: Cartel, Pinnacle

Single (12"): released on Situation 2, May'85 Dist: Cartel, Pinnacle

DESIRE.
Tracks: / Heartache (UK club mix) / Message / Desire / Flame / Immigrant.
Cassette single: released on Beggars Banquet, Nov'86 by Beggars Banquet Records. Dist: WEA

Single (7"): released on Beggars Banquet, Dec'85 by Beggars Banquet Records. Dist: WEA

Single (12"): released on Beggars Banquet, Dec'85 by Beggars Banquet Records. Dist: WEA

Single (7"): released on Situation 2, Nov'85 Dist: Cartel, Pinnacle

Single (12"): released on Situation 2, Nov'85 Dist: Cartel, Pinnacle

DESIRE(COME AND GET IT).
Tracks: / Desire(come and get it) / Message / Sapphire scavenger / New horizons.
Single (7"): released on Beggars Banquet, Oct'86 by Beggars Banquet Records. Dist: WEA

Single (12"): released on Beggars Banquet, Oct'86 by Beggars Banquet Records. Dist: WEA

DISCOVER.
Tracks: / Heartache / Over the rooftops / Kick / White Horse / Wait and see / Desire / Beyond doubt / Sweetest thing / Maid of Sker / Brand new moon.
Album: released on Beggars Banquet, Jul'86 by Beggars Banquet Records. Dist: WEA

Cassette: released on Beggars Banquet, Jul'86 by Beggars Banquet Records. Dist: WEA

Compact disc: released on Beggars Banquet, Oct'86 by Beggars Banquet Records. Dist: WEA

IMMIGRANTS.
Album: released on Situation 2, Jun'85 Dist: Cartel, Pinnacle

Cassette: released on Situation 2, Jun'85 Dist: Cartel, Pinnacle

INFLUENZA Relapse.
Single (7"): released on Situation 2, Apr'84 Dist: Cartel, Pinnacle

MOTION OF LOVE, THE.
Double-pack single: released on Beggars Banquet, Aug'87 by Beggars Banquet Records. Dist: WEA

Double-pack single: released on Beggars Banquet, Aug'87 by Beggars Banquet Records. Dist: WEA

PROMISE.
Album: released on Situation 2, Oct'83 Dist: Cartel, Pinnacle

SCREAMING.
Single (7"): released on Situation 2, May'83 Dist: Cartel, Pinnacle

Single (12"): released on Situation 2, May'83 Dist: Cartel, Pinnacle

SHAME.
Single (7"): released on Situation 2, May'84 Dist: Cartel, Pinnacle

Single (12"): released on Situation 2, May'84 Dist: Cartel, Pinnacle

SHAVIN MY NECK.
Single (7"): released on Situation 2, May'82 Dist: Cartel, Pinnacle

Single (12"): released on Situation 2, Jun'82 Dist: Cartel, Pinnacle

SWEETEST THING.
Tracks: / Sweetest thing / Psycho II.
Single (7"): released on Beggars Banquet, Mar'86 by Beggars Banquet Records. Dist:

WEA

Single (12"): released on Beggars Banquet, Mar'86 by Beggars Banquet Records. Dist: WEA

General Caine

HAIRDOOZ.
Tracks: / Hairdooz / Crack kills applejack.
Single (7"): released on Motown, Nov'86 by Motown Records. Dist: BMG Distribution

Single (12"): released on Motown, Nov'86 by Motown Records. Dist: BMG Distribution

IN FULL CHILL.
Tracks: / Hairdooz / Wrassle / Buffaloes / Can't let go / All the way up / Crack killed Applejack / Ticket, The / Cuttin' it up / General speaks, The.
Album: released on Motown, Feb'87 by Motown Records. Dist: BMG Distribution

Cassette: released on Motown, Feb'87 by Motown Records. Dist: BMG Distribution

General Echo

12" OF PLEASURE.
Album: released on Greensleeves, Sep'80 by Greensleeves Records. Dist: BMG, Jetstar, Spartan

AFRIKA'S NATIONAL HERO.
Single 10": released on Mandingo, Nov'82 Dist: Jetstar

HOTEL FEE.
Single (12"): released on Greensleeves, Jan'80 by Greensleeves Records. Dist: BMG, Jetstar, Spartan

General & Killerwatt

MINDER.
Single (12"): released on Cool Ghoul, Nov'85 by Cool Ghoul Records. Dist: Rough Trade, Cool Ghoul

General Lafayette

FOR THE GIRL WHO COULD'T FIND LOVE.
Tracks: / For the girl who couldn't find love / For the girl who couldn't find love (solo mix).
Single (7"): released on Plaza, May'87 by Plaza Records. Dist: Spartan

HEARTACHE.
Tracks: / Heartache / Beyond doubt / Deli babies.
Single (7"): released on Beggars Banquet, May'86 by Beggars Banquet Records. Dist: WEA

Single (12"): released on Beggars Banquet, May'86 by Beggars Banquet Records. Dist: WEA

REGGAE THE LONELY TRUMPET.
Single (7"): released on Plaza, Nov'82 by Plaza Records. Dist: Spartan

Single (12"): released on Plaza, Nov'82 by Plaza Records. Dist: Spartan

General, Mikey

DANCE HALL VIBES.
Tracks: / Dance hall vibes / Margaret.
Single (12"): released on Digikal, Oct'86 by Digikal Records. Dist: Revolver

I SAY NO.
Tracks: / I say no / Rose ann.
Single (12"): released on MGR, Dec'85 Dist: Jetstar Records

KUFF'N DEM.
Tracks: / Kuff'n dem.
Single (12"): released on Digikal, Mar'87 by Digikal Records. Dist: Revolver

SINGER WITH THE FLAVOUR.
Single (12"): released on Jah Life, Jun'85 by Jah Life Records. Dist: Jetstar

SOUND BOY BURIAL (General, Mikey & Andrew Paul).
Album: released on Digikal, Nov'86 by Digikal Records. Dist: Revolver

SOUND DOCTOR (General, Mikey & Andrew Paul).
Tracks: / Sound doctor / Jump and shout.
Single (12"): released on Fashion, Dec'85 by Fashion Records. Dist: PRT, Jetstar

General Public

ALL THE RAGE.
Album: released on Virgin, Oct'84 by Virgin Records. Dist: EMI, Virgin Distribution

Cassette: released on Virgin, Oct'84 by Virgin Records. Dist: EMI, Virgin Distribution

FAULTS AND ALL.
Tracks: / Faults and all / Taking the day off.
Single (7"): released on Virgin, Sep'86 by Virgin Records. Dist: EMI, Virgin Distribution

Single (12"): released on Virgin, Sep'86 by Virgin Records. Dist: EMI, Virgin Distribution

HAND TO MOUTH.
Tracks: / Come again / Faults and all / Forward as one / Murder / Cheque in the post / Too much or nothing / Love without the fun / Conversation / Never all there / Cry on your own shoulder.
Album: released on Virgin, Oct'86 by Virgin Records. Dist: EMI, Virgin Distribution

Cassette: released on Virgin, Oct'86 by Virgin Records. Dist: EMI, Virgin Distribution

Compact disc: released on Virgin, Nov'86 by Virgin Records. Dist: EMI, Virgin Distribution

TENDERNESS.
Single (12"): released on Virgin, Mar'85 by Virgin Records. Dist: EMI, Virgin Distribution

General Saint

ANOTHER ONE BITES THE DUST (General Saint & Clint Eastwood).
Single (7"): released on Greensleeves, Jun'81 by Greensleeves Records. Dist: BMG, Jetstar, Spartan

STOP THAT TRAIN(SINGLE) (seeEastwood,Clint&General Saint) (General Saint & Clint Eastwood).

General Strike

DANGER IN PARADISE.
Cassette: released on Touch, Jan'85 by Touch Records. Dist: Rough Trade, Cartel

General T

SHOWCASE (General T/Sister Candy/Colonel Flux).
Album: released on Raiders, Nov'84 Dist: Jetstar

General Tree

EVERYTHING SO-SO.
Album: released on World Enterprise, Jul'86 Dist: Jetstar

GHOST RIDER.
Album: released on Sunset, Aug'85 Dist: EMI

HEART MIND AND SOUL.
Album: released on Black Scorpio, Jul'85 by Black Scorpio Records. Dist: Jetstar

HORSEMAN STYLE.
Single (12"): released on Jammy's, Sep'84 by Jammy's Records. Dist: Jetstar

YOUNGER HORSEMAN, THE.
Album: released on Sunset, Mar'85 Dist: EMI

General Turbo

I'VE BEEN GIFTED.
Tracks: / I've been gifted / General Turbo.
Single (12"): released on Turbo, Jul'86 Dist: Jetstar

General Twilight

HIGHWAY LOVER.
Single (12"): released on Marlon Ranks, Jan'85 by Marlon Ranks Records. Dist: Jetstar

PAMELA.
Single (12"): released on Marlon Ranks, May'84 by Marlon Ranks Records. Dist: Jetstar

General Wolf

I BELIEVE IN LOVE.
Tracks: / I believe in love / Take a dream.

Generation, A

GENERATION, A/CANAL/ASHES AND DIAMONDS original soundtracks (Various Artists).
Album: released on That's Entertainment, Apr'83 by That's Entertainment Records. Dist: Pinnacle, PRT

Generation Band

CALL OF THE WILD.
Album: released on Palo Alto (Italy), Jan'85

Generation X

BEST OF GENERATION X, THE.
Album: released on Chrysalis, Nov'85 by Chrysalis Records. Dist: CBS

Cassette: released on Chrysalis, Nov'85 by Chrysalis Records. Dist: CBS

DANCING WITH MYSELF/UNTOUCHABLES/ROCK ON/KING ROCKER.
Single (7"): released on Chrysalis, Jan'81 by Chrysalis Records. Dist: CBS Deleted '85.

DANCING WITH MYSELF/UGLY RASH.
Single (7"): released on Chrysalis, Nov'80 by Chrysalis Records. Dist: CBS Deleted '85.

Single (12"): released on Chrysalis, Oct'80 by Chrysalis Records. Dist: CBS

Single (12"): released on Chrysalis, Jan'81 by Chrysalis Records. Dist: CBS

GENERATION X.
Album: released on Chrysalis, Mar'78 by Chrysalis Records. Dist: CBS

Cassette: released on Chrysalis, Mar'78 by Chrysalis Records. Dist: CBS

KING ROCKER.
Tracks: / King Rocker / Valley of the dolls.
Single (7"): released on Old Gold, Feb'87 by Old Gold Records. Dist: Lightning, Jazz Music, Spartan, Counterpoint

Single (7"): released on Chrysalis, Jan'79 by Chrysalis Records. Dist: CBS

KING ROCKER/ GIMME SOME TRUTH.

KISS ME DEADLY.
Album: released on Chrysalis, Jan'81 by Chrysalis Records. Dist: CBS

ORIGINAL GENERATION X.
Album: released on MBC, Jun'87 Dist: Pinnacle

THIS HEAT/TRYING FOR KICKS/FRIDAYS ANGELS.
Single (7"): released on Chrysalis, Jun'79 by Chrysalis Records. Dist: CBS

VALLEY OF THE DOLLS.
Album: released on Chrysalis, '79 by Chrysalis Records. Dist: CBS

Cassette: released on Chrysalis, '79 by Chrysalis Records. Dist: CBS

Genesis

ABACAB.
Album: released on Charisma, Sep'81 bv Virgin Records. Dist: EMI

Cassette: released on Charisma, Sep'81 by Virgin Records. Dist: EMI

Compact disc: released on Charisma, Sep'81 by Virgin Records. Dist: EMI

Compact disc: released on Charisma, '83 by Virgin Records. Dist: EMI

Single (7"): released on Charisma, Aug'81 by Virgin Records. Dist: EMI

AND THEN THERE WERE THREE.
Tracks: / Scenes from a nights dream / Snowbound undertow / Ballad of brig / Burning rope / Deep in the mother load / Down and out / Follow you follow me / Lady lies / Many too many / Say it's all right joe.
Notes: Digital Stereo.
Compact disc: released on Charisma, Dec'83 by Virgin Records. Dist: EMI

Album: released on Charisma, Sep'83 by Virgin Records. Dist: EMI

Cassette: released on Charisma, Sep'83 by Virgin Records. Dist: EMI

Compact disc: released on Charisma, Sep'83 by Virgin Records. Dist: EMI

DUCHESS.
Single (7"): released on Charisma, May'80 by Virgin Records. Dist: EMI

DUKE.
Compact disc: released on Charisma, Apr'85 by Virgin Records. Dist: EMI

Album: released on Charisma, Sep'83 by Virgin Records. Dist: EMI

Cassette: released on Charisma, Sep'83 by Virgin Records. Dist: EMI

FOLLOW YOU FOLLOW ME.
Single (7"): released on Old Gold, Jul'82 by Old Gold Records. Dist: Lightning, Jazz Music, Spartan, Counterpoint

FOXTROT.
Tracks: / Watcher of the skies / Time table / Get 'em out by friday / Can-utility and the coastliners / Horizons / Supper's ready / Lover's leap / Guaranteed eternal sanctuary(The) / Ikhnanton and Itsacon and their band of merry men / How dare be so beautiful / Willow farm / Apocalypse in 9 / 8 / As sure as eggs is eggs.
Compact disc: released on Charisma, Jul'86 by Virgin Records. Dist: EMI

Album: released on Charisma, Sep'83 by Virgin Records. Dist: EMI

Cassette: released on Charisma, Sep'83 by Virgin Records. Dist: EMI

FOXTROT / SELLING ENGLAND BY THE POUND.
Cassette: released on Charisma, Mar'83 by Virgin Records. Dist: EMI

GENESIS.
Tracks: / Mama / Illegal alien / That's all / Taking it all too hard / Just a job to do / Home by the sea / Second home by the sea / It's gonna get better / Carpet crawlers.
Compact disc: released on Charisma, Dec'83 by Virgin Records. Dist: EMI

Album: released on Charisma, Sep'83 by Virgin Records. Dist: EMI

GENESIS, ORIGINAL SOUNDTRACK.
Notes: Music by Ravi Shankar
Album: released on Milan France, Jun'86

Cassette: released on Milan France, Jun'86

I KNOW WHAT I LIKE.
Single (7"): released on Old Gold, Jul'82 by Old Gold Records. Dist: Lightning, Jazz Music, Spartan, Counterpoint

ILLEGAL ALIEN.
Single (7"): released on Charisma, Jan'84 by Virgin Records. Dist: EMI

Single (12"): released on Charisma, Jan'84 by Virgin Records. Dist: EMI

Picture disc single: released on Charisma, Jan'84 by Virgin Records. Dist: EMI

INTERVIEW PICTURE DISC.
Album: released on Baktabak, May'87 by Baktabak Records. Dist: Arabesque

IN TOO DEEP.
Tracks: / In too deep / Do the neurotic.
Single (7"): released on Charisma, Aug'86 by Virgin Records. Dist: EMI

Single (12"): released on Charisma, Aug'86 by Virgin Records. Dist: EMI

INVISIBLE TOUCH.
Tracks: / Invisible touch / Last domino (The).
Album: released on Charisma, Dec'86 by Virgin Records. Dist: EMI

Cassette: released on Charisma, Dec'86 by Virgin Records. Dist: EMI

Compact disc: released on Charisma, Dec'86 by Virgin Records. Dist: EMI

Single (7"): released on Virgin, May'86 by Virgin Records. Dist: EMI, Virgin Distribution

Single (12"): released on Virgin, May'86 by Virgin Records. Dist: EMI, Virgin Distribution

KEEP IT DARK.
Single (7"): released on Charisma, Oct'81 by Virgin Records. Dist: EMI

Single (12"): released on Charisma, Oct'81 by Virgin Records. Dist: EMI

LAMB LIES DOWN ON BROADWAY, THE.
Tracks: / Lamb lies down on broadway, The / Fly on a windshield / Broadway melody of 1974 / Cuckoo cocoon / In the cage / Grand parade of lifeless packaging, The / Back in NYC / Hairless heart / Count out time / Carpet crawl / Chamber of 32 doors, The / Lilywhite Lilith.. / Waiting room, The / Anyway / Here comes the supernatural anaesthetist / Lamia, The / Silent sorrow in empty boats / Colony of slippermen, The / Ravine / Light dies down on Broadway, The / Riding the scree / In the rapids / It.
Notes: Double Compact Disc
Compact disc: released on Charisma, '86 by Virgin Records. Dist: EMI

Album: released on Charisma, Sep'83 by Virgin Records. Dist: EMI

Cassette: released on Charisma, Sep'83 by Virgin Records. Dist: EMI

LAND OF CONFUSION.
Tracks: / Land of confusion / Feeding the fire / Do the neurotic.
Single (7"): released on Charisma, Nov'86 by Virgin Records. Dist: EMI

Single (12"): released on Charisma, Nov'86 by Virgin Records. Dist: EMI

Compact disc single: released on Virgin, Nov'86 by Virgin Records. Dist: EMI, Virgin Distribution

LIVE The mama tour.
Notes: There are 10 Tracks on this live recording playing time of 102 minutes.
Video-cassette (VHS): released on Virgin, Jan'86 by Virgin Records. Dist: EMI, Virgin Distribution

LIVE.
Tracks: / Watcher of the skies / Get 'em out by friday / Return of the giant hogweed (The) / Musical box / Knife(The).
Compact disc: released on Charisma, Jul'87 by Virgin Records. Dist: EMI

Album: released on Charisma, Feb'86 by Virgin Records. Dist: EMI

Cassette: released on Charisma, Feb'86 by Virgin Records. Dist: EMI

MAMA.
Single (7"): released on Charisma, Aug'83 by Virgin Records. Dist: EMI

Single (12"): released on Charisma, Aug'83 by Virgin Records. Dist: EMI

NURSERY CRYMES.
Tracks: / Musical box(The) / For absent friends / Return of the great hogweed(The) / Seven stones / Harold the Barrell / Harlequin(The) / Fountain of salmancia.
Compact disc: released on Charisma, Sep'85 by Virgin Records. Dist: EMI

Album: released on Charisma, Feb'84 by Virgin Records. Dist: EMI

Cassette: released on Charisma, Feb'84 by Virgin Records. Dist: EMI

PAPERLATE.
Single (7"): released on Charisma, Sep'83 by Virgin Records. Dist: EMI

ROCK ROOTS.
Album: released on Decca, May'76 by Decca Records. Dist: Polygram

Cassette: released on Decca, May'76 by Decca Records. Dist: Polygram Deleted '85.

SECONDS OUT.
Compact disc: released on Charisma, Nov'85 by Virgin Records. Dist: EMI

Album: released on Charisma, Sep'83 by Virgin Records. Dist: EMI

Cassette: released on Charisma, Sep'83 by Virgin Records. Dist: EMI

Cassette: released on Charisma, Sep'83 by Virgin Records. Dist: EMI

Selling England by the pound / Foxtrot

SELLING ENGLAND BY THE POUND.
Tracks: / Dancing with moonlit knight / I know what i like in your wardrobe / Firth of fifth / More Fool me / Battle of Epping Forest(The) / After the ordeal / Cinema show(The) / Aisle of plenty.
Notes: Originally released in 1973
Compact disc: released on Charisma, Feb'86 by Virgin Records. Dist: EMI

Album: released on Charisma, Oct'86 by Virgin Records. Dist: EMI

Cassette: released on Charisma, Oct'86 by Virgin Records. Dist: EMI

THREE SIDES LIVE.
Tracks: / Behind the lines / Duchess / Me and Sarah Jane / Follow you Follow me / One for the vine / Fountain of salmacis / It / Watcher of the skies / Turn it on again / Do do / Abacab / Misunderstanding / In the cage / Cinem show / Slipperman / Afterglow.
Notes: Double Compact Disc
Compact disc: released on Charisma, Apr'85 by Virgin Records. Dist: EMI

Video-cassette (VHS): released on Thorn-Emi, Jan'86

Album: released on Charisma(Import), Aug'82 by Virgin Records. Dist: EMI

Cassette: released on Charisma(Import), Aug'82 by Virgin Records. Dist: EMI

Album: released on Charisma, '83 by Virgin Records. Dist: EMI

Cassette: released on Charisma, '83 by Virgin Records. Dist: EMI

THROWING IT ALL AWAY.
Tracks: / Throwing it all away / I'd rather be you / Invisible touch".
Single (7"): released on Virgin, Jun'87 by Virgin Records. Dist: EMI, Virgin Distribution

Single (12"): released on Virgin, Jun'87 by Virgin Records. Dist: EMI, Virgin Distribution

THROWING IT ALL AWAY (LIVE).
Tracks: / Throwing it all away (live) / I'd rather you / Invisible touch (live).
Cassette single: released on Virgin, 20 Jun'87 by Virgin Records. Dist: EMI, Virgin Distribution

TONIGHT, TONIGHT, TONIGHT.
Tracks: / Tonight,tonight,tonight / In the glow of the night / Paperlate **.
Single (7"): released on Virgin, Mar'87 by Virgin Records. Dist: EMI, Virgin Distribution

Single (12"): released on Virgin, Mar'87 by Virgin Records. Dist: EMI, Virgin Distribution

Compact disc single: released on Virgin, Mar'87 by Virgin Records. Dist: EMI, Virgin Distribution

TRESPASS.
Tracks: / Looking for someone / White mountain / Visions of angels / Stagnation / Dusk / Knife.
Compact disc: released on Charisma, '86 by Virgin Records. Dist: EMI

Album: released on Charisma, Mar'83 by Virgin Records. Dist: EMI

Cassette: released on Charisma, Mar'83 by Virgin Records. Dist: EMI

TRICK OF THE TAIL.
Tracks: / Dance on a volcano / Entangled / Squonk / Mad man moon / Robbery, assault and battery / Ripples / Trick of the tail, A / Los Endos.
Compact disc: released on Charisma, '86 by Virgin Records. Dist: EMI

TRICK OF THE TAIL, A.
Album: released on Charisma, Sep'83 by Virgin Records. Dist: EMI

Cassette: released on Charisma, Sep'83 by Virgin Records. Dist: EMI

Compact disc: released on Charisma, Sep'83 by Virgin Records. Dist: EMI

WHEN THE SOUR TURNS TO SWEET.
Compact disc: released on Metal Masters, '86 by Razor Records. Dist: Pinnacle

WHERE THE SOUR TURNS SWEET.
Notes: Mini LP...
Album: released on Metal Masters, Apr'86 by Razor Records. Dist: Pinnacle

Album: released on Razor, Oct'87 by Razor. Dist: Pinnacle

WHERE THE SUN TURNS TO SWEET
"Genesis to Revelation".
Tracks: / Silent sun, The / That's me / Where the sour turns to sweet / In the beginning / Fireside song / Serpent, The / Am I very wrong / In the wilderness / Conqueror, The / In hiding / One day / Window / In limbo / Silent sun / Place to call my own, A / Winter's tale, A / One eyed hound.
Compact disc: released on Transatlantic, Jul'87 by Transatlantic Records. Dist: IMS-Polygram

WIND AND WUTHERING.
Tracks: / Eleventh earl of mar / One for the vine / Your own special way / Wot Gorilla / All in a mouse's night / Blood on the rooftops / Unquiet slumbers for the sleepers / In that quiet earth / Afterglow.
Compact disc: released on Charisma, Apr'86 by Virgin Records. Dist: EMI

Album: released on Charisma, Sep'83 by Virgin Records. Dist: EMI

Cassette: released on Charisma, Sep'83 by Virgin Records. Dist: EMI

Genesis Gospel Singers

N'TUTU.
Album: released on Africagram, Jun'84 by Cherry Red Records. Dist: Pinnacle

Single (7"): released on Africagram, Feb'84 by Cherry Red Records. Dist: Pinnacle

Single (12"): released on Africagram, Feb'84 by Cherry Red Records. Dist: Pinnacle

Gene Syndrome

25 OR 624.
Tracks: / 25 or 624 / And she's following.
Single (7"): released on Toadstall, Oct'86

Single (12"): released on Toadstall, Oct'86

Genetics of Environment

GENETICS OF ENVIRONMENT Eysenck, Proff. H.J (Eysenck, Proff. H.J.).
Cassette: released on Psychology, Oct'81

Geney, Michel & Claude

MUSETTE EN FLEUR.
Tracks: / Musette en fleur / Bocage Printanier / Schneewaltzer / Festival Fisa / Rose Champetre / Accordeon joyeux / Rapide digitale / La savoyarde / Echo champetre / Musette en montagne / Sur les deux rives / Verte valle.
Notes: Retail price given by ARC excluding P & P (via Mail Oder) is 5.95. Mail order distribution address: Accordion Record Club, 146 Birmingham Road, Kidderminster, Worcs. DY10 2SL. Tel: 0562 - 746105
Album: released on Accordion Record Club, Jul'86 by Accordion Record Club Records. Dist: Accordion Record Club

Cassette: released on Accordion Record Club, Jul'86 by Accordion Record Club Records. Dist: Accordion Record Club

Genghis Khan

LOVE YOU.
Single (7"): released on Wabbit, May'83 by Wabbit Records. Dist: Pinnacle

MEXICO.
Cassette: by Sonet Records. Dist: PRT

MONGOL NATION.
Single (7"): released on Wabbit, May'83 by Wabbit Records. Dist: Pinnacle

Genius of Rap

GENIUS OF RAP (Various Artists).
Album: released on Blatant, Jul'87 by Castle Communications. Dist: PRT

Cassette: released on Blatant, Jul'87 by Castle Communications. Dist: PRT

Genocide

GENOCIDE ep.
Single (7"): released on Safari, '80 by Safari Records. Dist: Pinnacle

IMAGES OF DELUSION.
Album: released on Safari, Nov'79 by Safari Records. Dist: Pinnacle

Genocides

HONEY THAT AIN'T NO ROMANCE.
Single (7"): released on Flicknife, Jul'83 by Flicknife Records. Dist: Spartan

IS THAT ALRIGHT.
Single (7"): released on Action, Oct'82 Dist: Rough Trade, Cartel

Genova, Jackie

WORK THAT BODY.
Album: released on Island, May'83 by Island Records. Dist: Polygram Deleted '87.

Cassette:

WORK THAT BODY INTO SKI SHAPE.
Album: released on Island, Nov'83 by Island Records. Dist: Polygram

Gentle Faith

GENTLE FAITH.
Album: released on Maranatha!, May'79 Dist: Kingsway Music, Pilgrim, Word Distribution

Gentle Giant

CIVILLIAN.
Cassette: released on Chrysalis, May'80 by Chrysalis Records. Dist: CBS

Album: released on Chrysalis, Apr'80 by Chrysalis Records. Dist: CBS

FREE HAND.
Album: released on Chrysalis, Aug'75 by Chrysalis Records. Dist: CBS

Album:

GREATEST HITS:GENTLE GIANT.
Album: released on Vertigo, Aug'81 by Phonogram Records. Dist: Polygram

Cassette: released on Vertigo, Aug'81 by Phonogram Records. Dist: Polygram

INTERVIEW.
Album: released on Chrysalis, Apr'76 by Chrysalis Records. Dist: CBS

Cassette: released on Chrysalis, Apr'76 by Chrysalis Records. Dist: CBS

'LIVE' PLAYING THE FOOL.
Double Album: released on Chrysalis, Jan'77 by Chrysalis Records. Dist: CBS

MISSING PIECE, THE.
Album: released on Chrysalis, Aug'77 by Chrysalis Records. Dist: CBS

OCTOPUS.
Album: released on Vertigo (Holland), Jul'84

Cassette: released on Vertigo (Holland). Jul'83

Gentlemen Prefer Blondes

GENTLEMEN PREFER BLONDES original London cast (Various Artists).
Album: released on That's Entertainment, Apr'83 by That's Entertainment Records. Dist: Pinnacle, PRT

Cassette: released on That's Entertainment, Apr'83 by That's Entertainment Records. Dist: Pinnacle, PRT

Gentle On My Mind

GENTLE ON MY MIND various artists (Various Artists).

Gentles, Bill

DANCE WITH ME.
Tracks: / Dance with me (Version).
Single (12"): released on Jama, Jan'86 by Jama Records.

EVER SINCE I MET YOU.
Single (12"): released on Echo, Feb'82 by Vista Sounds. Dist: Jazz Music

WANT TO BE LOVED, I.
Album: released on Third World, Feb'79 Dist: Jetstar Distribution

Gentle Touch

DREAM OF YOU.
Single (7"): released on Tristar, Nov'83 by Tristar Records. Dist: Pinnacle

Gentiman Gerald

ANYONE FOR TENNIS.
Single (7"): released on Dingles, Jul'81 by Dingles Records. Dist: Projection

Gentry, Bobbie

All I have to do is dream

ALL I HAVE TO DO IS DREAM (Gentry, Bobbie & Glen Campbell).
Cassette: released on Music For Pleasure, Jan'83 by EMI Records. Dist: EMI

BEST OF, THE.
Album: released on EMI (Germany), Aug'83 by EMI Records. Dist: Conifer

Gents

FRIDAY ON MY MIND.
Single (7"): released on Lambs To The Slaughter, Sep'86 by Prism Records. Dist: Pinnacle, Red Rhino, Cartel

Single (12"): released on Lambs To The Slaughter, Sep'86 by Prism Records. Dist: Pinnacle, Red Rhino, Cartel

GENTS, (THE).
Album: released on Lambs To The Slaughter, Aug'85 by Prism Records. Dist: Pinnacle, Red Rhino, Cartel

GIVE IT TO ME.
Tracks: / At the dance.
Single (7"): released on Prism, Feb'86 by Prism Records.

Single (12"): released on Prism, Feb'86 by Prism Records.

NEW DIRECTION.
Single (7"): released on Lambs To The Slaughter, May'85 by Prism Records. Dist: Pinnacle, Red Rhino, Cartel

REVENGE.
Single (7"): released on Posh, Aug'83 by Posh Records. Dist: Pinnacle

Single (7"): released on Mega, May'83 Dist: Jetstar Distribution

SCHOOLDAYS.
Single (7"): released on Kosmik, Jul'82 by Kosmik Records. Dist: PRT

SHOUT.
Single (7"): released on Lambs To The Slaughter, Mar'85 by Prism Records. Dist: Pinnacle, Red Rhino, Cartel

STAY WITH ME.
Single (12"): released on Prism, Sep'85 by Prism Records.

Single (7"): released on Prism, Sep'85 by Prism Records.

Gentz

STAND BY ME.
Single (7"): released on Shockrock (Ireland), Jun'83

Genuine Houserockin Music

GENUINE HOUSEROCKIN MUSIC Various Artists (Various Artists).
Album: released on Sonet, Mar'87 by Sonet Records. Dist: PRT

Geordie

GEORDIE FEATURING BRIAN JOHNSON (Geordie Featuring Brian Johnson).
Album: released on Red Bus, Jan'81 by Red Bus Records. Dist: PRT

NO SWEAT.
Album: released on Neat, May'85 by Neat Records. Dist: Pinnacle, Neat

NUTBUSH CITY LIMITS.
Single (7"): released on Armageddon, Apr'82 by Armageddon Records. Dist: Revolver, Cartel, Pinnacle

Geordie Aid

TRY GIVING IT EVERYTHING.
Single (7"): released on Geordie Aid, Aug'85 by Geordie Aid Records. Dist: Pinnacle

George Davis Is Innocent

GEORGE DAVIS IS INNOCENT O.K. Various artists (Various Artists).
Album: released on Sweet Folk All, May'81 by Sweet Folk All Records. Dist: Sweet Folk All, Roots, Celtic Music, Dragon, Impetus, Projection, Chris Wellard, Festival Records

George & Earl

GOING STEADY WITH THE BLUES.
Album: released on Bear Family, Jun'85 by

Bear Family Records. Dist: Rollercoaster Distribution, Swift

George & Jackie

DIANA.
Single (7"): released on Black Joy, Dec'81 Dist: Jetstar

THIRD WORLD.
Single (12"): released on Black Joy, Nov'82 Dist: Jetstar

George, Lowell

THANKS I'LL EAT IT HERE.
Album: released on Warner Brothers, Apr'79 by Warner Bros Records. Dist: WEA

Cassette: released on Warner Brothers, Apr'79 by Warner Bros Records. Dist: WEA

George, Robin

DANGEROUS MUSIC.
Album: released on Bronze, Feb'85 by Polygram Records. Dist: Polydor

Cassette: released on Bronze, Feb'85 by Polygram Records. Dist: Polydor

DON'T TURN AWAY.
Single (7"): released on Bronze, Aug'85 by Polygram Records. Dist: Polydor

Single (12"): released on Bronze, Aug'85 by Polygram Records. Dist: Polydor

HEARTLINE.
Single (12"): released on Bronze, Mar'85 by Polygram Records. Dist: Polydor

Single (12"): released on Bronze, Mar'85 by Polygram Records. Dist: Polydor

SPY.
Single (7"): released on Bronze, Jan'85 by Polygram Records. Dist: Polydor

Single (12"): released on Bronze, Jan'85 by Polygram Records. Dist: Polydor

George, Sophia

FINAL DECISION.
Tracks: / Final decision / Final decision(version) / Genuine.
Single (7"): released on Winner, 20 Jun'87 by Creole Records. Dist: Jetstar, PRT

Single (12"): released on Winner, 20 Jun'87 by Creole Records. Dist: Jetstar, PRT

FRESH.
Album: released on Winner, Feb'86 by Creole Records. Dist: Jetstar, PRT

LAZY BODY.
Tracks: / Can't live without you.
Single (7"): released on Winner, Apr'86 by Creole Records. Dist: Jetstar, PRT

Single (12"): released on Winner, Apr'86 by Creole Records. Dist: Jetstar, PRT

George, Sophie

FINAL DECISION.
Single (12"): released on Winner, Aug'87 by Creole Records. Dist: Jetstar, PRT

GIRLIE GIRLIE.
Single (7"): released on Winner, Nov'85 by Creole Records. Dist: Jetstar, PRT

Single (12"): released on Winner, Nov'85 by Creole Records. Dist: Jetstar, PRT

George, Wally

WAL-LY WAL-LY.
Album: released on Rhino (USA), Feb'85 by Rhino Records (USA).

Georgiades, Michael

NATURAL PROGRESSIONS (see Leadon, Bernie).

Georgia Grinders

GEORGIA GRINDERS AND JIM SNYDER (Georgia Grinders & Jim Snyder).
Album: released on Stomp Off, Jun'86 by Stomp Off Records. Dist: Jazz Music Distribution

Georgia II

AS TEARS GO BY.
Single (7"): released on PRT, May'83 by PRT Records. Dist: PRT

Single (12"): released on PRT, May'83 by PRT Records. Dist: PRT

FLAG, (THE).
Single (7"): released on PRT, Jan'83 by PRT Records. Dist: PRT

Single (12"): released on PRT, Jan'83 by PRT Records. Dist: PRT

Georgia Melodians

GEORGIA MELODIANS 1924 VOL.1,(THE).
Cassette: released on Retrieval, Apr'79 by Retrieval Records. Dist: Retrieval, VJM, Swift, Record Sales(Chris Wellard), Jazz Music

GEORGIA MELODIANS 1924-6 VOL.2, (THE).
Album: released on Retrieval, Apr'79 by Retrieval Records. Dist: Retrieval, VJM, Swift, Record Sales(Chris Wellard), Jazz Music

Georgia Satellites

BATTLESHIP CHAINS (KICK AND LICK REMIX).
Tracks: / Battleship chains (kick and lick remix) / Hard luck boy.
Single (7"): released on Elektra (USA), Apr'87 by Elektra/Asylum/Nonesuch Records. Dist: WEA

Single (12"): released on Elektra (USA), Apr'87 by Elektra/Asylum/Nonesuch Records. Dist: WEA

GEORGIA SATELLITES.
Tracks: / Keep your hands to yourself / Railroad steel / Battleship chains / Red lights / Myth of love (The) / I can't stand the pain / Golden light / Over and over / Nights of mystery / Every picture tells a story.
Album: released on Elektra (USA), Nov'86 by Elektra/Asylum/Nonesuch Records. Dist: WEA

Cassette: released on Elektra (USA), Nov'86 by Elektra/Asylum/Nonesuch Records. Dist: WEA

GEORGIA SATELLITES.
Compact disc: by WEA Records. Dist: WEA

KEEP THE FAITH.
Album:

Compact disc:

Cassette: released on Making Waves, Jul'87 by Making Waves Records.

KEEP YOUR HANDS TO YOURSELF.
Tracks: / Can't stand the pain.
Single (7"): released on Elektra (USA), Jan'87 by Elektra/Asylum/Nonesuch Records. Dist: WEA

Single (12"): released on Elektra, Aug'87 by WEA Records. Dist: WEA

Single (7"): released on Elektra, Aug'87 by WEA Records. Dist: WEA

Georgia Sea Island Songs

GEORGIA SEA ISLAND SONGS (Various Artists).
Tracks: / Moses / Kneebone / Sheep, sheep, don't you know the road / Live humble / Daniel / O Death / Read 'em John / Beulah land / Buzzard lope, The / Raggy Levi / Ain't I right / See Aunt Dinah / Walk, Billy Abbot / Reg'lar reg'lar rollin' under / Pay me / Carrie Belle / Laz'rus / Titanic, The.
Album: released on New World (USA), Dec'86 by New World Records (USA). Dist: Conifer

Georgie & Jackie

SING JUST FOR YOU.
Album: released on G&J, Dec'84 by G&J Records. Dist: Vista Sounds Records, G.R.I. Records

Georgio

SEXAPPEAL.
Tracks: / Sexappeal / Sexappeal (instrumental).
Single (7"): released on Motown, Mar'87 by Motown Records. Dist: BMG Distribution

Single (12"): released on Motown, Mar'87 by Motown Records. Dist: BMG Distribution

Geraldine

HEART OF AFRICA.
Single (7"): released on Magnet, Dec'83 by Magnet Records. Dist: BMG

IT'S ONLY LOVE.
Album: released on Magnet, Nov'83 by Magnet Records. Dist: BMG

Cassette: released on Magnet, Nov'83 by Magnet Records. Dist: BMG

LOVE ME TENDER.
Tracks: / Love me tender / You light up my life / He was beautiful (Cavatina) / Hopelessly devoted to you / Tammy / Nobody does it better / True love / Ben / I will wait for you / Jean / Secret love / Sunshine on my shoulders.
Album: released on Magnet, Jan'86 by Magnet Records. Dist: BMG

Cassette: released on Magnet, Jan'86 by Magnet Records. Dist: BMG

ROSE OF ALLENDALE.
Single (7"): released on Magnet, Dec'84 by Magnet Records. Dist: BMG

WILL YOU GO LASSIE GO.
Single (7"): released on Magnet, Oct'83 by Magnet Records. Dist: BMG

Geraldo

DANCE BAND YEARS - THE 1940'S (Geraldo & His Orchestra & Skyrockets).
Album: released on Saville, Jun'82 by Conifer Records. Dist: Conifer

GERALDO & AL BOWLLY (Geraldo & Al Bowlly).

GERALDO-THE MAN AND HIS MUSIC (Geraldo & His Orchestra).
Album: released on President, Feb'84 by President Records. Dist: Taylors, Spartan

Cassette: released on President, Jun'85 by President Records. Dist: Taylors, Spartan

GOLDEN AGE OF GERALDO.
Album: released on Golden Age, Mar'86 by Music For Pleasure Records. Dist: EMI

Cassette: released on Golden Age, Mar'86 by Music For Pleasure Records. Dist: EMI

HEART AND SOUL (Geraldo & His Orchestra).
Album: released on Saville, Apr'83 by Conifer Records. Dist: Conifer

JEALOUSY (Geraldo & His Gaucho Tango Orchestra).
Album: released on Joy, Aug'83 by President Records. Dist: Jazz Music, Swift, President Distribution

MEMORIES OF GERRY (Geraldo & His Orchestra).
Album: released on Old Bean, Aug'85 Dist: Jazz Music

Cassette: released on Old Bean, Aug'85 Dist: Jazz Music

SERENADE IN THE NIGHT (Geraldo & His Gaucho Tango Orchestra).
Album: released on Decca (Recollections), Jul'84 by Decca Recollections. Dist: Polygram, IMS

SINCERELY YOURS (Geraldo & His Orchestra).
Album: released on Decca (Reflections), Feb'82 by Decca Records. Dist: Polygram, IMS

TIP-TOP TUNES.
Tracks: / In a little Spanish town / Nearness of you / Top hat / Autumn concerto / Hallelujah / Signature tune / My heart stood still / There's a small hotel / Heather of the hill / Rockin' through Dixie / Nature boy / What is this thing called love? / I'm on a see-saw / So many times have I cried over you / When Johnny comes marching home / Begin the beguine / Isle of Innisfree / Arkansas traveller.
Album: released on Conifer Happy Days, Sep'86 by Conifer Records. Dist: Conifer, Chris Wellard, Swift, Jazz Music

Cassette: released on Conifer Happy Days, Sep'86 by Conifer Records. Dist: Conifer, Chris Wellard, Swift, Jazz Music

UNISSUED RECORDINGS (Geraldo & His Orchestra).
Album: released on Halcyon (USA), Sep'84 by Halcyon Records (USA). Dist: Jazz Music, Conifer, Taylors

Gerechtigkeits Liga

HYNOYISCHER EXISTENZIALISMUS.
Album: by SPK Records. Dist: Rough Trade, Cartel Deleted Apr'86.

Gerhard, Wolfgang

JAZZ MEETS FLAMENCO.
Album: released on Polydor (Germany), Sep'83 Dist: IMS-Polygram

German Brass

GERMAN BRASS (ZUNFTIGE BLASMUSIK) Various artists (Various Artists).
Tracks: / Ja, in der Birkenau...(...da ist der himmel blau) / Haxenschmeisser Polka / Ochsentreiber glaopp / Posaunisten vor / Waldgeist / Der ratata hat apfel g'stohln / Amboss polka / Schimmel-Galopp / Der wamper gust / Tiroler holzhackerbuam / Stockergassi.
Notes: Superb album of traditional German Brass music from four of that country's leading bands featured are: Otto Ebner und Sein Bellnhauser Musikanten, Heinz Muller und Seine Ruhmannsfeldener Blaskapelle.
Album: released on Polydor (Germany), Feb'86 Dist: IMS-Polygram

Cassette: released on Polydor (Germany), Feb'86 Dist: IMS-Polygram

Compact disc: released on Polydor (Germany), Feb'86 Dist: IMS-Polygram

German Folk Music

SUPER HIT PARADE.
Album: released on Polydor (Germany), Apr'86 Dist: IMS-Polygram

Cassette: released on Polydor (Germany), Apr'86 Dist: IMS-Polygram

Germinal

DIN.
Album: released on Latent, Nov'84 Dist: Rough Trade

Germino, Mark

LONDON MOON AND BARNYARD REMEDIES.
Tracks: / Political / Oriental drag / Barnyard (Rhapsody in brown) / God ain't no stained glass window / Sally Baker's (low tar) dream / Broken man's lament / We got away / Immigrant shuffle.
Album: released on RCA, Jan'87 by RCA Records. Dist: RCA, Roots, Swift, Wellard, Chris, I & B, Solomon & Peres Distribution

Cassette: released on RCA, Jan'87 by RCA Records. Dist: RCA, Roots, Swift, Wellard, Chris, I & B, Solomon & Peres Distribution

LONDON MOON & BARNYARD REMEDIES.
Tracks: / Political / Oriental drag / Barnyard / God ain't no stained glass window / Sally Baker's low tar dream / Broken man's lament / We got away / Immigrant shuffle.
Compact disc: released on RCA, Oct'86 by RCA Records. Dist: RCA, Roots, Swift, Wellard, Chris, I & B, Solomon & Peres Distribution

POLITICAL.
Tracks: / Political / Oriental drag / Broken mans's lament **.
Single (7"): released on RCA, Mar'87 by RCA Records. Dist: RCA, Roots, Swift, Wellard, Chris, I & B, Solomon & Peres Distribution

Single (12"): released on RCA, Mar'87 by RCA Records. Dist: RCA, Roots, Swift, Wellard, Chris, I & B, Solomon & Peres Distribution

Germs

GERMICIDE.
Cassette: released on Reach Out International, May'83 Dist: Red Rhino, Cartel

Gerry & The Holograms

GERRY & THE HOLOGRAMS.
Single (7"): released on Absurd, Sep'82 by Absurd. Dist: Pinnacle, Rough Trade

Gerry & The Pacemakers

20 YEAR ANNIVERSARY ALBUM.
Album: released on Deb, '83 by Deb Records. Dist: Spartan

BEST OF.
Album: released on Nut, '77 by EMI Records. Dist: EMI

Cassette: released on Nut, '77 by EMI Records. Dist: EMI

E.P COLLECTION,THE.
Tracks: / How do you do it? / Away from you / I like it / Chills / You'll never walk alone / Shot of rhythm and blues, A / You've got what I like / I'm the one / Don't let the sun catch you crying / Where have you been all my life / Maybellene / You're the reason / It's gonna be all right / I'll wait for you / Ferry cross the Mersey / You win again / Reelin' and rockin' / Whole lotta shakin' goin' on / Skinny Lizzie / My babe / Away from you / What'd I say.
Notes: 22-Track mastered.Contains three number ones and four other big hits,together with three very rare tracks.
Album: released on See For Miles, Jun'87 by See For Miles Records. Dist: Pinnacle

FERRY ACROSS THE MERSEY.
Tracks: / It's still rock'n'roll to me / I'm the one / Unchained melody / Roll over Beethoven / Imagine / Running man / Just the way you are / How do you do / Ferry across the Mersey.
Album: released on Showcase, Apr'86 Dist: Counterpoint

Cassette: released on Showcase, Apr'86 Dist: Counterpoint

Single (7"): released on SMP, '84 Dist: Jetstar, PRT

Single (7"): released on Creole, '82 by Creole Records. Dist: Rhino, PRT

Single (7"): released on Columbia, '82 by EMI Records. Dist: EMI

Single (7"): released on Deb, '83 by Deb Records. Dist: Spartan

FERRY CROSS THE MERSEY/DON'T LET THE SUN CATCH YOU CRYING.
Single (7"): released on J.B., '80 Dist: Warren, Mojo Distribution, Jetstar, Lightning, Arawak, Soundoff

Single (7"): released on Old Gold, '83 by Old Gold Records. Dist: Lightning, Jazz Music, Spartan, Counterpoint

GERRY AND THE PACEMAKERS.
Cassette: released on Timeless Treasures, Jul'86 Dist: Counterpoint Distribution

Album: released on EMI (Holland), '83 by EMI Records. Dist: Conifer

HIT SINGLES ALBUM.
Tracks: / You'll never walk alone / How do you do it / Away from you / I like it / Baby you're so good to me / It's happened to me / It's all right / I'm the one / You've got what I like / Don't let the sun catch you crying / Show me that you care / It's gonna be all right / It's just because / Ferry cross the Mersey / You you you / I'll be there / Baby you're so good to me / I am your driver / Fine line / Face to face / Shatterproof / Shine shine / Lesson in love / One night (for lovers) / Stay alone / Temptation / She says / Hunter, The.
Notes: For the first time ever these 8 singles have been chronologically packaged together with their flip sides on one album. Gerry & The Pacemakers were the first of the so called Mersybeat acts to top the chart (only just beating the Beatles) and the only group at that time to take all their first 3 singles to the top. 6 of their 8 singles released during this period also made it into the top 25 of the US chart.
Album: released on EMI, Jan'86 by EMI Records. Dist: EMI

Cassette: released on EMI, Jan'86 by EMI Records. Dist: EMI

Video-cassette (VHS): released on Polygram Music, Dec'84 by Polygram Records. Dist: Polygram

HOW DO YOU DO IT?.

Single (7"): released on EMI Golden 45's, '84 by EMI Records. Dist: EMI

Single (7"): released on EMI, '77 by EMI Records. Dist: EMI

OH MY LOVE/IF.
Single (7"): released on Deb, '83 by Deb Records. Dist: Spartan

SINGLES PLUS, THE.
Tracks: / How do you do it / Away from you / I like it / It's happened to me / You'll never walk alone / It's all right / I'm the one / You've got what I like / Don't let the sun catch you crying / Show me that you care / It's gonna be alright / It's just because / Ferry cross the mersey / You, you, you / I'll be there / Baby you're so good to me / Walk hand in hand / Dreams / La la la / Without you / Girl on a swing / Fool to myself.
Compact disc: released on EMI, May'87 by EMI Records. Dist: EMI

SINGLES PLUS,THE.
Compact disc: released on EMI, '87 by EMI Records. Dist: EMI

UNCHAINED MELODY.
Single (7"): released on Deb, '82 by Deb Records. Dist: Spartan

VERY BEST OF GERRY & THE PACEMAKERS.
Album: released on Music For Pleasure, '84 by EMI Records. Dist: EMI

Cassette: released on Music For Pleasure, '84 by EMI Records. Dist: EMI

YOU'LL NEVER WALK ALONE.
Single (7"): by Creole Records. Dist: Rhino, PRT

Single (7"): released on Old Gold, '83 by Old Gold Records. Dist: Lightning, Jazz Music, Spartan, Counterpoint

Gershwin

AN AMERICAN IN PARIS.
Compact disc: released on RCA, '83 by RCA Records. Dist: RCA, Roots, Swift, Wellard, Chris, I & B, Solomon & Peres Distribution

GERSHWIN'S GREATEST HITS Various artists (Various Artists).
Album: released on BBC, '78 by BBC Records & Tapes. Dist: EMI, PRT,

Cassette: released on CBS, '83 by CBS Records. Dist: CBS

Gershwin, George

50TH ANNIVERSARY.
Album: released on Halcyon (USA), May'87 by Halcyon Records (USA). Dist: Jazz Music, Conifer, Taylors

Cassette: released on Halcyon (USA), May'87 by Halcyon Records (USA). Dist: Jazz Music, Conifer, Taylors

AN AMERICAN IN PARIS/CUBAN OVERTURE/PORGY AND BESS.
Compact disc: released on RCA, '83 by RCA Records. Dist: RCA, Roots, Swift, Wellard, Chris, I & B, Solomon & Peres Distribution

GERSHWIN, GEORGE Various Artists.
Album: released on Golden Age, '84 by Music For Pleasure Records. Dist: EMI

Cassette: released on Golden Age, '84 by Music For Pleasure Records. Dist: EMI

PLAYS GERSHWIN.
Cassette: released on Orchid Music, '82 by Bibi. Dist: Pinnacle

TWO SIDES OF GEORGE GERSHWIN,THE.
Album: released on Halcyon (USA), '83 by Halcyon Records (USA). Dist: Jazz Music, Conifer, Taylors

Gershwhin, George

HITS OF GEORGE GERSHWIN 50th Anniversary album.
Notes: 50th anniversary album. Mono.
Album: released on Halcyon (USA), Feb'87 by Halcyon Records (USA). Dist: Jazz Music, Conifer, Taylors

Cassette: released on Halcyon (USA), Feb'87 by Halcyon Records (USA). Dist: Jazz Music, Conifer, Taylors

Gertrude Gooseberry

GERTRUDE GOOSEBERRY & BELINDA BLACKCURRANT (Various Artists).
Cassette: released on Tell-a-tale (Cassettes), '84

Gertrude Stein

GERTRUDE STEIN,GERTRUDE STEIN (Caroll, Pat).
Cassette: released on Caedmon(USA), '81 by Caedmon (USA) Records. Dist: Gower, Taylors, Discovery

Gerty, Ric

BITTEN ZUM TANZ-IN STRICT TEMPO RHYTHM.
Album: released on TWS (Germany), '85 Dist: WRD

DANCE AROUND THE CLOCK-IN STRICT TEMPO RHYTHM.
Album: released on TWS (Germany), '85 Dist: WRD

Geschlekt Akt

FOREPLAY (EP).
Single (12"): released on Criminal Damage, '84 by Criminal Damage Records. Dist: Backs, Cartel

Get by in Portuguese

GET BY IN PORTUGUESE.
Double cassette: released on BBC Publications, Apr'82 Dist: Record and Tape Sales Distribution, Taylor, H.R., Solomon & Peres Distribution

Get fit with...

GET FIT WITH THE GREEN GODDESS (Moran, Diana).
Album: released on BBC, '83 by BBC Records & Tapes. Dist: EMI, PRT,

Cassette: released on BBC, '83 by BBC Records & Tapes. Dist: EMI, PRT,

Get Happy Band

SAM MORGAN'S JAZZ BAND AND GET HAPPY BAND.
Album: released on VJM, '79 by Wellard, Chris Distribution. Dist: Wellard, Chris Distribution

Get on down

GET ON DOWN (Various Artists).
Album: released on Battersea, '83 by Battersea Records. Dist: Pinnacle

Cassette: released on Battersea, '83 by Battersea Records. Dist: Pinnacle

Get on up

GET ON UP (Various Artists).
Album: released on RCA, '83 by RCA Records. Dist: RCA, Roots, Swift, Wellard, Chris, I & B, Solomon & Peres Distribution

Cassette: released on RCA, '83 by RCA Records. Dist: RCA, Roots, Swift, Wellard, Chris, I & B, Solomon & Peres Distribution

Get right with God

GET RIGHT WITH GOD (Various Artists).
Album: released on Krazy Kat, '83 Dist: Jazz Music, Swift, Chris Wellard, H.R. Taylor, Charly, Hotshot, IRS Distribution

Get Smart

GET SMART.
Album: released on Nervous, Apr'87 by Nervous Records. Dist: Nervous, Rough Trade

Getting the fear

LAST SALUTE.
Single (7"): released on RCA, '84 by RCA Records. Dist: RCA, Roots, Swift, Wellard, Chris, I & B, Solomon & Peres Distribution

Single (12"): released on RCA, '84 by RCA Records. Dist: RCA, Roots, Swift, Wellard, Chris, I & B, Solomon & Peres Distribution

Get Wise

GET WISE Various artists.
Tracks: / Mission impossible / Long remembered thunder / Yellow hill / Childhood meditations / Others / Throw it away / Samba ingles / Vanessa / King of the fools / Get wise / We'll be back / That's why it isn't love / So coole.
Album: released on Portrait, Aug'86 by CBS Records. Dist: CBS

Getz-Gilberto

GETZ-GILBERTO COLLECTION.
Album: released on Deja Vu, Nov'85 by Deja Vu Records. Dist: Counterpoint Distribution, Record Services Distribution (Ireland)

Cassette: released on Deja Vu, Nov'85 by Deja Vu Records. Dist: Counterpoint Distribution, Record Services Distribution (Ireland)

Getz, Stan

AT STORYVILLE.
Tracks: / Thou swell / Song is you, The / Parker 51 / Mosquito knees / Budo / Pennies from Heaven.
Compact disc: released on Vogue, Dec'86 Dist: Discovery, Jazz Music, PRT, Swift

AT THE OPERA HOUSE (Getz, Stan & J J Johnson).
Tracks: / Billie's bounce / My funny valentine / Crazy rhythm / Blues in the closet / Yesterdays / It never entered my mind.
Notes: Classic Norman Granz production.With these concert recordings,Granz started the highly successful but short-lived Getz/Johnson discography.It's a major triumph of his formula:"Put the soloists together then get out of the way and let them play". Recorded September & October 1957. Digitally remastered. 73 minutes playing time.
Compact disc: released on Verve (USA), May'87 by Polydor. Dist: Polygram

BEST OF....
Album: released on CBS, '80 by CBS Records. Dist: CBS

BIG BAND BOSSA NOVA.
Compact disc: released on Polydor, Aug'87 by Polydor Records. Dist: Polygram, Polydor

BOSSA NOVA YEARS,THE.
Boxed set: released on Verve (USA), '85 by Polydor. Dist: Polygram

BROTHERS, (THE).
Compact disc: released on Carrere, Apr'87 by Carrere Records. Dist: PRT, Spartan

COMPACT JAZZ.
Compact disc: released on Verve, Jul'87 by Phonogram Records. Dist: Polygram

DESAFINADO (Getz, Stan & Charlie Byrd).
Compact disc: released on Verve, Jan'83 by Phonogram Records. Dist: Polygram

DESAFINDO (JAZZ SAMBA) (Getz, Stan & Charlie Byrd).
Compact disc: released on Verve, '83 by Phonogram Records. Dist: Polygram

DOLPHIN,THE.
Notes: This was Getz's first album for Concord and recorded about 1980. Supported by Lou Levy, piano; Monty Budwig, bass and Jake Hanna on drums. Featured tracks are: A Time For Love" - Johnny Mandell, "Joy Spring" - Clifford Brown, "Close Enough For Love" the theme used in the film "Agatha", and the title track "The Dolphin", a great bossa-nova track.
Album: released on Concord Jazz, '81 by Concord Jazz Records (USA). Dist: IMS, Polygram

Compact disc: released on Concord Jazz(USA), Jul'87 by Concord Jazz Records (USA). Dist: IMS, Polygram

EARLY DAYS,THE In Scandinavia (Getz, Stan & Oscar Pettiford).
Album: released on Rarities, '81

Album: released on Rarities, '81

FOCUS.
Tracks: / I'm late, I'm late / Her / Pan / I remember when / Night rider / Once upon a time / Summer afternoon.
Compact disc: released on Verve, Oct'84 by Phonogram Records. Dist: Polygram

Compact disc: released on Verve, '84 by Phonogram Records. Dist: Polygram

GETZ AU GO GO.
Tracks: / Singing song / Telephone song / One mote samba / Here's that rainy day / Corcovado / It might as well be spring / Voce e eu / Summer-time / Six nix pix clix / Only trust your heart.
Compact disc: released on Verve, Sep'84 by Phonogram Records. Dist: Polygram

Album: released on Verve (USA), '85 by Polydor. Dist: Polygram

Compact disc: released on Verve (USA), '85 by Polydor. Dist: Polygram

GETZ/GILBERTO COLLECTION,THE (Getz, Stan & Jaoa Gilberto).
Cassette: released on Deja Vu, '85 by Deja Vu Records. Dist: Counterpoint Distribution, Record Services Distribution (Ireland)

GILBERTO/GETZ (Getz, Stan & Astrud Gilberto).
Compact disc: released on Verve, '83 by Phonogram Records. Dist: Polygram

GILBERTO/GETZ.

GREAT ENGLISH CONCERT,THE (Getz, Stan/Coleman Hawkins/Roy Eldridge).
Album: released on Jazz Groove, '82 Dist: Jazz Music

GREAT ENGLISH CONCERT, (THE) (see Hawkins, Coleman) (Getz, Stan/Coleman Hawkins/Roy Eldridge).

HAMPTON & GETZ (Getz, Stan & lionel Hampton).
Compact disc: released on Polydor, Aug'87 by Polydor Records. Dist: Polygram, Polydor

JAZZ SAMBA (Getz, Stan & Charlie Byrd).
Compact disc: by Phonogram Records. Dist: Polygram

JAZZ SAMBA ENCORE (Getz, Stan & Luis Bonfa).
Tracks: / Sambalero / So danco samba / O morro noa tem vez / Insensatez / Samba de duas notas / Mania de Maria / Saudade vem correndo / Um abraco no getz / Ebony samba.
Compact disc: released on Verve, Apr'86 by Phonogram Records. Dist: Polygram

Album: released on Verve (USA), '84 by Polydor. Dist: Polygram

LAURINDO ALMEIDA.
Tracks: / Minima moca / Once again / Winter moor / Do what you do, do / Sambra de Sahra / Maracuta-too.
Compact disc: released on Verve, Dec'86 by Phonogram Records. Dist: Polygram

Compact disc: released on Verve, '84 by Phonogram Records. Dist: Polygram

LAURINDO ALMEIDA (Getz, Stan & Luis Bonfa).

LINE FOR LYONS (Getz, Stan & Chet Baker).
Notes: See also under Baker, Chet.
Compact disc: released on Vogue, '86 Dist: Discovery, Jazz Music, PRT, Swift

Album: released on Sonet, '83 by Sonet Records. Dist: PRT

Compact disc: released on Sonet, Jul'87 by Sonet Records. Dist: PRT

LIVE AT THE VILLAGE VANGUARD (Getz, Stan & Chet Baker).
Album: released on Ingo, '81 Dist: Jazz Horizons, Jazz Music, Celtic Music

MIDEM-LIVE 80 (Getz, Stan/Paul Horn/Mike Carson).
Album: released on Gateway (USA), '83 by Gemcom Inc.(USA) Records.

MOONLIGHT IN VERMONT (Getz, Stan & Johnny Smith).
Album:

OPUS DE BOP.
Album: released on Savoy (France), '85

PEACOCK (Getz, Stan Presents Jimmie Rowles).
Tracks: / I'll never be the same / Lester left town / Body and soul / What am I here for? / Serenade to Sweden / Chess players / Peacocks / My Buddy / Hour of parting / Rose Marie / This is all I ask / Skylark / Mosiac/Would you like to take a walk / I wanted to say / I thought about you / Yesterdays dreams / Falling in love / Voyage.
Album: released on CBS, Jul'86 by CBS Records. Dist: CBS

Cassette: released on CBS, Jul'86 by CBS Records. Dist: CBS

Album: released on Blackhawk, Sep'86 by Blackhawk Records (USA). Dist: IMS-Polygram

Cassette: released on Blackhawk, Sep'86 by Blackhawk Records (USA). Dist: IMS-Polygram

POETRY (Getz, Stan & Albert Dailey).
Album: released on Elektra(Musician), '84 by WEA Records. Dist: WEA

PORTRAITS (Getz, Stan, Quartz).

Album: released on Lotus, '81 Dist: Counterpoint

PURE GETZ (Getz, Stan Quartet).
Tracks: / On the up and up / Blood count / Very early / Sippin' at bells / I wish I knew / Come rain or come shine / Tempus fugit.
Compact disc: released on Concord Jazz(USA), Dec'86 by Concord Jazz Records (USA). Dist: IMS, Polygram

Album: released on Concord Jazz, '82 by Concord Jazz Records (USA). Dist: IMS, Polygram

Cassette: released on Concord Jazz, '82 by Concord Jazz Records (USA). Dist: IMS, Polygram

SILVER COLLECTION, THE (Getz, Stan & Oscar Peterson).
Compact disc: released on Polydor, '86 by Polydor Records. Dist: Polygram, Polydor

STAN GETZ.
Album: released on Queen-Disc, '81 Dist: Celtic Music, JSU, Jazz Horizons, Jazz Music

STAN GETZ AT STORYVILLE.
Album: released on Vogue, '78 Dist: Discovery, Jazz Music, PRT, Swift

STAN GETZ & BOB BROOKMEYER (Getz, Stan & Bob Brookmeyer).
Album: released on Verve (France), '84

STAN GETZ & MILES DAVIS (Getz, Stan & Miles Davis).
Album: released on Kings Of Jazz, '81 Dist: Jazz Horizons, Jazz Music, Celtic Music

STAN GETZ SPECIAL.
Album: released on For Collectors, '83 Dist: Jazz Horizons

STEAMER,THE.
Album: released on Verve, '82 by Phonogram Records. Dist: Polygram

SWEET RAIN.
Tracks: / Litha / O Grande amor / Sweet rain / Con aima / Windows / There will never be another you.
Compact disc: released on Verve, Apr'84 by Phonogram Records. Dist: Polygram

Album: released on Verve, '76 by Phonogram Records. Dist: Polygram

Compact disc: released on Verve, '84 by Phonogram Records. Dist: Polygram

TENOR CONTRASTS (Getz, Stan & James Moody).
Album: released on Esquire, '79 by Titan International Productions. Dist: Jazz Music, Cadillac Music, Swift, Wellard, Chris, Backs, Rough Trade, Revolver, Nine Mile

TWO SIDES OF STAN GETZ.
Album: released on Unique Jazz, Nov'86 Dist: Swift, Jazz Music, Jazz Horizons

VOYAGE.
Tracks: / I wanted to say / I thought about you / Yesterdays / Dreams / Falling in love / Voyage.
Notes: Personnel: Stan Getz,Kenny Barron,George Mraz,Victor Lewis
Compact disc: released on Blackhawk, Mar'87 by Blackhawk Records (USA). Dist: IMS-Polygram

WALKMAN JAZZ.
Cassette: released on Polydor, Jun'87 by Polydor Records. Dist: Polygram, Polydor

WEST COAST JAZZ.
Album: released on Verve (USA), '81 by Polydor. Dist: Polygram

YESTERDAY.
Album: released on Jazz Live, '81

Geuter, Andrew

FORTUNE MY FOE.
Album: released on Broadside, '81 by Broadside Records. Dist: Celtic Distributions, H.R. Taylor, Jazz Music, Projection, Jazz Services Unlimited Dist. (JSU)

Cassette: released on Broadside, '81 by Broadside Records. Dist: Celtic Distributions, H.R. Taylor, Jazz Music, Projection, Jazz Services Unlimited Dist. (JSU)

Geyer, Renee

SING TO ME.
Album: released on WEA, '85 by WEA Records. Dist: WEA

Geza X

HUNGARIAN.
Single (7"): released on Alternative Tentacles, Feb'83 by Alternative Tentacles Records. Dist: Rough Trade, Pinnacle

G-Force

WHITE KNUCKLES.
Single (7"): released on Jet, Nov'80 by Jet Records. Dist: CBS

G For Giraffe

SCIENTIFIC/GUILTY.
Single (7"): released on Amidisque, Dec'83 by Amidisque Records. Dist: RCA, Pinnacle

Ghiglioni, Tiziana

SOUNDS OF LOVE.
Album: released on Soul Note, Nov'83 Dist: Harmonia Mundi Distributors

Ghost

FOR ONE SECOND.
Album: released on Bam Caruso, May'87 by Bam Caruso Records. Dist: Rough Trade, Revolver, Cartel

Ghostbusters

GHOSTBUSTERS-MUSIC FROM THE FILM Various Artists (Various Artists).

Album: released on Arista, Sep'84 by Arista Records. Dist: RCA

Cassette: released on Arista, Sep'84 by Arista Records. Dist: RCA

Ghost Dance

GRIP OF LOVE.
Single (7"): released on Karbon, Sep'86 by Karbon Records. Dist: Pinnacle, Red Rhino, Cartel

Single (12"): released on Karbon, Sep'86 by Karbon Records. Dist: Pinnacle, Red Rhino, Cartel

HEARTFUL OF SOUL.
Tracks: / Heartful of soul / Can the can / Radar love.
Single (7"): released on Karbon, Jul'86 by Karbon Records. Dist: Pinnacle, Red Rhino, Cartel

RIVER OF NO RETURN.
Tracks: / Grip of love / Last train / Deeper blue, A / Grip of love (A cheaper blues version).
Single (12"): released on Karbon, Apr'86 by Karbon Records. Dist: Pinnacle, Red Rhino, Cartel

WORD TO THE WISE, A (EP).
Single (12"): released on Karbon, Aug'87 by Karbon Records. Dist: Pinnacle, Red Rhino, Cartel

Ghost Music

LOVE YOU & LEAVE YOU.
Single (7"): released on VP, Mar'85 by VP Records. Dist: Pinnacle

Ghost Of An American...

I HEAR VOICES.
Single (7"): released on ., 13 Jun'87

Single (12"): released on ., 13 Jun'87

Ghostriders

BAPTISM OF FIRE.
Single (12"): released on Criminal Damage, Jul'84 by Criminal Damage Records. Dist: Backs, Cartel

Ghosts Of Christmas Past

GHOSTS OF CHRISTMAS PAST Various Artists (Various Artists).
Album: released on Crepescule, Dec'86 by Island Records. Dist: Polygram, Pinnacle

Album: released on Les Disques Du Crepescule, Dec'86 Dist: Rough Trade, Pinnacle, Island, Polygram

Ghosts of dance

GHOSTS OF DANCE.
Single (7"): released on Plastic Canvas, Sep'82 Dist: Pinnacle

Ghost Town

GHOST TOWN A ballet by Richard Rodgers (Rodgers, Richard).
Notes: Orchestrated by Hans Spialek. Conducted by John Mauceri. This is the world premier recording of a major work by Richard Rogers. He composed the piece for the Ballet Russe and it was given its premiere at the Metropolitan Opera House on 12, November 1939. The original orchestrations by the great Hans Spialek (who orchestrated shows by George Gershwin, Jerome Kern, Rodgers and Hart, Cole Porter etc.) have recently been discovered and restored and were used in this recording with the co-operation of the Richard Rodgers Estate. This then is the authentic 1939 sound, as with the On Your Toes recent Broadway and London productions and TER's recording which used the original 1939 Hans Spialek's orchestrations. John Mauceri is one of those rare gifted conductors who can cross over from conducting serious classical works as well as Broadway Musicals. All of his conducting in the major opera houses such as The Royal Opera House, La Scala or the Metropolitan Opera, has been critically acclaimed. He will be making his debut with the Vienna State Opera and Paris Opera in 1987. He has recently been appointed to be the Musical Director of The Scottish Opera, taking over from Sir Alexander Gibson in 1987. Coupled with Ghost Town on this album are the two other ballets by Richard Rodgers. The World Premiere Complete Recordings of Slaughter on 10th Avenue and Princesse Zenobia. Both recordings were orchestrated by Hans Spialek and conducted by John Muceri. The recordings were produced by Norman Newell (Slaughter on 10th Avenue and Princesse Zenobia) and John Yap (Ghost Town) and were engineered by John Kurlander. As with past recordings, the album has been licenced to Polygram Records in USA for release in June on the Polydor label in the United States. It will be simultaneously released here on the TER label.
Compact disc: released on TER, Dec'86 Dist: Pinnacle

Album: released on TER, Jun'86 Dist: Pinnacle

Cassette: released on TER, Jun'86 Dist: Pinnacle

Ghost Train

HOPE AND GLORY.
Tracks: / Killing time.
Single (7"): released on Kingdom Come, May'86 Dist: Fast Forward

Ghoulies

DOGGED BY DOGMA.
Album: released on Lounging, Jun'82 by Lounging Records. Dist: Revolver, Cartel

Giancarlo Nicolai Trio

GIANCARLO NICOLAI TRIO.
Album: released on Leo Records, Jan'87 by Leo Records. Dist: Leo, Impetus

Giant Haystacks

BABY I NEED YOU.
Single (7"): released on BSB, Jul'83

IT'S OK FOR SANTA.
Single (7"): released on Mach 1, Dec'83 by Mach 1 Records. Dist: PRT

Single (7"): released on Mach 1, Nov'84 by Mach 1 Records. Dist: PRT

Giant Sand

BALLAD OF A THIN LINE MAN.
Album: released on Zippo, Sep'86

VALLEY OF RAIN.
Album: released on Zippo, Feb'86

Cassette: released on Zippo, Feb'86

Giant Sandworms

DON'T TURN AWAY.
Tracks: / Longsleeves.
Single (7"): released on One Guitar, Jan'86

Giants Of Jazz

GIANTS OF JAZZ Various Artists (Various Artists).
Album: released on George Wein Concord Jazz (USA), Jul'84 by Concord Jazz Records (USA). Dist: IMS, Polygram

GIANTS OF JAZZ, THE.
Tracks: / Straight, no chaser / Thelonius / Sweet and lovely / Don't blame me / I'll wait for you / Epistrophy.
Notes: Personnel: Dizzy Gillespie/Thelonius Monk/Kai Winding/Sonny Stitt/Art Blakey/ Al McKibbon.
Compact disc: released on Concord Jazz(USA), Jan'87 by Concord Jazz Records (USA). Dist: IMS, Polygram

GIANTS OF JAZZ VOLUME 1 Various Artists (Various Artists).
Album: released on Gateway (USA), '84 by Gemcom Inc.(USA) Records.

GIANTS OF TRADITIONAL JAZZ Various artists (Various Artists).
Notes: Mutt Carey & His Group, Sidney Bechet & His Group, Joe Marsala & His Group, Wild Bill Davison & His Group, Ben Pollack & His Group.
Album: released on Savoy (France), Feb'85

Double Album:

Giants Of Jazz & Blues

GIANTS OF JAZZ AND BLUES (Various Artists).
Album: released on Masters (Holland), Jan'87

Cassette: released on Masters (Holland), Jan'87

Gibb, Andy

ANDY GIBB'S GREATEST HITS ?.

Album: released on RSO, Feb'81

Cassette: released on RSO, Feb'81

Gibb, Barry

NOW VOYAGER.
Compact disc: by Polydor Records. Dist: Polygram, Polydor

Gibb, Maurice

HOLD HER IN YOUR HAND.
Single (7"): released on Audiotrax, Sep'84 by Audiotrax. Dist: PRT

Single (12"): released on Audiotrax, Sep'84 by Audiotrax. Dist: PRT

Gibbons, Carroll

BODY & SOUL (Gibbons, Carroll/Savoy Hotel Orpheans/Playmates).
Album: released on Joy, Nov'82 by President Records. Dist: Jazz Music, Swift, President Distribution

Cassette: released on Joy, Jun'85 by President Records. Dist: Jazz Music, Swift, President Distribution

BRIGHTER THAN THE SUN.
Tracks: / You're gonna lose your gal / One morning in May / May I ? / Beat O' my heart / So help me / I saw stars / For all we know / All my life / You're the kind of a baby for me / Kiss by kiss / Sailin' on the Robert E'Lee / One hour with you / What makes you so adorable / By special permission of the copyright owners (I love you) / After tonight we say goodbye / I wish I knew a bigger word than love / What more can I ask / Brighter than the sun / It's gonna be you / Oceans of time.
Album: released on Conifer, Jan'86 by Conifer Records. Dist: Conifer

Cassette: released on Conifer, Jan'86 by Conifer Records. Dist: Conifer

CARROLL GIBBONS STORY, (THE).
Album: released on World (Retrospect Series), Feb'84

Cassette: released on World (Retrospect Series), Feb'84

CARROLL RE-CALLS THE TUNES.
Tracks: / Lady is a tramp, The / Sweet Sue just you / California here I come / Babette / I can't give you anything but love / Dinah / Ain't misbehavin' / Stormy weather / Exactly like you / Oh me, oh my / They did'nt believe me / Cheek to cheek / In the still of the night / Two sleepy people / Rosalie / Solitude / Time on my hands / Manhatten holiday / Bubbling over / I cried for you / Somebody loves me / These foolish things / I'll see you in my dreams / Diane / I'll see you again / Kiss me again / Alice blue gown / Speak to me love / Marcheta / Ain't misbehavin' / Honeysuckle rose / I've got a feeling I'm falling / Keepin' out of mischief now / Summer rain / Smoke gets in your eyes / Way you look tonight, The / Moonbeams dance / I want the waiter.
Album: released on EMI Retrospect, Jul'86 by EMI Records. Dist: EMI

Cassette: released on EMI Retrospect, Jul'86 by EMI Records. Dist: EMI

DANCING IN THE DARK (Gibbons, Carroll & The Hotel Orpheans).
Tracks: / Snuggled on your shoulder / All of a sudden / What a life / Old man of the mountain, The / Blues in my heart / Goopy geer (he plays piano and he plays by ear) / Love me tonight / With love in my heart / Sweet and lovely / Keepin' out of mischief now / Actions speak louder than words / My silent love / Dancing in the dark / I heard / Bidin' my time / I wanna be loved / Cat and the fiddle medley: / Great big bunch of you / As time goes by.
Album: released on Saville, '86 by Conifer Records. Dist: Conifer

Cassette: released on Saville, '86 by Conifer Records. Dist: Conifer

DANCING IN THE DARK (Gibbons, Carroll & The Savoy Hotel Orpheans).
Album: released on Saville, Apr'83 by Conifer Records. Dist: Conifer

GOLDEN AGE OF CARROLL GIBBONS, (THE) (Gibbons, Carroll/Boyfriends/Savoy Hotel Orpheans).
Album: released on Golden Age, Apr'85 by Music For Pleasure Records. Dist: EMI

Cassette: released on Golden Age, Apr'85 by Music For Pleasure Records. Dist: EMI

NEW MAYFAIR DANCE ORCHESTRA, 1928-1930, (THE) (Gibbons, Carroll/Ray Noble).
Album: released on Saville, Nov'83 by Conifer Records. Dist: Conifer

ON THE AIR (Gibbons, Carroll & The Savoy Hotel Orpheans).
Album: released on President Evergreen, Jul'84

Cassette: released on President, Jun'85 by President Records. Dist: Taylors, Spartan

ON THE AIR-... The Hartley's Jam Broadcasts 1943-45 (Gibbons, Carrol & The Boy-

Straight from the shoulder (right from the heart) / You turned your head / Other peoples babies / Dinah / What a difference a day made / Pardon my southern accent / Heat wave.
Album: released on EMI Retrospect, Oct'86 by EMI Records. Dist: EMI

Gibbons, Steve

ON THE LOOSE (Gibbons, Steve Band).
Album: released on Magnum Force, Apr'86 by Magnum Music Group Ltd. Dist: Magnum Music Group Ltd, PRT, Spartan

PERSONAL PROBLEM.
Single (7"): released on Aura, Feb'86 by Holywood Nites Distribution. Dist: Pinnacle

Gibbons, Steve Band

SAINTS & SINNERS.
Album: released on RCA, Oct'81 by RCA Records. Dist: RCA, Roots, Swift, Wellard, Chris, I & B, Solomon & Peres Distribution

Cassette: released on RCA, Oct'81 by RCA Records. Dist: RCA, Roots, Swift, Wellard, Chris, I & B, Solomon & Peres Distribution

Gibb, Robin

BOYS (do fall in love).
Single (7"): released on Polydor, Jun'84 by Polydor Records. Dist: Polygram, Polydor

Single (12"): released on Polydor, Jun'84 by Polydor Records. Dist: Polygram, Polydor

HOW OLD ARE YOU.
Compact disc: by Polydor Records. Dist: Polygram, Polydor

LIKE A FOOL.
Tracks: / Possession.
Single (7"): released on Polydor, Apr'86 by Polydor Records. Dist: Polygram, Polydor

friends Featuring Anne Lenner).
Tracks: / Who? / Smoke gets in your eyes / Don't let it bother you / I saw stars / Messengers / Walking the chalk line / I'll see you again / Love is in the air / Coffee in the morning / Tea for two / Continental, The / Lost in a fog / Take a number from one to ten / If the moon turns green /
Single (12"): released on Polydor, Apr'86 by Polydor Records. Dist: Polygram, Polydor

SECRET AGENT.
Compact disc: released on Polydor, Jul'84 by Polydor Records. Dist: Polygram, Polydor

WALLS HAVE EARS.
Compact disc: released on Polydor, Nov'85 by Polydor Records. Dist: Polygram, Polydor

Gibbs, Joe

AFRICAN DUB (1) (Gibbs, Joe/Professionals).
Album: released on Lightning, '78 by Lightning Records. Dist: Jetstar

AFRICAN DUB (2) (Gibbs, Joe/Professionals).
Album: released on Lightning, '78 by Lightning Records. Dist: Jetstar

MAJESTIC DUB.
Album: released on Laser, Jul'79 by Mainline Record Company. Dist: Mainline

Album: released on Blue Moon, Feb'85 Dist: Magnum Music Group Ltd, PRT, Spartan

Gibbs, Terry

FEBRUARY 19TH, 1963 (Gibbs, Terry Quartet).
Album: released on From The Jazz Vault, Oct'80 by Damont Records. Dist: Swift, Taylor, H.R.

JAZZ PARTY (Gibbs, Terry & Buddy De Franco).
Album: released on Palo Alto (Italy), Jul'86

Cassette: released on Palo Alto (Italy), Jul'86

JAZZ PARTY - FIRST TIME TOGETHER (Gibbs, Terry & Buddy De Franco).
Album: released on Palo Alto (Italy), Jan'84

Cassette: released on Palo Alto (Italy), Jan'84

TAKE IT FROM ME (Gibbs, Terry Quartet).
Album: released on Jasmine, Sep'82 by Jasmine Records. Dist: Counterpoint, Lugtons, Taylor, H.R., Wellard, Chris, Swift, Cadillac

Cassette: released on Jasmine, Sep'82 by Jasmine Records. Dist: Counterpoint, Lugtons, Taylor, H.R., Wellard, Chris, Swift, Cadillac

TERRY.
Album: released on Jasmine, Feb'83 by Jasmine Records. Dist: Counterpoint, Lugtons, Taylor, H.R., Wellard, Chris, Swift, Cadillac

Gibson Brothers

CUBA.
Album: released on Island, Jul'79 by Island Records. Dist: Polygram

Cassette: released on Island, May'81 by Island Records. Dist: Polygram Deleted '85.

MY HEART'S BEATING (Tic tac).
Single (7"): released on Stiff, Jun'83 by Stiff Records. Dist: EMI, Record Services Distribution (Ireland)

Single (12"): released on Stiff, Jun'83 by Stiff Records. Dist: EMI, Record Services Distribution (Ireland)

ON THE RIVIERA.
Cassette: released on Island, Aug'80 by Island Records. Dist: Polygram

PARTY TONIGHT.
Tracks: / B'Lola.
Single (7"): released on Streetwave, Jul'86 by Streetwave Records. Dist: PRT Distribution

Single (12"): released on Streetwave, Jul'86 by Streetwave Records. Dist: PRT Distribution

Gibson, Chris

SLEEPS DARK & SILENT GATE.
Single (7"): released on Atmospheric, Mar'82

Gibson, Debbie

ONLY IN MY DREAMS.
Single (7"): released on Atlantic, Aug'87 by WEA Records. Dist: WEA

Single (12"): released on Atlantic, Aug'87 by WEA Records. Dist: WEA

Gibson, Don

15 GREAT HITS.
Album: released on RCA (Germany), Oct'84

Cassette: released on RCA (Germany), Oct'84

20 OF THE BEST.
Album: released on RCA International, Aug'82

Album: released on RCA International, Aug'82

Cassette: released on RCA International, Aug'82

Cassette: released on RCA International, Aug'82

COUNTRY NUMBER ONE.
Cassette: released on Warwick, Feb'80 Dist: Multiple Sound Distributors

DON GIBSON COLLECTION, THE.
Tracks: / Oh lonesome me / Snap your fingers / Just one time / Take these chains from my heart / Sweet dreams / Release me / Blue blue day / Funny familiar forgotten feelings / Kawliga.
Album: released on Castle Collectors, Jul'87 by Castle Communications Records. Dist: Pinnacle

Cassette: released on Castle Collectors, Jul'87 by Castle Communications Records. Dist: Pinnacle

Compact disc: released on Castle Collectors, Jul'87 by Castle Communications Records. Dist: Pinnacle

DON GIBSON & LOS INDIOS TABAJARAS (Gibson, Don & Los Indios Tabajaras).
Tracks: / I can't tell my heart that / Cryin' heart blues / My adobe hacienda / Address unknown / That's how it goes / When will this end / So how come (no one loves me) / What about me / I couldn't care less / Same old trouble, The / Hurtin' inside / Fireball mail / Above and beyond / Camptown races.
Album: released on Bear Family, Aug'86 by Bear Family Records. Dist: Rollercoaster Distribution, Swift

EARLY DAYS.
Tracks: / Automatic mama / Why am I so lonely / I lost my love / Cloudy skies / Dark future / Blue million tears, A / Just let me love you / Roses are red / ed lips white lies and blue hours / I love no one but you / Caroline breakdown / Wigglewag.
Album: released on Bear Family, Aug'86 by Bear Family Records. Dist: Rollercoaster Distribution, Swift

LEGEND IN HIS OWN TIME.
Double Album: released on Cambra, Apr'85 by Cambra Records. Dist: IDS, Conifer

Double cassette: released on Cambra, Apr'85 by Cambra Records. Dist: IDS, Conifer

ROCKIN' ROLLIN' GIBSON VOLUME 2.
Album: released on Bear Family, Sep'84 by Bear Family Records. Dist: Rollercoaster Distribution, Swift

ROCKIN' ROLLIN' GIBSON.
Album: released on Bear Family, Sep'84 by Bear Family Records. Dist: Rollercoaster Distribution, Swift

SEA OF HEARTBREAK.
Tracks: / Please help me I'm falling.
Single (7"): released on Old Gold, Oct'86 by Old Gold Records. Dist: Lightning, Jazz Music, Spartan, Counterpoint

Single (7"): released on Pastafont, Mar'84 by Pastafont Records.

THAT GIBSON BOY.
Tracks: / Even tho' / It's my way / Midnight / As much / Do you think / Didn't work out, did it? / Won't cha' come back to me / I wish it had been a dream / Ages and ages ago / Almost / It has to be / Foggy river.
Album: released on RCA, Jan'87 by RCA Records. Dist: RCA, Roots, Swift, Wellard, Chris, I & B, Solomon & Peres Distribution

Cassette: released on RCA, Jan'87 by RCA Records. Dist: RCA, Roots, Swift, Wellard, Chris, I & B, Solomon & Peres Distribution

YOU WIN AGAIN.
Album: released on Sundown, Aug'85 by Magnum Music Group Ltd. Dist: Magnum Music Group Ltd, PRT Distribution, Spartan Distribution

Gibson, Wayne

UNDER MY THUMB.
Single (7"): released on Kingdom, Dec'83 by Kingdom Records. Dist: Kingdom

Gidden, Yvonne

IN ORBIT (mega mix).
Single (12"): released on Electricity, Jan'84 by Electricity Records. Dist: PRT

Gidea Park

BEACH BOY GOLD.
Single (7"): released on Stone, May'81

BEACH BOY GOLD PART 2.
Single (7"): released on Polo, Jun'82 by Polo Records. Dist: PRT

Single (12"): released on Polo, Jun'82 by Polo Records. Dist: PRT

GIDEA PARK.
Album: released on Polo, Oct'81 by Polo Records. Dist: PRT

LIGHTNIN STRIKES.
Single (7"): released on Polo, Jan'82 by Polo Records. Dist: PRT

Single (12"): released on Polo, Jan'82 by Polo Records. Dist: PRT

RUN BABY RUN.
Tracks: / Don't look back.
Single (7"): released on Mix Factory, Apr'86 Dist: Creole Distribution, PRT Distribution

SEASONS OF GOLD (Four Seasons medley).
Single (7"): released on Polo, Sep'81 by Polo Records. Dist: PRT

Single (12"): released on Polo, Sep'81 by Polo Records. Dist: PRT

Gift

CRASHING DOWN.
Single (7"): released on Venus, Sep'82 by Miaow. Dist: Cartel

Gifted Children

PAINTING BY NUMBERS.
Single (7"): released on Whaam, May'81 Dist: Pinnacle

Gift Of Allen

CRYING IN THE RAIN.
Tracks: / Crying in the rain / You're the best girl in the world.
Notes: Blue Hat distribution: Blue Hat Records, PO Box 1, Bradford-on-Avon, Wilts.
Single (7"): released on Blue Hat, Jun'87 by Blue Hat Records. Dist: Blue Hat

Single (7"): released on Blue Hat, 13 Jun'87 by Blue Hat Records. Dist: Blue Hat

Gift of music

GIFT OF MUSIC Various Artists (Various Artists).
Boxed set: released on Pickwick, Oct'82 by Pickwick Records. Dist: Pickwick Distribution, Prism Leisure Distribution, Lugtons

Boxed set: released on Pickwick, Oct'82 by Pickwick Records. Dist: Pickwick Distribution, Prism Leisure Distribution, Lugtons

GIFT OF MUSIC Menuhin, Yehudi (Menuhin, Yehudi).
Cassette: released on Seminar Cassettes, Oct'81 by Seminar Cassettes. Dist: Davidson Distribution, Eastern Educational Products Distrib., Forlaget Systime Distribution, Laser Books Ltd Distribution, MacDougall Distribution, Talktapes Distribution, Watkins Books Ltd Distribution, Norton, Jeff Distribution

Gifts of legends

GIFTS OF LEGENDS Ayrton, Michael (Ayrton, Michael).
Cassette: released on Seminar Cassettes, Oct'81 by Seminar Cassettes. Dist: Davidson Distribution, Eastern Educational Products Distrib., Forlaget Systime Distribution, Laser Books Ltd Distribution, MacDougall Distribution, Talktapes Distribution, Watkins Books Ltd Distribution, Norton, Jeff Distribution

Giggetty

BLACK COUNTRY CHRISTMAS.
Single (7"): released on Revolver, Nov'80 by Revolver Records. Dist: Revolver, Cartel

Gigi

GIGI Original Film Soundtrack.
Tracks: / Overture / Thank heaven for little girls / Parisians (The) / Waltz at Maxim's (She's not thinking of me) / Night they invented champagne (The) / I remember it well / Say a prayer for me tonight / I'm glad i'm not young anymore / Gigi (Gaston's Soliloquy) / Finale.
Notes: Film soundtrack: Louis Jourdan, Maurice Chevalier, Betty Wand & Hermione Gingold. Conducted by : Andre Previn Songs by : Frederick Loewe & Alan Jay Lerner
Compact disc: released on CBS, Mar'87 by CBS Records. Dist: CBS

GIGI Original Broadway cast recording (Various Artists).
Tracks: / Overture / Thank heaven for little girls / It's a bore / Earth and other minor things, The / Paris is Paris again / She is not thinking of me / I remember it well / Night they invented champagne, The / Gigi / Contract, The / In this wide, wide world / I'm glad I'm not young anymore / Finale / Thank heaven for little girls (reprise).
Album: released on RCA, Jan'87 by RCA Records. Dist: RCA, Roots, Swift, Wellard, Chris, I & B, Solomon & Peres Distribution

Cassette: released on RCA, Jan'87 by RCA Records. Dist: RCA, Roots, Swift, Wellard, Chris, I & B, Solomon & Peres Distribution

GIGI Original soundrack.
Album: released on CBS, Jul'86 by CBS Records. Dist: CBS

Cassette: released on CBS, Jul'86 by CBS Records. Dist: CBS

GIGI-LONDON STAGE PRODUCTION Original cast recording (Various Artists).
Album: released on Safari, Nov'85 by Safari Records. Dist: Pinnacle

Cassette: released on Safari, Nov'85 by Safari Records. Dist: Pinnacle

Gigli, Benjamino

GREAT VOICES OF THE CENTURY.
Album: released on Bulldog, Mar'85 by Bulldog Records. Dist: President Distribution, Spartan, Swift, Taylor, H.R.

Gigli, Suzanne

BOYS DO IT.
Single (7"): released on Lamborghini, Nov'84 by Lamborghini Records. Dist: PRT

Single (12"): released on Lamborghini, Nov'84 by Lamborghini Records. Dist: PRT

Gigolo

DRY BONES.
Single (7"): released on Channel, May'82 by Channel Records. Dist: Pinnacle
Cat. no: **CHAN 002**

Gigolo and gigolette

GIGOLO AND GIGOLETTE Maugham, Somerset (Burden, Hugh).
Cassette: released on Talking Tape, '84

Gigolo & Gigolette

GIGOLO & GIGOLETTE Maugham, Somerset (Burden, Hugh).
Cassette: released on Talking Tape Company, Sep'84 by Talking Tape Company Records.

Gilbert, Andrew

WONDERLAND BY NIGHT Plays the Kawai 900 organ.
Tracks: / Danke Schon / Love me tender / Wonderland by night / How can I tell you ? / Shadow of your smile, The / Riders in the sky / September in the rain / You make me feel brand new / Red Sarafan, The / Ave Maria / Don't it make my brown eyes blue / I can't give you anything but love / Bali Ha'i.
Album: released on Grosvenor, Feb'82 by Grosvenor Records. Dist: Taylors

Gilbert, Bruce

SHIVERING MAN, THE.
Album: released on Mute, Mar'87 Dist: Spartan Distribution, Rough Trade Distribution, Cartel Distribution

THIS WAY.
Album: released on Mute, Aug'84 Dist: Spar-

tan Distribution, Rough Trade Distribution, Cartel Distribution

Gilbert, Lewis & Mills

MZUI.
Album: released on Cherry Red, May'82 by Cherry Red Records. Dist: Pinnacle

Gilberto, Astrud

ASTRUD GILBERTO.
Cassette: released on Audio Fidelity, Oct'84 Dist: PRT

ASTRUD GILBERTO ALBUM.
Tracks: / Once I loved / Agua de beber / How insensitive / Meditation / Roses and roses / O morro (nao tem vez) / Dindi / Photograph / Dreamer / So finha de ser com voce / All that's left to say goodbye.
Compact disc: released on Verve, Nov'84 by Phonogram Records. Dist: Polygram

ASTRUD GILBERTO ALBUM.
Tracks: / Once I loved / Agua de beber / How Insensitive / Meditation / And roses and roses / O morro (nao tem vez) / Dindi / Photograph / Dreamer / So finha de ser com voce / All that's left to say goodbye.
Compact disc: released on Verve, Nov'84 by Phonogram Records. Dist: Polygram

BEST OF ASTRUD GILBERTO.
Album: released on Verve (Holland), Nov'85 by Phonogram Records. Dist: Polygram

Cassette: released on Verve (Holland), Nov'85 by Phonogram Records. Dist: Polygram

BEST OF ASTRUD GILBERTO.
Tracks: / Stay / Call me / Meditation / Light of my life / How insensitive / It might as well be spring / Here's that rainy day / Agoe de beber / Beach samba / One note samba / My foolish heart / Certain smile, A / Girl from Ipanema, The / Shadow of your smile, The.
Album: released on Verve (Import), Oct'82

Cassette: released on Verve (Import). Oct'82

COMPACT JAZZ.
Compact disc: released on Verve, Jul'87 by Phonogram Records. Dist: Polygram

ESSENTIAL ASTRUD GILBERTO.
Tracks: / Take me to Aruanda / Bim bom / So nice (summer samba) / One note samba / O Ganso / Tristeza / Fly me to the moon / It might as well be spring / Manha de carnival / Girl from Ipanema, The / Meditation / O morro nao tem vez / Corcovado / Certain smile, A / Beach samba (bossa no paia) / Agua de beber / Goodbye sadness.
Album: released on Verve, Sep'84 by Phonogram Records. Dist: Polygram

Cassette: released on Verve, Sep'84 by Phonogram Records. Dist: Polygram

GETTING OVER YOU.
Tracks: / Young love of my life.
Single (7"): released on PRT, Sep'84 by PRT Records. Dist: PRT

LOOK TO THE RAINBOW.
Album: released on Polydor, Aug'86 by Polydor Records. Dist: Polygram, Polydor

Cassette: released on Polydor, Aug'86 by Polydor Records. Dist: Polygram. Polydor

Compact disc: released on Polydor, Aug'86 by Polydor Records. Dist: Polygram, Polydor

MUSIC FOR THE MILLIONS.
Tracks: / Once I loved / Auga de beber / Meditation / Roses and roses / How insensitive / O morro / Dindi / Photograph / Dreamer / So tinha de ser com voce / All that's left is to say goodbye.
Album: released on Verve (Holland), Jul'84 by Phonogram Records. Dist: Polygram

Cassette: released on Verve (Holland), Jul'84 by Phonogram Records. Dist: Polygram

PLUS (Gilberto, Astrud & James Last).
Notes: For full information see under: Last, James & Astrud Gilberto.

SHADOW OF YOUR SMILE.
Album: released on Verve (USA), Jun'82 by Polydor. Dist: Polygram

THAT GIRL FROM IPANEMA.
Tracks: / Girl from Ipanema, The / Meu piao / Far away / We'll make today last night again / Black magic / All I've got / Love for sale / Wanting you / Puppy song, The / Mamae eu quero / Chica chica boom chic.
Compact disc: released on Bellaphon, '86 by Bellaphon Records. Dist: IMS-Polygram

Album: released on Phoenix, Oct'82 by Audio Fidelity Enterprises. Dist: Stage One, Lugtons

THIS IS ASTRUD GILBERTO.
Album: released on Verve (Germany). Apr'85

WALKMAN JAZZ.
Cassette: released on Polydor, Jun'87 by Polydor Records. Dist: Polygram, Polydor

Gilberto, Joao

BRASIL.
Album: released on Mercury, Apr'82 by Phonogram Records. Dist: Polygram Distribution

GETZ/GILBERTO (Gilberto, Joao & Stan Getz).
Album: released on Verve, Aug'81 by Phonogram Records. Dist: Polygram

GILBERTO AND JOBIM.
Tracks: / Manha de Carnaval / O pato / Corcovado / Trevo de quarto folhas / Un abraco no bonfa / Se e' tarde me perdoa / Discussao / A felicidade / Amor certinho / Outra vez / Samba de uma nota so / Doralice / So em teus bracos / Meditacao / Felicidade, A.
Album: released on EMI (Italy), Dec'86 by EMI Records. Dist: Conifer

GILBERTO/GETZ (Gilberto, Joao & Stan Getz).
Tracks: / Girl from Ipenema / Doralice / Paro muchachar / Desafinado / Meu Caracado / Corcovado / So danco samba / O grande amor / Viva Sohando.
Compact disc: released on Verve, Mar'83 by Phonogram Records. Dist: Polygram

Compact disc: released on Verve, '83 by Phonogram Records. Dist: Polygram

Gilbert & Sullivan

D'OYLY CARTE 1875-1975.
Album: released on Decca, Jan'79 by Decca Records. Dist: Polygram

GILBERT & SULLIVAN OVERTURES G & S festival orchestra (Gilbert & Sullivan Overtures).
Album: released on PRT, Oct'84 by PRT Records. Dist: PRT

Cassette: released on PRT, Oct'84 by PRT Records. Dist: PRT

GILBERT & SULLIVAN SPECTACULAR
Various artists (Various Artists).
Album: released on Spot, Aug'83 by Pickwick Records. Dist: H.R. Taylor, Lugtons

Cassette: released on Spot, Aug'83 by Pickwick Records. Dist: H.R. Taylor, Lugtons

IOLANTHE.
Album: released on Decca, Jul'79 by Decca Records. Dist: Polygram

IOLANTHE (D'OYLY CARTE OPERA COMPANY).
Double Album: released on Decca, '82 by Decca Records. Dist: Polygram

Double cassette: released on Decca, '82 by Decca Records. Dist: Polygram

MIKADO.
Double Album: released on Decca, Apr'79 by Decca Records. Dist: Polygram

MIKADO (VIDEO).
Notes: Released on Savoy Video

PATIENCE.
Double Album: released on Decca, Jul'79 by Decca Records. Dist: Polygram

PIRATES OF PENZANCE.
Double Album: released on Decca, Apr'79 by Decca Records. Dist: Polygram

Princess Ida.

PRINCESS IDA.
Double Album: released on Decca, Jul'79 by Decca Records. Dist: Polygram

Album: by Decca Records. Dist: Polygram Deleted '8.

SAVOY OPERA.
Boxed set: released on Decca, '79 by Decca Records. Dist: Polygram

Boxed set: released on Decca, '79 by Decca Records. Dist: Polygram

TRIAL BY JURY.
Double Album: by EMI Records. Dist: EMI

WORLD OF GILBERT & SULLIVAN - VOL.1.
Cassette: released on Decca, '79 by Decca Records. Dist: Polygram

Album: released on World of Learning, '69 by World Of Learning Records. Dist: World Of Learning

WORLD OF GILBERT & SULLIVAN - VOL.2.
Cassette: released on Decca, '79 by Decca Records. Dist: Polygram

Album: released on World of Learning, '69 by World Of Learning Records. Dist: World Of Learning

WORLD OF GILBERT & SULLIVAN - VOL.3.
Album: released on World of Learning, '71 by World Of Learning Records. Dist: World Of Learning

YEOMAN OF THE GUARD & THE GONDOLIERS EXCERPTS.
Double cassette: released on Ditto, '83 by Pickwick Records. Dist: H.R. Taylor

YEOMAN OF THE GUARD & BALLET SUITE.
Cassette: released on Decca, Sep'79 by Decca Records. Dist: Polygram

Gilde Duo

TYROLEAN VAGABOND.
Tracks: / Snow waltz.
Single (7"):

Gilder, Nick

YOU REALLY ROCK ME.
Single (7"): released on Speed, Nov'82

Gildo, Rex

GEH NICHT.
Tracks: / Geh nicht vorbei (walk on by) / Speedy Gonzales / Oh oh candy lips / Liebe kaelter als eis (Devil in disguise) / Leider leider (Dear one) / Wenn es sein muss kann ich treu sein / Sieben wochen nach Bombay (I'm gonna get married) / Rexy zaehl auf mich (count on me) / Das ende der liebe (Tell Laura I love her) / Denk an mich in der ferne (Put your head on my shoulder) / Du eine (Dear someone) / Ich moecht in deinen armen sein / Glueck gohoert dazu / Du nennist alle maenner / Darling (You call everybody darling) / Dein zu sein (We got love) / Lass mich gehn (Turn me loose).
Album: released on Electrola, Feb'82 by Bear Family Records. Dist: Rollercoaster Distribution, Swift

Giles, Chris

CHRIS GILES PLAYS THE WERSI GALAXY.
Tracks: / Theme from "Shaft" / Even now / At the sign of the swingin' cymbal / Ballade pour Adeline / Fanfare for the common man / Overture poet and peasant / Soul limbo / Romance / Bel viso / L'amour de plein ete / Rinky dink / Hooked on romance.
Album:

Giles Cooper

UNDER THE LOOFAH TREE.
Cassette: released on BBC, May'84 by BBC Records & Tapes. Dist: EMI, PRT, Pye

Giles, Eddie

THAT'S HOW STRONG MY LOVE IS.
Single (7"): released on Charly, Jul'80 by Charly Records. Dist: Charly, Cadillac

Giles, Giles & Fripp

CHEERFUL INSANITY OF.....
Tracks: / Saga of Rodney Toady, The / North meadow / Newly weds / One in a million / Call tomorrow / Digging my lawn / Little children / Crukster, The / Thursday morning / Just George / How do they know / Elephant song / Sun is shining, The / Suite No.1 / Erudite eyes.
Album: released on Editions EG, Apr'82 by Virgin Records. Dist: EMI

Gilfellon, Tom

LOVING MAD TOM.
Album: released on Leader, Apr'65 Dist: Jazz Music, Projection

Gilgamesh

ANOTHER FINE TUNE YOU GOT ME INTO.
Tracks: / Bobberty theme from something else, waiting / Play time / Underwater song / Foel'd again / T.N.T.F.X. / Darker, brighter.
Album: released on Charly, Feb'79 by Charly Records. Dist: Charly, Cadillac

Gil, Gilberto

MINHA IDEOLOGIA NOITE NEON.
Tracks: / Minha ideologia, minha religiao / Nos barracos da cidade (barracos) / Roque santeiro, o rock / Seu Olhar / Febril / Touches pas a mon pote / Logos versus logo / Oracao pela libertacao da Africa do sul / Cliche do cliche / Casinha feliz / Duas luas.
Album: released on WEA, Jul'86 by WEA Records. Dist: WEA

NIGHTINGALE.
Album: released on Elektra, '79 by WEA Records. Dist: WEA

REALCE.
Album: released on WEA (France), Mar'85 Dist: Celtic Music Distribution, Swift

TODA MENINA BAINA.
Single (7"): released on WEA, Jul'85 by WEA Records. Dist: WEA Deleted '86.

Single (12"): released on WEA, Jul'85 by WEA Records. Dist: WEA

TOUCHES PAS MON POTE.
Tracks: / Toda menina baina / Polco.
Single (7"): released on WEA International, Jun'86

Single (12"): released on WEA International, Jun'86

Gillan

DOUBLE TROUBLE.
Double Album: released on Virgin, Oct'81 by Virgin Records. Dist: EMI, Virgin Distribution

Double cassette: released on Virgin, Oct'81 by Virgin Records. Dist: EMI, Virgin Distribution

FUTURE SHOCK.
Cassette: released on Virgin, Apr'81 by Virgin Records. Dist: EMI, Virgin Distribution

GLORY ROAD.
Album: released on Virgin, Mar'84 by Virgin Records. Dist: EMI, Virgin Distribution

Cassette: released on Virgin, Mar'84 by Virgin Records. Dist: EMI, Virgin Distribution

LIVING FOR THE CITY.
Single (7"): released on Virgin, Aug'82 by Virgin Records. Dist: EMI, Virgin Distribution

Picture disc single: released on Virgin, Aug'82 by Virgin Records. Dist: EMI, Virgin Distribution

LONG GONE.
Single (7"): released on Virgin, Oct'82 by Virgin Records. Dist: EMI, Virgin Distribution

ROCKS ON! (Gillan/Dean).
Album: released on Thunderbolt, Aug'84 by Magnum Music Group Ltd. Dist: Magnum Music Group Ltd, PRT Distribution, Spartan Distribution

Gill, Andy

DISPOSSESSION.
Single (12"): released on Survival, Aug'87 by Survival Records. Dist: Backs, Cartel Distribution

Gillan, Ian

GILLAN (Gillan ,Ian Band).
Album: released on Flyover, Feb'79 by Flyover Records. Dist: Flyover Records

LIVE AT THE BUDOKAN (Gillan ,Ian Band).
Album: released on Island, May'78 by Island Records. Dist: Polygram

WHAT I DID ON MY VACATION.
Tracks: / On the rocks / Scarabus / Money lender / Puget sound / Mad Elaine / Time and again / Vengeance / No easy way / If I sing softly / I'll rip your spine out / New Orleans / Mutually assured destruction / Unchain your brain / You're so right / No laughing in heaven / Long gone / If you believe me / Trouble / Bluesy blue sea / Lucille.
Album: released on 10, Jun'86 by 10 Records. Dist: Virgin, EMI

Cassette: released on 10, Jun'86 by 10 Records. Dist: Virgin, EMI

Compact disc: released on 10, Jun'86 by 10 Records. Dist: Virgin, EMI

Gillan, Pauline

HEARTS OF FIRE (Gillan, Pauline Band).
Album: released on Powerstation Records, Nov'85 by Powerstation Records. Dist: Pinnacle

ONE MORE TIME.
Single (12"): released on Bullet, Oct'84 Dist: Bullet Distribution

Gillard ,Pip

WHY CAN'T YOU LOVE ME.
Single (7"): released on Plus One, Aug'84 by Plus One Records. Dist: Cartel

Gillespie, Cherry

WHY?.
Single (7"): released on BBC, Aug'84 by BBC Records & Tapes. Dist: EMI, PRT, Pye

Gillespie, Dana

BELOW THE BELT.
Album: released on Ace, Jan'85 by Ace Records. Dist: Pinnacle, Swift, Hotshot, Cadillac

DANA GILLESPIE'S BLUE JOB.
Album: released on Ace, Nov'82 by Ace Records. Dist: Pinnacle, Swift, Hotshot, Cadillac

IT BELONGS TO ME.
Compact disc: released on Bellaphon, '86 by Bellaphon Records. Dist: IMS-Polygram

Gillespie, Dizzy

1948-52.
Album: released on Queen-Disc (Import), Apr'81

20 GOLDEN PIECES OF.
Album: released on Bulldog, Jul'82 by Bulldog Records. Dist: President Distribution, Spartan, Swift, Taylor, H.R.

AFRO CUBAN BOP (Gillespie, Dizzy & His Orchestra).
Album: released on Jazz Live, Apr'81

AFRO CUBAN JAZZ MOODS (Gillespie, Dizzy & Machito).
Album: released on Pablo (USA), '82 by Pablo Records (USA). Dist: Wellard, Chris, IMS-Polygram, BMG

Cassette: released on Pablo (USA), '82 by Pablo Records (USA). Dist: Wellard, Chris, IMS-Polygram, BMG

Album: released on Pablo, '82 by Pablo Records. Dist: Wellard, Chris, IMS-Polygram, BMG

Cassette: released on Pablo, '82 by Pablo Records. Dist: Wellard, Chris, IMS-Polygram, BMG

AN ELECTRIFYING EVENING.
Album: released on Verve, May'82 by Phonogram Records. Dist: Polygram

AT NEWPORT.
Album: released on Verve, Aug'81 by Phonogram Records. Dist: Polygram

AT THE MONTREUX JAZZ FESTIVAL 1975 (Gillespie, Dizzy Big Band).
Album: released on Pablo, '82 by Pablo Records. Dist: Wellard, Chris, IMS-Polygram, BMG

Cassette: released on Pablo, '82 by Pablo Records. Dist: Wellard, Chris, IMS-Polygram, BMG

BEBOP ENTERS SWEDEN 1947-49 (Gillespie, Dizzy Big Band).
Album: released on Dragon, Jul'82 by Dragon Records. Dist: Jazz Music, Projection, Cadillac

BEST OF DIZZY GILLESPIE, THE.
Album: released on Pablo (USA), '82 by Pablo Records (USA). Dist: Wellard, Chris, IMS-Polygram, BMG

Cassette: released on Pablo (USA), '82 by Pablo Records (USA). Dist: Wellard, Chris, IMS-Polygram, BMG

BIG BAND 1968.
Album: released on Beppo, Mar'77

BIRK'S WORKS.
Album: released on Duke, May'83

BIRKS WORKS.
Album: released on Duke, Jun'86 by Melodisc Records. Dist: Jazz Horizons, Jazz Music, Celtic Music, JSU, Swift

BODY AND SOUL (Gillespie, Dizzy & his Orchestra With Sarah Vaughan).
Album: released on Bulldog, Oct'85 by Bulldog Records. Dist: President Distribution, Spartan, Swift, Taylor, H.R.

Cassette: released on Bulldog, Oct'85 by Bulldog Records. Dist: President Distribution, Spartan, Swift, Taylor, H.R.

CARTER, GILLESPIE INC (Gillespie, Dizzy & Benny Carter).
Cassette: released on Pablo, '82 by Pablo Records. Dist: Wellard, Chris, IMS-Polygram, BMG

CHAMP 1951-1952, THE.
Album: released on Jazz Anthology, Mar'85 Dist: Discovery, Swift

Charlie Parker & Dizzy Gillespie

CLOSER TO THE SOURCE.
Tracks: / Could it be you / It's time for love / Closer to the source / You're No.1 in my book / Iced tea / Just before dawn / Textures.
Album: released on Atlantic, Jul'86 by WEA Records. Dist: WEA

Cassette: released on Atlantic, Jul'86 by WEA Records. Dist: WEA

COMPLETE PLEYEL CONCERT, THE.
Double Album: released on Vogue (France), Mar'84 Dist: Discovery, Jazz Music, PRT, Swift

CONCERT MASSEY HALL TORONTO (MAY 15, 1953) (Gillespie, Dizzy & Charlie Parker).

CONFIRMATION (Gillespie, Dizzy/Sonny Berman).

DEE GEE DAYS.
Album: released on Savoy, Sep'78

DEEGEE DAYS.
Tracks: / Tin Tin Deo / Birk's works / We love to boogie / Lady be good / Champ / I'm in a mess / School days / Swing low sweet cadillac / Bopsie's blues / I couldn't beat the rap / Caravan / Nobody knows / Bluest blues / On the sunny side of the street / Stardust / Time on my hands / Blue skies / Umbrella man / Confessin' / Ooh-shoo-be-doo-bee / They can't take that away from me.
Album: released on Savoy (France), Feb'85

Compact disc: released on RCA, Mar'86 by RCA Records. Dist: RCA, Roots, Swift, Wellard, Chris, I & B, Solomon & Peres Distribution

DIGITAL AT MONTREUX 1980.
Album: released on Pablo, '82 by Pablo Records. Dist: Wellard, Chris, IMS-Polygram, BMG

Cassette: released on Pablo, '82 by Pablo Records. Dist: Wellard, Chris, IMS-Polygram, BMG

DIZ DELIGHTS (Gillespie, Dizzy & His Orchestra).
Tracks: / 52nd street theme / Night in Tunisia / Anthropology / Ow / Oop-pop-a-da / Two bass hit / Stay on it / Woodyn' you / Cool breeze / Manetca / Good bait / Ool-ya-koo.
Album: released on RCA, Jul'86 by RCA Records. Dist: RCA, Roots, Swift, Wellard, Chris, I & B, Solomon & Peres Distribution

Cassette: released on RCA, Jul'86 by RCA Records. Dist: RCA, Roots, Swift, Wellard, Chris, I & B, Solomon & Peres Distribution

DIZZY (Gillespie, Dizzy Big 7).
Compact disc: released on Pablo (USA), May'86 by Pablo Records (USA). Dist: Wellard, Chris, IMS-Polygram, BMG

DIZZY & DOUBLE SIX OF PARIS.
Compact disc: released on Philips (Germany), '86

DIZZY GILESPIE BID BAND (Gillespie, Dizzy Big Band).

DIZZY GILLESPIE... Sonny Stitt, Kai Winding, A.Blakey, T.Monk, Al McKibbon (Gillespie, D/S.Stitt/K.Winding/A.Blakey/T.Monk/A.McKibbon).
Album: released on Lotus, Sep'86 Dist: Counterpoint

DIZZY GILLESPIE.
Album: released on Lotus, Sep'86 Dist: Counterpoint

DIZZY GILLESPIE (1946-49).
Tracks: / Minor walk / Guarachi guaro / Duff capers / Lover come back to me / I'm boppin' too / Overtime / Victory ball / Swedish suite / St.Louis blues / Katy / Jump did-le-ba / Hey pet, let's eat mo'meat! / Jumpin' with symphony Sid / In the land of Ooh-bla-dee / 52nd street theme / Night in Tunisia, A / Ol' man rebop / Anthropology / Ow! / Oop-pop-a-da / Two bass hit / Stay on it / Algo bueno (Woody'n'you) / Cool breeze / Cubana be / Cubana bop / Manteca / Good bait / Ool-ya-koo.
Album: released on Jazz Tribune (USA), Sep'86 Dist: Discovery

Cassette: released on Jazz Tribune (USA), Sep'86 Dist: Discovery

DIZZY GILLESPIE (1946-1949).
Album: released on RCA (France), '83 by RCA Records. Dist: Discovery

DIZZY GILLESPIE AND GIANTS OF JAZZ.
Album: released on Concord, Sep'84 by Import Records. Dist: IMS, Polygram

DIZZY GILLESPIE BIG BAND (Gillespie, Dizzy Big Band).
Notes: With Chubby Jackson Sextet/James Moody 1948
Album: released on Dragon, Jul'82 by Dragon Records. Dist: Jazz Music, Projection, Cadillac

DIZZY GILLESPIE & CHARLIE PARKER (Gillespie, Dizzy & Charlie Parker).
Album: released on EMI Europe, Jun'84 by EMI Records. Dist: Conifer

Cassette: released on EMI Europe, Jun'84 by EMI Records. Dist: Conifer

DIZZY GILLESPIE COLLECTION.
Album: released on Deja Vu, Nov'85 by Deja Vu Records. Dist: Counterpoint Distribution, Record Services Distribution (Ireland)

Cassette: released on Deja Vu, Nov'85 by Deja Vu Records. Dist: Counterpoint Distribution, Record Services Distribution (Ireland)

Cassette: released on Deja Vu, Aug'85 by Deja Vu Records. Dist: Counterpoint Distribution, Record Services Distribution (Ireland)

DIZZY GILLESPIE JAM.
Album: released on Pablo, '82 by Pablo Records. Dist: Wellard, Chris, IMS-Polygram, BMG

Cassette: released on Pablo, '82 by Pablo Records. Dist: Wellard, Chris, IMS-Polygram, BMG

DIZZY GILLESPIE'S BIG FOUR.
Album: released on Pablo, '82 by Pablo Records. Dist: Wellard, Chris, IMS-Polygram, BMG

Cassette: released on Pablo, '82 by Pablo Records. Dist: Wellard, Chris, IMS-Polygram, BMG

DIZZY GILLESPIE SEXTET (Gillespie, Dizzy Sextet).
Album: released on Vogue Jazz (France), May'84

DIZZY GILLESPIE & THE DOUBLE SIX OF PARIS.
Album: released on Mercury (Import), Oct'82

DIZZY GILLESPIE VOL 3.
Album: released on Jazz Reactivation, May'83 Dist: PRT

DIZZY GILLESPIE VOL 2.
Album: released on Jazz Reactivation, May'83 Dist: PRT

DIZZY GILLESPIE VOL1.
Album: released on Jazz Reactivation, Jan'82 Dist: PRT

DIZZY IN PARIS.
Compact disc: released on Vogue (France), Dec'85 Dist: Discovery, Jazz Music, PRT, Swift

DIZZY ON THE FRENCH RIVIERA.
Album: released on Philips, Sep'84 Dist: IMS-Polygram

Cassette: released on Philips, Sep'84 Dist: IMS-Polygram

DIZZY'S DELIGHT.
Album: released on Phoenix, May'79 by Audio Fidelity Enterprises. Dist: Stage One, Lugtons

DIZZY'S PARTY.
Album: released on Pablo (USA), May'82 by Pablo Records (USA). Dist: Wellard, Chris, IMS-Polygram, BMG

Cassette: released on Pablo (USA), May'82 by Pablo Records (USA). Dist: Wellard, Chris, IMS-Polygram, BMG

ENDURING MAGIC.
Tracks: / Blue and boogie / Thrill is gone, The / Yale blue blues / Take the 'A' train / Love for sale / Street of dreams / Jew's harp.
Notes: Live recordings made between 1970 and 1985 and dedicated to the memory of Billy Strayhorn and Duke Ellington. Personnel: Dizzy Gillespie-trumpet and Jew's harp/Dwike Mitchell-piano/ Willie Ruff-bass and French horn.
Album: released on Blackhawk, Jan'87 by Blackhawk Records (USA). Dist: IMS-Polygram

FREE RIDE.
Album: released on Pablo (USA), May'82 by Pablo Records (USA). Dist: Wellard, Chris, IMS-Polygram, BMG

Cassette: released on Pablo (USA), May'82 by Pablo Records (USA). Dist: Wellard, Chris, IMS-Polygram, BMG

GIANT, THE.
Notes: With Johnny Griffin etc.
Compact disc: released on Accord (France), '86 Dist: Discovery, Target

GILLESPIE JAM SESSIONS, THE.
Double Album: released on Verve, Aug'76 by Phonogram Records. Dist: Polygram

GOOD BAIT.
Album: released on Spotlite, May'83 by Spotlite Records. Dist: Cadillac, Jazz Music Spotlite

GREAT DIZZY GILLESPIE, THE.
Album: released on Joker (Import), Apr'81

GROOVIN' HIGH (Gillespie, Dizzy & His Sextets).
Album: released on Musicraft (USA), Oct'86 by Discovery Records (USA). Dist: Flexitron Distributors Ltd, Swift Distribution

IT HAPPENED ONE NIGHT (Gillespie, Dizzy/Ella Fitzgerald/Charlie Parker).

JAZZ MATURITY...WHERE ITS COMMING FROM (Gillespie, Dizzy/Roy Eldridge).
Album: released on Pablo (USA), May'82 by Pablo Records (USA). Dist: Wellard, Chris, IMS-Polygram, BMG

Cassette: released on Pablo (USA), May'82 by Pablo Records (USA). Dist: Wellard, Chris, IMS-Polygram, BMG

JUST BOP (Gillespie, Dizzy Sextet).
Album: released on Queen-Disc, Apr'81 Dist: Celtic Music, JSU, Jazz Horizons, Jazz Music

LIVE AT THE SHRINE AUDITORIUM (Gillespie, Dizzy Big Band).
Album: released on Queen-Disc (Import), Apr'81

MONTEREY 1961.
Album: released on Jazz-Legacy, Sep'79

MONTREUX 1980.
Compact disc: released on Pablo (USA), Apr'87 by Pablo Records (USA). Dist: Wellard, Chris, IMS-Polygram, BMG

NEW FACES.
Tracks: / Birk's works / Lorraine / Tin Tin Deo Tenor song / Ballad fiesta mojo / Every mornin'.
Compact disc: released on GRP (USA), Jul'85 by GRP Records (USA). Dist: IMS, Polygram

Album: released on GRP (USA), Jul'85 by GRP Records (USA). Dist: IMS, Polygram

Cassette: released on GRP (USA), Jul'85 by GRP Records (USA). Dist: IMS, Polygram

Compact disc: released on GRP (USA), Jul'85 by GRP Records (USA). Dist: IMS, Polygram

N.Y.C. 1952.
Album: released on Lotus (Import), Apr'81

ONE BASS HIT (Gillespie, Dizzy & His Orchestra).
Album: released on Musicraft (USA), Oct'86 by Discovery Records (USA). Dist: Flexitron Distributors Ltd, Swift Distribution

OOP-BOP SH'BAM (LIVE).
Album: released on Nostalgia (Sweden), Oct'82 by Wellard, Chris Distribution. Dist: Wellard, Chris Distribution

OO POP A DA (Gillespie, Dizzy Quartet).
Album: released on Affinity, Oct'85 by Charly Records. Dist: Charly, Cadillac

OSCAR PETERSON AND DIZZY GILLESPIE (Gillespie, Dizzy/Oscar Peterson).
Album: released on Pablo (USA), May'82 by Pablo Records (USA). Dist: Wellard, Chris, IMS-Polygram, BMG

Cassette: released on Pablo (USA), May'82 by Pablo Records (USA). Dist: Wellard, Chris, IMS-Polygram, BMG

Phoenix jazz fifth anniversary album

PLAYS AND RAPS IN HIS GREATEST CONCERT.
Album: released on Pablo, Jul'82 by Pablo Records. Dist: Wellard, Chris, IMS-Polygram, BMG

Cassette: released on Pablo, Jul'82 by Pablo Records. Dist: Wellard, Chris, IMS-Polygram, BMG

PLEYEL CONCERT 1953.
Tracks: / Champ, The / Tin tin dayo / They can't take that away from me / Good bait / Bluest blues, The / Birks works / I can't get started / On the sunny side of the street / Mon homme / Swing low sweet....Cadillac / School days / Ooshoo-be-do-be.
Compact disc: released on Vogue, Dec'86 Dist: Discovery, Jazz Music, PRT, Swift

PORTRAIT OF DUKE ELLINGTON, A (Gillespie, Dizzy & His Orchestra).
Album: released on Verve (USA), Jun'84 by Polydor. Dist: Polygram

Compact disc: released on Verve, Nov'84 by Phonogram Records. Dist: Polygram

PORTRAIT OF DUKE ELLINGTON.
Compact disc: released on Verve, Oct'84 by Phonogram Records. Dist: Polygram

PROFESSOR BOP.
Tracks: / Blue and boogie / Groovin' high / Dizzy atmosphere / All the things you are / Hot house / Ooh bop sh'bam / Our delight / Things to come / Ray's idea / Ray's idea / Emanon / Good dues blues.
Album: released on Charly, Mar'87 by Charly Records. Dist: Charly, Cadillac

Cassette: released on Charly, Mar'87 by Charly Records. Dist: Charly, Cadillac

Album: released on Atlantis, 11 Apr'87 by Charly Records. Dist: Charly

QUINTET IN EUROPE.
Album: released on Unique Jazz (Import), '81

QUINTET OF THE YEAR, THE (Gillespie, Dizzy/Parker/Powell/Mingus & Roach).
Album: released on Joker, '79 Dist: Counterpoint, Mainline, Record Services Distribution (Ireland)

SAVOY SESSION, THE (Gillespie, Dizzy & Dee Dee Days).
Double Album: released on Savoy (USA), Mar'85 by Arista Records. Dist: Polygram, Swift

SMALL GROUPS 1945-6, THE.
Album: released on Phoenix, Apr'81 by Audio Fidelity Enterprises. Dist: Stage One, Lugtons

SONNY SIDE UP (Gillespie, Dizzy & Sonny Rollins).
Notes: see also under Rollins,Sonny & Dizzy Gillespie
Compact disc: released on Polydor, Feb'87 by Polydor Records. Dist: Polygram, Polydor

SUMMERTIME (Gillespie, Dizzy & Mongo Santamaria).

Page 408

Album: released on Pablo (USA), '82 by Pablo Records (USA). Dist: Wellard, Chris, IMS-Polygram, BMG

Cassette: released on Pablo (USA), '82 by Pablo Records (USA). Dist: Wellard, Chris, IMS-Polygram, BMG

SWEET SOUL.
Album: released on Gateway (USA), Nov'79 by Gemcom Inc.(USA) Records.

Album: released on Pathe Marconi(France), Jan'85

Cassette: released on Pathe Marconi(France), Jan'85

SWING LOW SWEET CADILLAC.
Album: released on Jasmine, Jun'82 by Jasmine Records. Dist: Counterpoint, Lugtons, Taylor, H.R., Wellard, Chris, Swift, Cadillac

Cassette: released on Jasmine, Jun'82 by Jasmine Records. Dist: Counterpoint, Lugtons, Taylor, H.R., Wellard, Chris, Swift, Cadillac

Album: released on Impulse, Oct'85 by Impulse Records. Dist: MCA, Polygram

SWING LOW SWEET CHARIOT.
VOLUME 2 (Gillespie, Dizzy, Miles Davis, Charlie Parker).

Gillespie, Hugh
CLASSIC RECORDINGS OF IRISH TRADITIONAL FIDDLE MUSIC.
Album: released on Topic, '81 Dist: Roots Distribution

Gillies, Samantha
LET ME FEEL IT.
Tracks: / (Remix).
Single (7"): released on Greyhound, Nov'86 by Greyhound Records. Dist: PRT, Greyhound

Single (12"): released on Record Shack, Mar'85 by Record Shack Records. Dist: PRT

Gilley, Mickey
20 GOLDEN SONGS.
Album: released on Astan, Nov'84 by Astan Records. Dist: Counterpoint

Cassette: released on Astan, Nov'84 by Astan Records. Dist: Counterpoint

DOWN THE LINE.
Album: released on Charly, Jan'81 by Charly Records. Dist: Charly, Cadillac

FROM PASADENA WITH LOVE.
Album: released on Sundown, Jun'85 by Magnum Music Group Ltd. Dist: Magnum Music Group Ltd, PRT Distribution, Spartan Distribution

Cassette: released on Sundown, Jun'85 by Magnum Music Group Ltd. Dist: Magnum Music Group Ltd, PRT Distribution, Spartan Distribution

MICKEY AT GILLEY'S.
Album: released on Checkmate, Apr'78 Dist: I & B

MICKEY GILLEY I love country.
Tracks: / Headache tomorrow, A (or a heartache tonight).
Album: released on CBS, Mar'87 by CBS Records. Dist: CBS

Cassette: released on CBS, Mar'87 by CBS Records. Dist: CBS

Cassette: released on Audio Fidelity, Oct'84 Dist: PRT

THAT'S ALL THAT MATTERS TO ME.
Album: released on Epic, Dec'80 by CBS Records. Dist: CBS

Gilliam, Roberta
ALL I WANT IS MY BABY.
Tracks: / All I want is my baby / Until we sleep / Murder / Love on the air / Blue light / Out of the blue / All lovers are deranged / You know I'm right / Cruise / Let's get metaphysical / Near the end.
Single (7"): released on Warner Bros., Jan'86 by Warner Bros Records. Dist: WEA

Compact disc: released on Harvest, Aug'84 by EMI Records. Dist: Roots, EMI

Single (7"): released on Warner Bros., Jan'86 by Warner Bros Records. Dist: WEA

Gillies, Alasdair
ALL MY LIFE'S A CIRCLE.
Album: released on Country House, Dec'83 by BGS Productions Ltd. Dist: Taylor, H.R., Record Merchandisers Distribution, Pinnacle, Sounds of Scotland Records

Cassette: released on Country House, Dec'83 by BGS Productions Ltd. Dist: Taylor, H.R., Record Merchandisers Distribution, Pinnacle, Sounds of Scotland Records

AMONG MY SOUVENIRS.
Tracks: / Take me home / I dream of Jeannie / Among my souvenirs / I will love you all my life / Tak a dram / Scarlet ribbons / Scotland my home / Banners of Scotland, The / Bonnie Mary of Argyle / Say you'll stay until tomorrow / Beautiful dreamer / More than yesterday / Maggie / Messin' about on the river.
Album: released on Scotdisc, Dec'86 Dist: Clyde Factors Distributors

Cassette: released on Scotdisc, Dec'86 Dist: Clyde Factors Distributors

Compact disc: released on Scotdisc, Dec'86 Dist: Clyde Factors Distributors

BY COOL SILOAN.
Single (7"): released on Country House, Oct'79 by BGS Productions Ltd. Dist: Taylor, H.R., Record Merchandisers Distribution, Pinnacle, Sounds of Scotland Records

FAREWELL MY LOVE.
Cassette: released on PRT, Jan'78 by PRT Records.

LIVE AT EDEN COURT THEATRE, INVERNESS.
Double Album: released on Country House, Nov'79 by BGS Productions Ltd. Dist: Taylor, H.R., Record Merchandisers Distribution, Pinnacle, Sounds of Scotland Records
Cat. no: BGC 239

Cassette: released on Country House, Nov'79 by BGS Productions Ltd. Dist: Taylor, H.R., Record Merchandisers Distribution, Pinnacle, Sounds of Scotland Records

SCOTCH ON THE ROCKS.
Album: released on Pye, Dec'76

Cassette: released on Pye, Dec'76

SCOTTISH TRILOGY.
Single (7"): released on Country House, Jun'82 by BGS Productions Ltd. Dist: Taylor, H.R., Record Merchandisers Distribution, Pinnacle, Sounds of Scotland Records

SILVER AND GOLD.
Album: released on Scotdisc, Sep'84 Dist: Clyde Factors Distributors

Cassette: released on Scotdisc, Sep'84 Dist: Clyde Factors Distributors

WALTZING ROUND SCOTLAND.
Album: released on Country House, Jun'82 by BGS Productions Ltd. Dist: Taylor, H.R., Record Merchandisers Distribution, Pinnacle, Sounds of Scotland Records

Cassette: released on Country House, Jun'82 by BGS Productions Ltd. Dist: Taylor, H.R., Record Merchandisers Distribution, Pinnacle, Sounds of Scotland Records

Gillies, Anne Lorne
BELOVED SCOTLAND.
Album: released on Lochshore, Jun'84 by Klub Records. Dist: PRT

Cassette: released on Lochshore, Jun'84 by Klub Records. Dist: PRT

HILLS OF LORNE, THE.
Album: released on Lochshore, Jul'82 by Klub Records. Dist: PRT

Cassette: released on Lochshore, Jul'82 by Klub Records. Dist: PRT

LEGENDS OF SCOTLAND.
Cassette: released on Lochshore, Mar'87 by Klub Records. Dist: PRT

MILESTONE.
Album: released on Lochshore, Nov'82 by Klub Records. Dist: PRT

Cassette: released on Lochshore, Nov'82 by Klub Records. Dist: PRT

SINGS...THE SONGS OF THE GAEL.
Album: released on Lochshore, Jul'82 by Klub Records. Dist: PRT

Cassette: released on Lochsnore, Jul'82 by Klub Records. Dist: PRT

Gillies, Corrine
YOU DON'T KNOW WHERE YOUR INTEREST LIES.
Single (7"): released on Soul Stop, Aug'82 by Soul Stop Record 3. Dist: Spartan

Gillies, Stuart
AMANDA.
Single (7"): released on Old Gold, Jul'82 by Old Gold Records. Dist: Lightning, Jazz Music, Spartan, Counterpoint

Gillliom, Bobby
GIMME A BREAK.
Single (12"): released on NYC, Sep'83

Gill, John
FINGER BUSTER.
Album: released on Stomp Off, Jun'86 by Stomp Off Records. Dist: Jazz Music Distribution

Gill, Johnny
CAN'T WAIT TILL TOMORROW.
Tracks: / One small night.
Single (7"): released on Cotillion, Jun'85 by WEA Records. Dist: WEA

Single (12"): released on Cotillion, Jun'85 by WEA Records. Dist: WEA

CHEMISTRY.
Tracks: / Half crazy / Can't wait till tomorrow / Don't take away my pride / One small light / Way that you love me, The / Because of you / Chemistry / I found love.
Album: released on Cotillion (Import), Apr'85 by Atlantic Records. Dist: WEA

HALF CRAZY.
Tracks: / Super love.
Single (7"): released on WEA, Sep'85 by WEA Records. Dist: WEA

Single (12"): released on WEA, Sep'85 by WEA Records. Dist: WEA

Gill, Mike
FLEUR BLANCHE.
Single (7"): released on Gee Bee Music, Oct'82 by Gee Bee Records. Dist: Spartan

L.A. 84.
Single (7"): released on Gee Bee Music, Oct'83 by Gee Bee Records. Dist: Spartan

Gillum, Jazz
1935-1946.
Notes: Recorded in mono.
Album: released on B.O.B., Jan'87 Dist: Swift

Gill, Vince
TURN ME LOOSE.
Single (7"): released on RCA, Mar'85 by RCA Records. Dist: RCA, Roots, Swift, Wellard, Chris, I & B, Solomon & Peres Distribution

VINCE GILL.
Album: released on RCA, Apr'85 by RCA Records. Dist: RCA, Roots, Swift, Wellard, Chris, I & B, Solomon & Peres Distribution

Cassette: released on RCA, Apr'85 by RCA Records. Dist: RCA, Roots, Swift, Wellard, Chris, I & B, Solomon & Peres Distribution

Gilmer, Jimmy
SUGAR SHACK.
Single (7"): released on Creole (Reissue), Aug'82 by Creole Records. Dist: PRT, Rhino

Gilmour, David
ABOUT FACE.
Tracks: / Until we sleep / Murder / Love on the air / Blue light / Out of the blue / All lovers are deranged / You know I'm right / Cruise / Let's get metaphysical / Near the end.
Notes: Produced by David Gilmour and Bob Ezrin. A 1984 Original Sound Recording made by Pink Floyd Music Ltd./EMI Records Ltd.
Album: released on Fame, Mar'87 by Music For Pleasure Records. Dist: EMI

Cassette: released on Fame, Mar'87 by Music For Pleasure Records. Dist: EMI

Album: released on Harvest, '84 by EMI Records. Dist: Roots, EMI

Cassette: released on Harvest, '84 by EMI Records. Dist: Roots, EMI

Compact disc: released on Harvest, '84 by EMI Records. Dist: Roots, EMI

DAVID GILMOUR.
Album: released on Fame (Harvest), '83 by Music For Pleasure Records. Dist: EMI

Cassette: released on Fame (Harvest), '83 by Music For Pleasure Records. Dist: EMI

LOVE ON THE AIR.
Single (7"): released on Harvest, '84 by EMI Records. Dist: Roots, EMI

Single (12"): released on Harvest, '84 by EMI Records. Dist: Roots, EMI

Gilmour, Jon
GONNA DIE WITH A SMILE IF IT KILLS ME.
Album: released on Philo (USA), Apr'86

Gilroy
HOW CAN YOU SAY IT SOBER.
Single (12"): released on Private Eye, '85 by Private Eye Records. Dist: Jetstar

Giltrap, Gordon
AIRWAVES.
Album: released on PVK, '82

CHI-MAI/AFTER THE STORM.
Single (7"): released on PVK, '81

ELEGY.
Album: released on Filmtrax, Jun'87 by Filmtrax Records. Dist: EMI

Cassette: released on Filmtrax, Jun'87 by Filmtrax Records. Dist: EMI

FEAR OF THE DARK.
Album: released on Electric-Cube, '81 by Dakota. Dist: PRT

Cassette: released on Electric-Cube, '81 by Dakota. Dist: PRT

HOCUS POCUS.
Single (7"): released on PVK, Jul'81

LIVE.
Album: released on Electric, Oct'81 by Dakota. Dist: PRT

MAGPIE RAG/GYPSY LANE.
Single (7"): released on PVK, Mar'81

PEACOCK PARTY.
Album: released on PVK, Feb'81

Cassette: released on PVK, Feb'81

PERILOUS JOURNEY.
Album: released on Electric-Cube, Oct'81 by Dakota. Dist: PRT

Cassette: released on Electric-Cube, Oct'81 by Dakota. Dist: PRT

PLATINUM COLLECTION.
Album: released on Cube (Platinum coll), Oct'81

Cassette: released on Cube (Platinum coll), Oct'81

SUNBURST/HEADWIND.
Single (7"): released on PVK, Feb'82

VISIONARY.
Album: released on Electric-Cube, Oct'81 by Dakota. Dist: PRT

Cassette: released on Electric-Cube, Oct'81 by Dakota. Dist: PRT

Giltrap, Joe
MR TAMBOURINE MAN (Giltrap, Joe Band).
Tracks: / Mr Tambourine man / When Margaret was 11.
Single (7"): released on Play, Jul'87 by Play Records. Dist: Spartan

Gina
CAN'T STOP.
Single (7"): released on President, Jun'87 by President Records. Dist: Taylors, Spartan

THIS LOVE/VERSION.
Single (12"): released on Judas, Jul'82

Gina X
DRIVE MY CAR.
Single (7"): released on Statik, Aug'84 Dist: Rough Trade Distribution, Stage One Distribution

Single (12"): released on Statik, Aug'84 Dist: Rough Trade Distribution, Stage One Distribution

HARLEY DAVIDSON(ENGLISH VERSION).
Single (7"): released on Statik, Oct'84 Dist: Rough Trade Distribution, Stage One Distribution

Single (12"): released on Statik, Oct'84 Dist: Rough Trade Distribution, Stage One Distribution

NICE MOVER.
Album: released on Statik, Jul'86 Dist: Rough Trade Distribution, Stage One Distribution

NO GDM.
Single (7"): released on Statik, Mar'85 Dist: Rough Trade Distribution, Stage One Distribution

Single (12"): released on Statik, Mar'85 Dist: Rough Trade Distribution, Stage One Distribution

YINGLISH.
Album: released on Statik, Nov'84 Dist: Rough Trade Distribution, Stage One Distribution

Cassette: released on Statik, Nov'84 Dist: Rough Trade Distribution, Stage One Distribu-

Gingerbread

CHRISTMAS TIME.
Single (7"): released on RCA, Nov'85 by RCA Records. Dist: RCA, Roots, Swift, Wellard, Chris, I & B, Solomon & Peres Distribution

Single (12"): released on RCA, Nov'85 by RCA Records. Dist: RCA, Roots, Swift, Wellard, Chris, I & B, Solomon & Peres Distribution

Gingerbread man

GINGERBREAD MAN, THE (Hampshire, Susan).
Cassette: released on Storytime Cassettes, Aug'83

Ginger, Debbie

DOLLY Partons greatest hits.
Cassette: released on Bibi, Jan'82

Ginger, William

TONIGHT IS MY NIGHT OUT.
Single (12"): released on Disco Rocker, May'82

Ginnette

SEA OF HEARTBREAK.
Single (7"): released on Pastafont, Apr'83 by Pastafont Records.

Gino Vess

PALE BLUE WINDSCREEN.
Single (12"): released on One Track, Jun'84 by One Track Records. Dist: Red Rhino Distribution, Cartel Distribution

Ginsberg, Alan

WORLDS GREATEST POETS America today.
Album: released on Peerless, Jan'75

Ginsburg, Arnie

CRUISIN' 1961 WMEX Boston.
Cassette: released on Increase(USA), Jun'87 by Quicksilver Records (USA).

G. I. Orange

FIGHT AWAY THE LOVER.
Single (7"): released on EMI, Jun'84 by EMI Records. Dist: EMI

Giordano, Steve

DAYBREAK.
Album: released on Muse, Apr'81 by Peerless Records. Dist: Lugtons Distributors

Giraffe In Flames

GIRAFFE IN FLAMES various artists (Various Artists).
Album: released on AAZ, Sep'85 by AAZ Records. Dist: Red Rhino, Cartel

Girard, Chuck

CHUCK GIRARD.
Album: released on Good News (USA), May'82 by Word Records. Dist: Word Distribution

Cassette: released on Good News (USA), May'82 by Word Records. Dist: Word Distribution

---

GLOW IN THE DARK.
Album: released on Good News (USA), May'82 by Word Records. Dist: Word Distribution

Cassette: released on Good News (USA), May'82 by Word Records. Dist: Word Distribution

---

NAME ABOVE ALL NAMES, THE.
Album: released on Myrrh, May'84 by Word Records. Dist: Word Distribution

Cassette: released on Myrrh, May'84 by Word Records. Dist: Word Distribution

---

STAND, THE.
Album: released on Myrrh, May'82 by Word Records. Dist: Word Distribution

Cassette: released on Myrrh, May'82 by Word Records. Dist: Word Distribution

---

TAKE IT EASY.
Album: released on Myrrh, May'82 by Word Records. Dist: Word Distribution

Cassette: released on Myrrh, May'82 by Word Records. Dist: Word Distribution

---

WRITTEN ON THE WIND.
Album: released on Good News (USA), May'82 by Word Records. Dist: Word Distribution

Cassette: released on Good News (USA), May'82 by Word Records. Dist: Word Distribution

Girl

SHEER GREED.
Album: released on Jet, Jan'80 by Jet Records. Dist: CBS

Cassette: released on Jet, Jan'80 by Jet Records. Dist: CBS

Girl Called Johnny

HELLO IT IS'NT ME.
Tracks: / Shallow.
Single (7"): released on 10, Nov'86 by 10 Records. Dist: Virgin, EMI

Single (12"): released on Ten, Nov'86

Girl Can't Help It

BABY DOLL.
Single (7"): released on Virgin, Oct'82 by Virgin Records. Dist: EMI, Virgin Distribution

Single (12"): released on Virgin, Oct'82 by Virgin Records. Dist: EMI, Virgin Distribution

Cassette: released on Chivers Audio Books, '81 by Chivers Sound & Vision. Dist: Chivers Sound & Vision

Girl Groups

GIRL GROUPS various artists (Various Artists).
Album: released on Mercury (USA), Nov'81 by Import Records. Dist: IMS Distribution, Polygram Distribution

Cassette: released on Mercury (USA), Nov'81 by Import Records. Dist: IMS Distribution, Polygram Distribution

---

GIRL GROUPS OF THE 60'S various artists (Various Artists).
Cassette: released on K-Tel Goldmasters, Aug'84 by K-Tel Records. Dist: K-Tel

---

GIRL GROUPS OF THE SIXTIES (Various Artists).
Compact disc: released on K-Tel, '86 by K-Tel Records. Dist: Record Merchandisers Distribution, Taylors, Terry Blood Distribution, Wynd-Up Distribution, Relay Distribution, Pickwick Distribution, Solomon & Peres Distribution, Polygram

---

GIRL GROUPS (THE STORY OF A SOUND) various artists (Various Artists).
Album: released on Motown, Mar'84 by Motown Records. Dist: BMG Distribution

Cassette: released on Motown, Mar'84 by Motown Records. Dist: BMG Distribution

Girl Guides

20 TRADITIONAL CRISTMAS CAROLS.
Album: by BBC Records & Tapes. Dist: EMI, PRT, Pye

SING FOR JOY.
Album: by BBC Records & Tapes. Dist: EMI, PRT, Pye

Girl Most Likely

GIRL MOST LIKELY , THE Musical (Various Artists).
Notes: Jane Powell in a delightful musical, as a girl who can't decide which of her 3 fiancees to marry!
Video-cassette (VHS): released on Video Collection, May'87 by Video Collection Records. Dist: Counterpoint

Girls

CLAP CLAP.
Single (7"): released on Aura, Jul'82 by Hollywood Nites Distribution. Dist: Pinnacle

---

GIRLS ABOUT TOWN various artists (Various Artists).
Album: released on Impact, Sep'85 by Ace Records. Dist: Rough Trade, Pinnacle, Swift, Backs, Counterpoint, Jungle, Hotshot, Cartel

---

GIRLS CAN'T HELP IT various artists (Various Artists).
Album: by Rhino Records (USA). Deleted Feb'85.

GIRLS, GIRLS, GIRLS various artists (Various Artists).
Cassette: released on Autograph, Apr'85 Dist: Record Services Distribution (Ireland)

GIRLS WITH SOUL various artists (Various Artists).
Album: released on Stax, Aug'81 by Ace Records. Dist: Pinnacle, Chris Wellard, IMS-Polygram

Cassette: released on Stax, Aug'81 by Ace Records. Dist: Pinnacle, Chris Wellard, IMS-Polygram

---

SALLY GO ROUND THE ROSES.
Single (7"): released on Aura, Aug'82 by Hol-

Girls are rockin'

GIRLS ARE ROCKIN', THE Various artists (Various Artists).
Album: released on White, Aug'87. Estim retail price in Sep'87 was £5.99.

Girls At Our Best

FAST BOYFRIENDS.
Single (7"): released on Happy Birthday, Oct'81 Dist: Stage One

---

GO FOR GOLD.
Single (7"): released on Happy Birthday, Jun'81 Dist: Stage One

---

HEAVEN.
Single (7"): released on Go Discs, May'82 by Go Discs Records. Dist: CBS Distribution

---

PEEL SESSION 17.2.81.
Single (12"): released on Strange Fruit, Jun'87 by Clive Selwood. Dist: Pinnacle

---

POLITICS.
Single (7"): released on Rough Trade, Nov'80 by Rough Trade Records. Dist: Rough Trade Distribution, Cartel Distribution

Girlschool

I'M THE LEADER OF THE GANG (I AM) (Girlschool & Gary Glitter).
Single (7"): released on GWR, May'86 by GWR Records. Dist: RCA

Single (12"): released on GWR, May'86 by GWR Records. Dist: RCA

PLAY DIRTY LIVE.
Notes: A live set from the UK's foremost all-girl heavy metal band, featuring 14 tracks mostly from their last album. 1984 production.
Video-cassette (VHS): released on Polygram, Jun'86 by Polygram Records. Dist: Polygram

Video-cassette [Betamax]: released on Polygram, Jun'86 by Polygram Records. Dist: Polygram

---

RACE WITH THE DEVIL.
Tracks: / 1-2-3-4 Rock & roll / Furniture fire / Take it all away / Kick it down / Kick it down / Midnight ride / Race with the devil / Play dirty / Yeah right / Emergency / Breakout (knob in the media) / Flesh and blood / Tush / Don't stop / Future flash / Rock me shock me / Screaming blue murder / Wild life / Bomber / Nothing to lose / Live with me / Like it like that / Tonight / Take it from me.
Album: released on Raw Power, Apr'86 Dist: Pinnacle

Cassette: released on Raw Power, Apr'86 Dist: Pinnacle

SCREAMING BLUE MURDER.
Album: released on Bronze, May'82 by Polygram Records. Dist: Polydor

Cassette: released on Bronze, May'82 by Polygram Records. Dist: Polydor Deleted '83.

TAKE IT ALL AWAY.
Single (7"): released on City, Sep'81 by City Records. Dist: Pinnacle

Girls Just Wanna Have Fun

GIRLS JUST WANNA HAVE FUN Original soundtrack.
Compact disc: by Phonogram Records. Dist: Polygram

Girl Talk

FALLING FOR YOU.
Single (7"): released on WEA, Jan'87 by WEA Records. Dist: WEA

Single (12"): released on WEA, Jan'87 by WEA Records. Dist: WEA

GIRL TALK (Various Artists).
Tracks: / Lullaby of Birdland / Easy to love / Foggy day, A / He's got the whole world in his hands / You're driving me crazy / Take the 'A' train / I hear music / For all we know / Route 66 / Is you is or is you ain't my baby / Out of this world / Old devil moon / You're blase / Tiptoe gently / From this moment on* / Misery * / Don't worry about me* / Sometimes I feel like a motherless child * / African mailman * / September in the rain *.
Album: released on Atlantis, Aug'87 by Charly Records. Dist: Charly

Cassette: released on Atlantis, Aug'87 by Charly Records. Dist: Charly

Compact disc: released on Charly, Aug'87 by Charly Records. Dist: Charly, Cadillac

---

I WILL GIVE YOU LOVE.
Tracks: / I will give you love / I will give you love (inst) / Drum me up some love (inst).
Single (7"): released on WEA, 13 Jun'87 by WEA Records. Dist: WEA

Single (12"): released on WEA, 13 Jun'87 by

Girl Who Pretended...

GIRL WHO PRETENDED TO BE A BOY (Fullerton, Fiona).
Cassette: released on Listen Productions, Nov'84 Dist: H.R. Taylor, Hayward Promotions Distribution

Girly

WORKING GIRL (ONE WAY LOVE AFFAIR).
Single (12"): released on ZYX (Germany), Nov'85 by ZYX Records. Dist: Greyhound

Girl Zone

GIRL ZONE Various artists (Various Artists).
Album: released on Impact, May'86 by Ace Records. Dist: Rough Trade, Pinnacle, Swift, Backs, Counterpoint, Jungle, Hotshot, Cartel
Cat. no: **ACT 008**

Single (7"): released on State, Dec'82 by State Records.

Gish,Lillian

TALE OF THE SHINING PRINCESS,THE Spoken Word.
Cassette: released on Caedmon(USA), Apr'83 by Caedmon (USA) Records. Dist: Gower, Taylors, Discovery

---

DUAS VOZES (Gismonti, Egberto & Nana Vasconcelos).
Tracks: / Aquarela do Brasil / Rio De Janeiro / Tomarapeba / Dancando / Fogueira / Bianca / Don Quixote / O Dia / A Noite.
Compact disc: released on ECM (Germany), Apr'86 by ECM Records. Dist: IMS, Polygram, Virgin through EMI

SANFONA.
Album: released on ECM, Dec'81 by ECM Records. Dist: IMS, Polygram, Virgin through EMI

SOL DO MEIO DIA.
Tracks: / Palacio de pinturas / Raga / Kalimba / Coracao / Cafe / Sapain / Dance solitaria No.2 / Baiao Malandro.
Notes: Personnel: Egberto Gismonti/Nana Vasconcelos/Ralph Towner/Collin Walcott/Jan Garbarek
Compact disc: released on ECM (Germany), Jun'86 by ECM Records. Dist: IMS, Polygram, Virgin through EMI

SOLO.
Tracks: / Selva Amazonica / Pau Rolou / And zero / Frevo / Salvador / Ciranda Nordestina.
Compact disc: released on ECM (Germany), Dec'85 by ECM Records. Dist: IMS, Polygram, Virgin through EMI

WORKS.
Tracks: / Loro / Gismonti / Mauro senise / Zeca assumpcao / Nene raga / Gismonti / Vasconcelos / Collin Walcott / Ciranda nordestina / Magico / Gismonti / Garbarek / Charlie Haden / Maracutu / Gismonti / Mauro senise / Zera assumpcao / Nene salvador.
Compact disc: released on ECM (Germany), Nov'84 by ECM Records. Dist: IMS, Polygram, Virgin through EMI

Cassette: released on ECM (Germany), Nov'83 by ECM Records. Dist: IMS, Polygram, Virgin through EMI

Album: released on ECM (Germany), Nov'84 by ECM Records. Dist: IMS, Polygram, Virgin through EMI

Gist

EMBRACE THE HERD.
Album: released on Rough Trade, May'83 by Rough Trade Records. Dist: Rough Trade Distribution, Cartel Distribution

---

FOOL FOR A VALENTINE.
Single (7"): released on Rough Trade, Feb'83 by Rough Trade Records. Dist: Rough Trade Distribution, Cartel Distribution

---

LOVE AT FIRST SIGHT.
Single (7"): released on Rough Trade, Jun'82 by Rough Trade Records. Dist: Rough Trade Distribution, Cartel Distribution

---

THIS IS LOVE.
Single (7"): released on Rough Trade, Nov'80 by Rough Trade Records. Dist: Rough Trade Distribution, Cartel Distribution

Giuffre, Jimmy

AD LIB (Giuffre, Jimmy 4, The).
Album: released on Verve, Mar'81 by Phonogram Records. Dist: Polygram

---

EASY WAY, THE (Giuffre, Jimmy Three).
Album: released on Verve (USA), Mar'82 by Polydor. Dist: Polygram

---

FOUR BROTHERS.
Album: released on Affinity, Dec'81 by Charly Records. Dist: Charly, Cadillac

IN CONCERT (Giuffre, Jimmy Trio).
Album: released on Unique Jazz, Apr'81 Dist: Swift, Jazz Music, Jazz Horizons

QUARTET IN PERSON.
Album: released on Verve (USA), Mar'83 by Polydor. Dist: Polygram

QUASAR (Giuffre, Jimmy 4, The).
Compact disc: released on Soul Note (Italy), '86 Dist: Harmonia Mundi Distributors

TANGENTS IN JAZZ.
Album: released on Affinity, Apr'81 by Charly Records. Dist: Charly, Cadillac

THESIS (Giuffre, Jimmy Three).
Album: released on Verve (USA), Jun'81 by Polydor. Dist: Polygram

WEST COAST SCENE (Giuffre, Jimmy/M. Paich Octet).

Giuffria
CALL TO THE HEART.
Single (7"): released on MCA, Mar'85 by MCA Records. Dist: Polygram, MCA

Single (12"): released on MCA, Mar'85 by MCA Records. Dist: Polygram, MCA

Double-pack single: released on MCA, Mar'85 by MCA Records. Dist: Polygram, MCA

GIUFFRIA.
Album: released on MCA, Mar'87 by MCA Records. Dist: Polygram, MCA

Cassette: released on MCA, Mar'87 by MCA Records. Dist: Polygram, MCA

Album: released on MCA, Feb'85 by MCA Records. Dist: Polygram, MCA

Cassette: released on MCA, Feb'85 by MCA Records. Dist: Polygram, MCA

SILK AND STEEL.
Album: released on MCA, Aug'86 by MCA Records. Dist: Polygram, MCA

Cassette: released on MCA, Aug'86 by MCA Records. Dist: Polygram, MCA

G. Kenny
CHAMPAGNE.
Tracks: / Champagne / What does it take / Hi, how ya doin?.
Single (7"): released on Arista, Nov'86 by Arista Records. Dist: RCA

Single (12"): released on Arista, Nov'86 by Arista Records. Dist: RCA

DUOTONES.
Tracks: / Don't make me wait for love / You make me believe / Slip of the tongue / What does it take to win your love / What does it take (to win your love) / Don't make me wait for love / Sade / Esther / Slip of the tongue / Songbird / Champagne / You make me believe / Midnight / Three of a kind.
Notes: see also under Kenny G
Compact disc: released on Arista, Dec'86 by Arista Records. Dist: RCA

Album: released on Arista, Sep'86 by Arista Records. Dist: RCA

Cassette: released on Arista, Sep'86 by Arista Records. Dist: RCA

G FORCE.
Album: released on Arista, Mar'84 by Arista Records. Dist: RCA

Cassette: released on Arista, Mar'84 by Arista Records. Dist: RCA

GRAVITY.
Album: released on Arista, May'85 by Arista Records. Dist: RCA

Cassette: released on Arista, May'85 by Arista Records. Dist: RCA

HI HOW YA DOIN'.
Single (7"): released on Arista, Mar'84 by Arista Records. Dist: RCA

Single (12"): released on Arista, Mar'84 by Arista Records. Dist: RCA

HI HOW YA DOIN' (REMIX).
Single (7"): released on Arista, Jun'84 by Arista Records. Dist: RCA

Single (12"): released on Arista, Jun'84 by Arista Records. Dist: RCA

Picture disc single: released on Arista, Aug'84 by Arista Records. Dist: RCA

LOVE ON THE RISE (G. Kenny & Kashif).
Single (7"): released on Arista, May'85 by Arista Records. Dist: RCA

Single (12"): released on Arista, May'85 by Arista Records. Dist: RCA

SONGBIRD.
Tracks: / Songbird / Midnight motion / Songbird (ext.)
Single (7"): released on Arista, May'87 by Arista Records. Dist: RCA

Single (12"): released on Arista, May'87 by Arista Records. Dist: RCA

SONGBIRD (FULL LENGTH VERSION).
Tracks: / Songbird / Midnight motion.
Single (7"): released on Arista, Jul'87 by Arista Records. Dist: RCA

WHAT DOES IT TAKE TO WIN YOUR LOVE.
Tracks: / What does it take to win your love / Songbird.
Single (7"): released on Arista, Aug'86 by Arista Records. Dist: RCA

Single (12"): released on Arista, Aug'86 by Arista Records. Dist: RCA

Glackin, Paddy
DOUBLIN (Glackin, Paddy & Paddy Keenan).
Album: released on Tara (Ireland), '82 by Tara Records. Dist: I & B Records Distribution, Record Services Distribution (Ireland), Roots Distribution

Cassette: released on Tara (Ireland), '82 by Tara Records. Dist: I & B Records Distribution, Record Services Distribution (Ireland), Roots Distribution

HIDDEN GROUND (Glackin, Paddy & Jolyon Jackson).
Album: released on Tara (Ireland), '82 by Tara Records. Dist: I & B Records Distribution, Record Services Distribution (Ireland), Roots Distribution

Cassette: released on Tara (Ireland), '82 by Tara Records. Dist: I & B Records Distribution, Record Services Distribution (Ireland), Roots Distribution

Gladiators
CAN'T STOP RIGHTNESS.
Single (12"): released on Hitbound, May'83 by Hitbound Records. Dist: Jetstar

MASS CHARLEY.
Single (12"): released on Sun Set, Jul'83 by Sun Set Records. Dist: Jetstar Distribution

NATURALITY.
Album: released on Frontline (USA), Feb'79 by Calvary Records Inc. (USA). Dist: EMI

SERIOUS THING.
Album: released on Nighthawk, Nov'84 by Faulty Products Distrib. Dist: Pinnacle, Swift

Glad Rags
GLAD RAGS Various composers (Labeque, Katia & Maria).
Tracks: / Rialto ripples / Honky-tonk-a-rhythmical absurdity / Carolina shout / Entertainer, The / Antoinette / Magnetic rag / Maple leaf rag / Elite syncopations / Strenuous life / Stop time / Bethena.
Notes: Featuring: Katia & Maria Labeque (Two pianos). Produced by John Mc Laughlin. All arrangements by Francois Jeanneau.
Compact disc: released on EMI, Dec'84 by EMI Records. Dist: EMI

Gladwin, Joe
WHAT HAVE THEY DONE TO MY CHRISTMAS.
Single (7"): released on Rialto, Nov'82 by Rialto Records. Dist: Pinnacle

Glahe, Wil
GOLD ALBUM.
Album: released on Teldec (Germany), Sep'84 by Import Records. Dist: IMS Distribution, Polygram Distribution

Cassette: released on Teldec (Germany), Sep'84 by Import Records. Dist: IMS Distribution, Polygram Distribution

Glaser, Jim
AT THE COUNTRY STORE.
Album: released on Country Store, Dec'85 by Starblend Records. Dist: PRT, Prism Leisure Corporation Records

Cassette: released on Country Store, Dec'85 by Starblend Records. Dist: PRT, Prism Leisure Corporation Records

MAN IN THE MIRROR.
Tracks: / When you're not a lady / You're gettin' to me again / You got me running / Pretend / Woman, woman / I'd love to see you again / Close friends / If I could only dance with you / Let me down easy / Stand by the road / Man in the mirror, The.
Album: released on MCA Import, May'86 by MCA Records. Dist: Polygram, IMS

MAN IN THE MIRROR, THE.
Album: released on Range, Apr'84 by PRT, Jetstar

PAST THE POINT OF NO RETURN.
Tracks: / Merry-go-round / Those days / Tough act to follow / love of my woman, The / Early morning love / You were gone before you said goodbye / I'll be your fool tonight / Past the point of no return / In another minute / It's not easy / If I don't love you.
Album: released on MCA Import, Mar'86 by MCA Records. Dist: Polygram, IMS

WHO WERE YOU THINKING OF.
Single (7"):

WOMAN WOMAN.
Single (7"): released on Range, Apr'84 Dist: PRT, Jetstar

Glaser, Tompall
NIGHTS ON THE BORDERLINE.
Tracks: / Night on the border / Mamma don't let you big boy play outside / I cried a mile (for your inch I laughed) / Put another log on the fire / Up where we belong / I don't care anymore / Auction, The / Lovely Lucy / Streets of Baltimore, The / Til the right one comes along.
Album: released on MCA Import, Mar'86 by MCA Records. Dist: Polygram, IMS

TOMPALL GLASER.
Album: released on MCA, Mar'87 by MCA Records. Dist: Polygram, MCA

Cassette: released on MCA, Mar'87 by MCA Records. Dist: Polygram, MCA

Glasgow
STRANDED.
Single (7"): released on Neat, May'84 by Neat Records. Dist: Pinnacle, Neat

Glasgow, Alex
NORTHERN DRIFT (Glasgow, Alex & Henry Livings).
Album: released on MWM, Jun'82 by Mawson & Wareham. Dist: Spartan Distribution, Jazz Music Distribution, JSU Distribution

SONGS OF ALEX GLASGOW.
Album: released on MWM, Jun'82 by Mawson & Wareham. Dist: Spartan Distribution, Jazz Music Distribution, JSU Distribution

SONGS OF ALEX GLASGOW, TWO.
Album: released on MWM, Jun'82 by Mawson & Wareham. Dist: Spartan Distribution, Jazz Music Distribution, JSU Distribution

SONGS OF ALEX GLASGOW, THREE (Glasgow, Alex & the Northern Sinfonia Orchestra).
Album: released on Rubber, Jun'82 by Rubber Records. Dist: Roots Distribution, Projection Distribution, Jazz Music Distribution, Celtic Music Distribution, JSU Distribution, Spartan Distribution

Glasgow Caledonian
FIDDLES GALORE.
Album: released on Lismor, Nov'76 by Lismor Records. Dist: Lismor, Roots, Celtic Music

IN CONCERT.
Album: released on Lismor, '84 by Lismor Records. Dist: Lismor, Roots, Celtic Music

Cassette: released on Lismor, '84 by Lismor Records. Dist: Lismor, Roots, Celtic Music

Glasgow, Cheryl
EVEN NOW (I NEED YOU).
Single (7"): released on Code, Jun'84 by Code Records. Dist: Jetstar, EMI

Single (12"): released on Code, Jun'84 by Code Records. Dist: Jetstar, EMI

GLUED TO THE SPOT.
Tracks: / Glued to the spot (instrumental) / Glued to the spot / Losing the battle.
Single (12"): released on Live, Jan'87 Dist: Jetstar, PRT

Single (12"): released on Live, Jul'87 Dist: Jetstar, PRT

Single (12"): released on Alive, Aug'87 Dist: WRPM

Glasgow, Deborah
DON'T STAY AWAY.
Tracks: / Don't stay away / Knight in shining armour / Don't stay away (P.A.Mix/instrumental).
Single (7"): released on UK Bubblers-Greensleeves, Mar'87

Single (12"): released on UK Bubblers-Greensleeves, Mar'87

KNIGHT IN SHINING ARMOUR.
Tracks: / Knight in shining armour / Knight in shining armour (inst).
Single (7"): released on UK Bubblers-Greensleeves, Oct'86

YOU'RE MY SUGAR.
Tracks: / You're my sugar / You're my sugar (inst).
Single (12"): released on UK Bubblers, May'86 by Greensleeves Records. Dist: RCA, Jetstar

Glasgow Islay...
IT'S GOODBYE TO CARE (Glasgow Islay Gailic Choir).
Album: released on Lochshore, Oct'83 by Klub Records. Dist: PRT

Cassette: released on Lochshore, Oct'83 by Klub Records. Dist: PRT

Glasgow Phoenix Choir
INSPIRATIONAL BEST, THE.
Album: released on Word 20, May'82

Cassette: released on Word 20, May'82

Glasgow Police
...MARCH PAST.
Album: by Wax Records. Dist: Pinnacle

Glasgow Police Pipe Band
SCOTLAND'S BEST VOL 1 (City Of Glasgow Police Pipe Band).
Album: released on Emerald (Ireland), Nov'84 by Emerald Records. Dist: I & B, Ross, PRT

Cassette: released on Emerald (Ireland), Nov'84 by Emerald Records. Dist: I & B, Ross, PRT

Glasgow Skye Pipe...
MEN FROM SKYE, THE (Glasgow Skye Pipe Band Association).
Album: released on Klub, Jul'81

Cassette: released on Klub, Jul'81

Glasgow & Strathclyde...
GLASGOW & STRATHCLYDE UNIVERSITY OTC PIPE BAND.
Cassette: released on Lismor, Jul'77 by Lismor Records. Dist: Lismor, Roots, Celtic Music

Glass Axe
GLASS AXE/WICKED PRINCE, THE (Dotrice, Michele).
Cassette: released on Listen Productions, Nov'84 Dist: H.R. Taylor, Hayward Promotions Distribution

Glass Beat Came
PLEASURE.
Tracks: / Tell me.
Single (7"): released on Influx, Dec'86 Dist: DMS, RCA

Glass House
CRUMBS OFF THE TABLE.
Single (7"): released on HDH(Holland/Dozier/Holland), Dec'84 by Demon Records. Dist: Pinnacle

DEATH IN A ROLLS ROYCE.
Single (7"): released on Coach House, Aug'82

Glass Museum
DAY TRIPPER.
Single (7"): released on RGM, Nov'83 by RGM Records. Dist: Pinnacle

Single (12"): released on RGM, Nov'83 by RGM Records. Dist: Pinnacle

FRIEND DEPARTED.
Single (7"): released on RGM, Mar'84 by RGM Records. Dist: Pinnacle

FUTURE.
Single (7"): released on RGM, Aug'83 by RGM Records. Dist: Pinnacle

Single (12"): released on RGM, Aug'83 by RGM Records. Dist: Pinnacle

GLASS MUSEUM.
Album: released on RGM, Jan'84 by RGM Records. Dist: Pinnacle

Glasso, Michael
SCENES.
Album: released on ECM (Germany), Mar'83 by ECM Records. Dist: IMS, Polygram, Virgin through EMI

Glass, Philip
DANCE PIECES.
Tracks: / In the upper room / Dance 1 / Dance II / Dance V / Dance VIII / Dance IX / Glasspieces / Glasspiece I / Glasspiece II / Glasspiece III.
Compact disc: released on CBS, Jun'87 by CBS Records. Dist: CBS

Album: released on CBS, May'87 by CBS Rec-

ords. Dist: CBS

Cassette: released on CBS, May'87 by CBS Records. Dist: CBS

FACADE.
Single (7"): released on Epic, May'83 by CBS Records. Dist: CBS

FREEZING (Glass, Philip & Linda Ronstadt).
Tracks: / Freezing / Lightning.
Single (7"): released on Portrait, May'86 by CBS Records. Dist: CBS

Single (12"): released on Portrait, May'86 by CBS Records. Dist: CBS

GLASSWORKS.
Album: released on CBS, Jun'82 by CBS Records. Dist: CBS

Cassette: released on CBS, Jun'82 by CBS Records. Dist: CBS

KOYAANISQATSI.
Tracks: / Opening / Vessels / Cloud / Pruitt egoe 5.15 / Closing.
Notes: All tracks published by: Dunvagen Music Publishers/MCPS
Compact disc: released on Island, Sep'86 by Island Records. Dist: Polygram

Album: released on Island, Jul'83 by Island Records. Dist: Polygram

Cassette: released on Island, Jul'83 by Island Records. Dist: Polygram

MISHIMA.
Compact disc: released on Nonsuch, Dec'85

MUSIC IN 12 PARTS.
Notes: i
Cassette: released on Charisma, Oct'86 by Virgin Records. Dist: EMI

NORTH STAR.
Tracks: / Etoile polaire (north star) / Victor's lament / River run / Mon pere - mon pere / Are years what / (For Marianne Moore) / Lady day / Ange des orages / Ave / IKook / Montage.
Album: released on Virgin, Oct'86 by Virgin Records. Dist: EMI, Virgin Distribution

Cassette: released on Virgin, Oct'86 by Virgin Records. Dist: EMI, Virgin Distribution

Compact disc: released on Virgin, Nov'86 by Virgin Records. Dist: EMI, Virgin Distribution

PHOTOGRAPHER, THE.
Album: released on Epic, Jun'83 by CBS Records. Dist: CBS

Cassette: released on Epic, Jun'83 by CBS Records. Dist: CBS Deleted '86.

SOLO MUSIC.
Album: released on Shandar, Mar'78

Glass Ties

VIEWS FROM OTHER BRIDGES.
Single (7"): released on EMI, Sep'82 by EMI Records. Dist: EMI

YOU YOU YOU.
Single (7"): released on EMI, Feb'83 by EMI Records. Dist: EMI

Single (12"): released on EMI, Feb'83 by EMI Records. Dist: EMI

Glass Tiger

DON'T FORGET ME WHEN I'M GONE.
Tracks: / Don't forget me when I'm gone / Ancient Evenings / Don't forget me when I'm gone (Death Mix).
Single (7"): released on Manhattan, Sep'86 by President Records. Dist: Jazz Music, Swift, Taylors, Chris Wellard

Single (12"): released on Manhattan, Sep'86 by President Records. Dist: Jazz Music, Swift, Taylors, Chris Wellard

SOMEDAY.
Tracks: / Someday (dub mix) / Vanishing tribe.
Single (7"): released on Manhattan, Jan'87 by President Records. Dist: Jazz Music, Swift, Taylors, Chris Wellard

Single (12"): released on Manhattan, Jan'87 by President Records. Dist: Jazz Music, Swift, Taylors, Chris Wellard

THIN RED LINE, THE.
Tracks: / Thin red line / Don't forget me when I'm gone / Closer to you / Vanishing tribe / Looking at a picture / Secret / Ancient evenings / Ecstasy / Someday / I will be there / You're what I look for.
Compact disc: released on EMI, Jan'87 by EMI Records. Dist: EMI

Album: released on Manhattan, Jul'86 by President Records. Dist: Jazz Music, Swift, Taylors, Chris Wellard

Cassette: released on Manhattan, Jul'86 by President Records. Dist: Jazz Music, Swift, Taylors, Chris Wellard

Compact disc: released on Capitol, Feb'87 by Capitol Records. Dist: EMI

Glass Torpedoes

TALL STORIES.
Single (7"): released on Leo, Apr'83 Dist: Recommended

Glaxo Babies

CHRISTINE KEELER.
Single (7"): released on Heartbeat, Aug'79 Dist: Revolver, Pinnacle

NINE MONTHS TO THE DISCO.
Album: released on Heartbeat, Oct'81 Dist: Revolver, Pinnacle

PUT ME ON THE GUEST LIST.
Album: released on Heartbeat, '82 Dist: Revolver, Pinnacle

SEVEN DAYS.
Album: released on Heartbeat, Apr'80 Dist: Revolver, Pinnacle

SHAKE THE FOUNDATIONS.
Single (7"): released on Heartbeat, Jun'80 Dist: Revolver, Pinnacle

Gleason, Jackie

PLAYS ROMANTIC JAZZ.
Album: released on Capitol, Oct'84 by Capitol Records. Dist: EMI

Cassette: released on Capitol, Oct'84 by Capitol Records. Dist: EMI

SILK'N'BRASS.
Tracks: / One of those songs (Girls of the Folies Bergere) / Girl from Ipanema, The / It's such a happy day / Everything's coming up roses / Real live girl / Starry eyed and breathless / You're nobody 'til somebody loves you / Begin to love / Shangri-La / If I ruled the world / Somebody else is taking my place.
Notes: Orchestra conducted by: Jackie Gleason:
Album: released on Capitol, Oct'86 by Capitol Records. Dist: EMI

Cassette: released on Capitol, Oct'86 by Capitol Records. Dist: EMI

SONGS AND STORY OF JACKIE GLEASON.
Album: released on EMI (Germany), '83 by EMI Records. Dist: Conifer

TORCH WITH THE BLUE FLAME, THE.
Tracks: / Let's face the music and dance / Just in time / But beautiful / Love letttrs / My heart reminds me / Again / I've grown accustomed to her face / Careless / My silent love / Fascination / Alone in the crown / Time.
Notes: Jackie Gleason, conductor, actor and comedian of the 50's/60's presents a selection of much loved, easy listening tracks including tracks 'Fascination', 'I've Grown Accustomed To Her Face' and 'Lets Face The Music And Dance'bu the famous writers of the day, plus some Gleason originals. This previously rare album makes excellent late night listening.
Album: released on Capitol, Dec'85 by Capitol Records. Dist: EMI

Cassette: released on Capitol, Dec'85 by Capitol Records. Dist: EMI

Glee Club

FIVE GO DOWN TO THE SEA.
Tracks: / Five go down to the sea.
Single (12"): released on Abstract, Aug'86 by Abstract. Dist: Pinnacle

LET MY PEOPLE TWIST!.
Single (7"): released on Venture, Jan'87 Dist: Revolver, Cartel

SOMETHING IN THE AIR.
Single (7"): released on Abacus, Sep'85 by Abacus. Dist: Spartan

Glenaruel Scottish...

REELIN' 'N' RAMBLIN'.
Album: released on Lismor, Oct'76 by Lismor Records. Dist: Lismor, Roots, Celtic Music

SCOTTISH COUNTRY DANCE.
Album: released on Lismor, Oct'79 by Lismor Records. Dist: Lismor, Roots, Celtic Music

Glenn & Chris

DIAMOND LIGHTS.
Tracks: / Diamond lights / Diamond lights (inst).
Picture disc single: released on Record Shack, Apr'87 by Record Shack Records. Dist: PRT

Picture disc single: released on Record Shack, Apr'87 by Record Shack Records. Dist: PRT

IT'S GOODBYE.
Single (7"): released on Record Shack, Aug'87 by Record Shack Records. Dist: PRT

Single (12"): released on Record Shack, Aug'87 by Record Shack Records. Dist: PRT

Glenn, Glen

EVERYBODY'S MOVIN' AGAIN'.
Album: released on Ace, Aug'84 by Ace Records. Dist: Pinnacle, Swift, Hotshot, Cadillac

GLEN GLENN STORY, THE.
Album: released on Ace, Aug'82 by Ace Records. Dist: Pinnacle, Swift, Hotshot, Cadillac

ROCKABILLY LEGEND.
Album: released on Sunjay, Jun'87

Glenn, John

BACK AGAIN (Glenn, John & Mainliners).
Album: released on Misty, Jun'76 by Hawk Records. Dist: I & B Distribution, Solomon & Peres Distribution

BEST OF JOHN GLENN.
Album: released on Homespun(Ireland), Jul'82 by Outlet Records. Dist: Outlet

Cassette: released on Homespun(Ireland), Jul'82 by Outlet Records. Dist: Outlet

COUNTRY STAR (Glenn, John & Mainliners).
Album: by Outlet Records. Dist: Outlet Deleted '82.

Cassette: released on Homespun(Ireland), '82 by Outlet Records. Dist: Outlet

LITTLE COUNTRY TOWN IN IRELAND (Glenn, John & Mainliners).
Album: released on Homespun(Ireland), '82 by Outlet Records. Dist: Outlet

Cassette: released on Homespun(Ireland), '82 by Outlet Records. Dist: Outlet

MAKE MINE COUNTRY STYLE (Glenn, John & Mainliners).
Album: released on Homespun(Ireland), '82 by Outlet Records. Dist: Outlet

Cassette: released on Homespun(Ireland), '82 by Outlet Records. Dist: Outlet

SUNNYSIDE OF THE MOUNTAIN (Glenn, John & Mainliners).
Album: released on Homespun(Ireland), '82 by Outlet Records. Dist: Outlet

Cassette: released on Homespun(Ireland), '82 by Outlet Records. Dist: Outlet

Glenn, Lloyd

AFTER HOURS.
Album: released on Pathe Marconi, Sep'84 Dist: Swift

BLUE IVORIES.
Album: released on Stockholm (Sweden), Feb'85 Dist: Swift Distribution

BLUES AND BOOGIE.
Album: released on Black And Blue, Jan'85 Dist: Swift, Discovery, Target

TEXAS MAN.
Album: released on Juke Box Lil (Sweden), Aug'85

Glenn Miller Story

GLENN MILLER STORY, ORIGINAL SOUNDTRACK.
Compact disc: released on MCA, Oct'85 by MCA Records. Dist: Polygram, MCA

Album: released on MCA, Apr'82 by MCA Records. Dist: Polygram, MCA

Cassette: released on MCA, Apr'82 by MCA Records. Dist: Polygram, MCA

Compact disc: released on MCA, Apr'82 by MCA Records. Dist: Polygram, MCA

Album: released on MCA Coral, Apr'82 by MCA Records. Dist: Polygram

Cassette: released on MCA Coral, Apr'82 by MCA Records. Dist: Polygram

Glenside Ceile Band

GLENSIDE CEILE BAND.
Cassette: released on Autograph, Apr'85 Dist: Record Services Distribution (Ireland)

Glimmer

GLIMMER Various artists.
Cassette: released on Bibi, Feb'82

Glindeman, Ib

IB GLINDEMAN AND HIS DANISH BIG BAND (Glindeman, Ib,and his Danish big band).
Album: released on Big Band International, Jul'82 Dist: Swift

Glinn, Lillian

LILLIAN GLINN: 1927-29.
Album: released on VJM, Apr'79 by VJM (UK) Records. Dist: Swift

Glitter Band

GLITTER BAND: GREATEST HITS.
Album: released on Bell, May'76 by Arista Records. Dist: Polygram

LIVE AT THE MARQUEE.
Album: released on Conquest, Jan'86 Dist: Red Rhino, Cartel

UNTIL THE NEXT TIME.
Single (7"): released on Polo, Mar'85 by Polo Records. Dist: PRT

Glitter, Gary

ALIVE AND KICKING.
Album: released on APK, Mar'85 Dist: Pinnacle

Cassette: released on APK, Mar'85 Dist: Pinnacle

ALWAYS YOURS.
Tracks: / Intro / Rock'n'roll / Do you want to touch? / Always yours / Hello I'm back / Leader of the gang / I belong to you / I love, you love, me love / Oh no / I'm not just a pretty face / When I'm on, I'm on / Wild horses.
Album: released on Dojo, Apr'86 by Castle Communications Records. Dist: Cartel

Cassette: released on Dojo, Apr'86 by Castle Communications Records. Dist: Cartel

ANOTHER ROCK 'N' ROLL CHRISTMAS.
Single (7"): released on Arista, Nov'84 by Arista Records. Dist: RCA

Single (7"): released on MLM, Nov'85

BOYS WILL BE BOYS.
Tracks: / Hair of the dog / Boys will be boys / Close to you / Crash, crash / Lets get sexy / Dance me up / When I'm on / Another rock and roll Christmas / Shout, shout, shout / If you want me.
Notes: Digital Stereo.
Compact disc: released on Arista, Dec'84 by Arista Records. Dist: RCA

Album: released on Arista, Dec'84 by Arista Records. Dist: RCA

Cassette: released on Arista, Dec'84 by Arista Records. Dist: RCA

Compact disc: released on Arista, Dec'84 by Arista Records. Dist: RCA

DANCE ME UP.
Picture disc single: released on Arista, Jun'84 by Arista Records. Dist: RCA

GARY GLITTER: GREATEST HITS.
Album: released on Bell, Apr'76 by Arista Records. Dist: Polygram

GARY GLITTER'S GOLDEN GREATS.
Album: released on GTO, Jul'77 by GTO Records. Dist: CBS

LIVE ROCK 'N' ROLL.
Tracks: / Live rock 'n' roll.
Single (12"): released on Illuminated, Jul'86 by IKF Records. Dist: Pinnacle, Cartel, Jetstar

LOVE COMES.
Single (7"): released on Arista, Apr'85 by Arista Records. Dist: RCA

Single (12"): released on Arista, Apr'85 by Arista Records. Dist: RCA

Picture disc single: released on Arista, Apr'85 by Arista Records. Dist: RCA

ROCK'N'ROLL.
Single (7"): released on Illuminated, Apr'85 by IKF Records. Dist: Pinnacle, Cartel, Jetstar

Single (12"): released on Illuminated, Apr'85 by IKF Records. Dist: Pinnacle, Cartel, Jetstar

SHOUT! SHOUT! SHOUT!.
Picture disc single: released on MLM-Arista, Sep'84

SIX TRACK HITS.
Extended-play record: released on Scoop 33, Sep'83 by Pickwick Records. Dist: H.R. Taylor

Cassette: released on Scoop 33, Sep'83 by Pickwick Records. Dist: H.R. Taylor

Globe & Pow Pow

CELEBRATE! (EVERYBODY).
Single (7"): released on Tommy Boy, May'85 by Warner Brothers. Dist: WEA Distribution

Single (12"): released on Tommy Boy, May'85 by Warner Brothers. Dist: WEA Distribution

Deleted '87.

Globestyle
GLOBESTYLE Worldwide - your guide (Various Artists).
Album: released on Globestyle, Mar'87 by Ace Records. Dist: Projection

Globe Unity Orchestra
GLOBE UNITY ORCHESTRA.
Album: released on ECM (Germany), May'83 by ECM Records. Dist: IMS, Polygram, Virgin through EMI

Gloria
AT HER BEST.
Album: released on Harp(Ireland), May'80 by Pickwick Records. Dist: Taylors

GLORIA.
Album: released on Release (Ireland), May'81

MISSISSIPPI.
Album: released on Harp(Ireland), Oct'81 by Pickwick Records. Dist: Taylors

ONE DAY AT A TIME.
Single (7"): released on Release (Ireland), Dec'78

ONE DAY AT A TIME & OTHER SONGS.
Album: released on Stoic (Ireland), Jul'84
Cat. no: BT 300
Cassette: released on Stoic (Ireland), Jul'84

G, Lorna
DID'NT I TELL YOU.
Single (12"): released on Ariwa, Jul'87 by Ariwa Records. Dist: Revolver, Cartel, Jetstar, Rough Trade

Glory
DOING THE BEST WITH MY LIFE.
Tracks: / Doing the best with my life / Playing with fire.
Single (7"): released on Top Flight, Aug'86 Dist: Making Waves

HEARTS WILL SING.
Single (7"): released on Riva, Aug'87 Dist: PRT

Single (12"): released on Riva, Aug'87 Dist: PRT

Glory Bells
CENTURY RENDEZVOUS.
Album: released on Thunderbolt, Aug'85 by Magnum Music Group Ltd. Dist: Magnum Music Group Ltd, PRT Distribution, Spartan Distribution

Glosters
GLOSTERS (28TH/61ST) REGT BAND & CORPS OF DRUMS (Glosters (28th/61st) Regt Band & Corps of Drums).
Album: released on Music Masters, Apr'83 by Music Masters Records. Dist: Taylors

Cassette: released on Music Masters, Apr'83 by Music Masters Records. Dist: Taylors

Gloucester Cathedral
CAROLS FOR CHRISTMAS.
Album: released on Abbey, Nov'79 by Abbey. Dist: PRT, Taylors, Gamut

Gloucestershire wildlife
GLOUCESTERSHIRE WILDLIFE TAPESTRY (Various Artists).
Album: released on Saydisc, Oct'79 by Saydisc Records. Dist: Essex, Harmonia Mundi, Roots, H.R. Taylor, Jazz Music, Swift, Projection, Gamut

Cassette: released on Saydisc, Oct'79 by Saydisc Records. Dist: Essex, Harmonia Mundi, Roots, H.R. Taylor, Jazz Music, Swift, Projection, Gamut

Glove
BLUE SUNSHINE.
Album: released on Wonderland, Aug'83 by Polydor Records. Dist: Polygram

Cassette: released on Wonderland, Aug'83 by Polydor Records. Dist: Polygram Deleted '85.

Glover, Roger
BUTTERFLY BALL, (THE).
Album: released on Safari, Nov'84 by Safari Records. Dist: Pinnacle

Cassette: released on Safari, Nov'84 by Safari Records. Dist: Pinnacle

MASK, THE.
Single (7"): released on Polydor, Jun'84 by Polydor Records. Dist: Polygram, Polydor

Gluch, Jeremy
I KNEW BUFFALO BILL (Gluch, Jeremy &

Nikki Sudden).
Notes: See also under Sudden,Nikki & Jeremy Gluch
Album: released on Flicknife, Mar'87 by Flicknife Records. Dist: Spartan

Cassette: released on Flicknife, Mar'87 by Flicknife Records. Dist: Spartan

Gluck, Jeremy
I KNEW BUFFALO BILL.
Tracks: / Looking for a place / Too long / Gone free / Hymn / Time undone / Gallery wharf / Four seasons of trouble / All my secrets.
Album:

THRILLING TALE OF BUFFALO BILL (Gluck, Jeremy & Friends).
Single (12"): released on Tuff Enuff, Aug'87 Dist: Pinnacle

Gluck, Jeremy & Friends
LOOKING FOR A PLACE TO FALL.
Single (12"): released on Tuff Enuff, Sep'87 Dist: Pinnacle

Glynn, Dominic
DR. WHO.
Tracks: / Dr Who / Dr. Who (Cosmic remix).
Single (7"): released on BBC, Nov'86 by BBC Records & Tapes. Dist: EMI, PRT

Single (12"): released on BBC, Nov'86 by BBC Records & Tapes. Dist: EMI, PRT

Cassette single: released on BBC, Nov'86 by BBC Records & Tapes. Dist: EMI, PRT,

GMC
FOOT ON THE ROCK.
Single (7"): released on Kaz, Aug'85 by Kaz Records. Dist: PRT

Single (12"): released on Kaz, Aug'85 by Kaz Records. Dist: PRT

G. Men
DARK TRAIN/LEFT OUT/GOTTA GO.
: released on Cro-Magnon, May'82

G. Morgan
TEA WITH MR. TIMOTHY (Read by Garard Green).
Cassette: released on Chivers Audio Books, '81 by Chivers Sound & Vision. Dist: Chivers Sound & Vision

G.Mountford/G.Durrell
WHY SAVE WILD ANIMALS.
Cassette: released on Seminar Cassettes, Oct'81

Gnass
FREE KINGS.
Single (7"): released on Ffang, Nov'82 Dist: IDS

GNT
ONE BY ONE.
Single (7"): released on Mausoleum, Jul'85 by Mausoleum Records. Dist: Pinnacle

Go 2
LAND AND WATER.
Single (7"): released on Polydor, Jul'83 by Polydor Records. Dist: Polygram, Polydor

LIKE MY OWN COMPANY I.
Single (7"): released on Polydor, Jan'83 by Polydor Records. Dist: Polygram, Polydor

MAN OUT OF THE JUNGLE.
Single (7"): released on Polydor, Mar'83 by Polydor Records. Dist: Polygram, Polydor

Goanna
SOLID ROCK.
Single (7"): released on WEA, Feb'83 by WEA Records. Dist: WEA

Goat
REAL KAVOOM EP.
Single (12"): released on Real Kavoom, Jul'82

Go-Betweens
BEFORE HOLLYWOOD.
Tracks: / Bad debt follows you / Two steps out / Before Hollywood / Dusty in here / Ask / Cattle and cane / By chance / As long as that / On my block / That way.
Notes: All music by Lindy Morrison/Grant McLennan/Robert Forster. Lyrics Grant McLennan, and Robert Forster. Produced by John Brand.
Album: released on Rough Trade, Sep'84 by Rough Trade Records. Dist: Rough Trade Distribution, Cartel Distribution

BYE BYE PRIDE.
Single (7"): released on Beggars Banquet, Aug'87 by Beggars Banquet Records. Dist: WEA

Single (12"): released on Beggars Banquet, Aug'87 by Beggars Banquet Records. Dist: WEA

CATTLE AND CANE.
Single (7"): released on Rough Trade, Feb'83 by Rough Trade Records. Dist: Rough Trade Distribution, Cartel Distribution

CUT IT OUT.
Tracks: / Cut it out / Time in the desert / Doo wop in "A" (bam boom).
Single (7"): released on Beggars Banquet, May'87 by Beggars Banquet Records. Dist: WEA

Single (12"): released on Beggars Banquet, May'87 by Beggars Banquet Records. Dist: WEA

HAMMER THE HAMMER.
Single (7"): released on Rough Trade, Jun'82 by Rough Trade Records. Dist: Rough Trade Distribution, Cartel Distribution

HEAD FULL OF STEAM.
Tracks: / Head full of steam / Don't let him come back / Wrong Road (The).
Single (7"): released on Beggars Banquet, May'86 by Beggars Banquet Records. Dist: WEA

Single (12"): released on Beggars Banquet, May'86 by Beggars Banquet Records. Dist: WEA

LEE REMICK.
Tracks: / Lee Remick / People say / Don't let him come back.
Single (12"): released on Situation 2, Nov'86 Dist: Cartel, Pinnacle

LIBERTY BELLE AND THE BLACK DIAMOND EXPRESS.
Tracks: / Spring rain / Ghost and the black hat / Wrong road (The) / To reach me / Twin layers of lightning / In the core of a flame / Head full of steam / Bow down / Palm down / Apology accepted.
Album: released on Beggars Banquet, Mar'86 by Beggars Banquet Records. Dist: WEA

Cassette: released on Beggars Banquet, Mar'86 by Beggars Banquet Records. Dist: WEA

LIBERTY BELLE & THE BLACK DIAMOND EXPRESS.
Tracks: / Spring rain / Ghost and the black hat (The) / Wrong road (The) / To reach me / Twin layers of lightning / In the core of a flame / Head full of steam / Bow down / Palm down / Apology accepted.
Compact disc: released on Beggars Banquet, Jul'86 by Beggars Banquet Records. Dist: WEA

MAN O' SAND TO GIRL O' SEA.
Single (7"): released on Rough Trade, Oct'83 by Rough Trade Records. Dist: Rough Trade Distribution, Cartel Distribution

RIGHT HERE.
Tracks: / Right here / When people are dead / Little romance, A / Don't call me gone / Little romance, A.
Single (7"): released on Beggars Banquet, Feb'87 by Beggars Banquet Records. Dist: WEA

Single (12"): released on Beggars Banquet, Feb'87 by Beggars Banquet Records. Dist: WEA

Double-pack single: released on Beggars Banquet, Feb'87 by Beggars Banquet Records. Dist: WEA

SEND ME A LULLABY.
Album: released on Rough Trade, Jun'82 by Rough Trade Records. Dist: Rough Trade Distribution, Cartel Distribution

SPRING HILL FAIR.
Album: released on Sire, Sep'84

SPRING RAIN.
Tracks: / Spring rain / Life at hand / Little Joe.
Single (7"): released on Beggars Banquet, Feb'86 by Beggars Banquet Records. Dist: WEA

Single (12"): released on Beggars Banquet, Feb'86 by Beggars Banquet Records. Dist: WEA

TALLULAH.
Tracks: / Right here / You tell me / Someone else's wife / I just get caught out / Cut it out / House that Jack Kerouac built / Bye bye pride / Spirit of a vampyre / Clarke sisters, The / Hope then strife.
Album: released on Beggars Banquet, Jun'87 by Beggars Banquet Records. Dist: WEA

Cassette: released on Beggars Banquet, Jun'87 by Beggars Banquet Records. Dist: WEA

Compact disc: released on Beggars Banquet,

Jun'87 by Beggars Banquet Records. Dist: WEA

TALLULAH,THE.
Compact disc: released on Beggars Banquet, '87 by Beggars Banquet Records. Dist: WEA

Godard Ca Vous Chante?
GODARD CA VOUS CHANTE? various artists.
Tracks: / Sonate en re mineur / Godard / Chest / Respect / Du cote des peudecerts / La croisiere immobile.
Notes: With: John Zorn/The Amati Ensemble/Arto Lindsay/Daniel Deshays/Caroline Gautier/Oliver Foy.
Album: released on Nato (France), Sep'86 by Disques Nato. Dist: Essex Record Distributors Ltd.

Godard, Vic
HOLIDAY HYMN.
Single (7"): released on EL-Benelux, Aug'85 Dist: Rough Trade

Single (12"): released on EL-Benelux, Aug'85 Dist: Rough Trade

RETROSPECTIVE, A (1977-81) (Godard, Vic & The Subway Sect).
Album: released on Rough Trade, Jan'85 by Rough Trade Records. Dist: Rough Trade Distribution, Cartel Distribution

SONGS FOR SALE (Godard, Vic & The Subway Sect).
Album: released on London, Jun'82 by London Records. Dist: Polygram

Cassette: released on London, Jun'82 by London Records. Dist: Polygram

STOP THAT GIRL (Godard, Vic & The Subway Sect).
Single (7"): released on Rough Trade, Jan'81 by Rough Trade Records. Dist: Rough Trade Distribution, Cartel Distribution

WHAT'S THE MATTER BOY.
Album: released on MCA, Jul'82 by MCA Records. Dist: Polygram, MCA

Cassette: released on MCA, Jul'82 by MCA Records. Dist: Polygram, MCA

Goddard, Vic
TROUBLE.
Album: released on Rough Trade, Apr'86 by Rough Trade Records. Dist: Rough Trade Distribution, Cartel Distribution

Godden, Lee
IF THIS IS TRUE.
Single (7"): released on Chart, Jul'84 by Chart Records. Dist: Pinnacle

NATURAL RHYTHM.
Album: released on Monarch, Oct'83 by Chart Records. Dist: Pinnacle

Goddo
IF TOMORROW NEVER COMES.
Single (7"): released on Attic, Apr'82 Dist: Pinnacle

PRETTY BAD BOYS.
Album: released on Attic, Jan'82 Dist: Pinnacle

Cassette: released on Attic, Jan'82 Dist: Pinnacle

God Emperor
GOD EMPEROR OF DUNE Herbert, Frank (Herbert, Frank).
Cassette: released on Caedmon(USA), Sep'82 by Caedmon (USA) Records. Dist: Gower, Taylors, Discovery

Godfathers
HIT BY HIT.
Album: released on Corporate Image, Nov'86 by Godfathers, The. Dist: Red Rhino. Cartel

LOVE IS DEAD.
Tracks: / Love is dead./ Angela.
Single (7"): released on Corporate Image, Feb'87 by Godfathers, The. Dist: Red Rhino, Cartel

Single (12"): by Godfathers, The. Dist: Red Rhino, Cartel

SUNARISE.
Tracks: / Sunarise.
Single (7"): released on Corporate Image, Aug'86 by Godfathers, The. Dist: Red Rhino, Cartel

Single (12"): released on Corporate Image, Aug'86 by Godfathers, The. Dist: Red Rhino, Cartel

THIS DAMNATION.
Tracks: / This damnation.

Single (12"): released on Corporate Image, Mar'86 by Godfathers, The. Dist: Red Rhino, Cartel

Godley & Creme

CHANGING FACES-THE VERY BEST OF... (Godley & Creme/10CC).
Tracks: / Dreadlock holiday / Wall Street Shuffle, The / Under your thumb / Life is a minestrone / An Englishman in New York / Art for art's sake / Donna / Snack attack / Cry / Things we do for love, The / Wedding bells / I'm Mandy, fly me / Good morning judge / Rubber bullets / Save a mountain for me / I'm not in love.
Album: released on Polydor, Oct'87 by Polydor Records. Dist: Polygram, Polydor

Cassette: released on Polydor, Oct'87 by Polydor Records. Dist: Polygram, Polydor

Compact disc: released on Polydor, Aug'87 by Polydor Records. Dist: Polygram, Polydor

Album: released on Polygram, Aug'87 by Polygram Records. Dist: Polygram

Cassette: released on Polygram, Aug'87 by Polygram Records. Dist: Polygram

CRY.
Tracks: / Cry / Love bombs.
Single (7"): released on Polydor, Aug'86 by Polydor Records. Dist: Polygram, Polydor

Single (12"): released on Polydor, Aug'86 by Polydor Records. Dist: Polygram, Polydor

HISTORY MIX (THE).
Tracks: / Wet rubber soup / Cry / Epanding business / Dare 'you' man (The) / Hum drum boys in Paris / Mountain tension.
Compact disc: released on Polydor, Aug'85 by Polydor Records. Dist: Polygram, Polydor

SNACK ATTACK.
Tracks: / Wet rubber soup.
Single (7"): released on Polydor, Aug'87 by Polydor Records. Dist: Polygram, Polydor

Single (12"): released on Polydor, Aug'87 by Polydor Records. Dist: Polygram, Polydor

UNDER MY THUMB.
Tracks: / Under my thumb / Wedding bells.
Single (7"): released on Old Gold, Mar'86 by Old Gold Records. Dist: Lightning, Jazz Music, Spartan, Counterpoint

God Loves Country Music

GOD LOVES COUNTRY MUSIC various artists (Various Artists).
Album: released on Marantha Music, May'82

Cassette: released on Marantha Music, May'82

God, Mother & Country

FOOT ON THE ROCK.
Single (7"): released on Kaz, Sep'85 by Kaz Records. Dist: PRT

Single (12"): released on Kaz, Sep'85 by Kaz Records. Dist: PRT

Godot

SOMETHIN'S MISSING.
Single (7"): released on Pinnacle, Aug'82 by Pinnacle Records. Dist: Pinnacle

Single 10": released on Pinnacle, Aug'82 by Pinnacle Records. Dist: Pinnacle

WAIT FOR.
Single (12"): released on Godot, Apr'82 by Godot Records. Dist: Pinnacle

Gods and ungods

GODS AND UNGODS OF IRELAND Various artists (Various Artists).
Cassette: released on Anvil, Jan'81 Dist: Anvil

God's Favourite Dog

GOD'S FAVOURITE DOG (Various Artists).
Album: released on Touch And Go, May'87 Dist: Rough Trade, Cartel

God's Gift

DISCIPLINE.
Single (7"): released on New Hormones, Oct'82 by New Hormones Records.

FOLIE A QUATRE.
Cassette: released on Pleasantly Surprised Tapes, Jul'85 Dist: Fast Forward, Spartan

GOD'S GIFT (EP).
Single (12"): released on New Hormones, Jul'81 by New Hormones Records.

Godspell

GODSPELL London cast (London Cast).
Album: released on Bell, '72 by Arista Records. Dist: Polygram

Gods's Toys

ALL THE BORN LOSERS.
Single (7"): released on Badge, Aug'80 by Carlin Music Corporation Records. Dist: RCA

Gods & ungods of Ireland

GODS & UNGODS OF IRELAND Various artists (Various Artists).

Godwin, Peter

DANCE EMOTIONS.
Album: released on Polydor (Holland), Apr'84

Godz

I'LL GET YOU ROCKIN'.
Album: released on Heavy Metal America, Nov'85 by FM-Revolver Records. Dist: EMI

NOTHING IS SACRED.
Album: released on RCA (Germany), '83

POWER ROCK FROM USA.
Album: released on RCA (Germany), '83

Goeyvaerts, Karel

LITANIES.
Notes: Performed by: Kristina Van Damme (piano) The Cincinatti Percussion Group BRT Philharmonic Orchestra Ensemble Der Blaue Reiter Elisabeth Chojnacka (harpsichord)
Double Album: released on Les Disques Du Crepuscule, Mar'87 Dist: Rough Trade, Pinnacle, Island, Polygram

Goffin, Louise

CARNIVAL.
Single (7"): released on WEA, Aug'87 by WEA Records. Dist: WEA

Single (12"): released on WEA, Aug'87 by WEA Records. Dist: WEA

Go Fundamental

FOUR TRACK EP.
Single (7"): released on Davinci, Oct'82

PEOPLE ON THE TOP FLOOR.
Single (7"): released on Arista, May'85 by Arista Records. Dist: RCA

Single (12"): released on Arista, May'85 by Arista Records. Dist: RCA

Gogmagog

I WILL BE THERE.
Single (12"): released on Food For Thought, Sep'85 by Food For Thought Records. Dist: Pinnacle

Go Go

GO GO various artists (Various Artists).
Album: released on Streetsounds, Feb'85

Cassette: released on Streetsounds, Feb'85

GO-GO-THE SOUND OF WASHINGTON DC various artists (Various Artists).
Album: released on London, May'85 by London Records. Dist: Polygram

Cassette: released on London, May'85 by London Records. Dist: Polygram Deleted '86.

Gogo crankin'

GOGO CRANKIN' Various artists (Various Artists).
Album: released on Fourth & Broadway, Apr'85 by Island Records. Dist: Polygram, EMI

Cassette: released on Fourth & Broadway, Apr'85 by Island Records. Dist: Polygram, EMI

Go Go Lorenzo

TOP, BOTTOM, SIDE AND REAR (Go Go Lorenzo & The Davis Pinckney Project).
Tracks: / Top, bottom, side and rear / Top, bottom, side and rear (inst).
Single (7"): released on Polydor, Apr'87 by Polydor Records. Dist: Polygram, Polydor

Single (12"): released on Polydor, Apr'87 by Polydor Records. Dist: Polygram, Polydor

YOU CAN DANCE (IF YOU WANT TO) (Go Go Lorenzo & The Davis Pinckney Project).
Tracks: / You can dance.
Single (7"): released on Boiling Point, Nov'86 by Polydor Records. Dist: Polygram

Single (12"): released on Boiling Point, Nov'86 by Polydor Records. Dist: Polygram

Go-go's

BEAUTY AND THE BEAT.
Album: released on I.R.S.(Independent Record Syndicate), Aug'81 by I.R.S.. Dist: MCA

Cassette: released on I.R.S.(Independent Record Syndicate), Aug'81 by I.R.S.. Dist: MCA

GIRL OF A THOUSAND LISTS.
Single (7"): released on I.R.S.(Independent Record Syndicate), Nov'82 by I.R.S.. Dist: MCA

TALK SHOW.
Album: released on I.R.S.(Independent Record Syndicate), May'84 by I.R.S.. Dist: MCA

Cassette: released on I.R.S.(Independent Record Syndicate), May'84 by I.R.S.. Dist: MCA

WE GOT THE BEAT.
Single (7"): released on Stiff, May'80 by Stiff Records. Dist: EMI, Record Services Distribution (Ireland)

Go Hole

FLIGHT OF ANGELS.
Single (7"): released on Big Pop, Aug'87 by Big Pop Records. Dist: Pinnacle

Goin' back home

GOIN' BACK HOME: CHICAGO BLUES MASTERS, VOL 3 Various artists (Various Artists).
Album: released on Rhythm & Blues, Feb'84

Going Back...

GOING BACK ON THE FARM CHICAGO BLUES 1940-1942 various artists (Various Artists).
Album: released on Travelin' Man, Nov'85

GOING BACK TO NEW ORLEANS Various artists (Various Artists).
Album: released on Sonet, Jan'79 by Sonet Records. Dist: PRT

Going Down...

GOING DOWN THE VALLEY (Various Artists).
Tracks: / I truly understand, you love another man / Old Joe Clark / Billy Grimes, The Rover / George Washington / Little Maud / Cotton-eyed Joe / Going down the valley / Cottage door, The / Carve that possum / Molly put the kettle on / Milwaukee blues / Corrina, Corrina / Katie dear (silver dagger) / New salty dog, A / Nancy Jane / Sweet rose of heaven / Banjo pickin' girl / Little Maggie.
Notes: Recorded in mono. Vocal and instrumental styles in Folk Music from the South.
Album: released on New World (USA), Mar'87 by New World Records (USA). Dist: Conifer

GOING DOWN TO LOUISIANA Various artists (Various Artists).
Album: released on White Label, Jul'79 by White Label Records. Dist: Jetstar

Going To...

GOING TO CALIFORNIA (Various Artists).
Album: released on JSP, Sep'84 by JSP Records. Dist: Swift, Projection

GOING TO NEW ORLEANS various artists (Various Artists).
Notes: Artists include: Lester Robertson/Billy Tate/Little Victor/Eddie Hudson/Tabby Thomas/Skinny Dynamo/Ernie Holland/Vince Monroe/Rockin' Sidney
Album: released on Flyright, Oct'86 by Flyright Records. Dist: Krazy Kat, Swift, Jazz Music

Going West

GOING WEST (Various Artists).
Album: released on Polygram (Import), May'83

Cassette: released on Polygram (Import), May'83

Golbey, Brian

COUNTRY MUSIC STORY.
Cassette: released on Ampro Cassettes, Sep'81

LAST TRAIN SOUTH (Golbey, Brian & Nick Strutt).
Album: released on Waterfront, Mar'86 by Waterfront Records. Dist: Rough Trade, Cartel, Projection, Roots

WHEN THE DEALINGS DONE (Golbey, Brian & Pete Stanley).
Album: released on Waterfront, Mar'84 by Waterfront Records. Dist: Rough Trade, Cartel, Projection, Roots

Gold

GOLD LIVE FROM MOSCOW.
Album: released on President, Nov'79 by President Records. Dist: Taylors, Spartan

HIGH TIME.
Single (7"): released on Sky-Hi, Oct'80 Dist: Pinnacle

LITTLE CLOSER TO FREEDOM, A.
Tracks: / Little closer to freedom, A / Un peu pres des etoiles.
Single (7"): released on WEA International, Feb'86 by WEA Records. Dist: WEA

Single (12"): released on WEA International, Feb'86 by WEA Records. Dist: WEA

SAIL AWAY.
Tracks: / Sail away / Josy-Ann.
Single (7"): released on WEA International, Jun'86 by WEA Records. Dist: WEA

Gold, Andrew

ALL THIS AND HEAVEN TOO.
Cassette: released on Asylum, Mar'78 by WEA Records. Dist: WEA

ANDREW GOLD.
Album: released on Asylum, Jun'76 by WEA Records. Dist: WEA

LONELY BOY.
Single (7"): released on Old Gold, Sep'85 by Old Gold Records. Dist: Lightning, Jazz Music, Spartan, Counterpoint

WHIRLWIND.
Album: released on Asylum, May'80 by WEA Records. Dist: WEA

Cassette: released on Asylum, May'80 by WEA Records. Dist: WEA

Gold, Angie

Anglia remix Vol.2

APPLAUSE.
Tracks: / Applause / Creature of the night.
Single (7"): released on Passion, Oct'86 by Skratch Records. Dist: PRT

Single (12"): released on Passion, Oct'86 by Skratch Records. Dist: PRT

EAT YOU UP.
Single (12"): released on Passion, Mar'85 by Skratch Records. Dist: PRT

THIRD FINGER LEFT HAND.
Tracks: / Third finger left hand / Landslide.
Single (7"): released on Passion, 20 Jun'87 by Skratch Records. Dist: PRT

Single (12"): released on Passion, 20 Jun'87 by Skratch Records. Dist: PRT

TIMEBOMB.
Single (12"): released on Passion, Oct'85 by Skratch Records. Dist: PRT

Gold, David

DANCE TO THE MUSIC.
Single (12"): released on Whiplash, May'84 by Whiplash Records. Dist: Amanda Records Distribution

Golden Age Of...

GOLDEN AGE OF BALLADS AND PARLOUR SONGS Various artists (Various Artists).
Tracks: / Come to the fair / Grandfather's clock / Parted / Leanin' / Love, could I only tell thee / Bloom is on the rye, The / Wrap me up in my tarpaulin jacket / Until / Volunteer organist, The / Think on me / Life's dream is o'er / As I sit here / My dreams / For you alone / Lo, here the gentle Lark / Bloom is on the Rye (my pretty Jane), The / Wrap me up in my Tarpaulin jacket / Until / Volunteer organist, The / Think on me / Life's dream is o'er / As I sit here / My dreams / For you alone / Lo, here the gentle lark / Come to the fair (from "Song of the fair") / Grandfather's clock / Parted / Leanin' / Love, could I only tell thee.
Notes: 15 examples of those meldies heard in Parlours and Drawing Rooms up and down the country in The Early Days of This Century. These tracks, recorded in the 30's and 40's, include performances from Peter Dawson, Isobel Baillie, Webster Booth and Owen Brannigan. Piano accompaniment on many tracks is by the late Gerald Moore.
Album: released on Golden Age, Jun'87 by Music For Pleasure Records. Dist: EMI

Cassette: released on Golden Age, Jun'87 by Music For Pleasure Records. Dist: EMI

GOLDEN AGE OF CHICAGO BLUES various artists (Various Artists).
Compact disc: released on Vogue, Jan'86 Dist: Discovery, Jazz Music, PRT, Swift

GOLDEN AGE OF CLASSIC BRITISH FILM THEMES OF 40'S & 50'S (Various Artists).
Tracks: / Way to the stars, The / Cornish rhapsody / Voice in the night, A / Warsaw concerto / Dream of Olwen and Incidental Music, The / Mansell concerto, The / Saga of Odette, The / Carriage and Pair / Long forgotten melody / Portrait of Clare / Beggar's theme, The / Voice in the night, A.
Notes: Tracks 5 - 10 performed by Charles Williams & his Orchestra. (P) Original Sound Recordings owned by EMI Records Ltd.
Album: released on Golden Age, Mar'87 by Music For Pleasure Records. Dist: EMI

Cassette: released on Golden Age, Mar'87 by Music For Pleasure Records. Dist: EMI

GOLDEN AGE OF DANCE BANDS, THE
Various Artists (Various Artists).
Tracks: / You and the night and the music / Blue skies are round the corner / Yes yes (my baby says "Yes") / She had to go and lose it at the Astor / Solitude / You gorgeous dancing doll / Hold my hand / Pennies from heaven / Dancing in the dark / Let's dance at the make-believe ballroom / Happy days are here again / Half of it dearie blues, The / I've got my love to keep me warm / Lambeth walk, The / I took my harp to a party / Here's to the next time.

GOLDEN AGE OF FEMALE VOICE (Various Artists).
Tracks: / Nightingale sang in Berkley Square, A / There goes that song again / When I grow too old to dream / I've told ev'ry little star / That old feeling / Stormy weather / Pu-leeze Mr Hemingway / Moment I saw you, The / Spread a little happiness / When you've got a little springtime in your heart / Says my heart / Night was made for love, The / These foolish things / Nightingale sang in Berkely Square, A / You've done something to my heart / Moon got in my eyes, The / Try a little tenderness / Wish me luck (as you wave me goodbye).
Album: released on Golden Age, Mar'87 by Music For Pleasure Records. Dist: EMI

Cassette: released on Golden Age, Mar'87 by Music For Pleasure Records. Dist: EMI

GOLDEN AGE OF GEORGE GERSHWIN (Various Artists).
Album: released on Golden Age, Jul'84 by Music For Pleasure Records. Dist: EMI

Cassette: released on Golden Age, Jul'84 by Music For Pleasure Records. Dist: EMI

GOLDEN AGE OF GOSPEL SINGING (Various Artists).
Notes: Featuring: Bessie Griffin, Angelic Gospel Singers etc.
Album: released on Folklyric (USA), Jul'87 by Arhoolie Records. Dist: Topic, Projection

GOLDEN AGE OF HOLLYWOOD STARS (Various Artists).
Double Album: released on United Artists, Mar'78

GOLDEN AGE OF JAZZ OF THE 30'S (Various Artists).
Album: released on Golden Age, Jul'83 by Music For Pleasure Records. Dist: EMI

Cassette: released on Golden Age, Jul'83 by Music For Pleasure Records. Dist: EMI

GOLDEN AGE OF MALE VOICE (Various Artists).
Tracks: / Goodnight Vienna / Don't let that moon get away / Music goes round and round, The / Me and my girl / My melancholy baby / Best things in life are free, The / Only a glass of champagne / On the Amazon / Putting on the Ritz / Change partners / Let's face the music and dance / Sixty seconds got together / Dancing in the dark / I'll see you again / What a little moonlight can do / You brought a new kind of love to me.
Album: released on Golden Age, Mar'87 by Music For Pleasure Records. Dist: EMI

Cassette: released on Golden Age, Mar'87 by Music For Pleasure Records. Dist: EMI

GOLDEN AGE OF MUSIC HALL (Various Artists).
Album: released on Rhapsody, '82 by President Records. Dist: Taylors, Swift, Jazz Music, Wellard, Chris

GOLDEN AGE OF NOEL COWARD, THE Coward, Noel (Coward, Noel).
Album: released on Golden Age, Jul'83 by Music For Pleasure Records. Dist: EMI

Cassette: released on Golden Age, Jul'83 by Music For Pleasure Records. Dist: EMI

GOLDEN AGE OF ROCK'N'ROLL (Various Artists).
Album: released on Oak, Oct'82 by Oak Records. Dist: Spartan Distribution, Pinnacle

GOLDEN AGE OF THE CHARLESTON (Various Artists).
Album: released on Golden Age, Jul'83 by Music For Pleasure Records. Dist: EMI

Cassette: released on Golden Age, Jul'83 by Music For Pleasure Records. Dist: EMI

GOLDEN AGE OF THE DANCE BAND (Various Artists).
Album: released on Golden Age, Jun'87 by Music For Pleasure Records. Dist: EMI

Cassette: released on Golden Age, Jun'87 by Music For Pleasure Records. Dist: EMI

THOSE DANCE BAND YEARS VOL.2 (Various Artists).
Album: released on World, Oct'76 Dist: Jetstar

THOSE DANCE BAND YEARS VOL.3 (Various Artists).
Album: released on World, Oct'76 Dist: Jetstar

THOSE DANCE BAND YEARS VOL.4 (Various Artists).
Album: released on World, Oct'76 Dist: Jetstar

THOSE DANCE BAND YEARS VOL.6 (Various Artists).
Album: released on World, Oct'76 Dist: Jetstar

THOSE DANCE BAND YEARS VOL.7 (Various Artists).
Album: released on World, Jan'77 Dist: Jetstar

THOSE DANCE BAND YEARS (Various Artists).
Album: released on World, Oct'76 Dist: Jetstar

Golden Ballads

GOLDEN BALLADS (Various Artists).
Cassette: released on Bravo, Feb'80 by Pickwick Records. Dist: Lugtons

Golden Child

GOLDEN CHILD Original Film Soundtrack (Various Artists).
Tracks: / Best man in the world / Deeper love / Love goes on (love theme from the Golden child) / Shame on you / Body talk / Chosen one, The (Let your love find) / Sardo and the child / Golden love / Confrontation.
Notes: The new Paramount picture 'The Golden Child' stars Eddy Murphy. The soundtrack to the film features some very strong songs, notably one from Ann Wilson of Heart, as well as incidental music from John Barry and Michel Colombier.
Compact disc: released on Capitol, Apr'87 by Capitol Records. Dist: EMI

Album: released on Capitol, Jan'87 by Capitol Records. Dist: EMI

Cassette: released on Capitol, Jan'87 by Capitol Records. Dist: EMI

Golden Classics

GOLDEN CLASSICS (Various Artists).
Album: released on Ronco, Nov'83

Cassette: released on Ronco, Nov'83

Golden Country

GOLDEN COUNTRY (Various Artists).
Album: released on Hallmark, Apr'81 by Pickwick Records. Dist: Pickwick Distribution, PRT, Taylors

Cassette: released on RCA/Camden, Apr'81

Golden Days...

GOLDEN DAYS OF JAZZ (Various Artists).
Album: released on RCA (Germany), '83

GOLDEN DAYS OF ROCK (Various Artists).
Cassette: released on Ampro Cassettes, Sep'81

Golden Decade

GOLDEN DECADE 1960-1 (Various Artists).
Album: released on Decca, Feb'77 by Decca Records. Dist: Polygram

GOLDEN DECADE 1964-5 (Various Artists).
Album: released on Decca, Feb'77 by Decca Records. Dist: Polygram

GOLDEN DECADE 1968-9 (Various Artists).
Album: released on Decca, Feb'77 by Decca Records. Dist: Polygram

Golden Dozen

GOLDEN DOZEN - VOLUME 2 Various artists (Various Artists).
Album: Dist: Swift

GOLDEN DOZEN - VOLUME 3 Various artists (Various Artists).
Album: Dist: Swift

GOLDEN DOZEN - VOLUME 4 Various artists (Various Artists).
Album: Dist: Swift

Golden dozen hits

GOLDEN DOZEN HITS Various artists (Various Artists).
Album: Dist: Swift

Golden Eagle Jazz Band

GOLDEN EAGLE JAZZ BAND.
Album: released on Stomp Off, Jun'86 by Stomp Off Records. Dist: Jazz Music Distribution

Golden Earring

2ND.LIVE.
Album: released on Polydor (Import), Sep'81

Cassette: released on Polydor (Import), Sep'81

CUT.
Album: released on Philips, Apr'83 Dist: IMS-Polygram

Cassette: released on Philips, Apr'83 Dist: IMS-Polygram

EIGHT MILES HIGH.
Compact disc: by Polydor Records. Dist: Polygram, Polydor

GOLDEN EARRING LIVE.
Double Album: released on Polydor, Sep'77 by Polydor Records. Dist: Polygram, Polydor

GRAB IT FOR A SECOND.
Album: by Polydor Records. Dist: Polygram, Polydor

GREATEST HITS: GOLDEN EARRING VOL.3.
Album: released on Polydor (Import), Mar'84

Cassette: released on Polydor (Import), Mar'84

GREATEST HITS:GOLDEN EARING.
Double Album: released on Polydor, Nov'80 by Polydor Records. Dist: Polygram, Polydor

Cassette: released on Polydor, Nov'80 by Polydor Records. Dist: Polygram, Polydor

MOONTAN.
Album: by Polydor Records. Dist: Polygram

Cassette: by Polydor Records. Dist: Polygram

NORTH SOUTH EAST WEST.
Album: released on Carrere, Apr'84 by Carrere Records. Dist: PRT, Spartan

Cassette: released on Carrere, Apr'84 by Carrere Records. Dist: PRT, Spartan

RADAR LOVE.
Tracks: / Radar love / Just like Vince Taylor.
Single (7"): released on Old Gold, Mar'86 by Old Gold Records. Dist: Lightning, Jazz Music, Spartan, Counterpoint

SWITCH.
Album: released on Karussell (Germany), Aug'82

Cassette: released on Karussell (Germany), Aug'82

TO THE HILT.
Album: released on Polydor (Germany), Oct'85 Dist: IMS-Polygram

WHEN THE LADY SMILES.
Single (7"): released on Carrere, Apr'84 by Carrere Records. Dist: PRT, Spartan

Single (12"): released on Carrere, Apr'84 by Carrere Records. Dist: PRT, Spartan

Golden Fiddle Orchestra

GOLDEN FIDDLE ORCHESTRA, THE.
Album: released on Lismor, Nov'82 by Lismor Records. Dist: Lismor, Roots, Celtic Music

Cassette: released on Lismor, Nov'82 by Lismor Records. Dist: Lismor, Roots, Celtic Music

MAGIC OF THE FIDDLE.
Album: released on Mountain, Jul'80 Dist: Mike's Country Music Room Distribution

Golden Gate Quartet

JUBILEE.
Album: released on Ibach (France), Aug'84 Dist: Studio Imports

Cassette: released on Ibach (France), Aug'84 Dist: Studio Imports

NEGRO SPIRITUALS.
Album: released on Happy Bird (Germany), Jun'83 Dist: Polygram, IMS

NO. 1'S (GREATEST HITS), THE.
Album: released on Ibach (France), May'84 Dist: Studio Imports

Cassette: released on Ibach (France), May'84 Dist: Studio Imports

SPIRITUALS.
Tracks: / King of kings (The) / Old time religion / Take my hand precious Lord / My Lord what a morning / Precious memories / For the rest of my life / Casey Jones / Somebody's knocking at your door / Rocks don't fall on me / Roll Jordan roll / Skip to my lou / When they ring the golden bells / Peace in the valley.
Album: released on EMI (Italy), Nov'86 by EMI Records. Dist: Conifer

Cassette: released on EMI (Italy), Nov'86 by EMI Records. Dist: Conifer

Golden Goose

GOLDEN GOOSE (Various Artists).
Cassette: released on Pickwick (Ladybird), Feb'83

Golden Greats

GOLDEN GREATS: 20 BIG BANDS 20 big bands (Various Artists).
Album: released on MCA, Oct'85 by MCA Records. Dist: Polygram, MCA

Cassette: released on MCA, Oct'85 by MCA Records. Dist: Polygram, MCA

Golden Hammond Organ

GOLDEN HAMMOND ORGAN FAVOURITES.
Album: released on Note, Sep'80 by EMI Records. Dist: EMI

Cassette: released on Note, Sep'80 by EMI Records. Dist: EMI

Golden Hits...

GOLDEN HITS OF THE 40'S various artists (Various Artists).
Tracks: / Rum and coca cola / That lucky old sun / Old buttermilk sky / Moonlight becomes you / Don't fence me in / I hear a rhapsody / Baby its cold outside / Time waits for no one / Trolley song (The) / It might as well be spring / I'm always chasing rainbows / Blues in the night / Whispering grass / Paper dolls.
Notes: A wonderfully nostalgic reminder of the million sellers of the 1940's when Americam popular music was attracting huge audiences in the UK. Among the million selling record hits are, 'Rum And Coca Cola' by the Andrew Sisters, 'Moonlight Becomes You' by Bing Crosby, 'Whispering Grass' by The Ink Spots, and 'Anniversary Song' by Al Jonson. Featured also are hits by Dick Haymes, Judy Garland, The Mills Brothers, Jimmy Dorsey, Woody Herman and Louis Armstrong.
Album: released on MCA, Mar'86 by MCA Records. Dist: Polygram, MCA

Cassette: released on MCA, Mar'86 by MCA Records. Dist: Polygram, MCA

GOLDEN HITS OF THE 50'S various artists (Various Artists).
Tracks: / Love is a many splendoured thing / Sweet old fashioned girl, A / Love letters in the sand / Eddie my love / Little things mean a lot / Its almost tomorrow / Unchained melody / May you always / Mr Wonderful / Day the rains came (The) / Tammy / Young love / Rock around the clock / When / Here comes summer / Peggy Sue.
Notes: With the coming of rock'n'roll the 50's generated a complete change in the direction of popular music. This strong album chronicles that change beginning with the close harmonies of The Four Aces' 'Love Is A Many Splendoured Thing', novelty of Teresa Brewer's 'A Sweet Old Fashioned Girl', the smooth tones of Pat Boone with 'Love Letters In The Sand' through to the frantic 'Rock Around The Clock' by Bill Hayley. In between are featured many other classic hits of the 50's including 'Mr Wonderful', 'Peggy Lee', 'Tammy' by Debbie Reynolds, 'Young Love' by Tab Hunter and 'Peggy Sue' by Buddy Holly. Sixteen classic hits which will be long remembered.
Album: released on MCA, Mar'86 by MCA Records. Dist: Polygram, MCA

Cassette: released on MCA, Mar'86 by MCA Records. Dist: Polygram, MCA

GOLDEN HITS OF THE 60'S VOLUME 1 various artists (Various Artists).
Tracks: / Sweet nuthins / Johnny will / Little bitty tear, A / Ginny come lately / Sella / Our day will come / Do diddley / Wipeout / Grazing in the grass / Clapping song (the) / Eve of destruction / 1-2-3 / Monday Monday / If only I had time / Midnight confessions / Born to be wild.
Album: released on MCA, Mar'86 by MCA Records. Dist: Polygram, MCA

Cassette: released on MCA, Mar'86 by MCA Records. Dist: Polygram, MCA

GOLDEN HITS OF THE 60'S VOLUME 2 various artists (Various Artists).
Tracks: / Speedy Gonzalez / Sealed with a kiss / All alone I am / Brown eyed handsome man / Mr. bass man / Deck of cards / Pipeline / Red sails in the sunset / Like a baby / Dedicated to the one I love / Bend me shape me / What a wonderful world / Macarthur Park / Little arrows / Dizzy / Tracy.
Album: released on MCA, Mar'86 by MCA Records. Dist: Polygram, MCA

Cassette: released on MCA, Mar'86 by MCA Records. Dist: Polygram, MCA

GOLDEN HITS OF THE 70'S various artists (Various Artists).
Tracks: / Wandrin' star / When Julie comes round / Hey girl don't bother me / Mama told me / Woodstock / Gypsy woman / Walkin' in the rain with the one I love / Entertainer (The) / If / Don't cry for me Argentina / Float on / Lonely girl / Morning dance.
Album: released on MCA, Mar'86 by MCA Records. Dist: Polygram, MCA

Cassette: released on MCA, Mar'86 by MCA Records. Dist: Polygram, MCA

Golden Horde

CHOCOLATE BISCUIT CONSPIRACY
Album: released on I.D., Feb'86 by I.D. Rec-

DIG THAT CRAZY GRAVE.
Single (7"): released on Hotwire, Feb'85 by Crashed Records. Dist: Rough Trade, Cartel

IN REALITY.
Tracks: / In reality.
Single (12"): released on Media Burn, Feb'86 by Rocks Off Record Emporium. Dist: Rough Trade Distribution, Cartel Distribution

Golden Hour...

GOLDEN HOUR OF BRASS BANDS various artists (Various Artists).
Cassette: released on PRT, Jan'72 by PRT Records. Dist: PRT

GOLDEN HOUR OF CHORAL CLASSICS various artists (Various Artists).
Album: released on Pye, '79

GOLDEN HOUR OF CLARINET JAZZ GIANTS various artists (Various Artists).
Album: released on Pye, '79

Cassette: released on PRT, '79 by PRT Records. Dist: PRT

GOLDEN HOUR OF SCOTTISH DANCE BANDS various Scottish dance bands (Various Artists).
Album: released on Pye, '79

GOLDEN HOUR OF SCOTTISH FAVOURITES various artists (Various Artists).
Album: released on Pye, Jul'75

GOLDEN HOUR OF TOP BRASS various artists (Various Artists).
Cassette: released on PRT, Sep'77 by PRT Records. Dist: PRT

GOLDEN HOUR OF TRADITIONAL JAZZ various artists (Various Artists).
Cassette: released on PRT, Mar'79 by PRT Records. Dist: PRT

Cassette: released on PRT, Sep'72 by PRT Records. Dist: PRT

GOLDEN HOUR OF TRADITIONAL JAZZ VOL.4 various artists (Various Artists).

GOLDEN HOUR PRESENTS BRASS SPECTACULAR various artists (Various Artists).
Album:

GOLDEN HOUR PRESENTS THE BEST OF THE BEATLES SONGS various artists (Various Artists).
Album: released on Pye, '79

GOLDEN HOUR PRESENTS THEMES IN BRASS various artists (Various Artists).
Album: released on Pye, '79

Golden Ladies Of Soul

GOLDEN LADIES OF SOUL.
Cassette: released on Pickwick, Sep'80 by Pickwick Records. Dist: Pickwick Distribution, Prism Leisure Distribution, Lugtons

Golden Music Box...

GOLDEN MUSIC BOX FAVOURITES (Bornard music box collection).
Album: released on Bornard Music Box Co.(USA), Nov'80

Cassette: released on Bornard Music Box Co.(USA), Nov'80

Golden Palaminos

GOLDEN PALAMINOS.
Album: released on Celluloid (France), Jul'85 by Island. Dist: Polygram

VISIONS OF EXCESS.
Album: released on Celluloid (France), Apr'86 by Island. Dist: Polygram

Golden Seal

GOLDEN SEAL, THE Original soundtrack.
Album: released on Compleat, Apr'84 by Compleat Records. Dist: PRT

Cassette: released on Compleat, Apr'84 by Compleat Records. Dist: PRT

Golden Sixties

GOLDEN SIXTIES - INSTRUMENTALS ON PARADE various artists (Various Artists).
Tracks: / Days of Pearly Spencer / Friday on my mind / San Francisco / You are my world / Happy together / Locomotion / Good vibration / California dreamin' / I started a joke / I'll be there / Massachussettes / Eloise.
Notes: Another keyboard genius from Europe, Jean Michel de France, featuring 12 fantastic 80's interpretations of 60's classic pop hots. Prophet 10, Oberheim, DX, Syntne DX7 and more.
Album: released on Teldec (Germany), Nov'85 by Import Records. Dist: IMS Distribution, Poly-

Page 416

Golden Songs...

GOLDEN SONGS FROM THE SILVER SCREEN (Various Artists).
Cassette: released on Music For Pleasure (Holland), Jan'80 by EMI Records. Dist: EMI Deleted Dec'81.

GOLDEN SONGS OF STAGE AND SCREEN various artists (Various Artists).
Tracks: / Around the world / Somewhere my love / Evergreen / Day by day / Summer knows (The) / Send in the clowns / Edelweiss / Somewhere / Long ago / People / Don't cry for me Argentina / Soliloquy / Where do I begin / Gonna build a mountain / Alfie / How to handle a woman / Sunrise, sunset.
Cassette: released on Hour Of Pleasure, Sep'86 by Music For Pleasure Records. Dist: EMI. Estim retail price in Sep'87 was £1.99.

Golden Soul

GOLDEN SOUL (Various Artists).
Album: released on Atlantic, Apr'77 by WEA Records. Dist: WEA

Cassette: released on Ampro Cassettes, Sep'81

Golden Syrup

LOVERS CONCERTO.
Single (7"): released on Code, Oct'83 by Code Records. Dist: Jetstar, EMI

Single (12"): released on Code, Oct'83 by Code Records. Dist: Jetstar, EMI

Golden Trumpets

GOLDEN TRUMPETS (Various Artists).
Compact disc: by Polydor Records. Dist: Polygram, Polydor

Golden Turkey Album

GOLDEN TURKEY ALBUM (THE) various artists (Various Artists).
Album: released on Rhino (USA), May'86 by Rhino Records (USA).

Goldfinger

GOLDFINGER James Bond Original Soundtrack.
Tracks: / Goldfinger / Into Miami / Golden girl / Alpine drive - Auric's factory / Death of Tilley / Odd Job's pressing engagement / Laser beam, The / Bond back in action again / Pussy Galore's flying circus / Teasing the Korean / Gassing the gangsters / Dawn raid on Fort Knox / Arrival of the bomb and countdown, The / Death of Goldfinger, The (End title).
Notes: Produced by Harry Saltzman & Cubby Broccoli. Published by SBK United Partnership.All titles composed by John Barry except 'Goldfinger' - Bricusse/Barry/Newley. Conducted by John Barry.
Album: released on Liberty, Jul'87 by Liberty-United. Dist: EMI

Cassette: released on Liberty, Jul'87 by Liberty-United. Dist: EMI

Album: released on Liberty (Germany), '83

Gold, Harry

LIVE IN LEIPZIG (Gold, Harry & His Pieces Of Eight).
Tracks: / Dixieland jamboree / Davenport blues / That's a plenty / Blue / Riverboat shuffle / At the jazzband hall / Paper doll / Farewell blues / Maryland / Jazz me blues / Some of these days / Big chief Battle-Axe.
Notes: Recorded at Leipzig, G.D.R. 4/9/84. Edited and re-mastered by Paul Adams.
Album: released on Lake, Jan'85 by Fellside Recordings. Dist: Jazz Music, Fellside

OCTAGONAL GOLD (Gold, Harry & His Pieces Of Eight).
Album: released on Black Lion, Jul'80 by Black Lion Records. Dist: Jazz Music, Chris Wellard, Taylor, H.R., Counterpoint, Cadillac

Goldie, Don

JAZZ EXPRESS.
Notes: Mono
Album: released on Jazzology, Jun'86 Dist: Jazz Music, Swift

Goldilocks...

GOLDILOCKS AND THE THREE BEARS (Various Artists).
Tracks: / Goldilocks and the three bears / Sleeping beauty, The / Cock, the mouse and the little red hen, The / Hansel and Gretal / Little Red Riding Hood.
Cassette: released on Tellastory, Dec'86 by Bartlett Bliss Productions. Dist: PRT Distribution, Hayward Promotions Distribution, H.R. Taylor Distribution

GOLDILOCKS & OTHER FAVOURITE STORIES for children aged 3-7 (Various Artists).

GOLDILOCKS & THE THREE BEARS various artists (Various Artists).
Cassette: released on Pickwick (Ladybird), Feb'83

Gold, Louise

PRACTICE PRACTICE.
Tracks: / Practice practice / Supersonic Sam's cosmic cafe.
Single (7"): released on PRT, Apr'86 by PRT Records. Dist: PRT

Goldman Band

PRIDE OF AMERICA.
Tracks: / Governor's Own (The) / Boston Commandery / Pathfinder of Panama (the) / Gate City / His Excellency / Chimes of Liberty (the) / Bonnie Annie Laurie / President's march (the) / Our Director / Pride of America (the) / Tabasco / Revival March / Grandioso / My Maryland / On Jerry shore / Gardes du corps / Serenade (the) / Sesquicentennial march.
Notes: Various American Marches played by the Goldman Band
Album: released on New World (USA), Apr'87 by New World Records (USA). Dist: Conifer

Goldman, Vivien

LAUNDERETTE.
Single (7"): released on Window, Aug'81 Dist: Rough Trade

Gold, Michelle

LOST IN LOVE.
Single (7"): released on Other End, Jul'85 by Other End Records. Dist: PRT Distribution

Single (12"): released on Other End, Jul'85 by Other End Records. Dist: PRT Distribution

Gold, Patti

AS LONG AS WE KEEP BELIEVING.
Single (7"): released on Button, Oct'83 by Musical Characters Records. Dist: Spartan

DON'T TAKE IT.
Single (7"): released on Button, Mar'84 by Musical Characters Records. Dist: Spartan

GOODBYE.
Tracks: / Goodbye / Give me your word.
Single (7"): released on Audiotrax, Jan'86 by Audiotrax. Dist: PRT

LADY LOVES TO DANCE.
Single (7"): released on Look, Sep'81 Dist: R. Smith & Co. Records, H.R. Taylor

Goldsboro, Bobby

BEST OF BOBBY GOLDSBORO.
Album: released on Music For Pleasure (Holland), Apr'83 by EMI Records. Dist: EMI

Cassette: released on Music For Pleasure (Holland), Apr'83 by EMI Records. Dist: EMI

GREATEST HITS:BOBBY GOLDSBORO.
Album: released on Sunset, '78 Dist: EMI

HONEY.
Single (7"): released on United Artists, Apr'68

SUMMER(THE FIRST TIME).
Album: released on Sunset, Sep'77 Dist: EMI

SUMMER(THE FIRST TIME)(7").
Single (7"): released on United Artists, Aug'78

Goldsbury, Mack

ANTHROPOLOGIC.
Album: released on Muse (Import), Apr'81

Goldsmith

LIFE IS KILLING ME.
Single (7"): released on Bedlam, Mar'83 Dist: Pinnacle

Goldsmith, Gerry

ISLAND IN THE STREAM.
Compact disc: released on Silva Screen, Jul'87 Dist: PRT

Goldsmith, Glen

I WON'T CRY.
Single (7"): released on RCA, Aug'87 by RCA Records. Dist: RCA, Roots, Swift, Wellard, Chris, I & B, Solomon & Peres Distribution

Single (12"): released on RCA, Aug'87 by RCA Records. Dist: RCA, Roots, Swift, Wellard, Chris, I & B, Solomon & Peres Distribution

Goldstein, Gil

WRAPPED IN A CLOUD.
Album: released on Muse (Import), '81

Goldthorp, Mark

FLIGHT COMMANDER SOLITUDE AND THE... (Goldthorp, Mark & Simon Hinkler).
Album: released on Golden Dawn, Feb'86 by Artery Records. Dist: Cartel

G'Ole

G'OLE Film soundtrack (Soundtrack).
Album: released on Charisma, Apr'83 by Virgin Records. Dist: EMI

Cassette: released on Charisma, Apr'83 by Virgin Records. Dist: EMI

Gol Gappas

DINNER WITH NOUGAT.
Tracks: / Dinner with nougat / Saint Lucky / Chicken pox / Albert Parker / Ice cream.
Single (12"): released on EL-Cherry Red, Apr'86 by Cherry Red Records. Dist: Pinnacle

WEST 14.
Tracks: / Roman.
Single (7"): released on EL, Nov'86 by El Records. Dist: Rough Trade, Cartel, Pinnacle

Goliard

FORTUNE MY FOE.
Album: released on Broadside, Jun'81 by Broadside Records. Dist: Celtic Distributions, H.R. Taylor, Jazz Music, Projection, Jazz Services Unlimited Dist. (JSU)

Cassette: released on Broadside, Jun'81 by Broadside Records. Dist: Celtic Distributions, H.R. Taylor, Jazz Music, Projection, Jazz Services Unlimited Dist. (JSU)

Golson, Benny

BLUES ON DOWN.
Double Album: released on Milestone, Apr'79 by Ace Records. Dist: PRT

GROOVIN' WITH GOLSON.
Album:

ONE MORE MEMORY (Golson, Benny Quintet with Curtis Fuller).
Album: released on Timeless (Holland), Apr'84 Dist: JSU Distribution, Jazz Music Distribution, Jazz Horizons Distribution, Cadillac, Celtic Music Distribution

PARIS/NEW YORK 1958.
Album: released on Swing Disque, May'87

TIME SPEAKS.
Tracks: / I'll remeber April / Time speaks / No dancin' / Jordu / Blues for Duane / Theme for Maxine.
Notes: With Freddie Hubbard,Woody Shaw & K. Barron
Compact disc: released on Timeless (Holland), Jan'87 Dist: JSU Distribution, Jazz Music Distribution, Jazz Horizons Distribution, Cadillac, Celtic Music Distribution

Album: released on Timeless (Holland), Aug'85 Dist: JSU Distribution, Jazz Music Distribution, Jazz Horizons Distribution, Cadillac, Celtic Music Distribution

Gomez, Eddie

MEZGO.
Tracks: / Me too / Capricious fantasy / Puccini's walk / Delgado / Caribbean morning / Scott David / Cello sonata in G Minor / 1st movement.
Album: released on Epic, Sep'86 by CBS Records. Dist: CBS

Cassette: released on Epic, Sep'86 by CBS Records. Dist: CBS

Moreover

Gomm, Ian

I LIKE YOU I DON'T LOVE YOU.
Single (7"): released on Albion, Jul'81 by Albion Records. Dist: Spartan, Pinnacle

IMAGES.
Tracks: / It's got to be magic / Little lost lamb / Lego / Modern soul / State I'm in, (The) / Cheap hearts hurt / Play on / Just images / What makes a man a... / TV Times / That girl / Beauty & the beast / Cry myself to sleep / Keep on dancing.
Album: released on Decal, Jan'87 by Charly Records. Dist: Charly

I'M IN A HEARTACHE.
Single (7"): released on Albion, Feb'83 by Albion Records. Dist: Spartan, Pinnacle

ITS GOT TO BE MAGIC.
Tracks: / I's got to be magic / Play on.
Single (7"): released on Decal, Sep'86 by Charly Records. Dist: Charly

LEAVE IT TO THE MUSIC.
Single (7"): released on Albion, Nov'82 by Albion Records. Dist: Spartan, Pinnacle

SHE'LL NEVER TAKE THE PLACE OF YOU.
Single (7"): released on Albion, Sep'82 by Albion Records. Dist: Spartan, Pinnacle

SUMMER HOLIDAY.
Album: released on Albion, '78 by Albion Records. Dist: Spartan, Pinnacle

VILLAGE CHOICE, THE.
Album: released on Albion, Oct'82 by Albion Records. Dist: Spartan, Pinnacle

Gonads

DELILAH.
Single (7"): released on Razor, Feb'83 by Razor. Dist: Pinnacle

LIVE:THE OFFICIAL BOOTLEG.
Double Album: released on Red Robin, Aug'84 by Syndicate.

PEACE ARTISTS(EP).
Single (7"): released on Secret, Jul'82 by Secret Records. Dist: EMI

PURE PUNK FOR ROW PEOPLE(EP).
Single (7"): released on Secret, Jul'82 by Secret Records. Dist: EMI

Gone

LET'S GET REAL, REAL GONE FOR A CHANGE.
Album: released on SST, Jul'86 by SST Records. Dist: Pinnacle

Gonella, Nat

GOLDEN AGE OF NAT GONELLA.
Album: released on Golden Age, Jul'85 by Music For Pleasure Records. Dist: EMI

Cassette: released on Golden Age, Jul'85 by Music For Pleasure Records. Dist: EMI

HOW'M I DOIN' (Gonella, Nat & His Georgians).
Tracks: / Ol man mose.
Album: released on Old Bean, May'87 Dist: Jazz Music

Cassette: released on Old Bean, May'87 Dist: Jazz Music

HOW'M I DOIN'? (Gonella, Nat & His Georgians).
Tracks: / How'm I doin'? / Mama don't allow it / Blue turning to grey / Lazy rhythm / Fan it / You rascal you / Get hot / Kickin' the gong around / Bye bye blues / Music goes round and around / Confessin' / Someone sold Gabriels horn / Lady be good / Lady be good / His old cornet / His old cornet / How long how long blues / I want to be happy / Sweet music man / Ol' man river / Swingin' to those lies (it's a sin to tell a lie).
Notes: 1936.
Album: released on Old Bean, Mar'87 Dist: Jazz Music

Cassette: released on Old Bean, Mar'87 Dist: Jazz Music

MISTER RHYTHM MAN (Gonella, Nat & His Georgians).
Album: released on EMI Retrospect, Oct'84 by EMI Records. Dist: EMI

Cassette: released on EMI Retrospect, Oct'84 by EMI Records. Dist: EMI

NAT GONELLA & HIS TRUMPET.
Album: released on Ace Of Clubs, '67 by Decca Records. Dist: Polygram

NAT GONELLA SCRAPBOOK, THE.
Album: released on Joy, May'85 by President Records. Dist: Jazz Music, Swift, President Distribution

NAT GONELLA STORY.
Album: released on Note, Feb'78 by EMI Records. Dist: EMI

NATURALLY.
Tracks: / Yeah man.
Album: released on Conifer, Jun'86 by Conifer Records. Dist: Conifer

Gone To Black

GONE TO BLACK.
Album: released on Probe Plus, Jul'82 by Probe Plus Records. Dist: Probe Plus Distribution

Gone To Earth

FOLK IN HELL.
Album: released on Probe Plus, Nov'86 by Probe Plus Records. Dist: Probe Plus Distribution

LIVE & BURIED.
Single (7"): released on Probe Plus, Nov'85 by Probe Plus Records. Dist: Probe Plus Distribution

Gone With The Wind

GONE WITH THE WIND Original soundtrack (Various Artists).
Tracks: / Main title / Scarlett & Rhett's first meeting / Ashley & Scarlett / Mammy / Christmas during the war in Atlanta / Atlanta in flames / Reconstruction / Ashley returns to Tara from the war prison / Scarlett makes her demands of Rhett / Scarlett's fall down the staircase / Bonnie's fatal pony ride / Finale.
Album: released on CBS, Jul'86 by CBS Records. Dist: CBS

Cassette: released on CBS, Jul'86 by CBS Records. Dist: CBS

GONE WITH THE WIND Original soundtrack.
Album: released on MGM(Germany), Jul'85

GONE WITH THE WIND (CD) Original soundtrack (Steiner, Max).
Tracks: / Main title (inc. Selznick trademark / Barbecue at twelve oaks / Ball, The / Ashley and Scarlett / Mammy / Christmas in Atlanta / Fall of the South / Intermission music / Sherman's march through Georgia / Ashley returns to Tara from the war / Scarlett and Rhett at Tara / Belle Watling / Rhett and Bonnie / Scarlett's fall - Rhett's remorse / Bonnie's death / Finale.
Notes: Composed and conducted by Max Steiner
Compact disc: released on Polydor, Jun'87 by Polydor Records. Dist: Polygram, Polydor

Gong

ANGELS EGGS.
Album: released on Charly, '82 by Charly Records. Dist: Charly, Cadillac

BREAKTHROUGH.
Tracks: / Siciliano / Circle dance / Aja's theme / Divertimento / Concerto for jazz clarinet and orchestra / Allegro / Adagio / Presto.
Album: released on Eulenspiegel (Germany), Feb'87

Cassette: released on Eulenspiegel (Germany), Feb'87

CAMEMBERT ELECTRIQUE.
Tracks: / Radio gnome / You can't kill me / I've bin stone before / Mister Long Shanks / Dynamite / Wet cheese delirium / Squeezing sponges over policemen's heads / Fohat digs holes in space / Tried so hard / Tropical fish / Gnome the second.
Compact disc: released on Charly, Mar'86 by Charly Records. Dist: Charly, Cadillac

Album: released on Charly, '85 by Charly Records. Dist: Charly, Cadillac

Cassette: released on Charly, '85 by Charly Records. Dist: Charly, Cadillac

EXPRESSO 2.
Album: released on Virgin, Feb'78 by Virgin Records. Dist: EMI, Virgin Distribution

FLYING TEAPOT.
Album: released on Charly, '85 by Charly Records. Dist: Charly, Cadillac

Cassette: released on Charly, '85 by Charly Records. Dist: Charly, Cadillac

GAZEUSE.
Album: released on Virgin, Mar'84 by Virgin Records. Dist: EMI, Virgin Distribution

GONG LIVE.
Double Album: released on Virgin, Aug'77 by Virgin Records. Dist: EMI, Virgin Distribution

MAGICK BROTHER.
Tracks: / Mystic sister:Magick brother / Magick brother / Glad to say to say / Rational anthem / Chainstore chant: pretty Miss Titty / Pretty miss titty / Fable of fredfish: Hope you feel OK / Hope you feel O.K. / Ego / Gong song / Princess dreaming / 5 & 20 schoolgirls / 'Cos you got green hair.
Notes: A "BYG" recording. Licensed from Charly Records International APS.
Compact disc: released on Charly, Nov'86 by Charly Records. Dist: Charly, Cadillac

Album: released on Affinity, Nov'77 by Charly Records. Dist: Charly, Cadillac

RADIO GNOME PT.1.
Album: released on Virgin, Mar'84 by Virgin Records. Dist: EMI, Virgin Distribution

RADIO GNOME PT.2.
Album: released on Virgin, Mar'84 by Virgin Records. Dist: EMI, Virgin Distribution

SHAMAL.
Album: released on Virgin, Mar'84 by Virgin Records. Dist: EMI, Virgin Distribution

WINGFUL OF EYES.
Compact disc: released on Virgin, Jan'87 by Virgin Records. Dist: EMI, Virgin Distribution

YOU.
Album: released on Virgin, Mar'84 by Virgin Records. Dist: EMI, Virgin Distribution

Gonks

GONKS ARE HERE FOR CHRISTMAS, THE.
Single (7"): released on WEA, Nov'85 by WEA Records. Dist: WEA

Single (12"): released on WEA, Nov'85 by WEA Records. Dist: WEA

Gonnella, Ron

FIDDLE GEMS.
Album: released on Lismor, Nov'76 by Lismor Records. Dist: Lismor, Roots, Celtic Music

FIDDLERS FANCY.
Album: released on Lismor, '75 by Lismor Records. Dist: Lismor, Roots, Celtic Music

PLAYS THE FIDDLES OF GOW, MARSHALL & SKINNER.
Album: released on Ross, '86 by Ross Records. Dist: Ross Distribution, Roots Distribution

Cassette: released on Ross, '86 by Ross Records. Dist: Ross Distribution, Roots Distribution

RON GONNELLA'S BURN'S NIGHT.

SCOTTISH FIDDLE MASTER.
Cassette: released on Lismor, Jul'80 by Lismor Records. Dist: Lismor, Roots, Celtic Music

Album: released on Lismor, Jul'80 by Lismor Records. Dist: Lismor, Roots, Celtic Music

Album: released on Lismor, Jul'77 by Lismor Records. Dist: Lismor, Roots, Celtic Music

TRIBUTE TO NIEL GOW.
Album: released on Lismor, Jun'78 by Lismor Records. Dist: Lismor, Roots, Celtic Music

Gonsalves, Paul

CLEOPATRA FEELIN' JAZZY.
Album: released on Jasmine, Aug'82 by Jasmine Records. Dist: Counterpoint, Lugtons, Taylor, H.R., Wellard, Chris, Swift, Cadillac

Cassette: released on Jasmine, Aug'82 by Jasmine Records. Dist: Counterpoint, Lugtons, Taylor, H.R., Wellard, Chris, Swift, Cadillac

Duke Ellington & Paul Gonsalves

GETTING TOGETHER.
Compact disc: released on Carrere, Apr'87 by Carrere Records. Dist: PRT, Spartan

GETTIN' TOGETHER.
Compact disc: released on Carrere(France), '86 by Carrere Records (France). Dist: PRT

JUST SITTIN' & A ROCKIN' (Gonsalves, Paul & Ray Nance).
Album: released on Black Lion, Apr'85 by Black Lion Records. Dist: Jazz Music, Chris Wellard, Taylor, H.R., Counterpoint, Cadillac

MEXICAN BANDIT MEETS PITSBURGH PIRATE (Gonsalves, Paul & Roy Eldridge).
Tracks: / 1.5400 North / I cover the waterfront / C jam blues / Body and soul / It's the talk of the town / Somebody loves me.
Notes: The first collaboration between these two important jazz soloists. Paul Gonsalves was a key member of Duke Ellington's Orchestra for most of his working life (he died in 1974, ten days after Ellington). Having started with Ellington as an average tenor player, he emerged as one of the greats. Roy Eldridge is to trumpet players what Lester Young was to tenor saxophonists. He is one of the most important trumpet soloists in jazz history. Having worked with Fletcher Henderson, Teddy Wilson, Benny Goodman, Gene Krupa, Artie Shaw and countless small groups, his wealth of experience is unrivalled. Recorded in New York, 1973.
Album: released on Arhoolie, Oct'86 by Arhoolie Records. Dist: Projection, Topic, Jazz Music, Swift, Roots

Cassette: released on Fantasy, Oct'86 by RCA Records. Dist: RCA, Jetstar

RARE PAUL GONSALVES SEXTET IN EUROPE 1963 (Gonsalves, Paul Sextet).
Album: released on Jazz Connoisseur, Apr'79 Dist: Jazz Horizons, Jazz Music, Swift, Wellard, Chris

SALT & PEPPER (Gonsalves, Paul & Sonny Stitt).
Cassette: released on Jasmine, Jun'82 by Jasmine Records. Dist: Counterpoint, Lugtons, Taylor, H.R., Wellard, Chris, Swift, Cadillac

Album: released on Jasmine, Jun'82 by Jasmine Records. Dist: Counterpoint, Lugtons, Taylor, H.R., Wellard, Chris, Swift, Cadillac

TELL IT THE WAY IT IS.
Album: released on Jasmine, Jun'82 by Jasmine Records. Dist: Counterpoint, Lugtons, Taylor, H.R., Wellard, Chris, Swift, Cadillac

Cassette: released on Jasmine, Jun'82 by Jasmine Records. Dist: Counterpoint, Lugtons, Taylor, H.R., Wellard, Chris, Swift, Cadillac

Gonsalvez, Paul

IT DOESN'T MEAN A THING (Gonsalvez, Paul/ Earl Hines).

Gonzales

JUST MY IMAGINATION.
Single (7"): by PRT Records. Dist: PRT

Single (12"): by PRT Records. Dist: PRT

Gonzales, Charlie

CHARLIE GONZALES.
Album: released on Krazy Kat (USA), Apr'87

Gonzalez

HAVEN'T STOPPED DANCING YET.
Tracks: / Haven't stopped dancing yet / An't no way to treat a lady.
Single (12"):

JUST MY IMAGINATION.
Single (7"): by PRT Records. Dist: PRT

Single (12"): by PRT Records. Dist: PRT

PIRATES.
Single (7"): released on Tooti Frooti, Jun'84 by PRT Records. Dist: PRT Distribution

Single (12"): released on Tooti Frooti, Jun'84 by PRT Records. Dist: PRT Distribution

Gooch, John

AS TIME GOES BY.
Album: released on President, Feb'84 by President Records. Dist: Taylors, Spartan

BRENDAN'S THEME.
Single (7"): released on President, Mar'84 by President Records. Dist: Taylors, Spartan

Goodacre, Tony

25TH ANNIVERSARY.
Album: released on Sylvantone, '84 Dist: Outlet Distribution, Sylvantone Distribution

Cassette: released on Sylvantone, '84 Dist: Outlet Distribution, Sylvantone Distribution

GRANDMA'S FEATHER BED.
Album: released on Outlet, '84 by Outlet Records. Dist: Outlet Distribution

Cassette: released on Outlet, '84 by Outlet Records. Dist: Outlet Distribution

GUERNSEY, I'LL KEEP COMING BACK TO YOU.
Single (7"): released on Homespun(Ireland), May'84 by Outlet Records. Dist: Outlet

MR COUNTRY MUSIC.
Album: released on Outlet, '84 by Outlet Records. Dist: Outlet Distribution

Cassette: released on Outlet, '84 by Outlet Records. Dist: Outlet Distribution

RECORDED LIVE IN ILKLEY.
Album: released on Sylvantone, '84 Dist: Outlet Distribution, Sylvantone Distribution

Cassette: released on Sylvantone, '84 Dist: Outlet Distribution, Sylvantone Distribution

RED ROSES.
Album: released on Sylvantone, '84 Dist: Outlet Distribution, Sylvantone Distribution

Cassette: released on Sylvantone, '84 Dist: Outlet Distribution, Sylvantone Distribution

ROAMIN' ROUND IN NASHVILLE.
Album: released on Outlet, '84 by Outlet Records. Dist: Outlet Distribution

Cassette: released on Outlet, '84 by Outlet Records. Dist: Outlet Distribution

SYVANTONE SHOWCASE, THE (Goodacre, Tony/Jeannie Dee/Stu Page/Remuda/Geoff Ashford).
Album: released on Sylvantone, Aug'85 Dist: Outlet Distribution, Sylvantone Distribution

Cassette: released on Sylvantone, Aug'85 Dist: Outlet Distribution, Sylvantone Distribution

THANKS TO THE HANKS.
Album: released on Outlet, '84 by Outlet Records. Dist: Outlet Distribution

Cassette: released on Outlet, '84 by Outlet Records. Dist: Outlet Distribution

TONY GOODACRE COLLECTION (THE).
Tracks: / Nashville marathon / It's almost tomorrow / Girl I used to know (A) / Workin' my way through a heartache / Have I told you lately that I loved you / Down in Waikiki / I wonder who' kissing her now / Man in the sky / Woman's touch (A) / No tomorrow for yesterdays dreams / Place in the choir / Mocking bird hill / You've made my life complete / Country music is my life / Ain't got nothing to wear.
Album:

Cassette: released on Sylvantone, Jan'86 Dist: Outlet Distribution, Sylvantone Distribution

WRITTEN IN BRITAIN.
Album: released on Sylvantone, '84 Dist: Outlet Distribution, Sylvantone Distribution

Cassette: released on Sylvantone, '84 Dist: Outlet Distribution, Sylvantone Distribution

YOU'VE MADE MY LIFE COMPLETE.
Album: released on Outlet, '84 by Outlet Rec-

ords. Dist: Outlet Distribution

Cassette: released on Outlet, '84 by Outlet Records. Dist: Outlet Distribution

Good, Bad & The Ugly

GOOD, BAD & THE UGLY Original film soundtrack (Various Artists).
Album: released on Liberty, May'85 by Liberty-United. Dist: EMI

Cassette: released on Liberty, May'85 by Liberty-United. Dist: EMI

Good Bye-ee

GOODBYE-EE (SUNG BY 14-18) 20 great hits from the war years (Various Artists).
Album: released on Magnet, Dec'75 by Magnet Records. Dist: BMG

Goodbye Look

HALF THE FUN OF THE CRIME.
Single (7"): released on PRT, Apr'85 by PRT Records. Dist: PRT

Single (12"): released on PRT, Apr'85 by PRT Records. Dist: PRT

Goodbye Mr Chips

GOODBYE MR CHIPS Original cast recoding featuring John Mills (Various Artists).
Album: released on That's Entertainment, Oct'82 by That's Entertainment Records. Dist: Pinnacle, PRT

Cassette: released on That's Entertainment, Oct'82 by That's Entertainment Records. Dist: Pinnacle, PRT

GOODBYE MR CHIPS (CASSETTE) Read by John Shedden (Shedden, John).
Cassette: released on Colophone, Feb'81 by Audio-Visual Library Services. Dist: Audio-Visual Library Services

Goodbye Mr Mackenzie

RATTLER (THE).
Tracks: / Rattler (The).
Single (7"): released on Precious Organisation, Aug'86

Goodbye To All That

GOODBYE TO ALL THAT (Various Artists).
Album: released on Red Flame-Ink, Sep'85

Goodbye to Berlin

GOODBYE TO BERLIN Isherwood, Christopher (Isherwood, Christopher).
Cassette: released on Caedmon(USA), Apr'85 by Caedmon (USA) Records. Dist: Gower, Taylors, Discovery

Good Grief

SWINGING ON A STAR.
Single (7"): released on Anytime Records, Oct'82 by Challenge. Dist: Pinnacle

Good Guys

EXTRA TERRESTRIAL SONG.
Single (7"): released on Public, Dec'82 by Patrick Cambell-Lyons. Dist: Spartan

Goodhand-Tait, Philip

TEACHING AN OLD DOG NEW .....
Cassette: released on Chrysalis, Sep'77 by Chrysalis Records. Dist: CBS

Goodie

YOU AND I/DO SOMETHING.
Single (7"): released on Total Experience, Feb'83 by Phonogram. Dist: Polygram

Single (12"): released on Total Experience, Feb'83 by Phonogram. Dist: Polygram

Gooding, Cuba

HAPPINESS IS JUST AROUND THE BEND.
Single (7"): released on London, Nov'83 by London Records. Dist: Polygram

Single (12"): released on London, Nov'83 by London Records. Dist: Polygram

Good Looks

EVERY DAY OF MY LIFE.
Single (7"): released on Radioactive, Apr'82

JIM'LL FIX IT/JIM HAS FIXED IT FOR YOU.
Single (7"): released on Radioactive, Mar'82

Goodluck, John

SPEED THE PLOUGH.
Album: released on Sweet Folk All, May'81 by Sweet Folk All Records. Dist: Sweet Folk All, Roots, Celtic Music, Dragon, Impetus, Projection, Chris Wellard, Festival Records

SUFFOLK MIRACLE, THE.
Album: released on Tradition, Aug'76 Dist: JSU, Cassion Distribution, Celtic Music, Jazz Music, Projection, Roots Records

Goodman, Benny

1937-38 3 LP box set.
Album: released on Verve, Dec'81 by Phonogram Records. Dist: Polygram

1937-39.
Album: released on Jazz Anthology, Mar'85 Dist: Discovery, Swift

1938-1939 NEWHOUSE PRESENT (Goodman, Benny His Orchestra,Trio & Quartet).
Album: released on Nostalgia, May'86 Dist: Jazz Music, Counterpoint

1938 CARNEGIE HALL JAZZ CONCERT.
Album: by CBS Records. Dist: CBS

20 GREATEST HITS.
Album: released on Astan, Nov'84 by Astan Records. Dist: Counterpoint

Cassette: released on Astan, Nov'84 by Astan Records. Dist: Counterpoint

40TH ANNIVERSARY CONCERT.
Cassette: released on London, May'78 by London Records. Dist: Polygram

ALL OF ME.
Album: released on Black Lion-Intercord, '82

Cassette: released on Black Lion-Intercord, '82

ALL THE CATS JOIN IN (BULLDOG).
Album: released on Bulldog, Oct'85 by Bulldog Records. Dist: President Distribution, Spartan, Swift, Taylor, H.R.

Cassette: released on Bulldog, Oct'85 by Bulldog Records. Dist: President Distribution, Spartan, Swift, Taylor, H.R.

ALL THE CATS JOIN IN.
Album: released on First Heard, May'85 by Submarine Records. Dist: Conifer, Taylors

Cassette: released on First Heard, May'85 by Submarine Records. Dist: Conifer, Taylors

ALTERNATE GOODMAN VOL.12.
Album: released on Nostalgia, May'86 Dist: Jazz Music, Counterpoint

ALTERNATE GOODMAN VOL. 10.
Album: released on Nostalgia, Mar'87 Dist: Jazz Music, Counterpoint

ALTERNATE GOODMAN VOL. 11.
Album: released on Nostalgia, Mar'87 Dist: Jazz Music, Counterpoint

BASEL, SWITZERLAND, 1959.
Album: released on Artistry, Nov'86 Dist: Jazz Music

BASIN STREET BLUES.
Album: released on Astan, Nov'84 by Astan Records. Dist: Counterpoint

Cassette: released on Astan, Nov'84 by Astan Records. Dist: Counterpoint

BENNY GOODMAN.
Album: released on Jazz Reactivation, Jul'82 Dist: PRT

BENNY GOODMAN (Goodman, Benny & Tommy Dorsey).
Notes: Mono recording.Previously unissued broadcast records 36-41.
Album: released on Jazz Archives, Jul'86 by Jazz Archives Records. Dist: Jazz Music

BENNY GOODMAN 1940.
Album: released on Aircheck, Apr'79

BENNY GOODMAN COLLECTION,
Album: released on Deja Vu, Aug'85 by Deja Vu Records. Dist: Counterpoint Distribution, Record Services Distribution (Ireland)

Cassette: released on Deja Vu, Aug'85 by Deja Vu Records. Dist: Counterpoint Distribution, Record Services Distribution (Ireland)

BENNY GOODMAN & HIS ORCHESTRA (Goodman, Benny & His Orchestra).
Compact disc: released on Delta, '86 by Delta Records. Dist: Target

BENNY GOODMAN IN HI FI.
Album: released on Capitol, Mar'85 by Capitol Records. Dist: EMI

Cassette: released on Capitol, Mar'85 by Capitol Records. Dist: EMI

BENNY GOODMAN MEMORIAL CASSETTE.
Cassette: released on Magic, Dec'86 Dist: Jazz Music, Submarine, Swift, Chris Wellard, Conifer

BENNY GOODMAN ORCHESTRA.
Album: released on Kings Of Jazz, Apr'81 Dist: Jazz Horizons, Jazz Music, Celtic Music

BENNY GOODMAN PLAYS CLASSICS.
Double Album: released on Teldec, Mar'87

Cassette: released on Teldec, Mar'87

Double compact disc: released on Teldec, Mar'87

BENNY GOODMAN SWINGS.
Album: released on Pathe MarconiFrance), Jun'85

BENNY GOODMAN VOL.1.
Album: released on Bright Orange, Apr'79 Dist: Swift

BENNY GOODMAN VOL.2.
Album: released on Bright Orange, Apr'79 Dist: Swift

BENNY GOODMAN WITH RED NICHOLS' ORCH..
Album: released on Decca, '79 by Decca Records. Dist: Polygram

BEST OF BENNY GOODMAN(THE).
Cassette: released on RCA, Mar'86 by RCA Records. Dist: RCA, Roots, Swift, Wellard, Chris, I & B, Solomon & Peres Distribution

Album: released on RCA, '84 by RCA Records. Dist: RCA, Roots, Swift, Wellard, Chris, I & B, Solomon & Peres Distribution

BEST OF NEWHOUSE, THE Camel caravan broadcasts 1938-39.
Album: released on Nostalgia (Sweden), '82 by Wellard, Chris Distribution. Dist: Wellard, Chris Distribution

BG 1938.
Album: released on Queendisc (Import), May'83 Dist: Cadillac

BIG CITY SWING.
Album: released on Decca, Oct'80 by Decca Records. Dist: Polygram

BREAKFAST BALL.
Cassette: released on Saville, Jan'86 by Conifer Records. Dist: Conifer

CAMEL CARAVAN BROADCASTS, VOL 3 (Goodman, Benny & His Orchestra).
Album: released on Soundcraft, Nov'86 Dist: Jazz Music

CAMEL CARAVAN BROADCASTS, VOL 2 (Goodman, Benny & His Orchestra).
Album: released on Soundcraft, Nov'86 Dist: Jazz Music

CAMEL CARAVAN BROADCASTS 1938 (Goodman, Benny & His Orchestra).
Album: released on Soundcraft, Nov'86 Dist: Jazz Music

CAMEL CARAVANS VOL.3 One o' clock jump.
Album: released on Giants of Jazz, Oct'85 by Hasmick Promotions Ltd.. Dist: Counterpoint, Jazz Music, Taylors, Swift, Mainline, Wellard, Chris

CAMEL CARAVAN VOL.1.
Album: released on Giants of Jazz, Mar'85 by Hasmick Promotions Ltd.. Dist: Counterpoint, Jazz Music, Taylors, Swift, Mainline, Wellard, Chris

CAMEL CARAVAN VOL.2.
Album: released on Giants of Jazz, Mar'85 by Hasmick Promotions Ltd.. Dist: Counterpoint, Jazz Music, Taylors, Swift, Mainline, Wellard, Chris

Charlie Christian with Benny Goodman Sextet & Orchestra

CLARINET A LA KING The alternate Goodman vol.II.
Album: released on Nostalgia (Sweden), '82 by Wellard, Chris Distribution. Dist: Wellard, Chris Distribution

CLARINETITIS.
Tracks: / Clarinetitis / After a while / Dinah / Jazz holiday, A / Jungle blues / Sheik of Arabay (The) / Shim-me-sha-wabble / How come you do me like you do? / Blue / Muskrat ramble / Room 1411 / That's a-plenty / Indiana / Shirt-tail stomp / Sugar / Crazy 'bout my girl / Woverine blues / Railroad man.
Album: released on Affinity, Jan'86 by Charly Records. Dist: Charly, Cadillac

Cassette: released on Affinity, Jan'86 by Charly Records. Dist: Charly, Cadillac

CLASSICS IN JAZZ.
Album: released on Swaggie (Australia), Jan'83

COMMAND PERFORMANCE.
Album: released on Swinghouse, '84 Dist: Jazz Music Distribution, Swift Distribution, Chris Wellard Distribution

COMPLETE SMALL COMBINATIONS Volumes 1 & 2.
Tracks: / After you've gone / Body and soul / Who? / Someday, sweetheart / China boy / More than you know / All my life / Oh, lady be good / Nobody's sweetheart / Too good to be true / Moonglow / Dinah / Vibraphone blues / Sweet Sue - just you / My melancholy baby / Tiger rag / Stompin' at the savoy / Whispering / Ida sweet as apple cider / Tea for two / Runnin' wild / Avalon / Handful of keys / Man I love (The).
Notes: Double album and cassette. Mono.
Album: released on Jazz Tribune (USA), Sep'86 Dist: Discovery

Double cassette: released on Jazz Tribune (USA), Sep'86 Dist: Discovery

COMPLETE SMALL COMBINATIONS (1935-37) VOL 1/2.
Album: released on RCA (France), '83 by RCA Records. Dist: Discovery

COMPLETE SMALL COMBINATIONS (1937-39) VOL 3/4.
Album: released on RCA (France), '83 by RCA Records. Dist: Discovery

DANCE AND SWING WITH BENNY GOODMAN.
Album: released on Nostalgia (Sweden), '82 by Wellard, Chris Distribution. Dist: Wellard, Chris Distribution

DURING THE FABULOUS FIFTIES.
Album: released on Giants of Jazz, Aug'79 by Hasmick Promotions Ltd.. Dist: Counterpoint, Jazz Music, Taylors, Swift, Mainline, Wellard, Chris

EARL, THE The alternate Goodman vol.V.
Album: released on Nostalgia (Sweden), '82 by Wellard, Chris Distribution. Dist: Wellard, Chris Distribution

FLYING HOME The alternate Goodman vol.II.
Album: released on Nostalgia (Sweden), '82 by Wellard, Chris Distribution. Dist: Wellard, Chris Distribution

FORMATIVE YEARS, THE.
Tracks: / That's a plenty / Clarietitis / Wolverine Blues / Room 1411 / Blue / Blue / Crazy 'bout my gal / Railroad man / Carolina in the morning / How come you do me like you do? / Basin street blues / I gotta right to sing / Your mother's son-in-law / Goergia jubilee / Junk man / Ol' Pappy / Moonglow / Nitwit Serenade / Bugle call rag.
Notes: Featuring Glenn Miller,Gene Krupa,Red Nichols,Jack Teagarden,Billie Holiday,Joe Sullivan and Many more Jazz greats.
Album: released on Decca, Jun'86 by Decca Records. Dist: Polygram

FRENESI The alternate Goodman vol.II.
Album: released on Nostalgia (Sweden), '82 by Wellard, Chris Distribution. Dist: Wellard, Chris Distribution

GET HAPPY.
Album: released on Saville, Apr'87 by Conifer Records. Dist: Conifer

Cassette: released on Saville, Apr'87 by Conifer Records. Dist: Conifer

GOODMAN ON THE AIR.
Album: released on Nostalgia (Sweden), '82 by Wellard, Chris Distribution. Dist: Wellard, Chris Distribution

GOODMAN TOUCH, THE.
Album: released on Swaggie (Australia), Jan'83

HIS ORCHESTRA, TRIO AND QUARTET.
Album: released on Nostalgia, '82 Dist: Jazz Music, Counterpoint

HIS STARS & HIS GUESTS.
Album: released on Queen-Disc, Apr'81 Dist: Celtic Music, JSU, Jazz Horizons, Jazz Music

INDISPENSABLE ALBUM 5/6(THE).
Notes: Double album

INDISPENSABLE BENNY GOODMAN VOLUMES 3&4 1936-1937.
Notes: Double album and Double cassette.Mono recording.

INDISPENSABLE BENNY GOODMAN Volumes 1 & 2 1935-36.
Tracks: / Blue skies / Dear old Southland / Sometimes I'm happy / King porter stomp / Between the devil and the deep blue sea / Madhouse / If I could be with you / When buddah smiles / Stompin' at the Savoy / Breakin' in a pair of shoes / I hope Gabriel likes my music / Mutiny in the parlour / 'Tain't no use / Bugle call rag / Jam session / Goodnight my love / Take another guess(Oh yes) / Did you mean it / When you and i were young,Maggie / Swing low,

Page 418

sweet chariot / He ain't got no rhythm / I want to be happy / Chloe / Rossetta / Peckin' / Can't we be friends? / I'm gonna clap my hands / Sing,sing,sing incorporating Christopher Columbus / Swing is here / Get happy / Christopher Columbus / I know that you know / Star dust / You forgot to remember / When it's sleepy time down south / House hop / I would do anything for you / I've found a new baby / Roll 'em / Swingtime in the Rockies / Pick yourself up / Changes / Down South camp metting / St. Louis blues / Love me or leave me / Bugle call rag / Bob White / Organ grinder's swing / Sugar foot stomp / Riffin' at the Ritz / Minnie the moocher's wedding day / Somebody loves me / Let that be a lesson to you / Pop-corn man / Loch Lomond / Camel hop / True confession / Life goes to a party / It's wonderful / Thank's for the memory / If dreams come true / Sweet stranger.
Album: released on Jazz Tribune (USA), Sep'86 Dist: Discovery

Double cassette: released on Jazz Tribune (USA), Sep'86 Dist: Discovery

Album: released on Jazz Tribune (USA), Sep'86 Dist: Discovery

Double cassette: released on Jazz Tribune (USA), Sep'86 Dist: Discovery

JAM.
Album: released on Swinghouse, '84 Dist: Jazz Music Distribution, Swift Distribution, Chris Wellard Distribution

Cassette: released on Swinghouse, '84 Dist: Jazz Music Distribution, Swift Distribution, Chris Wellard Distribution

JAM SESSION (Goodman, Benny, All Stars).
Cassette: released on Ditto, Sep'86 by Pickwick Records. Dist: H.R. Taylor

JENNY The alternate Goodman vol.IV.
Album: released on Nostalgia (Sweden), '82 by Wellard, Chris Distribution. Dist: Wellard, Chris Distribution

JUMPIN' AT THE WOODSIDE.
Album: released on Giants of Jazz, Jan'87 by Hasmick Promotions Ltd.. Dist: Counterpoint, Jazz Music, Taylors, Swift, Mainline, Wellard, Chris

Cassette: released on Giants of Jazz, Jan'87 by Hasmick Promotions Ltd.. Dist: Counterpoint, Jazz Music, Taylors, Swift, Mainline, Wellard, Chris

JUMPIN' AT THE WOODSIDE (ALTERNATE GOODMAN VOL.1).
Album: released on Nostalgia (Sweden), '82 by Wellard, Chris Distribution. Dist: Wellard, Chris Distribution

KING OF SWING 1958-67.
Notes: Double LP
Album: released on Meteor, Aug'86 by Magnum Music Group Ltd. Dist: Magnum Music Group Ltd, PRT Distribution, Spartan Distribution

Album: released on CBS(Import), Jun'86 by CBS Records. Dist: Conifer, Discovery, Swift

Album: released on Musidisc (France), Oct'83 Dist: Discovery Distribution, Swift Distribution

KING PORTER STOMP.
Tracks: / Someday,Sweetheart / Madhouse / Sandman / If I could be with you one hour tonight / When Buddha smiles / Hunkadola / I'm living in a great big way / Dixieland band(The) / Japanese Sandman / You're a heavenly thing / Restless / Always / Ballad in Blue / Dear old Southland / Sometimes I'm Happy / King porter stomp / Between the devil and the deep blue sea / After you've gone / Body and Soul.
Album: released on Dance Band Days, Jun'86 Dist: Geoff's Records International

Cassette: released on Dance Band Days, Jun'86 Dist: Geoff's Records International

Album: released on Saville, Jun'86 by Conifer Records. Dist: Conifer

Cassette: released on Saville, Jun'86 by Conifer Records. Dist: Conifer

LET'S DANCE.
Album: released on Jazz Live, Apr'81

LET'S DANCE (EMI).
Album: released on EMI Europe, Jun'84 by EMI Records. Dist: Conifer

Cassette: released on EMI Europe, Jun'84 by EMI Records. Dist: Conifer

LIVE AT CARNEGIE HALL 40th Anniversary concert.
Tracks: / Let's Dance / I've found a new baby / Send in the clowns / Loch Lomond / Stardust / I love a piano / Roll 'em / King porter stomp / Rocky raccoon / Yesterday / That's a plenty / How high the moon / Moonglow / Oh lady be good / Jersey bounce / Someone to watch over me / Please don't talk to me when i'm gone / Benny Goodman Medley / Sing,Sing,Sing & Christopher columbus / Goodbye.
Compact disc: released on London, Jun'86 by London Records. Dist: Polygram

LONDON DATE.
Album: released on Sonic, Jul'76

MEMORIAL.
Notes: Unissued recordings 1943-46-61
Album: released on Magic, Jul'86 Dist: Jazz Music, Submarine, Swift, Chris Wellard, Conifer

Cassette: released on Magic, Jul'86 Dist: Jazz Music, Submarine, Swift, Chris Wellard, Conifer

MEMORIES OF THE SIXTIES.
Album: released on Bulldog, Mar'82 by Bulldog Records. Dist: President Distribution, Spartan, Swift, Taylor, H.R.

Cassette: released on Bulldog, Mar'82 by Bulldog Records. Dist: President Distribution, Spartan, Swift, Taylor, H.R.

MORE OF THE FABULOUS FIFTIES.
Album: released on Giants of Jazz, Aug'79 by Hasmick Promotions Ltd.. Dist: Counterpoint, Jazz Music, Taylors, Swift, Mainline, Wellard, Chris

NIGHT WITH BENNY GOODMAN, A.
Album: released on Jazz Live, Oct'86

OH MR GOODMAN.
Album: released on Swinghouse, Apr'79 Dist: Jazz Music Distribution, Swift Distribution, Chris Wellard Distribution

Cassette: released on Swinghouse, Oct'84 Dist: Jazz Music Distribution, Swift Distribution, Chris Wellard Distribution

ONE O'CLOCK JUMP (Goodman, Benny Caravans).
Album: released on Giants of Jazz, Oct'85 by Hasmick Promotions Ltd.. Dist: Counterpoint, Jazz Music, Taylors, Swift, Mainline, Wellard, Chris

ORCHESTRA AND GROUPS.
Album: released on Rarities, Apr'81

ORCHESTRAS & GROUPS.
Album: released on Rarities, Apr'81

ORIGINAL SOUNDS OF THE SWING ERA VOL.6.
Album: released on RCA (Germany), '83

PERMANENT GOODMAN, THE A portrait of music 1926-45.
Notes: 3 LP box set.
Album: released on Nostalgia, Mar'87 Dist: Jazz Music, Counterpoint

PLAYS GERSHWIN.
Album: released on CBS, May'83 by CBS Records. Dist: CBS

Cassette: released on CBS, May'83 by CBS Records. Dist: CBS

RARE BROADCASTING TANSCRIPTIONS 1935.
Album: released on Jazz Anthology, Apr'85 Dist: Discovery, Swift

REHEARSAL SESSIONS 1940.
Album: released on Jazz Document, Jul'82 Dist: Jazz Music

ROLL 'EM.
Album: released on Submarine, Oct'86 by Submarine Records. Dist: Wellard, Chris Distribution, Conifer Distribution, H.R. Taylor Distribution

Cassette: released on Submarine, Oct'86 by Submarine Records. Dist: Wellard, Chris Distribution, Conifer Distribution, H.R. Taylor Distribution

ROLL 'EM (Goodman, Benny, All Stars).
Tracks: / Airmail special / Don't be that way / Between the devil and the deep blue sea / Flying home / Roll 'em boogie.
Album: released on Swinghouse, Mar'87 Dist: Jazz Music Distribution, Swift Distribution, Chris Wellard Distribution

Cassette: released on Swinghouse, Mar'87 Dist: Jazz Music Distribution, Swift Distribution, Chris Wellard Distribution

ROYAL FLUSH The alternate Goodman vol.VIII.
Album: released on Nostalgia (Sweden), '82 by Wellard, Chris Distribution. Dist: Wellard, Chris Distribution

ROYAL FLUSH (ASTAN).
Album: released on Astan, Nov'84 by Astan Records. Dist: Counterpoint

Cassette: released on Astan, Nov'84 by Astan Records. Dist: Counterpoint

SELECT (Goodman, Benny(Quintet & Sextet)).
Cassette: released on Swinghouse, Dec'85 Dist: Jazz Music Distribution, Swift Distribution, Chris Wellard Distribution

SELECTET.
Album: released on Swinghouse, Feb'81 Dist: Jazz Music Distribution, Swift Distribution, Chris Wellard Distribution

SESSION (Goodman, Benny, All Stars).
Tracks: / Go, Margot, go / Get happy / Raising the riff / Billie's bounce / Ten-bone / Honeysuckle rose / Slipped disc / Breakfast feud.
Album: released on Swinghouse, Mar'87 Dist: Jazz Music Distribution, Swift Distribution, Chris Wellard Distribution

Cassette: released on Swinghouse, Mar'87 Dist: Jazz Music Distribution, Swift Distribution, Chris Wellard Distribution

SMALL GROUPS (1947-49).
Album: released on Swaggie (Australia), Jan'83

SMALL GROUPS VOL.1.
Album: released on Giants of Jazz, Jan'85 by Hasmick Promotions Ltd.. Dist: Counterpoint, Jazz Music, Taylors, Swift, Mainline, Wellard, Chris

SOMETIMES I'M HAPPY.
Album: released on Joker, Apr'81 Dist: Counterpoint, Mainline, Record Services Distribution (Ireland)

SWING GOES ON, THE.
Album: released on EMI (Germany), '83 by EMI Records. Dist: Conifer

SWINGIN' THROUGH THE YEARS.
Album: released on Giants of Jazz, Aug'79 by Hasmick Promotions Ltd.. Dist: Counterpoint, Jazz Music, Taylors, Swift, Mainline, Wellard, Chris

SWINGS.
Album: released on Pathe MarconiFrance), May'85

SWING WITH BENNY GOODMAN & HIS ORCHESTRA.
Album: released on CBS(France), May'85 by CBS Records. Dist: Conifer, Discovery, Swift

Cassette: released on CBS(France), May'85 by CBS Records. Dist: Conifer, Discovery, Swift

S'WONDERFUL SWING.
Tracks: / Seven come eleven / Great day / Lonely moments / Oh baby / Moon-faced and starry-eyed / Cu-tu-gu-ru / S'Wonderful / Linda / Clarinet a la King / Maybe you'll be there / Mahzel / Sing, sing, sing.
Album: released on First Heard, Jul'86 by Submarine Records. Dist: Conifer, Taylors

Cassette: released on First Heard, Jul'86 by Submarine Records. Dist: Conifer, Taylors

THIS IS BENNY GOODMAN.
Tracks: / King porter stomp / Sometimes I'm happy / When Buddha smiles / Stompin' at the Savoy / I know that you know / These foolish things remind me of you / Down south camp meeting / You turned the tables on me / Moonglow / Goodnight my love / Never should have told you / Sing,Sing,Sing / Changes / Afraid to dream / Avalon / Sugarfoot Stomp / Don't be that way / One o'clock jump / I let a song go out of my heart / And the Angels sing.
Notes: Double Album
Album: released on RCA, Jul'86 by RCA Records. Dist: RCA, Roots, Swift, Wellard, Chris, I & B, Solomon & Peres Distribution

Cassette: released on RCA, Jul'86 by RCA Records. Dist: RCA, Roots, Swift, Wellard, Chris, I & B, Solomon & Peres Distribution

THIS IS BENNY GOODMAN VOL 2.
Album: released on RCA (Germany), '83

THIS IS BENNY GOODMAN VOL 1.
Album: released on RCA (Germany), '83

TOGETHER AGAIN.
Album: released on RCA (France), Jun'84 by RCA Records. Dist: Discovery

UNHEARD BENNY GOODMAN, THE - VOL.9, 1947-1955.
Album: released on Blu-Disc (USA), Jan'87 Dist: Jazz Music

UNHEARD BENNY GOODMAN, THE - VOL.7, 1941-1942.
Album: released on Blu-Disc (USA), Jan'87 Dist: Jazz Music

UNHEARD BENNY GOODMAN, THE - VOL.8, 1936-1955.
Album: released on Blu-Disc (USA), Jan'87 Dist: Jazz Music

UNISSUED RADIO MATERIAL 1943.
Album: released on Queen-Disc, Apr'81 Dist: Celtic Music, JSU, Jazz Horizons, Jazz Music

V DISCS 1943/44.
Album: released on Jazz Society, Mar'87 Dist: Jazz Music, Swift

VOLUME 2.
Album: released on Jazz Anthology, Mar'85 Dist: Discovery, Swift

WAR YEARS, THE 1943/44/45.
Album: released on Jazz Anthology, Apr'85 Dist: Discovery, Swift

Goodmans Caravans

VOLUME 4.
Album: released on Jasmine, May'86 by Jasmine Records. Dist: Counterpoint, Lugtons, Taylor, H.R., Wellard, Chris, Swift, Cadillac

Good Missionaries

FIRE FROM HEAVEN.
Album: released on Deptford Fun City, Aug'79 by Faulty Products Records. Dist: Faulty Products Records, Pinnacle

Good Morning

GOOD MORNING BLUES "VAR GOD DROJ" Featuring Claes Jansson etc (Various Artists).
Album: released on Phontastic (Sweden), '82 by Wellard, Chris Distribution. Dist: Wellard, Chris Distribution

GOOD MORNING MR PRESLEY (Various Artists).
Album: released on Grunt Grunt A Go-Go, Jul'85 Dist: Backs, Cartel

Good News

MAKIN' IT.
Single (7"): released on Humber, Jun'84 by Humber Records. Dist: Humber

Single (12"): released on Humber, Jun'84 by Humber Records. Dist: Humber

SEE THE MARINERS.
Tracks: / See the mariners / Jambo.
Single (7"): released on Humber, Jan'86 by Humber Records. Dist: Humber

Good Old Days

GOOD OLD DAYS, THE Various artists with Leonard Sachs.
Album: released on Pye Special, Mar'76

Good Old Way

GOOD OLD WAY (SAMPLER) (Various Artists).
: released on Topic, '81 Dist: Roots Distribution

Good Ol' Persons

I CAN'T STAND TO RAMBLE.
Album: released on Kaleidoscope (USA), Feb'85 by Flying Fish Records (USA). Dist: Flying Fish (USA)

Good Rats

FROM RATS TO RICHES.
Album: released on Radar, '78 by WEA Music Ltd. Dist: WEA, PRT

Goodrum, Randy

SOLITARY NIGHTS.
Tracks: / It's like you never left at all / Software / Mr.Sandman / Holdin' out for love / Silhouette / Dolph / Solitary nights / Lady in the doorway, The / Little Bird / S soft your goodbye.
Notes: "Solitary Nights"is the complete"do-it-yourself"album by a man who waited almosttoo long to expose his great talents under his own name.Until this moment Randy had contended himself by writing songs for others,such George Benson and Kenny Rogers.Benson's "20-20 Vision"is one of his.Here is new voice with an entirely personal musical approach,based on catchy melodies with intriguing and intelli- gent lyrics.As well as singing and playing all the instruments,he also handled the actual recording using the ultimate harware techniques.Of the ten songs,nineare by Randy Goodrum.
Album: released on GRP (USA), Feb'86 by GRP Records (USA). Dist: IMS, Polygram

Compact disc: released on GRP (USA), Feb'86 by GRP Records (USA). Dist: IMS, Polygram

Goodson, Ida

IDA GOODSON SINGS AND PLAYS CHURCH MUSIC....
Notes: Full title: "Sings and plays church music and songs from the south".
Album: released on CSA, Jan'87 by CSA Records. Dist: PRT, Jetstar

Good Vibrations

GOOD VIBRATIONS Sounds of top 40 radio 1964-67 (Various Artists).

Goodwin, Jim

JIM GOODWIN & FRIENDS.
Album: released on Berkeley Rhythm, Jul'82 Dist: Jazz Music

Goodwin, Ken

MAKE SOMEONE HAPPY.
Album: released on President, '82 by President Records. Dist: Taylors, Spartan

Cassette: released on President, '82 by President Records. Dist: Taylors, Spartan

MERRY CHRISTMAS DARLING.
Album: released on President, Nov'79 by President Records. Dist: Taylors, Spartan

Goodwin, Mabel

"JAN STEWER" RECITATIONS.
Cassette: released on Folktracks, Nov'79 by Folktracks Cassettes. Dist: Folktracks

Goodwin, Ron

ADVENTURE AND EXCITEMENT (Goodwin, Ron & His Orchestra).
Tracks: / Theme from The Adventures Of Black Beauty / Battle Of Britain / Theme from The Trap / Trap, The / Theme from Lawrence Of Arabia / Lawrence of Arabia / First of The Few / Theme from Ben Hur / Ben Hur / Theme from The Big Country / Big Country, The / Magnificent seven / Headless horesmen (The) / Lara's theme from Dr. Zhivago / Music of Richard Rogers (The) / Carousel waltz, Oklahoma (The) / Oklahoma / Galloping Home / Those magnificent men...... / Theme from Battle of Britain / Trap (The) / Lawrence of Arabia / Spitfire prelude and fugue / Ben Hur / 633 Squadron / Lancelot & Guinevere / Big country (The) / Aces high (Luftwaffe march) / Luftwaffe March / Theme from The Battle of Britain / Magnificent Seven, The / Headless horseman, The / "Lara's Theme" from Dr.Zhivago / Theme from "Where Eagles Dare" / Where Eagles Dare / Suite from "Monte Carlo Or Bust" / Monte Carlo Or Bust / Carousel waltz, The / Oklahoma.
Album: released on EMI, Apr'87 by EMI Records. Dist: EMI

Cassette: released on EMI, Apr'87 by EMI Records. Dist: EMI

CHRISTMAS WONDERLAND (Goodwin, Ron & His Orchestra).
Album: released on Columbia, Dec'85 by EMI Records. Dist: EMI

Cassette: released on Columbia, Dec'85 by EMI Records. Dist: EMI

CONDUCTS THE NEW ZEALAND SYMPHONY ORCH..
Album: released on Columbia, Oct'84 by EMI Records. Dist: EMI

Cassette: released on Columbia, Oct'84 by EMI Records. Dist: EMI

DRAKE 400 (CONCERT SUITE).
Album: released on Chandos, Aug'84 by Chandos Records. Dist: Harmonia Mundi, Taylors

Cassette: released on Chandos, Aug'84 by Chandos Records. Dist: Harmonia Mundi, Taylors

LEGEND OF THE GLASS MOUNTAIN.
Album: released on EMI, Nov'80 by EMI Records. Dist: EMI

Cassette: released on EMI, Nov'80 by EMI Records. Dist: EMI

LOVE ALBUM, THE.
Album: released on MFP, Jul'85 by EMI Records. Dist: EMI

Cassette: released on MFP, Jul'85 by EMI Records. Dist: EMI

RON GOODWIN PLAYS BACHARACH AND DAVID.
Cassette: released on Ideal(Tapes), Jul'84 Dist: EMI

Goody, Kim

DON'T TURN AROUND.
Tracks: / Don't turn around / I need time.
Single (7"): released on Polydor, Mar'87 by Polydor Records. Dist: Polygram, Polydor

Goombay Dance Band

DON'T YOU CRY CAROLINE.
Single (7"): released on Starblend, Dec'84 by Starblend Records. Dist: PRT Distribution

GOOMBAY DANCE BAND 4 track cassette EP.
Cassette: released on Epic, Aug'82 by CBS Records. Dist: CBS

TYPICAL JAMAICAN MESS, A.
Tracks: / Typical Jamaican mess, A / Canta Di Legua.
Single (7"): released on WEA International, May'86

Single (12"): released on WEA International, May'86

Goonies

GOONIES Original sound track (Various Artists).
Album: released on Epic, Nov'85 by CBS Records. Dist: CBS

Cassette: released on Epic, Nov'85 by CBS Records. Dist: CBS

Goons

BLOODNOCK'S ROCK 'N' ROLL/I LOVE YOU.
Single (7"): released on Decca, Oct'75 by Decca Records. Dist: Polygram

DARK SIDE OF THE GOONS.
Album: released on One Up, Nov'80 by EMI Records.

Cassette: released on One Up, Nov'80 by EMI Records.

FIRST MEN OF THE GOON.
Album: released on Note, May'79 by EMI Records. Dist: EMI

Cassette: released on EMI, May'79 by EMI Records. Dist: EMI

GOON SHOW CLASSICS VOL.1.
Album: released on BBC, Sep'81 by BBC Records & Tapes. Dist: EMI, PRT, Pye

Cassette: released on BBC, Sep'81 by BBC Records & Tapes. Dist: EMI, PRT, Pye

GOON SHOW CLASSICS VOL.3.

GOON SHOW CLASSICS VOL.4.
Album: released on BBC, Sep'81 by BBC Records & Tapes. Dist: EMI, PRT, Pye

Cassette: released on BBC, Sep'81 by BBC Records & Tapes. Dist: EMI, PRT, Pye

GOON SHOW CLASSICS VOL.2.
Album: released on BBC, Sep'81 by BBC Records & Tapes. Dist: EMI, PRT, Pye

Cassette: released on BBC, Sep'81 by BBC Records & Tapes. Dist: EMI, PRT, Pye

Album: released on BBC, Sep'81 by BBC Records & Tapes. Dist: EMI, PRT, Pye

GOON SHOW CLASSICS VOL.6.
Album: released on BBC, '79 by BBC Records & Tapes. Dist: EMI, PRT, Pye

Cassette: released on BBC, '79 by BBC Records & Tapes. Dist: EMI, PRT, Pye

GOON SHOW CLASSICS VOL.7.
Album: released on BBC, Sep'80 by BBC Records & Tapes. Dist: EMI, PRT, Pye

Cassette: released on BBC, Sep'80 by BBC Records & Tapes. Dist: EMI, PRT, Pye

GOON SHOW CLASSICS VOL.8.
Album: released on BBC, Sep'81 by BBC Records & Tapes. Dist: EMI, PRT, Pye

Cassette: released on BBC, Sep'81 by BBC Records & Tapes. Dist: EMI, PRT, Pye

GOON SHOW CLASSICS VOL.9.
Album: released on BBC, Sep'82 by BBC Records & Tapes. Dist: EMI, PRT, Pye

Cassette: released on BBC, Sep'82 by BBC Records & Tapes. Dist: EMI, PRT, Pye

GOON SHOW CLASSICS VOL.10.
Album: released on BBC, Oct'83 by BBC Records & Tapes. Dist: EMI, PRT, Pye

Cassette: released on BBC, Oct'83 by BBC Records & Tapes. Dist: EMI, PRT, Pye

GOON SHOW CLASSICS VOL.11.
Album: released on BBC, Oct'85 by BBC Records & Tapes. Dist: EMI, PRT, Pye

Cassette: released on BBC, Oct'85 by BBC Records & Tapes. Dist: EMI, PRT, Pye

GOON SHOW CLASSICS VOL.5.
Album: released on BBC, Sep'81 by BBC Records & Tapes. Dist: EMI, PRT, Pye
Cat. no: **REB 339**

GOON SHOW GREATS.
Album: released on Parlophone, Oct'79 by EMI Records. Dist: EMI

Cassette: released on Parlophone, Oct'79 by EMI Records. Dist: EMI

GOON SHOW, THE.
Album: released on MFP, Jan'84 by EMI Records. Dist: EMI

Cassette: released on MFP, Jan'84 by EMI Records. Dist: EMI

LAST GOON SHOW OF ALL.
Album: released on BBC, Oct'77 by BBC Records & Tapes. Dist: EMI, PRT, Pye

MICHAEL PARKINSON MEETS THE GOONS.
Album: released on BBC, Sep'81 by BBC Records & Tapes. Dist: EMI, PRT, Pye

VERY BEST OF THE GOONS.
Album: released on EMI, Dec'74 by EMI Records. Dist: EMI

Cassette: released on EMI, Dec'74 by EMI Records. Dist: EMI

WORLD OF THE GOONS.
Album: released on Decca, Jan'80 by Decca Records. Dist: Polygram

Cassette: released on Decca, Jan'80 by Decca Records. Dist: Polygram

YING TON SONG/I'M WALKING BACKWARDS.
Single (7"): released on Decca, Jul'73 by Decca Records. Dist: Polygram

Goon Squad

EIGHT ARMS TO HOLD YOU.
Single (7"): released on Epic, Sep'85 by CBS Records. Dist: CBS Deleted '86.

Single (12"): released on Epic, Sep'85 by CBS Records. Dist: CBS Deleted '86.

Goose Girl

GOOSE GIRL.
Cassette: released on Pickwick (Tell-a-tale), Oct'84 by Pickwick Records. Dist: Pickwick Distribution

Gorby, Sarah

RUSSUE ETERNELLE (RUSSIAN AND GYPSY SONGS).
Album: released on Arion (France), Jun'79 Dist: Conifer, Discovery

Gordan, Joe

JOE GORDAN & SALLY LOGAN (Gordan, Joe & Sally Logan).
Album: released on Lismor, '75 by Lismor Records. Dist: Lismor, Roots, Celtic Music

Gordon, Alistair

TOUCH AND GO.
Single (7"): released on Rainbow, Jun'85 Dist: I & B, CBS

Gordon, Curtis

ROCK ROLL JUMP & JIVE.
Album: released on Bear Family, Jun'85 by Bear Family Records. Dist: Rollercoaster Distribution, Swift

YOU AIN'T SEEN NOTHIN' YET.
Tracks: / Rompin' and stompin' / Caffeine and nicotine / Baby, baby me / Tell 'em no / Divided heart / Little Bo-Peep / I'd like to tell you / You crazy, crazy moon / I'd do it for you / You ain't seen nothin' yet / If you tell me one more lie / Greatest sin, (The) / Rocky road of love / What's a little pride / Where'd ja get so much of / I just don't love you anymore.
Album: released on Bear Family, May'87 by Bear Family Records. Dist: Rollercoaster Distribution, Swift

YOU AIN'T SEEN NOTHIN' YET.
Album: released on Bear Family, Jul'87 by Bear Family Records. Dist: Rollercoaster Distribution, Swift

Gordon, Dexter

BLUES AND BALLADS.
Album: by Sonet Records. Dist: PRT

BLUES WALK.
Album: released on Black Lion, Sep'85 by Black Lion Records. Dist: Jazz Music, Chris Wellard, Taylor, H.R., Counterpoint, Cadillac

BOUNCIN' WITH DEX.
Album: released on Steeplechase Import, Mar'77

CHASE, THE.
Album: released on Spotlite, '83 by Spotlite Records. Dist: Cadillac, Jazz Music, Spotlite

CLUBHOUSE.
Album: released on Liberty-United, Jun'80 by EMI Records. Dist: EMI

DADDY PLAYS THE HORN.
Tracks: / Confirmation / Number four / Darn that dream / Autumn in New Yorks / Daddy plays the horn / You can depend on me.
Compact disc: released on Charly, Jan'87 by Charly Records. Dist: Charly, Cadillac

Album: released on Affinity, '83 by Charly Records. Dist: Charly, Cadillac

DAY IN COPENHAGEN, A (Gordon, Dexter & Slide Hampton).
Tracks: / My blues / You don't know what love is / New thing, A / What's new / Shadow of your smile, The / Day in Vienna, A.
Notes: Recorded in 1969 this was the first Dexter album to be arranged around the frame of three horns,drafted by Slide Hampton. Features three Slide Hampton original compositions and three standards.Dexter Gordon has received much acclaim in recent months for his performance in the film 'Around Midnight' in which he starred.
Compact disc: released on MPS Jazz, May'87

DEXTER BLOWS HOT AND COOL.
Compact disc: released on Boplicity, May'87 by Boplicity Records. Dist: Ace Records, Pinnacle

DEXTER BLOWS HOT & COLD.
Album: released on Boplicity, Jul'84 by Boplicity Records. Dist: Ace Records, Pinnacle

DEXTER CALLING.
Tracks: / Soul sister / Modal mood / I want more / End of a love affair / Clear the dex / Ernie's tune / Smile / Landslide / Soul sister / Modal mood / I want more / End of a love affair / Clear the dex / Ernie's tune / Smile / Landslide.
Compact disc: released on Manhattan-Blue Note, Jun'87 by EMI America Records (USA). Dist: EMI

DEXTER GORDON/KENNY DORHAM (Gordon, Dexter & Kenny Dorham).
Album: released on Jazz Reactivation, Jul'82 Dist: PRT

DOIN' ALRIGHT.
Cassette: released on Blue Note, Apr'87 by EMI Records. Dist: EMI

Album: released on Blue Note, Apr'87 by EMI Records. Dist: EMI

GETTIN' AROUND.
Tracks: / Manha de carnaval / Who can I turn to? / Heartaches / Shiny stockings / Everybody's somebody's fool / Le coiffeur / Very saxily yours / Flick of a trick.
Notes: * Extra tracks on CD only.
Album: released on Blue Note, Jul'87 by EMI Records. Dist: EMI

Compact disc: released on Manhattan-Blue Note, Jun'87 by EMI America Records (USA). Dist: EMI

Album: released on Blue Note, Aug'87 by EMI Records. Dist: EMI

GO!.
Tracks: / Cheesecake / Guess I'll hang out my tears to dry / Second balcony jump / Love for sale / Where are you? / Three o'clock in the morning.
Compact disc: released on EMI, Mar'87 by EMI Records. Dist: EMI

Album: released on Blue Note, Apr'85 by EMI Records. Dist: EMI

Cassette: released on Blue Note, Sep'87 by EMI Records. Dist: EMI. Estim retail price in Sep'87 was £5.99.

GOTHAM CITY.
Album: released on CBS, Feb'81 by CBS Records. Dist: CBS

HUNT, THE (see Gray, Wardell) (Gordon, Dexter & Wardell Gray).

I WANT MORE.
Album: released on Steeplechase Import, May'81

LIVE With Georges Arvanitas Trio (Gordon, Dexter/Sonny Grey).
Album: released on Spotlite, '83 by Spotlite Records. Dist: Cadillac, Jazz Music, Spotlite

LIVE AT THE AMSTERDAM PARADISO.
Album: released on Affinity, Aug'79 by Charly Records. Dist: Charly, Cadillac

LONG TALL DEXTER.
Album:

MONTMARTRE VOL.1.
Album: released on Black Lion, Jan'85 by Black Lion Records. Dist: Jazz Music, Chris Wellard, Taylor, H.R., Counterpoint. Cadillac

MOVE.
Album: released on Spotlite, '83 by Spotlite Records. Dist: Cadillac, Jazz Music, Spotlite

NIGHTS AT THE KEYSTONE.
Tracks: / Sophisticated lady / It's you or no one / Antabus / Easy Living / Tangerine / More than you know.
Notes: Double Album,Double Cassette.Dexter Gordon released a string on the Blue Note label in the sixties.recorded in 1978 and 1979 at San Francisco's famous Key- stone Korner,this live 2-record set captures the Dexter Gordon Quartet in top form responding to the warm crown with incredible musicianship.The quartet features George Cable on piano,Rufus Reid on bass and Eddie Gladden on drums,andthis album will be the first release from Dexter Gordon for a number of years.
Album: released on Blue Note, Dec'85 by EMI Records. Dist: EMI

Cassette: released on Blue Note, Dec'85 by EMI Records. Dist: EMI

ONE FLIGHT UP.
Tracks: / Tanya / Coppin'The Haven / Darn that Dream.
Notes: The tenor saxophone pioneer Dexter Gordon is accompanied by Donald Byrd and Kenny Drew in this,his second Paris session for Blue Note.The three performancesare lengthy

and swinging with a special aura of intimacy. This album introduced Byrd's "Tanya" which remains in Gordon's repertoire to this day.
Album: released on Blue Note, Dec'85 by EMI Records. Dist: EMI

OTHER SIDE OF ROUND MIDNIGHT, THE.
Tracks: / Round Midnight / Berangere's nightmare / Call sheet blues / What is this thing called love / Tivoli / Society red / As time goes by / It's only a paper moon / Round midnight (2).
Notes: This is the alternative soundtrack to the movie "Round Midnight" which opened in the West End during November 1986. As well as performances by the great Dexter Gordon who stars in the movie, it also contains music by Herbie Hancock and a performance by Bobby McFerrin.
Album: released on Blue Note, Dec'86 by EMI Records. Dist: EMI

OTHER SIDE OF ROUND MIDNIGHT (THE).
Tracks: / Round midnight / Berangere's nightmare / Call sheet blues / What is this thing called love.. / Tivoli / Society red / As time goes by / It's only a paper moon / Round midnight.
Compact disc: released on EMI, Mar'87 by EMI Records. Dist: EMI

OUR MAN IN PARIS.
Tracks: / Scrapple from the apple / Willow weep for me / Broadway / Stairway to the stars / Night in Tunisia, A / Our love is here to stay / Like someone to love.
Compact disc: released on EMI, Mar'87 by EMI Records. Dist: EMI

Album: released on Blue Note, Oct'84 by EMI Records. Dist: EMI

Cassette: released on Blue Note, Sep'87 by EMI Records. Dist: EMI. Estim retail price in Sep'87 was £5.99.

SAVOY MASTER TAKES 1945-47.
Tracks: / Dexter's cuttin'out / Dewxter's Minor Mad / Long tall Dexter / Dexter rides again / I can't escape from you / Dexter digs / Settin'the pace / So easy / Dexter's riff / Dexter's mood / Dextrose / Index / Dextivity / Blow Mr.Dexter / Dexter's Deck.
Notes: MONO Recording.
Album: released on RCA, Mar'86 by RCA Records. Dist: RCA, Roots, Swift, Wellard, Chris, I & B, Solomon & Peres Distribution

Cassette: released on RCA, Mar'86 by RCA Records. Dist: RCA, Roots, Swift, Wellard, Chris, I & B, Solomon & Peres Distribution

SOPHISTICATED GIANT.
Tracks: / Laura / Moontrane, The / Red top / Fried bananas / You're blase / How insensitive.
Album: released on CBS, Jul'87 by CBS Records. Dist: CBS

Cassette: released on CBS, Jul'87 by CBS Records. Dist: CBS

STRINGS & THINGS.
Album: released on Steeplechase(USA), Jun'81

SWINGIN' AFFAIR, A.
Album: released on Blue Note (USA Import), Sep'84

SWISS NIGHTS VOL.3.
Album: released on Steeplechase, Sep'79

Gordon, Eric

DAY AND DARKNESS/FOR YOUR LOVE.
Single (12"): released on Eric, Apr'83 by Eric Records. Dist: Jetstar

JUST DO ME RIGHT.
Single (12"): released on NK, Jul'85

LONELY LONELY.
Single (12"): released on NK, Nov'84

Gordon, Frank

CINEMA ORGAN ENCORES.
Notes: Cinema organ encores-Ritz,Birkenhead;Odeon,Manchester.
Album: released on Deroy, May'86 by Deroy Records. Dist: Jazz Music, Swift

CLARION ECHOES.
Compact disc: released on Soul Note (Italy), '86 Dist: Harmonia Mundi Distributors

Gordon, Gay

ESSENTIAL WALLY PARTY MEDLEY, THE (Gordon, Gay & The Mince Pies).
Tracks: / Here we go, here we go / Can Can / Simple simon / Conga / Gay Gordons / Knees up mother brown / National Anthem / Night Is Young, The / Auld Lang Syne / Happy Birthday / For He's A Jolly Good Fellow / 21 Today / Congratulations.
Single (7"): released on Lifestyle, Nov'86 by Zomba Records. Dist: CBS, PRT, RCA

Gordon, Harry

HARRY GORDON.
Album: released on Retro, Mar'81 by Retro Records. Dist: Retro

Gordon Highlanders

GORDON HIGHLANDERS, (THE).
Album: released on Teldec (Germany), Jul'84 by Import Records. Dist: IMS Distribution, Polygram Distribution

PRIDE O' THEM A', (THE).
Album: released on Major Richards, Feb'79 by Major Richards Records. Dist: Taylors

Cassette: released on Major Richards, Feb'79 by Major Richards Records. Dist: Taylors

Gordon, Joe

CROOKIT BAWBEE (Gordon, Joe & Sally Logan).
Album: released on Klub, Oct'85

Cassette: released on Klub, Oct'85

END OF A PERFECT DAY, (THE) (Gordon, Joe & Sally Logan).
Album: released on Klub, Oct'82

Cassette: released on Klub, Oct'82

FAVOURITES (Gordon, Joe & Sally Logan).
Album: released on Klub, May'81

Cassette: released on Klub, May'81

JOE GORDON & SALLY LOGAN (Gordon, Joe & Sally Logan).
Album: released on Lismor, '75 by Lismor Records. Dist: Lismor, Roots, Celtic Music

LOOKIN' GOOD.
Album: released on Contemporary (USA), Apr'82 Dist: Fantasy (USA) Distribution

MOONLIGHT AND ROSES (Gordon, Joe & Sally Logan).
Album: released on Neptune, Jun'78 by Lismor. Dist: Spartan

Single (7"): released on Coda, Jun'84 by Coda Records. Dist: Pinnacle, Cartel. WEA, Roots

MOONLIGHT & ROSES (Gordon, Joe & Sally Logan).

TOGETHER (Gordon, Joe & Sally Logan).
Album: released on Lismor, Nov'76 by Lismor Records. Dist: Lismor, Roots, Celtic Music

Album: released on Lismor, Nov'76 by Lismor Records. Dist: Lismor, Roots, Celtic Music

Gordon, Michael

FEELING OF LOVE.
Tracks: / Feeling of love / Feeling of love (PA mix).
Single (12"): released on Fine Style, May'87 by Fine Style Records. Dist: Revolver, Jetstar, PRT, Cartel

LOVE IS IN THE AIR.
Tracks: / Love Is In The Air.
Single (7"): released on Fine Style, Mar'86 by Fine Style Records. Dist: Revolver, Jetstar, PRT, Cartel

MAGIC FEELING.
Tracks: / Magic Feeling / Magic instrumental.
Single (7"): released on Fine Style, Sep'86 by Fine Style Records. Dist: Revolver, Jetstar, PRT, Cartel

Single (12"): released on Fine Style, Sep'86 by Fine Style Records. Dist: Revolver, Jetstar, PRT, Cartel

MASTER PERFORMANCE VOL 1: THE PIANO OF MICHAEL GORDON.
Cassette: released on AIM (Budget Cassettes), Aug'83

READY AND WAITIN' FOR YOU.
Tracks: / Ready and waiting for you (Instrumental).
Single (12"): released on Fine Style, Dec'86 by Fine Style Records. Dist: Revolver, Jetstar, PRT, Cartel

READY & WAITING FOR YOU.
Tracks: / Ready & waiting for you / Ready & waiting for you (PA mix).

Gordon, Peter

DEUTSCHE ANGST (Gordon, Peter & Lawrence Weiner).
Single (7"): released on Les Disques Du Crepescule, May'82 Dist: Rough Trade, Pinnacle, Island, Polygram

INNOCENT.
Tracks: / Day the Devil comes to getcha / Romance / Double / That Hat / St.Cecilia / Afternoon Drive / Diamond Lane / Announcement / Psycho / Heaven.
Album: released on CBS, Jul'86 by CBS Records. Dist: CBS

Cassette: released on CBS, Jul'86 by CBS Records. Dist: CBS

Gordon, Rabbi Joseph

COMPETITION.
Single (7"): released on Bam Caruso, Jan'85 by Bam Caruso Records. Dist: Rough Trade, Revolver, Cartel

Gordon, Rob

FOURTH CALEDONIAN BALL (Gordon, Rob & His Band).
Album: released on Fellside (Cumbria), '83 by Fellside Records. Dist: Roots, Projection, CM, Jazz Music

Gordon, Robert

ARE YOU GONNA BE THE ONE?.
Album: released on RCA, Jul'81 by RCA Records. Dist: RCA, Roots, Swift, Wellard, Chris, I & B, Solomon & Peres Distribution

Cassette: released on RCA, Jul'81 by RCA Records. Dist: RCA, Roots, Swift, Wellard, Chris, I & B, Solomon & Peres Distribution

BAD BOY.
Cassette: released on RCA, Feb'80 by RCA Records. Dist: RCA, Roots, Swift, Wellard, Chris, I & B, Solomon & Peres Distribution

Gordon, Rosco

BEST OF ROSCO GORDON: VOL 1.
Album: released on Ace, Nov'80 by Ace Records. Dist: Pinnacle, Swift, Hotshot, Cadillac

JUST A LITTLE BIT.
Single (7"): released on Charly, Jul'80 by Charly Records. Dist: Charly, Cadillac

KEEP ON DOGGIN'.
Album: released on R & B, Aug'81 by Red Bus. Dist: PRT

LEGENDARY SUN PERFORMERS, (THE).
Album: released on Charly, Nov'77 by Charly Records. Dist: Charly, Cadillac

MEMPHIS MASTERS, (THE).
Album: released on Ace, Aug'82 by Ace Records. Dist: Pinnacle, Swift, Hotshot, Cadillac

NO MORE DOGGIN'.
Album: released on Charly, Mar'83 by Charly Records. Dist: Charly, Cadillac

ROSCO ROCKS AGAIN.
Album: released on JSP, May'83 by JSP Records. Dist: Swift, Projection

Gordon, Steve

DANCE OF FLIES (Gordon, Steve & John Shanahan).
Album: released on Sweet Folk and Country, May'66 Dist: Chris Wellard Distribution

Gordon the Moron

FIT FOR NOTHING.
Single (7"): released on Rabid, Sep'82 by Rabid Records. Dist: Pinnacle, Rough Trade

Gordon, Vin

KOJO HOY.
Single (12"): released on Hugo Music, May'82 Dist: Jetstar

SEVEN ELEVEN.
Single (12"): released on Jaydee, Dec'82 by Jaydee Records. Dist: Jetstar

Gore

HEART GORE.
Album: released on Eksakt (Holland), Apr'87 by Eksakt Records (Holland). Dist: Red Rhino, Cartel

Gorehounds

BIG SPUD EP.
Single (12"): released on Idol, Apr'87 Dist: Rough Trade, Cartel

Gore, Lesley

GOLDEN HITS: LESLEY GORE.
Album: released on Mercury (USA), Aug'87 by Import Records. Dist: IMS Distribution, Polygram Distribution

Cassette: released on Mercury (USA), Aug'87 by Import Records. Dist: IMS Distribution, Polygram Distribution

IT'S MY PARTY.
Tracks: / Love on a mountain top.
Single (7"): released on Creole, Aug'82 by Creole Records. Dist: Rhino, PRT

Single (7"): released on Old Gold, Jan'85 by Old Gold Records. Dist: Lightning, Jazz Music, Spartan, Counterpoint

Gorky Park

GORKY PARK Original film soundtrack.
Album: released on TER, Jan'84 Dist: Pinnacle

Gorl, Robert

DARLING DON'T LEAVE ME.
Single (7"): released on Mute, Feb'84 Dist: Spartan Distribution, Rough Trade Distribution, Cartel Distribution

Single (12"): released on Mute, Feb'84 Dist: Spartan Distribution, Rough Trade Distribution, Cartel Distribution

MIT DIR.
Single (7"): released on Mute, Mar'83 Dist: Spartan Distribution, Rough Trade Distribution, Cartel Distribution

NIGHTFUL OF TENSION.
Album: released on Stumm, Mar'84

Cassette: released on Stumm, Mar'84

Gorman, Micheal

BONNIE KATE: TECHNIQUES OF IRISH FIDDLE PLAY.
Cassette: released on Folktracks, Nov'79 by Folktracks Cassettes. Dist: Folktracks

MOUNTAIN ROAD: IRISH REELS AND JIGS.
Cassette: released on Folktracks, Nov'79 by Folktracks Cassettes. Dist: Folktracks

Gorme, Eydie

BLAME IT ON THE BOSSA NOVA.
Single (7"): released on Old Gold, Apr'83 by Old Gold Records. Dist: Lightning, Jazz Music, Spartan, Counterpoint

COME IN FROM THE RAIN.
Album: released on President, Mar'85 by President Records. Dist: Taylors, Spartan

Cassette: released on President, Mar'85 by President Records. Dist: Taylors, Spartan

EYDIE GORME VAMPS THE ROARING 20'S.
Album: released on Memoir, Nov'84 by Memoir Records. Dist: PRT Distribution

Cassette: released on Memoir, Nov'84 by Memoir Records. Dist: PRT Distribution

I STILL BELIEVE IN LOVE (see Lawrence, Steve) (Gorme, Eydie & Steve Lawrence).

I WANT TO STAY HERE (Gorme, Eydie & Steve Lawrence).
Single (7"): released on Old Gold, Apr'83 by Old Gold Records. Dist: Lightning, Jazz Music, Spartan, Counterpoint

ON STAGE.
Album: released on Jasmine, Oct'84 by Jasmine Records. Dist: Counterpoint, Lugtons, Taylor, H.R., Wellard, Chris, Swift, Cadillac

OUR LOVE IS HERE TO STAY (Gorme, Eydie & Steve Lawrence).
Album:

SINGS/CANTA.
Compact disc: released on President, Jan'87 by President Records. Dist: Taylors, Spartan

SINGS SHOW STOPPERS.
Tracks: / Johnny One Note / I Don't Care / You're Just In Love / My Funny Valentine / You Can't Get A Man With A Gun / Always True To You In My Fashion / Guys And Dolls / I Can't Say No / Hello Young Lovers / Thou Sweet / I'm Gonna wash That Man Right Out Of My hair / Baubles Bangles And Beads.
Album: released on Memoir, Jul'86 by Memoir Records. Dist: PRT Distribution

Cassette: released on Memoir, Jul'86 by Memoir Records. Dist: PRT Distribution

SINGS SHOWSTOPPERS.
Album: released on Memoir, Jan'87 by Memoir Records. Dist: PRT Distribution

TOMAME O DEJAME.
Album: released on President, May'85 by President Records. Dist: Taylors, Spartan

Gorp

WILD WALK SIDEWAYS.
Album: released on Beat Bop, Mar'83

Gosdin, Vern

I CAN TELL BY THE WAY YOU DANCE.
Single (7"): released on Compleat, Aug'84 by Compleat Records. Dist: PRT

THERE IS A SEASON.
Album: released on Compleat, Sep'84 by Compleat Records. Dist: PRT

Cassette: released on Compleat, Sep'84 by Compleat Records. Dist: PRT

Go Service

IT MAKES ME REALISE.
Single (12"): released on Dreamworld, Sep'85 by TV Personalities, The. Dist: Rough Trade

Go South
GO SOUTH various artists (Various Artists).
Album: released on Earthworks, Jun'85 by Earthworks Records. Dist: Earthworks Distributors, Rough Trade, Cartel. Projection

Gospel at Colonus
GOSPEL AT COLONUS, (THE) Original cast recording (Various Artists).
Album: released on Warner Bros., Nov'84 by Warner Bros Records. Dist: WEA

Cassette: released on Warner eros., Nov'84 by Warner Bros Records. Dist: WEA

Gospel cannonball
GOSPEL CANNONBALL Various artists (Various Artists).
Album: released on Maranatha, May'85

Cassette: released on Maranatha, May'85

Gospel caravan
GOSPEL CARAVAN Various artists (Various Artists).
Album: released on Auvidis (France), May'85 Dist: Discovery

Cassette: released on Auvidis (France), May'85 Dist: Discovery

Gospel Road
GOSPEL ROAD, (THE) Original soundtrack (Cash, Johnny).
Double Album: released on CBS, '73 by CBS Records. Dist: CBS

Gospel Ship
GOSPEL SHIP Various Artists (Various Artists).
Tracks: / Amazing Grace / Poor Pilgrim / Testimony / Why must I wear this shroud? / Testimony / When Jesus Christ was born on Earth / Old Gospel Ship, The / When the Stars begin to fall / Hick's Farewell / See that my grave is kept clean / I am a poor wayfaring stranger / Little family, The / Jim And Me / Airplane Ride, The / Guide Me, O Thou Great Jehovah / Testimony of Pioneer religion.
Notes: Producer/Programmer:Alan Lomax.Recording Engineer:John Dikline.
Album: released on New World (USA), Jul'86 by New World Records (USA). Dist: Conifer

Gospel songs
GOSPEL SONGS Various artists (Various Artists).
Cassette: released on K-Tel, Aug'84 by K-Tel Records. Dist: Record Merchandisers Distribution, Taylors, Terry Blood Distribution, Wynd-Up Distribution, Relay Distribution, Pickwick Distribution, Solomon & Peres Distribution, Polygram

Gossip Girls
LILAC DREAMS.
Album: released on Backs, Feb'85 by Backs Records. Dist: Backs, Cartel

Single (7"): released on Music In Motion, Aug'84 Dist: PRT Distribution

Gotham
GOTHAM.
Album: released on Direction, Nov'83 by CBS Records. Dist: CBS

Gotham Gospel
GOTHAM GOSPEL VOLUME 1.
Notes: Includes: Violinaires, National Clouds.
Album: released on Krazy Kat (USA), Apr'87

Gotham House Party
GOTHAM HOUSE PARTY Various artists (Various Artists).
Tracks: / Drinking beer / Stomp / Roly Poly Mama / That's right / Mel's jump / Dual trumpet blues / I'm free / Hey Everybody / I ain't mad at you / House party / Corn pone / Danny's Blues / Red hot boogie.
Notes: Sampler Anthology of R&B Sax-Led Combos.All Tracks previously unissued. MONO recording.
Album: released on Krazy Kat, Oct'86 Dist: Jazz Music, Swift, Chris Wellard, H.R. Taylor, Charly, Hotshot, IRS Distribution

GOTHAM HOUSE PARTY (Various Artists).

Gothenburg Brass Band
GOTHENBURG BRASS BAND.
Album: released on Polyphonic, Jun'87 by Polyphonic Records. Dist: Taylors

Cassette: released on Polyphonic, Jun'87 by Polyphonic Records. Dist: Taylors

Gothic
GOTHIC Original Soundtrack.
Album: released on Virgin, Feb'87 by Virgin Records. Dist: EMI, Virgin Distribution

Cassette: released on Virgin, Feb'87 by Virgin Records. Dist: EMI, Virgin Distribution

Compact disc: released on Virgin, Apr'87 by Virgin Records. Dist: EMI, Virgin Distribution

Gothic Girls
GLASS BABY.
Single (12"): released on Backs, Apr'84 by Backs Records. Dist: Backs, Cartel

OUTRAGE.
Single (7"): released on Backs, May'83 by Backs Records. Dist: Backs, Cartel

Gothique
KRISTIANA.
Cassette: released on GEEC, Feb'84 by GEEC Records. Dist: GEEC Records

Gotta Go Go
GOTTA GO GO Various artists (Various Artists).
Notes: Artists include: Kurtis Blow, Chuck Brown, Little Benny & The Masters, Trouble Funk, Redds & The Boys.
Album: released on Streetsounds, Jun'86

Cassette: released on Streetsounds, Apr'86

Gottsching, Manuel
E2 E4.
Album: released on Inteam, Apr'84 by Inteam Records. Dist: Impex Distribution

Goulder, Dave
REQUIEM FOR STEAM Railway songs.
Album: released on Big Ben, Apr'81 by Big Ben Records. Dist: Spartan, Taylor, H.R.

Gould, Kevin
CLEAR VISION.
Album: by Pilgrim Records. Dist: Rough Trade, Cartel

Gouldman, Graham
ANIMALYMPICS.
Album: released on Mercury, Apr'80 by Phonogram Records. Dist: Polygram Distribution

Gould, Morton
DIGITAL SPACE.
Double Album: released on Varese, Dec'79 Dist: Swift

Goulet, Robert
AS TIME GOES BY.
Album: released on Memoir, Jan'87 by Memoir Records. Dist: PRT Distribution

CLOSE TO YOU.
Album: released on President, May'85 by President Records. Dist: Taylors, Spartan

ROBERT GOULET: GREATEST HITS.
Album: released on CBS Cameo, Mar'83 by CBS Records. Dist: CBS Deleted '87.

Cassette: released on CBS Cameo, Mar'83 by CBS Records. Dist: CBS

Govan Gaelic Choir
GOVAN GAELIC CHOIR.
Album: released on Lismor, Jun'75 by Lismor Records. Dist: Lismor, Roots, Celtic Music

Govan, James
I'M IN NEED.
Tracks: / Jealous kind / Uphill climb / Tell you about my girl / Starting all over again / Oh what a price / Help me in need / Love (I thought I would never find love) / Don't give up the ship / You left the water running / We had it all.
Album: released on Charly, Jul'87 by Charly Records. Dist: Charly, Cadillac

Government Issue
BOYCOTT STAB.
Album: released on Fountain Of Youth, May'85 Dist: Rough Trade, Cartel

FUN JUST NEVER STOPS, (THE).
Album: released on Homestead, Jul'85 Dist: Rough Trade, Cartel, Shigaku

GOVERNMENT ISSUE 5TH.
Album: released on Fountain Of Youth, Oct'86 Dist: Rough Trade, Cartel

Gowan
KEEP UP THE FIGHT.
Single (7"): released on CBS, Apr'83 by CBS Records. Dist: CBS

STRANGE ANIMAL.
Album: released on CBS, Aug'85 by CBS Records. Dist: CBS

Cassette: released on CBS, Aug'85 by CBS Records. Dist: CBS

Gowan, Larry
GOWAN.
Album: released on CBS, May'83 by CBS Records. Dist: CBS

Cassette: released on CBS, May'83 by CBS Records. Dist: CBS

Go West
BANGS AND CRASHES.
Tracks: / We close our eyes - the total overhang mix / Man in my mirror / Goodbye girl / S.O.S. - the perpendicular mix / Eye to eye - the horizontal mix / Ball of confusion / Call me - the indiscriminate mix / Haunted / Missing person / Don't look down - the statospheric mix / One way street / Innocence - the desperation mix.
Notes: Produced by Gary Stevenson and Tony Wilson. Double LP & Cassette.
Album: released on Chrysalis, May'86 by Chrysalis Records. Dist: CBS

Cassette: released on Chrysalis, May'86 by Chrysalis Records. Dist: CBS

Compact disc: released on Chrysalis, Aug'86 by Chrysalis Records. Dist: CBS

CALL ME.
Single (7"): released on Chrysalis, Apr'85 by Chrysalis Records. Dist: CBS

Single (12"): released on Chrysalis, Apr'85 by Chrysalis Records. Dist: CBS

DANCING ON THE COUCH.
Compact disc: released on Chrysalis, '87 by Chrysalis Records. Dist: CBS

Album: released on Chrysalis, May'87 by Chrysalis Records. Dist: CBS

Cassette: released on Chrysalis, May'87 by Chrysalis Records. Dist: CBS

DON'T LOOK DOWN-THE SEQUEL.
Single (7"): released on Chrysalis, Nov'85 by Chrysalis Records. Dist: CBS

Single (12"): released on Chrysalis, Nov'85 by Chrysalis Records. Dist: CBS Deleted '86.

GOODBYE GIRL.
Single (7"): released on Chrysalis, Jul'85 by Chrysalis Records. Dist: CBS

Single (12"): released on Chrysalis, Jul'85 by Chrysalis Records. Dist: CBS

GO WEST.
Tracks: / We close our eyes / Don't look down / Call me / Eye to eye / Haunted.
Compact disc: released on Chrysalis, Jun'85 by Chrysalis Records. Dist: CBS

Album: released on Chrysalis, Apr'85 by Chrysalis Records. Dist: CBS

Cassette: released on Chrysalis, Apr'85 by Chrysalis Records. Dist: CBS

Compact disc: released on Chrysalis, Apr'85 by Chrysalis Records. Dist: CBS

I WANT TO HEAR IT FROM YOU.
Tracks: / I want to hear it from you / Crossfire / True colours.
Single (7"): released on Chrysalis, Apr'87 by Chrysalis Records. Dist: CBS

Single (7"): released on Chrysalis, Apr'87 by Chrysalis Records. Dist: CBS

Single (12"): released on Chrysalis, Apr'87 by Chrysalis Records. Dist: CBS

Compact disc single: released on Chrysalis, Apr'87 by Chrysalis Records. Dist: CBS

KING IS DEAD, THE.
Single (7"): released on Chrysalis, Aug'87 by Chrysalis Records. Dist: CBS

Single (12"): released on Chrysalis, Aug'87 by Chrysalis Records. Dist: CBS

Single (12"): released on Chrysalis, Aug'87 by Chrysalis Records. Dist: CBS

Cassette single: released on Chrysalis, Aug'87 by Chrysalis Records. Dist: CBS

TRUE COLOURS.
Tracks: / XL5.
Single (7"): released on Chrysalis, Nov'86 by Chrysalis Records. Dist: CBS

Single (12"): released on Chrysalis, Nov'86 by Chrysalis Records. Dist: CBS

WE CLOSE OUR EYES.
Single (7"): released on Chrysalis, Feb'85 by Chrysalis Records. Dist: CBS

Single (12"): by Chrysalis Records. Dist: CBS

Goya, Francis
DE MOOISTE GITAARSUCCESSEN VAN FRANCIS GOYA.
Album: released on Music For Pleasure (Holland), Dec'86 by EMI Records. Dist: EMI

Cassette: released on Music For Pleasure (Holland), Dec'86 by EMI Records. Dist: EMI

QUIET MOMENTS (Goya, Francis & His Orchestra).
Double Album: released on Starblend, Nov'83 by Starblend Records. Dist: PRT Distribution

Double cassette: released on Starblend, Nov'83 by Starblend Records. Dist: PRT Distribution

Goykovich, Dusko
AFTER HOURS.
Album: released on Enja (Germany), Jan'82 by Enja Records (W.Germany). Dist: Cadillac Music

G.Q.
DISCO NIGHTS.
Album: released on Arista, Sep'79 by Arista Records. Dist: RCA

DISCO NIGHTS (ROCK FREAK).
: released on Arista, Feb'79 by Arista Records. Dist: RCA

Single (12"): released on Arista, Feb'79 by Arista Records. Dist: RCA

FACE TO FACE.
Album: released on Arista, Oct'81 by Arista Records. Dist: RCA

MAKE MY DREAM A REALITY.
Single (7"): released on Arista, May'79 by Arista Records. Dist: RCA

Single (12"): released on Arista, May'79 by Arista Records. Dist: RCA

SHAKE/SKIN YOU'RE IN.
Single (7"): released on Arista, Nov'81 by Arista Records. Dist: RCA

Single (12"): released on Arista, Nov'81 by Arista Records. Dist: RCA

SITTING IN THE PARK.
Single (7"): released on Arista, Jul'80 by Arista Records. Dist: RCA

Single (12"): released on Arista, Jul'80 by Arista Records. Dist: RCA

TWO.
Album: released on Arista, Feb'80 by Arista Records. Dist: RCA Deleted '83.

Grab Grab the Haddock
I'M USED NOW.
Single (12"): released on Cherry Red, Feb'85 by Cherry Red Records. Dist: Pinnacle

LAST FOND GOODBYE.
Single (7"): released on Cherry Red, Apr'85 by Cherry Red Records. Dist: Pinnacle

Single (12"): released on Cherry Red, Apr'85 by Cherry Red Records. Dist: Pinnacle

Grable, Betty
RARE RECORDINGS.
Album: released on Sandy Hook, Aug'79

Grab This & Dance
GRAB THIS AND DANCE (Various Artists).
Album: released on Club, Jun'87 by Phonogram Records. Dist: Polygram

G'Race
DR RHYTHM.
Single (7"): released on WEA Int, May'84

Single (12"): released on WEA Int, May'84

GRACE LIVE.
Album: released on Clay, Nov'81 by Clay Records. Dist: Pinnacle

MANHATTAN.
Single (7"): released on WEA Int, Feb'84

Grace, Brendan
FATHER OF THE BRIDE.
Single (7"): released on Ritz, Oct'84 by Outlet Records. Dist: Outlet, Prism Leisure Distribution, Record Services Distribution (Ireland), Roots

HUMOURS OF IRELAND.
Single (7"): released on Bottler, Mar'83 Dist: Spartan, I & B

Grace & Favour
ON THE REBOUND.
Single (7"): released on Playfar, Sep'82 by Playfar Records. Dist: Spartan

Grace, John
PRIVATE PARTS.
Album: released on Sweet Folk All, May'81 by Sweet Folk All Records. Dist: Sweet Folk All, Roots, Celtic Music, Dragon, Impetus, Projection, Chris Wellard, Festival Records

STORIES AND SONGS OF: PORTLAND BILL, THE.
Tracks: / Guided tour, The / Gone fishing / Beachcombing / Kite flying / Football / Foggy day, The / Bad dogger / Garden party, The.
Cassette: released on Tellastory, Dec'86 by Bartlett Bliss Productions. Dist: PRT Distribution, Hayward Promotions Distribution, H.R. Taylor Distribution

Gracie, Charlie
AMAZING GRACIE.
Album: released on Charly, Feb'82 by Charly Records. Dist: Charly, Cadillac

CHARLIE GRACIE'S EARLY RECORDINGS.
Album: released on Revival, Sep'79 Dist: Lightning, Swift

LIVE AT THE STOCKTON GLOBE AUGUST 26TH 1957.
Album: released on Rollercoaster, May'83 by Rollercoaster Records. Dist: Swift Distribution, Rollercoaster Distribution

ROCKIN' PHILADELPHIA.
78 rpm record: released on Magnum Force, Jul'82 by Magnum Music Group Ltd. Dist: Magnum Music Group Ltd, PRT, Spartan

Graduate
ACTING MY AGE.
Tracks: / Elvis should play Ska / Watching your world / Love that is bad / Julie Julie / Bad dreams / Acting my age / Sick and tired / Ever met a day / Dancing nights / Sut up.
Album: released on PRT, Jul'86 by PRT Records. Dist: PRT

Cassette: released on PRT, Jul'86 by PRT Records. Dist: PRT

Album: released on Precision, May'80 by PRT Records. Dist: PRT

Cassette: released on Precision, May'80 by PRT Records. Dist: PRT

GRADUATE, THE Original soundtrack featuring Simon & Garfunkel.
Album: released on CBS, Feb'84 by CBS Records. Dist: CBS

Cassette: released on CBS, Feb'84 by CBS Records. Dist: CBS

TROUBLED SON.
Single (7"): released on Graduate, Dec'82 by Graduate Records. Dist: Nine Mile, Cartel

Graebe, Martin
JACK IN THE GREEN.
Cassette: released on Folktracks, Nov'79 Dist: Roots

Graffia
CYMER DI.
Single (7"): released on Magic, Aug'80 Dist: Jazz Music, Submarine, Swift, Chris Wellard, Conifer

Graff, Rein De
DRIFTIN' ON A REED.
Album: released on Timeless, Apr'81

MODAL SOUL (Graff, Rein De & Dick Vennick).

Graf, Rolf
RIGHT FROM THE START.
Tracks: / Right from the start / Maxine.
Single (7"): released on Carrere, Jul'86 by Carrere Records. Dist: PRT, Spartan

Single (12"): released on Carrere, Jul'86 by Carrere Records. Dist: PRT, Spartan

SHINE.
Tracks: / Shine / Walk right in.
Single (7"): released on Broken Hill, Oct'86 by Carrere Records-Broken Hill (USA). Dist: PRT

Single (12"): released on Broken Hill, Oct'86 by Carrere Records-Broken Hill (USA). Dist: PRT

Graham, Billy
CRUSADE MEMORIES.
Album: released on Word 20, May'82

Cassette: released on Word 20, May'82

Graham, D'ancey
ALLUMA.
Album: released on Shibui, Jan'85 by Stage One Records. Dist: Pinnacle

Graham, Dave
IRISH REELS, JIGS, HORNPIPES & AIRS (Graham, Dave/Dave Evans/Dan Ar Brass/Duck Baker).
Album: released on Kicking Mule, Sep'79 by Sonet. Dist: Roots, PRT-Pye Distribution

Graham, Davey
ALL THAT MOODY.
Tracks: / Fingerbuster / Blue raga / To find the sun / Tristano, etc / Anji / Travelling man / Sunshine raga / Kim / Jenra / La Morena / Preacher blues.
Notes: Davey Graham, plus Keshav Sathe (tabla and tambura, Roger Bunn bass). Eastern influenced blues by this famous guitarist. Eron Records, 27 Balmoral Road, Deal,Kent CT14 8BX.
Cassette: released on Eron, Sep'85 by Eron Records. Dist: Eron Records

Album: released on Eron, Sep'85 by Eron Records. Dist: Eron Records

COMPLETE GUITARIST, THE.
Album: released on Kicking Mule, Jan'78 by Sonet. Dist: Roots, PRT-Pye Distribution

FOLK, BLUES AND ALL POINTS BETWEEN.
Album: released on See For Miles, May'85 by See For Miles Records. Dist: Pinnacle

Graham, David
DANCETIME AT THE TOWER.
Album: released on Grosvenor, Dec'86 by Grosvenor Records. Dist: Taylors

DAVID GRAHAM PLAYS THE BLACKPOOL TOWER WURLITZER....
Notes: Full title: "David Graham plays the Blackpool Tower Wurlitzer-Promenade".
Album: released on Grosvenor, Nov'86 by Grosvenor Records. Dist: Taylors

Cassette: released on Grosvenor, Nov'86 by Grosvenor Records. Dist: Taylors

Graham, Davy
FOLK BLUES AND ALL POINTS IN BETWEEN.
Tracks: / Leaving blues / Cocaine / Rock me baby / Moanin' / Skillet / Ain't nobody's business if i do / Maajun(a taste of tangier) / I can't keep from crying sometimes / Goin' down slow / Better git in your soul / Freight train blues / Both sides now / No preacher blues / Bad boy blues / I'm ready / Hoochie coochie man / Blue raga.
Album: released on See For Miles, Aug'86 by See For Miles Records. Dist: Pinnacle

Graham, Eileen
LAST ROAD.
Single (7"): released on Diversion, Dec'80 by Dingle's.

Grahame, Kenneth
WIND IN THE WILLOWS Spoken Word.
Album: released on Red Bus, Mar'84 by Red Bus Records. Dist: PRT

Cassette: released on Red Bus, Mar'84 by Red Bus Records. Dist: PRT

Grahame, Loretta
YOUNG FREE & SINGLE.
Single (12"): released on Intense, Feb'83 by Intense Records. Dist: PRT, Kingdom

Graham, Jaki
BREAKING AWAY.
Tracks: / Set me free / Breaking away / Still in love / Love under moonlight / Lets get blue / Stop the world / Luv 2 much / Love of your life, The / Closest one, The / Step right up / Mated / Love me tonight.
Compact disc: released on EMI, Dec'86 by EMI Records. Dist: EMI

Album: released on EMI, Sep'86 by EMI Records. Dist: EMI

Cassette: released on EMI, Sep'86 by EMI Records. Dist: EMI

Single (7"): released on EMI, Jul'86 by EMI Records. Dist: EMI

Single (12"): released on EMI, Jul'86 by EMI Records. Dist: EMI

HEAVEN KNOWS.
Tracks: / Round and around / Heaven knows / Could it be I'm falling in love (Duet with David Grant) / I fell for you / Hold on / Facts of love / You're mine / Loving you (duet with Dereck Bramble) / What's the name of your game / Stay the way you are.
Album: released on Fame, Jun'87 by Music For Pleasure Records. Dist: EMI

Cassette: released on Fame, Jun'87 by Music For Pleasure Records. Dist: EMI

Album: released on EMI, Jul'85 by EMI Records. Dist: EMI

Cassette: released on EMI, Jul'85 by EMI Records. Dist: EMI

Single (12"): released on EMI, Aug'85 by EMI Records. Dist: EMI

HEAVEN KNOWS (FEELS SO GOOD).
Single (12"): released on EMI, Jun'84 by EMI Records. Dist: EMI

Single (7"): released on EMI, Jun'84 by EMI Records. Dist: EMI

LET'S GET BLUE.
Tracks: / Let's get blue / Still in love / Love under midnight / Love 2 much (Too much)(12" mix) / Still in (dub).
Single (12"): released on EMI, Mar'87 by EMI Records. Dist: EMI

MATED (see Grant, David) (Graham, Jaki & David Grant).

MEGAMIX.
Tracks: / Set me free / Closest one, The / Step right up / Closest one, The (2).
Single (12"): released on EMI, Nov'86 by EMI Records. Dist: EMI

ROUND AND ROUND.
Single (7"): released on EMI, Jun'85 by EMI Records. Dist: EMI

Single (12"): released on EMI, Jun'85 by EMI Records. Dist: EMI

SET FREE.
Tracks: / Step right up / Breaking away / Set me free / Mated / Heaven knows / Round & around / Could it be I'm falling in love.
Video-cassette (VHS): released on PMI, Nov'86 by PMI Records. Dist: EMI

Video-cassette [Betamax]: released on PMI, Nov'86 by PMI Records. Dist: EMI

SET ME FREE.
Tracks: / Set me free / Stop the world.
Notes: Seven tracks including Set me free/Round and Around/Step right up.
Video-cassette (VHS): released on PMI, Nov'86 by PMI Records. Dist: EMI

Single (7"): released on EMI, Apr'86 by EMI Records. Dist: EMI

Single (12"): released on EMI, Apr'86 by EMI Records. Dist: EMI

STEP RIGHT UP.
Tracks: / Step right up / Closest one, The.
Single (7"): released on EMI, Nov'86 by EMI Records. Dist: EMI

Single (12"): released on EMI, Nov'86 by EMI Records. Dist: EMI

STILL IN LOVE (LIGHTS DOWN MIX).
Tracks: / Still in love (lights down mix) / Love too much (too much mix).
Single (12"): released on EMI, Feb'87 by EMI Records. Dist: EMI

Single (7"): released on EMI, Feb'87 by EMI Records. Dist: EMI

Graham, Kenny
BATTLE ROYAL (Graham, Kenny & Ronnie Scott).
Album: released on Esquire, May'81 by Titan International Productions. Dist: Jazz Music, Cadillac Music, Swift, Wellard, Chris, Backs, Rough Trade, Revolver, Nine Mile

CARIBBEAN SUITE/AFRO KADABRA (Graham's, Kenny Afro-Cubists).
Tracks: / Jump for Joe / Night in Tunisia, A / Take the 'A' train / Flamingo / Keni B'sindika / Afro-Kadabra / Mango walk / Bongo chant / Saga boy / Dance of the Zombies / Wha' huppin' sah? / Tempo medio lento / Beguine / Haitian Ritual.
Album: released on Esquire, Jul'87 by Titan International Productions. Dist: Jazz Music, Cadillac Music, Swift, Wellard, Chris, Backs, Rough Trade, Revolver, Nine Mile

MANGO WALK (Graham, Kenny & His Afro Cubists).
Album: released on Esquire, Apr'79 by Titan International Productions. Dist: Jazz Music, Cadillac Music, Swift, Wellard, Chris, Backs, Rough Trade, Revolver, Nine Mile

Graham, Larry
FIRED UP.
Album: released on Warner Bros., Jun'85 by Warner Bros Records. Dist: WEA

Cassette: released on Warner Bros., Jun'85 by Warner Bros Records. Dist: WEA

I'M SICK AND TIRED.
Single (7"): released on Warner Bros., Aug'83 by Warner Bros Records. Dist: WEA

Single (12"): released on Warner Bros., Aug'83 by Warner Bros Records. Dist: WEA

JUST BE MY LADY.
Album: released on Warner Bros., Jun'81 by Warner Bros Records. Dist: WEA

Graham, Len
WIND AND WATER Traditional songs, ballads and lilts.
Album: released on Topic, '81 Dist: Roots Distribution

YE LOVERS ALL.
Album: released on Claddagh, Feb'85 by Claddagh Records. Dist: I & B, Record Services Distribution (Ireland), Roots, Topic, Impetus, Projection, CM

Graham, Lorita
BABY I LOVE YOU SO (Graham, Lorita & Colourbox).
Tracks: / Baby I love you so / Look's like we're shy one horse..
Single (7"): released on 4AD, Apr'86 by 4AD Records. Dist: Rough Trade

Single (12"): released on 4AD, Apr'86 by 4AD Records. Dist: Rough Trade

Grahamophones
CHINESE LAUNDRY BLUES.
Tracks: / Chinese laundry blues / I would sooner be a crooner.
Single (7"): released on President, Jul'87 by President Records. Dist: Taylors, Spartan

WE'RE TOPS ON SATURDAY NIGHT.
Tracks: / Chinese laundry blues / Blue moon / We're tops on Saturday night / I would sooner be a crooner / Isn't this a lovely day / Who stole my heart away / Nobody's sweetheart / You rascal you / Stars fell on Alabama / When can I have a banana again / Room with a view / Deep purple / Puttin' on the ritz / Mr Wu's xylophone blues.
Album: released on President, Jun'87 by President Records. Dist: Taylors, Spartan

Cassette: released on President, Jun'87 by President Records. Dist: Taylors, Spartan

Graham, Tony
KISS THE BOYS.
Single (7"): released on Greyhound, Sep'84 by Greyhound Records. Dist: PRT, Greyhound

Single (12"): released on Greyhound, Sep'84 by Greyhound Records. Dist: PRT, Greyhound

Grainer, Ron
EDWARD & MRS. SIMPSON (Grainer, Ron Orchestra).
Album: released on RK, '78

TALES OF THE UNEXPECTED (Grainer, Ron Orchestra).
Single (7"): released on RK, May'82

Grainger, Al
SUSHEA.
Single (7"): released on Ash, Apr'84 by Ash Records. Dist: Ash

Grainger, Percy
GRAINGER PLAYS GRAINGER & GRIEG.
Album: released on RCA, Apr'79 by RCA Records. Dist: RCA, Roots, Swift, Wellard, Chris, I & B, Solomon & Peres Distribution

ROOM MUSIC TIT BITS AND....
Cassette: released on RCA, Apr'79 by RCA Records. Dist: RCA, Roots, Swift, Wellard, Chris, I & B, Solomon & Peres Distribution

Album: released on RCA, Apr'79 by RCA Records. Dist: RCA, Roots, Swift, Wellard, Chris, I & B, Solomon & Peres Distribution

SALUTE TO PERCY GRAINGER.
Album: released on Decca, '69 by Decca Records. Dist: Polygram

Grainger, Richard
HERBS ON THE HEART.
Album: released on Fellside, May'85 by Fellside Records. Dist: Roots, Jazz Music, Celtic Music, Projection

Grammacks
ROOTS CARIBBEAN ROCK (Grammacks feat. Jeff Joseph).

Gramm, Lou
MIDNIGHT BLUE.
Tracks: / Midnight blue / Chain of love.
Single (7"): released on Atlantic, Mar'87 by WEA Records. Dist: WEA

Single (12"): released on Atlantic, Mar'87 by WEA Records. Dist: WEA

READY OR NOT.
Album: released on Atlantic, Feb'87 by WEA Records. Dist: WEA

Cassette: released on Atlantic, Feb'87 by WEA Records. Dist: WEA

Compact disc: released on Atlantic, Apr'87 by WEA Records. Dist: WEA

Grammy R & B Songs

GRAMMY R & B SONGS 1960'S-1970'S Various Artists (Various Artists).
Notes: Artists include: Lionel Richie, Diana Ross, Michael Jackson. Digital stereo.
Compact disc: released on Motown, Feb'85 by Motown Records. Dist: BMG Distribution

Grammy Winners

GRAMMY WINNERS various artists (Various Artists).
Album: released on Denon, Mar'82 by Denon Records. Dist: Harmonia Mundi

Grandad & Adam

TALL STORY.
Single (7"): released on Look, Mar'82 Dist: R. Smith & Co. Records, H.R. Taylor

Grand Airs Of Conemara

GRAND AIRS OF CONEMARA various traditional Irish songs (Various Artists).
Album: released on Topic, '81 Dist: Roots Distribution

MORE GRAND AIRS FROM CONNEMARA Various artists (Various Artists).
Album: released on Topic, '81 Dist: Roots Distribution

Grand Chinese Orchestra

CHINESE FLUTE CONCERTOS.
Album: released on Lyrichord (USA), May'82 by Lyrichord Records (USA). Dist: Flexitron Distributors Ltd

Grand Dominion Jazz Band

GRAND DOMINION JAZZ BAND,THE.
Album: released on GHB, Jun'86 Dist: Jazz Music, Swift

Grand Funk

CAUGHT IN THE ACT.
Double Album: released on Capitol, Nov'75 by Capitol Records. Dist: EMI

Grand Funk Railroad

COLLECTION: GRAND FUNK RAILROAD.
Album: released on EMI (Germany), '83 by EMI Records. Dist: Conifer

LIVE ALBUM.
Double Album: released on Capitol, '71 by Capitol Records. Dist: EMI

Grand, Johnny

PARADE OF BROKEN HEARTS.
Album: released on Lismor, Apr'77 by Lismor Records. Dist: Lismor, Roots, Celtic Music

Grand Mal

BINGE PURGE.
Album: released on Fountain Of Youth, Jul'85 Dist: Rough Trade, Cartel

Grand Mamou Orchestra

CAJUNS, VOL.2, THE.
Album: released on Sonet, '73 by Sonet Records. Dist: PRT

Grand Man

GRAND MAN Catherine Cookson (Jameson, Susan).
Cassette: released on Chivers Audio Books, '81 by Chivers Sound & Vision. Dist: Chivers Sound & Vision

Grandmaster Caz

WILD STYLE THEME RAP 1 (Grandmaster Caz & Chris Stein).
Single (12"): released on Animal, Sep'83 by Chrysalis Records. Dist: Polygram

Grandmaster Chilly T

ROCK THE MESSAGE RAP.
Single (12"): released on Eclipse, May'83 by Decca Records. Dist: Polygram

Grandmaster Flash

BA DOP BOOM BANG.
Compact disc: released on Elektra (USA), Mar'87 by Elektra/Asylum/Nonesuch Records. Dist: WEA

Album: released on Elektra (USA), Mar'87 by Elektra/Asylum/Nonesuch Records. Dist: WEA

Cassette: released on Elektra (USA), Mar'87 by Elektra/Asylum/Nonesuch Records. Dist: WEA

GREATEST MESSAGES.
Cassette: released on Sugar Hill USA, Jun'84 by MCA Records. Dist: Roots Distribution, Mike's Country Music Room Distribution, Projection Distribution, PRT Distribution

Album: released on Sugar Hill USA, Jun'84 by MCA Records. Dist: Roots Distribution, Mike's Country Music Room Distribution, Projection Distribution, PRT Distribution

MESSAGE, THE.
Album: released on Sugar Hill USA, Oct'82 by MCA Records. Dist: Roots Distribution, Mike's Country Music Room Distribution, Projection Distribution, PRT Distribution

Cassette: released on Sugar Hill USA, Oct'82 by MCA Records. Dist: Roots Distribution, Mike's Country Music Room Distribution, Projection Distribution, PRT Distribution

MESSAGE, THE (12").
Single (12"): released on Sugar Hill USA, Aug'82 by MCA Records. Dist: Roots Distribution, Mike's Country Music Room Distribution, Projection Distribution, PRT Distribution

NEW YORK,NEW YORK.
Single (12"): released on Sugar Hill USA, May'83 by MCA Records. Dist: Roots Distribution, Mike's Country Music Room Distribution, Projection Distribution, PRT Distribution

Single (7"): released on Sugar Hill USA, May'83 by MCA Records. Dist: Roots Distribution, Mike's Country Music Room Distribution, Projection Distribution, PRT Distribution

SCORPIO.
Single (7"): released on Sugar Hill USA, Dec'82 by MCA Records. Dist: Roots Distribution, Mike's Country Music Room Distribution, Projection Distribution, PRT Distribution

Single (7"): released on Sugar Hill USA, Dec'82 by MCA Records. Dist: Roots Distribution, Mike's Country Music Room Distribution, Projection Distribution, PRT Distribution

SIGN OF THE TIMES(EDIT).
Single (7"): released on Elektra, Jan'85 by WEA Records. Dist: WEA

Single (12"): released on Elektra, Jan'85 by WEA Records. Dist: WEA Deleted '86.

SOURCE, THE.
Tracks: / Street scene / Style(Peter Gunn theme)MS Thang / P.L.U.(Peace, Love and Unity) / Throwin' down / Behind closed doors / Larry's dance theme(part2) / Lies / Fastest man alive / Freelance.
Album: released on Elektra (USA), Apr'86 by Elektra/Asylum/Nonesuch Records. Dist: WEA

Cassette: released on Elektra (USA), Apr'86 by Elektra/Asylum/Nonesuch Records. Dist: WEA

STYLE(PETER GUNN THEME).
Tracks: / Style(Peter Gun theme) / Style(Peter Gunn theme)instrumental / Style(Peter Gunn theme)Remix.
Single (7"): released on Elektra (USA), May'86 by Elektra/Asylum/Nonesuch Records. Dist: WEA

Single (12"): released on Elektra (USA), May'86 by Elektra/Asylum/Nonesuch Records. Dist: WEA

THEY SAID IT COULDN'T BE DONE.
Album: released on Elektra, Feb'85 by WEA Records. Dist: WEA

Cassette: released on Elektra, Feb'85 by WEA Records. Dist: WEA

U KNOW WHAT TIME IT IS?.
Tracks: / U know what time it is? / Bus dis (woo).
Single (7"): released on Elektra (USA), Mar'87 by Elektra/Asylum/Nonesuch Records. Dist: WEA

Single (12"): released on Elektra (USA), Mar'87 by Elektra/Asylum/Nonesuch Records. Dist: WEA

WHITE LINES Don't do it.
Single (12"): released on Blatant, Jun'87 by Castle Communications. Dist: PRT

Single (7"): released on Blatant, Aug'87 by Castle Communications. Dist: PRT

Picture disc single: released on Blatant, Aug'87 by Castle Communications. Dist: PRT

Grandmaster Melle Mel

BEAT STREET.
Single (12"): released on Sugar Hill USA, Jun'84 by MCA Records. Dist: Roots Distribution, Mike's Country Music Room Distribution, Projection Distribution, PRT Distribution

BEATSTREET BREAKDOWN.
Single (7"): released on Atlantic, Jun'84 by WEA Records. Dist: WEA Deleted '86.

Single (12"): released on Atlantic, Jun'84 by WEA Records. Dist: WEA

CONTINUOUS WHITE LINES.
Single (12"): released on Sugar Hill USA, Oct'84 by MCA Records. Dist: Roots Distribution, Mike's Country Music Room Distribution, Projection Distribution, PRT Distribution

JESSE (Grandmaster Richie Rich).
Single (7"): by MCA Records. Dist: Roots Distribution, Mike's Country Music Room Distribution, Projection Distribution, PRT Distribution

Single (12"): by MCA Records. Dist: Roots Distribution, Mike's Country Music Room Distribution, Projection Distribution, PRT Distribution

PUMP ME UP.
Single (7"): released on Sugar Hill USA, Mar'85 by MCA Records. Dist: Roots Distribution, Mike's Country Music Room Distribution, Projection Distribution, PRT Distribution

Single (12"): released on Sugar Hill USA, Mar'85 by MCA Records. Dist: Roots Distribution, Mike's Country Music Room Distribution, Projection Distribution, PRT Distribution

Picture disc single: released on Sugar Hill USA, Mar'85 by MCA Records. Dist: Roots Distribution, Mike's Country Music Room Distribution, Projection Distribution, PRT Distribution

STEP OFF.
Single (12"): released on Sugar Hill USA, Dec'84 by MCA Records. Dist: Roots Distribution, Mike's Country Music Room Distribution, Projection Distribution, PRT Distribution

STEP OFF (PART 1).
Single (12"): released on Sugar Hill USA, Dec'84 by MCA Records. Dist: Roots Distribution, Mike's Country Music Room Distribution, Projection Distribution, PRT Distribution

Single (7"): released on Sugar Hill USA, Dec'84 by MCA Records. Dist: Roots Distribution, Mike's Country Music Room Distribution, Projection Distribution, PRT Distribution

STEPPING OFF.
Cassette: released on Sugar Hill USA, May'85 by MCA Records. Dist: Roots Distribution, Mike's Country Music Room Distribution, Projection Distribution, PRT Distribution

Album: released on Sugar Hill USA, May'85 by MCA Records. Dist: Roots Distribution, Mike's Country Music Room Distribution, Projection Distribution, PRT Distribution

VICE.
Single (7"): released on Sugar Hill USA, Nov'85 by MCA Records. Dist: Roots Distribution, Mike's Country Music Room Distribution, Projection Distribution, PRT Distribution

WE DON'T WORK FOR FREE.
Single (12"): released on Sugar Hill USA, Sep'84 by MCA Records. Dist: Roots Distribution, Mike's Country Music Room Distribution, Projection Distribution, PRT Distribution

Single (7"): released on Sugar Hill USA, Sep'84 by MCA Records. Dist: Roots Distribution, Mike's Country Music Room Distribution, Projection Distribution, PRT Distribution

WHITE LINES(DON'T DO IT).
Picture disc single: released on Sugar Hill USA, Jul'84 by MCA Records. Dist: Roots Distribution, Mike's Country Music Room Distribution, Projection Distribution, PRT Distribution

Single (7"): released on Sugar Hill USA, Nov'83 by MCA Records. Dist: Roots Distribution, Mike's Country Music Room Distribution, Projection Distribution, PRT Distribution

Single (12"): released on Sugar Hill USA, Nov'83 by MCA Records. Dist: Roots Distribution, Mike's Country Music Room Distribution, Projection Distribution, PRT Distribution

WORK PARTY.
Album: released on Sugar Hill USA, Oct'84 by MCA Records. Dist: Roots Distribution, Mike's Country Music Room Distribution; Projection Distribution, PRT Distribution

Cassette: released on Sugar Hill USA, Oct'84 by MCA Records. Dist: Roots Distribution, Mike's Country Music Room Distribution, Projection Distribution, PRT Distribution

WORLD WAR THREE.
Single (7"): released on Sugar Hill USA, Jul'85 by MCA Records. Dist: Roots Distribution, Mike's Country Music Room Distribution, Projection Distribution, PRT Distribution

Single (12"): released on Sugar Hill USA, Jul'85 by MCA Records. Dist: Roots Distribution, Mike's Country Music Room Distribution, Projection Distribution, PRT Distribution

Single (12"): released on Sugar Hill USA, Jul'85 by MCA Records. Dist: Roots Distribution, Mike's Country Music Room Distribution, Projection Distribution, PRT Distribution

Grandmaster Richie Rich

DON'T BE FLASH.
Tracks: / Don't be flash / Flash scratch / Bonus beats.
Notes: See under Rich,Richie.
Single (12"): released on Spin-Off's, Nov'86 Dist: Spin-Off

Grandmothers

LOOKING UP GRANNY'S DRESS.
Album: released on Teldec (Germany), May'84 by Import Records. Dist: IMS Distribution, Polygram Distribution

Grand Night For Singing

GRAND NIGHT FOR SINGING various artists (Various Artists).
Album: released on CBS, Jan'80 by CBS Records. Dist: CBS

Cassette: released on CBS, Jan'80 by CBS Records. Dist: CBS

Grandpa Neil

LITTLE BOY THAT SANTA CLAUS FORGOT.
Single (7"): released on Chick, Nov'82 Dist: Pinnacle

Grand Prix

FIRST ALBUM, THE.
Album: released on RCA, Oct'80 by RCA Records. Dist: RCA, Roots, Swift, Wellard, Chris, I & B, Solomon & Peres Distribution

Cassette: released on RCA, Oct'80 by RCA Records. Dist: RCA, Roots, Swift, Wellard, Chris, I & B, Solomon & Peres Distribution

GIVE ME WHAT'S MINE.
Single (7"): released on Chrysalis, May'83 by Chrysalis Records. Dist: CBS

SAMURAI.
Album: released on Chrysalis, Jun'83 by Chrysalis Records. Dist: CBS

Cassette: released on Chrysalis, Jun'83 by Chrysalis Records. Dist: CBS

THERE FOR NONE TO SEE.
Album: released on RCA, Mar'82 by RCA Records. Dist: RCA, Roots, Swift, Wellard, Chris, I & B, Solomon & Peres Distribution

Cassette: released on RCA, Mar'82 by RCA Records. Dist: RCA, Roots, Swift, Wellard, Chris, I & B, Solomon & Peres Distribution

Grange Hill Cast

YOU KNOW THE TEACHER (SMASH HEAD).
Tracks: / You know the teacher (Smash head) / Don't stop.
Single (7"): released on BBC, Nov'86 by BBC Records & Tapes. Dist: EMI, PRT, Pye

Single (12"): released on BBC, Nov'86 by BBC Records & Tapes. Dist: EMI, PRT, Pye

Granlan, Tom

STARSTRUCK.
Single (7"): released on Peach River, Mar'82 by Peach River Records. Dist: PRT

Grant, Alex of Srathspey

DE'IL IN THE KITCHEN, THE.
Cassette: released on Folktracks, Nov'79 by Folktracks Cassettes. Dist: Folktracks

Grant Amy

AGE TO AGE.
Album: released on Myrrh, May'82 by Word Records. Dist: Word Distribution

Cassette: released on Myrrh, May'82 by Word Records. Dist: Word Distribution

CHRISTMAS ALBUM.
Album: released on Myrrh, Nov'84 by Word Records. Dist: Word Distribution

COLLECTION: AMY GRANT.
Tracks: / Old man's rubble / My father's eyes / El Shaddai.
Notes: After nine successful albums this is the first "best of...."release in Amy's career. It is a gathering of all her favourite songs from the first 10 years plus new tracks written especially for this album:
Album: released on Myrrh, Oct'86 by Word Records. Dist: Word Distribution

Cassette: released on Myrrh, Oct'86 by Word Records. Dist: Word Distribution

IN CONCERT.
Double Album: released on Myrrh, May'82 by Word Records. Dist: Word Distribution

Double cassette: released on Myrrh, May'82 by Word Records. Dist: Word Distribution

NEVER ALONE.
Album: released on Myrrh, May'82 by Word Records. Dist: Word Distribution

Cassette: released on Myrrh, May'82 by Word Records. Dist: Word Distribution

UNGUARDED.
Album: released on A&M, Sep'85 by A&M Records. Dist: Polygram

Cassette: released on A&M, Sep'85 by A&M Records. Dist: Polygram

Album: released on Myrrh, Aug'85 by Word Records. Dist: Word Distribution

Cassette: released on Myrrh, Aug'85 by Word Records. Dist: Word Distribution

Grant, Angus

HIGHLAND FIDDLE.
Album: released on Topic, '81 Dist: Roots Distribution

Grant, David

CHANGE.
Tracks: / Change / Change (Alternate Mix)* / Change (Dub version)* / Fire me up.
Single (7"): released on Polydor, Jul'87 by Polydor Records. Dist: Polygram, Polydor

Single (12"): released on Polydor, Jul'87 by Polydor Records. Dist: Polygram, Polydor

CLOSE TO YOU.
Tracks: / Goodbye love / Close to you.
Single (7"): released on Chrysalis, Mar'86 by Chrysalis Records. Dist: CBS

Single (12"): released on Chrysalis, Mar'86 by Chrysalis Records. Dist: CBS

COULD BE I'M FALLING IN LOVE.
Single (7"): released on Chrysalis, Mar'85 by Chrysalis Records. Dist: CBS

Single (12"): released on Chrysalis, Mar'85 by Chrysalis Records. Dist: CBS

DAVID GRANT.
Album: released on Chrysalis, Oct'83 by Chrysalis Records. Dist: CBS

Cassette: released on Chrysalis, Oct'83 by Chrysalis Records. Dist: CBS

HOPES AND DREAMS.
Album: released on Chrysalis, May'85 by Chrysalis Records. Dist: CBS

Cassette: released on Chrysalis, May'85 by Chrysalis Records. Dist: CBS

LOVE WILL FIND A WAY.
Single (7"): released on Chrysalis, Oct'83 by Chrysalis Records. Dist: CBS

Single (12"): released on Chrysalis, Oct'83 by Chrysalis Records. Dist: CBS

MATED (Grant, David & Jaki Graham).
Single (7"): released on EMI, Nov'85 by EMI Records. Dist: EMI

Single (12"): released on EMI, Nov'85 by EMI Records. Dist: EMI

ORGANISE.
Single (7"): released on Chrysalis, Feb'84 by Chrysalis Records. Dist: CBS

Single (12"): released on Chrysalis, Feb'84 by Chrysalis Records. Dist: CBS

STOP AND GO.
Single (7"): released on Chrysalis, Apr'83 by Chrysalis Records. Dist: CBS

Single (12"): released on Chrysalis, Apr'83 by Chrysalis Records. Dist: CBS Deleted '85.

TAKE US BACK.
Tracks: / Take us back / Tell me.
Single (7"): released on Polydor, Mar'87 by Polydor Records. Dist: Polygram, Polydor

Single (12"): released on Polydor, Mar'87 by Polydor Records. Dist: Polygram, Polydor

Grant, Earl

HOUSE OF BAMBOO.
Tracks: / House of Bamboo / Fever / Mission impossible / Crickets sing for Anna Maria,The.
Single (12"): released on London, Sep'86 by London Records. Dist: Polygram

Grant, Eddy

ALL THE HITS.
Album: released on K-Tel, Nov'84 by K-Tel Records. Dist: Record Merchandisers Distribution, Taylors, Terry Blood Distribution, Wynd-Up Distribution, Relay Distribution, Pickwick Distribution, Solomon & Peres Distribution, Polygram

Cassette: released on K-Tel, Nov'84 by K-Tel Records. Dist: Record Merchandisers Distribution, Taylors, Terry Blood Distribution, Wynd-Up Distribution, Relay Distribution, Pickwick Distribution, Solomon & Peres Distribution, Polygram

BABY COME BACK.
Single (7"): released on Ice, Feb'85 by Ice Records. Dist: RCA

Single (12"): released on Ice, Feb'85 by Ice Records. Dist: RCA

BORN TUFF.
Tracks: / Dance party / Next time around / Come along to my place / Melody of the night / Born tuff / Blood money / Village life / Funny little groove / In L.A. / She's standing at the corner.
Album: released on Ice, Aug'86 by Ice Records. Dist: RCA

Cassette: released on Ice, Aug'86 by Ice Records. Dist: RCA

Compact disc: released on Ice, Aug'86 by Ice Records. Dist: RCA

BOYS IN THE STREET.
Single (7"): released on Ice, Oct'84 by Ice Records. Dist: RCA

Single (12"): released on Ice, Oct'84 by Ice Records. Dist: RCA

CAN'T GET ENOUGH.
Album: released on Ice, May'83 by Ice Records. Dist: RCA

Cassette: released on Ice, May'83 by Ice Records. Dist: RCA

CAN'T GET ENOUGH OF YOU.
Single (7"): released on Ensign, Mar'81 by Ensign Records. Dist: CBS Distribution

Single (12"): released on Ensign, Mar'81 by Ensign Records. Dist: CBS Distribution

DANCE PARTY.
Tracks: / Dance party / Rock you good.
Single (7"): released on Ice, Jul'86 by Ice Records. Dist: RCA

Single (12"): released on Ice, Jul'86 by Ice Records. Dist: RCA

ELECTRIC AVENUE.
Single (7"): released on Ice, Jan'83 by Ice Records. Dist: RCA

Single (12"): released on Ice, Jan'83 by Ice Records. Dist: RCA

GOING FOR BROKE.
Album: by Ice Records. Dist: RCA Deleted Jun'84.

Cassette: released on Ice, Jun'84 by Ice Records. Dist: RCA

I DON'T WANNA DANCE.
Single (7"): released on Ice, Sep'82 by Ice Records. Dist: RCA

Single (12"): released on Ice, Sep'82 by Ice Records. Dist: RCA

I DON'T WANNA DANCE (VIDEO).
Tracks: / I don't wanna dance / Electric Avenue.
Video-cassette (VHS): released on Gold Rushes, Mar'87 by Video Collection Records. Dist: Counterpoint

I LOVE YOU YES I LOVE YOU.
Single (7"): released on Ensign, Jul'81 by Ensign Records. Dist: CBS Distribution

Single (12"): released on Ensign, Aug'81 by Ensign Records. Dist: CBS Distribution

KILLER ON THE RAMPAGE.
Album: released on Ice, Nov'82 by Ice Records. Dist: RCA

Cassette: released on Ice, Nov'82 by Ice Records. Dist: RCA

LIVE AT NOTTING HILL.
Album: released on Ice, Dec'81 by Ice Records. Dist: RCA

Cassette: released on Ice, Dec'81 by Ice Records. Dist: RCA

LIVE AT NOTTING HILL CARNIVAL.
Album: released on Ice, Dec'84 by Ice Records. Dist: RCA

Cassette: released on Ice, Dec'84 by Ice Records. Dist: RCA

LIVE IN LONDON.
Tracks: / Killer on the rampage / Too young to fall in love / War party / Romancing the stone / Do you fee my love / I don't wanna dance / Born tuff / Hello Africa / Baby come back / Walking on sunshine / Electric avenue / Living on the frontline / Genocide / Dance party.
Notes: Eddy Grant performing his latest and greatest song in front of over 40,000 people - the largest outdoor audience seen in London for many years. Recorded in 24 track stereo and digital mixed by eddy himself in his famous studio in Barbados to give superb live hi-fi sound.
Video-cassette (VHS): released on PMI, Jul'86 by PMI Records. Dist: EMI

ROMANCING THE STONE.
Single (7"): released on Ice, May'84 by Ice Records. Dist: RCA

Single (12"): released on Ice, May'84 by Ice Records. Dist: RCA

TILL I CAN'T TAKE LOVE NO MORE.
Single (7"): released on Ice, Oct'83 by Ice Records. Dist: RCA

Single (12"): released on Ice, Oct'83 by Ice Records. Dist: RCA

TIME TO LET GO.
Single (7"): released on Ice, Nov'81 by Ice Records. Dist: RCA

Single (12"): released on Ice, Nov'81 by Ice Records. Dist: RCA

WALKING ON SUNSHINE.
Album: released on Ice, Feb'83 by Ice Records. Dist: RCA

Cassette: released on Ice, Feb'83 by Ice Records. Dist: RCA

WAR PARTY (Bajan remix).
Single (7"): released on Ice, Apr'83 by Ice Records. Dist: RCA

Single (12"): released on Ice, Apr'83 by Ice Records. Dist: RCA

Grant, Gogi

GRANTED.... IT'S GOGI.
Tracks: / By myself / Day you came along, The / That's my desire / That's my desire / No fool like an old fool / I'm a dreamer,aren't we all / Don't be that way / I'm getting sentimental over you / I wished on the moon / Bibbidi-bobbidi-boo / Would I love you(love you,love you) / I'm confessin'(that I love you) / You're getting to be a habit with me.
Album: released on RCA, Jun'87 by RCA Records. Dist: RCA, Roots, Swift, Wellard, Chris, I & B, Solomon & Peres Distribution

Cassette: released on RCA, Jun'87 by RCA Records. Dist: RCA, Roots, Swift, Wellard, Chris, I & B, Solomon & Peres Distribution

WAYWARD WIND.
Single (7"): released on Old Gold, Jul'82 by Old Gold Records. Dist: Lightning, Jazz Music, Spartan, Counterpoint

Grant, Kitty

GLAD TO KNOW YOU.
Single (7"): released on Leo, Jun'83 Dist: Recommended

Grant, Lou

LOU GRANT SINGS YOUR RADIO FAVOURITES.
Tracks: / Candy kisses / Five little fingers / Just lovin' you / Jean / No one will ever know / Rose of Tralee, The / Tribute to Jock Stein, A / Careless hands / When I leave the world behind / Yer mither / When the gold in your hair turns to silver / Still / Turn your radio on / We will make love / Tribute to Jock Stein, A.
Album: released on Country House, Dec'86 by BGS Productions Ltd. Dist: Taylor, H.R., Record Merchandisers Distribution, Pinnacle, Sounds of Scotland Records

Cassette: released on Country House, Dec'86 by BGS Productions Ltd. Dist: Taylor, H.R., Record Merchandisers Distribution, Pinnacle, Sounds of Scotland Records

Grant, Manson

AWARD WINNERS (Grant, Manson & The Dynamos Showband).
Tracks: / Heartaches by the number / I won't go huntin' with you Jake / Legend in my time, A / Weatherman, The / Legend in my time, A.
Cassette: released on Ross, Dec'86 by Ross Records. Dist: Ross Distribution, Roots Distribution

Album: released on Ross, '86 by Ross Records. Dist: Ross Distribution, Roots Distribution

COUNTRY STARS (Grant, Manson & The Dynamos Showband).
Album: released on Ross, '86 by Ross Records. Dist: Ross Distribution, Roots Distribution

Cassette: released on Ross, '86 by Ross Records. Dist: Ross Distribution, Roots Distribution

COUNTRYWIDE REQUESTS (Grant, Manson & The Dynamos).
Album: released on Ross, '86 by Ross Records. Dist: Ross Distribution, Roots Distribution

Cassette: released on Ross, '86 by Ross Records. Dist: Ross Distribution, Roots Distribution

HAPPY HEART (Grant, Manson & The Dynamos).
Album: released on Ross, '86 by Ross Records. Dist: Ross Distribution. Roots Distribution

Cassette: released on Ross, '86 by Ross Records. Dist: Ross Distribution, Roots Distribution

MANSON GRANT & THE DYNAMOS SHOWBAND (Grant, Manson & The Dynamos Showband).
Album: released on Ross, '86 by Ross Records. Dist: Ross Distribution, Roots Distribution

Cassette: released on Ross, '86 by Ross Records. Dist: Ross Distribution, Roots Distribution

ON THE COUNTRY TRAIL.
Album: released on Ross, '86 by Ross Records. Dist: Ross Distribution, Roots Distribution

Cassette: released on Ross, '86 by Ross Records. Dist: Ross Distribution, Roots Distribution

SING ANOTHER SONG.
Album: released on Ross, '86 by Ross Records. Dist: Ross Distribution, Roots Distribution

Cassette: released on Ross, '86 by Ross Records. Dist: Ross Distribution, Roots Distribution

Grant, Rudy

FUNNY GIRL.
Single (7"): released on Ice, Mar'82 by Ice Records. Dist: RCA

Single (12"): released on Ice, Feb'82 by Ice Records. Dist: RCA

HARRISONS CAVE, BARBADOS.
Album: released on Seara, Feb'85 by Seara Records. Dist: Jetstar

MASH IN GUYANA.
Tracks: / Mash in Guyana / Mash in Guyana (version).
Single (12"): released on Seara, Jul'87 by Seara Records. Dist: Jetstar

WOMAN.
Single (7"): released on Ice, Nov'81 by Ice Records. Dist: RCA

Single (12"): released on Ice, Nov'81 by Ice Records. Dist: RCA

Grants

SLANGEVA.
Single (7"): released on REL, '79 Dist: Roots

Grants, Manson

COUNTRYWIDE REQUEST (Grants, Manson/Dynamos).
Album: released on Ross, Jul'84 by Ross Records. Dist: Ross Distribution, Roots Distribution

Cassette: released on Ross, Jul'84 by Ross Records. Dist: Ross Distribution, Roots Distribution

Grants piping...

GRANTS PIPING CHAMPIONSHIP (MARCH, STRATHSPEY & REEL) Various Artists (Various Artists).
Album: released on Lismor, Jul'84 by Lismor Records. Dist: Lismor, Roots, Celtic Music

Cassette: released on Lismor, Jul'84 by Lismor Records. Dist: Lismor, Roots, Celtic Music

GRANTS PIPING CHAMPIONSHIP (PIOBAIREACHD) Various Artists (Various Artists).
Album: released on Lismor, Jul'84 by Lismor Records. Dist: Lismor, Roots, Celtic Music

Cassette: released on Lismor, Jul'84 by Lismor Records. Dist: Lismor, Roots, Celtic Music

GRANTS WHISKY PIPING CHAMPIONSHIPS VOLUME 1 Various Artists (Various Artists).
Album: released on Lismor, Dec'79 by Lismor Records. Dist: Lismor, Roots, Celtic Music

GRANTS WHISKY PIPING CHAMPIONSHIPS VOLUME 2 Various Artists (Various Artists).
Album: released on Lismor, Dec'79 by Lismor Records. Dist: Lismor, Roots, Celtic Music

Grant, Steve

CONVICTION.
Single (7"): released on Record Shack, Jun'85 by Record Shack Records. Dist: PRT

Single (12"): released on Record Shack, Jun'85 by Record Shack Records. Dist: PRT

RUN FOR COVER.
Single (7"): released on Record Shack, Aug'84 by Record Shack Records. Dist: PRT

Single (12"): released on Record Shack, Aug'84 by Record Shack Records. Dist: PRT

Granz, Norman

JAM SESSION NUMBER 3.
Album: released on Verve (USA), Sep'81 by

Polydor. Dist: Polygram

Grapes of wrath

GRAPES OF WRATH Steinbeck, John.
Album: released on Caedmon(USA), '79 by Caedmon (USA) Records. Dist: Gower, Taylors, Discovery

Cassette: released on Caedmon(USA), '78 by Caedmon (USA) Records. Dist: Gower, Taylors, Discovery

Grappelli, Stephane

50TH ANNIVERSARY CONCERT (see Reinhardt, Django).

50TH ANNIVERSARY OF THE QUINTET OF THE HOT CLUB OF FRANCE.
Album: released on Vogue, Oct'84 Dist: Discovery, Jazz Music, PRT, Swift

80.
Album: released on Barclay (France), Mar'83 by Decca Records. Dist: IMS, Discovery, Conifer, Swift, Polygram

Cassette: released on Barclay (France), Mar'83 by Decca Records. Dist: IMS, Discovery, Conifer, Swift, Polygram

AFTERNOON IN PARIS.
Tracks: / Autumn leaves / This can't be love / Time after time / Undercided / Tangerine / Chicago / Manoir de mes rev / Daphne / Misty / Afternoon in Paris.
Compact disc: released on MPS(France), May'85

Album: released on MPS Jazz, May'81

AT THE WINERY.
Tracks: / You are the sunshine of my life / Love for sale / Angel's camp / Willow weep for me / Chicago / Talking a chance on love / Minor swing / Let's fall in love / Just you, just me.
Notes: Personnel: Stephane Grappelli - violin & electric viola / John Etheridge - guitar / Martin Taylor - guitar / Jack Sewing - bass.
Album: released on Concord, Mar'81 by Import Records. Dist: IMS, Polygram

Compact disc: released on Concord Jazz(USA), Jul'87 by Concord Jazz Records (USA). Dist; IMS, Polygram

BEST OF STEPHANE GRAPPELLI, (THE).
Album: released on Black Lion-Intercord, '82

CONVERSATIONS.
Compact disc: released on Fantasy (USA), Nov'86 by Fantasy Inc USA Records. Dist: IMS, Polygram

CRAZY RHYTHM.
Compact disc: released on Vogue, '86 Dist: Discovery, Jazz Music, PRT, Swift

DJANGO REINHARDT WITH STEPHANE GRAPPELLI (see Reinhardt, Django).

FASCINATING RHYTHM.
Compact disc: released on The Compact Collection, Sep'87 by Conifer Records. Dist: Conifer Distribution

FASCINATIN' RHYTHM.
Album: by EMI Records. Dist: EMI

FOR ALL SEASONS.
Album: released on EMI, Jun'85 by EMI Records. Dist: EMI

Cassette: released on EMI, Jun'85 by EMI Records. Dist: EMI

Compact disc: released on EMI, Jun'85 by EMI Records. Dist: EMI

GOLDEN HOUR OF STEPHANE G.
Cassette: released on PRT, Mar'78 by PRT Records. Dist: PRT

HOMAGE TO DJANGO REINHARDT VOLUME 2.
Album: released on Joker, Apr'81 Dist: Cadillac, Zodiac Distribution, Jazz Horizons, Jazz Music, JSU, Celtic Music

HOMAGE TO DJANGO REINHARDT.
Album: released on Joker, Apr'81 Dist: Cadillac, Zodiac Distribution, Jazz Horizons, Jazz Music, JSU, Celtic Music

HOT CLUB OF LONDON VOLUME 1.
Album: released on Black Lion, Sep'85 by Black Lion Records. Dist: Jazz Music, Chris Wellard, Taylor, H.R., Counterpoint, Cadillac

I HEAR MUSIC.
Album: released on RCA International, Oct'80

Cassette: released on RCA International, Oct'80

IMPROVISATIONS.
Double Album: released on Barclay, Mar'83 by Decca Records. Dist: Polygram, Discovery, Conifer, IMS, Swift

I REMEMBER DJANGO.
Album: released on Black Lion, Jan'85 by Black Lion Records. Dist: Jazz Music, Chris Wellard, Taylor, H.R., Counterpoint, Cadillac

JEALOUSY.
Album: released on EMI, '73 by EMI Records. Dist: EMI

Cassette: released on EMI, Dec'73 by EMI Records. Dist: EMI

JOUE GEO GERSHWIN AT C.PORTER.
Compact disc: released on Music Disc (France), Dec'85 Dist: IMS-Polygram Distribution

JUST ONE OF THOSE THINGS.
Album: released on H.M.V., Apr'84 by EMI Records. Dist: EMI

Cassette: released on H.M.V., Apr'84 by EMI Records. Dist: EMI

Album: released on Black Lion, Sep'85 by Black Lion Records. Dist: Jazz Music, Chris Wellard, Taylor, H.R., Counterpoint, Cadillac

LIVE IN COPENHAGEN.
Compact disc: released on Pablo, Aug'86 by Pablo Records. Dist: Wellard, Chris, IMS-Polygram, BMG

LIVE IN SAN FRANCISCO.
Tracks: / I've got rhythm / Fascinating rhythm / Let's fall in love / Swing '42 / Honeysuckle Rose / You are the sunshine of my life / Minor swing / Here, there and everywhere / St Louis blues / Them there eyes / After you've gone.
Notes: Personnel: Stephane Grappelli - violin / Martin Taylor - electric guitar / Diz Disley - acoustic guitar / Jack Sewing - bass.
Album: released on Blackhawk, Jul'87 by Blackhawk Records (USA). Dist: IMS-Polygram

MAGIC OF STEPHANE GRAPPELLI, (THE).
Album: released on Spot, Jun'85 by Pickwick Records. Dist: H.R. Taylor, Lugtons

Cassette: released on Spot, Jun'85 by Pickwick Records. Dist: H.R. Taylor, Lugtons

NORWEGIAN WOOD (see Duran, Elena).

NORWEGIAN WOOD.
Album: released on RCA, Oct'81 by RCA Records. Dist: RCA, Roots, Swift, Wellard, Chris, I & B, Solomon & Peres Distribution

Cassette: released on RCA, Oct'81 by RCA Records. Dist: RCA, Roots, Swift, Wellard, Chris, I & B, Solomon & Peres Distribution

PARIS ENCOUNTER.
Album: by WEA Records. Dist: WEA

PLAYS JEROME KERN.
Notes: Legendary jazz violinist Stephane Grapelli's first album for GRP celebrates the music of Jerome Kern. CD contains 2 extra tracks.
Album: released on GRP (USA), May'87 by GRP Records (USA). Dist: IMS, Polygram

Cassette: released on GRP (USA), May'87 by GRP Records (USA). Dist: IMS, Polygram

Compact disc: released on GRP (USA), May'87 by GRP Records (USA). Dist: IMS, Polygram

QUINTETTE DU HOT CLUB DE FRANCE.
Compact disc: released on Vogue, Jan'86 Dist: Discovery, Jazz Music, PRT, Swift

REUNION, THE.
Tracks: / I'm coming Virginia / Time after time / La chanson de rue / Too marvellous for words / It don't mean a thing / Makin' whoopee / After you've gone / Flamingo / Star eyes / Folks who live on the hill, (The).
Notes: Personnel : Stephane Grappelli - violin / George Shearing - piano / Andrew Simpkins - bass / Rusty Jones - drums. Recorded 11.4.76 at MPS Studio, Villengen.
Compact disc: released on Verve, Nov'84 by Phonogram Records. Dist: Polygram

Album: released on MPS (Germany), Apr'85 Dist: IMS-Polygram Distribution, Parnote Distribution (Formerly MDC)

Album: released on MPS Jazz, May'81

RHYTHM IS OUR BUSINESS (see Reinhardt, Django).

RHYTHM IS OUR BUSINESS.
Album: released on Decca (Rock Echoes), Nov'82 by Decca Records. Dist: Polygram, IMS

Cassette: released on Decca (Rock Echoes), Nov'82 by Decca Records. Dist: Polygram, IMS

STEFF AND SLAM.
Notes: With Slam Stewart - bass.
Compact disc: released on Black & Blue (France), '86 Dist: Swift, Target, Discovery

STEPHANE GRAPPELLI PLAYS COLE PORTER.
Double Album: released on Musidisc (France), Oct'83 Dist: Discovery Distribution, Swift Distribution

STEPHANE GRAPPELLI/JEAN-LUC PONTY.
Compact disc: released on Accord (France), '86 Dist: Discovery, Target

STEPHANE GRAPPELLI LIVE AT THE CARNEGIE HALL.
Album: released on Doctor Jazz (USA), Oct'83 by Doctor Jazz Records. Dist: CBS

Cassette: released on Doctor Jazz (USA), Oct'83 by Doctor Jazz Records. Dist: CBS

STEPHANE GRAPPELLI 1973.
Album: released on Pye, '73

STEPHANOVA.
Album: released on Concord Jazz(USA), Oct'83 by Concord Jazz Records (USA). Dist: IMS, Polygram

Compact disc: released on Concord Jazz(USA), Oct'83 by Concord Jazz Records (USA). Dist: IMS, Polygram

STRICTLY FOR THE BIRDS.
Album: by EMI Records. Dist: EMI

Cassette: released on EMI, May'80 by EMI Records. Dist: EMI

STRUTTIN' OUT.
Double Album: released on Decca, Jul'84 by Decca Records. Dist: Polygram

STRUTTIN' OUT (see Reinhardt, Django).

TALK OF THE TOWN.
Album: released on Black Lion, Sep'85 by Black Lion Records. Dist: Jazz Music, Chris Wellard, Taylor, H.R., Counterpoint, Cadillac

TEA FOR TWO.
Cassette: released on EMI, Oct'78 by EMI Records. Dist: EMI

Album: released on EMI, Jan'78 by EMI Records. Dist: EMI

Cassette: released on EMI, Jan'78 by EMI Records. Dist: EMI

TIVOLI GARDENS,COPENHAGEN(79).
Compact disc: released on Pablo (USA), May'86 by Pablo Records (USA). Dist: Wellard, Chris, IMS-Polygram, BMG

TIVOLI GARDENS, COPENHAGEN.
Album: released on Pablo, '82 by Pablo Records. Dist: Wellard, Chris, IMS-Polygram, BMG

Cassette: released on Pablo, '82 by Pablo Records. Dist: Wellard, Chris, IMS-Polygram, BMG

TOGETHER (see Reinhardt, Django).

TOP HAT.
Notes: For full details see under 'Menuhin,Sir Yehudi and Stepane Grappelli'. Made famous by Fred Astaire.

TRIBUTE TO DJANGO.
Album: released on Barclay (France), Feb'83 by Decca Records. Dist: IMS, Discovery, Conifer, Swift, Polygram

Cassette: released on Barclay (France), Feb'83 by Decca Records. Dist: IMS, Discovery, Conifer, Swift, Polygram

TWO-FER, (A).
Album: released on Muse, May'83 by Peerless Records. Dist: Lugtons Distributors

TWO OF A KIND.
Notes: For full details see under Asmussen,Svend and Stephane Grappelli.

VENUPELLI BLUES.
Album: released on Pathe MarconiFrance), Feb'87

VENUPELLI BLUES.
Tracks: / I can't give you anything but love / My one and only love / After you've gone / Undecided / Venupelli blues / I'll never be the same / Tea for two.
Compact disc: released on Affinity, Mar'87 by Charly Records. Dist: Charly, Cadillac

Album: released on Affinity, Aug'79 by Charly Records. Dist: Charly, Cadillac

VINTAGE 1981.
Album: released on Concord, Dec'81 by Import Records. Dist: IMS, Polygram

VIOLINS NO END.
Album: released on Pablo (USA), Mar'85 by Pablo Records (USA). Dist: Wellard, Chris, IMS-Polygram, BMG

Cassette: released on Pablo (USA), Mar'85 by Pablo Records (USA). Dist: Wellard, Chris, IMS-Polygram, BMG

VIOLINSPIRATION.
Tracks: / Lover come back to me / Sweet Lorraine / Shine / Solitude / Ain't misbehavin / Souvenir de villinger / Hot lips / My heart stood still / Nearness of you, The / Joy / Nightingale sang in Berkely square,A / Cherokee / Lover man.
Album: released on Memoir, Dec'85 by Memoir Records. Dist: PRT Distribution

Cassette: released on Memoir, Dec'85 by Memoir Records. Dist: PRT Distribution

Album: released on MPS Jazz, May'81

VIOLIN SUMMIT.
Album: released on MPS (Germany), Sep'84 Dist: IMS-Polygram Distribution, Parnote Distribution (Formerly MDC)

WALKMAN JAZZ.
Cassette: released on Polydor, Jun'87 by Polydor Records. Dist: Polygram, Polydor

Compact disc: released on Polydor, Jul'87 by Polydor Records. Dist: Polygram, Polydor

YOUNG DJANGO.
Tracks: / Djangology / Sweet chorus / Minor swing / Are you in the mood / Galerie St. Hubert / Tears / Swing guitars / Oriental Shuffle / Blues for Django and Stephane.
Compact disc: released on Polydor, May'84 by Polydor Records. Dist: Polygram, Polydor

Album: released on MPS Jazz, May'81

Grassl, De Alex

SOUTHERN EXPOSURE.
Compact disc: released on Windham Hill, Jan'86 Dist: AM

Grassroots

FEELING SO BLUEGRASS.
Album: released on Champ, Jan'82 by Champ Records. Dist: Champ

Grateful Dead

AMERICAN BEAUTY.
Album: released on Warner Brothers, Jan'77 by Warner Bros Records. Dist: WEA

AOXOMOXOA.
Album: released on Warner Brothers, Jan'77 by Warner Bros Records. Dist: WEA

BLUES FOR ALLAH.
Album: released on United Artists, Oct'75

EUROPE 72.
Triple album / cassette: released on Warner Brothers, Jan'72 by Warner Bros Records. Dist: WEA

FROM THE MARS HOTEL.
Compact disc: released on Mobile Fidelity Sound, Dec'85 by Mobile Fidelity Records.

GO TO HEAVEN.
Album: released on Arista, May'80 by Arista Records. Dist: RCA

GRATEFUL DEAD.
Album: released on Edsel, Feb'87 by Demon Records. Dist: Pinnacle, Jazz Music, Projection

IN THE DARK.
Album: released on Arista, Oct'87 by Arista Records. Dist: RCA

Cassette: released on Arista, Oct'87 by Arista Records. Dist: RCA

Compact disc: released on Arista, Aug'87 by Arista Records. Dist: RCA

LIVE DEAD.
Double Album: released on Warner Brothers, Jan'72 by Warner Bros Records. Dist: WEA

SHAKEDOWN STREET.
Album: released on Arista, Jan'78 by Arista Records. Dist: RCA

SKELETONS IN THE CLOSET.
Album: released on Thunderbolt, Oct'86 by Magnum Music Group Ltd. Dist: Magnum Music Group Ltd, PRT Distribution, Spartan Distribution

STEAL YOUR FACE.
Album: released on United Artists, Jun'76

TERRAPIN STATION.
Tracks: / Estimated prophet / Dancing in the streets / Passenger / Samson & Delilah / Sunrise / Lady with a fan / Terrapin station / Terrapin / Terrapin transit / At a siding / Terrapin fever / Refrain.
Album: released on Arista, Jan'87 by Arista Records. Dist: RCA

Cassette: released on Arista, Jan'87 by Arista Records. Dist: RCA

TOUCH OF GREY.
Tracks: / My brother Esau.
Single (7"): released on Arista, Aug'87 by Arista Records. Dist: RCA

Single (12"): released on Arista, Aug'87 by Arista Records. Dist: RCA

WAKE OF FLOOD/ FROM MARS HOTEL.
Album: released on United Artists, Feb'77

WHAT A LONG STRANGE TRIP ITS BEEN.
Album: released on Warner Brothers, Feb'78 by Warner Bros Records. Dist: WEA

Gravedigger
WAR GAMES.
Album: released on Noise, Feb'86 by Dorane. Dist: Revolver, Cartel

Gravenites Nick
MONKEY MEDICINE (Gravenites Nick/John cipolina Band).

Graves
WE'RE GONNA HAVE A BALL.
Album: released on Cow Boy, Sep'79 by Cowboy Records. Dist: Jetstar

Graves, Robert
I CLAUDIUS (Jacobi, Derek).
Cassette: released on Argo (Spokenword), Jul'82 by Decca Records. Dist: Polygram

Gravestone
BACK TO ATTACK.
Album: released on Powerstation Records, Sep'86 by Powerstation Records. Dist: Pinnacle

CREATING A MONSTER.
Album: released on Powerstation Records, Mar'87 by Powerstation Records. Dist: Pinnacle

Gravine, Anita
I ALWAYS KNEW.
Album: released on Stash, Mar'87 Dist: Swift Distribution, Jazz Music Distribution, Jazz Horizons Distribution, Celtic Music Distribution, Cadillac, JSU Distribution, Zodiac Distribution

Gray, Barry
JOE 90 (Gray, Barry Orchestra).
Tracks: / Joe 90(86 Dance mix) / Captain Scarlet theme / Joe 90(Original version).
Single (7"): released on PRT, May'86 by PRT Records. Dist: PRT

Single (12"): released on PRT, May'86 by PRT Records. Dist: PRT

NO STRINGS ATTACHED (Gray, Barry Orchestra).
Album: released on PRT, Sep'81 by PRT Records. Dist: PRT

Cassette: released on PRT, Sep'81 by PRT Records. Dist: PRT

THUNDERBIRDS (Gray, Barry Orchestra).
Single (7"): released on PRT, Jun'81 by PRT Records. Dist: PRT

Gray Bunnies
GRAY BUNNIES.
Single (12"): Dist: Spartan

Gray, Doble
DRIFT AWAY.
Tracks: / Drift away / In crowd, the.
Single (7"): released on MCA, 20 Jun'87 by MCA through Polygram, MCA
Cat. no: MCA 1154
Single (12"): released on Old Gold, Jul'84 by Old Gold Records. Dist: Lightning, Jazz Music, Spartan, Counterpoint

IN CROWD.
Single (7"): released on Decca, Mar'82 by Decca Records. Dist: Polygram

OUT ON THE FLOOR.
Single (7"): released on Inferno, Oct'83 by Inferno Records. Dist: Inferno, Cartel, Pinnacle

Single (12"): released on Inferno, Oct'83 by Inferno Records. Dist: Inferno, Cartel, Pinnacle

SINGS FOR IN CROWDERS THAT GO-GO.
Album: released on Kent, Aug'87 by Ace Records. Dist: Pinnacle. Estim retail price in Sep'87 was £5.67.

Gray, Dolores
WARM BRANDY.
Album: released on Capitol, Oct'84 by Capitol Records. Dist: EMI

Cassette: released on Capitol, Oct'84 by Capitol Records. Dist: EMI

Gray, Dorian
PROMISE OF LOVE.
Single (7"): released on Leeds Independent,

Sep'85 by Revolver Records. Dist: Cartel

Graye, Tony
OH GEE (Graye, Tony Quartet/Quintet).
Album: released on Zim, Apr'81 Dist: JSU, Jazz Horizons, Jazz Music, Swift

Gray, Glen
1939 (Gray, Glen & The Casa Loma Orchestra).
Album: released on Circle(USA), Jun'86 by Jazzology Records (USA). Dist: Jazz Music, Swift, Chris Wellard

GLEN GRAY & THE CASA LOMA ORCHESTRA, 1943-46 (Gray, Glen & The Casa Loma Orchestra).
Album: released on London, Oct'79 by London Records. Dist: Polygram

Jonah Jones Quartet/Glen Gray & The Casa Loma Orchestra
ONE NIGHT STAND WITH GLEN GRAY & CASA LOMA ORCHESTRA (Gray, Glen & The Casa Loma Orchestra).
Album: released on Sandy Hook, Apr'79

SOLO SPOTLIGHT (Gray, Glen & The Casa Loma Orchestra).
Tracks: / Golden earrings / Street of dreams / Blue star (The Medic theme) / My foolish heart / Love letters / Around the world in 80 days / Was I to blame for falling in love with you / Stella by starlight / Beautiful love / When fall in love / I don't stand a ghost of a chance with you / Love me.
Notes: Spectacular big band sound consisting of a variety of powerful uptempo swingers and mellow mood arrangments. Featuring individually talented instrumentalists who each have their own reputation as a star performer. As the title suggest the album showcased Glen Gary's various instrumentalists in solo spotlight. Ideal for both listening and dancing.
Album: released on Capitol, Jan'86 by Capitol Records. Dist: EMI

Cassette: released on Capitol, Jan'86 by Capitol Records. Dist: EMI

SWING GOES ON, VOL 1, (THE).
Album: released on EMI (Germany), '83 by EMI Records. Dist: Conifer

SWINGIN DECADE (Gray, Glen & The Casa Loma Orchestra).
Tracks: / Apple honey / Midnight sun / Mission to Moscow / Harlem Nocturne / Jack the bear / Champ,The / Blues Rhapsody / Malibu / Opus no.1 / Sherwood's forest / Oh what a beautiful mornin / Intermission riff.
Notes: Glen Gary and the Casa Loma Orchestra bring us a selection of well recorded big band arrangements. This was one of the few postwar, genuine stereo recordings by a big band.
Album: released on Capitol, Dec'85 by Capitol Records. Dist: EMI

Cassette: released on Capitol, Dec'85 by Capitol Records. Dist: EMI

THEMES OF THE GREAT BANDS.
Album: released on Capitol T (USA), Jun'83 Dist: Conifer

Album: released on Capitol(USA), Mar'84 by Capitol (USA) Records. Dist: EMI

Gray, Gregory
STRAWBERRIES.
Tracks: / Strawberries / Meanwhile.
Single (7"): released on CBS, Jan'86 by CBS Records. Dist: CBS

Single (12"): released on CBS, Jan'86 by CBS Records. Dist: CBS

THINK OF SWANS.
Tracks: / Life of Reilly / James Bond / Speechless / Life & times / Books read twice / Johnny Purify / Sensual / Charlie gets hurt / Strawberries / Seatown.
Album: released on CBS, Mar'86 by CBS Records. Dist: CBS

Cassette: released on CBS, Mar'86 by CBS Records. Dist: CBS

Gray, Jerry
BIG DANCE TONIGHT (Gray, Jerry & His Orchestra).
Album: released on Jasmine, Mar'84 by Jasmine Records. Dist: Counterpoint, Lugtons, Taylor, H.R., Wellard, Chris, Swift, Cadillac

UNCOLLECTED(1952),THE.
Album: released on Hindsight(UK), Jun'86 Dist: Jazz Music

Gray, Jimmie
KOOL PEOPLE.
Single (12"): released on JKO, Oct'82 by JKO Records. Dist: Pinnacle

Gray, Les
DON'T YOU SAY IT.
Single (7"): released on Runaway, Jun'82

Gray, Mark
FEELING INSIDE,THE.
Tracks: / Please be love / She will / You're the reason / Born to be a music man / Strong heart dance with me / Back when love was enough / I need you again / Walkin after midnight / That feeling inside.
Album: released on CBS, Mar'86 by CBS Records. Dist: CBS

Cassette: released on CBS, Mar'86 by CBS Records. Dist: CBS

Gray, Mel American Pie
SCHOOL'S OUT.
Single (7"): released on Cool, Aug'81

Gray, Owen
BATTLE OF THE GIANTS, ROUND ONE (Gray, Owen & Pluggy Satchmo).
Album: released on Vista Sounds, '83 by Vista Sounds Records. Dist: Jetstar

BATTLES OF THE GIANTS, ROUND 1 (Gray, Owen & Pluggy Satchmo).
Album: released on Vista Sounds, '83 by Vista Sounds Records. Dist: Jetstar

CUPID.
Album: released on Melodisc, Nov'84 by Spartan Records. Dist: Spartan Distribution

DREAMS.
Album: released on Blue Mountain, 11 Apr'87 Dist: Jetstar

ETHIOPIA.
Single (12"): released on King Jam, Sep'85 by King Jam Records. Dist: Jetstar

HE'LL HAVE TO GO TO HELL.
Single (12"): released on Face Int, May'84 Dist: Jetstar

HIT AFTER HIT: VOL 4.
Album: released on Vista Sounds, '83 by Vista Sounds Records. Dist: Jetstar

I'M STANDING IN HIS WAY.
Single (12"): released on Revolutionary Sounds, Nov'85

LITTLE GIRL.
Album: released on Vista Sounds, Sep'84 by Vista Sounds Records. Dist: Jetstar

MY BEST FRIEND.
Single (12"): released on Sapphire, Nov'82 by Sapphire Records. Dist: Jetstar

Oldies but goldies
OLDIES BUT GOODIES (Gray, Owen & Delroy Wilson).
Album: released on Vista Sounds, '83 by Vista Sounds Records. Dist: Jetstar

Cassette: released on Vista Sounds, '83 by Vista Sounds Records. Dist: Jetstar

OWEN GRAY MEETS MAX ROMEO (Gray, Owen & Max Romeo).
Album: released on Culture Press, Dec'84 by Vista Sounds Records. Dist: Jetstar, Rough Trade

SEXUAL HEALING.
Single 10": released on Pama, Nov'82 by Pama Records. Dist: Pama, Enterprise, Jetstar

STAND BY ME.
Album: released on Hitbound, Mar'86 by Hitbound Records. Dist: Jetstar

WATCH THIS SOUND.
Cassette: released on Skynote, Sep'86 Dist: Sidewalk Records

Album: released on Skynote, Apr'85 Dist: Sidewalk Records

WATCH THIS SOUND.

Grayson, Kathryn
20 GOLDEN FAVOURITES BY KATH-RYN GRAYSON.
Album: released on Bulldog, Mar'84 by Bulldog Records. Dist: President Distribution, Spartan, Swift, Taylor, H.R.

Grayson, Larry
TERRY WOGAN.
Single (7"): released on Monarch, Jul'83 by Chart Records. Dist: Pinnacle

Gray, Wardell
ALUMNI MASTERS, (THE) (Gray, Wardell & Ben Webster).
Album: released on Jazz Live. Apr'81

HUNT, THE (Gray, Wardell & Dexter Gordon).
Double Album: released on Savoy, '78

LIVE JAM SESSION AT TRADEWINDS.
Album: released on Jam Session (USA), Apr'81 Dist: Jazz Music, Jazz Horizons

WARDELL GRAY.
Album: released on Spotlite, '83 by Spotlite Records. Dist: Cadillac, Jazz Music, Spotlite

Grease
GREASE Original film soundtrack (Various Artists).
Double Album: released on RSO, Jan'84

GREASE (VIDEO) (Various Artists).
Video-cassette (VHS): released on CIC Video, Apr'87 by CBS Records. Dist: CBS, Pickwick Distribution

Grease 2
GREASE 2 Original film soundtrack (Various Artists).
Album: released on RSO, Jun'82

Cassette: released on RSO, Jun'82

Grease Band
AMAZING GREASE.
Album: released on Charly, May'79 by Charly Records. Dist: Charly, Cadillac

Great acoustics
GREAT ACOUSTICS Various artists (Various Artists).
Album: released on Philo (USA), Sep'85

Great American
GREAT AMERICAN COUNTRY HITS various session artists (Various session artists).
Cassette: released on Aim, Feb'83 Dist: H.R. Taylor

Great Australian Legend
GREAT AUSTRALIAN LEGEND with Martyn Wyndham-Read & Trevor Lucas (Various Artists).
Album: released on Topic, '81 Dist: Roots Distribution

Great bands of Ulster
GREAT BANDS OF ULSTER: VOL 1 Various bands (Various bands).
Album: released on Peres Bands(Ireland), Oct'81 by Solomon & Peres Distribution. Dist: Spartan

Great big bands
GREAT BIG BANDS Various big bands (Various bands).
Double Album: released on Musidisc (France), Aug'63 Dist: Discovery Distribution, Swift Distribution

Great bluesmen
GREAT BLUESMEN Various artists.
Double Album: released on Vanguard (France), Dec'83

GREAT BLUES MEN: VOL 2 Various artists (Various Artists).
Cassette: released on PRT, Jun'79 by PRT Records. Dist: PRT

Great blues singers
GREAT BLUES SINGERS Various Artists (Various Artists).
Album: released on Joker, '79 Dist: Counterpoint, Mainline, Record Services Distribution (Ireland)

Great Bone
OSSIFIED.
Cassette: released on Slob, Feb'84 by Slob Records. Dist: Falling A Distribution

THOSE DAYS OF YORG.
Cassette: released on Slob, Feb'84 by Slob Records. Dist: Falling A Distribution

Great British Dance Bands
JEROME KERN CENTENARY various artists (Various dance bands).
Album: released on EMI Retrospect, Jan'85 by EMI Records. Dist: EMI

Cassette: released on EMI Retrospect, Jan'85 by EMI Records. Dist: EMI

Album: released on EMI Retrospect, Jan'85 by EMI Records. Dist: EMI

Cassette: released on EMI Retrospect, Jan'85 by EMI Records. Dist: EMI

PLAY COLE PORTER various artists (Various dance bands).
Double Album: released on World Records, Aug'80 Dist: Polygram

Album: released on EMI Retrospect, Aug'85 by EMI Records. Dist: FMI

Cassette: released on EMI Retrospect, Aug'85 by EMI Records. Dist: EMI

PLAY GEORGE GERSHWIN 1920-28 various dance bands (Various dance bands).
Double Album: released on World Records, Oct'77 Dist: Polygram

PLAY HARRY WARREN I'll string along with you (Various dance bands).
Album: Dist: Polygram

PLAY LONDON PRIDE (1925-1949) various dance bands (Various dance bands).
Cassette: released on EMI Retrospect, Aug'84 by EMI Records. Dist: EMI

Album: released on EMI Retrospect, Aug'84 by EMI Records. Dist: EMI
Cat. no: **EG 260 157 1**

PLAY RODGERS & HART various dance bands (Various dance bands).
Album: released on World Records, Apr'80 Dist: Polygram

PLAY THE HITS OF JIMMY KENNEDY & MICHAEL CARR various dance bands (Various dance bands).
Cassette: released on World Records, Mar'80 Dist: Polygram

Album: released on World Records, Mar'80 Dist: Polygram

PLAY THE HITS OF THE 60'S & 70'S various dance bands (Various dance bands).
Album: released on World Records, Oct'80 Dist: Polygram

Cassette: released on World Records, Oct'80 Dist: Polygram

PLAY THE MUSIC OF HARRY WARREN various dance bands (Various dance bands).
Album: Dist: Polygram

PLAY THE MUSIC OF IRVING BERLIN various dance bands (Various dance bands).
Album: Dist: Polygram

PLAY THE MUSIC OF NACIO HERB BROWN various dance bands (Various dance bands).
Album: Dist: Polygram

PLAY THE MUSIC OF NOEL COWARD various dance bands (Various dance bands).
Album: released on World Records, '78 Dist: Polygram

PLAY THE MUSIC OF VIVIAN ELLIS (1926-1937) various dance bands (Various dance bands).
Album: Dist: Polygram

VOICES OF... various dance bands (Various dance bands).
Album: Dist: Polygram

Great British MC's

GREAT BRITISH MC'S various artists (Various Artists).

Great British Number Ones

GREAT BRITISH NUMBER ONES (VOL.1) various original artists (Various original artists).
Double Album: released on Cambra, '83 by Cambra Records. Dist: IDS, Conifer

Double cassette: released on Cambra, '83 by Cambra Records. Dist: IDS, Conifer

GREAT BRITISH NUMBER ONES (VOL.2) various original artists (Various original artists).
Double cassette: released on Cambra, Aug'83 by Cambra Records. Dist: IDS, Conifer

Double Album: released on Cambra, Aug'83 by Cambra Records. Dist: IDS, Conifer

GREAT BRITISH NUMBER ONES (VOL.3) various original artists (Various original artists).
Double Album: released on Cambra, Apr'85 by Cambra Records. Dist: IDS, Conifer

Double cassette: released on Cambra, Apr'85 by Cambra Records. Dist: IDS, Conifer

GREAT BRITISH NUMBER ONES (VOL.4) various original artists (Various original artists).
Double Album: released on Cambra, Nov'83 by Cambra Records. Dist: IDS, Conifer

Double cassette: released on Cambra, Nov'83 by Cambra Records. Dist: IDS, Conifer

Great British Pop

GREAT BRITISH POP Rock group hits of the mid 60's (Various Artists).
Album: released on Old Gold, Nov'86 by Old Gold Records. Dist: Lightning, Jazz Music, Spartan, Counterpoint

Cassette: released on Old Gold, Nov'86 by Old Gold Records. Dist: Lightning, Jazz Music, Spartan, Counterpoint

Album: released on Fashion, Dec'84 by Fashion Records. Dist: PRT, Jetstar

Great British Rock'n'Roll

GREAT BRITISH ROCK'N'ROLL ROCKABILLY various original artists (Various original artists).
Cassette: released on RCA International, Jul'80

GREAT BRITISH ROCK'N'ROLL ROCKABILLY VOL.II various original artists (Various original artists).
Cassette: released on RCA International, Sep'81

Album: released on RCA International, Sep'81

Great cinema themes

GREAT CINEMA THEMES Various artists (Various Artists).
Boxed set: released on DGG, Mar'85 by Polydor Records. Dist: Polygram

Great classical...

GREAT CLASSICAL MASTERPIECES: SPRING Various artists (Various Artists).
Album: released on K-Tel, Mar'85 by K-Tel Records. Dist: Record Merchandisers Distribution, Taylors, Terry Blood Distribution, Wynd-Up Distribution, Relay Distribution, Pickwick Distribution, Solomon & Peres Distribution, Polygram

Cassette: released on K-Tel, Mar'85 by K-Tel Records. Dist: Record Merchandisers Distribution, Taylors, Terry Blood Distribution, Wynd-Up Distribution, Relay Distribution, Pickwick Distribution, Solomon & Peres Distribution, Polygram

GREAT CLASSICAL MASTERPIECES: SUMMER Various artists (Various Artists).
Album: released on K-Tel, Mar'85 by K-Tel Records. Dist: Record Merchandisers Distribution, Taylors, Terry Blood Distribution, Wynd-Up Distribution, Relay Distribution, Pickwick Distribution, Solomon & Peres Distribution, Polygram

Cassette: released on K-Tel, Mar'85 by K-Tel Records. Dist: Record Merchandisers Distribution, Taylors, Terry Blood Distribution, Wynd-Up Distribution, Relay Distribution, Pickwick Distribution, Solomon & Peres Distribution, Polygram

Great Country...

GREAT COUNTRY FESTIVAL various artists (Various Artists).
Album: released on Mercury, Mar'81 by Phonogram Records. Dist: Polygram Distribution

GREAT COUNTRY HITS OF THE 70'S various artists (Various Artists).
Cassette: released on VFM Cassettes, May'79

GREAT COUNTRY MUSIC SHOW various original artists (Various original artists).
Double Album: released on Ronco, Nov'82

Double cassette: released on Ronco, Nov'82

GREAT COUNTRY STARS Various Artists (Various Artists).
Tracks: / Rhinestone cowboy / Talking in your sleep / Riders in the sky / If you ain't lovin(you ain't livin) / Wabash Cannonball / Country Willie / United we stand / I still miss someone / Orange blossom special / Gambler's guitar / One woman man / Eery time two fools collide / Sing me an old fashioned love song / Wild side of life,The / Tip of my fingers / Harper valley PTA / High noon / Angel of the morning / King of the road / Act naturally / Ode to Billy Joe.
Cassette: released on Hour Of Pleasure, Jan'86 by Music For Pleasure Records. Dist: EMI

Great dames...

GREAT DAMES OF ROCK 'N' ROLL Various artists (Various Artists).
Album: released on Spectra, May'82 by Spectra Records. Dist: Pinnacle

Great Divide

GOT TO BE LOVE.
Single (12"): released on Blue Murder, Oct'84 by Great Divide Records. Dist: Backs, Cartel

WHO BROKE THE LOVE BANK.
Single (7"): released on Wimp, Dec'82 by Wimp Records. Dist: Backs, Cartel

Great Escape, The

GREAT ESCAPE, (THE) Brickhill, Paul (Todd, Richard).
Cassette: released on Listen For Pleasure, May'84 by MFP Records. Dist: EMI

Greatest Ceilidhband...

YREATEST CEILIDHBAND YOU EVER SAW various artists (Various Artists).

Album: released on Milstream (Sweden), Jan'85 Dist: Celtic Music Distribution

Greatest Country Duets

GREATEST COUNTRY DUETS various artists (Various Artists).
Album: released on Epic, Mar'84 by CBS Records. Dist: CBS

Cassette: released on Epic, Mar'84 by CBS Records. Dist: CBS

Greatest Esquire...

JAZZ OF WORLD WAR II various artists (Various Artists).
Album: released on Joker, Apr'81 Dist: Counterpoint, Mainline, Record Services Distribution (Ireland)

Greatest Folk...

GREATEST FOLK SINGERS OF THE SIXTIES various artists (Various Artists).
Double Album: released on Vanguard (USA), Nov'84

Greatest Hi-NRG Hits

GREATEST HI-NRG HITS various artists (Various Artists).
Album: released on ERC, Aug'84 by ERC Records. Dist: PRT

Cassette: released on ERC, Aug'84 by ERC Records. Dist: PRT

Greatest Hits

GREATEST HITS OF 1986 (Various Artists).
Album: released on Telstar, Nov'86 by Telstar Records. Dist: RCA Distribution

Cassette: released on Telstar, Nov'86 by Telstar Records. Dist: RCA Distribution

GREATEST HITS OF 1985 various artists (Various Artists).
Double Album: released on Telstar, Nov'85 by Telstar Records. Dist: RCA Distribution

Double cassette: released on Telstar, Nov'85 by Telstar Records. Dist: RCA Distribution

Greatest Jazz...

GREATEST JAZZ CONCERT IN THE WORLD various artists (Various Artists).
Double Album: released on Pablo (USA), '82 by Pablo Records (USA). Dist: Wellard, Chris, IMS-Polygram, BMG

Greatest Movie Themes

GREATEST MOVIE THEMES various artists (Various Artists).
Cassette: released on AIM (Budget Cassettes), Feb'83

Greatest Rap Hits

GREATEST RAP HITS VOL.2 various artists (Various Artists).
Album: released on Sugarhill (USA), Apr'82 by PRT Records. Dist: PRT Distribution

Cassette: released on Sugarhill (USA), Apr'82 by PRT Records. Dist: PRT Distribution

Greatest Recordings...

GREATEST RECORDINGS OF THE BROADWAY MUSICAL THEATRE Archive collection (Various Artists).
Boxed set: released on Franklin Mint Record Society, '84

Greatest Show On Legs

BALLOON CHA-CHA.
Single (7"): released on Index, Mar'82 by Index Records. Dist: Swift

Greatest Singers

Compact disc: released on Motown, Mar'86 by Motown Records. Dist: BMG Distribution

GREATEST SONGS(WRITTEN BY HOLLAND,DOZIER,HOLLAND) Original Artists (Various Artists).
Tracks: / You can't hurry love / Reach out I'll be there / How sweet it is(to be loved by you) / You keep me hangin on / Standing in the shadows of love / Heatwave / Where did our love go / Take me in your arms (rock me a little while) / Stop in the name of love / It's the same old song / Heaven must have sent you / Baby love / I can't help myself / Reflections / This old heart of mine(is weak for you) / I hear a symphony / Baby I need your loving / My world is empty without you / Can I get a witness / Come see about me.
Compact disc: released on Motown, Mar'86 by Motown Records. Dist: BMG Distribution

GREATEST SONGS(WRITTEN BY SMOKEY ROBINSON) Original Artists (Various Artists).
Tracks: / Tracks of my tears,The / My girl / Ooo baby baby / My guy / Shop around / Get ready / You really got a hold on me / Way you do the thing you do,The / Going to a go-go / Ain't that peculiar / I second that emotion / Don't look back / More love / Tears of a clown,The / Cruisin / Being with you.

GREATEST SINGERS,GREATEST SONGS various artists (Various Artists).
Double Album: released on MFP, Sep'81 by EMI Records. Dist: EMI

Double cassette: released on MFP, Sep'81 by EMI Records. Dist: EMI

Greatest Songs

GREATEST SONGS BY HOLLAND/DOZIER/HOLLAND various artists (Various Artists).
Compact disc: released on Motown, Jun'85 by Motown Records. Dist: BMG Distribution

GREATEST SONGS (ORIGINAL ARTISTS) Written by Ashford & Simpson (Various Artists).
Tracks: / Ain't no mountain high enough / You're all I need to get by / Love woke me up this morning / Reach out and touch (somebody's hand) / Ain't nothing like the real thing / Didn't you Know (you'd have to cry sometime) / Remember me / Your precious love / Some things you never get used to / Destination: Anywhere / Surrender / What you gave me / I can't give back the love I feel for you / I wouldn't change the man he is / Just say, just say / Silly wasn't it / Boss,The / God lovin ain't easy fo come by / It's my house.

Compact disc: released on The Compact Collection, Sep'87 by Conifer Records. Dist: Conifer Distribution

CLOWN, (THE).
Single (7"): released on Headline, Jun'82 by Creole Records. Dist: PRT

COME ON DOWN.
Album: released on Homestead, Feb'86 Dist: Rough Trade, Cartel, Shigaku

GIVE ME BACK MY FREEDOM.
Single (7"): released on PVK, Mar'81

IN THE SKIES.
Tracks: / In the skies / Slabo day / Fool no more,A / Funky chunk / Tribal dance / Seven stars / Just for you / Proud pinto / Apostle.
Notes: Music by Peter A.Green. Lyrics by :- J.S.Green, Peter A.Green. Produced by Peter-Vernon-Kell.
Compact disc: released on Creole, May'79 by Creole Records. Dist: Rhino, PRT

KOLORS.
Album: released on Headline, Nov'83 by Creole Records. Dist: PRT

Cassette: released on Headline, Nov'83 by Creole Records. Dist: PRT

LITTLE DREAMER.
Album: released on PVK, Apr'80

PROMISED LAND.
Single (7"): released on PVK, Jul'81

WATCHA GONNA DO?.
Album: released on PVK, Mar'81

WHITE SKY.
Tracks: / Time for me to go / Shining star / Clown,The / White sky-(love that evil woman) / It's gonna be me / Born on the wild side / Fallin apart / Indian lover / Just another guy.
Notes: From his early work in 1966 with John Mayall's Bluebreakers, when he replaced Eric Clapton who had left the group to form cream, to his own highly successful band Fleetwood Mac, Peter Green grew to become Britain's top blues guitarist vocalist and writer. When singles success came with 'Albatross and 'Man of the world' - Green's time had truely arrived. However, Peter decided to drop out of the fame and subsequent fortune, giving his royalties to charity and leaving Fleetwood Mac. Since then (1970) his movements are few and his output little buthappily, he began recording again in 1979. Following our welcome success recently with the C.D. of his 1979 comeback album 'In the skies', we have now the LP, 'White sky'. Recorded in the winter of 81/82, it is a superb collection of tracks produced by Green himself and Geoff Robinson.
Album: released on Teldec (Germany), Nov'85 by Import Records. Dist: IMS Distribution, Polygram Distribution

Album: released on Headline, Jun'82 by Creole Records. Dist: PRT

Cassette: released on Headline, Jun'82 by Creole Records. Dist: PRT

Green, Ruby

PANIC WHEN THE SUN GOES DOWN see Katzman, Nick (Green, Ruby & Nick Katzman).

Green Rushes

GREEN RUSHES (Adair, Peter).
Cassette: released on Colophone Audio Visual, Feb'81 by Audio-Visual Library Services. Dist: Audio-Visual Library Services

Page 428

Greatest Western...

GREATEST WESTERN THEMES,THE (Various Artists).
Compact disc: released on K-Tel, Nov'86 by K-Tel Records. Dist: Record Merchandisers Distribution, Taylors, Terry Blood Distribution, Wynd-Up Distribution, Relay Distribution, Pickwick Distribution, Solomon & Peres Distribution, Polygram

Great Gates 1949-1952

GREAT GATES 1949-1952(EARLY WEST COAST R&B) (Various Artists).
Album: released on Krazy Kat (USA), Jan'86

Great Guitars

AT THE WINERY.
Tracks: / You took advantage of me / So dance Samba / Sheik of Araby / Straighten up and fly right / Just in time / Talk of the town,The / Broadway / Air mail special / Body and soul.
Notes: Personnel: Charlie Byrd-guitar/Barney Kessel-guitar/Herb Ellis-guitar/Joe Burd-bass/Jimmie Smith-drums.
Compact disc: released on Concord Jazz(USA), Sep'86 by Concord Jazz Records (USA). Dist: IMS, Polygram

STRAIGHT TRACKS.
Album: released on Concord, Mar'79 by Import Records. Dist: IMS, Polygram

Great Harp Players

GREAT HARP PLAYERS (1927-30) various artists (Various Artists).
Album: released on Matchbox (Bluesmaster), May'83

Great Jam Sessions

GREAT JAM SESSIONS VOL.1 various artists (Various Artists).
Album: released on Joker, Apr'81 Dist: Counterpoint, Mainline, Record Services Distribution (Ireland)

Great Jazz...

GREAT JAZZ LADIES VOL.1 various artists (Various Artists).
Album: released on Kings Of Jazz, Jul'82 Dist: Jazz Horizons, Jazz Music, Celtic Music

GREAT JAZZ PIANOS(1926-1940) various artists (Various Artists).
Album: released on Joker, Apr'81 Dist: Counterpoint, Mainline, Record Services Distribution (Ireland)

GREAT JAZZ SOLOS REVISITED various artists (Various Artists).
Album: released on Wave, Apr'79 by Charly Records. Dist: Charly

GREAT JAZZ TRUMPETS (1924-1937) various artists (Various Artists).
Album: released on Joker, Apr'81 Dist: Counterpoint, Mainline, Record Services Distribution (Ireland)

STANDARD COLLECTION (Various Artists).
Tracks: / Autumn in New York / Caravan.
Compact disc: released on Denon, May'86 by Denon Records. Dist: Harmonia Mundi

Great Jazz Trio

CHAPTER 11.
Album: released on East Wind, Sep'81 by East Wind Records. Dist: PRT

Great Leap Forward, The

CONTROLLING THE EDGES OF TONE.
Single (12"): released on Ron Johnson, Feb'87 by Ron Johnson Records. Dist: Nine Mile Distribution, Cartel Distribution

Great Marches...

GREAT MARCHES OF THE WORLD various artists (Various Artists).
Album: released on Decca, Feb'81 by Decca Records. Dist: Polygram

Great Military Bands

GREAT MILITARY BANDS various bands (Various bands).
Double cassette: released on Pickwick (Ditto series), Jan'83

Great Outdoors

MAKING ALLOWANCES FO THE JARGON.
Album: released on Upright, Feb'86 by Upright Records. Dist: Cartel, Rough Trade

WORLD AT MY SHOES.
Single (7"): released on Upright, Sep'85 by Upright Records. Dist: Cartel, Rough Trade

Great Plains

NAKED AT THE BUY, SELL AND TRADE..
Album: released on Homestead, May'86 Dist: Rough Trade, Cartel, Shigaku

Great Revival

GREAT REVIVAL various artists (Various Artists).
Album: released on Esquire, Jul'79 by Titan International Productions. Dist: Jazz Music, Cadillac Music, Swift, Wellard, Chris, Backs, Rough Trade, Revolver, Nine Mile

Great Rock'n'Roll...

GREAT ROCK'N'ROLL LOVE SONGS various artists (Various Artists).
Cassette: released on K-Tel Goldmasters, Aug'84 by K-Tel Records. Dist: K-Tel

Great Singers...

GREAT SINGERS OF THE FIFTIES various singers (Various Artists).
Album: released on Jazz Greats, Jan'79 Dist: Swift

GREAT SINGERS OF YESTERYEAR Various Artists (Various Artists).
Tracks: / Mad dogs and Englishmen / MRS.Worthington / We'll gather lilacs / If you were the only girl in the world / Puttin on the Ritz / My Melancholy baby / Goodnight sweetheart / Sing as we go / Wish me luck(As you wave me goodbye) / River stay way from my door / Just a-wearyin for you / Loiuse / You brought a new kind of love to me / I'll see you again / Let the people sing / You forget your gloves / Goodnight Vienna / Red hot Mama / Some of these days / Mr.Wu's an air raid warden now / Look for the silver lining / Fascinating rhythm.
Cassette: released on Hour Of Pleasure, Oct'86 by Music For Pleasure Records. Dist: EMI

Great Society

CONSPICUOUS ONLY IN IT'S ABSENCE (Great Society with Grace Slick).
Album: released on CBS, Feb'80 by CBS Records. Dist: CBS

Cassette: released on CBS, Feb'80 by CBS Records. Dist: CBS

Great Songs...

GREAT SONGS FROM DISNEY MOVIES various artists (Various Artists).
Album: released on World Records, Jun'78 Dist: Polygram

GREAT SONGS OF SCOTLAND various artists (Various Artists).
Album: released on Academy Sound & Vision, May'82 by Academy Sound & Vision Records. Dist: Pinnacle

Cassette: released on Academy Sound & Vision, May'82 by Academy Sound & Vision Records. Dist: Pinnacle

Great Sounds...

GREAT SOUNDS OF THE 1920'S various artists (Various Artists).
Boxed set: released on ASV Living Era, Oct'82 by ASV Records. Dist: PRT

Great Swing Jam Sessions

GREAT SWING JAM SESSIONS VOL.2 various artists (Various Artists).
Album: released on Joker, Apr'81 Dist: Counterpoint, Mainline, Record Services Distribution (Ireland)

Great Traditional marches

GREAT TRADITIONAL MARCHES various artists (Various Artists).
Double Album: released on EMI (Germany) '83 by EMI Records. Dist: Conifer

Great Unknown...

GREAT UNKNOWN SOUL CLASSICS Various Artists (Various Artists).
Album: released on Cascade, Sep'86 by Ace Records. Dist: Pinnacle

Cassette: released on Cascade, Sep'86 by Ace Records. Dist: Pinnacle

Great Unwashed

YELLOW RAIN.
Tracks: / Yellow rain / Fire burns.
Single (7"):

Great Verve songbook

GREAT VERVE SONGBOOK (Various Artists).
Album: released on Verve, '81 by Phonogram Records. Dist: Polygram

Great vocalists

GREAT VOCALISTS (Various Artists).
Album: released on Joker, '81 Dist: Counterpoint, Mainline, Record Services Distributior (Ireland)

Great Welsh...

GREAT WELSH MALE VOICE CHOIR TRADITION Various choirs (Various Artists).
Double Album: released on Decca, Jan'80 by Decca Records. Dist: Polygram

GREAT WELSH MALE VOICE CHOIR various choirs (Various Artists).
Cassette: released on Decca, Jan'80 by Decca Records. Dist: Polygram

Great Western...

GREAT WESTERN FILM THEMES COLLECTION (Various Artists).
Double Album:

GREAT WESTERN MOVIE THEMES various artists (Various Artists).
Cassette: released on VFM, May'85 by VFM Records. Dist: Taylors, Wynd-Up Distribution

GREAT WESTERN THEMES Various artists (Various Artists).
Album: released on EMI (Holland), '83 by EMI Records. Dist: Conifer

Great White

FACE THE DAY Chainsaw edit:.
Single (7"): released on Capitol, Jan'87 by Capitol Records. Dist: EMI

Single (12"): released on Capitol, Jan'87 by Capitol Records. Dist: EMI

GREAT WHITE.
Album: released on EMI, Mar'84 by EMI Records. Dist: EMI Deleted '86.

Cassette: released on EMI, Mar'84 by EMI Records. Dist: EMI

ONCE BITTEN.
Tracks: / Lady red light / Gonna getcha / Rock me / All over now / Fast road / What do you do (live) / Face the day (U.S. Radio blues version) / Gimme some lovin'.
Album: released on Capitol, Sep'87 by Capitol Records. Dist: EMI

Cassette: released on Capitol, Sep'87 by Capitol Records. Dist: EMI

ROCK ME.
Single (7"): released on Capitol, Aug'87 by Capitol Records. Dist: EMI

Single (12"): released on Capitol, Aug'87 by Capitol Records. Dist: EMI

Greaves John

KEW RHONE (Greaves John & Peter Belgvad).
Album: released on Virgin, Apr'86 by Virgin Records. Dist: EMI, Virgin Distribution

Grebenshohikov, Boris

SUBWAY CULTURE.
Notes: For full information see under: Kuryohkin, Sergey/Boris Grebenshohikov,

Greco, Buddy

AT MISTER KELLY'S.
Album: released on Jasmine, Jun'83 by Jasmine Records. Dist: Counterpoint, Lugtons, Taylor, H.R., Wellard, Chris, Swift, Cadillac

FOR ONCE IN MY LIFE.
Album: released on Bulldog, Jul'82 by Bulldog Records. Dist: President Distribution, Spartan, Swift, Taylor, H.R.

Greco, Juliette

DISQUE D'OR.
Album: released on Pathe MarconiFrance), Jan'85

Cassette: released on Pathe MarconiFrance), Jan'85

Greece

FOLK MUSIC OF CYPRUS various artists (Various Artists).
Album: released on Lyrichord (USA), Oct'81 by Lyrichord Records (USA). Dist: Flexitron Distributors Ltd

GOLDEN SOUVENIRS FROM GREECE various artists (Various Artists).
Album: released on Philips (Europe), Mar'83

Cassette: released on Philips (Europe), Mar'83

GREECE IS.. Popular & folk dances (Various Artists).
Album: released on EMI (Greece), May'83 by EMI Records. Dist: Conifer

Cassette: released on EMI (Greece), May'83 by EMI Records. Dist: Conifer

GREEK FOLK MUSIC various artists (Various Artists).
Album: released on Lyrichord (USA), Oct'81 by Lyrichord Records (USA). Dist: Flexitron Distributors Ltd

GREEK MUSIC FROM THE ISLE OF CRETE various artists (Various Artists).
Album: released on Lyrichord (USA), Oct'81 by Lyrichord Records (USA). Dist: Flexitron Distributors Ltd

MEMORIES OF GREECE various artists (Various Artists).
Cassette: released on Bravo, Feb'80 by Pickwick Records. Dist: Lugtons

MUSIC OF THE GREEK ORTHODOX LITURGY various artists (Various Artists).
Album: released on Lyrichord, Oct'81 Dist: Roots

VARIOUS DANCE SONGS & MELODIES various artists (Various Artists).
Album: released on Topic, '81 Dist: Roots Distribution

Greek bouzoukee

GREEK BOUZOUKEE Various artists (Various Artists).
Album: released on Nonesuch Explorer (USA), Jul'84

Green, Al

AL GREEN EXPLORES YOUR MIND.
Cassette: released on London, Dec'74 by London Records. Dist: Polygram

AL GREEN: GREATEST HITS.
Album: released on Telefunken (Germany), Aug'81 Dist: Decca Distribution, IMS, Polygram

Cassette: released on Telefunken (Germany), Aug'81 Dist: Decca Distribution, IMS, Polygram

BELLE ALBUM,THE.
Album: released on Hi, Feb'86 by Demon Records. Dist: Pinnacle

BELLE ALBUM, (THE).
Album: released on Cream, Sep'79 Dist: Global Records Distribution

BEST OF.
Album: released on Hi, Jul'86 by Demon Records. Dist: Pinnacle

CALL ME.
Album: released on London, '73 by London Records. Dist: Polygram

Album: released on Hi(USA), Jun'85 by London Records. Dist: Polygram

CREAM OF AL GREEN, (THE).
Album: released on Hi-Cream, Jan'80 by Hi-Cream Records. Dist: PRT

Cassette: released on Hi-Cream, Jan'80 by Hi-Cream Records. Dist: PRT

EXPLORES YOUR MIND.
Tracks: / Sha-la-la / Take me to the river / God blessed our love / City,The / One nite stand / I'm hooked on you / Stay with me forever / Hangin'on / School days.
Compact disc: released on Demon, Sep'86 by Demon Records. Dist: Pinnacle

FULL OF FIRE.
Tracks: / There's no way / I'd fly away / Full of fire / Together again / Soon as I get home / Let it shine / Glory, glory / That's the way it is / Always.
Album: released on Hi, May'86 by Demon Records. Dist: Pinnacle

GET NEXT TO YOU.
Album: released on Hi(UK), Mar'86 by London Records. Dist: Polygram

GOING AWAY.
Album: released on A&M, Nov'85 by A&M Records. Dist: Polygram

Cassette: released on A&M, Nov'85 by A&M Records. Dist: Polygram

GREATEST HITS:AL GREEN.
Album: released on Hi, Feb'87 by Demon Records. Dist: Pinnacle

Cassette: released on Hi, Feb'87 by Demon Records. Dist: Pinnacle

GREEN IS BLUE.
Album: released on Hi(UK), Mar'86 by London Records. Dist: Polygram

HAVE A GOOD TIME.
Album: released on Hi, Jul'86 by Demon Records. Dist: Pinnacle

HIGHER PLANE.
Album: released on Hi, Nov'85 by Demon Records. Dist: Pinnacle

Album: released on Hi-Cream, Feb'82 by Hi-Cream Records. Dist: PRT

Cassette: released on Hi-Cream, Feb'82 by Hi-Cream Records. Dist: PRT

I'M STILL IN LOVE WITH YOU.
Album: released on Hi(USA), Jun'85 by London Records. Dist: Polygram

Cassette: released on London, '72 by London Records. Dist: Polygram

IS LOVE.
Album: released on Hi, Jul'86 by Demon Records. Dist: Pinnacle

LET'S STAY TOGETHER.
Tracks: / Let's stay together / I've never found a girl / How you leaving / It ain't no fun to me / Talk to me, talk to me / Old time lovin / Judy / What is this feelin / Tomorrow's dream / How can you mend a broken heart / La-la for you.
Compact disc: released on Hi, Jul'86 by Demon Records. Dist: Pinnacle

Album: released on London, '72 by London Records. Dist: Polygram

Album: released on Hi-Demon, Feb'85 Dist: Cartel, Rough Trade, Counterpoint

Single (7"): released on Hi, Sep'85 by Demon Records. Dist: Pinnacle

Single (12"): released on Hi, Sep'85 by Demon Records. Dist: Pinnacle

LIGHT, THE.
Album: released on A&M, Nov'85 by A&M Records. Dist: Polygram

Cassette: released on A&M, Nov'85 by A&M Records. Dist: Polygram

LIVING FOR YOU.
Album: released on Hi, Nov'85 by Demon Records. Dist: Pinnacle

LORD WILL MAKE A WAY, THE.
Album: released on Hi, Jul'86 by Demon Records. Dist: Pinnacle

LORD WILL MAKE A WAY, (THE).
Album: released on Myrrh, May'82 by Word Records. Dist: Word Distribution

Cassette: released on Myrrh, May'82 by Word Records. Dist: Word Distribution

NEVER MET NOBODY LIKE YOU.
Single (7"): released on Hi, Feb'85 by Demon Records. Dist: Pinnacle

PRECIOUS LORD.
Album: released on Hi-Cream, Nov'82 by Hi-Cream Records. Dist: PRT

Album: released on Hi(USA), Jun'85 by London Records. Dist: Polygram

SOUL SURVIVOR.
Tracks: / Everything's gonna be alright / Jesus will fix it / You know and I know / So real to me / Introduction - soul survivor / Soul survivor / You've got a friend / He ain't heavy / 23rd Psalm.
Notes: 'Soul Survivor' finds Al Green in the company of Billy Preston (who sings and plays organ on 'You've Got A Friend') producer/musicians Paul Zaleski and Errol Thomas (who produced the bulk of this album during sessions in Memphis) and others.
Album: released on A&M, Mar'87 by A&M Records. Dist: Polygram

Cassette: released on A&M, Mar'87 by A&M Records. Dist: Polygram

SPOTLIGHT ON AL GREEN.
Double Album: released on PRT, Oct'81 by PRT Records. Dist: PRT Deleted '85.

Double cassette: released on PRT, Oct'81 by PRT Records. Dist: PRT

TIRED OF BEING ALONE.
Single (7"): released on Flashback, Jan'83 by Flashback Records/PRT Records. Dist: Mainline, PRT

Single (7"): released on Hi-Cream, Jan'80 by Hi-Cream Records. Dist: PRT

Single (7"): by Hi-Cream Records. Dist: PRT

Single (12"): by Hi-Cream Records. Dist: PRT

TOKYO - LIVE.
Double Album: released on Hi-Cream, Jul'81 by Hi-Cream Records. Dist: PRT Deleted '85.

Double cassette: released on Hi-Cream, Jul'81 by Hi-Cream Records. Dist: PRT

TRUE LOVE.
Tracks: / True love / You brought the sunshine / Going away.
Single (7"): released on A&M, Jan'86 by A&M Records. Dist: Polygram

Single (12"): released on A&M, Jan'86 by A&M Records. Dist: Polygram

TRUST IN GOD.
Tracks: / Don't make you wanna go home / No not one / Trust in god / Lean on me / Ain't no mountain high enough / Up the ladder to the roof / Never met nobody like you / Holy spirit / All we need is a little more love.

Page 430

Album: released on Hi-Cream, Feb'85 by Hi-Cream Records. Dist: PRT

Greenbaum, Norman
SPIRIT IN THE SKY.
Tracks: / Spirit in the sky / Milk cow.
Single (7"): released on Old Gold, May'86 by Old Gold Records. Dist: Lightning, Jazz Music, Spartan, Counterpoint

Single (7"): released on Reprise, Jul'81 by WEA Records. Dist: WEA

Single (7"): released on Old Gold, Sep'85 by Old Gold Records. Dist: Lightning, Jazz Music, Spartan, Counterpoint

Greenbelt fringe '84
GREENBELT FRINGE '84 Various artists (Various Artists).
Cassette: released on Plankton, Aug'84 by Plankton Records. Dist: Cantio (Sweden)

Green, Bennie
Biographical Details: See also under Ammons, Gene.
BLOWS HIS HORN.
Album: released on Fantasy Inc USA, Feb'86 by Fantasy Inc USA Records. Dist: IMS, Polygram

PAYNE, TERRY, GREEN - THE CONNECTION (Green, Bennie/Cecil Payne/Clark Terry).
Trombone by three

Green, Benny
CONNECTION, (THE).
Double Album: released on Vogue, Sep'75 Dist: Discovery, Jazz Music, PRT, Swift

Green, Bunky
PLACES WE'VE NEVER BEEN.
Album: released on Vanguard, Jan'80 by PRT Records. Dist: PRT

Green, Candy
LADY IN RED.
Album: released on JSP, Mar'82 by JSP Records. Dist: Swift, Projection

Green, Carl
THING IS... (Green, Carl & The Scene).
Album: released on RCA, Oct'81 by RCA Records. Dist: RCA, Roots, Swift, Wellard, Chris, I & B, Solomon & Peres Distribution

Cassette: released on RCA, Oct'81 by RCA Records. Dist: RCA, Roots, Swift, Wellard, Chris, I & B, Solomon & Peres Distribution

Green, Dotty
I CAUGHT YOU OUT.
Single (7"): released on Hot Melt, Nov'85 by Hot Melt Records. Dist: Pinnacle, Spartan

Single (12"): released on Hot Melt, Nov'85 by Hot Melt Records. Dist: Pinnacle, Spartan

I WANT YOU.
Tracks: / I want you / Melt down dub mix / I want you.
Single (12"): released on Hot Melt, Apr'87 by Hot Melt Records. Dist: Pinnacle, Spartan

Single (7"): released on Hot Melt, Nov'86 by Hot Melt Records. Dist: Pinnacle, Spartan

Single (12"): released on Hot Melt, Nov'86 by Hot Melt Records. Dist: Pinnacle, Spartan

Greene, Sarah
EENY MEENIE.
Single (7"): released on Lamborghini, Nov'83 by Lamborghini Records. Dist: PRT

Greenfield, Dave
FIRE AND WATER (Greenfield, Dave & Jean Jacques Burnel).
Album: released on Epic, Nov'83 by CBS Records. Dist: CBS Deleted '86.

Cassette: released on Epic, Nov'83 by CBS Records. Dist: CBS

RAIN, DOLE AND TEA (Greenfield, Dave & Jean Jacques Burnel).
Single (7"): released on Epic, Feb'84 by CBS Records. Dist: CBS

Greenfield Leisure
THOSE FAR-OFF SUMMERS (EP).
Single (12"): released on Strange Orchestra, Feb'82 Dist: Pinnacle, IKF Distribution

Green Fields of Tong
POLAND.
Single (7"): released on Speed, Nov'82

Green, Garard
FLIP THE STORY OF A SEAL.
Album: released on Chivers Audio Books, Jan'81 by Chivers Sound & Vision. Dist: Chivers Sound & Vision

Green, George
JAMMIN' THE BOOGIE (Green, George & Bob Hall).
Album: released on Black Lion, Jun'78 by Black Lion Records. Dist: Jazz Music, Chris Wellard, Taylor, H.R., Counterpoint, Cadillac

Green, Grant
BORN TO BE BLUE.
Album: released on Blue Note, Sep'85 by EMI Records. Dist: EMI

Cassette: released on Blue Note, Sep'87 by EMI Records. Dist: EMI. Estim retail price in Sep'87 was £5.49.

FEELIN' THE SPIRIT.
Tracks: / Just a closer walk with thee / Joshua fit de battle of Jerico / Nobody knows the trouble I've seen / Go down Moses / Sometimes I feel like a motherless child / Deep river.
Compact disc: released on Blue Note, Aug'87 by EMI Records. Dist: EMI

Compact disc: released on Blue Note, Aug'87 by EMI Records. Dist: EMI

GRANTSTAND.
Tracks: / Grantstand / My funny valentine / Blues in Maude's flat / Old folks / Grantstand / My funny valentine / Blues in Maude's flat / Old folks / Green's greenery.
Album: released on Blue Note, Nov'86 by EMI Records. Dist: EMI

Album: released on Manhattan, Nov'86 by President Records. Dist: Jazz Music, Swift, Taylors, Chris Wellard

Compact disc: released on Blue Note, Sep'87 by EMI Records. Dist: EMI. Estim retail price in Sep'87 was £11.99.

IDLE MOMENTS.
Tracks: / Idle moments / Jean De Fleur / Django / Nomad.
Album: released on Blue Note, Sep'87 by EMI Records. Dist: EMI

IRON CITY.
Album: released on Muse, Apr'81 by Peerless Records. Dist: Lugtons Distributors

LAST SESSION.
Tracks: / Wave / Just the way you are / Easy / Empanada / Night time in the switching yard / Three times a lady.
Album: released on Atlantis, Apr'87 by Charly Records. Dist: Charly

Cassette: released on Atlantis, Apr'87 by Charly Records. Dist: Charly

Green grow the laurels
GREEN GROW THE LAURELS Country singers from the south.
Album: released on Topic, '81 Dist: Roots Distribution

GREEN GROW THE LAURELS: SONGS OF FALSE LOVE & TRUE Various artists (Various Artists).
Cassette: released on Folktracks, Nov'79 by Folktracks Cassettes. Dist: Folktracks

Greenhill Singers
CHRISTMAS LIGHT.
Single (7"): released on Greenhill, Nov'85 by Greenhill Records. Dist: PRT

Greenhouse Of Terror
COMPULSION.
Tracks: / Compulsion.
Single (12"): released on Racket, Feb'86 Dist: Rough Trade

Green Howards
GREEN HOWARDS, XIX (Green Howards Regimental Band).
Album: released on Music Masters, Jan'83 by Music Masters Records. Dist: Taylors

Cassette: released on Music Masters, Jan'83 by Music Masters Records. Dist: Taylors

Green Ice
GREEN ICE Original film soundtrack.
Album: released on Polydor, May'81 by Polydor Records. Dist: Polygram, Polydor

Cassette: released on Polydor, May'81 by Polydor Records. Dist: Polygram, Polydor

Green, Ivy
WHATEVER THEY HYPE.
Album: released on Sirco, May'86 Dist: Red Rhino, Cartel

Album: released on Revolver, Oct'86 by Revol-

---

ver Records. Dist: Revolver, Cartel

Green, Jack
LATEST GAME.
Tracks: / Sweet Lover / Latest game / Television / Loving & knowing / You didn't have to love me / Amerian fool / Win your love / Right now / Difficult to care / I've had enough.
Album: released on Revolver, Jan'87 by Revolver Records. Dist: Revolver, Cartel

Album: released on Revolver, Jan'87 by Revolver Records. Dist: Revolver, Cartel

Green, Jesse
NICE AND SLOW.
Single (7"): released on Red Bus, Aug'87 by Red Bus Records. Dist: PRT

NICE AND SLOW (REMIX).
Single (7"): released on Atlas, Aug'87 by Atlas Records. Dist: PRT

Cassette single: released on Atlas, Aug'87 by Atlas Records. Dist: PRT

NICE & SLOW.
Tracks: / Nice & slow / Gimmi gimmi your loving.
Single (7"): released on Atlas, Jul'87 by Atlas Records. Dist: PRT

Single (12"): released on Atlas, Jul'87 by Atlas Records. Dist: PRT

YOUR LOVE.
Tracks: / Your love / Your love(Instrumental) / Your love.
Single (7"): released on BMW, Oct'86 by M.I.S., PRT

Single (12"): released on BMW, Oct'86 by M.I.S., PRT

Single (7"): released on BMW, Oct'86 by M.I.S., PRT

Single (12"): released on BMW, Oct'86 by M.I.S., PRT

Green, Keith
FOR HIM WHO HAS NO EARS TO HEAR.
Album: released on Sparrow, May'82 by Word Records. Dist: Spartan

Cassette: released on Sparrow, May'82 by Word Records. Dist: Spartan

JESUS COMMANDS US TO GO.
Album: released on Birdwing, Nov'84 by Word Records. Dist: Word Distribution

Cassette: released on Birdwing, Nov'84 by Word Records. Dist: Word Distribution

KEITH GREEN COLLECTION, (THE).
Album: released on Sparrow, May'82 by Word Records. Dist: Spartan

Cassette: released on Sparrow, May'82 by Word Records. Dist: Spartan

NO COMPROMISE.
Album: released on Sparrow, May'82 by Word Records. Dist: Spartan

Cassette: released on Sparrow, May'82 by Word Records. Dist: Spartan

SONGS FOR THE SHEPHERD.
Album: released on Sparrow, May'85 by Word Records. Dist: Spartan

Cassette: released on Sparrow, May'85 by Word Records. Dist: Spartan

Green, Leroy
ONLY YOU.
Single (12"): released on MK, Dec'85

Green, Lil
FOREMOTHERS, VOLUME 5.
Cassette: released on Rosetta, Dec'86 Dist: WRPM Distribution, Jazz Music Distribution, JSU Distribution, Swift Distribution

Green, Lloyd
GREEN VELVET.
Album: released on President, Oct'82 by President Records. Dist: Taylors, Spartan

LLOYDS OF NASHVILLE.
Album: released on Release (Ireland), May'81

STAINLESS STEEL.
Album: released on Pye International, Apr'78

STEELIN' FEELIN'S.
Album: released on Checkmate, Apr'78 Dist: I & B

STEEL RIDES.
Album: released on Monument, Apr'76 by CBS

Records. Dist: CBS Distribution

TEN SHADES OF GREEN.
Album: released on Checkmate, Apr'77 Dist: I & B

Green metal

GREEN METAL Various artists (Various Artists).
Album: released on Metal Masters, Sep'85 by Razor Records. Dist: Pinnacle

Green, Mick

PAINKILLER.
Album: released on Thunderbolt, Aug'86 by Magnum Music Group Ltd. Dist: Magnum Music Group Ltd, PRT Distribution, Spartan Distribution

Green On Red

BORN TO FIGHT.
Tracks: / Born to fight / Don't shine your light on me / While the widow weeps*.
Single (7"): released on Mercury, Jun'87 by Phonogram Records. Dist: Polygram Distribution

Single (12"): released on Mercury, Jun'87 by Phonogram Records. Dist: Polygram Distribution

CLARKSVILLE.
Tracks: / Clarksville / No drinkin' / Broken.
Notes: 'Broken'-extra track available on 12" version only.
Single (7"): released on Mercury, Feb'87 by Phonogram Records. Dist: Polygram Distribution

Single (12"): released on Mercury, Feb'87 by Phonogram Records. Dist: Polygram Distribution

GAS, FOOD AND LODGING.
Album: released on Zippo, May'85

Single (7"): released on Torso, Nov'85 by Torso Records. Dist: Rough Trade, Cartel, EMI

GRAVITY TALKS.
Album: released on Slash, Jan'87 by London Records. Dist: Polygram

Cassette: released on Slash, Jan'87 by London Records. Dist: Polygram

Cassette: released on Slash, Jan'87 by London Records. Dist: Polygram

GRAVITY TALKS.
Album: released on Slash (USA), '83

GREEN ON RED.
Album: released on Demon, Jun'85 by Demon Records. Dist: Pinnacle

KILLER INSIDE ME,(A).
Album: released on Mercury, Mar'87 by Phonogram Records. Dist: Polygram Distribution

Cassette: released on Mercury, Mar'87 by Phonogram Records. Dist: Polygram Distribution

Compact disc: released on Mercury, May'87 by Phonogram Records. Dist: Polygram Distribution

NO FREE LUNCH.
Album: released on Mercury, Oct'85 by Phonogram Records. Dist: Polygram Distribution

Cassette: released on Mercury, Oct'85 by Phonogram Records. Dist: Polygram Distribution

Green, P

CASE FOR THE BLUES,A.
Album: released on Nightflite, Feb'86 by Adrian Owlett. Dist: Charly, Spartan

Greenpeace: the album

GREENPEACE: THE ALBUM Various artists (Various Artists).
Album: released on Towerbell, Jul'85 by Towerbell Records. Dist: EMI

Cassette: released on Towerbell, Jul'85 by Towerbell Records. Dist: EMI

Green, Peter

BLUE GUITAR.
Album:

Cassette: released on Creole, Nov'81 by Creole Records. Dist: Rhino, PRT

CASE FOR THE BLUES, A.
Album: released on Nightflite, Aug'87 by Adrian Owlett. Dist: Charly, Spartan

Greenslade, Arthur

COUNTRY STRINGS.
Tracks: / One day at a time / Lucille / You needed me / Duelling Banjos / Welcome to my world / Blue eyes cry in the rain / Devil went down to Georga,The / For the good times / Stand by your man / What I've got in mind / Convoy / Don't it make my brown eyes blue.
Album: released on Conifer, Jan'86 by Conifer Records. Dist: Conifer

Cassette: released on Conifer, Jan'86 by Conifer Records. Dist: Conifer

Greensleeves Sampler

GREENSLEEVES SAMPLER (Various Artists).
Notes: One track each from twelve of the best selling albums on the Greensleeves label.Artists include: Dennis brown, Black Uhuru, Gregory Isaacs, Burning spear, Eek- a mouse etc.
Album: released on Greensleeves, Jun'87 by Greensleeves Records. Dist: BMG, Jetstar, Spartan

Cassette: released on Greensleeves, Jun'87 by Greensleeves Records. Dist: BMG, Jetstar, Spartan

Compact disc: released on Greensleeves, Jun'87 by Greensleeves Records. Dist: BMG, Jetstar, Spartan

Green, Steve

FOR GOD AND GOD ALONE.
Notes: This album has been number one in the American Christian music charts for four months now and when you listen to it you will know why. One obvious reason why this is so is because part of the album was recorded in London with the NationalPhilharmonic Orchestra. Steve has sung previously with the Bill Gaither trio and Whiteheart, but he has blossomed as a solo singer with his distinctive vocals complimenting the majestic arrangements. It is our March praise and worship Album of the month which shows just how highly we rate this album.
Album: released on Birdwing, Feb'87 by Word Records. Dist: Word Distribution

Cassette: released on Birdwing, Feb'87 by Word Records. Dist: Word Distribution

HE HOLDS THE SKY.
Notes: The marvellous tenor, Steve Green, brings us this his second album, and once again there is a wealth of fine songs here which give a strong platform for the 'Best male vocalist' Dove Award winner to display his phenomenal talent. Greg Nelson who produced Steve's debut album, is producer here. Once again the sound is huge with lavis orchestral accompainiments and punchy, tight rhythm sections enhanced by superb choral support giving real drama to the music. Steve Green isa genuine and sincere young man with a voice of rare quality.
Album: released on Birdwing, Feb'86 by Word Records. Dist: Word Distribution

Cassette: released on Birdwing, Feb'86 by Word Records. Dist: Word Distribution

Green Telescope, The

FACE IN A CROWD.
Tracks: / Face in a crowd / Thoughts of a madman.
Single (7"): released on Wump, Aug'86 Dist: Fast Forward, Cartel

Green, Tim

WHO CAN TELL?.
Single (7"): released on Rabid, Sep'82 by Rabid Records. Dist: Pinnacle, Rough Trade

Green velvet

GREEN VELVET Various artists (Various Artists).
Album: released on Ronco, Nov'83

Cassette: released on Ronco, Nov'83

Boxed set: released on Telstar, Nov'84 by Telstar Records. Dist: RCA Distribution

Boxed set: released on Telstar, Nov'84 by Telstar Records. Dist: RCA Distribution

Compact disc: released on Telstar, Jul'87 by Telstar Records. Dist: RCA Distribution

MORE GREEN VELVET (IRISH SONGS) Various artists (Various Artists).
Album: released on Telstar, Nov'85 by Telstar Records. Dist: RCA Distribution

Cassette: released on Telstar, Nov'85 by Telstar Records. Dist: RCA Distribution

Compact disc: released on Telstar, Jul'87 by Telstar Records. Dist: RCA Distribution

Greenwell, Peter

PETER GREENWELL IN CABARET.
Album: released on Souvenir, Dec'84

Green Willow Band

COTSWOLD MUSIC.
Album: released on Sweet Folk All, May'81 by Sweet Folk All Records. Dist: Sweet Folk All, Roots, Celtic Music, Dragon, Impetus, Projection, Chris Wellard, Festival Records

Greenwood, Lee

CHRISTMAS TO CHRISTMAS.

GREATEST HITS:LEE GREENWOOD.
Tracks: / Fool's gold / Somebody's gonna love you / It turns me inside out / She's lying / Dixie road / Ain't no trick (It takes magic) / Ring on her finger, time on her hands / I.O.U. / Going, going, gone. / God bless the U.S.A..
Album: released on MCA Import, Mar'86 by MCA Records. Dist: Polygram, IMS

INSIDE AND OUT.
Album: released on MCA, Feb'83 by MCA Records. Dist: Polygram, MCA

LOVE WILL FIND ITS WAY TO YOU.
Album: released on MCA, Mar'87 by MCA Records. Dist: Polygram, MCA

Cassette: released on MCA, Mar'87 by MCA Records. Dist: Polygram, MCA

SOMEBODY'S GONNA LOVE YOU.
Tracks: / I.O.U. / Somebody's gonna love you / Going, going, gone / Call it what you want to (It's still love) / Barely holding on / Love won't let us say goodbye / Ladies love / Wind beneath my wings,The / Think about the good times / Someone who remembers.
Compact disc: released on MCA, Jan'86 by MCA Records. Dist: Polygram, MCA

Album: released on MCA, Feb'84 by MCA Records. Dist: Polygram, MCA

Cassette: released on MCA, Feb'84 by MCA Records. Dist: Polygram, MCA

STREAMLINE.
Tracks: / Streamline / Lonely people / I don't mind the thorns(If you're the rose) / Hearts aren't meant to break(They're meant to love) / Little at a time,A / Breakin' even / Don't underestimate my love for you / Same old song / Will to love,The / Leave my heart the way you found it.

WIND BENEATH MY WINGS, (THE).
Album: released on MCA, Jul'84 by MCA Records. Dist: Polygram, MCA

Cassette: released on MCA, Jul'84 by MCA Records. Dist: Polygram, MCA

Greer, Gail

IN HEAT (Greer, Gail and Torso).
Single (7"): released on Identity, Oct'82 by Identity Records. Dist: IDS

INSEPARABLE.
Single (7"): released on Identity, Jan'83 by Identity Records. Dist: IDS

Greer, John

BEST OF JOHN GREER.
Album: released on Homespun(Ireland), '82 by Outlet Records. Dist: Outlet

Cassette: released on Homespun(Ireland), '82 by Outlet Records. Dist: Outlet

COUNTRY REQUESTS.
Album: released on Homespun(Ireland), Nov'76 by Outlet Records. Dist: Outlet

COUNTRY SIDE OF JOHN GREER, (THE).
Album: released on Outlet (Ireland), Sep'75

IRISH SONGS, COUNTRY STYLE.
Album: released on Homespun(Ireland), '82 by Outlet Records. Dist: Outlet

Cassette: released on Homespun(Ireland), '82 by Outlet Records. Dist: Outlet

KEEP IT COUNTRY.
Album: released on Homespun(Ireland), '82 by Outlet Records. Dist: Outlet

Cassette: released on Homespun(Ireland), '82 by Outlet Records. Dist: Outlet

OLD COUNTRY CHURCH.
Album: released on Homespun(Ireland), Feb'78 by Outlet Records. Dist: Outlet

ROSES FOR MAMA.
Album: released on Homespun(Ireland), '82 by Outlet Records. Dist: Outlet

Cassette: released on Homespun(Ireland), '82 by Outlet Records. Dist: Outlet

Single (7"): released on Homespun(Ireland), Nov'83 by Outlet Records. Dist: Outlet

SINGIN' ON A SUNDAY.
Album: released on Homespun(Ireland), '82 by Outlet Records. Dist: Outlet

Cassette: released on Homespun(Ireland), '82 by Outlet Records. Dist: Outlet

TEDDY BEAR.
Single (7"): released on Homespun(Ireland), Feb'81 by Outlet Records. Dist: Outlet

WHAT A FRIEND WE HAVE IN JESUS.
Album: released on Homespun(Ireland), Dec'82 by Outlet Records. Dist: Outlet

Cassette: released on Homespun(Ireland), Dec'82 by Outlet Records. Dist: Outlet

Greeting Number 4

CIVILISED TO DEATH.
Single (12"): released on Very Mouth, Aug'85 by Very Mouth Records. Dist: Cartel

CONDITION.
Single (7"): released on Very Mouth, Feb'83 by Very Mouth Records. Dist: Cartel

Greger, Max

BEST OF GLENN MILLER, THE.
Tracks: / Serenade in blue / Snrise Serenade / String of pearls,A / Little brown jug / I know why / Chattanooga choo choo / American patrol / Moonlight Serenade / St.Louis blues march / Tuxedo Junction / Stairway to the stars / Pennsylvania 6,5000 / Johnson rag / Moonlight sonata / Song of the Volga boatman / Boatman / Bungle call rag / Anvil chorus / Tiger rag.
Compact disc: released on Polydor, Sep'85 by Polydor Records. Dist: Polygram, Polydor

CLASSICS FOR DANCING.
Tracks: / Pizzicati / Cha-cha-cha / Melodie in F.Rumba / Mozart symphony no.40. Samba / Furst Igor ballet music. Rumba / Liszt Liebestraum.Shuffle / Offenbach Barcarole. Slow rock / Mozart Eine Kleine Nachmusik. Disco / Afforderung Zum Tanz. Foxtrott / Poeme. Langsamer Waltz / Bizet's Carmen. Tango / Chopin Etude. Langsammer' Foxtrott / Dvorak Humoreske. Quickstep / Strauss. Vienna Waltz / Brahms Ungarisc Her Tanz Nr 5. Disc..
Notes: Popular classic in strict dance tempo.
Compact disc: released on Polydor (Germany), Sep'84 Dist: IMS-Polygram

Album: released on Polydor (Germany), Sep'74 Dist: IMS-Polygram

Cassette: released on Polydor (Germany), Sep'74 Dist: IMS-Polygram

DANCE APPEAL.
Album: released on Polydor (Germany), Oct'82 Dist: IMS-Polygram

Cassette: released on Polydor (Germany), Oct'82 Dist: IMS-Polygram

EMOTIONS OF LOVE.
Tracks: / Emotions of love / Do you really want to hurt me / Hard to say I'm sorry / It's raining again / Words / Major Tom(Vollig losgelost) / Tu, Soltanto tu / Adios amor / Save your love / Arrivederci Claire / Heartbreaker / Amore mio.
Notes: Digital Stereo.
Album: released on Polydor (Germany), Aug'83 Dist: IMS-Polygram

Cassette: released on Polydor (Germany), Aug'83 Dist: IMS-Polygram

Compact disc: released on Polydor (Germany), Aug'83 Dist: IMS-Polygram

EUROPEAN JAZZ SOUNDS (Greger, Max & His Orchestra).
Tracks: / Discussion / Bluer than blue / Revelation / You're the one / Sax life / Carrera / Portrait in smoke / Meet BB / M G Blues / Boomerang.
Album: released on Polydor (Germany), Nov'86 Dist: IMS-Polygram

HALLO MAX.
Album: released on Polygram (Germany), Dec'86 by Polygram Records. Dist: Polygram

MANIMUM (BIG BAND JAZZ).
Tracks: / Salute to Miles / Falling in love / One for Cann / Piece for two / Senor Bailey / Bossa fluta / Early blues / Take the A-train.
Compact disc: released on Polydor (Germany), Feb'86 Dist: IMS-Polygram

MAX GREGER.
Album: released on Polydor (Holland), Jun'83

Cassette: released on Polydor (Holland), Jun'83

MAX GREGER PLAYS THE BEST OF GLENN MILLER..
Album: released on Polydor (Germany), Nov'85 Dist: IMS-Polygram

Cassette: released on Polydor (Germany), Nov'85 Dist: IMS-Polygram

MAXIMUM (Greger, Max Big Band).
Album: released on Polydor (Germany), Sep'85 Dist: IMS-Polygram

SUPERB DANCE MIX.
Album: released on Polydor (Germany), Apr'85 Dist: IMS-Polygram

Cassette: released on Polydor (Germany), Apr'85 Dist: IMS-Polygram

Compact disc: released on Polydor (Germany), Apr'85 Dist: IMS-Polygram

SUPER DANCE MIX (Greger, Max & His Orchestra).
Tracks: / Playa blanca / Time after time / Guardian angel / Black & white / Holiday / Ci sara / Footloose / Memories / Self control / Dream Waltz / Rio Chico / B-R Boogie.
Compact disc: released on Polydor, Jun'85 by Polydor Records. Dist: Polygram, Polydor

TANZEN '87.
Album: released on Polygram (Germany), Dec'86 by Polygram Records. Dist: Polygram

TANZEN, TANZEN, TANZEN..
Tracks: / DA da da ich lieb dich nicht / Der Kommissar / Du bist mein erster gedanke / Rosemarie / Una notte speciale / Felicita / Crbonara / On the road again / Hip hap hop / Ebony & Ivory / Carbonara.
Compact disc: released on Polydor (Germany), Jan'84 Dist: IMS-Polygram

TANZEN, TANZEN, TANZEN.
Compact disc: released on Polydor (Germany), '84 Dist: IMS-Polygram

WIJ DANSEN VOL 7.
Album: released on Polydor (Holland), Feb'85

Cassette: released on Polydor (Holland), Feb'85

WIJ DANSEN VOL 8.
Album: released on Polydor (Holland), Feb'85

Cassette: released on Polydor (Holland), Feb'85

Gregg, Hubert

THANKS FOR THE MEMORY.
Album: released on BBC, Oct'77 by BBC Records & Tapes. Dist: EMI, PRT, Pye

Gregg, John

COME BACK MARIANNE.
Single (7"): released on Magic Moon, Sep'80 Dist: Pinnacle

Gregg, Jonathan

I DON'T WANT TO BE ALONE TONIGHT.
Tracks: / I don't want to be alone tonight / Is this love that I'm feeling.
Single (7"): released on Tembo, Aug'86 by Tembo (Canada). Dist: IMS Distribution, Polygram Distribution

YOUNG HEARTS.
Tracks: / Young hearts / Young hearts.
Single (7"): released on Tembo, May'86 by Tembo (Canada). Dist: IMS Distribution, Polygram Distribution

Single (12"): released on Tembo, May'86 by Tembo (Canada). Dist: IMS Distribution, Polygram Distribution

Gregoris

GREGORIS TRAVELLING.
Album: released on Sonet, Nov'83 by Sonet Records. Dist: PRT

Gregory, Dennis

LOVE'S GONNA LOVE.
Single (12"): released on Sound City, Nov'85 by Sound City Records. Dist: Jetstar

OH YOUNG LADY.
Tracks: / Oh young lady / Young lady (Dub).
Single (12"): released on Sound City, Jul'86 by Sound City Records. Dist: Jetstar

TONIGHT I'M STAYING HERE WITH YOU.
Single (7"): released on Sound City, Apr'85 by Sound City Records. Dist: Jetstar

Gregory, Glen

WHEN YOUR HEART RUNS OUT OF TIME (Gregory, Glen and Claudia Brucken).
Single (7"): released on ZTT, Aug'85 by Island Records. Dist: Polygram

Single (12"): released on ZTT, Aug'85 by Island Records. Dist: Polygram Deleted '87.

Gregory, John

I WRITE THE SONGS (Gregory, John and his cascading strings).
Album: released on Dakota, Feb'84 by Dakota Records. Dist: PRT

Gregory, Tony

I DON'T WANNA BE LONELY.
Single (12"): released on TGM, Sep'84 by TGM Records. Dist: Jetstar Distribution

Gregson, Clive

HOME AND AWAY (Gregson, Clive & Christine Collister).
Album: released on Cooking Vinyl, Jan'87 Dist: Nine Mile, Cartel, Red Rhino

Cassette: released on Cooking Vinyl, Jan'87 Dist: Nine Mile, Cartel, Red Rhino

HOME IS WHERE THE HEART IS.
Single (7"): released on Demon, Apr'85 by Demon Records. Dist: Pinnacle

STRANGE PERSUASIONS.
Album: released on Demon, Apr'85 by Demon Records. Dist: Pinnacle

Cassette: released on Demon, Apr'85 by Demon Records. Dist: Pinnacle

Gregson, John

WINGS OF SOUND (Gregson, John and his orchestra).
Album: released on Dakota, May'85 by Dakota Records. Dist: PRT

Greinke, Jeff

PLACES OF NOTILITY.
Album: released on Dossier, Jun'87 Dist: Red Rhino, Cartel

Greko, Keith

KEITH GREKO.
Notes: Featuring Louis Bellson/Bud Shank/joe Henderson Etc.
Album: released on Concept, Jul'86 Dist: Jazz Music, Swift, Chris Wellard, Polygram

LAST TRAIN OUTTA FLAGSTAFF.
Notes: Artists include Louie Bellson/Bud Shank/David Friesen ETC.
Album: released on Concept, Oct'86 Dist: Jazz Music, Swift, Chris Wellard, Polygram

Gremlins

GREMLINS (Baker, Tom).
Cassette: released on Whinfrey Strachan, Jan'85 Dist: Whinfrey Strachan

GREMLINS Various artists (Various Artists).
Single (12"): released on Buena Vista, Oct'84 by Walt Disney Productions. Dist: Pickwick Distribution, PRT

Cassette: released on Geffen, Dec'84 by Geffen Records. Dist: WEA, CBS

GREMLINS, THE (Various Artists).
Album: released on Geffen, Dec'84 by Geffen Records. Dist: WEA, CBS

Grenadier Guards

1685-1985.
Tracks: / Windsor Flourish / Plovtsian dances / Grenadiers / Soldiers Chorus from 'The Decembrists' / Battle hymn / Man o' brass / Grenadiers march / Armenian Dances / It's a grand night for singing / British Grenadiers.
Album: released on Polyphonic, Mar'86 by Polyphonic Records. Dist: Taylors

BEST OF BRITISH, THE.
Album: released on Unicorn Kanchana, May'83 by Unicorn Records Ltd. Dist: Harmonia Mundi (UK) Limited Distr.

Cassette: released on Unicorn Kanchana, May'83 by Unicorn Records Ltd. Dist: Harmonia Mundi (UK) Limited Distr.

CHRISTMAS FROM THE GUARDS.
Album: released on Parade, Oct'80 Dist: MSD

Cassette: released on Parade, Oct'80 Dist: MSD

DRUMS AND FIFES Combined corps of drums 1st/2nd Batallion.
Cassette: released on Bandleader, May'83 by Bandleader Records. Dist: PRT

DRUMS AND FIFES (The 1st and 2nd Battalion of Grenadier Guards) (Grenadier Guards Band).
Tracks: / British Grenadiers / Girl I left behind me / Goodbye dolly / Garry Owen / Pack up your troubles / Lilliburlero / Great Escape / Hazlemere / Old grey mare / Brazil / See the conquering hero / Scipio / Red cloak / Army & Marine / Goodbye Dolly Gray.
Compact disc: released on Bandleader, Nov'86 by Bandleader Records. Dist: PRT

DRUMS AND FIFES Combined corps of drums 1st/2nd Batallion.
Album: released on Bandleader, Apr'83 by Bandleader Records. Dist: PRT

FOCUS ON THE GRENADIER GUARDS.
Double Album: released on Decca, May'78 by Decca Records. Dist: Polygram

MARCHING THROUGH THE YEARS (Grenadier Guards Band).
Tracks: / Children of the regiment / Admiral of the air / Washington grays / Bridge too far, A / Army and Marine / In the Dolomites / In storm and sunshine / Kennebec / Marching through the years / Birdcage Walk / Red Men's march, The / Man O'Brass / Raiders of the Lost Ark / Piper in the meadow, The / True comrades-in-arms / Robinson's grand entree / Independentia / On the square.

Notes: Recorded digitally in Abbey Road's 'Studio Number One'. Director of Music: Lt. Col. D.R. Kimberley MBE, FTCL, LRAM, ARCM, LGSM, psm.
Album: released on Grasmere, Jun'87 by Grasmere Records. Dist: EMI

Cassette: released on Grasmere, Jun'87 by Grasmere Records. Dist: EMI

MARCH SPECTACULAR.
Album: released on Bandleader (Military), Apr'83

Album: released on Bandleader (Military), Apr'83

NATIONAL ANTHEMS OF THE WORLD.
Album: released on Decca, Jun'78 by Decca Records. Dist: Polygram

TERCENTENARY GALA CONCERT.
Album: released on Polyphonic, Mar'86 by Polyphonic Records. Dist: Taylors

Cassette: released on Polyphonic, Mar'86 by Polyphonic Records. Dist: Taylors

TROOPING THE COLOUR.
Album: released on Major, Jun'78 by Major Records. Dist: Pinnacle

Cassette: released on Major Richards, Jun'78 by Major Richards Records. Dist: Taylors

WORLD OF SOUSA MARCHES, THE (Grenadier Guards Band).
Album: released on Decca, Jun'76 by Decca Records. Dist: Polygram

Cassette: released on Decca, Jun'76 by Decca Records. Dist: Polygram

WORLD OF THE GRENADIER GUARDS.
Album: released on Decca, '73 by Decca Records. Dist: Polygram

WORLD'S GREATEST MARCHES, THE.
Cassette single: released on Parade, Nov'79 Dist: MSD

YANKEE DOODLE DANDY (Grenadier Guards Band).
Album: released on Major Richards, Apr'83 by Major Richards Records. Dist: Taylors

Grenfell, Joyce

COLLECTION: JOYCE GRENFELL.
Album: released on One Up, Oct'76 by EMI Records.

JOYCE GRENFELL TALKING.
Album: released on Cube, Oct'81 by Dakota Records. Dist: PRT

KEEPSAKE.
Tracks: / Mad about the boy / Sigh no more / Ziguener / I'd follow my secret heart / Parisian Pierrot / Someday I'll Find you / Matelot / I'll see you again / Useful and Acceptable gifts / Two character studies,The American Mother/The Village Mother / Keepsake / Maud / Yellow rose of Texas, The / All the pretty little horses / I don't 'arf love you / Narcissus / If love were all / Someday I'll find you(Noel Coward Gems) / Matelot (Noel Coward Vocal Gems) / Party's over, The / I'm going to see you today / Drifting / There's nothing new to tell you.
Album: released on EMI Retrospect, Jul'86 by EMI Records. Dist: EMI

Cassette: released on EMI Retrospect, Jul'86 by EMI Records. Dist: EMI

NEW JOYCE GRENFELL COLLECTION.
Cassette: released on EMI, Apr'78 by EMI Records. Dist: EMI

SECOND COLLECTION, THE.
Album: released on Encore, Jun'79 by EMI Records. Dist: EMI

Cassette: released on Encore, Jun'79 by EMI Records. Dist: EMI

Gresley Male Voice choir

BEGONE DULL CARE.
Album: released on Bandleader, Sep'84 by Bandleader Records. Dist: PRT

Grey, Al

AL GREY & JASPER THILO QUINTET (Grey, Al & Jasper Thilo Quintet).
Album: released on Storyville, Jul'87 by Storyville Records. Dist: Jazz Music Distribution, Swift Distribution, Chris Wellard Distribution, Counterpoint Distribution

AL GREYS ALL STARS.
Album: released on Traveller's Products, Apr'79 Dist: Swift

JAZZ AT THE PHILHARMONIC 1983.
Album: released on Pablo, May'83 by Pablo Records. Dist: Wellard, Chris, IMS-Polygram, BMG

JUST JAZZ (Grey, Al & Buddy Tate).
Notes: For full information see under: Tate, Buddy/Al Grey.

LIVE AT RICKS (Grey, Al & Jimmy Forrest).
Album: released on Aviva(USA), Dec'79 Dist: Jazz Music, Swift

LIVE IN CHICAGO (see Forrest, Jimmy & Al Grey) (Grey, Al & Jimmy Forrest).

LIVE IN CHICAGO (Grey, Al & Jimmy Forrest).
Album: released on Aviva(USA), Apr'79 Dist: Jazz Music, Swift

Grey Al & JJ Johnson

THINGS ARE GETTING BETTER ALL THE TIME.
Album: released on Pablo, May'84 by Pablo Records. Dist: Wellard, Chris, IMS-Polygram, BMG

Cassette: released on Pablo, May'84 by Pablo Records. Dist: Wellard, Chris, IMS-Polygram, BMG

Album: released on Pablo (USA), May'84 by Pablo Records (USA). Dist: Wellard, Chris, IMS-Polygram, BMG

Cassette: released on Pablo (USA), May'84 by Pablo Records (USA). Dist: Wellard, Chris, IMS-Polygram, BMG

Grey Fox, The

GREY FOX, THE Original Soundtrack.
Tracks: / Big ride, The / Main titles / Oyster bed sequence / Nickleodeon sequence / Oregon robberry (The) / Ride through colors / Country store sequence / Ride to Kamloops / Golf waltz, A / Sweet Betsy from Pike / Grey Fox Theme (the) / Meeting tram at Ducks Siding / Kate's waltz / Miner's confessions to Kate / Chase (the) / End titles.
Notes: Original soundtrack recording composed & conducted by Michael Conway Baker. Traditional Irish music composed & performed by the Chieftains.
Compact disc: released on DRG (USA), Apr'87 by DRG Records. Dist: Conifer, RCA

ORIGINAL S/T.
Album: released on DRG (USA), Apr'84 by DRG Records. Dist: Conifer, RCA

Grey, Gregory

SENSUAL.
Tracks: / Sensual / Johnny Purify.
Single (7"): released on CBS, Apr'86 by CBS Records. Dist: CBS

Greyhound

BLACK AND WHITE/ MOON RIVER.
Single (7"): released on Old Gold, Apr'83 by Old Gold Records. Dist: Lightning, Jazz Music, Spartan, Counterpoint

MOON RIVER PLUS THREE VARIOUS ARTISTS.
Single (7"): released on Trojan, Aug'81 by Trojan Records. Dist: PRT, Jetstar

Grey Madeleine

CHANTS D'AUVERGNE.
Album: released on World, Jun'74 Dist: Jetstar

Grey, Owen

FORWARD ON THE SCENE.
Album: released on Third World, Jan'78 Dist: Jetstar Distribution

GREEN GRASS OF JAMAICA.
Single (12"): released on Sapphire, Feb'83 by Sapphire Records. Dist: Jetstar

LAST NIGHT.
Single (12"): released on Barry U, Dec'86 Dist: Jetstar

OWEN SINGS BOB MARLEY.
Album: released on Sarge, Jun'84 by Sarge Records. Dist: Jetstar

ROLLING STONE/ROLLING DUB.
Single (7"): released on Pama, Nov'81 by Pama Records. Dist: Pama, Enterprise, Jetstar

ROOM AT THE TOP.
Album: released on World Enterprise, Nov'86 Dist: Jetstar

SHAKE YOU DOWN.
Single (12"): released on Barry U, Dec'86 Dist: Jetstar

SOMETHING TO REMIND ME/ GIRL WHAT.
78 rpm record: released on Pama, Oct'82 by Pama Records. Dist: Pama, Enterprise, Jetstar

SWING HIGH WITH OWEN/PUT YOUR MONEY WHERE YOUR MOUTH IS.
Single (12"): released on Speciality, Nov'83 by Relic Records. Dist: Swift

Grey Parade

ASLEEP.
Tracks: / Asleep / House of steel.
Single (7"): released on Numa, Jan'86 by Numa Records. Dist: PRT Distribution

Single (12"): released on Numa, Jan'86 by Numa Records. Dist: PRT Distribution

EXTERIORS/ INTERIORS.
Single (12"): released on Rialto, Jun'83 by Rialto Records. Dist: Pinnacle

REASON, THE.
Album: released on Plan B, Jun'85 by Plan B Records. Dist: Cartel

Grey Roman

SHAKEDOWN.
Single (12"): released on FFT, May'84 by Food For Thought Records. Dist: Pinnacle

Grey Sara & Ellie Ellis

BREATH OF FRESH AIR, A.
Album: released on Fellside, Jan'83 by Fellside Records. Dist: Roots, Jazz Music, Celtic Music, Projection

MAKING THE AIR RESOUND.
Album: released on Fellside, May'85 by Fellside Records. Dist: Roots, Jazz Music, Celtic Music, Projection

Grey, Sonny

LIVE (Grey, Sonny/Dexter Gordon).

LIVE (Grey, Sonny/Dexter Gordon).
Album: released on Spotlite, Jan'83 by Spotlite Records. Dist: Cadillac, Jazz Music, Spotlite

Gribbin, Tom

GUNS OF BRIXTON (Gribbin, Tom & The Saltwater Cowboys).
Single (7"): released on Country Roads Records, Jun'81 by Country Roads Records. Dist: Stage One

SON OF LIGHTENING.
Album: released on Country Roads Records, Nov'81 by Country Roads Records. Dist: Stage One

USEPPA ISLAND RENDEVOUS (Gribbin, Tom & The saltwater Band).

USEPPA ISLAND RENDEVOUS (Gribbin, Tom & The saltwater Band).
Album: released on Range, May'84 Dist: PRT, Jetstar

Gridley, Andrew

LOST IN TIME REFLECTIONS.
Single (7"): released on ADG, Jul'83 by ADG Records. Dist: ADG Records

Single (7"): released on ADG, Jul'83 by ADG Records. Dist: ADG Records

Greig, Stan

BLUES EVERY TIME.
Tracks: / Love for sale / Honky tonk train blues / Take Five / Willow weep for me.
Album: released on Calligraph, Aug'86 by Calligraph Records. Dist: PRT

Greig, Stan Trio

BLUES EVERY TIME.
Album: released on Calligraph, Sep'85 by Calligraph Records. Dist: PRT

Grier, Sonja

LOVE FLIGHT 109.
Tracks: / Love flight 109 / Love flight 109 (dub).
Single (7"): released on RCA, Jul'87 by RCA Records. Dist: RCA, Roots, Swift, Wellard, Chris, I & B, Solomon & Peres Distribution

Single (12"): released on RCA, Jul'87 by RCA Records. Dist: RCA, Roots, Swift, Wellard, Chris, I & B, Solomon & Peres Distribution

Griffin, Billy

BELIEVE IT OR NOT.
Tracks: / Believe it or not / E.S.P.
Single (7"): released on Atlantic, Nov'86 by WEA Records. Dist: WEA

Single (12"): released on Atlantic, Nov'86 by WEA Records. Dist: WEA

BE WITH ME.
Album: released on CBS, Feb'83 by CBS Records. Dist: CBS

Single (7"): released on CBS, Mar'83 by CBS Records. Dist: CBS

Single (12"): released on CBS, Mar'83 by CBS Records. Dist: CBS

GIRL IS FINE (THE).
Tracks: / Girl is fine / E.S.P.
Single (7"): released on Atlantic, Apr'87 by

WEA Records. Dist: WEA

Single (12"): released on Atlantic, Apr'87 by WEA Records. Dist: WEA

HOLD ME TIGHTER IN THE TRAIN.
Single (7"): released on Old Gold, Sep'85 by Old Gold Records. Dist: Lightning, Jazz Music, Spartan, Counterpoint

SWINGIN' (THE).
Album: released on Kingdom Gate, Jun'87

SYSTEMATIC.
Album: released on CBS, Jul'85 by CBS Records. Dist: CBS

Griffin Brothers

RIFFIN' WITH THE GRIFFIN BROTHERS ORCHESTRA (Griffin Brothers Orchestra).
Double Album: released on Ace, Mar'85 by Ace Records. Dist: Pinnacle, Swift, Hotshot, Cadillac

Griffin, Johnny

BLOWING SESSION, A.
Album: released on Blue Note (USA), Sep'84

FLY MISTER FLY With the Joe Morris Orchestra.
Album: released on Saxonograph (Sweden), Jun'85

GRIFF AND LOCK (Griffin, Johnny & Eddie Lockjaw Davis).
Album:

INTRODUCING JOHNNY GRIFFIN.
Tracks: / Mil dew / Chicago calling / These foolish things / Boy next door / Nice and easy / It's alright with me / Lover man / Way you look tonight, The / Cherokee.
Notes: Produced by Alfred lion, produced for release by Michael Cuscuna. (P) 1987 Manhattan Records, a division of Capitol Records Inc.
Compact disc: released on Manhattan-Blue Note, May'87 by EMI America Records (USA). Dist: EMI

Album: released on Blue Note, Jul'85 by EMI Records. Dist: EMI

JAMFS ARE COMING, THE (Griffin, Johnny and Art Taylor Quartet).
Album: released on Timeless(import), Apr'81 Dist: Cadillac

JOHNNY GRIFFIN.
Album: released on Horo, Oct'79 Dist: Cadillac Music

JOHNNY GRIFFIN MEETS DEXTER GORDON (Griffin, Johnny and Dexter Gordon).
Album: released on Lotus (Import), Apr'81

LITTLE GIANT, THE.
Compact disc: released on JVC Fantasy (Japan), '86

YOU LEAVE ME BREATHLESS.
Album: released on Black Lion, Apr'85 by Black Lion Records. Dist: Jazz Music, Chris Wellard, Taylor, H.R., Counterpoint, Cadillac

Griffin, Reggie

MIRADA ROCK (Griffin, Reggie and Technofunk).
Single (12"): released on Sugar Hill USA, Jan'83 by MCA Records. Dist: Roots Distribution, Mike's Country Music Room Distribution, Projection Distribution, PRT Distribution

Griffin, Sylvia

WHITE HUNTER.
Single (7"): released on Magnet, Jan'84 by Magnet Records. Dist: BMG

Single (12"): released on Magnet, Jan'84 by Magnet Records. Dist: BMG

Griffin, Vincent

TRADITIONAL FIDDLE MUSIC FROM COUNTY CLARE.
Album: released on Topic, '81 Dist: Roots Distribution

Griffith, Albert

COUNTRY LIVING (Griffith, Albert & The Gladiators).
Album: released on Heartbeat (USA), Dec'85 Dist: Mike's Country Music Room Distribution, Swift, Projection, Topic, Jetstar, Ruff Lion Distribution

Griffith, Nanci

FROM A DISTANCE.
Tracks: / From a distance / Sing one for sister.
Single (7"): released on MCA, Jul'87 by MCA Records. Dist: Polygram, MCA

LAST OF THE TRUE BELIEVERS.
Compact disc: released on Philo, Dec'86 Dist:

Roots

LONE STAR STATE OF MIND.
Tracks: / Lone star state of mind / Cold hearts/closed minds / From a distance / Beacon street / Nickel dreams / Sing one for sister / Ford econoline / Trouble in the fields / Love in a memory / Let it shine on me / There's a light beyond these woods (Mary Margaret).
Album: released on MCA, Apr'87 by MCA Records. Dist: Polygram, MCA

Cassette: released on MCA, Apr'87 by MCA Records. Dist: Polygram, MCA

Compact disc: released on MCA, Jul'87 by MCA Records. Dist: Polygram, MCA

NANCI GRIFFITH.
Album: released on Rounder Europa, Mar'87

ONCE IN A VERY BLUE MOON.
Album: released on Philo (USA), Dec'85

Compact disc: released on Philo (USA), Dec'86

Griffith Park Collection

GRIFFITH PARK COLLECTION.
Compact disc: released on Elektra(Musician), Jul'84 by WEA Records. Dist: WEA

Griffiths, Albert

COUNTRY LIVING (Griffiths, Albert & The Gladiators).
Notes: See also under Gladiators,& Albert Griffiths
Album: released on Rounder Europa, Feb'87

Griffiths, Derek

HEADS & TAILS.
Album: released on BBC, Feb'80 by BBC Records & Tapes. Dist: EMI, PRT, Pye

Cassette: released on BBC, Feb'80 by BBC Records & Tapes. Dist: EMI, PRT, Pye

Griffiths, Hugh

BIG, WE BIG.
Single (12"): released on Scorpio, Oct'84 by Scorpio Records. Dist: Jetstar

DON'T YOU EVER LEAVE.
Single (12"): released on Gamble, Dec'84 by Gamble Records. Dist: Jetstar

MEMORIES.
Album: released on Blue Mountain, Jul'87 Dist: Jetstar

MOTHER AFRICA.
Album: released on Steppers, Mar'87

MR WALKER.
Album: released on Vista Sounds, Sep'84 by Vista Sounds Records. Dist: Jetstar

SEXY LADY.
Single (12"): released on Greensleeves, Sep'83 by Greensleeves Records. Dist: BMG, Jetstar, Spartan

SPLENDID THINGS.
Single (12"): released on Uptempo, Nov'83 by Uptempo Records. Dist: Jetstar Distribution

STUCK ON YOU.
Single (12"): released on Jedi, Oct'84 Dist: Jetstar

THEM R A TEASE.
Tracks: / Them nah please.
Single (12"): released on Pioneer International, Dec'86 by Pioneer International Records. Dist: Jetstar

Griffiths, Marcia

DON'T EVER LEAVE.
Single (12"): released on Sheba, Sep'81

I LOVE MUSIC.
Album: released on Mountain Sounds, Nov'86

IT HURTS TO BE ALONE.
Single (12"): released on Solomonic, Jan'84 by Solomonic Records. Dist: Jetstar, Pinnacle

Single (12"): released on Solomonic, Jan'84 by Solomonic Records. Dist: Jetstar, Pinnacle

NATURALLY.
Album: released on Skynote, Aug'78 Dist: Sidewak Records

ROCK MY SOUL.
Album: released on Pioneer International, Dec'84 by Pioneer International Records. Dist: Jetstar

SWEET BITTER LOVE.
Album: released on Trojan, '83 by Trojan Records. Dist: PRT, Jetstar

---

UNTRUE LOVE.
Single (12"): released on Intense, Dec'82 by Intense Records. Dist: PRT, Kingdom

Griffiths, Roni

BEST PART OF BREAKING UP.
Single (7"): released on Vanguard, Mar'83 by PRT Records. Dist: PRT

Single (12"): released on Vanguard, Mar'83 by PRT Records. Dist: PRT

BREAKING MY HEART.
Single (7"): released on Vanguard, Apr'83 by PRT Records. Dist: PRT

Single (12"): released on Vanguard, Apr'83 by PRT Records. Dist: PRT

RONI GRIFFITHS.
Album: released on Vanguard, Jul'82 by PRT Records. Dist: PRT

Album: released on Vanguard, Jul'82 by PRT Records. Dist: PRT

Griff, Zaine

ASHES AND DIAMONDS.
Album: released on Automatic, Sep'80 Dist: WEA, Independant

Grimes, Carol

CAROL GRIMES.
Album: by Charly Records. Dist: Charly, Cadillac

EYES WIDE OPEN.
Compact disc: released on TM Records. '86

Grimes, Tiny

FRANKIE AND JOHNNY BOOGIE.
Album: released on Black & Blue RCA (France), Nov'85 by RCA Records. Dist: Discovery

ONE IS NEVER TOO OLD TO SWING (Grimes, Tiny and Roy Eldridge).
Album: released on Sonet, Jan'78 by Sonet Records. Dist: PRT

PROFOUNDLY BLUE.
Album: released on Muse (Import), Apr'81

TINY GRIMES VOLUME 1-1949-1952.
Tracks: / Tiny's jump / Hey Hey / Why did you waste my time / St Louis Blues / Drinking Beer / My Baby's Left me / Frankie & Johnnie Boogie-1 / Hey Mr.J.B / Battle of the mass / I'm in love with you baby / My baby's cool / Hawaiian boogie / No hug no kiss / Frankie & Johnnie boogie-2.
Notes: Mono recording.
Album: released on Krazy Kat, Oct'86 Dist: Jazz Music, Swift, Chris Wellard, H.R. Taylor, Charly, Hotshot, IRS Distribution

VOLUME 1.
Album: released on Krazy Kat, Dec'86 Dist: Jazz Music, Swift, Chris Wellard, H.R. Taylor, Charly, Hotshot, IRS Distribution

VOLUME 2 1949-55.
Album: released on Krazy Kat, Oct'87 Dist: Jazz Music, Swift, Chris Wellard, H.R. Taylor, Charly, Hotshot, IRS Distribution. Estim retail price Jan'87 was £9.20.

Grimethorpe Colliery Band

BAND OF THE YEAR.
Album: released on RCA, May'77 by RCA Records. Dist: RCA, Roots, Swift, Wellard, Chris, I & B, Solomon & Peres Distribution

CLASSICS FOR BRASS.
Album: released on Decca, May'77 by Decca Records. Dist: Polygram

FIREBIRD.
Album: released on Polyphonic, Sep'82 by Polyphonic Records. Dist: Taylors

Cassette: released on Polyphonic, Jan'83 by Polyphonic Records. Dist: Taylors

GRIMETHORPE COLLIERY BAND.
Album: Dist: R. Smith & Co. Records, H.R. Taylor

GRIMETHORPE SPECIAL.
Album: released on Headline, Aug'77 by Creole Records. Dist: PRT

KING SIZE BRASS.
Album: released on Polyphonic, Jun'80 by Polyphonic Records. Dist: Taylors

Cassette: released on Parade, Mar'81 by MSD

POP GOES THE POST HORN.
Album: by Grosvenor Records. Dist: Taylors

RAISE YOUR BANNERS HIGH.
Single (7"): released on Rough Trade, Oct'85

Distribution, Cartel Distribution

Grimm
FAIRY TALES Various artists (Various Artists).
Cassette: released on Argo, Nov'84 by Decca Records. Dist: Polygram

Grimm Brothers
FOUR OF YOUR FAVOURITE STORIES FROM... (Various Artists).
Album: released on Tempo, Nov'79 by Warwick Records. Dist: Multiple Sound Distributors

Cassette: released on Tempo, Nov'79 by Warwick Records. Dist: Multiple Sound Distributors

GRIMM BROTHERS FAIRY TALES VOL 2 (Gordon, Hannah).
Album: released on Pinnacle, '79 by Pinnacle Records. Dist: Pinnacle

GRIMM BROTHERS FAIRY TALES VOL 1 (Gordon, Hannah).
Album: released on Pinnacle, '79 by Pinnacle Records. Dist: Pinnacle

MORE GRIMMS FAIRY TALES (Various Artists).
Cassette: released on Argo, Apr'85 by Decca Records. Dist: Polygram

SNOW WHITE AND ROSE RED (Various Artists).
Album: released on Tempo, Nov'79 by Warwick Records. Dist: Multiple Sound Distributors

Cassette: released on Tempo, Nov'79 by Warwick Records. Dist: Multiple Sound Distributors

SNOW WHITE AND ROSE RED (Various Artists).

Grimm, Roland
SELFISH AMERICAN BITCH.
Tracks: / Selfish American bitch / Demolition.
Single (7"): released on U-Turn, Jul'87

Grimms Fairy Tales
GRIMMS FAIRY TALES VOL 1 (Various Artists).
Cassette: released on VFM Cassettes, Jan'85

HOW MUCH IS THAT DOGGIE (Various Artists).
Cassette: released on Bibi, Jan'82

Grim Reaper
FEAR NO EVIL.
Album: released on Ebony, Jun'85 by Ebony Records. Dist: Pinnacle, Ebony

SEE YOU IN HELL.
Album: released on Ebony, Nov'83 by Ebony Records. Dist: Pinnacle, Ebony

Grind
ORIGINAL BROADWAY CAST (Various Artists).
Album: released on TER, Sep'85 Dist: Pinnacle

Cassette: released on TER, Sep'85 Dist: Pinnacle

Grine, Janny
LIKE THE WIND.
Album: released on Birdwing, Mar'84 by Word Records. Dist: Word Distribution

Cassette: released on Birdwing, Mar'84 by Word Records. Dist: Word Distribution

Grine, Joe
LIFE/WELL PLEASED AND SATISFIED.
Single (12"): released on Exclusive, Aug'82 Dist: Jetstar

Grip
KEEPING THE PEACE/MUSICLAND.
Single (7"): released on Gripping Youth, Aug'82 Dist: Cartel

Grippe, Ragner
SAND.
Album: released on Shandar, Mar'78

Grisman, Dave
KALEIDOSCOPE.
Album: released on Kaleidoscope, Sep'79

Grisman's, Dave
ACOUSTIC CHRISTMAS.
Album: released on Rounder (USA), Jan'84 Dist: Mike's Country Music Room Distribution, Jazz Music Distribution, Swift Distribution, Roots Records Distribution, Projection Distribution, Topic Distribution

Gritzbach, George
SWEEPER.
Album: released on Kicking Mule (USA), Nov'79 by Kicking Mule Records (USA). Dist: Topic, Projection

Grobschnitt
BALLERMAN.
Double Album: released on Logo, '79 by Logo Records. Dist: Roots, BMG

ILLEGAL.
Album: released on Brah, May'81

MERRY GO ROUND.
Album: released on Brain, Jan'80

RAZZIA.
Album: released on Brain (Germany), Aug'85

ROCKPOMMELS LAND.
Album: released on Logo, '79 by Logo Records. Dist: Roots, BMG

SOLAR MUSIC-LIVE.
Album: released on Brain, Jan'79

Grogan, Ali
LLIW HEULWEN.
Album: released on Sain, Jul'85 Dist: Roots

Grogan, Claire
LOVE BOMB.
Tracks: / Love bomb / I love the way you beg.
Single (7"): released on London, 23 May'87 by London Records. Dist: Polygram

Single (12"): released on London, 23 May'87 by London Records. Dist: Polygram

Groove Control
DO IT ANYWAY.
Single (12"): released on Nunk, Nov'84 by Nunk. Dist: Lightning

Groove Farm
SORE HEADS & HAPPY HEARTS (EP).
Single (7"): released on Raving Pop Blast, Mar'87 Dist: Revolver, Cartel

Groove Juice Special
HIT THAT JACK JIVE.
Album: released on Groove PR, Jul'82 by Beggars Banquet Records. Dist: WEA, PRT

Groove Jumping
GROOVE JUMPING various artists (Various Artists).
Tracks: / Ride and roll / No good lover / Strange kind of feeling / Bottle it up and go / Boot 'em up / Dead broke / Speed King / Smack dab in the middle / Lawdy Miss Mary / Worried 'bout you baby / Dat dat de dum dum / Mr Bear / Radar / How come?.
Album: released on Detour, Dec'86 by Detour Records. Dist: Swift, RCA, Jazz Music, Projection

Album: released on Detour, Feb'84 by Detour Records. Dist: Swift, RCA, Jazz Music, Projection

Groove Masters
SUNSHINE ON A BLUE DAY.
Single (7"): released on Electricity, Jun'84 by Electricity Records. Dist: PRT

Single (12"): released on Electricity, Jun'84 by Electricity Records. Dist: PRT

Groovey
GROOVEY (Various Artists).
Album: released on Four Leaf Clover, Jul'87 Dist: Jazz Music, Swift

Groovy, Paul
ANDY WATCHOUT (Groovy, Paul & The Pop Art Experience).
Tracks: / Andy Watchout.
Notes: See also under Pop Art Experience,& Paul Groovy
Single (7"): released on Bite Back, Mar'87 Dist: Backs, Cartel

Groovy, Winston
AFRICAN GIRL.
Album: released on Blue Moon, Apr'84 Dist: Magnum Music Group Ltd, PRT, Spartan

DON'T BLAME ME.
Single (12"): released on Time, Oct'80 Dist: Jetstar Distribution

FREE THE PEOPLE.
Album: released on Pama, Apr'84 by Pama Records. Dist: Pama, Enterprise, Jetstar

From We Met.
FROM WE MET.
Single (12"): released on Three Kings, Nov'83 by Three Kings Records. Dist: Jetstar Distribution

I REALLY LOVE YOU.
Single (12"): released on Dancebeat, Jan'84 by Dancebeat Records. Dist: Jetstar

LIVING IN A DREAM.
Single (12"): released on Sound City, Nov'84 by Sound City Records. Dist: Jetstar

NIGHT SHIFT.
Single (7"): released on Jive, Apr'85 by Zomba Records. Dist: RCA, PRT, CBS

Single (12"): released on Jive, Apr'85 by Zomba Records. Dist: RCA, PRT, CBS

Single (12"): released on Sound City, Mar'85 by Sound City Records. Dist: Jetstar

PARADISE IN YOUR EYES.
Single (12"): released on Dafala, Nov'83

PLEASE DON'T MAKE ME CRY.
Single (7"): released on Sound City, Nov'83 by Sound City Records. Dist: Jetstar

Single (12"): released on Sound City, Nov'83 by Sound City Records. Dist: Jetstar

PLEASE DON'T MAKE ME CRY (EP).
Single (7"): released on Trojan, Nov'83 by Trojan Records. Dist: PRT, Jetstar

Single (12"): released on Trojan, Nov'83 by Trojan Records. Dist: PRT, Jetstar

ROCK ME TONIGHT.
Single (12"): released on Jive, Sep'85 by Zomba Records. Dist: RCA, PRT, CBS

Single (7"): released on Jive, Sep'85 by Zomba Records. Dist: RCA, PRT, CBS

SO IN LOVE WITH YOU.
Single (7"): released on Top Ranking, Nov'82

SOMETHING ON THE SIDE.
Single (12"): released on Sound City, Feb'84 by Sound City Records. Dist: Jetstar

YOU MADE LOOK IT SO EASY.
Tracks: / You made it look so easy / Easy(Version).
Single (12"): released on WG, Jun'86 Dist: Jetstar

Gross, Henry
WILD ONE.
Tracks: / Wild one / Don't call it love.
Single (7"): released on Sonet, Aug'87 by Sonet Records. Dist: PRT

Grossman, Stefan
AUNT MOLLY'S MURRAY FARM.
Album: released on Sonet, '73 by Sonet Records. Dist: PRT

COUNTRY BLUES GUITAR.
Album: released on Kicking Mule, Aug'77 by Sonet. Dist: Roots, PRT-Pye Distribution

GRAMERCY PARK SHEIK.
Album: released on Sonet Records. Dist: PRT

HOT DOGS.
Album: released on Transatlantic, Oct'80 by Transatlantic Records. Dist: IMS-Polygram

HOW TO PLAY BLUES GUITAR.
Album: released on Kicking Mule, '78 by Sonet. Dist: Roots, PRT-Pye Distribution

HOW TO PLAY BLUES GUITAR VOL.2.
Album: released on Kicking Mule, '78 by Sonet. Dist: Roots, PRT-Pye Distribution

JOHN RENBOURN & STEFAN GROSSMAN (see Renbourn, John) (Grossman, Stefan and John Renbourn).
Album: released on Kicking Mule, '78 by Sonet. Dist: Roots, PRT-Pye Distribution

KICKING MULE (Grossman, Stefan and John Renbourn).

THREE KINGDOMS.
Notes: with John Renbourne.
Album: released on Sonet, Mar'87 by Sonet Records. Dist: PRT

UNDER THE VOLCANO.
Album: released on Kicking Mule, Feb'80 by Sonet. Dist: Roots, PRT-Pye Distribution

YAZOO BASIN BOOGIE.
Album: released on Kicking Mule, Jan'78 by Sonet. Dist: Roots, PRT-Pye Distribution

Grossman, Steve
TERRA FIRMA.
Album: released on PM, Jan'80

Way Out West
WAY OUT WEST VOL.1.
Album: released on Red, Jan'87 Dist: Projection, Jazz Horizons

WAY OUT WEST VOL. 2.
Album: released on Red, Jan'87 Dist: Projection, Jazz Horizons

Grosswendt, Martin
DOG ON A DANCE FLOOR.
Album: released on Philo, Sep'79 Dist: Roots

Grosz, Marty
ACOUSTIC GUITAR DUETS (Grosz, Marty & Wayne Wright).
Album: released on Aviva(USA), Apr'79 Dist: Jazz Music, Swift

CHICAGO 1957 (Grosz, Marty & His Honoris Causa Jazz Band).
Album: released on Collectors Items, Jul'86 Dist: Jazz Music, Swift, Chris Wellard

DICK WELLSTOOD & MARTY GROSZ (Grosz, Marty/Dick Wellstood).
Album: released on Aviva(USA), Apr'79 Dist: Jazz Music, Swift

Groucutt, Kelly
KELLY.
Album: released on RCA, Mar'82 by RCA Records. Dist: RCA, Roots, Swift, Wellard, Chris, I & B, Solomon & Peres Distribution

LET THE KIDS DO IT.
Single (7"): released on Riva, Jan'83 Dist: PRT

WE LOVE ANIMALS.
Single (7"): released on Premier, May'85 by Premier Records. Dist: CBS

Groundhogs
BACK AGAINST THE WALL.
Compact disc: released on Magnum, Jul'87 by Bulldog Records. Dist: Spartan

HOGGIN' THE STAGE.
Album: released on Psycho, Apr'84 Dist: Funhouse, Rough Trade

MOVING FAST, STANDING STILL.
Tracks: / Hunt part one(The) / Hunt part two(The) / Hunt part three(The) / Hunt part four (The) / Ain't gonna cry no more / 3 x 7 / Morning Eyes / Dog me bitch / T.S Instrumental / You don't love me / Razors edge / I Confess / Born to be with you / One more chance / Someone to love me / Protector(The) / Supersdead / Moving fast, standing still / I Want you to love me / When you gotta a good friend.
Album: released on Raw Power, May'86 Dist: Pinnacle

Cassette: released on Raw Power, May'86 Dist: Pinnacle

RAZOR'S EDGE.
Album: released on Conquest, May'85 Dist: Red Rhino, Cartel

SPLIT.
Tracks: / Split-Parts One two three four / Cherry Red / Year in the life,A / Junkman groundhog.
Notes: Original catalogue number,LBR 1017(album),TCLBR 1017(cassette).
Album: released on Liberty-United, Apr'80 by EMI Records. Dist: EMI

Cassette: released on Liberty-United, Aug'80 by EMI Records. Dist: EMI

THANK CHRIST FOR THE BOMB.
Tracks: / Strange town / Darkness is no friend / Soldier / Thank Christ for the bomb / Ship on the ocean / Garden / Status people / Rich man,poor man / Eccentric man.
Notes: All titles composed by McPhee,all titles published by United Partnership Ltd.
Album: released on Fame, May'86 by Music For Pleasure Records. Dist: EMI

Ground Zero
PINK.
Album: released on Reflex, Nov'85

Group
AMERICAN.
Single (7"): released on Jive, Apr'84 by Zomba Records. Dist: RCA, PRT, CBS

Single (12"): released on Jive, Apr'84 by Zomba Records. Dist: RCA, PRT, CBS

I DON'T LIKE TO LOSE.
Single (7"): released on Soul Supply, Dec'84 by High Energy Records. Dist: Charly

IRON CHAIN.
Single (7"): released on Jive, Sep'84 by Zomba Records. Dist: RCA, PRT, CBS

Single (12"): released on Jive, Sep'84 by Zomba Records. Dist: RCA, PRT, CBS

TECHNOLOGY/YOU'RE MY FLAG.
Single (7"): released on Jive, Sep'83 by Zomba Records. Dist: RCA, PRT, CBS

Single (12"): released on Jive, Sep'83 by Zomba Records. Dist: RCA, PRT, CBS

VICTIMS OF CIRCUMSTANCE.
Single (7"): released on Jive, Jun'84 by Zomba Records. Dist: RCA, PRT, CBS

Single (12"): released on Jive, Jun'84 by Zomba Records. Dist: RCA, PRT, CBS

Group therapy

ARTY-FACT/DRUG CHIC.
Single (7"): released on Kamera, Jul'82

Grove,Fred

SANACO.
Cassette: released on Soundings, Mar'85 Dist: Soundings

Groves,Edgel

FOOTPRINTS IN THE SAND.
Single (7"): released on Chips, Aug'81 by PRT. Dist: PRT

Grown Up Strange

ON A WING AND A PRAYER.
Tracks: / On a wing and a prayer.
Single (12"): released on Ugly Man, Nov'86 Dist: Cartel

GRP

GRP LIVE IN SESSION Various artists (Various Artists).
Tracks: / Rio funk / "St.Elsewhere",(Theme from) / Theme from"St. Elsewhere" / Mountain dance / Oasis / Rit variations(The) / Reverend lee / Dolphin dreams.
Notes: Featuring Dave Grusin,Lee Ritenour,Dave Valentin,Diane Schuur.
Album: released on GRP (USA), Dec'85 by GRP Records (USA). Dist: IMS, Polygram

Cassette: released on GRP (USA), Dec'85 by GRP Records (USA). Dist: IMS, Polygram

Compact disc: released on GRP (USA), Dec'85 by GRP Records (USA). Dist: IMS, Polygram

GRP NEW MAGIC DIGITAL SAMPLER Various artists (Various Artists).
Notes: Sampler Includes: Artists: Dave Grusin, Diane Schuur, Special EFX, Stephane Grappelli, Eddie Danies, The Duke Ellingon Orchestra, David Benoit, The Chick Corea Elektric Band.
Compact disc: released on GRP (USA), Jul'87 by GRP Records (USA). Dist: IMS, Polygram

GRP ROADTRACKS Various artists (Various Artists).
Tracks: / Power wave / Essence / Elektrik city / Can't believe that you're in love with me,I / Uptown east / Rio funk / Circle dance / Times of my life / Can't change my heart / Can't change my heart / Shuffle city / Harlequin / Harlequin.
Notes: A special cassette compilation for European release only,twelve representative tracks from GRP catalogue,60 minutes playing time,produced on chrome tape. Distinctive packaging to ensure good visibility.
Cassette: released on GRP (USA), Oct'86 by GRP Records (USA). Dist: IMS, Polygram

GRP ROADTRACKS (Various Artists).
Cassette: released on GRP (USA), Oct'86 by GRP Records (USA). Dist: IMS, Polygram

NEW AGE IN JAZZ.
Tracks: / Early a.m attitude / She could be mine / Heart is a lonely hunter / Mozaik / Dolphin dreams / Rio funk / Birk's works / Opening night / Very nice indeed / Fountain of you.
Notes: Superb collection from the "Master of Sound" GRP Records. Featuring tracks by Dave Grusin, Lee Ritenour, Dizzy Gillespie, Billy Cobham and others, this is an ideal demonstration CD and a great introduction to the GRP sound.
Compact disc: released on GRP (USA), Jun'86 by GRP Records (USA). Dist: IMS, Polygram

Grubbs, Earl & Carl

NEPTUNE.
Album: released on Muse, Apr'81 by Peerless Records. Dist: Lugtons Distributors

Grumbleweeds

COME ON DOWN T'BREAD SHOP.
Single (7"): released on MFP, Mar'81 by EMI Records. Dist: EMI

GRUMBLEWEEDS, THE.
Cassette: released on BBC, Nov'79 by BBC Records & Tapes. Dist: EMI, PRT, Pye

LET THE GOOD TIMES ROLL.
Tracks: / Let the good times roll / Dizzy / Womans intuition / Let your love flow / Rose has to die,A / Little bit wiser,A / Hands accross the sea / One little smile / Party times / More I see you, The / Whispers / Hold out / Live it down / All for the sake of rock n roll.

Album: released on K-Tel, Oct'86 by K-Tel Records. Dist: Record Merchandisers Distribution, Taylors, Terry Blood Distribution, Wynd-Up Distribution, Relay Distribution, Pickwick Distribution, Solomon & Peres Distribution, Polygram

Cassette: released on K-Tel, Oct'86 by K-Tel Records. Dist: Record Merchandisers Distribution, Taylors, Terry Blood Distribution, Wynd-Up Distribution, Relay Distribution, Pickwick Distribution, Solomon & Peres Distribution, Polygram

SHALL I GIVE YOU A NUDGE.
Single (7"): released on MFP, May'81 by EMI Records. Dist: EMI

WOMEN'S INTUITION.
Tracks: / Women's intuition / That's all I have to say.
Single (7"): released on Spirit, Jul'86 by Spirit Records. Dist: WEA

WORRAVAGORRINMEPOCKIT.
Album: released on MFP, Aug'81 by EMI Records. Dist: EMI

Grummit, John & Maureen

FREE TO FLY.
Cassette: released on Vision, Jul'85 Dist: Vision

Grundy, Eddie

LAMBS TO THE SLAUGHTER.
Single (7"): released on Dingles, Jul'81 by Dingles Records. Dist: Projection

POOR PIG.
Single (7"): released on Foxy, Nov'82 by Foxy. Dist: PRT

Gruntz, George

THEATRE (Gruntz, George Concert Jazz Band '83).
Album: released on ECM (Germany), Jun'84 by ECM Records. Dist: IMS, Polygram, Virgin through EMI

Grupo Raiz

AMANECERES.
Album: released on Monitor, Jan'84 Dist: Bulldog

Cassette: released on Monitor (USA), Jan'84

VOL 2 POR AMERICA DEL CENTRO.
Album: released on Monitor, Jan'84 Dist: Bulldog

Grusin, Dave

AND THE NY-LA DREAM BAND.
Album: released on GRP (USA), Jun'84 by GRP Records (USA). Dist: IMS, Polygram

Cassette: released on GRP (USA), Jun'84 by GRP Records (USA). Dist: IMS, Polygram

Compact disc: released on GRP (USA), Jun'84 by GRP Records (USA). Dist: IMS, Polygram

AND THE NY-LA DREAM BAND.
Album: released on GRP (USA), Jun'84 by GRP Records (USA). Dist: IMS, Polygram

Cassette: released on GRP (USA), Jun'84 by GRP Records (USA). Dist: IMS, Polygram

Compact disc: released on GRP (USA), Jun'84 by GRP Records (USA). Dist: IMS, Polygram

CINEMAGIC (Grusin, Dave & R.P.O.).
Tracks: / An actor's life / It might be you(Tootsie) / Heaven can wait / On golden pond / Condor (Three Days of the Condor) / Heart is a lonely hunter, The / Opening theme from the Goonies / Champ, The / Mountain dance* / Letting go * / PLO camp entrance * / Little drummer girl *.
Notes: A digital showcase of all Dave Grusin's most memorable motion picture film themes. Recorded with the prestigious London Symphony Orchestra including key musicians Tom Scott,Lee Ritenour,Harvey Mason,Ernie Watts &,of course,Dave Grusin on keyboards.
Album: released on GRP (USA), May'87 by GRP Records (USA). Dist: IMS, Polygram

Cassette: released on GRP (USA), May'87 by GRP Records (USA). Dist: IMS, Polygram

Compact disc: released on GRP (USA), May'87 by GRP Records (USA). Dist: IMS, Polygram

DAVE GRUSIN & NY-LA DREAM BAND (Grusin, Dave & NY-LA Dream Band).
Tracks: / Shuffle City / Countdown / Serengitti walk / Champ / What matters most / Number 8 / Three days of the condor / Summer sketches '82.
Compact disc: released on GRP (USA), Aug'84 by GRP Records (USA). Dist: IMS, Polygram

DISCOVERED AGAIN.
Album: released on Sheffield Treasury, Oct'82

HARKEQUIN (Grusin, Dave & Lee Ritenour).

HARLEQUIN (Grusin, Dave & Lee Ritenour).
Tracks: / Harlequin / Early A.M attitude / San ysidro / Before it's to late / Cat's of Rio / Grid-lock / Silent message / Bird (The).
Cassette: released on GRP (USA), Jul'85 by GRP Records (USA). Dist: IMS, Polygram

Compact disc: released on GRP (USA), Jul'85 by GRP Records (USA). Dist: IMS, Polygram

KALEIDOSCOPE.
Album: released on Japanese Import, May'79

MOUNTAIN DANCE.
Tracks: / Rag bag / Friends and strangers / City lights / Rondo-"If you hold out your hand" / Mountain dance / Thanksong / Capitain Caribe / Either way.
Compact disc: released on GRP (USA), Sep'85 by GRP Records (USA). Dist: IMS, Polygram

Album: released on GRP (USA), Sep'85 by GRP Records (USA). Dist: IMS, Polygram

Compact disc: released on GRP (USA), Sep'85 by GRP Records (USA). Dist: IMS, Polygram

NIGHT LINES.
Tracks: / Secret place / Night-lines / Kitchen dance / Somewhere between old and New York / Bossa barbeque / Power Wave / Thankful N' thoughtful / Theme from St. Elsewhere / Haunting me.
Notes: Two LP/Compact disc set.'Night lines' is Grammy Award winner Dave Grusin's firststudio albumin two years and it is unlike any previous Dave Grusin album ever recorded.Joining Dave Grusin are vocalist Phoebe Snow,song-writer vocalist Rand Goodrum and saxophonist David Sanborn.Digital Stereo.
Compact disc: released on GRP (USA), Sep'84 by GRP Records (USA). Dist: IMS, Polygram

Album: released on GRP (USA), Sep'84 by GRP Records (USA). Dist: IMS, Polygram

Cassette: released on GRP (USA), Sep'84 by GRP Records (USA). Dist: IMS, Polygram

Compact disc: released on GRP (USA), Sep'84 by GRP Records (USA). Dist: IMS, Polygram

ONE OF A KIND.
Album: released on GRP (USA), Mar'85 by GRP Records (USA). Dist: IMS, Polygram

Cassette: released on GRP (USA), Mar'85 by GRP Records (USA). Dist: IMS, Polygram

OUT OF THE SHADOWS.
Album: released on Arista, Jun'82 by Arista Records. Dist: RCA

Gryce, Gigi

NEW FORMULAS FROM THE JAZZ LAB see Byrd, Donald (Gryce, Gigi & Donald Byrd).

RAT RACE BLUES, THE.
Album: released on New Jazz (USA), Feb'84 by Fantasy Records. Dist: RCA

SIGNALS (Gryce, Gigi/Duke Jordan/Hal Overton).
Album:

Gryphon

MIDNIGHT MUSHRUMPS.
Tracks: / Midnight mushrumps / Ploughboys dream(The) / Last flash of gaberdine tailor (The) / Gulland rock / Dubbel dutch / Ethelion.
Notes: Richard Harvey:recorders(sopranino,descant,treble & tenor),Krumhorns(soprano, alto & tenor),Harmonium,Pipe Organ,Grand Piano,Harpischord,Electric Pianos,Toy Piano,Keyboard Glockenspiel,Mandolin,Vocals. Brian Gulland:Bassoon,Bass krumhorn,Tenor Recorder,All Keyboards on 'Gulland Rock',Vocals,Laugh & Candlestick Rotation. Graeme Taylor:Guitars(acoustic,semi-acoustic,classical,electric & 12-string) Vocals and r a i n c o a t Philip Nestor:Bass Guitars,Vocals. David Oberle:Drums,Timpani,Percussion,Lead Vocals,Headache and Candlestick. Produced by Gryphon.Recorded at The Chipping Norton Recording Studio,OXON.1974.
Album: released on Conifer, Aug'86 by Conifer Records. Dist: Conifer

G&S Festival

GONDOLIERS/RUDDIGORE (G&S Festival Chorus & Orchestra).
Album: released on PRT, Oct'84 by PRT Records. Dist: PRT

Cassette: released on PRT, Oct'84 by PRT Records. Dist: PRT

G-Squad

IN MY MIND/ROOM FULL OF PAPER.
Single (7"): released on SMT, Sep'81
Cat. no: **SMT 007**

GTR

GTR.
Tracks: / When the heart rules the mind / Hunter(The) / Here I wait / Sketches in the sun / Jekyll & Hyde / You can still get through through / Reach out (Never say no) / Toe the line / Hackett to bits / Imagining.
Album: released on Arista, Jul'86 by Arista Records. Dist: RCA

Cassette: released on Arista, Jul'86 by Arista Records. Dist: RCA

Compact disc: released on Arista, Jul'86 by Arista Records. Dist: RCA

WHEN THE HEART RULES THE MIND.
Tracks: / When the heart rules the mind / Reach out(Never say no) / Sketches in the sun / Hackett to bits.
Single (7"): released on Arista, May'86 by Arista Records. Dist: RCA

Single (12"): released on Arista, May'86 by Arista Records. Dist: RCA

Picture disc single: released on Arista, Sep'86 by Arista Records. Dist: RCA

GT'S

BOYS HAVE FEELINGS TOO.
Single (7"): released on Stiff, Feb'80 by Stiff Records. Dist: EMI, Record Services Distribution (Ireland)

Guadalcanal Diary

JAMBOREE.
Tracks: / Pray for rain / Cattle prod / Jamboree / Fear of god / Man hunt / Spirit train / Lonely street / Country club gun / Trouble / Michael rockefeller / Please stop me / See more,I / Dead eyes.
Album: released on Elektra (USA), Jul'86 by Elektra/Asylum/Nonesuch Records. Dist: WEA

Cassette: released on Elektra (USA), Jul'86 by Elektra/Asylum/Nonesuch Records. Dist: WEA

WALKING IN THE SHADOW OF THE BIG MAN.

Album: released on Elektra, Aug'85 by WEA Records. Dist: WEA

Album: released on Hybrid, Feb'85 by Statik Records. Dist: Pinnacle

WATUSI RADIO.
Single (7"): released on Elektra, Aug'85 by WEA Records. Dist: WEA

Guana Batz

CAVE.
Single (7"): released on Big Beat, Apr'84 by Ace Records. Dist: Projection, Pinnacle

HELD DOWN AT LAST.
Album: released on I.D., Jul'85 by I.D. Records. Dist: Revolver, Cartel

I'M ON FIRE.
Tracks: / I'm on fire.
Single (7"): released on I.D., Jun'86 by I.D. Records. Dist: Revolver, Cartel

Single (12"): released on I.D., Jun'86 by I.D. Records. Dist: Revolver, Cartel

LIVE OVER LONDON.
Album: released on I.D., Jun'87 by I.D. Records. Dist: Revolver, Cartel

LOAN SHARKS.
Tracks: / Radio sweetheart.
Single (7"): released on I.D., Dec'86 by I.D. Records. Dist: Revolver, Cartel

LONE SHARKS.
Album: released on I.D., Oct'86 by I.D. Records. Dist: Revolver, Cartel

Cassette: released on I.D., Oct'86 by I.D. Records. Dist: Revolver, Cartel

ROCK THIS TOWN.
Tracks: / Rock this town / Just love me.
Single (7"): released on I.D., 23 May'87 by I.D. Records. Dist: Revolver, Cartel

SEETHROUGH.
Tracks: / Seethrough / Batman(Live) / Side blues.
Single (12"): released on I.D., Feb'86 by I.D. Records. Dist: Revolver, Cartel

YOU'RE SO FINE/ROCKIN' IN MY COFFIN/JUNGLE RUMBLE/GUANA ROCK.
Single (7"): released on Big Beat, Nov'83 by Ace Records. Dist: Projection, Pinnacle

Guaraldi, Vince

FLOWER IS A LOVESOME THING, A (Guaraldi, Vince & Trio).
Album:

Guardian Angel
CRUCIAL LOVING/SPIRIT.
Single (7"): released on Solid Groove, Jul'82
Dist: Jetstar, Pinnacle

Single (12"): released on Solid Groove, Jul'82
Dist: Jetstar, Pinnacle

LOVES ALIVE AND KICKING / WOMAN AT.
Single (12"): released on Cavalis, Oct'80 by
Cavalis. Dist: Cavalis, Pinnacle

Guardian Angels
GUARDIAN ANGELS, THE.
Album: released on Chrysalis, Apr'85 by Chrysalis Records. Dist: CBS

Cassette: released on Chrysalis, Apr'85 by
Chrysalis Records. Dist: CBS

Guards Spectacular
SCARBOROUGH FAIR.
Album: released on Major Richards, Jan'78 by
Major Richards Records. Dist: Taylors

Guarnieri, Johnny
JOHNNY GUARNIERI PLAYS FATS WALLER.
Album: released on Taz Jazz, Jan'79 Dist:
Swift Distribution

SUPERSTRIDE.
Album: released on Taz Jazz, Jan'79 Dist:
Swift Distribution

Gubal
MY LIFE/LIVE DUB.
Single (12"): released on Vision, Aug'82 Dist:
Vision

Guduil
POOT.
Single (12"): released on Backs, Jul'85 by
Backs Records. Dist: Backs, Cartel

Guernica
GUERNICA.
Tracks: / Guernica.
Single (12"): released on Idol, Mar'87 Dist:
Rough Trade, Cartel

Guest Stars
GUEST STARS, THE.
Album: released on Guest Stars, Jul'84 Dist:
WRPM, IMS, Polygram

Cassette: released on Guest Stars, Jul'84 Dist:
WRPM, IMS, Polygram

OUT AT NIGHT.
Tracks: / Montezuma's mother / Miles apart /
Amy's bounce / What means love / Wind is getting angry.(The) / Song of the bridge / Uranus
in jeopardy / Birds of a feather.
Notes: Second album from the all girl band The
Guest Stars who have been touring non- stop
since their debut album release in July '84.Their
first LP received excel-lent reviews and opened
the eyes of various promoters who became
eager to book the band.Their appeal is diverse
offering music from Avant-Garde to Afro-Cuban
F   l.
Personnel:Deidre Cartwright/Laka Daisical/Ruthie Smith/Josefina Cupido/Linda Da Mango.
Album: released on Guest Stars, Dec'85 Dist:
WRPM, IMS, Polygram

Cassette: released on Guest Stars, Dec'85
Dist: WRPM, IMS, Polygram

Guetary, Georges
GEORGES GUETARY.
Album: released on EMI (France), '83 by EMI
Records. Dist: Conifer

Guide to better listening
GUIDE TO BETTER LISTENING (A) Narrators:Peter Goodchild & Caroline Grant.
Album: released on Decca, '79 by Decca Records. Dist: Polygram

Guiding star
COME SING WITH US.
Single (7"): released on Eagle (West Germany), Dec'81 by Bear Family Records. Dist:
Stage One

Guido
I'M ALONE.
Tracks: / I'm alone.
Single (7"): released on ., Mar'87

Guldoni, Jean
CRIME PASSIONNEL Music by Astor Piazzolla/Text by Pierre Philippe.
Album: released on Phonogram (France),
Jul'83

Cassette: released on Phonogram (France),
Page 436

Jul'83

Guilbeau, Gib
TOE TAPPIN' MUSIC.
Album: released on Shiloh, May'79

Guillory, Isaac
SOLO.
Album: released on Graffitti, Jun'86 by Rialto
Records. Dist: Projection

Guillotine
GUILLOTINE Various artists (Various artists).
Album: released on Virgin, Apr'86 by Virgin
Records. Dist: EMI, Virgin Distribution

Guiness album
GUINESS ALBUM OF HITS OF THE 70'S
Various artists (Guiness album of hits of the
70's).
Album: released on CBS, Dec'80 by CBS Records. Dist: CBS

Cassette: released on CBS, Dec'80 by CBS
Records. Dist: CBS

Guinn
GUINN.
Tracks: / Dreamin' / Open your door / Can't live
without you,I / Slow down / Sincerely / People
will be people / Give everything you got for love.
Album: released on Motown, Jun'86 by Motown Records. Dist: BMG Distribution

Cassette: released on Motown, Jun'86 by Motown Records. Dist: BMG Distribution

OPEN YOUR DOOR.
Tracks: / Open your door / Sincerely.
Single (7"): released on Motown, Apr'86 by Motown Records. Dist: BMG Distribution

Single (12"): released on Motown, Apr'86 by
Motown Records. Dist: BMG Distribution

PEOPLE WILL BE PEOPLE.
Tracks: / People will be people / Dreamin'
Single (7"): released on Motown, Jul'86 by Motown Records. Dist: BMG Distribution

Single (12"): released on Motown, Jul'86 by
Motown Records. Dist: BMG Distribution

Guitar...
GUITAR ALBUM Various artists (Various Artists).
Album: released on CBS, Nov'81 by CBS Records. Dist: CBS

Cassette: released on CBS, Nov'81 by CBS
Records. Dist: CBS

GUITAR GENIUS Various artists (Various Artists).
Album: released on Charly, Jul'85 by Charly
Records. Dist: Charly, Cadillac

GUITAR GOLD Various artists (Various Artists).
Album: released on Effects Gold, Nov'80 by
Ronco Records. Dist: Ronco Records

Cassette: released on Effects Gold, Nov'80 by
Ronco Records. Dist: Ronco Records

GUITAR SONGS OF PAPUA NEW GUINEA Played by Blasius To Una Turtavu.
Album: released on Lyrichord, Mar'83 Dist:
Roots

**GUITAR SPECTACULAR Various session
artists (Various Artists).**
Cassette: released on AIM (Budget Cassettes), Feb'83

GUITAR SPECTRUM (Various Artists).
Cassette: released on Pye, Sep'79

**GUITAR STAR Anthology-various artists
(Various Artists).**
Album: released on Red Lightnin', Sep'82 by
Red Lightnin' Records. Dist: Roots, Swift, Jazz
Music, JSU, Pinnacle, Cartel, Wynd-Up Distribution

**GUITAR THE PIANO AND YOU Various
artists (Various Artists).**
Album: released on Cambra, '83 by Cambra
Records. Dist: IDS, Conifer

Cassette: released on Cambra, '83 by Cambra
Records. Dist: IDS, Conifer

GUITAR WARS Various artists (Various Artists).
Album: released on CBS, Feb'83 by CBS Records. Dist: CBS

Guitar and the gun
GUITAR AND THE GUN Various artists.
Album: released on Africagram, Sep'83 by
Cherry Red Records. Dist: Pinnacle

**GUITAR AND THE GUN VOL 2 Various
artists.**
Album: released on Africagram, Jan'85 by
Cherry Red Records. Dist: Pinnacle

Guitar Gable
COOL CALM COLLECTED.
Tracks: / This should go on forever / Goodbye
baby / Life problem / Congo mombo / Have
mercy on me / String bean / Walking in the park
/ Please operator / Mary Lou / No matter who /
Walking with the kings / Irene / Long way from
home / Cool calm collected.
Album: released on Flyright, Oct'86 by Flyright
Records. Dist: Krazy Kat, Swift, Jazz Music

COOL, CALM, COLLECTED.
Album: released on Flyright, May'84 by Flyright
Records. Dist: Krazy Kat, Swift, Jazz Music

Guitar in my hands
GUITAR IN MY HANDS,VOLUME 2 Various artists (Various Artists).
Album: released on Moonshine, Nov'86 Dist:
Projection Distribution

TEXAS BLUES GUITAR 49-66 Various artists.
Album: released on Moonshine, Feb'85 Dist:
Projection Distribution

Guitar Junior
CRAWL, THE.
Album: released on Charly, Mar'84 by Charly
Records. Dist: Charly, Cadillac

Guitar Pete's Axe Attack
DEAD SOLDIER'S REVENGE.
Album: released on Heavy Metal America, '85
by FM-Revolver Records. Dist: EMI

NITEMARE.
Album: released on Homestead, Sep'86 Dist:
Rough Trade, Cartel, Shigaku

Guitars and Drums
BELIEVE IT OR NOT.
Single (12"): released on Guitar Masters, '84
Dist: Guitar Masters

Guitar Slim
BATTLE OF THE BLUES.
Single (7"): released on Ace, Feb'87 by Ace
Records. Dist: Pinnacle, Swift, Hotshot, Cadillac

CAROLINA BLUES.
Album: released on Arhoolie, '81 by Arhoolie
Records. Dist: Projection, Topic, Jazz Music,
Swift, Roots

GREENSBORO ROUNDER.
Notes: MONO Recording.
Album: released on Flyright, Jul'86 by Flyright
Records. Dist: Krazy Kat, Swift, Jazz Music

GREENSBORO' ROUNDER.
Album: released on Flyright, '79 by Flyright
Records. Dist: Krazy Kat, Swift, Jazz Music

RED CADILLAC & CRAZY CHICKS.
Album: released on Sundown, May'86 by Magnum Music Group Ltd. Dist: Magnum Music
Group Ltd, PRT Distribution, Spartan Distribution

THINGS THAT I USED TO DO,THE.
Album: released on Ace(Rare Masters), '84 by
Ace Records. Dist: Pinnacle, Swift, Hotshot

Guitars Unlimited
**GUITARS UNLIMITED   Various artists
(Various Artists).**
Notes: Artists include:Ulf Wakenius/Peter
Almqvist
Album: released on Sonet, Jun'86 by Sonet
Records. Dist: PRT

Album: by Sonet Records. Dist: PRT

Gulda, Friedrich
MUSIC OF OUR TIME.
Double Album: released on MPS Jazz, '81

Gulf Coast Seven
**GULF COAST 7/ORIGINAL JAZZ
HOUNDS 1923/7.**
Album: released on VJM, '79 by Wellard, Chris
Distribution. Dist: Wellard, Chris Distribution

Gulgowski, Wlodek
HOME.
Album: released on Amigo, Jul'87 Dist: Red
Rhino, Cartel

Gullin, Lars
GREAT LARS GULLIN.
Album: released on Dragon, '82 by Dragon
Records. Dist: Jazz Music, Projection, Cadillac

LARS GULLIN VOL.3 1954-55.
Album: released on Dragon, Jul'87 by Dragon
Records. Dist: Jazz Music, Projection, Cadillac

Gullin, Peter
ADVENTURES (Gullin, Peter Quartet).
Album: released on Phontastic, '86 Dist: Wellard, Chris

PETER GULLIN QUARTET, THE (Gullin,
Peter Quartet).
Album: released on Phontastic, Mar'87 Dist:
Wellard, Chris

Gullin, The Great Lars
1955/1956 VOLUME 1.
Notes: With Chet Baker/Dick Twardzik.
Album: released on Dragon, Jun'86 by Dragon
Records. Dist: Jazz Music, Projection, Cadillac

VOLUME 2 1953.
Album: released on Dragon, Jun'86 by Dragon
Records. Dist: Jazz Music, Projection, Cadillac

Gulliver in Lilliput
GULLIVER IN LILLIPUT (Duncan, Frank).
Cassette: released on Pinnacle, '79 by Pinnacle Records. Dist: Pinnacle

Gullivers Travels
GULLIVERS TRAVELS (Hart, Derek).
Cassette: released on Kiddy Kassettes, '77

Cassette: released on Tellastory, '80 by Bartlett Bliss Productions. Dist: PRT Distribution,
Hayward Promotions Distribution, H.R. Taylor
Distribution

Cassette: released on VFM, '85 by VFM Records. Dist: Taylors, Wynd-Up Distribution

Gulyayeu, Yuri
FOLK SONGS.
Cassette: released on Melodiya (USSR),
Feb'79 Dist: T.B.C Distribution

Gumdrop
GUMDROP Biro, Val (Brairs, Richard).
Cassette: released on Times Cassettes, '82 by
Ivan Berg. Dist: Pinnacle

Gun
RACE WITH THE DEVIL.
Single (7"): released on Old Gold, '82 by Old
Gold Records. Dist: Lightning, Jazz Music,
Spartan, Counterpoint

Gun Club
BIRTH,THE DEATH,THE GHOST,THE.
Album: released on ABC, '84 Dist: CBS, Pinnacle

Cassette: released on ABC, '84 Dist: CBS, Pinnacle

DANSE KALINDA BOOM Live in pandoras
box.
Album: released on Road Runner, Dec'85

FIRE OF LOVE.
Notes: Limited Edition of 3000 in Blue Vinyl.
Album: released on New Rose, Jan'86 Dist:
Rough Trade, Cartel

Album: released on Beggars Banquet, '82 by
Beggars Banquet Records. Dist: WEA

Cassette: released on Beggars Banquet, '82 by
Beggars Banquet Records. Dist: WEA

Single (7"): released on Animal, '82 by Chrysalis Records. Dist: Polygram

GHOST ON THE HIGHWAY.
Single (7"): released on Beggars Banquet, '82
by Beggars Banquet Records. Dist: WEA

HOUSE OF HIGHLAND AVENUE.
Single (7"): released on Animal, '83 by Chrysalis Records. Dist: Polygram

Single (12"): released on Animal, '83 by Chrysalis Records. Dist: Polygram

LAS VEGAS STORY.
Album: released on Animal, '84 by Chrysalis
Records. Dist: Polygram

LOVE SUPREME LIVE MATERIAL '82.
Album: released on Eva-Lolita, Nov'85 Dist:
Pinnacle

MIAMI.
Album: released on Animal, '82 by Chrysalis
Records. Dist: Polygram

TWO SIDES OF THE BEAST.
Tracks: / Sex Beat (Live) / Walking with the
beast / Like calling up thunder / Mother of earth
run through the jungle / Eternally is here / Las
Vegas Story, The / Death party (12" version) /
Seven miles with the devil (live) / Bo Diddley's

Postage & Packing

1. **PAYMENT DUE WITHIN 15 DAYS**
2. Payment to be made in Pounds Sterling only.
3. Please return the attached remittance advice with your payment.
4. In the event of any query, please contact the Customer Services Department and quote th

a gunslinger (live) / Preaching blues (live) / Good-bye Johnny (Live) / Going down the red river (Live).
Album: released on Dojo, Apr'86 by Castle Communications Records. Dist: Cartel

Album: released on Dojo, '85 by Castle Communications Records. Dist: Cartel

Gunfire & Piano's
GUNFIRE AND PIANO'S Various artists (Various Artists).
Album: released on Situation 2, Apr'86 Dist: Cartel, Pinnacle

Album: released on Situation 2, Apr'86 Dist: Cartel, Pinnacle

Gung-ho
PLAY TO WIN (ENGLISH VERSION).
Tracks: / Play to win (English version) / Ike Gung-ho.
Single (7"): released on Magnet, May'87 by Magnet Records. Dist: BMG

Single (12"): released on Magnet, May'87 by Magnet Records. Dist: BMG

Gunn, Ben
FERGIE'S FUSILIERS.
Tracks: / Fergie's Fusiliers / Jack Stein tartan, The.
Single (7"): released on Klub, Mar'86

VIVA SCOTLAND.
Single (7"): released on Lismor, '82 by Lismor Records. Dist: Lismor, Roots, Celtic Music

Gunne, Jo Jo
RUN RUN RUN.
Single (7"): released on Asylum, '76 by WEA Records. Dist: WEA

Gunning, Sarah Ogun
GIRL OF CONSTANT SORROW, A.
Album: released on Topic, '81 by Roots Distribution

Gun Shy
JUST TO BE YOUR SECRET.
Tracks: / Just to be your secret / Jumping off the train.
Single (7"): released on MCA, Jul'87 by MCA Records. Dist: Polygram, MCA

Single (12"): released on MCA, Jul'87 by MCA Records. Dist: Polygram, MCA

Guns'n'Roses
APPETITE FOR DEMOLITION.
Album: released on Geffen, Jul'87 by Geffen Records. Dist: WEA, CBS

APPETITE FOR DESTRUCTION.
Tracks: / Welcome to the jungle / It's so easy / Nightrain / Out ta get me / Mr. Brownstone / Paradise city / My Michelle / Think about you / Sweet child o'mine / You're crazy / Anything goes / Rocket queen.
Album: released on Geffen, Aug'87 by Geffen Records. Dist: WEA, CBS

Cassette: released on Geffen, Aug'87 by Geffen Records. Dist: WEA, CBS

IT'S SO EASY.
Tracks: / It's so easy / Mr. Brownstone.
Single (7"): released on Geffen, 20 Jun'87 by Geffen Records. Dist: WEA, CBS

Gunson, David
WHAT GOES UP MIGHT COME DOWN.
Album: released on Big Ben, '82 by Big Ben Records. Dist: Spartan, Taylor, H.R.

Cassette: released on Big Ben, '82 by Big Ben Records. Dist: Spartan, Taylor, H.R.

Gunter, Hardrock
BOOGIE WOOGIE ON A SATURDAY NIGHT.
Album: released on Charly, '84 by Charly Records. Dist: Charly, Cadillac

JUKEBOX HELP ME FIND MY....
Single (7"): released on Rollercoast, '80

Gurdev & Raj
PUNJABI MUNDDA PAAVEY BHAN-GRA.
Tracks: / Kurri jaandi walaiti disco punjabi mundda paavey bhangra / Akhh da ishara maar gidde wich nachie kurri / Gaddi jat di jaandi toor-ran pat di / Saahnun nach ke dakha mutyare (duet) / Dudh vee naku ghee vee naklee (duet) / Veer daivin tun sah nu rabba / Mitran di awaajsun ke (duet) / Nashe di ae laur dooja sohriyan da pind (duet) / Billo waikh ke gulabi mukh tera.
Notes: Music: Kuljit Bhamra.

IRH - 70 South Road, Southall, Middlesex UB1 1RH.
Cassette: released on IRH, Nov'86 by IRH Records. Dist: IRH

Gurdjieff the man
GURDJIEFF THE MAN (Bennett, J.G.).
Cassette: released on Seminar Cassettes, '81 by Seminar Cassettes. Dist: Davidson Distribution, Eastern Educational Products Distrib., Forlaget Systime Distribution, Laser Books Ltd Distribution, MacDougall Distribution, Talktapes Distribution, Watkins Books Ltd Distribution, Norton, Jeff Distribution

Gurkhas,The
GURKHAS,THE.
Album: released on Polyphonic, '83 by Polyphonic Records. Dist: Taylors

Gurney slade
GURNEY SLADE.
Single (7"): released on PRT, '83 by PRT Records. Dist: PRT

Guru Guru
HOT ON SPOT/IN BETWEEN (Guru Guru & Ultrepe).
Album: released on United Dairies, Jun'87 Dist: Rough Trade, Indies

Guru Guru Sun Band
HEY DU.
Album: released on Brain, '80

Gurus Disciples & Ashrams
GURUS DISCIPLES & ASHRAMS (Brent, Peter).
Cassette: released on Seminar Cassettes, '81 by Seminar Cassettes. Dist: Davidson Distribution, Eastern Educational Products Distrib., Forlaget Systime Distribution, Laser Books Ltd Distribution, MacDougall Distribution, Talktapes Distribution, Watkins Books Ltd Distribution, Norton, Jeff Distribution

Guru Wierdbrain
GURU WIERDBRAIN, THE.
Album: released on WEA Ireland, Jul'87 by WEA Records. Dist: Celtic Distributions, Projection, I & B

Cassette: released on WEA Ireland, Jul'87 by WEA Records. Dist: Celtic Distributions, Projection, I & B

Gurvitz, Adrian
CLASSIC.
Single (7"): released on RAK, '82 by RAK. Dist: EMI

CORNER OF LOVE.
Single (7"): released on RAK, '83 by RAK. Dist: EMI

KICK OFF YOUR MUDDY BOOTS.
Album: released on Threshold, '75 by Threshold Records. Dist: Decca Distribution, Polygram Distribution

PALACE SIGN.
Single (7"): released on RAK, '82 by RAK. Dist: EMI

YOUR DREAM.
Single (7"): released on RAK, '82 by RAK. Dist: EMI

G.U.S. Band
BANDOLOGY (G.U.S. Footwear Band).
Album: released on One Up, Jul'88 by EMI Records.

BEST OF BRASS (G.U.S. Footwear Band).
Album: released on Starline, '70 by EMI Records. Dist: EMI

CELEBRATION GOLDEN JUBILEE (G.U.S. Footwear Band).
Album: released on Chandos, Apr'83 by Chandos Records. Dist: Harmonia Mundi, Taylors

Cassette: released on Chandos, Apr'83 by Chandos Records. Dist: Harmonia Mundi, Taylors

GOING HOME (G.U.S. Footwear Band).
Album: released on Studio 2, Jun'75

LAND OF HOPE AND GLORY (G.U.S. Footwear Band).
Album: released on Columbia, '70 by EMI Records. Dist: EMI

QUARTETS FOR BRASS (G.U.S. Band Quartet).
Album: released on Polyphonic, Feb'80 by Polyphonic Records. Dist: Taylors

TRIBUTE TO ERIC BALL, A.
Album: released on Top Brass, Oct'80 by PRT Records. Dist: PRT Distribution

Gussie P
BURIAL DUB.
Album: released on Digikal, Feb'87 by Digikal Records. Dist: Revolver

Gustafsson, Rune
HIMSELF.
Album: released by Sonet Records. Dist: PRT

JUST THE WAY YOU ARE (Gustafsson, Rune & Niels-Henning Orsted-Pederson).
Album: released on Sonet, Oct'81 by Sonet Records. Dist: PRT

SWEETEST SOUNDS, THE (Gustafsson, Rune & Zoot Sims).
Album: released on Sonet, Feb'80 by Sonet Records. Dist: PRT

Gutbucket, Arnold
MARY ROSE (Gutbucket, Arnold & Humphrey Camelfoot).
Single (7"): released on Bucket, Oct'82

Guthrie, Arlo
ALICE'S RESTAURANT.
Album: released by WEA Records. Dist: WEA

ARLO GUTHRIE.
Album: released on Reprise, Jul'74 by WEA Records. Dist: WEA

ARLO GUTHRIE & PETE SEEGER IN CONCERT (Guthrie, Arlo & Pete Seeger).
Double Album: released on Reprise, May'75 by WEA Records. Dist: WEA

HOBO'S LULLABY.
Album: released by WEA Records. Dist: WEA

LAST OF THE BROOKLYN COWBOYS.
Album: released on Reprise, Aug'77 by WEA Records. Dist: WEA

POWER OF LOVE.
Album: released on Warner Brothers, Jul'81 by Warner Bros Records. Dist: WEA

Guthrie, Gwen
AIN'T NOTHING GOIN' ON BUT THE RENT.
Tracks: / Ain't nothing goin' on but the rent / Passions eyes.
Single (7"): released on Boiling Point, Jul'86 by Polydor Records. Dist: Polygram

Single (12"): released on Boiling Point, Jul'86 by Polydor Records. Dist: Polygram

CLOSE TO YOU.
Tracks: / Close to you / You touch my life / Save your love for me.
Single (12"): released on Polydor, Sep'86 by Polydor Records. Dist: Polygram, Polydor

Single (7"): released on Polydor, Sep'86 by Polydor Records. Dist: Polygram, Polydor

FRIENDS AND LOVERS See Gardiner, Boris (Guthrie, Gwen & Boris Gardiner).
Single (7"): released on Creole, Aug'87 by Creole Records. Dist: Rhino, PRT

Single (12"): released on Creole, Aug'87 by Creole Records. Dist: Rhino, PRT

GOOD TO GO LOVER.
Tracks: / Close to you / Outside in the rain / Good to go lover / You touch my life / Ain't nothing goin' on but the rent / I still want you / Stop holding back / Passion eyes.
Notes: Double album.
Album: released on Polydor, Oct'86 by Polydor Records. Dist: Polygram, Polydor

Cassette: released on Polydor, Oct'86 by Polydor Records. Dist: Polygram, Polydor

Compact disc: released on Polydor, Oct'86 by Polydor Records. Dist: Polygram, Polydor

GOOD TO GO LOVER (SINGLE).
Tracks: / Good to go lover / Outside in the rain (US remix).
Single (7"): released on Boiling Point, Feb'87 by Polydor Records. Dist: Polygram

Single (12"): released on Boiling Point, Feb'87 by Polydor Records. Dist: Polygram

JUST FOR YOU.
Album: released on Fourth & Broadway, Apr'87 by Island Records. Dist: Polygram, EMI

Cassette: released on Fourth & Broadway, Apr'87 by Island Records. Dist: Polygram, EMI

Album: released on Fourth & Broadway, Mar'85 by Island Records. Dist: Polygram, EMI

Cassette: released on Fourth & Broadway, Mar'85 by Island Records. Dist: Polygram, EMI

LOVE IN MODERATION.
Single (7"): released on Fourth & Broadway,

Jan'85 by Island Records. Dist: Polygram, EMI

Single (12"): released on Fourth & Broadway, Jan'85 by Island Records. Dist: Polygram, EMI Deleted '97.

OUTSIDE IN THE RAIN.
Tracks: / I still want you.
Single (7"): released on Boiling Point, Nov'86 by Polydor Records. Dist: Polygram

Single (12"): released on Boiling Point, Nov'86 by Polydor Records. Dist: Polygram

PORTRAIT.
Album: released on Island, Aug'83 by Island Records. Dist: Polygram

Cassette: released on Island, Aug'83 by Island Records. Dist: Polygram

SEVENTH HEAVEN.
Tracks: / Seventh heaven / It should have been you / Getting hot.
Notes: Extra track included
Single (7"): released on Fourth & Broadway, Sep'86 by Island Records. Dist: Polygram, EMI

Single (12"): released on Fourth & Broadway, Sep'86 by Island Records. Dist: Polygram, EMI

Guthrie, Gwyneth
WHITE WITCH Spoken Word.
Cassette: released on Colophone, Nov'81 by Audio-Visual Library Services. Dist: Audio-Visual Library Services

Guthrie, Woody
POOR BOY.
Album: released on Transatlantic, Oct'81 by Logo Records. Dist: Roots Distribution, RCA Distribution

SONGS FROM BOUND TO GLORY.
Album: released on Warner Brothers, Jun'77 by Warner Bros Records. Dist: WEA

TRIBUTE TO WOODIE GUTHRIE, A Various artists (Various Artists).
Album: released by CBS Records. Dist: CBS

WOODY GUTHRIE.
Album: released on Pye, '79

Guy, Barry
APPLICATION, INTERACTION AND... (see Stevens, John) (Guy, Barry/John Stevens/Trevor Watts).

ENDGAME (Guy, Barry & Howard Riley & John Stevens & Trevor Watts).
Album: released on Japo, Nov'79 by ECM (Germany). Dist: IMS, Polygram

ISKRA 1903 (see under Rutherford, Paul) (Guy, Barry/Paul Rutherford/Derek Bailey).

NO FEAR (see Stevens, John) (Guy, Barry/John Stevens/Trevor Watts).

ODE TO JAZZ ORCHESTRA (Guy, Barry & The London Jazz Comp Orchestra).
Double Album: released on Incus, Nov'79 Dist: Jazz Music, Cadillac

SOLO BRASS IMPROVISATIONS.
Album: released on Incus, Nov'76 Dist: Jazz Music, Cadillac

Guy, Buddy
BREAKING OUT.
Album: released on JSP, Mar'84 by JSP Records. Dist: Swift, Projection

BUDDY GUY.
Album: released on Chess(USA), Apr'83 by Sugar Hill (USA). Dist: PRT, Swift

CHESS MASTERS.
Album: released on Chess, Jan'87 by Charly Records. Dist: Charly, Swift, PRT, Discovery, IMS, Polygram

Cassette: released on Chess, Jan'87 by Charly Records. Dist: Charly, Swift, PRT, Discovery, IMS, Polygram

COMPLETE D.J. PLAY MY BLUES, THE.
Compact disc: released on JSP, Jun'87 by JSP Records. Dist: Swift, Projection

DJ PLAY MY BLUES.
Album: released on JSP, Oct'82 by JSP Records. Dist: Swift, Projection

DOLLAR DONE FELL, THE.
Album: released on JSP, Jan'82 by JSP Records. Dist: Swift, Projection

DRINKING TNT AND SMOKING DYNAMITE (Guy, Buddy & Junior Wells).
Album: released on Sonet, Jul'84 by Sonet Records. Dist: PRT

DRINKIN' TNT AND SMOKIN DYNAMITE (Guy, Buddy/Junior Wells & others).
Tracks: / Ah'w baby / Everything gonna be al-

right / How can one woman be so mean / Checking on my baby / When you see the little tears from my eyes / My younger days.
Album: released on Red Lightnin', Sep'82 by Red Lightnin' Records. Dist: Roots, Swift, Jazz Music, JSU, Pinnacle, Cartel, Wynd-Up Distribution

GOT TO USE YOUR HOUSE.
Album: released on Blues Ball, Sep'79 Dist: Swift

HOT AND COOL.
Album: released on Vanguard, Apr'78 by PRT Records. Dist: PRT

IN THE BEGINNING.
Album: released on Red Lightnin', Sep'82 by Red Lightnin' Records. Dist: Roots, Swift, Jazz Music, JSU, Pinnacle, Cartel, Wynd-Up Distribution

I WAS WALKING THROUGH THE WOODS.
Album: released on Chess, Oct'86 by Charly Records. Dist: Charly, Swift, PRT, Discovery, IMS, Polygram

LIVE AT CHICAGO 1979.
Tracks: / Buddy's blues parts 1 & 2 / I've got a right to love my woman / Tell me what's inside of you (2 versions) / Done gone over you / Things I used to do, The / You don't know how I feel / Dollar done sell, The / Don't answer the door.
Compact disc: released on JSP, Dec'86 by JSP Records. Dist: Swift, Projection

LIVE AT THE CHECKERBOARD LOUNGE 1979.
Compact disc: released on JSP, Sep'86 by JSP Records. Dist: Swift, Projection

ORIGINAL BLUES BROTHERS - LIVE (Guy, Buddy & Junior Wells).
Album: released on Blue Moon, Sep'83 Dist: Magnum Music Group Ltd, PRT, Spartan

TEN BLUE FINGERS.
Album: released on JSP, Feb'85 by JSP Records. Dist: Swift, Projection

Guy, Phil

BAD LUCK BOY (Guy, Phil & Buddy Guy).
Album: released on JSP, Aug'83 by JSP Records. Dist: Swift, Projection

IT'S A REAL MUTHA FUCKA.
Album: released on JSP, Sep'85 by JSP Records. Dist: Swift, Projection

PHIL GUY (Guy, Phil & Buddy Guy).
Album: released on JSP, Aug'82 by JSP Records. Dist: Swift, Projection

Guy, Philip

TOUGH GUY (Guy, Philip & The Chicago Machine).
Tracks: / Inlation / You made your move too soon / Frosty / She's fine / Like ice around my heart / Feeling sexy / Chicken shack / Down home blues.
Album: released on Red Lightnin', Jan'87 by Red Lightnin' Records. Dist: Roots, Swift, Jazz Music, JSU, Pinnacle, Cartel, Wynd-Up Distribution

Guys & Dolls

BEST OF GUYS & DOLLS, THE.
Album: released on Spot, Feb'84 by Pickwick Records. Dist: H.R. Taylor, Lugtons

Cassette: released on Spot, Feb'84 by Pickwick Records. Dist: H.R. Taylor, Lugtons

BREAKOUT.
Single (7"): released on Moon, Jul'83 by Moon Records. Dist: PRT Distribution

FREEZE.
Single (7"): released on Moon, Nov'83 by Moon Records. Dist: PRT Distribution

GUYS AND DOLLS Original Broadway Cast (Various Artists).
Album: released on Hallmark, Sep'86 by Pickwick Records. Dist: Pickwick Distribution, PRT, Taylors

Cassette: released on Hallmark, Sep'86 by Pickwick Records. Dist: Pickwick Distribution, PRT, Taylors

GUYS AND DOLLS Original cast.
Album: released on MCA, Mar'82 by MCA Records. Dist: Polygram, MCA

Cassette: released on MCA, Mar'82 by MCA Records. Dist: Polygram, MCA

Album: released on Chrysalis, May'82 by Chrysalis Records. Dist: CBS

Cassette: released on Chrysalis, May'82 by Chrysalis Records. Dist: CBS

Album: released on Reprise, Aug'81 by WEA Records. Dist: WEA

SPOTLIGHT ON GUYS & DOLLS.
Double Album: released on PRT, Oct'81 by PRT Records. Dist: PRT

Double cassette: released on PRT, Oct'81 by PRT Records. Dist: PRT

THERE'S A WHOLE LOT OF LOVING.
Single (7"): released on Magnet, Sep'81 by Magnet Records. Dist: BMG

Guys With Soul

GUYS WITH SOUL Various artists (Various Artists).
Album: released on Stax, Sep'81 by Ace Records. Dist: Pinnacle, Chris Wellard, IMS-Polygram

Cassette: released on Stax, Sep'81 by Ace Records. Dist: Pinnacle, Chris Wellard, IMS-Polygram

Gwalia Male Choir

TRAVELLING.
Tracks: / Yankee Doddle / Rose of Tralee / Marching song / Nant Y Myndd / Stodole Pumpa / Erisk-ay love lilt, The / Heimat / Long day closes, The / Down among the dead men / Chocoloza / Das Morgenrot / La Vergine / Silver birch, The / Steal away / Nos a bore / Calm is the sea / Nava Nagila.
Notes: Bob Barratt/Pianist Gwawr Owen/. Conductor: Wendy Halden:
Album: released on Grasmere, Nov'86 by Grasmere Records. Dist: EMI

Cassette: released on Grasmere, Nov'86 by Grasmere Records. Dist: EMI

Gwendal

GWENDAL.
Double Album: released on Pathe Marconi-France), Jan'85

Cassette:

Gwillan's Harp

GWILLAN'S HARP Ursuala K LeGuin Spoken word.
Album: released on Caedmon(USA), Jan'78 by Caedmon (USA) Records. Dist: Gower, Taylors, Discovery

Cassette: released on Caedmon(USA), Jan'78 by Caedmon (USA) Records. Dist: Gower, Taylors, Discovery

Gymslips

48 CRASH.
Single (7"): released on Abstract, Oct'82 by Abstract. Dist: Pinnacle

BIG SISTER.
Single (7"): released on Abstract, Jan'83 by Abstract. Dist: Pinnacle

EVIL EYE.
Single (7"): released on Abstract, Apr'85 by Abstract. Dist: Pinnacle

Single (12"): released on Abstract, Apr'85 by Abstract. Dist: Pinnacle

ROBOT MAN.
Single (7"): released on Abstract, Jul'83 by Abstract. Dist: Pinnacle

Gynaecologists

RED PULLOVER.
Single (7"): released on Teesbeat, Sep'81 by Smellytapes. Dist: Red Rhino Distribution, Indies Distribution, Self Distribution, Bullet Distribution

Gyngell, Denise

YOU BROKE MY HEART IN 17 PLACES.
Single (7"): released on Loose End, Jun'84 by MCA Records. Dist: CBS, MCA

Single (12"): released on Loose End, Jun'84 by MCA Records. Dist: CBS, MCA

Gypsy...

GYPSY BARON Various artists (Various Artists).
Album: released on Teldec (Germany), Jun'81 by Import Records. Dist: IMS Distribution, Polygram Distribution

Cassette: released on Teldec (Germany), Jun'81 by Import Records. Dist: IMS Distribution, Polygram Distribution

GYPSY GUITAR GENIUS Various artists (Various Artists).
Album: released on Topline, Jul'85 by Charly Records. Dist: Charly Distribution

Cassette: released on Topline, Jul'85 by Charly Records. Dist: Charly Distribution

GYPSY VIOLIN SUMMIT Various artists (Various Artists).
Album: released on MPS Jazz, May'81

I'M A WINNER (Gypsy & Freddie Perez).
Single (7"): released on Personal, Mar'85 by Personal Records. Dist: PRT

SINKING SHIP, THE.
Tracks: / Sinking ship, The / On the park way.
Single (12"): released on Hot Vinyl, Aug'86 by Hot Vinyl Records. Dist: Jetstar

Gyrations...

GYRATIONS ACROSS THE NATIONS Various artists (Various Artists).
Album: released on Hybrid, Oct'85 by Statik Records. Dist: Pinnacle

GYRATIONS ACROSS THE NATIONS VOL.2 Various artists (Various Artists).
Album: released on Hybrid, Feb'86 by Statik Records. Dist: Pinnacle

Gyro

CENTRAL DETENTION CENTRE.
Single (7"): released on Rabid, Sep'82 by Rabid Records. Dist: Pinnacle, Rough Trade

H

H2O

ALL THAT GLITTERS.
Single (7"): released on RCA, Oct'83 by RCA Records. Dist: RCA, Roots, Swift, Wellard, Chris, I & B, Solomon & Peres Distribution

Single (12"): released on RCA, Oct'83 by RCA Records. Dist: RCA, Roots, Swift, Wellard, Chris, I & B, Solomon & Peres Distribution

BLUE DIAMOND.
Tracks: / Hip corporation / Blue diamond / Blue diamond / Go on / I fought the law.
Notes: I fought the law is an extra track only available on 12" version
Single (7"): released on Legend, Feb'87 by Legend Records. Dist: EMI, Legend Distribution, Island

Single (12"): released on Legend, Feb'87 by Legend Records. Dist: EMI, Legend Distribution, Island

Compact disc single: released on Island, May'87 by Island Records. Dist: Polygram

FAITH.
Album: released on RCA, Jun'84 by RCA Records. Dist: RCA, Roots, Swift, Wellard, Chris, I & B, Solomon & Peres Distribution

Cassette: released on RCA, Jun'84 by RCA Records. Dist: RCA, Roots, Swift, Wellard, Chris, I & B, Solomon & Peres Distribution

I DREAM TO SLEEP.
Single (7"): released on RCA, Apr'83 by RCA Records. Dist: RCA, Roots, Swift, Wellard, Chris, I & B, Solomon & Peres Distribution

Single (12"): released on RCA, Apr'83 by RCA Records. Dist: RCA, Roots, Swift, Wellard, Chris, I & B, Solomon & Peres Distribution

JUST OUTSIDE OF HEAVEN.
Single (7"): released on RCA, Jul'83 by RCA Records. Dist: RCA, Roots, Swift, Wellard, Chris, I & B, Solomon & Peres Distribution

Single (12"): released on RCA, Jul'83 by RCA Records. Dist: RCA, Roots, Swift, Wellard, Chris, I & B, Solomon & Peres Distribution

Picture disc single: released on RCA, Aug'83 by RCA Records. Dist: RCA, Roots, Swift, Wellard, Chris, I & B, Solomon & Peres Distribution

WHO'LL STOP THE RAIN?.
Single (7"): released on RCA, May'84 by RCA Records. Dist: RCA, Roots, Swift, Wellard, Chris, I & B, Solomon & Peres Distribution

Single (12"): released on RCA, May'84 by RCA Records. Dist: RCA, Roots, Swift, Wellard, Chris, I & B, Solomon & Peres Distribution

YOU TAKE MY BREATH AWAY.
Single (7"): released on RCA, Dec'84 by RCA Records. Dist: RCA, Roots, Swift, Wellard, Chris, I & B, Solomon & Peres Distribution

Single (12"): released on RCA, Dec'84 by RCA Records. Dist: RCA, Roots, Swift, Wellard, Chris, I & B, Solomon & Peres Distribution

Habichuela, Pepe

A MANDELI.
Tracks: / Resuene / Al aire / El dron / Guadiana / Del cerro / Mi tierra / Boabdil / A mandeli / Mandeli, A.
Notes: Pepe Habichuela was born into a renowned flamenco family in 1944, and has now become the leading new guitarist in Spain, forging new directions in flamenco while securing his position as the leading virtuoso of this glorious tradional form.

Album: released on Hannibal, '84 by Hannibal Records. Dist: Charly, Harmonia Mundi, Projection, Celtic Music, Swing

Hackberry Ramblers

LOUISIANA CAJUN MUSIC.
Album: released on Arhoolie, May'81 by Arhoolie Records. Dist: Projection, Topic, Jazz Music, Swift, Roots

HACKER ILK.

Notes: Six studies in English folk song.
Album: released on Nato (France), Sep'86 by Disques Nato. Dist: Essex Record Distributors Ltd.

Hacker, Marilyn

POETRY AND VOICE OF MARILYN HACKER.
Album: released on Caedmon(USA), Nov'76 by Caedmon (USA) Records. Dist: Gower, Taylors, Discovery

Hackett, Bobby

AT NICK'S 1944 (Hackett, Bobby & His Orchestra).
Album: released on Commodore Classics, '87 by Teldec Records (Germany). Dist: Conifer, IMS, Polygram

BOBBY HACKETT & HIS ORCHESTRA 1943 (Hackett, Bobby & His Orchestra).
Notes: Mono.
Album: released on Jazzology, Jun'86 Dist: Jazz Music, Swift

BOBBY SEXTET HACKETT'S (Hackett, Bobby Sextet).
Notes: Featuring Bob Wilber, Urbie Green, Dave McKenna
Album: released on Storyville, May'86 by Storyville Records. Dist: Jazz Music Distribution, Swift Distribution, Chris Wellard Distribution, Counterpoint Distribution

BUTTERFLIES AIRS.
Album: released on Honeydew, Oct'79 Dist: Swift, JSU

IN A MELLOW MOOD.
Album: released on Capitol (France), Oct'84 by Capitol Records. Dist: Conifer

Cassette: released on Capitol (France), Oct'84 by Capitol Records. Dist: Conifer

JACK TEAGARDEN & BOBBY HACKETT ALL STARS 1963 (Hackett, Bobby & Jack Teagarden).
Album: released on Shoestring, Apr'79 by Shoestring Records. Dist: Shoestring

JAM SESSION (see Condon, Eddie).

JAZZ ULTIMATE (Hackett, Bobby & Jack Teagarden).
Tracks: / Indiana (Come back home in Indiana) / Oh baby / It's wonderful / I found a new baby / Sunday / Baby, won't you please come home / Everybody loves my baby / Mama's gone, good bye / Way down yonder in new orleans / 55th and Broadway / 'S wonderful.
Notes: From 'S Wonderful by the ever popular George and Ira Gershwin to '55th and Broadway' - a Hackett/Teagarden original. This album forms a very good Capitol jazz LP in the Dixieland vein.
Album: released on Capitol, Jan'86 by Capitol Records. Dist: EMI

Cassette: released on Capitol, Jan'86 by Capitol Records. Dist: EMI

JULY 25TH, 1960.
Album: released on From The Jazz Vault, Oct'80 by Damont Records. Dist: Swift, Taylor, H.R.

LIVE AT THE ROOSEVELT GRILL-MELODY IS A MUST.
Album: released on Phontastic, May'86 Dist: Wellard, Chris

LIVE FROM MANASSAS (Hackett, Bobby, Vic Dickenson, Maxine Sullivan).
Album: released on Jazzology, Feb'87 Dist: Jazz Music, Swift

LIVE FROM THE VOYAGER ROOM - VOL.2.
Album: released on Shoestring, Apr'81 by Shoestring Records. Dist: Shoestring

LIVE FROM THE VOYAGER ROOM (Hackett, Bobby & His Jazz Band).
Album: released on Shoestring, Apr'81 by

Shoestring Records. Dist: Shoestring

MELODY IS A MUST VOL. 2 Live at the Roosevelt Grill.
Album: released on Phontastic, Mar'87 Dist: Wellard, Chris

Hackett, Rene

NOTHING/ARMOUR.
Single (7"): released on 4AD, Oct'81 by 4AD Records. Dist: Rough Trade

Hackett, Steve

BAY OF KINGS.
Album: released on Lamborghini, Nov'83 by Lamborghini Records. Dist: PRT

Cassette: released on Lamborghini, Nov'83 by Lamborghini Records. Dist: PRT

CURED.
Album: released on Charisma, Mar'84 by Virgin Records. Dist: EMI

Cassette: released on Charisma, Mar'84 by Virgin Records. Dist: EMI

DEFECTOR.
Album: released on Charisma, Mar'83 by Virgin Records. Dist: EMI

Cassette: released on Charisma, Mar'83 by Virgin Records. Dist: EMI

DOLL THAT'S MADE IN JAPAN.
Single (7"): released on Lamborghini, Aug'84 by Lamborghini Records. Dist: PRT

Single (12"): released on Lamborghini, Aug'84 by Lamborghini Records. Dist: PRT

PLEASE DON'T TOUCH.
Album: released on Charisma, Sep'83 by Virgin Records. Dist: EMI

SPECIAL MORNINGS.
Album: released on Charisma, Sep'83 by Virgin Records. Dist: EMI

TILL WE HAVE FACES.
Tracks: / Let me count the ways / Doll that's made in Japan, A / Myopia / What's my name / Rio connection, The / Taking the easy way out / When you wish upon a star / Duel / Matilda Smith-Williams' home for the aged.

Compact disc: released on Lamborghini, Oct'84 by Lamborghini Records. Dist: PRT

Album: released on Lamborghini, Sep'84 by Lamborghini Records. Dist: PRT

Cassette: released on Lamborghini, Sep'84 by Lamborghini Records. Dist: PRT

VOYAGE OF THE ACOLYTE.
Tracks: / Ace of wands / Hands of the priestess, Part 1 / Tower struck down, A / Hands of the priestess, Part 2 / Hermit, The / Star of Sirius / Lovers, The / Shadow of the Hierophant.
Notes: Originally released October 1975
Album: released on Charisma, Oct'86 by Virgin Records. Dist: EMI

VOYAGE OF THE ACOLYTE/PLEASE DON'T TOUCH.
Double cassette: released on Charisma, Mar'83 by Virgin Records. Dist: EMI

Hackney Five-0

BETWEEN THE FLOORS.
Album: released on Midnight Music, Apr'86 by Midnight Music Records. Dist: Rough Trade Distribution, Cartel Distribution

CATALOGUE (OF TROUBLE AND THE BLUES).
Tracks: / Catalogue (of trouble and the blues) / Gorilla / Dalston (express version) / I'm so lonesome I could cry.
Single (12"): released on Midnight Music, Feb'86 by Midnight Music Records. Dist: Rough Trade Distribution, Cartel Distribution

Hadden, Rothfield & Carr

WHEN THESE SHOES WERE NEW.
Album: released on Lismor, Jun'85 by Lismor Records. Dist: Lismor, Roots, Celtic Music

Cassette: released on Lismor, Jun'85 by Lismor Records. Dist: Lismor, Roots, Celtic Music

Haden

FOLK SONGS (Haden/ Garbarek/ Gismonti).
Album: released on ECM (Import), Apr'81 by ECM Records. Dist: IMS, Polygram, Virgin through EMI

Haden, Charlie

AS LONG AS THERE'S MUSIC (Haden, Charlie/ Hampton Hawes).
Album: released on Music-Projection, May'81

BALLAD OF THE FALLEN.
Tracks: / El Segadors / If you want to write to me / Ballad of the fallen / Grandola vila morena / Introduction to people / People united will never be defeated / Silence / Too late / La pasionara / La santa espina.
Notes: Digital stereo. For their 1982 tour and the recording of this album, Charlie Haden reassembled the Liberation Music Orchestra maintaining the tradition of political jazz initiated in the late sixties. Despite it's political statement this is a highly listenable album of music based around popular latin folk and political songs.
Compact disc: released on ECM (Germany), Sep'84 by ECM Records. Dist: IMS, Polygram, Virgin through EMI

BALLAD OF THE FALLEN, THE.
Album: released on ECM (Germany), Oct'83 by ECM Records. Dist: IMS, Polygram, Virgin through EMI

CLOSENESS.
Album: released on Horizon, Nov'76 by A&M Records. Dist: CBS

GOLDEN NUMBER, THE.
Album: released on Horizon, Jan'78 by A&M Records. Dist: CBS

LIBERATION MUSIC ORCHESTRA.
Album: released on Jasmine, Aug'82 by Jasmine Records. Dist: Counterpoint, Lugtons, Taylor, H.R., Wellard, Chris, Swift, Cadillac

Cassette: released on Jasmine, Aug'82 by Jasmine Records. Dist: Counterpoint, Lugtons, Taylor, H.R., Wellard, Chris, Swift, Cadillac

QUARTET WEST.
Album: released on Verve (Germany), Aug'87

Cassette: released on Verve (Germany), Aug'87

Compact disc: released on Verve (Germany), Aug'87

Haden, Charlie Quartet West

CHARLIE HADEN QUARTET WEST.
Album: released on Verve (USA), Aug'87 by Polydor. Dist: Polygram

Cassette: released on Verve (USA), Aug'87 by Polydor. Dist: Polygram

Compact disc: released on Verve (USA), Aug'87 by Polydor. Dist: Polygram

Hades

RESISTING SUCCESS.
Album: released on Roadrunner, Aug'87 by Roadrunner Records (Germany). Dist: Pinnacle

Hadley, Bob

RAVEN.
Album: released on Kicking Mule, Jan'79 by Sonet. Dist: Roots, PRT-Pye Distribution

TUNES FROM THE WELL.
Album: released on Kicking Mule, Jan'78 by Sonet. Dist: Roots, PRT-Pye Distribution

Haeffner, Nick

GREAT INDOORS.
Album: released on Bam Caruso, May'87 by Bam Caruso Records. Dist: Rough Trade, Revolver, Cartel

MASTER, THE.
Tracks: / Master, The.
Single (12"): released on Bam Caruso, Jun'86 by Bam Caruso Records. Dist: Rough Trade, Revolver, Cartel

Haefner, Nick

BACK IN TIME FOR TEA.
Tracks: / Mean guitar / Every time you say goodbye.
Single (12"): released on Bam Caruso, Jan'87 by Bam Caruso Records. Dist: Rough Trade, Revolver, Cartel

Hafler Trio

BANG AN OPEN LETTER.
Album: released on Double Vision, Jun'84 by Double Vision Records. Dist: Rough Trade, Cartel

SEA ORGANISATION, THE.
Tracks: / Sea organisation, The.
Single 10": released on Touch, Nov'86 by Touch Records. Dist: Rough Trade, Cartel

THREE WAYS OF SAYING TWO THE NETHERLAND LECTURES.
Album: released on Charm, Sep'86 Dist: Jetstar

Hagar

THROUGH THE FIRE (Hagar, Schon, Aaronson, Shrieve).
Album: released on Geffen, May'84 by Geffen Records. Dist: WEA, CBS

Hagar, Sammy

COLLECTION: SAMMY HAGAR.
Album: released on EMI (Germany), Jan'83 by EMI Records. Dist: Conifer

GIVE TO LIVE.
Tracks: / When the hammer falls.
Single (7"): released on Geffen, Aug'87 by Geffen Records. Dist: WEA, CBS

Single (12"): released on Geffen, Aug'87 by Geffen Records. Dist: WEA, CBS

LOOKING BACK.
Tracks: / I'll fall in love again / There's only one way to rock / Heavy metal / Remember the heros / Baby's on fire / Three lock box / Two sides of love / I can't drive 55 / I don't need love / Voa.
Album: released on Geffen, Jan'87 by Geffen Records. Dist: WEA, CBS

Cassette: released on Geffen, Jan'87 by Geffen Records. Dist: WEA, CBS

NINE ON A TEN SCALE.
Album: released on Fame, May'83 by Music For Pleasure Records. Dist: EMI

Cassette: released on Fame, May'83 by Music For Pleasure Records. Dist: EMI

SAMMY HAGAR.
Tracks: / When the hammer falls / Hands and knees / Give to live / Boy's night out / Returning home / Standin' at the same old crossroads / Privacy / Back into you / Eagles fly / What they gonna say now.
Album: released on Geffen, Jul'87 by Geffen Records. Dist: WEA, CBS

Cassette: released on Geffen, Jul'87 by Geffen Records. Dist: WEA, CBS

Compact disc: released on Geffen, Jul'87 by Geffen Records. Dist: WEA, CBS

STANDING HAMPTON.
Tracks: / There's only one way to rock / Baby's on fire / Can't get loose / I'll fall in love again / Baby's on fire / Can't get loose / I'll fall in love again / Heavy metal / Baby its' you / Surrender / Inside lookin' in / Sweet hitchhiker / Piece of my heart.
Album: released on Geffen, Sep'86 by Geffen Records. Dist: WEA, CBS

Cassette: released on Geffen, Sep'86 by Geffen Records. Dist: WEA, CBS

STREET MACHINE.
Tracks: / Never say die / This planet's on fire (burn to hell) / Wounded in love / Falling in love / Growing pains / Child to man / Trans am (Highway wonderland) / Feels like love / Plain Jane.
Album: released on Revolver, Mar'87 by Revolver Records. Dist: Revolver, Cartel

Album: released on Revolver, Jun'86 by Revolver Records. Dist: Revolver, Cartel

THREE LOCK BOX.
Tracks: / Three lock box / Remote love / Remember the heroes / Your love is driving me crazy / In the rrom / Rise of the animal / I wouldn't change a thing / Growing up / Never give up / I don't need love.
Album: released on Geffen, Sep'86 by Geffen Records. Dist: WEA, CBS

Cassette: released on Geffen, Sep'86 by Geffen Records. Dist: WEA, CBS

Album: released on Geffen, Dec'82 by Geffen Records. Dist: WEA, CBS

Cassette: released on Geffen, Dec'82 by Geffen Records. Dist: WEA, CBS

TWO SIDES OF LOVE.
Single (7"): released on Geffen, Aug'84 by Geffen Records. Dist: WEA, CBS

VOA.
Tracks: / I can't drive / Swept away / Rock is in my blood / Two sides of love / Dick in the dirt / Voa / Don't make me wait / Burnin' down the city.
Album: released on Geffen, Sep'86 by Geffen Records. Dist: WEA, CBS

Cassette: released on Geffen, Sep'86 by Geffen Records. Dist: WEA, CBS

WINNER TAKES IT ALL (THE).
Tracks: / Winner takes it all (The) / Fight (The).
Single (7"): released on CBS, Apr'87 by CBS Records. Dist: CBS

YOUR LOVE IS DRIVING ME MAD.
Single (7"): released on Geffen, Jan'83 by Geffen Records. Dist: WEA, CBS

Hagar The Womb

FUNNERY IN A NUNNERY.
Single (12"): released on Abstract, Feb'85 by Abstract. Dist: Pinnacle

WORD OF THE WOMB (EP).
Single (12"): released on Mortarhate, Jan'84 by Dorane Ltd.

Hagen, Nina

ZARAH.
Single (7"): released on CBS, Feb'84 by CBS Records. Dist: CBS

Haggard, H Rider

KING SOLOMON'S MINES.
Cassette: released on Argo, Nov'84 by Decca Records. Dist: Polygram

Haggard, Merle

AMBER WAVES OF GRAIN.
Tracks: / Amber waves of grain / Tulare dust / Mama tried the farmer's daughter / Okie from Muskogee's coming home (The) / I wish things were simple / Working man's blues / Always late with your kisses / American waltz.
Album: released on Epic, May'86 by CBS Records. Dist: CBS

Cassette: released on Epic, May'86 by CBS Records. Dist: CBS

AT THE COUNTRY STORE.
Album: released on Country Store, Dec'85 by Starblend Records. Dist: PRT, Prism Leisure Corporation Records

Cassette: released on Country Store, Dec'85 by Starblend Records. Dist: PRT, Prism Leisure Corporation Records

BEST OF MERLE HAGGARD.
Compact disc: released on Capitol, Mar'87 by Capitol Records. Dist: EMI

BRANDED MAN.
Album: released on Capitol, Apr'85 by Capitol Records. Dist: EMI

Cassette: released on Capitol, Apr'85 by Capitol Records. Dist: EMI

CAPITOL COUNTRY CLASSICS.
Album: released on Capitol, Jan'80 by Capitol Records. Dist: EMI

Cassette: released on Capitol, Jan'80 by Capitol Records. Dist: EMI

EPIC COLLECTION (RECORDED LIVE).
Album: released on Epic, Jan'84 by CBS Records. Dist: CBS

Cassette: released on Epic, Jan'84 by CBS Records. Dist: CBS

FRIEND OF CALIFORNIA, A.
Album: released on CBS(Import), Sep'86 by CBS Records. Dist: Conifer, Discovery, Swift

Cassette: released on CBS, Sep'86 by CBS Records. Dist: CBS

GOING WHERE THE LONELY GO.
Album: released on Epic, Dec'82 by CBS Records. Dist: CBS

GREATEST HITS:MERLE HAGGARD.
Tracks: / I think I'll just stay here and drink / I'm always on a mountain when I fall / Red bandana / Way I am (The) / It's been a great afternoon / Ramblin' fever / Misery and gin / My own kind of hat / If were not back in love by Monday / Rainbow stew.
Album: released on MCA Import, Mar'86 by MCA Records. Dist: Polygram, IMS

HEART TO HEART (Haggard, Merle & Leona Williams).
Album: released on Mercury, Aug'83 by Phonogram Records. Dist: Polygram Distribution

Cassette: released on Mercury, Aug'83 by Phonogram Records. Dist: Polygram Distribution

I'M A LONESOME FUGITIVE.
Album: released on See For Miles, Sep'86 by See For Miles Records. Dist: Pinnacle

KERN RIVER.
Cassette: released on Epic, May'85 by CBS Records. Dist: CBS

MERLE HAGGARD I love country.
Tracks: / Place to fall apart, A / Place to fall apart, A.
Album: released on CBS, Sep'86 by CBS Records. Dist: CBS

MERLE HAGGARD SINGS COUNTRY FAVOURITES.
Tracks: / She thinks I still care / Mom and dad's waltz / Makin' believe / Moanin' the blues / Lovesick blues / Blues stay away from me / You've still got a place in my heart / Right or wrong / Mule skinner blues / Green green grass of home / Folsom prison blues / Walking the floor over you / Son of Hickory Holler's tramp, The / Long black limousine / San Antonio Rose / Take me back to Tulsa / Waiting for a train / This cold war / Little ole wine drinker me / Today I started loving you again.
Album: released on Capitol, May'87 by Capitol Records. Dist: EMI

Cassette: released on Capitol, May'87 by Capitol Records. Dist: EMI

MY FAREWELL TO ELVIS.
Album: released on MCA Import, Mar'86 by MCA Records. Dist: Polygram, IMS

PONCHO AND LEFTY.
Album: released on Epic, Feb'83 by CBS Records. Dist: CBS

RAINBOW STEW.
Cassette: released on MCA, Mar'82 by MCA Records. Dist: Polygram, MCA

SERVING 190 PROOF.
Album: released on MCA, Aug'81 by MCA Records. Dist: Polygram, MCA

Cassette: released on MCA, Aug'81 by MCA Records. Dist: Polygram, MCA

SONGS FOR THE MAMA THAT TRIED.
Tracks: / When God comes and gathers his jewels / Supper time / He walks with me / Softly and tenderly / Why me / Where no one stands alone / One day at a time / What a friend we have in Jesus / Swing low sweet chariot / Old rugged cross (The) / Keep on the sunny side.
Album: released on MCA Import, Mar'86 by MCA Records. Dist: Polygram, IMS

SONGWRITER.
Tracks: / Footlights / It's been a great afternoon / My own kind of hat / Life's just not the way it used to be / I think I'll just stay here and drink / Ramblin' fever / Make-up and faded blue jeans / Red bandana / From Graceland to the promise land / Rainbow stew.
Album: released on MCA Import, Mar'86 by MCA Records. Dist: Polygram, IMS

SWINGING DOOR.
Tracks: / Swinging doors / If I could be him / Longer you wait (The) / I'll look over you / I can't stand me / Girl turned ripe (The) / Bottle let me down (The) / No more you and me / Someone else you've known / High on a hilltop / This towns not big enough / Shade tree.
Album: released on See For Miles, Jun'86 by See For Miles Records. Dist: Pinnacle

TASTE OF YESTERDAY'S WINE, A (Haggard, Merle & George Jones).
Album: released on Epic, Oct'82 by CBS Records. Dist: CBS

Cassette: released on Epic, Oct'82 by CBS Records. Dist: CBS

Album: released on Hallmark, Sep'85 by Pickwick Records. Dist: Pickwick Distribution, PRT, Taylors

Cassette: released on Hallmark, Sep'85 by Pickwick Records. Dist: Pickwick Distribution, PRT, Taylors

TO ALL THE GIRLS I'VE LOVED BEFORE.
Album: released on Premier, Feb'87 by Premier Records. Dist: CBS

Cassette: released on Premier, Feb'87 by Premier Records. Dist: CBS

VERY BEST OF MERLE HAGGARD.
Tracks: / Everybody's had the blues / If we make it through December / It's not love (but it's not bad) / Old man from the mountain / Carolyn / I's all in the movies / Movin' on / Fightin' side of me (The) / Mama tried / Okie from Muskogee / Workin' man blues / I wonder if they ever think of me / Things aren't funny anymore / Roots of my raising (The) / Always wanting you.
Compact disc: released on Capitol, Apr'87 by Capitol Records. Dist: EMI

Haggart, Bob

CENTURY PLAZA (Haggart, Bob & World's Greatest Jazz Band).
Album: released on World Jazz, Jan'75 by World Jazz Records. Dist: World Jazz, JSU, Jazz Music

HARK THE HERALD ANGELS SWING (Haggart, Bob & World's Greatest Jazz Band).
Album: released on World Jazz, Jan'75 by World Jazz Records. Dist: World Jazz, JSU, Jazz Music

IN CONCERT VOL 1 MASSEY HALL (Haggart, Bob & World's Greatest Jazz Band).
Album: released on World Jazz, Jan'75 by World Jazz Records. Dist: World Jazz, JSU, Jazz Music

Maxine Sullivan with The Bob Haggart Quintet

PLAY COLE PORTER (Haggart, Bob & Yank Lawson).

PORTRAIT OF BIX, A.
Album: released on Jazzology, Jan'87 Dist: Jazz Music, Swift

VOL.2 CARN HALL & MAXINE (Haggart, Bob & World's Greatest Jazz Band).
Album: released on World Jazz, Jan'75 by World Jazz Records. Dist: World Jazz, JSU, Jazz Music

Hague, Mel

MEL HAGUE LIVE.
Album: released on Look, Jan'80 Dist: R. Smith & Co. Records, H.R. Taylor

MEL HAGUE & THE NEW WESTERNAIRES (Hague, Mel & The New Westernaires).
Album: released on Look, Aug'77 Dist: R. Smith & Co. Records, H.R. Taylor

OLD GRAVEL BOOTS.
Album: released on Look, Nov'79 Dist: R. Smith & Co. Records, H.R. Taylor

Ha Ha Ha

UP AND DOWN.
Tracks: / Up and down / Resuene (Solea) / Al aire (sulerias) / El Dron (Fandangos) / Guadiana (Jaleos) / Del Cerro (Tangos) / Mi tierra (Granaina) / Boabdil (Bulerias) / A Mandeli (Rumba).
Single (7"): released on Hobby Horse, Jan'86 by Revolver Records. Dist: Cartel

Album: released on Hannibal, '84 by Hannibal Records. Dist: Charly, Harmonia Mundi, Projection, Celtic Music, Roots

Ha-Ha-Mono

RUN FOR MILES.
Single (7"): released on Northeast Music, Jul'83 by Northeast Music Records. Dist: Northeast Music Distribution, Pinnacle

Hahn, Carol

DO YOUR BEST.
Single (7"): released on Malaco, May'83 by Malaco Records. Dist: Charly

Single (12"): released on Malaco, May'83 by Malaco Records. Dist: Charly

Hahn, Jerry Quintet

JERRY HAUN QUINTET.
Album: released on Arhoolie, May'81 by Arhoolie Records. Dist: Projection, Topic, Jazz Music, Swift, Roots

Haider, Joe

JOE HAIDER.
Album: released on Calig, Jul'82 Dist: JSU

Haig, Al

BE BOP KEYBOARDS MASTERS.
Double Album: released on Vogue Jazz, May'83

EXPRESSLY ELLINGTON (Haig, Al Quartet).
Album: released on Spotlite, Jan'83 by Spotlite Records. Dist: Cadillac, Jazz Music, Spotlite

INVITATION (Haig, Al Trio).
Album: released on Spotlite, Jan'83 by Spotlite Records. Dist: Cadillac, Jazz Music, Spotlite

MANHATTAN MEMORIES (Haig, Al Trio & Quartet).
Album: released on Sea Breeze, Mar'87 Dist: Swift

MEETS THE MASTER SAXES VOL 3.
Album: released on Spotlite, Jan'83 by Spotlite Records. Dist: Cadillac, Jazz Music, Spotlite

MEETS THE MASTER SAXES VOL 1.
Album: released on Spotlight, Jan'83 by PRT Records. Dist: PRT

MEETS THE MASTER SAXES VOL 2.
Album: released on Spotlite, Jan'83 by Spotlite Records. Dist: Cadillac, Jazz Music, Spotlite

PIANO INTERPRETATIONS.
Album: released on Sea Breeze, Aug'79 Dist: Swift

PORTRAIT OF BUD POWELL, A.
Album: released on Interplay, Sep'79 by Interplay Records. Dist: Jazz Music, Swift

QUINTET OF THE YEAR REVISITED.
Album: released on Spotlight, Mar'83 by PRT Records. Dist: PRT

SOLITAIRE.
Album: released on Spotlite, '83 by Spotlite Records. Dist: Cadillac, Jazz Music, Spotlite

SPECIAL BREW (Haig, Al & Jimmy Raney 4).
Album: released on Spotlite, '83 by Spotlite Records. Dist: Cadillac, Jazz Music, Spotlite

STABLEMATES (Haig, Al / Jon Eardley).

Halgh, Robert & Sema
THREE SEASONS ONLY.
Album: released on Le Rey, May'84

Halg, Paul
BIG BLUE WORLD.
Single (7"): released on Factory Benelux, Jun'84 by Rough Trade Records. Dist: Cartel

Single (12"): released on Factory Benelux, Jun'84 by Rough Trade Records. Dist: Cartel

BLUE FOR YOU.

Single (7"): released on Operation Twilight, Dec'82

HEAVEN HELP YOU NOW.
Single (7"): released on Operation Afterglow, Sep'85 Dist: Pinnacle

Single (12"): released on Operation Afterglow, Sep'85 Dist: Pinnacle

HEAVEN SENT.
Single (7"): released on Les Disques Du Crepuscule, Sep'84 Dist: Rough Trade, Pinnacle, Island, Polygram

JUSTICE.
Single (7"): released on Operation Twilight, Aug'82

LOVE ETERNAL.
Tracks: / Love eternal.
Single (7"): released on Operation Afterglow, Feb'86 Dist: Pinnacle

Single (12"): released on Operation Afterglow, Feb'86 Dist: Pinnacle

ONLY TRUTH.
Cassette: released on Les Disques Du Crepuscule, Oct'84 Dist: Rough Trade, Pinnacle, Island, Polygram

ONLY TRUTH, THE.
Single (7"): released on Les Disques Du Crepuscule, Sep'84 Dist: Rough Trade, Pinnacle, Island, Polygram

Single (7"): released on Les Disques Du Crepuscule, Sep'84 Dist: Rough Trade, Pinnacle, Island, Polygram Deleted '85.

ONLY TRUTH(US REMIX), THE.
Single (12"): released on Les Disques Du Crepuscule, Oct'84 Dist: Rough Trade, Pinnacle, Island, Polygram

RHYTHM OF LIFE.
Album: released on Crepescule, Oct'83 by Island Records. Dist: Polygram, Pinnacle

Cassette: released on Crepescule, Oct'83 by Island Records. Dist: Polygram, Pinnacle

RHYTHM OF LIFE(REMIXES).
Album: released on Factory Benelux, Jun'84 by Rough Trade Records. Dist: Cartel

RUNNING AWAY.
Single (7"): released on Operation Twilight, Jun'82

SENSE OF FUN.

Album: released on Operation Afterglow, Nov'85 Dist: Pinnacle

WARP OF PURE FUN, THE.
Compact disc: released on Les Disques Du Crepuscule, Feb'87 Dist: Rough Trade, Pinnacle, Island, Polygram

Hall Variety
HAIL VARIETY various artists (Various Artists).
Album: released on Save The Children Fund, Mar'83

Cassette: released on Save The Children Fund, Mar'83

.Haines, Alan
KING ARTHUR AND HIS KNIGHTS.
Cassette: released on Tellastory, Dec'86 by Bartlett Bliss Productions. Dist: PRT Distribution, Hayward Promotions Distribution, H.R. Taylor Distribution

Haines Gang
SO HOT/CLOSE SHAVE(EXTENDED MIX).
Single (7"): released on London, Oct'83 by London Records. Dist: Polygram

Single (12"): released on London, Oct'83 by London Records. Dist: Polygram

Haines, Perry
WHAT'S WHAT/WHAT'S FUNK.
Single (7"): released on Fetish, Nov'81 by Fetish Records. Dist: Cartel, Pinnacle

Hain, Kit
PERFECT TIMING/FLY BY NIGHT.
Single (7"):

SCHOOL FOR SPIES.
Album: released on Mercury, Nov'83 by Phonogram Records. Dist: Polygram Distribution

Cassette: released on Mercury, Nov'83 by Phonogram Records. Dist: Polygram Distribution

SLOW MOVES.
Single 10": released on Mercury, Mar'84 by Phonogram Records. Dist: Polygram Distribution

SPIRITS WALKING OUT.
Album: released on Deram, Nov'81 by Decca Records. Dist: Polygram

Cassette: released on Deram, Nov'81 by Decca Records. Dist: Polygram

Hain, Marshall
DANCING IN THE CITY.
Tracks: / Dancing in the alley.
Single (7"): released on Columbia, Aug'87 by EMI Records. Dist: EMI

Single (12"): released on Columbia, Aug'87 by EMI Records. Dist: EMI

Hair
DISCO SPECTACULAR (Various Artists).
Album: released on RCA, May'79 by RCA Records. Dist: RCA, Roots, Swift, Wellard, Chris, I & B, Solomon & Peres Distribution

LONDON CAST (Various Artists).
Album: by Polydor Records. Dist: Polygram, Polydor

Haircut 100
FAVOURITE SHIRTS(BOY MEETS GIRL).
Single (7"): released on Lightning, Jul'84 by Lightning Records. Dist: Jetstar

PELICAN WEST.
Album: released on Haircut 100, Feb'82 by Arista Records. Dist: RCA

Cassette: released on Haircut 100, Feb'82 by Arista Records. Dist: RCA

Album: released on Fame (Arista), Mar'84 by Music For Pleasure Records. Dist: EMI

Cassette: released on Fame (Arista), Mar'84 by Music For Pleasure Records. Dist: EMI

TOO UP TWO DOWN.
Single (7"): released on Polydor, Jun'84 by Polydor Records. Dist: Polygram, Polydor

Single (12"): released on Polydor, Jun'84 by Polydor Records. Dist: Polygram, Polydor

Hairman, Robt
AFRICA'S ON FIRE.
Single (7"): released on McDonald Brothers, Jul'84

Single (7"): released on MCA, Jul'84 by MCA Records. Dist: Polygram, MCA

Single (12"): released on MCA, Jul'84 by MCA Records. Dist: Polygram, MCA

Hairston, Curtis
CHILLIN' OUT.
Tracks: / Hold on (for me).
Single (7"): released on Atlantic, Nov'86 by WEA Records. Dist: WEA

Single (12"): released on Atlantic, Nov'86 by WEA Records. Dist: WEA

CURTIS HAIRSTON.
Tracks: / Chillin' out / Let's make love tonight / You're my shining star / Hold on (for me) / All we have is love / Take charge / Morning after, the / Let me change your mind.
Single (7"): released on Atlantic, Jan'87 by WEA Records. Dist: WEA

Cassette: released on Atlantic, Jan'87 by WEA Records. Dist: WEA

I WANT YOU all tonight.
Single (7"): released on RCA, Oct'83 by RCA Records. Dist: RCA, Roots, Swift, Wellard, Chris, I & B, Solomon & Peres Distribution

Single (12"): released on RCA, Oct'83 by RCA Records. Dist: RCA, Roots, Swift, Wellard, Chris, I & B, Solomon & Peres Distribution

Single (7"): released on RCA, Jun'85 by RCA Records. Dist: RCA, Roots, Swift, Wellard, Chris, I & B, Solomon & Peres Distribution

Single (12"): released on RCA, Jun'85 by RCA Records. Dist: RCA, Roots, Swift, Wellard, Chris, I & B, Solomon & Peres Distribution

MORNING AFTER, THE.
Single (7"): released on Atlantic, Feb'87 by WEA Records. Dist: WEA

Single (12"): released on Atlantic, Feb'87 by WEA Records. Dist: WEA

Haiti
DIVINE HORSEMEN The voodoo gods of Haiti.
Album: released on Lyrichord (USA), Oct'81 by Lyrichord Records (USA). Dist: Flexitron Distributors Ltd

MERINGUES AND FOLK BALLARDS OF HAITI.
Album: released on Lyrichord (USA), Oct'81 by Lyrichord Records (USA). Dist: Flexitron Distributors Ltd

RITUAL DREAMS OF HAITI Voodoo trance magic.
Album: released on Lyrichord (USA), Oct'81 by Lyrichord Records (USA). Dist: Flexitron Distributors Ltd

Hakon Graf
HIDEAWAY.
Cassette: released on Strawberry, Jul'83 Dist: Pinnacle

Haland, Bjoro
MY NASHVILLE ALBUM.
Album: released on Igus, Apr'81 by Klub. Dist: PRT, Musac Distribution Ltd (Scotland)

Cassette: released on Igus, Apr'81 by Klub. Dist: PRT, Musac Distribution Ltd (Scotland)

TO MY FRIENDS.
Album: released on Klub, Sep'80

Cassette: released on Klub, Sep'80

Halcox, Pat All Stars
SEVENTH AVENUE.
Album: released on Plant Life Jazz, Nov'81

Halcyon Dance Orchestra
MY BLUE HEAVEN.
Album: released on Halcyon (USA), Mar'79 by Halcyon Records (USA). Dist: Jazz Music, Conifer, Taylors

Haldra and Woody
UP WHERE WE BELONG/THE POEM.
Single (7"): released on WKS, Oct'73 by WKS Records. Dist: Jetstar Distribution

Hale, Barry
CHRISTMAS STORY/TELL ME WHERE.
Single (7"): released on Scarecrow, Dec'83 Dist: Jazz Music

COME ON BABY.
Single (7"): released on Scarecrow, Apr'84 Dist: Jazz Music

HEY GIRL/BE MY GUEST.
Single (7"): released on Revolver, Sep'81 by Revolver Records. Dist: Revolver, Cartel

KEEP YOUR CB RADIO SWITCHED ON.
Single (7"): released on Scarecrow, Oct'82 Dist: Jazz Music

Hale, Binnie
GOLDEN AGE OF BINNIE HALE & BOBBIE HOWES (Hale, Binnie & Bobby Howes).
Album: released on Golden Age, Mar'86 by Music For Pleasure Records. Dist: EMI

Cassette: released on Golden Age, Mar'86 by Music For Pleasure Records. Dist: EMI

Hale, Corky
HARP BEAT.
Tracks: / Nothing higher.
Album: released on Affinity, Apr'86 by Charly Records. Dist: Charly, Cadillac

Cassette: released on Affinity, Apr'86 by Charly Records. Dist: Charly, Cadillac

SO MUCH IN LOVE Roof garden.
Tracks: / So much in love / Roof garden.
Notes: Double A Side
Single (12"): released on Affinity, Mar'86 by Charly Records. Dist: Charly, Cadillac

Hale, Richard
TOGETHER (Hale, Richard and Maureen Hart).
Album: released on Klub, Nov'84

Cassette: released on Klub, Nov'84

Haley, Bill
16 GREATEST HITS, THE (Haley, Bill & The Comets).
Tracks: / Rock around the clock / See you later alligator / Shake,rattle and roll / Razzle dazzle / Saints rock 'n' roll,The / Skinny minnie / Rock-a-beatin' boogie / Rip it up / Rudy's rock / Jenny jenny / Kansas city / Rock the joint / Yakety sax / Johnny B. Good / Whole lotta shakin' goin' on / What'd I say.
Compact disc: released on Bescol, May'87 Dist: Target

20 GOLDEN PIECES OF (Haley, Bill & The Comets).
Album: released on Bulldog, Sep'82 by Bulldog Records. Dist: President Distribution, Spartan, Swift, Taylor, H.R.

6 TRACK HITS (Haley, Bill & The Comets).
Extended-play record: released on Scoop 33, Aug'83 by Pickwick Records. Dist: H.R. Taylor

Cassette: released on Scoop 33, Aug'83 by Pickwick Records. Dist: H.R. Taylor

BEST OF (Haley, Bill & The Comets).
Cassette: released on Creole, Jul'84 by Creole Records. Dist: Rhino, PRT

BIGGEST HITS (Haley, Bill and his comets).
Cassette: released on Speciality, '74 by Relic Records. Dist: Swift

Cassette: released on Cambra, '83 by Cambra Records. Dist: IDS, Conifer

BILL HALEY AND HIS COMETS.
Cassette: released on Audio Fidelity, Oct'84 Dist: PRT

BILL HALEY AND THE COMETS (Haley, Bill & Caterina Valente).

BILL HALEY COLLECTION (THE).
Album: released on Deja Vu, Jul'86 by Deja Vu Records. Dist: Counterpoint Distribution, Record Services Distribution (Ireland)

Cassette: released on Deja Vu, Jul'86 by Deja Vu Records. Dist: Counterpoint Distribution, Record Services Distribution (Ireland)

BILL HALEY'S SCRAPBOOK (Haley, Bill & Caterina Valente).
Album: released on Buddah, Jul'85

Cassette: released on Buddah, Jul'85

BOOGIE WITH BILL HALEY (Haley, Bill and his comets).
Album: released on Topline, Jan'85 by Charly Records. Dist: Charly Distribution

Cassette: released on Topline, Jan'85 by Charly Records. Dist: Charly Distribution

CRAZY MAN CRAZY (Haley, Bill and his comets).
Single (7"): released on Sonet, Jun'74 by Sonet Records. Dist: PRT

EVERYONE CAN ROCK'N'ROLL (Haley, Bill and his comets).
Single (7"): released on Sonet, Feb'81 by Sonet Records. Dist: PRT

EVERYONE CAN ROCK'N'ROLL.
Album: released on Sonet, Jun'80 by Sonet Records. Dist: PRT

FROM THE ORIGINAL MASTER TAPES.
Tracks: / Rock around the clock / Thirteen women / Shake, rattle and roll / A.B.C. boogie / Happy baby / Dim, dim the lights / Birth of the boogie / Mambo rock / Two hound dogs / Razzle dazzle / R.O.C.K. / Saints rock 'n' roll / Burn that candle / See you later Alligator / Paper boy (The) / Rudy's rock / Hot dog buddy buddy / Rip it up / Don't knock the clock
Compact disc: released on MCA, Sep'85 by MCA Records. Dist: Polygram, MCA

FROM THE ORIGINAL MASTER TAPES.
Compact disc: released on MCA, Sep'85 by MCA Records. Dist: Polygram, MCA

GOD BLESS ROCK'N'ROLL.
Single (7"): released on Sonet, Feb'82 by Sonet Records. Dist: PRT

GOLDEN GREATS: BILL HALEY.
Album: released on MCA, Jul'85 by MCA Records. Dist: Polygram, MCA

Cassette: released on MCA, Jul'85 by MCA Records. Dist: Polygram, MCA

GOLDEN HITS: BILL HALEY.
Album: released on MCA, Feb'84 by MCA Records. Dist: Polygram, MCA

Cassette: released on MCA, Feb'84 by MCA Records. Dist: Polygram, MCA

GOLDEN HITS/ROCK AROUND THE CLOCK.
Double cassette: released on MCA, Sep'84 by MCA Records. Dist: Polygram, MCA

GREATEST HITS:BILL HALEY & THE COMETS (Haley, Bill & The Comets).
Tracks: / Rock around the clock / Burn that candle / Forty cups of coffee / Two hound dogs / Shake, rattle and roll / Thirteen women / Saints rock 'n' roll / Rock you later Alligator / Don't knock the rock / Mambo rock / Corrine, Corrina / Calling all comets / Skinny Minnie / Rockin' thru' the rye / ABC boogie / Razzle-dazzle / R.O.C.K...
Compact disc: released on MCA, Feb'85 by MCA Records. Dist: Polygram, MCA

Compact disc: released on MCS Look Back, Jul'87

Album: released on Polydor (Italy), Sep'84

Cassette: released on Polydor (Italy), Sep'84

HAIL HAIL ROCK'N'ROLL (Haley, Bill and his comets).
Single (7"): released on Sonet, Feb'81 by Sonet Records. Dist: PRT

HILLBILLY HALEY.
Album: released on Rollercoaster, Nov'84 by Rollercoaster Records. Dist: Swift Distribution, Rollercoaster Distribution

JUST ROCK'N'ROLL.
Album: released on Sonet, '73 by Sonet Records. Dist: PRT

KING OF ROCK'N'ROLL, THE (Haley, Bill & The Comets).
Compact disc: released on Bellaphon, '86 by Bellaphon Records. Dist: IMS-Polygram

KING'S OF ROCK.
Album: released on Polydor (Import) Feb'82

Cassette: released on Polydor (Import), Feb'82

LIVE IN SWEDEN (Haley, Bill and his comets).
Cassette: released on Speciality, '74 by Relic Records. Dist: Swift

MR. ROCKIN'ROLLIN'-THE ESSENTIAL BILL HALEY (Haley, Bill and his comets).
Album: released on Charly, '84 by Charly Records. Dist: Charly, Cadillac

Cassette: released on Charly, '84 by Charly Records. Dist: Charly, Cadillac

ORIGINAL, THE 1954-57 (Haley, Bill & The Comets).
Album: released on Hallmark, Mar'87 by Pickwick Records. Dist: Pickwick Distribution, Taylors

Cassette: released on Hallmark, Mar'87 by Pickwick Records. Dist: Pickwick Distribution, PRT, Taylors

REAL ROCK DRIVE/LIVE IT UP (Haley, Bill and his comets).
Single (7"): released on Rollercoaster, Jan'80

Page 442

---

by Rollercoaster Records. Dist: Swift Distribution, Rollercoaster Distribution

R.O.C.K..
Album: released on Sonet, Oct'76 by Sonet Records. Dist: PRT

ROCK AROUND THE CLOCK (Haley, Bill & The Comets).
Album: released on Spot, Feb'83 by Pickwick Records. Dist: H.R. Taylor, Lugtons

Cassette: released on Spot, Feb'83 by Pickwick Records. Dist: H.R. Taylor, Lugtons

ROCK AROUND THE CLOCK.
Tracks: / Rock around the clock.
Compact disc: released on Decca (Germany), Dec'85 by Decca Records. Dist: Polygram, IMS

Album: released on Astan, Dec'85 by Astan Records. Dist: Counterpoint

Single (7"): released on MCA, Feb'81 by MCA Records. Dist: Polygram, MCA

Single (7"): released on Old Gold, Jul'82 by Old Gold Records. Dist: Lightning, Jazz Music, Spartan, Counterpoint

ROCK AROUND THE CLOCK (Haley, Bill and his comets).
Album: released on Orchid Music, Feb'82 by Bibi. Dist: Pinnacle

ROCKET 88 (Haley, Bill & The Saddlemen).
Single (7"): released on Thumbs Up, Feb'81 Dist: Spartan Distribution

ROCK'N'ROLL STAGE SHOW (Haley, Bill & His comets).
Album: released on Charly, Aug'83 by Charly Records. Dist: Charly, Cadillac

ROCK ROLLIN' BILL HALEY (Haley, Bill & His comets).
Album: released on MCA (USA), Sno'84

ROCK THE JOINT (Haley, Bill & The Comets).
Album: released on Rollercoaster, Jun'85 by Rollercoaster Records. Dist: Swift Distribution, Rollercoaster Distribution

Single (7"): released on Rollercoaster, Sep'84 by Rollercoaster Records. Dist: Swift Distribution, Rollercoaster Distribution

RUDY'S ROCK (Haley, Bill & His comets).
Single (7"): released on Revival, Jul'82 Dist: Lightning, Swift

SCRAPBOOK (Haley, Bill & The Comets).
Album: released on Buddah, Jul'85

Cassette: released on Buddah, Jul'85

SEE YOU LATER ALLIGATOR (Haley, Bill & The Comets).
Single (7"): released on Old Gold, Jul'82 by Old Gold Records. Dist: Lightning, Jazz Music, Spartan, Counterpoint

TRIBUTE TO BILL HALEY (Haley, Bill and his comets).
Album: released on MCF, '83

Cassette: released on MCF, '83

TWISTIN' KNIGHTS OF THE ROUND TABLE (Haley, Bill & His comets).
Album: released on PRT International, May'81

WHY DO I CRY OVER YOU.
Single (7"): released on Rollercoaster, '79 by Rollercoaster Records. Dist: Swift Distribution, Rollercoaster Distribution

WHAT DO YOU WANT TO MAKE THOSE EYES....
Single (7"): released on Weasel, Aug'83 by Weasel Records. Dist: Spartan

WHY CAN'T THEY LEAVE HIM ALONE.
Tracks: / Why can't they leave him alone / I'm just hearing you out.
Single (7"): released on RCA, Jul'87 by RCA Records. Dist: RCA, Roots, Swift, Wellard, Chris, I & B, Solomon & Peres Distribution

HALF A SIXPENCE Original London cast.
Album: released on That's Entertainment, Aug'83 by That's Entertainment Records. Dist: Pinnacle, PRT

Cassette: released on That's Entertainment, Aug'83 by That's Entertainment Records. Dist: Pinnacle, PRT

HALF GENTLEMEN.
Album: released on Armageddon, May'83 by Armageddon Records. Dist: Revolver, Cartel,

---

Pinnacle

HORRIBLE.
Album: released on Press, Jul'86 by Press Records.

LOUD.
Album: released on Armageddon, May'82 by Armageddon Records. Dist: Revolver, Cartel, Pinnacle

OUR SOLAR SYSTEM.
Album: released on Iridescence, Dec'84 by Iridescence Records. Dist: Rough Trade, Cartel

SING NO EVIL.
Album: released on Iridescence, Dec'84 by Iridescence Records. Dist: Rough Trade, Cartel

Album: released on Iridescence, Dec'84 by Iridescence Records. Dist: Rough Trade, Cartel

SPY.
Single (7"): released on Armageddon, May'81 by Armageddon Records. Dist: Revolver, Cartel, Pinnacle

BACK IN THE D.H.S.S.
Album: released on Probe Plus, Mar'87 by Probe Plus Records. Dist: Probe Plus Distribution

Cassette: released on Probe Plus, Mar'87 by Probe Plus Records. Dist: Probe Plus Distribution

BACK IN THE DHSS.
Single (7"): released on Probe Plus, Nov'85 by Probe Plus Records. Dist: Probe Plus Distribution

DICKIE DAVIES EYES.
Tracks: / Dickie Davies eyes / I left my heart (in Papworth General) / Bastard son of Dean Friedman, The.
Notes: with extra track on 12": version only
Single (7"): released on Probe Plus, Oct'86 by Probe Plus Records. Dist: Probe Plus Distribution

Single (12"): released on Probe Plus, Oct'86 by Probe Plus Records. Dist: Probe Plus Distribution

TRUMPTON RIOTS.
Tracks: / Trumpton Riots / Trumpton riots / Ducks Prague away kit / Architecture morality / Ted and Alice / 1966 and all that / Albert Hammond bootleg.
Single (7"): released on Probe Plus, Mar'86 by Probe Plus Records. Dist: Probe Plus Distribution

Single (12"): released on Probe Plus, Mar'86 by Probe Plus Records. Dist: Probe Plus Distribution

HALF MOON STREET Original Soundtrack (Richard Harvey).
Tracks: / Half moon Street / Half moon Street.
Notes: Composed by Richard Harvey
Album: released on Milan, Sep'86, IMS Distribution, Conifer Distribution, Discovery Distribution

Cassette: released on Milan France, Sep'86

CAN'T YOU WAIT TILL I GET YOU HOME.
Album: released on Collectors, Oct'84 by Castle Communications Records. Dist: PRT, Pinnacle, Jazz Music

FREEDOM FIGHTER.
Single (12"): released on Greensleeves, Jul'85 by Greensleeves Records. Dist: BMG, Jetstar, Spartan

GO BACK HOME.
Single (12"): released on Hawkeye, Jun'85 by Hawkeye Records. Dist: Hawkeye, Lightning (WEA) Distribution, Jetstar, PRT

GREETINGS.
Single (12"): released on Power House, Jul'86 by Power House Records. Dist: Jetstar

Album: released on Power House, Nov'86 by Power House Records. Dist: Jetstar

HOLD ON.
Single (12"): released on Jedi, Apr'85 Dist: Jetstar

IN FINE STYLE.
Album: released on Sonic Sounds, Aug'84 by Sonic Sound Records. Dist: Jetstar

JOINT FAVOURITES (Half Pint & Michael Palmer).
Tracks: / Joint favourites.
Notes: Contains two tracks by each artist, including the Half Pint single 'Freedom Fighter'.

Produced by Myrie Lewis and Errol Marshall, 'Joint Favourites' featuresTony Asher on keyboards.
Album: released on Greensleeves, Jan'86 by Greensleeves Records. Dist: BMG, Jetstar, Spartan

Album: released on Greensleeves, Jan'86 by Greensleeves Records. Dist: BMG, Jetstar, Spartan

MONEY MAN SKANK.
Album: released on Jammy's, Jun'84 by Jammy's Records. Dist: Jetstar

MR LANDLOR.
Single (12"):

NIGHT LIFE LADY.
Tracks: / Night life lady.
Single (12"): released on Island, Mar'86 by Island Records. Dist: Polygram

ONE IN A MILLION.
Album: released on Greensleeves, Oct'84 by Greensleeves Records. Dist: BMG, Jetstar, Spartan

POLITICAL FICTION.
Single (12"): released on Sun Set, Sep'84 by Sun Set Records. Dist: Jetstar Distribution

SALLY.
Single (12"): released on Jedi, Oct'84 Dist: Jetstar

HALFWAY HOUSE ORCHESTRA 1925/8, THE.
Album: released on VJM, Apr'79 by VJM (UK) Records. Dist: Swift

HALFWAY HOUSE ORCHESTRA & NEW ORLEANS OWLS - VOL.2.
Album: released on VJM, Apr'79 by Wellard, Chris Distribution. Dist: Wellard, Chris Distribution

ARMOUR (Halkett, Rene & David Jay).
Single (7"): released on 4AD, Dec'81 by 4AD Records. Dist: Rough Trade

ADELAIDE HALL.
Album: released on Monmouth, Mar'79

THERE GOES THAT SONG AGAIN.
Album: released on Decca, Nov'80 by Decca Records. Dist: Polygram

WHISPERING GRASS (Hall, Adelaide, Issy Bonn, Dorothy Carless, Benny Lee).
Notes: For full information see under Dorothy Carless.

4 TRACK CASSETTE EP.
Cassette: released on RCA, May'83 by RCA Records. Dist: RCA, Roots, Swift, Wellard, Chris, I & B, Solomon & Peres Distribution

TALK OF THE TOWN (Hall, Andrew, Society Jazz Band Of New Orleans).
Album: released on Shalom, Jul'82 Dist: Kingsway Distribution

ANGEL IN THE MORNING.
Single (12"): released on Reggae, Mar'83 by Reggae Records. Dist: Jetstar, Morpheus Distribution

ANYONE WHO HAD A HEART.
Single (12"): released on Germaine, Dec'85 by Germaine Records. Dist: Jetstar

BEST THING FOR ME, THE.
Tracks: / Best thing for me, The.
Single (7"): released on Germaine, Oct'86 by Germaine Records. Dist: Jetstar

Single (12"): released on Germaine, Oct'86 by Germaine Records. Dist: Jetstar

EIGHT LITTLE NOTES.
Tracks: / Eight little notes.
Album: released on Germaine, Dec'85 by Germaine Records. Dist: Jetstar

HEART MADE OF STONE.
Tracks: / Heart made of stone / Heart made of stone / Heart made of stone (alternative version) / Its hard to believe.
Single (7"): released on Trojan, Sep'86 by Trojan Records. Dist: PRT, Jetstar

Single (12"): released on Trojan, Sep'86 by Trojan Records. Dist: PRT, Jetstar

I WANT TO KNOW WHAT LOVE IS.
Single (12"): released on Germaine, Mar'85 by Germaine Records. Dist: Jetstar

JUST YOU JUST ME.
Album: released on Germaine, Feb'87 by Germaine Records. Dist: Jetstar

SMILE.
Tracks: / Smile / Smile.
Single (7"): released on Germaine, Jun'86 by Germaine Records. Dist: Jetstar

Single (12"): released on Germaine, Jun'86 by Germaine Records. Dist: Jetstar

Hallberg, Bengt

A.D 1980 (Hallberg, Bengt/Arne Dommerus).

DIALOGUE IN SWING (Hallberg, Bengt & Ove Lind).
Album: released on Phontastic (Sweden), '82 by Wellard, Chris Distribution. Dist: Wellard, Chris Distribution

DOWNTOWN MEETINGS.
Album: released on Phontastic (Sweden), '82 by Wellard, Chris Distribution. Dist: Wellard, Chris Distribution

EGENHANDIGT.
Album: released on Phontastic (Sweden), '82 by Wellard, Chris Distribution. Dist: Wellard, Chris Distribution

EVERGREENS (Hallberg, Bengt/Ove Lind/Staffan Broms).
Album: released on Phontastic, '82 Dist: Wellard, Chris

Cassette: released on Phontastic, '82 Dist: Wellard, Chris

EVERGREENS 2 (Hallberg, Bengt/Ove Lind/Staffan Broms).
Album: released on Phontastic (Sweden), '82 by Wellard, Chris Distribution. Dist: Wellard, Chris Distribution

Cassette: released on Phontastic (Sweden), '82 by Wellard, Chris Distribution. Dist: Wellard, Chris Distribution

GYLLENE CIRKELN 1962.
Album: released on Dragon, Jul'87 by Dragon Records. Dist: Jazz Music, Projection, Cadillac

HALLBERG'S HOT ACCORDION In the foreground.
Album: released on Phontastic (Sweden), '82 by Wellard, Chris Distribution. Dist: Wellard, Chris Distribution

HALLBERG TOUCH, THE.
Album: released on Phontastic (Sweden), '82 by Wellard, Chris Distribution. Dist: Wellard, Chris Distribution

POWERHOUSE-KRAFTVERK (Hallberg, Bengt/Arne Dommerus).
Album: released on Photographer, Jan'85 Dist: Jetstar

SONG FOR YOU, A.
Album: released on Phontastic (Sweden), '82 by Wellard, Chris Distribution. Dist: Wellard, Chris Distribution

Cassette: released on Phontastic (Sweden), '82 by Wellard, Chris Distribution. Dist: Wellard, Chris Distribution

SWEDISH JINGLES (Hallberg, Bengt/Svenska Truddelutter/Arne Domnerus).
Album: released on Phontastic (Sweden), '82 by Wellard, Chris Distribution. Dist: Wellard, Chris Distribution

TWO OF A KIND (Hallberg, Bengt/Karin Krog).
Album: released on Four Leaf Clover, Dec'82 Dist: Jazz Music, Swift

Hall, Big John

CELEBRATION OF PRAISE.
Album: by Pilgrim Records. Dist: Rough Trade, Cartel

IF GOD IS DEAD.
Album: by Pilgrim Records. Dist: Rough Trade, Cartel

LIFE IN JESUS' NAME.
Album: by Pilgrim Records. Dist: Rough Trade, Cartel

Hall, Bob

JAMMIN' THE BOOGIE (see Green, George) (Hall, Bob & George Green).

ROLL AND SLIDE (Hall, Bob & Dave Peabody).
Album: released on Appaloosa (Italy), Dec'84

SURVIVORS (Hall, Bob & Dave Kelley).
Album: released on Appaloosa (Import), May'81

Hall, Daryl

DREAMTIME.
Tracks: / Dreamtime / Dreamtime.
Single (7"): released on RCA, Jul'86 by RCA Records. Dist: RCA, Roots, Swift, Wellard, Chris, I & B, Solomon & Peres Distribution

Single (12"): released on RCA, Jul'86 by RCA Records. Dist: RCA, Roots, Swift, Wellard, Chris, I & B, Solomon & Peres Distribution

I WASN'T BORN YESTERDAY.
Tracks: / I wasn't born yesterday / What's gonna happen to us / Dreamtime*.
Single (7"): released on RCA, Nov'86 by RCA Records. Dist: RCA, Roots, Swift, Wellard, Chris, I & B, Solomon & Peres Distribution

Single (12"): released on RCA, Nov'86 by RCA Records. Dist: RCA, Roots, Swift, Wellard, Chris, I & B, Solomon & Peres Distribution

SACRED SONGS.
Album: released on RCA, Jul'84 by RCA Records. Dist: RCA, Roots, Swift, Wellard, Chris, I & B, Solomon & Peres Distribution

THREE HEARTS IN THE HAPPY ENDING MACHINE.
Tracks: / Dreamtime / Only a vision / I wasnt born yesterday / Someone like you / Next step / For you / Foolish pride / Right as rain / Let it out / What's going to happen to us.
Album: released on RCA, Aug'86 by RCA Records. Dist: RCA, Roots, Swift, Wellard, Chris, I & B, Solomon & Peres Distribution

Cassette: released on RCA, Aug'86 by RCA Records. Dist: RCA, Roots, Swift, Wellard, Chris, I & B, Solomon & Peres Distribution

Compact disc: released on RCA, Aug'86 by RCA Records. Dist: RCA, Roots, Swift, Wellard, Chris, I & B, Solomon & Peres Distribution

Hall, Ed

THIS IS JAZZ VOL.3.
Tracks: / This is Jazz / This is Jazz, Vol. 3.
Album: released on Storyville, Jun'86 by Storyville Records. Dist: Jazz Music Distribution, Swift Distribution, Chris Wellard Distribution, Counterpoint Distribution

Hall, Edmond

AT THE CLUB HANGOVER 1954.
Album: released on Storyville (USA), Jul'82 by Moss Music Group Records (USA). Dist: Discovery Distribution, Jazz Music Distribution, Swift Distribution, Chris Wellard Distribution, JSU Distribution, Celtic Music Distribution

TAKE IT EDMOND HALL WITH YOUR CLARINET.
Album: released on Queen-Disc (Import), Apr'81

TWO OF A KIND (Hall, Edmond Quartet & Teddy Wilson).
Album: released on Commodore Classics, May'87 by Teldec Records (Germany). Dist: Conifer, IMS, Polygram

Halleymites

WE ARE THE HALLEYMITES.
Single (7"): released on Red Bus, Nov'85 by Red Bus Records. Dist: PRT

Halley, Paul

NIGHTWATCH.
Album: released on Gramavision (USA), Jul'83 by Gramavison Records (USA). Dist: PRT, IMS, Polygram

Hall, Frieda

PHANTOM FINGERS OF FRIEDA HALL.
Album: released on Look, Nov'79 Dist: R. Smith & Co. Records, H.R. Taylor

Hall, Henry

GOLDEN AGE OF HENRY HALL,THE.
Album: released on Golden Age, Jul'84 by Music For Pleasure Records. Dist: EMI

HELP YOURSELF TO HAPPINESS (Hall, Henry and the BBC Dance Orchestra).
Album: released on Saville, Apr'83 by Conifer Records. Dist: Conifer

HELP YOURSELF TO HAPPINESS (Hall, Henry & His BBC Dance Orchestra).
Tracks: / You (just wonderful you) / Moon / Singing in the moonlight / Love is the sweetest thing / Maree / Always in my heart / Nobody else but Elsie / Lying in the hay / Turning of the tide / Hazel eyes / Help yourself to happiness / Clouds will soon roll by, The / Bahama mama / Wanderer / Marching along together / How can you say no / My extraordinary gal / Downhearted / Same old moon / Keep your last goodnight for me.
Album: released on Saville, '86 by Conifer Records. Dist: Conifer

Cassette: released on Saville, '86 by Conifer Records. Dist: Conifer

HENRY HALL & BBC DANCE ORCHESTRA (Hall, Henry & BBC Dance Orchestra).
Cassette: released on World Records, May'79 Dist: Polygram

HENRY HALL & THE BBC DANCE ORCHESTRA.
Album: released on World, '71 Dist: Jetstar

HERE'S TO THE NEXT TIME (Hall, Henry and the BBC Dance Orchestra).
Album: released on President, Mar'85 by President Records. Dist: Taylors, Spartan

LA DI DA DI DA (Hall, Henry Orchestra).
Single (7"): released on Music For Living, Nov'82 by Music For Living Records. Dist: Stage One Distribution

Single (12"): released on Music For Living, Nov'82 by Music For Living Records. Dist: Stage One Distribution

THIS IS HENRY HALL.
Double Album: released on World Records, Jun'78 Dist: Polygram

WHAT A PERFECT COMBINATION (Hall, Henry & His BBC Dance Orchestra).
Tracks: / Twenty million people / In a little second hand store / Day you came along, The / Thanks / Thats another Scottish story / Roaming / On a steamer over / I'll string along with you / Little valley in the mountains / Love in bloom / With my eyes wide open i'm dreaming / How's chances? / What a perfect combination / In the moonlight / My darling / Just so you'll remember.
Notes: Personnel: Henry Hall directing: Frank Wilson, Arthur Williams, Andy Hodgkiss (trumpets). Bill Mulraney, Eric Tann (trombones). Burton Gillis, Freddy Williams (clarinets and alto saxophone). Eddie Cromar (clarinet, alto & baritone saxophone). Cyril Hellier, Joseph Hitchenor, Bert Powell (violins). Jack Philips, Bert Read (pianos). George Dickinson (guitar). Theo Farrar (string- bass, or brass-bass where audible). Len Bermon (drums).
Album: released on Saville, Oct'86 by Conifer Records. Dist: Conifer

Cassette: released on Saville, Oct'86 by Conifer Records. Dist: Conifer

Hall, Herb

In New Orleans

OLD TYME MODERN (Hall, Herb Quartet).
Album: released on Sackville, Apr'81 Dist: JSU, Jazz Music, Jazz Horizons, Cadillac Music, Celtic Music, Swift

Halliday, Johnny

SOUVENIRS, SOUVENIRS.
Compact disc: released on Vogue, Dec'86 Dist: Discovery, Jazz Music, PRT, Swift

Halliday, R

SEA SONGS, SHANTIES AND SAILTALK (Halliday, R.F.P).
Cassette: released on Folktracks, Nov'79 by Folktracks Cassettes. Dist: Folktracks

Hallifax, Kelvin

WHITE BOY IN EUROPE.
Tracks: / White boy in Europe.
Single (12"): released on Teldec (Import), Mar'86

Halliwell, Nick

IT'LL END IN TEARS (Halliwell, Nick & the Gift).
Single (7"): released on Office Box, Aug'84 by Office Box Records. Dist: Red Rhino Distribution, Cartel Distribution

Hall, Jim

Biographical Details: See also under Carter, Ron.

CIRCLES.
Album: released on Concord Jazz, Nov'81 by Concord Jazz Records (USA). Dist: IMS, Polygram

CONCIERTO.
Tracks: / Two's blues / Answer is yes / Concierto De Arranjuez / You'd be so nice to come home to.
Album: released on CTI (Musidisc France), Feb'84 by Polydor Records. Dist: IMS, Polygram

Compact disc: released on CTI (Musidisc France), Feb'84 by Polydor Records. Dist: IMS, Polygram

FIRST EDITION (see Shearing, George) (Hall, Jim & George Shearing).

JIM HALL & RED MITCHELL (Hall, Jim & Red Mitchell).
Album: released on Artists House, May'81 Dist: JSU, Swift

JIM HALL'S THREE (Hall, Jim , Trio).
Tracks: / Hide & seek / Skylark / Bottlenose blues / And I do / All the things you are / Poor butterfly / Three.
Notes: Personnel: Jim Hall - guitar
Steve LaSpina- bass
Akira Tana- drums
Jim Hall's fifth recording for Concord featuring three standards and four original compositions. The track "Bottlenose blues" features the first recordingof Jim on the 12 string guitar.
Compact disc: released on Concord Jazz(USA), Mar'87 by Concord Jazz Records (USA). Dist: IMS, Polygram

Hallmark Of Harmony

YOUR ALL-TIME BARBERSHOP FAVOURITES.
Tracks: / (Keep your) sunnyside up / My old Dutch / Medley (Junction 33) / American trilogy / Bye bye blackbird / If you had all the world and its gold / Cockney Medley / Sweet Adeline / Red and yellow motor (Times square) / Medley / (Keep your) Sunnyside up / My old dutch / Junction 33 - medley / It's a good day, Zip a dee doo dah / American trilogy / Bye bye blackbird / If you had all the world and its gold / Cockney medley / Hello, hello, who's your lady friend / Don't dilly dally on the way / Any old iron / Call round any old time / Who were you with last night / Home town / I'm Henery the Eighth I am / It's a great big shame / Maybe it's because I'm a Londer / Sweet Adeline / Times square - red and yellow motor / Toot toot tootsie goo'bye / Goodbye my lady love.
Album: released on MFP, Jun'87 by EMI Records. Dist: EMI

Cassette: released on MFP, Jun'87 by EMI Records. Dist: EMI

YOUR ALL TIME BARBERSHOP FAVOURITES.
Album: released on MFP, Jun'87 by EMI Records. Dist: EMI

Hall, Mike

ONCE IN A WHILE.
Tracks: / Once in a while / Zing went the strings of my heart / You'll never know / Ponciana / Summertime / I won't send roses / Brazil / Come prima / Louisana samba / Way we were (The) / Music,music,music / Once in a lifetime.
Cassette: released on Audicord, '87 Dist: H.R. Taylor

Hall & Oates

20 CLASSIC TRACKS (Hall, Daryl & John Oates).
Album: released on Meteor, Nov'86 by Magnum Music Group Ltd. Dist: Magnum Music Group Ltd, PRT Distribution, Spartan Distribution

Cassette: released on Meteor, Nov'86 by Magnum Music Group Ltd. Dist: Magnum Music Group Ltd, PRT Distribution, Spartan Distribution

Compact disc: released on Meteor, Nov'86 by Magnum Music Group Ltd. Dist: Magnum Music Group Ltd, PRT Distribution, Spartan Distribution

ABANDONED LUNCHEONETTE (Hall, Daryl & John Oates).
Album: released on Atlantic, '74 by WEA Records. Dist: WEA

Cassette: released on Atlantic, Aug'76 by WEA Records. Dist: WEA

ADULT EDUCATION (Hall, Daryl & John Oates).
Single (7"): released on RCA, Mar'84 by RCA Records. Dist: RCA, Roots, Swift, Wellard, Chris, I & B, Solomon & Peres Distribution

Single (12"): released on RCA, Mar'84 by RCA Records. Dist: RCA, Roots, Swift, Wellard, Chris, I & B, Solomon & Peres Distribution

ALONG THE RED LEDGE (Hall, Daryl & John Oates).
Album: released on RCA, Jun'83 by RCA Records. Dist: RCA, Roots, Swift, Wellard, Chris, I & B, Solomon & Peres Distribution

BEAUTY ON A BACK STREET (Hall, Daryl & John Oates).
Album: released on RCA, Jul'84 by RCA Records. Dist: RCA, Roots, Swift, Wellard, Chris, I & B, Solomon & Peres Distribution

BIGGER THAN BOTH OF US (Hall, Daryl & John Oates).
Album: released on RCA International, Mav'81

DARYL HALL & JOHN OATES (Hall, Daryl & John Oates).
Album: released on Happy Bird (Germany), Jun'83 Dist: Polygram, IMS

Album: released on RCA, '84 by RCA Records. Dist: RCA, Roots, Swift, Wellard, Chris, I & B, Solomon & Peres Distribution

DARYL HALL & JOHN OATES (Hall, Daryl & John Oates).

EARLY YEARS, THE (Hall, Daryl & John Oates).
Tracks: / Reason why, The / Lot of changes comin', A / In honour of a lady / Deep river blues / If that's what makes you happy / Provider, The / They needed each other / Angelina / I'll be by

/ Perkiomen / Past times behind.
Album: released on Showcase, Apr'86 Dist: Counterpoint

Cassette: released on Showcase, Apr'86 Dist: Counterpoint

FAMILY MAN (Hall, Daryl & John Oates).
Single (7"): released on RCA, Apr'83 by RCA Records. Dist: RCA, Roots, Swift, Wellard, Chris, I & B, Solomon & Peres Distribution

Single (12"): released on RCA, Apr'83 by RCA Records. Dist: RCA, Roots, Swift, Wellard, Chris, I & B, Solomon & Peres Distribution

H20 (Daryl Hall & John Oates).
Tracks: / Maneater / Crime pays / One on one / Art of heartbreak / Open all night / Family man / Italian girls / Guessing games / Delayed reaction / At tension / Go solo.
Album: released on RCA, Oct'82 by RCA Records. Dist: RCA, Roots, Swift, Wellard, Chris, I & B, Solomon & Peres Distribution

Cassette: released on RCA, Oct'82 by RCA Records. Dist: RCA, Roots, Swift, Wellard, Chris, I & B, Solomon & Peres Distribution

Compact disc: released on RCA, Oct'82 by RCA Records. Dist: RCA, Roots, Swift, Wellard, Chris, I & B, Solomon & Peres Distribution

HALL & OATES (Hall, Daryl & John Oates).
Compact disc: released on Intertape, Jul'87 Dist: Target

HALL & OATES AT THE APOLLO (Hall, Daryl & John Oates).
Notes: With David Ruffin and Eddie Kendrick.
Compact disc: released on RCA, Feb'86 by RCA Records. Dist: RCA, Roots, Swift, Wellard, Chris, I & B, Solomon & Peres Distribution

I CAN'T GO FOR THAT (Hall, Daryl & John Oates).
Single (7"): released on RCA, Jan'82 by RCA Records. Dist: RCA, Roots, Swift, Wellard, Chris, I & B, Solomon & Peres Distribution

Single (12"): released on RCA, Jan'82 by RCA Records. Dist: RCA, Roots, Swift, Wellard, Chris, I & B, Solomon & Peres Distribution Deleted '85.

KISS ON MY LIST (Hall, Daryl & John Oates).
Single (7"): released on RCA, May'82 by RCA Records. Dist: RCA, Roots, Swift, Wellard, Chris, I & B, Solomon & Peres Distribution

LIVE AT THE APOLLO (Hall, Daryl & John Oates).
Album: released on RCA, Sep'85 by RCA Records. Dist: RCA, Roots, Swift, Wellard, Chris, I & B, Solomon & Peres Distribution

LIVE AT THE APOLLO (VIDEO) (Hall, Daryl & John Oates).
Video-cassette (VHS): released on RCA/Columbia, May'87

LIVE TIME (Hall, Daryl & John Oates).
Album: released on RCA, Jun'83 by RCA Records. Dist: RCA, Roots, Swift, Wellard, Chris, I & B, Solomon & Peres Distribution

MANEATER (Hall, Daryl & John Oates).
Tracks: / Maneater / I can't go for that.
Single (7"): by Old Gold Records. Dist: Lightning, Jazz Music, Spartan, Counterpoint

METHOD OF MODERN LOVE (Hall, Daryl & John Oates).
Single (7"): released on RCA, Jan'85 by RCA Records. Dist: RCA, Roots, Swift, Wellard, Chris, I & B, Solomon & Peres Distribution

Single (12"): released on RCA, Jan'85 by RCA Records. Dist: RCA, Roots, Swift, Wellard, Chris, I & B, Solomon & Peres Distribution

NITE AT THE APOLLO LIVE, A (Hall, Daryl & John Oates with The Temptations).
Single (7"): released on RCA, Sep'85 by RCA Records. Dist: RCA, Roots, Swift, Wellard, Chris, I & B, Solomon & Peres Distribution

Single (12"): released on RCA, Sep'85 by RCA Records. Dist: RCA, Roots, Swift, Wellard, Chris, I & B, Solomon & Peres Distribution
Cat. no: **PT 49936**

NO GOODBYES (Hall, Daryl & John Oates).
Album: released on Atlantic, Feb'77 by WEA Records. Dist: WEA

ONE ON ONE (Hall, Daryl & John Oates).
Single (7"): released on RCA, Jan'83 by RCA Records. Dist: RCA, Roots, Swift, Wellard, Chris, I & B, Solomon & Peres Distribution

Single (12"): released on RCA, Jan'83 by RCA Records. Dist: RCA, Roots, Swift, Wellard, Chris, I & B, Solomon & Peres Distribution

OUT OF TOUCH (Hall, Daryl & John Oates).
Single (7"): released on RCA, Sep'84 by RCA Records. Dist: RCA, Roots, Swift, Wellard, Chris, I & B, Solomon & Peres Distribution

Single (12"): released on RCA, Sep'84 by RCA Records. Dist: RCA, Roots, Swift, Wellard, Chris, I & B, Solomon & Peres Distribution

PAST TIMES BEHIND (Hall, Daryl & John Oates).
Album: released on Chelsea, Apr'77 by Pye Records. Dist: Pye

PRIVATE EYES (Hall, Daryl & John Oates).
Tracks: / Private Eyes / Looking for a good sign / I can't go for that (no can do) / Mano a Mano / Did it in a minute / Head above water / Tell me what you want / Friday let me down / Unguarded minute / Your imagination / Some men.
Compact disc: released on RCA, Dec'84 by RCA Records. Dist: RCA, Roots, Swift, Wellard, Chris, I & B, Solomon & Peres Distribution

PROVIDER, THE (Hall, Daryl & John Oates).
Album: released on Thunderbolt, Jun'84 by Magnum Music Group Ltd. Dist: Magnum Music Group Ltd, PRT Distribution, Spartan Distribution

REALLY SMOKIN' (Hall, Daryl & John Oates).
Single (12"): released on Fashion, Feb'85 by Fashion Records. Dist: PRT, Jetstar

Album: released on Thunderbolt, Oct'85 by Magnum Music Group Ltd. Dist: Magnum Music Group Ltd, PRT Distribution, Spartan Distribution

ROCK 'N' SOUL PART 1 (Hall, Daryl & John Oates).
Tracks: / Sare smile / She's gone / Rich girl / Kiss in my list / You make my dreams / Private eyes / I can't go for that (no can do) / Maneater / One on one / Wait for me / Say it isn't / Adult education.
Album: released on RCA, Oct'84 by RCA Records. Dist: RCA, Roots, Swift, Wellard, Chris, I & B, Solomon & Peres Distribution

Cassette: released on RCA, Oct'84 by RCA Records. Dist: RCA, Roots, Swift, Wellard, Chris, I & B, Solomon & Peres Distribution

Compact disc: released on RCA, Oct'84 by RCA Records. Dist: RCA, Roots, Swift, Wellard, Chris, I & B, Solomon & Peres Distribution

SAY IT ISN'T SO (Hall, Daryl & John Oates).
Single (7"): released on RCA, Oct'83 by RCA Records. Dist: RCA, Roots, Swift, Wellard, Chris, I & B, Solomon & Peres Distribution

SHE'S GONE (Hall, Daryl & John Oates).
Single (7"): released on Atlantic, Jul'81 by WEA Records. Dist: WEA

VOICES (Hall, Daryl & John Oates).
Tracks: / How does it feel to be back / Big kids / I hear the voices / Hard to be in love with you / Kiss on my list / Gotta lotta nerve / You've lost that lovin feelin / You make my dreams / Diddy doo wop / Everytime you go away / Africa.

Compact disc: released on RCA, '86 by RCA Records. Dist: RCA, Roots, Swift, Wellard, Chris, I & B, Solomon & Peres Distribution

WHOLE OATS (Hall, Daryl & John Oates).
Album: released on Atlantic, Sep'76 by WEA Records. Dist: WEA

X-STATIC (Hall, Daryl & John Oates).
Album: released on RCA International (USA), Sep'81 by RCA Records. Dist: RCA

YOUR IMAGINATION (Hall, Daryl & John Oates).
Single (7"): released on RCA, Jun'82 by RCA Records. Dist: RCA, Roots, Swift, Wellard, Chris, I & B, Solomon & Peres Distribution

Single (12"): released on RCA, Jun'82 by RCA Records. Dist: RCA, Roots, Swift, Wellard, Chris, I & B, Solomon & Peres Distribution

Hallom, Gerry

RUN A MINUTE, A.
Album: released on Fellside, May'85 by Fellside Records. Dist: Roots, Jazz Music, Celtic Music, Projection

TRAVELLIN' DOWN THE CASTLEREAGH.
Album: released on Fellside (Cumbria), '83 by Fellside Records. Dist: Roots, Projection, CM, Jazz Music

Halloran, John

STEPHEN FOSTER SINGS (Halloran, John, Singers).
Album: released on Tradition, Nov'74 Dist: JSU, Cassion Distribution, Celtic Music, Jazz Music, Projection, Roots Records

Halloween 1

HALLOWEEN 1 original soundtrack (Various Artists).
Album: released on Celine(West Germany), Jan'86 Dist: Silva Screen

Halloween 2

HALLOWEEN 2 original soundtrack (Various Artists).
Album: released on Celine(West Germany), Jan'86 Dist: Silva Screen

Hallow's Eve

TALES OF TERROR.
Album: released on Roadrunner (Dutch), Jun'85 Dist: Pinnacle

Hall, Pam

DEAR BOOPSIE.
Single (7"): released on Blue Mountain, Aug'86 Dist: Jetstar

Cassette: released on Blue Mountain, Aug'86 Dist: Jetstar

HOW GLAD I AM.
Tracks: / Hot hot loving.
Single (12"): released on Blue Trac, Aug'87 by Blue Mountain Records. Dist: Jetstar

LATE AT NIGHT.
Single (7"): released on Malaco, Jan'84 by Malaco Records. Dist: Charly

Single (12"): released on Malaco, Jan'84 by Malaco Records. Dist: Charly

NOT ONLY MY WIFE.
Single (12"): released on Unknown, Mar'86

PERFIDIA.
Album: released on World Enterprise, Nov'86 Dist: Jetstar

PERFIDIA, THE.
Tracks: / Perfidia, The / Come in a dis.
Single (12"): released on World Enterprise, Nov'86 Dist: Jetstar

PERFILLA Instrumental version.
Single (12"): released on Mobiliser, Feb'84 by Jetstar Records. Dist: Jetstar Distribution

SUPPLY AND DEMAND (Hall, Pam Mark).
Album: released on Reunion, Aug'85

Cassette: released on Reunion, Aug'85

Hall, Patrick

WITHOUT YOU.
Single (12"): released on A.Small, Mar'83

Hall, Randy

BELONG TO YOU, I.
Album: released on MCA, Aug'84 by MCA Records. Dist: Polygram, MCA

Cassette: released on MCA, Aug'84 by MCA Records. Dist: Polygram, MCA

Hall, Robin

HIGHLANDS & LOWLANDS (Hall, Robin & Jimmy Mc Gregor).

TWO HEIDS ARE BETTER THAN YIN (Hall, Robin & Jimmy Mc Gregor).
Album: released on Bulldog Records, Jul'82

Hall, Roy

DIGGIN' THE BOOGIE.
Album: released on Charly, Feb'84 by Charly Records. Dist: Charly, Cadillac

Hall, Tom

GREATEST HITS:TOM HALL (Hall, Tom T.).
Album: released on Mercury (USA), Sep'83 by Import Records. Dist: IMS Distribution, Polygram Distribution

GREATEST HITS: TOM T. HALL VOL.2 (Hall, Tom T.).
Album: released on Mercury (USA), Sep'83 by Import Records. Dist: IMS Distribution, Polygram Distribution

GREATEST HITS: TOM T. VOL.3 (Hall, Tom T.).
Album: released on Mercury (USA), Sep'83 by Import Records. Dist: IMS Distribution, Polygram Distribution

NATURAL DREAMS (Hall, Tom T.).
Album: released on Mercury, Sep'84 by Phonogram Records. Dist: Polygram Distribution
Cat. no: **MERL 47**

Compact disc: released on Mercury, Sep'84 by Phonogram Records. Dist: Polygram Distribution

P.S I LOVE YOU (Hall, Tom T.).
Single (7"): released on Phonogram, Oct'84 by Phonogram Records. Dist: Polygram

WHO DO YOU PRAY FOR (Hall, Tom T.).
Single (7"): released on Range, Oct'83 Dist: PRT, Jetstar

WORLD CLASS COUNTRY (Hall, Tom T.).
Album: released on Range, Jan'85 Dist: PRT, Jetstar

Hall, Tom T.

CLASSIC TOM T.HALL..
Tracks: / I washed my face in the morning dew / Ballad of forty dollars / Home coming / Week in a country jail,A / Salute to a switchblade / Year that Clayton Delaney died,The / Me and Jesus / Old dogs, children and watermelon wine / Ravishing Ruby / I love / That song is driving me crazy / Country is / Faster horses (The cowboy and the poet) / Your man loves you honey / Fox on the run / PS. I love you.
Notes: A definitive compilation of Tom T.Hall has been long sought after by his many British fans. 'Classic Tom T.Hall' is that album. Detailed sleeve notes by Tony Byworth and a run down of US catalogue numbers and chart positions is in- cluded.
Album: released on Mercury, May'87 by Phonogram Records. Dist: Polygram Distribution
Cat. no: **PRICE 104**

Cassette: released on Mercury, May'87 by Phonogram Records. Dist: Polygram Distribution

IN CONCERT.
Tracks: / Country is / Ballad of forty dollars / Year that Clayton Delaney died, The / Foggy Mountain breakdown / I know you're married (but I love you still) / Don't tell Ruby where I'm at / Your man loves you honey / I like beer / I took a memory to lunch / Sneaky snake / I love / Old dogs, children and watermelon wine.
Album: released on RCA, Mar'86 by RCA Records. Dist: RCA, Roots, Swift, Wellard, Chris, I & B, Solomon & Peres Distribution

Cassette: released on RCA, Mar'86 by RCA Records. Dist: RCA, Roots, Swift, Wellard, Chris, I & B, Solomon & Peres Distribution

LOVE LETTERS IN THE SAND.
Tracks: / Love letters in the sand / Song in a sea shell.
Single (7"): released on Mercury, Oct'86 by Phonogram Records. Dist: Polygram Distribution

STORY TELLER AND THE BANJO MAN, THE (Hall, Tom T. & Earl Scruggs).
Album: released on CBS, Aug'82 by CBS Records. Dist: CBS

Cassette: released on CBS, Aug'82 by CBS Records. Dist: CBS

Hall, Tony

FIELDVOLE MUSIC.
Album: released on Free Reed, Sep'79 by Free Reed Records. Dist: Roots, Projection, Hobgoblin Records, Oblivion

Hallyday, Johnny

TRIFFT DIE RATTLES.
Album: released on Bear Family, Mar'84 by Bear Family Records. Dist: Rollercoaster Distribution, Swift

Halpin, Kieran

BELIEVING.
Single (7"): released on CMS, Dec'84 by CMS Records. Dist: Celtic Music

LIVE AND KICKING.
Cassette: released on Celtic Music, Aug'85 by Celtic Music Distribution. Dist: Celtic Music, Jazz Music, Projection, Roots

MAN WHO LIVES IN BOTTLES, THE.

Album: released on Celtic Music, Jan'84 by Celtic Music Distribution. Dist: Celtic Music, Jazz Music, Projection, Roots

PORT OF CALL (Halpin, Kieran/Tom McConville).
Album: released on Rubber, Jun'82 by Rubber Records. Dist: Roots Distribution, Projection

Distribution, Jazz Music Distribution, Celtic Music Distribution, JSU Distribution, Spartan Distribution

STREETS OF EVERYWHERE, THE (Halpin, Kieran/Tom McConville).
Album: released on Black Crow, Jun'82 by Mawson & Wareham Records. Dist: Projection

Album: released on Black Crow, Jun'82 by Mawson & Wareham Records. Dist: Projection

Hambi

25 TEARS A DAY.
Single (7"): released on MCA, Sep'84 by MCA Records. Dist: Polygram, MCA

Single (12"): released on MCA, Sep'84 by MCA Records. Dist: Polygram, MCA Deleted '85.

I DON'T WANT TO LOSE YOU.
Tracks: / I don't want to lose you / Julie.
Single (7"): released on Harry Barter Productions, Jan'86 by Harry Barter Productions. Dist: PRT

Single (12"): released on Harry Barter Productions, Jan'86 by Harry Barter Productions. Dist: PRT

Hambi & the Dance

HEARTACHE.
Album: released on Virgin, May'82 by Virgin Records. Dist: EMI, Virgin Distribution

Cassette: released on Virgin, May'82 by Virgin Records. Dist: EMI, Virgin Distribution

Hamblen, Stuart

THIS OLD HOUSE HAS GOT TO GO.
Album: released on Stetson, 11 Apr'87 by Hasmick Promotions Ltd.. Dist: Counterpoint Distribution, H.R. Taylor Distribution, Swift Distribution, Chris Wellard Distribution

Cassette: released on Stetson, 11 Apr'87 by Hasmick Promotions Ltd.. Dist: Counterpoint Distribution, H.R. Taylor Distribution, Swift Distribution, Chris Wellard Distribution

Hamburg Radio...

FESTIVAL OF STRAUSS (Hamburg Radio Symphony Orchestra).
Album: released on Spot, Aug'83 by Pickwick Records. Dist: H.R. Taylor, Lugtons

Cassette: released on Spot, Aug'83 by Pickwick Records. Dist: H.R. Taylor, Lugtons

Hamdi, Baligh

INDO-ARABIC VARIATIONS (Hamdi, Baligh & Magid Khan).
Album: released on Sunset (France), Mar'85 Dist: IMS-Polygram Distribution

Hamefarers

BREATH O' SHETLAND.
Cassette: released on Accordion Record Club, Jul'86 by Accordion Record Club Records. Dist: Accordion Record Club

BREATH O' SHETLAND, A.
Album: released on Ross, '86 by Ross Records. Dist: Ross Distribution, Roots Distribution

Cassette: released on Ross, '86 by Ross Records. Dist: Ross Distribution, Roots Distribution

Hamel, Peter Michael

ORGANUM.
Album: released on Kuckuck (Germany), Jul'86

Cassette: released on Kuckuck (Germany), Jul'86

Hamill, Chris

ANGIE.
Single (7"): released on Random, Apr'81 Dist: Pinnacle

Single (7"): released on Solid Rock, Feb'83 Dist: Word Distribution

Hamill, Claire

24 HOURS FROM TULSA.
Single (7"): released on Beggars Banquet, Apr'83 by Beggars Banquet Records. Dist: WEA

Single (12"): released on Beggars Banquet, Apr'83 by Beggars Banquet Records. Dist: WEA

DENMARK.
Single (7"): released on Coda, Jul'84 by Coda Records. Dist: Pinnacle, Cartel, WEA, Roots

Single (12"): released on Coda, Jul'84 by Coda Records. Dist: Pinnacle, Cartel, WEA, Roots

DOOMSDAY, THE (EP).
Tracks: / Doomsday, The / Glastonbury (Jerusalem) / Tides / Spring awaken, lark rise / Stars.
Single (7"): released on Coda, Nov'86 by Coda Records. Dist: Pinnacle, Cartel, WEA, Roots

IF YOU'D ONLY TALK TO ME.
Single (7"): released on Coda, May'85 by Coda Records. Dist: Pinnacle, Cartel, WEA, Roots

Single (12"): released on Coda, May'85 by Coda Records. Dist: Pinnacle, Cartel, WEA, Roots

MOON IS A POWERFUL LOVER, A.
Single (12"): released on Coda, Jun'84 by Coda Records. Dist: Pinnacle, Cartel, WEA, Roots

Single (7"): released on Coda, Jun'84 by Coda Records. Dist: Pinnacle, Cartel, WEA, Roots

OCTOBER.
Album: released on Beggars Banquet, Mar'83 by Beggars Banquet Records. Dist: WEA

Cassette: released on Beggars Banquet, Mar'83 by Beggars Banquet Records. Dist: WEA

ONE HOUSE LEFT STANDING.
Album: released on Beggars Banquet, Mar'83 by Beggars Banquet Records. Dist: WEA

Cassette: released on Beggars Banquet, Mar'83 by Beggars Banquet Records. Dist: WEA

PALM OF MY HAND.
Single (7"): released on Coda, Nov'83 by Coda Records. Dist: Pinnacle, Cartel, WEA, Roots

Single (12"): released on Coda, Nov'83 by Coda Records. Dist: Pinnacle, Cartel, WEA, Roots

TOUCH PAPER.
Tracks: / Moon is a powerful lover / Denmark / Two fools in a storm / First night in New York / Come along brave lads / Jump / In the palm of my hand / Gonna be the one / Ultra-violet light / Once is not enough.
Compact disc: released on Coda, Oct'84 by Coda Records. Dist: Pinnacle, Cartel, WEA, Roots

Album: released on Coda, Sep'84 by Coda Records. Dist: Pinnacle, Cartel, WEA, Roots

Cassette: released on Coda, Sep'84 by Coda Records. Dist: Pinnacle, Cartel, WEA, Roots

Compact disc: released on Coda, Sep'84 by Coda Records. Dist: Pinnacle, Cartel, WEA, Roots

VOICES.
Album: released on Coda, Apr'86 by Coda Records. Dist: Pinnacle, Cartel, WEA, Roots

Cassette: released on Coda, Apr'86 by Coda Records. Dist: Pinnacle, Cartel, WEA, Roots
Cat. no: **NAGEC 8**
Compact disc: released on Coda, Apr'86 by Coda Records. Dist: Pinnacle, Cartel, WEA, Roots

Hamilton, Andy

SUPERCHART SAX.
Album: released on Ronco, Nov'81

Cassette: released on Ronco, Nov'81

Hamilton, Bob

DANCE PARTY.

Hamilton, Chico

MAN FROM TWO WORLDS.
Album: released on Jasmine, Aug'82 by Jasmine Records. Dist: Counterpoint, Lugtons, Taylor, H.R., Wellard, Chris, Swift, Cadillac
Cat. no: **JAS 48**
Cassette: released on Jasmine, Aug'82 by Jasmine Records. Dist: Counterpoint, Lugtons, Taylor, H.R., Wellard, Chris, Swift, Cadillac

MAY 19TH & 20TH, 1959 (Hamilton, Chico Quintet).
Album: released on From The Jazz Vault, Oct'80 by Damont Records. Dist: Swift, Taylor, H.R.

PASSIN' THRU (Hamilton, Chico Quintet).
Album: released on Jasmine, Jun'82 by Jasmine Records. Dist: Counterpoint, Lugtons, Taylor, H.R., Wellard, Chris, Swift, Cadillac

Cassette: released on Jasmine, Jun'82 by Jasmine Records. Dist: Counterpoint, Lugtons, Taylor, H.R., Wellard, Chris, Swift, Cadillac

Hamilton, Colbert

COLBERT HAMILTON & THE HELL RAZORS (Hamilton, Colbert & the Hell Razors).
Album: released on Fearless, Jul'84 by Fearless Records. Dist: Spartan, Cartel

LONG BLACK SHINY CAR (Hamilton, Colbert & the Hell Razors).
Single (7"): released on Rewind, Aug'84 by Rewind Records. Dist: Spartan

Hamilton, David

CINEMA ORGAN ENCORES.
Album: released on Deroy, Jun'81 by Deroy Records. Dist: Jazz Music, Swift

MELODY LINGERS ON Sounds on the Conn. Vol.1.
Cassette: released on Audio-Impact, Jun'81 Dist: H.R. Taylor

SOUNDS OF CONN vol.1.
Cassette: released on Amberlee, Oct'80 by Amberlee Records. Dist: Amberlee Records, H.R. Taylor

Hamilton, George

16 GREAT PERFORMANCES (Hamilton IV, George).
Album: released on ABC, Apr'76 Dist: CBS, Pinnacle

20 OF THE BEST (Hamilton IV, George).
Album: released on RCA, Mar'84 by RCA Records. Dist: RCA, Roots, Swift, Wellard, Chris, I & B, Solomon & Peres Distribution

Cassette: released on RCA, Mar'84 by RCA Records. Dist: RCA, Roots, Swift, Wellard, Chris, I & B, Solomon & Peres Distribution

BEST OF GEORGE HAMILTON IV (Hamilton IV, George).
Album: released on Victor, '74

BLUEGRASS GOSPEL (Hamilton 1V, George).
Album: released on Lamb & Lion, May'82 by Word Records. Dist: Word Distribution

Cassette: released on Lamb & Lion, May'82 by Word Records. Dist: Word Distribution

CUTTING ACROSS THE COUNTRY (Hamilton IV, George).
Album: released on RCA, Feb'81 by RCA Records. Dist: RCA, Roots, Swift, Wellard, Chris, I & B, Solomon & Peres Distribution

ENGLAND (Hamilton IV, George).
Single (7"): released on MRE, Sep'82

FAMOUS COUNTRY MUSIC MAKERS-COAST TO COAST (Hamilton IV, George).
Tracks: / Marie Laveau / Faster horses / Long black veil / Vince / Old gang's gone, The / Put a little lovin' on me / Little bit later on down the line, A / Hillbilly hell / Jackson / Back home in Huntsville again / I've got a thing about trains / Last dance at the Old Texas moon / One among the three of us / Singer of sad songs / Wilma Lou / Cowboys and daddies / Alimony / Air conditioner song, The / Daddy what if / Sunday mornin' down / You made a believer out me / Dropkick me Jesus (through the goalposts of life) / Wonderful soup stone, The / Bird named yesterday, A / Vegas / High plains jamboree / They covered up the old swimmin' hole / Woman in every man's life, The / Up against the wall Redneck mother / If you think I'm crazy / Amarillo highway / Great snowman, The / Redneck hippie.
Double Album: released on RCA, '79 by RCA Records. Dist: RCA, Roots, Swift, Wellard, Chris, I & B, Solomon & Peres Distribution

HYMMS COUNTRY STYLE (Hamilton IV, George).
Album: released on Word, Apr'85 by Word Records. Dist: Word Distribution, CBS

Cassette: released on Word, Apr'85 by Word Records. Dist: Word Distribution, CBS

MUSIC MAN'S DREAMS (Hamilton IV, George).
Album: released on Range, '84 Dist: PRT, Jetstar

NATIVIDAD (Hamilton IV, George).
Single (7"): released on MCPA, Dec'80

ONE DAY AT A TIME (Hamilton IV, George).
Album: released on Word, May'85 by Word Records. Dist: Word Distribution, CBS

Cassette: released on Word, May'85 by Word Records. Dist: Word Distribution, CBS

SONGS FOR A WINTERS NIGHT (Hamilton IV, George).
Album: released on Ronco, Oct'82

Cassette: released on Ronco, Oct'82

WAY OLD FRIENDS DO (Hamilton IV, George).

Hamilton IV, George

AT THE COUNTRY STORE.
Album: released on Starblend Country Store, Aug'86 by Starblend Records. Dist: PRT Distribution

Cassette: released on Starblend Country Store, Aug'86 by Starblend Records. Dist: PRT Distribution

CANADIAN PACIFIC.
Album: released on RCA/Camden, Sep'86

GEORGE HAMILTON 1V.
Tracks: / Till I gain control again / Can't remember, can't forget / Early morning rain / I will love you all my life / Break my mind / Good ole boys like me / Cornbread, beans and sweet potato pie / Canadian Pacific / Dirty old man / Blue train (of the heartbreak line) / Suzanne / 10 degrees and getting colder / Anyway / She's a little bit country / Streets of London / Countryfield / Let's get together* / West Texas highway / Back where it's at / Country music in my soul.
Notes: All produced by Bob Ferguson except * produced by Ronny Light.
Album: released on MFP, Mar'87 by EMI Records. Dist: EMI

Cassette: released on MFP, Mar'87 by EMI Records. Dist: EMI

GEORGE HAMILTON IV.
Tracks: / Abilene / Forever young / You're the best thing.
Notes: Produced by Billy Strange the album contains new recordings of several of the artists biggest hits including 'Abilene' and 'Early Morning Rain'.
Album: released on MCA, Mar'86 by MCA Records. Dist: Polygram, MCA
Cat. no: **MCF 3314**
Cassette: released on MCA, Mar'86 by MCA Records. Dist: Polygram, MCA

Hamilton, Jeff

INDIANA (Hamilton, Jeff Quintet).
Album: released on Concord Jazz, Jul'82 by Concord Jazz Records (USA). Dist: IMS, Polygram

Hamilton, Jimmy

IT'S ABOUT TIME.
Album: released on Fantasy (USA), Feb'86 by Fantasy Inc USA Records. Dist: IMS, Polygram

Hamilton, Joe

DO WHAT YOU DO DO WELL (Hamilton, Joe E.).
Album: released on Homespun(Ireland), '82 by Outlet Records. Dist: Outlet

Cassette: released on Homespun(Ireland), '82 by Outlet Records. Dist: Outlet

MOCKING BIRD HILL (Hamilton, Joe E.).
Album: released on Ara (Ireland), Jul'83 Dist: Outlet, I & B, EMI (Ireland)

Cassette: released on Ara (Ireland), Jul'83 Dist: Outlet, I & B, EMI (Ireland)

SING ME A GOOD OLD COUNTRY SONG (Hamilton, Joe E.).
Album: released on Homespun(Ireland), '82 by Outlet Records. Dist: Outlet

Cassette: released on Homespun(Ireland), '82 by Outlet Records. Dist: Outlet

Hamilton, John

THEM CHANGES (Hamilton, John & Doris Allen).
Single (7"): released on Charly, Mar'81 by Charly Records. Dist: Charly, Cadillac

Hamilton, Kenny

RIGHT HERE IS WHERE YOU BELONG.
Album: released on Scorpio, Feb'86 by Scorpio Records. Dist: Jetstar

Hamilton Pops Orchestra

DANCE PARTY.
Cassette: released on Chevron, Nov'84 Dist: Multiple Sound Distributors

Cassette: released on Chevron, Nov'84 Dist: Multiple Sound Distributors

Hamilton, Roy

HOLD ONTO THIS MOOD (REMIX).
Tracks: / Hold onto this mood (remix) / Hold onto this mood (inst).
Single (12"): released on Fourth & Broadway, Jun'87 by Island Records. Dist: Polygram, EMI

HOLD ONTO THIS MOOD.
Tracks: / Hold onto this mood / Hold onto this mood (inst).
Single (7"): released on Fourth & Broadway, 23 May'87 by Island Records. Dist: Polygram, EMI

Single (12"): released on Fourth & Broadway, 23 May'87 by Island Records. Dist: Polygram, EMI

HOLD TIGHT.
Single (7"): released on PRT, Apr'84 by PRT Records. Dist: PRT

HOW DO YOU DO Instrumentl mix.
Single (7"): released on PRT, Jul'83 by PRT Records. Dist: PRT

Hamilton, Russ

WE WILL MAKE LOVE/RAINBOW.
Single (7"): released on Old Gold, Jul'82 by Old Gold Records. Dist: Lightning, Jazz Music, Spartan, Counterpoint

Hamilton Sara & David

LIVE.
Album: released on Innovation, Oct'84 by Innovation Records. Dist: Jetstar

Hamilton, Scott

APPLES & ORANGES.
Album: released on Concord, Dec'81 by Import Records. Dist: IMS, Polygram

GRAND APPEARANCE, THE (Hamilton Scott Quartet).
Album: released on Progressive, Apr'81 by Progressive Records. Dist: Jetstar

HAMILTON, SCOTT & RUBY BRAFF (Hamilton, Scott & Ruby Braff).
Album: released on Phontastic, Nov'86 Dist:

Wellard, Chris

MAJOR LEAGUE (Hamilton, Scott, Jake Hanna, Dave McKenna).
Tracks: / Swinging at the Copper Rail / Pretty girl is like a melody, A / Cocktails for two / I'm through with love / Linger awhile / September in the rain / This is all I ask / It all depends on you / April in Paris.
Album: released on Concord Jazz(USA), Sep'86 by Concord Jazz Records (USA). Dist: IMS, Polygram

Cassette: released on Concord Jazz(USA), Sep'86 by Concord Jazz Records (USA). Dist: IMS, Polygram

RGHT TIME (THE).
Album: released on Concord Jazz(USA), Feb'87 by Concord Jazz Records (USA). Dist: IMS, Polygram

RIGHT TIME, THE (Hamilton, Scott Quintet).
Tracks: / Just in time / If I love again / Sleep / Eventide / All through the night / Skylark / Stealing port.
Compact disc: released on Concord Jazz(USA), Jul'87 by Concord Jazz Records (USA). Dist: IMS, Polygram

SCOTT HAMILTON QUINTET IN CONCERT, THE (Hamilton, Scott Quintet).
Album: released on Concord, Feb'84 by Import Records. Dist: IMS, Polygram

SCOTT HAMILTON & WARREN VACHE (Hamilton Scott & Warren Vache).
Album: released on Concord, Apr'79 by Import Records. Dist: IMS, Polygram

SCOTTS BUDDY (Hamilton Scott & Buddy Tate).
Album: released on Concord, May'81 by Import Records. Dist: IMS, Polygram

SECOND SET, THE.
Album: released on Concord, Nov'84 by Import Records. Dist: IMS, Polygram

SECOND SET (THE).
Tracks: / All the things you are / Time after time / Taps Miller / All too soon / How insensitive / I never knew / For all we know / Jumpin' the blues.
Notes. This album captures the second set of an impeccable live performance by the Scott Hamilton Quintet. Scott's band swings through a beautiful set of standards with the precision of the Benny Goodman quartet and the fire of Count Basie's Kansas City Seven.
Compact disc: released on Concord Jazz(USA), May'85 by Concord Jazz Records (USA). Dist: IMS, Polygram

Hamlet
HAMLET William Shakespeare (Derek Jacobi Timothy west and Barbara Jefford).
Album: released on Argo, Jul'82 by Decca Records. Dist: Polygram

Cassette: released on MFP, Nov'77 by EMI Records. Dist: EMI

Hamlisch, Marvin
ENTERTAINER.
Single (7"): released on MCA, Jun'83 by MCA Records. Dist: Polygram, MCA

ENTERTAINER (STING THEME), THE.
Single (7"): released on MCA, Feb'74 by MCA Records. Dist: Polygram, MCA

ORDINARY PEOPLE THEME.
Single (7"): released on Planet, Apr'81 Dist: WEA

Hammatan
NITE OF BLISS.

Single (7"): released on Lagos, Sep'80

Hammer
CONTRACT WITH HELL.
Album: released on Ebony, Apr'85 by Ebony Records. Dist: Pinnacle, Ebony

Hammer, Jan
CROCKETT'S THEME.
Single (7"): released on MCA, Aug'87 by MCA Records. Dist: Polygram, MCA

Single (12"): released on MCA, Aug'87 by MCA Records. Dist: Polygram, MCA

MIAMI VICE THEME.
Single (7"): released on MCA, Sep'85 by MCA Records. Dist: Polygram, MCA

UNTOLD PASSION (Hammer Jan & Neil Schon).
Album: released on CBS, Nov'82 by CBS Records. Dist: CBS

Hammet Vic
CINEMA ORGAN ENCORES.

Album: released on Deroy, Jun'81 by Deroy Records. Dist: Jazz Music, Swift

Cassette: released on Deroy, Jun'81 by Deroy Records. Dist: Jazz Music, Swift

Hammill, Peter
AND CLOSE AS THIS.
Tracks: / Too many of my yesterdays / Faith / Empire of delight / Silver / Beside the one you love / Other old cliches / Confidente / Sleep now.
Album: released on Virgin, Nov'86 by Virgin Records. Dist: EMI, Virgin Distribution

Cassette: released on Virgin, Nov'86 by Virgin Records. Dist: EMI, Virgin Distribution

BLACK BOX, A.
Album: released on Mercury, Jun'83 by Phonogram Records. Dist: Polygram Distribution

CHAMELEON IN THE SHADOW OF THE NIGHT/ The silent corner and the empty stage.
Album: released on Charisma, Mar'83 by Virgin Records. Dist: EMI

ENTER K Patience.
Notes: Gatefold Doublepack album and cassette.
Album: released on Spartan, Jan'86 by Spartan Records. Dist: Spartan

Cassette: released on Spartan, Jan'86 by Spartan Records. Dist: Spartan

Album: by Naive. Dist: Spartan

FILM NOIR/ SEVEN WONDERS.
Single (7"): released on Naive, Sep'83 by Naive. Dist: Spartan

FOOLS MATE.
Album: released on Charisma, Sep'83 by Virgin Records. Dist: EMI

FUTURE NOW (THE).
Album: released on Charisma, Oct'86 by Virgin Records. Dist: EMI

IN CAMERA.
Album: by Polydor Records. Dist: Polygram, Polydor

JUST GOOD FRIENDS.
Single (7"): released on Charisma, May'85 by Virgin Records. Dist: EMI

LOVE SONGS, THE.
Album: released on Charisma, Aug'84 by Virgin Records. Dist: EMI

MARGIN, THE (Hammill, Peter And the K Group).
Album: released on Foundry, Feb'85 by Foundry Records. Dist: Virgin, EMI

MARGIN,THE (Hammill, Peter And the K Group).

NADIR BIG CHANCE.
Album: released on Charisma(Import), Mar'83 by Virgin Records. Dist: EMI

PAINTING BY NUMBERS.
Tracks: / Painting by numbers / Hit me where you live.
Single (7"): released on Foundry, Mar'86 by Foundry Records. Dist: Virgin, EMI

Cassette: released on Foundry, Mar'86 by Foundry Records. Dist: Virgin, EMI

SILENT CORNER AND THE EMPTY STAGE.
Album: released on Charisma, Oct'86 by Virgin Records. Dist: EMI

SITTING TARGETS.
Album: released on Virgin, Jun'81 by Virgin Records. Dist: EMI, Virgin Distribution

SKIN.
Album: released on Foundry-Charisma, Jul'86 by Foundry Records. Dist: Virgin, EMI

Cassette: released on Foundry-Charisma, Jul'86 by Foundry Records. Dist: Virgin, EMI

Hammond, Albert
IT NEVER RAINS IN SOUTHERN CALERFORNIA.
Single (7"): released on Old Gold, Jul'82 by Old Gold Records. Dist: Lightning, Jazz Music, Spartan, Counterpoint

Hammond, Beres
ALL BECAUSE I'M LONELY.
Single (12"): released on Charm, May'87 by Jetstar

BERES HAMMOND.
Cassette: released on Charm, Dec'86 Dist: Jetstar

GROOVY LITTLE THING.
Single (12"): released on Harmony House,

Jun'85 by Harmony House Records. Dist: Jetstar

IRE AND MELLO/ IRE VERSION.
Single (12"): released on Londisc, Jan'84 by Londisc Records.

LET ME LOVE YOU/ LOVE SOUND.
Single (7"): released on Nighthawk, Aug'83 by Faulty Products Records. Dist: Pinnacle, Swift

SHE LOVES ME NOW.
Tracks: / She loves me now.
Single (12"): released on Greensleeves, Mar'86 by Greensleeves Records. Dist: BMG, Jetstar, Spartan

STUCK ON YOU.
Single (12"): released on Revue, Jan'85 by Revue Records. Dist: Creole

SUNSHINE PEOPLE.
Tracks: / Sunshine people / Holy mountain lion.
Single (12"): released on Hawkeye, Jun'86 by Hawkeye Records. Dist: Hawkeye, Lightning (WEA) Distribution, Jetstar, PRT

WHAT ONE DANCE CAN DO.
Tracks: / What one dance can do.
Single (12"): released on Revue, Apr'86 by Revue Records. Dist: Creole

Single (12"): released on Revue, Oct'85 by Revue Records. Dist: Creole

Hammond Doug
ALONE.
Album: released on Scarecrow, Apr'81 Dist: Jazz Music

Hammond, John
HAMMONDS HITS FOR THE HIGHWAY.
Cassette: released on Aim, Feb'83 Dist: H.R. Taylor

JOHN HAMMOND LIVE.
Album: released on Spindrift, Mar'84 Dist: Roots

MILEAGE.
Album: released on Sonet, Jun'80 by Sonet Records. Dist: PRT

SPIRITUALS TO SWING (1938-9).
Double Album: released on Vogue, Sep'78 Dist: Discovery, Jazz Music, PRT, Swift

SPOONFUL.
Album: released on Edsel, Apr'84 by Demon Records. Dist: Pinnacle, Jazz Music, Projection

Hammonds Sauce Works
BRASS ABLAZE.
Album: released on Polyphonic, Oct'80 by Polyphonic Records. Dist: Taylors

Cassette: released on Polyphonic, Mar'81 by Polyphonic Records. Dist: Taylors

SPECTACULAR BRASS.
Album: released on Polyphonic, Feb'80 by Polyphonic Records. Dist: Taylors

Cassette: released on Polyphonic, Jul'81 by Polyphonic Records. Dist: Taylors

Hampshire & Dorset
PAST AND PRESENT MUSIC (Hampshire & Dorset Band).
Album: released on Music Masters, Jun'82 by Music Masters Records. Dist: Taylors

Hampshire, Susan
SNOW WHITE Story told by Susan Hampshire.
Cassette: released on Storytime Cassettes, Aug'83

Hampshire Youth Concert
RHAPSODY IN BRASS.
Album: released on Solent, Aug'84 by Solent Records.

Hampton, Lionel
1944-1945 (Hampton, Lionel & His Orchestra).
Album: released on Solid Sender, Apr'81 Dist: Jazz Music

ALIVE AND JUMPING (Hampton, Lionel, Milt Buckner & All Stars).
Album: released on MPS Jazz, Jun'81

ALL AMERICAN AWARD CONCERT.
Album: released on Jasmine, Mar'84 by Jasmine Records. Dist: Counterpoint, Taylor, H.R., Wellard, Chris, Swift, Cadillac

AS TIME GOES BY.
Album: released on Sonet, '78 by Sonet Records. Dist: PRT

AS TIME GOES BY (Hampton, Lionel & Svend Asmussen).
Tracks: / Flying home / Midnight sun / Rose room / As time goes by / Air mail special / Avalon.
Compact disc: released on Sonet, Oct'86 by Sonet Records. Dist: PRT

Album: released on Sonet, Mar'87 by Sonet Records. Dist: PRT

AT NEWPORT '78 (Hampton, Lionel, All Star Band).
Album: released on Timeless, Apr'81

BLACKOUT.
Album: released on Gateway, Sep'83 by Kingdom. Dist: Pinnacle

BOOGIE WOOGIE ALBUM, THE.
Album: released on Telefunken (Germany), Apr'83 Dist: Decca Distribution, IMS, Polygram

COBB'S IDEA.
Album: released on Happy Bird (Germany), Jun'83 Dist: Polygram, IMS

Cassette: released on Happy Bird (Germany), Jun'83 Dist: Polygram, IMS

COMPLETE 1953 PARIS SESSIONS, THE.
Double Album: released on Vogue, Mar'77 Dist: Discovery, Jazz Music, PRT, Swift

COMPLETE LIONEL HAMPTON Volume 1 & 2.
Tracks: / Rhythym, rhythym / China stomp / I know that you know / Confessin' / Drum stomp / Piano stomp / I surrender dear / Object of my affection / Ring dem bells / Don't be that way / I'm in the mood for swing / Shoe shiner's drag / Any time at all / Muskrat ramble / Down home jump / Rock hill special / Fiddle diddle / My last affair / Jivin' the vibes / Mood that I'm in / Hampton stomp / Buzzin' around with the bee / Whoa babe / Stompology / On the sunny side of the street / Judy / Baby wont you please come home / Everybody loves my baby / After you've gone / I just couldn't take it baby / You're my ideal / Sun will shine tonight.
Album: released on RCA, Dec'85 by RCA Records. Dist: RCA, Roots, Swift, Wellard, Chris, I & B, Solomon & Peres Distribution

Cassette: released on RCA, Dec'85 by RCA Records. Dist: RCA, Roots, Swift, Wellard, Chris, I & B, Solomon & Peres Distribution

COMPLETE PARIS SESSION.
Tracks: / September in the rain / Free press / Always / Real crazy / More crazy / Completely crazy / I only have eyes for you.
Compact disc: released on Vogue (France), May'85 Dist: Discovery, Jazz Music, PRT, Swift

FLYING HOME (Hampton, Lionel & His Quartet).
Album: released on Mercury (USA), Nov'83 by Import Records. Dist: IMS Distribution, Polygram Distribution

FLYING HOME.
Album: released on Astan (USA), Mar'85

FLYIN' HOME.
Notes: O.C.I. = Oliver Crombie Imports.
Compact disc: released on Dunhill Compact Classics (USA), '86

HAMP IN HAARLEM (Hampton, Lionel & His Giants of Jazz).
Album: released on Timeless, Apr'81

HAMP THE CHAMP (Hampton, Lionel & His Orchestra).
Tracks: / Whoa babe / On the sunny side of the street / Shine / Don't be that way / I'm in the mood for swing / Muskrat ramble / Shoe shiner's drag / Shufflin' at the Hollywood / When lights are low / Hot mallets / Flying home / Jivin' with Jarvis / Three quarter boogie.
Album: released on RCA, Jul'86 by RCA Records. Dist: RCA, Roots, Swift, Wellard, Chris, I & B, Solomon & Peres Distribution

Cassette: released on RCA, Jul'86 by RCA Records. Dist: RCA, Roots, Swift, Wellard, Chris, I & B, Solomon & Peres Distribution

HAMPTOLOGIA - VOL.1.
Album: released on Polydor (Import), Feb'82

HAMPTOLOGIA - VOL.2.
Album: released on Polydor (Import), Feb'82

HAMPTON & GETZ (Hampton, Lionel & Stan Getz).

IN CONCERT.
Album: released on Jazz Live, Apr'81

IN PARIS - 1956.
Album: released on Swing Disque, May'87

IN THE BAG.
Tracks: / In the bag / Dig those vibes / Jack the fox boogie / How high the moon / Million dollar smile / Turkey hop / Double talk / Empty glass / Hamp's gumbo / Mingus fingers / Three minutes on 52nd Street / Hamp's got a Duke / Dancing on the ceiling / Blues for little 'T' / Memories of

you / Silver slipper.
Album: released on Affinity, Dec'85 by Charly Records. Dist: Charly, Cadillac

Cassette: released on Affinity, Dec'85 by Charly Records. Dist: Charly, Cadillac

JAM BAND.
Album: released on First Heard, '84 by Submarine Records. Dist: Conifer, Taylors

JAY BIRD.
Album: released on Black Lion-Intercord, '82

Cassette: released on Black Lion-Intercord, '82

JAZZ AMBASSADORS, THE.
Album: released on Polydor, '79 by Polydor Records. Dist: Polygram, Polydor

JIVING THE BLUES.
Album: released on Swinghouse, '84 Dist: Jazz Music Distribution, Swift Distribution, Chris Wellard Distribution

LEAPIN' WITH LIONEL (Hampton, Lionel & His Orchestra).
Album: released on Affinity, Nov'83 by Charly Records. Dist: Charly, Cadillac

LIONEL HAMPTON (Hampton, Lionel & His Orchestra).
Album: released on Bright Orange, Apr'79 Dist: Swift

LIONEL HAMPTON COLLECTION (THE).
Album: released on Deja Vu, Jul'86 by Deja Vu Records. Dist: Counterpoint Distribution, Record Services Distribution (Ireland)

Cassette: released on Deja Vu, Jul'86 by Deja Vu Records. Dist: Counterpoint Distribution, Record Services Distribution (Ireland)

LIONEL HAMPTON PRESENTS.
Album: released on Who's Who, Nov'79

LIONEL HAMPTON & THE JUST JAZZ ALL STARS (Hampton, Lionel & The Just Jazz All Stars).
Compact disc: released on Vogue, Dec'86 Dist: Discovery, Jazz Music, PRT, Swift

LIONEL HAMPTON - VOL.1 (Hampton, Lionel & The Just Jazz All Stars).
Album: released on Jazz Reactivation, Jan'82 Dist: PRT

LIONEL HAMPTON - VOL.2.
Album: released on Jazz Reactivation, May'83 Dist: PRT

LIVE AT CARNEGIE HALL Lionel Hampton 50th anniversary concert (Hampton, Lionel & His Orchestra).
Album: released on Carosello, Feb'83 Dist: Jazz Music, Jazz Horizons

LIVE AT THE MUZEVAL (Hampton, Lionel & His Band).
Album: released on Timeless, Apr'81

LIVE IN PARIS - VOL.1.
Album: released on Joker (Import), Apr'81

LIVE IN PARIS - VOL.2.
Album: released on Joker, Apr'81 Dist: Cadillac, Zodiac Distribution, Jazz Horizons, Jazz Music, JSU, Celtic Music

MADE IN JAPAN.
Album: released on Timeless (Holland), Aug'85 Dist: JSU Distribution, Jazz Music Distribution, Jazz Horizons Distribution, Cadillac, Celtic Music Distribution

Cassette: released on Timeless (Holland), Aug'85 Dist: JSU Distribution, Jazz Music Distribution, Jazz Horizons Distribution, Cadillac, Celtic Music Distribution

MASTERPIECES.
Album: released on Saar Giants Of Jazz (Italy), Sep'85 Dist: Mainline

Cassette: released on Saar Giants Of Jazz (Italy), Sep'85 Dist: Mainline

MESS IS HERE, THE Live '44-'45.
Album: released on Solid Sender, Jun'78 Dist: JSU, Jazz Music

MESS IS HERE (THE) 1944-445.
Notes: Mono
Album: released on Magic, Jan'86 Dist: Jazz Music, Submarine, Swift, Chris Wellard, Conifer

Cassette: released on Magic, Jan'86 Dist: Jazz Music, Submarine, Swift, Chris Wellard, Conifer

Album: released on Giants of Jazz, Oct'85 by Hasmick Promotions Ltd.. Dist: Counterpoint, Jazz Music, Taylors, Swift, Mainline, Wellard, Chris

NEWPORT UPROAR.
Album: released on RCA, Feb'86 by RCA Records. Dist: RCA, Roots, Swift, Wellard, Chris, I & B, Solomon & Peres Distribution

Cassette: released on RCA, Feb'86 by RCA Records. Dist: RCA, Roots, Swift, Wellard, Chris, I & B, Solomon & Peres Distribution

NEW YORK BLACKOUT.
Album: released on Pathe MarconiFrance), Jan'85

Cassette: released on Pathe MarconiFrance), Jan'85

PLAY BRASSENS (Hampton, Lionel & Friends).
Album: released on IMS(Import), Mar'84 by Polydor Records. Dist: IMS, Polygram

RING DEM VIBES.
Album: released on Barclay, Nov'79 by Decca Records. Dist: Polygram, Discovery, Conifer, IMS, Swift

SOUL OF LIONEL HAMPTEN, THE.
Album: released on Joker, Apr'81 Dist: Cadillac, Zodiac Distribution, Jazz Horizons, Jazz Music, JSU, Celtic Music

STARDUST (Hampton, Lionel All Stars).
Album: released on Jasmine, Jun'85 by Jasmine Records. Dist: Counterpoint, Lugtons, Taylor, H.R., Wellard, Chris. Swift. Cadillac

VIBERATIONS.
Album: released on Giants of Jazz, Oct'85 by Hasmick Promotions Ltd.. Dist: Counterpoint Jazz Music, Taylors, Swift, Mainline, Wellard, Chris

YOU BETTER KNOW IT!!.
Album: released on Jasmine, Jun'82 by Jasmine Records. Dist: Counterpoint, Lugtons, Taylor, H.R., Wellard, Chris, Swift, Cadillac

Cassette: released on Jasmine, Jun'82 by Jasmine Records. Dist: Counterpoint, Lugtons, Taylor, H.R., Wellard, Chris, Swift, Cadillac

Hampton, Slide

1969 (Hampton, Slide Quartet).
Album: released on Pathe MarconiFrance), Sep'84

DAY IN COPENHAGEN, A (see Gordon, Dexter).

Hampton Strings

QUIET NIGHTS IN.
Double Album: released on Cambra, '83 by Cambra Records. Dist: IDS, Conifer

Double cassette: released on Cambra, '83 by Cambra Records. Dist: IDS, Conifer

Hancock, Herbie

BEST OF HERBIE HANCOCK.
Album: released on CBS, Nov'84 by CBS Records. Dist: CBS

Cassette: released on CBS, Nov'84 by CBS Records. Dist: CBS

BY ALL MEANS (Hancock, Herbie & Alphonse Mouzon).
Album: released on MPS Jazz, Apr'81

EMPYREAN ISLES.
Album: released on Blue Note, Oct'85 by EMI Records. Dist: EMI

FEETS DON'T FAIL ME NOW.
Tracks: / You bet your love / Trust me / Tell everybody / Ready or not / Honey from the jar / Knee deep.
Compact disc: released on CBS, Sep'85 by CBS Records. Dist: CBS

FUTURE SHOCK.
Album: released on CBS, 11 Apr'87 by CBS Records. Dist: CBS

Cassette: released on CBS, 11 Apr'87 by CBS Records. Dist: CBS

Album: released on CBS, Aug'83 by CBS Records. Dist: CBS

Cassette: released on CBS, Aug'83 by CBS Records. Dist: CBS

HANCOCK, HERBIE AND THE ROCKIT BAND (Hancock, Herbie & The Rockit Band).
Video-cassette (VHS): released on CBS, Oct'84 by CBS Records. Dist: CBS

HARDROCK.
Single (7"): released on CBS, Aug'84 by CBS Records. Dist: CBS

Single (12"): released on CBS, Aug'84 by CBS Records. Dist: CBS

HEADHUNTERS.
Notes: Digital stereo
Compact disc: released on CBS, Jul'84 by CBS Records. Dist: CBS

HERBIE HANCOCK: GREATEST HITS.
Album: released on CBS, Jan'80 by CBS Records. Dist: CBS

Cassette: released on CBS, Jan'80 by CBS Records. Dist: CBS

HOT AND HEAVY.
Album: released on Star Jazz USA, Apr'86 by Charly Records. Dist: Charly Distribution

Cassette: released on Star Jazz USA, Apr'86 by Charly Records. Dist: Charly Distribution

Album: released on Premier, '84 by Premier Records. Dist: CBS

Cassette: released on Premier, '84 by Premier Records. Dist: CBS

Album: released on Chase Music, Nov'84 by Chase Records. Dist: PRT

Cassette: released on Chase Music, Nov'84 by Chase Records. Dist: PRT

I THOUGHT IT WAS YOU.
Single (7"): released on CBS, May'82 by CBS Records. Dist: CBS

Single (7"): released on Old Gold, Sep'85 by Old Gold Records. Dist: Lightning, Jazz Music, Spartan, Counterpoint

MAIDEN VOYAGE.
Tracks: / Maiden voyage / Eye of the hurricane, The / Little one, The / Survival of the fittest / Dolphin dance.
Album: released on Blue Note, May'85 by EMI Records. Dist: EMI

Cassette: released on Blue Note, May'85 by EMI Records. Dist: EMI

Cassette: released on Blue Note (France), Mar'84 Dist: Conifer

Compact disc: released on Blue Note, Sep'87 by EMI Records. Dist: EMI. Estim retail price in Sep'87 was £11.99.

Cassette: released on Blue Note, Sep'87 by EMI Records. Dist: EMI. Estim retail price in Sep'87 was £5.99.

MR HANDS.
Cassette: released on CBS, Nov'80 by CBS Records. Dist: CBS

MY POINT OF VIEW.
Album: released on Blue Note, Oct'84 by EMI Records. Dist: EMI

PIANO, THE.
Album: released on Japanese Import, Jan'80

PRISONER, THE.
Tracks: / I have a dream / Prisoner, The / Firewater / He who lives in fear / Promise of the sun / I have a dream / Prisoner, The / Firewater / He who lives in fear / Promise of the sun.
Compact disc: released on Manhattan-Blue Note, Aug'87 by EMI America Records (USA). Dist: EMI

Album: released on Blue Note, Sep'87 by EMI Records. Dist: EMI. Estim retail price in Sep'87 was £5.99.

QUARTET.
Album: released on CBS, '84 by CBS Records. Dist: CBS

ROCK IT.
Tracks: / Rock it / You bet your love / I thought it was you.
Single (12"): released on Old Gold, Feb'86 by Old Gold Records. Dist: Lightning, Jazz Music, Spartan, Counterpoint

SOUND SYSTEM.
Tracks: / Hardrock / Metal beat / Karabali / People are changing / Sound system.
Compact disc: released on CBS, Dec'85 by CBS Records. Dist: CBS

SOUND-SYSTEM.
Tracks: / Hardrock / Metal beat / Karabali / Junku / People are changing / Sound-system / Rockit / Autodrive / Future shock / TFS / Rough / Chameleon.
Album: released on CBS, Aug'86 by CBS Records. Dist: CBS

Cassette: released on CBS, Aug'86 by CBS Records. Dist: CBS

SPEAK LIKE A CHILD.
Tracks: / Riot / Speak like a child / First trip / Toys / Godbye to childhood / Sorcerer (The).
Compact disc: released on EMI, Mar'87 by EMI Records. Dist: EMI

Album: released on Blue Note, Jul'85 by EMI Records. Dist: EMI

SUNLIGHT.
Album: released on CBS, Jul'78 by CBS Records. Dist: CBS

Cassette: released on CBS, Jul'78 by CBS Records. Dist: CBS

TAKING OFF.
Tracks: / Watermelon man / Three bags full / Empty pockets / Maze, The / Driftin' / Alone and I.
Notes: Certainly a prophetic title for Herbie Hancock's first album. Aided by an all star front line of Freddie Hubbard and Dexter Gordon, Hancock's first date displays unusual maturity, lyricism and a strong sense of funk within the jazz context. Highlights include the initial recording of 'Watermelon Man' and other bluesy items such as 'Empty Pockets' and 'Three Bags Full'.
Album: released on Blue Note, May'86 by EMI Records. Dist: EMI

TAKIN' OFF.
Tracks: / Watermelon man / Three bags full / Empty pockets / Maze, The / Driftin' / Alone and I.
Compact disc: released on Manhattan-Blue Note, May'87 by EMI America Records (USA). Dist: EMI

Cassette: released on Blue Note, Sep'87 by EMI Records. Dist: EMI. Estim retail price in Sep'87 was £5.99.

THIRD PLANE (Hancock, Herbie/Ron Carter/Tony Williams).
Compact disc: released on Carrere(France), '86 by Carrere Records (France). Dist: PRT

THRUST.
Album: released on CBS, Oct'74 by CBS Records. Dist: CBS

Hancock, Hunter

BLUES & RHYTHM MIDNIGHT MATINEE (Hancock, Hunter Presents Various Artists).
Album: released on Route 66 (Sweden), Aug'85 by Mr. R&B Records. Dist: Swift Distribution, Cadillac, Jazz Music Distribution

CRUISIN' 1959 KGFJ Los Angeles.
Cassette: released on Increase(USA), Jun'87 by Quicksilver Records (USA).

Hancock, John

MISSIPPI MOTION A legacy in river ragtime.
Album: released on Stomp Off, Mar'87 by Stomp Off Records. Dist: Jazz Music Distribution

Hancock, Keith

KEITH HANCOCK.
Album: released on Greenwich Village, Jan'87 by Sweet Folk All Records. Dist: Roots, Projection, Lightning, Celtic Music, Wellard, Chris

Hancock, Tony

BEST OF..., THE.
Album: released on Hallmark, Jan'72 by Pickwick Records. Dist: Pickwick Distribution, PRT, Taylors

HANCOCK.
Cassette: released on Marble Arch, Nov'71 Dist: Taylors

HANCOCK'S HALF HOUR.
Album: released on BBC, Oct'83 by BBC Records & Tapes. Dist: EMI, PRT, Pye

Cassette: released on BBC, Oct'83 by BBC Records & Tapes. Dist: EMI, PRT, Pye

Album: released on BBC, Oct'84 by BBC Records & Tapes. Dist: EMI, PRT Pye

Cassette: released on BBC, Oct'84 by BBC Records & Tapes. Dist: EMI, PRT, Pye

Album: released on BBC, Oct'81 by BBC Records & Tapes. Dist: EMI, PRT, Pye

Cassette: released on BBC, Oct'81 by BBC Records & Tapes. Dist: EMI, PRT, Pye

Album: released on BBC, Oct'82 by BBC Records & Tapes. Dist: EMI, PRT, Pye

Cassette: released on BBC, Oct'82 by BBC Records & Tapes. Dist: EMI, PRT, Pye

Album: released on BBC, Nov'80 by BBC Records & Tapes. Dist: EMI, PRT, Pye

Cassette: released on BBC, Nov'80 by BBC Records & Tapes. Dist: EMI, PRT, Pye

LIFT & TWELVE ANGRY MEN, THE
Soundtracks from two TV programmes.
Album: released on BBC, Nov'76 by BBC Records & Tapes. Dist: EMI, PRT, Pye

UNIQUE HANCOCK.
Album: released on BBC, Jan'74 by BBC Records & Tapes. Dist: EMI, PRT, Pye

Cassette: released on BBC, Jan'79 by BBC Records & Tapes. Dist: EMI, PRT Pye

WORLD OF....
Cassette: released on Decca, Jan'79 by Decca Records. Dist: Polygram

WORLD OF TONY HANCOCK, THE.
Album: released on World of Learning, Oct'75 by World Of Learning Records. Dist: World Of

Learning

Handbells

HANDBELLS IN HARMONY.
Album: released on Saydisc, May'79 by Saydisc Records. Dist: Essex, Harmonia Mundi, Roots, H.R. Taylor, Jazz Music, Swift, Projection, Gamut

Handbells In Harmony

SOUNDS IN BRASS HARMONY.
Cassette: released on Saydisc, May'79 by Saydisc Records. Dist: Essex, Harmonia Mundi, Roots, H.R. Taylor, Jazz Music, Swift, Projection, Gamut

Handle, Johnny

COLLIER LAD, THE.
Album: released on Topic, Jan'81 Dist: Roots Distribution

Handley, Guthrie

WHERE WAS (Handley, Guthrie & Wayne Hussey).
Tracks: / Where was / Ha ha world / Four boats still negative*.
Single (7"): released on Lambs To The Slaughter, Jun'87 by Prism Records. Dist: Pinnacle, Red Rhino, Cartel

Single (12"): released on Lambs To The Slaughter, Jun'87 by Prism Records. Dist: Pinnacle, Red Rhino, Cartel

Hands, Brian

LURE OF THE SOUTH SEAS (Hands, Brian Concert Orchestra).
Album: released on Viking, Feb'79 Dist: Harmonia Mundi Distributors

Cassette: released on Viking, Jan'78 Dist: Harmonia Mundi Distributors

Handson & Davis

TONIGHT Love will make it right.
Single (12"): released on ZYX (Germany), Nov'85 by ZYX Records. Dist: Greyhound

Handy, Capt. John

Biographical Details: see under - Kid Sheik.

ALL ABOARD (Handy, Capt. John & His New Orleans Stompers).
Album: released on GHB, Jun'86 Dist: Jazz Music, Swift

CAPT. JOHN HANDY/GEOFF BULL/BARRY MARTYN'S BAND (Handy, Capt. John, Geoff Bull, Barry Martyn).
Album: released on GHB, Feb'87 Dist: Jazz Music, Swift

Handy, John

HARD WORK.
Album: released on Impulse, Aug'76 by Impulse Records. Dist: MCA, Polygram

RIGHT THERE.
Album: released on Gull, Apr'84 by Gull Records. Dist: Pinnacle

Handy, John 'Cap'n'

WITH THE CLAUDE HOPKINS BAND.
Album: released on RCA (France), Feb'85 by RCA Records. Dist: Discovery

Handy, John & Mabel

JOHN & MABEL HANDY MEMORIAL ALBUM.
Album: released on Nola, Apr'79 Dist: JSU, Jazz Music, Cadillac, Chris Wellard

Hang eleven

HANG ELEVEN (MUTANT SURF PUNKS) Various Artists (Various Artists).
Album: released on Anagram, Aug'85 by Cherry Red Records. Dist: Pinnacle

Hangman's...

LOVE IS BLUE (Hangman's Beautiful Daughters).
Tracks: / Love is blue / Popular trend / Jonathan / Don't ask my name.
Single (12"): released on Dreamworld, Mar'87 by TV Personalities, The. Dist: Rough Trade

Hang The Dance

HORSE FLESH.
Tracks: / Horse flesh.
Single (12"):

LAUGHING JACK SAID.
Single (7"): released on Well Hung, Apr'85 Dist: Red Rhino, Cartel

Hanly, Mick

AS I WENT OVER BLACKWATER.
Album: released on Mulligan, Sep'80 by Topic Records. Dist: Roots Distribution, Jazz Music Distribution, JSU Distribution, I & B Distribution, Projection Distribution, Wynd-Up Distribution, Celtic Distributions

Cassette: released on Mulligan, Sep'80 by Topic Records. Dist: Roots Distribution, Jazz Music Distribution, JSU Distribution, I & B Distribution, Projection Distribution, Wynd-Up Distribution, Celtic Distributions

Hanna, Fred

IRISH FAMILY FAVOURITES.
Album: released on Victor, '73

Hanna, George

ON THE SHORES OF LOUGH NEAGH
Traditional songs of a Tyrone Family (Hanna, George & Sarah Anne O'Neill).
Album: released on Topic, '81 Dist: Roots Distribution

Hanna, Roland

INFORMAL.
Album: released on Hi-Fly (Switzerland), Dec'79 Dist: Jazz Horizons

NEW YORK JAZZ QUARTET.
Album: released on Beehive (USA), Apr'84 by Cadillac Records. Dist: JSU

Hanna, Sir Roland

SWING ME NO WALTZES.
Album: released on Storyville, Nov'86 by Storyville Records. Dist: Jazz Music Distribution, Swift Distribution, Chris Wellard Distribution, Counterpoint Distribution

SWING ME NO WALTZES.
Album: released on Storyville, Jun'86 by Storyville Records. Dist: Jazz Music Distribution, Swift Distribution, Chris Wellard Distribution, Counterpoint Distribution

SWING ME NO WALTZES.
Album: released on Storyville, '79 by Storyville Records. Dist: Jazz Music Distribution, Swift Distribution, Chris Wellard Distribution, Counterpoint Distribution

THIS MUST BE LOVE (Hanna, Sir Roland, George Moraz, Ben Riley).
Album: released on Audiophile, Jun'86 by Jazzology Records (USA). Dist: Jazz Music, Swift

Hanoi Rocks

ALL THOSE WASTED YEARS.
Album: released on Lick, Jul'86 by Cherry Bombz. Dist: Pinnacle

Cassette: released on Lick, Mar'87 by Cherry Bombz. Dist: Pinnacle

BACK TO MYSTERY CITY.
Album: released on Lick, Jul'86 by Cherry Bombz. Dist: Pinnacle

Album: released on Lick, Jun'83 by Cherry Bombz. Dist: Pinnacle

Cassette: released on Lick, Jun'83 by Cherry Bombz. Dist: Pinnacle

BANGKOK SHOCKS SAIGON SHAKES.
Album: released on Lick, Aug'83 by Cherry Bombz. Dist: Pinnacle

Cassette: released on Lick, Aug'83 by Cherry Bombz. Dist: Pinnacle

BEST OF.
Album: released on Hanoi Rocks, Dec'85 by Hanoi Rocks Records. Dist: Pinnacle

Cassette: released on Hanoi Rocks, Dec'85 by Hanoi Rocks Records. Dist: Pinnacle

DEAD BY CHRISTMAS.
Tracks: / Oriental beat(live) / Back to Mystery city / Love's an injection / Lightning bar blues / Mental beat / Malibu beach(Calypso) / M.C.Baby / Village girl / 40 Taxi driver / Tragedy / Visitor(live) / Ice cream summer / Whispers in the dark / Cheyenne / No law and order / Fallen star / Dead by Christmas / Lost in the city / Don't never leave me(live) / Under my wheels(live) / I feel alright(live).
Notes: Double LP and cassette. Bar code:5013428 140161. Side 1:Tracks 1,2,Pub.1985. Tracks 3,4,5,Pub. 1983. Side 2:Tracks 1,3,4,5,Pub. 1983. Tracks 2 Pub.1982. Side 3: Tracks 1 Pub.1985. Tracks2 Pub.1984. Tracks 3,4,5,6, Pub.1983. Side 4: Tracks 1,2, Pub.1983. Tracks 3,4,5, Pub.1985. The recordings are Licensed from Hanoi Rocks. Design & Art Direction: Rocks. This compilation (C) 1986 Castle Communications PLC,Unit 7, 271 Merton Road, London,SW18 5JS.
Album: released on Raw Power, Apr'86 Dist: Pinnacle

Cassette: released on Raw Power, Apr'86 Dist: Pinnacle

HANOI ROCKS.
Album: released on Lick, Jul'86 by Cherry Bombz. Dist: Pinnacle

MALIBU BEACH.
Tracks: / Malibu beach.
Single (12"): released on Lick, Oct'86 by Cherry Bombz. Dist: Pinnacle

Single (7"): released on Licks, May'83

MALIBU BEACH/REBEL ON THE RUN.
Single (12"): released on Licks, '83

Single (7"): released on Licks. Jun'83

ORIENTAL BEAT.
Album: released on Lick, Jul'86 by Cherry Bombz. Dist: Pinnacle

Cassette: released on Lick, Aug'83 by Cherry Bombz. Dist: Pinnacle

ROCK'N'ROLL DIVORCE.
Album: released on Bootlick, Dec'86 Dist: Jungle, Cartel

SELF DESTRUCTION BLUES.
Album: released on Lick, Jul'86 by Cherry Bombz. Dist: Pinnacle

Cassette: released on Lick, Aug'83 by Cherry Bombz. Dist: Pinnacle

TWO STEPS FROM THE MOVE.
Album: released on CBS, Oct'84 by CBS Records. Dist: CBS

Cassette: released on CBS, Oct'84 by CBS Records. Dist: CBS

UNTIL I GET YOU/TRAGEDY/ORIENTAL.
Single (7"): released on Licks, Aug'83

Single (12"): released on Licks, Aug'82

UNTIL I GOT YOU.
Tracks: / Until I got you.
Single (7"): released on Lick, Dec'86 by Cherry Bombz. Dist: Pinnacle

Single (12"): released on Lick, Dec'86 by Cherry Bombz. Dist: Pinnacle

UP AROUND THE BEND.
Single (7"): released on CBS, Jun'84 by CBS Records. Dist: CBS

Single (12"): released on CBS, Jun'84 by CBS Records. Dist: CBS

Single (7"): released on CBS, Jun'84 by CBS Records. Dist: CBS

Hans Andersen

HANS ANDERSEN Original London cast featuring Tommy Steele.
Album: released on Pye, Jan'78

Hans Christian Andersen

HANS C.ANDERSEN FAIRY TALES (Various Artists).
Cassette: released on Bibi, Feb'82

HANS CHRISTIAN ANDERSEN 2 Various artists (Various Artists).
Cassette: released on VFM Cassettes, Jan'85

HANS CHRISTIAN ANDERSEN FAIRY TALES Read by Wendy Craig.
Cassette: released on Listen For Pleasure, Oct'82 by MFP Records. Dist: EMI

HANS CHRISTIAN ANDERSEN 1 Various artists (Various Artists).
Cassette: released on VFM Cassettes, Jan'85

Hansel and Gretel

HANSEL AND GRETEL (TELL-A-TALE SERIES Various artists.
Cassette: released on Pickwick (Ladybird), '83

Hans, Hans Raj

IK KURHI MENOON RANJION FAKIR KARGAYEE.
Tracks: / Giddhe wich melene ni / Kiddi chhetin hundian jawan kurhian / Ik kurhi menoon ranjion fakir kargayee / Tere pyar 'ch kasuti har paegi / Ve tuttie taria / Khirh khirh hasdi day / Ni toon larh farhley sohney saijjana da / Sohnian ni tere sohnay nainan / Uchi peengh na charhayin mutiare / Tere binan asin kehrhe marchale.
Notes: Musicby Kuljit Bhamra. Produced and distributed by Diamond Disc Productions, 20 Cranleigh Gardens, Southall, Middlesex. Tel: 01 574 4103. Designed by B. Sathi.
Cassette: released on Diamond Discs, Nov'86 by Diamond Discs Records. Dist: Diamond Discs Records

Hanshaw Annette

ANNETTE HANSHAW 1926.VOL1.
Album: released on Fountain, Apr'79 by Retrieval Records. Dist: Jazz Music, Swift, VJM, Wellard, Chris, Retrieval

ANNETTE HANSHAW 1927.VOL2.
Album: released on Fountain, Apr'79 by Retrieval Records. Dist: Jazz Music, Swift, VJM, Wellard, Chris, Retrieval

LOVABLE AND SWEET.
Album: released on World Records, May'77 Dist: Polygram

SHE'S GOT IT (1920-30'S).
Album: released on World Records, Oct'77 Dist: Polygram

SWEETHEART OF THE TWENTIES.(1926-28).
Album: released on Halcyon (USA), Dec'82 by Halcyon Records (USA). Dist: Jazz Music, Conifer, Taylors

VOL 3.
Album: released on Fountain, May'86 by Retrieval Records. Dist: Jazz Music, Swift, VJM, Wellard, Chris, Retrieval

Hanson & Davies

COME TOGETHER.
Single (12"): released on Fresh (USA), Aug'87 Dist: Pinnacle

Hanson, John

DANCIN YEARS/WHITE HORSE INN.
Album: released on Philips, Feb'75 Dist: IMS-Polygram

JOHN HANSON FOVOURITES.
Album: released on Phonogram, Jul'84 by Phonogram Records. Dist: Polygram

Cassette: released on Phonogram, Jul'84 by Phonogram Records. Dist: Polygram

JOHN HANSON SINGS 20 SHOWTIME GREATS.
Album: released on K-Tel, Oct'77 by K-Tel Records. Dist: Record Merchandisers Distribution, Taylors, Terry Blood Distribution, Wynd-Up Distribution, Relay Distribution, Pickwick Distribution, Solomon & Peres Distribution, Polygram

JOHN HANSON SINGS SONGS FROM HIS SHOWS.
Album: released on Philips, May'76 Dist: IMS-Polygram

SPOTLIGHT ON JOHN HANSON.
Album: released on Philips, Jul'77 Dist: IMS-Polygram

STUDENT PRINCE/VAGABOND KING.
Album: released on Pye Special, Mar'78

VAGABOND KING, THE.
Album: released on Flashback, Oct'85 by Flashback Records/PRT Records. Dist: Mainline, PRT

Cassette: released on Flashback, Oct'85 by Flashback Records/PRT Records. Dist: Mainline, PRT

Hansson, Bo

LORD OF THE RINGS.
Album: released on Charisma, Sep'83 by Virgin Records. Dist: EMI

MAGICIAN'S HAT.
Album: released on Charisma, Sep'83 by Virgin Records. Dist: EMI

Cassette: released on Charisma, Sep'83 by Virgin Records. Dist: EMI

Hanvey, Bobbie

BALLAD OF HURRICANE HIGGINS.
Single (7"):

MOTTONBURN STREAM & WHEEN MORE.
Album: released on Outlet, Apr'80 by Outlet Records. Dist: Outlet Distribution

Cassette: released on Outlet, Apr'80 by Outlet Records. Dist: Outlet Distribution

Hanwell band

BLAZING BRASS.
Cassette: released on Oak, Sep'82 by Oak Records. Dist: Spartan Distribution, Pinnacle

Happel,Harry

INTRODUCTION.
Album: released on Timeless(import), '81 Dist: Cadillac

INTRODUCTION: NORTH SEA HIGH LIGHTS.
Album: released on Spotlite, Mar'83 by Spotlite Records. Dist: Cadillac, Jazz Music, Spotlite

Happiness Ad

GEBURAH.
Tracks: / Geburah / Alone inside.
Single (7"): released on Flexible Response, Oct'86 Dist: Red Rhino, Cartel

Page 448

Happiness add

LOVE CAN BE CRUEL.
Single (7"): released on Off-Beat, Jun'85 by Off-Beat Records. Dist: Jetstar Distribution

Happy accordion hits

HAPPY ACCORDION HITS Various artists.
Album: released on Austrophon Diepholz(Germany), Jul'83

Cassette: released on Austrophon Diepholz(Germany), Jul'83

Happy days are here again

HAPPY DAYS ARE HERE AGAIN Various artists.
Album: released on EMI Retrospect, Aug'85 by EMI Records. Dist: EMI

Cassette: released on EMI Retrospect, Aug'85 by EMI Records. Dist: EMI

Happy End, The

RESOLUTION.
Album: released on Cooking Vinyl, Aug'87 Dist: Nine Mile, Cartel, Red Rhino

Cassette: released on Cooking Vinyl, Aug'87 Dist: Nine Mile, Cartel, Red Rhino

THERE'S NOTHING QUITE LIKE MONEY.
Album: released on Circus, Oct'85 Dist: Circus, Recommended

Happy families

HAPPY FAMILIES Various artists.
Album: released on Shangri-La, Nov'84 by Shangri-La records. Dist: PRT

Cassette: released on Shangri-La, Nov'84 by Shangri-La records. Dist: PRT

Happy families stories

HAPPY FAMILIES STORIES Mrs Wobble and the Waitress.
Cassette: released on Tellastory, Mar'83 by Bartlett Bliss Productions. Dist: PRT Distribution, Hayward Promotions Distribution, H.R. Taylor Distribution

Happy family

PURITANS(EP).
Single (7"): released on 4AD, Apr'82 by 4AD Records. Dist: Rough Trade

Happy Few

HUNTER/HEAVEN IS SO DIFFICULT.
Single (7"): released on Smug, Jun'82

Happy Mondays

FORTY FIVE (EP).
Single (7"): released on Factory, Sep'85 by Factory Records. Dist: Cartel, Pinnacle

FREAKY DANCING.
Tracks: / Freaky dancing.
Single (7"): released on Factory, Jun'86 by Factory Records. Dist: Cartel, Pinnacle

Single (12"): released on Factory, Jun'86 by Factory Records. Dist: Cartel, Pinnacle

SQUIRREL & G-MAN, TWENTY FOUR, PARTY PEOPLE, PLASTIC FACE....
Notes: Debut album produced by John Cale, featuring the single 'Tart Tart'
Album: released on Factory, Apr'87 by Factory Records. Dist: Cartel, Pinnacle

SQUIRRELL & G MAN 24 hour party people plastic face can't smile etc..
Album: released on Factory, May'87 by Factory Records. Dist: Cartel, Pinnacle

TART TART.
Tracks: / Tart, Tart.
Single (12"): released on Factory, Mar'87 by Factory Records. Dist: Cartel, Pinnacle

Happy people

LOVE POTION/DON'T STOP ME.
Single (7"): released on Solid Gold, Oct'81 Dist: MCA

Happy Prince

CHILDREN'S OPERA, THE (Happy Prince, The).
Album: released on Decca, '79 by Decca Records. Dist: Polygram

HAPPY PRINCE BY OSCAR WILDE.
Cassette: released on Talking Tape Company, Sep'84 by Talking Tape Company Records.

Cassette: released on Kiddy Kassettes, Feb'81

Happy refugees

LAST CHANCE SALOON.
Album: released on Gymnasium, Jul'84 Dist: Red Rhino, Cartel

Happy Together

HAPPY TOGETHER Various Artists (Various Artists).
Tracks: / I fought the law / Tell him / Birds and the bees,The / Single girl / Letter, The / She'd rather be with me / Double shot of my baby's love / It ain't me babe / Cinnamon cinder / Lightnin' Strikes / New Yorks a lonely town / Happy together / I fought the law / Tell him / Birds and the bees,The / Single girl / Letter,The / She'd rather be with me / Double shot of my baby's love.
Album: released on Topline, Sep'86 by Charly Records. Dist: Charly Distribution

Cassette: released on Topline, Sep'86 by Charly Records. Dist: Charly Distribution

Happy traum

BRIGHT MORNING STARS.
Single (7"): released on Waterfront, Mar'84 by Waterfront Records. Dist: Rough Trade, Cartel, Projection, Roots

Happy Truama

RELAX YOUR MIND.
Album: released on Pye, '74

Happy Yodellers

HAPPY YODELLERS Various Artists (Various Artists).
Tracks: / Tiroler Bravour-Jodler / Dort Wo Die Isar Fliebt / Immer Wann Der Morgen kommt / Heut'Bin Ich So Jodel Verliebt / Der Konigs-Jodler / Rob'n Auf Der Roten Wand / Mei Vata is a Appenzeller / Die Kasermandin / Am Morgen Wenn Di Sonne Lacht / Me liab / Schatzeri,Machs Fernsteri Auf Wenn Ich Auf Hohen Bergen Steh.
Notes: A fine album of Austrian Yodelling.
Album: released on Polydor (Germany), Apr'86 Dist: IMS-Polygram

Cassette: released on Polydor (Germany), Apr'86 Dist: IMS-Polygram

Harbour lights

RUB A DUB FEELING.
Single (12"): released on Jaguar, Oct'84 by Jaguar Records. Dist: Jetstar

Harbour, Pearl

PEARL HARBOUR AND THE EXPLOSIONS (Harbour, Pearl and the Explosions).
Album: released on Warner Brothers, Jan'80 by Warner Bros Records. Dist: WEA

Harbour, Sydney

KILL THE WEATHER MAN.
Single (7"): released on Reject, Apr'84 by Reject Records.

Hardcastle, Paul

19.
Single (7"): released on Chrysalis, Apr'85 by Chrysalis Records. Dist: CBS

Single (12"): released on Chrysalis, Apr'85 by Chrysalis Records. Dist: CBS

DON'T WASTE MY TIME.
Tracks: / Don't waste my time / Moonhopper / Loitering with intent.
Single (7"): released on Chrysalis, Jan'86 by Chrysalis Records. Dist: CBS

Single (12"): released on Chrysalis, Jan'86 by Chrysalis Records. Dist: CBS

FOOLIN' YOURSELF.
Tracks: / Foolin' yourself / King Tut / Strollin.
Single (7"): released on Chrysalis, Jun'86 by Chrysalis Records. Dist: CBS

Single (12"): released on Chrysalis, Jun'86 by Chrysalis Records. Dist: CBS

JUST FOR MONEY.
Single (7"): released on Chrysalis, Nov'85 by Chrysalis Records. Dist: CBS

Single (12"): released on Chrysalis, Nov'85 by Chrysalis Records. Dist: CBS

PAPA'S GOT A BRAND NEW PIGBAG.
Single (7"): released on Kaz, Jul'85 by Kaz Records. Dist: PRT

Single (12"): released on Kaz, Jul'85 by Kaz Records. Dist: PRT

PAUL HARDCASTLE.
Tracks: / In the beginning / 19 / King Tut / Don't waste my time / Central park / Just for money / Moonchopper / Better / Strollin' / Rain forest.
Compact disc: released on Chrysalis, Apr'86 by Chrysalis Records. Dist: CBS

Album: released on Chrysalis, Nov'85 by Chrysalis Records. Dist: CBS

Cassette: released on Chrysalis, Nov'85 by Chrysalis Records. Dist: CBS

RAIN FOREST.
Single (12"): released on Bluebird, Aug'84 by Bluebird Records. Dist: EMI, Jetstar

Single (7"): released on Bluebird, Jun'85 by Bluebird Records. Dist: EMI, Jetstar

Single (12"): released on Bluebird, Jun'85 by Bluebird Records. Dist: EMI, Jetstar

WIZARD,THE.
Tracks: / Wizard,The(part 1) / Wizard,The(part 2).
Single (7"): released on Chrysalis, Sep'86 by Chrysalis Records. Dist: CBS

Single (12"): released on Chrysalis, Sep'86 by Chrysalis Records. Dist: CBS

YOU'RE THE ONE FOR ME.
Single (12"): released on Total Control, Mar'84

ZERO ONE.
Tracks: / Forest fire / Panic / Rain forest / Sound chaser / Zero one / Ready-ready go / Drum beat / Hip-hop beat.
Compact disc: released on Bluebird-10, Jul'86 by Bluebird Records. Dist: Virgin Records, EMI, Jetstar

Album: released on Bluebird, Feb'85 by Bluebird Records. Dist: EMI, Jetstar

Hard Corps

DIRTY.
Single (12"): released on Survival, Aug'84 by Survival Records. Dist: Backs, Cartel Distribution

JE SUIS PASSEE.
Single (7"): released on Polydor, May'85 by Polydor Records. Dist: Polygram, Polydor

Single (12"): released on Polydor, May'85 by Polydor Records. Dist: Polygram, Polydor

Single (12"): released on Immaculate, May'85 by Immaculate Records. Dist: Cartel

LUCKY CHARM.
Single (7"): released on Trans Global, 30 May'87

Single (12"): released on Trans Global, 30 May'87

TO BREATHE.
Single (7"): released on Polydor, Oct'85 by Polydor Records. Dist: Polygram, Polydor

Single (12"): released on Polydor, Oct'85 by Polydor Records. Dist: Polygram, Polydor

Harden, Wilbur

COUNTDOWN (Harden, Wilbur & John Coltrane).
Notes: For full details see under **Coltrane, John.**

SAVOY SESSIONS (Harden, Wilbur & John Coltrane).
Double Album: released on Savoy, Sep'78

Hard Grindin' Bluesman

HARD GRINDIN' BLUESMAN Various artists.
Album: released on Krazy Kat (USA), Jan'85

Hardhats

TEAR DOWN THE HOUSE Wrecking crew mix.
Single (12"): released on G&M, Aug'87 Dist: PRT

Hardie, Ian

BREATH OF FRESH AIRS,A.
Tracks: / Cheviot blast / Poetic Milkman,The / Bull ring,The / Omnibus,The / Junction pool,The (The timeless clock) / Duke's Dyke,The / Damside hornpipe,The (The Eight-sided square) Bowmont water / Pipemaj. Rev Joe Brown(Boder Worthie's Club) / Cleek,The / Catch-a penny fox (The flooded goat) / Red herring,The / Old bean waltz(Venchen circle) / Hospital wood / North to England(Auchope Carin0 / Hoselaw chapel / Schoolroom pipers (The black hag) / Yetholm Haugh / Late white swan,The(Tobermory wedding) / Leg-up ,The / Tanners swee / Hen hole,The / (Ambon of Torwooklee.).
Album: released on Greentrax, Oct'86 by Greentrax Records. Dist: Projection, CM, Gordon Duncan Distribution, Rough Trade, Nine Mile, Cartel

Cassette: released on Greentrax, Oct'86 by Greentrax Records. Dist: Projection, CM, Gordon Duncan Distribution, Rough Trade, Nine Mile, Cartel

Hardin, Eddie

DAWN TIL DUSK.
Album: released on Coda, Apr'86 by Coda Records. Dist: Pinnacle, Cartel, WEA, Roots

Cassette: released on Coda, Apr'86 by Coda Records. Dist: Pinnacle, Cartel, WEA, Roots

Compact disc: released on Coda, Jul'86 by Coda Records. Dist: Pinnacle, Cartel, WEA, Roots

GOOD MORNING TO YOU.
Single (7"): released on President, Sep'85 by President Records. Dist: Taylors, Spartan

RED NOSE CITY.
Tracks: / Red nose city / Caribbean nights.
Single (7"): released on President, Jul'87 by President Records. Dist: Taylors, Spartan

WIND IN THE WILLOWS Musical production of (Hardin, Eddie & Zak Starkey).
Album: released on President, Jun'85 by President Records. Dist: Taylors, Spartan

Harding, Carolyn

MOVIN' ON.
Tracks: / Movin' on / Memories.
Single (7"): released on Magnetic Dance, Jul'87 by Magnetic Dance Records. Dist: BMG

Single (12"): released on Magnetic Dance, Jul'87 by Magnetic Dance Records. Dist: BMG

Harding, Mike

BEST OF MIKE HARDING, THE.
Album: released on Rubber, Apr'85 by Rubber Records. Dist: Roots Distribution, Projection Distribution, Jazz Music Distribution, Celtic Music Distribution, JSU Distribution, Spartan Distribution

Cassette: released on Rubber, Apr'85 by Rubber Records. Dist: Roots Distribution, Projection Distribution, Jazz Music Distribution, Celtic Music Distribution, JSU Distribution, Spartan Distribution

BEST OF MIKE HARDING-VOLUME TWO,THE.
Album: released on Rubber, May'86 by Rubber Records. Dist: Roots Distribution, Projection Distribution, Jazz Music Distribution, Celtic Music Distribution, JSU Distribution, Spartan Distribution

Cassette: released on Rubber, May'86 by Rubber Records. Dist: Roots Distribution, Projection Distribution, Jazz Music Distribution, Celtic Music Distribution, JSU Distribution, Spartan Distribution

BOMBER'S MOON.
Tracks: / January man / And the band played waltzing Matilda / Good morning morning / Factory / Bomber's moon / Small high window / God help the poor / Accrington pals,The / Thirty nights / These poor hands / Back of the back of the moon.
Album: released on Moonraker, Apr'86, Projection Distribution

Cassette: released on Moonraker, Apr'86, Projection Distribution

FLAT DOGS AND SHAKY PUDDEN.
Album: released on BBC, Apr'83 by BBC Records & Tapes. Dist: EMI, PRT, Pye

Cassette: released on BBC, Apr'83 by BBC Records & Tapes. Dist: EMI, PRT, Pye

FOO FOO SHUFFLEWICK AND HER EXOTIC BANANA.
Tracks: / Foo Foo Shufflewick and her exotic Banana / I am dancing alone in the night / Dracula and the trendies / Hotel Transylvania, The / Ronald Reagan, my hero / God meets Ronnie / Son et lumiere / Sao Bras Albuferia.
Notes: Mike's latest comedy album recorded live at the Leeds Grand Theatre on Mike's 'One For The Road' tour 1985. A volume seller for Christmas. Note the lower dealer price for cassette.
Album: released on Moonraker, Nov'86, Projection Distribution

Cassette: released on Moonraker, Nov'86, Projection Distribution

KOMIC KUTS.
Album: released on Philips, Oct'79 Dist: IMS-Polygram

Cassette: released on Philips, Oct'79 Dist: IMS-Polygram

LANCASHIRE LAD, A.
Album: released on Leader, '81 Dist: Jazz Music, Projection

MIKE HARDING'S BACK.
Album: released on Rubber, Jun'82 by Rubber Records. Dist: Roots Distribution, Projection Distribution, Jazz Music Distribution, Celtic Music Distribution, JSU Distribution, Spartan Distribution

MRS' ARDIN'S KID.
Album: released on Rubber, Jun'82 by Rubber Records. Dist: Roots Distribution, Projection Distribution, Jazz Music Distribution, Celtic Music Distribution, JSU Distribution, Spartan Distribution

Cassette: released on Rubber, Jun'82 by Rubber Records. Dist: Roots Distribution, Projection Distribution, Jazz Music Distribution, Celtic Music Distribution, JSU Distribution, Spartan

Distribution

OLD FOUR EYES IS BACK.
Cassette: released on Philips, May'77 Dist: IMS-Polygram

ONE MAN SHOW.
Album: released on Philips, Sep'84 Dist: IMS-Polygram

Cassette: released on Philips, Sep'84 Dist: IMS-Polygram

Cassette: released on Philips, Jun'76 Dist: IMS-Polygram

ON THE TOUCHLINE.
Cassette: released on Philips, Jul'79 Dist: IMS-Polygram

RED SPECS ALBUM, THE.
Album: released on Polydor, Aug'83 by Polydor Records. Dist: Polygram, Polydor

Cassette: released on Polydor, Aug'83 by Polydor Records. Dist: Polygram, Polydor

ROCHDALE COWBOY.
Single (7"): released on Rubber, Jun'75 by Rubber Records. Dist: Roots Distribution, Projection Distribution, Jazz Music Distribution, Celtic Music Distribution, JSU Distribution, Spartan Distribution

ROCHDALE COWBOY RIDES AGAIN, THE.
Album: released on Rubber, Jun'82 by Rubber Records. Dist: Roots Distribution, Projection Distribution, Jazz Music Distribution, Celtic Music Distribution, JSU Distribution, Spartan Distribution

ROLL OVER CECIL SHARPE.
Tracks: / Buggeri,Buggeri,Buggeri / Just can't beat this family life / Yorkshireman in the court of King Ronnie,The / 3-Legged pig,The / Roll over Cecil Sharpe / K-Tel folk song PLC. Inc..
Album: released on Moonraker, Apr'86, Projection Distribution

Cassette: released on Moonraker, Apr'86, Projection Distribution

Album: released on Moonraker, Feb'85, Projection Distribution

ROOTED.
Tracks: / Buckets of blue steam and square bubbles / Leroy and the foreman / When the Martians land in Huddersfield / Rooted / She'll be right mate / West-Yorkshire Dobra-playin' hippy cowboy,The / Wath on dearne blues.
Album: released on Moonraker, Apr'86, Projection Distribution

Cassette: released on Moonraker, Apr'86, Projection Distribution

TAKE YOUR FINGERS OFF IT.
Tracks: / Australia / Hail glorious St.Margaret / Take your fingers off it / Captain Legless meets Superdrunk / Ghost of the cafe Gungha Din,The / Crumpsall kid, The / Quasimodo meets the Virgin Mary / Viking helmet,The.
Album: released on Moonraker, Apr'86, Projection Distribution

Cassette: released on Moonraker, Apr'86, Projection Distribution

Hardin, Tim

MEMORIAL ALBUM.
Album: released on Polydor (Import), Feb'82

Hardin & York

FOR THE WORLD.
Album: released on See For Miles, Jan'85 by See For Miles Records. Dist: Pinnacle

Hardline

HARDLINE.
Album: released on Mausoleum, Oct'84 by Mausoleum Records. Dist: Pinnacle

Hard Luck Blues

HARD LUCK BLUES Lissie Miles, Susie Smith & other artists.
Album: released on VJM, '74 by Wellard, Chris Distribution. Dist: Wellard, Chris Distribution

Hardman, Bill

HOME.
Album: released on Muse, Apr'81 by Peerless Records. Dist: Lugtons Distributors

Hardman, Rosemary

SECOND SEASON CAME, THE.
Album: released on Leader, '81 Dist: Jazz Music, Projection

Hardman, Rosie

EAGLE OVER BLUE MOUNTAIN.
Album: released on Plantlife, Nov'81

STOPPED IN MY TRACKS.
Album: released on Plant Life, Nov'81 Dist: Roots

WEAKNESS OF EVE, THE.
Album: released on Plant Life, Jul'83 Dist: Roots

Hard Rock

FEEL NO WAY.
Single (12"): released on Inner Light, May'84 by Inner Light Records. Dist: Jetstar

HARD ROCK Various artists.
Album: released on Vertigo, Dec'81 by Phonogram Records. Dist: Polygram

Cassette: released on Vertigo, Dec'81 by Phonogram Records. Dist: Polygram

YOU'RE DRIVING ME CRAZY.
Single (12"): released on Omega, Oct'85 by Omega Records. Dist: Jetstar Distribution

Hard Rock'83

HARD ROCK'83 Various artists.
Album: released on Vertigo, Mar'84 by Phonogram Records. Dist: Polygram

Cassette: released on Vertigo, Mar'84 by Phonogram Records. Dist: Polygram

Hard Rock Soul Movement

BEAT IS MINE,THE.
Tracks: / Beat is mine.The / Double Def fresh (The get stupid fresh mix).
Single (12"): released on Elite, Jul'86 Dist: PRT

DO IT ANYWAY YOU WANNA.
Single (12"): released on Elite, Oct'85 Dist: PRT

DOUBLE DEFRESH.
Tracks: / Double Defresh / Def Hypnosis.
Single (12"): released on Elite, Feb'86 Dist: PRT

ELAWEAZER JUST A SKEEZER.
Tracks: / Elaweazer just a skeezer / Elaweazer just a skeezer (dub mix).
Single (12"): released on Serious, Jun'87 by Serious Records. Dist: PRT

Single (7"): released on Serious, Jun'87 by Serious Records. Dist: PRT

FUNKY GROOVE.
Tracks: / Funky Groove / Funky Groove(Alternative mix).
Single (7"): released on Streetwave, Oct'86 by Streetwave Records. Dist: PRT Distribution

Single (12"): released on Streetwave, Oct'86 by Streetwave Records. Dist: PRT Distribution

Hard Times

HARD TIMES Various Artists (Various Artists).
Tracks: / From my heart / Say you're leavin / Hard times / Bad to make a woman mad / Talk fast / Way I feel,The / Call my job / Figure head / You better stop / Puppy Howl / Rambling woman / Foot race / Honky Tonk / You can't love me / I know better / Money is the name of the game.
Album: released on Flyright, Oct'86 by Flyright Records. Dist: Krazy Kat, Swift, Jazz Music

HARD TIMES various artists (Various Artists).
Album: released on Flyright, Mar'85 by Flyright Records. Dist: Krazy Kat, Swift, Jazz Music

NEVER GIVE IN.
Single (7"): released on E & F, 30 May'87 by Supreme Records. Dist: PRT

Single (12"): released on E & F, 30 May'87 by Supreme Records. Dist: PRT

OCTOBER DAWN.
Single (7"): released on Edit, Jul'83 by Edit Records. Dist: Stage One

Hardware

DANCE.
Single (7"): released on Reset, Jul'85 by Vince Clarke/Eric Radcliffe. Dist: Spartan

Single (12"): released on Reset, Jul'85 by Vince Clarke/Eric Radcliffe. Dist: Spartan

Hardy, Francoise

GOLDEN HOUR PRESENTS THE BEST OF FRANCOISE HARDY.
Album: released on Golden Hour, '74 by PRT Records. Dist: PRT

Cassette: released on Golden Hour, '74 by PRT Records. Dist: PRT

GREATEST HITS:FRANCOISE HARDY.
Compact disc: released on Vogue (France), Jun'84 Dist: Discovery, Jazz Music, PRT, Swift

HIT PARADE OF FRANCOISE HARDY, THE.
Album: released on Vogue (France), Dec'84 Dist: Discovery, Jazz Music, PRT, Swift

Cassette: released on Vogue (France), Dec'84 Dist: Discovery, Jazz Music, PRT, Swift

Hardy, Thomas

IMAGINATIVE WOMAN, AN.
Cassette: released on Talking Tape, Sep'84

MAYOR OF CASTERBRIDGE, VOLUME 1,THE.
Notes: Read by : John Rowe. Michael Henchard, successful corn-merchant, respected citizen and mayor of Casterbridge, has striven to shake off the tainting horror of an aberration in his past. But years of industry, abstinence and applicationcannot save him from his own history, and the flaws that mar his great spirit serve only to drag him back into the mire of drink and despair. The grand trag-edy is firmly rooted in Hardy's beloved Wessex, from the prosperous market town of the title to hte dismal hut on Egdon heath where the story closes. Thomas Hardy (1840-1928) trained as an architect and practised in Dorchester, the modelfor Casterbridge, before devoting himself entirely to writing. The Mayor Of Casterbridge is produced by Betty Davies. 2 volumes: 9 cassettes. listening time12 hours 30 minutes. Cover to cover cassettes limited, Dene House, lockeridge, Marborough, Wiltshire.
Cassette: released on Cover to Cover, Sep'86 by Cover to Cover Cassettes. Dist: Conifer

THREE STRANGERS read by Richard Morant.
Cassette: released on Talking Tape Company, '84 by Talking Tape Company Records.

Hargreaves, Dale

EASTERN SIDE.
Single (7"): released on Zap International, Oct'83 Dist: PRT

SCARED TO DEATH EP (Hargreaves, Dale & His Flamingos).
Single (7"): released on Lightbeat, May'82 by Lightbeat Records. Dist: Pinnacle

Single (7"): released on Safari, Aug'82 by Safari Records. Dist: Pinnacle

Hargreaves, Jack

COUNTRY WALKING.
Album: released on Response, Feb'81 by Priority Records. Dist: BMG

KNOW YOUR DOG.
Album: released on Response, Feb'81 by Priority Records. Dist: BMG

KNOW YOUR FISH.
Album: released on Response, Feb'81 by Priority Records. Dist: BMG

Cassette: released on Response, Apr'81 by Priority Records. Dist: BMG

KNOW YOUR PONY.
Album: released on Response, Feb'81 by Priority Records. Dist: BMG

Haricots Rouges

AU JAM POTATOES, (LES) (1972).
Album: released on Pragmaphone, Aug'77 Dist: Cadillac

Harlandic Male...

SINCE MAGGIE & OTHER IRISH FAVOURITES (Harlandic Male Voice Choir).
Album: released on Emerald City (USA), Mar'84 by Atlantic.

Cassette: released on Emerald City (USA), Mar'84 by Atlantic.

SINGS MAGGIE (Harlandic Male Voice Choir).
Tracks: / Maggie / Star of the county down / Off in the stilly night / Danny boy / She moved thru' the fair / Molly Malone-(Medley) Mick Magillian / I'll take you home again Kathleen / Trotin to the fair / Eilean Aroon / Kathleen Mavoureen / (Medley):If you're Irish - When Irish eyes are smiling / In the gloaming.
Notes: All titles trad. arr: By John Anderson. Published by Emerald Music Ltd: Except side 2) track 6: Leonard Gould/Bolttler:
Album: released on Emerald (Ireland), Jan'84 by Emerald Records. Dist: I & B, Ross, PRT

Harle, John

HABENERA.
Album: released on Hannibal, Jul'87 by Hannibal Records. Dist: Charly, Harmonia Mundi, Projection, Celtic Music, Roots

Harlem

HARLEM various artists (Various Artists).
Album: released on Lake, May'85 by Fellside Recordings. Dist: Jazz Music, Fellside

HARLEM (1926-57) various artists (Various Artists).
Album: released on RCA (France), '83 by RCA Records. Dist: Discovery

HARLEM COMES TO LONDON Original Artists (Various Artists).
Album: released on World Records, Mar'78 Dist: Polygram

HARLEM HEAVIES (R&B '54-62) various artists (Various Artists).
Album: released on Moonstone, May'85 by Ampersand Music Ltd. Dist: Belwin Mills Music Ltd., ILA Distribution

Harlem Hamfats

HOT CHICAGO JAZZ-BLUES & JIVE 1936-37..
Album: released on Folklyric (USA), Oct'86 by Arhoolie Records. Dist: Topic, Projection

I'M SO GLAD.
Album: released on Queen Disc (USA), Jan'84

Harlem Hit Parade

HARLEM HIT PARADE Old town blues vol.2 (Various Artists).
Album: released on Ace, Apr'87 by Ace Records. Dist: Pinnacle, Swift, Hotshot, Cadillac

Harlem Lullaby

HARLEM LULLABY Various Artists (Various Artists).
Album: released on Hep, Apr'86 by H.R. Taylor Records. Dist: Jazz Music, Cadillac Music, JSU, Taylors, Wellard, Chris, Zodiac, Swift, Fast Forward

Harlem Roots

BIG BAND,THE.
Notes: With Duke & his Orchestra and Count Basie & his Orchestra.
Album: released on Storyville, May'86 by Storyville Records. Dist: Jazz Music Distribution, Swift Distribution, Chris Wellard Distribution, Counterpoint Distribution

HEADLINERS,THE.
Notes: With Fats Waller/ Louis Jordan/ Louis Armstrong.
Album: released on Storyville, May'86 by Storyville Records. Dist: Jazz Music Distribution, Swift Distribution, Chris Wellard Distribution, Counterpoint Distribution

JIVIN' TIME.
Notes: Featuring Nat Cole; Bob Howard; Red Allen; Rosetta Tharpe; With Lucky Millinder orchestra; June Rechmond, Dorothy Dandridge; Mabel.
Album: released on Storyville, May'86 by Storyville Records. Dist: Jazz Music Distribution, Swift Distribution, Chris Wellard Distribution, Counterpoint Distribution

RHYTHM IN HARMONY.
Notes: With Mills Bros./Delta Rhythm Boys.
Album: released on Storyville, May'86 by Storyville Records. Dist: Jazz Music Distribution, Swift Distribution, Chris Wellard Distribution, Counterpoint Distribution

Harlem Shuffle

HARLEM SHUFFLE Sixties soul classics (Various Artists).
Tracks: / Gimme little sign / Dancin' holiday / Love makes the world go round / Spring / Expressway to your heart / Oo wee baby I love you / Baby I'm yours / Cool jerk / Get on up / And get away / Duck, The / I know / Snake, The / Harlem shuffle / Hello stranger / Oh how happy / Oogum boogum song / Bounce / Backfield in motion / Make me your baby / You can make it if you try.
Compact disc: released on Charly, Apr'87 by Charly Records. Dist: Charly, Cadillac

Album: released on Charly(R&B), Aug'86 by Charly Records. Dist: Charly, Cadillac

Cassette: released on Charly, Apr'87 by Charly Records. Dist: Charly, Cadillac

Harlem Spirit

DANCING CHEEK TO CHEEK.
Single (7"): released on Fusion, Apr'84 by Fusion Records. Dist: Jetstar

Single (7"): released on Fusion, Apr'84 by Fusion Records. Dist: Jetstar

HOW SWEET IT IS.
Single (7"): released on Fusion, Oct'83 by Fusion Records. Dist: Jetstar

SUSSED.
Album: released on Fusion, Apr'86 by Fusion Records. Dist: Jetstar

WHY CAN'T WE BE LOVERS.
Single (7"): released on MVM, Feb'83

Harlequin

ONE FALSE MOVE.
Album: released on Heavy Metal America, Jun'84 by FM-Revolver Records. Dist: EMI

Harlequin Four's

SET IT OFF.
Tracks: / Set it off / Mastermind Remix.
Single (7"): released on Champion, Jul'86 by Champion Records. Dist: RCA

Single (12"): released on Champion, Jul'86 by Champion Records. Dist: RCA

Harleqyn

BURN.
Tracks: / Burn.
Single (7"): released on Starlight, Nov'86 by Starlight Records. Dist: Jetstar Distribution

Harley, Steve

BALLERINA.
Single (7"): released on Stiletto, Jul'83 by Fast Records. Dist: Cartel Distribution

Cassette: released on Stiletto, Jul'83 by Fast Records. Dist: Cartel Distribution

BEST OF..., THE (Harley, Steve & Cockney Rebel).
Album: released on Fame (EMI), May'82 by Music For Pleasure Records. Dist: EMI

Cassette: released on Fame (EMI), May'82 by Music For Pleasure Records. Dist: EMI

COLLECTION: STEVE HARLEY.
Album: released on EMI (Germany), '83 by EMI Records. Dist: Conifer

FACE TO FACE (Harley, Steve & Cockney Rebel).
Album: released on EMI (Germany), May'83 by EMI Records. Dist: Conifer

Cassette: released on EMI (Germany), May'83 by EMI Records. Dist: Conifer

HEARTBEAT LIKE THUNDER.
Tracks: / Heartbeat like thunder / Warm my cold heart.
Single (7"): released on RAK, Apr'86 by RAK. Dist: EMI

Single (12"): released on RAK, Apr'86 by RAK. Dist: EMI

IRRESISTABLE.
Tracks: / Irresistable / Lucky man.
Single (7"): released on RAK, Jun'86 by RAK. Dist: EMI

Single (12"): released on RAK, Jul'86 by RAK. Dist: EMI

LIVE FROM LONDON.
Notes: One-time Cockney Rebel leader perfmorming a selection of his best known work with that band and beyond, including: "Mr.Soft" and "Make Me Smile". 1984 production. Type of recording: Live. Total playing time: 60 minutes.
Video-cassette (VHS): released on Polygram, Oct'86 by Polygram Records. Dist: Polygram

MAKE ME SMILE (Harley, Steve & Cockney Rebel).
Single (7"): released on EMI, Oct'80 by EMI Records. Dist: EMI

Single (7"): released on Old Gold, Oct'83 by Old Gold Records. Dist: Lightning, Jazz Music, Spartan, Counterpoint

Harmonaires

FIRST LOVE.
Tracks: / Bye bye blues / Harmonica boy / Harmonoogie / Shoe shine boy / Tribute to Stephen Foster / Lullaby of birdland/Hello Dolly / Peg o my heart / Canadian sunset / Time I get to Phoenix / Five foot two / Perfidia / 12th street / Swedish rhapsody / Hot spud.
Cassette: released on Accordion Record Club, Jul'86 by Accordion Record Club Records. Dist: Accordion Record Club

Harmonica Blues

HARMONICA BLUES 1936-40 (Various Artists).
Notes: Mono.
Album: released on Wolf, Mar'87 Dist: Jazz Music, Swift

SUCKIN' AND BLOWIN'.
Album: released on Sunflower, Oct'82 Dist: Pinnacle

Harmonica Frank

HARMONICA FRANK.
Album: released on Puritan, Apr'79 Dist: Swift

Harmonica Showcase

HARMONICA SHOWCASE various artists (Various Artists).
Album: released on Matchbox, Sep'85 Dist: Projection

Harmony

HARMONY HOLIDAY various artists (Various Artists).
Album: released on MWM, Jun'82 by Mawson & Wareham. Dist: Spartan Distribution, Jazz Music Distribution, JSU Distribution

Harper, Addie

ADDIE HARPER AND THE WICK TRIO (Harper, Addie & The Wick Trio).
Album: released on Country House, Dec'83 by BGS Productions Ltd. Dist: Taylor, H.R., Record Merchandisers Distribution, Pinnacle, Sounds of Scotland Records

Cassette: released on Country House, Dec'83 by BGS Productions Ltd. Dist: Taylor, H.R., Record Merchandisers Distribution, Pinnacle, Sounds of Scotland Records

ON THE ROAD BY THE RIVER (Harper, Addie & The Wick Band).
Tracks: / Tribute to Allan Michael / Patches march / McNeil's march / Road by the river, The / Wind that blew, The / John Keith Laing / More than yesterday / Dumfries polka, The / Who at my door is standing / Edinburgh Caithness gathering waltz / Maid of the hill, The / Keep your feet still George Hinney / Primrose and the daffodil, The / John Gunn's anniversary / Snouts and ears / Geordie the boatman / Wattens welcome to the Queen Mother / When the gold in your hair turns to grey / Waterfall 99 / Elaine / Addie Harper of Wick / Standing stones / Caledonia march / Peat bog, The / Lilting fisherman / Boys of the town / Scotland my home / Crags of tumbledown mountain.
Album: released on Scotdisc, Jun'87 Dist: Clyde Factors Distributors

Cassette: released on Scotdisc, Jun'87 Dist: Clyde Factors Distributors

PRIDE OF THE NORTH, THE (Harper, Addie & The Wick Band).
Album: released on Ross, '86 by Ross Records. Dist: Ross Distribution, Roots Distribution

Cassette: released on Ross, '86 by Ross Records. Dist: Ross Distribution, Roots Distribution

Harper, Bill

BILLY HARPER QUINTET (Harper, Bill Quintet).
Album: released on Soul Note, Sep'79 Dist: Harmonia Mundi Distributors

BLACK SAINT IN EUROPE (Harper, Bill Quintet).
Album: released on Black Saint, Jul'78 Dist: Projection, IMS, Polygram, Chris Wellard, Harmonia Mundi, Swift

Harper, Billy

KNOWLEDGE OF SELF.
Album: released on Denon, Mar'82 by Denon Records. Dist: Harmonia Mundi

SORAN BUSHI.
Tracks: / Trying to get ready/Loverhood.
Compact disc single: released on Denon, Nov'84 by Denon Records. Dist: Harmonia Mundi

SORAN -BUSHI B.H.
Album: released on Denon, Mar'82 by Denon Records. Dist: Harmonia Mundi

Harper, Charlie

FREAKED.
Single (7"): released on Ramkup, Jul'81 Dist: Pinnacle

NEW BARBARIANS (Harper, Charlie Urban Dogs).
Single (7"): released on Fall Out, Nov'82 Dist: Swift, Red Rhino, Cartel

Harper, Don

COMBO (Harper, Don - Denny Wright Duo, Trio, Quartet, Sextet).
Album: released on One Up, Feb'78 by EMI Records.

SONG FOR ALICE.
Album: released on Avan-Guard, Aug'86 by Vanguard Records. Dist: Conifer, Discovery

Cassette: released on Avan-Guard, Aug'86 by Vanguard Records. Dist: Conifer, Discovery

Harper, Jeanette

PICK ME UP AND PUT ME IN YOUR POCKET.
Single (7"): released on Dawn, Jul'83

Harper, Roy

BORN IN CAPTIVITY.
Notes: Classic 'Demo' RH.
Album: released on Awareness, Apr'87 by Awareness. Dist: EMI

Cassette: released on Awareness, Apr'87 by Awareness. Dist: EMI

BULLINAMINGVASE.
Tracks: / One of those days in England / These last days / Cherishing the lonesome / Naked flame / Watford gap / One of those days in England (parts 2-10) / One of those days in England / These last days / Cherishing the lonesome / Naked flame / Breakfast with you / One of those days in England (parts 2-10).
Album: released on Harvest, Jun'87 by EMI Records. Dist: Roots, EMI

Cassette: released on Harvest, Jun'87 by EMI Records. Dist: Roots, EMI

COME OUT FIGHTING GHENGIS SMITH.
Album: released on Embassy, Jun'77 by CBS Records. Dist: CBS

ELIZABETH.
Single (7"): released on Second Sight, Mar'85

FLAT, BAROQUE AND BERSERK.
Album: released on Harvest, Jul'85 by EMI Records. Dist: Roots, EMI

FOLKJOKEOPUS.
Notes: LP includes 'McGoohans blues' & 'She's the one'
Album: released on Awareness, Apr'87 by Awareness. Dist: EMI

Cassette: released on Awareness, Apr'87 by Awareness. Dist: EMI

HQ.
Tracks: / Game (parts I-V), The / Spirit lives, the / Grown ups are just silly children / Referendum (legend) / Forget me not / Hallucinating light / When an old cricketer leaves the crease.
Notes: Original catalogue number: SHSP 4046 (album); TCSHSP 4046 (cassette)
Album: released on Harvest, Jun'85 by EMI Records. Dist: Roots, EMI

Cassette: released on Harvest, Jun'85 by EMI Records. Dist: Roots, EMI

IN BETWEEN EVERY LINE.
Tracks: / One of those days in England / Short and sweet / Referendum / Highway blues / True story / Game, the / One man rock and roll man / Hangman.
Album: released on EMI, Jun'86 by EMI Records. Dist: EMI

Cassette: released on EMI, Jun'86 by EMI Records. Dist: EMI

I STILL CARE.
Single (7"): released on Public, Feb'83 by Patrick Cambell-Lyons. Dist: Spartan

LIFEMASK.
Notes: The latest R.H. re-issue includes: Highway blues,The Lords prayer, Little lady, Bank of the dead. Cassette includes $ extra tracks.
Album: released on Awareness, Apr'87 by Awareness. Dist: EMI

Cassette: released on Awareness, Apr'87 by Awareness. Dist: EMI

NO ONE EVER GETS OUT ALIVE.
Single (7"): released on Public, Oct'82 by Patrick Cambell-Lyons. Dist: Spartan

SOPHISTICATED BEGGAR.
Cassette: released on Autograph, Apr'85 Dist: Record Services Distribution (Ireland)

Album: released on Big Ben, Jun'85 by Big Ben Records. Dist: Spartan, Taylor, H.R.

STORMCOCK.
Notes: A milestone in 20th century composing & recording and an album for all generations, past, present & future.
Album: released on Awareness, Apr'87 by Awareness. Dist: EMI

Cassette: released on Awareness, Apr'87 by Awareness. Dist: EMI

UNKNOWN SOLDIER, THE.
Album: released on Harvest, Apr'80 by EMI Records. Dist: Roots, EMI

WHATEVER HAPPENED TO 1214 A.D. (Harper, Roy with Jimmy Page).

WORK OF HEART.
Notes: 1982/3 Sunday Times LP of the year (alongside Chris De Burgh)
Album: released on Awareness, Apr'87 by Awareness. Dist: EMI

Cassette: released on Awareness, Apr'87 by Awareness. Dist: EMI

Harpes Indiennes

INDIAN HARPS OF SOUTH AMERICA.
Tracks: / Perriquera / El colas / Limena / Carretaguy / Preludio / El Tilingo / Crepusculo Andino / Concierto en la llanura / Llegada / Puerto Mitanda / Alma, corazon y vida / El Siquisiri / La cosas del cine / Maria Chuchena / Las Virgenes del sol / Colorado.
Notes: Superb album of South American harp music.
Album: released on Sunset (France), Apr'86 Dist: IMS-Polygram Distribution

Compact disc: released on Sunset (France), Apr'86 Dist: IMS-Polygram Distribution

Harpo, Slim

SHAKE YOUR HIPS.
Tracks: / Wonderin' blues / Baby scratch my back / I'm gonna miss you / Rain'in in my heart / We're two of a kind / I need money / Shake your hips / Midnight blues / Harpo's blues / Buzzin' / My little queen bee / I love the life I'm livin'.
Album: released on Flyright, Oct'86 by Flyright Records. Dist: Krazy Kat, Swift, Jazz Music

Harrell, Bill

BALLADS & BLUEGRASS (Harrell, Bill/Virginians).
Album: released on Adelphi, May'81 by Adelphi Records. Dist: Jetstar

Harrell, Tom

PLAY OF LIGHT, THE.
Album: released on Blackhawk, Aug'86 by Blackhawk Records (USA). Dist: IMS-Polygram

Cassette: released on Blackhawk, Aug'86 by Blackhawk Records (USA). Dist: IMS-Polygram

TOM HARRELL.
Notes: Tom Harrell with: Kenny Garrett/Kenny Barron/Ray Drammond
Album: released on Criss Cross, Jul'86 Dist: Jazz Music, Jazz Horizons, Cadillac

Harrier

OUT ON THE STREET.
Single (7"): released on Neon, Mar'84 by Neon Records. Dist: Neon, Pinnacle

Harries, Clive

ORGAN MUSIC FROM CHRISTCHURCH PRIORY.
Album: released on Alpha, Aug'82 by Alpha Records. Dist: H.R. Taylor, Gamut

Harriot, Derrick

EIGHTEEN WITH A BULLET.
Tracks: / Eighteen with a bullet/ (version).
Single (12"): released on Trojan, Sep'86 by Trojan Records. Dist: PRT, Jetstar

Harriott, Derrick

CARIBBEAN STYLE.
Single (12"): released on Sarge, Jul'84 by Sarge Records. Dist: Jetstar

CHECKING OUT.
Single (12"): released on Hawkeye, Jul'85 by Hawkeye Records. Dist: Hawkeye, Lightning (WEA) Distribution, Jetstar, PRT

GREATEST REGGAE HITS.
Album: released on Trojan, Feb'85 by Trojan Records. Dist: PRT, Jetstar

HOMELY GIRL.
Single (12"): released on Crystal, Oct'83 by Crystal Records. Dist: Jetstar, Revolver, Cartel

I'M YOUR PUPPET.
Single (12"): released on Hawkeye, Dec'81 by Hawkeye Records. Dist: Hawkeye, Lightning (WEA) Distribution, Jetstar, PRT

SONGS FOR MIDNIGHT LOVERS.
Album: released on Trojan, Feb'85 by Trojan Records. Dist: PRT, Jetstar

SWEETHEART.
Single (12"): released on Crystal, Jul'82 by Crystal Records. Dist: Jetstar, Revolver, Cartel

Harriott, Joe

JUMP FOR ME (Harriott, Joe & The Tony Kinsey Trio).
Tracks: / Last resort / Best behaviour / How deep is the ocean? / Get happy / Jump for me / Can't we be friends / Raymond / Nice work if you can get it / Chirracahaua / Teddi / Song is you, The / It don't mean a thing.
Album: released on Esquire, Jul'87 by Titan International Productions. Dist: Jazz Music, Cadillac Music, Swift, Wellard, Chris, Backs, Rough Trade, Revolver, Nine Mile

Harris, Anita

ANNIVERSARY WALTZ.
Single (7"): released on Old Gold, Apr'83 by Old Gold Records. Dist: Lightning, Jazz Music, Spartan, Counterpoint

Harris, Barry

AT THE JAZZ WORKSHOP.
Notes: With Sam Jones & Louis Hayes
Compact disc: released on JVC Fantasy (Japan), '86

BARRY HARRIS PLAYS BARRY HARRIS.
Album: released on Xanadu, Mar'79 Dist: Discovery, Jazz Horizons, Jazz Music, Swift

Harris, Beaver

360 DEGREE MUSICAL EXPERIMENT.
Album: released on Soul Note, Sep'79 Dist: Harmonia Mundi Distributors

Harris, Betty

RIDE YOUR PONY.
Single (7"): released on Charly, Jul'80 by Charly Records. Dist: Charly, Cadillac

Harris, Bill

ACES AT THE DEUCES (Harris, Bill/Charlie Ventura).
Album: released on Phoenix, Apr'81 by Audio Fidelity Enterprises. Dist: Stage One, Lugtons

BILL HARRIS & FRIENDS.
Album: released on Fantasy (USA), Feb'84 by Fantasy Inc USA Records. Dist: IMS, Polygram

LIVE AT THE 3 DEUCES (Harris, Bill/Charlie Ventura).
Album: released on Phoenix, Apr'81 by Audio Fidelity Enterprises. Dist: Stage One, Lugtons

PHOENIX JAZZ FIFTH ANNIVERSARY ALBUM (Harris, Bill/Dizzy Gillespie/Eddie Costa/Coleman Hawkins).
Album: released on Phoenix, Apr'81 by Audio Fidelity Enterprises. Dist: Stage One, Lugtons

Harris, Chopper

ESCARGOT A LA BONGO.
Single (7"): released on Utopia, Aug'83

Single (12"): released on Utopia, Aug'83

Harris, Dana

BEASTY MAN.
Tracks: / Beasty man.
Single (7"): released on Aura, Feb'86 by Hollywood Nites Distribution. Dist: Pinnacle

Harris, Diana

FAME LOVE.
Single (7"): released on Aura, Apr'85 by Hollywood Nites Distribution. Dist: Pinnacle

Harris, Eddie

EDDIE (Harris, Eddie, Ralph Armstrong, Sherman Ferguson).
Album: released on Timeless, Oct'86

EXODUS TO JAZZ.
Tracks: / Exodus / Alicia / Gone home / A.T.C. / A.M. Blues / Little girl blue / Velocity / W.P..
Notes: An original Vee Jay recording.
Album: released on Charly, Apr'87 by Charly Records. Dist: Charly, Cadillac

Cassette: released on Charly, Apr'87 by Charly Records. Dist: Charly, Cadillac

STEPS UP (Harris, Eddie quartet).
Album: released on Steeplechase(USA), Sep'81

Harris, Elena

IMAGINATION (Come on rescue me)....
Single (7"): released on Rhythmic, Oct'85 by Rhythmic Records. Dist: Havoc Distribution

Harris, Emmylou

13.
Album: released on Warner Brothers, 11 Apr'87 by Warner Bros Records. Dist: WEA

Cassette: released on Warner Brothers, 11 Apr'87 by Warner Bros Records. Dist: WEA

BALLAD OF SALLY ROSE, (THE).
Album: released on Warner Bros., Feb'85 by Warner Bros Records. Dist: WEA

Cassette: released on Warner Bros., Feb'85 by Warner Bros Records. Dist: WEA

BLUE KENTUCKY GIRL.
Album: released on Warner Brothers, Jun'79 by Warner Bros Records. Dist: WEA Deleted '85.

Cassette: released on Warner Brothers, Jun'79 by Warner Bros Records. Dist: WEA

CHRISTMAS ALBUM, (THE) (light of the stable).
Album: released on Warner Bros., Nov'79 by Warner Bros Records. Dist: WEA

Cassette: released on Warner Bros., Nov'79 by Warner Bros Records. Dist: WEA

ELITE HOTEL.
Album: released on Reprise, Jan'76 by WEA Records. Dist: WEA

Cassette: released on Reprise, Jan'76 by WEA Records. Dist: WEA Deleted '86.

Cassette: released on Warner Bros., Oct'82 by Warner Bros Records. Dist: WEA

LEGENDARY 'GLIDING BIRD' ALBUM, (THE).
Album: released on PRT Distribution, Apr'79

Cassette: released on PRT Distribution, Apr'79

LIVE (Harris, Emmylou/Gram Parsons).
Album: released on Sundown, Nov'83 by Magnum Music Group Ltd. Dist: Magnum Music Group Ltd, PRT Distribution, Spartan Distribution

LUXURY LINER.
Cassette: released on Warner Bros., Oct'82 by Warner Bros Records. Dist: WEA

MR. SANDMAN.
Single (7"): released on Warner Bros., Feb'81 by Warner Bros Records. Dist: WEA

ON THE RADIO.
Single (7"): released on Warner Bros., May'84 by Warner Bros Records. Dist: WEA

PROFILE - BEST OF EMMYLOU HARRIS.
Tracks: / One of these days / Sweet dreams / To daddy / C'est la vie / Making believe / Easy from now on / Together again / If I could only win your love / Too far gone / Two more bottles of wine / Boulder to Birmingham / Hello stranger.
Notes: Digital stereo
Compact disc: released on Warner Bros., Jul'84 by Warner Bros Records. Dist: WEA

Album: released on Warner Bros., '83 by Warner Bros Records. Dist: WEA Deleted '86.

Cassette: released on Warner Bros., '83 by Warner Bros Records. Dist: WEA

TRIO (Harris, Emmylou, Dolly Parton, Linda Rondstadt).
Notes: For full details of this recording see under **Parton, Dolly.**

WHITE SHOES.
Tracks: / Drivin' wheel / Pledging my love / In my dreams / White shoes / On the radio / It's only Rock 'n' Roll / Diamonds are a girl's best friend / Good news / Baby better start turnin' em down / Like an old fashioned waltz.
Compact disc: released on Warner Bros., Jan'84 by Warner Bros Records. Dist: WEA

Album: released on Warner Bros., Oct'83 by Warner Bros Records. Dist: WEA Deleted '86.

Cassette: released on Warner Bros., Oct'83 by Warner Bros Records. Dist: WEA Deleted '86.

Harris, Gene

GENE HARRIS TRIO PLUS ONE, THE.
Tracks: / Gene's lament / Misty / Uptown sop / Things ain't what they used to be / Yours is my heart alone / Battle hymn of the Republic.
Notes: Gene's debut album as a leader of Concord, a joyful, soulful performance captured live at New York's blue Note. From the opening note of Ray Brown's composition "Gene's Lament", you'll find yourself rockin' and clappin' to the beat. Personnel: Gene Harris-piano/Ray Brown-bass/Mickey Roker-drums/Special guest: Stanley Turrentine-tenor saxophone.
Album: released on Concord Jazz(USA), Oct'86 by Concord Jazz Records (USA). Dist: IMS, Polygram

PLUS ONE.
Compact disc: released on Jazz (USA), Apr'87

Harris, Gerard

JOSEPH'S PAST.
Album: released on Move, Jun'86 by Charly Records. Dist: Charly Distribution, Fast Forward Distribution, Cartel Distribution

Harris, Jack

JACK HARRIS & HIS ORCHESTRA 1937-1939 (Harris, Jack & his orchestra).
Album: released on World, Feb'75 Dist: Jetstar

Harris, Jerry

I'M SO GLAD.
Single (12"): released on Procedure, Nov'85

Harris, Jet

DIAMONDS (Harris, Jet/Tony Meehan).
Single (7"): released on Decca, Oct'80 by Decca Records. Dist: Polygram

Single (7"): released on Old Gold, Oct'83 by Old Gold Records. Dist: Lightning, Jazz Music, Spartan, Counterpoint

REMEMBERING (Harris, Jet/Tony Meehan).
Album: released on Decca, Sep'76 by Decca Records. Dist: Polygram

Cassette: released on Decca, Sep'76 by Decca Records. Dist: Polygram

Harris, Jody

IT HAPPENED ONE NIGHT.
Tracks: / It happened one night / I'm after hours again / Mystic mints / Money talks / You better read before you sign / Fairly modern / My Uncle Bill / Coal black mamas.
Album: released on Press, Jul'86 by Press Records.

Harris, Joey

JOEY HARRIS & THE SPEEDSTARS (Harris, Joey/Speedstars).
Album: released on MCA, Mar'84 by MCA Records. Dist: Polygram, MCA

Cassette: released on MCA, Mar'84 by MCA Records. Dist: Polygram, MCA

Harris, Johnny Ray

ROCKING IN LOUISIANA VOL.2 (Harris, Johnny Ray & Jimmy Wray).
Album: released on White, Jul'87

Harris, Keith

AREN'T I LUCKY (Harris, Keith & Orville).
Album: released on BBC, Apr'84 by BBC Records & Tapes. Dist: EMI, PRT, Pye

Cassette: released on BBC, Apr'84 by BBC Records & Tapes. Dist: EMI, PRT, Pye

Harris, Keith & Orville

AT THE END OF THE RAINBOW.
Album: released on BBC, May'83 by BBC Records & Tapes. Dist: EMI, PRT, Pye

BEIN' GREEN.
Single (7"): released on BBC, May'84 by BBC Records & Tapes. Dist: EMI, PRT, Pye

COME TO MY PARTY.
Single (7"): released on BBC, Nov'83 by BBC Records & Tapes. Dist: EMI, PRT, Pye

ORVILLE'S SONG.
Single (7"): released on BBC, Nov'82 by BBC Records & Tapes. Dist: EMI, PRT, Pye

SUPERDUCK.
Single (7"): released on BBC, Nov'84 by BBC Records & Tapes. Dist: EMI, PRT, Pye

WHITE CHRISTMAS.
Single (7"): released on Columbia, Nov'85 by EMI Records. Dist: EMI

Picture disc single: released on Columbia, Dec'85 by EMI Records. Dist: EMI

WILL YOU STILL LOVE ME IN THE MORNING.
Single (7"): released on BBC, Apr'83 by BBC Records & Tapes. Dist: EMI, PRT, Pye

Harris, Lenny

LONG AFTER TONIGHT IS ALL OVER.
Single (7"): released on Soul Stop, Feb'84 by Soul Stop Record 3. Dist: Spartan

Harris, Major

ALL MY LIFE.
Single (7"): released on London, Nov'83 by London Records. Dist: Polygram

Single (12"): released on London, Nov'83 by London Records. Dist: Polygram

I WANT YOUR LOVE.
Single (7"): released on Buzz Int., Feb'84

Single (12"): released on Buzz Int., Feb'84

Harrison

NO REFRAIN.
Single (7"): released on Skipping Rope, Dec'84 by Harrison Records.

Harrison, Geoff

EVE OF DESTRUCTION.
Single (7"): released on Banana, Apr'84 Dist: Pinnacle, Fresh

Harrison, George

ALL THINGS MUST PASS.
Tracks: / I'd have you anytime / My sweet lord / Wah-wah / Isn't it a pity / What is life / If not for you / Behind that locked door / Let it down / Run of the mill / Beware of darkness / Apple scruffs / Ballad of Sir Frankie Crisp (Let it roll) / Awaiting on you all / All things must pass / I dig love / Art of dying / Isn't it a pity / Hear me lord / Out of the blue / It's Johnny's birthday / Plug me in / I remember jeep / Thanks for the pepperoni.
Double compact disc: released on EMI, May'87 by EMI Records. Dist: EMI

Triple album / cassette: released on Parlophone, '71 by EMI Records. Dist: EMI

ALL THOSE YEARS AGO.
Single (7"): released on Dark Horse, May'81 by George Harrison. Dist: WEA

BEST OF GEORGE HARRISON, THE.
Tracks: / Something / If I needed someone / Here comes the sun / Here comes the sun / Taxman / Think for yourself / For you blue / While my guitar gently weeps / My sweet Lord / Give me love (give me peace on earth) / You / Bangla Desh / Dark horse / What is life.
Compact disc: released on Parlophone, May'87 by EMI Records. Dist: EMI

Album: released on MFP, Oct'81 by EMI Records. Dist: EMI

Cassette: released on MFP, Oct'81 by EMI Records. Dist: EMI

DARK HORSE.
Album: released on EMI (Germany), Aug'83 by EMI Records. Dist: Conifer

GEORGE HARRISON.
Tracks: / Love comes to everyone / Not guilty / Here comes the moon / Soft Hearted Hana / Blow away / Faster / Dark sweet lady / Your love is forever / Soft touch / If you believe*.
Notes: All words and music by George Harrison (C) 1979 Ganga Publishing BV, except* Words and music by George Harrison and Gary Wright (C) 1979 Ganga Publishing, BV. BMI/High Wave Music ASCAP. Produced by George Harrison anf Russ Titelman.
Album: released on Dark Horse, Mar'79 by George Harrison. Dist: WEA

Cassette: released on Dark Horse, Apr'79 by George Harrison. Dist: WEA

LIVING IN THE MATERIAL WORLD.
Album: released on EMI (Germany), Jun'83 by EMI Records. Dist: Conifer

MY SWEET LORD.
Single (7"): released on Apple, Nov'76 Dist: EMI
Cat. no: **R 5884**
Single (7"): released on EMI (Germany), Apr'83 by EMI Records. Dist: Conifer

TEARDROPS.
Single (7"): released on Dark Horse, Jul'81 by George Harrison. Dist: WEA

WAKE UP MY LOVE.
Single (7"): released on Dark Horse, Nov'82 by George Harrison. Dist: WEA

WONDERWALL.
Album: released on EMI (France), '83 by EMI Records. Dist: Conifer

Harrison, Harry

OFF THE CUFF.
Album: released on Broadside, Jun'81 by Broadside Records. Dist: Celtic Distributions, H.R. Taylor, Jazz Music, Projection, Jazz Services Unlimited Dist. (JSU)

Cassette: released on Broadside, Jun'81 by Broadside Records. Dist: Celtic Distributions, H.R. Taylor, Jazz Music, Projection, Jazz Services Unlimited Dist. (JSU)

Harrison, Kevin

FLY.
Single (7"): released on Glass, Jun'82 by Glass Records. Dist: Nine Mile, Rough Trade, Red Rhino, Play It Again Sam

INSCRUTABLY OBVIOUS.
Album: released on Cherry Red, Oct'81 by Cherry Red Records. Dist: Pinnacle

Harrison, Michelle

BEING IN LOVE.
Single (12"): released on Lion Kingdom, Jun'84 by Lion Kingdom Records. Dist: Jetstar, Pinnacle

DON'T TAKE LOVE SO EASY.
Single (12"): released on Lion Kingdom, May'83 by Lion Kingdom Records. Dist: Jetstar, Pinnacle

Harrison, Noel

WINDMILLS OF YOUR MIND.
Single (7"): released on Reprise, Jul'81 by WEA Records. Dist: WEA

Single (7"): released on Old Gold, Jul'82 by Old Gold Records. Dist: Lightning, Jazz Music, Spartan, Counterpoint

Harrison, Peter

NICE 'N' EASY.
Album: released on Grosvenor, Jun'81 by Grosvenor Records. Dist: Taylors

SALLEY IN OUR ALLEY.
Album: released on Plant Life, Nov'81 Dist: Roots

Harrison, Rex

HIS FAVOURITE SONGS.
Album: released on Pye, Jan'79

Harrison, Russ

PLAYING AT TRAINS.
Single (12"): released on Sincere Sounds, May'87

Harrison, Valerie

FOOL'S PARADISE.
Tracks: / Fool's paradise / Let's get funky.
Single (12"): released on Blackbeat, Aug'86 Dist: Jetstar

LITTLE BIT MORE, A (Harrison, Valerie & Bill Campbell).
Tracks: / Little bit more, A / You're so good.
Single (12"): released on Blackbeat, Nov'86 Dist: Jetstar

ON MY OWN (Harrison, Valerie & Bill Campbell).
Notes: For full details see under Bill Campbell.

Harrison, Wilbert

LOVIN' OPERATOR.
Album: released on Charly(R&B), May'85 by Charly Records. Dist: Charly, Cadillac

SMALL LABELS.
Tracks: / This woman of mine / Letter edged in black / Gin & coconut milk / Nobody knows my trouble / Calypso man / Cool water / After graduation / Off to work again / Off to school again / I'm broke / Mama mama mama / New York World's fair / Baby move on / You're still my baby / Please forgive me / Poison ivy.
Album: released on Krazy Kat (USA) Jun'86

Harris, Phil

ALICE FAYE & PHIL HARRIS: TWO COMPLETE RADIO BROADCASTS (see Faye, Alice) (Harris, Phil & Alice Faye).

BEST OF PHIL HARRIS,(THE).
Album: released on RCA International, Oct'80

Cassette: released on RCA International, Oct'80

TWO COMPLETE BROADCASTS (Harris, Phil & Alice Faye).
Album: released on Radio Archives, Jun'79 Dist: Jazz Music, Swift

UNCOLLECTED (1933), THE.
Notes: Mono
Album: released on Hindsight(UK), Jun'86 Dist: Jazz Music

Harris, Richard

MACARTHUR PARK.
Single (7"): released on Old Gold (Reissue), Jul'82

Harris, Rolf

COOJEE BEAR AND THE MONSTER.
Album: released on Solid, Mar'85 by Solid Records. Dist: Graduate, Spartan

Cassette: released on Solid, Mar'85 by Solid Records. Dist: Graduate, Spartan

HEY JIMMY JOHNSON.
Single (7"): released on RHE Records, Nov'81

ROLF ON SATURDAY.
Cassette: released on BBC, Apr'79 by BBC Records & Tapes. Dist: EMI, PRT, Pye Deleted May'81.

TOMMY (FROM '88 PINE').
Tracks: / Tommy.
Single (7"): released on Tembo, Nov'86 by Tembo (Canada). Dist: IMS Distribution, Polygram Distribution

Harris, Roy

BITTER & THE SWEET, THE.
Album: released on Topic, '81 Dist: Roots Distribution

BY SANDBANK FIELDS (songs & ballads).
Album: released on Topic, '81 Dist: Roots Distribution

CHAMPIONS OF FOLLY.
Album: released on Topic, '81 Dist: Roots Distribution

RAMBLING SOLDIER, THE.
Cassette: released on Fellside, Jul'87 by Fellside Records. Dist: Roots, Jazz Music, Celtic Music, Projection

Album: released on Fellside (Cumbria), '83 by Fellside Records. Dist: Roots, Projection, CM, Jazz Music

UTTER SIMPLICITY.
Tracks: / Jackie Munro / Golden glove, The / Rolling down to old Maui / Clear away the morning dew / I reckon I've served me time / Silver Queen / Young Roger Esq. / Budgie weed / Capt. Wedderburn's courtship / Tom Brown's stormy old weather / When we raced the Robin adair / Bright fields of England.
Notes: Accompanied by: Jill & Bernard Blackwell, Steve Hicks and Ann Dickinson. Recorded and produced by Paul Adams. Recorded January and June 1985.
Album: released on Fellside, May'85 by Fellside Records. Dist: Roots, Jazz Music, Celtic Music, Projection

Harris, Sam

I'D DO IT ALL AGAIN.
Tracks: / I'd do it all again / Rescue, The.
Single (7"): released on Motown, May'86 by Motown Records. Dist: BMG Distribution

Single (12"): released on Motown, May'86 by Motown Records. Dist: BMG Distribution

OVER THE RAINBOW.
Single (7"): released on Motown, Mar'85 by Motown Records. Dist: BMG Distribution

Single (12"): released on Motown, Mar'85 by Motown Records. Dist: BMG Distribution

SAM HARRIS.
Tracks: / Out of control / Sugar don't bite / I've heard it all before / Hearts of fire / I will not wait for you / Pretender / Don't look in eyes / You keep me hangin' on / Inside of me / Over the rainbow.
Compact disc: released on Motown, Aug'85 by Motown Records. Dist: BMG Distribution

Album: released on Motown, Oct'84 by Motown Records. Dist: BMG Distribution

Cassette: released on Motown, Oct'84 by Motown Records. Dist: BMG Distribution

SAM-I-AM.
Tracks: / I'll do it all again / Forever for you / Heart of the machine / Rescue, The / Suffer the innocent / Ba-doom ba-doom / Don't want to give up on love / In your eyes / Always / Bells, The / I need you / Stay with me.
Album: released on Motown, Jul'86 by Motown Records. Dist: BMG Distribution

Cassette: released on Motown, Jul'86 by Motown Records. Dist: BMG Distribution

SUGAR DON'T BITE.
Single (7"): released on Motown, Oct'84 by Motown Records. Dist: BMG Distribution

Single (12"): released on Motown, Oct'84 by Motown Records. Dist: BMG Distribution

Harris, Simon

BEATS, BREAKS AND SCRATCHES.
Album: released on Music Of Life, Jun'87 Dist: Streetwave

Harris, Stewart

LOVIN' OR LEAVIN'.
Tracks: / Lovin' or leavin'.
Single (7"): released on Network, Oct'86 by Epic. Dist: PRT, CBS

Harris, Sue

AMONG THE ATTRACTIONS (Harris, Sue & John Kirkpatrick).
Album: released on Topic, Jul'76 Dist: Roots Distribution

HAMMERS & TONGUES.
Album: released on Free Reed, Jan'87 by Free Reed Records. Dist: Roots, Projection, Hobgoblin Records, Oblivion

ROSE OF BRITAIN'S ISLE.
Album: released on Topic, Jun'74 Dist: Roots Distribution

Harris, Sue & Alan

HOW TO MAKE A BAKEWELL TART.
Album: released on Free Reed, Nov'77 by Free Reed Records. Dist: Roots, Projection, Hobgoblin Records, Oblivion

Harris, Thurston

LITTLE BITTY PRETTY ONE.
Tracks: / Over & over / Little bitty pretty one / Do what you did / Hey baby Leeba / You don't know / I'm asking forgiveness / hey little girl / Send me some lovin' / Only one love / Tell me so / Fine fine frame / Cross my heart / My love will last / I got loaded at Smokey Joe's joint.
Album: released on Stateside, Apr'87 Dist: EMI

Cassette: released on Stateside, Apr'87 Dist: EMI

Harris, Wee Willie

GOES APE.
Album: released on Ace, Oct'86 by Ace Records. Dist: Pinnacle, Swift, Hotshot, Cadillac

Harris, Woody

AMERICAN GUITAR SOLOS.
Album: released on Arhoolie, May'81 by Arhoolie Records. Dist: Projection, Topic, Jazz Music, Swift, Roots

BLOOMFIELD & HARRIS (see Bloomfield, Mike) (Harris, Woody & Mike Bloomfield).

Harris, Wynonie

BATTLE OF THE BLUES (Harris, Wynonie & Roy Brown).
Tracks: / Mr. Blues is coming to town / Good rocking tonight / Rock Mr. Blues / Bloodshot eyes / Just like two drops of water / Luscious woman / Lovin' machine / Keep on churnin' (till the butter comes) / Good morning judge / Quiet whiskey / Down boy down / Cadillac baby / Too much lovin' ain't no good / Hard luck blues / My gal from kokomo / Big town / Rock-a-bye baby / Black diamond / Ain't no rockin' no more / Fannie Brown got married / Shake 'em up baby / Good looking and foxy too.
Compact disc: released on Charly, Dec'86 by Charly Records. Dist: Charly, Cadillac

MR. BLUES COMIN' TO TOWN.
Album: released on Route 66, Apr'79

PLAYFUL BABY.
Album: released on Route, May'86 by Route Records. Dist: Jetstar Distribution

ROCK MR. BLUES.
Album: released on Charly(R&B), Jul'85 by Charly Records. Dist: Charly, Cadillac

Cassette: released on Charly(R&B), Jul'85 by Charly Records. Dist: Charly, Cadillac

Harrogate

HARROGATE DISTRICT, THE various artists (Various Artists).
Cassette: released on Audiocord Cassettes, May'83

Harrow, David

BITE THE HAND THAT FEEDS YOU (Harrow, David & Pinkie MacLure).

NO EASY TARGETS.
Single (12"): released on Red Flame, Oct'84 by Red Flame Records. Dist: Nine Mile, Cartel

OUR LITTLE GIRL.
Single (7"): released on Red Flame 10, Nov'83

Single (12"): released on Red Flame 10, Nov'83

SUCCESSION, THE.
Album: released on 10 Red Flame, Dec'83 by Red Flame Records. Dist: Rough Trade, Cartel

Harrow, Nancy

WILD WOMEN DON'T HAVE THE BLUES.
Album: released on Candid, Dec'85 Dist: Counterpoint, Cadillac

Harry, Debbie

FREE TO FALL.
Tracks: / Free to fall / Secret life.
Single (7"): released on Chrysalis, Feb'87 by Chrysalis Records. Dist: CBS

Single (12"): released on Chrysalis, Feb'87 by Chrysalis Records. Dist: CBS

FRENCH KISSING IN THE USA.
Single (7"): released on Chrysalis, Nov'86 by Chrysalis Records. Dist: CBS

Single (12"): released on Chrysalis, Nov'86 by Chrysalis Records. Dist: CBS

IN LOVE WITH LOVE.
Tracks: / In love with love / French kissin' (French).
Single (7"): released on Chrysalis, Apr'87 by Chrysalis Records. Dist: CBS

Single (12"): released on Chrysalis, Apr'87 by Chrysalis Records. Dist: CBS

KOO KOO.
Album: released on Chrysalis, Aug'81 by Chrysalis Records. Dist: CBS

Cassette: released on Chrysalis, Aug'81 by Chrysalis Records. Dist: CBS

ROCKBIRD.
Tracks: / I want you / French kissin' / Buckle up / In love with love / You got me in trouble / Free to fall / Rockbird / Secret life / Beyond the limit.
Notes: Produced by: Seth Justman.
Album: released on Chrysalis, Nov'86 by Chrysalis Records. Dist: CBS

Cassette: released on Chrysalis, Nov'86 by Chrysalis Records. Dist: CBS

Compact disc: released on Chrysalis, Nov'86 by Chrysalis Records. Dist: CBS

Hart, Billy

OSHUMARE.
Album: released on Gramavision (USA), Dec'85 by Gramavison Records (USA). Dist: PRT, IMS, Polygram

Hart, Bob

SONGS FROM SUFFOLK.
Album: released on Topic, '81 Dist: Roots Distribution

Hart, Corey

ANGRY YOUNG MAN.
Tracks: / Angry young man / Angry young men (Dub version).
Single (7"): released on EMI America, Nov'86 by EMI Records. Dist: EMI

Single (12"): released on EMI America, Nov'86 by EMI Records. Dist: EMI

BOY IN THE BOX.
Tracks: / Boy in the box / Komrade Kiev / Never surrender / Sunny place-shady people / Eurasian eyes / Everything in my heart / Silent talking / Waiting for you / Water from the moon.
Compact disc: released on EMI, Dec'85 by EMI Records. Dist: EMI

Album: released on EMI, Oct'85 by EMI Records. Dist: EMI

Cassette: released on EMI, Oct'85 by EMI Records. Dist: EMI

CAN'T HELP FALLING IN LOVE.
Tracks: / Can't help falling in love / Broken arrow / My brothers leaving today.
Notes: My brother's leaving today - extra track available on 12" version only.
Single (7"): released on EMI America, Feb'87 by EMI Records. Dist: EMI

Single (12"): released on EMI America, Feb'87 by EMI Records. Dist: EMI

FIELDS OF FIRE.
Tracks: / I am by your side / Dancing with my mirror / Take my heart / Angry young man / Goin' home / I can't help falling in love with you / Political cry / Is it too late? / Jimmy Rae / Blind faith.
Album: released on EMI America, Oct'86 by EMI Records. Dist: EMI

Cassette: released on EMI America, Oct'86 by EMI Records. Dist: EMI

Compact disc: released on EMI America, Oct'86 by EMI Records. Dist: EMI

NEVER SURRENDER.
Single (7"): released on EMI America, '85 by EMI Records. Dist: EMI

Single (12"): released on EMI America, '85 by EMI Records. Dist: EMI

SUNGLASSES AT NIGHT.
Single (7"): released on EMI America, '84 by EMI Records. Dist: EMI

Hart, Dicky

HUNGRY FOR YOU (Hart, Dicky & The Palpitations).
Single (7"): released on Medikal, '84

Harte, Ciaran

LOVE IS STRANGE.
Single (7"): released on Glass, '82 by Glass Records. Dist: Nine Mile, Rough Trade, Red Rhino, Play It Again Sam

Harte, Frank

DUBLIN STREET SONGS.
Album: Dist: Roots Distribution

FRANK HARTE & LISTENING TO MY SONG.
Album: released on Mulligan, '79 by Topic Records. Dist: Roots Distribution, Jazz Music Distribution, JSU Distribution, I & B Distribution, Projection Distribution, Wynd-Up Distribution, Celtic Distributions

THROUGH DUBLIN CITY.
Album: released on Topic, '81 Dist: Roots Distribution

Hart, Elroy

NORTH FLORIDA FIVES (Hart, Elroy & Fats Jefferson).
Album: released on Flyright, '79 by Flyright Records. Dist: Krazy Kat, Swift, Jazz Music

Hart family

HART TO HART.
Album: released on Sweet Folk All, '81 by Sweet Folk All Records. Dist: Sweet Folk All, Roots, Celtic Music, Dragon, Impetus, Projection, Chris Wellard, Festival Records

Hartford, John

ANNUAL WALTZ.
Tracks: / Annual waltz / All in my love for you.
Single (7"): released on MCA, May'87 by MCA Records. Dist: Polygram, MCA

Single (12"): released on MCA, 11 Apr'87 by MCA Records. Dist: Polygram, MCA

ANNUAL WALTZ (LP) (Hartford, John & The Hartford String Band).
Tracks: / All in my love for you / Ohio river rag / Annual waltz / Gone, gone, gone / Love wrote this song / Learning to smile all over again / Pennington bend / Here's to your dreams / Short life of trouble / Living in the Mississippi valley.
Cassette: released on MCA, 11 Apr'87 by MCA Records. Dist: Polygram, MCA

GUM TREE CANOE.
Album: released on Sundown, 11 Apr'87 by

Magnum Music Group Ltd. Dist: Magnum Music Group Ltd, PRT Distribution, Spartan Distribution

SLEEPIN' ON THE CUMBERLAND.
Album: released on Flying Fish (USA), '79 by Flying Fish Records (USA). Dist: Roots, Projection

Harth, Alfred

EARTH, THE.
Album: released on ECM (Germany), '84 by ECM Records. Dist: IMS, Polygram, Virgin through EMI

Hart, John

BLOWIN' MAN, THE.
Album: released on Sonet, '81 by Sonet Records. Dist: PRT

Hartley, Trevor

CAN YOU FEEL THE LOVE.
Tracks: / Can you feel the love / Can you feel the love (Instrumental).
Single (12"): released on Sir George, Apr'86 by Sir George Records. Dist: Jetstar, Pinnacle

PACK YOUR THINGS AND GO.
Single (12"): released on Tanga Music, Dec'82

WARM LOVE.
Single (7"): released on Top Ranking, Feb'83

Single (12"): released on Top Ranking, Feb'83

Hartly, Trevor

CALL ON ME.
Tracks: / Call on me / Call on me.
Single (7"): released on Virgin, Oct'86 by Virgin Records. Dist: EMI, Virgin Distribution

Single (12"): released on Virgin, Oct'86 by Virgin Records. Dist: EMI, Virgin Distribution

IT MUST BE LOVE.
Tracks: / It must be love / It must be love (version).
Single (12"): released on Unity Sound, Apr'87 Dist: Jetstar

Hartman, Dan

I CAN DREAM ABOUT YOU.
Tracks: / We are the young / I can dream about you / Shy hearts / I'm not a rolling stone / Rage to live / Name of the game / Power of a good love / Second nature / I can't get enough / Electricity.
Compact disc: released on MCA, May'85 by MCA Records. Dist: Polygram, MCA

Album: released on MCA, Jan'85 by MCA Records. Dist: Polygram, MCA

Cassette: released on MCA, Jan'85 by MCA Records. Dist: Polygram, MCA

Compact disc: released on MCA, Jan'85 by MCA Records. Dist: Polygram, MCA

Single (12"): released on MCA, Sep'85 by MCA Records. Dist: Polygram, MCA

Single (7"): released on MCA, Aug'85 by MCA Records. Dist: Polygram, MCA

Single (12"): released on MCA, Aug'85 by MCA Records. Dist: Polygram. MCA

INSTANT REPLAY.
Tracks: / Instant replay / Countdown-this is it / Double-O-Love / Chocolate box / Love is a natural / Time and space.
Cassette: released on Blue Sky, Feb'86 by CBS Records. Dist: CBS

Album: released on Blue Sky, Feb'86 by CBS Records. Dist: CBS

WAITING TO SEE YOU.
Tracks: / Waiting to see you.
Single (12"): released on Epic, Aug'86 by CBS Records. Dist: CBS

WE ARE YOUNG.
Compact disc: by MCA Records. Dist: Polygram, MCA

Hartman, John

IMPULSE (Hartman, John & John Coltrane).
Notes: For full details see under John Coltrane.

Hartman, Johnny

ONCE IN EVERY LIFE.
Album: released on Beehive (USA), Apr'84 by Cadillac Records. Dist:

UNFORGETTABLE SONGS.
Album: released on Jasmine, Mar'85 by Jasmine Records. Dist: Counterpoint, Lugtons, Taylor, H.R., Wellard, Chris, Swift, Cadillac

Hartman, Lisa

WHERE THE BOYS ARE.
Single (7"): released on RCA, Jul'84 by RCA Records. Dist: RCA, Roots, Swift, Wellard, Chris, I & B, Solomon & Peres Distribution

Hartman's Eart Breakers

HOT HILLBILLY RHYTHM FROM THE 1930'S (Lou, Betty).
Album: released on Rambler, Jul'81 Dist: Swift

Hart, Maureen

HEY LORD, IT'S ME.
Tracks: / Hey Lord, it's me / Sweet dreams.
Album: released on Klub, Nov'86

Cassette: released on Klub, Nov'86

Single (7"):

Hart, Paul

HALLEY'S COMET.
Single (7"): released on Columbia, '85 by EMI Records. Dist: EMI

Hart, Philip

ANGEL.
Tracks: / Angel / Angel.
Single (7"): released on Sonet, Jan'86 by Sonet Records. Dist: PRT

Single (12"): released on Simba, Nov'83 by Simba Records. Dist: Jetstar

EVERYTHING TO ME.

Single (7"): released on Sonet, '84 by Sonet Records. Dist: PRT

Hart, Tim

DRUNKEN SAILOR,THE/FROGGY'S COURTING.
Single (7"): released on MFP, '83 by EMI Records. Dist: EMI

DRUNKEN SALIOR & OTHER KIDS SONGS.
Album: released on Music For Pleasure (Holland), '83 by EMI Records. Dist: EMI

Cassette: released on Music For Pleasure (Holland), '83 by EMI Records. Dist: EMI

FAVOURITE CHILDRENS SONGS.
Album: released on MFP, '85 by EMI Records. Dist: EMI

Cassette: released on MFP, '85 by EMI Records. Dist: EMI

FOLK SONGS OF OLDE ENGLAND (Hart, Tim & Maddy Prior).
Album: released on Mooncrest, '83 by Mooncrest Records. Dist: PRT Distribution

Cassette: released on Mooncrest, '83 by Mooncrest Records. Dist: PRT Distribution

Album: released on Mooncrest, '83 by Mooncrest Records. Dist: PRT Distribution

MY VERY FAVOURITE NURSEY RHYME RECORD.
Album: released on MFP, '81 by EMI Records. Dist: EMI

Cassette: released on MFP, '81 by EMI Records. Dist: EMI

SUMMER SOLSTICE (Hart, Tim & Maddy Prior).
Tracks: / False knight on the road / Bring us in good ale / Of all the birds / I live not where I love / Ploughboy and the cockney, The / Westron Wynde / Sorry the day I was married / Dancing at Whitsun / Fly up my cock / Cannily cannily / Adam catched Eve / Three drunk maidens / Serving girls holiday.
Cassette: released on Mooncrest, Aug'86 by Mooncrest Records. Dist: PRT Distribution
Cat. no: **ZCEST 12**

SUMMER SOLSTICE (Hart, Tim & Maddy Prior).
Album: released on Mooncrest, '83 by Mooncrest Records. Dist: PRT Distribution

TIM HART.
Album: released on Chrysalis, '79 by Chrysalis Records. Dist: CBS

Cassette: released on Chrysalis, '79 by Chrysalis Records. Dist: CBS

Harum Scarum

DOGMAN.
Album: released on Au-Go-Go (Australia), Oct'86 by Au-Go-Go Records (Australia). Dist: Rough Trade, Cartel

Harvest

HARVEST Various artists (Various Artists).
Album: released on Broadside, Jun'81 by Broadside Records. Dist: Celtic Distributions, H.R. Taylor, Jazz Music, Projection, Jazz Services Unlimited Dist. (JSU)

Cassette: released on Broadside, Jun'81 by Broadside Records. Dist: Celtic Distributions, H.R. Taylor, Jazz Music, Projection, Jazz Services Unlimited Dist. (JSU)

Harvey, Alex

ANTHOLOGY.
Cassette: released on Sahara, Jan'86

BEST OF THE SENSATIONAL ALEX HARVEY BAND, THE (Harvey, Alex Band).
Album: released on RCA, May'84 by RCA Records. Dist: RCA, Roots, Swift, Wellard, Chris, I & B, Solomon & Peres Distribution

Cassette: released on RCA, May'84 by RCA Records. Dist: RCA, Roots, Swift, Wellard, Chris, I & B, Solomon & Peres Distribution

BEST OF THE SENSATIONAL ALEX HARVEY BAND, (THE) (Harvey, Alex Sensational Band).
Compact disc: released on K-Tel, Jun'87 by K-Tel Records. Dist: Record Merchandisers Distribution, Taylors, Terry Blood Distribution, Wynd-Up Distribution, Relay Distribution, Pickwick Distribution, Solomon & Peres Distribution, Polygram

Album: released on K-Tel, Jul'87 by K-Tel Records. Dist: Record Merchandisers Distribution, Taylors, Terry Blood Distribution, Wynd-Up Distribution, Relay Distribution, Pickwick Distribution, Solomon & Peres Distribution, Polygram

Cassette: released on K-Tel, Jul'87 by K-Tel Records. Dist: Record Merchandisers Distribution, Taylors, Terry Blood Distribution, Wynd-Up Distribution, Relay Distribution, Pickwick Distribution, Solomon & Peres Distribution, Polygram

COLLECTION: ALEX HARVEY (Harvey, Alex Sensational Band).
Tracks: / 25 Dollars for a message / Tale of the giant stoneater, The / Action strasse / Gang bang / Next / Give my compliments to the chef / Framed / Tomorrow belongs to me / Dance to your daddy / Sergeant fury / Sultan's choice / Delilah (Live) / Soul in chains / Faith healer / Boston tea party / Vambo, part 1 / Dogs of war / There's no lights on the Christmas tree mother / Giddy up a ding dong.
Album: released on Castle Collectors, Sep'86 by Castle Communications Records. Dist: Pinnacle

Cassette: released on Castle Collectors, Sep'86 by Castle Communications Records. Dist: Pinnacle

Compact disc: released on Collector Series, '86 by Castle Communications Records. Dist: PRT, Pinnacle, RCA, Ariola

DOCUMENT.
Cassette: released on Aura, Apr'86 by Hollywood Nites Distribution. Dist: Pinnacle

FOURPLAY (Harvey, Alex Band).
Album: released on Sahara, Nov'84

FRAMED (Harvey, Alex Band, The).
Compact disc: released on Samurai, '86 Dist: Pinnacle

FRAMED (Harvey, Alex Band).
Album: released on Sahara, Nov'84

FRAMED.
Cassette: released on Samurai, Jul'86 Dist: Pinnacle

IMPOSSIBLE DREAM, THE.
Cassette: released on Samurai, May'86 Dist: Pinnacle

Cassette: released on Samurai, May'86 Dist: Pinnacle

IMPOSSIBLE DREAM, THE (Harvey, Alex Band).
Album: released on Sahara, Nov'84

LEGEND (Harvey, Alex Sensational Band).
Compact disc: released on Samurai, '86 Dist: Pinnacle

LEGEND, THE (Harvey, Alex Band).
Album: released on Sahara, Nov'85

LIVE (Harvey, Alex Sensational Band).
Compact disc: released on Samurai, '86 Dist: Pinnacle

LIVE (Harvey, Alex Band).
Album: released on Sahara, Apr'86

Picture disc album: released on Sahara, Apr'86

Cassette: released on Sahara, Apr'86

LIVE (Harvey, Alex Sensational Band).
Tracks: / Compliments to the chef / Delilah / Faith healer / Fanfare (justly, skilfully, magnanimously) / Framed / Tomahawk kid / Vambo.
Album: released on Fame, Oct'86 by Music For Pleasure Records. Dist: EMI

NEXT (Harvey, Alex Band, The).
Tracks: / Swampsnake / Gang bang / Faith healer, The / Giddy up a ding dong / Next / Vambo marble eye / Last of the teenage parts 1 2 3, The.

Notes: (P) 1973 Original Sound Recordings owned by Canalfleet Ltd. trading as Samurai Records.
Picture disc album: released on Samurai, May'86 Dist: Pinnacle

Album: released on Fame, Mar'87 by Music For Pleasure Records. Dist: EMI

Cassette: released on Fame, Mar'87 by Music For Pleasure Records. Dist: EMI

Compact disc: released on Samurai, '86 Dist: Pinnacle

PENTHOUSE TAPES (Harvey, Alex Band).
Album: released on Sahara. Nov'84

PENTHOUSE TAPES, THE (Harvey, Alex Sensational Band).
Compact disc: released on Samurai, '86 Dist: Pinnacle

POET AND I.
Single (7"): released on Powerstation Records, Nov'83 by Powerstation Records. Dist: Pinnacle

ROCKDRILL (Harvey, Alex Band).
Album: released on Sahara, Nov'84

SENSATIONAL ALEX HARVEY BAND (Harvey, Alex Band).
Album: released on Sahara Nov'84

SOLDIER ON THE WALL, THE.
Album: released on Power Supply, Nov'83

Cassette: released on Power Supply, Nov'83

TOMORROW BELONGS TO ME (Harvey, Alex Band).
Album: released on Sahara, Nov'84

Harvey, Bobby

GLENNEAGLES FAVOURITES (Harvey, Bobby Band).
Album: released on Lochshore, Apr'87 by Klub Records. Dist: PRT

Cassette: released on Lochshore, Apr'87 by Klub Records. Dist: PRT

Harvey, Jancis

PORTRAIT OF JANCIS HARVEY, A.
Album: released on Westwood, May'77 by Westwood Records. Dist: Jazz Music, H.R. Taylor, JSU, Pinnacle, Ross Records

Harvey, Jane

IT NEVER ENTERED MY MIND (Harvey, Jane with Ray Ellis & His Orchestra).
Album: released on Discovery (USA), Jan'84

Cassette: released on Discovery (USA), Jan'84

Harvey, Kitty

FOGGY DEW, THE (Harvey, Kitty/Cliff Yeldman).
Cassette: released on Folktracks, Nov'79 by Folktracks Cassettes. Dist: Folktracks

Harvey, Richard

ELEGY.
Single (7"): released on ASV, Nov'85 by Academy Sound & Vision Records. Dist: Pinnacle Deleted Jul'87.

Harvey, Steve

SOMETHING SPECIAL.
Single (7"): released on London, May'83 by London Records. Dist: Polygram

Single (12"): released on London, May'83 by London Records. Dist: Polygram

TONIGHT.
Single (7"): released on London, Oct'83 by London Records. Dist: Polygram

Single (12"): released on London, Oct'83 by London Records. Dist: Polygram

Harvey & The Wallbangers

ALLEZ BANANES.
Album: released on Hubba Discs, May'85 by Hubba Discs Records. Dist: PRT

Cassette: released on Hubba Discs, May'85 by Hubba Discs Records. Dist: PRT

PARK THE TIGER (EP).
Tracks: / I ain't got you / Tons & tons of sunshine / Dancing in the backroom / Devil went down to Georgia / Like I should.
Single (7"): released on Hubba Discs, May'86 by Hubba Discs Records. Dist: PRT

WALLBANGERS A-GOGO.
Album: released on Hubba Discs, May'85 by Hubba Discs Records. Dist: PRT

Cassette: released on Hubba Discs, May'85 by Hubba Discs Records. Dist: PRT

Page 454

Harwoods

IT'S A MODERN ROMANCE.
Single (7"): released on Tembo, Jul'85 by Tembo (Canada). Dist: IMS Distribution, Polygram Distribution

Single (12"): released on Tembo, Jul'85 by Tembo (Canada). Dist: IMS Distribution, Polygram Distribution

Hashim

UK FRESH '86 - THE ANTHEM.
Tracks: / UK Fresh '86 - The Anthem / (Remix).
Single (12"): released on Streetwave, Jul'86 by Streetwave Records. Dist: PRT Distribution

WE'RE ROCKIN' THE PLANET.
Tracks: / We're rockin' the planet / We're rockin' the planet (Inst) / Bonus beats.
Single (12"): released on ZYX (Germany), Feb'86 by ZYX Records. Dist: Greyhound

Hashimoto, Ichiko

ICHIKO.
Notes: (L.O.E. Entertainment Ltd., 159 Broadhurst Gardens, London NW6 3AU. Tel: 01-328-6100/6215/6228)
Album: released on Pan East, Jul'86 by L.O.E. Records. Dist: Nine Mile, PRT, Cartel

Cassette: released on Pan East, Jul'86 by L.O.E. Records. Dist: Nine Mile, PRT, Cartel

Compact disc: released on Pan East, Jul'86 by L.O.E. Records. Dist: Nine Mile, PRT, Cartel

Haskins, Chris

CRESCENT CITY BLUES.
Album: released on Black Lion, Oct'82 by Black Lion Records. Dist: Jazz Music, Chris Wellard, Taylor, H.R., Counterpoint, Cadillac

Hassan, Nazia

DISO DEEWANE.
Album: released on H.M.V., May'83 by EMI Records. Dist: EMI

Hass, E.A.

INCOGNITO MOSQUITO PRIVATE INSECTIVE.
Cassette: released on Caedmon(USA), Apr'85 by Caedmon (USA) Records. Dist: Gower, Taylors, Discovery

Hasselgard, Stan

JAMMIN' AT JUBILEE.
Notes: With B. Eckstine; Wardell Gray; Barney Kessel; Jackie Mills; J. Rowles; Benny Goodman Septet 1948.
Album: released on Dragon, Jun'86 by Dragon Records. Dist: Jazz Music, Projection, Cadillac

JAZZ CLARINET OF... STOCKHOLM/N.Y. 1945/48, THE (Hasselgard, Ake 'Stan').
Album: released on Dragon, Jun'86 by Dragon Records. Dist: Jazz Music, Projection, Cadillac

Hassell

FOURTH WORLD POSSIBLE MUSICS (Hassell/Eno).
Tracks: / Chemistry / Delta rain dream / Griot (over contageous magic) / Ba-benzele / Rising thermal 14 degrees 16N, 32 degrees 28E / Charm over Burundi cloud.
Compact disc: released on Editions EG, Jan'87 by Virgin Records. Dist: EMI

Album: released on Editions EG, Jan'87 by Virgin Records. Dist: EMI

Hassell, John

DREAM THEORY IN MALAYA/POSSIBLE MUSICS Fourth World Vol.1/2.
Double cassette: released on Editions EG, Apr'82 by Virgin Records. Dist: EMI

Hassell, Jon

AKA/DABARI/JAVA.
Album: released on Editions EG, Jan'87 by Virgin Records. Dist: EMI

DREAM THEORY IN MAYLAYA.
Album: released on Editions EG, Jan'87 by Virgin Records. Dist: EMI

EARTHQUAKE ISLAND.
Album: released on Tomato, Mar'79

POSSIBLE MUSICS (Hassell, Jon/Brian Eno).
Album: released on Editions EG, May'79 by Virgin Records. Dist: EMI

POWER SPOT.
Tracks: / Power spot / Passage D E / Solaire / Miracle steps / Wing melodies / elephant and the orchid, The / Air.
Notes: Produced and Engineered by: Brian Eno & Daniel Lanois: Robert Palmer in the New York Times has compared the flexibility of Hassell's style with that of Miles Daves. They both play the trumpet, Palmer said,"as expressively and as intimately as a great singer uses his voice." Moreover, they are both "visionary composers who use their knowledge of American traditions and the musics of the world to create vivid landscapes that seem to palpitate with a life of their own". Personel: Jon Hassel - trumpet/J A Deane - acoustic and electronic percussion, alto flute/Jean-Philippe Rykiel - electronic keyboards, facsimile bass, percussion, strings, etc/Michael Brook - guitar, electronic treatments/Richard Horowitz -electronic keyboards/Brian Eno - electronic bass/Richard Armin, Paul Armin - Raad electro - acoustic strings/Miguel Frasconi-Flute.
Album: released on ECM (Germany), Oct'86 by ECM Records. Dist: IMS, Polygram, Virgin through EMI

Compact disc: released on ECM (Germany), Oct'86 by ECM Records. Dist: IMS, Polygram, Virgin through EMI

Hasson, Gemma

LOVE IS THE ONLY WAY.
Single (7"): released on Ritz, Dec'84 by Outlet Records. Dist: Outlet, Prism Leisure Distribution, Record Services Distribution (Ireland), Roots

Hastings, Lennie

ALWAYS THE BEST (Hastings, Lennie Quintet).
Notes: Featuring:- Digby Fairweather/J.Parker
Album: released on Dawn Club, Dec'86 Dist: Cadillac, Swift, JSU

Hatchetmen

CHOPPIN' AROUND.
Album: released on Big Beat, Mar'85 by Ace Records. Dist: Projection, Pinnacle

Hatchett, Molly

FLIRTING WITH DISASTER.
Album: released on Epic, Oct'79 by CBS Records. Dist: CBS

Hatchett's Swingtette

IN THE MOOD.
Album: released on Decca (Recollections), Jul'81 by Decca Recollections. Dist: Polygram, IMS

Hatfield & The North

HATFIELD AND THE NORTH.
Compact disc: released on Virgin, Jul'87 by Virgin Records. Dist: EMI, Virgin Distribution

ROTTERS CLUB, THE.
Tracks: / Share it / Lounging there trying / John Wayne socks psychology on the jaw (Big) / Chaos at the greasy spoon / Yes-no interlude, The / Fitter Stoke has a bath / Didn't matter anyway / Underdub / Mumps / Your Majesty is like a cream donut (quiet and loud) / Lumps / Prenut.
Compact disc: released on Virgin, Jun'87 by Virgin Records. Dist: EMI, Virgin Distribution

Hatrik

BEAST, THE.
Album: released on Road Runner, Dec'85

Hauand, Ali

VITAMINS A & D.
Album: released on Ring (Import), Jul'78

Haunted

HAUNTED, THE.
Album: released on Psycho, Sep'83 Dist: Funhouse, Rough Trade

Haunted Staircase

FLUTTERS.
Single (7"): released on Rabbit, Sep'84 by Rabbit Records. Dist: Pinnacle

Haunter of the dark

HAUNTER OF THE DARK (McCallum, David).
Cassette: released on Caedmon(USA), May'80 by Caedmon (USA) Records. Dist: Gower, Taylors, Discovery

Haunting melodies

HAUNTING MELODIES Various artists (Various Artists).
Album: released on Nouveau, Jan'84

Cassette: released on Nouveau, Jan'84

Hause, Alfred

TANGO A LA CARTE.
Tracks: / Es wird in hundert jahren wieder / So ein fruhling sein / Regentropfen / Schoner Gigolo, Armer Gigolo / La Cumparsita / Blue tango / Jalousie / Ole Guapa / Tango de sudsee / Tango Notturno / Florentinische nachte / In einer kelinen konditorei / Ich kusse ihre hand, Madame / Tango continento / Blauer Himmel.
Notes: Digital Stereo. Excellent album for lovers of ballroom dancing. Alfred Hause is one of the leading exponents of Tango and Latin and dance music.
Compact disc:

Album:

Cassette:

TANGOS OF THE WORLD (Hause, Alfred & Gregor, Max).
Tracks: / Adios Pampa Mia / Tango Du Reve (Traumtango) / Tango Notturno / Blauer Himmel / Perlenfischer / Lover's tango / Tango D'Albeniz / Rio Chico / Keep on dancin' / Evita / Carmen / Hey Jude / La Violetera / El Amanccar / La rosita / Poema.
Notes: A selection of tangos from around the world played by two leading exponents of modern dance music. A must for the 'Come Dancing' fraternity.
Compact disc: released on Polydor (Germany), May'85 Dist: IMS-Polygram

Hausen, Ana

PROFESSIONALS.
Single (7"): released on Human, Jul'81 Dist: Roots, Stage One

Hauses Hohner

MUSIC FOR ACCORDION ORCHESTRA NO.3 (Hauses Hohner, Das Orchestra).
Album: released on ARC (Accordion Records), May'84 Dist: Accordion Record Club

Have a great party...

HAVE A GREAT PARTY WITH THEM INDOORS(PARTY SINGALONG) Various artists (Various Artists).
Album: released on Innovative Music Production, Dec'84 by Pickwick Records. Dist: Taylors

Cassette: released on Innovative Music Production, Dec'84 by Pickwick Records. Dist: Taylors

Have A Nice Day

ANOTHER DAY, ANOTHER DOLLAR.
Single (7"): released on Temple, Aug'86 by Temple Records. Dist: Roots Distribution, Folksound Distribution, Celtic Music Distribution, Projection Distribution

Single (12"): released on Temple, Aug'86 by Temple Records. Dist: Roots Distribution, Folksound Distribution, Celtic Music Distribution, Projection Distribution

Have a rotten Christmas

HAVE A ROTTEN CHRISTMAS Various artists (Various Artists).
Album: released on Rot, Nov'84 by Rot Records. Dist: Red Rhino Through Cartel Distributions

Havens, Richie

DEATH AT AN EARLY AGE.
Single (7"): released on Connexion, Jun'83 Dist: PRT

Hawaii

MUSIC OF HAWAII Various artists (Various Artists).
Tracks: / Sweet Leilani / Song of the Islands / Haole hula / Bali ha'i / Now is the hour / Song of old Hawaii, A / Blue Hawaii / Hawaii war chant / Beyond the reef / Keep your eyes on the hands / Hawaiin wedding song,The / Aloha oe.
Notes: The ever-popular Hawaiian music - every track evocative of that romantic set of Islands. A 1985 compilation of the best from Hawaii. Get your travel brochuresout when listening to this one.
Album: released on RCA (Germany), Nov'85

Cassette: released on RCA (Germany), Nov'85

NATIVES ARE RESTLESS, THE.

Album: released on Eva-Lolita, Dec'85 Dist: Pinnacle

Hawaiian memories

HAWAIIAN MEMORIES Various artists (Various Artists).
Cassette: released on AIM (Budget Cassettes), Feb'83

Hawaiian pure gold

HAWAIIAN PURE GOLD Various artists (Various Artists).
Album: released on RCA International, Jul'80

Cassette: released on RCA International, Jul'80

Hawes, Annett

LET'S DANCE.
Album: released on Skynote, Jan'85 Dist: Sidewalk Records

Hawes, Hampton

ALL NIGHT SESSION.
Album: released on Contemporary, May'87 by Contemporary Records. Dist: Pinnacle

ALL NIGHT SESSION VOL. 1.
Tracks: / Jordu / Groovin' high / takin' care / Broadway / Hampton's Pulpit.
Album: released on Contemporary, Aug'86 by Contemporary Records. Dist: Pinnacle

EVERYBODY LIKES HAMPTON HAWES.
Album: released on Contemporary, Apr'82 by Contemporary Records. Dist: Pinnacle

FOR REAL.
Tracks: / Hip / Wrap your trouble in dreams / crazeology / numbers game / for real / I love you.
Album: released on Contemporary, Jan'86 by Contemporary Records. Dist: Pinnacle

"FOUR".
Album: released on Contemporary, May'86 by Contemporary Records. Dist: Pinnacle

GREENLEAVES OF SUMMER, THE.
Album: released on Contemporary (USA), Nov'83 Dist: Fantasy (USA) Distribution

HAMPTON HAWES.
Album: released on Concord Jazz(USA), Sep'83 by Concord Jazz Records (USA). Dist: IMS, Polygram

HAMPTON HAWES MEMORIAL ALBUM, THE.
Album: released on Xanadu (Import), Jul'82

KEY FOR TWO.
Album: released on Affinity, Aug'79 by Charly Records. Dist: Charly, Cadillac

LITTLE COPENHAGEN NIGHT MUSIC, A.
Album: released on Freedom, Jan'79 by Logo Records. Dist: RCA, Discovery, Wellard, Chris

LIVE AT THE JAZZ SHOWCASE CHICAGO VOL.1.
Album: released on Enja (Germany), Jan'82 by Enja Records (W.Germany). Dist: Cadillac Music

SEANCE, THE.
Album: released on Contemporary, Mar'79 by Contemporary Records. Dist: Pinnacle

SPANISH STEPS.
Album: released on Black Lion, Jan'85 by Black Lion Records. Dist: Jazz Music, Chris Wellard, Taylor, H.R., Counterpoint, Cadillac

THIS IS HAMPTON HAWES VOL.2.
Album: released on Contemporary (USA), Sep'81 Dist: Fantasy (USA) Distribution

TRIO VOL.1, THE.
Compact disc: released on JVC Fantasy (Japan), May'87

VOL 2 (Hawes, Hampton Trio).
Compact disc: released on JVC Fantasy (Japan), '86

VOLUME 1:THE TRIO.
Album: released on Contemporary, Mar'86 by Contemporary Records. Dist: Pinnacle

ALL NIGHT SESSION! VOLUME 2 (Hawes, Hampton Quartet).
Album: released on Contemporary, May'87 by Contemporary Records. Dist: Pinnacle

Hawke, Elmer

CHEERS (Hawke, Elmer & The Brewery Boys).
Single (7"): released on Wye, Nov'85 Dist: Pinnacle, Projection

TELL ME.
Single (7"): released on Hollywood, Sep'84 by Hollywood Records. Dist: Pinnacle

Hawkey, Andrew

AND THIS.....
Single (12"): released on Solar Sound, Sep'83 Dist: Chris Wellard

Hawkins, Buzz

DANCER.
Single (7"): released on Smile, Jul'81 by Smile Records. Dist: Spartan

Hawkins, Coleman

ALLSTARS.
Compact disc: released on Carrere, Apr'87 by Carrere Records. Dist: PRT, Spartan

ALL STAR SESSION.
Album: released on Jazz Bird, '82 Dist: Cassion (Melandy)

Cassette: released on Jazz Bird, '82 Dist: Cassion (Melandy)

BEAN-A-RE-BOP.
Album: released on Queen-Disc, Sep'79 Dist: Celtic Music, JSU, Jazz Horizons, Jazz Music

BEAN & BEN (Hawkins, Coleman & Ben Webster).
Album: released on Harlequin, Oct'83 by Harlequin Records. Dist: Swift, Jazz Music, Wellard, Chris, IRS, Taylor, H.R.

BODY AND SOUL.
Tracks: / Meet Doctor Foo / Fine dinner / She's funny that way / Body and soul / When day is done / Sheik of Araby, The / My blue heaven / Bouncing with Bean / Say it isn't so / Sotlite / April in Paris / How strange / Half step down please / Angel face / Jumping for Jane / I love you / There will never be another you / Little girl blue / Dinner for one, please James / I never knew / His very own blues / Thirty nine inches / Bean stalks again / I'm shooting high / Have you met Miss Jones? / Day you came along, The / Essence of you, The / Spotlite.
Album: released on RCA, Feb'87 by RCA Records. Dist: RCA, Roots, Swift, Wellard, Chris, I & B, Solomon & Peres Distribution

Cassette: released on RCA, Feb'87 by RCA Records. Dist: RCA, Roots, Swift, Wellard, Chris, I & B, Solomon & Peres Distribution

BODY & SOUL AT THE BAYOU CLUB: VOL 2 (Hawkins, Coleman & Roy Eldridge).
Album: released on Vogue (France), Jan'85 Dist: Discovery, Jazz Music, PRT, Swift

CENTERPIECE.
Album: released on Phoenix, Apr'81 by Audio Fidelity Enterprises. Dist: Stage One, Lugtons

CHOCOLATE DANDIES (1940),LEONARD FEATHER'S ALL STARS (1943).
Album: released on Commodore Classics, May'87 by Teldec Records (Germany). Dist: Conifer, IMS, Polygram

Compact disc: released on Commodore Classics, May'87 by Teldec Records (Germany). Dist: Conifer, IMS, Polygram

CLASSIC TENORS (Hawkins, Coleman & Lester Young).
Album: released on Joker, Apr'81 Dist: Cadillac, Zodiac Distribution, Jazz Horizons, Jazz Music, JSU, Celtic Music

Album: released on Doctor Jazz, Oct'83

Cassette: released on Doctor Jazz, Oct'83

COLEMAN HAWKINS.
Album: released on Queen-Disc, Apr'81 Dist: Celtic Music, JSU, Jazz Horizons, Jazz Music

Album: released on MFP (France), Apr'84 by EMI Records. Dist: EMI

Cassette: released on MFP (France), Apr'84 by EMI Records. Dist: EMI

COLEMAN HAWKINS: 1940-43.
Album: released on Commodore Class, Dec'84 by Teldec Records (Germany). Dist: Conifer, IMS, Polygram

COLEMAN HAWKINS ENCOUNTERS BEN WEBSTER.
Compact disc: released on Verve, Oct'84

COLEMAN HAWKINS IN CONCERT.
Album: released on Phoenix, Apr'81 by Audio Fidelity Enterprises. Dist: Stage One, Lugtons

COLEMAN HAWKINS PLAYS THE WINDY CITY.
Album: released on Spotlite, '83 by Spotlite Records. Dist: Cadillac, Jazz Music, Spotlite

COLEMAN HAWKINS & THE EARL HINES TRIO, 1965 (Hawkins, Coleman & The Earl Hines Trio).
Album: released on Pumpkin, Apr'79 Dist: Jazz Music, Wellard, Chris, Cadillac

COLEMAN HAWKINS & THE EARL HINES TRIO 1965 see Hines, Earl Trio (Hawkins, Coleman/ Earl Hines Trio).

DESAFINADO (Hawkins, Coleman Sextet).
Album: released on Jasmine, Jun'82 by Jasmine Records. Dist: Counterpoint, Lugtons, Taylor, H.R., Wellard, Chris, Swift, Cadillac

Cassette: released on Jasmine, Jun'82 by Jasmine Records. Dist: Counterpoint, Lugtons, Taylor, H.R., Wellard, Chris, Swift, Cadillac

Album: released on Impulse, Oct'85 by Impulse Records. Dist: MCA, Polygram

DISORDER AT THE BORDER.
Album: released on Spotlite, '83 by Spotlite Records. Dist: Cadillac, Jazz Music, Spotlite

DUKE ELLINGTON MEETS COLEMAN HAWKINS.
Album: released on Jasmine, Jun'82 by Jasmine Records. Dist: Counterpoint, Lugtons, Taylor, H.R., Wellard, Chris, Swift, Cadillac

Cassette: released on Jasmine, Jun'82 by Jasmine Records. Dist: Counterpoint, Lugtons, Taylor, H.R., Wellard, Chris, Swift, Cadillac

DUTCH TREAT.
Album: released on Xanadu, Jul'82 Dist: Discovery, Jazz Horizons, Jazz Music, Swift

ENCOUNTERS BEN WEBSTER.
Tracks: / Blues for Yolande / It never entered my mind / Rosita / You'd be so nice to come home to / Prisoner of love / tangerine / shine of harvest moon.
Compact disc: released on Verve, Oct'84 by Phonogram Records. Dist: Polygram

ESSENTIAL COLEMAN HAWKINS, THE.
Album: released on Verve, May'82 by Phonogram Records. Dist: Polygram

FAVOURITES.
Album: released on Phoenix, Apr'81 by Audio Fidelity Enterprises. Dist: Stage One, Lugtons

GENIUS OF, THE.
Album: released on Verve, Jan'86 by Phonogram Records. Dist: Polygram

Cassette: released on Verve, Jan'86 by Phonogram Records. Dist: Polygram

Compact disc: released on Verve, Jan'86 by Phonogram Records. Dist: Polygram

GOOD OL' BROADWAY.
Album: released on Fantasy Inc USA, Jun'86 by Fantasy Inc USA Records. Dist: IMS, Polygram

GREAT ENGLISH CONCERT, (THE) (Hawkins, Coleman/Stan Getz/Roy Eldridge).
Album: released on Jazz Groove, Jul'82 Dist: Jazz Music

HAWK.
Album: released on Shoestring, Apr'81 by Shoestring Records. Dist: Shoestring

HAWK AND ROY (Hawkins, Coleman & Roy Eldridge).
Album: released on Phoenix, Apr'81 by Audio Fidelity Enterprises. Dist: Stage One, Lugtons

HAWK IN HOLLAND, (THE).
Album: released on Jasmine, Feb'83 by Jasmine Records. Dist: Counterpoint, Lugtons, Taylor, H.R., Wellard, Chris, Swift, Cadillac

HAWKINS IN GERMANY (Hawkins, Coleman/Bud Powell).
Album: released on Black Lion, Jan'86 by Black Lion Records. Dist: Jazz Music, Chris Wellard, Taylor, H.R., Counterpoint, Cadillac

HAWKS TALKS, (THE).
Album: released on Affinity, Jun'85 by Charly Records. Dist: Charly, Cadillac

HAWK TALKS.
Album: released on Jasmine, Dec'83 by Jasmine Records. Dist: Counterpoint, Lugtons, Taylor, H.R., Wellard, Chris, Swift, Cadillac

HAWK VARIATIONS.
Notes: Mono.
Album: released on Swingtime, Jan'86 Dist: Jazz Music Distribution

HIGH AND MIGHTY HAWK, THE.
Tracks: / Get set / You've changed / Ooh-wee, Miss G.P.! / Vignette / My one and only love / Bird of prey blues.

IMMORTAL COLEMAN HAWKINS, THE.
Notes: With Roy Eldridge, Earl Hines trio.
Album: released on Pumpkin, Nov'86 Dist: Jazz Music, Wellard, Chris, Cadillac

INDISPENSABLE COLEMAN HAWKINS, (THE).
Album: released on RCA (France), Nov'84 by RCA Records. Dist: Discovery

LESTER YOUNG/COLEMAN HAWKINS (Hawkins, Coleman & Lester Young).
Album: released on Spotlite, '83 by Spotlite Records. Dist: Cadillac, Jazz Music, Spotlite

MARCH 21 & 25, 1963 (Hawkins, Coleman & His Orchestra).
Album: released on Jazz Vault, Oct'80 Dist: Jazz Music, JSU, Taylor, H.R.

MASTERS OF JAZZ VOL.12.
Album: released on Storyville, May'86 by Storyville Records. Dist: Jazz Music Distribution, Swift Distribution, Chris Wellard Distribution, Counterpoint Distribution

MEMORIAL.
Album: released on Joker Import, Apr'81

PIANO REFLECTIONS (Hawkins, Coleman/Duke Ellington).
Album: released on MFP (France), May'84 by EMI Records. Dist: EMI

SIRIUS.
Album: released on Pablo, '82 by Pablo Records. Dist: Wellard, Chris, IMS-Polygram, BMG
Cat. no: **2310 707**

Cassette: released on Pablo, '82 by Pablo Records. Dist: Wellard, Chris, IMS-Polygram, BMG

SOUL.
Album: released on Prestige (USA), Aug'84

SWINGVILLE 2005 (Hawkins, Coleman All Stars).
Album:

TENOR TRIUMVERATE (Hawkins, Coleman/Chu Berry/Lester Young).
Album: released on Queen-Disc, '81 Dist: Celtic Music, JSU, Jazz Horizons, Jazz Music

TODAY AND NOW (Hawkins, Coleman Quartet).
Album: released on Jasmine, Aug'82 by Jasmine Records. Dist: Counterpoint, Lugtons, Taylor, H.R., Wellard, Chris, Swift, Cadillac

Cassette: released on Jasmine, Aug'82 by Jasmine Records. Dist: Counterpoint, Lugtons, Taylor, H.R., Wellard, Chris, Swift, Cadillac

TOGETHER (Hawkins, Coleman & Lester Young).
Album: released on Jazz Live, Apr'81

VERY SAXY.
Album: released on Fantasy Inc USA, Jun'86 by Fantasy Inc USA Records. Dist: IMS, Polygram

WRAPPED TIGHT.
Album: released on Jasmine, Sep'82 by Jasmine Records. Dist: Counterpoint, Lugtons, Taylor, H.R., Wellard, Chris, Swift, Cadillac

Cassette: released on Jasmine, Sep'82 by Jasmine Records. Dist: Counterpoint, Lugtons, Taylor, H.R., Wellard, Chris, Swift, Cadillac

Hawkins, Edwin

BEST OF (Hawkins, Edwin Singers).
Album: released on Buddah, Jul'85

Cassette: released on Buddah, Jul'85

IMAGINE HEAVEN.
Album: released on IMS(Import), Mar'82 by Polydor Records. Dist: IMS, Polygram

LIVE WITH THE OAKLAND SYMPHONY ORCHESTRA.
Album: released on Myrrh, May'82 by Word Records. Dist: Word Distribution

Cassette: released on Myrrh, May'82 by Word Records. Dist: Word Distribution

Hawkins & Eldridge

EUROPEAN CONCERT (Hawkins & Eldridge Quintet).
Album: released on Unique Jazz, Nov'86 Dist: Swift, Jazz Music, Jazz Horizons

Hawkins, Erskine

COMPLETE ERSKINE HAWKINS - VOL 1/2 1938-1939.
Double Album: released on RCA (France), '83 by RCA Records. Dist: Discovery

ONE NIGHT STAND - 1946.
Album: released on Joyce, Jul'82

SNEAKIN' OUT.
Album: released on First Heard, Sep'79 by Submarine Records. Dist: Conifer, Taylors

Cassette: released on First Heard, Oct'84 by Submarine Records. Dist: Conifer, Taylors

TUXEDO JUNCTION.
Album: released on First Heard, May'79 by Submarine Records. Dist: Conifer, Taylors

Hawkins, Hawkshaw

16 GREATEST HITS.
Album: released on Starday, Apr'87

Cassette: released on Starday, Apr'87

Hawkins, Ronnie

HAWK, THE.
Album: released on Liberty, Jan'80 by Liberty-United. Dist: EMI

Album: released on Magnum Force, Apr'84 by Magnum Music Group Ltd. Dist: Magnum Music Group Ltd, PRT, Spartan

ROCKIN'.
Album: released on Pye International, Jan'78

RRRRACKETT TIME (Hawkins, Ronnie & The Hawks).
Album: released on Charly, Feb'80 by Charly Records. Dist: Charly, Cadillac

SINGS THE SONGS OF HANK WILLIAMS.
Album: released on PRT, Jul'83 by PRT Records. Dist: PRT

Cassette: released on PRT, Jul'83 by PRT Records. Dist: PRT

Hawkins, Roy

HIGHWAY 59.
Album: released on Ace, May'84 by Ace Records. Dist: Pinnacle, Swift, Hotshot, Cadillac

WHY DO EVERYTHING HAPPEN TO ME.
Album: released on Route 66, Jun'80

Hawkins, Screaming Jay

FRENZY.
Album: released on Edsel, Mar'86 by Demon Records. Dist: Pinnacle, Jazz Music, Projection

Cassette: released on Edsel, Mar'86 by Demon Records. Dist: Pinnacle, Jazz Music, Projection

Album: released on Edsel, Sep'82 by Demon Records. Dist: Pinnacle, Jazz Music, Projection

LIVE.
Album: released on Midnight (USA), Mar'86

SCREAMIN' THE BLUES.
Album: released on Red Lightnin', Sep'82 by Red Lightnin' Records. Dist: Roots, Swift, Jazz Music, JSU, Pinnacle, Cartel, Wynd-Up Distribution

Hawkins, Ted

BAD DOG.
Tracks: / Bad dog.
Single (12"): released on Gull, Jan'87 by Gull Records. Dist: Pinnacle

HAPPY HOUR.

Album: released on Windows On The World, Mar'87 by Windows On The World Records. Dist: PRT

Cassette: released on Windows On The World, Mar'87 by Windows On The World Records. Dist: PRT

ON THE BOARDWALK.
Album: released on Unamerican Activities, Aug'86 by Hotshot Records. Dist: Cartel, Projection, Red Rhino, Hotshot

Cassette: released on Unamerican Activities, Aug'86 by Hotshot Records. Dist: Cartel, Projection, Red Rhino, Hotshot

WATCH YOUR STEP.
Compact disc: released on W.O.T.W., Mar'87 Dist: Pinnacle

Single (12"): released on Gull, Feb'86 by Gull Records. Dist: Pinnacle

WATCH YOUR STEP.
Tracks: / Watch your step / Bring it home Daddy / If you love me / Don't lose your cool / Lost ones, The / Who got my natural comb? / Peace & Happiness / Sweet Baby / Stop your crying / Put in a cross / Sorry you're sick / Watch your step (Band version) / TWA / I gave up all I had / Stay close to me / Sweet Baby / Bring it home Daddy.
Album: released on Windows On The World, Nov'86 by Windows On The World Records. Dist: PRT

Single (12"): released on Windows On The World, Feb'85 by Windows On The World Records. Dist: PRT

WATCH YOUR STEP (ACOUSTIC).
Tracks: / Watch your step (Acoustic) / Sweet Baby / Watch your step.
Single (7"): released on W.O.W., Oct'86 by W.O.W. Records. Dist: Jetstar

Hawkins, Tramaine

TRAMAINE.
Album: released on Light USA, May'82 by Lexicon Music. Dist: Word Distribution

Cassette: released on Light USA, May'82 by Lexicon Music. Dist: Word Distribution

Hawkins, Walter

1927-29 (Hawkins, Walter 'Buddy Boy').
Album: released on Matchbox (Bluesmaster), Jan'83

JESUS CHRIST IS THE WAY (Hawkins, Walter & The Family).
Album: released on Light USA, May'82 by Lexicon Music. Dist: Word Distribution

Cassette: released on Light USA, May'82 by Lexicon Music. Dist: Word Distribution

LOVE ALIVE (Hawkins, Walter & The Love Centre Choir).
Album: released on Light USA, May'82 by Lexicon Music. Dist: Word Distribution

Cassette: released on Light USA, May'82 by Lexicon Music. Dist: Word Distribution

LOVE ALIVE 3.
Album: released on Light USA, Apr'85 by Lexicon Music. Dist: Word Distribution

Cassette: released on Light USA, Apr'85 by Lexicon Music. Dist: Word Distribution

LOVE ALIVE II (Hawkins, Walter & The Love Centre Choir).
Album: released on Light USA, May'82 by Lexicon Music. Dist: Word Distribution

Cassette: released on Light USA, May'82 by Lexicon Music. Dist: Word Distribution

Hawklords

25 YEARS ON.
Album: released on Charisma, Sep'83 by Virgin Records. Dist: EMI

Cassette: released on Charisma, Sep'83 by Virgin Records. Dist: EMI

WHO'S GONNA WIN THE WAR.
Single (7"): released on Flicknife, Jun'82 by Flicknife Records. Dist: Spartan

Hawk, Robert

WHOSE LAND IS THIS.
Single (7"): released on Raw, Apr'82 by Raw Records. Dist: Spartan

Hawks

HAWKS.
Album: released on Pathe MarconiFrance), Apr'85

Hawks, Tony

TOGETHER.
Single (7"): released on Hobo, Feb'85 by Hobo Records. Dist: Hobo

Hawk The Slayer

HAWK THE SLAYER Original Soundtrack.
Album: released on Chips, Nov'80 by PRT. Dist: PRT

Hawkwind

ANGELS OF DEATH.
Tracks: / Angel voices / Nuclear drive / Rocky paths / Solitary mind games / Living on a knife edge / Fahrenheit 451 / Looking in the future / Choose your masks / Joker at the gate, The / Waiting for tomorrow / Last Messiah, The / Arrival in Utopia / Virgin of the world / Angels of death.
Album: released on RCA, Jan'87 by RCA Records. Dist: RCA, Roots, Swift, Wellard, Chris, I & B, Solomon & Peres Distribution

Cassette: released on RCA, Jan'87 by RCA Records. Dist: RCA, Roots, Swift, Wellard, Chris, I & B, Solomon & Peres Distribution

ANTHOLOGY.
Album: released on Samurai, Nov'86 Dist: Pinnacle

Picture disc album: released on Samurai, Nov'86 Dist: Pinnacle

ANTHOLOGY VOL. 3.
Cassette: released on Samurai, Jul'86 Dist: Pinnacle

ANTHOLOGY - VOLUME 1.
Compact disc: released on Samurai, '86 Dist: Pinnacle

ANTHOLOGY - VOLUME 2.
Compact disc: released on Samurai, '86 Dist: Pinnacle

Album: released on Samurai, Mar'86 Dist: Pinnacle

Cassette: released on Samurai, Mar'86 Dist: Pinnacle

ASTOUNDING SOUNDS, AMAZING MUSIC.

Album: released on Charisma, '83 by Virgin Records. Dist: EMI

Cassette: released on Charisma, '83 by Virgin Records. Dist: EMI

BRING ME THE HEAD OF YURI GEGARIN Live at the Empire Pool - 1973.
Tracks: / Gaga / Egg (The) / Organe accumulator / Wage war / Urban guerilla / Master of the universe / Welcome to the future / Sonic attack / Silver machine.
Notes: Live at the Empire Pool, 1973. A "Demi-Monde" recording. Licensed from Charly Records International APS.
Compact disc: released on Charly, Nov'86 by Charly Records. Dist: Charly, Cadillac

Album: released on Demi Monde, '85 Dist: Charly

CHOOSE YOUR MASQUES.
Album: released on RCA, '82 by RCA Records. Dist: RCA, Roots, Swift, Wellard, Chris, I & B, Solomon & Peres Distribution

Cassette: released on RCA, '82 by RCA Records. Dist: RCA, Roots, Swift, Wellard, Chris, I & B, Solomon & Peres Distribution

CHRONICLE OF THE BLACK SWORD.
Tracks: / Song of the swords / Shade gate / Sea king / Pulsing cavern / Elric the enchanter / Nedle gun / Zarzinia / Demise / Sleep of a thousand tears / chaos army / Horn of Destiny.
Compact disc: released on Flicknife, '86 by Flicknife Records. Dist: Spartan

Album: released on Flicknife, Nov'85 by Flicknife Records. Dist: Spartan

Cassette: released on Flicknife, Nov'85 by Flicknife Records. Dist: Spartan

Video-cassette (VHS): released on Jettisoundz, Aug'86 Dist: Red Rhino, Cartel

CHURCH OF HAWKWIND.
Album: released on RCA, '82 by RCA Records. Dist: RCA, Roots, Swift, Wellard, Chris, I & B, Solomon & Peres Distribution

DOREMI FASOL LATIDO.
Album: released on Liberty, '85 by Liberty-United. Dist: EMI

Cassette: released on Liberty, '85 by Liberty-United. Dist: EMI

FRIENDS AND RELATIONS.
Tracks: / Who's gonna win the war / Golden void / Robot / Neesh / Good girl bad girl / Valium ten / Human Beings / Time Centre.
Notes: Side one recorded 'live' 1977-1978. Side two recorded 1982.
Album: released on Flicknife, Mar'82 by Flicknife Records. Dist: Spartan

HALL OF THE MOUNTAIN GRILL.
Album: released on Fame, '85 by Music For Pleasure Records. Dist: EMI

Cassette: released on Fame, '85 by Music For Pleasure Records. Dist: EMI

Album: released on Liberty, '85 by Liberty-United. Dist: EMI

Cassette: released on Liberty, '85 by Liberty-United. Dist: EMI

HAWKWIND.
Album: released on Liberty, '80 by Liberty-United. Dist: EMI

Album: released on Liberty, '84 by Liberty-United. Dist: EMI

Cassette: released on Liberty, '84 by Liberty-United. Dist: EMI

Picture disc single: released on Liberty, '84 by Liberty-United. Dist: EMI

HAWKWIND COLLECTION, THE Parts 1 & 2.
Tracks: / You shouldn't do that / We do it / Bring it on home / Silver machine / Born to go / Dealing with the devil / Urban guerilla / Masters of the universe / Who's gonna win the war / Hash cake'77 / Motorhead / Quark strangeness and charm / Douglas in the jungle / Space is deep / Earth calling / Angels of death / Spirit of the age / Ghost dance.
Notes: All tracks licensed from Canal Fleet Ltd. Art direction/design & illustration: Shoot That Tiger. (C) 1986. Matrix number: 5 013428 131 480.
Double cassette: released on Castle Collectors, Sep'86 by Castle Communications Records. Dist: Pinnacle

Double Album: released on Castle Collectors, Sep'86 by Castle Communications Records. Dist: Pinnacle

Compact disc: released on Castle, Dec'86 by Castle Records. Dist: Pinnacle

INDEPENDENT DAYS - VOL.2.
Album: released on Flicknife, Nov'86 by Flicknife Records. Dist: Spartan

Cassette: released on Flicknife, Nov'86 by Flicknife Records. Dist: Spartan

INDEPENDENTS DAY (6 TRACK).
Tracks: / Hurry on sundown / Motorway City / Motorhead / Over the top / Who's gonna win the war? / Social alliance.
Notes: 10" LP.
Album: released on Flicknife, Jun'84 by Flicknife Records. Dist: Spartan

Album: released on Flicknife, '84 by Flicknife Records. Dist: Spartan

IN SEARCH OF SPACE.
Album: released on Liberty, '85 by Liberty-United. Dist: EMI

Cassette: released on Liberty, '85 by Liberty-United. Dist: EMI

IN THE BEGINNING.

Album: released on Demi Monde, '85 Dist: Charly

LEVITATION.
Compact disc: released on Castle Classics, Jul'87 by Castle Communications. Dist: BMG

LIVE '70/73.
Tracks: / Sonic attack (1972) / Seven by seven (1972) / Wage ware (1973) / Urban guerilla (1973) / Only dreaming (1971) / Hurry on a sundown / In the egg (1973) / Orgone accumilater (1972) / Welcome to the future (1973) / Master of the universe (1970).
Album: released on Dojo, Apr'86 by Castle Communications Records. Dist: Cartel

MASTER OF THE UNIVERSE.
Tracks: / Masters of the universe / Brainstorm / Sonic attack / Orgone accumulator / It's so easy / Lost Johnny / Masters of the universe / Brainstorm / Sonic attack / Orgone accumulator / It's so easy / Lost Johnny.
Notes: Original Sound Recordings made by Liberty Records, a division of Capitol Records Inc.
Album: released on Liberty, Jun'87 by Liberty-United. Dist: EMI

Cassette: released on Liberty, Jun'87 by Liberty-United. Dist: EMI

Album: released on Fame (United Artists), '82 by Music For Pleasure Records. Dist: EMI

Cassette: released on Fame (United Artists), '82 by Music For Pleasure Records. Dist: EMI

MOTORHEAD.
Tracks: / Motorhead / Hurry on sundown.
Single (7"): released on Flicknife, Jul'86 by Flicknife Records. Dist: Spartan

MOTORHEAD/VALIUM 10.
Single (12"): released on Flicknife, '82 by Flicknife Records. Dist: Spartan

MOTORWAY CITY/MASTER OF THE UNIVERSE.
Single (7"): released on Flicknife, '83 by Flicknife Records. Dist: Spartan

NEEDLE GUN.
Single (7"): released on Flicknife, '85 by Flicknife Records. Dist: Spartan

Single (12"): released on Flicknife, '85 by Flicknife Records. Dist: Spartan

NIGHT OF THE HAWKS (EP) The earth ritual preview.
Tracks: / Night of the hawks / Green finned demon / Dream dancers / Dragons & fables.
Single (7"): released on Flicknife, Jan'84 by Flicknife Records. Dist: Spartan

OUT AND IN TAKES.
Tracks: / Turner Point / Waiting for tomorrow / Cajun jinx / Solitary mind games / Starflight / Ejection / Assassins of Allah / Flight to Maputo / Confrontation / 5/4 / Ghost dance.
Album: released on Flicknife, Apr'87 by Flicknife Records. Dist: Spartan

Cassette: released on Flicknife, Apr'87 by Flicknife Records. Dist: Spartan

Compact disc: released on Flicknife, May'87 by Flicknife Records. Dist: Spartan

OVER THE TOP.
Single (12"): released on Flicknife, Nov'81 by Flicknife Records. Dist: Spartan

PXR 5.
Album: released on Charisma, Mar'84 by Virgin Records. Dist: EMI

Cassette: released on Charisma, Mar'84 by Virgin Records. Dist: EMI

QUARK, STRANGENESS AND CHARM.
Tracks: / Spirit of the age / Damnation alley / Fable of a failed race / Quark / Strangeness and charm / Hassan 1 sahba / Forge of vulcan, The / Days of the underground / Iron dream, The.
Album: released on Charisma, Oct'86 by Virgin Records. Dist: EMI

Cassette: released on Charisma, Oct'86 by Virgin Records. Dist: EMI

Cassette: released on Charisma, Mar'83 by Virgin Records. Dist: EMI

RIDICULE.
Album: released on Obsession, Nov'85 Dist: Jungle Distribution, Cartel Distribution

ROADHAWKS.
Album: released on Fame (Liberty), Apr'84 by Music For Pleasure Records. Dist: EMI

Cassette: released on Fame (Liberty), Apr'84 by Music For Pleasure Records. Dist: EMI

Album: released on EMI (Germany), '83 by EMI Records. Dist: Conifer

SILVER MACHINE.
Tracks: / Silver machine.

Single (7"): released on Samurai, May'86 Dist: Pinnacle

Picture disc single: released on Samurai, May'86 Dist: Pinnacle

Single (12"): released on Samurai, May'86 Dist: Pinnacle

Picture disc single: released on RCA, Sep'82 by RCA Records. Dist: RCA, Roots, Swift, Wellard, Chris, I & B, Solomon & Peres Distribution

Single (7"): released on United Artists, Dec'82

Single (12"): released on United Artists, Jan'83

Picture disc single: released on United Artists, Dec'82

SONIC ATTACK.
Album: released on RCA, Oct'81 by RCA Records. Dist: RCA, Roots, Swift, Wellard, Chris, I & B, Solomon & Peres Distribution Deleted '85.

Cassette: released on RCA, Oct'81 by RCA Records. Dist: RCA, Roots, Swift, Wellard, Chris, I & B, Solomon & Peres Distribution

SPACE RITUAL VOL.2.
Compact disc: released on Magnum Force, Apr'87 by Magnum Music Group Ltd. Dist: Magnum Music Group Ltd, PRT, Spartan

Album: released on APK, Mar'85 Dist: Pinnacle

Cassette: released on APK, Mar'85 Dist: Pinnacle

TEXT OF THE FESTIVAL, THE.
Tracks: / Master of the universe / Dreaming / Shouldn't do that / Hurry on a sundown / Paranoia / See it as you really are / I do it / Come home / Sound shouldn't / Improvise / Compromise / Reprise.
Double Album: released on Jams, '83

Album: released on Illuminated, Feb'85 by IKF Records. Dist: Pinnacle, Cartel, Jetstar

THIS IS HAWKWIND,DO NOT PANIC.
Album: released on Flicknife, Nov'84 by Flicknife Records. Dist: Spartan

WARRIOR ON THE EDGE OF TIME.
Album: released on Liberty, Jun'85 by Liberty-United. Dist: EMI

Cassette: released on Liberty, Jun'85 by Liberty-United. Dist: EMI

ZAROZINIA.
Tracks: / Zarozinia / Assault and battery / Sleep of a thousand tears.
Single (7"): released on Flicknife, Mar'86 by Flicknife Records. Dist: Spartan

Single (12"): released on Flicknife, Mar'86 by Flicknife Records. Dist: Spartan

ZONES.
Tracks: / Zones / Dangerous vision / Running through the back brain / Island, The / Motorway city / Utopia 84 / Sociat alliance / Sonic attack / Dream worker / Bainstorm.
Album: released on Flicknife, Oct'83 by Flicknife Records. Dist: Spartan

Cassette: released on Flicknife, Oct'83 by Flicknife Records. Dist: Spartan

ZOO.
Single (12"): released on Flicknife, Dec'83 by Flicknife Records. Dist: Spartan

Hawkwind, Friends...

HAWKWIND, FRIENDS & RELATIONS various artists (Various Artists).
Album: released on Flicknife, Apr'85 by Flicknife Records. Dist: Spartan

Haworth, Bryn

GAP, THE.

Album: released on Chapel Lane, Dec'83 Dist: RCA

Cassette: released on Chapel Lane, Dec'83 Dist: RCA

PASS IT ON.
Cassette: released on Chapel Lane, Dec'83 Dist: RCA

Album: released on Chapel Lane, Dec'83 Dist: RCA

WINGS OF THE MORNING.
Album: released on Chapel Lane, Dec'83 Dist: RCA

Cassette: released on Chapel Lane, Dec'83 Dist: RCA

Hawthorn Scottish Band

SCOTTISH GEMS.
Album: released on Emerald, Jan'71 by Emerald Records. Dist: Ross, PRT, Solomon & Peres Distribution

Hawthorn, Vaughan
SUSE JE.
Album: released on Audio, Aug'87 by Relic. Dist: Swift

Cassette: released on Audio, Aug'87 by Relic. Dist: Swift

Compact disc: released on In Touch, Aug'87 by In Touch Records. Dist: Spartan

Haxby, Strensall
MACK THE KNIFE.
Tracks: / Mack the knife / Here I am. Single (7"): released on Mr. Sam Music, Jul'86 Dist: MIS-EMI Distribution

Haycock's Climax, Pete
SUNBIRD.
Single (7"): released on Nu-Disk, Jun'85

TOTAL CLIMAX.
Album: released on Nu-Disk, Jun'85

Cassette: released on Nu-Disk, Jun'85

YOUNG EXECUTIVE.
Single (7"): released on Nu-Disk, Oct'85

Hay, Colin James
CAN I HOLD YOU.
Tracks: / Can I hold you / Nature of the beast. Single (7"): released on Epic, May'87 by CBS Records. Dist: CBS

Single (12"): released on Epic, May'87 by CBS Records. Dist: CBS

HOLD ME.
Tracks: / Home sweet home / Hold me. Single (7"): released on Epic, Jan'87 by CBS Records. Dist: CBS

Single (12"): released on Epic, Jan'87 by CBS Records. Dist: CBS

Single (7"): released on Epic, Feb'87 by CBS Records. Dist: CBS

LOOKING FOR JACK.
Tracks: / Hold me / Can I hold you / Looking for Jack / Master of crime / These are our finest days / Puerto Rico / Ways of the world / I don't need you anymore / Circles Erratica / Fisherman's friend / Nature of the beast. Notes: Nature of the beast is an extra track only available on the cassette. Album: released on Epic, Mar'87 by CBS Records. Dist: CBS

Cassette: released on Epic, Mar'87 by CBS Records. Dist: CBS

Compact disc: released on Epic, Mar'87 by CBS Records. Dist: CBS

Haydock Male Voice Choir
HAYDOCK SOUND, THE.
Album: released on Grosvenor, Feb'77 by Grosvenor Records. Dist: Taylors

Hayes, Clancy
OH BY JINGO.
Album: Dist: Projection, Swift, Cadillac

Hayes, Edgar
1937-1938 (Hayes, Edgar & His Orchestra). Album: released on Swing Fan, May'86 Dist: Jazz Music Distribution

Hayes, Isaac
BEST OF SHAFT Original soundtrack.
Tracks: / Theme from Shaft / Walk from Regio's / Ellie's love theme / Cafe Regio's / Early Sunday morning / Soulsville / Bumpy's blues / Do your thing / End theme, The. Notes: From the man who invented 'symphonic soul' and influenced a whole generation of 70's soul acts, as well as countless TV and movie soundtracks, Isaac Hayes is an enduring force. The title track from this album reached the number one spot in the US singles chart and number three in the UK. Theme from 'Shaft' was also covered by Eddie & The Soul Band last year and reached number 13 in the UK charts.
Album: released on Stax, Jun'86 by Ace Records. Dist: Pinnacle, Chris Wellard, IMS-Polygram

Album: released on Stax, Oct'81 by Ace Records. Dist: Pinnacle, Chris Wellard, IMS-Polygram

Cassette: released on Stax, Oct'81 by Ace Records. Dist: Pinnacle, Chris Wellard, IMS-Polygram

BEST OF VOL.2 (THE).
Compact disc: released on London, Apr'87 by London Records. Dist: Polygram

HEY GIRL.
Tracks: / Ike's rap / Hey Fred (You need a sunbed)

Page 458

HIS GREATEST HITS.
Album: released on Stax, Nov'80 by Ace Records. Dist: Pinnacle, Chris Wellard, IMS-Polygram

HOT BUTTERED SOUL.
Album: released on Stax, Aug'81 by Ace Records. Dist: Pinnacle, Chris Wellard, IMS-Polygram

Cassette: released on Stax, Aug'81 by Ace Records. Dist: Pinnacle, Chris Wellard, IMS-Polygram

LIVE AT THE SAHARA TAHOE.
Tracks: / Theme from "Shaft" / Come on, The / Light my fire / Ike's rap / Never can say goodbye / Windows of the world / Look of love (The) / Ellie's love theme / Use me / Do your thing / Theme from "The Men" / It's too late / Rock me baby / Stormy monday blues / Type thang / First time ever I saw your face, The / Ike's rap VI / Ain't no sunshine / Feelin' alright. Notes: Recorded at the height of his popularity and featuring his best known material. Album: released on Stax, Nov'86 by Ace Records. Dist: Pinnacle, Chris Wellard, IMS-Polygram

Cassette: released on Stax, Nov'86 by Ace Records. Dist: Pinnacle, Chris Wellard, IMS-Polygram

MAN & A WOMEN, A (Hayes, Isaac & Dionne Warwick).
Double Album: released on ABC, Mar'77 Dist: CBS, Pinnacle

SHAFT (SELECTION FROM SOUND TRACK).
Album: released on Stax, Oct'81 by Ace Records. Dist: Pinnacle, Chris Wellard, IMS-Polygram

Cassette: released on Stax, Oct'81 by Ace Records. Dist: Pinnacle, Chris Wellard, IMS-Polygram

SHAFT, THEME FROM.
Single (7"): released on Stax, Mar'82 by Ace Records. Dist: Pinnacle, Chris Wellard, IMS-Polygram

Single (7"): released on Old Gold, Sep'85 by Old Gold Records. Dist: Lightning, Jazz Music, Spartan, Counterpoint

THEME FROM SHAFT.
Single (7"): released on Stax, Aug'87 by Ace Records. Dist: Pinnacle, Chris Wellard, IMS-Polygram

TO BE CONTINUED.
Album: released on Stax, Oct'81 by Ace Records. Dist: Pinnacle, Chris Wellard, IMS-Polygram

Cassette: released on Stax, Oct'81 by Ace Records. Dist: Pinnacle, Chris Wellard, IMS-Polygram

U-TURN.
Tracks: / If you want my lovin', do me right / Flash backs / You turn me on / Ike's rap VIII / Can't take my eyes off you / Thing for you / Thank God for love.
Album: released on CBS, Dec'86 by CBS Records. Dist: CBS

Hayes, Louis
REAL THING, THE.
Album: released on Muse, Apr'81 by Peerless Records. Dist: Lugtons Distributors

Hayes, Lynda
DON'T YOU LOVE ME ANYMORE.
Single (7"): released on Safari, Jul'84 by Safari Records. Dist: Pinnacle

Single (7"): released on Safari, Jul'84 by Safari Records. Dist: Pinnacle

Single (12"): released on Safari, Sep'84 by Safari Records. Dist: Pinnacle

Hayes, Tubby
AFTER LIGHTS OUT (Hayes, Tubby Quintet).
Album: released on Jasmine, Mar'83 by Jasmine Records. Dist: Counterpoint, Lugtons, Taylor, H.R., Wellard, Chris, Swift, Cadillac

MEXICAN GREEN (Hayes, Tubby, Quartet).
Album: released on Mole, Jan'81 by Mole Records. Dist: Mole Music Co., Spartan Distribution

TRIBUTE, A Live at the Golden Slipper-1963 (Hayes, Tubby Quintet).
Album:

TUBBS (Hayes, Tubby Quintet).
Album: released on Spotlite, '83 by Spotlite Records. Dist: Cadillac, Jazz Music, Spotlite

TUBBS' TOURS.
Album: released on Mole, Jul'81 by Mole Records. Dist: Mole Music Co., Spartan Distribution

TUBBY HAYES QUINTET, THE (Hayes, Tubby Quintet).

TUBBY'S GROOVE (Hayes, Tubby, Quartet).
Album: released on Jasmine, Feb'83 by Jasmine Records. Dist: Counterpoint, Lugtons, Taylor, H.R., Wellard, Chris, Swift, Cadillac

WHERE AM I GOING TO LIVE 1969.
Album: released on Harlequin, Jan'86 by Harlequin Records. Dist: Swift, Jazz Music, Wellard, Chris, IRS, Taylor, H.R.

Hayford, Jack
PRIESTS & KINGS.
Album: released on Word, Jun'85 by Word Records. Dist: Word Distribution, CBS

Cassette: released on Word, Jun'85 by Word Records. Dist: Word Distribution, CBS

Hayman, June
JUNE 1.
Album: released on Lochshore, Jun'85 by Klub Records. Dist: PRT

Cassette: released on Lochshore, Jun'85 by Klub Records. Dist: PRT

Haymes, Dick
FOR YOU, FOR ME, FOR EVERMORE.
Album: released on Audiophile, Jun'86 by Jazzology Records (USA). Dist: Jazz Music, Swift

GOLDEN GREATS: DICK HAYMES.
Album: released on MCA, Oct'85 by MCA Records. Dist: Polygram, MCA

Cassette: released on MCA, Oct'85 by MCA Records. Dist: Polygram, MCA

GREAT SONG STYLISTS (VOL.1), THE.
Album: released on Apex, Apr'83 Dist: Jazz Music, Swift

LAST GOODBYE.
Album: released on Ballad (Import), Jun'83

LOVE LETTERS.
Album: released on Memoir, Oct'85 by Memoir Records. Dist: PRT Distribution

MOONDREAMS.
Album: released on Capitol (France), '83 by Capitol Records. Dist: Conifer

POLKA DOTS AND MOONBEAMS.
Album: released on Memoir, Jan'87 by Memoir Records. Dist: PRT Distribution

POLKA DOTS AND MOON BEAMS.
Tracks: / Too late now / Little bit independant, A / I wish I didn't love you so / Spring will be a little late this year / Count every star / Laura... / It's magic / Polka dots and moonbeams / Song is you, The / They didn't believe me / Sunday morning or always / I guess I'll have to dream the rest / How are things in Glocca Morra? / My prayer.
Album: released on Memoir, Jul'86 by Memoir Records. Dist: PRT Distribution

Cassette: released on Memoir, Jul'86 by Memoir Records. Dist: PRT Distribution

RAIN OR SHINE.
Album: released on Capitol, Aug'78 by Capitol Records. Dist: EMI

SINGS IRVING BERLIN.
Album: released on MCA, Feb'84 by MCA Records. Dist: Polygram, MCA

Cassette: released on MCA, Feb'84 by MCA Records. Dist: Polygram, MCA

SOMETHING TO REMEMBER YOU BY (Haymes, Dick & Helen Forrest).
Album: released on Cambra, Apr'85 by Cambra Records. Dist: IDS, Conifer

Cassette: released on Cambra, Apr'85 by Cambra Records. Dist: IDS, Conifer

SPECIAL MAGIC, THE.
Album: released on Standing Room Only, Apr'79

V DISC YEARS, THE.
Album: released on Standing Room Only, Apr'79

VIC DAMONE & DICK HAYMES (Haymes, Dick & Vic Damone).
Album: released on Jazz Greats, Jan'79 Dist: Swift

Haymes, Joe
RAY NOBLE & JOE HAYMES 1935 (Haymes, Joe & Ray Noble).
Album: released on Aircheck (USA), Apr'79

Dist: Swift, Jazz Music

Haynes, Roy
OUT OF THE AFTERNOON (Haynes, Roy Quartet).
Album: released on Jasmine, Jun'82 by Jasmine Records. Dist: Counterpoint, Lugtons, Taylor, H.R., Wellard, Chris, Swift, Cadillac

Cassette: released on Jasmine, Jun'82 by Jasmine Records. Dist: Counterpoint, Lugtons, Taylor, H.R., Wellard, Chris, Swift, Cadillac

WE THREE (Haynes, Roy Trio).
Compact disc: released on Carrere, Apr'87 by Carrere Records. Dist: PRT, Spartan

Haynes, Steve
PICTURE PUZZLE.
Single (7"): released on Harbour, Jan'80 by Harbour Records. Dist: Wellard, Chris

Haysi Fantayzee
HOLY JOE.
Single (7"): released on Regard, Oct'82

Single (12"): released on Regard, Oct'82

Picture disc single: released on Regard, Nov'82

JOHN WAYNE IS BIG LEGGY.
Single (7"): released on Regard, Jun'82

Single (12"): released on Regard, Jun'82

Picture disc single: released on Regard, Jun'82

SHINY SHINY.
Single (7"): released on Regard, Jan'83

Single (12"): released on Regard, Jan'83

Picture disc single: released on Regard, Jan'83

SISTER FRICTION.
Picture disc single: released on Regard, Jul'83

Single (7"): released on Regard, May'83

Single (12"): released on Regard, May'83

Hayward, Andrew
TELEPHONE BOX (EP) (see also Panic Buttons) (Hayward, Andrew & Panic Buttons).
Single (7"): released on Twist & Shout, Jul'80

Hayward, Charles
BATTERIES, (LES) (Hayward, Charles 'Drum Trio').
Album: released on Ayaa Disques, Sep'86 by Recommended Records. Dist: Recommended, Rough Trade, Cartel

Hayward, Dennis
CARRY ON DANCING (Hayward's, Dennis Organisation).
Album: released on Savoy, May'86

SEQUENCE TIME.
Album: released on Savoy, Sep'86

Hayward, Justin
BEST IS YET TO COME, (THE).

Single (7"): released on Towerbell, Nov'85 by Towerbell Records. Dist: EMI

BLUE JAYS (Hayward, Justin & John Lodge).
Album: released on Threshold, Nov'84 by Threshold Records. Dist: Decca Distribution, Polygram Distribution

Cassette: released on Threshold, Nov'84 by Threshold Records. Dist: Decca Distribution, Polygram Distribution

FOREVER AUTUMN.
Tracks: / Forever autumn / Fighting machine, The. Notes: From Jeff Wayne's "War Of The Worlds"
Single (7"): released on Old Gold, Jan'87 by Old Gold Records. Dist: Lightning, Jazz Music, Spartan, Counterpoint

MOVING MOUNTAINS.
Tracks: / One again / Take your chances / Moving mountains / Silver-bird / Is it just a game / Lost and found / Goodbye / Who knows / Best is yet to come, The.
Compact disc: released on Towerbell, Sep'85 by Towerbell Records. Dist: EMI

Album: released on Towerbell, Sep'85 by Towerbell Records. Dist: EMI

Cassette: released on Towerbell, Sep'85 by Towerbell Records. Dist: EMI

SILVERBIRD.
Single (7"): released on Towerbell, Aug'85 by Towerbell Records. Dist: EMI

Cassette: released on Towerbell, Aug'85 by Towerbell Records. Dist: EMI

SONGWRITER.
Album: released on Deram, Feb'77 by Decca Records. Dist: Polygram

STAR COPS It won't be easy.
Tracks: / Star cops / Outer space.
Single (7"): released on BBC, Jul'87 by BBC Records & Tapes. Dist: EMI, PRT, Pye

Single (12"): released on BBC, Jul'87 by BBC Records & Tapes. Dist: EMI, PRT, Pye

Hayward, Peter

ELEGANCE.
Album: released on Grosvenor, Jun'81 by Grosvenor Records. Dist: Taylors

HAYWARD'S CHOICE.
Album: released on Grosvenor, Oct'82 by Grosvenor Records. Dist: Taylors

HORIZONS.
Album: released on Grosvenor, May'86 by Grosvenor Records. Dist: Taylors

MIDNIGHT BLUES.
Album: released on Grosvenor, May'86 by Grosvenor Records. Dist: Taylors

OVERTURE.
Album: released on Grosvenor, Feb'82 by Grosvenor Records. Dist: Taylors

RHYTHMS OF LIFE.
Cassette: released on Grosvenor, May'86 by Grosvenor Records. Dist: Taylors

SOUND OF MUSICALS.
Album: released on Grosvenor, Mar'82 by Grosvenor Records. Dist: Taylors

Haywoode

ARRIVAL.
Tracks: / Roses / Getting closer / Single handed / I can't let you go / Jelly baby / You'd better not fool around / I wanna be your lover / Time like this, A / Missing you / Under fire.
Album: released on CBS, Jul'86 by CBS Records. Dist: CBS

Cassette: released on CBS, Jul'86 by CBS Records. Dist: CBS

I CAN'T LET YOU GO.
Tracks: / My kind of hero.
Single (7"): released on CBS, Aug'86 by CBS Records. Dist: CBS

Single (12"): released on CBS, Aug'86 by CBS Records. Dist: CBS

Single (7"): released on CBS, Sep'84 by CBS Records. Dist: CBS

Single (12"): released on CBS, Sep'84 by CBS Records. Dist: CBS

I'M YOUR PUPPET.
Tracks: / I'm your puppet / Take me up to heaven.
Single (7"): released on CBS, Feb'87 by CBS Records. Dist: CBS

Single (12"): released on CBS, Feb'87 by CBS Records. Dist: CBS

ROSES.
Tracks: / Tease me.
Single (7"): released on CBS, May'86 by CBS Records. Dist: CBS

Single (12"): released on CBS, May'86 by CBS Records. Dist: CBS

YOU'D BETTER NOT FOOL AROUND.
Tracks: / Missing you.
Single (7"): released on CBS, Mar'86 by CBS Records. Dist: CBS

Single (12"): released on CBS, Mar'86 by CBS Records. Dist: CBS

Haywood, Leon

IT'S ME AGAIN.
Album: released on Casablanca(Holland), Sep'83 Dist: IMS, Polygram

Hayworth, Rita

RITA HAYWORTH.
Album: released on Deja Vu, Jan'87 by Deja Vu Records. Dist: Counterpoint Distribution, Record Services Distribution (Ireland

Cassette: released on Deja Vu, Jan'87 by Deja Vu Records. Dist: Counterpoint Distribution, Record Services Distribution (Ireland)

Hazan

DREAMER DEVANE.
Single (7"): released on EMI, May'83 by EMI Records. Dist: EMI

Single (12"): released on EMI, May'83 by EMI Records. Dist: EMI

Haza, Ofra

GALBI.
Tracks: / I'm nin' alu.
Single (12"): released on Ace, Jun'86 by Ace Records. Dist: Pinnacle, Swift, Hotshot, Cadillac

HIGH.
Single (7"): released on CBS, May'83 by CBS Records. Dist: CBS

YEMENITE SONGS.
Compact disc: released on Globestyle, May'87 by Ace Records. Dist: Projection

Album: released on Globestyle, Nov'85 by Ace Records. Dist: Projection

Haze

CELLAR REPLAY.
Tracks: / Night / I fear that I'll.... / Survive / Portrait / Firkin of mead, A / Take me home / Aardvarks anonymous / Turn around / Unto the dawn / In the light / Dig them mushrooms / Anonymous Aardvarks.
Notes: Paul Chisnell-percussion, vocals/Chris McMahon-Basses, keyboards, vocals/Paul McMahon-vocals, guitars.
Cassette: released on Gabadon, Apr'85 by Gabadon Records. Dist: Pinnacle

C'EST LA VIE.
Tracks: / Rogers revenge / Don't leave me here / Fallen leaves / Load / Mairage / For whom / Hum, The / Gabadon.
Notes: Paul Chisnell-percussion, vocals/Chris McMahon-Basses,keyboards/Paul McMahon-vocals & guitars. Produced and engineered by Haze, with assistance from Brian. Recorded in the Cellar Studio, 14th January 1984 to 16th February 1984. Cut at PRT. Pressed by Standard Pressings, Concett. Sleeve concept and design Brian.
Album: released on Gabadon, Apr'84 by Gabadon Records. Dist: Pinnacle

HDH Presents...

HDH PRESENTS THE HITS OF HOT WAX & INVICTUS RECORDS (Various Artists).
Compact disc: released on HDH(Holland/Dozier/Holland), Dec'86 by Demon Records. Dist: Pinnacle

H.D.Q.

HUNG, DRAWN & QUARTERED.
Album: released on Endangered Musik, May'86 by Endangered Musik Records. Dist: Revolver

Head

I AM THE KING.
Tracks: / I am the king / Killing time.
Single (7"): released on Demon, May'87 by Demon Records. Dist: Pinnacle

Single (12"): released on Demon, May'87 by Demon Records. Dist: Pinnacle

I CAN'T STOP.
Tracks: / I can't stop / Me & Mrs Jones / Ditchin' ma babee*.
Single (7"): released on Demon, Jul'87 by Demon Records. Dist: Pinnacle

Single (12"): released on Demon, Jul'87 by Demon Records. Dist: Pinnacle

SNOG ON THE ROCKS,A.
Album: released on Demon, Jun'87 by Demon Records. Dist: Pinnacle

Cassette: released on Demon, Jun'87 by Demon Records. Dist: Pinnacle

Compact disc: released on Demon, Jun'87 by Demon Records. Dist: Pinnacle

Head Cleaners

DISINFECTION (EP).
Single (7"): released on Xcentric Noise, Feb'82 by Xcentric Noise Records & Tapes Records. Dist: Cartel

INFECTION GROWS (EP).
Single (7"): released on Xcentric Noise, Oct'83 by Xcentric Noise Records & Tapes Records. Dist: Cartel

Head, Hands & Feet

OLD SOLDIERS NEVER DIE.
Album: released on Atlantic, '74 by WEA Records. Dist: WEA

Headhunters

IMPOSSIBLE.
Single (7"): released on Shout, Dec'83 by Shout Records. Dist: Rough Trade, Cartel

INDUSTRIAL WARFARE.
Album: released on Shout, Aug'83 by Shout Records. Dist: Rough Trade, Cartel

WAY OF THE SOUTH.
Single (12"): released on Quiet, Jun'86 by Quiet Records. Dist: Nine Mile, Cartel

WIPE OUT THE FUNK.
Single (12"): released on Shout, Oct'82 by Shout Records. Dist: Rough Trade, Cartel

Headline hits

HEADLINE HITS Various artists (Various Artists).
Album: released on K-Tel, Sep'83 by K-Tel Records. Dist: Record Merchandisers Distribution, Taylors, Terry Blood Distribution, Wynd-Up Distribution, Relay Distribution, Pickwick Distribution, Solomon & Peres Distribution, Polygram

Cassette: released on K-Tel, Sep'83 by K-Tel Records. Dist: Record Merchandisers Distribution, Taylors, Terry Blood Distribution, Wynd-Up Distribution, Relay Distribution, Pickwick Distribution, Solomon & Peres Distribution, Polygram

Head, Murray

BETWEEN US.
Album: released on Philips (France), Feb'85

Cassette: released on Philips (France), Feb'85

FIND THE CROWD.
Album: released on Mercury (France)_, Feb'85

Cassette: released on Mercury (France)_, Feb'85

HOW MANY WAYS?.
Album: released on Music Lovers, Apr'81 by Music Lovers Records. Dist: Music Lovers

IN THE HEART OF YOU.
Tracks: / In the heart of you / Fear and ambition / Wanderer*.
Single (7"): released on Virgin, Jan'87 by Virgin Records. Dist: EMI, Virgin Distribution

Single (12"): released on Virgin, Jan'87 by Virgin Records. Dist: EMI, Virgin Distribution

OLD SOHO.
Single (7"): released on Music Lovers, Sep'81 by Music Lovers Records. Dist: Music Lovers

ONE NIGHT IN BANGKOK.
Single (7"): released on RCA, Oct'84 by RCA Records. Dist: RCA, Roots, Swift, Wellard, Chris, I & B, Solomon & Peres Distribution

Single (12"): released on RCA, Oct'84 by RCA Records. Dist: RCA, Roots, Swift, Wellard, Chris, I & B, Solomon & Peres Distribution

PITY THE CHILD.
Tracks: / Pity the child / Deal / One night in Bangkok.
Single (7"): released on RCA, Jun'86 by RCA Records. Dist: RCA, Roots, Swift, Wellard, Chris, I & B, Solomon & Peres Distribution

Single (12"): released on RCA, Jun'86 by RCA Records. Dist: RCA, Roots, Swift, Wellard, Chris, I & B, Solomon & Peres Distribution

RESTLESS.
Album: released on Virgin, May'84 by Virgin Records. Dist: EMI, Virgin Distribution

Cassette: released on Virgin, May'84 by Virgin Records. Dist: EMI, Virgin Distribution

SAY IT ISN'T SO.
Compact disc: released on Island, Apr'87 by Island Records. Dist: Polygram

SOME PEOPLE.
Tracks: / Maybe tomorrow.
Single (7"): released on Virgin, Mar'86 by Virgin Records. Dist: EMI, Virgin Distribution

SOONER OR LATER.
Compact disc: released on Virgin, Feb'87 by Virgin Records. Dist: EMI, Virgin Distribution

Album: released on Virgin, Feb'87 by Virgin Records. Dist: EMI, Virgin Distribution

Cassette: released on Virgin, Feb'87 by Virgin Records. Dist: EMI, Virgin Distribution

VOICES.
Album: released on Mercury (France)_, Feb'85 Cat. no: 6313045

Cassette: released on Mercury (France)_, Feb'85

Head Of David

DOGBREATH.
Album: released on Blast First, Jun'86 by Sonic Youth Records. Dist: Rough Trade, Nine Mile, Red Rhino, Cartel

LP.
Album: released on Blast First, Sep'86 by Sonic Youth Records. Dist: Rough Trade, Nine Mile, Red Rhino, Cartel

SHIT HITS THE FAN, THE.
Album: released on Blast First, Jul'87 by Sonic Youth Records. Dist: Rough Trade, Nine Mile, Red Rhino, Cartel

Headon, Topper

DRUMMIN' MAN.
Single (7"): released on Mercury, Jun'85 by Phonogram Records. Dist: Polygram Distribution

Cassette: released on Mercury, Jun'85 by Phonogram Records. Dist: Polygram Distribution

Single (12"): released on Mercury, Jun'85 by Phonogram Records. Dist: Polygram Distribution

I'LL GIVE YOU EVERYTHING.
Tracks: / You're so cheeky.
Single (7"): released on Mercury, Feb'86 by Phonogram Records. Dist: Polygram Distribution

Single (12"): released on Mercury, Feb'86 by Phonogram Records. Dist: Polygram Distribution

WAKING UP.
Tracks: / Leave it to luck / I'll give you everything / Home for Donna / Got to keep on going / Dancing / Pleasure & pain / Time is tight / When you're down / Just another hit / Monkey on my back.
Notes: Topper Headon's first album after his move as drummer/writer with the Clash. A brilliant album inspiring all Soul music lovers and Clash fans alike. Featuring vocals by Jimmy Helms.
Album: released on Mercury, Jan'86 by Phonogram Records. Dist: Polygram Distribution

Cassette: released on Mercury, Jan'86 by Phonogram Records. Dist: Polygram Distribution

Headpins

HEAD OVER HEELS.
Tracks: / Still the one / Death of me / Stayin' all night / Hot stuff / Chain gang / Never come down from the danger zone / Don't matter what you say / Be with you / Afraid of the dark (you're only) / Burnin' at both ends.
Album: released on MCA, Aug'87 by MCA Records. Dist: Polygram, MCA

Cassette: released on MCA, Aug'87 by MCA Records. Dist: Polygram, MCA

LINE OF FIRE.
Album: released on MCA, Mar'84 by MCA Records. Dist: Polygram, MCA

Cassette: released on MCA, Mar'84 by MCA Records. Dist: Polygram, MCA Deleted '85.

Headquarters

IN MY ENGLAND.
Tracks: / In my ngland / Beauty and the blind / All fall down.
Notes: 33 rpm
Single (7"): released on Cottage Pie, Mar'87 Dist: Roots

NEW YORK RUNAROUND.
Single (7"): released on Skeleton, Apr'80 by Skeleton Records. Dist: Cartel, Probe

Headroom, Max

CHRISTMAS SANTA CLAUS (YOU'RE A LOVELY GUY).
Tracks: / Christmas Santa Calus (you're a lovely guy) / Gimme shades.
Single (7"): released on Chrysalis, Dec'86 by Chrysalis Records. Dist: CBS

Heads

AZTEC LIGHTNING.
Tracks: / Mayan interlude.
Single (7"): released on BBC, Jun'86 by BBC Records & Tapes. Dist: EMI, PRT, Pye

Headset One

HEADSET ONE (Various Artists).
Album: released on Deadman's Curve, Jan'87 by Dave Henderson.

Heads of Agreement

LOOSE TALK.
Single (7"): released on Admin B., Oct'82 by Admin B..

Heads Together

FUNKY STUFF.
Album: released on SRT, '75 by SRT Records. Dist: Pinnacle, Solomon & Peres Distribution, SRT Distribution, H.R. Taylor Distribution, PRT Distribution

Head to Head

SHANTY SHANTY.
Single (7"): released on Hollywood, Oct'85 by Hollywood Records. Dist: Pinnacle

Healy-Duffy

MEMORIES OF SLIGO.
Album: released on Topic, '81 Dist: Roots Distribution

Healy, Tim

IF YOU COULD READ MY MIND.
Tracks: / Take your last chance on me.
Single (7"): released on Columbia, Mar'86 by EMI Records. Dist: EMI

STICK YA JOB.
Single (7"): released on Spartan, Mar'85 by Spartan Records. Dist: Spartan

Heaney, Joe

IRISH TRADITIONAL SONGS IN GAELIC & ENGLISH.
Album: released on Topic, '81 Dist: Roots Distribution

SONGS IN IRISH - VOL.2.
Album: released on Gael-Linn (Ireland), '77 by Gael Linn Records. Dist: Roots, Projection, Celtic Music, Jazz Music

Heard, Jack

SEX MACHINE.
Single (7"): released on DB, Jul'86 by DB Records. Dist: Pinnacle

Heard, John

LONDON CONCERT, THE (Heard, John, Oscar Peterson & Louis Bellson).
Double Album: released on Pablo (USA), '82 by Pablo Records (USA). Dist: Wellard, Chris, IMS-Polygram, BMG

Double cassette: released on Pablo (USA), '82 by Pablo Records (USA). Dist: Wellard, Chris, IMS-Polygram, BMG

Heard, Mark

ASHES & LIGHT.
Album: released on Myrrh, Jan'85 by Word Records. Dist: Word Distribution

Cassette: released on Myrrh, Jan'85 by Word Records. Dist: Word Distribution

Hear'N'Aid

HEAR'N'AID Various artists (Various Artists).
Tracks: / Up to the limit (live) / Hungry for heaven (Live) / Can you see me / Heaven's on fire (Live) / On the road (Live) / Distant early warning (Live) / Zoo (Live) / Go for the throat.
Notes: An all star album for famine relief featuring six previously unreleased tracks-guaranteed to appeal to rock and metal fans every where, except major press. Promotion and marketing support for the release of this album.
Album: released on Vertigo, Jun'86 by Phonogram Records. Dist: Polygram

SESSIONS, THE.
Notes: The recording of the famine relief single "Stars", which a transatlantic host of top heavy metal musicians, including Dio, Judas Priest and Iron Maiden. 1986 production. Total playing time: 30 minutes.
Video-cassette (VHS): released on Virgin Video, Sep'86 by Virgin Records. Dist: EMI

STAR.
Tracks: / Four and a half minute news.
Notes: All proceeds will be distributed by USA for Africa to aid famine relief.
Single (7"): released on Vertigo, Apr'86 by Phonogram Records. Dist: Polygram

Single (12"): released on Vertigo, Apr'86 by Phonogram Records. Dist: Polygram

Hearne, Tony

GOTTA GET YOU HOME TONIGHT.
Single (12"): released on Neville King, Nov'84 by Neville King Records. Dist: Jetstar

WITHOUT YOU I'D GO CRAZY.
Single (12"): released on Neville King, Sep'84 by Neville King Records. Dist: Jetstar

Heart

ALONE.
Tracks: / Alone / Barracuda / Magic man.
Single (7"): released on Capitol, May'87 by Capitol Records. Dist: EMI

Single (12"): released on Capitol, May'87 by Capitol Records. Dist: EMI

Cassette single: released on Capitol, 30 May'87 by Capitol Records. Dist: EMI

BAD ANIMALS.
Tracks: / Who will you run to / Alone / There's the girl / I want you so bad / Wait for an answer / Bad animals / You ain't so tough / Strangers of the heart / Easy target / RSVP.
Notes: This is the second album from heart, their first has so far achieved Silver status in the UK, and sold over four million units in the America. Heart features the unique songwriting talents of Ann and Nancy Wilson who have composed some of the most melodic rock tunes of the 70's and 80'. [EMI release sheet, May 1987]
Album: released on Capitol, May'87 by Capitol Records. Dist: EMI

Cassette: released on Capitol, May'87 by Capitol Records. Dist: EMI

DOG AND THE BUTTERFLY.
Tracks: / Cook with fire / High time / Hijinx / Straight on / Dog and butterfly / Lighter touch / Nada one / Mistral wind.
Album: released on Portrait, Aug'86 by CBS Records. Dist: CBS

Cassette: released on Portrait, Aug'86 by CBS Records. Dist: CBS

DREAMBOAT ANNIE.
Album: released on Arista, Oct'76 by Arista Records. Dist: RCA

Cassette: released on Arista, Oct'76 by Arista Records. Dist: RCA

HEART.
Tracks: / If looks could kill / What about love? / Never / These dreams / Wolf / All eyes / Nobody home / Nothin' at all / What he don't know / Shell shock / Tell it like it is / Barracuda / Straight on / Dog & butterfly / Even it up / Bebe Le Strange / Sweet darlin' / I'm down / Long tall Sally / Unchained melody / Rock and roll.
Compact disc: released on Capitol, Feb'86 by Capitol Records. Dist: EMI

Album: released on Capitol, Oct'85 by Capitol Records. Dist: EMI

Cassette: released on Capitol, Oct'85 by Capitol Records. Dist: EMI

Album: released on Epic, Sep'87 by CBS Records. Dist: CBS

Cassette: released on Epic, Sep'87 by CBS Records. Dist: CBS

HEART OF ROCK'N'ROLL Various artists (Various Artists).
Album: released on K-Tel, Feb'83 by K-Tel Records. Dist: Record Merchandisers Distribution, Taylors, Terry Blood Distribution, Wynd-Up Distribution, Relay Distribution, Pickwick Distribution, Solomon & Peres Distribution, Polygram

Cassette: released on K-Tel, Feb'83 by K-Tel Records. Dist: Record Merchandisers Distribution, Taylors, Terry Blood Distribution, Wynd-Up Distribution, Relay Distribution, Pickwick Distribution, Solomon & Peres Distribution, Polygram

LITTLE QUEEN.
Tracks: / Little queen / Treat me well / Say hello / Cry to me / Go on cry / Barracuda / Love alive / Sylvan song / Dream of the archer / Kick it out.
Compact disc: released on Portrait, May'87 by CBS Records. Dist: CBS

Album: released on Portrait, Jun'86 by CBS Records. Dist: CBS

Cassette: released on Portrait, Jun'86 by CBS Records. Dist: CBS

MAGAZINE.
Compact disc: released on Capitol, Mar'87 by Capitol Records. Dist: EMI

NEVER.
Single (7"): released on Capitol, Oct'85 by Capitol Records. Dist: EMI

Single (12"): released on Capitol, Oct'85 by Capitol Records. Dist: EMI

NOTHIN' AT ALL (REMIX).
Tracks: / Wolf.
Single (7"): released on Capitol, May'86 by Capitol Records. Dist: EMI

Single (12"): released on Capitol, May'86 by Capitol Records. Dist: EMI

THESE DREAMS.
Tracks: / These dreams / If looks could kill / Live version / Shell shock / What about love ? / Heart of darkness.
Single (7"): released on Capitol, Mar'86 by Capitol Records. Dist: EMI

Double-pack single: released on Capitol, Mar'86 by Capitol Records. Dist: EMI

Single (12"): released on Capitol, Mar'86 by Capitol Records. Dist: EMI

WHAT ABOUT LOVE?.
Single (7"): released on Capitol, Jul'85 by Capitol Records. Dist: EMI

Heartbeats

HERE COME THE JETS.
Single (7"): released on RCA, Oct'82 by RCA Records. Dist: RCA, Roots, Swift, Wellard, Chris, I & B, Solomon & Peres Distribution

I'LL BE TRUE.
Single (7"): released on RCA, Jul'82 by RCA Records. Dist: RCA, Roots, Swift, Wellard, Chris, I & B, Solomon & Peres Distribution

MAGIC MAN.
Single (7"): released on RCA, Apr'83 by RCA Records. Dist: RCA, Roots, Swift, Wellard, Chris, I & B, Solomon & Peres Distribution

Heartbreakers

HEARTBREAKERS Various artists (Various Artists).
Notes: Double album including: Whitney Houston/Dire Straits/Level 42.
Album: released on Starblend, Aug'86 by Starblend Records. Dist: PRT Distribution

Cassette: released on Starblend, Aug'86 by Starblend Records. Dist: PRT Distribution

Album: released on K-Tel, Feb'83 by K-Tel Records. Dist: Record Merchandisers Distribution, Taylors, Terry Blood Distribution, Wynd-Up Distribution, Relay Distribution, Pickwick Distribution, Solomon & Peres Distribution, Polygram

Cassette: released on K-Tel, Feb'83 by K-Tel Records. Dist: Record Merchandisers Distribution, Taylors, Terry Blood Distribution, Wynd-Up Distribution, Relay Distribution, Pickwick Distribution, Solomon & Peres Distribution, Polygram

Cassette: released on Aim (Budget Cassettes), Sep'83

HEARTBREAKERS Original soundtrack.
Album: released on Ariola (Germany), May'84

LIVE AT MAX'S, KANSAS CITY.
Album: released on Beggars Banquet, Sep'79 by Beggars Banquet Records. Dist: WEA

Heartfixers

COOL ON IT.
Album: released on Landslide, Oct'86 by Dorane Ltd.

LIVE AT THE MOONSHADOW.
Album: released on LM/LD, Jul'86 Dist: Compendium International Distribution

Heartland Consort

HEARTLAND CONSORT.
Album: released on Enja (Germany), Feb'85 by Enja Records (W.Germany). Dist: Cadillac Music

Heart Of Darkness

HEART OF DARKNESS Conrad, Joseph (Scofield, Paul).
Cassette: released on Argo, Apr'85 by Decca Records. Dist: Polygram

Heart On Fire

YOU PROMISED ME A CAMERA.
Tracks: / Heaven / Starting line / Because you care.
Single (12"): released on Midnight Music, Jul'86 by Midnight Music Records. Dist: Rough Trade Distribution, Cartel Distribution

Hearts Of Love

HEARTS OF LOVE Various artists (Various Artists).
Album: released on PRT, Feb'84 by PRT Records. Dist: PRT

Cassette: released on PRT, Feb'84 by PRT Records. Dist: PRT

Hearts On Fire

DREAMS OF LEAVING.
Album: released on Midnight Music, Sep'85 by Midnight Music Records. Dist: Rough Trade Distribution, Cartel Distribution

YOU MAY NOT KNOW.
Single (12"): released on Midnight, Sep'85

Heart Throbs

HEART THROBS Various artists (Various Artists).
Tracks: / Why / Venus / De de dina / Tiger / Houndog man / More than I can say / Rubber ball / Night has a 1000 eyes, The / Forget him / Wild one / Volare.
Album: released on Topline, Oct'86 by Charly Records. Dist: Charly Distribution

TOY.
Tracks: / Toy / Make my day / I, the jury.
Single (12"): released on In Tape, Jun'87 by In Tape Records. Dist: Red Rhino, Cartel

Single (7"): released on In Tape, Jun'87 by In Tape Records. Dist: Red Rhino. Cartel

Heart To Heart

HEART TO HEART Various artists (24 love song duets) (Various Artists).
Notes: Including: Phil Collins/Marilyn Martin, David Grant/Jakie Graham.
Album: released on K-Tel, Mar'86 by K-Tel Records. Dist: Record Merchandisers Distribution, Taylors, Terry Blood Distribution, Wynd-Up Distribution, Relay Distribution, Pickwick Distribution, Solomon & Peres Distribution, Polygram

Cassette: released on K-Tel, Mar'86 by K-Tel Records. Dist: Record Merchandisers Distribution, Taylors, Terry Blood Distribution, Wynd-Up Distribution, Relay Distribution, Pickwick Distribution, Solomon & Peres Distribution, Polygram

Album: released on Spot, Feb'83 by Pickwick Records. Dist: H.R. Taylor,

Cassette: released on Spot, Feb'83 by Pickwick Records. Dist: H.R. Taylor,

THREE CHORD TRICK.
Single (7"): released on EMI, May'84 by EMI Records. Dist: EMI

Single (12"): released on EMI, May'84 by EMI Records. Dist: EMI

Hearty, Trevor

CLOSER TOGETHER.
Single (12"): released on Pressure, Dec'84 Dist: Priority

Heat

LOVE DANCE.
Single (7"): released on MCA, Jan'85 by MCA Records. Dist: Polygram, MCA

Heat & Dust

HEAT & DUST Original soundtrack (Various Artists).
Album: released on That's Entertainment, Apr'83 by That's Entertainment Records. Dist: Pinnacle, PRT

Heaters

CARMEN.
Single (7"): released on Precinct, Jul'81 Dist: Indies

Heat From The Street

HEAT FROM THE STREET Various Artists (Various Artists).
Album: released on Charisma, Mar'81 by Virgin Records. Dist: EMI

Heath Brothers

MARCHING ON!.
Album: released on Strata East(France), Aug'84

Heath, Edward

JOY OF CHRISTMAS, THE.
Album: released on Music For Pleasure, Sep'84 by EMI Records. Dist: EMI

Cassette: released on Music For Pleasure, Sep'84 by EMI Records. Dist: EMI

Heath, Elra

CHRIST IN COMPETITION.
Album: by Pilgrim Records. Dist: Rough Trade, Cartel

Heathen

BREAKING THE SILENCE.
Album: released on MFN, Aug'87 by Music For Nations Records. Dist: Pinnacle

Heath, Jimmy

JIMMY.
Album: released on Muse (Import), Apr'81

Heath, Ted

AT THE LONDON PALLADIUM.
Album: released on Jasmine, Feb'83 by Jasmine Records. Dist: Counterpoint, Lugtons, Taylor, H.R., Wellard, Chris, Swift, Cadillac

AT THE LONDON PALLADIUM VOL.3 (Heath, Ted & His Music).
Album: released on Jasmine, Jun'83 by Jasmine Records. Dist: Counterpoint, Lugtons, Taylor, H.R., Wellard, Chris, Swift, Cadillac

BIG BAND FAVOURITES (Heath, Ted & His Music).
Cassette: released on Decca, Aug'84 by Decca Records. Dist: Polygram

BIG BAND SOUND OF TED HEATH.
Notes: Direction by Don Lusher.
Album: released on Intersound, Dec'86 by Intersound Records. Dist: Jazz Music

COAST TO COAST (Heath, Ted & His Music).
Tracks: / St. Louis blues / Charleston / In San Francisco (I left my heart) / Chicago / Manhattan serenade / Alabamy bound / I've got a gal in Kalamazoo / Oh Susannah / Moonlight in Vermont / Lullaby of Broadway / Allentown jail / Jersey bounce.
Compact disc: released on London, Jul'87 by

London Records. Dist: Polygram

FATS WALLER ALBUM.
Album: released on Jasmine, Feb'83 by Jasmine Records. Dist: Counterpoint, Lugtons, Taylor, H.R., Wellard, Chris, Swift, Cadillac

FOCUS ON TED HEATH.
Double Album: released on Phase 4, May'78

Cassette: released on Decca, May'78 by Decca Records. Dist: Polygram

GOLDEN AGE OF TED HEATH, THE.
Double Album: released on Horatio Nelson, Nov'85 Dist: PRT

Cassette: released on Horatio Nelson, Nov'85 Dist: PRT

HITS I MISSED (Heath, Ted & His Music).

Album: released on Jasmine, Mar'83 by Jasmine Records. Dist: Counterpoint, Lugtons, Taylor, H.R., Wellard, Chris, Swift, Cadillac

KERN FOR MODERNS (Heath, Ted & His Music).
Album: released on Jasmine, Jun'83 by Jasmine Records. Dist: PRT

LATINO (Heath, Ted & Edmundo Ros).
Album: released on Decca (Elite), Mar'83 by Decca Records. Dist: Polygram, IMS

LISTEN TO MY MUSIC.
Album: released on Decca (Elite), Nov'82 by Decca Records. Dist: Polygram, IMS Deleted '86.

Cassette: released on Decca (Elite), Nov'82 by Decca Records. Dist: Polygram, IMS

OLDE ENGLYSHE (Heath, Ted & His Music).
Album: released on Jasmine, Mar'83 by Jasmine Records. Dist: Counterpoint, Lugtons, Taylor, H.R., Wellard, Chris, Swift, Cadillac

RODGERS FOR MODERNS (Heath, Ted & His Music).
Album: released on Jasmine, Dec'83 by Jasmine Records. Dist: Counterpoint, Lugtons, Taylor, H.R., Wellard, Chris, Swift, Cadillac

SENTIMENTAL JOURNEY.
Album: released on Polydor (France), May'84 Dist: Polygram

Cassette: released on Polydor (France), May'84 Dist: Polygram

SHALL WE DANCE (Heath, Ted & His Music).
Album: released on Jasmine, Jun'83 by Jasmine Records. Dist: Counterpoint, Lugtons, Taylor, H.R., Wellard, Chris, Swift, Cadillac

SPOTLIGHT ON SIDEMEN (Heath, Ted & His Music).
Album: released on Jasmine, Dec'83 by Jasmine Records. Dist: Counterpoint, Lugtons, Taylor, H.R., Wellard, Chris, Swift, Cadillac

STRICTLY INSTRUMENTAL (Heath, Ted & His Music).
Album: released on Decca, Nov'84 by Decca Records. Dist: Polygram

STRIKE UP THE BAND.
Album: released on Jasmine, Feb'83 by Jasmine Records. Dist: Counterpoint, Lugtons, Taylor, H.R., Wellard, Chris, Swift, Cadillac

SWING SESSION (Heath, Ted & His Music).
Album: released on Jasmine, Jun'83 by Jasmine Records. Dist: Counterpoint, Lugtons, Taylor, H.R., Wellard, Chris, Swift, Cadillac

TED HEATH AT THE BBC.
Album: released on BBC, Sep'83 by BBC Records & Tapes. Dist: EMI, PRT,

Cassette: released on BBC, Sep'83 by BBC Records & Tapes. Dist: EMI, PRT,

TED HEATH RECALLS THE FABULOUS DORSEYS (Heath, Ted & His Music).
Album: released on Jasmine, Mar'85 by Jasmine Records. Dist: Counterpoint, Lugtons, Taylor, H.R., Wellard, Chris, Swift, Cadillac

Cassette: released on Jasmine, Mar'85 by Jasmine Records. Dist: Counterpoint, Lugtons, Taylor, H.R., Wellard, Chris, Swift, Cadillac

TED HEATH SWINGS IN HI-STEREO (Heath, Ted & His Music).
Album: released on Jasmine, Mar'83 by Jasmine Records. Dist: Counterpoint, Lugtons, Taylor, H.R., Wellard, Chris, Swift, Cadillac

Heat Is On

HEAT IS ON Various artists (Various Artists).
Album: released on Red Stripe, Jul'81 Dist: Sonet, PRT

Heat Of Soul

HEAT OF SOUL VOLUME1 (Various Artists).
Album: released on Master Sound, Mar'87 by CBS Records. Dist: CBS

Cassette: released on Master Sound, Mar'87 by CBS Records. Dist: CBS

Heatwave

BOOGIE NIGHTS.
Single (7"): released on Epic, Nov'82 by CBS Records. Dist: CBS

Single (7"): released on Old Gold, Jun'84 by Old Gold Records. Dist: Lightning, Jazz Music, Spartan, Counterpoint

CENTRAL HEATING.
Album: released on GTO, Apr'78 by GTO Records. Dist: CBS

Cassette: released on GTO, Apr'78 by GTO Records. Dist: CBS

GANGSTERS OF THE GROOVE.
Tracks: / Groove line / Mind blowing decisions / Too hot to handle.
Single (12"): released on Old Gold, Feb'86 by Old Gold Records. Dist: Lightning, Jazz Music, Spartan, Counterpoint

GREATEST HITS:HEATWAVE.
Album: released on Epic, '84 by CBS Records. Dist: CBS

Cassette: released on Epic, '84 by CBS Records. Dist: CBS

HEATWAVE (EP).
Cassette: released on Epic, Aug'82 by CBS Records. Dist: CBS

HOT PROPERTY.
Album: released on GTO, May'79 by GTO Records. Dist: CBS

Cassette: released on GTO, May'79 by GTO Records. Dist: CBS

MAXIMUM HEAT.
Album: released on Hallmark, Nov'83 by Pickwick Records. Dist: Pickwick Distribution, PRT, Taylors

Cassette: released on Hallmark, Nov'83 by Pickwick Records. Dist: Pickwick Distribution, PRT, Taylors

Heaven

IN THE BEGINNING.
Single (7"): released on RCA, Aug'82 by RCA Records. Dist: RCA, Roots, Swift, Wellard, Chris, I & B, Solomon & Peres Distribution

ROCK SCHOOL.
Single (7"): released on CBS, Apr'84 by CBS Records. Dist: CBS

Single (12"): released on CBS, Apr'84 by CBS Records. Dist: CBS

TWILIGHT OF MISCHIEF.
Album: released on RCA, Sep'82 by RCA Records. Dist: RCA, Roots, Swift, Wellard, Chris, I & B, Solomon & Peres Distribution

Cassette: released on RCA, Sep'82 by RCA Records. Dist: RCA, Roots, Swift, Wellard, Chris, I & B, Solomon & Peres Distribution

Heaven1

WHERE ANGELS FEAR TO TREAD.
Album: released on CBS, Jun'84 by CBS Records. Dist: CBS

Cassette: released on CBS, Jun'84 by CBS Records. Dist: CBS Deleted '86.

Heaven 17

AND THAT'S NO LIE.
Single (7"): released on Virgin, Jan'85 by Virgin Records. Dist: EMI, Virgin Distribution Deleted '85.

Single (12"): released on Virgin, Jan'85 by Virgin Records. Dist: EMI, Virgin Distribution

COME LIVE WITH ME.
Single (7"): released on B.E.F., Jun'83 by Virgin Records. Dist: EMI, CBS

Single (12"): released on B.E.F., Jun'83 by Virgin Records. Dist: EMI, CBS

CONTENDERS.
Tracks: / Diary of the contender.
Single (7"): released on Virgin, Oct'86 by Virgin Records. Dist: EMI, Virgin Distribution

Single (12"): released on Virgin, Oct'86 by Virgin Records. Dist: EMI, Virgin Distribution

CRUSHED BY THE WHEEL OF INDUSTRY.
Single (7"): released on Virgin, Aug'83 by Virgin Records. Dist: EMI, Virgin Distribution

Single (12"): released on Virgin, Aug'83 by Virgin Records. Dist: EMI, Virgin Distribution

ENDLESS.
Tracks: / Heaven 17 megamix / We live so fast / Penthouse and pavement / Let me go / Temptation / Who'll stop the rain / Fascist groove thang (We don't need this) / Let's all make a bomb (new version) / Counterforce / Crushed by the wheels of industry / And that's no lie / Sunset now / Play to win / Height of the fighting (he-la-hu) / I'm your money / Song with no name (new version).
Notes: 68 minutes of Heaven 17. A-sides, B-sides & 12" re-mixes as they have never been heard before. Double play cassette lasts 85 minutes encased in a special limited edition box with booklet.
Compact disc: released on B.E.F., Jun'86 by Virgin Records. Dist: EMI, CBS

Double cassette: released on B.E.F., Jun'86 by Virgin Records. Dist: EMI, CBS

FOOLISH THING TO DO.
Tracks: / My sensitivity.
Single (7"): released on Virgin, Apr'86 by Virgin Records. Dist: EMI, Virgin Distribution

Single (12"): released on Virgin, Apr'86 by Virgin Records. Dist: EMI, Virgin Distribution

HEIGHT OF THE FIGHTING(HE LA HU).
Single (12"): released on Virgin, Feb'82 by Virgin Records. Dist: EMI, Virgin Distribution

HOW MEN ARE.
Tracks: / Five minutes to midnight / Sunset now / This is mine / Fuse / Shame is on the rocks / Skin I'm in, The / Flamedown / Reputation / And that's no lie.
Compact disc: released on Virgin, Jul'87 by Virgin Records. Dist: EMI, Virgin Distribution

Album: released on Virgin, Oct'84 by Virgin Records. Dist: EMI, Virgin Distribution

Cassette: released on Virgin, Oct'84 by Virgin Records. Dist: EMI, Virgin Distribution

INDUSTRIAL REVOLUTION.
Video-cassette (VHS): released on Virgin, Jan'84 by Virgin Records. Dist: EMI, Virgin Distribution

LET ME GO.
Single (7"): released on Virgin, Oct'82 by Virgin Records. Dist: EMI, Virgin Distribution

Single (12"): released on Virgin, Oct'82 by Virgin Records. Dist: EMI, Virgin Distribution

LUXURY GAP.
Compact disc: released on Virgin, '83 by Virgin Records. Dist: EMI, Virgin Distribution

Album: released on Virgin, '83 by Virgin Records. Dist: EMI, Virgin Distribution

Cassette: released on Virgin, '83 by Virgin Records. Dist: EMI, Virgin Distribution

PENTHOUSE AND PAVEMENT.
Tracks: / (We don't need this) fascist groove thang / Penthouse and pavement / Soul warfare / Geisha boys and temple girls / Let's all make a bomb / Height of the fighting / Song with no name / Play to win / We're going to live for a very long time.
Album: released on Virgin, Apr'86 by Virgin Records. Dist: EMI, Virgin Distribution

Cassette: released on Virgin, Apr'86 by Virgin Records. Dist: EMI, Virgin Distribution

Compact disc: released on Virgin, Jul'87 by Virgin Records. Dist: EMI, Virgin Distribution

Single (12"): released on Virgin, Oct'81 by Virgin Records. Dist: EMI, Virgin Distribution

Single (7"): released on Virgin, Oct'81 by Virgin Records. Dist: EMI, Virgin Distribution

Album: released on Virgin, Sep'81 by Virgin Records. Dist: EMI, Virgin Distribution

Cassette: released on Virgin, Sep'81 by Virgin Records. Dist: EMI, Virgin Distribution

PLAY TO WIN.
Single (7"): released on Virgin, Jul'81 by Virgin Records. Dist: EMI, Virgin Distribution

Single (12"): released on Virgin, Jul'81 by Virgin Records. Dist: EMI, Virgin Distribution

PLEASURE ONE.
Tracks: / Contenders / Trouble / Somebody / If I were you / Low society / Red / Look at me / Move out.
Album: released on Virgin, Nov'86 by Virgin Records. Dist: EMI, Virgin Distribution

Cassette: released on Virgin, Nov'86 by Virgin Records. Dist: EMI, Virgin Distribution

Compact disc: released on Virgin, Nov'86 by Virgin Records. Dist: EMI, Virgin Distribution

SUNSET NOW.
Single (7"): released on Virgin, Aug'84 by Virgin Records. Dist: EMI, Virgin Distribution Deleted '85.

Single (12"): released on Virgin, Aug'84 by Virgin Records. Dist: EMI, Virgin Distribution

THIS IS MINE.
Single (7"): released on Virgin, Oct'84 by Virgin Records. Dist: EMI, Virgin Distribution

Single (12"): released on Virgin, Oct'84 by Virgin Records. Dist: EMI, Virgin Distribution

TROUBLE.
Single (7"): released on Virgin, Jan'87 by Virgin Records. Dist: EMI, Virgin Distribution

Single (12"): released on Virgin, Jan'87 by Virgin Records. Dist: EMI, Virgin Distribution

WE DON'T NEED THIS FACIST GROOVE THING.
Single (7"): released on Virgin, Mar'81 by Virgin Records. Dist: EMI, Virgin Distribution

Heavenly Bodies

HEAVENLY BODIES Original Soundtrack (Various Artists).
Album: released on Epic, May'85 by CBS Records. Dist: CBS Deleted '87.

Cassette: released on Epic, May'85 by CBS Records. Dist: CBS

Heavenly Gospel Singers

1935-1940.
Album: released on Heritage, Jan'85 by Heritage Records. Dist: Chart

Heaven's Gate

HEAVENS GATE Original soundtrack.
Album: released on EMI (Holland), Jun'84 by EMI Records. Dist: Conifer

Cassette: released on EMI (Holland), Jun'84 by EMI Records. Dist: Conifer

Heavy

HEAVY Various groups (Various Artists).
Album: released on K-Tel, Jan'83 by K-Tel Records. Dist: Record Merchandisers Distribution, Taylors, Terry Blood Distribution, Wynd-Up Distribution, Relay Distribution, Pickwick Distribution, Solomon & Peres Distribution, Polygram

Cassette: released on K-Tel, Jan'83 by K-Tel Records. Dist: Record Merchandisers Distribution, Taylors, Terry Blood Distribution, Wynd-Up Distribution, Relay Distribution, Pickwick Distribution, Solomon & Peres Distribution, Polygram

Heavy D. & The Boys

MR.BIG STUFF.
Tracks: / Mr.Big Stuff / Mr.Big stuff (instrumental).
Single (7"): released on MCA, Nov'86 by MCA Records. Dist: Polygram, MCA

Single (12"): released on MCA, Nov'86 by MCA Records. Dist: Polygram, MCA

Heavy duty

HEAVY DUTY Various artists (Various Artists).
Album: released on Fame, May'85 by Music For Pleasure Records. Dist: EMI

Cassette: released on Fame, May'85 by Music For Pleasure Records. Dist: EMI

Heavy duty breaks

HEAVY DUTY BREAKS Various artists (Various Artists).

Album: released on Illuminated, Dec'84 by IKF Records. Dist: Pinnacle, Cartel, Jetstar

Cassette: released on Illuminated, Dec'84 by IKF Records. Dist: Pinnacle, Cartel, Jetstar

HEAVY DUTY BREAKS.
Single (12"): released on Illuminated, Feb'85 by IKF Records. Dist: Pinnacle, Cartel, Jetstar

Heavy Jelly

TAKE ME DOWN TO THE WATER.
Album: released on Psycho, Nov'84 Dist: Funhouse, Rough Trade

Heavy Metal

HEAVY METAL AMERICA various artists (Various Artists).
Album: released on Heavy Metal America, Apr'85 by FM-Revolver Records. Dist: EMI

Cassette: released on Heavy Metal America, Apr'85 by FM-Revolver Records. Dist: EMI

HEAVY METAL HEROES (VOL 2) various artists (Various Artists).
Album: released on Heavy Metal, Dec'82 by FM-Revolver Records. Dist: EMI

HEAVY METAL MONSTERS various artists (Various Artists).
Double Album: released on Cambra, Mar'85 by Cambra Records. Dist: IDS, Conifer

Double cassette: released on Cambra, Mar'85 by Cambra Records. Dist: IDS, Conifer

HEAVY METAL RECORDS (A TASTY TASTER) various artists (Various Artists).
Album: released on Heavy Metal, Dec'84 by FM-Revolver Records. Dist: EMI

Cassette: released on Heavy Metal, Dec'84 by FM-Revolver Records. Dist: EMI

HEAVY METAL THUNDER various artists (Various Artists).
Album: released on Carrere, Aug'82 by Carrere Records. Dist: PRT, Spartan

Cassette: released on Carrere, Aug'82 by Carrere Records. Dist: PRT, Spartan

HI DE HI various artists (Various Artists).
Album: released on BBC, Nov'81 by BBC Records & Tapes. Dist: EMI, PRT,

Cassette: released on BBC, Nov'81 by BBC Records & Tapes. Dist: EMI, PRT.

Heavy Metal Kids
CHELSEA KIDS.
Album: released on Razor, Aug'87 by Razor. Dist: Pinnacle

Heavy Pettin'
LOVE TIMES LOVE.
Single (7"): released on Polydor, Mar'84 by Polydor Records. Dist: Polygram, Polydor Deleted '84.

Single (12"): released on Polydor, Mar'84 by Polydor Records. Dist: Polygram, Polydor Deleted '84.

Picture disc single: released on Polydor, Mar'84 by Polydor Records. Dist: Polygram, Polydor

ROCK AIN'T DEAD.
Tracks: / Rock ain't dead / Sole survivor / China boy / Lost in love / Northwinds / Angel / Heart attack / Dream time / Walkin' with the angels / Throw a party / Crazy.
Compact disc: released on E.G., Jul'85 by Virgin Records. Dist: Virgin, EMI

ROLL THE DICE.
Single (7"): released on Neat, Aug'82 by Neat Records. Dist: Pinnacle, Neat

ROMEO.
Tracks: / Romeo / Don't call it love / City girl*.
Notes: * = Extra track on 12" only
Single (7"): released on Polydor, Apr'87 by Polydor Records. Dist: Polygram, Polydor

Single (12"): released on Polydor, Apr'87 by Polydor Records. Dist: Polygram, Polydor

SOLE SURVIVOR.
Single (7"): released on Polydor, Jun'85 by Polydor Records. Dist: Polygram, Polydor

Single (12"): released on Polydor, Jun'85 by Polydor Records. Dist: Polygram, Polydor

Heavy Rock
HEAVY ROCK (Various Artists).
Album: released on Vertigo, '81 by Phonogram Records. Dist: Polygram

Cassette: released on Vertigo, Jun'81 by Phonogram Records. Dist: Polygram

Heavy Traffic
HEAVY TRAFFIC STARRING "V" (Heavy Traffic Starring "V").
Tracks: / If you're gonna mess with me / S.O.S. (help me boy) / Jealousy / Fire is gone, The / Hand made love / Let's go crazy / You can't hurt me no more / Coming down with love / Promises in the dark / Deep in it.
Album: released on Atlantic, Apr'87 by WEA Records. Dist: WEA

Cassette: released on Atlantic, Apr'87 by WEA Records. Dist: WEA

Heavy Way
HEAVY WAY, THE Various hard-rock bands (Various Artists).
Tracks: / Last in line / Gotta let go / Seven seas / Between the wheels / Digital bitch / Rockin' all over the world / Breakout / Eternal dark / Lonely is the hunter / This month's massiah / Don't say make me / Rocker, The.
Notes: Strong compilation of international hard-rock bands. Distinctive sleeve. Total playing time 60 minutes.
Compact disc: released on Vertigo (Holland), Nov'84

Hebb, Bobby
SUNNY.
Single (7"): released on Old Gold, Jan'85 by Old Gold Records. Dist: Lightning, Jazz Music, Spartan, Counterpoint

Hebe
HEBE.
Album: released on H.M.V., Nov'85 by EMI

Records. Dist: EMI

Cassette: released on H.M.V., Nov'85 by EMI Records. Dist: EMI

Hebert, Adam
BEST OF ADAM HEBERT.
Album:

Hedda Gabler
HEDDA GABLER Plowright, J. (Ibsen, Henrik).
Album: released on Caedmon(USA), '74 by Caedmon (USA) Records. Dist: Gower, Taylors, Discovery

Cassette: released on Caedmon(USA), '74 by Caedmon (USA) Records. Dist: Gower, Taylors, Discovery

Hedgehog Pie
HEDGEHOG PIE.
Album: released on Rubber, Jun'82 by Rubber Records. Dist: Roots Distribution, Projection Distribution, Jazz Music Distribution, Celtic Music Distribution, JSU Distribution, Spartan Distribution

JUST ACT NORMAL.
Album: released on Rubber, Jun'82 by Rubber Records. Dist: Roots Distribution, Projection Distribution, Jazz Music Distribution, Celtic Music Distribution, JSU Distribution, Spartan Distribution

Hedgehoppers Anonymous
IT'S GOOD NEWS WEEK.
Single (7"): released on Old Gold, Apr'83 by Old Gold Records. Dist: Lightning, Jazz Music, Spartan, Counterpoint

Hedger, Alison
MARY ROSE SONG.
Single (7"): released on Golden Apple, Oct'82 by Golden Apple Records. Dist: Mary Rose Marketing Co.

Hedges, Chuck
CLARINET CLIMAX (Hedges, Chuck & Allan Vache).
Album: released on Jazzology (USA), Mar'84 Dist: Jazz Music, Swift

Hedges, Michael
AERIAL BOUNDARIES.
Compact disc: released on Windham Hill, Jan'86 Dist: AM

Album: released on Windham Hill, Nov'85 Dist: AM

Cassette: released on Windham Hill, Nov'85 Dist: AM

WATCHING MY LIFE GO BY.
Album: released on Windham Hill, Aug'87 Dist: AM

Cassette: released on Windham Hill, Aug'87 Dist: AM

Compact disc: released on Windham Hill, Aug'87 Dist: AM

Hedone
SENSIBLE.
Single (7"): released on On Gowa Power, Jun'84

Hee Bee Gee Bees
439 GOLDEN GREATS.
Album: released on Heebeegeebees, Sep'81 by Original. Dist: RCA

Cassette: released on Heebeegeebees, Sep'81 by Original. Dist: RCA

BORING SONGS (/Dead Cicada).
Notes: The Hee Bee Gee Bees under pseudonyms of Status Quid & The Beagles doing more send-ups of well-known groups.
Single (7"): released on Heebeegeebees, Nov'81 by Original. Dist: RCA

PURPLE PAINTS.
Single (7"): released on 10, Sep'85 by 10 Records. Dist: Virgin, EMI

RADIO ACTIVE.
Album: released on BBC, May'83 by BBC Records & Tapes. Dist: EMI, PRT,

Cassette: released on BBC, May'83 by BBC Records & Tapes. Dist: EMI, PRT,

TOO DEPRESSED TO COMMIT SUICIDE.
Single (7"): released on Heebeegeebees, Jan'83 by Original. Dist: RCA

Heera
JAGH WALA MELA.
Tracks: / Jithon de lachhi roj langdee / Mor nak wich coca paa glya / Nach lal haan diye / Dil

---

mera lal gayee / Jagh wala mela / 'Elna de naal ayee mitro / Munda moh lila / Sadaa putt rehan vasde / Lagdee too bottle jahee / Ter akh di ishare / Sajna da chhala mordke / Tere nee nashile naina ne.
Notes: Music composed and directed by Kuljit Bhamra. Distributed by Diamond Disc Productions UK, 20 Cranleigh Gardens, Southall, Middlesex. Tel: 01 574 4103.
Album: released on Diamond Discs, Nov'84 by Diamond Discs Records. Dist: Diamond Discs Records

Heffernen, Honor
STORMY WATERS.
Album: released on WEA Ireland, Jul'87 by WEA Records. Dist: Celtic Distributions, Projection, I & B

Cassette: released on WEA Ireland, Jul'87 by WEA Records. Dist: Celtic Distributions, Projection, I & B

Heff, Klaus
STERNENTANZA.
Album: released on Sky (Germany), Mar'84

Heffner, Nick
SNEAKY MOTHERS (THE).
Tracks: / Sneaky mothers (The) / Parking lot (The):World spinning sadley.
Notes: Double 'A' side
Single (7"): released on Bam Caruso, Apr'87 by Bam Caruso Records. Dist: Rough Trade, Revolver, Cartel

Heftl, Neal
BAND WITH YOUNG IDEAS, THE (Hefti, Neal & His Orchestra).
Album: released on Jasmine, Sep'83 by Jasmine Records. Dist: Counterpoint, Lugtons, Taylor, H.R., Wellard, Chris, Swift, Cadillac

Hefty Jazz
George Chisholm,Keith Smith and Hefty Jazz

Hegamin, Lucille
BLUE FLAME.
Album: released on VJM, Apr'79 by Wellard, Chris Distribution. Dist: Wellard, Chris Distribution

Hegarty, Dermot
21 YEARS.
Album: released on Harp(Ireland), Jul'81 by Pickwick Records. Dist: Taylors

CONNEMARA BY THE LAKE.
Album: released on Harp(Ireland), May'80 by Pickwick Records. Dist: Taylors

FAVOURITE TRADITIONAL MELODIES.
Album: released on Harp(Ireland), Aug'83 by Pickwick Records. Dist: Taylors

Cassette: released on Harp(Ireland), Aug'83 by Pickwick Records. Dist: Taylors

HITS OF IRELAND'S DERMOT HEGARTY - VOL.3.
Album: released on Release, Nov'76 by Release Records. Dist: I & B, Wynd-Up Distribution, Taylors, Solomon & Peres Distribution

IRISH STARTIME.
Album: released on Shannon, '78

Album: released on Irish Startime, Jan'78 Dist: I & B

Heibel
YEAH, EVERYTHING'S GREAT.
Album: released on Children Of The Revolution, Nov'86 by Revolver Records. Dist: Revolver, Cartel

Heidi
HEIDI By Johanna Spyri (Dench, Judi).
Double cassette: released on Argo (Spokenword), Jul'82 by Decca Records. Dist: Polygram

HEIDI By Johanna Spyri (Clark, Petula).
Double cassette: released on Listen For Pleasure, Oct'82 by MFP Records. Dist: EMI

RELATIONSHIPS.
Tracks: / Lizzie Anne.
Single (7"): released on Splinter, Mar'86 by Splinter

Heidt, Horace
1939 (Heidt, Horace & His Musical Knights).
Album: released on Hindsight(USA), Mar'84 by Hindsight Records (USA). Dist: Swift, Charly

Heild, Hehemiah
YOUR BODY'S HERE WITH ME.
Single (12"): released on Joe Gibbs, Sep'83 by Joe Gibbs Records. Dist: Jetstar

---

Helloo, Ronald
IN TIMES OF PANIC.
Single (7"): released on Amphibious, Jun'82

Heinz
JUST LIKE EDDIE.
Single (7"): released on Decca, Mar'82 by Decca Records. Dist: Polygram

Single (7"): released on Old Gold, Oct'83 by Old Gold Records. Dist: Lightning, Jazz Music, Spartan, Counterpoint

REMEMBERING.
Album: released on Decca, Jun'77 by Decca Records. Dist: Polygram

Heinz & The Tornados
HEINZ & THE TORNADOS.
Album: released on Decca (Rock Echoes), Mar'82 by Decca Records. Dist: Polygram, IMS

Cassette: released on Decca (Rock Echoes), Mar'82 by Decca Records. Dist: Polygram, IMS

Heinz & The Wild Boys
THAT'S THE WAY IT WAS.
Album: released on Rock Machine, Jan'87 by Razor Records. Dist: Pinnacle

Heir Apparent
GRACEFUL INHERITANCE.
Album: released on Black Dragon, Feb'86 by Black Dragon Records. Dist: Rough Trade

Heist
HEIST.
Single (12"): released on NV, Feb'86 Dist: Rough Trade Distribution, Cartel Distribution

Heist, Marco Van
SONG FOR THE FALKLANDS.
Single (7"): released on Disques Markel, Jun'82

Helaire, Nonc
FOR KOONASSES ONLY - VOLUME 1.
Album:

FOR KOONASSES ONLY - VOLUME 2.
Album:

Helden
HOLDING ON.
Single (7"): released on Zica, Nov'83 by Zica Records. Dist: Spartan

Single (12"): released on Zica, Nov'83 by Zica Records. Dist: Spartan

Heldon
HELDON 1.
Album: released on Cobra, Sep'79 by Cobra Records. Dist: Projection, EMI

INTERFACE.
Album: released on Cobra, Sep'79 by Cobra Records. Dist: Projection, EMI

STAND BY.
Album: released on Egg, Nov'79 Dist: Red Rhino, Cartel

UN REVE SANS CONSEQUENCE SPECIAL.
Album: released on Cobra, Sep'79 by Cobra Records. Dist: Projection, EMI

Helena
BE SOFT WITH ME TONIGHT.
Tracks: / Be soft with me tonight / Love that's real.
Single (7"): released on Arista, Feb'87 by Arista Records. Dist: RCA

Single (12"): released on Arista, Feb'87 by Arista Records. Dist: RCA

Cassette: released on BBC, May'80 by BBC Records & Tapes. Dist: EMI, PRT,

I WANT YOU.
Tracks: / Love that's real.
Single (7"): released on Arista, Sep'86 by Arista Records. Dist: RCA

Single (12"): released on Arista, Sep'86 by Arista Records. Dist: RCA

Helen & The Horns
FREIGHT TRAIN.
Single (7"): released on Thin Sliced, Feb'84 by Thin Sliced Records. Dist: Rough Trade Distribution, Cartel Distribution

HELEN AND THE HORNS.
Album: released on Rockin' Ray, Mar'85 Dist: Backs, Cartel Distribution

Helfer, Erwin
BOOGIE PIANO - CHICAGO-STYLE.
Album: released on Big Bear, '82 by Big Bear Records. Dist: Big Bear, Swift

Helgason, Johann
TAKE YOUR TIME.
Single (7"): released on Steinar, Nov'84

Helius Creed
X-RATED FAIRY TALES.
Album: released on Fundamental, Aug'86 by Fundamental Records. Dist: Red Rhino, Cartel

Helix
GIMME GOOD LOVIN'.
Picture disc single: released on Capitol, Jan'85 by Capitol Records. Dist: EMI

LONG WAY TO HEAVEN.
Album: released on Capitol, Sep'85 by Capitol Records. Dist: EMI

Cassette: released on Capitol, Sep'85 by Capitol Records. Dist: EMI

NO REST FOR THE WICKED.
Album: released on Capitol, Aug'83 by Capitol Records. Dist: EMI Deleted '85.

Cassette: released on Capitol, Aug'83 by Capitol Records. Dist: EMI

VIDEO EP.
Video-cassette (VHS): released on PMI, Jun'86 by PMI Records. Dist: EMI

Video-cassette (Betamax): released on PMI, Jun'86 by PMI Records. Dist: EMI

WHITE LACE AND BLACK LEATHER.
Album: released on Logo, Jun'82 by Logo Records. Dist: Roots, BMG

Hell
SAVE US (FROM THOSE WHO WOULD SAVE US).
Single (7"): by Deadly Weapon Records. Dist: Pinnacle

Hellanbach
BIG...H, (THE).
Album: released on Neat, '85 by Neat Records. Dist: Pinnacle, Neat

NOW HEAR THIS.
Album: released on Neat, '85 by Neat Records. Dist: Pinnacle, Neat

Hellborg, Jonas
AXIS.
Album: released on Eight Music, Jun'86

Hell Can Be Heaven
HELL CAN BE HEAVEN Original cast recording (Various Artists).
Album: released on TER, Dec'83 Dist: Pinnacle

Cassette: released on TER, Dec'83 Dist: Pinnacle

Hell comes to your house
HELL COMES TO YOUR HOUSE Various artists (Various Artists).
Album: released on Riot City, Jun'82 by Riot City Records. Dist: Revolver

Album: released on Music For Nations, Jul'84 by Music For Nations Records. Dist: Pinnacle

Cassette: released on Music For Nations, Jun'85 by Music For Nations Records. Dist: Pinnacle

Heller, Martin
FOUR FEATHERS.
Cassette: released on Colophone, Jun'81 by Audio-Visual Library Services. Dist: Audio-Visual Library Services

Hellion
HELLION.
Album: released on Music For Nations, Jan'84 by Music For Nations Records. Dist: Pinnacle

SCREAMS IN THE NIGHT.
Album: released on Music For Nations, Mar'87 by Music For Nations Records. Dist: Pinnacle

Hell is always today
HELL IS ALWAYS TODAY (Mackenzie, Michael).
Cassette: released on Colophone, Jun'81 by Audio-Visual Library Services. Dist: Audio-Visual Library Services

Hello
GLAM YEARS 1971-1979, THE.
Tracks: / New York groove / Love stealer /

Game's up / Good old USA / Round and round / You move me / C'mon / Machine-gun hustle / Oh Caroline / Shine on silver light / Tell him / Star studded sham / Let it rock / Seven rainy days / Whole lotta woman / 99 ways / Back seat talking / Dean / You shot me down / Feel this thing.
Album: released on Biff, Sep'87 by Blaylock Management Ltd.. Dist: Revolver

NEW YORK GROOVE.
Single (7"): released on Old Gold, Jan'85 by Old Gold Records. Dist: Lightning, Jazz Music, Spartan, Counterpoint

Hello Dolly
HELLO DOLLY Original film soundtrack.
Album: released on Polydor (Italy), May'84

Cassette: released on Polydor (Italy), May'84

Helloise
COSMOGONY.
Tracks: / Cosmogony / Broken hearts / Run a mile / Die hard / Ready for the night / For a moment / Gates of heaven / Hard life.
Album: released on WEA, Mar'86 by WEA Records. Dist: WEA

Cassette: released on WEA, Mar'86 by WEA Records. Dist: WEA

Hell on earth
HELL ON EARTH Various heavy metal groups (Various Artists).
Album: released on Music For Nations, Nov'83 by Music For Nations Records. Dist: Pinnacle

Helloween
HELLOWEEN Mini LP.
Album:

KEEPER OF THE SEVEN KEYS.
Album:

WALLS OF JERICHO.
Album: released on Noise, Dec'85 by Dorane. Dist: Revolver, Cartel

Hell's Belles
BARRICADES.
Single (7"): released on Raw Power, Feb'86 Dist: Pinnacle

Single (12"): released on Raw Power, Feb'86 Dist: Pinnacle

HELL'S BELLES.
Tracks: / Looks like love / Overload / Desire me / Screaming for mercy / Hell's belles / Barricades / Strange love / Dirty girls / Storm break loose / Long legs.
Notes: Bar code: 5 013428 140154 All tracks written by Hell's Belles. Produced by Phil McWalter and John A Rivers for lateral management international. All songs published by Castle Communications PLC except for the title track.
Album: released on Raw Power, Apr'86 Dist: Pinnacle

Cassette: released on Raw Power, Apr'86 Dist: Pinnacle

Hells bent on rockin'
HELLS BENT ON ROCKIN' Various artists (Various Artists).
Album: released on Nervous, May'85 by Nervous Records. Dist: Nervous, Rough Trade

Hellstar
REMNANTS OF WAR.
Album: released on Noise, Jul'86 by Dorane. Dist: Revolver, Cartel

Helms, Jimmy
GONNA MAKE YOU AN OFFER.
Single (7"): released on Cube, Jan'84 by Dakota Records. Dist: PRT

Single (12"): released on Cube, Jan'84 by Dakota Records. Dist: PRT

Helmut & Elisabeth
GENTLE BREEZE.
Album: released on Key, May'79 by Key Records. Dist: Spartan

Helpin, Kieran
MAN WHO LIVES IN BOTTLES, (THE).
Album: released on Celtic Music, Mar'84 by Celtic Music Distribution. Dist: Celtic Music, Jazz Music, Projection, Roots

Help me make it...
HELP ME MAKE IT THROUGH THE NIGHT Various artists (Various Artists).
Album: released on MFP, Jul'85 by EMI Records. Dist: EMI

Cassette: released on MFP, Jul'85 by EMI Records. Dist: EMI

Helstar
BURNING STAR.
Album: released on Music For Nations, Apr'84 by Music For Nations Records. Dist: Pinnacle

Helvette Underground
HELVETTE UNDERGROUND Various artists (Various Artists).
Cassette: released on Helvette Underground, Nov'84 by Helvette Underground Records. Dist: Falling A Distribution, Backs, Cartel

Hemet High Jazz Band
TIME AFTER TIME.
Album: released on AM-PM USA, Aug'84 Dist: Swift

Hemifran, Vykort
HEMIFRAN, VYKORT Various artists (Various Artists).
Album: released on ARC (Accordion Records), '84 Dist: Accordion Record Club

Hemlock Cock & Bull Band
ALL BUTTONED UP.
Album: released on Topic Records, Jul'81

Hemphill, Julius
BUSTER BEE (Hemphill, Julius & Oliver Lake).
Album: released on Sackville, Dec'79 Dist: JSU, Jazz Music, Jazz Horizons, Cadillac Music, Celtic Music, Swift

COON BID'NESS.
Album: released on Freedom, May'79 by Logo Records. Dist: RCA, Discovery, Wellard, Chris

LIVE IN NEW YORK.
Album: released on Red Records, May'79

RAW MATERIALS AND RESIDUALS.
Album: released on Black Saint, Jul'78 Dist: Projection, IMS, Polygram, Chris Wellard, Harmonia Mundi, Swift

Rio Boye & The Gotham Minstrels
RIO BOI & THE GOTHAM MINSTRELS.

ROI BOYE & THE GOTHAM MINSTRELS.
Double Album: released on Sackville, Jul'86 Dist: JSU, Jazz Music, Jazz Horizons, Cadillac Music, Celtic Music, Swift

Double Album: released on Sackville, Apr'81 Dist: JSU, Jazz Music, Jazz Horizons, Cadillac Music, Celtic Music, Swift

Henderson, Bill
TRIBUTE TO JOHNNY MERCER, (A).
Album: released on Discovery (USA), Jan'84

Cassette: released on Discovery (USA), Jan'84

Henderson, Finis
FINIS.
Album: released on Motown, Jul'83 by Motown Records. Dist: BMG Distribution

Cassette: released on Motown, Jul'83 by Motown Records. Dist: BMG Distribution

SKIP TO MY LOU.
Single (7"): released on Motown, Jul'83 by Motown Records. Dist: BMG Distribution

Single (12"): released on Gordy (USA), Jun'83 by Motown Records. Dist: RCA

Henderson, Fletcher
1950.
Album: released on Solid Sender, Apr'81 Dist: JSU, Jazz Music

CROWN KING OF SWING,THE.
Tracks: / After you've gone / Stardust / Tiger rag / Somebody stole my gal / You rascal you / Blue rhythm / Sugar foot stomp / Low down on the bayou / Twelfth street rag / Milenberg joys.
Album: released on Savoy (USA), Nov'85 by Arista Records. Dist: Polygram, Swift

Cassette: released on Savoy (USA), Nov'85 by Arista Records. Dist: Polygram, Swift

DIXIE STOMPERS, THE (1925-26).
DIXIE STOMPERS, THE (1927-28).
Album: released on Swaggie (Australia), Jan'83

DIXIE STOMPERS, THE (1925-26).
Album: released on Swaggie (Australia), Jan'83

END OF AN ERA VOLUME 1,THE.
Album: released on Swingtime, Jun'86 Dist: Jazz Music Distribution

FLETCHER HENDERSON'S ORCHESTRA 1923/24.
Album: released on VJM, Apr'79 by Wellard, Chris Distribution. Dist: Wellard, Chris Distribu-

tion

FLETCHER HENDERSON'S ORCHESTRA 1924/6.
Album: released on VJM, Apr'79 by Wellard, Chris Distribution. Dist: Wellard, Chris Distribution

FLETCHER HENDERSON STORY.
Album: released on CBS(Import), Jun'86 by CBS Records. Dist: Conifer, Discovery, Swift

FLETCHER HENDERSON ORCHESTRA.
Album: released on Joker, Apr'81 Dist: Counterpoint, Mainline, Record Services Distribution (Ireland)

FLETCHER HENDERSON & CONNIE'S INN ORCHESTRA 1931.
Album: released on Swing Classics (Import), Jul'82 Dist: Jazz Music Distribution, Swift

FLETCHER HENDERSON 1926-30.
Album: released on VJM, Apr'79 by Wellard, Chris Distribution. Dist: Wellard, Chris Distribution

FLETCHER HENDERSON & HIS ORCHESTRA 1923/5.
Album: released on Fountain, Apr'79 by Retrieval Records. Dist: Jazz Music, Swift, VJM, Wellard, Chris, Retrieval

INDISPENSABLE FLETCHER HENDERSON (1927-36).
Tracks: / Shufflin' Sadie / St.Louis Shuffle / St.Louis Shuffle... / Variety stomp / Variety Stomp. / Sugar foot stomp / Roll on Mississippi, roll on. / Moan, you moaners / Singing the blues / Oh, it looks like rain / Sweet music / My sweet tooth says I wanna / Malinda's Wedding Day / Strangers / Take me away from the river / I wanna count sheep / Poor old Joe / Hocus Pocus / Phantom fantasie / Harlem madness / Tidal wave / I'm a fool for loving you / Jangled nerves / Where there's you there's me / Do you or don't you love me / Grand terrace rhythm / Riffin' / Mary had a little lamb / Shoe shine boy / Sing, sing, sing. / Until today / Knock, knock who's there / Jim town blues / You can depend on me.
Notes: Double Album; Double Cassette; Mono.
Double Album: released on Jazz Tribune (USA), Sep'86 Dist: Discovery

Double cassette: released on Jazz Tribune (USA), Sep'86 Dist: Discovery

INDISPENSABLE FLETCHER HENDERSON (1927-1936), THE.
Double Album: released on RCA (France), '83 by RCA Records. Dist: Discovery

LOUIS ARMSTRONG & FLETCHER HENDERSON 1924/5.
Album: released on VJM, Jun'73 by Wellard, Chris Distribution. Dist: Wellard, Chris Distribution

ON COLUMBIA.
Album: released on USA Import, Aug'81

PATHE SESSIONS, THE (1923-25 - WITH HIS ORCHESTRA).
Album: released on Swaggie (Australia), Jan'83

RARE FLETCHER HENDERSON MASTERPIECES.
Album: released on VJM, Apr'79 by Wellard, Chris Distribution. Dist: Wellard, Chris Distribution

VERY FIRST & THE RAREST, THE.
Album: released on Jazz Live, Apr'81

WILD PARTY.
Album: released on Hep, Mar'85 by H.R. Taylor Records. Dist: Jazz Music, Cadillac Music, JSU, Taylors, Wellard, Chris, Zodiac, Swift, Fast Forward

Henderson, Greg
DREAMIN'.
Single (7"): released on Greyhound, Sep'84 by Greyhound Records. Dist: PRT, Greyhound

DREAMIN'/DREAMIN'(INSTRUMENTAL).
Single (12"): released on Greyhound, Nov'82 by Greyhound Records. Dist: PRT, Greyhound

Henderson, Joe
BARCELONA.
Album: released on Enja (Germany), Jan'82 by Enja Records (W.Germany). Dist: Cadillac Music

INNER URGE.
Album: released on Blue Note (USA), Sep'84

IN 'N' OUT.
Album: released on Blue Note (USA), Sep'84
Cat.no: BST 84166

IN'N'OUT.
Tracks: / In'n'out / Punjab / Serenity / Short story / Brown's Town.
Notes: Produced by Alfred Lion

Compact disc: released on Manhattan-Blue Note, Apr'87 by EMI America Records (USA). Dist: EMI

MIRROR MIRROR (Henderson, Joe & Chick Corea).
Album: released on MPS Jazz, May'81

MODE FOR JOE.
Album: released on Blue Note, Apr'85 by EMI Records. Dist: EMI

MYSTIFIED (Henderson, Joe, Tom, Rick Laird & Ron Steen).
Album: released on Timeless(import), Apr'81 Dist: Cadillac

OUR THING.
Tracks: / Teeter totter / Pedro's time / Our thing / Black road / Escape.
Notes: The collaboration of Joe Henderson and Kenny Dorham always produced electrifyingand complex, but always appealing straight ahead jazz. On this, their rarest ofalbums with Andrew Hill on piano, they move through Dorham's marvellous, intir- cate 'Escape' and the funky title tune and Latin cooker 'Pedro's Time'.
Album: released on Blue Note, Dec'85 by EMI Records. Dist: EMI

RELAXIN' AT CAMARILLO.
Album: released on Contemporary Jazz, Jul'81

SOFT FOCUS (Henderson, Joe, Tom, Rick Laird & Ron Steen).
Album: released on Timeless(import), Apr'81 Dist: Cadillac

STATE OF THE TENOR LIVE AT THE VILLAGE, THE.
Tracks: / Boo boo's birthday / Cheryl / Y ya la quiero / Soulville / Portrait / Bead game, The / All the things you are.
Compact disc: released on Manhattan-Blue Note, Jun'87 by EMI America Records (USA). Dist: EMI

STATE OF THE TENOR (THE).
Tracks: / Boo Boo's birthday / Cheryl / Ya la Quiero / Soulville / Portrait / Bead game (The).
Notes: The first volume of tenor saxophonist Joe Henderson's live Village Vanguard recording, accompanied only by bassist Ron Carter and drummer Al Foster, has already been critically acclaimed as his finest album and one of the most important albums in the history of Blue Note Records. Volume2, concieved simultaneously with the first album, is equally strong and daring, but it is not so challenging that it loses it's appeal in the process. Horace Silver's "Soulville" is a silky, sensual performance in the hands of this great tenor saxophonist. Charlie Mingus' ."Portrait" is a moving ballad of classic dimension, while Henderson's own "Ya la Quiero" is a rousing Latin cooker. Also featured are compositions by Thelonious Monk and Charlie Parker.
Album: released on Blue Note, Mar'87 by EMI Records. Dist: EMI

Henderson, Kelvin

DOOR IS ALWAYS OPEN, THE.
Single (7"): released on Buffalo (UK), Mar'79

FROM A JACK TO A KING.
Single (7"): released on Country Roads Records, Jun'81 by Country Roads Records. Dist: Stage One

HEADLITES.
Album: released on Country Roads Records, Nov'81 by Country Roads Records. Dist: Stage One

Henderson, Maggie

RAGTIME (Henderson, Maggie & F.Harris).
Album: released on BBC, Oct'74 by BBC Records & Tapes. Dist: EMI, PRT.

Henderson, Michael

FICKLE.
Album: released on Buddah, Jul'83 Dist: Swift, Jazz Music, PRT

FICKLE/INSTRUMENTAL VERSION.
Single (7"): released on Buddah, May'83 Dist: Swift, Jazz Music, PRT

Single (12"): released on Buddah, May'83 Dist: Swift, Jazz Music, PRT

GOIN' PLACES.
Album: released on Buddah, Jan'78 Dist: Swift, Jazz Music, PRT

IN THE NIGHT TIME.
Album: released on Buddah, Sep'78 Dist: Swift, Jazz Music, PRT

WIDE RECEIVER.
Album: released on Buddah, Oct'80 Dist: Swift, Jazz Music, PRT

WIDE RECEIVER/I CAN'T HELP IT.
Single (7"): released on Buddah, Sep'80 Dist: Swift, Jazz Music, PRT

Single (12"): released on Buddah, Sep'80 Dist: Swift, Jazz Music, PRT

Henderson, Murray

WORLD'S GREATEST PIPERS VOL.4, THE.
Album: released on Lismor, Jul'87 by Lismor Records. Dist: Lismor, Roots, Celtic Music

Henderson, Phil

SECRET PICTURES.
Tracks: / Secret pictures / Deckchairs in the rain.
Single (7"): released on Splash, Oct'86 by Splash Records. Dist: CBS

Hendon Band

BRASS SENTIMENTAL STYLE.
Album: released on Chandos, Aug'81 by Chandos Records. Dist: Harmonia Mundi, Taylors

Cassette: released on Chandos, Aug'81 by Chandos Records. Dist: Harmonia Mundi, Taylors

Hendricks, Barbara

NEGRO SPRITUALS.
Album: released on EMI, Nov'83 by EMI Records. Dist: EMI

Cassette: released on EMI, Nov'83 by EMI Records. Dist: EMI

Hendricks, Jon & Co

LOVE.
Tracks: / Royal garden blues / Bright moments / Willie's tune / Good ol' lady / Lil darlin' / I'll die happy / Love (Berkshire blues) / Tell me the truth / Swinging groove merchant(groove merchant),The / Angel eyes / In a Harlem airshaft (Harlem airshaft).
Notes: Artists: Michele Hendricks/Judity Hendricks/Bob Gurland/Leslie Dorsey. Produced by Jon Hendricks.
Album: released on Muse (USA), Sep'86 by Muse Records (USA). Dist: Conifer Distribution, Jazz Music Distribution

Cassette: released on Muse (USA), Sep'86 by Muse Records (USA). Dist: Conifer Distribution, Jazz Music Distribution

Hendriks, Gijs Quartet

CLOSE TO THE EDGE.
Album: released on Timeless, Sep'86

CLOSE TO THE EDGE..
Album: released on Timeless, Apr'81

DOM ROCKET.
Album: released on Timeless, Sep'86

DOM ROCKET.
Album: released on Timeless, Apr'81

Hendrix, Jimi

10TH ANNIVERSARY BOX.
Boxed set: released on Polydor, Sep'80 by Polydor Records. Dist: Polygram, Polydor

20 GOLDEN PIECES OF JIMI HENDRIX.
Album: released on Bulldog Records, Jul'82

20 GOLDEN PIECES OF JIMI HENDRIX: VOL 2.
Album: released on Bulldog Records, Nov'82

ALL ALONG THE WATCH TOWER (Hendrix Experience, Jimi).
Single (7"): released on Old Gold, Jul'84 by Old Gold Records. Dist: Lightning, Jazz Music, Spartan, Counterpoint

ARE YOU EXPERIENCED.
Tracks: / Foxy lady / Manic depression / Red house / Can you see me / Love or confusion / I don't live today / May this be love / Fire / 3rd stone from the sun / Remember / Are you experienced.
Compact disc: released on Track, Apr'85 by Polydor Records. Dist: Polygram

ARE YOU EXPERIENCED?.
Album: released on Polydor, Nov'81 by Polydor Records. Dist: Polygram, Polydor

Album: released on Polydor, Sep'85 by Polydor Records. Dist: Polygram, Polydor

Cassette: released on Polydor, Sep'85 by Polydor Records. Dist: Polygram, Polydor

Compact disc: released on Polydor, Sep'85 by Polydor Records. Dist: Polygram, Polydor

AT ISLE OF WIGHT.
Album: released on Polydor, Apr'84 by Polydor Records. Dist: Polygram, Polydor

Cassette: released on Polydor, Apr'84 by Polydor Records. Dist: Polygram, Polydor

AXIS BOLD AS LOVE.
Album: released on Polydor, Aug'83 by Polydor Records. Dist: Polygram, Polydor

Cassette: released on Polydor, Aug'83 by Polydor Records. Dist: Polygram, Polydor

BAND OF GYPSIES.
Compact disc: released on Track, Jul'84 by Polydor Records. Dist: Polygram

BAND OF GYSIES.
Album: released on Track, Aug'83 by Polydor Records. Dist: Polygram

Cassette: released on Track, Aug'83 by Polydor Records. Dist: Polygram

Compact disc: released on Track, Jul'84 by Polydor Records. Dist: Polygram

BEST OF JIMI HENDRIX, THE.
Tracks: / Who knows / Machine gun / Hear my train a'comin' / Foxy lady / Power to love / Message of love / Voodoo child / Stone free / Ezy ryder.
Compact disc: released on EMI, May'87 by EMI Records. Dist: EMI

CONCERTS.
Album: released on CBS, Sep'84 by CBS Records. Dist: CBS

Cassette: released on CBS, Sep'84 by CBS Records. Dist: CBS Deleted '87.

COSMIC TURNAROUND.
Album: released on Audio Fidelity, Feb'82 Dist: PRT

Cassette: released on Audio Fidelity, Feb'82 Dist: PRT

CRASH LANDING.
Album: released on Polydor, Mar'83 by Polydor Records. Dist: Polygram, Polydor

Cassette: released on Polydor, Mar'83 by Polydor Records. Dist: Polygram, Polydor

CRASH LANDING/MIDNIGHT LIGHTNING.
Cassette: released on Polydor, Jun'83 by Polydor Records. Dist: Polygram, Polydor

CRY OF LOVE.
Album: released on Polydor, '74 by Polydor Records. Dist: Polygram, Polydor

Cassette: released on Polydor, '74 by Polydor Records. Dist: Polygram, Polydor

Album: released on Polydor, Sep'85 by Polydor Records. Dist: Polygram, Polydor

Cassette: released on Polydor, Sep'85 by Polydor Records. Dist: Polygram, Polydor

ELECTRIC LADYLAND VOL 1.
Album: released on Polydor, '74 by Polydor Records. Dist: Polygram, Polydor Deleted '83.

ELECTRIC LADYLAND VOL 2.
Album: released on Polydor, '74 by Polydor Records. Dist: Polygram, Polydor

ELECTRIC LADYLAND.
Tracks: / And the gods made love / Electric ladyland / Voodoo Chile / Crosstown traffic / Still raining / House burning down / Along the watchtower / Long hot summer night / Little Miss Strange / Come on / Gipsy eyes / Burning of the midnight lamp / Rainy day / 1983 / Moon turn the tides / Gently away.
Double compact disc: released on Track, Nov'84 by Polydor Records. Dist: Polygram

Album: released on Polydor, Jan'84 by Polydor Records. Dist: Polygram, Polydor

Cassette: released on Polydor, Jan'84 by Polydor Records. Dist: Polygram, Polydor

Compact disc: released on Polydor, Jan'84 by Polydor Records. Dist: Polygram, Polydor

ESSENTIAL JIMI HENDRIX, (THE).
Double Album: released on Polydor, Jul'78 by Polydor Records. Dist: Polygram, Polydor

Double cassette: released on Polydor, Jul'78 by Polydor Records. Dist: Polygram, Polydor Deleted '86.

EXPERIENCE.
Compact disc: released on Bulldog, Jan'87 by Bulldog Records. Dist: President Distribution, Spartan, Swift, Taylor, H.R.

EXPERIENCE Original sound track from the motion picture (Hendrix,Jimi accompanied by Mitch Mitchell and Noel Redding).
Album: released on Bulldog, Jul'82 by Bulldog Records. Dist: President Distribution, Spartan, Swift, Taylor, H.R.

FREE SPIRIT..
Album: released on Phoenix, Dec'81 by Audio Fidelity Enterprises. Dist: Stage One,

FREE SPIRIT.
Album: released on Thunderbolt, Jun'87 by Magnum Music Group Ltd. Dist: Magnum Music Group Ltd, PRT Distribution, Spartan Distribution

GANGSTER OF LOVE.
Tracks: / Gangster of love / Let me go / Voice in the wind / Two + one goes / Good times / She's so fine / Soul food / Freedom and you / Win your love / Voices.
Album: released on Topline, Jan'86 by Charly Records. Dist: Charly Distribution

Cassette: released on Topline, Jan'86 by Charly Records. Dist: Charly Distribution

GANGSTER OF LOVE..
Album: released on Charly, Jul'85 by Charly Records. Dist: Charly, Cadillac

Cassette: released on Charly, Jul'85 by Charly Records. Dist: Charly, Cadillac

HENDRIX IN THE WEST.
Album: released on Polydor, '74 by Polydor Records. Dist: Polygram, Polydor

HEY JOE..
Album: released on Polydor (Import), Oct'83

Cassette: released on Polydor (Import), Oct'83

HEY JOE.
Single (7"): released on Polydor/Dreyfus (USA), Sep'80 by Polygram Records. Dist: Polygram

IN THE BEGINNING.
Album: released on Premier, '84 by Premier Records. Dist: CBS

Cassette: released on Premier, '84 by Premier Records. Dist: CBS

JIMI HENDRIX.
Notes: Number of tracks: Type of recordin: Documentary. Total playing time: 98 minutes
Video-cassette (VHS): released on Warner Home Video, Jun'86 by Warner Bros Records. Dist: WEA

Video-cassette [Betamax]: released on Warner Home Video, Jun'86 by Warner Bros Records. Dist: WEA

JIMI HENDRIX..
Album: released on Dakota, Oct'82 by Dakota Records. Dist: PRT

Cassette: released on Dakota, Oct'82 by Dakota Records. Dist: PRT

JIMI HENDRIX ALBUM, (THE).
Album: released on Contour, Nov'83 by Pickwick Records. Dist: Pickwick Distribution, PRT

Cassette: released on Contour, Nov'83 by Pickwick Records. Dist: Pickwick Distribution, PRT

JIMI HENDRIX LIVE.
Album: released on Polydor (Import), Mar'84

Cassette: released on Polydor (Import), Mar'84

JIMI HENDRIX: PROFILE.
Album: released on Teldec (Germany), Dec'81 by Import Records. Dist: IMS Distribution, Polygram Distribution

Cassette: released on Teldec (Germany), Dec'81 by Import Records. Dist: IMS Distribution, Polygram Distribution

JIMI HENDRIX: VOL 1.
Cassette: released on Audio Fidelity, Oct'84 Dist: PRT

JIMI HENDRIX: VOL 2.
Cassette: released on Audio Fidelity, Oct'84 Dist: PRT

JIMI HENDRIX:VOL 3.
Cassette: released on Audio Fidelity, Oct'84 Dist: PRT

JIMI PLAYS MONTEREY.
Tracks: / Killing floor / Foxey lady / Like a rolling stone / Rock me baby / Hey Joe / Can you see me / Wind cries Mary,The / Purple Haze / Wild thing.
Album: released on Polydor, Feb'86 by Polydor Records. Dist: Polygram, Polydor

Cassette: released on Polydor, Feb'86 by Polydor Records. Dist: Polygram, Polydor

Compact disc: released on Polydor, Feb'86 by Polydor Records. Dist: Polygram, Polydor

JOHNNY B.GOODE.
Tracks: / Voodoo Chile / Johnny B.Goode / All along the watchtower / Star spangled banner,The / Machine Gun.
Album: released on Fame, Aug'86 by Music For Pleasure Records. Dist: EMI

Cassette: released on Fame, Aug'86 by Music For Pleasure Records. Dist: EMI

Album: released on Fame, Oct'86 by Music For Pleasure Records. Dist: EMI

JOHNNY B. GOODE (VIDEO).
Notes: Released on Virgin/PVG . 25 minutes

KISS THE SKY.
Tracks: / Are you experienced / I don't live today / Voodoo Chile / Stepping stone / Castles made

of sand / Killing floor / Purple haze / Red house / Crowntown traffic / All along the watchtower.
Compact disc: released on Polydor, Jan'85 by Polydor Records. Dist: Polygram, Polydor

Album: released on Polydor, Nov'84 by Polydor Records. Dist: Polygram, Polydor Deleted '86.

Cassette: released on Polydor, Nov'84 by Polydor Records. Dist: Polygram, Polydor

Compact disc: released on Polydor, Nov'84 by Polydor Records. Dist: Polygram, Polydor

LEGENDARY JIMI HENDRIX, (THE).
Album: released on Polydor (Import), Oct'82

Cassette: released on Polydor (Import), Oct'82

LEGENDS OF ROCK.
Album: released on Telefunken (Germany), Apr'84 Dist: Decca Distribution, IMS Polygram

LEGEND, THE.
Album: released on Arcade Music Gala, Apr'86 Dist: Stage One

Cassette: released on Arcade Music Gala, Apr'86 Dist: Stage One

LIVE AT WINTERLAND.
Album: released on Polydor, Jul'87 by Polydor Records. Dist: Polygram, Polydor

Cassette: released on Polydor, Jul'87 by Polydor Records. Dist: Polygram, Polydor

MOODS.
Album: released on Phoenix, Oct'82 by Audio Fidelity Enterprises. Dist: Stage One, Lugtons

MORE EXPERIENCE.
Album: released on Bulldog Records, Jul'82

PLAYS BERKELEY.
Notes: Number of tracks:9. Type of recording: Live. Total playing time: 50 minutes.
Video-cassette (VHS): released on Palace, Jan'86 Dist: PVG

PURPLE HAZE (Hendrix Experience, Jimi).
Single (7"): released on Old Gold, Jul'84 by Old Gold Records. Dist: Lightning, Jazz Music, Spartan, Counterpoint

RAINBOW BRIDGE.
Compact disc: released on Reprise, Jan'87 by WEA Records. Dist: WEA

RAINBOW BRIDGE Soundtrack.
Album: released on Reprise, '74 by WEA Records. Dist: WEA

Cassette: released on Reprise, '74 by WEA Records. Dist: WEA

RARE HENDRIX.
Album: released on Enterprise, '76 by President Records. Dist: President Distribution, Jazz Music, Taylors, Spartan

RE-EXPERIENCED.
Double Album: released on Polydor (Import), May'83

REPLAY ON.
Album: released on Sierra, May'86 by Sierra Records. Dist: WEA

Cassette: released on Sierra, May'86 by Sierra Records. Dist: WEA

ROOTS OF HENDRIX.
Album: released on Phoenix, Oct'82 by Audio Fidelity Enterprises. Dist: Stage One, Lugtons

SINGLES ALBUM, THE.
Tracks: / Hey Joe / Stone free / Purple haze / wind cries Mary / 51st Anniversary / Highway Chile / Burning of the midnight lamp / Stars that play with laughing Sam's dice / All along the watchtower / Long hot summer night / Crosstown traffic / Let me light your fire.
Compact disc: released on Polydor, Apr'86 by Polydor Records. Dist: Polygram, Polydor

Album: released on Polydor, Feb'83 by Polydor Records. Dist: Polygram, Polydor

Cassette: released on Polydor, Feb'83 by Polydor Records. Dist: Polygram, Polydor

SMASH HITS.
Tracks: / Burning of the midnight lamp, The / Can you see me / 51st anniversary / Fire / Foxy lady / Hey, Joe / Highway Chile / Manic depression / Midnight lamp, The / Purple haze / Stars that play with laughing Sam's dice / Stone free.
Compact disc: released on Tracks, Feb'85

Album: released on Track, Aug'83 by Polydor Records. Dist: Polygram

Cassette: released on Track, Aug'83 by Polydor Records. Dist: Polygram

SOUNDTRACK RECORDINGS.
Album: released on Reprise, '79 by WEA Records. Dist: WEA

STONE FREE.
Album: released on Polydor, Nov'83 by Polydor Records. Dist: Polygram, Polydor

Cassette: released on Polydor, Nov'83 by Polydor Records. Dist: Polygram, Polydor

STRANGE THINGS.
Tracks: / fool for you baby / Oddball / Simon says / Come on baby part 1 / Come on baby part 2 / Blues blues / lime line / Good feeling / go go shoes part 1 / Bring my baby back / Psycho / Day Tripper / Happy Birthday / Don't accuse me / Welcome home / Hornets nest / Flashing / Strange things.
Album: released on Showcase, Apr'86 Dist: Counterpoint

Cassette: released on Showcase, Apr'86 Dist: Counterpoint

SUPERSTAR (MUSIC FOR THE MILLIONS).
Album: released on Polydor (Holland), Feb'85

Cassette: released on Polydor (Holland), Feb'85

TOMORROW NEVER KNOWS.
Album: released on Happy Bird (Germany), Jul'84 Dist: Polygram, IMS

Cassette: released on Happy Bird (Germany), Jul'84 Dist: Polygram, IMS

VOODOO CHILE.
Album: released on Polydor (Import), Feb'82

Cassette: released on Polydor (Import), Feb'82

Album: released on Polydor, Nov'83 by Polydor Records. Dist: Polygram, Polydor

Cassette: released on Polydor, Nov'83 by Polydor Records. Dist: Polygram, Polydor

Single (12"): released on Polydor, Sep'82 by Polydor Records. Dist: Polygram, Polydor

VOODOO CHILE (Hendrix Experience, Jimi).
Single (7"): released on Old Gold, Jul'84 by Old Gold Records. Dist: Lightning, Jazz Music, Spartan, Counterpoint

WAR HEROES.
Album: released on Polydor, Aug'83 by Polydor Records. Dist: Polygram, Polydor
Cat. no: **SPELP 4**
Cassette: released on Polydor, Aug'83 by Polydor Records. Dist: Polygram, Polydor Deleted '86.

WOKE UP THIS MORNING AND FOUND MYSELF DEAD.
Compact disc: released on Red Lightnin', Nov'86 by Red Lightnin' Records. Dist: Roots, Swift, Jazz Music, JSU, Pinnacle, Cartel, Wynd-Up Distribution

Album: released on Red Lightnin', Sep'82 by Red Lightnin' Records. Dist: Roots, Swift, Jazz Music, JSU, Pinnacle, Cartel, Wynd-Up Distribution

Hendrix, Karen

SAY IT AIN'T TRUE.
Tracks: / Say it ain't true / Say it ain't true (Instrumental).
Single (7"): released on Carrere, Jun'86 by Carrere Records. Dist: PRT, Spartan

Single (12"): released on Carrere, Jun'86 by Carrere Records. Dist: PRT, Spartan

Hendryx, Nona

ART OF DEFENCE, THE.
Tracks: / I sweat (going through the motions) / Soft targets / Life, (The) / I want you.
Album: released on RCA, May'84 by RCA Records. Dist: RCA, Roots, Swift, Wellard, Chris, I & B, Solomon & Peres Distribution

Cassette: released on RCA, May'84 by RCA Records. Dist: RCA, Roots, Swift, Wellard, Chris, I & B, Solomon & Peres Distribution

FEMALE TROUBLE.
Tracks: / I know what you need(Pygmys confessions) / Big fun / Baby go-go / Rhythm of change / Why should I cry / Too hot to handle / Winds of change(Mandela to Mandela) / Female trouble / Drive me wild.
Notes: Executive producers: Nona Hendryx & Dan Hartman.
Album: released on EMI America, Jun'87 by EMI Records. Dist: EMI

Cassette: released on EMI America, Jun'87 by EMI Records. Dist: EMI

Compact disc: released on EMI, '87 by EMI Records. Dist: EMI

Compact disc: released on EMI America, Jun'87 by EMI Records. Dist: EMI

HEAT, THE.
Album: released on RCA, Sep'85 by RCA Records. Dist: RCA, Roots, Swift, Wellard, Chris, I & B, Solomon & Peres Distribution

Single (12"): released on RCA, Sep'85 by RCA Records. Dist: RCA, Roots, Swift, Wellard, Chris, I & B, Solomon & Peres Distribution

IF LOOKS COULD KILL (D.O.A.).
Tracks: / If looks could kill (D.O.A) / Het - part 2 (The).
Single (7"): released on RCA, Sep'85 by RCA Records. Dist: RCA, Roots, Swift, Wellard, Chris, I & B, Solomon & Peres Distribution

Single (12"): released on RCA, Sep'85 by RCA Records. Dist: RCA, Roots, Swift, Wellard, Chris, I & B, Solomon & Peres Distribution

I SWEAT.
Single (7"): released on Arista, Jul'85 by Arista Records. Dist: RCA

Single (12"): released on Arista, Jul'85 by Arista Records. Dist: RCA

I SWEAT (GOING THROUGH THE MOTIONS).
Single (7"): by RCA Records. Dist: RCA, Roots, Swift, Wellard, Chris, I & B, Solomon & Peres Distribution

Single (12"): by RCA Records. Dist: RCA, Roots, Swift, Wellard, Chris, I & B, Solomon & Peres Distribution Deleted '85.

KEEP IT CONFIDENTIAL/DUMMY UP.
Single (7"): released on RCA, Aug'83 by RCA Records. Dist: RCA, Roots, Swift, Wellard, Chris, I & B, Solomon & Peres Distribution

Single (12"): released on RCA, Aug'83 by RCA Records. Dist: RCA, Roots, Swift, Wellard, Chris, I & B, Solomon & Peres Distribution

WHY SHOULD I CRY.
Tracks: / Why should I cry / Funkyland / Why should I cry (boo-hoo mix)* / Why should I cry (dub boo-hoo mix)*.
Single (7"): released on EMI America, May'87 by EMI Records. Dist: EMI

Single (12"): released on EMI America, May'87 by EMI Records. Dist: EMI

Single (12"): released on EMI America, 23 May'87 by EMI Records. Dist: EMI

Henley, Don

Biographical Details: This American singer, drummer and songwriter had been a member of **Linda Ronstadt's** backing group prior to becoming a member of the **Eagles** in 1971. **Henley** and guitarist / keyboardist **Glenn Frey** were the nucleus of the **Eagles**, being the only two players who remained in the band from start to finish; the pair wrote the lions share of the material, and split most of the lead vocal duties between the two of them. After 1980's live album, the bugely successful group gradually drifter apart, although no official split was announced. **Henley** & **Frey** both went on to achieve substantial solo success, starting in 1982.

BOYS IN SUMMER.
Single (7"): released on Geffen, Dec'84 by Geffen Records. Dist: WEA, CBS Deleted '86.

Single (12"): released on Geffen, Dec'84 by Geffen Records. Dist: WEA, CBS Deleted '86.

BUILDING THE PERFECT BEAST.
Tracks: / Boys of summer, The / You can't make love / Man with a mission / You're not drinking enough / Not enough love in the world / Building the perfect beast / All she wants to do is dance / Sunset grill / Drivin' with your eyes closed / Land of the living.
Album: released on Geffen, Sep'86 by Geffen Records. Dist: WEA, CBS

Cassette: released on Geffen, Sep'86 by Geffen Records. Dist: WEA, CBS

Compact disc: released on Geffen, Feb'87 by Geffen Records. Dist: WEA, CBS

DIRTY LAUNDRY/LILAH/THEM AND US.
Single (7"): released on Elektra, Jan'83 by WEA Records. Dist: WEA

Single (12"): released on Elektra, Jan'83 by WEA Records. Dist: WEA

Single (12"): released on Elektra, Jan'83 by WEA Records. Dist: WEA

I CAN'T STAND STILL.
Album: released on Asylum, Feb'83 by WEA Records. Dist: WEA

JOHNNY CAN'T READ.
Single (7"): released on WEA, Sep'82 by WEA Records. Dist: WEA

NOT ENOUGH LOVE IN THE WORLD.
Single (7"): released on Geffen, Jul'85 by Geffen Records. Dist: WEA, CBS Deleted '86.

UNCLOUDED DAY.
Single (7"): released on Elektra, May'83 by WEA Records. Dist: WEA

Single (12"): released on Elektra, May'83 by WEA Records. Dist: WEA

Hennings, Nancy

TIBETAN SPELLS 11 See Wolff, Henry.

Henreid, Polar

TOMORROW HAS BEEN CANCELLED.
Single (7"): released on Deluxe, Dec'83 by Deluxe Records. Dist: Pinnacle

Henrietta Rollins

DRIVE BY SHOOTING.
Notes: Better known as Henry Rollins, leader of Black Flag. New solo album.
Album: released on Texas Records, Aug'87 Dist: Sonet Distribution

Henry, Clarence

LITTLE GREEN FROG (Henry, Clarence 'Frogman').
Tracks: / Loving cajun style (cajun honey) / Cheatin' traces / Ain't got no home (1) / Think it over / Baby ain't that love / Heartaches by number / Have you ever been lonely / Little green frog / You can't hide a tear / I told my pillow / I might as well / Don't take it so hard / Tore up over you / Ain't got no home / Ain't got no home (2).
Album: released on Bear Family, Sep'87 by Bear Family Records. Dist: Rollercoaster Distribution, Swift. Estim retail price in Aug'87 was £8.99.

Henry, Clarence 'Frogman'

AIN'T GOT NO HOME.
Single (7"): released on Creole, Aug'82 by Creole Records. Dist: Rhino, PRT

AIN'T GOT NO HOME (CHESS).
Single (7"): released on Chess, Jul'85 by Charly Records. Dist: Charly, Swift, PRT, Discovery, IMS, Polygram

BUT I DO.
Single (7"): released on Juke Box, Mar'82

BUT I DO (CREOLE).
Single (7"): released on Creole, Aug'82 by Creole Records. Dist: Rhino, PRT

BUT I DO/YOU ALWAYS HURT THE ONE YOU LOVE.
Single (7"): released on Flashback, Jan'83 by Flashback Records/PRT Records. Dist: Mainline, PRT

LEGENDARY CLARENCE 'FROGMAN' HENRY.
Album: released on Silvertown, Nov'83 by Silvertown Records.

Cassette: released on Silvertown, Nov'83 by Silvertown Records.

NEW RECORDINGS.
Album: released on Clarence Frogman Henry, Apr'79 Dist: Swift

THAT OLDE PIANO.
Single (7"): released on Rockney, Aug'83 by Rockney Records. Dist: EMI

YOU ALWAYS HURT THE ONE YOU LOVE.
Single (7"): released on Creole, Aug'82 by Creole Records. Dist: Rhino, PRT

Henry, Ernie

LAST CHORUS.
Album: released on Riverside (USA), Feb'84 Dist: Fantasy (USA) Distribution

PRESENTING ERNIE HENRY.
Album: released on Riverside (USA), Aug'84 Dist: Fantasy (USA) Distribution

Henry, Georgie

I SEE YOU MY LOVE.
Single (12"): released on Ruddy Tee, Jun'82

Henry, Haywood

GENTLE MONSTER, THE.
Notes: Featuring Joe Newman/Hank Jones.
Album: released on Uptown (USA), Nov'86 by Uptown Records. Dist: Jazz Music

Henry IV

HENRY IV PART 1 By William Shakespeare (Complete text) (Various Artists).
Cassette: released on Argo (Spokenword), Oct'83 by Decca Records. Dist: Polygram

HENRY IV PART II By William Shakespeare (complete text) (Various Artists).
Cassette: released on Argo (Spokenword), Nov'83 by Decca Records. Dist: Polygram

Henry, Lenny

MOLE IN THE HOLE.
Single (7"): released on Jet, Mar'81 by Jet Records. Dist: CBS

STAND UP...GET DOWN.
Album: released on Chrysalis, Nov'84 by Chrysalis Records. Dist: CBS

Cassette: released on Chrysalis, Nov'84 by Chrysalis Records. Dist: CBS

Henry, Milton
WHO DO YOU THINK I AM.
Album: released on Wackies, Jul'85 by Wackies Records. Dist: Jetstar

Henry, Paul
WAITING AT THE CROSSROADS.
Single (7"): released on Pal, Nov'81

Henry's Cat
HENRY'S CAT Stories from the TV series (Godfrey, Bob).
Album: released on BBC, Sep'83 by BBC Records & Tapes. Dist: EMI, PRT.

Cassette: released on BBC, Sep'83 by BBC Records & Tapes. Dist: EMI, PRT.

Henry's Herd
MUH SONG, THE.
Tracks: / Muh song, the / Daisy's rag.
Single (7"): released on Sierra, Jul'86 by Sierra Records. Dist: WEA

Single (12"): released on Sierra, Jul'86 by Sierra Records. Dist: WEA

Henry VII
HENRY VII (Tell-A-Tale).
Cassette: released on Pickwick (Tell-a-tale), Mar'84 by Pickwick Records. Dist: Pickwick Distribution

Hensel, Carol
CAROL HENSEL'S EXERCISE & DANCE VOL.2.
Album: released on Satril, Oct'82 by Satril Records. Dist: PRT

Hensley, Ken
FREE SPIRIT.
Album: released on Bronze, Mar'81 by Polygram Records. Dist: Polydor

Cassette: released on Bronze, Mar'81 by Polygram Records. Dist: Polydor

SYSTEM, THE.
Single (7"): released on Bronze, Apr'81 by Polygram Records. Dist: Polydor Deleted '81.

Hentschel, David
EDUCATING RITA (Film music).
Album: released on Mercury, Jun'83 by Phonogram Records. Dist: Polygram Distribution

EDUCATING RITA/I CAN'T DANCE.
Single (7"): released on Mercury, May'83 by Phonogram Records. Dist: Polygram Distribution

Hepburns
GOALMOUTH INCIDENT.
Tracks: / Made up / World is, The / Pier head / Bath house, The.
Single (12"): released on Cherry Red, May'87 by Cherry Red Records. Dist: Pinnacle

Hepcat, Harry
GO CAT GO.
Album: released on Dee-Jay Jamboures, Aug'85

Hep Cat Hop
HEP CAT HOP (NERVOUS).
Album: released on Nervous, Jul'84 by Nervous Records. Dist: Nervous, Rough Trade

HEP CAT HOP (ROCKHOUSE) (Various Artists).
Album: released on Rockhouse, Jun'83 by Rockhouse Records. Dist: Swift Distribution, Charly Distribution

Hep Cats Session
HEP CATS SESSION (Various Artists).
Album: released on Charly, Feb'82 by Charly Records. Dist: Charly, Cadillac

Heptics
SPEND SOME TIME TOGETHER.
Single (12"): released on Starlight, Aug'85 by Starlight Records. Dist: Jetstar Distribution

Heptones
22 GOLDEN HITS.
Album: released on TTLP, Jan'86 Dist: Jetstar

BACK ON TOP.
Album: released on Vista Sounds, '83 by Vista Sounds Records. Dist: Jetstar

---

BETTER DAYS.
Album: released on Import Music Service (IMS), Mar'81 Dist: Concord Jazz Distributions, Pablo, Polygram

CHANGING TIME.
Album: released on Thunderbolt, Aug'87 by Thunderbolt Records. Dist: Jetstar Distribution. Estim retail price in Sep'87 was £7.99.

IN A DANCE HALL STYLE.
Album: released on Vista Sounds, '83 by Vista Sounds Records. Dist: Jetstar

IN MY TIME.
Single (12"): released on MM Music, Jul'85

LEGENDS FROM STUDIO 1.
Album: released on Trenchtown, Jun'85 by Trenchtown Records. Dist: Jetstar

ONE STEP AHEAD.
Single (12"): released on Move, Oct'85 by Charly Records. Dist: Charly Distribution, Fast Forward Distribution, Cartel Distribution

SEA OF LOVE/LOVING YOU ALRIGHT.
Single (12"): released on Supertone, May'83 by Supertone Records. Dist: Jetstar Distribution

SUSPICIOUS MINDS.
Tracks: / Suspicious minds / Crystal blue persuasion.
Single (12"): released on Paradise, Mar'86 Dist: Jetstar,   WEA

SWING LOW.
Album: released on Burning Sounds, Sep'85 by Ross, Bill/Burning Sounds Records. Dist: PRT

YOU DECORATED MY HEART.
Single (12"): released on Art & Craft, Mar'83 Dist: Jetstar

Hepworth Band
MARCHING WITH HEPWORTH.
Album: released on Look, Nov'79 by R. Smith & Co. Records, H.R. Taylor

Herald, Ted
DIE SINGLES 1958-60.
Album: released on Bear Family, Aug'87 by Bear Family Records. Dist: Rollercoaster Distribution, Swift. Estim retail price in Aug'87 was £13.50.

Herb Dust
HERB DUST VOL 1 (Various Artists).
Album: released on Kingdom, Sep'83 by Kingdom Records. Dist: Kingdom

Herbeck, Ray
1942 (Herbeck, Ray & His Modern Music With Romance).
Album: released on Circle(USA), Jun'86 by Jazzology Records (USA). Dist: Jazz Music, Swift, Chris Wellard

Herbert, Michael
RAMPIN' CAT, THE.
Album: released on Free Reed, Sep'79 by Free Reed Records. Dist: Roots, Projection, Hobgoblin Records, Oblivion

Herbert The Hedgehog
HERBERT THE HEDGEHOG Vols. 1-4.
Cassette: released on Herbert The Hedgehog, Nov'82

Herbert, Victor
MELACHRINO PRESENTS IMMORTAL MELODIES OF... ...Victor Herbert & Sigmund Romberg.
Album: released on Decca, Oct'74 by Decca Records. Dist: Polygram

Herbolzheimer, Peter
FAT MAN BOOGIE.
Album: released on East Wind, Oct'85 by East Wind Records. Dist: PRT

JAZZ GALA CONCERT VOL.3.
Compact disc: released on Bellaphon (Germany), '86 by Bellaphon Records. Dist: Target, JSU

JAZZ GALA CONCERT VOL.2.
Compact disc: released on Bellaphon (Germany), '86 by Bellaphon Records. Dist: Target, JSU

Herbrucken, Das
MUSIC FOR ACCORDION ORCH. NO.2.
Album: released on Accordion Record Club, '84 by Accordion Record Club Records. Dist: Accordion Record Club

Herd
FROM THE UNDERWORLD.
Single (7"): released on Old Gold, Jul'82 by Old Gold Records. Dist: Lightning, Jazz Music,

---

Spartan, Counterpoint

I DON'T WANT OUR LOVIN' TO DIE.
Single (7"): released on Old Gold, Jul'82 by Old Gold Records. Dist: Lightning, Jazz Music, Spartan, Counterpoint

Here And Now
BEEN AND GONE.
Album: released on Cold Harbour, May'86 Dist: Pinnacle, Probe Plus Distribution, Cartel, M.I.S., EMI, DMS, RCA,

BEEN AND GONE (VIDEO).
Notes: The band **Here And Now** recorded live on stage at Dingwall's in London. Footage of interviews between musical tracks. 1986 Production. total playing time: 45 mins.
Video-cassette (VHS): released on Jettisoundz, Aug'86 Dist: Red Rhino, Cartel

CHARTBUSTERS VOL.2.
Album: released on Here & Now, Mar'86 Dist: Spartan

Cassette: released on Here & Now, Mar'86 Dist: Spartan

CHARTBUSTERS VOL.3.
Album: released on Here & Now, Jun'86 Dist: Spartan

Cassette: released on Here & Now, Jun'86 Dist: Spartan

FANTASY SHIFT.
Album: released on Chick, Aug'85 Dist: Pinnacle

THEATRE.
Album: released on Conquest, May'85 Dist: Red Rhino, Cartel

Here Comes Christmas
HERE COMES CHRISTMAS (Various Artists).
Album: released on Kiddicraft, Oct'81 by MacDonald Educational Records. Dist: H.R. Taylor

Cassette: released on Kiddicraft, Oct'81 by MacDonald Educational Records. Dist: H.R. Taylor

Here Comes Garfield
HERE COMES GARFIELD (Various Artists).
Album: released on Epic, Dec'83 by CBS Records. Dist: CBS

Hereford Cathedral Choir
CAROLS FROM.....
Album: released on Alpha, Oct'81 by Alpha Records. Dist: H.R. Taylor,

Cassette: released on Alpha, Oct'81 by Alpha Records. Dist: H.R. Taylor,

Here's A Health...
SONGS OF GOOD COMPANY (Here's A Health To The Grog).
Cassette: released on Folktracks, Nov'79 by Folktracks Cassettes. Dist: Folktracks

Here's Johnny
HELLZ A POPPIN'.
Tracks: / Hellz a poppin' / Absence of malica.
Single (7"): released on RCA, May'86 by RCA Records. Dist: RCA, Roots, Swift, Wellard, Chris, I & B, Solomon & Peres Distribution

Single (12"): released on RCA, May'86 by RCA Records. Dist: RCA, Roots, Swift, Wellard, Chris, I & B, Solomon & Peres Distribution

IDLE WIND.
Single (7"): released on RCA, Oct'85 by RCA Records. Dist: RCA, Roots, Swift, Wellard, Chris, I & B, Solomon & Peres Distribution

Single (12"): released on RCA, Oct'85 by RCA Records. Dist: RCA, Roots, Swift, Wellard, Chris, I & B, Solomon & Peres Distribution

I FALL APART.
Single (7"): released on RCA, Jul'85 by RCA Records. Dist: RCA, Roots, Swift, Wellard, Chris, I & B, Solomon & Peres Distribution

Single (12"): released on RCA, Jul'85 by RCA Records. Dist: RCA, Roots, Swift, Wellard, Chris, I & B, Solomon & Peres Distribution

LOVE YOU TO DEATH.
Single (7"): released on RCA, Mar'86 by RCA Records. Dist: RCA, Roots, Swift, Wellard, Chris, I & B, Solomon & Peres Distribution

Single (12"): released on RCA, Mar'86 by RCA Records. Dist: RCA, Roots, Swift, Wellard, Chris, I & B, Solomon & Peres Distribution

MERRY HELL.
Tracks: / Hellzapoppin' / Absence of malice / Torture garden / Your room / Love you to death / Idlewild / Open minded / Reckless / How do you sleep / I fall apart.

Album: released on RCA, Apr'86 by RCA Records. Dist: RCA, Roots, Swift, Wellard, Chris, I & B, Solomon & Peres Distribution

Cassette: released on RCA, Apr'86 by RCA Records. Dist: RCA, Roots, Swift, Wellard, Chris, I & B, Solomon & Peres Distribution

Here's To The Ladies
HERE'S TO THE LADIES (Various Artists).
Album: released on RCA International, Oct'82

Cassette: released on RCA International, Oct'82

Heresy
HERESY/CONCRETE SOX (Heresy/Concrete Sox).
Album: released on Earache, Mar'87 by Earache Records. Dist: Revolver, Cartel

Heretic
BURNT AT THE STAKE.
Album: released on Thunderbolt, Apr'84 by Magnum Music Group Ltd. Dist: Magnum Music Group Ltd, PRT Distribution, Spartan Distribution

TORTURE KNOWS NO BOUNDARY.
Album: released on Roadrunner (Dutch), Feb'87 Dist: Pinnacle

Here We Go
HERE WE GO (Various Artists).

Herion, Trevor
BEAUTY LIFE.
Album: released on Interdisc, Oct'83 by Interdisc Records. Dist: Island, EMI

Heritage
CELTIC MYSTERY.
Tracks: / Julia Delaney's / Ready for the night / It'll be too late / Grass roots / Love is just around the corner / Cooley's / Celtic mystery / Emigrant's tale / Sligo fair / Queen of the rushes / Tatter Jack Walsh / Chicago jig, The.
Album: released on Raglan (Ireland), Aug'87 Dist: Polygram

Cassette: released on Raglan (Ireland), Aug'87 Dist: Polygram

SOME RANTIN' ROVIN' FUN.
Album: released on No Bad, Feb'81 by No Bad Records. Dist: Pinnacle, Wynd-Up Distribution (Scotland)

STRANGE PLACE TO BE.
Single (7"): released on Rondelet, Apr'81 Dist: Spartan Distribution

WHEN THE DANCIN' IT'S A DONE.
Album: released on No Bad, Feb'81 by No Bad Records. Dist: Pinnacle, Wynd-Up Distribution (Scotland)

Heritage Jazz Band
AT CARNEGIE HALL.
Album: released on Viko, Apr'79

NEW ORLEANS.
Album: released on Vogue (France), Dec'84 Dist: Discovery, Jazz Music, PRT, Swift

Hermann, Bernard
CITIZEN KANE.
Album: released on Red Seal, Jan'75 by RCA Records. Dist: RCA

Herman's Hermits
GREATEST HITS:HERMAN'S HERMITS.
Album: released on EMI (Germany), '83 by EMI Records. Dist: Conifer

I'M INTO SOMETHING GOOD.
Single (7"): released on EMI Golden 45's, Jul'84 by EMI Records. Dist: EMI

NO MILK TODAY.
Single (7"): released on EMI (France), Apr'83 by EMI Records. Dist: Conifer

THERE'S A KIND OF HUSH All over the world.
Tracks: / There's a kind of hush / No milk today.
Single (7"): released on RAK, Nov'86 by RAK. Dist: EMI

VERY BEST OF HERMAN'S HERMITS.
Album: released on Music For Pleasure (Holland), Oct'84 by EMI Records. Dist: EMI

Cassette: released on Music For Pleasure, Oct'84 by EMI Records. Dist: EMI

Hermans Vision
PARTY.
Single (7"): released on Hermans Vision, Mar'84 Dist: Pinnacle

---

Herman, Woody

1943-1946 Various discs (Herman, Woody & His Orchestra).

1943-1946 Various discs.
Album: released on Solid Sender, Apr'81 Dist: JSU, Jazz Music

1944 AND 1946 (Herman, Woody & His Orchestra).
Album: released on Solid Sender, Apr'81 Dist: JSU, Jazz Music

1945 BAND IN HI FI.
Album: released on Fanfare, Apr'79 by Ferroway/Fanfare Records. Dist: PRT

1949-THE CALIFORNIA CONCERTS (Herman, Woody & His Orchestra).
Album: released on Artistry, '86 Dist: Jazz Music

50TH ANNIVERSARY TOUR (Herman, Woody Big Band).
Tracks: / It don't mean a thing (if it ain't got that swing) / What's new / Pools / Blues for red / Conga / Central park west / Fried buzzard / Epistophy.
Album: released on Concord Jazz(USA), Aug'86 by Concord Jazz Records (USA). Dist: IMS, Polygram

Cassette: released on Concord Jazz(USA), Aug'86 by Concord Jazz Records (USA). Dist: IMS, Polygram

AND THE FOUR BROTHERS LIVE.
Album: released on Queen-Disc, Apr'81 Dist: Celtic Music, JSU, Jazz Horizons, Jazz Music

AT THE HOLLYWOOD PALLADIUM.
Album: released on Solid Sender, Apr'81 Dist: JSU, Jazz Music

BAND THAT PLAYS THE BLUES, THE.
Tracks: / At the woodchopper's ball / Dallas blues / Blues upstairs / Blues downstairs / Casbah blues / Blue prelude / Herman at the Sherman / Golden wedding / Blue flame / Fur trapper's ball / Bishop's blues / Woodsheddin' with Woody / Blues in the night / 'Tis autumn / String of pearls, A / Who dat up dere / String of pearls, A.
Notes: Licensed from MCA Records Ltd.
Cassette: released on Affinity, Sep'86 by Charly Records. Dist: Charly, Cadillac

Album: released on Affinity, Apr'84 by Charly Records. Dist: Charly, Cadillac

CALEDONIA.
Album: released on Astan (USA), Mar'85

CONCORD JAM VOL.1.
Album: released on Concord, Mar'81 by Import Records. Dist: IMS, Polygram

CRAZY RHYTHM.
Album: released on IMS(Import), Nov'82 by Polydor Records. Dist: IMS, Polygram

Cassette: released on IMS(Import), Nov'82 by Polydor Records. Dist: IMS, Polygram

EARLY AUTUMN.
Album: released on Pathe MarconiFrance), Jan'85

FAN IT.
Album: released on Swinghouse, '84 Dist: Jazz Music Distribution, Swift Distribution, Chris Wellard Distribution

FIRST SESSION 1937 (Herman, Woody & His Orchestra).
Album: released on Circle(USA), Feb'87 by Jazzology Records (USA). Dist: Jazz Music, Swift, Chris Wellard

FOUR BROTHERS AT THE ROYAL ROOST.
Album: released on Jazz Live, Oct'86

GIANT STEPS.
Compact disc: released on Fantasy (USA), Nov'86 by Fantasy Inc USA Records. Dist: IMS, Polygram

GREATEST HITS:WOODY HERMAN.
Album: released on Realm, '74 by Realm. Dist: CBS

HERDMAN HERD.
Album: released on Bright Orange, Apr'79 Dist: Swift

HEY, HEARD THE HERD.
Album: released on Verve (USA), Sep'81 by Polydor. Dist: Polygram

HOLLYWOOD PALLADIUM 1948.
Album: released on Hep, Apr'81 by H.R. Taylor Records. Dist: Jazz Music, Cadillac Music, JSU, Taylors, Wellard, Chris, Zodiac, Swift, Fast Forward

IN DISCO ORDER VOL.2.
Album: released on Ajax, Jul'77

IN ENGLAND 1959.
Album: released on Jazz Groove, Aug'81 Dist: Jazz Music

IT POURS.
Album: released on First Heard, '84 by Submarine Records. Dist: Conifer, Taylors

JUKE BOX (Herman, Woody & His First Herd).
Tracks: / Red top / Put that ring on my finger / Great Northern / Walking my baby bacj home / Golden wedding (la cinquantaine) / Atcheson, Topeka & the Santa Fe / Till the end of time / Perdido / It must be jelly / Superman with a horn / Day by day / Ee-ba-lee-ba / Wild root / Blue flame theme.
Album: released on First Heard, Nov'85 by Submarine Records. Dist: Conifer, Taylors

Cassette: released on First Heard, Nov'85 by Submarine Records. Dist: Conifer, Taylors
Cat. no: **CFH 36**

JULY 30TH 1959.
Album: released on From The Jazz Vault, Oct'80 by Damont Records. Dist: Swift, Taylor, H.R.

JUMPIN' WITH WOODY HERMAN'S FIRST HERD.
Album: released on Joker, Apr'81 Dist: Counterpoint, Mainline, Record Services Distribution (Ireland)

LIVE AT CONCORD '81.
Album: released on Concord Jazz(USA), Sep'82 by Concord Jazz Records (USA). Dist: IMS, Polygram

Cassette: released on Concord Jazz(USA), Sep'82 by Concord Jazz Records (USA). Dist: IMS, Polygram

LIVE AT MONTEREY That's jazz (6).
Album: released on Atlantic, Jul'76 by WEA Records. Dist: WEA

LIVE IN NEW ORLEANS.
Album: released on Giants of Jazz, Oct'84 by Hasmick Promotions Ltd.. Dist: Counterpoint, Jazz Music, Taylors, Swift, Mainline, Wellard, Chris

OMAHA NEBRASKA 1954.
Album: released on Swing World, '84 Dist: Jazz Music Distribution, Swift Distribution, Projection Distribution, Chris Wellard Distribution

Cassette: released on Swing World, '84 Dist: Jazz Music Distribution, Swift Distribution, Projection Distribution, Chris Wellard Distribution

PRE-HERDS.
Tracks: / I've got you under my skin / It must be jelly ('cause jam don't shake like that) / Basie's basement / Do nothing till you hear from me / As long as Ilive / Cherry / Ingie speaks / I ain't got nothin' but the blues / I get a kick out of you / I'll get by / Irresistible you / Cryin' sands / Noah / Perdido / Milkman, keep those bottles quiet / Goin' home.
Album: released on Affinity, Sep'86 by Charly Records. Dist: Charly, Cadillac

Cassette: released on Affinity, Sep'86 by Charly Records. Dist: Charly, Cadillac

Album: released on Affinity, Oct'86 by Charly Records. Dist: Charly, Cadillac

PRE HERDS (BULLDOG).
Album: released on Bulldog, Nov'83 by Bulldog Records. Dist: President Distribution, Spartan, Swift, Taylor, H.R.

PRESENTS A GREAT AMERICAN EVENING VOL.3.
Album: released on Concord Jazz(USA), Sep'83 by Concord Jazz Records (USA). Dist: IMS, Polygram

Cassette: released on Concord Jazz(USA), Sep'83 by Concord Jazz Records (USA). Dist: IMS, Polygram

RHAPSODY IN WOOD.
Album: released on First Heard, '84 by Submarine Records. Dist: Conifer, Taylors

ROAD BAND.
Album: released on Capitol, Jul'85 by Capitol Records. Dist: EMI

Cassette: released on Capitol, Jul'85 by Capitol Records. Dist: EMI

ROADBAND 1948.
Album: released on Hep, Apr'81 by H.R. Taylor Records. Dist: Jazz Music, Cadillac Music, JSU, Taylors, Wellard, Chris, Zodiac, Swift, Fast Forward

SECOND HERD LIVE IN HOLLYWOOD.
Album: released on Queen-Disc, Apr'81 Dist: Celtic Music, JSU, Jazz Horizons, Jazz Music

SWING GOES ON, THE (VOL.4).
Album: released on EMI (Germany), '83 by EMI Records. Dist: Conifer

THIRD HERD, THE.
Album: released on Discovery (USA), Jan'84 by Discovery Records (USA). Dist: Swift, Flexitron-Audio, Jazz Music

Cassette: released on Discovery (USA), Jan'84 by Discovery Records (USA). Dist: Swift, Flexitron-Audio, Jazz Music

THUNDERING HERD-LIVE.
Album: released on Meteor, Aug'86 by Magnum Music Group Ltd. Dist: Magnum Music Group Ltd, PRT Distribution, Spartan Distribution

THUNDERING HERDS.
Notes: 3 LP set.
Album: released on CBS(Import), Jun'86 by CBS Records. Dist: Conifer, Discovery, Swift

UNCOLLECTED WOODY HERMAN & HIS FIRST HERD.
Album: released on Hindsight(UK), May'79 Dist: Jazz Music

V-DISC YEARS VOL.1.
Notes: Mono.
Album: released on Hep, Sep'86 by H.R. Taylor Records. Dist: Jazz Music, Cadillac Music, JSU, Taylors, Wellard, Chris, Zodiac, Swift, Fast Forward

V DISC YEARS VOL. 2.
Album: released on Hep, Mar'87 by H.R. Taylor Records. Dist: Jazz Music, Cadillac Music, JSU, Taylors, Wellard, Chris, Zodiac, Swift, Fast Forward

WOODY & FRIENDS.
Album: released on Concord, Dec'81 by Import Records. Dist: IMS, Polygram

WOODY HERMAN.
Album: released on Jazz Reactivation, Jul'82 Dist: PRT

WOODY HERMAN (Herman, Woody (Members Of Orch.)).
Album: released on Bright Orange, Apr'79 Dist: Swift

WOODY HERMAN 1936-37 VOL.1.
Album: released on Ajax, Apr'79

WOODY HERMAN 1938-9 VOL.3.
Album: released on Ajax, Apr'79

WOODY HERMAN 1939 VOL.4.
Album: released on Ajax, Apr'79

WOODY HERMAN 1939 VOL.5.
Album: released on Ajax, Apr'79

WOODY HERMAN 1940-41 VOL.9.
Album: released on Ajax, Apr'79

WOODY HERMAN 1940 VOL.8.
Album: released on Ajax, Apr'79

WOODY HERMAN 1940 VOL.6.
Album: released on Ajax, Apr'79

WOODY HERMAN 1940 VOL.7.
Album: released on Ajax, Apr'79

WOODY HERMAN COLLECTION.
Album: released on Deja Vu, Nov'85 by Deja Vu Records. Dist: Counterpoint Distribution, Record Services Distribution (Ireland)

Cassette: released on Deja Vu, Nov'85 by Deja Vu Records. Dist: Counterpoint Distribution, Record Services Distribution (Ireland)

WOODY HERMAN & HIS FIRST HERD 1944.
Album: released on London, Oct'79 by London Records. Dist: Polygram

WOODY HERMAN & HIS ORCH. 1948.
Album: released on First Heard, Apr'79 by Submarine Records. Dist: Conifer, Taylors

WOODY HERMAN & HIS ORCH. 1946.
Album: released on First Heard, Apr'79 by Submarine Records. Dist: Conifer, Taylors

WOODY HERMAN & HIS THIRD HERD.
Album: released on Rarities, Apr'81

WOODY HERMAN PRESENTS VOL.2.
Album: released on Concord, Apr'82 by Import Records. Dist: IMS, Polygram

Cassette: released on Concord, Apr'82 by Import Records. Dist: IMS, Polygram

WOODY HERMAN & THE THIRD HERD.
Cassette: released on Swing World, Feb'83 Dist: Jazz Music Distribution, Swift Distribution, Projection Distribution, Chris Wellard Distribution

WOODY HERMAN & THE WOODCHOPPERS.
Album: released on Submarine, May'81 by Submarine Records. Dist: Wellard, Chris Distribution, Conifer Distribution, H.R. Taylor Distribution

WOODY'S WINNERS.
Album: released on CBS, Feb'84 by CBS Records. Dist: CBS Deleted '87

Album: released on CBS, Feb'84 by CBS Records. Dist: CBS

WORLD CLASS (Herman, Woody Big Band).
Tracks: / Four brothers / Rockin' chair / Claw, The / Woody's lament / Peanut vendor / Crystal silence / Greasy sack blues / Perdido.
Notes: Recorded live at Japan's Annex jazz festival in 1982. Woody's world class band features guest tenor saxophonists Al Cohn, Med flory, Sal Nistico and Flip Philips. this Woody Herman album captures completely the real big band sound - the excitement of the solos, the section work, interplay, and the surging explosive power that one expects from this legendary band.
Compact disc: released on Concord Jazz(USA), May'85 by Concord Jazz Records (USA). Dist: IMS, Polygram

Album: released on Concord Jazz(USA), Jun'84 by Concord Jazz Records (USA). Dist: IMS, Polygram

Cassette: released on Concord Jazz(USA), Jun'84 by Concord Jazz Records (USA). Dist: IMS, Polygram

Herman Ze German

HERMAN ZE GERMAN & FRIENDS.

WIPE OUT (Herman Ze German & Friends).
Tracks: / Wipe out / Pancake.
Single (7"): released on Capitol, Mar'86 by Capitol Records. Dist: EMI

Hermes, Corrine

SI LA VIE EST CADEAUX.
Single (7"): released on Polydor, Apr'83 by Polydor Records. Dist: Polygram, Polydor

WORDS OF LOVE.
Single (7"): released on Polydor, May'83 by Polydor Records. Dist: Polygram, Polydor

Hermine

LONELY AT THE TOP.
Album: released on Salome, Aug'84 by Salome Records. Dist: Rough Trade, Cartel

TORTURE.
Single (7"): released on Human, Jul'81 Dist: Roots, Stage One

TV LOVERS.
Single (7"): released on Human, Jul'81 Dist: Roots, Stage One

WORLD ON MY PLATES, THE.
Album: released on Crammed Discs, Apr'82 Dist: Rough Trade, Nine Mile, Cartel

Hernandez, Patrick

GOODBYE.
Single (7"): released on Delivery, Nov'81

Single (12"): released on Delivery, Nov'81

PATRICK HERNANDEZ.
Album: released on Gem, Jan'80 by Gem Records. Dist: RCA

Hernandez, Wayne

LET ME CALL YOU ANGEL.
Tracks: / Let me call you angel / Must be dreaming.
Single (7"): released on Epic, 20 Jun'87 by CBS Records. Dist: CBS

Single (12"): released on Epic, 20 Jun'87 by CBS Records. Dist: CBS

Single (12"): released on Epic, Jul'87 by CBS Records. Dist: CBS

Herne, Tony

SHAKE YOU DOWN.
Tracks: / Shake you down / Shake you down (Instrumental).
Single (12"): released on Fresh, Jan'87 Dist: Jetstar

Heroes

BABY'S HAD A TASTE.
Single (7"): released on Carrere, Jul'81 by Carrere Records. Dist: PRT, Spartan

RUSSIA AND AMERICA Why can't we be friends.
Single (7"): released on Calibre, Jun'84 by Calibre Records. Dist: PRT

Single (12"): released on Calibre, Jun'84 by Calibre Records. Dist: PRT

Herold, Helmuth

ARPA MONICA Harmonica.
Album: released on ARC (Accordion Records), '84 Dist: Accordion Record Club

Herold, Ted

DIE SINGLES 1958-1960.
Tracks: / Ich brauch' keinen ring / Lover doll / So schon ist nur die allererste liebe / Wunderbar wie du heut' wieder kusst / Hula rock / Dixieland rock / Dein kleiner bruder / Texas baby / Ich bin ein mann / Carolin / Hey baby / Kuss mich / Isabell / Crazy boy / Moonlight / 1:0 / Sunshine baby / Hast du funf minuten zeit / Auch du wirst gehn' / Hey little girl / Lonely / Oh so sweet / Nur sie / Wunderland.
Compact disc: released on Bear Family, Jul'87 by Bear Family Records. Dist: Rollercoaster Distribution, Swift. Estim retail price in Aug'87 was £13.50.

ICH BIN EIN MANN.
Album: released on Polydor, Oct'80 by Polydor Records. Dist: Polygram, Polydor

ICH HAB' EIN SWEETHEART.
Album: released on Polydor, Sep'81 by Polydor Records. Dist: Polygram, Polydor

IDOLS.
Album: released on Polydor, Oct'80 by Polydor Records. Dist: Polygram, Polydor

ORIGINALE.
Album: released on Polydor, Oct'80 by Polydor Records. Dist: Polygram, Polydor

ROCK AND ROLL PARTY (Herold, Ted & Andersen).
Double Album: released on Polydor, Nov'80 by Polydor Records. Dist: Polygram, Polydor

ROCK & ROLL PARTY (Herold, Ted & Andersen).

SING AND SWING MIT TED.
Album: released on Polydor, Feb'82 by Polydor Records. Dist: Polygram, Polydor

Herring, Albert

HERRING,ALBERT (Glyndebourne Festival Opera).
Notes: Glyndebourne festival opera production of Benjamin Britten's opera,with the London Philharmonic Orchestra and star solo artists.
Video-cassette (VHS): released on Thorn-Emi, Jun'86

Herring, Annie

KIDS OF THE KINGDOM.
Album: released on Birdwing, May'82 by Word Records. Dist: Word Distribution

Cassette: released on Birdwing, May'82 by Word Records. Dist: Word Distribution

SEARCH DEEP INSIDE.
Album: released on Sparrow, May'82 by Word Records. Dist: Spartan

Cassette: released on Sparrow, May'82 by Word Records. Dist: Spartan

Herrmann, Bernard

PORTRAIT OF ALFRED HITCHCOCK.
Album: released on Decca (France), Feb'85 by Decca Records. Dist: Discovery

Hersch,Fred Trio

HORIZONS.
Album: released on Concord Jazz(USA), Jul'85 by Concord Jazz Records (USA). Dist: IMS, Polygram

Herte, Kim

DANCE WITH A STRANGER (Herte, Kim & The Federation).
Tracks: / Dance with a stranger (East rap mix) / Dance with a stranger (7" radio mix) / Anything lying on the floor (inst.).
Single (7"): released on Big Top, Nov'86 Dist: Cartel

DO YOU WANNA DANCE(WITH ME).
Single (12"): released on RMO, May'85 by RMO Records. Dist: Jetstar

Single (7"): released on Londisc, Jun'85 by Londisc Records.

Single (12"): released on Londisc, Jun'85 by Londisc Records.

IT AIN'T HEAVY.
Tracks: / It ain't heavy / It ain't heavy (house mix).
Single (7"): released on Nine O Nine, Jul'87 by Creole Records. Dist: Rhino, PRT

IT AIN'T HEAVY.
Tracks: / It ain't heavy / It ain't heavy (house mix).
Single (7"): released on Nine O Nine, Jul'87 by Creole Records. Dist: Rhino, PRT

Single (12"): released on Nine O Nine, Jul'87 by Creole Records. Dist: Rhino, PRT

IT AIN'T HEAVY (EXTENDED MIX).
Tracks: / It ain't heavy (extended mix) / It ain't heavy / It ain't heavy (house mix).
Single (12"): released on Nine O Nine, Jul'87 by Creole Records. Dist: Rhino, PRT

Hertfordshire Musicale

YOUR FAVOURITE CHRISTMAS CAROL.
Cassette: released on Chevron, Nov'84 Dist: Multiple Sound Distributors

He Said

HAIL.
Album: released on Mute, Nov'86 Dist: Spartan Distribution, Rough Trade Distribution, Cartel Distribution

Cassette: released on Mute, Nov'86 Dist: Spartan Distribution, Rough Trade Distribution, Cartel Distribution

Compact disc: released on Mute, Nov'86 Dist: Spartan Distribution, Rough Trade Distribution, Cartel Distribution

ONLY ONE 1.
Single (7"): released on Mute, Oct'85 Dist: Spartan Distribution, Rough Trade Distribution, Cartel Distribution

Single (12"): released on Mute, Oct'85 Dist: Spartan Distribution, Rough Trade Distribution, Cartel Distribution

PALE FEET.
Tracks: / Pulling three G's.
Single (7"): released on Mute, Aug'86 Dist: Spartan Distribution, Rough Trade Distribution, Cartel Distribution

Single (12"): released on Mute, Aug'86 Dist: Spartan Distribution, Rough Trade Distribution, Cartel Distribution

PUMP.
Tracks: / Pump (Inst) / To and fro.
Single (7"): released on Mute, Apr'86 Dist: Spartan Distribution, Rough Trade Distribution, Cartel Distribution

Single (12"): released on Mute, Apr'86 Dist: Spartan Distribution, Rough Trade Distribution, Cartel Distribution

Hesernen, Honor

DANNY BOY.
Single (7"): released on Palace, Mar'83 Dist: PVG

He She Him

TRY A LITTLE TENDERNESS.
Single (7"): released on Loose End, Jul'83 by MCA Records. Dist: CBS, MCA

Hession, Carl

ECHOES OF IRELAND.
Tracks: / Rare ould times, The / Maggie / Red is the rose / Rose of Tralee / Slieve na mban / Fields of Athenry / Old rustic bridge, The / Echoes / Danny boy / Isle of Inisfree / Cliffs of Dooneen / Boulavogue / When you were sweet sixteen / Bunch of thyme / Banks of my own lovely Lee / I'll take you home again Kathleen / Galway bay / Forty shades of green / Cuaichin ghleann neifin / Wild colonial boy / Green glens of Antrim / Mountains of Mourne / Come back Paddy Reilly.
Album: released on Raglan (Ireland), Jun'87 Dist: Polygram

Cassette: released on Raglan (Ireland), Jun'87 Dist: Polygram

Hester, Benny

NOBODY KNOWS ME LIKE YOU.
Album: released on Myrrh, May'82 by Word Records. Dist: Word Distribution

Cassette: released on Myrrh, May'82 by Word Records. Dist: Word Distribution

Hewett, Howard

I'M FOR REAL.
Tracks: / I'm for real / Eye on you.
Single (7"): released on Elektra (USA), Aug'86 by Elektra/Asylum/Nonesuch Records. Dist: WEA

Single (12"): released on Elektra (USA), Aug'86 by Elektra/Asylum/Nonesuch Records. Dist: WEA

STAY (AFTER MIDNIGHT MIX).
Tracks: / Stay (after midnight mix) / Eye on you.
Single (7"): released on Elektra (USA), Feb'87 by Elektra/Asylum/Nonesuch Records. Dist: WEA

Single (12"): released on Elektra (USA), Feb'87 by Elektra/Asylum/Nonesuch Records. Dist: WEA

Hewick, Kevin

FEATHERING THE NEST.
Single (7"): released on Cherry Red, May'83 by Cherry Red Records. Dist: Pinnacle

OPHELIA'S DRINKING.
Single (7"): released on Factory, Feb'82 by Factory Records. Dist: Cartel, Pinnacle

SUCH HUNGER FOR LOVE.
Album: released on Cherry Red, May'83 by Cherry Red Records. Dist: Pinnacle

THIS COVER KEEPS REALITY UNREAL (Hewick, Kevin & the sound).
Single (12"): released on Cherry Red, Feb'84 by Cherry Red Records. Dist: Pinnacle

Hewitt, Ben

FOR QUITE A WHILE.
Tracks: / For quite a while / I saw Linda yesterday.
Single (7"): released on Pinner, Feb'87 by Pinner Records. Dist: Rough Trade, Cartel. Backs

GOOD TIMES AND SOME MIGHTY FINE ROCK 'N' ROLL.
Album: released on Bear Family, Nov'85 by Bear Family Records. Dist: Rollercoaster Distribution, Swift

Hewitt, Garth

ALIEN BRAIN.
Album: released on Myrrh, Aug'85 by Word Records. Dist: Word Distribution

Cassette: released on Myrrh, Aug'85 by Word Records. Dist: Word Distribution

BEST OF GARTH HEWITT, THE.
Album: released on Myrrh, May'82 by Word Records. Dist: Word Distribution

Cassette: released on Myrrh, May'82 by Word Records. Dist: Word Distribution

DID HE JUMP OR WAS HE PUSHED.
Cassette: released on Pathe Marconi, Sep'79 Dist: Swift Deleted '81.

HUNGRY WIND.
Single (7"): released on Blue Moon, Dec'83 Dist: Magnum Music Group Ltd, PRT, Spartan

IM GRATEFUL.
Album: released on Myrrh, May'82 by Word Records. Dist: Word Distribution

Cassette: released on Myrrh, May'82 by Word Records. Dist: Word Distribution

LOVE SONG FOR THE EARTH.
Cassette: released on Myrrh, May'82 by Word Records. Dist: Word Distribution

PORTFOLIO.
Album: released on Myrrh, Mar'87 by Word Records. Dist: Word Distribution

Cassette: released on Myrrh, Mar'87 by Word Records. Dist: Word Distribution

Hewson, Pete

TAKE MY HAND.
Single (7"): released on Reset, Aug'83 by Vince Clarke/Eric Radcliffe. Dist: Spartan

Single (12"): released on Reset, Aug'83 by Vince Clarke/Eric Radcliffe. Dist: Spartan

Hewwett, Howard

I COMMIT TO LOVE.
Tracks: / I'm for real / Last forever / Committ to love,I / In a crazy way / Love don't wanna wait / Got 2 go,I / Eye on you / Let's try it all over again / Say Amen.
Album: released on Elektra (USA), Sep'86 by Elektra/Asylum/Nonesuch Records. Dist: WEA

Cassette: released on Elektra (USA), Sep'86 by Elektra/Asylum/Nonesuch Records. Dist: WEA

Hex

YOU ARE NOT ALONE (Hex, Oi Polloi, Stalag 17, Symbol Of Freedom).
Notes: You are not alone EP.

Hex & Feed Your Head

NOTHING VENTURED NOTHING GAINED.
Extended-play record: released on Words of Wisdom, 30 May'87

Hey Day

COME AND GO.
Tracks: / Come and Go / This change of yours (vocal).
Single (7"): released on EMI, Feb'86 by EMI Records. Dist: EMI

Single (12"): released on EMI, Feb'86 by EMI Records. Dist: EMI

Heydayat, Dashiel

OBSOLETE (see also Daevid Allen) (Heydayat, Dashiel & Daevid Allen).

Heyderdahl, Dr Thor

ACHIEVEMENT.
Cassette: released on Seminar Cassettes, Oct'81 by Seminar Cassettes. Dist: Davidson Distribution, Eastern Educational Products Distrib., Forlaget Systime Distribution, Laser Books Ltd Distribution, MacDougall Distribution, Talktapes Distribution, Watkins Books Ltd Distribution, Norton, Jeff Distribution

Hey Elastica

IN ON THE OFF BEAT.
Album: released on Virgin, Mar'84 by Virgin Records. Dist: EMI, Virgin Distribution

Cassette: released on Virgin, Mar'84 by Virgin Records. Dist: EMI, Virgin Distribution Deleted '85.

SUCK A LITTLE HONEY.
Single (7"): released on Virgin Music, Mar'83 by Virgin Records. Dist: EMI

Single (12"): released on Virgin Music, Mar'83 by Virgin Records. Dist: EMI

Heyerdahl, Thor

KON-TIKI EXPEDITION.
Notes: Read by Tim Piggott-Smith. The Kon-Tiki Expedition is an enthralling, true adventure story which tells how six young men defied expert advice and crossed the Pacific on a balsa-wood raft to test a theory. The dangers they encountered, not only on the voyage itself, from storms and sharks, but also their shipwreck and arrival on a remote Pacific Island, have become part of sea-faring legends. Running time: 3 hours approx.
Cassette: released on Listen For Pleasure, Feb'87 by MFP Records. Dist: EMI

Heyler, Jack

LET YOURSELF GO also see Tudor, Stanley (Heyler, Jack & Stanley Tudor).
Album: released on Crystal, Jan'74 by Crystal Records. Dist: Jetstar, Revolver, Cartel

Heyward, Nick

GOODBYE YESTERDAY.
Tracks: / Goodbye yesterday / We've all been kissed / Goodbye Yesterday (Instrumental).
Single (12"): released on Arista, Jun'86 by Arista Records. Dist: RCA

LAURA.
Single (7"): released on Arista, May'85 by Arista Records. Dist: RCA

Picture disc single: released on Arista, May'85 by Arista Records. Dist: RCA

Single (12"): released on Arista, May'85 by Arista Records. Dist: RCA

LOVE ALL DAY.
Single (7"): released on Arista, May'84 by Arista Records. Dist: RCA

Single (12"): released on Arista, May'84 by Arista Records. Dist: RCA

NORTH OF A MIRACLE.
Notes: Digital Stereo recording.
Compact disc: released on Arista, Apr'84 by Arista Records. Dist: RCA

Album: released on Arista, Oct'83 by Arista Records. Dist: RCA

Cassette: released on Arista, Oct'83 by Arista Records. Dist: RCA

Compact disc: released on Arista, Apr'84 by Arista Records. Dist: RCA

OVER THE WEEKEND.
Tracks: / Over the weekend / Cry just a bit / Cry just a bit(God knows I love you).
Single (7"): released on Arista, Apr'86 by Arista Records. Dist: RCA

Single (12"): released on Arista, Apr'86 by Arista Records. Dist: RCA

PART 1.
Notes: The videos from the Haircut 100 hits of the early 1980's,plus a selection of Heywards subsequent solo singles,and interview footage with the artist. 1986 compilation,playing time of 50 minutes.
Video-cassette (VHS): released on Virgin Music, Jul'86 by Virgin Records. Dist: EMI

POSTCARDS FROM HOME.
Tracks: / Over the weekend / Move it up / Goodbye yesterday / Again in my heart / We've been kissed / Pray for a miracle / Now you've gone / Come on baby run / Teach till you reach / Cry just a bit.
Cassette: released on Arista, Sep'86 by Arista Records. Dist: RCA

Compact disc: released on Arista, Sep'86 by Arista Records. Dist: RCA

Album: released on Arista, Sep'86 by Arista Records. Dist: RCA

WARNING SIGN.
Single (7"): released on Arista, Oct'84 by Arista Records. Dist: RCA

Single (12"): released on Arista, Oct'84 by Arista Records. Dist: RCA

WARNING SIGN (EXT. REMIX).
Single (12"): released on Arista, Oct'84 by Arista Records. Dist: RCA

Heywood, Colin
DREAM LOVER.
Single (7"): released on Crash, Jan'83 by Satril Records. Dist: PRT

NO EASY WAY TO LOVE.
Tracks: / No easy way to love / Together.
Single (7"): released on Spartan, Apr'86 by Spartan Records. Dist: Spartan

SAFETY IN NUMBERS.
Single (7"): released on Monarch, Oct'83 by Chart Records. Dist: Pinnacle

Heywood, Eddie
BIGGEST LITTLE BAND OF THE FORTIES.
Album: released on Commodore Classics, May'87 by Teldec Records (Germany). Dist: Conifer, IMS, Polygram

BIGGEST LITTLE BIG BAND OF THE FORTIES, THE.
Album: released on Teldec (Germany), Sep'83 by Import Records. Dist: IMS Distribution, Polygram Distribution

HGB
CHASE THE NIGHT AWAY.
Single (7"): released on Backshot, Nov'81 Dist: MK

Hiatt, John
BACK TO NORMAL.
Single (7"): released on MCA, Feb'81 by MCA Records. Dist: Polygram, MCA

BACK TO THE WAR.
Single (7"): released on MCA, Oct'80 by MCA Records. Dist: Polygram, MCA

BRING THE FAMILY.
Compact disc: released on Demon, Jun'87 by Demon Records. Dist: Pinnacle

Album: released on Demon, May'87 by Demon Records. Dist: Pinnacle

Cassette: released on Demon, May'87 by Demon Records. Dist: Pinnacle

Cassette: released on Demon, Jun'87 by Demon Records. Dist: Pinnacle

SHE LOVES THE JERK.
Single (7"): released on Geffen, Feb'84 by Geffen Records. Dist: WEA, CBS

SHE SAID THE SAME THINGS TO ME.
Single (7"): released on Geffen, Jan'85 by Geffen Records. Dist: WEA, CBS

SLUG LINE.
Album: released on MCA, Aug'79 by MCA Records. Dist: Polygram, MCA

SNAKE CHARMER.
Tracks: / Snake charmer / This is your day.
Single (7"): released on Atlantic, Mar'85 by WEA Records. Dist: WEA

THANK YOU GIRL.
Tracks: / Thank you girl / My girl.
Single (7"): released on Demon, May'87 by Demon Records. Dist: Pinnacle

TWO BIT MONSTERS.
Album: released on MCA, Oct'80 by MCA Records. Dist: Polygram, MCA

WARMING UP THE ICE AGE.
Tracks: / Usual (The) / Crush (The) / When we ran / She said the same things to me / Living a little, laughing a little / Zero house / Warming up the ice age / I'm a real man / Number one honest game / Got a gun,I.
Album: released on Geffen, Sep'86 by Geffen Records. Dist: WEA, CBS

Cassette: released on Geffen, Sep'86 by Geffen Records. Dist: WEA, CBS

Hiawatha
HIAWATHA Original cast (Various Artists).
Album: released on Multi-Media, Apr'82 by Multi Media Tapes Dist: Pinnacle, Conifer Distribution, H.R. Taylor Distribution, Stage One Distribution

Cassette: released on Multi-Media, Apr'82 by Multi Media Tapes Dist: Pinnacle, Conifer Distribution, H.R. Taylor Distribution, Stage One Distribution

Hibbler, Al
GOLDEN GREATS: AL HIBBLER.
Tracks: / Unchained Melody / On a slow boat to china / Pennies from heaven / Don't get around much anymore / I'll never smile again / All or nothing at all / You'll never know / Trees / Very thought of you(The) / Stardust / Stormy

weather / 11th Hour Medley / He / After the lights go down low / September in the rain / Stella by starlight.
Notes: It was during the mid-fifties the smooth voiced Al Hibbler found fame and chart success with a number of MCA recordings.A star from the decade of ballad singers(Nat Cole,Dean Martin,Perry Como,ETC)were at their height,Al Hibbler proved withhis versions of 'Unchained Melody','Stardust','He','Stormy Weather','The Very Thought Of You'and many other great songs of the day,that he ranked with the very best.His versions of Unchained Melody'is regarded as the classic and opensthis strong collection.
Album: released on MCA, Feb'86 by MCA Records. Dist: Polygram, MCA

Cassette: released on MCA, Feb'86 by MCA Records. Dist: Polygram, MCA

UNCHAINED MELODY.
Single (7"): released on Old Gold, Jul'82 by Old Gold Records. Dist: Lightning, Jazz Music, Spartan, Counterpoint

Hickory Dickory Dock
HICKORY DICKORY DOCK (Various Artists).
Cassette: released on Bibi, Oct'81

Album: released on K-Tel, Mar'85 by K-Tel Records. Dist: Record Merchandisers Distribution, Taylors, Terry Blood Distribution, Wynd-Up Distribution, Relay Distribution, Pickwick Distribution, Solomon & Peres Distribution, Polygram

Hickory Lake
EASY COME EASY GO.
Album: released on Champ, '82 by Champ Records. Dist: Champ

Cassette: released on Champ, '82 by Champ Records. Dist: Champ

Hickory Rockabilly
HICKORY ROCKABILLY (Various Artists).
Tracks: / Hey Mae / Hey you there / I ain't gonna waste my time / I've got a brand new baby.
Single (7"): released on Magnum Force, Jan'87 by Magnum Music Group Ltd. Dist: Magnum Music Group Ltd, PRT, Spartan

Hickory Wind
CROSSING DEVIL'S BRIDGE.
Album: released on Flying Fish (USA), May'79 by Flying Fish Records (USA). Dist: Roots, Projection

WEDNESDAY NIGHT WALTZ, AT THE.
Album: released on Adelphi(USA), May'81 by Adelphi Records (USA). Dist: Projection, Swift

Hicks, Bob & friends
TEXAS CRAPSHOOTER.
Album: released on County (USA), May'79 Dist: Mike's Country Music Room Distribution, Projection, Swift

Hicks, Claire
PUSH (IN THE BUSH) (Hicks, Claire & Love Exchange).
Single (7"): released on Epic, Feb'85 by Epic Records. Dist: CBS

Single (12"): released on Epic, Feb'85 by Epic Records. Dist: CBS

Hicks, Dan
IT HAPPENED ONE BITE.
Album: released on Edsel, Mar'86 by Demon Records. Dist: Pinnacle, Jazz Music, Projection

RICH AND HAPPY IN HICKSVILLE - THE VERY BEST OF (Hicks, Dan & His Hot Licks).
Tracks: / You got to believe / Walkin' one and only / O'Reilly at the bar / Moody Richard (the innocent bystander) / Flight of the fly / I scare myself / Laughing song, The / Canned music / I'm an old cowhand (from the Rio Grande) / Woe the luck / Cowboys dream no.19 / Lonely madman / My old timey baby / Vivando / Payday blues / Sure hard mile / Euphonious walk, The / It's not my time to go.
Album: released on See For Miles, Apr'86 by See For Miles Records. Dist: Pinnacle

Hicks, Don
DON HICKS AND HIS HOT LICKS-ORIGINAL RECORDING (Hicks, Don & his hot licks).
Album: released on Edsel, Apr'85 by Demon Records. Dist: Pinnacle, Jazz Music, Projection

Hidden Charms
HISTORY.
Album: released on Volume (Sweden), Jan'87

LOVERS ROCK/CLUB MIX.
Single (7"): released on PRT, Sep'83 by PRT Records. Dist: PRT

Single (12"): released on PRT, Sep'83 by PRT Records. Dist: PRT

RUN FOR YOUR MONEY/I'M FINE.
Single (7"): released on PRT, Mar'83 by PRT Records. Dist: PRT

Single (12"): released on PRT, Mar'83 by PRT Records. Dist: PRT

Hidden voices
HIDDEN VOICES Various artists.
Album: released on Leo, Sep'84 Dist: Recommended

Hide my eyes
HIDE MY EYES Read by Bernard Archard.
Cassette: released on Chivers Audio Books, Aug'81 by Chivers Sound & Vision. Dist: Chivers Sound & Vision

Hiding in the hangar
HIDING IN THE HANGER Various artists.
Cassette: released on Cockpit, Apr'84 Dist: Vibes

Hi-Fi
LIVE EP (demonstration record).
Single (12"): released on Butt, Apr'82 by Butt Records. Dist: Counterpoint

MOODS FOR MALLARDS.
Tracks: / Walk away / Blue shirt / Holding out for rain / Throw a line / Knocking on your door / Desire / Time after Time / Alcohol / When you were mine.
Album: released on Shanghai, Aug'86

Hi-Fi Rock 'N' Roll Party
HI-FI ROCK 'N' ROLL PARTY Various artists (Various Artists).
Notes: Artists include: Jerry Bryne/Little Richard/Everly Brothers/Chordettes/Jesse Belvin/Chiffons/Marathons/Frankie Ford/Link Wray/Johnny Tillotson/Dion & the Belmonts/Jackie Wilson/Etc.
Compact disc: released on Ace, May'86 by Ace Records. Dist: Pinnacle, Swift, Hotshot, Cadillac

Higelin, Jaques
CAVIAR POUR LES AUTR.
Compact disc: released on EMI (France), May'86 by EMI Records. Dist: Conifer

Higgins, Alex "Hurricane"
147 - LIFE'S IN THE POCKET.
Single (7"): released on Solid, Dec'83 by Solid Records. Dist: Graduate, Spartan

Higgins, Baz
BINGO.
Single (12"): released on Mordent Music, Feb'85

Higgins, Bertie
KEY LARGO.
Album: released on Epic, Jun'82 by CBS Records. Dist: CBS

Cassette: released on Epic, Jun'82 by CBS Records. Dist: CBS

PIRATES AND POETS.
Album: released on Epic, Aug'83 by CBS Records. Dist: CBS

Cassette: released on Epic, Aug'83 by CBS Records. Dist: CBS

Higgins, Billy
SOLDIER, THE.
Album: released on Timeless, '81

Higgins, Chuck
BIP BOP BOM/TOO SMART.
Single (7"): released on Rollin' Rock, Jun'80

IS A PH.D.
Album: released on Rollin' Rock (USA), Oct'86 by Rondelet Music And Records. Dist: Jazz Music Distribution, Pinnacle, Swift Distribution

Album: released on Rollin, Jun'80

PACHUKO HOP.
Album: released on Ace, Sep'83 by Ace Records. Dist: Pinnacle, Swift, Hotshot, Cadillac

Higgins, Jack
TOUCH THE DEVIL.
Cassette: released on Listen For Pleasure, Mar'85 by MFP Records. Dist: EMI

Higgins, Lizzie
PRINCESS OF THE THISTLE.
Album: released on Topic, '81 Dist: Roots Distribution

UP AND AWA' WI' THE LAVEROCK.
Album: released on Topic, '81 Dist: Roots Distribution

WHAT A VOICE.
Album: released on Lismor, Jun'85 by Lismor Records. Dist: Lismor, Roots, Celtic Music

Cassette: released on Lismor, Jun'85 by Lismor Records. Dist: Lismor, Roots, Celtic Music

Higgins, Mark
O FOR THE WING OF A DOVE.
Single (7"): released on Pip, Sep'82 by PRT Records. Dist: PRT

Higgs, Joe
TRIUMPH.
Album: released on Alligator, Nov'85 Dist: Jetstar

WAGE A WAR.
Single (12"): released on Harry, Nov'84 by Harry Records. Dist: Jetstar

High 5
COLD STEEL GANG.
Tracks: / Cold steel gang / Confessions / Turn this car around / On the banks.
Single (7"): released on Probe Plus, Nov'83 by Probe Plus Records. Dist: Probe Plus Distribution

High Bees
SHE'S KILLING TIME.
Single (12"): released on Supreme International, Oct'85 by Supreme International Records. Dist: Fast Forward Distributors, Cartel Distribution

SOME INDULGENCE.
Single (12"): released on Supreme International, Apr'85 by Supreme International Records. Dist: Fast Forward Distributors, Cartel Distribution

High Commissioner
HIGH COMMISSIONER, (THE) Cleary, Jon (Wheeler, Peter).
Special: released on Soundings, Feb'85 Dist: Soundings

High country
LAST TRAIN TO GLORY.
Album: released on Pilgrim, '79 by Pilgrim Records. Dist: Rough Trade, Cartel

ON THE ROAD.
Album: released on Shiloh, Sep'79

High Fashion
FEELIN' LUCKY.
Album: released on Capitol, Aug'82 by Capitol Records. Dist: EMI

Cassette: released on Capitol, Aug'82 by Capitol Records. Dist: EMI

High Five
DOWN IN THE NO-GO.
Notes: Following the release of their 'Achingly Addictive'single,'Cold Steel Gang' The High Five release their debut album'Down In The No-Go'.
Album: released on No-Go, Apr'86 Dist: EMI

Cassette: released on No-Go, Apr'86 Dist: EMI

WORKING FOR THE MAN.
Single (7"): released on Big Village, Oct'84 by Big Village Records.

High flying irish...
HIGH FLYING IRISH SHOWBANDS Various artists (Various Artists).
Album: released on Spot, Feb'83 by Pickwick Records. Dist: H.R. Taylor.

Cassette: released on Spot, Feb'83 by Pickwick Records. Dist: H.R. Taylor.

High Inergy
FIRST IMPRESSIONS/COULD THIS BE LOVE.
Single (7"): released on Motown, Jun'82 by Motown Records. Dist: BMG Distribution

HE'S A PRETENDER (2 PARTS).
Single (7"): released on Gordy (USA), Feb'83 by Motown Records. Dist: RCA

Single (12"): released on Gordy (USA), Feb'83 by Motown Records. Dist: RCA

HIGH INERGY.
Album: released on Motown, Oct'81 by Motown Records. Dist: BMG Distribution

HOLD ON.
Album: released on Motown, Oct'81 by Motown Records. Dist: BMG Distribution

HOLD ON TO MY LOVE.
Single (7"): released on Motown, Oct'81 by Motown Records. Dist: BMG Distribution

I JUST WANNA DANCE WITH YOU.
Single (7"): released on Motown, Oct'81 by Motown Records. Dist: BMG Distribution

MAKE ME YOURS/I LOVE MAKIN' LOVE.
Single (7"): released on Motown, Oct'81 by Motown Records. Dist: BMG Distribution

SO RIGHT.
Album: released on Motown, Aug'82 by Motown Records. Dist: BMG Distribution

High Jinks
IF IT COULD BE LIKE THIS FOREVER.
Tracks: / If it could be like this forever / If it could be like this forever (Christmas mix).
Single (7"): released on Arista, Dec'86 by Arista Records. Dist: RCA

High, Judy
FRENCH NITES.
Single (7"): released on Spirit, May'85 by Spirit Records. Dist: WEA

PUSH JUST LITTLE BIT HARDER/WHEN YOURE WITH THE ONE YOU WANT.
Single (7"): released on Spirit, Nov'83 by Spirit Records. Dist: WEA

Single (12"): released on Spirit, Nov'83 by Spirit Records. Dist: WEA

High Kings of Tara
HIGH KINGS OF TARA Various artists.
Album: released on Tara (Ireland), '82 by Tara Records. Dist: I & B Records Distribution, Record Services Distribution (Ireland), Roots Distribution

Cassette: released on Tara (Ireland), '82 by Tara Records. Dist: I & B Records Distribution, Record Services Distribution (Ireland), Roots Distribution

Highland driving
HIGHLAND DRIVING (Various Artists).
Cassette: released on EMI, May'79 by EMI Records. Dist: EMI

Highland magic
HIGHLAND MAGIC (Various Artists).
Cassette: released on Lismor, Jul'84 by Lismor Records. Dist: Lismor, Roots, Celtic Music

Highland Strathspey
FIDDLES OF THE HIGHLAND STRATHSPEY & REEL SOCIETY, THE.
Album: released on Lismor, Nov'76 by Lismor Records. Dist: Lismor, Roots, Celtic Music

High Level Ranters
BONNY PIT LADDIE, THE.
Album: released on Topic, '81 Dist: Roots Distribution

BORDER SPIRIT.
Album: released on Topic, Nov'86 by Roots Distribution

ENGLISH SPORTING BALLADS.
Cassette: released on Broadside, Jun'81 by Broadside Records. Dist: Celtic Distributions, H.R. Taylor, Jazz Music, Projection, Jazz Services Unlimited Ltd. (JSU)

FOUR IN A BAR.
Album: released on Topic, '81 Dist: Roots Distribution

HIGH LEVEL.
Album: released on Leader, '81 Dist: Jazz Music, Projection

KEEP YOUR FEET STILL GEORDIE HINNIE.
Album: released on Leader, '81 Dist: Jazz Music, Projection

LADS OF NORTHUMBRIA, THE.
Album: released on Leader, '81 Dist: Jazz Music, Projection

MILE TO RIDE, A.
Album: released on Leader, '81 Dist: Jazz Music, Projection

NORTHUMBERLAND FOREVER.
Album: released on Topic, '81 Dist: Roots Distribution

RANTING LADS.
Album: released on Topic, '81 Dist: Roots Distribution

High Life Stars
ONE.
Album: released on Flying Elephant, Feb'84 Dist: Rough Trade, Cartel

Highlights...
HIGHLIGHTS WEMBLEY COUNTRY MUSIC FESTIVALS (Various Artists).
Cassette: released on Pickwick, Mar'84 by Pickwick Records. Dist: Pickwick Distribution, Prism Leisure Distribution,

Highly Strung
DON'T LET IT END.
Tracks: / Don't let end / Flame's lit(The).
Single (7"): released on Spartan, Jul'86 by Spartan Records. Dist: Spartan

High On The Hog
HOGTIED.
Album: released on Sweet Folk All, May'81 by Sweet Folk All Records. Dist: Sweet Folk All, Roots, Celtic Music, Dragon, Impetus, Projection, Chris Wellard, Festival Records

High Road to China
HIGH ROAD TO CHINA Original film soundtrack (Various Artists).
Album: released on A & R, '84 Dist: Spartan

High school confidential
HIGH SCHOOL CONFIDENTIAL (Various original artists).
Album: released on RCA, Dec'82 by RCA Records. Dist: RCA, Roots, Swift, Wellard, Chris, I & B, Solomon & Peres Distribution

Cassette: released on RCA, Dec'82 by RCA Records. Dist: RCA, Roots, Swift, Wellard, Chris, I & B, Solomon & Peres Distribution

Highs in the mid-sixties
HIGHS IN THE MID-SIXTIES (VOL 1 - LA '65) Teenage rebellion (Various Artists).
Album: released on Archive International Productions, Dec'83 Dist: Pacific

HIGHS IN THE MID-SIXTIES (VOL 2 - LA '66) Riot on sunset strip (Various Artists).
Album: released on Archive International Productions, Dec'83 Dist: Pacific

HIGHS IN THE MID-SIXTIES (VOL 3 - LA '67) Mondo Hollywood a go-go (Various Artists).
Album: released on Archive International Productions, Dec'83 Dist: Pacific

High Society
GOTTA GET OUT OF THIS RUT.
Single (7"): released on Eagle (London), Aug'81 by Eagle Records (London). Dist: Stage One

HIGH SOCIETY Original Cast Recording (Various Artists).
Tracks: / Overture / How do you spell Ambassador? / Give him the oo-la-la / Who wants to be a millionaire / Little one / Hey, good looking / I love you Samantha / Ball medley / Well did you evah? / Most gentlemen don't like love / Now you has jazz / In the still of the night / True love / True love / Finale / High society / Weel did you evah?
Notes: Major new London musical featuring the sensational music of Cole Porter, following successful season at the Leicester Haymarket Musical stars Trevor Eve, Stephen Rea, Natasha Richardson and Angela Richards. [EMI release sheet,April 87].
Album: released on Columbia, Jan'87 by EMI Records. Dist: EMI

Cassette: released on Columbia, Jan'87 by EMI Records. Dist: EMI

Compact disc: released on Columbia, Jan'87 by EMI Records. Dist: EMI

Cassette: released on Capitol, Nov'61 by Capitol Records. Dist: EMI

I NEVER GO OUT IN THE RAIN.
Single (7"): released on Eagle (London), Sep'80 by Eagle Records (London). Dist: Stage One

High Spirits
HIGH SPIRITS Original London cast.
Album: released on Flashback, Nov'85 by Flashback Records/PRT Records. Dist: Mainline, PRT

Cassette: released on Flashback, Nov'85 by Flashback Records/PRT Records. Dist: Mainline, PRT

High Tide
DANCING IN MY MIND.
Single (7"): released on WEA, Jan'82 by WEA Records. Dist: WEA

HIGH TIDE.
Tracks: / Blankman cries again / Joke(The) / Saneonymous.
Notes: Produced by High Tide & George Chkiantz.
Album: released on Psycho, May'84 Dist: Funhouse, Rough Trade

SEA SHANTIES.
Tracks: / Futilists lament / Death warmed up / Pushed,But not forgotten / Walking down their outlook / Missing out / Nowhere.
Album: released on Psycho, May'84 Dist: Funhouse, Rough Trade

High Times...
HIGH TIMES ALL-STAR EXPLOSION Various artists (Various Artists).
Album: released on Alligator, Nov'85 Dist: Jetstar

Hightower, Rosetta
EVERLASTING LOVE (see also Henry Turtle).
Single (7"): released on Riviera, Jan'85 by Riviere Records. Dist: M.I.S.

RIDE A WILD HORSE (see also Henry Turtle).
Single (7"): released on Riviera, Dec'84 by Riviere Records. Dist: M.I.S.

WE FOUND LOVE TODAY.
Single (7"): released on Mirage, Feb'81 Dist: Pinnacle

High Voltage
JUNKANOO-OO-OO.
Single (7"): released on Audiotrax, Aug'85 by Audiotrax. Dist: PRT

LOVE IS THE MESSAGE.
Single (12"): released on KRP, Dec'83 by High Energy Records. Dist: PRT

LOVE IS THE MESSAGE.
Single (12"): released on KRP, Mar'84 by High Energy Records. Dist: PRT

LOVE IS THE MESSAGE (87).
Single (12"): released on ISR, Jul'87 by ISR Records. Dist: DMS, RCA

Highwayman
HIGHWAYMAN (Various Artists).
Album: released on CBS, Jun'85 by CBS Records. Dist: CBS

Cassette: released on CBS, Jun'85 by CBS Records. Dist: CBS

Highwaymen
MICHAEL.
Tracks: / Michael / Tom Dooley.
Single (7"): released on Old Gold, Mar'87 by Old Gold Records. Dist: Lightning, Jazz Music, Spartan, Counterpoint

Highwaymen Ride Again
HIGHWAYMEN RIDE AGAIN I love country (Various Artists).
Tracks: / Twentieth century is almost over, The / How do you feel about foolin' around / Heroes / Down to her socks / Blackjack county chains / They're all the same to me / Whiter shade of pale, A / Last cowboy song, The / Ballad of forty dollars, The / Pilgrim, The / Casey's last ride / Under the gun / Eye of the storm / Why baby why / Whiter shade of pale, A.
Album: released on CBS, Mar'87 by CBS Records. Dist: CBS

Cassette: released on CBS, Mar'87 by CBS Records. Dist: CBS

Highways
HIGHWAYS Great songs of the American truck drivers (Various Artists).
Album: released on Mercury (USA), Mar'83 by Import Records. Dist: IMS Distribution, Polygram Distribution

Cassette: released on Mercury (USA), Mar'83 by Import Records. Dist: IMS Distribution, Polygram Distribution

Highwind
HIGHWIND.
Cassette: released on EMI International, Sep'79 by EMI Records. Dist: Conifer

High wind in Jamaica
HIGH WIND IN JAMAICA (read by Anthony Quale) (Hughes, R).
Album: released on Caedmon(USA), '78 by Caedmon (USA) Records. Dist: Gower, Taylors, Discovery

Cassette: released on Caedmon(USA), Jan'78 by Caedmon (USA) Records. Dist: Gower, Taylors, Discovery

Hi-Gloss
YOU'LL NEVER KNOW.
Album: released on Epic, Sep'81 by CBS Records. Dist: CBS

Cassette: released on Epic, Sep'81 by CBS Records. Dist: CBS

Single (7"): released on Epic, Jul'81 by CBS

Single (12"): released on Epic, Jul'81 by CBS Records. Dist: CBS

Higsons
CONSPIRACY.
Single (7"): released on Waap, Apr'82 by Waap Records. Dist: Cartel

CURSE OF THE HIGSONS (THE).
Album: released on Upright, Apr'87 by Upright Records. Dist: Cartel, Rough Trade

GOT TO LET THIS HEAT OUT.
Single (7"): released on Waap, Jul'83 by Waap Records. Dist: Cartel

I DON'T WANT TO LIVE WITH MONKEYS.
Single (7"): released on Romans In Britain, Jul'81 Dist: Rough Trade Distribution

LOST AND LONELY.
Single (7"): released on Waap, Dec'81 by Waap Records. Dist: Cartel

MUSIC TO WATCH GIRLS BY.
Single (7"): released on Upright, Sep'84 by Upright Records. Dist: Cartel, Rough Trade

Single (12"): released on Upright, Sep'84 by Upright Records. Dist: Cartel, Rough Trade

PUSH OUT THE BOAT.
Single (7"): released on Waap, Oct'83 by Waap Records. Dist: Cartel

RUN ME DOWN.
Single (7"): released on 2-Tone, Feb'83 by Chrysalis Records. Dist: Polygram Deleted '85

Single (12"): released on 2-Tone, Feb'83 by Chrysalis Records. Dist: Polygram

TAKE IT.
Single (7"): released on R4, Jul'85 by R & R. Dist: EMI

Single (12"): released on R4, Jul'85 by R & R. Dist: EMI

Hi-Jinx
STREAMLINING SONG, THE.
Single (7"): released on South Bank, Jul'84

Hi-Life International
COMME CI COMME CA.
Single (12"): released on Sterns, Dec'84 by Sterns Records. Dist: Sterns/Triple Earth Distribution

MUSIC TO WAKE THE DEAD.
Album: released on Sterns African, Nov'83 by Sterns African Records. Dist: Stern's Distribution, Rough Trade Distribution

NA WA FOR YOU.
Album: released on Sterns, Mar'85 by Sterns Records. Dist: Sterns/Triple Earth Distribution

NA WA FOR YOU.
Tracks: / Na Wa for you / Comme ci comme ca / Obrempong ahyease / Harmattan joy / Awo de me / Rice water / Seventeen / Come to Africa.
Notes: The second album from Britain's hardest working African outfit confirms their reputation for dance floor action.".....simply sparkles with purity of sounds" (West Africa)

TRAVEL AND SEE (Ghana/U.K).
Tracks: / All that glitters / Travel & See / Wish you were here / Abrokyire Abrabo / De tell you mama,I / Salaam alekum / For better for worse / Your touch is so warm.
Notes: Music to wake the dead ,from the London based band.A tight set of upbeat high- life and soukous,numbers."....the band that will make you bop till you drop" (Time Out).
Album: released on Sterns, Sep'86 by Sterns Records. Dist: Sterns/Triple Earth Distribution

Hi-Liters
DANCE ME TO DEATH.
Single (7"): released on Pinner, Jul'84 by Pinner Records. Dist: Rough Trade, Cartel, Backs

Hill 16
HILL 16.
Album: released on Meadow Walk, Jun'85 by Meadow Walk Records. Dist: Making Waves

Hillage, Steve
ALONE/FRAME BY FRAME.
Single (7"): released on Virgin, Apr'83 by Virgin Records. Dist: EMI, Virgin Distribution

Single (12"): released on Virgin, Apr'83 by Virgin Records. Dist: EMI, Virgin Distribution

FISH RISING.
Tracks: / Solar musick siute / Fish / Meditation of the snake / Salmon,(The) / Aftaglid.

Notes: Originally Virgin:V 2301 released 1975.
Album: released on Virgin, Mar'86 by Virgin Records. Dist: EMI, Virgin Distribution

Cassette: released on Virgin, Mar'86 by Virgin Records. Dist: EMI, Virgin Distribution

Compact disc: released on Virgin, 20 Jun'87 by Virgin Records. Dist: EMI, Virgin Distribution

GREEN.
Album: released on Virgin, Mar'84 by Virgin Records. Dist: EMI, Virgin Distribution

KAMIKAZE EYES/BEFORE THE WORLD.
Single (7"): released on Virgin, Jan'83 by Virgin Records. Dist: EMI, Virgin Distribution

Single (12"): released on Virgin, Jan'83 by Virgin Records. Dist: EMI, Virgin Distribution

L.
Tracks: / Hurdy gurdy man / Hurdy gurdy glissando / Elecktrick Gypsies / Om Nama Shivaya / Luna musick suite / It's all too much.
Notes: Originally Virgin:V 2066 released 1976.
Album: released on Virgin, Mar'84 by Virgin Records. Dist: EMI, Virgin Distribution

Cassette: released on Virgin, Mar'84 by Virgin Records. Dist: EMI, Virgin Distribution

Compact disc: released on Virgin, 20 Jun'87 by Virgin Records. Dist: EMI, Virgin Distribution

LIVE HERALD.
Album: released on Virgin, '79 by Virgin Records. Dist: EMI, Virgin Distribution

MOTIVATION RADIO.
Album: released on Virgin, Mar'84 by Virgin Records. Dist: EMI, Virgin Distribution

OPEN.
Album: released on Virgin, Mar'84 by Virgin Records. Dist: EMI, Virgin Distribution

RAINBOW DOME MUSICK.
Album: released on Virgin, May'79 by Virgin Records. Dist: EMI, Virgin Distribution

Hill, Andrew

LIVE AT MONTREAUX.
Album: released on Freedom, Jan'79 by Logo Records. Dist: RCA, Discovery, Wellard, Chris

POINT OF DEPARTURE.
Album: released on Blue Note (USA), Sep'84

SOLO PIANO.
Album: released on Artists House, May'81 Dist: JSU, Swift

Hill, Benny

LAUGH ALONG WITH BENNY HILL.
Cassette: released on Pickwick (Ditto series), Jan'83

THIS IS BENNY HILL.
Album: released on EMI, Feb'81 by EMI Records. Dist: EMI

Cassette: released on EMI, Feb'81 by EMI Records. Dist: EMI

WORLD OF.....
Album: released on World of Learning, '71 by World Of Learning Records. Dist: World Of Learning

Hillbilly Hop

HILLBILLY HOP Various artists (Various Artists).
Tracks: / Courtin' in the rain / Flirting with you / Skinnie Minnie / 8 more miles to Louisville / Mississippi / Texas vs. Alaska / Steel guitar rag / Four aces and a queen / Lie Detector / My heart, my heart / Kiss me like crazy / Crawdad song / All alone / Happy go lucky / 40th & Plum.
Notes: Artists:Arlie Duff,Jack Bradshaw,T.Inman,Lonnie Glosson,Wayne Raney,Red Foley, Grandpa Jones,Lawton Williams.
Album: released on Charly, Jul'86 by Charly Records. Dist: Charly, Cadillac

Hillbilly Rock

HILLBILLY ROCK (Various original artists).
Album: released on Charly, Feb'82 by Charly Records. Dist: Charly, Cadillac

Hill, Buck Quartet

SCOPE.
Album: released on Steeplechase, Sep'79

Hill, Dan

BEST OF DAN HILL, THE.
Album: released on 20th Century, Oct'80 Dist: RCA, IMS-Polygram

Cassette: released on 20th Century, Oct'80 Dist: RCA, IMS-Polygram

IT'S A LONG ROAD.
Single (7"): released on That's Entertainment, Feb'83 by That's Entertainment Records. Dist: Pinnacle, PRT

LONGER FUSE.
Album: released on 20th Century, Mar'78 Dist: RCA, IMS-Polygram

LOVE IN THE SHADOWS.
Album: released on PRT, Feb'84 by PRT Records. Dist: PRT

Cassette: released on PRT, Feb'84 by PRT Records. Dist: PRT

SOMETIMES WHEN WE TOUCH.
Single (7"): released on 20th Century, Jul'81 Dist: RCA, IMS-Polygram

T'S A LONG ROAD.

YOU PULLED ME THROUGH.
Single (7"): released on PRT, Jan'84 by PRT Records. Dist: PRT

Hiller, Holger

BUNCH OF FOULNESS IN THE PIT, A.
Album: released on Cherry Red, Feb'84 by Cherry Red Records. Dist: Pinnacle

HOLGER HILLER.
Album: released on Cherry Red, Feb'84 by Cherry Red Records. Dist: Pinnacle

JONNY.
Single (12"): released on Cherry Red, Feb'84 by Cherry Red Records. Dist: Pinnacle

OBEN IM ECK.
Album: released on Mute, Nov'86 Dist: Spartan Distribution, Rough Trade Distribution, Cartel Distribution

Cassette: released on Mute, Nov'86 Dist: Spartan Distribution, Rough Trade Distribution, Cartel Distribution

Compact disc: released on Mute, Nov'86 Dist: Spartan Distribution, Rough Trade Distribution, Cartel Distribution

WHIPPETS.
Single (12"): released on Mute, Mar'87 Dist: Spartan Distribution, Rough Trade Distribution, Cartel Distribution

Hill, Geoffrey

POETRY & VOICE OF GEOFFREY HILL, THE.
Album: released on Caedmon(USA), Jul'79 by Caedmon (USA) Records. Dist: Gower, Taylors, Discovery

Hill, Lonnie

COULD IT BE LOVE.
Tracks: / Could it be love / Step on out.
Single (7"): released on 10, May'86 by 10 Records. Dist: Virgin, EMI

Single (12"): released on 10, May'86 by 10 Records. Dist: Virgin, EMI

GALVASTON BAY.
Tracks: / Galvaston Bay / My sweet love.
Single (7"): released on 10, Jun'86 by 10 Records. Dist: Virgin, EMI

Single (12"): released on 10, Jun'86 by 10 Records. Dist: Virgin, EMI

YOU GOT ME RUNNING.
Tracks: / Keep on dancing / Step on out / Mr Music man / Something special to me / Galveston bay / Could it be love / My sweet love / Close to you / You got me running / Hard times.
Album: released on 10, Jul'86 by 10 Records. Dist: Virgin, EMI

Cassette: released on 10, Jul'86 by 10 Records. Dist: Virgin, EMI

Hillman, Chris

DESERT ROSE.
Album: released on Spindrift, Nov'84 Dist: Roots

Hill, Michael P

SHE'S MY QUEEN.
Single (12"): released on Big Top, Aug'87 Dist: Cartel

Hill, Noel

IG CNOC NA GRAI (Hill, Noel & Tony McMahon).

Hillsbrough Crew

STEEL CITY.
Tracks: / Steel city / Move on up.
Single (7"): released on Virgin, Dec'86 by Virgin Records. Dist: EMI, Virgin Distribution

Single (12"): released on Virgin, Dec'86 by Virgin Records. Dist: EMI, Virgin Distribution

Hills & Home

HILLS & HOME (Thirty years of bluegrass) (Various Artists).
Tracks: / Why did you wonder? / Pathway of teardrops, A / Blue ridge cabin home / Daniel prayed / Love please come home / You'd better wake up / Your old stand by / Twenty-one years / Springhill disaster / Old age / Blackberry blossom / Hold watcha got / Diesel train / Pathway of teardrops, A / Hills and home / Raise a ruckus tonight / Fox on the run / Dill pickles rag / Body and soul / Dill pickles rag.
Notes: Featuring: Bill Monroe and his Blue Grass Boys/Lester Flatt, Earl Scruggs and the Foggy Mountain Boys/The Stanley Brothers and the Clinch Mountain Boys/Don Reno, Red Smiley and the Tennessee Cut Ups/Mac Wiseman and the Country Boys/Jim Eanes and the Shenandoah Valley Boys/The Lonesome Pine Fiddlers/Bill Clifton and the Dixie Mountain Boys/Bill Baker, Jimmy Martin and the Sunny Mountain Boys/Dave Woolum and his Kentucky Mountain Boys/Jim Jesse and the Virginia Boys/The Osborne Brothers/The Country Gentlemen/The Lonesome River Boys/Emerson and Waldron/The New Grass Revival/Bluegrass Allstars.
Album: released on New World (USA), Dec'86 by New World Records (USA). Dist: Conifer

Hillsiders

DAY IN THE COUNTRY, A.
Album: released on LP, '79 by LP Records. Dist: Pinnacle

DRIVER GET ME HOME ON TIME.
Single (7"): released on Live Prom, '80

HILLSIDERS, THE.
Album: released on LP, '81 by LP Records. Dist: Pinnacle

SHE WAS MY ONLY ONE.
Single (7"): released on Live Prom, '81

Hillstreet

YOU PICK ME UP.
Single (7"): released on K West, Aug'87 by Creole Records. Dist: Rhino, PRT

Single (12"): released on K West, Aug'87 by Creole Records. Dist: Rhino, PRT

Hill, Teddy

TEDDY HILL & CAB CALLOWAY.
Album: released on Queen-Disc, Apr'81 Dist: Celtic Music, JSU, Jazz Horizons, Jazz Music

Hill, Tiny

1943/4 (Hill, Tiny & his Orchestra).
Album: released on Circle(USA), Mar'84 by Jazzology Records (USA). Dist: Jazz Music, Swift, Chris Wellard

Hill, Tony

CUCKOO CLOCK (Hill, Tony & the Hillmans).
Single (7"): released on Blue Hat, Dec'82 by Blue Hat Records. Dist: Blue Hat

H.M.S. PINAFORE MEDLEY (Hill, Tony & the Hillmans).
Single (7"): released on Blue Hat, Oct'84 by Blue Hat Records. Dist: Blue Hat

I'M A PIRATE KING.
Single (7"): released on Blue Hat, Apr'83 by Blue Hat Records. Dist: Blue Hat

OLD KING COLE.
Single (7"): released on Blue Hat, Sep'83 by Blue Hat Records. Dist: Blue Hat

TERRY WOGAN'S PARTY.
Single (7"): released on Blue Hat, May'84 by Blue Hat Records. Dist: Blue Hat

Hill, Vince

20 GOLDEN FAVOURITES.
Album: released on Note, Apr'80 by EMI Records. Dist: EMI

BRAVO POUR LA MUSICA.
Single (7"): released on Everest (Premier), Mar'83 by Everest Records. Dist: Pinnacle

EDELWEISS.
Single (7"): released on Old Gold, Jul'82 by Old Gold Records. Dist: Lightning, Jazz Music, Spartan, Counterpoint

FREEWAY SONGS.
Cassette: released on Mobile, '78

HIS GREATEST HITS.
Tracks: / Take me to your heart again / Importance of your love (The) / Little Bluebird / Somewhere my love / Love letter's in the sand / Doesn't anybody know my name? / Here, there and everywhere / Wives and lovers / Girl talk / Merci cherie / Heartaches / Roses of picardy / Moonlight and roses / Look around(And you'll find me there) / Love story / They long to be Close to you / Danny boy / You're my world / Time for us, A / Spanish eyes.

Cassette: released on Hour Of Pleasure, May'86 by Music For Pleasure Records. Dist: EMI

I'M THE SINGER.
Album: released on Premier, May'85 by Premier Records. Dist: CBS

Cassette: released on Premier, May'85 by Premier Records. Dist: CBS

LOVE & EMOTIONS.
Cassette: released on Hallmark, Mar'81 by Pickwick Records. Dist: Pickwick Distribution, PRT, Taylors

LOVING FEELINGS.
Cassette: released on Autograph, Apr'85 Dist: Record Services Distribution (Ireland)

PRAY FOR LOVE.
Single (7"): released on Multi-Media, May'82 by Multi Media Tapes Records. Dist: Pinnacle, Conifer Distribution, H.R. Taylor Distribution, Stage One Distribution

SINGS THE GREAT SONGS OF TODAY.
Album: released on Spot, Sep'84 by Pickwick Records. Dist: H.R. Taylor, Lugtons

Cassette: released on Spot, Sep'84 by Pickwick Records. Dist: H.R. Taylor, Lugtons

VINCE HILL.
Cassette: released on Ideal(Tapes), Jun'81 Dist: EMI

WHILE THE FEELING'S GOOD.
Album: released on Everest (Premier), '83 by Everest Records. Dist: Pinnacle

Cassette: released on Everest (Premier), '83 by Everest Records. Dist: Pinnacle

Hill, Z.Z.

BEST OF Z.Z.HILL.
Compact disc: released on Malaco, Apr'87 by Malaco Records. Dist: Charly

BLUESMASTER.
Album: released on Malaco, Dec'84 by Malaco Records. Dist: Charly

CHEATING IN THE NEXT ROOM.
Single (7"): released on Malaco, Jun'82 by Malaco Records. Dist: Charly

DOWN HOME.
Album: released on Malaco, May'82 by Malaco Records. Dist: Charly

Cassette: released on Malaco, May'82 by Malaco Records. Dist: Charly

DUES PAID IN FULL.
Album: released on Kent, Apr'84 by Ace Records. Dist: Pinnacle

GREATEST HITS:Z Z HILL.
Tracks: / Next room(The) / Down Home Blues / Please Don't let our good thing end / Right arm for your love / Open house at my house / Someone else is steppin' in / Shade tree mechanic / Three into two won't go / Stop you from givin' me the blues / Friday is my day.
Notes: Culled from the late Z.Z's six Malaco albums dating from 1980,these tracks high-light the man as one of the great modern Soul/Blues/Gospel singers and endorce what a sad loss his was.
Album: released on Malaco, Sep'86 by Malaco Records. Dist: Charly

I'M A BLUES MAN.
Album: released on Malaco, Nov'83 by Malaco Records. Dist: Charly

IN MEMORIAM.
Album: released on Malaco, Jun'85 by Malaco Records. Dist: Charly

MAN NEEDS A WOMAN, A.
Tracks: / Blues at the opera(Communication in regards to circumstances / Act 1, Scene 1 - It Ain't no use / Act 1, Scene 2 - Ha Ha(Laughing song) / Act 2, Scene 1 - Second chance / Act 2, Scene 2 - Our love is getting better / Act 3 - Finale,Faithful and true / Chockin' kind (The) / Hold back (One man at a time) / Man needs a woman, (A woman needs a man) / Early in the morning / Think I'd do it, I.
Album: released on Topline, May'86 by Charly Records. Dist: Charly Distribution

Cassette: released on Topline, May'86 by Charly Records. Dist: Charly Distribution

WHO'S THRILLING YOU Is Killing Me.
Tracks: / Am I groovin' you / 'Cause I love you / Love in the street / Don't need half a love,I / Ain't nothing you can do / I've got to get you back / Two sides to every story / That ain't the way to make love / Keep on lovin' you,I / Look what you've done / Whoever's thrilling you(Is killing me) / My turn.
Album: released on Stateside, Sep'86 Dist: EMI

Cassette: released on Stateside, Sep'86 Dist: EMI

Z.Z. HILL.
Album: released on Malaco, May'82 by Malaco Records. Dist: Charly

Cassette: released on Malaco, May'82 by Malaco Records. Dist: Charly

Hi-Los
HI-LO'S BACK AGAIN, THE.
Album: released on Memoir, Oct'85 by Memoir Records. Dist: PRT Distribution

Hilton Fyle Band
FRESH.
Album: released on Nadiya, Jun'87

Hilton, Ronnie
VERY BEST OF RONNY HILTON - 16 FAVOURITES OF THE 50'S.
Album: released on EMI, Feb'84 by EMI Records. Dist: EMI

Cassette: released on EMI, Feb'84 by EMI Records. Dist: EMI

Himber, Richard
1940 (Himber, Richard & His Orchestra).
Notes: Mono.
Album: released on Circle(USA), Jan'87 by Jazzology Records (USA). Dist: Jazz Music, Swift, Chris Wellard

Hinchcliffe, Frank
IN SHEFFIELD PARK.
Album: released on Topic, '81 Dist: Roots Distribution

Hindle Pickets and TBE
PART OF THE UNION.
Single (7"): released on Catch 22, Aug'84 by Catch 22. Dist: Red Rhino, Cartel

Hinds, Donna
SPECIAL PRAYER.
Tracks: / Special prayer. / From me to you.
Single (7"): released on Multi, Dec'86

Hinds, Errol
HO WHAT A SATURDAY NIGHT.
Single (12"): released on Witty, May'85 by Witty Records. Dist: Jetstar

Hindsight
HEAVEN'S JUST A BREATH AWAY.
Tracks: / Heaven's just a breath away / Come's the sunshine / Small change (Corn Exchange mix) / Heaven's just a breath away (heaven can wait).
Single (7"): Dist: Virgin

Single (12"): released on Circa, May'87 Dist: Virgin

Double-pack single: released on Circa, May'87 Dist: Virgin

SMALL CHANGE.
Tracks: / Small change / Be free.
Single (7"): released on Circa, Nov'86 Dist: Virgin

Single (12"): released on Circa, Nov'86 Dist: Virgin

Hinds, Justin
TRAVEL WITH LOVE.
Album: released on Nighthawk, Aug'85 by Faulty Products Records. Dist: Pinnacle, Swift

Hinds, Ornell
TOGETHER AGAIN (See Chandell, Tim) (Hinds, Ornell & Tim Chandell).
Album: released on Orbitone, Nov'80 by Orbitone Records. Dist: Jetstar Distribution

Hine, Eric
EXPECTATION Brave new world.
Single (7"): released on Radioactive, Jul'82

NOT FADE AWAY.
Single (7"): released on Radioactive, Apr'81

Single (12"): released on Radioactive, Apr'81

Hine, Graham
BOWERY FANTASY.
Album: released on Blue Goose, May'79 Dist: Projection, Swift

Hine, John
SILVER AND WHITE.
Cassette: released on One Key, Nov'84

Hine, Rupert
IMMUNITY.
Compact disc: released on A&M, Feb'81 by A&M Records. Dist: Polygram

---

Cassette: released on A&M, Feb'81 by A&M Records. Dist: Polygram

LIVING IN A SIN.
Single (7"): released on A&M, Apr'83 by A&M Records. Dist: Polygram

Cassette: released on A&M, Apr'83 by A&M Records. Dist: Polygram

WAVING NOT DROWNING.
Album: released on A&M, Apr'82 by A&M Records. Dist: Polygram

WILDEST WISH TO FLY, THE.
Album: released on Island, Feb'85 by Island Records. Dist: Polygram

Cassette: released on Island, Feb'85 by Island Records. Dist: Polygram

Hines, Carl
AN EVENING WITH CARL HINES.
Double Album: released on Vogue Jazz (France), May'83

Hines, Carlton
SHE LOVES ME.
Tracks: / She loves me / She loves me(DUB) / Jah Bull / Conference table(Dub).
Single (12"): released on Island, Nov'86 by Island Records. Dist: Polygram

Hines, Earl
1965.
Album: released on Pathe Marconi(France), Sep'84

AT CLUB HANGOVER VOL.5.
Album: released on Storyville, Sep'86 by Storyville Records. Dist: Jazz Music Distribution, Swift Distribution, Chris Wellard Distribution, Counterpoint Distribution

AT HOME.
Album: released on Delmark, Jan'74 Dist: Projection, Swift, Cadillac

BIG BAND.
Album: released on Golden Era, Jul'82 by Import Records. Dist: Wellard, Chris, Swift

BLUES AND THINGS (Hines, Earl with Jimmy Rushing).
Album: released on Swaggie (Australia), Jan'83

BLUES FOR GARROWAY.
Album: released on Pathe Marconi(France), Dec'84

Cassette: released on Pathe Marconi(France), Dec'84

BLUE SKIES (Hines, Earl "Fatha", Et Son Orchestre).
Tracks: / Jazz is his old lady and my old man / Just squeeze me / Yellow days / Deed I do / Blue skies / Hey love / Make it easy on yourself / Feelings.
Album: released on MFP Jazz Club, Feb'87 by EMI Records. Dist: EMI

COLEMAN HAWKINS & THE EARL HINES TRIO 1965 (Hines, Earl, Trio/ Coleman Hawkins).
Album: released on Pumpkin, Apr'79 Dist: Jazz Music, Wellard, Chris, Cadillac

COLEMAN HAWKINS & THE EARL HINES TRIO, 1965 (see Hawkins, Coleman) (Hines, Earl & Coleman Hawkins).

COLLECTION: EARL HINES.
Album: released on Deja Vu, May'86 by Deja Vu Records. Dist: Counterpoint Distribution, Record Services Distribution (Ireland)

Cassette: released on Deja Vu, May'86 by Deja Vu Records. Dist: Counterpoint Distribution, Record Services Distribution (Ireland)

DEEP FOREST.
Album: released on Black Lion, Oct'82 by Black Lion Records. Dist: Jazz Music, Chris Wellard, Taylor, H.R., Counterpoint, Cadillac

Cassette: released on Black Lion, Jan'83 by Black Lion Records. Dist: Jazz Music, Chris Wellard, Taylor, H.R., Counterpoint, Cadillac

DINAH.
Album: released on RCA (France), Oct'85 by RCA Records. Dist: Discovery

DIXIELAND BAND.
Album: released on Joker, Dec'79 Dist: Counterpoint, Mainline, Record Services Distribution (Ireland)

EARL HINES AND HIS ALL STARS (Hines, Earl & His All Stars).
Notes: Featuring Dicky Wells.
Album: released on Storyville, Jun'86 by Storyville Records. Dist: Jazz Music Distribution, Swift Distribution, Chris Wellard Distribution, Counterpoint Distribution

---

EARL HINES IN NEW ORLEANS.
Album: released on Sonet, Jan'76 by Sonet Records. Dist: PRT

EARL MEET SWEETS AND JAWS.
Album: released on Mercury (USA), Jul'83 by Import Records. Dist: IMS Distribution, Polygram Distribution

EARL'S BACKROOM AND COZY'S CARAVAN (Hines, Earl & Cozy Cole).
Album: released on Affinity, Dec'86 by Charly Records. Dist: Charly, Cadillac

EARL'S BACKROOM & COZY'S CARAVAN (Hines, Earl Quartet & Cozy Cole Septet).
Tracks: / Brussels' hustle / Oooh! / Backroom at the villa d'este / Caravan / Phatz' blues / Margie.
Notes: See also under Cozy Cole Septet Tracks 1-3 Earl Hines Quartet Tracks 4-6 Cozy Cole Septet Licensed from Decca Records Ltd. A Felsted recording.
Album: released on Affinity, Nov'86 by Charly Records. Dist: Charly, Cadillac

HINES '74.
Compact disc: released on Black & Blue (France), May'87 Dist: Swift, Target, Discovery

HINES' 74.
Compact disc: released on Black And Blue (France), Apr'87 Dist: Swift, Discovery, Target

HINES PLAYS HINES.
Album: released on Swaggie (Australia), Jan'83

INDISPENSABLE EARL HINES, THE VOL. 5/6.
Double Album: released on RCA (France), Jan'83 by RCA Records. Dist: Discovery

INDISPENSABLE, THE VOL.1/2.
Album: released on RCA (France), Jan'83 by RCA Records. Dist: Discovery

INDISPENSABLE VOL.3/4, THE.
Album: released on RCA (France), Jan'83 by RCA Records. Dist: Discovery

IN NEW ORLEANS.
Album: released on Up International Apr'81

IT DOESN'T MEAN A THING (Hines, Earl/ Paul Gonsalvez).
Album: released on Black Lion, Sep'85 by Black Lion Records. Dist: Jazz Music, Chris Wellard, Taylor, H.R., Counterpoint, Cadillac

I'VE GOT THE WORLD ON A STRING.
Album: released on Joker, Apr'81 Dist: Counterpoint, Mainline, Record Services Distribution (Ireland)

LEGENDARY LITTLE THEATRE CONCERT OF 1964 VOL.1.
Tracks: / Stealin' apples / Fats Waller Medley;Ain't misbehavin'/Two sleepy people / Fats Waller Medley;Ain't Misbehavin' / Fats Waller Medley;Two sleepy people / Fats Waller Medley;Keepin' out of mischief now / Fats Waller Medley;Jitterbug waltz / Fats Waller Medley;Honeysuckle rose / Fats Waller Medley;Lulu's back in town / Sweet Lorraine/Mandy,Make up your mind / Medley;Tangerine/Speak low/Continental.
Album: released on Deluxe (Avan-Guard), Aug'86 Dist: Conifer

LIVE IN ORANGE.
Album: released on Black & Blue (France), Jun'84 Dist: Swift, Target, Discovery

MASTER'S OF JAZZ.
Album: released on Storyville, May'86 by Storyville Records. Dist: Jazz Music Distribution, Swift Distribution, Chris Wellard Distribution, Counterpoint Distribution

ONCE UPON A TIME.
Album: released on Jasmine, Aug'82 by Jasmine Records. Dist: Counterpoint, Lugtons, Taylor, H.R., Wellard, Chris, Swift, Cadillac

Cassette: released on Jasmine, Aug'82 by Jasmine Records. Dist: Counterpoint, Lugtons, Taylor, H.R., Wellard, Chris, Swift, Cadillac

Album: released on Impulse, Oct'85 by Impulse Records. Dist: MCA, Polygram

PLAYS COLE PORTER.
Album: released on Swaggie (Australia), Jan'83

PLAYS DUKE ELLINGTON VOL.4.
Album: released on Swaggie (Australia), Jan'83

PLAYS DUKE ELLINGTON VOL.1.
Album: released on Swaggie (Australia), Jan'83

PLAYS DUKE ELLINGTON VOL.2.
Album: released on Swaggie (Australia), Jan'83

PLAYS DUKE ELLINGTON VOL.3.
Album: released on Swaggie (Australia), Jan'83

PLAYS GEORGE GERSHWIN.
Album: released on Carosello, Feb'83 Dist: Jazz Music, Jazz Horizons

Album: released on Swaggie (Australia), Jan'83

SAN FRANCISCO- OCT. 1957.
Album: released on Kings Of Jazz, Apr'81 Dist: Jazz Horizons, Jazz Music, Celtic Music

SPONTANEOUS EXPLORATIONS.
Album: released on Joker, Apr'81 Dist: Counterpoint, Mainline, Record Services Distribution (Ireland)

Swingin' the '20s
TEA FOR TWO.
Album: released on Black Lion, Jan'85 by Black Lion Records. Dist: Jazz Music, Chris Wellard, Taylor, H.R., Counterpoint, Cadillac

TIN ROOF BLUES (Hines, Earl , Muggsy Spanier).
Double Album: released on Vogue Jazz (France), May'83

TIN ROOF BLUES (see Spanier, Muggsy) (Hines, Earl & Muggsy Spanier).

TOUR DE FORCE.
Album: released on Black Lion, Sep'85 by Black Lion Records. Dist: Jazz Music, Chris Wellard, Taylor, H.R., Counterpoint, Cadillac

WALTZING MATILDA.
Album: released on Swaggie (Australia), Jan'83

Hines, Justin
SITTING IN THE JUNGLE (Hines, Justin & The Dominos).
Tracks: / Sitting in the jungle / I follow the rainbow
Single (12"): released on Jay Dee, Jan'87 by Jaydoe Records. Dist: Jetstar

Hines, Marcia
TAKE IT FROM THE BOYS.
Album: released on Logo, Mar'82 by Logo Records. Dist: Roots, BMG

Cassette: released on Logo, Mar'82 by Logo Records. Dist: Roots, BMG

Hinge & Bracket
DEAR LADIES.
Album: released on BBC, Apr'83 by BBC Records & Tapes. Dist: EMI, PRT, Pye

Cassette: released on BBC, Apr'83 by BBC Records & Tapes. Dist: EMI. PRT. Pye

Hino-Kikuchi Quintet
HINO-KIKUCHI QUINTET.
Notes: Tracks include:Tender Passion,Long Trip,H.G.,Pretty.
Compact disc: released on Denon, May'86 by Denon Records. Dist: Harmonia Mundi

Hino, Terumasa
TARO'S MOOD.
Album: released on Enja (Germany), Jan'82 by Enja Records (W.Germany). Dist: Cadillac Music

TERUMASA HINO.
Notes: Tracks include:Alone Together,Satsuki,Make Left.
Compact disc: released on Denon, May'86 by Denon Records. Dist: Harmonia Mundi

VIBRATIONS.
Album: released on Enja (Germany), Jan'82 by Enja Records (W.Germany). Dist: Cadillac Music

Hinton, Milt
JUST THE TWO OF US (Hinton, Milt and Art Hodes).
Album: released on Muse, Aug'82 by Peerless Records. Dist: Lugtons Distributors

Hip Hop
HIP HOP Various artists (Various Artists).
Cassette: released on Charisma, Dec'84 by Virgin Records. Dist: EMI

HIP HOP 16 (Various Artists).
Album: released on Streetsounds, Feb'87

Cassette: released on Streetsounds, Feb'87

HIP HOP 17 (Various Artists).
Album: released on Streetsounds, Jul'87

Cassette: released on Streetsounds, Jul'87

Hipsway

ASK THE LORD.
Tracks: / Ask the lord / Are you ready to listen / Pain machine.
Single (7"): released on Mercury, Apr'86 by Phonogram Records. Dist: Polygram Distribution

Single (12"): released on Mercury, Apr'86 by Phonogram Records. Dist: Polygram Distribution

BROKEN YEARS.
Single (12"): released on Mercury, Jun'85 by Phonogram Records. Dist: Polygram Distribution

HIPSWAY.
Tracks: / Honeythief,The / Ask the lord / Bad thing longing / Upon a thread / Long white car / Broken years,The / Tinder / Forbidden / Set this day apart.
Album: released on Mercury, Apr'86 by Phonogram Records. Dist: Polygram Distribution

Cassette: released on Mercury, Apr'86 by Phonogram Records. Dist: Polygram Distribution

Compact disc: released on Mercury, Apr'86 by Phonogram Records. Dist: Polygram Distribution

HONEY THIEF.
Tracks: / Honey Thief / Wild sorrow.
Single (7"): released on Mercury, Feb'86 by Phonogram Records. Dist: Polygram Distribution

Single (12"): released on Mercury, Feb'86 by Phonogram Records. Dist: Polygram Distribution

LONG WHITE CAR.
Tracks: / Ring out the bell / Tinder.
Single (7"): released on Mercury, Aug'86 by Phonogram Records. Dist: Polygram Distribution

Single (12"): released on Mercury, Aug'86 by Phonogram Records. Dist: Polygram Distribution

Hirax

HATE FEAR & POWER.
Album: released on Roadrunner (Dutch), Oct'86 Dist: Pinnacle

Hi Records

HI RECORDS : THE EARLY YEARS (Various Artists).
Album: released on Hi, May'87 by Demon Records. Dist: Pinnacle

Hired Man

HIRED MAN Various artists (Various Artists).
Album: released on Polydor, Nov'84 by Polydor Records. Dist: Polygram, Polydor

Cassette: released on Polydor, Nov'84 by Polydor Records. Dist: Polygram, Polydor

Hiroshima

ANOTHER PLACE.
Tracks: / One wish / Save yourself for me / Another place / I do remember / Game, The / Undercover / Stay away / What's it to ya / Touch and go.
Album: released on Epic, Jun'86 by CBS Records. Dist: CBS

Cassette: released on Epic, Jun'86 by CBS Records. Dist: CBS

GO.
Album: released on Epic (USA), Aug'87 by CBS Records. Dist: CBS

ODORI.
Album: released on Arista, Nov'80 by Arista Records. Dist: RCA

SEND YOUR LOVE TO ME.
Tracks: / Another place.
Single (7"): released on Epic, Apr'86 by CBS Records. Dist: CBS

Hirt, Al

AL HIRT.
Cassette: released on Audio Fidelity, Oct'84 Dist: PRT

SOLID GOLD BRASS.
Cassette: released on RCA International, Jun'82

His Latest Flame

SOMEBODY'S GONNA GET HURT.
Tracks: / All the same to me / Somebody's gonna get hurt (Inst).
Single (7"): released on Go Discs, May'86 by Go Discs Records. Dist: CBS Distribution

Single (12"): released on Go Discs, May'86 by Go Discs Records. Dist: CBS Distribution

STOP THE TIDE.
Tracks: / Wake up (and smell the coffee).
Single (7"): released on Go Discs, Sep'86 by Go Discs Records. Dist: CBS Distribution

Single (12"): released on Go Discs, Sep'86 by Go Discs Records. Dist: CBS Distribution

His Monkey Wife

HIS MONKEY WIFE Original cast (Various Artists).
Album: released on President, Jan'74 by President Records. Dist: Taylors, Spartan

Historic Recordings...

HISTORIC RECORDINGS FROM THE 1930'S (Various Artists).
Notes: Mono
Album: released on Folklyric (USA), Dec'86 by Arhoolie Records. Dist: Topic, Projection

History Of...

HISTORY OF ATLANTIC Various artists (Various Artists).
Cassette: released on Atlantic, Apr'83 by WEA Records. Dist: WEA

HISTORY OF LATINO ROCK Various artists (Various Artists).
Album: released on Rhino (USA), Jul'84 by Rhino Records (USA).

HISTORY OF TAMOKI WAMBESI Various artists (Various Artists).
Album: released on Wambesi, Aug'85 by Wambesi records. Dist: Jetstar

HISTORY OF THE ENGLISH DERBY (History of the English Derby).
Album: released on Replay, Aug'79 by Creole Records. Dist: CBS

HISTORY OF THE WORLD CUP (History of the World Cup).
Notes: Narated by Jack Charlton. Includes Free Full Colour Poster featuring all fixtures, K.O.times, and photos of every team squad taking part.
Album: released on BBC, May'86 by BBC Records & Tapes. Dist: EMI, PRT, Pye

Cassette: released on BBC, May'86 by BBC Records & Tapes. Dist: EMI, PRT, Pye

History Reflected

HISTORY REFLECTED, ELIZABETH 1, THE ARMADA 1588 various artists (Various Artists).
Cassette: released on Argo, Oct'84 by Decca Records. Dist: Polygram

HISTORY REFLECTED - WORLD WARS 1914/1939 Various artists (Various Artists).
Cassette: released on Argo, Mar'84 by Decca Records. Dist: Polygram

His Way With The Girls

HIS WAY WITH THE GIRLS Various artists (Various Artists).
Album: released on Soul Supply, Dec'86 by High Energy Records. Dist: Charly

Hit Action

HIT ACTION Various artists (Various Artists).
Album: released on Warwick, Nov'85 Dist: Multiple Sound Distributors

Cassette: released on Warwick, Nov'85 Dist: Multiple Sound Distributors

Hitchcock

ALFRED HITCHCOCK'S FILM MUSIC Original Soundtrack (Alfred Hitchcock's Film Music).
Tracks: / Prelude / City, The - Marion, Marion & Sam / Temptation / Flight - Patrol car, Car lot, Package, Rainstorm / Hotel room, Window, Parlour / Madhouse, The / Peephole, The / Finale / Main titles / Abduction of George Kaplan / Elevator, The / Murder at the U.N. / Mount Rushmore / Finale.
Compact disc: released on Milan France, Sep'86

Hitchcock, Carol

GET READY.
Tracks: / Get ready / More than words can say.
Single (7"): released on A&M, Apr'87 by A&M Records. Dist: Polygram

Single (12"): released on A&M, Apr'87 by A&M Records. Dist: Polygram

Hitchcock, Robyn

AMERICA/ IT WAS THE NIGHT.
Single (7"): released on Albion, Mar'82 by Albion Records. Dist: Spartan, Pinnacle

BELLS OF RHYMNEY.
Single (12"): released on Midnight Music, Dec'84 by Midnight Music Records. Dist: Rough Trade Distribution, Cartel Distribution

BLACK SNAKE DIAMOND ROLE.
Album: released on Aftermath, May'86 by Aftermath Records. Dist: Cartel

Album: released on Armageddon, Jun'81 by Armageddon Records. Dist: Revolver, Cartel, Pinnacle

BRENDA'S IRON SLEDGE.
Tracks: / Only the stones remain / Pit of souls (parts 1-4).
Single (12"): released on Midnight Music, Feb'86 by Midnight Music Records. Dist: Rough Trade Distribution, Cartel Distribution

EATEN BY HER OWN DINNER.
Tracks: / Grooving on an inner plane / Messages of dark / Bandoned brain, The / Happy the golden prince.
Single (12"): released on Midnight Music, Oct'86 by Midnight Music Records. Dist: Rough Trade Distribution, Cartel Distribution

Single (7"): released on Midnight Music, Nov'82 by Midnight Music Records. Dist: Rough Trade Distribution, Cartel Distribution

ELEMENT OF LIGHT.
Compact disc: released on Midnight, Dec'86

EXPLODING IN SILENCE (Hitchcock, Robyn & The Egyptians).
Album: released on Relativity (USA), Feb'86 Dist: Pinnacle, Rough Trade, Cartel

EXPLODING IN SILENCE.
Album: released on Midnight Music, Mar'86 by Midnight Music Records. Dist: Rough Trade Distribution, Cartel Distribution

Cassette: released on Midnight Music, Mar'86 by Midnight Music Records. Dist: Rough Trade Distribution, Cartel Distribution

FEGMANIA.
Compact disc: released on Midnight, '86

Album: released on Midnight Music, Mar'85 by Midnight Music Records. Dist: Rough Trade Distribution, Cartel Distribution

GOTTA LET THIS HEN OUT!.
Album: released on Midnight Music, Nov'85 by Midnight Music Records. Dist: Rough Trade Distribution, Cartel Distribution

Cassette: released on Midnight Music, Nov'85 by Midnight Music Records. Dist: Rough Trade Distribution, Cartel Distribution

Compact disc: released on Midnight Music, Oct'86 by Midnight Music Records. Dist: Rough Trade Distribution, Cartel Distribution

GROOVY DECAY.
Album: released on Midnight Music (Holland), Dec'85

Album: released on Albion, May'82 by Albion Records. Dist: Spartan, Pinnacle

HEAVEN.
Single (12"): released on Midnight Music, May'85 by Midnight Music Records. Dist: Rough Trade Distribution, Cartel Distribution

IF YOU WERE A PRIEST (Hitchcock, Robyn & The Egyptians).
Tracks: / Crawling glass fish, The.
Single (7"): released on Midnight Music, Oct'86 by Midnight Music Records. Dist: Rough Trade Distribution, Cartel Distribution

IF YOU WERE A PRIEST.
Single (7"): released on Glass Fish, Jan'87 Dist: Rough Trade

Single (12"): released on Glass Fish, Jan'87 Dist: Rough Trade

INVISIBLE HITCHCOCK (Hitchcock, Robyn & The Egyptians).
Album: released on Glass Fish, Jun'86 Dist: Rough Trade

I OFTEN DREAM OF TRAINS (Hitchcock, Robyn & The Egyptians).
Compact disc: released on Midnight Music, Oct'86 by Midnight Music Records. Dist: Rough Trade Distribution, Cartel Distribution

Album: released on Midnight Music, Aug'84 by Midnight Music Records. Dist: Rough Trade Distribution, Cartel Distribution

LET THIS MAN OUT.
Album: released on Midnight Music, Oct'85 by Midnight Music Records. Dist: Rough Trade Distribution, Cartel Distribution

MAN WHO INVENTED HIMSELF.
Single (7"): released on Armageddon, Apr'81 by Armageddon Records. Dist: Revolver, Cartel, Pinnacle

NIGHTRIDE TO TRINIDAD/ KINGDOM OF....
Single (12"): released on Albion, May'83 by Albion Records. Dist: Spartan, Pinnacle

Hitch, Curtis

CURTIS HITCH & HOAGY CARMICHAEL 1923-28 (Hitch, Curtis & Hoagy Carmichael).
Album: released on Fountain, Apr'79 by Retrieval Records. Dist: Jazz Music, Swift, VJM, Wellard, Chris, Retrieval

Hitchhikers Guide...

HITCHHIKERS GUIDE TO THE GALAXY Various artists (Various Artists).
Double Album: released on Original, Apr'80 Dist: RCA Distribution, Jazz Music Distribution, PRT Distribution

HITCH-HIKERS GUIDE TO THE GALAXY VOL.2 Various artists (Various Artists).
Album: released on Original, Nov'80 Dist: RCA Distribution, Jazz Music Distribution, PRT Distribution

Hi Tension

HAPPY.
Single (7"): released on Streetwave, Oct'84 by Streetwave Records. Dist: PRT Distribution

Single (12"): released on Streetwave, Oct'84 by Streetwave Records. Dist: PRT Distribution

HOW D'YOU FEEL.
Single (7"): released on EMI, May'82 by EMI Records. Dist: EMI

Single (12"): released on EMI, May'82 by EMI Records. Dist: EMI

Hitler, Bing

BING HITLER LIVE AT THE TRON.
Tracks: / Scotland pch aye / Sheep song.
Album: released on Jammy, Oct'86 by Jammy Records. Dist: Jammy

Cassette: released on Jammy, Oct'86 by Jammy Records. Dist: Jammy

Hitlist

GOOD EVENING YUGOSLAVIA.
Album: released on Virgin, Apr'86 by Virgin Records. Dist: EMI, Virgin Distribution

Cassette: released on Virgin, Apr'86 by Virgin Records. Dist: EMI, Virgin Distribution

INTO THE FIRE.
Tracks: / Total isolation.
Single (7"): released on Virgin, Mar'86 by Virgin Records. Dist: EMI, Virgin Distribution

Single (12"): released on Virgin, Mar'86 by Virgin Records. Dist: EMI, Virgin Distribution

OKAY FOR YOU.
Tracks: / High treason.
Single (12"): released on Virgin, Apr'86 by Virgin Records. Dist: EMI, Virgin Distribution

Single (7"): released on Virgin, Apr'86 by Virgin Records. Dist: EMI, Virgin Distribution

Hitman, Howie Tee

(BANG ZOOM) LET'S GO-GO (Real Roxanne) (Hitman, Howie Tee & Real Roxanne).

Hitmen

AIM FOR THE FEET.
Album: released on Urgent, Oct'80 Dist: CBS

Cassette: released on Urgent, Oct'80 Dist: CBS

Hit Mix '86

HIT MIX '86 (Various Artists).
Album: released on Stylus, Nov'86 Dist: Pinnacle, Terry Blood Distribution, Stylus Distribution

Cassette: released on Stylus, Nov'86 Dist: Pinnacle, Terry Blood Distribution, Stylus Distribution

Hit Parade

FOREVER.
Tracks: / Forever / Stop.
Single (7"): released on JSH, Jun'84 Dist: Red Rhino, Cartel

I GET SO SENTIMENTAL.
Tracks: / I get so sentimental / Sue.
Single (7"): released on JSH, Apr'87 Dist: Red Rhino, Cartel

MY FAVOURITE GIRL.
Tracks: / My favourite girl / It rained on Monday afternoon.
Single (7"): released on JSH, Oct'84 Dist: Red Rhino, Cartel

SEE YOU IN HAVANA.
Tracks: / See you in Havana / Wipe away the tears.
Single (7"): released on JSH, Jul'86 Dist: Red Rhino, Cartel

SUN SHINES IN GERRARDS CROSS, THE.
Tracks: / Sun shines in Gerrards Cross / You hurt me too.
Single (7"): released on JSH, Mar'85 Dist: Red Rhino, Cartel

YOU DIDN'T LOVE ME THEN.
Tracks: / You didn't love me then.
Single (7"): released on JSH, Oct'85 Dist: Red Rhino, Cartel

Hits

HITS 1 Various original artists (Various original artists).
Album: released on CBS-WEA, Nov'84 by WEA Records. Dist: WEA

Cassette: released on CBS-WEA, Nov'84 by WEA Records. Dist: WEA

HITS 2 Various artists (Various Artists).
Double Album: released on CBS-WEA, Apr'85 by WEA Records. Dist: WEA

Double cassette: released on CBS-WEA, Apr'85 by WEA Records. Dist: WEA

HITS 3 Various artists (Various Artists).
Double Album: released on WEA, Nov'85 by WEA Records. Dist: WEA

Double cassette: released on WEA, Nov'85 by WEA Records. Dist: WEA

HITS 4 Various artists (Various Artists).
Tracks: / Sun always shines on TV / You little theif / I'm your man / Manic monday / Borderline / Digging your scene / Imagination / Chain reaction / How will I know / If you were here tonight / System addict / Don't waste my time / (Nothing serious) just buggin' / Alice, I want you just for me! / Eloise / Suspicious minds / Rise / Hit that perfect beat / It's alright (baby's coming back) / West end girls / Kyrie / Captain of her heart / Radio Africa / Silent running (on dangerous ground) / No one is to blame / Come hell or waters high / Hounds of love / Calling America.
Album: released on CBS, Mar'86 by CBS Records. Dist: CBS

Cassette: released on CBS, Mar'86 by CBS Records. Dist: CBS

HITS 4 (VIDEO) Various artists (Various Artists).
Notes: Number of tracks:14. Type of recording: compilation. Total playing time: 55 minutes.
Video-cassette (VHS): released on RCA, Apr'86 by RCA Records. Dist: RCA, Roots, Swift, Wellard, Chris, I & B, Solomon & Peres Distribution

HITS 4 VIDEO SELECTION (Various Artists).
Video-cassette (VHS): released on PMI, '86 by PMI Records. Dist: EMI

HITS 5 (Various Artists).
Album: released on RCA (Special Imports Service), Nov'86

Cassette: released on RCA (Special Imports Service), Nov'86

Compact disc: released on RCA (Special Imports Service), Nov'86

HITS CORRUPTION Various artists (Various Artists).
Tracks: / Orgasam way / Touch you / Pearl and the swine ad / Holy ground / No sense at all / Poetry / Christ was a conservative / Batter matter / Everything's brilliant the poem / Heartbreak hotel / Down the yard / Help / Top comedian / Poetry / Interview.
Album: released on Hits & Corruption, Oct'86 Dist: Rough Trade, Cartel

Cassette: released on Hits & Corruption, Oct'86 Dist: Rough Trade, Cartel

HITS GREATEST STIFFS Various Artists (Various Artists).
Album: released on Stiff, Oct'77 by Stiff Records. Dist: EMI, Record Services Distribution (Ireland)

Cassette: released on Stiff, Oct'77 by Stiff Records. Dist: EMI, Record Services Distribution (Ireland)

HITS HITS HITS Various artists (Various Artists).
Album: released on Telstar, Oct'84 by Telstar Records. Dist: RCA Distribution

Cassette: released on Telstar, Oct'84 by Telstar Records. Dist: RCA Distribution

HITS REVIVAL (Various Artists).
Tracks: / Reet petite / Wonderful world / Lean on me / Everything I own / Loving you is sweeter than ever / You can't hurry love / It's a mans mans world / I heard it through the grapevine / Dancing in the street / What's going on / You keep me hanging on / Whispering bells / Let's stay together / Harlem shuffle / (Get up I feel like being a) Sex machine / I get the sweetest feeling.
Album: released on K-Tel, Jun'87 by K-Tel Records. Dist: Record Merchandisers Distribution, Taylors, Terry Blood Distribution, Wynd-Up Distribution, Relay Distribution, Pickwick Distribution, Solomon & Peres Distribution, Polygram

Cassette: released on K-Tel, Jun'87 by K-Tel Records. Dist: Record Merchandisers Distribution, Taylors, Terry Blood Distribution, Wynd-Up Distribution, Relay Distribution, Pickwick Distribution, Solomon & Peres Distribution, Polygram

Compact disc: released on K-Tel, Jun'87 by K-Tel Records. Dist: Record Merchandisers Distribution, Taylors, Terry Blood Distribution, Wynd-Up Distribution, Relay Distribution, Pickwick Distribution, Solomon & Peres Distribution, Polygram

HITS THAT MADE JOHN DENVER Various session artists (Various Session Artists).
Cassette: released on AIM (Budget Cassettes), Feb'83

HITS THAT MISSED Various artists (Various Artists).
Album: released on Red Lightnin', Sep'82 by Red Lightnin' Records. Dist: Roots, Swift, Jazz Music, JSU, Pinnacle, Cartel, Wynd-Up Distribution

HITS YOU MISSED VOL.1 Various artists (Various Artists).
Album: released on Viking, Mar'86 Dist: Harmonia Mundi Distributors

Hits For...

HITS FOR CHILDREN Various session artists (Various Session Artists).
Cassette: released on AIM (Budget Cassettes), Feb'83

HITS FOR KIDS Various artists (Various Artists).
Double cassette: released on Pickwick (Ditto series), Jan'83

HITS FOR LOVERS Various artists (Various Artists).
Tracks: / Saving all my love for you / See the day / What's love got to do with it / Sexual healing / If you were here tonight / Sweetest Taboo / Who's zoomin' who? / Saturday love / Power of love / All cried out / Missing you / When love breaks down / Penny lover / Still / New York eyes / Every time you go away.
Album: released on Epic, Feb'86 by CBS Records. Dist: CBS

Cassette: released on Epic, Feb'86 by CBS Records. Dist: CBS

Hits From...

HITS FROM HEAVEN Various artists (Various Artists).
Album: released on Rhino (USA), Jul'84 by Rhino Records (USA).

HITS FROM ROCK MUSICALS Various artists (Various Artists).
Album: released on Spot, Feb'83 by Pickwick Records. Dist: H.R. Taylor, Lugtons

Cassette: released on Spot, Feb'83 by Pickwick Records. Dist: H.R. Taylor, Lugtons

HITS FROM THE HOUSE OF SHAKA Various artists (Various Artists).
Album: released on Shaka, Jan'87 by Shaka Records. Dist: Jetstar

HITS FROM THE SILVER SCREEN Various artists (Various Artists).
Cassette: released on Ampro Cassettes, Sep'81

HITS FROM THE SWINGING SIXTIES Various artists (Various Artists).
Double Album: released on MFP, Sep'81 by EMI Records. Dist: EMI

Cassette: released on MFP, Sep'81 by EMI Records. Dist: EMI

MORE HITS FROM RADIO 1 Various artists (Various Artists).
Double Album: released on BBC, '79 by BBC Records & Tapes. Dist: EMI, PRT, Pye

Cassette: released on BBC, Nov'79 by BBC Records & Tapes. Dist: EMI, PRT, Pye

Hits of...

20 ORIGINAL TRACKS OF THE 60'S various artists (Various Artists).
Cassette: released on WEA, Apr'83 by WEA Records. Dist: WEA

HITS OF 1960 Various artists (Various Artists).
Tracks: / Hit and miss / Ain't misbehavin' / Someone else's baby / What do you want / Poor me / Shakin' all over / Starry eyed / Seven little girls sitting in the back seat / Tell Laura I love her / Apache / Please don't tease / I love you / Nine times out of ten / Summer place, A / Walk don't run / Standing on the corner / Pistol packing mama / Three steps to heaven / Walking to New Orleans / As long as he needs me / Teen beat / McDonald's cave / Portrait of my love / Train of love / Who could be bluer?.
Cassette: released on Hour Of Pleasure, '86 by Music For Pleasure Records. Dist: EMI

HITS OF 1961 Various artists (Various Artists).
Tracks: / Rubber ball / Weekend / She-she little Sheila / Piltdown rides again / Mountain's high / Let there be drums / You're sixteen, you're beautiful (and you're mine) / I'm a moody guy / You don't know / Walkin' back to happiness / Don't treat her like a child / Pasadena / You're driving me crazy / Easy going me / Lonely pup (in a christmas shop) / FBI / Kon-Tike / My kind of girl / Theme for a dream / I love how you love me / Black stockings / Tibute to Buddy Holly / Michael row the boat ashore / Hundred pounds of clay / African waltz / Moon river.
Cassette: released on Hour Of Pleasure, '86 by Music For Pleasure Records. Dist: EMI

HITS OF 1962 Various artists (Various Artists).
Tracks: / When my little girl is smiling / Softly as I leave you / Right said Fred / Cindy's birthday / Little Miss Lonely / Guitar tango / What now my love / Lovesick blues / Hole in the ground, The / Must be Madison / Baby take a bow / Let's talk about love / Our favourite melodies / Nut rocker / Drums are my beat / Jambalaya (on the Bayou) / Clown shoes / Sharing you / James Bond theme, The (Dr.No) / Norman / As you like it / Up on the roof / I remember you / Tell me what he said / Wonderful land / Theme from Dr.Kildare.
Cassette: released on Hour Of Pleasure, Sep'86 by Music For Pleasure Records. Dist: EMI. Estim retail price in Sep'87 was £1.99.

HITS OF 1963 Various artists (Various Artists).
Tracks: / How do you do it / Do you want to know a secret / If you've got make a fool of somebody / Stay / Hippy, hippy shake / I'll never get over you / Hello little girl / Foot tapper / Night has a thousand eyes / My way / My little girl / Surfin' USA / Little town flirt / We are in love / Hungry for love / Searchin' / First time, The / Dance on / Don't you think it's time / I'll keep you satisfied / Confessin' (that I love you) / I like it / Bad to me / Cruel sea, The / I (who have nothing) / I'm telling you now / I'm in love / From Russia with love.
Cassette: released on Hour Of Pleasure, Sep'86 by Music For Pleasure Records. Dist: EMI. Estim retail price in Sep'87 was £1.99.

HITS OF 1964 (Various Artists).
Cassette: released on Hour Of Pleasure, Jun'87 by Music For Pleasure Records. Dist: EMI. Estim retail price in Sep'87 was £1.99.

HITS OF 83 various artists (Various original artists).
Album: released on Ronco, Nov'83

Cassette: released on Ronco, Jan'83

HITS OF CD Various artists (Various Artists).
Compact disc: released on Phonogram Import, Jan'84

HITS OF CD VOL.3 Various artists (Various Artists).
Compact disc: released on Phonogram, Sep'85 by Phonogram Records. Dist: Polygram

HITS OF CLIFF RICHARD Various session artists (Various Session Artists).
Cassette: released on AIM (Budget Cassettes), Feb'83

HITS OF SWINGIN' SIXTIES VOL.2 Various artists (Various Artists).
Tracks: / Born to be wild / Eve of destruction / Hey there lonely girl / Moody river / Heather honey / Dedicated to the one I love / Wipe out / If I only had time / Itsy bitsy teeny weeny yellow polka dot bikini / All alone am I / Baby my heart / California dreamin' / Clapping song / I'm sorry / Learning the game / Warmed over kisses / Tracy / Words of love / I saw her again / Everybody / Speedy gonzales / Baby, I don't care / Little bitty tear / Like a baby / Too many rivers.
Album: released on Cambra, Sep'86 by Cambra Records. Dist: IDS, Conifer

Cassette: released on Cambra, Sep'86 by Cambra Records. Dist: IDS, Conifer

HITS OF THE 50'S various artists (Various Artists).
Cassette: released on Pickwick, Jul'82 by Pickwick Records. Dist: Pickwick Distribution, Prism Leisure Distribution, Lugtons

HITS OF THE 60'S various artists (Various Artists).
Cassette: released on EMI, Jul'80 by EMI Records. Dist: EMI

HITS OF THE 60'S various artists (Various Artists).
Album: released on Spot, Sep'84 by Pickwick Records. Dist: H.R. Taylor, Lugtons

Cassette: released on Spot, Sep'84 by Pickwick Records. Dist: H.R. Taylor, Lugtons

HITS OF THE 60'S AND 70'S various artists (Various Artists).
Cassette: released on Pickwick, Feb'80 by Pickwick Records. Dist: Pickwick Distribution, Prism Leisure Distribution, Lugtons

HIT'S OF THE 60'S - EASY LISTENING STYLE (Various Artists).
Tracks: / Ma cherie amour / Windmills of your mind / This guy's in love with you / Man without love, A / Release me / It must be him / Albatross / Fool on the hill, The / Hey Jude / Michelle / Up, up and away / Somethin' stupid / Raindrops keep fallin' on my head / Love is blue / Whiter shade of pale, A / Classical gas.
Compact disc: released on London, Jul'87 by London Records. Dist: Polygram

HITS OF THE 70'S various artists (Various Artists).
Album: released on Spot, Sep'84 by Pickwick Records. Dist: H.R. Taylor, Lugtons

HITS OF THE 80'S -CHART INVADERS various artists (Various Artists).
Album: released on Everest (Premier), '82 by Everest Records. Dist: Pinnacle

Cassette: released on Everest (Premier), '82 by Everest Records. Dist: Pinnacle

HITS OF THE FORTIES-THE VOCALISTS various artists (Various Artists).
Album: released on Decca, Mar'82 by Decca Records. Dist: Polygram

Cassette: released on Decca, Mar'82 by Decca Records. Dist: Polygram

HITS OF THE FORTIES VOL.2 various artists (Various Artists).

HITS OF THE FORTIES VOL.3 various artists (Various Artists).
Double Album: released on Decca, Oct'81 by Decca Records. Dist: Polygram

HITS OF THE FORTIES VOL.4 various artists (Various Artists).
Album: released on Decca, Mar'84 by Decca Records. Dist: Polygram

Cassette: released on Decca, Mar'84 by Decca Records. Dist: Polygram

HITS OF THE THIRTIES various artists (Various Artists).
Album: released on Decca, Nov'82 by Decca Records. Dist: Polygram

HITS OF THE THIRTIES VOL.3 various artists (Various Artists).
Album: released on Decca, Sep'84 by Decca Records. Dist: Polygram

HITS"THE HITS OF WORLD WAR II" various artists (Various Artists).
Boxed set: released on World Records, Dec'81 Dist: Polygram

Cassette: released on World Records, Dec'81 Dist: Polygram

Hits Of The...

HITS OF THE FIFTIES Various artists (Various Artists).
Compact disc: released on Mercury (Germany), '86 by Phonogram Records. Dist: Polygram Distribution

Cassette: released on Spot, Sep'84 by Pickwick Records. Dist: H.R. Taylor, Lugtons

HITS OF THE FIFTIES Various artists (Various Artists).
Tracks: / Whatever will be (Que sera sera) / I believe / Cry / Stranger in paradise / Swinging the blues / This ole house / On the street where you live / Diana / (How much is that) doggy in the window / Wonderful, wonderful / Man that got away / Rawhide / Yellow rose of Texas / White sports coat (and a pink carnation) / We will make love / Secret love / Little white cloud / Answer me, my love / I walk the line / Blue suede shoes / Start movin' (in my direction) / Heart aches by the number / Battle of New Orleans / Waterloo.
Album: released on Castle Collectors, Sep'86 by Castle Communications Records. Dist: Pinnacle

Cassette: released on Castle Collectors, Sep'86 by Castle Communications Records. Dist: Pinnacle

HITS OF THE SCREAMING SIXTIES Various original artists (Various original artists).
Album: released on Warwick, Oct'82 Dist: Multiple Sound Distributors

Cassette: released on Warwick, Oct'82 Dist: Multiple Sound Distributors

HITS OF THE SEVENTIES (Various Artists).
Tracks: / Midnight at the oasis / Love I lost, The / Rock your baby / Feelings / Patches / I'm a woman / Satisfaction guaranteed / Don't let me be misunderstood / Witch Queen of New Orleans, The / Indian reservation / Love the one you're with / Behind closed doors / Hey girl, don't bother me / I just can't help believing.
Compact disc: by Object Enterprises Ltd. Dist: Counterpoint Distribution

HITS OF THE SIXTIES Various artists (Various Artists).
Tracks: / Universal soldier / Hold me / Baby please don't go / Crying game, The / Waterloo sunset / America / Flowers in the rain / Itchy-coo park / Needles and pins / She's not there / First cut is the deepest / Homburg / If paradise is half as nice / Baby, now that I've found you / Out of time / Go now / Shakin' all over / Man of the world / I can't let Maggie go / With a little help from my friends / I like it / Exerpt from a teenage opera / Do you want to know a secret.

Page 474

Album: released on Castle Collectors, May'86 by Castle Communications Records. Dist: Pinnacle

Cassette: released on Castle Collectors, May'86 by Castle Communications Records. Dist: Pinnacle

HITS OF THE SIXTIES USA (Various Artists).
Tracks: / Needles & pins / Yakety yak / Tennessee waltz, The / Letter, The / Zip-a-de-doo-dah / Rebel rouser / Charlie Brown / Let's twist again / Rockin pneumonia & the boogie woogie flu / Under the boardwalk / Twist, The / He's so fine / Hucklebuck / When a man loves a woman / Young girl / Peppermint twist / Da doo ron ron / Tom Dooley / Smoke gets in your eyes / Run to him / Ballad of the Green berets / Twist twist senora / On Broadway / Maria.
Compact disc: by Object Enterprises Ltd. Dist: Counterpoint Distribution

HITS OF THE SWINGIN' SIXTIES VOL.1 Various artists (Various Artists).
Tracks: / Monday, monday / Dizzy / Woodstock / Here comes that feeling / Little arrows / Johnny will / Brown eyed handsome man / Ginny come lately / Heartaches / As usual / Hello dolly / Hush' not a word to Mary / Folk singer / Creeque alley / Lady luck / Sheila / What a wonderful world / Red sails in the sunset / Bo Diddley / Main attraction / 1-2-3 / When you ask about love / Rock around the clock / Speak to me pretty / Deck of cards / Ginny come lately.
Album: released on Cambra, Sep'86 by Cambra Records. Dist: IDS, Conifer

Cassette: released on Cambra, Sep'86 by Cambra Records. Dist: IDS, Conifer

HITS OF THE SWINGING SIXTIES VOL.2 various artists (Various original artists).
Album: released on Cambra, '83 by Cambra Records. Dist: IDS, Conifer

Hits On...

HITS ON 33 Various Artists (Various Artists).
Double Album: released on Ronco, Aug'81

Double cassette: released on Ronco, Aug'81

HITS ON CD VOL 2 Various Artists (Various Artists).
Compact disc: by Phonogram Records. Dist: Polygram Distribution

HITS ON CD VOL 3 Various Artists (Various Artists).
Compact disc: by Phonogram Records. Dist: Polygram

HITS ON CD VOL 4 (Various Artists).
Tracks: / St Elmo's fire / Everybody wants to rule the world / I'll be good / Single life / Desire / Jealousy / Burning flame / Let him go / Silent night.
Compact disc: released on Mercury (USA), Jun'86 by Import Records. Dist: IMS Distribution, Polygram Distribution

HITS ON CD VOL 5 Various artists (Various Artists).
Tracks: / You don't have to cry / Your wildest dreams / Mine all mine / Honeythief, The / Venus / Birth of rock and roll / Born yesterday / Two fools in love / Rock me baby / I engineer / Ain't nothin' goin' on but the rent / Seer, The / Mothers talk / I'd lie to you for your love / Burnin' love / Hear'n'aid.
Compact disc: released on Mercury (USA), Jan'87 by Import Records. Dist: IMS Distribution, Polygram Distribution

HITS ON CD VOL.6 (Various Artists).
Tracks: / Don't leave me this way / You give love a bad name / Word up / You're in the army now / Slow rivers / This is the world calling / Victory / Stay with me / Running the endless mile / More than physical / Outside in the rain / Breakout / Smoking gun / Walk the way the wind blows / Ain't got my eyes on you.
Compact disc: released on Mercury, Apr'87 by Phonogram Records. Dist: Polygram Distribution

HITS ON FIRE Various artists (Various Artists).
Album: released on Ronco, Jul'83

Cassette: released on Ronco, Jul'83

YITS ON CD Various Artists (Various Artists).
Compact disc: by Phonogram Records. Dist: Polygram

Hit Songs...

HIT SONGS AND HOT SONGS Various artists (Various Artists).
Album: released on Nostalgia (Sweden), Jan'82 by Wellard, Chris Distribution. Dist: Wellard, Chris Distribution

HIT SONGS OF THE 50'S Various artists (Various Artists).
Album: released on Decca (Recollections), Apr'85 by Decca Recollections. Dist: Polygram, IMS

Cassette: released on Decca (Recollections), Apr'85 by Decca Recollections. Dist: Polygram, IMS

HIT SONGS OF THE SIXTIES Various artists (Various Artists).
Double cassette: released on Pickwick (Ditto series), Jul'82

Hits Unlimited

NON-STOP DISCO PARTY.
Cassette: released on Chevron, Aug'85 Dist: Multiple Sound Distributors

WILD BOYS, THE.
Cassette: released on Chevron, Feb'85 Dist: Multiple Sound Distributors

Hits Video

HITS VIDEO 5, THE (Various Artists).
Video-cassette (VHS): released on CBS, Dec'86 by CBS Records. Dist: CBS

HITS VIDEO, THE Various artists (Various Artists).
Video-cassette (VHS): released on CBS-Fox, Jan'86 by CBS Records. Dist: CBS, Fox

TAKE 2 Various artists (Various Artists).
Video-cassette (VHS): released on Virgin Video, Jun'86 by Virgin Records. Dist: EMI

Video-cassette [Betamax]: released on Virgin Video, Jun'86 by Virgin Records. Dist: EMI

Hive

KINGDOM RISE,KINGDOM FALL.
Single (12"): released on Hum Music, Apr'85 Dist: Red Rhino, Cartel

Hizer,Mike

COME OUTSIDE (Hizer,Mike and the Barrow boys).
Single (7"): released on Sierra, Aug'85 by Sierra Records. Dist: WEA Deleted '86.

HMS Bounty

GIRL.
Single (7"): released on Cherry Red, Jun'85 by Cherry Red Records. Dist: Pinnacle

HMS Pinafore

HMS PINAFORE various artists (Various Artists).
Double Album: released on EMI, '74 by EMI Records. Dist: EMI

HMS PINAFORE/PIRATES OF PENZANCE various artists (Various Artists).
Cassette: released on Pickwick, Jul'82 by Pickwick Records. Dist: Pickwick Distribution, Prism Leisure Distribution, Lugtons

Hoax

BLIND PANIC.
Extended-play record: released on Hologram, Mar'82 by Aardvark. Dist: Wynd-Up Distribution

Hoban,John

MUSIC FOR HOLY WEEK AND EASTER.
Album: released on Abbey, Mar'80 by Abbey. Dist: PRT, Taylors, Gamut

Hoban, Russell

BEDTIME FOR FRANCES.
Tracks: / Bedtime for Frances / Best friends for Frances / Baby sister for Frances, A / Birthday for Frances, A.
Notes: Read by Jill shilling. the music for the songs was specially composed by Stephen Higgs who accompanies Jill Shilling on guitar.
Cassette: released on Tellastory, Apr'87 by Bartlett Bliss Productions. Dist: PRT Distribution, Hayward Promotions Distribution, H.R. Taylor Distribution

Hobbies of Today

IN MY MINDS EYE.
Tracks: / You.
Single (7"): released on Rune, Jan'86 by Hobbies Of Today. Dist: Rune Distribution

Hobbs/Adams/Bryars

ENSEMBLE PIECES.
Album: released on Editions EG, Jan'87 by Virgin Records. Dist: EMI

Hockensmith, Hadley

HEART SONG.
Notes: Hockensmith, on this Meadowlark album, plays guitar, guitar synthesiser and bass. He is a renowned and well respected musician having played with many top artists as a session musician over the years. Several years ago, Hadley Hockensmith and other session musicians decided to form their own band, Koinonia, who have gone on to international success. Hockensmith now has the opportunity to play in a different area than he would with Koinonia. This album comes up to the high standard one expects from Meadowlark records as they are all digitally mastered to complement the Meadowlark music.
Album: released on Meadowlark, Jan'87 by Sparrow Records. Dist: Word Distribution

Cassette: released on Meadowlark, Jan'87 by Sparrow Records. Dist: Word Distribution

Hockridge, Edmund

MAKE IT EASY ON YOURSELF (Hockridge, Edmund with Peter Knight Orch).
Album: released on President Evergreen, Oct'84

SINGS HITS FROM VARIOUS MUSICALS.
Album: released on Flashback, Nov'85 by Flashback Records/PRT Records. Dist: Mainline, PRT

Cassette: released on Flashback, Nov'85 by Flashback Records/PRT Records. Dist: Mainline, PRT

Hodes, Art

ART HODES PLAYS BESSIE.
Album: released on Euphonic, Mar'79 by Euphonic Records. Dist: Jazz Music, Swift

ART OF HODES, THE.
Album: released on Euphonic, Apr'79 by Euphonic Records. Dist: Jazz Music, Swift

ECHOES OF CHICAGO (Hodes, Art and His Windy City Seven).
Album: released on Jazzology, Aug'79 Dist: Jazz Music, Swift

JUST THE TWO OF US see Hinton, Milt (Hodes, Art and Milt Hinton).
Album: released on Muse, Aug'82 Dist: JSU Distribution, Jazz Horizons Distribution, Jazz Music Distribution, Celtic Music Distribution

LIVE AT HANRATTY'S,NEW YORK CITY.
Album: released on Must(import), '81

SELECTIONS FROM THE GUTTER.
Album: released on Storyville, Nov'86 by Storyville Records. Dist: Jazz Music Distribution, Swift Distribution, Chris Wellard Distribution, Counterpoint Distribution

SOME LEGENDARY ART (Hodes, Art Quintet).
Album: released on Audiophile, Jul'87 by Jazzology Records (USA). Dist: Jazz Music, Swift

Hodges and Ellington

SIDE BY SIDE.
Compact disc: released on Verve, Jan'86 by Phonogram Records. Dist: Polygram

Hodges Brothers

WATERMELON HANGIN.
Album: released on Arhoolie, May'81 by Arhoolie Records. Dist: Projection, Topic, Jazz Music, Swift, Roots

Hodges, Carl

BLUES ALL AROUND MY BED Blues roots vol.2.
Notes: See under: Blues Roots Vol.2.

Hodges, Johnny

2 OR 3 SHADES OF BLUE.
Album: released on RCA, Feb'86 by RCA Records. Dist: RCA, Roots, Swift, Wellard, Chris, I & B, Solomon & Peres Distribution

Cassette: released on RCA, Feb'86 by RCA Records. Dist: RCA, Roots, Swift, Wellard, Chris, I & B, Solomon & Peres Distribution

AT THE SPORTPLAST BERLIN.
Album:

Album: released on Pablo, Jan'82 by Pablo Records. Dist: Wellard, Chris, IMS-Polygram, BMG

BACK TO BACK (Hodges, Johnny & Duke Ellington).

BIG SOUND, THE (Hodges Johnny and the Ellington men).
Album: released on Verve (France), Feb'84

DUKES IN BED.
Album: released on Import Music Service (IMS), Dec'79 Dist: Concord Jazz Distributions, Pablo, Polygram

EVERYBODY KNOWS.
Album: by Jasmine Records. Dist: Counterpoint, Lugtons, Taylor, H.R., Wellard, Chris, Swift, Cadillac

JOHNNY HODGES VOL 1.
Album: released on Jazz Reactivation, Jan'82 Dist: PRT

JOHNNY HODGES VOL 1 1937-38.
Album: released on Ajax, Apr'79

JOHNNY HODGES VOL 2 1939.
Album: released on Ajax, Apr'79

JOHNNY HODGES VOL 2.
Album: released on Jazz Reactivation, May'83 Dist: PRT

JOHNNY HODGES VOL 3.
Album: released on Ajax (USA), Apr'79 Dist: Swift

JOHNNY HODGES VOL 4.
Album: released on Ajax (USA), Apr'79 Dist: Swift

JOHNNY HODGES WILD BILL DAVIS 1965-1966 (Hodges Johnny & Wild Bill Davis).
Album: released on RCA (France), Jan'83 by RCA Records. Dist: Discovery

MAN AND HIS MUSIC, A (Hodges, Johnny & Charlie Shavers).
Album: released on Storyville, May'86 by Storyville Records. Dist: Jazz Music Distribution, Swift Distribution, Chris Wellard Distribution, Counterpoint Distribution

MASTERS OF JAZZ VOL.9.
Album: released on Storyville, May'86 by Storyville Records. Dist: Jazz Music Distribution, Swift Distribution, Chris Wellard Distribution, Counterpoint Distribution

MELLOW TONW.
Album: released on Vogue Jazz (France), May'83

NOT SO DUKISH.
Album: released on Verve (USA), Dec'81 by Polydor. Dist: Polygram

RABBITS WORK.

RABBITS WORK VOL 5.
Album: released on Verve (USA), Jun'81 by Polydor. Dist: Polygram

SMOOTH ONE, THE.
Album: released on Verve (Polydor-Germany), Aug'79 by Polydor Records (Germany). Dist: Polygram

Hodgeson, Roger

IN THE EYE OF THE STORM.
Tracks: / Had a dream (sleeping with the enemy) / In jepardy / Lovers in the wind / Hooked on a problem / Give me love give me life / I'm not afraid / Only because of you.
Compact disc: released on A&M, Dec'84 by A&M Records. Dist: Polygram

Album:

Hodgson, Roger

HAD A DREAM.
Single (7"):

IN JEOPARDY.
Single (7"):

Hoeke, Rob

JUMPIN ON THE 88.
Album: released on Oldie Blues Holland, Mar'84

Hoff, Ernst Van't

HERE WE ARE (Hoff, Ernst Van't & Dick Wille Brandts).
Album: released on Hep, Apr'81 by H.R. Taylor Records. Dist: Jazz Music, Cadillac Music, JSU, Taylors, Wellard, Chris, Zodiac, Swift, Fast Forward

Hoffmann, Herbert M

CHRISTMAS CAROLS FOR CHURCH ORGAN.
:

Cassette: released on Chevron, Nov'84 Dist: Multiple Sound Distributors

Hoffman, Peter

ROCK CLASSICS.
Tracks: / House of the rising sun / Scarborough fair / Sun ain't gonna shine any more / Long and winding road / Macarthur park / Sailing / Nights in white satin / Yesterday / Say goodbye to hollywood / Bridge over troubled water.
Compact disc: released on CBS, Aug'85 by CBS Records. Dist: CBS

Compact disc: released on CBS, Aug'85 by CBS Records. Dist: CBS

Album: released on CBS, May'83 by CBS Records. Dist: CBS

Hoffnung

SPEECH AT OFORD UNIVERSTITY 1958.
Cassette: released on BBC, Jan'79 by BBC Records & Tapes. Dist: EMI, PRT, Pye

Hoffnung, Gerard
HOFFNUNG.
Double Album: released on BBC, Jan'74 by BBC Records & Tapes. Dist: EMI, PRT, Pye

Hoffpauir, Sleepy
FIDDLES TRADITIONAL CAJUN MUSIC.
Album:

SLEEPY HOFFPAUIR FIDDLES TRADITIONAL CAJUN MUSIC.
Album: released on Swallow, Feb'79

Hofmann, Peter
NIGHTS IN WHITE SATIN/SAILING.
Single (7"): released on CBS, May'83 by CBS Records. Dist: CBS

SUN AINT GONNA SHINE ANY MORE/SAY GOODBYE TO HOLLYWOOD.
Single (7"): released on CBS, Oct'83 by CBS Records. Dist: CBS

Hofner, Adolph
SOUTH TEXAS SWING.
Album: released on Arhoolie, May'81 by Arhoolie Records. Dist: Projection, Topic, Jazz Music, Swift, Roots

Hogan, Anne
KICKABYES.
Album: released on Double Vision, Jun'85 by Double Vision Records. Dist: Rough Trade, Cartel

Hogan, Jimmy
TRIO IRISH DANCE MUSIC.
Cassette: released on Folktracks, Nov'79 Dist: Roots

Hogay and the...
LAST FOOTBALL SONG, THE (Hogay and the Terrace Choir).
Single (7"): released on Silvertown, Jun'84 by Silvertown Records.

Hoggard, Jay
LOVE SURVIVES.
Album: released on Gramavision (USA), May'83 by Gramavision Records (USA). Dist: PRT, IMS, Polygram

RAINFOREST.
Album: released on Contemporary Jazz, Jul'81

Hogg, Smokey
GOIN' BACK HOME.
Album: released on Krazy Kat (USA), Mav'84
Album: released on Krazy Kat (USA), May'84

Hoglund, Ola
ALLT UNDER HIMMELENS FASTE (Hoglund, Ola/Arne Domnerus).
Album: released on Phontastic, May'86 Dist: Wellard, Chris

Hogshead
ROCKIN IN THE COUNTRY.
Album: released on Rollercoaster, Sep'84 by Rollercoaster Records. Dist: Swift Distribution, Rollercoaster Distribution

Hohki, Kazuko
KAZUKO HOHKI SINGS BRIDGITTE BARDOT.
Album: released on Essex, Apr'87 by Essex Records. Dist: Jazz Music

Hohner Accordian...
ACCORDIAN IN CONCERT (Hohner Accordian Orchestra Augsberg).
Album: released on ARC (Accordion Records), Jan'84 Dist: Accordion Record Club

Ho Ho Kam
DON'T YOU KNOW.
Tracks: / Envy your innocence.
Single (7"): released on Numa, Aug'86 by Numa Records. Dist: PRT Distribution

Single (12"): released on Numa, Aug'86 by Numa Records. Dist: PRT Distribution

HARLEQUIN TEARS.
Tracks: / To sleep.
Single (7"): released on Numa, Jun'86 by Numa Records. Dist: PRT Distribution

Single (12"): released on Numa, Jun'86 by Numa Records. Dist: PRT Distribution

Album: released on Numa, Aug'85 by Numa Records. Dist: PRT Distribution

KING.

Page 476

Single (7"): released on Numa, Nov'84 by Numa Records. Dist: PRT Distribution

Hokey Cokey
HOKEY COKEY (Various Artists).
Album: released on BBC, May'85 by BBC Records & Tapes. Dist: EMI, PRT, Pye

Hokum Hotshots
MAYBE IT'S THE BLUES.
Album: released on Celp, Mar'84 Dist: Harmonia Mundi

Holbrook, Robin
FRIENDLY ISLE.
Single (7"): released on Solent, Aug'84 by Solent Records.

Hold Down a Chord
HOLD DOWN A CHORD (Various Artists).
Album: released on BBC Publications, Jun'83 Dist: Record and Tape Sales Distribution, Taylor, H.R., Solomon & Peres Distribution

Holden, Ron
LOVE YOU SO.
Single (7"): released on Reviva, Jul'82

Holder, Ace
ROCKIN THIS JOINT TONITE.
Album: released on JSP, Feb'79 by JSP Records. Dist: Swift, Projection

Holdsworth, Alan
METAL FATIGUE.
Album: released on Enigma, Feb'86 by Enigma Records. Dist: Rough Trade, Cartel, EMI

SAND.
Album: released on Enigma (Europe), Aug'87 by Enigma Records. Dist: Rough Trade, Cartel, EMI

Holiday, Billie
16 CLASSIC TRACKS.
Album: released on MCA, Jun'82 by MCA Records. Dist: Polygram, MCA

Cassette: released on MCA, Jun'82 by MCA Records. Dist: Polygram, MCA

1942 - 1951 - 1954.
Album: released on Capitol (France), '83 by Capitol Records. Dist: Conifer

2 LP.
Double Album: released on Carrere(France), Apr'84 by Carrere Records (France). Dist: PRT

ALL OF ME.
Album: released on Happy Bird (Germany), Jul'84 Dist: Polygram, IMS

AN EVENING WITH LADY DAY.
Album: released on Jazz Bird, Jan'82 Dist: Cassion (Melandy)

AT STORYVILLE.
Album: released on Black Lion-Intercord, Jan'82

B.H STORY VOLUME 1.
Album: released on CBS, Jan'73 by CBS Records. Dist: CBS

BILLIE ELLA LENA SARAH (Holiday Ella Fitzgerald Lena Horne Sarah Vaugh).
Album: released on CBS, Mar'81 by CBS Records. Dist: CBS

BILLIE HOLIDAY.
Compact disc: released on CBS, May'87 by CBS Records. Dist: CBS

BILLIE HOLIDAY 30'S.
Album: released on Lotus, Aug'86 Dist: Counterpoint

Cassette: released on Lotus, Aug'86 Dist: Counterpoint

BILLIE HOLIDAY 40'S.
Album: released on Lotus, Aug'86 Dist: Counterpoint

Cassette: released on Lotus, Aug'86 Dist: Counterpoint

BILLIE HOLIDAY 50'S.
Album: released on Lotus, Aug'86 Dist: Counterpoint

Cassette: released on Lotus, Aug'86 Dist: Counterpoint

BILLIE HOLIDAY AT MONTEREY 1958.
Tracks: / Ain't nobody's business but my own / Willow weep for me / When your lover has gone / God bless the child / I only have eyes for you / Good morning heartache / Them there eyes / Billie's blues / Oh, what a little moonlight can do / Trav'lin light / Lover come back to me.

Notes: This album is a true event! Unearthed after more than 20 years, this first-time release of Billie Holiday at the 1st Monterey Jazz festival is a rare historic record and treat. Captured "live" in stereo outdoors in October 1958 (pre-stereo days) via an experimental stereo model recorder the quality is astounding. Remastered in   digital.
Personnel: Billie Holiday/Mal Waldron/Eddie Khan/Dick Berk.
Album: released on Blackhawk, Sep'86 by Blackhawk Records (USA). Dist: IMS-Polygram

Cassette: released on Blackhawk, Sep'86 by Blackhawk Records (USA). Dist: IMS-Polygram

BILLIE HOLIDAY (CD).
Compact disc: released on Deja Vu, Jul'87 by Deja Vu Records. Dist: Counterpoint Distribution, Record Services Distribution (Ireland)

BILLIE HOLIDAY COLLECTION, THE.
Album: released on Deja Vu, Aug'85 by Deja Vu Records. Dist: Counterpoint Distribution, Record Services Distribution (Ireland)

Cassette: released on Deja Vu, Aug'85 by Deja Vu Records. Dist: Counterpoint Distribution, Record Services Distribution (Ireland)

BILLIE HOLIDAY LIVE.
Album: released on Phoenix, Oct'82 by Audio Fidelity Enterprises. Dist: Stage One. Lugtons

BILLIE HOLIDAY SONGBOOK, THE.
Album: released on Verve, Aug'85 by Phonogram Records. Dist: Polygram

Cassette: released on Verve, Aug'85 by Phonogram Records. Dist: Polygram

BILLIE HOLIDAY STORY, THE - VOL 3.
Double Album: released on CBS, Jan'87 by CBS Records. Dist: CBS

BILLIE HOLIDAY STORY, THE - VOL 2.
Double Album: released on CBS, Jan'87 by CBS Records. Dist: CBS

BILLIE'S BLUES.
Tracks: / I'm a fool to want you / Glad to be unhappy / Sailboat in the moonlight / When a woman loves a man / I'll never be the same / Let's call the whole thing off / Summertime / Am I blue / I cover the waterfront / Billie's blues.
Album: released on CBS, Mar'86 by CBS Records. Dist: CBS

Cassette: released on CBS, Mar'86 by CBS Records. Dist: CBS

Album: released on Vanguard, Aug'86 by PRT Records. Dist: PRT

Cassette: released on Vanguard, Aug'86 by PRT Records. Dist: PRT

Album: released on Bulldog Records, Jul'82

Album: released on Astan, Nov'84 by Astan Records. Dist: Counterpoint

BODY AND SOUL.
Album: released on Verve (Import), Oct'82

COMPACT JAZZ.
Compact disc: released on Verve, Jul'87 by Phonogram Records. Dist: Polvgram

ESSENTIAL...., THE.
Album: released on Verve (USA), Mar'83 by Polydor. Dist: Polygram

FINE AND MELLOW.
Notes: Volume 1 (1939)
Album: released on Commodore Classics, May'87 by Teldec Records (Germany). Dist: Conifer, IMS, Polygram

Compact disc: released on Commodore Classics, May'87 by Teldec Records (Germany). Dist: Conifer, IMS, Polygram

FINE AND MELLOW 1939 1944.
Album: released on Commodore Classics, Aug'82 by Teldec Records (Germany). Dist: Conifer, IMS, Polygram

FINE & MELLOW.
Album: released on Cambra, Apr'85 by Cambra Records. Dist: IDS, Conifer

GOD BLESS THE CHILD.
Double Album: released on CBS, Jan'74 by CBS Records. Dist: CBS

GOLDEN GREATS: BILLIE HOLIDAY.
Album: released on MCA, Jul'85 by MCA Records. Dist: Polygram, MCA

GOLDEN YEARS 1933-41, THE.
Album: released on CBS, Dec'85 by CBS Records. Dist: CBS Deleted '86.

Cassette: released on CBS, Dec'85 by CBS Records. Dist: CBS

GOOD MORNING HEARTACHE.
Album: released on Hallmark, Jul'87 by Pickwick Distribution. Dist: Pickwick Distribution, PRT, Taylors

---

Cassette: released on Hallmark, Jul'87 by Pickwick Records. Dist: Pickwick Distribution, PRT, Taylors

GREATEST HITS: BILLIE HOLIDAY VOL.2.
Album: released on Masters (Holland), Apr'87

Cassette: released on Masters (Holland), Apr'87

GREATEST HITS: BILLIE HOLIDAY VOL.1.

I GOT THE RIGHT TO SING.
Album: released on Joker, Apr'81 Dist: Cadillac, Zodiac Distribution, Jazz Horizons, Jazz Music, JSU, Celtic Music

I'LL BE SEEING YOU.
Album: released on Commodore Classics, May'87 by Teldec Records (Germany). Dist: Conifer, IMS, Polygram

Compact disc: released on Commodore Classics, May'87 by Teldec Records (Germany). Dist: Conifer, IMS, Polygram

I'LL BE SEEING YOU (1944).
Album: released on Commodore Classics, Jan'85 by Teldec Records (Germany). Dist: Conifer, IMS, Polygram

IMMORTAL SESSIONS.
Album: released on Storyville, May'86 by Storyville Records. Dist: Jazz Music Distribution, Swift Distribution, Chris Wellard Distribution, Counterpoint Distribution

IMMORTAL, THE.
Album: released on Joker (Import), Apr'81

I WONDER WHERE YOUR LOVE IS GONE.
Cassette: released on Giants of Jazz, Oct'86 by Hasmick Promotions Ltd . Dist: Counterpoint, Jazz Music, Taylors, Swift, Mainline, Wellard, Chris

I WONDER WHERE YOUR LOVE HAS GONE.

LADY AND THE LEGEND VOL 3, THE.
Album: released on Rhapsody, Sep'84 by President Records. Dist: Taylors, Swift, Jazz Music, Wellard, Chris

LADY AND THE LEGEND VOL 2 1952-1956, THE.
Album: released on Rhapsody, Sep'84 by President Records. Dist: Taylors, Swift, Jazz Music, Wellard, Chris

LADY AND THE LEGEND VOL 1 1949-1951, THE.
Album: released on Rhapsody, Sep'84 by President Records. Dist: Taylors, Swift, Jazz Music, Wellard, Chris

LADY DAY/LADY IN SATIN.
Album: released on CBS(Blue Diamond), Jun'85 by CBS Records. Dist: CBS

LADY IN SATIN.
Album: released on CBS Cameo, Mar'83 by CBS Records. Dist: CBS

LADY OF THE BLUES.
Tracks: / God bless the child / Them there eyes / T'aint nobody's business if I do / My man / You're driving me crazy / Billie's blues / He's funny that way / Miss Brown to you / No detour ahead / Don't explain / Lover man / All of me / Daddy he can't make no time / Tenderly.
Album: released on Showcase, Apr'86 Dist: Counterpoint

Cassette: released on Showcase, Apr'86 Dist: Counterpoint

LADY SINGS THE BLUES.
Compact disc: released on Card/Grand Prix, Apr'87 Dist: Target

Album: released on Verve, Apr'82

LAST RECORDING.
Album: released on Import Music Service (IMS), Dec'79 Dist: Concord Jazz Distributions, Pablo, Polygram

LEGEND OF BILLIE HOLIDAY.
Tracks: / That ole devil called love / Lover man (oh where can you be) / Don't explain / Good morning heartache / There is no greater love / Easy living / Solitude / Porgy / My man / Them there eyes / Now or never / Ain't nobody's business if I do / Somebody's on my mind / Keep's on raining / You're my thrill / God bless the child.
Album: released on MCA, Nov'85 by MCA Records. Dist: Polygram, MCA

Cassette: released on MCA, Nov'85 by MCA Records. Dist: Polygram, MCA

Compact disc: released on MCA, Nov'85 by MCA Records. Dist: Polygram, MCA

LIVE 1953.
Album: released on Rarities, Apr'81

LIVE & RARE 1937-56.

Compact disc: released on Delta, '86 by Delta Records. Dist: Target

MASTERS OF JAZZ VOL.3.
Album: released on Storyville, May'86 by Storyville Records. Dist: Jazz Music Distribution, Swift Distribution, Chris Wellard Distribution, Counterpoint Distribution

MISS BROWN TO YOU.
Album: released on Swinghouse, Jan'84 Dist: Jazz Music Distribution, Swift Distribution, Chris Wellard Distribution

Mississippi delta blues

NEW ORLEANS (Holiday, Billie & Louis Armstrong).
Notes: For full details see under ARMSTRONG, Louis.

PORGY.
Album: released on Happy Bird (Germany), Jul'84 Dist: Polygram, IMS

RADIO & TV BROADCASTS.
Album: released on Uni/Base, Apr'81 Dist: Jazz Music, Jazz Horizons

REPLAY ON.
Album: released on Sierra, Aug'85 by Sierra Records. Dist: WEA

SAINT LOUISE BLUES (Holiday, Billie & Bessie Smith).
Notes: For full information see under: Smith, Bessie/Billie Holiday.

SILVER COLLECTION, THE.

SILVER COLLECTION, THE.
Tracks: / I wished on the moon / Moonlight in vermont / Say it isn't so / Love is here to stay / Darn that dream / But not for me / Body and soul / Comes love / They can't take that away from me / Let's call the whole thing off / Gee baby ain't I good for you / Embraceable you / All or nothing at all / We'll be together again.
Compact disc: released on Verve, Nov'84 by Phonogram Records. Dist: Polygram

Compact disc: released on Verve, Nov'84 by Phonogram Records. Dist: Polygram

SONGS FOR DISTINGUE LOVERS.
Album: released on Verve (USA), Oct'84 by Polydor. Dist: Polygram

Cassette: released on Verve (USA), Oct'84 by Polydor. Dist: Polygram

SONGS FOR DISTINGUISHED LOVERS.
Tracks: / Day in day out / Foggy day, A / Star fell on Alabama / One for my baby / Just one of those things / I didn't know what time it was.
Compact disc: released on Verve, Apr'84 by Phonogram Records. Dist: Polygram

STORYVILLE.
Album: released on Star Jazz USA, Apr'86 by Charly Records. Dist: Charly Distribution

Cassette: released on Star Jazz USA, Apr'86 by Charly Records. Dist: Charly Distribution
Cat. no: **SJAZZC 3**
Cassette: released on Chase Music, Nov'84 by Chase Records. Dist: PRT

STRANGE FRUIT.
Album: released on Storyville, Sep'86 by Storyville Records. Dist: Jazz Music Distribution, Swift Distribution, Chris Wellard Distribution, Counterpoint Distribution

TENDERLY.
Album: released on Happy Bird (Germany), Jul'84 Dist: Polygram, IMS

THAT OLE DEVIL CALLED LOVE.
Single (7"): released on MCA, Oct'85 by MCA Records. Dist: Polygram, MCA

VOL 2.
Album: released on MCA, Feb'84 by MCA Records. Dist: Polygram, MCA

Cassette: released on MCA, Feb'84 by MCA Records. Dist: Polygram, MCA

VOLUME 3.
Album: released on Queen, Jun'86 Dist: Jazz Music

WALKMAN JAZZ.
Cassette: released on Polydor, Jun'87 by Polydor Records. Dist: Polygram, Polydor

Holiday For Strings...

HOLIDAY FOR STRINGS & BRASS.
Tracks: / Holiday for strings / Stripper, The / Lisbon Antigua / You make me feel so young / I only have eyes for you / It could happen to you / Sophisticated lady / Orange Blossom special / Autimn leaves / Zambezi / Blue tango / April in Portugal / All my loving / Moon of Manakoora / Samba De Orfeu.
Album: released on Memoir, Jan'87 by Memoir Records. Dist: PRT Distribution

Cassette: released on Memoir, Jan'87 by Memoir Records. Dist: PRT Distribution

Holiday Hits

HOLIDAY HITS Various artists (Various Artists).
Tracks: / Wake me up before you go go / Respectable / Venus / Don't leave me this way / Dr. Beat / Fresh / Call me / Hooray, hooray, it's a holi-holiday / Barbados / D.I.S.C.O. / Dolce vita / Brother Louie / Everybody salsa / My toot toot / Give it up / Live is life.
Album: released on CBS, Jun'87 by CBS Records. Dist: CBS

Album: released on CBS, Jun'87 by CBS Records. Dist: CBS

Compact disc: released on CBS, Jul'87 by CBS Records. Dist: CBS

Holiday, Jimmy

EVERYBODY NEEDS HELP.
Tracks: / Baby boy's in love / Yesterday died / Man ain't nothin' without a woman (A) / I'm in love with you / Spread your love / Baby I love you / In the eyes of my girl / I don't want to hear it / Turning point, The / I'm gonna help hurry my brothers home / We forgot about love / Everybody needs help / Ready, willing and able / I've got to live while I can / I'm gonna use what I got (to get what I need) / Beauty of a girl in love, The.
Album: released on Stateside, Sep'86 Dist: EMI

Cassette: released on Stateside, Sep'86 Dist: EMI

Holiday Patrons

HOTTEST TIME OF THE YEAR.
Single (7"): released on Rod, Aug'85

Holland

EARLY WARNING.
Album: released on Ebony, Jun'84 by Ebony Records. Dist: Pinnacle, Ebony

Holland, Dave

JUMPIN' IN (Holland, Dave Quintet).
Album: released on ECM (Germany), Apr'84 by ECM Records. Dist: IMS, Polygram, Virgin through EMI

LIFE CYCLE Solo cello.
Album: released on ECM (Germany), Apr'83 by ECM Records. Dist: IMS, Polygram, Virgin through EMI

SEEDS OF TIME (Holland, Dave Quintet).
Tracks: / Uhren / Homecoming / Perspicuity / Celebration / World protection blues / Gridlock / Walk-a-way / Good doctor (The) / Double vision.
Notes: Personnel: Dave Holland - bass/Steve Coleman -alto and soprano saxophones, flutes/Julian Priester - trombone/Marvin 'Smitty' Smith -drums, percussion/ Kenny Wheeler - trumpet, cornet, pocket trumpet, fluegelhorn.
Compact disc: released on ECM (Germany), Aug'85 by ECM Records. Dist: IMS, Polygram, Virgin through EMI

VOLUME 1 (see also Sam Rivers) (Holland, Dave & Sam Rivers).
Album: released on Impro-arts, Jul'78 Dist: Projection

VOLUME 2 (see also Sam Rivers) (Holland, Dave & Sam Rivers).
Album: released on Impro-arts, Jul'78 Dist: Projection

Holland/Dozler

WHY CAN'T WE BE LOVERS.
Single (7"): released on HDH(Holland/Dozier/Holland), Feb'85 by Demon Records. Dist: Pinnacle

Holland, Jools

CRAZY OVER YOU.
Single (7"): released on I.R.S.(Independent Record Syndicate), Oct'83 by I.R.S.. Dist: MCA

Holland, Lys

MAN OF HONOUR, A.
Cassette: released on Soundings, Mar'85 Dist: Soundings

Holland, Maggie

SHORT CUT, A (Holland, Maggie & Jon Moore).
Album: released on Rogue, Sep'86 by Fast Forward Records. Dist: Nine Mile Distribution, Cartel Distribution

STILL PAUSE.
Album: released on Rogue, Jun'86 by Fast Forward Records. Dist: Nine Mile Distribution, Cartel Distribution

Holley, Lyin' Joe

SO COLD IN THE USA.
Album: released on JSP, Mar'82 by JSP Records. Dist: Swift, Projection

Holliday, Doc

DANGER ZONE.
Album: released on Razor, Jul'86 by Razor. Dist: Pinnacle

RIDES AGAIN.
Album: released on A&M, Jun'82 by A&M Records. Dist: Polygram

Holliday, Jennifer

AND I'M TELLING YOU I'M NOT GOING.
Single (7"): released on Geffen, Aug'82 by Geffen Records. Dist: WEA, CBS

FEEL MY SOUL.
Tracks: / Just let me wait / I am ready now / This game of love / I am love / Shine a light / Just for a while / My sweet delight / Change is gonna come / This day.
Album: released on Geffen, Sep'86 by Geffen Records. Dist: WEA, CBS

Cassette: released on Geffen, Sep'86 by Geffen Records. Dist: WEA, CBS

I AM CHANGING.
Single (7"): released on Geffen, Oct'82 by Geffen Records. Dist: WEA, CBS

I AM LOVE.
Single (7"): released on Geffen, Feb'84 by Geffen Records. Dist: WEA, CBS

Single (12"): released on Geffen, Feb'84 by Geffen Records. Dist: WEA, CBS

SHINE A LIGHT.
Single (7"): released on Geffen, Oct'83 by Geffen Records. Dist: WEA, CBS

Holliday, Johnny

CRUISIN' 1964 WHK Cleveland.
Cassette: released on Increase(USA), Jun'87 by Quicksilver Records (USA).

Holliday, Judy

HOLLIDAY WITH MULLIGAN (Holliday, Judy and Gerry Mulligan).
Tracks: / What's the rush / Loving you / Lazy / It must be christmas / Party's over (The) / It's bad for me / Supper time / Pass that peace pipe / I've got a right to sing the blues / Summer's over / Blue prelude.
Album: released on DRG (USA), Mar'87 by DRG Records. Dist: Conifer, RCA

Cassette: released on DRG (USA), Mar'87 by DRG Records. Dist: Conifer, RCA

Holliday, Michael

STORY OF MY LIFE, THE.
Single (7"): released on Old Gold (Reissue), Jul'82

VERY BEST OF MICHAEL HOLLIDAY, THE 16 favourites of the 50's.
Album: released on Music for Pleasure, Feb'84 by EMI Records. Dist: MFP Distribution

Cassette: released on Music for Pleasure, Feb'84 by EMI Records. Dist: MFP Distribution

Holliday, Oliver

DO WHAT YOU DO.
Single (7"): released on In Records, Jun'84 by In Records. Dist: Cunning Stunts Distributor

Hollies

20 GOLDEN GREATS.
Tracks: / Air that I breathe (The) / Carrie Anne / Bus stop / Listen to me / Look through any window / I can't let go / Long cool woman in a red dress / Here I go again / I can't tell the bottom from the top / I'm alive / Yes I will / Stay / Sorry Suzanne / Gasoline Alley bred / We're through / Jennifer Eccles / Stop stop stop / On a carousel / Just one look / He ain't heavy, he's my brother.
Compact disc: released on EMI, Mar'87 by EMI Records. Dist: EMI

Album: released on EMI, '85 by EMI Records. Dist: EMI

Cassette: released on EMI, '85 by EMI Records. Dist: EMI

Album: released on Capitol, Aug'79 by Capitol Records. Dist: EMI

: released on Capitol, Aug'79 by Capitol Records. Dist: EMI

AN HOUR OF THE HOLLIES.
Tracks: / Stop, stop, stop / Gasoline alley bred / Searchin' / Listen to me / What kind of boy / Rockin' robin / Come on back / Memphis Tennessee / Too young to be married / Dear Eloise / He ain't heavy, he's my brother / Sweet little sixteen / Nobody / Hey Willy / Just like me, (Ain't that) / Sorry Suzanne / Lucille / Keep off that friend of mine / On a carousel / Pay you back with interest / Clown / If I needed someone / Blowing in the wind.
Cassette: released on Hour Of Pleasure, Sep'87 by Music For Pleasure Records. Dist: EMI. Estim retail price in Sep'87 was £1.99.

ANOTHER NIGHT.
Album: released on Polydor, Feb'75 by Polydor Records. Dist: Polygram, Polydor

BEST OF THE HOLLIES EPS, THE.
Tracks: / Here I go again / You know he did / What kind of boy / Look through any window / What kind of love / When I'm not there / Rockin' robin / Lucille / Memphis / Just one look / I'm alive / Come on back / We're through / I've got a way of my own / So lonely / To you my love / Whatcha gonna do 'bout it / Too much monkey business / Come on home / I can't let go / Baby that's all / I'm talking about you (remix version).
Cassette: released on Nut, Mar'81 by EMI Records. Dist: EMI

BUS STOP.
Single (7"): released on EMI (Holland), Jul'84 by EMI Records. Dist: Conifer

CRAZY STEAL, A.
Album: released on Polydor, Apr'78 by Polydor Records. Dist: Polygram, Polydor

EP COLLECTION, THE.
Album: released on See For Miles, 11 Apr'87 by See For Miles Records. Dist: Pinnacle

GREATEST HITS:HOLLIES.
Album: released on EMI (Holland), '83 by EMI Records. Dist: Conifer

HE AIN'T HEAVY HE'S MY BROTHER.
Single (7"): released on Past Masters, Aug'82

HE AIN'T HEAVY HE'S MY BROTHER/BUS STOP.
Single (7"): released on Old Gold, Oct'83 by Old Gold Records. Dist: Lightning, Jazz Music, Spartan, Counterpoint

HOLLIES LIVE HITS.
Album: released on Polydor, Mar'77 by Polydor Records. Dist: Polygram, Polydor

HOLLIES, THE.
Album: released on MFP, Sep'85 by EMI Records. Dist: EMI

Cassette: released on MFP, Sep'85 by EMI Records. Dist: EMI

LIVE.
Album: released on Polydor, Feb'82 by Polydor Records. Dist: Polygram, Polydor

Cassette: released on Polydor, Feb'82 by Polydor Records. Dist: Polygram, Polydor

LONG COOL WOMAN IN A BLACK DRESS.
Tracks: / Long cool woman in a black dress / He ain't heavy he's my brother / King Midas in reverse / Blowin' in the wind / Stop, stop, stop / Mighty Quinn / I can't let go / Carrie Anne / Dear Eloise / Hey Willy.
Album: released on Music For Pleasure (Holland), Jan'86 by EMI Records. Dist: EMI

Cassette: released on Music For Pleasure (Holland), Jan'86 by EMI Records. Dist: EMI

NOT THE HITS AGAIN.
Tracks: / Wings / It's in her kiss / You'll be mine / Take your time / I am a rock / Honey & wine / Very last day (The) / It's only make believe / That's my desire / So lonely / Now's the time / Hard, hard year / Put yourself in my place / Please don't feel too bad / Nitty gritty-Something's got a hold on me / You better move on / I take what I want / Talkin 'bout you / Candy man / Set me free / Set me free / Lawdy Miss Clawdy / Sweet little sixteen.
Album: released on See For Miles, Feb'86 by See For Miles Records. Dist: Pinnacle

OTHER SIDE OF THE HOLLIES.
Cassette: released on Parlophone, Aug'78 by EMI Records. Dist: EMI

REUNION OF THE HEART.
Tracks: / Reunion of the heart / Too many hearts get broken / Hollie dazy (medley).
Single (7"): released on Columbia, Mar'87 by EMI Records. Dist: EMI

Single (12"): released on Columbia, Mar'87 by EMI Records. Dist: EMI

RUSSIAN ROULETTE.
Album: released on Polydor, Nov'76 by Polydor Records. Dist: Polygram, Polydor

STOP IN THE NAME OF LOVE.
Single (7"): released on WEA Int, Jul'83

STOP STOP STOP.
Album: released on Starline, '71 by EMI Records. Dist: EMI

THIS IS IT.
Tracks: / You gave me strength / You're all woman* / This is it.
Single (7"): released on Columbia, Jan'87 by EMI Records. Dist: EMI

Single (12"): released on Columbia, Jan'87 by EMI Records. Dist: EMI

TOO MANY HEARTS GET BROKEN.
Single (7"): released on Columbia, May'85 by EMI Records. Dist: EMI

Single (12"): released on Columbia, May'85 by EMI Records. Dist: EMI

Holloway, Elaine

MR. CHRISTMAS.
Single (7"): released on State, Nov'81 by State Records.

Holloway, Loleatta

CRY TO ME.
Single (7"): released on RCA, Jun'84 by RCA Records. Dist: RCA, Roots, Swift, Wellard, Chris, I & B, Solomon & Peres Distribution

Single (12"): released on RCA, Jun'84 by RCA Records. Dist: RCA, Roots, Swift, Wellard, Chris, I & B, Solomon & Peres Distribution

LOVE SENSATION.
Single (7"): released on Salsoul, Jan'84

Single (12"): released on Salsoul, Jan'84

Holloway, Red

RED HOLLOWAY AND COMPANY.
Tracks: / But not for me / Caravan / Passion flower / Blues for Q.M. / Well you needn't / What's new / Summertime / Tokyo Express.
Notes: Personnel: Red Holloway - tenor & alto saxophones / Cedar Walton - Piano / Richard Reid - bass / Jimmie Smith - drums.
Album: released on Concord Jazz(USA), Jul'87 by Concord Jazz Records (USA). Dist: IMS, Polygram

Cassette: released on Concord Jazz(USA), Jul'87 by Concord Jazz Records (USA). Dist: IMS, Polygram

Compact disc: released on Concord Jazz(USA), Jul'87 by Concord Jazz Records (USA). Dist: IMS, Polygram

Holloway, Stanley

BEST OF STANLEY HOLLOWAY.
Album: released on Encore, '78 by EMI Records. Dist: EMI

Cassette: released on Encore, '78 by EMI Records. Dist: EMI

BRAHN BOOTS.
Album: released on Decca, May'82 by Decca Records. Dist: Polygram

Cassette: released on Decca, May'82 by Decca Records. Dist: Polygram

WORLD OF STANLEY HOLLOWAY, THE.
Album: released on World of Learning, '71 by World Of Learning Records. Dist: World Of Learning

Hollow Crown

HOLLOW CROWN (AN ENTERTAINMENT ON THE THEME OF THE MONARCHY) With Doroth Tutin,Max Adrian,Richard Johnson & John Barton.
Cassette: released on Argo (Spokenword), Jul'82 by Decca Records. Dist: Polygram

Hollowell, Terri

JUST STAY WITH ME.
Single (7"): released on Amigo, Jan'81 Dist: Red Rhino, Cartel

JUST YOU AND ME.
Album: released on RK, Apr'80

Hollow, Ken

BRING HER BACK HOME TO ME.
Single (7"): released on Dingles, Jun'81 by Dingles Records. Dist: Projection

Hollwood musicals

HOLLYWOOD MUSICALS Medley.
Single (7"): released on RCA, Dec'83 by RCA Records. Dist: RCA, Roots, Swift, Wellard, Chris, I & B, Solomon & Peres Distribution

Holly, Buddy

Biographical Details: This American singer, songwriter and guitarist was one of the all-time greats of rock 'n' roll and pop music. Born Charles Hardin Holley (the 'e' of his surname was later dropped) in Lubbock, Texas in September 1936, Buddy took up singing and guitar-playing at school. He played regularly with his drumming schoolfriend **Jerry Allison**, and the pair formed a professional partnership in 1957. They then formed a group called **the Crickets**, whose line-up was in 1957. In that year, the combo released the final verion of a song Holly had been offering to various unenthusiastic record labels for several months-"That'll Be The Day" proved to be worth waiting for, eventually reaching No.1 on both the US and UK. "That'll Be The Day" was a bright , uplifting record; it made stars of the Crickets and especially leader Buddy Holly. For complicated contractual reasons, subsequent disc were separated into Buddy Holly releases and Crickets releases although the same musicians performed on the records. By the end of 1958, Holly & the Crickets had achieved success with "Peggy Sue", "Oh Boy!", "Listen To Me", "Maybe Baby", "Rave On", "Think It Over" and "Early In The Morning"; most of these were bigger in Britain than in America. The singer parted company with his group during 1958, but he continued using the old group name with some newly recurted Crickets (including the future country music superstar **Waylon Jennings**). In February 1959, while travelling on a private plane from concert venue in Iowa to another in North Dakota, the 22 year old Holly was killed as the small aircraft crashed into a frozen cornfield during a heavy snowstorm. The accedent also claimed the lives of two other rock 'n' roll stars **The Big Bopper** and **Ritchie Valens**, as well as that of the pilot. At the time of his tragically early death, Buddy was suffering a lull of his career fortunes. It is highly probable that this loll would only have been temporary, judging by the unreleased records and unfinished demos that were posthumously embellished by producer **Norman Petty** and unleashed onto the marketplace. The first posthumous record was **Paul Anka's** song "It Doesn't Matter Anymore", which reached No.1 in Britain and No.13 in the States. Numerous other tracks appeared over the next few years, achieving considerable commercial success in the UK. Although Buddy Holly is revered by American pop historians, it is in Britain that his status has become truly legendary; for it was the fledging UK pop Sixties. **Adam Faith** closely imitated his distinctive vocal hiccup, **the Hollies** named themselves after him and countless artists recorded remakes of his hits. It could be argued that Buddy Holly was the first pop star, as opposed to rock 'n' roll star - i.e. the first to combine the raw energy of rock'n'roll with a fine melodic sensibiity - and **Paul McCartney** has always been particularly keen to acknowledge the debt that **the Beatles** owed to him. McCartney purchased the publishing rights to Buddy Holly's catalogue in 1976, organised a 'Buddy Holly week' in September of that year the 40th Anniversary of the artists' birth; this became an annual event. A TV - advertised "20 Golden Greats" collection topped the British LP chart in 1978.

20 GOLDEN GREATS (Holly, Buddy & The Crickets).
Album: released on MCA Coral, '79 by MCA Records. Dist: Polygram

Cassette: released on MCA Coral, '79 by MCA Records. Dist: Polygram

20 LOVE SONGS.
Album: released on MFP (MCA), Sep'82 by EMI Records. Dist: EMI

Cassette: released on MFP (MCA), Sep'82 by EMI Records. Dist: EMI

23 ALL TIME GREATEST HITS.
Album: released on Astan, Nov'84 by Astan Records. Dist: Counterpoint

Cassette: released on Astan, Nov'84 by Astan Records. Dist: Counterpoint

BABY BABY.
Single (7"): released on MCA, Aug'85 by MCA Records. Dist: Polygram, MCA

BEST OF BUDDY HOLLY,THE.
Compact disc: released on Grand Prix, '86 by Grand Prix Records. Dist: Cartel

Album: released on Hallmark, Sep'86 by Pickwick Records. Dist: Pickwick Distribution, PRT, Taylors

Cassette: released on Hallmark, Sep'86 by Pickwick Records. Dist: Pickwick Distribution, PRT, Taylors

BROWN EYED HANDSOME MAN.
Single (7"): released on MCA, Aug'85 by MCA Records. Dist: Polygram, MCA

BUDDY HOLLY.
Tracks: / Early in the morning / Now we're one / It's so easy / Lonesome tears / Heartbeat / Well all right / Love's made a fool of you / Wishing / Reminiscing / It doesn't matter anymore / Come back baby / True love ways / That's my desire / Moondreams / Raining in my heart / Valley of tears / Baby let's play house / I'm gonna love you too / Peggy Sue / Look at me / Listen to me / Rave on / Valley of tears / Ready Teddy / Empty cup / Everyday / It's too late / Mailman bring me no more blues / Look at me / Words of love / Think it over / Baby I don't care / Fools paradise / Little baby.
Notes: Reissued material from the Coral vaults.
Album: released on MCA, Nov'86 by MCA Records. Dist: Polygram, MCA

Cassette: released on MCA, Nov'86 by MCA Records. Dist: Polygram, MCA

Album: released on MCA, Jan'86 by MCA Records. Dist: Polygram, MCA

Cassette: released on MCA, Aug'86 by MCA Records. Dist: Polygram, MCA

Album: released on MCA Coral, Mar'79 by MCA Records. Dist: Polygram

Cassette: released on MCA Coral, Mar'79 by MCA Records. Dist: Polygram

Album: released on Pickwick, Sep'80 by Pickwick Records. Dist: Pickwick Distribution, Prism Leisure Distribution, Lugtons

Cassette: released on Pickwick, Sep'80 by Pickwick Records. Dist: Pickwick Distribution, Prism Leisure Distribution, Lugtons

Album: released on MCA Coral, '83 by MCA Records. Dist: Polygram

Cassette: released on MCA Coral, '83 by MCA Records. Dist: Polygram

Cassette: released on Cambra, '83 by Cambra Records. Dist: IDS, Conifer

BUDDY HOLLY AND THE CHIRPING CRICKETS.
Tracks: / Oh boy / Not fade away / You've got love / Maybe baby / It's too late / Tell me how / That'll be the day / I'm looking for someone to love / Empty cup / Send me some loving / Last night / Rock me my baby.
Album: released on MCA, Nov'86 by MCA Records. Dist: Polygram, MCA. Estim retail price in Jul'87 was £3.48.

Cassette: released on MCA, Nov'86 by MCA Records. Dist: Polygram, MCA

BUDDY HOLLY-HISTORICAL RECORDINGS Undubbed and unreleased versions.
Album: released on Nor-va-jak, Jul'87

BUDDY HOLLY ROCKS.
Album: released on Charly, May'85 by Charly Records. Dist: Charly, Cadillac

BUDDY HOLLY & THE CRICKETS (Holly, Buddy & The Crickets).
Tracks: / Raining in my heart / Baby won't you come out tonight / Modern Don Juan / Mailman bring me no more blues / Love's made a fool of you / You've got love / Girl on my mind / That'll be the day (Nashville Recording) / Blue days-black nights / Midnight shift / I'm gonna love you too / Don't come back knockin' / Fool's paradise / An empty cup (and a broken date) / Rock around the Ollie Vee(version 1) / Think it over / It's not my fault / I guess I was just a fool / I'm gonna set my foot down / Rock a bye rock / Because I love you / You're the one / Ready Teddy / Send me some lovin / Lonesome tears / Rock around the Ollie Vee (version 2) / Reminiscing / Love's made a fool of you (without Holly) / When you ask about love (without Holly) / Baby my heart (without Holly).
Notes: Double album and cassette.
Double Album: released on Cambra, Sep'86 by Cambra Records. Dist: IDS, Conifer

Double cassette: released on Cambra, Sep'86 by Cambra Records. Dist: IDS, Conifer

CHIRPING CRICKETS (Holly, Buddy & The Crickets).
Album: released on MCA Coral, '83 by MCA Records. Dist: Polygram

Cassette: released on MCA Coral, '83 by MCA Records. Dist: Polygram

FOR THE FIRST TIME ANYWHERE.
Tracks: / Rock-a-bye rock / Maybe baby / I'm gonna set my foot down / Because I love you / Changing all those changes / That's my desire / Baby won't you come out tonight? / It's not my fault / Brown-eyed handsome man / Bo Diddley.
Compact disc: released on MCA, Sep'87 by MCA Records. Dist: Polygram, MCA

FOR THE FIRST TIME ANYWHERE (Holly, Buddy & The Crickets).
Tracks: / Rock-a-bye rock / Maybe baby (1st version) / Because I love you / I'm gonna set my foot down / Changing all those changes / That's my desire / Baby won't you come out tonight / It's not my fault / Brown eyed handsome man / Bo Diddley.
Album: released on MCA Coral, Mar'83 by MCA Records. Dist: Polygram

Cassette: released on MCA Coral, Mar'83 by MCA Records. Dist: Polygram

Compact disc: released on MCA, Jul'87 by MCA Records. Dist: Polygram, MCA

FROM THE ORIGINAL MASTER TAPES.
Album: released on MCA, Sep'85 by MCA Records. Dist: Polygram, MCA

GOLDEN GREATS: BUDDY HOLLY.
Album: released on MCA, Jul'85 by MCA Records. Dist: Polygram, MCA

Cassette: released on MCA, Jul'85 by MCA Records. Dist: Polygram, MCA

GOOD ROCKIN' TONIGHT.
Extended-play record: released on Bear Family, Sep'79 by Bear Family Records. Dist: Rollercoaster Distribution, Swift

GREATEST HITS:BUDDY HOLLY.
Album: released on MCA Coral, Aug'81 by MCA Records. Dist: Polygram

Cassette: released on MCA Coral, Aug'81 by MCA Records. Dist: Polygram

Compact disc: released on MCA Coral, Aug'81 by MCA Records. Dist: Polygram

GREATEST HITS/LOVE SONGS.
Cassette: released on MCA (Twinpax Cassettes), Sep'84

IT DOESN'T MATTER ANYMORE.
Single (7"): released on Old Gold, Apr'83 by Old Gold Records. Dist: Lightning, Jazz Music, Spartan, Counterpoint

Single (7"): released on MCA, Aug'85 by MCA Records. Dist: Polygram, MCA

LEGEND.
Album: released on MCA Coral, Mar'82 by MCA Records. Dist: Polygram

Cassette: released on MCA Coral, Mar'82 by MCA Records. Dist: Polygram

LEGENDARY BUDDY HOLLY, THE.
Album: released on Hallmark, Oct'87 by Pickwick Records. Dist: Pickwick Distribution, PRT, Taylors

Cassette: released on Hallmark, Oct'87 by Pickwick Records. Dist: Pickwick Distribution, PRT, Taylors

MAYBE BABY.
Single (7"): released on MCA, Sep'84 by MCA Records. Dist: Polygram, MCA

NASHVILLE SESSIONS, THE.
Album: released on MCA Coral, '83 by MCA Records. Dist: Polygram

Cassette: released on MCA Coral, '83 by MCA Records. Dist: Polygram

NASHVILLE SESSIONS.
Tracks: / You are my one desire / Blue days black nights / Modern Don Juan / Rock around with Ollie Vee / Midnight shift / Don't come back knockin / Girl on my mind / Love me.
Album: released on MCA, Nov'86 by MCA Records. Dist: Polygram, MCA

Cassette: released on MCA, Nov'86 by MCA Records. Dist: Polygram, MCA

OH BOY.
Single (7"): released on MCA, Aug'85 by MCA Records. Dist: Polygram, MCA

ONVERGETELIJKE HITS.
Album: released on Music for Pleasure (Holland), Apr'83 Dist: Conifer Distribution

PEGGY SUE.
Single (7"): released on MCA, Aug'85 by MCA Records. Dist: Polygram, MCA

PEGGY SUE/EVERYDAY.
Single (7"): released on Old Gold, Jul'82 by Old Gold Records. Dist: Lightning, Jazz Music, Spartan, Counterpoint

RAVE ON.
Single (7"): released on MCA, Aug'85 by MCA Records. Dist: Polygram, MCA

RAVE ON/TRUE LOVE WAYS.
Single (7"): released on Old Gold, Apr'83 by Old Gold Records. Dist: Lightning, Jazz Music, Spartan, Counterpoint

REAL BUDDY HOLLY STORY,THE.
Tracks: / Peggy Sue / That'll be the day / Well alright / Oh boy / It doesn't matter anymore / Maybe baby.
Notes: Paul McCartney's film of the life and music of Buddy Holly. Includes rare film and music of Buddy Holly, Elvis Presley, Paul McCartney, The Rolling stones, TheEverly Brothers, Little Richard, Chuck Berry, etc. Released to coincide with the anniversary of Buddy Holly's fiftieth birthday on 7th September 1986. De-luxepackaging on initial quantity includes gatefold wallet/box and American style car number plate. Package also includes 2 audio cassettes featuring 28 originalBuddy Holly Recordings. Number of tracks: 28. Type of recording: Compilation. Total playing time: 90 minutes.
Video-cassette (VHS): released on PMI, Sep'86 by PMI Records. Dist: EMI

Video-cassette [Betamax]: released on PMI, Sep'86 by PMI Records. Dist: EMI

REMINISCING.
Single (7"): released on MCA, Aug'85 by MCA Records. Dist: Polygram, MCA

ROCK AROUND WITH (Holly, Buddy & The Crickets).
Cassette: released on Cambra, May'84 by Cambra Records. Dist: IDS, Conifer

ROCK AROUND WITH BUDDY HOLLY.
Album: released on Cambra, Oct'86 by Cambra Records. Dist: IDS, Conifer

SINGLES COLLECTION.
Boxed set: released on MCA, Aug'85 by MCA Records. Dist: Polygram, MCA

SOMETHING SPECIAL FROM BUDDY HOLLY.
Tracks: / Good rockin' tonight / Rip it up / Blue monday / Honky tonk / Blue suede shoes / Shake, rattle and roll / Ain't got no home / Holly hop / Brown-eyed handsome man / Bo diddley / Gone (take 1) / Gone (take 2) / Have you ever been lonely (take 1) / Have you ever been lonely (take 2) / Have you ever been lonely (take 3).
Album: released on Rollercoaster, Sep'86 by Rollercoaster Records. Dist: Swift Distribution, Rollercoaster Distribution

THAT'LL BE THE DAY.
Tracks: / That'll be the day / I'm looking for some one to love / It doesn't matter anymore / Raining in my heart / That'll be the day / Rock me baby / Peggy Sue / Everyday / Oh boy / Not fade away / May be baby / Tell me how / Rave on / Ready Teddy / Think it over / It's so easy / It doesn't matter anymore / Raining in my heart / True love ways / Word of love / Reminiscing / Baby I don't care / Brown eyed handsome man / Bo diddley.
Single (7"): released on MCA, Aug'86 by MCA Records. Dist: Polygram, MCA

Single (12"): released on MCA, Aug'86 by MCA Records. Dist: Polygram, MCA

Single (7"): released on MCA, Aug'86 by MCA Records. Dist: Polygram, MCA

Single (7"): released on MCA, Aug'85 by MCA Records. Dist: Polygram, MCA

THINK IT OVER.
Single (7"): released on MCA, Aug'85 by MCA Records. Dist: Polygram, MCA

TRUE LOVE WAYS.
Single (7"): released on MCA, Aug'85 by MCA Records. Dist: Polygram, MCA

Holly, Jan

SITTING ON TOP OF THE WORLD.
Album: released on Horatio Nelson, Nov'85 Dist: PRT

Cassette: released on Horatio Nelson, Nov'85 Dist: PRT

SITTIN' ON TOP OF THE WORLD.
Tracks: / Too much too soon / I can feel your leavin' comin' on / You're my fantasy / Woman / Sitting on top of the world / No getting over you / Lonely nights / Singing the blues again / Broke up / Wish me love / You wrote the book / Do you ever think of me and Amarillo.
Album: released on Horatio Nelson, Jul'86 Dist: PRT

Cassette: released on Horatio Nelson, Jul'86 Dist: PRT

Holly & the Italians

RIGHT TO BE ITALIAN, THE.
Album: released on Virgin, May'81 by Virgin Records. Dist: EMI, Virgin Distribution

TELL THAT GIRL TO SHUT UP.
Single (7"): released on Oval, Jul'82 by Oval Records. Dist: Pinnacle

Holly Twins

I WANT ELVIS FOR CHRISTMAS.
Single (7"): released on Rock Star, Dec'80 Dist: Lightning, Swift Distribution, Superdisc Distribution

Hollywood!

FUNK ME JACK ME.
Single (12"): released on Kool Kat, Apr'87 by Kool Kat Records. Dist: PRT

HOLLYWOOD The Collection (London Festival Orchestra).
Tracks: / Man and a woman, A / Il silenzio / Love story / An affair to remember / Hello young lovers / Sound of music, The / Moon river / La ronde / Tara's theme / Three coins in a fountain / Shane / Anything goes / Dancing in the dark / Days of wine and roses / Love is a many splendoured thing / Tammy / Pennies from heaven / It's magic / Magnificent seven, The / High noon.
Compact disc: released on The Collection, Apr'87 by Object Enterprises Ltd. Dist: Counterpoint Distribution

HOLLYWOOD CAVALCADE various artists (Various Artists).
Notes: Legendary Hollywood Artists - Collectors Edition Series - Original recordings Mid price release.
Album: released on Meteor, Jan'86 by Magnum Music Group Ltd. Dist: Magnum Music Group Ltd, PRT Distribution, Spartan Distribution

HOLLYWOOD HILLBILLIES (Various Artists).
Album: released on See For Miles, Jul'87 by See For Miles Records. Dist: Pinnacle

HOLLYWOOD HIT PARADE Various artists (Various Artists).
Album: released on RCA, Feb'84 by RCA Records. Dist: RCA, Roots, Swift, Wellard, Chris, I & B, Solomon & Peres Distribution

Cassette: released on RCA, Feb'84 by RCA Records. Dist: RCA, Roots, Swift, Wellard, Chris, I & B, Solomon & Peres Distribution

HOLLYWOOD MUSICALS-MGM/UA Various original artists (Various original artists).
Album: released on SPI Milan, Jul'85 Dist: Silva Screen

Cassette: released on SPI Milan, Jul'85 Dist: Silva Screen

HOLLYWOOD SINGS (Various Artists).
Notes: Inc. songs sung by: Al Jolson, Marlene Deitrich, James Stewart, Gloria Swanson, Rudolph Valentino, Joan Crawford, Fred Astaire, Ginger Rogers, Eddie Cantor, Maurice Chevalier.
Compact disc: released on ASV, Feb'87 by Academy Sound & Vision Records. Dist: Pinnacle

HOLLYWOOD TO LAS VEGAS (Various Artists).
Notes: Double cassette.
Cassette: released on Ditto, May'87 by Pickwick Records. Dist: H.R. Taylor

Hollywood Argyles

HOLLYWOOD ARGYLES Featuring Gary Paxton.
Album: released on Rebel (Australia), Feb'84 Dist: Swift

Hollywood Beyond

COLOUR OF MONEY.
Tracks: / Colour of money / Hollywood beyond.
Single (7"): released on WEA, Jun'86 by WEA Records. Dist: WEA

Single (12"): released on WEA, Jun'86 by WEA Records. Dist: WEA

IF.
Tracks: / Opening scenario / Vision of love / After midnight / Save me / Crimes of passion / What's the colour of money? / No more tears / Metal on glass / Shadows I remember / Hollywood beyond.
Album: released on WEA, Jun'87 by WEA Records. Dist: WEA

Cassette: released on WEA, Jun'87 by WEA Records. Dist: WEA

Compact disc: released on WEA, Jun'87 by WEA Records. Dist: WEA

NO MORE TEARS.
Tracks: / No more tears / No time for losers.
Single (7"): released on WEA, Sep'86 by WEA Records. Dist: WEA

Single (12"): released on WEA, Sep'86 by WEA Records. Dist: WEA

SAVE ME.
Tracks: / Save me / No more tears.
Single (7"): released on WEA, Apr'87 by WEA Records. Dist: WEA

Single (12"): released on WEA, Apr'87 by WEA Records. Dist: WEA

Hollywood Brats

HOLLYWOOD BRATS.
Album: released on Cherry Red, '82 by Cherry Red Records. Dist: Pinnacle

THEN HE KISSED ME.
Single (12"): released on Cherry Red, Apr'84 by Cherry Red Records. Dist: Pinnacle

Hollywood, D.J.

UM TANG UM TANG/ TO WHOEVER IT MAY CONCERN..
Tracks: / Um tang um tang/ to whoever it may concern / Um tang tang (Instrumental).
Single (7"): released on Crossover-Serious, Sep'86 by Serious Records. Dist: PRT

Single (12"): released on Crossover-Serious, Sep'86 by Serious Records. Dist: PRT

Hollywood Killers

BUTTERFLY/KILLER'S WAIL.
Single (7"): released on Creole, Nov'82 by Creole Records. Dist: Rhino, PRT

Hollywood Studio Orches-

18 FAMOUS FILM & TV THEMES.
Compact disc: released on The Compact Collection, Sep'87 by Conifer Records. Dist: Conifer Distribution

22 FAMOUS WESTERN FILM TRACKS.
Compact disc: released on The Compact Collection, Sep'87 by Conifer Records. Dist: Conifer Distribution

BROADWAY MEMORIES 22 unforgettable melodies.
Compact disc: released on The Compact Collection, Sep'87 by Conifer Records. Dist: Conifer Distribution

SWING AND SWEET FROM HOLLYWOOD AND 52ND STREET.
Compact disc: released on The Compact Collection, Sep'87 by Conifer Records. Dist: Conifer Distribution

Holman, Bill

FABULOUS BILL HOLMAN ORCHESTRA.
Album: released on Sackville, Apr'81 Dist: JSU, Jazz Music, Jazz Horizons, Cadillac Music, Celtic Music, Swift

FABULOUS BILL HOLMAN, THE.
Album: released on Jasmine, Feb'83 by Jasmine Records. Dist: Counterpoint, Lugtons, Taylor, H.R., Wellard, Chris, Swift, Cadillac

GROUP ACTIVITY.
Album: released on Affinity, Jul'81 by Charly Records. Dist: Charly, Cadillac

Holman, Eddie

HEY THERE LONELY GIRL.
Single (7"): released on Old Gold, Jul'82 by Old Gold Records. Dist: Lightning, Jazz Music, Spartan, Counterpoint

I SURRENDER.
Single (7"): released on Kent, Jun'85 by Ace Records. Dist: Pinnacle

UNITED.
Album: released on New Cross, Jun'85 by Charly Records. Dist: Charly

Holman, Libby

LEGENDARY...., THE.
Album: released on Monmouth, May'79

SOMETHING TO REMEMBER HER BY.
Album: released on Monmouth, Mar'79

Holm, Dallas & Praise

CHANGE THE WORLD.
Notes: Dallas Hlom's first Dayspring release makes a strong statement, both musically and spiritually. Change the World is not a light hearted album. Musically it iscompetent and cohesive. Lyrically it's tough. In the past couple of years the massage of Dallas Holm and Praise has been deeling with holiness and separation from the world -'finding out what discipleship is really about'.
Album: released on Day Spring, Jun'86 by Word Records. Dist: Word Distribution, CBS

Cassette: released on Day Spring, Jun'86 by Word Records. Dist: Word Distribution, CBS

Holmes, Groove

CRY THE BLUES (see also Jimmy Witherspoon) (Holmes, Groove & Jimmy Witherspoon).
Album: released on Bulldog Records, Jul'82

GOOD VIBRATIONS.
Album: released on Muse (Import), Apr'81

Holmes, Hoe

AFTER DAWNING (see also Len Graham) (Holmes, Hoe & Len Graham).
Album: released on Topic, Feb'79 Dist: Roots Distribution

Holmes, Ian

IAN HOLMES & HIS SCOTTISH DANCE BAND (Holmes, Ian & Scottish Dance Band).
Album: released on Lismor, Oct'77 by Lismor Records. Dist: Lismor, Roots, Celtic Music

Cassette: released on Lismor, Oct'77 by Lismor Records. Dist: Lismor, Roots, Celtic Music

IDEAL HOMES (Holmes, Ian & Scottish Dance Band).
Album: released on Lismor, Jul'87 by Lismor Records. Dist: Lismor, Roots, Celtic Music

LET'S DANCE IN STRICT TEMPO (Holmes, Ian & Scottish Dance Band).
Album: released on Lismor, May'79 by Lismor Records. Dist: Lismor, Roots, Celtic Music

MORE SOUNDS SCOTTISH (Holmes, Ian & Scottish Dance Band).
Tracks: / Reels / Boston two step / Waltz / Polka / Accordion Duet / Johnstone fig, The / 6/8 Marches / Military two step / March, Strathspey & reel.
Notes: Retail price given by ARC excluding P & P (via mail order) is 4.99. Mail order distribution address: Accordion Records Club, 146 Birmingham Road, Kidderminster, Worcs. DY10 2SL. Tel: 0562-746105.
Album: released on Accordion Record Club, Jul'86 by Accordion Record Club Records. Dist: Accordion Record Club

TO DANCE TO (Holmes, Ian & Scottish Dance Band).
Tracks: / Solway reel / Sepherd's crook / Round reel of eight / Rose of Benbecula / Bonnie Anne / Winding nith,The / Laird of Dochart's reel / MacDonald of Sleat / Bonnie Brix / Whitesands jig / Macneil of Barra / Doon Hame / Rouken Glen / Lamont of Inveryne.
Album: released on Accordion Record Club, Jul'86 by Accordion Record Club Records. Dist: Accordion Record Club

Holmes, Joe

CHASTE MUSES, BARDS AND SAGES.
Album: released on Free Reed, Sep'79 by Free Reed Records. Dist: Roots, Projection, Hobgoblin Records, Oblivion

Holmes, Robert

INTERNATIONAL SUNSHINE.
Tracks: / International sunshine / Monkey song, The.
Single (7"): released on Virgin, Jun'87 by Virgin Records. Dist: EMI, Virgin Distribution

Single (12"): released on Virgin, Jun'87 by Virgin Records. Dist: EMI, Virgin Distribution

Holmes, Rupert

ADVENTURE.
Album: released on MCA, Nov'80 by MCA Records. Dist: Polygram, MCA

ESCAPE (PINA COLADA SONG).
Single (7"): released on Old Gold, Jan'85 by Old Gold Records. Dist: Lightning, Jazz Music, Spartan, Counterpoint

PARTNERS IN CRIME.
Tracks: / Escape (the pina colada song) / Partners in crime / Nearsighted / Lunch hour / Drop it / Him / Asworing machine / People that you never get to love (The) / Get outta yourself / In you I trust.
Notes: All songs written and arranged by Rupert Holmes. Produced by Rupert Holmes and Jim Boyer for the Holmes Line of records Inc. Original Sound Recordings made by Infinity Records. MCA are the exclusive licensees for United Kingdom. Published 1979 Infinity Records Inc.
Album: released on MCA, Mar'87 by MCA Records. Dist: Polygram, MCA

Cassette: released on MCA, Mar'87 by MCA Records. Dist: Polygram, MCA

Single (7"): released on Autonomy, Oct'82

SONGWRITERS FOR THE STARS 1 (see also Jimmy Webb) (Holmes, Rupert & Jimmy Webb).
Album: released on Polydor (Norway), Oct'83

Holmes, Watson

CINEMA ORGAN ENCORES.
Album: released on Deroy, Jun'81 by Deroy Records. Dist: Jazz Music, Swift

WURLITZER ORGAN ENCORES.
Album: released on Deroy, May'86 by Deroy Records. Dist: Jazz Music, Swift

Holm, Lars

FOLKLORISTICA On the free bass accordion.
Album: released on ARC (Accordion Records), '84 Dist: Accordion Record Club

Holm, Lasse

CANNELLONI MACARONI (PIZZERIA FANTASIA).
Tracks: / Cannelloni macaroni (pizzeria fantasia) / Such a miracle.
Single (7"): released on Sonet, Nov'86 by Sonet Records. Dist: PRT

Holocaust

COMING THROUGH.
Single (12"): released on Phoenix, Apr'82 by Audio Fidelity Enterprises. Dist: Stage One, Lugtons

HEAVY METAL MANIA.
Single (12"): released on Phoenix, Jul'80 by Audio Fidelity Enterprises. Dist: Stage One, Lugtons

NO MANS LAND.
Album: released on Phoenix, Apr'84 by Audio Fidelity Enterprises. Dist: Stage One, Lugtons

Hologram

HOLOCAUST LIVE.

Album: released on Phoenix, May'83 by Audio Fidelity Enterprises. Dist: Stage One, Lugtons

Holoway, Mike

DON'T LET LIFE GET YOU DOWN.
Single (7"): released on Smike, Nov'83 by Smike Records. Dist: Pinnacle

HERE I AM (Holoway, Mike & Kids).
Single (7"): released on Simon, Aug'83 by Supertunes Records. Dist: Pinnacle

Holt, David
REEL AND ROCK.
Album: released on Flying Fish (USA), Apr'86 by Flying Fish Records (USA). Dist: Roots, Projection

Holt, Errol
DANGER ZONE.
Single (12"): released on African Museum, Jun'82 Dist: Jetstar

Holt, John
1000 VOLTS OF HOLT.
Album: released on Trojan, Jul'84 by Trojan Records. Dist: PRT, Jetstar

Cassette: released on Trojan, Jul'84 by Trojan Records. Dist: PRT, Jetstar

16 SONGS FOR SOULFUL LOVERS.
Album: released on Prism, Nov'86 by Prism Records.

Cassette: released on Prism, Nov'86 by Prism Records.

2000 VOLTS OF HOLT.
Tracks: / Doctor love / Yester-me, yester-you, yesterday / Touch me in the morning / Keep on moving / I will / Alfie / I'll take a melody / My guiding star / On a clear day you can see forever / Peace and love / Take away my heart Teresa / For the love of you.
Album: released on Trojan, Feb'86 by Trojan Records. Dist: PRT, Jetstar

Cassette: released on Trojan, Feb'86 by Trojan Records. Dist: PRT, Jetstar

20 GOLDEN LOVE SONGS.
Tracks: / Never never never / I'd love you to want me / Killing me softly with her song / You will never find another love like mine / When I fall in love / I'll take a melody / Just the way you are / Too good to be forgotten / Doctor love / Help me make it through the night / Stoned out of my life / Touch me in the morning / I'll be lonely / Too much love / Love so right / Rainy night in Georgia / If I were a Carpenter / Everybody's talkin / Baby don't get hooked on me / Last farewell, The.
Album: released on Trojan, Feb'86 by Trojan Records. Dist: PRT, Jetstar

Cassette: released on Trojan, Feb'86 by Trojan Records. Dist: PRT, Jetstar

Album: released on Trojan, '83 by Trojan Records. Dist: PRT, Jetstar

20 GOLDEN LOVE SONGS.

3000 VOLTS OF HOLT.
Album: released on Trojan, '83 by Trojan Records. Dist: PRT, Jetstar

Cassette: released on Trojan, '83 by Trojan Records. Dist: PRT, Jetstar

DRESS UP YOURSELF.
Single (12"): released on Chartsounds, Dec'84 by Chartsounds Records. Dist: Jatstar

DUSTY ROADS.
Album: released on Trojan, '83 by Trojan Records. Dist: PRT, Jetstar

EASY LOVING.
Single (12"): released on Uptempo, Sep'85 by Uptempo Records. Dist: Jetstar Distribution

FAT SHE FAT.
Single (12"): released on Greensleeves, Sep'82 by Greensleeves Records. Dist: BMG, Jetstar, Spartan

FOR LOVERS AND DANCERS.
Album: released on Trojan, Nov'84 by Trojan Records. Dist: PRT, Jetstar

Cassette: released on Trojan, Nov'84 by Trojan Records. Dist: PRT, Jetstar

FROM ONE EXTREME TO ANOTHER
(Holt, John & Horace Andy).
Album: released on Beta, Jul'86 Dist: Jetstar

FURTHER YOU LOOK, THE.
Album: released on Trojan, '83 by Trojan Records. Dist: PRT, Jetstar

GHETTO QUEEN.
Single (7"): released on Creole, Oct'81 by Creole Records. Dist: Rhino, PRT

Single (12"): released on Creole, Oct'81 by Creole Records. Dist: Rhino, PRT

GREATEST HITS: JOHN HOLT.
Album: released on Prince Buster, Dec'84 by Prince Buster Records. Dist: Jetstar

HELP ME MAKE IT THROUGH THE NIGHT.
Single (7"): released on Old Gold (Reissue), Apr'83

HOLT GOES DISCO.
Album: released on Trojan, '83 by Trojan Records. Dist: PRT, Jetstar

IF YOU WERE MY LOVER.
Single (12"): released on Black Joy, Nov'84 Dist: Jetstar

I JUST CALLED TO SAY I LOVE YOU.
Single (12"): released on JKH, Oct'84 by JKH Records. Dist: Jetstar

I LOVE YOU BABY.
Tracks: / I love you baby / I love music.
Single (12"): released on Natty Congo, Apr'86 by Natty Congo Records. Dist: Jetstar

JAZZY LADY.
Single (12"): released on JKH, Nov'84 by JKH Records. Dist: Jetstar

JUST THE TWO OF US.
Album: released on CSA, Oct'82 by CSA Records. Dist: PRT, Jetstar

Cassette: released on CSA, Oct'82 by CSA Records. Dist: PRT, Jetstar

LEAN ON ME.
Single 10": released on Chartsounds, Dec'84 by Chartsounds Records. Dist: Jetstar

LET IT GO ON.
Album: released on Trojan, '83 by Trojan Records. Dist: PRT, Jetstar

LIVE IN LONDON.
Album: released on Very Good Music, Nov'84 by Very Good Music Records. Dist: Jetstar

LIVING LEGEND.
Album: released on Classic, May'86 Dist: Jetstar

LOVE I CAN FEEL.
Single (7"): released on Arrival, Oct'83 by Arrival. Dist: Revolver, Cartel

LOVE I CAN FEEL, A.
Album: released on Trojan, Feb'85 by Trojan Records. Dist: PRT, Jetstar

LOVE TO SHAVE (Holt, John & Alton Ellis).
Tracks: / Love to shave.
Single (12"): released on Basket, Mar'86 Dist: Jetstar

MR BIG BOSS.
Single (12"): released on Creole, May'83 by Creole Records. Dist: Rhino, PRT

NEVER GONNA GIVE YOU UP.
Tracks: / Never gonna give you up / Going steady.
Single (12"): released on King Jam, Jun'86 by King Jam Records. Dist: Jetstar

NEXT TEARDROP.
Single (7"): released on Jackpot, Oct'83

O.K. FRED.
Album: released on Spartan, Feb'87 by Spartan Records. Dist: Spartan

Cassette: released on Spa...n, Feb'87 by Spartan Records. Dist: Spartan

POLICE IN HELICOPTER.
Album: released on Greensleeves, Aug'83 by Greensleeves Records. Dist: BMG, Jetstar, Spartan

Single (12"): released on Greensleeves, May'83 by Greensleeves Records. Dist: BMG, Jetstar, Spartan

PRETTY GIRL.
Single (12"): released on Three Kings, Oct'85 by Three Kings Records. Dist: Jetstar Distribution

PRIVATE DOCTOR.
Single (12"): released on Greensleeves, Sep'83 by Greensleeves Records. Dist: BMG, Jetstar, Spartan

PURE GOLD.
Album: released on Vista Sounds, Mar'85 by Vista Sounds Records. Dist: Jetstar

REGGAE CHRISTMAS ALBUM, THE.
Album: released on Trojan, Nov'86 by Trojan Records. Dist: PRT, Jetstar

Cassette: released on Trojan, Nov'86 by Trojan Records. Dist: PRT, Jetstar

ROOTS OF HOLT.
Album: released on Trojan, '83 by Trojan Records. Dist: PRT, Jetstar

SHE'S A RISER.
Tracks: / She's a riser / She's a riser (version).
Single (12"): released on Blue Trac, Nov'86 by Blue Mountain Records. Dist: Jetstar

SWEETIE COME BRUSH ME.

Single (12"): released on Creole, Jun'82 by Creole Records. Dist: Rhino PRT

THIS OLD HEART OF MINE.
Single (12"): released on Arts & Crafts, Nov'84 Dist: Jetstar

TONIGHT I'M GONNA HOLD YOU.
Single (12"): released on Tapta, Apr'87

TOO MUCH LOVE.
Single (7"): released on Trojan, Sep'84 by Trojan Records. Dist: PRT, Jetstar

Single (12"): released on Trojan, Sep'84 by Trojan Records. Dist: PRT, Jetstar

VIBES.
Album: released on Lego Sound, Sep'85 by Lego Sound Records. Dist: Jetstar

WILD FIRE (see also Dennis Brown) (Holt, John & Dennis Brown).
Single (12"): released on Yvonne's Special, Aug'85

YOU POUR SUGAR ON ME.
Single (12"): released on Sure, Jul'85

YOU'RE EVERYTHING TO ME (Holt, John & June Powell).
Tracks: / You're everything to me / I'll be everything to you.
Single (12"): released on Trojan, Nov'86 by Trojan Records. Dist: PRT, Jetstar

Holton, Gary
CATCH A FALLING STAR.
Single (7"): released on Magnet, Nov'84 by Magnet Records. Dist: BMG

Single (12"): released on Magnet, Nov'84 by Magnet Records. Dist: BMG

PEOPLE IN LOVE.
Tracks: / People in love / Angel.
Single (7"): released on Acts International, Jul'86 Dist: PRT

Single (12"): released on Acts International, Jul'86 Dist: PRT

RUBY (DON'T TAKE YOUR LOVE TO TOWN) (see also Casino Steel) (Holton, Gary & Casino Steel).
Single (7"): released on Pinnacle, Jan'84 by Pinnacle Records. Dist: Pinnacle

Holt, Peter
HAPPY TOGETHER.
Album: released on Grosvenor, May'86 by Grosvenor Records. Dist: Taylors

Holts, Roosevelt
ROOSEVELT HOLTS AND FRIENDS.
Album: released on Arhoolie, May'81 by Arhoolie Records. Dist: Projection, Topic, Jazz Music, Swift, Roots

Holy Bible, The
HOLY BIBLE, THE (Various Artists).
Notes: Old and new Testaments, read over 60 Cassettes in 15 Box Sets. Available individually at 6.00 each or as a complete set.
Cassette: released on Signal, Nov'86

Holy Modal Rounders
LAST ROUND.
Album: released on Adelphi, May'81 by Adelphi Records. Dist: Jetstar

Holy Terror
TERROR AND SUBMISSION.
Album:

Holy Toy
PANZER AND RABBITS.
Album: released on Sonet, Dec'84 by Sonet Records. Dist: PRT

PERFECT DAY.
Single (12"): released on Uniton Records, Sep'84 Dist: Cartel

SOLDIER TOY.
Single (12"): released on Uniton Records, Sep'84 Dist: Cartel

WARSZAWA.
Album: released on Uniton Records, Sep'84 Dist: Cartel

Cassette: released on Uniton Records, Sep'84 Dist: Cartel

WHY NOT IN CHOIR.
Album: released on Sonet, Feb'86 by Sonet Records. Dist: PRT

Hom Bru
OBADEEA.
Album:

Home...
HOME FROM HOME Various artists (Various Artists).
Album: released on Ogun, Jun'79 Dist: Jazz Music, JSU, Cadillac

HOME GROWN ROCKABILLY Various artists (Various Artists).
Album: released on Rockhouse, Dec'84 Dist: Pinnacle

HOME MADE EARLY ROCK & ROLL Various artists (Various Artists).
Album: released on White Label (Holland), Mar'84 Dist: CSA, PRT

HOME NEWCASTLE Various artists (Various Artists).
Album: released on Mawson & Wareham, Nov'83 by Mawson & Wareham Records. Dist: Roots, Celtic Music, Spartan, Jazz Music, Projection

Home & Garden
HISTORY OF GEOGRAPHY.
Album: released on Deadman's Curve, Sep'86 by Dave Henderson

Homer's Odyssey
CALYPSO CHRISTMAS PACKAGE.
Album: released on Renoh, Dec'84 by Renoh. Dist: Jetstar

Home Service
ALL RIGHT JACK.
Album: released on Hobson's Choice, Feb'87 Dist: Projection

ALRIGHT JACK.
Album: released on Spindrift, Apr'86 by Roots

Cassette: released on Spindrift, Apr'86 by Roots

DOING THE INGLISH.
Tracks: / Bramsley.
Single (7"): released on Luggage, Aug'81 by Luggage. Dist: Multicord

HOME SERVICE, THE.
Album: released on Jigsaw, Jun'84 Dist: Roots, Pinnacle, Projection

MYSTERIES EP, THE Shey Fan Yan Ley.
Tracks: / Shey fan yan ley / We sing Alleluiah / Sheperds arise / Lewk up lewk up. / God / Creation / Serpents dance / Cain and Abel (don't be an outlaw) / Arrest, The / Appearance of the archangel / Journey to Bethlehem / Nativity, The / Herod / Entry to Jerusalem / Kings, The / Betrayal and denial (all in a morning) / Scourging / Judgement (the wheel) / God / Road to Calvary, The / Trial, The / Moon shines bright and we all sing alleluia, The / Wondrous love / Death of Mary / Coronation of the virgin / Lyke wake dirge / Shepherds arise.
Single (7"): released on Coda, Jan'86 by Coda Records. Dist: Pinnacle, Cartel, WEA, Roots

Album: released on Coda, Dec'86 by Coda Records. Dist: Pinnacle, Cartel, WEA, Roots

Cassette: released on Coda, Dec'86 by Coda Records. Dist: Pinnacle, Cartel, WEA, Roots

MYSTERIES, THE.
Tracks: / God / Creation / Serpants dance / Cain and Abel / Appearance of the Archangel / Journey to Bethlehem / Nativity (lay me low) / Herod / Kings, The / Shephards arise / Entry to Jerusalem / Betrayal and denial / Arrest, The / Scourging (all the morning part 2) / Trial, The (Lewk up-Lewk up) / Road to Calvary, The / Crucifixion / Moon shines bright, The / We sing alleluja / God / Wonderous love / Death of Mary / Coronation of the virgin / Lyke wake dirge / Judgement (The wheel).
Album: released on Coda, Jan'85 by Coda Records. Dist: Pinnacle, Cartel, WEA, Roots

Cassette: released on Coda, Jan'85 by Coda Records. Dist: Pinnacle, Cartel, WEA, Roots

ONLY MEN FALL IN LOVE.
Single (7"): released on Situation 2, Jul'81 Dist: Cartel, Pinnacle

SORROW.
Tracks: / Sorrow.
Single (7"): released on Making Waves, Jun'86 by Making Waves Records.

Homesick James
HOMESICK JAMES AND SNOOKY PRYOR (Homesick James and Snooky Pryor).
Album: released on Big Bear, Jan'82 by Big Bear Records. Dist: Big Bear, Swift

Homespun...
HOMESPUN COUNTRY SHOWTIME

Various artists (Various Artists).
Tracks: / It's hard to be humble / Teddy bear / Hey good lookin' / When it's springtime in the Rockies / Be careful of stone that you throw / I have a dream / Kingdom I call home / I dreamed about mama last night / Heart you break will be your own, The / Angeline would you like to dance again / Roses for mama / Jimmy quit the drinking / You need me / Little Rosa / Back home again / Kentucky in the morning.
Album: released on Homespun(Ireland), '82 by Outlet Records. Dist: Outlet

HOMESPUN FEAST OF IRISH FOLK Various artists (Various Artists).
Tracks: / Dublin in the rare Oul times / Bunch of thyme / Green fields of France / High reel / Wind in the willow / Mary from Dungloe / Spancil hill / Two jigs / And the band played waltzing Matilda / Nancy Spain / Four green fields / Gentle Annie / Rambles of spring / Town I love so well.
Album: released on Homespun(Ireland), Jul'83 by Outlet Records. Dist: Outlet

Cassette: released on Homespun(Ireland), Jul'83 by Outlet Records. Dist: Outlet

HOMESPUN'S COUNTRY HALL OF FAME Various artists (Various Artists).
Tracks: / Harper Valley PTA / China doll / Truck drivin' woman / Church courtroom and then goodbye / Door is always open, The / Mississippi / Blue eyes crying in the rain / Lucille / Little isle of green / Union mare and confederate gray / Jeannie Norman / Silver threads and golden needles / My son calls another man daddy / What's wrong with the way that we're doing it now / Once a day / Sunny side of the mountain / Back home again / I'll settle for old Ireland.
Album: released on Homespun(Ireland), '82 by Outlet Records. Dist: Outlet

Cassette: released on Homespun(Ireland), '82 by Outlet Records. Dist: Outlet

Home-T

DO YOU BELIEVE.
Tracks: / Land of Rydim.
Single (12"): released on Taxi, Sep'85 by Taxi Records. Dist: Jetstar Distribution

MR.CONSULAR (Home-T & Yellowman).
Tracks: / Could it be I'm falling in love / What's going on.
Single (12"): released on Island, May'85 by Island Records. Dist: Polygram

Home Wreckers

JACKIN'.
Tracks: / Jackin' (base mix) / Build your own house beats / Jackin' (Emu style).
Single (12"): released on Champion, Jan'87 by Champion Records. Dist: RCA

Homi & Jarvis

FRIEND OF A FRIEND.
Tracks: / I'm in love again / I told you so / Believe in yourself / If you see him / It didn't work out that way / Love's taking over / Run that by me / Some hearts.
Album: released on GRP (USA), Jul'84 by GRP Records (USA). Dist: IMS, Polygram

Homnick/Winter/Dixon

WHOOPIN'.
Notes: See under Winter/Dixon/Homnick

Honda, Minako

GOLDEN DAYS.
Tracks: / Golden days / Crazy nights.
Single (7"): released on Columbia, May'87 by EMI Records. Dist: EMI

Honda, Toshiyuki

DREAM (Honda, Toshiyuki, Chick Corea, Miroslav Vitous, Roy Haynes).
Compact disc: released on Toshiba-EMI, May'87

MODERN.
Compact disc: released on Eastworld, '86 by Eastworld Records (Japan). Dist: Target

SHANGRI-LA.
Compact disc: released on Eastworld, '86 by Eastworld Records (Japan). Dist: Target

Hondo

FALLOUT.
Tracks: / Can't turn you round.
Single (7"): released on Hondo, Mar'84 by Hondo Records. Dist: Rough Trade, Indies

Honduras and Nicaragua

PATRIA.
Album: released on Lyrichord (Import), May'83

Honest Doc & Mr. Driver

SPELL, THE.
Tracks: / Spell, The / Now spell house.
Single (12"): released on Jaxx, 13 Jun'87

Honey At The Core

HONEY AT THE CORE (Various Artists).
Cassette: released on Honey At The Core, Nov'86 Dist: Cartel

Honey Boy

LONELY.
Tracks: / Gaye.
Single (12"): released on Starline, May'83 by EMI Records. Dist: EMI

MOVE CLOSER.
Tracks: / Fantasy woman.
Single (12"): released on Londisc, Apr'85 by Londisc Records.

SWEET CHERRIES.
Tracks: / Sweet cherries (sweet honey version).
Single (12"): released on BB, Jul'84 Dist: Jetstar

WHAT'S YOUR NAME.
Tracks: / What's your name / Rock me baby.
Single (12"): released on World, May'86 Dist: Jetstar

Honeybus

I CAN'T LET MAGGIE GO.
Tracks: / Jesamine.
Single (7"): released on Old Gold (Reissue), Oct'83

I CAN'T LET MAGGIE GO..
Tracks: / Tender are.....
Single (7"): released on Decca (Recollections), Mar'82 by Decca Recollections. Dist: Polygram, IMS

Honeycombs

HAVE I THE RIGHT.
Tracks: / That's the way.
Single (7"): released on Flashback, Apr'79 by Flashback Records/PRT Records. Dist: Mainline, PRT

Single (7"): released on Old Gold (Reissue), Apr'83

MEEK AND HONEY.
Album: released on PRT, Jul'83 by PRT Records. Dist: PRT

Cassette: released on PRT, Jul'83 by PRT Records. Dist: PRT

Honey Cone

GIRLS IT AIN'T EASY.
Album: released on HDH(Holland/Dozier/Holland), May'84 by Demon Records. Dist: Pinnacle

WANT ADS.
Tracks: / Girls it ain't easy.
Single (7"): released on HDH(Holland/Dozier/Holland), May'84 by Demon Records. Dist: Pinnacle

Honey Drippers

SEA OF LOVE.
Tracks: / Rockin' at midnight.
Single (7"): released on Es Paranza (USA), Feb'85 by Atlantic Records. Dist: Polygram, Atlantic

VOLUME 1.
Tracks: / I get a thrill / Sea of love / I got a woman / Young boy blues / Rockin' at midnight.
Album: by Atlantic Records. Dist: Polygram, Atlantic

Cassette: released on Es Paranza (USA), Jan'84 by Atlantic Records. Dist: Polygram, Atlantic

Honeygale, Martin

FLIPPIN AWAY.
Single (12"): released on LGR, May'87 Dist: Jetstar

Honeygale, Peter

BE MY LADY.
Tracks: / Be my lady / Be my lady (dub).
Single (12"): released on Streetside, Aug'86 Dist: Jetstar Distribution

Honey Hush

GET AWAY GIRL.
Tracks: / She's so fine.
Single (7"): released on Rockhouse, Jun'83 by Rockhouse Records. Dist: Swift Distribution, Charly Distribution

Honeymooners

ANOTHER FIT OF LAUGHTER.
Single (7"): released on Mr. Ridiculous, Jun'87 by Mr. Ridiculous Records. Dist: Fast Forward Distributors, Cartel Distribution

Honeymoon Killers

ROUTE NATIONALE 7.
Single (7"): released on Crammed Discs (Belgium), Mar'82 Dist: Rough Trade, Nine Mile, Cartel

TUERS DE LA LUNE DE MIEL, (LES).
Album: released on Crammed Discs (Belgium), Apr'82 Dist: Rough Trade, Nine Mile, Cartel

WAIT AND SEE.
Tracks: / Lady and the pig man.
Single (7"): released on Crammed Discs (Belgium), May'83 Dist: Rough Trade, Nine Mile, Cartel

Honeymoon Suite

BAD ATTITUDE.
Tracks: / Bad attitude / Wounded.
Single (7"): released on WEA, Feb'86 by WEA Records. Dist: WEA

BIG PRIZE,THE.
Tracks: / Bad attitude / Feel it again / Lost and found / What does it take / One by one / Wounded / words in the wind / All along you knew / Once the feeling / Take my hand.
Album: released on WEA, Mar'86 by WEA Records. Dist: WEA

Cassette: released on WEA, Mar'86 by WEA Records. Dist: WEA

FEEL IT AGAIN.
Tracks: / Feel it again / One by one.
Single (7"): released on WEA, Mar'86 by WEA Records. Dist: WEA

Single (12"): released on WEA, Mar'86 by WEA Records. Dist: WEA

WAVE BABIES.
Tracks: / It's your heart.
Single (7"): released on WEA, Jul'85 by WEA Records. Dist: WEA

Honeytree

EVERGREEN.
Tracks: / Evergreen / It's only right / Here I am (Lovely Jesus) / Ruth / I am your servant / Rattle me, shake me / Searchlight / Say you told me so / Sometimes I need you / Lullaby in Jesus name.
Album: released on Myrrh, May'82 by Word Records. Dist: Word Distribution

Cassette: released on Myrrh, May'82 by Word Records. Dist: Word Distribution

Hong Kong Flew-Lawrence

DANCING ON A BASSLINE.
Tracks: / Dancing on a bassline.
Single (12"): released on Ariwa, Jun'86 by Ariwa Records. Dist: Revolver, Cartel, Jetstar, Rough Trade

Hong Kong Syndicat

BERLIN.
Tracks: / Berlin (dub version).
Single (12"): released on Sire, Apr'84

TOO MUCH.
Notes: Pic bag
Single (7"): released on E & F, 23 May'87 by Supreme Records. Dist: PRT

Single (12"): released on E & F, 23 May'87 by Supreme Records. Dist: PRT

Single (7"): released on E & F, 13 Jun'87 by Supreme Records. Dist: PRT

Single (12"): released on E & F, 13 Jun'87 by Supreme Records. Dist: PRT

Honkers & Screamers

HONKERS & SCREAMERS Various artists (Various Artists).
Album: released on Savoy, Aug'79

Honky

HONKY !.
Tracks: / You got it / Sexy lady / I'll survive / Can't sit down / Highfalutin' / Do It / Pour it on / Give it all you've got / Stretch it out / Pour it on slowly....
Album: released on Creole, Jan'79 by Creole Records. Dist: Rhino, PRT

Honky Tonk...

HONKY TONK DEMOS Various artists (Various Artists).
Album: released on Oval, May'82 by Oval Records. Dist: Pinnacle

HONKY TONK FREEWAY Original motion picture soundtrack (Various Artists).
Tracks: / Honky tonk freeway / You're crazy but I like you / Diamond trinkets / Faster faster / My man ain't man enough for me / Love keeps bringing me down / At the diner (instrumental) / Years from now / Ticlaw.
Album: released on Capitol, Oct'81 by Capitol Records. Dist: EMI

HONKY TONKIN' Various artists (Various Artists).
Album: released on Flyright, Oct'83 by Flyright Records. Dist: Krazy Kat, Swift, Jazz Music

HONKY TONK JUMP PARTY Various artists (Various Artists).
Tracks: / Honky tonk Part 1 / Jump children(vooit vooit) / House party / Strato cruiser / Breaking up the house / Good morning judge / Special delivery stomp / Club Savoy / Hucklebuck with Jimmy / Flying home / Joe Joe jump / Mighty mighty man / Deacon moves in,The / I want you to be my baby / Joops jump / Train kept a-rollin', The / Have mercy baby / Harlem noctutne / Kidney stew / Bloodshot eyes / Love don't love nobody / Honky tonk Part2.
Compact disc: released on Charly, Aug'86 by Charly Records. Dist: Charly, Cadillac

HONKY TONK PARTY TIME Various session artists (Various Artists).
Cassette: released on Aim (Budget Cassettes), Feb'83

Honolulu M Daffodils

GUITARS OF THE OCEAN.
Album: released on Hybrid, Mar'87 by Statik Records. Dist: Pinnacle

Honor Roll

HONOR ROLL Various original artists (Various Artists).
Tracks: / I've been working on the railroad / Just before midnight / Still water / Heavens full of joy / Y'know what I mean / Snow in lovers lane / Ain't gonna get fooled again / Easy walker / Don't panic / Frou frou / Summer nights / Button up your lip / Why not / Blue swing five / Five O'clock rush.
Album: released on Jazz Vault, Oct'80 Dist: Jazz Music, JSU, Taylor, H.R.

Honsinger, Tristan

CONCERT EXTRACTS.
Album: released on Incus, Nov'76 Dist: Jazz Music, Cadillac

Hood, Claire

LITTLE CHRISTMAS.
Single (7"): released on Spectra, Nov'81 by Spectra Records. Dist: Pinnacle

Hood, Morag

SNOW MOUNTAIN Read by Morag Hood.
Boxed set: released on Colophone, Feb'81 by Audio-Visual Library Services. Dist: Audio-Visual Library Services

Hoodoo Gurus

BITTER SWEET.
Single (7"): released on Chrysalis, Oct'85 by Chrysalis Records. Dist: CBS

BLOW YOUR COOL.
Tracks: / Out that door / What's my scene / Good times / I was the one / Hell for leather / Where nowhere is / Middle of the land / Come on / My caravan / On my street / Party machine.
Notes: Produced by Mark Opitz and the Gurus
Album: released on Big Time, May'87 by Mainline Record Company. Dist: Mainline

Cassette: released on Big Time, May'87 by Mainline Record Company. Dist: Mainline

GOOD TIMES.
Tracks: / Good times / On my street.
Single (7"): released on Chrysalis, Jul'87 by Chrysalis Records. Dist: CBS

Single (12"): released on Chrysalis, Jul'87 by Chrysalis Records. Dist: CBS

I WANT YOU BACK.
Single (7"): released on Demon, Jan'85 by Demon Records. Dist: Pinnacle

MARS NEEDS GUITARS.
Tracks: / Bittersweet / Poisen pen / In the wild / She / Death-defying / Like wow / Wipeout / Hayride to hell / Show some emotion / Other side of paradise / Mars needs guitars.
Compact disc: released on Chrysalis, Jul'86 by Chrysalis Records. Dist: CBS

Album: released on Chrysalis, Oct'85 by Chrysalis Records. Dist: CBS

Cassette: released on Chrysalis, Oct'85 by Chrysalis Records. Dist: CBS

MY GIRL.
Single (7"): released on Demon, Jun'85 by Demon Records. Dist: Pinnacle

STONEAGE ROMEOS.
Album: released on Demon, Dec'84 by Demon Records. Dist: Pinnacle

Hood, The

TOUGH GUYS DON'T DANCE.
Tracks: / Tough guys don't dance / Tough guys don't dance (dub).
Single (12"): released on Les Disques Du Crepuscule, Dec'86 Dist: Rough Trade, Pinnacle, Island, Polygram

Hooghuys Organ

HOOGHUYS ORGAN.
Album: released on Joy, '74 by President Records. Dist: Jazz Music, Swift, President Distribution

Hooked On...

HOOKED ON NUMBER ONES Various artists (Various Artists).
Compact disc: released on K-Tel, '86 by K-Tel Records. Dist: Record Merchandisers Distribution, Taylors, Terry Blood Distribution, Wynd-Up Distribution, Relay Distribution, Pickwick Distribution, Solomon & Peres Distribution, Polygram

Album: released on K-Tel, Nov'84 by K-Tel Records. Dist: Record Merchandisers Distribution, Taylors, Terry Blood Distribution, Wynd-Up Distribution, Relay Distribution, Pickwick Distribution, Solomon & Peres Distribution, Polygram

Cassette: released on K-Tel, Nov'84 by K-Tel Records. Dist: Record Merchandisers Distribution, Taylors, Terry Blood Distribution, Wynd-Up Distribution, Relay Distribution, Pickwick Distribution, Solomon & Peres Distribution, Polygram

Single (7"): released on Record Shack, Nov'84

Single (12"): released on Record Shack, Nov'84 by Record Shack Records. Dist: PRT

HOOKED ON SWING (Various Artists).
Compact disc: released on K-Tel, May'87 by K-Tel Records. Dist: Record Merchandisers Distribution, Taylors, Terry Blood Distribution, Wynd-Up Distribution, Relay Distribution, Pickwick Distribution, Solomon & Peres Distribution, Polygram

Hooked On Hits

HOOKED ON HITS Various Artists (Various Artists).
Compact disc: released on K-Tel, Aug'87 by K-Tel Records. Dist: Record Merchandisers Distribution, Taylors, Terry Blood Distribution, Wynd-Up Distribution, Relay Distribution, Pickwick Distribution, Solomon & Peres Distribution, Polygram

Hooker, Earl

BROWNIE MCGEE, SONNY TERRY WITH EARL HOOKER (Hooker, Earl with Brownie McGee & Sonny Terry).

CALLING ALL BLUES (Hooker, Earl & Magic Sam).
Tracks: / Rockin' wild / Bule Guitar / Blues In D natural / Calling all blues / Swear to tell the truth / Rockin' with the Kid-Galloping horses / Universal rock: Earl Hooker / My love is your love / Mr. Charlie / Square dance rock / Every night / About this time / Blue light boogie / You don't have to work: Magic Sam.
Album: released on Charly, Oct'86 by Charly Records. Dist: Charly, Cadillac

FIRST AND THE LAST RECORDING.
Album: released on Arhoolie, May'81 by Arhoolie Records. Dist: Projection, Topic, Jazz Music, Swift, Roots

HOOKER N STEVE.
Album: released on Arhoolie, May'81 by Arhoolie Records. Dist: Projection, Topic, Jazz Music, Swift, Roots

LEADING BRAND, THE (Hooker Earl & Jodie Williams).
Album: released on Red Lightnin', Oct'82 by Red Lightnin' Records. Dist: Roots, Swift, Jazz Music, JSU, Pinnacle, Cartel, Wynd-Up Distribution

PLAY YOUR GUITAR, MR.HOOKER.
Album: released on Black Magic (Belgium), Dec'85 Dist: Swift

THERES A FUNGUS AMUNG US.
Album: released on Red Lightnin', Oct'82 by Red Lightnin' Records. Dist: Roots, Swift, Jazz Music, JSU, Pinnacle, Cartel, Wynd-Up Distribution

TWO BUGS AND A ROACH.
Album: released on Arhoolie, May'81 by Arhoolie Records. Dist: Projection, Topic, Jazz Music, Swift, Roots

Hooker, John Lee

20 BLUES GREATS.
Album: released on Deja Vu, Nov'85 by Deja Vu Records. Dist: Counterpoint Distribution, Record Services Distribution (Ireland)

Cassette: released on Deja Vu, Nov'85 by Deja Vu Records. Dist: Counterpoint Distribution, Record Services Distribution (Ireland)

BLACK RHYMES N BLUES.
Album: released on Festival (France), Nov'84 Dist: Discovery, Red Lightnin' Distribution, Swift

BLUES BEFORE SUNRISE.
Album: released on Masters (Holland), Jan'87

Cassette: released on Masters (Holland), Jan'87

Album: released on Astan, Nov'84 by Astan Records. Dist: Counterpoint

BOOGIE CHILLUN.
Tracks: / Dimples / Every night / Little wheel / You can lead me baby / I love you honey / Maudie / I'm in the mood / Boogie Chillun / Hobo blues / Crawlin' kingsnake / Drive me away / Solid sender / No shoes / Want and blues / Will the circle be unbroken / I'm goin' upstairs / Boom boom / Bottle up and go / This is hip / Big legs, tight skirt / It serves me right to suffer / Your baby ain't sweet like mine.
Compact disc: released on Charly, Mar'86 by Charly Records. Dist: Charly, Cadillac

BURNIN'.
Tracks: / Boom boom / Process / Lost a good girl / New Leaf,A / Blues before sunrise / Let's make it / I got a letter / Thelma / Drug store woman / Keep your hands to yourself / What do you say.
Album: released on Topline, May'87 by Charly Records. Dist: Charly Distribution

Cassette: released on Topline, May'87 by Charly Records. Dist: Charly Distribution

CHESS MASTERS JOHN LEE HOOKER.
Album: released on Chess(USA), Apr'82 by Sugar Hill (USA). Dist: PRT, Swift

CREAM, THE.
Album: released on Tomato, Mar'79

DIMPLES/BOOM BOOM/ONIONS.
Single (7"): released on Charly, Jul'80 by Charly Records. Dist: Charly, Cadillac

DO THE BOOGIE.
Album: released on Happy Bird (Germany), Jul'84 Dist: Polygram, IMS

EVERYBODY ROCKIN.
Album: released on Charly, Mar'81 by Charly Records. Dist: Charly, Cadillac

HOOKERED ON BLUES.
Album: released on JSP, Aug'83 by JSP Records. Dist: Swift, Projection

HOUSE OF THE BLUES.
Compact disc: released on Vogue, Dec'86 Dist: Discovery, Jazz Music, PRT, Swift

Album: released on Chess, Oct'87 by Charly Records. Dist: Charly, Swift, PRT, Discovery, IMS, Polygram

Cassette: released on Chess, Oct'87 by Charly Records. Dist: Charly, Swift, PRT, Discovery, IMS, Polygram

HOUSE RENT BOOGIE.
Tracks: / Mambo chillun / Time is marching / Unfriendly woman / I'm so worried baby / Baby Lee / Road is so rough, The / Trouble blues / Everybody rockin' / I'm so excited / Crawlin' black spider / Little fine woman / Rosie Mae / You've taken my woman / Mama you've got a daughter / House rent boogie / I'm a stranger / I'm mad again / Hard hearted woman / I wanna walk / Run on / Blues before sunrise / Onions.
Compact disc: released on Charly, Feb'87 by Charly Records. Dist: Charly, Cadillac

I FEEL GOOD.
Album: released on Jewel, Sep'79

IT SERVES YOU RIGHT.
Album: released on Jasmine, Feb'84 by Jasmine Records. Dist: Counterpoint, Lugtons, Taylor, H.R., Wellard, Chris, Swift, Cadillac

JOHN LEE HOKER VOL 1.
Album: released on Ace(Cadet), May'81 by Ace Records. Dist: Pinnacle, Swift, Hotshot

MOANIN AND STONY BLUES (Hooker, John Lee/ Paul Harold/ Ralph Wills).
Double Album: released on Gusto (USA), Oct'79 by Gusto Records (USA). Dist: Crusader

MOANIN THE BLUES.
Album: released on Charly, Nov'81 by Charly Records. Dist: Charly, Cadillac

NEVER GET OUT OF THESE BLUES ALIVE.
Tracks: / Bumblebee bumblebee / Hit the road / Country boy / Booggee with the hook / If you take care of me I'll take care of you / T-B-Sheets / Letter to my baby / Never get out of these blues alive / Baby, I love you / Lonesome mood.

Album: released on See For Miles, Mar'87 by See For Miles Records. Dist: Pinnacle

NO FRIEND AROUND.
Album: released on Red Lightnin', Sep'82 by Red Lightnin' Records. Dist: Roots, Swift, Jazz Music, JSU, Pinnacle, Cartel, Wynd-Up Distribution

ORIGINAL AMERICAS FOLK BLUES FESTIVAL (Hooker, John Lee & Memphis Walker).

Compact disc: by Polydor Records. Dist: Polygram, Polydor

PLAYS AND SINGS THE BLUES.
Album: released on Chess, Apr'87 by Charly Records. Dist: Charly, Swift, PRT, Discovery, IMS, Polygram

Cassette: released on Chess, Apr'87 by Charly Records. Dist: Charly, Swift, PRT, Discovery, IMS, Polygram

SITTIN HERE THINKING.
Album: released on Muse, Apr'81 Dist: JSU Distribution, Jazz Horizons Distribution, Jazz Music Distribution, Celtic Music Distribution

Album: released on Muse, Apr'81 Dist: JSU Distribution, Jazz Horizons Distribution, Jazz Music Distribution, Celtic Music Distribution

Album: released on Happy Bird (Germany), Jul'83 Dist: Polygram, IMS

SOLID SENDER.
Album: released on Charly(R&B), Jul'84 by Charly Records. Dist: Charly, Cadillac

TANTALIZING WITH THE BLUES.
Album:

THIS IS HIP.
Album: released on Charly(R&B), Jan'85 by Charly Records. Dist: Charly, Cadillac

Hooker, Steve Shakers

REELY GONE.
Album: released on Lolita, May'84 by Lolita Records. Dist: Rough Trade, Cartel

Hookline & Silverfish

GOOD DEEDS.
Tracks: / Good deeds / Hope.
Notes: Double A side single. Self - 0734 341694
Single (7"): released on Shrubbery, Feb'87 by Shrubbery Records. Dist: Shrubbery

Hook'N'Pull Gang

POUR IT DOWN YER THROAT.
Tracks: / Pour it down yer throat.
Single (7"): released on Bitch Hog, Mar'87 by Bitch Hog Records. Dist: Fast Forward, Cartel

Hooley, Terry

LAUGH AT ME.
Single (7"): released on Fresh, Apr'81 Dist: Jetstar

Hooper, Eddie

KEEP YOUR WOMAN SATISFIED.
Single (7"): released on Half Moon, Sep'82 by Rondelet Music And Records. Dist: Spartan

Hooper, Neil

ONLY WHEN I'M LONELY.
Tracks: / Only when I'm lonely / Only when 'm lonely (inst.).
Single (7"): released on Tux, Nov'86

Hoopes, Ronnie

RESPECT FOR A GREAT TRADITION.
Album: released on Revelation, Apr'81

Hoorah, Boys Hoorah.

HOW THE WEST WAS WON.
Tracks: / How the west was won / You love me, I love me..
Single (7"): released on Pressgang, Apr'86 Dist: Jetstar, Cartel

Hooray for Hollywood

HOORAY FOR HOLLYWOOD (Various film artists) (Various Artists).
Album: released on RCA International (USA), Oct'80 by RCA Records. Dist: RCA

HOORAY FOR HOLLYWOOD (Various film artists) (Various Artists).
Cassette: released on RCA International, Oct'80

Hooray & The Henrys

ALL STUCK UP/ A CHAPS TALE.
Single (7"): released on Works, Dec'83 Dist: PRT

Hooter

ALL YOU ZOMBIES.
Tracks: / All you zombies / Where the children go.
Single (7"): released on CBS, Jul'86 by CBS Records. Dist: CBS

Single (12"): released on CBS, Aug'86 by CBS Records. Dist: CBS

Hooters

ALL YOU ZOMBIES.
Single (7"): released on CBS, Jun'85 by CBS Records. Dist: CBS

AND WE DANCED.
Tracks: / And we dance / She comes in colours / Blood from a stone.
Single (12"): released on CBS, Jun'86 by CBS Records. Dist: CBS

Single (7"): released on CBS, May'86 by CBS Records. Dist: CBS

Single (12"): released on CBS, May'86 by CBS Records. Dist: CBS

NERVOUS NIGHT.
Album: released on CBS, Sep'85 by CBS Records. Dist: CBS

Hope, Ellie

LUCKY/SHAKE.
Single (7"): released on Polo, Jan'83 by Polo Records. Dist: PRT

Hope, Johnny

WEEKEND SERENADE/CONFIDENTIAL.
Single (12"): released on Orbitone, May'82 by Orbitone Records. Dist: Jetstar Distribution

Hope, Lynn

AND HIS TENOR SAX.
Album: released on Pathe Marconi, Sep'84 Dist: Swift

MORROCCO.
Album: released on Saxonograph (Sweden), Aug'85

Hope, Marie

FREE PEOPLE.
Tracks: / Free people / Free people.
Single (12"):

Hope Of Glory

HOPE OF GLORY.
Album: by Pilgrim Records. Dist: Rough Trade, Cartel

Hope, Peter

DRY HIP ROTATION (Hope, Peter & Jonathan S.Podmore).
Album: released on Native, Jan'87 by Native Records. Dist: Red Rhino, Cartel

KITCHENETTE (Hope, Peter & J. F. Podmore).
Tracks: / Industrial fatality / Kitchenette version / Kitchenette.
Notes: See also under J.F.Podmore.
Single (12"): released on Native, Feb'87 by Native Records. Dist: Red Rhino, Cartel

LEATHER HANDS (Hope, Peter & R H Kirk).
Single (12"): released on Double Vision, Nov'85 by Double Vision Records. Dist: Rough Trade, Cartel

Single (12"): released on Double Vision, Oct'85 by Double Vision Records. Dist: Rough Trade, Cartel

TOO HOT (Hope, Peter & David Harrow).
Single (12"): released on Ink, Jun'85 by Red Flame. Dist: Rough Trade, Cartel, Pinnacle

Hopeton Junior

COUNTRY MAN.
Single (12"): released on Look To Afrika, Sep'84 by Look To Afrika Records. Dist: Jetstar

Hop Flop And Fly

HOP FLOP AND FLY (Various Artists).
Album: released on Sun, May'85 by Charly Records. Dist: Charly Distribution

Hopkins, Anthony

DISTANT STAR.
Tracks: / Distant star / Ordinary man.
Single (7"): released on Juice, Dec'86 by IRS. Dist: A&M, CBS

Hopkins, Barry

ANYTIME YOU WANT ME.
Tracks: / Anytime you want me / If I could live on your street.
Single (7"): released on Good, Mar'86 Dist: M.I.S., EMI

Single (7"): released on Good, Oct'85 Dist: M.I.S., EMI

Hopkins, Claude

CLAUDE HOPKINS.
Album: released on Jazz Archives, Jul'86 by Jazz Archives Records. Dist: Jazz Music

HARLEM 1934 (Hopkins, Claude & His Orchestra).
Album: released on Swing Classics, May'86 Dist: Jazz Music Distribution, Swift

HARLEM 1934 (Hopkins, Claude Orchestra).
Album: released on Swing Classics, Apr'78 Dist: Jazz Music Distribution, Swift

SOLILOQUY.
Album: released on Sackville, Jul'86 Dist: JSU, Jazz Music, Jazz Horizons, Cadillac Music, Celtic Music, Swift

Album: released on Sackville, Apr'81 Dist: JSU, Jazz Music, Jazz Horizons, Cadillac Music, Celtic Music, Swift

Hopkins, Lightnin'

52-53.
Album: released on Blues Classics (USA), Mar'85 by Arhoolie Records. Dist: Topic, Jazz Music, Projection

Ball & chain

BIG BOY CRUDUP & LIGHTNING HOPKINS (Hopkins, Lightnin' & Big Boy Crudup).
Album: released on Krazy Kat (USA), Nov'83

BLUE LIGHTNING.
Album: released on Jewel, Sep'79

BLUES IN MY BOTTLE.
Album: released on Prestige, Jun'84 by Prestige Records (USA). Dist: RCA, JSU, Swift

BLUES UNDERGROUND.
Album: released on D/D (US), Mar'79 Dist: Swift

DIRTY BLUES.
Album: released on Mainstream, Jan'73

DOWNHOUSE BLUES.
Album: released on JSP, Apr'84 by JSP Records. Dist: Swift, Projection

EARLY RECORDINGS.
Album: released on Arhoolie, May'81 by Arhoolie Records. Dist: Projection, Topic, Jazz Music, Swift, Roots

EARLY RECORDINGS VOL 2 (Hopkins, Lightnin' & Big Boy Crudup).
Album: released on Arhoolie, May'81 by Arhoolie Records. Dist: Projection, Topic, Jazz Music, Swift, Roots

ELECTRIC LIGHTNIN.
Album: released on JSP, Jan'84 by JSP Records. Dist: Swift, Projection

GREAT ELECTRIC SHOW AND DANCE, THE.
Album: released on Jewel, Sep'79

GREAT SONG OF.
Album: released on Astan, Nov'84 by Astan Records. Dist: Counterpoint

IN BEREKELEY.
Album: released on Arhoolie, May'81 by Arhoolie Records. Dist: Projection, Topic, Jazz Music, Swift, Roots

LEGACY OF THE BLUES VOL 2.
Album: released on Sonet, Jan'74 by Sonet Records. Dist: PRT

LIGHTNIN.
Album: released on Tomato, Mar'79

LIGHTNIN HOPKINS.
Album: released on Joker, Apr'81 Dist: Cadillac, Zodiac Distribution, Jazz Horizons, Jazz Music, JSU, Celtic Music

LIGHTNIN HOPKINS AND HIS GUITAR.
Album: released on Arhoolie, May'81 by Arhoolie Records. Dist: Projection, Topic, Jazz Music, Swift, Roots

LIGHTNIN HOPKINS HIS BROTHERS AND BARBARA DANE.
:

Album: released on Arhoolie, May'81 by Arhoolie Records. Dist: Projection, Topic, Jazz Music, Swift, Roots
Cat. no: **ARHOOLIE 1022**
Album: released on Arhoolie, May'81 by Arhoolie Records. Dist: Projection, Topic, Jazz Music, Swift, Roots

LIGHTNIN' IN NEW YORK.
Album: released on Candid, Dec'85 Dist: Counterpoint, Cadillac

LIGHTNIN STRIKES BACK.
Album: released on Arhoolie, May'81 by Arhoolie Records. Dist: Projection, Topic, Jazz Music, Swift, Roots

LIVE AT THE BIRD LOUNGE HOUSTON.
Album: released on Astan, Nov'84 by Astan Records. Dist: Counterpoint

Cassette: released on Astan, Nov'84 by Astan Records. Dist: Counterpoint

MOVE ON OUT.
Tracks: / Fishing clothes / Wig wearing woman / Vietnam blues - parts 1 & 2 / Play with your poodle / Back door friend / Gamblers blues / Move on out - part 1 / Breakfast time / Mr. Charlie - parts 1 & 2 / Long way from home / Move on out - part 2 / Moaning blues / Found my baby crying / Ride in your automobile.
Album: released on Charly, Jan'87 by Charly Records. Dist: Charly, Cadillac

SINGS THE BLUES.
Album: released on EMI (France), '83 by EMI Records. Dist: Conifer

STRUMS THE BLUES.
Album: released on EMI (France), '83 by EMI Records. Dist: Conifer

TALKING SOME SENSE.
Album: released on Jewel, Sep'79

TEXAS BLUES MAN.
Album: released on Arhoolie, May'81 by Arhoolie Records. Dist: Projection, Topic, Jazz Music, Swift, Roots

TEXAS BLUESMAN, THE.
Album: released on Arhoolie, Jul'87 by Arhoolie Records. Dist: Projection, Topic, Jazz Music, Swift, Roots

Hopkins, Linda

HOW BLUE CAN YOU GET.
Cassette: released on Palo Alto (USA), Jul'86 by Palo Alto Records. Dist: Conifer

Album: released on Palo Alto (Italy), Jan'84

Hopkins, Pickford Gary

WHY.
Tracks: / Why / Why - The story.
Single (7"): released on Spartan, Apr'87 by Spartan Records. Dist: Spartan

Single (12"): released on Spartan, Apr'87 by Spartan Records. Dist: Spartan

Hopkins, Sam 'Lightnin'

AT HIS NATURAL BEST.
Album: released on Rhapsody, Oct'80 by President Records. Dist: Taylors, Swift, Jazz Music, Wellard, Chris

LIVE AT THE BIRD LOUNGE.
Album: released on Bulldog, Jul'82 by Bulldog Records. Dist: President Distribution, Spartan, Swift, Taylor, H.R.

Hopper/Dean/Gowen/Sheen

ROGUE ELEMENT.
Album: released on Ogun, May'79 Dist: Jazz Music, JSU, Cadillac

Hopper, Hugh

1984.
Album: released on Atmosphere, Mar'80 by E.S.S.P..

MERCY DASH (Hopper, Hugh/ Keith Tippett/ Joe Gallivan/ Elton Dean).
Notes: For full information see under: Tippett, Keith/Gallivan, Joe/etc.

MONSTER BAND.
Album: released on Atmosphere, Jul'79 by E.S.S.P..

Hop Skip & Jump

HOP SKIP AND JUMP Various artists (Various Artists).
Tracks: / Hop skip and jump / R'n'roll Santa / Fifty megatons / Nicotine / Shortnin' bread / I don't need no more / Pretty baby rock / I ain't gonna be around / Rock'n chair rock / Knock off the rock / Motorcycle Mike / Run here honey / Rockin little mama / Roll over Beethoven.
Album: released on Esoldun, Dec'86 by Esoldun Records. Dist: Swift

Hordern, Michael

JUST SO STORIES, VOL 2 Kipling, Rudyard (Hordern, Michael/Barbara Jefford/Richard Johnson).
Double cassette: released on Argo (Spokenword), May'83 by Decca Records. Dist: Polygram

JUST SO STORIES, VOL 2 Kipling, Rudyard (Hordern, Michael/Barbara Jefford/Richard Johnson).

Hordern, Sir Michael

PARADISE POSTPONED.
Album: released on Listen For Pleasure, Nov'86 by MFP Records. Dist: EMI

Horea, Crishan

MAGIC OF THE PAN PIPES, THE.
Album: released on Polydor, Mar'83 by Polydor Records. Dist: Polygram, Polydor

Cassette: released on Polydor, Mar'83 by Polydor Records. Dist: Polygram, Polydor

Horizon

SILENT MOON.
Compact disc: released on Delta, Oct'86 by Delta Records. Dist: Target

SUNSHINE REGGAE.
Single (7"): released on Orbit, Jun'84 by Orbit Records. Dist: PRT Distribution

Horizons

STAGE STRUCK.
Single (7"):

Horne, Jimmy 'Bo'

YOU'RE SO GOOD TO ME.
Single (12"): released on Sunny View, Jan'84 by Sunny View Records. Dist: PRT Distribution

Horne, Kenneth

BEST OF ROUND THE HORNE, THE.
Album: released on BBC, Sep'75 by BBC Records & Tapes. Dist: EMI, PRT, Pye

BEYOND OUR KEN Excerpts from BBC Radio series.
Album: released on Note, '80 by EMI Records. Dist: EMI

Horne, Lena

20 GOLDEN PIECES OF LENA HORNE.
Album: released on Bulldog Records, Jul'82

Album: released on Bulldog Records, Jul'82

...AT THE WALDORF ASTORIA.
Album: released on RCA, Nov'80 by RCA Records. Dist: RCA, Roots, Swift, Wellard, Chris, I & B, Solomon & Peres Distribution

Cassette: released on RCA, Nov'80 by RCA Records. Dist: RCA, Roots, Swift, Wellard, Chris, I & B, Solomon & Peres Distribution

FABULOUS...., THE.
Album: released on Cambra, Feb'85 by Cambra Records. Dist: IDS, Conifer

Cassette: released on Cambra, Feb'85 by Cambra Records. Dist: IDS, Conifer

FRANK SINATRA & LENA HORNE (see Sinatra, Frank) (Horne, Lena & Frank Sinatra).

GIVE THE LADY WHAT SHE WANTS.
Album: released on RCA, Oct'84 by RCA Records. Dist: RCA, Roots, Swift, Wellard, Chris, I & B, Solomon & Peres Distribution

Cassette: released on RCA, Oct'84 by RCA Records. Dist: RCA, Roots, Swift, Wellard, Chris, I & B, Solomon & Peres Distribution

JAZZ MASTERS.
Album: released on DRG (USA), Aug'83 by DRG Records. Dist: Conifer, RCA

LENA A NEW ALBUM.
Album: released on RCA, Nov'76 by RCA Records. Dist: RCA, Roots, Swift, Wellard, Chris, I & B, Solomon & Peres Distribution

LENA & GABOR With Gabor szabo.
Album: released on Rhapsody, May'80 by President Records. Dist: Taylors, Swift, Jazz Music, Wellard, Chris

LENA HORNE Great performers series.
Album: released on Jazz Greats, Jan'79 Dist: Swift

Cassette: released on Audio Fidelity, Oct'84 Dist: PRT

LENA HORNE & FRANK SINATRA (Horne, Lena & Frank Sinatra).
Album: released on Astan, Nov'84 by Astan Records. Dist: Counterpoint

Cassette: released on Astan, Nov'84 by Astan Records. Dist: Counterpoint

LENA HORNE & PEARL BAILY.

Album: released on Jazz Greats, Jan'79 Dist: Swift

LENA....LIVE & LOVELY.
Tracks: / I concentrate on you / I get the blues when it rains / I've grown accustomed to his face / I got rhythm / I'm confessin'(that I love you) / I want to be happy / I surrender dear / I've found a new baby / I understand / I let a song go out of my heart / I ain't got nobody(and nobody cares about me) / I only have eyes for you.
Album: released on RCA, Jun'87 by RCA Records. Dist: RCA, Roots, Swift, Wellard, Chris, I & B, Solomon & Peres Distribution

Cassette: released on RCA, Jun'87 by RCA Records. Dist: RCA, Roots, Swift, Wellard, Chris, I & B, Solomon & Peres Distribution

Horne, Marilyn

BEAUTIFUL DREAMER.
Tracks: / Jeannie with the light brown hair / Beautiful dreamer / If you've only got a moustache / Camptown races / Sometimes I feel like a motherless child / I've just come from the fountain / Lord's prayer (The) / Shenandoah / Billy boy / Go way from my window / Simple gifts / Ching-a-ring-chaw / Long time ago / I bought me a cat / I bought me a cat / At the river / You're a grand old flag / When Johnny comes marching home / God bless America / I didn't raise my boy to be a soldier / Battle hymn of the republic.
Notes: Marilyn Horne is considered to be one of the great American singers, and in this new recording is heard performing American popular songs. The programme has been sung by Marilyn Horne on American television shows entitled "Marilyn Horne's American Songbook".
Album: released on Decca International, Nov'86 by Decca Records. Dist: Polygram, IMS

Horner, Yvette

CLASSICS OF MUSETTE VOL.7.
Album: released on CBS(France), Jun'84 by CBS Records. Dist: Conifer, Discovery, Swift

Cassette: released on CBS(France), Jun'84 by CBS Records. Dist: Conifer, Discovery, Swift

PLUS GRANDES VALSES MUSETTES, (LES).
Tracks: / Reine de musette / En glissant / Gigolette / Tonnerre de musette / Geraldine / Les halles / La valse de as / Folie musette / Joli perroquet / Tristan des fauvourgs / Ronce des nieges / Ballade sur les touches.
Album: released on Music For Pleasure (Holland), Jan'86 by EMI Records. Dist: EMI

Cassette: released on Music For Pleasure (Holland), Jan'86 by EMI Records. Dist: EMI

TANGOS.
Album: released on Pathe MarconiFrance), Dec'84

Cassette: released on Pathe MarconiFrance), Dec'84

Horn, Paul

INSIDE THE CATHEDRAL.
Album: released on Kuckuck (USA), Feb'87 Dist: Celestial Harmonies Distribution

Cassette: released on Kuckuck (USA), Feb'87 Dist: Celestial Harmonies Distribution

INSIDE THE GREAT PYRAMID.
Notes: Double album
Album: released on Kuckuck, Feb'87 Dist: PRT

Cassette: released on Kuckuck, Feb'87 Dist: PRT

Compact disc: released on Kuckuck, Feb'87 Dist: PRT

INSIDE THE GREAT PYRAMIND.
Tracks: / Prologue / Inside / Mantra I / Meditation / Mutaz Mahal / Unity / Agra vibrations / Akasha / Jumma / Shah Jahan / Mantra II / Duality / Ustad Isa / Mantra III.
Compact disc: released on Kuckuck (Germany), Jan'86

INSIDE THE TAL MAHAL.
Album: released on Kuckuck, May'87 Dist: PRT

Hornsby, Bruce

EVERY LITLE KISS (Hornsby, Bruce & The Range).
Tracks: / Every little kiss / River runs low,The / Way it is,The(instrumental).
Single (7"): released on RCA, Sep'86 by RCA Records. Dist: RCA, Roots, Swift, Wellard, Chris, I & B, Solomon & Peres Distribution

Single (12"): released on RCA, Sep'86 by RCA Records. Dist: RCA, Roots, Swift, Wellard, Chris, I & B, Solomon & Peres Distribution

MANDOLIN RAIN (Hornsby, Bruce & The Range).
Tracks: / Mandolin rain / Red planes, the / Way it is, The / Every little kiss.
Notes: The way it is/Every little kiss - these two extra tracks are only available on the 12" version.
Single (7"): released on RCA, Feb'87 by RCA Records. Dist: RCA, Roots, Swift, Wellard, Chris, I & B, Solomon & Peres Distribution

Single (12"): released on RCA, Feb'87 by RCA Records. Dist: RCA, Roots, Swift, Wellard, Chris, I & B, Solomon & Peres Distribution

WAY IT IS ,THE (Hornsby, Bruce & The Range).
Album: released on RCA, Jan'86 by RCA Records. Dist: RCA, Roots, Swift, Wellard, Chris, I & B, Solomon & Peres Distribution

Cassette: released on RCA, Jan'86 by RCA Records. Dist: RCA, Roots, Swift, Wellard, Chris, I & B, Solomon & Peres Distribution

Compact disc: released on RCA, Jan'86 by RCA Records. Dist: RCA, Roots, Swift, Wellard, Chris, I & B, Solomon & Peres Distribution

WAY IT IS ,THE (Hornsby, Bruce & The Range).
Tracks: / Way it is,The / Red plains,The / Wild frontier,The.
Single (7"): released on RCA, Jul'86 by RCA Records. Dist: RCA, Roots, Swift, Wellard, Chris, I & B, Solomon & Peres Distribution

Single (12"): released on RCA, Jul'86 by RCA Records. Dist: RCA, Roots, Swift, Wellard, Chris, I & B, Solomon & Peres Distribution

Hornweb Sax Quartet

KINESIS.
Notes: M. Archer, D. Saw, N. Manning, V. Middleton.
Album: released on Cadillac, Jan'87 by Cadillac Records. Dist: Cadillac

Horovitz, Joseph

RUMPOLE OF THE BAILEY.
Tracks: / Rumpole of the Bailey / Soft-shoe shuffle / Les girls.
Single (7"): released on Columbia, Jan'87 by EMI Records. Dist: EMI

Horovitz, Wayne

PRESIDENT (THE).
Album: released on Dossier, Feb'87 Dist: Red Rhino, Cartel

Horseguards London 1978

BEATING THE RETREAT.
Album: released on Major Richards, May'78 by Major Richards Records. Dist: Taylors

Cassette: released on Major Richards, Jun'78 by Major Richards Records. Dist: Taylors

Horseman

HORSE MOVE.
Cassette single: released on Raiders, May'85 Dist: Jetstar

Horseman, Daddy

CHICKEN FLAP (Horseman, Daddy & Ricky Ranking).
Single (12"): released on Magic Shoot, Sep'85 Dist: Jetstar

WARM UP.
Single (12"): released on Rusty International, May'85 by Rusty International Records. Dist: Jetstar Distribution

Horsemouth

REGGAE MUSIC/I WANT TO BE WITH YOU.
Single (12"): released on Horsemouth, Apr'82 Dist: Jetstar, Rough Trade

Horslips

BELFAST GIG, THE.
Album: released on Oats (Ireland), Jan'85

BEST OF HORSLIPS Traditional Irish rock music.
Album: released on Oats (Ireland), Aug'82

Cassette: released on Oats (Ireland), Aug'82

DRIVE THE COLD WINTER AWAY.
Album: released on Oats, Nov'76 Dist: Roots Distribution, I & B Distribution

FOLK COLLECTION.
Album: released on Stoic (Ireland), Aug'84

Cassette: released on Stoic (Ireland), Aug'84

HORSLIPS HISTORY.
Album: released on Oats (Ireland), Jan'85

MAN WHO BUILT AMERICA, THE.
Cassette: released on Outlet, Jul'87 by Outlet Records. Dist: Outlet Distribution

MAN WHO BUILT AMERICA.
Cassette: released on DJM, Jan'79 by DJM Records. Dist: CBS, Polygram

SHORT STORIES/TALL TALES.
Album: released on Mercury, Jan'80 by Phonogram Records. Dist: Polygram Distribution

TAIN, THE.
Album: released on Oats-DJM, '79

Cassette: released on Oats-DJM, '79

TRACKS FROM THE VAULTS.
Album: released on Oats (Ireland), Jan'78

UNFORTUNATE CUP OF TEA.
Album: released on Oats (Ireland), '74

Horsthuis, Maurice

CHANTENAY 80.
Tracks: / Chantenay 80 (1re, 2e, 3e parties).
Album: released on Nato (France), Sep'86 by Disques Nato. Dist: Essex Record Distributors Ltd.

Horton, Johnny

BATTLE OF NEW ORLEANS.
Single (7"): released on Old Gold, Jul'82 by Old Gold Records. Dist: Lightning, Jazz Music, Spartan, Counterpoint

JOHNNY HORTON.
Cassette: released on Audio Fidelity, Oct'84 Dist: PRT

MORE SPECIALS.
Album: released on Stetson, 11 Apr'87 by Hasmick Promotions Ltd.. Dist: Counterpoint Distribution, H.R. Taylor Distribution, Swift Distribution, Chris Wellard Distribution

Cassette: released on Stetson, 11 Apr'87 by Hasmick Promotions Ltd.. Dist: Counterpoint Distribution, H.R. Taylor Distribution, Swift Distribution, Chris Wellard Distribution

ROCK'N'ROLLIN' JOHNNY HORTON.
Album: released on CBS, Sep'84 by CBS Records. Dist: CBS

Horton, Pug

DON'T GO AWAY With Bob Wilber,Roland Hanna,Milt Hinton.
Album: released on Bodeswell, May'81

Horton, Shaky

SOUL OF BLUES HARMONICA, THE.
Album: released on Chess, Oct'87 by Charly Records. Dist: Charly, Swift, PRT, Discovery, IMS, Polygram

Cassette: released on Chess, Oct'87 by Charly Records. Dist: Charly, Swift, PRT, Discovery, IMS, Polygram

Horton, Walter

60'S GREATEST HITS (Horton, Walter & Carey Bell).
Album: released on Sonet, '76 by Sonet Records. Dist: PRT

AN OFFER YOU CAN'T REFUSE (Horton, Walter & Paul Butterfield).
Album: released on Red Lightnin', '82 by Red Lightnin' Records. Dist: Roots, Swift, Jazz Music, JSU, Pinnacle, Cartel, Wynd-Up Distribution

CAN'T KEEP LOVIN' YOU.
Album: released on Blind Pig (USA), Jul'84 by Blind Pig Records (USA). Dist: Topic, Projection

DEEP BLUES HARMONICA OF WALTER HORTON, THE.
Album: released on JSP, Jun'84 by JSP Records. Dist: Swift, Projection

WALTER HORTON.
Album: released on Black Magic, Nov'86 Dist: Swift

Hosanna

HOSANNA Various artists.
Album: released on Marantha Music, May'82

Cassette: released on Marantha Music, May'82

Host

TRYAL.
Album: released on Aura, Oct'84 by Hollywood Nites Distribution. Dist: Pinnacle

WALK ON LOVE.
Single (7"): released on Aura, Jan'85 by Hollywood Nites Distribution. Dist: Pinnacle

Hostages

GOING UP IN THE WORLD.
Single (7"): released on EMI, Aug'84 by EMI Records. Dist: EMI

Single (12"): released on EMI, Aug'84 by EMI Records. Dist: EMI Deleted '86.

HERE'S THE PEOPLE/IN A MINUTE.
Single (7"): released on This, Mar'82

Hot...

HOT AS I AM (Various Artists).
Album: released on Rambler, Feb'82 Dist: Swift

HOT BOPPIN' GIRLS (Various Artists).
Album: released on Supersonic, Jun'87

HOT BUBBLEGUM (Various Artists).
Album: released on K-Tel, Jun'81 by K-Tel Records. Dist: Record Merchandisers Distribution, Taylors, Terry Blood Distribution, Wynd-Up Distribution, Relay Distribution, Pickwick Distribution, Solomon & Peres Distribution, Polygram

Cassette: released on K-Tel, Jun'81 by K-Tel Records. Dist: Record Merchandisers Distribution, Taylors, Terry Blood Distribution, Wynd-Up Distribution, Relay Distribution, Pickwick Distribution, Solomon & Peres Distribution, Polygram

HOT CHILLS AND COLD THRILLS (Various Artists).
Album: released on Kent, Jun'84 by Ace Records. Dist: Pinnacle

HOT DANCE MUSIC IN CUBA 1909-37 Various Artists (Various Artists).
Notes: Artists:Colmbo y Garcia, Pablo Venuzuela, Antonio Romeu, Verar Del Real, Sexteto-Habanero, Sexteto Nacional, Guarteto Machin, Matamoros-Gueto, Trio Matamoros, Enrique Bryon, Estrellas Habaneros, Paulina Alvarez.
Album: released on VJM, Jun'86 by Wellard, Chris Distribution. Dist: Wellard, Chris Distribution

HOT HITS VOLUME 1. Various Artists (Various Artists).
Album: released on Dance Network, Nov'85 by Dance Network Records. Dist: Backs, Cartel

HOT JUMPIN R'N'ROLL Various artists (Various Artists).
Tracks: / Mad house jump / Slow down baby / Kansas city dog / Fool mule / Skinny Ginny / Humdinger / Fugitive, The / R'n'roll call / Horse, The / Teen town hop / Good golly Miss Molly / Frieda Frieda / Atlanta boogie / House near the track, The.
Album: released on Esoldun, Dec'86 by Esoldun Records. Dist: Swift

HOT LADIES OF ROCK (Various original artists).
Album: released on Hallmark, Oct'82 by Pickwick Records. Dist: Pickwick Distribution, PRT, Taylors

Cassette: released on Hallmark, Oct'82 by Pickwick Records. Dist: Pickwick Distribution, PRT, Taylors

HOT LINE (Various original artists).
Album: released on K-Tel, Feb'83 by K-Tel Records. Dist: Record Merchandisers Distribution, Taylors, Terry Blood Distribution, Wynd-Up Distribution, Relay Distribution, Pickwick Distribution, Solomon & Peres Distribution, Polygram

HOT MUSIC FROM CUBA - 1909-1953 (VOL.16) Various Artists (Various Artists).
Album: released on Harlequin, Jun'86 by Harlequin Records. Dist: Swift, Jazz Music, Wellard, Chris, IRS, Taylor, H.R.

HOT ROCKIN' PICKS (Various Artists).
Album: released on Goldband, Sep'84 by Charly Records. Dist: Charly

HOT SHOE SHOW (Various Artists).
Album: released on BBC, Jun'83 by BBC Records & Tapes. Dist: EMI, PRT, Pye

HOT SHOTS Various artists (Various Artists).
Double Album: released on Pickwick, Sep'80 by Pickwick Records. Dist: Pickwick Distribution, Prism Leisure Distribution, Lugtons

Cassette: released on Pickwick, Sep'80 by Pickwick Records. Dist: Pickwick Distribution, Prism Leisure Distribution, Lugtons

HOT SHOWER Various Artists (Various Artists).
Album: released on RCA, May'82 by RCA Records. Dist: RCA, Roots, Swift, Wellard, Chris, I & B, Solomon & Peres Distribution

Cassette: released on RCA, May'82 by RCA Records. Dist: RCA, Roots, Swift, Wellard, Chris, I & B, Solomon & Peres Distribution

HOT SOUTHERN BOPPERS Various Artists (Various Artists).
Tracks: / Chains of love / Bop bop baby / Don't need your lovin' baby / Take me to that place / My gal Mary-Ann / She's mu baby / Come on little mama / Tryin' to get to you / Take and give / She's gone away / Do what I do / Red cadillac & a black mustache / Eight wheel / Rock boppin' baby.
Album: released on Sun, Jan'86 by Charly Records. Dist: Charly Distribution

Album: released on Sun, Jan'86 by Charly Records. Dist: Charly Distribution

HOT YOU'RE HOT Various Original artists (Various original artists).
Cassette: released on Island, Sep'81 by Island Records. Dist: Polygram

Hot Aire

HOT AIRE Various artists.
Album: released on Halcyon (USA), Dec'82 by Halcyon Records (USA). Dist: Jazz Music, Conifer, Taylors

HOT AIRE (AMERICAN HOT HANDS OF THE TWENTIES) Various Artists (Various Artists).
Tracks: / Hot aire / If I had a girl like you / Darkktown shuffle / I'm goin' out if Lizzie comes in / Keep on croonin'a tune / Melancholy Lou / Don't wake me up, let me dream / Paddlin' Madelin' home / Breezin' along with the breeze / How many times / Tiger rag / Does she love me ? - Positively. Absolutele / What do I care what somebody said / You don't like it - not much / Swanee shore / Sugar babe I'm leavin' / When the morning glories wake up in the morning / Baltimore.
Album: released on Halcyon (USA), Mar'86 by Halcyon Records (USA). Dist: Jazz Music, Conifer, Taylors

Hot Antic Jazz Band

I GOT THE STINGER.
Album: released on Stomp Off, Jan'84 by Stomp Off Records. Dist: Jazz Music Distribution

VOLUME 2'.
Album: released on Stomp Off, Jun'86 by Stomp Off Records. Dist: Jazz Music Distribution

VOLUME 3'.
Album: released on Stomp Off, Jun'86 by Stomp Off Records. Dist: Jazz Music Distribution

Hot Butter

POPCORN.
Single (7"): released on Old Gold, Jan'85 by Old Gold Records. Dist: Lightning, Jazz Music, Spartan, Counterpoint

Hot Chocolate

CHANCES.
Single (7"): released on RAK, Sep'82 by RAK. Dist: EMI

CICERO PARK.
Album: released on RAK, Jul'74 by RAK. Dist: EMI

CLASS.
Album: released on Fame, Sep'84 by Music For Pleasure Records. Dist: EMI

Cassette: released on Fame, Sep'84 by Music For Pleasure Records. Dist: EMI

EMMA.
Single (7"): released on RAK, Mar'74 by RAK. Dist: EMI

EVERY 1'S A WINNER.
Tracks: / Every 1's a winner (groove mix) / So you win again.
Single (7"): released on EMI, Mar'87 by EMI Records. Dist: EMI

Single (12"): released on EMI, Mar'87 by EMI Records. Dist: EMI

GIRL CRAZY.
Single (7"): released on RAK, Apr'82 by RAK. Dist: EMI

GOING THROUGH THE MOTIONS.
Album: released on RAK, Jul'79 by RAK. Dist: EMI

GREATEST HITS:HOT CHOCOLATE.
Tracks: / Love is life / You could've been a lady / I believe (in love) / You'll always be a friend / Brother Louie / Rumours / Emma / Cheri babe / Disco queen / Child's prayer,A / You sexy thing / Don't stop it now / Man to man / Heaven in the back seat of my cadillac.
Album: released on RAK, Oct'76 by RAK. Dist: EMI

Cassette: released on RAK, Oct'76 by RAK. Dist: EMI

GREATEST HITS VIDEO:HOT CHOCOLATE.
Notes: Released on Video Collection

HEARTACHE NO.9.
Tracks: / Heartache no.9 / One life / Extended mix / Heartache no.9 (Dub).
Single (7"): released on RAK, Mar'86 by RAK. Dist: EMI

Single (12"): released on RAK, Mar'86 by RAK. Dist: EMI

HOT CHOCOLATE.
Album: released on RAK, Oct'75 by RAK. Dist: EMI

HOT CHOCOLATE'S GREATEST HITS.
Tracks: / Love is life / You could've been a lady / I believe in love / You'll always be a friend / Brother Louie / Rumours / Emma / Cheri babe / Disco queen / Child's prayer, A / You sexy thing / Don't stop it now / Man to man / Heaven is in the back seat of my cadillac.
Notes: Mono.
Album: released on MFP, Sep'87 by EMI Records. Dist: EMI

I'M SORRY.
Single (7"): released on RAK, Nov'83 by RAK. Dist: EMI

IT STARTED WITH A KISS.
Single (7"): released on RAK, Jun'82 by RAK. Dist: EMI

MAN TO MAN.
Album: released on RAK, Jul'76 by RAK. Dist: EMI

Cassette: released on RAK, Jul'76 by RAK. Dist: EMI

TEARS ON THE TELEPHONE.
Single (7"): released on RAK, Sep'83 by RAK. Dist: EMI

TWENTY HOTTEST HITS.
Album: released on EMI, Nov'79 by EMI Records. Dist: EMI

Cassette: released on EMI, Nov'79 by EMI Records. Dist: EMI

VERY BEST OF HOT CHOCOLATE, THE.
Album: released on EMI, Feb'87 by EMI Records. Dist: EMI

Cassette: released on EMI, Feb'87 by EMI Records. Dist: EMI

Compact disc: released on EMI, Feb'87 by EMI Records. Dist: EMI

VERY BEST OF HOT CHOCO-LATE,THE.
Tracks: / It started with a kiss / So you win again / I gave you my heart (Didn't I) / No doubt about it / Brother Louie / Tears on the telephone / Chances / You could've been a lady / Every 1's a winner / Girl crazy / You sexy thing / I'll put you together again / Are you getting enough happiness / Emma / What kinda boy you're lookin' for (girl) / Heaven is in the back seat of my cadillac. Notes: Composers: Tracks: 1,6,9,10,11,13,15,16 - E.Brown. Track. 2 - Island Music Ltd. Tracks:3,4 - Rak Publishers Ltd. Track: 12 - Dick James Music Ltd. Produced by Mickie Most. A Mickie Most Production. Cassette: released on Ranking Joe, Nov'86 by Ranking Joe Records. Dist: Jetstar

VERY BEST OF... (VIDEO).
Video-cassette (VHS): released on Video Collection, May'87 by Video Collection International Ltd . Dist: Counterpoint

YOU SEXY THING.
Tracks: / You sexy thing / Every 1's a winner.
Single (7"): released on EMI, Jan'87 by EMI Records. Dist: EMI

Single (12"): released on EMI, Jan'87 by EMI Records. Dist: EMI

YOU SEXY THING (EXT REPLAY MIX).
Tracks: / You sexy thing (ext replay mix) / Megamix-Emma / So you win again / You sexy thing / Every 1's a winner / You could've been a lady / Heaven is in the back seat of my Cadillac / Every 1's a winner.
Single (12"): released on EMI, Jan'87 by EMI Records. Dist: EMI

Hot Club
DIRT THAT SHE WALKS IN IS SACRED GROUND.
Single (7"): released on RAK, Aug'82 by RAK. Dist: EMI

I GOT RHYTHM (see also Stephane Grappelli) (Hot Club & Stephane Grappelli).
Album: released on Black Lion, Aug'74 by Black Lion Records. Dist: Jazz Music, Chris Wellard, Taylor, H.R., Counterpoint, Cadillac

IT AIN'T ME GIRL.
Single (7"): released on RAK, Jul'83 by RAK. Dist: EMI

Single (12"): released on RAK, Jul'83 by RAK. Dist: EMI

Hot Club de France
PARISIAN SWING.
Album: released on Ace Of Diamonds, '65 by Decca Records. Dist: Polygram

SWING 35-39 (Hot Club de France 5).
Album: released on Eclipse, '70 by Decca Records. Dist: Polygram

SWING 35-39 (Hot Club de France 5).
Cassette: released on Eclipse, Jan'75 by Decca Records. Dist: Polygram

Hot Club Quintet
1935 AND 1936 IN PARIS.
Album: released on Old Bean, Aug'87 Dist: Jazz Music. Estim retail price in Sep'87 was £5.25.

Cassette: released on Old Bean, Aug'87 Dist: Jazz Music. Estim retail price in Sep'87 was £5.25.

Hot Cotton Jazz Band
STOMPIN' ROOM ONLY - VOLUME 1..
Album: released on GHB, Jun'86 Dist: Jazz Music, Swift

TAKE YOUR TOMORROW.
Album: Dist: Jazz Music, Swift Deleted Jun'86.

Hot Cuisine
ONE NIGHT STAND.
Tracks: / One night stand.
Single (12"): released on Soul Supply, Apr'86 by High Energy Records. Dist: Charly

WHO'S BEEN KISSING YOU.
Single (12"): released on ISR, May'87 by ISR Records. Dist: DMS, RCA

Hotel Complex
FROZEN CHICKEN LIVES,A.
Album: released on Gymnasium, Mar'86 Dist: Red Rhino, Cartel

Hotel New Hampshire
HOTEL NEW HAMPSHIRE Original motion picture soundtrack.
Album: released on EMI, Nov'84 by EMI Records. Dist: EMI

Cassette: released on EMI, Nov'84 by EMI Records. Dist: EMI

Hotels, Motels...
HOTELS, MOTELS AND ROADSHOWS Various original artists (Various Artists).

Hotfoot
HOTFOOT.
Album: released on WEA Ireland, Mar'87 by WEA Records. Dist: Celtic Distributions, Projection, I & B

Cassette: released on WEA Ireland, Mar'87 by WEA Records. Dist: Celtic Distributions, Projection, I & B

Album: released on WEA Ireland, Mar'87 by WEA Records. Dist: Celtic Distributions, Projection, I & B

Cassette: released on WEA Ireland, Mar'87 by WEA Records. Dist: Celtic Distributions, Projection, I & B

Hotfoot Gale
MACHINE GUN BOOGIE.
Single (7"): released on JJ, Dec'82 Dist: Stage One

Hot Gossip
BREAK ME INTO LITTLE PIECES.
Single (7"): released on Fanfare, Jun'84 by Ferroway/Fanfare Records. Dist: PRT

Single (12"): released on Fanfare, Jun'84 by Ferroway/Fanfare Records. Dist: PRT

DON'T BEAT AROUND THE BUSH.
Single (7"): released on Fanfare, Nov'84 by Ferroway/Fanfare Records. Dist: PRT

Single (12"): released on Fanfare, Nov'84 by Ferroway/Fanfare Records. Dist: PRT

GEISHA BOYS & TEMPLE GIRLS.
Album: released on Dindisc, Nov'81 by Virgin Records. Dist: Virgin, EMI

Hot House
DON'T COME TO STAY.
Tracks: / Don't come to stay / Me and you.
Single (7"): released on RCA, Nov'86 by RCA. Roots, Swift, Wellard, Chris, I & B, Solomon & Peres Distribution

Single (12"): released on Construction, Nov'86 Dist: PRT

Single (7"): released on Construction, Nov'86 Dist: PRT

WAY WE TALK, THE.
Single (7"): released on Construction, Aug'87 Dist: PRT

Single (12"): released on Construction, Aug'87 Dist: PRT

Hothouse Flowers
LOVE DON'T WORK THIS WAY.
Tracks: / Love don't work this way / Freedom / See-line woman.
Single (7"): released on Mother, May'87 Dist: Island Distribution

Single (12"): released on Mother, May'87 Dist: Island Distribution

Hothouse Species
TRUST.
Single (7"): released on Compulsive, Apr'82 Dist: Rough Trade

Hotlegs
NEANDERTHAL MAN.
Single (7"): released on Old Gold, Jul'82 by Old Gold Records. Dist: Lightning, Jazz Music, Spartan, Counterpoint

Hot Licks
D.A.N.C.E..
Single (7"): released on Eagle (London), Mar'82 by Eagle Records (London). Dist: Stage One

Single (12"): released on Eagle (London), Mar'82 by Eagle Records (London). Dist: Stage One

Hotline
FEEL SO STRONG.
Single (7"): released on Red Bus, May'83 by Red Bus Records. Dist: PRT

Single (12"): released on Red Bus, May'83 by Red Bus Records. Dist: PRT

FELL SO STRONG.

HANG UP.
Single (7"): released on President, Sep'83 by President Records. Dist: Taylors, Spartan

HELP.
Single (7"): released on Red Bus, Mar'84 by Red Bus Records. Dist: PRT

ROCK THIS HOUSE.
Single (12"): released on Rhythm King, 30 May'87 Dist: Rough Trade, Cartel

Hot'n'Horrid
TOURISTS MAKE THWE TREES GROW.
Single (12"): released on Tim, Jul'87 Dist: Backs, Cartel Distribution

Hot Pursuit
VICTIM OF THE BEAT.
Tracks: / Victim of the beat / Victim of the beat (Dub mix).
Single (12"): released on Genie, Sep'86 by Genie Records. Dist: Spartan, CBS

Hot Rize
TRADITIONAL TIES.
Album: released on Sugarhill (USA), May'86 by PRT Records. Dist: PRT Distribution

Hot Rox
SUMMER FEVER (PUTS YOUR EMOTIONS IN MOTION).
Single (7"): released on CBS, Jun'84 by CBS Records. Dist: CBS

Single (12"): released on CBS, Jun'84 by CBS Records. Dist: CBS

Hot Sax Band
RED HOT SAX.
Album: released on Avon, Jul'86 by Avon Records. Dist: Counterpoint

Cassette: released on Avon, Jul'86 by Avon Records. Dist: Counterpoint

Hot Shot
I FOUND MORE LOVE.
Single (7"): released on Justice, Feb'85 by Pinnacle

Single (12"): released on Justice, Feb'85 by Pinnacle

SEXY TOUCH (MEDLEY).
Single (12"): released on Inferno, Nov'84 by Inferno Records. Dist: Inferno, Cartel, Pinnacle

Hot Streak
BODY WORK.
Tracks: / Body work / Body work (inst).
Single (7"): released on Boiling Point, Sep'86 by Polydor Records. Dist: Polygram

Single (12"): released on Boiling Point, Sep'86 by Polydor Records. Dist: Polygram

Hot Stuff
HOT STUFF.
Album: released on Crystal Clear, Dec'80 by Crystal Records. Dist: Revolver, Cartel

HOT STUFF Various artists (Various Artists).
Cassette: released on Bi Bi(Budget Cassettes), Jan'83

JACK IN THE BOX Featuring Lee Vanderbilt.
Single (7"): released on Sharpville Music, Oct'85

Single (7"): released on Sharpville Music, Oct'85

Hot Syndicate
TAKE ME BACK.
Single (12"): released on Suburn, Jan'84

HOTT
SPACE CIRCUS.
Single (12"): released on Hippo, Aug'84 by Hippo Records. Dist: PRT

Hotta Clapps Band
KNOWING IT ALL.
Single (12"): released on Spy, Mar'84 by Spy Records. Dist: Jetstar Distribution

Hottest Hits
HOTTEST HITS Various artists (Various Artists).

HOTTEST HITS VOL 1 Various artists.
Album: released on Treasure Isle, Aug'84 by Treasure Isle Records. Dist: Jetstar

Hot Tuna
BURGERS.
Tracks: / True religion / Highway song / 99 Blues / Sea child / keep on truckin' / Water song / Ode for Billy Dean / Let us get together right down here / Sunny day strut.
Notes: Tracks: 1,2,4,6,7,9 - Fish Scent Music Co. 3 - Southern Music. 8 - Robbins Music
Double Album: released on RCA (Special Imports Service), Jul'84

DOUBLE DOSE.
Album: released on RCA (Germany), '83

HISTORIC HOT TUNA.
Compact disc: by Pacific Records (USA). Dist: Atlantic

HOPPKORU.
Tracks: / Santa Claus retreat / Watch the north wind rise / It's so easy / Bowlegged woman, knock kneed man / Drivin' around / I wish you would / I can't be satisfied / I'm talking 'bout you / Extrication love song / Song from the stainless cymbal.
Album: released on RCA (Germany), Jan'83

Hotvills
AROUND THE WORLD.
Tracks: / Orange blossom special / O bayuro do mar / Sambalina / Hora staccato / Le retour des hirondelles / Danse du sabre / Tarantelle / Yiddishe momme / Yosel Yossel / El manisero / Nocturnal ballade / 12th street rag.
Notes: Retail price given by ARC excluding P & P (via mail order) is 5.95. Mail order distribution address: Accordion Record Club, 146 Birmingham road, Kidderminster Worcs. DY10 2SL. Tel: 0562 - 746105.
Album: released on Accordion Record Club, Jul'86 by Accordion Record Club Records. Dist: Accordion Record Club

DIXIELAND ALBUM,THE.
Tracks: / Tiger rag / How high the moon / Mus-kat ramble / Caravan / When the saints / Hotvill's Boogie / Down by the riverside / Margie / Alexander's ragtime / Sweet Georgie Brown / Dans les rues d'antibes.
Album: released on Accordion Record Club, Jul'86 by Accordion Record Club Records. Dist: Accordion Record Club

HOTVILLS.
Tracks: / Reminiscene / Reballade cha cha / Camboudery Orage slow fox trot / Nuit de camargue / Soleil / Canaville / Canadienne / Musette / Campagnon mon ami / Chanson non engagee / Ceux qui s'aiment.
Album: released on Accordion Record Club, Jul'86 by Accordion Record Club Records. Dist: Accordion Record Club

Hot Vultures
UP THE LINE.
Album: released on Plant Life, Nov'81 Dist: Roots

VULTURAMA-HOT VULTURES 20 BEST.
Cassette: released on Rogue, Nov'83 by Fast Forward Records. Dist: Nine Mile Distribution, Cartel Distribution

Houdini, Wilmouth
BARBADOS BLUES (Houdini, Wilmouth & Sam Manning).
Notes: For full details see under: Manning, Sam/Wilmouth Houdini.

TRINIDAD CALYPSOS FROM THE 30'S.
Album: released on Folklyric (USA), Mar'85 by Arhoolie Records. Dist: Topic, Projection

Houdusse, Patrick.

PATRICK HOUDUSSE.
Tracks: / Les triolets / I love samba / Quand vient le soir / I feel blue / Bolero de Patrick / March de radio-may enne / La grande valse / Un Francais a Madrid / Tango bleu, blanc, rouge / Morena de la plaza / Coupe de pouce / Accordeon en fete.
Album: released on Accordion Record Club, Jul'86 by Accordion Record Club Records. Dist: Accordion Record Club

Houghton Band

AN EVENING WITH HOUGHTON BAND.
Album: released on Fellside, Jan'83 by Fellside Records. Dist: Roots, Jazz Music, Celtic Music, Projection

DANCE AND ENJOY THE PRIDE OF LANCASHIRE.
Album: released on Fellside, Jan'83 by Fellside Records. Dist: Roots, Jazz Music, Celtic Music, Projection

HOUGHTON BAND, AN EVENING WITH.
Album: released on Fellside, Oct'80 by Fellside Records. Dist: Roots, Jazz Music, Celtic Music, Projection

PLAYS YOUR REQUESTS.
Album: released on Fellside, May'85 by Fellside Records. Dist: Roots, Jazz Music, Celtic Music, Projection

Houghton Weavers

ALIVE AND KICKING.
Album: released on EMI, Sep'81 by EMI Records. Dist: EMI

Cassette: released on EMI, Sep'81 by EMI Records. Dist: EMI

BLACKPOOL BELLE.
Tracks: / Blackpool Belle / That stranger is a friend.
Notes: Grasmere Music-59 Marlpit Lane, Coulsdon, Surrey, CR3 2HF
Single (7"): released on Langdale, Mar'87

CLATTER O' CLOGS.
Album: released on Folk Heritage, Jul'82 by Folk Heritage Records. Dist: Roots, Wynd-Up Distribution, Jazz Music, Folk Heritage

Cassette: released on Folk Heritage, Jul'82 by Folk Heritage Records. Dist: Roots, Wynd-Up Distribution, Jazz Music, Folk Heritage

HOWFEN WAKES.
Album: released on Folk Heritage, Jul'82 by Folk Heritage Records. Dist: Roots, Wynd-Up Distribution, Jazz Music, Folk Heritage

Cassette: released on Folk Heritage, Jul'82 by Folk Heritage Records. Dist: Roots, Wynd-Up Distribution, Jazz Music, Folk Heritage

IN CONCERT..
Album: released on Folk Heritage, Jul'82 by Folk Heritage Records. Dist: Roots, Wynd-Up Distribution, Jazz Music, Folk Heritage

Cassette: released on Folk Heritage, Jul'82 by Folk Heritage Records. Dist: Roots, Wynd-Up Distribution, Jazz Music, Folk Heritage

IN THE RARE OLD TIMES.
Album: released on HW, Apr'83 by EMI Records. Dist: EMI

Cassette: released on HW, Apr'83 by EMI Records. Dist: EMI

IT'S GOOD TO SEE YOU.
Album: released on Folk Heritage, Jul'86 by Folk Heritage Records. Dist: Roots, Wynd-Up Distribution, Jazz Music, Folk Heritage

Cassette: released on Folk Heritage, Jul'86 by Folk Heritage Records. Dist: Roots, Wynd-Up Distribution, Jazz Music, Folk Heritage

SIT THI DEAWN.
Album: released on Folk Heritage, Jul'82 by Folk Heritage Records. Dist: Roots, Wynd-Up Distribution, Jazz Music, Folk Heritage

Cassette: released on Folk Heritage, Jul'82 by Folk Heritage Records. Dist: Roots, Wynd-Up Distribution, Jazz Music, Folk Heritage

UP YOUR WAY.
Album: released on EMI, Sep'80 by EMI Records. Dist: EMI

Cassette: released on EMI, Sep'80 by EMI Records. Dist: EMI

Houliston, Max

MAX HOULESTON'S SCOTTISH BAND SHOW.
Tracks: / Mountain tay,The / Waiting for Sheila / Amazing Grace / Boys from county Armagh,The.
Cassette: released on Highlander, Jun'86 Dist: PRT

Houl Yer Whist

ON BOYNE'S RED SHORE.
Album: released on Archive, Jul'84 Dist: Polydor

Cassette: released on Archive, Jul'84 Dist: Polydor

Hound of the Baskervilles

HOUND OF THE BASKERVILLES Sir Arthur Conan Doyle.

HOUND OF THE BASKERVILLES Hugh Burden.
Cassette: released on Listen For Pleasure, Nov'77 by MFP Records. Dist: EMI

Hourglass

SOUL OF TIME, THE.
Album: released on See For Miles, Sep'85 by Charly Records. Dist: Spartan

Hour In The Shower

WE ARE THE WORLD.
Tracks: / We are the world / We are the world (Orchestra version) / We are the world (Global Mix).
Single (7"): released on Absolute, Jan'86 by Absolute. Dist: Spartan

Single (12"): released on Absolute, Jan'86 by Absolute. Dist: Spartan

House at Pooh Corner

HOUSE AT POOH CORNER A.A. Milne read by C. Channing.
Cassette: released on Caedmon(USA), Oct'81 by Caedmon (USA) Records. Dist: Gower, Taylors, Discovery

HOUSE AT POOH CORNER READ BY LIONEL JEFFERIES.

HOUSE AT POOH CORNER READ BY NORMAN SHELLEY.
Cassette: released on Argo (Spokenword), Nov'83 by Decca Records. Dist: Polygram

House Band

HOUSE BAND, THE.
Album: released on Topic, Nov'86 Dist: Roots Distribution

HOUSE BAND, THE.
Album: released on Topic, Mar'85 Dist: Roots Distribution

PACIFIC.
Tracks: / Pacific / Diamantina Drover / Joy after sorrow / In at the deep end / Old manriver / Pit stands idle, The / Going places / For the sake of example / Blazing Ruse.
Album: released on Topic, Mar'87 Dist: Roots Distribution

House, George

GEORDIERAMA (see also Mike Neville) (House, George & Mike Neville).
Album: released on MWM, Jun'82 by Mawson & Wareham. Dist: Spartan Distribution, Jazz Music Distribution, JSU Distribution

LARN YERSEL GEORDIE (see also Mike Neville) (House, George & Mike Neville).
Album: released on MWM, Jun'82 by Mawson & Wareham. Dist: Spartan Distribution, Jazz Music Distribution, JSU Distribution

Cassette: released on MWM, Jun'82 by Mawson & Wareham. Dist: Spartan Distribution, Jazz Music Distribution, JSU Distribution

NEW IMPROVED GEORDIERAMA (see also Mike Neville) (House, George & Mike Neville).
Album: released on MWM, Jun'82 by Mawson & Wareham. Dist: Spartan Distribution, Jazz Music Distribution, JSU Distribution

Household Cavalry

BEATING THE RETREAT.
Album: released on Major, May'78 by Major Records. Dist: Pinnacle

Househunters

CUTICLES.
Tracks: / Cuticles / Shopping city.
Single (12"): released on 53rd & 3rd, Jul'86 by Fast Forward Records. Dist: Fast Forward, Cartel

Housemartins

CARAVAN OF LOVE.
Tracks: / Caravan of love / When I first met Jesus / We shall not be moved* / So much in love* / Heaven help us all*.
Single (7"): released on Go Discs, Nov'86 by Go Discs Records. Dist: CBS Distribution

Single (12"): released on Go Discs, Nov'86 by Go Discs Records. Dist: CBS Distribution

FIVE GET OVER EXCITED.
Tracks: / Five get over excited / Rebel without the airplay / So glad / Hopelessly devoted to them.
Single (7"): released on Go Discs, May'87 by Go Discs Records. Dist: CBS Distribution

Single (12"): released on Go Discs, May'87 by Go Discs Records. Dist: CBS Distribution

FLAG DAY.
Single (7"): released on Go Discs, Oct'85 by Go Discs Records. Dist: CBS Distribution

Single (12"): released on Go Discs, Oct'85 by Go Discs Records. Dist: CBS Distribution

HAPPY HOUR.
Tracks: / Happy hour / Mighty ship,The / Sitting on a fence / He ain't heavy, he's my brother.
Single (7"): released on Go Discs, May'86 by Go Discs Records. Dist: CBS Distribution

Single (12"): released on Go Discs, May'86 by Go Discs Records. Dist: CBS Distribution

LONDON 0 HULL 4.
Tracks: / Happy hour / Get up off our knees / Flag day / Anxious / Reverends revenge / Sitting on a fence / Sheep / Over there / Think for a minute / We're not deep / Lean on me / Freedom / I'll be your shelter (just like a shelter).
Album: released on Go Discs, Jun'86 by Go Discs Records. Dist: CBS Distribution

Cassette: released on Go Discs, Jun'86 by Go Discs Records. Dist: CBS Distribution

Compact disc: released on Chrysalis, Jan'86 by Chrysalis Records. Dist: CBS

ME AND THE FARMER.
Single (7"): released on Go Discs, Aug'87 by Go Discs Records. Dist: CBS Distribution

Single (12"): released on Go Discs, Aug'87 by Go Discs Records. Dist: CBS Distribution

SHEEP.
Tracks: / Sheep / Drop down dead.
Single (7"): released on Go Discs, Feb'86 by Go Discs Records. Dist: CBS Distribution

Single (12"): released on Go Discs, Feb'86 by Go Discs Records. Dist: CBS Distribution

THINK FOR A MINUTE.
Tracks: / Think for a minute / Who needs the limelight / I smell winter / Joy, joy ,joy / Rap around the clock.
Single (7"): released on Go Discs, Sep'86 by Go Discs Records. Dist: CBS Distribution

Single (12"): released on Go Discs, Sep'86 by Go Discs Records. Dist: CBS Distribution

Housemaster Boyz

HOUSE NATION (Housemaster Boyz & The Rude Boy Of House).
Tracks: / House nation / Track'n the house / Acahouse.
Single (7"): released on Magnet, Apr'87 by Magnet Records. Dist: BMG

Single (12"): released on Magnet, Apr'87 by Magnet Records. Dist: BMG

Single (12"): released on Magnetic Dance, Aug'87 by Magnetic Dance Records. Dist: BMG

House of cards

HOUSE OF CARDS Jilly Cooper (Gordon, Hannah).
Cassette: released on Pickwick Talking Books, '83

House Of Darkness

HOUSE OF DARKNESS Conrad, Joseph (Scofield, Paul).
Cassette: released on Argo, Apr'85 by Decca Records. Dist: Polygram

House Of Love

SHINE ON.
Single (7"): released on Creation, 23 May'87 Dist: Rough Trade, Cartel

House of the Seven Flies

HOUSE OF THE SEVEN FLIES Read by Valentine Dyall.
Cassette: released on Chivers Audio Books, Aug'81 by Chivers Sound & Vision. Dist: Chivers Sound & Vision.

House Party

HOUSE PARTY (Various Artists).
Album: released on Creole, Nov'85 by Creole Records. Dist: Rhino, PRT

House, Son

IN CONCERT.
Album: released on Blue Moon, Dec'84 Dist: Magnum Music Group Ltd, PRT, Spartan

House Sound Of Chicago

HOUSE SOUND OF CHICAGO (VOL.2) (Various Artists).
Tracks: / Pleasure control / No way back / Work the box / J.B. piano traxx / House music anthem-move your body, The / What's up Rocky / Thank ya / Can you feel it / R U hot enough / 7 ways to jack / Ride the rhythm / Washing machine / Give yourself to me / When you hold me / House beat box / We're rocking down the house / Dum dum / What is house? / Jungle, The.
Notes: This double album features 19 more 'Ways To Jack' and follows up the highly successful volume one which spawned smash hit singles from Farley 'Jackmaster' Funk and Steve 'Silk' Hurley.
Double Album: released on London, Apr'87 by London Records. Dist: Polygram

Cassette: released on London, Apr'87 by London Records. Dist: Polygram

Compact disc: released on Trax, 30 May'87 by Trax Records. Dist: EMI

HOUSE SOUND OF CHICAGO Various artists (Various Artists).
Tracks: / Jack your body / Mystery of love / Shadows of your love / Love can't turn around / Music is the key / Move your body / Anthem.
Notes: The first album compilation to feature 'House Music'- The modern club sound of Chicago which has been the subject of much coverage in the UK Music press.
Album: released on London, Sep'86 by London Records. Dist: Polygram

Cassette: released on London, Sep'86 by London Records. Dist: Polygram

House Trax

HOUSE TRAX (Various Artists).
Album: released on Dance Music, Jun'87

Cassette: released on Dance Music, Jun'87

House with the green...

HOUSE WITH THE GREEN SHUTTERS Read by Tom Watson.
Cassette: released on Colophone Audio Visual, Feb'81 by Audio-Visual Library Services. Dist: Audio-Visual Library Services

Houston,Bee

BEE HOUSTON,HIS GUITAR AND BAND.
Album: released on Arhoolie, May'81 by Arhoolie Records. Dist: Projection, Topic, Jazz Music, Swift, Roots

Houston, Cissy

MAMA'S COOKIN'.
Tracks: / Midnight train to Georgia / Nothing can stop me / Making love / It's not easy / Any guy / Long and winding road, The / Don't wonder why / I just don't know what to do with myself / This empty place / Only time you say you love me, The / I love you / Will you love me tomorrow / I'll be there / Be my baby / I believe / Down in the boondocks.
Notes: Produced by Bob Finiz, Charles Koppelman and Donald Rubin.
Album: released on Charly, Jun'87 by Charly Records. Dist: Charly, Cadillac

Cassette: released on Charly, Jun'87 by Charly Records. Dist: Charly, Cadillac

WITH YOU I COULD HAVE IT ALL.
Tracks: / With you I could have it all / What you gonna do / (Dance Mix) / Ballad.
Compact disc: released on Creole, Feb'86 by Creole Records. Dist: Rhino, PRT

Single (12"): released on Creole, Feb'86 by Creole Records. Dist: Rhino, PRT

Single (7"): released on Glitter, Sep'85 Dist: Creole, PRT

Single (12"): released on Glitter, Sep'85 Dist: Creole, PRT

Houston, Clint

INSIDE THE PLACE OF THE ELLIPTIC.
Album: released on Timeless(import), Sep'86 Dist: Cadillac

INSIDE THE PLAIN OF THE ELLIPTIC.
Album: released on Timeless(import), May'81 Dist: Cadillac

Houston, David

BEST OF DAVID HOUSTON, THE.
Album: released on First Base, Mar'85 Dist: Spartan

MY WOMAN'S GOOD TO ME.
Single (7"): released on First Base, Mar'85 Dist: Spartan

Houston, Joe

EARTHQUAKE.
Album:

ROCKIN' AT THE DRIVE-IN.

Album: released on Ace, Nov'84 by Ace Records. Dist: Pinnacle, Swift, Hotshot, Cadillac

Houston Jump

HOUSTON JUMP (Various Artists).
Album: released on Krazy Kat, Dec'82 Dist: Jazz Music, Swift, Chris Wellard, H.R. Taylor, Charly, Hotshot, IRS Distribution

Houston, Larry

LET'S SPEND SOME TIME TOGETHER.
Single (7"): released on Inferno, Apr'83 by Inferno Records. Dist: Inferno, Cartel, Pinnacle

PROMISE.
Single (12"): released on Inferno, Apr'83 by Inferno Records. Dist: Inferno, Cartel, Pinnacle

Houston, Steve

POWER AND THE PREACHER, THE.
Album: released on Myrrh, Apr'85 by Word Records. Dist: Word Distribution

Cassette: released on Myrrh, Apr'85 by Word Records. Dist: Word Distribution

Houston, Thelma

96 TEARS.
Single (7"): released on RCA, Sep'81 by RCA Records. Dist: RCA, Roots, Swift, Wellard, Chris, I & B, Solomon & Peres Distribution

Single (12"): released on RCA, Sep'81 by RCA Records. Dist: RCA, Roots, Swift, Wellard, Chris, I & B, Solomon & Peres Distribution

ANY WAY YOU LIKE IT.
Album: released on Motown, Aug'82 by Motown Records. Dist: BMG Distribution

Cassette: released on Motown, Aug'82 by Motown Records. Dist: BMG Distribution

BREAKWATER CAT.
Cassette: released on RCA, Mar'80 by RCA Records. Dist: RCA, Roots, Swift, Wellard, Chris, I & B, Solomon & Peres Distribution

DON'T LEAVE ME THIS WAY.
Single (7"): released on Motown, Oct'81 by Motown Records. Dist: BMG Distribution

Single (7"): released on Motown, Apr'85 by Motown Records. Dist: BMG Distribution

Single (12"): released on Motown, Apr'85 by Motown Records. Dist: BMG Distribution

IF YOU FEEL IT.
Single (7"): released on RCA, May'81 by RCA Records. Dist: RCA, Roots, Swift, Wellard, Chris, I & B, Solomon & Peres Distribution

Single (12"): released on RCA, May'81 by RCA Records. Dist: RCA, Roots, Swift, Wellard, Chris, I & B, Solomon & Peres Distribution

I GUESS IT MUST BE LOVE.
Single (7"): released on MCA, Feb'85 by MCA Records. Dist: Polygram, MCA

Cassette: released on MCA, Feb'85 by MCA Records. Dist: Polygram, MCA

I'VE GOT THE MUSIC IN ME (Houston, Thelma & Pressure Cooker).
Album: released on Sheffield Treasury, Oct'82

NEVER GONNA BE ANOTHER ONE.
Album: released on RCA, Jun'81 by RCA Records. Dist: RCA, Roots, Swift, Wellard, Chris, I & B, Solomon & Peres Distribution

Cassette: released on RCA, Jun'81 by RCA Records. Dist: RCA, Roots, Swift, Wellard, Chris, I & B, Solomon & Peres Distribution

SUNSHOWER.
Album: released on Motown, Oct'81 by Motown Records. Dist: BMG Distribution

Cassette: released on Motown, Oct'81 by Motown Records. Dist: BMG Distribution

YOU USED TO HOLD ME SO TIGHT.
Single (7"): released on MCA, Nov'84 by MCA Records. Dist: Polygram, MCA

Single (12"): released on MCA, Nov'84 by MCA Records. Dist: Polygram, MCA

Houston, Whitney

DIDN'T WE ALMOST HAVE IT ALL.
Single (7"): released on Arista, Aug'87 by Arista Records. Dist: RCA

Single (12"): released on Arista, Aug'87 by Arista Records. Dist: RCA

GREATEST LOVE OF ALL.
Tracks: / Greatest love of all / Thinking about you / Shock me.
Single (7"): released on Arista, Mar'86 by Arista Records. Dist: RCA

Single (12"): released on Arista, Mar'86 by Arista Records. Dist: RCA

HOLD ME (Houston, Whitney & Teddy Pendergrass).
Tracks: / Hold me / Love.
Single (7"): released on Elektra (USA), Jan'86 by Elektra/Asylum/Nonesuch Records. Dist: WEA

HOW WILL I KNOW.
Tracks: / How will I know / Someone for me.
Single (7"): released on Arista, Jan'86 by Arista Records. Dist: RCA

Single (12"): released on Arista, Jan'86 by Arista Records. Dist: RCA

I WANNA DANCE WITH SOMEBODY.
Tracks: / I wanna dance with somebody / I wanna dance with somebody (remix) / I wanna dance with somebody (dub) / Moment of truth.
Compact disc single: released on Arista, May'87 by Arista Records. Dist: RCA

Single (7"): released on Arista, 23 May'87 by Arista Records. Dist: RCA

Single (12"): released on Arista, 23 May'87 by Arista Records. Dist: RCA

NO.1 VIDEO HITS, THE.
Video-cassette (VHS): released on RCA, Dec'86 by RCA Records. Dist: RCA, Roots, Swift, Wellard, Chris, I & B, Solomon & Peres Distribution

NO.1 VIDEO HITS,THE.
Notes: Number of tracks: 4. Type of recording: EP. Total playing time: 18 minutes.
Video-cassette (VHS): released on RCA, Oct'86 by RCA Records. Dist: RCA, Roots, Swift, Wellard, Chris, I & B, Solomon & Peres Distribution

SAVING ALL MY LOVE FOR YOU.
Single (7"): released on Arista, Oct'85 by Arista Records. Dist: RCA

Single (12"): released on Arista, Oct'85 by Arista Records. Dist: RCA

SOMEONE FOR ME.
Single (7"): released on Arista, Apr'85 by Arista Records. Dist: RCA

Single (12"): released on Arista, Apr'85 by Arista Records. Dist: RCA

WHITNEY.
Album: released on Arista, 30 May'87 by Arista Records. Dist: RCA

Cassette: released on Arista, 30 May'87 by Arista Records. Dist: RCA

Compact disc: released on Arista, 30 May'87 by Arista Records. Dist: RCA

WHITNEY HOUSTON.
Tracks: / How will I know / Take good care of my heart / Greatest love of all / Hold me / You give good love / Thinking about you / Someone for me / Saving all my love for you / Nobody loves me like you do.
Compact disc: released on Arista, Aug'86 by Arista Records. Dist: RCA

Album: released on Arista, Dec'85 by Arista Records. Dist: RCA

Cassette: released on Arista, Dec'85 by Arista Records. Dist: RCA

YOU GIVE GOOD LOVE.
Single (7"): released on Arista, Jul'85 by Arista Records. Dist: RCA

Single (12"): released on Arista, Jul'85 by Arista Records. Dist: RCA

Howard, Austin

I'M THE ONE WHO REALLY LOVES YOU.
Tracks: / I'm the one who really loves you / I'm the one who really loves you (Instrumental).
Single (7"): released on 10, Aug'86 by 10 Records. Dist: Virgin, EMI

Single (12"): released on 10, Aug'86 by 10 Records. Dist: Virgin, EMI

Howard, Billy

TRUCKIN' WITH SANTA.
Single (7"): released on Hat Factory, Dec'82 Dist: Stage One

Howard, Bob

CHRONLOGICAL STUDY VOL 3.

CHRONOLOGICAL STUDY VOL 1.
Album: released on Rarities, Apr'81

CHRONOLOGICAL STUDY VOL 2.
Album: released on Rarities, Apr'81

Album: released on Rarities, Apr'81

CHRONOLOGICAL STUDY VOL 4.
Album: released on Rarities, Apr'81

CHRONOLOGICAL STUDY VOL 5 Final volume.
Album: released on Rarities, Apr'81

Howard Brothers

PLEASURE OF PAIN.
Tracks: / Pleasure of pain / Shakin' All over / How was I to know / Road Warrior.
Single (12"): released on Hallelujah Sounds, May'86 Dist: Nine Mile, Rough Trade, Cartel

Howard, Camille

BROWN GAL 1946/1950 (Howard, Camille, Dorothy Donegan, Lil Armstrong).
Notes: Mono
Album: released on Krazy Kat, Jan'87 Dist: Jazz Music, Swift, Chris Wellard, H.R. Taylor, Charly, Hotshot, IRS Distribution

Howard, Dave Singers

ROCK ON.
Tracks: / Rock On.
Single (7"): released on Fun After All, Oct'86 Dist: Pinnacle

Single (12"): released on Fun After All, Oct'86 Dist: Pinnacle

WHOISHE?.
Single (12"): released on Hallelujah Sounds, Nov'85 Dist: Nine Mile, Rough Trade, Cartel

YON YONSON.
Single (12"): released on Hallelujah Sounds, 20 Jun'87 Dist: Nine Mile, Rough Trade, Cartel

Howard, Eddy

1949-1953 (Howard, Eddy & His Orchestra).
Album: released on Circle(USA), Oct'86 by Jazzology Records (USA). Dist: Jazz Music, Swift, Chris Wellard

Howard, George

ASPHALT GARDENS.

ASPHALT GARDENS.
Album: released on Palo Alto (USA), Dec'85 by Palo Alto Records. Dist: Conifer

Cassette: released on Palo Alto (USA), Dec'85 by Palo Alto Records. Dist: Conifer

Album: released on Palo Alto (Italy), Jan'84

Cassette: released on Palo Alto (Italy), Jan'84

NICE PLACE TO BE, A.
Tracks: / No no / Jade's world / Sweetest taboo / Nice place to be, A / Let's live in harmony / Pretty face / Spenser for hire / Stanley's groove.
Compact disc: released on MCA, Apr'87 by MCA Records. Dist: Polygram, MCA

Album: released on MCA, Feb'87 by MCA Records. Dist: Polygram, MCA

Cassette: released on MCA, Feb'87 by MCA Records. Dist: Polygram, MCA

STEPPIN'OUT.
Album: released on Palo Alto (Italy), Jul'86

Cassette: released on Palo Alto (Italy), Jul'86

STEPPIN' OUT.
Album: released on Palo Alto (Italy), Jul'84

Howard, Jan

JAN HOWARD.
Album: released on MCA, Mar'87 by MCA Records. Dist: Polygram, MCA

Cassette: released on MCA, Mar'87 by MCA Records. Dist: Polygram, MCA

Howard, John

IN AT THE DEEP END.
Single (7"): released on Loose, Oct'84 by Loose Records. Dist: Nine Mile, Cartel

NOTHING MORE TO SAY (BUT GOODBYE).
Single (7"): released on Loose, Mar'84 by Loose Records. Dist: Nine Mile, Cartel

Howard, Johnny

IRVING BERLIN HIT PARADE (Howard, Johnny Orchestra & Singers).
Album: released on Dansan, Jul'80 by Spartan Records. Dist: Spartan

PLAYS COLE PORTER.
Cassette: released on Dansan, Apr'80 by Spartan Records. Dist: Spartan

Howard, Maxine

LOVE ME NOW.
Single (12"): released on Streetwave, Sep'85 by Streetwave Records. Dist: PRT Distribution

Howard, Miki

COME SHARE MY LOVE.
Tracks: / Come share my love / Love will find a way / Imagination / Come back to me lover / I can't wait (to see you alone) / I surrender / Mr friend / You better be ready to love me / Do you want my love.
Album: released on Atlantic, Feb'87 by WEA Records. Dist: WEA

Cassette: released on Atlantic, Feb'87 by WEA Records. Dist: WEA

IMAGINATION.
Tracks: / Imagination / You better be ready to love me.
Single (7"): released on Atlantic, Apr'87 by WEA Records. Dist: WEA

Single (12"): released on Atlantic, Apr'87 by WEA Records. Dist: WEA

Howard, Paul

UNIFICATION (Howard, Paul & Joe Clack).
Single (12"): released on Davy Lamp, 20 Jun'87 Dist: Jungle, Cartel

Howard, Roland

SOME VELVET MORNING (Howard, Roland & Lydia Lunch).
Tracks: / Some velvet morning / Fell in love with a ghost,I.
Notes: Originally a hit for Lee Hazlewood & Nancy Sinatra.
Single (12"): released on 4AD, Jan'86 by 4AD Records. Dist: Rough Trade

Howard's, Kid

N.O.-THE LEGENDS LIVE (Howard's, Kid New Orleans Band).
Notes: Mono recording.
Album: released on Jazzology, Jun'86 Dist: Jazz Music, Swift

Howard The Duck

HOWARD THE DUCK ORIGINAL SOUNDTRACK (Various Artists).
Album: released on MCA, Nov'86 by MCA Records. Dist: Polygram, MCA

Cassette: released on MCA, Nov'86 by MCA Records. Dist: Polygram, MCA

Howard, Tom

HARVEST (THE) (Howard, Tom (Solo Piano)).
Notes: Highlights six original compositions by Tom Howard as well as new arrangements. Tracks include:Humble yourself in the sight of the lord,Seek ye first,A shield about us.
Album: released on Maranatha Music, May'86

Cassette: released on Maranatha Music, May'86

ONE BY ONE.
Album: released on Word, Jul'85 by Word Records. Dist: Word Distribution, CBS

Cassette: released on Word, Jul'85 by Word Records. Dist: Word Distribution, CBS

How Can You Buy..?

HOW CAN YOU BUY KILLARNEY ? Various artists (Various Artists).
Tracks: / If you're Irish with my Shillelegh / Forty shades of green / Spinning Wheel(The) / Rose of Tralee / Old Refrain(The) / How can you buy Killarney ? / Boys of County Armagh / Hold ground / Wild Rover(The) / I'll tell me ma / If you're Irish when Irish eyes are smiling Patse Fegan / Mother's love a blessing,A / Galway Bay / Mother Machree / How are things in Gloccamorra ? / Baird of Armagh / Mary of Dungloe / By the bright silv'ry light.
Album: released on Emerald (Ireland), May'85 by Emerald Records. Dist: I & B, Ross, PRT

Cassette: released on Emerald (Ireland), May'85 by Emerald Records. Dist: I & B, Ross, PRT

Howcher

COLDER THAN COLDEST SEA.
Single (7"): released on RAK, Oct'84 by RAK. Dist: EMI

Howdy Boys

SUNDAY.
Extended-play record: released on Despatch, Sep'82

Howe, Catherine

HARRY.
Single (7"): released on RCA, Oct'84 by RCA Records. Dist: RCA, Roots, Swift, Wellard, Chris, I & B, Solomon & Peres Distribution

Album: released on Victor, '74

Howe, James

HOWLIDAY INN.

Cassette: released on Caedmon(USA), May'85 by Caedmon (USA) Records. Dist: Gower, Taylors, Discovery

Howell, Peg Leg

1928-29.
Album: released on Matchbox, Jan'83 by Saydisc Records. Dist: Roots, Projection, Jazz Music, JSU, Celtic Music

VOL.1 1926-27.
Tracks: / Sadie Lee blues / Too tight blues / Moanin' and Groanin' blues / Hobo blues / Peg Leg stomp / Doin' wrong / Skin game blues / Coal man blues / Tishamingo blues / New prison blues / Fo'day blues / New jelly roll blues / Beaver slide rag / Papa stobb blues.
Notes: The 1928/28 recordings of Peg Leg Howell were issued on MSE 205 and we now complete his output with his earlier recordings.His Blues are simple and affecting but often have unusual lyrics and imaginative guitar accompaniments.He drew on country songs,ballads,white folk pieces,blue lyrics and field hollers and crea- ted a remarkably consistent repertoire. Recorded in Mono.
Album: released on Matchbox, Aug'86 by Saydisc Records. Dist: Roots, Projection, Jazz Music, JSU, Celtic Music

Howe of Fife Dance Band

HOWE OF FIFE DANCE BAND.
Cassette: released on Springthyme, '83 by Springthyme Records. Dist: Folksound Distribution

Howe, Steve

BEGINNINGS.
Album: released on Atlantic, Oct'75 by WEA Records. Dist: WEA

How Fear Came

HOW FEAR CAME Read by Michael Palin.
Cassette: released on Listen Productions, Nov'84 Dist: H.R. Taylor, Hayward Promotions Distribution

Howland, Chris

FRAULEIN.
Album: released on Bear Family, Mar'84 by Bear Family Records. Dist: Rollercoaster Distribution, Swift

Howling

HOWLING II,THE Original Soundtrack.
Notes: Artists include Steve Parsons & Babel.
Album: released on Filmtrax, Nov'85 by Filmtrax Records. Dist: EMI

Cassette: released on Filmtrax, Nov'85 by Filmtrax Records. Dist: EMI

Howling Wilf

CRY WILF (Howling Wilf & The Vee Jays).
Album: released on Big Beat, Aug'86 by Ace Records. Dist: Projection, Pinnacle

Howlin' Wolf

Biographical Details: See under Wolf, Howlin'

20 BLUES GREATS.
Album: released on Deja Vu, Nov'85 by Deja Vu Records. Dist: Counterpoint Distribution, Record Services Distribution (Ireland)

Cassette: released on Deja Vu, Nov'85 by Deja Vu Records. Dist: Counterpoint Distribution, Record Services Distribution (Ireland)

ALL NIGHT BOOGIE.
Album: released on Masters (Holland), Apr'87

Cassette: released on Masters (Holland), Apr'87

Album: released on Blue Moon, Nov'84 Dist: Magnum Music Group Ltd, PRT, Spartan

CAN'T PUT ME OUT.
Album: released on Blues Ball, Aug'81 Dist: Swift

CHESS MASTERS Vol 3.
Album: released on Chess, May'83 by Charly Records. Dist: Charly, Swift, PRT, Discovery, IMS, Polygram

CHESS MASTERS.
Double Album: released on Chess, Jun'81 by Charly Records. Dist: Charly, Swift, PRT, Discovery, IMS, Polygram

CHESS MASTERS-HOWLIN' WOLF Vol 2.
Double Album: released on Chess, Apr'82 by Charly Records. Dist: Charly, Swift, PRT, Discovery, IMS, Polygram

GOING BACK HOME.
Album: released on Syndicate Chapter, Sep'82 Dist: JSU Distribution, Projection Distribution, Red Lightnin' Distribution, Swift Distribution

GOLDEN CLASSICS.
Album: released on Astan, Nov'84 by Astan Records. Dist: Counterpoint

Cassette: released on Astan, Nov'84 by Astan Records. Dist: Counterpoint

HIS GREATEST HITS VOL.1.
Album: released on Chess, Aug'86 by Charly Records. Dist: Charly, Swift, PRT, Discovery, IMS, Polygram

Cassette: released on Chess, Aug'86 by Charly Records. Dist: Charly, Swift, PRT, Discovery, IMS, Polygram

HOWLIN' WOLF-LONDON SESSIONS.
Album: released on Chess, Apr'82 by Charly Records. Dist: Charly, Swift, PRT, Discovery, IMS, Polygram

LEGENDARY SUN PERFORMERS, THE.
Album: released on Pye, '74

LONDON SESSIONS, THE.
Notes: Featuring no less than Eric Clapton,Steve Winwood,Bill Wyman and Charlie Watts, here these pop greats team up with their blues hero and get back to the roots that started them all on the road to fame and fortune.
Album: released on Chess, Dec'85 by Charly Records. Dist: Charly, Swift, PRT, Discovery, IMS, Polygram

Compact disc: released on Vogue (France), Dec'85 Dist: Discovery, Jazz Music, PRT, Swift

MOANIN' IN THE MOONLIGHT.
Album: released on Chess, Apr'87 by Charly Records. Dist: Charly, Swift, PRT, Discovery, IMS, Polygram

Cassette: released on Chess, Apr'87 by Charly Records. Dist: Charly, Swift, PRT, Discovery, IMS, Polygram

OFF THE RECORD.
Album: released on Chess, Jan'87 by Charly Records. Dist: Charly, Swift, PRT, Discovery, IMS, Polygram

Cassette: released on Chess, Jan'87 by Charly Records. Dist: Charly, Swift, PRT, Discovery, IMS, Polygram

RIDIN' IN THE MOONLIGHT.
Album: released on Ace, May'82 by Ace Records. Dist: Pinnacle, Swift, Hotshot, Cadillac

ROCKIN' CHAIR ALBUM, THE.
Compact disc: released on Vogue, Dec'86 Dist: Discovery, Jazz Music, PRT, Swift

SAM'S BLUES.
Album: released on Charly, Jun'76 by Charly Records. Dist: Charly, Cadillac

WE THREE KINGS.
Album: released on Syndicate Chapter, Sep'82 Dist: JSU Distribution, Projection Distribution, Red Lightnin' Distribution, Swift Distribution

WOLF, THE.
Album: released on Blue Moon, Apr'84 Dist: Magnum Music Group Ltd, PRT, Spartan

How Long..?

HOW LONG HAS THIS BEEN GOING ON ? Various artists (Various Artists).
Notes: Artists include:S.Vaughan,O.Peterson,Joe Pass,Louie Bellson,Ray Brown.

How The West Was Won

HOW THE WEST WAS WON (Various Artists).
Tracks: / Overture / How the west was won / Bereavement and fulfilment / River pirates (The) / Home in the meadow / Cleve and the mule / Raise a ruckus tonight / Come share my life / Marriage proposal (The) / Entr'acte / Cheyennes / He's Linus' boy / Climb a higher hill / What was your name in the states / No, goodbye / Finale.
Notes: Film soundtrack composed and conducted by Alfred Newman. Featuring Debbie Reynolds.
Compact disc: released on CBS, Mar'87 by CBS Records. Dist: CBS

Compact disc: released on CBS, Apr'87 by CBS Records. Dist: CBS

HOW THE WEST WAS WON Original Soundtrack.
Album: released on CBS, Jul'86 by CBS Records. Dist: CBS

Cassette: released on CBS, Jul'86 by CBS Records. Dist: CBS

How to...

HOW TO CHANGE IDEAS (De Bono, Ted).
Cassette: released on Seminar Cassettes, Oct'81 by Seminar Cassettes. Dist: Davidson Distribution, Eastern Educational Products Distrib., Forlaget Systime Distribution, Laser Books Ltd Distribution, MacDougall Distribution, Talktapes Distribution, Watkins Books Ltd Distribution, Norton, Jeff Distribution

HOW TO GIVE YOURSELF A STEREO CHECKOUT Narrated by Jack De Manio & Elizabeth Knight.
Album: released on Decca, '67 by Decca Records. Dist: Polygram

HOW TO PICK A WINNER Seahorns soul farm vol.2 (Various Artists).
Tracks: / Lovely woman / How to pick a winner / Fairchild / Just like a woman / I love you still / Man of the street / Here comes that hurt again / You got to love me / Natural soul brother / Goodbye / Cheatin' woman / Don't set me back / Did you have fun / All I want is you / Sadie mae / You lie so much.
Album: released on Charly, May'87 by Charly Records. Dist: Charly, Cadillac

Cassette: released on Charly, May'87 by Charly Records. Dist: Charly, Cadillac

How We Live

ALL THE TIME IN THE WORLD.
Tracks: / All the time in the world / Lost at sea.
Single (7"): released on Portrait, May'87 by CBS Records. Dist: CBS

Single (7"): released on Portrait, Apr'87 by CBS Records. Dist: CBS

Single (12"): released on Portrait, Apr'87 by CBS Records. Dist: CBS

DRY LAND.
Tracks: / Working girl / All the time in the world / Dry land / Games in Germany / India / Rainbow room,The / Lost at sea / In the city / Working town / Beat in the heart,A.
Album: released on Portrait, Jun'87 by CBS Records. Dist: CBS

Cassette: released on Portrait, Jun'87 by CBS Records. Dist: CBS

Compact disc: released on Portrait, Jun'87 by CBS Records. Dist: CBS

WORKING GIRL.
Tracks: / Working girl / In the city.
Single (7"): released on Portrait, Jul'87 by CBS Records. Dist: CBS

Single (12"): released on Portrait, Jul'87 by CBS Records. Dist: CBS

Hoyland, George

TWO GRENODIDE SWORD DANCE MUSICIANS.
Cassette: released on Folktracks, Nov'79 by Folktracks Cassettes. Dist: Folktracks

Hoyte, Janice

I AM A DO RIGHT GIRL.
Album: released on SRT, Apr'78 by SRT Records. Dist: Pinnacle, Solomon & Peres Distribution, SRT Distribution, H.R. Taylor Distribution, PRT Distribution

LIVE IT UP (2 parts).
Single (7"): released on PRT, Sep'83 by PRT Records. Dist: PRT

Single (12"): released on PRT, Sep'83 by PRT Records. Dist: PRT

H.R.H.

OLD MAN OF LOCHNAGAR H.R.H. The Prince of Wales (Peter Ustinov).
Album: released on Multi-Media, Apr'82 by Multi Media Tapes Records. Dist: Pinnacle, Conifer Distribution, H.R. Taylor Distribution, Stage One Distribution

Cassette: released on Multi-Media, Apr'82 by Multi Media Tapes Records. Dist: Pinnacle, Conifer Distribution, H.R. Taylor Distribution, Stage One Distribution

Huang Chung

HUANG CHUNG.
Album: released on Arista, Mar'82 by Arista Records. Dist: RCA

ISN'T IT ABOUT TIME WE WERE ON T.V..
Single (7"): released on Rewind, Apr'80 by Rewind Records. Dist: Spartan

Huband, John

JOHN HUBAND & THE TAYSIDE SOUND.
Album: released on Ross, '86 by Ross Records. Dist: Ross Distribution, Roots Distribution

Cassette: released on Ross, '86 by Ross Records. Dist: Ross Distribution, Roots Distribution

JOHN HUBAND & THE TAYSIDE SOUND.
Notes: Retail price given by ARC excluding P & P (via mail order)is 4.99. Mail order distribution address:Accordion Record Club,146 Birmingham Road, Kidderminster,Worcs. DY10 2SL. TEL: 0562 746105

Hubback, Steve

BE ALRIGHT WHEN I'M DEAD.
Tracks: / Shipbuilding* / Dangerous work* / Wreck* / Tempted*.
Album: released on Dossier, Feb'87 Dist: Red Rhino, Cartel

Hubbard, Freddie

ARTISTRY OF FREDDIE HUBBARD, THE.
Album: released on Jasmine, Mar'83 by Jasmine Records. Dist: Counterpoint, Lugtons, Taylor, H.R., Wellard, Chris, Swift, Cadillac

BEST OF,THE.
Album: released on Pablo, Oct'84 by Pablo Records. Dist: Wellard, Chris, IMS-Polygram, BMG

BLUE SPIRITS.
Tracks: / Soul surge / Cunga black / Outer forces / Blue spirits / Jodo / Melting pot, The / True colors.
Compact disc: released on Manhattan-Blue Note, Jun'87 by EMI America Records (USA). Dist: EMI

BORN TO BE BLUE.
Album: released on Pablo, Jul'82 by Pablo Records. Dist: Wellard, Chris, IMS-Polygram, BMG

Cassette: released on Pablo, Jul'82 by Pablo Records. Dist: Wellard, Chris, IMS-Polygram, BMG

BORN TO BE BLUE (Hubbard, Freddie & Orchestra).
Compact disc: released on Pablo (USA), May'86 by Pablo Records (USA). Dist: Wellard, Chris, IMS-Polygram, BMG

HERE TO STAY.
Album: released on Blue Note, Sep'85 by EMI Records. Dist: EMI

HUB CAP.
Album: released on Blue Note, Apr'85 by EMI Records. Dist: EMI. Estim retail price in Jul'87 was £3.99.

HUB-TONES.
Tracks: / You're my everything / Phrophet / Hub-tones / Lament for Booker / For Spee's sake / Phrophet Jennings.
Compact disc: released on Blue Note, Jul'87 by EMI Records. Dist: EMI

Compact disc: released on Manhattan-Blue Note, Jul'87 by EMI America Records (USA). Dist: EMI

HUB-TUNES.
Album: released on Blue Note, Oct'85 by EMI Records. Dist: EMI

LIFE FLIGHT.
Tracks: / Battlescar galorica / Saint's homecoming song, A / Melting pot / Life flight / Battlescar Galorica / Saint's homecoming song, A / Melting pot / Life flight.
Album: released on Manhattan-Blue Note, Jul'87 by EMI America Records (USA). Dist: EMI

Compact disc: released on Manhattan-Blue Note, Sep'87 by EMI America Records (USA). Dist: EMI

LITTLE NIGHT MUSIC, A.
Compact disc: released on Fantasy (USA), Nov'86 by Fantasy Inc USA Records. Dist: IMS, Polygram

LIVE,THE HAGUE,1980.
Album: released on Pablo, '82 by Pablo Records. Dist: Wellard, Chris, IMS-Polygram, BMG

Cassette: released on Pablo, '82 by Pablo Records. Dist: Wellard, Chris, IMS-Polygram, BMG

LOVE CONNECTION,THE.
Cassette: released on CBS, Oct'79 by CBS Records. Dist: CBS

OUTPOST.
Album: released on Enja (Germany), Jan'82 by Enja Records (W.Germany). Dist: Cadillac Music

RED CLAY.
Album: released on CTI (Musidisc France), Feb'84 by Polydor Records. Dist: IMS, Polygram

RIDE LIKE THE WIND.
Notes: Digital stereo.
Compact disc: released on Elektra(Musician), Jul'84 by WEA Records. Dist: WEA

Video-cassette (VHS): released on Chris Wellard, Sep'86 Dist: Independent Video Sales

Compact disc: released on Elektra(Musician), Jul'84 by WEA Records. Dist: WEA

SPLASH.
Album: released on Fantasy, Dec'81 by RCA Records. Dist: RCA, Jetstar

SWEET RETURNS.
Compact disc: released on Elektra(Musician),

Sep'84 by WEA Records. Dist: WEA

Hubbards Cubbard

HUBBARD'S CUBBARD.
Album: released on Coda Landscape, Feb'84 by Coda Records. Dist: WEA

Compact disc: released on Coda Landscape, Feb'84 by Coda Records. Dist: WEA

SHRINK RAP.
Compact disc: by Coda Records. Dist: Pinnacle, Cartel, WEA, Roots

Album: released on Coda Landscape, Aug'85 by Coda Records. Dist: WEA

Cassette: released on Coda, Aug'85 by Coda Records. Dist: Pinnacle, Cartel, WEA, Roots

Compact disc: released on Coda Landscape, Aug'85 by Coda Records. Dist: WEA

Single (12"): released on Coda Landscape, Apr'85 by Coda Records. Dist: WEA

Hubert The Tree

DIG ME UP.
Single (7"): released on Lambs To The Slaughter, Nov'85 by Prism Records. Dist: Pinnacle, Red Rhino, Cartel

LET'S GO BONKERS FOR CHRISTMAS.
Tracks: / Let's go bonkers for christmas.
Single (7"): by Prism Records.

WAAAAARGH WOOO WOOOO WOOO YEAH BABY.
Album: released on Lambs To The Slaughter, Sep'85 by Prism Records. Dist: Pinnacle, Red Rhino, Cartel

Hubner, Abbi

LOW DOWN WIZZARDS.
Album: released on Stomp Off, Jun'86 by Stomp Off Records. Dist: Jazz Music Distribution

Hucko, Peanuts

JAM WITH PEANUTS (Hucko, Peanuts and his All Stars).

Album: released on Swinghouse, '84 Dist: Jazz Music Distribution, Swift Distribution, Chris Wellard Distribution

PEANUTS HUCKO WITH HIS QUARTET & ORCHESTRA (Hucko, Peanuts & His Quartet & Orchestra).
Notes: Plays tribute to Goodman.
Cassette: released on Holmia Cassettes, Jun'86 Dist: Jazz Music, Wellard, Chris

PEANUTS HUCKO WITH HIS PIED PIPER QUINTET (Hucko,Peanuts and his Pied Piper Quintet).
:

Album: released on World Jazz, Apr'81 by World Jazz Records. Dist: World Jazz, JSU, Jazz Music

SOUNDS OF THE JAZZ GREATS, THE.
Album: released on Zodiac, May'81 Dist: Jazz Music

STEALIN' APPLES (Hucko, Peanuts and his All Stars).
Album: released on Zodiac, Jun'83 Dist: Jazz Music

Huddersfield...

CAROLS ALBUM, THE (Huddersfield Choral Society).
Tracks: / I saw three ships come sailing in / Joy to the world / Away in a manger / God rest you merry gentlemen / It came upon the midnight clear / Shepherd's farewell, The / Good christian men / Good king Wenceslas / Once in royal David's city / We three kings of orient are / In the bleak midwinter / O come, o come emanuel / While shepherds watched their flocks by night / First Noel, The / Silent night (still the night) / Angels from the realms of glory / As with gladness men of old / Hark the herald angels sing / O come all ye faithful / Unto us is born a son / It came upon the midnight clear.
Notes: Conducted by Owain Arwel Highes/David Bell (organ)
Album: released on EMI, Dec'86 by EMI Records. Dist: EMI

Compact disc: released on EMI, Dec'86 by EMI Records. Dist: EMI

Album: released on EMI, Nov'86 by EMI Records. Dist: EMI

CHRISTMAS IF FOREVER (Huddersfield Choir).
Album: released on Audio Fidelity, Oct'84 Dist: PRT

Cassette: released on Audio Fidelity, Oct'84 Dist: PRT

HYMNS ALBUM,THE (Huddersfield Choral Society).
Tracks: / O worship the king / Praise,My soul,The king of Heaven / Lord's my Shepherd,I'll not want (The) / O Sacred Head!Sore wounded / When I survey the wonderous cross / Christ the lord is risen today! / Immortall,Invisible,God only wise / Aide with me / Crown him with many crowns / Chtistians awake,Salute the happy morn / City of God,How broad and far / Hallelujah! Sing to Jesus / God so loved the world / There is a green hill far away / Jesu,Lover of my soul / Guide me ,O thou great Jehovah / Eternal father,strong to save / Day thou gavest,Lord,is ended, the.
Album: released on His Master's Voice, Mar'86 by EMI Records. Dist: EMI

Cassette: released on His Master's Voice, Mar'86 by EMI Records. Dist: EMI

Compact disc: released on H.M.V., Apr'86 by EMI Records. Dist: EMI

Hudd, Roy

ROY HUDD'S VERY OWN MUSIC HALL.
Album: released on Flashback, Oct'85 by Flashback Records/PRT Records. Dist: Mainline, PRT

Cassette: released on Flashback, Oct'85 by Flashback Records/PRT Records. Dist: Mainline, PRT

Hudik Big Band

LIVE AT MONTREUX.
Album: released on Dragon, Jun'86 by Dragon Records. Dist: Jazz Music, Projection, Cadillac

LIVE AT MONTREUX.
Album: released on Dragon, Jan'85 by Dragon Records. Dist: Jazz Music, Projection, Cadillac

Hudson Country Players

INSTRUMENTAL COUNTRY.
Tracks: / Me and Bobby McGee / She called me baby / Blue bayou / Woman to woman / I'm having your baby / Ruby don't take your love to town / She's got you / Together again / Everytime you touch me I get high / Four walls / Happiest girl in the whole USA / Almost persuaded / Lovin' her was easier / Jolene / Desperado / Jamestown ferry / My love.
Album: released on Showcase, Oct'86 Dist: Counterpoint

Hudson, Dave

WHO BABY.
Single (12"): released on Red Man, May'84 by Red Man Records. Dist: Jetstar

Hudson, Dean

MORE 1941 & 1948 (Hudson, Dean & His Orchestra).
Album: released on Circle(USA), Jun'86 by Jazzology Records (USA). Dist: Jazz Music, Swift, Chris Wellard

Hudson, Jack

SUNDAY MORNING COMING DOWN.
Album: released on Folk Heritage, Jul'82 by Folk Heritage Records. Dist: Roots, Wynd-Up Distribution, Jazz Music, Folk Heritage

Hudson, Keith

BLACK MORPHOLOGIST OF REGGAE, (THE).
Album: released on Vista Sounds, '83 by Vista Sounds Records. Dist: Jetstar

RASTA COMMUNICATION.
Album: released on Greensleeves, Sep'79 by Greensleeves Records. Dist: BMG, Jetstar, Spartan

STEAMING JUNGLE.
Album: released on Vista Sounds, '83 by Vista Sounds Records. Dist: Jetstar

Cassette: released on Vista Sounds, '83 by Vista Sounds Records. Dist: Jetstar

Hudson, Laurice

AUTOMATIC LOVER.
Single (7"): released on Carrere, Apr'84 by Carrere Records. Dist: PRT, Spartan

Single (12"): released on Carrere, Apr'84 by Carrere Records. Dist: PRT, Spartan

Hudsons

ONE'S MAN MEAT.
Tracks: / One man's meat / Heat got you down.
Single (7"): released on Wheelchair, Jan'86

Single (12"): released on Wheelchair, Jan'86

Hudson, Will

EASY ROCKER.
Album: released on Sounds Of Swing, Jul'82

Hue and Cry

HERE COMES EVERYBODY.
Tracks: / Here comes everybody.
Single (12"): released on Stampede, Feb'86 Dist: Rough Trade Distribution

I REFUSE.
Tracks: / I refuse / Joe and Josephine.
Cassette single: released on Circa, Feb'87 Dist: Virgin

Single (7"): released on Circle(USA), Dec'86 by Jazzology Records (USA). Dist: Jazz Music, Swift, Chris Wellard

Single (12"): released on Circa, Dec'86 Dist: Virgin

LABOUR OF LOVE.
Tracks: / Labour of love / Wide screen / Goodbye to me *.
Single (7"): released on Circa, Jun'87 Dist: Virgin

Single (12"): released on Circa, Jun'87 Dist: Virgin

Hues Corporation

ROCK THE BOAT.
Tracks: / Rock the boat / Turn the beat around.
Single (7"): released on Old Gold, Nov'86 by Old Gold Records. Dist: Lightning, Jazz Music, Spartan, Counterpoint

Single (7"): released on RCA, Nov'84 by RCA Records. Dist: RCA, Roots, Swift, Wellard, Chris, I & B, Solomon & Peres Distribution

Single (7"): released on Soul Train, Jul'81 Dist: BMG

Huffey, Winston

YOU FACE LOOK GOOD.
Single (12"):

Hug, Armand

1968 PIANO SOLOS.
Album: released on Nola, Apr'79 Dist: JSU, Jazz Music, Cadillac, Chris Wellard

ARMAND HUG OF NEW ORLEANS: 1971.
Album: released on Swaggie (Australia), Jan'83

ARMAND HUG OF NEW ORLEANS: 1974.
Album: released on Swaggie (Australia), Jan'83

ARMAND HUG PLAYS JELLY ROLL MORTON.
Album: released on Swaggie (Australia), Jan'83

HUGGIN' THE KEYS.
Album: released on Swaggie (Australia), Jan'83

Huge Corporation Presents

HUGE CORPORATION PRESENTS Various artists (Various Artists).
Tracks: / Sun in splendour / Warm is my farm / Throwing Stones / Warts.
Notes: Self-143 Station road,Wigston,Leceister.Tel:(0533) 880686.
Single 10": released on Huge Corporation, Jun'86 by Huge Corporation Records. Dist: Huge Corporation

Huggy Boys's favourite...

HUGGY BOYS'S FAVOURITE OLDIES FROM CADDY RECORDS Various artists (Various Artists).
Album: released on Ace, Aug'83 by Ace Records. Dist: Pinnacle, Swift, Hotshot, Cadillac

Hughes, Carolyne

BLACKDOG AND SHEEPCROOK.
Cassette: released on Folktracks, Nov'79 by Folktracks Cassettes. Dist: Folktracks

Hughes, Clifford

ABIDE WITH ME.
Album: released on Lismor, Nov'76 by Lismor Records. Dist: Lismor, Roots, Celtic Music

SONG FOR YOU, (A).
Album: released on Lismor, May'75 by Lismor Records. Dist: Lismor, Roots, Celtic Music

Hughes, David

RUSSELL SQUARE (Hughes, David & Mick Linnard).

WORLD OF GREAT CLASSIC SONGS OF LOVE.
Album: released on World of Learning, '73 by World Of Learning Records. Dist: World Of Learning

Hughes, Emlyn

AT CHRISTMAS TIME (Hughes, Emlyn & Suzanne Dando).
Single (7"): released on Sub Zero, Nov'85 Dist: PRT Distribution

Hughes, Gary

SACRED CITIES.
Album: released on AIC, Apr'86 Dist: Pinnacle, PRT

Cassette: released on AIC, Apr'86 Dist: Pinnacle, PRT

Hughes, Glen

PLAY ME OUT.
Album: released on Safari, Apr'78 by Safari Records. Dist: Pinnacle

Hughes, Howard

BUFFALO BILL PART 1 (Hughes, Howard & The Western Approaches).
Tracks: / Buffalo Bill Part 1.
Single (7"): released on Abstract, Jul'86 by Abstract. Dist: Pinnacle

Single (12"): released on Abstract, Jul'86 by Abstract. Dist: Pinnacle

WEST OF PECO'S (Hughes, Howard & TWA).
Tracks: / West of Peco's.
Single (7"): released on Abstract, Mar'86 by Abstract. Dist: Pinnacle

Single (12"): released on Abstract, Mar'86 by Abstract. Dist: Pinnacle

Hughes, Jimmy

SHOT OF RHYTHM AND BLUES, (A).
Single (7"): released on Charly, Jul'80 by Charly Records. Dist: Charly, Cadillac

SOUL NEIGHBOURS (Hughes, Jimmy & Joe Simon).
Album: released on Charly(R&B), Nov'84 by Charly Records. Dist: Charly, Cadillac

Hughes, Ken

WE ARE HERE TO MANDELA'S FREE (Hughes, Ken & The Non Stop Pickets).
Tracks: / We are here to Mandela's free / Auta.
Single (7"): released on TFI, Jul'86 Dist: Revolver Distribution, Cartel Distribution

Hughes, Peter

JUST FOR YOU.
Album: released on Maestro, Jul'86 by Maestro Records.

Hughes, Spike

1930 VOLUME 2 (Hughes, Spike & His Dance Orchestra & His Three Blind Mice).
Album: released on Fountain, Jun'86 by Retrieval Records. Dist: Jazz Music, Swift, VJM, Wellard, Chris, Retrieval

SPIKE HUGHES (Hughes, Spike & His All-American Orchestra).
Album: released on Jasmine, Feb'83 by Jasmine Records. Dist: Counterpoint, Lugtons, Taylor, H.R., Wellard, Chris, Swift, Cadillac

Hughes, Ted

POETRY & VOICE OF TED HUGHES.
Cassette: released on Caedmon(USA), Sep'77 by Caedmon (USA) Records. Dist: Gower, Taylors, Discovery

Hughes, Tom

AND HIS BORDER FIDDLE.
Album: released on Springthyme Records, Oct'86 by Springthyme Records. Dist: Jazz Music Distribution, Projection Distribution, Roots Distribution

Cassette: released on Springthyme Records, Oct'86 by Springthyme Records. Dist: Jazz Music Distribution, Projection Distribution, Roots Distribution

TOM HUGHES & HIS BORDER FIDDLE (Hughes, Tom & His Border Fiddle).
Album: released on Springthyme, '83 by Springthyme Records. Dist: Jazz Music Distribution, Projection Distribution, Roots Distribution

Cassette: released on Springthyme, '83 by Springthyme Records. Dist: Jazz Music Distribution, Projection Distribution, Roots Distribution

Hughes, Tony

C'EST LA VIE.
Album: released on Folk Heritage, Jul'82 by Folk Heritage Records. Dist: Roots, Wynd-Up Distribution, Jazz Music, Folk Heritage

Hugill, Stan

ABOARD THE CUTTY SARK.
Album: released on Greenwich Village, May'81 by Sweet Folk All Records. Dist: Roots, Projection, Lightning, Celtic Music, Wellard, Chris

RATCLIFFE HIGHWA & THE SHANTYMENT.

Cassette: released on Folktracks, Nov'79 by Folktracks Cassettes. Dist: Folktracks

REMINISCES.
Album: released on Greenwich Village, Jun'81 by Sweet Folk All Records. Dist: Roots, Projection, Lightning, Celtic Music, Wellard, Chris

Hug me

HUG ME Stren, Patti (Danner, Blythe).
Cassette: released on Caedmon(USA), '84 by Caedmon (USA) Records. Dist: Gower, Taylors, Discovery

Hula

BLACK POP WORKOUT.
Single (12"): released on Red Rhino, Sep'82 by Red Rhino Records. Dist: Red Rhino, Cartel

BLACK WALL BLUE.
Single (12"): released on Red Rhino, Sep'86 by Red Rhino Records. Dist: Red Rhino, Cartel

CUT FROM INSIDE.
Album: released on Red Rhino, '84 by Red Rhino Records. Dist: Red Rhino, Cartel

CUT ME LOOSE.
Single (12"): released on Red Rhino, Aug'87 by Red Rhino Records. Dist: Red Rhino, Cartel

FEVER CAR.
Single (12"): released on Red Rhino, Sep'84 by Red Rhino Records. Dist: Red Rhino, Cartel

FREEZE OUT.
Tracks: / Freeze out.
Single (12"): released on Red Rhino, Mar'86 by Red Rhino Records. Dist: Red Rhino, Cartel

GET THE HABIT.
Single (12"): released on Red Rhino, Jun'85 by Red Rhino Records. Dist: Red Rhino, Cartel

GING GANG GOOLEY.
Single (7"): released on Crash, Oct'82 by Satril Records. Dist: PRT

MURMUR.
Album: released on Red Rhino, Nov'84 by Red Rhino Records. Dist: Red Rhino, Cartel

NO ONE LEAVES THE FEVER CAR.
Single (12"): released on Red Rhino, Nov'84 by Red Rhino Records. Dist: Red Rhino, Cartel

ONE THOUSAND HOURS.
Album: released on Red Rhino, Feb'86 by Red Rhino Records. Dist: Red Rhino, Cartel

POISON.
Single (7"): released on Red Rhino, Mar'87 by Red Rhino Records. Dist: Red Rhino, Cartel

Single (12"): released on Red Rhino, Mar'87 by Red Rhino Records. Dist: Red Rhino, Cartel

SHADOW LAND.
Album: released on Red Rhino, Sep'86 by Red Rhino Records. Dist: Red Rhino, Cartel

VOICE.
Album: released on Red Rhino, May'87 by Red Rhino Records. Dist: Red Rhino, Cartel

Cassette: released on Red Rhino, May'87 by Red Rhino Records. Dist: Red Rhino, Cartel

WALK ON STALKS OF SHATTERED GLASS.
Single (12"): released on Red Rhino, Oct'85 by Red Rhino Records. Dist: Red Rhino, Cartel

Hulbert, Jack

CICELY COUTNEIDGE & JACK HULBERT.
Album: released on World, '68 Dist: Jetstar

Hull, Alan

MALVINAS MELODY.
Single (7"): released on Black Crow, Oct'83 by Mawson & Wareham Records. Dist: Projection

ON THE OTHER SIDE.
Album: released on Black Crow, Nov'83 by Mawson & Wareham Records. Dist: Projection

PIPEDREAM.
Album: released on Charisma, Mar'83 by Virgin Records. Dist: EMI

Cassette: released on Charisma, Mar'83 by Virgin Records. Dist: EMI

Hull, Rod & Emu

BIG BLOW FOR ROD, A.
Cassette: released on VFM, Aug'85 by VFM Records. Dist: Taylors, Wynd-Up Distribution

CHANGED PLACES.
Cassette: released on VFM, Aug'85 by VFM Records. Dist: Taylors, Wynd-Up Distribution

GROTBAGS MOVING DAY.
Cassette: released on VFM, Aug'80 by VFM Records. Dist: Taylors, Wynd-Up Distribution

LITTLE LOST DOG, THE.
Cassette: released on VFM, Aug'85 by VFM Records. Dist: Taylors, Wynd-Up Distribution

SUPER EMU.
Cassette: released on VFM, Aug'85 by VFM Records. Dist: Taylors, Wynd-Up Distribution

WINDY DAY, A.
Cassette: released on VFM, Aug'85 by VFM Records. Dist: Taylors, Wynd-Up Distribution

Human Arts Ensemble

HUMAN ARTS ENSEMBLE VOLUME 1.
Album: released on Circle, May'79 Dist: Jazz Music

HUMAN ARTS ENSEMBLE VOLUME 2.
Album: released on Circle, May'79 Dist: Jazz Music

Human Beinz

EVOLUTIONS.
Tracks: / Face, the / My animal / Everytime woman / Close your eyes / If you don't mind Mrs.Applebee / Cement / Two of a kind / April 15th.
Album: released on Decal, Oct'86 by Charly Records. Dist: Charly

Human Chains

HUMAN CHAINS.
Tracks: / Freely / My Girl / Antonia / Elderberries / La La La / Grinding to the miller men / Hollyhocks / Golden slumbers / Further away / Suguxhama / Jolobe / Ikebana / Bon / Nancy D / Death.
Notes: Human Chains are Django Bates and Steve Arguelles both of whom are members of Loose Tubes.Both Django and Steve are at the forefront of a new wave of British modern jazz,creating accessible music that has potential to crossover to a mass audience. This is Human Chain' debut album and features with one exception,compositions composed by Django and Steve.
Album: released on Loose Tubes, Oct'86 Dist: IMS-Polygram

Human League

BOYS AND GIRLS.
Single (7"): released on Virgin, Feb'81 by Virgin Records. Dist: EMI, Virgin Distribution

CRASH.
Album: released on Virgin, May'86 by Virgin Records. Dist: EMI, Virgin Distribution

Cassette: released on Virgin, May'86 by Virgin Records. Dist: EMI, Virgin Distribution

Compact disc: released on Virgin, May'86 by Virgin Records. Dist: EMI, Virgin Distribution

DARE.
Album: released on Virgin, Oct'81 by Virgin Records. Dist: EMI, Virgin Distribution

Cassette: released on Virgin, Oct'81 by Virgin Records. Dist: EMI, Virgin Distribution

Compact disc: released on Virgin, Oct'81 by Virgin Records. Dist: EMI, Virgin Distribution

DON'T YOU WANT ME.
Single (7"): released on Virgin, Nov'81 by Virgin Records. Dist: EMI, Virgin Distribution

Single (12"): released on Virgin, Nov'81 by Virgin Records. Dist: EMI, Virgin Distribution

EMPIRE STATE HUMAN.
Single (7"): released on Virgin, Sep'79 by Virgin Records. Dist: EMI, Virgin Distribution

FASCINATION.
Single (12"): released on John Webster, May'83 by John Webster Records. Dist: Pinnacle

HOLIDAY 80.
Single (7"): released on Virgin, Apr'80 by Virgin Records. Dist: EMI, Virgin Distribution

HUMAN.
Tracks: / Human.
Single (7"): released on Virgin, Aug'86 by Virgin Records. Dist: EMI, Virgin Distribution

Single (12"): released on Virgin, Aug'86 by Virgin Records. Dist: EMI, Virgin Distribution

HYSTERIA.
Tracks: / I'm coming back / I love you too much / Rock me again & again / Louise / Lebanon,The / Betrayed / Sign, The / So hurt / Life on your own / Don't you know I want you.
Compact disc: released on Virgin, Jul'87 by Virgin Records. Dist: EMI, Virgin Distribution

Album: released on Virgin, Jul'84 by Virgin Records. Dist: EMI, Virgin Distribution

Cassette: released on Virgin, Jul'84 by Virgin Records. Dist: EMI, Virgin Distribution

I NEED YOUR LOVING.
Tracks: / I need your loving / I need your loving(Mix).
Single (7"): released on Virgin, Nov'86 by Virgin Records. Dist: EMI, Virgin Distribution

Single (12"): released on Virgin, Nov'86 by Virgin Records. Dist: EMI, Virgin Distribution

LEBANON, THE.
Single (7"): released on Virgin, Apr'84 by Virgin Records. Dist: EMI, Virgin Distribution

Single (12"): released on Virgin, Apr'84 by Virgin Records. Dist: EMI, Virgin Distribution

LIFE ON YOUR OWN.
Single (12"): released on Virgin, Jun'84 by Virgin Records. Dist: EMI, Virgin Distribution

Single (7"): released on Virgin, Jun'84 by Virgin Records. Dist: EMI, Virgin Distribution Deleted '85.

LOUISE.
Single (7"): released on Virgin, Oct'84 by Virgin Records. Dist: EMI, Virgin Distribution

Single (12"): released on Virgin, Oct'84 by Virgin Records. Dist: EMI, Virgin Distribution

LOVE ACTION (I BELIEVE IN LOVE).
Single (12"): released on Virgin, Jul'81 by Virgin Records. Dist: EMI, Virgin Distribution

Single (7"): released on Virgin, Jul'81 by Virgin Records. Dist: EMI, Virgin Distribution

ONLY AFTER DARK.
Single (7"): released on Virgin, May'80 by Virgin Records. Dist: EMI, Virgin Distribution

OPEN YOUR HEART.

SOUND OF THE CROWD.
Single (7"): released on Virgin, Apr'81 by Virgin Records. Dist: EMI, Virgin Distribution

Single (12"): released on Virgin, May'81 by Virgin Records. Dist: EMI, Virgin Distribution

Human Orchestra

HUMAN ORCHESTRA, THE various rhythm quartets (Various Artists).
Album: released on Clanka Lanka, Jun'85 by Mr. R&B Records. Dist: Swift

Human Sexual Response

ANDY FELL.
Single (7"): released on Don't Fall Off The Mountain, Oct'81 by Don't Fall Off The Mountain Records. Dist: Pinnacle, Rough Trade, Nine Mile, Indies

FIGURE 14.
Album: released on Don't Fall Off The Mountain, Feb'81 by Don't Fall Off The Mountain Records. Dist: Pinnacle, Rough Trade, Nine Mile, Indies

GUARDIAN ANGEL.
Single (7"): released on Don't Fall Off The Mountain, Mar'81 by Don't Fall Off The Mountain Records. Dist: Pinnacle, Rough Trade, Nine Mile, Indies

IN A ROMAN MOOD.
Album: released on Don't Fall Off The Mountain, Sep'81 by Don't Fall Off The Mountain Records. Dist: Pinnacle, Rough Trade, Nine Mile, Indies

WHAT DOES SEX MEAN TO ME.
Single (7"): released on Don't Fall Off The Mountain, Jan'81 by Don't Fall Off The Mountain Records. Dist: Pinnacle, Rough Trade, Nine Mile, Indies

Human Switchboard

COFFEE BREAK.
Cassette: released on Reach Out Int, '83

Humblebums

HUMBLEBUMS.
Album: released on Transatlantic, Jun'81 by Transatlantic Records. Dist: IMS-Polygram

Cassette: released on Transatlantic, Jun'81 by Logo Records. Dist: Roots Distribution, RCA Distribution

Humble Pie

BACK HOME AGAIN.
Album: released on Immediate, Jul'76 by Castle Communications. Dist: Cartel

COLLECTION: HUMBLE PIE (CD).
Tracks: / Bang / Natural born boogie / I'll go alone / Buttermilk boy / Desperation / Nitty little number like you / Wrist job / Stick shift / Growing closer / As safe as yesterday / Heartbeat / Down home again / Take me back / Only you can see / Silver tongue / Every mother's son / Sad bag of shakey Jake / Cold lady / Home and away / Light of love.
Compact disc: released on Collector Series, '86 by Castle Communications Records. Dist: PRT, Pinnacle, RCA, Ariola

COLLECTION: HUMBLE PIE.
Double Album: released on Castle Communications, Nov'85 by Castle Communications. Dist: Cartel, Pinnacle, Counterpoint

Double cassette: released on Castle Communications, Nov'85 by Castle Communications. Dist: Cartel, Pinnacle, Counterpoint

EAT IT.
Double Album: released on A&M, '73 by A&M Records. Dist: Polygram

NATURAL BORN BUGIE.
Single (7"): released on Immediate, Feb'83 by Castle Communications. Dist: Cartel

Single (7"): released on Old Gold, Sep'85 by Old Gold Records. Dist: Lightning, Jazz Music, Spartan, Counterpoint

PERFORMANCE - ROCKIN' THE FILMORE.
Album: released on A&M, '74 by A&M Records. Dist: Polygram

Double cassette: released on A&M, '74 by A&M Records. Dist: Polygram

SMOKIN'.
Album: released on A&M, '74 by A&M Records. Dist: Polygram

Humbug

WEARING SUSPENDERS.
Single (7"): released on Castle, Aug'81 by Castle Records. Dist: Pinnacle

Hume, Irene

PRELUDE.
Album: released on Filmtrax, Jun'87 by Filmtrax Records. Dist: EMI

Cassette: released on Filmtrax, Jun'87 by Filmtrax Records. Dist: EMI

Humes, Helen

E-BABA-LE-BA-THE R&B YEARS.
Tracks: / I would if I could / Keep your mind on me / Fortune tellin' man / Suspicious blues / Sad feeling / Rock me to sleep / This love of mine / He may be yours / E-BaBa-Le-Ba / If I could be with you / Ain't gonna quit you baby / Helen's advice / Knockin' myself out / Airplane blues.
Album: released on RCA, Oct'86 by RCA Records. Dist: RCA, Roots, Swift, Wellard, Chris, I & B, Solomon & Peres Distribution

Cassette: released on RCA, Oct'86 by RCA Records. Dist: RCA, Roots, Swift, Wellard, Chris, I & B, Solomon & Peres Distribution

HELEN.
Album: released on Muse (Import), '81

HELEN HUMES.
Album: released on Black Lion, Sep'85 by Black Lion Records. Dist: Jazz Music, Chris Wellard, Taylor, H.R., Counterpoint, Cadillac

HELEN HUMES & THE MUSE ALL STARS.
Album: released on Muse, Apr'81 by Peerless Records. Dist: Lugtons Distributors

LET THE GOOD TIMES ROLL.
Album: released on Black & Blue RCA (France), Nov'85 by RCA Records. Dist: Discovery

SWING WITH.... (Humes, Helen & Wynton Kelly).
Album: released on Contemporary(Import), May'83 Dist: IMS, Polygram

T'AIN'T NOBODY'S BIZ-NESS IF I DO.
Album: released on Contemporary, Mar'87 by Contemporary Records. Dist: Pinnacle

Album: released on Contemporary, Dec'81 by Contemporary Records. Dist: Pinnacle

Hummingbird

HUMMINGBIRD.
Album: released on A&M, '79 by A&M Records. Dist: Polygram

Humpe Humpe

3 OF US.
Single (7"): released on WEA Int, Jun'85

Humperdinck, Engelbert

16 GREATEST LOVE SONGS.
Album: released on Contour, Jul'84 by Pickwick Records. Dist: Pickwick Distribution, PRT

Cassette: released on Contour, Jul'84 by Pickwick Records. Dist: Pickwick Distribution, PRT

CLOSE TO YOU.

Compact disc: released on Chrysalis, '87 by Chrysalis Records. Dist: CRS.

ENGELBERT HUMPERDINCK'S GREATEST HITS.
Tracks: / Release me / Man without love / Way it used to be / Quando quando quando / Everybody knows we're through / There's a kind of hush / There goes my everything / Les bicyclettes de Belsize / I'm a better man for having loved you / Winter world of love / My world / Ten guitars / Am I that easy to forget / Last waltz.
Compact disc: released on London, Feb'87 by London Records. Dist: Polygram

ENGELBERT HUMPERDINCK COLLECTION ,THE.
Album: released on Telstar, Mar'87 by Telstar Records. Dist: RCA Distribution

GETTING SENTIMENTAL.
Album: released on Telstar, Apr'85 by Telstar Records. Dist: RCA Distribution

Cassette: released on Telstar, Apr'85 by Telstar Records. Dist: RCA Distribution

Compact disc: released on Telstar, Jul'85 by Telstar Records. Dist: RCA Distribution

GREATEST HITS:ENGELBERT HUMPERDINCK.
Album: released on Decca, Nov'80 by Decca Records. Dist: Polygram

Cassette: released on Decca, Nov'80 by Decca Records. Dist: Polygram

LAST WALTZ.
Single (7"): released on Old Gold, Oct'83 by Old Gold Records. Dist: Lightning, Jazz Music, Spartan, Counterpoint

Single (7"): released on Decca, Aug'67 by Decca Records. Dist: Polygram

LOVE LETTERS.
Double cassette: released on Decca, Aug'84 by Decca Records. Dist: Polygram

MUSIC FOR THE MILLIONS.
Album: released on Unknown, Apr'83

Cassette: released on Unknown, Apr'83

RELEASE ME.
Album: released on Contour, Sep'81 by Pickwick Records. Dist: Pickwick Distribution, PRT

Cassette: released on Contour, Sep'81 by Pickwick Records. Dist: Pickwick Distribution, PRT

Single (7"): released on Decca, Jan'67 by Decca Records. Dist: Polygram

Single (7"): released on Old Gold, Oct'83 by Old Gold Records. Dist: Lightning, Jazz Music, Spartan, Counterpoint

STAR COLLECTION.
Album: released on Decca (Holland), Mar'85 by Decca Records. Dist: Polygram, IMS

Cassette: released on Decca (Holland), Mar'85 by Decca Records. Dist: Polygram, IMS

TO ALL THE GIRLS I LOVED BEFORE.
Single (7"): released on Warwick, Jun'84 by Multiple Sound Distributors

VERY BEST OF ENGELBERT HUMPERDINCK.
Album: released on MFP, Jan'80 by EMI Records. Dist: EMI

Cassette: released on Decca, Dec'76 by Decca Records. Dist: Polygram

WORLD OF......HE.
Album: released on Arcade Music Gala, Apr'86 Dist: Stage One

Cassette: released on Arcade Music Gala, Apr'86 Dist: Stage One

Humphrey, Bobbi
NOW WAY.
Tracks: / Now way / Now way (Instrumental).
Single (7"): released on Club, Sep'86 by Phonogram Records. Dist: Polygram

Single (12"): released on Club, Sep'86 by Phonogram Records. Dist: Polygram

Humphrey, Percy
PERCY HUMPHREY & HIS CRESCENT CITY JOYMAKERS (Humphrey, Percy & His Crescent City Joymakers).
Notes: Mono recording.
Album: released on GHB, Jun'86 Dist: Jazz Music, Swift

PERCY HUMPHREY'S HOT SIX.
Album: released on CSA, Jan'87 by CSA Records. Dist: PRT, Jetstar

Humphries, Barry
HOUSEWIFE SUPERSTAR.

Album: released on Charisma, Mar'83 by Virgin Records. Dist: EMI

Cassette: released on Charisma, Mar'83 by Virgin Records. Dist: EMI

SOUND OF EDNA,THE.
Album: released on Charisma, Oct'86 by Virgin Records. Dist: EMI

Hunger
STRICTLY FROM HUNGER.
Album: released on Psycho, Sep'83 Dist: Funhouse, Rough Trade

Hunger Project
SAME INSIDE.
Single (7"): released on Latent, Nov'84 Dist: Rough Trade

Hungry For Hits
HUNGRY FOR HITS various artists (Various Artists).
Album: released on K-Tel, May'84 by K-Tel Records. Dist: Record Merchandisers Distribution, Taylors, Terry Blood Distribution, Wynd-Up Distribution, Relay Distribution, Pickwick Distribution, Solomon & Peres Distribution, Polygram

Cassette: released on K-Tel, May'84 by K-Tel Records. Dist: Record Merchandisers Distribution, Taylors, Terry Blood Distribution, Wynd-Up Distribution, Relay Distribution, Pickwick Distribution, Solomon & Peres Distribution, Polygram

Hunniford, Gloria
TASTE OF HUNNI, A.
Album: released on Ritz, Sep'82 by Outlet Records. Dist: Outlet, Prism Leisure Distribution, Record Services Distribution (Ireland), Roots

Cassette: released on Ritz, Sep'82 by Outlet Records. Dist: Outlet, Prism Leisure Distribution, Record Services Distribution (Ireland), Roots

Hunningale, Peter
FOOL FOR YOU (Hunningale, Peter & The Night Flight Band).
Tracks: / Fool for you / Let's get it together.
Single (12"): released on Street Vibes, Dec'86 Dist: Jetstar Distribution

GIVING MYSELF AWAY.
Single (12"): released on Street Vibes, Jun'85 Dist: Jetstar Distribution

GOT TO KNOW YOU.
Single (12"): released on Street Vibes, Aug'84 Dist: Jetstar Distribution

UNTAMED LOVE.
Tracks: / Untamed love / Untamed love (Dub).
Single (7"): released on Cosmic, Sep'86 Dist: DMS, RCA

Single (12"): released on Cosmic, Sep'86 Dist: DMS, RCA

Hunny Yum
DIDDUMS (Hunny Yum & Q.T Bum Fairies).
Single (7"): released on Cat Tracks, Nov'81 Dist: Pinnacle

Huns
GENE VINCENT'S 115TH DREAM.
Album: released on Hits & Corruption, Jul'85 Dist: Rough Trade, Cartel

Hunt, Declan
26 IRISH REPUBLICAN SONGS.
Tracks: / 3rd Wear Cork brigade / James Connolly / Maurice O'Neill / Rising of the moon / Grave of wolfe tone / Signal fires / Sean Tracy / Arbour hill / Foggy dew / Follow me up to Carlow / Boy called Williams, A / Hurrah for the volunteers / Old how th gun / Broad black brimmer / Kevin Barry / Fergal O'Hanlon / Connolly was there / Lay him away on the hillside / Irish volunteers / Rebel heart / Boys of Killmichael / Soldiers of '22 / Valley of knockanure / Old Fenian gun / God save Ireland / West awake, The.
Cassette: released on Derry, Jul'87 by Outlet Records. Dist: Outlet Records

Hunter
DREAMS OF ORDINARY MEN.
Notes: Australian band who toured Europe with Tina Turner.
Album: released on Polydor, Jun'87 by Polydor Records. Dist: Polygram, Polydor

Cassette: released on Polydor, Jun'87 by Polydor Records. Dist: Polygram, Polydor

Compact disc: released on Polydor, Jun'87 by Polydor Records. Dist: Polygram, Polydor

Compact disc: released on Polydor, 20 Jun'87 by Polydor Records. Dist: Polygram, Polydor

DREAMS OF ORDINARY MEN

(SINGLE).
Tracks: / Dreams of ordinary men / Start it up.
Single (7"): released on Polydor, 23 May'87 by Polydor Records. Dist: Polygram, Polydor

Single (12"): released on Polydor, 23 May'87 by Polydor Records. Dist: Polygram, Polydor

Hunter, Alastair
SCOTTISH RAMBLE, A (Hunter, Alastair & The Scottish Dance Band).
Album: released on One Up, May'78 by EMI Records.

Hunter, Alberta
CHICAGO-THE LIVING LEGENDS (Hunter, Alberta & Lovie Austin).
Album: released on Prestige, Jun'84 by Prestige Records (USA). Dist: RCA, JSU, Swift

GLORY OF(THE).
Album: released on CBS(Import), Jun'86 Dist: Conifer, Discovery, Swift

LEGENDARY, THE.
Album: released on DRG (USA), Jul'83 by DRG Records. Dist: Conifer, RCA

Cassette: released on DRG (USA), Jul'83 by DRG Records. Dist: Conifer, RCA

THIRTIES, THE.
Album: released on Stash, Mar'87 Dist: Swift Distribution, Jazz Music Distribution, Jazz Horizons Distribution, Celtic Music Distribution, Cadillac, JSU Distribution, Zodiac Distribution

Hunter, Andy
KING FAREWEEL.
Album: released on Lismor, '84 by Lismor Records. Dist: Lismor, Roots, Celtic Music

Cassette: released on Lismor, '84 by Lismor Records. Dist: Lismor, Roots, Celtic Music

Hunter, Chris
EARLY DAYS.
Album: released on Original, Sep'81 Dist: RCA Distribution, Jazz Music Distribution, PRT Distribution

Hunter, George
BOASTING.
Single (12"): released on Dread At The Controls, Dec'82 Dist: Dub Vendor, Virgin Records, EMI

Hunter, Ian
ALL THE GOOD ONES ARE TAKEN.
Album: released on CBS, Aug'83 by CBS Records. Dist: CBS Deleted '85.

Cassette: released on CBS, Aug'83 by CBS Records. Dist: CBS

SHORT BACK AND SIDES.
Album: released on Chrysalis, Aug'81 by Chrysalis Records. Dist: CBS

WELCOME TO THE CLUB.
Double Album: released on Chrysalis, May'80 by Chrysalis Records. Dist: CBS

YOU'RE NEVER ALONE WITH A SCHIZOIPHRENIC.
Album: released on Chrysalis, May'79 by Chrysalis Records. Dist: CBS

Hunter, Ivory Joe
ARTISTRY OF IVORY JOE HUNTER, THE.
Album: released on Bulldog Records, '82

Hunter, Joe
7TH STREET BOOGIE (Hunter, Ivory Joe).
Album: released on Route 66, Jun'80

THIS IS IVORY JOE (Hunter, Ivory Joe).
Album: released on Ace, Mar'84 by Ace Records. Dist: Pinnacle, Swift, Hotshot, Cadillac

Hunter, John
TRAGEDY.
Single (7"): released on Epic, Jan'85 by CBS Records. Dist: CBS

Hunter, Karen
YOUNG TRADITIONALIST.
Album: released on Lismor, May'83 by Lismor Records. Dist: Lismor, Roots, Celtic Music

Cassette: released on Lismor, May'83 by Lismor Records. Dist: Lismor, Roots, Celtic Music

Hunter, Leeford
SU SU-SU.
Single (7"): released on Small Acts, Oct'84 by Small Acts Records. Dist: Jetstar

---

Hunter, Robert
ROCK COLUMBIA.
Compact disc: by Pacific Records (USA). Dist: Atlantic

Hunters and collectors
CARRY ME.
Single (7"): released on Epic, Aug'84 by CBS Records. Dist: CBS

Single (12"): released on Epic, Aug'84 by CBS Records. Dist: CBS

JAWS OF LIFE.
Album: released on Epic, Sep'84 by CBS Records. Dist: CBS

Cassette: released on Epic, Sep'84 by CBS Records. Dist: CBS

Hunters Club
YOU AIN'T SEEN NOTHING YET.
Tracks: / You ain't seen nothing yet / Trashcan.
Single (7"): released on Trashcan, Apr'87

Hunter, Tab
YOUNG LOVE.
Single (7"): released on Old Gold, Jul'82 by Old Gold Records. Dist: Lightning, Jazz Music, Spartan, Counterpoint

Hunting Lodge
NOMAD LODGE.
Album: released on Side Effects, Jul'85 by SPK Records. Dist: Rough Trade, Cartel

Hunting Of The Shark
HUNTING OF THE SHARK various artists (Various Artists).
Cassette: released on Anvil, Jan'81 Dist: Anvil

Hunting Party
HUNTING PARTY ep.
Single (7"): released on Movement, Sep'85 Dist: Cartel Distribution

Hunting the Bismarck
HUNTING THE BISMARCK Forester, C.S (Andrew , Harry).

Huntington, Eddie
MEET MY FRIEND.
Tracks: / Meet my friend / Meet my friend (instrumental friend) / Meet my friend / Meet my friend (version).
Single (7"): released on Passion, Jul'87 by Skratch Records. Dist: PRT

Single (12"): released on Passion, Jul'87 by Skratch Records. Dist: PRT

Single (7"): released on Passion, Jul'87 by Skratch Records. Dist: PRT

Single (12"): released on Passion, Jul'87 by Skratch Records. Dist: PRT

Hunt, Irvine
TALES OF MANLAFF AND TOEWOMAN.
Album: released on Sweet Folk, May'81 Dist: Roots Distribution

Huntsmen
ROUTE 66.
Album: released on Lucky, Oct'80 by Lucky Records.

Hunt, Tommy
WORK SONG, THE.
Single (7"): released on Kent, Jun'85 by Ace Records. Dist: Pinnacle

YOUR MAN.
Album: released on Kent, Oct'86 by Ace Records. Dist: Pinnacle

Hurley, Armando
MUSIC CHANGE THE WORLD (Hurley, Armando & Friends).
Tracks: / Music change the world / Circus world.
Notes: Proceeds to YMCA anti-drugs campaign.
Single (7"): released on YMCA, Aug'86 by YMCA. Dist: RCA

Single (7"): released on Priority, Jan'86 by Priority Records. Dist: RCA

Hurley, Bill
DOUBLE AGENT.
Album: released on Demon, May'85 by Demon Records. Dist: Pinnacle

RECONSIDER ME.
Single (7"): released on Demon, Jul'85 by Demon Records. Dist: Pinnacle

Hurley, Red

HEY.
Single (7"):

HIT SINGLES.
Album: released on Play, Nov'76 by Play Records. Dist: Spartan

SINCERELY.
Album: released on Harp(Ireland), Jul'80 by Pickwick Records. Dist: Taylors

Cassette: released on Harp(Ireland), Jul'80 by Pickwick Records. Dist: Taylors

Hurley, Steve 'Silk'

JACK YOUR BODY.
Tracks: / Jack your body / Dub your body.
Single (7"): released on London, Jan'87 by London Records. Dist: Polygram

Single (12"): released on London, Jan'87 by London Records. Dist: Polygram

Hurrah!

BOXED.
Album: released on Kitchenware, Nov'85 by Kitchenware Records. Dist: Cartel, CBS, Polygram, RCA-Ariola Distribution

GLORIA.
Single (12"): released on Kitchenware, May'85 by Kitchenware Records. Dist: Cartel, CBS, Polygram, RCA-Ariola Distribution

Single (7"): released on Kitchenware, Feb'85 by Kitchenware Records. Dist: Cartel, CBS, Polygram, RCA-Ariola Distribution

Single (12"): released on Kitchenware, Feb'85 by Kitchenware Records. Dist: Cartel, CBS, Polygram, RCA-Ariola Distribution

HIP-HIP.
Single (7"): released on Kitchenware, Nov'84 by Kitchenware Records. Dist: Cartel, CBS, Polygram, RCA-Ariola Distribution

HOW MANY RIVERS.
Tracks: / How many rivers / Three wishes / If it rains*.
Single (7"): released on Kitchenware, 23 May'87 by Kitchenware Records. Dist: Cartel, CBS, Polygram, RCA-Ariola Distribution

Single (12"): released on Kitchenware, 23 May'87 by Kitchenware Records. Dist: Cartel, CBS, Polygram, RCA-Ariola Distribution

IF I COULD KILL.
Tracks: / If I could kill / Tell me about your problems / Girl of my dreams*.
Single (7"): released on Kitchenware, Dec'86 by Kitchenware Records. Dist: Cartel, CBS, Polygram, RCA-Ariola Distribution

Single (12"): by Kitchenware Records. Dist: Cartel, CBS, Polygram, RCA-Ariola Distribution

SUN SHINES HERE.
Single (7"): released on Kitchenware, Dec'83 by Kitchenware Records. Dist: Cartel, CBS, Polygram, RCA-Ariola Distribution

SWEET SANITY.
Tracks: / Sweet sanity / Heart and hands / Don't need food*.
Single (7"): released on Kitchenware, Feb'87 by Kitchenware Records. Dist: Cartel, CBS, Polygram, RCA-Ariola Distribution

Single (12"): released on Kitchenware, Feb'87 by Kitchenware Records. Dist: Cartel, CBS, Polygram, RCA-Ariola Distribution

TELL GOD I'M HERE.
Tracks: / I would if I could / Better time / Sweet sanity / Celtic / Walk in the park / How many rivers? / If love could kill / Miss this kiss / How high the moon / Mr. Sorrowful.
Album: released on Kitchenware, Feb'87 by Kitchenware Records. Dist: Cartel, CBS, Polygram, RCA-Ariola Distribution

Cassette: released on Kitchenware, Feb'87 by Kitchenware Records. Dist: Cartel, CBS, Polygram, RCA-Ariola Distribution

Compact disc: released on Kitchenware, Feb'87 by Kitchenware Records. Dist: Cartel, CBS, Polygram, RCA-Ariola Distribution

Compact disc: released on Kitchenware, Feb'87 by Kitchenware Records. Dist: Cartel, CBS, Polygram, RCA-Ariola Distribution

Compact disc: released on Kitchenware, '87 by Kitchenware Records. Dist: Cartel, CBS, Polygram, RCA-Ariola Distribution

WHO'D OF THOUGHT.
Single (7"): released on Kitchenware, Oct'84 by Kitchenware Records. Dist: Cartel, CBS, Polygram, RCA-Ariola Distribution

Single (12"): released on Kitchenware, Oct'84 by Kitchenware Records. Dist: Cartel, CBS, Polygram, RCA-Ariola Distribution

Hurray For Hollywood

HURRAY FOR HOLLYWOOD various artists (Various Artists).
Album: released on Astan, Nov'84 by Astan Records. Dist: Counterpoint

Cassette: released on Astan, Nov'84 by Astan Records. Dist: Counterpoint

Hurricane

TAKE WHAT YOU WANT.
Album: released on Roadrunner (Dutch), Jul'86 Dist: Pinnacle

Hurt & Husband

HOLY COW.
Single (7"): released on Mosa, Nov'81 Dist: Pinnacle

Hurt, John

AVALON BLUES (Hurt, John Mississippi).
Album: released on Heritage, Jan'82 by Heritage Records. Dist: Chart

BEST OF (Hurt, John Mississippi).
Double Album: released on Vanguard, '74 by PRT Records. Dist: PRT

Hurt, John Mississippi

SHAKE THAT THING.
Tracks: / Candy man / My creole belle / Make me a pallet on your floor / Shake that thing / I'm satisfied / Salty dog / Nobody's business but mine / Angels laid him away (The) / Casey Jones - talkin' Casey / Baby what's wrong with you / Lonesome blues.
Notes: Legendary blues artist - Unreleased material - Extensive sleeve notes.
Album: released on Blue Moon, Jan'86 Dist: Magnum Music Group Ltd, PRT, Spartan

Husby, Per

DEDICATIONS (Husby, Per Orchestra).
Album: released on Affinity, May'85 by Charly Records. Dist: Charly, Cadillac

Hush

AMERICAN GIRL.
Tracks: / Callin' you / Midnight train / Take it while you can / Don't say goodbye / You really should be swingin' / Winter love / Radio station / Son of an old rock'n'roller / Alright on the night / Singin' the blues / American girl / I do love you.
Single (7"): released on PVK, Oct'85

Album: released on PVK, Feb'87

HEARTS ON FIRE.
Single (7"): released on Spirit, Oct'83 by Spirit Records. Dist: WEA

Single (12"): released on Spirit, Oct'83 by Spirit Records. Dist: WEA

SINGIN' THE BLUES.
Tracks: / Singing the blues / Don't say goodbye / Singin' the blues / Don't say good bye.
Single (7"): released on PVK, Jan'86

SON OF AN OLD ROCK AND ROLLER.
Single (7"): released on Brilliant, Dec'81 by PVK. Dist: Spartan

Husker Du

CANDY APPLE GREY.
Tracks: / Crystal / Don't want to know if you are lonely / I don't know for sure / Sorry somehow / Too far down / Hardly getting over it / Dead set on destruction / Eiffel Tower high / No promise have I made / All this I've done for you.
Album: released on Warner Bros., Apr'86 by Warner Bros Records. Dist: WEA

Cassette: released on Warner Bros., Apr'86 by Warner Bros Records. Dist: WEA

COULD YOU BE THE ONE.
Tracks: / Could you be the one / Everytime.
Single (12"): released on Warner Brothers, Jan'87 by Warner Bros Records. Dist: WEA

DON'T WANT TO KNOW IF YOUR LONELY.
Tracks: / Don't want to know if your lonely / All work no play / Helter skelter.
Single (7"): released on Warner Bros., Feb'86 by Warner Bros Records. Dist: WEA

Single (12"): released on Warner Bros., Feb'86 by Warner Bros Records. Dist: WEA

EIGHT MILES HIGH.
Single (7"): released on SST, Apr'84 by SST Records. Dist: Pinnacle

EVERYTHING FALLS APART.
Album: released on Reflex (USA), Jul'83

FLIP YOUR WIG.
Cassette: released on SST, Apr'86 by SST Records. Dist: Pinnacle

Album: released on SST, Oct'85 by SST Records. Dist: Pinnacle

ICE COLD ICE.
Tracks: / Ie cold ice / Gotta lotta.
Single (7"): released on Warner Bros., 20 Jun'87 by Warner Bros Records. Dist: WEA

Single (12"): released on Warner Bros., 20 Jun'87 by Warner Bros Records. Dist: WEA

MAKES NO SENSE AT ALL.
Single (7"): released on SST, Sep'85 by SST Records. Dist: Pinnacle

METAL CIRCUS.
Tracks: / Metal circus.
Cassette single: released on SST, Mar'86 by SST Records. Dist: Pinnacle
Cat. no: **SST 020 C**
Single (12"): released on SST, Dec'83 by SST Records. Dist: Pinnacle

NEW DAY RISING.
Album: released on SST, Feb'85 by SST Records. Dist: Pinnacle

SORRY SOMEHOW.
Tracks: / Sorry somehow / All this I've done for you / Flexible flyer / Celibated summer.
Single (7"): released on WEA Int, Sep'86

Single (12"): released on WEA Int, Sep'86

WAREHOUSE SONGS AND STORIES.
Tracks: / These important years / Charity, charity, prudence and hope / Standing in the rain / Back from somewhere / Ice cold ice / You're a soldier / Could you be the one / Too much spice / Friend, you've got to fall / She floated away / Bed of nails / Tell you why tomorrow / It's not peculiar / Actual condition / No reservations / Turn it around / She's a woman / Up in the air / You can live at home.
Double Album: released on Warner Brothers, Jan'87 by Warner Bros Records. Dist: WEA

Special: released on Warner Brothers, Jan'87 by Warner Bros Records. Dist: WEA

ZAN ARCADE.
Album: released on SST, Nov'84 by SST Records. Dist: Pinnacle

Husky, Ferlin

FAVOURITES OF....
Album: released on Starday, Apr'87

Cassette: released on Starday, Apr'87

FERLIN HUSKY.
Album: released on MCA, Mar'87 by MCA Records. Dist: Polygram, MCA

Cassette: released on MCA, Mar'87 by MCA Records. Dist: Polygram, MCA

Husky, Tommy

DOUBLE EDGE BLADE.
Album: released on Nevis, Feb'80 Dist: H.R. Taylor

Hussain, Zakir

MAKING MUSIC (Hussain, Zakir & John McLaughlin).
Tracks: / Making music / Zakir / Water girl / Toni / Anisa / Sunjog / You and me / Sabah.
Notes: Personnel: Zakir Hussain - tabla, percussion, voice / Hariprasad Chaurasia - flutes / John McLaughlin - acoustic guitar / Jan Garbarek - tenor and soprano saxophones.
Album: released on ECM (Germany), Jul'87 by ECM Records. Dist: IMS, Polygram, Virgin through EMI

Compact disc: released on ECM (Germany), Jul'87 by ECM Records. Dist: IMS, Polygram, Virgin through EMI

Hussars

CHARGE OF THE LIGHT BRIGADE.
Single (7"): released on RK, Sep'82

Hussey, Winston

GHETTO MAN PROBLEM.
Album: released on Live & Learn, Nov'85 Dist: Jetstar

JOE GRINE LAST NIGHT.
Single (12"): released on Greensleeves, Jun'83 by Greensleeves Records. Dist: BMG, Jetstar, Spartan

Hutch

GOLDEN AGE OF HUTCH (THE).
Tracks: / O kay baby / Don't blame me / Murder in the moonlight / May I have the next romance with you / Remember me / Foggy day, A / Sing my heart / Goodnight my love / It's d'lovely / I wont tell a soul / I'll remember / There goes my dream / Imagination / Nearness of you (The) / Best things in life are free (The) / Room five hundred and four.
Album: released on Golden Age, Sep'86 by Music For Pleasure Records. Dist: EMI

Cassette: released on Golden Age, Sep'86 by Music For Pleasure Records. Dist: EMI

Hutch, Billy

CHANGE OF TIME.
Album: released on Firm, Dec'84 by Firm Records. Dist: Jetstar

Hutcherson, Bobby

COLOUR SCHEMES.
Tracks: / Recorda-me / Bemsha swing / Rosemary, Rosemary / Second-hand brown / Whisper not / Colour scheme / Remember / Never let me go.
Notes: Personnel: Bobby Hutcherson - vibraphone and marimba/Mulgrew Miller - piano/John Heard - bass/Billy Higgins - drums/Airto - percussion. Recorded Berkeley CA 1985. Recommended tracks: 'Recorda-Me' and 'Rosemary, Rosemary'. Bobby Hutcherson has been a major exponent of the vibraphone and marimba for many years. A musician who embraces a broad musical spectrum, showing both respect for the past and present.
Album: released on Fantasy (USA), Jun'86 by Fantasy Inc USA Records. Dist: IMS, Polygram

Cassette: released on Fantasy (USA), Jun'86 by Fantasy Inc USA Records. Dist: IMS, Polygram

DIALOGUE.
Tracks: / Catta / Idle while / Les noirs marchant / Dialogue / Ghetto lights / Jasper / Catta / Idle while / Les Noirs merchant / Dialogue / Ghetto lights / Jasper.
Compact disc: released on Manhattan-Blue Note, Jun'87 by EMI America Records (USA). Dist: EMI

FOUR SEASONS.
Tracks: / I mean you / All of you / Spring is here / Star eyes / If I were a bell / Summertime / Autumn leaves.
Compact disc: released on Timeless (Holland), Jan'87 Dist: JSU Distribution, Jazz Music Distribution, Jazz Horizons Distribution, Cadillac, Celtic Music Distribution

Album: released on Timeless (Holland), Aug'85 Dist: JSU Distribution, Jazz Music Distribution, Jazz Horizons Distribution, Cadillac, Celtic Music Distribution

GOOD BAIT.
Tracks: / Love samba / Good bait / Highway one / Montgomery / Spring is here / Israel.
Compact disc: released on JVC Fantasy (Japan), '86

Album: released on Fantasy (USA), Jun'86 by Fantasy Inc USA Records. Dist: IMS, Polygram
Cat. no: **LLP 501**
Cassette: released on Fantasy (USA), Jun'86 by Fantasy Inc USA Records. Dist: IMS, Polygram

HAPPENINGS.
Tracks: / Aquarian moon / Bouquet / Rojo / Maiden voyage / Head start / When you are near / Omen.
Compact disc: released on Manhattan-Blue Note, May'87 by EMI America Records (USA). Dist: EMI

TOTAL ECLIPSE.
Album: released on Blue Note, Jul'85 by EMI Records. Dist: EMI

Hutchings, Ashley

COMPLEAT DANCING MASTER, THE (Hutchings, Ashley. Et Al).
Tracks: / Beginning of the world, The / Stantipes / Trotto / Nonesuch / Cuckholds all awry / Dashing white sergeant, the / Devil among the tailors, the / Beatrice / Haste to the wedding / Triumph, the / Off she goes / Long odds / Mr.Cosgill's delight / Bonny breast knot / Double lead through / Barley break / Cussion dance / Arbeau and capriol / Hare's maggot, the.
Notes: Re-issue, originally released in 1974. Interpretations of traditional dance tunes, with readings on the subject of dance from Michael Gough, Bernard Hepton, Sarah Badel, Michael Hordern and Alec McCowen from the writings of Chaucer, Dickens, Shakespeare etc. Music by Phillip Picket, John Kirkpatrick, etc.
Album: released on Hannibal, Jan'87 by Hannibal Records. Dist: Charly, Harmonia Mundi, Projection, Celtic Music, Roots

MORRIS ON (Hutchings, Ashley/Thompson/Nicol).
Tracks: / Bean setting / Shooting / I'll go and list for a sailor / Princess royal / Cuckoos nest / Morris off / Morris call / Greensleeves / Nutting girl, The / Old woman tossed up in a blanket / Shepherd's hey / Trunkles / Staines morris / Lads a bunchum / Young Collins / Vandals of Hammerwich / Willow tree.
Notes: Re-issue, originally released 1971. Full list of artists included: Hutchings, Ashley/Thompson/Nicol/Mattacks/Kirkpatrick/Dransfield.
Album: released on Hannibal, Jan'87 by Hannibal Records. Dist: Charly, Harmonia Mundi, Projection, Celtic Music, Roots

Album: released on Island, May'80 by Island Records. Dist: Polygram

Hutchinson, Leslie

HUTCH AT THE PIANO.
Double Album: released on World, Feb'75 Dist: Jetstar

MAGIC OF HUTCH, (THE).
Album: released on Joy, Feb'83 by President Records. Dist: Jazz Music, Swift, President Distribution

MOONLIGHT COCKTAIL.
Album: released on EMI Retrospect, Mar'85 by EMI Records. Dist: EMI

Cassette: released on EMI Retrospect, Mar'85 by EMI Records. Dist: EMI

YOU AND THE NIGHT AND THE MUSIC.
Album: released on Saville, Feb'87 by Conifer Records. Dist: Conifer

Cassette: released on Saville, Feb'87 by Conifer Records. Dist: Conifer

YOU AND THE NIGHT AND THE MUSIC].
Tracks: / She's my secret passion / Out of nowhere / Close your eyes / Life is just a bowl of cherries / Maybe I love you too much / My wishing song / Did you ever see a dream walking? / Close your eyes / That's love / I travel alone / I saw stars / As I sit here / June in January / I only have eyes for you / Blue moon / You and the night and the music / Love is everywhere / Wake / Two tired eyes / Kiss me goodbye.
Album: released on Saville, Feb'87 by Conifer Records. Dist: Conifer

Hutch, Willie

IN AND OUT.
Album: released on Motown, Feb'83 by Motown Records. Dist: BMG Distribution

Cassette: released on Motown, Feb'83 by Motown Records. Dist: BMG Distribution

Single (7"): released on Motown, Nov'82 by Motown Records. Dist: BMG Distribution

Single (12"): released on Motown, Nov'82 by Motown Records. Dist: BMG Distribution

IN TUNE.
Album: released on Whitefield, Feb'79

KEEP ON JAMMIN.
Single (7"): released on Motown, Jun'85 by Motown Records. Dist: BMG Distribution

Single (12"): released on Motown, Jun'85 by Motown Records. Dist: BMG Distribution

MAKING A GAME OUT OF LOVE.
Album: released on Motown, Jul'85 by Motown Records. Dist: BMG Distribution

Cassette: released on Motown, Jul'85 by Motown Records. Dist: BMG Distribution

PARTY DOWN.
Single (7"): released on Motown, Feb'83 by Motown Records. Dist: BMG Distribution

Single (12"): released on Motown, Feb'83 by Motown Records. Dist: BMG Distribution

Hutson, Leroy

PARADISE.
Album: released on Elektra, Nov'82 by WEA Records. Dist: WEA

Hutto, J.B.

BLUES FOR FONESSA.
Album: released on Amugo, Sep'79

BLUESMASTER.
Album: released on JSP, Aug'85 by JSP Records. Dist: Swift, Projection

HAWK SQUAT.
Album: released on Delmark, '74 Dist: Projection, Swift, Cadillac

J.B. HUTTO LIVE: VOL 1.
Album: released on Charly, Apr'80 by Charly Records. Dist: Charly, Cadillac

LIVE AT SANDY'S JAZZ REVIVAL (Hutto, J.B. & The Housebreakers).
Album: released on Baron, Apr'79 Dist: Swift

SLIDESLINGER (Hutto, J.B. & The New Hawks).
Album: released on Rounder (USA), Jan'84 Dist: Mike's Country Music Room Distribution, Jazz Music Distribution, Swift Distribution, Roots Records Distribution, Projection Distribution, Topic Distribution

SLIDEWINDER.
Album: released on Delmark, '74 Dist: Projection, Swift, Cadillac

SLIPPIN' & SLIDIN' (Hutto, J.B. & The New Hawks).
Album: released on Demon, Mar'84 by Demon Records. Dist: Pinnacle

Hutton, Joe

BONNY NORTH TYNE.
Album: Dist: Roots Distribution

JOE HUTTON OF COQUETDALE.
Album: released on MWM, Jun'82 by Mawson & Wareham. Dist: Spartan Distribution, Jazz Music Distribution, JSU Distribution

Cassette: released on MWM, Jun'82 by Mawson & Wareham. Dist: Spartan Distribution, Jazz Music Distribution, JSU Distribution

NORTHUMBRIAN SMALL PIPES.
Album: released on MWM, May'83 by Mawson & Wareham. Dist: Spartan Distribution, Jazz Music Distribution, JSU Distribution

Hutton, June

AFTERGLOW (Hutton, June & The Boys Next Door).
Tracks: / Never in a million years / Gone with the wind / Until the real thing comes along / I should care / It's the talk of the town / You're getting to be a habit with me / Day by day / East of the sun (west of the moon) / Taking a chance on love / I hadn't anyone till you / My baby just cares for me / Dream a little dream of me.
Notes: This album, much sought after by collectors, has also received noticeable airplay over the years on Alan Dell's BBC Radio 2 programme. Never previously available in the UK as a 12" album, it has only ever graced the British record shelf once before as an abridged 10" version during the 50's. June Hutton, ex- singer with the popular 50's group, the Pied Pipers, is here teamed with arranger/conductor husband, Axel Stordahl, noted for his work with Sinatra during the 40's, to bring a collection of classic love songs.
Album: released on Capitol, Feb'87 by Capitol Records. Dist: EMI

Cassette: released on Capitol, Feb'87 by Capitol Records. Dist: EMI

Huxley, Craig

GENESIS PROJECT.
Compact disc: released on Sonic Atmospheres, '86 Dist: Target

IN A CHORD (Huxley, Craig & Georgia Kelly).
Notes: See also under Georgia Kelly
Compact disc: released on Sonic Atmospheres, '86 Dist: Target

Huygen, Michel

CAPTURING HOLOGRAMS.
Album: released on Jive Electro, Sep'84 by Zomba Records. Dist: RCA

Cassette: released on Jive Electro, Sep'84 by Zomba Records. Dist: RCA

Hybrid Kids

CLAWS.
Album: released on Cherry Red, '82 by Cherry Red Records. Dist: Pinnacle

COLLECTION OF CLASSIC MUTANTS.
Album: released on Cherry Red, Jan'80 by Cherry Red Records. Dist: Pinnacle

DO YOU THINK I'M SEXY?.
Single (7"): released on Cherry Red, Mar'82 by Cherry Red Records. Dist: Pinnacle

HAPPY XMAS WAR IS OVER.
Single (7"): released on Cherry Red, Dec'80 by Cherry Red Records. Dist: Pinnacle

Hyde, Alex

ALEX HYDE VOLUME 1 - 1924 Doowacka-doo from Germany.
Album: released on Harlequin, Nov'85 by Harlequin Records. Dist: Swift, Jazz Music, Wellard, Chris, IRS, Taylor, H.R.

ALEX HYDE VOLUME 2 - 1925 Jazz and hot dance from Germany.
Album: released on Harlequin, Nov'85 by Harlequin Records. Dist: Swift, Jazz Music, Wellard, Chris, IRS, Taylor, H.R.

Hyde Park After Dark

HYDE PARK AFTER DARK Various artists (Various Artists).
Album: released on Beehive (USA), Apr'84 by Cadillac Records. Dist: JSU

Hyde, Pat

MELANCHOLY BABY.
Single (7"): released on Zodiac, Feb'81 Dist: Jazz Music

Hyde, Paul

HERE'S THE WORLD FOR YA (Hyde, Paul & The Payolas).
Single (7"): released on A&M, May'85 by A&M Records. Dist: Polygram

Hydravian

HYDRAVION.
Album: released on Cobra, May'79 by Cobra Records. Dist: Projection, EMI

Hykes, David

CURRENT CIRCULATION (Hykes, David & The Harmonic Choir).
Album: released on Celestial Harmonies, Feb'85 by TM Records. Dist: PRT

HARMONIC MEETINGS (Hykes, David & The Harmonic Choir).
Double Album: released on Celestial Harmonies, Jul'87 by TM Records. Dist: PRT

Hyland, Brian

ITSY BITSY TEENY WEENY YELLOW POLKA DOT BIKINI.
Tracks: / Itsy bitsy teeny weeny yellow polka dot bikini / Susie darlin'.
Single (7"): released on Old Gold, Apr'86 by Old Gold Records. Dist: Lightning, Jazz Music, Spartan, Counterpoint

JOKER WENT WILD.
Single (7"): released on Neil Rushden (Import), Mar'83

SEALED WITH A KISS.
Single (7"): released on Old Gold, Jul'82 by Old Gold Records. Dist: Lightning, Jazz Music, Spartan, Counterpoint

Hylton, Jack

BANDS THAT MATTER.
Album: released on Eclipse, '70 by Decca Records. Dist: Polygram

BAND THAT JACK BUILT.
Album: released on World, '73 Dist: Jetstar

BREAKAWAY (Hylton, Jack & His Orchestra).
Album: released on Joy, Nov'82 by President Records. Dist: Jazz Music, Swift, President Distribution

GOLDEN AGE OF JACK HYLTON, (THE).
Album: released on Golden Age, Jul'84 by Music For Pleasure Records. Dist: EMI

Cassette: released on Golden Age, Jul'84 by Music For Pleasure Records. Dist: EMI

GOOD NEWS (Hylton, Jack & His Orchestra).
Album: Dist: Polygram

I'M IN A DANCING MOOD (Hylton, Jack & His Orchestra).
Tracks: / I'll never say "never again" again / She's a latin from Manhatten / About a quarter to nine / Rose room / I'm in a dancing mood / At the balalaika / Boo-hoo / September in the rain / Love live and rule my heart / Girls were made to love and kiss / Nice people / You must have been a beautiful baby / Jeepers creepers / Beer barrel polka / My prayer / Day in, day out / So deep is the night / Roadhouse revels / Rosita / Let the people sing.
Notes: A brand new 20 track compilation from Jack Hylton & His Orchestra, one of the pioneers of British dance music. This selection taken from the period between 1935 and 1940, demonstrates the talent of Jack Hylton through varied tempos and well known dance tunes. Contains classic tracks such as: 'Beer Barrel Polka', 'Jeepers Creepers', 'You Must Have Been A Beautiful Baby', 'September In The Rain' and many more.
Album: released on EMI Retrospect, Mar'86 by EMI Records. Dist: EMI

Cassette: released on EMI Retrospect, Mar'86 by EMI Records. Dist: EMI

JACK HYLTON.
Album: released on World, '70 Dist: Jetstar

JACK HYLTON & HIS ORCHESTRA: VOL 2 (Hylton, Jack & His Orchestra).
Album: released on Monmouth, Mar'79

JACK HYLTON & HIS ORCHESTRA: VOL 1 (Hylton, Jack & His Orchestra).
Album: released on Monmouth, Mar'79

JACK HYLTON & HIS ORCHESTRA (Hylton, Jack & His Orchestra).
Album: released on Jasmine, Mar'83 by Jasmine Records. Dist: Counterpoint, Lugtons, Taylor, H.R., Wellard, Chris, Swift, Cadillac

Album: released on Ace Of Clubs, '66 by Decca Records. Dist: Polygram

JACK'S BACK (Hylton, Jack & His Orchestra).
Album: released on ASV Living Era, Nov'82 by ASV Records. Dist: PRT

Cassette: released on ASV Living Era, Nov'82 by ASV Records. Dist: PRT

LOVABLE & SWEET.
Album: released on Old Bean, Feb'85 Dist: Jazz Music

PLYS DE SYLVA, BROWN & HENDERSON.
Album: released on World, Nov'74 Dist: Jetstar

SWING (Hylton, Jack & His Orchestra).
Album: released on Saville, Jul'83 by Conifer Records. Dist: Conifer

TALK OF THE TOWN.
Cassette: released on Saville, Jan'86 by Conifer Records. Dist: Conifer

Album: released on Saville, Jan'84 by Conifer Records. Dist: Conifer

TALK OF THE TOWN (Hylton, Jack & His Orchestra).

Hylton, Sheila

FALLING IN LOVE.
Single (7"): released on Sunset, Dec'83 Dist: EMI

LET'S DANCE.
Single (12"): released on Sunset, Jul'83 Dist: EMI

LOVE DON'T LIVE HERE ANYMORE.
Single (12"): released on Kerry Blue, Mar'82

Hyman, Dick

DICK HYMAN & HIS TRIO (Hyman, Dick & His Trio).
Album: released on Grape-Vine, Mar'79 Dist: RCA, Swift

DICK HYMAN PIANO SOLOS.
Album: released on Monmouth, Mar'79

SAY IT WITH MUSIC (Hyman, Dick & The Perfect Jazz Repertory Company).
Album: released on World Jazz, May'81 by World Jazz Records. Dist: World Jazz, JSU, Jazz Music

Hyman, Phyllis

BEST OF PHYLLIS HYMAN.
Album: released on Arista, Sep'86 by Arista Records. Dist: RCA

Cassette: released on Arista, Sep'86 by Arista Records. Dist: RCA

GODDESS OF LOVE.
Album: released on Arista, Jun'83 by Arista Records. Dist: RCA

Cassette: released on Arista, Jun'83 by Arista Records. Dist: RCA

LIVING ALL ALONE.
Tracks: / Living all alone / First time together / If you want me / Slow dancin' / Old friend / You just don't know / Ain't you had enough love / Screaming at the moon / What you won't do for love.
Notes: Executive producers Kenneth Gamble, Leon A Huff and Thom Bell. Original sound recording made by Assorted Music Inc.
Album: released on PIR, Aug'86

Cassette: released on PIR, Aug'86

SCREAMIN' AT THE MOON.
Tracks: / Screamin' at the moon / Ain't you had enough.
Single (7"): released on Philadelphia International, Mar'87 by CBS Records. Dist: CBS

Single (12"): released on Philadelphia International, Mar'87 by CBS Records. Dist: CBS

SCREAMING AT THE MOON (EXT REMIX).
Tracks: / Screaming at the moon (ext remix) / Screaming at the moon / Ain't you had enough love / Ain't you had enough love (ext) / Ain't you had enough love (percussapella version).
Special: released on Philadelphia International, Apr'87 by CBS Records. Dist: CBS

YOU KNOW HOW TO LOVE ME.
Tracks: / You know how to love me / We should be lovers / Riding the tiger.
Single (7"): released on Arista, Aug'86 by Arista Records. Dist: RCA

Single (12"): released on Arista, Aug'86 by Arista Records. Dist: RCA

Album: released on Arista, Mar'80 by Arista Records. Dist: RCA

Hymns...

HYMNS FOR ALL SEASONS Volume 1 (Various Artists).
Tracks: / When morning gilds the skies / Praise my soul, the King of Heaven / Rejoice, the Lord is King / Great is thy faithfulness / God of Abraham praise (The) / O love that will not let me go / Jesus shall reign.
Album: released on Word, Apr'86 by Word Records. Dist: Word Distribution, CBS

HYMNS OF PRAISE STRINGS Various artists (Various Artists).
Album: released on Marantha Music, May'82
Cat. no: **MM 0085**
Cassette: released on Marantha Music, May'82

HYMNS TRIUMPHANT various artists (Various Artists).
Album: released on Warwick, Nov'85 Dist: Multiple Sound Distributors

Cassette: released on Warwick, Nov'85 Dist: Multiple Sound Distributors

HYMNS TRIUMPHANT, 2 Various artists (Various Artists).
Album: released on Birdwing, Jan'85 by Word Records. Dist: Word Distribution

Cassette: released on Birdwing, Jan'85 by Word Records. Dist: Word Distribution

Compact disc: released on Birdwing, Jan'85 by Word Records, Dist: Word Distribution

HYMNS TRIUMPHANT VOLUME 2 (Various Artists).
Compact disc: by Word Records. Dist: Word Distribution, CBS

Hynes, Des
MUSIC FOR IRISH DANCING.

Tracks: / Miss McCloud's reel / Sally Gardens / Humour of Bandon / Rocky road to Dublin / Off she goes / Queen of the fair / Sunshine hornpipe / St Patrick's day / Blackbird (The) / Job of journeywork / Garden of daises.
Album: released on Accordion Record Club, Jul'86 by Accordion Record Club Records. Dist: Accordion Record Club

Cassette: released on Accordion Record Club, Jul'86 by Accordion Record Club Records. Dist: Accordion Record Club

Hypertension
CAN YOU FEEL IT?.
Single (7"): released on ERC, Oct'82 by ERC Records. Dist: PRT

Single (12"): released on ERC, Oct'82 by ERC Records. Dist: PRT

Hypnomatics
PERFECT STRANGER.
Single (7"): released on Cryptic, Jul'85 Dist: Red Rhino Through Cartel Distributions

Single (12"): released on Cryptic, Jul'85 Dist: Red Rhino Through Cartel Distributions

Hypocrite inna...
HYPOCRITE INNA DANCE HALL STYLE Various artists (Various Artists).
Album: released on Empire, Oct'84 by Empire Records. Dist: Backs, Cartel, Jetstar

Hypothetical Prophets
AROUND THE WORLD WITH THE PROPHETS.
Album: released on Epic, Jun'83 by CBS Records. Dist: CBS

Cassette: released on Epic, Jun'83 by CBS Records. Dist: CBS

Album: released on Hypothetical, Nov'82 by Initial Records. Dist: Pinnacle

PERSON TO PERSON.
Single (7"): released on Epic, Apr'83 by CBS Records. Dist: CBS

Single (12"): released on Epic, Apr'83 by CBS Records. Dist: CBS

WALLENBERG.
Single (12"): released on Hypothetical, Apr'82 by Initial Records. Dist: Pinnacle

Hysteria
BEHIND THE VEIL.
Single (12"): released on Sculpture, Oct'84 Dist: Revolver, Cartel

Hysterics
FIVE TRACKS OF LAUGHTER.
Single (7"): released on KA, Nov'82

HYSTERICS.
Album: released on KA, Oct'82

Cassette: released on KA, Oct'82

I

IAI Festival
IAI FESTIVAL various artists (Various Artists).
Album: released on Improvising Artists, '78 Dist: Swift

I Am
I AM II various artists (Various Artists).
Album: released on Maranatha!, Jun'85 Dist: Kingsway Music, Pilgrim, Word Distribution

Cassette: released on Maranatha!, Jun'85 Dist: Kingsway Music, Pilgrim, Word Distribution

I Am Slam
I AM SIAM.
Album: released on CBS, Mar'85 by CBS Records. Dist: CBS

Cassette: released on CBS, Mar'85 by CBS Records. Dist: CBS

TALK TO ME (I CAN HEAR YOU KNOW).
Single (7"): released on CBS, Jan'85 by CBS Records. Dist: CBS

Single (12"): released on CBS, Jan'85 by CBS Records. Dist: CBS

I Am The Doorway
I AM THE DOORWAY King, Stephen (Bishop, Ed.).
Cassette: released on Pickwick Talking Books, '83

I Am Woman
I AM WOMAN various artists (Various original artists).

Ian, Janis
BEST OF...,THE.
Album: released on CBS, Dec'80 by CBS Records. Dist: CBS

Cassette: released on CBS, Dec'80 by CBS Records. Dist: CBS

BETWEEN THE LINES.
Album: released on CBS, Jun'76 by CBS Records. Dist: CBS

Cassette: released on CBS, Jun'76 by CBS Records. Dist: CBS

JANIS IAN.
Album: released on CBS, Sep'78 by CBS Records. Dist: CBS

Cassette: released on CBS, Sep'78 by CBS Records. Dist: CBS

MIRACLE ROW.
Album: released on CBS, Mar'77 by CBS Records. Dist: CBS

Cassette: by CBS Records. Dist: CBS

NIGHT RAINS.
Album: released on CBS, Mar'83 by CBS Records. Dist: CBS

Cassette: released on CBS, Mar'83 by CBS Records. Dist: CBS

REMEMBER YESTERDAY, I.
Single (7"): released on CBS, Oct'81 by CBS Records. Dist: CBS

Ian & Margaret
THAT'S LIFE.

Album: released on Joy, '74 by President Records. Dist: Jazz Music, Swift, President Distribution

Ian's Blue Van
PASS THE PEAS.
Single (7"): released on Buypheu, Sep'84 by Fast Forward Records. Dist: Cartel

Ian & the Muscletones
HUMAN SACRIFICE.
Album: released on Appaloosa, Feb'81 Dist: Roots, Folksound, JSU, Projection, Celtic Music, Chris Wellard

Ibanez, Paco
LOS UNOS POR LOS OTROS.
Album: released on Polydor, Jul'76 by Polydor Records. Dist: Polygram, Polydor

PACO IBANEZ' POETRY AND MUSIC.
Album: released on Polydor, Jun'76 by Polydor Records. Dist: Polygram, Polydor

I Believe
I BELIEVE 20 All time gospel greats (Various Artists).
Album: released on Creole, Nov'83 by Creole Records. Dist: Rhino, PPT

I Benjaman
FRACTION OF JAH ACTION.
Album: released on Lipp, Nov'83 by Lipp Records. Dist: PRT, Lipp

GIVE LOVE A TRY.
Single (12"): released on Lion Kingdom, Jul'82 by Lion Kingdom Records. Dist: Jetstar, Pinnacle

JAH WORLD WILL KEEP ON TURNING
(I Benjaman & Michelle Harrison).
Single (12"): released on Lion Kingdom, Jan'83 by Lion Kingdom Records. Dist: Jetstar, Pinnacle

Ibrahim, Abdullah
DUKES' MEMORIES (Ibrahim, Abdullah & Dollar Brand).
Notes: See also under Dollar Brand.
Compact disc: released on Black & Blue (France), '86 Dist: Swift, Target, Discovery

WATER FROM AN ANCIENT WELL
(Ibrahim, Abdullah & Ekaya).
Tracks: / Mandela / Song for Sathima / Manenberg revisited / Tuang Guru / Water from an ancient well / Wedding, The / Mountain, The / Sameeda.
Compact disc: released on Blackhawk, Mar'87 by Blackhawk Records (USA). Dist: IMS-Polygram

Ibsen, Henrik
AN ENEMY OF THE PEOPLE.
Album: released on Caedmon(USA), '74 by Caedmon (USA) Records. Dist: Gower, Taylors, Discovery

Cassette: released on Caedmon(USA), '74 by Caedmon (USA) Records. Dist: Gower, Taylors, Discovery

I can count
I CAN COUNT Various artists (Various Artists).
Cassette: released on Invicta, Jul'84 by Audio-Visual Productions. Dist: Spartan

I Can Crawl
DESERT.
Album: released on Hybrid, Oct'86 by Statik Records. Dist: Pinnacle

HIT THE MISTY MOUNTAIN.
Single (12"): released on Zinger, Jul'87 by Zinger Records. Dist: Pinnacle

Icarus
STATE OF MIND.
Album: released on Russian Roulette, Sep'84 by Leo. Dist: Impetus Distribution

I Catch
MY DARLIN, I.
Single (7"): released on Excellent, Jun'85 by

Survival Records. Dist: Pinnacle

Single (12"): released on Excellent, Jun'85 by Survival Records. Dist: Pinnacle

Icebreakers...
PLANET MARS DUB (Icebreakers With The Diamonds).
Album: released on Frontline (USA), Jun'78 by Calvary Records Inc. (USA). Dist: EMI

Ice Club
DANCE.
Single (7"): released on Lost Moments, Mar'85 Dist: Backs, Cartel

Single (12"): released on Lost Moments, Mar'85 Dist: Backs, Cartel

Ice Dance Orchestra
ICE DANCE.
Double Album: released on Avon, Jul'86 by Avon Records. Dist: Counterpoint

Double cassette: released on Avon, Jul'86 by Avon Records. Dist: Counterpoint

Icehouse
CRAZY.
Tracks: / Crazy / Completely gone.
Single (7"): released on Chrysalis, Jul'87 by Chrysalis Records. Dist: CBS

Single (12"): released on Chrysalis, Jul'87 by Chrysalis Records. Dist: CBS

DON'T BELIEVE ANY MORE.
Single (7"): released on Chrysalis, Jun'84 by Chrysalis Records. Dist: CBS

Cassette: released on Chrysalis, Jun'84 by Chrysalis Records. Dist: CBS

HEY LITTLE GIRL.
Single (7"): released on Chrysalis, Jan'83 by Chrysalis Records. Dist: CBS

Single (12"): released on Chrysalis, Jan'83 by Chrysalis Records. Dist: CBS

ICEHOUSE.
Album: released on Chrysalis, Jun'81 by Chrysalis Records. Dist: CBS

Cassette: released on Chrysalis, Jun'81 by Chrysalis Records. Dist: CBS

Single (7"): released on Chrysalis, Jan'82 by Chrysalis Records. Dist: CBS Deleted '83.

Cassette: released on Chrysalis, Jan'82 by Chrysalis Records. Dist: CBS

LIVE IN MOTION.
Tracks: / Uniform / Street cafe / Hey little girl / Glam / Trojan blue / Great southern land / Love in motion / Mysterious thing / One by one / Goodnight Mr Matthews.
Compact disc: released on Chrysalis, Jan'86 by Chrysalis Records. Dist: CBS

MEASURE FOR MEASURE.
Tracks: / No promises / Cross the border / Spanish gold / Paradise / Flame, The / Regular boys / Mr Big.
Album: released on Chrysalis, May'86 by Chrysalis Records. Dist: CBS

Cassette: released on Chrysalis, May'86 by Chrysalis Records. Dist: CBS

NO PROMISES.
Tracks: / No promises / Perfect crime (The).
Single (7"): released on Chrysalis, Feb'86 by Chrysalis Records. Dist: CBS

Single (12"): released on Chrysalis, Feb'86 by Chrysalis Records. Dist: CBS

Compact disc: released on Carrere, Apr'87 by Carrere Records. Dist: PRT, Spartan

PARADISE.
Tracks: / Paradise / Baby you're so strange /

Hey little girl.
Single (7"): released on Chrysalis, Aug'86 by Chrysalis Records. Dist: CBS

Single (12"): released on Chrysalis, Aug'86 by Chrysalis Records. Dist: CBS

PRIMATIVE MAN.
Album: released on Chrysalis, Sep'82 by Chrysalis Records. Dist: CBS

Cassette: released on Chrysalis, Sep'82 by Chrysalis Records. Dist: CBS

SIDEWALK.
Tracks: / Take the town / This time / Someone like you / Stay close / Tonight / Don't believe anymore.
Notes: Digital stereo
Compact disc: released on Chrysalis, Oct'84 by Chrysalis Records. Dist: CBS

Album: released on Chrysalis, Jun'84 by Chrysalis Records. Dist: CBS

Cassette: released on Chrysalis, Jun'84 by Chrysalis Records. Dist: CBS

Compact disc: released on Chrysalis, Jun'84 by Chrysalis Records. Dist: CBS

STREET CAFE.
Single (7"): released on Chrysalis, Apr'83 by Chrysalis Records. Dist: CBS Deleted '84.

Cassette: released on Chrysalis, Apr'83 by Chrysalis Records. Dist: CBS

TAKING THE TOWN.
Single (7"): released on Chrysalis, Apr'84 by Chrysalis Records. Dist: CBS

Cassette: released on Chrysalis, Apr'84 by Chrysalis Records. Dist: CBS

Iceland
FOLK SONGS OF ICELAND.
Album: released on Lyrichord (USA), Oct'81 by Lyrichord Records (USA). Dist: Flexitron Distributors Ltd

Iceni Childrens...
NURSERY RHYME TIME (Iceni Childrens Choir).
Album: released on Victor, Oct'74

Ice Nine
ANOTHER LOVE AFFAIR.
Single (7"): released on Clockwork, Jan'84 by Clockwork Records. Dist: Stage One

I'cess
LOOK PON SHE.
Single (7"): released on Uptempo, Nov'84 by Uptempo Records. Dist: Jetstar Distribution

Ice-T
MAKE IT FUNKY.
Tracks: / Make it funky / Sex.
Single (7"): released on Sire, Jul'87

Single (12"): released on Sire. Jul'87

RHYME PAYS.
Tracks: / Intro*/Rhyme pays / 6'n the mornin' / Make it funky / Somebody gotta do it (pimpin' ain't easy!!!) / 409 / I love ladies / Sex / Pain / Squeeze the trigger.
Album: released on Sire, Jul'87

Cassette: released on Sire, Jul'87

Album: released on Sire, Aug'87

Cassette: released on Sire, Aug'87

Ice The Falling Rain
LIFE'S ILLUSION 2 parts.
Single (7"): released on Future, Nov'83 Dist: Pinnacle

Ice Time

ICE TIME various artists (Various Artists).
Album: released on BBC '78 by BBC Records & Tapes. Dist: EMI, PRT,

Cassette: released on BBC, '78 by BBC Records & Tapes. Dist: EMI, PRT,

Icicle Works

ALL THE DAUGHTERS.
Single (7"): released on Beggars Banquet, May'85 by Beggars Banquet Records. Dist: WEA

Single (12"): released on Beggars Banquet, May'85 by Beggars Banquet Records. Dist: WEA

BIRDS FLY WHISPER TO A SCREAM.
Single (7"): released on Situation 2, Jun'83 Dist: Cartel, Pinnacle Deleted '87.

Single (12"): released on Situation 2, Jun'83 Dist: Cartel, Pinnacle

Single (12"): by WEA Records. Dist: WEA

Single (12"): released on Beggars Banquet, Aug'84 by Beggars Banquet Records. Dist: WEA

EVANGELINE.
Tracks: / Evangeline / Everybody loves to play the fool / Waiting in the wings.
Single (7"): released on Beggars Banquet, Jan'87 by Beggars Banquet Records. Dist: WEA

Single (12"): released on Beggars Banquet, Jan'87 by Beggars Banquet Records. Dist: WEA

HOLLOW HORSE.
Single (7"): released on Beggars Banquet, Sep'84 by Beggars Banquet Records. Dist: WEA

Single (12"): released on Beggars Banquet, Sep'84 by Beggars Banquet Records. Dist: WEA Deleted '87.

ICICLE WORKS, THE.
Tracks: / Reap the rich harvest.
Album: released on Beggars Banquet, Mar'84 by Beggars Banquet Records. Dist: WEA

Cassette: released on Beggars Banquet, Mar'84 by Beggars Banquet Records. Dist: WEA

ICICLE WORKS, THE.
Tracks: / Chop the tree / Love is a wonderful colour / As the dragonfly flies / Lover's day / In the cauldron of love / Out of season / Factory in the desert / Birds fly / Nirvana.
Album: released on Beggars Banquet, Jul'86 by Beggars Banquet Records. Dist: WEA

Cassette: released on Beggars Banquet, Jul'86 by Beggars Banquet Records. Dist: WEA

Compact disc: released on Beggars Banquet, Jul'86 by Beggars Banquet Records. Dist: WEA

IF YOU WANT TO DEFEAT THE ENEMY SING HIS SONG.
Tracks: / Hope springs eternal / Travelling chest / Sweet Thursday / Up here in the north of England / Who do you want for your love / When you were mine / Evangeline / Truck driver's lament / Understanding Jane / Walking with a mountain / Please don't let it rain on my parade * / Everybody loves to play the fool / I never saw my hometown 'till I went around the world / Into the mystic.
Compact disc: released on Beggars Banquet, Apr'87 by Beggars Banquet Records. Dist: WEA

Album: released on Beggars Banquet, Apr'87 by Beggars Banquet Records. Dist: WEA

Album: released on Beggars Banquet, Apr'87 by Beggars Banquet Records. Dist: WEA

LOVE IS A WONDERFUL COLOUR.
Picture disc single: released on Beggars Banquet, Aug'84 by Beggars Banquet Records. Dist: WEA

Single (7"): released on Beggars Banquet, Nov'83 by Beggars Banquet Records. Dist: WEA

Single (12"): released on Beggars Banquet, Nov'83 by Beggars Banquet Records. Dist: WEA

NIRVANA.
Single (7"): released on Troll Kitchen, Oct'82

SEVEN HORSES.
Double-pack single: released on Beggars Banquet, Jun'85 by Beggars Banquet Records. Dist: WEA

Single (12"): released on Beggars Banquet, Jun'85 by Beggars Banquet Records. Dist: WEA

SEVEN SINGLES DEEP.
Tracks: / Hollow horse / Love is a wonderful colour / Birds fly / All the daughters / When it all comes down / Seven horses / Rapids.
Album: released on Beggars Banquet, Mar'86 by Beggars Banquet Records. Dist: WEA

Cassette: released on Beggars Banquet, Mar'86 by Beggars Banquet Records. Dist: WEA

Compact disc: released on Beggars Banquet, Mar'86 by Beggars Banquet Records. Dist: WEA

SMALL PRICE OF A BICYCLE, THE.

UNDERSTANDING JANE.
Tracks: / Understanding Jane / I never saw my home town 'till I went around the world / Seven horses - live / Perambulator - live / Rapids - live.
Cassette: released on Beggars Banquet, Jul'86 by Beggars Banquet Records. Dist: WEA

UP HERE IN THE NORTH OF ENGLAND.
Tracks: / Up here in the north of England / Sea songs / Nature's way / It makes no difference / Way laid.
Single (12"): released on Situation 2, Dec'86 Dist: Cartel, Pinnacle

WHEN IT ALL COMES DOWN.
Single (7"): released on Beggars Banquet, Oct'85 by Beggars Banquet Records. Dist: WEA

Single (12"): released on Beggars Banquet, Oct'85 by Beggars Banquet Records. Dist: WEA

WHO DO YOU WANT FOR YOUR LOVE.
Tracks: / Who do you want for your love / Understanding Jane - live / Should I stay or should I go / Roadhouse blues.
Single (7"): released on Beggars Banquet, Sep'86 by Beggars Banquet Records. Dist: WEA

Single (12"): released on Beggars Banquet, Sep'86 by Beggars Banquet Records. Dist: WEA

Cassette: released on Beggars Banquet, Sep'86 by Beggars Banquet Records. Dist: WEA

Icons

$ + 3.
Tracks: / Lots of money / Priveledge and easy / Walk / Nothin' left to save.
Album: released on Press, Jun'86 by Press Records.

ART IN THE DARK.
Tracks: / Number / Lots of money / Trouble in Havana / Nothin' left to save / Try / Tonight - there's a sign / Girl is mine (The) / Chains / Privilege and easy / Privelege and easy.
Album: released on Press, Jul'86 by Press Records.

Cassette: released on Press, Jul'86 by Press Records.

LOTS OF MONEY.
Tracks: / Walk / Nothin' left to save.
Single (12"): released on Press, Jul'86 by Press Records.

Icons of Filth

BRAIN DEATH ep.
Extended-play record: released on Mortarhate, Mar'85 by Dorane Ltd.

FILTH AND THE FURY, THE.
Single (7"): released on Mordam, Sep'85 Dist: Rough Trade Distribution

FILTH & THE FURY, THE.
Single (7"): released on Mortarhate, Feb'86 by Dorane Ltd.

ONWARD CHRISTIAN SOLDIERS.
Album: released on Motette, Mar'84 Dist:

ICQ

FLIGHT OF VENDOHAIR.
Single (12"): released on Unsquare, Jul'84 by Unsquare Records. Dist: Gipsy

Ideal

DER ERNST DES LEBENS.

SERIOUSNESS OF LIFE, THE.
Album: released on WEA, Jun'82 by WEA Records. Dist: WEA

Ideal Band

MEASURE OF FREEDOM, A.
: released on L.I.S.Records, '84

Ideal Giants

ALPHIBIAN CULT E.P. (Ideal Giants & Fabulous Salamander).
Tracks: / Civillian.
Single (7"): released on Amphibian, Sep'86 by Red Rhino Records. Dist: Cartel Red Rhino

Single (7"): released on Revolver, Mar'86 by Revolver Records. Dist: Revolver, Cartel

Ideal Guest House

IDEAL GUEST HOUSE various artists (Various Artists).
Cassette: released on Shelter, Oct'86

Idee Fixe

EASY MADONNA.
Single (7"): released on Button, Jul'84 by Musical Characters Records. Dist: Spartan

Identity Crisis

ELOISE.
Single (7"): released on FMR, Sep'82 Dist: Spartan

Ides Of March

ON THE FACE.
Tracks: / On the face.
Single (12"): released on RS, Dec'86 Dist: Revolver Distribution, Cartel Distribution

I Didn't Give A Damn...

I DIDN'T GIVE A DAMN IF WHITES BOUGHT IT,VOL.1 various artists (Various Artists).
Album: released on Red Lightnin', Oct'84 by Red Lightnin' Records. Dist: Roots, Swift, Jazz Music, Pinnacle, Cartel, Wynd-Up Distribution

I DIDN'T GIVE A DAMN IF WHITES BOUGHT IT,VOL.2 various artists (Various Artists).
Album: released on Red Lightnin', Oct'84 by Red Lightnin' Records. Dist: Roots, Swift, Jazz Music, Pinnacle, Cartel, Wynd-Up Distribution

I DIDN'T GIVE A DAMN IF WHITES BOUGHT IT, VOL.4 various artists (Various Artists).

I DIDN'T GIVE A DAMN IF WHITES BOUGHT IT,VOL.5 various artists (Various Artists).

I DIDN'T GIVE A DAMN IF WHITES BOUGHT IT, VOL.2 various artists (Various Artists).

Idle Eyes

TOKYO ROSE.
Tracks: / Unform.
Single (7"): released on WEA, Jan'86 by WEA Records. Dist: WEA

Idle Race

LIGHT AT THE END OF THE ROAD.
Tracks: / End of the road / Morning sunshine / Lady who said she could fly / Happy birthday-the birthday / Girl at the window / Big chief wooley bosher / Here we go round the lemon tree / My father's son / Skeleton and the roundabout / Come with me / Going home / Mr Corow and Sir Norman / Please no more sad songs / Follow me, follow / On with the show / Lucky man / Imposters of life's magazine / Days of the broken arrows.
Album: released on See For Miles, '86 by See For Miles Records. Dist: Pinnacle

Idles

AGROCULTURE.
Album: released on Upright, Mar'87 by Upright Records. Dist: Cartel, Rough Trade

Idle Strand

CUT AND RUN.
Album:

Idol, Billy

BILLY IDOL.
Tracks: / Come, come on / White wedding-part 1+2 / Hot in the city / Dead on arrival / Nobody's business / Love calling / Hole in the wall / Shooting stars / It'so cruel / Congo man.
Album: released on Chrysalis, Jul'82 by Chrysalis Records. Dist: CBS

Cassette: released on Chrysalis, Jul'82 by Chrysalis Records. Dist: CBS

Compact disc: released on Chrysalis, Jul'82 by Chrysalis Records. Dist: CBS

DANCING WITH MYSELF.
Single (12"): released on Chrysalis, Oct'83 by Chrysalis Records. Dist: CBS

DON'T NEED A GUN.
Tracks: / Don't need a gun / Fatal charm.
Single (7"): released on Chrysalis, Feb'87 by Chrysalis Records. Dist: CBS

Single (12"): released on Chrysalis, Feb'87 by Chrysalis Records. Dist: CBS

EYES WITHOUT A FACE.
Single (7"): released on Chrysalis, May'84 by Chrysalis Records. Dist: CBS

Single (12"): released on Chrysalis, May'84 by Chrysalis Records. Dist: CBS

Single (7"): released on Chrysalis, Aug'84 by Chrysalis Records. Dist: CBS

INTERVIEW BY KRIS NEEDS.
Album: released on Lip Service, Nov'86

MONY MONY.
Single (7"): released on Chrysalis, Sep'81 by Chrysalis Records. Dist: CBS Deleted '85.

Single (12"): released on Chrysalis, Sep'81 by Chrysalis Records. Dist: CBS

REBEL YELL.
Compact disc: by Chrysalis Records. Dist: CBS

REBEL YELL.
Single (7"): released on Chrysalis, Aug'85 by Chrysalis Records. Dist: CBS

Single (12"): released on Chrysalis, Aug'85 by Chrysalis Records. Dist: CBS

Album: released on Chrysalis, Jan'86 by Chrysalis Records. Dist: CBS

Cassette: released on Chrysalis, Jan'86 by Chrysalis Records. Dist: CBS

Compact disc: released on Chrysalis, Jan'86 by Chrysalis Records. Dist: CBS

SWEET 16.
Tracks: / Sweet 16 / Beyond belief.
Single (7"): released on Chrysalis, 30 May'87 by Chrysalis Records. Dist: CBS

Single (12"): released on Chrysalis, 30 May'87 by Chrysalis Records. Dist: CBS

TO BE A LOVER.
Tracks: / All summer single.
Single (7"): released on Chrysalis, Sep'86 by Chrysalis Records. Dist: CBS

Single (12"): released on Chrysalis, Sep'86 by Chrysalis Records. Dist: CBS

VITAL IDOL.
Tracks: / Dancing with myself / White wedding parts 1+2 / Flesh for fantasy / Catch my fall / Mony mony / Love calling (dub) / Hot in the city.
Compact disc: released on Chrysalis, '86 by Chrysalis Records. Dist: CBS

Album: released on Chrysalis, Jun'85 by Chrysalis Records. Dist: CBS

Cassette: released on Chrysalis, Jun'85 by Chrysalis Records. Dist: CBS

VITAL IDOL (VIDEO).
Video-cassette (VHS): released on Chrysalis, Jan'86 by Chrysalis Records. Dist: CBS

WHIPLASH SMILE.
Tracks: / World's forgotten boy / Don't need a gun / Beyond belief / Fatal charm / All summer single / One night, one chance / To be a lover / Soul standing by / Sweet sixteen / Man for all seasons.
Compact disc: released on Chrysalis, Nov'86 by Chrysalis Records. Dist: CBS

WHIPLASH SMILE (ALBUM)*.
Notes: All songs produced by Keith Forsey.
Album: released on Chrysalis, Oct'86 by Chrysalis Records. Dist: CBS

Cassette: released on Chrysalis, Oct'86 by Chrysalis Records. Dist: CBS

WHITE WEDDING.
Single (7"): released on Chrysalis, Jun'85 by Chrysalis Records. Dist: CBS

Single (12"): released on Chrysalis, Jun'85 by Chrysalis Records. Dist: CBS

Single (12"): released on Chrysalis, Sep'83 by Chrysalis Records. Dist: CBS

Idol Flowers

ALL I WANT IS YOU.
Single (7"): released on Miles Ahead, Jan'84 Dist: Pinnacle

Idol Race

LIGHT AT THE END OF THE ROAD.
Album: released on See For Miles, Jul'86 by See For Miles Records. Dist: Pinnacle

Idol Rich

BLAZE OF LOVE.
Single (7"): released on Dork, Nov'84 by Dork Records. Dist: Probe, Cartel

PESO TRAIL.
Single (7"): released on Dork, Sep'84 by Dork Records. Dist: Probe, Cartel

Idols

IDOLS various artists.
Cassette: released on K-Tel Goldmasters,

Aug'84 by K-Tel Records. Dist: K-Tel

YOU/ GIRL THAT I LOVE.
Single (7"):

Idrah

GOING DOWN.
Single (12"): released on Idrah, Sep'82 Dist: Jetstar

If...

IF IT SELLS IT SMELLS Various artists (Various Artists).
Single (12"): released on Pink, Oct'86 by Pink Records. Dist: Rough Trade

IF IT'S LOUD WE'RE PROUD various artists (Various Artists).
Album: released on Mausoleum, Jun'84 by Mausoleum Records. Dist: Pinnacle

IF IT'S NOT A HIT I'LL EAT MY HAT Various artists (Various Artists).
Tracks: / Hound dog / Pledging my love / I love my baby / I wanna ramble / Farther up the road / Keep on diggin' / To the end / Texas flood / Okie dokie stomp / Taxi blues / Spunky onions / Blue Monday / Funny how time slips away / Treat her right.
Album: released on Ace, Nov'85 by Ace Records. Dist: Pinnacle, Swift, Hotshot, Cadillac

IF PATRIOTIC SENTIMENT IS WANTED Various artists (Gilbert & Sullivan).
Album: released on Decca, Aug'77 by Decca Records. Dist: Polygram Deleted '81.

Cassette: released on Decca, Aug'77 by Decca Records. Dist: Polygram Deleted '83.

IF THEY COULD SEE ME NOW A night of 100 stars (Various Artists).
Notes: A unique event in London's theatre history has been captured on disc by That's Entertainment Records. On February 26th 1984,over 100 celebrities from film,radio and TV gathered at the Theatre Royal,Drury Lane for a gala charity show called'If they could see me now'.The event was to raise funds for ASBAH,a charity devoted to the cause of spina bifida and hydrocephalus.These celebrities performed a number of well-known show songs from such writers as Lerner & Loewe,Rodgers & Hart,Noel Coward,Stephen Sondheim,Cole Porter and Frank Loesser.Some of the shows represented are Guys & Dolls, 42nd. Street,Stop the World I Want To Get Off and A Little Night Music. This LP release presents highlights from the evening and is a lovely recording featuring artists such as Joss Ackland/Margaret Courtenay/Liz Robertson/Sheridan Morley/Miriam Karlin/George Sewell/Frank Finlay/Simon Callow/Virginia McKenna/Tim Curry & Christopher Reeve.
Album: released on TER, Jan'86 Dist: Pinnacle

IF YOU CAN'T PLEASE YOURSELF YOU CAN'T PLEASE YOUR SOUL various artists (Various Artists).
Album: released on EMI, Sep'85 by EMI Records. Dist: EMI

Cassette: released on EMI, Sep'85 by EMI Records. Dist: EMI

TEA BREAK OVER-BACK ON YOUR HEADS.
Album: released on Gull, Feb'75 by Gull Records. Dist: Pinnacle

If All Else Fails

DISTINCT.
Single (7"): released on Fail, Jan'82 Dist: Rough Trade

Ifield, Frank

20 GOLDEN GREATS.
Album: released on Platinum, Mar'86 by Geoffs Records.

Cassette: released on Platinum, Mar'86 by Geoffs Records.

Album: released on K-Tel, Nov'81 by K-Tel Records. Dist: Record Merchandisers Distribution, Taylors, Terry Blood Distribution, Wynd-Up Distribution, Relay Distribution, Pickwick Distribution, Solomon & Peres Distribution, Polygram

Cassette: released on K-Tel, Nov'81 by K-Tel Records. Dist: Record Merchandisers Distribution, Taylors, Terry Blood Distribution, Wynd-Up Distribution, Relay Distribution, Pickwick Distribution, Solomon & Peres Distribution, Polygram

CRAWLING BACK.
Single (7"): released on PRT, Jan'82 by PRT Records. Dist: PRT

GOLDEN HITS: FRANK IFIELD.
Double Album: released on MFP, Apr'81 by EMI Records. Dist: EMI Deleted '84.

Cassette: released on MFP, Apr'81 by EMI Records. Dist: EMI

HIS GREATEST HITS.
Tracks: / I remember you / Gotta get a date / She taught me how to yodel / Go tell it on the mountain / I'm confessin' (that I love you) / Mule train / Wolverton mountain / Angry at the big oak tree / Wayward wind / Funny how time slips away / Riders in the sky / Scarlet ribbons / Lovesick blues / Nobody's darlin' but mine / Lucky devil / Summer is over / I should care / Call her your sweetheart / Paradise / No one will ever know / Happy go lucky me / Waltzing Matilda / Young love / Cool water / Don't blame me.
Cassette: released on Hour Of Pleasure, '86 by Music For Pleasure Records. Dist: EMI

I REMEMBER YOU.
Single (7"): released on Old Gold, Jul'82 by Old Gold Records. Dist: Lightning, Jazz Music, Spartan, Counterpoint

Cassette: released on VFM, '78 by VFM Records. Dist: Taylors, Wynd-Up Distribution

PORTRAIT OF FRANK IFIELD.
Album: released on PRT, Jan'83 by PRT Records. Dist: PRT

Cassette: released on PRT, Jan'83 by PRT Records. Dist: PRT

SOMEONE TO GIVE MY LOVE TO.
Album: released on Spark, '74 by Spark Records. Dist: PRT

TOUCH THE MORNING.
Single (7"): released on PRT, Mar'83 by PRT Records. Dist: PRT

Ifill, Gloria

ALL NIGHT LONG.

Single (12"): released on Trindisc, Mar'84 by Trindisc Records. Dist: Jetstar, Pinnacle, Rough Trade, Cartel

If You're Irish

IF YOU'RE IRISH VOL.1 various artists (Various Artists).
Cassette: released on Homespun(Ireland), May'84 by Outlet Records. Dist: Outlet

IF YOU'RE IRISH VOL.2 various artists (Various Artists).
Cassette: released on Homespun(Ireland), Mar'85 by Outlet Records. Dist: Outlet

IF YOU'RE IRISH VOL.3 various artists (Various Artists).
Cassette: released on Homespun(Ireland), Jun'85 by Outlet Records. Dist: Outlet

Igadasha, Johnny

ALL NIGHT LONG.
Single (12"): released on House Of Asher, Nov'83 by House Of Asher Records. Dist: Jetstar

Iggy and Stooges

FUN HOUSE.
Album: released on Elektra, Mar'77 by WEA Records. Dist: WEA

STOOGES, THE.
Album: released on Elektra, Mar'77 by WEA Records. Dist: WEA

Iglesias, Julio

1100 BEL AIR PLACE.
Tracks: / All of you / Two lovers / Bambou medley / Air that I breathe, The / Last time, The / Moonlight lady / When I fall in love / Me va, me va / If / To all the girls I've loved before.
Compact disc: released on CBS, Sep'86 by CBS Records. Dist: CBS

Album: released on CBS, Aug'84 by CBS Records. Dist: CBS

Cassette: released on CBS, Aug'84 by CBS Records. Dist: CBS

24 GREATEST SONGS, THE.
Notes: Double CD Tracks include: Quieriеme mucho, Abrazame, Manuelo etc.
Compact disc: released on CBS, Mar'87 by CBS Records. Dist: CBS

AMERICA.
Tracks: / Ay ay ay / Alma llanera / Caminito / Recuerdos de ipacarai / Historia de un amor / Obsesion / Sombras / Cancion de orfeo / Guantanamera / Vaya cos dios / Moliendo cafe.
Compact disc: released on CBS, Mar'87 by CBS Records. Dist: CBS

BEGIN THE BEGUINE.
Tracks: / Begin the beguine / Quiereme / Me Olvide De Vivir / Por un poco de tu amour / Grande, grande, grande / Como tu / Guantanamera / Quiereme mucho / Hey / Un dia ty, un dia yo / Soy un truhan, soy un senor / Candilejas / El amor / 33 anos / Isla en el sol.
Album: released on CBS, Nov'81 by CBS Records. Dist: CBS

Cassette: released on CBS, Nov'81 by CBS Records. Dist: CBS

Album: released on World, Feb'84 Dist: Jetstar

Cassette: released on World, Feb'84 Dist: Jetstar

Compact disc: released on CBS, Aug'87 by CBS Records. Dist: CBS

DE NINA A MUJER.
Compact disc: released on CBS, Mar'87 by CBS Records. Dist: CBS

EMOCIONES.
Compact disc: by CBS Records. Dist: CBS

EN CONCIERTO.
Album: released on CBS, Dec'83 by CBS Records. Dist: CBS

Cassette: by CBS Records. Dist: CBS

FLOR DE PIEL, A.
Tracks: / Flor de piel, A / Vivi (I need) / Dicen / Manuela / Un adios a media voz / Te quiero asi (if I love you so) / Por el amou de una mujer / Desde que tu te has ido / Aun me queda la esperanza / En cualquier parte (another time, another place).
Compact disc: released on CBS, Aug'87 by CBS Records. Dist: CBS

FOREVER AND EVER.
Single (7"): released on CBS, Jun'83 by CBS Records. Dist: CBS

HEY.
Album: released on CBS, Sep'80 by CBS Records. Dist: CBS

Single (7"): released on CBS, Mar'83 by CBS Records. Dist: CBS

I'VE GOT YOU UNDER MY SKIN.
Single (7"): released on CBS, Sep'85 by CBS Records. Dist: CBS

JULIO.
Album: released on CBS, Jun'83 by CBS Records. Dist: CBS

Cassette: released on CBS, Jun'83 by CBS Records. Dist: CBS

MOMENTS.
Compact disc: released on CBS, '83 by CBS Records. Dist: CBS

POR UNA MUJER.
Tracks: / Un canto a galicia / Hombre solitario / Veces Llegan, A / Cartas / Rio rebelde / Si volvieras otra vez / Por una mujer / No soy de aqui / En un rincon / Del desvan / Sweet Caroline / Como el al camino / Vivir (I need).
Compact disc: released on CBS, Aug'87 by CBS Records. Dist: CBS

SOY JULIO IGLESIAS.
Tracks: / Dieciseis anos / Nina / Una leyenda / Asi nacemos / Vete ya / Vivencias / En una cuidad / Culaquiera / Soy / Minueto / Mi amour es mas joven que yo.
Compact disc: released on CBS, Aug'87 by CBS Records. Dist: CBS

THREE GOLD ALBUMS.
Album: released on CBS, Dec'82 by CBS Records. Dist: CBS

TO ALL THE GIRLS I'VE LOVED BEFORE (Iglesias, Julio & Willie Nelson).

Igloos

WOLF.
Single (7"): released on Fresh, Apr'81 Dist: Jetstar

Ignerents

RADIO INTERFERENCE.
Single (7"): released on Rundown, Dec'79 by Rundown Records. Dist: Pinnacle, Rough Trade

Single (7"): released on Ace, Feb'80 by Ace Records. Dist: Pinnacle, Swift, Hotshot, Cadillac

Igors Night Off

WE'RE HAVING A PARTY.
Single (7"): released on Make A Way, Apr'85 Dist: Pinnacle

I Got Rhythm

I GOT RHYTHM various artists (Various Artists).
Album: released on Kicking Mule, '79 by Sonet. Dist: Roots, PRT-Pye Distribution

Igus Orchestra

SCOTLAND FOR ME.
Album: released on Igus, Apr'87 by Klub. Dist: PRT, Musac Distribution Ltd (Scotland)

Cassette: released on Igus, Apr'87 by Klub. Dist: PRT, Musac Distribution Ltd (Scotland)

Compact disc: released on Igus, 20 Jun'87 by Klub. Dist: PRT, Musac Distribution Ltd (Scotland)

TASTE OF SCOTLAND.
Album: released on Igus, Apr'87 by Klub. Dist: PRT, Musac Distribution Ltd (Scotland)

Cassette: released on Igus, Apr'87 by Klub. Dist: PRT, Musac Distribution Ltd (Scotland)

Compact disc: released on Igus, 20 Jun'87 by Klub. Dist: PRT, Musac Distribution Ltd (Scotland)

I Have To...

I HAVE TO PAINT MY FACE various artists (Various Artists).
Album: released on Arhoolie, May'81 by Arhoolie Records. Dist: Projection, Topic, Jazz Music, Swift, Roots

Iheka-Chama

MANDINGO TRIBE.
Album: released on Clappers, Apr'84 by Clappers Records. Dist: Jetstar

Ijahman

ARE WE A WARRIOR.
Album: released on Island, Sep'79 by Island Records. Dist: Polygram

CULTURE COUNTRY.
Album: released on Tree Roots, Aug'87 by Tree Roots Records. Dist: Jetstar. Estim retail price in Sep'87 was £5.99.

HAILE I HYMN.
Album: released on Island, Jun'78 by Island Records. Dist: Polygram

Cassette: released on Island, Jun'78 by Island Records. Dist: Polygram

I Jahman Levi

AFRICA.
Album: released on Tree Roots, Jul'84 by Tree Roots Records. Dist: Jetstar

Cassette: released on Tree Roots, Jul'84 by Tree Roots Records. Dist: Jetstar

Ijahman & Madge

HOLD ON HONEY.
Single (12"): released on Jahmani, Nov'85

I DO.
Single (12"): released on Jahmani, May'85

IN THE NIGHT.
Single (12"): released on Tree Roots, Aug'87 by Tree Roots Records. Dist: Jetstar

MY LOVE.
Tracks: / Chariot of love.
Single (12"): released on Jah Man, Nov'86 by Jah Man Records. Dist: Jetstar

Ijog & The Tracksuits

BEDROOM TUNE.
Single (7"): released on Tyger, Feb'82

Ik

WHEN THE RIVER BREAKS.
Single (7"): released on Off-Beat, Jul'85 by Off-Beat Records. Dist: Jetstar Distribution

Single (12"): released on Off-Beat, Jul'85 by Off-Beat Records. Dist: Jetstar Distribution

Ikafa Lelah

DISCO 2000/TOGETHER IN LOVE.
Single (7"): released on Hobo, May'79 by Hobo Records. Dist: Hobo

Ikettes

FINE, FINE, FINE.
Album: released on Kent, Jan'87 by Ace Records. Dist: Pinnacle

I Know How

I KNOW HOW (Various Artists).
Single (7"): released on First Night, Jun'87 by Safari Records. Dist: Pinnacle

Ikon Ad

DON'T FEED US SHIT ep.
Single (7"): released on Radical Change, Aug'82 by Backs Records. Dist: Backs, Cartel

LET THE VULTURES FLY ep.
Single (7"): released on Radical Change, Jun'83 by Backs Records. Dist: Backs, Cartel

Ilana

PAPER CHASE (Ilana & The Champagne Dance Orchestra).
Single (7"): released on Stagecoach, May'82

I-Lands

IN THE RAIN.
Tracks: / In the rain / Velvet glove / Summer-

time No. 1.
Single (7"): released on Little Prince, Nov'85
Dist: Probe, Cartel

Single (7"): released on Little Prince, Nov'84
Dist: Probe, Cartel

I-Level

GIVE ME.
Single (7"): released on Virgin, Aug'82 by Virgin Records. Dist: EMI, Virgin Distribution

Single (12"): released on Virgin, Aug'82 by Virgin Records. Dist: EMI, Virgin Distribution Deleted '85.

I LEVEL.
Album: released on Virgin (Front Line), Jul'83

IN THE RIVER.
Single (7"): released on Virgin, Jun'84 by Virgin Records. Dist: EMI, Virgin Distribution

IN THE SAND.
Single (7"): released on Virgin, Feb'85 by Virgin Records. Dist: EMI, Virgin Distribution

MINEFIELD/NUMBER4/GIVE ME.
Single (7"): released on Virgin (USA), Apr'83 by Virgin Records. Dist: CBS

OUR SONG.
Single (7"): released on Virgin, Jul'84 by Virgin Records. Dist: EMI, Virgin Distribution

SHAKE.
Album: released on Virgin, Feb'85 by Virgin Records. Dist: EMI, Virgin Distribution

Cassette: released on Virgin, Feb'85 by Virgin Records. Dist: EMI, Virgin Distribution

STONE HEART.
Single (7"): released on Virgin, Aug'83 by Virgin Records. Dist: EMI, Virgin Distribution

TEACHER/ALL MY LOVE.
Single (7"): released on Virgin, Jun'83 by Virgin Records. Dist: EMI, Virgin Distribution

Ilkeston Brass Band

ILKESTON BRASS BAND.
Album: released on Pye, Oct'79

Illapu

ILLAPU, VOL 2: RAZA BRAVA.
Album: released on Monitor (USA). Jan'84

Cassette: released on Monitor (USA). Jan'84

I'll dance til...

I'LL DANCE TIL DE SUN BREAKS THROUGH Ragtime from 1898-1923 (Various Artists).
Album: released on Saydisc, Nov'83 by Saydisc Records. Dist: Essex, Harmonia Mundi, Roots, H.R. Taylor, Jazz Music, Swift, Projection, Gamut

Cassette: released on Saydisc, Nov'83 by Saydisc Records. Dist: Essex, Harmonia Mundi, Roots, H.R. Taylor, Jazz Music, Swift, Projection, Gamut

Illimani, Inti

CHILE.
Album: released on Xtra, Jun'75 by Relic Records. Dist: Swift

Illsley, John

NEVER TOLD A SOUL.
Compact disc: by Phonogram Records. Dist: Polygram

Single (7"): released on Vertigo, May'84 by Phonogram Records. Dist: Polygram

Single (12"): released on Vertigo, May'84 by Phonogram Records. Dist: Polygram

Album: released on Vertigo, Jun'84 by Phonogram Records. Dist: Polygram

Cassette: released on Vertigo, Jun'84 by Phonogram Records. Dist: Polygram

Compact disc: released on Vertigo, Jun'84 by Phonogram Records. Dist: Polygram

I'll take you there

I'LL TAKE YOU THERE Second Rosco show (Various Artists).
Album: released on Atlantic, Jun'74 by WEA Records. Dist: WEA

Illusion

I LIKE IT LOUD.
Tracks: / I like it loud / Heartbeat (the call) / Call in the law / Heart attack / I can't wait / Call me up / Shake / Red light / Get to you / Lifetime.
Album: released on Geffen, Nov'86 by Geffen Records. Dist: WEA, CBS

Cassette: released on Geffen, Nov'86 by Geffen Records. Dist: WEA, CBS

OUT OF THE MIST.

Album: released on Island, Mar'77 by Island Records. Dist: Polygram Deleted '79.

WHY CAN'T WE LIVE TOGETHER?.
Single (7"): released on PRT, Jun'82 by PRT Records. Dist: PRT

Single (12"): released on PRT, Jun'82 by PRT Records. Dist: PRT Deleted '85.

Illusion Orchestra

AUTUMN LEAVES.
Single (7"): released on R & B, Nov'82 by Red Bus. Dist: PRT

Single (12"): released on R & B, Nov'82 by Red Bus. Dist: PRT

Illusions From...

ILLUSIONS FROM THE CRACKLING VOID (Various Artists).
Album: released on Bam Caruso, May'87 by Bam Caruso Records. Dist: Rough Trade, Revolver, Cartel

Illustrated Man

JUST ENOUGH.
Single (7"): released on Parlophone, Jun'84 by EMI Records. Dist: EMI

Single (12"): released on Parlophone, Jun'84 by EMI Records. Dist: EMI Deleted '87.

Illustrious Cutlery

SCARECROW.
Single (7"): released on North West, Aug'87 by North West Records. Dist: Red Rhino Distribution, Cartel Distribution

Single (12"): released on North West, Aug'87 by North West Records. Dist: Red Rhino Distribution, Cartel Distribution

Iluwata

YESTERME YESTERYOU YESTERDAY.
Single (12"): released on Natty Congo, Dec'83 by Natty Congo Records. Dist: Jetstar

Il Y A Volkswagens

KILL MYSELF.
Single (7"): released on Mechanical Reproductions, Aug'81 Dist: Rough Trade

I'm

I'M COMING FROM SECLUSION Various Artists (Various Artists).
Album: released on Collectors Items, Apr'79 Dist: Jazz Music, Swift, Chris Wellard

Image

YOU MAKE ME FEEL.
Single (7"): released on Bowler Music, Feb'82

Images

IMAGES.
Notes: With Mara, James Llewelyn Kiek, Jim Denly, Danny Thompson etc.
Album: released on Plantlife, Jan'87

IMAGES Various orchestras (Various Orchestras).
Album: released on K-Tel, Sep'83 by K-Tel Records. Dist: Record Merchandisers Distribution, Taylors, Terry Blood Distribution, Wynd-Up Distribution, Relay Distribution, Pickwick Distribution, Solomon & Peres Distribution, Polygram

Cassette: released on K-Tel, Sep'83 by K-Tel Records. Dist: Record Merchandisers Distribution, Taylors, Terry Blood Distribution, Wynd-Up Distribution, Relay Distribution, Pickwick Distribution, Solomon & Peres Distribution, Polygram

Imagination

BODY TALK.
Tracks: / Tell me do you want my love / Flashback / I'll always love you (but don't look back) / In and out of love / Body talk / So good, so right / Burnin' up.
Compact disc: released on Red Bus, '86 by Red Bus Records. Dist: PRT

Single (7"): released on R & B, May'81 by Red Bus. Dist: PRT

Single (12"): released on R & B, May'81 by Red Bus. Dist: PRT

Album: released on R & B, Oct'81 by Red Bus. Dist: PRT

Cassette: released on R & B, Oct'81 by Red Bus. Dist: PRT

Compact disc: released on R & B, Oct'81 by Red Bus Records. Dist: PRT

CHANGES.

Single (7"): released on R & B, Nov'82 by Red Bus. Dist: PRT

Single (12"): released on R & B, Nov'82 by Red Bus. Dist: PRT

Picture disc single: released on R & B, Dec'82 by Red Bus. Dist: PRT

FLASHBACK.
Single (7"): released on R & B, Nov'81 by Red Bus. Dist: PRT

Single (12"): released on R & B, Nov'81 by Red Bus. Dist: PRT

FOUND MY GIRL.
Single (7"): released on R & B, Apr'85 by Red Bus. Dist: PRT

Single (12"): released on R & B, Apr'85 by Red Bus. Dist: PRT

I'LL ALWAYS LOVE YOU.
Single (7"): released on R & B, Nov'81 by Red Bus. Dist: PRT

IMAGINATION GOLD.
Compact disc: by Red Bus Records. Dist: PRT

Album: released on R & B, Nov'84 by Red Bus. Dist: PRT

Cassette: released on R & B, Nov'84 by Red Bus. Dist: PRT

Cassette: released on R & B, Nov'84 by Red Bus. Dist: PRT

Compact disc: released on R & B, Nov'84 by Red Bus Records. Dist: PRT

IMAGINATION IN CONCERT (VIDEO).
Video-cassette (VHS): released on Video Collection, May'87 by Video Collection International Ltd.. Dist: Counterpoint

IN AND OUT OF LOVE.
Single (7"): released on R & B, Sep'81 by Red Bus. Dist: PRT

Single (12"): released on R & B, Sep'81 by Red Bus. Dist: PRT

IN THE HEAT OF THE NIGHT.
Album: released on R & B, Sep'82 by Red Bus. Dist: PRT

Cassette: released on R & B, Sep'82 by Red Bus. Dist: PRT

Single (7"): released on R & B, Sep'82 by Red Bus. Dist: PRT

Single (12"): released on R & B, Sep'82 by Red Bus. Dist: PRT

JUST AN ILLUSION.
Single (7"): released on R & B, Feb'82 by Red Bus. Dist: PRT

Single (12"): released on R & B, Feb'82 by Red Bus. Dist: PRT

LAST DAYS OF SUMMER.
Single (7"): released on R & B, Aug'85 by Red Bus. Dist: PRT

Single (12"): released on R & B, Aug'85 by Red Bus. Dist: PRT

LAST TIME, THE.
Tracks: / Touch.
Single (7"): released on RCA, Aug'87 by RCA Records. Dist: RCA, Roots, Swift, Wellard, Chris, I & B, Solomon & Peres Distribution

Single (12"): released on RCA, Aug'87 by RCA Records. Dist: RCA, Roots, Swift, Wellard, Chris, I & B, Solomon & Peres Distribution

LOOKING AT MIDNIGHT.
Single (7"): released on R & B, May'83 by Red Bus. Dist: PRT

Single (12"): released on R & B, May'83 by Red Bus. Dist: PRT

MUSIC AND LIGHTS.
Single (12"): released on R & B, Jun'82 by Red Bus. Dist: PRT

NEW DIMENSION.
Single (7"): released on R & B, Oct'83 by Red Bus. Dist: PRT

Single (12"): released on R & B, Oct'83 by Red Bus. Dist: PRT

NIGHT DUBBING.
Album: released on R & B, May'83 by Red Bus. Dist: PRT

Cassette: released on R & B, May'83 by Red Bus. Dist: PRT

SCANDALOUS.
Album: released on R & B, Nov'83 by Red Bus. Dist: PRT

Cassette:

released on R & B, Nov'83 by Red Bus. Dist: PRT

STATE OF LOVE.
Single (7"): released on R & B, May'84 by Red Bus. Dist: PRT

Single (12"): released on R & B, May'84 by Red Bus. Dist: PRT

Picture disc single: released on R & B, May'84 by Red Bus. Dist: PRT

SUNSHINE.
Tracks: / Sunshine / Triology / Streetmix (medley) / Body talk (live version).
Single (7"): released on R & B, Apr'86 by Red Bus. Dist: PRT

Single (12"): released on R & B, Apr'86 by Red Bus. Dist: PRT

Double-pack single: released on R & B, Apr'86 by Red Bus. Dist: PRT

THANK YOU MY LOVE.
Single (7"): released on R & B, Oct'84 by Red Bus. Dist: PRT

Single (12"): released on R & B, Oct'84 by Red Bus. Dist: PRT

Picture disc single: released on R & B, Feb'85 by Red Bus. Dist: PRT

Imagination Brass

ZOOM ZOOM.
Tracks: / Zoom zoom / Zoom zoom (inst).
Single (7"): released on Bumble Bee, Jul'87 by CSA Records. Dist: PRT, Jetstar, CSA

Single (12"): released on Bumble Bee, Jul'87 by CSA Records. Dist: PRT, Jetstar, CSA

Imaginations

IMAGINATIONS - FURTHER REFLECTIONS Various Artists (Various Artists).
Album: released on CBS, Oct'83 by CBS Records. Dist: CBS

Cassette: released on CBS, Oct'83 by CBS Records. Dist: CBS

Imajinca

VERY FIRST VIDEO KISS, (THE).
Single (7"): released on A Record Company, Jun'84 by A Record company. Dist: CBS

Imanuel, Eli

EASY LOVER.
Single (12"): released on Silver Camel, Jan'82 Dist: Jetstar, Rough Trade

I'm Dead

SECOND IDENTITY.
Single (7"): released on Goldhanger, Jun'83 by Goldhanger Records. Dist: Rough Trade

I'm getting my act...

I'M GETTING MY ACT TOGETHER Original cast (Various Artists).
Album: released on That's Entertainment, Apr'83 by That's Entertainment Records. Dist: Pinnacle, Gamut

Imitation Life

ICE CUBES AND SUGAR.
Album: released on New Rose, Sep'86 Dist: Rough Trade, Cartel

Imlach, Hamish

MURDERED BALLADS.
Album: released on Xtra, Feb'74 by Relic Records. Dist: Swift

ODD RARITY.
Album: released on Xtra, '74 by Relic Records. Dist: Swift

SONNY'S DREAM.
Album: released on Lismor, Jun'85 by Lismor Records. Dist: Lismor, Roots, Celtic Music

Cassette: released on Lismor, Jun'85 by Lismor Records. Dist: Lismor, Roots, Celtic Music

Im-mac Logic

BOLERO.
Single (12"): released on Assorted Images, May'84 by Graduate Records. Dist: Graduate

Immaculate Fools

COMIC TRAGEDY.
Tracks: / Tragic comedy / Tragic comedy / Dub poets (live) / All fall down.
Notes: All fall down is an extra track available on 12" version only.
Single (7"): released on A&M, Feb'87 by A&M Records. Dist: Polygram

Single (12"): released on A&M, Feb'87 by A&M Records. Dist: Polygram

DUMB POET.
Tracks: / Never give less than everything / Tragic Comedy / One minute / Dumb poet / So much here / Wish you were here / Don't drive the hope from my heart / Pretty prize now / Stay away.
Notes: Their long awaited second album.Their album received excellent critical reactions, including a coveted 5 star review in Sounds. Ten wonderfully textured songs, spotlighting the lyrical and musical dexterity of a very unique U.K. band. In cludes their recent single 'Tragic Comedy'. The cassette and C.D. feature a bonus track.
Album: released on A&M, Apr'87 by A&M Records. Dist: Polygram

Cassette: released on A&M, Apr'87 by A&M Records. Dist: Polygram

Compact disc: released on A&M, Apr'87 by A&M Records. Dist: Polygram

HEARTS OF FORTUNE.
Album: released on A&M, Apr'85 by A&M Records. Dist: Polygram

Cassette: released on A&M, Apr'85 by A&M Records. Dist: Polygram

HEARTS OF FORTUNE (SINGLE).
Single (7"): released on A&M, May'85 by A&M Records. Dist: Polygram

Single (12"): released on A&M, May'85 by A&M Records. Dist: Polygram

IMMACULATE FOOLS.
Single (7"): released on A&M, Jan'85 by A&M Records. Dist: Polygram

Single (12"): released on A&M, Jan'85 by A&M Records. Dist: Polygram

NEVER GIVE LESS.
Tracks: / Never give less / She fools everyone / Love bites.
Single (7"): released on A&M, May'87 by A&M Records. Dist: Polygram

Single (12"): released on A&M, May'87 by A&M Records. Dist: Polygram

NOTHING MEANS NOTHING.
Single (7"): released on A&M, Sep'84 by A&M Records. Dist: Polygram

Single (12"): released on A&M, Sep'84 by A&M Records. Dist: Polygram

SAVE IT (re-recorded version).
Gatefold sleeve: released on A&M, Oct'85 by A&M Records. Dist: Polygram

Single (12"): released on A&M, Oct'85 by A&M Records. Dist: Polygram

WISH YOU WERE HERE.
Tracks: / Pretty prize now.
Single (7"): released on A&M, Aug'87 by A&M Records. Dist: Polygram

Single (12"): released on A&M, Aug'87 by A&M Records. Dist: Polygram

Immediate Singles

IMMEDIATE SINGLES Various artists (Various Artists).
Tracks: / Little miss understood / Much to say / I'm not saying / Last mile, The / Someone's gonna get their head kicked in tonite / Man of the world / Out of time / Time / Sitting on a fence / I'm your witchdoctor / Itchycoo park / Lazy Sunday / Hang on Sloopy / Natural born boogie / Angel of the morning / First cut is the deepest / America / Second amendment / Ars longa vita brevis / Acceptance brandenburger / Half as nice / Bend me, shape me.
Compact disc: released on Collector Series, '86 by Castle Communications Records. Dist: PRT, Pinnacle, RCA, Ariola

IMMEDIATE SINGLES COLLECTION Various Artists (Various Artists).
Double Album: released on Castle Communications, Nov'85 by Castle Communications. Dist: Cartel, Pinnacle, Counterpoint

Double cassette: released on Castle Communications, Nov'85 by Castle Communications. Dist: Cartel, Pinnacle, Counterpoint

Immediate Story

IMMEDIATE STORY Various Artists (Various Artists).
Album: released on Virgin, Jun'80 by Virgin Records. Dist: EMI, Virgin Distribution

Imminent

IMMINENT EPISODE ONE: ENGLAND-THE SUMMER OF 1985 Various artists (Various Artists).
Notes: Artists include: Yeah yeah Noh, Eric Random, Terry and Gerry.
Album: released on Food, Nov'85 by Food Records. Dist: Rough Trade, Cartel, WEA

IMMINENT FIVE (Various Artists).
Notes: inc. Primitives, BMX Bandits, Yeah Jazz.
Album: released on Food, Mar'87 by Food Records. Dist: Rough Trade, Cartel, WEA

IMMINENT VOL.2 Various artists (Various Artists).
Notes: Includes: Hula, 400 Blows, Stingrays.
Album: released on Food, May'86 by Food Records. Dist: Rough Trade, Cartel, WEA

IMMINENT VOL.3 Various artists (Various Artists).
Notes: Including: Eugene Chadbourne, Bunnydrums.
Album: released on Food, May'86 by Food Records. Dist: Rough Trade, Cartel, WEA

IMMINENT VOLUME 4 various artists (Various Artists).
Album: released on Food, Oct'86 by Food Records. Dist: Rough Trade, Cartel, WEA

Immortals

NO TURNING BACK.
Tracks: / No turning back (Chocks away mix).
Single (7"): released on MCA, May'86 by MCA Records. Dist: Polygram, MCA

Single (12"): released on MCA, May'86 by MCA Records. Dist: Polygram, MCA

Impact

PUNK CHRISTMAS.
Single (7"): released on Cyanide, Nov'83

Impact Auto Edit

IMPACT AUTO EDIT Various artists (Various Artists).
Tracks: / Impact auto edit / Inc hula / Sonic youth / Portion control.
Single (12"): released on Impact, Jan'86 by Ace Records. Dist: Rough Trade, Pinnacle, Swift, Backs, Counterpoint, Jungle, Hotshot, Cartel

Impatience

SLICE ME NICE.
Single (12"): released on Proto, Sep'84 by Proto Records. Dist: WEA

Imperial Metals

CHECKMATE.
Album: released on Two-Ten, '79 by Two-Ten Records. Dist: H.R. Taylor

Imperial Musicians

IMPERIAL MUSICIANS 1951-1962 The rhythm in rhythm & blues (Various Artists).
Tracks: / Blue monday / Shufflin' fox / Bumpity bump / Sleepwalking woman / Great big eyes / Come on pts.1 & 2 / I hear you knocking / Snag-a-tooth Jeannie / That's how you got killed before / Domino stomp / I've been walkin' / Bobby sox ramble / Deacon rides again.
Album: released on EMI America (Stateside), Jul'87 by EMI Records. Dist: EMI

Cassette: released on EMI America (Stateside), Jul'87 by EMI Records. Dist: EMI

Imperial Pompadours

ERSATZ.
Album: released on Demon, Dec'82 by Demon Records. Dist: Pinnacle

Imperial Rockabillies

IMPERIAL ROCKABILLIES VOLUME 1 Various Artists (Various Artists).
Album: released on Imperial(France), '83 by K-Tel Records. Dist: K-Tel, Taylors, Polygram

IMPERIAL ROCKABILLIES VOLUME 2 Various Artists (Various Artists).
Album: released on Imperial(France), '83 by K-Tel Records. Dist: K-Tel, Taylors, Polygram

Album: released on United Artists, May'79

IMPERIAL ROCKABILLIES VOLUME 3 Various Artists (Various Artists).
Album: released on United Artists, Aug'80

Album: released on Imperial(France), '83 by K-Tel Records. Dist: K-Tel, Taylors, Polygram

Imperials

FOLLOW MAN WITH MUSIC.
Album: released on Word, '74 by Word Records. Dist: Word Distribution, CBS

LET THE WIND BLOW.
Album: released on Myrrh, Aug'85 by Word Records. Dist: Word Distribution

Cassette: released on Myrrh, Aug'85 by Word Records. Dist: Word Distribution

ONE MORE SONG FOR YOU.
Album: released on Day Spring, May'82 by Word Records. Dist: Word Distribution, CBS

Cassette: released on Day Spring, May'82 by Word Records. Dist: Word Distribution, CBS

PRIORITY.
Album: released on Day Spring, May'82 by Word Records. Dist: Word Distribution. CBS

Cassette: released on Day Spring, May'82 by Word Records. Dist: Word Distribution, CBS

TIME TO GET IT TOGETHER.
Album: released on Key, '74 by Key Records. Dist: Spartan

Imperiet

PEACE.
Tracks: / Wild world / Blue heaven blues.
Single (7"): released on Mistlur, Mar'86 Dist: Nine Mile Distribution, Cartel Distribution

Single (12"): released on Mistlur, Mar'86 Dist: Nine Mile Distribution, Cartel Distribution

Impett, Jonathan

TRUMPET COLLECTION (Impett, Jonathan & The Clarion Ensemble).
Notes: Trumpet family instruments from the baroque to the present day with singer and accompaniment by a variety of keyboards, sackbut and cello.
Cassette: released on Amon Ra, Sep'87 by Saydisc Records. Dist: H.R. Taylor, Gamut, PRT, Jazz Music, Essex Record Distributors Ltd., Projection, Swift

Impi

IMPI.
Single (7"): released on Jive, Sep'82 by Zomba Records. Dist: RCA, PRT, CBS

Single (12"): released on Jive, Sep'82 by Zomba Records. Dist: RCA, PRT, CBS

Implied Consent

NOBODY IN PARTICULAR.
Single (7"): released on In Tape, Feb'84 by In Tape Records. Dist: Red Rhino, Cartel

Implosion

IMPLOSION Hayward, John (Foster, Barry).
Album: released on Dicomus, May'81

Importance Of Being...

IMPORTANCE OF BEING EARNEST, THE Wilde, Oscar (Gielgud, Sir John & Dame Edna Evans).
Notes: Cast includes:John Worthing-Sir John Gielgud/Algernon Moncrieff-Roland Culver/Lady Bracknell-Dame Edna Evans/Hon. Gwendolen Fairfax-Pamela Brown/Cecily Cardew-Celia Johnson/Miss Prism-Jean Cadell/Rev. Canon Chausuble,D.D.-Aubrey Mather/Merriman-Brewster Mason/Lane-Peter Sallis.
Compact disc: released on Listen For Pleasure, Jul'86 by MFP Records. Dist: EMI

Impossible Dreamers

AUGUST AVENUE.
Single (7"): released on RCA, Sep'85 by RCA Records. Dist: RCA, Roots, Swift, Wellard, Chris, I & B, Solomon & Peres Distribution

Single (12"): released on RCA, Sep'85 by RCA Records. Dist: RCA, Roots, Swift, Wellard, Chris, I & B, Solomon & Peres Distribution

HOUSE BUILT ON SAND.
Single (7"): released on Arcadia, Oct'84 Dist: Cartel

Single (12"): released on Arcadia, Oct'84 Dist: Cartel

I HAVE LOVE IN MY HANDS.
Tracks: / I have love in my hands.
Single (7"): released on RCA, Mar'87 by RCA Records. Dist: RCA, Roots, Swift, Wellard, Chris, I & B, Solomon & Peres Distribution

Single (12"): by RCA Records. Dist: RCA, Roots, Swift, Wellard, Chris, I & B, Solomon & Peres Distribution

LIFE ON EARTH.
Single (7"): released on 1982-100, Mar'82

RUNNING FOR COVER.
Tracks: / Running for cover / Wayfaring stranger / This land of woe.
Single (7"): released on RCA, Oct'86 by RCA Records. Dist: RCA, Roots, Swift, Wellard, Chris, I & B, Solomon & Peres Distribution

Single (12"): released on RCA, Oct'86 by RCA Records. Dist: RCA, Roots, Swift, Wellard, Chris, I & B, Solomon & Peres Distribution

SAY GOODBYE TO NO-ONE.
Tracks: / Say goodbye to no-one / Twisted shapes of all my mistakes / Rainbow warrior / Twisted shapes of all my mistakes / Rainbow warrior.
Single (7"): released on RCA, May'86 by RCA Records. Dist: RCA, Roots, Swift, Wellard, Chris, I & B, Solomon & Peres Distribution

Single (12"): released on RCA, May'86 by RCA Records. Dist: RCA, Roots, Swift, Wellard, Chris, I & B, Solomon & Peres Distribution

Impossible years

SCENES WE'D LIKE TO SEE.
Album: released on Dreamworld, Jun'85 by TV Personalities, The. Dist: Rough Trade

Imposter

PEACE IN OUR TIME.
Single (7"): released on Imposter, May'84 by Imposter Records. Dist: RCA

PILLS AND SOAP.
Single (7"): released on Imp, Jun'83 by Demon. Dist: Pinnacle

Single (7"): released on Edsel, Aug'83 by Demon Records. Dist: Pinnacle, Jazz Music, Projection

Impression

MIGHTY REAL.
Single (7"): released on New Language, Nov'85

Single (12"): released on New Language, Nov'85

Impressions

16 GREATEST HITS.
Album: released on ABC, '77 Dist: CBS, Pinnacle

BEST OF THE IMPRESSIONS.
Album: released on ABC, '77 Dist: CBS, Pinnacle

FAN THE FIRE.
Album: released on 20th Century, Sep'81 Dist: RCA, IMS-Polygram

Cassette: released on 20th Century, Sep'81 Dist: RCA, IMS-Polygram

FAN THE FIRE (SINGLE).
Single (7"): released on 20th Century, Aug'81 Dist: RCA, IMS-Polygram

Single (12"): released on 20th Century, Aug'81 Dist: RCA, IMS-Polygram

FINALLY GOT MYSELF TOGETHER.
Album: released on Buddah, Sep'74 Dist: Swift, Jazz Music, PRT

IMPRESSIONS Various artists (Various Artists).
Tracks: / Oxygene (Part 4) / La serenissima / Toccata / Chi mai / St. Elsewhere / Parisienne walkways / Theme from 'Travelling Man' / Road, The / Howard's way / Gentle touch, The / Robin (the hooded man) / Shadows / Black Tower, The / Merry Christmas Mr. Lawrence / Axel F..
Album: released on K-Tel, Jan'87 by K-Tel Records. Dist: Record Merchandisers Distribution, Taylors, Terry Blood Distribution, Wynd-Up Distribution, Relay Distribution, Pickwick Distribution, Solomon & Peres Distribution, Polygram

Cassette: released on K-Tel, Jan'87 by K-Tel Records. Dist: Record Merchandisers Distribution, Taylors, Terry Blood Distribution, Wynd-Up Distribution, Relay Distribution, Pickwick Distribution, Solomon & Peres Distribution, Polygram

Compact disc: released on K-Tel, Jan'87 by K-Tel Records. Dist: Record Merchandisers Distribution, Taylors, Terry Blood Distribution, Wynd-Up Distribution, Relay Distribution, Pickwick Distribution, Solomon & Peres Distribution, Polygram

IMPRESSIONS, (THE).
Album: released on Kent, Sep'83 by Ace Records. Dist: Pinnacle

KEEP ON PUSHING.
Album: released on Kent, Oct'83 by Ace Records. Dist: Pinnacle

NEVER ENDING IMPRESSIONS, (THE).
Album: released on Kent, Oct'83 by Ace Records. Dist: Pinnacle

ORIGINALS.
Double Album: released on ABC, Nov'76 Dist: CBS, Pinnacle

PEOPLE GET READY.
Album: released on Kent, Nov'83 by Ace Records. Dist: Pinnacle

RIGHT ON TIME.
Album: released on Charly, Nov'83 by Charly Records. Dist: Charly, Cadillac

WE'RE A WINNER.
Album: released on ABC, '77 Dist: CBS, Pinnacle

YOUR PRECIOUS LOVE.
Tracks: / Sweet was the wind / For your

precious love / Lover's lane / Don't drive me away / Gift of love, The / At the county fair / Come back my love / At the county fair / Come back my love / Love me / Little young lover / Lonely one / Long time ago, A / Senorita, I love you / Say that you love me / New love (I found a love).
Album: released on Topline, Aug'87 by Charly Records. Dist: Charly Distribution

Cassette: released on Topline, Aug'87 by Charly Records. Dist: Charly Distribution

Album: released on Charly, Nov'81 by Charly Records. Dist: Charly, Cadillac

Album: released on Topline, Aug'87 by Charly Records. Dist: Charly Distribution. Estim retail price in Sep'87 was £2.99.

Cassette: released on Topline, Aug'87 by Charly Records. Dist: Charly Distribution. Estim retail price in Sep'87 was £2.99.

Impressions of...
IMPRESSIONS OF DON WILLIAMS Various Session Artists (Various Artists).
Cassette: released on AIM (Budget Cassettes), Feb'83

Imprints
IT'S OVER.
Single (7"): released on Jammy, Jun'82 by Jammy Records. Dist: Jammy

Improve your driving
IMPROVE YOUR DRIVING Various Artists (Various Artists).
Cassette: released on Times Cassettes, Jan'79 by Ivan Berg. Dist: Pinnacle

Impulse
ACT ON IMPULSE.
Single (7"): released on Polydor, Jan'83 by Polydor Records. Dist: Polygram, Polydor

Single (12"): released on Polydor, Jan'83 by Polydor Records. Dist: Polygram, Polydor

PRIZE, (THE).
Single (7"): released on Polydor, May'83 by Polydor Records. Dist: Polygram, Polydor

Single (12"): released on Polydor, May'83 by Polydor Records. Dist: Polygram, Polydor

WILL YOU LOVE.
Tracks: / Will you love (Instrumental).
Single (7"): released on Willowdene, Aug'86 Dist: Spartan

Single (12"): released on Willowdene, Aug'86 Dist: Spartan

Impulsively
IMPULSIVELY Various Artists (Various Artists).
Double Album: released on Impulse, '77 by Impulse Records. Dist: MCA, Polygram

Imrie, Jim
I'LL TAKE YOU HOME AGAIN, KATHLEEN.
Cassette: released on Country House, Jul'85 by BGS Productions Ltd. Dist: Taylor, H.R., Record Merchandisers Distribution, Pinnacle, Sounds of Scotland Records

YOURS IN SONG.
Album: released on Country House, Sep'84 by BGS Productions Ltd. Dist: Taylor, H.R., Record Merchandisers Distribution, Pinnacle, Sounds of Scotland Records

Cassette: released on Country House, Sep'84 by BGS Productions Ltd. Dist: Taylor, H.R., Record Merchandisers Distribution, Pinnacle, Sounds of Scotland Records

Imruh-Asha, Rass
TRIBUTE TO SELASSIE 1.
Album: released on House Of Asher, Jul'85 by House Of Asher Records. Dist: Jetstar

I'm so hollow
EMOTION SOUND EMOTION.
Album: released on Illuminated, Jan'85 by IKF Records. Dist: Pinnacle, Cartel, Jetstar

I'm sorry I'll read...
I'M SORRY I'LL READ THAT AGAIN Various Artists (Various Artists).
Album: released on BBC, '78 by BBC Records & Tapes. Dist: EMI, PRT, Pye

Cassette: released on BBC, '78 by BBC Records & Tapes. Dist: EMI, PRT, Pye

I'm Talking
DO YOU WANNA BE.
Single (7"): released on London, Oct'86 by London Records. Dist: Polygram

Single (12"): released on London, Oct'86 by

London Records. Dist: Polygram

IN2XS
LOVE WILL COME/BUTTER WOULDN'T.
Single (7"): released on Lightbeat, Aug'82 by Lightbeat Records. Dist: Pinnacle

MAMA DON'T DANCE/IN THE BEGINNING.
Single (7"): released on Lightbeat, Apr'83 by Lightbeat Records. Dist: Pinnacle

In a Dance Hall
IN A DANCE HALL (Various Artists).
Album: released on Photographers, Jul'87

In and out of town
IN AND OUT OF TOWN Various Artists (Various Artists).
Album: released on Out Of Town, '81

Inane
MORE MUSIC.
Special: released on Subway Organisation, Oct'83 Dist: Revolver, Cartel

Inca Babies
BIG JUGULAR.
Single (12"): released on Black Lagoon, May'84 by Black Lagoon Records. Dist: Red Rhino, Cartel

GRUNT CADILLAC HOTEL.
Single (7"): released on Black Lagoon, Mar'83 by Black Lagoon Records. Dist: Red Rhino, Cartel

INTERIOR,(THE).
Single (7"): released on Black Lagoon, Nov'83 by Black Lagoon Records. Dist: Red Rhino, Cartel

JUDGE,THE.
Single (7"): released on Black Lagoon, Aug'84 by Black Lagoon Records. Dist: Red Rhino, Cartel

OPIUM DEM.
Album: released on Black Lagoon, Jun'87 by Black Lagoon Records. Dist: Red Rhino, Cartel

RUMBLE.
Album: released on Black Lagoon, Jan'85 by Black Lagoon Records. Dist: Red Rhino, Cartel

SURFIN' IN LOCUST LAND.
Single (12"): released on Black Lagoon, Sep'85 by Black Lagoon Records. Dist: Red Rhino, Cartel

THIS TRAIN.
Album: released on Black Lagoon, Sep'86 by Black Lagoon Records. Dist: Red Rhino, Cartel

In Camera
FIN.
Single (12"): released on 4AD, Apr'82 by 4AD Records. Dist: Rough Trade

Incantation
CACHARPAYA/ON THE WINGS OF A CONDOR.
Single (7"): released on Beggars Banquet, Sep'82 by Beggars Banquet Records. Dist: WEA

Single (12"): released on Beggars Banquet, Sep'82 by Beggars Banquet Records. Dist: WEA

CANARIOUS.
Single (7"): released on Coda, Nov'84 by Coda Records. Dist: Pinnacle, Cartel, WEA, Roots

CANARIOUS/EL CONDOR PASA/ATAHUALLPA/BUSCADO.
Single (7"): released on Beggars Banquet, Dec'83 by Beggars Banquet Records. Dist: WEA Deleted '85.

Single (12"): released on Beggars Banquet, Dec'83 by Beggars Banquet Records. Dist: WEA Deleted '87.

DANCE OF THE FLAMES.
Album: released on Beggars Banquet, Dec'83 by Beggars Banquet Records. Dist: WEA

Cassette: released on Beggars Banquet, Dec'83 by Beggars Banquet Records. Dist: WEA

Compact disc: released on Beggars Banquet, Dec'83 by Beggars Banquet Records. Dist: WEA

Album: released on Beggars Banquet, Dec'83 by Beggars Banquet Records. Dist: WEA

MUSIC OF ANDES.
Album: released on Coda, Nov'85 by Coda Records. Dist: Pinnacle, Cartel, WEA, Roots

Cassette: released on Coda, Nov'85 by Coda Records. Dist: Pinnacle, Cartel, WEA, Roots

MUSIC OF THE ANDES.
Compact disc: released on Coda, Feb'86 by Coda Records. Dist: Pinnacle, Cartel, WEA, Roots

ON EARTH AS IT IS IN HEAVEN.
Tracks: / On earth as it is in heaven (Theme from the mission) / Canto del agua.
Single (7"): released on Filmtrax, Nov'86 by Filmtrax Records. Dist: EMI

PANPIPES OF THE ANDES.
Tracks: / On the wind of a condor / Sonccuiman / Skuriadas / High flying bird / Winds of the mountain / Amores ahllaras / El pajaro morgador / Condor dance / Cacharpaya / Papel de plata / Friends of the Andes.
Album: released on Coda, Mar'86 by Coda Records. Dist: Pinnacle, Cartel, WEA Roots

Cassette: released on Coda, Mar'86 by Coda Records. Dist: Pinnacle, Cartel, WEA, Roots

PAN PIPES OF THE ANDES.
Album: released on Beggars Banquet, Nov'82 by Beggars Banquet Records. Dist: WEA

Compact disc: released on Beggars Banquet, Nov'82 by Beggars Banquet Records. Dist: WEA

PIPE DANCE.
Single (7"): released on Beggars Banquet, Dec'84 by Beggars Banquet Records. Dist: WEA

SIKURIADES/ITALIQUE.
Single (7"): released on Beggars Banquet, Mar'83 by Beggars Banquet Records. Dist: WEA

Single (12"): released on Beggars Banquet, Mar'83 by Beggars Banquet Records. Dist: WEA

VIRGINS OF THE SUN.
Tracks: / Brass band / Virgins of the sun / Solo harpist / Sacsaywaman / Adios, pueblo de mi waycho / Chupsizinatay yacu / Noches de luna / Festival in Laja / Selection of sekuris / Indian street musician / Aguita de putina / Chofercito / Los senors de potasi / Brass band.
Compact disc: released on Coda, Jan'85 by Coda Records. Dist: Pinnacle, Cartel, WEA, Roots

Album: released on Coda, Nov'84 by Coda Records. Dist: Pinnacle, Cartel, WEA, Roots

Cassette: released on Coda, Nov'84 by Coda Records. Dist: Pinnacle, Cartel, WEA, Roots

Album: released on Coda, Nov'84 by Coda Records. Dist: Pinnacle, Cartel, WEA, Roots

Incas, Los
EL CONDOR PASA.
Double Album: released on Phonogram, Aug'75 by Phonogram Records. Dist: Polygram

EL VIENTO.
Album: released on Festival, '74 Dist: Swift

LOS INCAS.
Album: released on Impact (import), Mar'79 Dist: IMS, Polygram

MUSIC OF THE ANDES.
Double Album: released on Abbum, '74

Ince, Jan
CATCHEE MONKEY.
Tracks: / Catchee monkey / Room in your heart.
Single (7"): released on Zapu, Apr'87

Single (12"): released on Zapu, Apr'87

Incest
INCEST Various artists.
Cassette: released on Complex(R.A.P.), Mar'85 Dist: Complex (R.A.P.), Red Rhino, Cartel

INCEST (Various Artists).
Cassette: released on Complex(R.A.P.), Mar'85 Dist: Complex (R.A.P.), Red Rhino, Cartel

In Chancery
JOHN GALSWORTHY (In Chancery (Forsyte saga)).
Notes: Full details see under Galsworthy, John.

Incognito
INCOGNITO.
Single (7"): released on Ensign, Jun'81 by Ensign Records. Dist: CBS Distribution

Single (12"): released on Ensign, Jun'81 by Ensign Records. Dist: CBS Distribution

London Records. Dist: Polygram

JAZZ FUNK.
Album: released on Ensign, Apr'81 by Ensign Records. Dist: CBS Distribution

Cassette: released on Ensign, Apr'81 by Ensign Records. Dist: CBS Distribution

NORTH LONDON BOY.
Single (7"): released on Ensign, Nov'81 by Ensign Records. Dist: CBS Distribution

Single (12"): released on Ensign, Nov'81 by Ensign Records. Dist: CBS Distribution

In comes I' Tom Fool
IN COMES I' TOM FOOL Various Artists (Various Artists).
Notes: Plough play - Barrow-on-Humber (Lincs)
Cassette: released on Folktracks, Nov'79 Dist: Roots

Incredible Blondes
WHERE DO I STAND.
Single (7"): released on No Strings, Feb'87 Dist: Rough Trade, Cartel

Incredible Casuals
THAT'S THAT.
Album: released on Demon, Mar'87 by Demon Records. Dist: Pinnacle

Incredible Hulk
INCREDIBLE HULK IN A GAME OF MONSTERS AND KINGS various artists (Various Artists).
Cassette: released on MFP, Oct'85 by EMI Records. Dist: EMI

Incredible Journey
INCREDIBLE JOURNEY, THE Burnford, Sheila (Cribbins, Bernard).
Cassette: released on Pickwick Talking Books, '83

Incredible Mr.Freeze
BACK TO THE SCENE OF THE CRIME.
Tracks: / Frozen theme.
Single (7"): released on London, Aug'86 by London Records. Dist: Polygram

Single (12"): released on London, Aug'86 by London Records. Dist: Polygram

Incredibles
HEART AND SOUL.
Album: released on Contemporary, Oct'74 by Contemporary Records. Dist: Pinnacle

Incredible String Band
5000 SPIRITS.
Album: released on Elektra, '73 by WEA Records. Dist: WEA

Album: released on Elektra, '73 by WEA Records. Dist: WEA

EARTHSPAN.
Album: released on Island, '74 by Island Records. Dist: Polygram Deleted '79.

HANGMAN'S BEAUTIFUL DAUGHTER.
Album: released on Island, '74 by Island Records. Dist: Polygram Deleted '79.

HARD ROPE & SILKEN TWINE.
Album: released on Island, '74 by Island Records. Dist: Polygram Deleted '79.

LIQUID ACROBAT AS REGARDS AIR.
Album: released on Island, '74 by Island Records. Dist: Polygram

NO RUINOUS FEUD.
Album: released on Island, '74 by Island Records. Dist: Polygram Deleted '79.

WEE TAM.
Album: released on Elektra, '73 by WEA Records. Dist: WEA

In Crowd
ADD A LITTLE LIGHT.
Single (12"): released on Smokey, Dec'82 Dist: Jetstar

BACK A YARD.
Single (12"): released on Revue, May'83 by Revue Records. Dist: Creole

HIS MAJESTY IS COMING.
Album: released on Cactus, Jun'78 by Creole Records. Dist: CBS

MAN FROM NEW GUINEA.
Cassette: released on Island, Oct'79 by Island Records. Dist: Polygram

Incubus
TO THE DEVIL A DAUGHTER.
Album: released on Guardian, Aug'84 by Guardian Records. Dist: Jazz Music, Pinnacle

Ind Coope...

GLASS OF BRASS, A (Ind Coope Burton Brewery Brass Band).
Album: released on Bandleader, Sep'84 by Bandleader Records. Dist: PRT

Cassette: released on Bandleader, Sep'84 by Bandleader Records. Dist: PRT

Indeep

GIRL'S GOT SOUL.
Single (7"): released on Becket, Jun'84

Single (12"): released on Becket, Jun'84

LAST NIGHT A DJ SAVED MY LIFE.
Single (7"): released on Sound Of New York, Jan'83 by Sound Of New York Records. Dist: PRT

Single (12"): released on Sound Of New York, Jan'83 by Sound Of New York Records. Dist: PRT

PYJAMA PARTY TIME.
Album: released on Becket, Apr'84

Cassette: released on Becket, Apr'84

RECORD KEEPS SPINNING.
Single (12"): released on Becket, Jan'84

Single (7"): released on Becket, Jan'84

WHEN BOY'S TALK.
Single (7"): released on Sound Of New York, Apr'83 by Sound Of New York Records. Dist: PRT

Single (12"): released on Sound Of New York, Apr'83 by Sound Of New York Records. Dist: PRT

Independents

FIRST TIME WE MET The greatest hits.
Tracks: / I found love on a rainy day / First time we met / I just want to be there / Leaving me / It's all over / Let this be a lesson to you / No wind no rain / Just as long as you need me (Parts 1&2) / Sara Lee / Baby I've been missing you / Couldn't hear nobody say (I love you like I do).
Notes: Courtesy of Gusto Records, under license from CBS Special Products, a service of CBS Records, a division of CBS Inc. This compilation (P) 1986 Charly Records Ltd(C) Charly Records Ltd.
Album: released on Charly, Nov'86 by Charly Records. Dist: Charly, Cadillac

Inder, Paul

EDIT.
Single (7"): released on Electro, Feb'82 Dist: Pinnacle

Inder, Paul Band

CHELSEA GIRL.
Single (7"): released on Hippodrome, Nov'83 Dist: EMI

Single (12"): released on Hippodrome, Nov'83 Dist: EMI

DON'T SAY GOODNIGHT.
Single (7"): released on Hippodrome, Apr'84 Dist: EMI

EDIT.
Single (7"): released on Electro, Feb'82 Dist: Pinnacle

Indestructable Beat

INDESTRUCTABLE BEAT OF SOWETO various artists (Various Artists).
Album: released on Earthworks Int., Sep'85 by Earthworks Records. Dist: Earthworks Distributors, Rough Trade, Cartel, Projection

Index

LOVE YOU'VE BEEN FAKIN'.
Single (7"): released on Excalibur, Aug'82 by Red Bus Records. Dist: PRT

Single (12"): released on Excalibur, Aug'82 by Red Bus Records. Dist: PRT

STARLIGHT.
Single (7"): released on Record Shack, Sep'81 by Record Shack Records. Dist: PRT

India

CLASSICAL MUSIC OF INDIA Master of the Sarangi (Various Artists).
Album: released on Nonesuch Explorer (USA), '79

FOLK MUSIC OF INDIA Orissa (Various Artists).
Album: released on Lyrichord (USA), Oct'81 by Lyrichord Records (USA). Dist: Flexitron Distributors Ltd

FOLK MUSIC OF INDIA-UTTAR PRADESH (Various Artists).
Album: released on Lyrichord (USA), Oct'81 by Lyrichord Records (USA). Dist: Flexitron Distributors Ltd

FOLK MUSIC OF INDIA ORISSA.
Album: released on Lyrichord (USA), Jan'82by Lyrichord Records (USA). Dist: Flexitron Distributors Ltd

FOLK MUSIC OF INDIA UTTAR PRADESH.
FOLK SONGS OF KASHMIR various artists (Various Artists).
Album: released on Lyrichord (USA), Oct'81 by Lyrichord Records (USA). Dist: Flexitron Distributors Ltd

FOLK SONGS OF NEPAL various artists (Various Artists).
Album: released on Lyrichord (USA), Oct'81 by Lyrichord Records (USA). Dist: Flexitron Distributors Ltd

INSTRUMENTAL DANCES OF INDIA various artists (Various Artists).
Album: released on Nonesuch Explorer (USA), Jul'84

LOWER CASTE RELIGIOUS MUSIC IN INDIA various artists (Various Artists).
Album: by Lyrichord Records (USA). Dist: Flexitron Distributors Ltd Deleted Oct'81.

MIDDLE CASTE RELIGIOUS MUSIC FROM INDIA various artists (Various Artists).
Album: released on Lyrichord (USA), Oct'81 by Lyrichord Records (USA). Dist: Flexitron Distributors Ltd

MUSIC OF INDIA Balachander & Sivaraman (Various Artists).
Album: released on Nonesuch Explorer (USA), '74

TALES FROM INDIA, VOL. 1 various artists (Various Artists).
Album: released on Anvil, Apr'80 Dist: Anvil

TALES FROM INDIA, VOL. 2 various artists (Various Artists).
Album: released on Anvil, Apr'80 Dist: Anvil

TRADITIONAL MUSIC OF INDIA various artists (Various Artists).
Album: released on Nonesuch Explorer (USA), Jul'84

Indiana Jones

INDIANA JONES & THE TEMPLE OF DOOM Original Soundtrack (Indiana Jones & The Temple of Doom).
Compact disc: released on Polydor, Aug'84 by Polydor Records. Dist: Polygram, Polydor

Album: released on Polydor, Jul'84 by Polydor Records. Dist: Polygram, Polydor Deleted '87.

Cassette: released on Polydor, Jul'84 by Polydor Records. Dist: Polygram, Polydor

Album: released on Disney, Oct'84 by BBC Records & Tapes. Dist: BBC Records & Tapes, PRT

Cassette: released on Disney, Oct'84 by BBC Records & Tapes. Dist: BBC Records & Tapes, PRT

Indian Monks

PAPPADUM PAPPADUM.
Single (7"): released on Battersea, Jul'83 by Battersea Records. Dist: Pinnacle

Single (12"): released on Battersea, Jul'83 by Battersea Records. Dist: Pinnacle

Indians

DANCE ON.
Album: released on Hawk, Jan'78 by Dolphin Records. Dist: I & B, Celtic Music, Solomon & Peres Distribution

Cassette: released on Hawk, Jan'78 by Dolphin Records. Dist: I & B, Celtic Music, Solomon & Peres Distribution

INDIAN COUNTRY.
Album: released on Hawk, '74 by Dolphin Records. Dist: I & B, Celtic Music, Solomon & Peres Distribution

INDIAN RESERVATION.
Album: released on Hawk, '74 by Dolphin Records. Dist: I & B, Celtic Music, Solomon & Peres Distribution

MAGNIFICENT SEVEN.
Album: released on Hawk, Jun'75 by Dolphin Records. Dist: I & B, Celtic Music, Solomon & Peres Distribution

Album: released on EMI, May'85 by EMI Records. Dist: EMI

Cassette: released on EMI, May'85 by EMI Records. Dist: EMI

WE'RE JUST INDIANS.
Album: released on Hawk, Sep'76 by Dolphin Records. Dist: I & B, Celtic Music, Solomon & Peres Distribution

Indians In Moscow

BIG WHEEL (EP).
Single (12"): released on Kennick Music, Sep'84

INDIANS IN MOSCOW.
Album: released on Kennick Music, Nov'84

Cassette: released on Kennick Music, Nov'84

I WISH I HAD.
Single (7"): released on Kennick Music, Mar'84

JACK PELTER & HIS SEX-CHANGE CHICKEN.
Single (7"): released on Kennick Music, Jun'84

Single (12"): released on Kennick Music, Jun'84

MIRANDA.
Single (7"): released on Kennick Music, Nov'83

NAUGHTY MIRACLE.
Single (7"): released on Kennick Music, Nov'83

Indian Summer

INDIAN SUMMER.
Album: released on Concord Jazz(USA), Oct'83 by Concord Jazz Records (USA). Dist: IMS, Polygram

Indiapop Compilation

INDIAPOP COMPILASION ALBUM various artists (Various Artists).
Album: released on Virgin, Jul'82 by Virgin Records. Dist: EMI, Virgin Distribution

Album: released on Virgin, Jul'82 by Virgin Records. Dist: EMI, Virgin Distribution

Indie Pop 20

INDIE TOP 20 (Various Artists).
Notes: Including: Erasure, New Order.
Cassette: released on Band Of Joy, Apr'87

Indifferent Dance

FLIGHT OF PURSUIT.
Single (7"): released on Centre, Oct'81 by Centre Records. Dist: Rough Trade

Indiscretion In Session

INDISCRETION IN SESSION various artists (Various Artists).
Album: released on Indiscreet, Feb'85 Dist: Red Rhino, Cartel

Indoor Games

ALL OF YOUR LIES.
Single (7"): released on Holyrood, May'83 by Holyrood Records. Dist: Pinnacle

Ind, Peter

AT THE DEN (Ind, Peter & Sal Mosca).
Album: released on Wave, Apr'79 by Charly Records. Dist: Charly

IMPROVISATIONS.
Album: released on Wave, Apr'79 by Charly Records. Dist: Charly

LOOKING OUT.
Album: released on Wave, Apr'79 by Charly Records. Dist: Charly

PETER IND SEXTET (Ind, Peter Sextet).
Album: released on Wave, Apr'79 by Charly Records. Dist: Charly

SOME HEFTY CATS (Ind, Peter & Dick Wellstood).
Album: released on Hefty Jazz, May'77 Dist: JSU, Swift, Wellard, Chris, Jazz Music, Cadillac Music

TIME FOR IMPROVISATIONS.
Album: released on Wave, Apr'79 by Charly Records. Dist: Charly

Indrax

STARLIGHT.
Single (7"): released on Record Shack, Sep'81 by Record Shack Records. Dist: PRT

Industrial Espionage

INDUSTRIAL ESPIONAGE (New York, Tokyo, Bonn, London) (Unknown).
Cassette: released on International Report, Oct'81 by Seminar Cassettes. Dist: Audio-Visual Library Services, Davidson Distribution, Eastern Educational Products Distrib., Forlaget Systime Distribution, MacDougall Distribution,

Records. Dist: EMI

Talktapes Distribution, Watkins Books Ltd Distribution, Norton, Jeff Distribution

Industrial Records Story

INDUSTRIAL RECORDS STORY various artists (Various Artists).
Album: released on Illuminated, Feb'85 by IKF Records. Dist: Pinnacle, Cartel, Jetstar

Industry

STATE OF THE NATION.
Single (7"): released on Capitol, Mar'84 by Capitol Records. Dist: EMI

Ineke, E

Free fair

In Embrace

INITIAL CARESS.
Single (12"): released on Glass, May'82 by Glass Records. Dist: Nine Mile, Rough Trade, Red Rhino, Play It Again Sam

LIVING DAYLIGHTS.
Single (7"): released on Glass, Sep'83 by Glass Records. Dist: Nine Mile, Rough Trade, Red Rhino, Play It Again Sam

PASSION FRUIT PASTELS.
Album: released on Glass, Mar'83 by Glass Records. Dist: Nine Mile, Rough Trade, Red Rhino, Play It Again Sam

ROOM UPSTAIRS, A.
Tracks: / Room upstairs, A / Room upstairs, A.
Single (7"): released on Glass, Dec'86 by Glass Records. Dist: Nine Mile, Rough Trade, Red Rhino, Play It Again Sam

Single (12"): released on Glass, Dec'86 by Glass Records. Dist: Nine Mile, Rough Trade, Red Rhino, Play It Again Sam

SHOUTING IN CAFES.
Single (7"): released on Cherry Red, Feb'85 by Cherry Red Records. Dist: Pinnacle

Single (12"): released on Cherry Red, Feb'85 by Cherry Red Records. Dist: Pinnacle

SONGS ABOUT SNOGGIN.
Album: released on Glass, Mar'87 by Glass Records. Dist: Nine Mile, Rough Trade, Red Rhino, Play It Again Sam

SUN BRINGS SMILES.
Single (7"): released on Glass, Feb'83 by Glass Records. Dist: Nine Mile, Rough Trade, Red Rhino, Play It Again Sam

THIS BRILLIANT EVENING.
Single (7"): released on Cherry Red, Oct'85 by Cherry Red Records. Dist: Pinnacle

Single (12"): released on Cherry Red, Oct'85 by Cherry Red Records. Dist: Pinnacle

TOO.
Album: released on Glass, Oct'83 by Glass Records. Dist: Nine Mile, Rough Trade, Red Rhino, Play It Again Sam

WHAT'S GOT INTO ME.
Single (7"): released on Glass, Jul'87 by Glass Records. Dist: Nine Mile, Rough Trade, Red Rhino, Play It Again Sam

YOU'RE HEAVEN SCENT.
Single (7"): released on Glass, Mar'84 by Glass Records. Dist: Nine Mile, Rough Trade, Red Rhino, Play It Again Sam

Single (12"): released on Glass, Mar'84 by Glass Records. Dist: Nine Mile, Rough Trade, Red Rhino, Play It Again Sam

In everything give thanks

IN EVERYTHING GIVE THANKS (SCRIPTURE SONGS) Various Artists (Various Artists).
Album: released on Dove, May'79 by Dove Records. Dist: Jetstar

In Excelsis

CARNIVAL OF DAMOCLES.
Single (7"): released on Jungle, Nov'83 by Jungle Records. Dist: Jungle, Cartel

LADDER OF LUST.
Single (12"): released on Jungle, Jun'84 by Jungle Records. Dist: Jungle, Cartel

ONE DAY.
Single (7"): released on In Ex, Oct'84 by In Ex Records. Dist: Red Rhino, Cartel

Single (12"): released on In Ex, Oct'84 by In Ex Records. Dist: Red Rhino, Cartel

PREY.
Album: released on Jungle, Feb'86 by Jungle Records. Dist: Jungle, Cartel

SWORD, (THE).
Single (12"): released on Jungle, Nov'83 by

Jungle Records. Dist: Jungle, Cartel

Infaction
LISTEN TO THE WISE MEN.
Single (7"): released on Lambs To The Slaughter, Jun'85 by Prism Records. Dist: Pinnacle, Red Rhino, Cartel

Infa Riot
KIDS OF THE 80'S.
Single (7"): released on Secret, Jul'82 by Secret Records. Dist: EMI

STILL OUT OF ORDER.
Album: released on Secret, Jul'82 by Secret Records. Dist: EMI

WINNER, THE.
Single (7"): released on Secret, Jul'82 by Secret Records. Dist: EMI

Infas
SOUND & FURY.
Album: released on Panache, Feb'84 by Panache Records. Dist: Island Deleted '85.

Cassette: released on Panache, Feb'84 by Panache Records. Dist: Island

SOUND & FURY (7").
Single (7"): released on Island, Mar'84 by Island Records. Dist: Polygram

Inferno
INFERNO Original Soundtrack (Emerson, Keith).
Album: released on Atlantic, Dec'80 by WEA Records. Dist: WEA

Inferno & Execute
SPLIT.
Album: released on Pusmort. Dec'86

Infinity
GRAND MIXER CUTS IT UP (Infinity feat. Grand Mixer).
Single (12"): released on Celluloid, Jul'83 by Charly Records. Dist: Charly

Influence
NO SURVIVORS.
Single (7"): released on Influence, May'83 by Rough Trade

Influx One
INFLUX ONE various independent groups (Various Artists).
Album: released on Zygo, Feb'81 by Zygo Records. Dist: Zygo Distribution

In fractured silence
IN FRACTURED SILENCE Various Artists (Various Artists).
Album: released on United Dairies, Aug'84 Dist: Rough Trade, Indies

Ingenbold, Ulrich
WINTEREISE (A winter journey) (Ingenbold, Ulrich & Hajo Weber).

Inge, William
BUS STOP & COME BACK LITTLE SHEBA William Inge.
Cassette: released on Caedmon(USA), Sep'85 by Caedmon (USA) Records. Dist: Gower, Taylors, Discovery

Ingram
NIGHT STALKERS.
Album: released on Other End, May'84 by Other End Records. Dist: PRT Distribution

WHEN YOU'RE HOT YOU'RE HOT.
Single (7"): released on Other End, May'84 by Other End Records. Dist: PRT Distribution

WITH YOU.
Single (7"): released on Other End, Jun'84 by Other End Records. Dist: PRT Distribution

Single (12"): released on Other End, Jun'84 by Other End Records. Dist: PRT Distribution

Ingram, James
ALWAYS.
Tracks: / Always (Instrumental).
Single (7"): released on Qwest, Jul'86 by WEA Records. Dist: WEA

Single (12"): released on Qwest, Jul'86 by WEA Records. Dist: WEA

BETTER WAY'.
Single (7"): released on MCA, Aug'87 by MCA Records. Dist: Polygram, MCA

Single (12"): released on MCA, Aug'87 by MCA Records. Dist: Polygram, MCA

IT'S YOUR NIGHT.
Tracks: / Party animal / Yh mo b there / She loves me (the best that I can be) / Try your love again / Whatever we imagine / One more rhythm / There's no easy way / It's your night / How do you keep the music playing?.
Compact disc: released on Qwest, '86 by WEA Records. Dist: WEA

Album: released on Warner Bros., Nov'83 by Warner Bros Records. Dist: WEA

Cassette: released on Warner Bros., Nov'83 by Warner Bros Records. Dist: WEA

IT'S YOUR NIGHT(B).
Single (12"): released on Warner Bros., Mar'85 by Warner Bros Records. Dist: WEA

Single (7"): released on Warner Bros., Mar'85 by Warner Bros Records. Dist: WEA

NEVER FELT SO GOOD.
Tracks: / Never felt so good / Red hot lover / Lately / Wings of my heart / Trust me / Tuff / Say hey / Love's been here and gone / Right back.
Album: released on Qwest, Aug'86 by WEA Records. Dist: WEA

Cassette: released on Qwest, Aug'86 by WEA Records. Dist: WEA

Compact disc: released on Warner Bros., '86 by Warner Bros Records. Dist: WEA

PARTY ANIMAL.
Single (7"): released on Qwest, Oct'83 by WEA Records. Dist: WEA

Single (12"): released on Qwest, Oct'83 by WEA Records. Dist: WEA

YAH MO BE THERE (Ingram, James/Michael McDonald).
Single (7"): released on Qwest, Jan'85 by WEA Records. Dist: WEA

Ingram, Johnny
CAN I TAKE YOU HOME TONIGHT?.
Single (7"): released on Mirror, Sep'85 by Priority Records. Dist: Priority Distribution

Single (12"): released on Mirror, Sep'85 by Priority Records. Dist: Priority Distribution

In harmony
IN HARMONY 2 Various Artists (Various Artists).
Album: released on CBS, Dec'81 by CBS Records. Dist: CBS

Cassette: released on CBS, Dec'81 by CBS Records. Dist: CBS

Inheritance
I STILL LOVE YOU.
Single (7"): released on Mynah, Nov'83 by Mynah Records. Dist: Mynah, ILA

In Hill House
SANCTUARY.
Single (7"): released on EMI, Sep'84 by EMI Records. Dist: EMI

Single (12"): released on EMI, Sep'84 by EMI Records. Dist: EMI

Single (7"): released on Seyscan, Mar'85 by Seyscan Records. Dist: Pinnacle

Ink Spots
20 GREATEST HITS.
Album: released on Nostalgia (USA), Dec'85 by Sonic Arts Corporation.

Cassette: released on Nostalgia (USA), Dec'85 by Sonic Arts Corporation.

BEST OF: THE INKSPOTS.
Cassette: released on Creole (Everest-Europa), Jul'84 by Creole Records. Dist: PRT, Rhino

Album: released on MFP, Sep'81 by EMI Records. Dist: EMI

Cassette: released on MFP, Sep'81 by EMI Records. Dist: EMI

GOLDEN GREATS: INK SPOTS.
Tracks: / If I didn't care / When swallows come / Back to capistrano / Whispering grass / Java jive / Do I worry / I don't want to set the world on fire / Don't get around much anymore / To each his own / I'll never smile again / Someone's rocking my dreamboat / We three / My prayer / Until the real thing comes along / No orchida for my lady / Gypsy, The / I'll get by / Maybe / You were only fooling / We'll meet again.
Notes: The Ink Spots had worldwide hits during the 30's and 40's. This new twenty track "Golden Greats" collection features virtually all their many classics.
Album: released on MCA, Feb'86 by MCA Records. Dist: Polygram, MCA

Cassette: released on MCA, Feb'86 by MCA Records. Dist: Polygram, MCA

GREATEST HITS: INK SPOTS.
Cassette: released on K-Tel Goldmasters, Sep'84 by K-Tel Records. Dist: K-Tel

INK SPOTS, THE.
Compact disc: released on K-Tel, '86 by K-Tel Records. Dist: Record Merchandisers Distribution, Taylors, Terry Blood Distribution, Wynd-Up Distribution, Relay Distribution, Pickwick Distribution, Solomon & Peres Distribution, Polygram

Album: released on Rhapsody, '74 by President Records. Dist: Taylors, Swift, Jazz Music, Wellard, Chris

JUST LIKE OLD TIMES.
Album: released on CBS, Mar'85 by CBS Records. Dist: CBS Deleted '87.

Cassette: released on CBS, Mar'85 by CBS Records. Dist: CBS

VERY BEST OF THE INKSPOTS.
Cassette: released on Hallmark, Jun'86 by Pickwick Records. Dist: Pickwick Distribution, PRT, Taylors

Cassette: released on Hallmark, Jun'86 by Pickwick Records. Dist: Pickwick Distribution, PRT, Taylors

VERY BEST OF THE INK SPOTS.
Compact disc:

VERY BEST OF THE INKSPOTS.
Compact disc: by DGR (Holland) Records. Dist: Target

Inmates
FIRST OFFENCE.
Album: released on Radar, Jan'80 by WEA Music Ltd. Dist: WEA, PRT

FIVE.
Album: released on Lolita, Dec'84 by Lolita Records. Dist: Rough Trade, Cartel

HEARTBEAT.
Single (7"): released on Radar, Apr'81 by WEA Music Ltd. Dist: WEA, PRT

ME AND THE BOYS.
Single (7"): released on WEA, Sep'81 by WEA Records. Dist: WEA

SHOT IN THE DARK.
Album: released on Radar, Sep'80 by WEA Music Ltd. Dist: WEA, PRT

Cassette: released on Radar, Sep'80 by WEA Music Ltd. Dist: WEA, PRT

Inna Feelings
BOYFRIEND.
Single (12"): released on Paradise, May'85 Dist: Jetstar, JSU, WEA

Inner Circle
BLAME IT ON THE SUN.
Album: released on Trojan, '83 by Trojan Records. Dist: PRT, Jetstar

GROOVIN' IN LOVE.
Tracks: / One way.
Single (12"): released on Charm, Jul'86 Dist: Jetstar

NEW AGE MUSIC.
Album: released on Island, Oct'80 by Island Records. Dist: Polygram

Cassette: released on Island, Oct'80 by Island Records. Dist: Polygram

SOMETHING SO GOOD.
Single: released on Carrere, Aug'82 by Carrere Records. Dist: PRT, Spartan

Inner City Express
SHOW ME WHERE YOUR FUNK IS.
Single (7"): released on Earlobe, Aug'81 by Earlobe Records. Dist: Pinnacle

Inner City Unit
BEER BACCY BINGO BENIDORM.
Album: released on Avatar, Sep'81 by Avatar Communications. Dist: CBS

MAXIMUM EFFECT, THE.
Album: released on Avatar, '82 by Avatar Communications. Dist: CBS

Cassette: released on Avatar, '82 by Avatar Communications. Dist: CBS

NEW ANATOMY.
Album: released on Demi Monde, Feb'85 Dist: Charly

Paradise Beach.
Single (7"): released on Riddle, Jul'80 by Riddle Records. Dist: Charly, Cartel

President's Tapes, The.
Album: released on Flicknife, Sep'85 by Flicknife Records. Dist: Spartan

Punkadelic.
Tracks: / Watching the grass grow / Space invaders / Polythene / Cars eat with autoface / God disco / Disco tango / Gas money / Alright on the flight / Blue rinse haggard robot / Bikborg.
Album: released on Flicknife, Jul'82 by Flicknife Records. Dist: Spartan

Album: released on Flicknife, Jul'82 by Flicknife Records. Dist: Spartan

Solitary Ashtray.
Single (7"): released on Riddle, Oct'79 by Riddle Records. Dist: Charly, Cartel

Inner City Unit & Nik Turner
BLOOD AND BONE.
Single (12"): released on Jettisoundz, Aug'83 Dist: Red Rhino, Cartel

Inner Force
CARNIVAL TIME.
Single (7"): released on Voida, Sep'84 by Voida Records. Dist: Jetstar

DON'T STOP I LIKE IT.
Single (12"): released on Voida, Oct'84 by Voida Records. Dist: Jetstar

HOLIDAY.
Single (7"): released on Music International, Aug'82 by Music International Records. Dist: Pinnacle

Inner Life
LET'S CHARGE IT UP.
Single (7"): released on Personal, Apr'85 by Personal Records. Dist: PRT

Single (12"): released on Personal, Apr'85 by Personal Records. Dist: PRT

NO WAY.
Single (12"): released on Personal, Apr'84 by Personal Records. Dist: PRT

Single (12"): released on Personal, Jun'84 by Personal Records. Dist: PRT

Inner Vibes
TRAIL AND CROSSES.
Tracks: / Me no respond.
Single (12"): released on Firehouse, May'86 Dist: Jetstar

Innes, Neil
DEAR FATHER CHRISTMAS.
Single (7"): released on Making Waves, Nov'85 by Making Waves Records.

HOW SWEET TO BE AM IDIOT.
Album: released on United Artists, Mar'75 Deleted '79.

HUMANOID BOOGIE.
Single (7"): released on PRT, Jan'84 by PRT Records. Dist: PRT

Single (12"): released on PRT, Jan'84 by PRT Records. Dist: PRT

OFF THE RECORD.
Album: released on MMC, Nov'83 by MMC Records. Dist: PRT Distribution, Pinnacle

THEM.
Single (7"): released on MMC, Mar'84 by MMC Records. Dist: PRT Distribution, Pinnacle

Inn Folk
ALL ALONG DOWN ALONG.
Cassette: released on Folktracks, Nov'79 by Folktracks Cassettes. Dist: Folktracks

Innocence & Experience
INNOCENCE & EXPERIENCE William Blake's poems of innocence & experience (Various Artists).
Album: released on Greenwich Village, Nov'79 by Sweet Folk All Records. Dist: Roots, Projection, Lightning, Celtic Music, Wellard, Chris

Innocents
ONE WAY LOVE.
Single (7"): released on Kingdom, Oct'80 by Kingdom Records. Dist: Kingdom

In progress
IN PROGRESS Various Artists (Various Artists).
Album: released on People Unite, Apr'84 by

People Unite Records. Dist: Jetstar, Rough Trade, Cartel, Pinnacle, Nine Mile

Insane

EL SALVADOR.
Single (7"): released on No Future, Jul'82 by No Future Records. Dist: Pinnacle, Rough Trade, Cartel

POLITICS.
Single (7"): released on Riot City, Oct'82 by Riot City Records. Dist: Revolver

WHY DIE.
Single (7"): released on Insane, Oct'82 by Insane Records. Dist: Cartel, Jungle

Insane Picnic

FOUR DAYS IN APRIL.
Cassette: released on Falling A, Nov'84 by Falling A Records. Dist: Falling A Distribution

MAGISTRATES & SAINTS.
Tracks: / Village boys / Ruin moon / Summer rain, The.
Single (12"): released on Waterfall, Oct'86 by Waterfall Records. Dist: Revolver, Cartel

ROMANCE.
Single (7"): released on Falling A, Oct'84 by Falling A Records. Dist: Falling A Distribution

Insanity

INSANITY 360 degree music experience (Various Artists).
Double Album: released on Black Saint Import, Jul'78

Insex

INNER SANCTION.
Single (7"): released on Dining Out, Jun'81 by Dining Out Records. Dist: IKF, Independent

LIFESPAN.
Single (7"): released on Dining Out, Jun'81 by Dining Out Records. Dist: IKF, Independent

Inside Moves

INSIDE MOVES Original soundtrack.
Album: released on Warner Brothers, Apr'81 by Warner Bros Records. Dist: WEA

Insignificance

INSIGNIFICANCE Shape of the Universe (Various Artists).
Album: released on ZTT, Aug'85 by Island Records. Dist: Polygram

Cassette: released on ZTT, Aug'85 by Island Records. Dist: Polygram Deleted '87.

Inspirational Choir

ABIDE WITH ME.
Tracks: / Sweet holy spirit.
Single (7"): released on Portrait, Dec'85 by CBS Records. Dist: CBS

Single (7"): released on Portrait, Nov'85 by CBS Records. Dist: CBS

HIGHER AND HIGHER.
Album: released on Portrait, Dec'86 by CBS Records. Dist: CBS

Cassette: released on Portrait, Dec'86 by CBS Records. Dist: CBS

IVE GOT A FEELING.
Single (7"): released on Portrait, Sep'85 by CBS Records. Dist: CBS

Single (12"): released on Portrait, Sep'85 by CBS Records. Dist: CBS

ONE LOVE.
Tracks: / Right there.
Single (7"): released on Portrait, Feb'86 by CBS Records. Dist: CBS

Single (12"): released on Portrait, Feb'86 by CBS Records. Dist: CBS

PICK ME UP.
Single (7"): released on Stiff, Nov'83 by Stiff Records. Dist: EMI, Record Services Distribution (Ireland)

Single (12"): released on Stiff, Nov'83 by Stiff Records. Dist: EMI, Record Services Distribution (Ireland)

SWEET INSPIRATION.
Tracks: / Sweet inspiration / People get ready / Up where we belong / One love / Jesus dropped the charges / I've got a feeling / You light up my life / Morning has broken / Amazing grace / What a friend we have in jesus / When he comes / od is / Abide with me.
Compact disc: released on CBS, Jan'86 by CBS Records. Dist: CBS

Album: released on Portrait, Nov'85 by CBS Records. Dist: CBS

(YOUR LOVE HAS LIFTED ME) HIGHER AND HIGHER.
Tracks: / (Your love has lifted me) Higher and higher / Amazing grace.
Single (7"): released on Portrait, Nov'86 by CBS Records. Dist: CBS

Single (12"): released on Portrait, Nov'86 by CBS Records. Dist: CBS

Inspiration Dance

INSPIRATION DANCE Various artists (Various Artists).
Album: released on Streetsounds. Sep'85

Instant Agony

FASHION PARADE.
Single (7"): released on Half Man-Half Biscuit, Feb'83 by Skeleton Records. Dist: Cartel

NICELY DOES IT.
Single (7"): released on Flicknife, Apr'84 by Flicknife Records. Dist: Spartan

NO SIGN OF LIFE.
Single (7"): released on Flicknife, Jul'83 by Flicknife Records. Dist: Spartan

THINK OF ENGLAND.
Single (7"): released on Half Man-Half Biscuit, Aug'82 by Skeleton Records. Dist: Cartel

Instant Disco

INSTANT DISCO Various artists (Various Artists).
Album: released on Pye, Nov'75 Deleted '78.

Instant Funk

FUNK IS ON, THE.
Album: released on Salsoul, Nov'80

INSTANT FUNK.
Album: released on Salsoul, Mar'83

WHY DON'T YOU THINK ABOUT ME.
Single (12"): released on Battersea, Jun'82 by Battersea Records. Dist: Pinnacle

Instant Replays

INSTANT REPLAYS Various artists (Various Artists).
Album: released on Polydor, Jan'78 by Polydor Records. Dist: Polygram, Polydor

Instant Sunshine

INSTANT SUNSHINE LP, THE Song for struggling supergroups.
Album: released on Note, Nov'80 by EMI Records. Dist: EMI Deleted '83.

Cassette: released on Note, Nov'80 by EMI Records. Dist: EMI

Instigators

BOOM.
Single (12"): released on Shuttle, Aug'83 Dist: RCA

HAWAII 5-0 THEME.
Single (7"): released on Shuttle, Apr'85 by RCA

Single (12"): released on Shuttle, Apr'85 by RCA

IT HAS TO BE SPOTTED.
Cassette: released on 96 Tapes, Mar'85 by 96 Tapes Records. Dist: Rough Trade, Cartel

NOBODY LISTENS ANYMORE.
Album: released on Bluurg, Jun'85 by Bluurg Records. Dist: Rough Trade, Nine Mile

PHOENIX.
Album: released on Bluurg, Jan'87 by Bluurg Records. Dist: Rough Trade, Nine Mile

Instrumental...

INSTRUMENTAL EXPLOSION Various artists (Various Artists).
Album: released on Diamond, Jun'78 by Diamond Records. Dist: Spartan Deleted May'79.

INSTRUMENTAL GOLD Various artists (Various Artists).
Special: released on Effects Gold, Nov'80 by Ronco Records. Dist: Ronco Records

Special: released on Effects Gold, Nov'80 by Ronco Records. Dist: Ronco Records

INSTRUMENTAL HITS (VOL.1) Various artists (Various Artists).
Double Album: released on Cambra, Aug'83 by Cambra Records. Dist: IDS, Conifer

Double cassette: released on Cambra, Aug'83 by Cambra Records. Dist: IDS, Conifer
Cat. no: CRT 077

INSTRUMENTALLY YOURS Various artists (Various Artists).
Double Album: released on Calibre, Oct'83 by Calibre Records. Dist: PRT

Double cassette: released on Calibre, Oct'83 by Calibre Records. Dist: PRT Deleted May'85.

INSTRUMENTAL RARITIES Various artists (Various Artists).
Album: released on See For Miles, Jan'85 by Charly Records. Dist: Spartan

INSTRUMENTAL REGGAE HITS Various artists (Various Artists).
Extended-play record: released on Trojan, May'83 by Trojan Records. Dist: PRT, Jetstar

INSTRUMENTAL ROCK Various artists (Various Artists).
Tracks: / Reveille rock / McDonalds cave / Let there be drums / Perfidia / You can't sit down (pt.2) / Memphis / Topsy (pt.2) / Bumble boogie / Raunchy / Bust out / F.B.I. / Walk don't run / Guitar boogie shuffle / Mexican / Saturday nite at the duckpond / Gypsy beat / Cruel sea / Trambone / Swingin' low / Beat girl (main title).
Notes: / A unique collection of the great instrumental gems that rocked the world during the turn of the 60's, 20 classics tracks from B.Bumble, Sandy Nelson, The Ventures, The Shadows, John Barry, Bert Weedon etc.
Album: released on MFP, Apr'86 by EMI Records. Dist: EMI

Cassette: released on MFP, Apr'86 by EMI Records. Dist: EMI

Instrumental magic

INSTRUMENTAL MAGIC Various Orchestras (Various Orchestras).
Album: released on Sonic, Nov'76

INSTRUMENTAL MAGIC VOLS 1&2 Various artists (Various Artists).
Double Album: released on Telstar, Jan'83 by Telstar Records. Dist: RCA Distribution

Double cassette: released on Telstar, Jan'83 by Telstar Records. Dist: RCA Distribution

INSTRUMENTAL MAGIC VOL.1 (Various Artists).
Compact disc: released on Telstar, Jul'87 by Telstar Records. Dist: RCA Distribution

INSTRUMENTAL MAGIC VOL.2.
Compact disc: released on Telstar, Jul'87 by Telstar Records. Dist: RCA Distribution

In Swing

DON'T YOU CALL MY NAME.
Tracks: / Reason why / Come on.
Single (7"): released on Inasense, Mar'86 by Inasense Records. Dist: Inasense

Intaferon

GET OUT OF LONDON.
Single (12"): released on Chrysalis, Aug'83 by Chrysalis Records. Dist: CBS

Intence

TRIADE.
Album: released on Sky (Germany), Aug'85

Intensified

INTENSIFIED Various artists (Various Artists).
Album: released on Island, Jul'79 by Island Records. Dist: Polygram

MORE INTENSIFIED VOL.2 (Various Artists).
Cassette: released on Island, Mar'80 by Island Records. Dist: Polygram

Album: released on Island, Mar'80 by Island Records. Dist: Polygram

MORE INTENSIFIED: VOL 2 Various artists (Various Artists).
Cassette: released on Island, Mar'80 by Island Records. Dist: Polygram

Intercommunal music

INTERCOMMUNAL MUSIC Various artists (Various Artists).
Album: released on Shandar Import, Mar'78 Deleted May'79.

Interface

AUTOMATION.
Single (7"): released on Blue Beat, May'82 by Blue Beat. Dist: Pinnacle

LOUDER THAN WORDS.
Single (7"): released on Clone, Mar'82 Dist: Spartan

Single (12"): released on Clone, Mar'82 Dist: Spartan

MEMORIES.
Single (7"): released on Embryo Arts, Dec'84

---

by Embryo Arts Records. Dist: Plankton Distribution

Intergalactic...

INTERGALACTIC TOURING BAND (Intergalactic touring band).
Album: released on Charisma, Dec'77 by Virgin Records. Dist: EMI Deleted May'79.

Interiors

INTERIORS.
Album: released on Windham Hill (Germany), Jul'86

Interlude Orchestra

ROMANTIC THEMES.
Tracks: / Only love / Hello / Woman in love / Why worry - local hero / Terms of endearment / September morn' / Somewhere / Samba pa ti / Theme from the Thornbirds / Arthur's theme / Out of Africa.
Compact disc: released on K-Tel, Jun'87 by K-Tel Records. Dist: Record Merchandisers Distribution, Taylors, Terry Blood Distribution, Wynd-Up Distribution, Relay Distribution, Pickwick Distribution, Solomon & Peres Distribution, Polygram

International...

INTERNATIONAL GATHERING OF THE CLANS Various artists (Various Artists).
Album: released on EMI, Jun'77 by EMI Records. Dist: EMI Deleted May'79.

INTERNATIONAL ROCKERS Various artists (Various Artists).
Album: released on Ethnic Fight, Aug'76 by Ethnic Fight Records. Dist: Spartan Deleted May'78.

INTERNATIONAL STARS OF TALK OF THE TOWN Various artists (Various Artists).
Double cassette: released on Double-Up, Jul'75 by EMI Records.

INTERNATIONAL VIRTUOSOS OF THE ACCORDION Various artists (Various Artists).
Album: released on ARC (Accordion Records), May'84 Dist: Accordion Record Club

International Athlete's

POWER FROM WITHIN'.
Tracks: / Power within' (Inst version).
Single (7"): released on BBC, Aug'86 by BBC Records & Tapes. Dist: EMI, PRT

Single (12"): released on BBC, Aug'86 by BBC Records & Tapes. Dist: EMI, PRT

International Blue Duo

INTRODUCING.
Album: released on Crosscut, Nov'84 Dist: Rollercoaster Distribution, Swift

International Breakdown

F.... BASTARDS.
Single (7"): released on Rebel, Nov'85 Dist: PRT

International Jazz Group

IN NEW YORK 1956/57.
Album: released on Swing Disque, May'87

International Pop

AL LAST(27 NON-STOP CLASSICS).
Album: released on Contour, Oct'74 by Pickwick Records. Dist: Pickwick Distribution, PRT
Cat. no: 2870 387

PERCUSSION AROUND THE WORLD.
Album: released on Phase 4, May'62

International Praise

INTERNATIONAL PRAISE Various Salvation Army Participants (Various Artists).
Album: released on Word, May'79 by Word Records. Dist: Word Distribution, CBS

International Report

POLLUTION AND INDUSTRY.
Cassette: released on International Report, Oct'81 by Seminar Cassettes. Dist: Audio-Visual Library Services, Davidson Distribution, Eastern Educational Products Distrib., Forlaget Systime Distribution, MacDougall Distribution, Talktapes Distribution, Watkins Books Ltd Distribution, Norton, Jeff Distribution

International Rescue

LIFE IN AN ELEVATOR.
Single (7"): released on Cowboy City, Sep'84 by Cowboy City Records. Dist: Rough Trade, Cartel

YOU NEED SHOES.
Single (7"): released on Cowboy City, Mar'84 by Cowboy City Records. Dist: Rough Trade, Cartel

Internationals

HOOTS MON.
Single (7"): released on Alan Wood, Nov'83 by

Alan Wood Records. Dist: Pinnacle

IT'S NOT UNUSUAL.
Single (7"): released on AWA, May'84 by AWA Records. Dist: Pinnacle

International Submarine
SAFE AT HOME.
Album: released on L.H.I., Jul'78 Deleted May'79.

Album: released on Stainless, Sep'85 by Sonet Records. Dist: PRT Distribution

International Velvet
INTERNATIONAL VELVET Original soundtrack.
Album: released on MGM, Aug'78 Dist: Polygram Distribution, Swift Distribution Deleted May'79.

Interplanetry Sound
CLOSE ENCOUNTERS.
Album: released on Hallmark, Apr'78 by Pickwick Records. Dist: Pickwick Distribution, PRT, Taylors Deleted May'79.

Interplay
PRETTY FACE(ZIZI JEANMARIE).
Single (7"): released on Carrere America (USA), Jan'82 by Polygram.

Single (12"): released on Carrere America (USA), Jan'82 by Polygram.

Intestines
LIFE IN A CARDBOARD BOX.
Single (7"): released on Alternative, Jan'81 Dist: PRT

In the....
IN THE GLENN MILLER MOOD Various Artists (Various Artists).
Cassette: released on AIM (Budget Cassettes), Feb'83

IN THE STILL OF THE NIGHT Various Artists (Various Artists).
Album: released on Capitol, Nov'81 by Capitol Records. Dist: EMI

Cassette: released on Capitol, Nov'81 by Capitol Records. Dist: EMI

In the beginning
IN THE BEGINNING Various Artists (Various Artists).
Album: released on Capitol, Sep'85 by Capitol Records. Dist: EMI

Cassette: released on Capitol, Sep'85 by Capitol Records. Dist: EMI

In the groove
IN THE GROOVE - THE 12 INCH DISCO PARTY Various Artists (Various Artists).
Album: released on Telstar, May'83 by Telstar Records. Dist: RCA Distribution

Cassette: released on Telstar, May'83 by Telstar Records. Dist: RCA Distribution

In the heat of the night
IN THE HEAT OF THE NIGHT Various Artists (Various Artists).
Double cassette: released on Cambra, '83 by Cambra Records. Dist: IDS, Conifer

In the house of dark...
IN THE HOUSE OF DARK MUSIC Lynch, Frances.
Double cassette: released on Colophone, Sep'81 by Audio-Visual Library Services. Dist: Audio-Visual Library Services

In the Nursery
DEUS EX MACHINA.
Single (12"): released on Ner, Mar'85 by New European Records/Death in June. Dist: Rough Trade, Cartel

STORY HORSE, THE.
Album: released on Sweatbox, Jul'87 by Sweatbox Records. Dist: Rough Trade, Cartel

Cassette: released on Sweatbox, Jul'87 by Sweatbox Records. Dist: Rough Trade, Cartel

TEMPER.
Single (12"): released on Sweatbox, Nov'85 by Sweatbox Records. Dist: Rough Trade, Cartel

TRINITY.
Single (12"): released on Sweatbox, Jun'87 by Sweatbox Records. Dist: Rough Trade, Cartel

TWINS.
Album: released on Sweatbox, Sep'86 by Sweatbox Records. Dist: Rough Trade, Cartel

---

WHEN CHERISHED DREAMS COME TRUE.
Album: released on Paragon, Jul'83 by Paragon Records. Dist: Paragon

WITNESS TO A SCREAM.
Single (7"): released on Paragon, Mar'84 by Paragon Records. Dist: Paragon

In The Summertime
IN THE SUMMERTIME various artists (Various Artists).
Compact disc: released on Bellaphon, '86 by Bellaphon Records. Dist: IMS-Polygram

In the world but not...
IN THE WORLD BUT NOT OF IT Van Renen, Daphne.
Cassette: released on Seminar Cassettes, Oct'81 by Seminar Cassettes. Dist: Davidson Distribution, Eastern Educational Products Distrib., Forlaget Systeme Distribution, Laser Books Ltd Distribution, MacDougall Distribution, Talktapes Distribution, Watkins Books Ltd Distribution, Norton, Jeff Distribution

Intl-Illimani
CANTO PARA UNA SEMILLA.
Album: released on Monitor (USA), Sen'84

Cassette: released on Monitor (USA), Sep'84

CANTO Y BAILE.
Tracks: / Mi chiquita / Dedica toria de un libro / Cantiga de la memoria rota / Bailando / Candidos / El colibri / El vals / La muerte no va conmigo / Danza de calaluna.
Notes: The music playes by Chilian folk group Inti-Illimani, at present in exile in Italy, is drawn mainly from Latin American Folk sources and performed on traditional instruments. Inti-Illimani tour all over Europe and have appeared here in the UK with guitarist John Williams.
Compact disc: released on Messidor (Germany), Jan'87 Dist: IMS Distribution, Polygram

RETURN OF THE CONDOR.
Album: released on BBC, May'84 by BBC Records & Tapes. Dist: EMI, PRT,

Cassette: released on BBC, May'84 by BBC Records & Tapes. Dist: EMI, PRT,

VIVA CHILE.
Tracks: / La fiesta de san benito / Longuita / Cancion del poder popular / Alturas / La segunda / Independancia / Cuenca de la C.U.T. / Tatai / Venceremos / Ramis / Rin del angelito / Subi-a / Simon Bolivar.
Cassette: released on EMI Europe, Sep'86 by EMI Records. Dist: Conifer

VOL 6/CANCION PARA MATAR UNA CULEBRA.
Album: released on Monitor (USA), Jan'84

Cassette: released on Monitor (USA), Jan'84

Intimate Disco
INTIMATE DISCO Various artists (Various Artists).
Album: released on Ebonite, Nov'77 Deleted May'79.

Intimate Moments
INTIMATE MOMENTS Original soundtrack.
Album: released on That's Entertainment, Apr'83 by That's Entertainment Records. Dist: Pinnacle, PRT

Intimate Obsessions
ASSASSIN.
Single (12"): released on Third Mind, Oct'85 by Third Mind Records. Dist: Backs, Cartel Distribution

EREBUS TO HADES.
Album: released on Third Mind, Jun'85 by Third Mind Records. Dist: Backs, Cartel Distribution

Intimate Strangers
BLUE HOUR.
Tracks: / Into the wilderness.
Single (7"): released on IRS, Nov'86 Dist: Polygram

Single (12"): released on IRS, Nov'86 Dist: Polygram

CHARM.
Tracks: / Let go / In the wilderness / Flame on / Deliverance / Child of the dust / Struck by lightning / My brilliant career / Raise the dragon / Blue hour / What are we waiting for.
Notes: Intimate strangers are Richard Spellman and Sean Lyons. This is their debut album "Charm".
Album: released on IRS, May'86 Dist: Polygram

Cassette: released on IRS, May'86 Dist: Polygram

IN THE WILDERNESS.
Single (7"): released on IRS, Oct'85 Dist: Poly-

---

gram

Single (12"): released on IRS, Oct'85 Dist: Polygram

LET GO.
Tracks: / My brilliant career / Set me free.
Single (7"): released on I.R.S.(Independent Record Syndicate), May'86 by I.R.S.. Dist: MCA

Single (12"): released on I.R.S.(Independent Record Syndicate), May'86 by I.R.S.. Dist: MCA

RAISE THE DRAGON.
Tracks: / Worlds apart.
Single (12"): released on IRS, Mar'86 Dist: Polygram

Single (12"): released on IRS, Mar'86 Dist: Polygram

Into A Circle
FOREVER.
Single (12"): released on Abstract, Jul'87 by Abstract. Dist: Pinnacle

Single (7"): released on Abstract, Aug'87 by Abstract. Dist: Pinnacle

Single (12"): released on Abstract, Aug'87 by Abstract. Dist: Pinnacle

INSIDE OUT.
Tracks: / Inside out / Reward / Flow / Field of sleep.
Single (7"): released on Abstract, Nov'86 by Abstract. Dist: Pinnacle

Into the night
INTO THE NIGHT, Original soundtrack.
Album:

Cassette:

In touch
IN TOUCH Various Artists (Various Artists).
Double Album: released on Starblend (Solitaire Collection), Nov'83 by Starblend Records. Dist: PRT Distribution

Cassette: released on Starblend (Solitaire Collection), Nov'83 by Starblend Records. Dist: PRT Distribution

Intransit
MICRO ON THE MOVE.
Single (7"): released on Embryo Arts, Aug'85 by Embryo Arts Records. Dist: Plankton Distribution

OUT OF THE DARK.
Cassette: released on Plankton, Apr'84 by Plankton Records. Dist: Cantio (Sweden)

Single (7"): released on Plankton, Dec'84 by Plankton Records. Dist: Cantio (Sweden)

Intrigue
HEAVEN MADE.
Single (7"): released on Project, Jun'85 by Marvin Howell. Dist: Polygram

Single (12"): released on Project, Jun'85 by Marvin Howell. Dist: Polygram

I LIKE IT.
Single (12"): released on Pressure, Feb'83 Dist: Priority

LET SLEEPING DOGS LIE.
Single (7"): released on Music Power, Sep'84 Dist: Greyhound, Jetstar Distribution

Single (12"): released on Music Power, Sep'84 Dist: Greyhound, Jetstar Distribution

NO TURNING BACK.
Single (12"): released on Music Power Records, Apr'84 Dist: Greyhound, Jetstar Distribution

NO TURNS BACK.
Single (7"): released on Music Power, Jun'84 Dist: Greyhound, Jetstar Distribution

Intro
HAUNTED COCKTAILS.
Single (7"):

LOST WITHOUT YOUR LOVE.
Single (7"):

Single (12"):

Introducing...
INTRODUCING THE YAHAMA ORGAN STARS Various artists (Various Artists).
Album: released on Ad-Rhythm, May'72 by Ad-Rhythm. Dist: Ad-Rhythm Deleted May'77.

Introspection
INTROSPECTION various artists (Various Artists).
Tracks: / Body and soul / Louise / Introspection

/ We speak / Strength and sanity / S'wonderful / Into the orbit / Race for space / II.V.I.
Notes: Neglected jazz figures of the 1950's and early 1960's.Mono.
Album: released on New World (USA), Dec'86 by New World Records (USA). Dist: Conifer

Introze
LAMBETH WALK.
Single (7"): released on Monarch, Nov'82 by Chart Records. Dist: Pinnacle

In Tua Nua
HEAVEN CAN WAIT.
Tracks: / Heaven can wait / Belt me.
Single (7"): released on Virgin, Mar'87 by Virgin Records. Dist: EMI, Virgin Distribution

Single (12"): released on Virgin, Mar'87 by Virgin Records. Dist: EMI, Virgin Distribution

SEVEN INTO THE SEA.
Tracks: / Ballad of Irish love.
Single (7"): released on Virgin, Jun'86 by Virgin Records. Dist: EMI, Virgin Distribution

Single (12"): released on Virgin, Jun'86 by Virgin Records. Dist: EMI, Virgin Distribution

SOMEBODY TO LOVE.
Single (7"): released on Island, Apr'85 by Island Records. Dist: Polygram

Single (12"): released on Island, Apr'85 by Island Records. Dist: Polygram

TAKE MY HAND.
Single (12"): released on Island, Nov'84 by Island Records. Dist: Polygram

Single (7"): released on Island, Jan'85 by Island Records. Dist: Polygram

VAUDEVILLE.
Album: released on Virgin, Apr'87 by Virgin Records. Dist: EMI, Virgin Distribution

Cassette: released on Virgin, Apr'87 by Virgin Records. Dist: EMI, Virgin Distribution

Compact disc: released on Virgin, May'87 by Virgin Records. Dist: EMI, Virgin Distribution

In Two a Circle
RISE.
Single (12"): released on Temple, Aug'86 by Temple Records. Dist: Roots Distribution, Folksound Distribution, Celtic Music Distribution, Projection Distribution

Single (12"): released on Temple, Dec'85 by Temple Records. Dist: Roots Distribution, Folksound Distribution, Celtic Music Distribution, Projection Distribution

Invaders From Mars
INVADERS FROM MARS various artists (Various Artists).
Album: released on Enigma, Nov'86 by Enigma Records. Dist: Rough Trade, Cartel, EMI

Invaders Steelband
DISTANT HORSES.
Album: released on Telefunken, Apr'77 Deleted May'79.

GIMME DAT.
Album: released on Telefunken, May'78 Deleted May'79.

Inveraray Castle Ceilidh
INVERARAY CASTLE CEILIDH (Various Artists).
Album: released on Nevis, May'77 Dist: H.R. Taylor

Cassette: released on Nevis, May'77 Dist: H.R. Taylor

Inversions
LOCO-MOTO.
Single (7"): released on Groove PR, Oct'81 by Beggars Banquet Records. Dist: WEA, PRT

Single (12"): released on Groove PR, Oct'81 by Beggars Banquet Records. Dist: WEA, PRT

Investigators
BABY IT'S YOURS.
Single (12"): released on Private Eye, Jun'85 by Private Eye Records. Dist: Jetstar

DOUBTS TO THE WIND.
Single (12"): released on Private Eye, Dec'84 by Private Eye Records. Dist: Jetstar

FIRST CASE.
Album: released on Ice Music, Oct'82 Dist: Jetstar

HOW COULD I LET YOU GET AWAY.
Single (12"): released on Plastic, '79 by Plastic Records. Dist: Pinnacle Deleted '80.

LIVING IN A WORLD OF MAGIC.
Single (12"): released on Private Eye, Jul'83 by Private Eye Records. Dist: Jetstar

LOVING FEELING/WHERE DO WE GO.
Single 10": released on Private Eye, Dec'82 by Private Eye Records. Dist: Jetstar

WOMAN I NEED YOUR LOVING.
Single (12"): released on Private Eye, Jun'84 by Private Eye Records. Dist: Jetstar

Invisible
LOVE ST.
Tracks: / Sunday / Twilight zone.
Single (12"): released on Midnight Music, Oct'86 by Midnight Music Records. Dist: Rough Trade Distribution, Cartel Distribution

Invisible Man
INVISIBLE MAN By H.G.Wells (Harper, Gerald).
Cassette: released on Pickwick Talking Books, '83

Invisible Man's Band
ALL NIGHT THING.
Single (7"): released on Island, Jun'80 by Island Music Records. Dist: Polygram Deleted '81.

Single (12"): released on Island, Jun'80 by Island Music Records. Dist: Polygram Deleted '81.

Invitation To Denon
INVITATION TO DENON PCM (digital) jazz (Various Artists).
Album: released on Denon, '82 by Denon Records. Dist: Harmonia Mundi

Invitro
IN VITRO.
Tracks: / Man and woman / I choose you / Some little something / Left me the night / I suffer / Erase the moon / Secretary / Agony of sophistication / Lightning in the dark / Not my friend / So tight.
Album: released on Manhattan, '87 by EMI Records. Dist: EMI

Cassette: released on Manhattan, '87 by EMI Records. Dist: EMI

In Vogue
SPIES ON THE WIRE.
Single (7"): released on Unit, Sep'84 by Unit Records. Dist: PRT

In With The Old
IN WITH THE OLD Original cast recording (Various Artists).
Album: released on That's Entertainment, Dec'86 by That's Entertainment Records. Dist: Pinnacle, PRT

Inxs
DON'T CHANGE/YOU NEVER USED TO CRY.
Single (7"): released on Mercury, Jun'83 by Phonogram Records. Dist: Polygram Distribution

Single (12"): released on Mercury, Jun'83 by Phonogram Records. Dist: Polygram Distribution

I SEND A MESSAGE.
Single (7"): released on Mercury, May'84 by Phonogram Records. Dist: Polygram Distribution

JUST KEEP WALKING.
Single (7"): by RCA Records. Dist: RCA, Roots, Swift, Wellard, Chris, I & B, Solomon & Peres Distribution Deleted Sep'81.

KISS THE DIRT (FALLING DOWN THE MOUNTAIN).
Tracks: / Six knots / One thing, The / Spy of love.
Single (7"): released on Mercury, Aug'86 by Phonogram Records. Dist: Polygram Distribution

Single (12"): released on Mercury, Aug'86 by Phonogram Records. Dist: Polygram Distribution

LISTEN LIKE THEIVES (SINGLE).
Tracks: / Begotten.
Single (7"): released on Mercury, Jun'86 by Phonogram Records. Dist: Polygram Distribution

Single (12"): released on Mercury, Jun'86 by Phonogram Records. Dist: Polygram Distribution

LISTEN LIKE THEIVES.
Tracks: / What you need / Listen like theives / Kiss the dirt (falling down the mountain) / Shine like it does / Good and bad times / Biting bullets / This time / Three sisters / Same direction / One x one / Red red sun.
Notes: The new album from Australia's top

band-Inxs. Initial quantities will be available in a gatefold sleeve with a free copy of Inxs's 1984 album "The Swing". Produced by Chris Thomas (Pretenders, Roxy, Sex Pistols)-A really powerful album of modern rock.
Album: released on Mercury, Jan'86 by Phonogram Records. Dist: Polygram Distribution

Cassette: released on Mercury, Jan'86 by Phonogram Records. Dist: Polygram Distribution

Compact disc: released on Mercury, Jan'86 by Phonogram Records. Dist: Polygram Distribution

LIVING INXS (VIDEO).
Video-cassette (VHS): released on Video Collection, May'87 by Video Collection International Ltd.. Dist: Counterpoint

ONE THING, THE.
Single (7"): released on Mercury, Sep'83 by Phonogram Records. Dist: Polygram Distribution

Single (12"): released on Mercury, Sep'83 by Phonogram Records. Dist: Polygram Distribution

ORIGINAL SIN.
Single (7"): released on Mercury, Feb'84 by Phonogram Records. Dist: Polygram Distribution

Single (12"): released on Mercury, Feb'84 by Phonogram Records. Dist: Polygram Distribution

SWING.
Compact disc: released on Mercury, Jul'86 by Phonogram Records. Dist: Polygram Distribution

SWING AND OTHER STORIES.
Notes: A band from Australia with a growing UK popularity cult and some recent chart success, here performing eleven recent tracks. 1985 production.   Number of tracks: 11
Video-cassette (VHS): released on Polygram, Aug'86 by Polygram Records. Dist: Polygram

SWING, THE.
Album: released on Mercury, May'84 by Phonogram Records. Dist: Polygram Distribution

Cassette: released on Mercury, May'84 by Phonogram Records. Dist: Polygram Distribution. Estim retail price in Aug'87 was £6.55.

Compact disc: released on Mercury, Jul'84 by Phonogram Records. Dist: Polygram Distribution

THIS TIME.
Tracks: / Original sin / Burn for you / Dancing on the jetty (live) / Burn for you.
Single (7"): released on Mercury, Feb'86 by Phonogram Records. Dist: Polygram Distribution

Double-pack single: released on Mercury, Feb'86 by Phonogram Records. Dist: Polygram Distribution

Single (12"): released on Mercury, Feb'86 by Phonogram Records. Dist: Polygram Distribution

UNDERNEATH THE COLOURS.
Album: released on RCA, Mar'82 by RCA Records. Dist: RCA, Roots, Swift, Wellard, Chris, I & B, Solomon & Peres Distribution

WHAT YOU NEED.
Tracks: / Sweet as sin / What you need (remix) / What you need (live) / One thing, The (live).
Single (7"): released on Mercury, Apr'86 by Phonogram Records. Dist: Polygram Distribution

Single (12"): released on Mercury, Apr'86 by Phonogram Records. Dist: Polygram Distribution

Inylmbo
SONGS OF THE BEMBA PEOPLE OF ZAMBIA.
Album: released on Ethnodisc, Jan'78

I.O.U.
NO ENTRY/HOT BLOOD.
Single (7"): released on DJM, Aug'79 by DJM Records. Dist: CBS, Polygram Deleted '80.

Ipanima Kaz
NIGHT KIXX.
Single (7"): released on Official, Jul'85 by Official Records. Dist: Revolver Distribution, Cartel Distribution

Ipetty Sipetty
IPETTY SIPETTY Scots children's rhyme. Aberdeen etc..
Cassette: released on Folktracks, Nov'79 Dist: Roots

Ipi Tombi
IPI TOMBI Original South African stage (Various Artists).
Album: released on Chant du Monde, Jan'76 Dist: Harmonia Mundi

IPI TOMBI (ORIGINAL STAGE PRODUCTION EXTRACTS) (Various Artists).
Album: released on Galaxy, Nov'79 by Galaxy Records. Dist: RCA, Red Lightnin' Distribution, Discovery, Swift

Cassette: released on Galaxy, Nov'79 by Galaxy Records. Dist: RCA, Red Lightnin' Distribution, Discovery, Swift

IPI TOMBI (STAGE CAST RECORDING) (Various Artists).
Album: released on Ipi Tombi, '79 Dist: Spartan

Cassette: released on Ipi Tombi, '79 Dist: Spartan

I Plee
ALL NIGHT LONG.
Single (12"): released on Daybreak, Jun'84 Dist: Jazz Horizons, Jazz Music

Ippu Do
LUNATIC MENU.
Album: released on Epic, Jan'83 by CBS Records. Dist: CBS

Ipso Facto
GIVE IT TO HER.
Single (12"): released on Zodiak, Sep'84 by Zodiak Records. Dist: Red Rhino, Cartel

GLASS TIGERS.
Single (12"): released on Zodiac, May'85 Dist: Jazz Music

MANNEQUIN.
Single (7"): released on If, Sep'84 by Zodiac Records. Dist: Red Rhino, Cartel

NOIR DIOR.
Single (7"): released on If, Sep'84 by Zodiac Records. Dist: Red Rhino, Cartel

I.Q.
BABEL IS NOW.
Single (7"): released on Jim White, Oct'84 by Jim White Records. Dist: Swift

Single (12"): released on Jim White, Oct'84 by Jim White Records. Dist: Swift

BARBELL IS IN.
Single (12"): released on Sahara, Oct'84

CORNERS/THE THOUSAND DAYS.
Single (7"): released on Sahara, Oct'85

Single (12"): released on Sahara, Oct'85

IT ALL STOPS HERE.
Single (7"): released on Samurai, May'86 Dist: Pinnacle

LIVING PROOF.
Album: released on Samurai, Nov'86 Dist: Pinnacle

NOMZAMO.
Notes: Produced by Ken Thomas
Album: released on Vertigo, 11 Apr'87 by Phonogram Records. Dist: Polygram

Cassette: released on Vertigo, 11 Apr'87 by Phonogram Records. Dist: Polygram

Compact disc: released on Vertigo, May'87 by Phonogram Records. Dist: Polygram

PASSING STRANGERS.
Tracks: / Passing strangers / Nomzamo / No lives lost.
Single (7"): released on Vertigo, May'87 by Phonogram Records. Dist: Polygram

Single (12"): released on Vertigo, May'87 by Phonogram Records. Dist: Polygram

PROMISES (AS THE YEARS GO BY).
Single (7"): released on Squawk, Aug'87 by Vertigo Records. Dist: Polygram Distribution

Single (12"): released on Squawk, Aug'87 by Vertigo Records. Dist: Polygram Distribution

TALES FROM THE LUSH ATTIC.
Album: released on One Shoe, Jun'84 by One Shoe Records. Dist: Pinnacle

TALES OF THE LUSH ATTIC.
Cassette: released on Samurai, May'86 Dist: Pinnacle

WAKE, THE.
Compact disc: released on Samurai, '86 Dist: Pinnacle

Ipi Tombi
Album: released on Sahara, Jun'85

Cassette: released on Sahara, Jun'85

IQ Zero
SHE'S SO RARE/CANDY DOLLS.
Single (7"): released on Logo, Jun'80 by Logo Records. Dist: Roots, BMG Deleted '80.

Irakere
CATALINA.
Tracks: / Aguanile bonko / Juana 1600 / El tata / Preludio a catalina / Rucu rucu a santa clara.
Notes: This Cuban All Star Band, founded in 1972, were a major attraction at the Ronnie Acott Afro-Cuban Festival last year and have been awarded a Grammy for the best Jazz Formation. Trumpet star Arturo Sandoval is featured soloist on four of the six tracks.
Album: released on Messidor (Germany), Jan'87 Dist: IMS Distribution, Polygram

CULPADELO GUAO.
Album: released on Messidor (Germany), May'87 Dist: IMS Distribution, Polygram

Iranian Music
FOLK MUSIC OF IRAN (Various Artists).
Album: released on Lyrichord (USA), Oct'81 by Lyrichord Records (USA). Dist: Flexitron Distributors Ltd

IRANIAN MUSIC (Various Artists).
Compact disc: Dist: Harmonia Mundi

LIVING TRADITION-MUSIC FROM IRAN (Various Artists).
Album: released on Argo, '71 by Decca Records. Dist: Polygram Deleted '81.

MUSIC OF IRAN-SANTUR RECITAL (Resteger-Nejad, Nasser).
Album: released on Lyrichord (USA), Oct'81 by Lyrichord Records (USA). Dist: Flexitron Distributors Ltd

MUSIC OF IRAN-THE TAR (Samandar, Bijan).
Album: released on Lyrichord (USA), Oct'81 by Lyrichord Records (USA). Dist: Flexitron Distributors Ltd

Album: released on Lyrichord (USA), Oct'81 by Lyrichord Records (USA). Dist: Flexitron Distributors Ltd

PERSIAN HERITAGE, A Classical music of Iran (Various Artists).
Album: released on Nonesuch, '79

I Refuse It
WE HATE YOU.
Tracks: / We hate you.
Single (7"): released on Toto, May'86 Dist: Revolver

Ireland...
IRELAND'S COUNTRY QUEENS Ann Breen, Leon, Margo, Philomena Begley (Various Artists).
Album: released on Homespun(Ireland), Dec'82 by Outlet Records. Dist: Outlet

Cassette: released on Homespun(Ireland), Dec'82 by Outlet Records. Dist: Outlet

IRELAND'S C & W CARNIVAL (Various Artists).
Album: released on Homespun(Ireland), '75 by Outlet Records. Dist: Outlet

IRELAND'S C & W CARNIVAL VOL.2 (Various Artists).
Album: released on Homespun(Ireland), Jul'76 by Outlet Records. Dist: Outlet

IRELAND'S C & W CARNIVAL VOL.3 (Various Artists).
Album: released on Homespun(Ireland), Jan'77 by Outlet Records. Dist: Outlet

IRELAND'S OWN (Various Artists).
Notes: Inc:Susan McCann, Margo, Ann Breen, Philomena Begley.
Cassette: released on Homespun(Ireland), Jun'87 by Outlet Records. Dist: Outlet

Ireland's Own Barnbrack
IRISH PARTY SING-A-LONG.
Tracks: / Irish rover / Good-bye Mick / Banana song / Green glens of Antrim / Boys from Co. Armagh / Irish eyes are smiling / Nancy Spain / Leaving of Liverpool / Musheen Durkin / Alley alley O / Uncle Nobby's steamboat / My Aunt Jane / Aul Lammas fair / Gentle Annie / A mother's love's a blessing / Good-bye Johnny dear / Gentle mother / Phil the fluter / Paddy Reilly / Slatterys mounted fut / Three counties meet

/ My Eileen is waiting / Homes of Donegal / Westmeath batchelor / If you're Irish / Dear oul Donegal / B for Barney / Doffer, (The) / Boston burglar / Moonshiner / Hills of Connemara / Home boys home / Courtin' in the kitchen / As I roved out.
Album: released on Homespun(Ireland), Jul'87 by Outlet Records. Dist: Outlet

Cassette: released on Homespun(Ireland), Jul'87 by Outlet Records. Dist: Outlet

I Remember Mama

I REMEMBER MAMA (Various Artists).
Compact disc: Dist: Pinnacle

I REMEMBER MAMA various artists (Various Artists).
Album: released on TER, Oct'85 Dist: Pinnacle

Cassette: released on TER, Oct'85 Dist: Pinnacle

Compact disc: released on TER, Oct'85 Dist: Pinnacle

Irene

IRENE Musical (Various Artists).
Notes: An Irish shopgirl moves into society, breaking hearts wherever she goes.
Video-cassette (VHS): released on Video Collection, May'87 by Video Collection International Ltd.. Dist: Counterpoint

IRENE Original cast recording of 1920 London Production (Various Artists).
Album: released on Monmouth, Mar'79

Irie, David

TRASH 'N' READY.
Tracks: / Didn't you say you love me.
Single (12"): released on Ace, May'86 by Ace Records. Dist: Pinnacle, Swift, Hotshot, Cadillac

Irie, Tippa

COMPLAIN NEIGHBOUR.
Single (7"): released on UK Bubblers, Jul'85 by Greensleeves Records. Dist: RCA, Jetstar

Single (12"): released on UK Bubblers, Jul'85 by Greensleeves Records. Dist: RCA, Jetstar

DANCE DOWN A YARD.
Tracks: / Dance down a yard / Dance up a lead.
Single (12"): released on UK Bubblers, Feb'87 by Greensleeves Records. Dist: RCA, Jetstar

DANCE MOVES (Irie, Tippa & Pato Banton).
Single (12"): released on UK Bubblers, Feb'86 by Greensleeves Records. Dist: RCA, Jetstar

HEARTBEAT.
Tracks: / Live as one.
Single (7"): released on UK Bubblers, Jun'86 by Greensleeves Records. Dist: RCA, Jetstar

Single (12"): released on UK Bubblers, Jun'86 by Greensleeves Records. Dist: RCA, Jetstar

HELLO DARLING.
Tracks: / Hello darling (Insrumental) / Hello darling (Jazz version).
Single (7"): released on UK Bubblers, Mar'86 by Greensleeves Records. Dist: RCA, Jetstar

Single (12"): released on UK Bubblers, Mar'86 by Greensleeves Records. Dist: RCA, Jetstar

IS IT REALLY HAPPENING TO ME.
Tracks: / Unlucky burglar / It's good to have the feeling / You're the best (86 remix / Telephone, The / Heatbeat / Robotic reggae / Married life / Football hooligan / Complain neighbour / Hello darling / Is it really happening to me.
Album: released on Greensleeves, Sep'86 by Greensleeves Records. Dist: BMG, Jetstar, Spartan

Cassette: released on Greensleeves, Sep'86 by Greensleeves Records. Dist: BMG, Jetstar, Spartan

Compact disc: released on Greensleeves, Sep'86 by Greensleeves Records. Dist: BMG, Jetstar, Spartan

IT'S GOOD TO HAVE THE FEELING YOU'RE THE BEST.
Single (7"): released on UK Bubblers, Mar'85 by Greensleeves Records. Dist: RCA, Jetstar

Single (12"): released on UK Bubblers, Mar'85 by Greensleeves Records. Dist: RCA, Jetstar

JUST A SPEAK.
Single (12"): released on UK Bubblers, Aug'84 by Greensleeves Records. Dist: RCA, Jetstar

PANIC PANIC.
Tracks: / Panic panic (Instrumental).
Single (7"): released on UK Bubblers, Nov'86 by Greensleeves Records. Dist: RCA, Jetstar

Single (12"): released on UK Bubblers, Nov'86 by Greensleeves Records. Dist: RCA, Jetstar

TELEPHONE, THE.
Single (7"): released on UK Bubblers, Oct'85 by Greensleeves Records. Dist: RCA, Jetstar

Single (12"): released on UK Bubblers, Oct'85 by Greensleeves Records. Dist: RCA, Jetstar

Irie, Tonto

GENERAL A GENERAL.
Single (12"): released on Jammy's, Sep'84 by Jammy's Records. Dist: Jetstar

NA GET NOTHING.
Tracks: / Two foot walk (Shaka Demus).
Single (12"): released on Jammy's, Oct'86 by Jammy's Records. Dist: Jetstar

NEW YORK LIFE.
Tracks: / New York life (Vocal) / New York life (instrumental) / New York life (version) / Slim belly man / Slim belly man (Version).
Single (7"): released on Island, Jul'87 by Island Records. Dist: Polygram

Single (12"): released on Island, Jul'87 by Island Records. Dist: Polygram

Irie, Welton

JAILHOUSE AFFAIR.
Single (12"): released on Black Roots, Nov'82 by Black Roots Records. Dist: Jetstar

Single (12"): released on Black Roots, Nov'82 by Black Roots Records. Dist: Jetstar

Irish...

GOLDEN HOUR PRESENTS IRISH SHOWBAND HITS (Various Artists).
Album: released on Golden Hour, Apr'76 by PRT Records. Dist: PRT Deleted '80.

IRISH CEILIDH DANCE TIME (Various Artists).
Album: released on Harp(Ireland), Aug'83 by Pickwick Records. Dist: Taylors

Cassette: released on Harp(Ireland), Aug'83 by Pickwick Records. Dist: Taylors

IRISH COLLECTION VOL.1 Various artists (Various Artists).
Tracks: / Tom Billy's jigs / Brian Boru's march / Dogs among the bushes / Jenny's wedding / Mrs MacDermott / Munster buttermilk / Wind that shakes the barley / Morning on a distant shore / Cathleen Henir's / Old torn petticoat / Dublin reel / Wind that shakes the barley / Belfast hornpipe / Ask me father / Finbar dwyers / Oak tree / Lark on the strand / Michael Murphy's hornpipes / Tripping up the stairs (a trip to Athlone).
Cassette: released on Polydor (Ireland), Aug'86 by Polydor Records. Dist: Polygram, I & B

IRISH COLLECTION VOL.2 Various artists (Various Artists).
Tracks: / Gypsy savey / Home by bearna / Siobhan ni dhuibhir / Lakes of coolfin / Wexford fishing song / Cunla / An bothan a ghaig fionnghuala / Boys of Mullabawn / Life is just that way / Eighteen years old / Nil se ina la / Cold blow and rainy night.
Cassette: released on Polydor (Ireland), Aug'86 by Polydor Records. Dist: Polygram, I & B

IRISH DANCING Ceoltoiri ros na ri (Various Artists).
Album: released on Outlet (Ireland), Jul'76

IRISH EXPLOSION (Various Artists).
Album: released on Ember, '79 by Bulldog Records. Dist: President Distribution, Spartan, Swift, Taylor, H.R.

IRISH FAVOURITES Irish favourites (Various Artists).
Tracks: / Irish rover, the / Ducks of Magherlin / Four strong winds / Finnegan's wake / Trip to Rathlin / Golden jubilee / Old maid in a garrett / Balliderry / Carrickfergus / Castle fo Dromore, the / Reilly's daughter / Gem of the Roe, the / whiskey your the devil / Green fields of France / Doffer's song / Roisin dubh / Leavin of Liverpool.
Album: released on Emerald (Ireland), May'85 by Emerald Records. Dist: I & B, Ross, PRT

Cassette: released on Emerald Gem, Aug'85 Dist: Spartan, MK

IRISH FESTIVAL (Various Artists).
Album: released on Mulligan (Ireland), Sep'80 by Topic Records. Dist: Roots Distribution, Jazz Music Distribution, JSU Distribution, I & B Distribution, Projection Distribution, Wynd-Up Distribution, Celtic Distributions

Cassette: released on Mulligan (Ireland), Sep'80 by Topic Records. Dist: Roots Distribution, Jazz Music Distribution, JSU Distribution, I & B Distribution, Projection Distribution, Wynd-Up Distribution, Celtic Distributions

IRISH PARTY REQUESTS (Various Artists).
Album: released on Homespun(Ireland), Aug'78 by Outlet Records. Dist: Outlet

IRISH PIPE MUSIC (Various Artists).
Album: released on Nonesuch Explorer (USA), Jul'84

IRISH PUB SONG TIME 20 songs (Various Artists).
Album: released on Homespun(Ireland), Dec'83 by Outlet Records. Dist: Outlet

Cassette: released on Homespun(Ireland), Dec'83 by Outlet Records. Dist: Outlet

IRISH REBEL SONGS (Various Artists).
Album: released on Ace Of Clubs, '63 by Decca Records. Dist: Polygram Deleted '81.

IRISH SING RUGBY SONGS (Various Artists).
Album: released on Sportsdisc, Jul'80 by Sportsdisc Records. Dist: H.R. Taylor, MIS-EMI Distribution

IRISH STARTIME TRADITIONAL (Various Artists).
Album: released on Irish Startime, Jan'78 Dist: I & B

REBEL SONGS OF IRELAND 2 (Various Artists).
Album: released on Release (Ireland), '79

Irish Country Four

SONGS, BALLADS & INSTRUMENTAL TUNES FROM ULSTER.
Album: released on Topic, '81 Dist: Roots Distribution

Irish Folk

IRISH FOLK (Various Artists).
Album: released on Accordion Record Club, '84 by Accordion Record Club Records. Dist: Accordion Record Club

IRISH FOLK COLLECTION, THE (Various Artists).
Cassette: released on Tara (Ireland), Oct'85 by Tara Records. Dist: I & B Records Distribution, Record Services Distribution (Ireland), Roots Distribution

IRISH FOLK FAVOURITES (Various Artists).
Album: released on Harp(Ireland), Feb'82 by Pickwick Records. Dist: Taylors

Cassette: released on Harp(Ireland), Feb'82 by Pickwick Records. Dist: Taylors

IRISH FOLK FESTIVAL (Various Artists).
Notes: Featuring: The dubliners, Planxty, Moving Hearth & Christie Moore.
Compact disc: released on Sound, '86 Dist: Target

IRISH FOLK HITS Various artists (Various Artists).
Tracks: / Old maid in a garrett / Curragh of Killen Dragoons, the / Rising of the moon, the / Enniskillen dragoons / Nightingale, the / Sergeant Bailey / Bold Donoghue / Come to the bower / Jolly tinker, the / Irish soldier, the.
Cassette: released on Marble Arch, Aug'86 Dist: Taylors

IRISH FOLK PUB SING-A-LONG (Various Artists).

Irish Guards Band

CHANGING OF THE GUARD.
Album: released on Bandleader, Apr'82 by Bandleader Records. Dist: PRT

Cassette: released on Bandleader, Apr'82 by Bandleader Records. Dist: PRT

DRUMS & PIPES OF THE 1ST. BTN..
Album: released on Music Masters, Apr'81 by Music Masters Records. Dist: Taylors

MARCHES FROM THE CLASSICS.
Album: released on Bandleader, Nov'84 by Bandleader Records. Dist: PRT

Cassette: released on Bandleader, Nov'84 by Bandleader Records. Dist: PRT

Irish Mists

MOUNTAINS OF MOURNE, THE.
Single (7"): released on Ritz, Jul'85 by Outlet Records. Dist: Outlet, Prism Leisure Distribution, Record Services Distribution (Ireland), Roots

Irish Music

FORGOTTEN IRELAND, THE (Demers, Mary Murphy).

IRELAND'S BEST (Various Artists).
Album: released on Homespun(Ireland), Oct'79 by Outlet Records. Dist: Outlet

Cassette: released on Homespun(Ireland), Oct'79 by Outlet Records. Dist: Outlet

IRELAND'S BEST 15 SONGS (Various Artists).
Album: released on Homespun(Ireland), Dec'83 by Outlet Records. Dist: Outlet

Cassette: released on Homespun(Ireland), Dec'83 by Outlet Records. Dist: Outlet

IRELAND'S BEST ON RELEASE VOL.2 (Various Artists).
Album: released on Release (Ireland), '74

IRELAND'S BEST ON RELEASE VOL.4 (Various Artists).
Album: released on Release (Ireland), '74

IRELANDS BEST ON RELEASE VOL.5 (Various Artists).
Album: released on Release (Ireland), '74
Cat. no: **BRL 4029**

IRELAND'S BEST ON RELEASE (Various Artists).
Album: released on Release (Ireland), '74

IRELAND'S BEST ON RELEASE VOL.3 (Various Artists).
Album: released on Release (Ireland), '74

IRELAND THE ETERNAL (Various Artists).
Album: released on Arion, Jun'79 Dist: Discovery

IRISH CHRISTMAS PARTY (Various Artists).
Album: released on Homespun(Ireland), '82 by Outlet Records. Dist: Outlet

Cassette: released on Homespun(Ireland), '82 by Outlet Records. Dist: Outlet

IRISH REELS, JIGS & OTHERS (DUCK BAKER ETC.) Arranged for the guitar (Various Artists).
Album: released on Kicking Mule, Oct'79 by Sonet. Dist: Roots, PRT-Pye Distribution

LARK IN THE MORNING (Various Artists).
Album: released on Tradition, Nov'74 Dist: JSU, Cassion Distribution, Celtic Music, Jazz Music, Projection, Roots Records

TRAVELLING PEOPLE OF IRELAND Irish tinker music (Various Artists).
Album: released on Lyrichord (USA), Oct'81 by Lyrichord Records (USA). Dist: Flexitron Distributors Ltd

Irish Traditional...

IRISH TRADITIONAL CONCERTINA STYLES Various artists (Various Artists).
Album: released on Topic Records, Sep'86

IRISH TRADITIONAL MUSIC & BALLADS Various artists (Various Artists).
Tracks: / Shores of Lough Brae / O'Carolan Tribute / Nancy Spain.

IRISH TRADITIONAL MUSIC & BALLADS Various artists (Various Artists).
Tracks: / Shores of Lough Brae, the.

IRISH TRADITIONAL MUSIC & BALLADS Various artists (Various Artists).
Tracks: / Brian Boru's march / Shores of Lough Brae, the / O'Carolan tribute / Nancy Spain / Brian Boru's march / Danny boy / Leaving of Nancy, the / Gill Aodain / Paddy's green shamrock shore / Gipsy Dave / Glenbeigh hornpipe. mountain lark / Old rustic bridge, the / Nil se ina la / Gill Chais / Fanny Poer / Banks of Claudy, the.
Cassette: released on Alpine, Aug'86 by President Records. Dist: IMS-Polygram

Irma La Douce

IRMA LA DOUCE Various artists (Various Artists).
Tracks: / Dis-donc, dis-donc / Meet Irma / Irma la douce/this is the story / Nestor the honest policeman / Our language of love / Our language of love/don't take all night / Market/our language of love, The / Easy living the hard way/our language of love / Escape / Our language of love/wedding ring / Return of Lord, The / In the tub with fieldglasses/our language of love / Goodbye Lord / I'm sorry Irma / Juke box/let's pretend love / Juke box/look again / But that's another story.
Album: released on CBS, Feb'87 by CBS Records. Dist: CBS

Cassette: released on CBS, Feb'87 by CBS Records. Dist: CBS

Iron Angel

WINGS OF WAR.
Album: released on Steamhammer, Jul'86

Iron Angels

HELLISH CROSSFIRE.
Album: released on Steamhammer, Jan'86
Cat. no: **SPV 08-1853**

Iron Butterfly

IN A GADDA DA VIDA.

Compact disc: released on Warner Bros., Jul'87 by Warner Bros Records. Dist: WEA

IN-A-GADDA-DA-VIDA.
Album: released on Atlantic, '74 by WEA Records. Dist: WEA

Page 506

Iron Eagle

IRON EAGLE original soundtrack.
Tracks: / One vision / Iron eagle / These are the good times / Maniac house / Intense / Hide in the rainbow / It's too late / Love can make you cry / This ragin fire.
Album: released on Capitol, May'86 by Capitol Records. Dist: EMI

Cassette: released on Capitol, May'86 by Capitol Records. Dist: EMI

Iron Fist

HOOKED ON ROCK.
Album: released on RCA, Apr'85 by RCA Records. Dist: RCA, Roots, Swift, Wellard, Chris, I & B, Solomon & Peres Distribution

Cassette: released on RCA, Apr'85 by RCA Records. Dist: RCA, Roots, Swift, Wellard, Chris, I & B, Solomon & Peres Distribution

Ironhorse

EVERYTHING IS GREY.
Album: released on Scotti Brothers (USA), Nov'80 by Epic Records. Dist: CBS

Iron Maiden

2 MINUTES TO MIDNIGHT.
Single (7"): released on EMI, Aug'84 by EMI Records. Dist: EMI

Single (12"): released on EMI, Aug'84 by EMI Records. Dist: EMI

ACES HIGH.
Picture disc single: released on EMI, Oct'84 by EMI Records. Dist: EMI

Single (12"): released on EMI, Oct'84 by EMI Records. Dist: EMI

Single (7"): released on EMI, Oct'84 by EMI Records. Dist: EMI

BEHIND THE IRON CURTAIN.
Video-cassette (VHS): released on PMI, Jun'86 by PMI Records. Dist: EMI

Video-cassette [Betamax]: released on PMI, Jun'86 by PMI Records. Dist: EMI

INTERVIEW PICTURE DISC.
Album: released on Baktabak, May'87 by Baktabak Records. Dist: Arabesque

IRON MAIDEN.
Tracks: / Prowler / Remember tomorrow / Running free / Phantom of the opera / Transylvania / Strange world / Charlotte the harlot / Iron Maiden.
Album: released on Fame (EMI), May'85 by Music For Pleasure Records. Dist: EMI

Cassette: released on Fame (EMI), May'85 by Music For Pleasure Records. Dist: EMI

Compact disc: released on Fame, Oct'87 by Music For Pleasure Records. Dist: EMI

KILLERS.
Tracks: / Ides of March / Wrathchild / Murders in the rue morgue / Another life / Genghis Khan / Innocent exile / Killers / Prodigal son / Purgatory / Drifter.
Album: released on Fame (EMI), May'85 by Music For Pleasure Records. Dist: EMI

Cassette: released on Fame (EMI), May'85 by Music For Pleasure Records. Dist: EMI

Compact disc: released on Fame, Oct'87 by Music For Pleasure Records. Dist: EMI

LIFE AFTER DEATH.
Tracks: / Number of the beast, The / Run for the hills / Running free / Flight of Icarus / 2 minutes to midnight.
Notes: Thirteen dizbusting tracks, plus amazing live antics, make up one of the heaviest and most exciting music videos of the year. During 1985 Maiden played four nights in Lough Beach and, fortunately for metal fans, the cameras were on hand to capture those shows. It's an awesome piece of work simply because the gfoup is so astounding on stage. Tracks include: The number of the beast/ Run for the hills/ Running free/ Flight of Icarus/ 2 minutes to midnight. HM fans will lap this up. Number of tracks: 13. Type of recording: live Total playing time: 90 minutes.
Video-cassette (VHS): released on PMI, Jun'86 by PMI Records. Dist: EMI

Video-cassette [Betamax]: released on PMI, Jun'86 by PMI Records. Dist: EMI

LIVE.
Video-cassette (VHS): released on PMI, Jun'86 by PMI Records. Dist: EMI

Video-cassette [Betamax]: released on PMI, Jun'86 by PMI Records. Dist: EMI

LIVE AFTER DEATH World slavery tour, The.
Tracks: / Aces high / Two minutes to midnight / Trooper,The / Revelations / Flight of Icarus / Time of the ancient mariner / Powerslave / Number of the beast, The / Hallowed be thy name / Iron maiden / Run to the hills / Running free.
Compact disc: released on EMI, Dec'85 by EMI Records. Dist: EMI

Double Album: released on EMI America (Stateside), Oct'85 by EMI Records. Dist: EMI

Double cassette: released on EMI America (Stateside), Oct'85 by EMI Records. Dist: EMI

NUMBER OF THE BEAST, THE.
Tracks: / Invaders / Children of the damned / Prisoner, The / 22, Acacia Avenue / Number of the beast, The / Run to the hills / Gangland / Hallowed be thy name.
Album: released on Fame, May'87 by Music For Pleasure Records. Dist: EMI

Cassette: released on Fame, May'87 by Music For Pleasure Records. Dist: EMI

NUMBER OF THE BEAST, THE.
Tracks: / Invaders / Children of the damned / Prisoner, The / 22 Acacia Avenue / Number of the beast, The / Run to the hills / Gangland / Hallowed be thy name.
Compact disc: released on EMI, Jan'87 by EMI Records. Dist: EMI

NUMBER OF THE BEAST.
Album: released on Fame, May'87 by Music For Pleasure Records. Dist: EMI

Cassette: released on Fame, May'87 by Music For Pleasure Records. Dist: EMI

NUMBER OF THE BEAST.
Single (7"): released on EMI, Apr'82 by EMI Records. Dist: EMI

Album: released on EMI, Mar'82 by EMI Records. Dist: EMI

Cassette: released on EMI, '82 by EMI Records. Dist: EMI

PIECE OF MIND.
Tracks: / Where eagles dare / Revelations / Flight of Icarus / Die with your boots on / Trooper, The / Still life / Quest for fire / Sun & steel / To tame a land.
Compact disc: released on EMI, '86 by EMI Records. Dist: EMI

Album: released on EMI, May'83 by EMI Records. Dist: EMI

Cassette: released on EMI, May'83 by EMI Records. Dist: EMI

POWERSLAVE.
Album: released on EMI, Sep'84 by EMI Records. Dist: EMI

Cassette: released on EMI, Sep'84 by EMI Records. Dist: EMI

Picture disc album: released on EMI, Sep'84 by EMI Records. Dist: EMI

Compact disc: released on EMI, Sep'84 by EMI Records. Dist: EMI

RUN FOR THE HILLS.
Single (7"): released on EMI, Jan'82 by EMI Records. Dist: EMI

Picture disc single: released on EMI, Jan'82 by EMI Records. Dist: EMI

RUNNING FREE.
Single (7"): released on EMI, Sep'85 by EMI Records. Dist: EMI

Single (12"): released on EMI, Sep'85 by EMI Records. Dist: EMI

RUN TO THE HILLS.
Video-cassette (VHS): released on Video Collection, Mar'87 by Video Collection International Ltd.. Dist: Counterpoint

Picture disc single: released on EMI, Dec'85 by EMI Records. Dist: EMI

Single (12"): released on EMI, Nov'85 by EMI Records. Dist: EMI

Single (12"): released on EMI, Nov'85 by EMI Records. Dist: EMI

SOMEWHERE IN TIME.
Tracks: / Caught somewhere in time / Wasted years / Sea of madness / Heaven can wait / Loneliness of the long distance runner (The) / Stranger in a strange land / Deja- vu / Alexander the great.
Compact disc: released on EMI, Oct'86 by EMI Records. Dist: EMI

Album: released on EMI, Jul'86 by EMI Records. Dist: EMI
Cat. no: **ZONE 1**
Cassette: released on EMI, Jul'86 by EMI Records. Dist: EMI

STRANGER IN A STRANGE LAND.
Tracks: / Stranger in a strange land / That girl / Juanita.
Single (12"): released on EMI, Nov'86 by EMI Records. Dist: EMI

TROOPER.
Single (7"): released on EMI, Jun'83 by EMI Records. Dist: EMI

Picture disc single: released on EMI, Jun'83 by EMI Records. Dist: EMI

VIDEO PIECES.
Video-cassette (VHS): released on PMI, Jun'86 by PMI Records. Dist: EMI

Video-cassette [Betamax]: released on PMI, Jun'86 by PMI Records. Dist: EMI

WASTED YEARS.
Tracks: / Wasted years / Reach out / Sherriff of Huddersfield (The).
Single (7"): released on EMI, Aug'86 by EMI Records. Dist: EMI

Single (12"): released on EMI, Aug'86 by EMI Records. Dist: EMI

Picture disc single: released on EMI, Aug'86 by EMI Records. Dist: EMI

WOMEN IN UNIFORM.
Single (7"): released on EMI, Sep'80 by EMI Records. Dist: EMI

Single (12"): released on EMI, Sep'80 by EMI Records. Dist: EMI

Iron Man

IRON MAN Hughes, Ted (Cribbins, Bernard).
Double cassette: released on Argo (Spokenword), Jul'82 by Decca Records. Dist: Polygram

Iron Muse

PANORAMA OF INDUSTRIAL FOLK MUSIC, A.
Album: released on Topic, May'81 Dist: Roots Distribution

I-Roy

CLASSIC I-ROY (THE).
Album: released on Mr. Tipsy, Apr'86

CRUCIAL CUTS.
Album: released on Virgin, Apr'83 by Virgin Records. Dist: EMI, Virgin Distribution

DREAD LOCKS IN JAMAICA.
Album: released on Love & Live, Feb'78

GODFATHER,(THE).
Album: released on Third World, May'78 Dist: Jetstar Distribution

OUTER LIMITS.
Album: released on Hawkeye, Mar'83 by Hawkeye Records. Dist: Hawkeye, Lightning (WEA) Distribution, Jetstar, PRT

Cassette: released on Hawkeye, Mar'83 by Hawkeye Records. Dist: Hawkeye, Lightning (WEA) Distribution, Jetstar, PRT

PRESENTING I-ROY.
Album: released on Trojan, May'83 by Trojan Records. Dist: PRT, Jetstar

I-Royals

CORONATION STREET.
Single (7"): released on Media Marvels, May'83 Dist: Pinnacle, Jetstar Distribution

Single (12"): released on Media Marvels, May'83 Dist: Pinnacle, Jetstar Distribution

Irrelevant Time

IF YOU WERE HERE.
Single (7"): released on Rhythmic, Aug'83 by Rhythmic Records. Dist: Havoc Distribution

Irsol

FIRST CONTACT.
Cassette: released on Adventures In Reality, Oct'84 by Backs Records. Dist: Cartel

HALF LIVE.
Cassette: released on Adventures In Reality, Oct'84 by Backs Records. Dist: Cartel

Irvine, Andrew

ANDREW I & PAUL B (see Brady, Paul) (Irvine, Andrew & Paul Brady).

Irvine, Andy

ANDY IRVINE & PAUL BRADY (Irvine, Andy/Paul Brady).
Album: released on Mulligan (Ireland), Sep'79 by Topic Records. Dist: Roots Distribution, Jazz Music Distribution, JSU Distribution, I & B Distribution, Projection Distribution, Wynd-Up Distribution, Celtic Distributions

Cassette: released on Mulligan (Ireland), Sep'79 by Topic Records. Dist: Roots Distribution, Jazz Music Distribution, JSU Distribution, I & B Distribution, Projection Distribution, Wynd-Up Distribution, Celtic Distributions

PATRICK STREET (Irvine, Andy, Jackie Daly, Kevin Burke, Arty McGlynn).
Album: released on WEA Ireland, Mar'87 by WEA Records. Dist: Celtic Distributions, Projection, I & B
Cat. no: **SIF 1071**
Album: released on WEA Ireland, Mar'87 by WEA Records. Dist: Celtic Distributions, Projection, I & B

RAINY SUNDAYS,WINDY DREAMS.
Album: released on Tara (Ireland), May'82 Dist: Stage One Distribution, Roots Records Distribution, I & B Distribution, Jazz Music Distribution, JSU Distribution, Projection Distribution, Celtic Music Distribution

Cassette: released on Tara (Ireland), May'82 Dist: Stage One Distribution, Roots Records Distribution, I & B Distribution, Jazz Music Distribution, JSU Distribution, Projection Distribution, Celtic Music Distribution

Irvine, Bill & Boggie

AT THE ROYAL ALBERT HALL.
Album: released on Dansan, Apr'78 by Spartan Records. Dist: Spartan

Cassette: released on Dansan, Apr'78 by Spartan Records. Dist: Spartan

Irvine, Weldon

IN HARMONY.
Album: released on Code O, Oct'75

Irving, Bobby

MISS MALIBU.
Single (12"): released on Jaguar, Oct'84 by Jaguar Records. Dist: Jetstar

Irving, Robert

NIGHTS AT THE BALLET.
Album: released on H.M.V., '68 by EMI Records. Dist: EMI

Isaac, Chris

GONE RIDIN'.
Tracks: / Gone ridin' / Talk to me.
Single (7"): released on Warner Bros., Jan'86 by Warner Bros Records. Dist: WEA

Isaacs, Barry

THIS TIME BABY.
Tracks: / This time baby / We're all in the rhythm.
Single (12"): released on Must Dance, Jul'86 by Must Dance Records. Dist: Jetstar Distribution

Isaacs, David

MORE LOVE.
Single (12"): released on Cartridge, May'82 by Cartridge. Dist: Jetstar

PLACE IN THE SUN.
Album: released on Culture Press, Dec'84 by Vista Sounds Records. Dist: Jetstar, Rough Trade

Isaacs, Dennis

SHE LOVES ME NOW.
Tracks: / She loves me now / Come dub me now.
Single (12"): released on Striker Lee, Mar'86 by Striker Lee Records. Dist: Jetstar Distribution

Isaacs, Gregory

ALL I HAVE IS LOVE.
Album: released on Trojan, Jul'84 by Trojan Records. Dist: PRT, Jetstar

Cassette: released on Trojan, Aug'84 by Trojan Records. Dist: PRT, Jetstar

ALL I HAVE IS LOVE, LOVE, LOVE.
Album: released on Tad's, Aug'86

Cassette: released on Tad's, Aug'86

BABY I LIED TO YOU.
Single (12"): released on Dynamite, Sep'84 by Dynamite Records. Dist: Jetstar

BANG BALLET.
Tracks: / Bang ballet.
Single (12"): released on Tad's, Jun'86

BEST OF GREGORY ISAACS.
Album: released on Channel 1, Sep'79 by Cha-Cha Records. Dist: Mojo

CHUNNIE YOU ARE NO.1.
Single (12"): released on GG'S, '79 by GG'S Records. Dist: Jetstar Deleted '80.

COOL DOWN THE PACE.
Single (7"): released on Island, Oct'84 by Island Records. Dist: Polygram Deleted '84.

Single 10": released on Island, Oct'82 by Island Records. Dist: Polygram

Single (12"): released on Island, Dec'82 by Island Records. Dist: Polygram

COOL RULER.
Album: released on Front line, Feb'79 by Virgin. Dist: EMI

CRUCIAL CUTS.
Album: released on Virgin, Apr'83 by Virgin Records. Dist: EMI, Virgin Distribution

Cassette: released on Virgin, Apr'83 by Virgin Records. Dist: EMI, Virgin Distribution

DISRESPECTFUL WOMAN.
Single (12"): released on Fidel, Nov'85 Dist: Cartel

DON'T BELIEVE IN HIM.
Single (12"): released on Silver Camel, Apr'83 Dist: Jetstar, Rough Trade

DOUBLE DOSE (Isaacs, Gregory & Sugar Minott).
Album: released on Blue Trac, Jan'87 by Blue Mountain Records. Dist: Jetstar

DREAM MY LIFE OVER.
Tracks: / Dream my life over.
Single (12"): released on African Museum, Sep'86 Dist: Jetstar

DRIFTING AWAY.
Single (12"): released on African Museum, Oct'84 Dist: Jetstar

EARLY YEARS, THE.
Album: released on Trojan, '83 by Trojan Records. Dist: PRT, Jetstar

EASY.
Album: released on Tad's, Apr'85

EXTRA CLASS.
Album: released on Vista Sounds, '83 by Vista Sounds Records. Dist: Jetstar

Cassette: released on Vista Sounds, '83 by Vista Sounds Records. Dist: Jetstar

EXTRA CLASSIC.
Cassette: released on Miccan, Sep'86 by Miccan Records. Dist: Jetstar Distribution

FOR EVERYONE.
Album: released on Success, Apr'80 Dist: Counterpoint Distribution Deleted '81.

GP.
Single (12"): released on African Museum, Mar'85 Dist: Jetstar

HARD DRUGS.
Tracks: / Hard drugs.
Single (12"): released on Tappa, Aug'86 Dist: Jetstar

IN PERSON.
Album: released on Trojan, '83 by Trojan Records. Dist: PRT, Jetstar

JUDGE NOT (see under Brown, Dennis).

JUDGE NOT (Isaacs, Gregory & Dennis Brown).
Album: released on Greensleeves, Aug'84 by Greensleeves Records. Dist: BMG, Jetstar, Spartan

JUST HAVIN' FUN.
Tracks: / Just havin' fun / Village (The).
Single (12"): released on Third World, Oct'86 Dist: Jetstar Distribution

KOOL RULER COME AGAIN.
Single (12"): released on Tad's, Dec'84

LET OFF SUPM (Isaacs, Gregory & Dennis Brown).
Single (12"): released on Greensleeves, May'85 by Greensleeves Records. Dist: BMG, Jetstar, Spartan

LIVE '84.
Album: released on Rough Trade, Oct'84 by Rough Trade Records. Dist: Rough Trade Distribution, Cartel Distribution

LIVE AT THE ACADEMY.
Compact disc: released on Kingdom Records, Jan'87 by Kingdom Records. Dist: Kingdom Records

LIVE AT THE ACADEMY.
Album: released on Kingdom Records, Oct'86 by Kingdom Records. Dist: Kingdom Records

LOSING WAIT.
Tracks: / Losing weight.
Single (12"): released on Blue Mountain, May'86 Dist: Jetstar

LOVER'S MAGIC.
Single (12"): released on Diamond C, Apr'84 by Diamond C Records. Dist: Jetstar

LOVER'S ROCK.
Cassette: released on Pre, Nov'82 by Charisma. Dist: Polygram

---

ME CAME AGAIN.
Single (12"): released on African Museum, Nov'84 Dist: Jetstar

MR. ISAACS.
Album: released on Vista Sounds, '83 by Vista Sounds Records. Dist: Jetstar

MR ISAACS
Cassette: released on Miccan, Sep'86 by Miccan Records. Dist: Jetstar Distribution

MUSICAL MURDER.
Single (12"): released on Blue Mountain, Jul'85 Dist: Jetstar

MUSICAL REVENGE.
Tracks: / Musical revenge / Musical revenge (version).
Single (12"): released on Tads, 23 May'87 by Tads Records. Dist: Jetstar Distribution

MY LOVE IS OVERDUE (Isaacs, Gregory/Trinity).
Single (12"): released on GG'S, Jul'84 by GG'S Records. Dist: Jetstar

NIGHT NURSE.
Album: released on Island, Aug'82 by Island Records. Dist: Polygram

Cassette: released on Island, Aug'82 by Island Records. Dist: Polygram

NO GOOD GIRL.
Tracks: / No good girl / Rockers non stop.
Single (12"): released on Greensleeves, Jun'86 by Greensleeves Records. Dist: BMG, Jetstar, Spartan

NO ONE BUT ME.
Single (12"): released on Fu-Manchu, Jun'84 by Fu-Manchu. Dist: Jetstar

OUT DEH.
Album: released on Island, Dec'84 by Island Records. Dist: Polygram

Cassette: released on Island, Dec'84 by Island Records. Dist: Polygram

PRIVATE BEACH PARTY.
Tracks: / Wish you were mine / Feeling Irie / Bits & pieces / Let off sum / No rushings / Private beach party / Better plant some loving / Got to be in tune / Special to me / Promise is a comfort.
Compact disc: released on Greensleeves, Jan'86 by Greensleeves Records. Dist: BMG, Jetstar, Spartan

Single (12"): released on Greensleeves, Jan'86 by Greensleeves Records. Dist: BMG, Jetstar, Spartan

Album: released on Greensleeves, Aug'85 by Greensleeves Records. Dist: BMG, Jetstar, Spartan

Cassette: released on Greensleeves, Aug'85 by Greensleeves Records. Dist: BMG, Jetstar, Spartan

REGGAE GREATS.
Album: released on Island, Jun'85 by Island Records. Dist: Polygram

Cassette: released on Island, Jun'85 by Island Records. Dist: Polygram

SENSATIONAL, THE.
Album: released on Vista Sounds, '83 by Vista Sounds Records. Dist: Jetstar

Cassette: released on Vista Sounds, '83 by Vista Sounds Records. Dist: Jetstar

SLUM DUB.
Album: released on Burning Sounds, Feb'85 by Ross, Bill/Burning Sounds Records. Dist: PRT

SOON FOREWARD.
Album: released on Front line, Aug'79 by Virgin. Dist: EMI

TALK DON'T BOTHER ME.
Album: released on Skengdom, Jul'87 by Skengdom Records. Dist: Jetstar

TICKLE ME.
Tracks: / Tickle me / Tickle me (Version).
Single (12"): released on Tappa, Nov'86 Dist: Jetstar

TOO LATE.
Single (12"): released on Londisc, Aug'84 by Londisc Records.

TWO BAD SUPERSTARS (Isaacs, Gregory & Dennis Brown).
Album: released on Burning Sounds, Feb'84 by Ross, Bill/Burning Sounds Records. Dist: PRT

Cassette: released on Burning Sounds, Feb'84 by Ross, Bill/Burning Sounds Records. Dist: PRT

Cat. no: BSC 1057

TWOP BAD SUPERSTARS (Isaacs, Gregory & Dennis Brown).

WHO CARES.
Single 10": released on Silver Camel, Apr'82 Dist: Jetstar, Rough Trade

Isaacs, Ike
LATIN GUITARS OF IKE ISAACS.
Album: released on Dansan, '78 by Spartan Records. Dist: Spartan

Isaacs, Mary
SO GOOD, SO RIGHT.
Album: released on Aqua-Gem, Nov'86 Dist: Jetstar

Isaacs, Owen
HEAVY LOAD.
Single (12"): released on Exclusive, Aug'82 Dist: Jetstar

MY STYLE.
Tracks: / My style / Come on.
Single (12"): released on Natami Music, Jan'86 Dist: Jetstar

Isaac, Tony
SQUADRON (Isaac, Tony band).
Single (7"): released on BBC, Oct'82 by BBC Records & Tapes. Dist: EMI, PRT

Isaak, Chris
BLUE HOTEL.
Tracks: / Blue hotel / Waiting for the rain to fall.
Single (12"): released on Warner Bros., Jul'87 by Warner Bros Records. Dist: WEA

Single (12"): released on Warner Bros., Jul'87 by Warner Bros Records. Dist: WEA

CHRIS ISAAK.
Album: released on Warner Bros., Mar'87 by Warner Bros Records. Dist: WEA

Cassette: released on Warner Bros., Mar'87 by Warner Bros Records. Dist: WEA

SILVERTONE.
Album: released on Warner Bros., Apr'85 by Warner Bros Records. Dist: WEA

YOU OWE ME SOME KIND OF LOVE.
Tracks: / You owe me some kind of love / Wit-chu to the train to fall.
Single (7"): released on Warner Brothers, Apr'87 by Warner Bros Records. Dist: WEA

Single (12"): released on Warner Brothers, Apr'87 by Warner Bros Records. Dist: WEA

Isaas, Barry
SHE IS READY.
Tracks: / She is ready / She is ready (Version).
Single (12"): released on ADA, Feb'86 Dist: Jetstar

Isalonisti
HUMORESQUE.
Tracks: / Souvenir / Whispering flowers / Czardas / Come away to Madrid / My sweet little friend / On the sea shore / My heart only calls to you / Humoresque / Slavonic dance no. 6 / Melody in F / Syncopation / Gypsey Capriccio / Poeme / Little Viennese march / Mill in the black forest / Maiden's prayer / We wander the world / Eight in the night / When a toreador falls in love.
Compact disc: released on Harmonia Mundi (France), Oct'86 Dist: Harmonia Mundi

Ish
ON THIS CORNER.
Tracks: / You're my only lover / I could love you / You're my favourite thing to do / On this corner / Holy nightyfeminity / More than I can bear / It ain't necessarily so / Chase the face.
Album: released on Geffen, Apr'86 by Geffen Records. Dist: WEA, CBS

Cassette: released on Geffen, Apr'86 by Geffen Records. Dist: WEA, CBS

YOU'RE MY ONLY LOVER.
Tracks: / You're my only lover / It ain't necessarily so.
Single (7"): released on Geffen, Apr'86 by Geffen Records. Dist: WEA, CBS

Isham, Mark
FILM MUSIC.
Compact disc: released on Windham Hill, Jan'86 Dist: AM

Album: released on Windham Hill, Nov'85 Dist: AM

Cassette: released on Windham Hill, Nov'85 Dist: AM

Compact disc: released on Windham Hill, Nov'85 Dist: AM

VAPOR DRAWINGS.
Notes: The first solo album from the composer/multi-instrumentalist, achieving a warm synthesis of jazz, rock and classical styles.
Compact disc: released on Windham Hill, Feb'86 Dist: AM

Album: released on Windham Hill, Nov'85 Dist: AM

Cassette: released on Windham Hill, Nov'85 Dist: AM

Compact disc: released on Windham Hill, Nov'85 Dist: AM

Isham, Mark & Art Lande
WE BEGIN.
Tracks: / Melancholy of departure, The / Ceremony in starlight / We begin / Lord Anenea / Surface and symbol / Sweet circle / Fanfare.
Notes: Personel: Art Lande - piano, synthesizer, percussion/Mark Isham - trumpet, fluegelhorn, piccolo trumpet, synthesizer, percussion.
Album: released on ECM (Germany), Jul'87 by ECM Records. Dist: IMS, Polygram, Virgin through EMI

Compact disc: released on ECM (Germany), Jul'87 by ECM Records. Dist: IMS, Polygram, Virgin through EMI

Ishmael & Andy
READY SALTED.
Album: released on Myrrh, '74 by Word Records. Dist: Word Distribution

Iskra jazz In Sweden
ISKRA JAZZ IN SWEDEN Various artists (Various Artists).
Double album: released on Caprice, Oct'77 by RCA Records. Dist: RCA

Island at the top...
ISLAND AT THE TOP OF THE WORLD (Ravenscroft, Thurl).
Album: released on Disneyland, Mar'75 by Disneyland-Vista Records (USA). Dist: BBC Records & Tapes, Rainbow Communications Ltd(Distribution)

Island story, The
ISLAND STORY, THE Various artists (Various Artists).
Tracks: / With or without you / Higher love / Virginia plain / Living in the past / All right now / Keep on running / Paper sun / Addicted to love / Slave to the rhythm / Annie I'm not your daddy / Cuba / Harlem shuffle, The / Israelites, The / My boy lollipop / Now that we've found love / No Woman,no cry / Love hurts / Up where we belong / Smoke gets in your eyes / Wild world / Eighteen with a bullet / Si tu dois parti / Morning has broken / World shut your mouth / Kissing with confidence / Too good to be forgotten / Video killed the radio star / This town ain't big enough for the both of us / Do anything you wanna do / Forgotten Town / Rage hand.
Double Album: released on Island, Jul'87 by Island Records. Dist: Polygram

Double cassette: released on Island, Jul'87 by Island Records. Dist: Polygram

Compact disc: released on Island, Jul'87 by Island Records. Dist: Polygram

Video-cassette (VHS): released on Island, Jul'87 by Island Records. Dist: Polygram

Isle of Man...
ISLE OF MAN TT RACES, 1967.
Double album: released on Taylors, Jul'77

Cassette: released on Taylors, Jul'77

Isle of Wight...
ISLE OF WIGHT: ATLANTA POP FESTIVAL Various artists (Various Artists).
Triple album / cassette: released on CBS, '74 by CBS Records. Dist: CBS

Isley Brothers
20 GOLDEN PIECES OF THE ISLEY BROTHERS.
Album: released on Bulldog, Apr'83 by Bulldog Records. Dist: President Distribution, Spartan, Swift, Taylor, H.R.

Cassette: released on Bulldog, Apr'83 by Bulldog Records. Dist: President Distribution, Spartan, Swift, Taylor, H.R.

3 & 3.
Album: released on Epic, Mar'81 by CBS Records. Dist: CBS

Cassette: released on Epic, Mar'81 by CBS Records. Dist: CBS Deleted '87.

BETWEEN THE SHEETS.
Single (7"): released on Epic, Jun'83 by CBS Records. Dist: CBS

Single (12"): released on Epic, Jun'83 by CBS Records. Dist: CBS Deleted '84.

Album: released on Epic, Jul'83 by CBS Records. Dist: CBS

Cassette: released on Epic, Jul'83 by CBS Records. Dist: CBS Deleted '85.

COLDER ARE MY NIGHTS.
Tracks: / Colder are my nights / Colder are my nights (Instrumental).
Single (7"): released on Warner Bros., Jan'86 by Warner Bros Records. Dist: WEA

Single (12"): released on Warner Bros., Jan'86 by Warner Bros Records. Dist: WEA

FLIPHITS.
Cassette: released on Motown, Jul'83 by Motown Records. Dist: BMG Distribution

FOREVER GOLD.
Album: released on Epic, '84 by CBS Records. Dist: CBS

Cassette: released on Epic, '84 by CBS Records. Dist: CBS

GO ALL THE WAY.
Album: released on Epic, May'80 by CBS Records. Dist: CBS

Cassette: released on Epic, May'80 by CBS Records. Dist: CBS

GRAND SLAM.
Album: released on Epic, Apr'81 by CBS Records. Dist: CBS

Cassette: released on Epic, Apr'81 by CBS Records. Dist: CBS

GREATEST MOTOWN HITS.
Album: released on Motown, Feb'87 by Motown Records. Dist: BMG Distribution

Cassette: released on Motown, Feb'87 by Motown Records. Dist: BMG Distribution

HARVEST FOR THE WORLD.
Tracks: / Harvest for the world.
Single (7"): released on Epic, Jun'86 by CBS Records. Dist: CBS

Single (7"): released on Epic, May'82 by CBS Records. Dist: CBS

Album: released on Epic, Jun'85 by CBS Records. Dist: CBS

Cassette: released on Epic, Jun'85 by CBS Records. Dist: CBS Deleted '87.

HEAT IS ON, (THE).
Album: released on Epic, Jun'75 by CBS Records. Dist: CBS

HIGHWAYS OF MY LIFE.
Single (7"): released on Old Gold, Apr'83 by Old Gold Records. Dist: Lightning, Jazz Music, Spartan, Counterpoint

I GUESS I'LL ALWAYS LOVE YOU.
Single (7"): released on Motown, Mar'83 by Motown Records. Dist: BMG Distribution

ISLEY BROTHERS: GREATEST HITS, VOL 1.
Album: released on Epic, Jun'84 by CBS Records. Dist: CBS

Cassette: released on Epic, Jun'84 by CBS Records. Dist: CBS

ITS A DISCO NIGHT.
Tracks: / It's a disco night / That lady / Summer breeze / It's your thing.
Single (12"): released on Old Gold, Feb'86 by Old Gold Records. Dist: Lightning, Jazz Music, Spartan, Counterpoint

LETS GO.
Tracks: / Surf and shout / Please please please / She's the one / Tango / What cha going to do / Staggerlee / You'll never leave him / Let's go let's go let's go / She's gone / Shake it with me baby / Long tall Sally / Do the twist / Who's that lady / My little girl / Love is a wonderful thing / Open up your eyes.
Notes: One of the longest lasting soul outfits ever. This brand new complation - features material from the early 60's- the band's years on United Artists. Includes their original version of " Who's that lady"- a song they later re-recorded and charted. Also features thier version of " Staggerlee" as seen on the 'Ready Steady Go' series of videos.
Album: released on Stateside, Mar'86 Dist: EMI

Cassette: released on Stateside, Mar'86 Dist: EMI

LIVE IT UP.
Album: released on Epic, Sep'74 by CBS Records. Dist: CBS

MASTERPIECE.
Tracks: / May I / My best was good enough / If leaving me is easy / You never know when you;re gonna fall in love / Stay gold / Colder are my nights / Come to me / Release your love / Most beautiful girl, The.
Album: released on Warner Bros., Dec'85 by Warner Bros Records. Dist: WEA

Cassette: released on Warner Bros., Dec'85 by Warner Bros Records. Dist: WEA

SIX TRACK HITS.
Extended-play record: released on Scoop 33, Sep'83 by Pickwick Records. Dist: H.R. Taylor

Cassette: released on Scoop 33, Sep'83 by Pickwick Records. Dist: H.R. Taylor

SMOOTH SAILIN'.
Tracks: / Everything is alright / Dish it out / It takes a good woman / Send a message / Smooth sailin' tonight / Somebody I used to know / Come my way / I wish.
Album: released on Warner Bros., Jul'87 by Warner Bros Records. Dist: WEA

Cassette: released on Warner Bros., Jul'87 by Warner Bros Records. Dist: WEA

SUPER HITS.
Album: released on Motown, Oct'81 by Motown Records. Dist: BMG Distribution

Cassette: released on Motown, Oct'81 by Motown Records. Dist: BMG Distribution

THAT LADY.
Single (7"): released on Old Gold, Apr'83 by Old Gold Records. Dist: Lightning, Jazz Music, Spartan, Counterpoint

THIS OLD HEART OF MINE.
Single (7"): released on Motown, Oct'81 by Motown Records. Dist: BMG Distribution

Album: released on Motown, Oct'81 by Motown Records. Dist: BMG Distribution

Cassette: released on Motown, Oct'81 by Motown Records. Dist: BMG Distribution

Single (7"): released on Motown, Jun'83 by Motown Records. Dist: BMG Distribution

TWIST AND SHOUT.
Cassette: released on Orchid Music, Feb'82 by Bibi. Dist: Pinnacle

WINNER TAKES ALL.
Double Album: released on Epic, Jul'79 by CBS Records. Dist: CBS

Cassette: released on Epic, Jul'79 by CBS Records. Dist: CBS

Isley Jasper Isley

BROADWAY'S CLOSER TO SUNSET BLVD.
Tracks: / Sex drive / Serve you right / I can't get over losin' you / Kiss and tell / Kiss and tell / Love is gonna last forever / Broadway's closer to sunset blvd / Look the other way / Break this chain / 450359-1.
Album: released on Epic, Jan'87 by CBS Records. Dist: CBS

Cassette: released on Epic, Jan'87 by CBS Records. Dist: CBS

CARAVAN OF LOVE.
Album: released on Epic, Oct'85 by CBS Records. Dist: CBS

Cassette: released on Epic, Oct'85 by CBS Records. Dist: CBS

Single (7"): released on Epic, Nov'85 by CBS Records. Dist: CBS

Single (12"): released on Epic, Nov'85 by CBS Records. Dist: CBS

DIFFERENT DRUMMER.
Tracks: / Different drummer / 8th wonder of the world / Blue rose / Do it right / Givin' you back the love / Once in a life time lady / For the sake of love / Brother to brother / I wanna be yours.
Album: released on Epic, May'87 by CBS Records. Dist: CBS

Cassette: released on Epic, May'87 by CBS Records. Dist: CBS

EIGHTH WONDER OF THE WORLD.
Tracks: / Eighth wonder of the world / Broadway's closer to Sunset Boulevard.
Single (7"): released on Epic, Apr'87 by CBS Records. Dist: CBS

Single (12"): released on Epic, Apr'87 by CBS Records. Dist: CBS

Single (12"): released on Epic, Jun'87 by CBS Records. Dist: CBS

INSATIABLE WOMAN.
Tracks: / Insatiable woman / Break this chain / Caravan of love / I can't get over losing you.
Single (7"): released on Epic, Feb'86 by CBS Records. Dist: CBS

Cassette: released on Epic, Feb'86 by CBS Records. Dist: CBS

Double-pack single: released on Epic, Feb'86 by CBS Records. Dist: CBS

Isley, Rem

WHEN ARE WE FATED IN ME YARD.
Single (12"): released on Dubplate, Jul'85 by Dubplate Records. Dist: Jetstar

ISM

CONSTANTINOPLE.
Album: released on Broken, Nov'84 by Broken Records. Dist: Stiff Records, EMI

Isol

WEATHERED STATUES.
Single (7"): released on Alternative Tentacles, Sep'82 by Alternative Tentacles Records. Dist: Rough Trade, Pinnacle

Isolation

MARIANNA.
Single (7"): released on What Records, Aug'85 Dist: Nine Mile, Cartel

Isotope

BEST OF ISOTOPE, THE Featuring Gary Boyle.
Album: released on Gull, '79 by Gull Records. Dist: Pinnacle

Cassette: released on Gull, '79 by Gull Records. Dist: Pinnacle

DEEP END.
Album: released on Gull, Sep'77 by Gull Records. Dist: Pinnacle

Cassette: released on Gull, Jun'76 by Gull Records. Dist: Pinnacle

ILLUSION.
Album: released on Gull, Sep'77 by Gull Records. Dist: Pinnacle

Cassette: released on Gull, '77 by Gull Records. Dist: Pinnacle

ISOTOPE.
Album: released on Gull, Sep'77 by Gull Records. Dist: Pinnacle

Cassette: released on Gull, '77 by Gull Records. Dist: Pinnacle

I Spit On Your Gravy

PIRANHA.
Tracks: / Piranha / Man's not a camel.
Single (7"): released on Virgin, Jul'87 by Virgin Records. Dist: EMI, Virgin Distribution

I-Spy Club

MEMORIES ARE MADE OF THIS.
Single (7"): released on State, Nov'82 by State Records.

ROSETTA BLUE.
Single (7"): released on State, Sep'82 by State Records.

Single (12"): released on State, Oct'82 by State Records.

Israel:

FLUTE MUSIC FROM ISRAEL Lehakat ha Nodomin.
Album: released on Arion (France), Aug'75 Dist: Conifer, Discovery

ISRAEL Songs & music celebrated by Robert Bahr.
Album: released on Festival, Jun'78 Dist: Swift

JEWISH SONGS Tzachi & Yael.
Album: released on CBS, '74 by CBS Records. Dist: CBS

SONGS AND DANCES FROM ISRAEL (Israel: Kol Aviv).
Album: released on Arion (France), Jun'79 Dist: Conifer, Discovery

Cassette: released on Arion (France), Jun'79 Dist: Conifer, Discovery

SONGS AND DANCES OF ISRAEL Various artists (Various Artists).
Album: released on Arion (France), Jul'84 Dist: Conifer, Discovery

Israel's Hope

INTRODUCING....
Tracks: / If you're happy and you know it / Butterfly song, The / O be careful little eyes / Heaven is a wonderful place / When I get to heaven / Today / Joy, joy down in my heart / Birdles in the treetops, The / Love him in the morning / It's a happy day / Make a joyful noise / Zaccheus was a wee little man / First John 4:7&8 / Climb, climb up sonshine mountain / This little light of mine / Give me oil in my lamp / Jesus loves the little children / Ha la la la / B-I-B-L-E, The / Love is the greatest gift of all / Jesus loves even me / Behold, what manner of love / Deep and wide / If you can sing a song / Tell me the stories of Jesus / Rejoice in the Lord always / Wise man built his house, The / Sandyland / Special specialities / Arky, arky / Jesus love me / Amen, praise the Lord / Clap'se hands / I will make you fishers of men.
Notes: Songs of prayer and praise from the Scripture, with strong roots in Hebrew folk music.
Album: released on Word, Jun'87 by Word Records. Dist: Word Distribution, CBS

Cassette: released on Word, Jun'87 by Word Records. Dist: Word Distribution, CBS

Album: released on Word, Jun'87 by Word Records. Dist: Word Distribution, CBS

Cassette: released on Word, Jun'87 by Word Records. Dist: Word Distribution, CBS

Issachar, Barry

TURN ME ON.
Single (12"): released on Black Music, Jun'82 by Black Music Records. Dist: Jetstar

Issachar, Hudlle

COVER LOVER.
Single (12"): released on Negus Roots, Aug'83 by Negus Roots Records. Dist: Jetstar

GHOSTBUSTERS.
Single (12"): released on Macabeen, Mar'85 by Macabeen Records. Dist: Jetstar

I Start Counting

CATCH THAT LOOK.
Tracks: / Catch that look / Cooler than Calcutta.
Single (7"): released on Mute, Aug'86 Dist: Spartan Distribution, Rough Trade Distribution, Cartel Distribution

Single (12"): released on Mute, Aug'86 Dist: Spartan Distribution, Rough Trade Distribution, Cartel Distribution

LETTERS TO A FRIEND.
Single (7"): released on Mute, Jun'84 Dist: Spartan Distribution, Rough Trade Distribution, Cartel Distribution

MY TRANSLUCENT HANDS (SINGLE).

MY TRANSLUCENT HANDS.
Album: released on Mute, Oct'86 Dist: Spartan Distribution, Rough Trade Distribution, Cartel Distribution

Single (7"): Dist: Spartan Distribution, Rough Trade Distribution, Cartel Distribution

STILL SMILING.
Single (7"): released on Mute, Apr'85 Dist: Spartan Distribution, Rough Trade Distribution, Cartel Distribution

Single (12"): released on Mute, Apr'85 Dist: Spartan Distribution, Rough Trade Distribution, Cartel Distribution

Istropolitana

BEATLES SEASONS, (THE) 4 concerti grossi (Istropolitana, Capella & Slovak Chamber Orchestra).
Tracks: / She loves you / Good night / We can work it out / Lady Madonna / Fool on the hill / Hard day's night, A / Michelle / Penny Lane / Long and winding road / Girl / Here comes the sun / Hey Jude / Carry that weight / And I love her / Help / Paperback writer / She's leaving home / Honey pie / Eight days a week / Yellow submarine.
Notes: Conducted by Richard Edlinger. A **Danubius Records**,publishing and filmworks, production. Arranged and adapted by Peter Breiner. A record of Beatles music in the form of concerti. Each concerto is a group of Beatles melodies under a season-related heading the headings are: **Spring awakening, Summer Joy, Autumn colours and Winter moods.**
Album: released on Columbia, Jun'87 by EMI Records. Dist: EMI

Cassette: released on Columbia, Jun'87 by EMI Records. Dist: EMI

Compact disc: released on Columbia, Jun'87 by EMI Records. Dist: EMI

It...

IT AIN'T HALF HOT MUM Various artists (Various Artists).
Album: released on EMI, Apr'75 by EMI Records. Dist: EMI Deleted '79.

IT HAPPENED THEN Various artists (Various Artists).
Album: released on PRT, Nov'84 by PRT Records. Dist: PRT

Cassette: released on PRT, Nov'84 by PRT Records. Dist: PRT

IT SOUNDS LIKE BIX Various artists (Various Artists).
Album: released on Broadway, Jan'79 Dist: Jetstar

IT TAKES TWO Various artists (Solitaire collection) (Various Artists).
Double Album: released on Starblend (Solitaire Collection), Nov'83 by Starblend Records.

Dist: PRT Distribution

Double cassette: released on Starblend (Solitaire Collection), Nov'83 by Starblend Records. Dist: PRT Distribution

IT TAKES TWO Various Motown artists (Various Artists).
Album: released on Motown, Oct'81 by Motown Records. Dist: BMG Distribution

Cassette: released on Motown, Oct'81 by Motown Records. Dist: BMG Distribution

IT WAS ONLY ROCK'N'ROLL Various artists (Various Artists).
Notes: 19 tracks by Bill Haley,little Richard,Sam the Sham,Swinging Blue Jeans,Jack Fender etc.
Compact disc: released on Delta, May'87 by Delta Records. Dist: Target

Italian Heroes

ALL FOR NOTHING.
Single (7"): released on Successful, Jun'85 Dist: Pinnacle

IT MUST BE THE LOVE.
Single (7"): released on Successful, Oct'83 Dist: Pinnacle

Italian Love Songs

ITALIAN LOVE SONGS Various artists (Various Artists).
Cassette: released on Aim (Budget Cassettes), Sep'83

Italo Boot Mix

ITALO BOOT MIX VOL.9 Various artists (Various Artists).
Album: released on ZYX (Germany), Aug'87 by ZYX Records. Dist: Greyhound. Estim retail price in Sep'87 was £5.75.

ITALO BOOT MIX VOLUME 4 Various artists (Various Artists).
Single (12"): released on ZYX (Germany), Jan'86 by ZYX Records. Dist: Greyhound

ITALO BOOT MIX VOLUME 5 Various artists (Various Artists).
Single (12"): released on ZYX (Germany), Mar'86 by ZYX Records. Dist: Greyhound

Itals

WHAT ABOUT ME?.
Single (12"): released on Bluesville International, Aug'84 Dist: Jetstar

It Bites

ALL IN RED.
Tracks: / All in red / Heartbreaker.
Single (7"): released on Virgin, Apr'86 by Virgin Records. Dist: EMI, Virgin Distribution

Single (12"): released on Virgin, Apr'86 by Virgin Records. Dist: EMI, Virgin Distribution

BIG LAD IN THE WINDMILL, THE.
Tracks: / I got you eating out of my hand / All in red / Whole new world / Screaming on the beaches / Turn me loose / Cold, tired & hungry / Calling all the heroes / You'll never go to heaven / Big lad in the windmill.
Album: released on Virgin, Jul'86 by Virgin Records. Dist: EMI, Virgin Distribution

Cassette: released on Virgin, Jul'86 by Virgin Records. Dist: EMI, Virgin Distribution

Compact disc: released on Virgin, Jul'86 by Virgin Records. Dist: EMI, Virgin Distribution

CALLING ALL THE HEROES.
Tracks: / Calling all the heroes / Strange but true.
Single (7"): released on Virgin, Jun'86 by Virgin Records. Dist: EMI, Virgin Distribution

Single (12"): released on Virgin, Jun'86 by Virgin Records. Dist: EMI, Virgin Distribution

OLD MAN AND THE ANGEL (THE).
Tracks: / Old man and the angel (The) / Castles.
Single (7"): released on Virgin, Apr'87 by Virgin Records. Dist: EMI, Virgin Distribution

Single (12"): released on Virgin, Apr'87 by Virgin Records. Dist: EMI, Virgin Distribution

Single (12"): released on Virgin, Apr'87 by Virgin Records. Dist: EMI, Virgin Distribution

WHOLE NEW WORLD.
Tracks: / Whole new world / Black December / Calling all the heroes.
Single (7"): released on Virgin, Oct'86 by Virgin Records. Dist: EMI, Virgin Distribution

Single (12"): released on Virgin, Oct'86 by Virgin Records. Dist: EMI, Virgin Distribution

Itchy Fingers

QUARK.
Album: released on Virgin, Jun'87 by Virgin Records. Dist: EMI, Virgin Distribution

Cassette: released on Virgin, Jun'87 by Virgin Records. Dist: EMI, Virgin Distribution

Itopia

SUNSHINE LOVE.
Single (12"): released on Wackies, Apr'85 by Wackies Records. Dist: Jetstar

YOU'VE LOST THAT LOVING FEELING.
Single (12"): released on Wackies, Nov'84 by Wackies Records. Dist: Jetstar

It's...

IT'S A CHILDRENS WORLD Folk Tales (It's a childrens world).
Album: released on Peerless, Jan'75 Deleted May'78.

IT'S A CRAMMED,CRAMMED,CRAMMED WORLD Various artists (Various Artists).
Album: released on Crammed Discs, Jun'84 Dist: Rough Trade, Nine Mile, Cartel

IT'S ALL ACCORDION TO WHAT YOU LIKE Various Midlands Artists (Various Artists).
Tracks: / Dizzy fingers / Musetta / For the good times Polish waltzes / Bavaian waltzes / Simonentta Ibiza / Georgia / Blues impromptu / Moonglow / C minor and ad lib / Autumn breezes / Funiculi / Polish / Bavarian / French / Telstar / Tulips from Amsterdam / Quando.
Album: released on Accordion Record Club, Sep'86 by Accordion Record Club Records. Dist: Accordion Record Club

IT'S ALWAYS FAIR WEATHER Original soundtrack.
Album: released on Polydor, May'74 by Polydor Records. Dist: Polygram, Polydor

IT'S CAJUN COUNTRY Various artists (Various Artists).
Album: released on Goldband, Feb'79 by Charly Records. Dist: Charly

IT'S FRESH VOLUME 1 (Various Artists).
Album: released on Tads, Feb'87 by Tads Records. Dist: Jetstar Distribution

IT'S NURSERY RHYME TIME Various artists (Various Artists).
Album: released on Fanfare, Sep'76 by Ferroway/Fanfare Records. Dist: PRT Deleted May'78.

IT'S ONLY ROCK'N'ROLL (Various Artists).
Tracks: / Long tall Sally / Wooly bully / Party doll / Mr Bassman / Duke of Earl / Let's twist again / Yakety yak / Blue moon / Running bear / Way down yonder in New Orleans / Personality / Willie & the hand jive.
Notes: These tracks have been re-recorded by the artist or one or more members of the original groups.
(P) & (C) 1987 K-Tel International (UK) Ltd.
Compact disc: released on K-Tel, Jun'87 by K-Tel Records. Dist: Record Merchandisers Distribution, Taylors, Terry Blood Distribution, Wynd-Up Distribution, Relay Distribution, Pickwick Distribution, Solomon & Peres Distribution, Polygram

IT'S ONLY ROCK 'N' ROLL(1957-1964) Various artists (Various Artists).
Album: released on Nut, May'79 by EMI Records. Dist: EMI

IT'S PARTY TIME Various artists (Various Artists).
Album: released on Decca, Nov'82 by Decca Records. Dist: Polygram

Cassette: released on Decca, Nov'82 by Decca Records. Dist: Polygram

IT'S PARTY TIME AGAIN Various artists (Various Artists).
Album: released on Decca, Dec'83 by Decca Records. Dist: Polygram

Cassette: released on Decca, Dec'83 by Decca Records. Dist: Polygram

IT'S ROCK AND ROLL (VOL 2) Various artists (Various Artists).
Album: released on BBC, Sep'78 by BBC Records & Tapes. Dist: EMI, PRT, Pye

Cassette: released on BBC, Sep'78 by BBC Records & Tapes. Dist: EMI, PRT, Pye

IT'S ROCK 'N' ROLL Various artists (Various Artists).
Album: released on BBC, Apr'77 by BBC Records & Tapes. Dist: EMI, PRT, Pye

Cassette: released on BBC, Apr'77 by BBC Records & Tapes. Dist: EMI, PRT, Pye

IT'S ROLLIN' ROCK Various artists (Various Artists).
Album: released on Rondelet (Rollin' Rock), Sep'82

IT'S SOMETHING ELSE (20 HITS FROM 50'S) (Various Artists).
Album: released on MFP, Aug'75 by EMI Records. Dist: EMI

IT'S TORTURE + 15 OTHER GREAT SOUL DESTROYERS Various artists (Various Artists).
Album: released on Kent, Sep'85 by Ace Records. Dist: Pinnacle

It's A Beautiful Day

IT'S A BEAUTIFUL DAY.
Album: released on CBS, Sep'79 by CBS Records. Dist: CBS

THOUSAND AND ONE NIGHTS, A.
Album: released on CBS, Mar'82 by CBS Records. Dist: CBS Deleted May'86

Cassette: released on CBS, Mar'82 by CBS Records. Dist: CBS

It's All Platinum

IT'S ALL PLATINUM.
Album: released on All Platinum, Apr'75 by PRT Records. Dist: PRT

It's A Secret

I CAN'T DANCE.
Tracks: / I can't dance / This goes anywhere.
Single (7"): released on GC, Nov'86 by GC Recordings. Dist: DMS, RCA

Single (12"): released on GC, Nov'86 by GC Recordings. Dist: DMS, RCA

It's Immaterial

BETTER IDEA.
Single (12"): released on Ark, Mar'85 Dist: ILA

ED'S FUNKY DINER.
Tracks: / Ed's funky diner / Friday night saturday morning / I mean after all it's only dead man's curve.
Single (7"): released on Siren, Jul'86 by Virgin Records. Dist: EMI

Single (12"): released on Siren, Jul'86 by Virgin Records. Dist: EMI

Single (7"): released on Siren, Oct'85 by Virgin Records. Dist: EMI

Single (12"): released on Siren, Oct'85 by Virgin Records. Dist: EMI

GIANT RAFT.
Single (7"): released on Wonderful World Of IDS, Oct'82

GIGANTIC RAFT.
Single (7"): released on Eternal, Feb'84 by Eternal Records. Dist: WEA

Single (12"): released on Eternal, Feb'84 by Eternal Records. Dist: WEA

IT'S IMMATERIAL.
Album: released on Ark, Mar'85 Dist: ILA

LIFE'S HARD AND THEN YOU DIE.
Tracks: / Driving away from home (Jim's tune) / Happy talk / Rope / Rope / Better idea, The / Space / Sweet life, The / Festival time / Ed's funky diner / Hang on sleepy town / Lullaby.
Compact disc: released on Siren, Nov'86 by Virgin Records. Dist: EMI

Cassette: released on Siren, Nov'86 by Virgin Records. Dist: EMI

Album: released on Siren, Nov'86 by Virgin Records. Dist: EMI

ROPE.
Tracks: / Rope / Festival time.
Single (7"): released on Siren, Feb'87 by Virgin Records. Dist: EMI

Single (12"): released on Siren, Feb'87 by Virgin Records. Dist: EMI

SPACE.
Single (7"): released on Siren, Nov'86 by Virgin Records. Dist: EMI

Single (12"): released on Siren, Nov'86 by Virgin Records. Dist: EMI

It's In The Mix

IT'S IN THE MIX Various artists (Various Artists).
Album: released on Calibre, Mar'83 by Calibre Records. Dist: PRT

IT'S IN THE MIX 1 Various artists (Various Artists).
Notes: Including Latin Rascals/Eruption/Newcleus
Album: released on Streetheat- Italoheat (Germany), Apr'86 Dist: Greyhound

IT'S IN THE MIX 2 Various artists (Various Artists).
Notes: Including Round one, Max Him, Ken Lazlo.
Album: released on Streetheat- Italoheat (Germany), Apr'86 Dist: Greyhound

IT'S IN THE MIX (VOL 2) Various artists (Various Artists).
Album: released on Calibre, Jul'83 by Calibre Records. Dist: PRT

Cassette: released on Calibre, Jul'83 by Calibre Records. Dist: PRT

IT'S IN THE MIX (VOL 3) Various artists (Various Artists).
Album: released on Calibre, Sep'83 by Calibre Records. Dist: PRT

Cassette: released on Calibre, Sep'83 by Calibre Records. Dist: PRT

IT'S IN THE MIX (VOL 4) Various artists (Various Artists).
Album: released on Calibre, Feb'84 by Calibre Records. Dist: PRT

Cassette: released on Calibre, Feb'84 by Calibre Records. Dist: PRT

Itturia, Manuel

SUPERB CHA-CHA.
Album: released on Code O, Jan'76

It Was Ten Years Ago Today

IT WAS TEN YEARS AGO TODAY Various artists (Various Artists).
Album: released on Konnexion, Aug'87 Dist: Roots, Pinnacle

Ivanhoe

IVANHOE Scott, Sir Walter (Fairbanks, Douglas Jnr).
Double Album: released on Caedmon(USA), May'79 by Caedmon (USA) Records. Dist: Gower, Taylors, Discovery

Double cassette: released on Caedmon(USA), May'78 by Caedmon (USA) Records. Dist: Gower, Taylors, Discovery

IVANHOE/ ROSE OF PERSIA Various artists (Various Artists).
Album: released on Dingles, Jun'84 by Dingle's Records. Dist: Projection

Ivor Novello

IVOR NOVELLO-SHOWTIME Various artists (Various Artists).
Double Album: released on Music For Pleasure, Feb'83 by EMI Records. Dist: EMI

Double cassette: released on Music For Pleasure, Feb'83 by EMI Records. Dist: EMI

Ivor the engine

IVOR THE ENGINE Stories from the BBC TV childrens series.
Album: released on BBC, Jul'84 by BBC Records & Tapes. Dist: EMI, PRT, Pye

Cassette: released on BBC, Jul'84 by BBC Records & Tapes. Dist: EMI, PRT, Pye

Ivory

LADY (IVORY).
Single (7"): released on Gomez, May'85 by M.I.S. Distribution. Dist: M.I.S.

YOU CAN'T FOOL EVERYBODY.
Single (7"): released on Gomez, Sep'83 by M.I.S. Distribution. Dist: M.I.S.

Ivory Coasters

MAKOSSA MUNGAKA.
Single (7"): released on Recreational, May'82 by Revolver Records. Dist: Rough Trade

Single (12"): released on Recreational, May'82 by Revolver Records. Dist: Rough Trade

Ivory Sessions

TIME FOR PEACE,A.
Tracks: / Abraham's Theme / Lord's prayer (The) / Hiding place / Amazing Grace.
Album: released on Maranatha Music, Jun'86

Cassette: released on Maranatha Music, Jun'86

Ivy Green

ALL ON THE BEAT.
Album: released on Circo, Jan'86 Dist: Red Rhino, Cartel

Ivy League

TOSSING & TURNING.
Single (7"): released on Flashback, Apr'79 by Flashback Records/PRT Records. Dist: Mainline, PRT

Iwamoto, Yoshikazu
WHEN THE BRIGHTNESS COMES.....
Album: released on Orchid, Jan'85 Dist: Impetus Distribution, Orchid

I Want..
I WANT ROCK Rockabilly compilation (Various Artists).
Album: released on White Label (Holland), Feb'85 Dist: CSA, PRT

Iyah Binghi Rockers
IYAH BINGHI ROCKERS SHOWCASE Various artists (Various Artists).
Album: released on Iyah Bingi, Sep'84 by Iyah Bingi Records. Dist: Jetstar, Kingdom, Iyah Bingi

Album: released on Pearl, Jun'76 by Pavillion (USA). Dist: Taylors, Swift

Ivan, Ranking
Single (12"): released on Disco Tex, Sep'84 by Disco Tex Records. Dist: Jetstar

I've Got The Bullets
IT SHOULD HAVE BEEN ME.
Single (7"): released on Epic, Feb'87 by CBS Records. Dist: CBS

Ives, Burl
ANIMAL FOLK.
Album: released on Castle Communications, May'74 by Castle Communications. Dist: Cartel, Pinnacle, Counterpoint Deleted May'76.

BRIGHT AND BEAUTIFUL.
Album: released on Word Twenty, May'85

Cassette: released on Word Twenty, May'85

CHIM CHIM CHEREE.
Album: released on Castle Communications, May'74 by Castle Communications. Dist: Cartel, Pinnacle, Countermint Deleted May'76

CHRISTMAS AT THE WHITE HOUSE.
Album: released on Caedmon(USA), May'79 by Caedmon (USA) Records. Dist: Gower, Taylors, Discovery

FAITH & JOY.
Album: released on Sacred, May'74 by Word Records.

LITTLE WHITE DUCK.
Album: released on Embassy, Jul'77 by CBS Records. Dist: CBS

LOVE AND JOY.
Album: released on Word, Jun'84 by Word Records. Dist: Word Distribution, CBS

Cassette: released on Word, Jun'84 by Word Records. Dist: Word Distribution, CBS

SHALL WE GATHER AT THE RIVER.
Album: released on Sacred, Mar'78 by Word records.

SONGS I SANG IN SUNDAY SCHOOL.
Album: released on Sacred, May'74 by Word Records.

STEPPING IN THE LIGHT.
Album: released on Word, Jun'84 by Word Records. Dist: Word Distribution, CBS

Cassette: released on Word, Jun'84 by Word Records. Dist: Word Distribution, CBS

TALENTED MAN, THE.
Album: released on Bulldog Records, Jul'82

Ivey, Lee
OLDER WOMEN (Ivey, Lee & Five Cents).
Single (7"): released on Dingles, Jun'84 by Dingle's Records. Dist: Projection

Jab Jab
KEEP ON SMILING.
Single (12"): released on Rip Off, Aug'85 Dist: Red Rhino, Cartel

Jab Jab Music
LONELINESS IS NOT HAPPINESS.
Single (7"): released on Shades, Aug'81 Dist: Pinnacle

Jacas, Jake
HOLD ME.
Single (7"): released on Motown, Jun'85 by Motown Records. Dist: BMG Distribution

Single (12"): released on Motown, Jun'85 by Motown Records. Dist: BMG Distribution

Jacetti, Roberto
I SAVE THE DAY (Jacetti, Roberto & The Scooters).
Single (7"): released on Carrere, Jun'84 by Carrere Records. Dist: PRT, Spartan

Single (12"): released on Carrere, Jun'84 by Carrere Records. Dist: PRT, Spartan

Jacinth, Joy
BABY BOY.
Single (7"): released on Zebratone, Mar'84 by Zebratone Records. Dist: Pinnacle

Jackals
ALL IN A DAY.
Tracks: / All in a day / Ringing in my ear / She just flies in / Baby let me follow you down.
Single (12"): released on Constitution, Jun'86 by Constitution Records. Dist: Rough Trade, Cartel

UNDERNEATH THE ARCHES.
Tracks: / Underneath the arches / Thunder machine.
Single (7"): released on Criminal Damage, Jun'86 by Criminal Damage Records. Dist: Backs, Cartel

WE ALL SIGN ON.
Single (7"): released on Constitution, Jul'87 by Constitution Records. Dist: Rough Trade, Cartel

Jackanory
JACKANORY:STORIES FROM LITTLENOSE (Grant, John).
Album: released on BBC, '79 by BBC Records & Tapes. Dist: EMI, PRT, Pye

Jackbeat
JACKBEAT Various artists (Various Artists).
Cassette: released on Rhythm King, Feb'87 Dist: Rough Trade, Cartel

JACKBEAT (Various Artists).
Album: released on Rhythm King, Dec'86 Dist: Rough Trade, Cartel

Jack & Chill
JACK THAT HOUSE BUILT (THE).
Tracks: / Jack that house built (The) / Jack that house dubbed (The).
Single (7"): released on 10, May'87 by 10 Records. Dist: Virgin, EMI

Single (12"): released on 10, May'87 by 10 Records. Dist: Virgin, EMI

Jackdaw With Crowbar
ICEBERG.
Single (12"): released on Ron Johnson, Aug'87 by Ron Johnson Records. Dist: Nine Mile Distribution, Cartel Distribution

Jacket, Illinois
BOTTOMS UP.
Album: released on Black & Blue (Franco), Nov'85 Dist: Swift, Target, Discovery

ILLINOIS FLIES AGAIN.
Tracks: / On a clear day (you can see forever) / Illinois jacket flies again / Robins nest / Watermelon man / I want a little girl / Pamaelas blues / Jan / Message, The / Bassoon blues / On broadway / Like young / Turnpike / Bonita.
Album: released on Arco, '86 by Charly Records. Dist: Charly

Jackhammer 5
ST.PETER'S EGG.
Single (12"): released on Cathexis, Oct'86 Dist: Fast Forward, Cartel

Jackie
LIKE I AM.
Single (7"): released on Hobbs, Sep'82 by Hobbs Music. Dist: Hobbs Music Distribution

Jackie & Roy
GLORY OF LOVE.
Album: released on Jasmine, Feb'84 by Jasmine Records. Dist: Counterpoint, Lugtons, Taylor, H.R., Wellard, Chris. Swift Cadillac

HIGH STANDARDS.
Album: released on Concord Jazz, Jul'82 by Concord Jazz Records (USA). Dist: IMS, Polygram

Jack & Jill
YOU.
Single (7"): released on Splash, Jan'85 by Splash Records. Dist: CBS

Jacko
T. JAM (CLUB MIX).
Single (12"): released on Hot Melt, Apr'87 by Hot Melt Records. Dist: Pinnacle, Spartan

Jack of all trades
JACK OF ALL TRADES Songs of various occupations (Various Artists).
Cassette: released on Folktracks, Nov'79 by Folktracks Cassettes. Dist: Folktracks

Jack on the rocks
JACK ON THE ROCKS 18 English sea songs (Various Artists).
Cassette: released on Folktracks, Nov'79 by Folktracks Cassettes. Dist: Folktracks

Jack Pack
SOUL IN THE BOX.
Single (7"): released on Dart, Jan'81 by President Records. Dist: Jazz Music, Swift

Jack, Ronnie
GOING FOR THE BIG ONE.
Single (7"): released on Ritz, Mar'81 by Outlet Records. Dist: Outlet, Prism Leisure Distribution, Record Services Distribution (Ireland), Roots

HEY MARY ANN.
Single (7"): released on Plaza, Oct'83 by Plaza Records. Dist: Spartan

MOTOR RIDING.
Single (7"): released on Plaza, Apr'82 by Plaza Records. Dist: Spartan

Jackson 5
20 GOLDEN GREATS.
Album: released on Motown, Oct'81 by Motown Records. Dist: BMG Distribution

Cassette: released on Motown, Oct'81 by Motown Records. Dist: BMG Distribution

ABC.
Album: released on Motown, Jun'82 by Motown Records. Dist: BMG Distribution

Cassette: released on Motown, Jun'82 by Motown Records. Dist: BMG Distribution

ANTHOLOGY Volumes 1 & 2.
Tracks: / I hear a symphony / Dancing machine / Body language / Got to be there / Rockin' robin / Ben / Daddy's home / ABC / I want you back / I'll be there / Sugar daddy / Maybe tomorrow / Mamas pearl / I am love / I am love / Teenage symphony / Skywriter / Hallelujah day / Bogie man / Let's get serious / Let me tickle your fancy / You're supposed to keep your love for me / Love don't want to leave / That's how love goes / Just a little bit of you / We're almost there / I wanna be where you are / Forever came today / All I do is think of you / I was made to love her / Whatever you got I want / Get it together.
Double compact disc: released on Motown, Oct'86 by Motown Records. Dist: BMG Distribution

Double compact disc: released on Motown, 20 Jun'87 by Motown Records. Dist: BMG Distribution

ANTHOLOGY.
Double Album: released on Motown, Oct'81 by Motown Records. Dist: BMG Distribution

Double cassette: released on Motown, Oct'81 by Motown Records. Dist: BMG Distribution

CHRISTMAS ALBUM.
Album: released on Motown, Nov'82 by Motown Records. Dist: BMG Distribution

Cassette: released on Motown, Nov'82 by Motown Records. Dist: BMG Distribution

DIANA ROSS PRESENTS THE JACKSON 5/A.B.C. 2 Classic albums.
Tracks: / Zip a dee doo dah / Nobody / I want you back / Can you remember / Standing in the shadows of love / You've changed / My cherie amour / Who's lovin' you / Chained / I'm losing you / Stand / Born to love you / Love you save / I found that girl / Young folks / Love you save, The / One more chance / 2-4-6-8 / Come 'round here I'm the one you need / Don't know why I love you / Never had a dream come true / True love can be beautiful / La la (means I love you) / I'll bet you / I found that girl / Young folks, The.
Compact disc: released on Motown, Nov'86 by Motown Records. Dist: BMG Distribution

DIANA ROSS PRESENTS THE JACKSON 5.
Album: released on Motown, Oct'81 by Motown Records. Dist: BMG Distribution

Cassette: released on Motown, Oct'81 by Motown Records. Dist: BMG Distribution

FLIPHITS (4 TRACK CASSETTE EP).
Cassette: released on Motown, Jul'83 by Motown Records. Dist: BMG Distribution

GREATEST HITS: JACKSON 5.
Album: released on Motown, Mar'82 by Motown Records. Dist: BMG Distribution

Cassette: released on Motown, Mar'82 by Motown Records. Dist: BMG Distribution

GREAT LOVE SONGS OF THE JACKSON 5.
Album: released on Motown, Nov'84 by Motown Records. Dist: BMG Distribution

Cassette: released on Motown, Nov'84 by Motown Records. Dist: BMG Distribution

I'LL BE THERE.
Single (7"): released on Motown (Re-issue), Jun'83

I WANT YOU BACK.
Single (7"): released on Motown (Re-issue), Oct'81

JACKSON 5, THE.
Album: released on Motown, '82 by Motown Records. Dist: BMG Distribution

Cassette: released on Motown, '82 by Motown Records. Dist: BMG Distribution

LOOKIN' THROUGH THE WINDOWS.
Album: released on Motown, Feb'83 by Motown Records. Dist: BMG Distribution

Cassette: released on Motown, Feb'83 by Motown Records. Dist: BMG Distribution

Single (7"): released on Motown (Re-issue), Oct'81

SKYWRITER.
Album: released on Motown, Nov'84 by Motown Records. Dist: BMG Distribution

Cassette: released on Motown, Nov'84 by Motown Records. Dist: BMG Distribution

THIRD ALBUM.
Album: released on Motown, Mar'82 by Motown Records. Dist: BMG Distribution

Cassette: released on Motown, Mar'82 by Motown Records. Dist: BMG Distribution

VERY BEST OF MICHAEL JACKSON & THE JACKSON 5.
Tracks: / One day in your life / Looking through the windows / Got to be there / Doctor my eyes / Ben / ABC / We're almost there / Skywriter / Rockin' robin / Happy / Ain't no sunshine / I'll be there / I want you back / Love you save, The / We've got a good thing going / Mamas pearl / Never can say goodbye / Hallelujah day.
Compact disc: released on Telstar, '86 by Telstar Records. Dist: RCA Distribution

Jackson, Banton, Evans
GENTLEMEN PREFER BLUES.
Album: released on Demi Monde, Apr'86 Dist: Charly

Jackson, Billy
HAVE A HAPPY CHRISTMAS (Jackson, Billy & Citizens Band).
Single (7"): released on London, Nov'83 by London Records. Dist: Polygram

Single (12"): released on London, Nov'83 by London Records. Dist: Polygram

MISTY MOUNTAIN (Jackson, Billy & Billy Ross).
Album: released on Iona, Jan'85 Dist: Folksound, Jazz Music, JSU, Swift, Celtic Music

Cassette: released on Iona, Jan'85 Dist: Folksound, Jazz Music, JSU, Swift, Celtic Music

WELLPARK SUITE, THE.
Album: released on Mill, Oct'85 Dist: Roots Distribution, Swift Distribution

Jackson, Bo Weavil
1926 Sam Butler.
Album: released on Matchbox (Bluesmaster), Jan'83

Jackson, Brian
1980 (see Scott-Heron, Gill) (Jackson, Brian & Gill Scott-Heron).

BOTTLE, THE (Jackson, Brian & Gill Scott-Heron).

Jackson, Chubby
CHOICE CUTS.
Notes: Including Chubby Jackson, Arnold Ross, George Wallington and Toots Thielemans.
Album: released on Esquire, Nov'86 by Titan International Productions. Dist: Jazz Music, Cadillac Music, Swift, Wellard, Chris, Backs, Rough Trade, Revolver, Nine Mile

Jackson, Chuck
GREAT CHUCK JACKSON, THE.
Album: released on Bulldog, Jul'82 by Bulldog Records. Dist: President Distribution, Spartan, Swift, Taylor, H.R.

MR EMOTION.
Album: released on Kent, Jan'85 by Ace Records. Dist: Pinnacle

Jackson, Cliff
CAROLINE SHOUT.

Album: released on Black Lion, Apr'85 by Black Lion Records. Dist: Jazz Music, Chris Wellard, Taylor, H.R., Counterpoint, Cadillac

CLIFF JACKSON & HIS CRAZY CATS.
Album: released on Fountain, Jul'81 by Retrieval Records. Dist: Jazz Music, Swift, VJM, Wellard, Chris, Retrieval

Jackson, David

LONG HELLO VOL 3.
Album: released on Butt, Mar'82 by Butt Records. Dist: Counterpoint

Jackson, Deon

HIS GREATEST.
Album: released on Solid Smoke (USA), Jul'84 Dist: Rhino

Jackson, Francis

YORK MINSTER ORGAN.
Album: released on Abbey, Jul'78 by Abbey. Dist: PRT, Taylors, Gamut

Jackson, Frankie

CAN'T WAIT TILL YOU GET HOME (Jackson, Frankie 'Halfpint').
Album: released on Collectors Items, Jul'86 Dist: Jazz Music, Swift, Chris Wellard

CAN'T YOU WAIT TILL YOU GET HOME (Jackson, Frankie 'Halfpint').
Album: released on Collectors Items, Oct'84 Dist: Jazz Music, Swift, Chris Wellard

Jackson, Franz

LET'S HAVE A PARTY.
Album: released on Pinnacle, Jul'82 by Pinnacle Records. Dist: Pinnacle

Jackson, Freddie

HAVE YOU EVER LOVED SOMEBODY.
Tracks: / Have you ever loved somebody / Tasty love (inst) / Have you ever loved somebody / Tasty love (inst) / Rock me tonight (for old time's sake) / Have you ever loved somebody (inst mix).
Single (7"): released on Capitol, Jan'87 by Capitol Records. Dist: EMI

Single (12"): released on Capitol, Jan'87 by Capitol Records. Dist: EMI

Single (7"): released on Capitol, Jan'87 by Capitol Records. Dist: EMI

HE'LL NEVER LOVE YOU LIKE I DO.
Tracks: / He'll never love you (like I do)(maserati mix) / I wanna say I love you / He'll never love you (like I do) / Tasty love / Have you ever loved someobody / Look around / Jam tonight / Just like the first time / I can't let you go / I don't want to lose your love.
Single (7"): released on Capitol, Apr'86 by Capitol Records. Dist: EMI

Single (12"): released on Capitol, Apr'86 by Capitol Records. Dist: EMI

JUST LIKE THE FIRST TIME.
Tracks: / You are my love / Tasty love / Have you ever loved somebody / Look around / Jam tonight / Just like the first time / I can't let you go / I don't want to lose your love / Janay / Still waiting / Janay / Still waiting / You are my love.
Compact disc: released on EMI, Jan'87 by EMI Records. Dist: EMI

Album: released on Capitol, Oct'86 by Capitol Records. Dist: EMI

Cassette: released on Capitol, Oct'86 by Capitol Records. Dist: EMI

ROCK ME TONIGHT.
Tracks: / He'll never love you (like I do) / Love is just a touch away / Iwanna say I love you / You are my lady / Rock me tonight (for old times sake) / Sing a song of love / Calling / Good morning heartache.
Compact disc: released on Capitol, Jan'86 by Capitol Records. Dist: EMI

Album: released on Capitol, May'85 by Capitol Records. Dist: EMI

Cassette: released on Capitol, May'85 by Capitol Records. Dist: EMI

ROCK ME TONIGHT (FOR OLD TIMES SAKE).
Tracks: / Rock me tonight (for old times sake) / Rock me tonight (for old times sake)(groove version).
Single (7"): released on Capitol, Feb'86 by Capitol Records. Dist: EMI

Single (12"): released on Capitol, Feb'86 by Capitol Records. Dist: EMI

Double-pack single: released on Capitol, Nov'85 by Capitol Records. Dist: EMI

TASTY LOVE.
Tracks: / Tasty love / I wanna say I love you.
Single (7"): released on Capitol, Sep'86 by Capitol Records. Dist: EMI

Single (12"): released on Capitol, Sep'86 by Capitol Records. Dist: EMI

YOU ARE MY LADY.
Single (7"): released on Capitol, Oct'85 by Capitol Records. Dist: EMI

Single (12"): released on Capitol, Oct'85 by Capitol Records. Dist: EMI

Jackson, George

CAIRITIONA (Jackson, George & Maggie McInnes).
Album: released on Iona, Jan'85 Dist: Folksound, Jazz Music, JSU, Swift, Celtic Music

Cassette: released on Iona, Jan'85 Dist: Folksound, Jazz Music, JSU, Swift, Celtic Music

Jackson, Glenda

READS FROM HER OWN STORYBOOK.
Double cassette: released on Argo (Spokenword), Jul'83 by Decca Records. Dist: Polygram

Jackson, Guy

RADIO ONE.
Single (7"): released on Rondelet, Oct'81 Dist: Spartan Distribution

Jackson, Janet

COME GIVE YOUR LOVE TO ME.
Single (7"): released on A&M, Jan'83 by A&M Records. Dist: Polygram

Single (12"): released on A&M, Jan'83 by A&M Records. Dist: Polygram

CONTROL (The Remixes).
Tracks: / Let's wait a while / Funny how time flies.
Compact disc: released on A&M, Mar'87 by A&M Records. Dist: Polygram

Single (7"): released on A&M, Oct'86 by A&M Records. Dist: Polygram

Single (12"): released on A&M, Oct'86 by A&M Records. Dist: Polygram

CONTROL.
Tracks: / Control / What have you done for me lately / You can be mine / Pleasure principle, The / When I think of you / He doesn't know I'm alive / Control / Pretty boy / Nasty (cool summer mix part 1).
Album: released on A&M, '86 by A&M Records. Dist: Polygram

Cassette: released on A&M, '86 by A&M Records. Dist: Polygram

Compact disc: released on A&M, '86 by A&M Records. Dist: Polygram

DON'T MESS UP THIS GOOD THING.
Single (7"): released on A&M, May'83 by A&M Records. Dist: Polygram

Single (12"): released on A&M, May'83 by A&M Records. Dist: Polygram

DREAM STREET.
Album: released on A&M, Oct'84 by A&M Records. Dist: Polygram

Cassette: released on A&M, Oct'84 by A&M Records. Dist: Polygram

JANET JACKSON.
Album: released on A&M, Jan'83 by A&M Records. Dist: Polygram

Cassette: released on A&M, Jan'83 by A&M Records. Dist: Polygram

LET'S WAIT AWHILE.
Tracks: / Let's wait awhile / Nasty (Cool summer mix Pt.1) / Nasty (original mix) / Control / Let's wait awhile (remix) / Nasty cool summer mix part1 (fade).
Double-pack single: released on Breakout, Mar'87 by A&M Records. Dist: Polygram

Single (7"): released on A&M, Mar'87 by A&M Records. Dist: Polygram

NASTY.
Tracks: / Nasty / You'll never find (a love like mine).
Single (7"): released on A&M, May'86 by A&M Records. Dist: Polygram

PLEASURE PRINCIPLE, THE.
Tracks: / Pleasure principle, The / Pleasure principle, The (remix edit) / Pleasure principle, The (edit).
Single (7"): released on Breakout, 30 May'87 by A&M Records. Dist: Polygram

Single (12"): released on Breakout, 30 May'87 by A&M Records. Dist: Polygram

Cassette single: released on Breakout, 30 May'87 by A&M Records. Dist: Polygram

TWO TO THE POWER (see Richard, Cliff) (Jackson, Janet & Cliff Richard).

WHAT HAVE YOU DONE FOR ME LATELY.
Tracks: / What have you done for me lately / Young love.
Single (7"): released on A&M, Mar'86 by A&M Records. Dist: Polygram

Single (12"): released on A&M, Mar'86 by A&M Records. Dist: Polygram

WHEN I THINK OF YOU.
Tracks: / When I think of you / Come give your love.
Single (7"): released on A&M, Jul'86 by A&M Records. Dist: Polygram

Single (12"): released on A&M, Jul'86 by A&M Records. Dist: Polygram

Jackson, Jermaine

BURNIN' HOT.
Single (7"): released on Motown, Oct'81 by Motown Records. Dist: BMG Distribution

DO WHAT YOU DO.
Single (7"): released on Arista, Jan'85 by Arista Records. Dist: RCA

Single (12"): released on Arista, Jan'85 by Arista Records. Dist: RCA

DO YOU REMEMBER ME.
Tracks: / Do you remember me (USA mix) / Voices in the dark.
Single (7"): released on Arista, May'86 by Arista Records. Dist: RCA

Single (12"): released on Arista, May'86 by Arista Records. Dist: RCA

Single (12"): released on Arista, Jul'86 by Arista Records. Dist: RCA

DYNAMITE.
Tracks: / Dynamite / Sweetest sweetest / Tell me I'm not dreaming (too good to be true) / Escape from the planet of the ant men / Come to me (one way or another) / Do what you do / Some things are private / Oh Mother.
Notes: Digital stereo
Compact disc: released on Arista, Mar'85 by Arista Records. Dist: RCA

Album: released on Arista, Mar'85 by Arista Records. Dist: RCA

Cassette: released on Arista, Mar'85 by Arista Records. Dist: RCA

Single (7"): released on Arista, Jul'84 by Arista Records. Dist: RCA

Single (12"): released on Arista, Jul'84 by Arista Records. Dist: RCA

DYNAMITE (JELLY BEAN REMIX).
Single (7"): released on Arista, May'85 by Arista Records. Dist: RCA

Single (12"): released on Arista, May'85 by Arista Records. Dist: RCA

I LIKE YOUR STYLE.
Album: released on Motown, Oct'81 by Motown Records. Dist: BMG Distribution

Cassette: released on Motown, Oct'81 by Motown Records. Dist: BMG Distribution

I'M JUST TOO SHY.
Single (7"): released on Motown, Nov'81 by Motown Records. Dist: BMG Distribution

I THINK IT'S LOVE.
Tracks: / I think it's love / Voices in the dark.
Single (7"): released on Arista, Feb'86 by Arista Records. Dist: RCA

Single (12"): released on Arista, Feb'86 by Arista Records. Dist: RCA

JERMAINE.
Album: released on Motown, Oct'81 by Motown Records. Dist: BMG Distribution

Cassette: released on Motown, Oct'81 by Motown Records. Dist: BMG Distribution

LET ME TICKLE YOUR FANCY.
Single (7"): released on Motown, Aug'82 by Motown Records. Dist: BMG Distribution

Single (12"): released on Motown, Aug'82 by Motown Records. Dist: BMG Distribution

LET'S GET SERIOUS.
Album: released on Motown, Oct'81 by Motown Records. Dist: BMG Distribution

Cassette: released on Motown, Oct'81 by Motown Records. Dist: BMG Distribution

Single (7"): released on Motown, Oct'81 by Motown Records. Dist: BMG Distribution

Album: released on Motown, Apr'85 by Motown Records. Dist: BMG Distribution

Cassette: released on Motown, Apr'85 by Motown Records. Dist: BMG Distribution

LITTLE GIRL DON'T YOU WORRY.
Single (7"): released on Motown, Oct'81 by Motown Records. Dist: BMG Distribution

Single (12"): released on Motown, Oct'81 by Motown Records. Dist: BMG Distribution

PARADISE IN YOUR EYES.
Single (7"): released on Motown, Feb'82 by Motown Records. Dist: BMG Distribution

PERFECT.
Single (7"): released on Arista, Aug'85 by Arista Records. Dist: RCA

Single (12"): released on Arista, Aug'85 by Arista Records. Dist: RCA

PRECIOUS MOMENTS.
Tracks: / Precious moments / Do you remember me / We never called it love / Give a little love / Lonely won't leave me alone.
Album: released on Arista, Jul'86 by Arista Records. Dist: RCA

Cassette: released on Arista, Jul'86 by Arista Records. Dist: RCA

Compact disc: released on Arista, Jul'86 by Arista Records. Dist: RCA

SWEETEST SWEETEST.
Single (7"): released on Arista, Apr'84 by Arista Records. Dist: RCA

Single (12"): released on Arista, Apr'84 by Arista Records. Dist: RCA

Picture disc single: released on Arista, Jun'84 by Arista Records. Dist: RCA

VERY SPECIAL PART.
Single (7"): released on Motown, Nov'82 by Motown Records. Dist: BMG Distribution

Single (12"): released on Motown, Nov'82 by Motown Records. Dist: BMG Distribution

WHEN THE RAIN BEGINS TO FALL (Jackson, Jermaine & Pia Zadora).
Single (7"): released on Arista, Sep'84 by Arista Records. Dist: RCA

Single (12"): released on Arista, Sep'84 by Arista Records. Dist: RCA

YOU LIKE ME DON'T YOU.
Single (7"): released on Motown, Oct'81 by Motown Records. Dist: BMG Distribution

Single (12"): released on Motown, Oct'81 by Motown Records. Dist: BMG Distribution

YOU MOVED A MOUNTAIN.
Single (7"): released on Motown, Apr'83 by Motown Records. Dist: BMG Distribution

YOU'RE SUPPOSED TO KEEP YOUR LOVE....
Single (7"): released on Motown, Oct'81 by Motown Records. Dist: BMG Distribution

Jackson, Jim

BEST OF 1928-30.
Album: released on Earl Archives, Jan'85 Dist: Swift, Jazz Music

BEST OF JIM JACKSON - 1928-1930.
Album: released on Earl Archives, Jan'87 Dist: Swift, Jazz Music

Jackson, Joe

BEAT CRAZY (Jackson,Joe,Band).
Album: released on A&M, Oct'80 by A&M Records. Dist: Polygram

Cassette: released on A&M, Oct'80 by A&M Records. Dist: Polygram

BIG WORLD.
Tracks: / Wild west / Right & wrong / (It's a) big world / Precious time / Tonight & forever / Shanghai sky / Fifty dollar love / We can't live together / Forty years / Soul kiss / Jet set, The / Tango Alantico / Home town / Man in the street.
Notes: The much awaited album from one of the UK's foremost songwriting and singing talents. "Big World" features no less than 15 brand new songs, including the single "Right And Wrong". Released as a 3 sided album (1), long playing chrome cassette, and CD, the vinyl version also includes a special fold out concertina-style booklet.
Album: released on A&M, Mar'86 by A&M Records. Dist: Polygram

Cassette: released on A&M, Mar'86 by A&M Records. Dist: Polygram

Compact disc: released on A&M, Mar'86 by A&M Records. Dist: Polygram

BODY AND SOUL.
Tracks: / Verdict / Cha cha loco / Not here, not now / You can't get what you want / You can't get what you want / Go for it / Loisaida / Happy ending / Be my number two / Heart of ice.
Notes: Digital stereo
Compact disc: released on A&M, Oct'84 by A&M Records. Dist: Polygram

Album: released on A&M, Oct'84 by A&M Records. Dist: Polygram

Cassette: released on A&M, Oct'84 by A&M Records. Dist: Polygram

BREAKING US IN TWO.
Single (12"): released on A&M, Feb'83 by A&M Records. Dist: Polygram

COSMOPOLITAN.
Single (7"): released on A&M, Aug'83 by A&M Records. Dist: Polygram

HOME TOWN.
Tracks: / Home town / Tango Atlantico.
Single (7"): released on A&M, May'86 by A&M Records. Dist: Polygram

Single (12"): released on A&M, May'86 by A&M Records. Dist: Polygram

JUMPING' JIVE.
Album: released on A&M, Jun'81 by A&M Records. Dist: Polygram

Cassette: released on A&M, Jun'81 by A&M Records. Dist: Polygram

LOOK SHARP.
Tracks: / One more time / Sunday papers / I she really going out with him / Happy loving couples / Throw it away / Baby stick around / Look sharp / Fools in love / (Do the) instant mash / Pretty girls / Got the time.
Compact disc: released on A&M, Nov'84 by A&M Records. Dist: Polygram

Album: released on Hallmark, Sep'84 by Pickwick Records. Dist: Pickwick Distribution, PRT, Taylors

Cassette: released on Hallmark, Sep'84 by Pickwick Records. Dist: Pickwick Distribution, PRT, Taylors

NIGHT AND DAY.
Compact disc: released on A&M, '83 by A&M Records. Dist: Polygram

Album: released on A&M, Jun'82 by A&M Records. Dist: Polygram

Cassette: released on A&M, Jun'82 by A&M Records. Dist: Polygram

RIGHT AND WRONG.
Tracks: / Right and wrong / Breaking us in two (live) / I'm the man (live0.
Single (7"): released on A&M, Apr'86 by A&M Records. Dist: Polygram

Single (12"): released on A&M, Apr'86 by A&M Records. Dist: Polygram

WILLPOWER.
Tracks: / No Pasaran / Solitude / Will Power / Nocturne / Symphony in one movement.
Compact disc: released on A&M, Apr'87 by A&M Records. Dist: Polygram

Album: released on A&M, 11 Apr'87 by A&M Records. Dist: Polygram

Cassette: released on A&M, 11 Apr'87 by A&M Records. Dist: Polygram

Jackson, John

BLUES & COUNTRY DANCE TUNES FROM VIRGINIA.
Album: released on Arhoolie, Oct'86 by Arhoolie Records. Dist: Projection, Topic, Jazz Music, Swift, Roots

BLUES FROM VIRGINIA.
Album: released on Arhoolie, May'81 by Arhoolie Records. Dist: Projection, Topic, Jazz Music, Swift, Roots

IN EUROPE.
Album: released on Arhoolie, May'81 by Arhoolie Records. Dist: Projection, Topic, Jazz Music, Swift, Roots

JOHN JACKSON.
Album: released on Rounder, May'79 Dist: Roots Distribution

JOHN JACKSON VOL.2.
Album: released on Arhoolie, May'81 by Arhoolie Records. Dist: Projection, Topic, Jazz Music, Swift, Roots

Jackson, Latoya

HEART DON'T LIE.
Single (7"): released on Epic, May'84 by CBS Records. Dist: CBS

Single (12"): released on Epic, May'84 by CBS Records. Dist: CBS

OPPS OH NO CLUB MIX.
Single (7"): released on Music Of Life, Oct'86 Dist: Streetwave

Single (12"): released on Music Of Life, Oct'86 Dist: Streetwave

Jackson, Lil'Son

BLUES COME TO TEXAS.
Album: released on Arhoolie, May'81 by Arhoolie Records. Dist: Projection, Topic, Jazz Music, Swift, Roots

ROCKIN' AN' ROLLIN'.
Album: released on Pathe Marconi, Sep'84 Dist: Swift

Jackson, Mahalia

20 GREATEST HITS.
Album: released on Masters (Holland), Apr'87

Cassette: released on Masters (Holland), Apr'87

20 GREATEST HITS.
Album: released on Astan, Nov'84 by Astan Records. Dist: Counterpoint

Cassette: released on Astan, Nov'84 by Astan Records. Dist: Counterpoint

GOSPEL.
Double Album: released on Vogue, Sep'77 Dist: Discovery, Jazz Music, PRT, Swift

IN THE UPPER ROOM.
Compact disc: released on Vogue, Jan'87 Dist: Discovery, Jazz Music, PRT, Swift

Compact disc: released on Vogue, '86 Dist: Discovery, Jazz Music, PRT, Swift

I'VE DONE MY WORK.
Album: released on Word, May'85 by Word Records. Dist: Word Distribution, CBS

Cassette: released on Word, May'85 by Word Records. Dist: Word Distribution, CBS

JESUS IS WITH ME.
Album: released on Astan, Nov'84 by Astan Records. Dist: Counterpoint

Cassette: released on Astan, Nov'84 by Astan Records. Dist: Counterpoint

MAHALIA JACKSON.
Album: released on CBS(Holland), Jun'84 by CBS Records. Dist: Discovery

Cassette: released on CBS(Holland), Jun'84 by CBS Records. Dist: Discovery

MAHALIA JACKSON COLLECTION, THE.
Album: released on Deja Vu, Aug'85 by Deja Vu Records. Dist: Counterpoint Distribution, Record Services Distribution (Ireland)

Cassette: released on Deja Vu, Aug'85 by Deja Vu Records. Dist: Counterpoint Distribution, Record Services Distribution (Ireland)

MAHALIA JACKSON VOL.1.
Album: released on Jazz Reactivation, Jan'82 Dist: PRT

MAHALIA JACKSON VOL.2.
Album: released on Jazz Reactivation, May'83 Dist: PRT

MY STORY.
Album: released on Astan, Nov'84 by Astan Records. Dist: Counterpoint

Cassette: released on Astan, Nov'84 by Astan Records. Dist: Counterpoint

MY TASK.
Album: released on World, May'85 Dist: Jetstar

Cassette: released on World, May'85 Dist: Jetstar

SILENT NIGHT.
Album: released on Teldec (Germany), Dec'81 by Import Records. Dist: IMS Distribution, Polygram Distribution

WARM & TENDER SOUL OF..., THE.
Double Album: released on Joker, Apr'81 Dist: Counterpoint, Mainline, Record Services Distribution (Ireland)

Album: released on Joker, Apr'81 Dist: Counterpoint, Mainline, Record Services Distribution (Ireland)

Album: released on Joker, Apr'81 Dist: Counterpoint, Mainline, Record Services Distribution (Ireland)

WHEN THE SAINT'S GO MARCHING IN.
Tracks: / I'm going to live the life I sing about in my song / When I wake up in glory / Jesus met the woman at the well / Oh Lord is it? / I will move on up a little higher / When the saints go marching in / Jesus out of the depths / Walk over God's heaven / Keep your hands on the plow / Didn't it rain.
Album: released on CBS, Jul'87 by CBS Records. Dist: CBS

Cassette: released on CBS, Jul'87 by CBS Records. Dist: CBS

Jackson, Marvin

OZARK ROCKABILLY.
Album: released on White label (Germany), Apr'85

Jackson, Michael

12" TAPE, THE.
Tracks: / Billie Jean / Beat it / Wanna be startin' somethin' / Thriller / P.Y.T. (pretty young thing).
Cassette: released on Epic, Sep'86 by CBS Records. Dist: CBS

18 GREATEST HITS (Jackson, Michael & Jackson Five).
Album: released on Telstar, Jul'83 by Telstar Records. Dist: RCA Distribution

Cassette: released on Telstar, Jul'83 by Telstar Records. Dist: RCA Distribution

18 GREATEST HITS (Jackson, Michael & Jackson Five).
Compact disc: released on Motown, May'84 by Motown Records. Dist: BMG Distribution

Compact disc: released on Motown, May'84 by Motown Records. Dist: BMG Distribution

AIN'T NO SUNSHINE.
Album: released on Motown, Jun'82 by Motown Records. Dist: BMG Distribution

Cassette: released on Motown, Jun'82 by Motown Records. Dist: BMG Distribution

Album: released on Blue Moon, Sep'83 Dist: Magnum Music Group Ltd, PRT, Spartan

Album: released on Astan, Nov'84 by Astan Records. Dist: Counterpoint

Cassette: released on Astan, Nov'84 by Astan Records. Dist: Counterpoint

AIN'T NO SUNSHINE/ I WANNA BE.
Single (7"): released on Motown, Oct'81 by Motown Records. Dist: BMG Distribution

ANTHOLOGY Volumes 1 & 2.
Tracks: / Got to be there / Rockin' Robin / Ain't no sunshine / Maria (you were the only one) / I wanna be where you are / Girl don't take your love from me / Love is here and now you're gone / Ben / People make the world go 'round / Shoo-be-doo-be-doo-da-day / With a child's heart / Everybody's somebody's fool / In our small way / All the things you are / You can cry on my shoulder / Maybe tomorrow / I'll be there / Never can say goodbye / It's too late to change the time / Dancing machine / When I come of age / Dear Michael / Music and me / You are there / One day in your life / Love's gone bad / That's what love is made of / Who's looking for a lover / Lonely teardrops / We're almost there / Take me back / Just a little bit of you / Melodie / I'll come home to you / If n'I was God / Happy (theme from "Lady sings the blues") / Don't let it get you down / Call on me / To make my father proud / Farewell my summer love.
Double compact disc: released on Motown, Jan'87 by Motown Records. Dist: BMG Distribution

BAD.
Tracks: / Bad / Way you make me feel, The / Speed demon / Liberian girl / Just good friends / Another part of me / Man in the mirror / I just can't stop loving you / Dirty Diana / Smooth criminal.
Album: released on Epic, Sep'87 by CBS Records. Dist: CBS

Cassette: released on Epic, Sep'87 by CBS Records. Dist: CBS

Compact disc: released on Epic, Sep'87 by CBS Records. Dist: CBS

BEN.
Single (7"): released on Motown, Oct'81 by Motown Records. Dist: BMG Distribution

Album: released on Motown, Oct'81 by Motown Records. Dist: BMG Distribution

Cassette: released on Motown, Oct'81 by Motown Records. Dist: BMG Distribution

Album: released on Motown, May'84 by Motown Records. Dist: BMG Distribution

Cassette: released on Motown, May'84 by Motown Records. Dist: BMG Distribution

BEST OF MICHAEL JACKSON.
Album: released on Motown, Oct'81 by Motown Records. Dist: BMG Distribution

Cassette: released on Motown, Oct'81 by Motown Records. Dist: BMG Distribution

DON'T STOP TIL YOU GET ENOUGH.
Single (7"): released on Epic, Apr'82 by CBS Records. Dist: CBS

EASE ON DOWN THE ROAD (Jackson, Michael & Diana Ross).
Single (7"): released on MCA, Jun'84 by MCA Records. Dist: Polygram, MCA

FAREWELL MY SUMMER LOVE.
Album: released on Motown, Aug'84 by Motown Records. Dist: BMG Distribution

Cassette: released on Motown, Aug'84 by Motown Records. Dist: BMG Distribution

Single (7"): released on Motown, May'84 by Motown Records. Dist: BMG Distribution

Single (12"): released on Motown, May'84 by Motown Records. Dist: BMG Distribution

FLIPHITS (EP).
Cassette: released on Motown, Jul'83 by Motown Records. Dist: BMG Distribution

FOREVER MICHAEL.
Album: released on Motown, Jun'83 by Motown Records. Dist: BMG Distribution

Cassette: released on Motown, Jun'83 by Motown Records. Dist: BMG Distribution

GIRL IS MINE, THE (Jackson, Michael & Paul McCartney).

GIRL YOU'RE SO TOGETHER.
Single (7"): released on Motown, Aug'84 by Motown Records. Dist: BMG Distribution

Cassette: released on Motown, Aug'84 by Motown Records. Dist: BMG Distribution

GOT TO BE THERE.
Album: released on Motown, Oct'81 by Motown Records. Dist: BMG Distribution

Cassette: released on Motown, Oct'81 by Motown Records. Dist: BMG Distribution

Single (7"): released on Motown, Oct'81 by Motown Records. Dist: BMG Distribution

Single (7"): released on Motown, Apr'85 by Motown Records. Dist: BMG Distribution

Single (12"): released on Motown, Apr'85 by Motown Records. Dist: BMG Distribution

GOT TO BE THERE/BEN 2 Classic albums.
Tracks: / Ain't no sunshine / I wanna be where you are / Girl don't take your love from me / In your own small way / Got to be there / Rockin' Robin / Love is here and now your gone / Wings of love / Maria, you were the only one / You've got a friend / Ben / Greatest show on earth / People make the world go round / We've got a good thing going / Eveybody's fool / My girl / What goes around comes around / In our small way / You can cry on my shoulders / Shoo be doo be doo da day.
Compact disc: released on Motown, Nov'86 by Motown Records. Dist: BMG Distribution

GREATEST HITS: MICHAEL JACKSON (Jackson, Michael & Jackson Five).
Album: released on Motown, Apr'84 by Motown Records. Dist: BMG Distribution

Cassette: released on Motown, Apr'84 by Motown Records. Dist: BMG Distribution

GREATEST ORIGINAL HITS (4 TRACK EP).
Single (7"): released on Epic, Mar'83 by CBS Records. Dist: CBS

GREAT LOVE SONGS OF MICHAEL JACKSON.
Album: released on Motown, Nov'84 by Motown Records. Dist: BMG Distribution

Cassette: released on Motown, Nov'84 by Motown Records. Dist: BMG Distribution

HAPPY/ WE'RE ALMOST THERE.
Single (7"): released on Motown, Jul'83 by Motown Records. Dist: BMG Distribution

Single (12"): released on Motown, Jul'83 by Motown Records. Dist: BMG Distribution

I JUST CAN'T STOP LOVING YOU (Jackson, Michael & Siedah Garrett).
Tracks: / I just can't stop loving you / Baby be mine.
Single (7"): released on Epic, Jul'87 by CBS Records. Dist: CBS

Single (7"): released on Epic, Aug'87 by CBS Records. Dist: CBS

Single (12"): released on Epic, Aug'87 by CBS Records. Dist: CBS

LOOKING BACK TO YESTERDAY.
Tracks: / When I come of age / Teenage symphony / I hear a symphony / Give me half a chance / Loves gone bad / Lonely teardrops / You're good for me / That's what love is made of / I like the way you are (don't change your love on me) / ho's lookin' for a lover / If I was God.
Album: released on Tamla Motown, Jul'86 by Motown Records. Dist: RCA Distribution

Cassette: released on Tamla Motown, Jul'86 by Motown Records. Dist: RCA Distribution

MAKING OF THRILLER.
Notes: For full details see under: Making Michael Jackson's Thriller

MICHAEL JACKSON.
Cassette: released on Epic, Dec'82 by CBS Records. Dist: CBS

MUSIC AND ME.
Album: released on Motown, Nov'84 by Motown Records. Dist: BMG Distribution

Cassette: released on Motown, Nov'84 by Motown Records. Dist: BMG Distribution

OFF THE WALL.
Tracks: / Don't stop til you get enough / Rock with you / Working day and night / Get on the floor / Off the wall / Girlfriend / She's out of my life / I can't help it / It's the falling in love / Burn this disco out.
Album: released on Epic, Nov'86 by CBS Records. Dist: CBS

Cassette: released on Epic, Nov'86 by CBS Records. Dist: CBS

Album: released on Epic, Aug'79 by CBS Records. Dist: CBS

Cassette: released on Epic, Aug'79 by CBS Records. Dist: CBS

Compact disc: released on Epic, '83 by CBS Records. Dist: CBS

Single (7"): released on CBS, Apr'82 by CBS Records. Dist: CBS

ONE DAY IN YOUR LIFE / TAKE ME BACK.
Single (7"): released on Motown, Oct'81 by Motown Records. Dist: BMG Distribution

ONE DAY IN YOUR LIFE.
Album: released on Motown, Oct'81 by Motown Records. Dist: BMG Distribution

Cassette: released on Motown, Oct'81 by Motown Records. Dist: BMG Distribution

P.Y.T (pretty young thing).
Single (7"): released on CBS, Mar'84 by CBS Records. Dist: CBS

ROCKIN' ROBIN/ LOVE IS HERE AND NOW.
Single (7"): released on Motown, Oct'81 by Motown Records. Dist: BMG Distribution

ROCK WITH YOU/ GET ON THE FLOOR.
Single (7"): released on CBS, Apr'82 by CBS Records. Dist: CBS

SAY SAY SAY/ ODE TO A KOALA BEAR (Jackson, Michael & Paul McCartney).
Single (7"): released on Parlophone, Oct'83 by EMI Records. Dist: EMI

Single (12"): released on Parlophone, Oct'83 by EMI Records. Dist: EMI

SINGLES PACK.
Single (7"): released on Epic, Nov'83 by CBS Records. Dist: CBS

THRILLER.
Tracks: / Wanna be startin' somethin' / Baby be mine / This girl is mine / Beat it / Billie jean / Thriller / Human nature / Pretty young thing / Lady in my life.
Compact disc: released on Epic, '83 by CBS Records. Dist: CBS

Album: released on Epic, Dec'82 by CBS Records. Dist: CBS

Cassette: released on Epic, Dec'82 by CBS Records. Dist: CBS

THRILLER/ THINGS I DO FOR YOU.
Single (12"): released on Epic, Nov'83 by CBS Records. Dist: CBS

WANNA BE STARTIN' SOMETHING.
Single (7"): released on Epic, Jun'83 by CBS Records. Dist: CBS

Single (12"): released on Epic, Jun'83 by CBS Records. Dist: CBS

WE'RE ALMOST THERE/ WE'VE GOT A....
Single (7"): released on Motown, Oct'81 by Motown Records. Dist: BMG Distribution

Single (12"): released on Motown, Oct'81 by Motown Records. Dist: BMG Distribution

Jackson, Mick

LET'S MAKE SUNSHINE.
Tracks: / Let's make sunshine / Something to remember you by.
Single (7"): released on Deja Vu, Mar'86 by Deja Vu Records. Dist: Counterpoint Distribution, Record Services Distribution (Ireland)

Single (12"): released on Deja Vu, Mar'86 by Deja Vu Records. Dist: Counterpoint Distribution, Record Services Distribution (Ireland)

THIS IS THE REAL THING/ GOOD LOVING.
Single (7"): released on PRT, Sep'82 by PRT Records. Dist: PRT

Single (12"): released on PRT, Sep'82 by PRT Records. Dist: PRT

Jackson, Millie

AN IMITATION OF LOVE.
Tracks: / Hot!Wild!Unrestricted crazy love / Wanna be your lover / Love is a dangerous game / Cover me (wall to wall) / Mind over matter / It's a thing / I need to be by myself / I fell in love.
Compact disc: released on Jive, Jan'87 by Zomba Records. Dist: RCA, PRT, CBS

Album: released on Jive, Nov'86 by Zomba Records. Dist: RCA, PRT, CBS

BEST OF MILLIE JACKSON, THE.
Album: released on Spring, Dec'76 by Polydor Inc.. Dist: Polygram Distribution

BEST OF MILLIE JACKSON.
Cassette: released on Spring, Dec'76 by Polydor Inc.. Dist: Polygram Distribution

CAUGHT UP.
Album: released on Polydor, Feb'75 by Polydor Records. Dist: Polygram, Polydor

Album: released on Important, Sep'85 Dist: EMI

Cassette: released on Important, Sep'85 Dist: EMI

E.S.P (Extra sexual perusation).
Album: released on Sire, Feb'84

Cassette: released on Sire, Feb'84

FEELIN' BITCHY.
Album: released on Spring, Oct'77 by Polydor Inc.. Dist: Polygram Distribution

Cassette: released on Spring, Oct'77 by Polydor Inc.. Dist: Polygram Distribution

FOR MEN ONLY.
Album: released on Spring, Jan'80 by Polydor Inc.. Dist: Polygram Distribution

Cassette: released on Spring, Jan'80 by Polydor Inc.. Dist: Polygram Distribution

FREE AND IN LOVE.
Album: released on Spring, May'76 by Polydor Inc.. Dist: Polygram Distribution

Cassette: released on Spring, May'76 by Polydor Inc.. Dist: Polygram Distribution

GET IT OUT CHA SYSTEM.
Cassette: released on Spring, Jul'78 by Polydor Inc.. Dist: Polygram Distribution

HARD TIMES.
Album: released on Spring, Oct'82 by Polydor Inc.. Dist: Polygram Distribution

Cassette: released on Spring, Oct'82 by Polydor Inc.. Dist: Polygram Distribution

HOT, WILD, UNRESTRICTED CRAZY LOVE.
Tracks: / Hot, wild, unrestricted carzy love / Hot, wild, unrestricted crazy love (instrumental).
Single (7"): released on Jive, Sep'86 by Zomba Records. Dist: RCA, PRT, CBS

Single (12"): released on Jive, Sep'86 by Zomba Records. Dist: RCA, PRT, CBS

HOUSE FOR SALE/ THERE YOU ARE.
Single (7"): released on Neil Rushden (Import), Mar'83

I FEEL LIKE WALKING IN THE RAIN.
Single (7"): released on Warner Bros., Mar'85 by Warner Bros Records. Dist: WEA

Single (12"): released on Warner Bros., Mar'85 by Warner Bros Records. Dist: WEA

I HAD TO SAY IT.
Cassette: released on Spring, Dec'80 by Polydor Inc.. Dist: Polygram Distribution

I WANNA KISS YOU ALL OVER.
Single (7"): released on Important, Mar'85 Dist: EMI

Single (12"): released on Important, Mar'85 Dist: EMI

LIVE & UNCENSORED.
Album: released on Polydor, Jan'80 by Polydor Records. Dist: Polygram, Polydor

Cassette: released on Polydor, Jan'80 by Polydor Records. Dist: Polygram, Polydor

Album: released on Important, Mar'85 Dist: EMI

LOVE IS A DANGEROUS GAME.
Compact disc single: by Zomba Records. Dist: RCA, PRT, CBS

LOVINGLY YOURS.
Album: released on Spring, Feb'77 by Polydor Inc.. Dist: Polygram Distribution

MOMENT'S PLEASURE, A.
Cassette: released on Spring, Apr'79 by Polydor Inc.. Dist: Polygram Distribution

STILL CAUGHT UP.
Album: released on Polydor, Sep'75 by Polydor Records. Dist: Polygram, Polydor

Album: released on Important, Sep'85 Dist: EMI

Cassette: released on Important, Sep'85 Dist: EMI

WANNA BE YOUR LOVER.
Tracks: / Wanna be you lover / Mind over matter.
Single (7"): released on Jive, 23 May'87 by Zomba Records. Dist: RCA, PRT, CBS

Single (12"): released on Jive, 23 May'87 by Zomba Records. Dist: RCA, PRT, CBS

Jackson, Milt

AT THE MONTREUX JAZZ FESTIVAL 1975 (Jackson, Milt, Big Four).
Cassette: released on Pablo, Jan'82 by Pablo Records. Dist: Wellard, Chris, IMS-Polygram, BMG

Album: released on Pablo, Jan'82 by Pablo Records. Dist: Wellard, Chris, IMS-Polygram, BMG

BAGS AND TRANE (Jackson, Milt & John Coltrane).
Album: released on Atlantic, Oct'80 by WEA Records. Dist: WEA

BAGS BAG.
Album: released on Pablo, Jan'82 by Pablo Records. Dist: Wellard, Chris, IMS-Polygram, BMG

Cassette: released on Pablo, Jan'82 by Pablo Records. Dist: Wellard, Chris, IMS-Polygram, BMG

BAGS MEETS WES (Jackson, Milt & Wes Montgomery).
Compact disc: released on JVC Fantasy (Japan), Nov'86

Album:

BALLADS AND BLUES.
Album: released on Atlantic, Mar'81 by WEA Records. Dist: WEA

BEST OF MILT JACKSON, THE.
Album: released on Pablo (USA), Jan'82 by Pablo Records (USA). Dist: Wellard, Chris, IMS-Polygram, BMG

Cassette: released on Pablo (USA), Jan'82 by Pablo Records (USA). Dist: Wellard, Chris, IMS-Polygram, BMG

BIG BAND VOL 1 (Jackson, Milt & Count Basie).
Tracks: / 9.20 special / Moonlight becomes you / Shiny stockings / Blues for me / Every tub / Easy does it / Lena and Lenny / Sunny side of the street / Back to the apple / I'll always be in love with you.
Compact disc: by Pablo Records (USA). Dist: Wellard, Chris, IMS-Polygram, BMG

BIG BAND, VOL.1, THE (Jackson, Milt & Count Basie).

BIG BAND VOL 2 (Jackson, Milt & Count Basie).
Compact disc: released on Pablo Jazz (USA), Apr'86 by United Artists. Dist: Swift

BIG MOUTH.
Album: released on Pablo, Jan'82 by Pablo Records. Dist: Wellard, Chris, IMS-Polygram, BMG

Cassette: released on Pablo, Jan'82 by Pablo Records. Dist: Wellard, Chris, IMS-Polygram, BMG

BIG THREE, THE (Jackson, Milt & Joe Pass & Ray Brown).
Compact disc: released on Pablo, Aug'86 by Pablo Records. Dist: Wellard, Chris, IMS-Polygram, BMG

BROTHER JIM.
Tracks: / Brother Jim / Ill wind / Rhythm-a-ning / Sudden death / How high the moon / Back to Bologna / Sleeves / Lullaby of the leaves / Weasel, The.
Notes: Recorded in New york city 17 may 1985
Album: released on Pablo (USA), Aug'86 by Pablo Records (USA). Dist: Wellard, Chris, IMS-Polygram, BMG

Cassette: released on Pablo (USA), Aug'86 by Pablo Records (USA). Dist: Wellard, Chris, IMS-Polygram, BMG

COMPLETE MILT JACKSON WITH HORACE SILVER.
Album: released on Fantasy Inc USA, Jun'86 by Fantasy Inc USA Records. Dist: IMS, Polygram

FEELINGS (Jackson, Milt & Strings).
Compact disc: released on Pablo (USA), May'86 by Pablo Records (USA). Dist: Wellard, Chris, IMS-Polygram, BMG

Album: released on Pablo, Jan'82 by Pablo Records. Dist: Wellard, Chris, IMS-Polygram, BMG

Cassette: released on Pablo, Jan'82 by Pablo Records. Dist: Wellard, Chris, IMS-Polygram, BMG

FROM OPUS DE JAZZ TO JAZZ SKY LINE.
Compact disc: released on RCA, Jan'87 by RCA Records. Dist: RCA, Roots, Swift, Wellard, Chris, I & B, Solomon & Peres Distribution

FROM OPUS DE JAZZ TO JAZZ SKYLINE.
Tracks: / Opus de funk / You leave me breathless / Opus and interlude / Opus pocus / Lover / Can't help lovin' that man / Lady is a tramp, The / Angel face / Sometimes I'm happy / What's new?.
Compact disc: released on RCA, Jan'87 by RCA Records. Dist: RCA, Roots, Swift, Wellard, Chris, I & B, Solomon & Peres Distribution

INVITATION.
Album:

IT DON'T MEAN A THING IF YOU CAN'T... (Jackson, Milt Quartet).
Album: released on Pablo, Mar'85 by Pablo Records. Dist: Wellard, Chris, IMS-Polygram, BMG

Cassette: released on Pablo, Mar'85 by Pablo Records. Dist: Wellard, Chris, IMS-Polygram, BMG

IT DON'T MEAN A THING (Jackson, Milt, Ray Brown Quartet).
Compact disc: released on Pablo, Aug'86 by Pablo Records. Dist: Wellard, Chris, IMS-Polygram, BMG

JACKSON.
Compact disc: released on Pablo (USA), May'86 by Pablo Records (USA). Dist: Wellard, Chris, IMS-Polygram, BMG

JAZZ 'N' SAMBA.
Album: released on Jasmine, Aug'82 by Jasmine Records. Dist: Counterpoint, Lugtons, Taylor, H.R., Wellard, Chris, Swift, Cadillac

Cassette: released on Jasmine, Aug'82 by Jasmine Records. Dist: Counterpoint, Lugtons, Taylor, H.R., Wellard, Chris, Swift, Cadillac

JAZZ SKYLINE, THE.
Tracks: / Lover / Can't help lovin' dat man / Lady is a tramp, the / Angel face / Sometimes I'm happy / What's new.
Album: released on RCA (France), Jul'86 by RCA Records. Dist: Discovery

LOOSE WALK (Jackson, Milt & Sonny Stitt).
Album: released on Palcoscenico (Italy), Jan'81 Dist: Jazz Music

MEMORIES OF THELONIOUS MONK.
Compact disc: released on Pablo (USA), May'86 by Pablo Records (USA). Dist: Wellard, Chris, IMS-Polygram, BMG

MILT JACKSON.
Tracks: / Lillie / Tahiti / What's new / Bag's groove / On the scene / Willow weep for me / Criss cross / Eronel / Misterioso / Evidence / Lillie (2) / Four in one.
Album: released on Blue Note, Jul'87 by EMI Records. Dist: EMI

MILT JACKSON & COMPANY.
Album: released on Pablo Jazz (USA), Oct'84 by United Artists. Dist: Swift

Milt Jackson/Ray Brown Jam

MILT JACKSON WITH THE THELONIUS MONK QUARTET.
Album: released on Blue Note (USA Import), Sep'84

NIGHT MIST.
Album: released on Pablo (USA), Jan'82 by Pablo Records (USA). Dist: Wellard, Chris, IMS-Polygram, BMG

Cassette: released on Pablo (USA), Jan'82 by Pablo Records (USA). Dist: Wellard, Chris, IMS-Polygram, BMG

OPUS DE JAZZ.
Notes: Artists include: Frank Wess (flute, tenor sax), Milt Jackson (vibes), Hank Jones (piano), Eddie Jones (bass), Kenny Clarke (drums). Opus De Jazz was not conceived to be a milestone album in jazz history. It just turned out to be a very significant and highly enjoyable chapter in the Milt Jackson story. Recorded New Jersey 1955.
Album: released on Savoy Jazz, Dec'85 by RCA Records (Germany). Dist: Conifer

SECOND NATURE, THE SAVOY SESSIONS.
Album:

SOUL BELIEVER.
Album: released on Pablo (USA), Jan'82 by Pablo Records (USA). Dist: Wellard, Chris, IMS-Polygram, BMG

Cassette: released on Pablo (USA), Jan'82 by Pablo Records (USA). Dist: Wellard, Chris, IMS-Polygram, BMG

SOUL FUSION (Jackson,Milt & Monty Alexander).

SOUL ROUTE (Jackson, Milt Quartet).
Compact disc: released on Pablo (USA), May'86 by Pablo Records (USA). Dist: Wellard, Chris, IMS-Polygram, BMG

Cassette: released on Pablo (USA), May'84 by Pablo Records (USA). Dist: Wellard, Chris, IMS-Polygram, BMG

STATEMENT (Jackson, Milt Quartet).
Album: released on Jasmine, Mar'85 by Jasmine Records. Dist: Counterpoint, Lugtons, Taylor, H.R., Wellard, Chris, Swift, Cadillac

TWO OF THE FEW (Jackson, Milt & Oscar Peterson).
Album: released on Pablo, May'83 by Pablo Records. Dist: Wellard, Chris, IMS-Polygram, BMG

Cassette: released on Pablo, May'83 by Pablo Records. Dist: Wellard, Chris, IMS-Polygram, BMG

VERY TALL (Jackson, Milt & Oscar Peterson).
Tracks:/ On Green dolphin street / Work song / Heartstrings / John Browns body / Wonderful guy / Reunion blues.
Compact disc: released on Verve, Jul'86 by Phonogram Records. Dist: Polygram

VOL.2-1978 (Jackson, Milt & Count Basie & The Big Band).
Compact disc: released on Pablo (USA), May'86 by Pablo Records (USA). Dist: Wellard, Chris, IMS-Polygram, BMG

Jackson, Neale
SCREAM IN VAIN.
Single (7"): released on Indiscreet, Feb'85 Dist: Red Rhino, Cartel

Jackson, Papa Charlie
MOSTLY NEW TO LP 1924-29.
Tracks:/ Salt Lake City blues / Mama don't allow it / I'm tired of fooling around with you / Bad luck woman blues / Corn liquor blues.
Album: released on Saydisc, Apr'87 by Saydisc Records. Dist: Essex, Harmonia Mundi, Roots, H.R. Taylor, Jazz Music, Swift, Projection, Gamut

Jackson, Paul
STORY OF GONE WITH THE WIND, THE.
Single (7"): released on Hippodrome, Oct'86 Dist: EMI

Single (12"): released on Hippodrome, Oct'86 Dist: EMI

Jackson, Python Lee
IN A BROKEN DREAM.
Cassette: released on VFM, May'79 by VFM Records. Dist: Taylors, Wynd-Up Distribution

Single (7"): released on Old Gold, Jul'82 by Old Gold Records. Dist: Lightning, Jazz Music, Spartan, Counterpoint

Jackson, Rebbie
CENTIPEDE.
Single (7"): released on CBS, Jan'85 by CBS Records. Dist: CBS

Single (12"): released on CBS, Jan'85 by CBS Records. Dist: CBS

REACTION.
Tracks:/ Reaction / Reaction (instrumental).
Single (7"): released on CBS, Sep'86 by CBS Records. Dist: CBS

Single (12"): released on CBS, Sep'86 by CBS Records. Dist: CBS

REACTIONS.
Tracks:/ Reaction / Ain't no way to love / Ticket to love / You don't know what you're missing / You send the rain away / If you don't call (you don't care) / Always wanting something / Tonight I'm yours / Lessons (in the line of love).
Album: released on CBS, Sep'86 by CBS Records. Dist: CBS

Cassette: released on CBS, Sep'86 by CBS Records. Dist: CBS

Jackson, R.G.
TRODDIN OUT OF BABYLON.
Single (12"): released on Black Music, Aug'82 by Black Music Records. Dist: Jetstar

Jackson, Ronald Shannon
DECODE YOURSELF.
Album: released on Island, Aug'85 by Island Records. Dist: Polygram

Jackson, R.Zee
HIT AFTER HIT - VOLUME 4.
Album: released on Vista Sounds, '83 by Vista Sounds Records. Dist: Jetstar

Cassette: released on Vista Sounds, '83 by Vista Sounds Records. Dist: Jetstar

REGGAE DISCO MEDLEY.
Single (12"): released on Echo, Feb'82 by Vista Sounds. Dist: Jazz Music

Jacksons
DESTINY.
Album: released on Epic, '84 by CBS Records. Dist: CBS

Cassette: released on Epic, '84 by CBS Records. Dist: CBS

IN CONCERT.
Video-cassette (VHS): released on VCL, Jan'84 by Elecstar Records. Dist: PRT

SHAKE YOUR BODY.
Single (7"): released on CBS, Apr'82 by CBS Records. Dist: CBS

STATE OF SHOCK (see also Mick Jagger).
Single (7"): released on Epic, Jun'84 by CBS Records. Dist: CBS

Single (12"): released on Epic, Jun'84 by CBS Records. Dist: CBS

TIME OUT FOR THE BURGLAR.
Tracks:/ Time out for the burglar / News at 11.
Single (12"): released on MCA, Feb'87 by MCA Records. Dist: Polygram, MCA

TORTURE.
Single (7"): released on Epic, Aug'84 by CBS Records. Dist: CBS Deleted '85.

Single (12"): released on Epic, Aug'84 by CBS Records. Dist: CBS

TRIUMPH.
Album: released on Epic, Jun'85 by CBS Records. Dist: CBS

Cassette: released on Epic, Jun'85 by CBS Records. Dist: CBS

VICTORY.
Tracks:/ Torture / Wait / One more chance / Be not always / State of shock / We can change the world / Hurt, The / Body.
Album: released on Epic, May'87 by CBS Records. Dist: CBS

Cassette: released on Epic, May'87 by CBS Records. Dist: CBS

Compact disc: by CBS Records. Dist: CBS

Jackson, Shannon
WHEN COLOURS PLAY.
Album: released on Caravan Of Dreams (USA), Jul'87 by Caravan Of Dreams Records (USA). Dist: IMS, Polygram

Jackson, Shawne
LOVELINE.
Single (7"): released on Loose End, May'83 by MCA Records. Dist: CBS, MCA

Single (12"): released on Loose End, May'83 by MCA Records. Dist: CBS, MCA

Jackson Sisters
I BELIEVE IN MIRACLES.
Tracks:/ I believe in miracles / Boy you're dynamite / Why can't we be more than friends.
Single (7"): released on Urban, Jun'87 by Polydor Records. Dist: Polygram

Single (12"): released on Urban, Jun'87 by Polydor Records. Dist: Polygram

Jackson, Steve 'Shade'
I ADMIRE YOU.
Single (12"): released on M&M, Jan'84 by M&M Records. Dist: Jetstar Distribution

Jackson, Stevie
GIVE ME A ROMANCE.
Tracks:/ Romantic mix-up.
Single (7"): released on Stage Show, Nov'86

Jackson, Stonewall
STONEWALL JACKSON.
Cassette: released on Audio Fidelity, Oct'84 Dist: PRT

UP AGAINST THE WALL.
Album: released on Allegiance, Apr'84 by PRT Records. Dist: PRT

Cassette: released on Allegiance, Apr'84 by PRT Records. Dist: PRT

WATERLOO.
Single (7"): released on Old Gold, Jul'82 by Old Gold Records. Dist: Lightning, Jazz Music, Spartan, Counterpoint

Jackson, Tom
GOOD MORNING AMERICA.
Single (7"): released on Magic, Feb'83 Dist: Jazz Music, Submarine, Swift, Chris Wellard, Conifer

Jackson, Tony
LOVE BLIND.
Single (7"): released on Cedar, Sep'84 by Cedar Records. Dist: PRT

Single (12"): released on Cedar, Sep'84 by Cedar Records. Dist: PRT

NEW YEARS RESOLUTION.
Single (7"): released on Cedar, Dec'84 by Cedar Records. Dist: PRT

Single (12"): released on Cedar, Dec'84 by Cedar Records. Dist: PRT

SNOWY WHITE CHRISTMAS.
Single (7"): released on Cedar, Oct'84 by Cedar Records. Dist: PRT

Single (12"): released on Cedar, Oct'84 by Cedar Records. Dist: PRT

STEPPIN' OUT OF THE GROOVE.
Single (7"): released on Switch, Aug'83 Dist: Backs, Cartel Distribution

SUMMER GROOVE.
Single (7"): released on Cedar, Jul'84 by Cedar Records. Dist: PRT

Single (12"): released on Cedar, Jul'84 by Cedar Records. Dist: PRT

Jackson, Walter
PORTRAIT OF WALTER JACKSON, A.
Album: released on Bluebird, Nov'84 by Bluebird Records. Dist: EMI, Jetstar

TOUCHING IN THE DARK.
Single (7"): released on Bluebird, Dec'84 by Bluebird Records. Dist: EMI, Jetstar

Single (12"): released on Bluebird, Dec'84 by Bluebird Records. Dist: EMI, Jetstar

Jackson, Wanda
2 SIDES OF WANDA.
Album: released on Capitol (France), '83 by Capitol Records. Dist: Conifer

BEST OF.
Album: released on EMI (Holland), '83 by EMI Records. Dist: Conifer

CLOSER TO JESUS.
Album: released on Word, May'82 by Word Records. Dist: Word Distribution, CBS

Cassette: released on Word, May'82 by Word Records. Dist: Word Distribution, CBS

COUNTRY GOSPEL.
Album: released on Word, May'82 by Word Records. Dist: Word Distribution, CBS

Cassette: released on Word, May'82 by Word Records. Dist: Word Distribution, CBS

EARLY.
Album: released on Bear Family, Mar'84 by Bear Family Records. Dist: Rollercoaster Distribution, Swift

GREATEST HITS:WANDA JACKSON.
Compact disc: released on MCS Look Back, Jul'87

HER GREATEST COUNTRY HITS.
Double Album: released on EMI (Holland), '83 by EMI Records. Dist: Conifer

LET'S HAVE A PARTY.
Tracks:/ Let's have a party / Rock your baby / Mean mean man / There's a party goin' / Fujiyama mama / Honey bop / Rip it up / Man we had a party / Hot dog that made him mad / You bug me bad / Who shot Sam / Tongue tied / Sparklin' brown eyes / Lost weekend / Brown-eyed handsome man / Honey don't / It doesn't matter anymore / Whole lotta shakin' goin' on / Long tall sally / Money honey / Searchin' / Hard headed woman / Slippin' & slidin' / Riot in cell

block no. 9 / I gotta know / Baby loves him / Let me explain / Savin' my love / Just a queen for a day / Cool love / Bye bye baby / Right or wrong.
Notes: Original Capitol recordings licensed from EMI Records Ltd. This compilation: P 1986 Charly Records Ltd C 1986 Charly Records Ltd
Double Album: released on Charly, May'87 by Charly Records. Dist: Charly, Cadillac

Cassette: released on Charly, May'87 by Charly Records. Dist: Charly, Cadillac

LOVIN' COUNTRY STYLE.
Album: released on Stetson, Oct'86 by Hasmick Promotions Ltd.. Dist: Counterpoint Distribution, H.R. Taylor Distribution, Swift Distribution, Chris Wellard Distribution

Cassette: released on Stetson, Oct'86 by Hasmick Promotions Ltd.. Dist: Counterpoint Distribution, H.R. Taylor Distribution, Swift Distribution, Chris Wellard Distribution

MY KIND OF GOSPEL.
Album: released on Sundown, Aug'86 by Magnum Music Group Ltd. Dist: Magnum Music Group Ltd, PRT Distribution, Spartan Distribution

MY TESTIMONY.
Album: released on Word, May'82 by Word Records. Dist: Word Distribution. CBS

Cassette: released on Word, May'82 by Word Records. Dist: Word Distribution. CBS

NOW I HAVE EVERYTHING.
Album: released on Myrrh, May'82 by Word Records. Dist: Word Distribution

Cassette: released on Myrrh, May'82 by Word Records. Dist: Word Distribution

RAVE ON.
Tracks:/ KTOP 166 / Breathless / Right or wrong / Stupid cupid / What in the world's come over you / I fall to pieces / Raining in my heart / Sweet dreams / Sweet nothings / Oh boy / Rave on.
Notes: Licensed from Kilo Music Ltd.
Album: released on Topline, Feb'87 by Charly Records. Dist: Charly Distribution

RIGHT OR WRONG.
Album: released on Capitol (France), '83 by Capitol Records. Dist: Conifer

ROCKABILLY FEVER.
Album: released on Magnum, Aug'85 by Bulldog Records. Dist: Spartan

ROCKIN' WITH WANDA.
Album: released on Capitol, Jul'77 by Capitol Records. Dist: EMI

Cassette: released on Capitol (France), '83 by EMI Records. Dist: Conifer

THERE'S A PARTY.
Album: released on Capitol (France), '83 by Capitol Records. Dist: Conifer

WANDA JACKSON.
Album: released on Capitol (France), '83 by Capitol Records. Dist: Conifer

Jackson, Willis
COOL GATOR.
Album:

GATOR HORN, THE.
Album: released on Muse (Import), Apr'81

LOCKIN' HORNS.
Album: released on Muse (Import), '81

NOTHING BUTT.
Album: released on Muse (Import), Feb'83

SINGLE ACTION.
Album: released on Muse (Import), Apr'81

Jack Star
ROCK THE AMERICAN WAY.
Album: released on Eva-Lolita, Dec'85 Dist: Pinnacle

Jacks, Terry
SEASONS IN THE SUN.
Single (7"): released on Old Gold, Mar'85 by Old Gold Records. Dist: Lightning, Jazz Music, Spartan, Counterpoint

Jacks, Tony
I HEAR A HEARTBEAT.
Single (7"): released on Strike, Nov'81 by Strike Records. Dist: Fresh Distribution, Rough Trade Distribution, Strike Distribution

Jack & The Beanstalk
JACK & THE BEANSTALK Various artists (Various Artists).
Cassette: released on Anvil, Jul'82 Dist: Anvil

Cassette: released on Pickwick (Ladybird).

Jack The Bear
SKIN & BONE.
Tracks: / Skin & bone / Carshunting / Cadillac.
Single (7"): released on Backs, 13 Jun'87 by Backs Records. Dist: Backs, Cartel

Jack the giant killer
JACK THE GIANT KILLER (Palin, Michael).
Cassette: released on Listen Productions, Nov'84 Dist: H.R. Taylor, Hayward Promotions Distribution

Jack the Lad
REGGAE MUSIC.
Single (7"): released on Outlook, Apr'83 by Brian Poole. Dist: Spartan Distribution

Single (12"): released on Outlook, Jul'83 by Brian Poole. Dist: Spartan Distribution

Jack Trax
JACK TRAX VOL.1 (Various Artists).
Album: released on Indigo (USA), Jul'87 by Indigo Records (USA). Dist: PRT

Cassette: released on Indigo (USA), Jul'87 by Indigo Records (USA). Dist: PRT

Jacobites
PIN YOUR HEART.
Single (12"): released on Glass, Sep'85 by Glass Records. Dist: Nine Mile, Rough Trade, Red Rhino, Play It Again Sam

ROBESPIERRE'S VELVET BASEMENT.
Album: released on Glass, Aug'85 by Glass Records. Dist: Nine Mile, Rough Trade, Red Rhino, Play It Again Sam

WHEN THE RAIN COMES.
Notes: Featuring Nikki Sudden, Dave Kusworth and Epic Soundtracks. Rock'n'roll troubadours, Keith Richards look-alikes, ragged romantics. How can you resist? Buy this record NOW!
Single (7"): released on Glass, Jan'86 by Glass Records. Dist: Nine Mile, Rough Trade, Red Rhino, Play It Again Sam

Single (12"): released on Glass, Jan'86 by Glass Records. Dist: Nine Mile, Rough Trade, Red Rhino, Play It Again Sam

YE JACOBITES BY NAME.
Album: released on Lismor, '84 by Lismor Records. Dist: Lismor, Roots, Celtic Music

Cassette: released on Lismor, '84 by Lismor Records. Dist: Lismor, Roots, Celtic Music

Jacobi, Wolfgang
WOLFGANG JACOBI (Various Artists).
Album: released on ARC (Accordion Records), '84 Dist: Accordion Record Club

Jacobs, David
SHOW SIDE OF DAVID JACOBS.
Album: released on BBC, Aug'84 by BBC Records & Tapes. Dist: EMI, PRT, Pye

Cassette: released on BBC, Aug'84 by BBC Records & Tapes. Dist: EMI, PRT, Pye

Jacobs, Little Walter
BLUE & LONESOME.
Album: released on Le Roi Du, Jul'79

SOUTHERN FEELING.
Album: released on Le Roi Du, Jul'79

Jacobs, Peter
COLBY'S MISSING MEMORY (Jacobs, Peter & Hanneke).
Notes: The second album featuring Peter & Hanneke Jacobs most recent charcater, Colby The Computer.
Album: released on Maranatha kids, Apr'86

Cassette: released on Maranatha kids, Apr'86

Jacques, Peter Band
WELCOME BACK.
Album: released on RCA, Mar'81 by RCA Records. Dist: RCA, Roots, Swift, Wellard, Chris, I & B, Solomon & Peres Distribution

Jacquet, Illinois
BIRTHDAY PARTY.
Album: released on JRC & JATH, Apr'81

BLUES AND SENTIMENTAL.
Album: released on Jazz Bird, '82 Dist: Cassion (Melandy)

Cassette: released on Jazz Bird, '82 Dist: Cassion (Melandy)

BLUES FROM LOUISIANA.
Album: released on JRC & JATH, Apr'81

GENIUS AT WORK.
Album: released on Black Lion, Jan'85 by Black Lion Records. Dist: Jazz Music, Chris Wellard, Taylor, H.R., Counterpoint Cadillac

GROOVIN'.
Album: released on Verve, Dec'81 by Phonogram Records. Dist: Polygram

ILLINOIS FLIES AGAIN.
Compact discs: released on Greenline, Mar'87 by Charly Records. Dist: Charly

ILLINOIS JACQUET.
Compact discs: released on Black And Blue (France), Apr'87 Dist: Swift, Discovery, Target

KID & THE BRUTE, THE (Jacquet, Illinois & Ben Webster).
Album: released on Verve, May'82 by Phonogram Records. Dist: Polygram

SWINGS THE THING.
Album: released on Verve, Aug'81 by Phonogram Records. Dist: Polygram

THOSE FLYIN', JUMPIN' AND GRUNTIN' SAXOPHONES.
Album: released on Queen Disc (USA), Nov'83

Jacquet, Russell
RUSS IN NICE.
Album: released on JRC & JATH, Apr'81

Jacqui & Birdie
HELLO FRIEND.
Album: released on Nevis, May'77 Dist: H.R. Taylor

Cassette: released on Nevis, May'77 Dist: H.R. Taylor

TIS A GIFT TO BE SIMPLE.
Album: released on Nevis, May'77 Dist: H.R. Taylor

Jacuzzi
HAPPENS ALL THE TIME.
Single (7"): released on Freeway, Jun'84 by Freeway. Dist: Revolver, Cartel

Jade
BOBBY'S GIRL.
Single (7"): released on Page One, Jan'84 by Page, Larry. Dist: PRT, Spartan

I CAN'T BELIEVE IT'S OVER.
Tracks: / I can't believe it's over / Blue jade.
Single (12"): released on Master Funk, Oct'86 by Master Funk Records. Dist: PRT

IF YOU'RE MAN ENOUGH.
Album: released on Road Runner, Nov'85

I'M A GIRL.
Single (7"): released on Page One, Jan'82 by Page, Larry. Dist: PRT, Spartan

LIAR.
Single (7"): released on Page One, Aug'83 by Page, Larry. Dist: PRT, Spartan

POSIN'.
Single (7"): released on Siam, Aug'81 by Siam Records. Dist: PRT

YOUNG LOVE.
Single (7"): released on Page One, Feb'83 by Page, Larry. Dist: PRT, Spartan

Jaderlund
KEJSARENS NYAKLADER.
Notes: With Norrstrom/Jormin/Jansson/Klinghagen
Album: released on Dragon, Jun'86 by Dragon Records. Dist: Jazz Music, Projection, Cadillac

Jade Warrior
HORIZEN.
Tracks: / Images of dune / Prescient dawn / Endless desert / Endless lives / Maker, The / Freman, The / People of the sand / Spice ritual / Sietch tabre / Journey on a dream / Giant beneath the sand / Prophet, The / Riding the maker / Caribbean wave / Horizen / East wind / Grey lake / Long wait at mount Li.
Notes: All compositions by Jade Warrior, published by Nada Pulse Music Productions Ltd, produced by Jade Warrior.
Album: released on Pulse, Jun'84 by Pulse Records.

REFLECTIONS.
Tracks: / English morning / Lady of the lake / Borne on the solar wind / Morning hymn / Bride of the summer / Soldiers song / Winters tale, A / Yellow eyes / Dark river / House of dreams.
Notes: All songs written & produced by Duhig, Havard & Field.
Album: released on Butt, Mar'82 by Butt Records.

Jad Fair
EVERYBODY KNEW .... BUT ME.
Album: released on Music Galore, Aug'85 by Shanghai records. Dist: Counterpoint Distribution

EVERYONE KNEW BUT ME.
Tracks: / I can't believe it's over / I do / Tony & The Boys.
Notes: 29 songs
Album: released on Press, Jul'86 by Press Records.

Single (7"): released on Funk Master, Oct'86 Dist: Jetstar

Single (12"): released on Funk Master, Oct'86 Dist: Jetstar

Jad W10
CELLAR DANCE.
Single (12"): released on Invitation Au Suicide, Jan'85 Dist: Rough Trade, Cartel

Jaffa, Max
MUSIC FOR A GRAND HOTEL (Jaffa, Max Orchestra).
Tracks: / Roses from the south / Gypsy carnival / Great waltz / Canto amoroso / Fascination / Scarborough fair / Some day I'll find you / Dobra Dobra / Gentle maiden / I dream of Jeanie / Memories of Richard Tauber / Adoration / Annen Polka / Victor Herbert Medley.
Compact disc: released on Valentine, Feb'86 by Valentine Records. Dist: PRT

PRELUDE TO ROMANCE (Jaffa, Max His Violin & Orchestra).
Album: released on Valentine, Apr'83 by Valentine Records. Dist: PRT

Cassette: released on Valentine, Apr'83 by Valentine Records. Dist: PRT

RELAX WITH THE MUSIC OF MAX JAFFA.
Tracks: / Vagabond king selection / Waltzing in the clouds / Lark in the clear air / Enough sadness and tears / Beautiful dreamer / Dobra Dobra / Great waltz selection / Forgotten dreams / Countess Maritza (The Czardas) / Last rose of summer / Ave Maria / Hungarian dance No.1 / Roses from the south / Melodies of Britain / Jeanie with the light brown hair / Fascination / I love the moon / Desert song (from 'The desert song') / Violin song from ('Tina') / Gypsy carnival / Serenade / Black eyes / Doina Voda / Souvenir D'Ukraine / Softly awakes my heart (Grand March) / Jeannie with the light brown hair.
Notes: As the title suggests a fabulous double album to relax to with the smooth sound of Max Jaffa and also featuring the Palm Court Trio (Jack Byfield - piano and Reginald Kilbey - cello). Plus a very strong sleeve design. A much requested album.
Album: released on MFP, Jun'87 by EMI Records. Dist: EMI

Double cassette: released on MFP, Jun'87 by EMI Records. Dist: EMI

Double cassette: released on MFP, Jun'87 by EMI Records. Dist: EMI

Jagged Edge
JAGGED EDGE Film Soundtrack.
Notes: 'Jagged Edge' directed by Richard Marquand, who was responsible for 'Eye Of The Needle' and 'Return Of The Jedi'. The film stars Jeff Bridges and Glenn Close and has music composed by John Barry.
Album: released on TER, Feb'86 Dist: Pinnacle

Jagger, Mick
LET'S WORK.
Single (7"): released on CBS, Aug'87 by CBS Records. Dist: CBS

Single (12"): released on CBS, Aug'87 by CBS Records. Dist: CBS

PRIMITIVE COOL.
Tracks: / Throwaway / Let's work / Radio control / Say you will / Primitive cool / Kow tow / Shoot off your mouth / Peace for the wicked / Party doll / War baby.
Album: released on CBS, Sep'87 by CBS Records. Dist: CBS

Cassette: released on CBS, Sep'87 by CBS Records. Dist: CBS

Compact disc: released on CBS, Sep'87 by CBS Records. Dist: CBS

SHE'S THE BOSS.
Tracks: / Lonely at the top / Half a loaf / Running out of luck / Turn the girl loose / Hard woman / Just another night / Lucky love / Secrets / She's the boss.
Compact disc: released on CBS, Jun'85 by CBS Records. Dist: CBS

Album: released on CBS, Mar'85 by CBS Records. Dist: CBS

Jaqs
EVENING STANDARDS.
Album: released on Island, Jan'80 by Island Records. Dist: Polygram

I NEVER WAS A BEACH BOY.
Single (7"): released on Island, Jan'81 by Island Records. Dist: Polygram

Jaguar
ARGUEMENT.
Album: released on Wackies, Mar'84 by Wackies Records. Dist: Jetstar

AXE CRAZY/WAR MACHINE.
Single (7"): released on Neat, Aug'82 by Neat Records. Dist: Pinnacle, Neat

BACK STREET WOMAN.
Single (7"): released on Heavy Metal, Nov'81 by FM-Revolver Records. Dist: EMI

POWER GAMES.
Album: released on Neat, Jan'85 by Neat Records. Dist: Pinnacle, Neat

THIS TIME.
Album: released on Music For Nations, Jul'87 by Music For Nations Records. Dist: Pinnacle

Jah Dave
FISHERMAN.
Single (12"): released on Ishence Musik, Jul'85 by Ishence Records. Dist: Jetstar

Single (12"): released on Ishence Musik, Jul'85 by Ishence Records. Dist: Jetstar

HOW LONG/PART 2.
Single (12"): released on Ishence Musik, May'83 by Ishence Records. Dist: Jetstar

INFORMER/TAKEN AWAY.
Single (12"): released on Solid Groove, Feb'83 Dist: Jetstar, Pinnacle

Jah Globe
MORE PEOPLE ARE WALKING.
Single (12"): released on Pyramid, Mar'84 Dist: Jetstar

Jahlib & Suns of Arda
MYSTERIES OF THE EAST.
Single (12"): released on Virgin, Jul'82 by Virgin Records. Dist: EMI, Virgin Distribution Deleted '82.

Jah Life
SMASHING SUPERSTARS.
Album: released on Vista Sounds, Jan'83 by Vista Sounds Records. Dist: Jetstar

Jah Lion
IN ACTION WITH THE REVOLUTIONARY BAND.
Album: released on Vista Sounds, Jan'83 by Vista Sounds Records. Dist: Jetstar

Jah Lloyd
SHAKE AND FLICKER.
Single (7"): released on Sheet, Jul'82 Dist: Rough Trade

Jah Pollack
HOUSE OF JAH/WILLIE BANG.
Single (12"): released on Conscious Man, Jul'82 Dist: Jetstar

Jah Scouse
MERGE.
Single (7"): released on Better Things, Apr'85 by Probe Records. Dist: Cartel

Jah Screechie
SHADOW MOVE.
Single (12"): released on Scom, Dec'84 by Scom Records. Dist: Jetstar

Jah Shaka
COMMANDMENTS OF DUB PART 3.
Album: released on Shaka, Jan'85 by Shaka Records. Dist: Jetstar

GOT TO KNOW.
Tracks: / Got to know.
Single (12"): released on Jah Shaka Music, Mar'86

JAH CHILDREN/JAH WORKS.
Single (12"): released on Jah Shaka, Sep'82 by Jah Shaka Records. Dist: Jetstar

JAH DUB CREATOR (COMMANDMENTS OF DUB PART 5).
Album: released on Shaka, Nov'86 by Shaka Records. Dist: Jetstar

LION YOUTH/BEYOND THE REALMS.

Single (12"): released on Jah Shaka, Nov'82 by Jah Shaka Records. Dist: Jetstar

REVELATION SONGS.
Album: released on Rough Trade, Jan'84 by Rough Trade Records. Dist: Rough Trade Distribution, Cartel Distribution

Jah Son

SHE LOVES A RUB A DUB.
Single (12"): released on Negus Roots, Apr'82 by Negus Roots Records. Dist: Jetstar

Jahson, David

PAST AND PRESENT.
Album: released on Spy, Nov'85 by Spy Records. Dist: Jetstar Distribution

REALLY WANT TO KNOW.
Single (12"): released on Spy, Mar'84 by Spy Records. Dist: Jetstar Distribution

Jah Stone

PINK EYE DISEASE/RHYTHMIC ROCK.
Single (12"): released on Regal, May'82

Jah Thomas

FRIDAY NIGHT JAMBOREE.
Single (12"): released on Silver Camel, Apr'83 Dist: Jetstar, Rough Trade

HAIL LYRICS FOR SALE/HAUL AND PULL UP.
Single (12"): released on Midnight Rock, Feb'83 Dist: Jetstar Distribution, Kingdom Distribution

MAKE A MOVE/DANCIN MOVE(WITH MICHAEL PALMER).
Single (12"): released on Midnight Rock, Jan'84 Dist: Jetstar Distribution, Kingdom Distribution

NAH FIGHT OVER WOMAN.
Album: released on Vista Sounds, May'83 by Vista Sounds Records. Dist: Jetstar

Jah Warriors

APARTHEID.
Single (7"): released on A Record Company, Oct'84 by A Record company. Dist: CBS

CAN'T TAKE NO MORE/IF YOU ONLY KNEW.
Single (12"): released on Bushman, Oct'82

NO ILLUSIONS.
Album: released on A Record Company, Oct'84 by A Record company. Dist: CBS

POOR MANS STORY.
Album: released on Vista Sounds, Feb'84 by Vista Sounds Records. Dist: Jetstar

WHATS THIS FEELING.
Single (7"): released on A Record Company, Sep'84 by A Record company. Dist: CBS

Jah Whoosh

DEH PON STREET AGAIN (Jah Whoosh & Zabandies).
Tracks: / Deh pon street again / Street dub.
Single (12"): released on Sky Juice, Nov'86 by Sky Juice Records. Dist: Jetstar

Jah Wobble

BETRAYEL/BATTLE OF BRITAIN.
Single (7"): released on Virgin, Apr'80 by Virgin Records. Dist: EMI, Virgin Distribution

BLOW OUT.
Single (12"): released on Lago, Nov'85 by Lago Records. Dist: Pinnacle, Rough Trade

FADING/NOCTURNAL.
Single (12"): released on Jah Wobble, May'82

HOW MUCH ARE THEY (EP) (Jah Wobble with Various Artists).
Single (12"): released on Island, Jul'81 by Island Records. Dist: Polygram

INVADERS OF THE HEART.
Single (7"): released on Lago, May'83 by Lago Records. Dist: Pinnacle, Rough Trade

LEGENG LIVES.
Album: released on Virgin, May'80 by Virgin Records. Dist: EMI, Virgin Distribution

LONG LONG WAY / ROMANY (Jah Wobble with Animal).
Single (12"): released on Jah, Oct'82 Dist: Jetstar

LOVE MYSTERY (Jah Wooble & Ollie Marland).
Single (7"): released on Island, Apr'85 by Island Records. Dist: Polygram

Single (12"): released on Island, Apr'85 by Island Records. Dist: Polygram Deleted '87.

NEON MOON (Jah Wooble & Ollie Marland).
Album: released on Island, May'85 by Island Records. Dist: Polygram Deleted '87.

Cassette: released on Island, May'85 by Island Records. Dist: Polygram Deleted '87.

SNAKE CHARMER (Jah Wooble/The Edge/Holger Czukay).
Album: released on Island, Oct'83 by Island Records. Dist: Polygram

Cassette: released on Island, Oct'83 by Island Records. Dist: Polygram

VOODOO.
Single (7"): released on Lago, Oct'84 by Lago Records. Dist: Pinnacle, Rough Trade

Jah Woosh

WHIP(2 PARTS).
Single (12"): released on Sky Juice, Oct'83 by Sky Juice Records. Dist: Jetstar

Ja Ja Ja

KATZ RAP.
Single (7"): released on Atatak, Aug'83 by Atatak Records. Dist: Rough Trade, Cartel

Jakata

GOLDEN GIRL.
Single (7"): released on Morocco, Apr'85

Single (12"): released on Morocco, Apr'85

HELL IS ON THE RUN.
Single (7"): released on Morocco, Sep'84

Single (12"): released on Morocco, Sep'84

LIGHT THE NIGHT.
Album: released on Morocco, Oct'84

Cassette: released on Morocco, Oct'84

Jake Porters combo .....

JAKE PORTERS COMBO RECORDS STORY VOL.2 Various artists (Various Artists).
Album: released on Ace, May'84 by Ace Records. Dist: Pinnacle, Swift, Hotshot, Cadillac

Jake Porters story

JAKE PORTERS STORY VOL.1 Various artists (Various Artists).
Album: released on ACE(Combo, USA), Oct'83 by Ace Records. Dist: Pinnacle, Swift, Hotshot

Jake The Pilgrim

GAIA.
Single (12"): released on Waterfall, Aug'87 by Waterfall Records. Dist: Revolver, Cartel

Jake Walk blues

JAKE WALK BLUES Various artists.
Album: released on Stash, Apr'81 Dist: Swift Distribution, Jazz Music Distribution, Jazz Horizons Distribution, Celtic Music Distribution, Cadillac, JSU Distribution, Zodiac Distribution

Jakko

CAN'T STAND THIS PRESSURE, I.
Single (7"): released on Stiff, Sep'84 by Stiff Records. Dist: EMI, Record Services Distribution (Ireland)

Single (12"): released on Stiff, Sep'84 by Stiff Records. Dist: EMI, Record Services Distribution (Ireland)

DANGEROUS DREAMS.
Tracks: / Dangerous dreams / Little town.
Single (7"): released on MDM, Oct'86 Dist: Siren, Virgin, EMI

Single (12"): released on MDM, Oct'86 Dist: Siren, Virgin, EMI

DANGEROUS DREAMS/OPENING DOORS.
Single (7"): released on Stiff, May'83 by Stiff Records. Dist: EMI, Record Services Distribution (Ireland)

Single (12"): released on Stiff, May'83 by Stiff Records. Dist: EMI, Record Services Distribution (Ireland)

GRAB WHAT YOU CAN.
Single (7"): released on Chiswick, Sep'82 by Chiswick Records. Dist: Pinnacle

Single (12"): released on Chiswick, Sep'82 by Chiswick Records. Dist: Pinnacle

JUDY GET DOWN.
Tracks: / Judy get down / This old man.
Single (7"): released on MDM, Jun'86 Dist: Siren, Virgin, EMI

Single (12"): released on MDM, Jun'86 Dist: Siren, Virgin, EMI

LEARNING TO CRY.
Tracks: / Learning to cry / Learning to cry Georgian mix.
Single (7"): released on MDM, Apr'86 Dist: Siren, Virgin, EMI

Single (12"): released on MDM, Apr'86 Dist: Siren, Virgin, EMI

NIGHT HAS A THOUSAND EYES.
Single (7"): released on Chiswick, Jan'82 by Chiswick Records. Dist: Pinnacle Deleted '82.

WHO'S FOOLING WHO.
Single (7"): released on Stiff, Mar'84 by Stiff Records. Dist: EMI, Record Services Distribution (Ireland)

Single (12"): released on Stiff, Mar'84 by Stiff Records. Dist: EMI, Record Services Distribution (Ireland)

Jakuzzi

RICHOCHET/HELIOTROPE.
Single (12"): released on Creole, Oct'81 by Creole Records. Dist: Rhino, PRT

Jali Musa Jawara

JALI MUSA JAWARA.
Album: released on Oval, Sep'86 Dist: Projection

Jam

ALL MOD CONS.
Album: released on Polydor, '78 by Polydor Records. Dist: Polygram, Polydor

Cassette: released on Polydor, '78 by Polydor Records. Dist: Polygram, Polydor

ALL MOD CONS/SETTING SONS.
Cassette: released on Polydor, Feb'83 by Polydor Records. Dist: Polygram, Polydor

BEAT SURRENDER/SHOPPING.
Single (7"): released on Polydor, Jan'83 by Polydor Records. Dist: Polygram, Polydor

Double-pack single: released on Polydor, Jan'83 by Polydor Records. Dist: Polygram, Polydor

COMPACT SNAP.
Tracks: / In the city / News of the world / Away from the numbers / All around the world / Modern world / Billy Hunt / Mr Clean / Bomb in Wardour Street / David Watt's / When you're young / Down in the tube station at midnight / Strange town / Butterfly collector / Smithersjones / Thick as thieves / Going underground / Eton rifles / Dreams of children / That's entertainment / Start / Man in the corner shop / Absolute beginners / Town called Malice / Tales from the riverbank / Precious / Funeral pyre / Bitterest pill I ever had to swallow / Beat surrender.
Notes: Digital Stereo
Compact disc: released on Polydor, Sep'84 by Polydor Records. Dist: Polygram, Polydor

DIG THE NEW BREED.
Album: released on Polydor, Jun'87 by Polydor Records. Dist: Polygram, Polydor

Cassette: released on Polydor, Jun'87 by Polydor Records. Dist: Polygram, Polydor

GIFT, THE.
Album: released on Polydor, Mar'82 by Polydor Records. Dist: Polygram, Polydor

Cassette: released on Polydor, Mar'82 by Polydor Records. Dist: Polygram, Polydor

GOING UNDERGROUND.
Single (7"): released on Polydor, Jan'83 by Polydor Records. Dist: Polygram, Polydor

IN THE CITY.
Album: released on Polydor, Aug'83 by Polydor Records. Dist: Polygram, Polydor

Cassette: released on Polydor, Aug'83 by Polydor Records. Dist: Polygram, Polydor

SETTING SONS..
Compact disc: by Polydor Records. Dist: Polygram, Polydor

SETTING SONS.
Album: released on Polydor, Nov'79 by Polydor Records. Dist: Polygram, Polydor

Cassette: released on Polydor, Nov'79 by Polydor Records. Dist: Polygram, Polydor

SNAP.
Double Album: released on Polydor, Oct'83 by Polydor Records. Dist: Polygram, Polydor

Double cassette: released on Polydor, Oct'83 by Polydor Records. Dist: Polygram, Polydor

SOUND AFFECTS.
Album: released on Polydor, Nov'80 by Polydor Records. Dist: Polygram, Polydor

Cassette: released on Polydor, Nov'80 by Polydor Records. Dist: Polygram, Polydor

SOUND AFFECTS/THE GIFT.
Double cassette: released on Polydor, Jun'83 by Polydor Records. Dist: Polygram, Polydor

THIS IS THE MODERN WORLD.
Album: released on Polydor, Apr'84 by Polydor Records. Dist: Polygram, Polydor

Cassette: released on Polydor, Apr'84 by Polydor Records. Dist: Polygram, Polydor

VIDEO SNAP.
Notes: Number of tracks: 15. Type of recording: Compilation. Total Playing Time: 60 minutes.
Video-cassette (VHS): released on Channel 5, Oct'86 Dist: W.H. Smiths

Jam '86

WE'VE GOT THE LOVE.
Tracks: / We've got the lore / Save love, save life.
Single (12"): released on Arista, Jun'86 by Arista Records. Dist: RCA

Album: released on Harlequin, Jun'86 by Harlequin Records. Dist: Swift, Jazz Music, Wellard, Chris, IRS, Taylor, H.R.

Jam Afrika

FEET UP.
Album: released on J-Culture, May'86 Dist: Jetstar

Jamaica

ROOTS OF REGGAE Music from Jamaica.
Album: released on Lyrichord (USA), Oct'81 by Lyrichord Records (USA). Dist: Flexitron Distributors Ltd

Cassette: released on Lyrichord (USA), Aug'82 by Lyrichord Records (USA). Dist: Flexitron Distributors Ltd

Jamaica Boys

LET ME HOLD YOU CLOSER.
Single (7"): released on Cool Tempo, Aug'85 by Chrysalis Records. Dist: CBS

Single (12"): released on Cool Tempo, Aug'85 by Chrysalis Records. Dist: CBS

Jamaica Girls

ROCK THE BEAT.
Single (7"): released on Becket, Oct'82

Single (12"): released on Becket, Oct'82

Jamaica Inn

JAMAICA INN READ BY TREVOR EVE Daphne Du Maurier.
Cassette: released on Listen For Pleasure, Apr'83 by MFP Records. Dist: EMI

Jamaica's greatest

JAMAICA'S GREATEST Various artists.
Album: released on Prince Buster, Feb'85 by Prince Buster Records. Dist: Jetstar

Jamal, Ahmad

AHMED JAMAL.
Album: released on Jazz Reactivation, Jul'82 Dist: PRT

AHMED JAMAL, THE BEST OF.
Album: released on 20th Century, Sep'81 Dist: RCA, IMS-Polygram

Cassette: released on 20th Century, Sep'81 Dist: RCA, IMS-Polygram

AT THE PERISHING.
Compact disc: released on Vogue, Dec'86 Dist: Discovery, Jazz Music, PRT, Swift

AT THE TOP POINCIANA REVISITED.
Album: released on Jasmine, Jun'82 by Jasmine Records. Dist: Counterpoint, Lugtons, Taylor, H.R., Wellard, Chris, Swift, Cadillac

Cassette: released on Jasmine, Jun'82 by Jasmine Records. Dist: Counterpoint, Lugtons, Taylor, H.R., Wellard, Chris, Swift, Cadillac

AWAKENING, THE (Jamal, Ahmad Trio).
Compact disc: released on MCA, Apr'87 by MCA Records. Dist: Polygram, MCA

Single (7"): released on Jim White, Aug'84 by Jim White Records. Dist: Swift

Album: released on Jasmine, Aug'82 by Jasmine Records. Dist: Counterpoint, Lugtons, Taylor, H.R., Wellard, Chris, Swift, Cadillac

Cassette: released on Jasmine, Aug'82 by Jasmine Records. Dist: Counterpoint, Lugtons, Taylor, H.R., Wellard, Chris, Swift, Cadillac

CONCERT MIDEM 81, IN (Jamal, Ahmad & Gary Burton).
Album: released on Gateway, '84 by Kingdom. Dist: Pinnacle

IN CONCERT (Jamal, Ahmad & Gary Burton).
Album: released on Gateway (USA), Jun'82 by Gemcom Inc.(USA) Records.

LIVE AT BUBBA'S.
Album: released on Gateway, Sep'83 by Kingdom. Dist: Pinnacle

NIGHT SONG.
Album: released on Motown, Oct'81 by Motown Records. Dist: BMG Distribution

ONE.
Album: released on One(Ahad), '79

Jambalaya

BUGGY FULL OF CAJUN MUSIC.
Album:

Jamboree

JAMBOREE Various session artists.
Cassette: released on AIM (Budget Cassettes), Feb'83

Jam Down

EXTRAORDINARY WOMAN.
Single (12"): released on Jam Down, Dec'83 by Jam Down Records. Dist: Jetstar

James

CHAIN MAIL.
Tracks: / Chain mail / Hup springs / Up rising.
Single (7"): released on Sire, Feb'86

Single (12"): released on Sire, Feb'86

FOLKLORE/WHAT'S THE WORLD/FIRE SO.... Cover design by Johnny (Hedgehog) Carroll.
Single (7"): released on Factory, Sep'83 by Factory Records. Dist: Cartel, Pinnacle

HYMN FROM A VILLAGE Cover design by Johnny (Hedgehog) Carroll.
Single (12"): released on Factory, Jun'85 by Factory Records. Dist: Cartel, Pinnacle

JIM 1 & JIM 2 Cover design by Johnny (Hedgehog) Carroll.

SO MANY WAYS.
Tracks: / So many ways / Withdrawn / Just hipper.
Single (7"): released on Sire, Jun'86

Single (12"): released on Sire, Jun'86

STUTTER.
Tracks: / Skullduggery / Scarecrow / So many ways / Just hip / John Yen / Summer songs / Really hard / Billy's shirts / Why so close / Withdrawn / Black hole.
Album: released on Sire, Jun'86

Cassette: released on Sire, Jun'86

James, Biby

IF I HAD YOU.
Tracks: / If I had you.
Single (12"): released on Toe, Apr'86 by Toe Records. Dist: Jetstar Distribution

James, Bob

ALL AROUND THE TOWN LIVE.
Tracks: / Touchdown / Stompin' / At the Savoy / Angela (theme from "Taxi") / We're all alone / Farandole / Westchester lady / Golden apple, The / Kari.
Album: released on CBS, Feb'81 by CBS Records. Dist: CBS

Cassette: released on CBS, Feb'81 by CBS Records. Dist: CBS

DOUBLE VISION (James, Bob & Sanborn, David).
Tracks: / Maputo / More than friends / Moontune / Since I fell for you / It's you / Never enough / You don't know me.
Album: released on Warner Bros., Jun'86 by Warner Bros Records. Dist: WEA

Cassette: released on Warner Bros., Jun'86 by Warner Bros Records. Dist: WEA

Compact disc: released on Warner Bros., Jun'86 by Warner Bros Records. Dist: WEA

HANDS DOWN.
Tracks: / Spunky / Macumba / Shamboozie / Janus / Roberta / It's only me.
Album: released on CBS, Jul'82 by CBS Records. Dist: CBS

Cassette: released on CBS, Jul'82 by CBS Records. Dist: CBS

LUCKY SEVEN.
Album: released on Tappan Zee, Sep'79

Cassette: released on CBS, '79 by CBS Records. Dist: CBS

OBSESSION.

Compact disc: released on Warner Brothers, Dec'86 by Warner Bros Records. Dist: WEA

SWAN, THE.
Album: released on CBS(France), Oct'85 by CBS Records. Dist: Conifer, Discovery, Swift

TOUCHDOWN.
Tracks: / Angela (theme from "Taxi") / Touchdown / I want to thank you (very much) / Sun runner / Caribbean nights.
Album: released on CBS, Jan'79 by CBS Records. Dist: CBS

TWO OF A KIND (James, Bob & Earl Klugh).
Album: released on Capitol, Nov'82 by Capitol Records. Dist: EMI

Cassette: released on Capitol, Nov'82 by Capitol Records. Dist: EMI

James Bond

JAMES BOND GREATEST HITS Various original artists (Various Artists).
Tracks: / James Bond theme / Kingston calypso / Under the Mango tree / From Russia with love / Goldfinger / 007 / Thunderball / You only live twice / On her majesty's service / We have all the time in the world / Diamonds are forever / Live and let die / Just a closer walk with thee / New second line / Bond meets solitaire / Man with the golden gun / Bond '77 / Moonraker / For your eyes only / James Bond theme.
Album: by Liberty-United. Dist: EMI

Cassette: released on Liberty, Mar'82 by Liberty-United. Dist: EMI

JAMES BOND THEMES Various artists (Various Artists).
Tracks: / James Bond theme, The / From Russia with love / Goldfinger / Thunderball / You only live twice / We have all the time in the world / Diamonds are for ever / Live and let die / Man with the golden gun, The / Nobody does it better / Moonraker / For your eyes only / All time high.
Compact disc: released on EMI, '87 by EMI Records. Dist: EMI

VIEW TO A KILL, A Original motion picture soundtrack (Various Artists).
Album: released on Parlophone, Jun'85 by EMI Records. Dist: EMI

Cassette: released on Parlophone, Jun'85 by EMI Records. Dist: EMI

James, Brian

WHY WHY WHY.
Single (7"): released on Illegal, Jan'82 by Faulty Products Records. Dist: Pinnacle, Lightning, Cartel

James, Charlie

EYE OF THE STORM.
Single (7"): released on Sour Grape, Aug'84 by Sour Grape Records. Dist: PRT

Single (12"): released on Sour Grape, Aug'84 by Sour Grape Records. Dist: PRT

James, Clive

CHARLES CHARMING'S CHALLENGES ON THE PATHWAY TO THE THRONE (James, Clive with Pamela Stephenson & Russell Davies).
Album: released on Arista, Jun'81 by Arista Records. Dist: RCA

James, Danny

ROCKIN' ROBIN.
Single (12"): released on Passion, Nov'83 by Skratch Records. Dist: PRT

James, Dave

CALCULATED RISK.
Album: released on Redbrick, Sep'83

James, David

ABSOLUTELY NOTHING.
Single (7"): released on Towerbell, Jan'82 by Towerbell Records. Dist: EMI

DRUM MACHINE.
Single (7"): released on Sirocco, Feb'85 by Sirocco Records. Dist: Pinnacle

ORIGINAL CUCKOO BIRD PINEAPPLE TRUCK.
Single (7"): released on Towerbell, Oct'81 by Towerbell Records. Dist: EMI

James Dean Of The...

JAMES DEAN OF THE DOLE QUEUE (Various Artists).
Album: released on Northwood, Nov'86 by Northwood Records. Dist: Backs-Cartel

James, Deeana

TO MY HEART.
Single (12"): released on Elite, Dec'86 Dist: PRT

James, Elmore

20 BLUES GREATS.
Album: released on Deja Vu, Nov'85 by Deja Vu Records. Dist: Counterpoint Distribution, Record Services Distribution (Ireland)

Cassette: released on Deja Vu, Nov'85 by Deja Vu Records. Dist: Counterpoint Distribution, Record Services Distribution (Ireland)

BEST OF ELMORE JAMES, THE.
Album: released on Ace, Mar'81 by Ace Records. Dist: Pinnacle, Swift, Hotshot, Cadillac

DONE SOMEBODY WRONG.
Single (7"): released on Charly, Mar'81 by Charly Records. Dist: Charly, Cadillac

DUST MY BROOM.
Album: released on Topline, Jan'85 by Charly Records. Dist: Charly Distribution

Cassette: released on Topline, Jan'85 by Charly Records. Dist: Charly Distribution

GOT TO MOVE.
Album: released on Charly, Mar'81 by Charly Records. Dist: Charly, Cadillac

GREATEST HITS:ELMORE JAMES.
Album: released on Masters (Holland), Jan'87

Cassette: released on Masters (Holland), Jan'87

JAMES/BRIM/JONES (James, Elmore, John Brim, Floyd Jones).
Notes: See also under John Brim and Floyd Jones.
Compact disc: released on Vogue, Dec'86 Dist: Discovery, Jazz Music, PRT, Swift

KING OF THE BOTTLENECK BLUES.
Tracks: / Wild about you baby / Mean and evil / My best friend / Dark and dreary / Hawaiian boogie / Blues before sunrise / Strange kinda feelin' / Sho 'nuff I do / I was a fool / Long tall woman / One more drink / Wild about you.
Album: released on Crown, Feb'86 by Ace Records. Dist: Pinnacle, Swift

Cassette: released on Crown, Feb'86 by Ace Records. Dist: Pinnacle, Swift

KING OF THE SLIDE GUITAR.
Album: released on Ace(Cadet), Apr'83 by Ace Records. Dist: Pinnacle, Swift, Hotshot

LET'S CUT IT.
Compact disc: released on Ace, Nov'86 by Ace Records. Dist: Pinnacle, Swift, Hotshot, Cadillac

ONE WAY OUT.
Album: released on Charly(R&B), '85 by Charly Records. Dist: Charly, Cadillac

Cassette: released on Charly(R&B), '85 by Charly Records. Dist: Charly, Cadillac

ORIGINAL METEOR & FLAIR SIDES (James, Elmore & his Broom Dusters).
Album: released on Ace, Aug'84 by Ace Records. Dist: Pinnacle, Swift, Hotshot, Cadillac

PICKIN' THE BLUES.
Tracks: / Dust my room / Look on yonder wall / It hurts me too / Coming home / Sky is crying (The) / Standing at the crossroads / Hand in hand / Mean mistreatin' mama / I done somebody wrong / Pickin' the blues / I believe.
Album: released on Showcase, Apr'86 Dist: Counterpoint

Cassette: released on Showcase, Apr'86 Dist: Counterpoint

RED HOT BLUES.
Album: released on Blue Moon, Nov'83 Dist: Magnum Music Group Ltd, PRT, Spartan

SHAKE YOUR MONEYMAKER.
Tracks: / Dust my broom / Twelve year old boy, The / Coming home / It hurts me too / Elmore's contribution to jazz / Cry for me baby / Take me where you go / Sky is crying, The / Held my baby last night / Knocking at your door / Rollin' and tumblin' / Done somebody wrong / Fine little mama / Shake your moneymaker / I need you / Can't stop lovin' my baby / Something inside of me / Person to person / Baby please set a date / One way out / Got to move / Talk to me baby (I can't hold out).
Compact disc: released on Charly, Dec'86 by Charly Records. Dist: Charly, Cadillac

TO KNOW A MAN.
Album: released on Line (West Germany), Feb'84

WHOSE MUDDY SHOES (James, Elmore and John Brim).
Album: released on Chess(USA), Apr'82 by Sugar Hill (USA). Dist: PRT, Swift

James, Etta

BLUES IN THE NIGHT (James, Etta & Eddie 'Cleanhead' Vinson).
Tracks: / Kidney stew / Railroad porter blues / Something's got a hold on me / Medley: at last / Trust in me / Sunday kind of love / I just wanna make love to you / Please send me someone to love / Love man / Misty.
Notes: Exciting new album from blues veternas Etta James and Eddie Vinson recorded live at Maula's club in Los Angeles. All star support from Red Holloway saxes. Jack McDuff - organ, Shuggie Otis - guitar and Paul Humphrey on drums.
Album: released on Fantasy, Nov'86 by RCA Records. Dist: RCA, Jetstar

Cassette: released on Fantasy, Nov'86 by RCA Records. Dist: RCA, Jetstar

CHESS MASTERS.
Album: released on Chess, Apr'81 by Charly Records. Dist: Charly, Swift, PRT, Discovery, IMS, Polygram

Album: released on Chess(USA), Apr'83 by Sugar Hill (USA). Dist: PRT, Swift

DEEP IN THE NIGHT.
Album: released on Warner Bros., Jul'78 by Warner Bros Records. Dist: WEA

ETTA JAMES AT LAST.
Album: released on Chess, Oct'87 by Charly Records. Dist: Charly, Swift, PRT, Discovery, IMS, Polygram

Cassette: released on Chess, Oct'87 by Charly Records. Dist: Charly, Swift, PRT, Discovery, IMS, Polygram

GOOD ROCKIN' MAMA.
Special: released on Ace(Cadet), May'81 by Ace Records. Dist: Pinnacle, Swift, Hotshot

Cassette: released on Ace, Feb'85 by Ace Records. Dist: Pinnacle, Swift, Hotshot, Cadillac

R & B DYNAMITE.
Notes: C0ompilation of early Etta James,taken from the sessions recorded for the Modern/RPM.20 tracks on the album,22 on cassette.Digitally re-mastered,one previously unreleased track.
Compact disc: released on Ace, May'87 by Ace Records. Dist: Pinnacle, Swift, Hotshot, Cadillac

Album: released on Ace, Jun'87 by Ace Records. Dist: Pinnacle, Swift, Hotshot, Cadillac

Cassette: released on Ace, Jun'87 by Ace Records. Dist: Pinnacle, Swift, Hotshot, Cadillac

R & B QUEEN.
Tracks: / My one and only / Pick-up / I'm a fool / By the light of the silvery moon / Come what may / That's all / Tough lover / Dance with me Henry / Tears of joy / Baby baby every night / Do something crazy / Market place.
Album: released on Crown, Feb'86 by Ace Records. Dist: Pinnacle, Swift

Cassette: released on Crown, Feb'86 by Ace Records. Dist: Pinnacle, Swift

TELL MAMA.
Single (7"): released on Chess, Jul'85 by Charly Records. Dist: Charly, Swift, PRT, Discovery, IMS, Polygram

TUFF LOVER.
Album: released on Ace, Jul'83 by Ace Records. Dist: Pinnacle, Swift, Hotshot, Cadillac

James, Freddie

GET UP & BOOGIE.

Album: released on Warner Bros., Jan'80 by Warner Bros Records. Dist: WEA

James Gang

TRUE STORY OF, THE.
Tracks: / Take a look around bluebird / Collage / Wrap city in English / Yadig woman / Ashes, the rain and I / It's all the same / Things I could be / Live my life again / I'll tell you why / Run run run / Midnight man.
Album: released on See For Miles, Mar'87 by See For Miles Records. Dist: Pinnacle

James, Harry

20 GOLDEN GREATS LIVE.
Cassette: released on Magic, Mar'87 Dist: Jazz Music, Submarine, Swift, Chris Wellard, Conifer

Cassette: released on Magic, May'87 Dist: Jazz Music, Submarine, Swift, Chris Wellard, Conifer

20 GOLDEN GREATS LIVE (James, Harry & His Music Makers).
Tracks: / Easy / My beloved is rugged / Rose Room / King Porter stomp / Your red wagon / Lady be good / Shiny stockings / Block party / Ultra / Jumping at the woodside / Flatbush Flanagan / Carnival / Dancing in the dark / Love & weather / Rockin' in Rhythm / Deep purple / Trumpet blues & cantabile / Lover come back to me.

20 GOLDEN PIECES OF HARRY JAMES (James, Harry Orchestra).
Album: released on Bulldog, Dec'81 by Bulldog Records. Dist: President Distribution, Spartan, Swift, Taylor, H.R.

Cassette: released on Bulldog, Feb'82 by Bulldog Records. Dist: President Distribution, Spartan, Swift, Taylor, H.R.

ARRANGEMENTS OF JIMMY MUNDY & ANDY GIBSON.
Album: released on Joyce (USA), May'84 Dist: Swift

ARRANGEMENTS OF RAINS, HOLMES, BILLY MAY ETC.
Album: released on Joyce (USA), May'84 Dist: Swift

BIG JOHN SPECIAL.
Album: released on Hep, Jun'82 by H.R. Taylor Records. Dist: Jazz Music, Cadillac Music, JSU, Taylors, Wellard, Chris, Zodiac, Swift, Fast Forward

CIRIBIRIBIN.
Album: released on Pathe MarconiFrance), Jun'85

CLEARWATER VOL.1.
Album: released on First Heard, Apr'85 by Submarine Records. Dist: Conifer, Taylors

CLEARWATER VOL.2.
Album: released on First Heard, Apr'85 by Submarine Records. Dist: Conifer, Taylors

CLEARWATER VOL.3 (James, Harry & His Music Makers).
Album: released on First Heard, Aug'85 by Submarine Records. Dist: Conifer, Taylors

COMIN' FROM GOOD PLACE (James, Harry & His Band).
Album: released on Sheffield Laboratories, Oct'82 by Sheffield Laboratories Records. Dist: Goldsmith, John Distribution

DOUBLE FEATURE.
Album: released on First Heard, Oct'84 by Submarine Records. Dist: Conifer, Taylors

Cassette: released on First Heard, Oct'84 by Submarine Records. Dist: Conifer, Taylors

FROM HOLLYWOOD.
Album: released on First Heard, '84 by Submarine Records. Dist: Conifer, Taylors

GLENN MILLER & HARRY JAMES BANDS (see Miller, Glenn) (James, Harry & Glenn Miller).

GOLDEN TRUMPET OF HARRY JAMES, THE (James, Harry & His Orchestra).
Tracks: / Ciribiribin / You made me love you / Two o'clock jump / I've heard that song before / Ultra / By the sleepy before / All or nothing at all / Cherry / Take the 'A' train / I heard you cried last night / Mole, The / Satin doll.
Compact disc: released on London, Jul'87 by London Records. Dist: Polygram

GREATEST HITS:HARRY JAMES (James, Harry Orchestra).
Compact disc: released on Bridge, Apr'87 Dist: CD Centre Distribution, Pinnacle, Target

Compact disc: released on Bridge, Apr'87 Dist: CD Centre Distribution, Pinnacle, Target

HARRY JAMES.
Album:

Cassette: released on Deja Vu, Jan'87 by Deja Vu Records. Dist: Counterpoint Distribution, Record Services Distribution (Ireland)

Album: released on Giants of Jazz, Apr'79 by Hasmick Promotions Ltd.. Dist: Counterpoint, Jazz Music, Taylors, Swift, Mainline, Wellard, Chris

HARRY JAMES AND HIS ORCHESTRA 1948-1949 (James, Harry & His Orchestra).
Album: released on Solid Sender, Apr'81 Dist: JSU, Jazz Music

HARRY JAMES AND HIS ORCHESTRA 1944-1945 (James, Harry & His Orchestra).
Album: released on Solid Sender, Apr'81 Dist: JSU, Jazz Music

HARRY JAMES & HIS MUSIC MAKERS (1942-7).
Album: released on First Heard, Jul'77 by Submarine Records. Dist: Conifer, Taylors

HARRY JAMES & HIS MUSIC MAKERS.
Album: released on Queen-Disc (Import), Apr'81

HARRY JAMES & HIS ORCHESTRA 1948-9 (James, Harry & His Orchestra).
Album: released on London, Oct'79 by London Records. Dist: Polygram

HARRY JAMES IN HI-FI.
Album: released on Capitol(USA), Mar'84 by Capitol (USA) Records. Dist: EMI

HARRY JAMES VOL.1 (James, Harry (Members of Orchestra)).
Album: released on Bright Orange, Apr'79 Dist: Swift

HARRY JAMES VOL.2.
Album: released on Bright Orange, Apr'79 Dist: Swift

HARRY'S CHOICE.
Album: released on Pathe MarconiFrance), Mar'85

Cassette: released on Pathe MarconiFrance), Mar'85

KING JAMES VERSION,THE (James, Harry & His Band).
Album: released on Sheffield Laboratories, Aug'82 by Sheffield Laboratories Records. Dist: Goldsmith, John Distribution

LIVE IN CONCERT (James, Harry & The Music Makers).
Album: released on Dance Band Days, Jun'86 Dist: Geoff's Records International

Cassette: released on Dance Band Days, Jun'86 Dist: Geoff's Records International

MEMORIAL.
Album: released on First Heard, '84 by Submarine Records. Dist: Conifer, Taylors

MEMORIAL ALBUM (THE).
Tracks: / Harry James reminisces / Back beat boogie (The) / Close to you / Dancing in the dark / King Porter stomp / Carnival / Man I love (The) / Flatbush Flanagan / Deep purple / Arrival (The) / Harry's blues / Dear old Southland / Trumpet blues and cantabile'.
Notes: Originally released in 1983 after the sad death of James in July that year, this collection will gladden his fan's hearts. Drevived from Harry's radio performances, every one a classic.
Album: released on First Heard, Nov'85 by Submarine Records. Dist: Conifer. Taylors

Cassette: released on First Heard, Nov'85 by Submarine Records. Dist: Conifer, Taylors

MUSICMAKING.
Album: released on First Heard, Oct'84 by Submarine Records. Dist: Conifer, Taylors

Cassette: released on First Heard, Oct'84 by Submarine Records. Dist: Conifer, Taylors

ONE NIGHT STAND (James, Harry & The Music Makers).
Album: released on Queen, Dec'79 Dist: Jazz Music

ONE NIGHT STAND WITH HARRY JAMES.
Album: released on Sandy Hook, Jan'79

ON THE AIR (James, Harry & His Orchestra).
Album: released on Aircheck, Feb'78

REMEMBER (James, Harry & His Music Makers).
Cassette: released on Magic, Aug'85 Dist: Jazz Music, Submarine, Swift, Chris Wellard, Conifer

SATURDAY NIGHT SWING.
Album: released on Giants of Jazz, Oct'84 by Hasmick Promotions Ltd.. Dist: Counterpoint, Jazz Music, Taylors, Swift, Mainline, Wellard, Chris

SEPTEMBER SONG.
Album: released on Astan (USA), Mar'85

SILVER COLLECTION, THE (James, Harry & His Orchestra).
Tracks: / Shiny stockings / Cotton tail / Lester leaps in / Take the 'A' train / Opus one / Cherokee / King Porter stomp / Flying home / In the mood / Tuxedo junction / One o'clock jump / She's gotta go / Mae and Ray / Sentimental journey / Ultra / Strictly instrumental / Crazy rhythm / Back beat boogie.
Notes: Digital stereo
Compact disc: released on Verve, Nov'84 by Phonogram Records. Dist: Polygram

SOUNDS FAMILIAR.
Album: released on Saville, Jun'82 by Conifer Records. Dist: Conifer

STILL HARRY AFTER ALL THESE YEARS.
Album: released on Sheffield Laboratories, Dec'80 by Sheffield Laboratories Records. Dist: Goldsmith, John Distribution

SWING GOES ON,THE vol 9.
Album: released on EMI (Germany), '83 by EMI Records. Dist: Conifer

SWINGIN' 'N' SWEET (James,Harry Octet).
Album: released on Giants of Jazz, Jul'84 by Hasmick Promotions Ltd.. Dist: Counterpoint, Jazz Music, Taylors, Swift, Mainline, Wellard, Chris

TEXAS CHATTER.
Album: released on Joker Import, Apr'81

TRUMPET BLUES.
Album: released on First Heard, '84 by Submarine Records. Dist: Conifer, Taylors

Cassette: released on First Heard, '84 by Submarine Records. Dist: Conifer, Taylors

TRUMPET TOAST (James, Harry & His Orchestra).
Album: released on MCA, Feb'84 by MCA Records. Dist: Polygram, MCA Deleted '86

Cassette: released on MCA, Feb'84 by MCA Records. Dist: Polygram, MCA Deleted '86.

TWO O'CLOCK JUMP (James, Harry Orchestra).
Album: released on Astan, Nov'84 by Astan Records. Dist: Counterpoint

Cassette: released on Astan, Nov'84 by Astan Records. Dist: Counterpoint

Album: released on Meteor, Aug'85 by Magnum Music Group Ltd. Dist: Magnum Music Group Ltd, PRT Distribution, Spartan Distribution

UNCOLLECTED HARRY JAMES & HIS ORCHESTRA,THE.
Album: released on Hindsight(USA), May'79 by Hindsight Records (USA). Dist: Swift, Charly

UNCOLLECTED (THE).
Album: released on Hindsight(UK), Apr'86 Dist: Jazz Music

James, Henry

TURN OF THE SCREW, THE (York, Suzannah).
Cassette: released on Argo (Cassettes), Sep'84 by Decca Records. Dist: Polygram

Cassette: released on Listen For Pleasure, Feb'81 by MFP Records. Dist: EMI

James, Hilary

MUSICAL MYSTERY TOUR (James, Hilary & Simon Mayor).
Cassette: released on Acoustics, Jul'87 by Acoustics Records. Dist: Cartel

James Homesick

HOME SWEET HOMESICK JAMES.
Album: released on Big Bear, Jan'82 by Big Bear Records. Dist: Big Bear, Swift

SHAKE YOUR MONEYMAKER (James Homesick and Snooky Pryor).
Album: released on Krazy Kat, Dec'84 Dist: Jazz Music, Swift, Chris Wellard, H.R. Taylor, Charly, Hotshot, IRS Distribution

James, Jimmy

DANCIN TILL DAWN.
Cassette: released on PRT, Jul'79 by PRT Records. Dist: PRT

LOVE FIRE.
Single (7"): released on ERC, Apr'84 by ERC Records. Dist: PRT

NOW IS THE TIME.
Tracks: / Now is the time / I'll go where your music takes me / Missing you.
Notes: Composed by Biddu. Produced and arranged by Keff McCulloch for Satril Records.
Single (7"): released on Nine O Nine, May'87 by Creole Records. Dist: Rhino, PRT

Single (12"): released on Nine O Nine, May'87 by Creole Records. Dist: Rhino, PRT

REACH OUT.
Single (7"): released on ERC, Aug'84 by ERC Records. Dist: PRT

James Jimmy Vagabounds

I'LL GO WHERE YOUR MUSIC TAKES ME.
Single (7"): released on Old Gold, Jul'82 by Old Gold Records. Dist: Lightning, Jazz Music, Spartan, Counterpoint

James John

ACCOUSTIC ELECTICA.
Album: released on Stoptime, Nov'84 by Stoptime Recordings. Dist: Roots Distribution, Projection Distribution, JSU Distribution

GUITAR JUMP.
Album: released on Kicking Mule, Sep'77 by Sonet. Dist: Roots, PRT-Pye Distribution

I GOT RHYTHM (James John & Sam Mitchell).
Album: released on Kicking Mule, Jan'78 by Sonet. Dist: Roots, PRT-Pye Distribution

LIVE IN CONCERT.
Album: released on Kicking Mule, Jan'78 by Sonet. Dist: Roots, PRT-Pye Distribution

James, Josie

CALL ME (WHEN YOU NEED MY LOVE).
Single (7"): released on TPL, Aug'85 Dist: PRT

DANCE YOU UP.
Tracks: / Dnce you up.
Single (7"):

Single (12"): released on Toadstall, Aug'86

James Keith

BEAUJOLAIS AND BALLERINAS/SPACE IN...
Single (7"): released on Keith James, Apr'82 by Keith James Records. Dist: Spartan

BOTTLE OF WINE A GUITAR BOX AND SAX.
Single (7"): released on Keith James, May'83 by Keith James Records. Dist: Spartan

KEEP IT TO YURSELF/BEHIND YOUR EYES.
Single (7"): released on Keith James, Jan'84 by Keith James Records. Dist: Spartan

LIFE IN A WESTERN WORLD.
Single (7"): released on Keith James, Feb'73 by Keith James Records. Dist: Spartan

ON THE REBOUND.
Album: released on Parole, Jan'82 by Parole Records. Dist: Cartel, Rough Trade, Faulty Products

ON THE REBOUND/GO FOR IT.
Single (7"): released on Paro, Aug'82 by Paro Records. Dist: Spartan

SNEAK A LITTLE TIME/DON'T LOSE THE OLD FOR THE NEW.
Single (7"): released on Keith James, Oct'83 by Keith James Records. Dist: Spartan

SWALLOW,THE.
Album: released on Keith James, May'83 by Keith James Records. Dist: Spartan

TEARS DON'T SEEM TO HURT ANYMORE.
Single (7"): released on Keith James, Oct'81 by Keith James Records. Dist: Spartan

James Lawrence

LATE NIGHT EXTRA (WURLITZER ORGAN BUCKINGHAM PALACE).
Album: released on Saydiscs, Jul'81

James, Marvin

HE-BE HAR-BE.
Tracks: / He-be har-be / He me and you.
Notes: Distribution by Self. Tel: 0634 43952
Single (7"): released on Havasong, Apr'86 Dist: Havasong

I'LL BE AROUND.
Single (12"): released on Hot Vinyl, Apr'87 by Hot Vinyl Records. Dist: Jetstar

LET ME DOWN EASY.
Tracks: / Let me down easy.
Single (12"): released on Hot Vinyl, Jun'86 by Hot Vinyl Records. Dist: Jetstar

MY DAD.
Tracks: / My Dad / Together in Iceland.
Single (7"): released on Havasong, Jan'87 Dist: Havasong

YOU'RE JUST LIKE A BUBBLE IN WINE.
Tracks: / You're just like a bubble in wine / Nothing to do.
Single (7"): released on Havasong, Oct'86 Dist: Havasong

James Michael St

THERE IS ONLY ONE LOVE.
Single (7"): released on WEA, Jul'85 by WEA Records. Dist: WEA

James Micky

MCGUIGAN.
Single (7"): released on Gem, Oct'85 by Gem Records. Dist: RCA

James M R

MORE GHOST STORIES READ BY MICHAEL HORDEN.
Cassette: released on Argo (Spokenword), Jun'84 by Decca Records. Dist: Polygram

James, Nick

JUST LIKE A YO YO.
Single (7"): released on Columbia, Aug'87 by EMI Records. Dist: EMI

Single (12"): released on Columbia, Aug'87 by EMI Records. Dist: EMI

Jameson, Derek

DO THEY MEAN US.
Tracks: / Do they mean us / Yes Virginia.
Single (7"): released on Polydor, Oct'86 by Polydor Records. Dist: Polygram, Polydor

Single (12"): released on Polydor, Oct'86 by Polydor Records. Dist: Polygram, Polydor

Album: released on Compact Organisation, Nov'84 Dist: PRT

YES VIRGINIA.
Tracks: / Yes Virginia / Do they mean us?.
Single (7"): released on Polydor, Nov'86 by Polydor Records. Dist: Polygram, Polydor

Single (12"): released on Polydor, Nov'86 by Polydor Records. Dist: Polygram, Polydor

Jameson Raid
HYPNOTISTS/GETTIN HOTTER.
Single (7"): released on Blackbird, Nov'80 by Blackbird Records. Dist: CBS Ireland Distribution, Polygram, Swift

James, Oscar
CARNIVAL JAM.
Single (12"): released on Flick, Aug'87 by Flick Records. Dist: Jetstar

LOVE RIDING HIGH.
Tracks: / Original fin / Love riding high.
Single (12"): released on 10, Oct'86 by 10 Records. Dist: Virgin, EMI

James & Percy
IF ONLY BEFORE.
Single (12"): by Code Green Records. Dist: Stage One

James, Phil
TWO OF US (THE).
Album: released on Park Heights, Nov'85 Dist: Jetstar Distribution

YOU AND I.
Tracks: / You and I / Run little girl.
Single (7"): released on LBA, Jun'86 by LBA Records.

James Phyllis St
AIN'T NO TURNING BACK.
Album: released on Motown, Nov'84 by Motown Records. Dist: BMG Distribution

CANDLELIGHT AFTERNOON.
Single (7"): released on Motown, Sep'84 by Motown Records. Dist: BMG Distribution

James, Rick
17.
Single (7"): released on Gordy (USA), Jul'84 by Motown Records. Dist: RCA

Single (12"): released on Gordy (USA), Jul'84 by Motown Records. Dist: RCA

BIG TIME/ISLAND LADY.
:

Single (7"): released on Motown, Oct'81 by Motown Records. Dist: BMG Distribution

BUSTIN OUT OF L SEVEN.
Album: released on Motown, Oct'81 by Motown Records. Dist: BMG Distribution

CAN'T STOP.
Single (7"): released on Gordy (USA), Mar'85 by Motown Records. Dist: RCA

Single (12"): released on Gordy (USA), Mar'85 by Motown Records. Dist: RCA

COLD BLOODED.
Album: released on Motown, Sep'83 by Motown Records. Dist: BMG Distribution

COLD BLOODED (2 PARTS).
Single (7"): released on Motown, Aug'83 by Motown Records. Dist: BMG Distribution

Single (12"): released on Motown, Aug'83 by Motown Records. Dist: BMG Distribution

COME GET IT.
Album: released on Motown, Oct'82 by Motown Records. Dist: BMG Distribution

Cassette: released on Motown, Oct'82 by Motown Records. Dist: BMG Distribution

DANCE WIT ME.
Single (7"): released on Motown, Jun'82 by Motown Records. Dist: BMG Distribution

Single (12"): released on Motown, Jun'82 by Motown Records. Dist: BMG Distribution

EBONY EYES/1,2,3, YOU HER AND ME/STANDING ON THE TOP (James, Rick and Friend).
Single (7"): released on Gordy (USA), Jan'84 by Motown Records. Dist: RCA

Single (12"): released on Gordy (USA), Jan'84 by Motown Records. Dist: RCA

FIRE IT UP.
Album: released on Motown, Oct'81 by Motown Records. Dist: BMG Distribution

FLAG, THE.
Tracks: / Freak flag / Forever and a day / Sweet and sexy / Free to be me / Save it for me / R U experienced / Funk in merica/Silly little man / Sow and easy / Oma raga / Painted pictures.
Album: released on Gordy (USA), Jun'86 by Motown Records. Dist: RCA

Cassette: released on Gordy (USA), Jun'86 by Motown Records. Dist: RCA

Compact disc: released on Gordy (USA), '86 by Motown Records. Dist: RCA

GARDEN OF LOVE.
Album: released on Motown, Oct'81 by Motown Records. Dist: BMG Distribution

GHETTO LIFE.
Single (7"): released on Motown, Jan'82 by Motown Records. Dist: BMG Distribution

Single (12"): released on Motown, Jan'82 by Motown Records. Dist: BMG Distribution

GIVE IT TO ME BABY/DON'T GIVE UP.
Single (7"): released on Motown, Oct'81 by Motown Records. Dist: BMG Distribution

Single (12"): released on Motown, Oct'81 by Motown Records. Dist: BMG Distribution

GLOW.
Album: released on Gordy (USA), May'85 by Motown Records. Dist: RCA

Cassette: released on Gordy (USA), May'85 by Motown Records. Dist: RCA

Single (7"): released on Gordy (USA), Jun'85 by Motown Records. Dist: RCA

Single (12"): released on Gordy (USA), Jun'85 by Motown Records. Dist: RCA

GREATEST HITS:RICK JAMES.
Tracks: / Super freak / You turn me on / You and I / Mary Jane / Ebony eyes / Give it to me baby / Dance wit me / Cold blooded / 17.
Album: released on Motown, Aug'86 by Motown Records. Dist: BMG Distribution

Cassette: released on Motown, Aug'86 by Motown Records. Dist: BMG Distribution

HARD TO GET/MY LOVE/GIVE IT ME.
Single (7"): released on Motown, Aug'82 by Motown Records. Dist: BMG Distribution

Single (12"): released on Motown, Aug'82 by Motown Records. Dist: BMG Distribution

REFLECTIONS OF RICK.
Tracks: / 17 / Oh what a night / You turn me on / Fire & desire / Bustin' out / You & I / Mary Jane / Dance wit' me / Give it to me baby / Super freak.
Compact disc: released on Motown, Nov'84 by Motown Records. Dist: BMG Distribution

Album: released on Motown, Aug'84 by Motown Records. Dist: BMG Distribution

Cassette: released on Motown, Aug'84 by Motown Records. Dist: BMG Distribution

Compact disc: released on Motown, Aug'84 by Motown Records. Dist: BMG Distribution

STREET SONGS.
Album: released on Motown, Oct'81 by Motown Records. Dist: BMG Distribution

Cassette: released on Motown, Oct'81 by Motown Records. Dist: BMG Distribution

STREET SONGS/THROWIN' DOWN 2 Classic albums.
Tracks: / Gve it to me baby / Ghetto life / Make love to me / Mr. Policeman / Super freak / Fire and desire / Call me / Below the funk (pass the J) / Dance wit' me / Money talks / Teardrops / Throwdown / Standing on the top / Hard to get / Standing on the top / Hard to get / Happy / 69 times / My love.
Compact disc: released on Motown, Dec'86 by Motown Records. Dist: BMG Distribution

SUMMER LOVE/GETTIN IT ON.
Single (7"): released on Motown, Oct'81 by Motown Records. Dist: BMG Distribution

Single (12"): released on Motown, Oct'81 by Motown Records. Dist: BMG Distribution

SUPER FREAK (PART 2).
Single (7"): released on Motown, Nov'82 by Motown Records. Dist: BMG Distribution

Single (12"): released on Motown, Nov'82 by Motown Records. Dist: BMG Distribution

SWEET AND SEXY THING.
Tracks: / Sweet and sexy thing.
Single (7"): released on Motown, Jun'86 by Motown Records. Dist: BMG Distribution

Single (12"): released on Motown, Jun'86 by Motown Records. Dist: BMG Distribution

THROWIN DOWN.
Album: released on Motown, Jun'82 by Motown Records. Dist: BMG Distribution

Cassette: released on Motown, Jun'82 by Motown Records. Dist: BMG Distribution

YOU AND I/HOLLYWOOD.
Single (7"): released on Motown, Oct'81 by Motown Records. Dist: BMG Distribution

YOU TURN ME ON.
Single (7"): released on Motown, Oct'84 by Motown Records. Dist: BMG Distribution

Single (12"): released on Motown, Oct'84 by Motown Records. Dist: BMG Distribution

James, Ronnie
TRYING TO BURN THE SUN (James, Ronnie Dio & Elf).

James, Sally
ONCE UPON A TIME STORIES.
Album: released on Super Tempo, May'84 by Multiple Sounds Records. Dist: Multiple Sound Distributors

Cassette: released on Super Tempo, May'84 by Multiple Sounds Records. Dist: Multiple Sound Distributors

James, Shirley
ASK ME TO STAY.
Single (7"): released on Black Jack, May'82 Dist: Jetstar, Spartan

RIGHT TIME OF THE NIGHT (James, Shirley & Danny Ray).
Single (7"): released on Black Jack, Sep'81 Dist: Jetstar, Spartan

Single (12"): released on Black Jack, Sep'81 Dist: Jetstar, Spartan

James Silk
C B CASANOVA.
Single (7"): released on Ramkup, Jul'81 Dist: Pinnacle

James, Skip
1931.
Album:

COMPLETE 1931 SESSIONS.
Album: released on Yazoo(USA), May'86

I'M SO GLAD.
Double Album: released on Vanguard, May'78 by PRT Records. Dist: PRT

James, Sonny
ALWAYS DANCING.
Album: released on Sounds Ultimate, May'85 Dist: PRT, H.R. Taylor

James Sonny Set
DANCE TO MY MUSIC.
Album: released on Sounds Ultimate, Sep'83 Dist: PRT, H.R. Taylor

James Stephen
I NEED YOU NOW.
Single (12"): released on Seven Leaves, May'85 by Seven Leaves Records. Dist: Jetstar

James Stuart
ONLY WHEN I LAUGH/KYPROS.
Single (7"): released on Radioactive, Sep'82

James Tina
SAN ANTONIO STROLL/LOVE IS A ROSE.
Single (7"): released on Emerald, Feb'81 by Emerald Records. Dist: Ross, PRT, Solomon & Peres Distribution

James, Tommy
MONY MONY (James, Tommy & The Shondells).
Single (7"): released on Old Gold, Jun'84 by Old Gold Records. Dist: Lightning, Jazz Music, Spartan, Counterpoint

MONY MONY/CRIMSON (James, Tommy & The Shondells).
Single (7"): released on Flashback, Jul'80 by Flashback Records/PRT Records. Dist: Mainline, PRT

SAY PLEASE/TWO TIME LOVER.
Single (7"): released on 21 Records, May'83 by Polydor Records. Dist: Polydor

SHORT SHARP SHOTS.
78 rpm record: released on PRT, Apr'83 by PRT Records. Dist: PRT

Cassette: released on PRT, Apr'83 by PRT Records. Dist: PRT

James, Tony
MEMORIES OF THE FABULOUS FOX VOL.2 (see Nourse,Everett/Tony James) (James, Tony/Everett Nourse).

MEMORIES OF THE FABULOUS FOX (see Nourse,Everett/Tony James) (James, Tony/Everett Nourse).

Jamil
SAVE IT FOR ME.
Single (7"): released on Nagla, Aug'87 by Nagla Records.

Jammers
BE MINE TONIGHT.
Single (7"): released on Salsoul, Dec'82

Single (12"): released on Salsoul, Dec'82

Jammin' For The Jackpot
JAMMIN' FOR THE JACKPOT (Various Artists).
Tracks: / Caravan / Casa Loma stomp / Dallas blues / Madhouse / Heebie jeebies / Pickin' the cabbage / Ebony silhouette / Jammin' for the jackpot / Toby / Blues of Avalon / Sensational mood / Original dixieland one-step / Atlanta low down / Auburn Avenue stomp / West end blues / Good feelin' blues.
Notes: Mono. Big bands and territory bands of the 30's
Album: released on New World (USA), Jul'86 by New World Records (USA). Dist: Conifer

Jamming
JAMMING! Various artists.
Album: released on Situation 2, Jun'84 Dist: Cartel, Pinnacle

Cassette: released on Situation 2, Jun'84 Dist: Cartel, Pinnacle

Jammy But Nice
JAMMY BUT NICE Various artists.
Album: released on Jammy, '80 by Jammy Records. Dist: Jammy

Jammy, Prince
PRESENTS MUSIC MAKER (Jammy, Prince & the Striker Lee Posse).
Album: released on Vista Sounds, Jul'84 by Vista Sounds Records. Dist: Jetstar

Jam sessions
JAM SESSIONS Various artists.
Album: released on Pablo (USA), '82 by Pablo Records (USA). Dist: Wellard, Chris, IMS-Polygram, BMG

Cassette: released on Pablo (USA), '82 by Pablo Records (USA). Dist: Wellard, Chris, IMS-Polygram, BMG

Janaway, Bruce
HORNED MOON Harmonica and guitar.
Cassette: released on Folktracks, Nov'79 by Folktracks Cassettes. Dist: Folktracks

Jan & Dean
20 ROCK'N'ROLL HITS.
Album: released on EMI (Germany), '83 by EMI Records. Dist: Conifer

FUN FUN FUN.
Tracks: / Ride the wild surf / Dead man's curve / Help me Rhonda / I get around / Drag city / Baby talk / Clementine / Surf city / Sidewalk surfin' / Little deuce coupe / Little old lady from Pasadena / Fun fun fun.
Album: released on Topline, Sep'86 by Charly Records. Dist: Charly Distribution

Cassette: released on Topline, Sep'86 by Charly Records. Dist: Charly Distribution

GREATEST HITS:JAN & DEAN.
Compact disc: released on MCS Look Back, Jul'87

JAN & DEAN.
Tracks: / Jan & Dean.
Cassette: released on Timeless Treasures, Jul'86 Dist: Counterpoint Distribution

JAN & DEAN STORY, THE.
Album: released on Creole, Nov'83 by Creole Records. Dist: Rhino, PRT

RIDE THE WIND SURF.
Cassette: released on Liberty-UA, Jun'81

SURF CITY.
Single (7"): released on Creole, Jul'80 by Creole Records. Dist: Rhino, PRT

Jane
GERMANIA.
Album: released on Polydor (Germany), Jul'83 Dist: IMS-Polygram

Cassette: released on Polydor (Germany), Jul'83 Dist: IMS-Polygram

IT'S A FINE DAY.
Single (7"): released on Cherry Red, May'83 by Cherry Red Records. Dist: Pinnacle

JANE.
Album: released on Brain, Mar'81

SING NO.9.
Album: released on Brain, Feb'80

Jane and Barton

JANE AND BARTON.
Album: released on Cherry Red, Sep'83 by Cherry Red Records. Dist: Pinnacle

Jane & Barton

I WANT TO BE WITH YOU.
Single (7"): released on Cherry Red, Sep'83 by Cherry Red Records. Dist: Pinnacle

Jane Eyre

JANE EYRE Original Soundtrack.
Album: released on That's Entertainment, Apr'83 by That's Entertainment Records. Dist: Pinnacle, PRT

Jane's Addiction

JANE'S ADDICTION.
Album: released on Triple XXX (USA), Aug'87 Dist: Pinnacle

Janes, Sam

Easter rebellion

Janette and the planets

NINE,NINE,NINE.
Single (7"): released on Dig This, Oct'84 by Dig This Records. Dist: ILA

Janice

BYE BYE.
Tracks: / Bye Bye.
Single (7"): released on Fourth & Broadway, Jul'86 by Island Records. Dist: Polygram, EMI

Single (12"): released on Fourth & Broadway, Jul'86 by Island Records. Dist: Polygram, EMI

Album: released on Arista, May'83 by Arista Records. Dist: RCA

Cassette: released on Arista, May'83 by Arista Records. Dist: RCA

Janie

SWINGING SANTA.
Single (7"): released on Mach, Nov'82

Jani & The planets

EXTRA TERRESTRIAL SONG.
Single (7"): released on Images, Jan'83 by MSD Records. Dist: PRT

Janitors

CHICKEN STOODGE.
Single (7"): released on In Tape, Jul'85 by In Tape Records. Dist: Red Rhino, Cartel

FAMILY FANTASTIC.
Single (7"): released on Abstract, 13 Jun'87 by Abstract. Dist: Pinnacle

Single (12"): released on Abstract, 13 Jun'87 by Abstract. Dist: Pinnacle

THUNDERHEAD.
Tracks: / Thunderhead.
Album: released on In Tape, Jul'86 by In Tape Records. Dist: Red Rhino, Cartel

Janitors, The

GOOD TO BE KING.
Tracks: / Good to be king.
Single (7"): released on In Tape, May'86 by In Tape Records. Dist: Red Rhino, Cartel

Jankel, Chas

CHAZ JANKEL.
Album: released on A&M, Oct'80 by A&M Records. Dist: Polygram

Cassette: released on A&M, Oct'80 by A&M Records. Dist: Polygram

I CAN GET OVER IT.
Single (12"): released on A&M, Oct'83 by A&M Records. Dist: Polygram

LOOKING AT YOU.
Single (7"): released on A&M, Jun'85 by A&M Records. Dist: Polygram

Single (7"): released on A&M, Jun'85 by A&M Records. Dist: Polygram

NUMBER 1.
Single (7"): released on A&M, Feb'85 by A&M Records. Dist: Polygram

Single (12"): released on A&M, Feb'85 by A&M Records. Dist: Polygram

WITHOUT YOU.
Single (12"): released on A&M, Jul'83 by A&M Records. Dist: Polygram

YOUR MY OCCUPATION (Jankel, Chas Featuring Brenda Jones).

Jankowski, Horst

HORST JANKOWSKI & HIS ORCHESTRA.
Album: released on Intersound, Sep'79 by Intersound Records. Dist: Jazz Music

PIANO INTERLUDE.
Album: released on Intersound, Oct'79 by Intersound Records. Dist: Jazz Music

WALK IN THE BLACK FOREST.
Single (7"): released on Old Gold, Jan'85 by Old Gold Records. Dist: Lightning, Jazz Music, Spartan, Counterpoint

Jannot, Veronique

DESIRE DESIRE (Jannot, Veronique & Laurent Voulzey).
Single (7"):

Janot, Johnny

EXPOSE YOURSELF TO CAJUN MUSIC.
Album:

Jansch, Bert

ESSENTIAL COLLECTION, THE (VOL. 2) Black water side.
Tracks: / Angie / My lover / Want my daddy now / First time ever I saw your face, The / Come back baby / Weeping willow blues / Little sweet sunshine, A / Black water side / Dissatisfied blues / Henry Martin / Woman like you, A / Miss Heather Rosemary Sewell / Birthday blues / Wishing well / Reynardine / Rosemary lane / Alman / Wayward child / Nobody's bar / Peregrinations / Bird song.
Compact disc: released on Transatlantic, Sep'87 by Transatlantic Records. Dist: IMS-Polygram

ESSENTIAL COLLECTION, THE (VOL. 1) Strolling down the highway.
Tracks: / Strolling down the highway / Running running from home / Oh how your love is strong / Needle of death / Tinker's blues / Courting blues / As the day grows longer now / Wheel, The / It don't bother me / Gardener, The / 900 miles / In this game / Casbah / Veronica / Nottamun town / Go your way my love / Love is teasing / I had no time / Ring a ding bird / I am lonely / Gardner, The / I have no time / Ring a ding bird.
Compact disc: released on Transatlantic, Jul'87 by Transatlantic Records. Dist: IMS-Polygram

FROM THE OUTSIDE.
Album: released on Mausoleum, Sep'85 by Mausoleum Records. Dist: Pinnacle

HEARTBREAK.
Album: released on Logo, '82 by Logo Records. Dist: Roots, BMG

THIRTEEN DOWN.
Album: released on Kicking Mule, Jul'80 by Sonet. Dist: Roots, PRT-Pye Distribution

Jansen

WORLDS IN A SMALL ROOM (Jansen/Barbieri).
Album: released on Pan East, Oct'86 by L.O.E. Records. Dist: Nine Mile, PRT, Cartel

Cassette: released on Pan East, Oct'86 by L.O.E. Records. Dist: Nine Mile, PRT, Cartel

Compact disc: released on Pan East, Oct'86 by L.O.E. Records. Dist: Nine Mile, PRT, Cartel

Jansen, Steve

STAY CLOSE (Jansen, Steve & Yukihiro Takahashi).

Jansson, Lena

PAY SOME ATTENTION TO ME (Jansson, Lena & Nils Lindberg Combo).
Album: released on Bluebell, Feb'87 Dist: Conifer, Jazz Music

Jansson, Tove

TALES FROM MOOMIN VALLEY.
Tracks: / Last dragon on the world, the / Invisible child, the / Cedric.
Notes: Approximate playing time One Hour
Cassette: released on Tellastory, Dec'86 by Bartlett Bliss Productions. Dist: PRT Distribution, Hayward Promotions Distribution, H.R. Taylor Distribution

Japan

ADOLESCENT SEX.
Album: released on Hansa, Sep'82 by Hansa Records. Dist: Polygram

Cassette: released on Ariola, Aug'83 Dist: RCA, Ariola

Cassette: released on Fame (Ariola), Sep'84 by Music For Pleasure Records. Dist: EMI

ALL TOMORROW'S PARTIES.
Single (7"): released on Hansa, Mar'83 by Hansa Records. Dist: Polygram

Single (12"): released on Hansa, Mar'83 by Hansa Records. Dist: Polygram

ART OF PARTIES.
Single (7"): released on Virgin, May'81 by Virgin Records. Dist: EMI, Virgin Distribution

Single (12"): released on Virgin, May'81 by Virgin Records. Dist: EMI, Virgin Distribution

ASSEMBLAGE extended cassette version.
:

Cassette: released on Hansa, Oct'82 by Hansa Records. Dist: Polygram

ASSEMBLAGE.
Album: released on Hansa, Sep'82 by Hansa Records. Dist: Polygram

Cassette: released on Hansa, Sep'82 by Hansa Records. Dist: Polygram

Album: released on Fame, Sep'85 by Music For Pleasure Records. Dist: EMI

Cassette: released on Fame, Sep'85 by Music For Pleasure Records. Dist: EMI

CANTON (Vision of China).
Single (7"): released on Virgin, Oct'81 by Virgin Records. Dist: EMI, Virgin Distribution

CANTONESE BOY.
Single (7"): released on Virgin, May'82 by Virgin Records. Dist: EMI, Virgin Distribution

Single (12"): released on Virgin, May'82 by Virgin Records. Dist: EMI, Virgin Distribution

CANTON/ VISIONS OF CHINA.
Single (12"): released on Virgin, May'83 by Virgin Records. Dist: EMI, Virgin Distribution

EUROPEAN SON.
Single (7"): released on Hansa, Jan'82 by Hansa Records. Dist: Polygram

Single (12"): released on Hansa, Jan'82 by Hansa Records. Dist: Polygram

EXORCISING GHOSTS.
Tracks: / Methods of dance / Swing / Gentlemen take polaroids / Quiet life / Foreign place, A / Night porter / My new career / Other side of life, The / Visions of China / Sons of pioneers / Talking drums / Art of parties, The / Taking islands in Africa / Voices raised in welcome, hands held in prayer / Life without buildings / Ghosts.
Compact disc: released on Virgin, Jan'85 by Virgin Records. Dist: EMI, Virgin Distribution

Album: released on Virgin, Dec'84 by Virgin Records. Dist: EMI, Virgin Distribution

Cassette: released on Virgin, Dec'84 by Virgin Records. Dist: EMI, Virgin Distribution

GENTLEMEN TAKE POLAROIDS.
Compact disc: released on Virgin, Apr'85 by Virgin Records. Dist: EMI, Virgin Distribution

Album: released on Virgin, Oct'80 by Virgin Records. Dist: EMI, Virgin Distribution

GHOSTS Version.
Single (12"): released on Virgin, Mar'82 by Virgin Records. Dist: EMI, Virgin Distribution

Single (7"): released on Virgin, Mar'82 by Virgin Records. Dist: EMI, Virgin Distribution

INSTANT FLASH.
Compact disc: released on Virgin, Oct'84 by Virgin Records. Dist: EMI, Virgin Distribution

I SECOND THAT EMOTION.
Tracks: / I second that emotion / Life in Tokyo.
Single (7"): by Old Gold Records. Dist: Lightning, Jazz Music, Spartan, Counterpoint

Single (7"): released on Hansa, Sep'82 by Hansa Records. Dist: Polygram

Single (12"): released on Hansa, Sep'82 by Hansa Records. Dist: Polygram

LIFE IN TOKYO.
Single (7"): released on Hansa, Sep'82 by Hansa Records. Dist: Polygram

Single (12"): released on Hansa, Sep'82 by Hansa Records. Dist: Polygram

NIGHTPORTER.
Single (7"): released on Virgin, Nov'82 by Virgin Records. Dist: EMI, Virgin Distribution

Single (12"): released on Virgin, Nov'82 by Virgin Records. Dist: EMI, Virgin Distribution

OBSCURE ALTERNATIVES.
Album: released on Fame (Ariola), Apr'84 by Music For Pleasure Records. Dist: EMI

Cassette: released on Fame (Ariola), Apr'84 by Music For Pleasure Records. Dist: EMI

OIL ON CANVAS.
Tracks: / Sons of pioneers / Cantonese boy / Visions of china / Ghosts / Voices raised in welcome, hands held in prayer / Nightporter / Still life in mobile homes / Methods of dance / Quiet life / Art of parties, The / Temple of dawn.
Compact disc: released on Virgin, Apr'85 by Virgin Records. Dist: EMI, Virgin Distribution

Video-cassette (VHS): released on Virgin, Jan'84 by Virgin Records. Dist: EMI, Virgin Distribution

Album: released on Virgin, Jun'83 by Virgin Records. Dist: EMI, Virgin Distribution

QUIET LIFE.
Album: released on Fame (Hansa), Sep'82 by Music For Pleasure Records. Dist: EMI

Cassette: released on Fame (Hansa), Sep'82 by Music For Pleasure Records. Dist: EMI

Single (7"): released on Hansa, Sep'82 by Hansa Records. Dist: Polygram

TIN DRUM.
Tracks: / Visions of China / Art of parties, The / Talking drum / Cantonese boy / Canton / Ghosts / Still life in mobile homes / Sons of pioneers.
Album: released on Virgin, Apr'86 by Virgin Records. Dist: EMI, Virgin Distribution

Cassette: released on Virgin, Apr'86 by Virgin Records. Dist: EMI, Virgin Distribution

Compact disc: released on Virgin, Apr'86 by Virgin Records. Dist: EMI, Virgin Distribution

Album: released on Virgin, Oct'81 by Virgin Records. Dist: EMI, Virgin Distribution

Album: released on Virgin, Oct'81 by Virgin Records. Dist: EMI, Virgin Distribution

VISIONS OF CHINA.
Single (7"): released on Virgin, Dec'84 by Virgin Records. Dist: EMI, Virgin Distribution

Single (12"): released on Virgin, Dec'84 by Virgin Records. Dist: EMI, Virgin Distribution

Japanese Music

BUDDIST CHANT.
Album: released on Lyrichord (USA), Oct'81 by Lyrichord Records (USA). Dist: Flexitron Distributors Ltd

HIROSHIMA MASSES,THE.
Album: released on Lyrichord (USA), Oct'81 by Lyrichord Records (USA). Dist: Flexitron Distributors Ltd

IMPERIAL COURT MUSIC OF JAPAN,THE.
Album: released on Lyrichord (USA), Oct'81 by Lyrichord Records (USA). Dist: Flexitron Distributors Ltd

JAPANESE FOLK MUSIC.
Album: released on Lyrichord (USA), Oct'81 by Lyrichord Records (USA). Dist: Flexitron Distributors Ltd

JAPANESE KABUTI NAGUATA MUSIC
Scenes from 'Dojoji' & 'Kagamijishi'.
Album: released on Lyrichord (USA), Oct'81 by Lyrichord Records (USA). Dist: Flexitron Distributors Ltd

JAPANESE KOTO CONSORT.
Album: released on Lyrichord (USA), Oct'81 by Lyrichord Records (USA). Dist: Flexitron Distributors Ltd

Album: released on Lyrichord (USA), Oct'81 by Lyrichord Records (USA). Dist: Flexitron Distributors Ltd

JAPANESE KOTO ORCHESTRA.
Album: released on Lyrichord (USA), Oct'81 by Lyrichord Records (USA). Dist: Flexitron Distributors Ltd

JAPANESE MASTERPIECES FOR THE KOTO.
Album: released on Lyrichord (USA), Oct'81 by Lyrichord Records (USA). Dist: Flexitron Distributors Ltd

JAPANESE MASTERPIECES FOR THE SHAKUHACHI.
Album: released on Lyrichord (USA), Oct'81 by Lyrichord Records (USA). Dist: Flexitron Distributors Ltd

Cassette: released on Lyrichord (USA), Aug'82 by Lyrichord Records (USA). Dist: Flexitron Distributors Ltd

JAPANESE NOH MUSIC.
Album: released on Lyrichord (USA), Oct'81 by Lyrichord Records (USA). Dist: Flexitron Distributors Ltd

JAPANESE SHAMISEN.
Album: released on Lyrichord (USA), Oct'81 by Lyrichord Records (USA). Dist: Flexitron Distributors Ltd

JAPANESE TEMPLE MUSIC.
Album: released on Lyrichord (USA), Oct'81 by Lyrichord Records (USA). Dist: Flexitron Distributors Ltd

JAPANESE TREASURERS.
Album: released on Lyrichord (USA), Oct'81 by Lyrichord Records (USA). Dist: Flexitron Distributors Ltd

JAPNESE KABUTI NAGUATA-SCENES FROM 'DOJOJI' & 'KAGAMIJISHI'.

JORURI-MUSIC OF THE JAPANESE BUNRAKU PUPPET THEATRE.
Album: released on Lyrichord (USA), Oct'81 by Lyrichord Records (USA). Dist: Flexitron Distributors Ltd

KOTO KUMUITA Classical song cycles by the great master composers of Japan.
Album: released on Lyrichord (USA), Oct'81 by Lyrichord Records (USA). Dist: Flexitron Distributors Ltd

SONGS FROM JAPAN various artists.
Cassette: released on RCA, Dec'79 by RCA Records. Dist: RCA, Roots, Swift, Wellard, Chris, I & B, Solomon & Peres Distribution

SOUL OF THE KOTO,THE.
Album: released on Lyrichord (USA), Oct'81 by Lyrichord Records (USA). Dist: Flexitron Distributors Ltd

SPIRITS OF SAMURAI.
Album: released on Lyrichord (USA), Oct'81 by Lyrichord Records (USA). Dist: Flexitron Distributors Ltd

TALES FROM...
Cassette: released on Anvil, Apr'80 Dist: Anvil

WHEN THE BRIGHTNESS COMES (Japan;Japanese solo Shakuhachi music).
Album: released on Orchid, Jan'85 Dist: Impetus Distribution, Orchid

ZEN,GOEIKA AND SHOMYO CHANTS.
Album: released on Lyrichord (USA), Oct'81 by Lyrichord Records (USA). Dist: Flexitron Distributors Ltd

Jap, Philip

BRAIN DANCE.
Single (7"): released on A&M, May'83 by A&M Records. Dist: Polygram

RED DOGS.
Single (7"): released on A&M, Feb'83 by A&M Records. Dist: Polygram

Single (12"): released on A&M, Feb'83 by A&M Records. Dist: Polygram

Jaqui

YOU MEAN EVERYTHING.
Single (7"): released on Code, Apr'84 by Code Records. Dist: Jetstar, EMI

Single (12"): released on Code, Apr'84 by Code Records. Dist: Jetstar, EMI

Jaramillo, Pepe

AN EVENING WITH.
Tracks: / Just for you / Love is in the air / Solitaire / Enterainer,The / It's impossible / How deep is your love / Breeze and I,The / That's when the music takes me / Don't stay away too long / Up, up and away / I only have eyes for you / Sing baby sing / Way we were,The / Maria / What a difference a day made / Tonight / Never on sunday / Laughter in the rain / Strangers in the night / She / Bimbo / My love / Old fashioned way,The / Rivers of Babylon / Distant Horizon / Fool on the hill,The.
Album: released on MFP, Jul'86 by EMI Records. Dist: EMI

Cassette: released on MFP, Jul'86 by EMI Records. Dist: EMI

..WITH HIS LATIN AMERICAN RHYTHMS.
Album: released on MFP, Sep'81 by EMI Records. Dist: EMI

Cassette: released on MFP, Sep'81 by EMI Records. Dist: EMI

Jara, Victor

MANIFIESTO.
Tracks: / Te Recuerdo Amanda / Canto Libre / Aquime quedo / Angelita huenuman / Ni chicha ni limona / La plegaria a un labrador / Cuando voy al trabajo / El derecho de vivir en paz / Vientos del pueblo / Manifiesto / La partida / Chile stadium.
Album: released on Conifer, Aug'86 by Conifer Records. Dist: Conifer

Jareba

ANOTHER STORY version.
Single (7"): released on Jade, Aug'82 by Jade Records. Dist: Jade

Jarmel,Maurice

LOVE'S A MANY SPLENDOURED THING.
Single (7"): released on Spin, Jan'85 by Symphola. Dist: Solomon & Peres Distribution

Jarmels

COMPLETE JARMELS,THE.
Album: released on Ace, Mar'86 by Ace Records. Dist: Pinnacle, Swift, Hotshot, Cadillac

Jarreau, Al

AL JARREAU.
Album: released on Disc AZ (France), Aug'84 Dist: Discovery

Cassette: released on Disc AZ (France), Aug'84 Dist: Discovery

ALL FLY HOME/THIS TIME.
Double cassette: released on WEA International, Nov'83 by WEA Records. Dist: WEA

BREAKIN' AWAY.
Compact disc: released on Warner Bros., '83 by Warner Bros Records. Dist: WEA

BREAKIN' AWAY.
Album: released on Warner Brothers, Aug'81 by Warner Bros Records. Dist: WEA

Cassette: released on Warner Brothers, Aug'81 by Warner Bros Records. Dist: WEA

Compact disc: released on Warner Brothers, '83 by Warner Bros Records. Dist: WEA

CLOSER TO YOUR LOVE.
Single (7"): released on WEA, Nov'81 by WEA Records. Dist: WEA

Single (12"): released on WEA, Nov'81 by WEA Records. Dist: WEA

GLOW.
Album: released on Reprise, Jul'77 by WEA Records. Dist: WEA

HIGH CRIME.
Tracks: / Raging waters / Imagination / Murphy's law / Tell me / After all / High crime / Let's pretend / Sticky Wicket / Love speaks louder than words / Fallin'.
Compact disc: released on WEA, Jan'85 by WEA Records. Dist: WEA

Album: released on WEA, Nov'84 by WEA Records. Dist: WEA

Cassette: released on WEA, Nov'84 by WEA Records. Dist: WEA

Compact disc: released on WEA, Nov'84 by WEA Records. Dist: WEA

IN LONDON.
Tracks: / Raging waters / Black and blues / I will be here for you / Let's pretend / High crime / Roof garden / Teach me tonight / We're in this love together.
Compact disc: released on WEA, Nov'85 by WEA Records. Dist: WEA

Video-cassette (VHS): released on WEA, Jun'86 by WEA Records. Dist: WEA

Video-cassette [Betamax]: released on WEA, Jun'86 by WEA Records. Dist: WEA

Album: released on WEA, Nov'85 by WEA Records. Dist: WEA

Cassette: released on WEA, Nov'85 by WEA Records. Dist: WEA

JARREAU.
Tracks: / Mornin' / Boogie down / I will be here for you / Save me / Step by step / Black and blues / Trouble in paradise / Not like this / Love is waiting.
Compact disc: released on WEA International, '84 by WEA Records. Dist: WEA

Album: released on WEA International, Apr'83 by WEA Records. Dist: WEA

Cassette: released on WEA International, Apr'83 by WEA Records. Dist: WEA

LET'S PRETEND.
Single (7"): released on Warner Bros., Jan'86 by Warner Bros Records. Dist: WEA

Single (12"): released on Warner Bros., Jan'86 by Warner Bros Records. Dist: WEA

LET'S PRETEND (LIVE).
Single (7"): released on Warner Bros., Sep'85 by Warner Bros Records. Dist: WEA

Single (12"): released on Warner Bros., Sep'85 by Warner Bros Records. Dist: WEA

L IS FOR LOVER.
Tracks: / Tell me what i gotta do / Says / Pleasure / Golden girl / Across the midnight sky / No ordinary romance / L is for lover / Real tight / L is for lover / No ordinary romance.
Album: released on WEA Int, Oct'86

Cassette: released on WEA Int, Oct'86

Compact disc: released on WEA Int, Oct'86

Single (7"): released on WEA Int, Oct'86

Single (12"): released on WEA Int, Oct'86

LOOK TO THE RAINBOW (LIVE).
Double Album: released on Warner Bros., May'77 by Warner Bros Records. Dist: WEA

MASQUERADE IS OVER, THE.
Album: released on Happy Bird (Germany), Jun'83 Dist: Polygram, IMS

Cassette: released on Happy Bird (Germany), Jun'83 Dist: Polygram, IMS

MOONLIGHTING.
Tracks: / Moonlighting / Golden girl (LP version).
Single (7"): released on WEA Int, Feb'87

Single (12"): released on WEA Int, Feb'87

MORNING/NOT LIKE THIS/ROOF GARDEN.
Single (12"): released on WEA, Apr'83 by WEA Records. Dist: WEA

RAGING WATERS.
Single (7"): released on Warner Bros., Apr'85 by Warner Bros Records. Dist: WEA

Single (12"): released on Warner Bros., Apr'85 by Warner Bros Records. Dist: WEA

REPLAY OF AL JARREAU.
Album: released on Sierra, Feb'85 by Sierra Records. Dist: WEA

Cassette: released on Sierra, Feb'85 by Sierra Records. Dist: WEA

SINGS BILL WITHERS.
Tracks: / Ain't no sunshine / Lean on me / Use me / Kissing my love / Grandma's hands / You / Lonely town, lonely street / That same love that made me laugh.
Album: released on Topline, Apr'87 by Charly Records. Dist: Charly Distribution

Cassette: released on Topline, Apr'87 by Charly Records. Dist: Charly Distribution

SPIRITS AND FEELINGS.
Album: released on Happy Bird (Germany), May'84 Dist: Polygram, IMS

TELL ME WHAT I GOTTA DO.
Tracks: / Tell me what I gotta do / Roof garden.
Single (7"): released on WEA Int, Apr'87

Single (12"): released on WEA Int, Apr'87

Single (12"): released on WEA Int, Nov'86

THIS TIME.
Album: released on WEA, Jun'80 by WEA Records. Dist: WEA

TROUBLE IN PARADISE/SAVE ME.
Single (7"): released on WEA Int, Jul'83

Single (12"): released on WEA Int, Jul'83

WE GOT BY.
Album: released on Reprise, Jun'77 by WEA Records. Dist: WEA

YOU.
Album: released on Platinum (W.Germany), Oct'85 Dist: Mainline

Cassette: released on Platinum (W.Germany), Oct'85 Dist: Mainline

Jarre, Jean Michel

CONCERTS IN CHINA.
Album: released on Polydor, May'82 by Polydor Records. Dist: Polygram, Polydor

Cassette: released on Polydor, May'82 by Polydor Records. Dist: Polygram, Polydor

Compact disc: released on Polydor, '83 by Polydor Records. Dist: Polygram, Polydor

EQUINOXE.
Compact disc: released on Polydor, '83 by Polydor Records. Dist: Polygram, Polydor

Album: released on Polydor, '78 by Polydor Records. Dist: Polygram, Polydor

Cassette: released on Polydor, '78 by Polydor Records. Dist: Polygram, Polydor

Compact disc: released on Polydor, '83 by Polydor Records. Dist: Polygram, Polydor

EQUINOXE (PART7/8).
Single (7"): released on Polydor, Jul'80 by Polydor Records. Dist: Polygram, Polydor

ESSENTIAL.
Compact disc: released on Polydor, '83 by Polydor Records. Dist: Polygram, Polydor

ESSENTIAL '76-'86, THE.
Compact disc: by Pacific Records (USA). Dist: Atlantic

ESSENTIAL, THE.
Album: released on Polydor, Oct'83 by Polydor Records. Dist: Polygram, Polydor

Compact disc: released on Polydor, Sep'84 by Polydor Records. Dist: Polygram, Polydor

FOURTH RENDEZ-VOUS.
Tracks: / Fourth rendez-vous / First rendez-vous / Rendez-vous IV (Special remix) / Rendez-vous IV (Original Mix) / (Moon Machine).
Single (7"): released on Disques Dreyfus, Oct'86 by Polydor Records. Dist: Polygram

Single (12"): released on Disques Dreyfus, Oct'86 by Polydor Records. Dist: Polygram

IN CONCERT LYON/HOUSTON.
Album: released on Polydor, Jul'87 by Polydor Records. Dist: Polygram, Polydor

Cassette: released on Polydor, Jul'87 by Polydor Records. Dist: Polygram, Polydor

JEAN-MICHEL JARRE IN CONCERT.
Compact disc: released on Dreyfus, Apr'87

MAGNETIC FIELDS.
Compact disc: released on Polydor, '83 by Polydor Records. Dist: Polygram, Polydor

Album: released on Polydor, May'81 by Polydor Records. Dist: Polygram, Polydor

Compact disc: released on Polydor, May'81 by Polydor Records. Dist: Polygram, Polydor

Cassette: released on Polydor, May'81 by Polydor Records. Dist: Polygram, Polydor

MAGNETIC FIELDS 2/MAGNETIC FIELDS 1.
Single (7"): released on Polydor, Jun'81 by Polydor Records. Dist: Polygram, Polydor

MAGNETIC FIELDS (PART 4).
Single (7"): released on Polydor, Nov'81 by Polydor Records. Dist: Polygram, Polydor

ORIENT EXPRESS/FISHING JUNKS.
Single (7"): released on Polydor, May'82 by Polydor Records. Dist: Polygram, Polydor

OXYGENE.
Compact disc: released on Polydor, '83 by Polydor Records. Dist: Polygram, Polydor

Album: released on Polydor, Aug'77 by Polydor Records. Dist: Polygram, Polydor

Cassette: released on Polydor, Aug'77 by Polydor Records. Dist: Polygram, Polydor

Compact disc: released on Polydor, '83 by Polydor Records. Dist: Polygram, Polydor

RENDEZVOUS.
Album: released on Polydor, Aug'86 by Polydor Records. Dist: Polygram, Polydor

Cassette: released on Polydor, Aug'86 by Polydor Records. Dist: Polygram, Polydor

Compact disc: released on Polydor, Aug'86 by Polydor Records. Dist: Polygram, Polydor

ZOOLOOK.
Tracks: / Ethnicolor / Diva / Zoolook / Wooloomooloo / Zoolookologie / Blah-blah / Ethnicolorll.
Compact disc: released on Disques Dreyfus, Nov'84 by Polydor Records. Dist: Polygram

Album: released on Polydor, Nov'84 by Polydor Records. Dist: Polygram, Polydor

Cassette: released on Polydor, Nov'84 by Polydor Records. Dist: Polygram, Polydor

Compact disc: released on Polydor, Nov'84 by Polydor Records. Dist: Polygram, Polydor

ZOOLOOKOLOGIE (REMIX).
Single (12"): released on Polydor, May'85 by Polydor Records. Dist: Polygram, Polydor

ZOOLOOK (REMIX).
Single (12"): released on Polydor, Jan'85 by Polydor Records. Dist: Polygram, Polydor

Jarre, Maurice

DOCTOR ZHIVAGO.
Album: released on Polydor, Jun'79 by Polydor Records. Dist: Polygram, Polydor

Virgin through EMI

DREAMSCAPE.
Compact disc: released on Sonic Atmospheres, '86 Dist: Target

LAWRENCE OF ARABIA Soundtrack (Jarre, Maurice & London Philharmonic Orchestra).
Album: released on Golden Guinea, '74 by PRT Records. Dist: PRT

LION OF THE DESERT (Jarre, Maurice & London Philharmonic Orchestra).
Album: released on RK, Jul'81

Jarrett, Keith

ARBOUR ZENA.
Tracks: / Dunes / Solara March / Mirrors.
Compact disc: released on ECM (Germany), Aug'85 by ECM Records. Dist: IMS, Polygram, Virgin through EMI

BACKHAND.
Album: released on Jasmine, Mar'83 by Jasmine Records. Dist: Counterpoint, Lugtons, Taylor, H.R., Wellard, Chris, Swift, Cadillac

BELONGING.
Tracks: / Spiral dance / Blossom / Long as you know you're living yours / Belonging / Windup, The / Solstice.
Compact disc: released on ECM (Germany), Jun'86 by ECM Records. Dist: IMS, Polygram, Virgin through EMI

BOP-BE.
Album: released on Jasmine, Jun'82 by Jasmine Records. Dist: Counterpoint, Lugtons, Taylor, H.R., Wellard, Chris, Swift, Cadillac

Cassette: released on Jasmine, Jun'82 by Jasmine Records. Dist: Counterpoint, Lugtons, Taylor, H.R., Wellard, Chris, Swift, Cadillac

CELESTIAL HAWK.
Cassette: released on ECM (Germany), Jul'85 by ECM Records. Dist: IMS, Polygram, Virgin through EMI

CHANGES.
Tracks: / Flying / Prism.
Compact disc: released on ECM (Germany), Oct'84 by ECM Records. Dist: IMS, Polygram, Virgin through EMI

COLOGNE CONCERT.
Compact disc: released on ECM (Germany) '83 by ECM Records. Dist: IMS, Polygram, Virgin through EMI

CONCERTS 3 LP digital box set.
Boxed set: released on ECM (Germany), Oct'82 by ECM Records. Dist: IMS, Polygram, Virgin through EMI

EYES OF THE HEART.
Tracks: / Eyes of the heart (part one) / Eyes of the heart (Part two).
Compact disc: released on ECM (Germany), Oct'85 by ECM Records. Dist: IMS, Polygram, Virgin through EMI

FACING YOU.
Tracks: / In front / Ritooria / Lalene / My lady: My child / Landscape for future earth / Starbright / Vapallia / Semblence.
Compact disc: released on ECM (Germany), Dec'85 by ECM Records. Dist: IMS, Polygram, Virgin through EMI

FORT YAWUH.
Album: released on Jasmine, Jun'82 by Jasmine Records. Dist: Counterpoint, Lugtons, Taylor, H.R., Wellard, Chris, Swift, Cadillac

Cassette: released on Jasmine, Jun'82 by Jasmine Records. Dist: Counterpoint, Lugtons, Taylor, H.R., Wellard, Chris, Swift, Cadillac

GURDJIEFF/SACRED HYMNS.
Tracks: / Reading of sacred books / Prayer & despair / Religious ceremony / Hymn / Orthodox hymn from Asia minor / Hymn for Good Friday / Hymn / Hymn for Easter Thursday / Hymn to the endless creator / Hymn from a great temple / Story of the resurrection of Christ, The / Holy affirming-holy denying-holy reconciling / Easter night procession / Meditation.
Compact disc: released on ECM (Germany), Jun'86 by ECM Records. Dist: IMS, Polygram, Virgin through EMI

INVOCATIONS/THE MOTH AND THE FLAME.
Tracks: / Invocations 1st-7th / Moth and the flame part 1-v, The.
Compact disc: released on EMI (Germany), Oct'85 by EMI Records. Dist: Conifer

MY SONG.
Tracks: / Questar / My song / Tabarka / Mandala / Journey home, The.
Compact disc: released on ECM (Germany), '84 by ECM Records. Dist: IMS, Polygram, Virgin through EMI

NUDE ANTS.
Tracks: / Chant of the soil / Innocence / Processional / Oasis / New dance / Sunshine song.
Compact disc: released on ECM (Germany), Jun'86 by ECM Records. Dist: IMS, Polygram, Virgin through EMI

SOLO CONCERTS.
Tracks: / Bremen, July 12, 1973 Part 1 / Bremen, July12, 1973, Part 2 / Lausanne, March 20, 1973.
Notes: Double compact disc
Compact disc: released on ECM (Germany), Jul'86 by ECM Records. Dist: IMS, Polygram, Virgin through EMI

SPHERES.
Tracks: / Spheres - 1st Movement / Spheres - 4th Movement / Spheres - 7th Movement / Spheres - 9th Movement.
Compact disc: released on ECM (Germany), Jul'86 by ECM Records. Dist: IMS, Polygram, Virgin through EMI

SPIRITS Volumes 1 & 2.
Album: released on ECM (Germany), Oct'86 by ECM Records. Dist: IMS, Polygram, Virgin through EMI

Compact disc: released on ECM (Germany), Oct'86 by ECM Records. Dist: IMS, Polygram, Virgin through EMI

STAIRCASE.
Tracks: / Staircase: Part 1; Part 2, Part 3 / Hourglass: Part 1, Part 2, / Sundial: Part 1, Part 2, Part 3 / Sand: Part 1, Part 2, Part 3.
Compact disc: released on ECM (Germany), Dec'85 by ECM Records. Dist: IMS, Polygram, Virgin through EMI

STANDARDS.
Cassette: released on ECM (Germany), Jun'84 by ECM Records. Dist: IMS, Polygram, Virgin through EMI

STANDARDS LIVE.
Tracks: / Stella by starlight / Wrong blues, The / Wrong blues, The / Falling in love with love / Too young to go steady / Way you look tonight, The / Old country, The.
Notes: This new album captures a stunning live performance of this highly celebrated trio in Paris during 1985. It includes such noteworthy compositions as 'Stella by Starlight' and 'The Way You Look Tonight' among others. Standards live, once again proves the subtle interplay of the trio which has often been compared to the legendary Bill Evans Trio. It throws new light on well known compositions from the 'Great American Songbook'. Personnel: Keith Jarrett
Album: released on ECM (Germany), Feb'86 by ECM Records. Dist: IMS, Polygram, Virgin through EMI

Compact disc: released on ECM (Germany), Feb'86 by ECM Records. Dist: IMS, Polygram, Virgin through EMI

STANDARDS VOL 1.
Album: released on ECM (Germany), Sep'83 by ECM Records. Dist: IMS, Polygram, Virgin through EMI

STANDARDS VOL 2.
Tracks: / So tender / Moon and sand / In love in vain / Never let me go / If i should lose you / I fall in love to easily.
Notes: IMS released Standards vol. 1 in September 1983 (ECM 1255). Volume 2 is from the same recording session with Jarrett ably supported by Gary Peacock and Jack Dejohnette.
Compact disc: released on ECM (Germany), May'85 by ECM Records. Dist: IMS, Polygram, Virgin through EMI

SURVIVOR'S SUITE.
Compact disc: released on ECM (Germany), Dec'85 by ECM Records. Dist: IMS, Polygram, Virgin through EMI

Cassette: released on ECM (Germany), Jul'85 by ECM Records. Dist: IMS, Polygram, Virgin through EMI

SURVIVORS SUITE.
Tracks: / Survivors suite, The / Beginning / Conclusion.

WORKS.
Tracks: / Country / Riootria / Journey, The / Staircase (part II) / String Quartet (2nd Movement) / Invocations / Nagoya part IIB (Encore).
Compact disc: released on ECM/Works (Germany), May'85 by ECM Records. Dist: IMS, Polygram, Virgin through EMI

Album: released on ECM (Germany), May'85 by ECM Records. Dist: IMS, Polygram, Virgin through EMI

Jarrett, Wayne

BILLY JEAN.
Single (12"): released on Kaya, May'84 by Kaya Records. Dist: Jetstar

BUBBLE UP.
Album: released on Wackies, Apr'84 by Wackies Records. Dist: Jetstar

CHIP IN.
Album: released on Greensleeves, Mar'82 by Greensleeves Records. Dist: BMG, Jetstar, Spartan

HOW CAN I LOVE ONE WOMAN.
Single (12"): released on Jedi, Sep'84 Dist: Jetstar

INNER CIRCLE.
Album: released on Ashantites, Mar'85 Dist: Jetstar

NICE AND EASY.
Single (12"): released on Jah Life, Jul'84 by Jah Life Records. Dist: Jetstar

SATTA DREAD.
Single (7"): released on Echo, Feb'82 by Vista Sounds. Dist: Jazz Music

YOUTH MAN.
Single (12"): released on Wackies, Apr'85 by Wackies Records. Dist: Jetstar

Jarrett, Winston

COME A ME.
Single (12"): released on Supertone, Sep'83 by Supertone Records. Dist: Jetstar Distribution

ROCKING VIBRATION.
Album: released on Culture Press, Mar'85 by Vista Sounds Records. Dist: Jetstar, Rough Trade

Jarrow 86

JARROW 86 Various Artists (Various Artists).
Notes: Track details not advised
Album: released on HHH Productions, Oct'86 by HHH Productions.

Jarvis, John

SO FA' SO GOOD.
Tracks: / Some kind of sunrise / Month of seasons, A / Best of both worlds / Scrumpy cider / Audrey / Can't turn my heart away / Framed in a still picture / Amber / Homecoming / Long awaited / Never delivered / Blue moon of Kentucky.
Album: released on MCA, Jul'87 by MCA Records. Dist: Polygram, MCA

Cassette: released on MCA, Jul'87 by MCA Records. Dist: Polygram, MCA

Compact disc: released on MCA, Jul'87 by MCA Records. Dist: Polygram, MCA

SOMETHING CONSTRUCTIVE.
Tracks: / Wide open spaces / Waiting / Solving a dream / Two moods / Dancing by candlelight / View from above, A / Southern hospitality / Something constructive / Long distances / Dancing by candlelight.
Album: released on MCA, Jul'87 by MCA Records. Dist: Polygram, MCA

Cassette: released on MCA, Jul'87 by MCA Records. Dist: Polygram, MCA

Compact disc: released on MCA, Jul'87 by MCA Records. Dist: Polygram, MCA

Jarvis, Steve

I DON'T GIVE A DAMN.
Single (7"): released on Marco Music, Jun'82

Jasmine Minks

1-2-3-4-5-6-7, ALL GOOD PREACHERS GO TO HEAVEN.
Album: released on Creation, Oct'84 Dist: Rough Trade, Cartel

COLD HEART.
Tracks: / Cold heart / World's no place / Forces network (AFM Version)* / You got me wrong*.
Single (7"): released on Creation, May'86 Dist: Rough Trade, Cartel

Single (12"): released on Creation, May'86 Dist: Rough Trade, Cartel

JASMINE MINKS.
Album: released on Creation, Jun'86 Dist: Rough Trade, Cartel

SUNSET.
Album: released on Creation, Oct'86 Dist: Rough Trade, Cartel

THINK.
Single (7"): released on Creation, Mar'84 Dist: Rough Trade, Cartel

WHAT'S HAPPENING.
Single (7"): released on Creation, Jun'85 Dist: Rough Trade, Cartel

WHERE TRAFFIC GOES.
Single (7"): released on Creation, Aug'84 Dist: Rough Trade, Cartel

Jason and the Scorchers

19TH NERVOUS BREAKDOWN.
Tracks: / 19th Nervous breakdown / Greetings from Nashville.
Single (7"): released on EMI America, Nov'86 by EMI Records. Dist: EMI

Single (12"): released on EMI America, Nov'86 by EMI Records. Dist: EMI

ABSOLUTELY SWEET MARIE.
Single (7"): released on EMI America, May'84 by EMI Records. Dist: EMI

Single (12"): released on EMI America, May'84 by EMI Records. Dist: EMI

FERVOR.
Album: released on EMI, Jun'84 by EMI Records. Dist: EMI

LOST AND FOUND.
Album: released on EMI, Feb'85 by EMI Records. Dist: EMI

Cassette: released on EMI, Feb'85 by EMI Records. Dist: EMI

SHOP IT AROUND.
Single (7"): released on EMI America, Jun'85 by EMI Records. Dist: EMI Deleted '86.

Special: released on EMI America, Jun'85 by EMI Records. Dist: EMI

Single (12"): released on EMI America, Jul'85 by EMI Records. Dist: EMI Deleted '86.

STILL STANDING.
Tracks: / Ghost town / Take me to your promised land / Golden ball and chain / Crashin' down / Shotgun blues / Good things come to those who wait / My heart still stands with you / 19th nervous breakdown / Ocean of doubt.
Compact disc: released on EMI America, Apr'87 by EMI Records. Dist: EMI

Album: released on EMI America, Oct'86 by EMI Records. Dist: EMI

Album: released on EMI America, Oct'86 by EMI Records. Dist: EMI

WHITE LIES.
Single (7"): released on EMI America, Mar'85 by EMI Records. Dist: EMI Deleted '86.

Single (12"): released on EMI America, Mar'85 by EMI Records. Dist: EMI Deleted '86.

Jason, David

CREATIVE RAGTIME VOL 6 (Jason, David and Neville Dickie).
Album: released on Euphonic, Apr'76 by Euphonic Records. Dist: Jazz Music, Swift

Jason, Kenny "Jammin"

CAN U DANCE.
Tracks: / Can U dance / Can U dance (dub inst).
Single (7"): released on Champion, Mar'87 by Champion Records. Dist: RCA

Single (12"): released on Champion, Mar'87 by Champion Records. Dist: RCA

CAN U DANCE (REMIX).
Tracks: / Can U dance (remix) / Can U dance (dub remix).
Single (12"): released on Champion, 13 Jun'87 by Champion Records. Dist: RCA

Jaspar, Bobby

4 FOUR SAX.
Album: released on Vogue Jazz, Apr'82

Jasper, Bobby

AT RONNIE SCOTTS - 1962 (Jaspar, Bobby Quartet).

NEW YORK 1956.
Album: released on Ace, Oct'86 by Ace Records. Dist: Pinnacle, Swift, Hotshot, Cadillac

Jaume, Andre

INCONTRU (Jaume, Andre Quartet/Tavagna).
Tracks: / Qualcosa di te / Que so voce muntagnole / U primu viaghju / U pinu tunisianu / Memoria / Paghella: Stamane e tre culombe / Paghella; Pecure cume le meie / Paghella: Veju nantu / Malamorte / Terzeti / Madrigale : Ecco bella / Ventu / Paghella u 26 di lugliu / Dopu ava.
Album:

Java

JAVANESE MUSIC FROM SURINAM.
Album: released on Lyrichord (USA), Oct'81 by Lyrichord Records (USA). Dist: Flexitron Distributors Ltd

MUSIC OF MYSTICAL ENCHANTMENT.
Album: released on Lyrichord (USA), Oct'81 by Lyrichord Records (USA). Dist: Flexitron Distributors Ltd

STREET MUSIC OF CENTRAL JAVA.
Album: released on Lyrichord, Oct'81 Dist: Roots

Jax

BITS AND PIECES.
Single (7"): released on Creole, Apr'80 by Creole Records. Dist: Rhino, PRT

Page 524

LICENSED TO CHILL.
Tracks: / Licensed to chill / Licensed to chill (dub mix).
Single (7"): released on Urban, Jul'87 by Polydor Records. Dist: Polygram

Single (12"): released on Urban, Jul'87 by Polydor Records. Dist: Polygram

Jaxon,Frankie

SATURDAY NIGHT SCRONTCH.
Album: released on Collectors Items, Feb'84 Dist: Jazz Music, Swift, Chris Wellard

Jayaraman,Lalguidi

SOUTH MEETS NORTH.
Album: released on Gramophone Co. of India, Feb'84 by Gramophone Company Of India, UK Branch. Dist: EMI, Sterns, Triple Earth

Cassette: released on Gramophone Co. of India, Feb'84 by Gramophone Company Of India, UK Branch. Dist: EMI, Sterns, Triple Earth

Jay Bee

TIME FOR LOVE.
Single (7"): released on JBM, May'85 Dist: T.One Records

Jay,David

NOTHING/ARMOUR.
Single (7"): released on 4AD, Oct'81 by 4AD Records. Dist: Rough Trade

Jay duck

JAY DUCK'S THEME (Jay duck and JD Revolution).
Single (7"): released on Magnet, Jul'83 by Magnet Records. Dist: BMG

Jay, Harry All Stars

LIQUIDATOR,THE/BOOK OF RULES.
Single (12"): released on Sunset, Jul'83 Dist: EMI

Jay, Julian

SUMMER LOVE.
Tracks: / Summer love / I don't think she's in love anymore.
Single (12"): released on Square Biz, Aug'86 Dist: Jetstar Distribution

Jayne,Lesley

ROCKING WITH MY RADIO/ISLE OF WIGHT.
Single (7"): released on BK, Jul'82

SAILING AWAY/HE'S TELLING ME LIES.
Single (7"): released on Miracle, Jan'83 by Gull Records. Dist: PRT Distribution

Jayston,Michael

HOW DO I LOVE THEE/CLASSICAL MEDLEY.
Single (7"): released on Flight, Nov'81 Dist: PRT

Jay & The Americans

GREATEST HITS:JAY & THE AMERICANS.
Compact disc: released on MCS Look Back, Jul'87

JAY AND THE AMERICANS.
Cassette: released on Timeless Treasures, Jul'86 Dist: Counterpoint Distribution

Jayvees

RIGHT BACK WHERE WE STARTED FROM.
Single (7"): released on V-Tone, Mar'81 by Relic. Dist: Swift

Jazateers

JAZZATEERS.
Album: released on Rough Trade, Jan'84 by Rough Trade Records. Dist: Rough Trade Distribution, Cartel Distribution

Jazawaki

DON'T PANIC.
Single (12"): released on Abstract, Dec'85 by Abstract. Dist: Pinnacle

Jazz

IT'S A WONDERFUL SOUND.
Album: released on Starfire, Apr'79

JAZZ '80 Various artists (Various Artists).
Double Album: released on Vogue Jazz (France), May'83

Double cassette: released on Vogue Jazz (France), May'83

JAZZ '81 Various artists (Various Artists).
Double Album: released on Vogue, Jul'81 Dist: Discovery, Jazz Music, PRT, Swift

Double cassette: released on Vogue, Jul'81 Dist: Discovery, Jazz Music, PRT, Swift

JAZZ AND COUNTRY IN THE MOVIES Original Soundtracks (Various Artists).
Album: released on SPI Milan (France), Aug'85 Dist: Silva Screen

JAZZ & CINEMA (Various Artists).
Album: released on CBS(France), Aug'84 by CBS Records. Dist: Conifer, Discovery, Swift

Cassette: released on CBS(France), Aug'84 by CBS Records. Dist: Conifer, Discovery, Swift

JAZZ FOR YOU - HOT, HEAVY & BLUE Various artists (Various Artists).
Double Album: released on Cambra, Mar'85 by Cambra Records. Dist: IDS, Conifer

Double cassette: released on Cambra, Mar'85 by Cambra Records. Dist: IDS, Conifer

JAZZ FROM CALIFORNIA Ben Pollack, Spanier, Brecht, Marsala.
Album: released on Jazz Archives, Jul'79 by Jazz Archives Records. Dist: Jazz Music

JAZZ FROM ST LOUIS 1924-1926 Various artists (Various Artists).
Album: released on Swaggie (Australia), Jan'83

JAZZ FROM THE GOLDEN ERA Various artists (Various Artists).
Album: released on VJM, Apr'79 by VJM (UK) Records. Dist: Swift

JAZZ GALA '80 Various artists (Various Artists).
Double Album: released on Gateway, Sep'83 by Kingdom. Dist: Pinnacle

JAZZ GIANTS PLAY LOVE SONGS Various artists (Various Artists).
Album: released on Cambra, Feb'85 by Cambra Records. Dist: IDS, Conifer

Cassette: released on Cambra, Feb'85 by Cambra Records. Dist: IDS, Conifer

JAZZ GIANTS, THE Various artists (Various Artists).
Album: released on Sackville, Apr'81 Dist: JSU, Jazz Music, Jazz Horizons, Cadillac Music, Celtic Music, Swift

JAZZ GOLD Various artists (Various Artists).
Special: released on Effects Gold, Nov'80 by Ronco Records. Dist: Ronco Records

Cassette: released on Effects Gold, '80 by Ronco Records. Dist: Ronco Records

JAZZ GUITAR ALBUM Burrell, Christian, Montgomery & other artists (Various Artists).
Double Album: released on Verve, Jan'76 by Phonogram Records. Dist: Polygram

JAZZ IN HARLEM (1926-31) Various artists (Various Artists).
Album: released on Arcadia, Apr'79 Dist: Cartel

JAZZ IN REVOLUTION Big Bands in the 1940's, The (Various Artists).
Tracks: / A-la-bridges / Dameron stomp / Saint, The / Elevation / Five o'clock shadow / Good jelly blues / Mingus fingers / Donna Lee / Perdido / Zonky / Tea for two / I can't get up the nerve / Mellow mood / Royal Roost / Chase, The.
Notes: Recorded in mono.
Album: released on New World (USA), Mar'87 by New World Records (USA). Dist: Conifer

JAZZ IN THE THIRTIES (1933-35) Various artists (Various Artists).
Double Album: released on WRC, Apr'76

JAZZ JUICE Various artists (Various Artists).
Album: released on Streetsounds, Sep'84

JAZZ LIFE Various artists (Various Artists).
Notes: Artists include: Charles Mingus, Eric Dolphy, Lucky Thompson, Booker Ervin, Max Roach etc.
Album: released on Candid, Dec'86 Dist: Counterpoint, Cadillac

JAZZ LIVE & RARE Various artists (Various Artists).
Notes: The first Esquire concert featuring Art Tatum, Coleman Hawkins, Billie Holiday etc. Recorded January 1944. Mono.
Compact disc: released on Delta, '86 by Delta Records. Dist: Target

JAZZ ME BLUES/THE CHICAGO CONNECTION (Jazz Me Blues & The Chicago Connection).
Tracks: / Jazz me blues / There'll be some changes made / Copenhagen / Trying to stop me crying / Bugle call rag / Downright disgusted / Milenberg joys / Wailin' blues / Baby won't you please come home? / Tillie's down town now / Fare thee well / My daddy rocks me (with one steady rock) / Prince of wails / I've found a new baby / Oh Suzanne, dust off that old pianna / Isn't there a little love (down in your heart for me)? / Barrel house stomp / I've found a new baby.
Album: released on Affinity, Apr'87 by Charly Records. Dist: Charly, Cadillac

JAZZ MEETING IN HOLLAND Various artists (Various Artists).
Notes: Artista include:Bud Freeman,J.McPartland,Ted Easton.
Album: released on Circle(USA), Jun'86 by Jazzology Records (USA). Dist: Jazz Music, Swift, Chris Wellard

JAZZ MONTEREY (1958-1980) Various artists (Various Artists).
Double Album: released on Palo Alto (Italy), Jan'85

JAZZ OFF THE AIR - VOL.1 Various artists (Various Artists).
Album: released on Spotlight, Jan'80 by PRT Records. Dist: PRT

JAZZ ON A SUMMERS DAY (Various Artists).
Notes: A documentary by Bert Stern of Newport Jazz Festival way back in 1958,featuring music varying from Lois Armstrong to R & B rocker Chuck Berry.1958 production. Recording time 85 minutes.
Video-cassette (VHS): released on Virgin Music, Oct'86 by Virgin Records. Dist: EMI

JAZZ PANORAMA OF THE TWENTIES - VOL.2 Charleston era, The (Various Artists).
Album: released on Joker, Apr'81 Dist: Cadillac, Zodiac Distribution, Jazz Horizons, Jazz Music, JSU, Celtic Music

JAZZ PIANO 2 Various artists (Various Artists).
Triple album / cassette: released on RCA (France), Nov'84 by RCA Records. Dist: Discovery

JAZZ PIANO ANTHOLOGY Various artists (Various Artists).
Tracks: / Sounds of africa / Keep out of the grass / Muscle shoals blues / Bear trap blues / In a mist / Honeysuckle rose / 57 Varieties / World is waiting for the sunrise(The) / Tiger rag / Liza / Boogie Woogie Prayer / Little joe from chicago / Didn't know what time it was,I / For miss black / Way back blues / Yearning for love / Round midnight / Thelonius / Back home again / Polka Dots and Moonbeams / In your own sweet way / Silver / Silver's blue / Billy boy / Billy boy / Pawn ticket / Splendid splinter / Port of call.
Notes: From 1 to 15:Historical recordings transcriptions of the originals on 78rpm. 2 LP set.
Album: released on CBS-Jazz Anthology USA, Jul'86 by CBS Records. Dist: CBS

JAZZ PIANO QUARTET (Jazz Piano Quartet).
Album: released on RCA (France), Feb'85 by RCA Records. Dist: Discovery

JAZZ REACTIVATION Various artists (Various Artists).
Album: released on Jazz Reactivation, Oct'84 Dist: PRT

Cassette: released on Jazz Reactivation, Oct'84 Dist: PRT

JAZZ SINGER Song from the film - Featuring Neil Diamond (Jazz Singer).
Album: released on Capitol, Nov'80 by Capitol Records. Dist: EMI

Double Album: released on Soundtrak, Oct'74

JAZZ SOUNDS OF THE TWENTIES Blues singers.
Album: released on Swaggie (Australia), Jan'83

JAZZ SOUNDS OF THE TWENTIES Dixieland bands.
Album: released on Swaggie (Australia), Jan'83

JAZZ SPECTACULAR.
Album: released on CBS, '84 by CBS Records. Dist: CBS

Cassette: released on CBS, '84 by CBS Records. Dist: CBS

JAZZ STREET (Various Artists).
Compact disc: released on CBS, May'87 by CBS Records. Dist: CBS

JAZZ WOMEN Feminist retrospective, A (Various Artists).
Double Album: released on Stash, Apr'81 Dist: Swift Distribution, Jazz Music Distribution, Jazz Horizons Distribution, Celtic Music Distribution, Cadillac, JSU Distribution, Zodiac Distribution

JAZZY LADIES Various artists (Various Artists).
Notes: O.C.I.= Oliver Crombie Imports.
Compact disc: released on Dunhill Compact Classics (USA), '86

Jazz Artists Guild

JAZZ LIFE, THE.
Album: released on Candid, May'86 Dist: Counterpoint, Cadillac

Jazz At...

JAZZ AT THE OPERA HOUSE various artists (Various Artists).
Album: released on CBS, Jul'83 by CBS Records. Dist: CBS

Cassette: released on CBS, Jul'83 by CBS Records. Dist: CBS

JAZZ AT THE PHILHARMONIC 1983 various artists (Various Artists).
Album: released on Pablo, Jul'83 by Pablo Records. Dist: Wellard, Chris, IMS-Polygram, BMG

JAZZ AT THE PHILHARMONIC,HARTFORD 1953 various artists (Various Artists).
Album: released on Pablo, Mar'85 by Pablo Records. Dist: Wellard, Chris, IMS-Polygram, BMG

Cassette: released on Pablo, Mar'85 by Pablo Records. Dist: Wellard, Chris, IMS-Polygram, BMG

JAZZ AT THE SANTA MONICA CIVIC various artists (Various Artists).
Album: released on Pablo, '82 by Pablo Records. Dist: Wellard, Chris, IMS-Polygram, BMG

JAZZ AT THE SANTA MONICA CIVIC 72 various artists (Various Artists).
Notes: Artists: Fetzgerald, Basie, Peterson, Eldridge.
Double compact disc: released on Pablo (USA), Jun'87 by Pablo Records (USA). Dist: Wellard, Chris, IMS-Polygram, BMG

Jazzateers

PRESSING ON.
Single (12"): released on Stampede, Jun'85 Dist: Rough Trade Distribution

SHOW ME THE DOOR/SIXTEEN REASONS.
Single (7"): released on Rough Trade, Jul'83 by Rough Trade Records. Dist: Rough Trade Distribution, Cartel Distribution

Jazz At The Philharmonic

AT THE MONTREUX JAZZ FESTIVAL 1975.
Album: released on Pablo (USA), '82 by Pablo Records (USA). Dist: Wellard, Chris, IMS-Polygram, BMG

Cassette: released on Pablo, '82 by Pablo Records. Dist: Wellard, Chris, IMS-Polygram, BMG

EXCITING BATTLE,STOCKHOLM '55,THE.
Album: released on Pablo (USA), '82 by Pablo Records (USA). Dist: Wellard, Chris, IMS-Polygram, BMG

Cassette: released on Pablo (USA), '82 by Pablo Records (USA). Dist: Wellard, Chris, IMS-Polygram, BMG

HARTFORD 1953.
Compact disc: released on Pablo (USA), Apr'87 by Pablo Records (USA). Dist: Wellard, Chris, IMS-Polygram, BMG

LIVE AT THE NICHIGEKI THEATRE,TOKYO.
Double Album: released on Pablo (USA), '82 by Pablo Records (USA). Dist: Wellard, Chris, IMS-Polygram, BMG

Double cassette: released on Pablo (USA), '82 by Pablo Records (USA). Dist: Wellard, Chris, IMS-Polygram, BMG

Jazz Band Ball

JAZZ BAND BALL VOL.12 various artists (Various Artists).
Album: released on Swaggie (Australia), Jan'83

Jazz Best

JAZZ BEST various artists (Various Artists).
Album: released on Verve, Apr'84 by Phonogram Records. Dist: Polygram

JAZZ BEST 20 immortal jazz standars (Original artists).
Compact disc: released on The Compact Collection, Sep'87 by Conifer Records. Dist: Conifer Distribution

JAZZ BEST VOL.2 various artists (Various Artists).
Album: released on Verve (Holland), Jul'84 by Phonogram Records. Dist: Polygram

Cassette: released on Verve (Holland), Jul'84 by Phonogram Records. Dist: Polygram

Jazz Butcher

CONSPIRACY.
Album: released on Glass, Oct'86 by Glass Records. Dist: Nine Mile, Rough Trade, Red Rhino, Play It Again Sam

Cassette: released on Glass, Oct'86 by Glass Records. Dist: Nine Mile, Rough Trade, Red

Rhino, Play It Again Sam

CONSPIRACY (EP) (Jazz Butcher Versus Max Eider).

HARD.
Tracks: / Hard / Grooving in the bus lane.
Single (7"): released on Glass, Mar'86 by Glass Records. Dist: Nine Mile, Rough Trade, Red Rhino, Play It Again Sam

Single (12"): released on Glass, Mar'86 by Glass Records. Dist: Nine Mile, Rough Trade, Red Rhino, Play It Again Sam

LIVE IN HAMBURG.
Album: released on Rebel, Dec'85 Dist: PRT

ANGELS.
Tracks: / Angels / Rebecca wants her bike back / Mersey*.
Single (7"): released on Glass, Nov'86 by Glass Records. Dist: Nine Mile, Rough Trade, Red Rhino, Play It Again Sam

Single (12"): released on Glass, Nov'86 by Glass Records. Dist: Nine Mile, Rough Trade, Red Rhino, Play It Again Sam

Jazz Classics

JAZZ CLASSICS VOLUME 1- NEW ORLEANS various artists.
Album: released on BBC, Feb'86 by BBC Records & Tapes. Dist: EMI, PRT, Pye

Cassette: released on BBC, Feb'86 by BBC Records & Tapes. Dist: EMI, PRT, Pye

JAZZ CLASSICS VOLUME 2 - CHICAGO various artists (Various Artists).
Album: released on BBC, Feb'86 by BBC Records & Tapes. Dist: EMI, PRT, Pye

Cassette: released on BBC, Feb'86 by BBC Records & Tapes. Dist: EMI, PRT, Pye

JAZZ CLASSICS VOLUME 3 - NEW YORK various artists (Various Artists).
Album: released on BBC, Feb'86 by BBC Records & Tapes. Dist: EMI, PRT, Pye

Cassette: released on BBC, Feb'86 by BBC Records & Tapes. Dist: EMI, PRT, Pye

Jazz Club

JAZZ CLUB various artists (Various Artists).
Album: released on Club, Aug'84 by Phonogram Records. Dist: Polygram

Cassette: released on Club, Aug'84 by Phonogram Records. Dist: Polygram

JAZZ CLUB 2 (Various Artists).
Album: released on Club, May'85 by Phonogram Records. Dist: Polygram

Cassette: released on Club, May'85 by Phonogram Records. Dist: Polygram

Jazz Collection

JAZZ COLLECTION various artists.
Notes: Artist incl: Woody Herman & his Orchestra, Duke Ellington & his Orchestra, Louis Armstrong, Tommy Dorsey & his Orchestra, Glenn Miller & his Orchestra. MONO.
Album: released on Deja Vu, Jul'86 by Deja Vu Records. Dist: Counterpoint Distribution, Record Services Distribution (Ireland)

Cassette: released on Deja Vu, Jul'86 by Deja Vu Records. Dist: Counterpoint Distribution, Record Services Distribution (Ireland)

Jazz Couriers

LAST WORD.
Album: released on Jasmine, Dec'83 by Jasmine Records. Dist: Counterpoint, Lugtons, Taylor, H.R., Wellard, Chris, Swift, Cadillac

THEME, THE.
Album: released on Jasmine, Feb'83 by Jasmine Records. Dist: Counterpoint, Lugtons, Taylor, H.R., Wellard, Chris, Swift, Cadillac

Jazz Dance

JAZZ DANCE various artists (Various Artists).
Tracks: / It's only paper moon / Jumpin' at the woodside / Sweet and lovely / Waltz i blew for yew / Sing, sing, sing / Bundle o' funk / Nature boy / World is waiting for the sunrise,The / Jitterbug waltz / Take the'A' Train / It's only paper moon.
Album: released on Pablo (USA), Dec'85 by Pablo Records (USA). Dist: Wellard, Chris, IMS-Polygram, BMG

JAZZ DANCE 1 Various artists (Various Artists).
Tracks: / Terrible T / Triple threat / Hold it / Love me or leave me / My baby just cares for me / Another one / Right down front / Tippin / Fever / Kidney stew.
Album: released on Atlantis, Jan'87 by Charly Records. Dist: Charly

Cassette: released on Atlantis, Jan'87 by Charly Records. Dist: Charly

JAZZ DANCE 1 (CD) (Various Artists).
Tracks: / Triple threat / Hold it / Love me or leave me / Another one / My baby just cares for me / Right down front / Fever / Kidney stew / Tippin / Boom boom / Kinda dukish (a)\(b) Rockin' in rhythm / Roof garden / Terrible T.
Notes: * Licensed from Charly International APS; ** Licensed from King Gusto Records; *** Licensed from Bethlehem Records; **** Licensed from Corky Hale.
Compact disc: released on Charly, Apr'87 by Charly Records. Dist: Charly, Cadillac

Jazzet Cinema

JAZZET CINEMA Various artists (Various Artists).
Tracks: / Singin' in the rain / All that jazz / Laura / On green dolphin street / Girl talk / Cheek to Cheek / Somewhere / Trolley song(The) / Way you look tonight(The) / Whistle while you work / People / Autumn leaves / Stormy weather / Who's afraid of the big bad wolf.
Album: released on CBS, Jul'86 by CBS Records. Dist: CBS

Cassette: released on CBS, Jul'86 by CBS Records. Dist: CBS

Jazz Festival

JAZZ FESTIVAL ALL STARS various artists (Various Artists).
Album: released on Jath, Dec'79 Dist: Jazz Horizons

Jazz Fiddlers

BRAG.
Album: released on Wam, May'87

Jazz Giants

JAZZ GIANTS Jazz Giants.
Album: released on Giants of Jazz, Jun'86 by Hasmick Promotions Ltd.. Dist: Counterpoint, Jazz Music, Taylors, Swift, Mainline, Wellard, Chris

Jazz Gillum

JAZZ GILLUM 1938-47.
Album: released on Travellin' Man, Jan'86 Dist: Jazz Music

Jazz Grass Ensemble

TICO BANJO.
Compact disc:

Jazz Hipsters

TENDER TRAP, THE.
Tracks: / Tender trap, The.
Single (7"): released on Axis, Jan'86 by Red Rhino Records. Dist: Cartel

Jazz & Hot Dance

JAZZ & HOT DANCE IN AUSTRALIA 1925-50 (Various Artists).
Album: released on Harlequin, Sep'85 by Harlequin Records. Dist: Swift, Jazz Music, Wellard, Chris, IRS, Taylor, H.R.

JAZZ & HOT DANCE IN CANADA 1916-1949 (Various Artists).
Album: released on Harlequin, May'86 by Harlequin Records. Dist: Swift, Jazz Music, Wellard, Chris, IRS, Taylor, H.R.

JAZZ & HOT DANCE IN CZECHOSLOVAKIA 1910-1946 (Various Artists).
Album: released on Harlequin, Jul'85 by Harlequin Records. Dist: Swift, Jazz Music, Wellard, Chris, IRS, Taylor, H.R.

JAZZ & HOT DANCE IN DENMARK 1909-1953 Various artists (Various Artists).
Notes: Artists: Lumbye, Cornelius & Schmidt, Waldemar Elberg, Otto Lington, Kat Julian,Erik Tuxen, Benny Carter/Ewans, Anker Skjoldborg, Roger Henrichsen, Leon Abbey, Svend Asmussen, Valaida Snow, Kordt Sisters, Harlem Kidies, Peter Rasmussen, Adrian Bentzen. MONO

Album: released on Harlequin, Jun'86 by Harlequin Records. Dist: Swift, Jazz Music, Wellard, Chris, IRS, Taylor, H.R.

JAZZ & HOT DANCE IN FINLAND 1929-1950 (Various Artists).
Album: released on Harlequin, Apr'85 by Harlequin Records. Dist: Swift, Jazz Music, Wellard, Chris, IRS, Taylor, H.R.

JAZZ & HOT DANCE IN INDIA VOL 4 1926-44 (Various Artists).
Album: released on Harlequin, Feb'85 by Harlequin Records. Dist: Swift, Jazz Music, Wellard, Chris, IRS, Taylor, H.R.

JAZZ & HOT DANCE IN MARTINIQUE 1929-1950 (Various Artists).
Album: released on Harlequin, Jul'85 by Harlequin Records. Dist: Swift, Jazz Music, Wellard, Chris, IRS, Taylor, H.R.

JAZZ & HOT DANCE IN SPAIN 1915-1947 Various artists (Various Artists).
Album: released on Harlequin, Jan'87 by Harlequin Records. Dist: Swift, Jazz Music, Wellard, Chris, IRS, Taylor, H.R.

JAZZ & HOT DANCE IN THE NETHERLANDS 1910-1950 (Various Artists).
Album: released on Harlequin, May'86 by Harlequin Records. Dist: Swift, Jazz Music, Wellard, Chris, IRS, Taylor, H.R.

Jazz Incorporated

WALKIN' ON.
Album: released on Dragon, Jun'86 by Dragon Records. Dist: Jazz Music, Projection, Cadillac

Album: released on Dragon, Jul'83 by Dragon Records. Dist: Jazz Music, Projection, Cadillac

Jazz Insects

GHOST TRAIN/ELEPHANTS.
Single (7"): released on Rococco, Mar'82 Dist: Pinnacle

Jazz Juice

JAZZ JUICE Various artists (Various Artists).
Notes: Artists include:Art Blakey,Miles Davis,Quartette Tres Bien,Airto,Gilberto Gil, Eddie Jefferson,Sergio Mendes.
Album: released on Streetsounds, Nov'85

Compact disc: released on Streetsounds, Nov'85

JAZZ JUICE.
Album: released on Streetsounds, Aug'85

JAZZ JUICE 2 Various artists (Various Artists).
Notes: Artists include:John Hendricks,Dianne Schuur,Pat Longo,Marcos Valle,Dirty Dozen Brass Band,Last Poets,Carmen McCrae,Oscar Brown jnr,Wood Herman Orchestra.
Album: released on Streetsounds, Jun'86

Cassette: released on Streetsounds, Jun'86

JAZZ JUICE 3 Various artists (Various Artists).
Album: released on Streetsounds, Sep'86

Cassette: released on Streetsounds, Sep'86

JAZZ JUICE 4 Various artists (Various Artists).
Album: released on Streetsounds, Dec'86

Cassette: released on Streetsounds, Dec'86

JAZZ JUICE 5 (Various Artists).
Album: released on Streetsounds, Jul'87

Cassette: released on Streetsounds, Jul'87

Jazz Messengers

AT THE CAFE BOHEMIA VOL.1.
Cassette: released on Blue Note, Apr'87 by EMI Records. Dist: EMI

Album: released on Blue Note, Apr'87 by EMI Records. Dist: EMI

AT THE CAFE BOHEMIA VOL.2.
Tracks: / Like someone in love / Yesterdays / Avila & Tequila / Sportin'crowd / I waited for you / Just one of those things* / Hanks symphony* / Gone with the wind.
Notes: This historic group(Art Blakely,Horace Silver,Hank Mobley,Denny Dorham and Doug Watkins) almost single-handedly develop modern hard bop and blue note sound.On this second album of their historic appearance at New York's Cafe Bohemia in 1955,they explore a variety of material from the cookin'Latin rythms to 'Avila And Tequila'to the bop classic 'Sportin' Crowd'to the standard ballards such as 'Yesterdays'.This live session sounds as fresh and vital as it did 30 years ago,when it set the trend for a new jazz sound that is still in force today.Produced by Alfred Lion.
Album: released on Blue Note, May'86 by EMI Records. Dist: EMI

Compact disc: released on Manhattan-Blue Note, May'87 by EMI America Records (USA). Dist: EMI

HORACE SILVER & THE JAZZ MESSENGERS (Jazz Messengers & Horace Silver).

NIGHT AT CAFE BOHEMIA WITH THE JAZZ MESSENGERS, A Volume 1.
Tracks: / Soft winds / Theme, The / Minor's holiday / Alone together / Prince Albert / Lady bird / What's new? / Decifering the message.
Compact disc: released on Manhattan, Jul'87 by EMI Records. Dist: EMI

Compact disc: released on Manhattan-Blue Note, Aug'87 by EMI America Records (USA). Dist: EMI

NIGHT IN TUNISIA, A (see Blakey, Art).

Jazz O'Maniacs

VOLUME 2.
Album: released on Stomp Off, Jun'86 by Stomp Off Records. Dist: Jazz Music Distribution

Jazz Singer

JAZZ SINGER Original Soundtrack.
Video-cassette (VHS): released on Thorn-Emi, Jan'84

Jazz Sluts

MAKING WAVES.
Tracks: / Marching dust / Morning after(The) / Roger Roger / Astral jogging / Riffers paradise / Seven sisters / Snake dance / H.H Boogie / Madagasca.
Compact disc: released on Coda, May'86 by Coda Records. Dist: Pinnacle, Cartel, WEA, Roots

Album: released on Coda, Oct'85 by Coda Records. Dist: Pinnacle, Cartel, WEA, Roots

Cassette: released on Coda, Oct'85 by Coda Records. Dist: Pinnacle, Cartel, WEA, Roots

Jazz Studio

JAZZ STUDIO 1 (Various Artists).
Album: released on Jasmine, Sep'83 by Jasmine Records. Dist: Counterpoint, Lugtons, Taylor, H.R., Wellard, Chris, Swift, Cadillac

JAZZ STUDIO TWO (Various Artists).
Album: released on Jasmine, Dec'83 by Jasmine Records. Dist: Counterpoint, Lugtons, Taylor, H.R., Wellard, Chris, Swift, Cadillac

Jazztet

MOMENT TO MOMENT.
Notes: With Art Farmer and Benny Golson.
Compact disc: released on Soul Note (Italy), '86 Dist: Harmonia Mundi Distributors

VOICES ALL.
Notes: With Art Farmer and Benny Golson.
Compact disc: released on Toshiba-EMI, '86

Jazz Warriors

OUT OF MANY ONE PEOPLE.
Tracks: / Warrors / In reference to our forefathers fathers dreams / Minor groove / Saint Maurice (of Aragon) / Many pauses.
Album: released on Antilles, Aug'87 by Island Records. Dist: Polygram

Cassette: released on Antilles, Aug'87 by Island Records. Dist: Polygram

Compact disc: released on Antilles, Aug'87 by Island Records. Dist: Polygram

Jazzy

WIDE-EYED BOY.
Tracks: / Wide-eyed boy / Tuesday.
Single (7"): released on Our own, Jan'87

Jazzy Jeff

GIRLS ARE NOTHING BUT TROUBLE (Jazzy Jeff & Fresh Prince).
Tracks: / Girls are nothing but trouble (Re-Mix) / Girls are nothing but trouble (Original mix).
Single (7"): released on Champion, Sep'86 by Champion Records. Dist: RCA

Single (12"): released on Champion, Sep'86 by Champion Records. Dist: RCA

KING HEROIN (DON'T MESS WITH HEROIN).
Single (7"): by Zomba Records. Dist: RCA

Single (12"): released on Jive Electro, Apr'85 by Zomba Records. Dist: RCA

MIX SO I CAN GO CRAZY.
Single (7"): released on Jive, Sep'85 by Zomba Records. Dist: RCA, PRT, CBS

Single (12"): released on Jive, Jul'85 by Zomba Records. Dist: RCA, PRT, CBS

ON FIRE.
Album: released on Jive, Nov'85 by Zomba Records. Dist: RCA, PRT, CBS

Cassette: released on Jive, Nov'85 by Zomba Records. Dist: RCA, PRT, CBS

J.B.'s

GRUNT (THE).
Tracks: / Grunt (The) (pt.1) / Grunt (The) (pt.2).
Single (7"): released on King (USA), Mar'87 by Gusto Records. Dist: Gusto Distribution, IMS, Swift

J.B's Allstars

ALPHABET ARMY.
Tracks: / Alphabet army / Alarm.
Single (7"): released on 2-Tone, Jan'86 by Chrysalis Records. Dist: Polygram

Single (12"): released on 2-Tone, Jan'86 by Chrysalis Records. Dist: Polygram

BACKFIELD IN MOTION.
Single (7"): released on RCA, Jan'84 by RCA Records. Dist: RCA, Roots, Swift, Wellard, Chris, I & B, Solomon & Peres Distribution

Single (12"): released on RCA, Jan'84 by RCA Records. Dist: RCA, Roots, Swift, Wellard, Chris, I & B, Solomon & Peres Distribution

ONE MINUTE EVERY HOUR.
Single (7"): released on RCA, Sep'83 by RCA Records. Dist: RCA, Roots, Swift, Wellard, Chris, I & B, Solomon & Peres Distribution

Single (12"): released on RCA, Sep'83 by RCA Records. Dist: RCA, Roots, Swift, Wellard, Chris, I & B, Solomon & Peres Distribution

SIGN ON THE DOTTED LINE.
Single (7"): released on RCA, May'84 by RCA Records. Dist: RCA, Roots, Swift, Wellard, Chris, I & B, Solomon & Peres Distribution

Single (12"): released on RCA, May'84 by RCA Records. Dist: RCA, Roots, Swift, Wellard, Chris, I & B, Solomon & Peres Distribution

J.C.M.B

ACNE GEL AND BRYLCREAM.
Tracks: / Dusty amplifiers / Crazy yo-yo song / Anyone seen my fuzzbox? / Extract's from Mit's special radio show / Up the tree house / Butlins at bognor / Why am I alone / Cassette 50 is crap / I slept in a haystack / Got chucked out of roy's caravan.
Notes: This four-piece British band originated in Hastings.Their original and current line-up is:'Jumbo'John-Vocals,Guitar;'Collossal'Criss-Bass,Vocals;'Mega'Mit - Keys,Vocals;'Big'Bruce-Drums;Vocals. "Acne and Brylcream"is their debut album,which reflects on their past and pres- ent experience of life.The band was formed when all found themselves together atthe same school and then they got to know each other.They started recording at John's house about 1983,andfinally decided to release "Acne Gel and Brylcream" in 1986.John was born in Hackney,London,Mit was born in Canada and Chris and Bruce were born in Hastings.
Album: released on Soft Cushion, Mar'86 by Soft Cushion Records. Dist: Soft Cushion

Cassette: released on Soft Cushion, Mar'86 by Soft Cushion Records. Dist: Soft Cushion

J, David

CROCODILE TEARS AND THE VELVET COSH.
Album: released on Glass, Mar'85 by Glass Records. Dist: Nine Mile, Rough Trade, Red Rhino, Play It Again Sam

DAVID J ON GLASS.
Cassette: released on Glass, Mar'86 by Glass Records. Dist: Nine Mile, Rough Trade, Red Rhino, Play It Again Sam

Album: released on Glass, Mar'86 by Glass Records. Dist: Nine Mile, Rough Trade, Red Rhino, Play It Again Sam

ETIQUETTE OF VIOLENCE.
Album: released on Situation 2, Nov'83 Dist: Cartel, Pinnacle

Album: released on Situation 2, Oct'83 Dist: Cartel, Pinnacle

I CAN'T SHAKE THIS SHADOW OF FEAR.
Single (7"): released on Glass, Oct'84 by Glass Records. Dist: Nine Mile, Rough Trade, Red Rhino, Play It Again Sam

Single (12"): released on Glass, Oct'84 by Glass Records. Dist: Nine Mile, Rough Trade, Red Rhino, Play It Again Sam

PROMISED LAND (J, David & J. Walkers).
Single (7"): released on Glass, Dec'83 by Glass Records. Dist: Nine Mile, Rough Trade, Red Rhino, Play It Again Sam

Single (12"): released on Glass, Dec'83 by Glass Records. Dist: Nine Mile, Rough Trade, Red Rhino, Play It Again Sam

V FOR VENDETTA.
Single (12"): released on Glass, Jun'84 by Glass Records. Dist: Nine Mile, Rough Trade, Red Rhino, Play It Again Sam

J.D. & Dallas

KEEP IT COUNTRY.
Album: released on Igus, Oct'81 by Klub. Dist: PRT, Musac Distribution Ltd (Scotland)

Jealous

ANOTHER BROKEN HEART.
Single (7"): released on KA, Jul'83

Jealous Girl

JEALOUS GIRL.
Single (7"): released on Zilch, May'82 by Zilch Records. Dist: Stage One

THREE DAYS AND RIKKI.
Single (7"): released on Zilch, Apr'82 by Zilch Records. Dist: Stage One

Jeanette

CRUSHED NICOTINE VIBRATO.
Single (7"): released on Survival, Jun'84 by Survival Records. Dist: Backs, Cartel Distribution

HAPPENING, THE.
Single (7"): released on Artic, Oct'84

HUM.
Album: released on Premonition, Nov'84 by Survival Records. Dist: Backs, Cartel

IN THE MORNING.
Single (12"): released on Survival, May'83 by Survival Records. Dist: Backs, Cartel Distribution

LADY BLUE.
Single (12"): released on Premonition, Jul'85 by Survival Records. Dist: Backs, Cartel

Jeanmaire, Zizi

ZIZI JEANMAIRE.
Album: released on Disc AZ (France), Aug'84 Dist: Discovery

Jeanneke Organ

SOUND OF JEANNEKE.
Album: released on Joy, '74 by President Records. Dist: Jazz Music, Swift, President Distribution

Jeannie's Beau

HAUNTING MY HOUSE.
Tracks: / Haunting my house / Love is the only way.
Single (7"): released on Sedition, Oct'86 Dist: PRT

Single (12"): released on Sedition, Oct'86 Dist: PRT

Jean Pierre & Vicky

LA MEME CHOSE.
Single (12"): released on Battersea, Aug'83 by Battersea Records. Dist: Pinnacle

Jeddah

ELEANOR RIGBY.
Single (7"): released on Death, Nov'83 by Death Records. Dist: Death, ILA

Jedson,Jon

JON,JEDSON JOURNEY,THE.
Album: released on President, Jul'79 by President Records. Dist: Taylors, Spartan

LET'S MAKE THE BEST OF TODAY.
Album: released on President, '79 by Presiden Records. Dist: Taylors, Spartan

MORE THAN EASY COUNTRY.
Cassette: released on Chevron, Nov'84 Dist: Multiple Sound Distributors

Jeep

FACTORY/FACTORY RE-VISITED(DISCO MIX).
Single (7"): released on Airport, Jul'83 Dist: Airport

HAPPY WANDERER/DO IT RIGHT.
Single (7"): released on Rough Trade, May'82 by Rough Trade Records. Dist: Rough Trade Distribution, Cartel Distribution

Jeeves

JEEVES-A GENTLEMAN'S PERSONAL GENTLEMAN various artists (Various Artists).
Cassette: released on Argo (Spokenword), Jul'82 by Decca Records. Dist: Polygram

JEEVES AND THE YULETIDE SPIRIT various artists (Various Artists).
Cassette: released on Talking Tape, '84

JEEVES STORIES various artists (Various Artists).
Cassette: released on Pickwick, '83 by Pickwick Records. Dist: Pickwick Distribution, Prism Leisure Distribution, Lugtons

Jeff and co.

SCRUFFY'S SONG/KNOCKING AT THE DOOR.
Single (7"): released on Sherpa, Nov'82 Dist: Stage One

Jefferson Airplane

2400 FULTON STREET The CD Collection.
Tracks: / It's no secret (Beginnings) / Come up the years (Beginnings) / My best friend (Beginnings) / Somebody to love (Beginnings) / Comin' back to me (Beginnings) / Embryonic journey (Beginnings) / She has funny cars (Beginnings) / Plastic fantastic lover (Psychedelia) / Wild tyme (Psychedelia) / Ballad of you & me & Pooneil (Psychedelia0 / Small package of value will come to you shortly (Psychedelia / White rabbit (Psychedelia) / Won't you try Saturday afternoon (Psychedelia) / Lather (Psychedelia) / We can be together (Revolution) / Crown of creation (Revolution) / Mexico (Revolution) / Wooden ships (Revolution) / Rejoyce (Revolution) / Volunteers (Revolution) / Pretty as you feel (Airplane parts) / Martha (Airplane parts) / Today (Airplane parts) / Third week in the Chelsea (airplane parts) / Let's get together (Beginnings) / Blues from an airplane (Beginnings) / J.P.P. MC step B. blues / Fat angel (Psychedelia) / Last wall of the castle (Psychedelia) / Greasy heart (Psychedelia) / Have you seen the saucers (Revolution) / Eat starch mom (Revolution) / Good shepherd (Airplane parts) / Eskimo blue day / Levi commercials, The (Airplane parts).
Compact disc: released on RCA, Jul'87 by RCA Records. Dist: RCA, Roots, Swift, Wellard, Chris, I & B, Solomon & Peres Distribution

Album: released on RCA, Jul'87 by RCA Records. Dist: RCA, Roots, Swift, Wellard, Chris, I & B, Solomon & Peres Distribution

Cassette: released on RCA, Jul'87 by RCA Records. Dist: RCA, Roots, Swift, Wellard, Chris, I & B, Solomon & Peres Distribution

AFTER BATHING AT BAXTERS.
Tracks: / Streetmasse:The ballad of you & me & Pooneil / Streetmasse:A small package of value will come to you,short! / Streetmasse:Young girl sunday blues / War is over:Martha, The / War is over:Wild tyme, The / Hymn to an older generation:The last wall of the castle / Hymn to an older generation:Rejoice / How suite is it:watch her ride / How suite is it:Spare chaynge / Shizo Forest love suite:Two heads / Shizo Forest love suite:Won't you try / Shizo Forest love suite:Saturday afternoon.
Album: released on RCA (Germany), May'83

BARK.
Tracks: / When the earth moves again / Feel so good / Crazy Miranda / Pretty as you feel / Wild turkey / Law man / Rock and Roll Island / Third week in the chelsea / Never argue with a german if you're tired or european song / Thunk / War movie.
Album: released on RCA (Special Imports Service), Jul'84

BEST OF JEFFERSON AIRPLANE, (THE).
Album: released on RCA (Germany), '83

Album: released on RCA, '84 by RCA Records. Dist: RCA, Roots, Swift, Wellard, Chris, I & B, Solomon & Peres Distribution

Cassette: released on RCA, '84 by RCA Records. Dist: RCA, Roots, Swift, Wellard, Chris, I & B, Solomon & Peres Distribution

BLESS ITS POINTED LITTLE HEAD.
Album: released on RCA (Germany), '83

CROWN OF CREATION.
Album: released on RCA (Germany), '83

Album: released on RCA, Oct'85 by RCA Records. Dist: RCA, Roots, Swift, Wellard, Chris, I & B, Solomon & Peres Distribution

Cassette: released on RCA, Oct'85 by RCA Records. Dist: RCA, Roots, Swift, Wellard, Chris, I & B, Solomon & Peres Distribution

EARLY FLIGHT.
Tracks: / High flyin'bird / Runnin'round this world / It's alright / In the morning / J.P.P. McStep B.Blues / Go to her / Up or down / Mexico / Have you seen the saucers.
Album: released on RCA (Germany), May'83

FLIGHT LOG(1966-76).
Tracks: / Come up the years / White rabbit / Comin' back to me / Won't you try(saturday afternoon) / Greasy heart / If you feel / Somebody to love -Live version / Wooden ships / Volunteers / Hesitation blues / Have you seen the stars tonite / Silver spoon / Feel so good / Pretty as you feel / Milk train / Ja Da (keep on truckin') / Come again toucan / Sketches of china / Genesis / Ride the tiger / Please come back (Live).
Notes: Selection of tracks from:(1) Jefferson airplane takes off 1966.(2,3)Surrealist-ic Pillow 1967.(4)After bathing at baxters 1967.(5,6)Crown of creation 1968. (7)Bless it's pointed little head 1969.(8,9)Volunteers 1969.(10)Hot tuna(by hot tuna,i.e Jorma Kaukonen & Jack Cassidy)1970.(11)Blows against the empire(by - Paul Kantner & Jefferson Starship)1970.(12)Sunflighter(by Paul Kantner,Grace Slik)1971.(13,14)Bark 1971 (15)Long john silver 1972. (16)Burgers(By Hot tuna) 1972.(17) Manhole(by Grace Slick) (18)Baron von toll booth and the chrome nun (by Paul Kantner,Grace Slick,David Freiberg)1973.(19)Quah(by Jorma Kaukonen withJim Hobson)1974.(20)Dragon fly(Jefferson Starship)1974.(21)Unreleased live perf-ormance 1976. 2 LP set.
Album: released on Grunt(USA), Jan'77 by RCA Records.

LONG JOHN SILVER.
Tracks: / Long john silver / Aerie (Gang of eagles) / Twilight double leader / Milk train / Son of Jesus(The) / Easter? / Trial by fire / Alexander the medium / Eat starch mom.
Album: released on RCA (Germany), May'83

ROCK GALAXY.
Album: released on RCA (Germany), '83

SURREALISTIC PILLOW.
Tracks: / She has funny cars / Somebody to love / My best friend / Today / Comin'back to me / 3/5 mile in 10 seconds / D.C.B.A-25 / How do you feel / White rabbit / Plastic fantastic love / Embryonic journey.
Notes: Produced by Rick Jarrard.
Album: released on RCA (Germany), May'83

Compact disc: released on RCA, Sep'84 by RCA Records. Dist: RCA, Roots, Swift, Wellard, Chris, I & B, Solomon & Peres Distribution

TAKES OFF.
Tracks: / Blues from an airplane / Let me in / Bringing me down / It's no secret / Tobacco road / Come up the years / Run around / Let's get together / Don't slip away / Chauffuer blues / And I like it.
Album: released on RCA (Germany), May'83

THIRTY SECONDS OVER WINTER-LAND.
Album: released on RCA (Germany), '83

VOLUNTEERS.
Album: released on RCA (Germany), '83

Album: released on RCA, Oct'85 by RCA Records. Dist: RCA, Roots, Swift, Wellard, Chris, I & B, Solomon & Peres Distribution

Cassette: released on RCA, Oct'85 by RCA Records. Dist: RCA, Roots, Swift, Wellard, Chris, I & B, Solomon & Peres Distribution

WHITE RABBIT.
Tracks: / White rabbit / Somebody to love.
Single (7"): released on Old Gold, Nov'86 by Old Gold Records. Dist: Lightning, Jazz Music, Spartan, Counterpoint

WHITE RABBIT (RE-ISSUE).
Tracks: / White rabbit / Somebody to love / She has funny cars* / Third week in the Chelsea.
Single (7"): released on Ariola, 30 May'87 Dist: RCA, Ariola

Single (12"): released on Ariola, 30 May'87 Dist: RCA, Ariola

WORST OF JEFFERSON AIRPLANE (The).
Tracks: / It's no secret / Blues from an airplane / Somebody to love / Today / White rabbit / Embryonic / Martha / Ballad of you & me & fooneil(The) / Crown of creation / Cushingura / Lather / Plastic Fantastic Lover / We can be together / Volunteers / Good shepherd.
Notes: This compilation (P) 1970 & (C) RCA Records Ltd,(P) Original Sound Recordings owned by RCA Records Ltd issued under exclusive licence to Music For Pleasure.
Album: released on Fame, Sep'86 by Music For Pleasure Records. Dist: EMI

Cassette: released on Fame, Sep'86 by Music For Pleasure Records. Dist: EMI

Jefferson, Blind Lemon

BLACK SNAKE MOAN, (THE).
Album: released on Joker (Import), Apr'81

BLIND LEMON JEFFERSON/SON HOUSE.
Album: released on Blue Moon, 11 Apr'87 Dist: Magnum Music Group Ltd, PRT, Spartan

COLLECTION: BLIND LEMON JEFFERSON.
Album: released on Deja Vu, Aug'86 by Deja Vu Records. Dist: Counterpoint Distribution, Record Services Distribution (Ireland)

Cassette: released on Deja Vu, Aug'86 by Deja Vu Records. Dist: Counterpoint Distribution, Record Services Distribution (Ireland)

KING OF THE COUNTRY BLUES.
Album: released on Yazoo(USA), Feb'85

REMAINING TITLES, (THE).
Album: released on Matchbox, Apr'84 by Saydisc Records. Dist: Roots, Projection, Jazz Music, JSU, Celtic Music

Jefferson, Carter

RISE OF ATLANTIS (THE).
Notes: With Terumasa Hino/Victor Lewis.
Album: released on Timeless(import), Sep'86 Dist: Cadillac

RISE OF ATLANTIS, (THE).
Album: released on Timeless, Apr'81

Jefferson, Eddie

LIVELIEST.
Album: released on Muse (Import), Apr'81

STILL ON THE PLANET.
Album: released on Muse (Import), Apr'81

THERE I GO AGAIN.
Album: released on Prestige (USA), May'84

THINGS ARE GETTING BETTER.
Album: released on Muse (Import), Apr'81

Jefferson, Marshall

HOUSE MUSIC ANTHEM (THE).
Tracks: / House music anthem (The) / Move your body.
Single (7"): released on Affair, Oct'86 Dist: DMS, RCA

Jefferson Starship

FREEDOM AT POINT ZERO.
Album: released on RCA, Jun'87 by RCA Records. Dist: RCA, Roots, Swift, Wellard, Chris, I & B, Solomon & Peres Distribution

FREEDOM AT POINT ZERO.
Tracks: / Jane / Lightning rose(carry the fire) / Things to come / Awakening / Girl with the hungry eyes / Just the same / Rock Music / Fading lady light / Freedom at point zero(Climbing tiger through the Sky).
Album: released on RCA, Sep'81 by RCA Records. Dist: RCA, Roots, Swift, Wellard, Chris, I & B, Solomon & Peres Distribution

Cassette: released on RCA, Sep'81 by RCA Records. Dist: RCA, Roots, Swift, Wellard, Chris, I & B, Solomon & Peres Distribution

GOLD.
Album: released on RCA (Germany), '83

Cassette: released on RCA (Germany), '83

JEFFERSON STARSHIP.
Notes: A live concert by one of San Francisco's longest-lived bands,formerly Jeferson Airplane.The songs delve from today back to the 50's hit like 'White Rabbit' 64 minutes playing time.
Video-cassette (VHS): released on RCA, Oct'84 by RCA Records. Dist: RCA, Roots, Swift, Wellard, Chris, I & B, Solomon & Peres Distribution

MODERN TIMES.
Tracks: / Find your way back / Stranger / Wild eyes (Angel) / Save your love / Modern times / Mary / Free / Alien / Stairway to cleveland (we do what we want).
Album: released on RCA, Sep'81 by RCA Records. Dist: RCA, Roots, Swift, Wellard, Chris, I & B, Solomon & Peres Distribution

Cassette: released on RCA, Sep'81 by RCA Records. Dist: RCA, Roots, Swift, Wellard, Chris, I & B, Solomon & Peres Distribution

NUCLEAR FURNITURE.
Tracks: / Layin'it on the line / No way out / Sorry me,Sorry you / Shining in the moonlight / Showdown / Champion.
Notes: Digital Stereo recording.
Compact disc: released on Baad, Oct'84 Dist: Pinnacle

Album: released on Grunt(USA), Jul'84 by RCA Records.

Cassette: released on Grunt(USA), Jul'84 by RCA Records.

Compact disc: released on Grunt(USA), Jul'84 by RCA Records.

RED OCTOPUS.
Tracks: / Fast buck freddie / Miracles / Git fiddler / Al garimasu (There is love) / Sweeter than honey / Play on love / Tumblin / I want to see another world / Sandalphon / There will be love.
Album: released on Fame, Jun'86 by Music For Pleasure Records. Dist: EMI

Cassette: released on Fame, Jun'86 by Music For Pleasure Records. Dist: EMI

Compact disc: released on RCA International, Oct'84

Album: released on RCA International, Oct'84

Cassette: released on RCA International, Oct'84

Compact disc: released on RCA International, Oct'84

WIND OF CHANGE.
Tracks: / Winds of change / Keep on dreamin' / Be my lady / I will stay / Out of control / Can't find love / Black widow / I came from the jaws of the dragon / Quit wasting time.
Notes: Digital stereo recording.
Compact disc: released on Grunt(USA), Oct'84 by RCA Records.

Album: released on Grunt(USA), Oct'84 by RCA Records.

Cassette: released on Grunt(USA), Oct'84 by RCA Records.

Jefferson, Thomas

IF I COULD BE WITH YOU (Jefferson, Thomas & His Dixieland Band).
Album: released on Nola, Apr'79 Dist: JSU, Jazz Music, Cadillac, Chris Wellard

THOMAS JEFFERSON & HIS DIXIELAND ALL STARS Featuring Sammy Rimington.
Cassette: released on Nola, May'87 Dist: JSU, Jazz Music, Cadillac, Chris Wellard

Jeffes, Simon

MUSIC FROM THE PENGUIN CAFE.
Album: released on Obscure, Mar'78 by Polydor Records. Dist: Polygram Distribution

Double cassette: released on Editions EG, Apr'82 by Virgin Records. Dist: EMI

Jeffreys

IT'S CHRISTMAS.
Single (7"): released on Go For It, Nov'83 by Go For It Records. Dist: ILA

Jeffreys, Garland

AMERICAN BOY AND GIRL.
Album: released on A&M, Sep'79 by A&M Records. Dist: Polygram

ESCAPE ARTIST.
Album: released on Epic, Mar'81 by CBS Records. Dist: CBS

GHOST WRITER.
Album: released on A&M, Apr'77 by A&M Records. Dist: Polygram

ONE EYED JACK.
Album: released on A&M, Apr'78 by A&M Records. Dist: Polygram

ROCK & ROLL ADULT.
Album: released on Epic, Jan'82 by CBS Records. Dist: CBS

Jeffries, Michael

RAZZLE DAZZLE (Jeffries, Michael & James Newton Howard).
Tracks: / Razzle dazzle / Half time / Razzle dazzle (Instrumental).
Single (7"): released on Warner Bros., May'86 by Warner Bros Records. Dist: WEA

Single (12"): released on Warner Bros., May'86 by Warner Bros Records. Dist: WEA

Jef Gilson

SOUL OF AFICA see also Singer Hal (Jef Gilson & Hal Singer).
Album: released on Chant du Monde, Feb'78 Dist: Harmonia Mundi

Jellybean

JUST VISITING THIS PLANET.
Album: released on Chrysalis(USA), Aug'87 by CBS. Dist: CBS

SIDEWALK TALK.
Tracks: / Sidewalk talk / Was dog a doughnut / Sidewalk talk (Funhouse remix) / Was dog a doughnut remix.
Single (7"): released on EMI America, Jan'86 by EMI Records. Dist: EMI

Single (12"): released on EMI America, Jan'86 by EMI Records. Dist: EMI

Single (12"): released on EMI America, Jan'86 by EMI Records. Dist: EMI

WOTUPSKI!?!.
Album: released on EMI America, Oct'84 by EMI Records. Dist: EMI

Cassette: released on EMI America, Oct'84 by EMI Records. Dist: EMI

Jelly Beans

YOU DON'T MEAN ME NO GOOD.
Single (7"): released on Inferno, Jul'80 by Inferno Records. Dist: Inferno, Cartel, Pinnacle

Jenkins, Billy

BEYOND E MAJOR.
Tracks: / Contry & Western / Blues, The / Heavy metal / Rock & Roll.
Album: released on Allmusic, May'85 by Allmusic Records. Dist: Backs, Cartel, Cadillac

Album: released on Allmusic, May'85 by Allmusic Records. Dist: Backs, Cartel, Cadillac

GREENWICH (Jenkins, Billy & The Voice Of God Collective).
Tracks: / Greenwich one way system / Dreadnought seaman's hospital / Rope / Arrival of the tourists / An empty river / Meridian council estate* / Discoboats at two o'clock.
Notes: Other musicians on this album are as follows: Dave Jago/trombone, Billy Jenkins/guitar, Steve Berry/double bass, Roy Dodds/drumkit, Dawson/percussion.
Album: released on Wood Wharf, Nov'85

PIANO SKETCHES, 1973-84.
Album: released on Wood Wharf, Nov'84

PIANO SKETCHES 1973-1984.
Tracks: / Cup of tea, A / Donkey droppings / My dead cleaning lady / Slimming advert / Helsinki waking up / Cooking oil / Ragtime / Fat people / 2nd April '78 / Snowbound / Young lovers / Laban Dance School early morning / Quiet Sunday afternoon, A / Jack Loussiers beard / Unborn child, The / Unborn child of the comedian, The / Invention.
Album: released on Wood Wharf, Sep'84

SOUNDS LIKE BROMLEY (Jenkins, Billy & The Voice Of God Collective).
Tracks: / High street/Saturday / Fat people / Parking meters / Sunday morning / Supermarkets / Council offices / Growing up in Bromley / Exodus from Bromley.
Notes: This is the first recording by the Voice of God Collective. Those taking part are listed in the 'tracks' section.
Album: released on Plymouth Sounds, Apr'82 by Plymouth Sounds Records. Dist: Backs, Cartel

UNCOMMERCIALITY.
Tracks: / Brilliant / Pharoah Sanders / Margaret's menstrual problem / Sade's lips / Spastics dancing / Bhopal.
Notes: Other musicians featuring on this album include: Dai Pritchard/alto, baritone sax, bass clarinet. Tim Matthewman/electric bass, Roy dodds/drums.
Album: released on Allmusic, Sep'86 by Allmusic Records. Dist: Backs, Cartel, Cadillac

Jenkins, Florence Foster

GLORY (???) OF THE HUMAN VOICE, (THE).
Album: released on RCA International, Jul'82

Cassette: released on RCA International, Jul'82

Jenkins, John

JENKINS, JORDAN & TIMMONS (Jenkins, John & Clifford Jordan & Bobby Timmons).
Album:

Jenkins, Leroy

GEORGE LEWIS.
Album: released on Black Saint, Jul'78 Dist: Projection, IMS, Polygram, Chris Wellard, Harmonia Mundi, Swift

LEGEND OF AL GLATSON, (THE).
Album: released on Black Saint, Apr'79 Dist: Projection, IMS, Polygram, Chris Wellard, Harmonia Mundi, Swift

REVOLUTIONARY ENSEMBLE.
Album: released on Enja (Germany), Jan'82 by Enja Records (W.Germany). Dist: Cadillac Music

SOLO CONCERT.
Album: released on India Navigation, May'78 by India Navigation Records. Dist: Cadillac, Projection, Swift

URBAN BLUES.
Album: released on Black Saint, May'85 Dist: Projection, IMS, Polygram, Chris Wellard, Harmonia Mundi, Swift

Jenkins, Martin

CARRY YOUR SMILE.
Album: released on Oblivion, Jan'85 Dist: Projection

Jenkins, Snuffy

CAROLINA BLUEGRASS.
Album: released on Arhoolie, May'81 by Arhoolie Records. Dist: Projection, Topic, Jazz Music, Swift, Roots

Jenni

JENNI Young, Vivien (Young, Vivien).
Double cassette: released on Soundings, Mar'85 Dist: Soundings

Jennings...

JENNINGS GOES TO SCHOOL Buckeridge, Anthony (Buckeridge, Anthony).
Cassette: released on Pinnacle, '79 by Pinnacle Records. Dist: Pinnacle

Jennings, Frank

ME AND MY GUITAR (Jennings, Frank Syndicate).
Cassette: released on Columbia, Apr'79 by EMI Records. Dist: EMI

ROSE OF EL PASO.
Tracks: / Rose of El Paso / Perfect stranger / I don't want to hear another she's leaving song / Love is a two-way street / Memories to burn / Colinda / When you finally realise you're on your own / Carmen / Till the water stops running / Ave Maria Morales.
Notes: One of our top long-established country music entertainers joins the Grasmere fold. Two years have elapsed since Frank's last sell-out L.P., and he now pres-ents a great cross section of bang up-to-date country music.
Album: released on Grasmere, Jul'86 by Grasmere Records. Dist: EMI

Cassette: released on Grasmere, Jul'86 by Grasmere Records. Dist: EMI

Jennings, Waylon

20 OUTLAW REUNION HITS (Jennings, Waylon & Willie Nelson).
Album: released on Astan, Nov'84 by Astan Records. Dist: Counterpoint

Cassette: released on Astan, Nov'84 by Astan Records. Dist: Counterpoint

AT THE COUNTRY STORE.
Album: released on Starblend Country Store, Aug'86 by Starblend Records. Dist: PRT Distribution

Cassette: released on Starblend Country Store, Aug'86 by Starblend Records. Dist: PRT Distribution

BLACK ON BLACK.
Album: released on RCA, May'82 by RCA Records. Dist: RCA, Roots, Swift, Wellard, Chris, I & B, Solomon & Peres Distribution Deleted '85.

Cassette: released on RCA, May'82 by RCA Records. Dist: RCA, Roots, Swift, Wellard, Chris, I & B, Solomon & Peres Distribution

BURNING MEMORIES.
Tracks: / Sally was a good old girl / Crying / Burning memories / It's so easy / White lightning / Abilene / Dream baby / Loves gonna live here / Big Mamou / Don't think twice it's alrigt.
Album: released on Showcase, Apr'86 Dist: Counterpoint

Cassette: released on Showcase, Apr'86 Dist: Counterpoint

COLLECTION: WAYLON JENNINGS.
Album: released on Castle Communications, Nov'85 by Castle Communications. Dist: Cartel, Pinnacle, Counterpoint

Cassette: released on Castle Communications, Nov'85 by Castle Communications. Dist: Cartel, Pinnacle, Counterpoint

DUKES OF HAZZARD.
Single (7"): released on RCA, May'82 by RCA Records. Dist: RCA, Roots, Swift, Wellard, Chris, I & B, Solomon & Peres Distribution

FILES: VOL 1.
Album: released on Bear Family, Feb'85 by Bear Family Records. Dist: Rollercoaster Distribution, Swift

FILES: VOL 13.
Album: released on Bear Family, Dec'85 by Bear Family Records. Dist: Rollercoaster Distribution, Swift

FILES: VOL 14.
Album: released on Bear Family, Dec'85 by Bear Family Records. Dist: Rollercoaster Distribution, Swift

FILES: VOL 15.
Album: released on Bear Family, Dec'85 by Bear Family Records. Dist: Rollercoaster Distribution, Swift

FILES: VOL 2.
Album: released on Bear Family, Feb'85 by Bear Family Records. Dist: Rollercoaster Distribution, Swift

FILES: VOL 3.
Album: released on Bear Family, Feb'85 by Bear Family Records. Dist: Rollercoaster Distribution, Swift

FILES: VOL 4.
Album: released on Bear Family, Mar'85 by Bear Family Records. Dist: Rollercoaster Distribution, Swift

FILES: VOL 5.
Album: released on Bear Family, Mar'85 by Bear Family Records. Dist: Rollercoaster Distribution, Swift

FILES: VOL 6.
Album: released on Bear Family, May'85 by Bear Family Records. Dist: Rollercoaster Distribution, Swift

FILES: VOL 7.
Album: released on Bear Family, May'85 by Bear Family Records. Dist: Rollercoaster Distribution, Swift

FILES: VOL 8.
Album: released on Bear Family, May'85 by Bear Family Records. Dist: Rollercoaster Distribution, Swift

FILES: VOL 9.
Album: released on Bear Family, Dec'85 by Bear Family Records. Dist: Rollercoaster Distribution, Swift

FOLK - COUNTRY.
Tracks: / Another bridge to burn / Stop the world (and let me off) / Cindy of New Orleans / Look into my teardrops / Down came the world / I don't mind / Just for you / Now everybody knows / That's the chance I'll have to take / What makes a man wander / I'm a man of constant sorrow / What's left of me.
Album: released on RCA, Jan'87 by RCA Records. Dist: RCA, Roots, Swift, Wellard, Chris, I & B, Solomon & Peres Distribution

Cassette: released on RCA, Jan'87 by RCA Records. Dist: RCA, Roots, Swift, Wellard, Chris, I & B, Solomon & Peres Distribution

GREATEST HITS: WAYLON JENNINGS VOL.2.
Album: released on RCA, Feb'85 by RCA Records. Dist: RCA, Roots, Swift, Wellard, Chris, I & B, Solomon & Peres Distribution

Cassette: released on RCA, Feb'85 by RCA Records. Dist: RCA, Roots, Swift, Wellard, Chris, I & B, Solomon & Peres Distribution

Compact disc: released on RCA, Feb'85 by RCA Records. Dist: RCA, Roots, Swift, Wellard, Chris, I & B, Solomon & Peres Distribution

GREATEST HITS:WAYLON JENNINGS.
Tracks: / Lonesome on'ly and mean / Ladies love outlaws / I've always been crazy / I'm a ramblin' man / Only daddy that'll walk the line / Amanda / Honky tonk heroes / Mammas don't let your babies grow up to be cowboys / Good hearted woman / Luckenbach / Texas (Back to the basics of love) / Are you sure Hank done it this way.
Compact disc: released on RCA, Sep'84 by RCA Records. Dist: RCA, Roots, Swift, Wellard, Chris, I & B, Solomon & Peres Distribution

Album: released on RCA (Germany), '83

Album: released on RCA, Sep'84 by RCA Records. Dist: RCA, Roots, Swift, Wellard, Chris, I & B, Solomon & Peres Distribution

Cassette: released on RCA, Sep'84 by RCA Records. Dist: RCA, Roots, Swift, Wellard, Chris, I & B, Solomon & Peres Distribution

Compact disc: released on RCA, Sep'84 by RCA Records. Dist: RCA, Roots, Swift, Wellard, Chris, I & B, Solomon & Peres Distribution

GREATEST HITS: WAYLON JENNINGS.

HANGIN' TOUGH.
Tracks: / Baker street / I can't help the way I don't feel about you / Rose in Paradise / Crying even don't come close / Chevy Van / Fallin' out / Deep in the west / Between fathers and sons / Crown Prince (The) / Defying Gravity (Executioner's song).
Album: released on MCA, Mar'87 by MCA Records. Dist: Polygram, MCA

Cassette: released on MCA, Mar'87 by MCA Records. Dist: Polygram, MCA

Compact disc: released on MCA, Apr'87 by MCA Records. Dist: Polygram, MCA

HITS VOLUME 2.
Tracks: / Looking gor Suzanne / Conversation / Waltz me to heaven / Dukes of Hazzard / Don't you think this outlaw bit's done got out of hand / I ain't livin' long like this / Come with me / America / Shine / Women do know how to carry on.
Compact disc: released on RCA International, Jun'85

IN THE BEGINNING.
Album: released on Bulldog, Nov'83 by Bulldog Records. Dist: President Distribution, Spartan, Swift, Taylor, H.R.

JUST TO SATISFY YOU (Jennings, Waylon & Willie Nelson).
Single (7"): released on RCA, May'82 by RCA Records. Dist: RCA, Roots, Swift, Wellard, Chris, I & B, Solomon & Peres Distribution

Single (7"): released on RCA, Oct'83 by RCA Records. Dist: RCA, Roots, Swift, Wellard, Chris, I & B, Solomon & Peres Distribution

LEAVIN' TOWN.
Tracks: / Leavin' town / Time to bum again / If you really want me to I'll go / Baby, don't be looking in my mind / That's alright / Time will tell the story / You're gonna wonder about me / For lovin' me / Anita, you're draming / Doesn't anybody know my name / Falling for you / I wonder just where I went wrong.
Album: released on RCA, Mar'86 by RCA Records. Dist: RCA, Roots, Swift, Wellard, Chris, I & B, Solomon & Peres Distribution

Cassette: released on RCA, Mar'86 by RCA Records. Dist: RCA, Roots, Swift, Wellard, Chris, I & B, Solomon & Peres Distribution

Album: released on RCA, Oct'84 by RCA Records. Dist: RCA, Roots, Swift, Wellard, Chris, I & B, Solomon & Peres Distribution

Cassette: released on RCA, Oct'84 by RCA Records. Dist: RCA, Roots, Swift, Wellard, Chris, I & B, Solomon & Peres Distribution

MOST WANTED NASHVILLE REBEL.
Album: released on RCA (S.I.S.), Aug'84

Cassette: released on RCA (S.I.S.), Aug'84

MUSIC MAN.
Album: released on RCA, Jul'80 by RCA Records. Dist: RCA, Roots, Swift, Wellard, Chris, I & B, Solomon & Peres Distribution

NEVER COULD TOE THE MARK.
Album: released on RCA, Aug'84 by RCA Records. Dist: RCA, Roots, Swift, Wellard, Chris, I & B, Solomon & Peres Distribution

Cassette: released on RCA, Aug'84 by RCA Records. Dist: RCA, Roots, Swift, Wellard, Chris, I & B, Solomon & Peres Distribution

OL'WAYLON.
Tracks: / Luckenbach / Texas (Back to the basics of love) / If you see me getting smaller / Lucille / Sweet Caroline / I Think I'm gonna kill myself / Belle of the ball / Medley of Elvis hits / That's all right / My baby left me / Till I gain control again / Brand new goodbye song / Satin sheets / This is getting funny (But there ain't nobody laughing).
Compact disc: released on RCA, Aug'85 by RCA Records. Dist: RCA, Roots, Swift, Wellard, Chris, I & B, Solomon & Peres Distribution

OL' WAYLON.
Album: released on RCA, Jun'77 by RCA Records. Dist: RCA, Roots, Swift, Wellard, Chris, I & B, Solomon & Peres Distribution Deleted '83.

Compact disc: released on RCA, Jun'77 by RCA Records. Dist: RCA, Roots, Swift, Wellard, Chris, I & B, Solomon & Peres Distribution

OUTLAWS' REUNION (Jennings, Waylon & Willie Nelson).
Album: released on Sundown, Sep'83 by Magnum Music Group Ltd. Dist: Magnum Music Group Ltd, PRT Distribution, Spartan Distribution

OUTLAWS' REUNION: VOL 2 (Jennings, Waylon & Willie Nelson).
Album: released on Sundown, Apr'84 by Magnum Music Group Ltd. Dist: Magnum Music Group Ltd, PRT Distribution, Spartan Distribution

RAVE ON.
Album: released on Bear Family, Sep'84 by Bear Family Records. Dist: Rollercoaster Distribution, Swift

REPLAY ON.
Album: released on Sierra, May'86 by Sierra Records. Dist: WEA

Cassette: released on Sierra, May'86 by Sierra Records. Dist: WEA

SINGER OF SAD SONGS.
Album: released on RCA International, Apr'80

Cassette: released on RCA International, Apr'80

TAKE IT TO THE LIMIT (Jennings, Waylon & Willie Nelson).
Album: released on CBS, Sep'83 by CBS Records. Dist: CBS

TAKER, (THE).
Album: released on Premier, '84 by Premier Records. Dist: CBS

Cassette: released on Premier, '84 by Premier Records. Dist: CBS

THIS TIME.
Album: released on Victor, Apr'74

TURN THE PAGE.
Album: released on RCA, Aug'85 by RCA Records. Dist: RCA, Roots, Swift, Wellard, Chris, I & B, Solomon & Peres Distribution

Cassette: released on RCA, Aug'85 by RCA Records. Dist: RCA, Roots, Swift, Wellard, Chris, I & B, Solomon & Peres Distribution

WAYLON.
Album: released on RCA, May'83 by RCA Records. Dist: RCA, Roots, Swift, Wellard, Chris, I & B, Solomon & Peres Distribution

Cassette: released on RCA, May'83 by RCA Records. Dist: RCA, Roots, Swift, Wellard, Chris, I & B, Solomon & Peres Distribution

WAYLON AND COMPANY.
Tracks: / Hold on I'm comin' / Leave them boys alone / Spanish Johnny / Just to satisfy you / So you want to be a cowboy singer / I may be used / Sight for sore eyes / I'll find it where I can / Conversation,The / Mason Dixon lines.
Notes: Artists include: Waylon Jennings/Jerry Reed/Hank Williams Jnr./Ernest Tubb/ Emmylou Harris/Willie Nelson/Tony White/James Garner/Mel Tills/Jessi Coulter.
Compact disc: released on RCA, Dec'84 by RCA Records. Dist: RCA, Roots, Swift, Wellard, Chris, I & B, Solomon & Peres Distribution

Album: released on RCA, Nov'83 by RCA Records. Dist: RCA, Roots, Swift, Wellard, Chris, I & B, Solomon & Peres Distribution

Cassette: released on RCA, Nov'83 by RCA Records. Dist: RCA, Roots, Swift, Wellard, Chris, I & B, Solomon & Peres Distribution

WAYLON MUSIC.
Double Album: released on RCA, Oct'80 by RCA Records. Dist: RCA, Roots, Swift, Wellard, Chris, I & B, Solomon & Peres Distribution

WAYLON & WILLIE (Jennings, Waylon & Willie Nelson).
Tracks: / Mammas, don't let your babies grow up to be cowboys / Year 2003 minus 25,The / Pick up the tempo / If you can touch her at all / Lookin' for a feeling / It's not supposed to be that way / I can get off on you / Don't cuss the fiddle / Gold dust woman / Couple more years,A / Wurlitzer prize,The (I don't want to get over you) / Mr.Shuk and Jive / Roman candles (Sittin' on) / Dock of the bay,The / Year that Clayton Delany died,The / Lady in the harbour / May I borrow some sugar from you / Last cowboy song / Heroes / Teddy bear song,The / Write your own songs / Old mother's locket trick,The.
Album: released on RCA, Mar'86 by RCA Records. Dist: RCA, Roots, Swift, Wellard, Chris, I & B, Solomon & Peres Distribution

Cassette: released on RCA, Mar'86 by RCA Records. Dist: RCA, Roots, Swift, Wellard, Chris, I & B, Solomon & Peres Distribution

Compact disc: released on RCA, Dec'84 by RCA Records. Dist: RCA, Roots, Swift, Wellard, Chris, I & B, Solomon & Peres Distribution

WILL THE WOLF SURVIVE.
Tracks: / Will the wolf survive / They ain't got em' all / Working without a net / Where does love go / Dog won't hunt,The / What you'll do when I,m gone / Suddenly single / Shadow of your distant friend,The / I've got me a woman / Devils right hand,The.
Notes: Waylon Jennings has now signed to MCA Records and we are proud to present his first album entitled 'Will the wolf survive'. Coproduced by Jimmy Bowen it features the following tracks:-
Album: released on MCA, Mar'86 by MCA Records. Dist: Polygram, MCA

Cassette: released on MCA, Mar'86 by MCA Records. Dist: Polygram, MCA

Compact disc: by MCA Records. Dist: Polygram, MCA

Jenny

UPTOWN DOWNTOWN.
Single (7"): released on PU, Dec'81

Jensen, Kris

LET'S SIT DOWN: A MILESTONE IN ROCK 'N' ROLL MUSIC, VOL 1.
Album: released on Hickory, Sep'84 by Bear Family Records. Dist: Tonal Distribution

TORTURE: A MILESTONE IN ROCK 'N' ROLL MUSIC, VOL 4.
Album: released on Hickory, Sep'84 by Bear Family Records. Dist: Tonal Distribution

Jensen, Theis

DANISH JAZZ: VOL 3.
Album: released on Storyville, Jul'82 by Storyville Records. Dist: Jazz Music Distribution, Swift Distribution, Chris Wellard Distribution, Counterpoint Distribution

Jeopardie, Jeff

2468 DOUBLE 9.
Tracks: / 2468 double 9.
Single (7"): released on Gull, Feb'86 by Gull Records. Dist: Pinnacle

Jeremiah in the...

JEREMIAH IN THE DARK WOODS
Ahlberg, Janet & Allan.
Cassette: released on Tellastory, Jun'83 by Bartlett Bliss Productions. Dist: PRT Distribution, Hayward Promotions Distribution, H.R. Taylor Distribution

Jeremy's Secret

KEY TO JEREMY'S SECRET.
Single (7"): released on Papier Mache, Jun'83 by Papier Mache Records. Dist: Rough Trade, Cartel

SNOWBALL EFFECT, (THE).
Album: released on Deep Six, May'84 Dist: Rough Trade, Cartel

Jerico Go

JERICO GO Various artists (Various Artists).
Album: released on DB, Nov'85 by DB Records. Dist: Pinnacle

Jerome

BETCHA.
Single (12"): released on Calibre, May'85 by Calibre Records. Dist: PRT

EXTRA SPECIAL.
Tracks: / Extra special / Extra special (Instrumental).
Single (7"): released on Calibre, Jan'86 by Calibre Records. Dist: PRT

Single (12"): released on Calibre, Jan'86 by Calibre Records. Dist: PRT

Single (7"): released on Calibre, Sep'85 by Calibre Records. Dist: PRT

Single (12"): released on Calibre, Sep'85 by Calibre Records. Dist: PRT

I'M INTO YOUR LOVE.
Single (7"): released on RCA, Jun'82 by RCA Records. Dist: RCA, Roots, Swift, Wellard, Chris, I & B, Solomon & Peres Distribution

Single (12"): released on RCA, Jun'82 by RCA Records. Dist: RCA, Roots, Swift, Wellard, Chris, I & B, Solomon & Peres Distribution

IN THE RIGHT DIRECTION.
Single (7"): released on Soto Sound, Jan'82 Dist: Soto Sound Distribution

Single (12"): released on Soto Sound, Jan'82 Dist: Soto Sound Distribution

LIVING A GOOD THING.
Single (7"): released on Calibre, Jun'84 by Calibre Records. Dist: PRT

Single (12"): released on Calibre, Jun'84 by Calibre Records. Dist: PRT

SOMETHING TO SAY ABOUT LOVE.
Single (7"): released on Calibre, Jan'85 by Calibre Records. Dist: PRT

Single (12"): released on Calibre, Jan'85 by Calibre Records. Dist: PRT

Jerome, Henry

1950/52.
Album: released on Circle(USA), Mar'84 by Jazzology Records (USA). Dist: Jazz Music, Swift, Chris Wellard

Jerome, Jerry Trio

JERRY JEROME TRIO.
Album: released on Vantage, Jun'86 Dist: Jazz Music

Jerome Kern

JEROME KERN & SILVER LINING Various artists (Various Artists).
Album: released on Arabesque, Nov'85 Dist: D Sharp Records, Pinnacle

Cassette: released on Arabesque, Nov'85 Dist: D Sharp Records, Pinnacle

Jerome, Steve

DON'T KEEP HAUNTING ME.
Single (7"): released on Needle, Aug'87 Dist: Pinnacle

Single (12"): released on Needle, Aug'87 Dist: Pinnacle

Jerry's Girls

JERRY'S GIRLS Original Cast Recording.
Tracks: / Jerry's girls / Put on your sunday clothes / It only takes a moment / Wherever he ain't / We need a little christmas / I won't send roses / Tap your troubles away / Two-a-day / Bosom buddies / Man in the moon,The / So long dearie / Take it all off / Shalom / Milk and honey / Showtum / If he walked into my life / Hello, Dolly / Nelson / Just go to the movies / Movies were movies / Look what happened to Mabel / Time heals everything / It's today / Mame / Kiss her now / That's how young I feel / Gooch's song / Before the parade passes by / I don't want to know / La cage aux folles / Song on the sand / I am what I am / Best of times,The / Jerry's turn.
Double compact disc: released on TER, May'85 Dist: Pinnacle

Double Album: released on TER, Mar'85 Dist: Pinnacle

Double cassette: released on TER, Mar'85 Dist: Pinnacle

Double compact disc: released on TER, Mar'85 Dist: Pinnacle

Jerry The Ferret

MUSIC GOES ON AND ON, THE.
Tracks: / Music goes on and on / Ginny / Ring road / Head in the clouds, Your.
Single (7"): released on Dead Horse, May'87 by Dead Horse Records. Dist: Dead Horse, Indies

ONE STEP FORWARD.
Tracks: / One step forward / I think you're lyin'.
Single (7"): released on Jerry The Ferret, Jan'87 by Dead Horse Records. Dist: Dead Horse, Indies

Jersey Artists

WE GOT THE LOVE (Jersey Artists For Mankind).
Tracks: / We got the love / Save love save life.
Single (7"): released on Arista, May'86 by Arista Records. Dist: RCA

Single (12"): released on Arista, May'86 by Arista Records. Dist: RCA

Jersey Hitchikers

YOU MAKE IT COME ALIVE.
Single (7"): released on Monarch, May'83 by Chart Records. Dist: Pinnacle

Jerusalem

JERUSALEM VOLUME II.
Album: released on Myrrh, May'82 by Word Records. Dist: Word Distribution

Cassette: released on Myrrh, May'82 by Word Records. Dist: Word Distribution

WARRIOR.
Album: released on Myrrh, May'82 by Word Records. Dist: Word Distribution

Cassette: released on Myrrh, May'82 by Word Records. Dist: Word Distribution

Jesrael

LET ME IN.
Single (7"): released on Solid Groove, Feb'82 Dist: Jetstar, Pinnacle

Jesse's Gang

CENTRE OF ATTRACTION.
Tracks: / Love's no mystery / Centre of attraction / Real love / Dreams / Your way / Noiz without words / Back-up / I'm back again / Do you know / My ride.
Album: released on Geffen, Aug'87 by Geffen Records. Dist: WEA, CBS

Cassette: released on Geffen, Aug'87 by Geffen Records. Dist: WEA, CBS

Album: released on Geffen, Aug'87 by Geffen Records. Dist: WEA, CBS

Cassette: released on Geffen, Aug'87 by Geffen Records. Dist: WEA, CBS

REAL LOVE.
Tracks: / Real love / My ride.
Single (7"): released on Geffen, Oct'86 by Geffen Records. Dist: WEA, CBS

Jesse, Steve

SHIFTING SANDS.
Single (7"): released on President, May'82 by President Records. Dist: Taylors, Spartan

SHUFFLE THE PACK.
Single (7"): released on President, Jul'81 by President Records. Dist: Taylors, Spartan

SLEEPLESS NIGHTS.
Single (7"): released on President, Jan'82 by President Records. Dist: Taylors, Spartan

Jessica's Tee Shirt

ETHIOPIA.
Single (7"): released on Rockstar, Mar'85

Jess & the Gingerbread

COUNTRY ROOTS.
Album: released on Tank, Dec'77 by Tank Records.

UNTIL IT'S TIME.
Album: released on Tank, Dec'77 by Tank Records.

Jester

KEMP'S JIG.
Album: released on Plant Life, Nov'81 Dist: Roots

Jesus Christ Superstar

JESUS CHRIST SUPERSTAR A rock opera (Various Artists).
Tracks: / Overture / Heave on their minds / What's the buzz/strange thing mystifying / Everything's all right / This Jesus must die / Hosanna / Simon Zealotes/Poor Jerusalem / Pilate's dream / Temple (The) / I don't know how to love him / Damned for all time/Blood money / Last supper (The) / Gethsemane (I only want to say) / Arrest (The) / Peter's denial / Pilate and Christ / King Herod's song / Judas' death / Trial before Pilate including the 39 lashes / Superstar / Crucifixion / John nineteen: forty-one.
Notes: A rock opera by Andrew Lloyd Webber and Tim Rice.
Compact disc: released on MCA, Apr'87 by MCA Records. Dist: Polygram, MCA

JESUS CHRIST SUPERSTAR Soundtrack.
Double Album: released on MCA, '74 by MCA Records. Dist: Polygram, MCA

JESUS CHRIST SUPERSTAR Original London Cast.
Album: released on MCA, '74 by MCA Records. Dist: Polygram, MCA

Compact disc: released on MCA, '74 by MCA Records. Dist: Polygram, MCA

JESUS CHRIST SUPERSTAR various artists (Various Artists).
Album: released on Deram, '73 by Decca Records. Dist: Polygram

JESUS CHRIST SUPERSTAR (ROCK OPERA) various artists (Various Artists).
Double Album: released on MCA, '74 by MCA Records. Dist: Polygram, MCA

Jesus Couldn't Drum

AUTUMN LEAVES.
Single (7"): released on Lost Moment, Aug'85

Single (12"): released on Lost Moment, Aug'85

ER......SOMETHING ABOUT A COW.
Album: released on Lost Moment, Jan'86

EVEN THE ROSES HAVE THORNS.
Single (7"): released on Lost Moments, Jul'84 Dist: Backs, Cartel

GOOD MORNING MR.SQUARE.
Album: released on Lost Moment, Jan'87

I'M A TRAIN.
Single (7"): released on Lost Moments, Nov'85 Dist: Backs, Cartel

Single (7"): released on Lost Moments, Nov'85 Dist: Backs, Cartel

Single (12"): released on Lost Moments, Nov'85 Dist: Backs, Cartel

Jesus Is The Answer

JESUS IS THE ANSWER various artists (Various Artists).
Album: released on Charly, Apr'85 by Charly Records. Dist: Charly, Cadillac

Jesus & Mary Chain

APRIL SKIES.
Tracks: / April skies / Kill Surf City / Who do you love* / Mushroom+ / Bo Diddley is Jesus+.
Notes: * = Extra track on 12" only + = Extra track in double pack
Single (7"): released on Blanco Y Negro, Apr'87 by WEA Records. Dist: WEA

Single (12"): released on Blanco Y Negro, Apr'87 by WEA Records. Dist: WEA

Double-pack single: released on Blanco Y Negro, Apr'87 by WEA Records. Dist: WEA

DARKLANDS.
Tracks: / April skies / Happy when it rains / Down on me / Deep one perfect / Fall / About you / Cherry came too / On the wall / Nine million rainy days.
Album: released on WEA, Aug'87 by WEA Records. Dist: WEA

Cassette: released on WEA, Aug'87 by WEA Records. Dist: WEA

Compact disc: released on WEA, Aug'87 by WEA Records. Dist: WEA

Album: released on Blanco Y Negro, Oct'87 by WEA Records. Dist: WEA

Cassette: released on Blanco Y Negro, Oct'87 by WEA Records. Dist: WEA

HAPPY WHEN IT RAINS.
Single (7"): released on Blanco Y Negro, Aug'87 by WEA Records. Dist: WEA

Single (12"): released on Blanco Y Negro, Aug'87 by WEA Records. Dist: WEA

INTERVIEW PICTURE DISC.
Album: released on Baktabak, Jun'87 by Baktabak Records. Dist: Arabesque

JUST LIKE HONEY.
Single (7"): released on Blanco Y Negro, Sep'85 by WEA Records. Dist: WEA

Single (12"): released on Blanco Y Negro, Sep'85 by WEA Records. Dist: WEA

NEVER UNDERSTAND.
Single (7"): released on Blanco Y Negro, Feb'85 by WEA Records. Dist: WEA

Single (12"): released on Blanco Y Negro, Feb'85 by WEA Records. Dist: WEA

PSYCHO CANDY.
Tracks: / Just like honey / Living end / Taste the floor / Hardest walk / Cut dead / In a hole / Taste of candy / Never understand / It's so hard / Inside me / Sowing seeds / My little underground / You trip me up / Something's wrong.
Compact disc: released on Blanco Y Negro, Oct'86 by WEA Records. Dist: WEA

Cassette: released on Blanco Y Negro, Sep'86 by WEA Records. Dist: WEA

Album: released on Blanco Y Negro, Nov'85 by WEA Records. Dist: WEA

SOME CANDY TALKING.
Tracks: / Some candy talking / Hit / Psycho candy / Taste of Cindy, A (Acoustic Version).
Single (7"): released on Blanco Y Negro, Jul'86 by WEA Records. Dist: WEA

Single (12"): released on Blanco Y Negro, Jul'86 by WEA Records. Dist: WEA

UPSIDE DOWN.
Tracks: / Upside down / Vegetable man.
Single (7"): released on Creation, Mar'86 Dist: Rough Trade, Cartel

YOU TRIP ME UP.
Single (7"): released on Blanco Y Negro, May'85 by WEA Records. Dist: WEA

Single (12"): released on Blanco Y Negro, May'85 by WEA Records. Dist: WEA

Jesus Of Nazareth

JESUS OF NAZARETH Sountrack to TV series.
Cassette: released on PRT, Apr'79 by PRT Records. Dist: PRT

J' Etais Au Bal

J' ETAIS AU BAL Various artists (Various Artists).
Album:

Jeter, Genobia

GENOBIA.
Tracks: / Sunshine / Peace of mind / Together / Blessing in disguise / I just want what's mine / We got love / All of my love / Take a look.
Album: released on RCA, Oct'86 by RCA Records. Dist: RCA, Roots, Swift, Wellard, Chris, I & B, Solomon & Peres Distribution

Cassette: released on RCA, Oct'86 by RCA Records. Dist: RCA, Roots, Swift, Wellard, Chris, I & B, Solomon & Peres Distribution

Jethro Tull

AQUALUNG.
Tracks: / Aqualung / Cross-eyed Mary / Cheap day return / Mother goose / Wond'ring aloud / Up to me / My God / Hymn 43 / Slipstream / Locomotive / Breath / Wind up.
Album: released on Chrysalis, '74 by Chrysalis Records. Dist: CBS

Cassette: released on Chrysalis, '74 by Chrysalis Records. Dist: CBS

Compact disc: by Chrysalis Records. Dist: CBS

BENEFIT.
Tracks: / With you there to help me / Nothing to say / Alive and well and living in / Son for Michael Collins / Jeffrey and me / To cry you a song / Time for everything, A / Inside / Play in time / Sossity / You're a woman.
Compact disc: released on Chrysalis, Jun'87 by Chrysalis Records. Dist: CBS

BROADSWORD & THE BEAST, THE.
Tracks: / Beastie / Clasp / Fallen on hard times / Flying colours / Slow marching / Broadsword / Pussy willow / Watching me watching you / Seal driver / Cheerio.
Notes: Produced by Paul Samwell-Smith.
Album: released on Chrysalis, Apr'82 by Chrysalis Records. Dist: CBS

Cassette: released on Chrysalis, Apr'82 by Chrysalis Records. Dist: CBS

Compact disc: released on Chrysalis, Apr'82 by Chrysalis Records. Dist: CBS

CORONACH.
Tracks: / Coronach / Jack Frost and the hooded crow.
Single (7"): released on Chrysalis, Jun'86 by Chrysalis Records. Dist: CBS

Cassette single: released on Chrysalis, Jun'86 by Chrysalis Records. Dist: CBS

HEAVY HORSES.
Tracks: / And the mouse police never sleeps / Acres wild / No lullaby / Moths / Journey man / Rover / One brown mouse / Heavy horses / Weathercock.
Compact disc: released on Crystal, '86 by Crystal Records. Dist: Jetstar, Revolver, Cartel

LIVING IN THE PAST.
Tracks: / Witch's promise, The.
Single (7"): released on Old Gold, Aug'87 by Old Gold Records. Dist: Lightning, Jazz Music, Spartan, Counterpoint

M.U.: BEST OF.
Tracks: / Teacher / Aqualung / Thick as a brick brick edit / Bungle in the jungle / Locomotive breath / Fat man / Living in the past / Passion play edit, A / Skating away (on the thin ice of the new day) / Rainbow blues / Nothing is easy.
Compact disc: released on Chrysalis, Dec'85 by Chrysalis Records. Dist: CBS

ORIGINAL MASTERS.
Tracks: / Living in the past / Aqualung / Too old to rock 'n' roll too young to die / Locomotive breath / Skating away on the thin ice of the new day / Bungle in the jungle / Sweet dreams / Songs from the wood / Witches promise / Thick as a brick / Minstrel in the gallery / Life's a long song.
Compact disc: released on Chrysalis, Apr'86 by Chrysalis Records. Dist: CBS

REPEAT.
Tracks: / Minstrel in the gallery / Cross-eyed Mary / New day yesterday, A / Bouree / Thick as a brick edit 4 / Warchild / Passion play edit 9 / To cry you a song / Too old to rock 'n' roll too young to die / Glory row.
Compact disc: released on Chrysalis, Apr'86 by Chrysalis Records. Dist: CBS

SLIPSTREAM.
Video-cassette (VHS): released on Chrysalis Video, Jan'84 by Chrysalis Records. Dist: CBS

SONGS FROM THE WOOD.
Tracks: / Songs from the wood / Jack in the green / Cup of wonder / Hunting girl / Ring out-Solstice bells / Velvet green / Whistler, The / Pibroch (cap in hand) / Fire at midnight.
Compact disc: released on Chrysalis, '86 by Chrysalis Records. Dist: CBS

THICK AS A BRICK.
Compact disc: released on Chrysalis, '86 by Chrysalis Records. Dist: CBS

THIS WAS.
Tracks: / My sunday feeling / Some day the sun won't shine / For you / Beggar's farm / Move on alone / Serenadeto a cuckoo / Dharma for one / It's breaking me / Cat's squirrel / Song for Jeffery, A / Round.
Compact disc: released on Chrysalis, '86 by Chrysalis Records. Dist: CBS

TOO OLD TO ROCK AND ROLL.
Tracks: / Quizz kid / Crazed institution / Salamander / Taxi grab / From a dead beat to an old greaser / Bad eyed and loveless / Big dipper / Too old to rock 'n' roll; too young to die / Pied piper / Chequered flag (dead of alive), The.
Compact disc: released on Chrysalis, '86 by Chrysalis Records. Dist: CBS

UNDER WRAPS.
Tracks: / Lap of luxury / Under wraps / European legacy / Later the same evening / Saboteur / Radio free Moscow / Nobody's car / Heat / Under wraps / Paparazzi / Apologee.
Notes: Cassette includes four extra tracks not available on album. Produced by Ian Anderson.
Album: released on Chrysalis, Sep'84 by Chrysalis Records. Dist: CBS

Cassette: released on Chrysalis, Sep'84 by Chrysalis Records. Dist: CBS

Compact disc: released on Chrysalis, Sep'84 by Chrysalis Records. Dist: CBS

Jets

ALLIGATOR EP.
Tracks: / Allegator EP.
Single (7"): released on Jetset, Mar'86 Dist: Rough Trade, Cartel

BLUE SKIES.
Single (7"): released on EMI, Jul'83 by EMI Records. Dist: EMI

CRUSH ON YOU.
Tracks: / Curiosity / Crush on you / You got it all / Love umbrella / Private number / Heart on the line / Right before my eyes / La la means I love you / Mesmerized / Crush on you / Right before my eyes / Crush on you (Instrumental) / Acopella.
Notes: Features their Top 5 smash "Crush On You". "Crush On You" features 4 U.S. Top 5singles. LP, Cassette and CD booklet contains full colour, fold out portraits of The Jets.
Album: released on MCA, Mar'87 by MCA Records. Dist: Polygram, MCA

Cassette: released on MCA, Mar'87 by MCA Records. Dist: Polygram, MCA

Compact disc: released on MCA, Mar'87 by MCA Records. Dist: Polygram, MCA

Single (7"): released on MCA, Apr'86 by MCA Records. Dist: Polygram, MCA

Single (12"): released on MCA, Apr'86 by MCA Records. Dist: Polygram, MCA

CURIOSITY.
Tracks: / Crush on you (crush mix)* / Curiosity / Love unbrella.
Notes: * = Extra track on 12" only.
Single (7"): released on MCA, Apr'87 by MCA Records. Dist: Polygram, MCA

Picture disc single: released on MCA, Apr'87 by MCA Records. Dist: Polygram, MCA

Single (12"): released on MCA, Apr'87 by MCA Records. Dist: Polygram, MCA

Single (7"): released on MCA, Feb'86 by MCA Records. Dist: Polygram, MCA

Single (12"): released on MCA, Feb'86 by MCA Records. Dist: Polygram, MCA

HEATWAVE.
Single (7"): released on PRT, Mar'84 by PRT Records. Dist: PRT

HEY BABY.
Single (7"): released on Soho, Jul'86

JAMES DEAN.
Single (7"): released on Soho, Jul'79

JETS.
Double-pack single: released on Fame (EMI), Sep'82 by Music For Pleasure Records. Dist: EMI Deleted '84.

Cassette: released on Fame (EMI), Sep'82 by Music For Pleasure Records. Dist: EMI

JETS,THE.
Tracks: / Curiosity / Crush on you.
Notes: Nine - piece from Minneapolis, all brothers and sisters. Album co-produced by Prince's engineer David Rivkin.
Album: released on MCA, Jun'86 by MCA Records. Dist: Polygram, MCA

Cassette: released on MCA, Jun'86 by MCA Records. Dist: Polygram, MCA

ORIGINAL TERMINAL BLOCK 4.
Single (7"): released on Good Vibration, '79 by Good Vibrations Records. Dist: Pinnacle, Rough Trade

PARTY DOLL.
Single (7"): released on PRT, Sep'84 by PRT Records. Dist: PRT

Single (12"): released on PRT, Sep'84 by PRT Records. Dist: PRT

PLATINUM HIGH SCHOOL (Jets, Johnny Storm & Shakin Stevens).
Album: released on Magnum Force, Nov'82 by Magnum Music Group Ltd. Dist: Magnum Music Group Ltd, PRT, Spartan

ROCKIN' AROUND THE CHRISTMAS TREE.
Single (7"): released on PRT, Nov'85 by PRT Records. Dist: PRT

SESSION OUT.
Album: released on Nervous, May'86 by Nervous Records. Dist: Nervous, Rough Trade

YOU GOT IT ALL.
Tracks: / You got it all / Heart on the line / Mix-doctor mix (feat Crush on you/Curiosity/Love umbrella)*.
Single (7"): released on MCA, 23 May'87 by MCA Records. Dist: Polygram, MCA

Single (12"): released on MCA, 23 May'87 by MCA Records. Dist: Polygram, MCA

Jetset, The

APRIL, MAY, JUNE AND THE JETSETS.

Album: released on Hi-Lo, Jan'87 by Hi-Lo Records. Dist: Nine Mile, Cartel

APRIL, MAY, JUNE AND THE JETSET.
Single (12"): released on Dance Network, Aug'85 by Dance Network Records. Dist: Backs, Cartel

BEST OF THE JETSET ep.
Single (7"): released on Dance Network, Oct'83 by Dance Network Records. Dist: Backs, Cartel

GO BANANAS.
Album: released on Dance Network, Mar'86 by Dance Network Records. Dist: Backs, Cartel

JUDY'S TOY BOX.
Single (7"): released on Dance Network, Feb'84 by Dance Network Records. Dist: Backs, Cartel

THERE GOES THE NEIGHBOUR.
Album: released on Dance Network, Mar'85 by Dance Network Records. Dist: Backs, Cartel

Jetstone

JU JU.
Tracks: / Ju Ju / Ju Ju (Remix) / Ju Ju (Inst Mix).
Single (7"): released on Carrere, Apr'86 by Carrere Records. Dist: PRT, Spartan

Single (12"): released on Carrere, Apr'86 by Carrere Records. Dist: PRT, Spartan

Jett, Joan

ALBUM (Jett, Joan and the Blackhearts).
Album: released on Epic, Sep'83 by CBS Records. Dist: CBS

Cassette: released on Epic, Sep'83 by CBS Records. Dist: CBS

BAD REPUTATION.
Album: released on Epic, Oct'82 by CBS Records. Dist: CBS Deleted '84.

Cassette: released on Epic, Oct'82 by CBS Records. Dist: CBS

GOOD MUSIC.
Single (7"): released on Polydor, Aug'87 by Polydor Records. Dist: Polygram, Polydor

Single (12"): released on Polydor, Aug'87 by Polydor Records. Dist: Polygram, Polydor

I LOVE PLAYING WITH FIRE (Jett, Joan & the Runaways).
Album: released on Cherry Red, Apr'82 by Cherry Red Records. Dist: Pinnacle

I LOVE ROCK AND ROLL (Jett, Joan and the Blackhearts).
Album: released on Epic, Apr'82 by CBS Records. Dist: CBS

Cassette: released on Epic, Apr'82 by CBS Records. Dist: CBS

I LOVE YOU LOVE ME LOVED (Jett, Joan and the Blackhearts).
Single (7"): released on Epic, Oct'84 by CBS Records. Dist: CBS

I NEED SOMEONE.
Single (7"): released on Epic, Apr'85 by CBS Records. Dist: CBS

Single (12"): released on Epic, Apr'85 by CBS Records. Dist: CBS

Jeunesse

I GET SO EXCITED.
Tracks: / I get so excited / Love attack.
Single (7"): released on Jive, Sep'86 by Zomba Records. Dist: RCA, PRT, CBS

Single (12"): released on Jive, Sep'86 by Zomba Records. Dist: RCA, PRT, CBS

Jeunnesse

MY LOVE CAN ONLY GET STRONGER.
Single (7"): released on R.E.D., Mar'84 by R.E.D. Records.

Jewel In The Crown

JEWEL IN THE CROWN TV Soundtrack.
Album: released on Chrysalis, Feb'84 by Chrysalis Records. Dist: CBS

Cassette: released on Chrysalis, Feb'84 by Chrysalis Records. Dist: CBS

Jewel Of The Nile

JEWEL OF THE NILE,THE Original soundtrack.
Notes: Artists include: Billy Ocean/Ruby Turner/Precious Wilson.
Album: released on Jive, Feb'86 by Zomba Records. Dist: RCA, PRT, CBS

Cassette: released on Jive, Jul'86 by Zomba Records. Dist: RCA, PRT, CBS

Jewel Spotlights

JEWEL SPOTLIGHTS, VOL.1 various artists (Various Artists).
Album: released on Jewel, Sep'79

Jewel, T. & L.T.C.

BELIEVE IT OR NOT.
Tracks: / Believe it or not / Believe it or not (Inst) Club mix.
Single (12"): released on Malaco Dance, Oct'86 Dist: PRT

Jewish Party

JEWISH PARTY various artists (Various Artists).
Album: released on Zomart, May'82 Dist: Pinnacle

Jewkes, Noel

LEGATO EXPRESS.
Album: released on Revelation, Apr'81

Jezzrell

ALL DEPENDS ON YOU.
Single (12"): released on Wackies, Apr'85 by Wackies Records. Dist: Jetstar

STOP PLAYUING TRICKS.
Single (12"): released on Wackies, Nov'83 by Wackies Records. Dist: Jetstar

J.F.A.

VALLEY OF THE YAKES.
Album: released on Fundamental, Jul'87 by Fundamental Records. Dist: Red Rhino, Cartel

J, Harry Allstars

LIQUIDATOR, (THE).
Single (7"): released on Old Gold, Jul'84 by Old Gold Records. Dist: Lightning, Jazz Music, Spartan, Counterpoint

Jiani, Carol

ASK ME.

Single (12"): released on Excaliber, Sep'82 by Red Bus Records. Dist: PRT

SUCH A JOY HONEY.
Tracks: / Such a joy honey / Such a joy honey (instrumental).
Single (7"): released on MCA, Mar'87 by MCA Records. Dist: Polygram, MCA

Jigsaw

LOVE ISN'T A HOME.
Single (7"): released on Splash, Jan'83 by Splash Records. Dist: CBS

SKY HIGH.
Tracks: / Sky high / Fly away.
Single (7"): released on Splash, Jul'86 by Splash Records. Dist: CBS

Single (12"): released on Splash, Jul'86 by Splash Records. Dist: CBS

JIH

BIG BLUE OCEAN.
Tracks: / Big blue ocean / Closer now / As you fall*.
Single (7"): released on Breadth Of Vision, Jan'87 Dist: Jetstar, Cartel, Jungle

Single (12"): released on Breadth Of Vision, Jan'87 Dist: Jetstar, Cartel, Jungle

SHADOW IN FULL, THE/BREADTH OF VISION.
Album: released on Jungle, Nov'86 by Jungle Records. Dist: Jungle, Cartel

THIS GIFT.
Tracks: / This gift / Shadow to fall.
Single (12"): released on Breadth Of Vision, Apr'86 Dist: Jetstar, Cartel, Jungle

Jimenez, Flaco

A TE DEJO EN SAN ANTONIO.
Album: released on Arhoolie, Jul'86 by Arhoolie Records. Dist: Projection, Topic, Jazz Music, Swift, Roots

FLACO JIMENEZ & HIS CONJUNTO.
Album: released on Arhoolie, May'81 by Arhoolie Records. Dist: Projection, Topic, Jazz Music, Swift, Roots

OPEN UP YOUR HEART.
Single (7"): released on Waterfront, Apr'85 by Waterfront Records. Dist: Rough Trade, Cartel, Projection, Roots

SAN ANTONIO SATURDAY NIGHT.
Notes: Including Flaco Jiminez
Album: released on Sonet, Jan'86 by Sonet Records. Dist: PRT

SAN ANTONIO SOUND, THE (Jimenez, Flaco Y Su Conjunto).
Album: released on Waterfront, Apr'85 by Waterfront Records. Dist: Rough Trade, Cartel, Projection, Roots

SONIDO DE SAN ANTONIO, EL.
Album: released on Arhoolie, May'81 by Arhoolie Records. Dist: Projection, Topic, Jazz Music, Swift, Roots

SON OF SANTIAGO.
Album: released on Waterfront, Oct'85 by Waterfront Records. Dist: Rough Trade, Cartel, Projection, Roots

Single (12"): released on Waterfront, Nov'85 by Waterfront Records. Dist: Rough Trade, Cartel, Projection, Roots

TEX MEX BREAKDOWN (Jimenez, Flaco Y Su Conjunto).
Album: released on Sonet, Nov'83 by Sonet Records. Dist: PRT

VIVA SEGUIN.
Album: released on Rogue, Jun'86 by Fast Forward Records. Dist: Nine Mile Distribution, Cartel Distribution

Jimenez, Santiago

SANTIAGO JIMENEZ WITH FLACO JIMENEZ.
Album: released on Arhoolie, May'81 by Arhoolie Records. Dist: Projection, Topic, Jazz Music, Swift, Roots

STRIKES AGAIN (Jimenez, Santiago Jnr).
Album: released on Arhoolie, Mar'85 by Arhoolie Records. Dist: Projection, Topic, Jazz Music, Swift, Roots

Jim & Jesse

EPIC BLUEGRASS HITS,THE.
Album: released on Rounder (USA), Dec'85 Dist: Mike's Country Music Room Distribution, Jazz Music Distribution, Swift Distribution, Roots Records Distribution, Projection Distribution, Topic Distribution

HANDFUL OF GOOD SEEDS, A (Jim & Jesse & the Virginia Boys).
Album: released on Canaan(USA), May'82 by Word Records. Dist: Word Distribution
Cat. no: **CGS 8512**
Cassette: released on Canaan(USA), May'82 by Word Records. Dist: Word Distribution

Jimmy, Bobby

ROACHES (Jimmy, Bobby & The Critters).
Tracks: / Roaches / Roaches (Instrumental).
Single (12"): released on Spartan, Aug'86 by Spartan Records. Dist: Spartan

Jimmy, Jimmy

HERE IN THE LIGHT.
Tracks: / Forget your sorrow / Sarah Moon / Silence / Here in the light / Lady / Following dreams / Passing dream / I met her in Paris / Love / Kettle's boiling,The.
Album: released on Epic, Mar'86 by CBS Records. Dist: CBS

Cassette: released on Epic, Mar'86 by CBS Records. Dist: CBS

I MET HER IN PARIS.
Single (12"): released on Epic, Jun'85 by CBS Records. Dist: CBS

SILENCE.
Tracks: / Silence / Songs from the street.
Single (7"): released on Epic, Feb'86 by CBS Records. Dist: CBS

Single (12"): released on Epic, Feb'86 by CBS Records. Dist: CBS

Jimmy The Hoover

TANTALISE.
Single (7"): released on Inner Vision, Jun'83 by CBS Records. Dist: CBS

Single (12"): released on Inner Vision, Jun'83 by CBS Records. Dist: CBS

Jingle Belles

CHRISTMAS SPECTRE.
Tracks: / Christmas spectre / This time next year.
Single (7"): released on Passion, Nov'86 by Skratch Records. Dist: PRT

Single (12"): released on Passion, Nov'86 by Skratch Records. Dist: PRT

Jingle Jangle

JINGLE JANGLE Original London cast (Featuring Norman Wisdom).
Album: released on That's Entertainment, May'83 by That's Entertainment Records. Dist: Pinnacle, PRT

Jing Ying Soloists

LIKE WAVES AGAINST THE SAND.
Tracks: / Chinese martial arts / Flower fair,The / Flowing streams,The / Night / Shenpadei folksong / Races,The / Love at the fair / Suzhou scenery / High moon,The / Like waves against the sand / Birdsong / Legend.
Notes: One of our most outstanding and surprising recordings on LP was 'Like Waves Agairist The Sand' by the Jing Ying Soloists and featuring traditional Chinese instruments and music in both solo and ensemble roles. When reviewed, Hi-Fi Newssaid 'I've never heard anything quite like this record -a dem-disc of the year -fantastic cleanliness of sound'. The transfer of this rrecording to CD. plus the addition of three further tracks which could not be fitted on the LP versionmakes for a 65 minute CD. of outstanding musical, technical and financial value.The evocative melodies and interesting rhythms of this traditional music are very approachable to the Western ear and full of surprises. The instrments usedare the Erhu(Tong Leung-tak) - a two stringed bowed instrument with a lovely mellow quality; the Pipa(Chan Man Gehong) - Chinese lute; Dizi(Lam Si Kwan) - Bamboo flutes with great expressive power and bright sonority; Yangqin(Chan Ki Cham) - the very versatile Chinese dulcimer played with two bamboo sticks; and the virtuoso Chinese percussion playing of Ho Man Chuen. CD. booklet in EnglishFrench and German.
Compact disc: released on Saydisc, May'86 by Saydisc Records. Dist: Essex, Harmonia Mundi, Roots, H.R. Taylor, Jazz Music, Swift, Projection, Gamut

Album: released on Saydisc, Nov'81 by Saydisc Records. Dist: Essex, Harmonia Mundi, Roots, H.R. Taylor, Jazz Music, Swift, Projection, Gamut

Cassette: released on Saydisc, Nov'81 by Saydisc Records. Dist: Essex, Harmonia Mundi, Roots, H.R. Taylor, Jazz Music, Swift, Projection, Gamut

Jin Records

JIN RECORDS - LOUISIANA BLUES (Various Artists).
Notes: Compilation featuring the best of Jin Records blues output. Artists include:Carol Fran, Rockin' Doopsie and Junior Cole.
Double Album: released on Ace, Aug'87 by Ace Records. Dist: Pinnacle, Swift, Hotshot, Cadillac

Jin Story

JIN STORY VOL.1 - BAYOU BOOGIE various artists (Various Artists).

Jive

JIVE, JIVE, JIVE,VOL.3 various artists (Various Artists).

Album: released on Jivin (Belguim), Feb'84

JIVE, JIVE, JIVE,VOL.4 various artists (Various Artists).
Album: released on Jivin (Belguim), May'84

JIVE, JIVE, JIVE,VOL.5 various artists (Various Artists).
Album: released on Jivin (Belguim), May'84

JIVE, JIVE, JIVE,VOL.6 various artists (Various Artists).
Album: released on Jivin (Belguim), May'84

Jive Alive

CHOO CHOO CH' BOOGIE.
Single (7"): released on Juke Box, Jun'84

Jive At Five

JIVE AT FIVE Various artists (Various Artists).
Album: released on New World (USA), Feb'87 by New World Records (USA). Dist: Conifer

Jive Bombers

BAD BOY.
Album:

THOSE BLOODSHOT EYES.
Single (7"): released on Meantime, Aug'81 Dist: Red Rhino, Cartel

Jive Electro

JIVE ELECTRO various artists (Various Artists).
Album: released on Jive, Oct'85 by Zomba Records. Dist: RCA, PRT, CBS

Cassette: released on Jive, Oct'85 by Zomba Records. Dist: RCA, PRT, CBS

Jive Five

OUR TRUE STORY.
Album: released on Ace, Aug'83 by Ace Records. Dist: Pinnacle, Swift, Hotshot, Cadillac

WAY BACK.
Album: released on Ambient Sound, Apr'85

Jive Marines

HOLIDAY SONG.
Single (7"): released on Rewind, Aug'82 by Rewind Records. Dist: Spartan

Jive Rap Attack

JIVE RAP ATTACK various artists (Various Artists).
Album: released on Jive, Aug'85 by Zomba Records. Dist: RCA, PRT, CBS

Cassette: released on Jive, Aug'85 by Zomba Records. Dist: RCA, PRT, CBS

Jive, Willie

MESSAGE IS CLEAR.
Single (7"): released on Cheapskate, Jan'82 by Cheapskate Records. Dist: RCA

Jivin' The Blues

JIVIN' THE BLUES various artists (Various Artists).
Album: released on Big Bear, '82 by Big Bear Records. Dist: Big Bear, Swift

J.J

BREAKDANCE HOLIDAY (J.J.'S Breakdance Krew).
Single (7"): released on Weasel, Apr'85 by Weasel Records. Dist: Spartan

FEELS LIKE I'M IN HEAVEN (J.J. and Trouble with Harry).
Single (7"): released on R.E.D., Sep'84 by R.E.D. Records.

NO PARTICULAR PLACE TO GO (J.J & The Rockets).

J. L.L. Cool

I NEED LOVE.
Single (7"): released on Def Jam (USA), Aug'87 by CBS Records. Dist: CBS

Single (12"): released on Def Jam (USA), Aug'87 by CBS Records. Dist: CBS

Joan Of Arc

TELL-A-TALE.
Cassette: released on Pickwick (Tell-a-tale), Mar'84 by Pickwick Records. Dist: Pickwick Distribution

Jobarteh, Malamini

JALIYA (GAMBIA).
Tracks: / Segou tutu / Mbassi / Solo / Bamba bojang / Tutu Jara / Fode kaba / Cheddo.
Notes: Traditional kora music from two of the Gambia's finest griots. A sensitive recording of this delicate instrument. '....one of the finest records of tradi-tional music to come our way in 1985. (Folk Roots)'
Album: released on Sterns, Sep'86 by Sterns Records. Dist: Sterns/Triple Earth Distribution

Jobim, Antonio Carlos

CERTAIN MISTER, A.
Cassette: released on Pickwick, May'80 by Pickwick Records. Dist: Pickwick Distribution, Prism Leisure Distribution, Lugtons

Album: released on Pickwick, May'80 by Pickwick Records. Dist: Pickwick Distribution, Prism Leisure Distribution, Lugtons

CERTAIN MR. JOBIM, A.
Compact disc: released on Discovery (USA), Dec'86 by Discovery Records (USA). Dist: Swift, Flexitron-Audio, Jazz Music

Album: released on Discovery (USA), Jan'84

Cassette: released on Discovery (USA), Jan'84

COMPOSER PLAYS,THE.
Tracks: / Girl from Ipenema,The / O morro / Auga de beber / Dreamer / Favela / Insensatez / Corcovado / One note samba / Meditation / Jazz samba / Chega de saudade / Des finado.
Compact disc: released on Polydor, Jul'85 by Polydor Records. Dist: Polygram, Polydor

PLAYS JOBIM.
Album: released on Verve (USA), Sep'84 by Polydor. Dist: Polygram

Cassette: released on Verve (USA), Sep'84 by Polydor. Dist: Polygram

WONDERFUL WORLD OF....,THE.
Tracks: / She's a carioca / Agua de beber / Felicidade,A / Dindi / Useless landscape / Favela.
Compact disc: released on Discovery (USA), Sep'86 by Discovery Records (USA). Dist: Swift, Flexitron-Audio, Jazz Music

WONDERFUL WORLD OF , THE.
Album: released on Discovery, Feb'84 Dist: PRT

Jobotti, Gerbina

MR BIG STUFF.
Tracks: / Mr Big Stuff / I've never been an angel (so love me for my faults) / Mr Big Stuff (7" mix).
Single (12"): released on Salome, Jul'87 by Salome Records. Dist: Rough Trade, Cartel

Single (7"): released on Salidu, Aug'87 by Salidu Records. Dist: PRT

Joboxers

BOXERBEAT.
Single (7"): released on RCA, Feb'83 by RCA Records. Dist: RCA, Roots, Swift, Wellard, Chris, I & B, Solomon & Peres Distribution

Single (12"): released on RCA, Feb'83 by RCA Records. Dist: RCA, Roots, Swift, Wellard, Chris, I & B, Solomon & Peres Distribution

IS THIS REALLY THE FIRST TIME.
Single (7"): released on RCA, Mar'85 by RCA Records. Dist: RCA, Roots, Swift, Wellard, Chris, I & B, Solomon & Peres Distribution

Single (12"): released on RCA, Mar'85 by RCA Records. Dist: RCA, Roots, Swift, Wellard, Chris, I & B, Solomon & Peres Distribution

JEALOUS LOVE.
Single (7"): released on RCA, Oct'83 by RCA Records. Dist: RCA, Roots, Swift, Wellard, Chris, I & B, Solomon & Peres Distribution

Single (12"): released on RCA, Oct'83 by RCA Records. Dist: RCA, Roots, Swift, Wellard, Chris, I & B, Solomon & Peres Distribution

JOHNNY FREINDLY.
Single (7"): released on RCA, Aug'83 by RCA Records. Dist: RCA, Roots, Swift, Wellard, Chris, I & B, Solomon & Peres Distribution

Single (12"): released on RCA, Aug'83 by RCA Records. Dist: RCA, Roots, Swift, Wellard, Chris, I & B, Solomon & Peres Distribution

JUST GOT LUCKY.
Single (7"): released on RCA, Jun'83 by RCA Records. Dist: RCA, Roots, Swift, Wellard, Chris, I & B, Solomon & Peres Distribution

LIKE GANGBUSTERS.
Tracks: / Just got lucky / Curious George / Crime of passion / She's got sex / Fully booked / Hide nor hair / Not my night / Boxerbeat / Crosstown walk up / Johnny Friendly.
Album: released on RCA, Sep'86 by RCA Records. Dist: RCA, Roots, Swift, Wellard, Chris, I & B, Solomon & Peres Distribution

Cassette: released on RCA, Sep'86 by RCA Records. Dist: RCA, Roots, Swift, Wellard, Chris, I & B, Solomon & Peres Distribution

SKIN & BONE.
Album: released on RCA, Apr'85 by RCA Records. Dist: RCA, Roots, Swift, Wellard, Chris, I & B, Solomon & Peres Distribution

Cassette: released on RCA, Apr'85 by RCA Records. Dist: RCA, Roots, Swift, Wellard, Chris, I & B, Solomon & Peres Distribution

Job Satisfaction

(STOCKHOLM, TOKYO, NEW YORK, LONDON).
Cassette: released on International Report, Oct'81 by Seminar Cassettes. Dist: Audio-Visual Library Services, Davidson Distribution, Eastern Educational Products Distrib., Forlaget Systime Distribution, MacDougall Distribution, Talktapes Distribution, Watkins Books Ltd Distribution, Norton, Jeff Distribution

Jobson, Richard

16 YEARS OF ALCHOHOL.
Album: released on Les Disques Du Crepuscle, Jan'87 Dist: Rough Trade, Pinnacle, Island, Polygram

BALLAD OF ETIQUETTE, THE.
Album: released on Cocteau, Jul'85 by Cocteau Records. Dist: Pinnacle, IDS

OTHER MAN,THE.
Album: released on Les Disques Du Crepuscule, Feb'86 Dist: Rough Trade, Pinnacle, Island, Polygram

Jo'burg hawk

JO'BURG HAWK.
Album: released on Charisma, Mar'84 by Virgin Records. Dist: EMI

Cassette: released on Charisma, Mar'84 by Virgin Records. Dist: EMI

Jock Strapp

COMPLEAT RUGBY SONGS.
Double Album: released on Sportsdisc, Nov'85 by Sportsdisc Records. Dist: H.R. Taylor, MIS-EMI Distribution

Double cassette: released on Sportsdisc, Nov'85 by Sportsdisc Records. Dist: H.R. Taylor, MIS-EMI Distribution

RUGBY SONGS VOL 2 (Jock Strapp Ensemble).
Album: released on Sportsdisc, Jul'80 by Sportsdisc Records. Dist: H.R. Taylor, MIS-EMI Distribution

RUGBY SONGS VOL 3 (Jock Strapp Ensemble).
Album: released on Sportsdisc, Jul'80 by Sportsdisc Records. Dist: H.R. Taylor, MIS-EMI Distribution

Jodie & Sherri

GYPSY BOY.
Single (12"): released on Splendid, Jan'85 by Splendid Records. Dist: Jetstar

Jodimars

WELL NOW DIG THIS.
Album: released on Bulldog, Jul'82 by Bulldog Records. Dist: President Distribution, Spartan, Swift, Taylor, H.R.

Cassette: released on Bulldog, Aug'82 by Bulldog Records. Dist: President Distribution, Spartan, Swift, Taylor, H.R.

Single (7"): released on President, Nov'79 by President Records. Dist: Taylors, Spartan

Jody

ACCIDENT.
Single (7"): released on Thunderbay, Apr'83 Dist: Spartan Distribution

YOU AND YOUR LOVE (ONE SIDED DISC) (Jody (Featuring Derek & Jude)).
Single (7"): released on Thunderbay, Apr'83 Dist: Spartan Distribution

Jody & Dee

SOME GIRLS (ONE SIDED SINGLE).
Single (7"): released on Thunderbay, Jan'83 Dist: Spartan Distribution

Joel, Billy

52ND STREET.
Album: released on CBS, Nov'85 by CBS Records. Dist: CBS

Cassette: released on CBS, Nov'85 by CBS Records. Dist: CBS

AN INNOCENT MAN.

AN INNOCENT MAN.
Compact disc: released on CBS, Aug'84 by CBS Records. Dist: CBS

Album: released on CBS, Sep'83 by CBS Records. Dist: CBS

Cassette: released on CBS, Sep'83 by CBS Records. Dist: CBS

Compact disc: released on CBS, Aug'84 by CBS Records. Dist: CBS

BILLY JOEL.
Cassette: released on CBS, Aug'82 by CBS Records. Dist: CBS

BILLY JOEL (3 LP BOX SET).
Album: released on CBS, Oct'79 by CBS Records. Dist: CBS

BRIDGE,THE.
Tracks: / Running on ice / This is the time / Matter of trust,A / Baby grand / Big man on Mulberry street / Temptation / Code of silence / Getting closer.
Album: released on CBS, Aug'86 by CBS Records. Dist: CBS

Cassette: released on CBS, Aug'86 by CBS Records. Dist: CBS

Compact disc: by CBS Records. Dist: CBS

CALIFORNIA FLASH.
Tracks: / Wonder woman / California flash / Revenge is sweet / Amplifier fire / Godzilla part 1 / Rolling home / Tear this castle down / Brain invasion.
Album: released on Showcase, Apr'86 Dist: Counterpoint

Cassette: released on Showcase, Apr'86 Dist: Counterpoint

CALIFORNIA FLASH.
Album: released on Platinum (W.Germany), Oct'85 Dist: Mainline

Cassette: released on Platinum (W.Germany), Oct'85 Dist: Mainline

COLD SPRING HARBOUR.
Album: released on CBS, Jan'84 by CBS Records. Dist: CBS

Cassette: released on CBS, Jan'84 by CBS Records. Dist: CBS

FOR THE LONGEST TIME CHRISTIE LEE.
Single (7"): released on CBS, Apr'84 by CBS Records. Dist: CBS

Single (12"): released on CBS, Apr'84 by CBS Records. Dist: CBS

GLASS HOUSE.
Tracks: / Through the long night / You maybe right / Don't ask me why / Sometimes a fantasy / It's still rock and roll to me / All for Leyna / I don't want to be alone / Sleeping with the television on / C'etait toi / Close to the borderline.
Compact disc: released on CBS, Nov'85 by CBS Records. Dist: CBS

Album: released on CBS, Mar'80 by CBS Records. Dist: CBS

GLASS HOUSES.
Tracks: / You may be right / Sometimes a fantasy / Don't ask me why / It's still rock'n'roll to me / All for Leyna / I don't want to be alone / Sleeping with the television on / C'etait toi (you were the one) / Close to the borderline / Through the long night.
Album: released on CBS, Nov'86 by CBS Records. Dist: CBS

Cassette: released on CBS, Nov'86 by CBS Records. Dist: CBS

GOODNIGHT SAIGON.
Single (7"): released on CBS, Feb'83 by CBS Records. Dist: CBS

GREATEST HITS: BILLY JOEL VOL.1 & 2.
Album: released on CBS, Jul'85 by CBS Records. Dist: CBS

Cassette: released on CBS, Jul'85 by CBS Records. Dist: CBS

Compact disc: released on CBS, Jul'85 by CBS Records. Dist: CBS

GREATEST HITS: BILLY JOEL VOL.1 & 2.
Tracks: / Piano man / Say goodbye to Hollywood / New York state of mind / Stranger,The / Just the way you are / Movin' out (Anothoy's song) / Only the good die young / She's always a woman / My life / Big shot / Honesty / You maybe right / It's still rock and roll to me / Pressure / Allen town / Goodnight saigon / Tell her about it / Uptown girl / Longest time,The / You're only human (Second wind) / Night is still young,The.

GREATEST ORIGINAL HITS (4 TRACK EP).
Single (7"): released on CBS, Mar'83 by CBS Records. Dist: CBS

INNOCENT MAN.
Single (12"): released on CBS, Jan'84 by CBS Records. Dist: CBS

LEAVE A TENDER MOMENT ALONE.
Single (7"): released on CBS, Jun'84 by CBS Records. Dist: CBS

Single (12"): released on CBS, Jun'84 by CBS Records. Dist: CBS

LIVE ON LONG ISLAND.
Video-cassette (VHS): released on CBS, Sep'84 by CBS Records. Dist: CBS

MATTER OF TRUST, A.
Tracks: / Matter of trust, A / Getting closer / Tell her about it / An innocent man.
Single (7"): released on CBS, Aug'86 by CBS Records. Dist: CBS

Single (12"): released on CBS, Sep'86 by CBS Records. Dist: CBS

MODERN WOMAN.
Tracks: / Modern woman / Sleeps with the television on / Night is still young / You're only human / Uptown girl / All for love.
Single (7"): released on CBS, Jun'86 by CBS Records. Dist: CBS

Single (12"): released on CBS, Jul'86 by CBS Records. Dist: CBS

Double-pack single: released on CBS, Jul'86 by CBS Records. Dist: CBS

NYLON CURTAIN.
Tracks: / Allentown / Laura / Pressure / Goodnight Saigon / She's right on time / Room of our own / Surprises / Scandinavian skies / Where's the orchestra.
Compact disc: released on CBS, Jan'83 by CBS Records. Dist: CBS

Album: released on CBS, Sep'82 by CBS Records. Dist: CBS

Cassette: released on CBS, Sep'82 by CBS Records. Dist: CBS

PIANO MAN.
Tracks: / Travelin' prayer / Ain't no crime / You're my home / Ballad of Billy The Kid,The / Worst comes to worst / Stop in Nevada / If I only had the words (To tell You) / Somewhere along the line / Captain Jack.
Compact disc: released on CBS, Sep'85 by CBS Records. Dist: CBS

Album: released on CBS, Mar'81 by CBS Records. Dist: CBS

Cassette: released on CBS, Mar'81 by CBS Records. Dist: CBS

Cassette: released on Epic, Feb'83 by CBS Records. Dist: CBS

SHE'S ALWAYS A WOMAN TO ME.
Tracks: / She's always a woman to me / Just the way you are.
Single (7"): released on CBS, Feb'86 by CBS Records. Dist: CBS

SONGS IN THE ATTIC.
Tracks: / Miami 2017 (seen the lights go out on broadway) / Summer, highland falls / Streetlife serenade / Los Angelenos / She's got a way / Everybody loves you now / Say goodbye to Hollywood / Captain Jack / You're my home / Ballad of Billy The Kid / I've loved these days.
Compact disc: released on CBS, May'87 by CBS Records. Dist: CBS

Album: released on CBS, Nov'83 by CBS Records. Dist: CBS

Cassette: released on CBS, Nov'83 by CBS Records. Dist: CBS

SPRING HARBOUR.
Compact disc: released on CBS, May'87 by CBS Records. Dist: CBS

STARING AT ME GIRL.
Single (12"): released on Leggo, Jul'82

STRANGER/INNOCENT MAN.
Album: released on CBS, Jul'87 by CBS Records. Dist: CBS

STRANGER, THE.
Tracks: / Just the way you are / Senes from an Italian restaurant / Vienna / Only the good die young / She's always a woman / Get it right the first time / Everybody has a dream / Movin' out (Anthony's song) / Stranger, the.
Album: released on CBS, May'87 by CBS Records. Dist: CBS

Cassette: released on CBS, May'87 by CBS Records. Dist: CBS

STRANGER,THE.
Tracks: / Movin' out / Just the way you are / Scenes from an Italian restaurant / Viena / Stranger / Only the good die young / She's always a woman / Get it right the first time / Everybody has a dream.
Compact disc: released on CBS, Dec'85 by CBS Records. Dist: CBS

Cassette: released on CBS, Dec'77 by CBS Records. Dist: CBS

STREETLIFE SERENADE.
Album: released on CBS, Mar'81 by CBS Records. Dist: CBS

Cassette: released on CBS, Mar'81 by CBS Records. Dist: CBS

Compact disc: released on CBS, Mar'87 by CBS Records. Dist: CBS

Tracks: / Los Angelinos / Great suburban showdown / Root beer rag / Roberta / Entertainer / Last of the big time spenders / Streetlife serenade / Weekend song / Souvenier / Mexican connection.

TELL HER ABOUT IT.
Single (12"): released on CBS, Aug'83 by CBS Records. Dist: CBS

THIS IS THE TIME.
Tracks: / This is the time.
Single (7"): released on CBS, Nov'86 by CBS Records. Dist: CBS

TURNSTILES.
Tracks: / I've loved these days / Mami 2017 (seen the lights go out on Broadway) / Angry young man / Say goodbye to Hollywood / James / New York State of mind / Prelude/Angry young man / Summer / Highland falls / All you wanna do is dance.
Compact disc: released on CBS, Mar'87 by CBS Records. Dist: CBS

Album: released on CBS, Nov'81 by CBS Records. Dist: CBS

Cassette: released on CBS, Nov'81 by CBS Records. Dist: CBS

UPTOWN GIRL.
Single (12"): released on CBS, Sep'83 by CBS Records. Dist: CBS

VIDEO ALBUM - VOL.1, THE.
Video-cassette (VHS): released on CBS, Nov'86 by CBS Records. Dist: CBS

Johal, H.S.

CHHAMAK JEHI MUTIAR (Johal, H.S. & Pali Cheema).
Tracks: / Chhamek jehi mutiar / Tut gayiaan choorian / Kardhi char gaye jawani / Maye ne maye / Chitti bag babey di noo / Lai gaye kadh kay kalja / Southall ch pawara paya goriay / Putt ney nishani jagg tey / Meri laggey bharjai / Sambh jawani noo.
Notes: Lyrics by Pali Cheema, composed by Kuljit Bhamra. Music Director Kuljit Singh Bhamra. Savera Investments, Unit 24, Vernon Buildings, Westbourne Street, High Wycombe, Bucks HP11 2PZ. Tel: 0494 25441/2.
Album: released on H S Johal, '86

Johansen, Glen

KILLER ON THE RAMPAGE.
Single (7"): released on Silvertown, Oct'83 by Silvertown Records.

Single (12"): released on Silvertown, Oct'83 by Silvertown Records.

Johansen, Henrik

DANISH JAZZ VOL 4.
Album: released on Storyville, Jul'82 by Storyville Records. Dist: Jazz Music Distribution, Swift Distribution, Chris Wellard Distribution, Counterpoint Distribution

Johansson, Ake

LIVE AT NEFERTITI.
Album: released on Dragon, Jul'83 by Dragon Records. Dist: Jazz Music, Projection, Cadillac

Johansson, Lasse

KING PORTER STOMP.
Album: released on Kicking Mule, Nov'80 by Sonet. Dist: Roots, PRT-

John

HELLO ALEXEI.
Single (7"): released on Red Door, Dec'84 by Red Door Records. Dist: Red Door

John, Elton

21 AT 33.
Tracks: / Changing the crown / Dear God / Give me the love / Little Jeannie / Never gonna fall in love again / Sartorial eloquence / Take me back / Two rooms at the end of the world / White lady white powder.
Compact disc: released on Rocket, '83 by Phonogram Records. Dist: Polygram Distribution

Album: released on Rocket, Jul'84 by Phonogram Records. Dist: Polygram Distribution

Cassette: released on Rocket, Jul'84 by Phonogram Records. Dist: Polygram Distribution

ACT OF WAR (John, Elton/Millie Jackson).
Single (12"): released on Rocket, Jun'85 by Phonogram Records. Dist: Polygram Distribution

ACT OF WAR (PART 5) (John, Elton/Millie Jackson).
Single (12"): released on Rocket, Jun'85 by Phonogram Records. Dist: Polygram Distribution

ALBUM, THE.
Album: released on Hallmark, Sep'81 by Pickwick Records. Dist: Pickwick Distribution, PRT, Taylors

Cassette: released on Hallmark, Sep'81 by Pickwick Records. Dist: Pickwick Distribution, PRT, Taylors

BENNIE AND THE JETS.
Single (7"): released on DJM, Sep'76 by DJM Records. Dist: CBS, Polygram

BITCH IS BACK.
Single (7"): released on DJM, Sep'78 by DJM Records. Dist: CBS, Polygram

BLUE EYES.
Single (7"): released on Rocket, Mar'82 by Phonogram Records. Dist: Polygram Distribution

BLUE MOVES.
Double Album: released on Rocket, Sep'84 by Phonogram Records. Dist: Polygram Distribution

Double cassette: released on Rocket, Sep'84 by Phonogram Records. Dist: Polygram Distribution

BORDER SONG.
Single (7"): released on DJM, Sep'78 by DJM Records. Dist: CBS, Polygram

BREAKING HEARTS.
Tracks: / Restless / Slow down Georgia / Who wears these shoes / Breaking hearts / Li'l refrigerator / Passengers / In neon / Burning bridges / Did he shoot her / Sad songs.
Notes: Digital stereo
Compact disc: released on Rocket, Aug'84 by Phonogram Records. Dist: Polygram Distribution

Album: released on Rocket, Jun'84 by Phonogram Records. Dist: Polygram Distribution

Cassette: released on Rocket, Jun'84 by Phonogram Records. Dist: Polygram Distribution

CANDLE IN THE WIND.
Single (7"): released on DJM, Sep'78 by DJM Records. Dist: CBS, Polygram

CAPTAIN FANTASTIC & THE BROWN DIRT COWBOY.
Tracks: / Captain Fantastic & The Brown Dirt Cowboy / Tower of Babel / Bitter fingers / Tell me when the whistle blows / Someone saved my life tonight / Gotta get a meal ticket / Better off dead / Writing / We all falll in love sometimes / Curtains.
Notes: Digital stereo
Compact disc: released on DJM, Oct'84 by DJM Records. Dist: CBS, Polygram

Album: released on DJM, May'81 by DJM Records. Dist: CBS, Polygram

Cassette: released on DJM, May'81 by DJM Records. Dist: CBS, Polygram

Compact disc: released on DJM, May'81 by DJM Records. Dist: CBS, Polygram

CARIBOU.
Tracks: / Bitch is back, The / Pinky Grimsby / Dixie Lily / Solar prestige / Gammon, A / Don't let the sun go down on me / Ticking.
Compact disc: released on DJM, Oct'86 by DJM Records. Dist: CBS, Polygram

Album: released on DJM, May'81 by DJM Records. Dist: CBS, Polygram

Cassette: released on DJM, May'81 by DJM Records. Dist: CBS, Polygram

CROCODILE ROCK.
Album: released on Karussell (Import), Mar'82

Cassette: released on Karussell (Import), Mar'82

Album: released on Karussell Gold (Germany), Aug'85

Cassette: released on Karussell Gold (Germany), Aug'85

Single (7"): released on DJM, Sep'78 by DJM Records. Dist: CBS, Polygram

CRY TO HEAVEN.
Tracks: / Cry to heaven / Candy by the pound / Rock'n'roll medley (live).
Single (7"): released on Rocket, Feb'86 by Phonogram Records. Dist: Polygram Distribution

Single (12"): released on Rocket, Feb'86 by Phonogram Records. Dist: Polygram Distribution

DANIEL.
Single (7"): released on DJM, May'78 by DJM Records. Dist: CBS, Polygram

DEAR GOD.
Single (7"): released on Rocket, Nov'80 by Phonogram Records. Dist: Polygram Distribution Deleted May'81.

DON'T LET THE SUN GO DOWN.
Single (7"): released on DJM, Sep'78 by DJM Records. Dist: CBS, Polygram

DON'T SHOOT ME I'M ONLY THE PIANO PLAYER.
Tracks: / Daniel / Teacher I need you / Elderberry wine / Blues for my baby and me / Midnight creeper / Have mercy on the criminal / I'm going to be a teenage idol / Texan love song / Crocodile rock / High flying bird.
Compact disc: released on DJM, Apr'86 by DJM Records. Dist: CBS, Polygram

Album: released on DJM, May'81 by DJM Records. Dist: CBS, Polygram

Cassette: released on DJM, May'81 by DJM Records. Dist: CBS, Polygram

ELTON JOHN.
Tracks: / Your song / I need you to turn to / Take me to the pilot / No shoe strings on Louise / First episode at Heinton / 60 years on / Border song / Greatest discovery / Cage, The / King must die, The.
Album: released on DJM, Apr'87 by DJM Records. Dist: CBS, Polygram

Cassette: released on DJM, Apr'87 by DJM Records. Dist: CBS, Polygram

Compact disc: released on DJM, Jun'87 by DJM Records. Dist: CBS, Polygram

Album: released on DJM, May'81 by DJM Records. Dist: CBS, Polygram

Cassette: released on DJM, May'81 by DJM Records. Dist: CBS, Polygram

Cassette: released on Cambra, '83 by Cambra Records. Dist: IDS, Conifer

ELTON JOHN LIVE COLLECTION, THE.
Album: released on Pickwick, Jan'79 by Pickwick Records. Dist: Pickwick Distribution, Prism Leisure Distribution,

Cassette: released on Pickwick, Jan'79 by Pickwick Records. Dist: Pickwick Distribution, Prism Leisure Distribution.

ELTON JOHN LIVE (NEW YORK 11/70).
Album: released on Hallmark, Jan'78 by Pickwick Records. Dist: Pickwick Distribution, PRT, Taylors

Cassette: released on Hallmark, Jan'78 by Pickwick Records. Dist: Pickwick Distribution, PRT, Taylors

EMPTY GARDEN.
Single (7"): released on Phonogram, May'82 by Phonogram Records. Dist: Polygram

EMPTY SKY.
Tracks: / Empty sky / Val Hala / Western ford gateway / Hymn 2000 / Lady what's tomorrow / Sails / Scaffold, The / Skyline pigeon / Gulliver / Hay chewed / Reprise.
Compact disc: released on DJM, Oct'86 by DJM Records. Dist: CBS, Polygram

Album: released on DJM, Apr'87 by DJM Records. Dist: CBS, Polygram

Cassette: released on DJM, Apr'87 by DJM Records. Dist: CBS, Polygram

Compact disc: released on DJM, Jun'87 by DJM Records. Dist: CBS, Polygram

Album: released on DJM, May'81 by DJM Records. Dist: CBS, Polygram

Cassette: released on DJM, May'81 by DJM Records. Dist: CBS, Polygram

FLAMES OF PARADISE See under Rush, Jennifer.
Tracks: / Flames of paradise / Call my name.
Single (7"): released on CBS, 30 May'87 by CBS Records. Dist: CBS

Single (12"): released on CBS, 30 May'87 by CBS Records. Dist: CBS

FOUR FROM FOUR EYES.
Cassette: released on DJM, '86 by DJM Records. Dist: CBS, Polygram

FOX, THE.
Tracks: / Breaking down barriers / Heart in the right place / Just like Belgium / Fox / Nobody wins / Fascist faces / Carla etude - fanfare / Chloe / Heels of the wind / Elton's song.
Compact disc: released on Rocket, '83 by Phonogram Records. Dist: Polygram Distribution

Album: released on Rocket, Jul'84 by Phonogram Records. Dist: Polygram Distribution

Cassette: released on Rocket, Jul'84 by Phonogram Records. Dist: Polygram Distribution

GOODBYE YELLOW BRICK ROAD.
Tracks: / Funeral for a friend / Love lies bleeding / Candle in the wind / Bennie and the jets / Goodbye yellow brick road / This song has no title / Grey seal / Jamaica jerk off / I've seen that movie too / Sweet painted lady / Ballad of Danny Bailey, The / Dirty little girl / All the girls love Alice / Your sister can't twist(but she can rock'n'roll) / Saturday nights alright for fighting / Roy Rogers / Social disease / Harmony.
Compact disc: released on DJM, Oct'84 by DJM Records. Dist: CBS, Polygram

Album: released on DJM, '76 by DJM Records. Dist: CBS, Polygram

Double Album: released on DJM, '76 by DJM Records. Dist: CBS, Polygram

Album: released on Platinum (W.Germany), Oct'85 Dist: Mainline

Double cassette: released on Platinum (W.Germany), Oct'85 Dist: Mainline

Single (7"): released on DJM, Sep'78 by DJM Records. Dist: CBS, Polygram

GREATEST HITS: ELTON JOHN VOL.2.
Album: released on DJM, Sep'77 by DJM Records. Dist: CBS, Polygram

Compact disc: released on DJM, Oct'85 by DJM Records. Dist: CBS, Polygram

Tracks: / Bitch is back / Lucy in the sky with diamonds / Sorry seems to be the hardest word / Don't got breaking my heart / Someone saved my life tonight / Philadelphia freedom / Island girl / Grow some funk of your own / Benny and the Jets / Pinball wizard.

GREATEST HITS:ELTON JOHN.
Tracks: / Your song / Honky cat / Goodbye yellow brick road / Saturday nights alright for fighting / Rocket man / Candle in the wind / Don't let the sun go down on me / Border song / Crocodile rock.
Compact disc: released on DJM, Oct'84 by DJM Records. Dist: CBS, Polygram

Album: released on EMI (Holland), '83 by EMI Records. Dist: Conifer

Album: released on DJM, Nov'75 by DJM Records. Dist: CBS, Polygram

GROW SOME FUNK OF YOUR OWN.
Single (7"): released on DJM, '78 by DJM Records. Dist: CBS, Polygram

HARMONY.
Single (7"): released on DJM, Oct'80 by DJM Records. Dist: CBS, Polygram

HEARTACHE ALL OVER THE WORLD.
Tracks: / Heartache all over the world / Highlander.
Single (7"): released on Rocket, Sep'86 by Phonogram Records. Dist: Polygram Distribution

Single (12"): released on Rocket, Sep'86 by Phonogram Records. Dist: Polygram Distribution

HONKY CAT.
Single (7"): released on DJM, Sep'78 by DJM Records. Dist: CBS, Polygram

HONKY CHATEAU.
Tracks: / Hnky cat / Mellow / I think I'm going to kill myself / Susie (dramas) / Rocket man / Salvation / Slaves / Amy / Mona Lisa and mad hatters / Hercules.
Album: released on DJM, Apr'87 by DJM Records. Dist: CBS, Polygram

Cassette: released on DJM, Apr'87 by DJM Records. Dist: CBS, Polygram

Compact disc: released on DJM, Jun'87 by DJM Records. Dist: CBS, Polygram

Album: released on DJM, May'81 by DJM Records. Dist: CBS, Polygram

Cassette: released on DJM, May'81 by DJM Records. Dist: CBS, Polygram

ICE ON FIRE.
Tracks: / This town / Cry to heaven / Soul glove / Nikita / Too young / Wrap her up / Satellite / Tell me what the papers say / Candy by the pound / Shoot down the moon.
Compact disc: released on Rocket, Nov'85 by Phonogram Records. Dist: Polygram Distribution

Album: released on Rocket, Nov'85 by Phonogram Records. Dist: Polygram Distribution

Cassette: released on Rocket, Nov'85 by Phonogram Records. Dist: Polygram Distribution

I'M STILL STANDING.
Single (7"): released on Rocket, Jul'83 by Phonogram Records. Dist: Polygram Distribution

Single (12"): released on Rocket, Jul'83 by Phonogram Records. Dist: Polygram Distribution

Picture disc single: released on Rocket, Jul'83 by Phonogram Records. Dist: Polygram Distribution

INTERVIEW PICTURE DISC.
Album: released on Baktabak, May'87 by Baktabak Records. Dist: Arabesque

I SAW HER STANDING THERE.
Single (7"): released on DJM, Mar'81 by DJM Records. Dist: CBS, Polygram

ISLAND GIRL.
Single (7"): released on DJM, Sep'78 by DJM Records. Dist: CBS, Polygram

JUMP UP.
Compact disc: released on Rocket, '83 by Phonogram Records. Dist: Polygram Distribution

Album: released on Rocket, Apr'82 by Phonogram Records. Dist: Polygram Distribution

Cassette: released on Rocket, Apr'82 by Phonogram Records. Dist: Polygram Distribution

KISS THE BRIDE.
Double-pack single: released on Rocket, Oct'83 by Phonogram Records. Dist: Polygram Distribution

LADY SAMANTHA.
Tracks: / Rock and roll Madonna / heneve you're ready we'll go steady again / Bad side of the moon / Jack rabbit / Into the old man's shoes / It's me that you need / Ho, ho, ho, who'd be a turkey at Christmas / Screw you / Skyline pigeon / Just like strange rain / Grey seal / Honey roll / Lady Samantha / Friends.
Album: released on DJM, Apr'87 by DJM Records. Dist: CBS, Polygram

Cassette: released on DJM, Apr'87 by DJM Records. Dist: CBS, Polygram

Compact disc: released on DJM, Jun'87 by DJM Records. Dist: CBS, Polygram

Album: released on DJM, May'81 by DJM Records. Dist: CBS, Polygram

Cassette: released on DJM, May'81 by DJM Records. Dist: CBS, Polygram

Single (7"): released on DJM, Sep'78 by DJM Records. Dist: CBS, Polygram

LEATHER JACKETS.
Album: released on Rocket, Oct'86 by Phonogram Records. Dist: Polygram Distribution

Cassette: released on Rocket, Oct'86 by Phonogram Records. Dist: Polygram Distribution

Compact disc: released on Rocket, Nov'86 by Phonogram Records. Dist: Polygram Distribution

LITTLE JEANNIE/CONQUER.
Single (7"): released on Rocket, May'80 by Phonogram Records. Dist: Polygram Distribution

LIVE IN AUSTRALIA.
Album: released on Rocket, Oct'87 by Phonogram Records. Dist: Polygram Distribution

Cassette: released on Rocket, Oct'87 by Phonogram Records. Dist: Polygram Distribution

Compact disc: released on Rocket, Aug'87 by Phonogram Records. Dist: Polygram Distribution. Estim retail price in Sep'87 was £17.99.

LIVE IN AUSTRALIA (VIDEO).
Video-cassette (VHS): released on Virgin, May'87 by Virgin Records. Dist: EMI, Virgin Distribution

LIVE IN CENTRAL PARK - NEW YORK.
Tracks: / Saturday nights alright for fighting / Little Jeannie / Benny and the Jets / Imagine / Someone saved my life tonight / Goodbye yellow brick road / Sorry seems to be the hardest word / Your song / Bite your lip/Get up and dance.
Notes: 13th September 1980 - Central Park, New York. 400,000 people - the largest concert audience in the USA since Woodstock. Nine film cameras - one mounted on a giant crane, one in a helicopter. Sound recordists manning 24 track equipment. All wait for one man - finally, Elton John bursts on stage, clad in one of the outrageous costumes he is to sport during this epic concert. The audience goes wild - join t h e m.
Number of tracks:9. Type of recording: Live. Total playing time: 60 minutes.
Video-cassette (VHS): released on VCL, Sep'86 by Elecstar Records. Dist: PRT

LONDON AND NEW YORK.
Album: released on Hallmark, Jan'78 by Pickwick Records. Dist: Pickwick Distribution, PRT, Taylors

Cassette: released on Hallmark, Jan'78 by Pickwick Records. Dist: Pickwick Distribution, PRT, Taylors

LOVE SONGS.
Tracks: / Blue eyes / Little Jeannie / Sartorial eloquence / Chloe / Song for Guy / Shine on through / Elton's song / Tonight / Sorry seems to be the hardest word / All quiet on the western front / Princess / Chameleon / Return to paradise / Someones final love song / Strangers / Never gonna fall in love again.
Compact disc: released on Rocket, '83 by Phonogram Records. Dist: Polygram Distribution

Album: released on Rocket, Feb'84 by Phonogram Records. Dist: Polygram Distribution

Cassette: released on Rocket, Feb'84 by Phonogram Records. Dist: Polygram Distribution

LOVING YOU IS SWEETER THAN EVER (John, Elton & Kiki Dee).
Single (7"): released on Ariola, Nov'81 Dist: RCA, Ariola

MADMAN ACROSS THE WATER.
Tracks: / Tiny dancer / Levon / Razor face / Madman across the water / Indian sunset / Holiday inn / Rotten peaches / All the nasties / Goodbye.
Compact disc: released on DJM, Oct'85 by DJM Records. Dist: CBS, Polygram

Album: released on DJM, Apr'87 by DJM Records. Dist: CBS, Polygram

Cassette: released on DJM, Apr'87 by DJM Records. Dist: CBS, Polygram

Compact disc: released on DJM, Jun'87 by DJM Records. Dist: CBS, Polygram

Album: released on DJM, May'81 Dist: Phonogram

Cassette: released on DJM, May'81 Dist: Phonogram

NEW COLLECTION, THE.
Album: released on Premier, '84 by Premier Records. Dist: CBS

Cassette: released on Premier, '84 by Premier Records. Dist: CBS

NEW COLLECTION, THE, VOL.2.
Album: released on Premier, '84 by Premier Records. Dist: CBS

Cassette: released on Premier, '84 by Premier Records. Dist: CBS

NIKITA.
Tracks: / Nikita.
Single (7"): released on Rocket, Sep'85 by Phonogram Records. Dist: Polygram Distribution

Single (12"): released on Rocket, Sep'85 by Phonogram Records. Dist: Polygram Distribution Deleted '87.

PHILADELPHIA FREEDOM.
Single (7"): released on DJM, Sep'78 by DJM Records. Dist: CBS, Polygram

PINBALL WIZARD.
Single (7"): released on DJM, Sep'78 by DJM Records. Dist: CBS, Polygram

ROCK OF THE WESTIES.
Tracks: / Yell help / Wednesday night / Ugly / Dan Dare (pilot of the future) / Island girl / Grow some funk of your own / I feel like a bullet (in the gun of Robert Ford) / Street kids / Hard luck story / Feed me / Billy Bones and the white bird.
Compact disc: released on DJM, '86 by DJM Records. Dist: CBS, Polygram

Album: released on DJM, May'81 by DJM Records. Dist: CBS, Polygram

Cassette: released on DJM, May'81 by DJM Records. Dist: CBS, Polygram

SEASONS... THE EARLY LOVE SONGS.
Cassette: released on Cambra, May'84 by Cambra Records. Dist: IDS, Conifer

SINGLE MAN, A.
Compact disc: by Phonogram Records. Dist: Polygram Distribution

Album: released on Rocket, Jun'83 by Phonogram Records. Dist: Polygram Distribution

Cassette: released on Rocket, Jun'83 by Phonogram Records. Dist: Polygram Distribution

SLOW RIVERS (John, Elton & Cliff Richard).
Tracks: / Slow rivers / Lord of the flies*.
Single (7"): released on Rocket, Nov'86 by Phonogram Records. Dist: Polygram Distribution

Single (12"): released on Rocket, Nov'86 by Phonogram Records. Dist: Polygram Distribution

SOMEONE SAVED MY LIFE.
Single (7"): released on DJM, Sep'78 by DJM Records. Dist: CBS, Polygram

SONG FOR GUY.
Single (7"): released on Phonogram, '78 by Phonogram Records. Dist: Polygram

STEP INTO CHRISTMAS.
Single (7"): released on DJM, Sep'78 by DJM Records. Dist: CBS, Polygram

SUPERIOR.
Compact disc: released on Rocket, '83 by Phonogram Records. Dist: Polygram Distribution

SUPERIOR SOUND OF ELTON JOHN 1970-1975.
Tracks: / Your song / Crocodile rock / Rocket man / Daniel / Saturday nights alright for fighting / Goodbye yellow brick road / Funeral for a friend / Love lies bleeding / Don't let the sun go down on me / Philadelphia freedom / Someone saved my life tonight / We all fall in love sometimes.
Compact disc: released on DJM, Oct'84 by DJM Records. Dist: CBS, Polygram

Single (7"): released on Rocket, Apr'83 by Phonogram Records. Dist: Polygram Distribution

TOO LOW FOR ZERO.
Compact disc: released on Rocket, '83 by Phonogram Records. Dist: Polygram Distribution

Album: released on Rocket, Jun'83 by Phonogram Records. Dist: Polygram Distribution

Cassette: released on Rocket, Jun'83 by Phonogram Records. Dist: Polygram Distribution

TUMBLEWEED CONNECTION.
Tracks: / Ballad of a well known gun / Come down in time / Country comfort / Son of your father / My fathers gun / Where to now St.Peter / Love song / Amoreena / Talking old soldiers / Burn down the mission / I'm going to be a teenage idol*.
Compact disc: released on DJM, Apr'86 by DJM Records. Dist: CBS, Polygram

Album: released on DJM, Apr'87 by DJM Records. Dist: CBS, Polygram

Cassette: released on DJM, Apr'87 by DJM Records. Dist: CBS, Polygram

Compact disc: released on DJM, Jun'86 by DJM Records. Dist: CBS, Polygram

Album: released on DJM, May'81 by DJM Records. Dist: CBS, Polygram

Cassette: released on DJM, May'81 by DJM Records. Dist: CBS, Polygram

VERY BEST OF ELTON JOHN, THE.
Album: released on Arcade Music Gala, Apr'86 Dist: Stage One

Cassette: released on Arcade Music Gala, Apr'86 Dist: Stage One

VICTIM OF LOVE.
Album: released on Rocket, Jul'84 by Phonogram Records. Dist: Polygram Distribution

Cassette: released on Rocket, Jul'84 by Phonogram Records. Dist: Polygram Distribution

VIDEO SINGLES, THE.
Video-cassette (VHS): released on Polygram/Spectrum, Jan'84 by Polygram Records. Dist: Polygram

WRAP HER UP.
Tracks: / Wrap her up / Restless.
Single (7"): released on Rocket, Dec'85 by Phonogram Records. Dist: Polygram Distribution

YOUR SONG.
Single (7"): released on DJM, Sep'78 by DJM Records. Dist: CBS, Polygram

Single (12"): released on DJM, Jun'77 by DJM Records. Dist: CBS, Polygram

YOUR SONG (LIVE).
Tracks: / Your song (live) / Don't let the sun go down on me / I need you to turn to* / Greatest discovery, The*.
Single (7"): released on Rocket, Jun'87 by Phonogram Records. Dist: Polygram Distribution

Single (12"): released on Rocket, Jun'87 by Phonogram Records. Dist: Polygram Distribution

John, Leee

ROCK ME SLOW.
Tracks: / Rock me slow / Rock me slow (instrumental) / Honey I'm yours.
Single (7"): released on R & B, Aug'86 by Red Bus. Dist: PRT

Single (12"): released on R & B, Aug'86 by Red Bus. Dist: PRT

John, Little Willie

GRITS AND SOUL.
Tracks: / All around the world / Need your love so bad / Fever / Do something for me / Suffering with the blues / I've been around / Person to person / Talk to me, talk to me / Let's rock while the rockin's good / Let them talk / Leave my kitten alone / Walk slow / My baby's in love with another guy / You hurt me / Big blue diamonds / Come back to me.
Notes: Original King recordings. Licensed from Gusto Records Inc., Nashville, Tennessee.
Album: released on Charly(R&B), Jul'85 by Charly Records. Dist: Charly, Cadillac

Cassette: released on Charly(R&B), Jul'85 by Charly Records. Dist: Charly, Cadillac

John, Mavis

HOW CAN I LOVE AGAIN.
Single (7"): released on Sonet, Jun'81 by Sonet Records. Dist: PRT

John, Michael
LOVE WILL TEAR US APART.
Single (7"): released on Loose, Sep'83 by Loose Records. Dist: Nine Mile, Cartel

Single (12"): released on Loose, Sep'83 by Loose Records. Dist: Nine Mile, Cartel

Johnny...
BEATNIK FLY (Johnny & The Hurricanes).
Single (7"): released on Decca, Mar'82 by Decca Records. Dist: Polygram

JOHNNY & THE HURRICANES (Johnny & The Hurricanes).
Album: released on Dakota (Countdown series), Oct'82 by Dakota Records. Dist: PRT

Cassette: released on Dakota (Countdown series), Oct'82 by Dakota Records. Dist: PRT

Album: released on London Rock Echoes Series, Nov'81

Album: released on Phoenix, Oct'82 by Audio Fidelity Enterprises. Dist: Stage One, Lugtons

RED RIVER ROCK (Johnny & The Hurricanes).
Single (7"): released on Dakota, Aug'82 by Dakota Records. Dist: PRT

Single (7"): released on Liberty-UA, Jul'84 Cat. no: 1A 006 99380
Single (7"): released on Old Gold, Jan'85 by Old Gold Records. Dist: Lightning, Jazz Music, Spartan, Counterpoint

REVEILLE ROCK (Johnny & The Hurricanes).
Single (7"): released on Creole, Aug'82 by Creole Records. Dist: Rhino, PRT

ROCKING GOOSE (Johnny & Hurricanes).
Single (7"): released on Dakota, Aug'82 by Dakota Records. Dist: PRT

Single (7"): released on Old Gold, Jan'85 by Old Gold Records. Dist: Lightning, Jazz Music, Spartan, Counterpoint

Johnny 7
PRESSURE'S TOO HOT.
Single (7"): released on Lost Moments, Dec'84 Dist: Backs, Cartel

Johnny B
TIME IS NOW.
Single (12"): released on MPD, Sep'82 Dist: Cartel Distribution

Johnny Hates Jazz
I DON'T WANT TO BE A HERO.
Single (7"): released on Virgin, Aug'87 by Virgin Records. Dist: EMI, Virgin Distribution

Single (12"): released on Virgin, Aug'87 by Virgin Records. Dist: EMI, Virgin Distribution

Cassette single: released on Virgin, Aug'87 by Virgin Records. Dist: EMI, Virgin Distribution

SHATTERED DREAMS.
Tracks: / Shattered dreams / My secret garden.
Single (7"): released on Virgin, Mar'87 by Virgin Records. Dist: EMI, Virgin Distribution

Single (12"): released on Virgin, Mar'87 by Virgin Records. Dist: EMI, Virgin Distribution

Johnny & Jazz
ME AND MY FOOLISH HEART.
Tracks: / Me and my foolish heart / Living in the past.
Single (7"): released on RAK, Mar'86 by RAK. Dist: EMI

Single (12"): released on RAK, Mar'86 by RAK. Dist: EMI

Johnny Otis Presents..
JOHNNY OTIS PRESENTS... various artists (Various Artists).
Album: released on Ace, Nov'83 by Ace Records. Dist: Pinnacle, Swift, Hotshot, Cadillac

Johnny & the Jailbirds
OUT ON BAIL.
Album: released on Charly, Apr'80 by Charly Records. Dist: Charly, Cadillac

Johnny The Priest
JOHNNY THE PRIEST Original London cast.
Album: released on That's Entertainment, Apr'83 by That's Entertainment Records. Dist: Pinnacle, Swift

Johnny & The Roccos
GOOD ROCKIN' TONIGHT.
Album: released on Magnum Force, 4 Nov'87 by Magnum Music Group Ltd. Dist: Magnum Music Group Ltd, PRT, Spartan

---

I HATE THE DISCO.
Tracks: / I hate the disco / Drip dry.
Single (7"): released on Off-Beat, Feb'86 by Off-Beat Records. Dist: Jetstar Distribution

SCOTS ON THE ROCKS.
Album: released on Magnum Force, Jul'82 by Magnum Music Group Ltd. Dist: Magnum Music Group Ltd, PRT, Spartan

TEARIN' UP THE BORDER.
Album: released on Off-Beat, Feb'86 by Off-Beat Records. Dist: Jetstar Distribution

Album: released on Off-Beat, Aug'85 by Off-Beat Records. Dist: Jetstar Distribution

John of Hildeshem
STORY OF THE THREE KINGS.
Cassette: released on Caedmon(USA), '84 by Caedmon (USA) Records. Dist: Gower, Taylors, Discovery

John, Paul...
JOHN, PAUL, GEORGE, RINGO & BERT
London cast (John, Paul, Ringo & Bert).
Cassette single: released on RSO, '74

John Paul II
JOHN PAUL II The visit of the Pope to Ireland.
Cassette: released on Outlet, Jan'80 by Outlet Records. Dist: Outlet Distribution

John, Phillipa
CARIBBEAN ENCOUNTER.
Notes: Read by Fiona Mathieson.
Cassette: released on Cover to Cover, Nov'86 by Cover to Cover Cassettes. Dist: Conifer

John, Robert
BACK ON THE STREET.
Album: released on EMI America, Feb'81 by EMI Records. Dist: EMI

BREAD AND BUTTER.
Single (12"): released on Motown, Mar'83 by Motown Records. Dist: BMG Distribution

Johns, Bibl
ABER NACHTS IN DER BAR.
Tracks: / Aber nachts in der bar / Es dreht sich die welt (Nicht nur um das geld) / Rocky Robby / Ricky Tick / Das....(Fing mit dem mondenschein am) / Wenn musik spielt / Mein herz ruft nach dir / Jacky, komm wieder / Junggesellen musst du fallen stellen / Junge, junge, das war wunderschon / Jimmy, oh Jimmy / Das kann gefahrlich sein / Ein Himmel ohne sterne / Ein morgen, ein mittag, ein abendkuss / Schenk mir was schones / Ich mocht' so gern nochmal bei dir sein.
Album: released on Bear Family, May'87 by Bear Family Records. Dist: Rollercoaster Distribution, Swift

Johns Children
LEGENDARY ORGASM ALBUM, THE.
Album: released on Cherry Red, '82 by Cherry Red Records. Dist: Pinnacle

Johns, Evan
EVAN JOHNS & THE H-BOMBS (Johns, Evan & The H-Bombs).
Album: released on Zippo, Feb'87

Johnson
CHAIN REACTION.
Tracks: / Chain reaction / Afraid to be real.
Single (7"): released on Total Control, Jun'86

Johnson, Anthony
A-YAH-WE-DEH.
Album: released on Jamming, Aug'85

A YA WE DEH (Johnson, Anthony & Tonto Rey).
Single (12"): released on Fu-Manchu, Jul'84 by Fu-Manchu. Dist: Jetstar

BABY WHY.
Single (12"): released on Midnight Rock, Dec'83 Dist: Jetstar Distribution, Kingdom Distribution

DANCE HALL VIBES.
Tracks: / Dance hall vibes / Rap up, mix up.
Single (12"): released on Unity, Apr'86 by Unity Records. Dist: Jetstar

DON'T LET ME DOWN.
Single (12"): released on Music Lovers, May'82 by Music Lovers Records. Dist: Music Lovers

---

DREADLOCKS FIGHT.
Single (12"): released on Rusty International, Feb'83 by Rusty International Records. Dist: Jetstar Distribution

GUN SHOT.
Album: released on Midnight Rock, '83 Dist: Jetstar Distribution, Kingdom Distribution

I'LL NEVER FALL IN LOVE AGAIN.
Single (12"): released on Rusty International, Oct'83 by Rusty International Records. Dist: Jetstar Distribution

I LOVE YOU GIRL.
Tracks: / I love you girl / Nah give up.
Single (12"): released on Look To Afrika, Feb'86 by Look To Afrika Records. Dist: Jetstar

JUST CALL ME.
Single (12"): released on Freedom Sounds, Sep'81 by Freedom Sounds Records. Dist: Jetstar

LET GO THIS ONE.
Single (12"): released on Greensleeves, Jan'82 by Greensleeves Records. Dist: BMG, Jetstar, Spartan

LOVE LOST.
Single (12"): released on Black Symbol, Feb'82 Dist: Jetstar

MEK WE GO A DANCE.
Single (12"): released on Black Roots, Jan'84 by Black Roots Records. Dist: Jetstar

NO MEN, NO GUY, NO BOY.
Tracks: / No men, no guy, no boy / Watch it.
Single (12"): released on Now Generation, Aug'86 Dist: Jetstar Distribution

ONCE MORE LOVING.
Album: released on Black Link Int., Oct'85 Dist: Jetstar

SINCE I MET YOU BABY.
Tracks: / Since I met you baby / Cassandra.
Single (12"): released on Shabrock, Jan'86 Dist: Jetstar

SITTING IN THE DARK.
Single (12"): released on Midnight Rock, Sep'84 Dist: Jetstar Distribution, Kingdom Distribution

STOP MY LOVING.
Single (12"): released on Rusty International, Aug'83 by Rusty International Records. Dist: Jetstar Distribution

STRICTLY RUB-A-DUB.
Single (12"): released on Midnight Rock, Sep'83 Dist: Jetstar Distribution, Kingdom Distribution

TAKE YOU TO THE SHOW.
Single (12"): released on Midnight Rock, Feb'83 Dist: Jetstar Distribution, Kingdom Distribution

TOO MUCH.
Single (12"): released on Oak Sound, Jul'82

Johnson, Bertie
NO WAY LOSE SIGHT OF JAH.
Single (12"): released on S&G, Jan'83 by Pinnacle

Johnson, Bob
KING OF ELFLANDS DAUGHTER, THE (Johnson, Bob & Peter Knight).
Album: released on Chrysalis, Aug'77 by Chrysalis Records. Dist: CBS

Johnson, Budd
BLUES A LA MODE (Johnson, Budd, His Septet & Quintet).
Tracks: / Foggy nights / Leave room in your heart for me / Destination blues / A la mode / Used blues / Blues by five.
Notes: Licensed from Decca Records Ltd. A Felsted recording. Copyright Control.
Album: released on Affinity, Nov'86 by Charly Records. Dist: Charly, Cadillac

IN MEMORY OF A VERY DEAR FRIEND (Johnson, Budd Quartet).
Album: released on Dragon, Jun'86 by Dragon Records. Dist: Jazz Music, Projection, Cadillac

Johnson, Bunk
1942 (Johnson, Bunk Jazz Band).
Album: released on Commodore Classics, Aug'82 by Teldec Records (Germany). Dist: Conifer, IMS, Polygram

BUNK JOHNSON BRASS & DANCE BAND.
Album: released on Storyville (Denmark), Jul'81

BUNK JOHNSON & HIS BAND (Johnson, Bunk & His Band).
Album: released on Nola, Apr'79 Dist: JSU, Jazz Music, Cadillac, Chris Wellard

---

BUNK JOHNSON & HIS BAND 1947 (Johnson, Bunk & His Band).
Cassette: released on Nola, May'87 Dist: JSU, Jazz Music, Cadillac, Chris Wellard

BUNK JOHNSON & HIS SUPERIOR JAZZ BAND.
Album: released on Contemporary(Import), Dec'81 Dist: IMS, Polygram

BUNK JOHNSON & LU WATTERS (Johnson, Bunk & Lu Watters).
Album: released on Contemporary(Import), May'83 Dist: IMS, Polygram

DOWN ON THE DELTA (Johnson, Bunk Band, Kid Rena's Band, Celestin's Original).
Tracks: / Tiger rag / Weary blues / Make me a pallet on the floor / Careless love / When the saints go marching in / Oh, didn't he ramble / Li'l Liza Jane / High society / Panama / Gettysburg march / Milenburg joys / Lowdown blues / High society / Clarinet marmalade / Weary blues / Get it right.
Notes: Full Group name: Bunk Johnson's Jazz Band/Kid Rena's Delta Jazz Band/Celestin's Original Tuxedo Orchestra.
Album: released on Esquire, Jul'87 by Titan International Productions. Dist: Jazz Music, Cadillac Music, Swift, Wellard, Chris, Backs, Rough Trade, Revolver, Nine Mile

NEW ORLEANS LEGENDS (Johnson, Bunk & Kid Ory).
Album: released on Joker, Sep'83 Dist: Cadillac, Zodiac Distribution, Jazz Horizons, Jazz Music, USA, Celtic Music

NEW YORK 1945 (Johnson, Bunk & His New Orleans Jazz Band).
Notes: With G.Lewis.
Album: released on Folklyric (USA), Sep'86 by Arhoolie Records. Dist: Topic, Projection

PURIST ISSUES, THE.
Album: released on Nola, Apr'79 Dist: JSU, Jazz Music, Cadillac, Chris Wellard

SPICY ADVICE (Johnson, Bunk & His Band).
Album: released on GHB, Jun'86 Dist: Jazz Music, Swift

Johnson, Carl
DON'T WANT TO BE ALONE.
Single (12"): released on B.B. Music, Mar'85 by B.B. Music Records. Dist: Jetstar

FATTY FATTY.
Tracks: / Fatty fatty / Fatty fatty (circa style).
Single (12"): released on Jumbo, Feb'87 Dist: Jetstar, East Anglian Productions

I WISH HE DIDN'T TRUST ME SO MUCH.
Single (12"): released on B.B. Music, Nov'85 by B.B. Music Records. Dist: Jetstar

Johnson, Chico
HULA HOOP.
Single (7"): released on Panther, Jun'84 by MCA Records. Dist: CBS

Single (12"): released on Panther, Jun'84 by MCA Records. Dist: CBS

LOOP DE LOOP WITH THE PEPPERMINT HOOP.
Single (7"): released on Tivoli, Oct'83 by Tivoli Records. Dist: Unknown

Single (12"): released on Tivoli, Oct'83 by Tivoli Records. Dist: Unknown

MISS THING.
Single (12"): released on Splash, Jan'85 by Splash Records. Dist: CBS

Johnson, David Earle
ROUTE TWO.
Album: released on Landslide (USA), Mar'85 Dist: Compendium, Rough Trade, Cartel

TIME IS FREE.
Album: released on Pye, '79

Johnson, D.E.
ROUTE TWO.
Notes: Features John Abercrombie.
Album: released on LM/LD, Jul'86 Dist: Compendium International Distribution

Johnson, Dick
SWING SHIFT (Johnson, Dick & Friends).
Album: released on Concord, Dec'81 by Import Records. Dist: IMS, Polygram

Johnson, Dink
DINK'S GOOD TIME MUSIC.
Album: released on Nola, Apr'79 Dist: JSU, Jazz Music, Cadillac, Chris Wellard

PROFESSORS - VOL.1 (Johnson, Dink & S.Brunson Campbell).
Album: released on Euphonic, Apr'79 by Euphonic Records. Dist: Jazz Music, Swift

PROFESSORS - VOL.2 (Johnson, Dink & S.Brunson Campbell).
Album: released on Euphonic, Apr'79 by Euphonic Records. Dist: Jazz Music, Swift

Johnson, Don

HEARTACHE AWAY.
Tracks: / Heartache away / Love roulette.
Single (7"): released on Epic, Nov'86 by CBS Records. Dist: CBS

Single (12"): released on Epic, Nov'86 by CBS Records. Dist: CBS

HEARTBEAT.
Tracks: / Heartbeat / Voice on a hotline / Last sound love makes, The / Lost in your eyes / Coco don't / Hartache away / Love roulette / Star tonight / Gotta get away / Can't take your money / Heartbeat / Can't take your memory.
Album: released on Epic, Nov'86 by CBS Records. Dist: CBS

Cassette: released on Epic, Nov'86 by CBS Records. Dist: CBS

Single (7"): released on Epic, Sep'86 by CBS Records. Dist: CBS

Single (12"): released on Epic, Sep'86 by CBS Records. Dist: CBS

Johnson, Eric

TONES.
Tracks: / Soulful terrain / Eerald eyes / Friends / Off my mind / Desert song, The / Trail of tears / Bristol shore / Zap / Victory.
Album: released on Warner Bros., Oct'86 by Warner Bros Records. Dist: WEA

Johnson, Frank

DIXIELAND JAZZ With his friends 1954-56.
Album: released on Swaggie (Australia), Jan'83

FRANK JOHNSON & HIS FABULOUS DIXIELANDERS 1951-55.
Album: released on Swaggie (Australia), Jan'83

FRANK JOHNSON'S FABULOUS DIXIELANDERS 1950.
Notes: Vocals: Warwick Dyer/Frank Johnson
Cassette: released on Swaggie (Australia), Jun'87

Johnson, Frankie Jr.

WHENEVER YOU CALL ME.
Tracks: / Whenever you call me / Whenever you call me (remix) / Whenever you call me (Instrumental remix).
Single (7"): released on Debut, Feb'86 by Skratch Music. Dist: PRT

Single (12"): released on Debut, Feb'86 by Skratch Music. Dist: PRT

Single (12"): released on Debut, Feb'86 by Skratch Music. Dist: PRT

Johnson, Graham

SONGMAKERS ALMANAC (Johnson, Graham & Anne Murray).
Notes: For full information see under: Murray, Anne.

Johnson, Herman

LOUISIANA COUNTRY BLUES (Johnson, Herman E.).
Album: released on Arhoolie, May'81 by Arhoolie Records. Dist: Projection, Topic, Jazz Music, Swift, Roots

Johnson, Howard

DOIN' IT MY WAY.
Album: released on A&M, Nov'83 by A&M Records. Dist: Polygram

Cassette: released on A&M, Nov'83 by A&M Records. Dist: Polygram

KEEPIN' LOVE NEW.
Album: released on A&M, Sep'82 by A&M Records. Dist: Polygram

SAY YOU WANNA.
Single (12"): released on Funk America, Jan'83 by A&M Records. Dist: CBS

SO FINE.
Notes: Full details see under BROTHERS JOHNSON "Stomp"

Johnson, James

HARLEM STRIDE PIANO SOLOS (Johnson, James P.).
Album: released on Swaggie (Australia), Jan'83

IT TAKES LOVE (Johnson, James P.).
Album: released on Kings Of Jazz, Apr'81 Dist: Jazz Horizons, Jazz Music, Celtic Music

JAMES P. JOHNSON 1921-26 (Johnson, James P.).

Johnson, James P.

AIN'TCHA GOT MUSIC.
Notes: Previously unissued solos and band sides featuring Tommy Dorsey, Harry Carney, B.Hackett etc.
Album: released on Pumpkin, Nov'86 Dist: Jazz Music, Wellard, Chris, Cadillac

Album: released on Pumpkin, Nov'86 Dist: Jazz Music, Wellard, Chris, Cadillac

FEELIN' BLUE.
Tracks: / All that I had is gone / Snowy morning blues / Chicago blues / Mournful tho'ts / Riffs / Feelin' blue / Put your mind right on it / Fare thee honey blues / You don't understand / You've got to be modernistic / Crying for the Carolines / What is this thing called love / Jingles / Go Harlem / Just a crazy song.
Album: released on Halcyon (USA), Feb'87 by Halcyon Records (USA). Dist: Jazz Music, Conifer, Taylors

Cassette: released on Submarine, Oct'86 by Submarine Records. Dist: Wellard, Chris Distribution, Conifer Distribution, H.R. Taylor Distribution

FROM RAGTIME TO JAZZ Piano solos.
Album: released on CBS, Jan'87 by CBS Records. Dist: CBS

Album: released on CBS(France), May'85 by CBS Records. Dist: Conifer, Discovery, Swift

JAMES P.JOHNSON 1928-31.
Notes: With Louisiana Sugar Babes 1928/Jimmy Johnson & Orch 1928-31/Jimmy Jonson & Band 1929/Jimmy Johnson & Clarence Williams 1930.
Album: released on Swaggie (Australia), Jun'87

JAMES P. JOHNSON & PERRY BRADFORD (Johnson, James P & Perry Bradford).
Album: released on Arcadia, Apr'79 Dist: Cartel

Johnson, J.C.

WE CALL IT CHRISTMAS (Johnson, J.C. & J.Kitchener).
Single (7"): released on Open Space, Nov'84 by Open Space Records. Dist: Pinnacle

Johnson, Jeff

NO SHADOW OF TURNING.
Notes: An acclaimed pianist/synthesiser player whose most recent album ('Icons') for his own label (Ark) was named a Campus Life record of the year.
Album: released on Meadowlark, Mar'86 by Sparrow Records. Dist: Word Distribution

Cassette: released on Meadowlark, Mar'86 by Sparrow Records. Dist: Word Distribution

Johnson, Jesse

BE YOUR MAN.
Single (7"): released on A&M, Apr'85 by A&M Records. Dist: Polygram

Single (12"): released on A&M, Apr'85 by A&M Records. Dist: Polygram

CAN YOU HELP ME (Johnson, Jesse Revue).
Single (7"): released on A&M, Jun'85 by A&M Records. Dist: Polygram

Single (12"): released on A&M, Jun'85 by A&M Records. Dist: Polygram
Cat. no: **AMY 259**

CRAZAY.
Tracks: / Crazay / I'm your man.
Single (7"): released on A&M, Nov'86 by A&M Records. Dist: Polygram
Cat. no: **AM 360**

Single (12"): released on A&M, Nov'86 by A&M Records. Dist: Polygram

JESSE JOHNSON'S REVUE.
Album: released on A&M, Nov'85 by A&M Records. Dist: Polygram

Cassette: released on A&M, Nov'85 by A&M Records. Dist: Polygram

SHE I CAN'T RESIST.
Tracks: / She I can't resist / She I can't resist (Version) / Crazay.
Notes: Crazay is an extra track which is only available on the 12" version.
Single (7"): released on A&M, Feb'87 by A&M Records. Dist: Polygram

Single (12"): released on A&M, Feb'87 by A&M Records. Dist: Polygram

SHOCKADELICA.
Tracks: / Change your mind / She / Addiction / Baby let's kiss / Better way / Tonight / Crazay / Do yourself a favour / Burn you up / Black in America.
Notes: When Jesse Johnson debuted as a solo artist in the USA last year, U.S. listeners responded by snapping up 700,000 copies of his first lp, "Jesse Johnson's Revue". This earned Johnson both a gold album and a place among a very select group - one of three acts in A & M's history to have won one with a debut lp. "Shockadelica" is a multi-format colelction of new songs, and on it the ace guitarist provces that players just get better. Johnson matches his outstanding guitar work with singing that's stronger than ever. In preparation for "Shockadelica", Johnson studied with one of L.A.'s top vocal coaches, Seth Riggs (whose other students include Michael Jackson). The training gives Jesse's vocals a new, dynamic edge. Growth since the last album is especially evident in Johnson's songwriting, which is an effective mix of urban contemporary and AOR tracks. Johnson produced "Shockadelica" with a high-tech attitude that's crisp, not slick. Among the stand out tracks is what has to got to be the hottest word of mouth single in a long time: "Crazay" featuring Jesse Johnson and Sly Stone. "Shockadelica" reflects years of excellent performances by Jesse Johnson, on his own and with Jimmy Jam and Morris Day in the Time.
Album: released on A&M, Oct'86 by A&M Records. Dist: Polygram

Cassette: released on A&M, Oct'86 by A&M Records. Dist: Polygram

Compact disc: released on A&M, Oct'86 by A&M Records. Dist: Polygram

Johnson, Jimmy

HEAP SEE.
Album: released on Blue Phoenix (France), Jan'85

Johnson, J J

AT THE OPERA HOUSE (see Getz, Stan).

CONCEPTS IN BLUE.
Album: released on Pablo, '82 by Pablo Records. Dist: Wellard, Chris, IMS-Polygram, BMG

Cassette: released on Pablo, '82 by Pablo Records. Dist: Wellard, Chris, IMS-Polygram, BMG

EMINENT, THE, VOL.1.
Album: released on Blue Note (USA Import), Sep'84

EMINENT, THE, VOL.2.
Album: released on Blue Note (USA Import), Sep'84

GREAT KAI AND J.J, THE (Johnson, J J & Kai Winding).
Album: released on Jasmine, Jun'82 by Jasmine Records. Dist: Counterpoint, Lugtons, Taylor, H.R., Wellard, Chris, Swift, Cadillac

Cassette: released on Jasmine, Jun'82 by Jasmine Records. Dist: Counterpoint, Lugtons, Taylor, H.R., Wellard, Chris, Swift, Cadillac

Album: released on Impulse, Oct'85 by Impulse Records. Dist: MCA, Polygram

J.J.!.
Album: released on RCA (France), '83 by RCA Records. Dist: Discovery

LIVE.
Album: released on Queen-Disc, Apr'81 Dist: Celtic Music, JSU, Jazz Horizons, Jazz Music

MAD BE-BOP.
Album:

THINGS ARE GETTING BETTER ALL THE TIME (Johnson, J J & Al Grey).

TOTAL J.J. JOHNSON, THE.
Album: released on RCA (France), Feb'85 by RCA Records. Dist: Discovery

TROMBONE BY THREE (Johnson, J J, Kai Winding, Bennie Green).
Album: released on Original Jazz Classics (USA), Jun'86 Dist: Fantasy (USA) Distribution, Chris Wellard Distribution, IMS-Polygram Distribution

TROMBONE BY THREE (Johnson, J J & Kai Winding).
Album: released on Prestige (USA), Aug'84

WE'LL BE TOGETHER AGAIN (Johnson, J J & Joe Pass).
Notes: Full details under Joe Pass.

YOKOHAMA CONCERT (Johnson, J J & Nat Adderley).
Album: released on Pablo, '82 by Pablo Records. Dist: Wellard, Chris, IMS-Polygram, BMG

Cassette: released on Pablo, '82 by Pablo Records. Dist: Wellard, Chris, IMS-Polygram, BMG

Johnson, Joe

BRADFORD (Johnson, Joe & The Hammond Works).
Tracks: / Bradford / Bradford's bouncing back.
Single (7"): released on Hit The Deck, Jun'87 by Hit The Deck Records. Dist: PRT

Johnson, Kenny

ALL THE KINGS HORSES.
Single (7"): released on OBM, Dec'82

BEST OF KENNY JOHNSON, THE.
Album: released on OBM, '82

LET ME HAVE YOU ONCE.
Album: released on OBM-RK, Jun'80

Johnson, Laurie

FIRST MEN IN THE MOON.
Album: released on Unicorn, May'81 Dist: Nine Mile, Cartel

MUSIC FROM THE AVENGERS, THE NEW AVENGERS & THE PROFFESIONAL With the London Studio Orchestra.
Album: released on KPM Ltd, Oct'80

PROFESSIONALS MAIN THEME (Johnson, Laurie Orchestra).
Single (7"): released on Unicorn, Mar'85 Dist: Nine Mile, Cartel

Johnson, Linton

BASS CULTURE (Johnson, Linton Kwesi).
Album: released on Island, May'80 by Island Records. Dist: Polygram

Cassette: released on Island, May'80 by Island Records. Dist: Polygram

DREAD BEAT AN BLOOD (Johnson, Linton Kwesi).
Album: released on Virgin, Jul'81 by Virgin Records. Dist: EMI, Virgin Distribution

LINTON KWESI JOHNSON LIVE (Johnson, Linton Kwesi).
Album: released on Rough Trade, Oct'85 by Rough Trade Records. Dist: Rough Trade Distribution, Cartel Distribution

LKJ IN DUB (Johnson, Linton Kwesi).
Album: released on Island, Nov'80 by Island Records. Dist: Polygram

MAKING HISTORY (Johnson, Linton Kwesi).

REGGAE GREATS (Johnson, Linton Kwesi).
Album: released on Island, May'85 by Island Records. Dist: Polygram

Cassette: released on Island, May'85 by Island Records. Dist: Polygram

Johnson, Lonnie

BLUES BY.
Album: released on Original Blues Classics (USA), May'84

BLUES OF LONNIE JOHNSON, THE 1937-8.
Album: released on Swaggie (Australia), Jan'83

IT FEELS SO GOOD.
Album: released on Queen-Disc, Apr'81 Dist: Celtic Music, JSU, Jazz Horizons, Jazz Music

LONNIE JOHNSON VOL 1 (1926-28).
Tracks: / When I was lovin' / Changed my mind blues / Sun to sun blues / Bed of sand / Lonesome jail blues / No good blues / Newport blues / Love story blues / Woman changed my life / Lonnies got the blues / You drove a good man away / Ball & chain blues / To do this you got to know / Superstitious blues / Cotton patch blues / Black bird blues / Unkind mama / Backwater blues / Crowing rooster blues.
Notes: There has been no blues singer to compare with Lonnie Johnson for diversity of experience and breadth of respect. As a recording artists he was one of the most popular of blues men, making a vast number of discs. His importance as a blues artist is without question, not only as a singer and guitarist, but also as an influence on his contempories.

ORIGINATOR OF MODERN GUITAR BLUES.
Album: released on Blues Boy, Aug'87 by Mr. R&B Records. Dist: Swift

Johnson, Lorenza

LOVE PAINS.
Single (12"):

Johnson, Louis

PASSAGE.
Album: released on A&M, Mar'81 by A&M Records. Dist: Polygram

Johnson, Luther

CHICKEN SHACK.
Album: released on Muse, Dec'79 by Peerless Records. Dist: Lugtons Distributors

CHICKEN SHACK (Johnson, Luther & Muddy Waters).
Album: released on Muse, Apr'81 by Peerless Records. Dist: Lugtons Distributors

Johnson, Lynton Kwesi

FORCES OF VICTORY.
Tracks: / Want fi goh rave / It noh funny / Sonny's lettah (anti-sus poem) / Independant inavenshan / Fite dem back / Reality poem / Forces of vicktry / Time come.
Album: released on Island, Oct'86 by Island Records. Dist: Polygram

Cassette: released on Island, Oct'86 by Island Records. Dist: Polygram

Johnson, Marc

BASS DESIRES.
Tracks: / Samurai hee-haw / Resolution / Black is the colour of my true loves hair / Bass desires / Wishing doll, A / Mojo highway / Thanks again.
Notes: This is the debut album of an exciting and powerful new group, led by bassist Marc Johnson who has worked with Bill Evans and is currently playing in John Abercrombie's trio. The music incorporates both jazz and rock idioms without ever sounding like a fusion band. Driven by the energetic guitars of Scofield and Frisell who also create interesting soundscapes with guitar synthesisers, the whole effect is highly original.
Personnel: Marc Johnson - bass, Bill Frisell - guitar, John Scofield - guitar, Peter Erskine - drums.
Album: released on ECM (Germany), Feb'86 by ECM Records. Dist: IMS, Polygram, Virgin through EMI

Compact disc: released on ECM (Germany), Feb'86 by ECM Records. Dist: IMS, Polygram, Virgin through EMI

Johnson, Marv

I'LL PICK A ROSE FOR MY ROSE.
Single (7"): released on Motown, Oct'81 by Motown Records. Dist: BMG Distribution

MOTOR CITY ROOTS - THE ROOTS OF DETROIT SOUL (Johnson, Marv & The Falcons).
Tracks: / You've got what it takes / You've got to move two mountains / Happy days / Come to me / He gave me you / Easier said (than done) / I need you / All the love I've got / You're so fine / Pow you're in love / You're mine / Teacher, The / Waiting for you / Goddess of angels / I plus love plus you / Country shack.
Album: released on Stateside, Sep'86 Dist: EMI

Cassette: released on Stateside, Sep'86 Dist: EMI

Johnson, Matt

BURNING BLUE SOUL.
Cassette: released on 4AD, Jun'84 by 4AD Records. Dist: Rough Trade

Johnson Mountain Boys

LET THE WHOLE WORLD TALK.
Album: released on Rounder Europa, Jun'87

LET THE WORLD TALK.
Notes: An album of traditional bluegrass music from the Johnson Moutain Boys,their sixth release since 1981.
Album: released on Rounder Europa, Jun'87

LIVE AT THE BIRCHMERE.
Album: released on Rounder (USA), Jul'84 Dist: Mike's Country Music Room Distribution, Jazz Music Distribution, Swift Distribution, Roots Records Distribution, Projection Distribution, Topic Distribution

WE'LL STILL SING ON.
Album: released on Rounder (USA), Dec'85 Dist: Mike's Country Music Room Distribution, Jazz Music Distribution, Swift Distribution, Roots Records Distribution, Projection Distribution, Topic Distribution

Johnson, Orlando

JUST A KISS.
Single (7"): released on Eden, Mar'85 by Eden Records. Dist: Pinnacle

Single (12"): released on Eden, Mar'85 by Eden Records. Dist: Pinnacle

TURN THE MUSIC ON (Johnson, Orlando & Trance).
Single (7"): released on Magnet, Jul'83 by Magnet Records. Dist: BMG

Single (12"): released on Magnet, Jul'83 by Magnet Records. Dist: BMG

Johnson, Paul

ARE WE STRONG ENOUGH.
Tracks: / Are we strong enough / Intimate friends / Where can you be.
Single (7"): released on CBS, Jul'87 by CBS Records. Dist: CBS

Single (12"): released on CBS, Jul'87 by CBS Records. Dist: CBS

Single (12"): released on CBS, Jul'87 by CBS Records. Dist: CBS

Extended-play record: released on CBS, Aug'87 by CBS Records. Dist: CBS

HALF A WORLD AWAY.
Tracks: / Half a world away / Where can you be / When love comes calling*.
Single (7"): released on CBS, May'87 by CBS Records. Dist: CBS

Single (12"): released on CBS, May'87 by CBS Records. Dist: CBS

Single (12"): released on CBS, 23 May'87 by CBS Records. Dist: CBS

PAUL JOHNSON.
Tracks: / When love comes calling / Calling / Fear of falling / New love / Every kinda people / Intimate friends / Burnin' / Heaven is 10 zillion light years away / Are we strong enough / Half a world away / Don't pass me by / Where can you be.
Album: released on CBS, 30 May'87 by CBS Records. Dist: CBS

Cassette: released on CBS, 30 May'87 by CBS Records. Dist: CBS

Compact disc: released on CBS, Jun'87 by CBS Records. Dist: CBS

WHEN LOVE COMES CALLING.
Tracks: / When love comes calling / Don't pass me by.
Single (7"): released on CBS, Jan'87 by CBS Records. Dist: CBS

Single (12"): released on CBS, Jan'87 by CBS Records. Dist: CBS

Johnson, Pete

ALL STAR SWING GROUPS (Johnson, Pete & Cozy Cole).

BOOGIE WOOGIE CLASSICS (Johnson, Pete/Albert Ammons).
Album: released on Blue Note (USA Import), Sep'84

MASTER OF BLUES & BOOGIE WOOGIE.
Album: released on Oldie Blues, Sep'79 Dist: Cadillac, Projection Distribution, Celtic Music Distribution, JSU Distribution, Swift Distribution

Johnson, Philip

YOUTH IN MOURNING.
Album: released on Namedrop Records, Jan'83 by Namedrop Records. Dist: Rough Trade

Johnson, Plas

ROCKIN' WITH THE PLAS.
Album: released on Capitol (France), '83 by Capitol Records. Dist: Conifer

Johnson, Robert

KING OF THE DELTA BLUES.
Album: released on CBS(Blue Diamond), Jun'85 by CBS Records. Dist: CBS

Cassette: released on CBS(Blue Diamond), Jun'85 by CBS Records. Dist: CBS

ROBERT JOHNSON.
Album: released on Deja Vu, Nov'85 by Deja Vu Records. Dist: Counterpoint Distribution, Record Services Distribution (Ireland)

Cassette: released on Deja Vu, Nov'85 by Deja Vu Records. Dist: Counterpoint Distribution, Record Services Distribution (Ireland)

Johnson, Syl

BRING OUT THE BLUES IN ME.
Tracks: / Brings out the blues in me / How you need to be loved / Last night was the night / Got my eyes on you / Liberated lady / Sock it to me / Is it because I'm black / Crazy people.
Album: released on Flyright, Apr'86 by Flyright Records. Dist: Krazy Kat, Swift, Jazz Music

IS IT BECAUSE I' BLACK.
Tracks: / Come on sock it to me / Dresses too short / I can take care of business / I'll take those skinny legs / I resign / Get ready / I feel an urge / I take care of homework / Is it because I'm black / Concrete reservation / Walk a mile in my shoes / I'm talkin' 'bout freedom / Right on.
Album: released on Charly, Aug'86 by Charly Records. Dist: Charly, Cadillac

LOVE CHIMES, THE.
Album: released on Hi, Jul'86 by Demon Records. Dist: Pinnacle

MS FINE BROWN FRAME.
Single (7"): released on Epic, Jan'73 by CBS Records. Dist: CBS

Single (12"): released on Epic, Jan'73 by CBS Records. Dist: CBS

Johnson, Tex

BODY SNATCH.
Single (12"): released on Lovely, Nov'83 Dist: Jetstar

CAN'T GET BY WITHOUT YOU.
Single (12"): released on Disco Tex, Jun'83 by Disco Tex Records. Dist: Jetstar

COLLECTION FOR LOVERS ONLY, THE.
Album: released on Disco Tex, Aug'86 by Disco Tex Records. Dist: Jetstar

CROWD OF PEOPLE.
Single (12"): released on Disco Tex, Sep'84 by Disco Tex Records. Dist: Jetstar

EVER SO HAPPY.
Tracks: / Ever so happy / Feeling happy.
Single (12"): released on Robin Hood, Mar'87

FAITHFULLY YOURS (Johnson, Tex & the Instigators).
Single (12"):

GIVE US A CHANCE.
Tracks: / Give us a chance / Hard road.
Single (12"): released on Sky Juice, Nov'86 by Sky Juice Records. Dist: Jetstar

KEEP ON LOVING ME.
Single (12"): released on Disco Tex, Nov'85 by Disco Tex Records. Dist: Jetstar

KNOCK A DANCE STYLE.
Single (12"): released on SD, Jun'82 by SD Records. Dist: Backs, Cartel

LOVE TO LOVE YOU.
Single (12"): released on Disco Tex, Jun'82 by Disco Tex Records. Dist: Jetstar

PILLOW TALK.
Single (12"): released on Disco Tex, Apr'82 by Disco Tex Records. Dist: Jetstar

STILL IN LOVE WITH YOU.
Single (12"): released on Disco Tex, Oct'85 by Disco Tex Records. Dist: Jetstar

WOMANISER.
Single (12"): released on Disco Tex, Dec'83 by Disco Tex Records. Dist: Jetstar

Johnson, T.J.

I CAN MAKE IT GOOD FOR YOU (Johnson, T.J. Band).
Single (7"): released on Switch, Jul'83 Dist: Backs, Cartel Distribution

Single (12"): released on Switch, Jul'83 Dist: Backs, Cartel Distribution

PRETTY LADY.
Single (7"): released on Switch, May'82 Dist: Backs, Cartel Distribution

Johnson, Troy

GETTING A GRIP ON LOVE.
Tracks: / You make me lose my head / If you've got the heart / Mesmerized / Just get a grip / It's my groove / It's you / Wonders of your love / Time will tell / Time will tell / Honest lover.
Album: released on Motown, Jul'86 by Motown Records. Dist: BMG Distribution

Cassette: released on Motown, Jul'86 by Motown Records. Dist: BMG Distribution

Johnson, Wayne

GRASSHOPPER (Johnson, Wayne Trio).
Album: released on Allegiance, Jul'84 by PRT Records. Dist: PRT

Cassette: released on Allegiance, Jul'84 by PRT Records. Dist: PRT

Johnson, Wilko

BOTTLE UP AND GO EP (Johnson, Wilko & Len Lewis Band).
Single (7"): released on Thunderbolt, Jul'83 by Magnum Music Group Ltd. Dist: Magnum Music Group Ltd, PRT Distribution, Spartan Distribution

DOWN BY THE WATERSIDE.
Single (7"): released on Rockburgh, Mar'80

ICE ON THE MOTORWAY.
Album: released on Nighthawk, Jan'81 by Faulty Products Records. Dist: Pinnacle, Swift

SOLID SENDERS.
Album: released on Virgin, Mar'85 by Virgin Records. Dist: EMI, Virgin Distribution

WATCH OUT.
Album: released on Waterfront, Jan'86 by Waterfront Records. Dist: Rough Trade, Cartel, Projection, Roots

Cassette: released on Waterfront, Jan'86 by Waterfront Records. Dist: Rough Trade, Cartel, Projection, Roots

Johns, Teddy

MORNINGTON CRESCENT.
Single (7"): Dist: PRT

Johnston, Annie

SONGS OF THE HEBRIDES.
Cassette: released on Folktracks, Nov'79 by Folktracks Cassettes. Dist: Folktracks

SOUTH UNIST & ERISKA, VOL.3.
Cassette: released on Folktracks, Nov'79 by Folktracks Cassettes. Dist: Folktracks

Johnstone, Arthur

GENERATIONS OF CHANGE.
Album: released on Lismor, Jun'85 by Lismor Records. Dist: Lismor, Roots, Celtic Music
Cat. no: LIFL 7007
Album: released on Lismor, Jun'85 by Lismor Records. Dist: Lismor, Roots, Celtic Music

Johnstone, Ian

SOME GUYS HAVE ALL THE LUCK.
Cassette: released on Chevron, Nov'82 Dist: Multiple Sound Distributors

Johnstone, Jim

COME DANCE WITH ME (Johnstone, Jim & Band).
Album: released on Lismor, Apr'77 by Lismor Records. Dist: Lismor, Roots, Celtic Music

DANCE TIME (Johnstone, Jim & His Band).
Album: released on Lismor, '84 by Lismor Records. Dist: Lismor, Roots, Celtic Music

Album: released on Lismor, '84 by Lismor Records. Dist: Lismor, Roots, Celtic Music

FAVOURITES.
Album: released on Ross, '86 by Ross Records. Dist: Ross Distribution, Roots Distribution

Cassette: released on Ross, '86 by Ross Records. Dist: Ross Distribution, Roots Distribution

JIM JOHNSTONE'S FAVOURITES (Johnstone, Jim & His Band).
Notes: Mail order distribution address: Accordion Record Club, 146 Birmingham Road, Kidderminster, Worcs DY10 2SL. Tel:0562-746105.

SCOTTISH WELCOME, A (Johnstone, Jim & Band).
Album: released on Lismor, '75 by Lismor Records. Dist: Lismor, Roots, Celtic Music

SOUND OF JIM JOHNSTONE AND HIS BAND,THE (Johnstone, Jim & His Band).
Album: released on Lismor, '79 by Lismor Records. Dist: Lismor, Roots, Celtic Music

SOUND OF JOHNSTONE, THE (Johnstone, Jim & Band).
Album: released on Note, Mar'78 by EMI Records. Dist: EMI

Johnstones

ANTHOLOGY.
Album: released on Transatlantic, Jun'78 by Transatlantic Records. Dist: IMS-Polygram

Johnston, Johnnie

HOP SCOTCH CHRISTMAS (Johnston, L).
Single (7"): released on Ross, Dec'83 by Ross Records. Dist: Ross Distribution, Roots Distribution

LITTLE OLE WINE DRINKER ME.
Album: released on Homespun(Ireland), Jun'83 by Outlet Records. Dist: Outlet

Cassette: released on Homespun(Ireland), Jun'83 by Outlet Records. Dist: Outlet

Johnston, Luther

DOIN' THE SUGAR TOO (Johnston, Luther JR).
Album: released on Blue Phoenix (France), Jan'85

Johnston, Sophie

HAPPY TOGETHER (Johnston, Sophie & Peter).
Tracks: / Happy together / Sold on you / Losing you / Losing you / Soy dance.
Single (7"): released on I Major, Aug'86 by I Major. Dist: I Major

Single (12"): released on I Major, Aug'86 by I Major. Dist: I Major

LOSING YOU (Johnston, Sophie & Peter).
Single (7"): released on Smash The Majors, Oct'85 Dist: M.I.S., EMI

TORN OPEN (Johnston, Sophie & Peter).
Tracks: / Torn open / Getting on.
Single (7"): released on I Major, 23 May'87 by I Major. Dist: I Major

Single (12"): released on I Major, 23 May'87 by I Major. Dist: I Major

John the Fish

COELACANTH.
Album: released on Sweet Folk All, May'81 by Sweet Folk All Records. Dist: Sweet Folk All, Roots, Celtic Music, Dragon, Impetus, Projection, Chris Wellard, Festival Records

John & The Night Riders

CHARGE OF THE NIGHTRIDERS.
Album: released on Rock House, Jan'85 Dist: Pinnacle

John & Yoko

SOMETIME IN NEW YORK CITY (John & Yoko With The Plastic Ono Band).
Tracks: / Sisters, O sisters / Attica state / Born in a prison / New York City / Sunday bloody Sunday / Luck of the Irish, The / John Sinclair / Angela / We're all water (with Elephants Memory & Invisible Strings) / Cold turkey / Don't worry Kyoko (with a cast of 1000's) / Well (baby please don't go) / Jamrag / Scumbag / Au / Woman is the nigger of the world.
Compact disc: released on EMI, Aug'87 by EMI Records. Dist: EMI

Double Album: released on Parlophone, Jan'72 by EMI Records. Dist: EMI

Compact disc: released on Parlophone, Aug'87 by EMI Records. Dist: EMI

LIVE JAM.
Tracks: / Cold turkey / Don't worry Kyoko / Well (baby please don't go) / Jamrag / Scumbag / AU.
Notes: Tracks 3-6 with Frank Zappa and the Mothers of Invemtion.
Compact disc: released on Parlophone, Aug'87 by EMI Records. Dist: EMI

Jo Jo

PINKMOUSE (ALLEZ).
Single (7"): released on Iguana, Aug'84 by Iguana Records. Dist: ILA, Grapevine

Jo Jo & The Real People

LADY MARMALADE.
Tracks: / Lady Marmalade / Seven times over.
Single (7"): released on Polydor, 13 Jun'87 by Polydor Records. Dist: Polygram, Polydor

Single (12"): released on Polydor, 13 Jun'87 by Polydor Records. Dist: Polygram, Polydor

Joker

BACK ON THE ROAD.
Single (7"): released on Lost Moments, Feb'85 Dist: Backs, Cartel

Jokers Wild

DON'T FALL IN LOVE.
Single (7"): released on Bold Reprieve, Sep'87 by Bold Reprieve Records. Dist: Pinnacle

Jolene

JOLENE WITH PART TWO.
Album: released on Country House, '81 by BGS Productions Ltd. Dist: Taylor, H.R., Record Merchandisers Distribution, Pinnacle, Sounds of Scotland Records

Cassette: released on Neptune, Aug'78 by Lismor. Dist: Spartan

TOGETHER AGAIN.
Album: released on Country House, Aug'80 by BGS Productions Ltd. Dist: Taylor, H.R., Record Merchandisers Distribution, Pinnacle, Sounds of Scotland Records

Cassette: released on Country House, Aug'80 by BGS Productions Ltd. Dist: Taylor, H.R., Record Merchandisers Distribution, Pinnacle, Sounds of Scotland Records

Jolie Blonde...

JOLIE BLONDE"ROCKS AND ROLLS various artists (Various Artists).
Album: released on Goldband, Sep'84 by Charly Records. Dist: Charly

Jolliffe, John

ALAMEIN.
Tracks: / Alamein / Ships in the night.
Single (7"): released on Carrere, Oct'86 by Carrere Records. Dist: PRT, Spartan

Single (12"): released on Carrere, Oct'86 by Carrere Records. Dist: PRT, Spartan

PLAYING WITH FIRE.
Tracks: / Playing with fire / Dancing with myself.
Single (7"): released on Carrere, Jun'86 by Carrere Records. Dist: PRT, Spartan

Single (12"): released on Carrere, Jun'86 by Carrere Records. Dist: PRT, Spartan

Joll, France

ATTITUDE.
Album: released on Epic, Nov'83 by CBS Records. Dist: CBS

Cassette: released on Epic, Nov'83 by CBS Records. Dist: CBS

Jolinder, Nils

SWEDISH POPULAR SONGS.
Album: released on Phontastic (Sweden), '82 by Wellard, Chris Distribution. Dist: Wellard, Chris Distribution

Joling, Gerard

LOVE IS IN YOUR EYES.
Single (7"): released on WEA, Aug'85 by WEA Records. Dist: WEA

TICKET TO THE TROPICS.
Tracks: / Ticket to the tropics / Communications.
Single (7"): released on WEA, Feb'86 by WEA Records. Dist: WEA

Jolley and Swain

BACK TRACKIN'.
Album: released on R & B, Jun'84 by Red Bus. Dist: PRT

Cassette: released on R & B, Jun'84 by Red Bus. Dist: PRT

Jolliffe, Steve

JAPANESE BUTTERFLY/NADA.
Album: released on Pulse, Jan'86 by Pulse Records.

JOURNEY'S OUT OF THE BODY.
Album: released on Nada Pulse Management, Feb'84 by Nada Pulse.

Jolly Jack

ROLLING DOWN TO OLD MAUI.
Album: released on Fellside, May'85 by Fellside Records. Dist: Roots, Jazz Music, Celtic Music, Projection

Jolly, Pete

JOLLY JUMPS IN.
Album: released on RCA (France), '83 by RCA Records. Dist: Discovery

Jolo

SOUL.
Tracks: / Soul (club mix) / Soul (instrumental) / Last call.
Single (12"): released on Greyhound, Jan'87 by Greyhound Records. Dist: PRT, Greyhound

Jolson, Al

20 GOLDEN GREATS VOL.1.
Cassette: released on Nostalgia (USA), Dec'85 by Sonic Arts Corporation.

20 GOLDEN GREATS VOL.2.
Cassette: released on Nostalgia (USA), Dec'85 by Sonic Arts Corporation.

AN EVENING WITH....
Album: released on ASA, Oct'86 by Asa Records. Dist: Jazz Music

Bing and Al volume 1

Bing and Al volume 2

Bing and Al volume 3

Bing and Al volume 4

Bing and Al volume 5

Bing and Al volume 6

JAZZ SINGER, THE.
Tracks: / California here I come / Pasadena / I'm sitting on top of the world / Blue river / Golden gate / Back in your own / My Mammy / Dirty hands / Dirty hands! Dirty face! / There's a rainbow round my shoulder / Sonny boy / I'm in seventh heaven / Little pal / Used to you / Why can't you / Liza / Let me sing and I'm happy / April showers / Rock-a-bye your baby with a dixie melody.
Notes: Eighteen tracks covering Jolson the performer, the writer and the star. Brian Rust has given us some excellent sleeve notes which really say it all.
Album: released on Submarine, Nov'85 by Submarine Records. Dist: Wellard, Chris Distribution, Conifer Distribution, H.R. Taylor Distribution

Cassette: released on Submarine, Nov'85 by Submarine Records. Dist: Wellard, Chris Distribution, Conifer Distribution, H.R. Taylor Distribution

ON THE AIR VO.5.
Album: released on Totem, Oct'86 Dist: Jazz Music, Projection, Swift

ON THE AIR VOL.2.
Album: released on Totem, Oct'86 Dist: Jazz Music, Projection, Swift

ON THE AIR VOL.3.
Album: released on Totem, Oct'86 Dist: Jazz Music, Projection, Swift

ON THE AIR VOL.4.
Album: released on Totem, Oct'86 Dist: Jazz Music, Projection, Swift

SONNY BOY.
Tracks: / I feel a song coming on / Isn't this a lovely day / I like to take orders from you / World is waiting for the sunrise, The / I'll see you in my dreams / Smoke gets in your eyes / Sonny boy / She's a latin from Manhattan / At sundown / My blue heaven / Night and day / Avalon / Cheek to cheek / I can't give you anything but love / Lady in red, The.
Album: released on Topline, May'87 by Charly Records. Dist: Charly Distribution

Cassette: released on Topline, May'87 by Charly Records. Dist: Charly Distribution

Album: released on Hallmark, Jul'86 by Pickwick Records. Dist: Pickwick Distribution, PRT, Taylors

Cassette: released on Hallmark, Jul'86 by Pickwick Records. Dist: Pickwick Distribution, PRT, Taylors

YOU AIN'T HEARD NOTHING YET.
Tracks: / California here I come / Sonny boy / April showers / Pasadena / When the red red robin comes bob bob bobbin' along / You made me love you / I'm ka-razy for you / You ain't heard nothin' yet / Swanee / When the little red roses get the blues for you / Rock-a-bye your baby with a dixie melody / Blue river / Used to you / Steppin' out / Spaniard that blighted my life, The / Golden gate / My Mammy.
Notes: What more is there to be said about this great man? 1986 is the 100th anniversary of his birth! The distinctive voice, like his songs, is quite timeless, and he was often referred to as "The worlds greatest entertainer", a total perfectionist who inspired many other singers - including the young Bing Crosby. It is hard to believe that even now his songs appeal to a wide cross section of age groups. Some of his greatest songs are featured on this disc - a sure-fire winner by any standards.
Album: released on ASV Living Era, Dec'85 by ASV Records. Dist: PRT

Cassette: released on ASV Living Era, Dec'85 by ASV Records. Dist: PRT

Jo Manu

HOT LIKE WE (Jo Manu & King Everal The Sham).
Tracks: / Hot like we / Hot like we (Version).
Single (12"): released on Java, Oct'86 Dist: Jetstar

Jonae, Gwen

RED LIGHT LOVER.
Single (7"): released on Carrere America (USA), Apr'83 by Polygram.

Single (12"): released on Carrere America (USA), Apr'83 by Polygram.

Jonah, Julian

HOT TO TOUCH.
Tracks: / Hot to touch / Dreaming.
Single (7"): released on Total Control, Jun'86

Single (12"): released on Total Control, Jun'86

Jon and the Nightriders

SPLASHBACK.
Extended-play record: released on Rock House, Nov'82 Dist: Pinnacle

SURF BEAT '80.
Album: released on Charly, Nov'81 by Charly Records. Dist: Charly, Cadillac

Jon and Vangelis

BEST OF.
Compact disc: released on Polydor, Sep'84 by Polydor Records. Dist: Polygram, Polydor

BEST OF JON AND VANGELIS, THE.
Album: released on Polydor, Aug'84 by Polydor Records. Dist: Polygram, Polydor

Cassette: released on Polydor, Aug'84 by Polydor Records. Dist: Polygram, Polydor

Compact disc: released on Polydor, Aug'84 by Polydor Records. Dist: Polygram, Polydor

FRIENDS OF MR. CAIRO, THE.
Album: released on Polydor, Jun'81 by Polydor Records. Dist: Polygram, Polydor

Cassette: released on Polydor, Jun'81 by Polydor Records. Dist: Polygram, Polydor

PRIVATE COLLECTION.
Album: released on Polydor, May'83 by Polydor Records. Dist: Polygram, Polydor

Cassette: released on Polydor, May'83 by Polydor Records. Dist: Polygram, Polydor

Compact disc: released on Polydor, '83 by Polydor Records. Dist: Polygram, Polydor

SHORT STORIES.
Album: released on Polydor, Jan'80 by Polydor Records. Dist: Polygram, Polydor Deleted '87.

Cassette: released on Polydor, Jan'80 by Polydor Records. Dist: Polygram, Polydor Deleted '86.

Compact disc: released on Polydor, Jan'80 by Polydor Records. Dist: Polygram, Polydor

SHORT STORIES/THE FRIENDS OF MR.CAIRO.
Cassette: released on Polydor, Aug'82 by Polydor Records. Dist: Polygram, Polydor

Jonas

BANG THE DRUM ALL DAY.
Single (7"): released on Lamborghini, Mar'85 by Lamborghini Records. Dist: PRT

DEDICATION SONG.
Single (7"): released on Lamborghini, Nov'83 by Lamborghini Records. Dist: PRT

LIPSTICK AND CANDY AND RUBBER SOLE SHOES.
Tracks: / Lipstick and candy and rubber sole shoes / Rock & roll school.
Single (7"): released on Genie, Aug'86 by Genie Records. Dist: Spartan, CBS

LITTLE QUENNIE/BABY CAN YOU ROCK.
Single (7"): released on Sundance, Feb'83 by Sundance Records. Dist: PRT Distribution

ROCK'N'ROLL SCHOOL.
Single (7"): released on Genie, Aug'85 by Genie Records. Dist: Spartan, CBS

Jonathan King Presents

JONATHAN KING PRESENTS ENTERTAINMENT USA 2 (Various Artists).
Album: released on Priority, Oct'86 by Priority Records. Dist: RCA

Cassette: released on Priority, Oct'86 by Priority Records. Dist: RCA

Jonathan Livingstone...

JONATHAN LIVINGSTONE SEAGULL Bach, Richard (Bach, Richard).
Cassette: released on Caedmon(USA), May'82 by Caedmon (USA) Records. Dist: Gower, Taylors, Discovery

JONATHAN LIVINGSTONE SEAGULL Original Sountrack.
Album: released on CBS, May'73 by CBS Records. Dist: CBS

Jones, Aled

ALED Music from the TV series.
Album: released on 10, Feb'87 by 10 Records. Dist: Virgin, EMI

Cassette: released on 10, Feb'87 by 10 Records. Dist: Virgin, EMI

Compact disc: released on 10, Feb'87 by 10 Records. Dist: Virgin, EMI

ALED JONES WITH THE BBC WELSH CHORUS.
Album: released on 10, Nov'85 by 10 Records. Dist: Virgin, EMI

Cassette: released on 10, Nov'85 by 10 Records. Dist: Virgin, EMI

Compact disc: released on 10-BBC, Dec'85

ALL THROUGH THE NIGHT.
Album: released on BBC, Jun'85 by BBC Records & Tapes. Dist: EMI, PRT, Pye

Cassette: released on BBC, Jun'85 by BBC Records & Tapes. Dist: EMI, PRT Pye

AN ALBUM OF HYMNS.
Cassette: released on Telstar, Nov'86 by Telstar Records. Dist: RCA Distribution

Compact disc: released on Telstar, Nov'86 by Telstar Records. Dist: RCA Distribution

Album: released on Telstar, Nov'86 by Telstar Records. Dist: RCA Distribution

Compact disc: by Telstar Records. Dist: RCA Distribution

AVA MARIA.
Album: released on Sain, Jul'85 by Sain Records. Dist: Projection, Sain

Single (7"): released on BBC, May'85 by BBC Records & Tapes. Dist: EMI, PRT, Pye

DIOLCH A CHAN.
Album: released on Sain, Jul'85 by Sain Records. Dist: Projection, Sain

MEMORY.
Single (7"): released on BBC, Jul'85 by BBC Records & Tapes. Dist: EMI, PRT, Pye

MORNING HAS BROKEN.
Tracks: / Morning has broken / How great thou art.
Single (7"): released on RCA, Nov'86 by RCA Records. Dist: RCA, Roots, Swift, Wellard, Chris, I & B, Solomon & Peres Distribution

PIE JESU.
Tracks: / Pie Jesu / Art thou troubled? / If I can help somebody / Zion hears the watchmen's voices / Jesu joy of mans desiring / Lullaby / I'll walk beside you / Crown of roses, The / I know that my redeemer liveth / Lausanne / God so loved the world / At the end of the day / Pie Jesu (faure) / Laudate dominum / Pie Jesu / Art thou troubled.
Single (7"): released on ASV, Jan'87 by Academy Sound & Vision Records. Dist: Pinnacle

Album: released on 10, Jun'86 by 10 Records. Dist: Virgin, EMI

Cassette: released on 10, Jun'86 by 10 Records. Dist: Virgin, EMI

Compact disc: released on 10, Jun'86 by 10 Records. Dist: Virgin, EMI

Single (7"): released on 10, May'86 by 10 Records. Dist: Virgin, EMI

SAILING.
Tracks: / Sailing / Scarborough Fair Canticle.
Single (7"): released on 10, Jul'87 by 10 Records. Dist: Virgin, EMI

Album: released on 10, Jul'87 by 10 Records. Dist: Virgin, EMI

Cassette: released on 10, Jul'87 by 10 Records. Dist: Virgin, EMI

SAILING (LP).
Compact disc: released on 10, Jul'87 by 10 Records. Dist: Virgin, EMI

TOO YOUNG TO KNOW.
Single (7"): released on Sain (Wales), Jun'85

WALKING IN THE AIR.
Single (7"): released on H.M.V., Oct'85 by EMI Records. Dist: EMI

Single (12"): released on H.M.V., Oct'85 by EMI Records. Dist: EMI

WHERE E'ER YOU WALK.
Album: released on 10, Feb'86 by 10 Records. Dist: Virgin, EMI

Cassette: released on 10, Feb'86 by 10 Records. Dist: Virgin, EMI

Compact disc: released on 10, Aug'86 by 10 Records. Dist: Virgin, EMI

WINTER STORY, A.
Tracks: / winter stor, A / Sion blewych coch.
Single (7"): released on H.M.V., Nov'86 by EMI Records. Dist: EMI

Single (12"): released on H.M.V., Nov'86 by EMI Records. Dist: EMI

Jones, Allan
DONKEY SERENADE - THE BEST OF.
Album: released on RCA, Aug'87 by RCA Records. Dist: RCA, Roots, Swift, Wellard, Chris, I & B, Solomon & Peres Distribution

Cassette: released on RCA, Aug'87 by RCA Records. Dist: RCA, Roots, Swift, Wellard, Chris, I & B, Solomon & Peres Distribution

Jones, Barbara
10 MILLION SELLERS IN REGGAE.
Album: released on Top Rank, Jan'86

BORROWED TIME.
Single (12"): released on Unknown, Jun'85

DEDICATED TO THE ONE I LOVE.
Album: released on Pioneer International, Mar'84 by Pioneer International Records. Dist: CBS, Essex

DON'T STAY AWAY.
Single (12"): released on Self Survivor, Apr'85 by Self Survivor Records. Dist: Jetstar

DREAM LOVER.
Single (12"): released on GG'S, Jul'82 by GG'S Records. Dist: Jetstar

FOR YOUR EYES ONLY.
Single (12"): released on GG'S, Jul'82 by GG'S Records. Dist: Jetstar

HAVE A GOOD TIME.
Single (12"): released on GG'S, '79 by GG'S Records. Dist: Jetstar

I CAN'T SAY GOODBYE TO YOU.
Single (12"): released on GG'S, Jul'82 by GG'S Records. Dist: Jetstar

NEED TO BELONG.
Album: released on EAD, Feb'86 by EAD Records. Dist: Jetstar

PLEASE MISTER, PLEASE.
Tracks: / Please mister, please / Mister (dub).
Single (12"): released on Charm, Nov'86 Dist: Jetstar

Cat. no: SC 7009

SINGLE GIRL.
Single (7"): released on Creole, Jun'83 by Creole Records. Dist: Rhino, PRT

Single (12"): released on Creole, Jun'83 by Creole Records. Dist: Rhino, PRT

TOMORROW IS FOREVER.
Single (12"): released on GG'S, Jun'82 by GG'S Records. Dist: Jetstar

WHY DID YOU LEAVE ME?.
Single (7"): released on GG'S, Feb'80 by GG'S Records. Dist: Jetstar

WILL IT LAST FOREVER?.
Album: released on GG'S, Aug'84 by GG'S Records. Dist: Jetstar

YOU'RE ALWAYS ON MY MIND.
Album: released on Dynamic, Nov'84 by Creole Records. Dist: CBS, Essex

Jones, Bobby
HILL COUNTRY SUITE.
Album: released on Enja (Germany), Jan'82 by Enja Records (W.Germany). Dist: Cadillac Music

SOUL SET FREE.
Album: released on Myrrh, May'82 by Word Records. Dist: Word Distribution

Cassette: released on Myrrh, May'82 by Word Records. Dist: Word Distribution

Jones, Brenda
YOUR MY OCCUPATION (Jones, Brenda Featuring Chas Jankel).
Tracks: / Your my occupation.
Single (7"): released on A&M, Aug'86 by A&M Records. Dist: Polygram

Single (12"): released on A&M, Aug'86 by A&M Records. Dist: Polygram

Jones, Bryan
BRYAN JONES BIG BAND (Jones, Bryan Big Band).
Album: released on Black Mountain, '82 by Black Mountain Records.

Jones, Byron
JUST BYRON.
Album: released on Grosvenor, Jun'81 by Grosvenor Records. Dist: Taylors

PLAYS THE CHRISTIE ORGAN, ASTRA THEATRE.
Notes: Full title: Plays the Christie organ, Astoria Theatre, Llandudno.
Album: released on Grosvenor, May'86 by Grosvenor Records. Dist: Taylors

PLAYS THE WERSI BETA - BEST WISHES.
Cassette: released on Grosvenor, Nov'86 by Grosvenor Records. Dist: Taylors

Jones, Carmell
REMARKABLE CARMELL JONES, (THE).
Album: released on Affinity, Nov'84 by Charly Records. Dist: Charly, Cadillac

Jones, Casey
STILL KICKIN'.
Album: released on Airwax (USA), Feb'84 Dist: Swift

Jones, Chris
NO MORE RANGE TO ROAM.
Album: released on Trailer, '81 Dist: Jazz Music, Celtic Music, JSU

Jones, Coley
COLEY JONES & THE DALLAS STRING BAND (Jones, Coley & The Dallas String Band).
Album: released on Matchbox (Bluesmaster), May'83

Jones & Crossland band
TOURNAMENT FOR BRASS.
Album: released on Grosvenor, Jun'81 by Grosvenor Records. Dist: Taylors

Jones, Curtis
CURTIS JONES IN LONDON.
Album: released on See For Miles, Aug'85 by Charly Records. Dist: Spartan

Jones, Davy
Manish Boys/Davy Jones & The Lower Third(EP)
YOU'VE GOT A HABIT OF LEAVING.
(Jones, Davy & The Lower Third).
Single (10"): released on Charly, Nov'82 by Charly Records. Dist: Charly, Cadillac

Jones, Dill
DILL JONES.
Album: released on Hep, Mar'87 by H.R. Taylor Records. Dist: Jazz Music, Cadillac Music, JSU, Taylors, Wellard, Chris, Zodiac, Swift, Fast Forward

UP JUMPED YOU WITH LOVE.
Album: released on Hep, Jul'87 by H.R. Taylor Records. Dist: Jazz Music, Cadillac Music, JSU, Taylors, Wellard, Chris, Zodiac, Swift, Fast Forward

Jones, Eddie
EDDIE JONES: 20 GUITAR GREATS.
Album: released on Everest (Premier), '83 by Everest Records. Dist: Pinnacle

Cassette: released on Everest (Premier), '83 by Everest Records. Dist: Pinnacle

Jones Elliot, Bryan
BALLAD OF SANTA CLAUS, (THE).
Single (7"): released on BBC, Nov'85 by BBC Records & Tapes. Dist: EMI, PRT, Pye

Jones, Elvin
BROTHER JOHN.
Album: released on Palo Alto (Italy), Jul'84

EARTH JONES.
Album: released on Palo Alto (Italy), Jul'86

Cassette: released on Palo Alto (Italy), Jul'86

Album: released on Palo Alto (Italy). Jan'84

Cassette: released on Palo Alto (Italy). Jan'84

ELVIN JONES.
Album:

JOHN COLTRANE MEMORIAL CONCERT.
Album: released on PM, Jan'80

LIVE AT THE VILLAGE VANGUARD.
Album: released on Enja (Germany), Jan'82 by Enja Records (W.Germany). Dist: Cadillac Music

MR THUNDER (Jones, Elvin Quartet).
Album: released on EWR, Jul'78

ON THE MOUNTAIN.
Album: released on PM, Jan'80

POLY CURRENTS.
Tracks: / Agenda / Agappe love / Mr.Jones / Yes / When.
Notes: In the late sixties and early seventies, Elvin Jones led a series of remarkable piano-less small groups with a mini saxophone section. This album features tenormen Joe Farrell and George Coleman and baritone saxophonist Pepper Adams. Guest artist Candido, the legendary conga drum master brings another dimension to Elvin's brilliant polyrhythmic drumming. Among the albums highlights are 'Mr.Jones' and Fred Tompkin's 'Yes'.
Album: released on Blue Note, Dec'85 by EMI Records. Dist: EMI

Album: released on Blue Note, Dec'85 by EMI Records. Dist: EMI

SKYSCRAPERS: VOL 1.
Album: released on Honeydew, Oct'79 Dist: Swift, JSU

SKYSCRAPERS: VOL 2.
Album: released on Honeydew, Oct'79 Dist: Swift, JSU

SKYSCRAPERS: VOL 3.
Album: released on Honeydew, Oct'79 Dist: Swift, JSU

SUMMIT MEETING.
Album: released on Vanguard, Jun'78 by PRT Records. Dist: PRT

TOGETHER (Jones, Elvin with Oregon).
Album: released on Vanguard, Jan'77 by PRT Records. Dist: PRT

Joneses
SUGAR PIE GUY.
Single (7"): released on Mercury, Mar'83 by Phonogram Records. Dist: Polygram Distribution

Single (12"): released on Mercury, Mar'83 by Phonogram Records. Dist: Polygram Distribution

Jones, Etta
IF YOU COULD SEE ME NOW.
Album: released on Muse, Apr'81 Dist: JSU Distribution, Jazz Horizons Distribution, Jazz Music Distribution, Celtic Music Distribution

MS JONES TO YOU.
Album: released on Muse, Apr'81 Dist: JSU Distribution, Jazz Horizons Distribution, Jazz

Music Distribution, Celtic Music Distribution

MY MOTHER'S EYES.
Album: released on Muse (Import), Apr'81

SAVE YOUR LOVE FOR ME.
Album: released on Muse (Import), May'81

SOMETHING NICE.
Album:

Jones, Floyd
BABY FACE LEROY & FLOYD JONES
(Jones, Floyd/Baby Face Leroy).
Album: released on Flyright, Oct'83 by Flyright Records. Dist: Krazy Kat, Swift, Jazz Music

FLOYD JONES & EDDIE TAYLOR
(Jones, Floyd & Eddie Taylor).
Album: released on Testament, May'86 Dist: Swift Distribution, Making Waves Distribution

JAMES/BRIM/JONES (Jones, Floyd, Elmore James, John Brim).
Notes: For full details see under Elmore James.

Jones, Frankie
BACK OFF.
Single (7"): released on Route, Oct'84 by Route Records. Dist: Jetstar Distribution

BEST OF FRANKIE JONES, THE.
Album: released on Trojan, Feb'87 by Trojan Records. Dist: PRT, Jetstar

GET OUT OF MY LIFE.
Single (12"): released on Greensleeves, May'85 by Greensleeves Records. Dist: BMG, Jetstar, Spartan

HELL IN THE DANCE (Jones, Frankie & Pad Anthony).
Single (12"): released on Top Rank, Nov'85

JAILHOUSE NO NICE.
Single (12"): released on Top Rank, Nov'85

LOVING ARMS.
Single (12"): released on Real Wax, Feb'85

MIX UP.
Single (12"): released on Village Roots, Sep'85 Dist: Jetstar

NO TOUCH THE RIDDUM.
Single (12"): released on Greensleeves, Nov'85 by Greensleeves Records. Dist: BMG, Jetstar, Spartan

OLD FIRE STICK.
Album: released on Power House, Nov'85 by Power House Records. Dist: Jetstar

PROBLEM.
Single (12"): released on Top Rank, May'85

RAM 17.
Tracks: / Ram 17 / Ram 17 instrumental.
Single (12"): released on Chart Hopper, Sep'86 Dist: Jetstar

SETTLE FE ME.
Single (12"): released on Bluesville International, Aug'84 Dist: Jetstar

SETTLEMENT.
Single (12"): released on Thunderbolt, Oct'84 by Magnum Music Group Ltd. Dist: Magnum Music Group Ltd, PRT Distribution, Spartan Distribution

SHOWDOWN VOL.2 (Jones, Frankie/Michael Palmer).
Album: released on Empire, Apr'84 by Empire Records. Dist: Backs, Cartel, Jetstar

THEM NICE.
Album: released on Harry, Oct'85 by Harry Records. Dist: Jetstar

WAR AND CRIME.
Single (12"): released on Gorgon, Oct'84 by Gorgon Records. Dist: Jetstar

Jones, George
Artist
Biographical Details: See also under Wynette, Tammy

15 GOLDEN CLASSICS VOL.1.
Album: released on Astan, Nov'84 by Astan Records. Dist: Counterpoint

Cassette: released on Astan, Nov'84 by Astan Records. Dist: Counterpoint

15 GOLDEN CLASSICS VOL.2.
Album: released on Astan, Nov'84 by Astan Records. Dist: Counterpoint

Cassette: released on Astan, Nov'84 by Astan Records. Dist: Counterpoint

16 GREATEST HITS.
Album: released on Starday, Apr'87

Cassette: released on Starday, Apr'87

20 GOLDEN PIECES OF GEORGE JONES.
Tracks: / Good year for the roses / Developing my pictures / Tender tears / Say it's not you / From here to the door / If my heart had windows / Favourite lies / Accidentally on purpose / Where grass won't grow / Sweet dreams / Things have gone to pieces / White lightning / 4-0-33 / Take me / I'm a people / I'm wasting good paper / Old brush arbors / Love bug / Walk through this world with me / Race is on, The.
Album: released on Bulldog, Feb'86 by Bulldog Records. Dist: President Distribution, Spartan, Swift, Taylor, H.R.

AT THE COUNTRY STORE.
Album: released on Country Store, Dec'85 by Starblend Records. Dist: PRT, Prism Leisure Corporation Records

Cassette: released on Country Store, Dec'85 by Starblend Records. Dist: PRT, Prism Leisure Corporation Records

BLUE MOON OF KENTUCKY.
Tracks: / I get lonely in a hurry / Love's gonna live here / Holiday for love / Imitation of love / Beggar to a king / What's money / She's lonesome again / Brown to blue / We could / Making the rounds / Lovin' lies / Same sweet girl / Please be my love / Blue moon of Kentucky / Yes I know why / Precious jewel / Matthew twenty four / Beacon in the night / I heard you crying in your sleep / In the shadow of a lie.
Notes: Original sound recordings made by Liberty records, advision of Capitol Records Inc. This compilation (P) 1987 EMI Records Ltd.
Album: released on Liberty (USA), Apr'87 Dist: United Artists

Cassette: released on Liberty (USA), Apr'87 Dist: United Artists

COLD COLD HEART.
Album: released on Allegiance, Apr'84 by PRT Records. Dist: PRT

Cassette: released on Allegiance, Apr'84 by PRT Records. Dist: PRT

DON'T STOP THE MUSIC.
Compact disc: released on Ace, Jun'87 by Ace Records. Dist: Pinnacle, Swift, Hotshot, Cadillac

GEORGE JONES I love country.
Tracks: / Why baby why / Tender years / Window up above, The / White lightnin' / Race is on, The / She thinks I still care / Her name is.... / I'm ragged but right / He stopped loving her today / Still doin' time / Shine on (Shine all your sweet love on me) / Radio lover / I always get lucky with you / Tennessee whiskey / If drinkin' don't kill me (her memory will) / She's my rock.
Album: released on Epic, Mar'87 by CBS Records. Dist: CBS

Cassette: released on Epic, Mar'87 by CBS Records. Dist: CBS

Album: released on CBS, Sep'86 by CBS Records. Dist: CBS

Cassette: released on Audio Fidelity, Oct'84 Dist: PRT

GEORGE JONES AND LADIES I love country (Jones, George & Ladies).
Tracks: / All fall down / Pair of old sneakers, A / Hallelujah, I love you so / Golden ring / All I want to do in life / We sure make good love / Daisy chain / That's good, that's bad / Here we are / Two storey house / Pair of old sneakers, A / If you can touch her at all / I've turned you to stone / Size seven round (made of gold) / Our love was ahead of its time / Slow burning fire / Best friends.
Album: released on Epic, Mar'87 by CBS Records. Dist: CBS

Cassette: released on Epic, Mar'87 by CBS Records. Dist: CBS

GEORGE JONES SALUTES HANK WILLIAMS & BOB WILLS.
Tracks: / Wedding bells / I just like this kind of living / You win again / I could never be ashamed of you / You're gonna change (or I'm gonna leave) / House without love / Your cheating heart / They'll never take her love from me / Mansion on the hill / Take these chains from my heart / Bubbles in my beer / Faded love / Roly poly / Trouble in mind / Take me back to Tulsa / Warm red wine, The / Time changes everything / Worried mind / Silver dew on the bluegrass tonight / San Antonio rose.
Notes: The king of country music, George Jones, plays tribute to the legendary Hank Williams and the king of western swing, Bob Wills. On this new compilation, George Jones covers hits made by these two pioneers of country music. This album makes a fitting companion to our previous George Jones compilation, "King of country music" (SLS 2600421/4).
Album: released on Liberty, Mar'86 by Liberty-United. Dist: EMI

Cassette: released on Liberty, Mar'86 by Liberty-United. Dist: EMI

GOOD OL' BOY.
Album: released on Sundown, Sep'84 by Magnum Music Group Ltd. Dist: Magnum Music Group Ltd, PRT Distribution, Spartan Distribution

GOOD YEAR FOR THE ROSES, A.
Tracks: / Where the grass won't grow / I'm a people / 4-0-33 / Things have gone to pieces / From here to the door / My favourite lies / Take me / White lightning / Tender years / Walk through this worlod with me / Say it's not you / Good year for the roses / Race is on, The / Developing my pictures / Old brush arbors.
Notes: All tracks licensed from the San Juan Music Group
Album: released on Showcase, '86 Dist: Counterpoint

Cassette: released on Showcase, '86 Dist: Counterpoint

Album: released on Premier, May'84 by Premier Records. Dist: CBS

Cassette: released on Premier, May'84 by Premier Records. Dist: CBS

GOOD YEAR FOR THE ROSES.
Tracks: / Good year for the roses, A / If my heart had windows / I'll share my world with you / I'm wasting good paper / Say it's not you / Accidently on purpose / Love bug / Where grass won't grow / 4033 / Things have gone to pieces / My favourite lies / From here to the door.
Album: released on Topline, Aug'87 by Charly Records. Dist: Charly Distribution. Estim retail price in Sep'87 was £2.99.

Cassette: released on Topline, Aug'87 by Charly Records. Dist: Charly Distribution

GREATEST HITS:GEORGE JONES & TAMMY WYNETTE (Jones, George & Tammy Wynette).
Cassette: released on Epic, Dec'77 by CBS Records. Dist: CBS

HE STOPPED LOVING HER.
Album: released on Premier, Feb'87 by Premier Records. Dist: CBS

Cassette: released on Premier, Feb'87 by Premier Records. Dist: CBS

JONES COUNTRY.
Album: released on Epic, Nov'83 by CBS Records. Dist: CBS

Cassette: released on Epic, Nov'83 by CBS Records. Dist: CBS

KING OF COUNTRY MUSIC.
Album: released on Liberty, Apr'84 by Liberty-United. Dist: EMI

Cassette: released on Liberty, Apr'84 by Liberty-United. Dist: EMI

KING & QUEEN OF COUNTRY MUSIC (Jones, George & Tammy Wynette).

LADIES CHOICE.
Album: released on Epic, Mar'85 by CBS Records. Dist: CBS

Cassette: released on Epic, Mar'85 by CBS Records. Dist: CBS Deleted May'87.

LIVE AT DANCETOWN USA.
Album: released on Del Rio, Nov'85 by Ace Records. Dist: Pinnacle, Swift, Counterpoint

LONE STAR LEGEND, THE.
Album: released on Ace, Apr'85 by Ace Records. Dist: Pinnacle, Swift, Hotshot, Cadillac

Cassette: released on Ace, Apr'85 by Ace Records. Dist: Pinnacle, Swift, Hotshot, Cadillac

MY VERY SPECIAL GUESTS.
Tracks: / Night life / Bartender's blues / Here we are / I've turned you to stone / It sure was good / I gotta get drunk / Proud Mary / Stranger in the house / I still hold her body / Will the circle be unbroken.
Album: released on Epic, Mar'86 by CBS Records. Dist: CBS

Cassette: released on Epic, Mar'86 by CBS Records. Dist: CBS

Album: released on Epic, May'79 by CBS Records. Dist: CBS

STILL THE SAME OLE ME.
Album: released on Epic, Jan'82 by CBS Records. Dist: CBS

Cassette: released on Epic, Jan'82 by CBS Records. Dist: CBS

STRANGERS, LOVERS AND FRIENDS.
Cassette: released on Ditto, May'87 by Pickwick Records. Dist: H.R. Taylor

TASTE OF YESTERDAY'S WINE, A (Jones, George & Merle Haggard).

TEXAS TORNADO.
Tracks: / White lightning / You gotta be my baby / What am I worth / Don't stop the music / Play it cool man / I'm gonna burn your playhouse down / Into my arms again / Let him know / Giveaway girl / All I want to do / My fool / Vitamins l-o-v-e.
Album: released on Crown, Feb'86 by Ace Records. Dist: Pinnacle, Swift

Cassette: released on Crown, Feb'86 by Ace Records. Dist: Pinnacle, Swift

TOGETHER AGAIN (Jones, George & Tammy Wynette).
Album: released on Epic, Jan'81 by CBS Records. Dist: CBS

Cassette: released on Epic, Jan'81 by CBS Records. Dist: CBS

WAYS OF THE WORLD.
Tracks: / Don't you ever get tired of hurting me / Open pity mind / On the banks of the ponchertrain / House without love is not a home, A / Ways of the world / Please don't let that woman get me / Yes I know why / Jonesy / Old brush arbor / Liberty / Jambalaya / Cold cold heart / Ragged but right / Tarnished angel / Your tender years / Wedding bells / Things have gone to pieces / World of forgotten people / From now on all of my friends are gonna be strangers / I can't escape from you.
Album: released on Starburst, Jul'87 by Starburst Records. Dist: CBS Distribution

Single (12"): released on Starburst, Jul'87 by Starburst Records. Dist: CBS Distribution

WHITE LIGHTNING.
Album: released on Ace, Sep'79 by Ace Records. Dist: Pinnacle, Swift, Hotshot, Cadillac

Album: released on Ace, Nov'84 by Ace Records. Dist: Pinnacle, Swift, Hotshot, Cadillac

Cassette: released on Ace, Nov'84 by Ace Records. Dist: Pinnacle, Swift, Hotshot, Cadillac

WHO'S GONNA FILL THEIR SHOES.
Album: released on CBS(Import), Sep'86 by CBS Records. Dist: Conifer, Discovery, Swift
Cat. no: **26696**

WINE COLOURED ROSES.
Tracks: / Wine coloured roses / I turn to you / Right left hand, The / Don't leave without taking your silver / Very best of me, The / Hopelessly yours / You never looked that good when you were mine / If only your eyes could lie / Ol' Frank / These old eyes have seen it all.
Album: released on Epic, Nov'86 by CBS Records. Dist: CBS

Cassette: released on Epic, Nov'86 by CBS Records. Dist: CBS

Jones Girls

ARTISTS SHOWCASE: JONES GIRLS.
Tracks: / You gonna make me love somebody else / 2 win u back / At peace with woman / Knockin' / Keep it comin' / Get as much love as you can / Life goes on / Nights over Egypt.
Album: released on Streetsounds, Jul'86

Cassette: released on Streetsounds, Jul'86

ON TARGET.
Album: released on RCA, Oct'83 by RCA Records. Dist: RCA, Roots, Swift, Wellard, Chris, I & B, Solomon & Peres Distribution

Cassette: released on RCA, Oct'83 by RCA Records. Dist: RCA, Roots, Swift, Wellard, Chris, I & B, Solomon & Peres Distribution

Single (7"): released on RCA, Oct'83 by RCA Records. Dist: RCA, Roots, Swift, Wellard, Chris, I & B, Solomon & Peres Distribution

Single (12"): released on RCA, Oct'83 by RCA Records. Dist: RCA, Roots, Swift, Wellard, Chris, I & B, Solomon & Peres Distribution

Jones, Glen

FINESSE.
Album: released on RCA, Nov'84 by RCA Records. Dist: RCA, Roots, Swift, Wellard, Chris, I & B, Solomon & Peres Distribution

Cassette: released on RCA, Nov'84 by RCA Records. Dist: RCA, Roots, Swift, Wellard, Chris, I & B, Solomon & Peres Distribution

I AM SOMEBODY.
Single (7"): released on RCA, Feb'83 by RCA Records. Dist: RCA, Roots, Swift, Wellard, Chris, I & B, Solomon & Peres Distribution

Single (12"): released on RCA, Feb'83 by RCA Records. Dist: RCA, Roots, Swift, Wellard, Chris, I & B, Solomon & Peres Distribution

TAKE IT FROM ME.
Tracks: / Stay / Set the night on fire / Love will show us how / Be my lady / Giving myself to you / All work and no play / Dangerous / Take it from me.
Album: released on RCA, Aug'86 by RCA Records. Dist: RCA, Roots, Swift, Wellard, Chris, I & B, Solomon & Peres Distribution

Cassette: released on RCA, Aug'86 by RCA Records. Dist: RCA, Roots, Swift, Wellard, Chris, I & B, Solomon & Peres Distribution

Jones, Gloria

TAINTED LOVE.
Single (7"): released on Inferno, Jan'82 by Inferno Records. Dist: Inferno, Cartel, Pinnacle

Single (12"): released on Inferno, Jan'82 by Inferno Records. Dist: Inferno, Cartel, Pinnacle

Single (7"): released on Soul Stop, Oct'84 by Soul Stop Record 3. Dist: Spartan

Single (7"): released on Rockhouse, Feb'83 by Rockhouse Records. Dist: Swift Distribution, Charly Distribution

WINDSTORM.
Album: released on Sidewalk, Mar'79 by Sidewalk Records. Dist: Mojo Distribution, Jetstar

Jones, Grace

FAME.
Album: released on Island, Jul'78 by Island Records. Dist: Polygram

I'M NOT PERFECT (BUT I'M PERFECT FOR YOU).
Tracks: / I'm not perfect (but I'm perfect for you) / Scary but fun / I'm not perfect (perfectly extended remix) / I'm not perfect (Instrumental version) / Scary but fun.
Notes: All tracks by Grace Jones and Bruce Woolley, and published by Bruce Woolley Music Ltd./CBS Songs Ltd.-Sonet Publications Ltd.
Single (7"): released on Manhattan, Nov'86 by President Records. Dist: Jazz Music, Swift, Taylors, Chris Wellard

Single (12"): released on Manhattan, Nov'86 by President Records. Dist: Jazz Music, Swift, Taylors, Chris Wellard

Picture disc single: released on Manhattan, Nov'86 by EMI Records. Dist: EMI

INSIDE STORY.
Tracks: / I'm not perfect (but I'm perfect for you) / Hollywood liar / Chan hitch-hikes to Shanghai / Victor should have been a jazz musician / Party girl / Crush / Barefoot in Beverly Hills / Scary but fun / White collar crime / Inside story.
Notes: Tracks 1-10 published by: Bruce Woolley Music Ltd./CBS Songs Ltd./ - Sonet Publications Ltd.
Compact disc: released on EMI, Dec'86 by EMI Records. Dist: EMI

Album: released on Manhattan, Nov'86 by EMI Records. Dist: EMI

Cassette: released on Manhattan, Nov'86 by EMI Records. Dist: EMI

INTERVIEW PICTURE DISC.
Album: released on Baktabak, May'87 by Baktabak Records. Dist: Arabesque

ISLAND LIFE.
Album: released on Island, Nov'85 by Island Records. Dist: Polygram

Cassette: released on Island, Nov'85 by Island Records. Dist: Polygram

ISLAND LIFE Best of Grace Jones.
Tracks: / Slave to the rhythm / Pull up to the bumper / Private life / La vie en rose / I need a man / My Jamaican guy / Walking in the rain / Libertango / Love is the drug / Do or die.
Compact disc: released on Island, Dec'85 by Island Records. Dist: Polygram

LIVING MY LIFE.
Tracks: / My Jamaican guy / Nipple to the bottle / Apple stretching, The / Everybody hold still / Cry now - laugh later / Inspiration / Unlimited capacity for love.
Notes: Produced by Chris Blackwell & Alex Sadkin
Album: released on Island, Feb'87 by Island Records. Dist: Polygram

Cassette: released on Island, Feb'87 by Island Records. Dist: Polygram

Album: released on Island, Nov'82 by Island Records. Dist: Polygram Deleted May'87.

Cassette: released on Island, Nov'82 by Island Records. Dist: Polygram

LOVE IS THE DRUG.
Tracks: / Love is the drug (remix) / Living my life / Apple stretching, The.
Single (7"): released on Island, Feb'86 by Island Records. Dist: Polygram

Single (12"): released on Island, Feb'86 by Island Records. Dist: Polygram

Picture disc single: released on Island, Feb'86 by Island Records. Dist: Polygram

Picture disc single: released on Island, Feb'86 by Island Records. Dist: Polygram

NIGHTCLUBBIN'.
Tracks: / Feel up / Walking in the rain / Pull up to the bumper / Use me / Art groupie / (Libertango) I've seen that face before / I've done it again.
Album: released on Island, Jan'87 by Island Records. Dist: Polygram

Cassette: released on Island, Jan'87 by Island Records. Dist: Polygram

Compact disc: released on Island, Jan'87 by Island Records. Dist: Polygram

ONE MAN SHOW, A.
Tracks: / Warm leatherette / Walking in the rain / Feel up / La vie en rose / Demolition man / Pull

up to the bumper / Private life / My Jamaican guy / Living my life / Libertango (I've seen that face before).
Video-cassette (VHS): released on Island Pictures, Nov'82 by Island Records. Dist: Polygram

PARTY GIRL Special remix.
Tracks: / Party girl (special remix) / White collar crime.
Single (7"): released on Manhattan, Mar'87 by President Records. Dist: Jazz Music, Swift, Taylors, Chris Wellard

Single (12"): released on Manhattan, Mar'87 by President Records. Dist: Jazz Music, Swift Taylors, Chris Wellard

Picture disc single: by President Records Dist: Jazz Music, Swift, Taylors, Chris Wellard

PORTFOLIO.
Tracks: / Send in the clowns / What I did for love / Tomorrow / La vie en rose / Sorry / That's the trouble / I need a man.
Notes: Produced by Tom Moulton for Bearr Junction productions.
Album: released on Island, Feb'87 by Island Records. Dist: Polygram

Cassette: released on Island, Feb'87 by Island Records. Dist: Polygram

Album: released on Island, Dec'77 by Island Records. Dist: Polygram

PRIVATE LIFE.
Tracks: / Private life (new "Groucho" remix) / My Jamaican guy / Feel up (vocal) / She's lost control again.
Single (7"): released on Island, May'86 by Island Records. Dist: Polygram

Single (12"): released on Island, May'86 by Island Records. Dist: Polygram

PULL UP TO THE BUMPER.
Tracks: / Pull up to the Bumper / La vie en rose.
Single (7"): released on Island, Jan'86 by Island Records. Dist: Polygram

Single (12"): released on Island, Jan'86 by Island Records. Dist: Polygram

Picture disc single: released on Island, Jan'86 by Island Records. Dist: Polygram

PULL UP TO THE BUMPER (CASSETTE).
Tracks: / Peanut butter (Pull up to the bumper inst.) / La vie en rose / Pull up to the bumper ("Groucho" remix) / Nipple to the bottle.
Cassette: released on Island, Jan'86 by Island Records. Dist: Polygram

SLAVE TO THE RHYTHM.
Compact disc: released on Island, Jul'87 by Island Records. Dist: Polygram
Cat. no: **CID 4011**
Album: released on ZTT, Nov'85 by Island Records. Dist: Polygram

Cassette: released on ZTT, Nov'85 by Island Records. Dist: Polygram

Single (7"): released on Island, Sep'85 by Island Records. Dist: Polygram

Single (12"): released on Island, Sep'85 by Island Records. Dist: Polygram

Picture disc single: released on ZTT, Oct'85 by Island Records. Dist: Polygram

WARM LEATHERETTE.
Tracks: / Warm leatherette / Private life / Rolling stone, A / Love is the drug / Hunter gets captured by the game, The / Bullshit / Breakdown / Pars.
Album: released on Island, Sep'86 by Island Records. Dist: Polygram

Cassette: released on Island, Sep'86 by Island Records. Dist: Polygram

Compact disc: released on Island, Sep'86 by Island Records. Dist: Polygram

Jones, Grandpa

16 GREATEST HITS.
Album: released on Starday, Apr'87

Cassette: released on Starday, Apr'87

20 OF THE BEST.
Album: released on RCA International, May'84

Cassette: released on RCA International, May'84 Deleted May'85.

MAN FROM KENTUCKY,(THE).
Album: released on Bulldog Records, Jul'82

Cassette: released on Bulldog Records, Jul'85

OTHER SIDE OF..., THE.
Album: released on King (USA), Apr'87 Dist: Gusto Distribution

Cassette: released on King (USA), Apr'87 Dist: Gusto Distribution

Jones, Hank

ARIGATO.
Album: released on Progressive (Import), Apr'81

BOP REDUX.
Album: released on Muse (Import), Apr'81

GROOVIN' HIGH.
Album: released on Muse (Import), Apr'81

I'M ALL SMILES (Jones, Hank & Tommy Flanagan).

JAZZ TRIO, (THE).
Album: released on Savoy (France), Oct'85

MOREOVER (Jones, Hank/Eddie Gomez/Al Foster).
Album: released on Phonogram (France), Oct'82

RELAXIN' AT CAMARILLO.
Notes: Artists include: Hank Jones (Piano); Bobby Jaspen (Flute); Paul Chambers (Bass); Kenny Clarke (Drums). This was Jones' last album as a leader for Savoy. Containing the great "Moonlight Becomes You" and Charlie Parker's "Relaxin' At Camarillo" it's as fresh-sounding today as when it first rolled off the Savoy presses thirty years ago. Recorded New Jersey 1956
Album: released on Savoy Jazz, Dec'85 by RCA Records (Germany). Dist: Conifer

Jones, Harley

VIRTUOSO ACCORDIONISTS (Jones, Harley & Maurice (NZ)).
Album: released on ARC (Accordion Records), May'84 Dist: Accordion Record Club

Jones, Howard

12 INCH ALBUM, THE.
Album: released on WEA, Nov'84 by WEA Records. Dist: WEA

Cassette: released on WEA, Nov'84 by WEA Records. Dist: WEA

ALL I WANT.
Tracks: / All I wnat / Roll up, right / Roll right up* / Don't want to fight@.
Single (7"): released on WEA, Sep'86 by WEA Records. Dist: WEA

Single (12"): released on WEA, Sep'86 by WEA Records. Dist: WEA

DREAM INTO ACTION.
Tracks: / Things can only get better / Life in one day / Dream into action / No one is to blame / Look mama / Assault and battery / Automaton / Is there a difference? / Elegy / Specialty / Why look for the key / Hunger for flesh.
Notes: Digital stereo recording.
Compact disc: released on WEA, Apr'85 by WEA Records. Dist: WEA

Album: released on WEA, Apr'85 by WEA Records. Dist: WEA

Cassette: released on WEA, Apr'85 by WEA Records. Dist: WEA

Compact disc: released on WEA, Apr'85 by WEA Records. Dist: WEA

HIDE AND SEEK.
Single (7"): released on WEA, Feb'84 by WEA Records. Dist: WEA

Single (12"): released on WEA, Feb'84 by WEA Records. Dist: WEA

HUMAN'S LIB.
Notes: Digital stereo.
Compact disc: released on WEA, Jun'84 by WEA Records. Dist: WEA

Album: released on WEA, Feb'84 by WEA Records. Dist: WEA

Cassette: released on WEA, Feb'84 by WEA Records. Dist: WEA

Compact disc: released on WEA, Jun'84 by WEA Records. Dist: WEA

LAST WORLD DREAM Live in concert.
Tracks: / Pearl in the shell / You know I love you...don't you? / Like to get to know you well / No one is to blame / Life in one day / Look mama / Will you still be there? / Always asking questions / Hide and seek / Dream into action / What is love? / New song / Things can only get better.
Notes: Directed by Wayne Isham. The stunning Music Video filmed at the NEC, Birmingham. Number of tracks: 13. Type of recording: live. Total playing time: 58 minutes.
Video-cassette (VHS): released on WEA, Oct'86 by WEA Records. Dist: WEA

Video-cassette [Betamax]: released on WEA, Oct'86 by WEA Records. Dist: WEA

LIFE IN ONE DAY.
Single (7"): released on WEA, Jun'85 by WEA Records. Dist: WEA

Single (12"): released on WEA, Jun'85 by WEA Records. Dist: WEA

LIKE TO GET TO KNOW YOU.
Video-cassette (VHS): released on Warner Bros., Oct'84 by Warner Bros Records. Dist: WEA

Single (7"): released on WEA, Jul'84 by WEA Records. Dist: WEA

Single (12"): released on WEA, Jul'84 by WEA Records. Dist: WEA

LITTLE BIT OF SNOW.
Tracks: / Little bit of snow / Let it flow / Will you still be there* / Hunger for the flesh (orchestral)* / ide and seek (orchestral)*.
Single (7"): released on WEA, Feb'87 by WEA Records. Dist: WEA

Single (12"): released on WEA, Feb'87 by WEA Records. Dist: WEA

LOOK MAMA.
Single (7"): released on WEA, Apr'85 by WEA Records. Dist: WEA

Single (12"): released on WEA, Apr'85 by WEA Records. Dist: WEA

NEW SONG.
Single (7"): released on WEA, Aug'83 by WEA Records. Dist: WEA

Single (12"): released on WEA, Aug'83 by WEA Records. Dist: WEA

NO ONE IS TO BLAME.
Tracks: / No one is to blame / Chase, The.
Single (7"): released on WEA, Feb'86 by WEA Records. Dist: WEA

Single (12"): released on WEA, Feb'86 by WEA Records. Dist: WEA

ONE TO ONE.
Tracks: / You know I love you, don't you / Balance of love, The / All I want / Where are we going / Don't want to fight anymore / Step into these shoes / Will you still be there? / Good luck bad luck / Give me strength / Ltle bit of snow.
Album: released on WEA, Oct'86 by WEA Records. Dist: WEA

Cassette: released on WEA, Oct'86 by WEA Records. Dist: WEA

Compact disc: released on WEA, Oct'86 by WEA Records. Dist: WEA

PEARL IN THE SHELL.
Single (12"): released on WEA, Apr'84 by WEA Records. Dist: WEA

THINGS CAN ONLY GET BETTER.
Single (7"): released on WEA, Jan'85 by WEA Records. Dist: WEA

Single (12"): released on WEA, Jan'85 by WEA Records. Dist: WEA

Picture disc single: released on WEA, Mar'85 by WEA Records. Dist: WEA

WHAT IS LOVE.
Single (7"): released on WEA, Nov'83 by WEA Records. Dist: WEA

Single (12"): released on WEA, Nov'83 by WEA Records. Dist: WEA

YOU KNOW I LOVE YOU DON'T YOU?.
Tracks: / You know I love you don't you / Dig this world deep / Dance in the field (mix).
Single (7"): released on WEA, Nov'86 by WEA Records. Dist: WEA

Jones, Ieuan

UNCOMMON HARP, THE.
Tracks: / Introduction, Cadenza & Rondo / On golden pond / Clair de Lune / Spanish romance / Hello / Chess / Rustle on spring, Op. 32. No.3 / Chi mai / Pavane pur une infante defunte / First waltz, Op.83.
Notes: Ieuan Jones plays regularly for The Queen Mother and has been appointed harpist to the House of Commons. Extra tracks on the Compact disc.
Album: released on BBC, Jun'87 by BBC Records & Tapes. Dist: EMI, PRT, Pye

Cassette: released on BBC, Jun'87 by BBC Records & Tapes. Dist: EMI, PRT, Pye

Compact disc: released on BBC, Jun'87 by BBC Records & Tapes. Dist: EMI, PRT, Pye

Jones, Isham

ISHAM JONES & HIS ORCHESTRA 1920-24.
Album: released on Retrieval, Apr'79 by Retrieval Records. Dist: Retrieval, VJM, Swift, Record Sales(Chris Wellard), Jazz Music

Jones,Ivan Boogaloo Joe

BLACK WHIP.
Album: released on Musicwise, Feb'84 Dist: Musicwise

Jones, Jack

DEAR HEART And other great songs of love.
Album: released on Memoir, Apr'86 by Memoir Records. Dist: PRT Distribution

Cassette: released on Memoir, Apr'86 by Memoir Records. Dist: PRT Distribution

DEJA VU.
Cassette: released on Polydor, Nov'82 by Polydor Records. Dist: Polygram, Polydor

Album: released on Polydor, Nov'82 by Polydor Records. Dist: Polygram, Polydor Deleted May'84.

FIRE AND RAIN.
Album: released on President, Mar'85 by President Records. Dist: Taylors, Spartan

Cassette: released on President, Mar'85 by President Records. Dist: Taylors, Spartan

GOLDEN CLASSICS.
Tracks: / Race is on / Bridge over troubled water / Lyin' eyes / My life / Beaking up is hard to do / Just the two of us / Chase the rainbows / Long and winding road / My fault / You've got a friend (medley).
Notes: All tracks licensed from Interworld Communications
Album: released on Unforgettable, Dec'86 by Castle Communications Records. Dist: Counterpoint

Cassette: released on Unforgettable, Dec'86 by Castle Communications Records. Dist: Counterpoint

GOLDEN GREATS: JACK JONES.
Album: released on MCA, Jul'85 by MCA Records. Dist: Polygram, MCA

Cassette: released on MCA, Jul'85 by MCA Records. Dist: Polygram, MCA

JACK JONES SPECIAL COLLECTION, (THE).
Album: released on RCA International, Apr'80

LOVE SONGS.
Album: released on MFP, Sep'85 by EMI Records. Dist: EMI

Cassette: released on MFP, Sep'85 by EMI Records. Dist: EMI

LYIN' EYES.
Single (7"): released on Applause, Mar'82 by Riva Records. Dist: WEA, Discovery

MAGIC MOMENTS.
Cassette: released on RCA, Jun'84 by RCA Records. Dist: RCA, Roots, Swift, Wellard, Chris, I & B, Solomon & Peres Distribution

MAKE IT WITH YOU.
Double Album: released on Cambra, Feb'85 by Cambra Records. Dist: IDS, Conifer

Double cassette: released on Cambra, Feb'85 by Cambra Records. Dist: IDS, Conifer

NOBODY DOES IT BETTER.
Album: released on Polydor, Sep'79 by Polydor Records. Dist: Polygram, Polydor

SONGS OF LOVE.
Album: released on Memoir, Jan'87 by Memoir Records. Dist: PRT Distribution

SPECIAL COLLECTION.
Cassette: released on RCA International, Apr'80

TOGETHER.
Album: released on Victor, May'73

VERY BEST OF JACK JONES, (THE).
Album: released on RCA, Jul'81 by RCA Records. Dist: RCA, Roots, Swift, Wellard, Chris, I & B, Solomon & Peres Distribution

Cassette: released on RCA, Jul'81 by RCA Records. Dist: RCA, Roots, Swift, Wellard, Chris, I & B, Solomon & Peres Distribution

Jones, Jackie

I WILL ALWAYS LOVE YOU (Jones, Jackie/Whitfield Batson).
Single (12"): released on Ruff Cutt, Aug'83

LOVE LIGHT.
Single (12"): released on Ital, Nov'82 Dist: Pinnacle

Jones, Janie

HOUSE OF THE JU-JU QUEEN (Jones, Janie & The Lash).
Single (7"): released on Beat Beat, Dec'83

Jones, Jill

JILL JONES.
Tracks: / Mia Bocca / G-spot / Violet blue / With you / All day, all night / For love / My man / Baby, you're a trip / Intro (baby you're a trip) / Mia bocca / G-Spot / Violet blue / With you / All day, all night / For love / My man / Baby, you're a trip.
Album: released on Paisley Park (usa), Jun'87 by WEA Records. Dist: WEA

Cassette: released on Paisley Park (usa), Jun'87 by WEA Records. Dist: WEA

Album: released on Paisley Park (usa), Jul'87 by WEA Records. Dist: WEA

Cassette: released on Paisley Park (usa), Jul'87 by WEA Records. Dist: WEA

MIA BOCA.
Tracks: / Mia boca / Bleaker Street.
Single (7"): released on Paisley Park (usa), Jun'87 by WEA Records. Dist: WEA

Single (12"): released on Paisley Park (usa), Jun'87 by WEA Records. Dist: WEA

Jones, Jimmy

BEST OF JIMMY JONES, THE.
Album: released on A.1, Nov'86 by A.1 Records. Dist: PRT

Cassette: released on A.1, Nov'86 by A.1 Records. Dist: PRT

GOOD TIMIN'.
Single (7"): released on Old Gold, Jul'84 by Old Gold Records. Dist: Lightning, Jazz Music, Spartan, Counterpoint

LIVE AT THE TALK OF EAST ANGLIA.
Album: released on Kin'ell Records. Nov'81

STRANDED.
Single (7"): released on Lark, Feb'83 by Lark Records. Dist: PRT

THAT'S THE NICEST THING.
Single (7"): released on Kin'ell, Nov'82

Jones, JJ

JOHNNY REMEMBER ME.
Single (7"): released on Rutland, May'83 by Rutland Records. Dist: Rutland Distribution

Jones, Jo

ESSENTIAL JO JONES, THE.
Double Album: released on Vogue Jazz (France), May'83

MAIN MAN, THE.
Album: released on Pablo (USA), '82 by Pablo Records (USA). Dist: Wellard, Chris, IMS-Polygram, BMG

Cassette: released on Pablo (USA), '82 by Pablo Records (USA). Dist: Wellard, Chris, IMS-Polygram, BMG

OUR MAN PAPA JO.
Album: released on Denon, Mar'82 by Denon Records. Dist: Harmonia Mundi

Jones, Johnny

HORSING AROUND (Jones, Johnny & The King Casuals).

JOHNNY JONES & BILLY BOY ARNOLD (Jones, Johnny & Billy Boy Arnold).
Album: released on Sonet, Feb'80 by Sonet Records. Dist: PRT

JOHNNY JONES V. TAMPA RED (Jones, Johnny & Tampa Red).
Album: released on Krazy Kat (USA), May'83

PURPLE HAZE (Jones, Johnny & The King Casuals).
Tracks: / Purple haze / Horsing around.
Single (7"): released on Cream, Mar'87 Dist: Global Records Distribution

Jones, John Paul

SAXY.
Album: released on Sarge, Jul'84 by Sarge Records. Dist: Jetstar

SCREAM FOR HELP.
Album: released on Atlantic, Apr'85 by WEA Records. Dist: WEA

Cassette: released on Atlantic, Apr'85 by WEA Records. Dist: WEA

Jones, Jonah

BUTTERFLIES IN THE RAIN (Jones, Jonah & His Swing Band).
Notes: Mono. 1944.

Album: released on Circle(USA), Jan'87 by Jazzology Records (USA). Dist: Jazz Music, Swift, Chris Wellard

HARLEM JUMP AND SWING (Jones, Jonah Sextet & Pete Brown Sextet).
Tracks: / There will never be another you / I can't believe that your in love with me / Used blues / Moonlight in Vermont / World is waiting for the sunrise, The / Tea for two / Delta blues / Beatle street blues / Down by the riverside / European blues / You're the cream in my coffee / Wrap your troubles in dreams.
Album: released on Affinity, '83 by Charly Records. Dist: Charly, Cadillac

JONAH JONES QUARTET/GLEN GRAY & THE CASA LOMA ORCHESTRA (Jones, Jonah & Glen Gray).
Tracks: / Baubles, bangles and beads / Echoes of Harlem / Two o'clock jump / I can't get started / Boy meets horn / Hot lips / After you've gone / West end blues / Ciribiribin / Tenderly / Sugar blues / Apollo jumps.
Notes: See also under Glen Gray. On this album, two capitol stars of the 50's and 60's are teamed together to present a string of exciting Big Band arrangements, Jonah Jones, a trumpeter, made many good selling albums with his quartet,while arranger/conductor Glen Gray was leader of the house Capitol Orchestra during the 50's and 60's. Together they swing through tunes by favourite composers.
Album: released on Capitol, Feb'87 by Capitol Records. Dist: EMI

Cassette: released on Capitol, Feb'87 by Capitol Records. Dist: EMI

JUMPING WITH A SHUFFLE.
Album: released on Capitol(USA), Mar'84 by Capitol (USA) Records. Dist: EMI

SWING STREET SHOWCASE (Jones, Jonah & Hot Lips Page).
Album: released on Commodore Classics, May'87 by Teldec Records (Germany). Dist: Conifer, IMS, Polygram

Album: released on Commodore Classics, Feb'84 by Teldec Records (Germany). Dist: Conifer, IMS, Polygram

Jones, Kim

GUESS WHO CARES.
Tracks: / Guess who cares / Anyway.
Album: released on Own, Mar'86 Dist: MIS-EMI Distribution

Jones, Klinte

IN THE HEAT OF THE NIGHT.
Single (12"): released on Personal, Aug'84 by Personal Records. Dist: PRT

Jones, Leath

BAD BOYS.
Single (7"): released on All That Records, Nov'81

Jones, "Little" Sonny

"LITTLE" SONNY JONES.
Notes: With Dave "Fat Man" Williams R & B Band.
Album: released on CSA, Jan'87 by CSA Records. Dist: PRT, Jetstar

Jones, Louise

IT AIN'T EASY.
Cassette: released on Music City, Jul'87 Dist: Ross Distribution

Jones, Mac

TRIBUTE TO BOB MARLEY.
Tracks: / Tribute to Bob Marley / Jah Jah Woman.
Single (7"): released on Instant, Feb'86 by Instant Records. Dist: Zodiac Distribution

Single (12"): released on Zodiac, Oct'86 Dist: Jazz Music

Jones, Matthew

MADE UP THE WORLD.
Tracks: / Made up the world / Pier head / Bath house, The.
Single (12"): released on Cherry Red, May'87 by Cherry Red Records. Dist: Pinnacle

Jones, Michael

PIANOSCAPES.
Album: released on Narada (Holland), Dec'84

Cassette: released on Narada (Holland), Dec'84

SEASCAPES.
Album: released on Narada (Holland), Dec'84

Cassette: released on Narada (Holland), Dec'84

Jones, Mose

BLACKBIRD.
Album: released on RCA, Feb'79 by RCA Records. Dist: RCA, Roots, Swift, Wellard, Chris, I & B, Solomon & Peres Distribution

Jones, Nic

BALLADS AND SONGS.
Album: released on Leader, Mar'85 Dist: Jazz Music, Projection

BANDOGGS.
Album: released on Trailer, '81 Dist: Jazz Music, Celtic Music, JSU

FROM THE DEVIL TO A STRANGER.
Album: released on Trailer, '81 Dist: Jazz Music, Celtic Music, JSU

PENGUIN EGGS.
Album: released on Topic, '81 Dist: Roots Distribution

SONGS OF A CHANGING WORLD (see Raven,Jon/Nic Jones/Tony Rose) (Jones, Nic/Jon Raven/Tony Rose).

Jones, Nigel

SENTINEL (Jones, Nigel Mazlyn).
Album: released on Avada, '79 Dist: Roots

Jones, Oran 'Juice'

1.2.1..
Tracks: / 1.2.1. / Here I go again / Curiosity.
Notes: * = Extra track on 12" only.
Single (7"): released on Def Jam (USA), Apr'87 by CBS Records. Dist: CBS

Single (12"): released on Def Jam (USA), Apr'87 by CBS Records. Dist: CBS

CURIOSITY.
Tracks: / Curiosity / Here I go again.
Single (7"): released on Def Jam (USA), Jan'87 by CBS Records. Dist: CBS

Single (12"): released on Def Jam (USA), Jan'87 by CBS Records. Dist: CBS

JUICE.
Tracks: / Rain, The / You can't hide from love / Here I go again / Curiosity / Your song / Love will find a way / It's yours / 1.2.1. / Two faces.
Album: released on Def Jam (USA), Jun'86 by CBS Records. Dist: CBS

Cassette: released on Def Jam (USA), Jun'86 by CBS Records. Dist: CBS

RAIN ,THE.
Tracks: / Rain, The / Your song.
Album: released on Def Jam (USA), Oct'86 by CBS Records. Dist: CBS

Jones, Paul

HIGH TIME.
Single (7"): released on Creole (Reissue), Aug'82 by Creole Records. Dist: PRT, Rhino

Jones, Philip

EASY WINNERS (Jones, Philip Brass Ensemble).
Cassette: released on Argo, '78 by Decca Records. Dist: Polygram

GRAND MARCH (Jones, Philip Brass Ensemble).
Compact disc: by Decca Records. Dist: Polygram

LOLLIPOPS (Jones, Philip Brass Ensemble).
Tracks: / London minatures / Londoner in New York / Flight of the bumble bee / Variations on a Tyrolean theme.
Compact disc: released on Claves, Nov'85 Dist: Gamut, Pinnacle, IMS, Polygram

WORLD OF BRASS.
Album: released on Decca, '74 by Decca Records. Dist: Polygram

WORLD OF THE TRUMPET.
Album: released on Decca, '74 by Decca Records. Dist: Polygram

Jones, Philly Joe

BLUES FOR DRACULA (Jones, Philly Joe Sextet).
Album: released on Original Jazz Classics (USA), Apr'86 Dist: Fantasy (USA) Distribution, Chris Wellard Distribution, IMS-Polygram Distribution

DAMERONIA.
Notes: Britt Woodman/Frank Wess/Cecil Payne
Album: released on Uptown (USA), Nov'86 by Uptown Records. Dist: Jazz Music

Album: released on Uptown (USA), Feb'83 by Uptown Records. Dist: Jazz Music

GREEN DOLPHIN STREET (see Evans, Bill).

LOOK STOP LISTEN (Jones, Philly Joe & Dameronia).
Notes: Featuring Johnny Griffin
Album: released on Uptown (USA), Nov'86 by Uptown Records. Dist: Jazz Music

MEAN WHAT YOU SAY.
Album: released on Sonet, Jan'78 by Sonet Records. Dist: PRT

ROUND MIDNIGHT.
Album: released on Lotus, Apr'81 Dist: Counterpoint

Slinger Cees, Philly Joe Jones ......

TRAILWAY EXPRESS.
Album: released on Black Lion, Jan'85 by Black Lion Records. Dist: Jazz Music, Chris Wellard, Taylor, H.R., Counterpoint, Cadillac

Jones, Quincy

BEST, THE.
Notes: Inc. Razzamatazz/Ai no corrida/Dude/Stuff like that/One hundred ways/Superstition.
Compact disc: released on A&M, Feb'85 by A&M Records. Dist: Polygram

Album: released on A&M, Feb'82 by A&M Records. Dist: Polygram

Cassette: released on A&M, Feb'82 by A&M Records. Dist: Polygram

BIRTH OF A BAND.
Compact disc: by Emarcy Records(USA). Dist: Polygram

BOSSA NOVA.
Album: released on Mercury (USA), Nov'83 by Import Records. Dist: IMS Distribution, Polygram Distribution

DEADEND WALKING IN SPACE.
Album: released on Platinum (W.Germany), Oct'85 Dist: Mainline

Cassette: released on Platinum (W.Germany), Oct'85 Dist: Mainline

DUDE, THE.
Tracks: / Ai no corrida / Dude, The / Just one / Betcha wouldnt hurt me / Something special / Razzamatazz / One hundred ways / Valas / Turn on the action.
Notes: Re-issue
Album: released on A&M, Apr'86 by A&M Records. Dist: Polygram

Cassette: released on A&M, Apr'86 by A&M Records. Dist: Polygram

Compact disc: released on A&M, '83 by A&M Records. Dist: Polygram

GREAT WIDE WORLD OF ..., THE.
Album: released on Mercury (USA), Nov'81 by Import Records. Dist: IMS Distribution, Polygram Distribution

GREAT WIDE WORLD, THE.
Tracks: / Lester leaps in / Ghana / Caravan / Everybody's blues / Cherokee (Indian love song) / Air mail special / They say it's wonderful / Chant of the weed / I never has seen snow.
Notes: Recorded 11/59. All star band sessions featuring Phil Woods, Lee Morgan, Art Farmer and many others
Compact disc: released on Emarcy(USA), Apr'85 by Emarcy Records(USA). Dist: Polygram

MELLOW MADNESS.
Album: released on A&M, Aug'75 by A&M Records. Dist: Polygram

MUSIC IN MY LIFE.
Album: released on Hallmark, Aug'83 by Pickwick Records. Dist: Pickwick Distribution, PRT, Taylors

Cassette: released on Hallmark, Aug'83 by Pickwick Records. Dist: Pickwick Distribution, PRT, Taylors

QUINCY JONES ALL STARS (Jones, Quincy All Stars).
Notes: With Art Farmer & Clifford Brown
Album: released on Esquire, Jul'86 by Titan International Productions. Dist: Jazz Music, Cadillac Music, Swift, Wellard, Chris, Backs, Rough Trade, Revolver, Nine Mile

QUINTESSENCE.
Album: released on Jasmine, Jan'85 by Jasmine Records. Dist: PRT

Album: released on Impulse, Oct'85 by Impulse Records. Dist: MCA, Polygram

QUINTESSENCE,THE.
Tracks: / Quintessence / Robot portrait / Little Karen / Straight,No chaser / For Lena and Lennie / Hard sock dance / Invitation / Twitch,The.
Compact disc: released on MCA, '87 by MCA Records. Dist: Polygram, MCA

SMACKWATER JACK.
Album: released on A&M, '74 by A&M Records Dist: Polygram

Cassette: released on A&M, '74 by A&M Records. Dist: Polygram Deleted '85.

SOUNDS...& STUFF LIKE THAT.
Album: released on A&M, Jun'78 by A&M Records. Dist: Polygram

Cassette: released on A&M, Jun'78 by A&M Records. Dist: Polygram

STUFF LIKE THAT.
Tracks: / Stuff like that / Ai no corrida / Rise / Feel so good.
Single (12"): released on Old Gold, Jan'87 by Old Gold Records. Dist: Lightning, Jazz Music, Spartan, Counterpoint

TAKE FIVE.
Album: released on Happy Bird (Germany), Aug'83 Dist: Polygram, IMS

Cassette: released on Happy Bird (Germany), Aug'83 Dist: Polygram, IMS

THIS IS HOW I FEEL.
Album: released on Jasmine, Feb'84 by Jasmine Records. Dist: Counterpoint, Lugtons, Taylor, H.R., Wellard, Chris, Swift, Cadillac

WALKING IN SPACE.
Album: released on A&M, '74 by A&M Records. Dist: Polygram

WE HAD A BALL.
Album: released on Philips (Timeless), Sep'84 Cat. no: **TIME 7**
Cassette: released on Philips (Timeless), Sep'84

Jones, Richard M.

CHICAGO JAZZ-VOL.2 (Jones, Richard M & Omar Simeon).
Album: released on Classic Jazz Masters, Dec'86 by Mainline Record Company. Dist: Mainline, Swift, Jazz Music

FROM N.O. TO CHICA (Jones, Richard M, Willie Hightower, Frankie Franko).
Album: released on Collectors Items, Jul'86 Dist: Jazz Music, Swift, Chris Wellard

Jones, Rickie Lee

CHUCK E'S IN LOVE.
Single (7"): released on Warner Brothers, Jun'79 by Warner Bros Records. Dist: WEA

GIRL AT HER VOLCANO.
Tracks: / Lush life / Walk away Rene / Hey bub / Rainbow sleeves / My funny valentine / Under the boardwalk / So long.
Album: released on Warner Brothers, Jun'83 by Warner Bros Records. Dist: WEA

Cassette: released on Warner Brothers, Jun'83 by Warner Bros Records. Dist: WEA

MAGAZINE.
Tracks: / Prelude to gravity / Gravity / Juke box fury / It must be love / Magazine / Real end, The / Deep space / Runaround Rorschachs / Theme for the Pope / Unsigned painting ,The / Wierd beast, The.
Compact disc: released on Warner Bros., Mar'86 by Warner Bros Records. Dist: WEA

Album: released on Warner Brothers, Oct'84 by Warner Bros Records. Dist: WEA

Cassette: released on Warner Brothers, Oct'84 by Warner Bros Records. Dist: WEA

PIRATES.
Tracks: / We belong together / Living it up / Skeletons / Woody and Dutch on the slow train to Peking / Pirates / Lucky guy / Traces of western slopes / Returns.
Compact disc: released on WEA, Jan'86 by WEA Records. Dist: WEA

Album: released on Warner Brothers, Jul'81 by Warner Bros Records. Dist: WEA

Cassette: released on Warner Brothers, Jul'81 by Warner Bros Records. Dist: WEA

RICKIE LEE JONES.
Tracks: / On Saturday afternoons in 1963 / Night train / Young blood / Easy money / Last chance Texaco / Danny's All Star Joint / Coolsville / Weasel and the white boy's cool / Company / After hours (12 bars past midnight).
Compact disc: released on Warner Bros., '83 by Warner Bros Records. Dist: WEA

Album: released on Warner Brothers, Jun'79 by Warner Bros Records. Dist: WEA

Double cassette: released on Warner Brothers, Nov'83 by Warner Bros Records. Dist: WEA

UNDER THE BOARDWALK.
Single (7"): released on Warner Brothers, Aug'83 by Warner Bros Records. Dist: WEA

Jones, Robin

EYE OF THE HURRICANE (Jones, Robin Quartet & Esmond Selwyn).
Album: released on Spotlite, '83 by Spotlite Records. Dist: Cadillac, Jazz Music, Spotlite

Jones, Rodney

ARTICULATION.
Album: released on Timeless, Sep'86

Album: released on Timeless, Apr'81

Jones, Ronnie

CAPTAIN OF HER HEART, THE.
Tracks: / Captain of her heart, The / Captain of her heart, The (1st dance mix) / Lovin you*.
Single (7"): released on Sublime, Mar'86 by Sublime Records. Dist: PRT Distribution

Single (12"): released on Sublime, Mar'86 by Sublime Records. Dist: PRT Distribution

Jones, Sam

BASSIST, THE.
Album: released on Discovery, Jun'83 Dist: PRT

SOMETHING IN COMMON.
Album: released on Muse (Import), Apr'81

Jones, Sebastian Graham

MUSIC FROM THE TRAVELLING MAN
(see Browne,Duncan & Sebastian Graham Jones).

Jones, Sherry

HANG ON SLOOPY.
Single (7"): released on Polo, Mar'82 by Polo Records. Dist: PRT

Single (12"): released on Polo, Mar'82 by Polo Records. Dist: PRT

Jones, Shirley

ALWAYS IN THE MOOD.
Tracks: / Do you get enough love / Breaking up / Last night I needed somebody / She knew about me / Always in the mood / I'll do anything for you / Surrender.
Album: released on PIR, Jul'86

Cassette: released on PIR, Jul'86

DO YOU GET ENOUGH LOVE.
Tracks: / Do you get enough love / We can work it out.
Single (7"): released on Philadelphia International, Jul'86 by CBS Records. Dist: CBS

Single (12"): released on Philadelphia International, Jul'86 by CBS Records. Dist: CBS

Jones, Spencer

HEAD OVER HEELS.
Single (7"): released on Polo, Mar'84 by Polo Records. Dist: PRT

Single (12"): released on Polo, Mar'84 by Polo Records. Dist: PRT

HOW HIGH.
Single (12"): released on Elite, Nov'82 Dist: PRT

HOW TO WIN YOUR LOVE.
Single (7"): released on Champion, Jan'86 by Champion Records. Dist: RCA

Single (12"): released on Champion, Jan'86 by Champion Records. Dist: RCA

I WANT YOU.
Single (12"): released on Elite, Dec'83 Dist: PRT

MISS FRIDAY.
Single (7"): released on Rise, Oct'86 by Steve O'Donnell/Colin Jennings. Dist: Pinnacle

Single (12"): released on Rise, Oct'86 by Steve O'Donnell/Colin Jennings. Dist: Pinnacle

Jones, Spike

BEST OF SPIKE JONES - VOL.2.
Album: released on RCA (Germany), '83

Bing Crosby with Spike Jones & Jimmy Durante

CAN'T STOP MURDERING.
Album: released on RCA (Germany), '83

GREATEST HITS:SPIKE JONES.
Cassette: released on Timeless Treasures, Jul'86 Dist: Counterpoint Distribution

I WENT TO YOUR WEDDING (Jones, Spike & His City Slickers).
Album: released on RCA International, '84 Cat. no: **NL 89310**
Cassette: released on RCA International, Nov'84

MURDERS THEM ALL.
Tracks: / Liebestraum / Blue Danube, The / Flight of the bumble bee / None but the lonely heart / Rhapsody from hunger / William Tell Overture / Carmen murdered / Dance of the hours / Glow worm, The / I kiss your hand madame / Love in bloom / Hotcha cornia / Black bottom / Hawiian war chant / I went to your wedding / I'm in the mood for love / That old black magic.
Double Album: released on RCA, Jul'86 by RCA Records. Dist: RCA, Roots, Swift, Wellard, Chris, I & B, Solomon & Peres Distribution

Cassette: released on RCA, Jul'86 by RCA Records. Dist: RCA, Roots, Swift, Wellard, Chris, I & B, Solomon & Peres Distribution

Double Album: released on RCA (France), Apr'84 by RCA Records. Dist: Discovery

ON THE AIR 1943 & 1944 (Jones, Spike & His City Slickers).
Album: released on Sandy Hook (USA), May'84 Dist: Swift, Jazz Music, IMS-Polygram

SPIKE JONES MURDERS AGAIN.
Album: released on RCA (Germany), '83

SPIKE JONES VOL 2.
Album: released on Harlequin, Dec'86 by Harlequin Records. Dist: Swift, Jazz Music, Wellard, Chris, IRS, Taylor, H.R.

STANDARD TRANSCRIPTION DISCS 1942-44 (Jones, Steve).
Album: released on Harlequin, Mar'86 by Harlequin Records. Dist: Swift, Jazz Music, Wellard, Chris, IRS, Taylor, H.R.

THANK YOU MUSIC LOVERS.
Album: released on Deja Vu, Oct'83 by Deja Vu Records. Dist: Counterpoint Distribution, Record Services Distribution (Ireland)

Cassette: released on Deja Vu, Oct'83 by Deja Vu Records. Dist: Counterpoint Distribution, Record Services Distribution (Ireland)

UNCOLLECTED, THE.
Album: released on Hindsight(UK), Apr'86 Dist: Jazz Music

Album: released on Hindsight(UK), Jun'85 Dist: Jazz Music

VOLUME 2.
Notes: Part 2 of the 16" Standard transcription discs
Album: released on Harlequin, Nov'86 by Harlequin Records. Dist: Swift, Jazz Music, Wellard, Chris, IRS, Taylor, H.R.

Jones, Steve

I NEED YOU.
Single (7"): released on P Flight, Dec'84

MERCY.
Tracks: / Mercy / Give it up / That's enough / Raining in my heart / With you or without you / Pleasure and pain / Pretty baby / Drugs suck / Through the night / Love letters.
Single (7"): released on I.R.S.(Independent Record Syndicate), Aug'87 by I.R.S.. Dist: MCA

Single (12"): released on I.R.S.(Independent Record Syndicate), Aug'87 by I.R.S.. Dist: MCA

Album: released on MCA, Apr'87 by MCA Records. Dist: Polygram, MCA

Cassette: released on MCA, Apr'87 by MCA Records. Dist: Polygram, MCA

Compact disc: released on MCA, Jun'87 by MCA Records. Dist: Polygram, MCA

Jones, Tamiko

I WANT YOU.
Single (12"): released on Hot Melt, Dec'86 by Hot Melt Records. Dist: Pinnacle, Spartan

Jones, Tammy

BEST OF TAMMY JONES, THE.
Cassette: released on Embassy, Feb'78 by CBS Records. Dist: CBS

COUNTRY GIRL.
Album: released on Blue Waters, Jun'85 Dist: M.I.S.

WEEKEND LOVING.
Album: released on Black Solidarity, Jun'85 by Black Solidarity Records. Dist: Jetstar

Jones, Terry

FAIRY TALES.
Cassette: released on Argo (Spokenword), Oct'85 by Decca Records. Dist: Polygram

Jones, Thad

ECLIPSE.
Album: released on Storyville, Nov'86 by Storyville Records. Dist: Jazz Music Distribution, Swift Distribution, Chris Wellard Distribution, Counterpoint Distribution

LIVE Live Jazzhus Slukefter, Tivoli (Jones, Thad, Eclipse).
Album: released on Metronome (Denmark), Jun'81 Dist: Jazz Music Distribution

MAGNIFICENT THAD JONES, THE.
Tracks: / April in Paris / Billie - doo / If I love again / If someone had told me / Thedia / I've got a crush on / Something to remember you by.
Compact disc: released on Blue Note, Aug'87 by EMI Records. Dist: EMI

MAGNIFICENT, THE.
Compact disc: released on Blue Note, Aug'87 by EMI Records. Dist: EMI

THAD JONES ECLIPSE (Jones, Thad, Eclipse).
Album: released on Metronome (Denmark), Jun'81 Dist: Jazz Music Distribution

THAD JONES & MEL LEWIS (Jones, Thad & Mel Lewis).

Album: released on Jazz Reactivation, Jul'82 Dist: PRT

Jones, Tom

6 TRACK HITS.
Extended-play record: released on Scoop 33, Sep'83 by Pickwick Records. Dist: H.R. Taylor

Cassette: released on Scoop 33, Sep'83 by Pickwick Records. Dist: H.R. Taylor

BOY FROM NOWHERE, A.
Tracks: / Boy from nowhere, A / I'll dress you in mourning / To be a matador / Dance with death.
Single (7"): released on Epic, Apr'87 by CBS Records. Dist: CBS

Single (12"): released on Epic, Mar'87 by CBS Records. Dist: CBS

COUNTRY.
Album: released on Mercury (Import), Oct'82

Cassette: released on Mercury (Import), Oct'82

COUNTRY SIDE OF TOM JONES, THE.
Album: released on RCA Camden, Mar'85 by RCA Records. Dist: Pickwick Distribution, Taylor, H.R.

Cassette: released on RCA Camden, Mar'85 by RCA Records. Dist: Pickwick Distribution, Taylor, H.R.

DARLIN'.
Tracks: / Darlin' / But I do / Lady lay down / No guarantee / What in the world's come over you / One night / Daughter's question, A / I don't want to know you that well / Dime Queen of Nevada / Things that matter most to me ,The / Come home Rhondda boy.
Album: released on Polydor, Oct'81 by Polydor Records. Dist: Polygram, Polydor Deleted '83.

Cassette: released on Polydor, Oct'81 by Polydor Records. Dist: Polygram, Polydor Deleted '83.

Compact disc: released on Polydor, Oct'81 by Polydor Records. Dist: Polygram, Polydor

Album: released on Mercury (USA), Aug'87 by Import Records. Dist: IMS Distribution, Polygram Distribution

Cassette: released on Mercury (USA), Aug'87 by Import Records. Dist: IMS Distribution, Polygram Distribution

DELILAH.
Album: released on Contour, Oct'82 by Pickwick Records. Dist: Pickwick Distribution, PRT

Cassette: released on Contour, Oct'82 by Pickwick Records. Dist: Pickwick Distribution, PRT

Single (7"): released on Decca, Feb'68 by Decca Records. Dist: Polygram

Single (7"): released on Old Gold, Oct'83 by Old Gold Records. Dist: Lightning, Jazz Music, Spartan, Counterpoint

GOLDEN HITS: TOM JONES.
Tracks: / Green green grass of home / I'm coming home / I'll never fall in love again / Not responsible / Help yourself / What's new pussycat / Love me tonight / It's not unusual.. / Funny familiar feelings / Detroit City / With these hands / Minute of your time / Without love / Delilah.
Album: released on Decca, Oct'80 by Decca Records. Dist: Polygram

Cassette: released on Decca, Oct'80 by Decca Records. Dist: Polygram

Compact disc: released on London, Mar'87 by London Records. Dist: Polygram

GREATEST HITS:TOM JONES.
Compact disc: released on Chrysalis, Jun'87 by Chrysalis Records. Dist: CBS

GREAT LOVE SONGS.
Album: released on Contour, May'87 by Pickwick Records. Dist: Pickwick Distribution, PRT

GREEN GRASS OF HOME.
Album: released on Decca (Holland), Feb'84 by Decca Records. Dist: Polygram, IMS

Cassette: released on Decca (Holland), Feb'84 by Decca Records. Dist: Polygram, IMS

Single (7"): released on Old Gold, Oct'83 by Old Gold Records. Dist: Lightning, Jazz Music, Spartan, Counterpoint

I'LL BE WHERE THE HEART IS.
Single (7"): released on Decca, Sep'83 by Decca Records. Dist: Polygram

I'LL DRESS YOU IN MOURNING.
Single (7"): released on Epic, Jul'87 by CBS Records. Dist: CBS

IT'S NOT UNUSUAL.
Tracks: / It's not unusual / Delilah / It's not unusual(extended)* / Land of 1000 dances(live mix)*.

Single (7"): released on London, May'87 by London Records. Dist: Polygram

Single (12"): released on London, May'87 by London Records. Dist: Polygram

Album: released on Contour, Mar'82 by Pickwick Records. Dist: Pickwick Distribution, PRT

Cassette: released on Contour, Mar'82 by Pickwick Records. Dist: Pickwick Distribution, PRT

Single (7"): released on Decca, Jan'65 by Decca Records. Dist: Polygram

IT'S NOT UNUSUAL - HIS GREATEST HITS.
Tracks: / It's not unusual / Green green grass of home / Help yourself / I'll never fall in love again (It looks like) / Not responsible / Love me tonight / Without love (there is nothing) / Delilah / What's new pussycat? / Detroit city / Once upon a time / Thunderball / Minute of your time, A / With these hands / Funny, familiar forgotten feelings / I'm coming home / You keep me hangin' on / It's not unusual/Land of 1000 dances..
Album: released on Decca, Jul'87 by Decca Records. Dist: Polygram

Cassette: released on Decca, Jul'87 by Decca Records. Dist: Polygram

Compact disc: released on Decca, Jul'87 by Decca Records. Dist: Polygram

LOVE SONGS.
Album: released on Arcade Music Gala, Apr'86 Dist: Stage One

Cassette: released on Arcade Music Gala, Apr'86 Dist: Stage One

MATADOR.
Album: released on Epic, Apr'87 by CBS Records. Dist: CBS

Cassette: released on Epic, Apr'87 by CBS Records. Dist: CBS

MUSIC FOR THE MILLIONS.
Album: released on Decca (Import), Mar'83 by Decca Records. Dist: Polygram, IMS

Cassette: released on Decca (Import), Mar'83 by Decca Records. Dist: Polygram, IMS

SINGS 24 GREAT STANDARDS.
Album: released on Decca, Dec'76 by Decca Records. Dist: Polygram

Cassette: released on Decca, Dec'76 by Decca Records. Dist: Polygram

SOMETHIN' 'BOUT YOU BABY I LIKE.
Album: released on Hallmark, Nov'83 by Pickwick Records. Dist: Pickwick Distribution, PRT, Taylors

Cassette: released on Hallmark, Nov'83 by Pickwick Records. Dist: Pickwick Distribution, PRT, Taylors

THIS IS TOM JONES.
Tracks: / Fly me to the moon / Little green apples / Wichita lineman / Sittin' on the dock of the bay / Dance of love / Hey Jude / Without you / That's all a man can say / That wonderful sound / Only once / Im a fool to want you / Let it be me.
Compact disc: released on Decca, Oct'85 by Decca Records. Dist: Polygram

Album: released on Contour, Aug'83 by Pickwick Records. Dist: Pickwick Distribution, PRT

Cassette: released on Contour, Aug'83 by Pickwick Records. Dist: Pickwick Distribution, PRT

TOM JONES ALBUM, THE.
Album: released on Decca, Sep'83 by Decca Records. Dist: Polygram

Cassette: released on Decca, Sep'83 by Decca Records. Dist: Polygram

TOM JONES - THE GREATEST HITS.
Album: released on Telstar, May'87 by Telstar Records. Dist: RCA Distribution

Cassette: released on Telstar, May'87 by Telstar Records. Dist: RCA Distribution

Compact disc: released on Telstar, May'87 by Telstar Records. Dist: RCA Distribution

WHAT'S NEW PUSSYCAT.
Single (7"): released on Decca (London), Aug'87 by Decca Records. Dist: Polygram, IMS

Jones, Tracy

HI EVERYBODY I'M TRACY JONES.
Album: released on SRT, Feb'77 by SRT Records. Dist: Pinnacle, Solomon & Peres Distribution, SRT Distribution, H.R. Taylor Distribution, PRT Distribution

Jones, Trevor

LAST PLACE ON EARTH.
Single (7"): released on Island, Mar'85 by Island Records. Dist: Polygram

Jones, Vivian

BANK ROBBERY.
Album:

COULD IT BE YOU (Jones, Vivian/Pieces).
Single (12"): released on Ironside, Jan'84 by Ironside Records. Dist: Jetstar

JAH WORKS.
Single (12"): released on Jah Shaka, Aug'87 by Jah Shaka Records. Dist: Jetstar

Album: released on Jah Shaka Music, Oct'87. Estim retail price in Sep'87 was £5.99.

LOAFING.
Single (7"): released on Rosie, Nov'82 by Rosie Records. Dist: PRT Distribution

MASH IT UP.
Single (12"): released on Ruff Cut, Nov'83 by Ruff Cut Records. Dist: Jetstar Distribution

MY BABY DON'T CARE.
Single (12"): released on Rosie, May'82 by Rosie Records. Dist: PRT Distribution

PHYSICAL.
Single (12"): released on Leo, Jun'85 Dist: Jazz Music, Chris Wellard

RED EYES.
Single (12"): released on Shaka, Dec'86 by Shaka Records. Dist: Jetstar

WHAT YOU GONNA DO.
Single (12"): released on Virgo, Aug'82

Jones, Winston

YOU ARE.
Single (12"): released on Vista Sounds, May'83 by Vista Sounds Records. Dist: Jetstar

Jones, Wizz

MAGICAL FLIGHT.
Album: released on Plant Life, Nov'81 Dist: Roots

Jonid & the Ids

FALSE PROMISES.
Single (7"): released on Prelude, May'82 by Prelude Records (USA).

Jon & The Nightriders

STAMPEDE!.
Album: released on Kix 4 U, Jul'87 by Kix 4u Records. Dist: Pinnacle

Jon & Vangelis

FRIENDS OF MR.CAIRO.
Compact disc: released on Polydor, '83 by Polydor Records. Dist: Polygram, Polydor

Compact disc: released on Polydor, '83 by Polydor Records. Dist: Polygram, Polydor

PRIVATE COLLECTION.
Compact disc: released on Polydor, '83 by Polydor Records. Dist: Polygram, Polydor

SHORT STORIES.
Tracks: / Curious electric / Each and every day / Bird song / I hear you now / Road / Far away in Bagdad / Love is / One more time / Thunder / Play within a play.
Compact disc: released on Polydor, '83 by Polydor Records. Dist: Polygram, Polydor

Album: released on Polydor, Jun'87 by Polydor Records. Dist: Polygram, Polydor

Cassette: released on Polydor, Jun'87 by Polydor Records. Dist: Polygram, Polydor

Jonzun Crew

LOST IN SPACE.
Album: released on 21 Records, Apr'83 by Polydor Records. Dist: Polydor Deleted '86

Cassette: released on 21 Records, Apr'83 by Polydor Records. Dist: Polydor

LOVIN'.
Single (7"): released on Tommy Boy, Feb'85 by Warner Brothers. Dist: WEA Distribution

Single (12"): released on Tommy Boy, Feb'85 by Warner Brothers. Dist: WEA Distribution

SPACE COWBOY.
Single (7"): released on 21 Records, Jul'83 by Polydor Records. Dist: Polydor

Single (12"): released on 21 Records, Jul'83 by Polydor Records. Dist: Polydor

Jonzun, Michael

BURNIN' UP.
Tracks: / Burnin' up / World is a battlefield, The / World is a battlefield, The (piano dub) / World is a battlefield, The (inst dub).

Single (7"): released on A&M, Aug'86 by A&M Records. Dist: Polygram

Single (12"): released on A&M, Aug'86 by A&M Records. Dist: Polygram

TIME IS RUNNING OUT (Jonzun, Michael/Jonzun Crew).
Single (7"): released on Tommy Boy, Aug'84 by Warner Brothers. Dist: WEA Distribution

Jookes

I JUST WANNA STAY HERE (and love you).
Single (7"): released on Hollywood, Jun'84 by Hollywood Records. Dist: Pinnacle

Jools

SINGING IN THE RAIN.
Single (7"): released on PRT, Jan'83 by PRT Records. Dist: PRT

Joolz

DENISE.
Single (12"): released on Abstract, Oct'83 by Abstract. Dist: Pinnacle

KISS, (THE).
Single (12"): released on Abstract, Jul'84 by Abstract. Dist: Pinnacle

LOVE IS (sweet romance).
Single (7"): released on EMI, Nov'85 by EMI Records. Dist: EMI

Single (7"): released on EMI, Nov'85 by EMI Records. Dist: EMI

MAD, BAD AND DANGEROUS TO KNOW.
Tracks: / Mad, bad and dangerous to know / Legend / Babies.
Single (7"): released on EMI, Aug'86 by EMI Records. Dist: EMI

Single (12"): released on EMI, Aug'86 by EMI Records. Dist: EMI

NEVER NEVER LAND.
Album: released on Abstract, May'85 by Abstract. Dist: Pinnacle

Joplin, Janis

GOLDEN HIGHLIGHTS OF JANIS JOPLIN.
Album: released on CBS(Import), Jun'86 by CBS Records. Dist: Conifer, Discovery, Swift

Cassette: released on CBS(Import), Jun'86 by CBS Records. Dist: Conifer, Discovery, Swift

I GOT DEM OL' COSMIC BLUES AGAIN MAMA.
Album: released on CBS, '83 by CBS Records. Dist: CBS

Cassette: released on CBS, '83 by CBS Records. Dist: CBS

IN CONCERT.
Tracks: / Down in me / Bye bye baby / All is loneliness / Piece of my heart / Road block / Flower in the sun / Summertime / Ego rock / Half moon / Kozmic blues / Move over / Try (just a little bit harder) / Get it while you can / Ball and chain.
Album: released on CBS, Sep'87 by CBS Records. Dist: CBS

Cassette: released on CBS, Sep'87 by CBS Records. Dist: CBS

JANIS JOPLIN: ANTHOLOGY.
Double Album: released on CBS, Jul'80 by CBS Records. Dist: CBS

JANIS JOPLIN: GREATEST HITS.
Album: released on CBS, Sep'82 by CBS Records. Dist: CBS

Cassette: released on CBS, Sep'82 by CBS Records. Dist: CBS

JANIS JOPLIN: IN CONCERT.
Double Album: released on CBS, '74 by CBS Records. Dist: CBS

PEARL.
Tracks: / Move over / Cry baby / Woman left lonely / Half moon / Buried alive in the blues / Me and Bobby Mc Gee / Mercedes Benz / Get it while you can / Trust me.
Compact disc: released on CBS, Dec'85 by CBS Records. Dist: CBS

Album: released on CBS, Jan'84 by CBS Records. Dist: CBS

Cassette: released on CBS, Jan'84 by CBS Records. Dist: CBS

Joplin, Scott

COLLECTION: SCOTT JOPLIN.
Album: released on Deja Vu, May'86 by Deja Vu Records. Dist: Counterpoint Distribution, Record Services Distribution (Ireland)

Cassette: released on Deja Vu, May'86 by Deja Vu Records. Dist: Counterpoint Distribution, Record Services Distribution (Ireland)

ELITE SYNCOPATION.
Album: released on Meteor, Apr'87 by Magnum Music Group Ltd. Dist: Magnum Music Group Ltd, PRT Distribution, Spartan Distribution

JOPLIN BOUQUET, (A) (Ann Charters).
Album: released on Sonet, '74 by Sonet Records. Dist: PRT

KING OF RAGTIME.
Album: released on Saar Giants Of Jazz (Italy), Sep'85 Dist: Mainline

Cassette: released on Saar Giants Of Jazz (Italy), Sep'85 Dist: Mainline

RAGTIME KING.
Album: released on Joker, Apr'81 Dist: Cadillac, Zodiac Distribution, Jazz Horizons, Jazz Music, JSU, Celtic Music

Jordanaires

SINGS ELVIS' GOSPEL FAVOURITES.
Notes: Top gospel quartet-Elvis Presley's vocal quartet
Album: released on Magnum Force, Jan'86 by Magnum Music Group Ltd. Dist: Magnum Music Group Ltd, PRT, Spartan

Jordan, Clifford

ADVENTURER.
Album: released on Muse, Apr'81 Dist: JSU Distribution, Jazz Horizons Distribution, Jazz Music Distribution, Celtic Music Distribution

BLOWING IN FROM CHICAGO (Jordan, Clifford/John Gilmore).
Album: released on Blue Note (USA Import), Sep'84

JENKINS, JORDAN & TIMMONS See under Jenkins, John.
Notes: For full information see JENKINS, John/Clifford Jordan & Bobby Timmins

NIGHT AT BOOMERS, (A) (Jordan, Clifford/C. Walton).
Album: released on Muse, Jun'77 by Peerless Records. Dist: Lugtons Distributors

NIGHT OF THE MARK VII.
Album: released on Muse, Apr'81 Dist: JSU Distribution, Jazz Horizons Distribution, Jazz Music Distribution, Celtic Music Distribution

ROYAL BALLADS (Jordan, Clifford Quartet).
Album: released on Criss Cross, Jul'87 Dist: Jazz Music, Jazz Horizons, Cadillac

Jordan, Danny

LADY IN MY LIFE.
Single (7"): released on Blue Note, Jun'85 by EMI Records. Dist: EMI

Single (12"): released on Blue Note, Jun'85 by EMI Records. Dist: EMI

Jordan, Duke

BLUE DUKE.
Album: released on RCA (France), Jun'84 by RCA Records. Dist: Discovery

CONNECTIONS, (THE)/LIAISONS DANGEREUSES, (LES).
Album: released on Vogue, Sep'75 Dist: Discovery, Jazz Music, PRT, Swift

DUKE JORDAN.
Album: released on Jazz-Legacy, Sep'79

DUKE'S ARTISTRY (Jordan, Duke Quartet).
Album: released on Steeplechase, Sep'79

FLIGHT TO JORDAN.
Compact disc: released on Blue Note, Aug'87 by EMI Records. Dist: EMI

GREAT SESSIONS, (THE) (Jordan, Duke Trio).
Album: released on Steeplechase(USA), Sep'81

JORDAN, ROUSE, TAYLOR - LES LIAISONS DANGEREUSES (Jordan, Duke/Rouse, Charlie).
Album: released on Jazz Reactivation, Jan'82 Dist: PRT

MIDNIGHT MOONLIGHT.
Album: released on Steeplechase, May'81

MURRAY HILL CAPER, (THE).
Album: released on Spotlite, '83 by Spotlite Records. Dist: Cadillac, Jazz Music, Spotlite

Jordan, Fred

SHROPSHIRE LAD, (THE) country songs.
Cassette: released on Folktracks, Nov'79 by

Folktracks Cassettes. Dist: Folktracks

SONGS OF A SHROPSHIRE FARM WORKER.
Album: released on Topic, '81 Dist: Roots Distribution

WHEN THE FROST IS ON THE PUMPKIN.
Album: released on Topic, '81 Dist: Roots Distribution

Jordan, Louis

1944/5 (Jordan, Louis & His Tympany Five).
Album: released on Circle(USA), Jun'84 by Jazzology Records (USA). Dist: Jazz Music Swift, Chris Wellard

20 GOLDEN GREATS LIVE.
Cassette: released on Magic, Mar'87 Dist: Jazz Music, Submarine, Swift, Chris Wellard, Conifer

BEST OF LOUIS JORDAN, (THE).
Album:

Cassette:

CHOO CHOO CH'BOOGIE (SINGLE).
Single (7"): released on Revival, Jul'82 Dist: Lightning, Swift

CHOO CHOO CH'BOOGIE.
Album: released on MFP, Apr'82 by EMI Records. Dist: EMI

Cassette: released on MFP, Apr'82 by EMI Records. Dist: EMI

COLLATES.
Album: released on Swinghouse, '84 Dist: Jazz Music Distribution, Swift Distribution, Chris Wellard Distribution

Cassette: released on Swinghouse, '84 Dist: Jazz Music Distribution, Swift Distribution, Chris Wellard Distribution

COUNT OF MONTE CRISTO (DUMAS).
Album: released on Caedmon(USA), Jan'78 by Caedmon (USA) Records. Dist: Gower, Taylors, Discovery

Cassette: released on Caedmon(USA), Jan'78 by Caedmon (USA) Records. Dist: Gower, Taylors, Discovery

GO BLOW YOUR HORN.
Album: released on EMI (France), '83 by EMI Records. Dist: Conifer

GO BLOW YOUR HORN PART II.
Album: released on Pathe Marconi, Sep'84 Dist: Swift

GOLDEN GREATS: LOUIS JORDAN.
Album:

Cassette:

GOOD TIMES.
Album: released on Swinghouse, '84 Dist: Jazz Music Distribution, Swift Distribution, Chris Wellard Distribution

Cassette: released on Swinghouse, '84 Dist: Jazz Music Distribution, Swift Distribution, Chris Wellard Distribution

GREAT RHYTHM & BLUES VOLUME 1.
Album: released on Bulldog Records, Jul'82

HOODOO MAN.
Album: released on Swingtime, Aug'86 Dist: Jazz Music Distribution

I BELIEVE IN MUSIC.
Album: released on Black & Blue (France), Dec'84 Dist: Swift, Target, Discovery

JIVIN' 1956-58 VOLUME 2.
Tracks: / Jamf, The / Saturday night fish fry / I never had a chance / Got my mojo working / Sunday / Sweet Lorraine / Slop, The / I hadn't anyone till you / Nearness of you, The / Because of you * / That's what true love can do* / I don't want to set the world on fire* / Day away from you, A* / I cried for you* / Man ain't a man, A / I've found my peace of mind / Sweet hunk of junk / I love you so / Wish i could make some money / Route 66.
Album: released on Bear Family, Mar'86 by Bear Family Records. Dist: Rollercoaster Distribution, Swift

JIVIN' 1956-58 VOLUME 1.
Tracks: / Big Bess / Ain't nobody here but us chickens / choo choo ch boogie / Knock me a kiss / Let the good times roll / Cladonia / Is you is or is you ain't ma baby / Beware brother beware / Don't let the sun catch you crying / I'm gona move to the outskirts of town / Salt pork west Virginia / Ruin Joe / Early in the morning / Cat scratchin / Morning light / Fire* / Rock doc / Ella Mae / I want to know* / I've found peace of mind* / Fire.
Album: released on Bear Family, Mar'86 by Bear Family Records. Dist: Rollercoaster Distribution, Swift

JIVIN' WITH JORDAN (Jordan, Louis & His Tympany Five).

Tracks: / At the swing cats ball / Doug the jitterbug / Honeysuckle Rose / But i'll be back / Your'e my meat / June tenth jamboree / What's the use of getting sober...... / Five guys named Moe / Is you is or is you ain't my baby / Buzz me / Salt pork,West Virginia / Reconversion blues / How long must I wait for you / That chick's too young to fry / No sale / All for the love of Lil / Texas & Pacific / Reet,petite & gone / Sure had a wonderful time / Open the door,Richard / Barnyard boogie / Early in the morning / Daddy -o / Onions / Psycho loco / Lemonade / Chartreuse / Fat Sam from Birmingham.
Notes: Licensed from MCA Records Ltd This cassette: P 1985 Charly Records Ltd C 1986 Charly Records Ltd Produced by Milt Gabler Compiled by Joop Visser
Cassette: released on Charly, Sep'87 by Charly Records. Dist: Charly, Cadillac

Double Album: released on Charly, May'85 by Charly Records. Dist: Charly, Cadillac

JUMPIN' STUFF (Jordan, Louis/Hot Lips Page/Don Byas).
Album: released on Rarities, Apr'81

JUMP & JIVE.
Album: released on JSP, Mar'84 by JSP Records. Dist: Swift, Projection

KNOCK ME OUT.
Album: released on Swingtime, Aug'86 Dist: Jazz Music Distribution

L. J. SWINGS (Jordan, Louis/Chris Barber).
Album: released on Black Lion, May'76 by Black Lion Records. Dist: Jazz Music, Chris Wellard, Taylor, H.R., Counterpoint, Cadillac

LOOK OUR SISTER.
Album: released on Krazy Kat, Jul'83 Dist: Jazz Music, Swift, Chris Wellard, H.R. Taylor, Charly, Hotshot, IRS Distribution

LOOK OUT (Jordan, Louis & His Tympany Five).
Album: released on Charly(R&B), Aug'83 by Charly Records. Dist: Charly, Cadillac

Cassette: released on Charly(R&B), '85 by Charly Records. Dist: Charly, Cadillac

LOUIS JORDAN & FRIENDS.
Album:

Album:

MORE...1944-1945 (Jordan, Louis & His Tympany Five).
Album: released on Circle, Jul'87 Dist: Jazz Music

PRIME CUTS.
Album: released on Swinghouse, Oct'84 Dist: Jazz Music Distribution, Swift Distribution, Chris Wellard Distribution

Cassette: released on Swinghouse, Oct'84 Dist: Jazz Music Distribution, Swift Distribution, Chris Wellard Distribution

REET PETITE & GONE.
Album: released on Krazy Kat, Mar'93 Dist: Jazz Music, Swift, Chris Wellard, H.R. Taylor, Charly, Hotshot, IRS Distribution

ROCK'N'ROLL CALL.
Tracks: / It's been said / Whatever Lola wants / Slo' smooth and easy / Bananas / Baby let's do it up / Chicken back / Baby you're just too much / Were can I go / Rock'n'roll call / Man ain't a man, A* / Texas stew* / Hard head.
Notes: Original RCA Victor/Vik Recordings
Album: released on Bear Family, Nov'86 by Bear Family Records. Dist: Rollercoaster Distribution, Swift

SOMEBODY DONE HOODOOED THE HOODOO.
Album: released on Jukebox Lil, Dec'86 Dist: Swift

Jordan, Sheila

CROSSING, THE.
Album: released on Blackhawk, Aug'86 by Blackhawk Records (USA). Dist: IMS-Polygram

OLD TIME FEELING (Jordan, Sheila/Harvie Swartz).
Album: released on Palo Alto (Italy), Jan'84

Jordan, Stanley

ELEANOR RIGBY.
Single (7"): released on Blue Note, Oct'85 by EMI Records. Dist: EMI

MAGIC TOUCH.
Tracks: / Eleanor Rigby / Freddy Freeloader / Round midnight / All the children / Lady in my life, The / Angel / Fundance / Return expedition / Child is born, A.
Compact disc: released on EMI, Jul'85 by EMI Records. Dist: EMI

Album: released on Blue Note, Apr'85 by EMI Records. Dist: EMI

STANDARDS VOL.1.
Tracks: / Sound of silence, The / Sunny / Georgia on my mind / Send one your love / Moon River / Guitar man / One bell less to answer / Because / My favourite things / Silent night.
Compact disc: released on Manhattan-Blue Note, May'87 by EMI America Records (USA). Dist: EMI

STANDARDS VOLUME 1.
Tracks: / Moon river / Guitar man / One less bell to answer / Because / My favourite things / Silent night / Sound of silence, The / Sunny / Georgia on my mind / Send one your love.
Notes: Produced by Stanley Jordan. Co-produced by Gene Lennon.
Album: released on Manhattan-Blue Note, Dec'86 by EMI America Records (USA). Dist: EMI

Jordinaires

SING ELVIS'S FAVORITE SPIRITUALS.
Album: released on Rockhouse, Sep'85 Dist: Pinnacle

Jorge, Ben

BEM-VINDA AMIZADE.
Tracks: / O dia o sol declarou o seu amor pela terra / Santa Clara clareou / Oe oe faz o carro de boi na estrada / Era uma vez um aposentado do marinherio / Lorraine / Curumin chama cunchata que von eontar / Katarina, Katarina / Ela mora em matogrosso fronteira com o paraguai / Para que digladiar / Luiz Wagner quitarreio.
Album: released on Som Livre (Brazil), Sep'83

BEN JORGE SONSUL.
Tracks: / Senhora dona da casa / A rainha foi embora / Irene Cara mia / My little brother / Obsessao meu amor / Bizantina bizancia / Pelos verdes mares / Me chamando de paixao / Os cavalheiros dorei Arthur / Abenco mamae abenco papa / Hooked on samba / A terra do filho do homen.
Album: released on Som Livre (Brazil), '84

Cassette: released on Som Livre (Brazil), '84

DAVIDA.
Album: released on Som Livre (Brazil), Aug'83

Jose, Charlie

BOSCASTLE BOW-WOW.
Cassette: released on Folktracks, Nov'79 by Folktracks Cassettes. Dist: Folktracks

Josef K

ANGLE.
Single (7"): released on Les Disques Du Crepuscule, Feb'82 Dist: Rough Trade, Pinnacle, Island, Polygram

CHANCE MEETING.
Single (7"): released on Postcard, May'81 by Alan Horne. Dist: Rough Trade

HEAVEN SENT.
Tracks: / Heaven sent.
Single (7"): released on Supreme, Mar'87 by Supreme Records. Dist: PRT Distribution

IT'S KINDA FUNNY.
Single (7"): released on Postcard, Dec'80 by Alan Horne. Dist: Rough Trade

ONLY FUN IN TOWN, (THE).
Album: released on Rough Trade, Jul'81 by Rough Trade Records. Dist: Rough Trade Distribution, Cartel Distribution

RADIO DRILL TIME.
Single (7"): released on Postcard, Aug'80 by Alan Horne. Dist: Rough Trade

Jose & Kazoo Band

KAZOO KAZOO.
Single (7"): released on Baby, Aug'82 by New Rose Records. Dist: Cartel

Single (12"): released on Baby, Aug'82 by New Rose Records. Dist: Cartel

Joseph & amazing....

JOSEPH & AMAZING TECHNICOLOR DREAMCOAT Original Cast (Various Artists).
Album: released on Polydor, Aug'83 by Polydor Records. Dist: Polygram, Polydor

Cassette: released on Polydor, Aug'83 by Polydor Records. Dist: Polygram, Polydor

JOSEPH & THE AMAZING TECHNICOLOR DREAMCOAT Various Artists (Various Artists).
Album:

Cassette:

Joseph, David

DEAR STAR.
Single (7"): released on Island, Oct'83 by Island Records. Dist: Polygram

Single (12"): released on Island, Oct'83 by Island Records. Dist: Polygram

JOYS OF LIFE.
Single (7"): released on Island, Jan'84 by Island Records. Dist: Polygram

Single (12"): released on Island, Jan'84 by Island Records. Dist: Polygram

JOYS OF LIFE, (THE).
Album: released on Island, Nov'83 by Island Records. Dist: Polygram

Album: released on Island, Nov'83 by Island Records. Dist: Polygram

NO TURNING BACK.
Single (7"): released on Fourth & Broadway, Aug'87 by Island Records. Dist: Polygram, EMI

Single (12"): released on Fourth & Broadway, Aug'87 by Island Records. Dist: Polygram, EMI

Joseph & Giselle

BUT YOU LOVE ME DADDY.
Single (7"): released on Button, Dec'82 by Musical Characters Records. Dist: Spartan

Joseph, Margie

KNOCKOUT.
Single (7"): released on Jive, Apr'83 by Zomba Records. Dist: RCA, PRT, CBS

Single (12"): released on Jive, Apr'83 by Zomba Records. Dist: RCA, PRT, CBS

MIDNIGHT LOVER.
Single (7"): released on Atlantic, Aug'84 by WEA Records. Dist: WEA Deleted '85.

Single (12"): released on Atlantic, Aug'84 by WEA Records. Dist: WEA

Joseph, Nerious

NO ONE NIGHT STAND.
Tracks: / No one night stand / Jealously.
Single (12"): released on Fine Style, Mar'87 by Fine Style Records. Dist: Revolver, Jetstar, PRT, Cartel

ROCK WITH ME BABY (Joseph, Nerious & Winsome).
Tracks: / Rock with me baby.
Single (12"): released on Fashion, Aug'86 by Fashion Records. Dist: PRT, Jetstar

YOU'RE MY SPECIAL LADY.
Single (12"): released on Fashion, Dec'85 by Fashion Records. Dist: PRT, Jetstar

Joseph, Steve

MY LIFE IS A SONG.
Single (7"): released on Songwriters Workshop, Feb'81 Dist: PRT

Joshua

SURRENDER.
Album: released on FM, Mar'86 by FM-Revolver Records. Dist: EMI

Jossiah

MAKE MY GOLD.
Single (7"): released on RPM, Apr'85 by RPM Records. Dist: PRT Distribution

Joubert Singers

STAND ON THE WORD.
Single (7"): released on 10, May'85 by 10 Records. Dist: Virgin, EMI

Single (12"): released on 10, May'85 by 10 Records. Dist: Virgin, EMI

Journey

BE GOOD TO YOURSELF.
Tracks: / Be good to yourself / Only the young / Anyway you want it* / Stone in love* / Seperate ways / After the fall* / Rubicon.
Single (7"): released on CBS, Apr'86 by CBS Records. Dist: CBS

Single (12"): released on CBS, Apr'86 by CBS Records. Dist: CBS

Picture disc single: released on CBS, Apr'86 by CBS Records. Dist: CBS

CAPTURED.
Tracks: / Majestic / Where were you / Just the same way / Line of fire / Lights / Stay awhile / Too late / Dixie highway / Feeling that way / Anytime / Do you recall / Walks like a lady / La do da / Lovin' touchin' / Squeezin' / Wheel in the sky / Any way you want it / Party's over (hopelessly in love), The.
Compact disc: released on CBS, May'87 by CBS Records. Dist: CBS

Album: released on CBS, Sep'87 by CBS Records. Dist: CBS

Cassette: released on CBS, Sep'87 by CBS Records. Dist: CBS

DEPARTURE.
Tracks: / Anyway you want it / Walks like a lady / Someday soon / People and places / Pecious time / Where were you / I'm cryin' / Line of fire /

Departure / Good morning girl / Stay a while / Homemade love.
Album: released on CBS, Feb'86 by CBS Records. Dist: CBS

Cassette: released on CBS, Feb'86 by CBS Records. Dist: CBS

ESCAPE.
Compact disc: released on CBS, May'87 by CBS Records. Dist: CBS

Album: released on CBS, Sep'81 by CBS Records. Dist: CBS

Cassette: released on CBS, Sep'81 by CBS Records. Dist: CBS

EVOLUTION.
Tracks: / Too late / Lovin' touchin' squeezin' / City of the angels / When you're alone it ain't easy / Sweet and simple / Lovin' you is easy / Just the same way / Do you recall? / Daydream / Lady Luck.
Compact disc: released on CBS, Mar'87 by CBS Records. Dist: CBS

Album: released on CBS, Jul'83 by CBS Records. Dist: CBS

Cassette: released on CBS, Jul'83 by CBS Records. Dist: CBS

FAITHFULLY.
Single (7"): released on CBS, Apr'83 by CBS Records. Dist: CBS

FRONTIERS.
Album: released on CBS, Feb'83 by CBS Records. Dist: CBS

Cassette: released on CBS, Feb'83 by CBS Records. Dist: CBS

FRONTIERS/ ESCAPE.
Album: released on CBS, Aug'87 by CBS Records. Dist: CBS

GIRL CAN'T HELP IT.
Tracks: / Girl can't help it / It could have been.
Single (7"): released on CBS, Nov'86 by CBS Records. Dist: CBS

INFINITY.
Album: released on Prix D'Ami (France), Sep'86

JOURNEY.
Cassette: released on CBS, Dec'82 by CBS Records. Dist: CBS

JOURNEY various artists (Various Artists).
Album: released on Towerbell, Aug'86 by Towerbell Records. Dist: EMI

Cassette: released on Towerbell, Aug'86 by Towerbell Records. Dist: EMI

RAISED ON RADIO.
Tracks: / Girl can't help it / Positive touch / Suzanne / Be good to yourself / Once you love somebody / Happy to give / Raised on radio / I'll be alright without you / It could have been you / Eyes of a woman, The / Why can't this night go on forever.
Album: released on CBS, May'86 by CBS Records. Dist: CBS

Compact disc: released on CBS, '86 by CBS Records. Dist: CBS

SEPARATE WAYS.
Single (7"): released on CBS, Feb'83 by CBS Records. Dist: CBS

Single (12"): released on CBS, Feb'83 by CBS Records. Dist: CBS

SUZANNE.
Tracks: / Suzanne / Ask the lonely / Raised on radio.
Single (7"): released on CBS, Jul'86 by CBS Records. Dist: CBS

Single (12"): released on CBS, Jul'86 by CBS Records. Dist: CBS

Journey to the centre...

JOURNEY TO THE CENTRE OF THE EARTH Verne, Jules (Pertwee, Jon).
Cassette: released on Pinnacle, '79 by Pinnacle Records. Dist: Pinnacle

Cassette: released on Og & Dells, Sep'84 by Og & Dells Records. Dist: Cartel Distribution

JOURNEY TO THE CENTRE OF THE EARTH Verne, Jules.
Cassette: released on Caedmon(USA), Jul'79 by Caedmon (USA) Records. Dist: Gower, Taylors, Discovery

Journey without maps

JOURNEY WITHOUT MAPS Various artists (Various Artists).
Double Album: released on 101 International, Mar'84

Jowe Head

PINCER MOVEMENT.
Album: released on Hedoniks, Mar'82 by Armageddon Records. Dist: Spartan

Jowell, Les

CY LAURY & LES JOWELL 1957 (Jowell, Les & Cy Laury).

Jowett, Les

LES JOWETT.
Album: released on Flyright, Jul'82 by Flyright Records. Dist: Krazy Kat, Swift, Jazz Music

Joy

LOST IN HONG KONG.
Tracks: / Lost in Hong Kong / Lucky star.
Single (12"): released on Teldec (Import), Mar'86

Single (7"): released on Conifer, Sep'85 by Conifer Records. Dist: Conifer

PARADISE ROAD.
Single (7"): released on Blue Chip, Jan'81 by Blue Chip Records. Deleted '81.

STATE OF INDEPENDENCE.
Single (7"): released on Island, Aug'82 by Island Records. Dist: Polygram Deleted '84.

Single (12"): released on Island, Aug'82 by Island Records. Dist: Polygram Deleted '84.

TOUCH BY TOUCH.
Tracks: / Touch by touch / Fire in the night.
Single (7"): released on Greyhound, Mar'87 by Greyhound Records. Dist: PRT, Greyhound

Joy, Benny

ROCKABILLY WITH BILLY JOY.
Album: released on White Label, Jul'79 by White Label Records. Dist: Jetstar

Joyce, James

JAMES JOYCE SOUNDBOOK.
Album: released on Caedmon(USA), May'80 by Caedmon (USA) Records. Dist: Gower, Taylors, Discovery

Cassette: released on Caedmon(USA), May'80 by Caedmon (USA) Records. Dist: Gower, Taylors, Discovery

Joyce, Rosalind

ARE YOU REALLY GOING.
Single (12"): released on Hartone, Aug'85 by Hartone Records. Dist: Jetstar

FRIENDS NOT LOVERS.
Tracks: / Friends not lovers / Friends not lovers (doin' fine mix).
Single (12"): released on Elite, Jan'87 Dist: PRT

Single (7"): released on Elite, Sep'86 Dist: PRT

Joyce, Rosaline

LOVERS SOUL.
Album: released on Jam Today, Oct'87 Dist: PRT, Jetstar. Estim retail price in Sep'87 was £5.99.

Cassette: released on Jam Today, Oct'87 Dist: PRT, Jetstar

Joy Circuit

DON'T TOUCH.
Single (7"): released on Pink Noise Product, Oct'85 Dist: Gipsy, CBS

Joy Division

ATMOSPHERE.
Single (12"): released on Factory, Oct'80 by Factory Records. Dist: Cartel, Pinnacle

CLOSER.
Compact disc: released on Factory Benelux, Apr'86 by Rough Trade Records. Dist: Cartel

Album: released on Factory, Jul'82 by Factory Records. Dist: Cartel, Pinnacle

Cassette: released on Factory, Nov'84 by Factory Records. Dist: Cartel, Pinnacle

LOVE WILL TEAR US APART/THESE DAYS.
Single (7"): released on Factory, Jun'80 by Factory Records. Dist: Cartel, Pinnacle

PEEL SESSION, THE.
Tracks: / Love will tear us apart / Twenty-four hours / Colony / Sound of music.
Single (12"): released on Strange Fruit, Sep'87 by Clive Selwood. Dist: Pinnacle

STILL.
Tracks: / Exercise one / Ice age / Sound of music, the / Glass / Only mistake, The / Walked in line / Kill, the / Something must break / Dead souls / Sister Ray / Shadowplay / Means to an end / Passover / New dawn fades / Transmission / Disorder / Isolation / Decades / Digital.
Double Album: released on Factory, Dec'86 by Factory Records. Dist: Cartel, Pinnacle

Special: released on Factory, Dec'86 by Factory Records. Dist: Cartel, Pinnacle

Cassette: released on Factory, Nov'84 by Factory Records. Dist: Cartel, Pinnacle

TRANSMISSION/NOVELTY.
Single (7"): released on Factory, '80 by Factory Records. Dist: Cartel, Pinnacle

Single (12"): released on Factory, '80 by Factory Records. Dist: Cartel, Pinnacle

UNKNOWN PLEASURES.
Tracks: / Disorder / Day of the lords / Candidate / Insight / New dawn fades / She's lost control / Shadow play / Wilderness / Interzone.
Compact disc: released on Factory, '86 by Factory Records. Dist: Cartel, Pinnacle

Album: released on Factory, Jul'82 by Factory Records. Dist: Cartel, Pinnacle

Cassette: released on Factory, Nov'84 by Factory Records. Dist: Cartel, Pinnacle

Joy, Jimmy

CHARLIE SPIVAK & JIMMY JOY.
Album: released on Aircheck (USA), Apr'79 Dist: Swift, Jazz Music

Joy, Lucia

I'M GONNA LEAVE YOU NOW.
Single (12"): released on ABL, Jun'83 by ABL Records. Dist: Jetstar

Joyner, Bruce

SLAVE OF EMOTION.
Album: released on Closer (France), Feb'85 Dist: Nine Mile, Cartel

SWIMMING WITH FRIENDS (Joyner, Bruce & The Plantations).
Album: released on Closer (France), Dec'86 Dist: Nine Mile, Cartel

Joy Of Christmas

JOY OF CHRISTMAS (Mitchell, Geoffrey).
Album: released on MFP, Sep'84 by EMI Records. Dist: EMI

Cassette: released on MFP, Sep'84 by EMI Records. Dist: EMI

JOY OF CHRISTMAS (Various Artists).
Album: released on Decca, '78 by Decca Records. Dist: Polygram

Joy Of Life

ENJOY.
Album: released on Ner, Aug'85 by New European Records/Death in June. Dist: Rough Trade, Cartel

Joy To The World

Christmas Music For Pipes & Organ

JOY TO THE WORLD.
Tracks: / O Sanctissima / Silent night / O Christmas tree / Jesu joy of man's desiring / Rudolph the red nosed reindeer / O gentle little Jesus / Come on shepherds / Joy to the world / Ave Marie / Wakeup all you shepherds / Jingle bells / On the Christmas tree / Come along children / First Nowell, The / Dance of the santons / O joyful night / Ring siegh bells / Angels from realms of glory / Song of Christmas / Holy child is born, The / Slent night / Jesu joy of man's desiring / Rudolph the red nosed reindeer / Ava maria / Jingle bells / Song for christmas / Joy to the world / First Noel / Come along children.
Notes: Beautiful music for Pan Pipes and Organ from world experts Georges Schmitt with Bernard Struber. The evocative sounds of the Pan Pipe are universally popular coupled with this selection of Christmas Music a successful release is assured.
Album: released on Saydisc, Sep'86 by Saydisc Records. Dist: Essex, Harmonia Mundi, Roots, H.R. Taylor, Jazz Music, Swift, Projection, Gamut

Cassette: released on Saydisc, Sep'86 by Saydisc Records. Dist: Essex, Harmonia Mundi, Roots, H.R. Taylor, Jazz Music, Swift, Projection, Gamut

Compact disc: released on Saydisc, Sep'86 by Saydisc Records. Dist: Essex, Harmonia Mundi, Roots, H.R. Taylor, Jazz Music, Swift, Projection, Gamut

JSP Sampler

JSP SAMPLER (CONTEMPORARY BLUES) (Various Artists).
Album: released on JSP, Sep'84 by JSP Records. Dist: Swift, Projection

J, Tommy

LOW PROFILE.
Tracks: / Low profile / Take one.
Single (12"): released on Silent, Apr'87 Dist: Stiff

Jubilee

JUBILEE Original soundtrack (Various Artists).
Tracks: / Deutscher girls / Plastic surgery / Paranoia blues / Right to work / Nine to five / Rule Britannia / Jerusalem / Wargasm in pornotopia / Slow water / Dover beach.
Album: released on E.G., Jan'87 by Virgin Records. Dist: Virgin, EMI

Album: released on Polydor, Apr'78 by Polydor Records. Dist: Polygram, Polydor

Judas Priest

6 TRACK HITS.
Extended-play record: released on Scoop 33, Sep'83 by Pickwick Records. Dist: H.R. Taylor

Cassette: released on Scoop 33, Sep'83 by Pickwick Records. Dist: H.R. Taylor

BEST OF JUDAS PRIEST.
Compact disc: released on Gull, May'87 by Gull Records. Dist: Pinnacle

Album: released on Gull, Feb'78 by Gull Records. Dist: Pinnacle

Cassette: released on Gull, Mar'78 by Gull Records. Dist: Pinnacle

BRITISH STEEL.
Album: released on CBS, Jan'84 by CBS Records. Dist: CBS

Cassette: released on CBS, Jan'84 by CBS Records. Dist: CBS

DEFENDERS OF THE FAITH.
Compact disc: released on CBS, Jul'84 by CBS Records. Dist: CBS

Cassette: released on CBS, Jan'84 by CBS Records. Dist: CBS

EVENING STAR.
Single (7"): released on Epic, Apr'82 by CBS Records. Dist: CBS

FREEWHEEL BURNING.
Single (7"): released on CBS, Jan'84 by CBS Records. Dist: CBS

Single (12"): released on CBS, Jan'84 by CBS Records. Dist: CBS

FUEL OF LIFE.
Video-cassette (VHS): released on CBS, Nov'86 by CBS Records. Dist: CBS

GREATEST ORIGINAL HITS 4 track cassette EP.
Cassette: released on CBS, Jan'83 by CBS Records. Dist: CBS

INTERVIEW PICTURE DISC.
Album: released on Baktabak, Jul'87 by Baktabak Records. Dist: Arabesque

JUDAS PRIEST.
Album: released on Shanghai, Aug'86

LIVE.
Video-cassette (VHS): released on CBS, Sep'84 by CBS Records. Dist: CBS

LIVING AFTER MIDNIGHT.
Single (7"): released on CBS, May'82 by CBS Records. Dist: CBS

LOCKED IN.
Tracks: / Locked in / Reckless.
Single (12"): released on CBS, May'86 by CBS Records. Dist: CBS

Gatefold sleeve: released on CBS, May'86 by CBS Records. Dist: CBS

POINT OF ENTRY.
Cassette: released on CBS, Feb'81 by CBS Records. Dist: CBS

PRIEST...LIVE.
Tracks: / Out in the cold / Heading out to the highway / Metal gods / Breaking the law / Love bites / Some heads are gonna roll / Sentinel, The / Private property / Rock you all around the world / Electric eye / Turbo lover / Freewheel burning / Parental guidance / Living after midnight / You've got another thing comin..
Album: released on CBS, Jun'87 by CBS Records. Dist: CBS

Cassette: released on CBS, Jun'87 by CBS Records. Dist: CBS

Compact disc: released on CBS, Jul'87 by CBS Records. Dist: CBS

ROCKA ROLLA.
Tracks: / One for the road / Rocka rolla / Winter / Deep freeze / Winter retreat / Cheater / Never satisfied / Run of the mill / Dying to meet you / Caviar and meths.
Notes: Licensed from Gull Records and not available in the UK for some time - Rocka RO Rolla - from the High Priests of Heavy Metal - Judas Priest. 10 great tracks recorded in 1974 featuring the unmistakable raw sound of an emerging super group. A fantastic modern sleeve design.
Album: released on Fame, Nov'85 by Music For Pleasure Records. Dist: EMI

Cassette: released on Fame, Nov'85 by Music For Pleasure Records. Dist: EMI

ROCKA-ROLLA.
Album: released on Gull, Sep'77 by Gull Records. Dist: Pinnacle

SAD WINGS OF DESTINY.
Album: released on Gull, Sep'77 by Gull Records. Dist: Pinnacle

SCREAMING FOR VENGEANCE.
Album: released on CBS, Jul'82 by CBS Records. Dist: CBS

SCREAMING VENGEANCE.
Tracks: / Hellion, The / Electric eye / Riding on the wind / Bloodstone / Pain and pleasure / (Take these) Chains) / Screaming for vengeance / You've got another thing comin' / Fever / Devil's child.
Album: released on CBS, Feb'86 by CBS Records. Dist: CBS

Cassette: released on CBS, Feb'86 by CBS Records. Dist: CBS

SIN AFTER SIN.
Album: released on CBS, Mar'81 by CBS Records. Dist: CBS

SOME HEADS ARE GONNA ROLL.
Single (7"): released on CBS, Mar'84 by CBS Records. Dist: CBS

Single (12"): released on CBS, Mar'84 by CBS Records. Dist: CBS

STAINED GLASS.
Album: released on CBS, Nov'81 by CBS Records. Dist: CBS

TAKE ON THE WORLD/STAR BREAKER.
Single (7"): released on CBS, May'82 by CBS Records. Dist: CBS

TURBO.
Tracks: / Turbo lover / Locked in / Private property / Parental guidance / Rock you all around the world / Out in the cold / Wild nights, hot and crazy days / Hot for love / Reckless.
Album: released on CBS, Apr'86 by CBS Records. Dist: CBS

Cassette: released on CBS, Apr'86 by CBS Records. Dist: CBS

Compact disc: released on CBS, '86 by CBS Records. Dist: CBS

TURBO LOVER.
Tracks: / Turbo lover / Hot for love.
Single (7"): released on CBS, Apr'86 by CBS Records. Dist: CBS

TYRANT.
Single (12"): released on Gull, Jun'83 by Gull Records. Dist: Pinnacle

UNITED/GRINDER.
Single (7"): released on CBS, Apr'82 by CBS Records. Dist: CBS

UNLEASHED IN THE EAST.
Album: released on CBS, Sep'79 by CBS Records. Dist: CBS

Judd, Martin

DA DA DA I DON'T LOVE YOU, YOU DON'T.
Single (7"): released on After Hours, Jul'82 Dist: CBS

Judds

DON'T BE CRUEL.
Tracks: / Don't be cruel / Sweetest gift, The (A Mothers smile).
Single (7"): released on RCA, Jan'87 by RCA Records. Dist: RCA, Roots, Swift, Wellard, Chris, I & B, Solomon & Peres Distribution

GIVE A LITTLE LOVE (Judds (Wynonna & Naomi)).
Tracks: / Turn it loose / Old pictures / Old pictures / Cow cow boogie / Maybe your baby's got the blues / I know where I'm going / Why don't you believe me / Sweetest gift, The (a mother's smile) / Give a little love to me / Had a dream (for the heart) / John Deere tractor / Isn't he a strange one / Blue Nun cafe / Change of heart / Don't be cruel / I'm falling in lovetonight.
Album: released on RCA, Jan'87 by RCA Records. Dist: RCA, Roots, Swift, Wellard, Chris, I & B, Solomon & Peres Distribution

Cassette: released on RCA, Jan'87 by RCA Records. Dist: RCA, Roots, Swift, Wellard, Chris, I & B, Solomon & Peres Distribution

Compact disc: released on RCA, '87 by RCA Records. Dist: RCA, Roots, Swift, Wellard, Chris, I & B, Solomon & Peres Distribution

I'M FALLING IN LOVE TONIGHT.
Single (7"): released on RCA, Apr'87 by RCA Records. Dist: RCA, Roots, Swift, Wellard, Chris, I & B, Solomon & Peres Distribution

MAMA HE'S CRAZY.
Single (7"): released on RCA, Oct'85 by RCA Records. Dist: RCA, Roots, Swift, Wellard, Chris, I & B, Solomon & Peres Distribution

ROCKIN WITH THE RHYTHM (Judds (Wynonna & Naomi)).
Tracks: / Have mercy / Grandpa (tell me 'bout the good old days) / Working in the coal mine / If I were you / Rockin' with the rhythm of the rain / Tears for you / Cry myself to sleep / River roll on / I wish she wouldn't treat you that way / Dream chaser.
Album: released on RCA, Apr'86 by RCA Records. Dist: RCA, Roots, Swift, Wellard, Chris, I & B, Solomon & Peres Distribution

Cassette: released on RCA, Apr'86 by RCA Records. Dist: RCA, Roots, Swift, Wellard, Chris, I & B, Solomon & Peres Distribution

WHY NOT ME.
Album: released on RCA, Mar'85 by RCA Records. Dist: RCA, Roots, Swift, Wellard, Chris, I & B, Solomon & Peres Distribution

Cassette: released on RCA, Mar'85 by RCA Records. Dist: RCA, Roots, Swift, Wellard, Chris, I & B, Solomon & Peres Distribution

Judge Dread

JERK YOUR BODY.
Tracks: / Jerk your body / Bring back the skins / Jerk your body / Bring back the skins.
Single (12"): released on Rhino, Jul'87 by Creole Records. Dist: PRT, Rhino

Single (7"): released on Rhino, Jul'87 by Creole Records. Dist: PRT, Rhino

LOST IN RUDENESS.
Single (7"): released on Creole, Dec'84 by Creole Records. Dist: Rhino, PRT

Single (12"): released on Creole, Dec'84 by Creole Records. Dist: Rhino, PRT

Jug Bands

JUG BANDS (Various Artists).
Album: released on Whoopee, Apr'79 by Whoopee Records. Dist: Whoopee Records, Waterfront Records, Jazz Music, JSU, Chris

Jugg

GOING OUT.
Single (7"): released on Stick It In Your Ear, Dec'82 Dist: Stick It In Your Ear

NOAH'S CASTLE.
Single (7"): released on Carrere America (USA), May'80 by Polygram.

Juggernauts

COME THROW YOURSELF UNDER THE....
Single (7"): released on Supreme International, Nov'84 by Supreme International Records. Dist: Fast Forward Distributors, Cartel Distribution

Juggernaut String band

GREASEY COAT.
Album: released on Waterfront, Mar'84 by Waterfront Records. Dist: Rough Trade, Cartel, Projection, Roots

Jugular Vein

WATERLOOK ROAD.
Album: released on Plastic, '79 by Plastic Records. Dist: Pinnacle

Juice

ANYTHING BUT LOVE.
Tracks: / Anything but love.
Single (7"): released on Spartan, Mar'86 by Spartan Records. Dist: Spartan

Single (12"): released on Spartan, Mar'86 by Spartan Records. Dist: Spartan

SPOTLITE OF LOVE.
Single (7"): released on Ecstasy, Aug'85 by Creole Records. Dist: CBS

Single (12"): released on Ecstasy, Aug'85 by Creole Records. Dist: CBS

YOU CAN'T HIDE FROM LOVE.
Tracks: / You can't hide from love / Curiosity.
Single (7"): released on Def Jam (USA), May'86 by CBS Records. Dist: CBS

Single (12"): released on Def Jam (USA), May'86 by CBS Records. Dist: CBS

Juice on the loose

ANY WAY THE WIND BLOWS.
Single (7"): released on Songwriters, Apr'80

Juicy

AFTER LOVING YOU.
Tracks: / After loving you / Private party / Sugar free.
Single (7"): released on Epic, Mar'87 by CBS Records. Dist: CBS

Single (12"): released on Epic, Mar'87 by CBS Records. Dist: CBS

ALL WORK NO PLAY.
Tracks: / All work no play / Serious.
Single (7"): released on Private I, 23 May'87 Dist: CBS

Single (12"): released on Private I, 23 May'87 Dist: CBS

BAD BOY.
Tracks: / Bad boy / Bad boy (dub mix).
Single (7"): released on Private Eye, Apr'86 by Private Eye Records. Dist: Jetstar

IT TAKES TWO.
Tracks: / Bad boy / It takes two / Love is good enough / Slow dancing / Nobody but you / Sugar free / Stay with me / Forever and ever.
Album: released on Epic, Mar'86 by CBS Records. Dist: CBS

Cassette: released on Epic, Mar'86 by CBS Records. Dist: CBS

SPREAD THE LOVE.
Tracks: / All work, no play / Show and tell / After loving you / Make you mine / Midnight fantasy / Serious / Spread the love / Private party.
Album: released on Epic, Apr'87 by CBS Records. Dist: CBS

Cassette: released on Epic, Apr'87 by CBS Records. Dist: CBS

SUGAR FREE.
Tracks: / Sugar free / Forever and ever / Bad boy*.
Single (7"): released on Private I Epic, Feb'86

Single (12"): released on Private I Epic, Feb'86

Juicy Lucy

WHO DO YOU LOVE?.
Single (7"): released on Bronze, Mar'81 by Polygram Records. Dist: Polydor

Juju Message

SEASONS.
Single (12"): released on Treacle, Nov'82

Ju-Ju Roots

JU JU ROOTS 1930'S-50'S (Various Artists).
Album: released on Rounder (USA), Jul'85 Dist: Mike's Country Music Room Distribution, Jazz Music Distribution, Swift Distribution, Roots Records Distribution, Projection Distribution, Topic Distribution

Juke box...

JUKE BOX FAVOURITES Various artists (Various Artists).
Cassette: released on K-Tel Goldmasters, Aug'84 by K-Tel Records. Dist: K-Tel

JUKE BOX HEROES, VOL 1 Various artists (Various Artists).
Album: released on WEA, Jul'85 by WEA Records. Dist: WEA

Cassette: released on WEA, Jul'85 by WEA Records. Dist: WEA

JUKE BOX HEROES, VOL 2 Various artists (Various Artists).
Album: released on WEA, Jul'85 by WEA Records. Dist: WEA

Cassette: released on WEA, Jul'85 by WEA Records. Dist: WEA

JUKE BOX HITS Various artists (Various Artists).
Double cassette: released on Pickwick (Ditto series), Jul'72

Album: released on K-Tel (Era), Jun'83 by K-Tel Records. Dist: K-Tel

Cassette: released on K-Tel (Era), Jun'83 by K-Tel Records. Dist: K-Tel

Cassette: released on K-Tel Goldmasters, Aug'84 by K-Tel Records. Dist: K-Tel

JUKE BOX HITS: VOL 4 Various artists (Various Artists).
Cassette: released on Autograph, Apr'85 Dist: Record Services Distribution (Ireland)

JUKE BOX HITS: VOL 5 Various artists (Various Artists).
Cassette: released on Autograph, Apr'85 Dist: Record Services Distribution (Ireland)

JUKE BOX HITS: VOL 6 Various artists (Various Artists).
Cassette: released on Autograph, Apr'85 Dist: Record Services Distribution (Ireland)

JUKE BOX JIVE Various artists (Various Artists).
Cassette: released on K-Tel Goldmasters, Aug'84 by K-Tel Records. Dist: K-Tel

JUKE BOX JIVE: HIGH SCHOOL CONFIDENTIAL Various artists (Various Artists).
Double Album: released on RCA, Dec'82 by RCA Records. Dist: RCA, Roots, Swift, Wellard, Chris, I & B, Solomon & Peres Distribution

Cassette: released on RCA, Dec'82 by RCA Records. Dist: RCA, Roots, Swift, Wellard, Chris, I & B, Solomon & Peres Distribution

JUKE BOX ROCK Various artists (Various Artists).
Cassette: released on K-Tel Goldmasters, Aug'84 by K-Tel Records. Dist: K-Tel

JUKE BOX ROCK 'N' ROLL Various artists (Various Artists).
Album: released on K-Tel (Era), Jun'83 by K-Tel Records. Dist: K-Tel

Cassette: released on K-Tel (Era), Jun'83 by K-Tel Records. Dist: K-Tel

JUKE BOX SATURDAY NIGHT Various artists (Various Artists).
Cassette: released on K-Tel Goldmasters, Aug'84 by K-Tel Records. Dist: K-Tel

JUKEBOX USA/JUKEBOX UK Various artists (Various Artists).
Cassette: released on Ditto, Jan'85 by Pickwick Records. Dist: H.R. Taylor

Jules

FRIENDS.
Single (7"): released on Tastey, Oct'83 by Jet Records. Dist: CBS Distribution

NOTHING TO ME.
Tracks: / Nothing to me / Nothing to me (dub mix).
Single (7"): released on Fifth Avenue, Feb'87 Dist: PRT

Julia & Company

BREAKIN' DOWN.
Single (7"): released on London, Mar'84 by London Records. Dist: Polygram

Single (12"): released on London, Mar'84 by London Records. Dist: Polygram

I'M SO HAPPY.
Single (7"): released on London, Feb'85 by London Records. Dist: Polygram

Single (12"): released on London, Feb'85 by London Records. Dist: Polygram

Julie

BIG TIME OPERATOR.
Tracks: / Big time operator / Can't get enough.
Single (7"): by Creole Records. Dist: Rhino, PRT Deleted May'87.

Single (12"): released on Creole, May'87 by Creole Records. Dist: Rhino, PRT

I CAN'T STAND THE PAIN.
Single (7"): released on Calibre, Mar'85 by Calibre Records. Dist: PRT

Single (12"): released on Calibre, Mar'85 by Calibre Records. Dist: PRT

I'M IN LOVE WITH MICHAEL JACKSON'S ANSWERPHONE.
Single (7"): released on Calibre, Oct'84 by Calibre Records. Dist: PRT

Single (12"): released on Calibre, Oct'84 by Calibre Records. Dist: PRT

Julien, Ivan

BLOW (Julien, Ivan & Eddy Louis).
Album: released on Barclay (Import), Nov'79

PORGY AND BESS.
Album: released on Barclay (Import), Nov'79

Julie & The Jems

1-2-3.
Single (7"): released on Utopia, Nov'82

Single (12"): released on Utopia, Nov'82

Julius Caesar

JULIUS CAESAR Dramatised biography by John Green (Rietty, Robert, narrator; Stephen Thorne, Caesar).
Cassette: released on History Makers, Jun'82 by Ivan Berg. Dist: Pinnacle

JULIUS CAESAR Shakespeare: complete text (Various Artists).
Double cassette: released on Argo (Spokenword), Nov'82 by Decca Records. Dist: Polygram

JULIUS CAESAR.
Cassette: released on Pickwick (Tell-a-tale), Mar'84 by Pickwick Records. Dist: Pickwick Distribution

Juluka

IMPI.
Single (7"): released on Safari, Jul'83 by Safari Records. Dist: Pinnacle

Single (12"): released on Safari, Jul'83 by Safari Records. Dist: Pinnacle

Picture disc single: released on Safari, Jul'83 by Safari Records. Dist: Pinnacle

SCATTERLINGS.
Single (7"): released on Safari, May'87 by Safari Records. Dist: Pinnacle

Single (12"): released on Safari, May'87 by Safari Records. Dist: Pinnacle

Album: released on Safari, Aug'83 by Safari Records. Dist: Pinnacle

SCATTERLINGS OF AFRICA.
Picture disc single: released on Safari, Jan'83 by Safari Records. Dist: Pinnacle

Single (12"): released on Safari, Jan'83 by Safari Records. Dist: Pinnacle

UMBAGANGA MUSIC.
Single (7"): released on Safari, Apr'83 by Safari Records. Dist: Pinnacle

Single (12"): released on Safari, Apr'83 by Safari Records. Dist: Pinnacle

Picture disc single: released on Safari, Apr'83 by Safari Records. Dist: Pinnacle

Julverne

A NEUF.
Album: released on Crammed UK, Sep'84 Dist: Rough Trade, Nine Mile, Cartel

Jump baby jump

JUMP BABY JUMP Various artists (Various Artists).
Album: released on Rockhouse, Mar'84 by Rockhouse Records. Dist: Swift Distribution, Charly Distribution

Jump children

JUMP CHILDREN Various artists (Various Artists).
Album: released on Charly(R&B), '85 by Charly Records. Dist: Charly, Cadillac

Cassette: released on Charly(R&B), '85 by Charly Records. Dist: Charly, Cadillac

Jumpin' Jack Flash

JUMPIN' JACK FLASH Original film soundtrack (Various Artists).
Tracks: / Set me free / Trick of the night, A / Misled / Rescue me / Jumpin' Jack Flash / You can't hurry love / Hold on / Window to the world / Breaking the code / Love music.
Album: released on Mercury, Apr'87 by Phonogram Records. Dist: Polygram Distribution

Cassette: released on Mercury, Apr'87 by Phonogram Records. Dist: Polygram Distribution

Compact disc: released on Mercury, Apr'87 by Phonogram Records. Dist: Polygram Distribution

Jumpin' The Blues

JUMPIN' THE BLUES various artists (Various Artists).
Tracks: / Damp rag / New kind of feelin' / Big Bob's boogie / Elephant rock / Riff, The / Fat man blues / There ain't enough room here to boogie / Dr Jives / Cadillac boogie / Tra-la-la / Race Horse / Pelican jump / Hi-Yo Silver / We're gonna rock this morning.
Album: released on Ace, Mar'84 by Ace Records. Dist: Pinnacle, Swift, Hotshot, Cadillac

JUMPIN THE BLUES VOL. 3 various artists (Various Artists).
Album: released on Ace, Mar'86 by Ace Records. Dist: Pinnacle, Swift, Hotshot, Cadillac

Album: released on Ace, Mar'85 by Ace Records. Dist: Pinnacle, Swift, Hotshot, Cadillac

JUMPIN' THE BLUES,VOL.2 various artists (Various Artists).

Jump Leads

FALSE KNIGHT.
Single (7"): released on Rogue, Feb'83 by Fast Forward Records. Dist: Nine Mile Distribution, Cartel Distribution

STAG MUST DIE, (THE).
Album: released on Ock, Dec'82 Dist: Jazz Music Distribution

Jump Squad

LORD OF THE DANCE.
Single (7"): released on 101, Aug'81 Dist: Spartan

Junction 16

TO THE SPANNER BORN.
Cassette: released on I'll Call You (Icy) Records, Oct'85 by I'll-Call-You (Icy) Records. Dist: I'll Call You

Junction Eleven

WICKED DAY.
Single (7"): released on LBA, Jun'84 by LBA Records.

June Brides

EVERY CONVERSTION.
Single (7"): released on Pink, Sep'84 by Pink Records. Dist: Rough Trade

IN THE RAIN.
Tracks: / In the rain / Every Conversation.
Single (12"): released on Pink, Apr'86 by Pink Records. Dist: Rough Trade

NO PLACE CALLED HOME.
Single (12"): released on In Tape, Oct'85 by In Tape Records. Dist: Red Rhino, Cartel

Single (7"): released on In Tape, Oct'85 by In Tape Records. Dist: Red Rhino, Cartel

THERE ARE EIGHT MILLION STORIES.
Album: released on Pink Label, Sep'85

THIS TOWN.
Tracks: / This Town / This Tape.
Single (7"): released on In Tape, Apr'86 by In Tape Records. Dist: Red Rhino, Cartel

THIS TOWN 12".
Tracks: / This Town / This Tape.
Single (12"): released on In Tape, Apr'86 by In Tape Records. Dist: Red Rhino, Cartel

Jung

REAL THING.
Single (7"): released on Sandwich, Feb'82 Dist: Rough Trade

Jungle Book

JUNGLE BOOK (James, Freddie & Una Stubbs).
Cassette: released on Whinfrey Strachan, Jan'85 Dist: Whinfrey Strachan

JUNGLE BOOK various artists (Various Artists).
Album: released on Disneyland, Dec'82 by Disneyland-Vista Records (USA). Dist: BBC Records & Tapes, Rainbow Communications Ltd(Distribution)

Cassette: released on Disneyland, Dec'82 by Disneyland-Vista Records (USA). Dist: BBC Records & Tapes, Rainbow Communications Ltd(Distribution)

Album: released on Disneyland, Dec'82 by Disneyland-Vista Records (USA). Dist: BBC Records & Tapes, Rainbow Communications Ltd(Distribution)

Album: released on Disneyland, Dec'82 by Disneyland-Vista Records (USA). Dist: BBC Records & Tapes, Rainbow Communications Ltd(Distribution)

JUNGLE BOOK, THE Kipling, Rudyard (Davies, Windsor).
Cassette: released on Listen For Pleasure, '83 by MFP Records. Dist: EMI

JUNGLE BOOK, THE Film sound track (Film soundtrack).
Album: released on Disney, Oct'84 by BBC Records & Tapes. Dist: BBC Records & Tapes, PRT

Cassette: released on Disney, Oct'84 by BBC Records & Tapes. Dist: BBC Records & Tapes, PRT

Jungle Heat

JUNGLE HEAT various artists (Various original artists).
Album: released on Warwick, Oct'82 Dist: Multiple Sound Distributors

Cassette: released on Warwick, Oct'82 Dist: Multiple Sound Distributors Deleted '83.

Jungle Juice

ALLEYOOP.
Single (7"): released on Radar, Sep'82 by WEA Music Ltd. Dist: WEA, PRT

Junglemania

ALPHABET ZOO.
Single (7"):

Junior

ACQUIRED TASTE.
Tracks: / Stone lover / Somebody / Not tonight / Oh Louise / Thing called love / Do you really want my love / Look what you've done to me / Come on over / Together.
Notes:
Track Details Not Advised
Album: released on London, Mar'86 by London Records. Dist: Polygram

Cassette: released on London, Mar'86 by London Records. Dist: Polygram

Compact disc: released on London, Apr'86 by London Records. Dist: Polygram

COME ON OVER 12".
Tracks: / Come On Over / Mama used To Say/Look what you've done.
Single (12"): released on London, Jan'86 by London Records. Dist: Polygram

COME ON OVER 7".
Tracks: / Come On Over / Mama used To Say? Look what you've done.
Single (7"): released on London, Jan'86 by London Records. Dist: Polygram

COMMUNICATION BREAKDOWN.
Single (7"): released on Mercury, Apr'83 by Phonogram Records. Dist: Polygram Distribution

Single (12"): released on Mercury, Apr'83 by Phonogram Records. Dist: Polygram Distribution

DO YOU REALLY WANT MY LOVE.
Single (7"): released on London, Jan'85 by London Records. Dist: Polygram

Single (12"): released on London, Jan'85 by London Records. Dist: Polygram

INSIDE LOOKIN' OUT.
Album: released on Mercury, Jun'83 by Phonogram Records. Dist: Polygram Distribution

Cassette: released on Mercury, Jun'83 by Phonogram Records. Dist: Polygram Distribution

MAMA USED TO SAY.
Single (7"): released on Mercury, Oct'84 by Phonogram Records. Dist: Polygram Distribution Deleted '86.

Single (12"): released on Mercury, Oct'84 by Phonogram Records. Dist: Polygram Distribution

OH LOUISE.
Single (7"): released on London, Nov'85 by London Records. Dist: Polygram

Single (12"): released on London, Nov'85 by London Records. Dist: Polygram

RUNNIN'.
Single (7"): released on Mercury, Aug'83 by Phonogram Records. Dist: Polygram Distribution

Single (12"): released on Mercury, Aug'83 by Phonogram Records. Dist: Polygram Distribution Deleted '84.

SOMEBODY.
Single (7"): released on London, Jul'84 by London Records. Dist: Polygram

Single (12"): released on London, Jul'84 by London Records. Dist: Polygram

YES (IF YOU WANT ME).
Tracks: / Yes (if you want me) / Not tonight.
Single (7"): released on London, Jul'87 by London Records. Dist: Polygram

Single (12"): released on London, Jul'87 by London Records. Dist: Polygram

Junior Choice

JUNIOR CHOICE Ed Stewarts Junior Choice (Various original artists).
Album: released on BBC, Jan'78 by BBC Records & Tapes. Dist: EMI, PRT,

JUNIOR CHOICE (FAVOURITE REQUESTS) various artists (Various original artists).
Cassette: released on BBC, Oct'80 by BBC Records & Tapes. Dist: EMI, PRT,

Junior English

HEY BABY.
Tracks: / Hey Baby / High Society.
Single (12"): released on International English, Mar'86 by International English Records. Dist: Jetstar

LONELINESS.
Single (12"): released on U Mat, Sep'85 Dist: Jetstar

NEVER TOO LATE.
Single (12"): released on International English, Apr'85 by International English Records. Dist: Jetstar

NEVER TOO LATE.
Tracks: / Something 'bout you baby I like / Take me away / Never too late / Falling in, falling out / Carol / Long ago / Mountain lady / Don't stop me now / Enough is enough / Riverside.
Compact disc: released on Vertigo, '83 by Phonogram Records. Dist: Polygram

Junior Jazz

JAZZ OFF THE AIR, VOL. 1 (Junior Jazz and Wnez).
Album: released on Spotlite, '83 by Spotlite Records. Dist: Cadillac, Jazz Music, Spotlite

Junior, Trevor

GHETTO LIVING.
Single (12"): released on Tonos, Jul'84 by Tonos Records. Dist: Jetstar Distribution

TIDAL WAVE.
Single (12"): released on Kings Of Jazz, May'85 Dist: Jazz Horizons, Jazz Music, Celtic Music

Junior, Wally Jump

JUMP BACK (Junior, Wally Jump & The Criminal Element).
Tracks: / Jummp back / Emu Dub Back, the.
Single (7"): released on Club, Aug'86 by Phonogram Records. Dist: Polygram

Single (12"): released on Club, Aug'86 by Phonogram Records. Dist: Polygram

TURN ME LOOSE.
Tracks: / Turn me loose / Cut me loose.
Single (7"): released on London, Feb'87 by London Records. Dist: Polygram

Single (12"): released on London, Feb'87 by London Records. Dist: Polygram

Junjo Presents..

JUNJO PRESENTS TWO BIG SOUND various artists (Various Artists).
Album: released on Greensleeves, May'83 by Greensleeves Records. Dist: BMG, Jetstar, Spartan

Junk

MESSIAHS OF THE POP RAUNCH.
Tracks: / Messiahs of the pop raunch / Your last breath was my first kiss / Cuckoo land.
Single (12"): released on Native, Jul'87 by Native Records. Dist: Red Rhino, Cartel

Junk, The

CUCKOOLAND.
Album: released on Native, Nov'86 by Native Records. Dist: Red Rhino, Cartel

Junkyard Band

WORD, THE.
Tracks: / Word, The.
Single (7"): released on Def Jam (USA), Aug'86 by CBS Records. Dist: CBS

Single (12"): released on Def Jam (USA), Aug'86 by CBS Records. Dist: CBS

Juno the Reaper

AS SEEN ON TV.
Single (7"): released on Sunny, Apr'82 by Sunny Records. Dist: PRT Distribution

Jupiter, Duke

LITTLE LADY.
Single (7"): released on Morocco, Jun'84

Single (12"): released on Morocco, Jun'84

WHITE KNUCKLE RIDE.
Album: released on Motown, Oct'84 by Motown Records. Dist: BMG Distribution

Cassette: released on Motown, Oct'84 by Motown Records. Dist: BMG Distribution

Jupiter Menace

JUPITER MENACE Original electronic soundtrack.
Album: released on Shanghai, Sep'84

Jupiter Red

SECRET AFFAIR.
Single (7"): released on Arrival, Oct'83 by Arrival. Dist: Revolver, Cartel

Jupp, Mickey

DON'T TALK TO ME.
Single (7"): released on Good Foot, Mar'81 by Good Foot Records (USA). Dist: Pinnacle

JUPPANESE.
Album: released on Stiff, '78 by Stiff Records. Dist: EMI, Record Services Distribution (Ireland)

ONLY FOR LIFE.
Single (7"): released on Towerbell, Aug'84 by Towerbell Records. Dist: EMI

Single (12"): released on Towerbell, Aug'84 by Towerbell Records. Dist: EMI

Jurgens, Dick

UNCOLLECTED DICK JURGENS & HIS ORCHESTRA,VOL 2, (THE).
Album: released on Fanfare, Jun'79 by Ferroway/Fanfare Records. Dist: PRT

Jurgens, Udo
UDO 1957-60.
Album: released on Polydor-Heciodor, '80

Juris, Vic
BLEECKER STREET.
Album: released on Muse (Import), Dec'82

HORIZON DRIVE.
Album: released on Muse (Import), Apr'81

Jury, The
JUST LIKE LOVERS.
Tracks: / Just like lovers / Ride your bike / Sardines.
Single (7"): released on Chrysalis, Aug'86 by Chrysalis Records. Dist: CBS

Just A Gigolo
JUST A GIGOLO Just a Gigolo.
Notes: Starring: David Bowie/Marlene Dietrich/Sydne Rome/Kim Novak/Marie Schnell/Curt Jurgens/David Hemmengs. Total playing minutes: 90 Minutes
Video-cassette (VHS): released on Cinema Features, Sep'86 Dist: VCL

Just A Ha Ha
LUCKY DAY.
Single (7"): released on PRT, Feb'84 by PRT Records. Dist: PRT

Single (12"): released on PRT, Feb'84 by PRT Records. Dist: PRT

Just, Barry
JUST BARRY.
Single (7"): released on Monarch, Aug'83 by

Chart Records. Dist: Pinnacle

Just Brothers
SLICED TOMATOES.
Single (7"): released on Inferno, Aug'83 by Inferno Records. Dist: Inferno, Cartel, Pinnacle

Just, Damian
I'M A MAN.
Tracks: / I'm a man / Sounds so fine.
Single (12"): released on Passion, May'87 by Skratch Records. Dist: PRT

Just For The Crack
LOVING YOU (Just For The Crack & Peter Welch).
Album: released on Heat, Aug'86 by Peter Welch. Dist: Gipsy, CBS

Cassette: released on Heat, Aug'86 by Peter Welch. Dist: Gipsy, CBS

Just Good Friends
ONE NIGHT.
Single (7"): released on Magnet, Mar'84 by Magnet Records. Dist: BMG

Single (12"): released on Magnet, Mar'84 by Magnet Records. Dist: BMG

Just go wild...
JUST GO WILD OVER ROCK 'N' ROLL
Various artists (Various Artists).
Album: released on Charly, Jul'81 by Charly Records. Dist: Charly, Cadillac

Just guitars
JUST GUITARS Various artists (Various Artists).

Album: released on CBS, May'84 by CBS Records. Dist: CBS

Cassette: released on CBS, May'84 by CBS Records. Dist: CBS

Justified Ancients
1987.
Album: released on KFL Communications, Jul'87

ALL YOU NEED IS LOVE.
Single (12"): released on Jams, 30 May'87

Single (7"): released on Jams, 30 May'87

Just-In-Case
MAGAZINE GIRL.
Single (7"): released on Thunderbay, Jul'83 Dist: Spartan Distribution

Just lovers
JUST LOVERS Various artists (Various Artists).
Album: released on Firm, Oct'85 by Firm Records. Dist: Jetstar

Just Say Yeh
JUST SAY YEH (Various Artists).
Album: released on Tanz, Nov'86 Dist: Red Rhino Distribution, Cartel Distribution

Just So Stories
JUST SO STORIES Kipling, Rudyard (Davis, David).
Cassette: released on Pinnacle, '79 by Pinnacle Records. Dist: Pinnacle

JUST SO STORIES, VOL 1 Kipling, Rudyard (Johnson, Richard/Barbara Jefford/Michael Horden).
Double cassette: released on Argo (Spokenword), Jul'82 by Decca Records. Dist: Polygram

Just when you thought...
JUST WHEN YOU THOUGHT IT WAS QUIET Various artists (Various Artists).
Album: released on Quiet, Apr'83 by Quiet Records. Dist: Nine Mile, Cartel

Just William stories
JUST WILLIAM STORIES Crompton, Richmal (Williams, Kenneth).
Double cassette: released on Argo (Spokenword), Jul'82 by Decca Records. Dist: Polygram

Juvet, Patrick
I LOVE AMERICA.
Album: released on Barclay (Import), Nov'79

LAURA: MUSIC FROM THE FILM.
Album: released on Mercury, Jun'82 by Phonogram Records. Dist: Polygram Distribution

PARIS BY NIGHT.
Album: released on Barclay, '79 by Decca Records. Dist: Polygram, Discovery, Conifer, IMS, Swift

JYL
JYL.
Album: released on Thunderbolt, Aug'86 by Magnum Music Group Ltd. Dist: Magnum Music Group Ltd, PRT Distribution, Spartan Distribution

K

K-9 Corporation
DOG TALK.
Single (7"): released on Capitol, Sep'83 by Capitol Records. Dist: EMI

Single (12"): released on Capitol, Sep'83 by Capitol Records. Dist: EMI

KAA Antelope
INDIAN TRILOGY (EP).
Single (7"): released on Sandwich, May'82 Dist: Rough Trade

Kabala
ASHEO ARA.
Single (12"): released on Ink, 23 May'87 by Red Flame. Dist: Rough Trade, Cartel, Pinnacle

ASHE WO ARO.
Tracks: / Ashewo ara / Voltan dance.
Single (7"): released on Ink, Jun'87 by Red Flame. Dist: Rough Trade, Cartel, Pinnacle

ASHE WO ARO / VOLTAN DANCE.
Single (12"): released on Red Flame, Oct'82 by Red Flame Records. Dist: Nine Mile, Cartel

GET BACK TO SUMMER.
Single (7"): released on Cabal, Aug'85 by Cabal Records. Dist: Spartan

Single (12"): released on Cabal, Aug'85 by Cabal Records. Dist: Spartan

WHAT LOVE IS.
Tracks: / What love is / Yo - yo dance.
Single (7"): released on Cabal, Mar'86 by Cabal Records. Dist: Spartan

Single (12"): released on Cabal, Mar'86 by Cabal Records. Dist: Spartan

YEN NBO OSE / YO YO DANCE.
Single (7"): released on 10 Red Flame, Nov'83 by Red Flame Records. Dist: Rough Trade, Cartel

Single (12"): released on 10 Red Flame, Nov'83 by Red Flame Records. Dist: Rough Trade, Cartel

YO YO DANCE.
Single (12"): released on Ink, Aug'87 by Red Flame. Dist: Rough Trade, Cartel, Pinnacle

Kabuki
I AM A HORSE / MY HAIR.
Single (7"): released on Kabaret Noir, Sep'82

KAD
SHAKIN' ALL OVER.
Single (7"): released on Shooting Star, Mar'83

Kadenza
LET'S DO IT.
Single (7"): released on PRT, Mar'83 by PRT Records. Dist: PRT

Single (12"): released on PRT, Mar'83 by PRT Records. Dist: PRT

LET'S STAY TOGETHER.
Single (7"): released on PRT, Sep'82 by PRT Records. Dist: PRT

Single (12"): released on PRT, Sep'82 by PRT Records. Dist: PRT

LIVING IN A BACK STREET / BACK STREET PRESSURE.
Single (7"): released on Calibre, Jan'84 by Calibre Records. Dist: PRT

Single (12"): released on Calibre, Jan'84 by Calibre Records. Dist: PRT

Kadettes
FIREBALL XL5 / MISSION IMPOSSIBLE.

Single (7"): released on Blank, Apr'82 by Blank Records. Dist: PRT, Taylor, H.R., Wynd-Up Distribution

Kaempfert, Bert
BERT KAEMPFERT.
Album: released on Polydor (Holland), Jun'83

Cassette: released on Polydor (Holland), Jun'83

Cassette: released on Polydor, Feb'83 by Polydor Records. Dist: Polygram, Polydor

BEST OF .....
Album: released on Polydor (Germany), Oct'82 Dist: IMS-Polygram

Cassette: released on Polydor (Germany), Oct'82 Dist: IMS-Polygram

BYE BYE BLUES.
Album: released on Polydor, '74 by Polydor Records. Dist: Polygram, Polydor

CHRISTMASTIDE.
Tracks: / Christmastide.
Compact disc: released on Polydor, Dec'85 by Polydor Records. Dist: Polygram, Polydor

DANKE SCHON.
Album: released on Polydor, Oct'80 by Polydor Records. Dist: Polygram, Polydor

Cassette: released on Polydor, Oct'80 by Polydor Records. Dist: Polygram, Polydor

FAMOUS SWING CLASSICS.
Tracks: / Woodchopper's ball (The) / Little brown jug / One o'clock jump / Lullaby of birdland / Two o'clock jump / Airmail special / Apple honey / Intermission riff / Jumpin' at the woodside / Mario / It's only a paper moon / In the mood / Opus one / Tuxedo junction / Night train / Perdido / Take the 'A' train / Skyliner / Honeysuckle rose.
Compact disc: released on Polydor, May'84 by Polydor Records. Dist: Polygram, Polydor

GREATEST HITS:BERT KAEMPFERT.
Compact disc: released on Polydor, Dec'85 by Polydor Records. Dist: Polygram, Polydor

HOURS OF THE STARS.
Album: released on Polydor (Germany), Sep'83 Dist: IMS-Polygram

Cassette: released on Polydor (Germany), Sep'83 Dist: IMS-Polygram

LIVE IN LONDON.
Tracks: / Bye bye blues / Tahitian sunset / All I never need is you / Strangers in the night / Afrikaan beat / Three o'clock in the morning / Take the 'A' train / Love / Swingin' safari, A / I cover the waterfront / Skyliner / Spanish eyes.
Notes: Digital stereo
Compact disc: released on Polydor, Apr'85 by Polydor Records. Dist: Polygram, Polydor

MOODS.
Album: released on Contour, Feb'82 by Pickwick Records. Dist: Pickwick Distribution, PRT

Cassette: released on Contour, Feb'82 by Pickwick Records. Dist: Pickwick Distribution, PRT

NOW AND FOREVER (Kaempfert, Bert and his Orchestra).
Album: released on Polydor, Jan'83 by Polydor Records. Dist: Polygram, Polydor

Cassette: released on Polydor, Jan'83 by Polydor Records. Dist: Polygram, Polydor Deleted '84.

RED ROSES FOR A BLUE LADY.
Tracks: / Red roses for a blue lady / African beat / Strangers in the night / Living it up / Mitternachts blues / World we knew (The) / Can't give you anything - but my love / Remember when / Moon over Naples / Swinging safari, A / Most beautiful girl (The) / That happy feeling / L-O-V-E / Wonderland by night / Bye bye blues / Danke schon.
Compact disc: released on Polydor, Dec'85 by Polydor Records. Dist: Polygram, Polydor

---

Album: released on Polydor (Holland), Jun'84

Cassette: released on Polydor (Holland), Jun'84

SILVER COLLECTION, THE.
Tracks: / Spanish eyes / Afrikaan beat / Wonderland by night / Why can't you and I add up to love / Manhattan merengue / Feelings / Hold back tomorrow / Island in the sun / Danke schon / Strangers in the night / Swinging safari / Sweet Caroline / Time to dream / Way we were (The) / Rhinestone cowboy / Red roses for a blue lady / Bye bye blues / Snowbird / Theme from shaft / Never my love / Headin' home / Raindrops keep fallin' on my head.
Compact disc: released on Polydor, Jan'85 by Polydor Records. Dist: Polygram, Polydor

SPANISH EYES.
Tracks: / Spanish eyes / Strangers in the night / That happy feeling / Red roses for a blue lady / Swingin' safari, A / Bye bye blues / Put your hand in the hand / Most beautiful girl (The) / Afrikaan beat / Feelings / Sweet Caroline / Rhinestone cowboy / What a difference a day makes / Remember when / L-O-V-E / Danke schon.
Compact disc: released on Polydor, Jan'83 by Polydor Records. Dist: Polygram, Polydor

SPRINGTIME.
Album: released on Polydor (Germany), Jun'81 Dist: IMS-Polygram

Cassette: released on Polydor (Germany), Jun'81 Dist: IMS-Polygram

STRANGERS IN THE NIGHT.
Compact disc: released on Polydor, Dec'85 by Polydor Records. Dist: Polygram, Polydor

Album: released on Contour, Jul'87 by Pickwick Records. Dist: Pickwick Distribution

SUPER STEREO SOUNDS OF BERT KAEMPFERT.
Album: released on Polydor, Mar'84 by Polydor Records. Dist: Polygram, Polydor

Cassette: released on Polydor, Mar'84 by Polydor Records. Dist: Polygram, Polydor

SWINGING SAFARI, A.
Tracks: / Afrikaan beat / Black beauty / Happy trumpeter / Market day / Similau / Skokiaan / Swingin' safari, A / Take me / That happy feeling / Tootie flutie / Wimoweh / Zambesi.
Compact disc: released on Polydor, May'85 by Polydor Records. Dist: Polygram, Polydor

THIS IS BERT KAEMPFERT.
Album: released on Arcade Music Gala, Apr'86 Dist: Stage One

Cassette: released on Arcade Music Gala, Apr'86 Dist: Stage One

WONDERLAND BY NIGHT.
Tracks: / Wonderland by night / Jumpin' at the woodside / Sugar bush / Afrikaan beat / Patapata / Lonely nightingale / Way we were (The) / Lullaby of birdland / Happy safari / In the mood / Happy trumpeter / Yellow bird / Baby elephant walk / Fly robin fly.
Compact disc: released on Polydor, Dec'85 by Polydor Records. Dist: Polygram, Polydor

Album: released on Polydor (Germany), Mar'83 Dist: IMS-Polygram

Cassette: released on Polydor (Germany), Mar'83 Dist: IMS-Polygram

Kaftan Kake
NICE VERY NICE / JAG UR (Kaftan Kake featuring Karan David).
Single (7"): released on Creole, Apr'82 by Creole Records. Dist: Rhino, PRT

Kah, Hubert
LIMOUSINE.
Tracks: / Limousine / Drowning.
Single (7"): released on MCA, Jan'87 by MCA Records. Dist: Polygram, MCA

Single (12"): released on MCA, Jan'87 by MCA Records. Dist: Polygram, MCA

TEN SONGS.
Tracks: / Pogo the clown / Lonesome cowboy / Drowning / Something I should know / Explain the world in a word / Love is so sensible / Get strange / That girl / Limousine / Under my skin.
Album: released on MCA, Feb'87 by MCA Records. Dist: Polygram, MCA

Cassette: released on MCA, Feb'87 by MCA Records. Dist: Polygram, MCA

Kahn Ali Akbar
AT SAN FANCISCO (Kahn Ali Akbar & Ravi Skanker).
Album: released on Gramophone Co. of India, Feb'84 by Gramophone Company Of India, UK Branch. Dist: EMI, Sterns, Triple Earth

Cassette: released on Gramophone Co. of India, Feb'84 by Gramophone Company Of India, UK Branch. Dist: EMI, Sterns, Triple Earth

Kahn Bismillah
RGS JAUNPURI & IMAN KALYAN.
Album: released on Gramophone Co. of India, Apr'84 by Gramophone Company Of India, UK Branch. Dist: EMI, Sterns, Triple Earth

Kahn, Chaka
BEST IN THE WEST/BE BOP MEDLEY.
Single (7"): released on Warner Bros., Feb'83 by Warner Bros Records. Dist: WEA

Single (12"): released on Warner Bros., Feb'83 by Warner Bros Records. Dist: WEA

CHAKA.
Album: released on Warner Bros., Jan'79 by Warner Bros Records. Dist: WEA

Cassette: released on Warner Bros., Jan'78 by Warner Bros Records. Dist: WEA

CHAKA KAHN.
Album: released on Warner Brothers, Jan'83 by Warner Bros Records. Dist: WEA

EYE TO EYE.
Single (7"): released on Warner Bros., Apr'85 by Warner Bros Records. Dist: WEA

Single (12"): released on Warner Bros., Apr'85 by Warner Bros Records. Dist: WEA

Kahondo Style
MY HEART'S IN MOTION.
Tracks: / Tokyo ando / Games with the lights / Barbaria / Last minute jingle / Jaws of glass / Holloway Road / Lonely teardrop / Ant by ant, leaf by leaf / Mongoose / Ghost of a flea / Programs on the air / My heart's in motion.
Album: released on Nato (France), Sep'86 by Disques Nato. Dist: Essex Record Distributors Ltd.

Kaiser, Henry
DEVIL IN THE DRAIN.
Album: released on SST, Oct'87 by SST Records. Dist: Pinnacle. Estim retail price in Sep'87 was £6.49.

IT'S A WONDERFUL LIFE.
Album: released on Metalanguage, Dec'84 by Metalanguage. Dist: Rough Trade, Cartel

Kaiser, Kurt
FATHER LIFT ME UP.
Album: released on Word, May'82 by Word Records. Dist: Word Distribution, CBS

Cassette: released on Word, May'82 by Word Records. Dist: Word Distribution, CBS

Kaiser, Roland
SANTA MARIA.
Single (7"): released on Proto, May'83 by Proto Records. Dist: WEA

Kaja

CRAZY PEOPLES RIGHT TO SPEAK.
Album: released on Parlophone, Sep'85 by EMI Records. Dist: EMI

Cassette: released on Parlophone, Sep'85 by EMI Records. Dist: EMI

SHOULDN'T DO THAT.
Single (7"): released on Parlophone, Aug'85 by EMI Records. Dist: EMI Deleted '86.

Single (12"): released on Parlophone, Aug'85 by EMI Records. Dist: EMI Deleted '86.

Special: released on Parlophone, Aug'85 by EMI Records. Dist: EMI

Kajagoogoo

BIG APPLE / MONOCHROMATIC / BIG APPLE (METROMIX).
Single (7"): released on EMI, Sep'83 by EMI Records. Dist: EMI

Single (12"): released on EMI, Sep'83 by EMI Records. Dist: EMI

TOO SHY.
Single (7"): released on EMI, Jan'83 by EMI Records. Dist: EMI

Single (12"): released on EMI, Jan'83 by EMI Records. Dist: EMI Deleted '87.

TURN YOUR BACK ON ME.
Single (7"): released on EMI, Apr'84 by EMI Records. Dist: EMI

Single (12"): released on EMI, Apr'84 by EMI Records. Dist: EMI Deleted '87.

Picture disc single: released on EMI, May'84 by EMI Records. Dist: EMI

VIDEO EP.
Video-cassette (VHS): released on PMI, Jun'86 by PMI Records. Dist: EMI

Video-cassette [Betamax]: released on PMI, Jun'86 by PMI Records. Dist: EMI

WHITE FEATHERS TOUR.
Video-cassette (VHS): released on PMI, Jun'86 by PMI Records. Dist: EMI

Video-cassette [Betamax]: released on PMI, Jun'86 by PMI Records. Dist: EMI

Kakoulli, Harry

BABY DON'T LIKE / JEALOUS MIND.
Single (7"): released on Strut, Apr'83 by Strut Records. Dist: Pinnacle

EVEN WHEN I'M NOT.
Album: released on Oval, May'82 by Oval Records. Dist: Pinnacle

I'M ON A ROCKET / I WANNA STAY.
Single (7"): released on Oval, May'82 by Oval Records. Dist: Pinnacle

LONELY BOY / I DON'T NEED YOU ANYMORE.
Single (7"): released on Strut, Jul'83 by Strut Records. Dist: Pinnacle

SHE'S MINE / IN DUB.
Single (7"): released on Connexion, Nov'83 Dist: PRT

Cat. no: NYC 103
Single (12"): released on Connexion, Nov'83 Dist: PRT

SUGAR DADDY.
Single (7"): released on Strut, Aug'84 by Strut Records. Dist: Pinnacle

Single (12"): released on Strut, Aug'84 by Strut Records. Dist: Pinnacle

WHY DON'T YOU COME BACK (see also Marsha Raven) (Kakoulli, Harry & Marsha Raven).
Single (7"): released on Ecstasy, Jul'85 by Creole Records. Dist: CBS

Single (12"): released on Ecstasy, Jul'85 by Creole Records. Dist: CBS

Kalabash

BETRAYED.
Single (12"): released on Kalabash, Dec'83 by Kalabash Records. Dist: Jetstar

Kalahari Surfers

LIVING IN THE HEART OF THE BEAST.
Album: released on Recommended, May'86 by Recommended Records. Dist: Recommended, Impetus, Rough Trade

SLEEP ARMED.
Tracks: / Prologue / Houghton parents / Healthy way of life / Potential aggressor / Remember the corporals / Golden Rendez vous / Leaders underground / This land / Hoe ry die boere" / Mafikeng road / Rademeyer's letter to his wife / Maids day off / Potential aggressor (2) / Greatest hits/tear gas / Brighter future.
Album: released on Recommended, Mar'87 by Recommended Records. Dist: Recommended, Impetus, Rough Trade

Kalambya Sisters

KATELINA / MBIE NUKE.
Single (12"): released on Zensor, Dec'83 by Zensor Records. Dist: Rough Trade

Kalapana, Harry

HAWAII DREAMS.
Notes: Waikiki Beach, Aloha Waikiki, Pacific Melody, The last Desert Melody etc.
Compact disc: released on Delta, '86 by Delta Records. Dist: Target

Kaleidoscope

BACON FROM MARS.
Album: released on Edsel, Aug'83 by Demon Records. Dist: Pinnacle, Jazz Music, Projection

FAINTLY BLOWING.
Album: released on Five Hours Back, Feb'87 by One Big Guitar / Zippo Records. Dist: Pinnacle, Revolver, Cartel

RAMPE' RAMPE'.
Album: released on Edsel, Jun'84 by Demon Records. Dist: Pinnacle, Jazz Music, Projection

TANGERINE DREAM.
Album: released on Five Hours Back, Feb'87 by One Big Guitar / Zippo Records. Dist: Pinnacle, Revolver, Cartel

Kale, J.J.

OKIE.
Album: released on Shelter, Aug'83

Cassette: released on Shelter, Aug'83

REALLY.
Album: released on Shelter, Aug'83

Cassette: released on Shelter, Aug'83

Kalevela

KALEVELA, THE (excerpts).
Cassette: released on Caedmon(USA), '82 by Caedmon (USA) Records. Dist: Gower, Taylors, Discovery

Kalima

FOUR SONGS EP - SPARKLE.
Single (12"): released on Factory, Jul'85 by Factory Records. Dist: Cartel, Pinnacle

NIGHT-TIME SHADOWS.
Tracks: / Mystic rhymes / After hours / Green Dolphin Street / Blackwater / In time / Father pants / Start the melody / Token freaky / Love suspended in time.
Album: released on Factory, Jul'86 by Factory Records. Dist: Cartel, Pinnacle

SMILING HOUR.
Single (7"): released on Factory, Nov'83 by Factory Records. Dist: Cartel. Pinnacle

Single (12"): released on Factory, Nov'83 by Factory Records. Dist: Cartel. Pinnacle

WEIRD FEELINGS.
Single (7"): released on Factory, May'87 by Factory Records. Dist: Cartel, Pinnacle

Single (12"): released on Factory, May'87 by Factory Records. Dist: Cartel, Pinnacle

WHISPERED WORDS.
Tracks: / Whispered words.
Single (12"): released on Factory, Mar'86 by Factory Records. Dist: Cartel, Pinnacle

WIERD READINGS.
Single (12"): released on Factory, 30 May'87 by Factory Records. Dist: Cartel, Pinnacle

Kalin Twins

WHEN.
Album: released on Bear Family, Mar'84 by Bear Family Records. Dist: Rollercoaster Distribution, Swift

Single (7"): released on Old Gold (Reissue), Jul'82

Kallen, Kitty

3 GREAT GIRLS (see 3 Great Girls) (Kallen, Kitty/Della Reese/Ann Margaret).

LITTLE THINGS MEAN A LOT.
Single (7"): released on Old Gold (Reissue), Jul'82

Kallmann, Gunter Choir

ELIZABETHAN SERANADE.
Album: released on Memoir, Oct'85 by Memoir Records. Dist: PRT Distribution

Cassette: released on Memoir, Oct'85 by Memoir Records. Dist: PRT Distribution

Kalnin, Teodor

TEODOR KALNIN CHOIR (LATVIAN RADIO).
Album: released on Melodiya (USSR), May'78 Dist: T.B.C Distribution

Kameleon

DANGER ZONE STRANGER ZONE.
Single (7"): released on Elite, Oct'81 Dist: PRT

Kamen, Nick

COME SOFTLY TO ME.
Tracks: / Miss you.
Single (7"): released on WEA, Aug'87 by WEA Records. Dist: WEA

Single (12"): released on WEA, Aug'87 by WEA Records. Dist: WEA

EACH TIME YOU BREAK MY HEART.
Tracks: / Each time you break my heart.
Single (7"): released on WEA, Oct'86 by WEA Records. Dist: WEA

LOVING YOU IS SWEETER THAN EVER.
Tracks: / Loving you is sweeter than ever / Baby after tonight.
Single (7"): released on WEA, Feb'87 by WEA Records. Dist: WEA

Single (12"): released on WEA, Feb'87 by WEA Records. Dist: WEA

NICK KAMEN.
Tracks: / Win your love / Open the door to your heart / Nobody else / Into the night / Come softly to me / Loving you is sweeter than ever / Each time you break my heart / Man in me, The / Any day now / Help me baby.
Album: released on WEA, Apr'87 by WEA Records. Dist: WEA

Cassette: released on WEA, Apr'87 by WEA Records. Dist: WEA

Compact disc: released on WEA, Apr'87 by WEA Records. Dist: WEA

NOBODY ELSE.
Tracks: / Nobody else / Any day now.
Single (7"): released on WEA, May'87 by WEA Records. Dist: WEA

Single (12"): released on WEA, May'87 by WEA Records. Dist: WEA

Kam, Ho Ho

SEVEN DEADLY SINS.
Album: released on Numa, Nov'86 by Numa Records. Dist: PRT Distribution

Cassette: released on Numa, Nov'86 by Numa Records. Dist: PRT Distribution

Kamikaze Pilots

SHARON SIGNS TO CHERRY RED.
Single (7"): released on Lowther, Apr'85

Kamikaze Sex Pilots

DARK NIGHT OF THE SOUL / RED INDIAN.
Single (7"): released on Lowther, Jun'83

Kaminsky, Max

JACK TEAGARDEN & MAX KAMINSKY (see also Jack Teagarden) (Kaminsky, Max & Jack Teagarden).
Album: released on Commodore Classics, Jul'82 by Teldec Records (Germany). Dist: Conifer, IMS, Polygram

Kamon, Karen

GIVE A LITTLE LOVE.
Tracks: / Give a little love / Heart over mind.
Single (7"): released on Atco, Jun'87 by Atlantic Records. Dist: WEA

Single (12"): released on Atco, Jun'87 by Atlantic Records. Dist: WEA

LOVERBOY.
Single (7"): released on CBS, Aug'84 by CBS Records. Dist: CBS

VOICES.
Tracks: / Lovesick / Give a little love / Fool for love / Love just ain't enough / Voices / All cried out / Strangeway / Heart over mind / Bop girl / Whatever we imagine.
Album: released on Atco, Apr'87 by Atlantic Records. Dist: WEA

Cassette: released on Atco, Apr'87 by Atlantic Records. Dist: WEA

Album: released on Atco (USA), 11 Apr'87 by Atlantic Records. Dist: WEA

Cassette: released on Atco (USA), 11 Apr'87

by Atlantic Records. Dist: WEA

Kamoze, Ini

CALL THE POLICE.
Single (7"): released on Island, Aug'85 by Island Records. Dist: Polygram

INI KAMOZE.
Album: released on Island, Jan'84 by Island Records. Dist: Polygram

Cassette: released on Island, Jan'84 by Island Records. Dist: Polygram

PIRATE.
Tracks: / Dream / Pirate / Betty Brown's mother / Queen of my house / R.O.U.G.H. / Gunshot / Burnin' / Pull the cork.
Album: released on Island, Aug'86 by Island Records. Dist: Polygram

Cassette: released on Island, Aug'86 by Island Records. Dist: Polygram

Single (12"): released on Island, Aug'86 by island Records. Dist: Polygram

STATEMENT.
Album: released on Island, Oct'84 by Island Records. Dist: Polygram

Kanawa, Kiri Te

60 MINUTES OF MUSIC.
Tracks: / O divine redeemer / Laudate dominium / Jesus que ma joie demeure / Sanctus / Panis angelicus / Ave Maria / Exsultate jubilate / Let the bright seraphim / Let their celestial concerts / Trumpet tune.
Cassette: released on Phillips France, Jul'86

BLUE SKIES (SINGLE).
Tracks: / Blue skies / Folks that live on the hill (The).
Single (7"): released on Decca, May'86 by Decca Records. Dist: Polygram

COME TO THE FAIR/FOLK SONGS & BALLADS.
Album: released on H.M.V., Jun'84 by EMI Records. Dist: EMI

Cassette: released on H.M.V., Jun'84 by EMI Records. Dist: EMI

I'M IN LOVE WITH A WONDERFUL GUY.
Tracks: / I'm in love with a wonderful guy / Honey bun.
Single (7"): released on CBS, Nov'86 by CBS Records. Dist: CBS

PUCCINI ARIAS.
Album: released on CBS(Masterworks), Jul'83 by CBS Records. Dist: CBS

Cassette: released on CBS(Masterworks), Jul'83 by CBS Records. Dist: CBS

ROYAL OCCASION, A (Kanawa, Kiri Te With National youth Choir of New Zealand).
Album: released on Tartar (New Zealand), Aug'83

Cassette: released on Tartar (New Zealand), Aug'83

SHEPERDS SONG(BAILERO).
Single (7"): released on Decca, May'83 by Decca Records. Dist: Polygram

Kanchan

KUCHH GABDAD HAI.
Tracks: / Kuchh gabdad hai / Chuk chuk gadi chali.
Single (12"): released on Sunbum, Mar'86 by Orbitone Records. Dist: Jetstar Distribution

KUCHI GATDAD HAI.
Album: released on Stereo, Apr'85 by Orbitone Records. Dist: Jetstar Distribution

Kanda Bongo Man

AMOUR FOU.
Album: released on Bongoman(Zaire), Jul'84

NON STOP NON STOP.
Tracks: / Iyole n'samba-carol / Ida / Djessy / Amina / Mazina.
Album: released on Globestyle, Jan'86 by Ace Records. Dist: Projection

Album: released on Globestyle, Nov'85 by Ace Records. Dist: Projection

Kandidate

I DON'T WANNA LOSE YOU.
Tracks: / I don't wanna lose you.
Single (7"): released on Old Gold, Mar'87 by Old Gold Records. Dist: Lightning, Jazz Music, Spartan, Counterpoint

Kane, A.R.

LOLITA.
Tracks: / Lolita / Sado-masochism is a must /

Butterfly collector.
Single (7"): released on 4AD, Jul'87 by 4AD Records. Dist: Rough Trade

LOLLITA.
Single (12"): released on One Little Indian, 23 May'87 by One Little Indian Records. Dist: Nine Mile Distribution, Cartel Distribution

WHEN YOU'RE SAD.
Single (12"): released on One Little Indian, Aug'87 by One Little Indian Records. Dist: Nine Mile Distribution, Cartel Distribution

Kane, D.J.

D.J.KANE & THE MILLIONAIRES (Kane, D.J. & the Millionaires).
Album: released on Radar, Feb'81 by WEA Music Ltd. Dist: WEA, PRT

Kane, Eden

BOYS CRY.
Single (7"): released on Old Gold, Jan'85 by Old Gold Records. Dist: Lightning, Jazz Music, Spartan, Counterpoint

WELL I ASK YOU.
Single (7"): released on Decca, Mar'82 by Decca Records. Dist: Polygram

Single (7"): released on Old Gold, Oct'83 by Old Gold Records. Dist: Lightning, Jazz Music, Spartan, Counterpoint

Kane Gang

BAD AND LOW DOWN WORLD OF THE KANE GANG (THE).
Tracks: / Gun law / Take this train / How much longer? / Loserville / Printers devil / Respect yourself - extended version / Closest thing to heaven / Small town creed / Crease in his hat.
Compact disc: released on Kitchenware, May'85 by Kitchenware Records. Dist: Cartel, CBS, Polygram, RCA-Ariola Distribution

Album: released on Kitchenware, Feb'85 by Kitchenware Records. Dist: Cartel, CBS, Polygram, RCA-Ariola Distribution

Cassette: released on Kitchenware, Feb'85 by Kitchenware Records. Dist: Cartel, CBS, Polygram, RCA-Ariola Distribution

BROTHER BROTHER.
Single (7"): released on Kitchenware, Jul'83 by Kitchenware Records. Dist: Cartel, CBS, Polygram, RCA-Ariola Distribution

Single (12"): released on Kitchenware, Jul'83 by Kitchenware Records. Dist: Cartel, CBS, Polygram, RCA-Ariola Distribution

CLOSEST THING TO HEAVEN.
Single (7"): released on Kitchenware, Jun'84 by Kitchenware Records. Dist: Cartel, CBS, Polygram, RCA-Ariola Distribution

Single (12"): released on Kitchenware, Jun'84 by Kitchenware Records. Dist: Cartel, CBS, Polygram, RCA-Ariola Distribution

GUN LAW.
Single (7"): released on Kitchenware, Feb'85 by Kitchenware Records. Dist: Cartel, CBS, Polygram, RCA-Ariola Distribution

Single (12"): released on Kitchenware, Feb'85 by Kitchenware Records. Dist: Cartel, CBS, Polygram, RCA-Ariola Distribution

MIRACLE.
Tracks: / Motortown / What time is it / Looking for gold / Take me to the world / King street rain / Don't look any further / Finer place, A / Let's get wet / Strictly love it ain't.
Notes: Produced by Pete Wingfield & The Kane Gang.
Album: released on Kitchenware, Jul'87 by Kitchenware Records. Dist: Cartel, CBS, Polygram, RCA-Ariola Distribution

Cassette: released on Kitchenware, Jul'87 by Kitchenware Records. Dist: Cartel, CBS, Polygram, RCA-Ariola Distribution

Compact disc: released on Kitchenware, Jul'87 by Kitchenware Records. Dist: Cartel, CBS, Polygram, RCA-Ariola Distribution

MOTORTOWN.
Tracks: / Motortown / Spend.
Single (7"): released on Kitchenware, 30 May'87 by Kitchenware Records. Dist: Cartel, CBS, Polygram, RCA-Ariola Distribution

Single (12"): released on Kitchenware, 30 May'87 by Kitchenware Records. Dist: Cartel, CBS, Polygram, RCA-Ariola Distribution

RESPECT YOURSELF.
Single (7"): released on Kitchenware, Oct'84 by Kitchenware Records. Dist: Cartel, CBS, Polygram, RCA-Ariola Distribution

Single (12"): released on Kitchenware, Oct'84 by Kitchenware Records. Dist: Cartel, CBS, Polygram, RCA-Ariola Distribution

SMALL TOWN CREED.
Single (7"): released on Kitchenware, Mar'84 by Kitchenware Records. Dist: Cartel, CBS, Polygram, RCA-Ariola Distribution

Single (12"): released on Kitchenware, Mar'84 by Kitchenware Records. Dist: Cartel, CBS, Polygram, RCA-Ariola Distribution

WHAT TIME IS IT.
Single (7"): released on Kitchenware, Aug'87 by Kitchenware Records. Dist: Cartel, CBS, Polygram, RCA-Ariola Distribution

Single (12"): released on Kitchenware, Aug'87 by Kitchenware Records. Dist: Cartel, CBS, Polygram, RCA-Ariola Distribution

Kane, Gary

ANYBODY ELSE BUT YOU (Kane, Gary & the Tornadoes).

Kane, General

GIRL PULLED THE DOG.
Single (7"): released on Motown, Aug'87 by Motown Records. Dist: BMG Distribution

Single (12"): released on Motown, Aug'87 by Motown Records. Dist: BMG Distribution

Kane, Madleen

PLAYING FOR TIME.
Single (7"): released on AMI, Sep'83 by AMI Records.

Kan Kan

CHANGING TRAINS (EP).
Single (12"): released on Dining Out, Feb'82 by Dining Out Records. Dist: IKF, Independent

INFORMER, THE (EP).
Single (12"): released on Illuminated, Oct'82 by IKF Records. Dist: Pinnacle, Cartel, Jetstar

Kansas

ALL I WANTED.
Tracks: / All I wanted / We're not alone anymore.
Single (7"): released on MCA, Jan'87 by MCA Records. Dist: Polygram, MCA

Single (12"): released on MCA, Jan'87 by MCA Records. Dist: Polygram, MCA

BEST OF.
Album: released on Epic, Sep'84 by CBS Records. Dist: CBS

Cassette: released on Epic, Sep'84 by CBS Records. Dist: CBS

BEST OF KANSAS (THE).
Tracks: / Carry on wayward son / Point of no return / Fight fire / No one together / Play the game tonight / Wall (The).
Compact disc: released on CBS, Nov'85 by CBS Records. Dist: CBS

DRASTIC MEASURES.
Album: released on Epic, Sep'83 by CBS Records. Dist: CBS

Cassette: by CBS Records. Dist: CBS

POWER.
Notes: The return of one of the American rock acts of the 70's with original singer Steve Walsh rejoining surviving members Phil Ehart (drums), and Rick Williams and the arrival of guitarist Steve Morse. The band that produced "Carry on wayward son" and "Dust in the wind" have teamed up with top producer Andrew Powell (formerly with Alan Parsons project).
Album: released on MCA, Dec'86 by MCA Records. Dist: Polygram, MCA

Cassette: released on MCA, Dec'86 by MCA Records. Dist: Polygram, MCA

Kansas City

Count Basie and Kansas City 7

KANSAS CITY 5 & 6(1938) (Kansas City 5 & 6 with Lester Young).
Album: released on Commodore Class, Dec'84 by Teldec Records (Germany). Dist: Conifer, IMS, Polygram

PREZ & FRIENDS ('44) (Kansas City 6 with Lester Young).
Album: released on Commodore Classics, Jan'85 by Teldec Records (Germany). Dist: Conifer, IMS, Polygram

Kansas Joe

BEST OF KANSAS JOE - VOL.1 - 1929-1935 (THE).
Notes: Mono
Album: released on Earl Archives, Jan'87 Dist: Swift, Jazz Music

Kantata

ASIKO.
Album: released on Oval, Jan'85 Dist: Projection

Single (12"): released on Oval, Jun'84 Dist: Projection

Kante, Mory

10 COLA NUTS.
Tracks: / 10 cola nuts / Kebendo / Kouma / Teri ya / Lele / Nonsense.
Notes: Mory Kante is a revered Mandingue musician from Guinea. He comes from a proud class of professional musicians who are regarded as being at the very top of Guinea society. The music is passed from one generation to another and is spiritual in content. Exciting vibrant music to dance to.
Album: released on Barclay (France), Jun'86 by Decca Records. Dist: IMS, Discovery, Conifer, Swift, Polygram

Cassette: released on Barclay (France), Jun'86 by Decca Records. Dist: IMS, Discovery, Conifer, Swift, Polygram

Compact disc: released on Philips (France), '86

PARIS A.
Tracks: / Ye ke ye ke / Gnaga lemba / Wari massilani / Ca va la bas / M'balou / Soumba.
Notes: New live album from Guinea's Mory Kante, offering more exciting and vibrant Africa dance music.
Album: released on Barclay (France), Sep'86 by Decca Records. Dist: IMS, Discovery, Conifer, Swift, Polygram

Cassette: released on Barclay (France), Sep'86 by Decca Records. Dist: IMS, Discovery, Conifer, Swift, Polygram

Kanute

AMAZING MIND.
Single (7"): released on EMI, Jan'85 by EMI Records. Dist: EMI

Single (12"): released on EMI, Jan'85 by EMI Records. Dist: EMI

Kapelle, Rote

IT MOVES...BUT DOES IT SWING?.
Tracks: / Marathon man / Jellystone Park / Anna / Acid face baby / Sunday / you don't know.
Notes: Recorded for BBC Radio One John Peel programme.
Extended-play record: released on In Tape, Jul'87 by In Tape Records. Dist: Red Rhino, Cartel

THESE ANIMALS ARE DANGEROUS.
Tracks: / These animals are dangerous / Sunday.
Single (7"): released on In Tape, Sep'86 by In Tape Records. Dist: Red Rhino, Cartel

Kapil, Sanjay

I WISH I COULD SEE MY EARTH.
Single (7"): released on JSO, Jul'81

Kapoor, Mahendra

BHABI GAL NA KARI.
Tracks: / Aj tenoon nachna pao / Bhabi gal na kiri / Ik chardi jawani / Gorian ghulab jayan gallan / Toon toon boley tar / Giddhe wich nachdi de / Saron de phool wargi / Kale doriach mukhra lukakey / Saun rabdi mauj lag javey / Mein ta peenia.
Notes: Savera/Multitone Records, Unit 24, Vernon Building, Westbourne Street, High Wycombe, Bucks. Music by Kuljit Bhamra. Lyrics by Baby Singh Mann.
Cassette: released on Severa-Multitone, Dec'86

Karajova, Nadka

LAMBKIN HAS COMMENCED BLEATING.
Single (7"): released on Folk Music Service, Mar'82 by Imp. Dist: Polygram

PAZARDJIK FOLK SONGS.
Album: released on Folk Music Service, Apr'82 by Imp. Dist: Polygram

Cassette: released on Folk Music Service, Apr'82 by Imp. Dist: Polygram

Karamel

IT'S OVER.
Single (12"): released on Red Man, Sep'83 by Red Man Records. Dist: Jetstar

Karamilo Petro

THIS IS PETRO KARAMILLO This is Petro Karamillo and his Latin American Rhythm.
Notes: Strict Tempo.
Album: released on Grosvenor, Dec'86 by Grosvenor Records. Dist: Taylors

Karas, Anton

WORLD OF ANTON KARAS.
Album: released on World of Learning, '71 by World Of Learning Records. Dist: World Of Learning

Karate Kid

KARATE KID Soundtrack with various artists.
Album: released on Casablanca, Aug'84 Dist: Polygram, Phonogram

Cassette: released on Casablanca, Aug'84 Dist: Polygram, Phonogram

KARATE KID PART II (THE) Original soundtrack (Karate Kid Part II).
Tracks: / Glory of love / Rock 'n' roll over you / Fish for life / Rock around the clock / Let me at 'em / This is the time / Earth angel / Love theme / Two looking at one / Storm (The).
Album: released on Warner Bros., Jun'86 by Warner Bros Records. Dist: WEA

Cassette: released on Warner Bros., Jun'86 by Warner Bros Records. Dist: WEA

Karbi, Ras

SEVEN SEALS,THE.
Album: released on Rockstone, Sep'84 by Rockstone Records. Dist: Jetstar Distribution

Karen

JUST FOR WHAT I AM.
Album: released on Beechwood, Jan'87 by Beechwood Records. Dist: Ross

Karlsson, Pelle

TEACH US YOUR WAY (Karlsson, Pelle & Evie).
Album: released on Word, May'81 by Word Records. Dist: Word Distribution, CBS

Cassette: released on Word, May'81 by Word Records. Dist: Word Distribution, CBS

Karn, Mick

AFTER A FASHION (Karn, Mick & Midge Ure).
Single (7"): released on Chrysalis, Jul'83 by Chrysalis Records. Dist: CBS

Single (12"): by Chrysalis Records. Dist: CBS

BUOY (Karn, Mick & David Sylvian).
Tracks: / Buoy / Dreams of Reason / Language of Ritual*.
Notes: * Extra track on 12" version only.
Single (7"): released on Virgin, Jan'87 by Virgin Records. Dist: EMI, Virgin Distribution

Single (12"): released on Virgin, Jan'87 by Virgin Records. Dist: EMI, Virgin Distribution

DREAMS OF REASON PRODUCE MONSTERS.
Tracks: / First impression / Language of ritual / Buoy / Land / Three fates (The) / When love walks in / Dream of reason / Answer.
Album: released on Virgin, Feb'87 by Virgin Records. Dist: EMI, Virgin Distribution

Cassette: released on Virgin, Feb'87 by Virgin Records. Dist: EMI, Virgin Distribution

Karrier

I'M BACK.
Single (7"): released on Unit, Sep'84 by Unit Records. Dist: PRT

Single (12"): released on Unit, Oct'84 by Unit Records. Dist: PRT

WAY BEYOND THE NIGHT.
Album: released on Unit, Mar'85 by Unit Records. Dist: PRT

Kartoon

AGE OF DANCING, THE.
Single (12"): released on Bronze, Jul'85 by Polygram Records. Dist: Polydor

Single (7"): released on Bronze, Jul'85 by Polygram Records. Dist: Polydor

OVERNIGHT SENSATION.
Single (7"): released on Bronze, Feb'85 by Polygram Records. Dist: Polydor

Single (12"): released on Bronze, Feb'85 by Polygram Records. Dist: Polydor

PRACTISING THE ART.
Album: released on Bronze, Apr'85 by Polygram Records. Dist: Polydor

Cassette: released on Bronze, Apr'85 by Polygram Records. Dist: Polydor

Kartoon Krew

BATMAN.
Tracks: / Batman.
Single (7"): released on Champion, Oct'86 by Champion Records. Dist: RCA

Single (12"): released on Champion, Oct'86 by Champion Records. Dist: RCA

INSPECTOR GADGET.
Single (7"): released on Champion, Nov'85 by

Champion Records. Dist: RCA

Single (12"): released on Champion, Nov'85 by Champion Records. Dist: RCA

Kasenetz-Katz

QUICK JOEY SMALL (Kasenetz-Katz singing orchestra circus).
Single (7"): released on Flashback, Jan'83 by Flashback Records/PRT Records. Dist: Mainline, PRT

Kashif

ARE YOU THE WOMAN.
Single (7"): released on Arista, Aug'84 by Arista Records. Dist: RCA

Single (12"): released on Arista, Aug'84 by Arista Records. Dist: RCA

BABY DON'T BREAK YOUR BABY'S HEART.
Single (7"): released on Arista, May'84 by Arista Records. Dist: RCA

Single (7"): released on Arista, May'84 by Arista Records. Dist: RCA

Single (12"): released on Arista, May'84 by Arista Records. Dist: RCA

CONDITION OF THE HEART.
Album: released on Arista, Nov'85 by Arista Records. Dist: RCA

Cassette: released on Arista, Nov'85 by Arista Records. Dist: RCA

I JUST GOTTA HAVE YOU.
Single (12"): released on Arista, Feb'83 by Arista Records. Dist: RCA

KASHIF.
Album: released on Arista, Mar'83 by Arista Records. Dist: RCA

SEND ME YOUR LOVE.
Album: released on Arista, Jun'84 by Arista Records. Dist: RCA

Kashkashian, Kim

ELEGIES (Kashkashian, Kim & Robert Levin).
Tracks: / Lacrymae op. 48 / Romance / Elegy / Alegie op. 44 / Romance oubliee / Adagio / Elegie.
Notes: Kim Kashkashian, viola, and Robert Levin, piano are two distinguished musicians from the classical music scene. Kim Kashkashian may rightly be called one of the best violinists of her generation. She is particulary interested in extending the repertoire for her instrument and performing pieces especially written for viola by notable contempory composers. She has played numerous concerts throughout Europe, the States and Japan and has performed with Gidon Kremer. Robert Levin has gained wide experience playing concerts at a variety of important fetivals both in Europe and the United States. He is a close associate of Gidon Kremer's Lockenhaus Festival in Germany. In addition to his concert and festival performances he also teaches Chamber Music, History and Theiry of Music at the New York State University. The programme here is an interesting selection of rarely performed compositions.
Album: released on ECM (Germany), Apr'86 by ECM Records. Dist: IMS, Polygram, Virgin through EMI

Compact disc: released on ECM (Germany), Apr'86 by ECM Records. Dist: IMS, Polygram, Virgin through EMI

Ka-Spel, Edward

CHYEKK CHINA DOLL.
Album: released on Torso, Mar'86 by Torso Records. Dist: Rough Trade, Cartel, EMI

Compact disc: released on Torso, Nov'86 by Torso Records. Dist: Rough Trade, Cartel, EMI

DANCE, CHINA DOLL.
Single (12"): released on In Phaze, Jun'84 by In Phaze Records. Dist: Rough Trade

EYES CHINA DOLL.
Album: released on Scarface, Aug'85 by Scarface Records. Dist: Cartel

LAUGH CHINA DOLL.
Album: released on In Phaze, Sep'84 by In Phaze Records. Dist: Rough Trade

Kas Product

BY PASS.
Album: released on RCA, Jul'83 by RCA Records. Dist: RCA, Roots, Swift, Wellard, Chris, I & B, Solomon & Peres Distribution

Cassette: released on RCA, Jul'83 by RCA Records. Dist: RCA, Roots, Swift, Wellard, Chris, I & B, Solomon & Peres Distribution

TRY OUT.
Album: released on RCA, Oct'82 by RCA Records. Dist: RCA, Roots, Swift, Wellard, Chris, I & B, Solomon & Peres Distribution

Cassette: released on RCA, Oct'82 by RCA Records. Dist: RCA, Roots, Swift, Wellard, Chris, I & B, Solomon & Peres Distribution

Kassap, Sylvain

L'ARLESIENNE.
Tracks: / Un ovillo de ternuras / Smogasbord / L'ile sonnante / Resonsnces / Lucille.
Album: released on Nato (France), Sep'86 by Disques Nato. Dist: Essex Record Distributors Ltd.

Kassav

AN-BA-CHEN'N LA.
Compact disc: by Sterns. Dist: Sterns, Triple Earth

KASSAV.
Album: released on GD Productions(Africa), Aug'85 by Sterns. Dist: Sterns, Triple Earth

Kasseya, Souzy

LE TELEPHONE SONNE.
Single (12"): released on Earthworks, Nov'84 by Earthworks Records. Dist: Earthworks Distributors, Rough Trade, Cartel, Projection

PHENOMENAL, THE.
Album: released on Earthworks, Jul'85 by Earthworks Records. Dist: Earthworks Distributors, Rough Trade, Cartel, Projection

Kassimi, Essa

AFGHAN LUTE, THE (Khan, Nazir).
Album: released on Arion, May'79 Dist: Discovery

Kasso

I LOVE THE PIANO.
Single (7"): released on Banana, Feb'84 Dist: Pinnacle, Fresh

Single (12"): released on Banana, Feb'84 Dist: Pinnacle, Fresh

NEW LIFE.
Single (7"): released on Banana, Jul'84 Dist: Pinnacle, Fresh

Kastrierte Philosophen

BETWEEN SHOOTINGS.
Album: released on What's So Funny About (Germany), May'87 Dist: Red Rhino, Cartel

INSOMNIA.
Album: released on What's So Funny, Aug'86

Katakukbey

GHANA O.K.!(GHANA BEYEYIE).
Album: released on Africagram, Feb'84 by Cherry Red Records. Dist: Pinnacle

Katch 22

WORKSHOP LIFE.
Single (7"): released on Mynah, Dec'84 by Mynah Records. Dist: Mynah, ILA

Kate visits the doctor

KATE VISITS THE DOCTOR (Snell, Nigel).
Cassette: released on Look & Listen, Nov'84 by Listen For Pleasure. Dist: EMI

Katmandu

THEME FROM DYNASTY.
Tracks: / Theme from Dynasty.
Single (7"): released on Lovebeat International, Mar'86

Single (12"): released on Lovebeat International, Mar'86

Katrina & The Waves

DO YOU WANT CRYING.
Single (7"): released on Capitol, Jul'85 by Capitol Records. Dist: EMI

Single (12"): released on Capitol, Jul'85 by Capitol Records. Dist: EMI

IS THAT IT?.
Tracks: / Is that it? / I really taught me to watusi.
Single (7"): released on Capitol, Apr'86 by Capitol Records. Dist: EMI

Single (12"): released on Capitol, Apr'86 by Capitol Records. Dist: EMI

KATRINA AND THE WAVES.
Album: by Capitol Records. Dist: EMI

LOVELY LINDSEY.
Tracks: / Lovely Lindsey / Cry for me.
Single (7"): released on Capitol, Oct'86 by Capitol Records. Dist: EMI

Single (12"): released on Capitol, Oct'86 by Capitol Records. Dist: EMI

PLASTIC MAN.
Single (7"): released on Silvertown, Mar'84 by Silvertown Records.

Single (12"): released on Silvertown, Mar'84 by Silvertown Records.

QUE TE QUIERO.
Single (7"): released on Capitol, Nov'85 by Capitol Records. Dist: EMI

Single (12"): released on Capitol, Nov'85 by Capitol Records. Dist: EMI

QUE TI QUIERO/ MACHINE GUN SMITH.
Single (7"): released on Silvertown, Nov'83 by Silvertown Records.

Single (12"): released on Silvertown, Nov'83 by Silvertown Records.

SUN STREAKED.
Tracks: / Sun streaked / One woman.
Single (7"): released on Capitol, Jun'86 by Capitol Records. Dist: EMI

Single (12"): released on Capitol, Jun'86 by Capitol Records. Dist: EMI

WALKING ON SUNSHINE.
Tracks: / Walking on sunshine / Red wine & whisky / Do you want crying / Que te quiro / Sun Street / Is that it.
Notes: A compilation of promotional video clips, live footage, and film featuring the band on tour. Includes the Top Ten hit 'Walking On Sunshine' and the current hit 'Sun Street'. Number of tracks: 6. Type of recording: Compilation. Total playing time: 30 minutes.
Video-cassette (VHS): released on PMI, Aug'86 by PMI Records. Dist: EMI

Single (7"): released on Capitol, Apr'85 by Capitol Records. Dist: EMI

Single (12"): released on Capitol, Apr'85 by Capitol Records. Dist: EMI

WAVES.
Tracks: / Is that it? / Tears for me / Sun Street / Lovely Lindsey / Riding shotgun / Sleep on my pillow / Money chair / Mr Star / Love that boy / Stop trying to prove.
Notes: Katrina & The Waves made a most impressive debut in 1985 with their first album and the Top 10 single 'Walking On Sunshine'. Since then they have toured America with the Beach Boys, Don Henley and Wham before returning to England to record their new album. The new album is produced by the same team as the last - Katrina & The Waves, Pat Collier & Scott Litt.
Album: released on Capitol, Apr'86 by Capitol Records. Dist: EMI

Cassette: released on Capitol, Apr'86 by Capitol Records. Dist: EMI

Compact disc: released on Capitol, Jul'86 by Capitol Records. Dist: EMI

Katz

VISIONS OF YOU.
Tracks: / Visions of you / Flight 2605.
Single (7"): released on Carrere, Jun'86 by Carrere Records. Dist: PRT, Spartan

Katz Ipanema

SISTER RESISTOR.
Single (7"): released on Official, May'87 by Official Records. Dist: Revolver Distribution, Cartel Distribution

Katzman, Nick

PANIC/ WHEN THE SUN GOES DOWN (Katzman, Nick & Ruby Green).
Album: released on Sonet, Jan'80 by Sonet Records. Dist: PRT

Kaukonen, Jorma

JORMA.

Album: released on RCA, Jan'80 by RCA Records. Dist: RCA, Roots, Swift, Wellard, Chris, I & B, Solomon & Peres Distribution

TOO HOT TO HANDLE.
Compact disc: by Pacific Records (USA). Dist: Atlantic

Kavana, Ron

ROLLIN' & COASTIN In search of America.
Album: released on Appaloosa, Jul'85 Dist: Roots, Folksound, JSU, Projection, Celtic Music, Chris Wellard

Kawasome, Masashi

NUAGE, (LE).
Notes: New Age music for piano, violin, flute, viola and voice.
Compact disc: released on Denon, May'86 by Denon Records. Dist: Harmonia Mundi

Kawere Boys Band

KENYAFRICA (VOL.5).
Album: released on Playasound, '74 Dist: Conifer, Discovery

Kayath, Marcelo

MARCELO KAYATH.
Album: released on Hyperion, Nov'86 by Hyperion Records. Dist: Taylors, PRT, Gamut

Kaye, Danny

BEST OF DANNY KAYE.
Album: released on MCA, Sep'82 by MCA Records. Dist: Polygram, MCA

Cassette: released on MCA, Sep'82 by MCA Records. Dist: Polygram, MCA

VERY BEST OF DANNY KAYE, THE 20 golden greats.
Tracks: / I'm Hans Christian Anderson / Inchworm / King's new clothes, The / Thumbelina / Ugly duckling, The / Wonderful Copenhagen / Tubby the tuba (parts 1 & 2) / Woody woodpecker song, The / Popo the puppet / I taut I taw a puddy tat (I thought I saw a pussy cat) / Ballin' the jack / Tchaikowsky / Civilization (bongo, bongo, bongo) / Molly Malone / Oh by jingo (oh by gee, your the only girl for me) / Candy kisses / St Louis blues / Manic depressive parents lobby number part I & part II.
Album: released on MCA, May'87 by MCA Records. Dist: Polygram, MCA

Cassette: released on MCA, May'87 by MCA Records. Dist: Polygram, MCA

Kaye, M.M.

ORDINARY PRINCESS, THE.
Cassette: released on Caedmon(USA), Sep'85 by Caedmon (USA) Records. Dist: Gower, Taylors, Discovery

Kaye, Sammy

ONE NIGHT STAND WITH SAMMY KAYE.
Album: released on Joyce (USA), May'84 Dist: Swift

PLAY 22 ORIGINAL BIG BAND RECORDINGS (Kaye, Sammy Orchestra).

Album: released on Hindsight(USA), Jun'84 by Hindsight Records (USA). Dist: Swift, Charly

SAMMY KAYE & HIS ORCH. WITH CLYDE MCCOY & HIS ORCH. (Kaye, Sammy Orchestra).
Album: released on Circle, Jul'87 Dist: Jazz Music

Kay, Janet

CAN'T GIVE IT UP/ IMAGINE THAT.
Single (12"): released on Solid Groove, Feb'83 Dist: Jetstar, Pinnacle

CAPRICORN WOMAN.
Album: released on Pressure, Mar'86 Dist: Priority

Album: released on Solid Groove, Mar'82 Dist: Jetstar, Pinnacle

ETERNALLY GRATEFUL.
Single (12"): released on Local, Aug'84 by Local Records. Dist: Pinnacle

FIGHT LIFE.
Single (12"): released on Soho, May'85

LOVIN YOU.
Single (12"): released on All Tone, 30 May'87 Dist: Jetstar

NO EASY WALK TO FREEDOM.
Single (7"): released on Local, Aug'87 by Local Records. Dist: Pinnacle

Single (12"): released on Local, Aug'87 by Local Records. Dist: Pinnacle

SILLY GAMES.
Tracks: / Silly games.
Single (12"): released on Pressure, Jun'86 Dist: Priority

Single (12"): released on Pressure, Dec'84 Dist: Priority

SO AMAZING (PART 2).
Tracks: / So amazing / Amazing dub.
Single (12"): released on Body Music, Apr'87 by Body Music Records. Dist: Jetstar

WHAT LOVE CAN DO/ LOVE DUNNIT.
Single (12"): released on Sarge, Sep'82 by Sarge Records. Dist: Jetstar

YOU BRING THE SUN OUT.
Single (12"): released on Arista, Jul'82 by Arista Records. Dist: RCA

Single (12"): released on Tom Tom, Aug'85 by Tom Tom Records. Dist: Jetstar Distribution

Kay, Kathie

FIRESIDE GIRL, THE.
Album: released on President, Feb'85 by President Records. Dist: Taylors, Spartan

KATHIE KAY.
Album: released on Scotdisc, Jul'85 Dist: Clyde Factors Distributors

Cassette: released on Scotdisc, Jul'85 Dist: Clyde Factors Distributors

MOTHER OF MINE/ OLD SCOTS MOTHER.
Single (7"): released on Country House, Jun'82 by BGS Productions Ltd. Dist: Taylor, H.R., Record Merchandisers Distribution, Pinnacle, Sounds of Scotland Records

SINGS.
Album: released on Country House, Dec'85 by BGS Productions Ltd. Dist: Taylor, H.R., Record Merchandisers Distribution, Pinnacle, Sounds of Scotland Records

Cassette: released on Country House, Dec'85 by BGS Productions Ltd. Dist: Taylor, H.R., Record Merchandisers Distribution, Pinnacle, Sounds of Scotland Records

SOMETHING FOR MUSIC.
Cassette: released on VFM, May'81 by VFM Records. Dist: Taylors, Wynd-Up Distribution

Kay, Ko Ko

KO KO KAY.
Album: released on Chess, Oct'87 by Charly Records. Dist: Charly, Swift, PRT, Discovery, IMS, Polygram

Cassette: released on Chess, Oct'87 by Charly Records. Dist: Charly, Swift, PRT, Discovery, IMS, Polygram

Kaz

MORE THAN I CAN SAY.
Single (7"): released on SMP, Mar'84 Dist: Jetstar, PRT

Single (12"): released on SMP, Mar'84 Dist: Jetstar, PRT

YOU TAKE MY BREATH AWAY/COLD EYES.
Single (7"): released on Passion, Oct'83 by Skratch Records. Dist: PRT

Kazino

AROUND MY DREAM.
Single (7"): released on Carrere, May'85 by Carrere Records. Dist: PRT, Spartan

Single (12"): released on Carrere, May'85 by Carrere Records. Dist: PRT, Spartan

Kazu Matsui Project

STANDING ON THE OUTSIDE.
Notes: Starr Marketing Services Ltd, 90 Queens Road, Twickenham, Middlesex. TW1 4ET. Tel: 01 891 6487.
Compact disc: released on Mobile Fidelity, Oct'86 by Mobile Fidelity Records.

KBC Band

IT'S NOT YOU, IT'S NOT ME.
Tracks: / It's not you, it's not me / It's not you, it's not me (Instr).
Single (7"): released on I.R.S.(Independent Record Syndicate), Jan'87 by I.R.S.. Dist: MCA

Single (12"): released on I.R.S.(Independent Record Syndicate), Jan'87 by I.R.S.. Dist: MCA

KBC BAND, THE.
Tracks: / Mariel / It's not you, it's not me / Hold me / Hold me / America / No more heartaches / Wrecking crew / When love comes / Dream motorcycle / Sayonara.
Album: released on Arista, Feb'87 by Arista Records. Dist: RCA

Cassette: released on Arista, Feb'87 by Arista Records. Dist: RCA

Compact disc: released on Arista, Feb'87 by Arista Records. Dist: RCA

K Creation

CHARIOTS OF FIRE / CHARMERS MOOD SAMBA.

Single (7"): released on KR, Oct'82 by KR Recordings Ltd. Dist: RCA, Revolver, Cartel

Single (12"): released on KR, Oct'82 by KR Recordings Ltd. Dist: RCA, Revolver, Cartel

K.C. & The Sunshine Band

ARE YOU READY.
Single (7"): released on CBS, Mar'84 by CBS Records. Dist: CBS

Single (12"): released on CBS, Mar'84 by CBS Records. Dist: CBS

BLOW YOUR WHISTLE.
Single (7"): released on President, Mar'74 by President Records. Dist: Taylors, Spartan

DO YOU WANNA GO PARTY.
Album: released on TK, Jul'79 Dist: CBS Distribution

GREATEST HITS: K.C. & THE SUNSHINE BAND.
Album: released on Epic, Oct'83 by CBS Records. Dist: CBS Deleted '87.

Cassette: released on Epic, Oct'83 by CBS Records. Dist: CBS

Album: released on Sunny View, Aug'84 by Sunny View Records. Dist: PRT Distribution

Cassette: released on Sunny View, Aug'84 by Sunny View Records. Dist: PRT Distribution

I'M SO CRAZY ABOUT YOU.
Single (7"): released on President, Mar'75 by President Records. Dist: Taylors, Spartan

QUEEN OF CLUBS/GET DOWN...
Single (7"): released on Old Gold, Jul'82 by Old Gold Records. Dist: Lightning, Jazz Music, Spartan, Counterpoint

K-Doe, Ernie

MOTHER IN LAW.
Tracks: / Mother in law / I cried my last tear / Certain girl, A / Te-ta-te-ta-ta / Wanted $10 000 reward / Hello my lover / Ain't it the truth / Popeye Joe / Real man / Heeby jeebies / Waitin' at the station / I'm the boss / Make you love me / Rub dub dub / I got to find somebody / Hurry up and know it.
Album: released on Stateside, Oct'86 Dist: EMI

Cassette: released on Stateside, Oct'86 Dist: EMI

Keaggy, Phil

GETTING CLOSER.
Notes: The latest album from this veteran of contempory Christian music, 'Getting Closer' is characterised by the compassion which has marked virtually all of Keaggy's recorded work over the past 15 years. The new album certainly comes closest of any of his records to capturing the dynamic guitar range he often displays in concert, but even when the lyrics are at their most searing, there's that unique, characteristic sweetness of spirit that comes from his heart to his listeners.
Album: released on Myrrh, Jul'86 by Word Records. Dist: Word Distribution

Cassette: released on Myrrh, Jul'86 by Word Records. Dist: Word Distribution

MASTER AND THE MUSICIAN,THE.
Album: released on Myrrh, May'82 by Word Records. Dist: Word Distribution

Cassette: released on Myrrh, May'82 by Word Records. Dist: Word Distribution

PH'LIP SIDE.
Album: released on Sparrow, May'82 by Word Records. Dist: Spartan

Cassette: released on Sparrow, May'82 by Word Records. Dist: Spartan

TOWN TO TOWN.
Album: released on Sparrow, May'82 by Word Records. Dist: Spartan

Cassette: released on Sparrow, May'82 by Word Records. Dist: Spartan

Keanan

WATERSPORT.
Single (12"): released on Awesome, Sep'85 by Awesome Records. Dist: Rough Trade, Cartel

Keane, Brian

BOLERO (Keane, Brian & Larry Coryell).
Compact disc: Dist: Swift, Target, Discovery

Keane,Dolores

SAIL OG RUA (Keane,Dolores and John Faulkner).
Album: released on Gael-Linn (Ireland), Feb'75 by Gael Linn Records. Dist: Roots, Projection, Celtic Music, Jazz Music

Cassette: released on Gael-Linn (Ireland), Feb'85 by Gael Linn Records. Dist: Roots, Projection, Celtic Music, Jazz Music

Keane Family

MUINTIT CHATHAIN.
Album: released on Gael-Linn (Ireland), Aug'85 by Gael Linn Records. Dist: Roots, Projection, Celtic Music, Jazz Music

Cassette: released on Gael-Linn (Ireland), Aug'85 by Gael Linn Records. Dist: Roots, Projection, Celtic Music, Jazz Music

Kean,Sherry

I WANT YOU BACK.
Single (7"): released on Capitol, Mar'84 by Capitol Records. Dist: EMI

Single (12"): released on Capitol, Mar'84 by Capitol Records. Dist: EMI

Kearns, Martyn

HEART OF BRAILLE.
Cassette: released on Press, Jul'86 by Press Records.

Keating John

SWING REVISITED (Keating,Johnny and his Band).
Album: released on Jasmine, Mar'83 by Jasmine Records. Dist: Counterpoint, Lugtons, Taylor, H.R., Wellard, Chris, Swift, Cadillac

THIS IS THE LONDON SYMPHONY ORCHESTRA (Keating John/London Symphony Orchestra).
Album: by EMI Records. Dist: EMI

Keaton,David

GLORIA/SPACE CONTROL.
Single (7"): released on Vogue, Nov'83 Dist: Discovery, Jazz Music, PRT, Swift

Single (12"): released on Vogue, Nov'83 Dist: Discovery, Jazz Music, PRT, Swift

Keats

KEATS.
Album: released on EMI, Aug'84 by EMI Records. Dist: EMI Deleted '86.

Cassette: released on EMI, Aug'84 by EMI Records. Dist: EMI Deleted '86.

TURN YOUR HEART AROUND.
Single (7"): released on EMI, Jul'84 by EMI Records. Dist: EMI

Keeble,Papa

GOOD THE BAD AND THE UGLY.
Single (7"): released on Carousel, Sep'82 by Carousel Records. Dist: Spartan, Rough Trade

Keegan, Josephine

JOSEPHINE KEEGAN & JIM MCKILLOP (Keegan, Josephine & Jim McKillop).
Album: released on Outlet (Ireland), Jul'83

Cassette: released on Outlet (Ireland), Jul'83

OLD FAVOURITES.
Album: released on Outlet, Aug'82 by Outlet Records. Dist: Outlet Distribution

Cassette: released on Outlet, Aug'82 by Outlet Records. Dist: Outlet Distribution

...ON THE FIDDLE.
Album: released on Outlet, Feb'83 by Outlet Records. Dist: Outlet Distribution

Cassette: released on Outlet, Feb'83 by Outlet Records. Dist: Outlet Distribution

TRADITIONAL IRISH MUSIC.
Album: released on Outlet, Mar'80 by Outlet Records. Dist: Outlet Distribution

Cassette: released on Outlet, Mar'80 by Outlet Records. Dist: Outlet Distribution

Keegaroos

WORLD CUP 82.
Single (7"): released on T.W., Jun'82 by T.W. Records. Dist: Cartel

Keel

BECAUSE THE NIGHT.
Tracks: / Beacause the night.
Single (7"): released on Vertigo, Mar'86 by Phonogram Records. Dist: Polygram

Single (12"): released on Vertigo, Mar'86 by Phonogram Records. Dist: Polygram

FINAL FRONTIER (THE).
Tracks: / Final frontier (The) / Rock and roll animal / Because the night / Here today, gone tomorrow / Arm and a leg / Raised on rock / Just another girl / Tears of fire / Nightfall / No pain no gain.
Notes: A mighty slab of magnificent metal, produced by legendary KISS-man Gene Simmons.
Album: released on Vertigo, Apr'86 by Phonogram Records. Dist: Polygram

Cassette: released on Vertigo, Apr'86 by Phonogram Records. Dist: Polygram

Compact disc: released on Vertigo, Apr'86 by Phonogram Records. Dist: Polygram

KEEL.
Tracks: / United nations / Somebody's waiting / Cherry lane / Calm before the storm / King of the rock / It's a jungle out there / I said the wrong thing to the right girl / Don't say you love me / If love is a crime (I wanna be convicted) / 4th of July.
Album: released on MCA, Jul'87 by MCA Records. Dist: Polygram, MCA

Cassette: released on MCA, Jul'87 by MCA Records. Dist: Polygram, MCA

Compact disc: released on MCA, Jul'87 by MCA Records. Dist: Polygram, MCA

LAY DOWN THE LAW.
Notes: Ron Keel's band's 1984 album.
Album: released on Shrapnel (USA), Aug'87

RIGHT TO ROCK, THE.
Album: released on Vertigo, Apr'85 by Phonogram Records. Dist: Polygram

Cassette: released on Vertigo, Apr'85 by Phonogram Records. Dist: Polygram

Keelers & Colliers

TYNESIDE.
Cassette: released on Folktracks, Nov'79 by Folktracks Cassettes. Dist: Folktracks

Keel, Howard

AND I LOVE YOU SO.
Compact disc: released on Warwick, Nov'86 Dist: Multiple Sound Distributors

Album: released on Warwick, Mar'84 by MSD Records. Dist: CBS

Cassette: released on Warwick, Mar'84 by MSD Records. Dist: CBS

BORN AGAIN.
Single (7"): released on Warwick, Apr'84 by MSD Records. Dist: CBS

JR WHO DO YOU THINK YOU ARE.
Tracks: / JR who do you think you are / I'll stay with you for a lifetime.
Single (7"): released on WEA, May'86 by WEA Records. Dist: WEA

REMINISCING.
Album: released on Telstar, Nov'85 by Telstar Records. Dist: RCA Distribution

Cassette: released on Telstar, Nov'85 by Telstar Records. Dist: RCA Distribution

REMINISCING - THE HOWARD KEEL.
Tracks: / Oklahoma medley / Some enchanted evening / This nearly was mine / I wont send roses / If ever I would leave you / Lamancha medley / You needed me / Love story / Yesterday / Something / Once upon a time / What are you doing for the rest of your life / Wave / Macarthur Park.
Compact disc: released on Telstar, Jan'86 by Telstar Records. Dist: RCA Distribution

Keenan, Brendan

BRENDAN KEENAN.
Album: released on Gael-Linn (Ireland), Feb'85 by Gael Linn Records. Dist: Roots, Projection, Celtic Music, Jazz Music

Cassette: released on Gael-Linn (Ireland), Feb'85 by Gael Linn Records. Dist: Roots, Projection, Celtic Music, Jazz Music

Keene, Tommy

PLACES THAT ARE GONE.
Tracks: / Places that are gone / Faith in love.
Single (7"): released on Geffen, Apr'86 by Geffen Records. Dist: WEA, CBS

SONGS FROM THE FILM.
Tracks: / Places that are gone / In our lives / Listen to me / Paper words / Godtown / Kill your sons / Call on me / As life goes on / My mother looked like Marilyn Monroe / Underworld / Astronomy / Story ends (The).
Album: released on Geffen, Mar'86 by Geffen Records. Dist: WEA, CBS

Cassette: released on Geffen, Mar'86 by Geffen Records. Dist: WEA, CBS

Keep

NOT SO WONDERFUL.
Single (7"): released on One By One Records, Sep'85 Dist: MIS-EMI Distribution

Keepin' the faith

KEEPIN' THE FAITH Various artists (Various Artists).
Album: released on PRT, Feb'84 by PRT Records. Dist: PRT

Cassette: released on PRT, Feb'84 by PRT Records. Dist: PRT

KEEPIN THE FAITH VOL 2 Various artists (Various Artists).
Album: released on PRT, Sep'84 by PRT Records. Dist: PRT

Keep It Dark
DON'T SURRENDER.
Tracks: / Don't surrender / Far from home / It's over.
Single (7"): released on Charisma, May'86 by Virgin Records. Dist: EMI

Single (12"): released on Charisma, May'86 by Virgin Records. Dist: EMI

DREAMER.
Tracks: / Dreamer / Outsider / What do we need.
Single (7"): released on Virgin, Mar'86 by Virgin Records. Dist: EMI, Virgin Distribution

Single (12"): released on Virgin, Mar'86 by Virgin Records. Dist: EMI, Virgin Distribution

FIRST DOWN AND TEN.
Album: released on Charisma, Jun'86 by Virgin Records. Dist: EMI

Cassette: released on Charisma, Jun'86 by Virgin Records. Dist: EMI

Keep on dancin'
KEEP ON DANCIN' Various artists (Various Artists).
Album: released on T. K. Records, Nov'81 by CBS Records. Dist: CBS Distribution

Cassette: released on T. K. Records, Nov'81 by CBS Records. Dist: CBS Distribution

Keep on trucking
KEEP ON TRUCKING Various artists (Various artists).
Album: released on RCA International, Oct'84

Cassette: released on RCA International, Oct'84

Keep smiling through
KEEP SMILING THROUGH Various artists (Various Artists).
Album: released on Golden Age, Apr'85 by Music For Pleasure Records. Dist: EMI

Cassette: released on Golden Age, Apr'85 by Music For Pleasure Records. Dist: EMI

Keep The...
KEEP THE GREY GULL FLYING 1924-1930 Various artists (Various Artists).
Cassette: released on Emporium Cassettes, Jul'86 by Emporium Cassettes Records. Dist: Jazz Music

KEEP THE HOME FIRES BURNING (Songs & Music Of The 1st WW) (Various Artists).
Tracks: / Here we are here we are / Goodbyee / Just before the battle / Your king and country want you / Trumpeter, The / Deathless army, The / Tramp, tramp, tramp / Keep the home fires burning / Boys of the old brigade / Boys in khaki, boys in blue / Colonel Bogey march / Pack up your troubles / It's a long way to Tipperary / Roses of Picardy / Passing review patrol / What has become of hindey dinky parlay voo.
Album: released on Saydisc, Sep'86 by Saydisc Records. Dist: Essex, Harmonia Mundi, Roots, H.R. Taylor, Jazz Music, Swift, Projection, Gamut

Cassette: released on Saydisc, Sep'86 by Saydisc Records. Dist: Essex, Harmonia Mundi, Roots, H.R. Taylor, Jazz Music, Swift, Projection, Gamut

Kelne Ahnung
PLASTIK.
Album: released on Passive, Mar'84 by Passive Records. Dist: Rough Trade, Cartel

PLASTIK C'EST CHIC.
Single (12"): released on Cherry Red, Apr'84 by Cherry Red Records. Dist: Pinnacle

Keith, Bill
BILL KEITH & JIM COLLIER (Keith, Bill & Jim Rooney).
Album: released on Hexagone, Sep'79 Dist: Projection

COLLECTION: BILL KEITH (Keith, Bill & Jim Rooney).
Album: released on Waterfront, Mar'84 by Waterfront Records. Dist: Rough Trade, Cartel, Projection, Roots

SOMETHING AULD, SOMETHING NEWGRASS, BORROWED, BLUEGRASS.
Album: released on Rounder, Jan'87 by Roots Unlimited

Keith & Darrell
WORK THAT BODY.
Single (7"): released on Motown, Jan'84 by RCA Records. Dist: RCA Distribution

Single (12"): released on Motown, Jan'84 by RCA Records. Dist: RCA Distribution

Keith, Leslie
BLACK MOUNTAIN BLUES.
Album: released on Sierra, Mar'79

Keith, Lex
LEX KEITH & HIS SCOTTISH COUNTRY BAND.
Cassette: released on Lismor, Jul'80 by Lismor Records. Dist: Lismor, Roots, Celtic Music

Keith, Penelope
STORYTIME TOP TEN VOL. 1.
Cassette: released on VFM Cassettes, Jan'85

STORYTIME TOP TEN VOL. 2.
Cassette: released on VFM Cassettes, Jan'85

STORYTIME TOP TEN VOL.10 (Keith, Penelope & Richard Briers).
Cassette: released on VFM Cassettes, Jan'85

Keith & Sonia
SHARING THE NIGHT.
Single (12"): released on Melody, Jul'83 by Melody Records. Dist: Jetstar Distribution

Keith & sonya
TWO TIME LOVERS.
Single (12"): released on Melodie, Dec'83 by Melodie Records. Dist: Jetstar Distribution

Kelday, Paul
BEYOND THE PERIMETERES.
Cassette: released on Kelday, Feb'84 by Kelday Records. Dist: Falling A Distribution

Keller, Jerry
HERE COMES SUMMER.
Single (7"): released on Old Gold, Jul'82 by Old Gold Records. Dist: Lightning, Jazz Music, Spartan, Counterpoint

Kellett Rowland
STREETS OF LEEDS, THE.
Cassette: released on Folktracks, Nov'79 by Folktracks Cassettes. Dist: Folktracks

Kelley, Peck
PECK KELLEY JAM - VOL 1 (Kelley, Peck & Dick Shannon Quartet).
Album: released on Commodore Classics, May'87 by Teldec Records (Germany). Dist: Conifer, IMS, Polygram

PECK KELLEY JAM - VOL 2 (Kelley, Peck & Dick Shannon Quartet).
Album: released on Commodore Classics, May'87 by Teldec Records (Germany). Dist: Conifer, IMS, Polygram

Kelli
DOUBLE DEALING.
Single (7"): released on Le Cam, Sep'84

Kelly
BREAKOUT.
Single (7"): released on Calibre Plus, Jul'84 by PRT Records. Dist: PRT

Single (12"): released on Calibre Plus, Jul'84 by PRT Records. Dist: PRT

Kelly, Badamas
ONE MAN ISN'T ENOUGH.
Single (12"): released on Big Top, Aug'87 Dist: Cartel

Kelly, Dave
CRYING IN THE RAIN (Kelly, Dave Band).
Tracks: / Crying in the rain.
Single (7"): released on BBC, Sep'86 by BBC Records & Tapes. Dist: EMI, PRT, Pye

DAVE KELLY BAND LIVE.
Album: released on Appaloosa, Jun'83 Dist: Roots, Hotshot, JSU, Projection, Celtic Music, Chris Wellard

FEELS RIGHT.
Album: released on Cool King, May'81 Dist: Pinnacle

HALCYON DAYS.
Album: released on Ethereal, Sep'84 by Ethereal Records. Dist: M.I.S.

HEART OF THE CITY (Kelly, Dave Band).
Album: released on Line, Jun'87

LONESOME MAN BLUES.
Tracks: / Lonesome man blues / Long hot summer.
Single (7"): released on BBC, May'86 by BBC Records & Tapes. Dist: EMI, PRT, Pye

Single (12"): released on BBC, May'86 by BBC

Records & Tapes. Dist: EMI, PRT, Pye

PUT YOUR MONEY WHERE YOUR MOUTH IS.
Single (7"): released on Cool King, Sep'81 Dist: Pinnacle

RETURN TO SENDER.
Single (7"): released on Cool King, Apr'81 Dist: Pinnacle

WHEN I'M DEAD AND GONE.
Single (7"): released on Cool King, Oct'82 Dist: Pinnacle

Kelly Frank
BARNET SONG.
Single (7"): released on Ritz, May'84 by Ritz Records. Dist: Spartan

CHRISTMAS COUNTDOWN.
Single (7"): released on Ritz, Nov'85 by Ritz Records. Dist: Spartan

Kelly Frankie
AIN'T THAT THE TRUTH.
Single (7"):

Single (12"): released on 10, Oct'85 by 10 Records. Dist: Virgin, EMI

Kelly, Gene
SINGIN' IN THE RAIN.
Album: released on Decca, Sep'78 by Decca Records. Dist: Polygram

Kelly, George
PLAYS THE MUSIC OF DON REDMAN.
Album: released on Stash, Mar'87 Dist: Swift Distribution, Jazz Music Distribution, Jazz Horizons Distribution, Celtic Music Distribution, Cadillac, JSU Distribution, Zodiac Distribution

Vasey, Al & George Kelly/Fessors Session Boys

Kelly, Georgia
IN A CHORD (Kelly, Georgia & Craig Huxley).

Kelly John
FIDDLE & CONCERTINA PLAYER.
Album: released on Freereed, Jan'81 by Topic Records. Dist: JSU

JOHN & JAMES KELLY (Kelly John & James).
Album:

Kelly, Kin
AIN'T TOO PROUD TO BEG.
Tracks: / Ain't too proud to beg / High dance, The.
Single (7"): released on Gipsy, Jul'87 by Gipsy Records. Dist: PRT

Single (12"): released on Gipsy, Jul'87 by Gipsy Records. Dist: PRT

EVERY HEART/HOPELESS LOVE.
Single (7"): released on Gipsy, Feb'83 by Gipsy Records. Dist: PRT

IF I COULD HEAR YOUR VOICE.
Single (7"): released on Gypsy, Nov'80 by Gipsy Records. Dist: Spartan

JEANNIE.
Single (7"): released on Gipsy, Mar'85 by Gipsy Records. Dist: PRT

JUST LIKE MARION/WHEN ROCK WAS KING.
Single (7"): released on Gypsy, Jul'81 by Gypsy Records. Dist: Spartan

KINETICS.
Album: released on Gipsy, Jan'81 by Gipsy Records. Dist: PRT

TO YOU.
Tracks: / To You / Hopeless love / To you / Hopeless love.
Single (7"): released on Gipsy, Jan'87 by Gipsy Records. Dist: PRT

Single (12"): released on Gipsy, Jan'87 by Gipsy Records. Dist: PRT

Notes: For full details see under Craig Huxley

Kelly, Grace
SNOWBIRD AND THE SUN BIRD Read by Grace Kelly.
Album: released on Conifer, Jan'83 by Conifer Records. Dist: Conifer

Kelly Jim
WATERMELON.
Single (12"): released on Lucky, Nov'82 by Lucky Records.

Kelly Marie
BORN TO BE ALIVE.
Tracks: / Born to be alive / Are you ready for love.
Single (12"): released on Passion, Dec'85 by Skratch Records. Dist: PRT

FEEL LIKE I'M IN LOVE.
Tracks: / Feel like I'm in love / Hot love.
Single (7"): released on Old Gold, Mar'86 by Old Gold Records. Dist: Lightning, Jazz Music, Spartan, Counterpoint

HALF WAY TO PARADISE.
Single (12"): released on Passion, Aug'87 by Skratch Records. Dist: PRT

Kelly, Pat
BEST OF PAT KELLY, THE.
Album: released on Vista Sounds, '83 by Vista Sounds Records. Dist: Jetstar

BRIDGE OVER TROUBLED WATER.
Tracks: / Bridge over troubled water / Bridge over troubled water (Instr).
Single (12"): released on Joe Frazer, Jan'87 by Joe Frazer Records. Dist: Jetstar

CAN WE MAKE LOVE TONIGHT.
Tracks: / Can we make love tonight / Can we make love tonight (version).
Single (12"): released on Body Music, 20 Jun'87 by Body Music Records. Dist: Jetstar

HEY BABY.
Single (7"): released on Ethnic, Jun'83 Dist: Kingdom

HOW I WISH IT WAS YOU.
Single (12"): released on Three Kings, Dec'85 by Three Kings Records. Dist: Jetstar Distribution

HOW LONG WILL IT TAKE (EP).
Single 10": released on Pama Oldies, Jul'82

LET ME HAVE THE CHANCE.
Tracks: / Let me have the chance.
Single (7"): released on Germaine, Nov'86 by Germaine Records. Dist: Jetstar

LET'S GET MARRIED / MARRIED VERSION.
Single (12"): released on Lola, Jul'82

LOVE THE WAY IT SHOULD BE.
Single (12"): released on Fashion, Nov'85 by Fashion Records. Dist: PRT, Jetstar

ONE IN A MILLION.
Album: released on Skynote, Jul'84 by Skynote Records. Dist: Jetstar

ONE IN A MILLION GIRL.
Single (12"): released on Paradise, Apr'82 Dist: Jetstar, JSU, WEA

ONE YOU LOVE, THE.
Single (12"): released on Jedi, Jun'84 Dist: Jetstar

ORDINARY MAN.
Album: released on Body Music, Aug'87 by Body Music Records. Dist: Jetstar

Album: released on Body Music, Aug'87 by Body Music Records. Dist: Jetstar

PAT KELLY AND FRIENDS.
Album: released on Chanan-Jah, Oct'84 by Chanan-Jah Records. Dist: Jetstar

READY TO LOVE YOU AGAIN.
Single (12"): released on World Enterprise, Jul'84 Dist: Jetstar

ROCK ME TONIGHT.
Single (12"): released on Paradise, May'75 Dist: Jetstar, JSU, WEA

ROSIE.
Single (12"): released on Top Lady, Dec'84

SISTER LOVE.
Single (12"): released on Ethnic, Aug'84 Dist: Kingdom

SREVOL.
Album: released on Ethnic, May'84 Dist: Kingdom

STILL WATER.
Single (12"): released on Ethnic, Jul'83 Dist: Kingdom

TALK ABOUT LOVE / I'VE BEEN TRYING.
Single (12"): released on Skynote, Nov'83 Dist: Sidewak Records

YOU MUST BELIEVE / BELIEVE IN DUB.
Single (12"): released on Ethnic, Dec'83 Dist: Kingdom

Kelly, Peck

PECK KELLY JAM VOL 1.
Album: released on Commodore Class, Feb'84 by Teldec Records (Germany). Dist: Conifer, IMS, Polygram

PECK KELLY JAM VOL 2.
Album: released on Commodore Classics, Feb'84 by Teldec Records (Germany). Dist: Conifer, IMS, Polygram

Kelly Phil

PHIL KELLY SINGS.
Album: released on Nevis, May'77 Dist: H.R. Taylor

PHIL KELLY SINGS (VOLUME 2).
Album: released on Nevis, May'77 Dist: H.R. Taylor

Kelly, Wynton

IN CONCERT (Kelly, Wynton & George Coleman).
Album: released on Affinity, Feb'81 by Charly Records. Dist: Charly, Cadillac

KELLY BLUE.
Compact disc: released on JVC Fantasy (Japan), May'87

Compact disc: released on Carrere, Apr'87 by Carrere Records. Dist: PRT, Spartan

LIVE IN BALTIMORE (Kelly, Wynton & George Coleman).
Album: released on Affinity, Apr'84 by Charly Records. Dist: Charly, Cadillac

WRINKLES (Kelly, Wynton & Friends).
Tracks: / Wrinkles / Autumn leaves / Temperance / Make the man love me / Joe's avenue / What know / Weird lullaby / Love, I've found you / June night.
Notes: Licensed from Vee Jay Records. This compilation (P) 1986 Charly Records Ltd./ (C) 1986 Charly Records Ltd.
Album: released on Affinity, May'86 by Charly Records. Dist: Charly, Cadillac

WYNTON KELLY.
Notes: With Kenny Byrrell, Paul Chambers and Philly Joe Jones.
Compact disc: released on JVC Fantasy (Japan), '86

WYNTON KELLY WITH BURRELL/CHAMBERS/JONES.
Compact disc: released on Carrere, Apr'87 by Carrere Records. Dist: PRT, Spartan

Kelsall, Phil

AT THE WURLITZER ORGAN-BLACKPOOL.
Tracks: / Day trip to Bangor, A / Radetsky March / Ballade pour Adeline / Day trip to Bangor, A / Happy together / Welcome to my heart (la felicidad) / Theme From Dallas / Theme from Knots Landing / Whats another year / I'm in the mood for dancing / Xanadu / Copacabana / Copacabana (at the) / Pigalle / Domino / Under Paris skies / Manhattan / Theme from 'New York' 'New York' / 42nd Street / Give my regards to Broadway / Yesterday / With a little help from my friends / Ticket to ride / Sabre dance / Old rugged cross, The / Toreador's march / To a wild rose / Annen polka / Twelfth street rag / Chiquitita / I have a dream / Winner takes it all / Play off / Thank you for the music / Liberty bell (the Monty Python theme) / Hopelessly devoted to you / Star Trek / Happy days / Thomas and Sarah / Lillie / I'm in favour of friendship / Red roses for a blue lady / Oh lady be good / You're the one that I want / Summer nights / Strangers in the night / Night and day / Night Fever / Blackpool bounce / Poeme / Secret love / Love is the sweetest thing / Love is in the air / Heaven can wait / Borsalino / We're all alone / Raining in my heart / Bright eyes / Magic of Paris, The / Cielito lindo / I will survive / Carnival is over, The / Night fever.
Notes: This is a double album. Producer-Bob Barratt, Recording Engineer-Stuart Eltham, Location Engineer-Graham Kirkby.
Double Album: released on MFP, Mar'87 by EMI Records. Dist: EMI

Cassette: released on MFP, Mar'87 by EMI Records. Dist: EMI

BLACKPOOL DANCE PARTY (Tower Ballroom, Blackpool featuring Wurlitzer Organ).
Album: released on Note, Mar'83 by EMI Records. Dist: EMI

Cassette: released on Note, Mar'83 by EMI Records. Dist: EMI

FASCINATION RHYTHM.
Tracks: / Wonderful / I got rhythm, fascinating rhythm / I feel pretty/Maria/Somewhere/Tonight / Cavalleria Rusticana / Eastenders / Crossroads / Howards way / Walking in the air / Westminster waltz / Over the waves / Donauwellen / You'll never know / My very good friend the milkman / Bei mir bist du schon / Only love / I won't send roses/Look what happened to Mabel / Rilley, Ace of spies / Archill Island / Maple leaf rag / We all stand together / I just called to say I love you / Kiss waltz, The/Sealed with a kiss/A kiss in the dark / Little orphan Annie / Hot carary/Loves makes the world go round.
Notes: Phil Kelsall is the number one name on the Wurlitzer Organ at the Tower Ballroom-Blackpool (as Reg Dixon used to be). He plays there everyday during the season and holds the crown as the best theatre organist in Britain today. His annual album have always sold well. Interest in Phil Kelsall is not limited only to Blackpool - out of season he tours the country playing for various organ clubs. Plenty of rhythm to be heard and also the subtler sounds that the Wurlitzer can produce. Band up-to-date repertoire,'Only love' from 'Mistral's Daughter', for example, and 'Mack & Mabel'.
Album: released on Columbia, Apr'86 by EMI Records. Dist: EMI

Cassette: released on Columbia, Apr'86 by EMI Records. Dist: EMI

IT'S JUST THE TIME FOR DANCING.
Tracks: / Bewitched / Love in bloom / Someone to watch over me / Here's that rainy day / La Golondrina / Cherry pink and apple blossom white / Porfavor / Skater's waltz, The / Spanish gypsy dance / Nagasaki / Sweet Georgia Brown / Little red monkey / On the prom-prom-promenade / Consider yourself / Garden in the rain, A / Rose of Washington Square / I'll string along with you / Girl From Ipanema / Destination love / Pink lady, The / Paradise / Wyoming lullaby / Bless 'em all / Band played on, The / Ash grove, The / Tip toe through the tulips / I don't know why (I just do) / My mammy / Scotch mist / Garden in the rain, A / Rose of Washington Square / Girl from Ipanema / Paradise / La Cumparsita / Little white lies / Happy feel / It's just the time for dancing / Mr. Sandman / Avalon / Crazy rhythm / Am I wasting my time on you? / Pal of my cradle days / Answer me.
Notes: Produced by Bob Barratt. Recording engineer-Stuart Eltham. Recorded at the Tower Ballroom Blackpool, by courtesy of First Leisure Corp. plc.
Cassette: released on Grasmere, May'87 by Grasmere Records. Dist: EMI

Album: released on Grasmere, Apr'87 by Grasmere Records. Dist: EMI

I'VE HEARD THAT SONG BEFORE.
Album: released on Note, Feb'84 by EMI Records. Dist: EMI

Cassette: released on Note, Feb'84 by EMI Records. Dist: EMI

MEET ME AT THE TOWER.
Album: released on Note, Jul'82 by EMI Records. Dist: EMI

Cassette: released on Note, Jul'82 by EMI Records. Dist: EMI

PARTY DANCE NIGHT.
Album: released on EMI, Apr'85 by EMI Records. Dist: EMI

Cassette: released on EMI, Apr'85 by EMI Records. Dist: EMI

PHIL KELSALL'S BLACKPOOL SING-SONG.
Album: released on Note, May'80 by EMI Records. Dist: EMI

THANK YOU FOR THE MUSIC.
Album: released on One Up, Aug'84 by EMI Records.

Kelson, Ran

HUNGRY FOR BLOOD.
Album: released on Ebony, Mar'86 by Ebony Records. Dist: Pinnacle, Ebony

Kemp, Hal

BUNNY BERIGAN VOL 1.
Album: released on Shoestring, Sep'79 by Shoestring Records. Dist: Shoestring

Kempion

Brummagem ballads

KEMPION.
Album: released on Broadside, Jun'81 by Broadside Records. Dist: Celtic Distributions, H.R. Taylor, Jazz Music, Projection, Jazz Services Unlimited Dist. (JSU)

Cassette: released on Broadside, Jun'81 by Broadside Records. Dist: Celtic Distributions, H.R. Taylor, Jazz Music, Projection, Jazz Services Unlimited Dist. (JSU)

STEAM BALLADS.
Album: released on Broadside, Jun'81 by Broadside Records. Dist: Celtic Distributions, H.R. Taylor, Jazz Music, Projection, Jazz Services Unlimited Dist. (JSU)

Cassette: released on Broadside, Jun'81 by Broadside Records. Dist: Celtic Distributions, H.R. Taylor, Jazz Music, Projection, Jazz Services Unlimited Dist. (JSU)

Kendall-Lane, Stephen

GHOSTHUNTER, THE.
Album: released on Design, Jul'84 by Breakaway Records. Dist: PRT, Stage One

Cassette: released on Design, Jul'84 by Breakaway Records. Dist: PRT, Stage One

Kendalls

BEST COUNTRY DUO 1978.
Album: released on Gusto (USA), Jul'79 by Gusto Records (USA). Dist: Crusader

FIRE AT FIRST SIGHT.
Album: released on MCA, Mar'87 by MCA Records. Dist: Polygram, MCA

Cassette: released on MCA, Mar'87 by MCA Records. Dist: Polygram, MCA

MOVIN' TRAIN.
Album: released on Mercury (USA), Dec'83 by Import Records. Dist: IMS Distribution, Polygram Distribution

THANK GOD FOR THE RADIO.
Single (7"): released on Gull, Jun'85 by Gull Records. Dist: Pinnacle

Kendricks, Eddie

KEEP ON TRUCKIN'.
Single (7"): released on Motown, May'83 by Motown Records. Dist: BMG Distribution

KEEP ON TRUCKIN' (PARTS 1 & 2).
Single (7"): released on Motown, Oct'81 by Motown Records. Dist: BMG Distribution

LOVE KEYS.
Album: released on Atlantic, Jul'81 by WEA Records. Dist: WEA

Cassette: released on Atlantic, Mar'81 by WEA Records. Dist: WEA

Kendricks, Ken

FEELS SO GOOD.
Tracks: / Feels so good / Feels so good (Instrumental).
Single (12"): released on Elite, Apr'86 Dist: PRT

Kenia

INITIAL THRILL.
Tracks: / Brincadera / Initial thrill / Doce doce / Sim ou nao / Sina / Don't let me be lonely tonight / Cruisin' / Captivated / Missing you.
Album: released on MCA, Jun'87 by MCA Records. Dist: Polygram, MCA

Cassette: released on MCA, Jun'87 by MCA Records. Dist: Polygram, MCA

Compact disc: released on MCA, Jun'87 by MCA Records. Dist: Polygram, MCA

Kennaway, Jane

DON'T DO IT.
Single (7"): released on I.O.U, Nov'83 by I.O.U. Records. Dist: I.O.U. Distribution, Pinnacle

I'M MISSING YOU.
Single (7"): released on I.O.U, Jun'83 by I.O.U. Records. Dist: I.O.U. Distribution, Pinnacle

Kennedy, Calum

CALUM KENNEDY SHOW,THE.
Tracks: / Hiking song,The / Mairi's wedding / Barnyards of Delgaty / o bin I were a Baron's heir / Waters of Kylesku,The / Gypsy Rover,The / Westering home / Home to Scotland / Song of the Clyde / Donald's toosers / Top of Ben Nevis / Heres to the hills / Mouth Music / Loch Maree Islands / Dark lights of old Aberdeen / These are my mountains / Brochan Lom / Mhic Iarla / Those brown eyes / Roolin' in the heather / Scotland the brave.
Cassette: released on Highlander, Jun'86 Dist: PRT

LEGENDS OF SCOTLAND.
Tracks: / Here's to the hills / Mouth Music / Comin' thro the rye / My Bonnie lies over the ocean / Loch Lomond / Annie Laurie / Bluebells of Scotland / Gypsy Rover / Laird of Drumblair / Calum's Ceilidh / Campbelltown loch / Brochan loh / Dark Island / Bratach bana / Donald where's you troosers / Top of Ben Nevis / Amazing Grace / Five lovely lassies from Bannion / Muirsheen Durkin / Bonnie lass O'Fyvie / Bridal path,The / Scarborough fair / Eilean Fraoich / Caristiona / Dark Lochagar / Ae fond kiss / Bonnie Kyleswater / Leanabh og / O Bin I were a Baron's heir.
Cassette: released on Lochshore, Jun'86 by Klub Records. Dist: PRT

Kennedy, Douglas

DUCKS AND BETTY (Kennedy, Douglas & Helen).
Cassette: released on Folktracks, Nov'79 by Folktracks Cassettes. Dist: Folktracks

Kennedy, Gene

ABERDEEN (Kennedy, Gene (The Diver)).
Single (7"): released on Rig, Aug'83 by Rig Records. Dist: Fast

Kennedy, Grace

ALL I WANT IS YOU.
Single (7"): released on Red Bus, Jul'83 by Red Bus Records. Dist: PRT

ONE VOICE.
Album: released on BBC, Jul'81 by BBC Records & Tapes. Dist: EMI, PRT,

Cassette: released on BBC, Jul'81 by BBC Records & Tapes. Dist: EMI, PRT,

TAKE IT OR LEAVE IT.
Tracks: / Take it or leave it / Take it or leave it (instrumental).
Single (7"): released on Nightmare, Feb'87 by Nightmare Records. Dist: PRT

Single (12"): released on Nightmare, Feb'87 by Nightmare Records. Dist: PRT

Kennedy, Hal

BEST OF HAL KENNEDY, THE.
Album: released on Canaan(USA), May'82 by Word Records. Dist: Word Distribution

Cassette: released on Canaan(USA), May'82 by Word Records. Dist: Word Distribution

Kennedy, Jackie

UNDER MY SPELL.
Single (12"): released on Stripe Line, Aug'83

Kennedy, Jayne

LOVE YOUR BODY.
Album: released on Compleat, Aug'83 by Compleat Records. Dist: PRT

Kennedy, Nigel

LET LOOSE.
Tracks: / Let loose / Zigane / Emotion / Before it's time / Way we were, The / Killer instinct / Impro 1 / Drive / Way outside.
Album: released on Columbia, Jun'87 by EMI Records. Dist: EMI

Cassette: released on Columbia, Jun'87 by EMI Records. Dist: EMI

Compact disc: released on Columbia, Jun'87 by EMI Records. Dist: EMI

Compact disc: released on Columbia, Jun'87 by EMI Records. Dist: EMI

LET LOOSE.
Compact disc: released on EMI, Jun'87 by EMI Records. Dist: EMI

STRAD JAZZ (Kennedy, Nigel & Peter Pettinger).
Tracks: / Body and soul / Autumn leaves / Swing '39 / Isn't she lovely / Lover man / Girl from Ipanema,The.

Kennedy, Norman

SCOTS SONGS AND BALLADS.
Album: released on Topic, '81 by Topic Records. Dist: JSU Distribution, Projection Distribution, Jazz Music Distribution

Kennedy, Wayne

SOMEDAY SOMEWAY.
Single (7"): released on Lark, Jan'84 by Lark Records. Dist: PRT

Kenny

BUMP.
Tracks: / Bump / Fancy pants.
Notes: Also contains:"Fancy pants" by Kenny
Single (7"): released on Old Gold, Apr'87 by Old Gold Records. Dist: Lightning, Jazz Music, Spartan, Counterpoint

FANCY PANTS.
Tracks: / Fancy pants / Bump.
Notes: Also contains:"The Bump" by Kenny
Single (7"): released on Old Gold, Apr'87 by Old Gold Records. Dist: Lightning, Jazz Music, Spartan, Counterpoint

Kenny, Gerard

CITY LIVING.
Album: released on RCA, Oct'81 by RCA Records. Dist: RCA, Roots, Swift, Wellard, Chris, I & B, Solomon & Peres Distribution

Cassette: released on RCA, Oct'81 by RCA Records. Dist: RCA, Roots, Swift, Wellard, Chris, I & B, Solomon & Peres Distribution

I'VE GROWN ACCUSTOMED TO HER FACE.
Single (7"): released on Starblend, Jul'83 by Starblend Records. Dist: PRT Distribution

LIVING ON MUSIC.
Album: released on RCA, Oct'80 by RCA Records. Dist: RCA, Roots, Swift, Wellard, Chris, I & B, Solomon & Peres Distribution

Cassette: released on RCA, Oct'80 by RCA Records. Dist: RCA, Roots, Swift, Wellard, Chris, I & B, Solomon & Peres Distribution

MADE IT THROUGH THE RAIN.

Single (7"): released on Impression, Jan'85 Dist: CBS

MUSIC OF GERARD KENNY, THE.
Album: released on Impression, Nov'84 Dist: CBS

Cassette: released on Impression, Nov'84 Dist: CBS

NEW YORK, NEW YORK.
Single (7"): released on RCA, Sep'78 by RCA Records. Dist: RCA, Roots, Swift, Wellard, Chris, I & B, Solomon & Peres Distribution

OTHER WOMAN,THE OTHER MAN.
Single (7"): released on Impression, Jan'84 Dist: CBS

WORLD FULL OF LAUGHTER.
Single (7"): released on Impression, Oct'84 Dist: CBS

Kenny's Window

KENNY'S WINDOW Maurice Sendak (Grimes, Tammy).
Album: released on Caedmon(USA), '78 by Caedmon (USA) Records. Dist: Gower, Taylors, Discovery

Cassette: released on Caedmon(USA), '78 by Caedmon (USA) Records. Dist: Gower, Taylors, Discovery

Kent 50

KENT 50 Various artists (Various Artists).
Notes: Artists include: Bobby Sheen/Dean Parrish/Chuck Jackson/Danny Monday/Jackie Wilson/Patti Austin/Lada Edmund/Maxine Brown Band/Showmen/Ike & Tina Turner/ Young Holt Trio/Tommy Hunt/Impressions/O'Jays/Otis Rush/Irma Thomas.
Album: released on Kent, Feb'86 by Ace Records. Dist: Pinnacle

Kent, Alexander

RICHARD BOLITHO MIDSHIPMAN.
Notes: Read by Anthony Valentine
Double cassette: released on Listen For Pleasure, Aug'86 by MFP Records. Dist: EMI

Kentigern

KENTIGERN.
Album: released on Topic, '81 by Topic Records. Dist: JSU Distribution, Projection Distribution, Jazz Music Distribution

Kent, Luther

IT'S IN THE BAG (Kent, Luther & Trick Band).
Album: released on Enja (Germany), Nov'84 by Enja Records (W.Germany). Dist: Cadillac Music

Kenton All Stars

JAZZ OFF THE AIR, VOL.2.
Album: released on Spotlite, '83 by Spotlite Records. Dist: Cadillac, Jazz Music, Spotlite

Kenton, Jackie

HEARTBREAKER.
Single (12"): released on Nature, Mar'83 Dist: Jetstar

Kenton, Janet

GOLDEN TOUCH.
Tracks: / Golden Touch / Lovely Life.
Single (12"): by High Power Records. Dist: Jetstar Deleted Nov'86.

HONESTLY.
Single (12"): released on Techniques, Aug'87 Dist: Jetstar Distribution

Kenton, Stan

1944.
Album: released on Swinghouse, '84 Dist: Jazz Music Distribution, Swift Distribution, Chris Wellard Distribution

Cassette: released on Swinghouse, '84 Dist: Jazz Music Distribution, Swift Distribution, Chris Wellard Distribution

1951 (Kenton, Stan & His Orchestra).
Album: released on First Heard, Sep'83 by Submarine Records. Dist: Conifer, Taylors

1962,VO.6 (Kenton, Stan & His Orchestra).
Album: released on Hindsight(USA), Mar'84 by Hindsight Records (USA). Dist: Swift, Charly

7.5 ON THE RICHTER SCALE (Kenton, Stan & His Orchestra).
Album: released on Jasmine, May'85 by Jasmine Records. Dist: Counterpoint, Lugtons, Taylor, H.R., Wellard, Chris, Swift, Cadillac

ADVENTURES IN BLUES, 1961.
Album: released on Creative World (USA), '85 Dist: Taylors, Chris Wellard, Swift

ADVENTURES IN JAZZ.
Album: released on Creative World (USA), '85 Dist: Taylors, Chris Wellard, Swift

ADVENTURES IN STANDARDS, 1961.
Album: released on Creative World (USA), '85 Dist: Taylors, Chris Wellard, Swift

ARTISTRY IN BOSSA NOVA, 1963.
Album: released on Creative World (USA), '85 Dist: Taylors, Chris Wellard, Swift

ARTISTRY IN RHYTHM.
Album: released on Creative World (USA), '85 Dist: Taylors, Chris Wellard, Swift

ARTISTRY IN TANGO.
Album: released on Gramercy 5, Mar'79 by Gramercy 5 Records. Dist: Swift

ARTISTRY IN VOICES & BRASS.
Album: released on Creative World (USA), '85 Dist: Taylors, Chris Wellard, Swift

BALLAD STYLE OF STAN KENTON (THE).
Notes: A 12 track album featuring the famed style of Stan Kenton. Scored by the foremost exponent of the style, Kenton himself, the album displays his distinctive piano style cushioned by beautifully played brass and reed sections. Warm, rich arrangements of standards including "How Deep Is The Ocean", "Then I'll Be Tired Of You" and "The End Of A Love Affair". A twofold appeal, providing rich designs for dancing and music for lazy listening. [EMI release sheet, May 1987]
Cassette: released on Capitol, May'87 by Capitol Records. Dist: EMI

Album: released on Capitol, May'87 by Capitol Records. Dist: EMI

BEST OF BRANT INN.
Album: released on First Heard, '84 by Submarine Records. Dist: Conifer, Taylors

BEST OF BRANT INN, THE (Kenton, Stan & His Orchestra).
Tracks: / Piano theme into the waltz of the prophets / Intermission riff / Reuben's blues / Genghiz khan / Begin the beguine / Artistry in Bolero - bossa nova / Eager beaver......
Cassette: released on First Heard, May'87 by Submarine Records. Dist: Conifer, Taylors

CARNEGIE (Kenton, Stan & His Orchestra).
Album: released on First Heard, Apr'81 by Submarine Records. Dist: Conifer, Taylors

CHRISTY YEARS, THE (1945-7).
Album: released on Creative World (USA), '85 Dist: Taylors, Chris Wellard, Swift

CITY OF GLASS AND THIS MODERN WORLD, THE.
Album: released on Creative World (USA), '85 Dist: Taylors, Chris Wellard, Swift

COLLECTOR'S CHOICE.
Album: released on Creative World (USA), '85 Dist: Taylors, Chris Wellard, Swift

CONCEPT ERA '56',THE.
Album: released on Artistry, Sep'86 Dist: Jazz Music

CONCEPT ERA VOL.2,THE.
Album: released on Artistry, Sep'86 Dist: Jazz Music

CONCERT ENCORES.
Album: released on First Heard, '84 by Submarine Records. Dist: Conifer, Taylors

Cassette: released on First Heard, '84 by Submarine Records. Dist: Conifer, Taylors

CONCERT IN PROGRESSIVE JAZZ, A.
Album: released on Creed, '85 Dist: Swift

CONTEMPORARY CONCEPTS.
Album: released on Creative World (USA), '85 Dist: Taylors, Chris Wellard, Swift

CUBAN FIRE, 1956.
Album: released on Creative World (USA), '85 Dist: Taylors, Chris Wellard, Swift

DEFINITIVE KENTON,THE.
Double Album: released on Artistry, Sep'86 Dist: Jazz Music

ENCORES.
Album: released on Creative World (USA), '85 Dist: Taylors, Chris Wellard, Swift

EUROPE '53 PART 1'.
Tracks: / Young blood / Collaboration / Love for sale / Walking shoes / Opus in pastels / Zoot / Twenty three degrees north - Eighty two degrees west / Solitaire / Intermission riff / Lover man / In a lighter vein.
Album: released on First Heard, Nov'85 by Submarine Records. Dist: Conifer, Taylors

Cassette: released on First Heard, Nov'85 by Submarine Records. Dist: Conifer, Taylors

Album: released on First Heard, Oct'84 by Submarine Records. Dist: Conifer, Taylors

Cassette: released on First Heard, Oct'84 by Submarine Records. Dist: Conifer, Taylors

EUROPE '53 PART 2'.
Tracks: / Portrait of a Count / Round Robin / Eager beaver / Frank speaking / Taboo / Taking a chance in love / I'll remember April / Great scott / My heart belongs to only you / How high the moon / Something cool / Concerto to end all concerto's.
Album: released on First Heard, Nov'85 by Submarine Records. Dist: Conifer, Taylors

Cassette: released on First Heard, Nov'85 by Submarine Records. Dist: Conifer, Taylors

FABULOUS ALUMNI OF STAN KENTON, THE.
Album: released on Creative World (USA), '85 Dist: Taylors, Chris Wellard, Swift

HOLLYWOOD BOWL, PART 1 (Kenton, Stan & June Christy).

HOLLYWOOD PALLADIUM CONCERTS 1944, THE.
Album: released on Queendisc (Import), '81 Dist: Cadillac

INNOVATIONS IN MODERN MUSIC, 1950.
Album: released on Creative World (USA), '85 Dist: Taylors, Chris Wellard, Swift

JAZZ COMPOSITIONS OF DEE BARTON, THE.
Album: released on Creative World, Apr'79 Dist: Taylors, Chris Wellard, Swift

KENTON AT THE TROPICANA.
Album: released on Creative World (USA), '85 Dist: Taylors, Chris Wellard, Swift

KENTON CONDUCTS THE JAZZ COMPOSTION OF DEE BARTON.
Album: released on Creative World (USA), '85 Dist: Taylors, Chris Wellard, Swift

KENTON IN CONCERT.
Notes: Live at the Albert Hall, London, 1956.
Double Album: released on Artistry, Sep'86 Dist: Jazz Music

KENTON IN STEREO.
Album: released on Creative World (USA), '85 Dist: Taylors, Chris Wellard, Swift

KENTON LIVE IN EUROPE.
Tracks: / Lush Life / Love for Sale / Turtle talk / My Old Flame / Tattooed Lady / I'm Glad There is You / Fire and Ice / Eager Beaver / Artistry in Rhythm.
Compact disc: released on London, Jan'86 by London Records. Dist: Polygram

KENTON PRESENTS, 1950.
Album: released on Creative World (USA), '85 Dist: Taylors, Chris Wellard, Swift

KENTON'S CHRISTMAS.
Album: released on Creative World (USA), '85 Dist: Taylors, Chris Wellard, Swift

KENTON SHOWCASE, 1953-4.
Album: released on Creative World (USA), '85 Dist: Taylors, Chris Wellard, Swift

KENTON TOUCH, 1958.
Album: released on Creative World (USA), '85 Dist: Taylors, Chris Wellard, Swift

KENTON/WAGNER, 1964.
Album: released on Creative World (USA), '85 Dist: Taylors, Chris Wellard, Swift

LIGHTER SIDE, THE.
Album: released on Creative World (USA), '85 Dist: Taylors, Chris Wellard, Swift

LIVE.
Album: released on Queen-Disc, Aug'81 Dist: Celtic Music, JSU, Jazz Horizons, Jazz Music

LIVE AT BRIGHAM YOUNG UNIVERSITY.
Album: released on Creed, '85 Dist: Swift

LIVE AT REDLANDS UNIVERSITY (Kenton, Stan & His Orchestra).
Album: released on Jasmine, '85 by Jasmine Records. Dist: Counterpoint, Lugtons, Taylor, H.R., Wellard, Chris, Swift, Cadillac

LIVE AT REDLANDS UNIVERSITY.
Album: released on Creative World (USA), '85 Dist: Taylors, Chris Wellard, Swift

LUSH INTERLUDE, 1958.
Album: Dist: Taylors, Chris Wellard, Swift

NEW CONCEPTS OF ARTISTRY IN RHYTHM (Kenton, Stan & His Orchestra).
Album: released on Capitol, Jul'85 by Capitol Records. Dist: EMI

Cassette: released on Capitol, Jul'85 by Capitol Records. Dist: EMI

Album: released on Creative World (USA), '85 Dist: Taylors, Chris Wellard, Swift

ONE NIGHT STAND WITH STAN KENTON.
Album: released on Joyce (USA), May'84 Dist: Swift

ON THE ROAD (Kenton, Stan & His Orchestra).
Album: released on Artistry, Sep'86 Dist: Jazz Music

PORTAITS ON STANDARDS, 1951-3.
Album: released on Creative World (USA), '85 Dist: Taylors, Chris Wellard, Swift

PROGRESSIVE JAZZ.
Album: released on Swing House (UK), Apr'85

Album: released on Swing House (UK), Apr'85

REISSUED COLLECTORS-THE KENTON ERA.
Album: released on Creative World (USA), '85 Dist: Taylors, Chris Wellard, Swift

RENDEZ-VOUS WITH KENTON.
Cassette:

Cassette: by Capitol (USA) Records. Dist: EMI

ROAD SHOW, THE (VOL.1).
Album: released on Creative World (USA), '85 Dist: Taylors, Chris Wellard, Swift

ROAD SHOW, THE (VOL.2).
Album: released on Creative World (USA), '85 Dist: Taylors, Chris Wellard, Swift

ROMANTIC APPROACH, THE.
Album: released on Creative World (USA), '85 Dist: Taylors, Chris Wellard, Swift

SKETCHES ON STANDARDS, 1953-4.
Album: released on Creative World (USA), '85 Dist: Taylors, Chris Wellard, Swift

SOME WOMEN I'VE KNOWN, 1944-5.
Album: released on Creative World (USA), '85 Dist: Taylors, Chris Wellard, Swift

SOPHISTICATED APPROACH.
Album: released on Creative World (USA), '85 Dist: Taylors, Chris Wellard, Swift

SOUND OF 62.
Album: released on First Heard, '84 by Submarine Records. Dist: Conifer, Taylors

STAGE DOOR SWINGS (Kenton, Stan & His Orchestra).
Tracks: / Lullaby of Broadway / Party's over,The / Baubles, bangles, and beads / Ev'ry time we say goodbye / Whatever Lola wants / Bali ha'i / Hey there / Younger than springtime / On the street where you live / I love Paris / All at once you love her / I've never been in love before.
Notes: Track 1 B.Feldman & Co/EMI Music Publ:/ Track 2 Startford Music Ltd./ Tracks 3,410,11: Chappell Music/ Tracks 5,7: CBS Songs Ltd./ Tracks6,8,9, Williamson Music/ Track 12,- Anglo Pic. Ltd: Tracks 1-6 Total Time 15.56/ Tracks 7-12 Total Time 15.48:
Album: released on Capitol, Jun'86 by Capitol Records. Dist: EMI

Cassette: released on Capitol, Jun'86 by Capitol Records. Dist: EMI

STAGE DOOR SWINGS, 1958.
Album: released on Creative World (USA), '85 Dist: Taylors, Chris Wellard, Swift

STANDARDS IN SILHOUETTE, 1959.
Album: released on Creative World (USA), '85 Dist: Taylors, Chris Wellard, Swift

STAN KENTON.
Compact disc: released on Deja Vu, Jan'86 by Deja Vu Records. Dist: Counterpoint Distribution, Record Services Distribution (Ireland)

Cassette: released on Deja Vu, Jan'86 by Deja Vu Records. Dist: Counterpoint Distribution, Record Services Distribution (Ireland)

Album: released on Bright Orange, Apr'79 Dist: Swift

STAN KENTON CONDUCTS THE LOS ANGELES.
Album: released on Creative World (USA), '85 Dist: Taylors, Chris Wellard, Swift

STAN KENTON IN HI FI.
Tracks: / Artistry jumps / Interlude / Intermission riff / Minor riff / Collaboration / Painted rhythm / Southern scandal / Peanut vendor,The / Eager Beaver / Concero to end all concertos / Artistry in boogie / lover / Unison riff.
Notes: Stan Kenton originally made recordings for Capitol Records in the 40's. This album highlighting the important segment of Stan Kenton's career during the postwar years, is made up of his original hits re-recorded in Hi-Fi in the

mid 50's.Including the well known 'Peanut Vendor' tune.
Album: released on Capitol, Jan'86 by Capitol Records. Dist: EMI

Cassette: released on Capitol, Jan'86 by Capitol Records. Dist: EMI

STAN KENTON/JEAN TURNER, 1963.
Album: released on Creative World (USA), '85 Dist: Taylors, Chris Wellard, Swift

STAN KENTONS GREATEST HITS.
Album: released on Music For Pleasure (Holland), Apr'83 by EMI Records. Dist: EMI

Cassette: released on Music For Pleasure (Holland), Apr'83 by EMI Records. Dist: EMI

TOGETHER AGAIN (Kenton, Stan & June Christy).
Album: released on Swinghouse, Oct'84 Dist: Jazz Music Distribution, Swift Distribution, Chris Wellard Distribution

Cassette: released on Swinghouse, Oct'84 Dist: Jazz Music Distribution, Swift Distribution, Chris Wellard Distribution

UNCOLLECTED STAN KENTON & HIS ORCHESTRA, THE.
Album: released on Hindsight(UK), May'79 Dist: Jazz Music

UNCOLLECTED,THE.
Album: released on Hindsight(UK), Apr'86 Dist: Jazz Music

Album: released on Hindsight(UK), Jun'85 Dist: Jazz Music

VOLUME II (1953-60).
Album: released on Creative World (USA), '85 Dist: Taylors, Chris Wellard, Swift

WEST SIDE STORY.
Album: released on Creed, '85 Dist: Swift

Kent Stop Dancing
KENT STOP DANCING various artists (Various Artists).
Album: released on Kent, Nov'84 by Ace Records. Dist: Pinnacle

KENT STOP DANCING-THE SEQUEL Compilation recording (Various Artists).
Notes: The follow up to "Kent Stop Dancing" (KENT 029). Features classic soul tracks from:The Snowmen,The Moving Sidewalks,The Knickerbockers, Ike & Tina Turner,Jackie Wilson,Timmy Shaw,The Platters,Johnny Williams Jr. etc.etc.
Album: released on Kent, Mar'87 by Ace Records. Dist: Pinnacle

Kent, Tommy
SUSIE DARLIN'.
Album: released on Polydor, Oct'80 by Polydor Records. Dist: Polygram, Polydor

Kentuck Country
KENTUCK COUNTRY various old time artists (Various Artists).
Album: released on Rounder (USA), Jan'84 Dist: Mike's Country Music Room Distribution, Jazz Music Distribution, Swift Distribution, Roots Records Distribution, Projection Distribution, Topic Distribution

Kentucky...
KENTUCKY FIDDLE BAND MUSIC various artists (Various Artists).
Album: released on Morning Star, '82 Dist: Projection Distribution

KENTUCKY ROCKABILLY various artists (Various Artists).

Kentucky Colonels
1966.
Album: released on Shiloh, May'79

NEW SOUND OF BLUEGRASS AMERICA, THE.
Album: released on Briar (USA), Apr'79 by Sierra Records. Dist: Mike's Country Music Room Distribution, Projection

ON STAGE.
Album: released on Rounder (USA), Jul'84 Dist: Mike's Country Music Room Distribution, Jazz Music Distribution, Swift Distribution, Roots Records Distribution, Projection Distribution, Topic Distribution

Kentucky County
BACK HOME AGAIN.
Album: released on Buffalo (UK), Mar'79

Kentucky Rock-A-Billy
KENTUCKY ROCK-A-BILLY Various artists (Various Artists).
Album: released on White, Feb'87

Album: released on White, Jul'79

Kenworthy Scofield
PIPE AND TABAR Moris, sword, etc, dances.
Cassette: released on Folktracks, Nov'79 Dist: Roots

Kenya
MWANA WAMBELE.
Album: released on Orchid, Jan'85 Dist: Impetus Distribution, Orchid

ROOTS. AFRICAN DRUMS (Kenya: National Dancing Team).
Album: released on Denon, Mar'82 by Denon Records. Dist: Harmonia Mundi

Kenya Partout
KENYA PARTOUT, VOL.1 various orchestras (Various Orchestras).
Album: released on Plaza, '74 by Plaza Records. Dist: Spartan

KENYA PARTOUT, VOL.2 various orchestras (Various Orchestras).
Album: released on Playasound, '74 Dist: Conifer, Discovery

KENYA PARTOUT, VOL.3 various orchestras (Various Orchestras).
Album: Dist: Conifer, Discovery

KENYA PARTOUT, VOL.4 various orchestras (Various Orchestras).
Album:

Kenyon, Carol
DANCE WITH ME.
Single (7"): released on A&M, May'84 by A&M Records. Dist: Polygram

GIVE ME ONE GOOD REASON.
Tracks: / Give me one good reason / Give me one good reason (inst).
Single (7"): released on Chrysalis, 23 May'87 by Chrysalis Records. Dist: CBS

Single (12"): released on Chrysalis, 23 May'87 by Chrysalis Records. Dist: CBS

Keogh, Paul
FROM THE GUITAR MAN WITH LOVE.
Album: released on Nouveau Music, '83 Dist: PRT Distribution

Cassette: released on Nouveau Music, '83 Dist: PRT Distribution

Kerner, Julia Ann
IT'S CHRISTMAS ALL OVER THE WORLD.
Tracks: / It's Christmas all over the world / Ooh it's Christmas.

Kern goes to Hollywood
KERN GOES TO HOLLYWOOD Original cast recording (Various Artists).
Album: released on Safari, Aug'85 by Safari Records. Dist: Pinnacle

Cassette: released on Safari, Aug'85 by Safari Records. Dist: Pinnacle

Kern, Jerome
ALL THE THINGS YOU ARE.
Album: released on Monmouth, Mar'79

GOLDEN AGE OF JEROME KERN, THE various Artists (Various Artists).
Album: released on Golden Age, Apr'85 by Music For Pleasure Records. Dist: EMI

JEROME KERN CENTENARY various artists (Various Artists).

Kerr
BACK AT YA.
Single (12"): released on Greyhound, Mar'84 by Greyhound Records. Dist: PRT, Greyhound

Kerrang Compilation
KERRANG COMPILATION Various artists (Various Artists).
Notes: Number of tracks: 20. Type of recordings: Compilation. Total playing time: 88 minutes.
Video-cassette (VHS): by PMI Records. Dist: EMI

Video-cassette [Betamax]: by PMI Records. Dist: EMI

Kerrang Kompilation
KERRANG KOMPILATION Various artists (Various Artists).
Album: released on Virgin-EMI, Jun'85 by EMI Records. Dist: EMI

Cassette: released on Virgin-EMI, Jun'85 by

EMI Records. Dist: EMI

Kerr, Bob Whoopee Band
BLUES JAZZ BOOGIE & RAGS.
Album: released on Whoopee, Jan'82 by Whoopee Records. Dist: Whoopee Records, Waterfront Records, Jazz Music, JSU, Chris

HARD PRESSED.
Album: released on Whoopee, Jan'82 by Whoopee Records. Dist: Whoopee Records, Waterfront Records, Jazz Music, JSU, Chris

REMEMBER REMEMBER/PLEASANT.
Single (7"): released on Whoopee, Oct'81 by Whoopee Records. Dist: Whoopee Records, Waterfront Records, Jazz Music, JSU, Chris

TAP DANCE MAN/5000 YEAR OLD ROCK (EP).
Single (7"): released on Whoopee, May'79 by Whoopee Records. Dist: Whoopee Records, Waterfront Records, Jazz Music, JSU, Chris

THINGS THAT GO BUMP IN THE NIGHT.
Album: released on Whoopee, Jan'82 by Whoopee Records. Dist: Whoopee Records, Waterfront Records, Jazz Music, JSU, Chris

WHOOPEE BAND, THE.
Album: released on Whoopee, Jan'82 by Whoopee Records. Dist: Whoopee Records, Waterfront Records, Jazz Music, JSU, Chris

Kerri & Mick
SONS & DAUGHTERS.
Single (7"): released on AI, Apr'84

Kerr, John
JOHN KERRS ISLAND.
Album: released on Harp(Ireland), Jul'81 by Pickwick Records. Dist: Taylors

MEMORIES OF ISLAND.
Album: released on Homespun(Ireland), Nov'84 by Outlet Records. Dist: Outlet

Cassette: released on Homespun(Ireland), Nov'84 by Outlet Records. Dist: Outlet

MY GREEN VALLEYS.
Cassette: released on Homespun(Ireland), Feb'79 by Outlet Records. Dist: Outlet

THREE LEAFED SHAMROCK.
Tracks: / Someone thinks of you to-night / Tree leaves of emerald green / Mulroy bay / Cork hornpipe,The / Boys of Bluehill / Mick McGilligan's daughter / Road to Creeslough / Father O'Flynn / Three leafed shamrock / Golden jubilee / Farewell Donegal / Goodbye Mick, goodbye Pat.
Album: released on Golden Guinea, Aug'86 by PRT Records. Dist: PRT

Kerr, Moira
BEST OF BOTH WORLDS, THE.
Album: released on Ross, '86 by Ross Records. Dist: Ross Distribution, Roots Distribution

Cassette: released on Ross, '86 by Ross Records. Dist: Ross Distribution, Roots Distribution

MINGULAY BOAT SONG/THE WATER IS WIDE.
Single (7"): released on Mayker, Nov'83

Kerry Fiddles
MUSIC FROM SLIABAH LUCHRA VOL 1.
Album: released on Topic, Jan'81 by Roots Distribution

Kerry, Pat
WON'T YOU BE THERE.
Single (7"): released on Keswick, Jan'81 by Loose Records. Dist: Pinnacle

Kershaw, Martin
DANCE OF THE MAGPIES.
Single (7"): released on Solid, Mar'85 by Solid Records. Dist: Graduate, Spartan

SOLITUDE.
Album: released on Solid Gold, Mar'85 Dist: MCA

Cassette: released on Solid Gold, Mar'85 Dist: MCA

Kershaw, Mary
LANCASHIRE SINGS AGAIN (Kershaw, Mary & Harvey).
Album: released on Topic, Jan'81 Dist: Roots Distribution

Kershaw, Nik
DANCIN GIRLS.

Single (7"):

Single (12"):

Picture disc single:

DON QUIXOTE.
Single (7"): released on MCA, Aug'85 by MCA Records. Dist: Polygram, MCA

Picture disc single: released on MCA, Aug'85 by MCA Records. Dist: Polygram, MCA

Single (12"): released on MCA, Aug'85 by MCA Records. Dist: Polygram, MCA

HUMAN RACING.
Tracks: / Dancing girls / Wouldn't it be good / Drum talk / Bogart / Gone to pieces / Shame on you / Cloak and dagger / Faces / I won't let the sun go down on me / Human racing.
Compact disc: released on MCA, Jan'85 by MCA Records. Dist: Polygram, MCA

Album: released on MCA, Feb'84 by MCA Records. Dist: Polygram, MCA

Cassette: released on MCA, Feb'84 by MCA Records. Dist: Polygram, MCA

Compact disc: released on MCA, Feb'84 by MCA Records. Dist: Polygram, MCA

Single (7"): released on MCA, Sep'84 by MCA Records. Dist: Polygram, MCA

Single (12"): released on MCA, Sep'84 by MCA Records. Dist: Polygram, MCA

Special: released on MCA, Sep'84 by MCA Records. Dist: Polygram, MCA

Picture disc single: released on MCA, Sep'84 by MCA Records. Dist: Polygram, MCA

Single (12"): released on MCA, Sep'84 by MCA Records. Dist: Polygram, MCA

HUMAN RACING.

I WON'T LET THE SUN GO DOWN ON ME.
Single (7"): released on MCA, Sep'83 by MCA Records. Dist: Polygram, MCA

NOBODY KNOWS.
Tracks: / Nobody knows / One of our fruit machines is missing.
Single (7"): released on MCA, Sep'86 by MCA Records. Dist: Polygram, MCA

Single (12"): released on MCA, Sep'86 by MCA Records. Dist: Polygram, MCA

RADIO MUSICOLA.
Album: released on MCA, Oct'86 by MCA Records. Dist: Polygram, MCA

Cassette: by MCA Records. Dist: Polygram, MCA

Compact disc: released on MCA, Dec'86 by MCA Records. Dist: Polygram, MCA

RADIO MUSICOLA (PICTURE DISC).
Picture disc single: released on MCA, Dec'86 by MCA Records. Dist: Polygram, MCA

RIDDLE.
Single (7"): released on MCA, Nov'84 by MCA Records. Dist: Polygram, MCA

Cassette: released on MCA, Dec'84 by MCA Records. Dist: Polygram, MCA

RIDDLE,THE.
Tracks: / Don Quixote / Know how / You might / Wild horses / Easy / Riddle,The / City of angels / Roses / Wide boy / Save the whale.
Compact disc: released on MCA, Jan'85 by MCA Records. Dist: Polygram, MCA

RIDDLE, THE.
Album: released on MCA, Nov'84 by MCA Records. Dist: Polygram, MCA

Cassette: released on MCA, Nov'84 by MCA Records. Dist: Polygram, MCA

Single (12"): released on MCA, Oct'84 by MCA Records. Dist: Polygram, MCA

Single (12"): released on MCA, Oct'84 by MCA Records. Dist: Polygram, MCA

SINGLE PICTURES.
Notes: Video EP with the promos for 'Wouldn't it be good', 'Dancing girls', and 'Don't let the sun go down on me', plus a live 'Human Racing' from Hammersmith. Number of tracks: 3. Type of recording: EP. Total Playing time: 20 minutes.
Video-cassette (VHS): released on CIC Video, Sep'84 by CBS Records. Dist: CBS, Pickwick Distribution

WHEN A HEART BEATS.
Single (7"): released on MCA, Nov'85 by MCA Records. Dist: Polygram, MCA

Single (12"): released on MCA, Nov'85 by MCA Records. Dist: Polygram, MCA

WIDE BOY.
Single (7"): released on MCA, Feb'85 by MCA Records. Dist: Polygram, MCA

Single (12"): released on MCA, Feb'85 by MCA Records. Dist: Polygram, MCA

WOULDN'T IT BE GOOD/MONKEY BUSINESS.
Single (7"): released on MCA, Jan'84 by MCA Records. Dist: Polygram, MCA

Single (12"): released on MCA, Jan'84 by MCA Records. Dist: Polygram, MCA

Kershaw, Rusty
CAJUN COUNTRY ROCKERS (VOLUME 3), THE (Kershaw, Rusty & Doug).
Album: released on Hockory, Sep'84 by Bear Family Records. Dist: Rollercoaster Distribution, Swift

LOUISIANNA MAN (Kershaw, Rusty & Doug).
Album: released on Sundown, Jul'85 by Magnum Music Group Ltd. Dist: Magnum Music Group Ltd, PRT Distribution, Spartan Distribution

MORE CAJUN COUNTRY ROCK (Kershaw, Rusty & Doug).
Album: released on Bear Family, Nov'84 by Bear Family Records. Dist: Rollercoaster Distribution, Swift

RUSTY & DOUG KERSHAW (Kershaw, Rusty & Doug).
Album: released on Flyright, Oct'86 by Flyright Records. Dist: Krazy Kat, Swift, Jazz Music

Kes
BARRY HINES.
Cassette: released on Listen For Pleasure, May'80 by MFP Records. Dist: EMI

HAYLEY'S EYES.
Single (7"): released on Plaza, Oct'85 by Plaza Records. Dist: Spartan

SOMEWHERE IN THE NIGHT.
Tracks: / Hayley's eyes / Somewhere in the night / Bird of prey.
Single (7"): released on Plaza, Jan'87 by Plaza Records. Dist: Spartan

Single (12"): released on Plaza, Feb'87 by Plaza Records. Dist: Spartan

Kesey, Ken
ONE FLEW OVER THE CUCKOO'S NEST.
Notes: Read by Michael Moriarty. Running time: 2 hours approx. Double cassette. Chief Bromden, a huge half-breed American Indian, whom the authorities believe is deaf and dumb, tells the story of a mental institution ruled by the formid- able Big Nurse. Into this terrifying grey world comes R.P. McMurphu, a brawling gambling man who wages total war on behalf of his cowed fellow inmates.
Double cassette: released on Listen For Pleasure, Sep'86 by MFP Records. Dist: EMI

Kessel, Barney
ARTISTRY OF BARNEY KESSEL, THE.
Compact disc: released on Fantasy (USA), Apr'87 by Fantasy Inc USA Records. Dist: IMS, Polygram

BLUE SOUL.
Album: released on Black Lion, Sep'85 by Black Lion Records. Dist: Jazz Music, Chris Wellard, Taylor, H.R., Counterpoint, Cadillac

EXPLORING THE SCENE (Kessel, Barney, Ray Brown, Shelley Manne).
Album: by Contemporary Records. Dist: Pinnacle

GREAT GUITARS AT CHARLIES GEORGETOWN (Kessel, Barney, Charlie Byrd, Herb Ellis).
Album: released on Concord Jazz, Apr'83 by Concord Jazz Records (USA). Dist: IMS, Polygram

Compact disc: released on Concord Jazz, Apr'83 by Concord Jazz Records (USA). Dist: IMS, Polygram

Cassette: released on Concord Jazz, Apr'83 by Concord Jazz Records (USA). Dist: IMS, Polygram

GREAT GUITARS AT THE WINERY (Kessel, Barney, Charlie Byrd, Herb Ellis).
Album: released on Concord Jazz, Nov'90 by Concord Jazz Records (USA). Dist: IMS, Polygram

IN CONCERT.
Compact disc: released on The Compact Collection, Sep'87 by Conifer Records. Dist: Conifer Distribution

JELLY BEANS (Kessel, Barney Trio).
Album: released on Concord, Dec'81 by Import

Records. Dist: IMS, Polygram

LET'S COOK.
Album: released on Contemporary, Jun'86 by Contemporary Records. Dist: Pinnacle

LIMEHOUSE BLUES (Kessel, Barney/Stephane Grappelli).
Album: released on Black Lion, Apr'85 by Black Lion Records. Dist: Jazz Music, Chris Wellard, Taylor, H.R., Counterpoint, Cadillac

PLAYS STANDARDS.
Compact disc: released on Carrere, Apr'87 by Carrere Records. Dist: PRT, Spartan

POLL WINNERS RIDE AGAIN, THE.
Compact disc: released on JVC Fantasy (Japan), May'87

SOLO.
Album: released on Concord Jazz, Oct'83 by Concord Jazz Records (USA). Dist: IMS, Polygram

SUMMERTIME IN MONTREUX.
Album: released on Black Lion, Sep'85 by Black Lion Records. Dist: Jazz Music, Chris Wellard, Taylor, H.R., Counterpoint, Cadillac

SWINGIN EASY.
Album: released on Black Lion, Jan'85 by Black Lion Records. Dist: Jazz Music, Chris Wellard, Taylor, H.R., Counterpoint, Cadillac

TO SWING OR NOT TO SWING.
Compact disc: released on JVC Fantasy (Japan), May'87

TWO WAY CONVERSATION (Kessel, Barney & Red Mitchell).
Album: released on Sonet, Mar'75 by Sonet Records. Dist: PRT

Kestral Kate
S.O.S.
Single (7"): released on Anderburr, Oct'84 by Anderburr. Dist: FRT

Cassette: released on Anderburr, Oct'84 by Anderburr. Dist: PRT

Ketcham, Charles
4 ALFRED HITCOCK FILMS (Ketcham, Charles & Utah Symphony Orchestra).
Album: released on TER, Sep'86 Dist: Pinnacle

Kevie Kev
ALL NIGHT LONG (WATERBED)/SWEET STUFF.
Single (12"): released on Sugar Hill USA, Dec'83 by MCA Records. Dist: Roots Distribution, Mike's Country Music Room Distribution, Projection Distribution, PRT Distribution

Kevin & The press gang
LOT TO LEARN/THATS HOW IT FEELS.
Single (7"): released on Posh, Aug'83 by Posh Records. Dist: Pinnacle

Kewi University Of Swing
BIGGLES/NURSE.
Single (7"): released on Idiot, Jul'83 by WEA Records. Dist: WEA

Key Of Dreams
AFRICA / SYNTHA JOY.
Single (7"): released on Baby, Feb'83 by New Rose Records. Dist: Cartel

Single (12"): released on Baby, Feb'83 by New Rose Records. Dist: Cartel

Keys Of Life
KEYS OF LIFE (Various Artists).
Album: released on Celestial Harmonies, Apr'87 by TM Records. Dist: PRT

Cassette: released on Celestial Harmonies, Apr'87 by TM Records. Dist: PRT

Compact disc: released on Celestial Harmonies, Jun'87 by TM Records. Dist: PRT

Keystones
WHITE CHRISTMAS.
Single (7"): released on Red Sky, Dec'84 by Red Sky Records. Dist: Red Sky, Projection, Celtic Music, Roots

Key, Troyce
I GOTTA NEW CAR (Key, Troyce & J.J Malone & The Rhythm Rockers).
Single (7"): released on Pinnacle, May'81 by Pinnacle Records. Dist: Pinnacle

I'VE GOTTA A NEW CAR (Key, Troyce & J.J Malone & The Rhythm Rockers).

YOUNGER THAN YESTERDAY (Key, Troyce & J.J Malone & The Rhythm Rockers).
Album: released on Red Lightnin', Nov'82 by Red Lightnin' Records. Dist: Roots, Swift, Jazz Music, JSU, Pinnacle, Cartel, Wynd-Up Distribution

Key West
FIRST INVASION.
Cassette: released on Mausoleum, May'84 by Mausoleum Records. Dist: Pinnacle

Khaled, Cheb
HADA RAYKOUM.
Album: released on Triple Earth, Nov'86 by Sterns Records. Dist: Sterns/Triple Earth Distribution

Khan, Amjad Ali
GULDASTA-E-RAGA.
Album: released on Gramophone Co. of India, Feb'84 by Gramophone Company Of India, UK Branch. Dist: EMI, Sterns, Triple Earth

Khan, Chaka
DESTINY.
Tracks: / Love a lifetime / Earth to Mickey / Watching the world / Other side of the world / My destiny / I can't be loved / It's you / So close / Tight fit / Who's it gonna be / Coltrane dreams.
Album: released on Warner Bros., Jul'86 by Warner Bros Records. Dist: WEA

Cassette: released on Warner Bros., Jul'86 by Warner Bros Records. Dist: WEA

Compact disc: released on Warner Bros., Jul'86 by Warner Bros Records. Dist: WEA

GOT TO BE THERE/PASS IT ON.
Single (7"): released on Warner Bros., Nov'82 by Warner Bros Records. Dist: WEA

I FEEL FOR YOU.
Tracks: / This si my night / Stonger tham before / My love is alive / Eye to eye / La flamme / I feel for you / Hold her / Through the fire / Caught in the act / Chinatown / This is my night / Stronger than before.
Compact disc: released on Warner Bros., Nov'84 by Warner Bros Records. Dist: WEA

Album: released on Warner Bros., Oct'84 by Warner Bros Records. Dist: WEA

Single (7"): released on Warner Bros., Oct'84 by Warner Bros Records. Dist: WEA

Single (12"): released on Warner Bros., Oct'85 by Warner Bros Records. Dist: WEA

KRUSH GROOVE (CAN'T STOP THE STREET).
Single (7"): released on Warner Bros., Sep'85 by Warner Bros Records. Dist: WEA

Single (12"): released on Warner Bros., Sep'85 by Warner Bros Records. Dist: WEA

LOVE OF A LIFETIME.
Tracks: / Love of a lifetime / Coltrane dreams.
Single (7"): released on Warner Bros., Jun'86 by Warner Bros Records. Dist: WEA

Single (12"): released on Warner Bros., Jun'86 by Warner Bros Records. Dist: WEA

NAUGHTY.
Album: released on Warner Brothers, Jan'80 by Warner Bros Records. Dist: WEA

Cassette: released on Warner Bros., Jun'80 by Warner Bros Records. Dist: WEA

THIS IS MY NIGHT.
Compact disc: released on Warner Bros., Feb'85 by Warner Bros Records. Dist: WEA

Single (7"): released on Warner Bros., Jan'85 by Warner Bros Records. Dist: WEA

Single (12"): released on Warner Bros., Jan'85 by Warner Bros Records. Dist: WEA

THROUGH THE FIRE.
Single (7"): released on Warner Bros., Aug'85 by Warner Bros Records. Dist: WEA

Single (12"): released on Warner Bros., Aug'85 by Warner Bros Records. Dist: WEA

WATCHING THE WORLD.
Tracks: / Watching the world / I can't be loved.
Single (7"): released on Warner Bros., Nov'86 by Warner Bros Records. Dist: WEA

Single (12"): released on Warner Bros., Nov'86 by Warner Bros Records. Dist: WEA

WHAT CHA GONNA DO FOR ME.

Album: released on Warner Brothers, Apr'81 by Warner Bros Records. Dist: WEA

Khan, Rufus & Chaka
AIN'T NOBODY/STOP ON BY/DON'T GO TO STRANGERS.
Single (7"): released on Warner Bros., Nov'83 by Warner Bros Records. Dist: WEA

Single (12"): released on Warner Bros., Nov'83 by Warner Bros Records. Dist: WEA

STOMPIN' AT THE SAVOY.
Album: released on Warner Bros., Sep'83 by Warner Bros Records. Dist: WEA

Cassette: released on Warner Bros., Sep'83 by Warner Bros Records. Dist: WEA

Khan, Shah
WORLD WILL END ON FRIDAY.
Album: released on Sky, Jan'78 by President Records.

Khan, Steve
EVIDENCE.
Album: released on Arista, Apr'81 by Arista Records. Dist: RCA

EYEWITNESS.
Album: released on Antilles, Dec'83 by Island Records. Dist: Polygram

Khar Tomb
SWAHILI LULLABY.
Single (7"): released on Whaam, May'83 by Pinnacle

Khord
AT HOME IN SCOTLAND.
Album: released on Country House, Sep'79 by BGS Productions Ltd. Dist: Taylor, H.R., Record Merchandisers Distribution, Pinnacle, Sounds of Scotland Records

Kla Zos
RAPE.
Single (7"): released on All The Madmen, Sep'84 by All The Madmen Records. Dist: Rough Trade, Cartel

Kick
I CAN'T LET GO.
Tracks: / I can't let go / Armchair politican.
Single (7"): released on Countdown, Feb'86 by Stiff Records. Dist: EMI, Swift

LETS GET BACK TOGETHER.
Single (7"): released on Footwear, Nov'84 Dist: Rough Trade, Cartel

Kicking mules...
KICKING MULES FLAT PICKING FESTIVAL Various original artists (Various original artists).
Album: released on Mule, Mar'77

Kick Partners
IT'S TOO LATE.
Single (7"): released on CM, May'85 Dist: PRT, Jetstar

JUST MY IMAGINATION.
Single (7"): released on Raw, Nov'83 by Raw Records. Dist: Spartan

Kick Reaction
YESTERDAY TODAY TOMORROW.
Tracks: / Yesterday today tomorrow / Stopping to speak / Friday away from the high street.
Single (12"): released on Precious Organisation, Feb'86

Kick up the arse
KICK UP THE ARSE, A VOLUME 1 Various artists (Various Artists).
Album: released on Rot, Oct'85 by Rot Records. Dist: Red Rhino Through Cartel Distributions

Kid
YOU DON'T LIKE MY MUSIC.
Single (7"): released on Excaliber, Jan'82 by Red Bus Records. Dist: WEA

Kid Creole
ANNIE I'M NOT YOUR DADDY (Kid Creole & The Coconuts).
Picture disc single: released on ZE, Sep'82 by Island Records. Dist: Polygram

BEST OF KID CREOLE, THE (Kid Creole & The Coconuts).
Album: released on Island, Sep'84 by Island Records. Dist: Polygram

Cassette: released on Island, Sep'84 by Island

Records. Dist: Polygram

CAROLINE WAS A DROPOUT (Kid Creole & The Coconuts).
Tracks: / Caroline was a dropout / You can't keep a good man down.
Single (7"): released on Sire, Jan'86

Single (12"): released on Sire, Jan'86

DON'T TAKE MY COCONUTS (Kid Creole & The Coconuts).
Single (7"): released on Island, Jul'84 by Island Records. Dist: Polygram

Single (12"): released on Island, Jul'84 by Island Records. Dist: Polygram

ENDICOTT (Kid Creole & The Coconuts).
Single (7"): released on Sire, May'85

Single (12"): released on Sire, May'85

FRESH FRUIT IN FOREIGN PLACES (Kid Creole & The Coconuts).
Tracks: / Going places / In the jungle / Animal crackers / I stand accused / Latin music / Musicana Americana / I am schweinerei / Gina Gina / With a girl like Mimi / Table manners / Dear Addy.
Album: released on Island, Jan'87 by Island Records. Dist: Polygram

Cassette: released on Island, Apr'87 by Island Records. Dist: Polygram

IN PRAISE OF OLDER WOMAN/OTHER CRIMES (Kid Creole & The Coconuts).
Album: released on Sire, Jul'85

Cassette: released on Sire, Jul'85

I, TOO, HAVE SEEN THE WOODS (Kid Creole & The Coconuts).
Tracks: / Begining, The / Buttermilk channel / Part of my design / Agony....ecstasy / Dancin' at the Bains Douches / El Hijo / Cold wave / End, The / So far, so good / Midsummer madness / Consider me / Boxed out / Call it a day.
Album: released on Sire, Jul'87

Cassette: released on Sire, Jul'87

Compact disc: released on Sire, Jul'87

LIVE AT HAMMERSMITH.
Video-cassette (VHS): released on Videoform, Jan'84

OFF THE COAST OF ME (Kid Creole & The Coconuts).
Album: released on ZE, Aug'82 by Island Records. Dist: Polygram

Cassette: released on ZE, Aug'82 by Island Records. Dist: Polygram

TROPICAL GANGSTERS (Kid Creole & The Coconuts).
Album: released on ZE, May'82 by Island Records. Dist: Polygram

Cassette: released on ZE, May'82 by Island Records. Dist: Polygram

WONDERFUL THING (Kid Creole & The Coconuts).
Single (12"): released on ZE, Aug'82 by Island Records. Dist: Polygram

Kidd, Carol

ALL MY TOMORROWS.
Tracks: / Don't worry about me / I'm all smiles / Autumn in New York / My funny valentine / Round Midnight / Dat Dere / Angel Eyes / When I dream / I thought about you / Folks who live on the hill, The / Haven't we met / All my tomorrows / Don't worry about me / I'm all smiles / Autumn in New York / My funny valentine / Round midnight / Dat dere / Angel eyes / When I dream / I thought about you / Folks who live on the hill, The / Haven't we met / All my tomorrows.
Album: released on Aloi, Jan'86 by Aloi Records. Dist: Aloi Records, Chris Wellard, IRS

Cassette: released on Aloi, Jan'86 by Aloi Records. Dist: Aloi Records, Chris Wellard, IRS

CAROL KIDD.
Tracks: / Then I'll be tired of you / We'll be together / You go to my head / It isn't so good it couldn't get better / More I see you, The / I've grown accustomed to your face / Yes, I know when I've had it / Waltz for Debbie / Never let me go / Like someone in love / Trouble is a man / I'm shadowing you / Spring can really hang you up the most / I like to recognise the tune.
Album: released on Aloi, Aug'84 by Aloi Records. Dist: Aloi Records, Chris Wellard, IRS

Cassette: released on Aloi, Aug'84 by Aloi Records. Dist: Aloi Records, Chris Wellard, IRS

NICE WORK If you can get it.
Tracks: / Nice work if you can get it / Havin' myself a time / Isn't it a pity / Bidin' my time / Sing for your supper / Daydream / I'll take romance / New York on Sunday / What is there to say / Mean to me / I guess I'll have to change my plan / Starting tomorrow / Confessions.
Album: released on Aloi, Jul'87 by Aloi Records. Dist: Aloi Records, Chris Wellard, IRS

KIDD GLOVE.
Album: released on Morocco, Apr'84

Cassette: released on Morocco, Apr'84

Kidd, Jeremy

PETALS AND ASHES.
Single (7"): released on Self Drive, Apr'85 Dist: Red Rhino, Cartel

Single (12"): released on Self Drive, Apr'85 Dist: Red Rhino, Cartel

Kidd, Johnny

BEST OF JOHNNY KIDD & THE PIRATES, THE (Kidd, Johnny & The Pirates).
Tracks: / Shot of rhythm and blues, A / Shakin' all over / Longing lips / Restless / Growl / I want that / Linda lu / You've got what it takes / Your cheatin' heart / I'll never get over you / Hungry for love / Shot of rhythm and blues, A / I can tell / Jealous girl / Shop around / Please don't touch / Always and ever.
Notes: A brand new 16 track compilation featuring the hits of Johnny Kidd - one of Britain's most influential rockers! Based on solid R & B - the same sound whichlater launched the 'British Beat Boom' with groups like the Beatles and the Stones - Kidd took the British rock scene by storm. Includes the ever popular hits 'Shakin' all over', 'You've got what it takes', 'I'll never get over you' and many more. Should enjoy wide appeal from those who remember him first time 'round and includes informative historical sleeve note for those wishing to discover the roots of British rock.
Album: released on EMI, Feb'87 by EMI Records. Dist: EMI

Cassette: released on EMI, Feb'87 by EMI Records. Dist: EMI

RARITIES (Kidd, Johnny & The Pirates).
Tracks: / I Know / Where are you / Little bit of soap, A / Oh boy / Steady date / More of the same / I just want to make love to you / This golden ring / Right string but the wrong yo yo / Can't turn you loose / Shakin' all over 65 / I hate getting up in the morning / Send for that girl / Hurry on back to love / You got what it takes / Fool, The / Ecstacy / Shop around / Weep no more, my baby / Whole lotta woman.
Album: released on See For Miles, Mar'87 by See For Miles Records. Dist: Pinnacle

SHAKIN' ALL OVER (Kidd, Johnny & The Pirates).
Single (7"): released on H.M.V., Jun'80 by EMI Records. Dist: EMI

SHAKIN' ALL OVER/ I'LL NEVER GET OVER YOU (Kidd, Johnny & The Pirates).
Single (7"): released on Old Gold, Oct'83 by Old Gold Records. Dist: Lightning, Jazz Music, Spartan, Counterpoint

Kiddo

GIVE IT UP/ TRY MY LOVING.
Single (12"): released on A&M, Apr'83 by A&M Records. Dist: Polygram

Kid Montana

REVISITING YALTA (EP).
Single (12"): released on Antler, Apr'84 by Antler Records (Belgium). Dist: Red Rhino, Cartel

TEMPEREMENTAL.
Album: released on Le Disques Du Crepuscule (Belgium), Jan'87

Kidnapped

KIDNAPPED Stevenson, R.L. (Fairbanks, Douglas Jnr).
Album: released on Caedmon(USA), Sep'80 by Caedmon (USA) Records. Dist: Gower, Taylors, Discovery

Cassette: released on Caedmon(USA), Sep'80 by Caedmon (USA) Records. Dist: Gower, Taylors, Discovery

KIDNAPPED (Pertwee, Jon).
Cassette: released on Pinnacle, Jan'79 by Pinnacle Records. Dist: Pinnacle

Kid 'N Play

LAST NIGHT.
Tracks: / Last night / Last night (inst).
Single (7"): released on Cool Tempo, Jul'87 by Chrysalis Records. Dist: CBS

Single (12"): released on Cool Tempo, Jul'87 by Chrysalis Records. Dist: CBS

Kid Ory

VOL. 1 LIVE AT CLUB HANGOVER.
Album: released on Dawn Club, Dec'86 Dist: Cadillac, Swift, JSU

VOL.2-LIVE AT CLUB HANGOVER.
Album: released on Dawn Club, Dec'86 Dist: Cadillac, Swift, JSU

VOL. 3-LIVE AT CLUB HANGOVER.
Album: released on Dawn Club, Dec'86 Dist: Cadillac, Swift, JSU

VOL.4-LIVE AT CLUB HANGOVER.
Album: released on Dawn Club, Dec'86 Dist: Cadillac, Swift, JSU

Kids Are United

KIDS ARE UNITED Various artists (Various Artists).
Album: released on Music For Nations, Jun'83 by Music For Nations Records. Dist: Pinnacle

Kids For Two Farthings

KIDS FOR TWO FARTHINGS (Kossoff, David).
Cassette: released on Chivers Audio Books, '81 by Chivers Sound & Vision. Dist: Chivers Sound & Vision

Kids From Fame

BEST OF FAME.
Tracks: / Starmaker / We got the power / Rock 'n' roll world / Take that first step / Body language / Hi-fidelity / Life is a celebration / Be your own herp / Friday night / Fame.
Compact disc: released on RCA, Oct'84 by RCA Records. Dist: RCA, Roots, Swift, Wellard, Chris, I & B, Solomon & Peres Distribution

BODY LANGUAGE/ LIFE IS A CELEBRATION.
Single (7"): released on RCA, Jun'83 by RCA Records. Dist: RCA, Roots, Swift, Wellard, Chris, I & B, Solomon & Peres Distribution

Single (12"): released on RCA, Jun'83 by RCA Records. Dist: RCA, Roots, Swift, Wellard, Chris, I & B, Solomon & Peres Distribution

FAME (TV series).
Album: released on BBC, Jun'82 by BBC Records & Tapes. Dist: EMI, PRT, Pye

Cassette: released on BBC, Jun'82 by BBC Records & Tapes. Dist: EMI, PRT, Pye

FRIDAY NIGHT/ COULD WE BE MAGIC.
Single (7"): released on RCA, Feb'83 by RCA Records. Dist: RCA, Roots, Swift, Wellard, Chris, I & B, Solomon & Peres Distribution

FROM FAME AGAIN.
Album: released on RCA, Jan'84 by RCA Records. Dist: RCA, Roots, Swift, Wellard, Chris, I & B, Solomon & Peres Distribution

Cassette: released on RCA, Jan'84 by RCA Records. Dist: RCA, Roots, Swift, Wellard, Chris, I & B, Solomon & Peres Distribution

HI FIDELITY/ I STILL BELIEVE IN YOU.
Single (7"): released on RCA, Jul'82 by RCA Records. Dist: RCA, Roots, Swift, Wellard, Chris, I & B, Solomon & Peres Distribution

KIDS FROM FAME (4 TRACK CASSETTE EP).
Cassette: released on RCA, May'83 by RCA Records. Dist: RCA, Roots, Swift, Wellard, Chris, I & B, Solomon & Peres Distribution

LIVE.
Album: released on BBC, Jan'84 by BBC Records & Tapes. Dist: EMI, PRT, Pye

Cassette: released on BBC, Jan'84 by BBC Records & Tapes. Dist: EMI, PRT, Pye

MANNEQUIN/ COME WHAT MAY.
Single (7"): released on RCA, Nov'82 by RCA Records. Dist: RCA, Roots, Swift, Wellard, Chris, I & B, Solomon & Peres Distribution

SONGS.
Album: released on BBC, May'83 by BBC Records & Tapes. Dist: EMI, PRT, Pye

Cassette: released on BBC, May'83 by BBC Records & Tapes. Dist: EMI, PRT, Pye

SONGS/ JUST LIKE YOU.
Single (7"): released on RCA, Aug'83 by RCA Records. Dist: RCA, Roots, Swift, Wellard, Chris, I & B, Solomon & Peres Distribution

STARMAKER.
Tracks: / Starmaker / Hi-fidelity.
Single (7"): released on Old Gold, Nov'86 by Old Gold Records. Dist: Lightning, Jazz Music, Spartan, Counterpoint

STARMAKER/ STEP UP TO THE MIKE.
Single (7"): released on RCA, Sep'82 by RCA Records. Dist: RCA, Roots, Swift, Wellard, Chris, I & B, Solomon & Peres Distribution

Kid Sheik

IN ENGLAND.
Notes: With S.Rimmington, Jack Wedell, B.Martin etc.
Album: released on GHB, Jan'87 Dist: Jazz Music, Swift

Kids In The Kitchen

SHINE.
Tracks: / Shine / Current stand / Change in mood / Places to go / Cynical / Something that you said / Bitter desire / My life / Not the way / How come.

Kids Praise Album

KIDS PRAISE ALBUM Various artists (Various Artists).
Album: released on Marantha Music, May'82

Cassette: released on Marantha Music, May'82

KIDS PRAISE ALBUM (2) Various artists (Various Artists).
Album: released on Marantha Music, May'82

Cassette: released on Marantha Music, May'82

Kid Thomas

ROCKIN' THIS JOINT TONIGHT.
Single (7"): released on JSP, Apr'84 by JSP Records. Dist: Swift, Projection

Single (7"): released on JSP, May'84 by JSP Records. Dist: Swift, Projection

Kiem

DON'T STOP.
Tracks: / Don't stop / Moneyman.
Single (7"): released on Torso, Jul'87 by Torso Records. Dist: Rough Trade, Cartel, EMI

MONEYMAN, THE.
Single (12"): released on Torso, Dec'86 by Torso Records. Dist: Rough Trade, Cartel, EMI

YOU SHOULD TRY.
Compact disc: released on Torso, Jul'87 by Torso Records. Dist: Rough Trade, Cartel, EMI

Kiener, Barry

INTRODUCING THE BARRY KIENER TRIO.
Album: released on Phoenix, Apr'81 by Audio Fidelity Enterprises. Dist: Stage One, Lugtons

Kihn, Greg

CITIZEN KIHN.
Album: released on EMI America, Apr'85 by EMI Records. Dist: EMI

Cassette: released on EMI America, Apr'85 by EMI Records. Dist: EMI

GREG KIHN.
Album: released on Polydor, Jan'74 by Polydor Records. Dist: Polygram, Polydor

GREG KIHN AGAIN.
Album: released on Beserkley (USA), Jan'79 by Beserkley Records. Dist: DMS, RCA

HAPPY MAN/ TROUBLE IN PARADISE (Kihn, Greg Band).
Single (7"): released on Beserkley (USA), Jul'83 by Beserkley Records. Dist: DMS, RCA

JEOPARDY/ FASCINATION.
Single (7"): released on Elektra, Mar'83 by WEA Records. Dist: WEA

KIHNSPIRACY (Kihn, Greg Band).
Compact disc: released on Beserkley (USA), Jan'84 by Beserkley Records. Dist: DMS, RCA

NEXT OF KIHN.
Album: released on Beserkley (USA), Mar'78 by Beserkley Records. Dist: DMS, RCA

POWER LINES.
Album: released on Polydor, Jan'74 by Polydor Records. Dist: Polygram, Polydor

WITH THE NAKED EYE.
Album: released on Beserkley (USA), Aug'79 by Beserkley Records. Dist: DMS, RCA

Kilbride, Pat

ROCK AND ROSES.

Album: released on Temple, Jan'83 by Temple Records. Dist: Roots Distribution, Folksound Distribution, Celtic Music Distribution, Projection Distribution

Kilburn & The High Roads

HANDSOME.
Album: released on Flashback, Nov'85 by Flashback Records/PRT Records. Dist: Mainline, PRT

Cassette: released on Flashback, Nov'85 by Flashback Records/PRT Records. Dist: Mainline, PRT

UPMINSTER KIDS.
Album: released on PRT, Jul'83 by PRT Records. Dist: PRT

Cassette: released on PRT, Jul'83 by PRT Records. Dist: PRT

Kilfernora Ceili Band

KILFERNORA CEILI BAND.
Album: released on Transatlantic, Jun'81 by Logo Records. Dist: Roots Distribution, RCA Distribution

Cassette: released on Transatlantic, Jun'81 by Logo Records. Dist: Roots Distribution, RCA Distribution

Kilgore Trout

STICK IT IN THE BANK MAN.
Tracks: / Quality control / English never listen / Bank / Right boys.

Killen-Handle

ALONG THE COALY TYNE.
Album: released on Topic, Jan'81 Dist: Roots Distribution

Killen, Louis

BALLADS AND BROADSIDES.
Album: released on Topic, Jan'81 Dist: Roots Distribution

Killer

READY FOR HELL.
Album: released on Mausoleum, May'84 by Mausoleum Records. Dist: Pinnacle

Cassette: released on Mausoleum, May'84 by Mausoleum Records. Dist: Pinnacle

SHOCK WAVES.
Album: released on Mausoleum, Apr'84 by Mausoleum Records. Dist: Pinnacle

Cassette: released on Mausoleum, Jul'84 by Mausoleum Records. Dist: Pinnacle

WALL OF SOUND.
Album: released on Mausoleum, May'84 by Mausoleum Records. Dist: Pinnacle

Cassette: released on Mausoleum, May'84 by Mausoleum Records. Dist: Pinnacle

Killer Dwarfs

KILLER DWARFS.
Album: released on Attic, Nov'83 Dist: Pinnacle

Killerman Jarrett

WAR IN SOUTH AFRICA.
Tracks: / War in South Africa / War in South Africa (Vocal dub Version).

Killigrew

CHRISTMAS CALYPSO/ HUSH.
Single (7"): released on Mont Music, Nov'82

Killing Joke

ADORATION.
Tracks: / Adoration / Exile / Ecstasy / Adoration.

BRIGHTER THAN A THOUSAND SUNS.
Album: released on E.G., Nov'86 by Virgin Records. Dist: Virgin, EMI

Cassette: released on E.G., Nov'86 by Virgin Records. Dist: Virgin, EMI

Compact disc: released on E.G., Nov'86 by Virgin Records. Dist: Virgin, EMI

EIGHTIES.
Single (12"): released on E.G., Mar'84 by Virgin Records. Dist: Virgin, EMI

FIRE DANCES.
Tracks: / Gathering / Fun and games / Rejuvenation / Frenzy / Harlequin / Feast of Blaze / Song and Dance / Dominator / Let's all go to the fire dances / Lust almighty.
Album: released on E.G., Jan'87 by Virgin Records. Dist: Virgin, EMI

Cassette: released on E.G., Jan'87 by Virgin Records. Dist: Virgin, EMI

Album: released on E.G., Jul'83 by Virgin Records. Dist: Virgin, EMI

Cassette: released on E.G., Jul'83 by Virgin Records. Dist: Virgin, EMI

HA-KILLING JOKE LIVE.
Special: released on Malicious Damage, Nov'82 Dist: Polygram

Cassette: released on Malicious Damage, Nov'82 Dist: Polygram

KILLING JOKE.
Tracks: / Requiem / War Dance / Tomorrow's World / Bloodsport / Wait / Complications / S.O.36 / Primitive.
Album: released on E.G., Jan'87 by Virgin Records. Dist: Virgin, EMI

Cassette: released on E.G., Jan'87 by Virgin Records. Dist: Virgin, EMI

Cassette: released on E.G., Oct'80 by Virgin Records. Dist: Virgin, EMI

KINGS AND QUEENS.
Single (7"): released on E.G., Mar'85 by Virgin Records. Dist: Virgin, EMI

Single (12"): released on E.G., Mar'85 by Virgin Records. Dist: Virgin, EMI

LOVE LIKE BLOOD, A.
Single (7"): released on E.G., Jan'85 by Virgin Records. Dist: Virgin, EMI

Single (12"): released on E.G., Jan'85 by Virgin Records. Dist: Virgin, EMI

LOVE LIKE BLOOD (GESTALT MIX).
Single (7"): released on E.G., Mar'85 by Virgin Records. Dist: Virgin, EMI

NIGHT TIME.
Tracks: / Night Time / Darkness Before Dawn / Love Like Blood / Kings and Queens / Tabazan / Multitudes / Europe / Eighties / Multitudes.
Album: released on E.G., Jan'87 by Virgin Records. Dist: Virgin, EMI

Cassette: released on E.G., Jan'87 by Virgin Records. Dist: Virgin, EMI

Compact disc: released on E.G., Jan'87 by Virgin Records. Dist: Virgin, EMI

REVELATIONS.
Tracks: / Hum / Empire Song / We have Joy / Chop-Chop / Pandys are Coming / Chapter III. / Have a Nice Day / Land of Milk and Honey / Good Samaritan / Dregs.
Album: released on E.G., Jan'87 by Virgin Records. Dist: Virgin, EMI

Cassette: released on E.G., Jan'87 by Virgin Records. Dist: Virgin, EMI

Album: released on Malicious Damage, Apr'82 Dist: Polygram

Cassette: released on Malicious Damage, Apr'82 Dist: Polygram

SANITY.
Tracks: / Sanity / Goodbye to the village.
Single (7"): released on E.G., Oct'86 by Virgin Records. Dist: Virgin, EMI

Single (12"): released on E.G., Oct'86 by Virgin Records. Dist: Virgin, EMI

WHAT'S THIS FOR?.
Tracks: / Fall of Because / Tension / Unspeakable / Butcher / Who Told You how / Follow the leader / Madness / Exit.
Album: released on E.G., Jan'87 by Virgin Records. Dist: Virgin, EMI

Cassette: released on E.G., Jan'87 by Virgin Records. Dist: Virgin, EMI

Album: released on E.G., Jun'81 by Virgin Records. Dist: Virgin, EMI

Cassette: released on E.G., Jun'81 by Virgin Records. Dist: Virgin, EMI

Killjoys

THIS IS NOT LOVE.
Single (7"): released on Clay, Dec'82 by Clay Records. Dist: Pinnacle

Killoran, Paddy

BACK IN TOWN.
Album: released on Shanachie, Sep'79 Dist: Sterns/Triple Earth Distribution, Roots

Kill Ugly Pop

CHURCH OF BLOODY DECEPTION,THE.
Tracks: / Church of bloody deception,The / Church of bloody deception,The (EP).

GATOR BREATH RIOT.
Single (12"): released on Fever, Aug'84 by Fever Records. Dist: Red Rhino, Cartel

PURPLE HAZE.
Single (7"): released on Fever, Aug'87 by Fever Records. Dist: Red Rhino, Cartel

Kilmarnock Concert Brass

SHADES OF BRASS.
Album: released on Chandos, Sep'83 by Chandos Records. Dist: Harmonia Mundi, Taylors

Cassette: released on Chandos, Sep'83 by Chandos Records. Dist: Harmonia Mundi, Taylors

Kilvert's Diary

HE BEING DEAD YET SPEAKETH (Davies, Timothy).
Double Album: released on Saydisc, Nov'80 by Saydisc Records. Dist: Essex, Harmonia Mundi, Roots, H.R. Taylor, Jazz Music, Swift, Projection, Gamut

Cassette: released on Saydisc, Nov'80 by Saydisc Records. Dist: Essex, Harmonia Mundi, Roots, H.R. Taylor, Jazz Music, Swift, Projection, Gamut

Kim, Andy

ROCK ME GENTLY.
Tracks: / Rock me gently / Games people play.
Notes: Also contains:"Games people play" by Joe South
Single (7"): released on Old Gold, Apr'87 by Old Gold Records. Dist: Lightning, Jazz Music, Spartan, Counterpoint

Kimball, Jeanette

SOPHISTICATED LADY.
Notes: Trios & Quartets.
Album: released on New Orleans, Sep'86 Dist: Swift, Zodiac Distribution, Jazz Music, JSU

Kimberly Rew

BIBLE OF BOP (THE).
Tracks: / Nightmare / Stomping / Nothing is gonna change / Fighting someone's war / My baby does her hairdo long / Walking in the dew / Fishing / Hey war pig.
Notes: With Robyn Hitchcock
Album: released on Press, Jul'86 by Press Records.

MY BABY DOES HER HAIRDO LONG.
Single (7"): released on Armageddon, Jul'81 by Armageddon Records. Dist: Revolver, Cartel, Pinnacle

STOMPING ALL OVER THE WORLD.
Single (7"): released on Armageddon, Jul'81 by Armageddon Records. Dist: Revolver, Cartel, Pinnacle

Kimber, William

ART OF WILLIAM KIMBER, THE.
Album: released on Topic, Jan'81 Dist: Roots Distribution

COUNTRY GARDENS, HEADINGTON'S MORRIS.
Cassette: released on Folktracks, Nov'79 by Folktracks Cassettes. Dist: Folktracks

Kimera

FEMME SAUVAGE.
Single (7"): released on TLO, Aug'87 Dist: PRT

Single (12"): released on TLO, Aug'87 Dist: PRT

HITS ON OPERA.
Album: released on Stylus, Oct'85 Dist: Pinnacle, Terry Blood Distribution, Stylus Distribution

Cassette: released on Stylus, Oct'85 Dist: Pinnacle, Terry Blood Distribution, Stylus Distribution

LOST OPERA (Kimera & The Operaiders).
Single (7"): released on Red Bus, Aug'84 by Red Bus Records. Dist: PRT

Single (12"): released on Red Bus, Aug'84 by Red Bus Records. Dist: PRT

LOST OPERATOR (THE) (Kimera & The Operaiders).
Tracks: / Lost operator (The) / Lost operator (The) -Dance Mix.
Single (12"): released on Carrere, May'86 by Carrere Records. Dist: PRT, Spartan

Kina

CERCANDO.
Album: released on Children Of The Revolution, Sep'86 by Revolver Records. Dist: Revolver, Cartel

Kincora, Ceili Band

CEOL TIRE.
Album: released on Shanachie, Jan'79 Dist: Sterns/Triple Earth Distribution, Roots

Kinder

MONKEY PUZZLE/ DOUBLE TALK.
Single (7"): released on Amidisque, Dec'83 by Amidisque Records. Dist: RCA, Pinnacle

Kindergarten

WARRIOR.
Single (7"): released on Diamond, Sep'85 by Revolver Records. Dist: Cartel

WORLD TURNED UPSIDE DOWN.
Tracks: / World turned upside down.
Single (12"): released on Diamond, Mar'86 by Revolver Records. Dist: Cartel

King

12" TAPE, THE.
Tracks: / Love and pride / Won't you hold my hand now / Alone without you / Taste of your tears (The) / Torture.
Cassette: released on CBS, Sep'86 by CBS Records. Dist: CBS

BITTER SWEET.
Tracks: / Alone without you / Platform one / I cringed,I died,I felt hot / Kfad wait for no one / 2 M B / These things / Taste of your tears / Torture / Sugar candy mountain / Buddahs / Mind yer toes.
Compact disc: released on CBS, Apr'86 by CBS Records. Dist: CBS

Album: released on CBS, Nov'85 by CBS Records. Dist: CBS

Cassette: released on CBS, Nov'85 by CBS Records. Dist: CBS

FROM STEPS IN TIME TO BITTER SWEEP.
Notes: Five tracks on this compilation,playing time 25 minutes.
Video-cassette (VHS): released on CBS-Fox, Jan'86 by CBS Records. Dist: CBS. Fox

LOVE AND PRIDE.
Single (7"): released on CBS, Jan'85 by CBS Records. Dist: CBS

STEPS IN TIME.
Album: released on CBS, Nov'84 by CBS Records. Dist: CBS

Cassette: released on CBS, Nov'84 by CBS Records. Dist: CBS

TORTURE.
Tracks: / Torture / Growing up with the king.
Single (7"): released on CBS, Dec'85 by CBS Records. Dist: CBS

Single (12"): released on CBS, Dec'85 by CBS Records. Dist: CBS

King, Albert

BEST OF, THE.
Compact disc: released on London, Apr'87 by London Records. Dist: Polygram

LAST SESSION, THE.
Notes: This previously unreleased album will excite a lot of people. The tapes had apparantly been sitting on a shelf for fifteen years, untouched and forgotten. The pairing of Albert King and John Mayall was an inspired one, King being the most influential guitar stylist of the modern blues era and Mayall being the chief conceptualist of the British revival of the 60's.Recorded August 1971. Personell: Albert King- Vocals, Lead Guitar\John Mayall-organ, piano,Harmonica,12 String Guitar\Larry Taylor-Bass\Ron Selico-Drums\Lee King-Rhythm Guitar\Kevin(last name unknown)-Organ, Piano\Clifford Solomon-Alto and tenor saxes\Ernie Watts-Tenor saxophone\Blue Mitchell-Trumpet
Album: released on Stax, Nov'86 by Ace Records. Dist: Pinnacle, Chris Wellard, IMS-Polygram

LAUNDROMAT BLUES.
Album: released on Edsel, Apr'84 by Demon Records. Dist: Pinnacle, Jazz Music, Projection

LIVE WIRE/BLUES POWER.
Compact disc: released on Mobile Fidelity, '86 by Mobile Fidelity Records.

NEW ORLEANS HEAT.
Tracks: / Get out of My Life Woman / Born Under a Bad Sign / Feeling, The / We All Wanna Boogie / Very thought of you (The) / I Got The Blues / I Get Evil / Angel of Mercy / Flat Tire.
Notes: Original Tomato recordings P 1978.
Compact disc: released on Charly, Jan'87 by Charly Records. Dist: Charly, Cadillac

SAN FRANCISCO 83.
Album: released on Fantasy, Nov'83 by RCA Records. Dist: RCA, Jetstar

Album: released on Carrere(France), Apr'84 by Carrere Records (France). Dist: PRT

King and I

KING AND I Original cast (Various Artists).
Album: released on MCA, Mar'82 by MCA Records. Dist: Polygram, MCA

Cassette: released on MCA, Mar'82 by MCA Records. Dist: Polygram, MCA

KING AND I Original film soundtrack.
Album: released on Capitol, Jan'58 by Capitol Records. Dist: EMI

KING AND I (1977 BROADWAY CAST) Original Soundtrack.
Album: released on RCA, Jan'79 by RCA Records. Dist: RCA, Roots, Swift, Wellard, Chris, I & B, Solomon & Peres Distribution

King Arthur

KING ARTHUR (Jones, Freddie).
Cassette: released on Squirrel, Nov'81

KING ARTHUR (Plummer, C).
Cassette: released on Caedmon(USA), '81 by Caedmon (USA) Records. Dist: Gower, Taylors, Discovery

KING ARTHUR AND HIS KNIGHTS Various artists (Various Artists).
Cassette: released on Tellastory, Jun'83 by Bartlett Bliss Productions. Dist: PRT Distribution, Hayward Promotions Distribution, H.R. Taylor Distribution

KING ARTHUR SOUNDBOOK Various artists (Various Artists).
Cassette: released on Caedmon(USA), '81 by Caedmon (USA) Records. Dist: Gower, Taylors, Discovery

King Austin

SOCA TAKING OVER.
Single (12"): released on Charlie's, Dec'84 by Charlie's Records. Dist: Jetstar

King Axe

ROCK THE WORLD.
Album: released on Roadrunner (Dutch), Jun'87 Dist: Pinnacle

King, B.B.

20 BLUES GREATS.
Album: released on Deja Vu, Nov'85 by Deja Vu Records. Dist: Counterpoint Distribution, Record Services Distribution (Ireland)

Cassette: released on Deja Vu, Nov'85 by Deja Vu Records. Dist: Counterpoint Distribution, Record Services Distribution (Ireland)

6 SILVER STRINGS.
Album:

Cassette:

AMBASSADOR OF THE BLUES.
Tracks: / Ambassador of the blues / You upset my baby / Sweet little angel / Three o'clock blues / Did you ever love a woman / B.B Blues / I can't lose / Five long years / Other night blues / I stay in the mood / Worst thing of my life / Pray for you.
Album: released on Crown, Feb'86 by Ace Records. Dist: Pinnacle, Swift

Cassette: released on Crown, Feb'86 by Ace Records. Dist: Pinnacle, Swift

BEST OF B.B. KING, THE.
Tracks: / Hummingbird / Cook county jail introduction / How blue can you get / Caldonia / Sweet sixteen / Ain't nobody home / Why I sing the blues / Thrill is gone, The / Nobody loves me but my mother.
Album: released on Fame (MCA), Jan'83 by Music For Pleasure Records. Dist: EMI

Cassette: released on Fame (MCA), Jan'83 by Music For Pleasure Records. Dist: EMI

Compact disc: released on MCA, Sep'87 by MCA Records. Dist: Polygram, MCA

BEST OF B. B. KING VOLUME 2 (THE).
Cassette: released on Ace, Jan'87 by Ace Records. Dist: Pinnacle, Swift, Hotshot, Cadillac

Album: released on Ace, Jan'87 by Ace Records. Dist: Pinnacle, Swift, Hotshot, Cadillac

Compact disc: by Ace Records. Dist: Pinnacle, Swift, Hotshot, Cadillac

BEST OF B. B. KING VOLUME 1 (THE).
Compact disc: released on Ace, Nov'86 by Ace Records. Dist: Pinnacle, Swift, Hotshot, Cadillac

BEST OF MEMPHIS MASTERS.
Cassette: released on Ace, Jan'85 by Ace Records. Dist: Pinnacle, Swift, Hotshot, Cadillac

BEST OF..., THE Volume 1.
Tracks: / Hummingbird / Cook county jail introduction / How blue can you get / Sweet sixteen / Why I sing the blues / Caldonia / Ain't nobody home / Thrill is gone, The / Nobody loves me but my mother.
Album: released on Ace, Dec'86 by Ace Records. Dist: Pinnacle, Swift, Hotshot, Cadillac

Cassette: released on Ace, Dec'86 by Ace Records. Dist: Pinnacle, Swift, Hotshot, Cadillac

BIM BAM / SHAKE HOLLER AND RUN.
Single (7"): released on Ace, May'81 by Ace Records. Dist: Pinnacle, Swift, Hotshot, Cadillac

COMPLETELY LIVE AND WELL.
Tracks: / Don't answer the door / Just a little love / My mood / Sweet little angel / Please accept my love / I want you so bad / Friends / Get off my back woman / Lets get down to business / Why I sing the blues / So exited / No good / You're losin' me / What happened / Confessin' the blues / Key to my kingdom / Crying won't help you now / You're mean / Thrill is gone (The).
Notes: Double Album.
Album: released on Charly, Nov'86 by Charly Records. Dist: Charly, Cadillac

Cassette: released on Charly, Nov'86 by Charly Records. Dist: Charly, Cadillac

COMPLETELY WELL.
Tracks: / So excited / No good / You're losin' me / What happened / Confessin' the blues / Key to my kingdom / Cryin' won't help you now / You're mean / Thrill is gone.
Compact disc: released on MCA, Jul'87 by MCA Records. Dist: Polygram, MCA

INCREDIBLE SOUL OF, THE.
Album: released on Musidisc (France), Oct'83 Dist: Discovery Distribution, Swift Distribution

KING OF THE BLUES GUITAR.
Album: released on Ace, Nov'85 by Ace Records. Dist: Pinnacle, Swift, Hotshot, Cadillac

LIVE (King, B.B., Pat Metheney, Dave Brubeck, Heath Bros).
Compact disc: released on Kingdom Jazz, Jan'87 by Kingdom Records. Dist: Kingdom Records

LIVE AT THE REGAL.
Album: released on Ace(MCA), Oct'83 by Ace Records. Dist: Pinnacle, Swift, Hotshot

LIVE IN LONDON.
Album: released on MCA, Apr'84 by MCA Records. Dist: Polygram, MCA

Cassette: released on MCA, Apr'84 by MCA Records. Dist: Polygram, MCA

MIDNIGHT BELIEVER.
Album: released on MCA, Jun'84 by MCA Records. Dist: Polygram, MCA

Cassette: released on MCA, Jun'84 by MCA Records. Dist: Polygram, MCA

NOW APPEARING AT OLE MISS.
Tracks: / (B.B King Blue Theme) Caldonia / Don't answer the door / You done lost your good thing now / I need love so bad / Nobody loves me but my mother hold on / I got some outside help (I don't really need) / Darlin' you know I love you / When I'm wrong / Thrill is gone (The) / Never make a move too soon / Three o'clock in the morning / Rock me baby / Guess who / I just can't leave your love-ove.
Notes: Double Album and Cassette.
Double Album: released on MCA, Feb'86 by MCA Records. Dist: Polygram, MCA

Digital audio tape: released on MCA, Feb'86 by MCA Records. Dist: Polygram, MCA

Album: released on MCA, Oct'81 by MCA Records. Dist: Polygram, MCA

ONE NIGHTER BLUES.
Notes: 16 tracks, 6 previously unissued and the remaining 10 very rare recordings from 1951-54.
Album: released on Ace, Apr'87 by Ace Records. Dist: Pinnacle, Swift, Hotshot, Cadillac

RAREST B.B. KING.
Album: released on Blues Boy, Aug'87 by Mr. R&B Records. Dist: Swift

ROCK ME BABY.
Album: released on Ace(Cadet USA), Oct'84 by Ace Records. Dist: Pinnacle. Swift, Hotshot

SIX SILVER STRINGS.
Tracks: / Six silver strings / Big boss man / In the midnight hour / Into the night / My Lucille / Memory blues / My guitar sings the blues / Double trouble.
Album: released on MCA, Sep'85 by MCA Records. Dist: Polygram, MCA

Album: released on Ace, Sep'86 by Ace Records. Dist: Pinnacle, Swift, Hotshot, Cadillac

Cassette: released on Ace, Sep'86 by Ace Records. Dist: Pinnacle, Swift, Hotshot, Cadillac

SPOTLIGHT ON LUCILLE.
Compact disc: released on Contemporary, Jan'87 by Contemporary Records. Dist: Pinnacle

Compact disc: released on Ace, Aug'86 by Ace Records. Dist: Pinnacle, Swift, Hotshot, Cadillac

STANDING ON THE EDGE OF LOVE.
Tracks: / Standing on the edge of love / Don't tell me nothing / Let yourself in for it **.
Single (7"): released on MCA, Mar'87 by MCA Records. Dist: Polygram, MCA

Single (12"): released on MCA, Mar'87 by MCA Records. Dist: Polygram, MCA

TAKE IT HOME.
Album:

Cassette:

King, Ben E.

BENNY & US See Average White Band.

DANCING IN THE NIGHT.
Tracks: / Dancing in the night (version).

Single (7"): released on Syncopate, 13 Jun'87 by EMI Records. Dist: EMI

Single (12"): released on Syncopate, 13 Jun'87 by EMI Records. Dist: EMI

GREATEST HITS: BEN E. KING.
Cassette: released on Dynamic, Oct'84 by Creole Records. Dist: CBS, Essex

HERE COMES THE NIGHT.
Album: released on Edsel, May'84 by Demon Records. Dist: Pinnacle, Jazz Music, Projection

SAVE THE LAST DANCE FOR ME.
Tracks: / Save the last dance for me / Wheel of love.
Single (7"): released on Manhattan, Jun'87 by EMI Records. Dist: EMI

Single (12"): released on Manhattan, Jun'87 by EMI Records. Dist: EMI

SPANISH HARLEM.
Tracks: / Spanish Harlem / First taste of love / Spanish Harlem / Stand by me/Don't play that song (medley).
Single (7"): released on Creole Classics, Mar'87 by Creole Records. Dist: PRT, Rhino

Single (12"): released on Creole Classics, Mar'87 by Creole Records. Dist: PRT, Rhino

Single (7"): released on Atlantic, Apr'87 by WEA Records. Dist: WEA

Single (12"): released on Atlantic, Apr'87 by WEA Records. Dist: WEA

SPANISH HARLEM / STAND BY ME.
Single (7"): released on Old Gold (Reissue), Jul'82

SPREAD MYSELF AROUND.
Single (7"): released on Bold Reprieve, May'87 by Bold Reprieve Records. Dist: Pinnacle

Single (12"): released on Bold Reprieve, May'87 by Bold Reprieve Records. Dist: Pinnacle

STAND BY ME.
Tracks: / Stand By Me / Yakkety Yak.
Single (7"): released on Atlantic, Jan'87 by WEA Records. Dist: WEA

Single (12"): released on Atlantic, Jan'87 by WEA Records. Dist: WEA

STAND BY ME (THE ULTIMATE COLLECTION).
Notes: Original tracks, now also on CD for the first time, including the no.1 hit.
Album: released on Atlantic, Feb'87 by WEA Records. Dist: WEA

Cassette: released on Atlantic, Feb'87 by WEA Records. Dist: WEA

Compact disc: released on Ce De International, Jul'87

STREET TOUGH.
Album: released on Atlantic, May'81 by WEA Records. Dist: WEA

ULTIMATE COLLECTION, THE.
Compact disc: released on Atlantic, Jul'87 by WEA Records. Dist: WEA

King, Bev

MARTY ROBBINS SCRAPBOOK (see also Joe Knight) (King, Bev & Joe Knight).

Album: released on Bear Family, Nov'85 by Bear Family Records. Dist: Rollercoaster Distribution, Swift

King, Bobby

BOBBY KING.
Album: released on Warner Brothers, Aug'81 by Warner Bros Records. Dist: WEA

CLOSE TO ME.
Single (7"): released on Motown, Aug'84 by Motown Records. Dist: BMG Distribution

Single (12"): released on Motown, Aug'84 by Motown Records. Dist: BMG Distribution

LOVE IN THE FIRE.
Album: released on Motown, Apr'84 by Motown Records. Dist: BMG Distribution

Cassette: released on Motown, Apr'84 by Motown Records. Dist: BMG Distribution

LOVEQUAKE.
Single (7"): released on Motown, Mar'84 by Motown Records. Dist: BMG Distribution

Single (12"): released on Motown, Mar'84 by Motown Records. Dist: BMG Distribution

King, Brenton

DON'T GIVE YOUR HEART AWAY.
Single (12"): released on The Foundation, May'84 by Foundation Records, The. Dist: Jetstar Distribution

NEVER GIVE UP.
Single (12"): released on Top Rank, Apr'85

King Brothers

6-5 JIVE.
Single (7"): released on Northwood, Mar'84 by Northwood Records. Dist: Backs-Cartel

IT'S PARTY TIME WITH .... (EP).
Single (7"): released on Northwood, Mar'85 by Northwood Records. Dist: Backs-Cartel

King, Calvin

NEVER GONNA FORGET YOU.
Tracks: / Never gonna forget you / Never gonna forget you (Disco Remix).
Single (12"): released on Elegance, Aug'86 by Elegance Records. Dist: Jetstar

THATS WHEN IT ALL STARTED.
Single (12"): released on Time, Oct'80 Dist: Jetstar Distribution

King, Carole

HER GREATEST HITS.
Album: released on Epic (Ode), Jul'83 by CBS Records. Dist: CBS

Cassette: released on Epic (Ode), Jul'83 by CBS Records. Dist: CBS

HER GREATEST HITS.
Tracks: / Jazzman / So far away / Sweet seasons / I feel the earth move / Brother brother / Only love is real / It's too late / Nightingale / Smackwater Jack / been to Caanan / Corazon / Believe in humility.
Compact disc: released on CBS, Mar'87 by CBS Records. Dist: CBS

IT MIGHT AS WELL RAIN UNTIL SEPTEMBER / ROAD TO NOWHERE.

Single (7"): released on Old Gold (Reissue), Oct'83

MUSIC.
Album: released on Epic (Ode), '83 by CBS Records. Dist: CBS

Cassette: released on Epic (Ode), '83 by CBS Records. Dist: CBS

PEARLS (SONGS OF GOFFIN AND KING).
Album: released on Fame (Capitol), May'82 by Music For Pleasure Records. Dist: EMI

Cassette: released on Fame (Capitol), May'82 by Music For Pleasure Records. Dist: EMI

SPEEDING TIME.
Tracks: / Computer eyes / Small Voice / Crying in the rain / Sacred of heart stone / Speeding time / Standin' on the borderline / So ready for love / Chalice borealis / Dancing / Alabastor lady.
Notes: Digital Stereo recording.
Compact disc: released on Atlantic, May'84 by WEA Records. Dist: WEA

TAPESTRY.
Tracks: / Feel the earth move / So far away / Beautiful way over yonder / You've got a friend / Where you lead / Will you love me tomorrow / Smack water Jack / Tapestry (you make me feel) like a woman.
Compact disc: released on CBS, '86 by CBS Records. Dist: CBS

Compact disc: released on Polydor, May'84 by Polydor Records. Dist: Polygram, Polydor

Album: released on Ode-Epic, '84

Cassette: released on Ode-Epic, '84

THOROUGHBRED.
Album: released on CBS, '84 by CBS Records. Dist: CBS

Cassette: released on CBS, '84 by CBS Records. Dist: CBS

King, Claude

CLAUDE KING'S BEST.
Album: released on Gusto (USA), '80 by Gusto Records (USA). Dist: Crusader

King, Clive

STIG OF THE DUMP.
Cassette: released on Cover to Cover, Jun'85 by Cover to Cover Cassettes. Dist: Conifer

King Crimson

BEAT.
Tracks: / Neal and Jack and Me / Heartbeat / Sartori in Tangier / Waiting Man / Neurotica / Two Hands / Howler / Requiem.
Album: released on E.G., Jan'87 by Virgin Records. Dist: Virgin, EMI

Cassette: released on E.G., Jan'87 by Virgin Records. Dist: Virgin, EMI

Compact disc: released on E.G., Jan'87 by Virgin Records. Dist: Virgin, EMI

COMPACT KING CRIMSON, THE.

Page 562

Album: released on E.G., Jan'86 by Virgin Records. Dist: Virgin, EMI

Cassette: released on E.G., Jan'86 by Virgin Records. Dist: Virgin, EMI

Compact disc: released on E.G., Jan'86 by Virgin Records. Dist: Virgin, EMI

DISCIPLINE.
Tracks: / Elephant Talk / Frame By Frame / Matte Kudasai / Indiscipline / Thela Run Ginjeet / Sheltering Sky (The) / Discipline.
Album: released on E.G., Jan'87 by Virgin Records. Dist: Virgin, EMI

Cassette: released on E.G., Jan'87 by Virgin Records. Dist: Virgin, EMI

Compact disc: by Virgin Records. Dist: Virgin, EMI

EARTHBOUND.
Album: released on Polydor, Oct'77 by Polydor Records. Dist: Polygram, Polydor

IN THE COURT OF THE CRIMSON KING.
Tracks: / 21st Century Schizoid Man / Mirrors / I Talk To the Wind / Epitaph-March For No Reason / Tomorrow And Tomorrow / Moonchild / Illusion / Court of the Crimson King / Return Of The Fire Witch / Dance of The Puppets.
Album: released on E.G., Jan'87 by Virgin Records. Dist: Virgin, EMI

Cassette: released on E.G., Jan'87 by Virgin Records. Dist: Virgin, EMI

Compact disc: by Virgin Records. Dist: Virgin, EMI

IN THE WAKE OF POSEIDON.
Tracks: / Peace A Beginning / Pictures Of A City / Cadence And Cascade / In The Wake Of Poseidon (Including Libra's Theme / Peace-A theme / Cat Food / Devil's Triangle / Merday Morn / Hand Of Sceiron / Garden Of Worm / Peace-An End.
Album: released on E.G., Jan'87 by Virgin Records. Dist: Virgin, EMI

Cassette: released on E.G., Jan'87 by Virgin Records. Dist: Virgin, EMI

Compact disc: released on E.G., Jan'87 by Virgin Records. Dist: Virgin, EMI

ISLANDS.
Tracks: / Formentera Lady / Sailor's Tale / Letter (The) / Ladies of The Road / Prelude / Islands.
Album: released on E.G., Jan'87 by Virgin Records. Dist: Virgin, EMI

Cassette: released on E.G., Jan'87 by Virgin Records. Dist: Virgin, EMI

Compact disc: released on E.G., Jan'87 by Virgin Records. Dist: Virgin, EMI

Album: released on Polydor, Apr'77 by Polydor Records. Dist: Polygram, Polydor

Cassette: released on Polydor, Apr'77 by Polydor Records. Dist: Polygram, Polydor

LARKS' TONGUES IN ASPIC.
Tracks: / Larks' Tongues In Aspic, Parts 1&2 / Book Of Saturday / Exiles / Easy Money / Talking drum (The).
Album: released on E.G., Jan'87 by Virgin Records. Dist: Virgin, EMI

Cassette: released on E.G., Jan'87 by Virgin Records. Dist: Virgin, EMI

Compact disc: released on E.G., Jan'87 by Virgin Records. Dist: Virgin, EMI

LIZARD.
Tracks: / Cirkus, Inc. Entry Of The Chameleons / Indoor Games / Happy Family / Lady Of The Dancing Water / Lizard Suite.
Album: released on E.G., Jan'87 by Virgin Records. Dist: Virgin, EMI

Cassette: released on E.G., Jan'87 by Virgin Records. Dist: Virgin, EMI

Compact disc: by Virgin Records. Dist: Virgin, EMI

RED.
Tracks: / Red / Fallen Angel / One More Red nightmare / Providence / Starless.
Album: released on E.G., Jan'87 by Virgin Records. Dist: Virgin, EMI

Cassette: released on E.G., Jan'87 by Virgin Records. Dist: Virgin, EMI

Compact disc: released on E.G., Jan'87 by Virgin Records. Dist: Virgin, EMI

Album: released on Polydor, Apr'77 by Polydor Records. Dist: Polygram, Polydor

Cassette: released on Polydor, Apr'77 by Polydor Records. Dist: Polygram, Polydor

SLEEPLESS.
Single (7"): released on E.G., Mar'84 by Virgin Records. Dist: Virgin, EMI

Single (12"): released on E.G., Mar'84 by Virgin Records. Dist: Virgin, EMI

STARLESS & BIBLE BLACK.
Album: released on Polydor, Mar'77 by Polydor Records. Dist: Polygram, Polydor

Cassette: released on Polydor, Mar'77 by Polydor Records. Dist: Polygram, Polydor

THREE OF A PERFECT PAIR.
Tracks: / Model man / Sleepless / Man with an open heart / Nuages / Dig me / No warning / Larks' toungues in aspic part 3 / Three of a perfect pair.
Album: released on E.G., Jan'87 by Virgin Records. Dist: Virgin, EMI

Cassette: released on E.G., Jan'87 by Virgin Records. Dist: Virgin, EMI

Compact disc: released on E.G., Jan'87 by Virgin Records. Dist: Virgin, EMI

Compact disc: released on E.G., Feb'84 by Virgin Records. Dist: Virgin, EMI

USA.
Album: released on Polydor, Dec'79 by Polydor Records. Dist: Polygram, Polydor

YOUNG PERSON'S GUIDE TO KING CRIMSON.
Double Album: released on Polydor, Mar'77 by Polydor Records. Dist: Polygram, Polydor

Cassette: released on Polydor, Mar'77 by Polydor Records. Dist: Polygram, Polydor

King Curtis

IT'S GREAT TO BE RICH (EP).
Single (12"): released on Red Lightnin', Jun'83 by Red Lightnin' Records. Dist: Roots, Swift, Jazz Music, JSU, Pinnacle, Cartel, Wynd-Up Distribution

SOUL GROOVE.
Tracks: / Blowin' off steam / Dark eyes / Who's sorry now / Sweet Georgia Brown / Sometimes I'm happy / Pickin' chicken / Soul groove part 1 / Soul groove part 2 / Clementine / Take me out to the ball game.

Album: released on Blue Moon, Jul'87 Dist: Magnum Music Group Ltd, PRT, Spartan

King, Danny & The Elves

CHRISTMASTIME IS HERE.
Single (7"): released on JPD, Dec'82 Dist: PRT

King, Denis Orchestra

WE'LL MEET AGAIN.
Single (7"): released on Multi Media Tapes, Jun'83 by Multi Media Tapes Records. Dist: Stage One Distribution, Conifer Distribution, H.R. Taylor Distribution, Pinnacle

King Diamond

ABIGAIL.
Album: released on Roadrunner (Dutch), May'87 Dist: Pinnacle

Compact disc: released on Roadrunner (Dutch), Jun'87 Dist: Pinnacle

FATAL PORTRAIT.
Album: released on Roadrunner (Dutch), Feb'86 Dist: Pinnacle

King Dice

CHILDREN'S HOUR, THE.
Single (7"): released on King Dice, Feb'85

Kingdom Come

CROWN OF THORNS.
Single (7"): released on Illegal, Feb'83 by Faulty Products Records. Dist: Pinnacle, Lightning, Cartel

Kingdoms

HEARTLAND.
Single (7"): released on Regard, Feb'84

Single (12"): released on Regard, Feb'84

King, Don

1-2 PUNCH.
Album: released on Double Vision, Jun'85 by Double Vision Records. Dist: Rough Trade, Cartel

King Dream Chorus

KING HOLIDAY (King Dream Chorus & The Holiday Crew).
Tracks: / King holiday / (Martin Luther King Tribute song).
Single (7"): released on Club, Feb'86 by Phonogram Records. Dist: Polygram

Single (12"): released on Club, Feb'86 by Phonogram Records. Dist: Polygram

King, Earl

GLAZED (King, Earl With Roomful Of Blues).
Album: released on Demon, Jan'87 by Demon Records. Dist: Pinnacle

LET THE GOOD TIMES ROLL.
Album: released on Ace, Jan'83 by Ace Records. Dist: Pinnacle, Swift, Hotshot, Cadillac

NEW ORLEANS ROCK 'N' ROLL.
Album: released on Sonet, Aug'77 by Sonet Records. Dist: PRT

STREET PARADE.
Album: released on Charly, Nov'81 by Charly Records. Dist: Charly, Cadillac

TRICK BAG The best of Earl King.
Tracks: / Trick bag / You better know / Things that I used to do for you,The / Always a first time / Mama & papa / Love me now / Mother's love / Come on(Pt.1) / Come on(Pt.2) / Don't cry my friend / Don't you lose it / We are just good friends / You're more to me than gold / Case of love, A.
Album: released on Stateside, Apr'87 Dist: EMI

Cassette: released on Stateside, Apr'87 Dist: EMI

Album: released on EMI (France), '83 by EMI Records. Dist: Conifer

King, Eileen

COUNTRY FLAVOUR, THE.
Album: released on Homespun(Ireland), '82 by Outlet Records. Dist: Outlet

Cassette: released on Homespun(Ireland), '82 by Outlet Records. Dist: Outlet

King, Ellie

SPECIAL OFFER.
Single (7"): released on Solid, Sep'82 by Solid Records. Dist: Graduate, Spartan

Single (12"): released on Solid, Sep'82 by Solid Records. Dist: Graduate, Spartan

King Errisson

LIVING IT UP ON JUPITER (2 Parts).
Single (7"): released on Half Moon, Feb'83 by Rondelet Music And Records. Dist: Spartan

King, Evelyn

ACTION (King, Evelyn 'Champagne').
Single (12"): released on RCA, Jan'84 by RCA Records. Dist: RCA, Roots, Swift, Wellard, Chris, I & B, Solomon & Peres Distribution

BACK TO LOVE.
Single (7"): released on RCA, Nov'82 by RCA Records. Dist: RCA, Roots, Swift, Wellard, Chris, I & B, Solomon & Peres Distribution

Single (12"): released on RCA, Nov'82 by RCA Records. Dist: RCA, Roots, Swift, Wellard, Chris, I & B, Solomon & Peres Distribution

CHAMPAGNE.
Album: released on RCA, Dec'83 by RCA Records. Dist: RCA, Roots, Swift, Wellard, Chris, I & B, Solomon & Peres Distribution

Cassette: released on RCA, Dec'83 by RCA Records. Dist: RCA, Roots, Swift, Wellard, Chris, I & B, Solomon & Peres Distribution

EVELYN KING (4 TRACK CASSETTE EP).
Cassette: released on RCA, May'83 by RCA Records. Dist: RCA, Roots, Swift, Wellard, Chris, I & B, Solomon & Peres Distribution

GET LOOSE.
Single (7"): released on RCA, Feb'83 by RCA Records. Dist: RCA, Roots, Swift, Wellard, Chris, I & B, Solomon & Peres Distribution

Single (12"): released on RCA, Feb'83 by RCA Records. Dist: RCA, Roots, Swift, Wellard, Chris, I & B, Solomon & Peres Distribution

Album: released on RCA, Sep'82 by RCA Records. Dist: RCA, Roots, Swift, Wellard, Chris, I & B, Solomon & Peres Distribution

Cassette: released on RCA, Sep'82 by RCA Records. Dist: RCA, Roots, Swift, Wellard, Chris, I & B, Solomon & Peres Distribution

GIVE IT UP (King, Evelyn 'Champagne').
Single (7"): released on CBS, Oct'85 by CBS Records. Dist: CBS

Single (12"): released on CBS, Oct'85 by CBS Records. Dist: CBS

GIVE ME ONE REASON (King, Evelyn 'Champagne').
Single (7"): released on RCA, Feb'85 by RCA Records. Dist: RCA, Roots, Swift, Wellard, Chris, I & B, Solomon & Peres Distribution

Single (12"): released on RCA, Feb'85 by RCA Records. Dist: RCA, Roots, Swift, Wellard, Chris, I & B, Solomon & Peres Distribution

HIGH HORSE (King, Evelyn 'Champagne').
Tracks: / High horse / Take a chance / High horse (remix)* / Shame*.
Single (7"): released on RCA, Mar'86 by RCA Records. Dist: RCA, Roots, Swift, Wellard, Chris, I & B, Solomon & Peres Distribution

Single (12"): released on RCA, Mar'86 by RCA Records. Dist: RCA, Roots, Swift, Wellard, Chris, I & B, Solomon & Peres Distribution

IF YOU WANT MY LOVIN'.
Single (7"): released on RCA, Sep'81 by RCA Records. Dist: RCA, Roots, Swift, Wellard, Chris, I & B, Solomon & Peres Distribution

Single (12"): released on RCA, Sep'81 by RCA Records. Dist: RCA, Roots, Swift, Wellard, Chris, I & B, Solomon & Peres Distribution

I'M IN LOVE.
Single (7"): released on RCA, Jun'81 by RCA Records. Dist: RCA, Roots, Swift, Wellard, Chris, I & B, Solomon & Peres Distribution

Single (12"): released on RCA, Jun'81 by RCA Records. Dist: RCA, Roots, Swift, Wellard, Chris, I & B, Solomon & Peres Distribution

Album: released on RCA, Jul'81 by RCA Records. Dist: RCA, Roots, Swift, Wellard, Chris, I & B, Solomon & Peres Distribution

Cassette: released on RCA, Jul'81 by RCA Records. Dist: RCA, Roots, Swift, Wellard, Chris, I & B, Solomon & Peres Distribution

LONG TIME COMING, A (King, Evelyn 'Champagne').
Tracks: / Chemistry of love / Change is gonna come / Spellbound / If you find the time / Slow down / If I let myself go / Your personal touch / I'm scared / High horse.
Album: released on RCA, Nov'85 by RCA Records. Dist: RCA, Roots, Swift, Wellard, Chris, I & B, Solomon & Peres Distribution

Cassette: released on RCA, Nov'85 by RCA Records. Dist: RCA, Roots, Swift, Wellard, Chris, I & B, Solomon & Peres Distribution

LOVE COME DOWN.
Tracks: / Love come down / Shame.
Single (7"): released on Old Gold, Apr'87 by Old Gold Records. Dist: Lightning, Jazz Music, Spartan, Counterpoint

Single (7"): released on RCA, Jul'82 by RCA Records. Dist: RCA, Roots, Swift, Wellard, Chris, I & B, Solomon & Peres Distribution

Single (12"): released on RCA, Jul'82 by RCA Records. Dist: RCA, Roots, Swift, Wellard, Chris, I & B, Solomon & Peres Distribution

SO ROMANTIC.
Tracks: / Show me / Heartbreaker / Till midnight / Just for the night / Give me one reason / Out of control / Talking in my sleep / So in love / I'm so romantic.
Compact disc: released on RCA, Jan'85 by RCA Records. Dist: RCA, Roots, Swift, Wellard, Chris, I & B, Solomon & Peres Distribution

Album: released on RCA, Sep'84 by RCA Records. Dist: RCA, Roots, Swift, Wellard, Chris, I & B, Solomon & Peres Distribution

Cassette: released on RCA, Sep'84 by RCA Records. Dist: RCA, Roots, Swift, Wellard, Chris, I & B, Solomon & Peres Distribution

SPIRIT OF THE DANCER.
Single (7"): released on RCA, Jan'82 by RCA Records. Dist: RCA, Roots, Swift, Wellard, Chris, I & B, Solomon & Peres Distribution

Single (12"): released on RCA, Jan'82 by RCA Records. Dist: RCA, Roots, Swift, Wellard, Chris, I & B, Solomon & Peres Distribution

YOUR PERSONAL TOUCH.
Single (7"): released on RCA, Oct'85 by RCA Records. Dist: RCA, Roots, Swift, Wellard, Chris, I & B, Solomon & Peres Distribution

Single (12"): released on RCA, Oct'85 by RCA Records. Dist: RCA, Roots, Swift, Wellard, Chris, I & B, Solomon & Peres Distribution

King Everal

COWBOY STYLE.
Single (12"): released on Cow Boy, Oct'83 by Cowboy Records. Dist: Jetstar

DREADLOCKS TIME (2 parts).
Single (7"): released on Jammy's, Oct'83 by Jammy's Records. Dist: Jetstar

HOT LIKE ME (King Everal The Sham & Jo Manu).

TONIGHT YOU'RE MINE.
Tracks: / Tonight you're mine / Tonight you're mine (version).
Single (12"): released on Super Power, Jun'87 by Super Power Records. Dist: Jetstar Distribution

WALK AND SKIP.
Single (12"): released on Sun Set, Sep'84 by Sun Set Records. Dist: Jetstar Distribution

King, Fillmore

KEEP ON DANCIN'.
Single (7"): released on Pinnacle, Apr'84 by Pinnacle Records. Dist: Pinnacle

KEPP ON DANCIN'.

Kingfishers Catch Fire

RADIO KAMPALA.
Tracks: / Radio Kampala / Battlescars.
Single (7"): released on Furry, Jul'86 Dist: Rough Trade, Cartel

King, Freddy

GIVES YOU A BONANZA OF INSTRUMENTALS.
Album: released on Crosscut, Nov'84 by IMS-Polygram Records. Dist: IMS, Polygram, Rollercoaster Distribution

ROCKIN' THE BLUES LIVE.
Album: released on Crosscut, Oct'83 by IMS-Polygram Records. Dist: IMS, Polygram, Rollercoaster Distribution

TAKIN' CARE OF BUSINESS.
Tracks: / I'm tore down / She put the whammy on me / Sen-sa-shun / Teardrops on your letter / Side tracked / Welfare, The (turns its back on you) / Stumble, The / Someday after a while (you'll be sorry) / Have you ever loved a woman / You know that you love me (but you never tell me so) / Hide away / I love the woman / San-ho-zay / Takin' care of business / High rise / You've got to love her with a feeling.
Notes: An original King recording. Licensed from Gusto Records Inc., Nashville, Tennessee.
Compact disc: released on Charly, Oct'86 by Charly Records. Dist: Charly, Cadillac

TAKING CARE OF BUSINESS.
Album: released on Charly(R&B), Jul'85 by Charly Records. Dist: Charly, Cadillac

Cassette: released on Charly(R&B), Jul'85 by Charly Records. Dist: Charly, Cadillac

King Gaillard

ROCKY ROAD TO DUBLIN.
Compact disc: released on Delta, Jan'86 by Delta Records. Dist: Target

King George

OH LORD.
Tracks: / OH Lord / You Are My Lady.
Single (12"): released on Top Rank, Jan'87

King, Greg Band

KIHNSPIRACY.
Tracks: / Jeopardy / Fascination / Tear that city down / Talkin' to myself / Can't love them all / I can't love tham all / I fall to pieces / Someday / Curious / Love never fails / How long.

King, Henry

JOE SANDERS & HENRY KING 1945.
Album: released on Aircheck, Apr'79

King Henrys consort

DANCERIE.
Single (7"): released on Rex, Jul'84 by Decca.

DANSERIE.
Single (7"): released on Eden, Sep'84 by Eden Records. Dist: Pinnacle

KING HENRYS CONSORT.
Album: released on Eden, Nov'84 by Eden Records. Dist: Pinnacle

THINGUMMY-JIG.
Single (7"): released on Eden, Dec'84 by Eden Records. Dist: Pinnacle

Single (7"): released on Rex, Jan'84 by Decca.

King & I

KING AND I (THE) Original Film Soundtrack (Various Artists).
Tracks: / Overture / I whistle a happy tune / My lord and master / Hello, young lovers / March of the Siamese children / Puzzlement, A / Getting to know you / We kiss in a shadow - I have dreamed / Shall Itell you what I think of you? / Something wonderful / Song of the King / Shall we dance? / Something wonderful (finale).
Compact disc: released on Capitol, Apr'87 by Capitol Records. Dist: EMI

King is dead

KING IS DEAD (Various artists) (Various Artists).
Album: released on Magnum Force, Nov'82 by Magnum Music Group Ltd. Dist: Magnum Music Group Ltd, PRT, Spartan

King, James

ANGELS KNOW, THE (King, James & the Lonewolves).
Single (12"): released on Swamplands, Jan'85

EASY LOVE.
Tracks: / Easy love / Heartbreak, sorrow and pain.
Single (7"): released on Expansion, Jun'87 Dist: PRT

TEXAS LULLABY (5 track ep) (King, James & the Lonewolves).
Single (12"): released on Thrush, Nov'83 Dist: Pinnacle

Cassette: released on Thrush, Feb'84 Dist: Pinnacle

King, John

TRUE LIFE COUNTRY MUSIC.
Single (7"):

King, Jonathan

EVERYONE'S GONE TO THE MOON.
Single (7"): released on Old Gold, Jul'82 by Old Gold Records. Dist: Lightning, Jazz Music, Spartan, Counterpoint

GIMME SOME.
Tracks: / Gimme some / Crying again / Royal Mix, The*.
Single (7"): released on Virgin, Sep'86 by Virgin Records. Dist: EMI, Virgin Distribution

Single (12"): released on Virgin, Sep'86 by Virgin Records. Dist: EMI, Virgin Distribution

KING SIZE KING.
Album: released on PRT, Nov'82 by PRT Records. Dist: PRT

Cassette: released on PRT, Nov'82 by PRT Records. Dist: PRT

SPACE ODDITY.
Single (7"): released on Epic, Apr'84 by CBS Records. Dist: CBS

Single (12"): released on Epic, Apr'84 by CBS Records. Dist: CBS

King Kobra

HOME STREET HOME.
Tracks: / Home street home / Iron Eagle (never say die).
Single (12"): released on FM-Revolver, Jan'87 by FM-Revolver Records. Dist: BMG (RCA/Ariola), Pathe Marconi, Polygram

IRON EAGLE.
Tracks: / Iron eagle (Never say die) / This raging fire.
Single (7"): released on Capitol, May'86 by Capitol Records. Dist: EMI

THRILL OF A LIFETIME.
Tracks: / Second time around / Dream on / Feel the heat / Thrill of a lifetime / Only the strong will survive / Iron eagle (never say die) / Home street home / Overnight sensation / Raise your hands to rock / Party animals.
Album: released on FM, Mar'87 by FM-Revolver Records. Dist: EMI

Cassette: released on FM, Mar'87 by FM-Revolver Records. Dist: EMI

King Kong

BIG HEAVY LOAD.
Album: released on World Enterprise, Nov'86 Dist: Jetstar

CAKE OF SUCCESS.
Tracks: / Cake of success / Predominat.
Single (12"): released on Now Generation, Nov'86 Dist: Jetstar Distribution

DANCE HALL SESSION.
Album: released on World Enterprise, Mar'86 Dist: Jetstar

DIGITAL.
Single (12"): released on Digikal, Apr'87 by Digikal Records. Dist: Revolver

DIGITAL (King Kong & Frankie Paul).
Tracks: / Digital / Rambo.
Single (12"): released on Digikal, Mar'87 by Digikal Records. Dist: Revolver

DO NOT GET HIGH.
Single (12"): released on Ottey's Promotion, Apr'87

GLAMOUR BOY IN MY LIFE.
Tracks: / Glamour boy in my life / Come right in / Identify me.
Single (12"): released on Striker Lee, Sep'86 by Striker Lee Records. Dist: Jetstar Distribution

Single (12"): released on Digikal, Nov'86 by Digikal Records. Dist: Revolver

IDENTIFY ME.
Album: released on Black Solidarity, Mar'87 by Black Solidarity Records. Dist: Jetstar

LEGAL.
Tracks: / Legal / Mix up.
Single (12"): released on Greensleeves, Mar'86 by Greensleeves Records. Dist: BMG, Jetstar, Spartan

MUST WORK ON SUNDAY.
Tracks: / Must work on Sunday / Outta me way.
Single (12"): released on Striker Lee, Mar'86 by Striker Lee Records. Dist: Jetstar Distribution

NICENESS.
Tracks: / Niceness / Name and number.
Single (12"): released on Sweetcorn, Sep'86 by Sweetcorn Records. Dist: Jetstar

PARO THEM PARO.
Tracks: / Paro them paro / Paronia.
Single (12"): released on Greensleeves, Sep'86 by Greensleeves Records. Dist: BMG, Jetstar, Spartan

RAGAMUFFIN A PASS.
Tracks: / Ragamuffin a pass / Girl then a come.
Single (12"): released on New Generation, Mar'87 Dist: Jetstar

SENSIMANIA IS WALKING.
Tracks: / Sensimania is walking / Digital sensimania.
Single (12"): released on Rem, Dec'85 Dist: Jetstar

TOOT TOOT TOO MUCH.
Single (7"): released on Zara, Sep'83 by Zara Records. Dist: Rough Trade

Single (12"): released on Zara, Sep'83 by Zara Records. Dist: Rough Trade

TROUBLE AGAIN.
Tracks: / Trouble again / Me lover.
Notes: Features 10 tracks including the popular single and title track 'Trouble again'.The album is produced by Kin Jammy.
Single (12"): released on Greensleeves, Jun'86 by Greensleeves Records. Dist: BMG, Jetstar, Spartan

Album: released on Greensleeves, Nov'86 by Greensleeves Records. Dist: BMG, Jetstar, Spartan

King Kurt

AMERICA.
Tracks: / America / High and mighty / America / America(dub mix) / Super sperm / AJ meets Davy mix / Hello baby / If I ruled the world / Respect to the king / AJ is cool / Summertime / Groove MC lullaby / Don't cha feel like making love.
Picture disc single: released on Polydor, Nov'86 by Polydor Records. Dist: Polygram, Polydor

Single (7"): released on Polydor, Oct'86 by Polydor Records. Dist: Polygram, Polydor

Single (12"): released on Polydor, Oct'86 by Polydor Records. Dist: Polygram, Polydor

BANANA BANANA.
Single (7"): released on Stiff, Jun'84 by Stiff Records. Dist: EMI, Record Services Distribution (Ireland)

Single (12"): released on Stiff, Jun'84 by Stiff Records. Dist: EMI, Record Services Distribution (Ireland)

BIG COCK.
Notes: Cassette includes two extra tracks: Banana/Slammers.
Album: released on Stiff, Feb'86 by Stiff Records. Dist: EMI, Record Services Distribution (Ireland)

Cassette: released on Stiff, Feb'86 by Stiff Records. Dist: EMI, Record Services Distribution (Ireland)

BILLY.
Single (7"): released on Stiff, Jun'85 by Stiff Records. Dist: EMI, Record Services Distribution (Ireland)

DESTINATION ZULU LAND.
Single (7"): released on Stiff, Sep'83 by Stiff Records. Dist: EMI, Record Services Distribution (Ireland)

Single (12"): released on Stiff, Sep'83 by Stiff Records. Dist: EMI, Record Services Distribution (Ireland)

KING KURT.
Album: released on Stiff, Dec'83 by Stiff Records. Dist: EMI, Record Services Distribution (Ireland)

LAND OF RING DANG DOO (THE).
Tracks: / Horatio / Gather your limbs / Land of Ring Dang Doo (The) / Zulu beat (live) / Zulu beat (live at the Reading Sexadrome) / Horatio (live at the Reading Sexadrome) / Gather your limbs (live at the Reading Sexadrome).
Notes: * = Extra track on 12" only
Single (7"): released on Polydor, Apr'87 by Polydor Records. Dist: Polygram, Polydor

Single (12"): released on Polydor, Apr'87 by Polydor Records. Dist: Polygram, Polydor

Double-pack single: released on Polydor, May'87 by Polydor Records. Dist: Polygram, Polydor

MACK THE KNIFE.
Single (7"): released on Stiff, Apr'84 by Stiff Records. Dist: EMI, Record Services Distribution (Ireland)

Single (12"): released on Stiff, Apr'84 by Stiff Records. Dist: EMI, Record Services Distribution (Ireland)

Picture disc single: released on Stiff, May'84 by Stiff Records. Dist: EMI, Record Services Distribution (Ireland)

ROAD TO RACK AND RUIN.
Single (7"): released on Stiff, Aug'85 by Stiff Records. Dist: EMI, Record Services Distribution (Ireland)

Single (12"): released on Stiff, Aug'85 by Stiff Records. Dist: EMI, Record Services Distribution (Ireland)

SLAMMERS.
Single (7"): released on Stiff, Nov'85 by Stiff Records. Dist: EMI, Record Services Distribution (Ireland)

Single (12"): released on Stiff, Nov'85 by Stiff Records. Dist: EMI, Record Services Distribution (Ireland)

ZULU BEAT.
Tracks: / Zulu beat / Rockin Kent / Ghost riders in the sky / Oedipus.
Single (7"): released on Thin Sliced, Jan'87 by Thin Sliced Records. Dist: Rough Trade Distribution, Cartel Distribution

Single (12"): released on Thin Sliced, Jan'87 by Thin Sliced Records. Dist: Rough Trade Distribution, Cartel Distribution

King Lear

KING LEAR Shakespear (Various Artists).
Cassette: released on Argo (Spokenword), Mar'83 by Decca Records. Dist: Polygram

King, Lisa

CAN'T HELP FALLING IN LOVE.
Single (7"): released on Trident, Oct'80 Dist: Stage One

King, Marcel

HOLLWOOD NIGHTS.
Single (12"): released on Debut-Passion, Mar'85

KEEP ON DANCING.
Single (12"): released on Factory, Mar'84 by Factory Records. Dist: Cartel, Pinnacle

REACH FOR LOVE(REMIX).
Single (12"): released on Factory, Mar'84 by Factory Records. Dist: Cartel, Pinnacle

Single (12"): released on Factory, Apr'85 by Factory Records. Dist: Cartel, Pinnacle

King, Mark

I FEEL FREE.
Single (7"): released on Polydor, Jun'84 by Polydor Records. Dist: Polygram. Polydor

Single (12"): released on Polydor, Jun'84 by Polydor Records. Dist: Polygram, Polydor

INFLUENCES.
Album: released on Polydor, Jul'84 by Polydor Records. Dist: Polygram, Polydor

Cassette: released on Polydor, Jul'84 by Polydor Records. Dist: Polygram. Polydor

King, Marva

FEELS RIGHT.
Album: released on Planet, Aug'81 Dist: WEA

King MC

WHAT HAVE YOU DONE FOR ME LATELY.
Tracks: / What have you done for me lately.
Single (7"): released on Important, May'86 Dist: EMI

Single (12"): released on Important, May'86 Dist: EMI

King, Morgana

EVERYTHING MUST CHANGE.
Compact disc: released on Muse (USA), Feb'86 by Muse Records (USA). Dist: Conifer Distribution, Jazz Music Distribution

Album: released on JSU-Swift, Apr'81

HIGHER GROUND.
Album: released on Muse, Apr'81 by Peerless Records. Dist: Lugtons Distributors

PORTRAITS.
Tracks: / What's going on/Save the children / You go to my head / Moment of truth / Time was

Page 564

(Duerme) / Send in the clowns / Lush life / You're not th kind / If you could see me know.
Notes: Personnel: Morgana King-Vocals/Joe Puma-Guitar/Ed Caccavale-Drums/Art Koenig-Bass/Jay Lonhart-Bass (track 2 & 6 only)/Ben Arnov-Keyboards/Clifford Carter-Synthesizer/John Kaye-Percussion. Produced by Mitch Farber 7 Chuck Irwin.
Album: released on Muse (USA), Aug'86 by Muse Records (USA). Dist: Conifer Distribution, Jazz Music Distribution

Cassette: released on Muse (USA), Aug'86 by Muse Records (USA). Dist: Conifer Distribution, Jazz Music Distribution

STRETCHIN' OUT.
Tracks: / What a difference a day made / Makin; whoopee / Them there eyes / I'm glad there is you / God bless the child / Could it be majic / All in love is fair/Feelings / Visions.
Album: released on Muse, Sep'86 by Peerless Records. Dist: Lugtons Distributors

Album: released on Muse, Apr'81 by Peerless Records. Dist: Lugtons Distributors

TASTE OF HONEY.
Album: released on Audio Fidelity, Mar'83 Dist: PRT

King, Natasha

AM.
Tracks: / AM / FM / Megamix.
Single (7"): released on Ecstasy, Feb'86 by Creole Records. Dist: CBS

Single (12"): released on Ecstasy, Feb'86 by Creole Records. Dist: CBS

King Obstinate

HUNGRY.
Tracks: / Hungry / Got a little something for you.
Single (12"): released on Hot Vinyl, Aug'86 by Hot Vinyl Records. Dist: Jetstar

King Of....

KING OF DRUMS Various artists (Various Artists).
Album: released on CBS(I love Jazz), Aug'84 by CBS Records. Dist: CBS

Cassette: released on CBS(I love Jazz), Aug'84 by CBS Records. Dist: CBS

KING OF ROCK 'N' ROLL, THE Various artists (Various Artists).
Album: released on Pickwick, Jun'85 by Pickwick Records. Dist: Pickwick Distribution, Prism Leisure Distribution, Lugtons

King of Hearts

QUEEN OF SPADES (2 parts).
Single (7"): released on Ritz, Feb'82 by Outlet Records. Dist: Outlet, Prism Leisure Distribution, Record Services Distribution (Ireland), Roots

King of Luxembourg

PICTURE OF DORIAN GRAY, A.
Tracks: / Picture of Dorian Gray, A / Hasta pronto / Lee Remick / Espadarte / Where are the prawns?.
Single (12"): released on EL, Mar'87 by El Records. Dist: Rough Trade, Cartel, Pinnacle

ROYAL BASTARD.
Tracks: / Picture of Dorian Gray / Valleri / Rubens Rooms(the) / Mad / Poptones / Something / Baby / Wedding of Ramona Blair / Happy together (prelude) / Liar liar.
Album: released on EL, May'87 by El Records. Dist: Rough Trade, Cartel, Pinnacle

VALLERI.
Tracks: / Valleri / Sketches of Luxemburg.
Single (7"): released on EL, Jul'86 by El Records. Dist: Rough Trade, Cartel, Pinnacle

King Of The Blues

KING OF THE BLUES Various artists (Various Artists).
Album: released on Topline, Aug'87 by Charly Records. Dist: Charly Distribution. Estim retail price in Sep'87 was £2.99.

Cassette: released on Topline, Aug'87 by Charly Records. Dist: Charly Distribution. Estim retail price in Sep'87 was £2.99.

King, P

HEY ROSALYN.
Single (7"): released on Red Bus, Jul'83 by Red Bus Records. Dist: PRT

King, Paul

FOLLOWING HEART.
Tracks: / Following heart / Brutality.
Single (7"): released on CBS, Jul'87 by CBS Records. Dist: CBS

Single (12"): released on CBS, Jul'87 by CBS Records. Dist: CBS

FOLLOW MY HEART.
Single (7"): released on CBS, Aug'87 by CBS Records. Dist: CBS

Single (7"): released on PRT, Aug'87 by PRT Records. Dist: PRT

Cassette single: released on CBS, Aug'87 by CBS Records. Dist: CBS

I KNOW.
Tracks: / I know / Some risks.
Single (12"): released on CBS, Apr'87 by CBS Records. Dist: CBS

I KNOW (REMIX).
Tracks: / I know (remix) / I know / Some risks.
Single (12"): released on CBS, Apr'87 by CBS Records. Dist: CBS

JOY.
Tracks: / Follow my heart / When you smile / I know / Pass on by / So brutal / It's up to you / One too many heartaches / Slow motion / Some risks / Glory's goal.
Album: released on CBS, May'87 by CBS Records. Dist: CBS

Cassette: released on CBS, May'87 by CBS Records. Dist: CBS

Album: released on CBS, Sep'87 by CBS Records. Dist: CBS

King, Pee Wee

BALLROOM KING.
Tracks: / Catty town / Plantation boogie / I don't mind / Blue Suede shoes / Steel rag guitar / Railroad boogie / Rootie tootie / Half a dozen boogie / Ballroom baby / Ten gallon boogie / Hoot scoot / Chew tobacco rag / Forty nine women / Indian giver / Bull fiddle boogie / Tweedle dee.
Album: released on Detour, Dec'86 by Detour Records. Dist: Swift, RCA, Jazz Music, Projection

BEST OF... (King, Pee Wee & Redd Stewart).
Notes: 10 tracks

ROMPIN',STOMPIN',SINGIN',SWINGIN'.
Album: released on RCA, Sep'84 by RCA Records. Dist: RCA, Roots, Swift, Wellard, Chris, I & B, Solomon & Peres Distribution

King Perry

KING PERRY 1947-1954.
Notes: Mono
Album: released on Krazy Kat, Jan'87 Dist: Jazz Music, Swift, Chris Wellard, H.R. Taylor, Charly, Hotshot, IRS Distribution

King, Peter

BAD MEMORY.
Tracks: / Bad memory.
Single (12"): released on Fashion, Mar'86 by Fashion Records. Dist: PRT, Jetstar

EAST 34TH STREET (King, Peter Quartet).
Album: released on Spotlite, '83 by Spotlite Records. Dist: Cadillac, Jazz Music, Spotlite

MY KIND OF COUNTRY.
Album: released on Tank, Dec'77 by Tank Records.

NEW BEGINNING (King, Peter Quartet/Quintet).
Album: released on Spotlite, '83 by Spotlite Records. Dist: Cadillac, Jazz Music, Spotlite

NITE LIFE.
Single (7"): released on 6AM, Sep'83

Single (12"): released on 6AM, Sep'83

SOMETHING WICKED.
Tracks: / Something wicked / Young blood.
Single (7"): released on Spirit, May'86 by Spirit Records. Dist: WEA

Single (12"): released on Spirit, May'86 by Spirit Records. Dist: WEA

STEP ON THE GAS.
Single (12"): released on Fashion, May'85 by Fashion Records. Dist: PRT, Jetstar

King Pleasure

KING PLEASURE SINGS/ANNIE ROSS SINGS (King Pleasure & Annie Ross).
Album:

King, Ray

WOMAN THAT UNDERSTANDS, A.
Single (7"): released on Big Bear, Jan'80 by Big Bear Records. Dist: Big Bear, Swift

King, Rob

YOU DON'T KNOW LIKE I KNOW.
Tracks: / You don't know like I know / Blues on.
Single (7"): released on Soul City, Jul'87 by Soul City Records. Dist: PRT

Single (12"): released on Soul City, Jul'87 by Soul City Records. Dist: PRT

Kings and Queens...

KINGS AND QUEENS OF ENGLAND
1,000 years of English monarchy.
Cassette: released on Sound Fact, Jul'81 by H.R. Taylor. Dist: Essex

KINGS AND QUEENS OF ENGLAND: BOOK 1 (Kings and queens of England: Book 1).
Cassette: released on Pickwick (Tell-a-tale), Mar'84 by Pickwick Records. Dist: Pickwick Distribution

KINGS AND QUEENS OF ENGLAND: BOOK 2 (Kings and queens of England: Book 2).
Cassette: released on Pickwick (Tell-a-tale), Mar'84 by Pickwick Records. Dist: Pickwick Distribution

King, Sasha

YOU CAN'T TURN ME AWAY.
Tracks: / You can't turn me away / You can't turn me away (club mix).
Single (12"): released on Londisc, Aug'86 by Londisc Records.

King's College

KINGSBRIDGE SONG CONTEST Performances by all competitors (Various Artists).
Cassette: released on Folktracks, Nov'79 by Folktracks Cassettes. Dist: Folktracks

Kings College Choir

CAROLS FROM KINGS.
Album: released on H.M.V., '69 by EMI Records. Dist: EMI

CHORAL FAVOURITES FROM KINGS COLLEGE.
Album: released on Columbia, Jul'79 by EMI Records. Dist: EMI

CHRISTMAS MUSIC FROM KINGS.
Album: released on EMI, '76 by EMI Records. Dist: EMI

CHRISTMAS MUSIC: MESSIAH.
Album: released on H.M.V., '69 by EMI Records. Dist: EMI

FESTIVAL OF LESSONS AND CAROLS.
Album: released on Contour, Oct'81 by Pickwick Records. Dist: Pickwick Distribution, PRT

Cassette: released on Contour, Oct'81 by Pickwick Records. Dist: Pickwick Distribution, PRT

Album: released on Argo, '78 by Decca Records. Dist: Polygram

WORLD OF CHRISTMAS.
Album: released on World of Learning, '70 by World Of Learning Records. Dist: World Of Learning

WORLD OF KINGS.
Album: released on World of Learning, '72 by World Of Learning Records. Dist: World Of Learning

King, Sid

BACK DOOR MAN.
Single (7"): released on Hot, Sep'80 by Hot Records. Dist: Rough Trade, Cartel

GONNA SHAKE THIS SHACK TONIGHT (King, Sid & The Five Strings).
Album: released on Bear Family, Sep'84 by Bear Family Records. Dist: Rollercoaster Distribution, Swift

LET'S GET LOOSE.
Album: released on Rockhouse, Jul'87 by Rockhouse Records. Dist: Swift Distribution, Charly Distribution

Album: released on Rockhouse, Aug'87 by Rockhouse Records. Dist: Swift Distribution, Charly Distribution

ROCKIN' ON THE RADIO (King, Sid & The Five Strings).
Album: released on Rollercoaster, Sep'84 by Rollercoaster Records. Dist: Swift Distribution, Rollercoaster Distribution

Kingsley, Ben

CRY, THE BELOVED COUNTRY.
Notes: Cry, the beloved country is the story of a simple Zulu parson's search for his delinquent son amidst the confusion of Johannesburg. It is told with simplicity, imagination and compassion, making it a deeply moving experience, whilst at the same time it approaches the racial problems of South Africa with intelligence and understanding. Written by Alan Paton Running time approx 2 hrs.
Cassette: released on Listen For Pleasure, Apr'87 by MFP Records. Dist: EMI

Kingsmen

BEST OF THE KINGSMEN, THE.
Album: released on Rhino (USA), Jan'86 by Rhino Records (USA).

LOUIE LOUIE Greatest hits.
Tracks: / Louie Louie / Money (that's what I want) / Jolly green giant / Death of an angel / Climb, The / Get out of my life woman / Little Latin lupe lu / Killer Joe / Annie Fanny / Long green / Little Sally tease / Trouble / If I need someone.
Album: released on Decal, Jan'87 by Charly Records. Dist: Charly

Single (7"): released on Old Gold, Jul'82 by Old Gold Records. Dist: Lightning, Jazz Music, Spartan, Counterpoint

Kingsnakes

ROUNDTRIP TICKET.
Album: released on New Rose, Aug'85 Dist: Rough Trade, Cartel

Single (7"): released on New Rose, Jun'85 Dist: Rough Trade, Cartel

Kings Of...

KINGS OF BLUES, THE Various artists (Various Artists).
Notes: Starr Marketing Services Ltd, 90 Queens Road, Twickenham, Middlesex. TW1 4ET. Tel: 01 891 6487
Compact disc: released on Bridge, Oct'86 Dist: CD Centre Distribution, Pinnacle, Target

KINGS OF COUNTRY & WESTERN Various artists (Various Artists).
Notes: Johnny Cash, Jerry Lee Lewis etc.
Compact disc: released on Bellaphon, Jan'86 by Bellaphon Records. Dist: IMS-Polygram

Compact disc: released on Bridge, Jan'86 Dist: CD Centre Distribution, Pinnacle, Target

KINGS OF DIXIELAND 20 Great Dixieland jazz hits (Various Artists).
Tracks: / Washington post march / Bill Bailey / Thunder and blazes / East side, West side / Wait 'till the sun shines Nellie / Daisy Bell / Tell me your dream / Careless love / Ramblin' wreck from Georgia Tech / Carry me back to old Virginny / New Washington and lee swing / Ida / Semper Fidelis / Give my regards to Broadway / Somebody stole my gal / Merry widow blues / Oh, dem golden slippers / Goodnight ladies / King fish blues / Battle hymn of the republic.
Compact disc: released on Hermes, Jun'87 by Nimbus Records. Dist: Target

KINGS OF DIXIELAND: VOL 1 Various artists (Various Artists).
Album: released on Bright Orange, Apr'79 Dist: Swift

KINGS OF DIXIELAND: VOL 2 Various artists (Various Artists).
Album: released on Bright Orange, Apr'79 Dist: Swift

KINGS OF DIXIELAND: VOL 3 Various artists (Various Artists).
Album: released on Bright Orange, Apr'79 Dist: Swift

KINGS OF DIXIELAND: VOL 4 Various artists (Various Artists).
Album: released on Bright Orange, Apr'79 Dist: Swift

KINGS OF DIXIELAND: VOL 5 Various artists (Various Artists).
Album: released on Bright Orange, Apr'79 Dist: Swift

KINGS OF DIXIELAND: VOL 6 Various artists (Various Artists).
Album: released on Bright Orange, Apr'79 Dist: Swift

KINGS OF ROCK Various artists (Various Artists).

KINGS OF ROCKABILLY Various artists (Various Artists).
Cassette: released on Ditto, May'86 by Pickwick Records. Dist: H.R. Taylor

KINGS OF SKIFFLE Various artists (Various Artists).
Double Album: released on Decca, '74 by Decca Records. Dist: Polygram

KINGS OF SOUL Various artists (Various Artists).
Notes: Sam & Dave, Percy Sledge, Aretha Franklin, Ben E. king, Brook Benton,Fontella Bass, Barbara Mason.
Compact disc: released on Bridge, Oct'86 Dist: CD Centre Distribution, Pinnacle, Target

KINGS OF SWING Various artists (Various Artists).
Notes: Orchestras of Benny Goodman, Harry James, Les Brown, Bob Crosby, Charley Barnet, and Tex Beneke.
Compact disc: released on Delta, Jan'86 by Delta Records. Dist: Target

Compact disc: released on Bridge, Apr'87 Dist: CD Centre Distribution, Pinnacle, Target

Album: released on Decca (Elite), Feb'82 by Decca Records. Dist: Polygram, IMS

KINGS OF THE BLUES Various artists (Various Artists).
Tracks: / Dust my broom / I wish you would / San-ho-zay / Open up baby / My back scratcher / Thug / I love you honey / Loose me / Born under a bad sign / Hide away / I ain't got you / Somebody loan me a dime / Part time love / I need your love so bad / Crawl, The / Honky tonk.
Notes: Brownie McGhee, Big Joe Williams, Lonnie Johnson, Sonny Terry, Champion Jack Dupree etc.
Compact disc: released on Bridge, Jan'86 Dist: CD Centre Distribution, Pinnacle, Target

Compact disc: released on Topline, May'87 by Charly Records. Dist: Charly Distribution

Album: released on Topline, Aug'87 by Charly Records. Dist: Charly Distribution

Cassette: released on Topline, Aug'87 by Charly Records. Dist: Charly Distribution

KINGS OF THE BLUES (II) Various artists (Various Artists).
Notes: Licensors. (a) Original FIRE recording via SANSU ENTERPRISES. Licensed from Charly Records International APS. (b) Original VEE JAY recording. Licensed from Charly Records International APS. (c) Original KING recording. Licensed from Gusto Records Inc. (d) Original JEWEL recording. Licensed from Charly Records International APS. (e) Original GOLDBAND recording. (f) Produced by Allen Toussaint for Sansu Enterprises Inc. Licensed from Charly Records International APS. (g) Licensed from Ala Enterprises Inc. (h) Original Sound Stage 7 recording. Licensed from Charly Records International APS.

Kings Of Oblivion

BIG FISH POPCORN.
Single (7"): released on Bam Caruso, 23 May'87 by Bam Caruso Records. Dist: Rough Trade, Revolver, Cartel

Kings Of Rock 'N' Roll

KINGS OF ROCK 'N' ROLL Various artists (Various Artists).
Notes: Bill Haley, Little Richard, Jerry Lee lewis etc
Compact disc: released on Bellaphon, Jan'86 by Bellaphon Records. Dist: IMS-Polygram

Compact disc: released on Bridge, Dec'85 Dist: CD Centre Distribution, Pinnacle, Target

KINGS OF ROCK 'N' ROLL - VOL.1 Various artists (Various Artists).
Notes: hits by Bill Haley & the Comets, bobby Vee, Bobby Rydell, tommy Roe, Little Richard etc.
Compact disc: released on Bridge, Jan'86 Dist: CD Centre Distribution, Pinnacle, Target

KINGS OF ROCK 'N' ROLL - VOL 2 Various artists (Various Artists).
Compact disc: released on Bridge, Oct'86 Dist: CD Centre Distribution, Pinnacle, Target

Kings Of Swing Orchestra

HOOKED ON SWING.
Tracks: / In the mood / I've got my love to keep me warm / Lullaby of Birdland / Sweet Georgia Brown / Bye bye blackbird / American patrol / Preacher, the / Cherokee / Johnsons rag / Caravan / Christopher Columbus / String of pearls / Take the "A" train / Down by the riverside / Opus one / In the mood (reprise) / I've got you under my skin / Saturday night is the lonliest night of the week / Day in - day out / High hopes / Just one of those things / Come fly with me / Witchcraft / All of me / Big bad Leroy Brown / Chicago / My kind of town / New York, New York / Serenade in blues / As time goes by / Stranger on the shore / Blue moon / Misty / Sentimental journey / You made me love you / Hello Dolly / Last time I saw Paris, The / S'wonderful, s'marvelous / It's de lovely / Mame / Lullaby of Broadway / Broadway / Get me to the church on time / I feel pretty / On the street where you live / Hello Dolly (reprise) / Chattanooga choo choo / Fascinating rhythm / Crazy rhythm / Little brown jug / Stomping at the Savoy / I've got a gal in Kalamazoo / What is this thing called love / Don't sit under the apple tree / Eager beaver / Perdido / Intermission riff / Birdland / C-jam blues / Chatanooga choo choo (reprise) / Don't get around much anymore / I'm beginning to see the light / Jersey bounce / After you've gone / Elmer's tune / Spirit is willing, The / My lean baby / Blues in the night / Don't get around much anymore (reprise) / East of the sun (and west of the moon) / Roses of Picardy / September in the rain / I'll remember you / For you / Continental, The / On a clear day you can see forever / Little white lies / I'll be around / East of the sun (and west of the moon) reprise / Begin the beguine / Old black magic, The / Mack the knife / Jeeper creepers / On the sunny side of the street / Margie / Jada / This can't be love / Johnny one note / Change partners / I'm putting all my eggs in one basket / Cabaret.
Notes: (P) & (C) 1987 K-Tel International (UK) Ltd.
Compact disc: released on K-Tel, Jun'87 by K-Tel Records. Dist: Record Merchandisers Distribution, Taylors, Terry Blood Distribution, Wynd-Up Distribution, Relay Distribution, Pickwick Distribution, Solomon & Peres Distribution, Polygram

SWITCHED ON SWING.
Album: released on K-Tel, Jun'82 by K-Tel Records. Dist: Record Merchandisers Distribution, Taylors, Terry Blood Distribution, Wynd-Up Distribution, Relay Distribution, Pickwick Distribution, Solomon & Peres Distribution, Polygram

Cassette: released on K-Tel, Jun'82 by K-Tel Records. Dist: Record Merchandisers Distribution, Taylors, Terry Blood Distribution, Wynd-Up Distribution, Relay Distribution, Pickwick Distribution, Solomon & Peres Distribution, Polygram

Single (7"): released on Philips, Mar'82 Dist: IMS-Polygram

Kings of the Orient

WHITE DOOR.
Single (7"): released on Clay, Oct'82 by Clay Records. Dist: Pinnacle

Single (12"): released on Clay, Oct'82 by Clay Records. Dist: Pinnacle

King, Solomon

SHE WEARS MY RING.
Tracks: / She wears my ring.
Single (7"): released on Old Gold, Mar'87 by Old Gold Records. Dist: Lightning, Jazz Music, Spartan, Counterpoint

Single (7"): released on Old Gold (Reissue), Jul'82

King Solomon's Mines

KING SOLOMON'S MINES Original Soundtrack.
Tracks: / Main title / Upside down people / crocodiles, The / pot luck / Forced flight / Dancing shots / Good morning / no pain / Ritual, The / No diamonds - Generique fin.
Notes: Latest remake of the adventure classic was dismissed as a 'Raiders Of The Last Ark' clone, despite being a box office success. However its orchestral score byveteran Jerry Goldsmith proves distinctive and should appeal to movie music buffs.
Album: released on Milan France, Apr'86

Cassette: released on Milan France, Apr'86

KING SOLOMON'S MINES Haggard, H. Rider (Anderson, Miles).
Double cassette: released on Argo, Jan'84 by Decca Records. Dist: Polygram

KING SOLOMON'S MINES Haggard, H. Rider (Jayston,Michael).
Cassette: released on Pinnacle, '79 by Pinnacle Records. Dist: Pinnacle

KING SOLOMON'S MINES Haggard, H. Rider (Young, John).
Cassette: released on Colophone Audio Visual, Feb'81 by Audio-Visual Library Services. Dist: Audio-Visual Library Services

King Sounds

BLACK AND WHITE.
Tracks: / Black and white / Black and white (Version).
Single (12"): released on King & I, Apr'86 Dist: Jetstar

GAMES PEOPLE PLAY.
Tracks: / Games people play / Games people play (version).
Single (12"): released on Viza, 23 May'87

BOOK OF RULES (King Sounds & The Israelites).
Single (12"): released on King 1, Oct'84

I DON'T WANT TO HURT YOU (King Sounds & The Israelites).
Tracks: / I don't want to hurt you.
Single (7"): released on King & I, Aug'86 Dist: Jetstar

THERE IS A REWARD (King Sounds & The Israelites).
Album: released on King and the I, Sep'85

YOU ARE MY PILOT (King Sounds & The Israelites).
Single (12"): released on King 1, Dec'83

King's Own...

TARTAN TOP TWENTY: VOL 1.
Album: released on Great Bands, Oct'81 by Decca Records. Dist: Polygram, Solomon & Peres Distribution

Cassette: released on Great Bands, Oct'81 by Decca Records. Dist: Polygram, Solomon & Peres Distribution

TARTAN TOP TWENTY: VOL 2.
Album: released on Great Bands, Oct'81 by Decca Records. Dist: Polygram, Solomon & Peres Distribution

Cassette: released on Great Bands, Oct'81 by Decca Records. Dist: Polygram, Solomon & Peres Distribution

King Sporty

DO YOU WANNA DANCE? (King Sporty & The Ex-tras).
Single (7"): released on Dancefloor, Sep'83 by Dancefloor Records. Dist: Vista Sounds Records, Jetstar

Single (12"): released on Dancefloor, Sep'83 by Dancefloor Records. Dist: Vista Sounds Records, Jetstar

MEET ME AT THE DISCO.
Single (7"): released on Dancefloor, May'83 by Dancefloor Records. Dist: Vista Sounds Records, Jetstar

King's Singers

ATLANTIC BRIDGE.
Cassette: released on Columbia, Sep'79 by EMI Records. Dist: EMI

CAPTAIN NOAH & FLOATING ZOO.
Album: released on Argo, '72 by Decca Records. Dist: Polygram

CHRISTMAS WITH THE KING'S SINGERS.
Album: released on MFP (EMI), Dec'82 by EMI Records. Dist: EMI

Cassette: released on MFP (EMI), Dec'82 by EMI Records. Dist: EMI

COLLECTIONS.
Album: released on MFP (EMI), Nov'82 by EMI Records. Dist: EMI

Cassette: released on MFP (EMI), Nov'82 by EMI Records. Dist: EMI

CONCERT COLLECTION.
Album: released on H.M.V., Mar'76 by EMI Records. Dist: EMI

Cassette: released on H.M.V., Mar'76 by EMI Records. Dist: EMI

DECK THE HALL.
Album: released on H.M.V., Nov'73 by EMI Records. Dist: EMI

HOME IS A SPECIAL KIND OF FEELING.
Single (7"): released on Masterchord, Mar'84 by Masterchord Records & Tapes. Dist: PRT

IN PERFECT HARMONY.
Tracks: / Ding a dong / Windmills of your mind, The / I'm a train / Fool on the hill / Java jive / Widdicombe Fair / Life on Mars / Horse with no name, A / She's leaving home / Morning has broken / Bye Bye Blues / Song and dance man / Travelin' Boy / It don't mean a thing (if it ain't got that swing) / Waltz in A flat major / Nimrod / Sympatique / Sgt Pepper Intro / Sunshine of your love / Building a wall / There are bad times just around corner / Bring me the sun again / God bless Joanna / Romance / Strawberry fields forever / Sweet gingerbread man / After the goldrush / For the peace of all mankind / Jimmy Brown song, The / Pantomime / Taste of Honey, A.
Album: released on Music For Pleasure, Apr'86 by EMI Records. Dist: EMI

Cassette: released on Music For Pleasure, Apr'86 by EMI Records. Dist: EMI

KIDS STUFF.
Album: released on EMI, Dec'86 by EMI Records. Dist: EMI

KING'S SINGERS BELIEVE IN MUSIC.
Tracks: / Something's coming / You needed me / All by myself / Short people / Lost in love / Betty Grable / Because / Della and the dealer / Music / I believe in music / I've got the music in me / Thank you for the music / Goodbye yellow brick road / Mahogony (theme from) / Save your kisses for me / Hasta Manana / Tea for two / We'll meet again / How did we fall in love / Copacabana (at the0.
Compact disc: released on H.M.V., May'87 by EMI Records. Dist: EMI

KING'S SINGERS, THE.
Album: released on Enterprise, '74 by President Records. Dist: President Distribution, Jazz Music, Taylors, Spartan

Album: released on One Up, Mar'76 by EMI Records.

LET'S BEGIN AGAIN.
Single (7"): released on Masterchord, Nov'83 by Masterchord Records & Tapes. Dist: PRT

REQUIEM FOR FATHER MALARCHY.
Album: released on Red Seal, Jul'76 by RCA Records. Dist: RCA

THIS IS THE KING'S SINGERS.
Tracks: / Im a train / Girl talk / Windmills of your mind / I love you, Samantha / Ring de banjo / God bless Joanne / Slow train / It was almost like a song / Strawberry fields forever / Gambler, The / Didn't we / After the goldrush / Dayton Ohio-1903 / With you on my mind / One of these songs / Transport of delight / I'll see you again / Life on mars.
Compact disc: released on H.M.V., May'87 by EMI Records. Dist: EMI

Album: released on EMI, Jul'80 by EMI Records. Dist: EMI

Cassette: released on EMI, Jul'80 by EMI Records. Dist: EMI

TRIBUTE TO THE COMEDIAN HARMONISTS.
Album: released on EMI, Jul'85 by EMI Records. Dist: EMI

Cassette: released on EMI, Jul'85 by EMI Records. Dist: EMI

VICTORIAN COLLECTION, THE.
Cassette: released on H.M.V., Jan'80 by EMI Records. Dist: EMI

Wind in the willows and the reluctant dragon

Kings's Row

KING'S ROW Original Film Score.
Notes: Digital Stereo.
Compact disc: released on That's Entertainment, Jul'84 by That's Entertainment Records. Dist: Pinnacle, PRT

Album: released on Chalfont (USA), Aug'80 by Varese Sarabande.

King, Stephen

THINNER.
Notes: Read by Paul Sorvino. Double Cassette.
Cassette: released on Listen For Pleasure, Aug'86 by MFP Records. Dist: EMI

Kingston Trio

BEST OF KINGSTON TRIO VOL.2.
Album: released on Capitol, Apr'81 by Capitol Records. Dist: EMI

TOM DOOLEY.
Tracks: / Tom Dooley.
Single (7"): released on Old Gold, Mar'87 by Old Gold Records. Dist: Lightning, Jazz Music, Spartan, Counterpoint

Album: released on Astan, Nov'84 by Astan Records. Dist: Counterpoint

Cassette: released on Astan, Nov'84 by Astan Records. Dist: Counterpoint

VERY BEST OF THE KINGSTON TRIO (THE).
Tracks: / Tom Dooley / Bad man's blunder / Tijuana trail (The) / Worried man, A / Everglades / Ally ally oxen free / Lemon tree / Jane Jane Jane / El Matador / Reverend Mr. Black / Desert Pete / Where have all the flowers gone / M.T.A. / Greenback dollar / Blowin' in the wind.
Notes: P 1987 Capitol Records Inc.
Compact disc: released on Capitol, May'87 by Capitol Records. Dist: EMI

King Stur-Guv Sounds

LIVE AT CLARENDON J.A..
Album: released on Vista Sounds, '83 by Vista Sounds Records. Dist: Jetstar

King Sun De Moet

HEY LOVE.
Tracks: / Hey love / Hey love (radio version) / Flame / Rhythm King / Priority.
Single (12"): released on RCA, May'87 by RCA Records. Dist: RCA, Roots, Swift, Wellard, Chris, I & B, Solomon & Peres Distribution

Single (7"): released on RCA, Jun'87 by RCA Records. Dist: RCA, Roots, Swift, Wellard, Chris, I & B, Solomon & Peres Distribution

King Sunny Ade

JU JU MUSIC.
Compact disc: released on Island, May'87 by Island Records. Dist: Polygram

King Swallow

SUBWAY JAM.
Single (12"): released on Seara, Jun'82 by Seara Records. Dist: Jetstar

Kingsway, Pete

TWO SHADES OF PETE KINGSWAY.
Album: released on Tank, Dec'77 by Tank Records.

King Tee

COOLEST, THE.
Single (12"): released on Techno-Hop (USA), Aug'87 Dist: Pinnacle

King, Terry

STAY WITH ME FOR CHRISTMAS.
Single (7"): released on Code, Oct'84 by Code Records. Dist: Jetstar, EMI

King, Tom

A.L.F.I.E..
Single (7"): released on Lamborghini, May'84 by Lamborghini Records. Dist: PRT

King, Tracy & Everton

HEAVEN (see Everton).

King Tubby

DUB FROM THE ROOTS.
Album: released on Striker Lee, Mar'85 by Striker Lee Records. Dist: Jetstar Distribution

KING AT THE CONTROLS.
Album: released on Vista Sounds, '83 by Vista Sounds Records. Dist: Jetstar

KING TUBBY THE DUBMASTER WITH THE WATERHOUSE POSSE.
Album: released on Vista Sounds, '83 by Vista Sounds Records. Dist: Jetstar

POETS OF DUB, (THE).
Album: released on Striker Lee, Mar'85 by Striker Lee Records. Dist: Jetstar Distribution

King, Will

BACK UP AGAINST THE WALL.
Album: released on RCA, May'85 by RCA Records. Dist: RCA, Roots, Swift, Wellard, Chris, I & B, Solomon & Peres Distribution

Cassette: released on RCA, May'85 by RCA Records. Dist: RCA, Roots, Swift, Wellard, Chris, I & B, Solomon & Peres Distribution

Single (7"): released on Total Experience, Jun'85 by Phonogram. Dist: Polygram

Single (12"): released on Total Experience, Jun'85 by Phonogram. Dist: Polygram

Kinika

JUNGLE FEVER.
Tracks: / Jungle fever / Scratch fever / Scratch fever (megamix) / Scratch fever (scratch mix) / Scratch fever (original mix).
Single (12"): released on Champion, May'87 by Champion Records. Dist: RCA

Kinks

100 MINUTES.
Cassette: released on PRT (100 Minute Series), Jun'82

ALL DAY AND ALL OF THE NIGHT.
Picture disc single: released on PRT, Oct'84 by PRT Records. Dist: PRT

ARTHUR OR THE DECLINE & FALL OF THE BRITISH EMPIRE.
Tracks: / Yes sir, no sir / Some mother's son / Drivin' / Brainwashed / Australia / Shangri la / Mr. Churchill says / She's bought a hat like Princess Marina / Young and innocent days / Nothing to say / Arthur / Victoria.
Compact disc: released on PRT, '86 by PRT Records. Dist: PRT

ARTHUR OR THE RISE AND FALL OF THE BRITISH EMPIRE.
Album: released on Pye, '74

BACKTRACKIN'.
Tracks: / You really got me / LoLa / Sunny Afternoon / All day and all of the night / Dedicated follower of fashion / Dead end street / Come dancing / Waterloo Sunset / Ape Man / Supersonic rocket ship.
Notes: Double Compact Disc.
Compact disc: released on Starblend, '86 by Starblend Records. Dist: PRT Distribution

BACKTRACKIN' - THE DEFINITIVE DOUBLE.......
Notes: Full title:- The Definitive Double Album Collection. Double LP and Cassette.
Album: released on Starblend, Dec'85 by Starblend Records. Dist: PRT Distribution

Cassette: released on Starblend, Dec'85 by Starblend Records. Dist: PRT Distribution

CANDY FROM MR. DANDY.
Album: released on PRT, Jul'83 by PRT Records. Dist: PRT

Cassette: released on PRT, Jul'83 by PRT Records. Dist: PRT

CELLULOID HEROES.
Album: released on RCA, Jul'84 by RCA Records. Dist: RCA, Roots, Swift, Wellard, Chris, I & B, Solomon & Peres Distribution

COLLECTION: KINKS.
Tracks: / Things are getting better / Apeman / Dedicated follower of fashion / Autumn almanac / Lola / All day and all of the night / You really got me / Set me free / Dancing in the street / Bald headed woman / Long tall Sally / Cadillac / Louie Louie / Creepin Jean / Wonder Boy / Act nice & gentle / Sittin' on my sofa / Too much monkey business / Beautiful Delilah / Tin soldier man / Victoria / Death of a clown / Wicked Anabella / Village green preservation society.
Album: released on Castle Communications, Nov'85 by Castle Communications. Dist: Cartel, Pinnacle, Counterpoint

Cassette: released on Castle Communications, Nov'85 by Castle Communications. Dist: Cartel, Pinnacle, Counterpoint

COME DANCING/NOISE.
Single (7"): released on Arista, Aug'83 by Arista Records. Dist: RCA

Single (12"): released on Arista, Aug'83 by Arista Records. Dist: RCA Deleted '84.

COME DANCING WITH THE KINKS Best of The Kinks 1977-86.
Album: released on Arista, Oct'86 by Arista Records. Dist: RCA

Cassette: released on Arista, Oct'86 by Arista Records. Dist: RCA

DEAD END STREET GREATEST HITS.
Double Album: released on PRT, Oct'83 by PRT Records. Dist: PRT

Double cassette: released on PRT, Oct'83 by PRT Records. Dist: PRT

DEDICATED FOLLOWER OF FASHION.
Tracks: / Dedicated follower of fashion / Autumn almanac.
Notes: Double A
Single (7"): released on PRT, May'86 by PRT Records. Dist: PRT

DO IT AGAIN.
Single (7"): released on Arista, Apr'85 by Arista Records. Dist: RCA

Single (12"): released on Arista, May'85 by Arista Records. Dist: RCA

EVERYBODY'S IN SHOWBIZ.
Album: released on RCA (Germany), '83

FACE TO FACE.
Cassette: released on PRT, Jun'80 by PRT Records. Dist: PRT

FACE TO FACE.
Tracks: / Party line / Rosy won't you please come home / Dandy / Too much on my mind / Session man / Rainy day in June / House in the country / Holiday in Waikiki / Most exclusive residence for sale / Fancy / Little Miss Queen of Darkness / You're looking fine / Sunny afternoon / I'll remember.
Compact disc: released on PRT, '86 by PRT Records. Dist: PRT

GIVE THE PEOPLE WHAT THEY WANT.
Album: released on Arista, Jan'82 by Arista Records. Dist: RCA

Cassette: released on Arista, Jan'82 by Arista Records. Dist: RCA

GREATEST HITS: KINKS.
Album: released on PRT, Nov'84 by PRT Records. Dist: PRT

Cassette: released on PRT, Nov'84 by PRT Records. Dist: PRT

GREATEST HITS:KINKS.
Tracks: / You really got me / All day and all of the night / Tired of waiting for you / Ev'rybody's gonna be happy / Set me free / See my friends / Till the end of the day / Dedicated followers of fashion / Sunny afternoon / Dead end street / Waterloo Sunset / Autumn Almanac / Wonder boy / Days / Plastic man / Victoria / Lola / Apeman.
Notes: Digital Stereo.
Compact disc: released on PRT, May'85 by PRT Records. Dist: PRT

HOW ARE YOU.
Tracks: / How are you / Killing time / This is sleazy town *.
Notes: * Extra track on 12" version only.
Single (7"): released on London, Dec'86 by London Records. Dist: Polygram

Single (12"): released on London, Dec'86 by London Records. Dist: Polygram

KINDA KINKS.
Tracks: / Look for me baby / Got my feet on the ground / Nothin' in the world can stop me worryin' 'bout that girl / Something better beginning / Naggin' woman / Wonder where my baby is tonight / Tired of waiting for you / Dancing in the street / So long / Don't ever change / Come on now / You shouldn't be sad.
Compact disc: released on PRT, '86 by PRT Records. Dist: PRT

Cassette: released on PRT, Jun'80 by PRT Records. Dist: PRT

KINKS ARE THE VILLAGE GREEN PRESREVATION SOCIETY, THE.
Album: released on PRT Flashback, Nov'85

Cassette: released on PRT Flashback, Nov'85

Album: released on PRT, Feb'81 by PRT Records. Dist: PRT

KINKS BOX SET, THE.
Boxed set: released on PRT, Nov'84 by PRT Records. Dist: PRT

Boxed set: released on PRT, Nov'84 by PRT Records. Dist: PRT

KINKS COLLECTION, THE.
Double Album: released on Pickwick, Jul'80 by Pickwick Records. Dist: Pickwick Distribution, Prism Leisure Distribution, Lugtons

Cassette: released on Pickwick, Jul'80 by Pickwick Records. Dist: Pickwick Distribution, Prism Leisure Distribution, Lugtons

KINKS FILE, THE.
Double Album: released on Pye, Nov'77
Cat. no: **FILD 001**
Cassette: released on PRT, Nov'77 by PRT Records. Dist: PRT

KINKS KONTROVERSY, THE.
Tracks: / Milk cow blues / Gotta get the first plane home / I am free / When I see that girl of mine / Till the end of the day / World keeps going round / I'm on an island / Where have all the good times gone / It's too late / What's in store for me? / You can't win.
Compact disc: released on PRT, '86 by PRT Records. Dist: PRT

KINKS KONTROVERSY.
Cassette: released on PYP, Jun'80 by WEA Records. Dist: WEA

KINKS LIVE AT THE KELVIN HALL.
Tracks: / All day and all of the night / Well respected man / You're looking fine / Sunny afternoon / Dandy / I'm on an island / Come on now / You really got me / Milk cow blues / Tired of waiting for you / Batman.
Compact disc: released on PRT, '86 by PRT Records. Dist: PRT

KINKS PART 1 Lola vs powerman & the moneygoround.
Tracks: / Contenders, the / Srangers / Denmark Street / Get back in line / Lola / Top of the pops / Moneygoround, The / This time tomorrow / Long way from home, A / Rats / Apeman / Powerman / Got to be free / Long way from home, A.
Compact disc: released on PRT, '86 by PRT Records. Dist: PRT

Album: released on Pye, '74

KINKS SOUNDTRACK FROM THE FILM PERCY.
Album: released on Pye, '74

KINKS, THE.
Cassette: released on PRT, Jun'80 by PRT Records. Dist: PRT

KOLLECTABLES.
Album: released on PRT, Nov'84 by PRT Records. Dist: PRT

Cassette: released on PRT, Nov'84 by PRT Records. Dist: PRT

KOVERS.
Album: released on PRT, Nov'84 by PRT Records. Dist: PRT

Cassette: released on PRT, Nov'84 by PRT Records. Dist: PRT

LIVE AT THE KELVIN HALL.
Album: released on Pye, Aug'80

LOLA.
Tracks: / Lola / Lola / Apeman.
Single (7"): released on Old Gold, Mar'86 by Old Gold Records. Dist: Lightning, Jazz Music, Spartan, Counterpoint

Cassette: released on Pickwick (Ditto series), Jul'82

LOLA/BERKLEY MEWS.
Single (7"): released on PRT, '74 by PRT Records. Dist: PRT

LOLA, PERCY & THE APEMAN COME FACE TO FACE WITH....
Notes: Full title: Lola, Pecry & the Apeman come face to face with the village green preservation society...something else.
Double Album: released on Golden Hour, Oct'74 by PRT Records. Dist: PRT

LOST AND FOUND.
Tracks: / Lost and found / Killing time / Ray Davies interview.
Single (7"): released on London, Mar'87 by London Records. Dist: Polygram

Cassette: by London Records. Dist: Polygram

MISFITS.
Album: released on Arista, May'78 by Arista Records. Dist: RCA

ONE FOR THE ROAD.
Double Album:

SCHOOLBOYS IN DISGRACE.
Album: released on RCA (Germany), '83

SHAPE OF THINGS TO COME.
78 rpm record: released on PRT, Apr'83 by PRT Records. Dist: PRT

Cassette: released on PRT, Apr'83 by PRT Records. Dist: PRT

SOAP OPERA.
Album: released on RCA (Special Imports Service), Jul'84

SOMETHING ELSE.
Album: released on PRT, Feb'81 by PRT Records. Dist: PRT

SPOTLIGHT ON THE KINKS.
Double Album: released on PRT, '80 by PRT Records. Dist: PRT

Double cassette: released on PRT, '80 by PRT Records. Dist: PRT

Album: released on PRT (Spotlight), Oct'82 by PRT Records. Dist: PRT

Cassette: released on PRT (Spotlight), Oct'82 by PRT Records. Dist: PRT

STATE OF CONFUSION.
Album: released on Arista, Jun'83 by Arista Records. Dist: RCA Deleted '85.

Cassette: released on Arista, Jun'83 by Arista Records. Dist: RCA

Single (7"): released on Arista, Mar'84 by Arista Records. Dist: RCA

Single (12"): released on Arista, Mar'84 by Arista Records. Dist: RCA

STORY OF: THE KINKS.
Notes: The story of one of Britain's most enduring rock bands, from 1964 to the presentday, and including classic hits like 'LOLA' and 'YOU REALLY GOT ME'. 1986 pro- duction. Type of recording: Documentary. Total playing time: 50 minutes.
Video-cassette (VHS): released on MGM, May'86 Dist: Polygram Distribution, Swift Distribution

SUNNY AFTERNOON.
Tracks: / Sunny Afternoon / Tired of waiting for you / Sittin' on my sofa.
Single (7"): released on Old Gold, Mar'86 by Old Gold Records. Dist: Lightning, Jazz Music, Spartan, Counterpoint

Single (7"): released on PRT, Jun'75 by PRT Records. Dist: PRT

THINK VISUAL.
Tracks: / Rock 'n' Roll cities / How are you / Think visual / Natural gift / Killing time / When you where a child / Working at the factory / Lost and found / Repetition / Welcome to sleazy town / Video shop, The.
Notes: The original Kinks recently signed to London records. Written and produced by Ray Davies.
Album: released on London, Nov'86 by London Records. Dist: Polygram

Cassette: released on London, Nov'86 by London Records. Dist: Polygram

Compact disc: released on London, Nov'86 by London Records. Dist: Polygram

TIRED OF WAITING FOR YOU.
Single (7"): released on Flashback, Jan'83 by Flashback Records/PRT Records. Dist: Mainline, PRT

WATERLOO SUNSET.
Single (7"): released on Flashback, Jun'80 by Flashback Records/PRT Records. Dist: Mainline, PRT

WORD OF MOUTH.
Album: released on Arista, Nov'84 by Arista Records. Dist: RCA

Cassette: released on Arista, Nov'84 by Arista Records. Dist: RCA

YOU REALLY GOT ME.
Album: released on Pye, May'80
Cat. no: **NSPL 18615**
Single (7"): released on Flashback, Apr'79 by Flashback Records/PRT Records. Dist: Mainline, PRT

Single (7"): released on PRT, Sep'83 by PRT Records. Dist: PRT

Single (12"): released on PRT, Sep'83 by PRT Records. Dist: PRT

Picture disc single: released on PRT, Sep'83 by PRT Records. Dist: PRT

Single (7"): released on Old Gold, Jun'84 by Old Gold Records. Dist: Lightning, Jazz Music, Spartan, Counterpoint

Cassette: released on PRT, May'80 by PRT Records. Dist: PRT

Kinky Foxx

SO DIFFERENT.
Single (7"): released on Sound Of New York, Dec'83 by Sound Of New York Records. Dist: PRT

Single (12"): released on Sound Of New York, Dec'83 by Sound Of New York Records. Dist: PRT

Kinnaird, Alison

HARPER'S GALLERY,THE.
Album: released on Temple, Jan'83 by Temple Records. Dist: Roots Distribution, Folksound Distribution, Celtic Music Distribution, Projection Distribution

HARP KEY ,THE.
Album: released on Mulligan, Sep'80 by Topic Records. Dist: Roots Distribution, Jazz Music Distribution, JSU Distribution, I & B Distribution, Projection Distribution, Wynd-Up Distribution, Celtic Distributions

Album: released on Temple, Jan'83 by Temple Records. Dist: Roots Distribution, Folksound Distribution, Celtic Music Distribution, Projection Distribution

MUSIC IN TRUST (Kinnaird, Alison & The Battlefield Band).
Cassette: released on Temple, May'86 by Temple Records. Dist: Roots Distribution, Folksound Distribution, Celtic Music Distribution, Projection Distribution

Kinney, Fern

BEAUTIFUL LOVE SONG/PIPIN' HOT.
Single (7"): released on Malaco, Mar'83 by Malaco Records. Dist: Charly

Single (12"): released on Malaco, Mar'83 by Malaco Records. Dist: Charly

FERN.
Album: released on WEA, Mar'81 by WEA Records. Dist: WEA

Cassette: released on WEA, Mar'81 by WEA Records. Dist: WEA

GROOVE ME.
Album: released on WEA, Jan'80 by WEA Records. Dist: WEA

Cassette: released on WEA, May'80 by WEA Records. Dist: WEA

I'M READY FOR YOUR LOVE.
Single (12"): released on Malaco, Dec'82 by Malaco Records. Dist: Charly

I'VE BEEN LONELY FOR SO LONG/LOVE ME...
Single (7"): released on WEA, Feb'81 by WEA Records. Dist: WEA

Single (12"): released on WEA, Mar'81 by WEA Records. Dist: WEA

TOGETHER WE ARE BEAUTIFUL.
Tracks: / Together we are beautiful / Love Town.
Single (7"): released on Old Gold, Mar'86 by Old Gold Records. Dist: Lightning, Jazz Music, Spartan, Counterpoint

Single (7"): released on WEA, Jan'80 by WEA Records. Dist: WEA

Kino

ROOM IN MY HEART.
Tracks: / Room in my heart / Ugh Ugh.
Single (7"): released on Chrysalis, Mar'86 by Chrysalis Records. Dist: CBS

Single (12"): released on Chrysalis, Mar'86 by Chrysalis Records. Dist: CBS

Kinross Festival

KINROSS FESTIVAL VOL.1 Various artists (Various Artists).
Album: released on Springthyme, Oct'86 by Springthyme Records. Dist: Jazz Music Distribution, Projection Distribution, Roots Distribution

Cassette: released on Springthyme, Oct'86 by Springthyme Records. Dist: Jazz Music Distribution, Projection Distribution, Roots Distribution

Kinsey, Tony

THAMES SUITE (Kinsey,Tony Big Band).
Album: released on Spotlite-Jazz, '83 by Spotlite Records. Dist: Cadillac, Jazz Music, Spotlite

Kintone

GOING HOME (AZANIA).
Tracks: / Going home / Freedom's song / Pennin / Looks like rain / Street market / Street market / After the storm / Song for nella / Ode to Joe.
Notes: In this album Kintone have created and evolved an entirely unique new sound melodic jazz in the truest sense of the word."...a gorgeous Synthesis of rollingAfrican rhythms and strong,jazzy melodics: (Blues & Soul)"

STATE OF EMERGENCY.
Tracks: / State of emergency.
Single (12"): released on KMC, Apr'86 Dist: Revolver, Cartel

Kipling, Anna

HAPPY ANNIVERSARY.
Tracks: / Happy anniversary / Where do you go.
Single (7"): released on MBS, Jul'87 Dist: PRT

Kipling, Rudyard

JUST SO STORIES (Various Artists).
Cassette: released on Cover to Cover, Jun'85 by Cover to Cover Cassettes. Dist: Conifer

KIM.
Notes: One of Rudyard Kipling's best-loved novels Kim,was published in 1901 and tells the story of an orphaned son of an sargeant in an Irish Regiment in India,who spends his childhood as a vagabond until he meets an Old Lama from Tibet and accompanies him on his travels.Read by Ben Cross the book presents a vivid picture India with its religions and superstitions. Running time approx 3 hours.
Cassette: released on Listen For Pleasure, Jul'86 by MFP Records. Dist: EMI

MORE JUNGLE BOOK STORIES (Richardson, Ian).
Double cassette: released on Argo (Spokenword), Jul'83 by Decca Records. Dist: Polygram

MORE JUST-SO STORIES (Davis, David).
Cassette: released on Pinnacle, '79 by Pinnacle Records. Dist: Pinnacle

Kipper

KIPPER various artists (Various Artists).
Cassette: released on Bibi, Feb'82

Kipper Family

EVER DECREASING CIRCLES.
Album: released on Dambuster, Dec'85 by Dambuster Records. Dist: Projection, Celtic Music, Roots

SINCE TIME IMMORAL.
Album: released on Dambuster, Feb'85 by Dambuster Records. Dist: Projection, Celtic Music, Roots

Kirby, John

JOHN KIRBY.
Tracks: / Ida / Peanut vendor / Revolutionary etude / Blue fantasy / Same old story (The) / Polonaise / Prelude for trumpet / Last night the nightingale woke me / I give you my word / Rustle of spring No.1 / Rehearsin for a nervous breakdown / Echoes of Harlem.
Album: released on Charly, Jan'87 by Charly Records. Dist: Charly, Cadillac

Cassette: by Charly Records. Dist: Charly, Cadillac

Kirby,Kathy

LET ME SING AND I'M HAPPY.
Album: released on President, Nov'83 by President Records. Dist: Taylors, Spartan

Cassette: released on President, Jan'84 by President Records. Dist: Taylors, Spartan

SECRET LOVE/YOU HAVE TO WANT TO...
Single (7"): released on Decca, Feb'82 by Decca Records. Dist: Polygram

Kirchner, Bill

WHAT IT IS TO BE FRANK (Kirchner, Bill Nonet).
Album: released on Sea Breeze, Mar'87 Dist: Swift

Kiri

BLUE SKIES.
Tracks: / Blue skies / Speak low / It might as well be spring / I Didn't Knowwhat time it was / Here's that rainy day / Yesterdays / So in love / How high the moon / True love / Gone with the wind / When I'm too old to dream / Folks who live on the hill (The).
Compact disc: released on Decca, Oct'85 by Decca Records. Dist: Polygram

Album: released on Decca, Oct'85 by Decca Records. Dist: Polygram

Cassette: released on Decca, Oct'85 by Decca Records. Dist: Polygram

Compact disc: released on Decca, Oct'85 by Decca Records. Dist: Polygram

Kirk,Andy

ANDY'S JIVE (Kirk,Andy and his Orchestra).
Album: released on Swinghouse, Dec'84 Dist: Jazz Music Distribution, Swift Distribution, Chris Wellard Distribution

CLOUDY (Kirk, Andy & His Twelve Clouds Of Joy).
Album: released on Hep, May'84 by H.R. Taylor Records. Dist: Jazz Music, Cadillac Music, JSU, Taylors, Wellard, Chris, Zodiac, Swift, Fast Forward

WALKIN' AND SWINGIN' (Kirk, Andy & His Twelve Clouds Of Joy).
Album: released on Affinity, Sep'83 by Charly Records. Dist: Charly, Cadillac

Kirkbymoorside Town...

MOORSIDE BRASS VOL 2.
Album: released on Look, Feb'84 Dist: R. Smith & Co. Records, H.R. Taylor

Kirkland,Eddie

PICK UP THE PIECES.
Album: released on JSP Records, Sep'81 by JSP Records. Dist: Jazz Music, Pinnacle

WAY IT WAS,THE.
Album: released on Red Lightnin', May'83 by Red Lightnin' Records. Dist: Roots, Swift, Jazz Music, JSU, Pinnacle, Cartel, Wynd-Up Distribution

AMONG THE MANY ATTRACTIONS AT THE SHOW.. (Kirkpatrick, John & Sue Harris).
Album: released on Topic, Jul'76 Dist: Roots Distribution

BALLAD OF THE BLACK COUNTRY.
Album: released on Broadside, Jun'81 by Broadside Records. Dist: Celtic Distributions, H.R. Taylor, Jazz Music, Projection, Jazz Services Unlimited Dist. (JSU)

Cassette: released on Broadside, Jun'81 by Broadside Records. Dist: Celtic Distributions, H.R. Taylor, Jazz Music, Projection, Jazz Services Unlimited Dist. (JSU)

BLUE BALLOON.
Tracks: / Noah / Blue balloon / Black against the snow / Don't shoot, I'm wearing my seat belt / Tunnel of love / Laundroloverette / Length of yarn, (A) / Hole in my heart / Dog's gone wild.
Album: released on Squeezer, Jun'87 by Topic Records. Dist: Roots Distribution, Projection Distribution

ENGLISH CANALS.
Album: released on Broadside, Jun'81 by Broadside Records. Dist: Celtic Distributions, H.R. Taylor, Jazz Music, Projection, Jazz Services Unlimited Dist. (JSU)

Cassette: released on Broadside, Jun'81 by Broadside Records. Dist: Celtic Distributions, H.R. Taylor, Jazz Music, Projection, Jazz Services Unlimited Dist. (JSU)

FACING THE MUSIC (Kirkpatrick, John & Sue Harris).
Album: released on Topic, '81 Dist: Roots Distribution

GOING SPARE.
Album: released on Free Reed, Jan'87 by Free Reed Records. Dist: Roots, Projection, Hobgoblin Records, Oblivion

Album: released on Freereed, '82 by Topic Records. Dist: JSU

JOGGING ALONG WITH ME REINDEER.
Single (7"): released on Dingles, Nov'80 by Dingles Records. Dist: Projection

PLAIN CAPERS.
Album: released on Freereed, Sep'79 by Topic Records. Dist: JSU

ROSE OF BRITAIN'S ISLE,THE.
Album: released on Topic, '81 Dist: Roots Distribution

SHREDS AND PATCHES (Kirkpatrick, John & Sue Harris).
Album: released on Topic, '81 Dist: Roots Distribution

THREE IN A ROW-ENGLISH MELODIAN.
Album: released on Squeezer, Nov'84 by Topic Records. Dist: Roots Distribution, Projection Distribution

THREE IN A ROW - THE ENGLISH MELODEON.
Tracks: / Queen of hearts, (The) / Dummy head / Chuntering Charlie / Round-bottomed wok, (The) / Wriggly-tin tattoo, (The) / Broken rifle, (The) / Blaze away / Sing a full song / Putney beach / Fulham gasworks / Fulham by gaslight / Walking up town / Siberian stomp, (The) / Nightingale sang in Berkeley Square / Find the lady.
Album: released on Squeezer, '84 by Topic Records. Dist: Roots Distribution, Projection Distribution

THREE IN A ROW: THE ENGLISH MELODEON.
Album: released on Squeezer, Nov'86 by Topic Records. Dist: Roots Distribution, Projection Distribution

Kirk,Richard

LEATHER HANDS (Kirk,Richard and Peter Hope).

Kirk, Richard H

BLACK JESUS VOICE.
Album: released on Rough Trade, Sep'86 by Rough Trade Records. Dist: Rough Trade Distribution, Cartel Distribution

HIPNOTIC.
Tracks: / Hipnotic.
Single (12"): released on Rough Trade, Sep'86 by Rough Trade Records. Dist: Rough Trade Distribution, Cartel Distribution

UGLY SPIRIT.
Album: released on Rough Trade, Nov'86 by Rough Trade Records. Dist: Rough Trade Distribution, Cartel Distribution

Kirk, Roland

DON'T YOU CRY,BEAUTIFUL EDITH.
Album: released on Verve (USA), Apr'83 by Polydor. Dist: Polygram

EARLY ROOTS.
Album: released on Affinity, Jun'84 by Charly Records. Dist: Charly, Cadillac

TEAR,THE.
Album: released on Atlantic, '79 by WEA Records. Dist: WEA

VIBRATION CONTINUES,THE.
Album: released on Atlantic, Jul'78 by WEA Records. Dist: WEA

WE FREE KINGS.
Compact disc: released on Polydor, Nov'86 by Polydor Records. Dist: Polygram, Polydor

Album: released on Mercury, Jun'83 by Phonogram Records. Dist: Polygram Distribution

Kirkwood, Diana

VALENTINO.
Tracks: / Valentino / You come into my life.
Single (7"): released on White Rock, Feb'86 Dist: PRT

Kirkwood,Pat

THANKS FOR THE MEMORY.
Album: released on BBC, Oct'77 by BBC Records & Tapes. Dist: EMI, PRT, Pye

Kirsh, Les

I'D BAKED YOU A CAKE.
Single (7"): released on Magic, Jul'84 Dist: Jazz Music, Submarine, Swift, Chris Wellard, Conifer

Kirton, Lew

DON'T WANNA WAIT.
Tracks: / Don't wanna wait / Stuck in the middle (Between two).
Single (7"): released on MCA, Jul'86 by MCA Records. Dist: Polygram, MCA

Single (12"): released on MCA, Jul'86 by MCA Records. Dist: Polygram, MCA

JUST CAN'T GET ENOUGH.
Single (7"): released on Epic, Dec'83 by CBS Records. Dist: CBS

Single (12"): released on Epic, Dec'83 by CBS Records. Dist: CBS

TALK TO ME.
Album: released on Epic, Jan'84 by CBS Records. Dist: CBS

Cassette: released on Epic, Jan'84 by CBS Records. Dist: CBS

Kismet

KISMET Original soundtrack (Various Artists).
Tracks: / Fate / Not since nineveh / Baubles,Bangles And Beads / Stranger in paradise / Gesticulate / Night of my nights / Bored / Olive tree (The) / Rahadlakum / And this is my beloved / Sands of time.
Compact disc: released on CBS, May'87 by CBS Records. Dist: CBS

Album: released on CBS, Jul'86 by CBS Records. Dist: CBS
Cat. no: **CBS 70287**
Cassette: released on CBS, Jul'86 by CBS Records. Dist: CBS

Kiss

ALIVE.
Compact disc: released on Casablanca, Apr'87 Dist: Polygram, Phonogram

Album: released on Casablanca, Sep'84 Dist: Polygram, Phonogram

Cassette: released on Casablanca, Sep'84

Dist: Polygram, Phonogram

ANIMALIZE.
Tracks: / I've had enough (Into the fire) / Heaven's on fire / Burn bitch burn / Get all you can take / Lonely is the hunter / Under the gun / Thrills of the night / While the city sleeps / Murder in high heels.
Notes: Digital stereo recording.
Compact disc: released on Vertigo, Nov'84 by Phonogram Records. Dist: Polygram

Album: released on Vertigo, Sep'84 by Phonogram Records. Dist: Polygram

Cassette: released on Vertigo, Sep'84 by Phonogram Records. Dist: Polygram

Compact disc: released on Vertigo, Sep'84 by Phonogram Records. Dist: Polygram

ANIMALIZE LIVE UNCENSORED.
Notes: 15 tracks on this live recording,playing time of 89 minutes.
Video-cassette (VHS): released on Embassy, Jan'86 by CBS Records. Dist: CBS

ASYLUM.
Tracks: / King of the mountain / Any way you slice it / Who wants to be lonely / Trial by fire / I'm alive / Love's a deadly weapon / Tears are falling / Secretly cruel / Radar for love / Uh! all night.
Compact disc: released on Mercury, Nov'85 by Phonogram Records. Dist: Polygram Distribution

Album: released on Vertigo, Sep'85 by Phonogram Records. Dist: Polygram

Cassette: released on Vertigo, Sep'85 by Phonogram Records. Dist: Polygram

Compact disc: released on Vertigo, Sep'85 by Phonogram Records. Dist: Polygram

BEST OF SOLO ALBUMS.
Album: released on Phonogram Import, Mar'81

CREATURES OF THE NIGHT.
Single (7"): released on Casablanca, Apr'83 Dist: Polygram, Phonogram

Single (12"): released on Casablanca, Apr'83 Dist: Polygram, Phonogram

DESTROYER.
Compact disc: released on Casablanca, Apr'87 Dist: Polygram, Phonogram

Album: released on Casablanca, Oct'83 Dist: Polygram, Phonogram

Cassette: released on Casablanca, Oct'83 Dist: Polygram, Phonogram

DOUBLE PLATINUM.
Tracks: / Strutter 78 / Do you love me / Hard woman / Calling Dr.Love / Let me go Rock 'n' Roll / Love gun / God of thunder / Firehouse / Hotter than hell / I want you / Deuce / 100,000 Years / Detroit rock city / She / Rock and Roll all nite / Beth / Makin' love / C'mon and love me / Cold gin / Black diamond.
Compact disc: released on Casablanca, Apr'87 Dist: Polygram, Phonogram

Album: released on Casablanca, Mar'85 Dist: Polygram, Phonogram

Cassette: released on Casablanca, Mar'85 Dist: Polygram, Phonogram

Compact disc: released on Casablanca, Mar'85 Dist: Polygram, Phonogram

DRESSED TO KILL.
Album: released on Casablanca, Feb'82 Dist: Polygram, Phonogram

Cassette: released on Casablanca, Feb'82 Dist: Polygram, Phonogram

DYNASTY.
Album: released on Casablanca, Oct'83 Dist: Polygram, Phonogram

Cassette: released on Casablanca, Oct'83 Dist: Polygram, Phonogram

ELDER, (THE).
Album: released on Casablanca, Nov'81 Dist: Polygram, Phonogram

Cassette: released on Casablanca, Nov'81 Dist: Polygram, Phonogram

HEAVEN'S ON FIRE.
Single (7"): released on Vertigo, Sep'84 by Phonogram Records. Dist: Polygram

Single (12"): released on Vertigo, Sep'84 by Phonogram Records. Dist: Polygram

HOTTER THAN HELL.
Album: released on Casablanca, Feb'82 Dist: Polygram, Phonogram

Cassette: released on Casablanca, Feb'82 Dist: Polygram, Phonogram

INTERVIEW PICTURE DISC.
Album: released on Baktabak, Jun'87 by Baktabak Records. Dist: Arabesque

KISS.
Album: released on Casablanca, Jul'84 Dist: Polygram, Phonogram

Cassette: released on Casablanca, Jul'84 Dist: Polygram, Phonogram

KISS ALIVE, 2.
Double Album: released on Casablanca, Feb'82 Dist: Polygram, Phonogram

Cassette: released on Casablanca, Feb'82 Dist: Polygram, Phonogram

LICK IT UP.
Compact disc: Dist: Polygram, Phonogram

Album: released on Mercury, Oct'83 by Phonogram Records. Dist: Polygram Distribution

Cassette: released on Mercury, Oct'83 by Phonogram Records. Dist: Polygram Distribution

LOVE GUN.
Album: released on Casablanca, Jul'84 Dist: Polygram, Phonogram

Cassette: released on Casablanca, Jul'84 Dist: Polygram, Phonogram

ROCK AND ROLL OVER.
Album: released on Casablanca, Feb'82 Dist: Polygram, Phonogram

Cassette: released on Casablanca, Feb'82 Dist: Polygram, Phonogram

TEARS ARE FALLING.
Single (7"): released on Vertigo, Oct'85 by Phonogram Records. Dist: Polygram

Single (12"): released on Vertigo, Oct'85 by Phonogram Records. Dist: Polygram

UNMASKED.
Tracks: / Is that you / Shandy / What makes the world go round / Talk to me / Naked city / Torpedo / Tomorrow / Two sides of the coin / She's no european / Easy as it seems / Tears are falling.
Notes: Digital stereo recording.
Compact disc: released on Casablanca, May'83 Dist: Polygram, Phonogram

Kissed Air

KARIBA.
Single (7"): released on Kabuki, May'82 by Gareth Ryan. Dist: Rough Trade

KAWARAYA.
Single (12"): released on Kabuki, Jul'83 by Gareth Ryan. Dist: Rough Trade

OUT OF THE NIGHT.
Single (7"): released on Kabuki, Nov'82 by Gareth Ryan. Dist: Rough Trade

Kissing Bandits

CAVEMAN.
Single (7"): released on Rogue, Mar'85 by Fast Forward Records. Dist: Nine Mile Distribution, Cartel Distribution

SHAKE SOME ACTION.
Single (7"): released on WEA, Mar'84 by WEA Records. Dist: WEA

Single (12"): released on WEA, Mar'84 by WEA Records. Dist: WEA

SUN BANDITS (THE).
Album: released on New Rose, Nov'85 Dist: Rough Trade, Cartel

Kissing Her...

KISSING HER AND CRYING FOR YOU Various artists (Various Artists).
Album: released on Kent, Apr'86 by Ace Records. Dist: Pinnacle

Kissing The Pink

CERTAIN THINGS ARE LIKELY.
Tracks: / One step / Never too late to love you / Certain things are likely / Dream dream / No-one's on the same side / I won't wait / Can you hear me / Jones / Identity card / One day.
Compact disc: released on Magnet, Nov'86 by Magnet Records. Dist: BMG

Album: released on Magnet, Nov'86 by Magnet Records. Dist: BMG

Cassette: released on Magnet, Nov'86 by Magnet Records. Dist: BMG

CERTAIN THINGS ARE LIKELY (SINGLE).
Tracks: / Certain things are likely (garage edit) / Certain things are likely (remix).
Single (7"):

Single (12"): released on Magnet, Feb'87 by Magnet Records. Dist: BMG

LAST FILM.
Single (7"): released on Magnet, Jan'83 by Magnet Records. Dist: BMG

Single (12"): released on Magnet, Jan'83 by Magnet Records. Dist: BMG

Double-pack single: released on Magnet, Jan'83 by Magnet Records. Dist: BMG

LOVE LASTS FOREVER.
Single (7"): released on Magnet, Jun'83 by Magnet Records. Dist: BMG

Single (12"): released on Magnet, Jun'83 by Magnet Records. Dist: BMG

Picture disc single: released on Magnet, Jun'83 by Magnet Records. Dist: BMG

MAYBE THIS DAY.
Single (7"): released on Magnet, Aug'83 by Magnet Records. Dist: BMG

Single (12"): released on Magnet, Aug'83 by Magnet Records. Dist: BMG

MR.BLUNT.
Single (7"): released on Magnet, May'82 by Magnet Records. Dist: BMG

Single (12"): released on Magnet, May'82 by Magnet Records. Dist: BMG

NAKED.
Album: released on Magnet, May'83 by Magnet Records. Dist: BMG

Cassette: released on Magnet, May'83 by Magnet Records. Dist: BMG

NEVER TOO LATE TO LOVE YOU.
Tracks: / Never too late to love you / Michael.

ONE STEP.
Tracks: / One step / Footsteps / Rain never stops, The*.
Single (7"): released on Magnet, Jul'87 by Magnet Records. Dist: BMG

Single (12"): released on Magnet, Jul'87 by Magnet Records. Dist: BMG

OTHER SIDE OF HEAVEN.
Single (7"): released on Magnet, Mar'85 by Magnet Records. Dist: BMG

Single (12"): released on Magnet, Mar'85 by Magnet Records. Dist: BMG

RADIO ON.
Single (7"): released on Magnet, Sep'84 by Magnet Records. Dist: BMG

Single (12"): released on Magnet, Sep'84 by Magnet Records. Dist: BMG

WATCHING THEIR EYES.
Single (7"): released on Magnet, Oct'82 by Magnet Records. Dist: BMG

Single (12"): released on Magnet, Oct'82 by Magnet Records. Dist: BMG Deleted '83.

WHAT NOISE.
Album: released on Magnet, Oct'84 by Magnet Records. Dist: BMG

Cassette: released on Magnet, Oct'84 by Magnet Records. Dist: BMG

Kiss kiss

KISS KISS Dahl, Roald (Gray, Charles).
Cassette: released on Pickwick Talking Books, '83

Kiss Kiss Bang Bang

HIGH HEELS.
Tracks: / High heels / Kiss me on my ....
Single (7"): released on Magnet, Jun'87 by Magnet Records. Dist: BMG

Single (12"): released on Magnet, Jun'87 by Magnet Records. Dist: BMG

Kiss Me Kate

KISS ME KATE Original Soundtrack (Various Artists).
Notes: 1953 Film soundtrack with: Howard Keel,Kathryn Grayson,Ann Miller,Keenan Wynn, James Whitmore,Tommy Rall etc. Conducted by Andre Previn Songs by Cole Porter
Compact disc: released on CBS, Mar'87 by CBS Records. Dist: CBS

KISS ME KATE Original Soundtrack.
Tracks: / Too darn hot / So in love / We open in venice / Why can't you behave / Were thine that special face / Tom,Dick or Harry / I've come to live it wealthy in padua / From this moment on / Always true to you in my fashion / I hate men / Where is the life that late I led / Brush up your Shakespeare / Kiss me Kate.
Album: released on CBS, Jul'86 by CBS Records. Dist: CBS

Cassette: released on CBS, Jul'86 by CBS Records. Dist: CBS

KISS ME KATE: REPRISE REPERTORY THEATRE Various artists (Various Artists).
Album: released on Reprise, Aug'81 by WEA Records. Dist: WEA

Kissoon, Katie

I NEED A MAN IN MY LIFE.
Single (7"): released on Jive, Jul'84 by Zomba Records. Dist: RCA, PRT, CBS

Single (12"): released on Jive, Jul'84 by Zomba Records. Dist: RCA, PRT, CBS

PENNY LOVER.
Single (7"): released on Jive, Jan'84 by Zomba Records. Dist: RCA, PRT, CBS

Picture disc single: released on Jive, Jan'84 by Zomba Records. Dist: RCA, PRT, CBS

Single (12"): released on Jive, Jan'84 by Zomba Records. Dist: RCA, PRT, CBS

YOU'RE THE ONE (YOU'RE MY NUMBER ONE).
Single (7"): released on Jive, Jan'83 by Zomba Records. Dist: RCA, PRT, CBS

Single (12"): released on Jive, Jul'83 by Zomba Records. Dist: RCA, PRT, CBS

Kissoon, Mac

GREATEST HITS:MAC & KATIE KISSOON (Kissoon, Mac & Katie).
Cassette: released on Autograph, Apr'85 Dist: Record Services Distribution (Ireland)

LAVENDER BLUE.
Single (7"): released on Crazy Viking, Oct'82 by Crazy Vikings Records. Dist: Pinnacle

LOVE AND UNDERSTANDING (Kissoon, Mac & Family).
Single (7"): released on Young Blood, Nov'81 by Young Blood Records. Dist: Pinnacle

MAC & KATIE KISSOON STORY, THE (Kissoon, Mac & Katie).
Album: released on State, Feb'78 by State Records.

SUGAR CANDY KISSES (Kissoon, Mac & Katie).
Extended-play record: released on Scoop, Oct'84

Cassette single: released on Scoop, Oct'84

Kiss That

KISS AND TELL.
Tracks: / Join us / Play cowboy / He said No! / I cant stand the rain / Can't stand the rain,I / March out / Little King / Highest rendezvous / Love only comes twice / Mullin.
Notes: Produced by Mick Ronson.
Album: released on Chrysalis, Jun'86 by Chrysalis Records. Dist: CBS

Cassette: released on Chrysalis, Jun'86 by Chrysalis Records. Dist: CBS

MARCH OUT.
Tracks: / March out / Simple girl.
Single (7"): released on Chrysalis, May'86 by Chrysalis Records. Dist: CBS

Single (12"): released on Chrysalis, May'86 by Chrysalis Records. Dist: CBS

Kiss The Blade

YOUNG SOLDIER.
Single (12"): released on Incision, Dec'86 by Incision Records. Dist: M.I.S., Revolver

Kiss the Bride

PARTY HAS BEGUN.
Single (12"): released on Incision, Jan'85 by Incision Records. Dist: M.I.S., Revolver

Kiss Yer Skull Goodbye

KISS YER SKULL GOODBYE Various artists (Various Artists).
Tracks: / Seven by seven / Time we left / Hard times / Beat, The / Take it for granted / Sleepless nights / Hide in the rain / In the fire / Because you lied / Temporary threshold shift.
Notes: Including Hawkwind, Atomic Rooster.
Album: released on Conifer, Jan'87 by Conifer Records. Dist: Conifer

Cassette: released on Conifer, Apr'86 by Conifer Records. Dist: Conifer

Kitamura, Eiji

SWING EIJI.
Album: released on Concord, Aug'81 by Import Records. Dist: IMS, Polygram

Kitaro

BEST OF KITARO.
Compact disc: released on Kuckuck, Feb'87 Dist: PRT

Album: released on Kuckuck, Feb'87 Dist: PRT
Cat. no: LPKUCK 073
Cassette: released on Kuckuck, Feb'87 Dist: PRT

Album: released on Kuckuck (Germany), Jul'86

Compact disc: released on Kuckuck (Germany), Jul'86

BEST SELECTION (THE).
Compact disc: released on Kuckuck (Germany), Jan'86

FROM THE FULL MOON STORY.
Tracks: / Krpa / Aurora / Hikari / Fuji / Full moon / Resurrection / From Astra / Heavenly illusion / New lights.
Notes: Latest release from Kitaro featuring tracks recorded between December 78 - Jan 79.
Album: released on Philips, Dec'85 Dist: IMS-Polygram

Compact disc: released on Philips, Dec'85 Dist: IMS-Polygram

KI.
Tracks: / Revelations / Stream of being / Kaleidoscope / Oasis / Sun / Endless water / Tree / Cloud.
Compact disc: released on Kuckuck (Germany), Jan'86

Compact disc: Dist: IMS-Polygram

Compact disc: released on Kuckuck (USA), May'87 Dist: Celestial Harmonies Distribution

LIVE IN ASIA.
Tracks: / Earth born / Caravansary / Theme of silk road / Cosmic live / Cloud / Japanese drums / Return to Russia / Straight away to Orion / Dawn in Malaysia.
Album: released on Polydor, Jan'86 by Polydor Records. Dist: Polygram, Polydor

Cassette: released on Polydor, Jan'86 by Polydor Records. Dist: Polygram, Polydor

Compact disc: released on Polydor, Jan'86 by Polydor Records. Dist: Polygram, Polydor

OASIS.
Tracks: / Rising sun / Moro-rism / New wave / Cosmic energy / Aqua / Moonlight / Shimmering horizon / Fragrance of nature / Innocent people / Oasis.
Album: released on Polydor, Jan'86 by Polydor Records. Dist: Polygram, Polydor

Cassette: released on Polydor, Jan'86 by Polydor Records. Dist: Polygram, Polydor

Compact disc: released on Polydor, Jan'86 by Polydor Records. Dist: Polygram, Polydor

SILK ROAD I.
Tracks: / Silk road theme / Bell tower / Heavenly father / Great river (The) / Great wall of China (The) / Flying celestial nymphy / Sild road fantasy / Shimmering light / Westbound time / Bodhisattva / Everlasting road.
Album: released on Polydor, Jan'86 by Polydor Records. Dist: Polygram, Polydor

Cassette: released on Polydor, Jan'86 by Polydor Records. Dist: Polygram, Polydor

Compact disc: released on Polydor, Jan'86 by Polydor Records. Dist: Polygram, Polydor

SILK ROAD II.
Tracks: / In the silence / Takla malikan desert / Eternal springs / Silver moon / Magical sand dance / Year 40080 / Time travel / Reicarnation / Dawning / Tienshan.
Album: released on Polydor, Jan'86 by Polydor Records. Dist: Polygram, Polydor

Cassette: released on Polydor, Jan'86 by Polydor Records. Dist: Polygram, Polydor

Compact disc: released on Polydor, Jan'86 by Polydor Records. Dist: Polygram, Polydor

SILK ROAD III.
Compact disc: by Polydor Records. Dist: Polygram, Polydor

SILK ROAD IV.
Compact disc: by Polydor Records. Dist: Polygram, Polydor

SILK ROAD SUITE (Kitaro & London Symphony Orchestra).
Album: released on Kuckuck (USA), Feb'87 Dist: Celestial Harmonies Distribution

Cassette:

SILVER CLOUD.
Tracks: / Earth born / Flying cloud / Dreams like yesterday / Never let you go / Noah's ark / Return to Russia / Panorama / Straight 'away to Orion.
Album: released on Polydor, Jan'86 by Polydor Records. Dist: Polygram, Polydor

Cassette: released on Polydor, Jan'86 by Polydor Records. Dist: Polygram, Polydor

Compact disc: released on Polydor, Jan'86 by Polydor Records. Dist: Polygram, Polydor

TEN KAI ASTRAL TRIP.
Compact disc: by Polydor Records. Dist: Polygram, Polydor

TENKU.
Tracks: / Tenku / Romance / Wings / Aura / Message from the Cosmos / Time traveller / Legend of the road / Milky way.
Album: released on Geffen, Oct'86 by Geffen Records. Dist: WEA, CBS

Cassette: released on Geffen, Oct'86 by Geffen Records. Dist: WEA, CBS

Compact disc: released on Geffen, Oct'86 by Geffen Records. Dist: WEA, CBS

TOWARDS THE WEST.
Album: released on Polydor, Jul'86 by Polydor Records. Dist: Polygram, Polydor

Cassette: released on Polydor, Jul'86 by Polydor Records. Dist: Polygram, Polydor

Compact disc: released on Polydor, Jul'86 by Polydor Records. Dist: Polygram, Polydor

TUNHAUNG.
Compact disc: released on Kuckuck (Germany), Jan'86

Compact disc: released on Kuckuck (USA), May'87 Dist: Celestial Harmonies Distribution

Kitchen, Geoff

JAZZ FOUNDATIONS.
Album: released on Swaggie (Australia), Jan'83

Kit Kat Band

HOT DANCE MUSIC 1925-1927.
Album: released on World, Aug'79 Dist: Jetstar

Kitsyke Will

DEVIL'S RIDE.
Album: released on Highway, '85 by Highway Records. Dist: Roots, Projection, Ross

Kitt, Eartha

AT HER VERY BEST.
Album: released on RCA, '84 by RCA Records. Dist: RCA, Roots, Swift, Wellard, Chris, I & B, Solomon & Peres Distribution

Cassette: released on RCA, '84 by RCA Records. Dist: RCA, Roots, Swift, Wellard, Chris, I & B, Solomon & Peres Distribution

BEST OF EARTHA KITT, THE.
Album: released on MCA, Sep'82 by MCA Records. Dist: Polygram, MCA

Cassette: released on MCA, Sep'82 by MCA Records. Dist: Polygram, MCA

CEST SI BON.
Album: released on IMS(Import), Mar'84 by Polydor Records. Dist: IMS, Polygram

I LOVE MEN.
Album: released on Record Shack, Oct'84 by Record Shack Records. Dist: PRT

Cassette: released on Record Shack, Oct'84 by Record Shack Records. Dist: PRT

Single (7"): released on Record Shack, Jun'84 by Record Shack Records. Dist: PRT

Single (12"): released on Record Shack, Jun'84 by Record Shack Records. Dist: PRT

LOVE FOR SALE.
Album: released on Capitol(USA), Mar'84 by Capitol (USA) Records. Dist: EMI

Cassette: released on Capitol(USA), Mar'84 by Capitol (USA) Records. Dist: EMI

ROMANTIC EARTHA KITT, THE.

SONGS.
Tracks: / Sing 'em low / Jonny, wenn du geburstag hast / Smoke gets in your eyes / Memphis blues (The) / Lullaby of birdland / Heel (The) / Apres moi / St. Louis blues / April in Portugal / I want to be evil / My heart belongs to daddy / Mambo de paree / Monotonous / C'est si bon / Let's do it / Lisbon Antigua / Do you remember? / Uska dara / Beale Street blues / Fascinating man / Looking for a boy / Just an old fashioned girl / Angelitos negros / Careless love / Under the bridges of Paris / If I can't take it with me / Day that the circus left town (The).
Album: released on RCA, Jul'86 by RCA Records. Dist: RCA, Roots, Swift, Wellard, Chris, I & B, Solomon & Peres Distribution

Cassette: released on RCA, Jul'86 by RCA Records. Dist: RCA, Roots, Swift, Wellard, Chris, I & B, Solomon & Peres Distribution

Album: released on RCA (Germany), '83

ST. LOUIS BLUES y.
Album: released on RCA (Germany), Jan'85

Cassette: released on RCA (Germany), Jan'85

THAT BAD EARTHA.
Album: released on RCA (Germany), '1

Cassette: released on RCA (Germany), '1

THIS IS MY LIFE.
Single (7"): released on Record Shack, Mar'86 by Record Shack Records. Dist: PRT

Single (7"): released on Record Shack, Mar'86 by Record Shack Records. Dist: PRT

WHERE IS MY MAN.
Single (7"): released on Record Shack, Nov'83 by Record Shack Records. Dist: PRT

Single (12"): released on Record Shack, Nov'83 by Record Shack Records. Dist: PRT

Kittrell, Christine

NASHVILLE R&B VOL.2.
Album: released on Krazy Kat, Dec'86 Dist: Jazz Music, Swift, Chris Wellard, H.R. Taylor, Charly, Hotshot, IRS Distribution

Kitty

BENJI.
Single (7"): released on L.O.E., Oct'82 Dist: PRT

Kix

COOL KIDS.
Single (7"): released on Atlantic, Jun'83 by WEA Records. Dist: WEA

FEAR OF FLYING.
Single (7"): released on Creole, Aug'8 by Creole Records. Dist: Rhino, PRT

MIDNITE DYNAMITE.
Album: released on Atlantic, Oct'85 by WEA Records. Dist: WEA

Kjeldsen, Mark

ARE YOU READY.
Single (7"): released on Backdoor, Jan'80 Dist: Polygram

K, Jon

ADOWA.
Album: released on Village Roots, Aug'87 Dist: Jetstar. Estim retail price in Sep'87 was £5.99.

Klang, Hugo

WHEEL OF FAT y.
Single (7"): released on Au-Go-Go (Australia), Oct'83 by Au-Go-Go Records (Australia). Dist: Rough Trade, Cartel

Klasicki, Vicki

WE'LL FIND OUR DAY (Klasicki, Vicki & Mike Holoway).
Single (7"): released on Simon, Aug'83 by Supertunes Records. Dist: Pinnacle

Klassix

KNOCK THREE TIMES.
Single (7"): released on JKO, Oct'82 by JKO Records. Dist: Pinnacle

PLEASE DON'T SMOKE.
Single (7"): released on JKO, Mar'85 by JKO Records. Dist: Pinnacle

WATCH THE WHITE BOY BOOGIE.
Single (12"): released on JKO, Jan'84 by JKO Records. Dist: Pinnacle

Klaxon 5

HOT HOUSE.
Single (7"): released on EL, Oct'84 by El Records. Dist: Rough Trade, Cartel, Pinnacle

Single (12"): released on EL, Oct'84 by El Records. Dist: Rough Trade, Cartel, Pinnacle

NEVER UNDERESTIMATE THE IGNORANCE OF THE RICH.
Tracks: / Never underestimate the ignorance of the rich / Great railway journeys.
Single (7"): released on EL, Nov'86 by El Records. Dist: Rough Trade, Cartel, Pinnacle

Klaxons

CLAP CLAP SOUND.
Single (7"): released on PRT, Jun'84 by PRT Records. Dist: PRT

Kleane, Dolores

FAREWELL TO EIRINN (Kleane, Dolores & John Faulkner/Eamonn Curran).
Album: released on Mulligan, Jul'81 by Topic Records. Dist: Roots Distribution, Jazz Music Distribution, JSU Distribution, I & B Distribution, Projection Distribution, Wynd-Up Distribution, Celtic Distributions

Kleeer

DE KLEEER TING.
Single (12"): released on Atlantic, Jun'81 by WEA Records. Dist: WEA

Single (7"): released on Atlantic, Jun'81 by WEA Records. Dist: WEA

GET READY.
Album: released on Web, Jun'83 by Web Records. Dist: ILA, PRT, Web

GET TOUGH.
Single (7"): released on Atlantic, Feb'81 by WEA Records. Dist: WEA

Single (7"): released on Atlantic, Feb'81 by WEA Records. Dist: WEA

INTIMATE CONNECTION.
Album: released on Atlantic, Mar'84 by WEA Records. Dist: WEA

KLEEER WINNERS.
Tracks: / Intimate connection / Take your heart away / Seeekret / Never cry again / Winners / Do kleer ting / Keep your body / Get tough / Open your mind / Wall to wall.
Album: released on Atlantic, Apr'86 by WEA Records. Dist: WEA

Cassette: released on Atlantic, Apr'86 by WEA Records. Dist: WEA

LICENSED TO DREAM.
Album: released on Alan Wood, Mar'81 by Alan Wood Records. Dist: Pinnacle

SEEKKRET.
Album: released on Atlantic, Jul'85 by WEA Records. Dist: WEA

Klein

DIRTY TALK (Klein & The M.B.O).
Single (7"): released on T.M.T., Nov'82 by T.M.T. Records. Dist: Unknown

Single (12"): released on T.M.T., Nov'82 by T.M.T. Records. Dist: Unknown

Kleinow, Pete

SNEAKY PETE (Kleinow, Sneaky Pete).
Album: released on Shiloh, May'79

Klemmer, John

BAREFOOT BALLET.
Tracks: / Barefoot ballet / Forest child / Crystal Fingers / Whisper to the wind / Poem painter / At 17 / Talking hands / Rain dancer / Naked / Barefoot ballet / Forest child / Crystal fingers / Whisper to the wind / Poem painter / At 17 / Talking hands / Rain dancer.
Compact disc: released on MCA, Apr'87 by MCA Records. Dist: Polygram, MCA

FINESSE.
Tracks: / Finesse / Man and woman / Sometimes / Greatest love of all (The) / Sun, the moon and the stars (The) / Beloved / But are you beautiful inside.
Notes: Digital Stereo.
Compact disc: released on Elektra Asylum, Jul'84 by Elektra/Asylum/Nonesuch Records. Dist: WEA

Album: released on Elektra, Feb'83 by WEA Records. Dist: WEA

Compact disc: released on Elektra Asylum, Jul'84 by Elektra/Asylum/Nonesuch Records. Dist: WEA

Klezmorim

EAST SIDE WEDDING.
Album: released on Arhoolie, May'81 by Arhoolie Records. Dist: Projection, Topic, Jazz Music, Swift, Roots

STREETS OF GOLD.
Album: released on Arhoolie, May'81 by Arhoolie Records. Dist: Projection, Topic, Jazz Music, Swift, Roots

Klo

FUN.
Single (7"): released on 101 International, Mar'84

Klobe Martin

TRONIC (Klobe Martin & Ralf Illenberger).
Album: released on Wundertute (W.Germany), Feb'85

Klockwerke

KLOCKWERKE MIND.
Single (7"): released on Trindisc, Aug'84 by Trindisc Records. Dist: Jetstar, Pinnacle, Rough Trade, Cartel

Klondike Peter

SOME OF THE FELLERS (Klondike Peter & The Huskies).
Album: released on Big Beat, May'80 by Ace Records. Dist: Projection, Pinnacle

Klones

DISCO RHYTHM.
Single (7"): released on Secret, Dec'81 by Se-

cret Records. Dist: EMI

Kloss, Arnold

STORY LINE.
Album: released on Daybreak, Oct'82 Dist: Jazz Horizons, Jazz Music

Kloss,Eric

CELEBRATION.
Album: released on Muse (Import), Apr'81

ONE TWO FREE.
Album: released on Muse (Import), Apr'81

Klovn,Svart

KNUST KNEKT.
Single (7"): released on Uniton Records, Sep'84 Dist: Cartel

Klugh, Earl

CRAZY FOR YOU.
Album: released on Liberty-United, Oct'81 by EMI Records. Dist: EMI

Cassette: released on Liberty-United, Oct'81 by EMI Records. Dist: EMI

DELTA LADY (Klugh, Earland David Matthews).
Album: released on PRT, Mar'83 by PRT Records. Dist: PRT

DELTA LADY Hsee Matthews, David) (Klugh, Earl & David Matthews).

DREAM COME TRUE.
Album: released on EMI (Germany), '83 by EMI Records. Dist: Conifer

FINGER PAINTINGS.
Album: released on Blue Note, Aug'77 by EMI Records. Dist: EMI

HEARTSTRING.
Tracks: / Heartstring / I'll see you again / Accoustic Lady parts 1&2 / Spanish night / Pretty world / Waiting for Cathy / Rayna / Heartstring (reprise).
Compact disc: released on EMI America, Apr'87 by EMI Records. Dist: EMI

HEART STRING.
Album: released on United Artists, Apr'79

HEART STRING/LATE NIGHT GUITAR.
Cassette: released on Liberty, Jun'83 by Liberty-United. Dist: EMI

Hotel California

LATE NIGHT GUITAR.
Album: released on United Artists, Dec'80

Album: released on EMI (Germany), '83 by EMI Records. Dist: Conifer

LIFE STORIES.
Tracks: / Traveller (The) / Just for your love / Second chances / For the love of you / Debra Anne / Santiago sunset / Sandman / Return of the rainmaker / Moon and the stars / Traveller, part II (The).
Album: released on Warner Bros., Sep'86 by Warner Bros Records. Dist: WEA

Cassette: released on Warner Bros., Sep'86 by Warner Bros Records. Dist: WEA

Compact disc: released on Warner Bros., Oct'86 by Warner Bros Records. Dist: WEA

LIVING INSIDE YOUR LOVE.
Album: released on Blue Note, Jan'77 by EMI Records. Dist: EMI Deleted '86.

LIVING INSIDE YOUR LOVE/FINGER PAINTINGS.
Cassette: released on Liberty, Jun'83 by Liberty-United. Dist: EMI Deleted '86.

LOW RIDE.
Tracks: / Back in Central Park / Be my love / Low ride / Just like yesterday / If you're still in love with me / I never thought I'd leave you / Christina / Night drive.
Compact disc: released on Capitol, Jan'84 by Capitol Records. Dist: EMI

Album: released on Capitol, May'83 by Capitol Records. Dist: EMI

Cassette: released on Capitol, May'83 by Capitol Records. Dist: EMI

Compact disc: released on Capitol, Jan'84 by Capitol Records. Dist: EMI

MAGIC IN YOUR EYES.
Album: released on United Artists, May'78 Deleted '86.

MAGIC IN YOUR EYES/DREAM COME TRUE.
Cassette: released on Liberty, Jun'83 by Liberty-United. Dist: EMI Deleted '86.

NIGHTSONGS.
Tracks: / Ain't misbehavin' / Theme from The Pawnbroker / Look of love (The) / Nature boy / Stay gold (Theme from The Outsiders) / Night song / See see rider / Certain smile, A / Shadow of your smile (The) / Theme from Picnic.
Compact disc: released on EMI, Apr'87 by EMI Records. Dist: EMI

Album: released on Capitol, Oct'84 by Capitol Records. Dist: EMI

Cassette: released on Capitol, Oct'84 by Capitol Records. Dist: EMI Deleted '86.

SODA FOUNTAIN SHUFFLE.
Compact disc: released on Warner Bros., Feb'87 by Warner Bros Records. Dist: WEA

Album: released on Warner Bros., May'85 by Warner Bros Records. Dist: WEA

Cassette: released on Warner Bros., May'85 by Warner Bros Records. Dist: WEA

TWO OF A KIND (Klugh,Earl and Bob James).
Album: released on Capitol, Nov'82 by Capitol Records. Dist: EMI

Cassette: released on Capitol, Nov'82 by Capitol Records. Dist: EMI

WISHFUL THINKING.
Album: released on Capitol, Mar'84 by Capitol Records. Dist: EMI

Cassette: released on Capitol, Mar'84 by Capitol Records. Dist: EMI Deleted '86.

Compact disc: released on Capitol, Mar'84 by Capitol Records. Dist: EMI

WORLD STAR.
Album: released on EMI (Holland), Jan'85 by EMI Records. Dist: Conifer

Cassette: released on EMI (Holland), Jan'85 by EMI Records. Dist: Conifer

Klymaxx

GIRLS IN THE BAND,THE.
Album: released on Elektra, Nov'83 by WEA Records. Dist: WEA

I MISS YOU.
Tracks: / I miss you / Video kid.
Single (7"): released on MCA, Jan'86 by MCA Records. Dist: Polygram, MCA

Single (12"): released on MCA, Jan'86 by MCA Records. Dist: Polygram, MCA

KLYMAXX.
Notes: Features the recent club hit 'Man size love' and forthcoming single 'sexy'. Producers include George Clinton, While Howard Hewitt (ex Shalamar) adds vocals on the ballad 'I'd still say yes'.
Album: released on MCA, Dec'86 by MCA Records. Dist: Polygram, MCA

Cassette: released on MCA, Dec'86 by MCA Records. Dist: Polygram, MCA

MAN IN MY LIFE/HEARTBREAKER.
Single (7"): released on Elektra, Jan'83 by WEA Records. Dist: WEA

Single (12"): released on Elektra, Jan'83 by WEA Records. Dist: WEA

MAN SIZE LOVE.
Tracks: / Man size love / Man size love (Dub mix).
Single (7"): released on MCA, Jan'87 by MCA Records. Dist: Polygram, MCA

Single (12"): released on MCA, Jan'87 by MCA Records. Dist: Polygram, MCA

MEETING IN THE LADIES ROOM.
Tracks: / Men all pause (The) / Lock and key / I miss you / Just our luck / Meeting in the ladies room / Video kid / Ask me no questions / Love bandit / I betcha.
Notes: Features the recent hit single 'I Miss You'. Album is already platinum in the US. Also includes their previous U.S hits 'The Men All Pause', 'Meeting In The Ladies Room', and 'Lock And Key'. An unusual group - six women who write, sing and play everything themselves - and look and sound great!
Album: released on MCA, Jun'86 by MCA Records. Dist: Polygram, MCA

Cassette: released on MCA, Jun'86 by MCA Records. Dist: Polygram, MCA

Compact disc: released on MCA, Jul'87 by MCA Records. Dist: Polygram, MCA

NEVER UNDERESTIMATE THE POWER OF A WOMAN.
Album: released on Solar, Jul'81 by MCA Records. Dist: Polygram Distribution

Cassette: released on Solar, Jul'81 by MCA Records. Dist: Polygram Distribution

WILD GIRLS/CAN'T LET LOVE JUST PASS.
Single (7"): released on Solar, Nov'82 by MCA Records. Dist: Polygram Distribution

Single (12"): released on Solar, Nov'82 by MCA Records. Dist: Polygram Distribution

K.M.R.

BREAKING OUT.
Single (7"): released on Cricket International, Oct'82 by Cricket International Records. Dist: Stage One

Knabel, Rudi

ZAMBER DER ZITHER.
Tracks: / Der dritte man / Wien, wien nur du allein / Wenn der herrgott net will / Hoppla-hop / Stell's meine ross 'in' stall / Wiener fiakerlied / La montanara-das lied der berge / Mein loisachtal / Zauber der berge / Grune almen / Abendstimmung / Die kleine serenade - serenade von Rudi Knabl.
Notes: Rudi Knabel, the famous Austrian zither player with a collection of his best recordings. 'Third Man' and 'La Montaranara-Das Lied Derv Berge' from 'Legend Of The Glass Mountain'
Album: released on Polydor (Germany), Sep'86 Dist: IMS-Polygram

Cassette: released on Polydor (Germany), Sep'86 Dist: IMS-Polygram

Knack

BUT THE LITTLE GIRLS UNDERSTAND.
Album: released on Capitol, Mar'80 by Capitol Records. Dist: EMI

GET THE KNACK.
Album: released on Fame (Capitol), Sep'82 by Music For Pleasure Records. Dist: EMI Deleted '84.

Cassette: released on Fame (Capitol), Sep'82 by Music For Pleasure Records. Dist: EMI

Knapp, James

FIRST AVENUE.
Album: released on ECM (Germany), Jul'81 by ECM Records. Dist: IMS, Polygram, Virgin through EMI

Knarren, Pete

MIDNIGHT BLUE.
Single (7"): released on EMI, Feb'83 by EMI Records. Dist: EMI

Kneller Hall R.M.S Band

HOME GROWN.
Tracks: / Celebration / Heroic march / Jubilee overture / Choc'late dancing / Prelude to comedy / Fantasia on the Dargason / Bond of friendship / Cavalry walk / Mad major / Royal Stuart / Prince / Royal standard / Sarafand / Silver salute.
Album: released on Polyphonic Digital, Sep'86

Cassette: released on Polyphonic Digital, Sep'86

Knepper, Jimmy

DREAM DANCING (Knepper, Jimmy Quintet).
Album: released on Criss Cross Jazz, Jan'87 Dist: Jazz Music, Jazz Horizons

IDOL OF THE FLIES.
Album: released on Affinity, May'82 by Charly Records. Dist: Charly, Cadillac

I DREAM TOO MUCH (Knepper, Jimmy Sextet).
Compact disc: released on Soul Note (Italy), '86 Dist: Harmonia Mundi Distributors

JUST FRIENDS (Knepper, Jimmy & Temperley Joe).
Album: released on Hep, Aug'79 by H.R. Taylor Records. Dist: Jazz Music, Cadillac Music, JSU, Taylors, Wellard, Chris, Zodiac, Swift, Fast Forward

PRIMROSE PATH (Knepper, Jimmy & Bobby Wellins).
Album: released on Hep, Jul'82 by H.R. Taylor Records. Dist: Jazz Music, Cadillac Music, JSU, Taylors, Wellard, Chris, Zodiac, Swift, Fast Forward

TELL ME (Knepper, Jimmy Sextet).
Album: released on Daybreak, Apr'81 Dist: Jazz Horizons, Jazz Music

Knight, Bobby

CREAM OF THE CROP.
Album: released on Pye, Oct'79

Knight, Brian

DARK HORSE, A.
Album: released on PVK, Apr'81

Knight, Frederick

I'VE BEEN LONELY SO LONG.
Single (7"): released on Stax, Aug'87 by Ace Records. Dist: Pinnacle, Chris Wellard, IMS-Polygram

KNIGHT RAP.
Album: released on Timeless, Aug'87

Knight, Gary

CRY WOLF.
Single (7"): released on Button, Oct'83 by Musical Characters Records. Dist: Spartan

PRIVATE EYE.
Single (7"): released on Works, Jun'84 Dist: PRT

Knight, Gladys

20 GOLDEN GREATS (Knight, Gladys & The Pips).
Album: released on Motown, Oct'81 by Motown Records. Dist: BMG Distribution

Cassette: released on Motown, Oct'81 by Motown Records. Dist: BMG Distribution

ALL THE GREATEST HITS (Knight, Gladys & The Pips).
Album: released on Motown, Apr'85 by Motown Records. Dist: BMG Distribution

Cassette: released on Motown, Apr'85 by Motown Records. Dist: BMG Distribution

BEFORE NOW AFTER THEN (Knight, Gladys & The Pips).
Album: released on Cambra, Apr'84 by Cambra Records. Dist: IDS, Conifer

Cassette: released on Cambra, Apr'84 by Cambra Records. Dist: IDS, Conifer

BEST OF.. (Knight, Gladys & The Pips).
Cassette: released on Buddah, Feb'76 Dist: Swift, Jazz Music, PRT

BEST OF GLADYS KNIGHT AND THE PIPS, THE (Knight, Gladys & The Pips).
Album: released on Buddah, Mar'76 Dist: Swift, Jazz Music, PRT

BEST THING THAT EVER HAPPENED TO ME (Knight, Gladys & The Pips).
Single (7"): released on Creole, Jan'83 by Creole Records. Dist: Rhino, PRT

BLESS THIS HOUSE (Knight, Gladys & The Pips).
Album: released on Buddah, Dec'84 Dist: Swift, Jazz Music, PRT

COLLECTION: GLADYS KNIGHT (4 LP SET) (Knight, Gladys & The Pips).
Special: released on Buddah, Sep'78 Dist: Swift, Jazz Music, PRT

COLLECTION: GLADYS KNIGHT.
Album: released on Starblend, Feb'85 by Starblend Records. Dist: PRT Distribution

Cassette: released on Starblend, Feb'85 by Starblend Records. Dist: PRT Distribution

EVERBODY NEEDS LOVE (Knight, Gladys & The Pips).

EVERY BEAT OF MY HEART.
Notes: Includes original hit material.
Album: released on Blue Moon, Mar'86 Dist: Magnum Music Group Ltd, PRT, Spartan

Album: released on Motown, '82 by Motown Records. Dist: BMG Distribution

Cassette: released on Motown, '82 by Motown Records. Dist: BMG Distribution

EVERY BEAT OF MY HEART (Knight, Gladys & The Pips).

FLIPHITS (Knight, Gladys & The Pips).
Cassette: released on Motown, Jul'83 by Motown Records. Dist: BMG Distribution

GLADYS KNIGHT & THE PIPS (Knight, Gladys & The Pips).

HELP ME MAKE IT THROUGH THE NIGHT (Knight, Gladys & The Pips).
Album: released on Motown, Jun'83 by Motown Records. Dist: BMG Distribution

Cassette: released on Motown, Jun'83 by Motown Records. Dist: BMG Distribution

Single (7"): released on Motown, Oct'81 by Motown Records. Dist: BMG Distribution

HERO (Knight, Gladys & The Pips).
Single (7"): released on CBS, Sep'83 by CBS Records. Dist: CBS Deleted '84.

Single (12"): released on CBS, Sep'83 by CBS Records. Dist: CBS

IMAGINATION (Knight, Gladys & The Pips).
Album: released on Buddah, Aug'74 Dist: Swift, Jazz Music, PRT

Album: released on Buddah, Jul'85 Dist: Swift, Jazz Music, PRT

Cassette: released on Buddah, Jul'85 Dist: Swift, Jazz Music, PRT

JUKE BOX GIANTS (Knight, Gladys & The Pips).
Album: released on Audio Fidelity, May'82 Dist: PRT

LOOKING BACK... "THE FURY YEARS" (Knight, Gladys & The Pips).
Album: released on Bulldog, Jul'82 by Bulldog Records. Dist: President Distribution, Spartan, Swift, Taylor, H.R.

MEMORIES OF THE WAY WERE.
Double Album: released on Buddah, Sep'79 Dist: Swift, Jazz Music, PRT

Cassette: released on Buddah, Nov'79 Dist: Swift, Jazz Music, PRT

MIDNIGHT TRAIN TO GEORGIA.
Album: released on Hallmark, Apr'81 by Pickwick Records. Dist: Pickwick Distribution, PRT, Taylors

Single (7"): released on Creole Replay, Aug'84 by Creole Records. Dist: PRT, Rhino

Cassette: released on Hallmark, Mar'81 by Pickwick Records. Dist: Pickwick Distribution, PRT, Taylors

MISS GLADYS KNIGHT.
Album: released on Buddah, Feb'79 Dist: Swift, Jazz Music, PRT

NEITHER ONE OF US.
Album: released on Motown, Mar'82 by Motown Records. Dist: BMG Distribution

Cassette: released on Motown, Mar'82 by Motown Records. Dist: BMG Distribution

NITTY GRITTY (Knight, Gladys & The Pips).
Album: released on Motown, Mar'82 by Motown Records. Dist: BMG Distribution

Cassette: released on Motown, Mar'82 by Motown Records. Dist: BMG Distribution

ON AND ON (Knight, Gladys & The Pips).
Cassette: released on Orchid Music, Feb'82 by Bibi. Dist: Pinnacle

ONE AND ONLY, THE (Knight, Gladys & The Pips).
Album: released on Buddah, May'78 Dist: Swift, Jazz Music, PRT

SEND THE OVERTIME FOR ME.
Single (7"): released on CBS, Apr'83 by CBS Records. Dist: CBS

Single (12"): released on CBS, Apr'83 by CBS Records. Dist: CBS

SPOTLIGHT ON GLADYS KNIGHT & THE PIPS.
Album: released on PRT, '80 by PRT Records. Dist: PRT

Cassette: released on PRT, '80 by PRT Records. Dist: PRT

STILL TOGETHER (Knight, Gladys & The Pips).
Album: released on Buddah, Mar'77 Dist: Swift, Jazz Music, PRT

TASTE OF BITTER LOVE (Knight, Gladys & The Pips).
Album: released on Hallmark, Nov'83 by Pickwick Records. Dist: Pickwick Distribution, PRT, Taylors

Cassette: released on Hallmark, Nov'83 by Pickwick Records. Dist: Pickwick Distribution, PRT, Taylors

TEEN ANGUISH (Knight, Gladys & The Pips).
Album: released on Charly, Jul'81 by Charly Records. Dist: Charly, Cadillac

VISIONS.
Album: released on CBS, Jun'83 by CBS Records. Dist: CBS Deleted '85.

Cassette: released on CBS, Jun'83 by CBS Records. Dist: CBS

WAY WE WERE, THE (Knight, Gladys & Bill Medley).
Single (7"): released on Flashback, Jul'80 by Flashback Records/PRT Records. Dist: Mainline, PRT

Single (7"): released on Old Gold, Apr'83 by Old Gold Records. Dist: Lightning, Jazz Music, Spartan, Counterpoint

Knight, Gladys & The Pips

ANTHOLOGY Volumes 1 & 2.
Tracks: / Every beat of my heart / Letter full of tears / Giving up / Just walk in my shoes / Do you love me just a little, honey / You don't love me no more / Take me in your arms and love / Everybody needs love / I heard it through the grapevine / End of our road, The / I know better / Don't let her take your love from me / All I could do was cry / It should have been me / I wish it would rain / Theme from "Valley of the Dolls" / Didn't you know (you'd have to cry sometime) / Got myself a good man / Nitty gritty, The / Friendship train / Tracks of my tears / You need love like I do (don't you?) / Every little bit hurts / If I were your woman / I don't want to do wrong / Oe less bell to answer / Is there a place (in his heart for me) / Master of my mind / No one could love you more / Can't give it up no more / For once in my life / Make me the woman that you go home to / Help me make it through the night / Neither one of us (wants to be the first to say goodbye) / Daddy could swear, I declare / All I need is time / Don';t tell me I'm crazy / Oh! what a love I have found / Only time you love me is when you're losing me, The / Between her goodbye and my hello.
Double compact disc: released on Motown, Jan'87 by Motown Records. Dist: BMG Distribution

Double compact disc: released on Motown, 20 Jun'87 by Motown Records. Dist: BMG Distribution

Album: released on Motown, Oct'81 by Motown Records. Dist: BMG Distribution

Cassette: released on Motown, Oct'81 by Motown Records. Dist: BMG Distribution

BROKEN PROMISES.
Tracks: / Operator / You broke your promise / Morning noon & night / Guess who / Love like mine, A / I really didn't mean it / One more lonely night / Come see about me / I can't stand by / I want that kind of love.
Album: released on Topline, Mar'87 by Charly Records. Dist: Charly Distribution

Cassette: released on Topline, Mar'87 by Charly Records. Dist: Charly Distribution

CHRISTMAS EVERYDAY.
Tracks: / Christmas everyday / Christmas every day (inst).
Single (7"): released on MCA, Nov'86 by MCA Records. Dist: Polygram, MCA

Single (12"): released on MCA, Nov'86 by MCA Records. Dist: Polygram, MCA

COMPACT COMMAND PERFORMANCES 17 Greatest Hits.
Tracks: / Everybody needs love / I heard it through the grapevine / End of our road / It should have been me / I wish it would rain / Didn't you know (you'd have to cry sometime) / Nitty gritty (the) / Friendship train / You need love like I do (don't you?) / If I were your woman / I don't want to do wrong / Make me the woman that you come home to / Help me make it through the night / Neither one of us (wants to be the first to say goodbye) / Daddy could swear,I do declare / All I need is time / Between her goodbye & my hello,
Compact disc: released on Motown, '86 by Motown Records. Dist: BMG Distribution

EARLY YEARS, THE Teen anguish.
Tracks: / If ever I should fall in love / Every beat of my heart / Either way I lose / It hurts so bad / Why don't you love me / Maybe, Maybe baby / Letter full of tears / Giving up / Go away, stay away / What will become of me / Queen of tears / Stop and get a hold of myself / Tell her you're mine / There will never be another love / Lovers always forgive / Who knows (I just can't trust you any more).
Notes: Licensed from Charly International APS. This CD (P) 1987 Charly Holdings Inc. (C) 1987 Charly Records Ltd.

GLADYS KNIGHT & THE PIPS.
Compact disc: released on Intertape, Jul'87 Dist: Target

Cassette: released on Ampro Cassettes, Sep'81

Album: released on Cambra, Apr'85 by Cambra Records. Dist: IDS, Conifer

Cassette: released on Cambra, Apr'85 by Cambra Records. Dist: IDS, Conifer

LOVING ON BORROWED TIME.
Tracks: / Loving on borrowed time / Angel of the city.
Single (7"): released on Epic, Aug'86 by CBS Records. Dist: CBS

NEITHER ONE OF US/ALL I NEED IS TIME 2 Classic albums.
Tracks: / Neither one of us (wants to be the first to say goodbye) / It's gotta be that way / For once in my life / This Child needs it's father / Who is she (and what is she to you) / And this is love / Daddy / Daddy could swear, I declare / Can't give it up no more / Don't it make you feel guilty / I'll be here (when you get home) / All I need is time / Heavy makes you happy / Only time you live me is when you're losing me (The) / Here I am again / There's a lesson to be learned / Oh what a love I have found / Singer (The) / Thankyou (falletin me be mice elf agin) / It's all over but the shoutin' / For once in my life / Only time you love me is when you're losing me, The / Singer, The.
Compact disc: released on Motown Records. Dist: BMG Distribution Deleted Nov'86.

REPLAY ON.
Album: released on Sierra, May'86 by Sierra Records. Dist: WEA

Cassette: released on Sierra, May'86 by Sierra Records. Dist: WEA

SEND IT TO ME.
Tracks: / Send it to me / Send it to me (acapella).
Single (7"): released on MCA, Mar'87 by MCA Records. Dist: Polygram, MCA

Single (12"): released on MCA, Mar'87 by MCA Records. Dist: Polygram, MCA

Knight, Jean

MR BIG STUFF.
Single (7"): released on Old Gold, Jan'87 by Old Gold Records. Dist: Lightning, Jazz Music, Spartan, Counterpoint

Single (7"): released on Stax, Mar'82 by Ace Records. Dist: Pinnacle, Chris Wellard, IMS-Polygram

Single (7"): released on Old Gold, Sep'85 by Old Gold Records. Dist: Lightning, Jazz Music, Spartan, Counterpoint

MR.BIG STUFF.
Tracks: / Mr.Big Stuff / Why I keep living these memories.
Single (7"): released on Stax, 13 Jun'87 by Ace Records. Dist: Pinnacle, Chris Wellard, IMS-Polygram

MR. BIG STUFF.
Album: released on Stax, Aug'87 by Ace Records. Dist: Pinnacle, Chris Wellard, IMS-Polygram. Estim retail price in Sep'87 was £4.90.

Knight, Jerry

I'M DOWN FOR THAT.
Single (12"): released on Funk America, Feb'83 by A&M Records. Dist: CBS

LOVE'S ON OUR SIDE.
Album: released on A&M, Mar'83 by A&M Records. Dist: Polygram

Knight, Joe

MARTY ROBBINS SCRAPBOOK (Knight, Joe & Bev King).

Knight, Pete

THAT'S ALRIGHT.
Album: released on Tank, Jun'79 by Tank Records.

Knight, Peter

BEST OF NOVELLO & COWARD (Knight, Peter & His Orchestra).
Tracks: / Ziguener / I'll follow my secret heart / Music in May / Violon began to play / Highwayman love / Room with a view / Party's over now / We'll gather lilacs.
Album: released on PRT Flashback, Jul'86

Cassette: released on PRT Flashback, Jul'86

Knight, Russ

CRUISIN' 1962 KLIF Dallas.
Cassette: released on Increase(USA), Jun'87 by Quicksilver Records (USA).

Knights, Don

CINEMA ORGAN ENCORES.
Album: released on Derry, Jun'81 by Outlet Records. Dist: Outlet Records

Knights & Emeralds

KNIGHTS AND EMERALDS Original soundtrack (Various Artists).
Notes: Artists include: Princess/Maxi Priest
Album: released on 10, Sep'86 by 10 Records. Dist: Virgin, EMI

Cassette: released on 10, Sep'86 by 10 Records. Dist: Virgin, EMI

Knight, Sonny

CONFIDENTIAL.
Album: released on Mr. R&B (Sweden), May'85 by Mr. R&B Records. Dist: Swift

Knitters

POOR LITTLE CRITTER ON THE ROAD.
Album: released on Slash, May'85 by London Records. Dist: Polygram

Knockout

NEVER.
Tracks: / Never / Perfect lover.
Single (7"): released on Karma, Jun'87 by Karma Records. Dist: PRT

Knopfler, David

BEHIND THE LINES.
Compact disc: released on Making Waves, May'85 by Making Waves Records.

Album:

Cassette:

Compact disc:

CUT THE WIRE.
Album: released on Greenhill, Mar'87 by Greenhill Records. Dist: PRT

Cassette: released on Greenhill, Mar'87 by Greenhill Records. Dist: PRT

HEART TO HEART.
Single (7"):

Single (12"):

MADONNA'S DAUGHTER.
Single (7"): released on Fast Alley, Jun'84 by Fast Alley Records. Dist: PRT

RELEASE.
Album: released on Peach River, Sep'83 by Peach River Records. Dist: PRT

Cassette: released on Peach River, Sep'83 by Peach River Records. Dist: PRT

SHOCKWAVE.
Single (7"): released on Making Waves, Feb'86 by Making Waves Records.

Single (12"): released on Making Waves, Feb'86 by Making Waves Records.

Single (7"): released on Pinnacle, Sep'85 by Pinnacle Records. Dist: Pinnacle

Single (12"): released on Pinnacle, Sep'85 by Pinnacle Records. Dist: Pinnacle

SOUL KISSING.
Single (7"): released on Peach River, Sep'83 by Peach River Records. Dist: PRT

Single (12"): released on Peach River, Sep'83 by Peach River Records. Dist: PRT

WHEN WE KISS.
Single (7"): released on Greenhill, Jan'87 by Greenhill Records. Dist: PRT

Single (12"): released on Greenhill, Jan'87 by Greenhill Records. Dist: PRT

Knopfler, Mark

Biographical Details: Mark Knopfler is the lead singer and driving force of Dire Straits. He is also one of the worlds greatest guitarists.

COMFORT AND JOY.
Single (7"): released on Vertigo, Jul'84 by Phonogram Records. Dist: Polygram

GOING HOME.
Tracks: / Going home / Wild theme / Smooching.
Single (7"): released on Vertigo, Sep'86 by Phonogram Records. Dist: Polygram

Single (12"): released on Vertigo, Sep'86 by Phonogram Records. Dist: Polygram

Single (7"): released on Vertigo, Feb'83 by Phonogram Records. Dist: Polygram

LOCAL HERO.
Album: released on Vertigo, Apr'83 by Phonogram Records. Dist: Polygram

Cassette: released on Vertigo, Apr'83 by Phonogram Records. Dist: Polygram

LOCAL HERO (THE).
Tracks: / Going home (theme from Local Hero).
Notes: Digital Stereo.

Compact disc: released on Vertigo, Jul'84 by Phonogram Records. Dist: Polygram

Compact disc: released on Vertigo, Jul'84 by Phonogram Records. Dist: Polygram

MUSIC FROM LOCAL HERO.
Album: released on Vertigo, Apr'83 by Phonogram Records. Dist: Polygram

Cassette: released on Vertigo, Apr'83 by Phonogram Records. Dist: Polygram

MUSIC FROM THE FILM CAL.
Compact disc: released on Vertigo, Nov'84 by Phonogram Records. Dist: Polygram

RELEASE PARIS.
Tracks: / Soul kissing / Come to me / Madonna's daughter / Girl and the paperboy (The) / Roman times / Sideshow / Little brother / Hey Henry / Grear divide (The) / Night train.
Album: released on Paris, Jun'86 Dist: Priority, RCA

Knot, Kenny

WATCH HOW THE PEOPLE DANCING.
Tracks: / Watch how the people dancing / A eeh do she.
Single (12"): released on Unity Sound, May'86 Dist: Jetstar

Knots In May

LIVING ON A GIRO.
Single (7"): released on Ritz, Apr'83 by Ritz Records. Dist: Spartan

Knotty Vision

KNOTTY VISION Various artists (Various Artists).
Album: released on Nighthawk, Mar'84 by Faulty Products Records. Dist: Pinnacle, Swift

Knowles, Pat

STANDARD SETTINGS.
Album: released on Fellside, '83 by Fellside Records. Dist: Roots, Jazz Music, Celtic Music, Projection

Knowles, Sonny

I'LL TAKE CARE OF YOUR CARES.
Tracks: / I'll take care of your cares / Behind the tear / Rare ould times / May i have the next dream with you / Solitaire / Can I forget you / Isadora / Roses of Picardy / Help me make it through the night / Delilah / You don't know me / Tell me / My lovely rose and you / My child.
Notes: Sonny Knowles is a romantic balladeer who is very popular on the cabaret circuitboth here and in Ireland. He has a warmth that makes him a favourite with that mass silent market.
Album: released on Polydor (Ireland), Mar'87 by Polydor Records. Dist: Polygram, I & B

Cassette: released on Polydor (Ireland), Mar'87 by Polydor Records. Dist: Polygram, I & B

Know Your Organ

KNOW YOUR ORGAN (Various Artists).
Album: released on Deroy, Jun'81 by Deroy Records. Dist: Jazz Music, Swift

Knox

GIGOLO AUNT.
Single (7"): released on Armageddon, Jul'81 by Armageddon Records. Dist: Revolver, Cartel, Pinnacle

PLUTONIUM EXPRESS.
Album: released on Razor, Sep'83 by Razor. Dist: Pinnacle

Knox, Buddy

GREATEST HITS: BUDDY KNOX.
Tracks: / Party doll / Rock-House / Maybellene / Storm clouds / Devil woman / Somebody touched me / Hula love / Rock your little baby to sleep / Lovey Dovey / Ling ting tong / I think I'm gonna kill myself / I washed my hands in muddy water / Travellin'.
Album: released on Charly, Apr'86 by Charly Records. Dist: Charly, Cadillac

Cassette: released on Charly, Apr'86 by Charly Records. Dist: Charly, Cadillac
Cat. no: **KTOP 142**
Album: released on Rockhouse, Mar'85 Dist: Pinnacle

LIBERTY TAKES.
Tracks: / Three eyed man / All by myself / Open your lovin' arms / She's gone / Now there's only me / Dear Abby / Three way love affair / Shadoroom / Tomorrow is a comin' / Hitch hike back to Georgia / Thanks a lot / Good lovin / All time loser / Lovey dovey / I got you / Ling ting tong.
Album: released on Charly, Oct'86 by Charly Records. Dist: Charly, Cadillac

PARTY DOLL.
Album: released on Pye International, Feb'78

SWEET COUNTRY MUSIC.
Album: released on Rock Star, Aug'87 Dist: Lightning, Swift Distribution, Superdisc Distribution

Knuckles, Frankie

YOU CAN'T HIDE FROM YOURSELF.
Tracks: / You can't hide from yourself (inst) / You can't hide from yourself (Chip E's house remix) / You can't hide from yourself (dub mix) / You can't hide from yourself / You can't hide from yourself(inst).
Single (7"): released on Portrait, Apr'87 by CBS Records. Dist: CBS

Single (12"): released on Portrait, Apr'87 by CBS Records. Dist: CBS

Single (12"): released on Portrait, May'87 by CBS Records. Dist: CBS

Knutt, Bobby

HELLO FETTLERS.
Album: released on Pye, Sep'79

Koffie

AND I'M TELLING YOU I'M NOT GOING.
Single (7"): released on Red Rooster, Nov'83 by Red Rooster Records. Dist: Pinnacle

Single (12"): released on Red Rooster, Nov'83 by Red Rooster Records. Dist: Pinnacle

Kofi

COUNTDOWN (Kofi & The Lovetones).
Single (7"): released on Electricity, Sep'84 by Electricity Records. Dist: PRT

Single (12"): released on Electricity, Sep'84 by Electricity Records. Dist: PRT

COUNTDOWN (1987 RE-RECORDING) (Kofi & The Lovetones).
Single (12"): released on Electricity, 23 May'87 by Electricity Records. Dist: PRT

Kojak & Mama Liza

SI DOWN PON IT.
Single (12"): released on Music Track, Nov'86 Dist: Jetstar Distribution

Koko Pop

BRAND NEW BEAT.
Single (7"): released on Motown, Oct'85 by Motown Records. Dist: BMG Distribution

Single (12"): released on Motown, Oct'85 by Motown Records. Dist: BMG Distribution

I'M IN LOVE WITH YOU.
Single (7"): released on Motown, Dec'84 by Motown Records. Dist: BMG Distribution

KOKO POP.
Album: released on Motown, Apr'85 by Motown Records. Dist: BMG Distribution

Cassette: released on Motown, Apr'85 by Motown Records. Dist: BMG Distribution

Kollo, Rene

HELLO MARY LOU.
Tracks: / Hello Mary Lou / Dich gibt's nur einmal / Eso beso / Du Casanova, du / Weit so weit / Davon traumen alle jungen leute / Auf der strasse meines lebens / Schone rose vom Rio Grande / Mandoline und roter wein / Sweet rosary / Sag nie goodbye / Meine grosse liebe wohnt in einer kleinen stadt / Traume weiter, sweet Sue / Peggy, Peggy / Ohne liebe is alles so traurig / Wie vom wind verweht.
Album: released on Bear Family, May'87 by Bear Family Records. Dist: Rollercoaster Distribution, Swift

Kondo, Toshinori

KONTON.
Tracks: / Sundown / Yami / Y.O.U. / Sandswitch / Yoyoyo / Gan.
Compact disc: released on Epic, '86 by CBS Records. Dist: CBS

Album: released on Epic, Sep'86 by CBS Records. Dist: CBS

Cassette: released on Epic, Sep'86 by CBS Records. Dist: CBS

Kongos, John

C.A.T.S. EYES.
Single (7"): released on Sierra, May'85 by Sierra Records. Dist: WEA

HE'S GONNA STEP ON YOU AGAIN.
Single (7"): released on Cube, Aug'82 by Dakota Records. Dist: PRT

TOKOLOSHE MAN.
Single (7"): released on Old Gold, Aug'82 by Old Gold Records. Dist: Lightning, Jazz Music, Spartan, Counterpoint Deleted Aug'82.

Konitz, Lee

4 FOUR SAX.
Double Album: released on Vogue Jazz, May'82

DOVE TAIL.
Tracks: / I want to be happy / Night has a thousand eyes / Counterpoint / Dovetail / Sweet Georgia Brown / Alone together / Cherokee / Penthouse serenade.
Album: released on Sunnyside (USA), Apr'84 Dist: Mole Jazz Distribution, Conifer Distribution

EZZTHETIC (Konitz, Lee & Miles Davis).
Notes: For full details see under Davis, Miles-Lee Konitz

FIGURE & SPIRIT (Konitz Lee Quintet).

FOUR KEYS (Konitz Lee/Matial Solal).
Album: released on MPS Jazz, May'81

GLAD KOONIX Live fron the Swedish tour 1983.
Album: released on Dragon, Jul'87 by Dragon Records. Dist: Jazz Music, Projection, Cadillac

IN SWEDEN 1951/53.
Album: released on Dragon, Jun'86 by Dragon Records. Dist: Jazz Music, Projection, Cadillac

KONITZ, LEE & WARNE MARSH VOL.3 (Konitz, Lee & Warne Marsh).
Notes: For full details see under Marsh, Warne

LEE KONITZ DUETS, THE.
Notes: With Jim Hall, Joe Henderson etc.
Compact disc: released on JVC Fantasy (Japan), May'87

LENNIE IN EUROPE (Konitz Lee/Tristano).
Album: released on Unique Jazz, Apr'81 Dist: Swift, Jazz Music, Jazz Horizons

LIVE AT THE MONTMARTRE CLUB (Konitz, Lee & Warne Marsh Quartet).
Notes: For full information see under: Marsh, Warne\lee Konitz Quintet.

LONDON CONCERT 1976 (Konitz,Lee and others).
Album: released on Wave, Apr'79 by Wave Records. Dist: JSU, Swift, Jazz Music, Cadillac, Chris Wellard

NONET,THE.
Album: released on Pye International, Feb'78

PYRAMID.
Album: released on Impro-arts, Jul'78 Dist: Projection

STEREOKONITZ.
Album: released on RCA (France), Oct'85 by RCA Records. Dist: Discovery

TIMESPAN text book solos.
Album: released on Wave, Dec'77 by Charly Records. Dist: Charly

VERY COOL.
Album: released on Verve, Nov'83 by Phonogram Records. Dist: Polygram

WILD AS SPRINGTIME.
Tracks: / She's as wild as Springtime / Hairy canary / Ez-thetic / Duende / Chopin Prelude No.20 / Spinning Waltz / Silly Samba / Hi, Beck / Ko.
Notes: Harold Danko - piano.
Album: released on GFM, Feb'87 by GFM Records. Dist: Fast Forward, Cartel, PRT, Projection

WILD AS SPRING TIME.
Album: released on GFM, Sep'84 by GFM Records. Dist: Fast Forward, Cartel, PRT, Projection

YES YES NONET (Konitz, Lee Nonet).
Album: released on Steeplechase, Sep'79

Konk

FOKA TOKA MOKA.
Single (7"): released on Konk, Feb'82

KONK PARTY.
Extended-play record: released on Konk, Dec'82

YO.
Album: released on Crepescule, Sep'83 by Island Records. Dist: Polygram, Pinnacle

YOUR LIFE.
Single (7"): released on Fourth & Broadway, Jun'84 by Island Records. Dist: Polygram, EMI

Single (12"): released on Fourth & Broadway, Jun'84 by Island Records. Dist: Polygram, EMI

Konstrucktivits

GLENASCANL.
Album: released on Sterile, Feb'86 Dist: Red Rhino Distribution, Cartel Distribution

Konstruktivitis

BLACK DECEMBER.
Album: released on Third Mind, Aug'84 by Third Mind Records. Dist: Backs, Cartel Distribution

Konte, Dembo

TANTANTE (Konte, Dembo & Kausu Kuyateh).
Album: released on Rogue, Mar'87 by Fast Forward Records. Dist: Nine Mile Distribution, Cartel Distribution

Konte Family

MANDINKA MUSIC.
Album: released on Virgin, Mar'82 by Virgin Records. Dist: EMI, Virgin Distribution

Kontikis

HAWAIIAN MEMORIES (Kontikis feat. Wout Steenhuis).
Album: released on Philips (Import), Apr'83
Cat. no: **9279 552**
Cassette: released on Philips (Import), Apr'83

Kontini, Finzy

CHA CHA CHA.
Tracks: / Cha cha cha / Bass and drums.
Single (12"): released on Carrere, Dec'85 by Carrere Records. Dist: PRT, Spartan

Kontiz, Lee

MOTION.
Tracks: / I remember you / All of me / Foolin' myself / You don't know what love is / You'd be so nice to come home to / Out of nowhere / I'll remember April / It's you or no one.
Notes: Personnel: Lee Konitz - alto sax / Sonny Dallas - bass / Elvin Jones - drums.
Album: released on Verve, Oct'84 by Phonogram Records. Dist: Polygram

Compact disc: released on Verve (USA), Jul'87 by Polydor. Dist: Polygram

Kontraband

NORTH STAR.
Album: released on Springthyme, Oct'86 by Springthyme Records. Dist: Jazz Music Distribution, Projection Distribution, Roots Distribution

Koobas, The

BARRICADES.
Album: released on Bam Caruso, Sep'86 by Bam Caruso Records. Dist: Rough Trade, Revolver, Cartel

Koo De Tah

TOO YOUNG FOR PROMISES.
Tracks: / Too young for promises / Dancing.
Single (7"): released on Mercury, Feb'86 by Phonogram Records. Dist: Polygram Distribution

Single (12"): released on Mercury, Feb'86 by Phonogram Records. Dist: Polygram Distribution

Kool, Bo

MONEY WE LOVE.
Single (12"): released on Tania Music, Oct'81

SPACE INVADER.
Single (12"): released on Master Funk, Mar'82 by Master Funk Records. Dist: PRT

Kool Moe Dee

GO SEE THE DOCTOR.
Tracks: / Go see the doctor (almost clean version) / Monster crack (radio edit).
Single (7"): released on Jive, Dec'86 by Zomba Records. Dist: RCA, PRT, CBS

Single (12"): released on Jive, Dec'86 by Zomba Records. Dist: RCA, PRT, CBS

KOOL MOE DEE.
Album: released on Jive, Jan'87 by Zomba Records. Dist: RCA, PRT, CBS

Cassette: released on Jive, Jan'87 by Zomba Records. Dist: RCA, PRT, CBS

Kool, Nat King

CHECKING OUT (Kool, Nat King & The Cool Runners).
Single (7"): released on Tia Wan, Sep'84

Kool & The Gang

AS ONE.
Compact disc: by Phonogram Records. Dist: Polygram

CELEBRATE.
Compact disc: by Phonogram Records. Dist: Polygram

Album: released on De-Lite, Dec'83 by Phonogram Records. Dist: Polygram

Cassette: released on De-Lite, Dec'83 by Phonogram Records. Dist: Polygram

Compact disc: released on De-Lite, Dec'83 by Phonogram Records. Dist: Polygram

CHERISH.
Single (7"): released on De-Lite, Apr'85 by Phonogram Records. Dist: Polygram

Single (12"): released on De-Lite, Apr'85 by Phonogram Records. Dist: Polygram

EMERGENCY.
Tracks: / Emergency / Fresh / Misled / Cherish / Surrender / Bad woman / You are the one.
Notes: Digital stereo.
Compact disc: released on De-Lite, Jan'85 by Phonogram Records. Dist: Polygram

Album: released on De-Lite, Nov'84 by Phonogram Records. Dist: Polygram

Cassette: released on De-Lite, Nov'84 by Phonogram Records. Dist: Polygram

Compact disc: released on De-Lite, Nov'84 by Phonogram Records. Dist: Polygram

FOREVER.
Album: released on Club, Dec'86 by Phonogram Records. Dist: Polygram

Cassette: released on Club, Dec'86 by Phonogram Records. Dist: Polygram

FOREVER.
Compact disc: released on Club, Dec'86 by Phonogram Records. Dist: Polygram

IN THE HEART.
Compact disc: by Phonogram Records. Dist:

Polygram

Album: released on De-Lite, Dec'83 by Phonogram Records. Dist: Polygram

Cassette: released on De-Lite, Dec'83 by Phonogram Records. Dist: Polygram

Compact disc: released on De-Lite, Dec'83 by Phonogram Records. Dist: Polygram

KOOL KUTS.
Album: released on De-Lite (USA), Nov'82 Dist: Polygram

Cassette: released on De-Lite (USA), Nov'82 Dist: Polygram

LADIES NIGHT.
Tracks: / Got you into my life / Hangin' out / If you feel like dancing / Ladies' night / Tonight's the night / Too hot.
Compact disc: released on De-Lite, '86 by Phonogram Records. Dist: Polygram

Album: released on De-Lite, Dec'83 by Phonogram Records. Dist: Polygram

Cassette: released on De-Lite, Dec'83 by Phonogram Records. Dist: Polygram

SOMETHING SPECIAL.
Tracks: / Steppin' out / Good time tonight / Take my heart / Be my lady / Get down on it / Pass it on / Stand up and sing / No show.
Compact disc: released on De-Lite, '86 by Phonogram Records. Dist: Polygram

Album: released on De-Lite, Mar'85 by Phonogram Records. Dist: Polygram

Cassette: released on De-Lite, Mar'85 by Phonogram Records. Dist: Polygram

SOMETHING SPECIAL.

STONE LOVE.
Single (7"): released on Club, Feb'87 by Phonogram Records. Dist: Polygram

Single (12"): released on Club, Feb'87 by Phonogram Records. Dist: Polygram

STONE LOVE.
Tracks: / Stone love / Dance champion / Get down on it (ext mix) ** / Ladies night (remix) **.
Single (7"): released on Club, Feb'87 by Phonogram Records. Dist: Polygram

Single (12"): released on Club, Feb'87 by Phonogram Records. Dist: Polygram

Double-pack single: released on Club, Mar'87 by Phonogram Records. Dist: Polygram

THROWDOWN MIX Hits medley.
Tracks: / Get down on it / Ladies night / Fresh / Big fun / Celebration / Victory (7" version) / Bad woman.
Single (7"): released on Club, Dec'86 by Phonogram Records. Dist: Polygram

Single (12"): released on Club, Dec'86 by Phonogram Records. Dist: Polygram

TWICE AS KOOL.
Double Album: released on De-Lite, May'83 by Phonogram Records. Dist: Polygram

Double cassette: released on De-Lite, May'83 by Phonogram Records. Dist: Polygram

VICTORY.
Tracks: / Victory / I.B.M.C. / Stone love / Forever / Holiday / Peace maker / Broadway / Special way / God's country / Victory / Bad woman.
Album: released on Club, Dec'86 by Phonogram Records. Dist: Polygram

Cassette: released on Club, Dec'86 by Phonogram Records. Dist: Polygram

Single (12"): released on Club, Dec'86 by Phonogram Records. Dist: Polygram

Single (7"): released on Club, Nov'86 by Phonogram Records. Dist: Polygram

Koran, The

KORAN, THE (Sheikh Mahamound Khalil Ah-Hosary).
Cassette: released on EMI, May'79 by EMI Records. Dist: EMI

Cassette: released on EMI, May'79 by EMI Records. Dist: EMI

Korberg, Tommy

ANTHEM.
Tracks: / Anthem / Mountain duet.
Single (7"): released on RCA, Nov'86 by RCA Records. Dist: RCA, Roots, Swift, Wellard, Chris, I & B, Solomon & Peres Distribution

Single (12"): released on RCA, Nov'86 by RCA Records. Dist: RCA, Roots, Swift, Wellard, Chris, I & B, Solomon & Peres Distribution

Korea music & dances

FOLK MUSIC FROM KOREA.
Album: released on Arion, Jun'79 Dist: Discovery

Korean

KOREAN COURT MUSIC.
Album: released on Lyrichord (USA), Oct'81 by Lyrichord Records (USA). Dist: Flexitron Distributors Ltd

KOREAN SOCIAL AND FOLK MUSIC.
Album: released on Lyrichord (USA), Oct'81 by Lyrichord Records (USA). Dist: Flexitron Distributors Ltd

Korgis

ALL THE LOVE IN THE WORLD.
Single (7"): released on Rialto, Jun'81 by Rialto Records. Dist: Pinnacle

BURNING QUESTIONS.
Single (7"): released on Marvellous, Oct'85 Dist: Sonet, PRT

Single (12"): released on Marvellous, Oct'85 Dist: Sonet, PRT

DON'T BELIEVE IN MAGIC.
Tracks: / Don't believe in magic / I'll be here.
Single (7"): released on Sonet, Jul'86 by Sonet Records. Dist: PRT

DON'T SAY THAT IT'S OVER.
Single (7"): released on Rialto, Sep'81 by Rialto Records. Dist: Pinnacle

EVERYBODY'S GOT TO LEARN SOMETIME.
Single (7"): released on Rialto, Apr'80 by Rialto Records. Dist: Pinnacle

IF IT'S ALRIGHT WITH YOU BABY.
Single (7"): released on Rialto, Jul'80 by Rialto Records. Dist: Pinnacle

I JUST CAN'T HELP IT.
Single (7"): released on Rialto, Jan'80 by Rialto Records. Dist: Pinnacle

IT WON'T BE THE SAME OLD PLACE.
Tracks: / It won't be the same old place / Climate of treason.
Single (7"): released on Sonet, Nov'86 by Sonet Records. Dist: PRT

KORGIS, THE.
Album: released on Rialto, Jul'79 by Rialto Records. Dist: Pinnacle

ROVERS RETURN.
Single (7"): released on Rialto, Nov'80 by Rialto Records. Dist: Pinnacle

STICKY GEORGE.
Album: released on Rialto, Jul'81 by Rialto Records. Dist: Pinnacle Deleted '85.
Cat. no: **ALTO 103**
Cassette: released on Rialto, Jul'81 by Rialto Records. Dist: Pinnacle

TRUE LIFE CONFESSIONS.
Single (12"): released on Sonet, Jun'85 by Sonet Records. Dist: PRT

Single (7"): released on Sonet, Jun'85 by Sonet Records. Dist: PRT

YOUNG & RUSSIAN.
Single (7"): released on Rialto, Oct'79 by Rialto Records. Dist: Pinnacle

Korner, Alexis

ALEXIS 1957 (with Cyril Davies).
Album: released on Krazy Kat (USA), Nov'84

BEIRUT.
Single (7"): released on Charisma, May'84 by Virgin Records. Dist: EMI

COLLECTION: ALEXIS KORNER.
Tracks: / She fooled me / Hoochie coochie man / Oh lord. don't let them drop that atom bomb on me / I got a woman / Corina Corina / Everyday I have the blues / Operator / Rosie / Polly put the kettle on / I see it / You don't miss your water till your well runs dry / Mighty mighty spade and whitey / Lo and behold / Louisiana blues / Oo whee baby / Rock me baby / Sweet sympathy / Country shoes.
Compact disc: released on Collector Series, '86 by Castle Communications Records. Dist: PRT, Pinnacle, RCA, Ariola

HAMMER AND NAILS.
Album: released on Thunderbolt, Jan'87 by Magnum Music Group Ltd. Dist: Magnum Music Group Ltd, PRT Distribution, Spartan Distribution

Cassette: released on Thunderbolt, Jan'87 by Magnum Music Group Ltd. Dist: Magnum Music Group Ltd, PRT Distribution, Spartan Distribution

JUVENILE DELINQUENT.
Album: released on Charisma, Jun'84 by Virgin Records. Dist: EMI

Cassette: released on Charisma, Jun'84 by Virgin Records. Dist: EMI

PARTS 1 & 2 1961 - 1972.
Tracks: / She fooled me / Hoochie coochie man / Oh lord don't let them drop that atomic bomb on me / I got a woman / Corina Corina / Everyday I have the blues / Operator / Rosie / Polly put the kettle on / I see it / You don't miss your water till your well runs dry / Mighty mighty spade and whitey / Lo and behold / Louisiana blues / Oo whe baby / Rock me baby / Sweet sympathy / Country shoes.
Notes: Compiled by Del Taylor. Produced by Adam Sieff. Digitally Re-Mastered by Matrix number: 5013428 131503. Double album and cassette.
Album: released on Castle Collectors, Sep'86 by Castle Communications Records. Dist: Pinnacle

Cassette: released on Castle Collectors, Sep'86 by Castle Communications Records. Dist: Pinnacle

PROFILE OF ALEXIS KORNER.
Cassette: released on Teldec (Germany), Jun'81 by Import Records. Dist: IMS Distribution, Polygram Distribution

Album: released on Teldec (Germany), May'81 by Import Records. Dist: IMS Distribution, Polygram Distribution

R & B FROM THE MARQUEE (Korner, Alexis & Blues Inc).
Album: released on Ace Of Clubs, Feb'84 by Decca Records. Dist: Polygram

TESTAMENT.
Compact disc: released on Thunderbolt, '86 by Magnum Music Group Ltd. Dist: Magnum Music Group Ltd, PRT Distribution, Spartan Distribution

Album: released on Thunderbolt, Jun'85 by Magnum Music Group Ltd. Dist: Magnum Music Group Ltd, PRT Distribution, Spartan Distribution

Cassette: released on Thunderbolt, Jun'85 by Magnum Music Group Ltd. Dist: Magnum Music Group Ltd, PRT Distribution, Spartan Distribution

Korn, Jiri

DAISY.
Single (7"): released on Code, Sep'84 by Code Records. Dist: Jetstar, EMI

Korshid, Omar

BELLY DANCE FROM LEBANON (Korshid, Omar & His Magic Guitar).
Cassette: released on EMI (Greece), May'79 by EMI Records. Dist: Conifer

Kosmin, Lee

WHAT'S IT TO YOU.
Single (7"): released on WEA Int, Jun'83

Kossoff, David

YOU HAVE A MINUTE LORD.
Album: released on BBC, May'78 by BBC Records & Tapes. Dist: EMI, PRT, Pye

Cassette: released on BBC, May'78 by BBC Records & Tapes. Dist: EMI, PRT, Pye

Kossoff, Paul

BACK STREET CRAWLER.
Tracks: / I'm ready / Time away / Molton gold / Bck street crawler / Tuesday morning.
Album: released on Island, Apr'87 by Island Records. Dist: Polygram

Cassette: released on Island, Apr'87 by Island Records. Dist: Polygram

BLUE SOUL.
Tracks: / Over the green hills: Part 1 / Worry / Moonshine / Trouble on double time / Crossroads / Oh I wept / We got time / Oh how we danced / Stealer, The / Hold on / Catch a train / Come together in the morning / Molten gold / I know why the sun don't shine / Tricky Dicky rides again / I'm ready / Blue soul.
Cassette: released on Island, Oct'86 by Island Records. Dist: Polygram

Album: released on Island, Apr'86 by Island Records. Dist: Polygram

CROYDON - JUNE 15TH 1975.
Double Album: released on Street Tunes, Sep'83 by Street Tunes Records. Dist: Pinnacle

HUNTER, THE.
Album: released on Street Tunes, Aug'83 by Street Tunes Records. Dist: Pinnacle

KOSS.
Compact disc: released on Castle Classics, Jul'87 by Castle Communications. Dist: BMG

Double Album: released on Street Tunes, Aug'83 by Street Tunes Records. Dist: Pinnacle

LEAVES IN THE WIND.
Album: released on Street Tunes, Aug'83 by Street Tunes Records. Dist: Pinnacle

MR BIG.
Cassette: released on Street Tunes, Nov'83 by Street Tunes Records. Dist: Pinnacle

Kostbanded

COTTON CLUB STOMP.
Album: released on Kenneth, Mar'87 Dist: Chris Wellard

Kotch

RUB A DUB OFFICER.
Single (12"): released on Macca Music, Oct'84 by Macca Music Records. Dist: Jetstar

Koto, Baba

LOVE HAS GOT A HOLD ON ME.
Tracks: / Love has got a hold on me.
Single (7"): released on Mr. Sam Music, Mar'87 Dist: MIS-EMI Distribution

Kotsonis, George

APHRODITE INHERITANCE, THE.
Album: released on BBC, Apr'79 by BBC Records & Tapes. Dist: EMI, PRT, Pye

Kottke, Leo

6 & 12 STRING GUITAR.
Album: released on Takoma (USA), Apr'84 Dist: Allegiance Distribution

Cassette: released on Takoma (USA), Apr'84 Dist: Allegiance Distribution

Album: released on Sonet, '79 by Sonet Records. Dist: PRT

BALANCE.
Cassette: released on Chrysalis, '79 by Chrysalis Records. Dist: CBS

BEST OF LEO KOTTKE (THE).
Tracks: / Stealing / Last steam engine train / Machine no. 2 / Cripple creek / Grim to the brim / Louise / Wheels / Poor boy / Morning is the long way home / Spanish Entemologist (The) / Pamela Brown / Bean time / Busted bicycle / Lost John / Living in the country / Stealing / Last steam engine train / Machine no.2 / Cripple creek / Grim to the brim / Louise / Wheels / Poor boy / Morning is the long way home / Spanish entomomlogist, The / Pamela Brown / Bean time / Busted bicycle / Lost John / Living in the country.
Compact disc: released on EMI, Apr'87 by EMI Records. Dist: EMI

BURNT LIPS.
Album: released on Chrysalis, Jan'79 by Chrysalis Records. Dist: CBS

GUITAR MUSIC.
Album: released on Chrysalis, Apr'81 by Chrysalis Records. Dist: CBS

LEO KOTTKE WITH PETER LANG & JOHN FAHEY.
Album: released on Sonet, '75 by Sonet Records. Dist: PRT

TIME STEP.
Album: released on Chrysalis, May'83 by Chrysalis Records. Dist: CBS

Koulsoum, Oum

AL ATLAL.
Cassette: released on EMI (Greece), May'79 by EMI Records. Dist: Conifer
Cat. no: **MC 33103**
Album: released on EMI (Greece), May'79 by EMI Records. Dist: Conifer

ALF LAYLAT WA LAYLAT.
Cassette: released on EMI (Greece), May'79 by EMI Records. Dist: Conifer

Album: released on EMI (Greece), May'79 by EMI Records. Dist: Conifer

AMAL HAYATI.
Cassette: released on EMI (Greece), May'79 by EMI Records. Dist: Conifer
Cat. no: **MC 33105**
Album: released on EMI (Greece), May'79 by EMI Records. Dist: Conifer

AROUH LEMIN.
Cassette: released on EMI (Greece), May'79 by EMI Records. Dist: Conifer
Cat. no: **MC 33127**
Album: released on EMI (Greece), May'79 by EMI Records. Dist: Conifer

FAKEROUNI.
Cassette: released on EMI (Greece), May'79 by EMI Records. Dist: Conifer

Album: released on EMI (Greece), May'79 by EMI Records. Dist: Conifer

HAGERTAK.
Cassette: released on EMI (Greece), May'79 by EMI Records. Dist: Conifer

Album: released on EMI (Greece), May'79 by EMI Records. Dist: Conifer

Page 574

HATHA LAYALTI.
Cassette: released on EMI (Greece), May'79 by EMI Records. Dist: Conifer

Album: released on EMI (Greece), May'79 by EMI Records. Dist: Conifer

INTA OMRI.
Cassette: released on EMI (Greece), May'79 by EMI Records. Dist: Conifer

Album: released on EMI (Greece), May'79 by EMI Records. Dist: Conifer

ROUBAIYAT AL KHAYAM.
Cassette: released on EMI (Greece), May'79 by EMI Records. Dist: Conifer

Album: released on EMI (Greece), May'79 by EMI Records. Dist: Conifer

YA THALMANI.
Cassette: released on EMI (Greece), May'79 by EMI Records. Dist: Conifer

Album: released on EMI (Greece), May'79 by EMI Records. Dist: Conifer

ZAKARIYAT.
Cassette: released on EMI (Greece), May'79 by EMI Records. Dist: Conifer

Album: released on EMI (Greece), May'79 by EMI Records. Dist: Conifer

Koumba

WE GO LEGGO.
Single (12"): released on Greensleeves, Nov'82 by Greensleeves Records. Dist: BMG, Jetstar, Spartan

Koush

HAPPINESS.
Single (12"): released on Koush, Jul'82

Kraan

KRAAN LIVE.
Double Album: released on Gull, May'78 by Gull Records. Dist: Pinnacle

Kraftwerk

AUTOBAHN.
Tracks: / Autobahn / Kometenmelodie 1 / Kometenmelodie 2 / Mitternacht / Morgenspaziergang.
Compact disc: released on EMI, Jul'87 by EMI Records. Dist: EMI

Album: released on Parlophone, Jun'85 by EMI Records. Dist: EMI

Cassette: released on Parlophone, Jun'85 by EMI Records. Dist: EMI

Album: released on EMI, Mar'82 by EMI Records. Dist: EMI

Cassette: released on EMI, Mar'82 by EMI Records. Dist: EMI

COMPUTER LOVE.
Single (7"): released on EMI Golden 45's, May'84 by EMI Records. Dist: EMI

COMPUTER WORLD.
Album: released on EMI, May'81 by EMI Records. Dist: EMI

Cassette: released on EMI, May'81 by EMI Records. Dist: EMI

Compact disc: released on EMI, May'81 by EMI Records. Dist: EMI

ELECTRIC CAFE.
Tracks: / Boing boom tschak / Techno pop / Musique non stop / Telephone call, The / Sex object / Electric cafe.
Notes: The album was preceded by single 'Musique non stop' released on 27th October. The album is packaged in a Deluxed gatefold sleeve featuring computer graphics as designed by the New York institute. The NYI is in the process of making a completely computer-generated video of the single track and this will be premiered at Electric Cafe in the UK. The album will be supported by a major marketing campaign including music press advertising and point-of-sale material and will be followed up by a second single in January prior to a UK tour.
Album: released on EMI, Nov'86 by EMI Records. Dist: EMI

Cassette: released on EMI, Nov'86 by EMI Records. Dist: EMI

Compact disc: released on EMI, Dec'86 by EMI Records. Dist: EMI

EXCELLER 8.
Album: released on Vertigo, Oct'75 by Phonogram Records. Dist: Polygram

MAN MACHINE.
Album: released on Fame (Capitol), Mar'85 by Music For Pleasure Records. Dist: EMI

Cassette: released on Fame (Capitol), Mar'85 by Music For Pleasure Records. Dist: EMI

Compact disc: released on EMI, Sep'84 by EMI Records. Dist: EMI

MUSIQUE NON STOP.
Tracks: / Musique non stop.
Single (7"): released on EMI, Oct'86 by EMI Records. Dist: EMI

Single (12"): released on EMI, Oct'86 by EMI Records. Dist: EMI

RADIO-ACTIVITY.
Tracks: / Radioactivity / Radioland / Airwaves / Intermission / News / Voice of energy, The / Antenna / Radio stars / Uranium / Transistor / Ohm sweet ohm / Geiger counter.
Album: released on Capitol, Jun'87 by Capitol Records. Dist: EMI

Cassette: released on Capitol, Jun'87 by Capitol Records. Dist: EMI

Compact disc: released on EMI, Apr'87 by EMI Records. Dist: EMI

Album: released on Fame, Jun'84 by Music For Pleasure Records. Dist: EMI

Cassette: released on Fame, Jun'84 by Music For Pleasure Records. Dist: EMI

RADIO AKTIVITAT.
Album: released on EMI Electrola (Germany), Jul'83 by EMI Records. Dist: Conifer

RALF & FLORIAN.
Album: released on Philips, Jan'74 Dist: IMS-Polygram

TELEPHONE CALL, THE.
Tracks: / Telephone call, The / Der telefon anruf (German version) / House phone.
Notes: House Phone is an extra track only available on the 12" version.
Single (7"): released on EMI, Feb'87 by EMI Records. Dist: EMI

Single (12"): released on EMI, Feb'87 by EMI Records. Dist: EMI

TOUR DE FRANCE.
Cassette single: released on EMI, Aug'83 by EMI Records. Dist: EMI

Single (7"): released on EMI, Aug'84 by EMI Records. Dist: EMI

Single (12"): released on EMI, Aug'84 by EMI Records. Dist: EMI

TRANS - EUROPE EXPRESS.
Tracks: / Europe endless / Hall of mirrors (The) / Showroom dummies / Trans - Europe express / Metal on metal / Franz Schubert / Endless endless.
Album: released on Fame, Jun'86 by Music For Pleasure Records. Dist: EMI

Cassette: released on Fame, Jun'86 by Music For Pleasure Records. Dist: EMI

Compact disc: released on EMI, Apr'87 by EMI Records. Dist: EMI

TRANS-EUROPE EXPRESS.
Album: released on Capitol, '85 by Capitol Records. Dist: EMI

Cassette: released on Capitol, '85 by Capitol Records. Dist: EMI

VARIOUS NUMBERS.
Double Album: released on Vertigo, '73 by Phonogram Records. Dist: Polygram

Krahmer, Carlo

CARLO KRAHMER MEMORIAL ALBUM.
Album: released on Esquire, Nov'77 by Titan International Productions. Dist: Jazz Music, Cadillac Music, Swift, Wellard, Chris, Backs, Rough Trade, Revolver, Nine Mile

KRAHMER'S, CARLO CHICAGOANS (Krahmer, Carlo Chicagoans).
Album: released on Esquire, Jun'86 by Titan International Productions. Dist: Jazz Music, Cadillac Music, Swift, Wellard, Chris, Backs, Rough Trade, Revolver, Nine Mile

Krakamaraka

EL VINO COLLAPSO.
Single (7"): released on Magic Moon, Jun'83 Dist: Pinnacle

K-Ram

MENAGE A TROIS.
Single (7"): released on Chrysalis, Apr'84 by Chrysalis Records. Dist: CBS

Single (12"): released on Chrysalis, Apr'84 by Chrysalis Records. Dist: CBS

Kramer, Billy J.

BAD TO ME (Kramer, Billy J. & The Dakotas).
Single (7"): released on Old Gold, Oct'83 by Old Gold Records. Dist: Lightning, Jazz Music, Spartan, Counterpoint

BEST OF BILLY J KRAMER, THE.
Album: released on Parlophone, Aug'84 by EMI Records. Dist: EMI

Cassette: released on Parlophone, Aug'84 by EMI Records. Dist: EMI

BILLY J KRAMER.
Album: released on EMI (Holland), '83 by EMI Records. Dist: Conifer

DO YOU WANT TO KNOW A SECRET (Kramer, Billy J. & The Dakotas).
Single (7"): released on Old Gold, Oct'83 by Old Gold Records. Dist: Lightning, Jazz Music, Spartan, Counterpoint

GREATEST HITS:BILLY J KRAMER.
Cassette: released on Autograph, Apr'85 Dist: Record Services Distribution (Ireland)

KRAMER VERSUS KRAMER.
Album: released on Attack, Oct'86 by Trojan Records. Dist: Trojan, Pinnacle, Red Rhino

LISTEN (Kramer, Billy J. & The Dakotas).
Album: released on See For Miles, Mar'82 by Charly Records. Dist: Spartan

Cassette: released on See For Miles, Aug'82 by Charly Records. Dist: Spartan

ROCK IT.
Single (7"): released on Runaway, Mar'82

YOU CAN'T LIVE ON MEMORIES.
Single (7"): released on RAK, Jun'83 by RAK. Dist: EMI

YOU'RE RIGHT I'M WRONG.
Single (7"): released on Runaway, Sep'82

Kramer & Wolmer

TWENTY FINGERS.
Album: released on ARC (Accordion Records), '84 Dist: Accordion Record Club

Krankies

FAN-DABI-DOZI.
Album: released on RCA, Nov'84 by RCA Records. Dist: RCA, Roots, Swift, Wellard, Chris, I & B, Solomon & Peres Distribution

Cassette: released on RCA, Nov'84 by RCA Records. Dist: RCA, Roots, Swift, Wellard, Chris, I & B, Solomon & Peres Distribution

HAND IN HAND AT CHRISTMAS.
Single (7"): released on Relax, Nov'84 Dist: CBS

IT'S FAN DABI DOBI.
Album: released on RCA, Dec'81 by RCA Records. Dist: RCA, Roots, Swift, Wellard, Chris, I & B, Solomon & Peres Distribution

Cassette: released on RCA, Dec'81 by RCA Records. Dist: RCA, Roots, Swift, Wellard, Chris, I & B, Solomon & Peres Distribution

KRANKIES GO TO HOLLYWOOD, THE.
Album: released on Relax, Oct'84 Dist: CBS

Cassette: released on Relax, Oct'84 Dist: CBS

TWO SIDES OF THE KRANKIES.
Album: released on MWM, Jun'82 by Mawson & Wareham. Dist: Spartan Distribution, Jazz Music Distribution, JSU Distribution

Kranz, George

DIN DAA DAA.
Single (7"): released on Fourth & Broadway, Sep'84 by Island Records. Dist: Polygram, EMI

Single (12"): released on Fourth & Broadway, Sep'84 by Island Records. Dist: Polygram, EMI

Krause, Dagmar

ANGEBOT & NACHFRAGE.
Notes: The same album as HNBL 1317 but entirely in German.
Album: released on Hannibal, Jan'87 by Hannibal Records. Dist: Charly, Harmonia Mundi, Projection, Celtic Music, Roots

Cassette: released on Hannibal, Jan'87 by Hannibal Records. Dist: Charly, Harmonia Mundi, Projection, Celtic Music, Roots

SUPPLY AND DEMAND.
Notes: A collection of brecht theatre songs with music by Kurt Weill and Hans Eisler.
Album: released on Hannibal, Jan'87 by Hannibal Records. Dist: Charly, Harmonia Mundi, Projection, Celtic Music, Roots

Cassette: released on Hannibal, Jan'87 by Hannibal Records. Dist: Charly, Harmonia Mundi, Projection, Celtic Music, Roots

Album: released on Hannibal, Mar'86 by Hannibal Records. Dist: Charly, Harmonia Mundi, Projection, Celtic Music, Roots

Cassette: released on Hannibal, Mar'86 by Hannibal Records. Dist: Charly, Harmonia Mundi, Projection, Celtic Music, Roots

Kraus, Peter

CONNIE FRANCIS & PETER KRAUS - VOL.2 (see Francis, Connie & Peter Kraus) (Kraus, Peter & Connie Francis).

DIE SINGLES 1956-1958.
Tracks: / Tutti frutti / Die strasse der vegessenen / O wie gut / Susie rock / Schau' keinen anderen mann an (tu' es nicht wieder) / Ten o'clock rock / Lass mich bitte nie allein / Liebelei / Ich will nicht wissen / Es fing so wunderbar an / Wenn teenager traumen / Mach dich schon / Hafen rock / Diana / So wie damals baby / I love you baby / Du sollst mein schicksal / Rosmarie / Hula baby / Mit siezehn / Du gehorst mir / Teenager melodie* / Ich mocht mit dir traumen*.
Notes: * With Micky Main
Compact disc: released on Bear Family, Jul'87 by Bear Family Records. Dist: Rollercoaster Distribution, Swift. Estim retail price in Aug'87 was £13.50.

DIE SINGLES 1956-58.
Album: released on Bear Family (Rollercoaster), Aug'87

PETER KRAUS UND DIE ROCKIES(SUNG IN GERMAN).
Album: released on Polydor, Sep'84 by Polydor Records. Dist: Polygram, Polydor

Kraut

AN ADJUSTMENT TO SOCIETY.
Album: released on Garage(USA Import), Aug'83 Dist: Indies, Cartel

Krcek, Jaroslav

RABA.
Album: released on Recommended, Mar'86 by Recommended Records. Dist: Recommended, Impetus, Rough Trade

Kreamcicle

NO NEWS IS NEWS.
Tracks: / No news is news.
Single (7"): released on Bluebird-10, Jul'86 by Bluebird Records. Dist: Virgin Records, EMI, Jetstar

Single (12"): released on Bluebird-10, Jul'86 by Bluebird Records. Dist: Virgin Records, EMI, Jetstar

Kreator

AFTER THE ATTACK.
Picture disc album:

ENDLESS PAIN.
Album:

PLEASURE TO KILL.
Album: released on Noise, Apr'86 by Dorane. Dist: Revolver, Cartel

Kreem

TRIANGLE OF LOVE.
Tracks: / Triangle of love / Triangle of love (vocal mix) / Uptown triangle beats.
Single (7"): released on Nine O Nine, Jun'87 by Creole Records. Dist: Rhino, PRT

Krein, Henry

ACCORDIAN MAGIC.
Cassette: released on Ampro Cassettes, May'79

Kremer, Gidon

EDITION LOCKENHAUS Vol. 1 & 2.
Tracks: / Quintet in F minor for piano and strings / Two songs from fiancailles pour rire / Conte fantastique d'apres une des histoires extraodinaires.. / Conte fantastique d'apres une des histoires extraodinaires.. / Le masque de la mort rouge / String quartet no. 1 / Tango from the soldier's tale / Concerto en re / Two waltzes for the flute, clarinet & piano / Two pieces for string octet op.11.
Notes: Lockenhaus is a small place near Vienna where Gidon Kremer organizes his annual chamber music festival. This 'Lockenhaus Edition' will be added to at regular intervals and will document all the exciting musical pieces from previous festivals; rather like books which appear in volumes and eventually make up a series. The musical combinations will conform to a theme. Every edition will be a self-contained unit. Edition Lockenhaus Vol. 1 & 2 have two units: one French and the other Slavonic. Besides some well-known pieces this double album contains some rarely performed compositions like Andre Caplet's 'Conte Fantastique' and Schostakowisch's two pieces for string octet. Double album and compact disc.
Double Album: released on ECM (Germany), Dec'85 by ECM Records. Dist: IMS, Polygram, Virgin through EMI

Double compact disc: released on ECM (Germany), Dec'85 by ECM Records. Dist: IMS, Polygram, Virgin through EMI

EDITION LOCKENHAUS Vol 3 (Kremer, Gidon & Valery Afanassiev).
Notes: Valery Afanassiev was born in Moscow in 1947. He began taking piano lessons at the age of six and in 1965 entered the Moscow Conservatory. In 1968 he won the first prize at the Bach competition in Leipzig and in 1972 the Queen Elizabeth competition in Brussels. He has toured extensively throughout Russia and Europe and the USA, working with major orchestras. Afanassiev's repertoire ranges from Froberger and Bach to modern composers such as Kagel and Crumb. He recently recorded Mozart's 'Kegel-Statt Trio' with Gidon Kremer and Kim Kashkashian for DG.
Album: released on ECM (Germany), Aug'86 by ECM Records. Dist: IMS, Polygram, Virgin through EMI

Compact disc: released on ECM (Germany), Aug'86 by ECM Records. Dist: IMS, Polygram, Virgin through EMI

Kress, Carl
TWO GUITARS (Kress, Carl/George Barnes).
Album: released on Stash, Apr'83 Dist: Swift Distribution, Jazz Music Distribution, Jazz Horizons Distribution, Celtic Music Distribution, Cadillac, JSU Distribution, Zodiac Distribution

Krew
PAPER HEROES.
Tracks: / Paper heroes / It's for you.
Single (7"): released on WEA, Apr'86 by WEA Records. Dist: WEA

Single (12"): released on WEA, Apr'86 by WEA Records. Dist: WEA

Krewman
ADVENTURES OF THE KREW MEN.
Album: released on Lost Moment, Aug'86

SWEET DREAMS.
Album: released on Lost Moment, May'87

Krew Men
I'M GONNA GET IT.
Single (7"): released on Lost Moment, Apr'85

RAMBLING.
Single (7"): released on Lost Moment, Jun'85

WHAT ARE YOU TODAY?.
Single (7"): released on Lost Moment, Nov'85

Single (12"): released on Lost Moment, Nov'85

Kriegal, Volker
HOUSEBOAT.
Album: released on MPS Jazz, May'81

LONG DISTANCE.
Album: released on MPS Jazz, May'81

MISSING LINK.
Double Album: released on MPS Jazz, May'81

STAR EDITION.
Double Album: released on MPS Jazz, May'81

Krieger, Bobby
VERSIONS.
Album: released on Shang Hai, Sep'84

Krimsky, Katrina
STELLA MALU (Krimsky, Katrina/Trevor Watts).
Album: released on ECM, Dec'81 by ECM Records. Dist: IMS, Polygram, Virgin through EMI

Krissl
LOVE MAKES A WOMAN.
Single (7"): released on Secret Rendezvous, Nov'85 Dist: EMI, Jetstar

Single (12"): released on Secret Rendezvous, Nov'85 Dist: EMI, Jetstar

Kriss Kross
HOTEL.
Single (12"): released on Midas, Jan'84 by Magnet Records. Dist: PRT Distribution

Kristofferson, Kris
FULL MOON.
Album: released on A&M, '73 by A&M Records. Dist: Polygram

HELP ME MAKE IT THROUGH THE NIGHT.
Album: released on CBS, '84 by CBS Records. Dist: CBS

Cassette: released on CBS, '84 by CBS Records. Dist: CBS

NATURAL ACT.
Album: released on A&M, Mar'82 by A&M Records. Dist: Polygram

Cassette: released on A&M, Mar'82 by A&M Records. Dist: Polygram

REPOSSESSED.
Tracks: / Anthem '84 / Heart (the) / This old road / Love is the way / Mean old man / Shipwrecked in the eighties / They killed him / What about me / El Gavilon (The hawk) / El Coyote.
Notes: In
Album: released on Mercury, Mar'87 by Phonogram Records. Dist: Polygram Distribution

Cassette: released on Mercury, Mar'87 by Phonogram Records. Dist: Polygram Distribution

Compact disc: released on Mercury, Mar'87 by Phonogram Records. Dist: Polygram Distribution

Songs of Kristofferson
STAR IS BORN, A.
Album: released on CBS, Feb'77 by CBS Records. Dist: CBS

Cassette: released on CBS, Feb'77 by CBS Records. Dist: CBS

WINNING HAND, THE (with Dolly Parton/Willie Nelson/Brenda Lee).
Album: released on Monument, Jan'83 by CBS Records. Dist: CBS Distribution

Cassette: released on Monument, Jan'83 by CBS Records. Dist: CBS Distribution

Kristofferson, Lee
FIRE.
Single (7"): released on Surrey Sound, Nov'80 Dist: Pinnacle

Krog, Karin
I REMEMBER YOU.
Album: released on Spotlite, '83 by Spotlite Records. Dist: Cadillac, Jazz Music, Spotlite

SOME OTHER SPRING (Krog, Karin & Dexter Gordon).
Album: released on Storyville, May'86 by Storyville Records. Dist: Jazz Music Distribution, Swift Distribution, Chris Wellard Distribution, Counterpoint Distribution

SONG FOR YOU, A (with Bengt Hallbergpiano).
Album: released on Phontastic (Sweden), '82 by Wellard, Chris Distribution. Dist: Wellard, Chris Distribution

Cassette: released on Phontastic (Sweden), '82 by Wellard, Chris Distribution. Dist: Wellard, Chris Distribution

SUCH WINTERS OF MEMORY (Krog, Karin/John Surman).
Album: released on ECM (Germany), Sep'83 by ECM Records. Dist: IMS, Polygram, Virgin through EMI

Krokus
ALIVE AND SCREAMIN'.
Tracks: / Long stick goes boom / Eat the rich / Screaming in the night / Hot shot city / Midnite maniac / Bedside radio / Lay me down / Stayed awake all night / Headhunter.
Album: released on Arista, Feb'87 by Arista Records. Dist: RCA

Cassette: released on Arista, Feb'87 by Arista Records. Dist: RCA

Compact disc: released on Arista, Feb'87 by Arista Records. Dist: RCA

BLITZ, THE.
Album: released on Arista, Aug'84 by Arista Records. Dist: RCA

Cassette: released on Arista, Aug'84 by Arista Records. Dist: RCA

CHANGE OF ADDRESS.
Tracks: / Now / Hot shot city / School's out / Let this love begin / Burning up the night / Say goodbye / World on fire / Hard luck hero / Long way from home.
Album: released on Ariola, Jun'86 Dist: RCA, Ariola

Cassette: released on Ariola, Jun'86 Dist: RCA, Ariola

HEADHUNTER.
Album: released on Arista, Apr'83 by Arista Records. Dist: RCA Deleted '85.

Cassette: released on Arista, Apr'83 by Arista Records. Dist: RCA

METAL RENDEZVOUS.
Album: released on Ariola, Sep'82 by Ariola

Cassette: released on Ariola, Sep'82 Dist: RCA, Ariola Deleted '83.

ONE VICE AT A TIME.
Album: released on Arista, Feb'82 by Arista Records. Dist: RCA

Cassette: released on Arista, Feb'82 by Arista Records. Dist: RCA Deleted '83.

PAINKILLER.
Album: released on Phonogram Import, Mar'81

PAY IT IN METAL.
Album: released on Philips (Europe), Aug'82

Kronos Quartet
KRONOS QUARTET.
Notes: Featuring the music of Peter Sculthorpe, Aulis Sallinen, Philip Glass, Conlon Nancarrow and Jimi Hendrix.
Album: released on Nonesuch, Jan'87

- Cassette: released on Nonesuch, Jan'87

Compact disc: released on Nonesuch, Jan'87

MUSIC BY BILL EVANS.
Tracks: / Waltz for Debbie / Very early / Nardis / Re: person I knew / Time remembered / Walking up / Turn out the stars / Five / Peace piece.
Notes: Kronos Quartet is a young adventurous San Francisco based ensemble with a swiftly growing international reputation. Formed in 1978, they specialize in contemporary composers such as John Cage, Terry Riley and Philip Glass. Of late their interest has been directed to the works of the great jazz composers. Their last album featured compositions by Thelonious Monk and Duke Ellington and this new album is dedicated to the music of Bill Evans. Kronos Quartet are joined on this recording by Eddie Gomez and Jim Hall. Gomez had along association with Bill Evans and is a natural choice for this project.
Album: released on Line (Germany). Oct'86

Cassette: released on Line (Germany). Oct'86

Kronstadt Uprising
PART OF THE GAME.
Single (7"): released on Dog Rock, Jul'85 by Dog Rock Records. Dist: Backs, Cartel

Krukutz
LOVE INSURANCE.
Single (7"): released on Ecstasy, Feb'85 by Creole Records. Dist: CBS

Single (12"): released on Ecstasy, Feb'85 by Creole Records. Dist: CBS

TAKE A CHANCE TO DANCE.
Single (12"): released on Bolts, Sep'87 by Bolts Records. Dist: PRT, Pinnacle

Krull
KRULL Original TV Soundtrack (London Symphony Orchestra).
Compact disc: released on Silva Productions, '86

Album: released on Silva Screen, Nov'86 by Silva Screen Records. Dist: Silva Screen

KRULL (JAMES HORNER) Original soundtrack (London Symphony Orchestra).
Album: released on Ades(France), Mar'84 Dist: IMS, Polygram, Studio Import & Export Distribution

Krumbach, Wilhelm
BACH VARIATIONS.
Cassette: released on Timeless, Oct'86

Krupa, Gene
44/46.
Album: released on Hep, Apr'81 by H.R. Taylor Records. Dist: Jazz Music, Cadillac Music, JSU, Taylors, Wellard, Chris, Zodiac, Swift, Fast Forward

ACE DRUMMER MAN (1943-47).
Album: released on Giants of Jazz, Aug'79 by Hasmick Promotions Ltd.. Dist: Counterpoint, Jazz Music, Taylors, Swift, Mainline, Wellard, Chris

DRUM BATTLE (Krupa, Gene & Buddy Rich).
Album: released on Verve, Oct'76 by Phonogram Records. Dist: Polygram

DRUM BOOGIE.
Tracks: / Opus 1 / Leave us leap / Drum boogie / Body and soul / Boogie blues / Massachusetts / How high the moon / Tuxedo junction / Dark eyes / That's what you think / Bolero at the savoy / Lover.
Notes: Mono.
Album: released on Verve (USA), Sep'86 by Polydor. Dist: Polygram

DRUMMER MAN.
Album: released on Polydor, '86 by Polydor Records. Dist: Polygram, Polydor

Cassette: released on Polydor, '86 by Polydor Records. Dist: Polygram, Polydor

Compact disc: released on Polydor, '86 by Polydor Records. Dist: Polygram, Polydor

DRUMMIN' MAN.
Album: released on CBS Cameo, Mar'83 by CBS Records. Dist: CBS

Cassette: released on CBS Cameo, Mar'83 by CBS Records. Dist: CBS

EXCITING GENE KRUPA, THE.
Album: released on Giants of Jazz, Oct'84 by Hasmick Promotions Ltd.. Dist: Counterpoint, Jazz Music, Taylors, Swift, Mainline, Wellard, Chris

GENE KRUPA.
Album: released on Swinghouse, Nov'86 Dist: Jazz Music Distribution, Swift Distribution, Chris Wellard Distribution

Album: released on Swinghouse, Nov'86 Dist: Jazz Music Distribution, Swift Distribution, Chris Wellard Distribution

Album: released on Swinghouse, '84 Dist: Jazz Music Distribution, Swift Distribution, Chris Wellard Distribution

Cassette: released on Swinghouse, '84 Dist: Jazz Music Distribution, Swift Distribution, Chris Wellard Distribution

Album: released on Verve, Apr'84 by Phonogram Records. Dist: Polygram

Cassette: released on Verve, Apr'84 by Phonogram Records. Dist: Polygram Deleted '86.

Album: released on Joker (Import), Apr'81

GENE KRUPA & BUDDY RICH - THE DRUM BATTLE (Krupa, Gene & Buddy Rich).

GENE KRUPA COLLECTION.
Album: released on Deja Vu, Feb'87 by Deja Vu Records. Dist: Counterpoint Distribution, Record Services Distribution (Ireland)

GENE KRUPA, LIONEL HAMPTON & TEDDY WILSON (Krupa, Gene, Lionel Hampton & Teddy Wilson).
Album: released on Verve (Import), Mar'81

GENE KRUPA ORCHESTRA & TRIO (Krupa, Gene Orchestra & Trio).
Album: released on Submarine, Oct'86 by Submarine Records. Dist: Wellard, Chris Distribution, Conifer Distribution, H.R. Taylor Distribution

GENE KRUPA ORCHESTRA (1941) (Krupa, Gene & His Orchestra).
Album: released on Jazz Live (Import), Apr'81

GENE KRUPA - VOL.1.
Album: released on Kings Of Jazz, Aug'81 Dist: Jazz Horizons, Jazz Music, Celtic Music

GENE KRUPA - VOL.10 (1940).
Album: released on Ajax (USA), Apr'79 Dist: Swift

GENE KRUPA - VOL.11 (1940-1).
Album: released on Ajax (USA), Apr'79 Dist: Swift

GENE KRUPA - VOL.1 (1935-8).
Album: released on Ajax (USA), Apr'79 Dist: Swift

GENE KRUPA - VOL.12 (1941).
Album: released on Ajax (USA), Apr'79 Dist: Swift

GENE KRUPA - VOL.13 (1941).
Album: released on Ajax (USA), Apr'79 Dist: Swift

GENE KRUPA - VOL.14 (1941).
Album: released on Ajax (USA), Apr'79 Dist: Swift

GENE KRUPA - VOL.2 (1938).
Album: released on Ajax (USA), Apr'79 Dist: Swift

GENE KRUPA - VOL.3 (1938).
Album: released on Ajax (USA), Apr'79 Dist: Swift

GENE KRUPA - VOL.4 (1939).
Album: released on Ajax (USA), Apr'79 Dist: Swift

GENE KRUPA - VOL.5 (1939).
Album: released on Ajax (USA), Apr'79 Dist: Swift

GENE KRUPA - VOL.6 (1939-40).
Album: released on Ajax (USA), Apr'79 Dist: Swift

GENE KRUPA - VOL.7 (1940).
Album: released on Ajax (USA), Apr'79 Dist: Swift

GENE KRUPA - VOL.8 (1940).
Album: released on Ajax (USA), Apr'79 Dist: Swift

GENE KRUPA - VOL.9 (1940).
Album: released on Ajax (USA), Apr'79 Dist: Swift

GENE'S BAND.
Album: released on First Heard, '84 by Submarine Records. Dist: Conifer, Taylors

KRUPA & RICH (Krupa, Gene & Buddy Rich).
Album: released on Verve (USA), May'84 by Polydor. Dist: Polygram

ORIGINAL DRUM BATTLE (Krupa, Gene & Buddy Rich).
Album: released on Verve (Import), Aug'81

PERDIDO (Krupa, Gene Quintet).
Tracks: / Theme-I never knew / Poor butterfly / Perdido (lost) / I'm getting sentimental over you / I can't get started / Big noise from Winnetka, The / Perdido.
Album: released on Swinghouse, Mar'87 Dist: Jazz Music Distribution, Swift Distribution, Chris Wellard Distribution

Cassette: released on Swinghouse, Mar'87 Dist: Jazz Music Distribution, Swift Distribution, Chris Wellard Distribution

Album: released on Submarine, Oct'86 by Submarine Records. Dist: Wellard, Chris Distribution, Conifer Distribution, H.R. Taylor Distribution

Cassette: released on Submarine, Oct'86 by Submarine Records. Dist: Wellard, Chris Distribution, Conifer Distribution, H.R. Taylor Distribution

PERDIDO.
Album: released on Swinghouse, Sep'81 Dist: Jazz Music Distribution, Swift Distribution, Chris Wellard Distribution

RADIO DISCS OF GENE KRUPA, THE.
Album: released on Joyce (USA Import), Jul'77

SUPERB PERFORMANCES (1945-1949) (Krupa, Gene & His Orchestra).
Album: released on First Heard, Jan'77 by Submarine Records. Dist: Conifer, Taylors

SWINGING BIG BANDS 1947-47, THE (Krupa, Gene & His Orchestra).
Album: released on Joker (Import), Apr'81

THAT DRUMMERS BAND (Krupa, Gene & His Orchestra).
Album: released on SOS, '74

Town hall concert 1945

WHAT'S THIS (1946-1947) (Krupa, Gene & His Orchestra).
Album: released on Hep, Jun'81 by H.R. Taylor Records. Dist: Jazz Music, Cadillac Music, JSU, Taylors, Wellard, Chris, Zodiac, Swift, Fast Forward

Kru-Pops

YUMMY YUMMY YUMMY.
Single (7"): released on Electric Bubble Gum, Dec'82 by Electric Bubble Gum Records. Dist: Pinnacle

Krupps

ENTERING THE ARENA.
Album: released on Statik, Jul'82 Dist: Rough Trade Distribution, Stage One Distribution

Krush Groove

KRUSH GROOVE Original film soundtrack.
Tracks: / Can't stop the street / I can't live without my radio / If I ruled the world / All you can eat / Feel the spin / Holly rock / She's on it / Love triangle / Tender love / Krush groovin'.
Album: released on Warner Bros., Mar'86 by Warner Bros Records. Dist: WEA

Cassette: released on Warner Bros., Mar'86 by Warner Bros Records. Dist: WEA

Krystol

PASSION FROM A WOMAN.
Tracks: / Passion from a woman / Love attack / Precious precious / All my love / I might fall in love with you / He's so jive / Baby make your mind up / Scared single.
Album: released on Epic, Sep'87 by CBS Records. Dist: CBS

Cassette: released on Epic, Sep'87 by CBS Records. Dist: CBS

PASSION FROM A WOMAN (7").
Single (7"): released on Epic, Aug'87 by CBS Records. Dist: CBS

PRECIOUS PRECIOUS.
Tracks: / Precious precious / He's so jive.
Single (7"): released on Epic, Nov'86 by CBS Records. Dist: CBS

Single (12"): released on Epic, Nov'86 by CBS Records. Dist: CBS

Kublai Khan

ANNIHILATION.
Tracks: / Death breath / Mongrel horde / Down to the inferno / Liars dice / Passing away/Kublaikhan / Clash of the swords / Battle hymn (the centurian).
Notes: Produced by Kublai Kahn & Peter Davis for Crazy Life Music. Recorded March 1987, Westwood Studio, Minnesota by Jonathon.
Album: released on Heavy Metal America, Jun'87 by FM-Revolver Records. Dist: EMI

Album: released on Heavy Metal America, '87 by FM-Revolver Records. Dist: EMI

Kudos

HOW CAN THIS BE LOVE.
Single (7"): released on Legacy, Oct'84 Dist: PRT

Single (12"): released on Legacy, Oct'84 Dist: PRT

I NEED YOU.
Single (7"): released on Peninsula, Oct'83 by Prism Records. Dist: Various Distribution

Kudos Point

NIGHT OF THE LONG KNIVES.
Single (7"): released on Deb, Apr'82 by Deb Records. Dist: Spartan

ZAMBIA.
Single (7"): released on Deb, Dec'82 by Deb Records. Dist: Spartan

Kuepper, Ed

ELECTRICAL STORM.
Album: released on Hot, May'86 by Hot Records. Dist: Rough Trade, Cartel

ROOMS OF THE MAGNIFICENT.
Album: released on Hot, Feb'87 by Hot Records. Dist: Rough Trade, Cartel

Kuhn, Paul

BLAUE WILDLEDER SCHUH.
Album: released on Bear Family, Mar'84 by Bear Family Records. Dist: Rollercoaster Distribution, Swift

PLAY GLENN MILLER & BENNY GOODMAN (Kuhn, Paul & His Orchestra).
Album: released on Dansan, Jul'80 by Spartan Records. Dist: Spartan

Kuhn, Steve

LAST YEAR'S WALTZ (Kuhn, Steve Quartet).
Album: released on ECM (Germany), Apr'82 by ECM Records. Dist: IMS, Polygram, Virgin through EMI

LIFE'S MAGIC (Kuhn, Steve Trio).
Notes: Personnel: Steve Kuhn, Ron Carter, Al Foster.
Album: released on Blackhawk, Apr'87 by Blackhawk Records (USA). Dist: IMS-Polygram

MOSTLY BALLADS.
Tracks: / Yesterdays gardenias / Tennessee waltz / Danny boy / Don't explain / Body and soul / Emily / Airegin / How high the moon.
Album: released on New World (USA), May'87 by New World Records (USA). Dist: Conifer
Cat. no: **NW 351**
Compact disc: released on New World (USA), May'87 by New World Records (USA). Dist: Conifer

Kull

EYE OF DESTRUCTION.
Single (7"): released on Bomb, Mar'84 Dist: Menace Breaker Distributors

Kumpf, Hans

ON A RUSSIAN TRIP.
Album: released on Leo, Sep'84 Dist: Jazz Music, Chris Wellard

Kunda, Toure

NATALIA.
Compact disc: by Charly Records. Dist: Charly

NATALIE.
Album: released on Celluloid, Apr'85 by Charly Records. Dist: Charly

Kuniyoshi-Kuhn

HANDSCAPES (Kuniyoshi-Kuhn, Akemi, Marcio Mattos, Eddie Prevost).
Album: released on Leo, Jan'87 Dist: Recommended

Kunz, Charlie

CLAP HANDS, HERE COMES CHARLIE.
Album: released on Decca (Recollections), Nov'83 by Decca Recollections. Dist: Polygram, IMS

DANCE YOUR WAY THROUGH THE THIRTIES (Kunz, Charlie & The Casani Club Orchestra).
Tracks: / Unless / There was an old woman / Learn to croon / Did my heart beat did I fall in love / Let's sit this one out / Did you ever see a dream walking / She fell for a feller from "Oopasala" / Dear stranger / When you're sixty / Moonstruck / By a waterfall / Roaming / Doggone I've done it / Lazybones / Memories of hours spent with you / I raised my hat / On the good ship lollipop / There's no green grass round the old north pole.
Album: released on Joy, May'87 by President Records. Dist: Jazz Music, Swift, President Distribution

DEAR STRANGER (Kunz, Charlie & The Casani Club Orchestra).
Album: released on Joy, Mar'87 by President Records. Dist: Jazz Music, Swift, President Distribution

FOCUS ON CHARLIE KUNZ.
Cassette: released on Decca, Oct'77 by Decca Records. Dist: Polygram

MUSIC FOR THE MILLIONS.
Album: released on Philips (Import), Mar'83

Cassette: released on Philips (Import), Mar'83

NO ONE BUT YOU.
Album: released on Decca, Feb'81 by Decca Records. Dist: Polygram

Cassette: released on Decca, Feb'81 by Decca Records. Dist: Polygram

WORLD OF CHARLIE KUNZ.
Album: released on World of Learning, '69 by World Of Learning Records. Dist: World Of Learning

Kunzel, Eric

ROUND UP.
Tracks: / Sounds of the west / Gioacchino Rossini / Magnificent seven (The) / Furies Suite (The) / Round up / How the west was won / Gunfight at the OK Corral / Pops Hoedown / Big country / High noon / Western medley / Themes from Silverado.
Compact disc: released on Telarc, Apr'87 by Audio-Technica US Inc. (USA). Dist: Conifer Distribution

Kursaal Flyers

BEST OF, THE.
Album: released on Teldec (Germany), Nov'83 by Import Records. Dist: IMS Distribution, Polygram Distribution

IN FOR A SPIN.
Album: released on Edsel, Jun'85 by Demon Records. Dist: Pinnacle, Jazz Music, Projection

MONSTER IN LAW.
Single (7"): released on Waterfront, Jun'85 by Waterfront Records. Dist: Rough Trade, Cartel, Projection, Roots

Kurtis, Gary

SHAPE I'M IN.
Tracks: / Shape I'm in (The) / Slow down.
Single (7"): released on Street Warrior, Jun'86 by Priority Records. Dist: BMG Distribution

Kuryokhin, Sergey

Sentenced to silence

SUBWAY CULTURE (Kuryokhin, Sergey & Boris Grebenshohikov).
Notes: Double album.
Album: released on Leo, Jan'87 Dist: Recommended

WAYS OF FREEDOM, THE.
Album: released on Leo, Sep'84 Dist: Jazz Music, Chris Wellard

Kuslap, Voldemar

FOLK SONGS.
Cassette: released on Melodiya (USSR), Feb'79 Dist: T.B.C Distribution

Kustbandet

KUSTBANDET (Coast line band).
Album: released on Kenneth, Jul'82 Dist: Chris Wellard

Kustom

LET THE GIRL DANCE.
Single (7"): released on Silhouette, Jan'82

Kusworth, Dave

BOUNTY HUNTERS, THE.
Notes: Debut album from Dave Kusworth's wonderful Bounty Hunters; as Jack Daniels soaked and Keith Richards influenced as his other outings with the Dogs D'Amour, the Jacobites and the Rag Dolls.
Album: released on Swordfish, May'87 Dist: Nine Mile Distribution, Cartel Distribution

JACOBITES (Kusworth, Dave & Nikki Sudden).

Kutash, Jeff

DOWN STREET (Kutash, Jeff/Dancin' Machine).
Single (7"): released on Magnet, Jul'83 by Magnet Records. Dist: BMG

Single (12"): released on Magnet, Jul'83 by Magnet Records. Dist: BMG

Kuti, Fela

ARMY ARRANGEMENT.
Tracks: / Army arrangement / Cross examination / Government chicken boy.
Notes: Recorded 1985.
Album: released on Barclay (France), Aug'86 by Decca Records. Dist: IMS, Discovery, Conifer, Swift, Polygram

Cassette: released on Barclay (France), Aug'86 by Decca Records. Dist: IMS, Discovery, Conifer, Swift, Polygram

Compact disc: by Charly Records. Dist: Charly

Compact disc: released on Barclay (France), Sep'87 by Decca Records. Dist: IMS, Discovery, Conifer, Swift, Polygram

BLACK PRESIDENT.
Album: released on Arista, Apr'81 by Arista Records. Dist: RCA

Cassette: released on Arista, Sep'83 by Arista Records. Dist: RCA

EVERYTHING SCATTER.
Album: released on Creole, '79 by Creole Records. Dist: Rhino, PRT

GENTLEMEN.
Album: released on Creole, '79 by Creole Records. Dist: Rhino, PRT

GREATEST HITS: FELA KUTI.
Album: released on EMI Nigeria, Jan'85 by EMI Records. Dist: Conifer

LADY.
Single (7"): released on EMI, Nov'83 by EMI Records. Dist: EMI

Single (12"): released on EMI, Nov'83 by EMI Records. Dist: EMI

LIVE IN AMSTERDAM.
Double Album: released on EMI, May'84 by EMI Records. Dist: EMI

Cassette: released on EMI, May'84 by EMI Records. Dist: EMI Deleted '86.

MUSIC IS THE WEAPON OF THE FUTURE.
Compact disc: released on Barclay (France), Sep'87 by Decca Records. Dist: IMS, Discovery, Conifer, Swift, Polygram

NO AGREEMENT.
Tracks: / No agreement / Dog eat dog.
Notes: The undisputed King of Highlife, the premier dance music of Nigeria, Fela Kuti's music is a fusion of highlife rhythms and jazz melodies, often with romantic or political lyrics. As a hero of the people and a political activist he has long been an embarrassment to the Nigerian authorities. He has been imprisoned for his radical views. Despite harrassment by the authorities, Kuti has managed to continue to cut ambitious multi-ethnic albums and undertake major international tours. In 1978 he brought to Europe his huge African 70 band which included 27 female dancers and singers - all of whom he married.
Album: released on Barclay (France), Aug'86 by Decca Records. Dist: IMS, Discovery, Conifer, Swift, Polygram

Cassette: released on Barclay (France), Aug'86 by Decca Records. Dist: IMS, Discovery, Conifer, Swift, Polygram

ORIGINAL SUFFERHEAD.
Album: released on Arista, Jan'82 by Arista Records. Dist: RCA

Cassette: released on Arista, Sep'83 by Arista Records. Dist: RCA

SHUFFERING AND SHMILING.
Tracks: / Shuffering and shmiling / Perambulator.
Notes: Recorded 1978.
Album: released on Barclay (France), Aug'86 by Decca Records. Dist: IMS, Discovery, Conifer, Swift, Polygram

Cassette: released on Barclay (France), Aug'86 by Decca Records. Dist: IMS, Discovery, Conifer, Swift, Polygram

TEACHER DON'T TEACH ME NONSENSE (Kuti, Fela Anikulapo).
Tracks: / Teacher don't teach me nonsense (instr) / Teacher don't teach me nonsense (vocal) / Look and laugh (instr) / Look and laugh (vocal).
Notes: Produced by Wally Badarou.
Album: released on Barclay-London, Dec'86 by Decca-London Records. Dist: Polygram

Cassette: released on Barclay-London, Dec'86 by Decca-London Records. Dist: Polygram

Compact disc: released on Barclay-London, Dec'86 by Decca-London Records. Dist: Polygram

TEACHER DON'T TEACH ME NON-SENSE.
Notes: Fela Kuti see under Kuti, Fela
Compact disc: released on London, Feb'87 by London Records. Dist: Polygram

ZOMBIE (Kuti, Fela/Africa 70).
Tracks: / Zombie / Monkey banana / Everythings scotter.
Notes: Recorded 1976.

K Wallis B

DIAMONDS (K Wallis B & The Dark Shades Of Night).
Tracks: / Diamonds / Man with the golden arm (main title theme) / Diamonds (Ext. dance mix).

Album: released on Barclay (France), Aug'86 by Decca Records. Dist: IMS, Discovery, Conifer, Swift, Polygram

Cassette: released on Barclay (France), Aug'86 by Decca Records. Dist: IMS, Discovery, Conifer, Swift, Polygram

Album: released on Creole, Nov'77 by Creole Records. Dist: Rhino, PRT

Single (7"): released on Vertigo, Jun'87 by Phonogram Records. Dist: Polygram

Single (12"): released on Vertigo, Jun'87 by Phonogram Records. Dist: Polygram

Kwan, Michael

COMPACT DISC GREATEST HITS.
Compact disc: released on Phonogram Import, '84

GREATEST HITS:MICHAEL KWAN.
Compact disc:

Kyle Creed

VIRGINIA REEL (Kyle Creed etc.).
Double Album: released on Leader, '81 Dist: Jazz Music, Projection

Kyser, Kay

DANCE DATE (Kyser, Kay/his orchestra).
Album: released on Big Band Archives, Jul'82

Kyte, Sydney

1931-1932 (Kyte, Sydney/his Piccadilly Hotel Band).
Album: released on World Records, Oct'80 Dist: Polygram

L.A.4

EXECUTIVE SUITE.
Album: released on Concord Jazz, Jun'83 by Concord Jazz Records (USA). Dist: IMS, Polygram

Cassette: released on Concord Jazz, Jun'83 by Concord Jazz Records (USA). Dist: IMS, Polygram

L.A.4.
Tracks: / Dindi / Rainbows / Rondo es pressivo / Manteca / St. Thomas / Concierto de aranjuez.
Compact disc: released on Concord Jazz(USA), Sep'86 by Concord Jazz Records (USA). Dist: IMS, Polygram

MONTAGE.
Album: released on Concord Jazz(USA), Nov'81 by Concord Jazz Records (USA). Dist: IMS, Polygram

ZACA.
Tracks: / Zaca.
Album: released on Concord Jazz(USA), Nov'80 by Concord Jazz Records (USA). Dist: IMS, Polygram

La Bamba
LA BAMBA Original soundtrack (Various Artists).
Tracks: / La Bamba / Come on / Ooh! my head / We belong together / Framed / Donna / Lonely teardrop / Crying, waiting, hoping / Summertime blues / Who do you love.
Album: released on London, Aug'87 by London Records. Dist: Polygram

Cassette: released on London, Aug'87 by London Records. Dist: Polygram

Compact disc: released on London, Aug'87 by London Records. Dist: Polygram

La Ban
LOVE IN SIBERIA.
Tracks: / Love in Siberia / It's a fantasy.
Single (7"): released on Creole, Feb'87 by Creole Records. Dist: Rhino, PRT

Single (12"): released on Creole, Feb'87 by Creole Records. Dist: Rhino, PRT

LaBarbera, Pat
PASS IT ON.
Album: released on PM, Jan'80

La Beef, Sleepy
AIN'T GOT NO HOME.
Album: released on Rockhouse, Sep'83 by Rockhouse Records. Dist: Swift Distribution, Charly Distribution

BEEFY ROCKABILLY.
Album: released on Charly, '74 by Charly Records. Dist: Charly, Cadillac

DOWNHOME ROCKABILLY.
Album: by Charly Records. Dist: Charly, Cadillac

EARLY RARE & ROCKIN' SIDES.
Album: released on Charly, Feb'80 by Charly Records. Dist: Charly, Cadillac

NOTHING BUT THE TRUTH.
Notes: New album from Arkansas legend Sleepy La Beef
Album: released on Rounder Europa, Apr'87

ROCKABILLY HEAVYWEIGHT.
Album: by Charly Records. Dist: Charly, Cadillac

SLEEPY LABEEF.
Notes: Another blighter with different records sharing the same title
Album: released on Ace, Sep'79 by Ace Records. Dist: Pinnacle, Swift, Hotshot, Cadillac
Album: released on Sonet-Rounder, Jun'81 by Sonet Records. Dist: PRT

Labelle, Patti
BEST OF PATTI LABELLE, THE.
Tracks: / Lady marmalade / You are my friend / Joy to have our love / Little girls / Music is my way of life / I don't go shopping / It's alright with me / Come what may.
Album: released on Epic, Aug'86 by CBS Records. Dist: CBS

IF YOU ONLY KNEW.
Single (7"): released on Philadelphia International, Mar'84 by CBS Records. Dist: CBS

Single (12"): released on Philadelphia International, Mar'84 by CBS Records. Dist: CBS

IM IN LOVE AGAIN.
Tracks: / I'm in love again / Lover man (oh where can you be) / Love, need and want you / If only you knew / Body language / I'll never, never give up / Love bankrupt / When am I gonna find true love.
Album: released on Philadelphia International, May'87 by CBS Records. Dist: CBS

Cassette: released on Philadelphia International, May'87 by CBS Records. Dist: CBS

KISS AWAY THE PAIN.
Tracks: / Kiss away the pain / Kiss away the pain (inst).
Single (7"): released on MCA, Mar'87 by MCA Records. Dist: Polygram, MCA

Single (12"): released on MCA, Mar'87 by MCA Records. Dist: Polygram, MCA

OH PEOPLE.
Tracks: / Oh people / Love attack.
Single (12"): released on MCA, Jul'86 by MCA Records. Dist: Polygram, MCA

Single (7"): released on MCA, Jul'86 by MCA Records. Dist: Polygram, MCA

OH PEOPLE (THE JIM MIX).
Tracks: / Oh people (the jim mix) / Love attack instrumental.
Single (12"): released on MCA, Aug'86 by MCA Records. Dist: Polygram, MCA

ON MY OWN (Labelle, Patti & Michael McDonald).
Tracks: / On my own / Stir it up.
Single (7"): released on MCA, Apr'86 by MCA Records. Dist: Polygram, MCA

Single (12"): released on MCA, Apr'86 by MCA Records. Dist: Polygram, MCA

POURIN' WHISKEY BLUES.
Single (7"): released on Milan, May'85, IMS Distribution, Conifer Distribution, Discovery Distribution

SOMETHING SPECIAL.
Tracks: / Something special / Something special accapella version.
Single (7"): released on MCA, Nov'86 by MCA Records. Dist: Polygram, MCA

Single (12"): released on MCA, Nov'86 by MCA Records. Dist: Polygram, MCA

WINNER IN YOU.
Tracks: / On my own / On my own / Something special (is gonna happen tonight) / Kiss away the pain / Twisted / You're mine tonight / Finally we're back together / Beat my heart like a drum / Sleep with me tonight / There's a winner in you.
Compact disc: released on MCA, '86 by MCA Records. Dist: Polygram, MCA

Labels Unlimited
LABELS UNLIMITED (THE SECOND RECORD COLLECTION) Various Artists.
Album: released on Cherry Red, '82 by Cherry Red Records. Dist: Pinnacle

LaBeque, Katia & Marielle
GLAD RAGS.
Album: released on EMI, Mar'83 by EMI Records. Dist: EMI

Cassette: released on EMI, Mar'83 by EMI Records. Dist: EMI

Labes, Jef
TELESTAR.
Single (7"): released on KA, Jul'83

La Boost
BEDASAN ON DACCA.
Tracks: / Ram it home.
Single (7"): released on Breakin, Sep'87 by Breakin Records.

Labours of Heracles
LABOURS OF HERACLES Various Artists (Various Artists).
Cassette: released on Anvil, Jul'82 Dist: Anvil

Labyrinth
LABYRINTH Film sound track (Bowie, David).
Tracks: / Underground / Into the labyrinth / Magic dance / Sarah / Chilly down / Hallucination / As the world falls down / Goblin battle, The / Within you / Thirteen o'clock / Home at last / Underground reprise.
Compact disc: released on EMI, '86 by EMI Records. Dist: EMI

La cage aux folles
BROADWAY CAST ALBUM.
Notes: Artists include: George Hearn, Gene Barry, John Weiner and Elizabeth Parrish.
Compact disc: released on RCA, '86 by RCA Records. Dist: RCA, Roots, Swift, Wellard, Chris, I & B, Solomon & Peres Distribution

Lacey, Marie
YOU'RE ENOUGH.
Album: by Pilgrim Records. Dist: Rough Trade, Cartel

La Chandra
SHY GIRL.
Tracks: / Shy girl (radio edit) / Shy girl (dub).
Single (7"): released on Syncopate, 23 May'87 by EMI Records. Dist: EMI

Single (12"): released on Syncopate, 23 May'87 by EMI Records. Dist: EMI

SHY GIRL (REMIX).
Tracks: / Shy girl (remix) / Shy girl (pianopella) / Shy girl (dance mix).
Single (7"): released on Syncopate, Jun'87 by EMI Records. Dist: EMI

Lack of knowledge
SENTINEL.
Single (12"): released on Chainsaw, Jul'85 by Chainsaw Records. Dist: Red Rhino, Cartel

SIRENS ARE BACK.
Album: released on Corpus Christi, Apr'85 by Exitstencil Music. Dist: Cartel

La Cosa Nostra
COSA NOSTRA, (LA).
Album: released on Crammed Discs, Oct'85 Dist: Rough Trade, Nine Mile, Cartel

LaCreme, Cathy
I MARRIED A CULT FIGURE FROM SALFORD.
Single (7"): released on Rock Steady, '80 by Rock Steady Records. Dist: Rough Trade Distribution, Indies Distribution, Cartel Distribution

Lacy Smith
SIDELINES.
Album: released on Impro-arts, Jul'78 Dist: Projection

Lacy, Steve
COMPANY 4 (Lacy, Steve/Derek Bailey).
Album: released on Incus, '78 Dist: Jazz Music, Cadillac

HOCUS POCUS.
Album: released on Himalaya, Oct'86 by Himalaya Records. Dist: Rough Trade, Cartel

MOON.
Album: released on Affinity, Jun'79 by Charly Records. Dist: Charly, Cadillac

RAPS.
Album: released on Adelphi, May'81 by Adelphi Records. Dist: Jetstar

STRAIGHT HORN OF STEVE LACY, THE.
Album: released on Candid, Dec'85 Dist: Counterpoint, Cadillac

Album: released on Candid, Jul'87 Dist: Counterpoint, Cadillac

TRICKLES.
Album: released on Black Saint, Jul'78 Dist: Projection, IMS, Polygram, Chris Wellard, Harmonia Mundi, Swift

TROUBLES (Lacy, Steve Quintet).
Album: released on Soul Note, Sep'79 Dist: Harmonia Mundi Distributors

Lacy Street Blues Band
LACY STREET BLUES BAND.
Album: released on Culture Press, Jul'85 by Vista Sounds Records. Dist: Jetstar, Rough Trade

L. A. Danny
COUNTRY LOVING.
Single (12"): released on The Foundation, Dec'83 by Foundation Records, The. Dist: Jetstar Distribution

Ladd, Cheryl
FASCINATED.
Video-cassette (VHS): released on PMI, Jun'86 by PMI Records. Dist: EMI

Video-cassette (Betamax): released on PMI, Jun'86 by PMI Records. Dist: EMI

Ladders
GOTTA SEE JANE.
Single (7"): released on Statik, Jun'83 Dist: Rough Trade Distribution, Stage One Distribution

Single (12"): released on Statik, Jun'83 Dist: Rough Trade Distribution, Stage One Distribution

Ladd's Black Aces
LADD'S BLACK ACES 1921-2 VOLUME 1.
Album: released on Retrieval, Apr'79 by Retrieval Records. Dist: Jazz Music, Swift, VJM, Wellard, Chris, Retrieval

LADD'S BLACK ACES 1922-3 VOLUME 2.

LADD'S BLACK ACES 1923-4 VOLUME 3.
Double Album: released on Fountain, Apr'79 by Retrieval Records. Dist: Jazz Music, Swift, VJM, Wellard, Chris, Retrieval

La-de-dah & others
LA-DE-DAH & OTHER NOVELTY HITS Various artists (Various Artists).
Tracks: / Running bear / Alley oop / La de dah / Nee nee na na nono / Muleskinner blues / Telephone man / Mr. Custer / Mr. Bassman / Sgt. Preston of the Yukon / Junk food junkie / Papa oo mow mow / Mr. Livingston.
Album: released on Topline, Jan'87 by Charly Records. Dist: Charly Distribution

Cassette:

Ladies Choice
FUNKY SENSATION.

Single (12"): released on LGR, Jan'86 Dist: Jetstar

Ladies sing the blues

LADIES SING THE BLUES Various Artists (Various Artists).
Double Album:

LADIES SING THE BLUES VOLUME 2 Various Artists (Various Artists).
Double Album:

Ladoux, Chris

RODEO'S SINGING BRONIC RIDER.
Album: released on Westwood, Jun'79 by Westwood Records. Dist: Jazz Music, H.R. Taylor, JSU, Pinnacle, Ross Records

L.A. Dream Team

KINGS OF THE WEST COAST.
Album: released on MCA, Oct'86 by MCA Records. Dist: Polygram, MCA

Cassette: released on MCA, Oct'86 by MCA Records. Dist: Polygram, MCA

NURSERY RHYMES.
Single (7"): released on MCA, Sep'86 by MCA Records. Dist: Polygram MCA

Single (12"): released on MCA, Sep'86 by MCA Records. Dist: Polygram, MCA

Lads

HERE WE GO (football anthem).
Single (7"): released on FA, May'84 by FA Records. Dist: Spartan

Lady Ann

INFORMER.
Single (12"): released on Joe Gibbs, Mar'83 by Joe Gibbs Records. Dist: Jetstar

MESSAGE TO EVERY HUSBAND.
Single (12"): released on Mobiliser, Feb'84 by Jetstar Records. Dist: Jetstar Distribution

Lady Anne

LADY ANNE YOU'RE SWEET.
Single (12"): released on Greensleeves, Oct'82 by Greensleeves Records. Dist: BMG, Jetstar, Spartan

Lady B

ATTRACTIVE YOUNG MAN WANTED.
Single (7"): released on RCA, Sep'83 by RCA Records. Dist: RCA, Roots, Swift, Wellard, Chris, I & B, Solomon & Peres Distribution

Single (12"): released on RCA, Sep'83 by RCA Records. Dist: RCA, Roots, Swift, Wellard, Chris, I & B, Solomon & Peres Distribution

Lady be good

LADY BE GOOD Original Cast (Various Artists).
Album: released on World, '74 Dist: Jetstar

Cassette: released on World Records, May'79 Dist: Polygram

Lady Hawke

LADY HAWKE Original Soundtrack.
Album: released on Atlantic, Aug'85 by WEA Records. Dist: WEA

Ladysmith Black Mambazo

HELLO MY BABY.
Tracks: / Hello my baby / King of Kings / Unomathemba* / At Golgotha*.
Notes: * = Extra track on 12" only.
Single (7"): released on Warner Brothers, Apr'87 by Warner Bros Records. Dist: WEA

Single (12"): released on Warner Brothers, Apr'87 by Warner Bros Records. Dist: WEA

INALA.
Album: released on Serengeti, Apr'87 Dist: RCA, Sterns/Triple Earth Distribution

Cassette: released on Serengeti, Apr'87 Dist: RCA, Sterns/Triple Earth Distribution

INDUKU ZETHU.
Album: released on Earthworks, Oct'84 by Earthworks Records. Dist: Earthworks Distributors, Rough Trade, Cartel, Projection

SHAKA ZULU.
Tracks: / Unomathemba / Hello my baby / At golgotha / King of kings / Earth is never satisfied, The / How long / Home of the heroes / These are the guys / Rain, rain beautiful rain / Who were you talking to.
Album: released on Warner Bros., Apr'87 by Warner Bros Records. Dist: WEA

Cassette: released on Warner Bros., Apr'87 by Warner Bros Records. Dist: WEA

Compact disc: released on Warner Bros., Apr'87 by Warner Bros Records. Dist: WEA

THAT'S WHY I CHOOSE YOU.
Tracks: / That's why I choose you / Pauline.
Single (7"): released on Serengeti, Mar'87 Dist: RCA, Sterns/Triple Earth Distribution

ULWANDLE OLUNCGWELE.
Compact disc: released on Serengeti, May'87 Dist: RCA, Sterns/Triple Earth Distribution

UNDUKU ZETHU.
Compact disc: released on Serengeti, May'87 Dist: RCA, Sterns/Triple Earth Distribution

Ladysmith, B M

INALA.
Compact disc: Dist: RCA, Sterns/Triple Earth Distribution

Lady & The Tramp

LADY AND THE TRAMP Original Soundtrack.
Album: released on Disney, Oct'84 by BBC Records & Tapes. Dist: BBC Records & Tapes, PRT

Cassette: released on Disney, Oct'84 by BBC Records & Tapes. Dist: BBC Records & Tapes, PRT

LADY AND THE TRAMP Various Artists (Various Artists).
Extended-play record: released on Disneyland, Dec'82 by Disneyland-Vista Records (USA). Dist: BBC Records & Tapes, Rainbow Communications Ltd(Distribution)

Cassette: released on Disneyland, Dec'82 Dist: EMI

LADY AND THE TRAMP (Scales, Prunella).
Special: released on Whinfrey Strachan, Jan'85 Dist: Whinfrey Strachan

LADY AND THE TRAMP (12") Various Artists (Various Artists).
Album: released on Disneyland, Dec'82 by Disneyland-Vista Records (USA). Dist: BBC Records & Tapes, Rainbow Communications Ltd(Distribution)

Special: released on Disneyland, Dec'82 by Disneyland-Vista Records (USA). Dist: BBC Records & Tapes, Rainbow Communications Ltd(Distribution)

Lady with Carnations

LADY WITH CARNATIONS (Geeson, Judy).
Cassette: released on Chivers Audio Books, '81 by Chivers Sound & Vision. Dist: Chivers Sound & Vision

Lafferty, Karen

BIRD IN A GOLDEN CAGE.
Album: released on Maranatha, May'79

LIFE PAGES LOVE OF THE AGES.
Album: released on Maranatha Music, May'82

Cassette: released on Maranatha Music, May'82

SWEET COMMUNION.
Album: released on Maranatha, May'79

L. A. Force

ACTION (night action).
Single (12"): released on Challenge, May'85 by Elite Records. Dist: Pinnacle

Lagoya, Alexandre

60 MINUTES OF MUSIC.
Tracks: / Asturia / Concerto de aranjuez / Recuerdos de la alhambra / Mallorca / Canarios / Pavane / Romanesca / Etude, op 35 no.17 / Lobos prelude no.1 / Lobos prelude no.2.
Notes: Popular guitar works.y
Cassette: released on Philips (France), Jul'86

Lagrene, Birell

15.
Album: released on Antilles, Aug'82 by Island Records. Dist: Polygram

Cassette: released on Antilles, Aug'82 by Island Records. Dist: Polygram

BIRELI SWING 81.
Album: released on Austrophon Diepholz(Germany), Jul'83

DOWN IN TOWN.
Album: released on Antilles, Nov'83 by Island Records. Dist: Polygram

Cassette: released on Antilles, Nov'83 by Island Records. Dist: Polygram Deleted '87

ROUTES TO DJANGO.
Tracks: / Night and day / All of me / My melancholy baby.
Compact disc: released on Polystar (Japan), '86 Dist: Target, Polygram

Compact disc: released on Antilles, '87 by Island Records. Dist: Polygram

Album: released on Antilles, Apr'82 by Island Records. Dist: Polygram

Lahm, David

REAL JAZZ FOR THE FOLKS WHO FEEL JAZZ.
Album: released on Palo Alto (Italy), Jan'84

Lahost

BIG SLEEP, (THE).
Single (7"): released on Quiet, Nov'85 by Quiet Records. Dist: Nine Mile, Cartel

Single (7"): released on Orbitone, Oct'85 by Orbitone Records. Dist: Jetstar Distribution

Laibach

BOJI.
Single (12"): released on Layla, Mar'84 by Layla Records. Dist: Rough Trade, Cartel

GEBURT EINER NATION.
Tracks: / Geburt einer nation / Leben heist leben.
Single (12"): released on Mute, Mar'87 Dist: Spartan Distribution, Rough Trade Distribution, Cartel Distribution

LIEBE, (DIE).
Single (12"): released on Cherry Red, Nov'85 by Cherry Red Records. Dist: Pinnacle

LIFE IS LIFE.
Tracks: / Life is life / Germania / Leben.
Single (7"): released on Mute, Jul'87 Dist: Spartan Distribution, Rough Trade Distribution, Cartel Distribution

Single (12"): released on Mute, Jul'87 Dist: Spartan Distribution, Rough Trade Distribution, Cartel Distribution

NOVA AKROPOLA.
Tracks: / IV personen / Nova akropola / Krvava fruda-plodna zemja / Vojna poena / Ti ki izzivas.
Album: released on Cherry Red, Dec'85 by Cherry Red Records. Dist: Pinnacle

OCCUPIED EUROPE TOUR '85.
Album: released on Side Effects, Jul'86 by SPK Records. Dist: Rough Trade, Cartel

OPUS DEI.
Album: released on Mute, Mar'87 Dist: Spartan Distribution, Rough Trade Distribution, Cartel Distribution

OPUS DE MONUMENTAL.
Tracks: / Reben heist reben / Geburt einer nation / Reben-tod / Opus dei / How the west was won.
Compact disc: released on Mute, Jun'87 Dist: Spartan Distribution, Rough Trade Distribution, Cartel Distribution

PANARAMA.
Single (12"): released on East-West Trading Company, May'84 by Cherry Red Records. Dist: Pinnacle

Laid Back

IT'S A SHAME.
Single (7"): released on WEA International, Aug'87 by WEA Records. Dist: WEA

SUNSHINE REGGAE.
Single (7"): released on Creole, Nov'83 by Creole Records. Dist: Rhino, PRT

Single (12"): released on Creole, Nov'83 by Creole Records. Dist: Rhino, PRT

WHITE HORSE.
Single (7"): released on Creole, Feb'84 by Creole Records. Dist: Rhino, PRT

Single (12"): released on Creole, Feb'84 by Creole Records. Dist: Rhino, PRT

Lai, Francis

FRANCIS LAI.
Cassette: released on Audio Fidelity, Oct'84 Dist: PRT

MAN, A WOMAN, AND A LOVE STORY, (A) (Lai, Francis/his orchestra).
Album: released on Spot, Oct'83 by Pickwick Records. Dist: H.R. Taylor, Lugtons

Cassette: released on Spot, Oct'83 by Pickwick Records. Dist: H.R. Taylor, Lugtons

Laila, Runa

SUPERUNA.
Album: released on H.M.V., '83 by EMI Records. Dist: EMI

Laine, Cleo

16 GOLDEN CLASSICS.
Tracks: / He was beautiful / People / Aquarius / Somewhere / Killing me softly / Send in the clowns / If / Don't cry for me Argentina / Just the way you are / Streets of London / When I need you / Let's have a quiet night in / Eleanor Rigby / I believe (when you fall in love) / You'll never walk alone / Feelings.
Notes: All tracks licensed from Sierra Records Ltd\Westminster Music Ltd. Design: Shoot that Tiger!; (c) 1986. Castle communications place, Unit 7, 271, Merton Road, London SW18 5JS: Bar code: 5\013428\920084
Album: released on Unforgettable, Dec'86 by Castle Communications Records. Dist: Counterpoint

Cassette: released on Unforgettable, Dec'86 by Castle Communications Records. Dist: Counterpoint

Compact disc: released on Unforgettable, '86 by Castle Communications Records. Dist: Counterpoint

BEST FRIENDS C (Laine, Cleo & John Williams).
Album: released on RCA, Sep'81 by RCA Records. Dist: RCA, Roots, Swift, Wellard, Chris, I & B, Solomon & Peres Distribution

Cassette: released on RCA, Sep'81 by RCA Records. Dist: RCA, Roots, Swift, Wellard, Chris, I & B, Solomon & Peres Distribution

Album: released on Magenta, Dec'81 Dist: Windham Hill

Cassette: released on Magenta, Dec'81 Dist: Windham Hill

CLEO AT CARNEGIE.
Tracks: / Any place.. /It's a grand night../Good morning/It's a.. / I'm shadowing you / Crazy rhythm / Primrose colour blue / We are the music makers / You spotted snakes / Methuselah / When I was one and twenty / Sing me no song/ Triboro' fair / You've got to do what you've got to do / He was beautiful / Turkish delight / Never let me go / Hoagy Carmichael Medley / I want to be happy.
Notes: 10th anniversary concert, recorded live at Carnegie Hall.
Compact disc: released on DRG (USA), Apr'87 by DRG Records. Dist: Conifer, RCA

Double Album: released on RCA, Jun'87 by RCA Records. Dist: RCA, Roots, Swift, Wellard, Chris, I & B, Solomon & Peres Distribution

Double cassette: released on RCA, Jun'87 by RCA Records. Dist: RCA, Roots, Swift, Wellard, Chris, I & B, Solomon & Peres Distribution

CLEO LIVE AT CARNEGIE.
Notes: The 10th Anniversary Concert.
Album: released on Towerbell, Sep'86 by Towerbell Records. Dist: EMI

Cassette: released on Towerbell, Sep'86 by Towerbell Records. Dist: EMI

COLETTE.
Album: released on Evolution, Sep'80 Dist: RCA, Folksound

Cassette: released on Evolution, Sep'80 Dist: RCA, Folksound

ESSENTIAL COLLECTION, THE.
Compact disc: released on Sierra, May'87 by Sierra Records. Dist: WEA

INCOMPARABLE CLEO LAINE, THE.
Album: released on Black Lion, Jul'80 by Black Lion Records. Dist: Jazz Music, Chris Wellard, Taylor, H.R., Counterpoint, Cadillac

IN CONCERT AT THE CARNEGIE.
Album: released on Sierra, Oct'85 by Sierra Records. Dist: WEA

Cassette: released on Sierra, Oct'85 by Sierra Records. Dist: WEA

IN RETROSPECT (Laine, Cleo & Johnny Dankworth).
Album: released on Polydor (Germany), May'83 Dist: IMS-Polygram

JAZZ FIRST (Laine, Cleo & Jean Luc Ponty).
Cassette: released on Timeless Treasures, Jul'86 Dist: Counterpoint Distribution

LIVE AT CARNEGIE HALL.
Double Album: released on Magenta, '82 Dist: Windham Hill

LOVER AND HIS LASS, (A).
Album: released on Esquire, Dec'76 by Titan International Productions. Dist: Jazz Music, Cadillac Music, Swift, Wellard, Chris, Backs, Rough Trade, Revolver, Nine Mile

OFF THE RECORD WITH CLEO LAINE.
Album: released on Sierra, Nov'84 by Sierra Records. Dist: WEA

Cassette: released on Sierra, Nov'84 by Sierra Records. Dist: WEA

ONE MORE DAY.
Album: released on Sepia, Feb'83 by Sepia Records. Dist: PRT

Cassette: released on Sepia, Feb'83 by Sepia Records. Dist: PRT

Album: released on DRG (USA), May'84 by DRG Records. Dist: Conifer, RCA

Cassette: released on DRG (USA), May'84 by DRG Records. Dist: Conifer, RCA

PLATINUM COLLECTION.
Cassette: released on Cube (Platinum coll), Oct'81

SMILIN' THROUGH (see Moore, Dudley/Cleo Laine) (Laine, Cleo & Dudley Moore).

STRICTLY FOR THE BIRDS (Laine, Cleo & Dudley Moore).
Single (7"): released on CBS, Nov'82 by CBS Records. Dist: CBS

THAT OLD FEELING.
Tracks: / That old feeling / Tenderly / I've got a crush on you / Once in a while / Imagination / It never entered my mind / Ain't misbehavin' / I didn't know about you / I never went away / It's not easy (to say I love you) / Alfie / I've got it bad and that ain't good / Everytime we say goodbye / Embraceable you / My funny valentine / It happens quietly / He needs me / You're looking at me.
Compact disc: released on Key West, Dec'86 Dist: PRT

Compact disc: released on The Collection, Apr'87 by Object Enterprises Ltd. Dist: Counterpoint Distribution

THEMES.
Album: released on Sierra, Oct'85 by Sierra Records. Dist: WEA

Cassette: released on Sierra, Oct'85 by Sierra Records. Dist: WEA

Wereld successen

WERELD SUCCESSEN (Laine, Cleo & John Williams).
Album: released on IMS(Import), Oct'82 by Polydor Records. Dist: IMS, Polygram

WORD SONGS.
Notes: Famous Philips recording of Cleo Laine singing the poetry of William Shakespeare T.S.Elliott, John Dunne, William Makepeace Thackery, Spike Milligan, Sir John Betjeman, Thomas Hardy and others, set to music by John Dankworth. "Word Songs"was always one of the most popular sections of Cleo's concert repertoire and hasnot been available on album for some years. Over one hour of music. Recorded January 1977 to February 1978.
Personnel: John Dankworth - soprano sax, alto sax, clarinet/Paul Hart - keyboard/Pete Morgan, Daryl Runswick - bass, bass guitar/Kenny Clare, Allan Ganley, Tony Kinsey - drums.
Compact disc: released on Philips, Apr'87 Dist: IMS-Polygram

Double Album: released on Red Seal, '78 by RCA Records. Dist: RCA

Cassette: released on Red Seal, '78 by RCA Records. Dist: RCA

Laine, Denny

HOMETOWN GIRL.
Tracks: / Hometown girl / Stay away.
Single (7"): released on President, May'86 by President Records. Dist: Taylors, Spartan

HOMETOWN GIRLS.
Album: released on President, Nov'85 by President Records. Dist: Taylors, Spartan

Cassette: released on President, Nov'85 by President Records. Dist: Taylors, Spartan

JAPANESE TEARS.
Album: released on Scratch, Dec'80

Single (7"): released on Scratch, Aug'82

LAND OF PEACE.
Tracks: / Land of peace / If I tried.
Single (7"): released on President, Nov'86 by President Records. Dist: Taylors, Spartan

SAY YOU DON'T MIND.
Single (7"): released on Scratch, Aug'82

WEEP FOR LOVE.
Album: released on President, May'85 by President Records. Dist: Taylors, Spartan

Cassette: released on President, May'85 by President Records. Dist: Taylors, Spartan

WHO MOVED THE WORLD.
Single (7"): released on Rock City, Nov'81 by Brian Adams. Dist: Pinnacle

Laine, Frankie

1947 (Laine, Frankie with Carl Fischer & Orch.).
Album: released on Hindsight(USA), Mar'84 by Hindsight Records (USA). Dist: Swift, Charly

ALL OF ME.
Album: released on Bulldog, Mar'82 by Bulldog Records. Dist: President Distribution, Spartan, Swift, Taylor, H.R.

Cassette: released on Bulldog, Mar'82 by Bulldog Records. Dist: President Distribution, Spartan, Swift, Taylor, H.R.

AMERICAN LEGEND.
Cassette: released on CBS, Feb'78 by CBS Records. Dist: CBS

ANSWER ME.
Single (7"): released on Bulldog, Apr'82 by Bulldog Records. Dist: President Distribution, Spartan, Swift, Taylor, H.R.

BEST OF.
Cassette: released on Creole (Everest-Europa), Jul'84 by Creole Records. Dist: PRT, Rhino

BEST OF FRANKIE LAINE.
Album: released on Music For Pleasure (Holland), Apr'83 by EMI Records. Dist: EMI

Cassette: released on Music For Pleasure (Holland), Apr'83 by EMI Records. Dist: EMI

FRANKIE LAINE.
Tracks: / I believe / Mule train / High noon / Jezebel / Answer me.
Album: released on Music For Pleasure (Holland), '86 by EMI Records. Dist: EMI

Cassette: released on Music For Pleasure (Holland), '86 by EMI Records. Dist: EMI

Album: released on Spot, Aug'83 by Pickwick Records. Dist: H.R. Taylor, Lugtons

Cassette: released on Spot, Aug'83 by Pickwick Records. Dist: H.R. Taylor, Lugtons

GOLDEN GREATS: FRANKIE LAINE.
Album: released on Polydor, May'83 by Polydor Records. Dist: Polygram, Polydor

Cassette: released on Polydor, May'83 by Polydor Records. Dist: Polygram, Polydor

GOLDEN YEARS, THE.
Album: released on Philips, Nov'84 Dist: IMS-Polygram

Cassette: released on Philips, Nov'84 Dist: IMS-Polygram

HIGH MOON.
Single (7"): released on CBS, Apr'82 by CBS Records. Dist: CBS

Single (7"): released on Old Gold, Jul'82 by Old Gold Records. Dist: Lightning, Jazz Music, Spartan, Counterpoint

HIS GREATEST HITS.
Tracks: / I believe / Moonlight gambler / Jealousy (jalousie) / Rain, rain, rain / Sixteen tons / Cry of the wilde goose, The / Granada / Don't fence me in / Rose, Rose I love you / Answer me / Woman in love, A / Wheel of fortune / Rawhide / Still runs cool water / Strange lady in town / Mule train / Hummingbird / Jezebel / There must be a reason / High noon.
Album: released on Warwick Reflections, Jun'86 by Warwick Records.

Cassette: released on Warwick Reflections, Jun'86 by Warwick Records.

MY FAVOURITES.
Album: released on Arcade Music Gala, Apr'86 Dist: Stage One

Cassette: released on Arcade Music Gala, Apr'86 Dist: Stage One

RAWHIDE.
Tracks: / Rawhide / Mule train / Moonlight gambler / I believe / Don't fence me in / Strange lady in town / Rose, Rose I love you / There must be a reason / Answer me (mutterlein) / Jezebel / High noon (do not forsake me) / Jealousy / Sixteen tons / Cool water / Wheel of fortune / Rain, rain, rain / Granada / Cry of the wild goose.
Single (7"): released on Old Gold, Jan'87 by Old Gold Records. Dist: Lightning, Jazz Music, Spartan, Counterpoint

Album: released on Showcase, Sep'86 Dist: Counterpoint

Cassette: released on Showcase, Sep'86 Dist: Counterpoint

SONGBOOK.
Boxed set: released on World Records, '81 Dist: Polygram

Boxed set: released on World Records, '81 Dist: Polygram

UNCOLLECTED, THE.
Album: released on Hindsight(UK), Apr'86 Dist: Jazz Music

WOMAN IN LOVE.
Single (7"): released on Old Gold, Jul'82 by Old Gold Records. Dist: Lightning, Jazz Music, Spartan, Counterpoint

Single (7"): released on Old Gold, Jul'82 by Old Gold Records. Dist: Lightning, Jazz Music, Spartan, Counterpoint

WORLD OF FRANKIE LAINE, THE.
Cassette: released on Ronco, Mar'82

Laine, John

SET ME FREE.
Tracks: / Set me free / Future song.

TEMPTATION.
Single (7"): released on Hollywood, May'84 by Hollywood Records. Dist: Pinnacle

Single (12"): released on Hollywood, May'84 by Hollywood Records. Dist: Pinnacle

Laing, Phil

DAY AFTER DAY.
Tracks: / Day after day / Don't say it's over.

Laing, Shona

NOT A KENNEDY Glad I'm....
Tracks: / Not a Kennedy / Resurrection.
Single (7"): released on Virgin, Jul'87 by Virgin Records. Dist: EMI, Virgin Distribution

Single (12"): released on Virgin, Jul'87 by Virgin Records. Dist: EMI, Virgin Distribution

Laird, Christopher

THREE MUSKHOUNDS.
Single (7"): released on BBC, Apr'85 by BBC Records & Tapes. Dist: EMI, PRT

Cassette: released on BBC, Apr'85 by BBC Records & Tapes. Dist: EMI, PRT

Laird, Skee

LOVELY LADY WITH A LOVELY VOICE.
Cassette: released on Nevis, Jan'80 Dist: H.R. Taylor

SKEE LAIRD SINGS COOL COUNTRY.
Album: released on Nevis, Apr'79 Dist: H.R. Taylor

Lalty, Pete

RASH ADVENTURE, A.
Album: released on Oblivion, Jan'85 Dist: Projection

Lakakis, Paul

BOOM BOOM (LET'S GO BACK TO MY ROOM).
Tracks: / Boom boom / Boom boom (inst).
Single (7"): released on Champion, May'87 by Champion Records. Dist: RCA

Single (12"): released on Champion, May'87 by Champion Records. Dist: RCA

Lake, Greg

GREG LAKE.
Album: released on Chrysalis, Oct'81 by Chrysalis Records. Dist: CBS

I BELIEVE IN FATHER CHRISTMAS.
Tracks: / I believe in Father Christmas / Humbug.
Single (7"): released on Manticore, Nov'82 by Atlantic Records. Dist: WEA

MANOEUVRES.
Album: released on Chrysalis, Jul'83 by Chrysalis Records. Dist: CBS

Cassette: released on Chrysalis, Jul'83 by Chrysalis Records. Dist: CBS

Lakeland

COUNTRY SPEECH, SONGS AND DANCES.
Cassette: released on Folktracks, Nov'79 by Folktracks Cassettes. Dist: Folktracks

Lakeman, Geoff

BUSHES AND BRIARS (Lakeman, Geoff/Barry Skinner).
Album: released on Fellside (Cumbria), May'83 by Fellside Records. Dist: Roots, Projection, CM, Jazz Music

Lake, Oliver

BUSTER BEE (Lake, Oliver & Julius Hemphill).

BUSTER BEE (see Hemphill, Julius) (Lake, Oliver & Julius Hemphill).
Album: released on Sackville, Apr'81 Dist: Jazz Music, Jazz Horizons, Cadillac Music, Celtic Music, Swift

CLEVONT FITZHUBERT (Lake, Oliver Quertet).
Album: released on Black Saint, Jul'82 Dist: Projection, IMS, Polygram, Chris Wellard, Harmonia Mundi, Swift

CONCERT A SPACE (Lake, Oliver & Joseph Bowie).
Album: released on Sackville, Apr'81 Dist: JSU, Jazz Music, Jazz Horizons, Cadillac Music, Celtic Music, Swift

HOLDING TOGETHER.
Album: released on Black Saint, Jul'78 Dist: Projection, IMS, Polygram, Chris Wellard, Harmonia Mundi, Swift

JUMP UP.
Album: released on Gramavision (USA), May'83 by Gramavison Records (USA). Dist: PRT, IMS, Polygram

PLUG IT (Lake,Oliver and Jump Up).
Album: released on Gramavision (USA), Dec'83 by Gramavison Records (USA). Dist: PRT, IMS, Polygram

Lakeside

FANTASTIC VOYAGE.
Album: released on Solar, Dec'80

KEEP ON MOVING STRAIGHT AHEAD.
Album: released on Solar, Mar'82

OUTRAGEOUS.
Single (7"): released on MCA, Apr'85 by MCA Records. Dist: Polygram, MCA

Single (12"): released on MCA, Apr'85 by MCA Records. Dist: Polygram, MCA

RAID.
Single (7"): released on Elektra, Mar'83 by WEA Records. Dist: WEA

Single (12"): released on Elektra, Mar'83 by WEA Records. Dist: WEA

Lake, Steve

IN EVERY LIFE.
Extended-play record: released on Not So Brave, May'85 Dist: Red Rhino Distribution, Cartel Distribution

MURDER VIOLENCE SEX DIVORCE.
Album: released on Not So Brave, Jun'85 Dist: Red Rhino Distribution, Cartel Distribution

WELCOME TO MONKEY HOUSE.
Single (12"): released on Not So Brave, Mar'84 Dist: Red Rhino Distribution, Cartel Distribution

Lake, Tim

SAME OLD ROADSIDE INN.
Album: released on Rounder, Sep'79 Dist: Roots Distribution

Lala

LOVE ME JUST A LITTLE.
Tracks: / Love me just a little / Love me just a little (inst).
Single (7"): released on Arista, Jul'87 by Arista Records. Dist: RCA

Single (12"): released on Arista, Jul'87 by Arista Records. Dist: RCA

Lalor, Dave

DARLING.
Tracks: / Darling / Take me back (Take me home).
Single (7"): released on S.R.S., Jun'87 by S.R.S. Records.

Lama

LOVE ON THE ROCKS.
Single (7"): released on Carrere, Mar'84 by Carrere Records. Dist: PRT, Spartan

Single (12"): released on Carrere, Mar'84 by Carrere Records. Dist: PRT, Spartan

Lamara

STAR OF THE SHOW.
Tracks: / Star of the show / Tanesia.

Lamarr, Chris

YOUNG AND FREE.
Single (7"): released on Crash, Jan'83 by Satril Records. Dist: PRT

Lamarr, Louise

STEVIE'S O.K.

Single (7"): released on Juice, Jan'83 by IRS. Dist: A&M, CBS

Lamb

YEAR OF JUBILEE.

Notes: Lamb's first album with Maranatha! Music and, therefore, the first album Word has distributed. Lamb is Joel Chernoff (all vocals and vocal arrangement, 6-string and 12-string acoustic guitars, keyboards, composer) and Rick 'Levi' Coghill (6-string, 12-string and high string acoustic guitars, all electric guitars, percussion, musical direction, producer). Lamb invite us to celebrate with them in the joyous spirit of revival contained in this offering of Messianic praise and worship.

Lamb, Annabel

HEARTLAND.
Single (7"): released on A&M, Apr'83 by A&M Records. Dist: Polygram

Single (12"): released on A&M, Apr'83 by A&M Records. Dist: Polygram

ONCE BITTEN.
Single (7"): released on A&M, Feb'83 by A&M Records. Dist: Polygram

Lamb, Annabelle

DIFFERENT DRUM.
Tracks: / Different drum / In the land of dreamy dreams / Lonely house*.
Single (7"): released on RCA, 13 Jun'87 by RCA Records. Dist: RCA, Roots, Swift, Wellard, Chris, I & B, Solomon & Peres Distribution

Single (12"): released on RCA, 13 Jun'87 by RCA Records. Dist: RCA, Roots, Swift, Wellard, Chris, I & B, Solomon & Peres Distribution

Lambe, Jeanie

MIDNIGHT SUN, (THE) (Lambe, Jeanie & Danny Moss Quartet).
Album: released on Zodiac, Sep'84 Dist: Jazz Music

SINGS THE BLUES.
Album: released on Zodiac, Dec'82 Dist: Jazz Music

Lambert

AT NEWPORT '63 (Lambert/Hendricks/Bavan).
Album: released on RCA (France), May'83 by RCA Records. Dist: Discovery

HAVIN' A BALL AT THE VILLAGE GATE (Lambert/Hendricks/Bavan).
Album: released on RCA (France), Oct'85 by RCA Records. Dist: Discovery

SING A SONG OF BASIE (Lambert/Hendricks/Ross).
Album: released on Jasmine, Jun'82 by Jasmine Records. Dist: Counterpoint, Lugtons, Taylor, H.R., Wellard, Chris, Swift, Cadillac

Cassette: released on Jasmine, Jun'82 by Jasmine Records. Dist: Counterpoint, Taylor, H.R., Wellard, Chris, Swift, Cadillac

SWINGERS, (THE) (Lambert/Hendricks/Ross).
Album: released on Affinity, Nov'84 by Charly Records. Dist: Charly, Cadillac

Lambert, Donald

GIANT STRIDE (Lambert, Donald & His Harlem Piano).

GIANT STRIDE.
Album: released on Jazzology, Aug'79 Dist: Jazz Music, Swift

HARLEM STRIDE CLASSICS 1960-62.
Album: released on Pumpkin, Apr'79 Dist: Jazz Music, Wellard, Chris, Cadillac

Lambert, Franz

56 HOLIDAY HITS.
Double Album: released on Philips (Germany), Apr'85

Double cassette: released on Philips (Germany), Apr'85

DIE SUPERHITS DER VOLKSMUSIK.
Tracks: / Die Fischerin vom bodensee / Hohe tannen / Schneewalzer / La montanara / Drei weibe birken / Heidi / Schutzenliesel / Rosamunde / La pastorella / Das alte forstehaus / Ja, mir san mit'm radl da / Kufsteiner lied / Treue bergvagabunden / Herz schmerz-polka.
Notes: Arranged by H W Scharnowski and H Jost. Engineered by W Pentinghaus. Produced by Franz Lambert. Recorded at Hermes Studios, Kamen. Franz lambert used the Wesi Delta and Wersi Galaxis Organ.

FIESTA BRASILIANA 28 Latin hits on organ.
Tracks: / Amoradaytsciou tschiou tschiou / Tico tico / La bamba / Watermelon man / Tequila / Island in the sun / La novia / Malaguena / Mexico / Carnavalito / A banda / La felicidad / O baiao bongo / Mambo nr 5 / Siboney mambo jambo / South of the border / Cuando sali de Cuba / Ave Maria no morro / Banana boat song / Patricia / Managua Nicaragua / Orgeo Negro / Cu cu rru cu cu paloma / El cumbanchero / Carneval Brasil / Brasil.

FRANZ LAMBERT.
Album: released on Teldec (Germany), Jul'84 by Import Records. Dist: IMS Distribution, Polygram Distribution

Cassette: released on Teldec (Germany), Jul'84 by Import Records. Dist: IMS Distribution, Polygram Distribution

GREATEST HITS:FRANZ LAMBERT.
Album: released on Philips (Import), Aug'81

Cassette: released on Philips (Import), Aug'81

HELLO,AMERICA.
Album: released on Teldec (Germany), Oct'83 by Import Records. Dist: IMS Distribution, Polygram Distribution

Cassette: released on Teldec (Germany), Oct'83 by Import Records. Dist: IMS Distribution, Polygram Distribution

HIGHLIGHTS.
Album: released on Teldec, Apr'81

Cassette: released on Teldec, Apr'81

KING OF HAMMOND.
Double Album: released on Philips (Germany), Jul'82

Double cassette: released on Philips (Germany), Jul'82

LA PARRANDA PARTY.
Album: released on EMI (Germany), May'83 by EMI Records. Dist: Conifer

LET'S HAVE A PARTY.
Album: released on Teldec (Germany), Sep'85 by Import Records. Dist: IMS Distribution, Polygram Distribution

POP ORGAN HIT PARADE-40 SUPER HITS.
Album: released on Note, Feb'79 by EMI Records. Dist: EMI

SUPERGOLD.
Double Album: released on EMI (Germany), May'83 by EMI Records. Dist: Conifer

SUPER PARTY.
Album: released on Import Music Service (IMS), Apr'81 Dist: Concord Jazz Distributions, Pablo, Polygram

Cassette: released on Polydor (Germany), Apr'81 Dist: IMS-Polygram

SYMPHONIE D'AMOUR.
Album: released on Teldec (Germany), Jul'83 by Import Records. Dist: IMS Distribution, Polygram Distribution

Cassette: released on Teldec (Germany), Jul'83 by Import Records. Dist: IMS Distribution, Polygram Distribution

TOP HITS 2.
Album: released on Teldec (Import), Feb'82

Cassette: released on Teldec (Import), Feb'82

TOP HITS 3.
Album: released on Teldec (Germany), Aug'82 by Import Records. Dist: IMS Distribution, Polygram Distribution

Cassette: released on Teldec (Germany), Aug'82 by Import Records. Dist: IMS Distribution, Polygram Distribution

Lambert,H

Adran Schubert & His Salon Orchestra

Lambert/Hendricks/Ross

SING ALONG WITH BASIE.
Compact disc: released on Vogue, May'87 Dist: Discovery, Jazz Music, PRT, Swift

Lamb, Natalie

NATALIE LAMB, SAMMY PRICE & THE BLUES (Lamb, Natalie, Sammy Price & The Blues).
Album: released on GHB, Jul'87 Dist: Jazz Music, Swift

Lambrettas

BEAT BOYS IN THE JET AGE.
Album: released on Rocket, Jul'80 by Phonogram Records. Dist: Polygram Distribution

KICK START.
Album: released on Razor, Aug'85 by Razor. Dist: Pinnacle

Lamb, Rose

SHOPPING AROUND.
Single (7"): released on V-Tone, Sep'81 by Relic. Dist: Swift

Lambs On The Green Hills

SONGS FROM COUNTY CLARE.
Album: released on Topic, May'81 by Topic Records. Dist: JSU Distribution, Projection Distribution, Jazz Music Distribution

Lamella

WASTING YOUR TIME.
Single (7"): released on Direct, Apr'81 Dist: Backs, Cartel

Lamond, Don

DON LAMOND & HIS BIG BAND EXTRAORDINARY.
Album: released on Progressive (Import), Feb'83

Lamont, Duncan

SUMMER SOUNDS.
Tracks: / Girl from Ipanema, The / Quiet nights of quiet stars / Shadow of your smile, The / Call me / Felicidade/Samba de orfeu / Destination love / Wave / My cherie amour / Mas que nada / Fool on the hill / Desafinado / Un homme et une femme / Meditation / How insensitive / Summer samba / Our day will come / Look of love, The / We've only just begun / Gentle one / Alone again.

LaMotta, Stephanie

I'M HERE AT LAST (so forget the past).
Single (7"): released on Zilch, Jun'82 by Zilch Records. Dist: Stage One

L'Amourder

RITUAL.
Album: released on Fun After All, Oct'86 Dist: Pinnacle

Lamour, Gina

CONTINENTAL, (THE).
Single (12"): released on Glamour, Aug'83 by Glamour Records. Dist: PRT

I WANT TO BE ALONE.
Single (7"): released on Glamour, Nov'83 by Glamour Records. Dist: PRT

MOVE OVER DARLING.
Single (7"): released on Glamour, Jul'83 by Glamour Records. Dist: PRT

Single (12"): released on Glamour, Aug'83 by Glamour Records. Dist: PRT

Single (7"): released on Glamour, Dec'83 by Glamour Records. Dist: PRT

YI YI YI YI I LIKE YOU VERY MUCH.
Single (7"): released on Calibre, Jun'84 by Calibre Records. Dist: PRT

Single (12"): released on Calibre, Jun'84 by Calibre Records. Dist: PRT

L'Amour, Rudi

CALL ME On your lonely nights.
Tracks: / Call me / Lonely nights.
Single (7"): released on Button, Jul'87 by Musical Characters Records. Dist: Spartan

Lamsie

ROSE.
Single (12"): released on White, Apr'85

La Muerte

EVERY SOUL OPPRESSED BY SIN.
Album: released on Big Disc, Feb'87 Dist: Pinnacle

PEEP SHOW.
Single (12"): released on Soundwork, Mar'86

Lana As Covergirl

STAY WITH ME.
Tracks: / Stay with me / I'm a winner.

Lancashire Fayre

LANCASHIRE FAYRE.
Album: released on Folk Heritage, Jul'82 by Folk Heritage Records. Dist: Roots, Wynd-Up Distribution, Jazz Music, Folk Heritage

NOT EASILY FORGOTTEN.
Tracks: / Best of order / Windhover / Not easily forgotten / Fleetwood fishermen / Hop, hop, hop / Lancashire lad / Smuggler / Lancashire scenes / Dawn brigade / John Willie's ferret / Ellison's tenement / Weaver, The / Bread and fishes / Lancashire's pride.
Notes: Recorded and produced by Paul adams in April 1985. All titles arranged by Lancashire Fayre. Artists: Paddy Rouse - xylophone/bodhran. Hazel Lees - mandolin/whistles. Stuart Lees - 6-string guitar. Will Layfield - 12-string guitar/banjo. Ewan Rowland - flute/whistles.

Lande

SKYLIGHT (Lande/Samuels/McCandless).
Album: released on ECM (Germany), Jun'82 by ECM Records. Dist: IMS, Polygram, Virgin through EMI

Album: released on ECM (Germany), Jun'82 by ECM Records. Dist: IMS, Polygram, Virgin through EMI

Landes, Dee

MY LOVER BOY.
Single (12"): released on Londisc, Sep'85 by Londisc Records.

Land, Harold

GROOVEYARD.
Album: released on Contemporary, Mar'79 by Good Time Jazz Records (USA). Dist: IMS, Polygram

HAROLD IN THE LAND OF JAZZ.
Album: released on Boplicity, Aug'85 by Boplicity Records. Dist: Ace Records, Pinnacle

Land Of Distraction

DISTRACTION.
Single (7"):

Single (12"):

Land O'heart's desire

LAND O'HEART'S DESIRE Various artists (Various Artists).
Cassette: released on Meridan, Mar'80 by Meridean Records. Dist: Taylors, Harmonia Mundi Distributors

Lan Doky, Niels trio

HERE OR THERE.
Notes: With Niels Henning O.P.\Alvin Queen
Album: released on Storyville, Nov'86 by Storyville Records. Dist: Jazz Music Distribution, Swift Distribution, Chris Wellard Distribution, Counterpoint Distribution

Landry, Art

1924-1927 (Landry, Art & His Orchestra).

Landsborough, Charlie

I WILL LOVE YOU ALL MY LIFE.
Single (7"): released on Pastafont, Feb'83 by Pastafont Records.

THANK YOU LORD.
Single (7"): released on Pastafont, Nov'82 by Pastafont Records.

Landscape

FROM THE TEA ROOMS OF MARS... To the hell holes of uranus.
Album: released on RCA, Mar'81 by RCA Records. Dist: RCA, Roots, Swift, Wellard, Chris, I & B, Solomon & Peres Distribution

Cassette: released on RCA, Mar'81 by RCA Records. Dist: RCA, Roots, Swift, Wellard, Chris, I & B, Solomon & Peres Distribution

LANDSCAPE.
Album: released on RCA, Sep'81 by RCA Records. Dist: RCA, Roots, Swift, Wellard, Chris, I & B, Solomon & Peres Distribution

Cassette: released on RCA, Sep'81 by RCA Records. Dist: RCA, Roots, Swift, Wellard, Chris, I & B, Solomon & Peres Distribution

MANHATTAN BOOGIE WOOGIE.
Album: released on RCA, Jul'82 by RCA Records. Dist: RCA, Roots, Swift, Wellard, Chris, I & B, Solomon & Peres Distribution

Cassette: released on RCA, Jul'82 by RCA Records. Dist: RCA, Roots, Swift, Wellard, Chris, I & B, Solomon & Peres Distribution

Landscape III

SO GOOD SO PURE SO KIND.
Single (7"): released on RCA, Feb'83 by RCA Records. Dist: RCA, Roots, Swift, Wellard, Chris, I & B, Solomon & Peres Distribution

Single (12"): released on RCA, Feb'83 by RCA Records. Dist: RCA, Roots, Swift, Wellard, Chris, I & B, Solomon & Peres Distribution

YOU KNOW HOW TO HURT ME.
Single (7"): released on RCA, Apr'83 by RCA Records. Dist: RCA, Roots, Swift, Wellard, Chris, I & B, Solomon & Peres Distribution

Single (12"): released on RCA, Apr'83 by RCA Records. Dist: RCA, Roots, Swift, Wellard, Chris, I & B, Solomon & Peres Distribution

Land's End

LAND'S END Various artists (Various Artists).
Cassette: released on Touch, Jul'85 by Touch Records. Dist: Rough Trade, Cartel

Lane, Arnold

BOOK OF SAND.
Single (7"): Dist: Rough Trade, Red Rhino, Cartel

Page 582

Lane, Patricia
I DREAMED A DREAM.
Tracks: / I dreamed a dream / I know.

Lane, Steve
IN CONCERT (Lane, Steve/Southern Stompers/Michele).
Album: released on VJM, May'74 by VJM (UK) Records. Dist: Swift

I'VE GOT FORD ENGINE 1969-72 (Lane, Steve/Southern Stompers).
Album: released on VJM, May'74 by VJM (UK) Records. Dist: Swift

MOVIN' ON (Lane, Steve/Famous Southern Stompers).
Album: released on VJM, Apr'79 by VJM (UK) Records. Dist: Swift

STEVE LANE & HIS FAMOUS SOUTHERN STOMPERS (Lane, Steve/Famous Southern Stompers).
Album: released on Stomp Off, Dec'82 by Stomp Off Records. Dist: Jazz Music Distribution

WEMBLEY WIGGLE (Lane, Steve/Southern Stompers).
Album: released on 77, May'74 by 77 Records. Dist: Chris Wellard, Cadillac Music, Jazz Music

Langa Langa Stars
LIKOMBE.
Album: released on Vercky's (Zaire), Jul'84 Dist: Earthworks Distributors, Rough Trade

MOYEBE (Langa Langa Stars & Choc Stars).
Album: released on Vercky's (Zaire), Jul'84 Dist: Earthworks Distributors, Rough Trade

Lang, Don
DON LANG GETS THE BUG (Lang, Don & His Frantic 5).
Album: released on Jam, Apr'79 Dist: Jazz Music

GETS THE BUG.
Album: released on Jam, Mar'87 Dist: Jazz Music

ROCK, ROCK, ROCK (Lang, Don & His Frantic 5).
Tracks: / Queen of the hop / Ramshackle daddy / 6-5 hand jive / Red planet rock / Texas tambourine / School day / Rock Mr Piper / Rock around the cookhouse / Rock-a-billy / Rock, rock, rock / 6-5 special / Four brothers / Come go with me / Tequila / Hey daddy / Rock and roll blues / Rock around the island / I want you to be my baby / See you Friday / They call him Cliff / Time machine / Witch doctor.
Album: released on See For Miles, Jun'83 by Charly Records. Dist: Spartan

TWENTY TOP TWENTY TWISTS (Lang, Don & The Twisters).
Album: released on See For Miles, Dec'84 by Charly Records. Dist: Spartan

Lang, Eddie
EDDIE LANG & LONNIE JOHNSON VOL.1.
Album: released on Swaggie (Australia), Jan'83

EDDIE LANG & LONNIE JOHNSON VOL.2.
Album: released on Swaggie (Australia), Jan'83

Langer, Clive
EVEN THOUGH.
Single (7"): released on Creation, Jun'87 Dist: Rough Trade, Cartel

I WANT THE WHOLE WORLD (Langer, Clive/The Boxes).
Album: released on Radar, May'79 by WEA Music Ltd. Dist: WEA, PRT

SPLASH (Langer, Clive/The Boxes).
Album:

Lange, Stevie
DON'T WANT TO CRY NO MORE.
Single (7"): released on Jive, Aug'83 by Zomba Records. Dist: RCA, PRT, ARA

REMEMBER MY NAME.
Single (7"): released on RCA, Nov'81 by RCA Records. Dist: RCA, Roots, Swift, Wellard, Chris, I & B, Solomon & Peres Distribution

Langford, Bonnie
JUST ONE KISS.
Single (7"): released on Tembo, Nov'84 by Tembo (Canada). Dist: IMS Distribution, Polygram Distribution

Lang, Gabby
1,2,3 O'CLOCK.
Single (7"): released on Excalibur, Feb'84 by Red Bus Records. Dist: PRT

Single (12"): released on Excalibur, Feb'84 by Red Bus Records. Dist: PRT

Langholm Town Band
MELODIES FROM THE MUCKLE TOON.
Album: released on Lake, Oct'80 by Fellside Recordings. Dist: Jazz Music, Fellside

Lang, K.D.
ANGELS WITH A LARIOT (Lang, K.D. & The Reclines).
Album: released on Warner Brothers, Feb'87 by Warner Bros Records. Dist: WEA

Cassette: released on Warner Brothers, Feb'87 by Warner Bros Records. Dist: WEA

Langley, Gerard
SIAMESE BOYFRIENDS (Langley, Gerard & Ian Kearey).
Album: released on Fire, Feb'87 by Twist and Shout Music. Dist: Nine Mile, Rough Trade, Cartel

Langley, Jerry
CHASING MY MOUTH AGAIN.
Single (7"): released on Monarch, Oct'82 by Chart Records. Dist: Pinnacle

Langleys
I'LL NEVER LET YOU DOWN AGAIN.
Single (7"): released on Triangle, Aug'85 by Triangle Records. Dist: Pinnacle

Lang, Peter
LEO KOTTKE WITH PETER LANG & JOHN FAHEY (see Kottke, Leo with Peter Lang & John Fahey).

Langstaff, John
AMERICAN & BRITISH FOLKSONGS.
Album: released on Tradition, Nov'74 Dist: JSU, Cassion Distribution, Celtic Music, Jazz Music, Projection, Roots Records

Lang, Thomas
HAPPY MAN (THE).
Tracks: / Happy man (The) / Envy / Injury / Logic / Sympathy / Sleep with me.
Single (12"): released on Epic, Mar'87 by CBS Records. Dist: CBS

Single (7"): released on Epic, May'87 by CBS Records. Dist: CBS

ME AND MRS JONES.
Tracks: / Me and Mrs Jones / Shoelaces.
Single (7"): released on Epic, Jul'87 by CBS Records. Dist: CBS

Single (12"): released on Epic, Jul'87 by CBS Records. Dist: CBS

Compact disc single: released on Epic, Jul'87 by CBS Records. Dist: CBS

SCALLYWAG JAZZ.
Tracks: / Fingers and thumbs / Happy man, The / Boys prefer / Me & Mrs Jones / Scallywag jaz / Shoelaces (Mrs Jones Part 2) / Strength / Sleep with me / Spirit / Injury.
Album: released on Epic, Jul'87 by CBS Records. Dist: CBS

Cassette: released on Epic, Jul'87 by CBS Records. Dist: CBS

Compact disc: released on Epic, Jul'87 by CBS Records. Dist: CBS

Compact disc: released on Epic, Aug'87 by CBS Records. Dist: CBS

Langton, Lloyd Group
DREAMS THAT FADE AWAY.
Single (7"): released on Albion, Jul'84 by Albion Records. Dist: Spartan, Pinnacle

OUTSIDE THE LAW.
Tracks: / Outside the law / Fire to four / Talk to you / Rocky paths / Space chase / Waiting for tomorrow / Mask of pain / Psydelic warlords.
Album: released on Flicknife, Dec'83 by Flicknife Records. Dist: Spartan

WIND OF CHANGE.
Single (7"): released on Flicknife, Jul'83 by Flicknife Records. Dist: Spartan

Language
WE'RE CELEBRATING.
Single (7"): released on Stiff, Mar'83 by Stiff Records. Dist: EMI, Record Services Distribution (Ireland)

Single (12"): released on Stiff, Mar'83 by Stiff Records. Dist: EMI, Record Services Distribution (Ireland)

Language courses
DAILY EXPRESS LANGUAGE COURSES (see under individual language, eg.Spanish).

LANGUAGE COURSE - AFRIKAANS (Linguaphone).
Boxed set: released on Linguaphone, Apr'82

LANGUAGE COURSE - AN ENGLISH CHILD IN FRANCE Beuret.
Cassette: released on Beuret Aug'83

LANGUAGE COURSE - ARABIC (Berlitz).

LANGUAGE COURSE - ARABIC (MODERN STANDARD) (Linguaphone).
Boxed set: released on Linguaphone, Apr'82

LANGUAGE COURSE - BUONGIORNO ITALIA BBC Publications.
Triple album / cassette: released on BBC Publications, Jun'83 Dist: Record and Tape Sales Distribution, Taylor, H.R., Solomon & Peres Distribution

Triple album / cassette: released on BBC Publications, Jun'83 Dist: Record and Tape Sales Distribution, Taylor, H.R., Solomon & Peres Distribution

LANGUAGE COURSE - CANTONESE (Teach yourself series) (Linguaphone).
Boxed set: released on Linguaphone, Apr'82

LANGUAGE COURSE - CHINESE (MANDARIN) (Linguaphone).
Boxed set: released on Linguaphone, Apr'82

LANGUAGE COURSE - CHINESE (Berlitz).

LANGUAGE COURSE - CZECH (Teach yourself series) (Linguaphone).
Boxed set: released on Linguaphone, Apr'82

LANGUAGE COURSE - DANISH (Linguaphone).
Boxed set: released on Linguaphone, Apr'82

LANGUAGE COURSE - DANISH (Teach yourself series) (Linguaphone).
Boxed set: released on Linguaphone, Apr'82

LANGUAGE COURSE - DIGAME BBC Publications.
Double Album: released on BBC Publications, Jun'83 Dist: Record and Tape Sales Distribution, Taylor, H.R., Solomon & Peres Distribution
Album: released on BBC Publications, Jun'83 Dist: Record and Tape Sales Distribution, Taylor, H.R., Solomon & Peres Distribution

Double cassette: released on BBC Publications, Jun'83 Dist: Record and Tape Sales Distribution, Taylor, H.R., Solomon & Peres Distribution

Cassette: released on BBC Publications, Jun'83 Dist: Record and Tape Sales Distribution, Taylor, H.R., Solomon & Peres Distribution

LANGUAGE COURSE - DUTCH (Linguaphone).
Boxed set: released on Linguaphone Apr'82

LANGUAGE COURSE - ENGLISH ('Audio active' course) (Linguaphone).
Boxed set: released on Linguaphone, Apr'82

LANGUAGE COURSE - ENSEMBLE BBC Publications.
Double Album: released on BBC Publications, Jun'83 Dist: Record and Tape Sales Distribution, Taylor, H.R., Solomon & Peres Distribution

Double cassette: released on BBC Publications, Jun'83 Dist: Record and Tape Sales Distribution, Taylor, H.R., Solomon & Peres Distribution

LANGUAGE COURSE - ENGLISH (ADVANCED) (Linguaphone).
Boxed set: released on Linguaphone, Apr'82

LANGUAGE COURSE - ENGLISH (INTERMEDIATE) (Linguaphone).
Boxed set: released on Linguaphone, Apr'82

LANGUAGE COURSE - ENGLISH (AS A FOREIGN LANGUAGE) (Linguaphone).
Boxed set: released on Linguaphone, Apr'82

LANGUAGE COURSE - FINNISH (Linguaphone).
Boxed set: released on Linguaphone, Apr'82

LANGUAGE COURSE - FRENCH ('Audio active' course) (Linguaphone).
Boxed set: released on Linguaphone, Apr'82

LANGUAGE COURSE - FRENCH ('Linguavision') (Linguaphone).
Special: released on Linguaphone, May'83

LANGUAGE COURSE - FRENCH (ROAD TO) (Linguaphone).
Cassette: released on Linguaphone, Apr'82

LANGUAGE COURSE - FRENCH AT HOME Harraps.
Boxed set: released on Harrap Languages, Apr'83

LANGUAGE COURSE - FRENCH (Travel pack) (Linguaphone).
Boxed set: released on Linguaphone, Apr'82

LANGUAGE COURSE - FRENCH (Berlitz).

LANGUAGE COURSE - FRENCH (Linguaphone).
Boxed set: released on Linguaphone, Apr'82

LANGUAGE COURSE - FRENCH (Sonodisc courses) (Linguaphone).
Boxed set: released on Linguaphone, Apr'82

LANGUAGE COURSE - FRENCH ('Breakthrough') (Pan).
Special: released on Pan, Dec'82

LANGUAGE COURSE - GET BY IN PORTUGUESE BBC Publications.
Cassette: released on BBC Publications, Jun'83 Dist: Record and Tape Sales Distribution, Taylor, H.R., Solomon & Peres Distribution

LANGUAGE COURSE - GERMAN (Linguaphone).
Boxed set: released on Linguaphone, Apr'82

LANGUAGE COURSE - GERMAN ('Breakthrough') (Pan).
Special: released on Pan, Dec'82

LANGUAGE COURSE - GERMAN, ROAD TO (Linguaphone).
Cassette: released on Linguaphone, Jul'82

LANGUAGE COURSE - GERMAN (Travel pack) (Linguaphone).
Boxed set: released on Linguaphone, Apr'82

LANGUAGE COURSE - GERMAN (Sonodisc courses) (Linguaphone).
Boxed set: released on Linguaphone, Apr'82

LANGUAGE COURSE - GET BY IN GREEK BBC Publications.
Cassette: released on BBC Publications, Jun'83 Dist: Record and Tape Sales Distribution, Taylor, H.R., Solomon & Peres Distribution

LANGUAGE COURSE - GET BY IN ITALIAN BBC Publications.
Cassette: released on BBC Publications, Jun'83 Dist: Record and Tape Sales Distribution, Taylor, H.R., Solomon & Peres Distribution

LANGUAGE COURSE - GERMAN ('Audio active' course) (Linguaphone).
Boxed set: released on Linguaphone, Apr'82

LANGUAGE COURSE - GET BY IN FRENCH BBC Publications.
Cassette: released on BBC Publications, Jun'83 Dist: Record and Tape Sales Distribution, Taylor, H.R., Solomon & Peres Distribution

LANGUAGE COURSE - GERMAN (Berlitz).

LANGUAGE COURSE - GET BY IN SPANISH BBC Publications.
Cassette: released on BBC Publications, Jun'83 Dist: Record and Tape Sales Distribution, Taylor, H.R., Solomon & Peres Distribution

LANGUAGE COURSE - GREEK (MODERN) (Linguaphone).
Boxed set: released on Linguaphone, Apr'82
Cat. no: No catalogue name

LANGUAGE COURSE - GREEK ('Breakthrough') (Pan).
Special: released on Pan, Dec'82
Cat. no: No catalogue number

LANGUAGE COURSE - GREAT BRITAIN (Berlitz).

LANGUAGE COURSE - GREEK (Berlitz).

LANGUAGE COURSE - HEBREW (MODERN) (Linguaphone).
Boxed set: released on Linguaphone, Apr'82
Cat. no: No catalogue number

LANGUAGE COURSE - HINDI (Linguaphone).
Boxed set: released on Linguaphone, Apr'82
Cat. no: No catalogue number

LANGUAGE COURSE - HONG KONG (Berlitz).

LANGUAGE COURSE - HUNGARIAN (Berlitz).

LANGUAGE COURSE - ICELANDIC (Linguaphone).
Boxed set: released on Linguaphone, Apr'82
Cat. no: No catalogue number

LANGUAGE COURSE - IMPROVE YOUR FRENCH Harraps.
Boxed set: released on Harrap Languages, Apr'83

LANGUAGE COURSE - IRISH (Linguaphone).

Boxed set: released on Linguaphone, Apr'82

LANGUAGE COURSE - ITALIAN ('Breakthrough') (Pan).
Special: released on Pan, Dec'82

LANGUAGE COURSE - ITALIAN (Berlitz).

LANGUAGE COURSE - ITALIAN (Linguaphone).
Boxed set: released on Linguaphone, Apr'82

LANGUAGE COURSE - ITALIAN (Travel pack) (Linguaphone).
Boxed set: released on Linguaphone, Apr'82

LANGUAGE COURSE - JAPANESE (Teach yourself series) (Linguaphone).
Boxed set: released on Linguaphone, Apr'82

LANGUAGE COURSE - JAPANESE (Berlitz).

LANGUAGE COURSE - JAPANESE (Linguaphone).
Boxed set: released on Linguaphone, Apr'82

LANGUAGE COURSE - KEIN PROBLEM BBC Publications.
Double Album: released on BBC Publications, Jun'83 Dist: Record and Tape Sales Distribution, Taylor, H.R., Solomon & Peres Distribution

Double cassette: released on BBC Publications, Jun'83 Dist: Record and Tape Sales Distribution, Taylor, H.R., Solomon & Peres Distribution

LANGUAGE COURSE - LAZY LANGUAGES.
Special: released on Lazy Languages, Apr'82 Dist: H.R. Taylor, Bond Street Music

LANGUAGE COURSE - LATIN AMERICAN (Berlitz).

LANGUAGE COURSE - L'ITALIA DAL VIVO BBC Publications.
Triple album / cassette: released on BBC Publications, Jun'83 Dist: Record and Tape Sales Distribution, Taylor, H.R., Solomon & Peres Distribution

Triple album / cassette: released on BBC Publications, Jun'83 Dist: Record and Tape Sales Distribution, Taylor, H.R., Solomon & Peres Distribution

LANGUAGE COURSE - MAKE SENTENCES IN FRENCH 2 Beuret.
Cassette: released on Beuret, Aug'83

LANGUAGE COURSE - MAKE SENTENCES IN FRENCH 1 Beuret.
Cassette: released on Beuret, Aug'83

LANGUAGE COURSE - MALAY (BAHASA MALAYSIA) (Linguaphone).
Boxed set: released on Linguaphone, Apr'82

LANGUAGE COURSE - MEXICAN (Berlitz).

LANGUAGE COURSE - NORWEGIAN (Linguaphone).
Boxed set: released on Linguaphone, Apr'82

LANGUAGE COURSE - PERSIAN (Teach yourself series) (Linguaphone).
Boxed set: released on Linguaphone, Apr'82

LANGUAGE COURSE - PORTUGUESE (Linguaphone).
Boxed set: released on Linguaphone, Apr'82

LANGUAGE COURSE - PORTUGESE (Berlitz).

LANGUAGE COURSE - POLISH (Linguaphone).
Boxed set: released on Linguaphone, Apr'82

LANGUAGE COURSE - POLISH (Berlitz).

LANGUAGE COURSE - RUSSIAN (Linguaphone).
Boxed set: released on Linguaphone, Apr'82

LANGUAGE COURSE - RUSSIAN (Berlitz).

LANGUAGE COURSE - RUSSIAN LANGUAGE & PEOPLE BBC Publications.
Double Album: released on BBC Publications, Jun'83 Dist: Record and Tape Sales Distribution, Taylor, H.R., Solomon & Peres Distribution

Double cassette: released on BBC Publications, Jun'83 Dist: Record and Tape Sales Distribution, Taylor, H.R., Solomon & Peres Distribution

LANGUAGE COURSE - SERBO-CROAT (Linguaphone).
Boxed set: released on Linguaphone, Apr'82

LANGUAGE COURSE - SINGAPORE (Berlitz).

LANGUAGE COURSE - SPANISH (Sonodisc course) (Linguaphone).
Boxed set:

LANGUAGE COURSE - SPANISH (LATIN-AMERICAN) (Linguaphone).
Boxed set: released on Linguaphone, Apr'82

LANGUAGE COURSE - SPANISH ('Audio active' course) (Linguaphone).
Boxed set: released on Linguaphone, Apr'82

LANGUAGE COURSE - SPANISH (ROAD TO) (Linguaphone).
Cassette: released on Linguaphone, Jul'82

LANGUAGE COURSE - SPANISH (Travel pack) (Linguaphone).
Boxed set: released on Linguaphone, Apr'82

LANGUAGE COURSE - SPANISH (CASTILIAN) (Linguaphone).
Boxed set: released on Linguaphone, Apr'82

LANGUAGE COURSE - SPANISH (Berlitz).

LANGUAGE COURSE - SPANISH ('Breakthrough') (Pan).
Special: released on Pan, Dec'82

LANGUAGE COURSE - SUR LE VIF BBC Publications.
Double Album: released on BBC Publications, Jun'83 Dist: Record and Tape Sales Distribution, Taylor, H.R., Solomon & Peres Distribution

Double cassette: released on BBC Publications, Jun'83 Dist: Record and Tape Sales Distribution, Taylor, H.R., Solomon & Peres Distribution

LANGUAGE COURSE - SWISS (Berlitz).

LANGUAGE COURSE - SWAHILI (Teach yourself series) (Linguaphone).
Boxed set: released on Linguaphone, Apr'82

LANGUAGE COURSE - SWAHILI (Berlitz).

LANGUAGE COURSE - SWEDISH (Linguaphone).
Boxed set: released on Linguaphone, Apr'82

LANGUAGE COURSE - THAILAND (Berlitz).

LANGUAGE COURSE - TURKISH (Berlitz).

LANGUAGE COURSE - WELSH (Linguaphone).
Boxed set: released on Linguaphone, Apr'82

Language From Memory

FORTUNE.
Single (7"): released on Towerbell, Jan'82 by Towerbell Records. Dist: EMI

Language Learning

LANGUAGE LEARNING Programmed instruction language learning.
Album: released on P.I.L.L., '75

Lanier & Co.

DANCING IN THE NIGHT.
Tracks: / Dancing in the night / Dancing in the night (inst).
Single (7"): released on Syncopate, 20 Jun'87 by EMI Records. Dist: EMI

Single (12"): released on Syncopate, 20 Jun'87 by EMI Records. Dist: EMI

I DON'T KNOW WHAT TO DO ABOUT YOU.
Tracks: / I don't know what to do about you.
Single (12"): released on Charly, Mar'87 by Charly Records. Dist: Charly, Cadillac

Lankchan, Hip

HIP LANKCHAN.
Album: released on JSP, Mar'82 by JSP Records. Dist: Swift, Projection

Lankester Brisley, Joyce

BEST OF MILLY MOLLY MANDY, THE.
Tracks: / Milly Molly Mandy And Dum Dum / Milly Molly Mandy finds a train / Milly Molly Mandy and the gang / Milly Molly Mandy goes sledging.
Cassette: released on Tellastory, Dec'86 by Bartlett Bliss Productions. Dist: PRT Distribution, Hayward Promotions Distribution, H.R. Taylor Distribution

MILLY MOLLY MANDY.
Tracks: / Milly Molly Mandy Has an adventure / Milly Molly Mandy and the golden wedding / Milly Molly Mandy acts for the pictures / Milly Molly Mandy finds a parcel.
Cassette: released on Tellastory, Dec'86 by Bartlett Bliss Productions. Dist: PRT Distribution, Hayward Promotions Distribution, H.R. Taylor Distribution

Lanphere, Don

STOP.
Album: released on Hep, Mar'87 by H.R. Taylor Records. Dist: Jazz Music, Cadillac Music, JSU, Taylors, Wellard, Chris, Zodiac, Swift, Fast Forward

Lanphere, Don Quintet

DON LOVES MIDGE.
Album: released on Hep, Aug'85 by H.R. Taylor Records. Dist: Jazz Music, Cadillac Music, JSU, Taylors, Wellard, Chris, Zodiac, Swift, Fast Forward

OUT OF NOWHERE.
Album: released on Hep, Aug'83 by H.R. Taylor Records. Dist: Jazz Music, Cadillac Music, JSU, Taylors, Wellard, Chris, Zodiac, Swift, Fast Forward

Lantier, Jack

FEMMES QUE VOUS ETES JOLIES.
Compact disc: released on Vogue, Jan'86 Dist: Discovery, Jazz Music, PRT, Swift

Lanza, Mario

20 GOLDEN FAVOURITES.
Album: released on RCA, '84 by RCA Records. Dist: RCA, Roots, Swift, Wellard, Chris, I & B, Solomon & Peres Distribution

Cassette: released on RCA, '84 by RCA Records. Dist: RCA, Roots, Swift, Wellard, Chris, I & B, Solomon & Peres Distribution

AN EVENING WITH MARIO LANZA.
Album: released on RCA/Camden, Apr'81

Cassette: released on RCA/Camden, Apr'81

ART & VOICE OF MARIO LANZA.
Triple album / cassette: released on Red Seal, '73 by RCA Records. Dist: RCA

BROADWAY HITS.
Album: released on RCA (Germany), '83

CHRISTMAS CAROLS.
Album: released on RCA, Nov'83 by RCA Records. Dist: RCA, Roots, Swift, Wellard, Chris, I & B, Solomon & Peres Distribution

Cassette: released on RCA, Nov'83 by RCA Records. Dist: RCA, Roots, Swift, Wellard, Chris, I & B, Solomon & Peres Distribution

CHRISTMAS HYMNS AND CAROLS.
Album: released on Pickwick, Oct'79 by Pickwick Records. Dist: Pickwick Distribution, Prism Leisure Distribution, Lugtons

Cassette: released on RCA Camden, '75 by RCA Records. Dist: Pickwick Distribution, Taylor, H.R.

COLLECTION: MARIO LANZA.
Boxed set: released on Red Seal, Nov'82 by RCA Records. Dist: RCA

Double Album: released on Cambra, Mar'85 by Cambra Records. Dist: IDS, Conifer

Double cassette: released on Cambra, Mar'85 by Cambra Records. Dist: IDS, Conifer

EXCLUSIVO.
Album: released on RCA (Brazil), Jan'84

Cassette: released on RCA (Brazil), Jan'84

FOREVER.
Tracks: / September song / Marachiare / Song of India / Day in day out / Song is you / Beloved / La danza / Mattinata / Maria mari / Guadeamus igitur / Thrill is gone / My romance / Rose Marie / Long ago / Falling in love with you / I'll be seeing you / Younger than springtime / Among my souvenirs.

HIS GREATEST HITS FROM OPERETTAS AND MUSICALS - VOL.III.
Album: released on RCA Classics, Aug'81

Cassette: released on RCA Classics, Aug'81 Deleted '85.

HIS GREATEST HITS FROM OPERETTAS AND MUSICALS - VOL.II.
Album: released on RCA Classics, Aug'81

Cassette: released on RCA Classics, Aug'81 Deleted '85.

I'LL SEE YOU IN MY DREAMS.
Album: released on Deja Vu, Oct'83 by Deja Vu Records. Dist: Counterpoint Distribution, Record Services Distribution (Ireland)

Cassette: released on Deja Vu, Oct'83 by Deja Vu Records. Dist: Counterpoint Distribution, Record Services Distribution (Ireland)

I'LL WALK WITH GOD.
Album: released on Red Seal, '74 by RCA Records. Dist: RCA

LEGENDARY MARIO LANZA, THE.
Album: released on K-Tel, Aug'81 by K-Tel Records. Dist: Record Merchandisers Distribution, Taylors, Terry Blood Distribution, Wynd-Up Distribution, Relay Distribution, Pickwick Distribution, Solomon & Peres Distribution, Polygram

Cassette: released on K-Tel, Aug'81 by K-Tel Records. Dist: Record Merchandisers Distribution, Taylors, Terry Blood Distribution, Wynd-Up Distribution, Relay Distribution, Pickwick Distribution, Solomon & Peres Distribution, Polygram

MAGIC MOMENTS WITH MARIO LANZA.
Cassette: released on RCA, May'85 by RCA Records. Dist: RCA, Roots, Swift, Wellard, Chris, I & B, Solomon & Peres Distribution

MARIO LANZA.
Double Album: released on Cambra, Aug'83 by Cambra Records. Dist: IDS, Conifer

Double cassette: released on Cambra, Aug'83 by Cambra Records. Dist: IDS, Conifer

PURE GOLD.
Album: released on RCA International, Apr'80

Cassette: released on RCA International, '84

SINGS OPERAS GREATEST HITS.
Double Album: released on Red Seal, '74 by RCA Records. Dist: RCA

STUDENT PRINCE, THE.
Album: released on RCA Classics, Aug'81

Cassette: released on RCA Classics, Aug'81

YOU DO SOMETHING TO ME.
Album: released on RCA Camden, '69 by RCA Records. Dist: Pickwick Distribution, Taylor, H.R.

Lanz, David

HEARTSOUNDS.
Album: released on Narada (Holland), Dec'84

Cassette: released on Narada (Holland), Dec'84

Lapotaire, Jane

I'LL PUT YOU TOGETHER AGAIN.
Single (7"): released on DJM, Nov'83 by DJM Records. Dist: CBS, Polygram

Laraaji

DAY OF RADIANCE.
Album: released on E.G., Jan'87 by Virgin Records. Dist: Virgin, EMI

Lara, Derek

COME ON OVER.
Single (12"): released on Plantation, Jan'82 Dist: Jetstar

HELLO STRANGER.
Single (7"): released on Pama, Nov'82 by Pama Records. Dist: Pama, Enterprise, Jetstar

Lara, Jennifer

BE YOUR LADY.
Tracks: / Be your lady / My man.
Single (12"): released on Uptempo, Nov'86 by Uptempo Records. Dist: Jetstar Distribution

ISLANDS IN THE STREAM (Lara, Jennifer & Delroy Wilson).

ROOTS DAUGHTER.
Single (12"): released on Londisc, Sep'84 by Londisc Records.

Larcarnge

LARCARNGE PLAYS AZNAVOUR (Larcarnge & Roland Shaw Orchestra).
Tracks: / Old fashioned way, The / Take me with you / Yesterday / Je taime / Whole world is singing my love, The / She / You've let yourself go / What makes a man / Love is new / To die of love / La boheme.

Larcarnge, Maurice

ACCORDEON AU SOLEILNET.
Album: released on ARC (Accordion Records), '84 Dist: Accordion Record Club

ACCORDEON TRADITIONNEL.
Album: released on ARC (Accordion Records), '84 Dist: Accordion Record Club

C'EST FETE A L'ACCORDEON.
Tracks: / Retour de biarritz / Seville en fete / La star musette / Valse Africaine / Le tango tango / Grisonnants / Accordeon super boogie / C'est la fete a l'accordeon / Echo montagnard / Le marin a casquette / Vichy musette / Souvenir paternel.

LARCANGE PLAYS TRENET (Larcarnge & Roland Shaw Orchestra).
Album: released on ARC (Accordion Records), '84 Dist: Accordion Record Club

Page 584

MARTELETTE.
Album: released on ARC (Accordion Records), '84 Dist: Accordion Record Club

MES TITRES EN OR.
Tracks: / Accordeon rockers / Pistonette / Perles de cristal / C'est ma marseillaise / Drole de rigolade / Reve de ballerine / Capricieusette / Accordeon steeple / Retour de biarritz / Accordeon dance / Operamusette.

PARIS ACCORDIONS.
Cassette: released on Gold Crown, Sep'79 by Decca Records. Dist: Polygram

Album: released on Gold Crown, Sep'79 by Decca Records. Dist: Polygram

SALUT L'ACCORDEON.
Tracks: / Operamusette / Oh un tango disco / Petite marquise / J'ai besoin de toi / La vie n'est pas foutue / Surprise polka / Vacances parade / Nostalgia printaniere / Ouvrir les yeux / Balapapa / Caroline / Belinda.

Largo
LARGO (Various Artists).
Notes: Double album and cassette.
Album: released on TM, May'87 by TM Records. Dist: PRT Distribution

Cassette: released on TM, May'87 by TM Records. Dist: PRT Distribution

Largo, Hugo
DRUM.
Album: released on Relativity (USA), Aug'87 Dist: Pinnacle

Laria, A.J.
A.J. LARIA AND WYNTON MARSALIS (Laria. A.J./Wynton Marsalis).
Cassette: released on Nola, Mar'87 Dist: JSU, Jazz Music, Cadillac, Chris Wellard

Lariat, Lash
BITTER TEARS (Lariat, Lash & The Long Riders).
Album: released on Big Beat, Mar'85 by Ace Records. Dist: Projection, Pinnacle

DOLE QUEUE BLUES (Lariat, Lash & The Long Riders).
Single (7"): released on Big Beat, Nov'85 by Ace Records. Dist: Projection, Pinnacle

Single (12"): released on Big Beat, Nov'85 by Ace Records. Dist: Projection, Pinnacle

Larkins, Ellis
SWINGING FOR HAMP (Larkins, Ellis/Tony Middleton).
Album: released on Concord Jazz, Nov'80 by Concord Jazz Records (USA). Dist: IMS, Polygram

Larkins, Percy
MUSIC OF PASSION (7").
Single (7"): released on Move, Jun'85 by Charly Records. Dist: Charly Distribution, Fast Forward Distribution, Cartel Distribution

MUSIC OF PASSION(LP).
Album: released on Move, Jul'85 by Charly Records. Dist: Charly Distribution, Fast Forward Distribution, Cartel Distribution

Lark In The Clear Air
LARK IN THE CLEAR AIR various artists (Various Artists).
Album: released on Topic, '81 Dist: Roots Distribution

Lark Rise To Candleford
LARK RISE TO CANDLEFORD (A country tapestry). (Various Artists).
Album: released on Charisma, Sep'83 by Virgin Records. Dist: EMI

Larks
ALL OR NOTHING GIRL.
Tracks: / All or nothing girl / Whatever you say / Parents:teachers *

BILLY GRAHAM.
Tracks: / Billy Graham / Maggie, Maggie, Maggie / Phantom of the bingo hall* / Larking with the larks

PAIN IN THE NECK.
Tracks: / Pain in the neck / Clean boy.
Single (7"): released on Exaltation, Feb'87 Dist: Pinnacle

Single (12"): released on Exaltation, Feb'87 Dist: Pinnacle

L'Armour, Gina
I'M GONNA MAKE YOU WANT ME.
Single (7"): released on Calibre, Aug'85 by Calibre Records. Dist: PRT

Single (12"): released on Calibre, Aug'85 by Calibre Records. Dist: PRT

Larner, Sam
GARLAND FOR SAM.
Album: released on Topic, '81 Dist: Roots Distribution

La Rock, Scott
CRIMINAL MINDED.
Compact disc: released on Westside, Aug'87 by Streetsounds Records. Dist: BMG

CRIMINAL MINDED (La Rock, Scott & Blastmaster KRS 1L).
Album: released on Westside, Aug'87 by Streetsounds Records. Dist: BMG

Cassette: released on Westside, Aug'87 by Streetsounds Records. Dist: BMG

La Rock, T
MIRACLE KING.
Album: released on 10, 30 May'87 by 10 Records. Dist: Virgin, EMI

Cassette: released on 10, 30 May'87 by 10 Records. Dist: Virgin, EMI

La Rose, Judy
LITTLE BIT OF LOVE.
Tracks: / Little bit of love / Little bit of love (Dub mix).
Single (7"): released on Champion, Nov'86 by Champion Records. Dist: RCA

Single (12"): released on Champion, Nov'86 by Champion Records. Dist: RCA

Larou, Lash
DON'T DRIVE DRUNK.
Single (12"): released on John Dread Production, Nov'85 Dist: Jetstar

Larry & Alvin
THROW ME.
Single (12"): released on Greensleeves, Sep'84 by Greensleeves Records. Dist: BMG, Jetstar, Spartan

Larry & The Blue Notes
MAJOR BILL TAPES - SIXTIES PUNK VOL.1.
Album: released on Big Beat, Oct'85 by Ace Records. Dist: Projection, Pinnacle

Larsen, Morton Gunnar
PLAYS ROBERTO CLEMENTINE....
Notes: Plays Roberto Clementine/ Poor Jimmy Green and Other Jazz Ragtime Compositions.

Larson, Claude
HIGH-TEC.
Album: released on Intersound, Dec'86 by Intersound Records. Dist: Jazz Music

Larson, Nicolette
FOOL ME AGAIN.
Single (7"): released on Warner Brothers, Mar'82 by Warner Bros Records. Dist: WEA

IN THE NICK OF TIME.
Album: released on Warner Brothers, Jan'80 by Warner Bros Records. Dist: WEA

NICOLETTE.
Album: released on Warner Brothers, '78 by Warner Bros Records. Dist: WEA

RADIOLAND.
Album: released on Warner Brothers, Jan'81 by Warner Bros Records. Dist: WEA

SAY WHEN.
Album:

Cassette:

YOU CAN'T SAY YOU DON'T LOVE ME ANYMORE.
Single (7"):

Lasalle, Denise
COME TO BED.
Single (7"): released on Malaco, May'83 by Malaco Records. Dist: Charly

Single (12"): released on Malaco, May'83 by Malaco Records. Dist: Charly

LADY IN THE STREET, A.
Album: released on Malaco, May'83 by Malaco Records. Dist: Charly

Cassette: released on Malaco, May'83 by Malaco Records. Dist: Charly

MY TOOT TOOT.
Album: released on Epic, Aug'85 by CBS Rec-

---

ords. Dist: CBS

Cassette: released on Epic, Aug'85 by CBS Records. Dist: CBS Deleted '87.

RAIN AND FIRE.
Tracks: / It be's that way sometimes / I'm sho gonna mess with yo man / What's goin' on in my house / Look what can happen to you... / Shame, shame, shame / Dip, bam, thank you maam / Learnin' how to cheat on you / Rain and fire / It takes you all night / Is he lovin' someone else tonight.

RIGHT PLACE, RIGHT TIME (Lasalle, Denise & Latimore).
Single (7"): released on Malaco, Jun'84 by Malaco Records. Dist: Charly

Single (12"): released on Malaco, Jun'84 by Malaco Records. Dist: Charly

Laser Reggae Hits
LASER REGGAE HITS Various artists (Various Artists).
Album: released on Blue Moon, Dec'82 by Magnum Music Group Ltd. PRT, Spartan

Lasha, Prince
INSIDE STORY.
Album: released on Enja (Germany), Jan'82 by Enja Records (W.Germany). Dist: Cadillac Music

JOURNEY TO ZOAR (Lasha, Prince & The Firebirds).
Album: released on Enja (Germany), Apr'82 by Enja Records (W.Germany). Dist: Cadillac Music

Lask
LASK, NICHOLS, BAUSCHULT.
Album: released on ECM (Germany), Apr'82 by ECM Records. Dist: IMS, Polygram, Virgin through EMI

SUCHT + ORDNUNG (Lask 2).
Album: released on ECM (Germany), Jun'84 by ECM Records. Dist: IMS, Polygram, Virgin through EMI

Lasley, David
WHERE DOES THE BOY HANG OUT?.
Single (7"): released on EMI America, Aug'84 by EMI Records. Dist: EMI

Single (7"): released on EMI America, '86 by EMI Records. Dist: EMI

La Sonora De Baru
RITMO TROPICAL.
Album: released on Globestyle, Jan'87 by Ace Records. Dist: Projection

L. A. Sounds
HITS HITS HITS.
Cassette: released on Chevron, Feb'85 Dist: Multiple Sound Distributors

HITS HITS HITS VOLUME 2.
Cassette: released on Chevron, Aug'85 Dist: Multiple Sound Distributors

WISHING YOU WERE HERE.
Cassette: released on Chevron, Feb'85 Dist: Multiple Sound Distributors

YOU TAKE ME UP.
Cassette: released on Chevron, Nov'84 Dist: Multiple Sound Distributors

L.A Splash
I DONT'T LIKE.
Single (7"): released on RCA, Apr'87 by RCA Records. Dist: RCA, Roots, Swift, Wellard, Chris, I & B, Solomon & Peres Distribution

Single (12"): released on RCA, Apr'87 by RCA Records. Dist: RCA, Roots, Swift, Wellard, Chris, I & B, Solomon & Peres Distribution

Lassiter
LASSITER Original soundtrack.
Album: released on That's Entertainment, Dec'84 by That's Entertainment Records. Dist: Pinnacle, PRT

Last Chant
RUN OF THE DOVE.
Single (7"): released on Chicken Jazz, Oct'81 by Chicken Jazz Records. Dist: Rough Trade

Last Dance
LAST DANCE Various Motown artists (Various Artists).
Album: released on Motown, Oct'81 by RCA Records. Dist: RCA Distribution

Cassette: released on Motown, Oct'81 by RCA Records. Dist: RCA Distribution

---

Last Dragon, The
LAST DRAGON, THE Original soundtrack.
Compact disc: by Motown Records. Dist: BMG Distribution

Last Few Days
PURE SPIRIT AND SALIVA LIVE.

Last Gang
SPIRIT OF YOUTH.
Single (7"): by Graduate Records. Dist: Nine Mile, Cartel

Last, James
ALL ABOARD WITH CAP'N JAMES.
Compact disc: by Polydor Records. Dist: Polygram, Polydor

Album: released on Polydor, Oct'84 by Polydor Records. Dist: Polygram, Polydor

Cassette: released on Polydor, Oct'84 by Polydor Records. Dist: Polygram, Polydor

Compact disc: released on Polydor, Oct'84 by Polydor Records. Dist: Polygram, Polydor

Album: released on Polydor (Germany), Sep'84 Dist: IMS-Polygram

Cassette: released on Polydor (Germany), Sep'84 Dist: IMS-Polygram

Compact disc: released on Polydor (Germany), Sep'84 Dist: IMS-Polygram

Album: released on Polydor (Germany), Jul'81 Dist: IMS-Polygram

Cassette: released on Polydor, Jul'81 by Polydor Records. Dist: Polygram, Polydor

AT ST. PATRICK'S CATHEDRAL, DUBLIN.
Compact disc: by Polydor Records. Dist: Polygram, Polydor

BEST FROM 150 GOLD, THE.
Album: released on Polydor, Aug'80 by Polydor Records. Dist: Polygram, Polydor

Cassette: released on Polydor, Aug'80 by Polydor Records. Dist: Polygram, Polydor

BISCAYA.
Compact disc: by Polydor Records. Dist: Polygram, Polydor

Album: released on Polydor (Germany), Jul'82 Dist: IMS-Polygram

Cassette: released on Polydor (Germany), Jul'82 Dist: IMS-Polygram

BLUEBIRD.
Compact disc: by Polydor Records. Dist: Polygram, Polydor

Cassette: released on Polydor, Nov'82 by Polydor Records. Dist: Polygram, Polydor

BY REQUEST.
Tracks: / Mornings at 7 (BBC ice skating theme) / Elvira Madigan (Dr Zhivago main theme) / Air that breathe (The) / Adagio from the New World Symphony / Lonely shepherd (The) / Roses of the south / Sabre dance / Lonely bull (The) / Tulips from Amsterdam / Seduction / Zipa dee doo dah / Spanish eyes / Valencia / That's life.
Notes: In 1967 James Last had his first chart album. Twenty years and 51 chart albums on, the phenomenon continues, with estimated worldwide sales of 45 million. With this 20th anniversary in mind, we have compiled this retrospective "By Request" album based on enquiries we constantly recieve, plus the most popular tracks chosen by his strong fan club.
Album: released on Polydor, Apr'87 by Polydor Records. Dist: Polygram, Polydor

Cassette: released on Polydor, Apr'87 by Polydor Records. Dist: Polygram, Polydor

Compact disc: released on Polydor, Apr'87 by Polydor Records. Dist: Polygram, Polydor

CARRIBEAN NIGHTS.
Album: released on Polydor, Oct'80 by Polydor Records. Dist: Polygram, Polydor

Cassette: released on Polydor, Oct'80 by Polydor Records. Dist: Polygram, Polydor

CHRISTMAS CLASSICS.
Compact disc: by Polydor Records. Dist: Polygram, Polydor

Album: released on Polydor, Nov'79 by Polydor Records. Dist: Polygram, Polydor

Cassette: released on Polydor, Nov'79 by Polydor Records. Dist: Polygram, Polydor

CHRISTMAS DANCING.
Compact disc: by Polydor Records. Dist: Polygram, Polydor

Album: released on Polydor (Germany), Nov'83 Dist: IMS-Polygram

Cassette: released on Polydor (Germany), Nov'83 Dist: IMS-Polygram

CHRISTMAS & JAMES LAST.
Album: released on Polydor, Nov'76 by Polydor Records. Dist: Polygram, Polydor

Cassette: released on Polydor, Nov'76 by Polydor Records. Dist: Polygram, Polydor

CHRISTMAS WITH JAMES LAST.
Tracks: / Frohliche weihnacht uberall / Suber glocke nie klingen / Schlittenfahrt zum weihnachtsmarkt / Die hirten / Ave Maria / Ofreude uber freude / In der Kathedrale / Heidsche bumbeidschi / Morgen, kinder, wird's was geben / Von himmel hoch / Stille nacht / Kirchenglocken zur weihnachtzeit.
Notes: Released for the german market last year, this extremely attractive collection of festive tunes will find a ready market amongst the UK James Last fans. Twelvesuperb tracks including 4 James Last original compositions.
Album: released on Polydor (Germany), Nov'86 Dist: IMS-Polygram

Cassette: released on Polydor (Germany), Nov'86 Dist: IMS-Polygram

Compact disc: released on Polydor (Germany), Nov'86 Dist: IMS-Polygram

CLASSICS UP TO DATE - VOL 3.
Compact disc: released on Polydor, Jul'84 by Polydor Records. Dist: Polygram, Polydor

CLASSICS UP TO DATE - VOL 2.
Cassette: released on Polydor, Nov'83 by Polydor Records. Dist: Polygram, Polydor

Compact disc: released on Polydor, Jul'84 by Polydor Records. Dist: Polygram, Polydor

CLASSICS UP TO DATE - VOL 5.
Compact disc: released on Polydor, Jul'84 by Polydor Records. Dist: Polygram, Polydor

CLASSICS UP TO DATE - VOL 1.
Cassette: released on Polydor, Nov'83 by Polydor Records. Dist: Polygram, Polydor

Compact disc: released on Polydor, Jul'84 by Polydor Records. Dist: Polygram, Polydor

CLASSICS UP TO DATE - VOL 4.
Compact disc: released on Polydor, Jul'84 by Polydor Records. Dist: Polygram, Polydor

CLASSICS UP TO DATE - VOL 6.
Tracks: / Eine kleine nachtmusik / Ballade / Sonata no.v cantible / Emperor quintet, The / Largo / Nordic ways / Allegro / Reverie / Presto / Theme from symphony no.1 promenade 9.
Cassette: released on Polydor, Jun'84 by Polydor Records. Dist: Polygram, Polydor

Compact disc: released on Polydor, Jun'84 by Polydor Records. Dist: Polygram, Polydor

CONCERT SUCCESSES.
Album: released on Polydor (Import), Mar'84

Cassette: released on Polydor (Import), Mar'84

COUNTRY & SQUARE DANCE PARTY.
Album: released on Polydor, Jan'74 by Polydor Records. Dist: Polygram, Polydor

Compact disc: released on Polydor, Sep'79 by Polydor Records. Dist: Polygram, Polydor

DE NEDERLANDSE SUCCESSEN.
Album: released on Polydor (Holland), Jul'84

Cassette: released on Polydor (Holland), Jul'84

DEUTSCHE VITA.
Notes: This album comprises of hits from the 50's, particularly those popular in Germany, with modern arrangements in the style of Whitney Houston and Matt bianco etc. An album produced for the German market but with good sales potential for the UK.

EVERYTHING COMES TO AN END ONLY A SAUSAGE HAS TWO.
Tracks: / Min hit heisst / Susi Schmidt / Aerobic erotic / Jenny Jones / Keine Sterne in anthem / Der Holzwurmblues / Alles hat ein ende nur die wurst hat zwei / Viva la Mexico / Ba-ba-bankuberfall / Lotti's loses lotterleben / Old MacDonald / Vampire (Venus) / Mein tuut tuut.
Album: released on Polydor (Germany), Apr'87 Dist: IMS-Polygram

Cassette: released on Polydor (Germany), Apr'87 Dist: IMS-Polygram

Compact disc: released on Polydor (Germany), Apr'87 Dist: IMS-Polygram

GALA.
Album: released on Polydor (Holland), Mar'87

Cassette: released on Polydor (Holland), Mar'87

GAMES THAT LOVERS PLAY.
Compact disc: by Polydor Records. Dist: Polygram, Polydor

Album: released on Polydor, Oct'84 by Polydor Records. Dist: Polygram, Polydor

Cassette: released on Polydor, Oct'84 by Polydor Records. Dist: Polygram, Polydor

GENTLEMAN OF MUSIC, THE.
Double Album: released on Polydor, Mar'83 by Polydor Records. Dist: Polygram, Polydor

Cassette: released on Polydor, Mar'83 by Polydor Records. Dist: Polygram, Polydor

HAMMOND A GO GO.
Compact disc: by Polydor Records. Dist: Polygram, Polydor

Cassette: released on Polydor, Oct'84 by Polydor Records. Dist: Polygram, Polydor

HANSIMANIA.
Album: released on Polydor, Nov'81 by Polydor Records. Dist: Polygram, Polydor

Cassette: released on Polydor, Nov'81 by Polydor Records. Dist: Polygram, Polydor

HAPPY CHRISTMAS WITH....
Album: released on Polydor (Germany), Nov'82 Dist: IMS-Polygram

Cassette: released on Polydor (Germany), Nov'82 Dist: IMS-Polygram

HAPPY LEHAR (Last, James Orchestra).
Cassette: released on Polydor, Oct'84 by Polydor Records. Dist: Polygram, Polydor

Compact disc: released on Polydor, Oct'84 by Polydor Records. Dist: Polygram, Polydor

HAPPY LEHAR.
Compact disc: by Polydor Records. Dist: Polygram, Polydor

IM ALLGAU (IN THE ALPS).
Tracks: / Polka party / Schnackl polka / Ich spiel fur mich / Der Lumpensammler / Auf dem hochsten berge / Frisch vom fass / Jodler / Wo der aurhahn baizt / De schean / Im schweinsgalopp / Schottisch / Frieden in den bergen / Der lustige fritz / Fesche jugend.
Notes: Digital stereo. This album features typical barbarian music using many traditional melodies played on typical instruments of the region.
Album: released on Polydor, Oct'84 by Polydor Records. Dist: Polygram, Polydor

Cassette: released on Polydor, Oct'84 by Polydor Records. Dist: Polygram, Polydor

Compact disc: released on Polydor, Oct'84 by Polydor Records. Dist: Polygram, Polydor

IN CONCERT.
Compact disc: by Polydor Records. Dist: Polygram, Polydor

IN RUSSIA.
Notes: Digital stereo.
Compact disc: released on Polydor, Aug'84 by Polydor Records. Dist: Polygram, Polydor
Cat. no: 821 113-2

INSTRUMENTALS FOR DANCING VOLS.1 & 2.
Double cassette: released on Polydor, Feb'83 by Polydor Records. Dist: Polygram, Polydor

INSTRUMENTALS IN LOVE VOLS.1 & 2.
Double cassette: released on Polydor, Feb'83 by Polydor Records. Dist: Polygram, Polydor

IN THE MOOD FOR TRUMPETS.
Compact disc: released on Polydor, Jul'84 by Polydor Records. Dist: Polygram, Polydor

JAMES LAST AT ST PATRICK'S CATHEDRAL, DUBLIN.
Tracks: / In the cathedral / Ave Maria / Conversation-Joseph Haydn trumpet concerto / An caoineadh / Scherzo from symphony no.2 / Away in the manger / Intermezzo of Notre Dame / Darkest midnight, The / Intermezzo from cavalleria rusticana / Holly and the ivy, The / Coulin / Seinn aililiu / Abide with me.
Notes: Digital stereo.

JAMES LAST AT ST.PATRICK'S CATHEDRAL DUBLIN.
Cassette: released on Polydor, Dec'84 by Polydor Records. Dist: Polygram, Polydor

Compact disc: released on Polydor, Dec'84 by Polydor Records. Dist: Polygram, Polydor

JAMES LAST IN CONCERT.
Album: released on Polydor, Oct'84 by Polydor Records. Dist: Polygram, Polydor

Cassette: released on Polydor, Oct'84 by Polydor Records. Dist: Polygram, Polydor

Compact disc: released on Polydor, Oct'84 by Polydor Records. Dist: Polygram, Polydor

JAMES LAST IN RUSSIA.
Album: released on Polydor, Oct'84 by Polydor Records. Dist: Polygram, Polydor

Cassette: released on Polydor, Oct'84 by Polydor Records. Dist: Polygram, Polydor

JAMES LAST IN SCOTLAND.
Album: released on Polydor, Nov'84 by Polydor Records. Dist: Polygram, Polydor Deleted Nov'84.

Cassette: released on Polydor, Nov'84 by Polydor Records. Dist: Polygram, Polydor

JAMES LAST LIVE IN LONDON.
Double Album: released on Polydor, Aug'78 by Polydor Records. Dist: Polygram, Polydor

JAMES LAST LIVE IN LONDON 78.
Cassette: released on Polydor, Jan'78 by Polydor Records. Dist: Polygram, Polydor

JAMES LAST PLAYS ROBERT STOLZ.
Tracks: / Two hearts in three - four time / My song of love / Love Vienna mine / Mood for lovers, The / Fair or dark, I love them all / You shall be king of my hearts / Say you, say you to me / You too / Goodbye / Spring time in Vienna / Gypsy violin / We are young, we are full of life / Charming weather / Where is it? / Earning for you / Vienna, where wine and waltz are flowing / Your eyes / Don't say goodbye / Come into the park of Sanssouci / Salome / Before my fathers house / Last rose is blooming, The.

JAMES LAST PLAYS THE GREATEAST SONGS OF THE BEATLES.
Tracks: / Eleanor Rigby / Hard day's night / Let it be / Penny Lane / She loves you / Michelle / Ob-la-di ob-la-dah / Hey Jude / Lady Madonna / All you need is love / Norwegian wood / Yesterday.

JAMES LAST - TANGO (Last, James Orchestra).
Album: released on Polydor, Aug'81 by Polydor Records. Dist: Polygram, Polydor

Cassette: released on Polydor, Aug'81 by Polydor Records. Dist: Polygram, Polydor

KAPT'N JAMES - TAKE ME WITH YOU.
Album: released on Polydor (Germany), Mar'83 Dist: IMS-Polygram

Cassette: released on Polydor (Germany), Mar'83 Dist: IMS-Polygram

LAST FOR EVER.
Double Album: released on Polydor, Oct'81 by Polydor Records. Dist: Polygram, Polydor

Double cassette: released on Polydor, Oct'81 by Polydor Records. Dist: Polygram, Polydor

LAST THE WHOLE NIGHT.
Album: released on Polydor, Aug'79 by Polydor Records. Dist: Polygram, Polydor

Cassette: released on Polydor, May'79 by Polydor Records. Dist: Polygram, Polydor

LEAVE THE BEST TO LAST.
Compact disc: by Polydor Records. Dist: Polygram, Polydor

Compact disc: released on Polydor, Sep'85 by Polydor Records. Dist: Polygram, Polydor

Album: released on Polydor, Sep'85 by Polydor Records. Dist: Polygram, Polydor

Cassette: released on Polydor, Sep'85 by Polydor Records. Dist: Polygram, Polydor

Compact disc: released on Polydor, Sep'85 by Polydor Records. Dist: Polygram, Polydor

LISTEN TO YOUR HEART (Last, James & Astrud Gilberto).
Tracks: / Listen to your heart / Champagne and Caviar.
Single (7"): released on Polydor, Jan'87 by Polydor Records. Dist: Polygram, Polydor

LONELY BULL, THE.
Tracks: / Lonely bull / Mornings at seven.
Single (7"): released on Polydor, Apr'87 by Polydor Records. Dist: Polygram, Polydor

MELODIES OF THE CENTURY.
Album: released on Polydor, Jun'82 by Polydor Records. Dist: Polygram, Polydor

Cassette: released on Polydor, Jun'82 by Polydor Records. Dist: Polygram, Polydor

MEMORIES OF RUSSIA.
Album: released on Polydor, Jan'74 by Polydor Records. Dist: Polygram, Polydor

MY FAVOURITE CLASSICS.
Album: released on Polydor, Apr'83 by Polydor Records. Dist: Polygram, Polydor

Cassette: released on Polydor, Apr'83 by Polydor Records. Dist: Polygram, Polydor

MY FAVOURITE FOLKSONGS.
Album: released on Polydor (Germany), Aug'83 Dist: IMS-Polygram

Cassette: released on Polydor (Germany), Aug'83 Dist: IMS-Polygram

MY FAVOURITE INSTRUMENTALS.
Album: released on Polydor, Apr'83 by Polydor Records. Dist: Polygram, Polydor

Cassette: released on Polydor, Apr'83 by Polydor Records. Dist: Polygram, Polydor

MY FAVOURITE LOVE SONGS.
Album: released on Polydor, Apr'83 by Polydor Records. Dist: Polygram, Polydor

Cassette: released on Polydor, Apr'83 by Polydor Records. Dist: Polygram, Polydor

MY FAVOURITE PARTY SONGS.
Cassette: released on Polydor, Apr'83 by Polydor Records. Dist: Polygram, Polydor

MY FAVOURITE ROMANTIC SONGS.
Cassette: released on Polydor, Apr'83 by Polydor Records. Dist: Polygram, Polydor

MY FAVOURITE SHANTIES.
Album: released on Polydor (Germany), Apr'83 Dist: IMS-Polygram

Cassette: released on Polydor (Germany), Apr'83 Dist: IMS-Polygram

MY FAVOURITE WORLD HITS.
Album: released on Polydor, Apr'83 by Polydor Records. Dist: Polygram, Polydor

Cassette: released on Polydor, Apr'83 by Polydor Records. Dist: Polygram, Polydor

NON STOP DANCING (83 party power).
Compact disc: released on Polydor, Sep'84 by Polydor Records. Dist: Polygram, Polydor

NON-STOP DANCING.
Compact disc: released on Polydor, Jan'83 by Polydor Records. Dist: Polygram, Polydor

NON STOP DANCING 18 (Last, James Orchestra).
Cassette: released on Polydor, Apr'77 by Polydor Records. Dist: Polygram, Polydor

NON STOP DANCING '85.
Tracks: / Reach out / Jump (for my love) / Dancing with tears in my eyes / Sad songs (say so much) / Such a shame / I won't let the sun go down on me / Magdalena / She bop / I just called to say I love you / Lonliness / Ghostbusters / Uauauaua / Catch me I'm falling / Oh Rosita / Wake me up before you go go / It's a hard life / Small town boy / Searchin' / Two tribes / When doves cry / 1,000 and 1 nights / Stuck on you / Exodus.
Album: released on Polydor, Feb'85 by Polydor Records. Dist: Polygram, Polydor

Cassette: released on Polydor, Feb'85 by Polydor Records. Dist: Polygram, Polydor

Compact disc: released on Polydor, Feb'85 by Polydor Records. Dist: Polygram, Polydor

NON STOP PARTY.
Album: released on Polydor, Aug'83 by Polydor Records. Dist: Polygram

Cassette: released on Polydor, Aug'83 by Polydor Records. Dist: Polygram

PARADISE.
Compact disc: by Polydor Records. Dist: Polygram, Polydor

Cassette: released on Polydor, Oct'84 by Polydor Records. Dist: Polygram, Polydor

PARTY POWER.
Tracks: / Best years of our lives, The / Shadows of the night / Hard to say I'm sorry / Eye of the tiger / Africa / Abracadabra / Words / Let's go dancing / Pass the dutchie / Sexual healing / Down under / Saddle up / Don't go.

PLUS (Last, James & Astrud Gilberto).
Tracks: / Samba do Soho / I'm nothing without you / Champlagne and Caviar / Listen to your heart / Moonrain / caravan / Amor essom / Saci / Forgive me / With love / Agua de Beber.
Album: released on Polydor, Jan'87 by Polydor Records. Dist: Polygram, Polydor

Cassette: released on Polydor, Jan'87 by Polydor Records. Dist: Polygram, Polydor

Compact disc: released on Polydor, Jan'87 by Polydor Records. Dist: Polygram, Polydor

POLKA PARTY.
Compact disc: by Polydor Records. Dist: Polygram, Polydor

Compact disc: released on Polydor, Oct'84 by Polydor Records. Dist: Polygram, Polydor

REFLECTIONS.
Cassette: released on Polydor, Sep'83 by Polydor Records. Dist: Polygram, Polydor

Compact disc: released on Polydor, Apr'84 by Polydor Records. Dist: Polygram, Polydor

ROMANTIC DREAMS.
Cassette: released on Polydor, Sep'80 by Polydor Records. Dist: Polygram, Polydor

Compact disc: released on Polydor, Jan'83 by Polydor Records. Dist: Polygram, Polydor

ROSE OF TRALEE.

Compact disc: by Polydor Records. Dist: Polygram, Polydor

Album: released on Polydor, Feb'84 by Polydor Records. Dist: Polygram, Polydor

Cassette: released on Polydor, Feb'84 by Polydor Records. Dist: Polygram, Polydor

ROSES FROM THE SOUTH.
Album: released on Polydor, Jan'81 by Polydor Records. Dist: Polygram, Polydor

Cassette: released on Polydor, Jan'81 by Polydor Records. Dist: Polygram, Polydor

Compact disc: released on Polydor, Aug'84 by Polydor Records. Dist: Polygram, Polydor

SCHLIESS DIE AUGEN.
Album: released on Polydor (Germany), Mar'82 Dist: IMS-Polygram

Cassette: released on Polydor (Germany), Mar'82 Dist: IMS-Polygram

SING MIT...8.
Album: released on Import Music Service (IMS), Mar'81 Dist: Concord Jazz Distributions, Pablo, Polygram

SING MIT LABDIE PUPPEN'TANZEN.
Album: released on Polydor (Germany), Feb'82 Dist: IMS-Polygram

Cassette: released on Polydor (Germany), Feb'82 Dist: IMS-Polygram

SKY BLUE.
Tracks: / Sky blue / An old folks get together / Three men in a boat / First meeting / Rio / Guido's love song / Hong Kong / Kowloon / New York - from Central Park to Tiffany's / Amsterdam / LH 903 diverted to Munich / On the beach / Journey to Greece / Finale.
Album: released on Polydor, Jul'85 by Polydor Records. Dist: Polygram, Polydor

Cassette: released on Polydor, Jul'85 by Polydor Records. Dist: Polygram, Polydor

Compact disc: released on Polydor, Jul'85 by Polydor Records. Dist: Polygram, Polydor

SUPERLAST - SUPERPARTY.
Tracks: / Juliet / Africa / Love is a stranger / Moonlight shadow / Living on video.
Album: released on Polydor (Germany), Apr'84 Dist: IMS-Polygram

Cassette: released on Polydor (Germany), Apr'84 Dist: IMS-Polygram

Compact disc: released on Polydor (Germany), Apr'84 Dist: IMS-Polygram

SWING WITH JAMES LAST.
Tracks: / Study in brown / Who cares? / Perdido / Barcarole / Peach, The / Nutcracker / All by myself / Heart and soul / Last but not least / Where or when / Heart of rock and roll.

TANGO.
Compact disc: released on Polydor, Jan'83 by Polydor Records. Dist: Polygram, Polydor

TRAUMSCHIFF (LOVEBOAT).
Tracks: / Traumschiff thema / Brasilien / Heidelinde / Bali / Dinner-marsch / Thailand / Mexico / Love theme / Ich habe das leben gelebt / Sadness.
Notes: This new album is the theme and background music to the successful German TV-Soap opera 'Loveboat'. James Last composed and arranged the score himself.
Album: released on Polydor (Germany), Jan'87 Dist: IMS-Polygram

Cassette: released on Polydor (Germany), Jan'87 Dist: IMS-Polygram

Compact disc: released on Polydor (Germany), Jan'87 Dist: IMS-Polygram

TRAUM WAS SCHONES.
Compact disc: released on Polydor Records. Dist: Polygram, Polydor

TRUMPET A GO GO.
Compact disc: by Polydor Records. Dist: Polygram, Polydor

Album: released on Polydor, Oct'84 by Polydor Records. Dist: Polygram, Polydor

Cassette: released on Polydor, Oct'84 by Polydor Records. Dist: Polygram, Polydor

VIVA VIVALDI.
Tracks: / Primavera (spring) / Springtime dream, A / Sicilian wedding / Largo / La cappella di venezia / La danza di Verona / La festa degli angeli / La strada d'amore / Piazza palermo / Winter / Addic mare / La stravaganza.

WESTERN PARTY.
Compact disc: by Polydor Records. Dist: Polygram, Polydor

WIR WOLLEN SPAB.
Album: released on Polydor (Germany), Feb'83 Dist: IMS-Polygram

Cassette: released on Polydor (Germany),

Feb'83 Dist: IMS-Polygram

Last Man In Europe
SONGS FROM THE ARK.
Album: released on Situation 2, May'82 Dist: Cartel, Pinnacle

Last of the mohicans
LAST OF THE MOHICANS, (THE) Various artists (Various Artists).
Cassette: released on Tell-A-tale (Cassettes), Sep'84

Last Party
MR. HURST.
Single (7"): released on Harvey, Feb'87 Dist: Revolver

Last place on earth
LAST PLACE ON EARTH, (THE) Original soundtrack.
Album: released on Island, Mar'85 by Island Records. Dist: Polygram Deleted May'87.

Cassette: released on Island, Mar'85 by Island Records. Dist: Polygram

Last Poets
OH MY PEOPLE.
Album: released on Celluloid, Apr'85 by Charly Records. Dist: Charly

Album: released on Celluloid-Carrere, Jun'84 by Celluloid. Dist: PRT, Spartan

Last Resort
WAY OF LIFE-SKINHEAD ANTHEMS, A.
Album: released on Last Resort, Apr'82 by Last Resort Records. Dist: Last Resort

Last Rites
FASCISM MEANS WAR.
Single (7"): released on Essential, Mar'84 Dist: Rough Trade

REACTION, (THE).
Album: released on Essential, Jun'84 Dist: Rough Trade

WE DON'T CARE.
Single (7"): released on Flicknife, Jun'83 by Flicknife Records. Dist: Spartan

Last, Robert
FOR DANCING.
Double Album: released on Decca (Germany), May'74 by Decca Records. Dist: Polygram, IMS

Last Rough Cause
SKINS 'N' PUNKS VOL.1 (Last Rough Cause/Society's Rejects).
Album: released on Oil, Oct'86 Dist: Revolver Distribution

Last, Roy
GOODTIMES AHEAD.
Album: released on Jax Pax, Dec'83 by Neon Records. Dist: Pinnacle

Last Starfighter, The
LAST STARFIGHTER, THE Original soundtrack.
Compact disc: released on Silva Screen, May'87 by Silva Screen Records. Dist: Silva Screen

Last Supper
LAST SUPPER Various artists (Various Artists).
Cassette: released on Adventures In Reality, Jul'84 by Backs Records. Dist: Cartel

Last Touch
LADIES OF GREY.
Album: released on Zilch, Jul'81 by Zilch Records. Dist: Stage One

Cassette: released on Zilch, Jul'81 by Zilch Records. Dist: Stage One

Last Words
ANIMAL WORLD.
Single (7"): released on Rough Trade, Aug'79 by Rough Trade Records. Dist: Rough Trade Distribution, Cartel Distribution

TODAYS KIDS.
Single (7"): released on Remand, Jan'80

TOP SECRET.
Single (7"): released on Armageddon, Jul'81 by Armageddon Records. Dist: Revolver, Cartel, Pinnacle

---

LAST YEAR WHEN I WAS YOUNG (Bennett, Hywel).
Cassette: released on Chivers Audio Books, May'81 by Chivers Sound & Vision. Dist: Chivers Sound & Vision

Laswell, Bill
BASELINES.
Album: released on Rough Trade, May'84 by Rough Trade Records. Dist: Rough Trade Distribution, Cartel Distribution

BEST OF.... (Laswell, Bill Material/Friends).
Album: released on Celluloid (France), Mar'85 by Island. Dist: Polygram

POINTS BLANK/METLABLE SNAPS (Laswell, Bill and John Zorn).
WORK SONG.
Single (12"): released on Rough Trade, Aug'84 by Rough Trade Records. Dist: Rough Trade Distribution, Cartel Distribution

Laszlo, Ken
TONIGHT.
Tracks: / Tonight (Italian mix) / Tonight (Instr) / Hey hey guy (remix) / Tonight (Instr.) / Tonight / Tonight instrumental.
Single (12"): released on Greyhound, Jan'87 by Greyhound Records. Dist: PRT, Greyhound

Lateef, Yusef
ANGEL EYES.
Double Album: released on Savoy (USA), Mar'85 by Arista Records. Dist: Polygram, Swift

CONTEMPLATION.
Album: released on Affinity, Sep'84 by Charly Records. Dist: Charly, Cadillac

GOLDEN FLUTE, (THE).
Album: released on Jasmine, Mar'83 by Jasmine Records. Dist: Counterpoint, Lugtons, Taylor, H.R., Wellard, Chris, Swift, Cadillac

GONG.
Double Album:

MORNING THE SAVOY SESSIONS.
Album:

SAX MASTERS.
Double Album: released on Vogue, Jan'76 Dist: Discovery, Jazz Music, PRT, Swift

YUSEF LATEEF.
Album: released on Jazz Reactivation, Jan'82 Dist: PRT

Latest
STARTING OVER.
Single (12"): released on Souled Out, Aug'84 by Souled Out Records. Dist: Pinnacle

Latimore
GOOD TIME MAN.
Album: released on Malaco, Jun'85 by Malaco Records. Dist: Charly

SINGING IN THE KEY OF LOVE.
Album: released on Malaco, Jul'82 by Malaco Records. Dist: Charly

Cassette: released on Malaco, Jul'82 by Malaco Records. Dist: Charly

Latin Electrica
LATIN ELECTRICA.
Single (7"): released on Nouveau, Jun'84

Single (12"): released on Nouveau, Jun'84

Latin For Dancing
LATIN FOR DANCING Various artists (Various Artists).
Album: released on Karussell (Germany), May'82

Cassette: released on Karussell (Germany), May'82

Latin Gold
LATIN GOLD Various artists (Various Artists).
Special: released on Effects Gold, Nov'80 by Ronco Records. Dist: Ronco Records

Cassette: released on Effects Gold, Nov'80 by Ronco Records. Dist: Ronco Records

Latin Quarter
AMERICAN FOR BEGINNERS.
Tracks: / American for beginners / Sadanista.

I TOGETHER.
Tracks: / I together / See him / Thin white duke*.
Single (7"): released on Rockin' Horse, Jun'87 by Arista Records. Dist: RCA Distribution

---

Single (12"): released on Rockin' Horse, Jun'87 by Arista Records. Dist: RCA Distribution

MICK AND CAROLINE.
Tracks: / I (together) / Remember / Freight elevator / Nomzamo / Negotiating with a loaded gun / Burn again / Love has gone / Night, The / Donovan's doorway / Men below, The.
Album: released on Arista, Jan'87 by Arista Records. Dist: RCA

Cassette: released on Arista, Jan'87 by Arista Records. Dist: RCA

Compact disc: released on Arista, Jan'87 by Arista Records. Dist: RCA

MODERN TIMES.
Tracks: / Modern times / No ordinary return / Radio Africa / Toulouse / America for beginners / Eddie / No rope as long as time / Seaport September / New millionaires / Truth about John / Cora / Modern times (single) / Thin white duke / No rope as long as time*.
Album: released on Rockin' Horse, Sep'85 by Arista Records. Dist: RCA Distribution

Cassette: released on Rockin' Horse, Sep'85 by Arista Records. Dist: RCA Distribution

Compact disc: released on Rockin' Horse, Sep'85 by Arista Records. Dist: RCA Distribution

NEW MILLIONAIRES, THE.
Single (7"): released on Rockin' Horse, Jun'85 by Arista Records. Dist: RCA Distribution

Single (12"): released on Rockin' Horse, Jun'85 by Arista Records. Dist: RCA Distribution

NO ROBE AS LONG AS TIME.
Tracks: / No robe as long as time / No ordinary return.

NO ROPE AS LONG AS TIME.
Single (7"): released on Rockin' Horse, Oct'85 by Arista Records. Dist: RCA Distribution

Single (12"): released on Rockin' Horse, Oct'85 by Arista Records. Dist: RCA Distribution

RADIO AFRICA.
Tracks: / Radio Africa / Voices inside / Toulouse .
Single (7"): released on Ignition, Oct'84 Dist: Lightning, Pinnacle

Single (7"): released on Rockin' Horse, Mar'85 by Arista Records. Dist: RCA Distribution

Single (12"): released on Rockin' Horse, Mar'85 by Arista Records. Dist: RCA Distribution

TOULOUSE.
Single (7"): released on Rockin' Horse, Jun'85 by Arista Records. Dist: RCA Distribution

Single (12"): released on Rockin' Horse, Jun'85 by Arista Records. Dist: RCA Distribution

Latouche, Panchita
SPEND SOME TIME WITH ME.
Single (7"): released on Paradise, May'82 Dist: Jetstar, JSU, WEA

Latter, Gene
ROCK BABY ROCK / SWEET SUGAR RAY.
Single (7"): released on Magnet, Jul'82 by Magnet Records. Dist: BMG

Lattisaw, Stacy
ATTACK OF THE NAME GAME.
Single (7"): released on Cotillion (Import), Nov'82 by Atlantic Records. Dist: WEA

BABY I LOVE YOU / WITH YOU.
Single (7"): released on Atlantic, Oct'81 by WEA Records. Dist: WEA

I'M NOT THE SAME GIRL.
Album: released on Cotillion, Aug'85 by WEA Records. Dist: WEA

JUMP INTO MY LIFE.
Tracks: / Jump into my life / Long shot.
Single (7"): released on Motown, Jan'87 by Motown Records. Dist: BMG Distribution

Single (12"): released on Motown, Jan'87 by Motown Records. Dist: BMG Distribution

JUMP TO THE BEAT.
Single (7"): released on Atlantic, Jun'80 by WEA Records. Dist: WEA

Single (12"): released on Atlantic, Jun'80 by WEA Records. Dist: WEA Deleted '84.

LET ME BE YOUR ANGEL.
Album: released on Atlantic, Jul'80 by WEA Records. Dist: WEA

Cassette: released on Atlantic, Jul'80 by WEA Records. Dist: WEA

LOVE ON A TWO WAY STREET / YOUNG GIRL.
Single (7"): released on Atlantic, Jul'81 by WEA Records. Dist: WEA

MILLION DOLLAR BASE / THE WAYS OF LOVE /HEY THERE LONELY BOY.
Single (7"): released on Cotillion (Import), Jan'84 by Atlantic Records. Dist: WEA

Single (12"): released on Cotillion (Import), Jan'84 by Atlantic Records. Dist: WEA

NAIL IT TO THE WALL.
Tracks: / Nail it to the wall / Nail it to the wall instrumental.

SNEAKIN' OUT / JUMP TO THE BEAT.
Single (7"): released on Cotillion (Import), Sep'82 by Atlantic Records. Dist: WEA

Single (12"): released on Cotillion (Import), Sep'82 by Atlantic Records. Dist: WEA

TAKE ME ALL THE WAY.
Tracks: / Just jump into my life / Hard way / Take me all the way / Little bit of heaven / long shot / Nail it to the wall / love me like the first time / You ain't leavin / Over the top / One more night.
Album: released on Motown, Nov'86 by Motown Records. Dist: BMG Distribution

Cassette: by Motown Records. Dist: BMG Distribution

WITH YOU.
Album: released on Atlantic, Jun'81 by WEA Records. Dist: WEA

Lauder, Sir Harry

GOLDEN AGE OF HARRY LAUDER, THE.
Album: released on Golden Age, Jul'83 by Music For Pleasure Records. Dist: EMI

Cassette: released on Golden Age, Jul'83 by Music For Pleasure Records. Dist: EMI

I LOVE A LASSIE.
Album: released on Pearl, Feb'80 by Pavillion (USA). Dist: Taylors, Swift

Lauer, Martin

TAXI NACH TEXAS.
Tracks: / Sacramento / Die letzte rose der prairie / Wenn ich ein cowboy war / Jim und Joe / Am lagerfeuer / Sein bestes pferd / Taxi nach texas / John Brown's baby / Silver dollars / Roll 'em over / Die blauen berge / Pierde und sattel / King John / Cowboy lady / Smoky / Wenn die sonne scheint in Texas.
Notes: Original Polydor Aufnashmen.

Laugh

PAUL MCCARTNEY.
Single (7"): released on Remorse, Aug'87 by Remorse Records. Dist: Revolver, Cartel

TAKE YOUR TIME YEAH.
Single (12"): released on Remorse, Nov'86 by Remorse Records. Dist: Revolver, Cartel

Laugh In

LAUGH IN Various artists (Various Artists).
Album: released on BBC, Dec'83 by BBC Records & Tapes. Dist: EMI, PRT, Pye

Cassette: released on BBC, Dec'83 by BBC Records & Tapes. Dist: EMI, PRT, Pye

Laughing Academy

SOME THINGS TAKE LONGER.
Album: released on Brand New, Jan'87 by Brand New Records. Dist: Ace Records, Chiswick Records, Pinnacle

SUSPICION.
Album: released on Braw Products, Jul'85 Dist: Fast Forward, Cartel

Laughing Accordian

LAUGHING ACCORDIAN Various session artists (Various Session Artists).
Cassette: released on AIM (Budget Cassettes), Feb'83

Laughing All The Way...

LAUGHING ALL THE WAY TO THE BANKS Various artists (Various Artists).
Album: released on Riverside, Sep'85 Dist: K-Tel, Jetstar

Laughing Apples

PRECIOUS FEELING.
Single (7"): released on Essential, Mar'82 Dist: Rough Trade

Laughing Clowns

ETERNALLY YOURS.
Single (7"): released on Hot, Mar'85 by Hot Records. Dist: Rough Trade, Cartel

Single (12"): released on Hot, Mar'85 by Hot Records. Dist: Rough Trade, Cartel

EVERYTHING THAT FLIES.
Single (12"): released on Red Flame, May'83 by Red Flame Records. Dist: Nine Mile, Cartel

GHOSTS OF AN EVIL WIFE.
Album: released on Hot, Aug'85 by Hot Records. Dist: Rough Trade, Cartel

HISTORY OF ROCK'N'ROLL.

LAUGHING CLOWNS.
Single (12"): released on M. Link, Aug'82

LAUGHTER AROUND THE TABLE.
Album: released on Red Flame, Aug'83 by Red Flame Records. Dist: Nine Mile, Cartel

LAW OF NATURE.
Album: released on Hot, Dec'84 by Hot Records. Dist: Rough Trade, Cartel

MAD FLIES MAD FLIES.
Single (7"): released on P. Melon, Aug'82

Laughing In Rhythm

LAUGHING IN RHYTHM Various artists (Various Artists).
Album: released on Stash, Apr'81 Dist: Swift Distribution, Jazz Music Distribution, Jazz Horizons Distribution, Celtic Music Distribution, Cadillac, JSU Distribution, Zodiac Distribution

Laughing Stock Of BBC

LAUGHING STOCK OF THE BBC Various artists (Various Artists).
Album: released on BBC, Apr'82 by BBC Records & Tapes. Dist: EMI, PRT, Pye

Cassette: released on BBC, Apr'82 by BBC Records & Tapes. Dist: EMI, PRT, Pye

Laughter And Tears...

LAUGHTER AND TEARS COLLECTION Various artists (Various Artists).
Album: released on WEA, Jun'83 by WEA Records. Dist: WEA

Cassette: released on WEA, Jun'83 by WEA Records. Dist: WEA

Laughter In The Garden

CLUTCH TIGHT.
Single (7"): released on Crash, Dec'83 by Satril Records. Dist: PRT
Cat. no: **CRA 601**

CORRIDOR OF STATUES.
Single (12"): released on Teatime, Aug'82

Launton Handbell Ringers

MODAL MELODIES.
Cassette: released on Saydisc, Jan'81 by Saydisc Records. Dist: Essex, Harmonia Mundi, Roots, H.R. Taylor, Jazz Music, Swift, Projection, Gamut

Album: released on Saydisc, Nov'80 by Saydisc Records. Dist: Essex, Harmonia Mundi, Roots, H.R. Taylor, Jazz Music, Swift, Projection, Gamut

Lauper, Cyndi

12" TAPE, THE.
Tracks: / Girls just want to have fun / Time after time / She bop / All through the night / Money changes everything.

ALL THROUGH THE NIGHT.
Single (12"): released on Portrait, Nov'84 by CBS Records. Dist: CBS

CHANGE OF HEART.
Tracks: / Change of heart / What a thrill / Heartbeat*.
Notes: * Extra track on 12" version only.
Single (7"): released on Portrait, Nov'86 by CBS Records. Dist: CBS

Single (7"): released on WEA, Jun'84 by WEA Records. Dist: WEA

Single (12"): released on WEA, Jun'84 by WEA Records. Dist: WEA

GIRLS JUST WANT TO HAVE FUN.
Single (7"): released on Portrait, Jan'84 by CBS Records. Dist: CBS Deleted '86.

Single (12"): released on Portrait, Jan'84 by CBS Records. Dist: CBS

MONEY CHANGES EVERYTHING.
Single (7"): released on Portrait, Feb'85 by CBS Records. Dist: CBS

Single (12"): released on Portrait, Feb'85 by CBS Records. Dist: CBS

SHE BOP.
Single (7"): released on Portrait, Aug'84 by CBS Records. Dist: CBS

Single (12"): released on Portrait, Aug'84 by CBS Records. Dist: CBS

Picture disc single: released on Portrait, Aug'84 by CBS Records. Dist: CBS

SHE'S SO UNUSUAL.
Compact disc: by CBS Records. Dist: CBS

Album: released on Portrait, Jan'84 by CBS Records. Dist: CBS

Cassette: released on Portrait, Jan'84 by CBS Records. Dist: CBS

TIME AFTER TIME.
Single (7"): released on Portrait, Mar'84 by CBS Records. Dist: CBS Deleted '87.

Single (12"): released on Portrait, Mar'84 by CBS Records. Dist: CBS Deleted '85.

Picture disc single: released on Portrait, Mar'84 by CBS Records. Dist: CBS

TRUE COLORS.
Tracks: / Change of heart / Maybe he'll know / Boy blue / True colors / Calm inside the storm / What's going on / Iko iko / Faraway nearby, The / 911 / One track mind / True colors (single) / Money changes everything (single) / Heading for the moon.

WHAT'S GOING ON.
Tracks: / What's going on.
Single (7"): released on Portrait, Feb'87 by CBS Records. Dist: CBS

Single (12"): released on Portrait, Mar'87 by CBS Records. Dist: CBS

Picture disc single: released on Portrait, Mar'87 by CBS Records. Dist: CBS

Laurel and Hardy

CLUNK CLICK/ YOU'RE NICKED.
Single (7"): released on CBS, Mar'83 by CBS Records. Dist: CBS

Single (12"): released on CBS, Mar'83 by CBS Records. Dist: CBS

DANGEROUS SHOES/ WRITE ME A LETTER.
Single (7"): released on Upright, Nov'83 by Upright Records. Dist: Cartel, Rough Trade

Single (12"): released on Upright, Nov'83 by Upright Records. Dist: Cartel, Rough Trade

GOLDEN AGE OF HOLLYWOOD COMEDY.
Album: released on United Artists, Nov'75

LOTS OF LOVING AND SHE'S GONE.
Single (12"): released on CBS, May'83 by CBS Records. Dist: CBS

Single (12"): released on CBS, May'83 by CBS Records. Dist: CBS

SHINE ON HARVEST MOON (Laurel & Hardy with Jean Parker).
Tracks: / Shine on harvest moon / Cuckoo song, The / World is waiting for the sunrise (The) / Cuckoo song, The.
Single (7"): released on Columbia, Nov'86 by EMI Records. Dist: EMI

TRAIL OF THE LONESOME PINE.
Single (7"): released on United Artists, Oct'75

WHAT A BARGAIN.
Album: released on Upright, Mar'87 by Upright Records. Dist: Cartel, Rough Trade

YOU'RE NICKED/ TELL HER I'M SORRY.
Single 10": released on Top Notch, Oct'82

Laurel & Hardy Music Box

LAUREL & HARDY MUSIC BOX Original Soundtrack (Various Artists).
Notes: Conductor: Ronnie Hazelhurst.
Album: released on Silva Screen, Jul'87 by Silva Screen Records. Dist: Silva Screen

Cassette: released on Silva Screen, Jul'87 by Silva Screen Records. Dist: Silva Screen

Laurels

ZOOM.
Single (12"): released on Happy, Sep'84 by Happy Records. Dist: Pinnacle

Laurence, Paul

HAVEN'T YOU HEARD.
Tracks: / Strung out / She's not a sleaze / You hooked me / Good & plenty / Racism / Haven't you heard / There ain't nothin' (like your lovin') / I'm sensitive.
Notes: Although a new name to many, Paul Laurence has been responsible for creating a distinctive and very influential sound over the past couple of years in his workwith Kashif, Melba Moore and Evelyn King. He composed and produced 'Rock Me Tonight' for Freddie Jackson, named by Billboard magazine as the no.1 Black Music single of 1985 after six weeks at no.1 on the Black Music charts, the longest run of any single by a new artist since 1977. A debut single by Paul laurence entitles "She's Not A Sleaze" was released late last year and performed well on the dance charts. Paul Laurence doesn't restrict the subject matter of his songs to the well-trodden romantic realm's of today's typical soulmusic but tackles issues like drug abuse on "Strung Out", prejudice on "Racism" and even offers a rather humerous approach to morality on "She's Not A Sleaze". However, with his Baptist Church choir background he can deliver a scorching ballad with the best of them when he chooses, "You Hooked Me" being a fine example. "Haven't You Heard" is produced by Paul Laurence.

SHE'S NOT A SLEAZE.
Single (7"): released on Capitol, Sep'85 by Capitol Records. Dist: EMI

Single (12"): released on Capitol, Sep'85 by Capitol Records. Dist: EMI

STRUNG OUT.
Tracks: / Strung out / I'm sensitive.

Laurence, Sherise

AMOUR DE MA VIE, (L').
Notes: Luxembourg Eurovision entry.

Laurens, Rose

AFRICA/ BROKEN HEART.
Single (7"): released on WEA, Oct'83 by WEA Records. Dist: WEA

AMERICAN LOVE.
Tracks: / American love / Quand tu pars.

Laurie, Annie

Creole gal

Laurie, Cy

DELVING BACK WITH CY (Laurie, Cy quartet\band).
Notes: Cy Laurie quartet with Fred Hunt, Les jowett. Cy Laurie band with Al Fairweather
Album: released on Esquire, Nov'86 by Titan International Productions. Dist: Jazz Music, Cadillac Music, Swift, Wellard, Chris, Backs, Rough Trade, Revolver, Nine Mile

SHADES OF CY.
Notes: with Hugh Rainey/Peter Corrigan/Steve Nice.

Album: released on Suntan, Mar'87 Dist: Jetstar Distribution

Laury, Cy

CY LAURY & LES JOWELL 1957 (Laury, Cy & Les Jowell).
Album: released on Flyright (USA), Jul'82 by Flyright Records. Dist: Swift, Jazz Music, Wellard, Chris, Cadillac

Lava

CRUISIN.
Album: released on Polydor (Import), Feb'82

PRIME TIME.
Album: released on Polydor, Jun'83 by Polydor Records. Dist: Polygram, Polydor

Cassette: released on Polydor, Jun'83 by Polydor Records. Dist: Polygram, Polydor

Laverne, Andy

LIQUID SILVER.
Notes: With John Abercrombie, Eddie Gomez, Peter Erskine and the Essex String Quartet.
Compact disc: released on DMP, '86 by DMP Records. Dist: Venture

Laverne Trio

See how it feels

Lavette, Betty

EASIER TO SAY.
Cassette: released on Charly, Jul'80 by Charly Records. Dist: Charly, Cadillac

I CAN'T STOP/ EITHER WAY WE LOSE.
Single (7"): released on Motown, Jul'82 by Motown Records. Dist: BMG Distribution

I'M IN LOVE.
Album: released on Charly, Jan'85 by Charly Records. Dist: Charly, Cadillac

TELL ME A LIE.
Album: released on Motown, Jan'82 by Motown Records. Dist: BMG Distribution

YOU SEEN ONE YOU SEEN 'EM ALL.
Single (7"): released on Motown, Mar'82 by Motown Records. Dist: BMG Distribution

Lavias

DO YOU WANNA DANCE (2 PARTS).
Single (7"): released on Golden Pyramid, Jul'83 by Golden Pyramid. Dist: Pinnacle

Lavilliers, Bernard
O GRINGO.
Album: released on IMS, Jun'81 by Polydor Records. Dist: IMS, Polygram

Lavin, Christine
FUTURE FOSSILS.
Compact disc: released on Philo (USA), '86

Album: released on Philo (USA), Sep'85

Lavitz, L
EXTENDED PLAY.
Tracks: / Certain people / Group therapy / Crystal / Between coming and going / Times square.
Album: released on Press, Jul'86 by Press Records.

Album: released on Press, Feb'85 by Press Records.

Lavitz, T
STORYTIME.
Compact disc: by Pacific Records (USA). Dist: Atlantic

Lawal, Gasper
ABIO SUNNI.
Album: released on Hotcap, Aug'85 Dist: Rough Trade, Cartel

KITA-KATA.
Single (12"): released on C.A.P., Dec'81 by C.A.P. Records. Dist: Stage One, Rough Trade

KOKOROKO.
Tracks: / Kokoroko.
Single (12"): released on Hot Cat, Sep'86 Dist: Rough Trade, Cartel

Law Lords
LIVINGSTONE RAP (Law Lords International).
Single (12"): released on Cherry Red, Jun'84 by Cherry Red Records. Dist: Pinnacle

Lawlor, Teresa
MOODS.
Album: released on WEA Ireland, Mar'87 by WEA Records. Dist: Celtic Distributions, Projection, I & B

Cassette: released on WEA Ireland, Mar'87 by WEA Records. Dist: Celtic Distributions, Projection, I & B

Lawndale
SASQUATCH ROCK.
Album: released on SST, Aug'87 by SST Records. Dist: Pinnacle

Lawnmower
CAT, THE.
Album: released on Fat Wallet, Aug'85 by Probe Plus Records. Dist: Cartel

Lawrence
HOLLAND SPECIAL.

Lawrence, Arnie
RENEWAL.
Album: released on Palo Alto (Italy) Jan'84

Lawrence, Dave
ONE MORE TEAR.
Single (7"): released on Admiral, Jan'83 by Admiral. Dist: PRT

Lawrence, Elliot
ELEVATION.
Album: released on First Heard, '84 by Submarine Records. Dist: Conifer, Taylors

PLAYS JOHNNY MANDEL.
Single (12"): released on Fantasy Inc USA, Feb'86 by Fantasy Inc USA Records. Dist: IMS, Polygram

Lawrence, Gary
GARY LAWRENCE & HIS SIZZLING SYCOPATORS.
Album: released on Blue Goose, May'79 Dist: Projection, Swift

Lawrence, Gertrude
WE WERE DANCING TONIGHT AT 8.30
Album: released on Monmouth, '74

Lawrence, Karen
RIP AND TEAR.
Tracks: / Rip side / Shot for the heart / Never enough / What a lovely way to go / Get it up get it right / Rip and tear / Tear side / Is this love / Wild heart / Kiss from a distance * / Out of the blue.

Album: released on FM-Revolver, Jul'86 by FM-Revolver Records. Dist: BMG (RCA/Ariola), Pathe Marconi, Polygram

Lawrence, Kenneth
MONEY GOT TO PAY.
Single (12"): released on Firm, Jun'83 by Firm Records. Dist: Jetstar

Lawrence, Lee
FASCINATION.
Album: released on President, Sep'83 by President Records. Dist: Taylors, Spartan

Cassette: released on President, Jan'84 by President Records. Dist: Taylors, Spartan

Lawrence of Arabia
LAWRENCE OF ARABIA Soundtrack.
Album: released on Golden Guinea, '74 by PRT Records. Dist: PRT

Lawrence, Stephanie
AM I ASKING TOO MUCH.
Single (7"): released on Sierra, Sep'85 by Sierra Records. Dist: WEA

Lawrence, Steve
BEST OF STEVE AND EYDIE, THE (Lawrence, Steve & Eydie Gorme).
Cassette: released on CBS Cameo, Aug'85 by CBS Records. Dist: CBS

I WANT TO STAY HERE (see Gorme, Eydie) (Lawrence, Steve & Eydie Gorme).
OUR LOVE IS HERE TO STAY (see Gorme, Eydie) (Lawrence, Steve & Eydie Gorme).
STILL BELIEVE IN LOVE, I (Lawrence, Steve & Eydie Gorme).
Album: released on President, Mar'85 by President Records. Dist: Taylors, Spartan

Cassette: released on President, Mar'85 by President Records. Dist: Taylors, Spartan

SYD LAWRENCE ORCHESTRA VOL 2 (Lawrence, Syd Orchestra).
Album: released on Celebrity, Mar'82 by Evolution Group records. Dist: Spartan

Cassette: released on Celebrity, Mar'82 by Evolution Group records. Dist: Spartan

WE GOT US (Lawrence, Steve & Eydie Gorme).
Album: released on Jasmine, Mar'84 by Jasmine Records. Dist: Counterpoint, Lugtons, Taylor, H.R., Wellard, Chris, Swift, Cadillac

WE'RE ALL ALONE.
Album: released on President, Mar'85 by President Records. Dist: Taylors, Spartan

Lawrence, Syd
BAND BEAT (Lawrence, Syd Orchestra).
Album: released on BBC, Oct'76 by BBC Records & Tapes. Dist: EMI, PRT, Pye

BIG BAND SWING.
Compact disc:

HOLLAND SPECIAL.
Tracks: / Als op capri de rozentuinen bloeien / Penny serenade / Weet je nog wel die avond in de regen? / Bloesem van seringen / Veel mooier dan het mooiste schildwerij / Groot Rotterdam & bouncin' in Bavaria / Als sterren flonk' rond aan de hemel staan / Diep in mijn hart / Twas eine zommernachtfeest / Denk jij nog aan di tijd?.
Notes: Twelve popular Dutch compositions arranged for big band and played in the style of Glenn Miller by the popular Syd Lawrence Orchestra. All titles are played in dance tempo.
Album:

Cassette:

Cassette: released on Philips Import, Mar'84

REMEMBER GLENN MILLER (Lawrence, Syd Orchestra).
Cassette: released on Ditto, Sep'83 by Pickwick Records. Dist: H.R. Taylor

RITUAL FIRE DANCE.
Album: released on Autograph, Apr'85 by Record Services Distribution (Ireland)

SWING CLASSICS (Lawrence, Syd Orchestra).
Album: released on Philips, Apr'82 by IMS-Polygram

Cassette: released on Philips, Apr'82 Dist: IMS-Polygram

Album: released on Philips, Jul'84 Dist: IMS-Polygram

Cassette: released on Philips, Jul'84 Dist: IMS-Polygram

SYD LAWRENCE & HIS ORCHESTRA (Lawrence, Syd Orchestra).

Album: released on Cambra, May'85 by Cambra Records. Dist: IDS, Conifer

Cassette: released on Cambra, May'85 by Cambra Records. Dist: IDS, Conifer

SYD LAWRENCE VOL 1.
Album: released on Everest (Premier), '82 by Everest Records. Dist: Pinnacle

Cassette: released on Everest (Premier), '82 by Everest Records. Dist: Pinnacle

Lawrie, Edwina
BYE BYE LOVE.
Single (7"): released on Springsong, Feb'83 by Springsong Records. Dist: Unknown

DARK GLASSES.
Single (7"): released on Panther, Aug'84 by MCA Records. Dist: CBS

Single (12"): released on Panther, Aug'84 by MCA Records. Dist: CBS

Laws, Eloise
LOVE FACTORY.
Single (7"): released on Inferno, Jul'80 by Inferno Records. Dist: Inferno, Cartel, Pinnacle

Lawson, Brenda
SWEET LOVE / GUTS.
Single (7"): released on Rough Cut, Dec'82

Lawson, Dennis
ULTRA FANTASTICO.
Single (7"): released on EMI, Apr'84 by EMI Records. Dist: EMI

Lawson-Haggart
BEST OF JAZZ IN THE TROC.
Album: released on World Jazz, Apr'81 by World Jazz Records. Dist: World Jazz, JSU, Jazz Music

Lawson, Tom
I'LL TAKE YOU HOME AGAIN KATHLEEN.
Single (7"): released on Klub, Aug'83

Lawson, Yank
CENTURY PLAZA.
Album: released on World Jazz, '75 by World Jazz Records. Dist: World Jazz, JSU, Jazz Music

HARK THE HERALD ANGELS SWING.
Album: released on World Jazz, '75 by World Jazz Records. Dist: World Jazz, JSU, Jazz Music

IN CONCERT VOL 1 MASSEY HALL.
Album: released on World Jazz, '75 by World Jazz Records. Dist: World Jazz, JSU, Jazz Music

PLAY COLE PORTER (Lawson, Yank & Bob Lawson).
PLAY COLE PORTER (see also Bob Haggart) (Lawson, Yank & Bob Haggart).
Album: released on World Jazz, Aug'75 by World Jazz Records. Dist: World Jazz, JSU, Jazz Music

PLAYS MOSTLY BLUES.
Notes: with Al Klink, G. Masso, B. Haggart etc.
Album: released on Audiophile, Jul'87 by Jazzology Records (USA). Dist: Jazz Music, Swift

Laws, Ronnie
EVERY GENERATION.
Album: released on United Artists, Feb'80

MIRROR TOWN.
Tracks: / Come to me / Misled / Tell me / Mirror town / Like a crazy man / Midnight side / Cold day / You have to be in love / Take a chance.
Album: released on CBS, Oct'86 by CBS Records. Dist: CBS

Cassette: released on CBS, Oct'86 by CBS Records. Dist: CBS

MR NICE GUY.
Album: released on Capitol, Sep'83 by Capitol Records. Dist: EMI

Cassette: released on Capitol, Sep'83 by Capitol Records. Dist: EMI

PRESSURE SENSITIVE (Laws, Ronnie & Pressure).
Tracks: / Always there / Momma / Never be the same / Tell me something good / Nothing to lose / Tidal wave / Why do you laugh at me / Mrs Mary's place.
Compact disc: released on EMI America, May'87 by EMI Records. Dist: EMI

RONNIE LAWS.
Tracks: / City girl / Always there / Love is here / Every generation / Paradise (you are) / Friends and strangers / In the groove / Stay awake / Saturday evening.

Compact disc: released on Capitol, Apr'87 by Capitol Records. Dist: EMI

Lawton, Jimmy
ARIZONA SUNDAY.
Album: released on Westwood, Jan'78 by Westwood Records. Dist: Jazz Music, H.R. Taylor, JSU, Pinnacle, Ross Records

Laycock, Tim
CAPERS AND RHYMES.
Album: released on Greenwich Village, May'81 by Sweet Folk All Records. Dist: Roots, Projection, Lightning, Celtic Music, Wellard, Chris

GIANT AT CERNE, THE.
Album: released on Dingles, Mar'84 by Dingles Records. Dist: Projection

Single (7"): released on Dingles, Mar'84 by Dingles Records. Dist: Projection

Laye, Evelyn
GOLDEN AGE OF EVELYN LAYE, THE.
Album: released on Golden Age, Jul'85 by Music For Pleasure Records. Dist: EMI

Cassette: released on Golden Age, Jul'85 by Music For Pleasure Records. Dist: EMI

Layne, Cynthia
STEALING LOVE.
Single (12"): released on Trindisc, Mar'84 by Trindisc Records. Dist: Jetstar, Pinnacle, Rough Trade, Cartel

Layton & Johnstone
AMERICAN DUETTISTS WITH PIANO.
Double Album: released on World, '74 Dist: Jetstar

Cassette: released on World Records, Jul'79 Dist: Polygram

SONG IS ENDED, THE.
Album: released on Joy, Jul'83 by President Records. Dist: Jazz Music, Swift, President Distribution

WHEN YOU'RE SMILING.
Tracks: / Wonder where my baby is tonight / My pal Harry / Meadow lark / Ramona / Dawning / After my laughter came tears / Sunny Skies / Get out and get under the moon / Was it a dream / Bluebird sing me a song / I'll never ask for more / Deep night / If I had a talking picture of you / Pro-ro-rollin' along / Stein song / When you're smiling / Harmony heaven / I gotta right to sing the blues / Lazybones / I like to go back in the evening / I wonder where my baby is tonight.
Album: released on Conifer, Sep'86 by Conifer Records. Dist: Conifer

Cassette: released on Conifer, Sep'86 by Conifer Records. Dist: Conifer

Lazenby, Keith
KISS THE NIGHT GOODBYE / HEARTS.
Single (7"): released on AKA, Aug'83 Dist: Stage One, IDS, Indies, Cartel

Lazlo & the Leopards
I CAN BE YOUR FRIEND.
Single (7"): released on Red Bus, Jun'84 by Red Bus Records. Dist: PRT

Lazlo, Viktor
BREATHLESS.
Single (7"): Don't say no.
Single (7"): released on Polydor, Aug'87 by Polydor Records. Dist: Polygram, Polydor

Single (12"): released on Polydor, Aug'87 by Polydor Records. Dist: Polygram, Polydor

Lazy Lester
LAZY LESTER-RIDES AGAIN.
Album: released on Blue Horizon, Oct'87 by Ace Records. Dist: Pinnacle. Estim retail price in Sep'87 was £5.67.

POOR BAY BLUES.
Album: released on Flyright, Jun'79 by Flyright Records. Dist: Krazy Kat, Swift, Jazz Music Cat. no: FLYRIGHT LP 544

THEY CALL ME LAZY.
Album: released on Flyright, Apr'77 by Flyright Records. Dist: Krazy Kat, Swift, Jazz Music

Lazzaro, Claude
TANGO (Lazzaro, Claude & Chorus).
Compact disc: released on Delta, Jan'86 by Delta Records. Dist: Target

Lea, Barbara
DO IT AGAIN.
Album: released on Audiophile, Jan'87 by Jazzology Records (USA). Dist: Jazz Music. Swift

Leace
JILL THE GROOVE.
Single (12"): released on Nine O Nine, Aug'87 by Creole Records. Dist: Rhino, PRT

Leadbelly
COLLECTION: LEADBELLY.
Album: released on Deja Vu, Oct'86 by Deja Vu Records. Dist: Counterpoint Distribution, Record Services Distribution (Ireland)

Cassette: released on Deja Vu, Oct'86 by Deja Vu Records. Dist: Counterpoint Distribution, Record Services Distribution (Ireland)

HIS GUITAR, HIS VOICE & HIS PIANO.
Album: released on Pathe Marconi(France), Sep'84

LAST SESSIONS (VOLUME 1).
Album: released on Spartan, Feb'87 by Spartan Records. Dist: Spartan

Cassette: released on Spartan, Feb'87 by Spartan Records. Dist: Spartan

LEADBELLY.
Album: released on EMI (France), '83 by EMI Records. Dist: Conifer

Leaders
MUDFOOT.
Tracks: / Miss Nancy / Elaborations / Midnite train / Freedom swing song / Song of her / Mudfoot / Cupid.
Notes: The Leaders are:- Arthur Blythe, Lester Bowie, Chico Freeman, Kirk Lightsey, Cecil McBee and Don Moye.
Album: released on Blackhawk, Jan'87 by Blackhawk Records (USA). Dist: IMS-Polygram

Compact disc: released on Blackhawk, Jul'87 by Blackhawk Records (USA). Dist: IMS-Polygram

Leadon, Bernie
NATURAL PROGRESSIONS (Leadon, Bernie/Michael Georgiades).
Album: released on Asylum, Aug'77 by WEA Records. Dist: WEA

Leadweight
LEADWEIGHT Various Artists (Various Artists).
Cassette: released on Neat, '85 by Neat Records. Dist: Pinnacle, Neat

Leaf, Ann
LIVE IN CONCERT - MAJESTIC PIPE ORGAN.
Album: released on Glass, Sep'80 by Amberlee Records. Dist: H.R. Taylor

MIGHTY WURLITZER, THE (Leaf, Ann & Gaylord Carter).
Tracks: / Great Day.

League of Gentlemen
LEAGUE OF GENTLEMEN, (THE).
Album: released on E.G., Mar'81 by Virgin Records. Dist: Virgin, EMI

Cassette: released on Editions EG, Apr'81 by Virgin Records. Dist: EMI

League of nations
MUSIC FOR THE NEW DEPRESSION.
Album: released on Glass, '83 by Glass Records. Dist: Nine Mile, Rough Trade, Red Rhino, Play It Again Sam

Album: released on Glass, Apr'84 by Glass Records. Dist: Nine Mile, Rough Trade, Red Rhino, Play It Again Sam

League Unlimited
LOVE AND DANCING (League Unlimited Orchestra).
Tracks: / Hard times / Love action (I believe in love) / Don't you want me / Things that dreams are made of / Do or die / Open your heart / Sound of the crowd, The / Seconds.
Compact disc: released on Virgin, '86 by Virgin Records. Dist: EMI, Virgin Distribution

Album: released on Virgin, Jun'82 by Virgin Records. Dist: EMI, Virgin Distribution

Cassette: released on Virgin, Jun'82 by Virgin Records. Dist: EMI, Virgin Distribution

Leahy, Geoff
1984.
Single (7"): released on K.Mosaic, Mar'84 Dist: Pinnacle

Lea, Jimmy
CITIZEN KANE.
Single (7"): released on Trojan, Nov'85 by Trojan Records. Dist: PRT, Jetstar

Leander, Zarah
ZARAH LEANDER'S GREATEST HITS (Various Artists).
Compact disc: released on Rouska, May'87 Dist: Red Rhino Distribution, Cartel Distribution

Leandre, Joelle
DOUZE SONS, (LES).
Tracks: / Pavane / Basses profondes / Pierrot / Ballde de chien / Cadenza rare / Trio en forme de bagatelle / Grand duo concertant / Les trois dames / Instant opus 3 / Sonate breve echappee / Seriozo (pour cordes et trombone) / Soupir.
Album: released on Nato (France), Sep'86 by Disques Nato. Dist: Essex Record Distributors Ltd.

Leandros, Vicky
GREEK SONGS (Leandros, Vicky/Nana Mouskouri/Demis Roussos).
Album: released on Philips, Jun'79 Dist: IMS-Polygram

LOVE IS ALIVE.
Album: released on Philips, Dec'81 Dist: IMS-Polygram

Cassette: released on Philips, Dec'81 Dist: IMS-Polygram

Leanne
FANTASY/LE DUB FANTASY.
Single (7"): released on Statik, Nov'82 Dist: Rough Trade Distribution, Stage One Distribution

Leao, Nara
GIRL FROM IPANEMA.
Tracks: / Little boat / Girl from Ipanema / Berimbau / Desafinado / Wave / Corcovado / Waters of March / Felicidade, A / Morning of the carnival / Chega de Saudade / Meditation / One note Samba / Agua de Beber / You and I / Samba do aviao / Que sera.
Notes: Outside of Brazil, Astrud Gilberto is probably the country's most famous songstress. But to Brazilians at home the name Nara Leao is the one who is acknowledged as the most authentic exponent of the Bossa Nova\Samba movement. She's the best. This digital recording features 16 popular Brazilian songs including the internationally known 'Girl from Ipanema', 'Desafinado' and 'One note Samba'. A great recording from an artiste who is sure to attract a lot of interest here by the release of this album.
Album: released on Polydor (Import), Nov'86

Cassette: released on Polydor (Import), Nov'86

Compact disc: released on Polydor (Import), Nov'86

Leapers, sleepers &...
LEAPERS, SLEEPERS & CREEPERS Various artists.
Album: released on Kent, Dec'84 by Ace Records. Dist: Pinnacle

Lear, Amanda
SECRET PASSION.
Album: released on Carrere, 11 Apr'87 by Carrere Records. Dist: PRT, Spartan

Cassette: released on Carrere, 11 Apr'87 by Carrere Records. Dist: PRT, Spartan

TAM TAM.
Album: released on Ariola (Germany), Jan'84

Cassette: released on Ariola (Germany), Jan'84

TIME'S UP/APHRODISIAC.
Single (12"): released on Carrere, Apr'87 by Carrere Records. Dist: PRT, Spartan

Learning & memory
LEARNING and MEMEORY by Tony Buzan (Maag, Peter & The London Symphony Orchestra).
Cassette: released on Psychology Today, Oct'81

Learning to control pain
LEARNING TO CONTROL PAIN by David Bresler.
Cassette: released on Psychology Today, Nov'81

Learning Tree, The
LEARNING TREE, THE 12 songs about the conservation of the environment.
Album: released on EMI, '74 by EMI Records.

Learn to drive
LEARN TO DRIVE.
Tracks: / Entire highway code, The / Rules of the road, The / Basic manoeuvres / Actual driving (est explained in detail, The.
Cassette: released on Learn To Drive, Oct'86 Dist: IMS-Polygram

Lea, Sandra
WHISPERING NIGHTS.
Single (7"): released on Rondercrest, Apr'81 by Rondercrest Records. Dist: M.I.S. Distribution

Leather chaps &...
LEATHER CHAPS AND LACE PETTICOATS various.
Album: released on Cherry Red, Jun'85 by Cherry Red Records. Dist: Pinnacle

Leather Nun
506.
Single (12"): released on Wire, Jul'85 Dist: Nine Mile, Cartel

ALIVE.
Album: released on Wire, Dec'85 Dist: Nine Mile, Cartel

GIMME GIMME GIMME.
Tracks: / Gimme Gimme Gimme (a man after midnight) / Lollipop / Gimme gimme gimme (Chopper mix) ".
Single (7"): released on Wire, May'86 Dist: Nine Mile, Cartel

Single (12"): released on Wire, May'86 Dist: Nine Mile, Cartel

GIMME, GIMME, GIMME (A MAN AFTER MIDNIGHT).
Tracks: / Gimme, Gimme, Gimme (A man after midnight) The rejected V. / Lollipop- Suckers Version / Gimme,Gimme, Gimme (A man after midnight) Chopper Mix.
Single (12"): released on Wire, Oct'86 Dist: Nine Mile, Cartel

I CAN SMELL YOUR THOUGHTS.
Tracks: / I can smell your thoughts (remix) / Falling apart / 506 (revisited)*
Single (12"): released on Wire, 23 May'87 Dist: Nine Mile, Cartel

Single (7"): released on Wire, 23 May'87 Dist: Nine Mile, Cartel

LUST GAMES.
Album: released on Wire, Nov'86 Dist: Nine Mile, Cartel

ON THE ROAD.
Tracks: / On the road / Desolation avenue / Sons of a good family".
Single (7"): released on Wire, Feb'86 Dist: Nine Mile, Cartel

Single (12"): released on Wire, Feb'86 Dist: Nine Mile, Cartel

PINK HOUSE.
Tracks: / Pink house / Speed of life / Lucky strike.
Single (7"): released on Wire, Nov'86 Dist: Nine Mile, Cartel

Single (12"): released on Wire, Nov'86 Dist: Nine Mile, Cartel

PRIME MOVER.
Tracks: / Prime mover / F.F.A.
Single (12"): released on Wire, Aug'86 Dist: Nine Mile, Cartel

PRIME MOVER/F.F.A..
Single (7"): released on Subterranean, Jan'84 by Subterranean Records. Dist: Rough Trade Distribution

SLOW DEATH.
Album: released on Criminal Damage, May'84 by Criminal Damage Records. Dist: Backs, Cartel

SLOW DEATH 5-TRACK MINI ALBUM.
Single (12"): released on Wire, Aug'86 Dist: Nine Mile, Cartel

STEEL CONSTRUCTION.
Album: released on Wire, Oct'87 Dist: Nine Mile, Cartel. Estim retail price in Sep'87 was £5.99

Cassette: released on Wire, Oct'87 Dist: Nine Mile, Cartel. Estim retail price in Sep'87 was £5.99

Leatherwolf
ENDANGERED SPECIES.
Album: released on Heavy Metal America, Jul'85 by FM-Revolver Records. Dist: EMI

Leatherwood, Stu
SO TELL ME WHO'S CRAZY.
Single (7"): released on Tellybell, Jun'85

Leaveners
BIRD OF FREEDOM.
Album: released on Burlington, Oct'86 by Plant Life Records. Dist: Jazz Music, Celtic Music, Clyde Factors Distributors, I.R.S., Projection, Wellard, Chris, Roots

Leaves
1966.
Album: released on Fan Club, May'84 by New Rose. Dist: Rough Trade, Cartel

HEY JOE.
Album: released on Line (West Germany), Feb'84

Leblanc, Shorty
Best of two Cajun greats

Lebow, Martee
LOVE'S A LIAR.
Tracks: / Where do I stand / Another lonely heart / Love's a liar / Maybe you'll remember / Learning the hard way / Hang on (to my reckless youth) / Fallen angel / Forbidden / I must be in love / One good reason.
Album: released on Atlantic, Jun'87 by WEA Records. Dist: WEA

Cassette: released on Atlantic, Jun'87 by WEA Records. Dist: WEA

Lebrijano, Juan Pena
ENCUENTROS.
Album: released on Globestyle, Oct'87 by Ace Records. Dist: Projection. Estim retail price in Sep'87 was £5.67.

Ledernacken
1ST LP.
Album:

BOOGALOO (THE).
Single (12"):

DRUMS OF MATUMBA.
Single (7"): released on Strikeback, Jun'85 by Strikeback Records. Dist: Rough Trade

ICH WILL DICH ESSEN.
Single (7"): released on Strikeback, Sep'84 by Strikeback Records. Dist: Rough Trade

Single (12"): released on Strikeback, Sep'84 by Strikeback Records. Dist: Rough Trade

I'M A DOG.
Tracks: / I'm a dog.
Single (12"): released on Hit The Deck, Aug'86 by Hit The Deck Records. Dist: PRT

MOCK AND GULLEY / AMOCK / RHYTHMUS / RAUSCH.
Single (7"): released on Empire, Feb'84 by Empire Records. Dist: Backs, Cartel, Jetstar

SHIMMY & SHAKE.
Tracks: / Shimmy & Shake / Money / Real treat.
Single (12"):

Ledin, Tomas
NEVER AGAIN (Ledin, Tomas & Agnetha).
Single (7"): released on Epic, Oct'82 by CBS Records. Dist: CBS

WHAT ARE YOU DOING TONIGHT.
Single (12"): released on Epic, Jul'83 by CBS Records. Dist: CBS

Ledwith Tony
IRISH MUSIC FROM THE FAVOURITE (Ledwith Tony & Jimmy powers).

Led Zeppelin
4 SYMBOLS.
Compact disc: released on Atlantic, '83 by WEA Records. Dist: WEA

Album: released on Atlantic, '74 by WEA Records. Dist: WEA

Cassette: released on Atlantic, '74 by WEA Records. Dist: WEA

CODA.
Compact disc: released on Atlantic, Jul'87 by WEA Records. Dist: WEA

Album: released on Swansong, Nov'82

Cassette: released on Swansong, Nov'82

HOUSES OF THE HOLY.
Compact disc:

Album: released on Atlantic, '74 by WEA Records. Dist: WEA
Cat. no: K 50014
Cassette: released on Atlantic, '74 by WEA Records. Dist: WEA

IN THROUGH THE OUT DOOR.
Tracks: / In the evening / South bound saurez / Fool in the rain / Hot dog / Carouselambra / All my love / I'm gonna crawl.
Compact disc: released on Swansong, Jan'86

Album: released on Swansong, Aug'79

Cassette: released on Swansong, Aug'79

LED ZEPPELIN.
Compact disc: released on Atlantic, Jan'87 by WEA Records. Dist: WEA

Album: released on Atlantic, '74 by WEA Records. Dist: WEA

Cassette: released on Atlantic, '74 by WEA Records. Dist: WEA

LED ZEPPELIN 2.
Tracks: / Whole lotta love / What is and what should be / Lemon song, The / Thank you / Heartbreaker / Livin' lovin' maid / (She's a woman) / Ramble on / Moby Dick / Bring it on home.
Compact disc: released on Atlantic, Dec'86 by WEA Records. Dist: WEA

Album: released on Atlantic, '74 by WEA Records. Dist: WEA

Cassette: released on Atlantic, '74 by WEA Records. Dist: WEA

LED ZEPPELIN 3.
Tracks: / Immigrant song / Friends / Celebration day / Since I've been loving you / Out on the tiles / Gallows pole / Tangerine / That's the way / Bron-y-aur stomp / Hats off to (Roy) Harper.
Compact disc: released on Atlantic, Jan'87 by WEA Records. Dist: WEA

Album: released on Atlantic, '74 by WEA Records. Dist: WEA

Cassette: released on Atlantic, '74 by WEA Records. Dist: WEA

PHYSICAL GRAFFITI.
Tracks: / Houses of the holy / Trampled under foot / Kashmir / Custard pie / Rover, The / In my time of dying.
Compact disc: released on Swansong, Jan'87

Double Album: released on Swansong, '75

Double cassette: released on Swansong, '75

PRESENCE.
Compact disc: released on Swansong, 20 Jun'87

Album: released on Swansong, Apr'76

Cassette: released on Swansong, Apr'76

SONG REMAINS THE SAME, THE.
Video-cassette (VHS): released on WHV, Feb'86

Compact disc: released on Swansong, Mar'87

Double compact disc: released on Swansong, Feb'87

Double Album: released on Swansong, Oct'76

Double cassette: released on Swansong, Oct'76

Lee, Albert

ALBERT LEE.
Album: released on Polydor, Aug'83 by Polydor Records. Dist: Polygram, Polydor

COUNTRY GUITAR MAN.
Album: released on Sundown, Nov'86 by Magnum Music Group Ltd. Dist: Magnum Music Group Ltd, PRT Distribution, Spartan Distribution

Cassette: released on Sundown, Nov'86 by Magnum Music Group Ltd. Dist: Magnum Music Group Ltd, PRT Distribution, Spartan Distribution

HIDING.
Tracks: / Country boy / Billy Tyler / Are you wasting my time / Now and then it's gonna rain / O a real good night / Setting me up / Ain't living long like this / Hiding / Hotel love / Come up and see me anytime.
Album: released on A&M, Apr'86 by A&M Records. Dist: Polygram

Cassette: released on A&M, Apr'86 by A&M Records. Dist: Polygram

SPEECHLESS.
Tracks: / T-bird to Vegas / Bullish boogie / 17th summer / Salt creek / Arkansas traveller / Cannonball / Romany rye / Erin / T-bird to Vegas / Bullish boogie / Seventeenth summer / Salt creek / Akansas traveler / Cannonball / Romany Rye / Erin.
Notes: Albert Lee- another highly distinguished guitarist, well-known for his work withDave Edmunds, Emmylou Harris, and most recently on the Everly Brothers reunion concerts and albums.
Compact disc: released on MCA Master Series, Feb'87 by MCA Records. Dist: Polygram

Album: released on MCA, Jul'87 by MCA Records. Dist: Polygram, MCA

Cassette: released on MCA, Jul'87 by MCA Records. Dist: Polygram, MCA

Compact disc: released on MCA, Jul'87 by MCA Records. Dist: Polygram, MCA

Lee, Alvin

FREE FALL.
Album: released on Avatar, Dec'80 by Avatar Communications. Dist: CBS

I DON'T WANNA STOP.
Single (7"): released on Avatar, Aug'81 by Avatar Communications. Dist: CBS

NUTBUSH CITY LIMITS.
Single (7"): released on Avatar, Mar'82 by Avatar Communications. Dist: CBS

ROCK'N'ROLL GUITAR PICKER (Lee, Alvin Band).
Single (7"): released on Avatar, Dec'81 by Avatar Communications. Dist: CBS

TAKE THE MONEY (Lee, Alvin Band).
Single (7"): released on Avatar, Aug'81 by Avatar Communications. Dist: CBS

Lee,Arthur

ARTHUR LEE.
Album: released on Beggars Banquet, Jul'81 by Beggars Banquet Records. Dist: WEA

Lee, Benny

WHISPERING GRASS (Lee, Benny/Adelaide Hall/Issy Bonn/Dorothy Carless).
Notes: For full information see under Dorothy Carless.
Single (7"): released on Old Gold, Oct'83 by Old Gold Records. Dist: Lightning, Jazz Music, Spartan, Counterpoint

Lee, Bill

SHE'S GOTTA HAVE IT.
Notes: For full information see **"She's gotta have it"**

Lee, Brenda

16 CLASSIC TRACKS.
Cassette: released on MFP, Feb'82 by EMI Records. Dist: EMI

AS USUAL.
Single (7"): released on MCA, '80 by MCA Records. Dist: Polygram, MCA

BEST OF BRENDA LEE, THE.
Tracks: / Sweet nothin's / I'm sorry / Emotions / Dum dum / Fool number one / You always hurt the one you love / Will you love me tomorrow / When i fall in love / I'll be seeing you / Speak to me pretty / Here comes that feeling / It started all over again / My colouring book / Someday you'll want me to want you / End of the world, The / All alone am i / Losing you / I wonder / My whole world / Sweet impossible you / As usual / Is it true / Think / Love letters / Too many rivers / Make the world go away / Crying time / Sweet dreams / Crying time / Sweet dreams / Yesterday / Always on my mind / For the good times / Feelings.
Notes: Now released on mid-line, the definite Brenda Lee album features this great artists 32 best knoen recording including all her many hits. DOUBLE ALBUM
Album: released on MCA, May'86 by MCA Records. Dist: Polygram, MCA

GOLDEN DECADE, THE.
Album: released on Charly, Jan'85 by Charly Records. Dist: Charly, Cadillac

HERE COMES THAT FELLING.
Album: released on Old Gold, Jul'82 by Old Gold Records. Dist: Lightning, Jazz Music, Spartan, Counterpoint

I'M SORRY.
Single (7"): released on Old Gold, Jul'82 by Old Gold Records. Dist: Lightning, Jazz Music, Spartan, Counterpoint

SWEET NOTHIN'S.
Single (7"): released on Old Gold, Jul'82 by Old Gold Records. Dist: Lightning, Jazz Music, Spartan, Counterpoint

WIEDERSEHN IST WUNDERSCHON.
Tracks: / Wiedersehn ist wunderschon / Ohne dich / Drei Rote / Ich will immer auf dich warten / No my boy / Darling bye bye / Geh nicht am gluck vorbei / Am strand von Hawaii / Kansas City / Darling was ist los mit dir / In meinen traumen / Wo und wann fangt die liebe an / Pourquoi Jamais / La premier fool / Nulla di me / Sono Sciocca.
Album: released on Bear Family, Feb'86 by Bear Family Records. Dist: Rollercoaster Distribution, Swift

WINNING HAND, THE.
Album: released on Monument, Jan'83 by CBS Records. Dist: CBS Distribution

Cassette: released on Monument, Jan'83 by CBS Records. Dist: CBS Distribution

Lee, Byron

ART OF MAS (Lee, Byron and The Dragonaires).
Album: released on Dynamic, Oct'77 by Creole Records. Dist: CBS, Essex

BEST OF CARNIVAL, THE (Lee, Byron and The Dragonaires).
Album: released on Dynamic, Aug'84 by Creole Records. Dist: CBS, Essex

CARNIVAL EXPERIENCE (Lee, Byron and The Dragonaires).
Album: released on Dynamic, Nov'79 by Creole Records. Dist: CBS, Essex

FEELING IT-SOFT MAN (Lee, Byron and The Dragonaires).
Single (12"): released on Dynamic, Jun'84 by Creole Records. Dist: CBS, Essex

HOT HOT HOT (Lee, Byron and The Dragonaires).
Single (12"): released on Dynamic, Aug'84 by Creole Records. Dist: CBS, Essex

JAMAICA'S GOLDEN HITS (Lee, Byron and The Dragonaires).
Cassette: released on Dynamic, Mar'87 by Creole Records. Dist: CBS, Essex

JAMAICA'S GOLDEN HITS(VOL.2) (Lee, Byron and The Dragonaires (And friends)).
Album: released on Dynamic, Feb'84 by Creole Records. Dist: CBS, Essex

Cassette: released on Dynamic, Feb'84 by Creole Records. Dist: CBS, Essex

JAMAICA'S GOLDEN HITS (VOL.2) (Lee, Byron and The Dragonaires).

MIGHTY SPARROW (Lee, Byron and The Dragonaires).
Album: released on Dynamic, Jun'76 by Creole Records. Dist: CBS, Essex

MORE CARNIVAL (Lee, Byron and The Dragonaires).
Album: released on Dynamic, Aug'78 by Creole Records. Dist: CBS, Essex

REGGAE INTERNATIONAL (Lee, Byron and The Dragonaires).
Album: released on Dynamic, Dec'76 by Creole Records. Dist: CBS, Essex

SOCA GIRL (Lee, Byron and The Dragonaires).
Tracks: / Soca girl (calypso version of girlie girlie) / Gimme soca.
Album: released on Dynamic, Sep'86 by Creole Records. Dist: CBS, Essex

Single (12"): released on Dynamic, Jan'86 by Creole Records. Dist: CBS, Essex

SOCA THUNDER (Lee, Byron and The Dragonaires).
Album: released on Dynamics, Jul'87

SOUL-SKA (Lee, Byron all stars).
Album: released on Vista Sounds, '83 by Vista Sounds Records. Dist: Jetstar

THIS IS CARNIVAL (Lee, Byron and The Dragonaires).
Album: released on Dynamic, Sep'76 by Creole Records. Dist: CBS, Essex

TINY WINEY (Lee, Byron and The Dragonaires).
Single (7"): released on Dynamic, Jan'85 by Creole Records. Dist: CBS, Essex

Single (12"): released on Dynamic, Jan'85 by Creole Records. Dist: CBS, Essex

WINE MISS TINY (Lee, Byron and The Dragonaires).
Album: released on Creole, Apr'85 by Creole Records. Dist: Rhino, PRT

Leecan & Cooksey

REMAINING TITLES, THE 1926-27.
Tracks: / Black cat bone blues / Dirty guitar blues / Dollar blues / Royal palm blues / Blue harmonica / Macon Georgia cut out.
Album: released on Saydisc, Apr'87 by Saydisc Records. Dist: Essex, Harmonia Mundi, Roots, H.R. Taylor, Jazz Music, Swift, Projection,

Lee,Christopher

TALES OF MYSTERY & HORROR (Edgar Allen Poe).
Cassette: released on Listen For Pleasure, Oct'82 by MFP Records. Dist: EMI

Lee, Curtis

UNDER THE MOON OF LOVE.
Single (7"): released on Rivival, Jun'81

Single (7"): released on Rivival, Aug'84

Lee, David H.

ME.
Album: released on Tank, Sep'79 by Tank Records.

Lee, Dee C

COME HELL OR WATERS HIGH.
Tracks: / Come hell or waters high / I don't miss.
Single (7"): released on CBS, Feb'86 by CBS Records. Dist: CBS

Single (12"): released on CBS, Feb'86 by CBS Records. Dist: CBS

HEY WHAT'D YA SAY.
Tracks: / Hey what'd ya say / Selina wow wow.
Single (7"): released on CBS, Jul'86 by CBS Records. Dist: CBS

Single (12"): released on CBS, Jul'86 by CBS Records. Dist: CBS

HOLD ON.
Tracks: / Hold on / Welcome.
Single (7"): released on CBS, May'86 by CBS Records. Dist: CBS

Single (12"): released on CBS, May'86 by CBS Records. Dist: CBS

SELINA WOW WOW.
Single (7"): released on CBS, Feb'84 by CBS Records. Dist: CBS

Single (12"): released on CBS, Feb'84 by CBS Records. Dist: CBS

SHRINE.
Tracks: / Shrine / Hey what'd ya say? / That's when something special starts / He's gone / Come hell or waters high / What about me / Still the children cry / Just my type / Holdon.
Album: released on CBS, Jul'86 by CBS Records. Dist: CBS

Cassette: released on CBS, Jul'86 by CBS Records. Dist: CBS

Compact disc: released on CBS, Jul'86 by CBS Records. Dist: CBS

YIPPEE-YI-YAY.
Single (7"): released on CBS, May'84 by CBS Records. Dist: CBS

Single (12"): released on CBS, May'84 by CBS Records. Dist: CBS

Lee, Des Band

DANCE DANCE DANCE.
Single (7"):

Lee, Dicky

I SAW LINDA YESTERDAY.
Tracks: / I saw Linda yesterday / For quite a while.
Single (7"): released on Pinner, Jan'87 by Pinner Records. Dist: Rough Trade, Cartel, Backs

Lee, Dino

KING OF WHITE TRASH.
Album: released on New Rose, Jun'85 Dist: Rough Trade, Cartel

Lee, Frankie

FACE IT.
Album: released on Demon, Feb'85 by Demon Records. Dist: Pinnacle

Lee, Freddie 'Fingers'

COME ON.
Album: released on Charly, Dec'79 by Charly Records. Dist: Charly, Cadillac

FREDDIE FINGERS LEE.
Album: released on Charly, '78 by Charly Records. Dist: Charly, Cadillac

OL' ONE EYES BACK.
Album: released on Charly, Nov'79 by Charly Records. Dist: Charly, Cadillac

ROCKIN' WITH MY PIANO.
Album: released on Magnum Force, Jul'82 by Magnum Music Group Ltd. Dist: Magnum Music Group Ltd, PRT, Spartan

Album: released on Rockstar, Sep'82

Lee, General

WHITE ON WHITE.
Album: released on Revolver, Jun'81 by Revolver Records. Dist: Revolver, Cartel

Lee, George

ANANSI (Lee's Anansi, George).
Album: released on Ebusia, Jan'85 by George Lee Records. Dist: Jetstar

Cassette: released on Ebusia, Jan'85 by George Lee Records. Dist: Jetstar

SEA SHELLS.
Single (12"): released on Ebusia, Sep'84 by George Lee Records. Dist: Jetstar

Lee, George E.

1927-29 (Lee, George E. & his Novelty Singing Orchestra).
Album: released on Fountain-Retrieval, Sep'86 by Retrieval Records. Dist: Retrieval, VJM, Swift, Jazz Music, Wellard, Chris

Lee,Jack

GREATEST HITS: JACK LEE.
Album: released on Lolita, Dec'84 by Lolita Records. Dist: Rough Trade, Cartel

HANGING ON THE TELEPHONE.
Single (7"): released on Disclexia, Sep'82 Dist: Pinnacle

JACK LEE.
Album: released on Eva-Lolita, Jan'86 Dist: Pinnacle

Lee, Jackie

DUCK, THE.
Single (7"): released on Old Gold, Jul'82 by Old Gold Records. Dist: Lightning, Jazz Music, Spartan, Counterpoint

RUPERT L.
Single (7"): released on PRT, Dec'85 by PRT Records. Dist: PRT

Lee, Johnny

DALLAS MAIN TITLE THEME.
Tracks: / Dallas main title theme / Theme from Dallas (Dallas dreams) / Loneliness in Lucy's eyes, The (the life Sue Ellen leads).
Single (7"): released on Warner Bros., Jan'86 by Warner Bros Records. Dist: WEA

JOHNNY LEE.
Cassette: released on Audio Fidelity, Oct'84 Dist: PRT

JOHNNY LEE & WILLIE NELSON (Lee, Johnny & Willie Nelson).
Album: released on Astan, Nov'84 by Astan Records. Dist: Counterpoint

Cassette: released on Astan, Nov'84 by Astan Records. Dist: Counterpoint

Lee, Julia

SNATCH AND GRAB IT.
Tracks: / Tonight's the night / My man stands out / It comes in like a lion / Don't come too soon / Don't save it too long (The money song) / You ain't got it no more / Chuck it (in a bucket) / Can't get enough of that stuff / All this beef and big red tomatoes / Last call for alcohol / Come on over to my house / Trouble in mind / Gotta gimme whatcha got / Snatch and grab it / Mama don't allow it / Ain't it a crime / Knock me a kiss / Take it or leave it / That's what I like / King size papa / I didn't like it the first time / Tell me daddy.
Notes: Original Capitol Recordings. Licensed from Capitol Records Inc. This CD (P) 1987Charly Records Ltd. (C) 1987 Charly Records Ltd.
Compact disc: released on Charly, May'87 by Charly Records. Dist: Charly, Cadillac

Lee, Julie

PARTY TIME.
Album: released on Capitol (France), '83 by Capitol Records. Dist: Conifer

TONIGHT'S THE NIGHT.
Album: released on Charly(R&B), Mar'82 by Charly Records. Dist: Charly, Cadillac

Cassette: released on Charly(R&B), Mar'82 by Charly Records. Dist: Charly, Cadillac

Leek, Andde

DANCING QUEEN.
Single (7"): released on Fascination, May'84 Dist: AM, CBS

Single (12"): released on Fascination, May'84 Dist: AM, CBS

SOUL DANCING.
Single (7"): released on Fascination, Oct'83 Dist: AM, CBS

Single (12"): released on Fascination, Oct'83 Dist: AM, CBS

Lee, Katrina

BORN TOO LATE.
Tracks: / Born too late / Fell into love.
Single (7"): released on Epic, Jul'86 by CBS Records. Dist: CBS

Single (12"): released on Epic, Jul'86 by CBS Records. Dist: CBS

Lee, Laura

RIP OFF.
Single (7"): released on HDH(Holland/Dozier/Holland), Jun'84 by Demon Records. Dist: Pinnacle

RIP OFF, THE.
Album: released on HDH(Holland/Dozier/Holland), Dec'84 by Demon Records. Dist: Pinnacle

Lee, Leapy

LITTLE ARROWS.
Single (7"): released on Old Gold, Jul'82 by Old Gold Records. Dist: Lightning, Jazz Music, Spartan, Counterpoint

Lee, Linford

MOTHER NATURE PLANNED IT SO.
Single (12"): released on Regal, Jun'82

Lee,Lonnie

GREATEST HITS: LONNIE LEE.
Album: released on Rebel (Australia), Feb'84 Dist: Swift

Lee, Maggie

RUNAROUND.
Single (7"): released on CBS, Jun'84 by CBS Records. Dist: CBS

Lee, Miriam

MEN IN MY LIFE, THE.
Single (7"): released on Passion, Sep'85 by Skratch Records. Dist: PRT

Single (12"): released on Passion, Sep'85 by Skratch Records. Dist: PRT

Lee, Peggy

16 GREATEST HITS.
Album: released on EMI (Holland), '83 by EMI Records. Dist: Conifer

ALL AGLOW AGAIN.
Album: released on Capitol, Jul'85 by Capitol Records. Dist: EMI

Cassette: released on Capitol, Jul'85 by Capitol Records. Dist: EMI

BEAUTY AND THE BEAT! (Lee, Peggy and George Shearing and The Quintet).
Tracks: / Do I love you / I lost my sugar in Salt Lake City / If dreams come true / All too soon / Mambo in Miami / Isn't it romantic / Blue prelude / You came a long way from St.Louis / Always true to you in my fashion / There'll be another spring / Get out of town / Satin doll.

BEAUTY & THE BEAT.
Album: released on Pathe MarconiFrance), Mar'85

Cassette: released on Pathe MarconiFrance), Mar'85

BEST OF PEGGY LEE, THE.
Album: released on Music For Pleasure, Apr'83 by EMI Records. Dist: EMI

Cassette: released on Music For Pleasure, Apr'83 by EMI Records. Dist: EMI

Album: released on MCA, Dec'81 by MCA Records. Dist: Polygram, MCA

Cassette: released on MCA, Dec'81 by MCA Records. Dist: Polygram, MCA

BLACK COFFEE.
Album: released on Jasmine, Aug'83 by Jasmine Records. Dist: Counterpoint, Lugtons, Taylor, H.R., Wellard, Chris, Swift, Cadillac

BLUES CROSS COUNTRY.
Album: released on Pathe MarconiFrance), Oct'84

Cassette: released on Pathe MarconiFrance), Oct'84

EASY LISTENING.
Album: released on Artistic (UK), Apr'85

Cassette: released on Artistic (UK), Apr'85

FEVER.
Tracks: / Fever / Ma, he's making eyes at me.
Notes: Also contains:"Ma, he's making eyes at me"
Single (7"): released on Old Gold, Apr'87 by Old Gold Records. Dist: Lightning, Jazz Music, Spartan, Counterpoint

Single (7"): released on EMI (France), Apr'83 by EMI Records. Dist: Conifer

Single (7"): released on EMI (Holland), Jul'84 by EMI Records. Dist: Conifer

Single (7"): released on EMI Golden 45's, Feb'85 by EMI Records. Dist: EMI

GOLDEN GREATS: PEGGY LEE.
Album: released on MCA, Jul'85 by MCA Records. Dist: Polygram, MCA

Cassette: released on MCA, Jul'85 by MCA Records. Dist: Polygram, MCA

IF YOU GO.
Album: released on Capitol, May'85 by Capitol Records. Dist: EMI

Cassette: released on Capitol, May'85 by Capitol Records. Dist: EMI

IS THAT ALL THERE IS?.
Single (7"): released on Capitol (Holland), Jul'84 by Capitol Records. Dist: Conifer

JUMP FOR JOY.
Tracks: / Jump for joy / Back in your own back yard / When my sugar walks down the street / I hear music / Just in time / Old devil moon / What a little moonlight can do / Four or five times / Music! Music! Music! / Cheek to cheek / Glory of love, The.
Notes: Originally released in 1958, 12 excellent up tracks. Lightheartedly backed by the legendary Nelson Riddle and his Orchestra. A swinging classic.
Album: released on Capitol T (USA), Dec'85 Dist: Conifer

MAN I LOVE, THE (Lee, Peggy, Orchestra conducted by Frank Sinatra).
Album: released on Capitol, Apr'84 by Capitol Records. Dist: EMI

Cassette: released on Capitol, Apr'84 by Capitol Records. Dist: EMI

PEGGY LEE COLLECTION, THE.
Cassette: released on Deja Vu, Aug'85 by Deja Vu Records. Dist: Counterpoint Distribution, Record Services Distribution (Ireland)

PEGGY LEE COLLECTION.
Album: released on Deja Vu, Nov'85 by Deja Vu Records. Dist: Counterpoint Distribution, Record Services Distribution (Ireland)

Cassette: released on Deja Vu, Nov'85 by Deja Vu Records. Dist: Counterpoint Distribution, Record Services Distribution (Ireland)

PETE KELLY'S BLUES (Lee, Peggy & Ella Fitzgerald).
Album: released on Jasmine, Sep'83 by Jasmine Records. Dist: Counterpoint, Lugtons, Taylor, H.R., Wellard, Chris, Swift, Cadillac

PRETTY EYES.
Tracks: / As you desire me / It could happen to you / Pretty eyes / Moments like this / Remind me / You fascinate me so / I wanna be loved / I'm walking through / I remember you / Too close for comfort / Fly with me to the moon (in other words) / Because I love him so.
Notes: This album sets Peggy Lee against string and flute arrangements through a selection of warm, misty songs. Billy May leads the orchestra in some expert stringarrangements- a refreshing change to his more familiar brass sound. Includes standards such as 'Too close for comfort' and 'Fly with me to the moon ', some- times lightly swung, sometimes reflective, but all sung in the incomparable Peggy Lee style.
Album: released on Capitol, May'86 by Capitol Records. Dist: EMI

Cassette: released on Capitol, May'86 by Capitol Records. Dist: EMI

RENDEZ-VOUS WITH.
Album: released on Capitol(USA), Mar'84 by Capitol (USA) Records. Dist: EMI

Cassette: released on Capitol(USA), Mar'84 by Capitol (USA) Records. Dist: EMI

SEA SHELLS.
Album: released on Jasmine, Oct'84 by Jasmine Records. Dist: Counterpoint, Taylor, H.R., Wellard, Chris, Swift, Cadillac

THINGS ARE SWINGIN'.
Tracks: / It's a wonderful world / Things are swinging / Alright, okay, you win / Ridin' high / It's been a long time / Lullaby in rhythm / Alone together / I'm beginning to see the light / It's a good, good night / You're getting to be a habit with me / You're mine, you / Life is for livin'.
Notes: One of Peggy Lee's most popular albums which has only been available for some time on import. This 5-star collection of swinging numbers includes 'Alright, okay you win', 'I'm beginning to see the light' and many more.
Album: released on Capitol, Dec'85 by Capitol Records. Dist: EMI

Cassette: released on Capitol, Dec'85 by Capitol Records. Dist: EMI

UNCOLLECTED.
Album: released on Hindsight(UK), Sep'86 Dist: Jazz Music

WITH THE DAVID BARBOUR AND BILLY MAY BANDS 1948.
Album: released on Hindsight(UK), Oct'86 Dist: Jazz Music

Lee, Philip John

FIVE SWORDS.
Album: released on Run River, Feb'87 by Run River Records. Dist: In-Market Ltd., PRT

Lee Roth, David

DAVID LEE ROTH (VIDEO).
Video-cassette (VHS): released on WEA, May'87 by WEA Records. Dist: WEA

Leer, Thomas

4 MOVEMENTS (EP).
Single (12"): released on Cherry Red, Jul'81 by Cherry Red Records. Dist: Pinnacle

ALL ABOUT YOU.
Single (7"): released on Cherry Red, Nov'82 by Cherry Red Records. Dist: Pinnacle

Single (12"): released on Cherry Red, Nov'82 by Cherry Red Records. Dist: Pinnacle

CONTRADICTIONS.
Album: released on Cherry Red, Jan'82 by Cherry Red Records. Dist: Pinnacle

HEARTBEAT.
Single (7"): released on Arista, Feb'85 by Arista Records. Dist: RCA

Single (12"): released on Arista, Feb'85 by Arista Records. Dist: RCA

Single (12"): released on Oblique-Arista, Mar'85

INTERNATIONAL.
Single (7"): released on Oblique, Jul'84 by Arista Records. Dist: Polygram Distribution

Single (12"): released on Oblique, Jul'84 by Arista Records. Dist: Polygram Distribution

Picture disc single: released on Oblique, Jul'84 by Arista Records. Dist: Polygram Distribution

NO.1.
Single (7"): released on Arista, May'85 by Arista Records. Dist: RCA

Single (12"): released on Arista, May'85 by Arista Records. Dist: RCA

SCALE OF TEN.
Album: released on Arista, Jun'85 by Arista Records. Dist: RCA

Cassette: released on Arista, Jun'85 by Arista Records. Dist: RCA

Lee, Rustie

INVITATION TO PARTY.
Album: released on Stylus, Nov'85 Dist: Pinnacle, Terry Blood Distribution, Stylus Distribution

Cassette: released on Stylus, Nov'85 Dist: Pinnacle, Terry Blood Distribution, Stylus Distribution

Leesha Paradise

STAND BY ME.
Single (7"): released on President, Sep'82 by President Records. Dist: Taylors, Spartan

Lees, Ian 'sludge'

CAN YOU DO THE BOOGIE.
Tracks: / Can you do the boogie / New hand jive.
Single (7"): released on Swoop, Jan'83 Dist: Le Matt Music Distribution

VIVA ENGLAND.
Single (7"): released on Lismor, Mar'82 by Lismor Records. Dist: Lismor, Roots, Celtic Music

Lee, Tim

CAN'T GET LOST WHEN YOU'RE GONE (Lee, Tim & Matt Piucci).
Album: released on Enigma (Europe), Nov'86 by Enigma Records. Dist: Rough Trade, Cartel, EMI

Lee, Toney

LOVE SO DEEP.
Single (7"): released on Design Communications, Aug'83

REACH OUT.
Single (7"): released on T.M.T., Jan'83 by T.M.T. Records. Dist: Unknown

Single (12"): released on T.M.T., Jan'83 by T.M.T. Records. Dist: Unknown

Lee, Tony

STREETS OF DREAMS.
Album: released on Lee Lambert, May'80 by Lee Lambert Records. Dist: Cadillac

Lee, Tony, Trio

BRITISH JAZZ ARTISTS VOL.1.
Album: released on Lee Lambert, May'80 by Lee Lambert Records. Dist: Cadillac

BRITISH JAZZ ARTISTS VOL.2 (Lee, Tony, Trio & Terry Smith).
Album: released on Lee Lambert, May'77 by Lee Lambert Records. Dist: Cadillac

Page 592

TONY LEE TRIO AND FRIENDS.
Album: released on Pye, Jul'79

Lee, Wilma
CARTER FAMILY'S GREATEST HITS
(Lee, Wilma/Stoney Cooper).
Notes: 10 tracks
Album: released on Starday, Apr'87

Cassette: released on Starday, Apr'87

Lefevre, Raymond
INTERPRETS JULIO IGLESIAS.
Compact disc: by Phonogram Records. Dist: Polygram

ORCHESTRA DEMONSTRATION.
Compact disc:

ORCHESTRA OPERAMANIA.
Compact disc:

SHEEP IN WOLVES CLOTHING (Lefevre, Raymond, & Broken hearts).
Album: released on Myrrh, Sep'85 by Word Records. Dist: Word Distribution

Cassette: released on Myrrh, Sep'85 by Word Records. Dist: Word Distribution

Left Bank
AND ONE DAY.
Tracks: / And one day / I can fly.
Single (7"): released on Bam Caruso, Apr'86 by Bam Caruso Records. Dist: Rough Trade, Revolver, Cartel

Left Banke
AND SUDDENLY ITS.
Album: released on Bam Caruso, Feb'84 by Bam Caruso Records. Dist: Rough Trade, Revolver, Cartel

HISTORY OF THE LEFT BANKE, THE.
Album: released on Rhino (USA), Jan'86 by Rhino Records (USA).

VOICES CALLING.
Album: released on Bam Caruso, Feb'87 by Bam Caruso Records. Dist: Rough Trade, Revolver, Cartel

WALK AWAY RENEE.
Single (7"): released on Bam Caruso, Feb'84 by Bam Caruso Records. Dist: Rough Trade, Revolver, Cartel

Left Hand Frank
CHICAGO BLUES (Left Hand Frank & Jimmy Rogers).
Album: released on JSP, Jan'82 by JSP Records. Dist: Swift, Projection

Left Hand Side
JIMMY JIMMY JIMMY.
Single (7"): released on Raffia, Aug'84 Dist: Spartan

Leftovers
KAISER BILLS' BATMAN.
Single (7"): released on Plazma, Nov'80

Lefturno
OUT OF SIGHT.
Single (7"):

Single (12"):

Legacy
DON'T WASTE THE NIGHT.
Single (7"): released on Epic, Jun'85 by CBS Records. Dist: CBS

Single (12"): released on Epic, Jun'85 by CBS Records. Dist: CBS

GUILTY.
Tracks: / Guilty / Guilty (inst).
Single (7"): released on EMI, Mar'87 by EMI Records. Dist: EMI

Single (12"): released on EMI, Mar'87 by EMI Records. Dist: EMI

VOICES CALLING.
Album: released on Bam Caruso, Apr'86 by Bam Caruso Records. Dist: Rough Trade, Revolver, Cartel

WALK AWAY RENEE.
Album: released on Bam Caruso, Apr'86 by Bam Caruso Records. Dist: Rough Trade, Revolver, Cartel

Legacy of Lies
SACRIFICE THE QUEEN.
Tracks: / Sacrifice The Queen / It's not really a revolution.
Notes: Free 7" + poster.

Single (12"): released on Quiet, Nov'86 by Quiet Records. Dist: Nine Mile, Cartel

YOU AND WHOSE ARMY.
Tracks: / You and whose army.
Single (12"): released on Quiet, Jun'86 by Quiet Records. Dist: Nine Mile, Cartel

Legacy of the blues
LEGACY OF THE BLUES (Various Artists).
Album: released on Sonet, '82 by Sonet Records. Dist: PRT

Legal Eagles
LEGAL EAGLES Original Soundtrack.
Album: released on MCA, Oct'86 by MCA Records. Dist: Polygram, MCA

Legal Limits
COVER GIRL.
Album: released on FM, Feb'86 by FM-Revolver Records. Dist: EMI

Legato
BUTTERCUP.
Single (12"): released on Unknown, Jun'85

FOOL FOR YOUR LOVE / I CARE.
Single (12"): released on Ital, Apr'82 Dist: Pinnacle

HELLO LOVE.
Single (12"): released on Sanity, Dec'82 by Sanity Records. Dist: Pinnacle, Jetstar

IT'S A SHAME.
Single (7"): released on Sanity, Jun'83 by Sanity Records. Dist: Pinnacle, Jetstar

Single (12"): released on Sanity, Jun'83 by Sanity Records. Dist: Pinnacle, Jetstar

LATELY.
Single (12"): released on Santic, Mar'82

Legator
HUMAN BEINGS.
Single (7"): released on V-Tone, May'82 by Relic. Dist: Swift

HUMAN BEINGS/LONG VERSION.
Single (12"): released on Focus, Sep'82 by Virgin. Dist: EMI

Legear
CRASHIN' DOWN.
Single (7"): released on Protot, Mar'85

Single (12"): released on Protot, Mar'85

Legend
BALLAD, THE.
Single (7"): released on Constrictor, Jun'87 Dist: Rough Trade, Red Rhino, Cartel

DEATH IN THE NURSERY.
Single (7"): released on Workshop, Sep'82

DESTROYS THE BLUES.
Single (7"): released on Creation, Oct'84 Dist: Rough Trade, Cartel

LEGEND Country and Western vocal group.
Album: released on Neptune, Oct'77 by Lismor. Dist: Spartan

Cassette: released on Neptune, Oct'77 by Lismor. Dist: Spartan

LOUISIANIA SATURDAY NIGHT.
Album: released on Neptune, Dec'79 by Lismor. Dist: Spartan

RING OF FIRE.
Album: released on Neptune, Dec'80 by Lismor. Dist: Spartan

Cassette: released on Neptune, Dec'80 by Lismor. Dist: Spartan

SOME OF US STILL BURN.
Single (12"): released on Vinyl Drip, Sep'85 Dist: Backs, Cartel

Legendary...
LEGENDARY BIG BANDS Various original bands (Various bands).
Album: released on Ronco, Apr'82

LEGENDARY COUNTRY & WESTERN HITS (Various Artists).
Cassette: released on Mercury (Germany), Apr'85 by Phonogram Records. Dist: Polygram Distribution

LEGENDARY SPECIALTY MISSING MASTERS (Various Artists).
Album: released on Sonet, Mar'84 by Sonet Records. Dist: PRT

Legendary Crane River...
KOLYER\SUNSHINE\DAVIES\ETC..
Album: released on Dawn Club, Dec'86 Dist: Cadillac, Swift,

LEGENDARY CRANE RIVER JAZZ BAND.
Album: released on Dawn Club, May'79 Dist: Cadillac, Swift,

Legendary Golden Vampires
CREEPING POISON.
Single (7"): released on Exile, Apr'85 by Exile Records. Dist: Pinnacle

GONE FOR GOOD.
Single (7"): released on Exile, Sep'85 by Exile Records. Dist: Pinnacle

TROUBLE BOUND EP.
Tracks: / Trouble Bound EP
Single 10": released on Exile, May'86 by Exile Records. Dist: Pinnacle

Legendary Lonnie
CONSTIPATION SHAKE/DEVILS GUITAR.
Single (7"): released on Nervous, Jun'81 by Nervous Records. Dist: Nervous, Rough Trade

ELEPHANT DANCE.
Single (7"): released on Rebound, May'85 by Rebound Records. Dist: Terry Blood Distribution

Legendary Pink Dots
ASYLUM.
Album: released on Play It Again Sam, Sep'85 Dist: Red Rhino, Cartel

BASILISK.
Album: released on Third Man Tapes, Jul'83

BRIGHTER NOW.
Album: released on In Phaze, Jan'82 by In Phaze Records. Dist: Rough Trade

CURIOUS GUY.
Tracks: / Curious guy.

CURSE.
Album: released on In Phaze, Aug'83 by In Phaze Records. Dist: Rough Trade

FACES IN THE FIRE.
Album: released on Play It Again Sam, Jan'84 Dist: Red Rhino, Cartel

ISLAND OF JEWELS.
Album: released on Play It Again Sam, Nov'86 Dist: Red Rhino, Cartel

LEGENDARY PINK DOTS.
Album: released on In Phaze, May'84 by In Phaze Records. Dist: Rough Trade

LOVERS.
Album: released on Terminal Kaleidoscope, May'85 Dist: Backs, Cartel Distribution

Legendary Stardust Cowboy
ROCK IT TO STARDOM.
Album: released on Amazing, Apr'85 by Big Beat Records. Dist: Pinnacle, Cartel, Jungle

Legend, Johnny
JOHNNY LEGEND AND HIS ROCK 'N' ROLL COMBO (Legend, Johnny & his R 'n' R Combo).
Album: released on Honeymoon, Jun'79 by Honeymoon Records. Dist: Lightning, Superdisc Distribution, Swift

ROCKABILLY RUMBLE (Legend, Johnny & his Skullcaps).
Album: released on Rondelet, Apr'81 Dist: Spartan Distribution

SOAKIN' THE BONE (Legend, Johnny & his Skullcaps).
Album: released on Rondelet, Nov'81 Dist: Spartan Distribution

SOUTH'S GONNA RISE AGAIN (Legend, Johnny & his Skullcaps).
Single (7"): released on Rondelet, Apr'81 Dist: Spartan Distribution

Legend of Jesse James
LEGEND OF JESSE JAMES (Various original artists).
Tracks: / Ride of the redlegs / Quantrill's Quebrillas / Six gun shooting / Have you heard the news / Heaven ain't ready for you yet / Help him Jesus / Old clay county, The / Riding with Jesse James / Hunt them down / Wish we were back in Missouri / Northfield the plan / Northfield the disaster / High walls / Death of me, The / Plot, The / One more shot.
Double Album: released on A&M, Nov'80 by A&M Records. Dist: Polygram

Double cassette: released on A&M, Nov'80 by

A&M Records. Dist: Polygram

Legends
LEGENDS Various artists (Various Artists).
Cassette: released on Cambra, Mar'85 by Cambra Records. Dist: IDS, Conifer

Cassette: released on Cambra, Mar'85 by Cambra Records. Dist: IDS, Conifer

LEGENDS (SOLITAIRE COLLECTION) Various artists (Various Artists).
Double Album: released on Starblend, Nov'83 by Starblend Records. Dist: PRT Distribution

Cassette: released on Starblend, Nov'83 by Starblend Records. Dist: PRT Distribution

LEGENDS VOL.1, THE (Various Artists).

LEGENDS VOL.2, THE (Various Artists).

Legends of the Clans
LEGENDS OF THE CLANS Various artists (Various Artists).

LEGENDS OF THE CLANS Various artists (Various Artists).
Cassette: released on Anvil, Jan'81 Dist: Anvil

Legend, The
EVERYTHING'S COMING UP ROSES.
Tracks: / Everything's coming up roses (6 track).
Single (12"): released on Vinyl Drip, Jul'86 Dist: Backs, Cartel

Legg, Adrian
FRETMELT.
Album: released on Spindrift, Mar'85 Dist: Roots

REQUIEM FOR A HICK.
Album: released on Westwood, Oct'77 by Westwood Records. Dist: Jazz Music, H.R. Taylor, JSU, Pinnacle, Ross Records

TECHNO PICKETS.
Album: released on Spindrift, Oct'83 Dist: Roots

Legge Wade
BE BOP KEYBOARD MASTERS.
Album: released on Vougue Jazz, May'83

Leggio Carmen Quartet
SMILE.
Album: released on Progressive, Apr'81 by Progressive Records. Dist: Jetstar

Legion Of Parasites
CRIMES AGAINST HUMANITY.
Single (12"): released on Fight Back, Aug'84 by Fight Back Records. Dist: Jungle, Cartel

Legrand, Michel
AFTER THE RAIN.
Album: released on Pablo, May'83 by Pablo Records. Dist: Wellard, Chris, IMS-Polygram, BMG

Cassette: released on Pablo, May'83 by Pablo Records. Dist: Wellard, Chris, IMS-Polygram, BMG

LEGRAND JAZZ.
Compact disc: released on Philips (France), '86

MICHEL LEGRAND.
Cassette: released on Audio Fidelity, Oct'84 Dist: PRT

Le Griffe
BREAKING STRAIN.
Album: released on Bullet, May'84 Dist: Bullet Distribution

FAST BIKES / WHERE ARE YOU NOW / THE ACTOR.
Single (7"): released on Bullet, Jan'83 Dist: Bullet Distribution

Single (12"): released on Bullet, Jan'83 Dist: Bullet Distribution

YOU'RE KILLING ME.
Single (7"): released on Bullet, Nov'83 Dist: Bullet Distribution

Single (12"): released on Bullet, Nov'83 Dist: Bullet Distribution

Legs Akimbo
GREASY JOE'S CAFE.
Single (7"): released on Vindaloo, Apr'80 by Vindaloo Records. Dist: WEA, Cartel

Legs Diamond

OUT ON BAIL.
Album: released on Music For Nations, Jun'85 by Music For Nations Records. Dist: Pinnacle

TURN TO STONE.
Tracks: / Turn to stone / Twisted love / Right between the eyes.

Le Guinn, Ursula

RIGEL 9, (THE) (see Bedford, David) (Le Guinn, Ursula & David Bedford).

Lehrer Tom

SONGS BY TOM LEHRER.
Album: released on Decca, Oct'81 by Decca Records. Dist: Polygram

Lehrman, Paul D.

CELTIC MACINTOSH, THE.
Tracks: / Irish washerwoman, The / An seaduine doite / O'Carolan's farewell / Repeal of the Union / Music in the glen / Old storyteller, The / Hewlett / Fisherman's wife, The / Chanter's song, The\Ulster hornpipe / Sheebeg sheemore / Trip to Sligo, The\Green sleeves / Gile mear.
Notes: An album of recordings featuring traditional and contemporary music from irelandand the British Isles, the world's first album produced entirely on a personal computer. The 'Celtic Macintosh' includes recordings of jigs, reels, hornpipes, airs and laments-all produces by a variety of computer synthesizer instruments and sound processors, under the control of an Apple Macintosh 512K computer and M.I.D.I. music software programmed by Paul D. Lehrman. Further information available from ESSP Distribution at the sound House, POB 37B, E. Molesey, Surrey, KT8 9JB Tel: 01-577 5818.
Cassette: released on E.S.S.P., Jan'87 by E.S.S.P. Records. Dist: E.S.S.P.

Leiber\Stoller

ONLY IN AMERICA.
Album: released on WEA, Jan'80 by WEA Records. Dist: WEA

Leibman, Dave

GUIDED DREAM (Leibman, Dave & Tolvan Big Band).
Album: released on Dragon, Jul'87 by Dragon Records. Dist: Jazz Music, Projection, Cadillac

Leige Lord

BURN TO MY TOUCH.
Album: released on Metal Blade, May'87 Dist: Enigma Distribution

Leigh, Carol

BLAME IT ON THE BLUES H (Leigh, Carol/Bob Helm/Ray Skjelbred).

GO BACK WHERE YOU STAYED LAST NIGHT.
Notes: Mono. With H.Smith/E.Carson

Volume 2

YOU'VE GOT TO GIVE ME SOME.
Notes: With Hal Smith/Knocky Parker

Leighton Bernie Quartet

BERNIE LEIGHTONS PLAYS DUKE ELLINGTON AT JIMMY WESTONS.
Album: released on Monmouth, Mar'79

Leisure process

ANXIETY/THE COMPANY.
Single (7"): released on Epic, May'83 by CBS Records. Dist: CBS

Single (12"): released on Epic, May'83 by CBS Records. Dist: CBS

CASHFLOW/THE EMIGRE.
Single (7"): released on Epic, Feb'83 by CBS Records. Dist: CBS

Single (12"): released on Epic, Feb'83 by CBS Records. Dist: CBS

Leitch, Peter

ON A MISTY NIGHT.
Album: released on Criss Cross, Jul'87 Dist: Jazz Music, Jazz Horizons, Cadillac

Leithaug, Solveig

IN THE WORLD.
Notes: Well known in her native Norway, Solveig is now spreading her ministry and music. Already, at the age of 20, her first Christian record has been in the top 20 of Norway's pop charts, and her first single reached number four. "In the world" is Solveig's first release and is somewhat reminiscent of Abba. The tracks were recorded in Norway with her vocals and the backing vocals being done in Los Angeles, including a duet with long-time friend Larry Norman. All the songs were written by Solveig (with English adaptions by various writers) and clearly show that she has some very important and poignent things to say.

Album: released on Day Spring, Feb'87 by Word Records. Dist: Word Distribution, CBS

Cassette: released on Day Spring, Feb'87 by Word Records. Dist: Word Distribution, CBS

Leitmotiv

BIG MONEY.
Tracks: / Big money.

CARESS & CURSE.
Album: released on Paragon, Jan'84 by Paragon Records. Dist: Paragon

SAY REMAIN.
Single (7"): released on Cryptic, Oct'85 Dist: Red Rhino Through Cartel Distributions

Single (12"): released on Cryptic, Oct'85 Dist: Red Rhino Through Cartel

SILENT RUN/LIVING IN A TIN.
Single (7"): released on Pax, Nov'83 by Pax Records. Dist: Red Rhino, Cartel

TO THE SUFFERING.
Single (7"): released on Reconciliation, Feb'85 by Anti system. Dist: Red Rhino, Cartel

Le Jete

LA CAGE AUX FOLLES.
Single (7"): released on Dance, Dec'83 by Dance Records. Dist: Pinnacle

Le Lu Lu

AFRICA.
Tracks: / Africa / Fragile thing / Blip Verts*.
Single (7"): released on Possum, Oct'86 Dist: DMS-RCA

Single (12"): released on Possum, Oct'86 Dist: DMS-RCA

Lemaire Phillipe

WHITE CHRISTMAS.
Cassette: released on Chevron, Nov'84 Dist: Multiple Sound Distributors

Lema, Ray

KINSHASA WASHINGTON DC PARIS.
Album: released on Celluloid (France), Jul'85 by Island. Dist: Polygram

MEDECINE.
Compact disc: by Charly Records. Dist: Charly

Lemarr Tony

1,2,3/LETS DANCE.
Single (7"): released on President, Nov'82 by President Records. Dist: Taylors, Spartan

COME BACK AGAIN/HIT MAN RUN MAN.
Single (7"): released on President, Nov'81 by President Records. Dist: Taylors, Spartan

SEA CRUISE/I WANNA THANK YOU.
Single (7"): released on President, May'82 by President Records. Dist: Taylors, Spartan

Le Mat

THOUGHTS OF THE FOOL / EV'RY DREAM.

Lemon Kittens

BIG DENTIST, THE.
Album: released on Illuminated, Jan'83 by IKF Records. Dist: Pinnacle, Cartel, Jetstar

CAKE BEAST.
Single (12"): released on United Dairies, May'82 Dist: Rough Trade, Indies

SPOON FED AND WRITHING (EP).
Single (7"): released on Whaam, Oct'82 Dist: Pinnacle

Lembo Recordings

LEMBO RECORDINGS, THE (Various Artists).
Album: released on White, May'87

Le Mesurier, John

NOT MUCH CHANGE (see Dunn,Clive & John Le Mesurier) (Le Mesurier, John & Clive Dunn).

Lemon hearts

SHAKE YOURSELF.
Tracks: / Shake yourself / Honey from the spoon / Fine love.
Single (7"): released on Epic, May'87 by CBS Records. Dist: CBS

Single (12"): released on Epic, May'87 by CBS Records. Dist: CBS

Single (7"): released on Step Forward, Oct'79 by Faulty Products Records. Dist: Faulty Products Distribution, Pinnacle

Lemon Pipers

GEEN TAMBOURINE/BLUEBERRY BLUE (EP).

GREEN TAMBOURINE.
Single (7"): released on Old Gold, Jul'84 by Old Gold Records. Dist: Lightning, Jazz Music, Spartan, Counterpoint

GREEN TAMBOURINE/BLUEBERRY BLUE (EP).
Single (7"): released on Flashback, Jul'80 by Flashback Records/PRT Records. Dist: Mainline, PRT

Lemon popsicle 6

LEMON POPSICLE 6 Various artists (Various Artists).
Album: released on Red Bus, Oct'85 by Red Bus Records. Dist: PRT

Lemons

MY FAVOURITE BAND.
Single (7"): released on Race, Aug'81

L'Empire Bakuba

AMOUR PROPRE.
Album: released on Vercky's (Zaire), Jul'84 Dist: Earthworks Distributors, Rough Trade

Lemuria

THUNDER IN YOUR LOVE.
Single (12"): released on Street Level, Nov'84

Lena

CONNECTION.
Tracks: / Connection / Connection (instrumental mix).

Lend An Ear

LEND AN EAR Various groups (Various Artists).
Album: released on Vroom, May'82

Lendor, Kim

JUST WHEN I NEEDED YOU MOST.
Tracks: / Just when I needed you most / Just when I needed you most (club mix acappella).
Single (7"): released on Crystal, 13 Jun'87 by Crystal Records. Dist: Jetstar, Revolver, Cartel

Single (12"): released on Crystal, 13 Jun'87 by Crystal Records. Dist: Jetstar, Revolver, Cartel

JUST WHEN I NEED YOU MOST.
Tracks: / Just when I need you most / Miss you (tough baby).
Single (7"): released on Crystal, Jul'87 by Crystal Records. Dist: Jetstar, Revolver, Cartel

Single (12"): released on Crystal, Jul'87 by Crystal Records. Dist: Jetstar, Revolver, Cartel

Lenihan Tom

SONGS TRADITIONAL IN WEST CLARE.
Album: released on Topic, Jan'81 Dist: Roots Distribution

Lennon And McCartney

LENNON AND MCCARTNEY SONGBOOK, THE (Various Artists).
Notes: Full title: The Lennon and McCartney songbook - with a little help from their friends. Artists include Roxy Music/Elton John/Michael Jackson.

Lennon, Charlie

EMIGRANT SUITE, THE.
Album: released on Gael-Linn (Ireland), Oct'85 by Gael Linn Records. Dist: Roots, Projection, Celtic Music, Jazz Music

Lennon, John

BORROWED TIME (Lennon, John & Yoko Ono).
Single (7"): released on Polydor, Mar'84 by Polydor Records. Dist: Polygram, Polydor

Single (12"): released on Polydor, Mar'84 by Polydor Records. Dist: Polygram, Polydor

DOUBLE FANTASY (Lennon, John & Yoko Ono).
Tracks: / Just like starting over / Kiss kiss kiss / Clean up time / Give me something / I'm losing you / I'm moving on / Beautiful boy (darling boy) / Watching the wheels / I'm your angel / Woman / Beautiful boys / Dear Yoko / Every man has a woman who loves / Hard times are over.
Album: released on Warner-Geffen, Nov'80 by Warner Bros Records. Dist: WEA

Cassette: released on Warner-Geffen, Nov'80 by Warner Bros Records. Dist: WEA

Compact disc: released on Warner-Geffen, Nov'80 by Warner Bros Records. Dist: WEA

GIVE PEACE A CHANCE.
Single (7"): released on EMI Golden 45's, Mar'84 by EMI Records. Dist: EMI

HAPPY XMAS (WAR IS OVER) / LISTEN THE SNOW IS FALLING.
Single (7"): released on Apple, Nov'81 Dist: EMI

IMAGINE.
Tracks: / Imagine / Crippled inside / Jealous guy / It's so hard / I don't want to be a soldier / Give me some truth / Oh my love / How do you sleep / How? / Oh Yoko!.
Compact disc: released on EMI, May'87 by EMI Records. Dist: EMI

Album: released on EMI, Jan'71 by EMI Records. Dist: EMI

IMAGINE-THE FILM.
Video-cassette (VHS): released on PMI, Jun'86 by PMI Records. Dist: EMI

Video-cassette [Betamax]: released on PMI, Jun'86 by PMI Records. Dist: EMI

IMAGINE/WORKING CLASS HERO.
Single (7"): released on Apple, Oct'75 Dist: EMI

I'M STEPPIN OUT.
Single (7"): released on Polydor, Jul'84 by Polydor Records. Dist: Polygram, Polydor

Single (12"): released on Polydor, Jul'84 by Polydor Records. Dist: Polygram, Polydor

INSTANT KARMA (Lennon, John & Yoko Ono).
Single (7"): released on EMI (France), Apr'83 by EMI Records. Dist: Conifer

I SAW HER STANDING THERE (Lennon, John & Elton John).
Single (7"): released on DJM, Mar'81 by DJM Records. Dist: CBS, Polygram

JEALOUS GUY.
Single (7"): released on Parlophone, Nov'85 by EMI Records. Dist: EMI

Single (12"): released on Parlophone, Nov'85 by EMI Records. Dist: EMI

JOHN LENNON 8 album box set.
Tracks: / Give peace a chance / New York city / It's so hard / Woman is the nigger of the world / Mother / Come together / Imagine / Cold turkey / Hound dog.
Boxed set: released on Geffen, Jan'81 by Geffen Records. Dist: WEA, CBS

Cassette: released on Parlophone, Jun'81 by EMI Records. Dist: EMI

JOHN LENNON COLLECTION, THE.
Album: released on EMI, Nov'82 by EMI Records. Dist: EMI

Cassette: released on EMI, Nov'82 by EMI Records. Dist: EMI

JOHN LENNON & PLASTIC ONO BAND.

JOHN LENNON/PLASTIC ONO BAND.
Tracks: / Mother / Hold on / I found out / Working class hero / Isolation / Remember / Love / Well well well / Look at me / God / My mummy's dead.
Compact disc: released on EMI, Jul'87 by EMI Records. Dist: EMI

Album: released on Frame, Jun'84 Dist: Jazz Music

Cassette: released on Frame, Jun'84 Dist: Jazz Music

LIVE IN NEW YORK CITY.
Tracks: / New York city / It's so hard / Woman is the nigger of the world / Well, well, well / Instant Karma (we all shine on) / Mother / Come together / Imagine / Cold turkey / Hound dog / Give peace a chance.
Compact disc: released on Parlophone, '86 by EMI Records. Dist: EMI

Album: released on Parlophone, Feb'86 by EMI Records. Dist: EMI

Cassette: released on Parlophone, Feb'86 by EMI Records. Dist: EMI

Video-cassette (VHS): released on PMI, Jun'86 by PMI Records. Dist: EMI

Video-cassette [Betamax]: released on PMI, Jun'86 by PMI Records. Dist: EMI

LOVE/GIVE ME SOME TRUTH.
Single (7"): released on Parlophone, Nov'82 by EMI Records. Dist: EMI

MENLOVE AVE.
Tracks: / Here we go again / Rock and roll people / Angel baby / My baby left me / To know her is to love her / Steel and glass / Scared / Old dirt road / Nobody loves you (when you're down and out) / Bless you.

Page 594

Album: released on Parlophone, Nov'86 by EMI Records. Dist: EMI

Cassette: released on Parlophone, Nov'86 by EMI Records. Dist: EMI

MENLOVE AVE.
Tracks: / Rock 'n' roll people / Angel baby / Since my baby left me / To know her is to love her / Steel and glass / Scared / Old dirt road / Nobody loves you (when you're down and out) / Bless you.
Compact disc: released on Parlophone, Apr'87 by EMI Records. Dist: EMI

MILK AND HONEY A HEART PLAY (Lennon, John & Yoko Ono).
Album: released on Polydor, Jan'84 by Polydor Records. Dist: Polygram, Polydor

Cassette: released on Polydor, Jan'84 by Polydor Records. Dist: Polygram, Polydor

Picture disc single: released on Polydor, Jan'84 by Polydor Records. Dist: Polygram, Polydor

Compact disc: released on Polydor, Jan'84 by Polydor Records. Dist: Polygram, Polydor

MIND GAMES.
Tracks: / Mind games / Tight as / Aisumasen (I'm sorry) / One day (at a time) / Bring on the Lucie (Freda Peeple) / Nutopian international anthem / Intuition / Out of the blue / Only people / I know (I know) / You are here / Meat city.
Compact disc: released on EMI, Jul'87 by EMI Records. Dist: EMI

Cassette: released on Music for Pleasure, Oct'80 by EMI Records. Dist: MFP Distribution

Compact disc: released on Parlophone, Aug'87 by EMI Records. Dist: EMI

MIND GAMES/NEAT CITY.
Single (7"): released on Parlophone, Jan'73 by EMI Records. Dist: EMI

NO 9 DREAM/ WHAT YOU GOT.
Single (7"): released on Apple, Jan'75 Dist: EMI

NOBODY TOLD ME/O SANITY (WITH YOKO ONO).
Single (7"): released on Polygram, Jan'84 by Polygram Records. Dist: Polygram

POWER TO THE PEOPLE/OPEN YOUR BOX.
Single (7"): released on Parlophone, Mar'71 by EMI Records. Dist: EMI

REFLECTIONS & POETRY.
Album: released on Silhouette (USA), Jun'84 Dist: Swift

ROCK'N'ROLL.
Tracks: / Be-bop-a-lula / Stand by me / Rip it up - ready teddy / You can't catch me / Ain't that a shame / Do you want to dance / Sweet little sixteen / Slippin' and slidin' / Peggy Sue / Bring it on home to me / Bony Moronie / Ya ya / Just because.
Compact disc: released on Parlophone, May'87 by EMI Records. Dist: EMI. Estim retail price in Sep'87 was £11.99.

Album: released on Music for Pleasure, Nov'81 by EMI Records. Dist: MFP Distribution

Cassette: released on Music for Pleasure, Nov'81 by EMI Records. Dist: MFP Distribution

SHAVED FISH.
Tracks: / Give peace a chance / Cold turkey / Instant karma / Power to the people / Mother / Woman is the nigger of the world / Imagine / Whatever gets you thru' the night / Mind games / #9 dream / Happy xmas (war is over) / Give peace a chance (reprise).
Compact disc: released on EMI, May'87 by EMI Records. Dist: EMI

Album: released on Reprise, Oct'75 by WEA Records. Dist: WEA

STAND BY ME/MOVE OVER MS L.
Single (7"): released on Apple, Apr'81 Dist: EMI

TWO MINUTES SILENCE.
Tracks: / Two minutes silence / Two minutes silence (dub).
Single (7"): released on Antar, 30 May'87 by Bam Caruso Records. Dist: Rough Trade, Revolver

WALLS AND BRIDGES.
Tracks: / Going down on love / Whatever gets you thru the night / Old dirt road / What you got / Bless you / Scared / # 9 dream / Surprise, surprise (sweet bird of paradox) / Steel and glass / Beef jerky / Nobody loves you (when you're down and out) / Ya ya.
Compact disc: released on Parlophone, Jul'87 by EMI Records. Dist: EMI

Album: released on Parlophone, Jan'85 by EMI Records. Dist: EMI

Cassette: released on Parlophone, Jan'85 by EMI Records. Dist: EMI

Compact disc: released on Parlophone Aug'87 by EMI Records. Dist: EMI

WATCHING THE WHEELS.
Single (7"): released on Geffen, Apr'81 by Geffen Records. Dist: WEA, CBS

WHATEVER GETS YOU THROUGH THE NIGHT.
Single (7"): released on Parlophone, Jan'74 by EMI Records. Dist: EMI

WOMAN/BEAUTIFUL BOYS.
Single (7"): released on Geffen, Jan'81 by Geffen Records. Dist: WEA, CBS

Lennon, Julian

BECAUSE.
Single (7"): released on EMI, Nov'85 by EMI Records. Dist: EMI

SAY YOU ARE WRONG.
Single (7"): released on Charisma, Feb'85 by Virgin Records. Dist: EMI

Single (12"): released on Charisma, Feb'85 by Virgin Records. Dist: EMI

SECRET VALUE OF DAYDREAMING.
Tracks: / Stick around / You get what you want / Let me tell you / I've seen your face / Coward till the end ? / This is my day / You didn't have to tell me / Everyday / Always think twice / I want your body.
Album: released on Charisma, '86 by Virgin Records. Dist: EMI

Cassette: released on Charisma, '86 by Virgin Records. Dist: EMI

Compact disc: released on Charisma, Jul'87 by Virgin Records. Dist: EMI

STICK AROUND.
Tracks: / Always think twice.
Single (7"): released on Charisma, Mar'86 by Virgin Records. Dist: EMI

Single (12"): released on Charisma, Mar'86 by Virgin Records. Dist: EMI

THIS IS MY DAY.
Tracks: / Everyday.
Single (7"): released on Charisma, May'86 by Virgin Records. Dist: EMI

TIME WILL TEACH US ALL.
Tracks: / Time will teach us all (inst).
Single (7"): released on EMI, Jul'86 by EMI Records. Dist: EMI

Single (12"): released on EMI, Jul'86 by EMI Records. Dist: EMI

TOO LATE FOR GOODBYES.
Single (7"): released on Charisma, Sep'84 by Virgin Records. Dist: EMI

Single (12"): released on Charisma, Sep'84 by Virgin Records. Dist: EMI

VALOTTE.
Compact disc: by Virgin Records. Dist: EMI

Single (7"): released on Charisma, Dec'84 by Virgin Records. Dist: EMI

Single (12"): released on Charisma, Dec'84 by Virgin Records. Dist: EMI

Picture disc single: released on Charisma, Dec'84 by Virgin Records. Dist: EMI

Album: released on Charisma, Oct'84 by Virgin Records. Dist: EMI

Cassette: released on Charisma, Oct'84 by Virgin Records. Dist: EMI

Compact disc: released on Charisma, Oct'84 by Virgin Records. Dist: EMI

Lennox-Martin, Anne

DON'T DILLY DALLY.

PRETTY PLOUGHBOY, THE (see also Sam Stephens).
Album: released on Dingles, '83 by Dingle's Records. Dist: Projection

PRETTY PLOUGHBOY,THE.
Album: released on Dingles, '83 by Dingles Records. Dist: Projection

TURN THE MUSIC ON (see also Sam Stephens).
Album: released on Dingles, '83 by Dingle's Records. Dist: Projection

Lenoir, J.B.

CHESS MASTERS.
Album: released on Chess, Jul'84 by Charly Records. Dist: Charly, Swift, PRT, Discovery, IMS, Polygram

NATURAL MAN.
Album: released on Chess, Oct'86 by Charly Records. Dist: Charly, Swift, PRT, Discovery, IMS, Polygram

ONE OF THESE MORNING (Lenoir, J.B./Willie Dixon).
Album: released on JSP, Sep'86 by JSP Records. Dist: Swift, Projection

Lenroy, Derek

DEEP MEDITATION (Lenroy, Derek & Ringo).
Single (12"): released on Body Music, Nov'82 by Body Music Records. Dist: Jetstar

I'LL NEVER LOVE AGAIN.
Single (12"): released on Raiders, Mar'85 Dist: Jetstar

Lenya, Lotte

SEPTEMBER SONG.
Album: released on CBS(Masterworks), Feb'85 by CBS Records. Dist: CBS

Cassette: released on CBS(Masterworks), Feb'85 by CBS Records. Dist: CBS

Leoi

YOU MEAN EVERYTHING TO ME.
Single (7"): released on BPOP, Oct'85

Single (12"): released on BPOP, Oct'85

Leom, Trisha

MY BOY LOLLIPOP.
Single (7"): released on Master Funk, Dec'81 by Master Funk Records. Dist: PRT

Leon

COUNTRY.
Album: released on Homespun(Ireland), '82 by Outlet Records. Dist: Outlet

Cassette: released on Homespun(Ireland), '82 by Outlet Records. Dist: Outlet

COWGIRL AND THE DANDY.
Album: released on Homespun(Ireland), '82 by Outlet Records. Dist: Outlet

Cassette: released on Homespun(Ireland), '82 by Outlet Records. Dist: Outlet

GREAT COUNTRY SINGER COUNTRY LOVE.
Album: released on Homespun(Ireland), '82 by Outlet Records. Dist: Outlet

Cassette: released on Homespun(Ireland), '82 by Outlet Records. Dist: Outlet

JEALOUS HEART.
Album: released on Homespun(Ireland), Jul'82 by Outlet Records. Dist: Outlet

Cassette: released on Homespun(Ireland), Jul'82 by Outlet Records. Dist: Outlet

Single (7"): released on Homespun(Ireland), Feb'83 by Outlet Records. Dist: Outlet

JEALOUS HEART (Leon & Johnnie Johnston).
Single (7"): released on Homespun(Ireland), Apr'83 by Outlet Records. Dist: Outlet

YOU MADE MY LIFE COMPLETE.
Single (7"): released on Homespun(Ireland) May'80 by Outlet Records. Dist: Outlet

Le One

INCOMMUNIQUE.
Single (7"): released on Ricochet, Nov'83 by Ricochet Records.

Single (12"): released on Ricochet, Nov'83 by Ricochet Records.

Leonhart, Jay

SALAMANDER PIE.
Compact disc: released on DMP, '86 by DMP Records. Dist: Venture

THERE'S GONNA BE TROUBLE.
Tracks: / Summers on the river / There's gonna be trouble / Ali Privaye / Life in the middle ages / Lonely rider / Jimmy don't go away / Confirmation / Couple from the Duluth / Smile / I got the blues / Down in the south / Patience / Blues for Donna.
Notes: Music composed by Charlie Parker (Atlantic Music Corp, BMI). Music composed by Jay Leonhart (Chancellor Music Ltd, BMI). Lyrics written by Jay Leonhart (Chancellor Music Ltd, BMI). Joe Beck-Guitar/Jay Leonhart-vocals, bass, acoustic guitar, synthesizer programming.
Album: released on Sunnyside (USA), Nov'86 Dist: Mole Jazz Distribution, Conifer Distribution

Leoni, Paul

FLIGHTS OF FANCY.
Tracks: / Light of experience / Feelings.
Compact disc: released on Nouveau Music, '86 Dist: PRT Distribution

Album: released on Nouveau Music, Jan'83 Dist: PRT Distribution

Cassette: released on Nouveau Music, Jan'83 Dist: PRT Distribution

Album: released on Nouveau Music, '83 Dist: PRT Distribution

Cassette: released on Nouveau Music, '83 Dist: PRT Distribution

Leon, Trisha

MY BOY LOLLIPOP.
Single (7"): released on Master Funk, Aug'87 by Master Funk Records. Dist: PRT

Leopard, The

GIUSEPPE DI LAMPEDUSA Read by John Houseman.
Cassette: released on Caedmon(USA), Aug'83 by Caedmon (USA) Records. Dist: Gower, Taylors, Discovery

Leo's Sunshipp

GIVE ME THE SUNSHINE.
Single (7"): released on Expansion, Aug'86 Dist: PRT

Lepke, Louis

ARGENTINA SURRENDER.
Single (12"): released on Exclusive, Jul'82 Dist: Jetstar

BACK OFF.
Single (12"): released on Music Works, Jan'83 Dist: Jetstar Distribution

Le Rock

LE ROCK / ANOTHER BOTTLE OF WINE.
Single (7"): released on OGP, May'83 Dist: Pinnacle

Leroi Brothers

AIN'T I'M A DOG.
Single (7"): released on Demon, May'84 by Demon Records. Dist: Pinnacle

CHECK THIS ACTION.
Album: released on Demon, Apr'84 by Demon Records. Dist: Pinnacle

FORGET ABOUT THE DANGER.
Album: released on Demon, Apr'85 by Demon Records. Dist: Pinnacle

PROTECTION FROM ENEMIES.
Album: released on Demon, Apr'85 by Demon Records. Dist: Pinnacle

Leroux, Gaston

PHANTOM OF THE OPERA.
Notes: Read by Anton Rodgers. Who is the Phantom of the Opera? What are his dark and deadly designs? And what ghastly secret lies beneath his mask? Beneath the Opera House in Paris, somewhere in the dark labyrinths hidden from the Public's eyes, the Phantom lurks, watching and waiting. In his crazed obsession to further the career of a beautiful young singer he will stop at nothing, not even murder. Running time: 3 hours approx.
Cassette: released on Listen For Pleasure, Feb'87 by MFP Records. Dist: EMI

Leroy, Baby Face

BABY FACE LEROY & FLOYD JONES (Leroy, Baby Face & Floyd Jones).
Album: released on Flyright, Oct'83 by Flyright Records. Dist: Krazy Kat, Swift, Jazz Music

BLUES IS KILLING ME (Leroy, Baby Face & Floyd Jones).
Album: released on Flyright, Oct'86 by Flyright Records. Dist: Krazy Kat, Swift, Jazz Music

Leroy Brothers

LUCKY LUCKY ME.
Album: released on New Rose, May'85 Dist: Rough Trade, Cartel

Leroy, Derek

LOVE HAS GONE AWAY.
Single (12"): released on Raiders, Sep'84 Dist: Jetstar

Le Rue

LE RUE.
Album: released on Unamerican Activities, Feb'87 by Hotshot Records. Dist: Cartel, Projection, Red Rhino, Hotshot

Lerwick Brass Band

UP-HELLY-AA (EP).
Single (7"): released on Galley, Feb'82 Dist: Galley

Les 4 Guitarists...

WORLD TOUR (Les 4 Guitarists De L' Apocalypso-Bar).
Album: released on Recommended, Jun'87 by Recommended Records. Dist: Recommended, Impetus, Rough Trade

Les Afferux

HELL IS PAVED WITH GOOD INTENTIONS.
Single (7"): released on Mamba, Oct'85 Dist: M.I.S.

Les Ambassadeurs

DANCE MUSIC FROM W'AFRICA.
Album: released on Rounder (USA), Jan'85 Dist: Mike's Country Music Room Distribution, Jazz Music Distribution, Swift Distribution, Roots Records Distribution, Projection Distribution, Topic Distribution

Les Compagnons...

LES COMPAGNONS DE LA CHANSON (Les Compagnons De La Chanson).
Album: released on EMI (France), Jun'83 by EMI Records. Dist: Conifer

Cassette: released on EMI (France), Jun'83 by EMI Records. Dist: Conifer

Lesear, Anne

TAKE HIM BACK (TAXI).
Single (7"): released on Allegiance, May'84 by PRT Records. Dist: PRT

Les Elite

PATHWAYS.
Album: released on Unicorn, 30 May'87 Dist: Nine Mile, Cartel

Les Enfants

TOUCHE.
Album: released on Chrysalis, Apr'85 by Chrysalis Records. Dist: CBS

Cassette: released on Chrysalis, Apr'85 by Chrysalis Records. Dist: CBS

Les Girls!

LES GIRLS! Various artists (Various Artists).
Album: released on Cambra, Aug'83 by Cambra Records. Dist: IDS, Conifer

Cassette: released on Cambra, Aug'83 by Cambra Records. Dist: IDS, Conifer

Lesley, Chris

TURNING TABLES (Lesley, Chris & Nick Hooper).
Album: released on Banana Enterprises, Feb'87 by Banana Enterprises. Dist: Banana Enterprises

Lesley, Jean

JEAN LESLEY & STETSON (Lesley, Jean & Stetson).
Album: released on Solent, Aug'84 by Solent Records.

Cassette: released on Solent, Aug'84 by Solent Records.

Lesley, Kim

STORE IT UP 'TIL MORNING (Lesley, Kim & Her All Stars).
Album: released on Zodiac, May'82 Dist: Jazz Music

Lesmana, Indra

FOR EARTH AND HEAVEN.
Tracks: / Stephanie / L.A. / Corrobores / Song for ... / For earth and heaven / Morro rock / Dancin' shore / First glance.
Album: released on MCA, Aug'86 by MCA Records. Dist: Polygram, MCA

Cassette: released on MCA, Aug'86 by MCA Records. Dist: Polygram, MCA

Compact disc: released on MCA, Jul'87 by MCA Records. Dist: Polygram, MCA

NO STANDING.
Album: released on Zebra, Feb'87 by Cherry Red Records. Dist: Pinnacle

Cassette: released on Zebra, Feb'87 by Cherry Red Records. Dist: Pinnacle

Les Miserables

LES MISERABLES Original London cast.
Tracks: / At the end of the day / I dreamed a dream / Lovely ladies / Who am I ? / Cme to me / Confrontation / Castle on a cloud / Master of the house / Stars / Look down / Little people / Red and black / Do you hear the people sing ? / I saw him once in my life / Heart full of love, A / One day more / On my own / Attack, The / Little fall of rain, A / Drink with me / Bring him home / Dog eats dog / Soliloquy / Empty chairs and empty tables / Wedding chorale / Beggars at the feast / Finale.
Notes: Featuring: Patti LuPone, Colm Wilkingson, Roger Allam, Rebecca Caine, Ian Tucker, Alun Armstrong etc. Cond.Martin Koch.Songs by Claude-Michel Schonberg, Alain Boubill and Jean-Marc Natel with English lyrics by Herbert Kretzmer.
Compact disc: released on First Night, '86 by Safari Records. Dist: Pinnacle

Album: released on Safari, Dec'85 by Safari Records. Dist: Pinnacle

Cassette: released on Safari, Dec'85 by Safari Records. Dist: Pinnacle

LES MISERABLES Original Paris cast recording (Les Miserables "Highlights").
Album: released on First Night, Jan'86 by Safari Records. Dist: Pinnacle

Cassette: released on First Night, Jan'86 by Safari Records. Dist: Pinnacle

LES MISERABLES (HIGHLIGHTS) Original French Cast Recording.
Compact disc: released on First Night, Jun'87 by Safari Records. Dist: Pinnacle

Lessing, Doris

Ancient ways to new freedom

GOLDEN NOTEBOOK, THE.
Cassette: released on Caedmon(USA), Apr'85 by Caedmon (USA) Records. Dist: Gower, Taylors, Discovery

Lester, Bob

ONE MORE TIME (Lester, Bob & The Moonglows).
Album: released on Relic (US), Mar'85

Lester, Ketty

LOVE LETTERS.
Single (7"): released on Old Gold, Jul'82 by Old Gold Records. Dist: Lightning, Jazz Music, Spartan, Counterpoint

Lester Square

PLUG, THE (Lester Square and the Square Deal Surfs).
Single (7"): released on Thin Sliced, Jul'84 by Thin Sliced Records. Dist: Rough Trade Distribution, Cartel Distribution

Single (12"): released on Thin Sliced, Jul'84 by Thin Sliced Records. Dist: Rough Trade Distribution, Cartel Distribution

Les Thugs

RADICAL HYSTERY.
Single (7"): released on Closer (France), Mar'86 Dist: Nine Mile, Cartel

Album: released on Closer (France), Mar'86 Dist: Nine Mile, Cartel

Lesueur, James

PRINCE DE L'ACCORDEON.
Tracks: / Piccolo rag / Valse emraude / Samba sympa / Matins qui chantent / Pistolette / Accordeonarama / Surprise Polka / La belle Mexicaine / Potion magique / Sambatucada / Accordeon en fete.
Album: released on Accordion Record Club, Jul'86 by Accordion Record Club Records. Dist: Accordion Record Club

Les uns et les Autres

LES UNS ET LES AUTRES Original film soundtrack (Various Artists).
Compact disc: released on RCA, '83 by RCA Records. Dist: RCA, Roots, Swift, Wellard, Chris, I & B, Solomon & Peres Distribution

LES UNS ET LES AUTRES Original Soundtrack.
Compact disc: released on RCA, '83 by RCA Records. Dist: RCA, Roots, Swift, Wellard, Chris, I & B, Solomon & Peres Distribution

Les Zazous

ANOTHER TOWN.
Tracks: / Another town / Against the tide / Today.
Single (7"): released on Spell, Mar'87

Let Flatt Get It

LET FLATT GET IT Various artists (Various Artists).
Album: released on Charly, May'86 by Charly Records. Dist: Charly, Cadillac

Lethal Poor

TRANCE FLOOR.
Single (12"): released on Lethal Productions, Sep'85 Dist: Rough Trade, Cartel

Lethal Weapon

LETHAL WEAPON Original soundtrack (Various Artists).
Album: released on Warner Brothers, Aug'87 by Warner Bros Records. Dist: WEA

Cassette: released on Warner Brothers, Aug'87 by Warner Bros Records. Dist: WEA

LETHAL WEAPON Original soundtrack (Various Artists).
Tracks: / Lethal weapon / Amanda / Meet Martin Riggs / Roger / Coke deal / Mr. Joshua / They've got my daughter / Desert, The / Nightclub / Weapon, The.
Album: released on Warner Brothers, Sep'87 by WEA Records. Dist: WEA

Cassette: released on Warner Brothers, Sep'87 by WEA Records. Dist: WEA

Lets.....

LET'S ALL GO TO MUSIC HALL Ted Ray & other artists.
Double Album: released on Argo, Aug'75 by Decca Records. Dist: Polygram Deleted '83.

LET'S ALL GO WILD The fampus rolin' rockabilly sound.
Album: released on Dial (Holland), Apr'79 Dist: Swift

LET'S BEAT IT various artists.
Album: released on CBS, Jun'85 by CBS Records. Dist: CBS

Cassette: released on CBS, Jun'85 by CBS Records. Dist: CBS

LET'S BREAK ! Various artists (Various Artists).
Video-cassette (VHS): released on Warner, Oct'84 by Warner Bros Records. Dist: WEA

LET'S DANCE TO THE 80'S Various artists (Various Artists).
Compact disc: released on Vogue, '86 Dist: Discovery, Jazz Music, PRT, Swift

LET'S FLAT GET IT Various artists (Various Artists).
Tracks: / Lets flat get it / Billy boy / Baby lets play house / Such a night / Once with you / Shape I'm in, The / Can'tcha see / Little ole you / I'd rather be lucky / Pretty blue jean baby / Mama mama / When I'm alone with you / You've got me lyin' / Satisfaction Guaranteed / Where did you stay last night / Talk about my baby.
Album: released on Charly, Apr'86 by Charly Records. Dist: Charly, Cadillac

LET'S GO ROCK AND ROLL Various artists (Various Artists).
Tracks: / Let's go rock and roll / Hot rod / Rock, rock, rock / Sixteen teens / R' n' roll march / Cow jumped over, The / Rock me a boogie / 24 Boys friends / Number 9 train / Wildcat tamer / Susie and Pat / Hey Hester / My girl across town / Take it home to Grandma.
Album: released on Esoldun, Dec'86 by Esoldun Records. Dist: Swift

LET'S HEAR IT FROM THE GIRLS Various artists (Various Artists).
Tracks: / Cloudbusting / We don't need another hero / Someone for me / You look good to me / Dare to dream / Pain / Light my fire / Holding out for a hero / After the love has gone / One dance won't do / This is my life / Sugar walls / Smooth operator / Love is a battlefield / That ole devil called love / See the day / Together we are beautiful / Power of love / I'll be your friend / Misty blue / Stir it up / Integrity / Automatic / I will survive / If you're ready (come go with me) / Let the four winds blow / In the shelter of your arms / Round and around.
Notes: Ever heard the sound 28 girls make when they get together? Then you have got to hear "Let's hear it from the girls",from Stylus. 28 hot selling girl singers sing their hits, for the first time in recorded history, on one unique double album set.
Album: released on Stylus, Apr'86 Dist: Pinnacle, Terry Blood Distribution, Stylus Distribution

Cassette: released on Stylus, Apr'86 Dist: Pinnacle, Terry Blood Distribution, Stylus Distribution

LET'S STOMP various artists.
Album: released on Edsel, Oct'82 by Demon Records. Dist: Pinnacle, Jazz Music, Projection

LET'S TRY ANOTHER IDEAL GUEST HOUSE (Various Artists).
Album: released on Shelter, Jun'87

Let's Active

BIG PLANS FOR EVERYBODY.
Tracks: / In little ways / Talking to myself / Writing on the book of last pages / Last chance town / Won't go wrong / Badger / Fell / Still dark out / Whispered news / Reflecting pool / Route 67.
Album: released on IRS, Jun'86 Dist: Polygram

Cassette: released on IRS, Jun'86 Dist: Polygram

CYPRESS.
Album: released on I.R.S.(Independent Record Syndicate), Sep'84 by I.R.S.. Dist: MCA

IN LITTLE WAYS.
Tracks: / Two you's.
Single (7"): released on IRS, Jun'86 Dist: Polygram

Single (12"): released on IRS, Jun'86 Dist: Polygram

Let's get dressed

LOVE ANOTHER WAY.
Single (7"): released on Fast, Mar'84 by Fast Forward Communications (Scotland). Dist: Cartel

Lets wreck mother

CUTS.
Single (12"): released on Flicknife, Jun'85 by Flicknife Records. Dist: Spartan

Letterman,The

LETTERMAN,THE The best of.
Compact disc: released on Capitol, '87 by Capitol Records. Dist: EMI

Lettermen

ALL TIME GREATEST HITS.
Tracks: / Goin' out of my head / Can't take my eyes off you / When I fall in love / Put your head on my shoulder / Love / Traces/Memories / Hurt so bad / Theme from a summer place / Sangria / Way you look tonight (The) / I believe.
Compact disc: released on EMI, Apr'87 by EMI Records. Dist: EMI

EVERGREEN.
Album: released on President, Mar'85 by President Records. Dist: Taylors, Spartan

Cassette: released on President, Mar'85 by President Records. Dist: Taylors, Spartan

Letters

NOBODY LOVES ME.
Single (7"): released on Heartbeat, '81 Dist: Revolver, Pinnacle

Letter to Brezhnev

LETTER TO BREZHNEV Original soundtrack (Various Artists).
Album: released on London, Nov'85 by London Records. Dist: Polygram

Cassette: released on London, Nov'85 by London Records. Dist: Polygram

Let the good times roll

LET THE GOOD TIMES ROLL Various artists.
Cassette: released on Cambra, '83 by Cambra Records. Dist: IDS, Conifer

Album: released on MFP, Feb'80 by EMI Records. Dist: EMI

Cassette: released on Gold, Apr'81 by Gold Records. Dist: President Distribution, Taylors

LET THE GOOD TIMES ROLL-EARLY ROCK CLASSICS 1952-58 Various artists
Album: released on Capitol, Nov'81 by Capitol Records. Dist: EMI

Cassette: released on Capitol, Nov'81 by Capitol Records. Dist: EMI

Let them eat cake

I GET STATIC.
Single (7"): released on PRT, Aug'84 by PRT Records. Dist: PRT

Single (12"): released on PRT, Aug'84 by PRT Records. Dist: PRT

Let The Music Scratch

LET THE MUSIC SCRATCH various artists (Various Artists).
Album: released on Streetwave, Jul'84 by Streetwave Records. Dist: PRT Distribution

Levaillant, Denis

BARIUM CIRCUS.
Tracks: / L'entree des athletes aux chevaux noirs / La trapeziste / Le jongleur masque / Les Equilibristes / La pantomime amoureuse / Les petits chiens gris / Le magicien / Le clown blanc / La parade des augustes / Le depart des fauves.
Album: released on Nato (France), Sep'86 by Disques Nato. Dist: Essex Record Distributors Ltd.

DIRECT.
Tracks: / Un jour sur les conseils de Paul... / Comme un duc / Lennie up / Thelonius melodius / Earl's pearls / Hi, Samson! / Les deux noms de bud / La derniere prise / Le rendez-vous (New York city, St.Mark's place) / Le jeune franc avec le vieux cecil / Le lendemain / Paul n'avait laisse aucune instruction pour refermer la ....
Album: released on Nato (France), Sep'86 by Disques Nato. Dist: Essex Record Distributors Ltd.

Levashov, Valentini

FOLK SONGS.

Cassette: released on Melodiya (USSR), Feb'79 Dist: T.B.C Distribution

Levay, Rik

MISS YOU/YOUR LOVE YOU GIVE.
Single (7"): released on Loose End, Aug'83 by MCA Records. Dist: CBS, MCA

Single (12"): released on Loose End, Aug'83 by MCA Records. Dist: CBS, MCA

Level 42

EARLY TAPES, THE (JULY/AUGUST, 1980).
Album: released on Polydor, Aug'83 by Polydor Records. Dist: Polygram, Polydor

Cassette: released on Polydor, Aug'83 by Polydor Records. Dist: Polygram, Polydor

INTERVIEW PICTURE DISC.
Album: released on Baktabak, May'87 by Baktabak Records. Dist: Arabesque

I SLEEP ON MY HEART.
Single (7"): released on Polydor, Nov'85 by Polydor Records. Dist: Polygram, Polydor Deleted '86.

Single 10": released on Polydor, Nov'85 by Polydor Records. Dist: Polygram, Polydor Deleted '86.

Single (12"): released on Polydor, Nov'85 by Polydor Records. Dist: Polygram, Polydor

IT'S OVER.
Tracks: / Physical presence.
Single (7"): released on Polydor, Aug'87 by Polydor Records. Dist: Polygram, Polydor

Single (12"): released on Polydor, Aug'87 by Polydor Records. Dist: Polygram, Polydor

LESSONS IN LOVE.
Tracks: / Hot water (live) / World machine.
Single (7"): released on Polydor, Apr'86 by Polydor Records. Dist: Polygram, Polydor

Single (12"): released on Polydor, Apr'86 by Polydor Records. Dist: Polygram, Polydor

LEVEL 42.
Compact disc: released on Polydor, Jul'84 by Polydor Records. Dist: Polygram, Polydor

Album: released on Polydor, Aug'81 by Polydor Records. Dist: Polygram, Polydor

Cassette: released on Polydor, Aug'81 by Polydor Records. Dist: Polygram, Polydor

PHYSICAL PRESENCE EP - FOLLOW ME.
Single (7"): released on Polydor, Jun'85 by Polydor Records. Dist: Polygram, Polydor

Single (12"): released on Polydor, Jun'85 by Polydor Records. Dist: Polygram, Polydor

PHYSICAL PRESENCE, A.
Double Album: released on Polydor, Jun'85 by Polydor Records. Dist: Polygram, Polydor

Compact disc: by Polydor Records. Dist: Polygram, Polydor

Double cassette: released on Polydor, Jun'85 by Polydor Records. Dist: Polygram, Polydor

PURSUIT OF ACCIDENTS, THE.
Compact disc: by Polydor Records. Dist: Polygram, Polydor

Album: released on Polydor, Sep'82 by Polydor Records. Dist: Polygram, Polydor

Cassette: released on Polydor, Sep'82 by Polydor Records. Dist: Polygram, Polydor

RUNNING IN THE FAMILY.
Tracks: / Running in the family / Dream crazy.
Single (7"): released on Polydor, Jan'87 by Polydor Records. Dist: Polygram, Polydor

Single (12"): released on Polydor, Jan'87 by Polydor Records. Dist: Polygram, Polydor

RUNNING IN THE FAMILY (LP).

Tracks: / Lessons in love / Children say / Running in the family / It's over / To be with you again / Two solitudes / Fashion fever / Sleepwalkers (The) / Freedom someday.
Album: released on Polydor, Mar'87 by Polydor Records. Dist: Polygram, Polydor

Cassette: released on Polydor, Mar'87 by Polydor Records. Dist: Polygram, Polydor

Compact disc: released on Polydor, Mar'87 by Polydor Records. Dist: Polygram, Polydor

SOMETHING ABOUT YOU.
Single (7"): released on Polydor, Sep'85 by Polydor Records. Dist: Polygram, Polydor Deleted '86.

Single (12"): released on Polydor, Sep'85 by Polydor Records. Dist: Polygram, Polydor

STANDING IN THE LIGHT.
Tracks: / Micro-Kid / Sun goes down / Out of sight, out of mind / Dance on heavy weather / Pharoah's dream of endless time / Standing in the light / I want eyes / People / Machine stops.
Compact disc: released on Polydor, '83 by Polydor Records. Dist: Polygram, Polydor

Album: released on Polydor, Aug'83 by Polydor Records. Dist: Polygram, Polydor

Cassette: released on Polydor, Aug'83 by Polydor Records. Dist: Polygram, Polydor

STRATEGY.
Album: released on Elite, Dec'81 Dist: PRT

TO BE WITH YOU AGAIN.
Tracks: / To be with you again / Micro kid (live) / Lessons in love (Shep Pettibone remix)*.
Notes: * = Extra track on 12" only.
Single (7"): released on Polydor, Apr'87 by Polydor Records. Dist: Polygram, Polydor

Single (12"): released on Polydor, Apr'87 by Polydor Records. Dist: Polygram, Polydor

TRUE COLOURS.
Compact disc: by Polydor Records. Dist: Polygram, Polydor

Album: released on Polydor, Sep'84 by Polydor Records. Dist: Polygram, Polydor

Cassette: released on Polydor, Sep'84 by Polydor Records. Dist: Polygram, Polydor

VIDEO SINGLES.
Notes: One of Britain's top funk/pop bands with five promos for familiar hit singles including 'Leaving me now' and 'Lessons in love'. 1986 compilation. Total playing time: 20 minutes.
Video-cassette (VHS): released on Polygram, Jul'86 by Polygram Records. Dist: Polygram

WORLD MACHINE.
Tracks: / World machine / Physical presence / Something about you / Leaving me now / I sleep on my heart / It's not the same for us / Good man in a storm / Coup d'etat / Lying still / Dream crazy / Love games (US remix) / Hot water (12" mix) / Sun goes down (living it up) (up front mix) / Chinese way (US mix) / I sleep on my heart (remix) / Something about you (Sisa mix).
Notes: A limited cassette version of the album "World machine" features the whole album on side one and a bonus side of 12" mixes on side two.
Compact disc: released on Polydor, Oct'85 by Polydor Records. Dist: Polygram, Polydor

Cassette: released on Polydor, May'86 by Polydor Records. Dist: Polygram, Polydor

WORLD MACHINE (U.S. EDITION).
Tracks: / Something about you / World machine / Physical presence / Leaving me now / Hot water / It's not the same for us / Good man in a storm / Chant has begun.
Notes: Limited U.S.edition. Available for a limited period only the U.S. Edition of "World Machine" which has now taken Level 42 into the top 30 stateside! Features two tracks not on the UK edition-"Hot Water" and "The Chant Has Begun".
Compact disc: released on Polydor, '86 by Polydor Records. Dist: Polygram, Polydor

Album: released on Polydor, May'86 by Polydor Records. Dist: Polygram, Polydor

Levert

BIG THROWDOWN, THE.
Album: released on Atlantic (USA), Aug'87 Dist: WEA

Album: released on Atlantic, Aug'87 by WEA Records. Dist: WEA

Cassette: released on Atlantic, Aug'87 by WEA Records. Dist: WEA

CASANOVA.
Single (7"): released on Atlantic, Aug'87 by WEA Records. Dist: WEA

Single (12"): released on Atlantic, Aug'87 by WEA Records. Dist: WEA

GOES MY MIND (POP POP POP POP).
Tracks: / Looking for love.
Single (7"): released on Atlantic, Oct'86 by WEA Records. Dist: WEA

Single (12"): released on Atlantic, Oct'86 by WEA Records. Dist: WEA

Levey, Stan

STANLEY THE STEAMER (Levey, Stan Sextet (featuring Dexter Gordon)).
Album: released on Affinity, May'82 by Charly Records. Dist: Charly, Cadillac

WEST COAST RHYTHM (see also Red Mitchell) (Levey, Stan & Red Mitchell).
Album: released on Affinity, '83 by Charly Records. Dist: Charly, Cadillac

Leviathan

BALLADS & SONGS OF THE WHALING TRADE.
Album: released on Wynd-up, '81 Dist: Wynd-Up Distribution

Leviev, Michael Quartet

BLUES FOR THE FISHERMAN.
Notes: Live at Ronnie Scotts (London), June 1980
Compact disc: released on Mole, May'87 by Mole Records. Dist: Mole Music Co., Spartan Distribution

TRUE BLUES.
Album: released on Mole Jazz, Jul'81 by Mole Jazz Records. Dist: Mole Jazz Distributors

Leviev, Milcho

BLUES FOR THE FISHERMAN (Leviev, Milcho, Quartet with Art Pepper).
Album: released on Mole Jazz, Aug'80 by Mole Jazz Records. Dist: Mole Jazz Distributors

MUSIC FOR BIG BAND AND SYMPHONY ORCHESTRA.
Album: released on Trend (USA), Jun'83 by Discovery Records. Dist: Flexitron Distributors Ltd, Swift

PLAYS THE MUSIC OF IRVING BERLIN.
Album: released on Discovery, Aug'83 Dist: PRT

Levi, Ijahman

CLOSER TO YOU/CRAZES.
Single (12"): released on Jahmania, Jul'82

I DO (Levi, Ijahman & maj).
Album: released on Jahmani, Nov'86

LEND A HAND/CLOSER TO YOU.
Single (7"): released on Tree Roots, Jun'82 by Tree Roots Records. Dist: Jetstar

Single (12"): released on Tree Roots, Jun'82 by Tree Roots Records. Dist: Jetstar

LILLY OF MY VALLEY.
Single (12"): released on Jahmani, Jun'85

MELLOW MUSIC.
Single (12"): released on Jah Man, May'84 by Jah Man Records. Dist: Jetstar

TELL IT TO THE CHILDREN.
Album: released on Tree Roots, Apr'82 by Tree Roots Records. Dist: Jetstar

Cassette: released on Tree Roots, Apr'82 by Tree Roots Records. Dist: Jetstar

Levine, James

PLAYS SCOTT JOPLIN.
Album: released on RCA (Germany), '83

Levine,Steve

BELIEVIN' IT ALL.
Single (7"): released on Chrysalis, Mar'84 by Chrysalis Records. Dist: CBS

Single (12"): released on Chrysalis, Mar'84 by Chrysalis Records. Dist: CBS

Levin, Marc

SOCIAL SKETCHES.
Album: released on Enja (Germany), Jan'82 by Enja Records (W.Germany). Dist: Cadillac Music

Levin, Robert

ELEGIES (Levin, Robert & Kim Kashkashian).
Notes: For full information see under "Kashkashian", Kim & Robert Levin.

Levi, Papa

BIG "N" BROAD.
Single (7"): released on Island, Oct'84 by Island Records. Dist: Polygram

Single (12"): released on Island, Oct'84 by Island Records. Dist: Polygram

BONNIE & CLYDE.
Single (7"): released on Island, Jun'84 by Island Records. Dist: Polygram

Single (12"): released on Island, Jun'84 by Island Records. Dist: Polygram

TROUBLE IN AFRICA.
Single (12"): released on Mango, Nov'85 by Inferno Records. Dist: Inferno

Album: released on Jah, Aug'87 Dist: Jetstar. Estim retail price in Sep'87 was £5.99.

Levi, Philip

MI GOD MI KING/INNA ME YARD.
Single (12"): released on Level Vibes, Jan'84 by Level Vibes Records. Dist: Jetstar

Levi, Sammy

IT A GO DONE.
Single (12"): released on Greensleeves, Mar'84 by Greensleeves Records. Dist: BMG, Jetstar, Spartan

Levi & the Rockats

LOUISIANA HAYRIDE.
Album: released on Rockhouse, Nov'82 by Rockhouse Records. Dist: Swift Distribution, Charly Distribution

Levy, Barrington

BARRINGTON LEVY.
Album: released on Clock Tower, Feb'84 by Clocktower Records. Dist: Jetstar

BARRINGTON LEVY MEETS FRANKIE PAUL (see also Frankie Paul) (Levy, Barrington & Frankie Paul).
Album: released on Arrival, Nov'84 by Arrival. Dist: Revolver, Cartel

BIG BOUT YA.
Single (12"): released on Corner Store, Sep'84

BLACK ROSE.
Single 10": released on Hitbound, Oct'83 by Hitbound Records. Dist: Jetstar

ENGLISHMAN.
Album: released on Greensleeves, Nov'79 by Greensleeves Records. Dist: BMG, Jetstar, Spartan

GET UP STAND UP.
Tracks: / Do the dance.
Single (12"): released on MGR, Dec'85 Dist: Jetstar Records

HERE I COME.
Album: released on Time, Nov'85 Dist: Jetstar Distribution

Cassette: released on Time, Nov'85 Dist: Jetstar Distribution

Single (7"): released on Time One, Dec'84 Dist: Jetstar Distribution

Single (12"): released on Time One, Dec'84 Dist: Jetstar Distribution

JAH BLACK.
Single (12"): released on Black Roots, Mar'84 by Black Roots Records. Dist: Jetstar

JUGGLING SOLDIER.
Single (12"): released on Live & Learn, May'86 Dist: Jetstar

LIFESTYLE.
Album: released on GG'S, Jun'84 by GG'S Records. Dist: Jetstar

MINI BUS (ON THE TELEPHONE).
Single (12"): released on Kingdom, Mar'84 by Kingdom Records. Dist: Kingdom

Single (7"): released on Kingdom, Mar'85 by Kingdom Records. Dist: Kingdom

MOMMY KISSING SANTA CLAUS.
Tracks: / Flash your dread.
Single (7"): released on Thunderbolt, Dec'85 by Magnum Music Group Ltd. Dist: Magnum Music Group Ltd, PRT Distribution, Spartan Distribution

MONEY MOVES.
Single (7"): released on London, May'85 by London Records. Dist: Polygram

Single (12"): released on London, May'85 by London Records. Dist: Polygram

MURDERER.
Single (12"): released on Jah Life, Mar'85 by Jah Life Records. Dist: Jetstar

ONE FOOT JO-JO.
Single (12"): released on Jah Life, Aug'84 by Jah Life Records. Dist: Jetstar

OPEN BOOK.
Single (12"): released on Oak Sound, Dec'82

PLEASE JAH JAH.
Single (12"): released on Volcano, Mar'84 by Volcano Records. Dist: Jetstar

POOR MAN STYLE.
Album: released on Trojan, '83 by Trojan Records. Dist: PRT, Jetstar

PRISON OVAL ROCK Master mix.
Single (12"): released on Green Shoes (Canada), Jan'84 by Green Shoes Records (Canada). Dist: Red Rhino, Cartel

REAL THING, THE.
Single (7"): released on Time, Aug'85 Dist: Jetstar Distribution

Single (12"): released on Time, Aug'85 Dist: Jetstar Distribution

ROBIN HOOD.
Album: released on Greensleeves, Jun'80 by Greensleeves Records. Dist: BMG, Jetstar, Spartan

STRUGGLER.
Tracks: / Struggler / Moonlight lover.
Single (7"): released on Time One, Mar'87 Dist: Jetstar Distribution

Single (12"): released on Time, Dec'86 Dist: Jetstar Distribution

TOMORROW IS ANOTHER DAY.
Single (12"): released on Greensleeves, Feb'82 by Greensleeves Records. Dist: BMG, Jetstar, Spartan

UNDER ME FANCY.
Single (12"): released on Time, Aug'84 Dist: Jetstar Distribution

WARM AND SUNNY DAY.
Single (12"): released on Cha-Cha, Apr'80 by Cha Cha. Dist: Jetstar

Single (12"): released on Chrysalis, Apr'86 by Chrysalis Records. Dist: CBS

HIP TO BE SQUARE.
Tracks: / Some of my lies are true.
Single (7"): released on Chrysalis, Nov'86 by Chrysalis Records. Dist: CBS

Single (12"): released on Chrysalis, Nov'86 by Chrysalis Records. Dist: CBS

HUEY LEWIS & THE NEWS.
Album: released on Chrysalis, Jul'80 by Chrysalis Records. Dist: CBS

HUEY LEWIS & THE NEWS.
Compact disc: by Chrysalis Records. Dist: CBS

IF THIS IS IT.
Single (7"): released on Chrysalis, Sep'84 by Chrysalis Records. Dist: CBS

Single (12"): released on Chrysalis, Sep'84 by Chrysalis Records. Dist: CBS

I WANT A NEW DRUG (CALLED LOVE).
Single (7"): released on Chrysalis, Mar'84 by Chrysalis Records. Dist: CBS

Single (12"): released on Chrysalis, Mar'84 by Chrysalis Records. Dist: CBS

PICTURE THIS.
Tracks: / Change of heart / Tattoo (giving it all up for love) / Hope you love me like you say you do / Workin' for a livin' / Do you believe in love / It is me / Whatever happened to me / Only one / Buzz buzz buzz.
Compact disc: released on Chrysalis, Jun'87 by Chrysalis Records. Dist: CBS

Album: released on Chrysalis, Feb'82 by Chrysalis Records. Dist: CBS

Compact disc: released on Chrysalis, Feb'82 by Chrysalis Records. Dist: CBS

POWER OF LOVE.
Single (7"): released on Chrysalis, Aug'85 by Chrysalis Records. Dist: CBS

Single (12"): released on Chrysalis, Aug'85 by Chrysalis Records. Dist: CBS

SIMPLE AS THAT.
Tracks: / Simple as that / Walking on a thin line / Do you believe in love* / Bad is bad* / Workin' for a livin'.
Single (7"): released on Chrysalis, Mar'87 by Chrysalis Records. Dist: CBS

Single (12"): released on Chrysalis, Mar'87 by Chrysalis Records. Dist: CBS

SPORTS.
Album: released on Chrysalis, Nov'84 by Chrysalis Records. Dist: CBS

Cassette: released on Chrysalis, Nov'84 by Chrysalis Records. Dist: CBS

Compact disc: released on Chrysalis, Nov'84 by Chrysalis Records. Dist: CBS

STUCK WITH YOU.
Tracks: / Don't ever tell me that you love me / Heart of rock'n'roll, The / Trouble in paradise.
Single (7"): released on Chrysalis, Aug'86 by Chrysalis Records. Dist: CBS

Single (12"): released on Chrysalis, Aug'86 by Chrysalis Records. Dist: CBS

Lewis Hugh X

GOODWILL AMBASSADOR.
Album: released on President, Dec'80 by President Records. Dist: Taylors, Spartan

Lewis, Jerry Lee

18 ORIGINAL SUN HITS.
Compact disc: released on Rhino, '86 by Creole Records. Dist: PRT, Rhino

20 SUPER HITS.
Compact disc: released on Bellaphon, Jan'86 by Bellaphon Records. Dist: IMS-Polygram

6 TRACK HITS.
Special: released on Scoop 33, Sep'83 by Pickwick Records. Dist: H.R. Taylor

Cassette: released on Scoop 33, Sep'83 by Pickwick Records. Dist: H.R. Taylor

AT THE COUNTRY STORE.
Album: released on Country Store, Apr'87 by Starblend Records. Dist: PRT, Prism Leisure Corporation Records

Cassette: released on Country Store, Apr'87 by Starblend Records. Dist: PRT, Prism Leisure Corporation Records

AT THE STAR CLUB HAMBURG.
: released on Mercury (USA), Oct'83 by Import Records. Dist: IMS Distribution, Polygram Distribution

BEST OF THE COUNTRY MUSIC HALL FAME HITS.
Album: released on Mercury, Apr'81 by Phonogram Records. Dist: Polygram Distribution

BREATHLESS/HIGH SCHOL CONFIDENTIAL.
Single (12"): released on Charly, Nov'83 by Charly Records. Dist: Charly, Cadillac

CHANTILLY LACE.
Single (7"): released on Sun, Jan'80 by Charly Records. Dist: Charly Distribution

COLLECTION-PARTS 1 & 2.
Tracks: / Be bop a lula / Dixie (instrumental) / Goodnight Irene / Great balls of fire / High school confidential / Lewis boogie / Matchbox / Money / Sixty minute man / Ubangi stomp / Whole lotta shakin'going on / Wine drinkin' spo-dee-o-dee / C.C.Rider / Good golly Miss Molly / Good rockin' tonight / Hang up my rock & roll shoes / Johnny B.Goode / Long gone lonesome blues / Mean woman blues / Pumpin' piano rock / Sweet little sixteen / What'd I say / Will the circle be unbroken / Let the good times roll.
Album: released on Castle Communications, Jul'86 by Castle Communications. Dist: Cartel, Pinnacle, Counterpoint

Cassette: released on Castle Communications, Jul'86 by Castle Communications. Dist: Cartel, Pinnacle, Counterpoint

COMPLETE LONDON SESSION VOL.1.
Tracks: / Drinkin' wine spo dee-o-dee / Music to the man. / Baby what you want me to do? / Bad moon rising / Sea cruise / I cant get no satisfaction / Jukebox / No headstone on my grave / Big Boss Man / Pledging my love / Dungaree Doll / Memphis Tennessee / I cant give you anything but love Baby..
Notes:
Mercury recordings. With guest Artists.
Album: released on Bear Family, Aug'86 by Bear Family Records. Dist: Rollercoaster Distribution, Swift

COMPLETE LONDON SESSION VOL.2.
Tracks: / Be bop a lula / Trouble in mind / Johnny B Goode / High school confidential / Early morning rain / Singin the Blues / Goldmine in the sky / Whole lotta shakin going on / Sixty minute Man / Down the line / What'd I say / Rock'n Roll medley.
Notes:
MERCURY RECORDINGS
Album: released on Bear Family, Aug'86 by Bear Family Records. Dist: Rollercoaster Distribution, Swift

DUETS (Lewis Jerry Lee & Friends).
Album: by Charly Records. Dist: Charly

ESSENTIAL JERRY LEE LEWIS, THE
20 original Rock 'n' Roll hits.
Tracks: / Down the line / Let the good times roll / Jambalaya / High school confidential / Jailhouse rock / Lewis boogie / Hound dog / What'd I say / Lovin' up a storm / Wild one / Great balls of fire / Singing the blues / Little Queenie / Mean woman blues / Sixty minute man / Lovesick blues / Breathless / It'll be me / Whole lotta shakin' goin' on / Don't be cruel.
Notes: Original Sun recordings. Licensed from Charly Records International APS. This cassette P 1978 Charly Holdings Inc. (C) 1986 Charly Records Ltd
Cassette: released on Charly, Nov'86 by Charly Records. Dist: Charly, Cadillac

FERRIDAY FIREBALL.
Tracks: / Lewis boogie / It'll be me / High school confidential / Whole lotta shakin' goin' on / Good rockin' tonight / Big legged woman / Great balls of fire / Drinkin' wine spo-dee-o-dee / Matchbox / You win again / Will the circle be unbroken / That lucky old sun / Crazy arms / Break up / Memory of you / Johnny B.Goode / Little Queenie / Milkshake madamoiselle / Big blon' baby / Breathless / Mean woman blues / Down the line / When the saints go marching in / End of the road / What'd I say.
Compact disc: released on Charly, Mar'86 by Charly Records. Dist: Charly, Cadillac

GOOD GOLLY MISS MOLLY.
Cassette: released on Bravo, Feb'80 by Pickwick Records. Dist

GOOD ROCKING TONIGHT.
Album: by Charly Records. Dist: Charly Distribution

GOOD ROCKIN' TONIGHT.
Cassette: released on Ditto, Sep'86 by Pickwick Records. Dist: H.R. Taylor

GREAT BALL OF FIRE, THE.
Tracks: / I'm feeling sorry / You're the only star (in my blue heaven) / I'll keep on loving you / Cool cool ways (Sexy ways) / Milkshake Mademoiselle / Mean woman blues / Great balls of fire / Turn around / Rock'n'roll baby / Ubangi stomp / Jambalaya (on the Bayou) / Down the line (go go go) / Breathless / Great balls of fire.
Album: released on Sun, Aug'86 by Charly Records. Dist: Charly Distribution

GREAT BALL OF FIRE, THE.
Album: released on Sun, Jun'82 by Charly Records. Dist: Charly Distribution

GREAT BALLS OF FIRE/WHOLE LOTTA SHAKIN.
Single (7"): released on Old Gold (Reissue), Jul'82

HIGH SCHOOL CONFIDENTIAL.
Single (7"): released on Sun, Jan'80 by Charly Records. Dist: Charly Distribution

I AM WHAT I AM.
Album: released on MCA, Jul'84 by MCA Records. Dist: Polygram, MCA

Cassette: released on MCA, Jul'84 by MCA Records. Dist: Polygram, MCA

Album: released on MCA, May'85 by MCA Records. Dist: Polygram, MCA

Cassette: released on MCA, May'85 by MCA Records. Dist: Polygram, MCA

JERRY LEE LEWIS.
Compact disc: released on Pickwick, Apr'86 by Pickwick Records. Dist: Pickwick Distribution, Prism Leisure Distribution,

Album: released on Elektra, Nov'81 by WEA Records. Dist: WEA

Album: released on Mercury, Nov'81 by Phonogram Records. Dist: Polygram Distribution

Cassette: released on Mercury, Nov'81 by Phonogram Records. Dist: Polygram Distribution

Cassette: released on Pickwick (Ditto series), Jul'82

Album: released on Cambra, Feb'85 by Cambra Records. Dist: IDS, Conifer

Cassette: released on Cambra, Feb'85 by Cambra Records. Dist: IDS, Conifer

JERRY LEE LEWIS COLLECTION.
Notes:
No Track details advised!
Album: released on Deja Vu, Jul'86 by Deja Vu Records. Dist: Counterpoint Distribution, Record Services Distribution (Ireland)

Cassette: released on Deja Vu, Jul'86 by Deja Vu Records. Dist: Counterpoint Distribution, Record Services Distribution (Ireland)

Double Album: released on Pickwick, Mar'86 by Pickwick Records. Dist: Pickwick Distribution, Prism Leisure Distribution,

JERRY LEE LEWIS & HIS PUMPING PIANO.
Album: released on Charly, Oct'75 by Charly Records. Dist: Charly, Cadillac

JERRY LEE LEWIS VOL.2.
Compact disc: released on Pickwick, Oct'86 by Pickwick Records. Dist: Pickwick Distribution, Prism Leisure Distribution,

JERRY LEE'S GREATEST.
Album: released on Charly, Feb'81 by Charly Records. Dist: Charly, Cadillac

KICKIN' UP A STORM.
Tracks: / Who will buy the wine / Frankie and Johnny / Home / Little Queenie / Friday night / Big blon' baby / Lovin' up a storm / Hillbilly fever / I could never be ashamed of you / It all depends (who will buy the wine) / I'll sail my ship alone / Bonnie B. / As long as I live / Night train to Memphis / Mexicali Rose / In the mood.
Album: released on Sun, Feb'87 by Charly Records. Dist: Charly Distribution

KILLER 1963-1968, THE.
Tracks: / Whole lotta shakin' goin' on / Crazy arms / Great balls of fire / High school confidential / I'll make it all up to you / Break up / Down the line / Hit the road Jack / End of the road / Your cheatin' heart / Wedding bells / Just because / Breathless / He took it like a man / Drinkin' wine spo dee o dee / Johnny B.Goode / Hallelujah I just love her so / You went back on your word / Pen & paper / Hole he said he'd dig for me, The / You win again / Fools like me / Hit the road Jack / I'm on fire(master) / I'm on fire** / She was my baby / Bread & butter man / I bet you're gonna like it / Got you on my mind / Mathilda / Corrine,Corrina / Sexy ways / Wild side of life, The / Mean woman blues(live) / High school confidential(live) / Money(live) / Matchbox(live) / What'd I say(Pts.1&2)(live) / Down the line(live) / Great balls of fire(live) / Good golly Miss Molly(live) / Lewis' boogie / Your cheatin' heart(live) / Hound dog(live) / Long tall Sally(live) / Whole lotta shakin' goin' on(live) / Jenny Jenny(live) / Who will the next fool be(live) / Memphis, Tennessee(live) / Hound dog(live) / Mean woman blues (2)(live) / High heel sneakers(live) / No particular place to go(live) / Together again(live) / Long tall Sally(2)(live) / Whole lotta shakin' goin' on(2)(live) / Flip,flop & fly / Don't let go / Maybelline / Roll over Beethoven / Just in time** / I believe in you / Herman,the hermit / Baby hold me close / Skid row** / This must be the place / Rockin' pneumonia & the boogie woogie flu / Seasons of my heart / Big boss man / Too young / Danny boy** / Crazy arms / City lights / Funny how time slips away / North to Alaska / Walk right in / Wolverton Mountain / King of the road / Detroit City / Ring of fire / Baby(you've got what it takes) / Green green grass of home / Sticks & stones / What a heck of a mess / Lincoln limousine / Rockin' Jerry Lee** / Memphis beat / Urge, The / Whenever you're ready / She thinks I still care / Memphis beat(take 1) / Memphis beat(take 2)** / Twenty four hours a day** / Swinging doors** / Little Queenie(live) / How's my X treating you(live) / Johnny B.Goode(live) / Green green grass of home(live) / What'd I say(pt.2)(live) / You win again(live) / I'll sail my ship alone(live) / Crying time(live) / Money(live) / Roll over Beethoven(live) / Swinging doors(string mix) / If I had it all to do over / Just dropped in / It's a hang up baby / Holdin' on / Hey baby / Dream baby / Treat her right / Turn on your lovelight / Shotgun man / All the good is gone / Another place,another time / Walking the floor over you / I'm a lonesome fugitive / Break my mind / Play me a song I can cry to / Before the next teardrop falls / All night long / We live in two different worlds now / What's made Milwaukee famous / On the back row / Slippin' around / She still comes around / Today I started loving you again / Louisiana / There stands the glass / I can't have a merry Christmas ,Mary(without you) / Out of my mind / I can't get over you / Listen, They're playing my song / Echoes / Release me / Let's talk about us to make love sweeter for you.
Notes: Original Smash/Mercury recordings. Contains 8 previously unissued tracks (tracks marked**). The first 2000 Boxsets included a bonus interview LP.
Boxed set: released on Bear Family, Sep'86 by Bear Family Records. Dist: Rollercoaster Distribution, Swift

KILLER 1969-1972, THE.
Notes: 11-LP box set.

KILLER 1973-1977, THE (12 unit box set).
Tracks: / Alcohol of fame, the / Tomorrow's taking my baby away / Mama's hands / What my woman can't do / Tell tale signs / Morning after baby let me down, the / I think I need to pray / I hate goodbyes / Where would I be / My cricket and me / Falling to the bottom / Gods were angry with me, the / Sometimes a memory isn't enough / Bluer words / He can't fill my shoes / I'm left you're right she's gone / Keep me from blowing away / Honky tonk wine / Room full of roses / Picture from lifes other side, A / I've forgot more about you than he'll ever know / Until the day forever ends / Boogie woogie country man / I can still hear the music in the rest room / Speak a little louder to us Jesus / Honey hush / Jesus is on the main line / Remember me / Shake rattle and roll / Love inflation / I don't want to be lonely tonight / Forever forgiving / Little peace and harmony, A / No one knows me / When I take my vacation in heaven / I'm still jealous of you / You ought to see my mind / Don't boogie woogie (when you say your prayers tonight) / Thanks for nothing / Red hot memories (ice cold beer) / I was sorta wonderin' / Jerry's place / That kind of fool / Your cheatin' heart / Crawdad song / House of blue lights, the / Goodnight Irene / Damn good country song, A / Lord what's left for me to do / Great balls of fire / One rose (thats left in my heart) / I'm knee deep in loving you / I can help (1 & 2) / Slippin' and slidin' / From a Jack to a King (1 & 2) / fter the fool you've made of me / Closest thing to you, the / I can't keep my hands off you / One rose (that's left in my heart) / Wedding bells / Fifties, the / Only love can get you in my door / Old country church, the / Harbour lights / Jerry Lee's rock'n'roll revival show / I sure miss those good old times / Let's put it all back together again / Country memories / As long as we live / Jealous heart / (You'd think by now) I'd be over you / Come on in / Who's sorry now / Let's say goodbye like we said hello / Georgia on my mind / What's so good about goodbye / Tennessee Saturday night / Ivory tears / Middle age crazy / Last letter, the / Last cheaters waltz, the / Let's live a little / I hate you / Before the night is over / Sittin' and thinkin' / Blue suede shoes / Lucille / Corrine Corrina / Don't let the stars get in your eyes / Sweet little sixteen / Life's railway to heaven / Sweet little sixteen / Ivory tears / You call everybody darling / Wild and wooly ways / I'll find it where I can / Lord I've tried everything but you / You're all too ugly tonight / Arkansas seesaw / Pee Wee's place / Drinkin' wine spo-dee-o-dee / Music man / Baby what do you want me to do / Bad moon rising / Sea cruise / (I can't get no) satisfaction / Jukebox / No headstone on my grave / Big boss man / Pledging my love / Dungaree doll / Memphis Tenessee / I can't give you anything but love baby / Be bop a lula / Trouble in mind / Johnny B Goode / High school confidential / Early morning rain / Singing the blues / oldmine in the sky / Whole lotta shakin' going on / Sixty minute man / Down the line / What'd I say / Rock'n'roll medley / Honey hush / Raining in my heartt / Margie / Silver threads among the gold / Silver threads among the gold / Cry / All over hell and half of Georgia / Isure miss those good old times / Take your time / Hold on I'm coming (fast version) / Haunted house, the (extended version) / Meat man / When a man loves a woman / Hold on I'm coming (slow version) / Just a little bit / Born to be a loser / Haunted house, the / Blueberry hill / Revolutionary man, the / Big blue diamond / That old bourbon street church / Jack Daniels (old number seven) / Why me Lord / Ride me down easy / Cold cold morning light.
Boxed set: released on Bear Family, Mar'87 by Bear Family Records. Dist: Rollercoaster Distribution, Swift

KILLER COUNTRY.
Album: released on Edsel, Jun'87 by Demon Records. Dist: Pinnacle, Jazz Music, Projection

KILLER PERFORMANCE, THE (VIDEO).
Notes: Originally a BBC Arena programme,this includes archive material stretching back to the 50's,plus live footage from a Bristol concert. Total playing time: 30 minutes.
Video-cassette (VHS): released on Virgin, Dec'84 by Virgin Records. Dist: EMI, Virgin Distribution

KILLER ROCKS ON, THE.
Album: released on Karussell (Germany), Oct'82

Cassette: released on Karussell (Germany), Oct'82

KILLER STRIKES, THE.
Album: released on Topline, Nov'84 by Charly Records. Dist: Charly Distribution

Cassette: released on Topline, Nov'84 by Charly Records. Dist: Charly Distribution

LIVE AT THE STAR CLUB HAMBURG.
Album: released on Philips (Timeless), Sep'84

Cassette: released on Philips (Timeless), Sep'84

MILESTONES.
Notes: Track details not advised.
Album: released on Rhino (USA), Jan'86 by Rhino Records (USA).

MOTIVE SERIES.
Album: released on Mercury, May'82 by Phonogram Records. Dist: Polygram Distribution

Cassette: released on Mercury, May'82 by Phonogram Records. Dist: Polygram Distribution

MY FINGERS DO THE TALKING FOREVER.
Single (7"): released on MCA, Feb'83 by MCA Records. Dist: Polygram, MCA

NUGGETS VOL 1.
Album: released on Charly, Mar'77 by Charly Records. Dist: Charly, Cadillac

NUGGETS VOL 2.
Album: released on Charly, Dec'77 by Charly Records. Dist: Charly, Cadillac

ORIGINAL JERRY LEE LEWIS, THE.
Album: released on Charly, Oct'76 by Charly Records. Dist: Charly, Cadillac

ORIGINAL JERRY LEE LEWIS, THE.
Tracks: / Crazy arms / End of the road / It'll be me / Whole lotta shakin' goin' on / You win again / Great balls of fire / Down the line / Beathless / High school confidential / Fools like me / Breakup / I'll make it all up to you / Lovin' up a storm / Big blon' baby / Livin' lovin' wreck / What'd I say.
Cassette: released on Charly, Sep'86 by Charly Records. Dist: Charly, Cadillac

PUMPIN PIANO CAT, THE.
Album: released on Sun, Jun'82 by Charly Records. Dist: Charly Distribution

PUMPIN' PIANO CAT, THE.
Tracks: / Born to lose / My Carolina sunshine girl / Long gone lonesome blues / Crazy arms / Silver threads among the gold / You're the only star (in my blue heaven) / End of the road / My old pal of yesterday / Little green valley / It'll be me / All night long / Pumpin piano rock / Sixty minute man / Lewis boogie.
Notes: Licensed from Charly Records International APS. This compilation (P) 1986 Charly Holdings Inc. (C) Charly Records Ltd.
Album: released on Sun, Jul'86 by Charly Records. Dist: Charly Distribution

RARE AND ROCKIN'.
Tracks: / It won't happen with me / Teenage letter / Pink pedal pushers / Hillbilly music / Deep elem blues / You win again / I'm feeling sorry / I'm the guilty one / It hurt me so / I love you because / Cold, cold heart / Whole lotta shakin' going on / In the mood / Great balls of fire / I forgot to remember to forget / Turn around / It all depends (on who will buy the wine) / It'll be me (slow version) / It'll be me (fast version) / Sixty minute man / Loving up a storm / Rockin' with red (she knows how to rock me) / Honey hush / Hound dog / Hang up my rock'n'roll shoes.
Notes: Original Sun Recordings. Licensed from Charly Records International APS. This CD P 1987 Charly Holdings Inc. This CD C 1987 Charly Records Ltd.
Compact disc: released on Sun, Apr'87 by Charly Records. Dist: Charly Distribution

RARE JERRY LEE LEWIS VOL 2.
Album: released on Charly, Oct'75 by Charly Records. Dist: Charly, Cadillac

RARE JERRY LEE LEWIS VOL 1.
Album: released on Charly, Oct'75 by Charly Records. Dist: Charly, Cadillac

SESSION, THE.
Compact disc: released on Mercury, May'85 by Phonogram Records. Dist: Polygram Distribution

SUN YEARS, THE.
Album: released on Sun, Mar'83 by Charly Records. Dist: Charly Distribution

THIRTIETH ANNIVERSARY.
Compact disc: released on Phonogram, Feb'87 by Phonogram Records. Dist: Polygram

TRIO PLUS.

Album: released on Sun, May'80 by Charly Records. Dist: Charly Distribution

WHEN TWO WORLDS COLIDE.
Album: released on Elektra, Apr'80 by WEA Records. Dist: WEA

WHOLE LOTTA SHAKIN' GOIN' ON.
Tracks: / You are my sunshine / Shame on you / I don't know anybody / Whole lotta shakin' goin' on / Drinkin' wine spo-dee-o-dee / When the saints go marching in / I'll be me / Deep Elem blues no.2 / Singing the blues / Honey hush / Lewis boogie / You win again / Hand me down my walking cane / Old time religion / Crawdad song (The).
Album: released on Sun, Jul'86 by Charly Records. Dist: Charly Distribution

Album: released on Sun, Jun'82 by Charly Records. Dist: Charly Distribution

WHOLE LOTTA SHAKIN GOING ON.
Single (7"): released on Sun, Jan'80 by Charly Records. Dist: Charly Distribution

WILD ONE AT HIGH SCHOOL HOP THE.
Album: released on Charly, Mar'84 by Charly Records. Dist: Charly, Cadillac

WILD ONE, THE.
Tracks: / Don't be cruel / Good rockin' tonight / Pink pedal pushers / Ooby dooby / Hound dog / Jailhouse rock / Real wild child / High school confidential / I forgot to remember to forget / Break up / Put me down / Milkshake Mademoisel / Carrying on (Sexy ways) / Let the good times roll / High school confidential.
Album: released on Sun, Aug'86 by Charly Records. Dist: Charly Distribution

Lewis, John

BRIDGE GAME (THE).
Tracks: / Prelude No:9 -One at heart / Fugue No:9-The game demand / Prelude No:4-Two clubs / Fugue No:4-A little slam in diamonds / Prelude No:5-One spade(Tears from children) / Fugue No:5-The preempt / Prelude No:16-One diamond / Fugue No:16-The takeout double / Fugue No:16-The takout double / Prelude No:8-Two clubs / Fugue No:8-The invitation to a slam.
Notes: Personnel:John Lewis-Piano/Joel Lester-Violin/Lois Martin-Viola/Scott Nickrenz-Viola/Howard Collins-Guitar/Marc Johnson-Bass. Composed by John Lewis (of the MJQ)"The Bridge Game" is a work based on J.S bach"The Well-Tempered Clavier"Book 1.This is a beautiful example of how classical &jazz can be brought together naturally without sounding contrived.
Album: released on Phillips Holland, Jun'86

Cassette: released on Phillips Holland, Jun'86

Compact disc: released on Phillips Holland, Jun'86

J S BACH PRELUDES AND FUGUES.
Tracks: / Prelude No:1 / Prelude No:2 / Prelude No:6 / Prelude No:7 / Prelude No:21 / Prelude No:22 / Fugue No:1 / Fugue No:2 / Fugue No:6 / Fugue No:7 / Fugue No:21 / Fugue No:22.
Notes: J S Bach preludes and fugues from the well tempered clavier book 1.
Compact disc: released on Phonogram Import, Jul'85

Album: released on Phonogram Import, Jul'85

Cassette: released on Phonogram Import, Jul'85

Compact disc: released on Phonogram Import, Jul'85

Lewis Johnny

GEORGIA SLIDE GUITAR.
Album: released on Arhoolie, May'81 by Arhoolie Records. Dist: Projection, Topic, Jazz Music, Swift, Roots

Lewis, Lena

MISSUS LA GROOVE.
Single (7"): released on Carrere, Jul'85 by Carrere Records. Dist: PRT, Spartan

Single (12"): released on Carrere, Jul'85 by Carrere Records. Dist: PRT, Spartan

Lewis, Lew

SAVE THE WAIL (Lewis, Lew Reformer).
Album: released on Stiff, Nov'79 by Stiff Records. Dist: EMI, Record Services Distribution (Ireland)

SHAME SHAME SHAME.
Single (12"): released on Waterfront, Aug'87 by Waterfront Records. Dist: Rough Trade, Cartel, Projection, Roots

Single (7"): released on Epic, Aug'87 by CBS Records. Dist: CBS

Lewis, Linda

CLASS STYLE.
Single (7"): released on Electricity, May'84 by Electricity Records. Dist: PRT

Single (12"): released on Electricity, May'84 by Electricity Records. Dist: PRT

Picture disc single: released on Electricity, May'84 by Electricity Records. Dist: PRT

Single (12"): released on Electricity, May'84 by Electricity Records. Dist: PRT

CLOSE THE DOOR TAKE YOUR HEART.
Single (7"): released on Epic, Apr'85 by CBS Records. Dist: CBS

TEAR AND A SMILE, A.
Album: released on Epic, Sep'83 by CBS Records. Dist: CBS

Cassette: released on Epic, Sep'83 by CBS Records. Dist: CBS

WOMAN OVERBOARD.
Gatefold sleeve:

Album: released on Arista, Apr'77 by Arista Records. Dist: RCA

Lewis, Lindell

EASY RIDER.
Single (12"): released on Sea View, Mar'84 by Sea View Records. Dist: Jetstar

Lewis, Lou

DON'T HIDE AWAY.
Tracks: / Don't let them fool you / Father of the fatherless / Sweet Lamb / Tapestry / Wedding song / Come to me / Kingdom song, The / Travelling along / High Priest / Don't hide away.
Notes: Available from Zimrah music, 39 union road, Exeter, Devon, EX4 6HU. Add 45p for P&P for cassette.
Cassette: released on Zimrah Music, Dec'86 Dist: Marshall Pickering

HEALING STREAM.
Tracks: / Healing stream / Feet on the rock / I feel lovely / Valleys / Eagles song / I know where you're coming from / Broken heart / Knowing that I need you / Breaking up / Suddenly (joy springs up).
Cassette: released on Zimrah Music, Dec'86 Dist: Marshall Pickering

WALLS.
Tracks: / Walls / I'm no hero / Don't try to hide / Expert, The / Mary's song / Winds of change / If just once in a while / Jacob's song / Hazel's song / Give it away.
Notes: Available from Zimrah Music, 39 Union Street, Exeter, Devon, EX4 6HN. (Add 45p for P&P per cassette.
Cassette: released on Cover to Cover, Dec'86 by Cover to Cover Cassettes. Dist: Conifer

Lewis, Meade Lux

JAZZ PIANO THE (Lewis, Meade Lux/Albert Ammons and Pete Johnson).
Album: released on Joker, Apr'81 Dist: Counterpoint, Mainline, Record Services Distribution (Ireland)

Lewis, Mel

20 YEARS AT THE VILLAGE VANGUARD (Lewis, Mel and the Jazz Orchestra).
Tracks: / All of me / Blue note / Butter / C-Jam blues / Dearly beloved / Interloper / Alone together / American express.
Album: released on Atlantic, Jun'87 by WEA Records. Dist: WEA

Cassette: released on Atlantic, Jun'87 by WEA Records. Dist: WEA

Lewis, Nigel

WHAT I FEEL NOW.
Album: released on Media Burn, Nov'86 by Rocks Off Record Emporium. Dist: Rough Trade Distribution, Cartel Distribution

Lewis, Philip

RHYTHM MANIACS SESSIONS 1929 VOL.1 (Lewis, Philip Rhythm Maniacs).
Album: released on Fountain-Retrieval, Jul'87 by Retrieval Records. Dist: Retrieval, VJM, Swift, Jazz Music, Wellard, Chris

Lewis, Ramsey

HIS GREATEST SIDES VOL.1.
Tracks: / High heel sneakers / Hang on sloopy / Dancing in the streets / Hard days night / Something you've got / In crowd / Wade in the water / Soul man / Since you've been gone / One,Two,Three / Les fleurs / Uptight,Everythings alright.
Album: released on Chess, Aug'86 by Charly Records. Dist: Charly, Swift, PRT, Discovery, IMS, Polygram

Cassette: released on Chess, Aug'86 by Charly Records. Dist: Charly, Swift, PRT, Discovery, IMS, Polygram

KEYS TO THE CITY.
Tracks: / Keys to the city / You're falling in love / 7-11 / Strangers / My love will lead you home / Melody of life / Shamballa / Love and understanding.
Album: released on CBS, May'87 by CBS Records. Dist: CBS

Cassette: released on CBS, May'87 by CBS Records. Dist: CBS

Lewis, Ramsey Trio

REUNION.
Tracks: / In crowd, The / (Song of) Delilah / Hello Cello / Hang on sloopy / Wind, The / Carmen / Horizons.
Album: released on CBS, Jan'84 by CBS Records. Dist: CBS

Cassette: released on CBS, Jan'84 by CBS Records. Dist: CBS

Lewis Sisters

MELTING POINT.
Tracks: / Melting point / Devil made me do it.
Single (7"): released on Riva, Oct'86 Dist: PRT

Single (12"): released on Riva, Oct'86 Dist: PRT

SO GOOD SO RIGHT.
Tracks: / So good so right / Dangerous.
Single (7"): released on Riva, Jan'87 Dist: PRT

SO GOOD SO RIGHT.
Single (12"): released on Riva, Feb'87 Dist: PRT

Lewis, Smiley

CALDONIA'S PARTY.
Tracks: / My baby was right / Gowing old / Low-down / Where were you / Dirty people / Sad life / Bee's boogie / Bells are ringing (The) / Bells are ringing, The / Gumbo blues / Ain't gonna do it / You're not the one / Big mamou / Caldonia's party / Oh baby / Playgirl / Blue Monday.
Album: released on KC, Oct'86 by KC Records. Dist: Cartel

DOWN YONDER.
Tracks: / Down the road / Rocks (The) / Rocks, The / Real gone lover / Lost weekend / Bumpity bump / Hear you knocking,I / I hear you knocking / Queen of hearts / Come on / Rootin'and Tootin' / One night / Shame,shame,shame / Please listen to me / Down yonder we go ballin' / Go on fool / Bad luck blues / Stormy monday nights.
Album: released on KC, Oct'86 by KC Records. Dist: Cartel

HOOK LINE & SINKER.
Tracks: / Lillie Mae / Gypsy blues / My baby was right / That certain door / It's music / Jailbird / Nobodys knows / Oh red / Can't stop loving you / No no / Hook line and sinker / If you ever used a woman / Standing on the corner / It's so peaceful / Slide me down / Don't jive me.
Album: released on KC, Oct'86 by KC Records. Dist: Cartel

I HEAR YOU KNOCKING.
Tracks: / I hear you knocking / One night / Down the road / Shame,shame,shame / She's got me hook,line & seeker / Tee-nah-nah / Down yonder(we go ballin') / Big Mamou / Caldonia's party / Bells are ringing, The / Someday / Jailbird / Real gone lover / Little Fernandez.
Album: released on Stateside, Apr'87 Dist: EMI

Cassette: released on Stateside, Apr'87 Dist: EMI

Lewis, Ted

IS EVERYBODY HAPPY.
Album: released on Halcyon (USA), Dec'86 by Halcyon Records (USA). Dist: Jazz Music, Conifer, Taylors

JAZZ HOLIDAY, A (Lewis, Ted & His Band).
Tracks: / Jazz holiday, A / Shimme sha wobble / My mama's in town / Say / Arabella / Glad rag doll / Bugle call rag / Bam bam bammy shore / Where'd you get those eyes? / Milenberg joys / She's funny that way / Camel walk / Hello Montreal / New St Louis blues / That certain party / Some of these days / Dark Town strutters ball.
Album: released on ASV, Mar'81 by Academy Sound & Vision Records. Dist: Pinnacle

VINTAGE SHOE BIZS GREATS also see Tucker, Sophie (Lewis, Ted & Tucker Sophie).
Album: released on Folkways (USA), Mar'84 by Folkways (USA) Records. Dist: Swift, Projection, Recommended

VOL.1 - IS EVERYBODY HAPPY\1920'S (Lewis, Ted & His Band).

Lewis, Vic

JAM SESSIONS The war years volume 1.
Tracks: / Yellow dog blues / Blues in E. / Johnny's idea / Wigmore jump / Wigmore blues / My blue heaven / Someday sweetheart / Ain't misbehavin' / Ja Da / Tea for two.
Notes: Mono recording.
Album: released on Harlequin, Jun'86 by Harlequin Records. Dist: Swift, Jazz Music, Wellard, Chris, IRS, Taylor,

JAM SESSIONS VOL.4 1942-43.
Album: released on Harlequin, Jan'87 by Harlequin Records. Dist: Swift, Jazz Music, Wellard, Chris, IRS, Taylor,

JAM SESSIONS VOLUME 6 1946-49.

Album: released on Harlequin, Apr'87 by Harlequin Records. Dist: Swift, Jazz Music, Wellard, Chris, IRS, Taylor, H.R.

JAM SESSIONS VOLUME 4.
Tracks: / Soft winds / What's new / Blues / I found a new baby / Washboard blues / Woo-Woo / Stardust / Cotton tail / Body and soul / Sweet Georgia Brown.
Notes: With Buddy Featherstonhaugh RAF Rhythm club sextet -1943-1944. Mono recording,not issued HMV sides but previously unissued tracks from broad- casts.
Album: released on Harlequin, Nov'86 by Harlequin Records. Dist: Swift, Jazz Music, Wellard, Chris, IRS, Taylor, H.R.

LEONARD FEATHER PRESENTS "JAZZ FROM BOTH SIDES" (Lewis, Vic & His Jazz Group & Jack Marshall & His Jazz Group).
Album: released on Concept, Jul'87 Dist: Jazz Music, Swift, Chris Wellard, Polygram

NEW YORK '38 (Lewis, Vic & his American Jazzmen).
Album: released on Esquire, Jan'86 by Titan International Productions. Dist: Jazz Music, Cadillac Music, Swift, Wellard, Chris, Backs, Rough Trade, Revolver, Nine Mile

PLAYS STAN KENTON 1948-54.
Album: released on Harlequin, Apr'87 by Harlequin Records. Dist: Swift, Jazz Music, Wellard, Chris, IRS, Taylor, H.R.

VIC LEWIS CONDUCTS-TEABREAK.
Album: released on Concept, Apr'86 Dist: Jazz Music, Swift, Chris Wellard Polygram

VIC LEWIS JAM SESSIONS VOL. 5 1938-46.
Album: released on Harlequin, 11 Apr'87 by Harlequin Records. Dist: Swift, Jazz Music, Wellard, Chris, IRS, Taylor, H.R.

VIC LEWIS JAM SESSIONS VOLUME 2, THE 1945.
Tracks: / Tri-colour blues / It's the talk of the town / Sam's blues (Fast and Slow versions) / Lady be good / Johnny's blues / Rose room / Ghost of a chance / Mean to me / Sweet Lorraine / Jazz me blues / Etude in ashes / I ain't gonna give nobody / Singing the blues / Riverboat shuffle / Peg O'my heart / Copenhagen / Round about eight / Etude in red / Fidgety feet.
Notes: Mono recording.
Album: released on Harlequin, Jun'86 by Harlequin Records. Dist: Swift, Jazz Music, Wellard, Chris, IRS, Taylor, H.R.

VIC LEWIS JAM SESSIONS VOLUME 4 (1945-46).
Tracks: / World is waiting for the sunrise, The / World is waiting for the sunrise (The) / Blues / I've found a new baby / I got rhythm.
Notes: Mono recording.
Album: released on Harlequin, Jun'86 by Harlequin Records. Dist: Swift, Jazz Music, Wellard, Chris, IRS, Taylor, H.R.

Ley, Eggy Hotshots

COME AND GET IT! (Ley, Eggy Hotshots & Fiona Duncan).
Album: released on Veloce, Jun'87

EGGY LEY'S HOTSHOTS.
Album: released on Wam, May'87

Ley,Tabu

AFRISA SELECTION (ZAIRE).
Tracks: / Amilo / Camarade de sous / Sanza misato / Ebeze.
Notes: The first British release from the legendary Tabu Ley-Rochereau is a power pack-ed album with a new flavour. ".....the sort of soul electricity one recalls on albums by Marvin Gaye and Diana Ross(New York Times)"
Album: released on Sterns, Sep'86 by Sterns Records. Dist: Sterns/Triple Earth Distribution

Leyton, John

BEST OF, THE.
Album: released on See For Miles, Aug'87 by See For Miles Records. Dist: Pinnacle. Estim retail price in Sep'87 was £5.67.

Compact disc: released on See For Miles, Sep'87 by See For Miles Records. Dist: Pinnacle. Estim retail price in Sep'87 was £11.89.

THE BEST OF.
Album: released on See For Miles, Aug'87 by See For Miles Records. Dist: Pinnacle

L, Gary

TIME (TO PARTY).
Tracks: / Time (to party) / Time (sensational mix).
Single (12"): released on Champion, Jan'87 by Champion Records. Dist: RCA

LGT

TOO LONG.
Tracks: / I want to be there / Portoriko / Slippin' away / In other words / Too long / Surrender to the heat / Bloodshot eyes / Soul on fire / Last song, The.
Album: released on EMI, Mar'83 by EMI Records. Dist: EMI

Cassette: released on EMI, Mar'83 by EMI Records. Dist: EMI

Liar

SET THE WORLD ON FIRE.
Album: released on Bearsville (USA), Feb'79 by Warner Bros Records. Dist: WEA

Liaz

MISSION IMPOSSIBLE.
Tracks: / Mission impossible / Mission impossible (house mix) / Mission impossible (secret agent mix).
Single (12"): released on Kool Kat, May'87 by Kool Kat Records. Dist: PRT

MISSION IMPOSSIBLE (THE IMPOSSIBLE 7" MIX).
Tracks: / Mission impossible (The impossible 7" mix) / Mission impossible (radio edit).
Single (7"): released on Kool Kat, 13 Jun'87 by Kool Kat Records. Dist: PRT

Single (12"): released on Kool Kat, 13 Jun'87 by Kool Kat Records. Dist: PRT

Liberace

AT THE PALLADIUM.
Album: released on MCA, Apr'87 by MCA Records. Dist: Polygram, MCA

Cassette: released on MCA, Apr'87 by MCA Records. Dist: Polygram, MCA

...AT THE PALLADIUM.
Tracks: / Rhapsody in blue/I got rhythm / Mack the knife / Tico tico / Me and my shadow / Last time I saw Paris (The)...Medley / Jalousie....medley / I'll be seeing you.
Cassette: released on MCA, Apr'87 by MCA Records. Dist: Polygram, MCA

Album: released on MCA, Apr'87 by MCA Records. Dist: Polygram, MCA

BEST OF LIBERACE.
Album: released on MCA, '83 by MCA Records. Dist: Polygram, MCA

Cassette: released on MCA, '83 by MCA Records. Dist: Polygram, MCA

BEST OF THE CLASSICS.
Album: released on AVI (USA), Jul'79 by A.V.I. Records. Dist: Target, PRT

Cassette: released on AVI (USA), Jul'79 by A.V.I. Records. Dist: Target, PRT

HERE'S LIBERACE.
Tracks: / Rhapsody in blue / I got rhythm / Mack the knife / Tico Tico / Last time I saw Paris, The (medley) / La Seine (medley) / Autumn leaves (les feuilles mortes) medley / Under Paris skies (medley) / Poor people of Paris, The (medley) / Can-can (medley) / Jalousie (jealousy) medley / Boogie woogie (medley) / You made me love you (I didn't want to do it) medley / Medley: the last time I saw Paris / Boogie woogie / Rhapsody in blue* / I got rhythm Mack the knife / Tico tico / Last time I saw Paris, The* / La Seine Autum leaves (Les feuilles mortes) / Under Paris skies / Poor people of Paris, The / Can-can / Jalousie (jealousy)* / Boogie woogie / You made me love you (I didn't want to do it).
Notes: *-Medley.
Compact disc: released on MCA, Aug'87 by MCA Records. Dist: Polygram, MCA

I'LL BE SEEING YOU.
Tracks: / I'll be seeing you / I'll be seeing you (B).
Single (7"): released on MCA, Mar'87 by MCA Records. Dist: Polygram, MCA

JUST FOR YOU.
Album: released on Golden Hour, Oct'76 by PRT Records. Dist: PRT

Cassette: released on PRT, Oct'76 by PRT Records. Dist: PRT

LIBERACE.
Album: released on AVI (USA), Aug'79 by A.V.I. Records. Dist: Target, PRT

TWAS THE NIGHT BEFORE CHRISTMAS.
Album: released on Audio Fidelity, Oct'84 Dist: PRT

Cassette: released on Audio Fidelity, Oct'84 Dist: PRT

WONDERFUL LIBERACE.
Album: released on Spot, Feb'84 by Pickwick Records. Dist: H.R. Taylor, Lugtons

Cassette: released on Spot, Feb'84 by Pickwick Records. Dist: H.R. Taylor, Lugtons

Liberation Suite

STRIDE FOR STRIDE.
Album: released on Chapel Lane, Dec'83 Dist: RCA

Cassette: released on Chapel Lane, Dec'83 Dist: RCA

Liberty

OUR VOICE IS TOMORROW'S HOPE.
Tracks: / Our voice is tomorrow's hope.
Single (7"): released on Mortarhate, Feb'86 by Dorane Ltd.

PEOPLE WHO CARE ARE ANGRY.
Album: released on Mortarhate, Oct'86 by Dorane Ltd.

Liberty Bell

J-BECK STORY VOL.2.
Album: released on EVA, Mar'84

Liberty Belles

LIBERTY BELLES Various artists (Various Artists).
Album: released on Stateside, Sep'85 Dist: EMI

Cassette: released on Stateside, Sep'85 Dist: EMI

Libra Libra

I LIKE IT.
Tracks: / I like it / I like it (Dub mix).
Single (7"): released on Champion, Jan'87 by Champion Records. Dist: RCA

Lichfield Cathedral Choir

EVENSONG FOR THE FEAST OF SAINT CHAD.
Album: released on Alpha, Aug'82 by Alpha Records. Dist: H.R. Taylor, Gamut

FROM DARKNESS INTO LIGHT Music from Advent and Christmas.
Album: released on Alpha, Oct'81 by Alpha Records. Dist: H.R. Taylor, Gamut

Cassette: released on Alpha, Oct'81 by Alpha Records. Dist: H.R. Taylor, Gamut

HEAR MY PRAYER.
Album: released on Alpha, Jul'83 by Alpha Records. Dist: H.R. Taylor. Gamut

SING XMAS CAROLS.
Album: released on Abbey, '74 by Abbey. Dist: PRT, Taylors, Gamut

Licks

1970'S.
Single (7"): released on Stortbeat, Nov'79 by Stortbeat Records. Dist: Spartan Distribution

Lick The Tins

BELLE OF BELFAST CITY (THE).
Tracks: / Belle of belfast city (The) / Calliope house.
Single (7"): released on Sedition, Aug'86 Dist: PRT

Single (12"): released on Sedition, Aug'86 Dist: PRT

BLIND MAN ON A FLYING HORSE, A.
Album: released on Sedition, May'87 Dist: PRT

Cassette: released on Sedition, May'87 Dist: PRT

CAN'T HELP FALLING IN LOVE.
Tracks: / Can't help falling in love / Bad dreams.
Single (7"): released on Sedition, Feb'87 Dist: PRT

Single (12"): released on Sedition, Feb'87 Dist: PRT

IN THE MIDDLE OF THE NIGHT.
Tracks: / In the middle of the night / Looks like you / Road to California.
Single (7"): released on Sedition, Mar'87 Dist: PRT

Single (12"): released on Sedition, Mar'87 Dist: PRT

Liebman, David

DOIN' IT AGAIN (Liebman, David Quartet).
Album: released on Timeless, Apr'81

DOUBLE EDGE (Liebman, David & Richard Beirach).

FORGOTTEN FANTASIES (Liebman, David & Richard Beirach).
Album: released on A&M, Jul'76 by A&M Records. Dist: Polygram

IF THEY ONLY KNEW.
Album: released on Timeless(import), '81 Dist: Cadillac

LIGHT'N UP PLEASE.
Album: released on Horizon, Apr'77 by A&M Records. Dist: CBS

OPAL HEART, THE (Liebman, David Quartet).
Album: released on Enja (Germany), Jan'82 by Enja Records (W.Germany). Dist: Cadillac Music

PENDULUM (Liebman, David Quartet).
Album: released on Artists House, May'81 Dist: JSU, Swift

QUEST.
Album: released on Palo Alto (Italy), Jan'85

Album: released on New Jazz (USA), Feb'84 by Fantasy Records. Dist: RCA

SWEET HANDS.
Album: by A&M Records. Dist: CBS

Liebrer, Franz

FAMOUS STRAUSS WALTZES (Liebrer, Franz Josef & His Viennese Orchestra).
Album: released on Dansan, Apr'81 by Spartan Records. Dist: Spartan

Liege Lord

FREEDOM'S RISE.
Album: released on Black Dragon, May'87 by Black Dragon Records. Dist: Rough Trade

Lie Lie, Bunny

I MISS YOU.
Single (12"): released on Sweetcorn, Oct'84 by Sweetcorn Records. Dist: Jetstar

LOVE ME GIRL.
Single (12"): released on Time, May'85 Dist: Jetstar Distribution

MIDNIGHT LOVING.
Album: released on Rusty International, May'84 by Rusty International Records. Dist: Jetstar Distribution

MRS BROWN.
Tracks: / Mrs Brown / My sound.
Single (12"): released on Sweetcorn, Jun'86 by Sweetcorn Records. Dist: Jetstar

Lies all lies

STILL NIGHT AIR.
Tracks: / Still night air / Armchair holiday.
Single (7"): released on Face, May'86 by Face Records & Music. Dist: T.One Records

Lieutenant pigeon

MOULDY OLD DOUGH.
Single (7"): released on Decca, Mar'82 by Decca Records. Dist: Polygram

Single (7"): released on Old Gold, Apr'82 by Old Gold Records. Dist: Lightning, Jazz Music, Spartan, Counterpoint

Life

ALL PLAYED OUT.
Tracks: / All played out / All played out (Dub Instrumental) / Bonus beat.
Single (7"): released on Lovebeat International, Mar'86

Single (12"): released on Lovebeat International, Mar'86

OPTIMISM.
Single (7"): released on Factory, Jul'85 by Factory Records. Dist: Cartel, Pinnacle

TELL ME.
Single (7"): released on Factory, Jul'84 by Factory Records. Dist: Cartel, Pinnacle

TOO LATE.
Single (7"): released on Media, Aug'80

WELL PLEASED AND SATISFIED.
Single (12"): released on Exclusive, Aug'82 Dist: Jetstar

Life Ahead Corporation

RICH MEN'S BURDEN.
Single (12"): released on Trust, Apr'85 by Fast. Dist: Cartel Distribution

Life and loves...

LIFE AND LOVES OF A SHE DEVIL Various artists (Various Artists).
Notes: Brilliant new music from the BBC serial starring Dennis Waterman.Includes the title song "Warm love gone cold" sung by Christine Collister.
Album: released on BBC, Oct'86 by BBC Records & Tapes. Dist: EMI, PRT, Pye

Cassette: released on BBC, Oct'86 by BBC Records & Tapes. Dist: EMI, PRT, Pye

Life and Mary Ann

LIFE AND MARY ANN Cookson, Catherine (James, Susan).
Cassette: released on Chivers Audio Books, Apr'81 by Chivers Sound & Vision. Dist: Chivers Sound & Vision

Life and Times
STRAWPLAIT & BONELACE.
Album: released on Fellside, May'85 by Fellside Records. Dist: Roots, Jazz Music, Celtic Music, Projection

Life at the top
LIFE AT THE TOP Various artists (Various Artists).
Album: released on Third Mind, Nov'84 by Third Mind Records. Dist: Backs, Cartel Distribution

Life Force
INVITATION.
Single (7"): released on Polo, Aug'84 by Polo Records. Dist: PRT

Single (12"): released on Polo, Aug'84 by Polo Records. Dist: PRT

MAN IN A MILLION.
Single (7"): released on Polo, Jun'85 by Polo Records. Dist: PRT

Single (12"): released on Polo, Jun'85 by Polo Records. Dist: PRT

REACH FOR THE STARS.
Single (7"): released on Polo, Jan'85 by Polo Records. Dist: PRT

Single (12"): released on Polo, Jan'85 by Polo Records. Dist: PRT

WHAT A WAY TO GO.
Single (7"): released on Polo, May'84 by Polo Records. Dist: PRT

Single (12"): released on Polo, May'84 by Polo Records. Dist: PRT

Life of Brian
LIFE OF BRIAN Original soundtrack.
Album: released on WEA, Oct'79 by WEA Records. Dist: WEA

Life Optimism
BETTER.
Single (7"): released on Factory, Sep'85 by Factory Records. Dist: Cartel, Pinnacle

Life's a riot...
LIFE'S A RIOT & THEN YOU DIE Various artists (Various Artists).
Album: released on Riot City, Mar'85 by Riot City Records. Dist: Revolver

Life Sentence
LIFE SENTENCE.
Notes: Chicago hardcore metal-punk, Produced by Barry Stern from Zoetrope.
Album: released on Walkthrufyre (USA), Aug'87

Lifesighs
GET SERIOUS.
Single (7"): released on Pressure, Oct'85 Dist: Priority

Single (12"): released on Pressure, Oct'85 Dist: Priority

Life Studies
HOMEWARD.
Single (7"): released on Occasion, Aug'83 by Occasion Records. Dist: Cartel Distribution

Life, the universe...
LIFE, THE UNIVERSE & EVERYTHING Adams, Douglas (Moore, Stephen).
Cassette: released on Listen For Pleasure, Oct'84 by MFP Records. Dist: EMI

Lift
UNITED STATES.
Tracks: / United States / L.I.F.T..
Single (7"): released on Magnet, Jun'87 by Magnet Records. Dist: BMG

Single (12"): released on Magnet, Jun'87 by Magnet Records. Dist: BMG

Lift Up
DIAMONDS NEVER MADE A LADY.
Tracks: / Diamonds never made a lady (extended mix) / Diamonds never made a lady (Inst).
Single (12"): released on Greyhound, Jan'87 by Greyhound Records. Dist: PRT, Greyhound

Ligament blub brothers
BIG SHOE BOY.
Tracks: / Big boy shoe.
Single (7"): released on Scrundespatch, Aug'86

Liggett, Otis
EVERY BREATH YOU TAKE.
Single (7"): released on Warehouse, Oct'83 by Warehouse Records. Dist: PRT

Single (12"): released on Warehouse, Oct'83 by Warehouse Records. Dist: PRT

Liggins, Joe
DARKTOWN STRUTTERS BALL (Liggins, Joe & His Honey Drippers).
Album: released on Jukebox Lil, Aug'81 Dist: Swift

GREAT RHYTHM & BLUES: VOL 6.
Album: released on Bulldog Records, Jul'82

Liggins, Joe & Jimmy
JOE & JIMMY LIGGINS.
Album: released on Sonet, '74 by Sonet Records. Dist: PRT

Liggins, Len
REMEDY FOR BAD NERVES, (A).
Single (7"): released on AAZ, Sep'85 by AAZ Records. Dist: Red Rhino, Cartel

Light
CONTRASTING STRANGERS.
Tracks: / Contrasting strangers.
Single (7"): released on Inevitable, Apr'86 by Inevitable Records. Dist: Rough Trade

Single (12"): released on Inevitable, Apr'86 by Inevitable Records. Dist: Rough Trade

CONTRASTING STRANGERS.
Single (7"): released on Inevitable, Jun'85 by Inevitable Records. Dist: Rough Trade

Single (12"): released on Inevitable, Jun'85 by Inevitable Records. Dist: Rough Trade

ILLUMINATION.
Tracks: / Pride of winning / Better things to cry for / 10 million years / old man roms / When daylight is over / Contrasting strangers / I'm thinking of you now / Something special / Masquerade / Precious is the pearl.
Album: released on Inevitable, Apr'86 by Inevitable Records. Dist: Rough Trade

Cassette: released on Inevitable, Apr'86 by Inevitable Records. Dist: Rough Trade

PRIDE IS WINNING.
Tracks: / Pride of winning / Ten million years
Single (7"): released on Inevitable, Jun'86 by Inevitable Records. Dist: Rough Trad

Single (12"): released on Inevitable, Jun'86 by Inevitable Records. Dist: Rough Trade

TURN OUT THE LIGHT.
Single (7"): released on Shock, Jan'80

Light A Big Fire
CHARLENE.
Tracks: / Charlene / Hunger / Shape I'm in.
Single (7"): released on Siren, Aug'86 by Virgin Records. Dist: EMI

Single (12"): released on Siren, Aug'86 by Virgin Records. Dist: EMI

GUNPOWDERS.
Notes: Mini LP
Album: released on Statik, Nov'85 Dist: Rough Trade Distribution, Stage One Distribution

I SEE PEOPLE.
Tracks: / I see people / Jonny on all fours / Mr. Twilight (live).
Single (7"): released on Siren, Mar'87 by Virgin Records. Dist: EMI

Single (12"): released on Siren, Mar'87 by Virgin Records. Dist: EMI

MR TWILIGHT.
Tracks: / Mr. Twilight / Lovers.
Single (7"): released on Siren, Nov'86 by Virgin Records. Dist: EMI

Single (12"): released on Siren, Nov'86 by Virgin Records. Dist: EMI

SURVEILLANCE.
Album: released on Siren, Apr'87 by Virgin Records. Dist: EMI

Light Blues
LIGHT BLUES SING JEROME KERN.
Album: released on Hyperion, Oct'84 by Hyperion Records. Dist: Taylors, PRT, Gamut

Light Factory
LIVE FACTORY/BUS STOPS.
Tracks: / Light factory / C'mon C'mon (We're down at the station) / Waiting at the bus-stop / (Climb onboard our) great big bus.
Notes: Produced by Nigel Palmer (Scarf Studios).Published by Sea Dream Music/Light Factory Productions.

Cassette: released on Plankton, Mar'86 by Plankton Records. Dist: Cantio (Sweden)

Lightfoot,Gordon
BEST OF.....
Album: released on Warner Brothers, May'81 by Warner Bros Records. Dist: WEA

Cassette: released on Warner Brothers, May'81 by Warner Bros Records. Dist: WEA

COLD ON THE SHOULDER.
Album: released on Reprise, Mar'75 by WEA Records. Dist: WEA

DREAM STREET ROSE.
Album: released on WEA, Jun'80 by WEA Records. Dist: WEA

Cassette: released on WEA, Jun'80 by WEA Records. Dist: WEA

EAST OF MIDNIGHT.
Tracks: / Stay loose / Morning glory / East of midnight / Lesson in love, A / Anything for love / Let it ride / Ecstacy made easy / You just gotta be / Passing ship, A / I'll tag along.
Album: released on Warner Bros., Oct'86 by Warner Bros Records. Dist: WEA

Cassette: released on Warner Bros., Oct'86 by Warner Bros Records. Dist: WEA

ENDLESS WIRE.
Album: released on Warner Brothers, Feb'78 by Warner Bros Records. Dist: WEA

Cassette: released on Warner Brothers, Feb'78 by Warner Bros Records. Dist: WEA

IF YOU COULD READ MY MIND.
Tracks: / If you could read my mind / Sundown.
Single (12"): released on Old Gold, Mar'86 by Old Gold Records. Dist: Lightning, Jazz Music, Spartan, Counterpoint

Album: released on Reprise, '74 by WEA Records. Dist: WEA

Single (7"): released on Reprise, '80 by WEA Records. Dist: WEA

SHADOWS.
Album: released on Warner Brothers, Feb'82 by Warner Bros Records. Dist: WEA

Cassette: released on Warner Brothers, Feb'82 by Warner Bros Records. Dist: WEA Deleted '83.

SUMMERTIME DREAM.
Cassette: released on Reprise, Jun'76 by WEA Records. Dist: WEA

SUNDOWN.
Album: released on Warner Bros., Jun'74 by Warner Bros Records. Dist: WEA

Cassette: released on Warner Bros., '80 by Warner Bros Records. Dist: WEA

Lightfoot, Papa George
NATCHEZ TRACE.
Album: released on Crosscut, Sep'84 by IMS-Polygram Records. Dist: IMS, Polygram, Rollercoaster Distribution

Lightfoot, Terry
AS TIME GOES BY.
Album: released on PRT, Feb'87 by PRT Records. Dist: PRT

Cassette: released on PRT, Feb'87 by PRT Records. Dist: PRT

AS TIME GOES BY A jazz entertainment (Lightfoot, Terry & his band).
Cassette: released on PRT, Jan'87 by PRT Records. Dist: PRT

CLEAR ROUND (Lightfoot, Terry & his band).
Album: released on Plant Life Jazz, Nov'81

IN CONCERT.
Double Album: released on Black Lion, May'79 by Black Lion Records. Dist: Jazz Music, Chris Wellard, Taylor, H.R., Counterpoint. Cadillac

LONESOME (Lightfoot, Terry & his band).
Tracks: / Lonesome / Bloodshot eyes.
Single (7"): released on PRT, Jan'87 by PRT

LONESOME.
Tracks: / Lonesome / Bloodshot eyes.
Single (7"): released on PRT, Feb'87 by PRT

Lighthouse Keepers
TALES OF THE UNEXPECTED.
Album: released on Hot, May'85 by Hot Records. Dist: Rough Trade, Cartel

Lighthouse, The
LIGHTHOUSE, THE/KIMOMO, THE

(H.E.BATES) Read by Martin Jarvis.
Cassette: released on Pickwick Talking Books, '83

Light Infantry bands...
LIGHT INFANTRY BANDS & BUGLES.
Album: released on Music Masters, Jun'83 by Music Masters Records. Dist: Taylors

Cassette: released on Music Masters, Jun'83 by Music Masters Records. Dist: Taylors

Lightning Slim
LIGHTNING SLIM.
Album: released on Flyright, Dec'86 by Flyright Records. Dist: Krazy Kat, Swift, Jazz Music

TRIP TO CHICAGO.
Notes: Mono recording.
Album: released on Flyright, Jul'86 by Flyright Records. Dist: Krazy Kat, Swift, Jazz Music

Lightnin' Rod
DORIELLA DU FONTANE (Lightnin' Rod & Jimi Hendrix).
Single (12"): released on Celp, Jun'84 Dist: Harmonia Mundi

Lightnin' Slim
HIGH & LOW DOWN.
Album: released on Sonet, '74 by Sonet Records. Dist: PRT

LONDON GUMBO.
Album: released on Sonet, Aug'78 by Sonet Records. Dist: PRT

Light of day
LIGHT OF DAY Original soundtrack (Various Artists).
Tracks: / Light of day / This means war / Twist it off / Cleveland rocks / Stay with me tonight / It's all coming down tonight / Rude mood / Only lonely / Rabbit's got the gun / You got no place to go / Elegy (instrumental).
Compact disc: released on Epic, May'87 by CBS Records. Dist: CBS

Light of the World
BEST OF LIGHT OF THE WORLD.
Album: released on Ensign, Nov'85 by Ensign Records. Dist: CBS Distribution

Cassette: released on Ensign, Nov'85 by Ensign Records. Dist: CBS Distribution

FAMOUS FACES.
Single (7"): released on EMI, Sep'82 by EMI Records. Dist: EMI

Single (7"): released on EMI, Aug'82 by EMI Records. Dist: EMI

JEALOUS LOVER.
Single (7"): released on EMI, Jul'83 by EMI Records. Dist: EMI

Single (12"): released on EMI, Jul'83 by EMI Records. Dist: EMI

LONDON TOWN '85.
Single (7"): released on Ensign, Jun'85 by Ensign Records. Dist: CBS Distribution

Single (12"): released on Ensign, Jun'85 by Ensign Records. Dist: CBS Distribution

REMIXED....
Album: released on Mercury, Jun'81 by Phonogram Records. Dist: Polygram Distribution

Light Princess, The
LIGHT PRINCESS, THE Read by Glynis Johns.
Cassette: released on Caedmon(USA), Aug'83 by Caedmon (USA) Records. Dist: Gower, Taylors, Discovery

Lightsey, Kirk
EVERYTHING HAPPENS TO ME (Lightsey, Kirk Trio).
Cassette: released on Timeless, Oct'86

LIGHSEY LIVE.
Tracks: / Pee Wee / Habiba / Trinkle tinkle / Spring is here / Fee Fi Fo Fum / Just one of those things.
Notes: Kirk Lightsey -piano.Recorded at the Baird Auditorium of the Smithsonian institution in Washington D.C on june 28 1985.
Compact disc: released on Sunnyside (USA), Nov'86 Dist: Mole Jazz Distribution, Conifer Distribution

LIGHTSEY.
Album: released on Sunnyside (USA), Apr'84 Dist: Mole Jazz Distribution, Conifer Distribution

LIGHTSEY 1 (Lightsey,Kirk Piano).
Tracks: / Fee-Fi-Fo-Fum / Habiba / Trinkle tinkle / Moon ra / Fresh air / Wild flower / Never let me go.
Notes: Kirk Lightsey on piano and flute.Re-

corded at Penthouse Recordings.
Album: released on Sunnyside (USA), Sep'86
Dist: Mole Jazz Distribution, Conifer Distribution

LIGHTSEY 2.
Album: released on Sunnyside (USA), Apr'84
Dist: Mole Jazz Distribution, Conifer Distribution

SHORTER BY TWO (Lightsey, Kirk/Harold Denko).
Album: released on Sunnyside (USA), Apr'84
Dist: Mole Jazz Distribution, Conifer Distribution

Light & Shade
L'AMOUR.
Single (7"): released on Light & Shade, Mar'85
by Light & Shade Records. Dist: M.I.S.

Light up the dynamite
LIGHT UP THE DYNAMITE Featuring Nick Lowe & Shakin' Stevens.
Album: released on Magnum Force, '83 by Magnum Music Group Ltd. Dist: Magnum Music Group Ltd, PRT, Spartan

Ligon, Bert
DANCING BARE (Ligon, Bert/Gary Willis/Jay Fort/K. Covington).
Album: released on Sea Breeze, Mar'87 Dist: Swift

Ligotage
FORGIVE AND FORGET-LIVE.
Album: released on Picasso, Dec'84 by Picasso Records. Dist: Pinnacle

Like
CONTRASTING STRANGERS.
Tracks: / Contrasting strangers / Monument / Thinking of you.
Single (7"): released on RCA, Feb'86 by RCA Records. Dist: RCA, Roots, Swift, Wellard, Chris, I & B, Solomon & Peres Distribution

Single (12"): released on RCA, Feb'86 by RCA Records. Dist: RCA, Roots, Swift, Wellard, Chris, I & B, Solomon & Peres Distribution

Lil'Ed
ROUGH HOUSEIN' (Lil'Ed & The Blues Imperials).
Album: released on Sonet, Oct'86 by Sonet Records. Dist: PRT

Cassette: released on Sonet, Oct'86 by Sonet Records. Dist: PRT

Liliput
EISGERWIND.
Single (7"): released on Rough Trade, Feb'81 by Rough Trade Records. Dist: Rough Trade Distribution, Cartel Distribution

LILIPUT.
Album: released on Rough Trade, '84 by Rough Trade Records. Dist: Rough Trade Distribution, Cartel Distribution

MATROSEN, DIE.
Single (7"): released on Rough Trade, Jul'80 by Rough Trade Records. Dist: Rough Trade Distribution, Cartel Distribution

SOME SONGS.
Album: released on Rough Trade, Dec'83 by Rough Trade Records. Dist: Rough Trade Distribution, Cartel Distribution

YOU DID IT.
Single (7"): released on Rough Trade, Jul'83 by Rough Trade Records. Dist: Rough Trade Distribution, Cartel Distribution

Lillo
YOU'RE A GOOD GIRL.
Single (12"): released on Capitol, Aug'83 by Capitol Records. Dist: EMI

Single (7"): released on Capitol, Aug'83 by Capitol Records. Dist: EMI

Lilly, Willy
LILLY, WILLY AND THE MAIL ORDER WITCH Bach, Othello (Grimes, Tammy).
Cassette: released on Caedmon(USA), '84 by Caedmon (USA) Records. Dist: Gower, Taylors, Discovery

Lilting Banshee
LILTING BANSHEE various artists (Various Artists).
Album: released on Saydisc, Sep'85 by Saydisc Records. Dist: Essex, Harmonia Mundi, Roots, H.R. Taylor, Jazz Music, Swift, Projection, Gamut

Cassette: released on Saydisc, Sep'85 by Saydisc Records. Dist: Essex, Harmonia Mundi, Roots, H.R. Taylor, Jazz Music, Projection, Gamut

Lilting banshee (The)
LILTING BANSHEE (THE) (Monger, Eileen).
Notes: For full details see under "Monger, Eileen"

Lima, Carlos Barbosa & Sha-
BRAZIL, WITH LOVE.
Tracks: / Luiza / Felicidade / Chovendo Na Rosiera / Garoto / Estrada Do Sol / Gabriella / Passatempo / Vou vivendo / Pretencioso / Carinhoso / Brejeiro / Apandhi-Te, Cavaquinha / Bambino / Odeon.
Album: released on Concord Jazz(USA), Jul'87 by Concord Jazz Records (USA). Dist: IMS, Polygram

Cassette: released on Concord Jazz(USA), Jul'87 by Concord Jazz Records (USA). Dist: IMS, Polygram

Compact disc: released on Concord Jazz(USA), Jul'87 by Concord Jazz Records (USA). Dist: IMS, Polygram

Limahl
COLOUR ALL MY DAYS.
Tracks: / Love in your eyes / Colour all my eyes / Nothing on earth(Can you keep me from you) / Tonight will be the night / Working out / Don't send for me / Shock / Outside to inside / Love will tear the soul / For my hearts sake.
Album: released on EMI, May'86 by EMI Records. Dist: EMI

Cassette: released on EMI, May'86 by EMI Records. Dist: EMI

DON'T SUPPOSE.
Album: released on EMI, Nov'84 by EMI Records. Dist: EMI

Cassette: released on EMI, Nov'84 by EMI Records. Dist: EMI

INSIDE TO OUTSIDE.
Tracks: / Inside to outside / Shock.
Single (7"): released on EMI, Sep'86 by EMI Records. Dist: EMI

Single (12"): released on EMI, Sep'86 by EMI Records. Dist: EMI

LOVE IN YOUR EYES.
Tracks: / Love in your eyes / Love will tear the soul.
Single (7"): released on EMI, Apr'86 by EMI Records. Dist: EMI

Single (12"): released on EMI, Apr'86 by EMI Records. Dist: EMI

Picture disc single: released on EMI, Apr'86 by EMI Records. Dist: EMI

NEVER ENDING STORY.
Single (7"): released on EMI, Sep'84 by EMI Records. Dist: EMI

Single (12"): released on EMI, Sep'84 by EMI Records. Dist: EMI

ONLY FOR LOVE.
Single (7"): released on EMI, Oct'83 by EMI Records. Dist: EMI Deleted '86.

Single (12"): released on EMI, Oct'83 by EMI Records. Dist: EMI Deleted '86.

Picture disc single: released on EMI, Oct'83 by EMI Records. Dist: EMI

TOO MUCH TROUBLE.
Single (7"): released on EMI, May'84 by EMI Records. Dist: EMI Deleted '86.

Single (12"): released on EMI, May'84 by EMI Records. Dist: EMI Deleted '86.

Picture disc single: released on EMI, May'84 by EMI Records. Dist: EMI

Limbo
MAN UNITED.
Single (7"): released on Weasel, Feb'85 by Weasel Records. Dist: Spartan

Lime
BEST OF LIME.
Tracks: / Angel eyes / Come and get your love / Take it up / Your love / Unexpected love / Your Love / Unexpected lovers / Babe we're gonna love tonight / Guilty.
Album: released on Polydor, Nov'85 by Polydor Records. Dist: Polygram, Polydor

Compact disc: by Polydor Records. Dist: Polygram, Polydor

LIME 2.
Album: released on Import Music Service (IMS), Nov'83 Dist: Concord Jazz Distributions, Pablo, Polygram

LIME 3.
Album: released on Import Music Service (IMS), Nov'83 Dist: Concord Jazz Distributions, Pablo, Polygram

SENSUAL SENSATION.
Album: released on Polydor (Italy), Nov'84

Cassette: released on Polydor (Italy), Nov'84

UNEXPECTED LOVERS.
Album: released on Polydor (Germany), Aug'85 Dist: IMS-Polygram

Single (7"): released on Boiling Point, Jul'85 by Polydor Records. Dist: Polygram

Single (12"): released on Boiling Point, Jul'85 by Polydor Records. Dist: Polygram Deleted '86.

YOUR LOVE.
Album: released on Polydor (Germany), Jun'84 Dist: IMS-Polygram

Limelight
ASHES TO ASHES.
Single (7"): released on Future Earth, Oct'82 by Future Earth Records. Dist: Red Rhino, Cartel

Limelight Orchestra
COLD WARRIOR.
Single (7"): released on BBC, Aug'84 by BBC Records & Tapes. Dist: EMI, PRT, Pye

SKORPION, (THE).
Single (7"): released on BBC, Jan'83 by BBC Records & Tapes. Dist: EMI, PRT, Pye

Lime Spiders
SLAVE GIRL.
Album: released on Hybrid, Oct'85 by Statik Records. Dist: Pinnacle

WIERDO LIBIDO.
Tracks: / Wierdo libido / My flash on you.
Single (12"): released on Zinger, Apr'87 by Zinger Records. Dist: Pinnacle

Lime Spiders, The
CAVE COMES ALIVE, THE.
Album: released on Virgin, Aug'87 by Virgin Records. Dist: EMI, Virgin Distribution

Cassette: released on Virgin, Aug'87 by Virgin Records. Dist: EMI, Virgin Distribution

Limit
LIMIT, (THE).
Album: released on Portrait, Feb'85 by CBS Records. Dist: CBS

Cassette: released on Portrait, Feb'85 by CBS Records. Dist: CBS Deleted '87.

SAY YEAH!.
Single (7"): released on Portrait, Dec'84 by CBS Records. Dist: CBS

Single (12"): released on Portrait, Dec'84 by CBS Records. Dist: CBS

SHE'S SO DIVINE.
Single (7"): released on Ariola, Feb'85 Dist: RCA, Ariola

Single (12"): released on Ariola, Feb'85 Dist: RCA, Ariola

SHOCK WAVES.
Single (7"): released on Survival, Jul'81 by Survival Records. Dist: Backs, Cartel Distribution

TAKE IT.
Single (7"): released on Survival, Nov'81 by Survival Records. Dist: Backs, Cartel Distribution

Limited warranty
LIMITED WARRANTY.
Tracks: / Last to know / Hit you from behind / This is serious / Beat down the door / Yesterday's news / Victory line / One of a kind / Never enough / Domestic / You can buy.

Limmie & Family Cooking
YOU CAN DO MAGIC.
Single (7"): released on Old Gold, Jan'85 by Old Gold Records. Dist: Lightning, Jazz Music, Spartan, Counterpoint

Lincoln, Abbey
AFFAIR.
Album: released on EMI (France), Jan'85 by EMI Records. Dist: Conifer

TALKING TO THE SUN.
Album: released on Enja (Germany), Nov'84 by Enja Records (W.Germany). Dist: Cadillac Music

THAT'S HIM.
Album: released on Riverside (USA), Feb'84 Dist: Fantasy (USA) Distribution

Lincoln, Charley
CHARLEY LINCOLN.
Album: released on Matchbox, Aug'83 by Saydisc Records. Dist: Roots, Projection, Jazz Music, JSU, Celtic Music

Lincoln, Mayorga
GROWING UP IN HOLLYWOOD TOWN.
WEST OF OZ (Lincoln, Mayorga & Amanda McBroom).

Lincoln, Prince
EXPERIENCE (Lincoln, Prince & The Royal Rasses).
Album: released on Vista Sounds, Jul'84 by Vista Sounds Records. Dist: Jetstar

REVOLUTIONARY MAN (Lincoln, Prince & The Royal Rasses).
Single (7"): released on Target, Aug'84 by Target Records. Dist: Spartan Distribution

Lincoln, Teddy
I COULD HAVE LOVED YOU.
Single (12"): released on Regal, Mar'82

PLAY WITH FIRE.
Single (12"): released on Selena, Feb'82 Dist: Jetstar

SEVENTEEN.
Single (12"): released on Regal, Jul'82

SLAVE.
Single (12"): released on Jah Life, Sep'85 by Jah Life Records. Dist: Jetstar

Linda & Raymondo
RIGHT TIME RIGHT PLACE.
Single (12"): released on Time, Nov'85 by Jetstar Distribution

Linda & the Prophets
WORK.
Single (12"): released on Survival, Apr'85 by Survival Records. Dist: Backs, Cartel Distribution

Lindberg, John
COMIN' & GOIN'.
Album: released on Leo, Sep'84 Dist: Recommended

DIMENSION 5 (Lindberg, John Quintet).
Album: released on Black Saint, Jul'82 Dist: Projection, IMS, Polygram, Chris Wellard, Harmonia Mundi, Swift

HAUNT OF THE UNRESOLVED.
Tracks: / Haunt of the unresolved-Part 1 / Haunt of the unresolved-Part 2.

Lind, Bob
ELUSIVE BUTTERFLY.
Single (7"): released on USA Import, '80

Lindenberg, Udo
GERMANS.
Tracks: / Germans / Shadow of your smile(The).
Single (7"): released on Rockin' Horse, Apr'85 by Arista Records. Dist: RCA Distribution

UDO LINDENBERG UND DAS PANIK ORCHESTRA.
Tracks: / Hoch im nordon / Ales klar auf der andrea doria / Honky Tonk show / Johnny Controlietti / Rudi ratlos / Bodo ballerman / Rock 'n' Roll arena in jena / Riki Mascratti / Guten tag ich heibe schmidt / Reeperbahn / New York(New York state of mind) / Baby,wenn ich down bin / Grande finale / Kann denn liebe sunde sein / Kugel im colt / Zwischen rhein und aufruhr.
Notes: Gesang:Udo Lindenberg und Leata Galloway:

Lindh, Bjorn J:Son
DAY AT THE SURFACE, A.
Album: released on Sonet, Jul'80 by Sonet Records. Dist: PRT

FROM HERE TO ETERNITY.
Single (7"): released on Sonet, May'83 by Sonet Records. Dist: PRT

TO BE CONTINUED.
Album: released on Sonet, Jul'82 by Sonet Records. Dist: PRT

WET WINGS.
Album: released on Sonet, May'81 by Sonet Records. Dist: PRT

Lindisfarne
BACK AND FOURTH.
Album: released on Mercury, Dec'83 by Phonogram Records. Dist: Polygram Distribution

Cassette: released on Mercury, Dec'83 by Phonogram Records. Dist: Polygram Distribu-

tion

DANCE YOUR LIFE AWAY.
Album: released on River City, Oct'86 Dist: RCA

Cassette: released on River City, Oct'86 Dist: RCA

DO WHAT I WANT.
Single (7"): released on LMP, Jan'83 Dist: BMG, PRT, RCA

FINEST HOUR.
Album: released on Charisma, Sep'83 by Virgin Records. Dist: EMI

Album: released on Charisma, Sep'83 by Virgin Records. Dist: EMI

FOG ON THE TYNE.
Tracks: / Meet me on the corner / Alright on the night / Uncle Sam / Together forever / January song / Peter Brophy don't care / City song / Passing Ghosts / Train in G major / Fog on the Tyne.
Notes: Originally released 1971.

FOG ON THE TYNE/NICELY OUT OF TUNE.
Double cassette: released on Charisma, Mar'83 by Virgin Records. Dist: EMI

I MUST STOP GOING TO PARTIES.
Single (7"): released on Hangover, Nov'81 by Hangover Records. Dist: Spartan

LADY ELEANOR.
Album: released on Hallmark, Aug'77 by Pickwick Records. Dist: Pickwick Distribution, PRT, Taylors

LINDISFARNE LIVE.
Album: released on Charisma, Sep'83 by Virgin Records. Dist: EMI

Cassette: released on Charisma, Sep'83 by Virgin Records. Dist: EMI

LINDISFARNE TASTIC LIVE.
Album: released on LMP, Sep'84 Dist: BMG, PRT, RCA

LINDISFARNTASTIC VOL.2.
Album: released on LMP, Nov'84 Dist: BMG, PRT, RCA

Cassette: released on LMP, Nov'84 Dist: BMG, PRT, RCA

LOVE ON THE RUN.
Tracks: / Love on the run / One hundred miles to Liverpool.
Single (7"): released on LMP, Feb'87 Dist: BMG, PRT, RCA

MEET ME ON THE CORNER.
Single (7"): released on Old Gold, Jul'82 by Old Gold Records. Dist: Lightning, Jazz Music, Spartan, Counterpoint

NEWS, THE.
Album: released on Mercury, Sep'79 by Phonogram Records. Dist: Polygram Distribution

NIGHTS.
Single (7"): released on LMP, Sep'82 Dist: BMG, PRT, RCA

SHINE ON.
Tracks: / Shine on.

SLEEPLESS NIGHTS.
Album: released on LMP, Oct'82 Dist: BMG, PRT, RCA

Cassette: released on LMP, Oct'82 Dist: BMG, PRT, RCA

Lindley, David
EL RAYO - X.
Album: released on Asylum, May'81 by WEA Records. Dist: WEA

LIVE (Lindley, David & El Rayo X).
Album: released on WEA (Germany). Oct'84

MR.DAVE.
Album: released on WEA, Jul'85 by WEA Records. Dist: WEA

WIN THIS RECORD.
Album: released on Asylum, Oct'82 by WEA Records. Dist: WEA

Lindo, Hopeton
SIDEWALK TRAVELLER.
Single (12"): released on Music Works, Dec'82 Dist: Jetstar Distribution

Lindon, Claudius
ARMS RACE.
Single (12"): released on Sanity, Apr'84 by Sanity Records. Dist: Pinnacle, Jetstar

Lindo, Neville
RUB A DUB COMMANDER.
Page 604

Single (12"): released on Negus Roots, Dec'84 by Negus Roots Records. Dist: Jetstar

You're My Doctor Girl
YOU'RE MY DOCTOR GIRL.
Single (12"): released on Negus Roots, Jul'85 by Negus Roots Records. Dist: Jetstar

Lind, Ove
DIALOGUE IN SWING (see Hallberg, Bengt) (Lind, Ove & Bengt Hallberg).
Album: released on Phontastic (Sweden), '82 by Wellard, Chris Distribution. Dist: Wellard, Chris Distribution

EVERGREENS.
Double Album: released on Phontastic (Sweden), '82 by Wellard, Chris Distribution. Dist: Wellard, Chris Distribution

Double cassette: released on Phontastic (Sweden), '82 by Wellard, Chris Distribution. Dist: Wellard, Chris Distribution

EVERGREENS 2.
Double Album: released on Phontastic (Sweden), '82 by Wellard, Chris Distribution. Dist: Wellard, Chris Distribution

Double cassette: released on Phontastic (Sweden), '82 by Wellard, Chris Distribution. Dist: Wellard, Chris Distribution

GERSHWIN - EVERGREEN.
Double Album: by Wellard, Chris Distribution. Dist: Wellard, Chris Distribution

Double cassette: by Wellard, Chris Distribution. Dist: Wellard, Chris Distribution

ONE MORNING IN MAY (Lind, Ove Quartet).
Album: released on Phontastic (Sweden), '82 by Wellard, Chris Distribution. Dist: Wellard, Chris Distribution

SUMMER NIGHT.
Album: released on Phontastic (Sweden), '82 by Wellard, Chris Distribution. Dist: Wellard, Chris Distribution

SWINGING DIXIELAND (Lind, Ove & The Phontastic Dixie Players).
Album: released on Phontastic (Sweden), '82 by Wellard, Chris Distribution. Dist: Wellard, Chris Distribution

Lindsay, Balford
JUST BECAUSE I LOVE YOU.
Single (12"): released on Londisc, Apr'85 by Londisc Records.

Lindsay, Jimmy
TURN OUT THE LIGHTS.
Single (12"): released on Music Hive. Mar'82

Lindsay, Julian
NETWORK 7 Theme from the TV series (Lindsay, Julian & Steve Levine).
Tracks: / Network 7 / Straight in straight out / 808°
Single (7"): released on Sierra, Jul'87 by Sierra Records. Dist: WEA

Single (12"): released on Sierra, Jul'87 by Sierra Records. Dist: WEA

Lindsay-Thomas, David
YOU OUGHTA BE IN PICTURES.
Single (7"): released on Modern (UK), May'83 Dist: WEA Distribution

Lindsey, Arto
ENVY (Lindsey, Arto & Ambitious lovers).
Tracks: / Cross your legs / Trouble maker / Pagode Americano / Nothings monstered / Crowning roar / Too many mansions / Let's be adult / Venus lost her shirt / My competition / Badu / Dora / Beberibe / Loas Coruleus.
Album: released on Editions EG, Jan'87 by Virgin Records. Dist: EMI

Album: released on Editions EG, Feb'85 by Virgin Records. Dist: EMI

Lindsey, Judy
FUJIYAMA MAMA.
Single (7"): released on Seville, Jul'83 by President Records. Dist: Jazz Music, Swift

Lindsey, Steve
SHE'S LOCKED UP MY LIFE IN HER SUITCASE.
Single (7"): released on Rialto, May'82 by Rialto Records. Dist: Pinnacle

Lindt, Virna
ATTENTION STOCKHOLM.
Single (7"): released on Compact Organisation, Jan'85 Dist: PRT

I EXPERIENCED LOVE.
Single (7"): released on Compact Organisation, Sep'84 Dist: PRT

Single (12"): released on Compact Organisation, Sep'84 Dist: PRT

INTELLIGENCE.
Single (7"): released on Compact Organisation, Jun'83 Dist: PRT

Single (12"): released on Compact Organisation, Jun'83 Dist: PRT

SHIVER.
Single (7"): released on Compact Organisation, Jan'85 Dist: PRT

Cassette: released on Compact Organisation, Jan'85 Dist: PRT

WHISTLEWIND.
Tracks: / Whistlewind.

YOUNG AND HIP.
Single (7"): released on Compact Organisation, Oct'81 Dist: PRT

Line Line
VISION.
Single (7"): released on New Dance, Jun'84 Dist: Rough Trade, Red Rhino, Cartel

Lines
HOUSE OF CRACKS.
Single (7"): released on Red, Mar'82 Dist: Projection, Jazz Horizons

Single (12"): released on Red, Mar'82 Dist: Projection, Jazz Horizons

ON THE AIR.
Single (7"): released on Red, May'80 Dist: Projection, Jazz Horizons

THERAPY.
Album: released on Fresh, Nov'81 Dist: Jetstar

TRANSIT.
Single (7"): released on Red, Aug'81 Dist: Projection, Jazz Horizons

Ling Family
SINGING TRADITIONS OF A SUFFOLK FAMILY.
Album: released on Topic, '81 Dist: Roots Distribution

Lingle, Paul
DANCE OF THE WITCH HAZELS AT THE JUG CLUB 1951.
Album: released on Euphonic, Sep'79 by Euphonic Records. Dist: Jazz Music, Swift

Linkmen
EVERY INCH A KING.
Single (7"): released on Kitchenware, Jan'85 by Kitchenware Records. Dist: Cartel, CBS, Polygram, RCA-Ariola Distribution

Single (12"): released on Kitchenware, Jun'84 by Kitchenware Records. Dist: Cartel, CBS, Polygram, RCA-Ariola Distribution

I'LL WIND.
Single (12"): released on Spice, Oct'85 Dist: Rough Trade, Cartel

Linnard, Mick
RUSSELL SQUARE (Linnard, Mick & David Hughes).
Album: released on Trailer, '81 Dist: Jazz Music, Celtic Music, JSU

Lino
WAKE UP LONDON.
Single (7"): released on Pok-A-Dot, Aug'81 by Pok-A-Dot Records. Dist: Pinnacle

Lins,Ivan
TOGETHER.
Tracks: / Open wings aka the smiling hour / Message / We are all the same tonight / Ant hill / New times / Starting over aka the island / Together / Dvorah,Dinorah / Holy flag procession / Believe what I say / Leave me / To despair never more / Someday-Vignette.
Notes: Superb album from Ivan Lins with special guests George Benson and singer Patti Austin.Recommended tracks "Together"featuring George Benson and "Believe what Isay" featuring Patti Austin.

Linton,Slim
GOING OUT OF MY MIND.
Tracks: / Going out of my mind / Test transmission.

TO BE TRUE (Linton,Slim & The Robotics).
Tracks: / To be true / Electro magnet.

Linx
GO AHEAD.
Album: released on Chrysalis, Oct'81 by Chrysalis Records. Dist: CBS Deleted '85.

Cassette: released on Chrysalis, Oct'81 by Chrysalis Records. Dist: CBS

INTUITION.
Tracks: / Wonder what you're doing now / I Won't forget / Intuition / There's love / Rise and shine / Throw away the key / Together we can shine / Count on me / Don't grt in my way.
Notes: Produced by Bob Carter,David Grant & Peter Martin for The Solid Foundation.
Album: released on Fame (Chrysalis), Nov'83 by Music For Pleasure Records. Dist: EMI

Cassette: released on Fame (Chrysalis), Nov'83 by Music For Pleasure Records. Dist: EMI

YOU'RE LYING.
Tracks: / You're lying / Intuition.
Single (7"): released on Old Gold, Feb'87 by Old Gold Records. Dist: Lightning, Jazz Music, Spartan, Counterpoint

YOU'RE LYING.
Tracks: / You're lying / Intuition / So this is romance / Throw away the key.
Single (7"): released on Old Gold, Jan'87 by Old Gold Records. Dist: Lightning, Jazz Music, Spartan, Counterpoint

Lionheart
DIE FOR LOVE.
Single (7"): released on Epic, Jan'85 by CBS Records. Dist: CBS

Lions
MARGARET THATCHER.
Tracks: / Margaret Thatcher / Living the good life.
Notes: Soho - 01-734 3465
Single (7"): released on Soho, 30 May'87

Single (12"): released on Soho, 30 May'87

Lions Breed
DAMN THE NIGHT.
Album: released on Earthshaker (Germany), Jun'85 by Earthshaker Records (Germany). Dist: IMS, Polygram

Lionspride
BREAKING OUT.
Album: released on Mausoleum, Oct'84 by Mausoleum Records. Dist: Pinnacle

Cassette: released on Mausoleum, Oct'84 by Mausoleum Records. Dist: Pinnacle

Lion Youth
ALECIA.
Single (12"): released on Virgo, Nov'81

DECELIA.
Single (12"): released on Freedom Sounds, Jun'82 by Freedom Sounds Records. Dist: Jetstar

LET ME ROCK YOU.
Single (12"): released on Sunsplash, Nov'83 by Sunsplash Records. Dist: Jetstar Distribution

LITTLE WOMAN.
Single (12"): released on Virgo, Mar'83

LOVE COMES AND GOES.
Album: released on Freedom Sounds, Dec'81 by Freedom Sounds Records. Dist: Jetstar

RAT A CUT BOTTLE.
Single (12"): released on Freedom Sounds, Sep'81 by Freedom Sounds Records. Dist: Jetstar

SANDRA.
Single (12"): released on Virgo, Aug'82

Lip Machine
ASTRONAUT.
Single (12"): released on Disposable Dance, Nov'85

OUR WORLD.
Tracks: / Our world / Lip machine.
Single (12"): released on DDT, 30 May'87 by D.D.T Records. Dist: Fast Forward, Cartel

ROCKET LOVE AND ASTRONUT.
Tracks: / Rocket love and astronut.

Lipman,Berry
NIGHT OUT WITH THE BERRY LIPMAN SINGERS AND ORCHESTRA.
Album: released on Dansan, Oct'79 by Spartan Records. Dist: Spartan

Lipps Inc.
FUNKY TOWN.
Single (7"): released on Old Gold, Jan'85 by Old Gold Records. Dist: Lightning, Jazz Music, Spartan, Counterpoint

Lipscombe,Mance
MANCE LISCOMBE VOL 4.
Album: released on Arhoolie, May'81 by Arhoolie Records. Dist: Projection, Topic, Jazz

Music, Swift, Roots

TEXAS BLUES.
Album: released on Arhoolie, May'81 by Arhoolie Records. Dist: Projection, Topic, Jazz Music, Swift, Roots

TEXAS SONGSTER VOL 2.
Album: released on Arhoolie, May'81 by Arhoolie Records. Dist: Projection, Topic, Jazz Music, Swift, Roots

TEXAS SONGSTER VOL 3.
Album: released on Arhoolie, May'81 by Arhoolie Records. Dist: Projection, Topic, Jazz Music, Swift, Roots

TEXAS SONGSTER VOL 6.
Album: released on Arhoolie, May'81 by Arhoolie Records. Dist: Projection, Topic, Jazz Music, Swift, Roots

YOU'LL NEVER FIND ANOTHER.
Album: released on Arhoolie, May'81 by Arhoolie Records. Dist: Projection, Topic, Jazz Music, Swift, Roots

TEXAS BLUES.
Album: released on Arhoolie, Jul'87 by Arhoolie Records. Dist: Projection, Topic, Jazz Music, Swift, Roots

Lipton, Celia

LONDON I LOVE, THE.
Album: released on Horatio Nelson, Nov'85 Dist: PRT

Cassette: released on Horatio Nelson, Nov'85 Dist: PRT

YOU'VE GOT YOUR OWN LIFE TO LIVE.
Tracks: / You've got your own life to live / I've got your number.
Single (7"): released on Premier, Feb'87 by Premier Records. Dist: CBS

Lipton,Sydney

1932-3 (Lipton,Sydney and his Orchestra).
Album: released on World Records, Sep'77 Dist: Polygram

BEAUTIFUL MELODIES FROM AROUND THE WORLD.
Album: released on Horatio Nelson, Nov'85 Dist: PRT

Cassette: released on Horatio Nelson, Nov'85 Dist: PRT

DANCING AT THE GROSVENOR HOUSE (Lipton,Sydney and his Orchestra).
Album: released on President, Feb'85 by President Records. Dist: Taylors, Spartan

Liquid Gold

DANCE YOURSELF DIZZY.
Single (7"): released on Polo, Feb'80 by Polo Records. Dist: PRT

Single (12"): released on Polo, Feb'80 by Polo Records. Dist: PRT

DON'T PANIC.
Single (7"): released on Polo, Mar'81 by Polo Records. Dist: PRT

Single (12"): released on Polo, Mar'81 by Polo Records. Dist: PRT

MR.GROOVY (IT FEELS SO NICE)/C'MON AND DANCE.
Single (7"): released on Creole, May'79 by Creole Records. Dist: Rhino, PRT

MY BABY'S BABY.
Single (7"): released on Polo, Jan'82 by Polo Records. Dist: PRT

Single (12"): released on Polo, Jan'82 by Polo Records. Dist: PRT

NIGHT THE WINE AND THE ROSES,THE.
Single (7"): released on Polo, Oct'80 by Polo Records. Dist: PRT

Single (12"): released on Polo, Oct'80 by Polo Records. Dist: PRT

ONE OF US FELL IN LOVE.
Single (7"): released on Polo, Oct'81 by Polo Records. Dist: PRT

Single (12"): released on Polo, Oct'81 by Polo Records. Dist: PRT

SUBSTITUTE.
Single (7"): released on Polo, May'80 by Polo Records. Dist: PRT

SUCCESSIVE REFLEXES.
Extended-play record: released on 99, Feb'82

TURN THE TABLES.
Single (7"): released on Ecstasy, Sep'84 by Creole Records. Dist: CBS

Single (12"): released on Ecstasy, Sep'84 by Creole Records. Dist: CBS

WHERE DID WE GO WRONG.
Single (7"): released on Polo, Jul'82 by Polo Records. Dist: PRT

Picture disc single: released on Polo, Jul'82 by Polo Records. Dist: PRT

Single (12"): released on Polo, Jul'82 by Polo Records. Dist: PRT

Lisa

ROCKET TO YOUR HEART remix.
Single (12"): released on Carrere America (USA), Apr'84 by Polygram.

Lisa Lisa & Cult Jam

ALL CRIED OUT.
Tracks: / All cried out / Behind my eyes / Can you feel that heat.

CAN YOU FEEL THE BEAT H (Lisa Lisa & Cult Jam with Full Force).
Single (7"): released on CBS, Oct'85 by CBS Records. Dist: CBS Deleted '86.

Single (12"): released on CBS, Oct'85 by CBS Records. Dist: CBS Deleted '86.

HEAD TO TOE.
Tracks: / Head to toe / Head to toe (version).
Single (12"): released on CBS, 20 Jun'87 by CBS Records. Dist: CBS

I WONDER IF I TAKE YOU HOME (Lisa Lisa & Cult Jam with Full Force).
Single (7"): released on CBS, Aug'85 by CBS Records. Dist: CBS Deleted '86.

Single (12"): released on CBS, Aug'85 by CBS Records. Dist: CBS Deleted '86.

Special: released on CBS, Aug'85 by CBS Records. Dist: CBS Deleted '86.

LISA LISA & CULT JAM WITH FULL FORCE (Lisa Lisa & Cult Jam with Full Force).
Album: released on CBS, Sep'85 by CBS Records. Dist: CBS

Cassette: released on CBS, Sep'85 by CBS Records. Dist: CBS

SPANISH FLY.
Tracks: / Everything will b-fine / Head to toe / Face in the crowd, A / Someone to love me for me / Talking nonsense / I promise you / Fool is born everyday, A / Lost in emotion / Playing with fire.
Album: released on CBS, May'87 by CBS Records. Dist: CBS

Cassette: released on CBS, May'87 by CBS Records. Dist: CBS

Compact disc: released on CBS, May'87 by CBS Records. Dist: CBS

Lisburn Railway...

LISBURN RAILWAY ST.PRESBYTERIAN CHURCH CHOIR (Lisburn Railway St.Presbyterian Church Choir).
Cassette: released on Praise, Sep'79 Dist: Outlet

Lise by Night

PHONE TO PHONE.
Single (7"): released on Manhattan, Aug'85 by EMI Records. Dist: EMI

Listen...

LISTEN MOVE AND DANCE NO.4 various artists (Various Artists).
Album: released on H.M.V., '66 by EMI Records. Dist: EMI

LISTEN MOVE AND DANCE NOS.1-3 various artists (Various Artists).
Album: released on H.M.V., Oct'74 by EMI Records. Dist: EMI

LISTEN THEY'RE PLAYING MY SONG various artists (Various Artists).
Cassette: released on AIM (Budget Cassettes), Feb'83

WHATEVER.
Single (7"): released on Listening Trees, Apr'85 by Listening Trees. Dist: Revolver, Cartel

Listen To..

LISTEN TO DR. JIVE various artists (Various Artists).
Album: released on Krazy Kat, Jan'84 Dist: Jazz Music, Swift, Chris Wellard, H.R. Taylor, Charly, Hotshot, IRS Distribution

LISTEN TO THE BANNED various artists (Various Artists).
Album: released on ASV, Sep'84 by Academy Sound & Vision Records. Dist: Pinnacle

Cassette: released on ASV, Sep'84 by Academy Sound & Vision Records. Dist: Pinnacle

Listen To The Bands

LISTEN TO THE BANDS Various artists (Various Artists).
Tracks: / Cross of honour / Arabella / Early one morning / Napoleon Galop / Flying Scot (The) / Novelty the faithful hussar / Farewell Waltz / Black Knight (The) / Skye boat song / Overture le carnaval Romain / Symphonic Foxtrot Samum / Semper Sousa / Webers last waltz / Bold Gendarmes (The) / Men of Harlech / Slaidburn / Tantalus Quelen / Sardust / Trombone trio / Battle of Britain / Beau ideal.
Notes: Especially compiled for MFP. This double album features seven Top Brass Bands including Brighouse & rastrick, G.U.S., Footwear, Cory Workmen's Band. A Wonderful collection of popular brass band tracks. A must for Brass Band enthusiasts.
Double Album: released on MFP, Jun'87 by EMI Records. Dist: EMI

Double cassette: released on MFP, Jun'87 by EMI Records. Dist: EMI

Double Album: released on MFP, Jun'87 by EMI Records. Dist: EMI

Listen With..

LISTEN WITH MOTHER various artists (Various Artists).
Album: released on BBC, Aug'84 by BBC Records & Tapes. Dist: EMI, PRT, Pye

Cassette: released on BBC, Aug'84 by BBC Records & Tapes. Dist: EMI, PRT, Pye

Lister,Johnny

O MEIN PAPA/FALKLAND SOUND.
Single (7"): released on Monarch, Nov'82 by Chart Records. Dist: Pinnacle

REGINA CAMPAGNOLA (Lister,Johnny and his shuffle band).
Single (7"): released on Masterchord, Aug'84 by Masterchord Records & Tapes. Dist: PRT

Lite band

EVERYBODY NEEDS SOMEBODY.
Tracks: / Everybody needs somebody / Heavy heavy.
Single (7"): released on Creole, Jul'87 by Creole Records. Dist: Rhino, PRT

Single (12"): released on Creole, Jul'87 by Creole Records. Dist: Rhino, PRT

Single (7"): released on Creole, Jul'87 by Creole Records. Dist: Rhino, PRT

Little Acorns

HOW LUCKY YOU ARE/THE MUGGER.
Single (7"): released on Last Straw, Jul'83 by Small Run Records. Dist: Pinnacle

Little America

LITTLE AMERICA.
Tracks: / You were right / That's the way it stays / Walk on fire / Perfect world / Lost along the way / Lies / Walk the land / Heroes / Underground / Out of bounds / Conversations / Standin' on top.
Album: released on Geffen, Apr'86 by Geffen Records. Dist: WEA, CBS

Cassette: released on Geffen, Apr'86 by Geffen Records. Dist: WEA, CBS

Little and Large

HE'S MY DAD/SPEND A LITTLE TIME.
Single (7"): released on EMI, Oct'82 by EMI Records. Dist: EMI

LIVE AT ABBEY ROAD.
Album: released on EMI, Sep'81 by EMI Records. Dist: EMI

Cassette: released on EMI, Sep'81 by EMI Records. Dist: EMI

SOOPERSONIC 'SYD SINGS'.
Album: released on Nevis, Nov'77 Dist: H.R. Taylor

TELEPHONE MAN.
Single (7"): released on Nevis, Nov'77 Dist: H.R. Taylor

Little Angel

BAD OR JUST NO GOOD.
Tracks: / Bad or just no good / Btter than the rest / Burning me / Reach for me.
Single (12"): released on L. A. Song Management, 23 May'87

Little Anthony

OUTSIDE LOOKIN' IN... (Little Anthony & The Imperials).
Album: released on Liberty, Oct'84 by Liberty-United. Dist: EMI

Cassette: released on Liberty, Oct'84 by Liberty-United. Dist: EMI

Little Benny

BUGGIN' OUT (Little Benny & The Masters).
Tracks: / Buggin' out / Buggin' out (inst).
Single (7"): released on Bluebird, Apr'87 by Bluebird Records. Dist: EMI, Jetstar

Single (7"): released on Bluebird, Aug'87 by Bluebird Records. Dist: EMI, Jetstar

Single (12"): released on Bluebird, Aug'87 by Bluebird Records. Dist: EMI, Jetstar

WHO COMES TO BOOGIE (Little Benny & The Masters).
Single (7"): released on Bluebird, Jan'85 by Bluebird Records. Dist: EMI, Jetstar

Single (12"): released on Bluebird, Jan'85 by Bluebird Records. Dist: EMI, Jetstar

Little Bird

ZOLA.
Single (7"): released on Magnus Music, Jun'84

Little Bit..

LITTLE BIT THIS, A LITTLE BIT THAT various artists (Various Artists).
Album: released on Joy, Jul'83 by President Records. Dist: Jazz Music, Swift, President Distribution

Little blue brontosaurus

LITTLE BLUE BRONTOSAURUS, (THE) Preiss, Byron/Stout, William (Irving, George S.).
Cassette: released on Caedmon(USA), '84 by Caedmon (USA) Records. Dist: Gower, Taylors, Discovery

LITTLE BLUE BRONTOSAURUS Irving, George.S (Priess, Byron/Stout, William).
Cassette: released on Caedmon(USA), '84 by Caedmon (USA) Records. Dist: Gower, Taylors, Discovery

Little, Booker

VICTORY AND SORROW.
Album: released on Affinity, May'84 by Charly Records. Dist: Charly, Cadillac

Little Brother

NO RELATION.
Tracks: / No relation.
Single (7"): released on Rouska, Apr'86 Dist: Red Rhino Distribution, Cartel Distribution

Little Caesar

LYING WOMAN...GOODBYE BABY.
Album: by Mr. R&B Records. Dist: Swift Distribution, Cadillac, Jazz Music Distribution

Little Charlie

ALL THE WAY CRAZY (Little Charlie & The Nightcats).
Notes: Available early April.
Album: released on Sonet, Apr'87 by Sonet Records. Dist: PRT

Little Clarkie

BUBBLE 'N' ROCK (Little Clarkie & The Offbeat Posse).
Single (12"): released on YND, Aug'87 Dist: Jetstar

LIVE STOCK PARTY (Little Clarkie And The Offbeat Posse).
Tracks: / Live stock party / Bounty hunter.
Single (12"): released on Jah Tubbys, Sep'86 by Jah Tubbys Records. Dist: Jetstar

SELECT HIM GOOD (Little Clarkie And The Offbeat Posse).
Tracks: / Select him good / Bless the selector / Select the rhythm.
Single (12"): released on Jah Tubbys, Jan'86 by Jah Tubbys Records. Dist: Jetstar

Little Club Jazz

LITTLE CLUB JAZZ Various artists (Various Artists).
Tracks: / My honey's loving arms / Rocky mountain blues / Herje Kati / Sister Kate (I wish that I could shimmy like my) / China boy / Square face / I got rhythm / Chasing shadows / Knock, knock / In a little gypsy tearoom / Bugle call rag / Jungle love / What's the use? / Clarinet marmalade / Beale Street Mama / Tapioca / Blues in my condition / Buglers dilemma.
Notes: Small Groups in the 30's. Mono.
Album: released on New World (USA), Sep'86 by New World Records (USA). Dist: Conifer

Little Drummer Girl, The

LITTLE DRUMMER GIRL, THE Le Carre, John.
Cassette: released on Listen For Pleasure, '83 by MFP Records. Dist: EMI

Little Egypt
I DO VOODOO.
Single (7"): released on Arrival, Jul'82 by Arrival. Dist: Revolver, Cartel

Little Esther
BAD BAAD GIRL.
Tracks: / Ring-a-ding doo / Aged & mellow blues / Ramblin' blues / Storm, The / Hollerin' and screamin' / Mainliner / Saturday night daddy / You took my love too fast / Last laugh blues / Flesh blood and Bones / Turn the lamps down low / Cherry wine / Hound dog / Looking for a man (to satisfy my soul) / Deacon moves in, The / I'm a bad bad girl.
Compact disc: released on Charly, Jan'87 by Charly Records. Dist: Charly, Cadillac

BAD BAD GIRL.
Album: released on Charly(R&B), Jul'85 by Charly Records. Dist: Charly, Cadillac

Cassette: released on Charly(R&B), Jul'85 by Charly Records. Dist: Charly, Cadillac

Little Eva
LLLLLOCO-MOTION.
Album: released on Decca (Rock Echoes), Apr'82 by Decca Records. Dist: Polygram, IMS

Cassette: released on Decca (Rock Echoes), Apr'82 by Decca Records. Dist: Polygram, IMS

LOCOMOTION.
Single (7"): released on Old Gold, Oct'83 by Old Gold Records. Dist: Lightning, Jazz Music, Spartan, Counterpoint

LOCO-MOTION, THE.
Tracks: / Loco-motion, The / Let's turkey trot / He is the boy / Keep your hands off my baby.
Single (7"): released on London, Sep'86 by London Records. Dist: Polygram

Single (12"): released on London, Sep'86 by London Records. Dist: Polygram

Single (7"): released on London, Mar'80 by London Records. Dist: Polygram

Little Feat
AS TIME GOES BY The best of Little Feat.
Tracks: / Dixie chicken / Willing / Rock 'n' Roll Doctor / Trouble / Sailin' shoes / Spanish moon / Feats don't fail me now / All that you dream / Long distance love / Mercenary territory / Old folks boogie / 20 million things.
Album: released on Warner Bros., Mar'86 by Warner Bros Records. Dist: WEA

Cassette: released on Warner Bros., Mar'86 by Warner Bros Records. Dist: WEA

AS TIME GOES BY(BEST OF).
Tracks: / Willing / Rock'n'Roll Doctor / Sailin' Shoes / Spanish moon / Feats don't fail me now / All that you dream / Long distance love / Mercenary territory / Old folks boogie / 20 million things / Dixie Chicken / Trouble.
Album: released on Warner Brothers, '74 by Warner Bros Records. Dist: WEA

DIXIE CHICKEN.
Album: released on Warner Brothers, '74 by Warner Bros Records. Dist: WEA

Single (7"): released on Warner Bros., Mar'75 by Warner Bros Records. Dist: WEA

DOWN ON THE FARM.
Album: released on Warner Bros., Oct'79 by Warner Bros Records. Dist: WEA

Cassette: released on Warner Bros., Oct'79 by Warner Bros Records. Dist: WEA

FEATS DON'T FAIL ME NOW.
Album: released on Atlantic, Sep'74 by WEA Records. Dist: WEA

HOY HOY.
Album: released on Warner Brothers, Aug'81 by Warner Bros Records. Dist: WEA

Cassette: released on Warner Brothers, '85 by Warner Bros Records. Dist: WEA

LITTLE FEAT.
Album: released on Warner Brothers, Jan'75 by Warner Bros Records. Dist: WEA

LITTLE FEAT & DIXIE CHICKEN.
Double Album: released on Warner, Oct'79 by Warner Bros Records. Dist: WEA

LTTLE FEAT & DIXIE CHICKEN.
SAILIN' SHOES. ·
Cassette: released on Warner Bros., '79 by Warner Bros Records. Dist: WEA

TIME LOVES A HERO.
Album: released on Warner Bros., May'77 by Warner Bros Records. Dist: WEA

Cassette: released on Warner Bros., May'77 by Warner Bros Records. Dist: WEA

WAITING FOR COLUMBUS.
Double Album: released on Warner Brothers, Feb'78 by Warner Bros Records. Dist: WEA

Cassette: released on Warner Bros., Feb'78 by Warner Bros Records. Dist: WEA

Littlefield, Willie
HAPPY PAY DAY (Littlefield, Little Willie).
Album: released on Ace, Aug'85 by Ace Records. Dist: Pinnacle, Swift, Hotshot, Cadillac

I'M IN THE MOOD (Littlefield, Little Willie).
Album: released on Oldie Blues (Holland), Feb'84

IT'S MIDNIGHT (Littlefield, Little Willie).
Album: released on Route 66, Jun'80

JUMPIN' WITH... (Littlefield, Little Willie).
Album: released on Ace(Cadet USA), Sep'84 by Ace Records. Dist: Pinnacle, Swift, Hotshot

KC LOVING (Littlefield, Little Willie).
Tracks: / Striking on you baby / Blood is redder than wine / KC loving / Pleading at midnight / Midnight hour was shining / Miss KC's fine / Rockabye baby / My best wishes and regards / Jim Wilson's boogie / Sitting on the curbstone / Please don't stop / Falling tears / Goofy dust blues / Don't take my heart little girl.
Album: released on KC, Oct'86 by KC Records. Dist: Cartel

Little Fish
FOUR HERTFORSHIRE FOLK SONGS.
Album: released on Plant Life, Nov'81

Little Foxes
CROSSED LINE.
Single (7"): released on C&D, Feb'83 by Phonogram Records. Dist: Polygram

GOLDEN BODIES.
Single (7"): released on C&D, Jul'83 by Phonogram Records. Dist: Polygram

Little Gerhard
IN DEUTSCHLAND.
Album: released on Bear Family, Oct'82 by Bear Family Records. Dist: Rollercoaster Distribution, Swift

Little Ginny
CHASING THE WIND.
Single (7"): released on Pastafont, Jul'82 by Pastafont Records.

Album: released on SRT, Mar'79 by SRT Records. Dist: Pinnacle, Solomon & Peres Distribution, SRT Distribution, H.R. Taylor Distribution, PRT Distribution

MY DIXIE DARLING.
Album: released on Pastafont, Jun'82 by Pastafont Records.

Single (7"): released on Pastafont, Sep'82 by Pastafont Records.

Little Grey Rabbit...
LITTLE GREY RABBIT STORIES (Whitfield, June).
Cassette: released on Pinnacle, '79 by Pinnacle Records. Dist: Pinnacle

LITTLE GREY RABBIT STORIES, MORE (Whitfield, June).
Cassette: released on Pinnacle, '79 by Pinnacle Records. Dist: Pinnacle

Little Harry
D.J CLASH, VOL.2 (Little Harry & Billy Boyo).

Little Henry & Tiger
LITTLE HENRY & THE TIGER various artists (Various Artists).
Cassette: released on Anvil, Jan'81 by Anvil

Little Heroes
ONE PERFECT DAY.
Single (7"): released on EMI, Jun'83 by EMI Records. Dist: EMI

YOUNG HEARTS.
Single (7"): released on EMI, Jan'83 by EMI Records. Dist: EMI

Little John
BEST OF LITTLE JOHN, THE.
Album: released on RM, Jun'85 by RM Records. Dist: Jetstar

BETTER YU GWAN.
Single (12"):

BRANDY (Little John & Billy Boyo).
Single (12"): released on Music Lovers, Oct'82 by Music Lovers Records. Dist: Music Lovers

BUBBLING STYLE.
Single (12"): released on Black Roots, Feb'85 by Black Roots Records. Dist: Jetstar

---

BUSHMASTER CONNE...'ION (Little John & Billy Boyo).
Single (12"):

CLARKE'S BOOTY.
Tracks: / Clarke's Booty / Have to girlie girlie.
Single (12"): released on Unity Sound, Feb'86 Dist: Jetstar

CLARK'S BOOTY.
Album: released on World Enterprise, Jul'86 Dist: Jetstar

DO MAMA.
Single (12"): released on Hawkeye, Jun'85 by Hawkeye Records. Dist: Hawkeye, Lightning (WEA) Distribution, Jetstar, PRT

DON'T WAIT TO BE LONELY.
Single (7"): released on Jamaica Sound, Jul'84 by Jamaica Sound Records. Dist: Jetstar

FORM A LINE.
Single (12"):

I DON'T WANT TO CRY OVER YOU.
Single (12"): released on Jah Bible, Nov'83 by Jah Bible Records. Dist: Jetstar

I HAVE WORK TO DO.
Single (12"): released on Gamble, Jul'83 by Gamble Records. Dist: Jetstar

JANET SINCLAIR (Little John & Billy Boyo).
Single (12"):

JOKER LOVER.
Single (12"):

JOYCE GONE.
Single (12"): released on Jah Guidance, Nov'83 by Jah Guidance Records. Dist: Jetstar

MIX UP.
Single (12"): released on Music Parade, Dec'83 by Music Parade Records. Dist: Jetstar Distribution

MY WOMAN IS CRYING.
Single (12"): released on Bebo, Mar'84 by Bebo Records. Dist: Jetstar

MY WOMAN IS CRYING.
Single (12"): released on Midnight Rock, Oct'83 Dist: Jetstar Distribution, Kingdom Distribution

POLICE PEGGY.
Single (12"): released on Greensleeves, Mar'85 by Greensleeves Records. Dist: BMG, Jetstar, Spartan

RIVER TO THE BANK.
Album: released on Power House, Dec'85 by Power House Records. Dist: Jetstar

SCHOOL GIRL.
Single (12"): released on Top Rank, Jun'85

SLICE OF THE CAKE.
Single (12"): released on Rockers Forever, May'85 Dist: Jetstar Distribution

STYLE.
Single (12"): released on Music Hawk, Nov'83 by Music Hawk Records. Dist: Jetstar Distribution

TEAR DOWN THE DANCE HELL.
Single (12"): released on M&M, Jan'85 by M&M Records. Dist: Jetstar Distribution

TO ALL THE POSSE.
Single (12"): released on Volcano, Mar'84 by Volcano Records. Dist: Jetstar

TRUE CONFESSION.
Album: released on Power House, Nov'84 by Power House Records. Dist: Jetstar

UNITE.
Album: released on Vista Sounds, May'84 by Vista Sounds Records. Dist: Jetstar

WALK AWAY.
Single (12"): released on Music Hawk, Aug'84 by Music Hawk Records. Dist: Jetstar Distribution

WARRIORS AND TROUBLE.
Album: released on World Enterprise, Aug'86 Dist: Jetstar

YES MAMA.
Single (12"): released on Live & Love, Feb'87 by Third World Records. Dist: Jetstar

YOUTH OF TODAY.
Single (12"): released on Skengdom, Feb'87 by Skengdom Records. Dist: Jetstar

Littlejohn, John
CHICAGO BLUES STARS.
Album: released on Arhoolie, May'81 by Arhoolie Records. Dist: Projection, Topic, Jazz

---

Music, Swift, Roots

Little Jump Joint
SULTANS OF THE SLIDE GUITAR.
Album: released on Blues Ball, Sep'79 Dist: Swift

Little Jump Joint
LITTLE JUMP JOINT Various artists (Various Artists).
Notes: Artists Include: Jimmy Payne & Dick Barton/Rich Miller/Carl Phillips/Jim Bissett/Etc:
Album: released on White Label, Oct'86 by White Label Records. Dist: Jetstar

Little Kurk
FRIEND THEM MATE.
Tracks: / Friend them mate / Don't touch the crack.
Single (12"): released on Jammy's, Jan'87 by Jammy's Records. Dist: Jetstar

Little Mac
MEAT AND GRAVY FROM CADILLAC BABY - VOL.3 (Little Mac, Eddie Boyd & L.C. McKinley).
Album: released on Red Lightnin', Aug'79 by Red Lightnin' Records. Dist: Roots, Swift, Jazz Music, JSU, Pinnacle, Cartel, Wynd-Up Distribution

Little, Marie
MARIE LITTLE.
Album: released on Leader, '81 Dist: Jazz Music, Projection

Little Me
LONDON CAST RECORDING.
Album: released on Flashback, Nov'85 by Flashback Records/PRT Records. Dist: Mainline, PRT

Cassette: released on Flashback, Nov'85 by Flashback Records/PRT Records. Dist: Mainline, PRT

Little Mermaid
LITTLE MERMAID Spoken word cassette for children.
Cassette: released on Tellastory, Dec'80 by Bartlett Bliss Productions. Dist: PRT Distribution, Hayward Promotions Distribution, H.R. Taylor Distribution

LITTLE MERMAID, THE Various artists (Various Artists).
Cassette: released on Pickwick (Ladybird), '83

Little Milton
ANNIE MAE'S CAFE.
Album: released on Malaco, Dec'86 by Malaco Records. Dist: Charly

HIS GREATEST HITS.
Album: released on Chess, Jan'87 by Charly Records. Dist: Charly, Swift, Discovery, IMS, Polygram

Cassette: released on Chess, Jan'87 by Charly Records. Dist: Charly, Swift, PRT, Discovery, IMS, Polygram

HIS GREATEST SIDES.
Cassette: released on Chess, Jan'87 by Charly Records. Dist: Charly, Swift, PRT, Discovery, IMS, Polygram

HIS GREATEST SIDES VOL 1.
Album: released on Chess, Jul'84 by Charly Records. Dist: Charly, Swift, PRT, Discovery, IMS, Polygram

LITTLE MILTON SINGS BIG BLUES.
Album: released on Chess, Oct'87 by Charly Records. Dist: Charly, Swift, PRT, Discovery, IMS, Polygram

Cassette: released on Chess, Oct'87 by Charly Records. Dist: Charly, Swift, PRT, Discovery, IMS, Polygram

PLAYING FOR KEEPS.
Album: released on Malaco, Dec'84 by Malaco Records. Dist: Charly

RAISE A LITTLE SAND.
Album: released on Red Lightnin', Sep'82 by Red Lightnin' Records. Dist: Roots, Swift, Jazz Music, JSU, Pinnacle, Cartel, Wynd-Up Distribution

SAM'S BLUES (Little Milton & Howlin' Wolf).
Album: released on Charly, Jun'76 by Charly Records. Dist: Charly, Cadillac

SAM'S BLUES.
Album: released on Charly, Jun'76 by Charly Records. Dist: Charly, Cadillac

WE'RE GONNA MAKE IT.
Album: released on Charly, Apr'87 by Charly Records. Dist: Charly, Swift, PRT, Discovery, IMS, Polygram

Cassette: released on Chess, Apr'87 by Charly Records. Dist: Charly, Swift, PRT, Discovery, IMS, Polygram

Little Miss Stories

LITTLE MISS STORIES Read by John Alderton and Pauline Collins.
Album: released on Ingot, Dec'83 by Ingot Records. Dist: PRT

Cassette: released on Ingot, Dec'83 by Ingot Records. Dist: PRT

Little Oz Stories

LITTLE OZ STORIES (L.Frank Baum) Read by Ray Bolger.
Cassette: released on Caedmon(USA), Aug'83 by Caedmon (USA) Records. Dist: Gower, Taylors, Discovery

Little Prince

LITTLE PRINCE, THE (Antoine De Saint Exupery) Read by Louis Jourdan.
Cassette: released on Caedmon(USA), Aug'83 by Caedmon (USA) Records. Dist: Gower, Taylors, Discovery

Little Ramblers

LITTLE RAMBLERS 1924/5 VOL 1, THE.
Album: released on VJM, Apr'79 by VJM (UK) Records. Dist: Swift

LITTLE RAMBLERS 1925/6 VOL 2, THE.
Album: released on VJM, Apr'79 by VJM (UK) Records. Dist: Swift

Little Red Riding Hood

AND OTHER FAVOURITE STORIES FOR....
Cassette: released on VFM, Jul'85 by VFM Records. Dist: Taylors, Wynd-Up Distribution

LITTLE RED RIDING HOOD.
Cassette: released on Tellastory, Oct'79 by Bartlett Bliss Productions. Dist: PRT Distribution, Hayward Promotions Distribution, H.R. Taylor Distribution

LITTLE RED RIDING HOOD Various artists (Various Artists).
Cassette: released on Pickwick (Ladybird), Feb'83

Little Red Schoolhouse

FOUR ICED PUNS EP.
Single (7"): released on T.I.M., Jun'87 by T.I.M. Records. Dist: Backs, Cartel Distribution

Single (12"): released on T.I.M., Jun'87 by T.I.M. Records. Dist: Backs, Cartel Distribution

Little Richard

16 GREATEST HITS, THE.
Tracks: / Long tall sally / Keep a knockin' / Good golly,miss molly / Girl can't help it, The / Tutti frutti / Lucille / Ooh my soul / Slippin' and slidin' / Baby face / Rip it up / Send me some lovin' / Hound dog / Cherry red / Short fat fanny / Money honey / Whole lotta shakin' goin' on.
Compact disc: released on Bescol, May'87 Dist: Target

16 ROCK AND ROLL CLASSICS.
Album: released on Arena, Feb'87 by Arena Records. Dist: Spartan

Cassette: released on Arena, Feb'87 by Arena Records. Dist: Spartan

20 CLASSIC CUTS.
Compact disc: released on Ace, Dec'86 by Ace Records. Dist: Pinnacle, Swift, Hotshot, Cadillac

20 LITTLE RICHARD ORIGINAL HITS.
Album: released on Speciality, Oct'76 by Relic Records. Dist: Swift

22 CLASSIC CUTS.
Album: released on Ace, Dec'86 by Ace Records. Dist: Pinnacle, Swift, Hotshot, Cadillac

Cassette: released on Ace, Dec'86 by Ace Records. Dist: Pinnacle, Swift, Hotshot, Cadillac

Compact disc: by Ace Records. Dist: Pinnacle, Swift, Hotshot, Cadillac

BABY FACE.
Single (7"): released on Creole, Aug'82 by Creole Records. Dist: Rhino, PRT

BEST OF.
Cassette: released on Creole (Everest-Europa), Jul'84 by Creole Records. Dist: PRT, Rhino

BY THE LIGHT OF THE SILVERY MOON.
Single (7"): released on Speciality (USA), '80 by Speciality Records (USA). Dist: Miracle Gospel Distribution, Zanita, Rex Inge

DOLLARS, DOLLARS AND MORE DOLLARS.
Album:

EARLY STUDIO OUTTAKES.
Album: released on Sunjay, Mar'87

FABULOUS LITTLE RICHARD.
Album: released on Ace, Feb'85 by Ace Records. Dist: Pinnacle, Swift, Hotshot, Cadillac

FRIENDS FROM THE BEGINNING (Little Richard & Jimi Hendrix).
Album: released on Ember, '74 by Pye Records. Dist: Pye

GET DOWN WITH IT.
Album: released on Edsel, Oct'82 by Demon Records. Dist: Pinnacle, Jazz Music, Projection

GIRL CAN'T HELP IT.
Single (7"): released on Creole (Reissue), Aug'82 by Creole Records. Dist: PRT, Rhino

GOLDEN HIGHLIGHTS OF LITTLE RICHARD.
Album: released on CBS(Import), Jun'86 by CBS Records. Dist: Conifer, Discovery, Swift

Cassette: released on CBS(Import), Jun'86 by CBS Records. Dist: Conifer, Discovery, Swift

GOOD GOLLY MISS MOLLY.
Single (7"): released on Old Gold, Jan'85 by Old Gold Records. Dist: Lightning, Jazz Music, Spartan, Counterpoint

Single (7"): released on Juke Box, Mar'82

Single (7"): released on Creole (Reissue), Aug'82 by Creole Records. Dist: PRT, Rhino

GREATEST HITS:LITTLE RICHARD.
Compact disc: released on MCS Look Back, Jul'87

GREATEST HITS: LITTLE RICHARD.
Cassette: released on CBS, Jun'84 by CBS Records. Dist: CBS

Cassette: released on K-Tel Goldmasters, Aug'84 by K-Tel Records. Dist: K-Tel

GREAT GOSH A'MIGHTY.
Tracks: / Great gosh a'mighty / Ride, The / Down and out in Beverly Hill.
Single (7"): released on MCA, May'86 by MCA Records. Dist: Polygram, MCA

Single (12"): released on MCA, May'86 by MCA Records. Dist: Polygram, MCA

HERE'S LITTLE RICHARD (Little Richard & His Band).
Album: released on Ace, Feb'85 by Ace Records. Dist: Pinnacle, Swift, Hotshot, Cadillac

HE'S GOT IT.
Album: released on Topline, Nov'84 by Charly Records. Dist: Charly Distribution

Cassette: released on Topline, Nov'84 by Charly Records. Dist: Charly Distribution

HIS BIGGEST HITS.
Album: released on Sonet, Jun'80 by Sonet Records. Dist: PRT

HIS GREATEST RECORDINGS.
Album: released on Ace, Jan'85 by Ace Records. Dist: Pinnacle, Swift, Hotshot, Cadillac

Cassette: released on Ace, Jan'85 by Ace Records. Dist: Pinnacle, Swift, Hotshot, Cadillac

I'M QUITTING SHOW BUSINESS.
Tracks: / I've just come from the mountain / Search me lord / Coming home / I'm quitting show business.
Extended-play record: released on Magnum Force, Jun'87 by Magnum Music Group Ltd. Dist: Magnum Music Group Ltd, PRT, Spartan

LIFETIME FRIEND.
Tracks: / Great gosh a'mighty / Operator / Somebody's comin' / Lifetime friends / Destruction / I found my way / World can't do me (The) / One ray of sunshine / Someone cares / Big house reunion.
Album: released on WEA, Nov'86 by WEA Records. Dist: WEA

Cassette: released on WEA, Nov'86 by WEA Records. Dist: WEA

Compact disc: released on WEA, Nov'86 by WEA Records. Dist: WEA

LITTLE RICHARD... (Little Richard & His Band).
Album: released on Sonet, May'80 by Sonet Records. Dist: PRT

LITTLE RICHARD.
Album: released on Deja Vu, Jan'87 by Deja Vu Records. Dist: Counterpoint Distribution, Record Services Distribution (Ireland)

Cassette: released on Deja Vu, Jan'87 by Deja Vu Records. Dist: Counterpoint Distribution, Record Services Distribution (Ireland)

Double Album: released on Cambra, Aug'83 by Cambra Records. Dist: IDS, Conifer

Double cassette: released on Cambra, Aug'83 by Cambra Records. Dist: IDS, Conifer

LITTLE RICHARD (CD).
Tracks: / Whole lotta shakin' / Rip it up / Baby face / Send me some lovin' / Send me some lovin' / Girl can't help it, The / Lucille / Ooh my soul / Jenny Jenny / Good golly Miss Molly / Tutti frutti / Long tall Sally / Keep a knockin' / Money honey / Hound dog / Groovy little Suzie / Dancing all around the world / Slippin' and slidin' / Lawdy Miss Clawdy / True fine mama / She's got it.
Compact disc: released on The Collection, Apr'87 by Object Enterprises Ltd. Dist: Counterpoint Distribution

LITTLE RICHARD - NOW.
Album: released on Creole, Oct'77 by Creole Records. Dist: Rhino, PRT

LUCILLE.
Album: released on Premier, '84 by Premier Records. Dist: CBS

Cassette: released on Premier, '84 by Premier Records. Dist: CBS

Cassette: released on Bravo, Feb'80 by Pickwick Records. Dist: Lugtons

Single (7"): released on Speciality (USA), '80 by Speciality Records (USA). Dist: Miracle Gospel Distribution, Zanita, Rex Inge

Single (7"): released on Old Gold, Jan'85 by Old Gold Records. Dist: Lightning, Jazz Music, Spartan, Counterpoint

OOH, MA SOUL!.
Album: released on Magnum Force, Nov'86 by Magnum Music Group Ltd. Dist: Magnum Music Group Ltd, PRT, Spartan

OOH MY SOUL.
Album: released on Charly, '83 by Charly Records. Dist: Charly, Cadillac

OPERATOR.
Tracks: / Operator / Big House Reunion.
Single (7"): released on WEA, Oct'86 by WEA Records. Dist: WEA

Single (12"): released on WEA, Oct'86 by WEA Records. Dist: WEA

REAL THING, THE.
Album: released on Magnum Force, Sep'83 by Magnum Music Group Ltd. Dist: Magnum Music Group Ltd, PRT, Spartan

RIP IT UP.
Tracks: / Rip it up / Jenny Jenny / Slippin' and slidin' / I don't know what you got / Send me some lovin' / Going home tomorrow / You better stop / Ooh my soul / Blueberry hill / Good golly miss Molly / Tutti frutti / Long tall Sally / Girl can't help it, The / She's got it / Lucille / Keep a knockin'.
Notes: Original Vee Jay recordings.
Compact disc: released on Topline, May'87 by Charly Records. Dist: Charly Distribution

Single (7"): released on Juke Box, Mar'82

ROCKIN' IN THE SEVENTIES.
Tracks: / Tutti frutti / Girl I Can't Help It / Lucille / Good golly Miss Molly / Long Tall Sally / Rip it up / Slippin'and slidin' / Ooh my soul / Keep a knockin' / Ready Teddy / She's got it / Bama lama bama loo / Send me some lovin' / Miss Ann / True fine Mama / Jenny Jenny.
Album: released on Charly, Aug'86 by Charly Records. Dist: Charly, Cadillac

Cassette: released on Charly, Aug'86 by Charly Records. Dist: Charly, Cadillac

ROCKIN''N'RAVIN' (Little Richard/Boots Brown And His Blockbusters).
Tracks: / Get rich quick / Why did you leave me / Taxi blues / Every hour / I brought it all on myself / Ain't nothin' happenin' / Thinkin' 'bout my mother / Please have mercy on me / Blockbuster / Hip boots / Shortnin' bread / Blue fairy boogie / Breakfast ball / Double clutch / Dynamite / Oh happy day.
Album: released on RCA, Oct'86 by RCA Records. Dist: RCA, Roots, Swift, Wellard, Chris, I & B, Solomon & Peres Distribution

Cassette: released on RCA, Oct'86 by RCA Records. Dist: RCA, Roots, Swift, Wellard, Chris, I & B, Solomon & Peres Distribution

ROCK'N'ROLL RESURRECTION.
Tracks: / Tutti frutti / Girl can't help it, The / Lucille / Good golly miss Molly / Long tall Sally / Rip it up / Slippin'n'slidin' / Keep a knockin' / Ready Teddy / She's got it / Bama lama bama loo / Send me some lovin' / Miss Ann / Ooh my soul / True fine mama / Jenny Jenny / By the light of the silvery moon / Baby face / All round the world / Can't believe you wanna leave.
Compact disc: released on Charly, Mar'87 by Charly Records. Dist: Charly, Cadillac

Album: released on Charly, Aug'86 by Charly Records. Dist: Charly, Cadillac

Cassette: released on Charly, Aug'86 by Charly Records. Dist: Charly, Cadillac

Cat. no: **TCCR 30258**

SINGS GOSPEL FAVOURITES.
Album: released on Bulldog Records, Jul'82

SOMEBODY'S COMING.
Tracks: / Somebody's coming / One ray of sunshine.
Single (7"): released on WEA, Jan'87 by WEA Records. Dist: WEA

TUTTI FRUTTI.
Compact disc: released on Delta, Apr'87 by Delta Records. Dist: Target

Single (7"): released on Old Gold, Jan'85 by Old Gold Records. Dist: Lightning, Jazz Music, Spartan, Counterpoint

UNRELEASED LITTLE RICHARD, THE.
Album: released on EMI (France), '83 by EMI Records. Dist: Conifer

VOLUME 2.
Album: released on Ace, Feb'85 by Ace Records. Dist: Pinnacle, Swift, Hotshot, Cadillac

WHOLE LOTTA SHAKIN.
Album: released on Bulldog, Jul'82 by Bulldog Records. Dist: President Distribution, Spartan, Swift, Taylor, H.R.

Cassette: released on Bulldog, Nov'82 by Bulldog Records. Dist: President Distribution, Spartan, Swift, Taylor, H.R.

Little River Band

BEGINNINGS.
Album: released on EMI (Holland), '83 by EMI Records. Dist: Conifer

COLLECTION: LITTLE RIVER BAND.
Album: released on EMI (Germany), '83 by EMI Records. Dist: Conifer

GREATEST HITS: LITTLE RIVER BAND.
Compact disc: released on Capitol, Mar'84 by Capitol Records. Dist: EMI

GREATEST HITS:LITTLE RIVER BAND.
Compact disc: released on Capitol, Mar'84 by Capitol Records. Dist: EMI

IT'S A LONG WAY THERE.
Album: released on EMI (Holland), '83 by EMI Records. Dist: Conifer

LITTLE RIVER BAND.
Album: released on Fame (EMI), Nov'83 by Music For Pleasure Records. Dist: EMI

Cassette: released on Fame (EMI), Nov'83 by Music For Pleasure Records. Dist: EMI

LIVE EXPOSURE.
Video-cassette (VHS): released on P. Morris Music, Jun'81

Video-cassette [Betamax]: released on P. Morris Music, Jun'81

OTHER GUY.
Single (7"): released on Capitol, Jan'83 by Capitol Records. Dist: EMI

SLEEPER CATCHER.
Album: released on ECM (Germany), Aug'83 by ECM Records. Dist: IMS, Polygram, Virgin through EMI

YOU'RE DRIVING ME OUT OF MY MIND.
Single (7"): released on Capitol, May'83 by Capitol Records. Dist: EMI

Little Roy

NATTY YARD.
Single (12"): released on Love Linch, Feb'82 Dist: Jetstar

WITHOUT MY LOVE.
Single (12"): released on Copasetic, Aug'81 Dist: Stage One

Little, Sharon

DON'T MASH UP CREATION.
Single (12"): released on One Love, Jun'82

Little shop of horrors

LITTLE SHOP OF HORRORS Original soundtrack (Various Artists).
Album: released on Geffen, Mar'87 by Geffen Records. Dist: WEA, CBS

Cassette: released on Geffen, Mar'87 by Geffen Records. Dist: WEA, CBS

Little Sonny

NEW KING OF THE BLUES HARMONICA.
Tracks: / Baby what you want me to do / Eli's pork chop / Hey little girl / Hot potato / Don't ask me no questions / Tomorrow's blues today / Back down yonder / Sad funk / Creeper return,

The.
Notes: Born Aaron Willis 1932, Little sonny is one of the great blues harmonica playersto have come out of detroit. This was his first album and mainly features his own compositions.
Album: released on Stax, Nov'86 by Ace Records. Dist: Pinnacle, Chris Wellard, IMS-Polygram

Cassette: released on Stax, Nov'86 by Ace Records. Dist: Pinnacle, Chris Wellard, IMS-Polygram

Little Steven

BITTER FRUIT.
Tracks: / Bitter fruit (No Pasaran mix) / Vote! / Bitter fruit (Cana no mas dub)* / Bitter fruit / Vote!.
Single (7"): released on Manhattan, Mar'87 by President Records. Dist: Jazz Music, Swift, Taylors, Chris Wellard

Single (12"): released on Manhattan, Mar'87 by President Records. Dist: Jazz Music, Swift, Taylors, Chris Wellard

Compact disc single: released on Manhattan, Apr'87 by President Records. Dist: Jazz Music, Swift, Taylors, Chris Wellard

BITTER FRUIT (PLATANO QUEMADO MIX).
Tracks: / Bitter fruit (Platano Quemado mix) / Vote! (part3) / Vote! (world war 3).
Single (12"): released on Manhattan, 23 May'87 by EMI Records. Dist: EMI

Compact disc single: released on Manhattan, 23 May'87 by EMI Records. Dist: EMI

FOREVER (Little Steven & The Disciples Of Soul).
Single (7"): released on EMI America, Nov'82 by EMI Records. Dist: EMI

FREEDOM NO COMPROMISE.
Tracks: / Freedom / Trail of broken treaties / Pretoria / Bitter fruit / No more party's / Can't you feel the fire / Native American / Sanctuary.
Notes: Little Steven, guitarist and one-time member of Bruce Springsteen's E-Street Band, was the co-ordinator of the highly successful "Sun City" project which spawned the hit single denouncing apartheid and show-business support of the South African political system. Honoured by the United Nations for his anti-apartheid work, Little Steven continues to voice his bitter social comment through his music. The entire album is composed, arranged and produced by Little Steven and the material deals with various political issues, much of it concerned with South Africa. The first single from the album is entitled "Bitter Fruit", and deals with the American involvement in Nicaragua. Ruben Blades assists Little Steven on lead vocals and the 12" version features and extendd mix with sensational trumpet and guitar solos over a blistering salsa-style dance remix. The single was released in April. Assisting on lead vocals on "Native America" is Bruce Springsteen, and Kenny Moore, who will be known to many for his keyboard work on Tina Turner's "Private Dancer" tour, assists with vocals on "Trail of Broken Treaties".[EMI release sheet, May 1987]
Album: released on Manhattan, Mar'87 by President Records. Dist: Jazz Music, Swift, Taylors, Chris Wellard

Cassette: released on Manhattan, Mar'87 by President Records. Dist: Jazz Music, Swift, Taylors, Chris Wellard

Compact disc: released on Manhattan, May'87 by President Records. Dist: Jazz Music, Swift, Taylors, Chris Wellard

LYIN' IN A BED OF FIRE (Little Steven & The Disciples Of Soul).
Single (7"): released on EMI America, Apr'83 by EMI Records. Dist: EMI

MEN WITHOUT WOMEN (Little Steven & The Disciples Of Soul).
Tracks: / Lyin' in a bed of fire / Save me / Inside of me / Men without women / Princess of Little Italy / Until the good is gone / Under the gun / Angel eyes / I've been waiting / Caravan / This time it's for real / Forever.
Notes: Little Steven and The Disciples Of Soul is the creation of guitarist, singer and songwriter Miama Steve Van Zandt. The first album release by the bandhas provided the foundation for an extraordinary film called "Men without women"shot by British film maker Derek Burbridge, "Men without women" tells the story of a rock and roll band and in doing so, expounds many of Miami Steve's unique rock and roll philosophies. The film was shot in and around New York City, and features a driving concert performance by Little Steven and his 11 piece band oftop flight American musicians. Locations include central park, Harlem and the streets of Manhattan. Number of tracks: 12. Type of recording: film. Total playing time: 90 minutes.
Video-cassette (VHS): released on EMI, Nov'82 by EMI Records. Dist: EMI

Video-cassette [Betamax]: released on EMI, Nov'82 by EMI Records. Dist: EMI

Album: released on EMI America, Oct'82 by EMI Records. Dist: EMI

Cassette: released on EMI America, Oct'82 by EMI Records. Dist: EMI

OUT OF THE DARKNESS.
Tracks: / Out of the darkness / Fear.
Single (7"): released on EMI America, Jan'86 by EMI Records. Dist: EMI

Single (7"): released on EMI America, Jun'84 by EMI Records. Dist: EMI

SOLIDARITY (Little Steven & The Disciples Of Soul).
Single (7"): released on EMI America, Aug'83 by EMI Records. Dist: EMI

Single (12"): released on EMI America, Aug'83 by EMI Records. Dist: EMI

VOICE OF AMERICA.
Album: released on EMI America, Jun'84 by EMI Records. Dist: EMI

Cassette: released on EMI America, Jun'84 by EMI Records. Dist: EMI

Little Tina & Flight '56

LITTLE TINA & FLIGHT '56.
Album: released on Rockhouse, Mar'85 Dist: Pinnacle

THIS LITTLE GIRL IS GONNA ROCK.
Album: released on Charly, '78 by Charly Records. Dist: Charly, Cadillac

Littleton, John

STEAL AWAY.
Album: released on Auvidis (France), May'85 Dist: Discovery

Cassette: released on Auvidis (France), May'85 Dist: Discovery

Little Walter

BEST OF....
Album: released on Chess, Apr'87 by Charly Records. Dist: Charly, Swift, PRT, Discovery, IMS, Polygram

Cassette: released on Chess, Apr'87 by Charly Records. Dist: Charly, Swift, PRT, Discovery, IMS, Polygram

BOSS BLUES HARMONICA.
Compact disc: released on Vogue, Dec'86 Dist: Discovery, Jazz Music, PRT, Swift

CHESS MASTERS.
Double Album: released on Chess, Apr'81 by Charly Records. Dist: Charly, Swift, PRT, Discovery, IMS, Polygram

Double Album: released on Chess(USA), May'83 by Sugar Hill (USA) Dist: PRT, Swift

CONFESSIN' THE BLUES.
Album: released on Chess, Oct'86 by Charly Records. Dist: Charly, Swift, PRT, Discovery, IMS, Polygram

ON THE ROAD AGAIN.
Album: released on Xtra, '79 by Relic Records. Dist: Swift

QUARTER TO TWELVE.
Album: released on Red Lightnin', Sep'82 by Red Lightnin' Records. Dist: Roots, Swift, Jazz Music, JSU, Pinnacle, Cartel, Wynd-Up Distribution

THUNDERBIRD.
Album: released on Syndicate Chapter, Sep'82 Dist: JSU Distribution, Projection Distribution, Red Lightnin' Distribution, Swift Distribution

WE THREE KINGS.
Album: released on Syndicate Chapter, Sep'82 Dist: JSU Distribution, Projection Distribution, Red Lightnin' Distribution, Swift Distribution

WE THREE KINGS (Little Walter, Howlin' Wolf & Muddy Waters).
Album: released on Syndicate, Sep'82

WINDY CITY BLUES (Little Walter/Otis Rush).
Notes: Recorded live in chicago. Top blues artists. Archive edition.
Album: released on Blue Moon, Feb'86 Dist: Magnum Music Group Ltd, PRT, Spartan

Little Willie John

GRITS AND SOUL.
Compact disc: released on Charly, Jan'87 by Charly Records. Dist: Charly, Cadillac

Little Women

LITTLE WOMEN Louisa May Alcott (Alcott, Louisa May).
Cassette: released on Argo, Mar'84 by Decca Records. Dist: Polygram

LITTLE WOMEN Narrator Elaine Stritch.
Cassette: released on Pinnacle, '79 by Pinnacle Records. Dist: Pinnacle

Litton, Andrew

GERSHWIN GOLD Gershwin 50th anniversary tribute (Litton, Andrew & Royal Philharmonic Orchestra).
Tracks: / Rhapsody in blue / Swanee / Nobody but you / Do it again / Clap yo' hands / Who cares? / Strike up the band / Sweet and low down / Somebody loves me / Bidin' my time / S'wonderful / That certain feeling / Do do do / Lady be good / Man I love, The / I'll build a stairway to paradise / Embraceable you / Fascinating rhythm / My one and only / Liza / I got rhythm.
Album: released on RPO, Jul'87 by Royal Philharmonic Orchestra Music. Dist: Academy Sound & Vision Records, PRT Distribution

Cassette: released on RPO, Jul'87 by Royal Philharmonic Orchestra Music. Dist: Academy Sound & Vision Records, PRT Distribution

Compact disc: released on RPO, Jul'87 by Royal Philharmonic Orchestra Music. Dist: Academy Sound & Vision Records, PRT Distribution

Live...

LIVE AND DIRECT - VOL.2 Various artists (Various Artists).
Album: released on Hawkeye, Mar'83 by Hawkeye Records. Dist: Hawkeye, Lightning (WEA) Distribution, Jetstar, PRT

Cassette: released on Hawkeye, Mar'83 by Hawkeye Records. Dist: Hawkeye, Lightning (WEA) Distribution, Jetstar, PRT

LIVE AND HEAVY Various artists (Various Artists).
Album: released on Nems, Nov'81 Dist: Castle Communications Records, Pinnacle Records

LIVE AT NEWPORT Various artists (Various Artists).
Album: released on Blue Moon, Jun'84 Dist: Magnum Music Group Ltd, PRT, Spartan

LIVE AT THE 101 Various artists (Various Artists).
Double Album: released on 101 International, Mar'84

Double cassette: released on 101 International, Mar'84

LIVE AT THE CAVERN Various artists (Various Artists).
Album: released on See For Miles, Sep'85 by Charly Records. Dist: Spartan

LIVE AT THE FESTIVAL (Live at the Festival).
Album: released on Enja (Germany), Feb'82 by Enja Records (W.Germany). Dist: Cadillac Music

LIVE AT THE HAIG, LOS ANGELES 1952 Various artists (Various Artists).
Album: released on Jamm Session, Apr'79

Album: released on Jamm Session, Apr'79

LIVE AT THE RAT Compilation of various artists (Various Artists).
Album: released on Rat Records, Aug'77

LIVE AT THE TRADEWINDS, INGLEWOOD 1952 Various artists (Various Artists).
Album: released on Jamm Session, Apr'79

LIVE A WEEK AT THE BRIDGE E16 Various artists (Various Artists).
Album: released on Bridgehouse, May'80 Dist: Pinnacle

LIVE CHICAGO BLUES - VOL.1 Various artists (Various Artists).
Album: released on Sonet, '78 by Sonet Records. Dist: PRT

LIVE CHICAGO BLUES - VOL.2 Various artists (Various Artists).
Album: released on Sonet, '78 by Sonet Records. Dist: PRT

LIVE CHICAGO BLUES - VOL.3 Various artists (Various Artists).
Album: released on Sonet, '78 by Sonet Records. Dist: PRT

LIVE FOR LIFE (Various Artists).
Tracks: / Love lessons / Lively up yourself / Ages of you / Howling wind / Amy / I been down so long / Hero takes a fall / Take your medicine / We got the beat / Tempted.
Notes: All proceeds from this album will be donated to the cancer research centre in the USA. Live tracks by Sting, The Bangles, Bob Marley, and The Alarm.
Album: released on I.R.S.(Independent Record Syndicate), Jun'86 by I.R.S.. Dist: MCA

Cassette: released on I.R.S.(Independent Record Syndicate), Jun'86 by I.R.S.. Dist: MCA

LIVE IN CONCERT Various artists (Various Artists).
Compact disc: released on Kingdom Records, '86 by Kingdom Records. Dist: Kingdom Records

Album: released on Kingdom, Jan'85 by Kingdom Records. Dist: Kingdom

Cassette: released on Kingdom, Jan'85 by Kingdom Records. Dist: Kingdom

LIVE IN LONDON - VOL.1 Various artists (Various Artists).
Album: released on Ace, Feb'84 by Ace Records. Dist: Pinnacle, Swift, Hotshot, Cadillac

LIVE-IN WORLD Anti heroin project (Various Artists).
Tracks: / Smack / Cold Turkeying / Hot line / End of the rainbow, The / Live-in world / It's not easy / Don't use drugs / Needle and the damage done (The) / Freak street\Skag / Suspended pool / Something better / You know it makes sense / Waiting in the dark / World spins so slow, The / Slay the dragon / Simple as that / Naughty atom bomb / Candles / Head full of shadows / Aqua / We came here to rock / Heroin / Little bit of snow / Never never / Hooked on love / Man's too strong, The / Blue (armed with love) / Something better / On the street / Magical / You know it makes sense / She's gonna love ya to death / Live-in world.
Notes: A double album project featuring major artists to support the fight against drugs in the UK. Includes the single 'Live-in world' which was released on oct. 27th. Royalties from the sale of this record will go to the Phoenix House Charity for recovery centres throughout the UK. Donated tracks from major artists include the following: Boon (Level 42) -'Head full of shadows', Paul McCartney-'Simple as that', Holly Johnson-'Slay the Dragon, Icicle works\Pete Wylie-'The needle and the damage done'. All the above are original tracks unreleased elsewhere. All major music and national papers have donated space to the project.
Single (7"): released on EMI, Oct'86 by EMI Records. Dist: EMI

Single (12"): released on EMI, Oct'86 by EMI Records. Dist: EMI

Double Album: released on EMI, Nov'86 by EMI Records. Dist: EMI

Double cassette: released on EMI, Nov'86 by EMI Records. Dist: EMI

Live at...

LIVE AT ALICE IN WONDERLAND (Various Artists).
Album: released on Flicknife, Aug'86 by Flicknife Records. Dist: Spartan

Cassette: released on Flicknife, Aug'86 by Flicknife Records. Dist: Spartan

LIVE AT ELECTRIC CIRCUS (Various Artists).
Album: released on Virgin, Apr'86 by Virgin Records. Dist: EMI, Virgin Distribution

LIVE AT SMALL'S PARADISE (Various Artists).
Notes: George 'harmonica' Smith, Rod Piazza, Bacon Fat, Pee Wee Crayton, J.D. Nicholson
Album: released on Blue Moon, Jun'86 Dist: Magnum Music Group Ltd, PRT, Spartan

LIVE AT THE ROCKHOUSE (Various Artists).
Notes: Artists include: Eddie Bond, Janice Martin etc.
Album: released on Rockhouse, Oct'86 by Rockhouse Records. Dist: Swift Distribution, Charly Distribution

LIVE AT THE ZAP CLUB (Various Artists).
Album: released on Zap Club, Nov'85

Live & Let Die

LIVE AND INDEPENDENT (VIDEO) At The Bay 63 (Various Artists).
Notes: Featuring Stump, Menticide, The Larks, June Brides, The Black Cillas, Blyth Power & Ghost Dance. Released on Nightingale Films

LIVE AND LEARN (Various Artists).
Notes: Artists: Mighty Diamonds, Junior Brammer, Ansel Meditation, Michael Prophet, Al Campbell, Don Carlos.
Album: released on CSA, Apr'86 by CSA Records. Dist: PRT, Jetstar

LIVE AND LET DIE James Bond Original Soundtrack (Various Artists).
Tracks: / Live and let die (main titles) / Just a closer walk with thee / New second line / Bond meets Solitaire / Whisper who dares / Snakes alive / Baron Samedi's dance of death / San Monique / Fillet of soul - New Orleans / Live and let die / Fillet of soul - Harlem / Bond drops in / If he finds it, kill him / Trespassers will be eaten / Solitaire gets her cards / Sacrifice / James Bond theme.
Notes: Produced by Harry Saltzman & Cubby Broccoli. All tracks composed by George Martin and published by SBK United Partnership except where otherwise stated.
Album: released on Liberty, Jul'87 by Liberty-United. Dist: EMI

Cassette: released on Liberty, Jul'87 by Liberty-United. Dist: EMI

Album: released on United Artists, '73

Lively Body

LIVELY BODY (Various Artists).
Album: released on Music Master, Mar'86 Dist: Jetstar Distribution

Liverpool...

LIVERPOOL 1963-1964 VOL.2 various artists (Various Artists).

Album: released on See For Miles, Dec'83 by Charly Records. Dist: Spartan

LIVERPOOL 1963-68 various artists (Various Artists).
Album: released on See For Miles, Jun'83 by See For Miles Records. Dist: Pinnacle

LIVERPOOL '63 -'68 (Various Artists).
Tracks: / Ferry cross the Mersey / Skinny Lizzie / Abyssinian secret / For no one / Sandy / It's too late now / Everything in the garden / Break away / Que sera sera / I really do / America / I gotta woman / Angel of love / I love her / Magic potion / First cut is the deepest / Why don't you love me / One way ticket / Don't you do it no more / How I won the war.
Album: released on See For Miles, Aug'86 by See For Miles Records. Dist: Pinnacle

LIVERPOOL/ANTHEM (Liverpool Football Team 1986).
Single (7"): released on Mean, Mar'83 by Mean Records. Dist: Spartan

LIVERPOOL(ANTHEM) (Liverpool Football Team 1986).
Single (7"): released on Mean, Mar'84 by Mean Records. Dist: Spartan

OFF TO DUBLIN (Liverpool Ceili Band).
Cassette: released on Polydor (Eire), Feb'85

SITTING ON TOP OF THE WORLD (Liverpool Football Team 1986).
Tracks: / Sitting on top of the world / Running like the wind.
Single (7"): released on Columbia, Apr'86 by EMI Records. Dist: EMI

UIVERPOOL SCENE - VOL 2 Various artists (Various Artists).
Album: released on See For Miles, Oct'86 by See For Miles Records. Dist: Pinnacle

Liverpool Cathedral

CHOIR OF LIVERPOOL METROPOLITAN CATHEDRAL.
Album: released on Abbey, '79 by Abbey. Dist: PRT, Taylors, Gamut

CHRISTMAS AT LIVERPOOL CATHEDRAL.
Album: released on Abbey, Nov'79 by Abbey. Dist: PRT, Taylors, Gamut

CHRISTMAS CAROLS.
Album: released on Alpha, Nov'81 by Alpha Records. Dist: H.R. Taylor, Gamut

CHRISTMAS MUSIC FROM...
Album: released on Abbey, Nov'79 by Abbey. Dist: PRT, Taylors, Gamut

FESTIVAL OF PRAISE ADVENT-ASCENSION.
Album: released on Abbey, Jan'77 by Abbey. Dist: PRT, Taylors, Gamut

SINGS.
Album: released on Abbey, '74 by Abbey. Dist: PRT, Taylors, Gamut

Liverpool Express

IF YOU'RE OUT THERE.
Single (7"): released on Direct, May'85 Dist: Backs, Cartel

SO WHAT/ROLL OVER.
Single (7"): released on Priority, Nov'83 by Priority Records. Dist: RCA

Liverpool Philharmonic

BY THE SLEEPY LAGOON AND OTHER ERIC COATES FAVOURITES.
Cassette: released on EMI, Nov'83 by EMI Records. Dist: EMI

GOD BLESS THE PRINCE OF WALES.
Single (7"): released on Chandos, Jul'81 by Chandos Records. Dist: Harmonia Mundi, Taylors

Live Sex

AN EXPRESSION OF FAITH.
Album: released on Very Mouth, Nov'85 by Very Mouth Records. Dist: Cartel

Live Skull

BRINGING HOME THE BAIT.
Album: released on Homestead, Sep'85 Dist: Rough Trade, Cartel, Shigaku

CLOUD ONE.
Album: released on Homestead, Sep'86 Dist: Rough Trade, Cartel, Shigaku

DON'T GET ANY ON YOU.
Album: released on Homestead, Aug'87 Dist: Rough Trade, Cartel, Shigaku

PUSHERMAN EP.
Single (7"): released on Homestead, Feb'87 Dist: Rough Trade, Cartel, Shigaku

RAISE THE MANIFESTATION.
Album: released on Homestead, Dec'86 Dist: Rough Trade, Cartel, Shigaku

Live Wire

IT'S FOR YOU.
Tracks: / It's for you.
Single (7"): released on BMW, Oct'86 Dist: M.I.S., PRT

Single (12"): released on BMW, Oct'86 Dist: M.I.S., PRT

Livin'..

LIVIN' THE NIGHTLIFE various artists (Various Artists).
Album: released on SMP, Mar'85 Dist: Jetstar, PRT

Living Chicago Blues

LIVING CHICAGO BLUES VOL.1 various artists (Various Artists).
Album: released on Sonet, Feb'79 by Sonet Records. Dist: PRT

LIVING CHICAGO BLUES VOL.2 various artists (Various Artists).
Album: released on Sonet, Feb'79 by Sonet Records. Dist: PRT

LIVING CHICAGO BLUES VOL.3 various artists (Various Artists).
Album: released on Sonet, Feb'79 by Sonet Records. Dist: PRT

LIVING CHICAGO BLUES VOL.4 various artists (Various Artists).
Album: released on Alligator-sonet, Jan'81

LIVING CHICAGO BLUES VOL.5 various artists (Various Artists).
Album: released on Alligator-sonet, Jan'81

LIVING CHICAGO BLUES VOL.6 various artists (Various Artists).
Album: released on Alligator-sonet, Jan'81

Living Daylight

COLLEEN.
Single (12"): released on Road Runner, Oct'85

Living Daylights

ANY WAY YOU WANT.
Album: released on Phase, May'84

HEART OF GOLD.
Single (7"): released on In Phaze, Jun'84 by In Phaze Records. Dist: Rough Trade

Single (12"): released on In Phaze, Jun'84 by In Phaze Records. Dist: Rough Trade

LIVING DAYLIGHTS Original soundtrack (Various Artists).
Album: released on Warner Brothers, Aug'87 by Warner Bros Records. Dist: WEA

Cassette: released on Warner Brothers, Aug'87 by Warner Bros Records. Dist: WEA

Compact disc: released on Warner Brothers, Aug'87 by Warner Bros Records. Dist: WEA

LIVING DAYLIGHTS, THE Original Sound Track (Various Artists).
Tracks: / Living daylights, The / Necros attacks / Sniper was a woman, The / Ice chase / Kara meets Bond / Koskov escapes / Where has every body gone / Into Vienna / Hercules takes off / Mujahadin and Opium / Inflight flight / If there was a man.
Notes: Inc. The Pretenders, A-Ha.
Compact disc: released on Warner Bros., Jul'87 by Warner Bros Records. Dist: WEA

Living Death

METAL REVOLUTION.
Tracks: / Killing machine / Grippin' a heart / Rulers must come / Screaming from a chamber / Intro / Shadow of the dawn / Panic and hysteria / Road of destiny / Deep in Hell.
Album: released on Earthshaker (Germany), Apr'86 by Earthshaker Records (Germany). Dist: IMS, Polygram

VENGEANCE OF HELL.
Album: released on Mausoleum, Oct'84 by Mausoleum Records. Dist: Pinnacle

WATCH OUT.
Album: released on Earthshaker (Germany), Jun'85 by Earthshaker Records (Germany). Dist: IMS, Polygram

Living In A Box

LIVING IN A BOX.
Tracks: / Living in a box / Penthouse Mix / Super Heroes / Living in a box / Love is the art / So the story goes / From beginning to end / Generate the wave / Scales of justice / Going for the big one / Human story / Can't stop the wheel / Living in a box (reprise).
Single (7"): released on Chrysalis, Mar'87 by Chrysalis Records. Dist: CBS

Single (12"): released on Chrysalis, Mar'87 by Chrysalis Records. Dist: CBS

Compact disc single: released on Chrysalis, Mar'87 by Chrysalis Records. Dist: CBS

Album: released on Chrysalis, Apr'87 by Chrysalis Records. Dist: CBS

Cassette: released on Chrysalis, Apr'87 by Chrysalis Records. Dist: CBS

Compact disc: released on Chrysalis, '87 by Chrysalis Records. Dist: CBS

SCALES OF JUSTICE.
Tracks: / Scales of justice / Ecstasy.
Single (7"): released on Chrysalis, 30 May'87 by Chrysalis Records. Dist: CBS

Single (12"): released on Chrysalis, 30 May'87 by Chrysalis Records. Dist: CBS

Cassette single: released on Chrysalis, 30 May'87 by Chrysalis Records. Dist: CBS

Living In Texas

AND DAVID CRIED.
Single (7"): released on Rhythmic, Aug'83 by Rhythmic Records. Dist: Havoc Distribution

COWBOY DREAM.
Album: released on Big Beat, Jun'87 by Ace Records. Dist: Projection, Pinnacle

COWBOY DREAM.
Album: released on Big Beat, Jun'87 by Ace Records. Dist: Projection, Pinnacle

GLAD BAD MAD AND SAD.
Single (12"): released on Chainsaw, Sep'85 by Chainsaw Records. Dist: Red Rhino, Cartel

GOD BLESS AMERICA.
Single (12"): released on Chainsaw, Aug'84 by Chainsaw Records. Dist: Red Rhino, Cartel

ITALIA LIVE '85.
Album: released on Latex, Jun'85 by Latex Records. Dist: Red Rhino, Cartel

KINGDOM.
Single (7"): released on Chainsaw, Feb'84 by Chainsaw Records. Dist: Red Rhino, Cartel

Single (12"): released on Chainsaw, Feb'84 by Chainsaw Records. Dist: Red Rhino, Cartel

LIVING IN TEXAS.
Album: released on Chainsaw, Nov'84 by Chainsaw Records. Dist: Red Rhino, Cartel

MY END OF HEAVEN.
Single (12"): released on Rebirth, Oct'83 Dist: Red Rhino, Cartel

Living Legends

POPE IS A DOPE, (THE).
Single (7"): released on Upright, May'82 by Upright Records. Dist: Cartel, Rough Trade

Living New Orleans Jazz

LIVING NEW ORLEANS JAZZ 1973 various artists (Various Artists).
Album: released on Smokey Mary, Apr'79 Dist: Swift

LIVING NEW ORLEANS JAZZ 1974 various artists (Various Artists).
Album: released on Smokey Mary, Apr'79 Dist: Swift

Livings, Henry

NORTHERN DRIFT (Livings, Henry & Alex Glasgow).
Album: released on MWM, Jun'82 by Mawson & Wareham. Dist: Spartan Distribution, Jazz Music Distribution, JSU Distribution

Living Sound

LET YOUR SPIRIT SING.
Album: released on Light USA, May'82 by Lexicon Music. Dist: Word Distribution

Cassette: released on Light USA, May'82 by Lexicon Music. Dist: Word Distribution

SPIDERMAN.
Single (7"): released on Dulcima, Sep'84 by Living Productions Records. Dist: H.R. Taylor

Livingston, Carlton

AIN'T GONNA FIGHT.
Single (12"): released on JB, Feb'83 by Mr. R&B Records. Dist: Swift

ARMAGIDEON TIME.
Single (7"): released on Dynamite, Aug'82 by Dynamite Records. Dist: Jetstar

CHALICE IN HAND.
Single (7"): released on Power House, Jun'82 by Power House Records. Dist: Jetstar

HUNDREDWEIGHT OF COLLIE WEED.
Single (12"): released on Greensleeves, Mar'84 by Greensleeves Records. Dist: BMG, Jetstar, Spartan

MARIE.
Single (7"): released on Power House, Feb'82 by Power House Records. Dist: Jetstar

MR MUSIC MAN.
Single (12"): released on Greensleeves, Jul'84 by Greensleeves Records. Dist: BMG, Jetstar, Spartan

RUMOURS.
Album: released on Bebo, Jul'84 by Bebo Records. Dist: Jetstar

SETTLE CROWD OF PEOPLE.
Single (12"): released on Technics, Nov'84 by Technics Records. Dist: Jetstar Distribution

TRODDING THROUGH THE JUNGLE.
Album: released on Dynamite, Jul'84 by Dynamite Records. Dist: Jetstar

WHEN I'M HOT.
Single (12"): released on What's Up Doc, Sep'84 by What's Up Doc Records. Dist: Jetstar

YES I FEEL.
Single (12"): released on Rosie Uprising, Sep'84 by Rosie Uprising Records. Dist: Jetstar Distribution

YOUR LOVING.
Single (12"): released on Time, Jun'84 Dist: Jetstar Distribution

Livingstone, Carly

CHILDREN OF THE MOUNTAIN.
Single (12"): released on GG'S, Sep'84 by GG'S Records. Dist: Jetstar

Livingstone, Dandy

A.M. LOVER / LOVER VERSION.
Single (7"): released on Mint Music, Oct'82

RUDY A MESSAGE TO YOU.
Special: released on Trojan, '83 by Trojan Records. Dist: PRT, Jetstar

SOMETIMES WHEN WE TOUCH / TUFF TUFF.
Single (7"): released on Cartridge, May'82 by Cartridge. Dist: Jetstar

SUZANNE BEWARE OF THE DEVIL.
Single (7"): released on Old Gold (Reissue), Apr'83

Lizard Train

13 HOUR DAYDREAM.
Single (12"):

Liz & The Sandpipers

LIZ & THE SANDPIPERS Various artists (Various Artists).
Cassette: released on Delyse, Mar'81 by Delyse Records. Dist: H.R. Taylor

Lizzy Borden

LIVE AT THE MURDERESS ROAD SHOW.
Album: released on Roadrunner (Dutch), Sep'86 Dist: Pinnacle

LOVE YOU TO PIECES.
Album: released on Road Runner, Jun'85

MENACE TO SOCIETY.
Album: released on Roadrunner (Dutch), Oct'86 Dist: Pinnacle

VISUAL LIES.
Compact disc: released on Road Runner, Sep'87. Estim retail price in Sep'87 was £12.99.

Album: released on Roadrunner, Oct'87 by Roadrunner Records (Germany). Dist: Pinnacle. Estim retail price in Sep'87 was £5.99.

Lizzy Lee Anne

WHISPERING ON THE PHONE.
Single (7"): released on Kick, Mar'84 by Mike Collier. Dist: Pinnacle

L. Jays

I'VE BEEN HURT / WORKING FOR YOUR LOVE.
Single (7"): released on S&D, Feb'82

LKT Band, The

BABY BE TRUE.
Single (12"): released on Clouds, Oct'85 by Clouds Records. Dist: Jetstar

LL Cool J

BIGGER AND DEFFER.
Tracks: / I'm bad / Get down / Bistol Hotel, The / My rhyme ain't done / 357-Break it on down /

Go cut creator go / Breakthrough,The / I need love / Ahh, let's get ill / Do wop,The / On the ill tip.
Album: released on Def Jam (USA), Jun'87 by CBS Records. Dist: CBS

Cassette: released on Def Jam (USA), Jun'87 by CBS Records. Dist: CBS

I CAN'T LIVE WITHOUT MY RADIO (SEPT 86).
Tracks: / I can't live without my radio / Rock bells / You'll rock * / El Shabazz *.
Single (7"): released on Def Jam (USA), Sep'86 by CBS Records. Dist: CBS

Single (12"): released on Def Jam (USA), Sep'86 by CBS Records. Dist: CBS

I CAN'T LIVE WITHOUT MY RADIO (JAN 86).
Tracks: / I can't live without my radio / I can't give you no more.
Single (7"): released on Def Jam (USA), Jan'86 by CBS Records. Dist: CBS

Single (12"): released on Def Jam (USA), Jan'86 by CBS Records. Dist: CBS

I'M BAD.
Tracks: / I'm bad / Get down / Dangerouse* / Rock the bells* / I can't live without my radio*.
Single (7"): released on Def Jam (USA), May'87 by CBS Records. Dist: CBS

Single (12"): released on Def Jam (USA), May'87 by CBS Records. Dist: CBS

Picture disc single: released on Def Jam (USA), Jun'87 by CBS Records. Dist: CBS

RADIO.
Tracks: / I cant live without my Radio. / You cant dance. / Dear Yvette / I can give you more / Dangerous / Rock the Bells / I need a beat / You'll rock. / I want you..
Album: released on Def Jam (USA), Feb'86 by CBS Records. Dist: CBS

Cassette single: released on Def Jam (USA), Feb'86 by CBS Records. Dist: CBS

ROCK THE BELLS.
Tracks: / Rock the bells / Rock the Bells / El Shabazz.
Single (7"): released on Def Jam (USA), Mar'86 by CBS Records. Dist: CBS

Single (12"): released on Def Jam (USA), Mar'86 by CBS Records. Dist: CBS

Lloyd, A. L.
English & Scottish folk ballads

Lloyd, Allen
I KEEP LOOKING AT YOU.
Single (7"): released on Epic, Mar'84 by CBS Records. Dist: CBS

Single (12"): released on Epic, Mar'84 by CBS Records. Dist: CBS

Lloyd, Carol
CAROL LLOYD.
Album: released on Philly World (USA), Apr'83
Cat. no: **PWLP 1004**

COME SEE ABOUT ME / I JUST WANT.....
Single (7"):

Single (12"):

Lloyd,Charles Quartet
NIGHT IN COPENHAGEN,A.
Album: released on Blue Note, Apr'85 by EMI Records. Dist: EMI

Lloyd & Charmain
REMEMBER THAT SUNDAY.
Single (7"): released on Dancebeat, Aug'81 by Dancebeat Records. Dist: Jetstar

Lloyd collection
MAGGIE'S FARM.
Tracks: / Maggie's Farm.
Single (7"): released on Mayday, Apr'86 Dist: Rough Trade

Lloyd & Devon
BUM BALL.
Single (12"): released on Rosie Uprising, Sep'84 by Rosie Uprising Records. Dist: Jetstar Distribution

Lloyd, Floyd
BETTER TO LAUGH THAN TO CRY.
Album: released on Vista Sounds, '83 by Vista Sounds Records. Dist: Jetstar

SWEET LADY/CHECK OUT YOUR MIND.
Single (7"): released on Echo, Mar'82 by Vista Sounds. Dist: Jazz Music

Single (12"): released on Echo, Mar'82 by Vista Sounds. Dist: Jazz Music

Lloyd, Frank Harmonica
FRANK LLOYD HARMONICA.
Album: released on Adelphi(USA), May'81 by Adelphi Records (USA). Dist: Projection, Swift

Lloyd, Geoff
AFTER LOVE/WHEN WE MEET.
Single (7"): released on Nectar, Feb'82 by Nectar Records. Dist: Pinnacle

Lloyd-Langton group
NIGHT AIR.
Album: released on Flicknife, Mar'85 by Flicknife Records. Dist: Spartan

Lloyd, Richard
FIELD OF FIRE (Richard Lloyd).
Notes:
Track details were not advised.
Album: released on Mistlur, Mar'86 Dist: Nine Mile Distribution, Cartel Distribution

Lloyd Webber, Andrew
VARIATIONS.
Tracks: / Introduction / Theme and variations 1-23.
Compact disc: released on MCA, Mar'87 by MCA Records. Dist: Polygram, MCA

VARIATIONS.
Tracks: / Introductions / Theme (Paganini Caprice in A minor No 24) and variation... / Variations 5 and 6 / Variation 7 / Variation 8 / Variation 9 / Variation 10 / Variations 11-15 / Variation 16 / Variations 14-15 varied / Variation 17 / Variation 18 / Variations 19, 20 and 6 varied / Variations 21 and 22 / Variation 23.
Notes: A renowned album which will benefit enormously from conversion to mid-line.
Album: released on MCA, May'86 by MCA Records. Dist: Polygram, MCA

Lloyd Webber, Julian
PIECES.
Tracks: / Nights in white satin / I know him so well / First time ever I saw your face (The) / Tonight I celebrate my love / Hello / Air on a G string / From suite no 3 in D / Up where we belong / Theme from Brideshead revisited / Theme from the Yellow book / Largo (from 'New World Symphony') / Cavatina (theme from 'The Deer Hunter') / Bright eyes.
Compact disc: released on Polydor, Aug'85 by Polydor Records. Dist: Polygram, Polydor

Llwybr Llaethog
DULL DI DRAIS.
Extended-play record: released on Anhrefn, Feb'87 Dist: Revolver, Cartel

Loaded Fourty Fours
THUNDERBIRDS ARE GO/T.V. CHILD.
Single (7"): released on XS, Oct'81 Dist: Fresh

Loake,Simon & Andrew
ROGUES MARCH.
Album: released on Sweet Folk All, Feb'81 by Sweet Folk All Records. Dist: Sweet Folk All, Roots, Celtic Music, Dragon, Impetus, Projection, Chris Wellard, Festival Records

Lobban,Sandra
MAKE YOU MY MAN/MAKE DUB.
Single (7"): released on Music Gallery, Sep'82

TIME IS FOR LOVE/LOVE VERSION.
Single (7"): released on Music Gallery, Dec'82

Lobi,Kakraba
XYLOPHONE PLAYER FROM GHANA.
Album: released on Tangent, Apr'81 Dist: Roots Distribution, Lugtons Distributors, Taylors, JSU Distribution, Spartan Distribution

Lobo
CARRIBEAN DISCO SHOW,THE.
Album: released on Polydor, Sep'81 by Polydor Records. Dist: Polygram, Polydor

Cassette: released on Polydor, Sep'81 by Polydor Records. Dist: Polygram, Polydor

SOCA CALYPSO.
Album: released on Phillips Holland, Jul'82

Cassette: released on Phillips Holland, Jul'82

Lobo(US)
I'D LOVE YOU TO LOVE ME.
Single (7"): released on USA Import, '75

I DON'T WANT TO WANT YOU/COME LOOKING FOR ME.
Single (7"): released on Young Blood, Jan'84 by Young Blood Records. Dist: Pinnacle

ME AND YOU AND A DOG NAMED BOO.
Single (7"): released on Old Gold, Sep'85 by Old Gold Records. Dist: Lightning, Jazz Music, Spartan, Counterpoint

Local boy makes good
HOROSCOPE/HYPNOTIC RHYTHM.
Single (7"): released on Arrival, Jan'82 by Arrival. Dist: Revolver, Cartel

Local Heroes SW9
DRIP DRY ZONE.
Album: released on Oval, May'82 by Oval Records. Dist: Pinnacle

HOW THE WEST WAS WON.
Album: released on Oval, May'82 by Oval Records. Dist: Pinnacle

Lochan
LOCHAN.
Album: released on Celtic Music, Mar'84 by Celtic Music Distribution. Dist: Celtic Music, Jazz Music, Projection, Roots

Lochies
HOME TO LEWIS.
Album: released on Lismor, '75 by Lismor Records. Dist: Lismor, Roots, Celtic Music

LEWIS FOLK.
Album: released on Lismor, '74 by Lismor Records. Dist: Lismor, Roots, Celtic Music

NORTH BY NORTH-WEST.
Album: released on Lismor, Nov'76 by Lismor Records. Dist: Lismor, Roots, Celtic Music

SLAINTE MHATH good health.
Album: released on Lismor, Jun'78 by Lismor Records. Dist: Lismor, Roots, Celtic Music

Cassette: released on Lismor, Jun'78 by Lismor Records. Dist: Lismor, Roots, Celtic Music

Loch ness monster
INDUSTRIAL POPPIES.
Notes:
Track details not advised.
Album: released on Hamster, Mar'86 by Hamster Records And Tapes. Dist: Backs, Cartel

Locke, Annie
LIVING EARTH (THE) (Annie Locke).
Tracks: / In a Crystal cave. / Crystal Moments / crystal Fairies / Crystal Waters / Once upon a time there was a kingdom.
Notes:
Peaceful, crystal clear music written with gentle synthsizer sounds for moments of rest and tranquillity. Composed and performed by Annie Locke, Inner Harmonies, 182 southfield Rd, London, W4 5LD Tel 10-995 9749. No catalogue number advised!
Cassette single: released on Inner Harmonies, Jun'86 Dist: Inner Harmonies

Locke brass consort
CONSTRASTS IN BRASS.
Album: released on Unicorn, Aug'78 Dist: Nine Mile, Cartel

JUBILANT BRASS.
Album: released on Red Seal, Jun'77 by RCA Records. Dist: RCA

Locke,Josef
WORLD OF JOSEF LOCKE TODAY,THE.
Album: released on World of Learning, '69 by World Of Learning Records. Dist: World Of Learning

Locke, Joseph
HEAR MY SONG.
Album: released on Music For Pleasure (Holland), Jul'83 by EMI Records. Dist: EMI

Cassette: released on Music For Pleasure (Holland), Jul'83 by EMI Records. Dist: EMI

Album: released on MWM, May'83 by Mawson & Wareham. Dist: Spartan Distribution, Jazz Music Distribution, JSU Distribution

Locke,Joy
NEVER GIVE YOUR HEART AWAY.
Single (7"): released on Cha-Cha, Sep'82 by Cha Cha. Dist: Jetstar

Locklin, Hank
20 OF THE BEST.
Album: released on RCA, '84 by RCA Records. Dist: RCA, Roots, Swift, Wellard, Chris, I & B, Solomon & Peres Distribution

Cassette: released on RCA, '84 by RCA Records. Dist: RCA, Roots, Swift, Wellard, Chris, I & B, Solomon & Peres Distribution

ALL KINDS OF EVERYTHING.
Album: released on topspin, Jul'79

FAMOUS COUNTRY MUSIC MAKERS.
Double Album: released on RCA, Sep'75 by RCA Records. Dist: RCA, Roots, Swift, Wellard, Chris, I & B, Solomon & Peres Distribution

FROM HERE TO THERE TO YOU.
Album: released on Bulldog, Jul'85 by Bulldog Records. Dist: President Distribution, Spartan, Swift, Taylor, H.R.

Cassette: released on Bulldog, Jul'85 by Bulldog Records. Dist: President Distribution, Spartan, Swift, Taylor, H.R.

IRISH SONGS COUNTRY STYLE.
Album: released on RCA, Nov'84 by RCA Records. Dist: RCA, Roots, Swift, Wellard, Chris, I & B, Solomon & Peres Distribution

Cassette: released on RCA, Nov'84 by RCA Records. Dist: RCA, Roots, Swift, Wellard, Chris, I & B, Solomon & Peres Distribution

MR.COUNTRY.
Album: released on Spot, Feb'83 by Pickwick Records. Dist: H.R. Taylor, Lugtons

Cassette: released on Spot, Feb'83 by Pickwick Records. Dist: H.R. Taylor, Lugtons

PLEASE HELP FROM FALLING. (Hank Locklin).
Tracks: / Pease help me from falling / Sea of heart.
Single (7"): released on Old Gold, Oct'86 by Old Gold Records. Dist: Lightning, Jazz Music, Spartan, Counterpoint

PLEASE HELP ME I'M FALLING (Hank Locklin).
Tracks: / Please help me I'm falling / Geisha girl / Send me the pillow / Its a little more like heaven / Let me be the one / Happy Birthday to me / Happy Journey / Down on my knees / Night life queen / Day time love affair / There never was a time / Baby I need you..
Notes:
There are two albums of this title by this person. The first was released in DEC 85,. CAT no 20068. The second was released later the following year, its CAT no was TOP 132.
Album: released on Topline, '86 by Charly Records. Dist: Charly Distribution

Album: released on Astan, Dec'85 by Astan Records. Dist: Counterpoint

Album: released on Astan, Nov'84 by Astan Records. Dist: Counterpoint

Cassette: released on Astan, Nov'84 by Astan Records. Dist: Counterpoint

WE'RE GONNA GO FISHIN'/PLEASE HELP ME I'M FALLING.
Single (7"): released on RCA, Oct'81 by RCA Records. Dist: RCA, Roots, Swift, Wellard, Chris, I & B, Solomon & Peres Distribution

Locks, Fred
BLACK STAR LINER.
Album: released on Vista Sounds, '83 by Vista Sounds Records. Dist: Jetstar

Cassette: released on Vista Sounds, '83 by Vista Sounds Records. Dist: Jetstar

GIVE JAH YOUR HEART & SOUL.
Single (12"): released on Blacker Dread, Oct'84

REDEMPTION.
Single (12"): released on Omega, Oct'85 by Omega Records. Dist: Jetstar Distribution

Lock Up Your Daughters
LOCK UP YOUR DAUGHTERS various artists (Various Artists).
Album: released on That's Entertainment, Apr'83 by That's Entertainment Records. Dist: Pinnacle, PRT

Cassette: released on That's Entertainment, Apr'83 by That's Entertainment Records. Dist: Pinnacle, PRT

Lockwood, Anna
GLASS WORLD.
Album: released on Tangent, Apr'81 Dist: Roots Distribution, Lugtons Distributors, Taylors, JSU Distribution, Spartan Distribution

Lockwood, Didier
NEW WORLD (Lockwood, Didier/Gordon Beck/Tony Williams/Niels Pedersen).
Album: released on JMS (France), Nov'84

Album: released on MPS Jazz, Jun'81

Lockwood, Neil
TELL TALE HEART.
Single (7"): released on Red Bus, Mar'83 by Red Bus Records. Dist: PRT

Single (12"): released on Red Bus, Mar'83 by

Lockwood, Robert Jnr.
BLUES LIVE IN JAPAN.
Album: released on Advent, Apr'79 Dist: Celtic Music, Projection, Swift

STEADY ROLLIN' MAN.
Album: released on Delmark, '74 Dist: Projection, Swift, Cadillac

Lockyer, Malcolm
CLASSICS IN THE MODERN MOOD
(Lockyer, Malcolm Orchestra).
Cassette: released on Kingfisher Cassettes, Nov'81 by Fraser-Peacock Associates Ltd. Dist: PRT

Loco Lotus
DETROIT.
Single (12"): released on Loco Records, Dec'84 by Loco Records. Dist: Loco Records

Locomotives, The
BOURGEOIS VOODOO.
Album: released on Big Beat, 7 Sep'87 by Ace Records. Dist: Projection, Swift

FROM THE FINEST ROLLING STOCK.
Album: released on Media Burn, Dec'86 by Rocks Off Record Emporium. Dist: Rough Trade Distribution, Cartel Distribution

Lodge, Ian
BABY JUMP TO IT.
Tracks: / Baby jump to it / One way out (remix).
Single (7"): released on ABR, Aug'87 by ABR Productions. Dist: Spartan. Pinnacle

SHE'S MAKING MOVIES.
Tracks: / She's making movies / There is only one way out / There's only one way out.
Single (7"): released on ABR, Jan'86 by ABR Productions. Dist: Spartan, Pinnacle

STAY.
Single (7"): released on ABR, Jun'85 by ABR Productions. Dist: Spartan, Pinnacle

WALKIN' TO THE BEAT.
Single (7"): released on President, Apr'84 by President Records. Dist: Taylors, Spartan

Single (12"): released on President, Apr'84 by President Records. Dist: Taylors, Spartan

Lodge, J.C.
GOT TO MAKE IT UP.
Single (12"): released on Londisc, Jan'84 by Londisc Records.

I BELIEVE IN YOU.
Album: released on Greensleeves, Aug'87 by Greensleeves Records. Dist: BMG, Jetstar, Spartan

Cassette: released on Greensleeves, Aug'87 by Greensleeves Records. Dist: BMG, Jetstar, Spartan

SOMEONE LOVES YOU HONEY.
Tracks: / Someone loves you honey / Stay in tonight.
Single (12"): released on Greensleeves, Nov'86 by Greensleeves Records. Dist: BMG, Jetstar, Spartan

Single (7"): released on Greensleeves, Sep'86 by Greensleeves Records. Dist: BMG, Jetstar, Spartan

Single (12"): Dist: Roots, Pinnacle, Projection

TOGETHER WE WILL STAY.
Tracks: / Together we will stay / Together we will stay (version).
Single (12"): released on Greensleeves, May'87 by Greensleeves Records. Dist: BMG, Jetstar, Spartan

Lodge, John
BLUE JAYS (see Hayward, Justin) (Lodge, John & Justin Hayward).

NATURAL AVENUE.
Tracks: / Intro to children of rock'n'roll / Natural avenue / Summer breeze / Carry me / Who could change / Broken dreams, hard road / Piece of my heart / Rainbow / Say you love me / Children of rock'n'roll / Street café.
Compact disc: released on London, Jul'87 by London Records. Dist: Polygram

STREET CAFE.
Single (7"): released on Decca, Oct'80 by Decca Records. Dist: Polygram

Lodge, June
GIVE MY HUSBAND A MESSAGE.
Tracks: / Give my husband a message / Selfish lover.
Single (7"): released on Hawkeye, Dec'85 by Hawkeye Records. Dist: Hawkeye, Lightning (WEA) Distribution, Jetstar, PRT

REVEALED (Lodge, June C).
Album: released on WKS, Apr'85 by WKS Records. Dist: Jetstar Distribution

STAY IN TONIGHT.
Single (7"): released on Joe Gibbs, Feb'82 by Joe Gibbs Records. Dist: Jetstar

Loeb, Caroline
C'EST LA OUATE(AND SO WHAT!).
Tracks: / C'est la ouate / And so what(English version) / C'est la ouate(Dean Anderson US dance remix) / Paresseuse dub *.
Single (12"): released on London, May'87 by London Records. Dist: Polygram

Single (7"): released on London, May'87 by London Records. Dist: Polygram

C'EST LA OUATE.
Tracks: / C'est la ouate / And so what.
Single (7"): released on Barclay, 23 May'87 by Decca Records. Dist: Polygram, Discovery, Conifer, IMS, Swift

Single (12"): released on Barclay, 23 May'87 by Decca Records. Dist: Polygram, Discovery, Conifer, IMS, Swift

Loesser, Frank
WHERE'S CHARLEY.
Album: released on Monmouth, Jun'79

Lofgren, Nils
AND GRIN.
Album: released on CBS, Oct'79 by CBS Records. Dist: CBS

ANYTIME AT ALL.
Tracks: / Anytime at all / New holes in old shoes.
Single (7"): released on Towerbell, Mar'86 by Towerbell Records. Dist: EMI

CODE OF THE ROAD.
Double Album: released on Towerbell, Apr'86 by Towerbell Records. Dist: EMI

Cassette: released on Towerbell, Apr'86 by Towerbell Records. Dist: EMI

CRY TOUGH.
Album: released on Fame, Jul'83 by Music For Pleasure Records. Dist: EMI

Cassette: released on Fame, Jul'83 by Music For Pleasure Records. Dist: EMI

DELIVERY NIGHT.
Single (7"): released on Towerbell, Nov'85 by Towerbell Records. Dist: EMI

Single (12"): released on Towerbell, Dec'85 by Towerbell Records. Dist: EMI

FLIP.
Album: released on Towerbell, Jun'85 by Towerbell Records. Dist: EMI

Cassette: released on Towerbell, Jun'85 by Towerbell Records. Dist: EMI

FLIP YA FLIP.
Single (7"): released on Towerbell, Jul'85 by Towerbell Records. Dist: EMI

Single (12"): released on Towerbell, Aug'85 by Towerbell Records. Dist: EMI

Single (12"): released on Towerbell, Aug'85 by Towerbell Records. Dist: EMI

NIGHT FADES AWAY.
Album: released on MCA, Feb'84 by MCA Records. Dist: Polygram, MCA

Cassette: released on MCA, Feb'84 by MCA Records. Dist: Polygram, MCA

NILS.
Album: released on A&M, Jun'79 by A&M Records. Dist: Polygram

Cassette: released on A&M, Jun'79 by A&M Records. Dist: Polygram

NILS LOFGREN.
Album: released on A&M, Apr'75 by A&M Records. Dist: Polygram

Cassette: released on A&M, Apr'75 by A&M Records. Dist: Polygram

NILS LOFGREN AND GRIN.
Tracks: / Soft fun & moon tears / Open wide / White lies / Take you to the movies tonight / Sometimes / Pioneer Mary / Heavy chevy / Lost a number / Ain't love nice / Rusty gun / If I were a song / Love again / We all sung together / Like rain / End unkind.
Album: released on CBS, Feb'86 by CBS Records. Dist: CBS

Cassette: released on CBS, Feb'86 by CBS Records. Dist: CBS

NILS LOFGREN & GRIN.
Cassette: released on CBS, Nov'79 by CBS Records. Dist: CBS

RHYTHM ROMANCE, A.
Album: released on A&M, Apr'82 by A&M Records. Dist: Polygram

Cassette: released on A&M, Apr'82 by A&M Records. Dist: Polygram

SECRETS IN THE STREET.
Single (7"): released on Towerbell, Jan'86 by Towerbell Records. Dist: EMI

Double-pack single: released on Towerbell, May'85 by Towerbell Records. Dist: EMI

Single (12"): released on Towerbell, May'85 by Towerbell Records. Dist: EMI

Single (12"): released on Towerbell, Jun'85 by Towerbell Records. Dist: EMI

WONDERLAND.
Tracks: / Across the tracks / Into the night / It's all over now / I wait for you / Daddy dream / Wonderland / Room without love / Confident girl / Lonesome ranger / Everybody wants / Deadline.
Album: released on MCA, Jun'87 by MCA Records. Dist: Polygram, MCA

Cassette: released on MCA, Jun'87 by MCA Records. Dist: Polygram, MCA

Album: released on MCA, Aug'83 by MCA Records. Dist: Polygram, MCA

Cassette: released on MCA, Aug'83 by MCA Records. Dist: Polygram, MCA

Album: released on MCA, Aug'87 by MCA Records. Dist: Polygram, MCA

Cassette: released on MCA, Aug'87 by MCA Records. Dist: Polygram, MCA

Lofsky, Lorne
IT COULD HAPPEN TO YOU.
Album: released on Pablo, '82 by Pablo Records. Dist: Wellard, Chris, IMS-Polygram, BMG

Cassette: released on Pablo, '82 by Pablo Records. Dist: Wellard, Chris, IMS-Polygram, BMG

Loft
UP THE HILL AND DOWN THE SLOPE.
Single (7"): released on Creation, Aug'85 Dist: Rough Trade, Cartel

Single (12"): released on Creation, '85 Dist: Rough Trade, Cartel

WHY DOES THE RAIN FALL?.
Single (7"): released on Creation, Sep'84 Dist: Rough Trade, Cartel

Lofton, Clarence
1935-6 RECORDINGS (Lofton, Cripple Clarence).
Album: released on Magpie, Feb'79 Dist: Projection

Log 10
STEP IN THE DARK.
Single (7"): released on Sonic, Jun'83

YOU'RE NOT THERE.
Single (7"): released on Sonic, May'84

Logan
STAB IN THE BACK.
Tracks: / Stab in back.
Single (7"): released on A.1, Mar'86 by A.1 Records. Dist: PRT

Single (12"): released on A.1, Mar'86 by A.1 Records. Dist: PRT

Logan, Johnny
HOLD ME NOW.
Tracks: / Hold me now / Living a lie / Hold me now / Stay / Foolish love / When your woman cries / I'm not in love / Helpless heart / What's another year / Living a lie / Such a lady / Hold me now / Stay / Foolish love / When your woman cries / I'm not in love / Helpless heart / What's another year / Heartbroken man / Living a lie / Such a lady.
Single (7"): released on Epic, May'87 by CBS Records. Dist: CBS

Album: released on Epic, Jul'87 by CBS Records. Dist: CBS

Cassette: released on Epic, Jul'87 by CBS Records. Dist: CBS

Compact disc: released on Epic, Jul'87 by CBS Records. Dist: CBS

HOLD ME NOW (LP).
Album: released on Epic, Jul'87 by CBS Records. Dist: CBS

Cassette: released on Epic, Jul'87 by CBS Records. Dist: CBS

I'M NOT IN LOVE.
Tracks: / I'm not in love / Such a lady.

Single (7"): released on Epic, Jul'87 by CBS Records. Dist: CBS

Single (12"): released on Epic, Jul'87 by CBS Records. Dist: CBS

Logan, Sally
CROOKIT BAWBEE (see Gordon, Joe) (Logan, Sally & Joe Gordon).

END OF A PERFECT DAY, (THE) (see Gordon, Joe) (Logan, Sally & Joe Gordon).

FAVOURITES (see Gordon, Joe) (Logan, Sally & Joe Gordon).

JOE GORDON & SALLY LOGAN (see Gordon, Joe) (Logan, Sally & Joe Gordon).

MONLIGHT AND ROSES (see Gordon, Joe) (Logan, Sally & Joe Gordon).

MOONLIGHT & ROSES (Logan, Sally & Joe Gordon).
Album: released on Neptune, Jun'78 by Lismor. Dist: Spartan

Cassette: released on Neptune, Jun'78 by Lismor. Dist: Spartan

TOGETHER (see Gordon, Joe) (Logan, Sally & Joe Gordon).

Loggerheads
FOUR WAYS TO COOK A GOOSE.
Extended-play record: released on Antenna, 23 May'87 Dist: Cartel

Loggins and Messina
SITTIN' IN.
Compact disc: released on Mobile Fidelity, '86 by Mobile Fidelity Records.

Loggins, Kenny
DANGER ZONE.
Tracks: / Danger zone / I'm gonna do it right.
Single (7"): released on CBS, Sep'86 by CBS Records. Dist: CBS

FOREVER.
Single (7"): released on CBS, Jun'85 by CBS Records. Dist: CBS

HIGH ADVENTURE.
Album: released on CBS, Dec'82 by CBS Records. Dist: CBS

I'M FREE (HEAVEN HELPS THE MAN).
Single (7"): released on CBS, Jun'84 by CBS Records. Dist: CBS

Single (12"): released on CBS, Jun'84 by CBS Records. Dist: CBS

I'M GONNA DO IT RIGHT.
Tracks: / I'm gonna do it right / Danger zone / Footloose / I'm freee.
Single (7"): released on CBS, Sep'86 by CBS Records. Dist: CBS

MEET ME HALF WAY.
Single (7"): released on CBS, 30 May'87 by CBS Records. Dist: CBS

VOX HUMANA.
Album: released on CBS, Jun'85 by CBS Records. Dist: CBS Deleted '87.

Cassette: released on CBS, Jun'85 by CBS Records. Dist: CBS

WELCOME TO HEARTLIGHT.
Single (7"): released on CBS, Jan'83 by CBS Records. Dist: CBS

Logic, Laura
PEDIGREE CHARM.
Album: released on Rough Trade, Aug'84 by Rough Trade Records. Dist: Rough Trade Distribution, Cartel Distribution

WONDERFUL OFFER.
Single (7"): released on Rough Trade, Oct'81 by Rough Trade Records. Dist: Rough Trade Distribution, Cartel Distribution

Logic System
BE YOURSELF.
Single (7"): released on EMI, Mar'82 by EMI Records. Dist: EMI

Single (12"): released on EMI, Mar'82 by EMI Records. Dist: EMI

Picture disc single: released on EMI, Mar'82 by EMI Records. Dist: EMI

Logue, Christopher
RED BIRD EP.
Single (12"): released on Evergreen, May'84

Lol
KEEP IT COMING.
Single (12"): released on Diamond C, Sep'84 by Diamond C Records. Dist: Jetstar

ONE DRAW.
Single (12"): released on Echo, Mar'82 by Vista Sounds. Dist: Jazz Music

Lois Sagar

STEPPING OUT WITH LOIS SAGAR.
Tracks: / Wonderful one / Snowbird / I may be wrong / April in Portugal / Lady is a tramp / Tears / Mistakes / Vaya con dios / Brazil / Quando,quando / Manana / Only you / Affair to remember / Alone / Gettin' sentimental over you / Loveliest night of the year / Merry widow / Love will find a way / Ari verdeci roma / Strangers in the night / Bunch of Thyme / Hurt / Una Paloma Blanca / Y viva espana / Can't help falling in love / Are you lonesome tonight / Unless / Hello dolly / Who's sorry now / Ma,he's making eyes at me / Blue moon / Again / I'm in the mood for love / Wheels / Never on a Sunday / In a little spanish town / You're sixteen / Singin' the blues / Raining in my heart / Side by side / Until it's time for you to go.
Cassette: released on Audicord, '87 Dist: H.R. Taylor

Lok

FUNHOUSE.
Single (7"): released on Fetish, May'81 by Fetish Records. Dist: Cartel, Pinnacle

Lola

WAX THE VAN.
Tracks: / Wax the van / Wax the van (dub).
Single (7"): released on Syncopate, Mar'87 by EMI Records. Dist: EMI

Single (12"): released on Syncopate, Mar'87 by EMI Records. Dist: EMI

Lolita

LOLITA Read by James Mason (Nabokov, Vladimir).
Cassette: released on Caedmon(USA), '82 by Caedmon (USA) Records. Dist: Gower, Taylors, Discovery

Lolitas

LOLITAS.
Notes: French Pop/Punk.
Album: released on New Rose, Jun'87 Dist: Rough Trade, Cartel

Lollar, Bobby

BAD BAD BOY.
Single (7"): released on Benton, Oct'83 by Benton Records. Dist: Swift

Lollipops and...

LOLLIPOPS AND FISH FINGERS In aid of the N.S.P.C.C. (Various Artists).
Album: released on MFP, Oct'84 by EMI Records. Dist: EMI

Cassette: released on MFP, Oct'84 by EMI Records. Dist: EMI

Lollipop Shoppe

JUST COLOUR.
Album: released on Big Beat, Aug'85 by Ace Records. Dist: Projection, Pinnacle

Lomax, Alan

MUDERERS' HOME AND BLUES IN THE MISSISSIPPI NIGHT.
Album: released on Vogue Jazz, Jun'83

Lombard

WINGS OF A DOVE.
Album: released on Kix 4 U, Oct'86 by Kix 4u Records. Dist: Pinnacle

Lombardo, Guy

UNCOLLECTED, THE.
Album: released on Hindsight(UK), Apr'86 Dist: Jazz Music

UNCOLLECTED..., THE.
Album: released on Hindsight(UK), Jun'85 Dist: Jazz Music

Lomond Cornkisters

BY BONNIE LOCH LEVEN.
Album: released on Ross, '86 by Ross Records. Dist: Ross Distribution, Roots Distribution

Cassette: released on Ross, '86 by Ross Records. Dist: Ross Distribution, Roots Distribution

Lomond Folk

BLENDED SCOTCH.
Album: by Lismor Records. Dist: Lismor, Roots, Celtic Music

Londis, Dee

MY LOVERBOY.
Single (12"): released on Londis. Oct'85

London

DON'T CRY WOLF.
Album: released on Axis, May'87 by Red Rhino Records. Dist: Cartel

NON STOP ROCK.
Album: released on Road Runner, Nov'85

London Boot mix

LONDON BOOT MIX various artists (Various Artists).
Tracks: / London boot mix (27 minute megamix).
Single (12"): released on ZYX (Germany), Feb'86 by ZYX Records. Dist: Greyhound

London Brass

IMPRESSIONS OF BRASS.
Compact disc: released on Hallmark, '86 by Pickwick Records. Dist: Pickwick Distribution, PRT, Taylors

London Cast

JESUS CHRIST SUPERSTAR London Cast.
Tracks: / Heaven on their minds / Everything's alright / This Jesus must die / Hosanna / Simon Zealotes / I don't know how to love him / Gethsemane / Pilate's dream / King Herods song / Could we start again please / Trial before Pilate / Superstar / John 19;41.
Compact disc: released on MCA, Aug'85 by MCA Records. Dist: Polygram, MCA

London Chamber Orchestra

GOSPEL ACCORDING TO SAINT LUKE.
Tracks: / Gospel according to Saint Luke / Passover.
Notes: From the BBC TV series.
Single (7"): released on BBC, Mar'87 by BBC Records & Tapes. Dist: EMI, PRT,

London Community Gospel

FEEL THE SPIRIT.
Tracks: / All to Jesus / O happy day.
Notes: On this new album we find a collection of the Choir's own material plus other songs which they have featured in concerts around Europe. Once again their album catches the energy and excitement that is associated with Black Gospel music but, more importantly, expected whenever you listen to the London Community Gospel Choir.
Album: released on Myrrh, Sep'86 by Word Records. Dist: Word Distribution

Cassette: released on Myrrh, Sep'86 by Word Records. Dist: Word Distribution

SING THE GOSPEL GREATS.
Album: released on MFP, Oct'85 by EMI Records. Dist: EMI

Cassette: released on MFP, Oct'85 by EMI Records. Dist: EMI

London Concert Artists

SWEET & LOW.
Album: released on ASV, Jun'81 by Academy Sound & Vision Records. Dist: Pinnacle

London Concert Orchestra

MAGIC OF STRAUSS.
Cassette: released on Ditto Cassettes, Sep'83

London Conference

MEDICINE THE HUMAN ASPECT.
Cassette: released on Seminar Cassettes, Oct'81 by Seminar Cassettes. Dist: Davidson Distribution, Eastern Educational Products Distrib., Forlaget Systime Distribution, Laser Books Ltd Distribution, MacDougall Distribution, Talktapes Distribution, Watkins Books Ltd Distribution, Norton, Jeff Distribution

London Cowboys

LONG TIME COMING, A.
Album: released on Radioactive, Nov'86

STREET FULL OF SOUL.
Single (7"): released on Flicknife, Apr'83 by Flicknife Records. Dist: Spartan

London Emmanuel Choir

BE MY SPIRIT.
Album: by Pilgrim Records. Dist: Rough Trade, Cartel

BE STILL MY SOUL.
Album: by Pilgrim Records. Dist: Rough Trade, Cartel

CAROLLING WITH THE LONDON EMMANUEL CHOIR.
Album: by Pilgrim Records. Dist: Rough Trade, Cartel

CHOICE IS YOURS BBC TV Songs of Praise (London Emmanual Choir/Toad Choir).
Tracks: / Onward Christian soldiers / In Heavenly love abiding / Eternal Father, strong to save / How sweet the name of Jesus sounds / King of love my shepherd is, The / When I survey the wondrous cross / Abide with me / Day Thou gavest, Lord, is ended / Hark how the adoring hosts above / Dear Lord and father of mankind / Love is come again / Thine is the glory / It is a thing most wonderful / Christ is made the sure foundation / Come let us to the Lord our God / Ye gates lift up your heads on high.
Album: by BBC Records & Tapes. Dist: EMI, PRT, Pye

CHURCH'S ONE FOUNDATION, THE.
Album: by Pilgrim Records. Dist: Rough Trade, Cartel

GIVE GOD THE GLORY.
Album: by Pilgrim Records. Dist: Rough Trade, Cartel

GLORY TO THE LORD.
Album: by Pilgrim Records. Dist: Rough Trade, Cartel

HALLELUJAH JUBILEE.
Album: released on Word, Mar'78 by Word Records. Dist: Word Distribution, CBS

HE IS THE WAY.
Album: by Pilgrim Records. Dist: Rough Trade, Cartel

LET THE WHOLE WORLD KNOW.
Album: by Pilgrim Records. Dist: Rough Trade, Cartel

PRAISE & REJOICE.
Album: by Pilgrim Records. Dist: Rough Trade, Cartel

SINGS 20 BEST LOVED HYMNS.
Album: by Pilgrim Records. Dist: Rough Trade, Cartel

TELL THE GOOD NEWS.
Album: by Pilgrim Records. Dist: Rough Trade, Cartel

WHISPERING HOPE.
Album: by Pilgrim Records. Dist: Rough Trade, Cartel

London Festival Orchestra

20 GOLDEN PIECES OF JOHANN STRAUSS.
Album: released on Bulldog, Oct'85 by Bulldog Records. Dist: President Distribution, Spartan, Swift, Taylor, H.R.

Cassette: released on Bulldog, Oct'85 by Bulldog Records. Dist: President Distribution, Spartan, Swift, Taylor, H.R.

CLASSIC COLLECTION The Collection.
Compact disc: by Object Enterprises Ltd. Dist: Counterpoint Distribution

Days of future passed

London Film Orchestra

ANNA OF THE FIVE TOWNS.
Single (7"): released on Sierra, Jan'85 by Sierra Records. Dist: WEA

London, Frank Kwame

JACK THE LAD.
Tracks: / Jack the lad / Jack the lad (version).
Single (12"): released on Creole, Jul'87 by Creole Records. Dist: Rhino, PRT

JACK THE LAD (VOCAL MIX).
Tracks: / Jack the lad (vocal mix) / Jack the lad (badger mix) / Jack the lad (dub mix).
Single (12"): released on Nine O Nine, Jul'87 by Creole Records. Dist: Rhino, PRT

London Jewish Male Choir

HEAR OUR VOICE.
Cassette: released on B'nai B'rith, Aug'85

London, Jimmy

I'M YOUR PUPPET.
Single (12"): released on Dancebeat, Jan'84 by Dancebeat Records. Dist: Jetstar

LET'S KEEP IT THAT WAY.
Single (12"): released on GG'S, Jun'84 by GG'S Records. Dist: Jetstar

London, Julie

ABOUT THE BLUES.
Album: released on Capitol(USA), Mar'84 by Capitol (USA) Records. Dist: EMI

Cassette: released on Capitol(USA), Mar'84 by Capitol (USA) Records. Dist: EMI

ALL THROUGH THE NIGHT.
Tracks: / I've got you under my skin / You do something to me / Get out of town / All through the night / So in love / At long last love / My heart belongs to daddy / Ev'ry time we say goodbye / In the still of the night.
Album: released on Capitol T (USA), Nov'85 Dist: Conifer

AROUND MIDNIGHT.
Album: released on Liberty, Jul'85 by Liberty-United. Dist: EMI

Cassette: released on Liberty, Jul'85 by Liberty-United. Dist: EMI

BEST OF JULIE LONDON,(THE).
Album: released on Liberty, Apr'84 by Liberty-United. Dist: EMI

Cassette: released on Liberty, Apr'84 by Liberty-United. Dist: EMI

CALENDAR GIRL.
Album: released on Edsel, May'83 by Demon Records. Dist: Pinnacle, Jazz Music, Projection

CRY ME A RIVER.
Single (7"): released on Edsel, Feb'83 by Demon Records. Dist: Pinnacle, Jazz Music, Projection

Picture disc single: released on Edsel, Feb'83 by Demon Records. Dist: Pinnacle, Jazz Music, Projection

CRY ME A RIVER.
Single (7"): released on EMI (France), Apr'83 by EMI Records. Dist: Conifer

JULIE.
Album: released on Capitol(USA), Mar'84 by Capitol (USA) Records. Dist: EMI

Cassette: released on Capitol(USA), Mar'84 by Capitol (USA) Records. Dist: EMI

JULIE AT HOME.
Tracks: / You'd be so nice to come to / Lonesome road / They didn't believe me / By myself / Thrill is gone / You've changed / Goodbye / Sentimental journey / Give me the simple life / You stepped out of a dream / Let there be love / Everything happens to me.
Album: released on Liberty, Oct'86 by Liberty-United. Dist: EMI

Cassette: released on Liberty, Oct'86 by Liberty-United. Dist: EMI

JULIE IS HER NAME.
Album: released on Edsel, May'83 by Demon Records. Dist: Pinnacle, Jazz Music, Projection

Album: released on EMI (Holland), May'83 by EMI Records. Dist: Conifer

Album: released on Music For Pleasure, Oct'84

Cassette: released on Music For Pleasure, Oct'84

JULIE IS HER NAME VOLUME II.
Tracks: / Blue moon / What is this thing called / How has this been going on / Too good to be true / Too good to be true / Spring is here / Goody goody / One i love belongs to some body else, The / If i'm lucky / Hot toddy / Little white lies / I guess i'll have to change my plans / I got lost in his arms.
Notes: Julie here employs a small, intimate group comprising of piano, bass and guitar to bring a superb late night listening album of quality songs.
Album: released on Capitol, Dec'85 by Capitol Records. Dist: EMI

Cassette: released on Capitol, Dec'85 by Capitol Records. Dist: EMI

LONDON BY NIGHT.
Album: released on Capitol(USA), Mar'84 by Capitol (USA) Records. Dist: EMI

Cassette: released on Capitol(USA), Mar'84 by Capitol (USA) Records. Dist: EMI

LONELY GIRL.
Album: released on Capitol, Oct'84 by Capitol Records. Dist: EMI

Cassette: released on Capitol, Oct'84 by Capitol Records. Dist: EMI

MAKE LOVE TO ME.
Album: released on Capitol, Oct'84 by Capitol Records. Dist: EMI

Cassette: released on Capitol, Oct'84 by Capitol Records. Dist: EMI

SOPHISTICATED LADY.
Album: released on Liberty, May'85 by Liberty-United. Dist: EMI

Cassette: released on Liberty, May'85 by Liberty-United. Dist: EMI

SWING ME AN OLD SONG.
Album: released on Pathe MarconiFrance), Mar'85

Cassette: released on Pathe MarconiFrance), Mar'85

YOUR NUMBER PLEASE.
Album: released on Capitol, Oct'84 by Capitol Records. Dist: EMI

Cassette: released on Capitol, Oct'84 by Capitol Records. Dist: EMI

London, Laurie

HE'S GOT THE WHOLE WORLD IN HIS HANDS.
Album: released on Bear Family, Mar'84 by Bear Family Records. Dist: Rollercoaster Distribution, Swift

London Live

LONDON LIVE Effects of London.
Notes: An audio souvenire of London life and sounds. Robin Lumley & Peter Willsher take you across London by sound, visiting the many fascinating aspects of life in the capital. This album, recorded entirely on location, givesa picture of Londonlife in sound, and through the miracle of digital sound recording techniques, even the humble tube train comes tolife on your stereo system at home, where you can re-live your London experiences after a visit, or be whetted into coming to London if you've never been.
Cassette: released on ASV Digital, Jul'87

Album: released on ASV Digital, Jul'87

London Male Welsh Choir

GOD BLESS THE PRINCE OF WALES.
Single (7"): released on PVK, Aug'81

SONGS OF THE VALLEYS.
Album: released on K-Tel, Jul'81 by K-Tel Records. Dist: Record Merchandisers Distribution Taylors, Terry Blood Distribution, Wynd-Up Distribution, Relay Distribution, Pickwick Distribution, Solomon & Peres Distribution, Polygram

Cassette: released on K-Tel, Jul'81 by K-Tel Records. Dist: Record Merchandisers Distribution, Taylors, Terry Blood Distribution, Wynd-Up Distribution, Relay Distribution, Pickwick Distribution, Solomon & Peres Distribution, Polygram

London Oratory Junior

LAETARE JERUSALEM.
Album: released on Abbey, Apr'79 by Abbey. Dist: PRT, Taylors, Gamut

London Pavilion

LONDON PAVILION Various artists (Various Artists).
Tracks: / Curtain / Valleri / Ruling class, The / Love / Fire / Paper wraps rock / Dreams of living / Never underestimate the ignorance of the rich / If you're missing someone / Libera me / Montague Terrace (in blue) / At the end of the corridor / How blue sky was.
Notes: 1986 original sound recording made by Cherry Red Records Ltd.

LONDON PAVILLION El in 1986 (Various Artists).
Album: released on EL, Jan'87 by El Records. Dist: Rough Trade, Cartel, Pinnacle

Cassette: released on EL, Jan'87 by El Records. Dist: Rough Trade, Cartel, Pinnacle

London Philharmonic

CHARIOTS OF FIRE Film score by Vangelis: LPO plus synths..
Album: released on Hallmark, Jun'82 by Pickwick Records. Dist: Pickwick Distribution, PRT, Taylors

Cassette: released on Hallmark, Jun'82 by Pickwick Records. Dist: Pickwick Distribution, PRT, Taylors

CLASSICAL GOLD.
Album: released on Ronco, Sep'78

CLASSICAL THEMES.
Album: released on Nouveau, Jun'83

Cassette: released on Nouveau, Jun'83

CLASSIC CASE OF FUNK H.
Compact disc: released on Reflection, '86 Dist: Taylor, H.R., MSD

Album: released on Warwick, Oct'82 Dist: Multiple Sound Distributors

Cassette: released on Warwick, Oct'82 Dist: Multiple Sound Distributors

DIAMOND SYMPHONIES Hits of Neil Diamond.
Album: released on Ronco, Nov'80

Cassette: released on Ronco, Nov'80

Dragon dance

HYMNS TRIUMPHANT.
Album: released on Sparrow, May'85 by Word Records. Dist: Spartan

Cassette: released on Sparrow, May'85 by Word Records. Dist: Spartan

HYMNS TRIUMPHANT (London Phil. Orch./National Phil. Orch.).
Album: released on Warwick, Nov'84 Dist: Multiple Sound Distributors

Cassette: released on Warwick, Nov'84 Dist: Multiple Sound Distributors

LOVE DUET.
Tracks: / Love duet / Ambush.
Notes: LSO conducted by Carl Davis. Torvill & dean's 'Fire & Ice'.
Single (7"): released on First Night, Nov'86 by Safari Records. Dist: Pinnacle

TORVILL & DEAN'S FIRE AND ICE.
Album: released on First Night, Nov'86 by Safari Records. Dist: Pinnacle

Cassette: released on First Night, Nov'86 by Safari Records. Dist: Pinnacle

WILLOW PATTERN DANCE.
Single (7"): released on Chrysalis, Nov'84 by Chrysalis Records. Dist: CBS

London Piano Accordeon

ACCORDEON PARADE.
Album: released on EMI Retrospect, May'84 by EMI Records. Dist: EMI

Cassette: released on EMI Retrospect, May'84 by EMI Records. Dist: EMI

LONDON PIANO ACCORDION BAND, THE.
Tracks: / In a little gypsy tea room / Isle of Capri / Rain / Wanderer / Dreaming / Wagon wheels / Rose of Italy (Rose of Tralee) / Marina waltz / Happy-go-lucky you and broken-hearted me / You were so charming / Play to me gypsy / It was a tango / Lonely little lady / Jump on the wagon / Sweet dreams pretty lady / Sleepy time in sleepy hollow / My wishing song / Little valley in the mountains.
Album: released on Joy, Aug'87 by President Records. Dist: Jazz Music, Swift, President Distribution

London Posse

LONDON POSSE (London Posse with Sipho).
Tracks: / London Posse / My beatbox reggae style.
Single (12"): released on Biglife, Jul'87 by Biglife Records. Dist: Rough Trade, Cartel

London PX

ARNOLD LAYNE Flexi disc.
Single (7"): released on Terraplane, Dec'82

ORDERS/EVICTION.
Single (7"): released on London PX, Jul'81

London Ragtime Orchestra

LONDON RAGTIME ORCHESTRA London Ragtime Orchestra.
Album: released on Stomp Off, Jun'86 by Stomp Off Records. Dist: Jazz Music Distribution

London Saxophone Quartet

LONDON SAXOPHONE QUARTET IN DIGITAL.
Album: released on Polyphonic, Apr'84 by Polyphonic Records. Dist: Taylors

Cassette: released on Polyphonic, Apr'84 by Polyphonic Records. Dist: Taylors

London shows

LONDON SHOWS The war years (Various Artists).
Tracks: / Are you havin any fun? / Run rabbit run / How beautiful you are / My heart belongs to daddy / Crash, bang, I wanna go home / Have you met Miss Jones / Who's taking you home tonight / Start the day right / As round and round we go-Your company's requested / This can't be love / Let the people sing / You done some thing to my heart / They call me a dreamer / We'll go smiling along / Cheerio' / Let's be buddies / But in the morning no! / Lambeth walk / Me & my girl / Waiting for Sally / Wrap yourself in cotton wool / Tahiti rendezvous / It's a million to one / Smiths & the Jones, The / Yankee doodle came to town.
Notes: A definite "Hits Of The Blitz" compilation, featuring unforgettable songs from a host of London shows at theatres who kept the "Business As Usual" notices up while the bombs dropped all around. A bevy of top composers are represented including Irving Berlin, Cole Porter, Noel Gaye, Richard Rodgers and Lorenz HartAmong the contributing shows are "The Little Dog Laughed", "Black Velvet", "Haw Haw" and "Gangway"; a perfect way to lift the gloom by raising the blackout curtains...... Recorded in mono.
Double Album: released on Recollections, Sep'86

Double cassette: released on Recollections, Sep'86

LONDON SHOWS- THE WAR YEARS Various artists (Various Artists).
Tracks: / Are you havin any fun / F.D.R. Jones / Run rabbit run / How beautiful you are / My heart belongs to daddy / Crash, bang I wanna go home / Have you met miss Jones / Who's taking you home tonight / Start the day right / As round and round we go / Your company's requested / This can't be love / Let the people sing / You done something to my heart / They call me a dreamer / We'll go smiling along / Cheerio / Let's be buddies / But in the morning no / It's d'lovely / Underneath the arches / Lambeth walk / Me & my girl / Waiting for Sally / Wrap yourself in cotton wool / Tahiti rendezvous / Swing bugler / There's something about that town / It's a million to one / Smiths and Jones (The) / Yankee doodle came to London town.
Album: released on Recollections, Sep'86

Cassette: released on Recollections, Sep'86

London Studio Symphony

NORTH BY NORTHWEST Digital filmscore series vol.1.
Album: released on Kanchana, Sep'80 Dist: Harmonia Mundi Distributors

WESTERN WORLD OF DIMITRI TIOMKIN.
Album: released on Unicorn Kanchana, Aug'81 by Unicorn Records Ltd. Dist: Harmonia Mundi (UK) Limited Distr.

London Symphony Orchestra

BAKER STREET.
Single (7"): released on Creole, Mar'81 by Creole Records. Dist: Rhino, PRT

BEST OF CLASSIC ROCK.
Album: released on K-Tel, Nov'82 by K-Tel Records. Dist: Record Merchandisers Distribution, Taylors, Terry Blood Distribution, Wynd-Up Distribution, Relay Distribution, Pickwick Distribution, Solomon & Peres Distribution, Polygram

Cassette: released on K-Tel, Nov'82 by K-Tel Records. Dist: Record Merchandisers Distribution, Taylors, Terry Blood Distribution, Wynd-Up Distribution, Relay Distribution, Pickwick Distribution, Solomon & Peres Distribution, Polygram

CLASSIC ROCK.
Album: released on Telstar/Telescope, Mar'87

Cassette: released on Telstar/Telescope, Mar'87

Compact disc: by K-Tel Records. Dist: Record Merchandisers Distribution, Taylors, Terry Blood Distribution, Wynd-Up Distribution, Relay Distribution, Pickwick Distribution, Solomon & Peres Distribution, Polygram

Album: released on K-Tel, Jul'78 by K-Tel Records. Dist: Record Merchandisers Distribution, Taylors, Terry Blood Distribution, Wynd-Up Distribution, Relay Distribution, Pickwick Distribution, Solomon & Peres Distribution, Polygram

Cassette: released on K-Tel, Oct'77 by K-Tel Records. Dist: Record Merchandisers Distribution, Taylors, Terry Blood Distribution, Wynd-Up Distribution, Relay Distribution, Pickwick Distribution, Solomon & Peres Distribution, Polygram

CLASSIC ROCK 2 The Second Movement.
Album: released on Telstar/Telescope, Mar'87

Cassette: released on Telstar/Telescope, Mar'87

CLASSIC ROCK 3 Rhapsody in black.
Album: released on Telstar/Telescope, Mar'87

Cassette: released on Telstar/Telescope, Mar'87

CLASSIC ROCK 4 Rock classics.
Album: released on Telstar/Telescope, Mar'87

Cassette: released on Telstar/Telescope, Mar'87

CLASSIC ROCK 5 Rock Symphonies.
Album: released on Telstar/Telescope, Mar'87

Cassette: released on Telstar/Telescope, Mar'87

CLASSIC ROCK CLASSICS.
Single (7"): released on Towerbell, Oct'82 by Towerbell Records. Dist: EMI

Single (12"): released on Towerbell, Oct'82 by Towerbell Records. Dist: EMI

CLASSIC ROCK SECOND MOVEMENT.
Cassette: released on K-Tel, Jan'79 by K-Tel Records. Dist: Record Merchandisers Distribution, Taylors, Terry Blood Distribution, Wynd-Up Distribution, Relay Distribution, Pickwick Distribution, Solomon & Peres Distribution, Polygram

E.T./EARTHBOUND.
Single (7"): released on MFP, Nov'82 by EMI Records. Dist: EMI

E.T./ESCORT THEME.
Single (7"): released on Towerbell, Dec'82 by Towerbell Records. Dist: EMI

FANTASY ALBUM.
Album: released on BBC, Nov'84 by BBC Records & Tapes. Dist: EMI, PRT, Pye

Cassette: released on BBC, Nov'84 by BBC Records & Tapes. Dist: EMI, PRT, Pye

FANTASY MOVIE THEMES.
Notes: With Roy Budd. full orchestral scores of 'Raiders of the lost ark', Indiana jones, Wild Geese, final conflict etc.
Compact disc: released on Hermes, Jan'86 by Nimbus Records. Dist: Target

FURTHER EXPERIMENTS WITH MICE.
Tracks: / Further experiments with mice / Decline and fall of a bridge.
Notes: London Symphony Orchestra Narrator John Dankworth.
Single (7"): released on Sepia, Jul'86 by Sepia Records. Dist: PRT

GLORIA/SHE'S OUT OF MY LIFE.
Single (7"): released on K-Tel, Nov'83 by K-Tel Records. Dist: Record Merchandisers Distribution, Taylors, Terry Blood Distribution, Wynd-Up Distribution, Relay Distribution, Pickwick Distribution, Solomon & Peres Distribution, Polygram

LSO BEETHOVEN COLLECTION.
Cassette: released on Pickwick, Dec'79 by Pickwick Records. Dist: Pickwick Distribution, Prism Leisure Distribution, Lugtons

MUSICAL FANTASY.
Album: released on Starblend, '83 by Starblend Records. Dist: PRT Distribution

Album: released on Starblend, Nov'83 by Starblend Records. Dist: PRT Distribution

Cassette: released on Starblend, Nov'83 by Starblend Records. Dist: PRT Distribution

Compact disc: released on Starblend, Nov'83 by Starblend Records. Dist: PRT Distribution

MUSIC FOR ROYAL OCCASIONS Conducted by Sir Alexander Gibson.
Album: released on Pickwick, Jul'81 by Pickwick Records. Dist: Pickwick Distribution, Prism Leisure Distribution, Lugtons

Cassette: released on Pickwick, Jul'81 by Pickwick Records. Dist: Pickwick Distribution, Prism Leisure Distribution, Lugtons

MUSIC YOU HAVE LOVED.
Compact disc: released on Pickwick, Oct'86 by Pickwick Records. Dist: Pickwick Distribution, Prism Leisure Distribution, Lugtons

Album: released on Spot, Feb'83 by Pickwick Records. Dist: H.R. Taylor, Lugtons

Cassette: released on Spot, Feb'83 by Pickwick Records. Dist: H.R. Taylor, Lugtons

Album: released on Spot, Feb'83 by Pickwick Records. Dist: H.R. Taylor, Lugtons

Cassette: released on Spot, Feb'83 by Pickwick Records. Dist: H.R. Taylor, Lugtons

Cassette: released on Pickwick, Feb'80 by Pickwick Records. Dist: Pickwick Distribution, Prism Leisure Distribution, Lugtons

NEW ROCK CLASSICS.
Album: released on Teldec (Germany), Dec'85 by Import Records. Dist: IMS Distribution, Polygram Distribution

Cassette: released on Teldec (Germany), Dec'85 by Import Records. Dist: IMS Distribution, Polygram Distribution

POWER OF CLASSIC ROCK.
Tracks: / Two Tribes-Relax / I want to know what love is / Drive / Purple Rain / Time after time / Born in the USA-Dancing in the dark / Power of love / Thriller / Total eclipse of the heart / Hello / Modern Girl.
Compact disc: released on Portrait, Jan'86 by CBS Records. Dist: CBS

Album: released on Portrait, Nov'85 by CBS Records. Dist: CBS

Cassette: released on Portrait, Nov'85 by CBS Records. Dist: CBS

ROCK CLASSICS.
Album: released on K-Tel, Jun'81 by K-Tel Records. Dist: Record Merchandisers Distribution, Taylors, Terry Blood Distribution, Wynd-Up Distribution, Relay Distribution, Pickwick Distribution, Solomon & Peres Distribution, Polygram

Cassette: released on K-Tel, Jun'81 by K-Tel Records. Dist: Record Merchandisers Distribution, Taylors, Terry Blood Distribution, Wynd-Up Distribution, Relay Distribution, Pickwick Distribution, Solomon & Peres Distribution, Polygram

ROCK SYMPHONIES.
Album: released on K-Tel, Aug'83 by K-Tel Records. Dist: Record Merchandisers Distribution, Taylors, Terry Blood Distribution, Wynd-Up Distribution, Relay Distribution, Pickwick Distribution, Solomon & Peres Distribution, Polygram

Cassette: released on K-Tel, Aug'83 by K-Tel Records. Dist: Record Merchandisers Distribution, Taylors, Terry Blood Distribution, Wynd-Up Distribution, Relay Distribution, Pickwick Dis-

tribution, Solomon & Peres Distribution, Polygram

SILK ROAD SUITE.
Album: released on Kuckuck (Germany), May'84

SPACE MOVIE THEMES.
Notes: Full orchestral scores of 'star Wars', the Empire strikes back', 'return of theJedi', 'superman' etc.
Compact disc: released on Hermes, Jan'86 by Nimbus Records. Dist: Target

STAR WARS.
Album: released on RSO, Sep'82
Cassette: released on RSO, Sep'82

STAR WARS (ORIGINAL SOUND-TRACK).
Cassette: released on 20th Century, Nov'79 Dist: RCA, IMS-Polygram

STRAUSS FAMILY.
Album: released on Polydor, '74 by Polydor Records. Dist: Polygram, Polydor

SWITCHED ON SULLIVAN.
Single (7"): released on Lancaster, Oct'82 by Lancaster Records. Dist: PRT

TESS Music by Philippe Sarde.
Album: released on MCA, May'81 by MCA Records. Dist: Polygram, MCA

London Underground
STRANGE/WHY DO FAT MAN HAVE.
Single 10": released on On-U-Sound, Apr'82 Dist: Rough Trade Distribution, Lightning

TRAIN OF THOUGHT.
Single (7"): released on Situation 2, Oct'81 Dist: Cartel, Pinnacle

WATCHING WEST INDIANS IN THE COLD.
Single 10": released on On-U-Sound, Mar'82 Dist: Rough Trade Distribution, Lightning

London Welsh Male...
SING THE SONGS OF OUR HOMELAND (see Welsh Guards) (London Welsh Male Voice Choir / Welsh Guards).
Tracks: March of the men of Harlech / Speed your journey / Deliah / Welsh rhapsody / Roman war song (A) / Annie's song / Huntsmen's chorus / Mae henwlad fy nhadau / Llanfair / Impossible dream (The) / Gwahoddiad / Arms park / Battle hymn of the republic / If I fell / Mor fawr wyt ti.
Notes: The very first time that both these London based 'bodies' have recorded together. It is very rare these days to find a new album of Military Band and Male Voice Choir together. The London Welsh Male Choir have previously had success with their album 'Songs From The Valleys' (out on K-Tel).

Lone Groover
JOHNNY MAKE YOU BAD SO.
Single (12"): released on Greensleeves, Feb'82 by Greensleeves Records. Dist: BMG, Jetstar, Spartan

LONE GROOVER (4 TRACK EP).
Single (7"): released on Charly, Jan'82 by Charly Records. Dist: Charly, Cadillac

Lone Justice
I FOUND LOVE.
Tracks: East of Eden / After the Flood / Ways to be wicked / Don't toss us away / Working late / Pass it on / Wait 'til we get home / Soap, soup and salvation / You are the light / Sweet, sweet baby(I'm falling).
Single (7"): released on Geffen, Feb'87 by Geffen Records. Dist: WEA, CBS

Double-pack single: released on Geffen, Feb'87 by Geffen Records. Dist: WEA, CBS

LONE JUSTICE.
Tracks: I found love / Shelter / Reflected / Beacon / Wheels / Belfry / Dreams come true / Gift, The / Inspiration / Dixie storms.
Album: released on Geffen, Apr'86 by Geffen Records. Dist: WEA, CBS

Cassette: released on Geffen, Apr'86 by Geffen Records. Dist: WEA, CBS

SHELTER.
Tracks: I found love / Shelter / Reflected / Beacon / Wheels / Belfry / Dreams come true / Gift, The / Inspiration / Dixie storms.
Album: released on Geffen, Nov'86 by Geffen Records. Dist: WEA, CBS

Cassette: released on Geffen, Nov'86 by Geffen Records. Dist: WEA, CBS

Compact disc: released on Geffen, Nov'86 by Geffen Records. Dist: WEA, CBS

SHELTER (SINGLE).
Tracks: Shelter / Can't look back / Belfry *

Single (7"): released on Geffen, Oct'86 by Geffen Records. Dist: WEA, CBS

Single (12"): released on Geffen, Oct'86 by Geffen Records. Dist: WEA, CBS

Lonely is an eyesore
LONELY IS AN EYESORE (Various Artists).
Album: released on 4AD, Jun'87 by 4AD Records. Dist: Rough Trade

Cassette: released on 4AD, Jun'87 by 4AD Records. Dist: Rough Trade

Compact disc: released on 4AD, Jun'87 by 4AD Records. Dist: Rough Trade

Lone Ranger
4 SEASON LOVER.
Single (12"): released on Silver Bullet, Feb'85 by Silver Bullet Records. Dist: Jetstar

COCONUT WOMAN/RUB-A-DUB TIME.
Single (12"): released on Claire, Jan'83 by Claire Records. Dist: Jetstar

LEARN TO DRIVE.
Album: released on Bebo's Music, Jul'85

ON THE OTHER SIDE OF DUB.
Album: released on Studio One, Sep'84 Dist: Jetstar

ROSEMARIE/YOU MAKE YOUR MISTAKES.
Single (7"): released on Bridgehouse, Nov'81 Dist: Pinnacle

SILENT FASHION/LOVER'S ROCK (PUDDY ROOTS).
Single (12"): released on Technics, Oct'83 by Technics Records. Dist: Jetstar Distribution

Lonesome Pine Fiddlers
14 MOUNTAIN SONGS.
Album: released on Starday, Apr'87

Cassette: released on Starday, Apr'87

Lonesome sundown
BEEN GONE TOO LONG.
Album: released on Sonet, Apr'80 by Sonet Records. Dist: PRT

LONESOME WHISTLER.
Tracks: Don't say a word / I stood by / California blues / Lonely lonely me / Give it up / Gonna stick to you baby / Lonesome whistler / Leave my money / My home is a prison / Lost without love / Mojo man / Don't go.
Album: released on Flyright, Oct'86 by Flyright Records. Dist: Krazy Kat, Swift, Jazz Music

Lonesome Tone
MUM, DAD, LOVE, HATE AND ELVIS.
Single (7"): released on Stiff, Oct'80 by Stiff Records. Dist: EMI, Record Services Distribution (Ireland)

Lonewolf
NOBODY'S MOVE.
Single (12"): released on Neat, Jan'85 by Neat Records. Dist: Pinnacle, Neat

Lone Wolf McQuade
LONE WOLF MCQUADE Original film soundtrack (De Masi, Francesco).
Album: released on TER, Nov'83 Dist: Pinnacle

Loney, Roy
FAST AND LOOSE.
Album: released on Lolita, Jun'84 by Lolita Records. Dist: Rough Trade, Cartel

LANA LEE/MAGDALENA/GOODNIGHT.
Single (7"): released on Rockhouse, Apr'83 by Rockhouse Records. Dist: Swift Distribution, Charly Distribution

LIVE.
Album: released on Lolita, Jun'84 by Lolita Records. Dist: Rough Trade, Cartel

OUT AFTER DARK.
Album: released on Solid Smoke, Sep'79 Dist: Projection, Swift

ROCK AND ROLL DANCE PARTY.
Album: released on Rockhouse(USA), Nov'82

Long, Annette
STAY WITH ME.
Album: released on Grosvenor, Jun'84 by Grosvenor Records. Dist: Taylors

Longfellow, Baron
AMOUR/CHICAGO'S QUEEN.
Single (7"): released on Polydor, Aug'81 by

Polydor Records. Dist: Polygram, Polydor

Long Good Friday
LONG GOOD FRIDAY Original soundtrack (Monkman, Francis).
Album: released on C.E.S., Sep'84 by C.E.S.Records. Dist: Spartan

Long Hello
LONG HELLO 4 Featuring Guy Evans.
Album: released on Shanghai, '82

VOLUME 1.
Album: released on Butt, Mar'82 by Butt Records. Dist: Counterpoint

VOLUME 3 (DAVID JACKSON).
Album: released on Butt, Mar'82 by Butt Records. Dist: Counterpoint

VOLUME TWO.
Album: released on Upper Class, Aug'86 by Chinless Productions. Dist: Spartan, Music Galore

Long Honeymoon
AMAZOON/AMAZOON (U RAP IT).
Single (7"): released on A&M, Apr'83 by A&M Records. Dist: Polygram

Single (12"): released on A&M, Apr'83 by A&M Records. Dist: Polygram

Longmire, Wilbert
BLACK IS THE COLOUR.
Single (12"): released on Streetwave, May'86 by Streetwave Records. Dist: PRT Distribution

Longpig
OF LOVE AND ADDICTION.
Album: released on Anagram, Mar'84 by Cherry Red Records. Dist: Pinnacle

WHY DO PEOPLE FIND EACH OTHER STRANGE.
Single (7"): released on Anagram, Mar'84 by Cherry Red Records. Dist: Pinnacle

Single (12"): released on Anagram, Mar'84 by Cherry Red Records. Dist: Pinnacle

Long Pursuit
LONG PURSUIT, THE Cleary, Jon (Dunbavan, Alan).
Special: released on Soundings, Mar'85 Dist: Soundings

Long Ryders
10-5-60.
Album: released on PVC, Nov'85 Dist: Pacific

Compact disc: released on Zippo, Aug'87

I HAD A DREAM.
Single (7"): released on Zippo, Mar'85

I WANT YOU BAD.
Tracks: I want you bad / Ring bells / State of my union".
Single (7"): released on Island, Jun'87 by Island Records. Dist: Polygram

Single (12"): released on Island, Jun'87 by Island Records. Dist: Polygram

LOOKING FOR LEWIS AND CLARKE.
Single (7"): released on Island, Sep'85 by Island Records. Dist: Polygram

Single 10": released on Island, Oct'85 by Island Records. Dist: Polygram

NATIVE SONS.
Album: released on Zippo, Oct'84

STATE OF OUR UNION.
Cassette: released on Island, Nov'85 by Island Records. Dist: Polygram

TWO FISTED TALES.
Tracks: Gunslinger man / I want you bad / Stitch in time, A / Light gets in the way / Prairie fire / Baby's in toyland / Long short story / Man of misery / Harriet Tubman's gonna carry me home / For the rest of my days / Spectacular fall.
Album: released on Island, Jun'87 by Island Records. Dist: Polygram

Cassette: released on Island, Jun'87 by Island Records. Dist: Polygram

Longsy D & Cutmaster MC
HIP HOP REGGAE.
Single (12"): released on VV Big, Aug'87 Dist: Jetstar

Long Tall Shorty
ON THE STREETS AGAIN.
Single (7"): released on Diamond, Jan'85 by Revolver Records. Dist: Cartel

WHAT'S GOING ON.
Single (7"): released on Diamond, May'86 by Revolver Records. Dist: Cartel

WIN OR LOSE/AIN'T DONE WRONG.
Single (7"): released on Ramkup, Nov'81 by Pinnacle

Long Tall Texans
SAINTS & SINNERS.
Single (12"): released on Razor, 13 Jun'87 by Razor. Dist: Pinnacle

SODBUSTERS.
Album: released on Razor, Jan'87 by Razor. Dist: Pinnacle

Longthorne, Joe
SINGER (THE).
Album: released on Great Britain, Jul'86 Dist: Taylors

Cassette: released on Great Britain, Jul'86 Dist: Taylors

Lonious Monster, The
NEXT SATURDAY AFTERNOON.
Album: released on Relativity (USA), Aug'87 Dist: Pinnacle

Look
DRUMMING UP LOVE.
Single (7"): released on Towerbell, Oct'83 by Towerbell Records. Dist: EMI

Look Back in Anger
CAPRICE.
Album: released on Criminal Damage, Jul'84 by Criminal Damage Records. Dist: Backs, Cartel

CAPRICE/MANNEQUIN.
Single (7"): released on Look Back in Anger, Aug'82 Dist: Menace Breaker Distributors

FLOWERS/INAMORTA/TORMENT.
Single (12"): released on Criminal Damage, Jan'84 by Criminal Damage Records. Dist: Backs, Cartel

Look before you leap
LOOK BEFORE YOU LEAP Original cast (Various Artists).
Single (7"): released on Royal, May'84 by Royal Records. Dist: Stage One Distribu'on

Look Of Love
LOOK OF LOVE (Various Artists).
Album: released on EMI, Nov'80 by EMI Records. Dist: EMI

Loons
SPLIT KNEE LOONS.
Single (7"): released on Avatar, Jul'81 by Avatar Communications. Dist: CBS

Loop
SIXTEEN DREAMS.
Single (12"): released on Head, Jan'87 by Head Records. Dist: Revolver, Cartel

SPINNING PARTS Parts 1 + 2.
Picture disc single: released on Head, Jan'87 by Head Records. Dist: Revolver, Cartel

Single (12"): released on Head, Jun'87 by Head Records. Dist: Revolver, Cartel

Loose Ends
BACKSHEESH MIXES, THE.
Tracks: Gonna make you mine West side mix) / choose me (Dave the blade mix) / Silent talking (album mix) / Nights of pleasure (7" mix) / Let's rock (7" remix).
Single (12"): released on Virgin, Dec'86 by Virgin Records. Dist: EMI, Virgin Distribution

HANGING ON A STRING.
Single (7"): released on Virgin, Feb'85 by Virgin Records. Dist: EMI, Virgin Distribution

Single (12"): released on Virgin, Feb'85 by Virgin Records. Dist: EMI, Virgin Distribution

LITTLE SPICE, A.
Tracks: Tell me what you want / Feels so right now / Let's rock so much love / Dial 999 / Music makes me higher / Choose me / Little spice, A
Album: released on Virgin, Apr'86 by Virgin Records. Dist: EMI, Virgin Distribution

Cassette: released on Virgin, Apr'86 by Virgin Records. Dist: EMI, Virgin Distribution

LOOSE ENDS.
Notes: One of Britain's top soul/dance groups with five tracks covering their career to date, including hits like 'HANGING ON A STRING' and new single 'STAY A WHILE CHILD', 1986 production.

Video-cassette (VHS): released on Virgin Music Video, Sep'86 by Virgin Records. Dist: EMI

LOOSE ENDS-ANTHOLOGY (Various Artists).
Album: released on Union Pacific, Sep'82 Dist: Swift, Jazz Music, Red Lightnin' Distribution

MAGIC TOUCH.
Single (7"): released on Virgin, Apr'85 by Virgin Records. Dist: EMI, Virgin Distribution

NIGHTS OF PLEASURE.
Tracks: / Night of pleasure / Let's rock.
Single (7"): released on Virgin, Nov'86 by Virgin Records. Dist: EMI, Virgin Distribution

Single (12"): released on Virgin, Nov'86 by Virgin Records. Dist: EMI, Virgin Distribution

OHH, YOU MAKE ME FEEL.
Single (7"): released on Virgin, Aug'87 by Virgin Records. Dist: EMI, Virgin Distribution

Single (12"): released on Virgin, Aug'87 by Virgin Records. Dist: EMI, Virgin Distribution

SLOW DOWN.
Tracks: / Slow down / Slow down (instrumental) / Gonna make you mine / Gonna make you mine / Slowdown.
Notes: *= extra tracks included in Double pack.
Single (7"): released on Virgin, Sep'86 by Virgin Records. Dist: EMI, Virgin Distribution

Single (12"): released on Virgin, Sep'86 by Virgin Records. Dist: EMI, Virgin Distribution

SO WHERE ARE YOU.
Compact disc: by Virgin Records. Dist: EMI, Virgin Distribution

Album: released on Virgin, Mar'85 by Virgin Records. Dist: EMI, Virgin Distribution

Cassette: released on Virgin, Mar'85 by Virgin Records. Dist: EMI, Virgin Distribution

STAY A LITTLE WHILE CHILD.
Tracks: / Stay a little while child / Gonna make you mine.
Single (7"): released on Virgin, May'86 by Virgin Records. Dist: EMI, Virgin Distribution

Single (12"): released on Virgin, May'86 by Virgin Records. Dist: EMI, Virgin Distribution

ZAGORA.
Tracks: / Stay a little while child / Be thankful (Mama's song) / Slow down / Ooh, you make me feel / Just a minute / Who are you? / I can't wait / Nights of pleasure / Let's get back to love / Rainbow/Take the 'A' train.
Album: released on Virgin, Jun'86 by Virgin Records. Dist: EMI, Virgin Distribution

Cassette: released on Virgin, Jun'86 by Virgin Records. Dist: EMI, Virgin Distribution

Compact disc: released on Virgin, Jun'86 by Virgin Records. Dist: EMI, Virgin Distribution

Loose Lips

MY PAST LIFE HAS GONE Featuring Helen Watson.
Album: released on Appaloosa, May'81 Dist: Roots, Folksound, JSU, Projection, Celtic Music, Chris Wellard

Loose Talk

DAN DARE/HOME PLANET.
Single (7"): released on Jet, Jul'82 by Jet Records. Dist: CBS

JUDGE DREAD/YOU YOU YOU.
Single (7"): released on Jet, Jan'83 by Jet Records. Dist: CBS

Loose Tubes

DELIGHTFUL PRECIPICE.
Tracks: / Sad Afrika / Delightful precipice / Shelley / Sosbun Brakk / Sunny / Hermeto's giant breakfast / Would I were.
Notes: Superb new album from Loose Tubes. "Delightful Precipice" was recorded at Angel Studios and goes a long way in capturing the spirit and energy of a live performance. The band are on tour throughout the UK during October.
Album: released on Loose Tubes, Oct'86 Dist: IMS-Polygram

Cassette: released on Loose Tubes, Oct'86 Dist: IMS-Polygram

LOOSE TUBES.
Tracks: / Eden Express / Rowing boat delineation egg / Descarge / Descarge occuriencia / Yellow hill / Mister Zee / Arriving.
Notes: Debut album from Loose Tubes - the dynamic 21 piece band currently taking the UK by storm. The guys are all dedicated musicians involvd in a variety of projects; from session work with major recording artists to work with their individual bands. Together they pool their diverse resources and make Loose Tubes a highly original statement.
Album: released on Loose Tubes, Feb'86 Dist: IMS-Polygram

Looters

CROSS THE BORDER (EP).
Tracks: / Cross the border / Streets are callin' (the) / Rise up / Being human.
Single (12"): released on Alternative Tentacles, Nov'86 by Alternative Tentacles Records. Dist: Rough Trade, Pinnacle

LOOTERS.
Tracks: / Looters.
Single (12"): released on Alternative Tentacles, Sep'86 by Alternative Tentacles Records. Dist: Rough Trade, Pinnacle

Lopez, Trini

20 GREATEST HITS.
Album: released on Masters (Holland), Jan'87 Cat. no: **MA 10685**
Cassette: released on Masters (Holland), Jan'87

GOODIES.
Notes: Incl. If Ihad a hammer, La Bamba, This land is your land, America.
Compact disc: released on Bellaphon, '86 by Bellaphon Records. Dist: IMS-Polygram

GREATEST HITS:TRINI LOPEZ.
Compact disc: released on Delta, '86 by Delta Records. Dist: Target

Compact disc: released on Delta, Feb'86 by Delta Records. Dist: Target

Compact disc: released on MCS Look Back, Jul'87

GREATEST HITS: TRINI LOPEZ.
Cassette: released on K-Tel Goldmasters, Aug'84 by K-Tel Records. Dist: K-Tel

HIS TOP HITS.
Cassette: released on Timeless Treasures, Jul'86 Dist: Counterpoint Distribution

IF I HAD A HAMMER/LA BAMBA.
Single (7"): released on Reprise, Jul'81 by WEA Records. Dist: WEA

IF I HAD A HAMMER/LA BAMBA (OLD GOLD).
Single (7"): released on Old Gold, Jul'82 by Old Gold Records. Dist: Lightning, Jazz Music, Spartan, Counterpoint

TRINI TRAX.
Single (7"): released on RCA, Nov'81 by RCA Records. Dist: RCA, Roots, Swift, Wellard, Chris, I & B, Solomon & Peres Distribution

Single (12"): released on RCA, Nov'81 by RCA Records. Dist: RCA, Roots, Swift, Wellard, Chris, I & B, Solomon & Peres Distribution

VERY BEST OF TRINI LOPEZ.
Album: released on K-Tel (Era), Jun'83 by K-Tel Records. Dist: K-Tel

Cassette: released on K-Tel (Era), Jun'83 by K-Tel Records. Dist: K-Tel

L'Orange mechanique

SYMPHONY.
Tracks: / Symphony.
Single (7"): released on Art Pop, Apr'86 by Art Pop Records. Dist: Rough Trade, Cartel, Pinnacle

Lorbass

WIE ES UNS GEFALLT.
Album: released on Burlington, Nov'81 by Plant Life Records. Dist: Jazz Music, Celtic Music, Clyde Factors Distributors, I.R.S., Projection, Wellard, Chris, Roots

WOHL BEKOMM'S.
Album: released on Burlington, Nov'81 by Plant Life Records. Dist: Jazz Music, Celtic Music, Clyde Factors Distributors, I.R.S., Projection, Wellard, Chris, Roots

Lorber, Jeff

FACTS OF LOVE.
Tracks: / Facts of love / Sand castles / Every woman needs.
Single (7"): released on Club, Mar'87 by Phonogram Records. Dist: Polygram

Single (12"): released on Club, Mar'87 by Phonogram Records. Dist: Polygram

Double-pack single: released on Club, Mar'87 by Phonogram Records. Dist: Polygram

PRIVATE PASSION.
Tracks: / Facts of love / True confessions / Jamaica / Back in love / Kristen / private passion / Sand castles / Keep on lovin' her / Midnight snack.
Notes: The new album from Jeff lorber features ex-Tower of power vocalist Michael Jeffries and newcomer karyn White on vocals, plus jeff's characteristic Jazz\funk keyboard work. Includes the single "Facts of love'.
Album: released on Club, Nov'86 by Phonogram Records. Dist: Polygram

Cassette: released on Club, Nov'86 by Phonogram Records. Dist: Polygram

SAND CASTLES.
Tracks: / Sand castles.
Single (7"): by Phonogram Records. Dist: Polygram

Single (12"): released on Club, Mar'87 by Phonogram Records. Dist: Polygram

STEP BY STEP.
Compact disc: by Phonogram Records. Dist: Polygram

Lorber, Larry

SHIVERS UP MY SPINE.
Single (7"): released on Numa, Oct'84 by Numa Records. Dist: PRT Distribution

Single (12"): released on Numa, Oct'84 by Numa Records. Dist: PRT Distribution

L'orchestre electronique

SOUND WAVES.
Compact disc: released on Nouveau Music, '86 Dist: PRT Distribution

Album: released on Nouveau Music, Jan'83 Dist: PRT Distribution

Cassette: released on Nouveau Music, Jan'83 Dist: PRT Distribution

Lord Arthur Saville's...

LOST HORIZON read by Michael Elder.
Cassette: released on Colophone, Jun'81 by Audio-Visual Library Services. Dist: Audio-Visual Library Services

OSCAR WILDE.
Cassette: released on Talking Tape Company, Jan'84 by Talking Tape Company Records.

Lord Buckley

BAD RAPPING.
Album: released on Demon, Jul'86 by Demon Records. Dist: Pinnacle

BLOWING HIS MIND.
Album: released on Demon, May'85 by Demon Records. Dist: Pinnacle

IN CONCERT.
Album: released on Demon Verbals, Sep'85 by Demon Records. Dist: Demon Records, Pinnacle

Lord Cloak Inner Force

FAT WOMAN.
Single (12"): released on Voida, Mar'85 by Voida Records. Dist: Jetstar

Lord C.M

C.M LORD.
Album: released on RCA, Mar'82 by RCA Records. Dist: RCA, Roots, Swift, Wellard, Chris, I & B, Solomon & Peres Distribution

Lord Diamond

MISS LORNA.
Single (7"): released on Jama, Sep'84 by Jama Records.

Single (12"): released on Jama, Sep'84 by Jama Records.

STOP KNOCKING ON WOOD.
Tracks: / Stop knocking on wood / Party people.
Single (12"): released on Jazz Star, Aug'86 Dist: Jetstar

Lord Emsworth

LORD EMSWORTH & THE GIRLFRIEND P.G. Wodehouse (Lord Emsworth & the Girlfriend).
Cassette: released on Talking Tape Company, '84 by Talking Tape Company Records.

Lord Eric

GETTIN SENTIMENTAL (ORGAN).
Album: released on Acorn, Dec'77 Dist: Folksound, Jazz Music

Lord God made...

LORD GOD MADE THEM ALL, THE (JAMES HERRIOT) Read by Christopher Timothy.
Cassette: released on Listen For Pleasure, Sep'82 by MFP Records. Dist: EMI

Lord Jon

COUNTRY DIARY OF AN EDWARDIAN LADY.
Album: released on Safari, Mar'84 by Safari Records. Dist: Pinnacle

Cassette: released on Safari, Mar'84 by Safari Records. Dist: Pinnacle

Single (7"): released on Safari, Mar'84 by Safari Records. Dist: Pinnacle

GEMINI SUITE.
Album: released on EMI (Germany), Jun'83 by EMI Records. Dist: Conifer

GEMINI SUITE THE.
Album: released on Safari, Nov'84 by Safari Records. Dist: Pinnacle

Cassette: released on Safari, Nov'84 by Safari Records. Dist: Pinnacle

Lord Laro

ROCKIN' SOCA.
Single (12"): released on Revue, Jan'85 by Revue Records. Dist: Creole

Lord & Mary Ann

LORD & MARY ANN By Catherine Cookson read by Susan Jameson.
Cassette: released on Chivers Audio Books, '81 by Chivers Sound & Vision. Dist: Chivers Sound & Vision

Lord Mountdrago

LORD MOUNTDRAGO Maugham, Somerset (Burden, Hugh).
Cassette: released on Talking Tape, '84

Lord Nelson

MI LOVER.
Tracks: / Mi lover / We like it.
Single (12"): released on Bumble Bee, Nov'86 by CSA Records. Dist: PRT, Jetstar, CSA

Lord Of Storm

SOME PEOPLE ARE SO REAL.
Single (12"): released on Offstreet, Aug'81 by Offstreet Records. Dist: EMI, Pinnacle

Lord Of The Rings

LORD OF THE RINGS various artists (Various Artists).
Album: released on BBC, Jul'81 by BBC Records & Tapes. Dist: EMI, PRT, Pye

Cassette: released on BBC, Jul'81 by BBC Records & Tapes. Dist: EMI, PRT, Pye

LORD OF THE RINGS Spoken Word (Spoken Word).
Album: released on Caedmon(USA), Jul'77 by Caedmon (USA) Records. Dist: Gower, Taylors, Discovery

Cassette: released on Caedmon(USA), Jul'77 by Caedmon (USA) Records. Dist: Gower, Taylors, Discovery

Lord Rockingham's

HOOTS MONN.
Single (7"): released on Decca, Mar'82 by Decca Records. Dist: Polygram

Lords

LIKE A VIRGIN.
Single (12"): released on Illegal, May'85 by Faulty Products Records. Dist: Pinnacle, Lightning, Cartel

Lord Sassafrass

POCCOMANIA JUMP.
Album: released on Scorpio, Mar'85 by Scorpio Records. Dist: Jetstar

Single (12"): released on Horseman, May'85 by Horseman Records. Dist: Jetstar

Lords of The New Church

IS NOTHING SACRED.
Album: released on I.R.S.(Independent Record Syndicate), Sep'83 by I.R.S.. Dist: MCA

Cassette: released on I.R.S.(Independent Record Syndicate), Sep'83 by I.R.S.. Dist: MCA

LORDS OF THE NEW CHURCH.
Compact disc: released on Illegal, Apr'87 by Faulty Products Records. Dist: Pinnacle, Lightning, Cartel

PSYCHO SEX.
Single (7"): released on New Rose, Sep'87 Dist: Rough Trade, Cartel

Single (12"): released on New Rose, Sep'87 Dist: Rough Trade, Cartel

REAL BAD TIME, THE.
Single (7"): released on Bondage International, Aug'87 Dist: Nine Mile, Cartel

Lord's Taverners

BEST OF TEST MATCH SPECIAL.
Notes: An amazing collection of memories from Bradman to Botham and featuring brand new recordings of John Arlott, Brian Johnston, Fred Trueman, Trevor Bailey and Christopher Martin-Jenkins.
Album: released on Haven, Dec'85 by MCA Records. Dist: CBS

Cassette: released on Haven, Dec'85 by MCA Records. Dist: CBS

Lord Tee

NEVER ENDING LOVE (Lord Tee & Weed).
Single (12"): released on Bluesville International, Aug'84 Dist: Jetstar

Lore and The Legends

ONE STEP AHEAD OF THE LAW.
Tracks: / Plains of Madalene / Just across the river / El bandito / Yankees in Houston / Taffeta memories / Saying goodbye to the west / One step ahead of the law / Silver spurs / Cowboy arms hotel / Parly gates / Sometimes it's hard to be a cowboy / Hairtrigger colts 44.
Album: released on Colt, Dec'86 Dist: Swift

Album: released on Nightflite, Aug'87 by Adrian Owlett. Dist: Charly, Spartan

Lorenco Marques

WARDROBES, (THE).
Single (7"): released on Siren, Sep'82

Loriana

HOLD A DAY HOLD A NIGHT.
Single (12"): released on Explicit, 20 Jun'87 by Explicit Records. Dist: Jetstar, EMI

HOLD THE DAY, HOLD THE NIGHT.
Tracks: / Hold the day, hold the night / Hold the day, hold the night (inst).
Single (7"): released on Explicit, 23 May'87 by Explicit Records. Dist: Jetstar, EMI

Single (12"): released on Explicit, 23 May'87 by Explicit Records. Dist: Jetstar, EMI

Loring, Gloria

FRIENDS AND LOVERS (Loring, Gloria/Carl Anderson).
Tracks: / Friends and lovers / You always knew.
Single (7"): released on Carrere, Sep'86 by Carrere Records. Dist: PRT, Spartan

Single (12"): released on Carrere, Sep'86 by Carrere Records. Dist: PRT, Spartan

Lori & Rafael

ALWAYS.
Single (12"): released on Roddy's Music, Aug'87 Dist: Jetstar Distribution

Lorries

CRAWLING MANTRA.
Tracks: / Crawling mantra / Hang man / All the same / Shout at the sky (live).
Single (7"): released on Red Rhino, Apr'87 by Red Rhino Records. Dist: Red Rhino, Cartel

Double-pack single: released on Red Rhino, Apr'87 by Red Rhino Records. Dist: Red Rhino, Cartel

Single (12"): released on Red Rhino, Apr'87 by Red Rhino Records. Dist: Red Rhino, Cartel

Los Angeles

CLOSE ENCOUNTERS/STAR WARS (Los Angeles Philharmonic Orchestra).
Cassette: released on Decca, Feb'78 by Decca Records. Dist: Polygram

Los Angeles, Paris, Moscow,

UNWILLING TO SCHOOL.
Cassette: released on International Report, Oct'81 by Seminar Cassettes. Dist: Audio-Visual Library Services, Davidson Distribution, Eastern Educational Products Distrib., Forlaget Systime Distribution, MacDougall Distribution, Talktapes Distribution, Watkins Books Ltd Distribution, Norton, Jeff Distribution

Los Angeles police band

LOS ANGELES POLICE BAND.
Tracks: / Mingulay boat song / Balmoral highlanders / Dorney Gerry / Lackland ferry / Flower of Scotland / Mairi's wedding / Sky boat song / Going home / Loch Lomond / Cock o' the north / Blue bonnets / Saints / Jesus Christ superstar / Marine corps hymn / Amazing Grace / Scotland the brave / We're no awa' to bide awa' / Auld Lang syne.
Album: released on Lismor, Nov'85 by Lismor Records. Dist: Lismor, Roots, Celtic Music

Cassette: released on Lismor, Nov'85 by Lismor Records. Dist: Lismor, Roots, Celtic Music

Los Angeles Zydeco Band

T-LOU.
Album: Dist: Swift

Los bravos

BLACK IS BLACK.
Tracks: / Black is black (20 years after remix) / Black is black (instrumental) / Black is black / I don't care.
Single (7"): released on Carrere, Sep'86 by Carrere Records. Dist: PRT, Spartan

Single (12"): released on Carrere, Sep'86 by Carrere Records. Dist: PRT, Spartan

Single (7"): released on Old Gold, Nov'86 by Old Gold Records. Dist: Lightning, Jazz Music, Spartan, Counterpoint

Los Calchakis

FLUTE INDIENNE, (LA).
Compact disc: by Polydor Records. Dist: Polygram, Polydor

Los Indios Tabajaros

MARIA ELENA.
Tracks: / Maria Elena / Ballard of the green berets.
Single (7"): released on Old Gold, Oct'86 by Old Gold Records. Dist: Lightning, Jazz Music, Spartan, Counterpoint

Los Lobos

AND A TIME TO DANCE.
Album: released on Slash, Jan'87 by London Records. Dist: Polygram

Album: released on Rough Trade, Apr'84 by Rough Trade Records. Dist: Rough Trade Distribution, Cartel Distribution

Cassette: released on Slash, Jan'87 by London Records. Dist: Polygram

BAMBA, (LA).
Tracks: / La Bamba / Charlena / Rip it up*.
Single (7"): released on Slash, Jul'87 by London Records. Dist: Polygram

Single (12"): released on Slash, Jul'87 by London Records. Dist: Polygram

BY THE LIGHT OF THE MOON.
Tracks: / One time one night / Shakin' shakin' shakes / Is this all there is / Prenda del Alma / All I wanted to do was dance / set me free (Rosa Lee) / Hardest time, The / My baby's gone / river of fools / Mess we're in, The / Tears of God.
Album: released on Slash, Jan'87 by London Records. Dist: Polygram. Estim retail price in 1 Feb'87 was £3.50.

Cassette: released on Slash, Jan'87 by London Records. Dist: Polygram

Compact disc: released on Polydor, Jan'87 by Polydor Records. Dist: Polygram, Polydor

DON'T WORRY BABY.
Single (7"): released on Slash-London, Mar'85

Single (12"): released on Slash-London, Mar'85

HOW WILL THE WOLF SURVIVE.
Tracks: / Don't worry baby / Matter of time, A / Corrida No.1 / our last night / Breakdown, The / I got loaded / Sere nata nortena / Evangeline / I got to let you know / Lil' king of everything / Will the wolf survive?.
Album: released on Slash, Jan'87 by London Records. Dist: Polygram

Cassette: released on Slash, Jan'87 by London Records. Dist: Polygram

Compact disc: released on Polydor, Jan'87 by Polydor Records. Dist: Polygram, Polydor

ONE TIME ONE NIGHT.
Tracks: / One time one night / River of fools / Anselma / Don't worry baby.
Notes: * = Extra track on 12" only
Single (7"): released on Slash, Apr'87 by London Records. Dist: Polygram

Single (12"): released on Slash, Apr'87 by London Records. Dist: Polygram

SET ME FREE (ROSA LEE).
Tracks: / Set me free (Rosa Lee) / Shakin' shakin' shakes / Preudeabelalama / Will the wolf survive.
Notes: "Will the wolf survive' is an extra track only available on 12" version.
Single (7"): released on Slash, Feb'87 by London Records. Dist: Polygram

Single (12"): released on Slash, Feb'87 by London Records. Dist: Polygram

WILL THE WOLF SURVIVE.
78 rpm record: released on Slash, May'85 by London Records. Dist: Polygram

Los Pinginos Del Morte

CORRIDOS FROM TEXAS.
Album: released on Arhoolie, May'81 by Arhoolie Records. Dist: Projection, Topic, Jazz Music, Swift, Roots

Loss, Joe

50 BIG BAND FAVOURITES (Loss, Joe & His Orchestra/Jack Parnell & His Orchestra).
Cassette: released on Trio, Nov'84 by MFP. Dist: EMI

50 FABULOUS YEARS.
Album: released on Note, Nov'80 by EMI Records. Dist: EMI

Cassette: released on Note, Nov'80 by EMI Records. Dist: EMI

BEST OF LATIN,THE.
Tracks: / La cumparsita (Tango) / Jealousy (Tango) / wheels (Cha cha) / Tea for two (Cha cha) / Quando caliente el sol (Rumba) / Girl form Ipanema,The (Bossa Nova) / Soul bossa nova / Best thing for you is me,The (Bossa nova) / Tequila / Sapnish gypsy dance (Paso doble) / March of the Matadors (Paso doble) / Roberta (Rumba) / La bamba (Rumba) / Guantanamera (Rumba) / Brazil (Samba) / Copacabana (Samba) / Banda,A (Banda) / Manolet (Merengue).
Notes: Featuring the best of the tangos, the cha cha, the samba, the rumbas, the paso dobles etc. for ballroom dancing. Including 3 tracks with vocals by Ross McManusfather of Elvis Costello. This compilation, personally selected by Joe Loss could truly be described as 'The Best Of Latin'.
Album: released on EMI, Dec'85 by EMI Records. Dist: EMI

Cassette: released on EMI, Dec'85 by EMI Records. Dist: EMI

BLACK & WHITE MINSTRELS & THE JOE LOSS ORCHESTRA (see Black & White Minstrels & Joe Loss Orchestra) (Loss, Joe Orchestra & Black & White Minstrels).

GOLDEN AGE OF, THE.
Album: released on Golden Age, Apr'85 by Music For Pleasure Records. Dist: EMI

Cassette: released on Golden Age, Apr'85 by Music For Pleasure Records. Dist: EMI

IN THE MOOD WITH JOE (Loss, Joe & His Orchestra).
Album: released on President, Nov'85 by President Records. Dist: Taylors, Spartan

ISN'T IT HEAVENLY (Loss, Joe & his band).
Tracks: / Smoke gets in your eyes / In other words we're through / When the new moon shines / I love you truly / Let's fall in love / La cocara cha / There's a ring around the moon / For you madonna / Stars fell on Alabama / Soon / Tina / One morning in May / Isn't it heavenly / Don't forget(1933 version) / Ending with a kiss / General's fast asleep, The / Continental, The / Under a blanket of blue.
Notes: Produced, Re-mastered, Compiled & Transferred by Colin Brown
Album: released on Conifer, Jun'86 by Conifer Records. Dist: Conifer

JOE LOSS PLAYS GLENN MILLER.
Tracks: / Moonlight Serenade / American patrol / At last / I've got a gal in Kalamazoo / Pennsylvania 6-5000 / Little brown jug / In the mood / Adios / Moonlight Cocktail / Jersey bounce / Tuxedo Junction / I know why / String of pearls, A / Serenade in blue / St. Louis blues / Chattanooga choo-choo / Bugle call rag / Frenesi / Elmer's tune / My guy's come back.
Cassette: released on Hour Of Pleasure, Oct'86 by Music For Pleasure Records. Dist: EMI

LET'S DANCE AT THE MAKE-BELEIVE BALLROOM 1934-1940 (Loss, Joe Band).
Double Album: released on World, Oct'77 Dist: Jetstar

Double Album: released on World Records, Oct'77 Dist: Polygram

MARCH OF THE MODS (Loss, Joe Orchestra).
Single (7"): released on Pop, Oct'64 by Magnet Records. Dist: RCA

PARTY DANCE TIME (Loss, Joe & His Orchestra).
Album: released on EMI Retrospect, Mar'84 by EMI Records. Dist: EMI

Cassette: released on EMI Retrospect, Mar'84 by EMI Records. Dist: EMI

PLAYS YOUR ALL TIME PARTY HITS (Loss, Joe & His Orchestra).
Double Album: released on MFP, Sep'81 by EMI Records. Dist: EMI

Double cassette: released on MFP, Sep'81 by EMI Records. Dist: EMI

REMEMBER ME? (Loss, Joe & His Orchestra).
Tracks: / There's a new world / Nice cup of tea, A / With plenty of money and you / Hometown / Ramona / Diane / Charmaine / Felix kept on walking / Sheik of araby, The / My blue heaven / Remember me? / Lullaby of Broadway / Tiptoe through the tulips / If I had a talking picture of you / I double dare you / All by yourself in the moonlight / Horsey, keep your tail up / Poor little Angeline / You're an education / Cry, baby, cry / Penny serenade / You go to my head / Chestnut tree, The / And the angels sing / Boom (Why does my heart go-) / Oh, you crazy moon / Scatterbrain / Oh Johnny, oh Johnny, oh.
Notes: Compiled and transferred by Chris Ellis
Album: released on Retrospect, Sep'86 by World Records.

Cassette: released on Retrospect, Oct'86 by World Records.

WHEELS CHA CHA (Loss, Joe Orchestra).
Single (7"): released on H.M.V., May'61 by EMI Records. Dist: EMI

Lost Boys

LOST BOYS Original soundtrack (Original Soundtrack).
Album: released on Atlantic, Aug'87 by WEA Records. Dist: WEA

Cassette: released on Atlantic, Aug'87 by WEA Records. Dist: WEA

YOU NEVER LOVE ME.
Tracks: / Feels like love / You never love me.
Single (7"): released on MCA, Mar'87 by MCA Records. Dist: Polygram, MCA

Single (12"): released on MCA, Mar'87 by MCA Records. Dist: Polygram, MCA

Lost Boys, The

LOST BOYS, THE Original Soundtrack (Original Soundtrack).
Tracks: / Good times / Lost in the shadows / Don't let the sun go down on me / Laying down the law / People are strange / Cry little sister / Power play / I still believe / Beauty has her way / To the shock of Miss Louise.
Album: released on Atlantic, Aug'87 by WEA Records. Dist: WEA

Cassette: released on Atlantic, Aug'87 by WEA Records. Dist: WEA

Lost Cheers

NO FIGHTING NO WAR.
Single (7"): released on Riot Clone, May'83 by Riot Clone Records. Dist: Cartel, Rough Trade

WOMANS PLACE/MANS DUTY.
Single (7"): released on Mortarhate, Feb'84 by Dorane Ltd.

Lost Cherees

ALL PART OF GROWING UP.
Album: released on Fight Back, Sep'84 by Fight Back Records. Dist: Jungle, Cartel

Lost Cherries

UNWANTED CHILDREN.
Single (12"): released on Mortarhate, Sep'85 by Dorane Ltd.

Lost Dreams

LOST DREAMS New Orleans vocal groups, The (Various Artists).
Tracks: / Drunk,drunk,drunk / Why fool yourself / Bluesy me / Lost dreams / Sunny side of the street / Eternally yours / Cotton picking hands / Later baby / Boom boom / Teardrop eyes / Ain't gonna do it / Shake the dice / Darling,please / Last ride.
Album: released on Stateside, Apr'87 Dist: EMI

Cassette: released on Stateside, Apr'87 Dist: EMI

Lost Empires

LOST EMPIRES Original soundtrack.
Album: released on TER, Nov'86 Dist: Pinnacle

Cassette: released on TER, Nov'86 Dist: Pinnacle

Compact disc: released on TER, Nov'86 Dist: Pinnacle

Lost Gringos

BARGELD / AMORE.
Single (7"): released on Atatak, Aug'83 by Atatak Records. Dist: Rough Trade, Cartel

NIPPON SAMBA (EP).
Single (12"): released on Atatak, Aug'83 by Atatak Records. Dist: Rough Trade, Cartel

TROCA TROCA.
Single (12"): released on Atatak, Jun'84 by Atatak Records. Dist: Rough Trade, Cartel

Lost In The Stars

LOST IN THE STARS Various artists (Various Artists).
Album: released on A&M, Nov'85 by A&M Records. Dist: Polygram

Cassette: released on A&M, Nov'85 by A&M Records. Dist: Polygram

Lost Jockey

ANIMAL BEHAVIOUR.
Album: released on Battersea, Jul'83 by Battersea Records. Dist: Pinnacle

Cassette: released on Battersea, Jul'83 by Battersea Records. Dist: Pinnacle

PROFESSOR SLACK.
78 rpm record: released on Operation Twilight, Jul'82

Lost Loved Ones

DARK THE.

Single (7"): released on Epic, Sep'84 by CBS Records. Dist: CBS

Single (12"): released on Epic, Sep'84 by CBS Records. Dist: CBS

RAISE THE FLAG.

Single (7"): released on Epic, Feb'85 by CBS Records. Dist: CBS

Single (12"): released on Epic, Feb'85 by CBS Records. Dist: CBS

Lost Roberts

HELP ME/SHELBY COUNTRY.

Single (7"): released on Rising River, Feb'82 Dist: Kingsley Sound & Vision

Lost Rough Cause

VIOLENT FEW THE (EP).

Single (7"): released on LRC, Sep'85 Dist: Jetstar, Cartel

Lost Soul

LOST SOUL Various artists (Various Artists).

Album: released on CBS, Jan'84 by CBS Records. Dist: CBS

Lost World

LOST WORLD Doyle,Sir Arthur Conan (Mason, James).

Cassette: released on Listen For Pleasure, Dec'80 by MFP Records. Dist: EMI

Lot 49

INNOCENT VICTIMS.

Single (7"): released on Magic Moon, May'83 Dist: Pinnacle

Single (12"): released on Magic Moon, May'83 Dist: Pinnacle

Lothar

THIS IS IT , MACHINES (Lothar and the hand people).

Tracks: / Machines / Today is only yesterday's tomorrow / That's another story / Sister lonely / Sex and violence / You won't be lonely / It comes on anyhow / Wedding night for those who love / Yes, I love you / This is it / This may be goodbye / Midnight ranger / Ha (ho) / Sdrawkcab / Space hymn.

Album: released on See For Miles, Aug'86 by See For Miles Records. Dist: Pinnacle

Lothian Dance Band

IN STRICT TEMPO.

Album: released on Lismor, Nov'81 Dist: Projection, Lismor, Cadillac Music, H.R. Taylor, Outlet

Cassette: released on Lismor, Nov'81 Dist: Projection, Lismor, Cadillac Music, H.R. Taylor, Outlet

PRESENTING THE LOTHIAN SCOTTISH DANCE BAND.

Album: released on REL, May'77

Cassette: released on REL, May'77

Lots of lovin'

LOTS OF LOVIN' Various artists (Various Artists).

Album: released on Three Star, Oct'86

Lot's of rockin'

LOT'S OF ROCKIN' Various artists (Various Artists).

Album: released on Collector (White Label Holland), Jan'85 Dist: Swift

Lotus Eaters

IT HURTS.

Single (7"): released on Sylvan, Feb'85 by Arista Records. Dist: Polygram Distribution

Single (12"): released on Sylvan, Feb'85 by Arista Records. Dist: Polygram Distribution

NO SENSE OF SIN.

Album: released on Sylvan, Jun'84 by Arista Records. Dist: Polygram Distribution

Cassette: released on Sylvan, Jun'84 by Arista Records. Dist: Polygram Distribution

OUT ON YOUR OWN.

Single (7"): released on Sylvan, Jun'84 by Arista Records. Dist: Polygram Distribution

Single (12"): released on Sylvan, Jun'84 by Arista Records. Dist: Polygram Distribution

SET ME APART.

Single (7"): released on Sylvan-Arista, Mar'84

Single (12"): released on Sylvan-Arista, Mar'84

Lotus Eater, (The)

LOTUS EATER, (THE) Maugham,W. Somerset (Howard, Alan).

Cassette: released on Caedmon(USA), May'82 by Caedmon (USA) Records. Dist: Gower, Taylors, Discovery

Loudermilk, John D.

TWELVE SIDES OF LOUDERMILK.

Tracks: / All of this for Sally / Angela Jones / Big daddy / Bully of the beach, The / He's just a scientist (that's all) / Rhythm and bluesy / Tobacco Road / Everybody knows / Goggle eye / This little bird / Road hog / Oh how sad.

Album: released on RCA, Jan'87 by RCA Records. Dist: RCA, Roots, Swift, Wellard, Chris, I & B, Solomon & Peres Distribution

Cassette: released on RCA, Jan'87 by RCA Records. Dist: RCA, Roots, Swift, Wellard, Chris, I & B, Solomon & Peres Distribution

Loudest Whisper

SPREAD YOUR WINGS.

Tracks: / Spread your wings.

Single (7"): released on Ritz, May'86 by Outlet Records. Dist: Outlet, Prism Leisure Distribution, Record Services Distribution (Ireland), Roots

Loudness

DISSOLUTION.

Album: released on Music For Nations, Jun'85 by Music For Nations Records. Dist: Pinnacle

Cassette: released on Music For Nations, Jun'85 by Music For Nations Records. Dist: Pinnacle

HURRICANE EYES.

Tracks: / S.D.I. / This lonely heart / Rock 'n' roll gypsy / In my dreams / Take me home / Strike of the sword / Rock this way / In this world beyond / Hungry hunter / So lonely.

Album: released on Atlantic, Jul'87 by WEA Records. Dist: WEA

Cassette: released on Atlantic, Jul'87 by WEA Records. Dist: WEA

Album: released on Atco, Aug'87 by Atlantic Records. Dist: WEA

Cassette: released on Atco, Aug'87 by Atlantic Records. Dist: WEA

LET IT GO.

Tracks: / Let it go / 1000 eyes / Ashes in the sky.

Single (7"): released on Atco, Oct'86 by Atlantic Records. Dist: WEA

Single (12"): released on Atco, Oct'86 by Atlantic Records. Dist: WEA

LIGHTNING STRIKES.

Tracks: / Let it go / Dark desire / Face to face / Who knows / Ashes in the sky / black star oblivion / Street life dream / Complication / Let it go / Dark desire / 1000 eyes / Face to face / Who knows / Ashes in the sky / Black star oblivion / Street life dream / Complication.

Compact disc: released on Atlantic, Dec'86 by WEA Records. Dist: WEA

Album: released on Atco, Jul'86 by Atlantic Records. Dist: WEA

ROADRACER.

Single (12"): released on Music For Nations, Jun'84 by Music For Nations Records. Dist: Pinnacle

THUNDER IN THE EAST.

Album: released on Music For Nations, Mar'85 by Music For Nations Records. Dist: Pinnacle

Loudon, Dorothy

BROADWAY BABY.

Tracks: / Broadway baby / It all depends on you / After you / It all belongs to me / Bobo's / Pack up your sins and go to the devil / Any place I hang my hat is home / I got lost in his arms / They say it's wonderful / Do it again / He was too good to me / I had myself a true love / Ten cents a dance.

Album: released on DRG (USA), Mar'87 by DRG Records. Dist: Conifer, RCA

Cassette: released on DRG (USA), Mar'87 by DRG Records. Dist: Conifer, RCA

Compact disc: released on DRG (USA), Apr'87 by DRG Records. Dist: Conifer, RCA

Loudspeaker

PSYCHOTIC MACHINE.

Single (12"): released on One Little Indian, Aug'87 by One Little Indian Records. Dist: Nine Mile Distribution, Cartel Distribution

Loughlin, K

ALL IRELAND CHAMPION TRADITIONAL ACCORDIONIST.

Album: released on Outlet, Mar'80 by Outlet Records. Dist: Outlet Distribution

Cassette: released on Outlet, Mar'80 by Outlet Records. Dist: Outlet Distribution

Loughlin, Kevin

FROM GLEN TO GLEN.

Album: released on Misty, Jun'77 by Hawk Records. Dist: I & B Distribution, Solomon & Peres Distribution

Loughsiders

LOUGHSIDERS, (THE).

Cassette: released on Outlet (Ireland), May'84

Louie Bluie

LOUIE BLUIE Original soundtrack.

Album: released on Arhoolie, Aug'85 by Arhoolie Records. Dist: Projection, Topic, Jazz Music, Swift, Roots

Louis, Arthur

COME ON AND LOVE ME.

Single (12"): released on Mainstreet, Aug'81 Dist: Stage One

STILL IT FEELS GOOD.

Single (7"): released on Mainstreet, Jul'81 Dist: Stage One

Louis, Eddy & Ivan Jullen

BLOW (see Julien, Ivan).

Louisiana

LOUISIANA Original soundtrack.

Album: released on CBS(France), May'84 by CBS Records. Dist: Conifer, Discovery, Swift

Cassette: released on CBS(France), May'84 by CBS Records. Dist: Conifer, Discovery, Swift

LOUISIANA BLUES Jin records (Various Artists).

Album: released on Ace, Aug'87 by Ace Records. Dist: Pinnacle, Swift, Hotshot, Cadillac

LOUISIANA BLUES Various artists (Various Artists).

Album: released on Arhoolie, May'81 by Arhoolie Records. Dist: Projection, Topic, Jazz Music, Swift, Roots

LOUISIANA BLUES-JIN RECORDS Various Artists (Various Artists).

Album: released on Ace, Aug'87 by Ace Records. Dist: Pinnacle, Swift, Hotshot, Cadillac

LOUISIANA R & B Various artists (Various Artists).

Album: released on Red Pepper, Jul'83 Dist: Jazz Music, Wellard, Chris

LOUISIANA SOUTHERN SOUL Various artists (Various Artists).

Album: released on Krazy Kat, Jul'85 Dist: Jazz Music, Swift, Chris Wellard, H.R. Taylor, Charly, Hotshot, IRS Distribution

Louisiana Cajun

LOUISIANA CAJUN SPECIAL NO.1 Harious artists (Various Artists).

Album: released on Ace, Jul'85 by Ace Records. Dist: Pinnacle, Swift, Hotshot, Cadillac

SPECIAL NO.2.

Album: released on Ace, '86 by Ace Records. Dist: Pinnacle, Swift, Hotshot, Cadillac

Louisiana explosive blues

LOUISIANA EXPLOSIVE BLUES Various artists (Various Artists).

Album: Dist: Swift

Louisiana Honeydrippers

BAYOU BLUEGRASS.

Album: released on Arhoolie, May'81 by Arhoolie Records. Dist: Projection, Topic, Jazz Music, Swift, Roots

Louisiana Playboys

CAJUN TOOT TOOT MUSIC.

Tracks: / Lucille / Lacassine special / I don't care / Canton two step / Zydeco et pas sale / Steel guitar rag / Sugar bee / Musicians waltz / Think about me baby / Wagonwheel special / Hathaway one step.

Album: released on JSP, Oct'85 by JSP Records. Dist: Swift, Projection

Louisiana Red

BLUES FROM THE HEART.

Album: released on JSP, Jan'83 by JSP Records. Dist: Swift, Projection

BLUES MAN.

Album: released on JSP, Jun'84 by JSP Records. Dist: Swift, Projection

HOT SAUCE.

Tracks: / Lightnin' bug / Alabama train / You're gonna need me, baby / Trouble all my days / Ride on, red, ride on / Whose ol' funky drawers is these / Wo-ho-ho baby / 'Let these' blues / Sometimes I wonder / Gonna move on down the line.

Album: released on Red Lightnin', Jul'87 by Red Lightnin' Records. Dist: Roots, Swift, Jazz Music, JSU, Pinnacle, Cartel, Wynd-Up Distribution

LOUISIANA RED AND SUGAR BLUE (Louisiana Red/Sugar Blue).

Album: released on Black Panther, Apr'79 by Black Panther Records. Dist: Pinnacle, Swift

LOWDOWN BACK PORCH BLUES, (THE).

Album: released on Vogue (France), Mar'84 Dist: Discovery, Jazz Music, PRT, Swift

Louis, Joe Hill

ONE MAN BAND 1949-56.

Album: released on Muskadine, Apr'79 Dist: Swift Distribution

Louis, Norma

THIS FEELING'S KILLING ME.

Single (12"): released on Challenge, Nov'81 by Elite Records. Dist: Pinnacle

Louis,Serge

SURPRISE.

Tracks: / El montal bonita / Le marin a casquette / Le tango de corinne / Surprise / Par amour / Tempo grand vitesse / Reine du musette / Amigo abel / La valse du papulo / La java du camionneur / Tango d'un soir des vacances / Creneau musette.

Album: released on Accordion Record Club, Jul'86 by Accordion Record Club Records. Dist: Accordion Record Club

Louistine

TAKE ME ON.

Album: released on Timeless, Jun'87

Lounge Lizards

BIG HEART (LIVE IN TOKYO).

Tracks: / Big heart / Hair street / Fat house / It could have been very very very beautiful / They were insane / Punch and Judy tango,The / Map of bubbles.

Notes: John Lurie - Alto Sax/Evan Lurie - Piano/Erik Sanko - Bass/Douglas Bowne - DrumsCurtis Fowlkes - Trombone/Roy Nathanson - Soprano, Alto, Tenor Saxes/Marc Ribot Guitar. Recorded at the Space Harjuku, Tokyo, 8th February 1986. Mixed at stu-dio Sky and Two Two One. Produced by John Lurie and Seigen Ono. Recorded and mixed by Seigen Ono. Big Heart and They Were Insane remixed by Jim Anderson at 39th Street Music. Photography by Perry Ogden. Drawing by James Nares. Designby Keith Davis. Dedicated to Miss Liz.

Album: released on Island, Jul'86 by Island Records. Dist: Polygram

Cassette: released on Island, Jul'86 by Island Records. Dist: Polygram

LIVE FROM THE DRUNKEN BOAT.

Album: released on Europa, Dec'83

LOUNGE LIZARDS, THE.

Album: released on E.G., Jan'87 by Virgin Records. Dist: Virgin, EMI

NO PAIN FOR CAKES.

Tracks: / My trip to Ireland / No pain for cakes / My clowns on fire / Carry me out / Bob and Nico / Tango no.3 determination for Rosa Parks / Magic of Palermo, The / Cue for passion / Where were you.

Notes: The Lounge Lizards are John Lurie (alto sax), Evan Laurie (piano), Roy Nathanson (reeds), Curtis Fowlkes (trombone), Marc Ribot (guitar, banjo), Erik Savko (bass), E.J.Rodriguez (percussion), Dougie Bowne (drums). Produced by John Lurie. Engineered by Seigen Ono.

Album: released on Antilles, Jun'87 by Island Records. Dist: Polygram

Cassette: released on Antilles, Jun'87 by Island Records. Dist: Polygram

Compact disc: released on Antilles, Jun'87 by Island Records. Dist: Polygram

Loussier, Jacques

AIR ON THE G-STRING.

Single (7"): released on Start, Mar'85 Dist: CBS, PRT

BACH TO THE FUTURE.

Album: released on Start, Nov'86 Dist: CBS, PRT

Cassette: released on Start, Nov'86 Dist: CBS, PRT

BACK TO THE FUTURE.

Compact disc: released on Start, '86 Dist: CBS, PRT

BASICALLY BACH.

Album: released on Decca, Oct'80 by Decca Records. Dist: Polygram

BEST OF PLAY BACH Vol. 1 & 2.

Album: released on Start, Mar'85 Dist: CBS, PRT

Cassette: released on Start, Mar'85 Dist: CBS, PRT

FOCUS ON JACQUES LOUSSIER.
Double Album: released on Decca, Sep'75 by Decca Records. Dist: Polygram

KEEP LOVE ALIVE/ WHISPERING HOPE (see Secombe, Harry) (Loussier, Jacques & Harry Secombe).
Single (7"): released on Starblend, Nov'82 by Starblend Records. Dist: PRT Distribution

PLAY BACH Volume 1 & 2.
Compact disc: released on Start, '86 Dist: CBS, PRT

PULSION.
Album: released on CBS, Mar'80 by CBS Records. Dist: CBS

REFLECTIONS OF BACH.
Compact disc: released on Start, May'87 Dist: CBS, PRT

Album: released on Start, May'87 Dist: CBS, PRT

Cassette: released on Start, May'87 Dist: CBS, PRT

Louvin Brothers

MY CHRISTIAN HOME.
Album: released on Starday, Apr'87

Cassette: released on Starday, Apr'87

Love

DA CAPO.
Album: released on Elektra, May'81 by WEA Records. Dist: WEA

FOREVER CHANGES.
Album: released on Elektra, Jan'84 by WEA Records. Dist: WEA

Cassette: released on Elektra, Jan'84 by WEA Records. Dist: WEA

LOVE.
Album: released on Edsel, Feb'87 by Demon Records. Dist: Pinnacle, Jazz Music, Projection

LOVE ALBUM, (THE) Various artists (Various Artists).
Album: released on Telstar, Nov'85 by Telstar Records. Dist: RCA Distribution

Cassette: released on Telstar, Nov'85 by Telstar Records. Dist: RCA Distribution

LOVE BALLADS Various artists (Various Artists).
Special: released on Streetsounds, Nov'84

Special: released on Streetsounds, Nov'84

LOVE HITS Various artists (Various Artists).
Special: released on Scoop 33, Mar'84 by Pickwick Records. Dist: H.R. Taylor

LOVE IS THE GAME Various artists (Various Artists).
Album: released on Calibre, Jun'83 by Calibre Records. Dist: PRT

Cassette: released on Calibre, Jun'83 by Calibre Records. Dist: PRT Deleted May'85.

LOVE LIVE.
Album: released on Teldec (Germany), May'84 by Import Records. Dist: IMS Distribution, Polygram Distribution

Love Affair

6 TRACK HITS.
Extended-play record: released on Scoop 33, Mar'84 by Pickwick Records. Dist: H.R. Taylor

Cassette single: released on Scoop 33, Mar'84 by Pickwick Records. Dist: H.R. Taylor

EVERLASTING LOVE.
Single (7"): released on Old Gold (Reissue), Jul'82

GREATEST HITS:LOVE AFFAIR.
Cassette: released on Autograph, Apr'85 Dist: Record Services Distribution (Ireland)

RAINBOW VALLEY.
Single (7"): released on Old Gold (Reissue), Jul'82

WITCH QUEEN OF NEW ORLEANS.
Single (12"): released on Hit The Deck, Apr'87 by Hit The Deck Records. Dist: PRT

Love and Money

ALL YOU NEED IS LOVE..AND MONEY.
Tracks: / Candybar express / River of people / Twisted / Pain in gun / Love and money / Dear John / Cheeseburger / You're beautiful / Temptation time.
Album: released on Mercury, '86 by Phonogram Records. Dist: Polygram Distribution

Cassette: released on Mercury, '86 by Phonogram Records. Dist: Polygram Distribution

Compact disc: released on Mercury, '86 by Phonogram Records. Dist: Polygram Distribution

CANDYBAR EXPRESS.
Tracks: / Candybar express,The / Love and money (Dub).
Single (7"): released on Mercury, Apr'86 by Phonogram Records. Dist: Polygram Distribution

Single (12"): released on Mercury, Apr'86 by Phonogram Records. Dist: Polygram Distribution

DEAR JOHN.
Tracks: / Dear John / Jane / Fame / Shape of things to come,The.
Single (7"): released on Mercury, Jul'86 by Phonogram Records. Dist: Polygram Distribution

Single (12"): released on Mercury, Jul'86 by Phonogram Records. Dist: Polygram Distribution

Love and Rockets

BALL OF CONFUSION.
Single (7"): released on Beggars Banquet, May'85 by Beggars Banquet Records. Dist: WEA

Single (12"): released on Beggars Banquet, May'85 by Beggars Banquet Records. Dist: WEA

EXPRESS.
Tracks: / It could be sunshine / Kundalini Express / All in my mind / Life in Laralay / Yin and Yang (the flower pot men) / Love me / All in my mind (Acoustic Version) / An American dream.
Album: released on Beggars Banquet, Oct'86 by Beggars Banquet Records. Dist: WEA

Cassette: released on Beggars Banquet, Oct'86 by Beggars Banquet Records. Dist: WEA

IF THERE'S A HEAVEN ABOVE.
Single (7"): released on Beggars Banquet, Aug'85 by Beggars Banquet Records. Dist: WEA

Single (12"): released on Beggars Banquet, Aug'85 by Beggars Banquet Records. Dist: WEA

KUNDALINI EXPRESS.
Tracks: / Kunealini express / Lucifer Sam / Holiday on the moon.
Single (12"): released on Beggars Banquet, May'87 by Beggars Banquet Records. Dist: WEA

SEVENTH DREAM OF TEENAGE HEAVEN.
Tracks: / If there's a heaven above / Private future,A / Dog-end of a day gone by,The / Game,The / Seventh dream of teenage heaven / Haunted when the minutes drag / Saudade.
Compact disc: released on Beggars Banquet, May'86 by Beggars Banquet Records. Dist: WEA

Album: released on Beggars Banquet, Oct'85 by Beggars Banquet Records. Dist: WEA

Cassette: released on Beggars Banquet, Oct'85 by Beggars Banquet Records. Dist: WEA

YIN AND YANG (THE FLOWER POT MAN).
Tracks: / Yin and Yang (The flower pot man) / Angels and Devils.

Love box

LOVE BOX Various artists (Various Artists).
Boxed set: released on Pickwick, Mar'83 by Pickwick Records. Dist: Pickwick Distribution, Prism Leisure Distribution,

Boxed set: released on Pickwick, Mar'83 by Pickwick Records. Dist: Pickwick Distribution, Prism Leisure Distribution,

LOVE BOX VOLUME 2 Various artists (Various Artists).
Boxed set: released on Impact, Sep'84 by Ace Records. Dist: Rough Trade, Pinnacle, Swift, Backs, Counterpoint, Jungle, Hotshot, Cartel

Double cassette: released on Impact, Sep'84 by Ace Records. Dist: Rough Trade, Pinnacle, Swift, Backs, Counterpoint, Jungle, Hotshot, Cartel

Love, Brad

I'LL BE YOUR WARRIOR.
Single (7"): released on MCA, Jan'83 by MCA Records. Dist: Polygram, MCA

Love Bug

YOU CAN COUNT ON ME.
Tracks: / You can count on me / You can't have it.
Single (7"): released on Roxy, May'86 by Ritz Records. Dist: Spartan Distribution

Lovebug Starski

AMITYVILLE.
Tracks: / Amityville (House on the Hill) / Amityville (Dub mix).

HOUSE ROCKER.
Tracks: / House rocker / Positive life / Baby tell me / Amityville (The House On The Hill) / Saturday night / Say what you wanna say / Eighth wonder / House rocker / House rocker (Concrete Mix) / House rocker / (Concrete mix).
Single (7"): released on Epic, '86 by CBS Records. Dist: CBS

Single (12"): released on Epic, '86 by CBS Records. Dist: CBS

Single (12"): released on Epic, '86 by CBS Records. Dist: CBS

SATURDAY NIGHT.
Tracks: / Saturday night / Positive life / Saturday night / Positive Life.
Single (7"): released on CBS, '86 by CBS Records. Dist: CBS

Single (12"): released on CBS, '86 by CBS Records. Dist: CBS

Love, Clayton

COME ON HOME BLUES.
Album: released on Red Lightnin', Sep'82 by Red Lightnin' Records. Dist: Roots, Swift, Jazz Music, JSU, Pinnacle, Cartel, Wynd-Up Distribution

Love,Darlene

CHRISTMAS (BABY PLEASE COME HOME).
Single (7"): released on Spector, Nov'82 Dist: Spec's Music Records (USA)

LIVE.

WHITE CHRISTMAS.
Single (7"): released on Phil Spector Int., Dec'82

Loved One

LOCATE & CEMENT.
Album: released on Metaphon, Jun'85

Love, Geoff

50 DANCING FAVOURITES (Love, Geoff & His Orchestra).
Cassette: released on MFP, Nov'84 by EMI Records. Dist: EMI

AN HOUR OF BIG WAR THEMES (Love, Geoff & His Orchestra).
Tracks: / Colonel Bogey / Theme from 'Lawrence Of Arabia' / Guns of Navarone,The / Battle of Britain / Longest day,The / Where eagles dare / 633 Squadron / Dam Busters,The / Great escape march,The / Green Berets,The / Cavatina / Winds of war,The / Colditz march / Sink the Bismark / Songs of the high seas / Beneath the southern cross / Guadalcanal march / 8th Army march / Theme from 'We'll meet again' / Theme from 'Is Paris Burning' / Theme from 'Reach for the sky'.

BEST OF BRITISH, (THE) (Love, Geoff Banjos).
Double Album: released on MFP, Oct'85 by EMI Records. Dist: EMI

Double cassette: released on MFP, Oct'85 by EMI Records. Dist: EMI

BIG BAND MOVIE THEMES (Love, Geoff & His Orchestra & Singers).
Album: released on MFP, Sep'75 by EMI Records. Dist: EMI

BIG BIG MOVIE THEMES (Love, Geoff & His Orchestra & Singers).
Album: released on MFP, Apr'77 by EMI Records. Dist: EMI

BIGGEST PUB PARTY IN THE WORLD,(THE).
Cassette: released on Note, Sep'81 by EMI Records. Dist: EMI

BIG LOVE MOVIE THEMES.
Album: released on MFP, Sep'71 by EMI Records. Dist: EMI

BIG TV THEMES ALBUM, (THE) (Love, Geoff & His Orchestra).
Album: released on Music for Pleasure, Oct'84 by EMI Records. Dist: MFP Distribution

Cassette: released on Music for Pleasure, Oct'84 by EMI Records. Dist: MFP Distribution

CLASSIC T.V. THEMES (Love, Geoff & His Orchestra & Singers).
Tracks: / Colditz / Edwardians,The (Upstairs, Downstairs) / Galloping home (Black Beauty) / Ironside / Alias Smith & Jones / Brothers,The / World of Sport / Cheyenne.. / Sucu Sucu (Top Secret) / Hawaii 5-0 / Bless this house / Sleepy shores (Owen MD) / Crossroads / Onedin line,The / Match of the day / Persuaders,The / Bonanza / We'll meet again / Eye level (Van Der Valk) / Pink Panther,The / Dick Barton / Return of the Saint / Good word,The (Nationwide).
Cassette: released on Hour Of Pleasure, '86 by Music For Pleasure Records. Dist: EMI

CLASSIC WAR THEMES (Love Geoff & LPO).
Album: released on MFP, Dec'79 by EMI Records. Dist: EMI

GREAT WESTERN THEMES (Love, Geoff & His Orchestra).
Tracks: / Big country,The / Fistful of dollars,A / Call of the faraway hill,The (Shane) / How the west was won / Green leaves of summer,The / Magnificent seven,The / For a few dollars more / Wild Bunch,The / Cat Ballou / Virginian,The / Maverick / Legend of Jesse James,The / Good, the bad and the ugly,The / Gunfight at the O.K. Corral / High noon / True grit / Once upon a time in the west / Man who shot liberty valance,The / Hombre / Big valley,The / Laramie / Gun law / Wagon train.

IN CONCERT WITH GEOFF LOVE (Love, Geoff & His Orchestra).
Tracks: / Skater's waltz, The / Minute waltz / Destiny / Invitation to the dance / Morning Peer Gynt suite no.1 op.46 / Elizabethan serenade / Largo / Moonlight sonata / Blue Danube, The / Sleeping Beauty, The / Merry Widow, the / Tales from the Vienna woods / Dusk / Overture-'The marriage of Figaro' k.v.492 / Air on a G-string / Clair de lune / Jesu joy of man's desiring. / Ave Maria.
Notes: Produced by Norman Newell.
Double album and cassette.
Album: released on MFP, May'87 by EMI Records. Dist: EMI

Cassette: released on MFP, May'87 by EMI Records. Dist: EMI

LAMBETH WALK (STREET PARTY).
Single (7"): released on Columbia, Nov'84 by EMI Records. Dist: EMI

MELODIES THAT LIVE FOREVER (Love, Geoff & His Orchestra).
Tracks: / Skaters waltz(The) / Minute waltz / Destiny / Invitation to the dance / Morning - Peer Gynt suite no. 1 Opus 46 / Elizabethan serenade / Largo / Moonlight sonata / Blue Danube (The) / Sleeping beauty (The) / Merry widow (The) / Tales from the Vienna woods / Dusk / Overture: The marriage of Figaro / Enigma variations no. 9 Nimrod / Air on a 'G' string / Clair de lune / Jesu, joy of man's desiring / Ave Maria.
Double Album: released on MFP, Apr'87 by EMI Records. Dist: EMI

NORTH & SOUTH OF THE BORDER (Love, Geoff Singers).
Tracks: / Blanket on the ground / Paper roses / Snowbird / Annie's song / Take me home country roads / San Antonio Rose / Peacful easy feeling / Behind closed doors / Jolene / Stand by your man / South of the border / How insensitive / Tangerine / Girl from Ipenema (The) / You belong to my heart / Maria Elena / Yours / Vaya con dios / Perfidia / Adios.
Cassette: released on Hour Of Pleasure, May'87 by Music For Pleasure Records. Dist: EMI. Estim retail price in Sep'87 was £1.99.

SING A-LONG-BANJO PARTY (Love, Geoff Banjos).
Double Album: released on EMI, Oct'83 by EMI Records. Dist: EMI

Double cassette: released on EMI, Oct'83 by EMI Records. Dist: EMI

SING-ALONG BANJO PARTY (VOL.2).
Album: released on MFP (EMI), Sep'82 by EMI Records. Dist: EMI

Cassette: released on MFP (EMI), Sep'82 by EMI Records. Dist: EMI

SINGALONG BANJO PARTY (VOL.1).
Double Album: released on Music for Pleasure, Apr'83 by EMI Records. Dist: MFP Distribution

Double cassette: released on Music for Pleasure, Apr'83 by EMI Records. Dist: MFP Distribution

SONGS THAT WON THE WAR (Love, Geoff Banjos).
Double Album: released on Music for Pleasure, May'84 by EMI Records. Dist: MFP Distribution

Double cassette: released on Music for Pleasure, May'84 by EMI Records. Dist: MFP Distribution

STRING OF PEARLS, A (Love, Geoff & His Orchestra & Singers).
Album: released on EMI, Oct'83 by EMI Records. Dist: EMI

Cassette: released on EMI, Oct'83 by EMI Records. Dist: EMI

SUPER THEMES (Love, Geoff & His Orchestra).
Tracks: / Superman / Incredible Hulk,The / Bionic woman,The / Spiderman / Blake 7 / Batman / Wonder woman / Six million dollar man / Dr.Who / Close Encounters of the third kind / Star wars / U.F.O. / Star Trek / Barbarella / Space 1999 / Thunderbirds / Also sprach zarathustra / Princess Leia's theme / Logan's run.

TAP DANCIN' TIME (Love, Geoff & His Orchestra).
Album: released on Multi Media Tapes, Apr'82 by Multi Media Tapes Records. Dist: Stage One Distribution, Conifer Distribution, H.R. Taylor Distribution, Pinnacle

Cassette: released on Multi Media Tapes, Apr'82 by Multi Media Tapes Records. Dist: Stage One Distribution, Conifer Distribution, H.R. Taylor Distribution, Pinnacle

WHEN I FALL IN LOVE (Love, Geoff Singers).
Tracks: / Imagine / What are you doing the rest of your life? / Moon river / If / I'm stone in love with you / When I fall in love / More I see you, The / I only have eyes for you / It's impossible / Annie's song / Without you / My eyes adored you / First time ever I saw your face, The / My cherie amour / Love story (where do I begin) / Something / Don't cry for me Argentina / Vincent / Killing me softly with his song / Snowbird / Send in the clowns / For one in my life / Michelle / You make me feel brand new / Just the way you are / Evergreen.
Notes: A superb collection of favourite love songs, 26 tracks which include 'Imagine' 'Vincent', 'Annie's Song' and 'Without You' to name but a few. All sung beauti fully by the ever popular Geoff Love Singers.
Double Album: released on MFP, Jun'87 by EMI Records. Dist: EMI

Double cassette: released on MFP, Jun'87 by EMI Records. Dist: EMI

WORLD'S GREATEST LOVE SONGS VOL.1.
Album: released on Music For Pleasure, May'80 by EMI Records. Dist: EMI

Cassette: released on Music For Pleasure, May'80 by EMI Records. Dist: EMI

YOUR HUNDRED FAVOURITE LOVE SONGS VOL 11 (Love, Geoff Singers).
Album: released on MFP, Mar'81 by EMI Records. Dist: EMI

YOUR HUNDRED FAVOURITE LOVE SONGS VOL 7 (Love, Geoff Singers).
Album: released on MFP, Sep'83 by EMI Records. Dist: EMI

Cassette: released on MFP, Sep'83 by EMI Records. Dist: EMI

YOUR HUNDRED FAVOURITE LOVE SONGS VOL 5 (Love, Geoff Singers).
Album: released on MFP, Nov'82 by EMI Records. Dist: EMI

Cassette: released on MFP, Nov'82 by EMI Records. Dist: EMI

YOUR HUNDRED FAVOURITE LOVE SONGS VOL 6 (Love, Geoff Singers).
Album: released on MFP, Jan'83 by EMI Records. Dist: EMI

Cassette: released on MFP, Jan'83 by EMI Records. Dist: EMI

YOUR HUNDRED INSTRUMENTAL FAVOURITES VOL 1 (Love, Geoff & His Orchestra).
Cassette: released on Music For Pleasure (Holland), Feb'81 by EMI Records. Dist: EMI

YOUR HUNDRED INSTRUMENTAL FAVOURITES VOL 5 (Love, Geoff & His Orchestra).
Album: released on MFP, Nov'82 by EMI Records. Dist: EMI

Cassette: released on MFP, Nov'82 by EMI Records. Dist: EMI

YOUR HUNDRED INSTRUMENTAL FAVOURITES VOL 6 (Love, Geoff & His Orchestra).
Album: released on MFP, Jan'83 by EMI Records. Dist: EMI

Cassette: released on MFP, Jan'83 by EMI Records. Dist: EMI

YOUR HUNDRED INSTRUMENTAL FAVOURITES VOL 7 (Love, Geoff & His Orchestra).
Album: released on MFP, Sep'83 by EMI Records. Dist: EMI

Cassette: released on MFP, Sep'83 by EMI Records. Dist: EMI

Love, Gerald

GOING TO PARTY (HEY JULEY).
Single (7"): released on Moltwo, May'84 by Moltwo Records. Dist: Jetstar Distribution

Love,Joe Ski

PEE-WEE'S DANCE.
Tracks: / Pee-Wee's dance / Pee-Wee's dance (Instrumental).

Lovejoys

GIMMEEBACK.
Single (12"): released on Wackies, Oct'83 by Wackies Records. Dist: Jetstar

LET ME ROCK YOU.
Single (12"): released on Solid Groove, Jul'82 Dist: Jetstar, Pinnacle

Loveless

KISS THAT CRAZY CORPSE.
Single (7"): released on Fragile, Aug'85 by Fragile Records. Dist: Cartel

TALES FROM THE GRAVE.
Cassette: released on Fragile, Aug'85 by Fragile Records. Dist: Cartel

Loveless, Patty

I DID.
Tracks: / I did / Lonely days lonely nights.
Single (7"): released on MCA, Jul'87 by MCA Records. Dist: Polygram. MCA

PATTY LOVELESS.
Tracks: / Lonely days, lonely nights / I did / You are everything / Blue is not a word / Slow healing heart / After all / Wicked ways / Half over you / Some blue moons ago / Sounds of Loneliness.
Album: released on MCA, Mar'87 by MCA Records. Dist: Polygram, MCA

Cassette: released on MCA, Mar'87 by MCA Records. Dist: Polygram, MCA

Lovelight

ACTIVATE.
Notes: Livelight's debut recording with word following their transfer from Window Records and word's re-release of their previous Window albums 'Sing Praises' and'Lovelight'. Although relatively new to the Christian Music scene. Lovelight have quickly established themselves as professioal in every sense of the word. They have a strong desire to present the Gospel and this is evident in the closeharmoney songs, harmoney sketches and straight talk. Buzz magazine.
Album: released on Day Spring, '86 by Word Records. Dist: Word Distribution, CBS

Cassette: released on Day Spring, '86 by Word Records. Dist: Word Distribution, CBS

LOVELIGHT.
Notes: This album is a re-release by this slick, close-harmoney trio, who are now sign-ed to word. Their clean-cut presentation and 'easy listening' music, with its Manhattan Transfer-type sound, make them a welcome contrast to other contempor- ary Gospel bands.

SING PRAISES.
Tracks: / Morning noon and night / When morning gilds the skies / Heaven came down / I wnat to praise you lord / Day thou gavest,The.
Notes: Another re-release from this group newly signed to Word. 'I have been really blessed as the love and joy of the Lord shines through Lovelight's ministry and SING PRAISES, their album of praise and workship' - Marilyn Baker.
Cassette: released on Day Spring, '86 by Word Records. Dist: Word Distribution. CBS

Love, Mary

YOU TURNED MY BITTER INTO SWEET.
Single (7"): released on Kent, Nov'82 by Ace Records. Dist: Pinnacle

Love & Mary Ann

LOVE & MARY ANN Catherine Cookson (Jameson, Susan).
Cassette: released on Chivers Audio Books, May'81 by Chivers Sound & Vision. Dist: Chivers Sound & Vision

Love, Mike

JINGLE BELL ROCK/LET'S PARTY.
Single (7"): released on Creole, Nov'83 by Creole Records. Dist: Rhino, PRT

Single (12"): released on Creole, Nov'83 by Creole Records. Dist: Rhino, PRT

LOOKING BACK WITH LOVE.
Album: released on Epic, Feb'82 by CBS Records. Dist: CBS

Love & Money

LOVE & MONEY.
Tracks: / Love & money / Home is where the heart is.
Single (7"): released on Mercury, Mar'87 by Phonogram Records. Dist: Polygram Distribution

Single (12"): released on Mercury, Mar'87 by Phonogram Records. Dist: Polygram Distribution

RIVER OF PEOPLE.
Tracks: / River of people / Desire / Candybar express*.
Notes: *=extra track on 12" version only.
Single (7"): released on Mercury, Jan'87 by Phonogram Records. Dist: Polygram Distribution

Single (12"): released on Mercury, Jan'87 by Phonogram Records. Dist: Polygram Distribution

Love On My Mind

LOVE ON MY MIND.
Tracks: / You taught me how to speak in love / Honey / I've got love on my mind / By the time I get to Phoenix / Softly as I leave you / I love you more and more everyday / Can't help falling in love / Put a little love in your heart / Tonight I celebrate my love / You're having my baby / Hurt / Something / Love Letters / When a woman loves a man / They long to be-close to you / Somethin' 'bout you baby I like.
Album: released on Memoir, Jan'87 by Memoir Records. Dist: PRT Distribution

Cassette: released on Memoir, Jan'87 by Memoir Records. Dist: PRT Distribution

Lover Boy

GET LUCKY.
Album: released on CBS, Feb'82 by CBS Records. Dist: CBS

Cassette: released on CBS, Feb'82 by CBS Records. Dist: CBS

GWAN GO DANCE.
Single (12"): released on Rocka, Nov'86 Dist: Revolver, Cartel

HEAVEN IN YOUR EYES.
Tracks: / Heaven in your eyes / Friday night / Loving every minute of it * / Heaven in your eyes / Friday night.
Notes: *= extra track on 12" version only.
Single (7"): released on CBS, Jan'87 by CBS Records. Dist: CBS

Single (12"): released on CBS, Jan'87 by CBS Records. Dist: CBS

KEEP IT UP.
Album: released on CBS, Aug'83 by CBS Records. Dist: CBS Deleted '85.

Cassette: released on CBS, Aug'83 by CBS Records. Dist: CBS

LOVERBOY.
Album: released on CBS, Mar'81 by CBS Records. Dist: CBS

THIS COULD BE THE NIGHT.
Tracks: / This could be the night / It's your life.

Lovers

LOVERS Various artists (Various Artists).
Album: released on Telstar, Nov'86 by Telstar Records. Dist: RCA Distribution

Cassette: released on Telstar, Nov'86 by Telstar Records. Dist: RCA Distribution

Lover Speaks

EVERY LOVER'S SIGN.
Tracks: / Every lover's sign / Every lover's sign (Dub Mix).
Single (7"): released on A&M, '86 by A&M Records. Dist: Polygram

Single (12"): released on A&M, '86 by A&M Records. Dist: Polygram

I CLOSE MY EYES AND COUNT TO TEN.
Tracks: / I close my eyes and count to ten / Never forget you.
Single (7"): released on A&M, Feb'87 by A&M Records. Dist: Polygram

Single (12"): released on A&M, Feb'87 by A&M Records. Dist: Polygram

LOVER SPEAKS,THE.
Notes: The Lovers Speaks are David Freeman (voice over and lyrics), and Joseph Hughes (instruments and music). They were 'discovered' by Dave Stewart of Eurythmics, who heard a demo of the duo. Dave played the tape to producer Jimmy Lovine, whowas then in London recording the Pretenders. This is the result. A quite exceptional debut album, which highlights the stunning song-writing that result-ed in their recent debut single 'No more I love yous' being a top 75 hit.
Album: released on A&M, '86 by A&M Records. Dist: Polygram

Cassette: released on A&M, '86 by A&M Records. Dist: Polygram

Compact disc: released on A&M, '86 by A&M Records. Dist: Polygram

NO MORE I LOVE YOUS.
Tracks: / No more I love yous / Of tears / This can't go on.
Single (7"): released on A&M, '86 by A&M Records. Dist: Polygram

Single (12"): released on A&M, '86 by A&M Records. Dist: Polygram

TREMBLE DANCING.
Tracks: / Tremble dancing / Still faking this art of love / This could be the night / It's your life.
Single (7"): released on A&M, '86 by A&M Records. Dist: Polygram

Single (12"): released on A&M, '86 by A&M Records. Dist: Polygram

Single (7"): released on CBS, '86 by CBS Records. Dist: CBS

Lovers Reggae

LOVERS REGGAE VOL.1 various artists (Various Artists).
Album: released on Vista Sounds, '83 by Vista Sounds Records. Dist: Jetstar

Lovesmith, Michael

AIN'T NOTHIN' LIKE IT.
Single (7"): released on Motown, Sep'85 by RCA Records. Dist: RCA Distribution

Single (12"): released on Motown, Sep'85 by RCA Records. Dist: RCA Distribution

BABY I WILL.
Single (7"): released on Motown, Jul'83 by RCA Records. Dist: RCA Distribution

Single (12"): released on Motown, Jul'83 by RCA Records. Dist: RCA Distribution

BREAK THE ICE.
Single (7"): released on Motown, Jul'85 by RCA Records. Dist: RCA Distribution

Single (12"): released on Motown, Jul'85 by RCA Records. Dist: RCA Distribution

I CAN MAKE IT HAPPEN.
Album: released on Motown, Sep'83 by RCA Records. Dist: RCA Distribution

Cassette: released on Motown, Sep'83 by RCA Records. Dist: RCA Distribution

Lovers Rock Collection

LOVERS ROCK COLLECTION VOLS. 1 & 2 various artists (Various Artists).
Album: released on Striker Lee, Aug'85 by Striker Lee Records. Dist: Jetstar Distribution

Lovers Roots

LOVERS ROOTS VOL.2 various artists.
Album: released on Vista Sounds, '83 by Vista Sounds Records. Dist: Jetstar

Love Sculpture

BLUES HELPING.
Album: released on Parlophone, '68 by EMI Records. Dist: EMI Deleted '86.

DAVE EDMUNDS - LOVE SCULPTURE YEARS Vol:1.
Tracks: / In the land of the few / Seagull / Nobody's talking / Why (how-now) / You can't catch me / Sabre dance / People, people / Brand new woman / River to another day / Think of love / Farandole.
Notes: A collection of 11 tracks from Love Sculpture - a trio headed by Dave Edmunds, recorded during 1968-70. Features songs from the album 'Forms and Feelings', including the classic 'Sabre Dance' as well as 3 tracks from singles which have become collectors' items. The ever popular, wild arrangement of Khachaturian's 'Sabre Dance' - here in a version lasting over 11 minutes - was a Top 5 UK hit for the group in 1968/9. An interesting 'blast from the past' to replace those worn out 60's pressings or for Edmunds' current followers to explore.
Album: released on Harvest, Feb'87 by EMI Records. Dist: Roots, EMI

Cassette: released on Harvest, Feb'87 by EMI Records. Dist: Roots, EMI

SABRE DANCE.
Single (7"): released on EMI Golden 45's, Mar'84 by EMI Records. Dist: EMI

SABRE DANCE/MY WHITE BICYCLE.
Single (7"): released on Old Gold, Oct'83 by Old Gold Records. Dist: Lightning, Jazz Music, Spartan, Counterpoint

RHYMES OF PASSION.
Album: released on Motown, Aug'85 by RCA Records. Dist: RCA Distribution

Cassette: released on Motown, Aug'85 by RCA Records. Dist: RCA Distribution

Love Song

FEEL THE LOVE.
Album: released on Good News (USA), May'82 by Word Records. Dist: Word Distribution

Cassette: released on Good News (USA), May'82 by Word Records. Dist: Word Distribution

LOVE SONG.
Album: released on Good News (USA), May'82 by Word Records. Dist: Word Distribution

Cassette: released on Good News (USA), May'82 by Word Records. Dist: Word Distribution

Love song duets

LOVE SONG DUETS Various artists (Various Artists).
Album: released on Motown, Apr'85 by RCA Records. Dist: RCA Distribution

Cassette: released on Motown, Apr'85 by RCA Records. Dist: RCA Distribution

Love Songs

LOVE SONGS (Various Artists).
Tracks: / Rainy night in Georgia / Love letter in

the sand / Save the last dance for me / Don't let the sun catch you crying / Dedicated to the one I love / Baby now that I've found you / Love I lost, The / I heard it through the grapevine / What becomes of the broken hearted / When a man loves a woman / My guy / If you dont know me by now / I just can't help believing / Cry.
Compact disc: released on The Collection, Apr'87 by Object Enterprises Ltd. Dist: Counterpoint Distribution

LOVE SONGS Various artists (Various Artists).
Album: released on Telstar, Dec'84 by Telstar Records. Dist: RCA Distribution

Cassette: released on Telstar, Dec'84 by Telstar Records. Dist: RCA Distribution

Double cassette: released on Pickwick (Ditto series), Jul'82

LOVE SONGS ALBUM Various artists (Various Artists).
Album: released on K-Tel, Oct'82 by K-Tel Records. Dist: Record Merchandisers Distribution, Taylors, Terry Blood Distribution, Wynd-Up Distribution, Relay Distribution, Pickwick Distribution, Solomon & Peres Distribution, Polygram

Cassette: released on K-Tel, Oct'82 by K-Tel Records. Dist: Record Merchandisers Distribution, Taylors, Terry Blood Distribution, Wynd-Up Distribution, Relay Distribution, Pickwick Distribution, Solomon & Peres Distribution, Polygram

LOVE SONGS VOL.2 Various artists (Various Artists).
Double cassette: released on Ditto Cassettes, Sep'83

Love Story

LOVE STORY Original soundtrack.
Album:

Cassette:

Love Symphony Orchestra

PENTHOUSE.
Album: released on Miracle, Apr'79 by Gull Records. Dist: PRT Distribution

Love themes

LOVE THEMES Various artists (Various Artists).
Cassette: released on AIM (Budget Cassettes), Feb'83

Love the reason

LOVE THE REASON Various artists (Various Artists).
Album: released on Respond, Oct'83 by Paul Weller. Dist: Polydor

Cassette: released on Respond, Oct'82 by Paul Weller. Dist: Polydor

Love, Timothy

DANCE AND REMEMBER CHARLIE KUNZ.
Tracks: / Pink elephants / You're dancing on my heart / Dear hearts and gentle people / You're adorable,'A' / It's only a paper moon / Roaming in the gloaming / You are my sunshine / Ain't she sweet / I Remember you / All alone / Beautiful dreamer / Shadow of your smile,The / Melody in f / Tea for two / I'm in the mood for love / English country garden / Memories / Maria / My Thanks to you / It's a sin to tell a lie / Sally.

DANCING WITH LOVE.
Tracks: / Broken doll, A\Baby face\Abie / My old man's a dustman\Come outside / That old lamplighter\Bachelor gay, A / Sleepy time down south\By the fireside / Run rabbit run\Pardon me pretty baby / Silver threads among the gold / Life is nothing without music\Paper roses / Am I wasting my time on you\That's what god made mothers for / Only your love / Smiling through\I'll always be in love with you / Till we meet again / Dream of Olwen, The / Love is all\I'll give you the Earth / Gipsy flower girl\Gwendolyne / Tango d'more / I'm happy when I'm hiking\Yodle-odle\John peel / Hold your hand out you naughty boy\My little wooden hut / Honeysuckle and the bee, The / Live laugh and love\dreaming / Maid of the mountains\Speak to me.
Album: released on Sounds Ultimate, Feb'87 Dist: PRT, H.R. Taylor

Love Tractor

THIS AIN'T NO OUTER SPACE SHIP.
Tracks: / Cartoon kiddies / Small town / Chilli part two / Night club scene / Outside with ma / Rudolf Nureyev / Beatle boots / Amusement park / Party train / We all loved each other so much.
Album: released on Big Time, Jun'87 by Mainline Record Company. Dist: Mainline

Cassette: released on Big Time, Jun'87 by Mainline Record Company. Dist: Mainline

WHEEL OF PLEASURE.
Tracks: / Neon lights / March / Jeb Pharoah's / Fun to be happy / Highland sweetheart / Spin your partner / Wheel of pleasure / Chilly Damn Willy / Slum dungeon / Seventeen days / Paint / Timerbland.

Album: released on DB (USA), Nov'84 Dist: Compendium International Distribution, Rough Trade, Cartel

Love Train

LOVE TRAIN-THE BEST OF PHILADELPHIA Various artists (Various Artists).
Album: released on Philadelphia International, Mar'83 by CBS Records. Dist: CBS

Cassette: released on Philadelphia International, Mar'83 by CBS Records. Dist: CBS Deleted May'85.

Lovett, Eddie

ALL FOR YOU.
Album: released on K & K, Nov'84 by K & K. Dist: Jetstar

GYPSY GIRL.
Single (12"): released on K & K, Dec'83 by K & K. Dist: Jetstar

MERRY CHRISTMAS.
Album: released on K & K, Dec'84 by K & K. Dist: Jetstar

ROCKERS FOR LOVERS.
Album: released on KR, Dec'81 by KR Recordings Ltd. Dist: RCA, Revolver, Cartel

Cassette: released on KR, Dec'81 by KR Recordings Ltd. Dist: RCA, Revolver, Cartel

SHINING STAR.
Single (7"): released on KR, Oct'81 by KR Recordings Ltd. Dist: RCA, Revolver, Cartel

Single (12"): released on KR, Oct'81 by KR Recordings Ltd. Dist: RCA, Revolver, Cartel

Lovett, Lyle

COWBOY MAN.
Tracks: / Waltzing fool (The) / An acceptable level of Ecstasy (the wedding song) / Closing down / Cowboy man / God will / Farther down Line, The / This old porch / Why I don't know / If I were the man you wanted / You can't resist it.
Compact disc: released on MCA, Apr'87 by MCA Records. Dist: Polygram, MCA

LYLE LOVETT.
Tracks: / Cowboy man / God will / Farther down theline / This old porch / Why I don't know / If I weren't the man you wanted / You can't resist it / Waltzing fool / An acceptable level of ecstasy (The wedding song) / Closing time.
Album: released on MCA, Mar'87 by MCA Records. Dist: Polygram, MCA

Cassette: released on MCA, Mar'87 by MCA Records. Dist: Polygram, MCA

YOU CAN'T RESIST IT.
Tracks: / You can't resist it / Closing time.
Single (7"): released on MCA, Jul'87 by MCA Records. Dist: Polygram, MCA

Love Unlimited

LOVE'S THEME (Love Unlimited Orchestra).
Single (7"): released on 20th Century, Aug'81 Dist: RCA, IMS-Polygram

WALKING IN THE RAIN WITH THE ONE I LOVE.
Single (7"): released on 20th Century, '80 Dist: RCA, IMS-Polygram

Lovich, Lene

ANGELS.
Single (7"): released on Stiff, Jan'80 by Stiff Records. Dist: EMI, Record Services Distribution (Ireland)

BIRD SONG.
Single (7"): released on Stiff, Sep'79 by Stiff Records. Dist: EMI, Record Services Distribution (Ireland)

DON'T KILL THE ANIMALS (Lovich, Lene & Nina Hagen).
Tracks: / Don't kill the animals / Don't kill the animals (Inst).
Notes: All proceeds to P.E.T.A.

FLEX.
Album: released on Stiff, Jan'80 by Stiff Records. Dist: EMI, Record Services Distribution (Ireland)

IT'S YOU,ONLY YOU(MEIN SCHMERZ).
Single (7"): released on Stiff, Oct'82 by Stiff Records. Dist: EMI, Record Services Distribution (Ireland)

LUCKY NUMBER.
Single (7"): released on Stiff, May'82 by Stiff Records. Dist: EMI, Record Services Distribution (Ireland)

NEW TOY.
Single (12"): released on Stiff, Feb'81 by Stiff Records. Dist: EMI, Record Services Distribution (Ireland)

Single (7"): released on Stiff, Feb'81 by Stiff Records. Dist: EMI, Record Services Distribution (Ireland)

NO MAN'S LAND.
Album: released on Stiff, Oct'82 by Stiff Records. Dist: EMI, Record Services Distribution (Ireland)

Cassette: released on Stiff, Oct'82 by Stiff Records. Dist: EMI, Record Services Distribution (Ireland)

STATELESS.
Album: released on Stiff, Apr'79 by Stiff Records. Dist: EMI, Record Services Distribution (Ireland)

WHAT WILL I DO WITHOUT YOU.
Single (7"): released on Stiff, Mar'80 by Stiff Records. Dist: EMI, Record Services Distribution (Ireland)

Lovie, Robert

NORTH EAST SHORE, THE.
Compact disc: released on Donside, Jan'87 Dist: Roots

Lovin Brothers

MY BABY'S GONE.
Album: released on Stetson, Oct'86 by Hasmick Promotions Ltd.. Dist: Counterpoint Distribution, H.R. Taylor Distribution, Swift Distribution, Chris Wellard Distribution

Cassette: released on Stetson, Oct'86 by Hasmick Promotions Ltd.. Dist: Counterpoint Distribution, H.R. Taylor Distribution, Swift Distribution, Chris Wellard Distribution

Lovindeer

BLUE DRAWS.
Single (12"): released on Sound Of Jamaica, Sep'84 Dist: Jetstar

COMING IN HOT.
Single (12"): released on Sound Of Jamaica, Sep'84 Dist: Jetstar

DISCO REGGAE JAM.
Album: released on TSOJ, Aug'85 by TSOJ Records. Dist: Jetstar

GOVERNMENT BOOPS.
Album: released on TSOJ, Dec'86 by TSOJ Records. Dist: Jetstar

LICKSHOT MAN.
Single (12"): released on Sound Of Jamaica, Oct'84 Dist: Jetstar

MAN SHORTAGE.
Tracks: / Man shortage / Bandooloo style.

SOCA NIGHTS.
Album: released on TSOJ, Dec'86 by TSOJ Records. Dist: Jetstar

Lovin' & Dreamin'

LOVIN' & DREAMIN' various artists (Various Artists).
Double cassette: released on Pickwick (Ditto series), Mar'83

Loving...

LOVING COUPLES Original Soundtrack (Loving Couples).
Album: released on Motown, Dec'81 by RCA Records. Dist: RCA Distribution

Cassette: released on Motown, Dec'81 by RCA Records. Dist: RCA Distribution

LOVING FIFTIES (Various Artists).
Notes: Including Connie Francis, Billy Fury.
Album: released on Trax Baby Boomer Classics, Apr'87

Cassette: released on Trax Baby Boomer Classics, Apr'87

LOVING SIXTIES (Various Artists).
Notes: Including Peter Sarstedt, The Fortunes.
Album: released on Trax Baby Boomer Classics, Apr'87

Cassette: released on Trax Baby Boomer Classics, Apr'87

LOVING YOU Original Soundtrack (Presley, Elvis).
Album: released on RCA, Sep'77 by RCA Records. Dist: RCA, Roots, Swift, Wellard, Chris, I & B, Solomon & Peres Distribution

Loving Awareness

LOVING AWARENESS.
Album: released on Morelove, Aug'76

Lovin' Spoonful

BEST IN THE WEST.
Album: released on Buddah(Kama Sutra), Apr'83

Cassette: released on Buddah(Kama Sutra), Apr'83

BEST OF:LOVIN' SPOONFUL.
Album: released on Teldec (Germany), Nov'81 by Import Records. Dist: IMS Distribution, Polygram Distribution

COLLECTION: LOVIN' SPOONFUL 20 Hits.
Album: released on Masters (Holland), Jan'87

Cassette: released on Masters (Holland), Jan'87

DAYDREAM.
Single (7"): released on Old Gold, Apr'83 by Old Gold Records. Dist: Lightning, Jazz Music, Spartan, Counterpoint

GREATEST HITS:LOVIN' SPOONFUL.
Album: released on Buddah, Jul'85 Dist: Swift, Jazz Music, PRT

Cassette: released on Buddah, Jul'85 Dist: Swift, Jazz Music, PRT

JUG BAND MUSIC.
Album: released on Edsel, '86 by Demon Records. Dist: Pinnacle, Jazz Music, Projection

SUMMER IN THE CITY.
Single (7"): released on Buddah, Jul'85 Dist: Swift, Jazz Music, PRT

Single (7"): released on Old Gold, Jul'84 by Old Gold Records. Dist: Lightning, Jazz Music, Spartan, Counterpoint

Single (7"): released on Flashback, Jan'83 by Flashback Records/PRT Records. Dist: Mainline, PRT

Single (7"): released on Buddah, Jun'80 Dist: Swift, Jazz Music, PRT

Low, David

DANCING FEET.
Cassette: released on Beechwood, Jan'87 by Beechwood Records. Dist: Ross

Lowdown Memphis Harmoni-

LOWDOWN MEMPHIS HARMONICA JAM 1950-1955 recordings (Various Artists).
Album: released on Nighthawk, Apr'79 by Faulty Products Records. Dist: Pinnacle, Swift

Lowe, Arthur

MR MEN SINGS.
Cassette: released on BBC, May'79 by BBC Records & Tapes. Dist: EMI, PRT, Pye

PIGWIG PAPERS.
Cassette: released on VFM Cassettes, Jan'85

Lowe, Frank

EXOTIC HEARTBREAK (Lowe, Frank Quintet).
Album: released on Soul Note, Jul'82 Dist: Harmonia Mundi Distributors

FLAM, THE with various artists.
Album: released on Black Saint (Italy), Jul'78 Dist: Target, Jazz Music, Harmonia Mundi

FRESH.
Album: released on Freedom, Mar'79 by Logo Records. Dist: RCA, Discovery, Wellard, Chris

Lowe, Jez

JEZ LOWE.
Album: released on Fellside, Jul'87 by Fellside Records. Dist: Roots, Jazz Music, Celtic Music, Projection

Album: released on Fellside (Cumbria), '83 by Fellside Records. Dist: Roots, Projection, CM, Jazz Music

OLD DURHAM ROAD, THE.
Album: released on Fellside (Cumbria), '83 by Fellside Records. Dist: Roots, Projection, CM, Jazz Music

TWO A ROUE (Lowe,Jez & Jake Walton).
Notes: Digitally mastered.
Album: released on Fellside, '86 by Fellside Records. Dist: Roots, Jazz Music, Celtic Music, Projection

Lowe, Nick

16 ALL-TIME LOWES.
Album: released on Demon, Nov'84 by Demon Records. Dist: Pinnacle

Cassette: released on Demon, Nov'84 by Demon Records. Dist: Pinnacle

20 ALL TIME LOWES.
Compact disc: released on Demon, '86 by Demon Records. Dist: Pinnacle

BORN A WOMAN (EP).
Single (7"): released on Stiff, May'77 by Stiff Records. Dist: EMI, Record Services Distribution (Ireland)

BURNING.
Single (7"): released on F-Beat, Feb'82 by F-Beat Records. Dist: RCA, Pinnacle

HALF A BOY & HALF A MAN.
Single (7"): released on F-Beat, May'84 by F-Beat Records. Dist: RCA, Pinnacle

Single (12"): released on F-Beat, May'84 by F-Beat Records. Dist: RCA, Pinnacle

I KNEW THE BRIDE.
Single (7"): released on F-Beat, Jul'85 by F-Beat Records. Dist: RCA, Pinnacle

Single (12"): released on F-Beat, Jul'85 by F-Beat Records. Dist: RCA, Pinnacle

JESUS OF COOL, THE.
Cassette: released on Radar, Mar'78 by WEA Music Ltd. Dist: WEA, PRT

L.A.F.F.
Single (7"): released on F-Beat, Aug'84 by F-Beat Records. Dist: RCA, Pinnacle

Single (12"): released on F-Beat, Aug'84 by F-Beat Records. Dist: RCA, Pinnacle

LIGHT UP THE DYNAMITE (Lowe, Nick & Shakin' Stevens).
Album: released on Magnum Force, '83 by Magnum Music Group Ltd. Dist: Magnum Music Group Ltd, PRT, Spartan

MY HEART HURTS.
Single (7"): released on F-Beat, Apr'82 by F-Beat Records. Dist: RCA, Pinnacle

NICK KNACK.
Compact disc: released on Demon, '86 by Demon Records. Dist: Pinnacle

NICK LOWE & HIS COWBOY OUTFIT.
Album: released on RCA, May'84 by RCA Records. Dist: RCA, Roots, Swift, Wellard, Chris, I & B, Solomon & Peres Distribution

Cassette: released on RCA, May'84 by RCA Records. Dist: RCA, Roots, Swift, Wellard, Chris, I & B, Solomon & Peres Distribution

RAGIN EYES.
Single (7"): released on F-Beat, Apr'83 by F-Beat Records. Dist: RCA, Pinnacle

Single (12"): released on F-Beat, Apr'83 by F-Beat Records. Dist: RCA, Pinnacle

ROSE OF ENGLAND.
Album: released on F-Beat, Sep'85 by F-Beat Records. Dist: RCA, Pinnacle

Cassette: released on F-Beat, Sep'85 by F-Beat Records. Dist: RCA, Pinnacle

SO IT GOES.
Single (7"): released on Stiff, Sep'76 by Stiff Records. Dist: EMI, Record Services Distribution (Ireland) Deleted '80

Lowe, Peter
ARABESQUE.
Single (7"): released on Beebee, Nov'83 by Grasmere Records. Dist: EMI

Lower Levels
GET IT.
Single (7"): released on Loppylugs, Jan'82 by Loppylugs Records. Dist: Pinnacle, Loppylugs

Lowes, Mundell
PORGY & BESS (Lowes, Mundell Jazzmen).
Album: released on RCA (France), '83 by RCA Records. Dist: Discovery

Low, Gary
I WANT YOU.
Single (7"): released on Savoir Faire, Aug'84

Single (12"): released on Savoir Faire, Aug'84

YOU ARE A DANGER.
Single (7"): released on Baby, Nov'83 by New Rose Records. Dist: Cartel

Single (12"): released on Baby, Nov'83 by New Rose Records. Dist: Cartel

Lowlife
LOGIC & LUST.
Single (7"): released on Clay, Nov'82 by Clay Records. Dist: Pinnacle

Single (12"): released on Clay, Nov'82 by Clay Records. Dist: Pinnacle

PERMANENT SLEEP.
Single (7"): released on Nightshift, '86 Dist: Fast Forward, Cartel

RAIN.
Notes: 6 Track Mini LP.
Single (7"): released on Nightshift, '86 Dist: Fast Forward, Cartel

---

VAIN DELIGHTS.
Tracks: / Vain delights / Hollow gut / Permanent sleep (Steel mix) / From side to side / Nightshift.
Single (12"): released on Lowlife, Dec'86

Low Noise
JUNGLELINE.
Single (7"): released on Happy Birthday, Sep'81 Dist: Stage One

Low Over Scandinavia
SAY SOMETHING NICE.
Single (7"): released on Trial, Apr'84 by Trial Records. Dist: Pinnacle

Low Profile
CALL ME.
Single (7"): released on Buzz, Aug'83

Single (12"): released on Buzz, Aug'83

Loyoyo
EXTRA WEAPONS.
Album: released on Floppy Discs, Apr'85 Dist: Rough Trade, Cartel

LPH
ONE MORE RUB-A-DUB.
Single (12"): released on Guinep Roots, Nov'84 by Guinep Roots. Dist: Jetstar

L.T.D.
LOVE TO THE WORLD.
Album: released on A&M, Nov'77 by A&M Records. Dist: Polygram

STOP ON BY.
Single (7"): released on Buzz Int., Jul'84

Single (12"): released on Buzz Int., Jul'84

TOGETHERNESS.
Album: released on A&M, Jun'78 by A&M Records. Dist: Polygram

L-Train
ACTION STYLE.
Single (7"): released on War, Jun'85 by War Records. Dist: PRT

Single (12"): released on War, Jun'85 by War Records. Dist: PRT

Lubich, Warren
ON THE AVENUE.
Album: released on Doric, Jan'77 by Amberlee Records. Dist: H.R. Taylor

WURLITZER ORGAN CALIFORNIA USA.
Album: released on Doric, Sep'80 by Amberlee Records. Dist: H.R. Taylor

Lucas, Carrie
PORTRAIT OF CARRIE.
Album: released on Solar, Oct'80 by MCA Records. Dist: Polygram Distribution

SHOW ME WHERE YOU'RE COMING FROM.
Single (7"): released on Solar, May'82 by MCA Records. Dist: Polygram Distribution

STREET CORNER SYMPHONY.
Album: released on RCA, Jul'78 by RCA Records. Dist: RCA, Roots, Swift, Wellard, Chris, I & B, Solomon & Peres Distribution

Lucas, Cheryl
CHAMPAGNE LADY.
Single (7"): released on Circle, Aug'83 Dist: Jazz Music

Single (12"): released on Circle, Aug'83 Dist: Jazz Music

Lucas, Matt
RIDE THAT TRAIN TONIGHT 17 tracks recorded 1959-65 & 1970-75.
Album: released on Charly, Aug'83 by Charly Records. Dist: Charly, Cadillac

Lucas, Nick
SINGING TROUBADOR, THE.
Album: released on ASV Living Era, May'83 by ASV Records. Dist: PRT

Cassette: released on ASV Living Era, May'83 by ASV Records. Dist: PRT

Lucas, Robin
FAVOURITE STORIES OF JESUS.
Cassette: released on Bibi, Jan'82

LITTLE GINGERBREAD MAN, THE (Lucas, Robin Childrens Theatre).
Cassette: released on Bibi, Jan'82

Luce, William
CURRER BELL, ESQ. (A solo portrait of Charlotte Bronte).
Double cassette: released on Caedmon(USA), Apr'85 by Caedmon (USA) Records. Dist: Gower, Taylors, Discovery

Lucia Joy
HEART & SOUL.
Single (12"): released on ABL, Jan'84 by ABL Records. Dist: Jetstar

Lucia, Paca de
PACA DE LUCIA.
Notes: For full details see under De Lucia, Paco

Lucia, Paco de
CASTRO MARIN.
Album: released on Philips, Dec'81 Dist: IMS-Polygram

Cassette: released on Philips, Dec'81 Dist: IMS-Polygram

ENTRE DOS AGUAS.
Album: released on Philips Import, Mar'84

Cassette: released on Philips Import, Mar'84

FABULOUS GUITAR OF PACO DE LUCIA.
Album: released on Polydor (France), May'84 Dist: Polygram

Cassette: released on Polydor (France), May'84 Dist: Polygram

HIT SOUNDTRACK, THE.
Album: released on Mercury, Sep'84 by Phonogram Records. Dist: Polygram Distribution

Cassette: released on Mercury, Sep'84 by Phonogram Records. Dist: Polygram Distribution

MOTIVE SERIES.
Album:

Cassette:

Lucia & Project 2
LA ISLA BONITA.
Tracks: / La Isla Bonita (rap version) / La Isla Bonita (version).
Single (7"): released on Nine O Nine, 30 May'87 by Creole Records. Dist: Rhino, PRT

Single (12"): released on Nine O Nine, 30 May'87 by Creole Records. Dist: Rhino, PRT

Lucienne
CARRIBEAN.
Single (7"): released on Pan, Feb'80

Luckhurst, Reg
DOWNHEARTED.
Single (7"): released on Lucky, Oct'80 by Lucky Records.

WAS IT RAIN.
Single (7"): released on Lucky, Oct'80 by Lucky Records.

YOUR CHEATIN' HEART.
Album: released on Lucky, Oct'80 by Lucky Records.

Luckhurts, Lucky
LONDON LIFE VOL.1.
Cassette: released on Folktracks, Nov'79 by Folktracks Cassettes. Dist: Folktracks

LONDON LIFE VOL.2.
Cassette: released on Folktracks, Nov'79 by Folktracks Cassettes. Dist: Folktracks

LONDON MUSIC HALL.
Cassette: released on Folktracks, Nov'79 by Folktracks Cassettes. Dist: Folktracks

Luckley, Stu & Bob Fox
NOWT SO GOOD'LL PASS (See Fox, Bob).

Lucky day
LUCKY DAY (Top American Bands of The 1920's) (Various Artists).
Tracks: / Sweet Georgia Brown / I'm gonna Charleston back to Charleston / Ukelele Lady / I love my baby (My baby loves me) / Bye bye blackbird / So is your old lady / Birth of the blues, The / Lady / Who / It all depends on you / Hallelujah / My blue heaven / South wind / Good news / I'm looking over a four leaf clover / She's got it / Sometimes I'm happy / My Melancholy baby / Singin' in the rain / Turn on the heat.
Album: released on Saville, '86 by Conifer Records. Dist: Conifer

Cassette: released on Saville, '86 by Conifer Records. Dist: Conifer

---

Lucky Saddles
BOTH HERE TODAY.
Single (7"): released on Albion, Aug'81 by Albion Records. Dist: Spartan, Pinnacle

Lucky Seven
GET LUCKY.
Album: released on Kix 4 U, Jul'87 by Kix 4u Records. Dist: Pinnacle

Lucy Show
ELECTRIC DREAMS.
Single (7"): released on Piggy Bank, May'84

EMPHEMERAL.
Single (7"): released on A&M, Jul'85 by A&M Records. Dist: Polygram

Single (12"): released on A&M, Jul'85 by A&M Records. Dist: Polygram

LEONARDO DA VINCI.
Single (7"): released on Shout, Dec'83 by Shout Records. Dist: Rough Trade. Cartel

MANIA.
Tracks: / Land & the life / View from the outside / Sojourn's end / Sad September / Million things / Sun & moon / Shame / Melody / Part of me now / New message.
Album: released on Big Time, Jun'87 by Mainline Record Company. Dist: Mainline

Cassette: released on Big Time, Jun'87 by Mainline Record Company. Dist: Mainline

MILLION THINGS, A.
Tracks: / Million things / Sojourn's end / Jam in E*.
Notes: * Extra track on 12" version.
Single (7"): released on Big Time, Aug'87 by Mainline Record Company. Dist: Mainline

Single (12"): released on Big Time, Aug'87 by Mainline Record Company. Dist: Mainline

SEE IT GOES.
Single (7"): released on Piggy Bank, Sep'84

Single (12"): released on Piggy Bank. Sep'84

UNDONE.
Album: released on A&M, Aug'85 by A&M Records. Dist: Polygram

Cassette: released on A&M, Aug'85 by A&M Records. Dist: Polygram

UNDONE (2).
Single (7"): released on A&M, Oct'85 by A&M Records. Dist: Polygram

Single (12"): released on A&M, Oct'85 by A&M Records. Dist: Polygram

Lucy, Tom
PARIS FRANCE.
Single (7"): released on Bridgehouse, Aug'82 Dist: Pinnacle

Luddites
ALTERED STATES.
Single (7"): released on Red Rhino, Mar'84 by Red Rhino Records. Dist: Red Rhino, Cartel

STRENGTH OF YOUR CRY (EP).
Single (7"): released on Xcentric Noise, Jul'83 by Xcentric Noise & Tapes Records. Dist: Cartel

Ludovico's Technique
LUDOVICO'S TECHNIQUE.
Album: released on New Rose, Mar'85 Dist: Rough Trade, Cartel

Ludus
DANGER CAME SMILING.
Single (7"): released on New Hormones, Sep'82 by New Hormones Records.

FOUR COMPOSITIONS.
Single (12"): released on New Hormones, Mar'80 by New Hormones Records.

MOTHERS HOUR.
Single (7"): released on New Hormones, Jul'81 by New Hormones Records.

MY CHERRY IS NOT SHERRY.
Single (7"): released on New Hormones, Jul'81 by New Hormones Records.

VISIT.
Single (12"): released on New Hormones, Jul'81 by New Hormones Records.

Ludwig, Gene
NOW'S THE TIME.
Album: released on Muse, Apr'81 by Peerless Records. Dist: Lugtons Distributors

Luft, Lorna
WHERE THE BOYS ARE.
Single (7"): released on Epic, Jun'84 by CBS Records. Dist: CBS

Single (12"): released on Epic, Jun'84 by CBS Records. Dist: CBS

Luin, Lars
HEAVY LOAD.
Single (12"): released on Emporium, Jul'82

Lukatch, Marla
RUSSIAN POPULAR SONGS.
Cassette: released on Melodiya (USSR), Feb'79 Dist: T.B.C Distribution

Luke, Robin
SUSIE DARLIN'.
Album: released on Dot, Sep'84

Lukk
ON THE ONE.
Single (7"): released on Important, Aug'85 Dist: EMI

Single (12"): released on Important, Aug'85 Dist: EMI

Lullababy
LULLABABY SOOTHING TAPE (Lullaby).
Cassette: released on Lullababy, May'85 by Mojo. Dist: Pinnacle

Lullaby of Broadway
LULLABY OF BROADWAY (Various Artists).
Album: released on Meteor, Apr'87 by Magnum Music Group Ltd. Dist: Magnum Music Group Ltd, PRT Distribution, Spartan Distribution

Lull & Others
LULL & OTHERS Saki (Burden, Hugh).
Cassette: released on Talking Tape Company, Aug'81 by Talking Tape Company Records.

Lulu
MY BOY LOLLIPOP.
Tracks: My boy lollipop / It's only love.
Single (7"): released on Jive, Nov'86 by Zomba Records. Dist: RCA, PRT, CBS

Single (12"):
Double-pack single: released on Jive, Nov'86 by Zomba Records. Dist: RCA, PRT, CBS

Special: released on Jive, Nov'86 by Zomba Records. Dist: RCA, PRT, CBS

SHOUT.
Album: released on Decca (Rock Echoes), Jun'83 by Decca Records. Dist: Polygram, IMS

Cassette: released on Decca (Rock Echoes), Jun'83 by Decca Records. Dist: Polygram, IMS Deleted '85.

Single (7"): released on Old Gold, Jun'84 by Old Gold Records. Dist: Lightning, Jazz Music, Spartan, Counterpoint

SHOUT (Lulu and the Luvvers).
Tracks: Shout / Forget me baby / Call me / Heatwave.
Single (7"): released on Decca, Jul'86 by Decca Records. Dist: Polygram

Single (12"): released on Decca, Jul'86 by Decca Records. Dist: Polygram

Single (7"): released on Decca, Mar'82 by Decca Records. Dist: Polygram

THAT'S SO.
Single (7"): released on Lifestyle, Mar'84 by Zomba Records. Dist: CBS, PRT, RCA

TO SIR WITH LOVE.
Single (7"): released on United Artists, '80

Lulu Kiss Me Dead
SPEAK TO ME.
Tracks: Speak to me / Someday soon.

ULTIMATE SOLUTION.
Single (7"): released on Situation 2, May'85 Dist: Cartel, Pinnacle

Single (12"): released on Situation 2, May'85 Dist: Cartel, Pinnacle

Luman, Bob
IS RED HOT.
Album: released on Seeburg, Jul'87

LET'S THINK ABOUT LIVING.
Album: released on Sundown, Aug'84 by Magnum Music Group Ltd. Dist: Magnum Music Group Ltd, Spartan Distribution

Single (7"): released on Sundown, Apr'85 by Magnum Music Group Ltd, PRT Distribution, Spartan Distribution

Page 622

tion

MORE OF THAT ROCKER.
Album:

MORE ROCK-A-BILLY ROCK (Luman, Bob & Friends).
Album: released on White Label, Feb'87 by White Label Records. Dist: Jetstar

ROCKER, THE.
Album:

STILL ROCKIN'.
Album: released on Bear Family, Nov'84 by Bear Family Records. Dist: Rollercoaster Distribution, Swift

STRANGER THAT FICTION.
Single (7"): released on Rollin' Rock, Jun'80

THAT'S ALRIGHT.
Single (7"): released on Rollin' Rock, Jun'80

Lumley, Joanna
TALES OF RUPERT BEAR Spoken Word.
Cassette: released on Pickwick Talking Books, '83

Lumumba
YELLOW MEALIE MEAL (Lumumba featuring Candry Ziqubu).
Tracks: Yellow mealie meal / Kiss kiss (sugar mama).
Single (7"): released on EMI, Feb'87 by EMI Records. Dist: EMI

Single (12"): released on EMI, Feb'87 by EMI Records. Dist: EMI

Luna
SPACE SPELL.
Album: released on Arhoolie, May'81 by Arhoolie Records. Dist: Projection, Topic, Jazz Music, Swift, Roots

Lunatic Fringe
FRINGE WITH THE FRINGE.
Single (7"): released on Children Of The Revolution, Jan'85 by Revolver Records. Dist: Revolver, Cartel

WHO'S IN CONTROL.
Extended-play record: released on Ressurection, Jul'82

Luna Twist
AFRICAN TIME.
Single (7"): released on Statik, Apr'82 Dist: Rough Trade Distribution, Stage One Distribution

Single (12"): released on Statik, Apr'82 Dist: Rough Trade Distribution, Stage One Distribution

LOOK OUT.
Single (7"): released on Statik, Mar'83 Dist: Rough Trade Distribution, Stage One Distribution

Single (12"): released on Statik, Mar'83 Dist: Rough Trade Distribution, Stage One Distribution

LUNA TWIST.
Album: released on Statik, Jul'83 Dist: Rough Trade Distribution, Stage One Distribution

Lunceford, Jimmie
COMPLETE, THE.
Notes: 4 L.P. set.
Album: released on CBS (Import), Jun'86 by CBS Records. Dist: Conifer, Discovery, Swift

GOLDEN SWING YEARS, THE (Lunceford, Jimmie & his orchestra).

GOLDEN SWING YEARS, (THE) (Lunceford, Jimmie & his orchestra).
Album: released on Storyville, Jul'81 by Storyville Records. Dist: Jazz Music Distribution, Swift Distribution, Chris Wellard Distribution, Counterpoint Distribution

JIMMIE LUNCEFORD & HIS ORCHESTRA (Lunceford, Jimmie & his orchestra).
Album: released on Jasmine, Sep'83 by Jasmine Records. Dist: Counterpoint, Lugtons, Taylor, H.R., Wellard, Chris, Swift, Cadillac

JIMMIE LUNCEFORD & HIS ORCHESTRA (Lunceford, Jimmie & his orchestra).
Album: released on Jazz Bird, '82 Dist: Cassion (Melandy)

Cassette: released on Jazz Bird, '82 Dist: Cassion (Melandy)

JIMMIE LUNCEFORD & HIS ORCHESTRA VOL. 2 (Lunceford, Jimmie & his orchestra).
Album: released on Hep, Mar'87 by H.R. Taylor Records. Dist: Jazz Music, Cadillac Music, JSU, Taylors, Wellard, Chris, Zodiac, Swift, Fast Forward

JIMMIE LUNCEFORD & LOUIS PRIMA 1945.
Album: released on Aircheck, Apr'79

JIMMIE LUNCEFORD VOLUME 1.
Album: released on Kings Of Jazz, Aug'81 Dist: Jazz Horizons, Jazz Music, Celtic Music

RUNNIN' A TEMPERATURE.
Tracks: Runnin' a temperature / Bird of paradise / Mood indigo / My melancholy baby / Yard dog mazurka / Coquette / Harlem shout / Unsophisticated Sue / Knock me a kiss / Stratosphere / Hittin' the bottle / Black and tan fantasy / Love nest / Sleepy time gal / Runnin' wild / Sweet Sue, just you / Avalon / Posin'.
Album: released on Affinity, Sep'86 by Charly Records. Dist: Charly, Cadillac

Cassette: released on Affinity, Sep'86 by Charly Records. Dist: Charly, Cadillac

Album: released on Affinity, Oct'86 by Charly Records. Dist: Charly, Cadillac

SWING GOES ON, (THE) VOLUME 7.
Album: released on EMI (Germany), '83 by EMI Records. Dist: Conifer

'TAIN'T WHAT YOU DO.
Album: released on Saar Giants Of Jazz (Italy), Sep'85 Dist: Mainline

Cassette: released on Saar Giants Of Jazz (Italy), Sep'85 Dist: Mainline

Lunceford, Jimmy
JIMMY LUNCEFORD & HIS ORCHESTRA 1945.
Album: released on First Heard, Apr'79 by Submarine Records. Dist: Conifer, Taylors

LITTLE JOHN etc. (1945).
Album: released on First Heard, Dec'77 by Submarine Records. Dist: Conifer, Taylors

NO TITLE ON FILE (Lunceford, Jimmy Orchestra).
Album: released on Jazz Live, Apr'81

STRICTLY LUNCEFORD (Lunceford, Jimmy Orchestra).
Album: released on Affinity (MCA), Sep'83

VOL.1 1934.
Notes: Mono.
Album: released on Hep, Nov'86 by H.R. Taylor Records. Dist: Jazz Music, Cadillac Music, JSU, Taylors, Wellard, Chris, Zodiac, Swift, Fast Forward

Lunch, Lydia
13:13.
Album: released on Situation 2, Jun'82 Dist: Cartel, Pinnacle

DEATH VALLEY (Lunch, Lydia/Sonic Youth).
Single (12"): released on Iridescence, Jan'85 by Iridescence Records. Dist: Rough Trade, Cartel

DROWNING OF LADY HAMILTON, (THE).
Album: released on Widowspeak, Jun'85 Dist: Rough Trade

IN LIMBO.
Album: released on Double Vision, Sep'84 by Double Vision Records. Dist: Rough Trade, Cartel

UNCENSORED.
Cassette: released on Widowspeak, Mar'85 Dist: Rough Trade

Lundy, Carmen
GOOD MORNING KISS.
Tracks: Time is love / Dindi / Lamp is low, The / Perfect stranger / Goodmorning kiss / Show me that you love me / Love for sale / Quiet times.
Notes: Carmen Lundy is a great new discovery and the hottest singer today on the comporary jazz scene. Her track from this, her debut album, "The Lamp Is Low" has been receiving an incredible amount of radio and club exposure and comparisons have already been made between her and Anita Baker. Like Anita, Carmen writes a great deal of her own material. Five of the tracks on this album are her own originals. Supported by an all-star line-up including Dizzy Gillespie protegy Jon Faddis and Carmen's brother Curtis Lundy, formerly with the Betty Carter Trio, this is a jazz album which has wide crossover appeal.
Album: released on Blackhawk, Apr'87 by Blackhawk Records (USA). Dist: IMS-Polygram

Cassette: released on Blackhawk, Apr'87 by Blackhawk Records (USA). Dist: IMS-Polygram

Lundy, Emmett W.
FIDDLE TUNES FROM GRAYSON COUNTY, VIRGINIA.
Album: released on String, '81 by Topic Records. Dist: Roots Distribution, Jazz Music Distribution, JSU Distribution, Projection Distribution, Swift Distribution

Lundy, Ted
LOVE SICK & SORROW (Lundy, Ted/Bob Paisley/Southern Mountain Boys).
Album: released on Rounder, Mar'79 Dist: Roots Distribution

Lupone, Patti
I DREAMED A DREAM.
Tracks: I dreamed a dream / J'ai reve d'une outrevre / One more day.
Single (7"): released on First Night, Dec'85 by Safari Records. Dist: Pinnacle .

Single (12"): released on First Night, Dec'85 by Safari Records. Dist: Pinnacle

Lurie, John
DOWN BY LAW.
Album: released on Made To Measure, 30 May'87 by Made To Measure Records. Dist: Pinnacle

STRANGER THAN PARADISE.
Album: released on Made To Measure, Mar'86 by Made To Measure Records. Dist: Pinnacle

Lurkers
DRAG YOU OUT.
Single (7"): released on Clay, Nov'82 by Clay Records. Dist: Pinnacle

Picture disc single: released on Clay, Nov'82 by Clay Records. Dist: Pinnacle

FINAL VINYL.
Single (12"): released on Clay, Mar'84 by Clay Records. Dist: Pinnacle

FRANKENSTEIN AGAIN.
Single (7"): released on Clay, Feb'83 by Clay Records. Dist: Pinnacle

FULHAM FALLOUT.
Album: released on Beggars Banquet, Jun'78 by Beggars Banquet Records. Dist: WEA

GOD'S LONELY MEN.
Album: released on Beggars Banquet, Apr'79 by Beggars Banquet Records. Dist: WEA

Cassette: released on Beggars Banquet, May'79 by Beggars Banquet Records. Dist: WEA

I DON'T NEED TO TELL HER.
Single (7"): released on Beggars Banquet, Aug'79 by Beggars Banquet Records. Dist: WEA

LAST WILL AND TESTAMENT.
Album: released on Beggars Banquet, Nov'80 by Beggars Banquet Records. Dist: WEA

LET'S DANCE NOW.
Single (7"): released on Clay, May'84 by Clay Records. Dist: Pinnacle

THIS DIRTY TOWN.
Single (7"): released on Clay, Jun'82 by Clay Records. Dist: Pinnacle

Lusardi, Linda
EYE CONTACT.
Tracks: Eye contact / Eye contact (Club Mix).
Single (7"): released on Polo, Oct'86 by Polo Records. Dist: PRT

Single (12"): released on Polo, Oct'86 by Polo Records. Dist: PRT

Lusher, Don
DON LUSHER BIG BAND (Lusher, Don Big Band).
Album: released on Chandos, Aug'81 by Chandos Records. Dist: Harmonia Mundi, Taylors

Cassette: released on Chandos, Aug'81 by Chandos Records. Dist: Harmonia Mundi, Taylors

DON LUSHER COLLECTION.
Album: released on One Up, May'76 by EMI Records.

DON LUSHER WITH BRIGHOUSE & RASTRICK BAND (Lusher, Don with Brighouse & Rastrick Band).
Album: released on Grosvenor, Jan'77 by Grosvenor Records. Dist: Taylors

Lustmord
PARADISE DISOWNED.
Album: released on Side Effects, Dec'86 by SPK Records. Dist: Rough Trade, Cartel

Lutcher, Joe
JOE JOE JUMP.
Album: released on Charly, Apr'82 by Charly Records. Dist: Charly, Cadillac

Lutcher, Nellie

MY PAPAS GOT TO HAVE EVERYTHING.
Album: released on Jukebox Lil, Jan'85 Dist: Swift

REAL GONE GAL.
Album: released on Stateside, Mar'85 Dist: EMI

Cassette: released on Stateside, Mar'85 Dist: EMI

Lute Group

LIKE AS THE LUTE DELIGHTS.
Album: released on Plantlife, Aug'85

Luton Girls Choir

BEST OF THE LUTON GIRLS CHOIR THE.
Cassette: released on Note, Sep'79 by EMI Records. Dist: EMI

Lux, Gary

CHILDREN OF THE WORLD.
Single (7"): released on Global, May'85 Dist: PRT

WEEKEND.
Single (7"): released on Global, Mar'85 Dist: PRT

Single (12"): released on Global, Mar'85 Dist: PRT

Luxon, Benjamin

AS TIME GOES BY.
Album: released on RCA, Jan'82 by RCA Records. Dist: RCA, Roots, Swift, Wellard, Chris, I & B, Solomon & Peres Distribution

Cassette: released on RCA, Jan'82 by RCA Records. Dist: RCA, Roots, Swift, Wellard, Chris, I & B, Solomon & Peres Distribution

Luxury

BURN ME UP/DON'T PRETEND.
Single (7"): released on Polydor, Jan'84 by Polydor Records. Dist: Polygram, Polydor

Luxury condos coming...

LUXURY CONDOS COMING TO YOUR NEIGHBOURHOOD SOON Various artists (Various Artists).
Album: released on Twin Tone, Aug'86

LW 5

GET TO KNOW YOU.
Album: released on Virgin, Nov'85 by Virgin Records. Dist: EMI, Virgin Distribution

Cassette: released on Virgin, Nov'85 by Virgin Records. Dist: EMI, Virgin Distribution

KILL OR BE KILLED.
Single (12"): released on Virgin, Oct'85 by Virgin Records. Dist: EMI, Virgin Distribution

RIPE FOR THE PICKING.
Single (7"): released on Virgin, Jun'85 by Virgin Records. Dist: EMI, Virgin Distribution

Single (12"): released on Virgin, Jun'85 by Virgin Records. Dist: EMI, Virgin Distribution

Lydon & O'Donnel

LYDON & O'DONNEL FAMILY ALBUM (Various Artists).
Album: released on McDonald, Dec'86 Dist: Pinnacle

Lye Lye,Bunny

100% LOVING.
Tracks: / 100% loving / Permanent love.
Single (12"): released on Rock Fort, Sep'86 Dist: Jetstar

Lyle Graham

MARLEY/DOWN THE SUBWAY.
Single (7"): released on Red Bus, Jun'83 by Red Bus Records. Dist: PRT

Lyle McGuiness Band

ACTING ON IMPULSE.
Album: released on Cool King, Jun'83 Dist: Pinnacle

ELISE/WHAT DOES IT TAKE.
Single (7"): released on Cool King, May'83 Dist: Pinnacle

Lyles, Cynthia

CROSSOVER.
Tracks: / Crossover / Crossover(Inst.).
Single (7"): released on GFM, Nov'86 by GFM Records. Dist: Fast Forward, Cartel, PRT, Projection

Single (12"): released on GFM, Nov'86 by GFM Records. Dist: Fast Forward, Cartel, PRT, Projection

Lymon, Frankie

I'M NOT A JUVENILE DELINQUENT (Lymon,Frankie & The Teenagers).
Single (7"): released on Lightning, Jan'80 by Lightning Records. Dist: Jetstar

WHY DO FOOLS FALL IN LOVE.
Album: released on Pye International, Jan'78

Single (7"): released on Lightning, Jan'80 by Lightning Records. Dist: Jetstar

Single (7"): released on Old Gold, Jul'84 by Old Gold Records. Dist: Lightning, Jazz Music, Spartan, Counterpoint

Lynam, Ray

BRAND NEW MR ME.
Album: released on Harp(Ireland), Jul'81 by Pickwick Records. Dist: Taylors

MONA LISA.
Tracks: / Mona Lisa's lost her smile / Road to Dundee,The / Too late / From now on / Wintertime / Devil inside,The / To be lovers / You put the blue in me / He stopped loving her today / Bluegrass Medley / I heard the bluebird sing / Nancy Myles.
Album: released on Ritz, Jun'86 by Outlet Records. Dist: Outlet, Prism Leisure Distribution, Record Services Distribution (Ireland), Roots

Cassette: released on Ritz, Jun'86 by Outlet Records. Dist: Outlet, Prism Leisure Distribution, Record Services Distribution (Ireland), Roots

MONA LISA LOST HER SMILE.
Tracks: / Mona Lisa lost her smile / Winter time.
Single (7"): released on Ritz, Aug'86 by Outlet Records. Dist: Outlet, Prism Leisure Distribution, Record Services Distribution (Ireland), Roots

SHADES OF RAY LYNAM.
Album: released on Ritz, Apr'86 by Outlet Records. Dist: Outlet, Prism Leisure Distribution, Record Services Distribution (Ireland), Roots
Cat. no: **RITZSP 414**
Cassette: released on Ritz, Apr'86 by Outlet Records. Dist: Outlet, Prism Leisure Distribution, Record Services Distribution (Ireland), Roots

TO BE LOVERS.
Tracks: / To be lovers / Winter time.
Single (7"): released on Ritz, Mar'86 by Outlet Records. Dist: Outlet, Prism Leisure Distribution, Record Services Distribution (Ireland), Roots

Lynch Bert & Hazel

MAMA DON'T LIKE IT/VERSION.
Single (12"): released on Sunburst, May'82 Dist: Sunburst Records

Lynch, Kenny

BETTER DAY A.
Single (7"): released on Spartan, Mar'85 by Spartan Records. Dist: Spartan

Single (12"): released on Spartan, Mar'85 by Spartan Records. Dist: Spartan

GOTTA GET UP.
Tracks: / Gotta get up / No.
Single (7"): released on Spartan, Mar'86 by Spartan Records. Dist: Spartan

Single (12"): released on Spartan, Mar'86 by Spartan Records. Dist: Spartan

HALF THE DAY'S GONE AND WE HAVEN'T....
Single (7"): released on Satril, Aug'83 by Satril Records. Dist: PRT

Single (12"): released on Satril, Aug'83 by Satril Records. Dist: PRT

HALF THE DAY'S GONE AND WE HAVEN'T EARNED A PENNY.
Cassette: released on Satril, Jul'83 by Satril Records. Dist: PRT

THEY DON'T KNOW YOU/AVERAGE MAN.
Single (7"): released on Satril, May'83 by Satril Records. Dist: PRT

Lynch, Lee

HERE I GO AGAIN/FAMOUS SHAMUS.
Single (7"): released on Ritz, Oct'83 by Ritz Records. Dist: Spartan

MOLLY MAGUIRE.
Single (7"): released on Ritz, Nov'85 by Ritz Records. Dist: Spartan

Lynham, Ray

COUNTRY FAVOURITES (Lynham, Ray & Hillbillies).
Cassette: released on Release (Ireland), May'77

COUNTRY STARS (Lynham, Ray & Begley Philomena).
Album: released on Homespun(Ireland), May'84 by Outlet Records. Dist: Outlet

Cassette: released on Homespun(Ireland), May'84 by Outlet Records. Dist: Outlet

FIRE OF TWO OLD FLAMES THE (Lynham, Ray & Philomena Begley).
Single (7"): released on Ritz, Sep'85 by Ritz Records. Dist: Spartan

GYPSY JOE & ME.
Album: by Pickwick Records. Dist: Taylors

MONA LISA'S LOST HER SMILE.
Single (7"): released on Ritz, Feb'85 by Ritz Records. Dist: Spartan

SHE SANG THE MELODY (Lynham, Ray & Philomena Begley).
Single (7"): released on Ritz, May'85 by Ritz Records. Dist: Spartan

WE GO TOGETHER AGAIN (Lynham, Ray & Philomena Begley).
Album: released on Sonus, Mar'84 by Sonus Records. Dist: Spartan

Cassette: released on Sonus, Mar'84 by Sonus Records. Dist: Spartan

WHAT A LIE/DON'T WANNA SEE ANOTHER.
Single (7"): released on Ritz, Apr'82 by Ritz Records. Dist: Spartan

Lynn

SOUNTRACK.
Album: released on Warner Brothers, Dec'75 by Warner Bros Records. Dist: WEA

Lynn, Alice

YOU KEEP ME HANGIN ON (Lynn, Alice & Buster Pearson).
Single (12"): released on Pavilion, Sep'82 by Pearl Opal Flapper. Dist: Taylors, Harmonia Mundi

Lynn, Andrea

FEEL YOUR LOVE.
Single (12"): released on Sanity, Aug'83 by Sanity Records. Dist: Pinnacle, Jetstar

Lynn, Barbara

YOU'LL LOSE A GOOD THING.
Single (7"): released on Oval, May'82 by Oval Records. Dist: Pinnacle

Lynn, Cheryl

AT LAST YOU'RE MINE.
Single (7"): released on Epic, Apr'85 by CBS Records. Dist: CBS

FIDELITY.
Single (7"): released on CBS, Jul'85 by CBS Records. Dist: CBS

Single (12"): released on CBS, Jul'85 by CBS Records. Dist: CBS

IF THIS WORLD WAS MINE (Lynn, Cheryl & Luther Vandross).
Single (7"): released on CBS, Jan'83 by CBS Records. Dist: CBS

Single (12"): released on CBS, Jan'83 by CBS Records. Dist: CBS

IT'S GONNA BE RIGHT.
Album: released on CBS, Aug'85 by CBS Records. Dist: CBS

Cassette: released on CBS, Aug'85 by CBS Records. Dist: CBS

PREPPIE.
Cassette: released on CBS, Dec'83 by CBS Records. Dist: CBS

Lynn,Ian

CELEBRATION.
Compact disc: released on MMC, '86 by MMC Records. Dist: PRT Distribution, Pinnacle

EARLY SHOW.
Tracks: / Do you see / Seven bridges / Golden days / Interlude no'5. / When winter comes / Smow mountain / Interlude no.6. / River,The / Interlude no.7 / Earth song.
Compact disc: released on MMC, '86 by MMC Records. Dist: PRT Distribution, Pinnacle

EARLY SNOW.
Album: released on MMC, Mar'85 by MMC Records. Dist: PRT Distribution, Pinnacle

FORGOTTEN SUMMER.
Tracks: / Another good reason / Another good reason / Forgotten summer / Grey sky blue / Some day soon / Sun dance / Waltz,The / First finale / Interludes 1-4.
Compact disc: released on MMC, '86 by MMC Records. Dist: PRT Distribution, Pinnacle

Album: released on MMC, Nov'83 by MMC Records. Dist: PRT Distribution, Pinnacle

PARTY IN THE RAIN (Lynn,Ian/Pete Brown).
Album: released on International Records & Tapes, May'83 by International Records & Tapes. Dist: Pinnacle

Lynn, Loretta

AT THE COUNTRY STORE.
Album: released on Country Store, Dec'85 by Starblend Records. Dist: PRT, Prism Leisure Corporation Records

Cassette: released on Country Store, Dec'85 by Starblend Records. Dist: PRT, Prism Leisure Corporation Records

COAL MINERS DAUGHTER.
Album: released on MCA Import, Mar'86 by MCA Records. Dist: Polygram, IMS

COUNTRY PARTNERS (Lynn, Loretta & Conway Twitty).
Tracks: / As soon as I hang up the phone / Don't mess up a good thing / Love's not where love should be / Two lonely people / I changed my way / Country bumpkin / Siders and snakes / I'm geeting tired of losing you / Sweet things I remember about you / It all falls down / Lifetime before,A.
Album: released on MCA Import, Mar'86 by MCA Records. Dist: Polygram, IMS

DYNAMIC DUO (Lynn, Loretta & Conway Twitty).
Album: released on Music for Pleasure, Jan'83 by EMI Records. Dist: MFP Distribution

Cassette: released on Music for Pleasure, Jan'83 by EMI Records. Dist: MFP Distribution

GOLDEN GREATS: LORETTA LYNN.
Tracks: / Before I'm over you / Wine women and song / Happy birthday / Blue Kentucky girl / You ain't woman enough / Don't come home a drinkin' / Fist city / Woman of the world (Leave my world alone) / Coalminer's daughter / One's on the way / Love is the foundation / Hey Loretta / Trouble in paradise / Somebody somewhere / She's got you / Out of my head (and back in bed).
Notes: Always a strong selling country artists, this fine new collection of sixteen Loretta Lynn hits will certainly continue the tradition. Featuring all the songs Loretta is renowned for her many fans can enjoy 'Coalminer's Daughter' 'Blue Kentucky Girl', 'Trouble In Paradise', 'Happy Birthday' and many others'. A strong value for money album from a Country Superstar.
Album: released on MCA, Feb'86 by MCA Records. Dist: Polygram, MCA

Cassette: released on MCA, Feb'86 by MCA Records. Dist: Polygram, MCA

GREAT COUNTRY HITS.
Album: released on MCA, May'85 by MCA Records. Dist: Polygram, MCA

Cassette: released on MCA, May'85 by MCA Records. Dist: Polygram, MCA

I REMEMBER PATSY.
Tracks: / She's got you / Walking after midnight / Why can't he be here / Faded love / I fall to pieces / Crazy / Sweet dreams / Back in baby's arms / Leavin' on your mind / I remember Patsy.
Album: released on MCA Import, Mar'86 by MCA Records. Dist: Polygram, IMS

JUST A WOMAN.
Tracks: / Stop the clock / Heart don't do this to me / Wouldn't it be great / When I'm in love all alone / I can't say it on the radio / I'll think of something / Adam's rib / Take me in your arms (and hold me) / Just a woman / One man band.
Album: released on MCA Import, Mar'86 by MCA Records. Dist: Polygram, IMS

SINGS.
Album: released on Stetson, Oct'86 by Hasmick Promotions Ltd.. Dist: Counterpoint Distribution, H.R. Taylor Distribution, Swift Distribution, Chris Wellard Distribution

Cassette: released on Stetson, Oct'86 by Hasmick Promotions Ltd.. Dist: Counterpoint Distribution, H.R. Taylor Distribution, Swift Distribution, Chris Wellard Distribution

SINGS COUNTRY.
Tracks: / Stand by your man / Snowbird / Minute you're gone / Rose garden / Crazy / Paper roses / You're the only good thing (That's happened to me) / Me and Bobby McGee / Send me the pillow (That you dream on) / Behind closed doors / I won't forget you / Race is on,The / (Hey won't you play) / Help me make it through the night.
Notes: Specially compiled for Music For Pleasure from the MCA catalogue, this LP features a unique collection of country standards performed in the inimitable style of Loretta Lynn. Loretta Lynn albums on Music For Pleasure are always bigsellers and this will be no exception. Fourteen great tracks including 'Stand By Your Man','Paper Roses','Rose Garden','Behind Closed Doors','Help Me Make It

Through The Night', and 'Me And Bobby McGee'.
Album: released on Music For Pleasure, Feb'86 by EMI Records. Dist: EMI

Cassette: released on Music For Pleasure, Feb'86 by EMI Records. Dist: EMI

VERY BEST OF CONWAY & LORETTA, THE (Lynn, Loretta & Conway Twitty).
Album: released on MCA Import, Mar'86 by MCA Records. Dist: Polygram, IMS

Lynn, Vera
16 GOLDEN CLASSICS.
Tracks: / Auf wiedersehn sweetheart / Yours / White cliffs of Dover, The (There'll be Bluebirds over) / My son my son / windsor waltz / Forget-me-not / Homing waltz, The / Who are we / Faithful hussar, The (don't cry my love) / Trasvellin' home / We'll meet again / As time goes by / When I grow too old to dream / Back in your own backyard / Far away places / Goodnight my love.
Notes: All tracks licensed from The Decca Records Co. Ltd\Design: Shoot that Tiger (c) 1986: Castle Communications place, Unit 7, 271, Merton Road, London SW18 5JS Bar code: 5013428920152.
Album: released on Unforgettable, Dec'86 by Castle Communications Records. Dist: Counterpoint

Cassette: released on Unforgettable, Dec'86 by Castle Communications Records. Dist: Counterpoint

20 FAMILY FAVOURITES.
Album: released on EMI, Nov'81 by EMI Records. Dist: EMI

Cassette: released on EMI, Nov'81 by EMI Records. Dist: EMI

20 GOLDEN PIECES OF VERA LYNN.
Album: released on Bulldog, Sep'85 by Bulldog Records. Dist: President Distribution, Spartan, Swift, Taylor, H.R.

Cassette: released on Bulldog, Sep'85 by Bulldog Records. Dist: President Distribution, Spartan, Swift, Taylor, H.R.

BEST OF.
Album: released on EMI (Holland), '83 by EMI Records. Dist: Conifer

COLLECTION: VERA LYNN.
Double Album: released on Castle Communications, Nov'85 by Castle Communications. Dist: Cartel, Pinnacle, Counterpoint

Double cassette: released on Castle Communications, Nov'85 by Castle Communications. Dist: Cartel, Pinnacle, Counterpoint

FOCUS ON VERA LYNN.
Double Album: released on Decca, Oct'77 by Decca Records. Dist: Polygram

Cassette: released on Decca, Oct'77 by Decca Records. Dist: Polygram

GOLDEN MEMORIES.
Album: released on Note, Nov'79 by EMI Records. Dist: EMI

GREATEST HITS: VERA LYNN.
Picture disc album: released on Astan, Dec'85 by Astan Records. Dist: Counterpoint

GREATEST HITS: VERA LYNN - VOL.1.
Album: released on Contour, Jun'81 by Pickwick Records. Dist: Pickwick Distribution. PRT

GREAT YEARS, THE.
Cassette: released on Decca, '79 by Decca Records. Dist: Polygram

HITS OF THE BLITZ.
Album: released on H.M.V., '62 by EMI Records. Dist: EMI

I LOVE THIS LAND.
Single (7"): released on State, Jun'82 by State Records.

IN CONCERT - GUARDS DEPOT CATERHAM (Lynn, Vera & The Woolf Phillips Orchestra).
Album: released on President Evergreen, Sep'84

REMEMBERS THE WORLD AT WAR.
Album: released on EMI, '74 by EMI Records. Dist: EMI

SINGING TO THE WORLD.
Album: released on Picadilly, Feb'81

Cassette: released on Picadilly, Feb'81

SPOTLIGHT ON VERA LYNN.
Double Album: released on PRT, Oct'84 by PRT Records. Dist: PRT

Double cassette: released on PRT, Oct'84 by PRT Records. Dist: PRT

STARLIGHT SERENADES.
Notes: For full information see under 'Starlight

Serenades'.

SWEETHEART OF THE FORCES.
Album: released on Decca (Holland), Apr'86 by Decca Records. Dist: Polygram, IMS

Cassette: released on Decca (Holland), Apr'86 by Decca Records. Dist: Polygram, IMS

THANK YOU FOR THE MUSIC.
Album: released on Pye Pop, Sep'79

Cassette: released on PRT, Sep'79 by PRT Records. Dist: PRT

Cassette: released on Spot, Jun'85 by Pickwick Records. Dist: H.R. Taylor, Lugtons

THIS IS VERA LYNN.
Album: released on EMI, Oct'80 by EMI Records. Dist: EMI

Cassette: released on EMI, Oct'80 by EMI Records. Dist: EMI

UNFORGETTABLE VERA LYNN, THE.
Double Album: released on MFP, Oct'85 by EMI Records. Dist: EMI

Double cassette: released on MFP, Oct'85 by EMI Records. Dist: EMI

VERA....
Cassette: released on Ideal(Tapes), Apr'80 Dist: EMI

VERA LYNN SONGBOOK, THE.
Boxed set: released on World Records, Dec'81 Dist: Polygram

Special: released on World Records, Dec'81 Dist: Polygram

WAR YEARS, THE.
Album: released on Decca, Jul'84 by Decca Records. Dist: Polygram

WE'LL MEET AGAIN.
Album: released on Decca, Oct'80 by Decca Records. Dist: Polygram

Cassette: released on Decca, Oct'80 by Decca Records. Dist: Polygram

WHITE CLIFFS OF DOVER.
Single (7"): released on EMI, May'84 by EMI Records. Dist: EMI

Lynott, Phil
OUT IN THE FIELDS (Lynott, Phil & Gary Moores).
Single (7"): released on 10, May'85 by 10 Records. Dist: Virgin, EMI

Single (12"): released on 10, May'85 by 10 Records. Dist: Virgin, EMI

PHILIP LYNOTT ALBUM, THE.
Album: released on Vertigo, Oct'82 by Phonogram Records. Dist: Polygram

Cassette: released on Vertigo, Oct'82 by Phonogram Records. Dist: Polygram

SOLO IN SOHO.
Album: released on Vertigo, Sep'85 by Phonogram Records. Dist: Polygram

Cassette: released on Vertigo, Sep'85 by Phonogram Records. Dist: Polygram

YELLOW PEARL.
Single (7"): released on Vertigo, Dec'81 by Phonogram Records. Dist: Polygram

Single (12"): released on Vertigo, Dec'81 by Phonogram Records. Dist: Polygram Deleted '85.

Lynott, Philip
KING'S CALL.
Tracks: / King's call / Yellow pearl / Dear miss lonely hearts'.
Notes: *=Extra track on 12" version only.
Single (7"): released on Vertigo, Jan'87 by Phonogram Records. Dist: Polygram

Single (12"): released on Vertigo, Jan'87 by Phonogram Records. Dist: Polygram

Lynton, Jackie
BIT NEAR THE MARK, A.
Album: released on Scratch, Dec'80

DAYDREAM.
Single (7"): released on Rock City, Aug'85 by Brian Adams. Dist: Pinnacle

Single (12"): released on Rock City, Aug'85 by Brian Adams. Dist: Pinnacle

Lynyrd skynyrd
ANTHOLOGY.
Tracks: / I ain't the one / Poison whiskey / Don't

ask me no questions / Needle and the spoon (The) / Roof gypsy roll / Honky tonk night time man / Cheatin' woman / Made in the shade / Saturday night special (live) / Sweet home Alabama / Searching / Down south Jukins / White dove / Free bird (live) / What's your name / One more time / Railroad song / Ballad of Curtis Loew (The) / T for Texas (live) (Blue yodel no. 1).
Notes: Bar code no. 5 013428 140314
Album: released on Raw Power, Mar'87 Dist: Pinnacle

Cassette: released on Raw Power, Mar'87 Dist: Pinnacle

FREEBIRD.
Single (12"):

Picture disc single:

Single (7"): released on Old Gold, Jul'84 by Old Gold Records. Dist: Lightning, Jazz Music, Spartan, Counterpoint

GIMME BACK MY BULLETS.
Album:

Cassette:

NUTHIN' FANCY.
Tracks: / Saturday night special / Cheatin' women / Railroad song / I'm a country boy / On the hunt / Am I losin' / Made in the shade / Whiskey rock-a-roller / Saturday night special / Cheatin' women / Railroad song / I'm a country boy / On the hunt / Am I losin' / Made in the shade / Whiskey rock-a-roller.
Compact disc: released on MCA, Aug'87 by MCA Records. Dist: Polygram, MCA

Album:

Cassette:

ONE MORE FROM THE ROAD.
Album:

Cassette:

PRONOUNCED LEH-NERD SKIN-NERD.
Album:

Cassette:

PRONOUNCED LEH-NERD SKIN-NERD / SECOND HELPING.
Double cassette: released on MCA (Twinpax Cassettes), Sep'84

SECOND HELPING.
Album:

Cassette:

SKYNYRD FIRST AND LAST.
Album:

Cassette

STREET SURVIVORS.
Album:

Cassette:

VERY BEST OF LYNYRD SKYNYRD
Gold and platinum.
Double Album:

Double cassette:

Lyon, Jimmy
FIRING LINE, THE.
Tracks: / Firing line, The / Wisdom.
Single (12"): released on Live, Dec'86 Dist: Jetstar, PRT

Lyons avenue jive
LYONS AVENUE JIVE Various artists (Various Artists).
Album: released on Ace, May'86 by Ace Records. Dist: Pinnacle, Swift, Hotshot, Cadillac

Lyons, Gerry
I AIN'T GOT NO WORK.
Single (12"): released on D.A.D., Jun'85 by D.A.D. Records. Dist: Jetstar

Lyons, Jimmy
GIVE IT UP (Lyons, Jimmy Quintet).
Compact disc: released on Black Saint (Italy), '86 Dist: Target, Jazz Music, Harmonia Mundi

OTHER AFTERNOONS.
Album: released on Affinity, Nov'79 by Charly Records. Dist: Charly, Cadillac

Lyons, John
MAY MORNING DEW, THE.
Album: released on Topic, '81 by Topic Records. Dist: JSU Distribution, Projection Distribution, Jazz Music Distribution

Lyons, Tim
GREEN LINNET, THE.
Album: released on Leader, '81 Dist: Jazz Music, Projection

Lyres
BOX SET, THE.
Album: released on New Rose, Jan'86 Dist: Rough Trade, Cartel

ON FYRE.
Album: released on New Rose, Sep'84 Dist: Rough Trade, Cartel

Someone who'll treat you right

Lyric By Nine
CITY LIFE.
Single (7"): released on Pregnant Turtle, Aug'84

Lyrics, Leslie
BLIND DATE.
Single (12"): released on UK Bubblers, Apr'85 by Greensleeves Records. Dist: RCA, Jetstar

Lysis, Roger Dean's
CYCLES.
Album: released on Mosaic, Aug'77 by Mosaic Records. Dist: Jazz Music Distribution, Impetus Distribution, JSU Distribution, Cadillac

LYSIS LIVE.
Album: released on Mosaic, '77 by Mosaic Records. Dist: Jazz Music Distribution, Impetus Distribution, JSU Distribution, Cadillac

Lytle, Johnny
FAST HANDS.
Album: released on Muse (Import), '81

GOOD VIBES.
Album: released on Muse, Aug'82 Dist: JSU Distribution, Jazz Music Distribution, Jazz Music Distribution, Celtic Music Distribution

VILLAGE CALLER.
Album: released on Riverside (USA), Aug'84 Dist: Fantasy (USA) Distribution

Lyttleton, Humphrey
1966.
Album: released on Harlequin, Jan'85 by Harlequin Records. Dist: Swift, Jazz Music, Wellard, Chris, IRS, Taylor, H.R.

BAD PENNY BLUES (THE BEST OF HUMPH 1949-1956).
Album: released on Cube, Jan'83 by Dakota Records. Dist: PRT

BEST OF THE.
Album: released on Black Lion, Apr'80 by Black Lion Records. Dist: Jazz Music, Chris Wellard, Taylor, H.R., Counterpoint, Cadillac

Cassette: released on Black Lion, Apr'80 by Black Lion Records. Dist: Jazz Music, Chris Wellard, Taylor, H.R., Counterpoint, Cadillac

BUDDY TATE WITH HUMPHREY.
Notes: For full details see under Tate, Buddy.

DELVING BACK WITH HUMPH.
Album: released on Esquire, Apr'79 by Titan International Productions. Dist: Jazz Music, Cadillac Music, Swift, Wellard, Chris, Backs, Rough Trade, Revolver, Nine Mile

DOGGIN AROUND.
Album: released on Wam, May'87

ECHOES OF HARLEM.
Album: released on Black Lion, Oct'82 by Black Lion Records. Dist: Jazz Music, Chris Wellard, Taylor, H.R., Counterpoint, Cadillac

ECHOES OF THE DUKE (Lyttleton Humphrey & His Band and Helen Shapiro).
Album: released on Calligraph, Sep'85 by Calligraph Records. Dist: PRT

HUMPH AT THE CONWAY.
Tracks: / Texas moaner / Coal black shine / Last smile blues / Elephant stomp blues / Wally plays the blues / My bucket's got a hole in it / I double dare you / That's the old man's blues / Feline stomp / St James infirmary / Memphis shake / Mo pas lemme cas.
Album: released on Calligraph, Mar'86 by Calligraph Records. Dist: PRT

HUMPH LIVE AT THE BULLS HEAD.
Tracks: / Now that we're here, let's go / Echoes
of Harlen / Doggin' arounds / Harbourfront
hangout / Miss Matilda / High society / Do nothing till you hear from me / Toot sweet / Three
little words / Caribana Queen.
Album: released on Calligraph, Nov'85 by Calligraph Records. Dist: PRT

IT SEEMS LIKE YESTERDAY.
Tracks: / Don't monkey with it / K.C. Blues /
Trog's blues / Blue blow blew..
Album: released on Calligraph, Jun'86 by Cal-
ligraph Records. Dist: PRT

Cassette: released on Calligraph, Jun'86 by
Calligraph Records. Dist: PRT

Album: released on Calligraph, Jun'85 by Cal-

ligraph Records. Dist: PRT

M & B JAM SESSION,THE.
Notes: With Digby, Roy Williams, Bruce Tur-
ner etc.
Album: released on Big Bear, Feb'87 by Big
Bear Records. Dist: Big Bear, Swift

ONCE IN A WHILE MIKE PAYNE.
Album: released on Black Lion, Jun'78 by Black
Lion Records. Dist: Jazz Music, Chris Wellard,
Taylor, H.R., Counterpoint, Cadillac

SIR HUMPH'S DELIGHT.
Album: released on Black Lion, Oct'79 by Black
Lion Records. Dist: Jazz Music, Chris Wellard,
Taylor, H.R., Counterpoint, Cadillac

SPREADING JOY.
Album: released on Black Lion, Feb'79 by
Black Lion Records. Dist: Jazz Music, Chris
Wellard, Taylor, H.R., Counterpoint, Cadillac

TRIBUTE TO HUMPH, A (VOLUME 1).
Album: released on Dormouse, Mar'84 by Dormouse Records. Dist: Swift

TRIBUTE TO HUMPH - VOL 4, A.
Album: released on Dormouse, Sep'86 by Dormouse Records. Dist: Swift

WORLD OF BUDDY BOLDEN, THE.
Album: released on Calligraph, Jan'87 by Calligraph Records. Dist: PRT

COLLECTIVE CALLS (URBAN) (Lytton,
Paul / Evan Parker).
Album: released on Incus, Nov'76 Dist: Jazz
Music, Cadillac

LIVE AT UNITY THEATRE (Lytton, Paul /
Evan Parker).
Album: released on Incus, Nov'76 Dist: Jazz
Music, Cadillac

RA 1+2 H (Lytton, Paul with Evan Parker).
Album: released on Ring, Jul'78 Dist: Cadillac

Album: released on Ring, Jul'78 Dist: Cadillac

M

M-80
M-80.
Album: released on Megaton, Jul'86 by Megaton Records. Dist: Rough Trade Distribution, Cartel Distribution

M80.
Album: released on Roadrunner (Dutch), Mar'85 Dist: Pinnacle

Maastrichts Salon...
BELLE EPOQUE, (LA) (Maastricht salon orchestra).
Tracks: / Florentiner Marsch / Veleta (The) / Muhle im schwarzwald (Die) / Auf der heide bluh'n die letzten rosen / Petite tonkinoise / Serenade / Funiculi-funicula / Carnaval des entants / Susi / Grossmutterchen / Jalouise / Czardasfurstin.
Notes: All the atmosphere of an afternoon in a Viennese cafe is created on this wonderful collection of salon favourites.
Album: released on Polydor (Germany), Apr'86 Dist: IMS-Polygram

Cassette: released on Polydor (Germany), Apr'86 Dist: IMS-Polygram

Compact disc: released on Polydor (Germany), Apr'86 Dist: IMS-Polygram

SERENATA.
Album:

Cassette:

Mabon, Willie
CHESS MASTERS...WILLIE MABON.
Album: released on Chess, Mar'85 by Charly Records. Dist: Charly, Swift, PRT, Discovery, IMS, Polygram

COMEBACK, THE.
Album: released on Big Bear, Apr'79 by Big Bear Records. Dist: Big Bear, Swift

I'M THE FIXER.
Album: released on Flyright, Oct'86 by Flyright Records. Dist: Krazy Kat, Swift, Jazz Music

Maboul, Aksak
ONZE DANSES POUR COMBATTRE LA MIGRAINE.
Album: released on Crammed UK, Sep'84 Dist: Rough Trade, Nine Mile, Cartel

UN PEU DE L'AME DES BANDITS.
Album: released on Crammed UK, Sep'84 Dist: Rough Trade, Nine Mile, Cartel

Mabsant
CHWAR'E CHWYLDRO.
Album: released on Gwerin, Feb'86 by Gwerin Records. Dist: Gwerin

Mabuse, Sipho
BURN OUT.
Tracks: / Burn out / Rise.
Single (7"): released on Virgin, 20 Jun'87 by Virgin Records. Dist: EMI, Virgin Distribution

Single (12"): released on Virgin, 20 Jun'87 by Virgin Records. Dist: EMI, Virgin Distribution

Single (7"): released on Important, Jul'85 Dist: EMI

Single (12"): released on Important, Jul'85 Dist: EMI

JIVE SOWETO.
Tracks: / Jive Soweto / Break dancing.
Single (7"): released on Important, Sep'86 Dist: EMI

JIVE SOWETO (Sipho Mabuse).
Tracks: / Jive Soweto / Break dancing.
Single (12"): released on Important, Sep'86 Dist: EMI

SHIKISHA.
Tracks: / Shikisha / Afrodizzia.

Single (7"): released on Virgin, Apr'87 by Virgin Records. Dist: EMI, Virgin Distribution

SIPHO MABUSE.
Tracks: / Shikisha / Rhythm lady / In the night / Path to freedom / Ti nyanga (African doctor) / Rum out / Let's get it on / Jive Soweto.
Compact disc: released on Virgin, Jun'07 by Virgin Records. Dist: EMI, Virgin Distribution

Album: released on Virgin, Jun'87 by Virgin Records. Dist: EMI, Virgin Distribution

Cassette: released on Virgin, Jun'87 by Virgin Records. Dist: EMI, Virgin Distribution

Macalla
MINA NA HEIREANN.
Album: released on Gael-Linn (Ireland), Feb'85 by Gael Linn Records. Dist: Roots, Projection, Celtic Music, Jazz Music

Cassette: released on Gael-Linn (Ireland), Feb'85 by Gael Linn Records. Dist: Roots, Projection, Celtic Music, Jazz Music

Mac...
See also under Mc...

MacAlpine...
PROJECT: DRIVER (MacAlpine, Aldridge, Rock, Sarzo).
Notes: Guitarist/Keyboard player Tony MacAlpine, Tommy Aldridge (ex Ozzie Osbourne) RoBRock and Rudy Sarzo (Quiet Riot, Whitesnake etc).

MacAlpine, Tony
MAXIMUM SECURITY.
Tracks: / Autumn lords / Hundreds of thousands / Tears of Sahara / Key to the city / Time and the test, The / The Kings cup, The / Sacred wonder / Etude 4 Opus 10 / Vision, The / Dreamstate / Porcelain doll.
Notes: Produced by Mike Varney. Features contributions by George Lynch from Dokken and Nightrangers Jeff Watson.
Compact disc: released on Vertigo, 20 Jun'87 by Phonogram Records. Dist: Polygram

Album: released on Vertigo, Jun'87 by Phonogram Records. Dist: Polygram

Cassette: released on Vertigo, Jun'87 by Phonogram Records. Dist: Polygram

Macao Combo
MACAO MACAO.
Single (7"): released on PRT, Jun'84 by PRT Records. Dist: PRT

Macattack
ART OF DRUMS.
Single (12"): released on Baad, '86 Dist: Pinnacle

Macaulay, Willie John
FROM SCOTLAND FOR YOU.
Cassette: released on Harmasala, Feb'87

MacBeath, Jimmy
STREET SINGER AND STORYTELLER-VOL.1.
Cassette: released on Folktracks, Nov'79 by Folktracks Cassettes. Dist: Folktracks

STREET SINGER AND STORYTELLER-VOL.2.
Cassette: released on Folktracks, Nov'79 by Folktracks Cassettes. Dist: Folktracks

STREET SINGER AND STORYTELLER-VOL.3.
Cassette: released on Folktracks, Nov'79 by Folktracks Cassettes. Dist: Folktracks

Macca B
WE'VE HAD ENOUGH.
Album: released on Ariwa, 30 May'87 by Ariwa Records. Dist: Revolver, Cartel, Jetstar, Rough Trade

Maccabees
MACCABEES various artists (Various Artists).

Album: released on Maccabees, Sep'84 by Maccabees Records. Dist: Jetstar

Macc Lads
BEER & SEX & CHIPS & GRAVY.
Album: by FM-Revolver Records. Dist: EMI Deleted Mar'87

BITTER,FIT CRACK.
Tracks: / Barrel's round / Guess me weight / Uncle Knobby / Maid of ale / Dan's big log / Got to be Gordon's / Bitter, fit crack / Julie the schooly / Doctor doctor / Torremolinos / Alo'teesha.
Album: released on FM, Aug'87 by FM-Revolver Records. Dist: EMI

EH UP!.
Tracks: / Eh up!.
Single (7"): released on Hetic house, '86 Dist: Probe Plus Distribution, Cartel

Single (12"): released on Hetic house, '86 Dist: Probe Plus Distribution, Cartel

MacCloud, Margaret
WEST OF WEST, A NEW SOUND TO GAELIC.
Cassette: released on Waverley, May'79 by EMI Records. Dist: EMI

MacColl, Calum
NGATIJIRRI SUNRISE (See Maddern, Eric) (MacColl, Calum & Eric Maddern).

MacColl, Ewan
BLOOD AND ROSES VOL.3 (MacColl, Ewan / Peggy Seeger).
Album: released on Plant Life, '82

BLOOD & ROSES VOLUME 1 (MacColl, Ewan / Peggy Seeger).
Album: released on Blackthorne, '82 Dist: Projection, Cadillac Music, Celtic Music, Roots

BLOOD & ROSES VOLUME 2 (MacColl, Ewan / Peggy Seeger).
Album: released on Blackthorne, '82 Dist: Projection, Cadillac Music, Celtic Music, Roots

BUNDOOK BALLADS.
Album: released on Topic, '81 by Topic Records. Dist: JSU Distribution, Projection Distribution, Jazz Music Distribution

CHORUS FROM THE GALLOWS.
Album: released on Topic, '81 by Topic Records. Dist: JSU Distribution, Projection Distribution, Jazz Music Distribution

CLASSIC SCOTS BALLADS.
Album: released on Traditional, Nov'74

COLD SNAP (MacColl, Ewan / Peggy Seeger).
Album: released on Blackthorne, '82 Dist: Projection, Cadillac Music, Celtic Music, Roots

DIFFERENT THEREFORE EQUAL (MacColl, Ewan / Peggy Seeger).
Album: released on Blackthorne, '82 Dist: Projection, Cadillac Music, Celtic Music, Roots

ENGLISH & SCOTTISH FOLK BALLADS (MacColl, Ewan / A. L. Lloyd).
Album: released on Topic, '74 by Topic Records. Dist: JSU Distribution, Projection Distribution, Jazz Music Distribution

HOT BLAST (MacColl, Ewan / Peggy Seeger).
Album: released on Blackthorne, '82 Dist: Projection, Cadillac Music, Celtic Music, Roots

JACOBITE REBELLIONS, (THE).
Album: released on Topic, '81 by Topic Records. Dist: JSU Distribution, Projection Distribution, Jazz Music Distribution

KILROY WAS HERE (MacColl, Ewan / Peggy Seeger).
Album: released on Blackthorne, '82 Dist: Projection, Cadillac Music, Celtic Music, Roots

MANCHESTER ANGEL, (THE).
Album: released on Topic, '81 by Topic Records. Dist: JSU Distribution, Projection Distribution, Jazz Music Distribution

SATURDAY NIGHT AT THE BULL AND MOUTH.
Album: released on Blackthorne, '82 Dist: Projection, Cadillac Music, Celtic Music, Roots

SONGS OF JACOBITE REBELL.
Album: released on Topic, '74 Dist: Roots Distribution

STEAM WHISTLE BALLADS.
Album: released on Topic, '81 by Topic Records. Dist: JSU Distribution, Projection Distribution, Jazz Music Distribution

WANTON MUSE.
Album: released on Argo, '72 by Decca Records. Dist: Polygram

MacColl, Kirsty
BERLIN.
Single (7"): released on Now, Aug'83 by North Of Watford Records. Dist: Wynd-Up Distribution

Single (12"): released on Now, Aug'83 by North Of Watford Records. Dist: Wynd-Up Distribution

DESPERATE CHARACTER.
Album: released on Polydor, Jul'81 by Polydor Records. Dist: Polygram, Polvdor

Single (7"): released on Polydor, Jul'81 by Polydor Records. Dist: Polygram, Polvdor

Single (7"): released on Stiff, Jun'85 by Stiff Records. Dist: EMI, Record Services Distribution (Ireland)

Single (12"): released on Stiff, Jun'85 by Stiff Records. Dist: EMI, Record Services Distribution (Ireland)

KIRSTY MACCOLL.
Album: released on Polydor, Mar'85 by Polydor Records. Dist: Polygram, Polvdor

Cassette: released on Polydor, Mar'85 by Polydor Records. Dist: Polygram, Polydor Deleted '86.

NEW ENGLAND, (A).
Single (7"): released on Stiff, Dec'84

Single (12"): released on Stiff, Dec'84

TERRY.
Single (7"): released on Stiff, Oct'83

Single (12"): released on Stiff, Oct'83

MacCulli, Finn
SINK YE SWIM YE.
Album: released on REL, '78

MacCullam, Hugh A
WORLD'S GREATEST PIPERS Volume 2.
Notes: Includes Marches,Strathspeys & reels,Airs,Jigs,Competition Marches,Hornpipes, Piobaireachd.

MacDiarmid, Hugh
LEGEND AND THE MAN, THE.
Album: released on Nevis, May'77 Dist: H.R. Taylor

MacDonald, Aimil
AIN'T NOBODY GONNA TOUCH MY BODY.
Single (7"): released on Spinach, Feb'81

MacDonald, Alastair J.
SURGE OF THE SEA,THE.
Cassette: released on Ross, Dec'85 by Ross Records. Dist: Ross Distribution, Roots Distribution

MacDonald, Angus
WORLD'S GREATEST PIPERS VOLUME 1,THE (MacDonald,Pipe Major Angus).
Album: released on Lismor, Nov'85 by Lismor Records. Dist: Lismor, Roots, Celtic Music

MacDonald, Donald
HERE COMES DONNY.
Album: released on Lismor, Jul'77 by Lismor Records. Dist: Lismor, Roots, Celtic Music

Cassette: released on Lismor, Jul'77 by Lismor Records. Dist: Lismor, Roots, Celtic Music

LARGE AS LIFE.
Album: released on Lismor, Aug'78 by Lismor Records. Dist: Lismor, Roots, Celtic Music

Cassette: released on Lismor, Aug'78 by Lismor Records. Dist: Lismor, Roots, Celtic Music

MacDonald, George
GOLDEN KEY, THE.
Cassette: released on Caedmon(USA), Sep'85 by Caedmon (USA) Records. Dist: Gower, Taylors, Discovery

MacDonald,Iain
BENEATH STILL WATERS.
Tracks: / Coldest night of the year / Maid of Islay / Bed of shifting stone / Do you think it's right / Iolaire,The / Santiago Stadium / Salt in the wind / No fun city/Free Nelson Mandella / Ask questions later? / All our dreams.
Album: released on Greentrax, Oct'86 by Greentrax Records. Dist: Projection, CM, Gordon Duncan Distribution, Rough Trade, Nine Mile, Cartel

Cassette: released on Greentrax, Oct'86 by Greentrax Records. Dist: Projection, CM, Gordon Duncan Distribution, Rough Trade, Nine Mile, Cartel

MacDonald, Jeanette
JEANETTE MACDONALD & NELSON EDDY (see also Nelson Eddy).
Album: released on RCA, '84 by RCA Records. Dist: RCA, Roots, Swift, Wellard, Chris, I & B, Solomon & Peres Distribution

Cassette: released on RCA, '84 by RCA Records. Dist: RCA, Roots, Swift, Wellard, Chris, I & B, Solomon & Peres Distribution

SINGS "SAN FRANSISCO" AND OTHER SILVER SCREEN FAVOURITES.
Album: released on Deja Vu, Oct'83 by RCA Records. Dist: RCA

Cassette: released on Deja Vu, Oct'83 by RCA Records. Dist: RCA

MacDonald, John
ROVING PLOUGHBOY, THE (MacDonald, John with daughter Ena).
Cassette: released on Folktracks, Nov'79 by Folktracks Cassettes. Dist: Folktracks

SINGING MOLECATCHER OF MORAYSHIRE, THE Scots Ballads, Bothy songs & Melodeon tunes.
Album: released on Topic, '81 by Topic Records. Dist: JSU Distribution, Projection Distribution, Jazz Music Distribution

Macdonald,Ralph
UNIVERSAL RHYTHM.
Album: released on London, Sep'84 by London Records. Dist: Polygram

Cassette: released on London, Sep'84 by London Records. Dist: Polygram

YOU NEED MORE CALYPSO.
Tracks: / You need more calypso / In the name of love.
Single (7"): released on London, Mar'86 by London Records. Dist: Polygram

Single (12"): released on London, Mar'86 by London Records. Dist: Polygram

MacDonald, Ranald
MACDONALD OF KEPPOCH SINGS.
Album: released on REL, '77 Dist: Roots

MacDonald Sisters
SONGS OF THE ISLANDS.
Album: released on Lismor, Apr'77 by Lismor Records. Dist: Lismor, Roots, Celtic Music

Cassette: released on Lismor, Apr'77 by Lismor Records. Dist: Lismor, Roots, Celtic Music

MacDonald, Skeets
GOING STEADY WITH THE BLUES.
Album: released on Capitol (France), '83 by Capitol Records. Dist: Conifer

Maceo & The Macs
CROSS THE TRACK (WE BETTER GO BACK EXT VERSION).
Tracks: / Cross the track (we better go back ext version) / Parrly part 1 / Soul power*.
Notes: * = Extra track on 12" only
Single (7"): released on Urban, Apr'87 by Polydor Records. Dist: Polygram

Single (12"): released on Urban, Apr'87 by Polydor Records. Dist: Polygram

Macero, Teo
IMPRESSIONS OF CHARLES MINGUS.
Album: released on Imported, Jun'84 Dist: Conifer

Macfarland, C
MAGGIE'S LETTER.
Single (12"): released on Sapphire, Nov'83 by Sapphire Records. Dist: Jetstar

Macfayden, Lain
CEOL MOR-CEOL BEAG.
Album: released on Temple(Scotland), Oct'85

MacGillivray,Iain
ROLLING HOME.
Album: released on Fellside, Jul'86 by Fellside Records. Dist: Roots, Jazz Music, Celtic Music, Projection

Cassette: released on Fellside, Jul'87 by Fellside Records. Dist: Roots, Jazz Music, Celtic Music, Projection

MacGregor, Freddie
GLAD YOU'RE HERE WITH ME.
Tracks: / Glad you're here with me / Push comes to shove.
Single (12"): released on R.A.S, May'86 by Greensleeves Records. Dist: RCA

MISERABLE WOMAN.
Tracks: / Miserable woman / Miserable woman (Version).
Single (12"): released on Greensleeves, Aug'86 by Greensleeves Records. Dist: BMG, Jetstar, Spartan

WINE OF VIOLENCE.
Tracks: / Wine of violence / Once a man.
Single (12"): released on Yashemabata, Jan'87 Dist: DMS-RCA

Mach 1
LOST FOR WORDS.
Album: released on Future Dance, Mar'85 Dist: Pinnacle

Machinations
PRESSURE SWAY Instrumental.
Single (12"): released on A&M, Jan'84 by A&M Records. Dist: Polygram

Machin, David
ICH LIEBE DICK.
Single (7"): released on PVK, Jul'81

SHOOT SHOOT JOHNNY.
Single (7"): released on PVK, May'82

Machito
AFRO-CUBAN JAZZ MOODS (Machito & Dizzy Gillespie).

AFRO-CUBOP (Machito & His Orchestra).
Album: released on Spotlite, '83 by Spotlite Records. Dist: Cadillac, Jazz Music, Spotlite

LIVE AT NORTH SEA 82 (Machito & His Salsa Big Band).
Album: released on Timeless, Apr'83

MUCHO MACHO MACHITO (Machito & His Afro Cuban Salseros).
Album: released on Pablo, '82 by Pablo Records. Dist: Wellard, Chris, IMS-Polygram, BMG

Cassette: released on Pablo, '82 by Pablo Records. Dist: Wellard, Chris, IMS-Polygram, BMG

SALSA BIG BAND 1982.
Album: released on Timeless (Holland), Aug'85 Dist: JSU Distribution, Jazz Music Distribution, Jazz Horizons Distribution, Cadillac, Celtic Music Distribution

Cassette: released on Timeless (Holland), Aug'85 Dist: JSU Distribution, Jazz Music Distribution, Jazz Horizons Distribution, Cadillac, Celtic Music Distribution

Macho Man
MACHO MAN.
Single (7"): released on Monarch, Aug'83 by Chart Records. Dist: Pinnacle

Macias, Enrico
ENRICO MACIAS.
Album: released on EMI (France), '83 by EMI Records. Dist: Conifer

MacIntosh, C.J.
TABLES ARE TURNING, THE.
Single (12"): released on Music Of Life, Aug'87 Dist: Streetwave

MacIntosh, Ian
LIVE IN GLASGOW.
Album: released on Kettle, Nov'79 Dist: JSU, Folksound, Celtic Music, MK

MacIntyre, Maurice
FORCES & FEELINGS.
Album: released on Delmark, '74 Dist: Projection, Swift, Cadillac

HUMILITY IN LIGHT OF CREATOR.
Album: released on Delmark, '74 Dist: Projection, Swift, Cadillac

Mac,Joy
INSEPARABLE.
Tracks: / Inseparable / Inseparable.
Single (7"): released on Sierra, '86 by Sierra Records. Dist: WEA

Single (12"): released on Sierra, '86 by Sierra Records. Dist: WEA

Macka-B
BIBLE READER.
Single (12"): released on Fashion, Jun'85 by Fashion Records. Dist: PRT, Jetstar

DON'T JUDGE ME.
Tracks: / Don't judge me / You are the ladies.
Single (12"): released on Ariwa, Nov'86 by Ariwa Records. Dist: Revolver, Cartel, Jetstar, Rough Trade

SIGN OF THE TIMES.
Album: released on Ariwa, '86 by Ariwa Records. Dist: Revolver, Cartel, Jetstar, Rough Trade

WETLOOK CRAZY.
Tracks: / Wetlook crazy / Down inna de jungle.
Single (12"): released on Ariwa, '86 by Ariwa Records. Dist: Revolver, Cartel, Jetstar, Rough Trade

Mackay, A.
IN SEARCH OF EDDIE RIFF.
Album: released on Polydor, Mar'77 by Polydor Records. Dist: Polygram, Polydor

MacKay, Rhona
SINGS AND PLAYS THE MUSIC OF THE HARP.
Album: released on Lismor, '84 by Lismor Records. Dist: Lismor, Roots, Celtic Music

Cassette: released on Lismor, '84 by Lismor Records. Dist: Lismor, Roots, Celtic Music

Mackenzie, Gisele
GISELE.
Album: released on RCA, Oct'84 by RCA Records. Dist: RCA, Roots, Swift, Wellard, Chris, I & B, Solomon & Peres Distribution

Cassette: released on RCA, Oct'84 by RCA Records. Dist: RCA, Roots, Swift, Wellard, Chris, I & B, Solomon & Peres Distribution

Tracks: / These foolish things remind me of you / You're my everything / Swingin' down the lane / On top of the world,alone / Don't worry 'bout me / Tiptoe thru the tulips / Everytime we say goodbye / Do you ever think of me / Between the devil & the deep blue sea / Beyond the sea / You are my lucky star / At sundown.

Mackenzie, Malcolm M.
MACKENZIES PIPES AND STRINGS (Mackenzie, Pipe Major Malcolm M.).
Compact disc: released on Lochshore, 20 Jun'87 by Klub Records. Dist: PRT

Album: released on Lochshore, Jun'85 by Klub Records. Dist: PRT

Mackenzies
MEALY MOUTH.
Single (12"): released on Ron Johnson, Feb'87 by Ron Johnson Records. Dist: Nine Mile Distribution, Cartel Distribution

Mack, Ida
IDA MAE MACK AND BESSIE TUCKER 1928 Recordings (Mack, Ida Mae/Bessie Tucker).
Album: released on Magpie, Jul'79 Dist: Projection

Mackintosh, Ken
VERY THOUGHT OF YOU, THE (Mackintosh, Ken & His Orchestra).
Album: released on President, Nov'85 by President Records. Dist: Taylors, Spartan

Mack,Jimmy & The Tropics
CHRISTMAS MEMORIES.
Tracks: / Christmas memories / Christmas memories (Inst.).
Single (12"): released on Suntan, '86 Dist: Jetstar Distribution

LATE IN THE EVENING.
Tracks: / Late in the evening / Late in the evening (Dub).
Single (12"): released on Suntan, '86 Dist: Jetstar Distribution

Mack, Joy
I NEED SOME MONEY.
Single (12"):

Mack, Le Roy
HOUND DOG RAMBLE.
Album: released on Briar (USA), Apr'79 by Sierra Records. Dist: Mike's Country Music Room Distribution, Projection

Mack, Lonnie
MEMPHIS.
Single (7"): released on Old Gold, Jul'82 by Old Gold Records. Dist: Lightning, Jazz Music, Spartan, Counterpoint

SECOND SIGHT.
Tracks: / Me and my car / Rock & Roll bones / Tough on me tough on you / Camp Washington Chill / Cincinatti / Rock people / Buffalo Woman / Ain't nobody / Back on the road again / Song I haven't sung, A.
Notes: Produced by lonnie Mack, associate producer Justin niebank.
Album: released on Sonet, Jan'87 by Sonet Records. Dist: PRT

STRIKE LIKE LIGHTNING.
Tracks: / Hound dog man / Satisfy Susie / Stop / Long way from Memphis / Double whammy / Strike like lightning / Falling back in love with you / If you have to know / You ain't got me / Oreo cookie blues.
Compact disc: by Sonet Records. Dist: PRT Deleted '86.

Album: released on Sonet, Aug'85 by Sonet Records. Dist: PRT

WHAM OF THAT MEMPHIS MAN, THE.
Album: released on Edsel, Apr'85 by Demon Records. Dist: Pinnacle, Jazz Music, Projection

Mack & Mabel
MACK & MABEL Original cast recording featuring Robert Preston.
Album: released on MCA, Oct'82 by MCA Records. Dist: Polygram, MCA

Cassette: released on MCA, Oct'82 by MCA Records. Dist: Polygram, MCA

Mack, Richie
IF I FELL.
Single (12"): released on S.Groove, Apr'83

MacLaine, Shirley
IN CONCERT.
Album: released on CBS Cameo, Aug'85 by CBS Records. Dist: CBS

Cassette: released on CBS Cameo, Aug'85 by CBS Records. Dist: CBS

Maclean, Alistair
GUNS OF NAVARONE, THE (READ BY PATRICK ALLEN).
Cassette: released on Listen For Pleasure, May'84 by MFP Records. Dist: EMI

MacLean, Calum
SCOTTISH ACCORDIAN HITS.
Album: released on Lismor, Jul'77 by Lismor Records. Dist: Lismor, Roots, Celtic Music

Cassette: released on Lismor, Jul'77 by Lismor Records. Dist: Lismor, Roots, Celtic Music

Cassette: released on Lismor, Jul'77 by Lismor Records. Dist: Lismor, Roots, Celtic Music

MacLean & MacLean
DOLLI PARTEN'S TITS.
Single (7"): released on Safari, May'81 by Safari Records. Dist: Pinnacle

TAKING THE 'O' OUT OF COUNTRY.
Album: released on Singing Dog, Jul'81

Cassette: released on Singing Dog, Jul'81

MacLeod, Bobby
AT THE DANCIN'.
Cassette: released on Emerald (Ireland), '81 by Emerald Records. Dist: I & B, Ross, PRT

GENUINE ARTICLE, THE.
Album: released on Lismor, '84 by Lismor Records. Dist: Lismor, Roots, Celtic Music

Cassette: released on Lismor, '84 by Lismor Records. Dist: Lismor, Roots, Celtic Music

MAN FROM TOBERMORY.
Cassette: released on Emerald (Ireland), Oct'81 by Emerald Records. Dist: I & B, Ross, PRT

WORLD OF SCOTLAND, THE (WITH OTHER ARTISTS).
Album: by World Of Learning Records. Dist: World Of Learning

MacLeod, Donald

PIPE TUNES HIGHLAND DANCING.
Album: released on Lismor, Jul'77 by Lismor Records. Dist: Lismor, Roots, Celtic Music

PIPE TUNES HIGHLAND DANCING.
Album: released on Lismor, Nov'77 by Lismor Records. Dist: Lismor, Roots, Celtic Music

POSITIVELY PIOBAIREACHD.
Album: released on Lismor, Jul'78 by Lismor Records. Dist: Lismor, Roots, Celtic Music

POSITIVELY PIOBAIR (MacLeod, Donald, Pipe Major).
Cassette: released on Lismor, Jul'78 by Lismor Records. Dist: Lismor, Roots, Celtic Music

MacLeod, Donnie

FAREWELL MY LOVE.
Album: released on Lismor, '83 by Lismor Records. Dist: Lismor, Roots, Celtic Music

Cassette: released on Lismor, '83 by Lismor Records. Dist: Lismor, Roots, Celtic Music

MacLeod, Jim

COME SCOTTISH COUNTRY DANCING WITH THE GREAT JIM MACLEOD.
Album: released on Decca, Sep'79 by Decca Records. Dist: Polygram

COULD I HAVE THIS DANCE (MacLeod, Jim & His Band).
Album: released on Ross, '86 by Ross Records. Dist: Ross Distribution, Roots Distribution

Cassette: released on Ross, '86 by Ross Records. Dist: Ross Distribution, Roots Distribution

DANCE PARTY FAVOURITES (MacLeod, Jim & His Band).
Compact disc: released on Scotdisc, May'87 Dist: Clyde Factors Distributors

JIM MACLEOD BAND WITH GUESTS.
Cassette: released on Beltona, Mar'80 by Decca Records. Dist: Polygram

JIM MACLEOD ENCORE MUSIC ALBUM (MacLeod, Jim & His Band).
Tracks: / Come to Fiona's wedding / Dan McKdowie's reel / Winding forth, The / Lights in Lochindaal / Bunesa (child in a manger) / Mull of the cool high bens / My Glasgow / Bonnie Dundee / John A Doig / Easdale house / Fare thee well Annabelle / Leaving Dundee / Captain McBrides hornpipe / Miss Claytons Hornpipe / Billy Cuthbertson / Navvie, The / I'd be a legend in my time / Moragis fairy glen / Staro' Rabbie Burns / Irish rover / Lovely banchory / Mrs Mary Prentice / Tambain's lum.
Cassette: released on Scotdisc, Jun'87 Dist: Clyde Factors Distributors

JIM MACLEOD'S SCOTTISH DANCE PARTY.
Tracks: / Come by the hills / Dashing white sergeant / St Ermins reel / Barbara A Stirling / A tune for Andy Burgess / Caddam woods / Miss Alison MacLeod / A tune for Donald McDonald / Do you think you could love again / Amazing Grace / Pittenweem Jo / Da tushker / Miss Susan Cooper / John Spence / Crusing down the river / Loch Lomond / After all these years / Morags fairy glen / Star O'Rabbie Burns / Rose of Allendale / Bugle horn (The) / Trip to Madeira (A) / Walter Simon of Perth / Leaving Dundee / Shufflin Sammy / Bluebell polka / Will you save the last dance for me / Just for old times sake.
Compact disc: released on Scotdisc, May'87 Dist: Clyde Factors Distributors

MAGIC SOUNDS OF JIM MACLEOD AND HIS BAND, THE (MacLeod, Jim & His Band).
Album: released on Music for Pleasure, May'83 by EMI Records. Dist: MFP Distribution

OUR KIND OF MUSIC (MacLeod, Jim & His Band).
Album: released on Decca, '78 by Decca Records. Dist: Polygram

SOUND OF SCOTLAND, THE (MacLeod, Jim & His Band).
Album: released on Klub, Jul'81

Cassette: released on Klub, Jul'81

SOUNDS SCOTTISH (MacLeod, Jim & His Band).
Cassette: released on Waverley, Oct'80 by EMI Records. Dist: EMI

SOUNDS SCOTTISH (PARTY NIGHT AT DUNBLANE HYDRO) (MacLeod, Jim & His Band).
Album: released on Waverley, Oct'80 by EMI Records. Dist: EMI

TAKE YOUR PARTNERS IT'S JIM.
Album: released on Decca, Jan'78 by Decca Records. Dist: Polygram

MacLeod, Margaret

WEST OF WEST.
Album: by EMI Records. Dist: EMI

MacLure, Pinkie

BITE THE HAND THAT FEEDS YOU (MacLure, Pinkie & David Harrow).
Single (12"): released on Ink, Jun'85 by Red Flame. Dist: Rough Trade, Cartel, Pinnacle

Mac Mac

SO SHY (Mac Mac - Jammolott kingdom).
Tracks: / So shy / So shy (inst) / So shy / Acapella Inst..
Single (7"): released on Creole, '86 by Creole Records. Dist: Rhino, PRT

Single (12"): released on Creole, '86 by Creole Records. Dist: Rhino, PRT

TAKE ME HOME LISA LISA (Mac Mac - Jammolott kingdom).
Single (7"):

Single (12"):

MacMunas Gang

TOWN CALLED BIG NOTHING, A.
Tracks: / Town called big nothing, A / Return to big nothing.
Single (7"): released on Demon, May'87 by Demon Records. Dist: Pinnacle

Single (12"): released on Demon, May'87 by Demon Records. Dist: Pinnacle

MacMurrough

CARRIG RIVER.
Tracks: / Carrig river / Follow me up to carlow / Sean dunnan gall / O'Sullivan's retreat / Johnny Shoemaker / Tunnel tigers / Reynard the fox / She moved through the fair / Tabhair dom do lamh / Rocky road to dublin / Diobhan ni dhuibhir / Courtown fishermen.
Cassette: released on Polydor (Ireland), Aug'86 by Polydor Records. Dist: Polygram, I & B

MacNab, Jim

CRYSTAL CHANDELIERS.
Album: released on Klub, May'79

Single (7"): released on Klub, Apr'79

MacNab, J.J.

DON'T TURN OUT THE LIGHT.
Album: released on Country House, Jun'81 by BGS Productions Ltd. Dist: Taylor, H.R., Record Merchandisers Distribution, Pinnacle, Sounds of Scotland Records

Cassette: released on Country House, Jun'81 by BGS Productions Ltd. Dist: Taylor, H.R., Record Merchandisers Distribution, Pinnacle, Sounds of Scotland Records

DO YOU RIGHT TONIGHT.
Single (7"): released on Country House, Oct'80 by BGS Productions Ltd. Dist: Taylor, H.R., Record Merchandisers Distribution, Pinnacle, Sounds of Scotland Records

MacNee, Patrick

KINKY BOOTS (see Blackman, Honor) (MacNee, Patrick & Honor Blackman).

MacNeice, Louis

FOUR TWENTIETH CENTURY POETS.
Cassette: released on Argo, Apr'85 by Decca Records. Dist: Polygram

MacNeil, Flora

CRAOBH NAN UBHAL.
Album: released on Tangent, Apr'81 Dist: Roots Distribution, Lugtons Distributors, Taylors, JSU Distribution, Spartan Distribution

MacNeill, Seumas

PURELY PIOBAIREACHD.
Album: released on Lismor, Nov'76 by Lismor Records. Dist: Lismor, Roots, Celtic Music

Macon, Uncle Dave

AT HOME - AT HOME, HIS LAST RECORDINGS, 1950.
Tracks: / Cumberland Mountain deer race / Rabbit in the pea patch / Bully of the town / Mountain dew / Old maid's love song / Rock of Ages / Keep my skillet good and greasy / Death of John Henry / That's where my money goes / Long John Green / Lady in the car / Cotton eyed Joe / Something's sure to tickle me / Chewing gum / All in down and out blues / Hungry hash house / Who mule / No one to welcome me home / Banjo solo / Jenny put the kettle on / Kissing in the sly.
Album: released on Bear Family, May'87 by Bear Family Records. Dist: Rollercoaster Distribution, Swift

MacOrlan, Pierre

CHANSONS DU QUAI DES BRUMES (MacOrlan, Pierre/Monique Morelli).
Album: released on Arion (France), May'79 Dist: Conifer, Discovery

MacPherson, Alexander A.

RULE BRITANNIA.
Album: released on Lismor, Jun'79 by Lismor Records. Dist: Lismor, Roots, Celtic Music

MacPherson,Fraser

I DIDN'T KNOW ABOUT YOU.
Album: released on Sackville, Jul'86 Dist: JSU, Jazz Music, Jazz Horizons, Cadillac Music, Celtic Music, Swift

JAZZ PROSE.
Album: released on Concord Jazz, Jul'85 by Concord Jazz Records (USA). Dist: IMS, Polygram

Cassette: released on Concord Jazz, Jul'85 by Concord Jazz Records (USA). Dist: IMS, Polygram

MacPherson, Sandy

I'LL PLAY FOR YOU.
Album: released on World Records, Aug'80 Dist: Polygram

Cassette: released on World Records, Aug'80 Dist: Polygram

MacRae, Dave

FORECAST (MacRae, Dave & John Yates).
Album: released on Tartar (New Zealand), '84

Cassette: released on Tartar (New Zealand), '84

MacRae, Donald

HEBRIDEAN JOURNEY.
Album: released on Lismor, May'77 by Lismor Records. Dist: Lismor, Roots, Celtic Music

Cassette: released on Lismor, May'77 by Lismor Records. Dist: Lismor, Roots, Celtic Music

MacRae,Gordon

MOTION PICTURE SOUNDSTAGE.
Tracks: / Singin' in the rain / Dancing in the dark / You're a sweetheart / Cabin in the sky / Hooray for love / Love is a many splendored thing / Jealousy / Pennies from heaven / Laura / Easy to love / Flirtation walk / Goodnight Sweetheart.
Notes: Orchestra conducted by: Van Alexander
Album: released on Capitol, Oct'86 by Capitol Records. Dist: EMI

Cassette: released on Capitol, Oct'86 by Capitol Records. Dist: EMI

OLD RUGGED CROSS (Macrae, Gordon and Jo Stafford).
Notes: Full details see under: Stafford, Jo.

Mac, Richie

OH SCENTED ROSE.
Single (12"): released on London Gemi, Jun'84 Dist: Pinnacle

Mac the Paperman

UP TO THE BOX.
Album: released on Dirtier Promotions, May'87 by Dirtier Promotions Records. Dist: Rare Sounds Distribution

Cassette: released on Dirtier Promotions, May'87 by Dirtier Promotions Records. Dist: Rare Sounds Distribution

M.A.D.

SUN FEAST.
Single (12"): released on Criminal Damage, Sep'84 by Criminal Damage Records. Dist: Backs, Cartel

Mad About Sunday

DRUNK.
Single (7"): released on Backs, May'83 by Backs Records. Dist: Backs, Cartel

Madagascar

MADAGASCAR Various Artists (Various Artists).
Compact disc: by Sterns Records. Dist: Sterns/Triple Earth Distribution

MAHALEO.
Album:

Madagasikara 1

MADAGASIKARA 1 Various Artists (Various Artists).
Tracks: / Afindrafindrao / King's song / Feam baliha / Dia Mahaory / Bonne annee amin ny tanana / Mamakivaky alankiminina / Fambolena eto Madagasikira / Nilentika/Tazana kely / Mahatsiarotsiaro fanina aeo zeho / Nametaa imaintso / Kilalao / Viavy Rosy.
Album: released on Globestyle, Oct'86 by Ace Records. Dist: Projection

Madagasikara 2

MADAGASIKARA 2 Various Artists (Various Artists).
Tracks: / Raha manina any / Ny any / Ento rora / Madirovalo / Mahaleo / Tsapika 2000 / Totoy tsara / Sarotra / Voromby (Oiseau de fer) / Aza mba manary toky / Malaza avaratna.
Album: released on Globestyle, Nov'86 by Ace Records. Dist: Projection

Madame Tussaud

ROCKIN' IN RHYTHM (Madame Tussaud's Dance Orchestra).
Tracks: / Rockin' in rhythm / Black eyed susan Brown / Jazz cocktail / My bluebird's singing the blues / Mood indigo / I raise my hat / Stevedore stomp / Roll up the carpet / Lightning / You're still in my heart / Wild goose chase / Sophisticated lady / Echoes of the jungle / Old man blues / We'll all go riding on a rainbow / Old fashioned sweethearts / Who walks in when I walk out ? / You're gonna lose your gal.
Album: released on Fountain-Retrieval, '86 by Retrieval Records. Dist: Retrieval, VJM, Swift, Jazz Music, Wellard, Chris

Madam X

HIGH IN HIGH SCHOOL.
Single (7"): released on Jet, Feb'85 by Jet Records. Dist: CBS

Special: released on Jet, Feb'85 by Jet Records. Dist: CBS

WE RESERVE THE RIGHT.
Album: released on Jet, Mar'85 by Jet Records. Dist: CBS

Cassette: released on Jet, Mar'85 by Jet Records. Dist: CBS

Mad Axeman

MAD AXEMAN.
Album: released on Mausoleum, May'85 by Mausoleum Records. Dist: Pinnacle

Mad Daddy's

APES GO WILD.
Album: released on New Rose, Jun'87 Dist: Rough Trade, Cartel

MUSIC FOR MEN.
Album: released on New Rose, Nov'85 Dist: Rough Trade, Cartel

Madder, Gaynor Rose

ARE YOU IN PAIN.
Single (7"): released on Ugly Man, Apr'87 Dist: Cartel

Single (12"): released on Ugly Man, Apr'87 Dist: Cartel

Maddern, Eric

NGATIJIRRI SUNRISE (Maddern, Eric & Calum MacColl).
Album: released on Ngati, Jun'85 by Ngati Records. Dist: Triple Earth

Maddison, Derek

I'LL GO WHERE THE MUSIC TAKES ME.
Single (7"): released on Fellside, Oct'80 by Fellside Records. Dist: Roots, Jazz Music, Celtic Music, Projection

Maddocks, John

GOOD VIBRATIONS (Maddocks, John & Jazz Maniacs).
Album: released on Folk Heritage, Jan'78 by Folk Heritage Records. Dist: Roots, Wynd-Up Distribution, Jazz Music, Folk Heritage

JUST GONE (Maddocks, John Jazzmen).
Album: released on Folk Heritage, Jul'82 by Folk Heritage Records. Dist: Roots, Wynd-Up Distribution, Jazz Music, Folk Heritage

Mad Dog

MAD DOG.
Notes: Mad Dog are the first signing to the new Stud Records label.
Album: released on Stud, Apr'87 by John Sherry.

Maddo, Oslbert

KING OF THE RING.
Single (12"): released on Sunsplash, Nov'83 by Sunsplash Records. Dist: Jetstar Distribution

Maddox Brothers & Rose

FAMILY FOLKS.
Album: released on CBS(USA), Sep'84 by Bear Family Records. Dist: Rollercoaster Distribution, Swift

MADDOX BROTHERS & ROSE 1946-1951 VOL.1.
Album: released on Arhoolie, May'81 by Arhoolie Records. Dist: Projection, Topic, Jazz Music, Swift, Roots

MADDOX BROTHERS & ROSE 1946-1951 VOL.2.
Album: released on Arhoolie, May'81 by Arhoolie Records. Dist: Projection, Topic, Jazz Music, Swift, Roots

ON THE AIR.
Album: released on Arhoolie, Feb'86 by Arhoolie Records. Dist: Projection, Topic, Jazz Music, Swift, Roots

Album: released on Arhoolie, May'84 by Arhoolie Records. Dist: Projection, Topic, Jazz Music, Swift, Roots

ROCKIN' ROLLIN' MADDOX BROTHERS & ROSE.
Album: released on Bear Family, Sep'84 by Bear Family Records. Dist: Rollercoaster Distribution, Swift

Maddox, Rose

BEAUTIFUL BOUQUET, A.
Album: released on Arhoolie, Jan'87 by Arhoolie Records. Dist: Projection, Topic, Jazz Music, Swift, Roots

Album: released on Arhoolie, Oct'86 by Arhoolie Records. Dist: Projection, Topic, Jazz Music, Swift, Roots

QUEEN OF THE WEST.
Album: released on Rounder (USA), Jan'84 Dist: Mike's Country Music Room Distribution, Jazz Music Distribution, Swift Distribution, Roots Records Distribution, Projection Distribution, Topic Distribution

SINGS BLUE GRASS.
Album: released on Stetson, Oct'86 by Hasmick Promotions Ltd.. Dist: Counterpoint Distribution, H.R. Taylor Distribution, Swift Distribution, Chris Wellard Distribution

Cassette: released on Stetson, Oct'86 by Hasmick Promotions Ltd.. Dist: Counterpoint Distribution, H.R. Taylor Distribution, Swift Distribution, Chris Wellard Distribution

Made In England

PROSPECTS.
Tracks: / Stay sharp / Prospects.
Notes: Featuring Ray Dorset
Single (7"): released on Red Bus, Feb'86 by Red Bus Records. Dist: PRT

STAY SHARP.
Single (7"): released on Red Bus, Aug'85 by Red Bus Records. Dist: PRT

Single (12"): released on Red Bus, Aug'85 by Red Bus Records. Dist: PRT

Made In Heaven

MADE IN HEAVEN 18 songs of pure inspiration (Various Artists).
Album: released on K-Tel, Jun'85 by K-Tel Records. Dist: Record Merchandisers Distribution, Taylors, Terry Blood Distribution, Wynd-Up Distribution, Relay Distribution, Pickwick Distribution, Solomon & Peres Distribution, Polygram

Cassette: released on K-Tel, Jun'85 by K-Tel Records. Dist: Record Merchandisers Distribution, Taylors, Terry Blood Distribution, Wynd-Up Distribution, Relay Distribution, Pickwick Distribution, Solomon & Peres Distribution, Polygram

Made To Measure

MADE TO MEASURE VOLUME 1 (Various Artists).
Album: released on Crammed Discs (Belgium), Mar'84 Dist: Rough Trade, Nine Mile, Cartel

Mad House

6.
Tracks: / 6 / 6#24.
Single (7"): released on Paisley Park (usa), Jun'87 by WEA Records. Dist: WEA

Single (12"): released on Paisley Park (usa), Jun'87 by WEA Records. Dist: WEA

MADHOUSE.
Single (12"): released on Homestead, Jun'85 Dist: Rough Trade, Cartel, Shigaku

Madigan, Gerry

TAKE ME BACK TO TULSA.
Single (7"): released on Homespun(Ireland), Sep'84 by Outlet Records. Dist: Outlet

Madison

BEST IN SHOW.
Tracks: / Oh rendezvous / Carry on / Hotel party / Drama / Shine / Give it back(remixed version) / Can't take it / World wide man / Out of the bunker / Mental masturbation.
Notes: All songs written by Madison. Produced & arranged by Anders Helmerson & Madison
Album: released on Sonet, Sep'86 by Sonet Records. Dist: PRT

Mad Jocks and Englishmen

GLORIA.
Single (7"): released on DPR, Apr'83 by DPR Records. Dist: Pinnacle

JUST LIKE KENNY.
Single (12"): released on Zuma, Mar'84 by Zuma Records. Dist: CBS, PRT

Single (12"): released on Zuma, Mar'84 by Zuma Records. Dist: CBS, PRT

Mad Lads

YOU BLEW IT.
Single (7"): released on Champion, Sep'85 by Champion Records. Dist: RCA

Single (12"): released on Champion, Sep'85 by Champion Records. Dist: RCA

Mad Max

MAD MAX-BEYOND THUNDERDOME Original motion picture soundtrack (Mad Max Beyond Thunderdome).
Album: released on Capitol, Aug'85 by Capitol Records. Dist: EMI

Cassette: released on Capitol, Aug'85 by Capitol Records. Dist: EMI

NIGHT OF PASSION.
Album: released on Roadrunner (Dutch), Jul'87 Dist: Pinnacle

ROLLIN THUNDER.
Album: released on Music For Nations, Aug'84 by Music For Nations Records. Dist: Pinnacle

STORMCHILD.
Album: released on Roadrunner (Dutch), Aug'85 Dist: Pinnacle

Mad Max 2

MAD MAX 2 Original motion picture soundtrack.
Album: released on That's Entertainment, Mar'02 by That's Entertainment Records. Dist: Pinnacle, PRT

Madness

7.
Album: released on Stiff, Oct'81

Cassette: released on Stiff, Oct'81

ABSOLUTELY.
Album: released on Stiff, Sep'80 by Stiff Records. Dist: EMI, Record Services Distribution (Ireland)

Cassette: released on Stiff, Sep'80 by Stiff Records. Dist: EMI, Record Services Distribution (Ireland)

BAGGY TROUSERS.
Single (7"): released on Stiff, Sep'80 by Stiff Records. Dist: EMI, Record Services Distribution (Ireland)

CARDIAC ARREST.
Single (7"): released on Stiff, Feb'82 by Stiff Records. Dist: EMI, Record Services Distribution (Ireland)

COMPLETE MADNESS.
Tracks: / Embarrassment / Shut up / My girl / Baggy trousers / It must be love / Prince, The / Bed & breakfast man / Night boat to Cairo / House of fun / One step beyond / Cardiac arrest / Grey day / Take it or leave it / In the city / Madness / Return of the Los Palmas 7.
Compact disc: released on Stiff, Jul'86 by Stiff Records. Dist: EMI, Record Services Distribution (Ireland)

Album: released on Stiff, Apr'82 by Stiff Records. Dist: EMI, Record Services Distribution (Ireland)

COMPLETE MADNESS(VIDEO).
Video-cassette (VHS): released on Stiff, Jan'84 by Stiff Records. Dist: EMI, Record Services Distribution (Ireland)

DRIVING IN MY CAR.
Single (7"): released on Stiff, Jun'82 by Stiff Records. Dist: EMI, Record Services Distribution (Ireland)

Picture disc single: released on Stiff, Jun'82 by Stiff Records. Dist: EMI, Record Services Distribution (Ireland)

Single (12"): released on Stiff, Jun'82 by Stiff Records. Dist: EMI, Record Services Distribution (Ireland)

EMBARRASSMENT.
Single (7"): released on Stiff, Nov'80 by Stiff Records. Dist: EMI, Record Services Distribution (Ireland)

GHOST TRAIN, THE.
Tracks: / Ghost train, The / maybe in another life / seven year scratch:*.
Single (7"): released on Zarjazz, Oct'86 by Virgin. Dist: EMI

Single (12"): released on Zarjazz, Oct'86 by Virgin. Dist: EMI

GREY DAY.
Single (7"): released on Stiff, Apr'81 by Stiff Records. Dist: EMI, Record Services Distribution (Ireland)

HOUSE OF FUN.
Single (7"): released on Stiff, May'82 by Stiff Records. Dist: EMI, Record Services Distribution (Ireland)

Picture disc single: released on Stiff, May'82 by Stiff Records. Dist: EMI, Record Services Distribution (Ireland)

IT MUST BE LOVE.
Single (7"): released on Stiff, Nov'81 by Stiff Records. Dist: EMI, Record Services Distribution (Ireland)

KEEP MOVING.
Album: released on Stiff, Feb'84 by Stiff Records. Dist: EMI, Record Services Distribution (Ireland)

Cassette: released on Stiff, Feb'84 by Stiff Records. Dist: EMI, Record Services Distribution (Ireland)

Picture disc album: released on Stiff, Jun'84 by Stiff Records. Dist: EMI, Record Services Distribution (Ireland)

MADNESS PRESENT THE RISE AND FALL.
Album: released on Stiff, Nov'82 by Stiff Records. Dist: EMI, Record Services Distribution (Ireland)

Cassette: released on Stiff, Nov'82 by Stiff Records. Dist: EMI, Record Services Distribution (Ireland)

MAD NOT MAD.
Tracks: / I'll compete / Yesterday's men / Uncle Sam / White heat / Mad not mad / Sweetest girl / Burning the boats / Tears you can't hide / Time / Coldest day.
Compact disc: released on Zarjazz, Jul'87 by Virgin. Dist: EMI

Album: released on Zarjazz, Oct'85 by Virgin. Dist: EMI

Cassette: released on Zarjazz, Oct'85 by Virgin. Dist: EMI

MICHAEL CAINE.
Single (7"): released on Stiff, Jan'84 by Stiff Records. Dist: EMI, Record Services Distribution (Ireland)

Single (12"): released on Stiff, Jan'84 by Stiff Records. Dist: EMI, Record Services Distribution (Ireland)

MY GIRL.
Single (7"): released on Stiff, Jan'80 by Stiff Records. Dist: EMI, Record Services Distribution (Ireland)

Single (12"): released on Stiff, Jan'80 by Stiff Records. Dist: EMI, Record Services Distribution (Ireland)

ONE BETTER DAY.
Picture disc single: released on Stiff, Jun'84 by Stiff Records. Dist: EMI, Record Services Distribution (Ireland)

ONE STEP BEYOND.
Cassette: released on Stiff, Oct'79 by Stiff Records. Dist: EMI, Record Services Distribution (Ireland)

Single (7"): released on Stiff, Oct'79 by Stiff Records. Dist: EMI, Record Services Distribution (Ireland)

Album: released on Stiff, Oct'79 by Stiff Records. Dist: EMI, Record Services Distribution (Ireland)

OUR HOUSE.
Single (7"): released on Stiff, Oct'82 by Stiff Records. Dist: EMI, Record Services Distribution (Ireland)

Picture disc single: released on Stiff, Oct'82 by Stiff Records. Dist: EMI, Record Services Distribution (Ireland)

Single (12"): released on Stiff, Nov'82 by Stiff Records. Dist: EMI, Record Services Distribution (Ireland)

PEEL SESSION 27.8.79.
Cassette single: released on Strange Fruit, 13 Jun'87 by Clive Selwood. Dist: Pinnacle

PRINCE (THE).
Tracks: / Madness.
Single (7"): released on Old Gold, Feb'87 by Old Gold Records. Dist: Lightning, Jazz Music, Spartan, Counterpoint

RETURN OF THE LOS PALMAS 7.
Single (7"): released on Stiff, Jan'81 by Stiff Records. Dist: EMI, Record Services Distribution (Ireland)

Single (12"): released on Stiff, Jan'81 by Stiff Records. Dist: EMI, Record Services Distribution (Ireland)

SHUT UP.
Single (7"): released on Stiff, Sep'81 by Stiff Records. Dist: EMI, Record Services Distribution (Ireland)

SUN AND THE RAIN.
Single (7"): released on Stiff, Oct'83 by Stiff Records. Dist: EMI, Record Services Distribution (Ireland)

Single (12"): released on Stiff, Oct'83 by Stiff Records. Dist: EMI, Record Services Distribution (Ireland)

Picture disc single: released on Stiff, Oct'83 by Stiff Records. Dist: EMI, Record Services Distribution (Ireland)

SWEETEST GIRL.
Tracks: / Sweetest girl / Jennie.
Single (7"): released on Zarjazz, Jan'86 by Virgin. Dist: EMI

Single (12"): released on Zarjazz, Jan'86 by Virgin. Dist: EMI

TOMORROW'S JUST ANOTHER DAY.
Single (7"): released on Stiff, Feb'83 by Stiff Records. Dist: EMI, Record Services Distribution (Ireland)

Single (12"): released on Stiff, Feb'83 by Stiff Records. Dist: EMI, Record Services Distribution (Ireland)

Picture disc single: released on Stiff, Feb'83 by Stiff Records. Dist: EMI, Record Services Distribution (Ireland)

UNCLE SAM.
Single (7"): released on Zarjazz, Oct'85 by Virgin. Dist: EMI

Single (12"): released on Zarjazz, Oct'85 by Virgin. Dist: EMI

UTTER MADNESS.
Album: released on Zarjazz, Nov'86 by Virgin. Dist: EMI

Cassette: released on Zarjazz, Nov'86 by Virgin. Dist: EMI

Compact disc: released on Zarjazz, Nov'86 by Virgin. Dist: EMI

Video-cassette (VHS): released on PVG, Jan'87

VICTORIA GARDENS.
Single (7"): released on Stiff, Apr'84 by Stiff Records. Dist: EMI, Record Services Distribution (Ireland)

WINGS OF A DOVE.
Single (7"): released on Stiff, Aug'83 by Stiff Records. Dist: EMI, Record Services Distribution (Ireland)

Single (12"): released on Stiff, Aug'83 by Stiff Records. Dist: EMI, Record Services Distribution (Ireland)

Picture disc single: released on Stiff, Aug'83 by Stiff Records. Dist: EMI, Record Services Distribution (Ireland)

WORK,REST AND PLAY MADNESS.
Single (7"): released on Stiff, Mar'80 by Stiff Records. Dist: EMI, Record Services Distribution (Ireland)

YESTERDAY'S MEN.
Single (7"): released on Zarjazz, Aug'85 by Virgin. Dist: EMI

Single (12"): released on Zarjazz, Aug'85 by Virgin. Dist: EMI

Madoc, Ruth

FOLLOWING A STAR (Madoc, Ruth and Children of Kings School).
Tracks: / Following a star.
Single (7"): released on Wattsco, Dec'86 Dist: PRT

Madonna

ANGEL.
Single (7"): released on Sire, Oct'85

Single (12"): released on Sire, Oct'85

BORDERLINE.
Tracks: / Borderline / Borderline / Physical attraction / Borderline,(DUB):*.
Single (7"): released on Sire, Jan'86

Single (7"): released on Sire, Jan'86

Single (7"): released on Sire, Jun'84

Single (12"): released on Sire, Jun'84

CRAZY FOR YOU.
Single (7"): released on Geffen, Jun'85 by Geffen Records. Dist: WEA, CBS

DRESS YOU UP.
Single (7"): released on Warner Brothers, Nov'85 by Warner Bros Records. Dist: WEA

Single (12"): by Warner Bros Records. Dist: WEA

Special: released on Warner Brothers, Nov'85 by Warner Bros Records. Dist: WEA

EVERYBODY.
Single (7"): released on Warner Brothers, Dec'82 by Warner Bros Records. Dist: WEA

Single (12"): released on Warner Brothers, Dec'82 by Warner Bros Records. Dist: WEA

GAMBLER.
Single (7"): released on Geffen, Oct'85 by Geffen Records. Dist: WEA, CBS

Single (12"): released on Geffen, Oct'85 by Geffen Records. Dist: WEA, CBS

HOLIDAY/THINK OF ME.
Single (7"): released on Sire, Nov'83

Single (12"): released on Sire, Nov'83

INTERVIEW PICTURE DISC.
Album: released on Baktabak, Jun'87 by Baktabak Records. Dist: Arabesque

INTO THE GROOVE.
Single (7"): released on Warner Brothers, Jul'85 by Warner Bros Records. Dist: WEA

Single (12"): released on Warner Brothers, Jul'85 by Warner Bros Records. Dist: WEA

Special: released on Warner Brothers, Jul'85 by Warner Bros Records. Dist: WEA

LA ISLA BONITA.
Tracks: La Isla Bonita (remix) / La Isla Bonita (instrumental).
Single (7"): released on Sire, Mar'87

Single (12"): released on Sire, Mar'87

LIKE A VIRGIN.
Tracks: / Material girl / Angel / Like a virgin / Over and over / Love don't live here anymore / Into the groove / Dress you up / Shoo-Bee-Doo / Pretender / Stay.
Compact disc: released on Sire, Sep'85

Album: released on Sire, Aug'85

Cassette: released on Sire, Aug'85

Single (7"): released on Sire, Sep'84

Single (12"): released on Sire, Sep'84

LIVE TO TELL.
Tracks: / Live to tell / Live to tell (inst).
Single (7"): released on Warner Bros., '86 by Warner Bros Records. Dist: WEA

Single (12"): released on Warner Bros., '86 by Warner Bros Records. Dist: WEA

LUCKY STAR.
Single (7"): released on Sire, Mar'84

Single (12"): released on Sire, Mar'84

MADONNA.
Tracks: / Lucky star / Borderline / Burning up / I know it / Holiday / Think of me / Physical attraction / Everybody.
Notes: Digital stereo
Compact disc: released on Sire, '84

Album: released on Sire, Sep'83

MATERIAL GIRL.
Single (7"): released on Warner Brothers, Feb'85 by Warner Bros Records. Dist: WEA

Single (12"): released on Warner Brothers, Feb'85 by Warner Bros Records. Dist: WEA

OPEN YOUR HEART.
Tracks: / Open your heart / Lucky star.
Single (7"): released on Sire, Nov'86

Single (12"): released on Sire, Nov'86

Single (7"): released on Virgin, Oct'81 by Virgin Records. Dist: EMI, Virgin Distribution

Single (12"): released on Virgin, Oct'81 by Virgin Records. Dist: EMI, Virgin Distribution

PAPA DON'T PREACH.
Tracks: / Papa doesn't preach / Ain't no big deal.
Single (7"): released on Sire, '86

Single (12"): released on Sire, '86

TRUE BLUE.
Tracks: / True blue / Holiday / True Blue / Holiday / Papa dont preach / Open your heart / White heart / Live to tell / Where's the party / True Blue / La Isla Bonita / Jimmy, Jimmy / Love makes the world go round.
Single (7"): released on Sire, Sep'86

Single (12"): released on Sire, Sep'86

Cassette single: released on Sire, Jul'86

Compact disc: released on Sire, Jul'86

Album: released on Sire, Jul'86

VIDEO EP (THE).
Notes: Number of tracks: 4. Type of recording: EP. Total playing time: 18 minutes.
Video-cassette (VHS): released on Warner music, '86 by Warner Bros Records. Dist: WEA

VIRGIN TOUR (THE).
Notes: Number of tracks: 10. Type of recording: Live. Total playing time: 50 minutes.
Video-cassette (VHS): released on WEA, '86 by WEA Records. Dist: WEA

Video-cassette [Betamax]: released on WEA, '86 by WEA Records. Dist: WEA

WHO'S THAT GIRL.
Tracks: / Who's that girl / White heat.
Single (7"): released on Sire, Jul'87

Single (12"): released on Sire, Jul'87

WILD DANCING (Madonna & Otto Wernherr).
Single (12"): released on Receiver, Feb'87 by Receiver Records. Dist: Pinnacle

---

Madore,Michel
LA CHAMBRE BUPTIALE.
Album: released on Egg, Apr'79 Dist: Red Rhino, Cartel

Mad Professor
DUB ME CRAZY.
Album: released on Ariwa, Oct'82 by Ariwa Records. Dist: Revolver, Cartel, Jetstar, Rough Trade

DUB ME CRAZY PART 5.
Album: released on Ariwa, Jan'85 by Ariwa Records. Dist: Revolver, Cartel, Jetstar, Rough Trade

JAH SHAKA MEETS MAD PROFESSOR AT ARIWA SOUNDS (Mad Professor & Jah Shaka).
Album: released on Ariwa, Apr'84 by Ariwa Records. Dist: Revolver, Cartel, Jetstar, Rough Trade

NEGUS ROOTS MEETS THE MAD PROFESSOR (Mad Professor & Negus Roots).
Album: released on Negus Roots, Mar'84 by Negus Roots Records. Dist: Jetstar

PROFESSOR CAPTURES PATO BANTON (Mad Professor & Pato Banton).
Album: released on Ariwa, Oct'85 by Ariwa Records. Dist: Revolver, Cartel, Jetstar, Rough Trade

SCHIZOPHRENIC DUB.
Album: released on Ariwa, Jul'86 by Ariwa Records. Dist: Revolver, Cartel, Jetstar, Rough Trade

STEPPING IN DUBWISE COUNTRY (Mad River).
Album: released on Ariwa, May'87 by Ariwa Records. Dist: Revolver, Cartel, Jetstar, Rough Trade

Mad River
MAD RIVER.
Album: released on Edsel, Mar'85 by Demon Records. Dist: Pinnacle, Jazz Music, Projection

PARADISE BAR & GRILL.
Cassette: released on Edsel, May'86 by Demon Records. Dist: Pinnacle, Jazz Music, Projection

Album: released on Edsel, May'86 by Demon Records. Dist: Pinnacle, Jazz Music, Projection

Madskwad
BELT HAS GOT TO STAY/WE ARE THE...
Single (7"): released on Lismor, May'82 by Lismor Records. Dist: Lismor, Roots, Celtic Music

---

Mad Violets
WORLD OF....
Album: released on Eva-Lolita, Jul'86 Dist: Pinnacle

Maegan
DOCTOR'S ORDERS.
Single (7"): released on Savoir Faire, May'84

Single (12"): released on Savoir Faire, May'84

Maelen,Jimmy
BEATS WORKIN'.
Album: released on Epic, Sep'80 by CBS Records. Dist: CBS

Maelov,Eddie
ANOTHER TEARDROP (Maelov,Eddie and Sunshine Patterson).
Single (7"): released on Human, Nov'81 Dist: Roots, Stage One

Single (12"): released on Human, Nov'81 Dist: Roots, Stage One

LINES/LAST BOUQUET (Maelov,Eddie and Sunshine Patterson).
Single (7"): released on Human, Jul'81 Dist: Roots, Stage One

Single (12"): released on Human, Jul'81 Dist: Roots, Stage One

Maestro Orchestra
PERSONAL CHOICE.
Notes: Directed by Tommy Sanderson. Track details not advised.
Album: released on Maestro, Oct'86 by Maestro Records.

Mae,Thelma
WONDERMAN LOVER.
Single (7"): released on Solid Groove, Sep'81 Dist: Jetstar, Pinnacle

Maffia
DA NI'M YN RHAN.
Album: released on Sain, '85 by Sain Records. Dist: Projection, Isain

Maffia Mr Huws
YR OCHOR ARALL.
Album: released on Sain, '85 Dist: Roots

Mafia, Leroy
LIFE IS JUST A DREAM (Leroy Mafia).
Tracks: / Life is just a dream / Anywhere you go.
Single (12"): released on Vena, Apr'86 by Vena Records. Dist: Jetstar

Magadini, Pete
BONES BLUES (Magadini,Pete,Quartet).
Notes: Track details not advised. Artists also include: Don Menza/ Dave Young/ Wray Downes/.
Album: released on Sackville, Jul'86 Dist: JSU, Jazz Music, Jazz Horizons, Cadillac Music, Celtic Music, Swift

Magazine
AFTER THE FACT.
Album: released on Virgin, May'82 by Virgin Records. Dist: EMI, Virgin Distribution

Cassette: released on Virgin, May'82 by Virgin Records. Dist: EMI, Virgin Distribution

MAGIC MURDER AND THE WEATHER.
Album: released on Virgin, Jun'81 by Virgin Records. Dist: EMI, Virgin Distribution

RAYS AND HAIL.
Compact disc: released on Virgin, Jun'87 by Virgin Records. Dist: EMI, Virgin Distribution

REAL LIFE.
Album: released on Virgin, Mar'84 by Virgin Records. Dist: EMI, Virgin Distribution

Magazine 60
DON QUICHOTTE.
Tracks: / Don Quichotte.
Single (7"): released on RCA, Jul'86 by RCA Records. Dist: RCA, Roots, Swift, Wellard, Chris, I & B, Solomon & Peres Distribution

Single (12"): released on RCA, Jul'86 by RCA Records. Dist: RCA, Roots, Swift, Wellard, Chris, I & B, Solomon & Peres Distribution

Magdalen College
NOW THE HOLLY (Magdalen College Choir Oxford).
Album: released on Abbey, '74 by Abbey. Dist: PRT, Taylors, Gamut

---

Mageean, J & A.
MAGEEAN/FITZSIMMONS (Mageean, J. & A.A. Fitzsimmons).
Album: released on Greenwich Village, Jan'87 by Sweet Folk All Records. Dist: Roots, Projection, Lightning, Celtic Music, Wellard, Chris

Mageean, Jim
CAPSTAN BAR, THE.
Album: released on Dingles, Mar'79 by Dingles Records. Dist: Projection

MAKE THE RAFTERS ROAR (Mageean, Jim & Johnny Collins).
Album: released on Sweet Folk All, May'81 by Sweet Folk All Records. Dist: Sweet Folk All, Roots, Celtic Music, Dragon, Impetus, Projection, Chris Wellard, Festival Records

OF SHIPS AND MEN.
Album: released on Greenwich Village, May'81 by Sweet Folk All Records. Dist: Roots, Projection, Lightning, Celtic Music, Wellard, Chris

STRONTRACE (Mageean, Jim & Johnny Collins).
Album: released on Greenwich Village, Jan'85 by Sweet Folk All Records. Dist: Roots, Projection, Lightning, Celtic Music, Wellard, Chris

Magee, Len
LEN MAGEE.
Album: released on Dove, May'79 by Dove Records. Dist: Jetstar

LOVE IS THE ANSWER.
Album: by Pilgrim Records. Dist: Rough Trade, Cartel

ONCE UPON A WINTER.
Album: by Pilgrim Records. Dist: Rough Trade, Cartel

PRAYER SONG VOL.1.
Album: released on Dove, May'79 by Dove Records. Dist: Jetstar

PRAYER SONG VOL.2.
Album: released on Dove, May'79 by Dove Records. Dist: Jetstar

PRESENCE OF YOUR SPIRIT.
Album: released on Dove, May'79 by Dove Records. Dist: Jetstar

PRICE OF PEACE, THE.
Album: released on Dove, May'79 by Dove Records. Dist: Jetstar

Maggie Maggie Maggie...
MAGGIE MAGGIE MAGGIE OUT OUT OUT Various artists (Various Artists).
Tracks: / Open your eyes / Government stinks / Women in disguise / Fuck religion, fuck politics, fuck the lot of you / Flood of lies / You'll never know / Crisis / Government policy / Warning / Kill the poor / Government downfall / Burn 'em down / Keep Britain untidy / Government's to blame / Police story / Give us a future.
Album: released on Anagram, Jun'87 by Cherry Red Records. Dist: Pinnacle

Cassette: released on Anagram, Jun'87 by Cherry Red Records. Dist: Pinnacle

Maggie May
MAGGIE MAY Original London cast (Various Artists).
Album: released on That's Entertainment, Apr'83 by That's Entertainment Records. Dist: Pinnacle, PRT

Cassette: released on That's Entertainment, Apr'83 by That's Entertainment Records. Dist: Pinnacle, PRT

Magic
MAGIC.
Album: released on Bullseye, Jul'79 Dist: Bullseye Music

Magical Brass
MAGICAL BRASS (Various Artists).
Cassette: released on Ampro Cassettes, Sep'81

Magical Michael
MILLIONAIRE.
Single (7"): released on Atomic, Aug'80 by Atomic Records. Dist: Pinnacle

Magical mull
MAGICAL MULL (Various Artists).
Cassette: released on Mull Recordings, Jan'87 by Mull Recordings. Dist: Ross Records, Sounds of Scotland Records

Magic Box
I HEARD IT THROUGH THE GRAPEVINE.
Single (12"): released on Kameleon, Feb'85

Magic Circle
MAGIC CIRCLE RECORD Featuring Paul Daniels (Various Artists).
Album: released on Technical, Dec'80 Dist: Stage One Distribution

Magician
HOUSE OF THE PURPLE MIST (1&2).
Single (7"): released on Hobo, Aug'79 by Hobo Records. Dist: Hobo

MAGICIAN.
Album: released on Hobo, May'79 by Hobo Records. Dist: Hobo

Magic Instrumentals
MAGIC INSTRUMENTALS Various artists (Various Artists).
Notes: Duane Eddy, Acker Bilk, Chris Barber etc.
Compact disc: released on Bridge, '86 Dist: CD Centre Distribution, Pinnacle, Target

Magic Machines
DANNY THE DUMPER TRUCK.
: released on Look & Listen, Nov'84 by Listen For Pleasure. Dist: EMI

MAGGIE THE MECHANICAL DIGGER.
Cassette: released on Look & Listen, Nov'84 by Listen For Pleasure. Dist: EMI

SIMON THE CEMENT MIXER.
Cassette: released on Look & Listen, Nov'84 by Listen For Pleasure. Dist: EMI

Magic Magic Co
TABLE TOP TAP.
Single (7"): released on It's Magic, Feb'84 by It's Magic Records. Dist: Pinnacle

Magic moments
MAGIC MOMENTS Various artists (Various Artists).
Tracks: / Make the world go away / Without you / We used to / Distant drums / That old feeling / Moon river / Catch a falling star / Moonlight Serenade / Cry me a river / Stormy weather / Solitude / Magic moments / Shadow of your smile / Light my fire / You win again / Make it with you.
Notes: Tracks 1, 9, 12, 13 - electronic Stereo, track 15 - mono.
Album: released on Music For Pleasure, Feb'87 by EMI Records. Dist: EMI

Cassette: released on Music For Pleasure, Feb'87 by EMI Records. Dist: EMI

MAGIC MOMENTS Various Artists (Various Artists).
Notes: Artists include: Hits of the 50's: Perry Como/Jonny Ray/etc
Album: released on Starblend, Oct'86 by Starblend Records. Dist: PRT Distribution

Cassette: released on Starblend, Oct'86 by Starblend Records. Dist: PRT Distribution

MAGIC MOMENTS.
Album: released on CBS, Nov'84 by CBS Records. Dist: CBS

Cassette: released on CBS, Nov'84 by CBS Records. Dist: CBS

MAGIC MOMENTS Various Artists (Various Artists).
Cassette: released on RCA, Jun'84 by RCA Records. Dist: RCA, Roots, Swift, Wellard, Chris, I & B, Solomon & Peres Distribution

MAGIC MOMENTS FROM THE 50'S (Various Artists).
Cassette: released on AIM (Budget Cassettes), Feb'83

Magic of Christmas
MAGIC OF CHRISTMAS (Various Artists).
Album: released on Audio Fidelity, Oct'84 Dist: PRT

Cassette: released on Audio Fidelity, Oct'84 Dist: PRT

Magic of Dance
MAGIC OF DANCE Magic of Dance (Various Artists).
Album: released on BBC, '79 by BBC Records & Tapes. Dist: EMI, PRT, Pye

Cassette: released on BBC, '79 by BBC Records & Tapes. Dist: EMI, PRT, Pye

Magic of Lassie
MAGIC OF LASSIE (Various Artists).
Album: released on Pickwick, May'79 by Pickwick Records. Dist: Pickwick Distribution, Prism Leisure Distribution, Lugtons

Cassette: released on Pickwick, May'79 by Pickwick Records. Dist: Pickwick Distribution, Prism Leisure Distribution, Lugtons

Magic of Paris
MAGIC OF PARIS (Various Artists).
Album: released on Note, Sep'81 by EMI Records. Dist: EMI Deleted '87.

Cassette: released on Note, Sep'81 by EMI Records. Dist: EMI

Magic of Torvill & Dean
MAGIC OF TORVILL & DEAN (Various Artists).
Album: released on Stylus, Aug'85 Dist: Pinnacle, Terry Blood Distribution, Stylus Distribution

Cassette: released on Stylus, Aug'85 Dist: Pinnacle, Terry Blood Distribution, Stylus Distribution

Magic of Vienna
MAGIC OF VIENNA, THE.
Album:

Magic Pan Flutes
MAGIC OF THE PAN FLUTE (THE).
Notes: Double album and cassette. Track details not advised.
Album: released on Avon, Aug'87 by Avon Records. Dist: Counterpoint

Cassette single: released on Avon, Jul'86 by Avon Records. Dist: Counterpoint

Magic Quern
MAGIC QUERN, THE Stories from Barra in Gaelic & English.
Cassette: released on Folktracks, Nov'79 by Folktracks Cassettes. Dist: Folktracks

Magic Roundabout
MAGIC ROUNDABOUT (Thompson, Eric).
Album: released on BBC, Oct'76 by BBC Records & Tapes. Dist: EMI, PRT, Pye

Cassette: released on BBC, Oct'76 by BBC Records & Tapes. Dist: EMI, PRT, Pye

Magic Sam
BLACK MAGIC.
Album: released on Delmark, '74 Dist: Projection, Swift, Cadillac

EASY BABY.
Album: released on Charly(R&B), Oct'85 by Charly Records. Dist: Charly, Cadillac

WEST SIDE SOUL (Magic Sam Blues Band).
Album: released on Delmark (USA), May'84 Dist: Swift

Magic Sounds
MAGIC SOUNDS OF THE EDINBURGH MILITARY TATTOO (Various Artists).
Album: released on MFP, May'83 by EMI Records. Dist: EMI

MAGIC SOUNDS OF THE PIPES (Various Artists).
Album: released on MFP, May'83 by EMI Records. Dist: EMI

Magic strings
FLOWERS.
Notes: Arranged and conducted by norman Candler.
Album: released on Intersound, Dec'86 by Intersound Records. Dist: Jazz Music

Magic touch, The
MAGIC TOUCH, THE Various Artists (Various Artists).
Album: released on Kent, Aug'86 by Ace Records. Dist: Pinnacle

Magic Toyshop, The
MAGIC TOYSHOP, THE Original soundtrack (Original Soundtrack).
Album: released on TER, Aug'87 Dist: Pinnacle

Cassette: released on TER, Aug'87 Dist: Pinnacle

Magma
MAGMA LIVE.
Album: released on Tomato, Mar'79

UDU WUDU.
Album: released on Tomato, Mar'79

Magna Carta
HIGHWAY TO SPAIN.
Single (7"): released on Recorded Delivery, Aug'81 Dist: RCA

LOVE IS FOREVER.
Single (7"): released on Mays, Apr'84 by Mays Records. Dist: Roots, Spartan, Projection

SEASONS.
Album: released on Vertigo (Import), Apr'83 Dist: IMS, Polygram

Cassette: released on Vertigo (Import), Apr'83 Dist: IMS, Polygram

SPOTLIGHT ON MAGNA CARTA.
Double Album: released on Philips, Jun'77 Dist: IMS-Polygram

Magnante, Charles
ACCORDIAN ENCORES.
Tracks: / Minute Waltz / Granada / Dance of the Dwarfs / I know that you know / Beer barrel Polka / Pavan & Ronda / Perpetual motion / Italian Medley / Waltz allegro / Waltz in B flat / Hora staccato / In a mist / Bach goes to town / Durand waltz / Reflections / Clarinet polka.
Cassette: released on Accordion Record Club, Jul'86 by Accordion Record Club Records. Dist: Accordion Record Club

CHARLES MAGNANTE, VIRTUOSO.
Tracks: / Marriage of Figaro / Piano concerto in B flat min / Blue Danube / Voices of spring / Bouree / Prelude in G minor / Capricco / Italian / Waltz in C sharp min / Prelude in E minor / Dance of the red flutes / Song of India.
Cassette: released on Accordion Record Club, Jul'86 by Accordion Record Club Records. Dist: Accordion Record Club

Magne, Michael
ELEMENT NO.1 La terre.
Album: released on Egg, Nov'79 by Barclay Records. Dist: Logo, RCA, Discovery

Magness, Ron
MIRACLES.
Single (7"): released on Towerbell, Jan'83 by Towerbell Records. Dist: EMI

STAND BY ME.
Single (7"): released on Towerbell, Sep'82 by Towerbell Records. Dist: EMI

Magnet Disco Magic
MAGNET DISCO MAGIC (Various Artists).
Album: released on MFP, Oct'79 by EMI Records. Dist: EMI

Magnetic Hits
MAGNETIC HITS (Various Artists).
Double Album: released on Cambra, Apr'85 by Cambra Records. Dist: IDS, Conifer

Cassette: released on Cambra, Apr'85 by Cambra Records. Dist: IDS, Conifer

Magnetic north
MAGNETIC NORTH Various Artists (Various Artists).
Cassette: released on Touch, Apr'86 by Touch Records. Dist: Rough Trade, Cartel

Magnificent 7
MAGNIFICENT 7 (THE) (Various Artists).
Album: released on ABC, Feb'87 Dist: CBS, Pinnacle

Magnificent Marches
MAGNIFICENT MARCHES various artists (Various Artists).
Album: released on Cambra, May'85 by Cambra Records. Dist: IDS, Conifer

Cassette: released on Cambra, May'85 by Cambra Records. Dist: IDS, Conifer

Magnificents
15 COOL JEWELS (Magnificents & The Rhythm Aces).
Album: released on Solid Smoke (USA), Feb'85 Dist: Rhino

Magnificent Seven
MAGNIFICENT SEVEN Bernstein.
Album: released on Sun Set, '70 by Sun Set Records. Dist: Jetstar Distribution

Magnolia Jazz band
MAGNOLIA JAZZ BAND.
Album: released on Stomp Off, Jun'86 by Stomp Off Records. Dist: Jazz Music Distribution

Magnum
11TH HOUR, THE.
Compact disc: released on Jet Caroline, Jan'87

ANTHOLOGY.
Tracks: / In the beginning / Lords of chaos / Kingdom of madness / Bringer, The / Greta adventures / Fire Bird / Foolish geart heart / Stayin' alive / If i could live forever / Reborn (live) / Changes (live) / Walking the straight line / We all play the game / Spirit, The / Prise, The / Vicious companions / Word, The / Hit & run / So far away.
Double Album: released on Raw Power, Apr'86 Dist: Pinnacle

Cassette: Dist: Pinnacle

Compact disc: released on Raw Power, May'86 Dist: Pinnacle

BACK TO EARTH.
Single (7"): released on Jet, Sep'82 by Jet Records. Dist: CBS

CHASE THE DRAGON.
Compact disc: released on Jet Caroline, Jan'87

Album: released on Jet, Jun'84 by Jet Records. Dist: CBS

Cassette: released on Jet, Jun'84 by Jet Records. Dist: CBS

ELEVENTH HOUR, THE.
Album: released on Jet, Jun'83 by Jet Records. Dist: CBS

Cassette: released on Jet, Jun'83 by Jet Records. Dist: CBS

JUST LIKE AN ARROW.
Single (7"): released on FM, Mar'85 by FM-Revolver Records. Dist: EMI

Single (12"): released on FM, Mar'85 by FM-Revolver Records. Dist: EMI

KINGDOM OF MADNESS.
Album: released on Jet, Aug'78 by Jet Records. Dist: CBS. Estim retail price in Jul'87 was £3.99.

Cassette: released on Jet, Aug'78 by Jet Records. Dist: CBS

Compact disc: released on Castle Classics, '86 by Castle Communications. Dist: BMG

LIGHTS BURNED OUT.
Single (7"): released on Jet, Feb'82 by Jet Records. Dist: CBS

MAGNUM II.
Tracks: / Great adventure / Changes / Battle (The) / If I could live forever / Reborn / So cold the night / Foolish heart / Stayin' alive / Firebird / All of my life.
Notes: Produced by: Leo Lyons
Album: released on Castle Classics, Mar'87 by Castle Communications. Dist: BMG

Album: released on JKH, Oct'79 by JKH Records. Dist: Jetstar

Cassette: released on Jet, Oct'79 by Jet Records. Dist: CBS

Compact disc: released on Castle Classics, '86 by Castle Communications. Dist: BMG

MARAUDER.
Tracks: / If I could live forever / Battle (the) / Foolish heart / In the beginning / Reborn / Changes / So cold the night / Lords of chaos.
Album: released on Castle Classics, Mar'87 by Castle Communications. Dist: BMG

Album: released on Jet, May'80 by Jet Records. Dist: CBS

Cassette: released on Jet, May'80 by Jet Records. Dist: CBS

Compact disc: released on Castle Classics, '86 by Castle Communications. Dist: BMG

MIDNIGHT.
Tracks: / Midnight / Back street kid.
Single (7"): released on Polydor, Oct'86 by Polydor Records. Dist: Polygram, Polydor

Single (12"): released on Polydor, Oct'86 by Polydor Records. Dist: Polygram, Polydor

OH LONELY NIGHT.
Tracks: / Oh lonely night / Le morts dansants(live) / Hold back your love(live).
Single (7"): released on Polydor, Jun'86 by Polydor Records. Dist: Polygram, Polydor

ON A STORYTELLERS NIGHT.
Tracks: / How far Jerusalem / Just like an arrow / Before first light / On a storytellers night / Les morts dansant / Endless love / Two hearts / Steal your heart / All England / Last Dance.
Album: released on FM, Mar'87 by FM-Revolver Records. Dist: EMI

Cassette: released on FM, Mar'87 by FM-Revolver Records. Dist: EMI

Compact disc: released on FM, Mar'87 by FM-Revolver Records. Dist: EMI

Album: released on FM, May'85 by FM-Revolver Records. Dist: EMI

Cassette: released on FM, May'85 by FM-Revolver Records. Dist: EMI

Picture disc single: released on FM, May'85 by FM-Revolver Records. Dist: EMI

Compact disc: released on FM, May'85 by FM-Revolver Records. Dist: EMI

Single (7"): released on FM, Jun'85 by FM-Revolver Records. Dist: EMI

Single (12"): released on FM, Jun'85 by FM-Revolver Records. Dist: EMI

SACRED HOUR, THE -LIVE.
Video-cassette (VHS): released on Embassy, Feb'86 by EBS Records. Dist: CBS

VIGILANTE.
Tracks: / Lonely night / Need a lot of love / Sometime love / Midnight(you won't be sleeping) / Red on the highway / Holy rider / When the world comes down / Vigilante / Back street kid.
Album: released on Polydor, Oct'86 by Polydor Records. Dist: Polygram, Polydor

Cassette: released on Polydor, Oct'86 by Polydor Records. Dist: Polygram, Polydor

Compact disc: released on Polydor, Oct'86 by Polydor Records. Dist: Polygram, Polydor

WHEN THE WORLD COMES DOWN.
Tracks: / Vigilante.
Single (7"): released on Polydor, Feb'87 by Polydor Records. Dist: Polygram, Polydor

Single (12"): released on Polydor, Feb'87 by Polydor Records. Dist: Polygram, Polydor

Magnum Force
SHARE MY LOVE.
Album: released on Bluebird, Nov'84 by Bluebird Records, Jan'86, Jetstar

Magnum Force Rockfile
MAGNUM FORCE ROCKFILE various artists (Various Artists).
Album: released on Magnum Force, Jul'82 by Magnum Music Group Ltd. Dist: Magnum Music Group Ltd, PRT, Spartan

Magnum Mysterium
MAGNUM MYSTERIUM (Various Artists).
Album: released on Kuckuck, Apr'87 Dist: PRT

Cassette: released on Kuckuck, Apr'87 Dist: PRT

Magnum PI
MAGNUM PI The american TV hits album (Various Artists).
Album: released on Indiana, Nov'86 Dist: PRT

Cassette: released on Indiana, Nov'86 Dist: PRT

Magnus Cathedral
CHOIR & ORGAN OF....
Album: released on Lismor, '75 by Lismor Records. Dist: Lismor, Roots, Celtic Music

Magnus, Nick
SUN ARISE.
Single (7"): released on Polydor, Jun'84 by Polydor Records. Dist: Polygram, Polydor

Magnusson, Bob
REVELATION.
Compact disc: released on Discovery (USA), Dec'86 by Discovery Records (USA). Dist: Swift, Flexitron-Audio, Jazz Music

SONG FOR JANET LEE (Magnusson, Bob Quintet).
Tracks: / Song for Janet / Waltz you saved, The / Poet, The / When it comes to pass / Peace of mind / Double play(a pitcher's delight).
Notes: Bob Magnusson-bass/Hubert Laws-flute/Bobby Shew-trumpet and flugelhorn/Peter Sprague-guitar/Billy Mintz-drums
Compact disc: released on Discovery (USA), Sep'86 by Discovery Records (USA). Dist: Swift, Flexitron-Audio, Jazz Music

Album: released on Discovery (USA), Nov'84 by Discovery Records (USA). Dist: Swift, Flexitron-Audio, Jazz Music

Maguire Gang
GIMME GOOD TIMES.
Single (7"): released on Real Feel, Jan'85 by Real Feel.

Maguire, John
COME DAY GO DAY GOD SEND SUNDAY.
Album: released on Leader, '81 Dist: Jazz Music, Projection

Mahal, Taj
SOOTHIN'.
Single (7"): released on Sonet, Aug'87 by Sonet Records. Dist: PRT

Single (12"): released on Sonet, Aug'87 by Sonet Records. Dist: PRT

TAJ.
Tracks: / Everybody is somebody / Paradise / Do I love her / Light of the pacific / Deed I do / Soothin' / Pillow talk / Local local girl / Kauai calypso / French letter.
Notes: Produced by Taj Mahal. Executive producer Jonathan F.P. rose.
Album: released on Sonet, Jan'87 by Sonet Records. Dist: PRT

Mahana
CRYSTAL CHANDELIERS.
Single (7"): released on Dawn, Nov'82

Mahavishnu
MAHAVISHNU.
Album: released on WEA, Jan'85 by WEA Records. Dist: WEA

Mahavishnu Orchestra
BIRDS OF FIRE.
Album: released on CBS, Nov'83 by CBS Records. Dist: CBS

Cassette: released on CBS, Nov'83 by CBS Records. Dist: CBS

Maher, Gina
BRIGHT SIDE UP.
Single (7"): released on Young Blood, Jul'85 by Young Blood Records. Dist: Pinnacle

Mah, Marcella
SHOA LIN.
Single (7"): released on Rebecca, Jan'82 by Rebecca Records. Dist: Pinnacle

Mah, Marchella
I'M YOURS MAYBE.
Tracks: / I'm tours maybe.
Single (7"): released on Pink Fly, Oct'86 Dist: Pinnacle

MAKE HAY WHILE THE SUN SHINES.
Tracks: / Make hay while the sun shines / Give it up.
Single (7"): released on Pink Fly, Jun'87 Dist: Pinnacle

Mahogany
RIDE ON THE RHYTHM.
Single (7"): released on Arista, Jan'83 by Arista Records. Dist: RCA

Single (12"): released on Arista, Jan'83 by Arista Records. Dist: RCA

Mahogany, Rush
LIVE (featuring Frank Marino).
Album: released on CBS, Mar'78 by CBS Records. Dist: CBS

Mahoney, Johnny
BABYLON.
Single (12"): released on Tchoupic Music, Jan'82

Mahoney, Tony
ALL NIGHT.
Single (12"): released on Tchoupic Music, Dec'81

Mahotella Queens
LIGHTS OF THE INDESTUCIBLE BEAT, THE.
Album: released on Earthworks, Feb'86 by Earthworks Records. Dist: Earthworks Distributors, Rough Trade, Cartel, Projection

PHEZULU EQHUDENI (Mahotella Queens, Mahlathanini & Other Stars).
Album: released on Carthage, Jul'87

Album: released on Earthworks, Apr'84 by Earthworks Records. Dist: Earthworks Distributors, Rough Trade, Cartel, Projection

Maiden Theatre Company
3 LITTLE PIGS.
Cassette: released on PRT, Nov'77 by PRT Records. Dist: PRT

ALADDIN.
Cassette: released on PRT, Nov'77 by PRT Records. Dist: PRT

SNOW WHITE.
Cassette: released on PRT, Nov'77 by PRT Records. Dist: PRT

Maiden Theatre Group
AUGUSTUS ANT.
Album: released on EMI, Mar'78 by EMI Records. Dist: EMI

GRUMBLEY.
Album: released on EMI, Mar'78 by EMI Records. Dist: EMI

Maid Of The Mountains
MAID OF THE MOUNTAINS 1917 Recording.
Album: released on World, '72 Dist: Jetstar

Maineeaxe
GAME, THE.
Single (7"): released on Powerstation Records, Oct'84 by Powerstation Records. Dist: Pinnacle

GIMME SOME GOLD.
Album: released on Powerstation Records, Feb'85 by Powerstation Records. Dist: Pinnacle

Cassette: released on Powerstation Records, Feb'85 by Powerstation Records. Dist: Pinnacle

GIMME YOUR LOVE.
Single (12"): released on Powerstation Records, Jan'85 by Powerstation Records. Dist: Pinnacle

GONNA MAKE YOU ROCK.
Single (7"): released on Powerstation Records, Jun'84 by Powerstation Records. Dist: Pinnacle

HOUR OF THUNDER, THE.
Album: released on Powerstation Records, Aug'86 by Powerstation Records. Dist: Pinnacle

SHOUT IT OUT.
Album: released on Powerstation Records, Jun'84 by Powerstation Records. Dist: Pinnacle

Mainers mountaineers
GOOD OLE MOUNTAIN MUSIC.
Album: released on King (USA), Apr'87 Dist: Gusto Distribution

Cassette: released on King (USA), Apr'87 Dist: Gusto Distribution

Maines Brothers
AMARILLO HIGHWAY.
Album: released on Country Roads Records, Nov'81 by Country Roads Records. Dist: Stage One

Main Event
MAIN EVENT various artists (Various original artists).
Album: released on K-Tel, May'79 by K-Tel Records. Dist: Record Merchandisers Distribution, Taylors, Terry Blood Distribution, Wynd-Up Distribution, Relay Distribution, Pickwick Distribution, Solomon & Peres Distribution, Polygram

Mainframe
5 MINUTES ON.
Tracks: / 5 minutes on / Eric's revenge.
Single (7"): released on Polydor, Jan'86 by Polydor Records. Dist: Polygram, Polydor

Single (12"): released on Polydor, Jan'86 by Polydor Records. Dist: Polygram, Polydor

RADIO.
Single (7"): released on MC2 Music, Apr'83

Main Ingredient
DO ME RIGHT.
Tracks: / Do me right / Do me right (Inst).
Single (7"): released on Cool Tempo, Jun'86 by Chrysalis Records. Dist: CBS

Single (12"): released on Cool Tempo, Jun'86 by Chrysalis Records. Dist: CBS

Mainline
ONE AND ONLY Jackson medley.
Single (12"): released on Malaco, Jun'84 by Malaco Records. Dist: Charly

Main Stream Power Band
BEST IN SWING, THE.
Album: released on MWM, Dec'86 by Mawson & Wareham. Dist: Spartan Distribution, Jazz Music Distribution, JSU Distribution

Main Street Piano Band
PIANO TO THE PEOPLE.
Album: released on Intersound, '86 by Intersound Records. Dist: Jazz Music

Main T. Posse
FICKLE PUBLIC SPEAKING.
Single (7"): released on Respond, May'83 by Paul Weller. Dist: Polydor

Single (12"): released on Respond, May'83 by Paul Weller. Dist: Polydor

Maire nl Chanthasalgh
NEW STRING HARP, THE.
Album: released on Temple, Jan'86 by Temple Records. Dist: Roots Distribution, Folksound Distribution, Celtic Music Distribution, Projection Distribution

Cassette: released on Temple, Jan'86 by Temple Records. Dist: Roots Distribution, Folksound Distribution, Celtic Music Distribution, Projection Distribution

Mairs, Julie
GIVE ME A SIGN.
Notes: Also on file as Mars, Julie
Album: released on Plant Life, Sep'84 Dist: Roots

Maisonettes
FOR SALE.
Album: released on Ready Steady Go, Nov'83

Cassette: released on Ready Steady Go, Nov'83

HEARTACHE AVENUE.
Single (7"): released on Graduate, Oct'82 by Graduate Records. Dist: Nine Mile, Cartel

Single (12"): released on Ready Steady Go, Jan'83

SAY IT AGAIN.
Single (7"): released on Ready Steady Go, Aug'83

Single (12"): released on Ready Steady Go, Aug'83

WHERE IS STAND.
Single (7"): released on Ready Steady Go, Mar'83

Mal Tal
AM I LOSING YOU FOREVER.
Single (7"): released on Virgin, Oct'85 by Virgin Records. Dist: EMI, Virgin Distribution Deleted '86.

Single (12"): released on Virgin, Oct'85 by Virgin Records. Dist: EMI, Virgin Distribution

BET THAT'S WHAT YOU SAY.
Single (7"): released on Injection Disco Dance, Aug'87 Dist: PRT

Single (12"): released on Injection Disco Dance, Aug'87 Dist: PRT

BODY AND SOUL.
Single (7"): released on Virgin, Jul'85 by Virgin Records. Dist: EMI, Virgin Distribution

Single (12"): released on Virgin, Jul'85 by Virgin Records. Dist: EMI, Virgin Distribution

FEMALE ISTITUTION.
Tracks: / Female Istitution / female intuition (Inst).
Single (7"): released on Virgin, Feb'86 by Virgin Records. Dist: EMI, Virgin Distribution

Single (12"): released on Virgin, Feb'86 by Virgin Records. Dist: EMI, Virgin Distribution

HISTORY.
Album: released on Virgin, Jun'85 by Virgin Records. Dist: EMI, Virgin Distribution

Cassette: released on Virgin, Jun'85 by Virgin Records. Dist: EMI, Virgin Distribution

Single (7"): released on Hot Melt, May'85 by Hot Melt Records. Dist: Pinnacle, Spartan

Single (12"): released on Hot Melt, May'85 by Hot Melt Records. Dist: Pinnacle, Spartan

WHAT GOES ON.
Single (7"): released on Electricity, Sep'84 by Electricity Records. Dist: PRT

Single (12"): released on Electricity, Sep'84 by Electricity Records. Dist: PRT

Maltchell, Graeme
FINE FETTLE.
Album: released on Lapwing, Jul'86 by Lapwing Records Ltd. Dist: Celtic Music, Projection, Roots Records, Ross, Gordon Duncan Distribution, Graham Tosh Distribution, Chans Records

Majaivana, Lovemore
AMANDLA.
Album: released on Zimbabwe, Aug'87 Dist: Revolver, Cartel. Estim retail price in Sep'87 was £5.99.

Majella
ISLE OF MY DREAMS.
Album: released on Klub, Nov'83

Cassette: released on Klub, Nov'83

OLD FLAME.
Album: released on Klub, Nov'86

SPINNING WHEEL.
Album: released on Hallmark, Feb'77 by Pickwick Records. Dist: Pickwick Distribution, PRT, Taylors

Single (7"): released on Klub, Oct'82

Majestics

I LOVE HER SO MUCH (IT HURTS).
Single (7"): released on Soul Supply, May'85 by High Energy Records. Dist: Charly

TUTTI FRUTTI.
Notes: From the BBC TV Series.
Album: released on BBC, Mar'87 by BBC Records & Tapes. Dist: EMI, PRT, Pye

Cassette: released on BBC, Mar'87 by BBC Records & Tapes. Dist: EMI, PRT, Pye

Majestic Singers

LOOK WHERE.
Album: released on Myrrh, Jun'85 by Word Records. Dist: Word Distribution

Cassette: released on Myrrh, Jun'85 by Word Records. Dist: Word Distribution

Majestic Wind Ensemble

PAN FLUTE FAVOURITES.
Tracks: / Day in the life, A / Something / Michelle / Yesterday / Strawberry fields forever / MacArthur Park / Don't cry for me Argentina / Feelings / Fool on the hill, The / Whiter shade of pale, A / She's out of my life / Unchained melody / Morning has broken / Nights in white satin / El condor pasa / Tara's theme / Let it be / I'm stone in love with you.
Album: released on Showcase, Oct'86 Dist: Counterpoint

Cassette: released on Showcase, Sep'86 Dist: Counterpoint

Majesty

NOTHING LASTS FOREVER.
Tracks: / Nothing lasts forever.
Single (7"): released on Bluebird, Jun'86 by Bluebird Records. Dist: EMI, Jetstar

Single (12"): released on Bluebird, Jun'86 by Bluebird Records. Dist: EMI, Jetstar

WISH YOU WERE HERE.
Tracks: / Wish you were here / Among the heroes.
Single (7"): released on Individual, Sep'86 by Individual Records. Dist: Pinnacle

Major Accident

FIGHT TO WIN.
Single (7"): released on Flicknife, Apr'83 by Flicknife Records. Dist: Spartan

LEADERS OF TOMORROW.
Single (7"): released on Flicknife, Jul'83 by Flicknife Records. Dist: Spartan

MR NOBODY.
Single (7"): released on Step Forward, Jan'83 by Faulty Products Records. Dist: Faulty Products Distribution, Pinnacle

PNEUMATIC PNEUROSIS.
Album: released on Flicknife, May'85 by Flicknife Records. Dist: Spartan

RESPECTABLE.
Single (7"): released on Flicknife, Apr'84 by Flicknife Records. Dist: Spartan

TORTURED TUNES LIVE - THE OFFICIAL BOOTLEG.
Album: released on Syndicate, Sep'84

Major Bill's Tezas

MAJOR BILL'S TEZAS ROCK 'N' ROLL Various artists (Various Artists).
Album: released on Sonet, Nov'79 by Sonet Records. Dist: PRT

Majority By Four

CAROLINE.
Single (7"): released on Waiting-In-Vain, Feb'80 by Waiting-In-Vain Records. Dist: December Songs, Independents Distribution

Major Lance

MONKEY TIME.
Album: released on Edsel, Jan'84 by Demon Records. Dist: Pinnacle, Jazz Music, Projection

Major Major Major

PARTY UP.
Tracks: / Party up / Fancy you wanting me.
Single (7"): released on A-Side, May'87 by Sonet Records. Dist: PRT

Single (12"): released on A-Side, May'87 by Sonet Records. Dist: PRT

Majors, Lee

UNKNOWN STUNTMAN.
Single (7"): released on Scotti Brothers (USA), Feb'83 by Scotti Brothers Records. Dist: Polydor

Major Tom

MISSING AMBASSADOR, (THE).
Cassette: released on Pickwick (Tell-a-tale), Oct'84 by Pickwick Records. Dist: Pickwick Distribution

Makaton Chat

FEDERAL STATE CHANCE.
Single (12"): released on Statik, Feb'83 Dist: Rough Trade Distribution, Stage One Distribution

STRANGE BEACH.
Album: released on Trans, Aug'83 by Trans Records. Dist: Statik, Stage One

Makaya & The Tsosis

MAKAYA & THE TSOSIS.
Album: released on Enja (Germany), Jan'82 by Enja Records (W.Germany). Dist: Cadillac Music

Makeba, Miriam

FORBIDDEN GAMES.
Album: released on RCA (Germany), Apr'83

VOICE OF AFRICA, (THE).
Album: released on RCA (Special Imports Service), Jul'84

Makeba, Myriam

PATA PATA/MALAIKA.
Compact disc: by Polydor Records. Dist: IMS, Polygram

Make it rock 'n' roll

MAKE IT ROCK 'N' ROLL Various artists (Various Artists).
Album: released on BBC, Mar'83 by BBC Records & Tapes. Dist: EMI, PRT, Pye

Cassette: released on BBC, Mar'83 by BBC Records & Tapes. Dist: EMI, PRT, Pye

Makem & Clancy

WE'VE COME A LONG WAY.
Tracks: / We've come a long way / Frog in the well, The / Roseville Fair / Drill ye tarriers drill / Coast of Malabar, The / Queen of Connemara / Highwayman, The / Fair & tender lady / Peg leg Jack / Parcel of rogues, A / Fagfaidh mise an baile seo / Golden / Mary Ellen Carter, The.
Notes: Makem & Clancy are a vastly experienced Irish folk duo who have toured successfully since the break up of the original Irish folk heroes The Clancy Brothers & Tommy Makem
Album: released on Polydor (Ireland), Mar'87 by Polydor Records. Dist: Polygram, I & B

Cassette: released on Polydor (Ireland), Mar'87 by Polydor Records. Dist: Polygram, I & B

WE'VE COME A LONG WAY.
Album: released on Shanachie (USA), Feb'87

Makem, Sarah

ULSTER BALLAD SINGER.
Album: released on Topic, '81 Dist: Roots Distribution

Makem, Tommy

COME FILL YOUR GLASS WITH US.
Album: released on Traditional, Nov'74

TOMMY MAKEM & LIAM CLANCY (Makem, Tommy & Liam Clancy).
Album: by CBS Records. Dist: CBS

Making Love to Lettuce

LETTUCE IN THE CARAVAN.
Tracks: / Summer Of '86 / Triffids / Two Cans Of Special Brew / I Tried To Make You Understand.
Album: released on Unknown, Nov'86

Making Thriller

MAKING MICHAEL JACKSON'S THRILLER (Making Michael Jackson's Thriller).
Video-cassette (VHS): released on Vestron, Oct'86

Making trax

MAKING TRAX - GREAT INSTRUMENTALS Various artists (Various Artists).
Album: released on Motown, Oct'84 by RCA Records. Dist: RCA Distribution

Cassette: released on Motown, Oct'84 by RCA Records. Dist: RCA Distribution

Makin' Time

FEELS LIKE IT'S LOVE.
Single (7"): released on Countdown, Oct'85 by Stiff Records. Dist: EMI, Swift

Single (12"): released on Countdown, Oct'85 by Stiff Records. Dist: EMI, Swift

HERE IS MY NUMBER.
Single (7"): released on Countdown, Jun'85 by Stiff Records. Dist: EMI, Swift

Single (12"): released on Countdown, Jun'85 by Stiff Records. Dist: EMI, Swift

NO LUMPS OF FAT OR GRISTLE GUARENTEED.
Album: released on Ready To Eat, Sep'86 by Making Time. Dist: Backs, Cartel

PUMP IT UP.
Tracks: / Pump it up / Once again / Walk a thin line / Eating up the gold.
Single (7"): released on Stiff, Apr'86 by Stiff Records. Dist: EMI, Record Services Distribution (Ireland)

Single (12"): released on Stiff, Apr'86 by Stiff Records. Dist: EMI, Record Services Distribution (Ireland)

RHYTHM 'N' SOUL.
Album: released on Countdown, Jun'85 by Stiff Records. Dist: EMI, Swift

Cassette: released on Countdown, Jun'85 by Stiff Records. Dist: EMI, Swift

TIME TROUBLE AND MONEY.
Album: released on Re-Elect The President, Mar'87 Dist: Backs, Cartel

Makossa, Jack E

OPERA HOUSE, THE.
Single (7"): released on Champion, Aug'87 by Champion Records. Dist: RCA

Single (12"): released on Champion, Aug'87 by Champion Records. Dist: RCA

Makowicz, Adam

INTERFACE (Makowicz, Adam Trio).
Compact disc: released on Sonet, Jul'87 by Sonet Records. Dist: PRT

Album: released on Sonet, Jul'87 by Sonet Records. Dist: PRT

Malach, Bob

SOME PEOPLE.
Album: released on MPS Jazz, Jun'81

Malachi Favors

NATURAL AND SPIRITUAL.
Album: released on Aeco, May'81 Dist: Projection

Malachy, Doris

BEST OF DORIS MALACHY, THE.
Album: released on Homespun(Ireland), Apr'79 by Outlet Records. Dist: Outlet

CONTINENTAL ACCORDION.
Album: released on Homespun(Ireland), Jun'79 by Outlet Records. Dist: Outlet

DANCING THROUGH IRELAND'S HITS.
Album: released on Homespun(Ireland), Jun'77 by Outlet Records. Dist: Outlet

IRISH PARTY SING ALONG.
Tracks: / McNamara's band / King of the fairies\Seven nights drunk\Spanish Lady / Curragh of kildare / Fields of Athenry / Jug of punch\Leavin' of liverpool\Holy ground / Wild rover\Love is teasin'\black velvet band / Courtin' in the kitchen\Lonesome boatman\Whiskey in the jar\ Slatteries mounted fut / Willie McBride / Inniskilling dragoons / Cliffs of Dooneen / Will ye go lassie go / Moonlight in Mayo / Molly Malone\Galway shawl / Belfast\Harvest home hornpipe\I'll tell ma\Irish rover / Carrickfergus\Rose of Tralee / Star of County Down / Are you right there Michael / Dingle regatta.
Notes: Produced by Cel Fay - Rod McVey, recorded at Outlet Int. Studios Belfast.
Album: released on Homespun(Ireland), Feb'87 by Outlet Records. Dist: Outlet

Cassette: released on Homespun(Ireland), Feb'87 by Outlet Records. Dist: Outlet

IRISH PUB SING-ALONG.
Album: released on Homespun(Ireland), Dec'83 by Outlet Records. Dist: Outlet

Cassette: released on Homespun(Ireland), Dec'83 by Outlet Records. Dist: Outlet

WALTZING THRO' IRELAND VOL 3.
Album: released on Homespun(Ireland), Aug'82 by Outlet Records. Dist: Outlet

Cassette: released on Homespun(Ireland), Aug'82 by Outlet Records. Dist: Outlet

WE ALL HAVE A SONG IN OUR HEARTS (Malachy, Doris Orchestra & Chorus).
Tracks: / We all have a song in our hearts / More than yesterday / Pal of my cradle days / I'll be your sweetheart if you'll be mine / Skye boat song / Lovely irish rose / Irish lullaby (to ra loo ra loo ra) / Cottage by the lee / If I had my life to live over / It's a spin to tell a lie / Bunch of violets / Spinning wheel / Joys of love / Mother's love's a blessing, A / Goodbye Jonny dear / Gentle mother.
Album: released on Homespun(Ireland), Dec'86 by Outlet Records. Dist: Outlet

Cassette: released on Homespun(Ireland), Dec'86 by Outlet Records. Dist: Outlet

Malandraki, Lilli

AN EVENING IN CRETE (Malandraki, Lilli & Donald Swann).
Album: released on World, '78 Dist: Jetstar

Malaria

MALARIA REVISISTED.
Cassette: released on Reach Out International, May'83 Dist: Red Rhino, Cartel

MY NEW DOG.
Single (12"): released on Les Disques Du Crepuscule, Sep'82 Dist: Rough Trade, Pinnacle, Island, Polygram

NEW YORK PASSAGE.
Single (12"): released on Jungle, Nov'82 by Jungle Records. Dist: Jungle, Cartel

WHITE WATER WHITE SEA.
Single (12"): released on Les Disques Du Crepuscule, Apr'82 Dist: Rough Trade, Pinnacle, Island, Polygram

Malcahy, Mick

MICK MULCAHY-ACCORDION.
Album: released on Gael-Linn (Ireland), Jan'77 by Gael Linn Records. Dist: Roots, Projection, Celtic Music, Jazz Music

Malcolm & Alwyn

LIVE.
Album: released on Marantha Music, May'82
Cat. no: **MRC 007**
Cassette: released on Marantha Music, May'82

Malcolm, Johnny

MASTER PERFORMANCE VOL.4.
Cassette: released on Aim (Budget Cassettes), Aug'83

Malcolm's Interview

YOU DON'T LISTEN.
Single (12"): released on Egg, Jun'85 Dist: Red Rhino, Cartel

Maldaur, Geoff

I AIN'T DRUNK (Maldaur, Geoff & The Nite-Lites).
Tracks: / Boogie chillun / Nobody knows (the way I feel this morning) / I ain't drunk / Natural ball / Down for the count / Meanest woman blues / As long as I'm moving / Caledonia / Sea sea rider.
Notes: Geoff and the band cover the entire gamut of jump blues from 1948 to 1949!
Album: released on Hannibal, Jun'86 by Hannibal Records. Dist: Charly, Harmonia Mundi, Projection, Celtic Music, Roots

Maldore, Michel

LA CHAMBRE NUPTIALE.
Album: released on Egg, Nov'79 Dist: Red Rhino, Cartel

Malfatti, Radu

FORMU.
Tracks: / Funf leichte stucke / Formu.
Album: released on Nato (France), Sep'86 by Disques Nato. Dist: Essex Record Distributors Ltd.

Malia, Dominic

SWEETIE.
Tracks: / Sweetie / Love's brown across the shore.
Single (7"): released on Mooncrest, Jul'87 by Mooncrest Records. Dist: PRT Distribution

Malibu

GIRLS CHAMP.
Tracks: / Girls champ / Body come down.
Single (12"): released on VIP, Sep'86 Dist: Jetstar Distribution

GOLDEN RULE.
Tracks: / Golden rule / One dance story.
Single (12"): released on Supreme, Aug'86 by Supreme Records. Dist: PRT Distribution

KEEP WALKING.
Single (7"): released on RCA, Jun'85 by RCA Records. Dist: RCA, Roots, Swift, Wellard, Chris, I & B, Solomon & Peres Distribution

Single (12"): released on RCA, Jun'85 by RCA Records. Dist: RCA, Roots, Swift, Wellard, Chris, I & B, Solomon & Peres Distribution

Malice
IN THE BEGINNING.
Album: released on Atlantic, Oct'85 by WEA Records. Dist: WEA

LICENCED TO KILL.
Album: released on Atlantic, Mar'87 by WEA Records. Dist: WEA

Cassette: released on Atlantic, Mar'87 by WEA Records. Dist: WEA

Malicorne
FIRST.
Album: released on Hexagone, Sep'79 Dist: Projection

SECOND.
Album: released on Hexagone, Sep'79 Dist: Projection

Malinga, Joe Group
SOUTHERN AFRICAN FORCE.
Album: released on Meteor (Switzerland), Nov'84 Dist: Cadillac

Malla, Boogsie
TALK ABOUT MY BABY.
Single (12"): released on Original Sounds, Sep'85 Dist: Jetstar Distribution

Mallan, Peter
BONNIE MARY OF ARGYLL.
Single (7"): released on Klub, Jul'81

FISHIN' SONG, THE.
Single (7"): released on Klub, Aug'79

LEGENDS OF SCOTLAND.
Album: released on Lochshore, Mar'87 by Klub Records. Dist: PRT

LONELY I WONDER.
Album: released on Igus, Nov'82 by Klub. Dist: PRT, Musac Distribution Ltd (Scotland)

Cassette: released on Igus, Nov'82 by Klub. Dist: PRT, Musac Distribution Ltd (Scotland)

RELAX WITH PETER MALLAN.
Album: released on Klub, Nov'79

Cassette: released on Klub, Nov'79

THESE ARE MY MOUNTAINS.
Album: released on Waverley, Jul'80 by EMI Records. Dist: EMI

Mallett
C.C. RIDER.
Single (7"): released on Rox, '80 by Rox Records. Dist: Spartan Distribution

Mallinder, Stephen
POW WOW PLUS.
Album: released on Double Vision, Oct'85 by Double Vision Records. Dist: Rough Trade, Cartel

TEMPERATURE DROP.
Single (12"): released on Fetish, Nov'81 by Fetish Records. Dist: Cartel, Pinnacle

Malloy, David
TOMMY PEOPLES (Malloy, Matt & Paul Brady).
Album: released on Mulligan, Nov'79 by Topic Records. Dist: Roots Distribution, Jazz Music Distribution, JSU Distribution, I & B Distribution, Projection Distribution, Wynd-Up Distribution, Celtic Distributions

Malmsteen, Yngwie
MARCHING OUT (Malmsteen, Yngwie & Rising Force).
Tracks: / Prelude / I'll see the light tonight / Don't let it end / Disciples of hell / I am a viking / Overture 1383 / Anguish and fear / On the run again / Soldier without faith / Caught in the middle / Marching out.
Album: released on Polydor, Aug'85 by Polydor Records. Dist: Polygram, Polydor

Cassette: released on Polydor, Aug'85 by Polydor Records. Dist: Polygram, Polydor

Compact disc: released on Polydor, Aug'85 by Polydor Records. Dist: Polygram, Polydor

RISING FORCE.
Album: released on Verve (France), May'85

TRILOGY.
Album: released on Polydor, Nov'86 by Polydor Records. Dist: Polygram, Polydor

Cassette: released on Polydor, Nov'86 by Polydor Records. Dist: Polygram, Polydor

Compact disc: released on Polydor, Nov'86 by Polydor Records. Dist: Polygram, Polydor

Malone, Bugsy & The Radix
CALL ME BABY.
Tracks: / Call me baby / Call me baby (Version).
Single (7"): released on Taurus, Aug'86 Dist: Jetstar

Malone, J.J.
I'VE GOT A NEW CAR (Malone, J.J. & Troyce Key & the Rhythm Rockers).
Album: released on Red Lightnin', Sep'82 by Red Lightnin' Records. Dist: Roots, Swift, Jazz Music, JSU, Pinnacle, Cartel, Wynd-Up Distribution

YOUNGER THAN YESTERDAY.
Album: released on Red Lightnin', May'83 by Red Lightnin' Records. Dist: Roots, Swift, Jazz Music, JSU, Pinnacle, Cartel, Wynd-Up Distribution

Maloney, Paddy
TIN WHISTLES (Maloney, Paddy/Sean Potts).
Album: released on Claddagh, Jun'75 by Claddagh Records. Dist: I & B, Record Services Distribution (Ireland), Roots, Topic, Impetus, Projection, CM

Cassette: released on Claddagh, Jun'75 by Claddagh Records. Dist: I & B, Record Services Distribution (Ireland), Roots, Topic, Impetus, Projection, CM

Malopoets
MALOPOETS.
Cassette: released on EMI America, Jun'85 by EMI Records. Dist: EMI

Maltese Falcon
METAL RUSH.
Album: released on Music For Nations, Oct'84 by Music For Nations Records. Dist: Pinnacle

Mama don't allow it
MAMA DON'T ALLOW IT Various Artists (Various Artists).
Album: released on Decca(American Recollections), Feb'84

Mamas Boys
BELFAST CITY BLUES.
Single (7"): released on Scoff, Apr'82 Dist: Rough Trade, Cartel

HARD'N'LOUD.
Single (12"): released on Jive, Nov'85 by Zomba Records. Dist: RCA, PRT, CBS

IN THE HEAT OF THE NIGHT.
Single (7"): released on Albion, Oct'82 by Albion Records. Dist: Spartan, Pinnacle

MAMA'S BOYS.
Album: released on Jive, Jul'84 by Zomba Records. Dist: RCA, PRT, CBS

Cassette: released on Jive, Jul'84 by Zomba Records. Dist: RCA, PRT, CBS

MAMA WE'RE ALL CRAZY NOW.
Single (12"): released on Jive, Aug'84 by Zomba Records. Dist: RCA, PRT, CBS

MIDNIGHT PROMISES.
Single (7"): released on Spartan, Jan'84 by Spartan Records. Dist: Spartan

Single (12"): released on Spartan, Jan'84 by Spartan Records. Dist: Spartan

NEEDLE IN THE GROOVE.
Single (7"): released on Ultranoise, Jan'83 by Ultranoise Records. Dist: Cartel

Single (12"): released on Ultranoise, Jan'83 by Ultranoise Records. Dist: Cartel

Picture disc single: released on Jive, Jun'85 by Zomba Records. Dist: RCA, PRT, CBS

PLUG IT IN.
Tracks: / In the heat of the night (short version) / Burnin' up / Needle in the grove / Reach for the top / Silence is out of fashion / Straight forward / Runaway dreams / Getting out / Belfast city blues.
Album: released on Castle Communications, Jul'86 by Castle Communications. Dist: Cartel, Pinnacle, Counterpoint

Cassette: released on Castle Communications, Jul'86 by Castle Communications. Dist: Cartel, Pinnacle, Counterpoint

Album: released on Albion, Oct'82 by Albion Records. Dist: Spartan, Pinnacle

Cassette: released on Albion, Apr'83 by Albion Records. Dist: Spartan, Pinnacle

POWER AND PASSION.
Album: released on Jive, Mar'85 by Zomba Records. Dist: RCA, PRT, CBS

Album: released on Jive, Mar'85 by Zomba Records. Dist: RCA, PRT, CBS

TURN IT UP.
Album: released on Spartan, Oct'83 by Spartan Records. Dist: Spartan

Mamas & Papas
20 GOLDEN HITS.
Album: released on ABC, Mar'82 Dist: CBS, Pinnacle

Cassette: released on ABC, Mar'82 Dist: CBS, Pinnacle

20 GREATEST HITS.
Album: released on MFP, Oct'80 by EMI Records. Dist: EMI

CALIFORNIA DREAMIN'.
Single (7"): released on Old Gold, Jul'82 by Old Gold Records. Dist: Lightning, Jazz Music, Spartan, Counterpoint

DEDICATED TO THE ONE I LOVE.
Single (7"): released on Old Gold, Jul'82 by Old Gold Records. Dist: Lightning, Jazz Music, Spartan, Counterpoint

GOLDEN GREATS: MAMAS & PAPAS.
Tracks: / Dedicated to the one I love / Monday Monday / Look through my window / California dreamin' / I call your name / My girl / Dream a little dream of me / Go where you wanna go / Got a feelin' / I saw her again last night / Words of love / Twelve thirty / Dancing in the street / Glad to be unhappy / Creeque Valley / Midnight voyage / Spanish Harlem / You baby / Do you wanna dance / Twist and shout.
Cassette: released on MCA, Jul'85 by MCA Records. Dist: Polygram, MCA

Compact disc: released on MCA, '86 by MCA Records. Dist: Polygram, MCA

Album: released on MCA, Jul'85 by MCA Records. Dist: Polygram, MCA

HITS OF GOLD.
Album: released on ABC, Aug'81 Dist: CBS, Pinnacle

Cassette: released on ABC, Aug'81 Dist: CBS, Pinnacle

IF YOU CAN BELIEVE YOUR EYES AND EARS.
Tracks: / Monday, monday / Straight shooter / Got a feelin' / I call your name / Do you wanna dance / Go where you wanna go / California dreamin' / Spanish Harlem / Somebody groovy / Hey girl / You baby / In crowd / Monday, Monday / Straight shooter / Got a feelin / I call your name / Do you wanna dance / Go where you wanna go / California dreamin' / Spanish Harlem / Somebody groovy / Hey girl / You baby / In crowd.
Compact disc: released on MCA, Aug'87 by MCA Records. Dist: Polygram, MCA

Mamba
PERCUSSIONS.
Tracks: / Variations / Ambiance 1 / Au-Dela / Ballade / Ambiance 2 / Mambalele / Rituel 11 / Maracas / Troisieme Monde / Rythmotom 1 / Ambiance 3 / Rythmotom 11 / Energy.
Notes: Disques Pierr Verany Chemin De La Bosque, 13090 Aix-En-Provence, France.
Compact disc: released on Disques Pierre Verany, Aug'86 by Disques Pierre Verany Records. Dist: Conifer

Mamelodi
JABULANI SATURDAY NIGHT.
Single (7"): released on Magnet, Sep'83 by Magnet Records. Dist: BMG

Mammath
ROCK ME.
Single (7"): released on Neat, Dec'84 by Neat Records. Dist: Pinnacle, Neat

Man
ALL IN THE GAME.
Tracks: / All in the game / All in the game (instrumental).
Single (7"): released on RCA, Mar'86 by RCA Records. Dist: RCA, Roots, Swift, Wellard, Chris, I & B, Solomon & Peres Distribution

Single (12"): released on King Buck, Jan'84 by King Buck Records. Dist: Jetstar

DO YOU LIKE IT HERE NOW, ARE YOU SETTLING IN?.
Album: released on Liberty-United, Aug'80 by EMI Records. Dist: EMI

FRIDAY 13TH.
Album: released on Picasso, Nov'85 by Picasso Records. Dist: Pinnacle

Cassette: released on Picasso, Dec'83 by Picasso Records. Dist: Pinnacle

GREEN FLY.
Tracks: / Rainbow eyes / Sospan fach / C'mon / Babe, I'm gonna leave you / 7171 551 / Back to the future / Ain't their fight / Keep on crinting / Intro\Kerosene / Four day Louise / California silks and satins.
Notes: Original sound recording made by EMI Recordings Ltd, licensed to Latymer- a division of cherry Red Records Ltd (1986).
Album: released on Latymer, Jan'87 Dist: Pinnacle

Man 2 man
MALE STRIPPER (Man 2 man meet man parrish).
Tracks: / Male stripper (UK love mix) / (Original US mix).
Single (12"): released on Bolts, Jul'86 by Bolts Records. Dist: PRT, Pinnacle

WHO KNOWS WHAT EVIL.
Tracks: / Who knows what evil / Man 2 man instrumental.
Single (7"): released on Nightmare, Nov'86 by Nightmare Records. Dist: PRT

Single (12"): released on Nightmare, Nov'86 by Nightmare Records. Dist: PRT

Managers
SHAKE IT UP SHAKE IT UP.
Single (7"): released on Sire, Jul'82

Single (12"): released on Sire, Jul'82

Man And A Woman
MAN AND A WOMAN (Film Soundtrack) (Various Artists).
Album: released on Sunset, Mar'77 Dist: EMI

Album: released on EMI, Nov'80 by EMI Records. Dist: EMI

Man behind the wheel, The
MAN BEHIND THE WHEEL, THE (Various Artists).
Album: released on Starday, Apr'87

Cassette: released on Starday, Apr'87

Mance, Junior
AT THE VILLAGE VANGUARD.
Compact disc: released on Carrere, Apr'87 by Carrere Records. Dist: PRT, Spartan

DEEP (Mance, Junior Trio).
Album: released on JSP, Mar'82 by JSP Records. Dist: Swift, Projection

TENDER TOUCH OF..., THE (Mance, Junior & Martin Rivera Duo).
Album: released on Nilva (Switzerland), Apr'84

Manchanile, Amanda
LOVE AUTOMATION.
Single (12"): released on Unit Dance, Jun'87 by Priority Records. Dist: RCA

Mancha, Steve
IT'S ALL OVER THE GRAPEVINE.
Tracks: / It's all over the grapevine / It's all over the grapevine (instrumental).
Single (7"): released on Columbia, Aug'86 by EMI Records. Dist: EMI

Single (12"): released on Columbia, Aug'86 by EMI Records. Dist: EMI

STANDING IN LINE.
Tracks: / Standing in line / Standing in line(instrumental).
Single (7"): released on Nightmare, Mar'87 by Nightmare Records. Dist: PRT

Single (12"): released on Nightmare, Mar'87 by Nightmare Records. Dist: PRT

Manchester boys choir
LITTLE DRUMMER BOY.
Single (7"): released on Spirit, Nov'85 by Spirit Records. Dist: WEA

NEW KIND OF CHRISTMAS, A.
Album: released on K-Tel, Nov'85 by K-Tel Records. Dist: Record Merchandisers Distribution, Taylors, Terry Blood Distribution, Wynd-Up Distribution, Relay Distribution, Pickwick Distribution, Solomon & Peres Distribution, Polygram

Cassette: released on K-Tel, Nov'85 by K-Tel Records. Dist: Record Merchandisers Distribution, Taylors, Terry Blood Distribution, Wynd-Up Distribution, Relay Distribution, Pickwick Distribution, Solomon & Peres Distribution, Polygram

SINGING FOR YOU.
Tracks: / Waltz of my heart / Chorus of ariel spirits / Count your blessings / Streamlet, The / Mary Stuart's prayer / Break o' day / Over the waves / This little light of mine / Gruss / Happy wanderer (the) / Tulerunt dominum meum / Stodola pumpa / Morgenblatter / Psalm 150.
Notes: From a modest beginning in 1981, the Manchester Boys Choir has developed to the 100+ singing boys now internationally recognised for the musical excellence. The choir's repertoire is as varied as the background of each choir member, all of whom are accepted without audition. Under their director of music Adrian P Jessett, the choir functions under the auspices of the City of Manchester Music Department.
Album: released on Grasmere, Jul'86 by Grasmere Records. Dist: EMI

Cassette: released on Grasmere, Jul'86 by Grasmere Records. Dist: EMI

Manchester, Melissa

MUSIC OF GOODBYE, THE (Manchester, Mellissa/Al Jarreau).
Tracks: / Music of goodbye (love theme out of Africa), The / Main title / I had a farm in Africa / Have you got a story for me.
Single (7"): released on MCA, Mar'86 by MCA Records. Dist: Polygram, MCA

Single (12"): released on MCA, Mar'86 by MCA Records. Dist: Polygram, MCA

YOU SHOULD HEAR HOW SHE TALKS ABOUT YOU.
Single (7"): released on Arista, Sep'82 by Arista Records. Dist: RCA

Manchester United

GLORY GLORY MAN UNITED.
Single (7"): released on EMI, May'83 by EMI Records. Dist: EMI

Picture disc single: released on EMI, May'83 by EMI Records. Dist: EMI

WE ALL FOLLOW MAN UNITED.
Picture disc single: released on Curb (USA), May'85 by Warner Bros Records. Dist: CBS, WEA

Mancini, Henry

AT THE MOVIES.
Tracks: / Moon river / Pink panther / Peter Gunn / Good, the bad and the ugly, The / Midnight cowboy / Magnificient seven / How soon / Shot in the dark (a) / Dear heart / Seventy six trombones / Days of wine and roses / Theme from shaft / Raindrops keep fallin' on my head.
Album: released on MFP, Sep'86 by EMI Records. Dist: EMI

Cassette: released on MFP, Sep'86 by EMI Records. Dist: EMI

BEST OF HENRY MANCINI, THE (Mancini, Henry & his orchestra).
Album: released on RCA/Camden, Jan'84

Cassette: released on RCA/Camden, Jan'84

BOLERO.
Single (7"): released on WEA, Mar'84 by WEA Records. Dist: WEA

DISCO DE OURO (Mancini, Henry & his orchestra).
Album: released on RCA/Brazil, Jan'84

MAGIC OF HENRY MANCINI, THE.
Album: released on Warner Brothers, Mar'84 by Warner Bros Records. Dist: WEA Deleted '87.

Cassette: released on Warner Bros., Mar'84 by Warner Bros Records. Dist: WEA

MAN AND HIS MUSIC, A.
Album: released on Cambra, Feb'85 by Cambra Records. Dist: IDS, Conifer

Cassette: released on Cambra, Feb'85 by Cambra Records. Dist: IDS, Conifer

MANCINI'S ANGELS.
Album: released on RCA, Aug'77 by RCA Records. Dist: RCA, Roots, Swift, Wellard, Chris, I & B, Solomon & Peres Distribution

MERRY MANCINI CHRISTMAS, A.
Album: released on RCA International (USA), Dec'81 by RCA Records. Dist: RCA

Cassette: released on RCA International (USA), Dec'81 by RCA Records. Dist: RCA

NIGHT VISITOR Film soundtrack.
Album: released on Citadel, Mar'79 Dist: Swift

Album: released on Citadel, Mar'79 Dist: Swift

PINK PANTHER THEME (Mancini, Henry & his orchestra).
Single (7"): released on USA Import, '75

PURE GOLD.
Tracks: / Moon river / Days of wine and roses / Charade / Moment to moment / Romeo and Julliet / Pink panther theme (the) / Mr Lucky / Baby elephant walk / Peter Gunn / It had better be tonight.
Notes: Digital stereo
Compact disc: released on RCA, Dec'84 by RCA Records. Dist: RCA, Roots, Swift, Wellard, Chris, I & B, Solomon & Peres Distribution

Album: released on RCA International (USA), Apr'80 by RCA Records. Dist: RCA

Cassette: released on RCA International (USA), Apr'80 by RCA Records. Dist: RCA

Compact disc: released on RCA (Italy), Apr'80

THIS IS HENRY MANCINI, VOL.2.
Album: released on RCA (Germany), Apr'81

THIS IS HENRY MANCINI, VOL.1.
Album: released on RCA (Germany), Apr'81

THORN BIRDS THEME (THE) (Mancini, Henry & his orchestra).
Tracks: / Thorn birds theme (the) / Love theme from the thorn birds.
Single (7"): released on WEA, Aug'86 by WEA Records. Dist: WEA

TOUCH OF EVIL Film soundtrack.
Album: released on Citadel, Mar'79 Dist: Swift

TRAIL OF THE PINK PANTHER (Mancini, Henry & his orchestra).
Album: released on Liberty, Dec'82 by Liberty-United. Dist: EMI

Cassette: released on Liberty, Dec'82 by Liberty-United. Dist: EMI

UNIQUELY MANCINI.
Album: released on Deja Vu, Oct'83 by Deja Vu Records. Dist: Counterpoint Distribution, Record Services Distribution (Ireland)

Cassette: released on Deja Vu, Oct'83 by Deja Vu Records. Dist: Counterpoint Distribution, Record Services Distribution (Ireland)

VERY BEST OF HENRY MANCINI, THE.
Album: released on RCA, '84 by RCA Records. Dist: RCA, Roots, Swift, Wellard, Chris, I & B, Solomon & Peres Distribution

Cassette: released on RCA, '84 by RCA Records. Dist: RCA, Roots, Swift, Wellard, Chris, I & B, Solomon & Peres Distribution

Mancrab

FISH FOR LIFE (from Karate Kid II).
Tracks: / Fish for life / Fish for life (instrumental).
Single (7"): released on 10, Aug'86 by 10 Records. Dist: Virgin, EMI

Single (12"): released on 10, Aug'86 by 10 Records. Dist: Virgin, EMI

Mandalaband

EYE OF WENDOR, THE.
Album: by Chrysalis Records. Dist: CBS

Mandell, Mike

SKY MUSIC.
Album: released on Vanguard, Jan'79 by PRT Records. Dist: PRT

Mandell, Robert

LORD IS MY SHEPHERD (Mandell, Robert & Leicester Childrens Choir).
Single (7"): released on Pressit, Jan'83 Dist: Taylor, H.R.

MUSICAL HIGHLIGHTS (Mandell, Robert Orch.).
Notes: Songs and music from: Annie get your gun, Oklahoma, My fair lady, Carousel, West-Side story, etc. With Ivor Emmanuel, Rosemary Squires etc.
Compact disc: released on Bridge, '86 Dist: CD Centre Distribution, Pinnacle, Target

Mandeville, John

TRAVELS OF SIR JOHN MANDEVILLE, THE.
Cassette: released on Anvil, Apr'80 Dist: Anvil

Mandible Rumpus

WHAT'S MY LINE.
Single (7"): released on Mayhem, Aug'82 by International Records & Tapes. Dist: Pinnacle

Mandingo

SAVAGE RITE.
Album: released on EMI, Nov'77 by EMI Records. Dist: EMI

Mandrake Paddle...

STRANGE WALKING MAN (Mandrake Paddle Steamer).
Single (7"): released on Bam Caruso, Jun'85 by Bam Caruso Records. Dist: Rough Trade, Revolver, Cartel

Mandrell, Barbara

BEST OF BARBARA MANDRELL (THE).
Tracks: / Woman to woman / Love is thin ice / Hold me / After the lovin' / Married but not to each other / Sleeping single in a double bed / That's what friends are for / Midnight angel / Standing room only / Tonight.
Album: released on MCA Import, Mar'86 by MCA Records. Dist: Polygram, IMS

CLEAN CUT.
Album: released on MCA, Apr'84 by MCA Records. Dist: Polygram, MCA

Cassette: released on MCA, Apr'84 by MCA Records. Dist: Polygram, MCA Deleted '85.

GET TO THE HEART.
Tracks: / I'm a believer / Fast lanes and country roads / I'd fall in love tonight / Don't look in my eyes / Angel in your arms / For your love / If they grew tired of my music / You only you / Survivors / When you get to the heart.
Album: released on MCA Import, Mar'86 by MCA Records. Dist: Polygram, IMS

GREATEST HITS:BARBARA MANDRELL.
Tracks: / I was country when country wasn't cool / Years / Wish you were here / Best of strangers (the) / Happy birthday dear heartache / (If loving you is wrong) I don't want to be right / Crackers / One of a kind pair of fools / In times like these / There's no love in Tennessee.
Album: released on MCA Import, Mar'86 by MCA Records. Dist: Polygram, IMS

SURE FEELS GOOD.
Tracks: / Just to satisfy you / You can't get there from here / It all came true / You keep me hangin' on / Child support / Angels love bad men / One of us is always leaving / Sunshine street / I'm glad I married you / Sure feels good / Just to satisfy you / You can't get there from here / It all came true / Hangin' on / Child support / Angels love bad men / One of us is always leaving / Sunshine street / I'm glad I married you / Sure feels good / If it don't come easy / Love me like you used to / I won't take less than your love / I wonder what he's doing tonight / I'll Tennessee you in / Allen / Temporaily blue / If I didn't love you / Heartbreaker / Hope you find what you're loving for.
Album: released on EMI America, Jul'87 by EMI Records. Dist: EMI

Cassette: released on EMI America, Jul'87 by EMI Records. Dist: EMI

Compact disc: released on EMI America, Jul'87 by EMI Records. Dist: EMI

Compact disc: released on EMI America, Aug'87 by EMI Records. Dist: EMI

Compact disc: released on EMI America, Aug'87 by EMI Records. Dist: EMI

Cassette: released on EMI America, Aug'87 by EMI Records. Dist: EMI

Album: released on EMI America, Aug'87 by EMI Records. Dist: EMI

Cassette: released on EMI America, Aug'87 by EMI Records. Dist: EMI

Mandrell, Louise

LOUISE MANDRELL.
Album: released on Epic, Apr'82 by CBS Records. Dist: CBS

Cassette: released on Epic, Apr'82 by CBS Records. Dist: CBS

Manfred Mann

R & B YEARS, THE.
Tracks: / Without you / Don't ask me what I say / I'm your king pin / Got my mojo working / Down the road apiece / Hoochie coochie / Can't believe it / Driva man / Hubble bubble (toil and trouble) / Smokestack lightning / It's gonna work out fine / Did you have to do that / Let's go get stoned / I put a spell on you / Why shouldn't we not / Bring it to Jerone / Poison ivy / Cock-a-hoop / You've got to take it.
Album: released on See For Miles, Nov'86 by See For Miles Records. Dist: Pinnacle

Album: released on See For Miles, Mar'82 by Charly Records. Dist: Spartan

Cassette: released on See For Miles, Mar'82 by Charly Records. Dist: Spartan

Manfredo Fest

JUNGLE KITTEN.
Single (7"): released on Bluebird, May'83 by Bluebird Records. Dist: EMI, Jetstar

Man Friday

PICKING UP SOUND 2 Parts (Man Friday & Jive Junior).
Single (12"): released on Malaco, Oct'83 by Malaco Records. Dist: Charly

Man From Delmonte

WATER IN MY EYES.
Tracks: / Bred by you.
Single (7"): released on Ugly Man, Aug'87 Dist: Cartel

Single (12"): released on Ugly Man, Aug'87 Dist: Cartel

Mangaroo, Danny

WHEN THINGS GO WRONG.
Single (12"): released on Joe Gibbs, Mar'84 by Joe Gibbs Records. Dist: Jetstar

Mangas, Yiorgos

YIOGOS MANGAS.
Album: released on Globestyle, Aug'87 by Ace Records. Dist: Projection

YIORGOS MANGAS.
Album: released on Globestyle, Aug'87 by Ace Records. Dist: Projection

Mangelsdorff

ETERNAL RHYTHM (Mangelsdorff/Don Cherry).
Album: released on MPS Jazz, May'81

WIDE POINT, THE (Mangelsdorff/Jones/Danielson).
Album: released on MPS Jazz, May'81

Mangelsdorff, Albert

LIVE IN TOKYO.
Album: released on Enja (Germany), Jan'82 by Enja Records (W.Germany). Dist: Cadillac Music

SPONTANEOUS.
Album: released on Enja (Germany), Jan'82 by Enja Records (W.Germany). Dist: Cadillac Music

TRILOGUE-LIVE.
Album: released on MPS Jazz, Jun'81

Mangione, Chuck

BEST OF CHUCK MANGIONE, (THE).
Album: released on Mercury (Holland), Jul'84 by Phonogram Records. Dist: Polygram Distribution

BEST OF, THE Walkman jazz series.
Cassette: released on Verve, May'87 by Phonogram Records. Dist: Polygram

BEST OF VOLUME 1.
Album: released on Mercury (Import), May'83

Cassette: released on Mercury (Import), May'83

COMPACT JAZZ.
Tracks: / Land of make believe / As long as we're together.
Compact disc: released on Phonogram, Jul'87 by Phonogram Records. Dist: Polygram

Cassette: released on Phonogram, Jul'87 by Phonogram Records. Dist: Polygram

FEELS SO GOOD.
Album: released on A&M, Apr'78 by A&M Records. Dist: Polygram

JOURNEY TO A RAINBOW.
Album: released on CBS, Jul'83 by CBS Records. Dist: CBS

Cassette: released on CBS, Jul'83 by CBS Records. Dist: CBS

LAND OF MAKE BELIEVE.
Tracks: / Legend of the one-eyed sailor / Lullaby for Nancy / Carol / El gato triste / Gloria from mass of St Bernard / As long as we're together / Land of make believe.
Notes: Jazz fluegelhor/trumpet star Chuck Mangione recorded live in concert with the Hamilton Philharmonic featuring Esther Satterfield with her superb rendition of the title track.
Compact disc: released on Phonogram Import, Jul'85

SAVE TONIGHT FOR ME.
Compact disc: released on CBS, May'87 by CBS Records. Dist: CBS

Manhattan

MANHATTAN Original soundtrack (Various Artists).
Compact disc: released on CBS, Jun'87 by CBS Records. Dist: CBS

Album: released on CBS, '79 by CBS Records. Dist: CBS

Manhattan collection

MANHATTAN COLLECTION (THE) Various artists (Various Artists).
Compact disc: released on Chord, Dec'86 by Chord Records. Dist: Charly

Manhattan Jazz Quintet

AUTUMN LEAVES.
Tracks: / Jordu / Recado bossa nova / Confirmation / Autumn leaves / Mood piece.
Notes: Following on from their award winning debut album, 'Autumn Leaves' is further proof that this group is one of the best to have emerged in recent years. Still strictly a studio band, their music is in the tradition of the hard bop tenor-trumpet quintets of the fifties and sixties, as heard on labels like Blue Note and Prestige. Personnel: Lew Soloff-trumpet/George Young-tenor sax/David Matthews-piano/Charnett Moffett-bass/Steve Gadd-drums.
Album: released on King (Japan), Jul'86 Dist: IMS, Polygram

LIVE.
Double Album: released on King (USA), Apr'87 Dist: Gusto Distribution

MANHATTAN JAZZ QUINTET.
Tracks: / Summertime / Rosario / Milestones / My favourite things / Airegin / Summer waltz.
Notes: Straight ahead Be-bop album from five of New York's top sidemen lead by David Matthews. As well as two original compositions by David Matthews, one each from Miles Davis and Sonny Rollins, the selection also includes two popular standards 'Summertime' and 'My Favourite Things'. This album won Swing Journal's 1984 Gold Disk award in Japan. Personnel: Lew Soloff-trumpet/George Young-tenor sax/David Matthews-piano/Charnett Moffett-bass/Steve Gadd-drums.
Album: released on King (Japan), Jul'86 Dist: IMS, Polygram

MY FUNNY VALENTINE.
Tracks: / Mr P.C. / Round midnight / On a clear day / New York state of mind / U blues.
Notes: New album from this quintet, who's forte is updating the sound of the best jazz tunes from the 50's and 60's. On *My funny valentine* they take on three jazz standards, two tunes associated with pop singers Barbara Streisand and Billy Joel and one original blues number from pianist David Matthews. Personnel: Lew Sollof-trumpet/George Young-Tenor sax/David Matthews-piano/Eddie Gomez-bass/Steve Gadd-drums.
Album: released on King (USA), Jan'87 Dist: Gusto Distribution

Manhattan Jazz Septet

MANHATTAN JAZZ SEPTET.
Album: released on Jasmine, Jun'83 by Jasmine Records. Dist: Counterpoint, Lugtons, Taylor, H.R., Wellard, Chris, Swift, Cadillac

Manhattans

6 TRACK HITS.
Extended-play record: released on Scoop 33, Sep'83 by Pickwick Records. Dist: H.R. Taylor Cat. no: **7 SR 5027**
Cassette: released on Scoop 33, Sep'83 by Pickwick Records. Dist: H.R. Taylor

AFTER MIDNIGHT.
Album: released on CBS, Aug'80 by CBS Records. Dist: CBS

BACK TO BASICS.
Tracks: / Change of heart / Where did we go wrong / All I need / I'm through trying to prove my love to you / Mr D.J. / Back into the night / Just like you / Maybe tomorrow / Don't look in my eyes / Neither one of us (wants to be the first to say goodbye).
Album: released on CBS, Dec'86 by CBS Records. Dist: CBS

Cassette: released on CBS, Dec'86 by CBS Records. Dist: CBS

BEST OF THE MANHATTANS, THE.
Album: released on CBS, '84 by CBS Records. Dist: CBS Deleted '86.

Cassette: released on CBS, '84 by CBS Records. Dist: CBS

FOREVER BY YOUR SIDE.
Album: released on CBS, Sep'83 by CBS Records. Dist: CBS

Cassette: released on CBS, Sep'83 by CBS Records. Dist: CBS

KISS AND SAY GOODBYE.
Single (7"): released on Old Gold, Apr'83 by Old Gold Records. Dist: Lightning, Jazz Music, Spartan, Counterpoint

MANHATTANS.
Album: released on CBS, Jul'76 by CBS Records. Dist: CBS

Manhattan Transfer

BEST OF MANHATTAN TRANSFER.
Tracks: / Tuxedo Junction / Boy from New York city / Twilight zone / Body and soul / Candy / Four brothers / Birdland / Gloria / Trickle trickle / Operator / Java jive / Nightingale sang in Berkeley Square (a).
Compact disc: released on Atlantic, '83 by WEA Records. Dist: WEA

Compact disc: released on Atlantic, '83 by WEA Records. Dist: WEA

BODIES AND SOULS.
Tracks: / Spice of life / This independence / Mystery / American pop / Soldier of fortune / Code of ethics / Malaise en malaise / Down south camp meetin' / Why not / Goodbye love / Night that monk returned to heaven (the).
Compact disc: released on Atlantic, Feb'84 by WEA Records. Dist: WEA

Album: released on Atlantic, Feb'84 by WEA Records. Dist: WEA Deleted '86.

Cassette: released on Atlantic, Feb'84 by WEA Records. Dist: WEA

Compact disc: released on Atlantic, Feb'84 by WEA Records. Dist: WEA

BOP DOO-WOPP.
Tracks: / Route 66 / My cat fell in the well / Duke of Dubuque (the) / How high the moon / Baby come back to me / Safronia B / Heart's desire / That't the way it goes / Unchained melody.
Notes: Digital stereo.
Compact disc: released on Atlantic, Feb'85 by WEA Records. Dist: WEA

Album: released on Atlantic, Feb'85 by WEA Records. Dist: WEA

Cassette: released on Atlantic, Feb'85 by WEA Records. Dist: WEA

Compact disc: released on Atlantic, Feb'85 by WEA Records. Dist: WEA

BOY FROM NEW YORK CITY.
Single (7"): released on WEA, Apr'81 by WEA Records. Dist: WEA

CHANSON D'AMOUR.
Single (7"): released on Old Gold, Sep'85 by Old Gold Records. Dist: Lightning, Jazz Music, Spartan, Counterpoint

COMING OUT.
Album: released on Atlantic, Aug'76 by WEA Records. Dist: WEA

Cassette: released on Atlanta Artists (USA), Aug'76 Dist: Polygram

INDEPENDENCE.
Single (7"): released on Atlantic, Oct'83 by WEA Records. Dist: WEA

Single (12"): released on Atlantic, Oct'83 by WEA Records. Dist: WEA

LIVE.
Tracks: / Four brothers / Rambo / (You should) Meet Benny Bailey / Airegin II / To you / Sing joy spring / Move / That's killer Joe / Duke of Dubuque,The / Gloria / On the boulevard / Shaker song,The / Ray's Rockhouse.
Album: released on Atlantic, Jun'87 by WEA Records. Dist: WEA

Cassette: released on Atlantic, Jun'87 by WEA Records. Dist: WEA

LIVE.
Album: released on Atlantic, '78 by WEA Records. Dist: WEA

Cassette: released on Atlantic, '78 by WEA Records. Dist: WEA

MANHATTAN TRANSFER.
Album: released on Atlantic, May'75 by WEA Records. Dist: WEA

MANHATTAN TRANSFER & GENE PISTILLI.
Album: released on MFP, Jul'78 by EMI Records. Dist: EMI

MECCA FOR MODERNS.
Cassette: released on Atlantic, May'81 by WEA Records. Dist: WEA

NIGHTINGALE SANG IN BERKELEY SQUARE, (A).
Single (7"): released on Atlantic, Dec'81 by WEA Records. Dist: WEA

PASTICHE.
Album: released on Atlantic, Feb'78 by WEA Records. Dist: WEA

Cassette: released on Atlantic, Oct'82 by WEA Records. Dist: WEA

SPICE OF LIFE.
Single (7"): released on Atlantic, Jan'84 by WEA Records. Dist: WEA

Single (12"): released on Atlantic, Jan'84 by WEA Records. Dist: WEA

VOCALESE.
Video-cassette (VHS): released on Atlantic, Jun'86 by WEA Records. Dist: WEA

Video-cassette [Betamax]: released on Atlantic, Jun'86 by WEA Records. Dist: WEA

Album: released on Atlantic, Aug'85 by WEA Records. Dist: WEA

Cassette: released on Atlantic, Aug'85 by WEA Records. Dist: WEA

Maniacs

OVERSAXED.
Album: released on Penthouse, Jan'85 by Penthouse Records. Dist: Pinnacle

SATURDAY NIGHT.
Single (12"): released on 25 West, Jun'84 by 25 West Records. Dist: Greyhound

Manifold, Keith

DANNY BOY.
Album: released on Westwood, Nov'76 by Westwood Records. Dist: Jazz Music, H.R. Taylor, JSU, Pinnacle, Ross Records

REMEMBERING.
Album: released on Westwood, '82 by Westwood Records. Dist: Jazz Music, H.R. Taylor, JSU, Pinnacle, Ross Records

TIME.
Album: released on Future Earth, Mar'84 by Future Earth Records. Dist: Red Rhino, Cartel

Manilla Road

MYSTIFICATION.
Album: released on Black Dragon, Jul'87 by Black Dragon Records. Dist: Rough Trade

Manilow, Barry

2.00 AM PARADISE CAFE (VIDEO).
Notes: Barry's tribute to the big band era. 56 minutes
Video-cassette (VHS): released on Video Collection, May'87 by Video Collection International Ltd.. Dist: Counterpoint

2AM PARADISE CAFE.
Album: released on Arista, Nov'84 by Arista Records. Dist: RCA

Cassette: released on Arista, Nov'84 by Arista Records. Dist: RCA

2AM PARADISE CAFE (7").
Single (7"): released on Arista, Aug'84 by Arista Records. Dist: RCA

ALL THE BEST BARRY/MANDY/THIS ONE'S FOR YOU/TRYING TO.
Triple album / cassette: released on Arista, Nov'80 by Arista Records. Dist: RCA

Triple album / cassette: released on Arista, Nov'80 by Arista Records. Dist: RCA

BARRY-LIVE IN BRITAIN.
Album: released on Arista, Apr'82 by Arista Records. Dist: RCA

Cassette: released on Arista, Apr'82 by Arista Records. Dist: RCA

BARRY MANILOW 1.
Album: released on Fame (Arista), May'83 by Music For Pleasure Records. Dist: EMI

Cassette: released on Fame (Arista), May'83 by Music For Pleasure Records. Dist: EMI

BERMUDA TRIANGLE.
Tracks: / Bermuda triangle / Lonely together.
Single (7"): released on Old Gold, Nov'86 by Old Gold Records. Dist: Lightning, Jazz Music, Spartan, Counterpoint

EVEN NOW.
Album: released on Arista, Apr'78 by Arista Records. Dist: RCA

Cassette: released on Arista, Apr'78 by Arista Records. Dist: RCA

HE DOESN'T CARE.
Tracks: / He doesn't care (but I do) / It's all behind us now / I'm your man.
Single (7"): released on RCA, Mar'86 by RCA Records. Dist: RCA, Roots, Swift, Wellard, Chris, I & B, Solomon & Peres Distribution

Single (12"): released on RCA, Mar'86 by RCA Records. Dist: RCA, Roots, Swift, Wellard, Chris, I & B, Solomon & Peres Distribution

I'M YOUR MAN.
Tracks: / I'm your man / He doesn't love you but I do.
Single (7"): released on RCA, May'86 by RCA Records. Dist: RCA, Roots, Swift, Wellard, Chris, I & B, Solomon & Peres Distribution

Single (12"): released on RCA, May'86 by RCA Records. Dist: RCA, Roots, Swift, Wellard, Chris, I & B, Solomon & Peres Distribution

IN CONCERT AT THE GREEK.
Notes: Number of tracks: 19. Type of recording: Live. Total playing time: 110 minutes.
Video-cassette (VHS): released on Guild Home Video, Jan'84 by Guild Records. Dist: Gold & Sons

IN SEARCH OF LOVE.
Single (7"): released on RCA, Nov'85 by RCA Records. Dist: RCA, Roots, Swift, Wellard, Chris, I & B, Solomon & Peres Distribution

Single (12"): released on RCA, Nov'85 by RCA Records. Dist: RCA, Roots, Swift, Wellard, Chris, I & B, Solomon & Peres Distribution

LIVE AT THE GREEK (VIDEO).
Notes: 110 minutes of the greatest hits.
Compact disc single:

MANDY.
Tracks: / Mandy / Copacabana.
Single (7"): released on Old Gold, Nov'86 by Old Gold Records. Dist: Lightning, Jazz Music, Spartan, Counterpoint

Album: released on Arista, Mar'75 by Arista Records. Dist: RCA

Cassette: released on Arista, Mar'75 by Arista Records. Dist: RCA

MANILOW.
Tracks: / At the dance / If you were here with me tonight / Sweet heaven / Ain't nothing like the real thing / It's a long way up / I'm your man / It's all behind us now / In search of love / He doesn't care (but I do) / Some sweet day.
Album: released on RCA, Nov'85 by RCA Records. Dist: RCA, Roots, Swift, Wellard, Chris, I & B, Solomon & Peres Distribution

Cassette: released on RCA, Nov'85 by RCA Records. Dist: RCA, Roots, Swift, Wellard, Chris, I & B, Solomon & Peres Distribution

Compact disc: released on RCA, Feb'86 by RCA Records. Dist: RCA, Roots, Swift, Wellard, Chris, I & B, Solomon & Peres Distribution

MANILOW LIVE.
Double Album: released on Arista, Nov'77 by Arista Records. Dist: RCA

Double cassette: released on Arista, Nov'77 by Arista Records. Dist: RCA

MANILOW MAGIC-THE BEST OF BARRY MANILOW.
Album: released on Arista, Feb'79 by Arista Records. Dist: RCA

Cassette: released on Arista, Feb'79 by Arista Records. Dist: RCA

MANILOW MIRACLES.
Boxed set: released on Arista, Dec'81 by Arista Records. Dist: RCA

Cassette: released on Arista, Dec'81 by Arista Records. Dist: RCA

ONE VOICE.
Album: released on Arista, Sep'79 by Arista Records. Dist: RCA

Cassette: released on Arista, Sep'79 by Arista Records. Dist: RCA

THIS ONE'S FOR YOU.
Album: released on Arista, Oct'76 by Arista Records. Dist: RCA

Cassette: released on Arista, Oct'76 by Arista Records. Dist: RCA

TOUCH MORE MAGIC, A.
Tracks: / You're looking hot tonight / Let's hang on / I wanna do it with you / I'm gonna sit right down and write myself a letter / Some kind of friend / Bermuda triangle / Stay / Put a quarter in the jukebox / Old songs / I made it through the rain / Lonely together / Even now / Memory / One voice.
Notes: Digital stereo.
Compact disc: released on Arista, Apr'84 by Arista Records. Dist: RCA

Compact disc: released on Arista, Apr'84 by Arista Records. Dist: RCA

Album: released on Arista, Sep'83 by Arista Records. Dist: RCA

Cassette: released on Arista, Sep'83 by Arista Records. Dist: RCA

TRYIN' TO GET THE FEELING.
Album: released on Fame (Arista), Nov'82 by Music For Pleasure Records. Dist: EMI

Cassette: released on Fame (Arista), Nov'82 by Music For Pleasure Records. Dist: EMI

YOU'RE LOOKIN' HOT TONIGHT (Live from Blenheim Palace).
Single (7"): released on Arista, Sep'83 by Arista Records. Dist: RCA

Man In Her Life, The

MAN IN HER LIFE, THE Ayers, Ruby M. (Ballard, Jane).

Manish Boys

I PITY THE FOOL (EP).
Single (7"): released on Charly, Nov'82 by Charly Records. Dist: Charly, Cadillac

MANISH BOYS/DAVY JONES & THE LOWER THIRD(EP) (Manish Boys/Davy Jones & Lower Third).
Extended-play record: released on See For Miles, Jun'85 by Charly Records. Dist: Spartan

Manitaza

GIMME WHAT I WANT.
Single (7"): released on Axe, Feb'82

Single (12"): released on Axe, Feb'82

Man jumping

AEROTROPICS.
Album: released on Cocteau, Jul'85 by Cocteau Records. Dist: Pinnacle, IDS

Single (12"): released on Cocteau, Apr'85 by Cocteau Records. Dist: Pinnacle, IDS

JUMP CUT.
Tracks: / Belle dux on the beach / Buzz buzz buzz goes the honeybee / World service / Walk on bye / Down the locale / Squeezi / Arotropics.
Album: released on Cocteau, Jan'85 by Cocteau Records. Dist: Pinnacle, IDS

WORLD SERVICE.
Compact disc: released on E.G., May'87 by Virgin Records. Dist: Virgin, EMI

Mankind

CHAIN REACTION.
Single (7"): released on Firebird, Mar'79 by Pinnacle Records. Dist: Pinnacle

DOCTOR WHO.
Single (7"): released on Motor, Jan'84 Dist: Pinnacle

Single (12"): released on Motor, Jan'84 Dist: Pinnacle

Mankind, Sidney

TRUTH, THE.
Single (12"): released on Musical Ambassador, Sep'82

Manklan

BOYS OF THE TERRITORY.
Single (12"): released on Wire, Jul'85 Dist: Nine Mile, Cartel

Manley, Cynthia

BACK IN MY ARMS AGAIN.
Single (7"): released on Atlantic, Mar'83 by WEA Records. Dist: WEA

Man & Me

GOOD COMPANION / YOU'RE MY.....
Single (7"): released on Solid Gold, Jan'82 Dist: MCA

Mannan

NIGHT PATROL.
Album: released on Artic, May'84

Mann, Carl

GONNA ROCK'N'ROLL TONIGHT.
Album: released on Charly, '78 by Charly Records. Dist: Charly, Cadillac

IN ROCKABILLY COUNTRY.
Album: released on Charly, Apr'81 by Charly Records. Dist: Charly, Cadillac

LEGENDARY SUN PERFORMERS.
Album: released on Charly, Nov'77 by Charly Records. Dist: Charly, Cadillac

LIKE MANN.
Album: released on Charly, Feb'81 by Charly Records. Dist: Charly, Cadillac

ROCKING MANN, (THE).
Tracks: / Mona Lisa / Foolish one / Pretend / Rockin' love / Some enchanted evening / I can't forget / South of the border / I'm coming home / Baby I don't care / Vanished / Wayward wind / Born to be bad / I ain't go no home / If I could change you / Mountain dew / When I grow too old to dream / Baby I don't care / I'm bluer than anyone can be / Walkin' and thinkin' / If I ever needed love / Island of love / Stop the world / Don't let the stars get in your eyes / Look at that moon / Too young / Because of you / Ain't you got no lovin' for me? / Kansas City / Blueberry Hill / Walkin' the dog / Ubangi stomp / Mona Lisa (reprise).
Double Album: released on Charly, Jun'87 by Charly Records. Dist: Charly, Cadillac

ROCKING MANN, THE.
Double Album: released on Charly, Jul'87 by Charly Records. Dist: Charly, Cadillac

Mann C.C.

HAVEN'T GOT THE TIME.
Single (7"): released on Movement 24, Feb'80

Mann, Clarence

I'LL BE AROUND.
Single (7"): released on Expansion, Nov'86 Dist: PRT

Mann, Dany

NA BABY, WEI GEHT'S.
Album: released on Polydor, Sep'81 by Polydor Records. Dist: Polygram, Polydor

Mann, Doug

SINGING STREET, THE.
Album: released on OK, May'83 Dist: Stage One Distribution

Cassette: released on OK, May'83 Dist: Stage One Distribution

STORY OF GREYFRIERS BOBBY, THE.
Single (7"): released on REL, '78 Dist: Roots

Manne, Shelly

AT THE BLACK HAWK VOL.3 (Manne, Shelly & His Men).
Album: released on Contemporary (USA), Dec'81 Dist: Fantasy (USA) Distribution

AT THE BLACK HAWK VOL.4 (Manne, Shelly & His Men).
Album: released on Contemporary (USA), Sep'82 Dist: Fantasy (USA) Distribution

AT THE BLACK HAWK VOL.2 (Manne, Shelly & His Men).
Album: released on Contemporary (USA), Jul'81 Dist: Fantasy (USA) Distribution

IN CONCERT AT CARMELO'S VOL 1 (Manne, Shelly Double Piano Jazz Quartet).
Tracks: / Sweet & lovely / Marilyn Monroe / Night has a thousand eyes, The / Strollin' / I'll take romance / Lennie's pennies.
Notes: Shelly Manne-Drums/Chuck Domanico-Bass/Alan Broadbent-Piano/Bill Mays-Piano.
Compact disc: released on Trend (USA), Sep'86 by Discovery Records. Dist: Flexitron Distributors Ltd, Swift

IN CONCERT AT CARMELO'S VOL 2 (Manne, Shelly Double Piano Jazz Quartet).
Tracks: / In your own street / Alone together / Midnight song for Thalia / Lament / Along came Betty.
Notes: Shelly Mann-drums/Chuck Domanico-bass/Alan Broadbent-piano/Bill Mays-piano.
Compact disc: released on Trend (USA), Sep'86 by Discovery Records. Dist: Flexitron Distributors Ltd, Swift

INTERPRETATIONS OF BACH AND MOZART (Manne, Shelly Jazz Quartet).
Tracks: / Bach - violin concerto in E major / Air from the suite in D / Mozart - Divertimento K 136 / Andante (from Concerto for piano and orch in C major 467).
Notes: Shelly Manne-drums/Mike Wofford-piano/Gary Foster-flute and sax/Chuck Domanico-bass.
Compact disc: released on Trend (USA), Sep'86 by Discovery Records. Dist: Flexitron Distributors Ltd, Swift

MANNE - THAT'S GERSHWIN (Manne, Shelly Quintet & Big Band).
Album: released on Discovery (USA), Nov'84 by Discovery Records (USA). Dist: Swift, Flexitron-Audio, Jazz Music

MORE SWINGING SOUNDS (Manne, Shelly & his men).
Album: released on Contemporary, Jan'86 by Contemporary Records. Dist: Pinnacle

MY FAIR LADY (Manne, Shelly & friends).
Compact disc: released on Mobile Fidelity, Oct'86 by Mobile Fidelity Records.

MY FAIR LADY (SONGS FROM) (Manne, Shelly & His Friends).
Cassette: released on MFP, Oct'81 by EMI Records. Dist: EMI

SHELLY MANNE & HIS FRIENDS (Manne, Shelly & His Friends).
Album: released on Doctor Jazz, Oct'83

Cassette: released on Doctor Jazz, Oct'83

TWO THREE FOUR.
Album: released on Jasmine, Sep'82 by Jasmine Records. Dist: Counterpoint, Lugtons, Taylor, H.R., Wellard, Chris, Swift, Cadillac

Cassette: released on Jasmine, Sep'82 by Jasmine Records. Dist: Counterpoint, Lugtons, Taylor, H.R., Wellard, Chris, Swift, Cadillac

WAY OUT WEST See Rollins, Sonny.

WEST COAST SOUND, THE (Manne, Shelly & his men).
Tracks: / Grasshopper / La mugura / Summer night / Afrodesia / You & the night & the music / Gazelle / Sweets / Spring is here / Mallets / You're getting to be a habit with me / You're my thrill / Fugue.
Album: released on Contemporary, Jan'86 by Contemporary Records. Dist: Pinnacle

Mann, Herbie

AT THE VILLAGE GATE.
Compact disc: released on Atlantic Jazz, Jul'87 by WEA Records. Dist: WEA

MEMPHIS UNDERGROUND.
Album: released on Atlantic, Jan'79 by WEA Records. Dist: WEA

Manning, Bernard

LIVE AT THE EMBASSY CLUB.
Album: released on President, May'77 by President Records. Dist: Taylors, Spartan

Manning, Sam

BARBADOS BLUES (Manning, Sam & Wilmoth Houdini).
Album: released on Collectors Items, Jul'86 Dist: Jazz Music, Swift, Chris Wellard

Album: released on Collectors Items, Oct'84 Dist: Jazz Music, Swift, Chris Wellard

Mann, John

AN EMINENT EXPERIENCE (Eminent 2000 Grand Theatre Organ).
Album: released on Grosvenor, Aug'82 by Grosvenor Records. Dist: Taylors

AN EMINENT MANN & HIS MUSIC (Eminent 2000 Grand Theatre Organ).
Album: released on Grosvenor, Jun'81 by Grosvenor Records. Dist: Taylors

Cassette: released on Grosvenor, Jun'81 by Grosvenor Records. Dist: Taylors

AN EMINENT OCCASION (Eminent 2000 Grand Theatre Organ).
Album: released on Grosvenor, '78 by Grosvenor Records. Dist: Taylors

CHRISTIE SOUND, THE.
Album: released on Grosvenor, Mar'82 by Grosvenor Records. Dist: Taylors

ENTERTAINS.
Notes: Excerts from live records at Huddersfield Town Hall.
Album: released on Grosvenor, May'86 by Grosvenor Records. Dist: Taylors

FOREVER MELODIES.
Tracks: / Snow bells / Cara mia / Caraquinto / Jesu joy of mans desiring / Cuckoo waltz / New York New York / One / La uran tango Argentin / St. Louis blues / Brighton sea step / Song on the sand / Swedish rhapsody / All I ask of you / Theme: Romeo & Juliet.
Cassette: released on Grosvenor, Jun'87 by Grosvenor Records. Dist: Taylors

Album: released on Grosvenor, Jun'87 by Grosvenor Records. Dist: Taylors

JOHN MANN ENTERTAINS.
Album: released on Grosvenor, Sep'85 by Grosvenor Records. Dist: Taylors

Cassette: released on Grosvenor, Sep'85 by Grosvenor Records. Dist: Taylors

Mann,Manfred

BEST OF:MANFRED MANN.
Album: released on Mercury (USA), Nov'81 by Import Records. Dist: IMS Distribution, Polygram Distribution

Cassette: released on Mercury (USA), Nov'81 by Import Records. Dist: IMS Distribution, Polygram Distribution

Album: released on Nut, Jul'77 by EMI Records. Dist: EMI

Album: released on Music for Pleasure (Holland), Apr'83 Dist: Conifer Distribution

Cassette: released on Music for Pleasure (Holland), Apr'83 Dist: Conifer Distribution

BLINDED BY THE LIGHT (Mann's, Manfred Earthband).
Single (7"): released on Bronze, '80 by Polygram Records. Dist: Polydor

BUDAPEST (Mann's, Manfred Earthband).
Cassette: released on Bronze, Feb'84 by Polygram Records. Dist: Polydor

Album: released on Bronze, Feb'84 by Polygram Records. Dist: Polydor

COLLECTION: MANFRED MANN.
Album: released on EMI (Germany), '83 by EMI Records. Dist: Conifer

CRIMINAL TANGO.
Album: released on Ten, Jul'86

Cassette: released on Ten, Jul'86

Compact disc: released on 10, Jul'86 by 10 Records. Dist: Virgin, EMI

DAVY'S ON THE ROAD AGAIN (Mann's, Manfred Earthband).
Single (7"): released on Bronze, Feb'84 by Polygram Records. Dist: Polydor

Single (12"): released on Bronze, Feb'84 by Polygram Records. Dist: Polydor

DEMOLITION MAN (Mann's, Manfred Earthband).
Single (7"): released on Bronze, Jan'83 by Polygram Records. Dist: Polydor

DO ANYTHING YOU WANNA DO.
Tracks: / Do anything you wanna do / Crossfire.
Single (7"): released on 10, Mar'86 by 10 Records. Dist: Virgin, EMI

Single (12"): released on 10, Mar'86 by 10 Records. Dist: Virgin, EMI

DO WAH DIDDY DIDDY.
Single (7"): released on Past Masters, Oct'82

DO WAH DIDDY DIDDY (2).
Single (7"): released on Old Gold, Oct'83 by Old Gold Records. Dist: Lightning, Jazz Music, Spartan, Counterpoint

GLORIFIED MAGNIFIED (Mann's, Manfred Earthband).
Album: released on Bronze, '81 by Polygram Records. Dist: Polydor

GOING UNDERGROUND.
Tracks: / Going underground / I shall be rescued.
Single (7"): released on 10, May'86 by 10 Records. Dist: Virgin, EMI

Single (12"): released on 10, May'86 by 10 Records. Dist: Virgin, EMI

GOOD EARTH, THE (Mann's, Manfred Earthband).
Album: released on Bronze, '81 by Polygram Records. Dist: Polydor

HITS 1966-69 (Manns, Manfred 'Earthband').
Album: released on Mercury, Apr'86 by Phonogram Records. Dist: Polygram Distribution

Cassette: released on Mercury, Apr'86 by Phonogram Records. Dist: Polygram Distribution

MANFRED MANN.
Album: released on EMI (Holland), '83 by EMI Records. Dist: Conifer

MANFRED MANN'S EARTHBAND (Mann's, Manfred Earthband).
Album: released on Bronze, '81 by Polygram Records. Dist: Polydor

MANNERISMS.
Album: released on Sonic, Jul'76

MESSIN' (Mann's, Manfred Earthband).
Album: released on Bronze, '81 by Polygram Records. Dist: Polydor

MIGHTY QUINN.
Single (7"): released on Old Gold, Jun'82 by Old Gold Records. Dist: Lightning, Jazz Music, Spartan, Counterpoint

NIGHTINGALES & BOMBERS (Mann's, Manfred Earthband).
Album: released on Bronze, '81 by Polygram Records. Dist: Polydor

PRETTY FLAMINGO.
Tracks: / Pretty flamingo / Come tomorrow.
Single (7"): released on Old Gold, Mar'87 by Old Gold Records. Dist: Lightning, Jazz Music, Spartan, Counterpoint

PRETTY FLAMINGO.
Single (7"): released on Lightning, '80 by Lightning Records. Dist: Jetstar

PRETTY FLAMINGO (2).
Single (7"): released on Old Gold, Oct'83 by Old Gold Records. Dist: Lightning, Jazz Music, Spartan, Counterpoint

Single (7"): released on Old Gold, May'84 by Old Gold Records. Dist: Lightning, Jazz Music, Spartan, Counterpoint

ROARING SILENCE, THE (Mann's, Manfred Earthband).
Album: released on Bronze, '81 by Polygram Records. Dist: Polydor

Album: released on Bronze, '81 by Polygram Records. Dist: Polydor

RUNNER, THE H (Mann's, Manfred Earthband).
Single (7"): by Polygram Records. Dist: Polydor

Single (12"): by Polygram Records. Dist: Polydor

SEMI-DETACHED SUBURBAN 20 GREAT HITS.
Cassette: released on EMI, Sep'79 by EMI Records. Dist: EMI

SINGLES ALBUM, THE.
Tracks: / Why should we not / Brother Jack / Cock a hoop / Now you're needing me / 5-4-3-2-1 / Without you / Hubble bubble / I'm your king pin / Do wah diddy diddy / What you gonna do / Sha la la / Joh Hardy / Come tomorrow / What

did I do wrong / Oh no not my baby / What am I doing wrong / If you gotta go, go now / Stay around / Pretty flamingo / You're standing by.
Notes: For the first time ever all of Manfred Mann's singles released during their years on the HMV label have been chronologically collected together on one album. It wasn't until '5-4-3-2-1' was released and selected as the signature tune to the overwhelmingly influential TV show, 'Ready, Steady Go' that the name of Manfred Mann featured in the Top 10, but for the next year and a half, the group were rarely absent from the charts. Of special consideration are the group's two chart topping singles 'Do Wah Diddy Diddy' and 'Pretty Flamingo' while 'If You Gotta Go, Go Now' was their first hit written by Bob Dylan.
Album: released on EMI, Jan'86 by EMI Records. Dist: EMI

Cassette: released on EMI, Jan'86 by EMI Records. Dist: EMI

SINGLES PLUS, THE.
Tracks: / Why should we not / Brother Jack / Cock a hoop / Now you're needing me / 5-4-3-2-1 / Without you / Hubble bubble (Toil and trouble) / I'm your kingpin / Do wah diddy diddy / What you gonna do / Sha la la / John Hardy / Come tomorrow / What did I do wrong / Oh no not my baby / What am I doing wrong / If you gotta go, go now / Stay around / Pretty flamingo / You're standing by / You gave me somebody to love / Poison ivy / Groovin' / Can't believe it / Did you have to do that?.
Compact disc: released on EMI, Jul'87 by EMI Records. Dist: EMI

SOLAR FIRE (Mann's, Manfred Earthband).
Album: released on Bronze, '81 by Polygram Records. Dist: Polydor

SOMEWHERE IN AFRIKA (Mann's, Manfred Earthband).
Album: released on Bronze, Jan'83 by Polygram Records. Dist: Polydor

Cassette: released on Bronze, Jan'83 by Polygram Records. Dist: Polydor

SOUL OF MANFRED MANN.
Tracks: / Abominable snowman (the) / I got you babe / Bare hugg / Spirit feel / Why should you not / L.S.D. / I can't get no satisfaction / God rest ye merry gentlemen / My generation / Mr Anello / Still I'm sad / Tengo, tengo / Brother Jack / Sack o' woe.
Album: released on See For Miles, Jul'86 by See For Miles Records. Dist: Pinnacle

SOUL OF MANN.
Album: released on See For Miles, Jun'85 by Charly Records. Dist: Spartan

VERY BEST OF MANFRED MANN (1963-1966).
Album: released on Music for Pleasure, May'84 by EMI Records. Dist: MFP Distribution

Cassette: released on Music for Pleasure, May'84 by EMI Records. Dist: MFP Distribution

Mann, Ritchie

WUNDERBAR.
Album: released on Sky, '78 by President Records.

Manone, Wingy

1947 (Manone, Wingy & Sidney Bechet).
Notes: MONO
Album: released on Jazz Archives, Jul'86 by Jazz Archives Records. Dist: Jazz Music

VOLUME 4.
Album: released on Little Gem (USA), Jul'84 Dist: Swift

WINGY MANONE & WILL BRADLEY (see Bradley, Will) (Manone, Wingy & Will Bradley).

Manowar

ALL MEN PLAY ON 10.
Single (12"): released on Ten, Aug'84

BATTLE HYMNS.
Album: released on Liberty, Aug'82 by Liberty-United. Dist: EMI

Cassette: released on Liberty, Aug'82 by Liberty-United. Dist: EMI Deleted '86.

BLOW YOUR SPEAKERS.
Tracks: / Blow your speakers / Violence and bloodshed.
Single (7"): released on Atlantic, 23 May'87 by WEA Records. Dist: WEA

Single (12"): released on Atlantic, 23 May'87 by WEA Records. Dist: WEA

DEFENDER.
Single (12"): released on Music For Nations, Oct'83 by Music For Nations Records. Dist: Pinnacle

FIGHTING THE WORLD.
Tracks: / Fighting the world / Blow your speakers / Carry on / Violence and bloodshed / Defender / Drums of doom / Holy war / Blackwind, fire and steel.
Album: released on Atlantic, Jan'87 by WEA Records. Dist: WEA

Cassette: released on Atlantic, Jan'87 by WEA Records. Dist: WEA

FIGHTING THE WORLD.
Album: released on Atco, Feb'87 by Atlantic Records. Dist: WEA

Cassette: released on Atco, Feb'87 by Atlantic Records. Dist: WEA

Compact disc: released on Atco, Jul'87 by Atlantic Records. Dist: WEA

HAIL TO ENGLAND.
Album: released on Music For Nations, Feb'84 by Music For Nations Records. Dist: Pinnacle

Cassette: released on Music For Nations, Feb'84 by Music For Nations Records. Dist: Pinnacle

INTO GLORY RIDES.
Album: released on Music For Nations, Jul'83 by Music For Nations Records. Dist: Pinnacle

Cassette: released on Music For Nations, Jul'83 by Music For Nations Records. Dist: Pinnacle

SIGN ON THE HAMMER.
Album: released on 10, Sep'84 by 10 Records. Dist: Virgin, EMI

Cassette: released on 10, Sep'84 by 10 Records. Dist: Virgin, EMI

Man Parrish

BOOGIE DOWN.
Single (7"): released on Polydor, Mar'85 by Polydor Records. Dist: Polygram, Polydor

Single (12"): released on Polydor, Mar'85 by Polydor Records. Dist: Polygram, Polydor

HIP HOP BE BOP.
Single (12"): released on Polydor, Mar'83 by Polydor Records. Dist: Polygram, Polydor Deleted '86.

Single (7"): released on Polydor, Mar'85 by Polydor Records. Dist: Polygram, Polydor

MALE STRIPPER.
Tracks: / Male stripper.
Single (7"): released on Bolts, Jan'87 by Bolts Records. Dist: PRT, Pinnacle

Single (12"): released on Bolts, Jan'87 by Bolts Records. Dist: PRT, Pinnacle

MAN PARRISH.
Album: released on Polydor, Apr'83 by Polydor Records. Dist: Polygram, Polydor

Cassette: released on Polydor, Apr'83 by Polydor Records. Dist: Polygram, Polydor

Mansell, Tony Singers

TRIBUTE TO SIMON & GARFUNKEL.
Cassette: released on Oak, Oct'82 by Oak Records. Dist: Spartan Distribution, Pinnacle

Mansfield, Darrell

HIGHER POWER.
Album: released on Marantha Music, May'82

Cassette: released on Marantha Music, May'82

Mansfield, Katherine

GARDEN PARTY, THE.
Cassette: released on Cover to Cover, Jun'85 by Cover to Cover Cassettes. Dist: Conifer

Manteau

PROMISES.
Single (7"): released on Riva, Oct'84 Dist: PRT

Mantilla, Ray

SYNERGY (Mantilla, Ray Space Station).
Notes: Guest: Steve Grossman.
Album: released on Red, Jan'87 Dist: Projection, Jazz Horizons

Mantler, Michael

ALIEN.
Tracks: / Part 1 / Part 2 / Part 3 / Part 4.
Notes: Austro-American trumpeter Michael Mantler is known for his unconventional projects. On his new album 'Alien' he performs with ex-Mother of Invention Don Preston, a specialist in synthesizer sounds and well-known for his work for Frank Zappa. 'Alien' sounds like the score for an imaginary film - the music has a mostly lyrical and dark character. Michael Mantler's immaculate trumpet playing unfolds over a startling variety of synthesizer sounds, carefully layered by Don Preston. An additional drum computer brings tension and drive. Personnel: Michael Mantler-trumpet/Don Preston-synthesizers.
Album: released on ECM (Germany), Dec'85 by ECM Records. Dist: IMS, Polygram, Virgin through EMI

Compact disc: released on ECM (Germany), Dec'85 by ECM Records. Dist: IMS, Polygram, Virgin through EMI

HAPLESS CHILD, THE.
Compact disc: released on ECM (Germany), Jul'87 by ECM Records. Dist: IMS, Polygram, Virgin through EMI

SOMETHING THERE.
Album: released on Watteau, Mar'83 by Armageddon Records. Dist: Stage One

Compact disc: released on ECM (Germany), Jul'87 by ECM Records. Dist: IMS, Polygram, Virgin through EMI

Man to Man

ENERGY IS EUROBEAT (Man to Man meets Man Parrish).
Single (7"): released on Bolts, May'87 by Bolts Records. Dist: PRT, Pinnacle

Single (12"): released on Bolts, May'87 by Bolts Records. Dist: PRT, Pinnacle

I NEED A MAN.
Tracks: / I need a man / Energy is Eurobeat / Male stripper (remix)*.
Single (7"): released on Bolts, 20 Jun'87 by Bolts Records. Dist: PRT, Pinnacle

Single (12"): released on Bolts, 20 Jun'87 by Bolts Records. Dist: PRT, Pinnacle

Single (12"): released on Bolts, Aug'87 by Bolts Records. Dist: PRT, Pinnacle

Manton

NO TREES IN BRIXTON.
Single (7"): released on Mainstream, Jun'81

Mantovani

16 GOLDEN CLASSICS.
Tracks: / Love story (theme from) / Lawrence of Arabia / Moon River / Smoke gets in your eyes / Good morning starshine / Sunrise sunset / Tulips from Amsterdam / Walk in the Black Forest, A / West side story (Maria\Somewhere) / Mona Lisa / When I fall in love / Summertime / Over the rainbow / Some enchanted evening / Lemon tree / Walk in the Black Forest, A / Taste of honey, A.
Notes: All tracks from Decca Records Ltd. Design: Shoot that tiger! (C) 1986 Castle Communications Place, Unit 7, 271, Merton Road, London SW18 5JS. Bar Code 5\013428\920138
Album: released on Unforgettable, Dec'86 by Castle Communications Records. Dist: Counterpoint

CASCADE OF PRAISE.
Album: released on Word, May'85 by Word Records. Dist: Word Distribution, CBS

Cassette: released on Word, May'85 by Word Records. Dist: Word Distribution, CBS

CHRISTMAS MAGIC.
Album: released on Audio Fidelity, Oct'84 Dist: PRT

Cassette: released on Audio Fidelity, Oct'84 Dist: PRT

COLLECTION: MANTOVANI (Mantovani & His Orchestra).
Compact disc: released on Castle Collectors, Jul'87 by Castle Communications Records. Dist: Pinnacle

ECHOES OF ITALY (Mantovani & His Orchestra & Laszlo Tabor & His Orchestra).
Tracks: / Torna a surriento / Italia mia / Mattinata / Carnival of Venice / O sole mio / Ciribiribin / Santa Lucia / Arrivaderci Roma / Funiculi, funicula / Summertime in Venice / Capriccio Italien / Vieni sul mar / Anema e core / Bella piccininia / Mamma.
Compact disc: released on London, Jul'87 by London Records. Dist: Polygram

EIN TRAUM FUR ZWEI (THE RED ALBUM).
Album: released on EEC Import (Limited Edition), Dec'82 Dist: IMS, Polygram

Cassette: released on EEC Import (Limited Edition), Dec'82 Dist: IMS, Polygram

EVERGREEN.
Album: released on Arcade Music Gala, Apr'86 Dist: Stage One

Cassette: released on Arcade Music Gala, Apr'86 Dist: Stage One

FROM MANTOVANI WITH LOVE.
Tracks: / Try to remember / It's impossible / My prayer / If I only had time / Loss of love / Gwendolyne / Rosy's theme / Love story theme / Little green apples / Last summer / Where have all the flowers gone / May each day.
Compact disc: released on Decca, Sep'85 by Decca Records. Dist: Polygram

GEMS FOREVER (Mantovani & His Orchestra).
Tracks: / All the things you are / True love / I could have danced all night / You kept coming back like a song / Woman in love, A / This nearly was mine / Summertime / Something to remember you by / Love letters / Nearness of you, The / An affair to remember / Hey there.
Compact disc: released on London, Jul'87 by London Records. Dist: Polygram

GOLDEN AGE OF THE YOUNG MANTOVANI 1935-1939, THE.
Tracks: / I wished on the moon / Please believe me / Cuban Pete / Serenade in the night / All alone in Vienna / Where are you / Blue Hawaii / You're laughing at me / Ten pretty girls / Waltz of the gipsies / Something to sing about / In my little red book / So little time (so much to do) / There's rain in my eyes / My prayer / Spider of the night.
Notes: (P) Original Sound Recordings owned by EMI Records Ltd. Mantovani & His Orchestra.

GOLDEN VIOLINS.
Album: released on Decca (Holland), Jul'84 by Decca Records. Dist: Polygram, IMS

Cassette: released on Decca (Holland), Jul'84 by Decca Records. Dist: Polygram, IMS

GREATEST GIFT IS LOVE, THE (Mantovani & His Orchestra).
Album: released on Decca, Dec'75 by Decca Records. Dist: Polygram

Cassette: released on Decca, Dec'75 by Decca Records. Dist: Polygram

GREAT MANTOVANI, THE.
Album: released on President Evergreen, Mar'85

GREAT MANTOVANI (THE).
Tracks: / Story of Three Loves / Dream of Olwen (the) / Around the World / Swan Lake waltz / Song of India / Moulin Rouge / Blue Danube (The) / Charmaine / Lonely ballerina / Stranger in paradise / Gigi / Tenderly / With these hands / Tonight.
Compact disc: released on President, Jan'87 by President Records. Dist: Taylors, Spartan

HOLY NIGHT.
Album: released on Audio Fidelity, Oct'84 Dist: PRT

Cassette: released on Audio Fidelity, Oct'84 Dist: PRT

INCOMPARABLE, THE (Mantovani & His Orchestra).
Album: released on Decca, '65 by Decca Records. Dist: Polygram

Cassette: released on Decca, '65 by Decca Records. Dist: Polygram

I WISH YOU LOVE.
Album: released on Contour, Sep'84 by Pickwick Records. Dist: Pickwick Distribution, PRT

Cassette: released on Contour, Sep'84 by Pickwick Records. Dist: Pickwick Distribution, PRT

LIVE AT THE FESTIVAL HALL VOL. 2.
Tracks: / Three coins in the fountain / Sound of music, The / Deep purple / What are you doing the rest of your life / Entertainer, The / Send in the clowns / Italian fantasy / Charmaine / Swedish rhapsody.
Compact disc: released on Bellaphon, '86 by Bellaphon Records. Dist: IMS-Polygram

LIVE AT THE FESTIVAL HALL VOL. 1.
Tracks: / Love is a many splendoured thing / Some enchanted evening / Summertime in Venice / Merry waltz / Cavatina / Autumn leaved / Elizabethan serenade / Big country, The.
Compact disc: released on Bellaphon, '86 by Bellaphon Records. Dist: IMS-Polygram

LIVE AT THE ROYAL FESTIVAL HALL (Mantovani & His Orchestra).
Tracks: / Charmaine and introduction / Love is a many splendoured thing / Some enchanted evening / Summertime in Venice / Merry waltz / Cavatina / Autumn leaves / Elizabethan serenade / Big country, The / Three coins in the fountain / Sound of music, The / Deep purple / What are you doing the rest of your life / Entertainer, The / Send in the clowns / Italian fantasy / Charmaine / Swedish rhapsody.

LOVE THEMES, THE.
Double Album: released on Horatio Nelson, Nov'85 Dist: PRT

Double cassette: released on Horatio Nelson, Nov'85 Dist: PRT

MAGIC OF MANTOVANI (Mantovani & His Orchestra).
Compact disc: released on K-Tel, '86 by K-Tel Records. Dist: Record Merchandisers Distribution, Taylors, Terry Blood Distribution, Wynd-Up Distribution, Relay Distribution, Pickwick Distribution, Solomon & Peres Distribution, Polygram

MANTOVANI.
Compact disc: released on Intertape, Jul'8 Dist: Target

Album: released on Teldec (Import), May'83

MANTOVANI FAVOURITES (Mantovani & His Orchestra).
Tracks: / Londonderry air / Walk in the Black Forest, A / Dream / Black eyes / Welcome home / Party's over (The) / Happy wanderer (The) / Till the end of time / Trumpeter's lullaby, A / Whiffenpoof song / Tulips from Amsterdam / Auld lang syne.
Compact disc: released on London, Feb'87 by London Records. Dist: Polygram

Album: released on Decca, Jul'77 by Decca Records. Dist: Polygram

Cassette: released on Decca, Jul'77 by Decca Records. Dist: Polygram

MANTOVANI & HIS ORCHESTRA - THE COLLECTION (Mantovani & His Orchestra).
Tracks: / Out of my dreams / Charmaine / Blue tango / Deep purple / Auf wiedersehn sweetheart / Whispering / Give my regards to Broadway / It takes two to tango / Over the rainbow / Trolley song, the / Diane / Wunderbar / Cabaret / Hernando's hideaway / Three o'clock in the morning / Skater's waltz, The / Harlem nocturne / Forgotten dreams / Anniversary waltz, The / Autumn leaves / Tulips from Amsterdam / Me and my shadow / Taste of honey, A / Jealousy / Home on the range / Jamaica farewell / April in Portugal / May each day.
Notes: The recordings are licensed from Decca Record Co. Design - Shoot That Tiger. This compilation (c) 1986. Castle Communications PLC, Unit 7, 271 Merton Road, London SW18 5JS. Bar code: 5 013428 131305

MANTOVANI MAGIC (Mantovani & His Orchestra).
Tracks: / Misty / Red roses for a blue lady / Chim chim cher-ee / Love me with all your heart / Goodnight sweetheart / Cara mia / I wish you love / Lover / Stardust / Mona Lisa / Most beautiful girl in the world / Auf wiederseh'n sweetheart.
Compact disc: released on London, Mar'87 by London Records. Dist: Polygram

Compact disc: released on Telstar, Jul'87 by Telstar Records. Dist: RCA Distribution

Album: released on Telstar, Nov'83 by Telstar Records. Dist: RCA Distribution

Cassette: released on Telstar, Nov'83 by Telstar Records. Dist: RCA Distribution

MANTOVANI ORCHESTRA.
Album: released on Dakota (Countdown series), Oct'82 by Dakota Records. Dist: PRT

Cassette: released on Dakota (Countdown series), Oct'82 by Dakota Records. Dist: PRT

MANTOVANI PLAYS ALL-TIME ROMANTIC HITS (Mantovani & His Orchestra).
Cassette: released on Decca, Apr'75 by Decca Records. Dist: Polygram

MANTOVANI PRESENTS HIS CONCERT SUCCESSES.
Tracks: / Charmaine / Die fledermaus overture / Moon river / Hora staccato / Aquarius / Autumn leaves / Gypsy carnival / Seventy-six trombones / Greensleeves / Capriccio Italien / Theme from the Virginian / Fantasy on Italian melodies / Charmaine reprise.

MANTOVANI'S MAGIC TOUCH (Mantovani & His Orchestra).
Double Album: released on Decca, '70 by Decca Records. Dist: Polygram

MANTOVANI TOUCH, THE (Mantovani & His Orchestra).
Cassette: released on Decca, Apr'72 by Decca Records. Dist: Polygram

MANTOVANI VOLUME IV.
Cassette: released on Audio Fidelity, Oct'84 Dist: PRT

MANTOVANI VOLUME I.
Cassette: released on Audio Fidelity, Oct'84 Dist: PRT

MANTOVANI VOLUME II.
Cassette: released on Audio Fidelity, Oct'84 Dist: PRT

MANTOVANI VOLUME III.
Cassette: released on Audio Fidelity, Oct'84 Dist: PRT

MEMORIES (Mantovani & His Orchestra).
Cassette: released on Decca, Mar'71 by Decca Records. Dist: Polygram

MORE MANTOVANI GOLDEN HITS (Mantovani & His Orchestra).
Album: released on Decca, Jun'76 by Decca Records. Dist: Polygram

Cassette: released on Decca, Jun'76 by Decca Records. Dist: Polygram

MUSICAL MOMENTS WITH MANTOVANI & HIS ORCHESTRA (Mantovani & His Orchestra).
Album: released on Decca, Nov'74 by Decca Records. Dist: Polygram

MUSIC FOR THE MILLIONS - SONGS OF PRAISE.
Album: released on Polydor (Holland), Jul'83

Cassette: released on Polydor (Holland), Jul'83

MUSIC FROM THE FILMS (Mantovani & His Orchestra).
Album: released on Decca, '58 by Decca Records. Dist: Polygram

Cassette: released on Decca, '58 by Decca Records. Dist: Polygram

MUSIC OF LOVE, THE.
Album: released on Contour, Feb'84 by Pickwick Records. Dist: Pickwick Distribution, PRT

Cassette: released on Contour, Feb'84 by Pickwick Records. Dist: Pickwick Distribution, PRT

STRAUSS WALTZES (Mantovani & His Orchestra).
Album: released on Decca, '58 by Decca Records. Dist: Polygram

Cassette: released on Decca, '58 by Decca Records. Dist: Polygram

THEATRE FAVOURITES.
Double Album: released on Decca, Jan'80 by Decca Records. Dist: Polygram

Double cassette: released on Decca, Jan'80 by Decca Records. Dist: Polygram

TREASURY OF MELODY.
Boxed set: released on World Records, Dec'81 Dist: Polygram

Special: released on World Records, Dec'81 Dist: Polygram

UNFORGETTABLE SOUND OF MANTOVANI.
Tracks: / Elizabethan serenade / Cara mia / I'll never fall in love again / Spanish eyes / Vaya con dios / Big country / Valencia / I love Paris / Good life / Golden earrings / Besame mucho / Smoke gets in your eyes / Give my regards to Broadway / Tico-tico / Eye level / Sweetest sounds / September song / Black eyes / In the still of the night / Try to remember / Sapateado / Perfidia / Till / Walk in the black forest / How are things in Glocca Morra / Days of wine and roses / Cabaret / Goodnight sweetheart.
Double Album: released on Decca, Apr'84 by Decca Records. Dist: Polygram

Double cassette: released on Decca, Apr'84 by Decca Records. Dist: Polygram

Compact disc: released on Decca, Apr'84 by Decca Records. Dist: Polygram

VERY BEST OF MANTOVANI, THE.
Tracks: / Charmaine / Swedish rhapsody / Lonely ballerina / Tonight / Theme from 'Exodus' / Hello young lovers / Red roses for a blue lady / Love is a many splendoured thing / And I love you so / Send in the clowns / Moulin rouge / Stardust / Some enchanted evening / Unchained melody / Way you look tonight, The / Edelweiss / Smoke gets in your eyes / More / Around the world / What a wonderful world.
Notes: Licensed from the Decca Record Co Ltd. (P) & (C) Warwick Records. A Warwick Leisure Product. Made and printed in the U.K. Bar code 5 012106 220058.

WORLD OF MANTOVANI (Mantovani & His Orchestra).
Album: released on Decca, '68 by Decca Records. Dist: Polygram

Cassette: released on Decca, '68 by Decca Records. Dist: Polygram

WORLD OF MANTOVANI - VOL.2 (Mantovani & His Orchestra).
Album: released on Decca, Sep'69 by Decca Records. Dist: Polygram

Cassette: released on Decca, Sep'69 by Decca Records. Dist: Polygram

YOUNG MANTOVANI 1935-1939, THE.
Album: released on World (Retrospect Series), Feb'84

Cassette: released on World (Retrospect Series), Feb'84

Mantovani & His Orchestra

AN EVENING WITH MANTOVANI.
Cassette: released on Decca, Oct'73 by Decca Records. Dist: Polygram

AS TIME GOES BY.
Album: released on Contour, May'87 by Pickwick Records. Dist: Pickwick Distribution, PRT

BEAUTIFUL MUSIC.
Album: released on Contour, Sep'81 by Pickwick Records. Dist: Pickwick Distribution, PRT

Cassette: released on Contour, Sep'81 by Pickwick Records. Dist: Pickwick Distribution, PRT

CONCERT SUCCESSES.
Tracks: / Die fledermaus / Moon river / 76 trombones / Hora staccato / Aquarius / Autumn leaves / Gypsy carnival / Fantasy on Italian melodies / Greensleeves / Capiccio Italien / Virginian / Charmaine.
Compact disc: released on London, '86 by London Records. Dist: Polygram

FARAWAY PLACES.
Double Album: released on Decca, Sep'78 by Decca Records. Dist: Polygram

Double cassette: released on Decca, Sep'78 by Decca Records. Dist: Polygram

FILM ENCORES.
Cassette: released on Decca, May'71 by Decca Records. Dist: Polygram

FILM FAVOURITES.
Double Album: released on Decca, May'80 by Decca Records. Dist: Polygram

Double cassette: released on Decca, May'80 by Decca Records. Dist: Polygram

FOCUS ON MANTOVANI.
Double Album: released on Decca, Sep'75 by Decca Records. Dist: Polygram

Double cassette: released on Decca, Sep'75 by Decca Records. Dist: Polygram

FROM MANTOVANI WITH LOVE.
Cassette: released on Decca, Sep'71 by Decca Records. Dist: Polygram

Compact disc: released on Decca, Sep'71 by Decca Records. Dist: Polygram

GOLDEN HITS: MANTOVANI.
Album: released on Decca, May'67 by Decca Records. Dist: Polygram

Cassette: released on Decca, May'67 by Decca Records. Dist: Polygram

Compact disc: released on Decca, May'67 by Decca Records. Dist: Polygram

HOLY NIGHT.
Album: released on Audio Fidelity, Dec'81 Dist: PRT

INCOMPARABLE.
Tracks: / Superman / Memory / I just called to say I love you / Amadeus suite / 007 Suite-James Bond Theme / 007 Suite-From Russia with love / 007 Suite-Never say never again / 007 Suite-Goldfinger / Canon / Nessun Dorma (Turandot) / Jerusalem / Chariots of fire.
Notes: (P) & (C) 1987 K-Tel International (UK) Ltd Conducted by Stanley Black.
Compact disc: released on K-Tel, May'87 by K-Tel Records. Dist: Record Merchandisers Distribution, Taylors, Terry Blood Distribution, Wynd-Up Distribution, Relay Distribution, Pickwick Distribution, Solomon & Peres Distribution, Polygram

KISMET.
Album: released on Decca, Sep'79 by Decca Records. Dist: Polygram Deleted May'82.

Cassette: released on Decca, Sep'79 by Decca Records. Dist: Polygram Deleted May'82.

LATIN RENDEZVOUS.
Album: released on Decca, May'63 by Decca Records. Dist: Polygram

LIFETIME OF MUSIC, A.
Double Album: released on Decca, May'80 by Decca Records. Dist: Polygram Deleted May'87.

Double cassette: released on Decca, May'80 by Decca Records. Dist: Polygram

MANHATTAN.
Album: released on Jasmine, Mar'85

MANTOVANI CHRISTMAS ALBUM.
Album: released on Contour, Oct'81 by Pickwick Records. Dist: Pickwick Distribution, PRT

Cassette: released on Contour, Oct'81 by Pickwick Records. Dist: Pickwick Distribution, PRT

MANTOVANI IN VIENNA.
Double Album: released on Decca, Sep'78 by Decca Records. Dist: Polygram

Double cassette: released on Decca, Sep'78 by Decca Records. Dist: Polygram

MANTOVANI MAGIC.
Album: released on Design, Apr'84 by Breakaway Records. Dist: PRT, Stage One

Cassette: released on Design, Apr'84 by Breakaway Records. Dist: PRT, Stage One

MANTOVANI ORCHESTRA.
Album: released on Phoenix, Jul'82 by Audio Fidelity Enterprises. Dist: Stage One, Lugtons

Double Album: released on Cambra, Apr'85 by Cambra Records. Dist: IDS, Conifer

Double cassette: released on Cambra, Apr'85 by Cambra Records. Dist: IDS, Conifer

Mantronix

ALBUM, THE.
Tracks: / Bassline / Needle to the groove / Mega-mix / Hardcore hip-hop / Ladies / Get stupid / Fresh - part 1 / Fresh is the word.

BASSLINE.
Tracks: / Bassline / Ladies - revised / Ladies instrumental* / Get stupid (fresh part 1)*.

LADIES.
Tracks: / Ladies / Ladies dub.

MUSIC MADNESS.
Album: released on 10, Dec'86 by 10 Records. Dist: Virgin, EMI

Cassette: released on 10, Dec'86 by 10 Records. Dist: Virgin, EMI

SCREAM (PRIMAL SCREAM EDIT).
Tracks: / Scream (primal scream edit) / Scream (dub).
Single (7"): released on 10, 13 Jun'87 by 10 Records. Dist: Virgin, EMI

Single (12"): released on 10, 13 Jun'87 by 10 Records. Dist: Virgin, EMI

WHO IS IT.
Tracks: / Who is it ? (Dance mix) / Who is it (Dub version) / Ladies (revised)* / Baseline (stretched).
Notes: *= extra track on 12" version only.
Single (7"): released on 10, Jan'87 by 10 Records. Dist: Virgin, EMI

Single (12"): released on 10, Jan'87 by 10 Records. Dist: Virgin, EMI

WHO IS IT?.
Single (12"): released on 10, Feb'87 by 10 Records. Dist: Virgin, EMI

Man two man

WHO KNOWS WHAT EVIL (FRIGHTMARE MIX).
Single (12"): released on Nightmare, Feb'87 by Nightmare Records. Dist: PRT

Manuel

BOLERO (Manuel & The Music of the Mountains).
Album: released on Music For Pleasure, Sep'84 by EMI Records. Dist: EMI

Cassette: released on Music For Pleasure, Sep'84 by EMI Records. Dist: EMI

FIESTA (Manuel & The Music of the Mountains).
Album: released on EMI, May'80 by EMI Records. Dist: EMI

Cassette: released on EMI, May'80 by EMI Records. Dist: EMI Deleted '83.

MAGIC OF MANUEL & THE MUSIC OF THE MOUNTAINS, THE.
Tracks: / Somewhere my love / Sunrise, sunset / Theme from "Love Story" / Shadow of your smile, The / Spanish harlem / Strangers in the night / If / Bali hai / El condor pasa / Cuando calienta el sol.
Notes: Produced by Norman Newell. (P) Original Sound Recordings made by EMI Records Ltd. This compilation (P) 1986 Music For Pleasure. Double LP set.

MANUEL.
Cassette: released on Ideal(Tapes), Apr'80 Dist: EMI

MATADOR (Manuel & The Music of the Mountains).
Single (7"): released on Multi-Media, Jun'82 by Multi Media Tapes Records. Dist: Pinnacle, Conifer Distribution, H.R. Taylor Distribution, Stage One Distribution

SPECTACULAR SOUND OF..., THE (Manuel & The Music of the Mountains).
Album: released on EMI, Nov'80 by EMI Records. Dist: EMI

Cassette: released on EMI, Nov'80 by EMI Records. Dist: EMI

SUPERNATURAL.
Double Album: released on EMI, Sep'79 by EMI Records. Dist: EMI

THIS IS DIGITAL RECORDING.
Album: released on EMI, Apr'80 by EMI Records. Dist: EMI Deleted '83.

Cassette: released on EMI, Apr'80 by EMI Records. Dist: EMI

VERY BEST OF MANUEL, THE.
Album: released on Columbia, Jul'76 by EMI Records. Dist: EMI

Cassette: released on Columbia, Jul'76 by EMI Records. Dist: EMI

Manuel, Ian

DALES OF CALEDONIA, THE.
Album: released on Topic, '81 by Topic Records. Dist: JSU Distribution, Projection Distribution, Jazz Music Distribution

FROSTY PLOUGHSHARE.
Album: released on Topic, '81 by Topic Records. Dist: JSU Distribution, Projection Distribution, Jazz Music Distribution

Man upstairs
CONSUMER SONG.
Tracks: / Consumer song.
Single (7"): released on Sideline, May'86 Dist: Nine Mile, Cartel

SAD IN MY HEART.
Single (7"): released on Sideline, Aug'85 Dist: Nine Mile, Cartel

Man With No Image
S.O.S.
Album: released on Yoff, Feb'87

Man With The...
HOOKED ON TIJUANA (Man With The Golden Horn).
Single (7"): released on Jive, Oct'83 by Zomba Records. Dist: RCA, PRT, CBS

Single (12"): released on Jive, Oct'83 by Zomba Records. Dist: RCA, PRT, CBS

Manylka, Zeke
COLD LIGHT OF DAY.
Single (7"): released on Polydor, Jun'85 by Polydor Records. Dist: Polygram, Polydor

Single (12"): released on Polydor, Jun'85 by Polydor Records. Dist: Polygram, Polydor

HEAVEN HELP US TRY.
Single (7"): released on Polydor, Jun'84 by Polydor Records. Dist: Polygram, Polydor

Single (12"): released on Polydor, Jun'84 by Polydor Records. Dist: Polygram, Polydor

Manzanera, Phil
801 LIVE.
Tracks: / Lagima / TNK (Tomorrow never knows) / East of asteroid / Rongwrong / Sombre reptiles / Baby's on fire / Diamond head / Miss Shapiro / You really got me / Third uncle.
Album: released on E.G., Jan'87 by Virgin Records. Dist: Virgin, EMI

Cassette: released on E.G., Jan'87 by Virgin Records. Dist: Virgin, EMI

DIAMOND HEAD.
Album: released on Polydor, Mar'77 by Polydor Records. Dist: Polygram, Polydor

GUITARISSIMO.
Album: released on E.G., Apr'87 by Virgin Records. Dist: Virgin, EMI

Cassette: released on E.G., Apr'87 by Virgin Records. Dist: Virgin, EMI

LISTEN NOW (Manzanera, Phil & Eight Hundred & One).
Album: released on Polydor, Oct'77 by Polydor Records. Dist: Polygram, Polydor

PRIMITIVE GUITARS.
Album: released on Editions EG, Jan'87 by Virgin Records. Dist: EMI

Album: released on Editions EG, Mar'82 by Virgin Records. Dist: EMI

PRIMITIVE GUITARS.
Cassette: released on Editions EG, Jan'87 by Virgin Records. Dist: EMI

Manzarek, Ray
WHEEL OF FORTUNE.
Single (7"): released on A&M, Jan'84 by A&M Records. Dist: Polygram

Maono
MAONO.
Album: released on Black Saint, Apr'79 Dist: Projection, IMS, Polygram, Chris Wellard, Harmonia Mundi, Swift

Maori Songs
MAORI LOVE SONGS Original Maori songs (Maori Love Songs).
Album: released on Viking, Feb'78 Dist: Harmonia Mundi Distributors

MAORI SONGS AND MUSIC FROM NEW ZEALAND (Maori Songs And Music From New Zealand).
Album: released on Exploring The World Of Music, Apr'76 Dist: Peerless (USA)

SONGS OF NEW ZEALAND (Maori Chorale).
Album: released on Viking, Jun'79 Dist: Harmonia Mundi Distributors

Mapangala, Samba
MALAKO (Mapangala, Samba & Orchestre

Virunga).
Single (12"): released on Earthworks, Aug'84 by Earthworks Records. Dist: Earthworks Distributors, Rough Trade, Cartel, Projection

Mapfumo, Thomas
ALL MY LIFE.
Single (12"): released on Rough Trade, Apr'86 by Rough Trade Records. Dist: Rough Trade Distribution, Cartel Distribution

CHIMURENGA FOR JUSTICE.
Album: released on Rough Trade, May'86 by Rough Trade Records. Dist: Rough Trade Distribution, Cartel Distribution

CHIMURENGA SINGLES, THE.
Album: released on Earthworks, Mar'84 by Earthworks Records. Dist: Earthworks Distributors, Rough Trade, Cartel, Projection

DANGEROUS LION.
Album: released on Earthworks, Mar'86 by Earthworks Records. Dist: Earthworks Distributors, Rough Trade, Cartel, Projection

HUPENYU WANGU.
Single (12"): released on Rough Trade, May'86 by Rough Trade Records. Dist: Rough Trade Distribution, Cartel Distribution

MABASA.
Album: released on Earthworks, Dec'84 by Earthworks Records. Dist: Earthworks Distributors, Rough Trade, Cartel, Projection

MR. MUSIC.
Album: released on Earthworks, Jul'85 by Earthworks Records. Dist: Earthworks Distributors, Rough Trade, Cartel, Projection

Maple leaf rag
MAPLE LEAF RAG (Various Artists).
Album: released on New World (USA), Jul'86 by New World Records (USA). Dist: Conifer

Maple Leaf Scottish...
WELCOME TO TAYSIDE.
Album: released on Thistle, '75

Mara
IMAGES.
Album: released on Plant Life, Jun'85 Dist: Roots

Marabar Caves
SALLY'S PLACE CREW.
Single (12"): released on Tiki, Feb'85 Dist: Nine Mile Distribution, Cartel Distribution

Marable Quartet, Lawrence
TENORMAN.
Album: released on Fresh Sounds, Aug'87 by Charly Records. Dist: Charly

Marainey
MARAINEY'S BLACK BOTTOM.
Album: released on Yazoo(USA), Feb'87

Maranatha:Men's chorus
MOVE INTO HIS PRESENCE.
Notes: Another of Maranatha's beautifully praise albums,this time with a male voice sound. Produced and arranged by Walt Harrah and including 'Glorify Thy Name','Seek Ye First','In His Time','Sing Hallelujah','Jesus,Name Above All Names','Humble Thyself In The Sight Of The Lord'.
Album: released on Maranatha!, Apr'86 Dist: Kingsway Music, Pilgrim, Word Distribution

Cassette: released on Maranatha!, Apr'86 Dist: Kingsway Music, Pilgrim, Word Distribution

Maranatha Singers
PRAISE 7.
Album: released on Maranatha Music, Nov'84

Cassette: released on Maranatha Music, Nov'84

PRAISE III.
Album: released on Maranatha Music, May'82

Cassette: released on Maranatha Music, May'82

PRAISE NINE.
Tracks: / Majesty / All hail King Jesus / Be exhalted O God / Meekness and majesty / How excellent your name / Thy word / Servant king, The / Unto the lord / We are here to praise you / May the fragrance of Jesus fill this place / He alone (deserves our praise) / I just want to praise you / Great are you lord / Great is thy name / You are the almighty king / When I look into your holiness / Lord have mercy on us / Change my heart, O God / Blessed by the lord God almighty.
Album: released on Maranatha, Jul'87

Cassette: released on Maranatha Jul'87

PRAISE STRINGS 8.
Notes: Praise Strings 8 features beautiful string arrangements of the 11 original songs from the popular Praise 8 album. The flowing of the Maranatha! Strings bring these songs of worship alive with the quality that soothes the spirit and inspires quiet reflections.
Album: released on Maranatha!, Oct'86 Dist: Kingsway Music, Pilgrim, Word Distribution

Cassette: released on Maranatha!, Oct'86 Dist: Kingsway Music, Pilgrim, Word Distribution

SCRIPTURE IN SONG.
Notes: Scripture In Song has been a pioneer worldwide in worship music since the late 1960's,sharing the finest new praise music from all over the world,particularly in Europe,Australia and New Zealand. Maranatha! Music has put together 16 songs from Scripture in Song favourites. These uplifting and inspirational songs of praise come alive through rich harmonies and beautifully orchestrated arrangements. These selections have a depth which sets them apart from the conventional 'chorus',and which draws the listener into deep sense of worship.
Cassette: released on Maranatha!, Oct'86 Dist: Kingsway Music, Pilgrim, Word Distribution

Album: released on Maranatha!, Oct'86 Dist: Kingsway Music, Pilgrim, Word Distribution

Mara, Nat & His Tahitians
TAHITI-VOILA.
Album: released on Viking, Feb'78 Dist: Harmonia Mundi Distributors

Marbles
ONLY ONE WOMAN.
Single (7"): released on Old Gold, Jul'82 by Old Gold Records. Dist: Lightning, Jazz Music, Spartan, Counterpoint

Marble Staircase
STILL DREAMING.
Single (7"): released on Whaam, Sep'83 Dist: Pinnacle

Marcel
I'VE BEEN A BAD BOY.
Single (7"): released on Red Bus, Oct'82 by Red Bus Records. Dist: PRT

Marcels
BLUE MOON.
Album: released on Emus, Sep'79 by Emus Records. Dist: Swift

Single (7"): released on Old Gold, Jul'82 by Old Gold Records. Dist: Lightning, Jazz Music, Spartan, Counterpoint

Marching Girls
TRUE LOVE.
Single (7"): released on Pop Aural, Jul'81 Dist: Fresh, Rough Trade, Swift, Spartan, Virgin

Marching up and down band
POP HERE THERE AND EVERYWHERE.
Album: released on Pip, Nov'84 by PRT Records. Dist: PRT

Marching with the guards
MARCHING WITH THE GUARDS Various Artists (Various Artists).
Cassette: released on Ditto, Aug'84 by Pickwick Records. Dist: H.R. Taylor

March, Peggy
WHERE DID OUR LOVE GO.
Tracks: / Where did our love go / Who needs you.
Single (7"): released on RCA, Aug'86 by RCA Records. Dist: RCA, Roots, Swift, Wellard, Chris, I & B, Solomon & Peres Distribution

Single (12"): released on RCA, Oct'86 by RCA Records. Dist: RCA, Roots, Swift, Wellard, Chris, I & B, Solomon & Peres Distribution

March, Stella
BARRIER TO LOVE.
Cassette: released on Soundings, Feb'85 Dist: Soundings

CARRIAGE FOR FIONA, A.
Cassette: released on Soundings, Mar'85 Dist: Soundings

March Violets
CROW BABY.
Single (7"): released on Rebel, May'83 Dist: PRT

Single (12"): released on Rebirth, Mar'85 Dist: Red Rhino, Cartel

DEEP.
Single (7"): released on Rebirth, Apr'85 Dist: Red Rhino, Cartel

Single (12"): released on Rebirth, Apr'85 Dist:

Red Rhino, Cartel

GROOVING IN THE GREEN.
Single (7"): released on Merciful Release, Nov'82 by Sisterhood Records. Dist: WEA

MARCH VIOLETS (EP).
Single (7"): released on Merciful Release, Aug'82 by Sisterhood Records. Dist: WEA

NATURAL HISTORY.
Album: released on Rebirth, Oct'84 Dist: Red Rhino, Cartel

SNAKEDANCE.
Single (7"): released on Rebirth, Jan'84 Dist: Red Rhino, Cartel

Single (12"): released on Rebirth, Jan'84 Dist: Red Rhino, Cartel

TURN TO THE SKY.
Tracks: / Turn to the sky / Never look / Deep.
Notes: 'Deep' available on 12" version only.
Single (7"): released on Rebirth-London, Feb'86

Single (12"): released on Rebirth-London, Feb'86

WALK IN THE SUN.
Single (7"): released on Rebirth, Jun'84 Dist: Red Rhino, Cartel

Single (12"): released on Rebirth, Jun'84 Dist: Red Rhino, Cartel

Marcos
FLAMENCO HORIZONS.
Single (7"): released on Stoptime, Apr'84

Marcovic gut sextet
MARCOVIC GUT SEXTET.
Cassette: released on Timeless, Oct'86

Marc & The Crucials
CHEEK TO CHEEK.
Single (7"): released on Astra, Dec'83 by Astra. Dist: Spartan

Marc & The Mambas
TORMENT AND TOREROS.
Album: released on Some Bizzare, Aug'83 by Charisma Records. Dist: EMI, CBS, Polygram

Cassette: released on Some Bizzare, Aug'83 by Charisma Records. Dist: EMI, CBS, Polygram

Marcus,P.J.
FOR YOUR SWEET INFORMATION.
Tracks: / For your sweet information / For your sweet information (Inst.).
Single (12"): released on ZYX (Germany), Mar'86 by ZYX Records. Dist: Greyhound

Mardells
ONE OF A MILLION.
Single (7"): released on Escape, May'82

Marden Hill
CURTAIN.
Tracks: / Curtain / Let's make Shane & Mackenzie.
Single (7"): released on EL, Nov'86 by El Records. Dist: Rough Trade, Cartel, Pinnacle

Mardi Gras in New Orleans
MARDI GRAS IN NEW ORLEANS Various artists (Various Artists).
Album: released on Mardi Gras, Feb'79 Dist: Making Waves

Mardis,Bobby
KEEP ON.
Tracks: / Keep on / Keep on (Inst.).
Single (12"): released on Bluebird-10, Feb'86 by Bluebird Records. Dist: Virgin Records, EMI, Jetstar

Marentic, James
NIMBUS.
Album: released on Discovery (USA), Aug'83

Maresca, Ernie
SHOUT (KNOCK YOURSELF OUT).
Single (7"): released on Seville, Feb'81 by President Records. Dist: Jazz Music, Swift

SHOUT SHOUT (KNOCK YOURSELF OUT).
Album: released on Seville, Nov'82 by President Records. Dist: Jazz Music, Swift

Margaret, Ann
3 Great girls

Margin Of Sanity

MARGIN OF SANITY.
Album: released on Chainsaw, Jan'87 by Chainsaw Records. Dist: Red Rhino, Cartel

Margo

18 IRISH SONGS.
Album: released on Ara (Ireland), Aug'82 Dist: Outlet, I & B, EMI (Ireland)

Cassette: released on Ara (Ireland), Aug'82 Dist: Outlet, I & B, EMI (Ireland)

ALL TIME HITS.
Album: released on Ara (Ireland), Oct'79 Dist: Outlet, I & B, EMI (Ireland)

COALMINERS DAUGHTER.
Single (7"): released on Homespun(Ireland), Apr'81 by Outlet Records. Dist: Outlet

COUNTRY GIRL.
Album: released on Homespun(Ireland), May'82 by Outlet Records. Dist: Outlet

Cassette: released on Homespun(Ireland), May'82 by Outlet Records. Dist: Outlet

COUNTRY STYLE.
Album: released on Ara (Ireland), Oct'79 Dist: Outlet, I & B, EMI (Ireland)

GREATEST HITS: MARGO VOL.2.
Cassette: released on Ara (Ireland), May'78 Dist: Outlet, I & B, EMI (Ireland)

IRISH REQUESTS.
Album: released on Ara (Ireland), Jul'79 Dist: Outlet, I & B, EMI (Ireland)

Cassette: released on Ara (Ireland), Jul'79 Dist: Outlet, I & B, EMI (Ireland)

MARGO'S FAVOURITES.
Album: released on Harp(Ireland), Jul'80 by Pickwick Records. Dist: Taylors

Cassette: released on Harp(Ireland), Jul'80 by Pickwick Records. Dist: Taylors

TOAST FROM AN IRISH COLLEEN.
Album: released on Stoic, Mar'84 by Stoic Records. Dist: Spartan Distribution

Cassette: released on Stoic, Mar'84 by Stoic Records. Dist: Spartan Distribution

TOAST TO CLADDAGH, A.
Album: released on Ara (Ireland), Jan'78 Dist: Outlet, I & B, EMI (Ireland)

Cassette: released on Ara (Ireland), Jan'78 Dist: Outlet, I & B, EMI (Ireland)

TRIP TO IRELAND.
Album: released on Homespun(Ireland), May'82 by Outlet Records. Dist: Outlet

Cassette: released on Homespun(Ireland), May'82 by Outlet Records. Dist: Outlet

Margolyes, Miriam

SNOW WHITE & THE SEVEN DWARFS
Read by Miriam Margolyes.
Cassette: released on Pickwick Talking Books, '83

Mariachis

MEXICO.
Album: released on Playasound (France), May'85

Cassette: released on Playasound (France), May'85

Mariachis Mexico

VIVA MEXICO.
Tracks: / Jarbe Tapatio / Las mananitas / El terreno / La Raspa / Las Coronelas / La bamba / La negra / El mariachi / El balachon / El barrilito / Las perlitas / El negro jose / Guada lajara / Alla en el rancho grande / Nereida / La bikina / Brujilla / El relicario / Cumpa chelo.
Notes: Recorded in Mexico city,here is one of the most famous Mariachis orchestras you can hear today. The music here is authentic and extremly listenable. Recommended tracks:'Jarabe Tapatio' and 'Cumpa Chelo'
Compact disc: released on Poldor Int., Dec'85

Mariano,Charlie

ALTO SAX-FOR YOUNG MODERNS
(Mariano,Charlie,Quartet).
Album: released on Affinity, Oct'82 by Charly Records. Dist: Charly, Cadillac

JYOTHI.
Tracks: / Voice solo.
Compact disc: released on ECM (Germany), Aug'86 by ECM Records. Dist: IMS, Polygram, Virgin through EMI

Album: released on ECM (Germany), Nov'83 by ECM Records. Dist: IMS, Polygram, Virgin through EMI

Marias,A.C.

JUST TALK.
Tracks: / Just talk / Just talk (Inst.).
Single (12"): released on Mute, Aug'86 Dist: Spartan Distribution, Rough Trade Distribution, Cartel Distribution

Maria, Tania

BRAZIL WITH MY SOUL.
Album: released on Barclay (Import), May'78

COME WITH ME.
Tracks: / Sangria / Embraceable you / Lost in Amazonia / Come with me / Sementes, Graines & Seeds / Nega / Euzinha / Its all over now.
Notes: Originally released in '83
Album: released on Concord Jazz, Mar'83 by Concord Jazz Records (USA). Dist: IMS, Polygram

Cassette: released on Concord Jazz, Mar'83 by Concord Jazz Records (USA). Dist: IMS, Polygram

Compact disc: released on Concord Jazz(USA), Jul'87 by Concord Jazz Records (USA). Dist: IMS, Polygram

LADY FROM BRAZIL (THE).
Tracks: / Lady from Brazil (the) / I should not call you / Tanoca vignette / Bronx / Just get up / Valeu / All gone love / It hurts so much.
Compact disc: released on EMI, Mar'87 by EMI Records. Dist: EMI

LIVE.
Album: released on Music Disc (France), Aug'83 Dist: IMS-Polygram Distribution

Cassette: released on Music Disc (France), Aug'83 Dist: IMS-Polygram Distribution

LOVE EXPLOSION.
Tracks: / Funky tambourim / It's all in my hands / You've got me feeling your love / Love explosion / Bela la bela / Rainbow of your love / Deep cove view / Pour toi.
Compact disc: released on Concord Jazz(USA), Dec'86 by Concord Jazz Records (USA). Dist: IMS, Polygram

Album: released on Concord Jazz Picante(USA), Jan'84 Dist: IMS, Polygram

Cassette: released on Concord Jazz Picante(USA), Jan'84 Dist: IMS, Polygram

MADE IN NEW YORK.
Album: released on Manhattan, Apr'85 by EMI Records. Dist: EMI

Cassette: released on Manhattan, Apr'85 by EMI Records. Dist: EMI

PIQUANT.
Album: released on Concord Jazz Picante(USA), May'81 Dist: IMS, Polygram

REAL TANIA MARIA-WILD, (THE).
Album: released on Concord Jazz Picante(USA), Feb'85 Dist: IMS, Polygram

Cassette: released on Concord Jazz Picante(USA), Feb'85 Dist: IMS, Polygram

TAURUS.
Album: released on Concord Jazz(USA), Mar'82 by Concord Jazz Records (USA). Dist: IMS, Polygram

Cassette: released on Concord Jazz(USA), Mar'82 by Concord Jazz Records (USA). Dist: IMS, Polygram

VIA BRAZIL (VOLUME 1).
Album: by Decca Records. Dist: Polygram, Discovery, Conifer, IMS, Swift

WILD.
Tracks: / Yatra-ta / Fiz a cama na varanda / Vem pra roda / Come with me / Funky tambourin / 2 am / Sangria.
Compact disc: released on Concord Jazz(USA), Nov'86 by Concord Jazz Records (USA). Dist: IMS, Polygram

Marie &...

SALTYHOUND (Marie & the Wildwood Flowers).
Single (12"): released on Ediesta, Nov'86 by Ediesta Records. Dist: Red Rhino, Cartel

YOU THROW MY LOVE.
Single (12"): released on TCD Music, Jan'82

Marie, Karena

RUNAWAY.
Single (7"): released on Cask, Apr'82 by Cask. Dist: Cask

Marie,Kelly

DON'T LET THE FLAME DIE OUT.
Single (7"): released on Passion, Jun'85 by Skratch Records. Dist: PRT

Single (12"): released on Passion, Jun'85 by Skratch Records. Dist: PRT

DON'T TAKE YOUR LOVE TO HOLLYWOOD.
Single (7"): released on Calibre Plus, Oct'82 by PRT Records. Dist: PRT

Single (12"): released on Calibre Plus, Oct'82 by PRT Records. Dist: PRT

FEELS LIKE I'M IN LOVE.
Tracks: / Feels like I'm in love / Shattered glass.
Single (7"): released on PRT, Sep'86 by PRT Records. Dist: PRT

Single (12"): released on PRT, Sep'86 by PRT Records. Dist: PRT

Album: released on Calibre, Nov'80 by Calibre Records. Dist: PRT

Single (7"): released on Calibre, May'80 by Calibre Records. Dist: PRT

Single (12"): released on Calibre, May'80 by Calibre Records. Dist: PRT

HANDS UP.
Tracks: / Hands up / Hands up (Inst.).
Single (12"): released on Passion, Jun'86 by Skratch Records. Dist: PRT

I'M ON FIRE.
Single (7"): released on Calibre Plus, Oct'84 by PRT Records. Dist: PRT

Single (12"): released on Calibre Plus, Oct'84 by PRT Records. Dist: PRT

I NEED YOUR LOVE.
Single (7"): released on Calibre Plus, Jan'82 by PRT Records. Dist: PRT

Single (12"): released on Calibre Plus, Jan'82 by PRT Records. Dist: PRT

LOVE'S GOT A HOLD ON YOU.
Single (7"): released on Calibre Plus, Jul'82 by PRT Records. Dist: PRT

Single (12"): released on Calibre Plus, Jul'82 by PRT Records. Dist: PRT

SILENT TREATMENT.
Single (7"): released on Calibre Plus, Sep'83 by PRT Records. Dist: PRT

Single (12"): released on Calibre Plus, Sep'83 by PRT Records. Dist: PRT

WHO'S THAT LADY WITH MY MAN.
Album: released on Pye, Jun'77

Marie, Rose

SO LUCKY.
Tracks: / So lucky / Danny Boy.
Single (7"): released on A.1, Mar'87 by A.1 Records. Dist: PRT

WHILE I WAS MAKING LOVE TO YOU (EP).
Single (7"): released on Ritz, Apr'82 by Ritz Records. Dist: Spartan

Marie Ward

MARIE WARD Original Soundtrack (Bernstein, Elmer).
Album: released on Colosseum(West Germany), Sep'86 Dist: Silva Screen

Marillion

1982-1986 THE VIDEOS.
Tracks: / Market Square heroes / He knows you know / Garden party / Assassing / Kayleigh / Lavender / Heart of Lothian / Lady Nina.
Notes: This video EP is a collection of all Marillion's hit singles,and one 'B' side,pur together in chronological order from 1982 through to 1986. Showing the band in all various stages of line-ups from beginning of 'Market Square Heroes' to the present day. None of the videos have ever been commercially available before. Total playing time :30 minutes.
Video-cassette (VHS): released on PMI, Jun'86 by PMI Records. Dist: EMI

Video-cassette [Betamax]: released on PMI, Jun'86 by PMI Records. Dist: EMI

ASSASSING.
Single (7"): released on EMI, May'84 by EMI Records. Dist: EMI

Single (12"): released on EMI, May'84 by EMI Records. Dist: EMI

Picture disc single: released on EMI, May'84 by EMI Records. Dist: EMI

CLUTCHING AT STRAWS.
Tracks: / Hotel hobbies / Warm wet circles / That time of the night(The short straw) / Going under / Just for the record / White Russian / Incommunicado / Torch song / Slainte mhath / Sugar mice / Last straw, the.
Album: released on EMI, Jun'87 by EMI Records. Dist: EMI

Cassette: released on EMI, Jun'87 by EMI Records. Dist: EMI

Compact disc: released on EMI, Jun'87 by EMI Records. Dist: EMI

Compact disc: released on EMI, Jun'87 by EMI Records. Dist: EMI

FUGAZI.
Tracks: / Assassing / Punch and Judy / Jigsaw / Emerald lies / She chameleon / Incubus / Fugazi.
Notes: Digital Stereo.
Compact disc: released on EMI, Aug'84 by EMI Records. Dist: EMI

Album: released on EMI, Mar'84 by EMI Records. Dist: EMI

Cassette: released on EMI, Mar'84 by EMI Records. Dist: EMI

Picture disc single: released on EMI, Mar'84 by EMI Records. Dist: EMI

Compact disc: released on EMI, Mar'84 by EMI Records. Dist: EMI

GARDEN PARTY.
Single (7"): released on EMI, Jun'83 by EMI Records. Dist: EMI

Single (12"): released on EMI, Jun'83 by EMI Records. Dist: EMI

Picture disc single: released on EMI, Jun'83 by EMI Records. Dist: EMI

GRENDEL;THE WEBB, THE.
Notes: Marillion and the video EP features two much sought after videos, 'The grendel' and 'The webb',both filmed at London's Hammersmith Odeon. The 17 minute epic of 'The grendel' was released on record on 25th October 1982 on 12" format only,and the 8 minute masterpiece of 'The webb' is taken from the now gold status album 'Scrit for a jester's tear'.This EP completes the collection for the devoted Marillion fans who undoubtedly secured the success of the 'Recital of the Script' 60 minute video,released in October 1983. Total playing time: 27 minutes.
Video-cassette (VHS): released on PMI, Jun'86 by PMI Records. Dist: EMI

Video-cassette [Betamax]: released on PMI, Jun'86 by PMI Records. Dist: EMI

HEART OF LOTHIAN.
Single (7"): released on EMI, Nov'85 by EMI Records. Dist: EMI

Single (12"): released on EMI, Nov'85 by EMI Records. Dist: EMI

Picture disc single: released on EMI, Nov'85 by EMI Records. Dist: EMI

HE KNOWS YOU KNOW.
Single (7"): released on EMI, Jan'83 by EMI Records. Dist: EMI

Single (12"): released on EMI, Jan'83 by EMI Records. Dist: EMI

INCOMMUNICADO.
Tracks: / Incommunicado / Going under / Sugar mice.
Extended-play record: released on EMI, May'87 by EMI Records. Dist: EMI

Single (12"): released on EMI, May'87 by EMI Records. Dist: EMI

Video-cassette (VHS): released on PMI, Sep'87 by PMI Records. Dist: EMI

INTERVIEW PICTURE DISC.
Album: released on Baktabak, Jul'87 by Baktabak Records. Dist: Arabesque

KAYLEIGH.
Single (7"): released on EMI, May'85 by EMI Records. Dist: EMI

Single (12"): released on EMI, May'85 by EMI Records. Dist: EMI

Picture disc single: released on EMI, May'85 by EMI Records. Dist: EMI

Picture disc single: released on EMI, Jun'85 by EMI Records. Dist: EMI

LAVENDER.
Single (7"): released on EMI, Aug'85 by EMI Records. Dist: EMI

Single (12"): released on EMI, Aug'85 by EMI Records. Dist: EMI

MARKET SQUARE HEROES.
Single (7"): released on EMI, Oct'82 by EMI Records. Dist: EMI

Single (12"): released on EMI, Oct'82 by EMI Records. Dist: EMI

MISPLACED CHILDHOOD.
Tracks: / Pseudo-silk kimono, The / Kayleigh / Lavender / Bittersuite / Heart of Lothian / Waterhole / Lords of the backstage / Blind curve / Childhood's end? / White feather.
Compact disc: released on EMI, Sep'85 by EMI Records. Dist: EMI

Album: released on EMI, Jun'85 by EMI Records. Dist: EMI

Cassette: released on EMI, Jun'85 by EMI Records. Dist: EMI

Picture disc album: released on EMI, Jun'85 by EMI Records. Dist: EMI

Compact disc: released on EMI, Jun'85 by EMI Records. Dist: EMI

PUNCH AND JUDY.
Single (7"): released on EMI, Jan'84 by EMI Records. Dist: EMI

Single (12"): released on EMI, Jan'84 by EMI Records. Dist: EMI

Picture disc single: released on EMI, Jan'84 by EMI Records. Dist: EMI

RECITAL OF SCRIPT.
Video-cassette (VHS): released on Thorn-Emi, Jan'84

RECITAL OF THE SCRIPT.
Notes: Number of tracks: 6. Type of recording: Live. Total playing time: 55 minutes.
Video-cassette (VHS): released on PMI, Jun'86 by PMI Records. Dist: EMI

Video-cassette [Betamax]: released on PMI, Jun'86 by PMI Records. Dist: EMI

REEL TO REEL.
Tracks: / Assassing / Incubus / Cinderella search / Emerald lies / Forgotten sons / Garden party / Market Square heroes.
Notes: First time on Fame - chart topping band Marillion. Recent smash hits,'Kayleigh' and 'Lavender Blue' have ensured the sucess of this album from 1984. the cassette includes an extra track - 'Emerald Lies'. Reproduced in the original sleeve.
Album: released on Fame, Nov'85 by Music For Pleasure Records. Dist: EMI

Cassette: released on Fame, Nov'85 by Music For Pleasure Records. Dist: EMI

SCRIPT FOR A JESTER'S TEAR.
Tracks: / He knows, you know / Web (The) / Garden party / Chelsea monday / Forgotten sons.
Compact disc: released on EMI, Feb'87 by EMI Records. Dist: EMI

Album: released on EMI, Mar'83 by EMI Records. Dist: EMI

Cassette: released on EMI, Mar'83 by EMI Records. Dist: EMI

Picture disc album: released on EMI, Jun'84 by EMI Records. Dist: EMI Deleted May'86.

SUGAR MICE.
Tracks: / Sugar mice / Tux on.
Single (7"): released on EMI, Jul'87 by EMI Records. Dist: EMI

Single (12"): released on EMI, Jul'87 by EMI Records. Dist: EMI

Compact disc single: released on EMI, Jul'87 by EMI Records. Dist: EMI

Picture disc single: released on EMI, Jul'87 by EMI Records. Dist: EMI

SUGAR MICE (12" VERSION).
Tracks: / Sugar mice / Sugar mice (album version) / Tux on.
Picture disc single: released on EMI, Jul'87 by EMI Records. Dist: EMI

Marilyn

CALLING YOUR NAME.
Single (7"): released on Mercury, Nov'83 by Phonogram Records. Dist: Polygram Distribution Deleted May'86.

CRY AND BE FREE.
Single (7"): released on Mercury, Feb'84 by Phonogram Records. Dist: Polygram Distribution

Single (12"): released on Mercury, Feb'84 by Phonogram Records. Dist: Polygram Distribution

YOU DON'T LOVE ME.
Single (7"): released on Love-Mercury, Apr'84

Single (12"): released on Love-Mercury, Apr'84

Marine

SAME BEAT.
Single (7"): released on Les Disques Du Crepuscule, May'82 Dist: Rough Trade, Pinnacle, Island, Polygram

Marine Girls

BEACH PARTY.
Tracks: / In love / Fridays / Tonight / Tonight? / Times we used to spend / Flying over Russia / Tutti lo sanno / All dressed up / Honey / Holiday song / He got the girl / Day/night dreams / Promises / Silent red / Dishonesty / 20,000 Leagues / Marine Girls.
Album: released on Cherry Red, Apr'87 by Cherry Red Records. Dist: Pinnacle

DON'T COME BACK.
Single (7"): released on Cherry Red, Jan'83 by Cherry Red Records. Dist: Pinnacle

LAZY WAYS.
Album: released on Cherry Red, Mar'83 by Cherry Red Records. Dist: Pinnacle

Cassette: released on Cherry Red, Mar'83 by Cherry Red Records. Dist: Pinnacle

ON MY MIND.
Single (7"): released on In Phaze, Jan'82 by In Phaze Records. Dist: Rough Trade

Single (7"): released on Cherry Red, May'82 by Cherry Red Records. Dist: Pinnacle

Mariner

TELECOMMUNICATION.
Single (7"): released on Tube, Jun'82 by Tony Hatch. Dist: Pinnacle

Marini, Marino

VOLARE.
Tracks: / Volare / Come'prima.
Single (7"): released on Old Gold, Mar'86 by Old Gold Records. Dist: Lightning, Jazz Music, Spartan, Counterpoint

Marino, Frank

FULL CIRCLE.
Notes: Solo album from Frank Marino (ex-Mahogany Rush).
Album: released on Grudge (USA), Aug'87

LIVE.
Album: released on CBS, Mar'78 by CBS Records. Dist: CBS

MAHOGANY RUSH 4.
Album: released on CBS, Dec'77 by CBS Records. Dist: CBS

THERE'S NO GOOD IN GOODBYE.
Album: by CBS Records. Dist: CBS

WHAT'S NEXT.
Album: released on CBS, May'80 by CBS Records. Dist: CBS

WORLD ANTHEM.
Album: released on CBS, Jul'77 by CBS Records. Dist: CBS

Marinos, George

RED MOON.
Album: released on Sonet, May'74 by Sonet Records. Dist: PRT

Marino the band

WANNA KEEP YOU SATISFIED.
Album: released on LRM, Apr'86 by Marino The Band. Dist: Spartan

Marionette

BLONDE SECRETS AND DARK BOMBSHELLS.
Album: released on Heavy Metal, Jul'85 by FM-Revolver Records. Dist: FMI

Cassette: released on Heavy Metal, Jul'85 by FM-Revolver Records. Dist: EMI

ON A NIGHT LIKE THIS.
Single (12"): released on FM, Jun'85 by FM-Revolver Records. Dist: EMI

Marion's flight

MARION'S FLIGHT Various Artists (Various Artists).
Extended-play record: released on Epigram, Jan'82 by Epigram Records. Dist: Rough Trade

Mark, Beer

DUST ON THE ROAD.
Album: released on My China, Jul'81

Mark E

LET'S GET MARRIED.
Single (12"): released on Dolphin, Apr'82

Markee

GOOD SENSIMANIA.
Single (12"): released on Horsemouth, Jul'83 Dist: Jetstar, Rough Trade

Mar Keys

LAST NIGHT.
Single (12"): released on Atlantic, Apr'80 by WEA Records. Dist: WEA

Mark, James & Julie

GOLDEN DUETS.
Single (7"): released on Rations, Nov'81

Mark,Louisa

SIXTH STREET.
Tracks: / Sixth Street / Sixth street (Inst.).
Single (12"): released on Bushay, Sep'86 Dist: Jetstar

Mark & Mambas

UNTITLED.
Album: released on Some Bizarre, Sep'82 by Virgin Records. Dist: EMI, CBS, Polygram

Cassette: released on Some Bizarre, Sep'82 by Virgin Records. Dist: EMI, CBS, Polygram

Markopoulos, Yannis

WHO PAYS THE FERRYMAN.
Cassette: released on BBC, May'78 by BBC Records & Tapes. Dist: EMI, PRT, Pye

Single (7"): released on Old Gold, Jan'85 by Old Gold Records. Dist: Lightning, Jazz Music, Spartan, Counterpoint

Marks Brothers

JOE JOE'S BAR.
Tracks: / Joe Joe's bar / Ronnie 'B' good.
Single (7"): released on Carrere, Jan'86 by Carrere Records. Dist: PRT, Spartan

Mark & Silly Buggers

OH DEAR I HAVE NO (SCRUPLES).
Single (12"): released on Zambi, Apr'82

Marks,Kenny

ATTITUDE.
Tracks: / Life after High School / Attitude / It doesn't hurt that much / Heroes / Friends.
Notes: Kenny Marks is carinf,energetic and straightforward. It al comes through in his contemporary music. With this release he pulls together a top notch band with some of the country's best musicians to communicate the Christian response to today's social pressures.
Album: released on Day Spring, May'86 by Word Records. Dist: Word Distribution, CBS

Marks, Louisa

6 SIX STREET.
Single (7"): released on Robot, May'79 Dist: Pinnacle

Single (12"): released on Robot, May'79 Dist: Pinnacle

ALL MY LOVING.
Single (12"): released on Code, Sep'84 by Code Records. Dist: Jetstar, EMI

BREAKOUT.
Album: released on Bushranger, Mar'85 Dist: Jetstar

CAUGHT YOU IN A LIE.
Tracks: / Caught you in a lie / Tribute to Muhammed Ali.
Single (12"): released on Code, Oct'86 by Code Records. Dist: Jetstar, EMI

Single (7"): released on Voyage International, Feb'82 by Code Records. Dist: PRT

Single (7"): released on Code, Mar'84 by Code Records. Dist: Jetstar, EMI

Single (12"): released on Code, Mar'84 by Code Records. Dist: Jetstar. EMI

FOOLISH FOOL.
Single (12"): released on Skynote, Nov'85 by Skynote Records. Dist: Jetstar

HELLO THERE (Marks, Louisa & The Zabandis).
Single (12"): released on Oak Sound, Jun'84

MUM AND DAD.
Single (7"): released on Bushay, Feb'82 Dist: Jetstar

Marksman

MARKSMAN, THE Original Soundtrack.
Album: released on BBC, Oct'87 by BBC Records & Tapes. Dist: EMI, PRT, Pye. Estim retail price in Sep'87 was £5.99.

Cassette: released on BBC, Oct'87 by BBC Records & Tapes. Dist: EMI, PRT, Pye. Estim retail price in Sep'87 was £5.99.

Mark T

FROM LITTLE EAST TO MID-WEST (Mark T and the Brickbats).
Album: released on Waterfront, Aug'87 by Waterfront Records. Dist: Rough Trade, Cartel, Projection, Roots. Estim retail price in Aug'87 was £5.99.

JOHNNY THERE (Mark T and the Brickbats).
Album: released on Fellside, Nov'86 by Fellside Records. Dist: Roots, Jazz Music, Celtic Music, Projection

Markus, Ben

SEE ME CRY.
Single (7"): by Ooze Records. Dist: PRT Distribution

Markusfeld, Alain

CONTEMPORUS.
Album: released on Egg, Nov'79 by Barclay Records. Dist: Logo, RCA, Discovery

PLATOCK.
Album: released on Egg, Nov'79 by Barclay Records. Dist: Logo, RCA, Discovery

Marlettes

BOTH SIDES OF THE MARLETTES.
Compact disc: released on Country House, Jun'82 by BGS Productions Ltd. Dist: Taylor, H.R., Record Merchandisers Distribution, Pinnacle, Sounds of Scotland Records

Cassette: released on Country House, Jun'82 by BGS Productions Ltd. Dist: Taylor, H.R., Record Merchandisers Distribution, Pinnacle, Sounds of Scotland Records

MORNING IN THE COUNTRY.
Album: released on Neptune, Jan'78 by Lismor. Dist: Spartan

Cassette: released on Neptune, Jan'78 by Lismor. Dist: Spartan

PURE LOVE.
Album: released on Scotdisc, Sep'84 Dist: Clyde Factors Distributors

Cassette: released on Scotdisc, Sep'84 Dist: Clyde Factors Distributors

TENNESSEE MOUNTAIN HOME.
Album: released on Lismor, Nov'76 by Lismor Records. Dist: Lismor, Roots, Celtic Music

Marley, Bob

20 GREATEST HITS (Marley, Bob & The Wailers).
Cassette: released on Blue Thumb, Oct'82

25 GREATEST HITS.
Double Album: released on Happy Bird (Germany), Jun'84 Dist: Polygram, IMS

Cassette: released on Happy Bird (Germany), Jun'84 Dist: Polygram, IMS

AFRICAN HERBSMAN (Marley, Bob & The Wailers).
Album: released on Fame (Trojan), Nov'83 by Music For Pleasure Records. Dist: EMI

Cassette: released on Fame (Trojan), Nov'83 by Music For Pleasure Records. Dist: EMI

Album: released on Trojan, Jul'84 by Trojan Records. Dist: PRT, Jetstar

Cassette: released on Trojan, Aug'84 by Trojan Records. Dist: PRT, Jetstar

BABYLON BY BUS (Marley, Bob & The Wailers).
Tracks: / Positive vibration / Funky reggae party / Exodus / Rat race / Lively up yourself / Rebel music (three o'clock road block) / War / No more trouble / Stir it up / Concrete jungle / Kinky reggae / Is this love? / Heathen / Jamming.
Compact disc: released on Island, Feb'87 by Island Records. Dist: Polygram

BEST RARITIES.
Album: released on Barclay (Import), Jul'82

Cassette: released on Barclay (Import), Jul'82

BOB MARLEY.
Compact disc: released on Intertape, Jul'87 Dist: Target

BOB MARLEY & THE WAILERS COLLECTION (Marley, Bob & The Wailers).
Tracks: / Soul shakedown party / Stop the train / Caution / Soul captives / Go tell it on the mountain / Can't you see / Soon come / Cheer up / Back out / Do it twice / Try me / It's alright / Sun is shining / No sympathy / My cup / Corner stone / No water / Soul almighty / Reaction / One love / Love and affection / Mega dog / Donna / Lonesome feeling / It hurts to be alone / Who feels it / Dancing Shoes.
Notes: All tracks licensed from The San Juan Music Group: Design: Shoot That Tiger! This compilation : 1985 Castle Communications Ltd,Unit 7, 271 Merton Road,London SW 18 5 JS. Bar code 5 013428 131237: Double Album-Double Cassette.
Album: released on Collectors, Apr'86 by Castle Communications Records. Dist: PRT, Pinnacle, Jazz Music

Cassette: released on Collectors, Apr'86 by Castle Communications Records. Dist: PRT, Pinnacle, Jazz Music

BOB MARLEY & THE WAILERS WITH PETER TOSH (Marley, Bob & The Wailers).
Album: released on Hallmark, Mar'81 by Pickwick Records. Dist: Pickwick Distribution, PRT,

Taylors

Cassette: released on Hallmark, Mar'81 by Pickwick Records. Dist: Pickwick Distribution, PRT, Taylors

BUFFALO SOLDIER (Marley, Bob & The Wailers).
Single (7"): released on Island, Apr'83 by Island Records. Dist: Polygram

Single (12"): released on Island, Apr'83 by Island Records. Dist: Polygram

BURNIN' (Marley, Bob & The Wailers).
Album: released on Island, Mar'87 by Island Records. Dist: Polygram

CATCH A FIRE (Marley, Bob & The Wailers).
Album: released on Island, Oct'86 by Island Records. Dist: Polygram

Cassette: released on Island, Oct'86 by Island Records. Dist: Polygram

CHANCES ARE.
Album: released on WEA, Oct'81 by WEA Records. Dist: WEA

Cassette: released on WEA, Oct'81 by WEA Records. Dist: WEA Deleted '85.

CLASSIC TRACKS (THE).
Album: released on Arena, Feb'87 by Arena Records. Dist: Spartan

Cassette: released on Arena, Feb'87 by Arena Records. Dist: Spartan

CONFRONTATION (Marley, Bob & The Wailers).
Tracks: / Chant down Babylon / Buffalo soldier / Jump Nyabinghi / Mix up, mix up / Give thanks and praises / Blackman redemption / Trenchtown / I know / Stiff necked fools / Rastaman live up.
Album: released on Island, Mar'87 by Island Records. Dist: Polygram

Cassette: released on Island, Mar'87 by Island Records. Dist: Polygram

Album: released on Island, Mar'87 by Island Records. Dist: Polygram

Cassette: released on Island, Mar'87 by Island Records. Dist: Polygram

Album: released on Island, May'83 by Island Records. Dist: Polygram

Cassette: released on Island, May'83 by Island Records. Dist: Polygram

COULD YOU BE LOVED (Marley, Bob & The Wailers).
Single (7"): released on Island, Nov'84 by Island Records. Dist: Polygram Deleted '87.

Single (12"): released on Island, Nov'84 by Island Records. Dist: Polygram Deleted '87.

Picture disc single: released on Island, Nov'84 by Island Records. Dist: Polygram

Single (7"): released on Island, May'80 by Island Records. Dist: Polygram

Single (12"): released on Island, May'80 by Island Records. Dist: Polygram

EARLY MUSIC (Marley, Bob & The Wailers).
Album: released on CBS, Nov'81 by CBS Records. Dist: CBS

Cassette: released on CBS, Nov'81 by CBS Records. Dist: CBS

ESSENTIAL BOB MARLEY, THE.
Album: released on Design, May'84 by Breakaway Records. Dist: PRT, Stage One

Cassette: released on Design, May'84 by Breakaway Records. Dist: PRT, Stage One

Picture disc album: released on Design, Jul'84 by Breakaway Records. Dist: PRT, Stage One

ETERNAL.
Double Album: released on Cambra, Mar'85 by Cambra Records. Dist: IDS, Conifer

Double cassette: released on Cambra, Mar'85 by Cambra Records. Dist: IDS, Conifer

EXODUS (Marley, Bob & The Wailers).
Tracks: / Natural mystic / So much things to say / Guiltiness / Heathen, The / Exodus / Jamming / Waiting in vain / Turn your lights down low / Three little birds / Obe love-people get ready.
Compact disc: released on Island, Jan'87 by Island Records. Dist: Polygram

Album: released on Island, Mar'87 by Island Records. Dist: Polygram

Cassette: released on Island, Mar'87 by Island Records. Dist: Polygram

Album: released on Island, Jan'78 by Island Records. Dist: Polygram

Cassette: released on Island, Mar'81 by Island Records. Dist: Polygram

GREATEST HITS: BOB MARLEY.
Album: released on Barclay (Import), Jul'82

Cassette: released on Barclay (Import), Jul'82

IN THE BEGINNING (Marley, Bob & The Wailers).
Album: released on Trojan, Jul'84 by Trojan Records. Dist: PRT, Jetstar

Cassette: released on Trojan, Jul'84 by Trojan Records. Dist: PRT, Jetstar

KAYA (Marley, Bob & The Wailers).
Tracks: / Easy skanking / Is this love / Sun is shining / Satisfy my soul / She's gone / Misty morning / Crisis / Kaya / Running away / Time will tell.
Album: released on Island, Nov'86 by Island Records. Dist: Polygram

Cassette: released on Island, Nov'86 by Island Records. Dist: Polygram

Compact disc: released on Island, Feb'87 by Island Records. Dist: Polygram

LEE PERRY SESSIONS (THE).
Album: released on Konnexion, Feb'87 Dist: Roots, Pinnacle

LEGEND.
Video-cassette (VHS): released on Island Pictures, Oct'84 by Island Records. Dist: Polygram

Album: released on Island, May'84 by Island Records. Dist: Polygram

Cassette: released on Island, May'84 by Island Records. Dist: Polygram

LEGEND (Marley, Bob & The Wailers).
Tracks: / Is this love / Jamming / No woman,no cry / Stir it up / Get up and stand up / Satisfy my soul / I shot the sheriff / One love-people get ready / Buffalo solider / Exodus / Redemption song / Could you be loved / Want more.
Compact disc: released on Island, Aug'85 by Island Records. Dist: Polygram

LEGENDARY, THE.
Album: released on Premier, '84 by Premier Records. Dist: CBS

Cassette: released on Premier, '84 by Premier Records. Dist: CBS

LIVE AT THE LYCEUM (Marley, Bob & The Wailers).
Tracks: / Trenchtown rock / Burnin' and lootin' / Them belly full / Lively up yourself / No woman no cry / I shot the sheriff / Get up stand up.
Compact disc: released on Island, Jan'87 by Island Records. Dist: Polygram

Album: released on Island, Sep'86 by Island Records. Dist: Polygram

Cassette: released on Island, Sep'86 by Island Records. Dist: Polygram

Compact disc: released on Island, Sep'86 by Island Records. Dist: Polygram

Compact disc: released on Blue Moon, Oct'86 Dist: Magnum Music Group Ltd, PRT, Spartan

LIVELY UP YOURSELF.
Album: released on Premier, Feb'87 by Premier Records. Dist: CBS

Cassette: released on Premier, Feb'87 by Premier Records. Dist: CBS

MELLOW MOOD (Marley, Bob & The Wailers).
Tracks: / There she goes again / Put it on / How many times / Mellow mood / Chances are / Hammer / Tell me / Touch me / Treat me right / Soul rebel.
Compact disc: released on Topline, Apr'87 by Charly Records. Dist: Charly Distribution

Album: released on Topline, Nov'84 by Charly Records. Dist: Charly Distribution

Cassette: released on Topline, Nov'84 by Charly Records. Dist: Charly Distribution

NATTY DREAD (Marley, Bob & The Wailers).
Compact disc: released on Island, Apr'87 by Island Records. Dist: Polygram

Album: released on Island, Mar'87 by Island Records. Dist: Polygram

Cassette: released on Island, Mar'87 by Island Records. Dist: Polygram

Album: released on Island, '75 by Island Records. Dist: Polygram

Cassette: released on Island, '75 by Island Records. Dist: Polygram

NATURAL MYSTIC (Marley, Bob & The Wailers).
Tracks: / Natural / Natural mystic (Version).
Single (12"): released on Daddy Kool, Jan'86 by Daddy Kool Records. Dist: Jetstar, Red Lightnin' Distribution

NO WOMAN NO CRY (Marley, Bob & The Wailers).
Single (12"): released on Island, Jun'81 by Island Records. Dist: Polygram

ONE LOVE.
Album: released on Platinum (W.Germany), Oct'85 Dist: Mainline

Cassette: released on Platinum (W.Germany), Oct'85 Dist: Mainline

Single (7"): released on Island, Apr'84 by Island Records. Dist: Polygram Deleted '87.

Single (12"): released on Island, Apr'84 by Island Records. Dist: Polygram

Picture disc single: released on Island, Apr'84 by Island Records. Dist: Polygram

PUT IT ON (Marley, Bob & The Wailers).
Tracks: / One love / Love and affection / Mega dog / Donna / Lonesome feeling / It hurts to be alone / Who feels it / Dancing shoes / You can't do that to me / Touch me / Put it on / How many times / There she goes / Mellow moods / Treat you right / Chances are / Soul rebel / Hammer.
Album: released on Showcase, Apr'86 Dist: Counterpoint

Cassette: released on Showcase, Apr'86 Dist: Counterpoint

RAINBOW COUNTRY.
Single (12"): released on Daddy Kool, Aug'85 by Daddy Kool Records. Dist: Jetstar, Red Lightnin' Distribution

RASTAMAN VIBRATION (Marley, Bob & The Wailers).
Compact disc: released on Island, Apr'87 by Island Records. Dist: Polygram

Album: released on Island, Mar'87 by Island Records. Dist: Polygram

Cassette: released on Island, Mar'87 by Island Records. Dist: Polygram

Album: released on Island, Jan'78 by Island Records. Dist: Polygram

Cassette: released on Island, May'81 by Island Records. Dist: Polygram

RASTA REVOLUTION (Marley, Bob & The Wailers).
Album: released on Trojan, Jul'84 by Trojan Records. Dist: PRT, Jetstar

Cassette: released on Trojan, Aug'84 by Trojan Records. Dist: PRT, Jetstar

Album: released on Fame, Jul'85 by Music For Pleasure Records. Dist: EMI

Cassette: released on Fame, Jul'85 by Music For Pleasure Records. Dist: EMI

REBEL MUSIC (Marley, Bob & The Wailers).
Tracks: / Rebel music(3 o'clock roadblock) / So much trouble in the world / Them belly full (but we hungry) / Rat race / War/No more trouble / Roots / Slave driver / Ride natty ride / Crazy Bladhead / Get up,stand up.
Notes: Photography Adrian Boot/Design Island Art: (c) 1986 Island Records Ltd
Album: released on Island, Jun'86 by Island Records. Dist: Polygram

Cassette: released on Island, Jun'86 by Island Records. Dist: Polygram

Compact disc: released on Island, '86 by Island Records. Dist: Polygram

REPLAY ON BOB MARLEY.
Album: released on Sierra, Feb'85 by Sierra Records. Dist: WEA

Cassette: released on Sierra, Feb'85 by Sierra Records. Dist: WEA

RIDING HIGH.
Album: released on Premier, '84 by Premier Records. Dist: CBS

Cassette: released on Premier, '84 by Premier Records. Dist: CBS

ROOTS.
Album: released on Blue Moon, Nov'86 Dist: Magnum Music Group Ltd, PRT, Spartan

Cassette: released on Blue Moon, Nov'86 Dist: Magnum Music Group Ltd, PRT, Spartan

SOUL REBEL (Marley, Bob & The Wailers).
Album: released on New Cross, Sep'81 by Charly Records. Dist: Charly

Cassette: released on Charly(R&B), Jan'82 by Charly Records. Dist: Charly, Cadillac

Album: released on Blue Moon, Jun'84 Dist: Magnum Music Group Ltd, PRT, Spartan

SOUL REBELS (Marley, Bob & The Wailers).
Album: released on Receiver, Feb'87 by Receiver Records. Dist: Pinnacle

SOUL SHAKEDOWN PARTY (Marley, Bob & The Wailers).
Single (7"): released on Trojan, Oct'83 by Trojan Records. Dist: PRT, Jetstar

Single (12"): released on Trojan, Oct'83 by Trojan Records. Dist: PRT Jetstar

SURVIVAL (Marley, Bob & The Wailers).
Tracks: / Ambush in the night / So much trouble / Africa unite / Babylon system / Ride Natty ride / One prop / Fighting against ism and skism / Top ranking / Wake up and live / Survival / Zimbabwe.
Compact disc: released on Island, Apr'87 by Island Records. Dist: Polygram

Album: released on Island, Mar'87 by Island Records. Dist: Polygram

Cassette: released on Island, Mar'87 by Island Records. Dist: Polygram

Album: released on Island, Oct'79 by Island Records. Dist: Polygram

Cassette: released on Island, May'81 by Island Records. Dist: Polygram

THANK YOU LORD (Marley, Bob & The Wailers).
Single (7"): released on Trojan, Jun'81 by Trojan Records. Dist: PRT, Jetstar

THREE LITTLE BIRDS (Marley, Bob & The Wailers).
Single (7"): released on Island, Jun'85 by Island Records. Dist: Polygram

Single (12"): released on Island, Jun'85 by Island Records. Dist: Polygram

Cassette: released on Island, Jul'85 by Island Records. Dist: Polygram

UPRISING.
Compact disc: by Polygram Records. Dist: Polygram

UPRISING (Marley, Bob & The Wailers).
Tracks: / Coming in from the cold / Real situation / Bad card / We and them / Work / Zion train / Pimpers paradise / Could you be loved / Forever loving Jah / Redemption song.
Compact disc: released on Island, Feb'87 by Island Records. Dist: Polygram

Album: released on Island, Jul'80 by Island Records. Dist: Polygram

Cassette: released on Island, Jul'80 by Island Records. Dist: Polygram Deleted Mar'81.

WAILERS LIVE (Marley, Bob & The Wailers).
Album: released on Island, Nov'75 by Island Records. Dist: Polygram

Marley, Rita

GOOD GIRLS CULTURE.
Single (7"): released on Island, Mar'85 by Island Records. Dist: Polygram
Cat. no: **IS 224**
Single (12"): released on Island, Mar'85 by Island Records. Dist: Polygram

HARAMBE.
Album: released on Teldec (Germany), May'84 by Import Records. Dist: IMS Distribution, Polygram Distribution

MUSIC FOR THE WORLD (Marley, Rita, J. Mowatt & M. Griffiths).
Single (12"): released on Shanachie, Aug'83 Dist: Sterns/Triple Earth Distribution, Roots

ONE DRAW.
Single (7"): released on Island, Nov'82 by Island Records. Dist: Polygram
Cat. no: **WIP 6841**
Single (12"): released on Island, Nov'82 by Island Records. Dist: Polygram

RITA MARLEY.

Album: released on Trident, Nov'80 Dist: Stage One

SO MUCH THINGS TO SAY.
Tracks: / So much things to say / So much things to say (version).
Single (12"): released on White Label, Jul'87 by White Label Records. Dist: Jetstar

WHO FEELS IT.
Album: released on Teldec (Germany), Apr'84 by Import Records. Dist: IMS Distribution, Polygram Distribution

Marley, Ziggy

HEY WORLD (Marley, Ziggy & the Melody makers).
Tracks: / Give a little love / Get up jah jah children / Hey world ! / Fight to survive / Freedom road / Say people / 666 / Police brutality / Lord we a come / Reggae revolution.
Notes: All tracks recorded in Jamaica except 1-5 (recorded at Mama Jo's studio L.A.)
Album: released on EMI America, Nov'86 by EMI Records. Dist: EMI

Cassette: released on EMI, Nov'86 by EMI Records. Dist: EMI

Marl, Marley

HE CUTS SO FRESH.
Tracks: / He cuts so fresh / Bass game.
Single (7"): released on MCA, 23 May'87 by MCA Records. Dist: Polygram, MCA

Single (12"): released on MCA, 23 May'87 by MCA Records. Dist: Polygram, MCA

Marlow, John

SISTER SOUL.
Single (7"): released on Situation 2, Dec'81 Dist: Cartel, Pinnacle

Marlow, Nicholas

CITY LIFE.
Single (7"): released on Avatar, Apr'82 by Avatar Communications. Dist: CBS

Single (12"): released on Avatar, Apr'82 by Avatar Communications. Dist: CBS

Marlow, Robert

CALLING ALL DESTROYERS.
Single (7"): released on Reset, May'85 by Vince Clarke/Eric Radcliffe. Dist: Spartan

CLAUDETTE.
Single (7"): released on Reset, Jul'84 by Vince Clarke/Eric Radcliffe. Dist: Spartan

Single (12"): released on Reset, Jul'84 by Vince Clarke/Eric Radcliffe. Dist: Spartan

FACE OF DORIAN GRAY.
Single (7"): released on Reset, Jul'83 by Vince Clarke/Eric Radcliffe. Dist: Spartan

Single (12"): released on Reset, Jul'83 by Vince Clarke/Eric Radcliffe. Dist: Spartan

I JUST WANNA DANCE.
Single (7"): released on Reset, Oct'83 by Vince Clarke/Eric Radcliffe. Dist: Spartan

Single (12"): released on Reset, Oct'83 by Vince Clarke/Eric Radcliffe. Dist: Spartan

Marmalade

6 TRACK HITS.
Extended-play record: released on Scoop 33, Aug'84 by Pickwick Records. Dist: H.R. Taylor

Cassette: released on Scoop 33, Aug'84 by Pickwick Records. Dist: H.R. Taylor

BACK ON THE ROAD.
Album: released on Decca, May'81 by Decca Records. Dist: Polygram

DOING IT ALL FOR YOU.
Album: released on Sky, Jan'79 by President Records.

GOLDEN SHREDS.
Single (7"): released on Sounds Right, Nov'85 Dist: MIS-EMI Distribution

Single (12"): released on Sounds Right, Nov'85 Dist: MIS-EMI Distribution

GREATEST HITS: MARMALADE - VOL.1.
Album: released on Zuma, May'85 by Zuma Records. Dist: CBS, PRT

Cassette: released on Zuma, May'85 by Zuma Records. Dist: CBS, PRT

HEARTBREAKER.
Single (7"): released on Just, Jun'84

OB-LA-DI, OB-LA-DA.
Cassette: released on Autograph, Apr'85 Dist: Record Services Distribution (Ireland)

Single (7"): released on Old Gold (Reissue), Jul'82

REFLECTIONS OF MY LIFE.
Single (7"): released on Decca, Oct'80 by Decca Records. Dist: Polygram

Single (7"): released on Old Gold (Reissue), Oct'83

Marmarosa, Dodo

CHICAGO SESSIONS.
Tracks: / Mellow mood / Cottage for sale / April played the fiddle / Everything happens to me / On Green Dolphin Street / Why do I love you / I thought about you / Me and my shadow / Tracy's blues / You call it madness / Gone with the wind / Someday / Automation / Dodo's tune / Analysis / Only a rose.
Compact disc: released on Charly, Dec'86 by Charly Records. Dist: Charly, Cadillac

Album: released on Arco, Dec'86 by Charly Records. Dist: Charly

DODO'S DANCE.
Album: released on Spotlite, '83 by Spotlite

Page 644

Records. Dist: Cadillac, Jazz Music, Spotlite

LIVE DODO.

Tracks: / C jam blues / Be bop / Deep purple / Rose room / How high the moon / Perdido / Great lie, The.
Cassette: released on Submarine, Oct'86 by Submarine Records. Dist: Wellard, Chris Distribution, Conifer Distribution, H.R. Taylor Distribution

Album: released on Swinghouse, Oct'79 Dist: Jazz Music Distribution, Swift Distribution, Chris Wellard Distribution

PIANO MAN.

Album: released on Phoenix, Apr'81 by Audio Fidelity Enterprises. Dist: Stage One, Luptons

Marocco, Frank Quintet

ROAD TO MAROCCO.
Album: released on ARC (Accordion Records), '84 Dist: Accordion Record Club

Maroon Dogs

DARK NIGHTS FALLING.
Single (7"): released on Dux, Aug'84 by Dux Records. Dist: Spartan

Marquee The Collection

MARQUEE THE COLLECTION 1958-1983 - VOL.1 Various artists (Various Artists).
Album: released on England, Jun'83 by Mean Records. Dist: Spartan

Cassette: released on England, Jun'83 by Mean Records. Dist: Spartan

MARQUEE THE COLLECTION 1958-1983 - VOL.2 Various artists (Various Artists).
Album: released on England, Jun'83 by Mean Records. Dist: Spartan

Cassette: released on England, Jun'83 by Mean Records. Dist: Spartan

MARQUEE THE COLLECTION 1958-1983 - VOL.3 Various artists (Various Artists).
Album: released on England, Jun'83 by Mean Records. Dist: Spartan

Cassette: released on England, Jun'83 by Mean Records. Dist: Spartan

MARQUEE THE COLLECTION 1958-1983 - VOL.4 Various artists (Various Artists).
Album: released on England, Jun'83 by Mean Records. Dist: Spartan

Cassette: released on England, Jun'83 by Mean Records. Dist: Spartan

Marquis De Sade

CRYSTAL GRIEFF.
Single (7"): released on Out Of Town, Jun'82

Marra, Michael

GAELS BLUES.
Album: released on Mink, Jun'85 Dist: Celtic Music Distribution

Marrett, Bunny

TIMES ARE GETTING HARDER.
Single (12"): released on Shoc-Wave, Aug'80 by Uniton Records. Dist: Pinnacle

Marriage Of Convenience

MY YOUNG DREAMS.
Single (7"): released on Stranglers Information Service, Oct'85 Dist: Pinnacle

Marriner, Neville

MORE AMADEUS (Marriner, Neville & Academy of St Martin in the Field).
Compact disc: by London Records. Dist: Polygram

Album: released on London, Aug'85 by London Records. Dist: Polygram

Cassette: released on London, Aug'85 by London Records. Dist: Polygram

NEVILLE MARRINER AND THE ACADEMY OF ST.MARTIN IN THE FIELDS.
Video-cassette (VHS): released on PMI, Aug'87 by PMI Records. Dist: EMI

Marriott, Steve

PACKET OF THREE.
Album: released on Aura, Apr'86 by Hollywood Nites Distribution. Dist: Pinnacle

Cassette: released on Aura, Apr'86 by Hollywood Nites Distribution. Dist: Pinnacle

WAT'CHA GONNA DO ABOUT IT.

Single (7"): released on Aura, Jan'85 by Hollywood Nites Distribution. Dist: Pinnacle

Mars

78.
Album: released on Widowspeak, Dec'86 Dist: Rough Trade

IN THE HEAT OF THE NIGHT.
Single (7"): released on Silicone, Sep'85 Dist: Stage One

PROJECT DRIVER.
Compact disc: released on Roadrunner (Dutch), Jun'87 Dist: Pinnacle

Marsala, Joe

1944 (Marsala, Joe & his band).
Album: released on Jazzology, Jun'86 Dist: Jazz Music, Swift

JOE MARSALA 1942.
Album: released on Aircheck, Apr'79

Marsalis, Branford

ROYAL GARDEN BLUE.
Tracks: / Swingin' at the haven / Dienda / Strike up the band / Emanon / Royal garden blues / Shadows / Wrath of Tain (The).
Compact disc: released on CBS, Mar'87 by CBS Records. Dist: CBS

ROYAL GARDEN BLUES.
Tracks: / Swingin at the haven / Dienda / Strike up the band / Emanon / Royal Garden blues / Shadows / Wrath of Tain (The).
Album: released on CBS, Nov'86 by CBS Records. Dist: CBS

SCENES IN THE CITY.
Album: released on CBS, May'84 by CBS Records. Dist: CBS

Marsalis, Wynton

AMERICAN HERO, AN.
Tracks: / One by one / My funny valentine / Round 'bout midnight / ETA / Time will tell / Blakey's theme.
Album: released on Kingdom Records, '86 by Kingdom Records. Dist: Kingdom Records

Compact disc: released on Kingdom Records, Nov'86 by Kingdom Records. Dist: Kingdom Records

BLACK CODE.
Tracks: / Black codes / For wee folks / Delfeayo's dilemma / Phryzzinian man / Aural oasis / Chambers of Tain / Blues.
Compact disc: released on CBS, '86 by CBS Records. Dist: CBS

BLACK CODES (from the underground).
Album: released on CBS, Nov'85 by CBS Records. Dist: CBS

Cassette: released on CBS, Nov'85 by CBS Records. Dist: CBS

CARNAVAL.
Tracks: / Variations on "Le Carnaval de Venise" / Grand Russian fantasia / Debutante, The / Believe me, if all those endearing young charms / Moto perpetuo / 'Tis the last rose of summer / Flight of the bumble bee / Napoli / Variations on a Neapolitan song / Fantasie brillante / Sometimes I feel like a motherless child / Valse brillante.
Album: released on CBS, Apr'87 by CBS Records. Dist: CBS

Cassette: released on CBS, Apr'87 by CBS Records. Dist: CBS

Compact disc: released on CBS, Apr'87 by CBS Records. Dist: CBS

FIRST RECORDINGS.
Tracks: / Angel eyes / Bitter dose / Wheel within a wheel / Gypsy.
Compact disc: released on Kingdom Records, '86 by Kingdom Records. Dist: Kingdom Records

Album: released on Gateway, Sep'83 by Kingdom. Dist: Pinnacle

HOT HOUSE FLOWERS.
Album: released on CBS, Nov'84 by CBS Records. Dist: CBS

Cassette: released on CBS, Nov'84 by CBS Records. Dist: CBS

Compact disc: released on CBS, Nov'84 by CBS Records. Dist: CBS

HUMMEL & HAYDN TRUMPET CONCERTOS.
Compact disc: released on CBS, Jul'84 by CBS Records. Dist: CBS

MARSALIS STANDARD TIME.

Tracks: / Caravan / April in Paris / Cherokee / Goodbye / New Orleans / Soon all will know / Foggy day (in London town) / Song is you, The / Memories of you / In the afterglow / Autumn leaves / Cherokee.
Album: released on CBS, Aug'87 by CBS Records. Dist: CBS

Cassette: released on CBS, Aug'87 by CBS Records. Dist: CBS

THINK OF ONE.
Album: released on CBS, Jul'83 by CBS Records. Dist: CBS

Cassette: released on CBS, Jul'83 by CBS Records. Dist: CBS Deleted '87.

WYNTON MARSALIS.
Album: released on CBS, Feb'82 by CBS Records. Dist: CBS

Marsden, Bernie

AND ABOUT TIME TOO.
Cassette: released on Parlophone, May'81 by EMI Records. Dist: EMI

LOOK AT ME NOW.
Album: released on Parlophone, Aug'81 by EMI Records. Dist: EMI

Cassette: released on Parlophone, Aug'81 by EMI Records. Dist: EMI

Marsden, Gerry

LENNON & McCARTNEY SONGBOOK BY G. MARSDEN, THE.
Album: released on K-Tel, Mar'85 by K-Tel Records. Dist: Record Merchandisers Distribution, Taylors, Terry Blood Distribution, Wynd-Up Distribution, Relay Distribution, Pickwick Distribution, Solomon & Peres Distribution, Polygram

Cassette: released on K-Tel, Mar'85 by K-Tel Records. Dist: Record Merchandisers Distribution, Taylors, Terry Blood Distribution, Wynd-Up Distribution, Relay Distribution, Pickwick Distribution, Solomon & Peres Distribution, Polygram

Marsden, Lynne

COCKTAILS FOR TWO.
Single (7"): released on Derelict, May'85 by Derelict Records. Dist: M.I.S.

Marseille

TOUCH THE NIGHT.
Album: released on Albion, Oct'84 by Albion Records. Dist: Spartan, Pinnacle

WALKING ON A HIGHWIRE.
Single (7"): released on Ultranoise, Sep'84 by Ultranoise Records. Dist: Spartan

Mars- Fenwick Band

ASH AIN'T NOTHING BUT TRASH.
Tracks: / Ash ain't nothing but trash / Smoking out the barons.
Single (7"): released on President, Jun'86 by President Records. Dist: Taylors, Spartan

Single (12"): released on President, Jun'86 by President Records. Dist: Taylors, Spartan

FIRE IN THE CITY.
Tracks: / Fire in the city / Raise the price / Lover not a fighter, A / T-Bird Ford / I lose again / What'cha gonna do / Poontang kid (The) / Hot lips / Hard luck and trouble / There's a party going on / Date with an angel, A / I need love / Ash ain't nothing but trash.
Album: released on President, Jan'87 by President Records. Dist: Taylors, Spartan

Cassette: released on President, Jan'87 by President Records. Dist: Taylors, Spartan

Single (7"): released on President, Feb'87 by President Records. Dist: Taylors, Spartan

Marshall, Al

BE MY GUEST.
Single (7"): released on Pavillion, Mar'82

Single (7"): released on Tent, Jun'83 by RCA Records. Dist: BMG Distribution

DANCE WITH ME.
Single (7"): released on Pavillion, Jun'82

Single (12"): released on Pavillion, Jun'82

I LIKE THE WAY YOU DANCE WITH ME.
Single (12"): released on Tent, Oct'82 by RCA Records. Dist: BMG Distribution

I'M GONNA MAKE THIS A NIGHT THAT YOU.....
Single (7"): released on Tent, Jan'83 by RCA Records. Dist: BMG Distribution

Single (12"): released on Tent, Jan'83 by RCA Records. Dist: BMG Distribution

Marshall, Billy
SONGS OF A SKYE MAN (Marshall, Billy (Uilleam)).
Album: released on Lismor, Jul'77 by Lismor Records. Dist: Lismor, Roots, Celtic Music

Cassette: released on Lismor, Jul'77 by Lismor Records. Dist: Lismor, Roots, Celtic Music

Marshall Doktors
WORRYING KIND, THE.
Single (7"): released on Rewind, Nov'80 by Rewind Records. Dist: Spartan

Marshall, Eddie
DANCE OF THE SUN (Marshall, Eddie, Bobby hutcherson,manny boyd,George Cables).
Album: released on Timeless, Apr'81

Marshall Hain
FREE RIDE.
Single (7"): released on Harvest, Jul'78 by EMI Records. Dist: Roots, EMI

Marshall, Jimmy
JIMMY MARSHALL.
Album: released on Nevis, May'77 Dist: H.R. Taylor

Marshall, Junior
MASSIVE MAN SKANK.
Single (12"): released on Roots Rockers, Oct'82

Marshall, Keith
BITTEREST TASTE.
Single (7"): released on Arrival, Apr'84 by Arrival. Dist: Revolver, Cartel

DEAN/ BEST OF ME.
Single (7"): released on Arrival, Jul'81 by Arrival. Dist: Revolver, Cartel

KEITH MARSHALL.
Album: released on Arrival, Jul'81 by Arrival. Dist: Revolver, Cartel

Cassette: released on Arrival, Jul'81 by Arrival. Dist: Revolver, Cartel

LIGHT YEARS/ THERE GOES MY HEART.
Single (7"): released on Arrival, May'82 by Arrival. Dist: Revolver, Cartel

ONLY CRYING.
Single (7"): released on Arrival, Mar'81 by Arrival. Dist: Revolver, Cartel

SILVER AND DIAMONDS.
Single (7"): released on Arrival, Jun'81 by Arrival. Dist: Revolver, Cartel

SINCE I LOST MY BABY.
Single (7"): released on Arrival, Apr'83 by Arrival. Dist: Revolver, Cartel

Marshall Larry
HAPPINESS.
Single (12"): released on Iyah Bingi, May'84 by Iyah Bingi Records. Dist: Jetstar, Kingdom, Iyah Bingi

I ADMIRE YOU (Larry Marshall).
Album: released on Java, Aug'86 Dist: Jetstar

Marshall, Louisa
STOP.
Single (7"): released on Bo-Peep, Feb'85 Dist: M.I.S.

Marshall, Lyn
COMPLETE YOGA.
Double Album: released on Sun Set, Mar'83 by Sun Set Records. Dist: Jetstar Distribution

EVERYDAY YOGA.
Album: released on BBC, Feb'83 by BBC Records & Tapes. Dist: EMI, PRT, Pye

Cassette: released on BBC, Feb'83 by BBC Records & Tapes. Dist: EMI PRT, Pye

YOGA (VOLUME 2).
Cassette: released on Sun Set, Sep'76 by Sun Set Records. Dist: Jetstar Distribution

Marshall, Merl D
MY OBSESSION.
Single (7"): released on WEA Int, Jun'85

Single (12"): released on WEA Int, Jun'85

Marshall, Mike
GATOR STRUT.
Album: released on Rounder (USA), Apr'85 Dist: Mike's Country Music Room Distribution,

---

Jazz Music Distribution, Swift Distribution, Roots Records Distribution, Projection Distribution, Topic Distribution

Marshall Tucker
BEST OF THE MARSHALL TUCKER BAND.
Album: released on Capricorn, Sep'79 by Polydor Records. Dist: Polygram

RUNNING LIKE THE WIND (Marshall Tucker Band).
Album: released on Warners, Jul'79

TOGETHER FOREVER.
Album: released on Capricorn, Jul'78 by Polydor Records. Dist: Polygram

Marshall, Wayne
GIVE ME THE FIX.
Single (12"): released on Jah Tubbys, Dec'85 by Jah Tubbys Records. Dist: Jetstar

I LOVE (Wayne Marshall).
Tracks: / I love / Fear of Jah Jah.
Single (7"): released on Greensleeves, Oct'86 by Greensleeves Records. Dist: BMG, Jetstar, Spartan

PON A LEVEL.
Tracks: / Pon a level / Dance baby dance / Pon a level (version).
Single (12"): released on Quadro Pack, Jul'87 by Quadro Pack Records. Dist: Jetstar, BMG

Marsh, Linda
HAPPY HEART.
Album: released on Tank, Dec'77 by Tank Records.

Marsh, Marne
HOT HOUSE (Marsh, Marne & Red Mitchell).
Notes: For full information see: Mitchell, Red & Warne Marsh

Marshmellow Overcoat
WHAT'S GOING ON/ TRAFFIC HUG/ HELL.
Single (12"): released on Skysaw, Mar'85 by Skysaw Records. Dist: Red Rhino, Cartel

Marsh, Warne
ALL MUSIC.
Album: released on Nessa, Mar'79 Dist: Projection, Swift

ART OF IMPROVISING, THE.
Album: released on Revelation, Apr'81

ART OF IMPROVISING VOL.2, THE.
Album: released on Revelation, Apr'81

ART PEPPER WITH WARNE MARSH
(see under Pepper,Art/Warne Marsh).

BACK HOLME (Marsh, Warne Quartet & Quintet).
Album: released on Criss Cross Jazz, Jan'87 Dist: Jazz Music, Jazz Horizons

JAZZ FROM THE EAST VILLAGE.
Album: released on Wave, Apr'79 by Wave Records. Dist: JSU, Swift, Jazz Music, Cadillac, Chris Wellard

LIVE AT THE MONTMARTE CLUB
(Marsh, Warne\Lee Konitz Quintet).
Notes: Mono Production.
Album: released on Storyville, Jun'86 by Storyville Records. Dist: Jazz Music Distribution, Swift Distribution, Chris Wellard Distribution, Counterpoint Distribution

LIVE AT THE MONTMARTRE CLUB
(Marsh, Warne\Lee Konitz Quintet).
Album: released on Storyville, Nov'86 by Storyville Records. Dist: Jazz Music Distribution, Swift Distribution, Chris Wellard Distribution, Counterpoint Distribution

LONDON CONCERT (Marsh, Warne\Lee Konitz).
Album: released on Wave, May'77 by Wave Records. Dist: JSU, Swift, Jazz Music, Cadillac, Chris Wellard

MARSH,WARNE/LEE KONITZ VOL 3
(Warne Marsh\ Lee Konitz).
Notes: No track details advised Mono Production
Album: released on Storyville, Jun'86 by Storyville Records. Dist: Jazz Music Distribution, Swift Distribution, Chris Wellard Distribution, Counterpoint Distribution

NE PLUS ULTRA.
Album: released on Revelation, Apr'81

REPORT OF THE SYMPOSIUM ON RELAXED IMPROVISATION VOLUME 1
(Marsh, Warne/Clare Fischer/Gary Foster).
Album: released on Revelation, Apr'81

WARNE MARSH.
Album: released on Wave, Apr'79 by Wave

Records. Dist: JSU, Swift, Jazz Music, Cadillac, Chris Wellard

WARNE MARSH QUINTET (Marsh, Warne Quintet).
Notes: Featuring Lee Konitz\Niels-Henning-Orsted-Pedersen
Album: released on Storyville, Nov'86 by Storyville Records. Dist: Jazz Music Distribution, Swift Distribution, Chris Wellard Distribution, Counterpoint Distribution

WARNE MARSH QUINTET (Marsh, Warne Quintet).
Notes: Featuring Lee Konitz/Niels Henning/Orsted Pedero
Album: released on Storyville (USA), Jun'86 by Moss Music Group Records (USA). Dist: Discovery Distribution, Jazz Music Distribution, Swift Distribution, Chris Wellard Distribution, JSU Distribution, Celtic Music Distribution

WARNE OUT.
Album: released on Flyright, Sep'80 by Flyright Records. Dist: Krazy Kat, Swift, Jazz Music

Mars, Johnny
BORN UNDER A BAD SIGN.
Single (7"): released on Ace, Oct'81 by Ace Records. Dist: Pinnacle, Swift, Hotshot, Cadillac

Single (7"): released on Lamborghini-Sundance, Jul'84 by Lamborghini Records. Dist: PRT

Single (7"): released on Lamborghini-Sundance, Jul'84 by Lamborghini Records. Dist: PRT

HOT LIPS BOOGIE.
Single (7"): by Sundance Records. Dist: PRT Distribution

JOHNNY MARS WITH MIGHTY MARS
(Mars, Johnny/Mighty Mars).
Album: released on JSP, Jan'82 by JSP Records. Dist: Swift, Projection

KING OF THE BLUES HARP.
Album: released on JSP, Aug'85 by JSP Records. Dist: Swift, Projection

LIFE ON MARS.
Album: released on Lamborghini, Jul'84 by Lamborghini Records. Dist: PRT

MIGHTY MARS.
Album: released on JSP, Jul'84 by JSP Records. Dist: Swift, Projection

OAKLAND BOOGIE, (THE).
Album: released on Big Bear, '82 by Big Bear Records. Dist: Big Bear, Swift

Mars, Julie
GIVE ME A SIGN.
Notes: Also on file as Mairs, Julie
Album: released on Plant Life, Mar'84 Dist: Roots

Marson, Stuart
NIGHT FALLS ON THE ORCHESTRA.
Album: released on Sweet Folk, Jul'85 Dist: Roots Distribution

Martell, Lena
100 MINUTES.
Cassette: released on PRT (100 Minute Series), Jun'82

6 TRACK HITS.
Special: released on Scoop 33, Sep'83 by Pickwick Records. Dist: H.R. Taylor

Cassette: released on Scoop 33, Sep'83 by Pickwick Records. Dist: H.R. Taylor

BEAUTIFUL SUNDAY.
Album: released on Ronco, Nov'80

Cassette: released on Ronco, Nov'80

BEST OF LENA MARTELL, THE.
Album: released on Pye, Oct'76

Cassette: released on Pye. Oct'76

BY REQUEST.
Album: released on Ronco, Mar'80

Cassette: released on Ronco, Mar'80

COLLECTION: LENA MARTELL.
Special: released on Pye, Sep'78

FEELINGS.
Album: released on Hallmark, Mar'81 by Pickwick Records. Dist: Pickwick Distribution, PRT, Taylors

Cassette: released on Hallmark, Mar'81 by Pickwick Records. Dist: Pickwick Distribution, PRT, Taylors

HELLO MISTY MORNING.
Album: released on Pye, Nov'77

Cassette: released on Pye. Nov'77

LENA MARTELL.
Album: released on Pickwick, Sep'80 by Pickwick Records. Dist: Pickwick Distribution, Prism Leisure Distribution, Lugtons

Cassette: released on Pickwick, Sep'80 by Pickwick Records. Dist: Pickwick Distribution, Prism Leisure Distribution, Lugtons

LENA MARTELL COLLECTION, THE.
Album: released on Ronco, Aug'79

LENA MARTELL IN CONCERT, ROYAL FESTIVAL HALL.
Album: released on Pye, Mar'79

Cassette: released on Pye, Mar'79

LENA MARTELL TODAY.
Album: released on Country House, Sep'84 by BGS Productions Ltd. Dist: Taylor, H.R., Record Merchandisers Distribution, Pinnacle, Sounds of Scotland Records

Cassette: released on Country House, Sep'84 by BGS Productions Ltd. Dist: Taylor, H.R., Record Merchandisers Distribution, Pinnacle, Sounds of Scotland Records

LENA'S MUSIC ALBUM.
Tracks: / Can't smile without you / As time goes by / Darlin' / Come to me / Forever in blue jeans / You / One day at a time / Say maybe / You needed me / Delta dawn / We love each other / Don't remember your name / Don't cry for me Argentina.
Compact disc: released on PRT, Oct'79 by PRT Records. Dist: PRT

Album: released on PRT, Oct'79 by PRT Records. Dist: PRT

LET THE MUSIC PLAY.
Album: released on One Up, Feb'80 by EMI Records.

LOVE ALBUM, THE.
Album: released on Pickwick, May'85 by Pickwick Records. Dist: Pickwick Distribution, Prism Leisure Distribution, Lugtons

Cassette: released on Pickwick, May'85 by Pickwick Records. Dist: Pickwick Distribution, Prism Leisure Distribution, Lugtons

MAGIC OF LENA MARTELL.
Cassette: released on PRT, Jan'75 by PRT Records. Dist: PRT

ONE DAY AT A TIME.
Single (7"): released on PRT, Oct'79 by PRT Records. Dist: PRT

Single (7"): released on Old Gold, Apr'83 by Old Gold Records. Dist: Lightning, Jazz Music, Spartan, Counterpoint

PRESENTING LENA MARTELL.
Album: released on Pye, Jan'74

Album: released on Flashback, Nov'85 by Flashback Records/PRT Records. Dist: Mainline, PRT

Cassette: released on Flashback, Nov'85 by Flashback Records/PRT Records. Dist: Mainline, PRT

SOMETHING SIMPLE.
Album: released on Decca (Elite), May'81 by Decca Records. Dist: Polygram, IMS

Cassette: released on Decca (Elite), May'81 by Decca Records. Dist: Polygram, IMS

SOMEWHERE IN MY LIFE TIME.
Album: released on Pye, Jan'78

SONGS.
Album:

SONGS OF LIFE/ SONGS OF LOVE.
Double Album: released on Ronco, Jul'82

Double cassette: released on Ronco, Jul'82

SPOTLIGHT ON LENA MARTELL.
Double Album: released on PRT, Jan'80 by PRT Records. Dist: PRT

Double cassette: released on PRT, Jan'80 by PRT Records. Dist: PRT

SPOTLIGHT ON...VOL.2.
Album: released on PRT (Spotlight), Oct'82 by PRT Records. Dist: PRT

Cassette: released on PRT (Spotlight), Oct'82 by PRT Records. Dist: PRT

THAT WONDERFUL SOUND OF LENA MARTELL.
Album: released on Pye, Apr'74

THIS IS LENA MARTELL.
Album: released on Pye, Jan'73

TOUCH OF LENA MARTELL.
Album: released on Pye, Jan'74

VERY SPECIAL LOVE FROM LENA.
Album: released on Pye, Mar'77

Cassette: released on Pye, Mar'77

YOU'RE MY HERO Wind beneath my wings, The.
Single (7"): released on Country House, Nov'84 by BGS Productions Ltd. Dist: Taylor, H.R., Record Merchandisers Distribution, Pinnacle, Sounds of Scotland Records

Martha & The Muffins

DANSEPARC Everyday it's tomorrow.
Single (7"): released on RCA, May'83 by RCA Records. Dist: RCA, Roots, Swift, Wellard, Chris, I & B, Solomon & Peres Distribution

Single (12"): released on RCA, May'83 by RCA Records. Dist: RCA, Roots, Swift, Wellard, Chris, I & B, Solomon & Peres Distribution

INSECT LOVE.
Single (7"): released on Dindisc, Oct'79 by Virgin Records. Dist: Virgin, EMI

METRO MUSIC.
Album: released on Virgin, Mar'84 by Virgin Records. Dist: EMI, Virgin Distribution

Cassette: released on Virgin, Mar'84 by Virgin Records. Dist: EMI, Virgin Distribution

TRANCE AND DANCE.
Album: released on Dindisc, Sep'80 by Virgin Records. Dist: Virgin, EMI

Cassette: released on Dindisc, Sep'80 by Virgin Records. Dist: Virgin, EMI

Martha & The Vandellas

DANCING IN THE STREET/ HEATWAVE.
Single (7"): released on Motown, Jun'83 by Motown Records. Dist: BMG Distribution

FORGET ME NOT/ I'M READY.
Single (7"): released on Motown, Mar'83 by Motown Records. Dist: BMG Distribution

GREATEST HITS: MARTHA & THE VANDELLAS.
Album: released on Motown, Mar'82 by RCA Records. Dist: RCA Distribution

Cassette: released on Motown, Mar'82 by RCA Records. Dist: RCA Distribution

JIMMY MACK/ THIRD FINGER LEFT HAND.
Single (7"): released on Motown, Oct'81 by Motown Records. Dist: BMG Distribution

Marthely, J P

RETE.
Compact disc: by Sterns. Dist: Sterns, Triple Earth

Martian School Girls

MOTION/ LA LA SONG.
Single (7"): released on Albion, Jun'81 by Albion Records. Dist: Spartan, Pinnacle

Martin, Ansell

I'LL BE IN THE JUNGLE.
Single (7"): by EMI Records. Dist: EMI

Martin, Benny

TENNESSEE JUBILEE.
Album: released on Sonet, Oct'76 by Sonet Records. Dist: PRT

Martin, Dadi

BODY POPPIN.
Single (7"): released on VP, Jun'84 by VP Records. Dist: Pinnacle

Single (12"): released on VP, Jun'84 by VP Records. Dist: Pinnacle

Martindale, Wink

DECK OF CARDS.
Single (7"): released on Old Gold, Jul'82 by Old Gold Records. Dist: Lightning, Jazz Music, Spartan, Counterpoint

Martin, Dean

BEST OF....
Album: released on EMI (Holland), '83 by EMI Records. Dist: Conifer

CHA CHA DE AMOR.
Album: released on Capitol, Oct'84 by Capitol Records. Dist: EMI

Cassette: released on Capitol, Oct'84 by Capitol Records. Dist: EMI

CLASSIC DINO, THE.
Album: released on Capitol, Jun'79 by Capitol Records. Dist: EMI

DEAN MARTIN.
Boxed set: released on World Records, Dec'81 Dist: Polygram

Cassette: released on World Records, Dec'81 Dist: Polygram

DEAN MARTIN SINGS.
Tracks: / I feel a song comin' on / Thats Amore / Come Back to sorrento.
Notes:
He sings in his own inimatable style. Recorded in 1955 when Martin was one half of the Jerry Lewis/ Dean Matin: comedy act. This album shows why Martin needed to break away from the mad antics of Lewis and follow his singing career more seriously, because he is a voice that is rich, Baritone, still loved by many today.
Album: released on Capitol T (USA), Dec'85 Dist: Conifer

DON'T GIVE UP ON ME/ DRINKING.
Single (7"): released on Warner Bros., Jul'83 by Warner Bros Records. Dist: WEA

EVERYBODY LOVES SOMETIME.
Compact disc: released on Hi Grade, '86 Dist: Target

EVERYBODY LOVES SOMEBODY.
Single (7"): released on Reprise (USA), '80 by WEA Records. Dist: WEA

Compact disc: released on The Compact Collection, Sep'87 by Conifer Records. Dist: Conifer Distribution

GENTLE ON MY MIND.
Album: released on Reprise, Jan'74 by WEA Records. Dist: WEA

MEMORIES ARE MADE OF THIS.
Compact disc: released on Card/Grand Prix, Apr'87 Dist: Target

MEMORIES ARE MADE OF THIS.
Tracks: / Memories are made of this / Return to me.
Notes: Also contains:"Return to me" by Dean Martin
Single (7"): released on Old Gold, Apr'87 by Old Gold Records. Dist: Lightning, Jazz Music, Spartan, Counterpoint

Album: released on MFP, Sep'81 by EMI Records. Dist: EMI

Cassette: released on MFP, Sep'81 by EMI Records. Dist: EMI

PRETTY BABY.
Album: released on Capitol(USA), Mar'84 by Capitol (USA) Records. Dist: EMI

Cassette: released on Capitol(USA), Mar'84 by Capitol (USA) Records. Dist: EMI

RETURN TO ME.
Tracks: / Memories are made of this / Return to me.
Notes: Also contains:"Memories are made of this" by Dean Martin
Single (7"): released on Old Gold, Apr'87 by Old Gold Records. Dist; Lightning, Jazz Music, Spartan, Counterpoint

RIO BRAVO.
Single (7"): released on EMI (France), Apr'83 by EMI Records. Dist: Conifer

SLEEP WARM.
Album: released on Capitol, Jul'85 by Capitol Records. Dist: EMI

Cassette: released on Capitol, Jul'85 by Capitol Records. Dist: EMI

VERY BEST OF DEAN MARTIN, THE.
Album: released on MFP, Sep'85 by EMI Records. Dist: EMI

Cassette: released on MFP, Sep'85 by EMI Records. Dist: EMI

Album: released on Capitol, Jul'83 by Capitol Records. Dist: EMI

Cassette: released on Capitol, Jul'83 by Capitol Records. Dist: EMI

WHEN YOU'RE SMILING.
Album: released on MFP, Sep'75 by EMI Records. Dist: EMI

WHITE CHRISTMAS (Martin, Dean & Nat King Cole).
Album: released on MFP (Capitol), Dec'82 by EMI Records. Dist: EMI

WINTER ROMANCE, A.
Album: released on Capitol, Oct'84 by Capitol Records. Dist: EMI

Cassette: released on Capitol, Oct'84 by Capitol Records. Dist: EMI

Martine

POLTERGEIST.
Single (7"): released on Ram, Dec'83 by Ram. Dist: PRT

Martin, Eric

ERIC MARTIN.
Album: released on Music For Nations, Dec'85 by Music For Nations Records. Dist: Pinnacle

INFORMATION.
Tracks: / Information / I cant stop the fire.
Single (7"): released on Food For Thought, Feb'86 by Food For Thought Records. Dist: Pinnacle

Martinez, Nigel

BEHIND MY BACK.
Single (12"): released on Pinnacle, Feb'83 by Pinnacle Records. Dist: Pinnacle

BETTER THINGS TO COME.
Album: released on State, Jul'78 by State Records.

Martin, George

BEATLES TO BOND & BACH.
Compact disc: released on Chrysalis, '87 by Chrysalis Records. Dist: CBS

OFF THE BEATLE TRACK (Martin, George Orchestra).
Album: released on See For Miles, Mar'82 by See For Miles Records. Dist: Pinnacle

Cassette: released on See For Miles, Mar'82 by See For Miles Records. Dist: Pinnacle

Martin, Horace

AFRICA IS CALLING/ SATURDAY NIGHT JAMBOREE.
Single (12"): released on African Youth Music, Apr'82

SUZIE.
Tracks: / Suzie / Give me the vibes.
Single (12"): released on Music Track, Jan'87 Dist: Jetstar Distribution

TALKIN BOUT BOOPS (Horace, Martin).
Tracks: / Talkin Bout Boops / Man Fi You.
Single (12"): released on Reggae City, May'86 by Reggae City Records. Dist: Jetstar

TYPE OF LOVING/MI LOVER (Martin, Horace & Tiger).
Tracks: / No wanga gut / Neighbourhood living / Type of loving/Mi lover.
Single (12"): released on Island, Jul'87 by Island Records. Dist: Polygram

V MAN.
Single (12"): released on High Power, Nov'85 by High Power Records. Dist: Jetstar

ZUGGY ZUGGY/SWEET SOMETHING.
Single (12"): released on Negus Roots, Jul'83 by Negus Roots Records. Dist: Jetstar

Martinique

NO REGRETS.
Single (12"): released on Young Blood, Mar'85 by Young Blood Records. Dist: Pinnacle

Martin, Janis

COMPLETE RCA JANIS MARTIN, THE.
Double Album: released on RCA, Aug'80 by RCA Records. Dist: RCA, Roots, Swift, Wellard, Chris, I & B, Solomon & Peres Distribution

FEMALE ELVIS COMPLETE RECORDINGS 1956-60, THE.
Tracks: / Drugstore rock 'n roll / Will you willyum / Love and kisses / My boy Elvis / Cracker Jack / Bang bang / Ooby dooby / Barefoot baby / Good love / Little bit / Two long years / All right baby / Billy boy my Billy boy / Let's elope baby / Love me love / Love me to pieces / William / Here today and gone tomorrow / Teen street / Hard times ahead / Cry guitar / Just squeeze me / One more year to go / Blues keep calling / Please be my love / I don't hurt anymore / Half loved / My confession / I'll never be free / Love me love (cha cha).
Compact disc: released on Bear Family, Jul'87 by Bear Family Records. Dist: Rollercoaster Distribution, Swift. Estim retail price in Aug'87 was £13.50.

Album: released on Bear Family (Rollercoaster), Aug'87. Estim retail price in Aug'87 was £13.50.

THAT ROCKIN GAL ROCKS ON.
Album: released on RCA, Sep'84 by RCA Records. Dist: RCA, Roots, Swift, Wellard, Chris, I & B, Solomon & Peres Distribution

THAT ROCKIN GAL SINGS MY BOY ELVIS.
Album: released on RCA, Sep'84 by RCA Records. Dist: RCA, Roots, Swift, Wellard, Chris, I & B, Solomon & Peres Distribution

Martin, Jimmy

WILL THE CIRCLE BE UNBROKEN.
Album: released on Gusto (USA), '80 by Gusto Records (USA). Dist: Crusader

Martin, Juan

CHI MAI.
Single (7"): released on PVK, Mar'84

DAVID'S SONG.
Single (7"): released on WEA, Nov'83 by WEA Records. Dist: WEA

FLIGHT TO PARADISE.
Tracks: / Flight to paradise / Desired.
Single (7"): released on WEA, Jan'85 by WEA Records. Dist: WEA

OLE-DON JUAN FLAMENCO.
Album: released on Note, Jun'77 by EMI Records. Dist: EMI

ROMANCE.
Cassette: released on EMI, Mar'84 by EMI Records. Dist: EMI

ROMEO & JULIET LOVE THEME.
Single (7"): released on WEA, Apr'84 by WEA Records. Dist: WEA

SERENADE (Martin, Juan & Royal Philharmonic Orchestra).
Album: released on K-Tel, Jan'84 by K-Tel Records. Dist: Record Merchandisers Distribution, Taylors, Terry Blood Distribution, Wynd-Up Distribution, Relay Distribution, Pickwick Distribution, Solomon & Peres Distribution, Polygram

Cassette: released on K-Tel, Jan'84 by K-Tel Records. Dist: Record Merchandisers Distribution, Taylors, Terry Blood Distribution, Wynd-Up Distribution, Relay Distribution, Pickwick Distribution, Solomon & Peres Distribution, Polygram

SOLO ALBUM, (THE).
Album: released on WEA, May'85 by WEA Records. Dist: WEA

Cassette: released on WEA, May'85 by WEA Records. Dist: WEA

Martin, Marilyn

MARILYN MARTIN (Marilyn Martin).
Tracks: / Body and the beat / Night moves / Too much too soon / Turn it on / Thank you / One step closer to you / Beauty or the beast / Move Closer / Te dream is always the same / Here is the news.
Album: released on Atlantic, Mar'86 by WEA Records. Dist: WEA

Cassette: released on Atlantic, Mar'86 by WEA Records. Dist: WEA

NIGHT MOVES (Marilyn Martin).
Tracks: / Night Moves / Wildest dreams.
Single (7"): released on Atlantic, May'86 by WEA Records. Dist: WEA

Single (12"): released on Atlantic, May'86 by WEA Records. Dist: WEA

Martin & Martin

JUST ANOTHER LITTLE GIRL.
Single (7"): released on Hippodrome, Apr'84 Dist: EMI

Martin, Mary

FALLING FOR YOU.
Tracks: / Falling for you / Falling for you (inst).
Single (7"): released on In Touch, Jul'87 by In Touch Records. Dist: Spartan

Single (12"): released on In Touch, Jul'87 by In Touch Records. Dist: Spartan

MARY MARTIN SINGS, RICHARD ROGERS PLAYS (Martin, Mary & Richard Rogers).
Album: released on RCA, Oct'84 by RCA Records. Dist: RCA, Roots, Swift, Wellard, Chris, I & B, Solomon & Peres Distribution

Cassette: released on RCA, Oct'84 by RCA Records. Dist: RCA, Roots, Swift, Wellard, Chris, I & B, Solomon & Peres Distribution

WRITING'S ON THE WALL, THE (Mary Martin).
Tracks: / Writings on the wall, The / Part 1 nst)/ Part 2 (Wall Mix).
Single (7"): released on Londisc, Nov'86 by Londisc Records.

Single (12"): released on Londisc, Nov'86 by Londisc Records.

Martin,Mel and the Listen

SHE WHO LISTENS (Mel Martin and the Listen).
Album: released on Move, Apr'86 by Charly Records. Dist: Charly Distribution, Fast Forward Distribution, Cartel Distribution

Martin, Mike

ON THE ROAD.

Page 646

Album: released on Flyright, Oct'79 by Flyright Records. Dist: Krazy Kat, Swift, Jazz Music

Martin, Moon
STREET FEVER.
Album: released on Capitol, Jan'81 by Capitol Records. Dist: EMI

Cassette: released on Capitol, Jan'81 by Capitol Records. Dist: EMI

Martin, Neil
INTRODUCING NEIL MARTIN.
Album: released on EMI, Apr'78 by EMI Records. Dist: EMI

Martin, Nicholas
HEY LOOK ME OVER.
Album: released on Grosvenor, Jun'83 by Grosvenor Records. Dist: Taylors

Cassette: released on Grosvenor, Aug'83 by Grosvenor Records. Dist: Taylors

Martino, Al
AL MARTINO.
Album: released on EMI (Germany), '83 by EMI Records. Dist: Conifer

BEST OF.
Album: released on EMI (Holland), '83 by EMI Records. Dist: Conifer

BEST OF AL MARTINO.
Album: released on Capitol, '70 by Capitol Records. Dist: EMI

HITS OF AL MARTINO, THE.
Album: released on MFP, Oct'85 by EMI Records. Dist: EMI

Cassette: released on MFP, Oct'85 by EMI Records. Dist: EMI

LOVE SONGS.
Album: released on Music For Pleasure (Capitol), Nov'83

Cassette: released on Music For Pleasure (Capitol), Nov'83

SPANISH EYES.
Album: released on Capitol, '66 by Capitol Records. Dist: EMI

Single (7"): released on EMI (Holland), Jul'84 by EMI Records. Dist: Conifer

VERY BEST OF AL MARTINO, THE.
Album: released on Capitol, May'84 by Capitol Records. Dist: EMI

Cassette: released on Capitol, May'84 by Capitol Records. Dist: EMI

VERY BEST OF AL MARTINO.
Album: released on Capitol, Oct'74 by Capitol Records. Dist: EMI

Martino, Pat
CONSCIOUSNESS (Pat Martino).
Tracks: / Impressions / Consciousness / Passata on guitar / Along came Betty / Along came Betty / Along came Betty / On the stairs / willow / Both sides now.
Notes:
Pat Martino(guitar), Eddie Green('Elec Piano', except Willow, Just percussion. Tyrone Brown, (Bass), Sherman Ferguson, (Drums and Perc). Engineer:Tony May: Recorded at Generation Sound Studio. Cover Photo and design: Ron Warwell. Produced by Michael Cuscuna/ Robert E Devere., Management. Port Washington. New Yrk.
Album: released on Muse Jazz (USA), Jan'86

Album: released on Muse (Import), Apr'81

EAST.
Album:

EXIT.
Album: released on Muse (Import), Apr'81

FOOTPRINTS.
Album: released on Muse (Import), Apr'81

LIVE.
Album: released on Muse (Import), Apr'81

STRINGS.
Notes:
TRACK DETAILS NOT ADVISED
Album:

WE'LL BE TOGETHER AGAIN.
Album: released on Muse (Import), Apr'81

Martino, Ramon
NO PROBLEM / MEMORIES OF ANADULSIA (Yoakam, Dwight).
Single (7"): released on Fringe, Apr'82 Dist: Pinnacle

Martin, Patrick D.
COMPUTER DATIN'.
Single (7"): released on Illegal, Oct'80 by Faulty Products Records. Dist: Pinnacle, Lightning, Cartel

Martin, Remy
I WANT YOU.
Single (12"): released on Cartridge, May'82 by Cartridge. Dist: Jetstar

Martin, Ricky
HOLD ME TIGHT.
Single (7"): released on Everest (Premier), Apr'83 by Everest Records. Dist: Pinnacle

Martin, Shane
I NEED YOU.
Single (12"): released on Neil Rushden (Import), Mar'83

Martin, Tony
20 GOLDEN PIECES OF TONY MARTIN.
Album: released on President, Oct'85 by President Records. Dist: Taylors, Spartan

Cassette: released on President, Oct'85 by President Records. Dist: Taylors, Spartan

BARRIERS.
Single (7"): released on Barrier, Mar'84

BEST OF TONY MARTIN, (THE).
Album: released on RCA, Oct'84 by RCA Records. Dist: RCA, Roots, Swift, Wellard, Chris, I & B, Solomon & Peres Distribution

Cassette: released on RCA, Oct'84 by RCA Records. Dist: RCA, Roots, Swift, Wellard, Chris, I & B, Solomon & Peres Distribution

TENEMENT SYMPHONY.
Album: released on RCA, Aug'87 by RCA Records. Dist: RCA, Roots, Swift, Wellard, Chris, I & B, Solomon & Peres Distribution

Cassette: released on RCA, Aug'87 by RCA Records. Dist: RCA, Roots, Swift, Wellard, Chris, I & B, Solomon & Peres Distribution

Marti, Virgilio
SALUDANDO A LOS RUMBEROS.
Album: released on Globestyle, Feb'87 by Ace Records. Dist: Projection

Marton, Sandy
CAMEL BY CAMEL.
Single (7"): released on Carrere, Sep'85 by Carrere Records. Dist: PRT, Spartan

PEOPLE FROM IBIZA.
Single (7"): released on Carrere, Oct'84 by Carrere Records. Dist: PRT, Spartan

Single (12"): released on Carrere, Oct'84 by Carrere Records. Dist: PRT, Spartan

Martyn, John
ANGELINE.
Notes:
EXTRA TRACK ON COMPACT DISC VERSION ONLY
Single (7"): released on Island, Feb'86 by Island Records. Dist: Polygram

Single (12"): released on Island, Feb'86 by Island Records. Dist: Polygram

Compact disc single: released on Island, Feb'86 by Island Records. Dist: Polygram

BLESS THE WEATHER.
Album: released on Island, '74 by Island Records. Dist: Polygram

ELECTRIC JOHN MARTYN, THE.
Album: released on Island, Oct'82 by Island Records. Dist: Polygram

Cassette: released on Island, Oct'82 by Island Records. Dist: Polygram

GLORIOUS FOOL.
Album: released on WEA, Sep'81 by WEA Records. Dist: WEA

Cassette: released on WEA, Sep'81 by WEA Records. Dist: WEA

GRACE & DANGER.
Album: released on Island, Oct'80 by Island Records. Dist: Polygram

Compact disc: released on Island, May'87 by Island Records. Dist: Polygram

Cassette: released on Island, May'81 by Island Records. Dist: Polygram

GUN MONEY / HISS ON THE TAPE.
Single (7"): released on WEA, Nov'82 by WEA Records. Dist: WEA

HISS ON THE TAPE / LIVIN' ALONE.
Single (7"): released on WEA, Oct'82 by WEA Records. Dist: WEA

INSIDE OUT.
Album: released on Island, '74 by Island Records. Dist: Polygram

LONDON CONVERSATION.
Album: released on Island, '74 by Island Records. Dist: Polygram

LONELY LOVE.
Tracks: / Lonely love / Sweet little Mystery / Fishermans Friend (12" Disc only).
Single (7"): released on Island, Mar'86 by Island Records. Dist: Polygram

Single (12"): released on Island, Mar'86 by Island Records. Dist: Polygram

ONE WORLD.
Tracks: / Dealer / One world / Smiling stranger / Big muff / Couldn't love you anymore / Certain surprise / Dancing / Small Hours.
Album: released on Island, Sep'86 by Island Records. Dist: Polygram

Cassette: released on Island, Sep'86 by Island Records. Dist: Polygram

Compact disc: released on Island, Sep'86 by Island Records. Dist: Polygram

OVER THE RAINBOW.
Single (7"): released on Island, Oct'84 by Island Records. Dist: Polygram

PHILENTROPY.
Tracks: / Make no mistake / Dont want to know / Root love / Lookin' on / Hung up / Johnnie too bad / Sunday's child / Smiling stranger.
Notes:
'Hung up' and 'Dont want to know' were recorded live at the Apollo Theatre, Oxford. 'Johnnie too bad' & 'Make no mistake' were recorded live at the Dome in Brighton, all in Autumn of 1982. 'Sunday's Child', 'Lookin on','Root Love' and ' Smiling Stranger' were recorded in London during Spring 1983. The Musicians: John Martyn(Vocals, Guitars); Alan Thomson(Bass Guitar),Jeffrey Allen(Drums); Danny Cummings(Percussion); Ronnie Leahy(Keyboards); (Brighton and Oxford). All tracks written and composed by John Martyn. All tracks Published by Island Music LTD. Except 'Root Love', by Warlock Music; and 'Hung Up' by Intersong LTD. All tracks licensed from Miracle Management.(C) 1985 Castle Communications PLC.Unit 7,271 Merton Rd, London SW18 5IS. Bar Code:5 013428 120262
Album: released on Dojo, Apr'86 by Castle Communications Records. Dist: Cartel

Cassette: released on Dojo, Apr'86 by Castle Communications Records. Dist: Cartel

Compact disc: released on Dojo, '86 by Castle Communications Records. Dist: Cartel

PIECE BY PIECE.
Tracks: Nighttime / Lonely love / Angeline / One step too far / Piece by piece / Serendipity / Who believes in angels / cover of mine / John Wayne.
Notes:
Produced by: John Martyn. Engineered by:Brian Young and Robin Rankin. Instrumentalist: John Martyn(Guitars and Synthasizer's);Foster Patterson(Keyboards and Backing Vocals); Alan Thompson(Fretless Bass); Danny Cummings(Percussion); Colin Tully(Sax).
Album: released on Island, Feb'86 by Island Records. Dist: Polygram

Cassette: released on Island, Feb'86 by Island Records. Dist: Polygram

Compact disc: released on Island, Jul'86 by Island Records. Dist: Polygram

PLEASE FALL IN LOVE WITH ME.
Single (7"): released on WEA, Aug'81 by WEA Records. Dist: WEA

ROAD TO RUIN, THE (Martyn, John & Beverley).
Album: released on Island, '74 by Island Records. Dist: Polygram

SAPPHIRE.
Album: released on Island, Nov'84 by Island Records. Dist: Polygram

Cassette: released on Island, Nov'84 by Island Records. Dist: Polygram

SO FAR SO GOOD.
Album: released on Island, Mar'77 by Island Records. Dist: Polygram

SOLID AIR.
Tracks: / Over the hill / Don't want to know / I'd rather be with the devil / Go down easy / Dreams by the sea / May you never / Man in the station (The) / Easy blues (The) / Solid Air.
Compact disc: released on Island, Feb'87 by Island Records. Dist: Polygram

Album: released on Island, Nov'86 by Island Records. Dist: Polygram

Cassette: released on Island, Nov'86 by Island Records. Dist: Polygram

STORMBRINGER (Martyn, John & Beverley).
Album: released on Island, '74 by Island Records. Dist: Polygram

SUNDAYS CHILD.
Album: released on Island, Jan'75 by Island Records. Dist: Polygram

TUMBLER, THE.
Album: released on Island, '74 by Island Records. Dist: Polygram

WELL KEPT SECRET.
Album: released on WEA, '83 by WEA Records. Dist: WEA

Martyn, Nicky
LAUGHTER SHOW.
Album: released on Nevis, May'79 Dist: H.R. Taylor

Martyr
FOR THE UNIVERSE.
Notes:
TRACK DETAILS NOT ADVISED

FOR THE UNIVERSE.
Album: released on Megaton, Sep'85 by Megaton Records. Dist: Rough Trade Distribution, Cartel Distribution

Marvelettes
ANTHOLOGY.
Album: released on Motown, Sep'82 by RCA Records. Dist: RCA Distribution

Cassette: released on Motown, Sep'82 by RCA Records. Dist: RCA Distribution

COMPACT COMMAND PERFORMANCES 23 greatest hits.
Tracks: / Please Mr. Postman / Twistin' postman / Playboy / Beechwood 4-5789 / Someday, someway / Strange I know / Locking up my heart / Forever / My daddy knows best / As long as I know he's mine / He's a good guy (yes he is) / You're my remedy / Too many fish in the sea / I'll keep holding on / Danger heartbreak dead ahead / Don't mess with Bill / Don't mess with Bill / You're the one / Hunter gets captured by the game, The / When you're young and in love / Day you take me on (you have to take the other), The / My baby must be a magician / Here I am baby / Destination anywhere.
Compact disc: released on Motown, Mar'87 by Motown Records. Dist: BMG Distribution

WHEN YOU'RE YOUNG AND IN LOVE.
Single (7"): released on Motown (Re-issue), Oct'81

Marvel-Masters
MARVEL-MASTERS VOL 1 Various artists (Various Artists).
Album: released on Cowboy Carl, Apr'79 Dist: Mike's Country Music Room Distribution, Swift, Tonal Distribution

Marvels
HEAVEN MUST HAVE SENT YOU / ANYMORE.
Single 10": released on Pama, Oct'82 by Pama Records. Dist: Pama, Enterprise, Jetstar

HE NEVER FAIL I YET / I'LL FOLLOW YOU.
Single (12"): released on Pama, Dec'82 by Pama Records. Dist: Pama, Enterprise, Jetstar

IN THE MIDDLE OF THE NIGHT.
Album: released on Nightowl, Jul'78

NEVER LET YOUR LOVE SLIP AWAY.
Tracks: / Never let your love slip away / Side B (dub).
Single (12"): released on Toptenner, May'86 Dist: Jetstar

STAY.
Tracks: / Stay / Stay (Dub).
Single (12"): released on Toptenner, May'86 Dist: Jetstar

Marvin, Hank
ALL ALONE WITH FRIENDS.
Album: released on Polydor, May'83 by Polydor Records. Dist: Polygram, Polvdor

Cassette: released on Polydor, May'83 by Polydor Records. Dist: Polygram, Polydor

HANK MARVIN.
Album: released on Columbia, '69 by EMI Records. Dist: EMI

HAWK AND THE DOVE / JANINE.
Single (7"): released on Polydor, Apr'83 by Polydor Records. Dist: Polygram, Polydor

INVISIBLE MAN / ALL ALONE WITH FRIENDS.
Album: released on Polydor, Jun'83 by Polydor Records. Dist: Polygram, Polydor

TROUBLE WITH ME IS YOU / CAPTAIN.....
Single (7"): released on Polydor, Feb'83 by
Polydor Records. Dist: Polygram. Polydor

WORDS AND MUSIC.
Album: released on Polydor, Aug'83 by Polydor Records. Dist: Polygram, Polydor Deleted '85.

Cassette: released on Polydor, Aug'83 by Polydor Records. Dist: Polygram, Polydor

Marvin, Lee
WANDERIN' STAR.
Single (7"): released on MCA (Re-issue), Jul'80

Marvin & Tige
MARVIN & TIGE Original Film Soundtrack.
Album: released on Capitol, Dec'83 by Capitol Records. Dist: EMI

Cassette: released on Capitol, Dec'83 by Capitol Records. Dist: EMI

Marvin, Welch & Farrar
STEP FROM THE SHADOW.
Tracks: / Marmaduke / Lady of the morning / Time to come, The / Lonesome mole / Black eyes / Brownie Kentucky / Skin deep / Faithful / You never can tell / Hard to live with / Music makes my day / Mistress fate and father time / Silvery rain / Wish you were here / Thousand conversations / Tiny Robin / Thank heavens i've got you / Please Mr please.
Album: released on See For Miles, Nov'86 by See For Miles Records. Dist: Pinnacle

Marx Brothers
3 HOURS, 59 MINUTES, 51 SECONDS.
Boxed set: released on Record & Tape Sales, Oct'79

Marx, Richard
DON'T MEAN NOTHING.
Tracks: / Don't mean nothing / Flame of love, The.
: released on Manhattan, Jul'87 by EMI Records. Dist: EMI

Single (12"): released on Manhattan, Jul'87 by EMI Records. Dist: EMI

RICHARD MARX.
Tracks: / Should've known better / Don't mean nothing / Endless summer nights / Lonely heart / Hold on to the nights / Have mercy / Remember Manhattan / Flame of love / Rhythm of life / Heaven only knows / Should've known better / Don't mean nothing / Endless summer nights / Lonely heart / Hold on to the nights / Have mercy / Remember Manhattan / Flame of love / Rhythm of life / Heaven only knows.
Album: released on Manhattan, Aug'87 by EMI Records. Dist: EMI

Cassette: released on Manhattan, Aug'87 by EMI Records. Dist: EMI

Compact disc: released on Manhattan, Aug'87 by EMI Records. Dist: EMI

Mary Jane Girls
ALL NIGHT LONG / MUSICAL LOVE.
Single (7"): released on Motown, Jun'83 by RCA Distribution

Single (12"): released on Motown, Jun'83 by RCA Records. Dist: RCA Distribution

BOYS / YOU ARE MY HEAVEN / ALL NIGHT LONG* / CANDY MAN*.
Single (7"): released on Motown, Sep'83 by RCA Records. Dist: RCA Distribution

Single (12"): released on Motown, Sep'83 by RCA Records. Dist: RCA Distribution

CANDY MAN.
Single (7"): released on Motown, Apr'83 by RCA Records. Dist: RCA Distribution

IN MY HOUSE.
Single (7"):

Single (12"):

MARY JANE GIRLS.
Album:

Single (12"):

ONLY FOR YOU.
Tracks: / In my house / Break it up / Shadow lover / Lonely for you / Wild and crazy love / Girlfriend / I betcha / Leather queen.
Compact disc: released on Motown, '86 by Motown Records. Dist: BMG Distribution

ONLY FOUR YOU.
Album:

Cassette:

Page 648

WALK LIKE A MAN.
Tracks: / Walk Like a Man / All night Long.
Notes:
Extra track on 12" version
Single (7"): released on Gordy (USA), Jul'86 by Motown Records. Dist: RCA

Single (12"): released on Gordy (USA), Jul'86 by Motown Records. Dist: RCA

WILD AND CRAZY LOVE.
Single (7"):

Single (12"):

Mary-Lou
HERE COMES THE NIGHT.
Single (7"): released on Modern (UK), Dec'84 Dist: WEA Distribution

LIPSTICK ON YOUR COLLAR / FEVER.
Single (7"):

WHERE THE BOYS ARE / LET'S DANCE.
Single (7"):

Mary O'Hara
ADVENTURES OF THE SCALLYWAG GANG.
Cassette: released on Tempo Storytime, May'84

Mary Poppins
MARY POPPINS Original soundtrack (Various Artists).
Album: released on Disneyland, Aug'82 by WEA Records. Dist: WEA

MARY POPPINS Various artists (Various Artists).
Album: released on Disneyland, Dec'82 by WEA Records. Dist: WEA

Cassette: released on Disneyland, Dec'82 Dist: EMI

Album: released on Disneyland, Dec'82 Dist: EMI

Picture disc album: released on Disneyland, Dec'82 by Disneyland-Vista Records (USA). Dist: BBC Records & Tapes, Rainbow Communications Ltd(Distribution)

Album: released on Disney, Oct'84 by BBC Records & Tapes. Dist: BBC Records & Tapes, PRT

Cassette: released on Disney, Oct'84 by BBC Records & Tapes. Dist: BBC Records & Tapes, PRT

Masal
BOOGY MAN.
Tracks: / Boogy man/ Youre the one (a side of 12" / Lets go crazy/ So mad so crazy (B side of 12").
Single (12"): released on Antler, Nov'86 by Antler Records (Belgium). Dist: Red Rhino, Cartel

STRANGER TO MYSELF / LIGHTNING.
Single (7"): released on Turbo, Oct'82 Dist: Jetstar

Masaki
DA-BA-DA.
Single (7"): released on L.O.E., Mar'86 Dist: PRT

Single (12"): released on L.O.E., Mar'86 Dist: PRT

Mascara
BAJA.
Single (12"): released on Personal, Oct'84 by Personal Records. Dist: PRT

SEE YOU IN L.A.
Album: released on Ensign, Aug'79 by Ensign Records. Dist: CBS Distribution

Mas, Carolyne
MAS HYSTERIA.
Album: released on Mercury (USA Import), Apr'81

Masco
AFRICAN LOVE.
Tracks: / African Love / Party jam.
Single (7"): released on City 1, Sep'86 by Priority Records, RCA

Single (12"): released on City 1, Sep'86 by Priority Records, RCA

PARTY JAM.
Tracks: / Party jam / Party jam (Inst).
Single (12"): released on Citybeat, Dec'86 Dist: WEA

Masdaki
BEEN.
Compact disc:

Masekela, Hugh
AFRICAN BREEZE.
Single (7"): released on Jive, Oct'85 by Zomba Records. Dist: RCA, PRT, CBS

Single (12"): released on Jive, Oct'85 by Zomba Records. Dist: RCA, PRT, CBS

BRING HIM BACK HOME.
Tracks: / Serengeti.
Single (7"): released on Atlantic, Feb'87 by WEA Records. Dist: WEA

DON'T GO LOSE IT BABY.
Single (7"): released on Jive, May'84 by Zomba Records. Dist: RCA

KE BALE There there go.
Tracks: / Ke bale / Bird on the wing.
Single (7"): released on Warner Bros., 13 Jun'87 by Warner Bros Records. Dist: WEA

Single (12"): released on Warner Bros., 13 Jun'87 by Warner Bros Records. Dist: WEA

LADY.
Single (7"): released on Jive Africa, Apr'85 by Zomba Records. Dist: RCA

Single (12"): released on Jive Africa, Apr'85 by Zomba Records. Dist: RCA

NOTICE TO QUIT.
Notes:
A musical Semi documentary of his country, South Africa, featuring the music of Jazz trumpeteer Hugh masekela, plus poetry and news footage. 1986 production
No   track   details
total playing time 52 minute
Video-cassette (VHS): released on Hendring Video, Sep'86 by Charly Records. Dist: Charly, PVG

PULA EA NA (IT'S RAINING).
Single (7"): released on Jive Africa, Nov'84 by Zomba Records. Dist: RCA

Single (12"): released on Jive Africa, Nov'84 by Zomba Records. Dist: RCA

TECHNO-BUSH.
Album: released on Jive Africa, Jun'84 by Zomba Records. Dist: RCA

Cassette: released on Jive Africa, Jun'84 by Zomba Records. Dist: RCA

TOMORROW (Masekela, Hugh, with Kalahari).
Tracks: / Bring him back home / Mayibuyi / Ke bale / London fog / Everybody's standing up / Bird on the wing / Something for nothing / Serengeti.
Album: released on WEA, Jan'87 by WEA Records. Dist: WEA

Cassette: released on WEA, Jan'87 by WEA Records. Dist: WEA

Compact disc: released on WEA, Jan'87 by WEA Records. Dist: WEA

WAITING FOR THE RAIN.
Album: released on Jive, May'85 by Zomba Records. Dist: RCA, PRT, CBS

Cassette: released on Jive, May'85 by Zomba Records. Dist: RCA, PRT, CBS

WIMOWEH (THE LION NEVER SLEEPS).
Single (7"): released on Jive Africa, Sep'84 by Zomba Records. Dist: RCA

Single (12"): released on Jive Africa, Sep'84 by Zomba Records. Dist: RCA

M.A.S.H.
M.A.S.H. Original Film Soundtrack.
Album: released on CBS, '84 by CBS Records. Dist: CBS

Cassette: released on CBS, '84 by CBS Records. Dist: CBS

THEME FROM M.A.S.H..
Single (7"): released on CBS, Apr'80 by CBS Records. Dist: CBS

Masi
FIRE IN THE RAIN.
Album: released on Roadrunner (Dutch), 30 May'87 Dist: Pinnacle

Mas, Jeanne
INTO THE NIGHT.
Single (7"): released on EMI, Aug'84 by EMI Records. Dist: EMI

Mas, Jean Pierre
JEAN PIERRE MAS & CESARIUS ALVIM (see also Cesarius Alvim). (Mas, Jean Pierre & Cesarius Alvim).

Album: released on Polydor, May'82 by Polydor Records. Dist: Polygram, Polydor

Maslak, Keshavan
BIG TIME (Maslak, Keshavan Quartet).
Album: released on Daybreak, Apr'83 Dist: Jazz Horizons, Jazz Music

BLASTER MASTER (Maslak, Keshavan with Charles Moffett).
Album: released on Black Saint, May'85 Dist: Projection, IMS, Polygram, Chris Wellard, Harmonia Mundi, Swift

HUMANPLEXITY.
Album: released on Leo, Sep'84 Dist: Recommended

LOVED BY MILLIONS.
Album: released on Leo, Sep'84 Dist: Recommended

Maslon, Jimmie
IT'S ME JIMMIE.
Album: released on Rollin, Jun'80

SALACIOUS ROCKABILLY CAT.
Album: released on Rollin, Jun'80

TURN ME ALL AROUND.
Single (7"): released on Rondelet, Apr'81 Dist: Spartan Distribution

YOUR WILDCAT WAYS (Maslon, Jimmie & Crazy Sounds).
Album: released on Rondelet, Apr'81 Dist: Spartan Distribution

Masne, Vincent Le
GUITARES (Masne, Vincent Le & Bertrand Porquet).
Album: released on Shandar, Mar'78

Mason
DOUBLE-X-POSURE.
Tracks: / Double-x-posure / Pour it on.
Single (7"): released on Elektra (USA), Apr'87 by Elektra/Asylum/Nonesuch Records. Dist: WEA

Single (12"): released on Elektra (USA), Apr'87 by Elektra/Asylum/Nonesuch Records. Dist: WEA

LIVING ON THE EDGE.
Album: released on Elektra (USA), Feb'87 by Elektra/Asylum/Nonesuch Records. Dist: WEA
Cat. no: K 960472-1

Cassette: released on Elektra (USA), Feb'87 by Elektra/Asylum/Nonesuch Records. Dist: WEA

Mason, Barbara
I'LL NEVER LOVE THE SAME WAY TWICE.
Tracks: / On and off / Playing with my feelings.
Single (7"): released on Bluebird, Apr'87 by Bluebird Records. Dist: EMI, Jetstar

Single (12"): released on Bluebird, Apr'87 by Bluebird Records. Dist: EMI, Jetstar

PIECE OF MY LIFE, A.
Album: released on Wmot, May'81

Album: released on Bluebird, Apr'85 by Bluebird Records. Dist: EMI, Jetstar

Cassette: released on Bluebird, Apr'85 by Bluebird Records. Dist: EMI, Jetstar

SHE'S GOT THE PAPERS BUT I'VE GOT THE MAN.
Tracks: / She's got the papers... / On and off.
Single (7"): released on Bluebird, 13 Jun'87 by Bluebird Records. Dist: EMI, Jetstar

TIED UP.
Album: released on Other End, Jun'84 by Other End Records. Dist: PRT Distribution

Mason, Barry
BERTIE THE BUS.
Single (7"): released on Mandal, May'83 by Mandal Records. Dist: Pinnacle

Mason, Dave
HEADKEEPER.
Album: by Island Records. Dist: Polygram

VERY BEST OF DAVE MASON.
Cassette: released on Blue Thumb, Feb'82

Mason & Fenn
PROFILES.
Album: released on Harvest, Aug'85 by Harvest Records. Dist: Roots, EMI

Cassette: released on Harvest, Aug'85 by EMI Records. Dist: Roots, EMI

Mason, James
Lolita

Mason, Jeff
STRANGEWAYS.
Tracks: / Strangeways / Made in Heaven.
Single (7"): released on Bitten By Sharks, Jan'87 by Bitten By Sharks Records. Dist: Bitten By Sharks Records

Mason, John
GREAT PERFORMANCE (Mason, John & the Scottish Fiddle Orchestra).
Album: released on Impression, Jul'84 Dist: CBS

Cassette: released on Impression, Jul'84 Dist: CBS

Mason, Nick
NICK MASON'S FICTITIOUS SPORTS.
Cassette: released on Harvest, May'81 by EMI Records. Dist: Roots, EMI

Mason, Rod
CARRY ME BACK.
Album: released on Wam, May'87

GREAT HAVING YOU AROUND.
Album: released on Black Lion, Apr'79 by Black Lion Records. Dist: Jazz Music, Chris Wellard, Taylor, H.R., Counterpoint, Cadillac

MEET ME WHERE THEY PLAY THE BLUES.
Album: released on Black Lion, Jun'78 by Black Lion Records. Dist: Jazz Music, Chris Wellard, Taylor, H.R., Counterpoint, Cadillac

PEARLS, THE Jelly Roll Morton Interpretations. (Mason, Rod Hot Seven).
Album: released on Black Lion, Jul'87 by Black Lion Records. Dist: Jazz Music, Chris Wellard, Taylor, H.R., Counterpoint, Cadillac

ROD MASON.
Album: released on Black Lion, Feb'80 by Black Lion Records. Dist: Jazz Music, Chris Wellard, Taylor, H.R., Counterpoint, Cadillac

Mason, Rod Hot Five
COME BACK SWEET PAPA.
Album: released on Black Lion, May'85 by Black Lion Records. Dist: Jazz Music, Chris Wellard, Taylor, H.R., Counterpoint, Cadillac

Jazz holiday

Mason, Sylvia
SHOPPING AROUND (Mason, Sylvia & the Sapphires).
Single (7"): released on Stiff, Jul'82 by Stiff Records. Dist: EMI, Record Services Distribution (Ireland)

SYLVIA MASON.
Album: released on Carrere, Mar'80 by Carrere Records. Dist: PRT, Spartan

Masquerade
DON'T BACK BACK.
Single (12"): released on Pirate, Sep'84 by Pirate Records. Dist: Jetstar

EVERYBODY SAY.
Tracks: / Everybody say / Everybody say (Version).
Single (12"): released on Streetwave, Jan'87 by Streetwave Records. Dist: PRT Distribution

ONE NATION.
Tracks: / one nation / One nation (Inst).
Cassette single: released on Streetwave, Dec'85 by Streetwave Records. Dist: PRT Distribution

Single (12"): released on Streetwave, Dec'85 by Streetwave Records. Dist: PRT Distribution

ONE NATION (ORIGINAL STREET MIX).
Tracks: / One Nation (Original street Mix) / Set it off (Original Full Versio).
Notes: Featuring dina carrol.
Single (12"): released on Streetwave, Jan'86 by Streetwave Records. Dist: PRT Distribution

(SOLUTION TO) THE PROBLEM.
Tracks: / (Solution to) the problem.
Single (7"): released on Streetwave, May'86 by Streetwave Records. Dist: PRT Distribution

Masqueraders
HOW.
Single (7"): released on Grape-Vine, Apr'80 Dist: RCA, Swift

Mass
LABOUR OF LOVE.
Album: released on 4AD, Sep'81 by 4AD Records. Dist: Rough Trade

METAL FIGHTER.
Album: released on Teldec (Germany), Feb'84

---

by Import Records. Dist: IMS Distribution, Polygram Distribution

Massed bands
FESTIVAL OF MUSIC (Massed Bands Of The RAF).
Album: released on Polyphonic, Dec'84 by Polyphonic Records. Dist: Taylors

Cassette: released on Polyphonic, Dec'84 by Polyphonic Records. Dist: Taylors

FESTIVAL OF MUSIC 1985 (Massed Bands Of The Royal Air Force).
Album: released on Polyphonic, Mar'86 by Polyphonic Records. Dist: Taylors

Cassette: released on Polyphonic, Mar'86 by Polyphonic Records. Dist: Taylors

GRAND MILITARY CONCERT (Massed bands of British Armed Forces).
Album: released on Grasmere, Sep'85 by Grasmere Records. Dist: Sell

Cassette: released on Grasmere, Sep'85 by Grasmere Records. Dist: Sell

HORSE GUARDS PARADE (Massed Bands Of The Royal Air Force).
Album: released on Bandleader, Jun'87 by Bandleader Records. Dist: PRT

Cassette: released on Bandleader, Jun'87 by Bandleader Records. Dist: PRT

MASSED BAND OF THE HOUSEHOLD CAVALRY (Massed band of the Household Cavalry).
Album: released on Bandleader, '84 by Bandleader Records. Dist: PRT

Cassette: released on Bandleader, '84 by Bandleader Records. Dist: PRT

TRIBUTE IN MUSIC, A (Massed Bands Of The Royal Air Force).
Album: released on Polyphonic, Sep'85 by Polyphonic Records. Dist: Taylors

Cassette: released on Polyphonic, Sep'85 by Polyphonic Records. Dist: Taylors

Massed English...
SPECTACULAR (Massed English male voice choirs).
Compact disc: released on Bandleader, '86 by Bandleader Records. Dist: PRT

Mass extension
HAPPY FEE.
Single (7"): released on Fourth & Broadway, Mar'85 by Island Records. Dist: Polygram, EMI

Single (12"): released on Fourth & Broadway, Mar'85 by Island Records. Dist: Polygram, EMI

Massey, Cal
BLUES TO COLTRANE.
Album: released on Candid, Jul'87 Dist: Counterpoint, Cadillac

Massey, Roy
MOONLIGHT AND ROSES.
Album: released on Alpha, Aug'82 by Alpha Records. Dist: H.R. Taylor, Gamut

Massive
MASSIVE (Various Artists).
Album: released on Virgin, May'85 by Virgin Records. Dist: EMI, Virgin Distribution

Cassette: released on Virgin, May'85 by Virgin Records. Dist: EMI, Virgin Distribution

Massive 2
MASSIVE 2 (Various Artists).
Tracks: / Kool noh / In the springtime / Heartbeat / Call on me / Tonight / Who the cap fits / Every thursday night / Hurt me.
Notes: Compilation album featuring 16 reggae hits. other artists: Cool Blood, Beres Hammond, Winsome Tiger, Home T4, Just Dale & The Robotics, Little Clarkie, Michael Gordon. Available on extended version cassette containing more than one hour of music.
Album: released on Virgin, Nov'86 by Virgin Records. Dist: EMI, Virgin Distribution

Cassette: released on Virgin, Nov'86 by Virgin Records. Dist: EMI, Virgin Distribution

Massive Dread
MASSIVE DREAD.
Album: released on His Majesty, Oct'81 by Pinnacle

NICE THEM UP.
Single (12"): released on Upfront, Sep'81 by Serious Records. Dist: PRT

Massive Horn
MERRY MELODIES.

Album: released on Top Notch, Dec'85

Massive Horns
COOL AND DEADLY.
Single (12"): released on Fashion, Jan'84 by Fashion Records. Dist: PRT, Jetstar

Masso, George Quintet
DIALOGUE AT CONDON'S (Al Klink, Lou Stein, Jack Lesberg, Bobby Rosengarden).
Album: released on World Jazz, May'81 by World Jazz Records. Dist: World Jazz, JSU, Jazz Music

Mass Production
DIAMOND CHIP.
Single (7"): released on Cotillion, Jun'81 by WEA Records. Dist: WEA

Single (12"): released on Cotillion, Jun'81 by WEA Records. Dist: WEA

SHE'S GOT TO HAVE IT.
Tracks: / She's got to have it / We bite.
Single (12"): released on Nine O Nine, May'87 by Creole Records. Dist: Rhino, PRT

TURN UP THE MUSIC.
Album: released on Cotillion, May'81 by WEA Records. Dist: WEA

Master Builder
MASTER BUILDER Ibsen, Henrik.
Album: released on Caedmon(USA), '74 by Caedmon (USA) Records. Dist: Gower, Taylors, Discovery

Cassette: released on Caedmon(USA), '74 by Caedmon (USA) Records. Dist: Gower, Taylors, Discovery

Master drummers of dagbon
MASTER DRUMMERS OF DAGBON.
Album: released on Rounder (USA), Jul'85 Dist: Mike's Country Music Room Distribution, Jazz Music Distribution, Swift Distribution, Roots Records Distribution, Projection Distribution, Topic Distribution

Master, Frankie
1941/2 (Master, Frankie & His Orchestra).
Album: released on Circle(USA), Mar'84 by Jazzology Records(USA). Dist: Jazz Music, Swift, Chris Wellard

Master Funk Band
MY BOY LOLLIPOP.
Single (12"): released on Master, Dec'81

Master Genius
LET'S DANCE.
Single (12"): released on Carrere, May'84 by Carrere Records. Dist: PRT, Spartan

Master Jam
DANCIN' ALL NIGHT.
Single (12"): released on Proto, Jan'83 by Proto Records. Dist: WEA

FREAK WITH YOU (2 Parts).
Single (12"): released on Proto, May'83 by Proto Records. Dist: WEA

Mastermind
UNCLE SAM WANTS YOU.
Single (7"): released on Half Moon, Sep'82 by Rondelet Music And Records. Dist: Spartan

Single (12"): released on Half Moon, Sep'82 by Rondelet Music And Records. Dist: Spartan

Mastermixers
MASTERMIXERS Various artists (Various Artists).
Album: released on Creole, Oct'81 by Creole Records. Dist: Rhino, PRT

Cassette: released on Creole, Oct'81 by Creole Records. Dist: Rhino, PRT

Master Mixes
MASTER MIXES (Various artists) (Various Artists).
Album: released on Prelude, Jul'82 Dist: CBS

Master of Country
MASTER OF COUNTRY Various artists (Various Artists).
Album: released on Music For Pleasure (Holland), Jan'85 by EMI Records. Dist: EMI

Cassette: released on Music For Pleasure (Holland), Jan'85 by EMI Records. Dist: EMI

Master of the game
MASTER OF THE GAME Television soundtrack (Television Sountrack).

Album: released on BBC, Sep'84 by BBC Records & Tapes. Dist: EMI, PRT, Pye

Master of the universe
MASTERS OF THE UNIVERSE Various artists (Various Artists).
Album: released on Spot, May'84 by Pickwick Records. Dist: H.R. Taylor, Lugtons

Cassette: released on Spot, May'84 by Pickwick Records. Dist: H.R. Taylor, Lugtons

Masterpiece
I CAN'T WAIT.
Single (7"): released on Serious, Jun'87 by Serious Records. Dist: PRT

Single (12"): released on Serious, Jun'87 by Serious Records. Dist: PRT

Masterpieces
MASTERPIECES FOR BRASS BAND Various artists (Various Artists).
Compact disc: released on Valentine, Feb'86 by Valentine Records. Dist: PRT

MASTERPIECES VOLUME 1 Various artists.
Album: released on Londisc, Apr'85 by Londisc Records.

Master, Sammy
ROCKIN RED WING.
Single (7"): released on Revival Record, Jun'82

Master Saxes
MASTER SAXES VOL.3 (various artists) (Various Artists).
Album: released on Spotlite, Jan'80 by Spotlite Records. Dist: Cadillac, Jazz Music, Spotlite

Master Series- Sampler
MASTER SERIES-SAMPLER Compilation (Various Artists).
Compact disc: released on MCA, Feb'87 by MCA Records. Dist: Polygram, MCA

Masters, Frank
1946-1947 (Masters, Frank & His Orchestra).
Album: released on Circle(USA), Jun'86 by Jazzology Records(USA). Dist: Jazz Music, Swift, Chris Wellard

Masters, Frankie
ACCENTUATE THE POSITIVE.
Album: released on Golden Era, Jul'82 by Import Records. Dist: Wellard, Chris, Swift

Mastership
ALIVE IN BRITAIN.
Single (12"): released on Londonium, Oct'84 Dist: Fast Forward, Cartel

Masters of...
MASTERS OF METAL (Various Artists).
Notes: Artists include Iron Maiden/Saxon/Whitesnake.
Album: released on K-Tel, Feb'86 by K-Tel Records. Dist: Record Merchandisers Distribution, Taylors, Terry Blood Distribution, Wynd-Up Distribution, Relay Distribution, Pickwick Distribution, Solomon & Peres Distribution, Polygram

Cassette: released on K-Tel, Feb'86 by K-Tel Records. Dist: Record Merchandisers Distribution, Taylors, Terry Blood Distribution, Wynd-Up Distribution, Relay Distribution, Pickwick Distribution, Solomon & Peres Distribution, Polygram

MASTERS OF THE BEAT Various artists (Various Artists).
Album: released on Tommy Boy, Nov'85 by Warner Brothers. Dist: WEA Distribution

Cassette: released on Tommy Boy, Nov'85 by Warner Brothers. Dist: WEA Distribution

MASTERS OF THE RAGTIME GUITAR Various original artists (Various original artists).
Album: released on Kicking Mule, Aug'77 by Sonet. Dist: Roots, PRT-Pye Distribution

Masters of Ceremony
SEXY.
Single (7"): released on London, Mar'87 by London Records. Dist: Polygram

Single (12"): released on London, Mar'87 by London Records. Dist: Polygram

Masters of the universe
HE MAN.
Single (7"): released on Telebell, Nov'85 by Towerbell Records. Dist: EMI

Master, The

MASTER, THE Coward, Noel (Lawrence, Gertrude).
Album: released on WMI (Retrospect), Apr'85

Cassette: released on WMI (Retrospect), Apr'85

Masterworks

MASTERWORKS An electronic adventure into the world of the classics (Various Artists).
Album: released on K-Tel, Oct'80 by K-Tel Records. Dist: Record Merchandisers Distribution, Taylors, Terry Blood Distribution, Wynd-Up Distribution, Relay Distribution, Pickwick Distribution, Solomon & Peres Distribution, Polygram

Maston, Jimmie

HAUNT YOU BABY ROCK, THE.
Single (7"): released on Rollin, Jun'80

Mata

ON YOUR BIKES.
Single (7"): released on Savoir Faire, Jul'83

Matadaruka

ODE TO JOHNNY DRUGHEAD.
Single (12"): released on Alligator, Nov'83 Dist: Jetstar

Matadi, Ronny

AUTOMATIC MAGIC.
Single (12"): released on Congo Matadi, Feb'83 by Congo Matadi Records. Dist: Jetstar

Matador

MATADOR Various Artist (Various Artists).
Tracks: / Overture / There's no way out of here / To be a Matador / I was born to me / Only other people / Manolete, Belmonte, Joselito. / Boy from nowhere, A / Wake up Madrid / I'll take you out to dinner / This incredible journey / Don't be deceived / I'll dress you in mourning / Dance with death / Panama hat, A.
Album: released on Epic, Jun'87 by CBS Records. Dist: CBS

Cassette: released on Epic, Jun'87 by CBS Records. Dist: CBS

Compact disc: released on Epic, Jun'87 by CBS Records. Dist: CBS

MATADOR (Various Artists).
Album: released on Epic, 30 May'87 by CBS Records. Dist: CBS

Cassette: released on Epic, 30 May'87 by CBS Records. Dist: CBS

TOUCH BEYOND CANNED LOVE, A.
Album: released on What's So Funny About (Germany), May'87 Dist: Red Rhino, Cartel

Mata Hari

MATA HARI Original soundtrack (Various Artists).
Album: released on Milan France, May'85

Matania, Tina

LOVE ME JUST A LITTLE MORE.
Single (7"): released on WSME, Apr'84 by Pressing Engagements. Dist: Pinnacle

Mataya

MUSIC MUSIC MUSIC.
Single (7"): released on Instant, Nov'82 by Instant Records. Dist: Cartel

Single (12"): released on Instant, Nov'82 by Instant Records. Dist: Cartel

Match

BOOM BOOM BORIS.
Single (7"): released on Red Bus, Jul'85 by Red Bus Records. Dist: PRT

Matchbox

CROSSED LINE.
Album: released on Magnet, Jul'83 by Magnet Records. Dist: BMG

Cassette: released on Magnet, Jul'83 by Magnet Records. Dist: BMG

FLYING COLOURS.
Album: released on Magnet, Sep'81 by Magnet Records. Dist: BMG

Cassette: released on Magnet, Sep'81 by Magnet Records. Dist: BMG

GOING DOWN TOWN.
Album: released on Magnum Force, Oct'85 by Magnum Music Group Ltd. Dist: Magnum Music Group Ltd, PRT, Spartan

Cassette: released on Magnum Force, Oct'85 by Magnum Music Group Ltd. Dist: Magnum

Music Group Ltd, PRT, Spartan

I WANT OUT.
Single (7"): released on Magnet, Jan'83 by Magnet Records. Dist: BMG

MATCHBOX.
Cassette: released on Magnet, Sep'79 by Magnet Records. Dist: BMG

MIDNITE DYNAMOS.
Album: released on Magnet, '83 by Magnet Records. Dist: BMG

Cassette: released on Magnet, '83 by Magnet Records. Dist: BMG

RIDERS IN THE SKY.
Album: released on Charly, '78 by Charly Records. Dist: Charly, Cadillac

SETTIN' THE WOODS ON FIRE.
Album: released on Chiswick, Apr'79 by Chiswick Records. Dist: Pinnacle

THOSE ROCKBILLY REBELS.
Album: released on Music For Pleasure (Holland), Nov'83 by EMI Records. Dist: EMI

Cassette: released on Music For Pleasure (Holland), Nov'83 by EMI Records. Dist: EMI

Matchroom Mob

SNOOKER LOOPY (Matchroom Mob with Chas & Dave).
Tracks: / Snooker loopy / Wallop (snookered).
Single (7"): released on Rockney, Apr'86 by Rockney Records. Dist: EMI

Single (12"): released on Rockney, Apr'86 by Rockney Records. Dist: EMI

Material

CIGURI.
Single (7"): released on Reds, Mar'82

Single (12"): released on Reds, Mar'82

ONE DOWN.
Album: released on Elektra(Import), Mar'83 by WEA Records. Dist: WEA

SECRET LIFE 1979-81.
Album: released on Jungle, Jul'86 by Jungle Records. Dist: Jungle, Cartel

TEMPORY MUSIC COMPILATION.
Album: released on Celluloid (France), Mar'85 by Island. Dist: Polygram

TEMPORY MUSIC TWO (4 tracks).
Single (12"): released on Fresh, Aug'81 Dist: Jetstar

Mathematiquo Moderne

LES VISITEURS DU SOIR.
Album: released on Celluloid, Jan'82 by Island Records. Dist: Polygram

Mathews, Mat

JUST LIKE THIS (Mathews, Mat(elect) & Roy Hansen (Acoustic)).
Album: released on ARC (Accordion Records), '84 Dist: Accordion Record Club

Mathews Southern Comfort

MATHEWS SOUTHERN COMFORT MEETS SOUTHERN COMFORT.
Cassette: released on See For Miles, Sep'87 by See For Miles Records. Dist: Pinnacle. Estim retail price in Sep'87 was £5.67.

Mathews, Tony

CONDITION BLUE.
Album: released on Sonet-Alligator, Jun'81 by Sonet Records. Dist: PRT

Mathieu, Mireille

LES CONTES DE CRI-CRI (Mathieu, Mireille & Placido Domingo).
Album: released on CBS(France), Oct'85 by CBS Records. Dist: Conifer, Discovery, Swift

Mathis, Cathy

LATE NIGHT HOUR.
Tracks: / Late night hour / Late night hour (inst).
Single (7"): released on Tabu, 30 May'87 by CBS Records. Dist: CBS Distribution

Single (12"): released on Tabu, 30 May'87 by CBS Records. Dist: CBS Distribution

Mathisen, Leo

DANISH JAZZ, VOL 2.
Album: released on Storyville, Jul'82 by Storyville Records. Dist: Jazz Music Distribution, Swift Distribution, Chris Wellard Distribution, Counterpoint Distribution

Mathis, Johnny

99 MILES FROM LA.
Album: released on Hallmark, Sep'81 by Pickwick Records. Dist: Pickwick Distribution, PRT, Taylors

Cassette: released on Hallmark, Sep'81 by Pickwick Records. Dist: Pickwick Distribution, PRT, Taylors

ALL FOR YOU.
Album: by CBS Records. Dist: CBS

Album: by CBS Records. Dist: CBS

Cassette: released on CBS, Jul'80 by CBS Records. Dist: CBS

BEST DAYS OF MY LIFE, (THE).
Album: released on CBS, Mar'79 by CBS Records. Dist: CBS

Cassette: released on CBS, Mar'79 by CBS Records. Dist: CBS

BEST OF JOHNNY MATHIS, (THE).
Compact disc: released on CBS, Aug'84 by CBS Records. Dist: CBS

CELEBRATION.
Album: released on CBS, Sep'81 by CBS Records. Dist: CBS

Cassette: released on CBS, Sep'81 by CBS Records. Dist: CBS

CHANTE NOEL.
Notes: Track details not advised
Album: released on CBS(Import), Jun'86 by CBS Records. Dist: Conifer, Discovery, Swift

CHRISTMAS EVE WITH JOHNNY MATHIS.
Tracks: / It's beginning to look like Christmas / Toyland / Most wonderful time of the year, it's the / Jingle bells / Christmas is for everyone / Where can I find Christmas / Every Christmas eve/Giving (Santa's theme) / Christmas waltz, the / We need a little Christmas / Carolling, carolling/Happy holiday.
Album: released on CBS, Dec'86 by CBS Records. Dist: CBS

Cassette: released on CBS, Dec'86 by CBS Records. Dist: CBS

GOT YOU WHERE I WANT YOU (Mathis, Johnny & Dionne Warwick).
Single (7"): released on CBS, Jan'83 by CBS Records. Dist: CBS

GREATEST HITS: JOHNNY MATHIS VOL 4.
Album: released on CBS, '84 by CBS Records. Dist: CBS

Cassette: released on CBS, Jan'77 by CBS Records. Dist: CBS

GREATEST ORIGINAL HITS.
Cassette: released on CBS, Jan'83 by CBS Records. Dist: CBS

HEARTFELT.
Album: released on President, Nov'80 by President Records. Dist: Taylors, Spartan

HEAVENLY.
Compact disc: released on Mobile Fidelity, '86 by Mobile Fidelity Records.

Cassette: released on Embassy, Jul'77 by CBS Records. Dist: CBS

HOLLYWOOD MUSICALS (Mathis, Johnny & Henry Mancini).
Tracks: / You stepped out of a dream / Taking a chance on love / When you wish upon a star / True love / Whistling away the dark / Time after time / It might as well be spring / I had the craziest dream / Long ago (and far away) / Crazy world / Johnny Burke/Jimmy Van Heusen medley / Moonlight becomes you/It could happen to you/but beautiful.
Album: released on CBS, Nov'86 by CBS Records. Dist: CBS

Cassette: released on CBS, Nov'86 by CBS Records. Dist: CBS

Compact disc: released on CBS, Nov'86 by CBS Records. Dist: CBS

I'M STONE IN LOVE WITH YOU.
Album: released on Hallmark, Nov'83 by Pickwick Records. Dist: Pickwick Distribution, PRT, Taylors

Cassette: released on Hallmark, Nov'83 by Pickwick Records. Dist: Pickwick Distribution, PRT, Taylors

Single (7"): released on CBS, May'82 by CBS Records. Dist: CBS

IN CONCERT (VIDEO) With Deniece Williams.
Notes: Silver Anniversary Concert
Video-cassette (VHS): released on Video Col-

lection, May'87 by Video Collection International Ltd.. Dist: Counterpoint

IT MIGHT AS WELL BE SPRING (Mathis, Johnny & Henry Mancini).
Tracks: / It might as well be spring / When a child is born.
Single (7"): released on CBS, Oct'86 by CBS Records. Dist: CBS

JOHNNY MATHIS COLLECTION.
Double Album: released on Pickwick, Mar'76 by Pickwick Records. Dist: Pickwick Distribution, Prism Leisure Distribution, Lugtons

Cassette: released on Pickwick, Dec'79 by Pickwick Records. Dist: Pickwick Distribution, Prism Leisure Distribution, Lugtons

JOHNNY MATHIS COLLECTION: VOL 2.
Double Album: released on Pickwick, Jul'77 by Pickwick Records. Dist: Pickwick Distribution, Prism Leisure Distribution, Lugtons

Cassette: released on Pickwick, Feb'80 by Pickwick Records. Dist: Pickwick Distribution, Prism Leisure Distribution, Lugtons

JOHNNY MATHIS SINGS OF LOVE.
Album: released on Hallmark, '72 by Pickwick Records. Dist: Pickwick Distribution, PRT, Taylors

JOHNNY MATHIS SINGS THE MUSIC OF BACHARACH & KAEMPFERT.
Double Album: released on CBS, '74 by CBS Records. Dist: CBS

KILLING ME SOFTLY.
Album: released on CBS, Mar'81 by CBS Records. Dist: CBS

Cassette: released on CBS, Mar'81 by CBS Records. Dist: CBS CBS Deleted '87.

LIVE.
Album: released on Hallmark, Oct'87 by Pickwick Records. Dist: Pickwick Distribution, PRT, Taylors

Cassette: released on Hallmark, Oct'87 by Pickwick Records. Dist: Pickwick Distribution, PRT, Taylors

LOVE SONGS.
Album: released on CBS, '79 by CBS Records. Dist: CBS

LOVE WON'T LET ME WAIT (Mathis, Johnny & Deniece Williams).
Single (7"): released on CBS, Mar'84 by CBS Records. Dist: CBS

MATHIS COLLECTION, (THE).
Cassette: released on CBS, Feb'78 by CBS Records. Dist: CBS

MATHIS MAGIC.
Album: released on CBS, Oct'79 by CBS Records. Dist: CBS

Cassette: released on CBS, Nov'79 by CBS Records. Dist: CBS

MISTY.
Album: released on Hallmark, Feb'77 by Pickwick Records. Dist: Pickwick Distribution, PRT, Taylors

MOST REQUESTED SONGS.
Compact disc: released on CBS, May'87 by CBS Records. Dist: CBS

NIGHT AND DAY.
Album: released on CBS, Nov'81 by CBS Records. Dist: CBS Deleted '86.

Cassette: released on CBS, Nov'81 by CBS Records. Dist: CBS

ONE LOVE.
Single (7"): released on CBS, May'83 by CBS Records. Dist: CBS

RIGHT FROM THE HEART.
Tracks: / Touch by touch / Love shock / Just one touch / Hooked on goodbye / I need you / Step by step / Right from the heart / Falling in love / Here we go again / hold on.
Compact disc: released on CBS, Dec'86 by CBS Records. Dist: CBS

Album: released on CBS, May'85 by CBS Records. Dist: CBS

Cassette: released on CBS, May'85 by CBS Records. Dist: CBS Deleted '87.

SIMPLE.
Tracks: / Simple / We were never really out of love.
Single (7"): released on CBS, May'86 by CBS Records. Dist: CBS

Single (12"): released on CBS, May'86 by CBS Records. Dist: CBS

Single (7"): released on CBS, Aug'84 by CBS Records. Dist: CBS

SO DEEP IN LOVE (Mathis, Johnny & De-niece Williams).
Single (7"): released on CBS, Jul'83 by CBS Records. Dist: CBS

SPECIAL PART OF ME, A.
Tracks: / Simple / Love won't let me wait / Best is yet to come / Lead me to your love / You're a special part of me / Love never felt so good / Priceless / One love / Right here and now.
Compact disc: released on CBS, Sep'84 by CBS Records. Dist: CBS

TEARS AND LAUGHTER.
Cassette: released on CBS, Feb'80 by CBS Records. Dist: CBS

THAT'S WHAT FRIENDS ARE FOR (Mathis, Johnny & Deniece Williams).
Album: released on CBS, Aug'78 by CBS Records. Dist: CBS

THIS GUY'S IN LOVE WITH YOU.
Album: released on Hallmark, Aug'75 by Pickwick Records. Dist: Pickwick Distribution, PRT, Taylors

UNFORGETTABLE: A TRIBUTE TO NAT KING COLE (Mathis, Johnny & Natalie Cole).
Album: released on CBS, Sep'83 by CBS Records. Dist: CBS

Cassette: released on CBS, Sep'83 by CBS Records. Dist: CBS

WHEN A CHILD IS BORN.
Notes:
Track details not advised
Album: released on Hallmark, Nov'85 by Pickwick Records. Dist: Pickwick Distribution, PRT, Taylors

Cassette: released on Hallmark, Nov'85 by Pickwick Records. Dist: Pickwick Distribution, PRT, Taylors

Album: released on CBS, '78 by CBS Records. Dist: CBS

WHEN WILL I SEE YOU AGAIN?.
Album: released on CBS, Jul'75 by CBS Records. Dist: CBS

YOU LIGHT UP MY LIFE.
Album: released on CBS, Oct'84 by CBS Records. Dist: CBS Deleted '87.

Cassette: released on CBS, Oct'84 by CBS Records. Dist: CBS

Mathis, Kathy
KATT WALK.
Tracks: / Automatic stop and go / Late night hour / Straight from the heart / Crunch / Katt walk / Baby I'm hooked / All to yourself / Now that you've gone / Olive branch (instrumental), The / Love festival.
Album: released on Tabu, Aug'87 by CBS Records. Dist: CBS Distribution

Cassette: released on Tabu, Aug'87 by CBS Records. Dist: CBS Distribution

LATE NIGHT HOUR.
Single (7"): released on Tabu, May'87 by CBS Records. Dist: CBS Distribution

Matic 16
GET MYSELF TOGETHER.
Single (7"): released on L C Outernational, Jan'83 by L C Outernational Records. Dist: Jetstar

Single (12"): released on L C Outernational, Jan'83 by L C Outernational Records. Dist: Jetstar

NO MONEY TODAY.
Single (12"): released on Regent, Oct'82 Dist: MIS-EMI Distribution

SAY YOU WANT ME.
Single (12"): released on Conqueror, Jul'83 Dist: Jetstar

Matinee Idols
LINE-UP.
Album: released on President, Jul'84 by President Records. Dist: Taylors, Spartan

WHO'LL BE THE NEXT IN LINE?.
Single (7"): released on President, Nov'83 by President Records. Dist: Taylors, Spartan

Matrix
HARVEST.
Album: released on Pablo (USA), '82 by Pablo Records (USA). Dist: Wellard, Chris, IMS-Polygram, BMG

Cassette: released on Pablo (USA), '82 by Pablo Records (USA). Dist: Wellard, Chris, IMS-Polygram, BMG

Matsubara, Masaki
BEEN.

Album: released on L.O.E, Jul'86 Dist: PRT

Cassette: released on L.O.E, Jul'86 Dist: PRT

Compact disc: released on L.O.E, Jul'86 Dist: PRT

DA-BA-DA.
Single (7"): released on L.O.E., Jul'86 Dist: PRT

Single (12"): released on L.O.E., Jul'86 Dist: PRT

Matsui, Kazu project
SANDING ON THE OUTSIDE.

Matsui, Keiko
DROP OF WATER.
Compact disc: by Pacific Records (USA). Dist: Atlantic

Matsu, Tokyo
COUNTRY LADY FROM JAPAN.
Album: released on Checkmate, Apr'78 Dist: & B

Matsutoya, Yumi
TRAIN OF THOUGHT.
Video-cassette (VHS): released on PMI, Jun'86 by PMI Records. Dist: EMI

Video-cassette [Betamax]: released on PMI, Jun'86 by PMI Records. Dist: EMI

Matt Bianco
CAN'T STAND IT ANYMORE.
Tracks: / Can't stand it anymore / Can't stand it anymore (inst.).
Single (7"): released on WEA, Feb'86 by WEA Records. Dist: WEA

Single (12"): released on WEA, Feb'86 by WEA Records. Dist: WEA

DANCING IN THE STREET.
Tracks: / Dancing in the street / Dancing in the street (inst) / Just can't stand it (live).
Single (7"): released on WEA, May'86 by WEA Records. Dist: WEA

Single (12"): released on WEA, May'86 by WEA Records. Dist: WEA

HALF A MINUTE.
Single (7"): released on WEA, Oct'84 by WEA Records. Dist: WEA

Single (12"): released on WEA, Oct'84 by WEA Records. Dist: WEA

MATT BIANCO.
Tracks: / Yeh yeh / Dancing in the street / Undercover / Fly by night / Smooth / I wonder / Just can't stand it / Summer song / Sweetest love affair / Up front.
Album: released on WEA, Apr'86 by WEA Records. Dist: WEA

Cassette: released on WEA, Apr'86 by WEA Records. Dist: WEA

Compact disc: released on WEA, Apr'86 by WEA Records. Dist: WEA

MORE THAN I CAN BEAR.
Single (7"): released on WEA, Feb'85 by WEA Records. Dist: WEA

Single (12"): released on WEA, Feb'85 by WEA Records. Dist: WEA

SNEAKING OUT THE BACKDOOR.
Picture disc single: released on WEA, May'84 by WEA Records. Dist: WEA

WHOSE SIDE ARE YOU ON ?.
Album: released on WEA, Aug'84 by WEA Records. Dist: WEA

Cassette: released on WEA, Aug'84 by WEA Records. Dist: WEA

Compact disc: released on WEA, Aug'84 by WEA Records. Dist: WEA

YEAH YEAH.
Single (7"): released on WEA, Sep'85 by WEA Records. Dist: WEA

Single (12"): released on WEA, Sep'85 by WEA Records. Dist: WEA

Mattea, Kathy
WALK THE WAY THE WIND BLOWS.

Album: released on Mercury, Apr'87 by Phonogram Records. Dist: Polygram Distribution

Cassette: released on Mercury, Apr'87 by Phonogram Records. Dist: Polygram Distribution

Compact disc: released on Mercury, May'87 by Phonogram Records. Dist: Polygram Distribution

Matthews, David
DELTA LADY (Matthews, David Orchestra).
Notes: Featuring Earl Klugh
Compact disc: released on Bellaphon, '86 by Bellaphon Records. Dist: IMS-Polygram

DELTA LADY (Matthews, David & Earl Klugh).
Album: released on PRT, Mar'83 by PRT Records. Dist: PRT

Cassette: released on PRT, Mar'83 by PRT Records. Dist: PRT

GRAND CROSS.
Album: released on PRT, Nov'83 by PRT Records. Dist: PRT

Cassette: released on PRT, Nov'83 by PRT Records. Dist: PRT

ICE FUSE ONE.
Album: released on PRT, May'85 by PRT Records. Dist: PRT

Matthews, Ian
HIT AND RUN.
Album: released on CBS, May'77 by CBS Records. Dist: CBS

JOURNEYS FROM GOSPEL OAK.
Album: released on Mooncrest, Aug'74 by Mooncrest Records. Dist: PRT Distribution

SPOT OF INTERFERENCE.
Album: released on Sundown, Jun'86 by Magnum Music Group Ltd. Dist: Magnum Music Group Ltd, PRT Distribution, Spartan Distribution

Matthews, Jessie
GOLDEN AGE OF JESSIE MATTHEWS.
Album: released on Golden Age, Mar'86 by Music For Pleasure Records. Dist: EMI

Cassette: released on Golden Age, Mar'86 by Music For Pleasure Records. Dist: EMI
Cat. no: GX 412541-4

JACK WHITING AND JESSIE MATTHEWS.
Album: released on Monmouth, Mar'79

TRIBUTE TO A STAR, A.
Album: released on Decca, Dec'81 by Decca Records. Dist: Polygram

Matthews,Ronnie
ROOTS,BRANCHES & DANCES.
Album: released on Beehive (USA), Dec'79 by Cadillac Records. Dist: JSU

Matthews Southern Comfort
LATER THAT SAME YEAR.
Album: released on MCA, '74 by MCA Records. Dist: Polygram, MCA

MEET SOUTHERN COMFORT.
Tracks: / Woodstock / Something in the way she moves / Blood red roses / And when she smiles (she makes the sun shine) / I've lost you / Once in a lifetime / Brand new Tennessee waltz(The) / To love / I sure like your smile / Wedding song(There is love) / I need help / April lady / I wanna be your mama again / Something said / Dreadful ballad of Willie Hurricane / Belle.
Album: released on See For Miles, Mar'87 by See For Miles Records. Dist: Pinnacle

Cassette: released on See For Miles, Mar'87 by See For Miles Records. Dist: Pinnacle

WOODSTOCK.
Single (7"): released on Old Gold, Jul'82 by Old Gold Records. Dist: Lightning, Jazz Music, Spartan, Counterpoint

Matthieu, Mireille
TOGETHER WE ARE STRONG (see Duffy, Patrick).
Single (7"): released on Arista, Apr'83 by Arista Records. Dist: RCA

Mattson,Dave
LEAD ME HOME.
Album: released on Myrrh, May'79 by Word Records. Dist: Word Distribution

Matty, Marie
DREAMING.
Tracks: / Dreaming / Dreaming (inst).
Single (12"): released on Londisc, Feb'86 by Londisc Records.

Matumbi
ALIVE AND KICKING.
Single (7"): released on MR, Jan'84 Dist: Jetstar Distribution, ILA Distribution

Single (12"): released on MR, Jan'84 Dist: Jetstar Distribution, ILA Distribution

BEST OF MATUMBI.

Album: released on Trojan, '83 by Trojan Records. Dist: PRT, Jetstar

IN DAYLIGHT.
Single (7"): released on Solid Groove, Jul'82 Dist: Jetstar, Pinnacle

Single (12"): released on Solid Groove, Jul'82 Dist: Jetstar, Pinnacle

TESTIFY.
Album: released on Solid Groove, '82 Dist: Jetstar, Pinnacle

Matusewitch, Sergei
ACCORDIAN-CONCERTINA RECITAL.
Album: released on ARC (Accordion Records), '84 Dist: Accordion Record Club

Maughan, Susan
BOBBY'S GIRL.
Single (7"): released on Old Gold, Jul'82 by Old Gold Records. Dist: Lightning, Jazz Music, Spartan, Counterpoint

Mau Maus
FACTS OF WAR.
Extended-play record: released on Paragon, Jun'83 by Paragon Records. Dist: Paragon

LIVE AT THE MARPLES.
Album: released on Pax, '84 by Pax Records. Dist: Red Rhino, Cartel

MY JUDGE AND JURY.
Album: released on Rebellion, Nov'84 Dist: Red Rhino, Cartel

NO CONCERN/CLAMPDOWN/WHY DO.
Single (7"): released on Pax, Nov'82 by Pax Records. Dist: Red Rhino, Cartel

RUN WITH THE PACK.
Album: released on Pax, Sep'84 by Pax Records. Dist: Red Rhino, Cartel

SCARRED FOR LIFE.
Single (12"): released on Rebellion, Jun'85 Dist: Red Rhino, Cartel

SOCIETY'S REJECTS.
Single (7"): released on Pax, Aug'82 by Pax Records. Dist: Red Rhino, Cartel

TEAR DOWN THE WALLS.
Single (7"): released on Rebellion, Aug'84 Dist: Red Rhino, Cartel

Maureen
LOVE IS ALL.
Single (7"): released on Klub, Apr'80

Mauriat, Paul
BRASIL EXCLUSIVAMENTE.
Album: released on Philips (Import), '78

BRAZILIAN LANDSCAPE.
Album: released on Philips (Import), '78

CLASSICS IN THE AIR.
Tracks: / Toccata and fugue in Dm / Canon / Symphony No. 9 (Choral) / La gazza ladra (Overture) / Liebestraum No. 3 / Barber of Seville, The (Overture) / La Traviata (Prelude) / Prelude in C / Symphony No. 40 (Minuet) / Moonlight sonata / Hungarian dance No. 5 / Sonata "Pathetique".
Notes: 11 popular classics given the contemporary orchestral treatment by Paul Mauriat.The CD has an additional track.
Album: released on Philips (France), Dec'85

Cassette: released on Philips (France), Dec'85

Compact disc: released on Philips (France), Dec'85

I LOVE BREEZE (Mauriat, Paul & His Orchestra).
Tracks: / Introduction prelude 59 / Ai no cafe terrasse / Mozart medley / I love breeze / Toccata / Best of French medley / Czardas / Love is blue / Penelope / El Bimbo.
Compact disc: released on Philips Import, '84

MAGIC (Mauriat, Paul & His Orchestra).
Tracks: / Come vorrei / Empty garden / New York New York / Hard to say I'm sorry / Sun river / Love is blue / Hot on the scent / Ebony and Ivory / I've never been to me / Even the nights are better / Morning hunt / Tug of war / Take it away.
Compact disc: released on Philips Import, '84

MAGIC LASER HITS.
Tracks: / Green lake, The / Summer has risen / L'amour c'est comme una cigarette / Flashdance..what a feeling / Baby come to me / Say say say / Elle est d'ailleurs / She works hard for the money / I guess that's why they call it the blues / Sunset opening / Total eclipse of the heart / Sunset opening / Physical / Ebony and ivory / Taste of the sixties / Guilty / One that you love, The / Up where we belong / Pour la plaisir.
Notes: 60 minutes of orchestral magic from Paul Mauriat. As well as Mauriat original com-

positions this album contains such popular hits as 'Ebony And Ivory', 'Say Say Say', 'She Works Hard For The Money' and 'Up Where We Belong'.

Compact disc: released on Philips (France), Aug'85

MUSIC OF PAUL MAURIAT (Mauriat, Paul & His Orchestra).
Double Album: released on Philips, '73 Dist: IMS-Polygram

PENELOPE (Mauriat, Paul & His Orchestra).
Tracks: / Penelope / Love is blue / El bimbo / Petit oiseau mecanique / inuetta / J n'pourrai / Jamais t'oublier / Petite melodie / Contigo mi vida / Hymne a l'amour / Il n'ya pas de fumes sans feu / Y'a le printemps / Pearl fisher / Toccata / Copacabana (at the copa) / Feelings / Speak softly love / Last tango in Paris / Pegase.
Compact disc: released on Philips Import, '84

SEVEN SEAS, THE.
Tracks: / Seven seas, The / So bad-pipes of peace / Thriller / An innocent man / Making love out of nothing at all / Baroque cantable / Say say say / Total eclipse of the heart / I like chopin / Thing of Laura / You flew into my life.
Notes: Popular contempory music given the full treatment from the famous Paul Mauriat Orchestra
Compact disc: released on Phonogram Import, Jul'85

TOUT POUR LA MUSIQUE.
Album: released on Philips (Europe), Aug'82

Cassette: released on Philips (Europe), Aug'82

WINDY (Mauriat, Paul & His Orchestra).
Tracks: / Windy / That's what friends are for / Nikita / Saving all my love for you / You are my world / Waiting / Day after day / Part time lover / Only love (l'amour en heritage) / Quoi / Sara / Say you, say me.
Notes: Latest album from arranger, composer and orchestra leader Paul Mauriat. 12 beautiful tunes including popular contempory hits 'That's What Friends Are For', 'Nikita', 'Part Time Lover', 'Only Love' and more.
Album: released on Polydor (France), Jul'86 Dist: Polygram

Cassette: released on Polydor (France), Jul'86 Dist: Polygram

Compact disc: released on Polydor (France), Jul'86 Dist: Polygram

Maurison, Oliver

IS LOVE.
Single (7"): released on Authentic, Jan'80 by MHB Records. Dist: Lightning

Single (12"): released on Authentic, Jan'80 by MHB Records. Dist: Lightning

Mauro, Turk

UNDERDOG, THE (Mauro, Turk\Al Cohn\Hugh Lawson\Bob Cranshaw).
Album: released on Storyville, Nov'86 by Storyville Records. Dist: Jazz Music Distribution, Swift Distribution, Chris Wellard Distribution, Counterpoint Distribution

Mauru,Turk

HEAVYWEIGHT.
Album: released on Phoenix, '81 by Audio Fidelity Enterprises. Dist: Stage One, Lugtons

Mave & Dave

DO YOU REALLY WANT MY LOVE.
Single (7"): released on Red Stripe, Nov'80 Dist: Sonet, PRT

Mawasi

BRIDGES.
Single (12"): released on Londisc, Apr'85 by Londisc Records.

Mawer, Ryan

ENCOUNTERS.
Cassette: released on Vision, Sep'84 Dist: Vision

Cassette: released on Vision, Jan'85 Dist: Vision

Max &...

AND GOD GAVE US MAX (Max & The Broadway Metal Choir).
Album: released on Powerstation Records, May'86 by Powerstation Records. Dist: Pinnacle

Maxie and Mitch

DOUBLE TROUBLE.
Album: released on Rubber, Jan'84 by Rubber Records. Dist: Roots Distribution, Projection Distribution, Jazz Music Distribution, Celtic Music Distribution, JSU Distribution, Spartan Distribution

Maximum Joy

DO IT TODAY/TOUCHDOWN.
Single (7"): released on Fontana, Aug'82 by Phonogram Records. Dist: Polygram

IN THE AIR/SIMMER TIL DONE.
Single (7"): released on Y, Jul'82

Single (12"): released on Y, Jul'82

STATION M.X.J.Y..
Album: released on Y, Oct'82

STRETCH/SILENT STREET.
Single (7"): released on Y, Oct'81

Single (12"): released on Y, Oct'81

WHITE AND GREEN PLACE/BUILDING BRIDGES.
Single (7"): released on Y, Feb'82

Single (12"): released on Y, Feb'82

WHY CAN'T WE LIVE TOGETHER.
Single (7"): released on Garage, Apr'83 by Garage Records. Dist: Pinnacle

Maximum Rock 'n' Roll

WELCOME TO 1984.
Album: released on Maximum Rock'n'Roll, Jun'84 Dist: Cartel

Maximus Three

MAXIMUS PARTY.
Single (12"): released on Eclipse, Feb'83 by Decca Records. Dist: Polygram

Maxine

1984/IN LOVE.
Album: released on Chrysalis, Jan'84 by Chrysalis Records. Dist: CBS

Single (12"): released on Chrysalis, Jan'84 by Chrysalis Records. Dist: CBS

TO KNOW YOU IS TO LOVE YOU.
Single (7"): released on Olympic, Oct'82 Dist: Cassion (Melandy) Distribution, Celtic Music Distribution

Maxine,Brian

HIGHWAY FEVER.
Single (7"): released on Subway, Jul'81 Dist: Revolver Distribution, Spartan Distribution

Maxwell,Bob

LOWLANDS AWAY.
Album: released on Music World, '76

Maxwells

COUNTRY STYLE.
Album: released on SRT, Oct'77 by SRT Records. Dist: Pinnacle, Solomon & Peres Distribution, SRT Distribution, H.R. Taylor Distribution, PRT Distribution

Mayall, John

BEHIND THE IRON CURTAIN.
Album: released on PRT, May'86 by PRT Records. Dist: PRT

Cassette: released on PRT, May'86 by PRT Records. Dist: PRT

BEYOND THE TURNING POINT.
Album: released on Polydor, '74 by Polydor Records. Dist: Polygram, Polydor

BLUES ALONE.
Album: released on Ace Of Clubs, '67 by Decca Records. Dist: Polygram

BLUESBREAKERS.
Album: released on Decca, '83 by Decca Records. Dist: Polygram

Album: released on Decca, '83 by Decca Records. Dist: Polygram

BLUES FROM LAUREL CANYON.
Album: released on Decca, '68 by Decca Records. Dist: Polygram

COLLECTION: JOHN MAYALL.
Tracks: / Key to love / Hideaway / Ramblin' on my mind / All your love / They call it stormy Monday / Hoochie coochie man / Crocodile walk / Crawling up a hill / Marsha's mood / Sonny boy blow / Looking back / Hard road, A / Super-natural (The) / You don't love me / Leaping Christine / Suspicions, part 2 / Picture on the wall / Death of J.B. Lenoir (The) / Sandy / Bear (The) / Walking on sunset / Fly tomorrow.
Compact disc: released on Collector Series, '86 by Castle Communications Records. Dist: PRT, Pinnacle, RCA, Ariola

CRUSADE (Mayall,John Bluesbreakers).
Album: released on Decca, '67 by Decca Records. Dist: Polygram

DIARY OF A BAND (Mayall,John Bluesbreakers).
Album: released on Decca, '68 by Decca Records. Dist: Polygram

EMPTY ROOMS.
Double Album: released on Polydor, Aug'74 by Polydor Records. Dist: Polygram, Polydor

GREATEST HITS: JOHN MAYALL.
Double Album: released on Polydor, Nov'80 by Polydor Records. Dist: Polygram, Polydor

Cassette: released on Polydor, Nov'80 by Polydor Records. Dist: Polygram, Polydor

HARD ROAD, A (Mayall,John Bluesbreakers).
Album: released on Decca, '67 by Decca Records. Dist: Polygram

JAZZ BLUES FUSION.
Album: released on Polydor, '74 by Polydor Records. Dist: Polygram, Polydor Deleted '87.

JOHN LEE BOOGIE.
Single (7"): released on DJM, Jun'81 by DJM Records. Dist: CBS, Polygram

JOHN MAYALL COLLECTION, THE.
Tracks: / Key to love / Hide away / Ramblin' on my mind / All your love / They call it stormy Monday / Hoochie coochie man / Crocodile walk (1st version) / Crawling up a hill / Crawling up a hill / Sonny boy blow / Looking back / Hard road, A / Supernatural / You don't love me / Leaping Christine / Suspicions / Picture on the wall / Death of J.B.Lenoir / Sandy / Bear, The / Walking on sunset / Fly tomorrow.
Double Album: released on Castle Communications, Apr'86 by Castle Communications. Dist: Cartel, Pinnacle, Counterpoint

Cassette: released on Castle Communications, Apr'86 by Castle Communications. Dist: Cartel, Pinnacle, Counterpoint

JOHN MAYALL PLAYS JOHN MAYALL.
Album: released on Decca, '65 by Decca Records. Dist: Polygram

JOHN MAYALL STORY,THE,VOL 1.
Album: released on Decca (Rock Echoes), Oct'83 by Decca Records. Dist: Polygram, IMS

LAST EDITION.
Album: released on Polydor, Jun'83 by Polydor Records. Dist: Polygram, Polydor

Cassette: released on Polydor, Jun'83 by Polydor Records. Dist: Polygram, Polydor

LAST OF THE BRITISH BLUES,THE.
Album: released on MCA, Feb'82 by MCA Records. Dist: Polygram, MCA

Cassette: released on MCA, Feb'82 by MCA Records. Dist: Polygram, MCA

LOOKING BACK.
Album: released on Decca, '69 by Decca Records. Dist: Polygram

MOVING ON.
Album: released on Polydor (Germany), Aug'85 Dist: IMS-Polygram

NOTICE TO APPEAR.
Album: released on ABC, Feb'76 Dist: CBS, Pinnacle

PRIMAL SOLOS.
Album: released on Decca, Apr'83 by Decca Records. Dist: Polygram

Cassette: released on Decca, Apr'83 by Decca Records. Dist: Polygram

RAW BLUES.
Album: released on Ace Of Clubs, '67 by Decca Records. Dist: Polygram

ROOM TO MOVE.
Album: released on IMS, Apr'84 by Polydor Records. Dist: IMS, Polygram

SOME OF MY BEST FRIENDS ARE BLUES.
Tracks: / All your love / It ain't right / You don't love me / Dust my blues / Oh pretty woman / My time after awhile / I can't quit you baby / Me and my women / Double trouble / So many roads / All my life.
Album: released on Charly, Apr'86 by Charly Records. Dist: Charly, Cadillac

TURNING POINT.
Album: released on Polydor, May'82 by Polydor Records. Dist: Polygram, Polydor

Cassette: released on Polydor, May'82 by Polydor Records. Dist: Polygram, Polydor

Compact disc: released on Polydor, Aug'87 by Polydor Records. Dist: Polygram, Polydor

WORLD OF JOHN MAYALL VOL 2.
Album: released on World of Learning, '71 by World Of Learning Records. Dist: World Of Learning

Mayana

SHAKIN' ALL OVER/SKIPS A BEAT.
Single (7"): released on Graffitti, Oct'83 by Rialto Records. Dist: Projection

Single (12"): released on Graffitti, Oct'83 by Rialto Records. Dist: Projection

SKIPS A BEAT/NO LOVE ON THE RUN.
Single (7"): released on Graffitti, Jul'83 by Rialto Records. Dist: Projection

Single (12"): released on Graffitti, Jul'83 by Rialto Records. Dist: Projection

May,Bill Quintet

THA'S DELIGHTS.
Album: released on Trend (USA), Jan'84 by Discovery Records. Dist: Flexitron Distributors Ltd, Swift

May, Billy

20 GOLDEN PIECES OF BILLY MAY.
Album: released on Bulldog, Nov'81 by Bulldog Records. Dist: President Distribution, Spartan, Swift, Taylor, H.R.

Cassette: released on Bulldog, Feb'82 by Bulldog Records. Dist: President Distribution, Spartan, Swift, Taylor, H.R.

BACCHANALIA! (May,Billy and his Orchestra).
Album: released on Capitol, Mar'85 by Capitol Records. Dist: EMI

Cassette: released on Capitol, Mar'85 by Capitol Records. Dist: EMI

BEST OF BILLY MAY AND HIS ORCHESTRA,THE (May,Billy and his Orchestra).
Album: released on Music For Pleasure (Holland), Apr'83 by EMI Records. Dist: EMI

Cassette: released on Music For Pleasure (Holland), Apr'83 by EMI Records. Dist: EMI

BILLY MAY'S BIG FAT BRASS.
Tracks: / Brassmen's holiday / Autumn leaves / Love is the thing / Ping pong / Moonlight becomes you / Pawn ticket / Solving the riddle / Invitation / Continental, The (You kiss while you're dancing) / Return of the zombie / On a little street in Singapore / Joom jooms.
Notes: A timely reissue of this Grammy award winning album from the creative Billy May and his brass ensemble. As usual, each track contains the humourous musical expression always present in Billy May's arrangements - a brief description of each is outlined on the sleeve, along with personnels. A good selection of well known tracks including some May originals, using just brass - no reeds - a refreshing change incorporating plenty of swingy inventions for brass.
Album: released on Capitol, May'86 by Capitol Records. Dist: EMI

Cassette: released on Capitol, May'86 by Capitol Records. Dist: EMI

BILLY MAY'S NAUGHTY OPERETTA (May,Billy and his Orchestra).
Album: released on Capitol, Feb'84 by Capitol Records. Dist: EMI

Cassette: released on Capitol, Feb'84 by Capitol Records. Dist: EMI

FANCY DANCIN'.
Album: released on Pathe MarconiEMI Europe), Mar'85

Cassette: released on Pathe MarconiFrance), Mar'85

I BELIEVE IN YOU.
Album: released on Bainbridge (France), May'85 Dist: Discovery

Cassette: released on Bainbridge (France), May'85 Dist: Discovery

SKYLINER.
Album: released on Golden Hour, Nov'77 by PRT Records. Dist: PRT

SORT-A-MAY (May,Billy and his Orchestra).
Album: released on Capitol, Mar'79 by Capitol Records. Dist: EMI

SWING GOES ON,THE VOL8.
Album: released on EMI (Germany), '83 by EMI Records. Dist: Conifer

YOU MAY SWING.
Album: released on Intersound, Dec'86 by Intersound Records. Dist: Jazz Music

May,Brian & friends

STAR FLEET PROJECT.
Album: released on EMI, Nov'83 by EMI Records. Dist: EMI

Cassette: released on EMI, Nov'83 by EMI Records. Dist: EMI

Page 652

Maycock, George Trio
GEORGE MAYCOCK TRIO
Album: released on King (USA), Jul'78 by Gusto Records. Dist: Gusto Distribution, IMS, Swift

Mayday
DAY AFTER DAY.
Single (7"): released on Reddingtons, May'80 Dist: Rough Trade

MAYDAY.
Album:

SAVE THE CHILDREN.
Single (7"): released on Ritz, Oct'85 by Outlet Records. Dist: Outlet, Prism Leisure Distribution, Record Services Distribution (Ireland), Roots

Mayer, John
ETUDES (Mayer, John & Indo Jazz Fusions).
Album: released on Sonet, '74 by Sonet Records. Dist: PRT

Mayer, Laurie
DUST IN THE WIND.
Tracks: / Dust in the wind / Bright blue Nile.
Notes: Double 'A' side
Single (7"): released on Y 11, 30 May'87 by Y 11 Records. Dist: Rough Trade, Cartel

Single (12"): released on Y 11, Jun'87 by Y 11 Records. Dist: Rough Trade, Cartel

Mayerl, Billy
KING OF SYNCOPATION.
Album: released on World, '73 Dist: Jetstar

Mayfair
SUMMERTIME CITY.
Single (7"): released on Mayfair, Jul'84 by Ross Records. Dist: Pinnacle

Mayfair Charm School
MONTAGUE TERRACE (IN BLUE).
Tracks: / Montague Terrace (in blue) / Little black dress.
Single (7"): released on EL, Nov'96 by El Records. Dist: Rough Trade, Cartel, Pinnacle

Mayfield, Curtis
BABY IT'S YOU.
Tracks: / Baby it's you / Breakin' in the streets.
Single (7"): released on 98-6, Nov'86

Single (12"): released on 98-6, Nov'86

GIVE YE GET TAKE AND HAVE.
Album: released on Buddah, Jul'76

HONESTY.
Album: released on Epic, Mar'83 by CBS Records. Dist: CBS

Cassette: released on Epic, Mar'83 by CBS Records. Dist: CBS

IT'S ALRIGHT/SUPERFLY.
Single (7"): released on Polydor, Oct'80 by Polydor Records. Dist: Polygram, Polydor

MOVE ON UP.
Single (7"): released on Flashback, Jan'83 by Flashback Records/PRT Records. Dist: Mainline, PRT

NEVER SAY YOU CAN'T SURVIVE.
Album: released on Curtom, Mar'77 Dist: WEA

Mayfield, Percy
HIT THE ROAD AGAIN.
Album: released on Timeless (Holland), Nov'85 Dist: JSU Distribution, Jazz Music Distribution, Jazz Horizons Distribution, Cadillac, Celtic Music Distribution

MY HEART IS ALWAYS SINGING SAD SONGS.
Album: released on Ace, Nov'85 by Ace Records. Dist: Pinnacle, Swift, Hotshot, Cadillac

Mayhem
BLOOD RUSH.
Single (7"): released on Vigilante, Mar'85 by Probe. Dist: Cartel

Single (12"): released on Vigilante, Mar'85 by Probe. Dist: Cartel

GENTLE MURDER.
Single (7"): released on Riot City, Aug'82 by Riot City Records. Dist: Revolver

GENTLE MURDER/LIE AND DIE/CLEAN CUT.
Single (7"): released on Riot City, Nov'83 by Riot City Records. Dist: Revolver

Mayhem and Psychosis
MAYHEM AND PSYCHOSIS VOL. 1 20 Psych pund classics from the 60's
Notes: Inc. Magic Plants, Chob.
Album: released on Roxy, Mar'87 by Ritz Records. Dist: Spartan Distribution

MAYHEM AND PSYCHOSIS VOL. 2 20 Psych punk classics from the 60's.
Notes: Inc. Them, Chocolate Moose.
Album: released on Roxy, Mar'87 by Ritz Records. Dist: Spartan Distribution

MAYHEM AND PSYCHOSIS (Various Artists).
Album: released on Roxys, Jan'86

MAYHEM AND PSYCHOSIS VOL.2 (Various Artists).
Album: released on Roxy, Jul'86 by Ritz Records. Dist: Spartan Distribution

Maynard, George
RUMPSY BUMPSY.
Cassette: released on Folktracks, Nov'79 by Folktracks Cassettes. Dist: Folktracks

YE SUBJECTS OF ENGLAND Traditional songs from Sussex.
Album: released on Topic, '81 Dist: Roots Distribution

Mayorga, Lincoln
GROWING UP IN HOLLYWOOD TOWN (Mayorga, Lincoln & Amanda McBroon).
Album: released on Sheffield Laboratories, Oct'82 by Sheffield Laboratories Records. Dist: Goldsmith, John Distribution

LINCOLN MAYORGA & DISTINGUISHED COLLEAGUES, VOL 3.
Album: released on Sheffield Laboratories, Oct'82 by Sheffield Laboratories Records. Dist: Goldsmith, John Distribution

WEST OF OZ (Mayorga, Lincoln & Amanda McBroon).
Album: released on Sheffield Laboratories, Oct'82 by Sheffield Laboratories Records. Dist: Goldsmith, John Distribution

Mayor, Ronnie
CAN'T WAIT 'TIL SUMMER COMES.
Single (7"): released on Do-It, Aug'81 by Do-It Records. Dist: Virgin, EMI

May, Phil & Fallen Angels
PHIL MAY & FALLEN ANGELS.
Album: released on Butt, Feb'05 by Butt Records. Dist: Counterpoint

Maypoles to mistletoe
MAYPOLES TO MISTLETOE Various artists (Various Artists).
Album: released on Leader, '81 Dist: Jazz Music, Projection

Mays, Bill Quintet
THAT'S DELIGHTS.
Tracks: / That's delight / Blues Marx / Mavrodaphne's dance / Goodbye California / S'wonderful / Goodbye.
Notes: Bill Mays - piano/Andy Simpkins - bass/Tom Harrell - flugelhorn/Ralph Moore - tenor sax/Shelly Mann - drums and percussion
Compact disc: released on Trend (USA), '86 by Discovery Records. Dist: Flexitron Distributors Ltd, Swift

May, Simon Orchestra
EASTENDERS.
Single (7"): released on BBC, Feb'85 by BBC Records & Tapes. Dist: EMI, PRT, Pye

HOLIDAY SUITE, THE.
Tracks: / Holiday suite, The. / Holiday tracks / Holiday club.
Single (7"): released on BBC, Mar'86 by BBC Records & Tapes. Dist: EMI, PRT, Pye

Single (12"): released on BBC, Mar'86 by BBC Records & Tapes. Dist: EMI, PRT, Pye

HOWARDS WAY.
Single (7"): released on BBC, Oct'85 by BBC Records & Tapes. Dist: EMI, PRT, Pye

SIMON'S WAY.
Tracks: / Howard's way / Variations on the theme of Howard's Way / Orrin New England / Frere / Abbey's theme / Tarrant set (the) / Barracuda / Always there / Anyone can fall in love / Warm light of a brand new day (The) / Holiday suite / Julia's theme / Eastenders.
Album: released on BBC, Sep'86 by BBC Records & Tapes. Dist: EMI, PRT, Pye

Mays, Lyle
LYLE MAYS.
Tracks: / Highland aire / Teiko / Slink / Mirror of the heart / Alaskan suite: Northern Lights invo-

cation ascent / Close to home.
Album: released on Geffen, May'86 by Geffen Records. Dist: WEA, CBS

Cassette: released on Geffen, May'86 by Geffen Records. Dist: WEA, CBS

Compact disc: released on Geffen, May'86 by Geffen Records. Dist: WEA, CBS

Maytals
54-46 WAS MY NUMBER.
Single (7"): released on Trojan, Apr'84 by Trojan Records. Dist: PRT, Jetstar

Single (12"): released on Trojan, Apr'84 by Trojan Records. Dist: PRT, Jetstar

Maytones
ONLY YOUR PICTURE.
Album: released on Vista Sounds, Dec'84 by Vista Sounds Records. Dist: Jetstar

Maytone, Vernon
MR POSTMAN.
Single (12"): released on Music Radics, Sep'84 by Music Radics Records. Dist: Jetstar Distribution

Maywood
MOTHER HOW ARE YOU TODAY?.
Single (7"): released on Logo, Jun'80 by Logo Records. Dist: Roots, BMG

Mazarati
MAZARATI.
Tracks: / Players ball / Lonely girl on Bourbon Street / 100 mph / Stroke / Suzy / Strawberry lover / I guess it's all over.
Album: released on Warner Bros., Apr'86 by Warner Bros Records. Dist: WEA

Cassette: released on Warner Bros., Apr'86 by Warner Bros Records. Dist: WEA

Maze
BACK IN STRIDE.
Single (7"): released on Capitol, Feb'85 by Capitol Records. Dist: EMI Deleted '86.

Single (12"): released on Capitol, Feb'85 by Capitol Records. Dist: EMI

CAN'T STOP THE MUSIC (Maze featuring Frankie Beverly).
Album: released on Capitol, Mar'85 by Capitol Records. Dist: EMI

Cassette: released on Capitol, Mar'85 by Capitol Records. Dist: EMI

GOLDEN TIME OF DAY (Maze featuring Frankie Beverly).
Album: released on Capitol, May'82 by Capitol Records. Dist: EMI

HAPPY FEELIN'S (VIDEO) Live in New Orleans.
Video-cassette (VHS): released on Video Collection, May'87 by Video Collection International Ltd. Dist: Counterpoint

INSPIRATION.
Album: by Capitol Records. Dist: EMI

I WANNA BE WITH YOU (Maze featuring Frankie Beverly).
Tracks: / I wanna be with you / I wanna be with you (instrumental).
Single (7"): released on Capitol, Aug'86 by Capitol Records. Dist: EMI

Single (12"): released on Capitol, Aug'86 by Capitol Records. Dist: EMI

JOY AND PAIN (Maze featuring Frankie Beverly).
Album: released on Capitol, Mar'82 by Capitol Records. Dist: EMI

Cassette: released on Capitol, Mar'82 by Capitol Records. Dist: EMI

LIVE IN LOS ANGELES (Maze featuring Frankie Beverly).
Tracks: / Running away / Too many games / I wanna thank you / You / Happy feelings / Feel that you're feeling / Joy and pain / Before I let go / Back in stride / I wanna be with you / Freedom (South Africa) / Dee's song / When you love someone.
Album: released on Capitol, Sep'86 by Capitol Records. Dist: EMI

Cassette: released on Capitol, Sep'86 by Capitol Records. Dist: EMI

LIVE IN NEW ORLEANS (Maze featuring Frankie Beverly).
Double Album: released on EMI, Jul'81 by EMI Records. Dist: EMI

Double cassette: released on EMI, Jul'81 by EMI Records. Dist: EMI

LIVE IN NEW ORLEANS

Video-cassette (VHS): released on PMI, Jun'86 by PMI Records. Dist: EMI

Video-cassette [Betamax]: released on PMI, Jun'86 by PMI Records. Dist: EMI

LOVE IS THE KEY.
Single (7"): released on Capitol, Apr'83 by Capitol Records. Dist: EMI

Single (12"): released on Capitol, Apr'83 by Capitol Records. Dist: EMI

MAZE.
Cassette: released on Capitol, Jun'83 by Capitol Records. Dist: EMI

MAZE (Maze featuring Frankie Beverly).
Album: released on Capitol, May'82 by Capitol Records. Dist: EMI

TOO MANY GAMES.
Single (7"): released on Capitol, Jul'85 by Capitol Records. Dist: EMI

Single (12"): released on Capitol, Jul'85 by Capitol Records. Dist: EMI

TOO MANY GAMES (Maze featuring Frankie Beverly).
Single (12"): released on Capitol, Aug'85 by Capitol Records. Dist: EMI

WE ARE ONE (Maze featuring Frankie Beverly).
Album: released on Capitol, May'83 by Capitol Records. Dist: EMI

Cassette: released on Capitol, May'83 by Capitol Records. Dist: EMI

WE ARE ONE / RIGHT ON TIME.
Single (7"): released on Capitol, Jun'83 by Capitol Records. Dist: EMI

Single (12"): released on Capitol, Jun'83 by Capitol Records. Dist: EMI

Mazel, Judy
LIFE IN THE SLIM LANE.
Album: released on CBS, Sep'83 by CBS Records. Dist: CBS

Cassette: released on CBS, Sep'83 by CBS Records. Dist: CBS Deleted '85.

Mazina
MAZINA (African music by two native musicians) (African music by two native musicians).
Album: released on Apollo. '69

Mazuhashi, Takashi
GON'S DELIGHT.
Album: released on Denon, Mar'82

Mazzy, Jimmy
Shake it down

Mbilabel / Tabu Ley
DANS KENYA ET CADANCE MUDANA.
Album: released on Genidia (Zaire), Mar'85 Dist: Earthworks Distributors, Rough Trade

M & B Jam Session
M & B JAM SESSION VOLUME 1, THE.
Album: released on Big Bear, Oct'85 by Big Bear Records. Dist: Big Bear, Swift

M'boom
COLLAGE.
Compact disc: released on Soul Note (Italy), '86 Dist: Harmonia Mundi Distributors

Album: released on Soul Note, May'85 Dist: Projection, Celtic Music, Chris Wellard

MBS
OUT OF THE BLUE / IN THE MORNING.
Single (12"): released on Star Track, Aug'83 Dist: Star Track Distribution

MC5
BABES IN ARMS.
Cassette: released on Reach Out Int, Jul'83

BACK IN THE USA.
Album: released on Atlantic, Feb'77 by WEA Records. Dist: WEA

Mc....
See also under Mac..

McAllndon, Hugh
DIAMOND GREEN.
Cassette: released on Outlet (Ireland), Feb'79

McAlister, Mike
I DON'T DIG IT / 21.
Single (7"): released on Rollin, Jun'80

McAloon-Rea

DROPS OF BRANDY.
Album: released on Topic, Jan'81 Dist: Roots Distribution

McAloon, Sean

DROPS OF BRANDY Traditional Irish (McAloon, Sean & John Rea).
Album: released on Topic, May'76 Dist: Roots Distribution

McAnally, Mac

MINIMUM LOVE.
Single (7"): released on Geffen, Apr'83 by Geffen Records. Dist: WEA, CBS

McAndless, Paul

NAVIGATOR.
Album: released on Landslide (USA), Mar'85 Dist: Compendium, Rough Trade, Cartel

McArthur, Helen

CHRISTMAS WITH BRASS.
Album: released on Note, Nov'77 by EMI Records. Dist: EMI

UPON THE MIDNIGHT CLEAR.
Album: released on Note, Jan'78 by EMI Records. Dist: EMI

McAslin, Mary

OLD FRIENDS.
Album: released on Philo, May'79 Dist: Roots

PRAIRIE IN THE SKY.
Album: released on Philo, May'79 Dist: Roots

WAY OUT WEST.
Album: released on Philo, May'79 Dist: Roots

McAvoy, Gerry

BASSICS.
Album: released on Bridgehouse, Dec'81 Dist: Pinnacle

McBain's Country...

ENGLISH FOLK DANCES (McBain's Country Dance Band).
Album: released on H.M.V., Oct'74 by EMI Records. Dist: EMI

McBain's Scottish...

MCBAIN'S SCOTTISH DANCING BAND (McBain's Scottish Dancing Band).
Double Album: released on Double 12. Mar'77

McBeath, Jimmy

BOUND TO BE A ROW.
Album: released on Topic, Jan'81 Dist: Roots Distribution

WILD ROVER NO MORE.
Album: released on Topic, Jan'81 Dist: Roots Distribution

McBee, Cecil

ALTERNATE SPACES.
Album: released on India, Jan'80 Dist: JSU

COMPASSION (McBee, Cecil Sextet).
Album: released on Enja (Germany), Jan'82 by Enja Records (W.Germany). Dist: Cadillac Music

FLYING OUT.
Album: released on India Navigation, Oct'84 by India Navigation Records. Dist: Cadillac, Projection, Swift

MUSIC FROM THE SOURCE (McBee, Cecil Sextet).
Album: released on Enja (Germany), Jan'82 by Enja Records (W.Germany). Dist: Cadillac Music

McBee, Hamper

RAW BASH.
Album: released on Rounder, Mar'79 Dist: Roots Distribution

McBennett, Helen

THAT'S WHEN THE MUSIC.
Album: released on Emerald, Feb'78 by Emerald Records. Dist: Ross, PRT, Solomon & Peres Distribution

McBride, Frankie

COULD I HAVE THIS DANCE.
Single (7"):

FIVE LITTLE FINGERS.
Album: released on Emerald (Ireland), Oct'81 by Emerald Records. Dist: I & B, Ross, PRT
Cat. no: GES 1097
Cassette: released on Emerald (Ireland), Oct'81 by Emerald Records. Dist: I & B, Ross,

Page 654

PRT
Cat. no: KGEC 1097

HOW ARE THINGS IN GLOCCA MORRA.
Single (7"): released on Emerald, Jun'67 by Emerald Records. Dist: Ross, PRT, Solomon & Peres Distribution

I'M BEING GOOD/ LAURA.
Single (7"):

JUST BEYOND THE MOON.
Single (7"):

VERY BEST OF FRANKIE MCBRIDE, THE.
Cassette: released on Music City, Jul'87 Dist: Ross Distribution

McBroom, Amanda

GROWING UP IN HOLLYWOOD TOWN (McBroom, Amanda & Mayorga Lincoln).
Album: released on Sheffield Laboratories, Oct'82 by Sheffield Laboratories Records. Dist: Goldsmith, John Distribution

GROWING UP IN HOLLYWOOD TOWN (see Mayorga, Lincoln) (McBroom, Amanda & Lincoln Mayorga).

WEST OF OZ (McBroom, Amanda & Mayorga Lincoln).
Album: released on Sheffield Laboratories, Aug'82 by Sheffield Laboratories Records. Dist: Goldsmith, John Distribution

WEST OF OZ (see Mayorga, Lincoln) (McBroom, Amanda & Lincoln Mayorga).

McCaffery, Frank

JEALOUS HEART.
Album: released on Release, Jun'78 by Release Records. Dist: I & B, Wynd-Up Distribution, Taylors, Solomon & Peres Distribution

McCaffey, Anne

WHITE DRAGON, THE.
Album: released on Caedmon(USA), Jul'79 by Caedmon (USA) Records. Dist: Gower, Taylors, Discovery

McCaffrey, Frank

CANDLELIGHT AND WINE.
Tracks: / Candlelight and wine / I'll take you home again Kathleen.
Single (7"): released on Ritz, Jan'87 by Outlet Records. Dist: Outlet, Prism Leisure Distribution, Record Services Distribution (Ireland), Roots

I'LL TAKE YOU HOME AGAIN KATHLEEN & OTHER.....
Album: released on Ritz, Jan'87 by Outlet Records. Dist: Outlet, Prism Leisure Distribution, Record Services Distribution (Ireland), Roots
Cassette: released on Ritz, Jan'87 by Outlet Records. Dist: Outlet, Prism Leisure Distribution, Record Services Distribution (Ireland), Roots

RING YOUR MOTHER WORE(THE).
Tracks: / Ring your mother wore(The) / Jody and the kid.
Single (7"): released on Ritz, Nov'85 by Outlet Records. Dist: Outlet, Prism Leisure Distribution, Record Services Distribution (Ireland), Roots

RING YOUR MOTHER WORE, THE.
Single (7"): released on Ritz, Nov'85 by Outlet Records. Dist: Outlet, Prism Leisure Distribution, Record Services Distribution (Ireland), Roots

McCaffrey, Leo

AN EVENING IN THE GLENS.
Album: released on Homespun(Ireland), Jan'82 by Outlet Records. Dist: Outlet
Cassette: released on Homespun(Ireland), Jan'82 by Outlet Records. Dist: Outlet

RATHLIN ISLAND/ MY LAGAN (EP).
Single (7"):

SOUVENIR OF IRELAND.
Cassette: released on Homespun(Ireland), May'84 by Outlet Records. Dist: Outlet

WEEKEND IN IRELAND.
Album: released on Emerald (Ireland), Oct'81 by Emerald Records. Dist: I & B, Ross, PRT
Cassette: released on Emerald (Ireland), Oct'81 by Emerald Records. Dist: I & B, Ross, PRT

McCain, Jerry

JERRY MCCAIN.
Album: released on White Label, Jul'79 by White Label Records. Dist: Jetstar

MIDNIGHT BEAT.
Tracks: / Honky tonk / Sugar baby / Homogenised love / Midnight beat / I don't care

---

where I get my loving / Love ain't nothing to play with / Juicy Lucy / Somebody's been talking / Soul spasm / I don't care where I get my loving / She's crazy 'bout entertainers / 728 Texas / Stick em up / Put it where I can get it.
Album: released on Charly, Jan'87 by Charly Records. Dist: Charly, Cadillac

McCalla, Dennis

PEACE MAKER.
Single (12"): released on Raintree, Mar'84 Dist: ILA

McCalla, Noel

BEGGIN (EP)/ AIN'T THAT PECULIAR.
Single (7"): released on Epic, Jun'80 by CBS Records. Dist: CBS

McCall, C.W.

CONVOY.
Single (7"): released on Old Gold, Jul'84 by Old Gold Records. Dist: Lightning, Jazz Music, Spartan, Counterpoint

McCall, Toussaint

NOTHING TAKES THE PLACE OF YOU.
Single (7"): released on Charly, Jul'80 by Charly Records. Dist: Charly, Cadillac

McCalmans

PEACE AND PLENTY.
Tracks: / Tullochgorum / Bells of the town(The) / Song of the plough / Colliery gate (The) / No you won't get me down in your mines / Black Bear(The) / Drover's lad (The) / Top House(The) / South Australia / Esikibo river / Blood red roses / Little Sally Rackett / Up and rin awa' Geordie / Mothers,Daughters,Wives / Highland road (The) / Barratt's privateers / Men of the sea / Song for Europe / Tae the weavers gin ye gang / Leave her Johnny.

SCOTTISH SONGS.
Tracks: / Farewell tae tarwathie / Smuggler / Mormond braes / Mingalay boat song.
Album: released on Ross, Dec'86 by Ross Records. Dist: Ross Distribution, Roots Distribution
Cassette: released on Ross, Dec'86 by Ross Records. Dist: Ross Distribution, Roots Distribution

McCandless, Paul

NAVIGATOR.
Notes: Solo from Oregon's woodwind specialist.

McCann, Phillip

WORLD'S MOST BEAUTIFUL MELODIES, THE.
Album: released on Chandos, Nov'85 by Chandos Records. Dist: Harmonia Mundi, Taylors
Cat. no: BBRD 1029
Cassette: released on Chandos, Nov'85 by Chandos Records. Dist: Harmonia Mundi, Taylors

McCann, Susan

AT HOME IN IRELAND.
Album: released on Homespun(Ireland), Nov'85 by Outlet Records. Dist: Outlet
Cassette: released on Homespun(Ireland), Nov'85 by Outlet Records. Dist: Outlet

BEST OF SUSAN MCCANN, THE.
Album: released on topspin, Apr'85

BEST OF..., THE.
Album: released on K-Tel, Apr'83 by K-Tel Records. Dist: Record Merchandisers Distribution, Taylors, Terry Blood Distribution, Wynd-Up Distribution, Relay Distribution, Pickwick Distribution, Solomon & Peres Distribution, Polygram
Cassette: released on K-Tel, Apr'83 by K-Tel Records. Dist: Record Merchandisers Distribution, Taylors, Terry Blood Distribution, Wynd-Up Distribution, Relay Distribution, Pickwick Distribution, Solomon & Peres Distribution, Polygram

BEST OF THE SIXTIES.
Cassette: released on Music City, Jul'87 Dist: Ross Distribution

BLUE JEAN.
Single (7"): released on Homespun(Ireland), Apr'85 by Outlet Records. Dist: Outlet

IRELAND'S OWN (McCann, Susan, Margo, Ann Breen, Philomena Begley).
Tracks: / Boys from Armagh / Cottage by the lee / Heaven around Galway Bay / Come my little son / Dear old Killarney / Rose of Clare / Old Claddagh Ring / Spinning wheel / Rose of Tralee / Danny boy / Village in Co.Tyrone / Girl from Donegal / Isle of Inisfree / Any Tipperary town / Old cross of Ardboe / That's an Irish lullaby.
Cassette: released on Homespun(Ireland), May'87 by Outlet Records. Dist: Outlet

ISLE OF IRELAND.
Album: released on topspin, Jun'85

Cassette: released on topspin. Jun'85

JOHNNY LOVELY JOHNNY.
Tracks: / Johnny lovely johnny / Where the river Shannon flows.

MERRY CHRISTMAS.
Cassette: released on Topspin (Ireland), Dec'85 Dist: I & B, Outlet, Shannon Distribution, S & P Distribution

SOMETIME WHEN WE TOUCH (McCann, Susan & Ronan Collins).
Cassette: released on Music City, Jul'87 Dist: Ross Distribution

SONGS JUST FOR YOU.
Tracks: / Could it be I don't belong here anymore / Have I told you lately that I love / This song is just for you / There goes my everything / Could I have this dance / Baby blue / Paper roses / Jelous Heart / Country roads / Remember you're mine.

STORYBOOK COUNTRY.
Album: released on topspin, May'81

TRIBUTE TO BUCK OWENS-LIVE AT THE GRAND.
Album: released on Homespun(Ireland), Dec'85 by Outlet Records. Dist: Outlet
Cassette: released on Homespun(Ireland), Dec'85 by Outlet Records. Dist: Outlet

WHEN THE SUN SAYS GOODBYE TO THE MOUNTAINS.
Album: released on Topspin (Ireland), Jul'85 Dist: I & B, Outlet, Shannon Distribution, S & P Distribution
Cassette: released on Topspin (Ireland), Jul'85 Dist: I & B, Outlet, Shannon Distribution, S & P Distribution
Single (7"): released on Homespun(Ireland), Nov'85 by Outlet Records. Dist: Outlet

McCarlos, Don

SWEET AFRICA/ SWEET ROOTS MUSIC.
Single (12"): released on Starlight, Jul'82 by Starlight Records. Dist: Jetstar Distribution

McCarroll, Andy

EPITAPH FOR A REBEL.
Album: by Pilgrim Records. Dist: Rough Trade, Cartel

McCarthy

FRANS HALS.
Tracks: / Frans Hals.
Single (7"): released on Pink, Mar'87 by Pink Records. Dist: Rough Trade
Single (12"): released on Pink, Mar'87 by Pink Records. Dist: Rough Trade

McCarthy, Keith

EVERYBODY RUDE.
Tracks: / Everybody rude / Rambo calypso.

McCartney, Paul

ANOTHER DAY/OH WOMAN OH WHY.
Single (7"): released on Parlophone, Mar'71 by EMI Records. Dist: EMI

BACK SEAT OF MY CAR/ HEART OF THE COUNTRY (McCartney, Paul & Linda).
Single (7"): released on EMI, Aug'71 by EMI Records. Dist: EMI

BAND ON THE RUN (McCartney, Paul & Wings).
Compact disc: by EMI Records. Dist: EMI
Album: released on Parlophone, Jan'85 by EMI Records. Dist: EMI
Cassette: released on Parlophone, Jan'85 by EMI Records. Dist: EMI

BAND ON THE RUN/ ZOO GANG (McCartney, Paul & Wings).
Single (7"): released on Parlophone, Jun'74 by EMI Records. Dist: EMI

COMING UP/ LUNCH BOX ODD SOX.
Single (7"): released on Parlophone, Apr'80 by EMI Records. Dist: EMI

EBONY & IVORY/ RAINCLOUDS (McCartney, Paul/Stevie Wonder).
Single (7"): released on Parlophone, Mar'82 by EMI Records. Dist: EMI
Single (12"): released on Parlophone, Mar'82 by EMI Records. Dist: EMI

GIRL IS MINE, THE (McCartney, Paul & Michael Jackson).
Single (7"): released on Epic, Nov'82 by CBS Records. Dist: CBS

GIVE MY REGARDS TO BROAD STREET.
Tracks: / No more lonely nights / Good say sun-

shine / Corridor music / Yesterday / Here,There and Everywhere / Wanderlust / Ballroom dancing / Silly love songs / Silly love songs (Reprise) / Not such a bad boy / So bad / No values / No more lonely nights (reprise) / For no-one / Eleanor Rigby / Eleanor's Dream / Long and winding road / No more lonely nights(play out version) / Goodnight princess.
Notes: Digital stereo recording.
Album: released on Parlophone, Oct'84 by EMI Records. Dist: EMI

Cassette: released on Parlophone, Oct'84 by EMI Records. Dist: EMI

Compact disc: released on Parlophone, Oct'84 by EMI Records. Dist: EMI

HELEN WHEELS/ COUNT MY DREAMER (McCartney, Paul & Wings).
Single (7"): released on EMI, Oct'73 by EMI Records. Dist: EMI

INTERVIEW PICTURE DISC.
Album: released on Baktabak, Jun'87 by Baktabak Records. Dist: Arabesque

JET/ LET ME ROLL IT (McCartney, Paul & Wings).
Single (7"): released on Parlophone, Feb'74 by EMI Records. Dist: EMI

MCCARTNEY.
Tracks: / Lovely Linda, The / That would be something / Valentine day / Every night / Hot as sun / Glasses / Junk / Man we was lonely / Oo you / Mamma Miss America / Teddy boy / Singalong junk / Maybe I'm amazed / Kreen-akrore.
Notes: Produced by Paul McCartney
Compact disc: released on Parlophone, Apr'87 by EMI Records. Dist: EMI

Album: released on Fame (Parlophone), Apr'84 by Music For Pleasure Records. Dist: EMI

Cassette: released on Fame (Parlophone), Apr'84 by Music For Pleasure Records. Dist: EMI

MCCARTNEY LL.
Tracks: / Coming up / Temporary secretary / On the way / Waterfalls / Nobody knows / Front parlour / Summers day song / Frozen jap / Bogey music / Darkroom / One of these days.
Album: released on Parlophone, May'80 by EMI Records. Dist: EMI

Cassette: released on Parlophone, May'80 by EMI Records. Dist: EMI

Album: released on Fame, Sep'87 by Music For Pleasure Records. Dist: EMI. Estim retail price in Sep'87 was £3.49.

Cassette: released on Fame, Sep'87 by Music For Pleasure Records. Dist: EMI. Estim retail price in Sep'87 was £3.49.

MY LOVE/ THE MESS (McCartney, Paul & Wings).
Single (7"): released on Parlophone, Mar'73 by EMI Records. Dist: EMI

NO MORE LONELY NIGHTS.
Single (7"): released on Parlophone, Sep'84 by EMI Records. Dist: EMI

Single (12"): released on Parlophone, Sep'84 by EMI Records. Dist: EMI

Compact disc: released on Parlophone, Sep'84 by EMI Records. Dist: EMI

NO MORE LONELY NIGHTS (SPECIAL DANCE MIX).
Single (12"): released on Parlophone, Nov'84 by EMI Records. Dist: EMI

ONLY LOVE REMAINS.
Tracks: / Only love remains / Tough on a tightrope.
Single (7"): released on Parlophone, Nov'86 by EMI Records. Dist: EMI

Single (12"): released on Parlophone, Nov'86 by EMI Records. Dist: EMI

PIPES OF PEACE.
Notes: See under compact disc section.
Album: released on Parlophone, Oct'83 by EMI Records. Dist: EMI

Cassette: released on Parlophone, Oct'83 by EMI Records. Dist: EMI

Compact disc: released on Parlophone, Oct'83 by EMI Records. Dist: EMI

PIPES OF PEACE/ SO BAD.
Single (7"): released on Parlophone, Dec'83 by EMI Records. Dist: EMI

PRESS.
Tracks: / Press / It's not true / Hanglide / Press (Dub) / Press (video Edit).

PRESS TO PLAY.
Tracks: / Strangehold / Good times coming/Feel the sun / Talk more talk / Footprints / Only love remains / Press / Pretty little head / Move over busker / Angry / However absurd.
Notes: Producers Paul McCartney and Hugh Padgham. All titles MPL Communications Ltd. Cleared copyright S.Robinson.

PRETTY LITTLE HEAD.
Tracks: / Pretty little head / Angry / Write away.
Cassette single: released on EMI, Nov'86 by EMI Records. Dist: EMI

RAM (McCartney, Paul & Linda).
Tracks: / Too many people / 3 legs / Ram on / Dear boy / Uncle Albert/ Admiral Halsey / Smile away / Heart of the country / Monkberry moon delight / Eat at home / Long haired lady / Ram on / Back seat of my car, The.
Compact disc: released on Capitol, Apr'87 by Capitol Records. Dist: EMI

Album: released on Parlophone, Jan'85 by EMI Records. Dist: EMI

Cassette: released on Parlophone, Jan'85 by EMI Records. Dist: EMI

RED ROSE SPEEDWAY (McCartney, Paul & Wings).
Album: released on Parlophone, Jan'85 by EMI Records. Dist: EMI

Cassette: released on Parlophone, Jan'85 by EMI Records. Dist: EMI

ROADSHOW (McCartney, Paul &Wings).
Video-cassette (VHS): released on Thorn-Emi, Jan'84

RUPERT AND THE FROG SONG.
Video-cassette (VHS): released on Virgin, May'85 by Virgin Records. Dist: EMI, Virgin Distribution

SALLY G/ JUNIORS FARM.
Single (7"): released on Parlophone, Nov'74 by EMI Records. Dist: EMI

SPIES LIKE US.
Single (7"): released on Parlophone, Nov'85 by EMI Records. Dist: EMI

Single (12"): released on Parlophone, Nov'85 by EMI Records. Dist: EMI

Picture disc single: released on Parlophone, Dec'85 by EMI Records. Dist: EMI

Picture disc single: released on Parlophone, Dec'85 by EMI Records. Dist: EMI

TAKE IT AWAY.
Single (12"): released on EMI (Germany), May'84 by EMI Records. Dist: Conifer

TAKE IT AWAY/ I'LL GIVE YOU A RING.
Single (7"): released on Parlophone, Jun'82 by EMI Records. Dist: EMI

Single (12"): released on Parlophone, Jun'82 by EMI Records. Dist: EMI

TEMPORARY SECRETARY/ SECRET FRIEND.
Single (12"): released on Parlophone, Sep'80 by EMI Records. Dist: EMI

TUG OF WAR.
Compact disc: by EMI Records. Dist: EMI

Album: released on Parlophone, Apr'82 by EMI Records. Dist: EMI

Cassette: released on Parlophone, Apr'82 by EMI Records. Dist: EMI

TUG OF WAR/ GET IT.
Single (7"): released on Parlophone, Sep'82 by EMI Records. Dist: EMI

WE ALL STAND TOGETHER (McCartney, Paul & The Frog Chorus).
Single (7"): released on Parlophone, Nov'85 by EMI Records. Dist: EMI

Picture disc single: released on Parlophone, Nov'85 by EMI Records. Dist: EMI

WONDERFUL CHRISTMAS TIME/ RUDOLPH THE RED NOSED REGGAE.
Single (7"): released on Parlophone, Nov'79 by EMI Records. Dist: EMI

McCaulay,Robin

ELOISE (McCaulay,Robin (Far corporation)).
Tracks: / Eloise / Don't say goodbye.

McCauley, Max

20 GOLDEN YODELS.
Album: released on Emerald, Jul'79 by Emerald Records. Dist: Ross, PRT, Solomon & Peres Distribution

McClain, Charly

WHO'S CHEATIN' WHO.
Single (7"): released on CBS, Apr'81 by CBS Records. Dist: CBS

McClaine, Carla

BRINGIN' ON BACK THE GOOD TIMES.
Single (7"): released on Runaway, Sep'81

McClain, Janice

JANICE MCCLAIN.
Tracks: / Passion and pain / When love calls / Second chance on love / Let's spend the night / Give a little bit of love / It's gonna come back to you / Hideaway / Rhythm of our love, The / Last goodbye.
Album: released on MCA, Feb'87 by MCA Records. Dist: Polygram, MCA

Cassette: released on MCA, Feb'87 by MCA Records. Dist: Polygram, MCA

PASSION AND PAIN.
Tracks: / Passion and pain / Passion and pain (Inst).
Single (7"): by MCA Records. Dist: Polygram, MCA

Single (12"): released on MCA, Mar'87 by MCA Records. Dist: Polygram, MCA

McClain, Marlon

SHAKE IT UP/ PASTEL.
Single (7"): released on Fantasy, Aug'81 by RCA Records. Dist: RCA, Jetstar

Single (12"): released on Fantasy, Aug'81 by RCA Records. Dist: RCA, Jetstar

McClary, Thomas

THIN WALLS.
Single (7"): released on Motown, Jan'85 by Motown Records. Dist: BMG Distribution

Single (12"): released on Motown, Jan'85 by Motown Records. Dist: BMG Distribution

McClatchy, Debby

APPLES IN WINTER.
Album: released on Plant Life, Nov'83 Dist: Roots

McClean, Hugh

THOMAS MCCLARY.
Album: released on Motown, Feb'85 by Motown Records. Dist: BMG Distribution

Cassette: released on Motown, Feb'85 by Motown Records. Dist: BMG Distribution

McClean, Jackie

CONSEQUENCE.
Album: released on Liberty-United, Jun'80 by EMI Records. Dist: EMI

TIPPIN' THE SCALES (Yoakam, Dwight).
Album: released on Blue Note, Apr'85 by EMI Records. Dist: EMI

McClean, Shirley

LET ME GO.
Single (12"): released on Lucky Dice, Nov'83 by Lucky Dice Records. Dist: Jetstar

McClelland, Harry

JESUS IS A FRIEND OF MINE.
Cassette: released on Praise, Jul'84 Dist: Outlet

STRANGER OF GALILEE.
Cassette: released on Praise, May'87 Dist: Outlet

TILL THE STORM PASSES BY.
Cassette: released on Praise (Ireland), Dec'85

McClen, Dee Dee

I'M IN LOVE.
Single (12"): released on Regal, Oct'82

McClennan, Tommy

BLUEBIRD.
Album: released on Black & White, Nov'77

McCleod, Enos

ME AND MI LOVER.
Single (12"): released on Bendown, Oct'84 by Bendown Records. Dist: Jetstar

McCleod, Jim

FAMILY FAVOURITES.
Album: released on Beltona, Apr'75 by Decca Records. Dist: Polygram

McCloud, Caspar

MESSIN AROUND.
Single (7"): released on Rock Steady, '79 by Rock Steady Records. Dist: Rough Trade Distribution, Indies Distribution, Cartel Distribution

McCloud, Emos

HEAD MISTRESS.
Single (7"): released on African Unity, Oct'83 by African Unity Records. Dist: Jetstar

McCloud, Jim

COME SCOTTISH COUNTRY DANCING.
Album: released on Decca, Oct'79 by Decca Records. Dist: Polygram

McClung, Tom

MOYALLAN BROWN RED.
Album: released on Outlet, May'80 by Outlet Records. Dist: Outlet Distribution

Cassette: released on Outlet, May'80 by Outlet Records. Dist: Outlet Distribution

McClure, Bobby

IT FEELS SO GOOD (TO BE BACK HOME).
Tracks: / It feels so good (to be back home) / You never miss your water / It feels so good (radio version).
Single (12"): released on Debut, Apr'87 by Skratch Music. Dist: PRT

McCluskey, John

FITBA' CRAZY.
Album: released on Nevis, May'77 Dist: H.R. Taylor

McClusky Brothers

AWARE OF ALL.
Tracks: / Aware of all / He's on the beach / Please go to sleep.
Single (12"): released on Thrush, Jul'86 Dist: Pinnacle

McConnell, Cathal

ON LOUGH ERNE'S SHORE.
Album: released on Topic, '81 by Topic Records. Dist: JSU Distribution, Projection Distribution, Jazz Music Distribution

TRADITIONAL IRISH SONGS (McConnell, Cathal/Robin Morton).
Album: released on Topic, Jul'76 by Topic Records. Dist: JSU Distribution, Projection Distribution, Jazz Music Distribution

McConnell, Rob

AGAIN ! (McConnell, Rob & The Boss Band).
Album: released on Pausa (France), May'85 Dist: Discovery Distribution

ALL IN GOOD TIME (McConnell, Rob & The Boss Band).
Album: released on Innovation (Canada), Sep'84 Dist: Mole Jazz

BIG BAND JAZZ (McConnell, Rob & The Boss Band).
Album: released on Pausa (France), May'85 Dist: Discovery Distribution

PRESENT PERFECT (McConnell, Rob & The Boss Band).
Compact disc: released on MPS, Dec'84

McConville, Tom

PORT OF CALL (McConville, Tom and Kieran Halpin).
Album: released on Rubber, Jun'82 by Rubber Records. Dist: Roots Distribution, Projection Distribution, Jazz Music Distribution, Celtic Music Distribution, JSU Distribution, Spartan Distribution

STREETS OF EVERYWHERE (McConville, Tom and Kieran Halpin).

McCookery,Helen Book

LEAVING YOU BABY.
Tracks: / Leaving you baby.
Single (12"): released on Pure Trash, Oct'86 Dist: Swift

McCook, Tommy

HOT LAVA (McCook, Tommy & The Skatalites).
Album: released on Third World, Nov'77 Dist: Jetstar Distribution

INSTRUMENTAL.
Album: released on Justice, Feb'78 Dist: Pinnacle

KING TUBBY AT DUB STATION (McCook, Tommy & The Aggrovators).
Album: released on Love & Live, Aug'78

McCoo, Marilyn

MARILYN & BILLY (McCoo, Marilyn & Billy Davis Junior).
Album: released on CBS, '78 by CBS Records. Dist: CBS

McCorkle, Susannah

QUALITY OF MERCER, THE.
Album: released on Black Lion, Apr'79 by Black Lion Records. Dist: Jazz Music, Chris Wellard, Taylor, H.R., Counterpoint, Cadillac

THERE WILL NEVER BE ANOTHER YOU The music of Harry Warren.
Album: released on World Records, Dec'76

McCormack, John

20 GOLDEN PIECES OF.
Album: released on Bulldog Records, Jul'82

COUNT JOHN MCCORMACK.
Boxed set: released on Pearl, Apr'79 by Pavillion (USA). Dist: Taylors, Swift

GOLDEN AGE OF..., THE
Album: released on Golden Age, Apr'85 by Music For Pleasure Records. Dist: EMI

Cassette: released on Golden Age, Apr'85 by Music For Pleasure Records. Dist: EMI

GOLDEN VOICE OF JOHN MCCOR-MACK (VOLUME 1).
Album: released on Dolphin, Aug'78

IRISH MINSTREL.
Album: released on Red Seal, Jun'84 by RCA Records. Dist: RCA

Cassette: released on Red Seal, Jun'84 by RCA Records. Dist: RCA

JOHN MCCORMACK.
Special: released on World Records, '81 Dist: Polygram

Special: released on World Records, '81 Dist: Polygram

JOHN MCCORMACK IN IRISH SONG.
Album: released on Rhapsody, '74 by President Records. Dist: Taylors, Swift, Jazz Music, Wellard, Chris

JOHN MCCORMACK SINGS BALLADS.
Album: released on Rhapsody, '74 by President Records. Dist: Taylors, Swift, Jazz Music, Wellard, Chris

LIGHT PATTERNS.
Album: released on Sheet, Apr'82 Dist: Rough Trade

...SINGS OF OLD SCOTLAND.
Album: released on World, Jan'80 Dist: Jetstar

SONGS OF JOHN MCCORMACK.
Album: released on Decca, '62 by Decca Records. Dist: Polygram

VOLUME ONE.
Album: released on Bulldog, May'85 by Bulldog Records. Dist: President Distribution, Spartan, Swift, Taylor, H.R.

VOLUME TWO.
Album: released on Bulldog, May'85 by Bulldog Records. Dist: President Distribution, Spartan, Swift, Taylor, H.R.

McCoury, Del

BLUEGRASS BAND.
Album: released on Arhoolie, May'81 by Arhoolie Records. Dist: Projection, Topic, Jazz Music, Swift, Roots

McCowan, Alex

DON QUIXOTE.
Cassette: released on Kiddy Kassettes, Aug'77

McCoy

OH WELL.
Album: released on Legacy, Nov'83 Dist: PRT

McCoy, George and Ethel

AT HOME WITH THE BLUES.
Album: released on Swingmaster, May'86 Dist: Jazz Music Distribution

McCoy, John

OH WELL / BECAUSE YOU LIED.
Single (7"): released on Legacy, Nov'83 Dist: PRT

SOUND OF THUNDER, THE.
Single (7"): released on Legacy, Oct'84 Dist: PRT

THINK HARD.
Album: released on Mausoleum, Apr'85 by Mausoleum Records. Dist: Pinnacle

Cassette: released on Mausoleum, Apr'85 by Mausoleum Records. Dist: Pinnacle

McCoy, Robert

BLUES AND BOOGIE WOOGIE CLASSICS.
Album: released on Oldie Blues, Sep'79 Dist: Cadillac, Projection Distribution, Celtic Music Distribution, JSU Distribution, Swift Distribution

McCoys

HANG ON SLOOPY.
Page 656

McCoy, Van

HUSTLE, THE / THE SHUFFLE.
Single (7"): released on Old Gold, Jul'82 by Old Gold Records. Dist: Lightning, Jazz Music, Spartan, Counterpoint

HUSTLE TO THE BEST OF VAN MCCOY.
Album: released on H & L, Feb'77 by H&L Records (USA).

McCracklin, Jimmy

BLAST 'EM DEAD.
Double Album: released on Ace, Jun'87 by Ace Records. Dist: Pinnacle, Swift, Hotshot, Cadillac

BLASTING THE BLUES.
Album: released on JSP, Jun'83 by JSP Records. Dist: Swift, Projection

BLUES AND SOUL.
Tracks: / Walk,The / Looking for a woman / That's the way(it goes) / Every night every day / I did wrong / had to get with it / Just got to know / Think / Get back / R M Blues / I don't care / I'll see it through / Pretty little sweet thing / What's going on / Stinger / You ain't nothing but a devil.
Album: released on Stateside, Oct'86 Dist: EMI

Cassette: released on Stateside, Oct'86 Dist: EMI

I'M GONNA HAVE MY FUN (McCracklin, Jimmy & His blues blasters).
Album: released on Route 66 (Sweden), May'86 by M. R&B Records. Dist: Swift Distribution, Cadillac, Jazz Music Distribution

ROCKIN' MAN.
Album: released on Route 66, Jun'80

YOU DECEIVED ME.
Album: released on Crown Prince (Sweden), May'86

McCrae, George

BEST OF GEORGE MCCRAE, THE.
Album: released on Jay Boy, Nov'76 by President Records.

GEORGE MCCRAE.
Album: released on TK, Jun'78 Dist: CBS Distribution

LET'S DANCE.
Tracks: / Let's Dance / Never forget your eyes.
Single (7"): released on President, Jan'86 by President Records. Dist: Taylors, Spartan

Single (12"): released on President, Jan'86 by President Records. Dist: Taylors, Spartan

LISTEN TO YOUR HEART.
Single (7"): released on President, Jun'84 by President Records. Dist: Taylors, Spartan

Single (12"): released on President, Jun'84 by President Records. Dist: Taylors, Spartan

LOVE'S BEEN GOOD TO ME.
Tracks: / Love's been good to me / Out of knowhere(into my life).
Single (7"): released on President, Sep'86 by President Records. Dist: Taylors, Spartan

ONE STEP CLOSER (TO LOVE) / IF IT WASN'T FOR YOU.
Single (7"): released on President, Feb'84 by President Records. Dist: Taylors, Spartan

Single (12"): released on President, Feb'84 by President Records. Dist: Taylors, Spartan

ONE STEP CLOSER TO LOVE.
Cassette: released on President, Mar'84 by President Records. Dist: Taylors, Spartan

OWN THE NIGHT.
Single (7"): released on President, Sep'84 by President Records. Dist: Taylors, Spartan

Single (12"): released on President, Sep'84 by President Records. Dist: Taylors, Spartan

ROCK YOUR BABY.
Tracks: / Rock your baby / Ooh baby.
Single (7"): released on Portrait, Feb'87 by CBS Records. Dist: CBS

Single (12"): released on Portrait, Feb'87 by CBS Records. Dist: CBS

Album: released on Hallmark, Apr'81 by Pickwick Records. Dist: Pickwick Distribution, PRT, Taylors

Cassette: released on Hallmark, Apr'81 by Pickwick Records. Dist: Pickwick Distribution, PRT, Taylors

TOGETHER (McCrae, George & Gwen).
Album: released on President, Dec'85 by

McCrae, Gwen

DO YOU KNOW WHAT I MEAN.
Single (7"): released on Sierra, Nov'84 by Sierra Records. Dist: WEA

Single (12"): released on Sierra, Nov'84 by Sierra Records. Dist: WEA Deleted '87.

McCroby, Ron

OTHER WHISTLER, THE.
Album: released on Concord Jazz(USA), Nov'84 by Concord Jazz Records (USA). Dist: IMS, Polygram

McCue, Bill

DREAMS OF CALEDONIA.
Album: released on MK, Jun'84
Cat. no: MK 1
Cassette: released on MK, Jun'84

LEGENDS OF SCOTLAND - BONNIE PRINCE CHARLIE.
Cassette: released on MK, Jun'84

LEGENDS OF SCOTLAND: MARY QUEEN OF SCOTS.
Cassette: released on MK, Jun'84

LEGENDS OF SCOTLAND: ROBERT BURNS.
Cassette: released on MK, Jun'84

LEGENDS OF SCOTLAND: ROBERT THE BRUCE.
Cassette: released on MK, Jun'84

TAM O'SHANTER.
Album: released on Lismor, Dec'79 by Lismor Records. Dist: Lismor, Roots, Celtic Music

McCulloch, Alan Band

SWEET DREAMS (EP).
Single (7"): released on Linden Sounds, Mar'84 by Linden Sounds Records. Dist: Pinnacle

McCulloch, Cecil

PICK 'EM UP (McCulloch, Cecil & Border Boys).
Single (7"): released on Detour, Feb'83

McCulloch, Gordeanna

GORDEANNA MCCULLOCH.
Album: released on Topic, '81 by Topic Records. Dist: JSU Distribution, Projection Distribution, Jazz Music Distribution

McCulloch, Ian

SEPTEMBER SONG.
Single (7"): released on Korova, Nov'84 Dist: WEA

Single (12"): released on Korova, Nov'84 Dist: WEA

McCullough, Andy

MUSIC OF THE ORIENT EXPRESS.
Album: released on Audiotrax, Aug'84 by Audiotrax. Dist: PRT

Cassette: released on Audiotrax, Aug'84 by Audiotrax. Dist: PRT

McCullough, Henry

HELL OF A RECORD.
Album: released on Teldec (West Germany), Jan'85

McCutchan, Philip

CAMERON'S CONVOY.
Cassette: released on Soundings, Mar'85 Dist: Soundings

McCutcheon, John

WINTER SOLSTICE.
Compact disc: released on Rounder (USA), Dec'86 Dist: Mike's Country Music Room Distribution, Jazz Music Distribution, Swift Distribution, Roots Records Distribution, Projection Distribution, Topic Distribution

Album: released on Rounder (USA), Jan'85 Dist: Mike's Country Music Room Distribution, Jazz Music Distribution, Swift Distribution, Roots Records Distribution, Projection Distribution, Topic Distribution

McCuy, Clyde

SUGAR BLUES (McCuy, Clyde & His Orchestra).
Notes: Mono. 1951.
Album: released on Circle(USA), Jan'87 by Jazzology Records (USA). Dist: Jazz Music, Swift, Chris Wellard

---

McDaniels, Gene

ANOTHER TEAR FALLS.
Tracks: / Hundred pounds of clay / Spanish Harlem / Walk with a winner / Point of no return, The / Chip chip / Hang on (just a little bit longer) / Tear, A / Tower of strength / Another tear falls / Raindrops / Forgotten man, (There goes) / It's a lonely town / Spanish lace / I don't want to cry / Cry,baby,cry / You can have her.
Notes: Licensed from: EMI Records Ltd This compilation : P 1986 Charly Records Ltd C 1986 Charly Records Ltd
Album: released on Charly, Aug'86 by Charly Records. Dist: Charly, Cadillac

McDermott, Josie

DARBY'S FAREWELL Trad songs played on flute & whistle, & songs from Sligo.
Album: released on Topic, '81 by Topic Records. Dist: JSU Distribution, Projection Distribution, Jazz Music Distribution

McDermott, Kevin

SUFFOCATION BLUES.
Album: released on No Strings, May'86 Dist: Rough Trade, Cartel

McDevitt, Chas

FREIGHT TRAIN (McDevitt, Chas & Nancy Whisky).
Single (7"): released on Old Gold, Jul'82 by Old Gold Records. Dist: Lightning, Jazz Music, Spartan, Counterpoint

TAKES YA BACK DON'T IT.
Album: released on Joy, Jun'76 by President Records. Dist: Jazz Music, Swift, President Distribution

McDonald, Alastair

ALASTAIR MCDONALD.
Album: released on Polydor, Oct'76 by Polydor Records. Dist: Polygram, Polydor

ALASTAIR MCDONALD SINGS ROBERT BURNS.
Album: released on Nevis, May'77 Dist: H.R. Taylor

BONNIE PRINCE CHARLIE.
Cassette: released on Nevis, Jan'80 Dist: H.R. Taylor

COLOMBE SHALOM / WHITE WINGS.
Single (7"): released on Corban, Oct'83 Dist: MK

MUSIC OF THE HIGHLANDS.
Tracks: / Gypsy laddie,The / Early morning worker,The / Jamie Raeburn / Melville Castle / Music of the highlands / Bonnie ship the diamond / Get up, get out / Exile song,The / Kirstean / Perfervidum / Rory mors lament.
Album: released on Emerald, Nov'84 by Emerald Records. Dist: Ross, PRT, Solomon & Peres Distribution

Cassette: released on Emerald, Nov'84 by Emerald Records. Dist: Ross, PRT, Solomon & Peres Distribution

SCOTLAND FIRST.
Cassette: released on Nevis, May'77 Dist: H.R. Taylor

SCOTLAND IN SONG.
Album: released on Nevis, May'81 Dist: H.R. Taylor

SCOTTISH BATTLE BALLADS.
Album: released on Nevis, Jan'80 Dist: H.R. Taylor

Cassette: released on Nevis, Jan'80 Dist: H.R. Taylor

SINGS ROBERT BURNS.
Cassette: released on Nevis, May'77 Dist: H.R. Taylor

WE'VE BEEN INVITED / BRUCE'S ADDRESS.
Single (7"): released on McCoochley Street, Apr'82 Dist: MK

McDonald, Alistair

BEST OF ALISTAIR MCDONALD, THE.
Album: released on Emerald, Aug'87 by Emerald Records. Dist: Ross, PRT, Solomon & Peres Distribution

Cassette: released on Emerald, Aug'87 by Emerald Records. Dist: Ross, PRT, Solomon & Peres Distribution

McDonald, Bobby

BOBBY MCDONALD/SAMMY RIMINGTON/LIZZIE MILES (McDonald, Bobby/Sammy Rimington/Lizzie Miles).
Cassette: released on Nola, Mar'87 Dist: JSU, Jazz Music, Cadillac, Chris Wellard

McDonald, Carl

STAR / SKANK IT RUB A DUB STYLE.
Single (12"): released on Makdon, Apr'82 by Makdon Records. Dist: Jetstar

McDonald, Country Joe

ANIMAL TRACKS.
Album: released on Animus, Aug'83 Dist: Rough Trade, Cartel

BEST OF COUNTRY JOE MCDONALD.
Album: released on Golden Hour, Apr'77 by PRT Records. Dist: PRT

BEST OF COUNTRY JOE MCDONALD.
Cassette: released on PRT, Apr'77 by PRT Records. Dist: PRT

BLOOD ON THE ICE.
Single (7"): released on Animus, Sep'83 Dist: Rough Trade, Cartel

COLLECTORS ITEMS.
Album: released on Rag Baby, Jul'81 Dist: Pinnacle, Red Lightnin' Distribution

ELECTRIC MUSIC.
Album: released on Vanguard, '74 by PRT Records. Dist: PRT

I FEEL LIKE I'M.
Album: released on Vanguard, '74 by PRT Records. Dist: PRT

ON MY OWN.
Album: released on Rag Baby, Sep'81 Dist: Pinnacle, Red Lightnin' Distribution

McDonald, Donny

DONNY MCDONALD WITH LIZZIE MILES, ROBICHAUX & RIMINGTON.
Album: released on Nola, Apr'79 Dist: JSU, Jazz Music, Cadillac, Chris Wellard

McDonald, Fergie

FERGIE MCDONALD & HIS HIGHLAND DANCE BAND.
Album: released on Grampian, '72 by Grampian Records. Dist: Grampian, Clyde Factors Distributors, Ross

SWING YOUR PARTNERS.
Album: released on Lismor, Nov'76 by Lismor Records. Dist: Lismor, Roots Celtic Music

THERE'S IRISH ON THE ISLANDS.
Album: released on Lismor, '83 Dist: Projection, Lismor, Cadillac Music, H.R. Taylor, Outlet

Cassette: released on Lismor, '83 Dist: Projection, Lismor, Cadillac Music, H.R. Taylor, Outlet

Album: released on RCA, Dec'81 by RCA Records. Dist: RCA, Roots, Swift, Wellard, Chris, I & B, Solomon & Peres Distribution

Cassette: released on RCA, Dec'81 by RCA Records. Dist: RCA, Roots, Swift, Wellard, Chris, I & B, Solomon & Peres Distribution

McDonald & Giles

MCDONALD & GILES.
Album: released on Polydor, Mar'77 by Polydor Records. Dist: Polygram, Polydor

McDonald, Joe

ARE YOU DIRTY / THE HIGHLAND TINKER (McDonald, Joe & The Highland Exposure Show).
Single (7"): released on Charly, Oct'83 by Charly Records. Dist: Charly, Cadillac

McDonald, Kathleen

SILVER VOICE OF HIGHLANDS.
Album: released on Emerald, '70 by Emerald Records. Dist: Ross, PRT, Solomon & Peres Distribution

McDonald, Michael

BEST OF MICHAEL MCDONALD, THE.
Album: released on WEA, Sep'86 by WEA Records. Dist: WEA

Cassette: released on WEA, Sep'86 by WEA Records. Dist: WEA

IF THAT'S WHAT IT TAKES.
Album: released on Warner Brothers, Aug'82 by Warner Bros Records Dist: WEA

Cassette: released on Warner Brothers, Aug'82 by Warner Bros Records. Dist: WEA

Compact disc: released on Warner Brothers, Aug'82 by Warner Bros Records. Dist: WEA

I GOTTA TRY, BELIEVE IN IT.
Single (7"): released on Warner Brothers, Jan'83 by Warner Bros Records. Dist: WEA
Cat. no: **W 9862**

I KEEP FORGETTIN'.
Tracks: / I keep forgetting / Losin' end.
Single (7"): released on Warner Bros., Jun'86 by Warner Bros Records. Dist: WEA

NO LOOKIN' BACK.
Tracks: / I gotta try.
Single (7"): released on Warner Bros., Oct'86 by Warner Bros Records. Dist: WEA

Single (12"): released on Warner Bros., Oct'86 by Warner Bros Records. Dist: WEA

Tracks: / No looking back / By heart / Bad times / Angel (I'll be your) / Any foolish thing / Our love / On your every word (I hang) / Lost in the parade / Don't let me down.
Compact disc: released on Warner Brothers, Feb'87 by Warner Bros Records. Dist: WEA

Album: released on Warner Brothers, Aug'85 by Warner Bros Records. Dist: WEA

Cassette: released on Warner Brothers, Aug'85 by Warner Bros Records. Dist: WEA

OUR LOVE Theme to No Mercy.
Tracks: / Our love / Don't let me down / Bad times.
Single (7"): released on Warner Bros., Mar'87 by Warner Bros Records. Dist: WEA

Single (12"): released on Warner Bros., Mar'87 by Warner Bros Records. Dist: WEA

SWEET FREEDOM.
Tracks: / Sweet freedom / I'll be your angel / Yah mo b there / I gotta try / I keep forgettin' / Our love / On my own / No lookin back / Any foolish thing / That's why / What a fool believes / I can let go now.
Album: released on Warner Bros., Nov'86 by Warner Bros Records. Dist: WEA

Cassette: released on Warner Bros., Nov'86 by Warner Bros Records. Dist: WEA

Compact disc: released on Warner Bros., Nov'86 by Warner Bros Records. Dist: WEA

Single (7"): released on MCA, Aug'86 by MCA Records. Dist: Polygram, MCA

YAH MO BE THERE (see Ingram,James/Michael McDonald) (McDonald, Michael/ James Ingram).

McDonald, Pete

END OF THE LINE.
Album: released on Creole, Sep'84 by Creole Records. Dist: Rhino, PRT

LADY OF MINE.
Single (7"): released on Creole, Aug'83 by Creole Records. Dist: Rhino, PRT

LOVE UNDECIDED.
Single (7"): released on Creole, Mar'85 by Creole Records. Dist: Rhino, PRT

McDonald, Ronald

PLAY LISTEN AND LEARN WITH ... VARIOUS ARTISTS.
Album: released on Spot, May'84 by Pickwick Records. Dist: H.R. Taylor, Lugtons

Cassette: released on Spot, May'84 by Pickwick Records. Dist: H.R. Taylor, Lugtons

McDonald,Skeets

DON'T LET THE STARS GET IN YOUR EYES.
Tracks: / Don't let the stars get in your eyes / Looking at the moon and wishing on star / Iam music / I've got to win your love again / I need your love / But i do / Be my life's companion / Heartbreaking one / All American boy,The / What a lonesome life it's been / I'll make believe / I can't hold a memory in my arms / Bless your little ol'heart(You're mine) / Big family trouble / Love that hurts me so,The / Today I'm movin' out.
Album: released on Bear Family, May'86 by Bear Family Records. Dist: Rollercoaster Distribution, Swift

ROCKIN' ROLLIN'.
Tracks: / You oughta see grandma rock / Heart breaking mama / I love you mama mia / Finger tips / Keep her off your mind / What am i doing here / I love you ,I love you / You gotta be my baby / Look who's crying now / You better not go / Let's spend some time with me / Let me know / Smoke comes out of my chimney(just the same) / I can't stand it any longer / Echo of your footsteps,The.
Notes: Original Capitol Recordings.
Album: released on Bear Family, May'86 by Bear Family Records. Dist: Rollercoaster Distribution, Swift

McDonnell-Morton

AN IRISH JUBILEE (TRADITIONAL IRISH SONGS).
Album: released on Topic, '81 Dist: Roots Distribution

McDowell, Fred

FRED MCDOWELL AND HIS BLUES BOYS.
Album: released on Arhoolie, May'81 by Arhoolie Records. Dist: Projection, Topic, Jazz Music, Swift, Roots

KEEP YOUR LAMP TRIMMED.
Album: released on Arhoolie, May'81 by Arhoolie Records. Dist: Projection, Topic, Jazz Music, Swift, Roots

MISS DELTA BLUES.
Album: released on Arhoolie, May'81 by Arhoolie Records. Dist: Projection, Topic, Jazz Music, Swift, Roots

MISS DELTA BLUES VOL 2.
Album: released on Arhoolie, May'81 by Arhoolie Records. Dist: Projection, Topic, Jazz Music, Swift, Roots

MISSISSIPPI DELTA BLUES (McDowell, Fred & Billie Holiday).
Album: released on Black Lion, Jul'87 by Black Lion Records. Dist: Jazz Music, Chris Wellard, Taylor, H.R., Counterpoint, Cadillac

STANDING AT THE BURYING GROUND (see also Jo Ann Kelly) (McDowell, Fred & Jo Ann Kelly).
Album: released on Red Lightning, Aug'84

McDowell,Fred Missisipi

DOSE OF DOUBLE DYNAMITE, A.
Album: released on Red Lightnin', Jan'86 by Red Lightnin' Records. Dist: Roots, Swift, Jazz Music, JSU, Pinnacle, Cartel, Wynd-Up Distribution

McDowell, Ronnie

ALL TIED UP IN LOVE.
Album: released on MCA, Mar'87 by MCA Records. Dist: Polygram, MCA

Cassette: released on MCA, Mar'87 by MCA Records. Dist: Polygram, MCA

McDuff,Jack

GEORGE BENSON & JACK MCDUFF Hsee Benson, George) (McDuff, Jack & George Benson).

HONEYDRIPPER,THE.
Album:

McElherron, Paddy

PADDY MCELHERRON.
Tracks: / My Donegal shore / Boys from co. Armagh / Cottage in old Donegal / Newry town / Far from Erin's shore / Going back to Castleblaney / Green glens of Antrim / Village in Co. Tyrone / Lovely Derry / Mountains of Mourne / Gallant John Joe / My lovely irish rose / Co. Cavan.
Cassette: released on Homespun(Ireland), Feb'87 by Outlet Records. Dist: Outlet

VILLAGE OF AVOCA (McElherron, Paddy & The Wildcountry Band).
Single (7"): released on Homespun(Ireland), Dec'84 by Outlet Records. Dist: Outlet

McEntire, Reba

AT THE COUNTRY STORE.
Album: released on Country Store, Apr'87 by Starblend Records. Dist: PRT, Prism Leisure Corporation Records

Cassette: released on Country Store, Apr'87 by Starblend Records. Dist: PRT, Prism Leisure Corporation Records

BEHIND THE SCENE.
Album: released on Mercury (USA), Dec'83 by Import Records. Dist: IMS Distribution, Polygram Distribution

GREATEST HITS:REBA MCENTIRE.
Tracks: / Just a little love / He broke your memory last night / How blue / Somebody should leave / Have I got a deal for you / Only in my mind / Whoever's in New England / Little rock / Waht am I gonna do about you / One promise too late.
Album: released on MCA, May'87 by MCA Records. Dist: Polygram, MCA

Cassette: released on MCA, May'87 by MCA Records. Dist: Polygram, MCA

Compact disc: released on MCA, May'87 by MCA Records. Dist: Polygram. MCA

HAVE I GOT A DEAL FOR YOU.
Tracks: / I'm in love all over / She's single again / Great divide,The / Have I got a deal for you / Red roses(wont work now) / Only on my mind / She's the one loving you now / Whose heartache os this anyway / I don't need nothin'you ain't got / Don't forget your way home.
Album: released on MCA Import, Mar'86 by MCA Records. Dist: Polygram, IMS

JUST A LITTLE LOVE.
Tracks: / Just a little love / Poison sugar / I'm getting over you / You always there for me / Every second someone breaks a heart / Tell me what's so good about goodbye / He broke your memory last night / If only / Congratulations / Silver eagle.
Album: released on MCA Import, Mar'86 by MCA Records. Dist: Polygram, IMS

MY KIND OF COUNTRY.
Tracks: / How blue / That's what he said / I want to hear it from you / It's not over(if I'm not over you) / Somebody should leave / Everything but my heart / Don't you believe him / Before I met you / He's only everything / You've got me (Right where you want me).
Album: released on MCA Import, Mar'86 by MCA Records. Dist: Polygram, IMS

REBA NELL MCENTIRE.
Tracks: / I've never stopped dreaming of you / Hold on / I know I'll have a better day tomorrow / Hold on / Don't say goodnight,say good morning / Muddy Mississippi / It's another silent night / Empty arms / Love is never easy / Waitin' for the sun to shine/Good friends.
Notes: A special collection of previously unreleased tracks.Reba McEntire is one of the brightest stars on today's American country scene.She won the 1984 and 1985 "Country Music Awards"as female vocalist of the year.
Album: released on Mercury (USA), Sep'86 by Import Records. Dist: IMS Distribution, Polygram Distribution

Cassette: released on Mercury (USA), Sep'86 by Import Records. Dist: IMS Distribution, Polygram Distribution

UNLIMITED.
Album: released on Mercury (USA), Mar'83 by Import Records. Dist: IMS Distribution, Polygram Distribution

WHAT AM I GOING TO DO ABOUT YOU.
Tracks: / What am I going to do about you / One promise too late.
Single (7"): released on MCA, Mar'87 by MCA Records. Dist: Polygram, MCA

WHAT AM I GONNA DO ABOUT YOU.
Tracks: / Why not tonight / What am I gonna do about you / Lookin' for a new love story / Take me back / My mind is on you / Let the music lift you up / I heard her cryin' / No such thing / One promise too late / Till it snows in Mexico.
Album: released on MCA, Nov'86 by MCA Records. Dist: Polygram, MCA

Cassette: released on MCA, Nov'86 by MCA Records. Dist: Polygram. MCA

WHOEVER'S IN NEW ENGLAND.
Tracks: / Can't stop now / You can take the wings off me / Whoever's in New England / I'll believe it when I feel it / I've seen better days / Little Rock / If you only knew / One thin dime / Don't touch me there / To make the same mistake again.
Compact disc: released on MCA, Feb'87 by MCA Records. Dist: Polygram, MCA

Album: released on MCA Import, Mar'86 by MCA Records. Dist: Polygram, IMS

McEvoy, Gloria

GOLDEN DUETS (McEvoy, Gloria & Johnny).
Album: released on Harp(Ireland), May'80 by Pickwick Records. Dist: Taylors

McEvoy, John

BEST OF JOHN MCEVOY.
Album: released on Heritage, Jun'76 by Heritage Records. Dist: Chart

McEvoy, Johnny

CHRISTMAS DREAMS.
Album: released on Hawk, Dec'76 by Dolphin Records. Dist: I & B, Celtic Music, Solomon & Peres Distribution

I'LL SPEND A TIME WITH YOU.
Album: released on Hawk, Aug'78 by Dolphin Records. Dist: I & B, Celtic Music, Solomon & Peres Distribution

JOHNNY MCEVOY.
Album: released on Halcyon, '74 by Halcyon Records. Dist: Jazz Music

JOHNNY MCEVOY GOES COUNTRY.
Album: released on Harp(Ireland), Jul'80 by Pickwick Records. Dist: Taylors

LEAVES IN THE WIND.
Album: released on Hawk, Jun'77 by Dolphin Records. Dist: I & B, Celtic Music, Solomon & Peres Distribution

LONG BEFORE YOUR TIME.
Album: released on Hawk, Sep'76 by Dolphin Records. Dist: I & B, Celtic Music, Solomon & Peres Distribution

MY FAVOURITE IRISH SONGS.
Album: released on Harp(Ireland), Jul'81 by Pickwick Records. Dist: Taylors

SINCE MAGGIE WENT AWAY.
Album: released on MCA, Sep'85 by MCA Records. Dist: Polygram, MCA

Cassette: released on MCA, Sep'85 by MCA

Records. Dist: Polygram, MCA

SINGS COUNTRY.
Album: released on Hawk, '74 by Dolphin Records. Dist: I & B, Celtic Music, Solomon & Peres Distribution

SONGS OF IRELAND.
Tracks: / Home boys home / Red is the rose / Black velvet band / Maggie / Good ship Kangaroo / Wild mountain thyme / I wish I had someone to love me / Town of ballybay / Molly,My Irish Molly / Rare old times,The / Streets of New York,The / Traveling people / Shores of America / Bunch of thyme / Irish soldier laddie / Song for Ireland.
Notes: Latest album by Ireland's premier vocalist,Johnny McEvoy,who has enjoyed phenom-enal succes in his home country for many years with over a million album sales to his credit.He has written songs for the Furey Brothers and Foster and Allen whilst his own records continually top the Irish charts.This new album features all his most requested songs from his large UK following.
Album: released on MCA, Jul'86 by MCA Records. Dist: Polygram, MCA

Cassette: released on MCA, Jul'86 by MCA Records. Dist: Polygram, MCA

SOUNDS LIKE MCEVOY.
Album: released on Hawk, '74 by Dolphin Records. Dist: I & B, Celtic Music, Solomon & Peres Distribution

WHERE MY EILEEN IS WAITING.
Album: released on Hawk, Aug'75 by Dolphin Records. Dist: I & B, Celtic Music, Solomon & Peres Distribution

McEwan, Billy

ORGAN POPS.
Cassette: released on Country House, Nov'79 by BGS Productions Ltd. Dist: Taylor, H.R., Record Merchandisers Distribution, Pinnacle, Sounds of Scotland Records

Album: released on BGS, Nov'79 by BGS Productions Ltd. Dist: BGS Distribution, Wynd-Up Distribution, Ross Records, Duncan, Gordon Distribution, Taylor, H.R., Record Merchandisers Distribution

McEwan, William

OLD RUGGED CROSS.
Album: released on Mawson & Wareham, Sep'83 by Mawson & Wareham Records. Dist: Roots, Celtic Music, Spartan, Jazz Music, Projection

McFadden & Whitehead

AIN'T NO STOPPIN'(AIN'T NO WAY).
Single (7"): released on Buddah, May'84 Dist: Swift, Jazz Music, PRT

Single (12"): released on Buddah, May'84 Dist: Swift, Jazz Music, PRT

AIN'T NO STOPPING US NOW.
Tracks: / Ain't no stopping us now / I've got love.
Single (7"): released on Streetwave, Sep'85 by Streetwave Records. Dist: PRT Distribution

Single (7"): released on Wynd-up, May'82 Dist: Wynd-Up Distribution

Single (7"): released on Old Gold, Jul'84 by Old Gold Records. Dist: Lightning, Jazz Music, Spartan, Counterpoint

I HEARD IT IN A LOVE SONG.
Album: released on Philadelphia International, Dec'80 by CBS Records. Dist: CBS

Cassette: released on Philadelphia International, Dec'80 by CBS Records. Dist: CBS

Single (7"): released on CBS, Sep'80 by CBS Records. Dist: CBS

MCFADDEN & WHITWHEAD.
Album: released on Philadelphia International, Jun'79 by CBS Records. Dist: CBS

McFarland, Billy

DOWN THE TRAIL OF ACHING HEARTS.
Album: released on Outlet, Jul'76 by Outlet Records. Dist: Outlet Distribution

JENIFER JOHNSON.
Single (7"): released on Homespun(Ireland), Feb'81 by Outlet Records. Dist: Outlet

RATHLIN ISLAND.
Single (7"): released on Homespun(Ireland), Apr'82 by Outlet Records. Dist: Outlet

WHEN THE HARVEST MOON IS SHINING.
Single (7"): released on Homespun(Ireland), Mar'84 by Outlet Records. Dist: Outlet

Mcfarland, Sandra

CRAZY IN LOVE.
Single (12"): released on Body Music, Jan'83 by Body Music Records. Dist: Jetstar

NEVER LOVE AGAIN.
Single (12"): released on Paradise, Mar'82 Dist: Jetstar, JSU, WEA

Mcfarland, Tom

TRAVELLIN' WITH THE BLUES.
Album: released on Arhoolie, May'81 by Arhoolie Records. Dist: Projection, Topic, Jazz Music, Swift, Roots

McFerrin, Bobby

BOBBY MCFERRIN.
Album: released on Elektra(Musician), Jun'82 by WEA Records. Dist: WEA

SPONTANEOUS INVENTIONS.
Tracks: / Scrapple from the apple / Honeysuckle rose / Bwee-Dop / Cara mia / Fascinating Rhythm / Itst bitsy spider / Thinkin' about your body / Drive / Opportunity / I got the feelin' / Walkin' / Blackbird / Manna Iguana.
Notes: Filmed live at the Aquarius Theatre,Holywood in february of this year.Features 5 tracks from the current album of the same name plus other classics.Released to coincide with his European tour.Vocally and visually his performances defy description-here are two recent US attempts:"His voice can sound like a walking bass or a growling trumpet,a bebop saxophone,an opera singer,a Beatle,a female rhythm and blues singer,a lead guitar,an air by Bach,or any of the above tandem.Meanwhile he mimes ,taps his feet,clicks his tongue and beats his chest"(Inter- national Tribune). "Calling Bobby McFerrin a singer is like calling The Grand Canyon a hole"(Cash- Box).

SPONTANEOUS INVENTIONS.
Tracks: / Thinkin' about your body / Turtle shoes / From me to you / There ya go / Cara mia / Another night in Tunisia / Opportunity / Walkin' / I hear music / Beverley Hills blues / Manana Iguana.
Album: released on Blue Note, Oct'86 by EMI Records. Dist: EMI

Compect disc: released on Blue Note, Oct'86 by EMI Records. Dist: EMI

Video-cassette (VHS): released on PMI, Nov'86 by PMI Records. Dist: EMI

THINKIN' ABOUT YOUR BODY For Debs.
Tracks: / Thinkin about your body (for Debs) / From me to you.
Single (7"): released on EMI, Dec'86 by EMI Records. Dist: EMI

VOICE, THE.
Album: released on Elektra(Musician), Aug'84 by WEA Records. Dist: WEA

Mcfly, Marty

JOHNNY B GOODE (Mcfly, Marty & the Starlighters).

McGann, Andy

ANDY MCGANN & PADDY REYNOLDS FIDDLE (McGann, Andy & Paddy Reynolds).
Album: released on Shanachie, Apr'77 Dist: Sterns/Triple Earth Distribution, Roots

IT'S A HARD ROAD TO TRAVEL.
Album: released on Shanachie, Sep'79 Dist: Sterns/Triple Earth Distribution, Roots

McGann brothers

SHAME ABOUT THE BOY.
Single (7"): released on Chrysalis, Sep'83 by Chrysalis Records. Dist: CBS

McGarity,Lou

SOME LIKE IT HOT & SOME LIKE IT BLUE (McGarity,Lou Big 5 and 7).
Cassette: released on Holmia Cassettes, Jun'86 Dist: Jazz Music, Wellard, Chris

McGarrigle, Kate & Anna

DANCER WITH BRUISED KNEES.
Album: released on Warner Brothers, Jan'77 by Warner Bros Records. Dist: WEA

FRENCH RECORD.
Tracks: / Entre la jeunesse et la sagesse / Complainte pour Ste. Catherine / Mais quant tu Danses / Chaminant a la ville / Excursion a Venise / En filant ma quenoille / La belle s'est etourdie / Naufragee du tendre / Avant la guerre / A boire / Prends ton monteau / Boire, A.
Notes: Originally produced for the french-speaking Quebec market. Includes the french tracks from the McGarrigles First two albums together with french versions of songs originally recorded in english.

Album: released on Hannibal, Jun'86 by Hannibal Records. Dist: Charly, Harmonia Mundi, Projection, Celtic Music, Roots

LOVE OVER AND OVER.
Album: released on Polydor, Apr'82 by Polydor Records. Dist: Polygram, Polydor

Cassette: released on Polydor, Apr'82 by Polydor Records. Dist: Polygram, Polydor

McGear, Mike

ALL THE WHALES IN THE OCEAN.
Single (7"): released on Carrere, May'80 by Carrere Records. Dist: PRT, Spartan

McGear & the Monarchists

NO LAR DI DAR(IS LADY DI).
Single (7"): released on Conn, Jul'81 by Conn Records. Dist: Spartan

McGee, Brownie

BROWNIE MCGEE, SONNY TERRY WITH EARL HOOKER (McGee, Brownie & Sonny Terry With Earl Hooker).
Album: released on See For Miles, Apr'87 by See For Miles Records. Dist: Pinnacle

I COULDN'T BELIEVE MY EYES (McGee, Brownie & Sonny Terry With Earl Hooker).

Tracks: / Black cat bone / Brownie's new blues / Poor man blues / Tell me why / My baby's so fine / You just usin' me for a convenience / Hole in the wall / Long way from home / Don't wait for me / I'm in love with you baby / Parcel post blues / When I was drinking / I couldn't believe my eyes / Life is a gamble / Don't mistreat me / Rock Island line.
Notes: All tracks produced by Ed Mitchell Original sound recordings made by ABC Blues-way/MCA Records Inc This compilation published 1987. See For Miles Records Ltd. Copyright 1987 See For Miles Miles Ltd A Colin Miles Compilation
Album: released on See For Miles, May'87 by See For Miles Records. Dist: Pinnacle

McGee, Francine

DELIRIUM.
Single (12"): released on Bluebird, Nov'83 by Bluebird Records. Dist: EMI, Jetstar

McGee, Holard

COOKIN' TIME.
Album: released on Hep, Apr'81 by H.R. Taylor Records. Dist: Jazz Music, Cadillac Music, JSU, Taylors, Wellard, Chris, Zodiac, Swift, Fast Forward

McGee, Jay W

WHEN WE PARTY(UPTOWN DOWN-TOWN).
Single (7"): released on Ensign, Sep'82 by Ensign Records. Dist: CBS Distribution

Single (12"): released on Ensign, Sep'82 by Ensign Records. Dist: CBS Distribution

McGee, Sam

COUNTRY GUITAR.
Album: released on Arhoolie, May'81 by Arhoolie Records. Dist: Projection, Topic, Jazz Music, Swift, Roots

McGettigan, John

JOHN MCGETTIGAN.
Album: released on Topic, '81 Dist: Roots Distribution

McGhee,Brownie

BEST OF BROWNIE MCGHEE.
Album: released on Storyville, May'86 by Storyville Records. Dist: Jazz Music Distribution, Swift Distribution, Chris Wellard Distribution, Counterpoint Distribution

BROWNIE BLUES.
Album: released on Prestige, Jun'84 by Prestige Records (USA). Dist: RCA, JSU, Swift

BROWNIE MCGEE WITH SONNY TERRY & SVEND ERIK NORREGARD.
Album: released on Storyville, Jul'81 by Storyville Records. Dist: Jazz Music Distribution, Swift Distribution, Chris Wellard Distribution, Counterpoint Distribution

Album: released on Storyville, Jul'81 by Storyville Records. Dist: Jazz Music Distribution, Swift Distribution, Chris Wellard Distribution, Counterpoint Distribution

LETS HAVE A BALL 1945-55 (McGhee,Brownie & his buddies).
Album: released on Magpie, Jan'79 Dist: Projection

MCGHEE & TERRY (McGhee,Brownie & Sonny Terry).
Album: released on Storyville, May'86 by Storyville Records. Dist: Jazz Music Distribution, Swift Distribution, Chris Wellard Distribution, Counterpoint Distribution

WALK ON (McGhee,Brownie & Sonny Terry).
Album: released on Bulldog Records, Jul'82 Cat. no: **BDL 1018**
Cassette: released on Bulldog, Jul'85 by Bulldog Records. Dist: President Distribution, Spartan, Swift, Taylor, H.R.

YOU HEAR ME TALKIN' (McGhee,Brownie & Sonny Terry).
Album: released on Muse, Apr'81 by Peerless Records. Dist: Lugtons Distributors

Album: released on Happy Bird (Germany), Aug'83 Dist: Polygram, IMS

McGhee, Dennis

EARLY RECORDINGS (McGhee, Dennis with Fruge, Courville).
Album: released on Morning Star, Apr'79 Dist: Projection Distribution

TRADITIONAL CAJUN FIDDLING (McGhee, Dennis/S.D. Courville).

Album: released on Morning Star, Apr'79 Dist: Projection Distribution

McGhee,Howard

COOKIN' TIME (McGhee,Howard Orchestra).
Album: released on Hep, Apr'79 by H.R. Taylor Records. Dist: Jazz Music, Cadillac Music, JSU, Taylors, Wellard, Chris, Zodiac, Swift, Fast Forward

DUSTY BLUE.
Tracks: / Dusty blue / Sound of music,The / I concentrate on you / Sleep talk / Part avenue petite / Flyin'colours / With malice / Groovin'high / Cottage for sale.
Notes: Licensed from Bethlehem Records.This compilation.(1986 Charly Records Ltd(c) 1986 Charly records.
Album: released on Affinity, May'86 by Charly Records. Dist: Charly, Cadillac

HEATS ON, THE (McGhee,Howard & Roy).
Album: released on Esquire, Jul'78 by Titan International Productions. Dist: Jazz Music, Cadillac Music, Swift, Wellard, Chris, Backs, Rough Trade, Revolver, Nine Mile

HERE COMES FREDDY (McGhee,Howard & Illinois Jacquet).
Album: released on Sonet, '76 by Sonet Records. Dist: PRT

LIVE AT EMERSON'S.
Album: released on Zim, Apr'81 Dist: JSU, Jazz Horizons, Jazz Music, Swift

MAGGIE.
Album:

MAGGIE'S BACK IN TOWN.
Album: released on Contemporary, Dec'81 by Contemporary Records. Dist: Pinnacle

SHADES OF BLUE.
Album: released on Black Lion, Jul'87 by Black Lion Records. Dist: Jazz Music, Chris Wellard, Taylor, H.R., Counterpoint, Cadillac

THAT BOP THING (McGhee,Howard, Quintet).
Album: released on Affinity, May'82 by Charly Records. Dist: Charly, Cadillac

TRUMPET AT TEMPO.
Album: released on Spotlite, '83 by Spotlite Records. Dist: Cadillac, Jazz Music, Spotlite

WISE IN TIME (McGhee, Howard & Teddy Edwards).
Album: released on Storyville, Nov'86 by Storyville Records. Dist: Jazz Music Distribution, Swift Distribution, Chris Wellard Distribution, Counterpoint Distribution

YOUNG AT HEART (McGhee, Howard & Teddy Edwards).
Album: released on Storyville, Sep'86 by Storyville Records. Dist: Jazz Music Distribution, Swift Distribution, Chris Wellard Distribution, Counterpoint Distribution

McGhee, J.

ONE DRAW.
Single (12"): released on Echo, Mar'82 by Vista Sounds. Dist: Jazz Music

McGhee, Wes

AIRMAIL.
Album: released on Terrapin Records, Feb'81

IT'S NO USE BEIN' A FAST DRAW.
Single (7"): released on Country Roads Records, Aug'81 by Country Roads Records. Dist: Stage One

LANDING LIGHTS.
Album: released on TRP, Jan'85 Dist: Charly

LONG NIGHTS AND BANJO MUSIC.
Album: released on Terrapin Records, Feb'81

...THANKS FOR THE CHICKEN.
Album: released on TRP, Aug'85 Dist: Charly

WHISKY IS MY DRIVER.
Single (7"): released on Terrapin Records, Feb'82

ZACATECAS.
Album: released on TRP, Oct'86 Dist: Charly

McGill, Alan

20 BEST LOVED GOSPEL SONGS.
Album: by Pilgrim Records. Dist: Rough Trade, Cartel

McGinn,Matt

SCREWTOPS ARE FALLING ON MY HEAD.
Cassette: released on Highlander, Jun'86 Dist: PRT

Album: released on Pye, Oct'75

TWO HEADED MAN STRIKES AGAIN.
Album: released on Emerald, Jul'74 by Emerald Records. Dist: Ross, PRT, Solomon & Peres Distribution

McGlohon, Loonis

LOONIS IN LONDON.
Album: released on Audiophile, Oct'83 by Jazzology Records (USA). Dist: Jazz Music, Swift

McGlynn,Arty

MCGLYNN'S FANCY.
Tracks: / Carolan's draught / Floating crowbar, The star of munster(The) / I wish my love was a red, red rose / Peter Byrne's fancy / Blackbird, The / Creeping Docken / Charles O'Connor / Jenny's welcome to charlie/the connecht heifers(Jig) / Arthur Darley(Jig) / Hills above Drumquin, The / Miss Monaghan/The flags of Dublin/Hand me down the tackle / Sally gardens, The / Sonny Brogan's fancy/Brian O'lynn/Ben Kelly's delight(Jigs).
Album: released on Emerald (Ireland), Jun'85 by Emerald Records. Dist: I & B, Ross, PRT

McGlynn, Fraser

REEL MCGLYNN, THE.
Cassette: released on Nabo, Mar'87 Dist: MK

McGlynn, Pat Band

PAT MCGLYNN BAND.
Picture disc album: released on Flyover, Apr'79 by Flyover Records. Dist: Flyover Records

McGoldrick,Anna

ANNA MCGOLDRICK (VOL.1).
Album: released on Bonus, Jan'76 Dist: I & B

VOICE OF IRELAND, THE.

Tracks: / Dear old Donegal / Forty shades of green / Paddy McGinty's goat / Danny boy / Humour is on me now(The) / Spinning wheel / Let him go,let him tarry / How are things in Glocca Morra / Mick McGilian's ball / Little town in the ould county down / Teddy O'Neale / Golden jubilee.
Cassette: released on Polydor (Ireland), Aug'86 by Polydor Records. Dist: Polygram, I & B

Cassette: released on Polydor (Eire), Feb'85

McGonagall, William

TRUTH AT LAST, THE.
Double cassette: released on Argo (Spokenword), May'83 by Decca Records. Dist: Polygram

McGorman, Sec

SONGS OF THE IRISH REPUBLIC.
Album: released on Derry, Oct'75 by Outlet Records. Dist: Outlet Records

McGough, Roger

SUMMER WITH MONIKA.
Album: released on Island, Sep'78 by Island Records. Dist: Polygram

McGovern, Jimmy

GATHERING.... (McGovern, Jimmy & his Country Dance Orchestra).
Double Album: released on AJP, May'77 by AJP Records.

JIMMY MCGOVERN AND HIS SCOTTISH DANCE BAND (McGovern, Jimmy and his Scottish Dance Band).
Cassette: released on AIM (Budget Cassettes), Feb'83

McGovern, Maureen

ACADEMY AWARD PERFORMANCE.
Album: released on 20th Century, Sep'75 Dist: RCA, IMS-Polygram

McGrae, Gwen

DOIN' IT / HEY WORLD.
Single (7"): released on Atlantic, Feb'83 by WEA Records. Dist: WEA

Single (12"): released on Atlantic, Feb'83 by WEA Records. Dist: WEA

KEEP THE FIRE BURNING / FUNKY.....
Single (7"): released on Atlantic, Oct'82 by WEA Records. Dist: WEA

Single (12"): released on Atlantic, Oct'82 by WEA Records. Dist: WEA

McGregor, Chris

IN HIS GOOD TIME.
Double Album: released on Blue Note, Jun'79 by EMI Records. Dist: EMI

PROCESSION.
Album: released on Ogun, '78 Dist: Jazz Music, JSU, Cadillac

McGregor, Freddie

ACROSS THE BORDER.
Album: released on RAS, Oct'84

Single (12"): released on Big Ship, Sep'84 by Big Ship Records. Dist: Jetstar

ALL IN THE SAME BOAT.

Tracks: / All in the same boat / Hungry belly pickney / Push come to shove / Jah a the don / I'm coming home / Glad you're here with me / I don't want to see you cry / Somewhere / Mama Mama / Peace in the valley.
Album: released on Real Authentic Sound, Sep'86

Cassette: released on Real Authentic Sound, Sep'86

Compact disc: released on R.A.S, May'87 by Greensleeves Records. Dist: RCA

BIG SHIP.
Single (12"): released on Greensleeves, Jun'82 by Greensleeves Records. Dist: BMG, Jetstar, Spartan

Single (12"): released on Intense, Sep'82 by Intense Records. Dist: PRT, Kingdom

CAN'T GET YOU OUT OF MY MIND.
Tracks: / Can't get you out of my mind.
Single (7"): released on Real Authentic Sound, Nov'86

Single (12"): released on Real Authentic Sound, Nov'86

COME ON OVER.
Album: released on Real Authentic Sound, Jun'86

FREDDIE.
Album: released on Vista Sounds, '83 by Vista Sounds Records. Dist: Jetstar

GUANTANAMERA.
Single (12"): released on Tads, May'84 by Tads Records. Dist: Jetstar Distribution

I JUST DON'T WANT TO BE LONELY.
Tracks: / I just don't want to be lonely / I just don't want to be lonely (version).
Single (7"): released on Germaine, 20 Jun'87 by Germaine Records. Dist: Jetstar

Single (12"): released on Germaine, Jun'87 by Germaine Records. Dist: Jetstar

I'M READY.
Album: released on Studio One, Sep'84 Dist: Jetstar

LOVE AT FIRST SIGHT.
Album: released on Vista Sounds, Dec'84 by Vista Sounds Records. Dist: Jetstar

LOVE BALLAD.
Single (7"): released on Fight, Feb'82 Dist: Jetstar

Single (12"): released on Fight, Feb'82 Dist: Jetstar

Single (12"): released on Exclusive, Mar'82 Dist: Jetstar

MASHING UP HER BRAIN.
Single 10": released on J & J, Jul'83 by J & J Records. Dist: Jetstar

NAME AND NUMBER.
Tracks: / Name and number / Name and number (version).
Single (12"): released on Tads, 23 May'87 by Tads Records. Dist: Jetstar Distribution

NEVER GET AWAY.
Single (12"): released on Spiderman, Jul'82

PRETTY WOMAN.

Single (12"): released on Hawkeye, Apr'83 by Hawkeye Records. Dist: Hawkeye, Lightning (WEA) Distribution, Jetstar, PRT

PUSH COMES TO SHOVE.
Tracks: / Push comes to shove / Glad you're here with me.
Single (12"): released on R.A.S, May'86 by Greensleeves Records. Dist: RCA

ROMAN SOLDIER.
Single 10": released on Hitbound, Oct'83 by Hitbound Records. Dist: Jetstar

ROOTS MAN SHANKING (McGregor, Freddie & Toyan).
Single (12"): released on Greensleeves, Feb'82 by Greensleeves Records. Dist: BMG, Jetstar, Spartan

SPECIAL LOVER.
Single (12"): released on Music Works, Dec'82 Dist: Jetstar Distribution

TOO LONG WILL BE TOO LATE (McGregor, Freddie & Jennifer Lara).
Single (12"): released on Tads, Dec'83 by Tads Records. Dist: Jetstar Distribution

McGregor, Jimmy

HIGHLANDS & LOWLANDS (McGregor, Jimmy & Robin Hall).
Album: released on Nevis, May'77 Dist: H.R. Taylor

KIDS STUFF (McGregor, Jimmy & Robin Hall).
Album: released on Eclipse, Oct'74 by Decca Records. Dist: Polygram

SCOTCH & IRISH (McGregor, Jimmy & Robin Hall).
Album: released on Eclipse, '70 by Decca Records. Dist: Polygram

SCOTLANDS BEST.
Album: released on Beltona, Dec'75 by Decca Records. Dist: Polygram

SCOTTISH CHOICE (McGregor, Jimmy & Robin Hall).
Album: released on Eclipse, '71 by Decca Records. Dist: Polygram

TWO HEIDS ARE BETTER THAN YIN (McGregor, Jimmy & Robin Hall).

McGregor, Mary

TORN BETWEEN TWO LOVERS.
Single (7"): released on Old Gold, Jul'84 by Old Gold Records. Dist: Lightning, Jazz Music, Spartan, Counterpoint

Single (7"): released on Ariola, Sep'82 Dist: RCA, Ariola

McGriff, Jimmy

ALL ABOUT MY GIRL.
Single (7"): released on EMI, Apr'83 by EMI Records. Dist: EMI

BLUES FOR MR.JIMMY.
Tracks: / Bump de bump de bump / Discotheque U.S.A / Cash box / Blues for Joe / Blues for Mr.Jimmy / Dog(You dog), The / Sho' nuff / Turn blue / Party's over(The).
Notes: One of the all-time great R 'n' B organ players.A re-issue of a much sought after collectors album.
Album: released on Stateside, Apr'86 Dist: EMI

Cassette: released on Stateside, Apr'86 Dist: EMI

COUNTDOWN.
Single (7"): released on Milestone, Nov'83 by Ace Records. Dist: PRT

SOUL SURVIVORS (McGriff,Jimmy & Hank Crawford).
Tracks: / Because of you / Frim fram sauce / Peeper,The / One mint julep / Second time around ,The / After supper.
Notes: Straight ahead Jazz/Blues playing from two master musicians who truely are soul Survivors.Both came through the 50s and 60s soul period.Crawford making a name for himself with the Ray Charles band and moving on to make countless recordingsfor Atlantic and CTI.McGriff following in the wake of fellow organist Jimmy Smi-th to emerge as one of the most popular organists of the period.His version of "I've got a woman" was a great favourite with the Mods.This album has a great Blue Note sound about it.Not suprising when you see that the engineer was Rudy Van Gelder!

STARTING FIVE, THE.
Album: released on Milestone, Oct'87 by Ace Records. Dist: PRT. Estim retail price in Oct'87 was £5.67.

STATE OF THE ART.
Tracks: / Headbender / Stormy weather / Cheesesteak / Don't ever doubt me / New wave blues / Slow gindin' / Hip hop bebop.
Notes: Along with Jimmy Smith,Jack McDuff and Richard 'Groove' Holmes,Jimmy McGriff is one of the great Jazz/R&B organists to have emerged from the 60's period.In 1962he had a top twenty US hit with his instrumental version of Ray Charles' "I've Got A Woman"and won a huge following with UK mods thanks to 'MG Blues'and other free-wheeling singles issued by SUE Records which were jazzier than Booker T & the MG's.This new album features material ranging from ballads to sythesized funk to classier jazz organ over a walking bass line.
Album: released on Fantasy (USA), Feb'86 by Fantasy Inc USA Records. Dist: IMS, Polygram

McGuigan, Paddy

MY COUNTRY, MY SONG, AND ME.
Album: released on Dolphin, Oct'75 Dist: I & B Records Distribution, Prism Leisure Corporation Records, Record Services Distribution (Ireland)

McGuigan, Pat

DANNY BOY.
Single (7"): released on Ritz, Jul'85 by Outlet Records. Dist: Outlet, Prism Leisure Distribution, Record Services Distribution (Ireland), Roots

McGuinness Flint

WHEN I'M DEAD AND GONE.
Single (7"): released on EMI Golden 45's, Jul'84 by EMI Records. Dist: EMI

McGuinness, Lyle Band

ELISE.
Single (7"): released on Cool King, May'83 Dist: Pinnacle

McGuire, Barry

BEST OF BARRY.
Album: released on Sparrow, May'82 by Word Records. Dist: Spartan

Cassette: released on Sparrow, May'82 by Word Records. Dist: Spartan

EVE OF DESTRUCTION.
Single (7"): released on Old Gold, Jul'82 by Old Gold Records. Dist: Lightning, Jazz Music, Spartan, Counterpoint

FINER THAN GOLD.
Album: released on Sparrow, May'82 by Word Records. Dist: Spartan

Cassette: released on Sparrow, May'82 by Word Records. Dist: Spartan

INSIDE OUT.
Album: released on Sparrow, May'82 by Word Records. Dist: Spartan

Cassette: released on Sparrow, May'82 by Word Records. Dist: Spartan

TO THE BRIDE (McGuire, Barry, The 2nd chapter of acts & the David band).
Album: released on Myrrh, May'82 by Word Records. Dist: Word Distribution

Cassette: released on Myrrh, May'82 by Word Records. Dist: Word Distribution

McGuire, Mo

TIME AND TIME AGAIN.
Single (7"): released on Derelict, Oct'85 by Derelict Records. Dist: M.I.S

McGuire, Sean

IRELAND'S CHAMPION FIDDLER.
Album: released on Outlet, Jun'77 by Outlet Records. Dist: Outlet Distribution

ON TWO LEVELS (McGuire, Sean and Josephine Keegan).
Album: released on Rubber, Jun'82 by Rubber Records. Dist: Roots Distribution, Projection Distribution, Jazz Music Distribution, Celtic Music Distribution, JSU Distribution, Spartan Distribution

McGuire Sisters

BEST OF THE MCGUIRE SISTERS, THE.
Album: released on MCA, May'82 by MCA Records. Dist: Polygram, MCA

Cassette: released on MCA, May'82 by MCA Records. Dist: Polygram, MCA

BST OF THE MCGUIRE SISTERS, THE.

JUST FOR OLD TIME'S SAKE.
Album: released on Jasmine, Oct'84 by Jasmine Records. Dist: Counterpoint, Lugtons, Taylor, H.R., Wellard, Chris, Swift, Cadillac

MAY YOU ALWAYS.
Single (7"): released on Old Gold, Jul'84 by Old Gold Records. Dist: Lightning, Jazz Music, Spartan, Counterpoint

McHugh, Maureen

JUBILEE PAEGEANT FAIR EP.
Single (7"): released on Keswick, '81 by Loose Records. Dist: Pinnacle

Mcldol, Richie

SKYE BOAT SONG.
Single (7"): released on Dork, Nov'84 by Dork Records. Dist: Probe, Cartel

McInnes Alyson

JUMP SHOUT BOOGIE.
Single (7"): released on Happy Face, Oct'81 by Happy Face Records. Dist: Red Rhino, Bullet Distribution, Pinnacle, PRT, Birds Nest

McIntire, Lani
HAWAIIAN MOONLIGHT (McIntire, Lani & his Hawaiian Orchestra).
Cassette: released on Bravo, Feb'80 by Pickwick Records. Dist: Lugtons

McIntyre
PEACE AND BLESSINGS (McIntyre, Maurice, Quartet).
Album: released on Soul Note, Sep'79 Dist: Harmonia Mundi Distributors

McIntyre, Hal
HAL McINTYRE & HIS ORCHESTRA.
Album: released on First Heard, Jul'77 by Submarine Records. Dist: Conifer, Taylors

McIntyre, Ken
INTRODUCING THE VIBRATIONS (McIntyre, Ken, Sextet).
Album: released on Steeplechase, Aug'77

LOOKING AHEAD (McIntyre, Ken & Eric Dolphy).
Album:

Mcisaac, Billy
LOVE ME LIKE YOU DID BEFORE.
Single (7"): released on Sedition, Jun'85 Dist: PRT

Single (12"): released on Sedition, Jun'85 Dist: PRT

McIvor, John
GATHERING OF THE CLANS, THE.
Album: released on Nevis, Jan'79 Dist: H.R. Taylor

Mckane, Lorraine
LET THE NIGHT TAKE THE BLAME.
Single (7"): released on Carrere, Jan'85 by Carrere Records. Dist: PRT, Spartan

Single (12"): released on Carrere, Jan'85 by Carrere Records. Dist: PRT, Spartan

Mckay, Curly
ON TOUR WITH CURLY MCKAY.
Album: released on Grampian, '73 by Grampian Records. Dist: Grampian, Clyde Factors Distributors, Ross

McKay, Freddie
CARDS ON THE TABLE/CARD TRICKS.
Single (12"): released on Castaff, Feb'84 by Castaff Records. Dist: Jetstar

DRUNKEN SAILOR.
Single (12"): released on Sky Juice, May'84 by Sky Juice Records. Dist: Jetstar

IN TIMES OF TROUBLE.
Single (12"): released on Live & Love, Apr'82 by Third World Records. Dist: Jetstar

MY LOVE FOR YOU.
Single (12"): released on Thunderbar, Sep'84 by Thunderbar Records. Dist: Jetstar Distribution

TRIBAL IN A YARD.
Album: released on Move, Jan'86 by Charly Records. Dist: Charly Distribution, Fast Forward Distribution, Cartel Distribution

McKay, Heather
HEATHER MCKAY SINGS.
Album: released on Grampian, '73 by Grampian Records. Dist: Grampian, Clyde Factors Distributors, Ross

Mckee, Mary
GREATER LOVE, A.
Album: by Pilgrim Records. Dist: Rough Trade, Cartel

MEANINGS OF MY LIFE.
Album: by Pilgrim Records. Dist: Rough Trade, Cartel

McKellar, Kenneth
HIGHWAY JOURNEY.
Tracks: / Down in the glen / Midges / My ain folk / Those happy days of summer / Farewell my love / Misty Islands of the highlands / Crookit bawbee / Aye waukin' / Dark island / Saturday dance / Leaving Isimore.
Album: released on Lismor, Nov'85 by Lismor Records. Dist: Lismor, Roots, Celtic Music

Cassette: released on Lismor, Nov'85 by Lismor Records. Dist: Lismor, Roots, Celtic Music

I BELONG TO SCOTLAND.
Album: released on Decca, Apr'78 by Decca Records. Dist: Polygram

IN SCOTLAND.

Album: released on Lismor, '83 by Lismor Records. Dist: Lismor, Roots, Celtic Music

Cassette: released on Lismor, '83 by Lismor Records. Dist: Lismor, Roots, Celtic Music

OPERATIC WORLD OF..., THE.
Album: released on Decca, Jan'80 by Decca Records. Dist: Polygram

ROAD TO THE ISLES, THE.
Album: released on Decca (Elite), Feb'85 by Decca Records. Dist: Polygram, IMS

Cassette: released on Decca (Elite), Feb'85 by Decca Records. Dist: Polygram, IMS

SACRED SONGS.
Album: by Decca Records. Dist: Polygram

SACRED SONGS FROM SCOTLAND.
Album: released on Word, May'85 by Word Records. Dist: Word Distribution, CBS

Cassette: released on Word, May'85 by Word Records. Dist: Word Distribution, CBS

SCOTLAND THE BRAVE.
Cassette: released on Ditto, Mar'86 by Pickwick Records. Dist: H.R. Taylor

SINGS ROBERT BURNS.
Cassette: released on Decca, Jul'78 by Decca Records. Dist: Polygram

WORLD OF KENNETH MCKELLAR VOL.2.
Album: released on World of Learning, '70 by World Of Learning Records. Dist: World Of Learning

WORLD OF NURSERY RHYMES, THE (McKellar, Kenneth & Vera Lynn).
Album: released on Decca, Nov'76 by Decca Records. Dist: Polygram

McKenna, Dave
CELEBRATION OF HOAGY CARMICHAEL.
Album: released on Concord Jazz(USA), Nov'83 by Concord Jazz Records (USA). Dist: IMS, Polygram

DANCING IN THE DARK.
Tracks: / By myself / Shine on your shoes, A / I see your face before me / Alone together / Me / I guess I'll have to change my pain / You and the night and the music / Dancing in the dark / Something to remember you by / Now sun in sky / Oh,but I do / Gal in calico, A.
Notes: What better combination could be found? The two-fisted,swing piano styling of the great Dave McKenna and eleven beautiful selections from the prolific Tin Pan Alley composer,Arthur Schwartz.
Album: released on Concord Jazz(USA), Feb'86 by Concord Jazz Records (USA). Dist: IMS, Polygram

Cassette: released on Concord Jazz(USA), Feb'86 by Concord Jazz Records (USA). Dist: IMS, Polygram

GROOVIN AT THE GRUNEWALD.
Album: released on Phontastic (Sweden), Jan'82 by Wellard, Chris Distribution. Dist: Wellard, Chris Distribution

KEY MAN THE.
Album: released on Concord Jazz(USA), Apr'85 by Concord Jazz Records (USA). Dist: IMS, Polygram

MY FRIEND THE PIANO.
Tracks: / Margie / Only trust your heart / Mean to me / Slowly / You're driving me crazy / Summer medley: guess I'll go back home this summer / Indian summer / Baby, baby all the time / Always medley: It's always you / Always / This is always.
Notes: Dave McKenna - piano.
Album: released on Concord Jazz(USA), Feb'87 by Concord Jazz Records (USA). Dist: IMS, Polygram

Compact disc: released on Concord Jazz(USA), Jul'87 by Concord Jazz Records (USA). Dist: IMS, Polygram

NO HOLDS BARRED (McKenna Dave Swing Six).
Album: released on Famous Door, Feb'79 Dist: Swift

OIL AND VINEGAR.
Album: released on Honey, Oct'79 Dist: MRC Distribution

ORIGINAL WILBER.
Album: released on Phontastic, Jan'82 Dist: Wellard, Chris

PIANO MOVER (McKenna Dave & Dick Johnson).
Album: released on Concord, May'81 by Import Records. Dist: IMS, Polygram

PLAYS THE MUSIC HARRY WARREN (McKenna Dave Trio).
Album: released on Concord Jazz(USA), Mar'82 by Concord Jazz Records (USA). Dist:

IMS, Polygram

RUBY BRAFF FEATURINF DAVE MCKENNA.
Album: released on Jasmine, Jun'84 by Jasmine Records. Dist: Counterpoint, Lugtons, Taylor, H.R., Wellard, Chris, Swift, Cadillac

McKenna, Joe
TRADITIONAL MUSIC OF IRELAND (McKenna Joe & Antoinette).
Album: released on Shanachie, Sep'79 Dist: Sterns/Triple Earth Distribution, Roots

McKenna, Virginia
TWO FACES OF LOVE.
Album: released on RIM, Mar'79 by Rediffusion. Dist: Jazz Music, Taylors Harmonia Mundi Distribution, Pinnacle

McKenzie, Bob & Doug
GREAT WHITE NORTH.
Album: released on Mercury (Import), Apr'82

TAKE OFF/ELRON MCKENZIE.
Single (7"): released on Phonogram, Apr'82 by Phonogram Records. Dist: Polygram

McKenzie,Candi
TURN ME UP.
Tracks: / Turn me up / Last dance,The.
Single (7"): released on WEA, Apr'86 by WEA Records. Dist: WEA

Single (12"): released on WEA, Apr'86 by WEA Records. Dist: WEA

McKenzie, Candy
IT MUST BE LOVE.
Single (7"): released on Elite, Jun'85 Dist: PRT

Single (12"): released on Elite, Jun'85 Dist: PRT

REMIND ME/DIFFERENT STYLE.
Single (7"): released on Intense, Oct'83 by Intense Records. Dist: PRT, Kingdom

Single (12"): released on Intense, Oct'83 by Intense Records. Dist: PRT, Kingdom

McKenzie, Duncan
ALL OF YOU OUT THERE/MAKING LOVE.
Single (7"): released on Outlook, Jul'83 by Brian Poole. Dist: Spartan Distribution

McKenzie, Maurice
WEE KIRKCUDBRIGHT CENTIPEDE THE.
Cassette: released on Emerald (Ireland), Oct'81 by Emerald Records. Dist: I & B, Ross, PRT

McKenzies
NEW BREED.
Tracks: / New breed.
Single (7"): released on Ron Johnson, Mar'86 by Ron Johnson Records. Dist: Nine Mile Distribution, Cartel Distribution

McKenzie,Scott
SAN FRANCISCO/JUST LIKE AN OLD TIME.
Single (7"): released on Old Gold (Reissue), Apr'83

SAN FRANCISCO (WEAR SOME FLOWERS).
Single (7"): released on CBS, Apr'82 by CBS Records. Dist: CBS

SECRET HOME.
Single (7"): released on Soul Stop, Mar'84 by Soul Stop Record 3. Dist: Spartan

McKenzies, Ranson
KEEP ON WORKING/ORANGE GROOVES (McKenzies, Ranson & Friends).
Single (12"): released on Smokey, May'82 Dist: Jetstar

McKenzies Sings Orbidoig
ICE CREAM FACTORY/EXCURSIONS.
Single (7"): released on WEA, Oct'82 by WEA Records. Dist: WEA

Single (12"): released on WEA, Oct'82 by WEA Records. Dist: WEA

McKenzie,Tony
LOLITA.
Tracks: / Lolita / This is the night of the party.
Single (7"): released on Portrait, Jan'86 by CBS Records. Dist: CBS

Single (12"): released on Portrait, Jan'86 by CBS Records. Dist: CBS

McKern Leo
TRAILS OF RUMPOLE THE.
Cassette: released on Listen For Pleasure, Aug'85 by MFP Records. Dist: EMI

McKillop, Jim
JIM MCKILLOP ON FIDDLE & JOSEPHINE KEEGAN ON PIANO (McKillop, Jim on Fiddle & Josephine Keegan on Piano).
Album: released on Outlet (Ireland), Jul'83

Cassette: released on Outlet (Ireland), Jul'83

McKinley,Ray
BLUE SKIES.
Album: released on First Heard, Jan'84 by Submarine Records. Dist: Conifer, Taylors

Cassette: released on First Heard, Jan'84 by Submarine Records. Dist: Conifer, Taylors

CLASS OF 49.
Album: released on Hep, Apr'81 by H.R. Taylor Records. Dist: Jazz Music, Cadillac Music, JSU, Taylors, Wellard, Chris, Zodiac, Swift, Fast Forward

DOWN THE ROAD APIECE (McKinley,Ray & his Orchestra).
Album: released on Dance Band Days, Jun'86 Dist: Geoff's Records International

Cassette: released on Dance Band Days, Jun'86 Dist: Geoff's Records International

GLENN MILLER STORY THE.
Album: released on RCA (Germany), Jan'83

RAY MCKINLEY & HIS MAGICIANS 1946-9 (McKinley,Ray & his Orchestra).
Album: released on First Heard, Apr'79 by Submarine Records. Dist: Conifer, Taylors

WILL BRADLEY & RAY MCKINLEY 1940/1.
Album: released on Aircheck, Apr'79

McKinney's Cotton Pickers
COMPLETE MCKINNEY'S COTTON PICKERS (1928-1929), THE.
Album: released on RCA (France), '83 by RCA Records. Dist: Discovery

COMPLETE MCKINNEY'S COTTON PICKERS, THE.
Album: released on RCA (France), '83 by RCA Records. Dist: Discovery

COMPLETE, VOL 5.
Album: released on RCA (France), Mar'84 by RCA Records. Dist: Discovery

McKone, Vivienne
NOBODY'S FOOL/ON THE OUTSIDE.
Single (7"): released on Cambra, Feb'83 by Cambra Records. Dist: IDS, Conifer

ONE IN A MILLION/NOBODY'S FOOL.
Single (7"): released on Cambra, Jan'83 by Cambra Records. Dist: IDS, Conifer

McKown, Gene
ROCKABILLY RHYTHM.
Single (7"): released on Rollin' Rock, Jun'80

McKuen, Rod
AT CARNEGIE HALL.
Double album: released on Warner, Jan'74 by Warner Bros Records. Dist: WEA

GREATEST HITS: ROD MCKUEN.
Album: released on EMI, Jan'73 by EMI Records. Dist: EMI

McKusick, Hal
JAZZ WORKSHOP.
Album: released on RCA (France), Jan'83 by RCA Records. Dist: Discovery

McLachlan, Ian
KINGS OF THE BUTTON KEYED BOX (McLachlan, Ian & Fergie MacDonald).
Album: released on Lismor, Jul'87 by Lismor Records. Dist: Lismor, Roots, Celtic Music

McLain, Charly
CHARLY MCLAIN I love country.
Tracks: / Sentimental ol' you / Fly into love / Dancing your memory away / With just one look in your eyes / Women get lonely / With you / Everyday love / Radio heart / Who's cheatin' who / Band of gold / Some hearts get all the breaks / You are my music, you are my song / Wen it's down to me and you / Someone just like you / Sleepin' with the radio on / Paradise tonight.
Album: released on CBS, Mar'87 by CBS Records. Dist: CBS

Cassette: released on CBS, Mar'87 by CBS Records. Dist: CBS

McLain, Tommy

BEFORE I GROW TOO OLD/SWEET DREAMS.
Single (7"): released on Oval, May'82 by Oval Records. Dist: Pinnacle

BEST OF TOMMY MCLAIN, THE.
Album: released on Jin, Feb'79 Dist: Swift

SWEET DREAMS/THINK IT OVER.
Single (7"): released on Oval, Aug'76 by Oval Records. Dist: Pinnacle

TOMMY MCLAIN.
Album: released on Jin, Feb'79 Dist: Swift

McLaren, Malcolm

BUFFALO GALS (McLaren,Malcolm & World Famous supreme team).
Single (7"): released on Charisma, Nov'82 by Virgin Records. Dist: EMI

CARMEN.
Single (7"): released on Charisma, Dec'84 by Virgin Records. Dist: EMI

Single (12"): released on Charisma, Dec'84 by Virgin Records. Dist: EMI

DOUBLE DUTCH.
Single (7"): released on Charisma, Jul'83 by Virgin Records. Dist: EMI

Single (12"): released on Charisma, Jul'83 by Virgin Records. Dist: EMI

DUCK FOR THE OYSTER.
Single (7"): released on Charisma, Sep'83 by Virgin Records. Dist: EMI

Single (12"): released on Charisma, Sep'83 by Virgin Records. Dist: EMI

DUCK ROCK.
Cassette: released on Charisma, May'83 by Virgin Records. Dist: EMI

Album: released on Charisma, May'83 by Virgin Records. Dist: EMI

DUCK ROCK CHEER.
Tracks: / Duck rock cheer / Boys chorus.
Single (7"): released on Charisma, Jan'86 by Virgin Records. Dist: EMI

Single (12"): released on Charisma, Jan'86 by Virgin Records. Dist: EMI

FANS.
Tracks: / Madam butterfly(Un bel di vedroma) / Fans(Nessun dorma) / Carmen(L'Oiseau rebelle) / Boys chorus(La sui monti dell'est) / Lauretta(O mio babbino caro) / Death of a butterfly(Tu tu piccola).
Compact disc: released on Charisma, Jan'85 by Virgin Records. Dist: EMI

Album: released on Charisma, Jan'85 by Virgin Records. Dist: EMI

Cassette: released on Charisma, Jan'85 by Virgin Records. Dist: EMI

MADAM BUTTERFLY.
Single (7"): released on Charisma, Sep'84 by Virgin Records. Dist: EMI

Single (12"): released on Charisma, Sep'84 by Virgin Records. Dist: EMI

Special: released on Charisma, Sep'84 by Virgin Records. Dist: EMI

Cassette: released on Charisma, Sep'84 by Virgin Records. Dist: EMI

SOWETO.
Single (7"): released on Charisma, Feb'83 by Virgin Records. Dist: EMI

Single (12"): released on Charisma, Feb'83 by Virgin Records. Dist: EMI

SWAMP THING.
Tracks: / Swamp thing / Duck rock cheer / Buffalo love / Supresto / B1 Bikini / Eiffel tower / Boom boom baby / Duck Rogers / Promises.
Album: released on Charisma, Nov'85 by Virgin Records. Dist: EMI

WOULD YA LIKE MORE SCRATCHIN'.
Album: released on Charisma, May'84 by Virgin Records. Dist: EMI

Cassette: released on Charisma, May'84 by Virgin Records. Dist: EMI

McLatchy, Debbie

LADY LUCK.
Album: released on Innisfree(USA), Sep'79 by Green Linnet (USA). Dist: Projection

McLaughlin, John

ADVENTURES IN RADIOLAND.
Tracks: / Wait, The / Just Ideas / Jozy / Half man, half cookie / Florianapolis / Gotta dance / Wall will fall, The / Reincarnation / Mitch match
Notes: Brand new album from guitar John McLaughlin. Digitally recorded and featuring new self-penned compositions. John also produced the album. Knowing the reputation that McLaughlin has and the high esteem in which he is held through his workwith the Mahavishnu Orchestra and earlier with musicians of the calibre of MilesDavis etc this new album is bound to attract alot of media attention. Personnel: Jonas Hallborg - bass / Bill Evans - saxes / Danny Gottlieb - drums / MitchellForman - keyboards / John McLaughlin - guitars.
Album: released on Polygram, Jul'87 by Polygram Records. Dist: Polygram

Cassette: released on Polygram, Jul'87 by Polygram Records. Dist: Polygram

Compact disc: released on Polygram, Jul'87 by Polygram Records. Dist: Polygram

BEST OF JOHN MCLAUGHLIN, THE.
Album: released on CBS, Jan'81 by CBS Records. Dist: CBS

BIRDS OF FIRE (McLaughlin, Mahavishnu, John).
Album: released on CBS, '73 by CBS Records. Dist: CBS

DEVOTION.
Album: by CBS Records. Dist: CBS

EXTRAPOLATION.
Album: released on Polydor, '69 by Polydor Records. Dist: Polygram, Polydor

FUSE ONE (see Clarke, Stanley) (McLaughlin, John/Stanley Clarke/Larry Coryell).

HANDFUL OF BEATY, A (McLaughlin, John & Shakti).
Album: released on CBS, Mar'77 by CBS Records. Dist: CBS

INNER MOUNTAIN FLAME (McLaughlin, Mahavishnu, John).
Album: released on CBS, '74 by CBS Records. Dist: CBS

INNER WORLDS.
Album: by CBS Records. Dist: CBS

MCLAUGHLIN, JOHN (WITH SHAKTI).
Album: released on CBS, Jun'76 by CBS Records. Dist: CBS

MY GOAL'S BEYOND (McLaughlin, Mahavishnu, John).
Album: by CBS Records. Dist: CBS

NATURAL ELEMENTS (McLaughlin, John & Shakti).
Album: released on CBS, Dec'77 by CBS Records. Dist: CBS

PASSION GRACE AND FIRE (McLaughlin, John/Al Di Meola/Paco De Lucia).
Album: released on Philips (Mercury), Jun'83

Cassette: released on Philips (Mercury), Jun'83

Compact disc: released on Philips (Mercury), Jun'83

THUNDERBYRD.
Album: by CBS Records. Dist: CBS

McLean, Don

AMERICAN PIE.
Compact disc: released on United Artists, Mar'87

Album: released on Fame (United Artists), May'82 by Music For Pleasure Records. Dist: EMI

Cassette: released on Fame (United Artists), May'82 by Music For Pleasure Records. Dist: EMI

Single (7"): released on EMI, Apr'83 by EMI Records. Dist: EMI

AMERICAN PIE (2 PARTS).
Single (7"): released on United Artists, Jan'84

CHAIN LIGHTNING.
Album: by EMI Records. Dist: Conifer

CRYING/GENESIS.
Single (7"): released on EMI, Apr'80 by EMI Records. Dist: EMI

DOMINION.
Double Album: released on EMI, Feb'83 by EMI Records. Dist: EMI

Double cassette: released on EMI, Feb'83 by EMI Records. Dist: EMI

GREATEST HITS: DON MCLEAN Then

and now.
Tracks: / He's got you / American pie / To have and to hold / Castles in the air / But she loves me / Superman's ghost / Vincent / And I love you so / Crying / Don't burn the bridge.
Compact disc: released on EMI, Jul'87 by EMI Records. Dist: EMI

HOMELESS BROTHER.
Album: released on United Artists, Nov'74

MUSIC OF DON MCLEAN, THE.
Tracks: / And I love you so / It's just the sun / Wonderful baby / Fools paradise / American pie / Left for dead on the road of love / Crying / Building my body / Dream lover / Prime time / Vincent.
Notes: Don Mclean rose to fame in early 70's with the epic 'American Pie'single and Followed it with his tribute to Van Gogh with the song "Vincent".The music of Don Mclean not only covers 11 great songs,but also provides an insight into the man himself with backstage interview footage by Paul Gambaccini.
Video-cassette (VHS): released on PMI, Jan'84 by PMI Records. Dist: EMI

Video-cassette [Betamax]: released on PMI, Jan'84 by PMI Records. Dist: EMI

Video-cassette (VHS): released on PMI, Jun'86 by PMI Records. Dist: EMI

Video-cassette [Betamax]: released on PMI, Jun'86 by PMI Records. Dist: EMI

MUSIC OF... (VIDEO), THE.
Notes: Inc. 'Vincent', 'American Pie', And I love you so' etc. 55 minute.
Video-cassette (VHS): released on Video Collection, May'87 by Video Collection International Ltd. Dist: Counterpoint

PLAYIN' FAVOURITES.
Album: released on United Artists, '73

SOLO.
Double Album: released on United Artists, Sep'76

TAPESTRY.
Album: released on United Artists, '72

Album: released on EMI (Holland), '83 by EMI Records. Dist: Conifer

Album: released on Fame (United Artists), Sep'84 by Music For Pleasure Records. Dist: EMI

VERY BEST OF DON MCLEAN.
Album: released on United Artists, Sep'80

Cassette: released on United Artists, Sep'80

VERY THOUGHT OF YOU/LEFT FOR DEAD.
Single (7"): released on EMI, Nov'82 by EMI Records. Dist: EMI

VINCENT.
Single (7"): released on USA Import, '80

McLean, Dougie

CRAIGE DHU.
Album: released on Dunkeld, '83 by Dunkeld Records. Dist: Projection

FIDDLE.
Album: released on Dunkeld, '84 by Dunkeld Records. Dist: Projection

SNAIGNOW.
Album: released on Plant Life, Nov'81 Dist: Roots

McLean, Jackie

BLUESNIK.
Album: released on Blue Note, Jan'85 by EMI Records. Dist: EMI

CONNECTION,THE (McLean,Jackie and Freddie Redd).
Album: released on Boplicity, Oct'83 by Boplicity Records. Dist: Ace Records, Pinnacle

FRICKLE SONANCE,A.
Album: released on Blue Note (USA Import), Sep'84

JACKIE MCLEAN & CO. various artists (Various Artists).
Album: released on Prestige (USA), Feb'84

JACKIE'S BAG.
Tracks: / Quadrangle / Blues Inn / Fidel / Appointment in Ghana / Ballad for Doll, A / Isle of Java / Street singer / Melonae's dance / Medina.
Album: released on Blue Note, Jul'85 by EMI Records. Dist: EMI

Compact disc: released on Blue Note, Sep'87 by EMI Records. Dist: EMI. Estim retail price in Sep'87 was £11.99.

LET FREEDOM RING.
Tracks: / Melody for Melonae / I'll keep loving you / Rene / Omega.

Compact disc: released on Manhattan-Blue Note, May'87 by EMI America Records (USA). Dist: EMI

Album: released on Blue Note, May'86 by EMI Records. Dist: EMI

LONG DRINK OF THE BLUES, A.
Album: released on Original Jazz Classics (USA), Jan'87 by Fantasy (USA) Distribution, Chris Wellard Distribution, IMS-Polygram Distribution

MCLEANS SCENE.
Album: released on Prestige (USA), Aug'84

NEW AND OLD GOSPEL.
Album: released on Blue Note, Jan'85 by EMI Records. Dist: EMI

ONE STEP BEYOND.
Tracks: / Saturday and sunday / Saturday and sunday (alternate take) / Frankenstein / Blue rondo / Ghost town / Saturday and sunday(alternate take) / Saturday and sunday (alternate take).
Album: released on Blue Note (USA Import), Sep'84

Compact disc: released on Blue Note, Aug'87 by EMI Records. Dist: EMI

Compact disc: released on Manhattan-Blue Note, Aug'87 by EMI America Records (USA). Dist: EMI
Cat. no: CDP-7 46821 2

SWING SWANG SWINGIN'.
Album: released on Boplicity, Sep'83 by Boplicity Records. Dist: Ace Records, Pinnacle

TRIBUTE TO CHARLIE PARKER FROM THE NEWPORT JAZZ FESTIVAL.
Album: released on RCA (France), '83 by RCA Records. Dist: Discovery

McLean, John

COME INTO THE GARDEN.
Single (12"): released on Black Starliner, Aug'85 by Black Starliner Records. Dist: Jetstar

OPEN MY HEART.
Single (7"): released on Roots Radical, Oct'84 by Roots Radical Records. Dist: Jetstar Distribution

Single (12"): released on Roots Radical, Oct'84 by Roots Radical Records. Dist: Jetstar Distribution

STARLINE/DANCE WITH ME/ROCK TO...
Single (12"): released on Music Lovers, Jul'82 by Music Lovers Records. Dist: Music Lovers

McLean, Norman

BONNIE DAYS OF SUMMER,THE.
Album: by Lismor Records. Dist: Lismor, Roots, Celtic Music

FLOWER OF SCOTLAND & THE BONNIE DAYS OF SUMMER.
Album: by Lismor Records. Dist: Lismor, Roots, Celtic Music

NORMAN MCLEAN SINGS.
Album: released on Lismor, '73 by Lismor Records. Dist: Lismor, Roots, Celtic Music

NORMAN MCLEAN SINGS VOL2.
Album: released on Lismor, Jul'77 by Lismor Records. Dist: Lismor, Roots, Celtic Music

Cassette: released on Lismor, Jul'77 by Lismor Records. Dist: Lismor, Roots, Celtic Music

McLean, Penny

LADY BUMP.
Album: released on Release, Oct'76 by Release Records. Dist: I & B, Wynd-Up Distribution, Taylors, Solomon & Peres Distribution

McLean, Ranchi

CINDERELLA/WALKING ON (McLean,Ranchi & the Revolutionaries).
Single (7"): released on Dart, Aug'83 by President Records. Dist: Jazz Music, Swift

McLelland, Sandy

CAN WE STILL BE FRIENDS (McLelland,Sandy & Backline).
Album: released on Mercury, May'79 by Phonogram Records. Dist: Polygram Distribution

NO TURNING BACK/TRIED TO WARN YOU.
Single (7"): released on Action, Jan'82 Dist: Rough Trade, Cartel

STAY CLEAN TONIGHT.
Single (7"): released on Action, Feb'81 Dist: Rough Trade, Cartel

TWO TIRED LOVERS/DAY YOU LEFT.
Single (7"): released on Action, Jul'82 Dist: Rough Trade, Cartel

McLellan, Tommy
COTTON PATCH BLUES.
Album: released on Travellin' Man, Nov'84 Dist: Jazz Music

McLeod, Bobby
SCOTTISH DANCE-ALONG, A.
Album: by Decca Records. Dist: Polygram

McLeod, Doug
NO ROAD BACK HOME.
Album: released on Making Waves, Sep'85 by Making Waves Records.

McLeod, Jim
JIM MCLEOD'S DANCE PARTY FAVOURITES.
Tracks: / Bluebell polka / Will you save the last dance just for me / Just for old times' sake / Come by the hills / Dashing white sergeant / Dashing white sergeant (encore) / Do you think you could love me again / Amazing grace / Pittenweem / Shetland reels / Cruising down the river / Loch Lomond / After all these years / Gay Gordons / Gay Gordons (encore) / Leaving dundee / Suffin' Sammy.
Album: on Scotdisc, Dec'86 Dist: Clyde Factors Distributers

Cassette: released on Scotdisc, Dec'86 Dist: Clyde Factors Distributors

NORTH OF THE BORDER Sequence dancing (McLeod, Jim & His Band & Bryan Smith).
Album: released on BS Production, Jul'87

SCOTTISH DANCE WORLD, THE (McLeod, Jim & His Band).
Album: released on World of Learning, '71 by World Of Learning Records. Dist: World Of Learning

McLeod, Rory
ANGRY LOVE.
Album: released on Forward Sounds, Jan'86 by Forward Sounds Records. Dist: Rough Trade, Cartel

KICKING THE SAWDUST.
Double Album: released on Forward Sounds, Mar'87 by Forward Sounds Records. Dist: Rough Trade, Cartel

McLinton, Delbert
FEELIN' ALRIGHT.
Album: released on Astan, Nov'84 by Astan Records. Dist: Counterpoint

Cassette: released on Astan, Nov'84 by Astan Records. Dist: Counterpoint

McMahon, Tommy
CLARE CONERTINAS (McMahon, Tommy & Terry O'Sullivan).
Album: released on Topic, '75 by Polygram Records.

McManus, Jill
SYMBOLS OF HOPI.
Album: released on Concord Jazz(USA), Jun'84 by Concord Jazz Records (USA). Dist: IMS, Polygram

McMaster, Andy
ANOTHER POLITICIAN.
Tracks: / Another politician / Normal street.
Notes: Pic bag
Single (7"): released on GFM, 30 May'87 by GFM Records. Dist: Fast Forward, Cartel, PRT, Projection

Single (12"): released on GFM, 30 May'87 by GFM Records. Dist: Fast Forward, Cartel, PRT, Projection

NO JOY.
Tracks: / No joy / Normal street.
Single (7"): released on GFM, 30 May'87 by GFM Records. Dist: Fast Forward, Cartel, PRT, Projection

M.C. Miker "G"
CELEBRATION RAP (M.C. Miker "G" & Deejay Sven).
Tracks: / Celebration rap / Play it loud.
Single (7"): released on Debut, Nov'86 by Skratch Music. Dist: PRT

Single (12"): released on Debut, Nov'86 by Skratch Music. Dist: PRT

McMinn, Don
HEARTACHE HOTEL (McMinn, Don & The Memphis Blues Revue).
Album: released on Exit, Mar'84 by Exit Records. Dist: Backs

McMorland, Alison
ALISON MCMORLAND & PETA WEBB.
Album: released on Topic, '81 Dist: Roots Distribution

Page 662

BELT WI' COLOURS THREE.
Album: released on Tangent, Apr'81 Dist: Roots Distribution, Lugtons Distributors, Taylors, JSU Distribution, Spartan Distribution

FUNNY FAMILY, THE.
Album: released on Big Ben, Apr'81 by Big Ben Records. Dist: Spartan, Taylor. H.R.

McNabb, Christine
YOU TOOK YOUR LOVE AWAY.
Single (12"): released on Rad's, Aug'84 by Rad's Records. Dist: Jetstar

McNabb, Michael
COMPUTER MUSIC.
Compact disc: released on Mobile Fidelity, Oct'86 by Mobile Fidelity Records.

McNairn, John
YESTERDAY IS OVER.
Single (7"): released on Individual, Aug'85 by Individual Records. Dist: Pinnacle

McNally, John
DANNY BOY AND OTHER FAVOURITES.
Cassette: released on Harp(Ireland), Jul'80 by Pickwick Records. Dist: Taylors

Album: released on Harp(Ireland), Jul'80 by Pickwick Records. Dist: Taylors

McNeal, Rita
FLYING ON YOUR OWN.
Tracks: / Flying on your own / She's called Nova Scotia.
Single (7"): released on 10, 20 Jun'87 by 10 Records. Dist: Virgin, EMI

McNeely, Big Jay
BEST OF, THE.
Album: released on Saxonograph (Sweden), Jan'86

BIG JAY MCNEELY MEETS THE PENGUINS.
Album: released on Ace, Apr'84 by Ace Records. Dist: Pinnacle, Swift, Hotshot, Cadillac

DEACON RIDES AGAIN.
Album: released on Pathe Marconi, Sep'84 Dist: Swift

FROM HARLEM TO CAMDEN.
Album: released on Ace, Aug'84 by Ace Records. Dist: Pinnacle, Swift, Hotshot, Cadillac

ROADHOUSE BOOGIE.
Album: released on Saxophonograph, May'85 Dist: Swift

McNeil, Bryan
UNSUNG HERO, THE.
Album: released on Temple, Mar'85 by Temple Records. Dist: Roots Distribution, Folksound Distribution, Celtic Music Distribution, Projection Distribution

McNeil, Finlay
FONN IS FURAN.
Album: released on Temple, Dec'82 by Temple Records. Dist: Rough Trade Distribution, Cartel Distribution

McNeil, Flora
SONGS IN SCOTS, GAELIC (OF BANA).
Cassette: released on Folktracks, Nov'79 by Folktracks Cassettes. Dist: Folktracks

McNeil, John
EMBARKATION.
Album: released on Steeplechase, Apr'79

FAUN (McNeil, John Quintet).
Album: released on Steeplechase, Sep'79

McNeil, Les
IF ONLY.
Single (12"): released on Ambac, Sep'83 by Ambac Records. Dist: Jetstar

LOVE MECHANIC.
Single (12"): released on Solid Groove, Feb'82 Dist: Jetstar, Pinnacle

McNeilstown Pipe Band
WORLD CHAMPIONS.
Album: released on Homespun(Ireland), Jun'79 by Outlet Records. Dist: Outlet

McNeil, Roddy
RODDY MCNEIL SINGS IT.
Album: released on Play, Jan'76 by Play Records. Dist: Spartan

McNeir, Ronnie
FOLLOW YOUR HEART.
Tracks: / Follow your heart / Everybody's in a hurry / Love's under suspect.
Single (7"): released on Expansion, Nov'86 Dist: PRT

LOVE SUSPECT.
Album: released on Expansion, Apr'87 Dist: PRT

McNichol, Evelyn
SACRED PIANO ARRANGEMENTS.
Album: by Pilgrim Records. Dist: Rough Trade, Cartel

TELL THE WORLD.
Album: released on Word, May'79 by Word Records. Dist: Word Distribution, CBS

McNichol, Kristy
FIRST LOVE (McNichol, Kristy/Christopher Atkins).
Single (7"): released on Polydor, Jan'83 by Polydor Records. Dist: Polygram, Polydor

McNiel, Les
AGAIN.
Single (12"): released on Ambassador, Jul'82 by Ambassador Records. Dist: Pinnacle, Jetstar

GODDESS OF LOVE.
Single (12"): released on Soul Patrol, Mar'84 by Soul Patrol Records. Dist: Jetstar

McNulty, Pat
PAT MCNULTY (UILLEANN PIPES).
Album: released on Silver Hill, Nov'76 Dist: Jazz Music

McPartland, Jimmy
ONE NIGHT STAND.
Notes: With Dick Wellstood
Album: released on Jazzology, Jan'87 Dist: Jazz Music, Swift

McPartland, Marian
ALONE TOGETHER (see Shearing, George).
Double Album:

AT HICKORY HOUSE.
Double Album:

JANUARY 6TH & 8TH 1964.
Album: released on From The Jazz Vault, Oct'90 by Damont Records. Dist: Swift, Taylor, H.R.

MUSIC OF LEONARD BERNSTEIN, (THE).
Album: released on Bainbridge (France), May'85 Dist: Discovery

Cassette: released on Bainbridge (France), May'85 Dist: Discovery

PERSONAL CHOICE.
Tracks: / I hear a rhapsody / Meditation / In your own sweet way / Sleepin' bee, A / I'm old fashioned / When the sun comes out / Tricotism / Melancholy mood.
Compact disc: released on Concord Jazz(USA), Mar'87 by Concord Jazz Records (USA). Dist: IMS, Polygram

Album: released on Concord Jazz(USA), Mar'83 by Concord Jazz Records (USA). Dist: IMS, Polygram

Cassette: released on Concord Jazz(USA), Mar'83 by Concord Jazz Records (USA). Dist: IMS, Polygram

WILLOW CREEK AND OTHER BALLADS.
Album: released on Concord Jazz(USA), Jul'85 by Concord Jazz Records (USA). Dist: IMS, Polygram

Album: released on Concord Jazz(USA), Jul'85 by Concord Jazz Records (USA). Dist: IMS, Polygram

McPartland, Marion
ELEGANT PIANO (see Wilson, Teddy).

McPeake Family
MCPEAKE FAMILY, THE.
Album: released on Topic, '81 Dist: Roots Distribution

WILD MOUNTAIN THYME.
Album: released on Topic, '74 Dist: Roots Distribution

McPeake Family Trio
JUG OF PUNCH, THE.
Cassette: released on Folktracks, Nov'79 by Folktracks Cassettes. Dist: Folktracks

McPeake (Snr), Frank
FRANK MCPEAKE (SNR).
Cassette: released on Folktracks, Nov'79 by Folktracks Cassettes. Dist: Folktracks

McPhail, Ian
ARGYLL'S FANCY (McPhail, Ian & His band).
Album: released on Lismor, Nov'85 by Lismor Records. Dist: Lismor, Roots, Celtic Music

McPhatter, Clyde
ROCK AND CRY.
Album: released on Charly(R&B), Apr'84 by Charly Records. Dist: Charly, Cadillac

Cassette: released on Charly(R&B), Apr'84 by Charly Records. Dist: Charly, Cadillac

McPhatter, Clyde & the Drifters
BIP BAM.
Album: released on Edsel, May'84 by Demon Records. Dist: Pinnacle, Jazz Music, Projection

McPhee, George
GEORGE MCPHEE PLAYS ORGAN OF PAISLEY ABBEY.
Album: released on Abbey, Jan'78 by Abbey. Dist: PRT, Taylors, Gamut

McPhee, Joe
VISITATION (McPhee, Joe/The Bill Smith ensamble).
Album: released on Sackville, Jul'86 Dist: JSU, Jazz Music, Jazz Horizons, Cadillac Music, Celtic Music, Swift

McPherson, Charles
NEW HORIZONS.
Album: released on Xanadu, Mar'79 Dist: Discovery, Jazz Horizons, Jazz Music, Swift

PROPHET, THE.
Album: released on Discovery (USA), Jan'84 by Discovery Records (USA). Dist: Swift, Flexitron-Audio, Jazz Music

McRae, Carmen
CARMEN MCRAE.
Cassette: released on Audio Fidelity, Oct'84 Dist: PRT

HEATWAVE (McRae, Carmen/Cal Tjader).
Album: released on Concord Jazz, Jul'82 by Concord Jazz Records (USA). Dist: IMS, Polygram

I HEAR MUSIC (see Connor, Chris) (McRae, Carmen & Chris Connor).

LIVE AT BUBBA'S.
Album: released on Gateway, Sep'83 by Kingdom. Dist: Pinnacle

MISS MAGIC.
Notes: O.C.I. = Oliver Crombie Imports. Tel: 01 455 0066.
Compact disc: released on Dunhill Compact Classics (USA), '86

RONNIE SCOTT'S PRESENTS CARMEN MCCRAE LIVE.
Album: released on Pye-Ronnie Scott, Jan'78

YOU'RE LOOKING AT ME.
Album: released on Concord Jazz(USA), Apr'84 by Concord Jazz Records (USA). Dist: IMS, Polygram

YOU'RE LOOKING FOR ME.
Tracks: / I'm an errand girl for rhythm / Beautiful moons ago / Firm fram sauce (The) / Come in and out of the rain / How does it feel? / If I had you / I can't see for lookin' / Sweet Lorraine / You're lookin' at me / Just you just me.
Compact disc: released on Concord Jazz(USA), Sep'86 by Concord Jazz Records (USA). Dist: IMS, Polygram

McRae, Malcolm
ART OF THE SOLO PIPER.
Album: released on Tartar (New Zealand), Aug'83

Cassette: released on Tartar (New Zealand), Aug'83

McRoby, Ron
PLAYS PUCCOLO.
Album: released on Concord Jazz, Apr'83 by Concord Jazz Records (USA). Dist: IMS, Polygram

Cassette: released on Concord Jazz, Apr'83 by Concord Jazz Records (USA). Dist: IMS, Polygram

McShann, Jay

BIG BAND THAT JUMPS.
Album: released on Black Lion, Sep'85 by Black Lion Records. Dist: Counterpoint, Jazz Music, Cadillac

BLUES & BOOGIE (McShann, Jay & Sammy Price).
Album: released on Philips (Holland), Apr'84

Cassette: released on Philips (Holland), Apr'84

CRAZY LEGS & FRIDAY STRUT (McShann, Jay & Buddy Tate).
Album: released on Sackville, Apr'81 Dist: Swift, Jazz Music, Jazz Horizons, Cadillac Music, Celtic Music

EARLY BIRD (McShann,Jay Orchestra).
Album: released on Spotlite, '83 by Spotlite Records. Dist: Cadillac, Jazz Music. Soollite

GOING TO KANSAS CITY (McShann,Jay & The All Stars).
Album: released on Swaggie(Australia), Jan'83 Dist: Jazz Music

HOOTIE'S KC BLUES (McShann,Jay Orchestra).
Album: released on Affinity, Sep'83 by Charly Records. Dist: Charly, Cadillac, Swift

JAY McSHANN/BUDDY TATE/JIMM GALLOWAY/DON THOM-PSON/CLARKE (Mcshann, Jay/Buddy Tate/Jimm Galloway/Don Thompson/Clarke).
KANSAS CITY HUSTLE.
Album: released on Sackville, Apr'81 Dist: Swift, Jazz Music, Jazz Horizons, Cadillac Music, Celtic Music

MAN FROM MUSKOGEE, (THE).
Album: released on Sackville, Apr'81 Dist: Swift, Jazz Music, Jazz Horizons, Cadillac Music, Celtic Music

MAN FROM MUSKOGEE (THE).
Tracks: / Vine Street boogie / Staggers (The) / Yardbird waltz / My Chile / Confessin' the blues / Moten swing / Man from Muskogee (The) / Blues for an old cat / I ain't mad at you / Do wah doo / Dexter blues.
Album: released on Affinity, '86 by Charly Records. Dist: Charly, Cadillac, Swift

TRIBUTE TO FATS WALLER, A.
Album: released on Sackville, Apr'81 Dist: Swift, Jazz Music, Jazz Horizons, Cadillac Music, Celtic Music

TUXEDO JUNCTION.
Album: released on Sackville, '81 Dist: Swift, Jazz Music, Jazz Horizons, Cadillac Music, Celtic Music

VINE STREET BOOGIE.
Tracks: / My chile / Hootie blues / Satin doll / I'm beginning to see the light / Vine street boogie / Confessin' the blues / Yardbird waltz / Hooties ignorant oil.
Album: released on Black Lion, Sep'87 by Black Lion Records. Dist: Counterpoint, Jazz Music, Cadillac. Estim retail price in Oct'87 was £5.73.

McShaw, Pinky

IT'S COMING SOON.
Single 7": released on Trance, Dec'84

Single 12": released on Trance. Dec'84

McTell, Blind Willie

1940: BLIND WILLIE MCTELL.
Tracks: / Chainey / Murderer's home / Kill it kid rag / I got to cross de river O'Jordan / Monologue / Old time religion, Amen / Will Fox / Dying crapshooter's blues / Amazing grace / Monologue / Medley / King Edward blues / Dollar boll weevil / I got to cross the River Jordan.
Album: released on Blue Moon, Jul'87 by Magnum Music Group Ltd. Dist: PRT. Estim retail price in Aug'87 was £6.39.

LEGENDARY LIBRARY OF CON-GRESS RECORDINGS 1940.
Album: released on Blue Moon, Oct'87 by Magnum Music Group Ltd. Dist: PRT

McTell, Ralph

71/72.
Album: released on Mays, '82 by Mays Records., Projection, Swift, Celtic Music, Cadillac, Ross, Duncans, Impetus

AT HIS BEST.
Album: released on Cambra, Feb'85 by Cambra Records. Dist: Celtic Music

Cassette: released on Cambra, Feb'85 by Cambra Records. Dist: Celtic Music

AT THE END OF A PERFECT DAY.
Tracks: / Streets of London / Scarborough fare / You've got a friend / Penny Lane / Lamplighter (The) (England 1914) / Last farewell (The) / Sailing / Beautiful dreamer / Homeward bound / Scarlet ribbons / I'll have to say I love you in a song / Morning has broken / Weather the storm / Those were the days / Barges / England.
Notes: Telstar have recorded Ralph McTell's new album 'At the end of a perfect day',a collection of songs of 'love and friendship'. There is a strong theme of 'Life in England' that runs through the album.Ralph McTells perhaps best known for his song 'The Streets of London' which tells of the harshness of city life,and in contrast to this he describes a country scene in 'Scarborough Fair'. There are songs about the England of days gone by with 'Those were the days' and 'The lamplighter (England 1914)'. 'At the end of a perfect day' includes 'The last farewell' and 'Homeward bound',making it an album with many popular songs.
Album: released on Telstar, Dec'85 by Telstar Records. Dist: BMGg*

Cassette: released on Telstar, Dec'85 by Telstar Records. Dist: BMGg*

BEST OF ALPHABET ZOO.
Album: released on MFP, Sep'84 by Music For Pleasure Records. Dist: EMI

Cassette: released on MFP, Sep'84 by Music For Pleasure Records. Dist: EMI

BRIDGE OF SIGHS.
Album: released on Mays, Jan'87 by Mays Records., Projection, Swift, Celtic Music, Cadillac, Ross, Duncans, Impetus

Cassette: released on Mays, Jan'87 by Mays Records., Projection, Swift, Celtic Music, Cadillac, Ross, Duncans, Impetus

ENGLAND.
Single 7": released on EMI, Jun'82 by EMI Records(UK). Dist: EMI

FERRYMAN, THE.
Album: released on Mays, Sep'87 by Mays Records., Projection, Swift, Celtic Music, Cadillac, Ross, Duncans, Impetus

I FALL TO PIECES.
Single 7": released on Mays, Nov'82 by Mays Records., Projection, Swift, Celtic Music, Cadillac, Ross, Duncans, Impetus

KENNY THE KANGAROO.
Single 7": released on Mays, Nov'82 by Mays Records., Projection, Swift, Celtic Music, Cadillac, Ross, Duncans, Impetus

Single 7": released on Mays, May'83 by Mays Records., Projection, Swift, Celtic Music, Cadillac, Ross, Duncans, Impetus

LOVE GROWS.
Album: released on Mays, '82 by Mays Records., Projection, Swift, Celtic Music, Cadillac, Ross, Duncans, Impetus

RALPH, ALBERT AND SYDNEY.
Album: released on Mays, Sep'87 by Mays Records., Projection, Swift, Celtic Music, Cadillac, Ross, Duncans, Impetus

RALPH MCTELL.
Album: released on Hallmark, Jul'78 by Pickwick Records.

RALPH MCTELL COLLECTION.
Double Album: released on Pickwick, Feb'78 by Pickwick Records. Dist: PRT, Prism Leisure

Cassette: released on Pickwick, Jul'80 by Pickwick Records. Dist: PRT, Prism Leisure

RIGHT SIDE UP.
Album: released on Warner Bros., Nov'76 by WEA Records. Dist: WEA

SLIDE AWAY THE SCREEN.
Album: released on Warner Bros., Apr'79 by WEA Records. Dist: WEA

Cassette: released on Warner Bros., Apr'79 by WEA Records. Dist: WEA

SONGS FROM ALPHABET ZOO.
Album: released on Mays, '83 by Mays Records., Projection, Swift, Celtic Music, Cadillac, Ross, Duncans, Impetus

Cassette: released on Mays, '83 by Mays Records., Projection, Swift, Celtic Music, Cadillac, Ross, Duncans, Impetus

STRANGER TO THE SEASON.
Single 7": released on Mays, Oct'83 by Mays Records., Projection, Swift, Celtic Music, Cadillac, Ross, Duncans, Impetus

STREETS.
Album: released on Warner Bros., Mar'75 by WEA Records. Dist: WEA

STREETS OF LONDON (7").
Single 7": released on Reprise (USA), Jul'81 by WEA Records. Dist: WEA

STREETS OF LONDON (LP 1).
Album: released on Hallmark, Aug'77 by Pickwick Records.

STREETS OF LONDON (LP 2).
Album: released on Transatlantic, Feb'81 by Logo Records. Dist: Roots, BMG, Celtic Music

Cassette: released on Transatlantic, Feb'81 by Logo Records. Dist: Roots, BMG, Celtic Music

TICKLE ON THE TUM (McTell, Ralph & Jacqui Redding).
Cassette: released on Mays, Nov'86 by Mays Records., Projection, Swift, Celtic Music, Cadillac, Ross, Duncans, Impetus

Album: released on Mays, Nov'86 by Mays Records., Projection, Swift, Celtic Music, Cadillac, Ross, Duncans, Impetus

WATER OF DREAMS.
Album: released on Mays, '82 by Mays Records., Projection, Swift, Celtic Music, Cadillac, Ross, Duncans, Impetus

WEATHER THE STORM.
Album: released on Mays, '82 by Mays Records., Projection, Swift, Celtic Music, Cadillac, Ross, Duncans, Impetus

WIND IN THE WILLOWS.
Single 7": released on Red Bus, May'84 by Red Bus Records. Dist: PRT

WINNERS SONG.
Single 7": released on Mays, Nov'84 by Mays Records., Projection, Swift, Celtic Music, Cadillac, Ross, Duncans, Impetus

McTells

JESSE MAN RAE.
Single 7": released on Frank, Aug'87 Dist: Backs*, Cartel

McVay

BOYS GO DANCING.
Single 7": released on RAK, Jul'84 by RAK Records. Dist: PRT

Single 12": released on RAK, Jul'84 by RAK Records. Dist: PRT Deleted '86.

McVay,Ray Orchestra

COME DANCING.
Album: released on Transatlantic, Mar'82 by Logo Records. Dist: Roots, BMG, Celtic Music

Cassette: released on Transatlantic, Mar'82 by Logo Records. Dist: Roots, BMG, Celtic Music

MUSIC FROM THE HIT PARADE.
Album: released on Dansan, Jul'80 by Spartan Records. Dist: Spartan, Taylors

TIME STEP.
Tracks: / Under the moon of love / When / That'll be the day / Stop! In the name of love / Ob li di,ob la da / Black is black / I only wanna be with you / Dancing Queen / Chanson d'amour / We've only just begun / Daddy cool / For ever and ever / That's the way(I like it).
Notes: All tracks licensed from Logo Records. Compiled by John Howard.
Album: released on Conifer, Jul'86 by Conifer Records. Dist: Conifer, Jazz Music

WORLD DISCO DANCIN' CHAMPION-SHIP.
Album: released on EMI, '78 by EMI Records(UK). Dist: EMI

WORLD OF LATIN DANCING.
Double Album: released on Philips, May'76 Dist: IMS-Polygram

McVea, Jack

1944-1947.
Album: released on Solid Sender, Apr'81 Dist: Jazz Music

COME BLOW YOUR HORN.
Album: released on Ace, Aug'85 by Ace Records. Dist: PRT, Pinnacle, Celtic Music, Cadillac, Jazz Music

NOTHIN' BUT JAZZ 1962 (McVea,Jack Quintet).
Notes: Re-issue of 1977 album. MONO.
Album: released on Harlequin, May'86 by Flyright Records. Dist: Swift, Jazz Music, Wellards, Cadillac, Taylors

OPEN THE DOOR RICHARD (McVea, Jack Allstars).
Album: released on Jukebox Lil, Jan'85 by Jukebox Lil. Dist: Swift, Celtic Music

TWO TIMIN' BABY (McVea,Jack & His door openers).
Album: released on Jukebox Lil, May'86 by Jukebox Lil. Dist: Swift, Celtic Music

McVeigh, Father Joe

SINGS.
Album: released on Release (Ireland), Jun'76 Dist: I & B, Wynd-Up, Solomon & Peres

McVey, Morgan

LOOKING GOOD DIVING.
Single 7": released on CBS, Jan'87 by CBS Records. Dist: CBS

Single 12": released on CBS, Jan'87 by CBS Records. Dist: CBS

McVicar

MCVICAR Film Soundtrack.
Album: released on Polydor, '80 by Polydor Records. Dist: Polygram, Polydor

Cassette: released on Polydor, '80 by Polydor Records. Dist: Polygram, Polydor

McVie. Christine

CHRISTINE MCVIE.
Tracks: / Love will show us how / Challenge / So excited / One in a million / Ask anybody / Got a hold on me / Who's dreaming this dream? / I'm the one / Keeping secrets / Smile I live for.
Notes: Digital stereo
Compact disc: released on Warner Bros., Sep'84 by WEA Records. Dist: WEA

Album: released on Warner Bros., Feb'84 by WEA Records. Dist: WEA

Cassette: released on Warner Bros., Feb'84 by WEA Records. Dist: WEA

GOT A HOLD ON ME.
Single 7": released on Warner Bros., Feb'84 by WEA Records. Dist: WEA

Single 12": released on Warner Bros., Feb'84 by WEA Records. Dist: WEA

LOVE WILL SHOW US HOW.
Single 7": released on Warner Bros., Apr'84 by WEA Records. Dist: WEA

VIDEO ALBUM, THE.
Video-cassette (VHS): released on Vestron Music, Oct'84 Dist: CBS

McVouty

SLIM & BAM.
Album: released on Hep Jazz, Apr'79 by H.R. Taylor Records. Dist: Celtic Music, Jazz Music, Taylors, Wellards, Zodiac, Swift, Fast Forward

McWilliams, David

DAYS OF PEARLY SPENCER.
Single 7": released on EMI (France), Apr'83 by EMI Records(UK). Dist: Conifer

DON'T DO IT FOR LOVE.
Album: released on EMI, '76 by EMI Records(UK). Dist: EMI

WOUNDED.
Album: released on Carmel UK, Jan'82 Dist: Pinnacle

McWilliams, Randy

DUMB ONE.
Single 7": released on Switch, Mar'84 by Cadillac Music., Cadillac

M.C. Shy D.

I'VE GOT TO BE TOUGH.
Tracks: / We don't play.
Single 12": released on Champion, Feb'87 by Champion Records. Dist: BMGg*

MDC

MILLIONS OF DAMN CHRISTIANS.
Album: released on We Bite, Nov'87 Dist: Revolver, Cartel

MILLIONS OF DEAD COCKS.
Album: released on Alternative Tentacles, Nov'82 by Alternative Tentacles Records. Dist: Rough Trade, Cartel

MULTI DEATH CORPORATION (EP).
Single 7": released on Crass, Jan'84 by Exit-stencil Music. Dist: Southern Record

SMOKE SIGNALS.
Album: released on Radical, Dec'86 by Radical Records. Dist: Cartel

Me And My Girl

ME AND MY GIRL Original cast Album (Various artists).
Tracks: / Overture / Weekend at Hareford, A / Thinking of no one but me / Family solicitor, The / Me and my girl / An English gentleman / You would if you could / Lambeth walk, The / Sun has got his hat on, The / Once you lose your heart / Take it on the chin / Song of Hareford / Love makes the world go round / Leaning on a lampost / If only you cared for me / Finale.
Album: released on That's Entertainment, 7 Nov'87 by That's Entertainment Records. Dist: Pinnacle

Cassette: released on That's Entertainment, 7 Nov'87 by That's Entertainment Records. Dist: Pinnacle

Compact disc: released on That's Entertainment, Oct'87 by That's Entertainment Records. Dist: Pinnacle. Estim retail price in Sep'87 was £11.99.

ME AND MY GIRL Original soundtrack (Various artists).
Compact disc: released on Manhattan, Apr'87 by EMI Records(UK). Dist: EMI

Album: released on Columbia, Mar'85 by EMI Records(UK). Dist: EMI

Cassette: released on Columbia, Mar'85 by EMI Records(UK). Dist: EMI

Me and You

ACCESS TO FILE.
Album: released on Tomorrow's High Today, Jul'87

WHO TOLD YOU SO.
Single 12": released on THT, Jul'82

Meadow Mist

CHRISTMAS ISN'T CHRISTMAS.
Single 7": released on Lorraine's, Nov'82 by Lorraine's Records.

LOVE YOUR NEIGHBOUR.
Single 7": released on Lorraine's, Nov'83 by Lorraine's Records.

Meadowlark sampler

MEADOWLARK SAMPLER Various artists (Various artists).
Notes: Selections from John Michael Talbot, Douglas Trowbridge, Justo Almario, Richard Souther and Jeff Johnson.
Album: released on Meadowlark, Mar'86 by Word Records(UK)Ltd.. Dist: Word, CBS

Cassette: released on Meadowlark, Mar'86 by Word Records(UK)Ltd.. Dist: Word, CBS

MEADOWLARK SAMPLER '86 (THE) (Various artists).
Notes: The Meadowlark Sampler is fast establishing a tradition of introducing a new Meadowlark product. The '86 Sampler is an invitation to share the quiet contemplative sounds of artists like John Michael Talbot, Richard Souther, Hadley Hockensmith, Billy Smiley and Amy Shreve.
Album: released on Meadowlark, Feb'87 by Word Records(UK)Ltd.. Dist: Word, CBS

Cassette: released on Meadowlark, Feb'87 by Word Records(UK)Ltd.. Dist: Word, CBS

Meal Ticket

KEEPIN' THE FAITH.
Album: released on Razor, Aug'87 by Razor. Dist: Pinnacle

Mean St. Dealers

BENT NEEDLES.
Album: released on Graduate, Nov'79 by Graduate Records., Cartel

Meanies

NO SLEEP TILL BEDTIME EP.
Single 7": released on Grinning Whale, Sep'87 Dist: Cartel, Fast Forward

Meanwhile back at...

MEANWHILE BACK AT THE GOGO Various Artists (Various artists).
Album: released on Kent, May'85 by Kent Records. Dist: Pinnacle, Cadillac, Jazz Music

MEANWHILE BACK AT THE RANCH BIG DAN IS FIGHTING FOR HIS LIFE (Various artists).
Album: released on Bam Caruso, May'87 by Bam Caruso Records. Dist: Celtic Music, Revolver, Cartel

Mearns, John

HAME AND GUID NICHT WITH JOHN MEARNS.
Album: released on Ross, Dec'84 by Ross Records. Dist: Ross, Taylors, Celtic Music, Roots

Cassette: released on Ross, Dec'84 by Ross Records. Dist: Ross, Taylors, Celtic Music, Roots

Meat Beat

SUCK HARD (Meat Beat Manifesto).
Tracks: / Suck hard.
Single 12": released on Sweatbox, Jul'87 by Sweatbox Records. Dist: Rough Trade, Cartel

Meat & Gravy

HITS THAT MISSED (Meat & Gravy from Cadillac Gravy Vol.2).
Album: released on Red Lightnin', Apr'79 by Red Lightnin' Records. Dist: Red Lightnin', Cadillac, Caroline, Hotshot, Lightning, Swift, Jazz Music, Projection

RECORDS WAS CHEAP TO MAKE THEN (Meat & Gravy from Cadillac Gravy Vol.1).
Album: released on Red Lightnin', Apr'79 by Red Lightnin' Records. Dist: Red Lightnin', Cadillac, Caroline, Hotshot, Lightning, Swift, Jazz Music, Projection

TRYING TO MAKE A LIVING (Meat & Gravy from Cadillac Gravy Vol.3).
Album: released on Red Lightnin', Apr'79 by Red Lightnin' Records. Dist: Red Lightnin', Cadillac, Caroline, Hotshot, Lightning, Swift, Jazz Music, Projection

Meat Mouth

MEAT MOUTH IS MURDER.
Tracks: / Meat mouth is murder.
Single 12": released on Factory, Sep'87 by Factory Records. Dist: Cartel, Pinnacle

MEATMOUTH MURDER.
Single 12": released on Ron Johnson, Aug'87 by Ron Johnson Records. Dist: Nine Mile, Cartel

Meat Puppets

HUEVOS.
Album: released on SST, Oct'87 by SST Records. Dist: Pinnacle. Estim retail price in Sep'87 was £6.49.

I CAN'T BE COUNTED ON.
Tracks: / I can't be counted on / Paradise.
Single 12": released on SST, 17 Oct'87 by SST Records. Dist: Pinnacle

MEAT PUPPETS.
Album: released on SST, Apr'84 by SST Records. Dist: Pinnacle

MIRAGE.
Album: released on SST, Jun'87 by SST Records. Dist: Pinnacle

Cassette: released on SST, Jun'87 by SST Records. Dist: Pinnacle

Compact disc: released on SST, Jul'87 by SST Records. Dist: Pinnacle

OUT MY WAY.
Album: released on SST, Sep'86 by SST Records. Dist: Pinnacle

Compact disc: released on SST, Sep'87 by SST Records. Dist: Pinnacle. Estim retail price in Sep'87 was £11.99.

UP ON THE SUN.
Album: released on SST, Apr'85 by SST Records. Dist: Pinnacle

Compact disc: released on SST, Aug'87 by SST Records. Dist: Pinnacle

Meat Whiplash

DON'T SLIP UP.
Single 7": released on Creation, Sep'85 Dist: Rough Trade, Cartel

Meatloaf

12" TAPE: MEATLOAF.
Tracks: / Bat out of hell / Dead ringer for love / Read 'em and weep / If you really want to / Razor's edge.
Cassette: released on Epic, Sep'86 by CBS Records. Dist: CBS

BAD ATTITUDE.
Tracks: / Bad attitude / Modern girl / Nowhere fast / Surf's up / Piece of the action / Jumpin' the gun / Cheatin' in your dreams / Don't leave your mark on me / Sailor to a siren.
Notes: Produced by Meat Loaf, Paul Jacobs and Mack. Original Recordings Produced by Alan Shacklock for Modern Media London Ltd.
Album: released on Fame, May'86 by Music For Pleasure Records. Dist: EMI

Cassette: released on Fame, May'86 by Music For Pleasure Records. Dist: EMI

Compact disc: released on Arista, Feb'85 by Arista Records. Dist: BMG

Album: released on Arista, Oct'84 by Arista Records. Dist: BMG

Cassette: released on Arista, Oct'84 by Arista Records. Dist: BMG

BAT OUT OF HELL.
Tracks: / You took the words right out of my mouth / Heaven can wait / All revved up with no place to go / Two out of three ain't bad / Bat out of hell / For crying out loud / Paradise a dashboard light / Praying for the end of time / Bat out of hell / Man and woman.
Compact disc: released on Epic, '83 by CBS Records. Dist: CBS

Album: released on Epic, Jan'78 by CBS Records. Dist: CBS

Cassette: released on Epic, '79 by CBS Records. Dist: CBS

Single 7": released on Arista, Oct'87 by Arista Records. Dist: BMG

Single 12": released on Arista, Oct'87 by Arista Records. Dist: BMG

BAT OUT OF HELL/ HIT OUT OF HELL.
Album: released on Epic, Aug'87 by CBS Records. Dist: CBS

BLIND BEFORE I STOP.
Tracks: / Execution day / Execution day / Rock'n' roll mercenaries / Getting away with murder / One more kiss (night of the soft parade / Blind before I stop / Burning down / Standing on the outside / Masculine / Man and a woman / Special girl / Rock 'n' roll here.
Single 7": released on Arista, Feb'87 by Arista Records. Dist: BMG

Single 12": released on Arista, Feb'87 by Arista Records. Dist: BMG

Single 12": released on Arista, Feb'87 by Arista Records. Dist: BMG

Album: released on Arista, Sep'86 by Arista Records. Dist: BMG

Cassette: released on Arista, Sep'86 by Arista Records. Dist: BMG

Compact disc: released on Arista, '86 by Arista Records. Dist: BMG

CHRIS TETLEY INTERVIEWS MEATLOAF.
Picture disc album: released on Music & Media, Oct'87 Dist: Spartan

DEAD RINGER.
Tracks: / Peel out / I,m gonna lover her for both of us / More than you deserve / I'll kill you if you don't come back / Read 'em and weep. / Nocturnal pleasure / Dead ringer for love / Everything is permitted.
Compact disc: released on Epic, Jul'86 by CBS Records. Dist: CBS

Compact disc: released on CBS, Nov'87 by CBS Records. Dist: CBS

Album: released on Epic, Nov'85 by CBS Records. Dist: CBS

Cassette:

GETTING AWAY WITH MURDER.
Tracks: / Getting away with murder / Scot free (remix) / Rock 'n' Roll hero / Getting away with murder / Rock 'n' roll hero.
Single 10": released on Arista, Nov'86 by Arista Records. Dist: BMG

Picture disc single: released on Arista, Nov'86 by Arista Records. Dist: BMG

Single 7": released on Arista, Nov'86 by Arista Records. Dist: BMG

Single 12": released on Arista, Nov'86 by Arista Records. Dist: BMG

GREATEST ORIGINAL HITS (4 Track EP).
Single 7": released on Epic, Mar'83 by CBS Records. Dist: CBS

HITS OUT OF HELL.
Tracks: / Bat out of hell / Read em' and weep / Midnight at the lost and found / To out of three ain't bad / Dead ringer for love / Modern girl / I'm gonna love her for both of us / You took the words right out of my mouth / Razor's edge / Paradise by the dashboard light.
Compact disc: released on Cleveland, Apr'85 by CBS Records. Dist: CBS

Video-cassette (VHS): released on Cleveland, Jan'86 by CBS Records. Dist: CBS

Album: released on Epic, Jan'85 by CBS Records. Dist: CBS

Cassette: released on Epic, Jan'85 by CBS Records. Dist: CBS

IF YOU REALLY WANT TO.
Single 7": released on Epic, Apr'83 by CBS Records. Dist: CBS

Single 12": released on Epic, Apr'83 by CBS Records. Dist: CBS

Picture disc single: released on Epic, Apr'83 by CBS Records. Dist: CBS

LIVE AT WEMBLEY.
Notes: Number of tracks: Type of recording: Live. Total playing time:
Video-cassette (VHS): released on Videoform, Jan'84 Dist: Gold, EMI

LIVE : MEATLOAF.
Compact disc: released on Arista, Oct'87 by Arista Records. Dist: BMG

Album: released on Arista, Oct'87 by Arista Records. Dist: BMG

Cassette: released on Arista, Oct'87 by Arista Records. Dist: BMG

MEATLOAF FEATURING STONEY & MEATLOAF.
Album: released on Prodigal, Oct'81 Dist: BMG

Cassette: released on Prodigal, Oct'81 Dist: BMG

MIDNIGHT AT THE LOST AND FOUND.
Tracks: / Razor's edge / Midnight at the Lost and found / Wolf at your door / Keep driving / Promised land, the / You never can be too sure about that girl / Priscilla / Don't you look at me like that / If you really want to / Fallen angel.
Album: released on Epic, Jan'87 by CBS Records. Dist: CBS

Cassette: released on Epic, Jan'87 by CBS Records. Dist: CBS

Album: released on Epic, Apr'83 by CBS Records. Dist: CBS

Cassette: released on Epic, Apr'83 by CBS Records. Dist: CBS

NOWHERE FAST.
Single 7": released on Arista, Dec'84 by Arista Records. Dist: BMG

Single 7": released on Arista, Dec'84 by Arista Records. Dist: BMG

Picture disc single: released on Arista, Dec'84 by Arista Records. Dist: BMG

PIECE OF THE ACTION.
Single 7": released on Arista, Mar'85 by Arista Records. Dist: BMG

Single 12": released on Arista, Mar'85 by Arista Records. Dist: BMG

Picture disc single: released on Arista, Mar'85 by Arista Records. Dist: BMG

RAZORS EDGE.
Single 7": released on Cleveland, Jan'84 by CBS Records. Dist: CBS

Single 12": released on Cleveland, Jan'84 by CBS Records. Dist: CBS

Single 7": released on Epic, Jun'83 by CBS Records. Dist: CBS

Single 12": released on Epic, Jun'83 by CBS Records. Dist: CBS

Picture disc single: released on Epic, Jun'83 by CBS Records. Dist: CBS

ROCK'N'ROLL MERCENARIES.
Tracks: / Rock 'n' roll mercenaries / Revolutions per minute.
Single 7": released on Arista, Aug'86 by Arista Records. Dist: BMG

Single 12": released on Arista, Aug'86 by Arista Records. Dist: BMG

Picture disc single: released on Arista, Aug'86 by Arista Records. Dist: BMG

Picture disc single: released on Arista, Sep'86 by Arista Records. Dist: BMG

Picture disc single: released on Arista, Sep'86 by Arista Records. Dist: BMG

SPECIAL GIRL.
Compact disc single: released on Arista, May'87 by Arista Records. Dist: BMG

WHAT YOU SEE IS WHAT YOU GET (Meatloaf(Feat Stoney)).
Single 7": released on Prodigal, Oct'81 Dist: BMG

Mecano

DONDE EST EL PAIS DE LAS HADES.
Album: released on CBS(Spain), Jan'84 by CBS Records. Dist: Counterpoint, Celtic Music, Jazz Music, Swift, Conifer

Cassette: released on CBS(Spain), Jan'84 by CBS Records. Dist: Counterpoint, Celtic Music, Jazz Music, Swift, Conifer

UNIVITED GUEST.
Single 7": released on CBS, Aug'83 by CBS Records. Dist: CBS

Mechall,Francois

CONVERSATIONS (Mechali,Francois/Beb Guerin).
Tracks: / Rappel / Grand II / Arca.
Album: released on Nato(France), Sep'86 by Disques Nato. Dist: Essex

GRANDIER VOLTIGEUR, (LE).
Tracks: / Offrande (1re partie: decocher) / Offrande (2e partie) / Arca / Duo / Ensemble 1 / Kenny Wheeler solo / Ensemble 2..

Album: released on Nato(France), Sep'86 by Disques Nato. Dist: Essex

Mechanical Instruments

MECHANICAL INSTRUMENTS From the Paul Corin collection vol.2.
Album: released on Response, Feb'81 by Priority Records. Dist: BMG, Taylors

MUSIC FOR THE MAGIC LANTERN.
Album: released on Saydisc, May'79 by Saydisc Records. Dist: Taylors, Jazz Music, Swift, Projection, Essex, Gamut, Harmonia Mundi, Celtic Music

PAUL CORIN COLLECTION.
Album: by Priority Records. Dist: BMG, Taylors

Mechanical Man

PRESSURE SITUATION.
Tracks: / Pressure situation / Don't I know / One way street.
Single 7": released on Arista, Jan'86 by Arista Records. Dist: BMG

Single 12": released on Arista, Jan'86 by Arista Records. Dist: BMG

Mechanical music hall

MECHANICAL MUSIC HALL Various artists (Various artists).
Cassette: released on Saydisc, Apr'81 by Saydisc Records. Dist: Taylors, Jazz Music, Swift, Projection, Essex, Gamut, Harmonia Mundi, Celtic Music

Mechanical Opera

MECHANICAL OPERA Various artists (Various artists).
Tracks: / La Traviata / Rigoletti / Nabucco / Il Travatore / Ernani / Rigoletto / Nabucco / Mikado / Pirates of Penzance / H.M.S. Pinafore / Les Huguenots / Robert La Diable / La fill du regiment / Linda di Chamounix / Lucia di Lammermoor / William Tell / Barber of Seville / I puritani / La sonnambula / Faust / Carmen / Czar & Carpenter / Marriage of Figaro / La Dame Blanche / Mignon / Lohengrin / Tannhauser / Les cloches de Corneville(Planquette) / Midsummer nights dream / Il Travatore / Ernani / La Traviata / I Lombardi / Rigoletto / Nabucco / Mikado, The / Pirates of Penzance, The / HMS Pinafore / Faust.
Notes: Operias from Verdi to Gilbert & Sullivan played by old musical boxes. 46 items including arias from tracks listed.
Album: released on Saydisc, Apr'87 by Saydisc Records. Dist: Taylors, Jazz Music, Swift, Projection, Essex, Gamut, Harmonia Mundi, Celtic Music

Cassette: released on Saydisc, Apr'87 by Saydisc Records. Dist: Taylors, Jazz Music, Swift, Projection, Essex, Gamut, Harmonia Mundi, Celtic Music

Compact disc: released on Saydisc, Apr'87 by Saydisc Records. Dist: Taylors, Jazz Music, Swift, Projection, Essex, Gamut, Harmonia Mundi, Celtic Music

Meco

ENCOUNTERS OF EVERY KIND.
Album: released on RCA, Apr'78 Dist: BMG
Cat. no: **XL 13050**

STAR WARS THEME.
Single 7": released on Millennium(USA), Oct'77 Dist: BMG, Polygram

Medals For Mothers

MEDALS FOR MOTHERS various artists (Various artists).
Album: released on Homespun(Ireland), '82 by Homespun Records. Dist: Homespun, Outlet

Cassette: released on Homespun(Ireland), '82 by Homespun Records. Dist: Homespun, Outlet

Medeiros, Glenn

NOTHING'S GONNA CHANGE MY LOVE FOR YOU.
Tracks: / Nothing's gonna change my love for you / You left the loneliest heart / Nothing's gonna change my love for you (ext. version) / Nothing's gonna change my love for you (instrumental).
Single 7": released on Mercury, Jul'87 by Phonogram Records. Dist: IMS, Polygram

Single 12": released on Mercury, Jul'87 by Phonogram Records. Dist: IMS, Polygram

Medema, Ken

KINGDOM IN THE STREETS.
Album: released on Word(UK), May'82 by Word Records(UK)Ltd.., CBS

Cassette: released on Word(UK), May'82 by Word Records(UK)Ltd.., CBS

LOOKING BACK.
Album: released on Word(UK), May'82 by Word Records(UK)Ltd.., CBS

Cassette: released on Word(UK), May'82 by Word Records(UK)Ltd.., CBS

Media

SOUTH COAST CITY ROCKERS.
Single 7": released on Brain Booster, Feb'80

T.V. KIDS.
Single 7": released on Brain Booster, Feb'80

Medical Students Sing..

MEDICAL STUDENTS SING RUGBY SONGS various artists (Various artists).
Album: released on Sportsdisc, Jul'80 by Sportsdisc Records.

Medicine Head

BEST OF MEDICINE HEAD.
Album: released on Polydor, Sep'81 by Polydor Records. Dist: Polygram, Polydor

Cassette: released on Polydor, Sep'81 by Polydor Records. Dist: Polygram, Polydor

Medieval

MEDIEVAL.
Notes: Mini album/cassette.
Album: released on New Renaissance(USA), Nov'87 Dist: Pinnacle

Cassette: released on New Renaissance(USA), Nov'87 Dist: Pinnacle

Medieval Players

AT MANERE MINSTRELSY.
Album: released on Plant Life, Jul'83 Dist: Jazz Music, Projection, Swift, Celtic Music, Cadillac, Ross, Duncans, Impetus

Meditation

STRANGER IN LOVE/UNITY.
Single 12": released on Kingdom, Oct'81 by Kingdom Records. Dist: Kingdom, PRT

Meditations

CARPENTER REBUILD.
Single 12": released on Jackal, Mar'82 Dist: Jazz Music

EASE UP FATTIE/SHADOW MAN.
Single 12": released on Greensleeves, Jul'83 by Greensleeves Records. Dist: BMG, Jetstar, Spartan

GREATEST HITS: MEDITATIONS.
Album: released on Greensleeves, Nov'84 by Greensleeves Records. Dist: BMG, Jetstar, Spartan

NO MORE FRIEND.
Single 12": released on Greensleeves, Jan'83 by Greensleeves Records. Dist: BMG, Jetstar, Spartan

SIT DOWN AND REASON.
Single 12": released on Jah Guidance, Nov'83 by Jah Guidance Records. Dist: Jetstar

WAKE UP.
Album: released on Third World, Apr'78 Dist: Jetstarr*

Mediterranean melody

MEDITERRANEAN MELODY Various artists (Various artists).
Cassette: released on Ampro Cassettes, Sep'81

Medium Medium

GLITTER HOUSE, (THE).
Album: released on Cherry Red, Oct'81 by Cherry Red Records. Dist: Pinnacle

HUNGRY SO ANGRY.
Single 7": released on Cherry Red, Feb'81 by Cherry Red Records. Dist: Pinnacle

THEM OR ME.
Single 7": released on APT, Jan'80 Dist: Swift

Medley, Bill

I'VE HAD THE TIME OF MY LIFE (Medley, Bill & Jennifer Warnes).
Tracks: / I've had the time of my life / Love is strange.
Single 7": released on RCA, Oct'87 Dist: BMG

THEIR TOP HITS (Medley, Bill & The Righteous Brothers).
Cassette: released on Timeless Treasures, Sep'87 Dist: Counterpoint, Jazz Music

Medlocke, Rick

RICK MEDLOCKE AND BLACKFOOT (Medlocke, Rick and Blackfoot).
Tracks: / Back on the streets / Staurday night / Closest thing to heaven / Silent type / Reckless boy / Private life / liar / Steady Rockin' / My wild romance / Rock 'N' Roll tonight.
Album: released on Atlantic, Jun'87 by WEA Records. Dist: WEA, Swift, Celtic Music

Cassette: released on Atlantic, Jun'87 by WEA Records. Dist: WEA, Swift, Celtic Music

Medway Powerhouse

MEDWAY POWERHOUSE VOL.1, THE Various artists (Various artists).
Album: released on Hangman, Aug'87 Dist: Revolver, Cartel. Estim retail price in Sep'87 was £5.99.

Medway sound

FROM THE WATERS OF THE MEDWAY.
Album: by BBC Records & Tapes. Dist: EMI

Meece, David

'7'.
Notes: David's new album has been a monumental creative effort both in songwriting and production, spanning two years from conception to completion. He secured the services of five award-winning producers, each of whom has produced the songs best suited to his particular production abilities - among them Brown Bannister, Skip Conte and Greg Nelson. The new album is filled with up-tempo techno-pop music and features high energy number's such as 'You Can Go', his new single co-written with Michael Card and Mike Hudson, and moving ballads such as 'I Can See(On Emmaus Road)', a powerful song Meece wrote with Gloria Gaither.
Album: released on Myrrh, Apr'86 by Word Records(UK)Ltd.. Dist: Word, CBS

Cassette: released on Myrrh, Apr'86 by Word Records(UK)Ltd.. Dist: Word, CBS

CANDLE IN THE RAIN.
Album: released on Myrrh, Nov'87 by Word Records(UK)Ltd.. Dist: Word, CBS

Cassette: released on Myrrh, Nov'87 by Word Records(UK)Ltd.. Dist: Word, CBS

Meechelle La Chaux

LOVE ME ALL OVER.
Tracks: / Love me all over.
Single 12": released on Preset, Mar'87 Dist: Pinnacle

M.E.F.F.

NEVER STOP.
Single 12": released on Respond, Sep'84 by Paul Weller. Dist: Polygram

Megadeath

KILLING IS MY BUSINESS AND BUSINESS IS GOOD.
Album: released on Music For Nations, May'85 by Music For Nations Records. Dist: Pinnacle

Compact disc: released on Music For Nations, Aug'87 by Music For Nations Records. Dist: Pinnacle

Compact disc: released on Music For Nations, Aug'87 by Music For Nations Records. Dist: Pinnacle

Megadeth

PEACE SELLS....BUT WHO'S BUYING.
Tracks: / Wake up dead / Conjuring, The / Peace sells / Devils Island / Good morning/Black friday / Bad omen / I ain't supersitious / My last words.
Album: released on Capitol, Nov'86 by Capitol Records. Dist: EMI

Cassette: released on Capitol, Nov'86 by Capitol Records. Dist: EMI

Megalamania

MEGALAMANIA (Various artists).
Album: released on Powerstation, Oct'86 by Powerstation Records. Dist: Red Rhino, Cartel

Megatone

OPEN ALL HOURS.
Album: released on Intersound, Jul'87 by Intersound Records. Dist: Jazz Music

Mehead

ELMER'S END.
Tracks: / Elmer's end / Mummy song / Oldest man in the world / Brain Collages.
Single 12": released on Makerite, 21 Nov'87, Cartel

Mehler and Nash

JAZZ PRAISE.
Album: released on Maranatha, Sep'85 by Word Records(UK)Ltd.. Dist: Word, CBS

Cassette: released on Maranatha, Sep'85 by Word Records(UK)Ltd.. Dist: Word, CBS

Meislin, Barbara

CARVINGS IN THE CANYON.
Album: released on Stash, Nov'87 Dist: Swift, Jazz Music, Jazz Horizons, Celtic Music, Cadillac, Zodiac

Meisner, Randy

ONE MORE SONG.
Album: released on Epic, Dec'80 by CBS Records. Dist: CBS

Cassette: released on Epic, Dec'80 by CBS Records. Dist: CBS

RANDY MEISNER.
Album: released on Asylum, Jun'78 by WEA Records. Dist: WEA

RANDY MEISNER (2).
Album: released on Epic, Oct'82 by CBS Records. Dist: CBS

Mekons

BEATEN AND BROKEN.
Tracks: / Beaten and broken / Chop that child in half / Hey Susan / Deep end.
Single 12": released on Sin, Feb'86 Dist: Red Rhino, Cartel

CRIME AND PUNISHMENT.
Tracks: / Crime and punishment.
Single 12": released on Sin, Jan'86 Dist: Red Rhino, Cartel

EDGE OF THE WORLD, THE.
Album: released on Sin, Jun'86 Dist: Red Rhino, Cartel

FAST PRODUCT.
Cassette: released on EMI, Nov'79 by EMI Records(UK). Dist: EMI

FEAR AND WHISKY.
Album: released on Sin, Aug'85 Dist: Red Rhino, Cartel

HELLO CRUEL WORLD.
Tracks: / Hello cruel world.
Single 7": released on Sin, Jun'86 Dist: Red Rhino, Cartel

HOLE IN THE GROUND.
Tracks: / Hole in the ground / Sin city / Prince of darkness.
Single 12": released on Cooking Vinyl, Sep'87 Dist: Nine Mile, Cartel, Celtic Music

HONKY TONKIN'.
Album: released on Sin, Mar'87 Dist: Red Rhino, Cartel

Cassette: released on Sin, Mar'87 Dist: Red Rhino, Cartel

MEKONS STORY.
Album: released on CNT, Nov'82 Dist: Rough Trade, Cartel

NEVER BEEN IN A RIOT.
Single 7": released on Fast, Sep'79 by Fast Forward Communications (Scotland). Dist: Cartel

SLIGHTLY SOUTH OF THE BORDER.
Tracks: / Sightly south of the border.
Single 10": released on Sincere Sounds, Sep'86

SPORTING LIFE.
Single 7": released on CNT, Nov'82 Dist: Rough Trade, Cartel

WHERE WERE YOU.
Single 7": released on Fast, Sep'79 by Fast Forward Communications (Scotland). Dist: Cartel

Mel & Kim

F.L.M. AND RESPECTABLE.
Video-cassette (VHS): released on Video Collection, Sep'87 by Video Collection International Ltd.. Dist: Counterpoint

F.L.M. (SINGLE).
Tracks: / F.L.M. / F.L.M. (remix).
Single 7": released on Supreme, Jun'87 by Supreme Records. Dist: PRT

Single 12": released on Supreme, Jun'87 by Supreme Records. Dist: PRT

F.L.M..
Album: released on Supreme, Apr'87 by Supreme Records. Dist: PRT

Cassette: released on Supreme, Apr'87 by Supreme Records. Dist: PRT

GREATEST HITS: MEL AND KIM.
Tracks: / Respectable / FLM (fun love and money) / I'm the one who really loves you / From a whisper, to a scream / Showing out / Respectable (remix) / Touch me / Do ya do ya (wanna please me) / I'm all you need / I want you to want me / Dream city / Nothing's gonna stop me now.
Notes: From the "Greatest Hits and Pics" series. The cassette is packaged with a 48-page colour book containing various pictures and facts. Contains six hit singles.
Cassette: released on Telstar, Nov'87 by Telstar Records. Dist: BMG*

RESPECTABLE.
Tracks: / Respectable (The tabloid mix) / Respectable (The 7"mix) / Respectable (Extra beats version).
Single 7": released on Supreme, Feb'87 by Supreme Records. Dist: PRT

Single 12": released on Supreme, Feb'87 by Supreme Records. Dist: PRT

Single 12": released on Supreme, Mar'87 by Supreme Records. Dist: PRT

Single 12": released on Supreme, Mar'87 by Supreme Records. Dist: PRT

SHOWING OUT.
Tracks: / Showing out / System.
Single 12": released on Supreme, Jan'87 by Supreme Records. Dist: PRT

I'M THE ONE WHO REALLY LOVES YOU.
Tracks: / I'm the one who really loves you.
Single 7": released on Supreme, Sep'87 by Supreme Records. Dist: PRT

Single 12": released on Supreme, Sep'87 by Supreme Records. Dist: PRT

SHOWING OUT.
Tracks: / Showing out / System (House version) / Showing out (Mortgage Mix).
Single 7": released on Supreme, Sep'86 by Supreme Records. Dist: PRT

Single 12": released on Supreme, Sep'86 by Supreme Records. Dist: PRT

Single 12": released on Supreme, Oct'86 by Supreme Records. Dist: PRT

Single 12": released on Supreme, Sep'86 by Supreme Records. Dist: PRT

Mel, Melle

MESSAGE II.
Single 7": released on Sugarhill, Jan'83 by MCA Records. Dist: Roots

Single 12": released on Sugarhill, Jan'83 by MCA Records. Dist: Roots

Mel & Tim

STARTING ALL OVER AGAIN.
Tracks: / Starting all over again / It hurts to want it so bad.
Single 7": released on Stax, Mar'82 by Ace Records. Dist: Pinnacle, Wellards, Swift, IMS, Polygram

Single 7": released on Stax, Sep'87 by Ace Records. Dist: Pinnacle, Wellards, Swift, IMS, Polygram

Melachrino, George

MELACHRINO MAGIC.
Cassette: released on Ditto, May'86 by Pickwick Records. Dist: Taylors

Melachrino Strings

BEYOND THE BLUE HORIZON.
Album: released on Warwick, Apr'79 by Warwick Records. Dist: CBS, MSD, Taylors, Solomon & Peres

Cassette: released on Warwick, Apr'79 by Warwick Records. Dist: CBS, MSD, Taylors, Solomon & Peres Deleted May'81.

GERSHWIN AND KERN GALA, A.
Album: released on Pressit, Oct'84 Dist: Taylors

Cassette: released on Pressit, Oct'84 Dist: Taylors
Cat. no: **LC C775**

ROMANTIC SERENADE.
Album: released on Pressit, Oct'84 Dist: Taylors

Cassette: released on Pressit, Oct'84 Dist: Taylors

STARDUST.
Album: released on Pressit, Oct'84 Dist: Taylors

Cassette: released on Pressit, Oct'84 Dist: Taylors

TIME FOR LOVING, A.
Double cassette: released on Pickwick(Ditto series), Jul'82 by Pickwick Records. Dist: PRT

Melanie

ARABESQUE.
Album: released on RCA, Aug'82 Dist: BMG

Cassette: released on RCA, Aug'82 Dist: BMG

BEST OF MELANIE.
Album: released on Buddah, Jul'85

Cassette: released on Buddah, Jul'85

BORN TO BE.
Album: released on Buddah, Aug'74

BRAND NEW KEY.
Single 7": released on Flashback, Jan'83 by Flashback Records/PRT Records. Dist: Mainline

CANDLES IN THE RAIN.
Album: released on Buddah, Aug'74

DIDN'T YOU EVER LOVE SOMEBODY.
Single 7": released on Neighborhood(USA), Nov'83 Dist: CBS

EVERY BREATH OF THE WAY.
Single 7": released on Neighborhood(USA), Sep'83 Dist: CBS

Single 12": released on Neighborhood(USA), Sep'83 Dist: CBS

Picture disc single: released on Neighborhood(USA), Sep'83 Dist: CBS

PROFILE: MELANIE.
Album: released on Teldec, Jul'81 Dist: Pinnacle, Celtic Music

Cassette: released on Teldec, Jul'81 Dist: Pinnacle, Celtic Music

SEVENTH WAVE.
Album: released on Neighborhood(USA), Nov'83 Dist: CBS

SPOTLIGHT ON MELANIE.
Double Album: released on PRT, Oct'81 by PRT Records.

Double cassette: released on PRT, Oct'81 by PRT Records.

Melba, Nellie

GREAT VOICES OF THE CENTURY.
Album: released on Bulldog, Mar'85 by Bulldog Records. Dist: President, Spartan, Swift, Taylors, Jazz Music

NELLIE MELBA.
Album: released on Bulldog, Feb'85 by Bulldog Records. Dist: President, Spartan, Swift, Taylors, Jazz Music

Meldonian, Dick

IT'S A WONDERFUL WORLD (Meldonian, Dick Trio).
Album: released on Statiras, Nov'87 by Statiras Records. Dist: Jazz Music

JERSEY SWING CONCERTS, (THE).
Album: released on Progressive(Import), Apr'83 Dist: Jazz Music

SOME OF THESE DAYS.
Album: released on Progressive(Import), Apr'81 Dist: Jazz Music

Melillo, Mike

SEPIA.
Album: released on Red, Jan'87 Dist: Cadillac, Jazz Horizons

Melis, Marcello

MARCELLO MELIS.
Album: released on Black Saint (Italy), Apr'79, Harmonia Mundi

NEW VILLAGE ON THE LEFT.
Album: released on Black Saint (USA Import), Aug'77

Melissa

GET YOUR LOVE RIGHT.
Single 7": released on Index, May'82 by Index Records. Dist: Swift

TEDDY BEAR.
Single 7": released on Identity, Oct'82 by Identity Records. Dist: Priority, BMG

Mellaa & Co

BE FREE.
Tracks: / Be free.
Single 12": released on Dancefloor(USA), Nov'87 Dist: Pinnacle

Melle Mel

WHITE LINES (DON'T DON'T DO IT) (see Grandmaster Flash) (Melle Mel & Grandmaster Flash).

Melle,Gill Quartet

QUADRAMA.
Album: released on Fantasy Inc USA, Feb'86 by Fantasy Inc USA Records. Dist: IMS, Polygram

Mellencamp, John Cougar

See also Cougar, John

AUTHORITY SONG.
Single 7": released on Riva, Feb'84 Dist: PRT

CHERRY BOMB.
Tracks: / Cherry bomb.
Single 7": released on Mercury, Nov'87 by Phonogram Records. Dist: IMS, Polygram

Single 12": released on Mercury, Nov'87 by Phonogram Records. Dist: IMS, Polygram

CRUMBLIN' DOWN.
Single 7": released on Riva, Nov'83 Dist: PRT

Single 12": released on Riva, Nov'83 Dist: PRT

JOHN COUGAR.
Compact disc: released on Riva, Jan'86 Dist: PRT

KID INSIDE.
Compact disc: released on Castle, Nov'86 by Castle Records. Dist: Pinnacle

LONELY OL' NIGHT.
Single 7": released on Riva, Oct'85 Dist: PRT

Single 12": released on Riva, Oct'85 Dist: PRT

LONESOME JUBILEE, THE.
Tracks: / Paper in fire / Down and out in paradise / Check it out / Real life, The / Cherry bomb / We are the people / Empty hands / Hard times for an honest man / Hot dogs and hamburgers / Rotty toot toot / Rooty toot toot.
Album: released on Mercury, Sep'87 by Phonogram Records. Dist: IMS, Polygram. Estim retail price in Sep'87 was £6.49.

Cassette: released on Mercury, Sep'87 by Phonogram Records. Dist: IMS, Polygram. Estim retail price in Sep'87 was £6.49.

Compact disc: released on Mercury, Sep'87 by Phonogram Records. Dist: IMS, Polygram

NOTHIN' MATTERS.
Tracks: / Hot night in a cold town / Ain't even done with the night / Don't misunderstand me / This time / Make me feel / To M.G. / (Wherever she may be) tonight / Wild angel / Cheapshot.
Compact disc: released on Riva, Jan'86 Dist: PRT

PAPER IN FIRE.
Tracks: / Paper in fire / Never too old.
Notes: * extra track on 12" version.
Single 7": released on Mercury, Sep'87 by Phonogram Records. Dist: IMS, Polygram

Single 12": released on Mercury, Sep'87 by Phonogram Records. Dist: IMS, Polygram

PINK HOUSES.
Single 7": released on Riva, Jun'84 Dist: PRT

ROCK IN THE USA.
Tracks: / Rock in the USA / Under the boardwalk.
Single 7": released on Riva, Apr'86 Dist: PRT

Single 12": released on Riva, Apr'86 Dist: PRT

SCARECROW.
Tracks: / Rain on the scarecrow / Grandmas's theme / Small town / Minutes to memories / Lonely ol' night / Face of the nation,The / Justice and independence '85 / Between a laugh and a tear / Rumbleseat / You've got to stand for something / R.O.C.K. in the U.S.A. / Kind of fella I am,The.
Compact disc: released on Riva, Nov'85 Dist: PRT

Album: released on Riva, Nov'85 Dist: PRT

Cassette: released on Riva, Nov'85 Dist: PRT

SMALL TOWN.
Single 7": released on Riva, Jan'86 Dist: PRT

Double-pack single: released on Riva, Jan'86 Dist: PRT

Single 12": released on Riva, Jan'86 Dist: PRT

Double-pack single: released on Riva, Jan'86 Dist: PRT

UH-HUH.
Compact disc: released on Riva, Aug'84 Dist: PRT

Album: released on Riva, Mar'84 Dist: PRT

Cassette: released on Riva, Mar'84 Dist: PRT

Compact disc: released on Riva, Mar'84 Dist: PRT

Mellow, Locksley

COME AND DINE WITH ME.
Single 12": released on Scarlet, Apr'82 by Scarlet Records. Dist: Cartel

ICE WATER.
Single 12": released on Scarlet, Jun'82 by Scarlet Records. Dist: Cartel

Mellow 'n' Roots

BRING BACK MY LOVE.
Single 12": released on K&K, Dec'84 by K&K Records. Dist: Jetstar

Mellow Rose

LET ME BE THE ONE.
Single 12": released on Nice, Nov'80

Mellstock Band

UNDER THE GREENWOOD TREE.
Tracks: / Arise and hail the joyful day / Morgianna / Pantaloon Quadrille,The / Hail happy morn / Kiss me my love and welcome / Awake and join the cheerful choir / Gipseys hornpipe,The / One-eyed fiddler,The / See heaven's high portals / I'm off to Charlestown / Awake ye mortals all / While shepherds watched / Fairy dance / Tink a tink / Behold the morning star.
Compact disc: released on Saydisc, Mar'87 by Saydisc Records. Dist: Taylors, Jazz Music, Swift, Projection, Essex, Gamut, Harmonia Mundi, Celtic Music

Album: released on Saydisc, Oct'86 by Saydisc Records. Dist: Taylors, Jazz Music, Swift, Projection, Essex, Gamut, Harmonia Mundi, Celtic Music

Cassette: released on Saydisc, Oct'86 by Saydisc Records. Dist: Taylors, Jazz Music, Swift, Projection, Essex, Gamut, Harmonia Mundi, Celtic Music

Melly, George

16 GOLDEN CLASSICS.
Tracks: / Mississippi mud / Hound dog / This train / Abdul Abulbul Amir / Mama don't allow it / Frankie and Johnnie / Send me to the 'lectric chair / I'm a ding dong daddy / My canary has circles under its eyes / Heebie jeebies / Black bottom / Sporting life / Ma Rainey's black bottom / St Louis blues / Spider crawl / Sent for you yesterday and here you come today.
Notes: Tracks 1 & 3 with Alex Welsh and his dixielanders; track 2 with Mick Mulligan's band & guests; 11 with Mick Mulligan & his band; 13 & 16 with mick Mulligan's band & guests. All tracks licensed from The Decca Record Co. Ltd. Design by Shoot That Tiger! (C) 1986 Castle communications Place, unit 7, 271, Merton Rd, London SW18 5JS. Bar Code 5\013428\920145

Album: released on Unforgettable, Dec'86 by Castle Communications Records. Dist: Counterpoint

HOMETOWN (Melly, George, with John Chilton's Feetwarmers).
Tracks: / Home town / I won't grow old / Sweet Georgia Brown / Home town / Boogie woogie man, The / I'm busy and you can't come in / It's de-lovely / My momma rocks me / Shaking the blues away / Draggin my heart around / Don't get around much anymore / I won't grow old / Thinking blues / Running wild.
Single 7": released on PRT, Nov'86 by PRT Records.

LET'S DO IT.
Album: released on Pye, Sep'80

Cassette: released on PRT, Sep'80 by PRT Records.

LIKE SHERRY WINE.
Album: released on PRT, Oct'81 by PRT Records.

Cassette: released on PRT, Oct'81 by PRT Records.

MAKIN' WHOOPEE.
Album: released on PRT, Mar'83 by PRT Records.

Cassette: released on PRT, Mar'83 by PRT Records.

Single 7": released on PRT, Apr'83 by PRT Records.

MANY MOODS OF MELLY, THE (Melly, George, with John Chilton's Feetwarmers).
Tracks: / Masculine woman, feminine men / It's the bluest kind of blues / Nobody's sweetheart / Drunk again / Kitchen man / St.Louis blues / Do your duty / As time goes by / Black mountain blues / Give her a little drop more / Send me to the 'lectric chair' / Happy feet.
Album: released on PRT, Oct'84 by PRT Records.

Cassette: released on PRT, Oct'84 by PRT Records.

Compact disc: released on PRT, Oct'84 by PRT Records.

MASCULINE WOMEN FEMININE MEN.
Single 7": released on PRT, Oct'84 by PRT Records.

MELLY IS AT IT AGAIN.
Album: released on Reprise (USA), Nov'76 by WEA Records. Dist: WEA

MELLY SINGS HOAGY.
Cassette: released on Ronnie Scott, Mar'78 Dist: Pye

RUNNING WILD (Melly, George, with John Chilton's Feetwarmers).
Album: released on PRT, Nov'86 by PRT Records.

Cassette: released on PRT, Nov'86 by PRT Records.

Compact disc: released on PRT, Nov'86 by PRT Records.

SINGS FATS WALLER AIN'T MISBEHAVIN.
Album: released on Pye, Mar'79

Cassette: released on Pye, Mar'79

SON OF NUTS.
Album: released on Warner Bros., May'73 by WEA Records. Dist: WEA

Melodeon greats

MELODEON GREATS Various artists (Various artists).
Album: released on Topic, May'81 by Topic Records. Dist: Jazz Music, Projection, Swift, Celtic Music, Cadillac, Ross, Duncans, Impetus

Melodeons

CLEVELAND LONG SWORD DANCE MUSIC.
Cassette:

Melodians

PREMEDITATION.
Album: released on Skynote, Sep'86 Dist: Sidewalk Records

SWEET SENSATION.
Album: released on Island, Feb'81 by Island Records. Dist: Polygram, Celtic Music

Melodic Clawhammer Banjo

MELODIC CLAWHAMMER BANJO-CHIEF O'NEILL'S FAVORITE Various artists (Various artists).
Album: released on Kicking Mule, Jan'78 Dist: Sonet, Projection, Swift, Celtic Music, Cadillac, Ross, Duncans, Impetus

Melodica Melodies

MELODICA MELODIES Various artists (Various artists).
Album: released on Trojan, May'83 by Trojan Records. Dist: Jetstar

Melodies for you

MELODIES FOR YOU (VOLUME 1) Various artists (Various artists).
:

Melody, Bobby

DREWS LAND ROCK.
Single 10": released on Pama Records, Jul'82

GOT TO BE SERTN.
Single 12": released on Music Works, Nov'82 Dist: Jetstar

KEEP ON TRYING.
Single 12": released on Negus Roots, Mar'82 by Negus Roots Records. Dist: Jetstar

KISSING AND LOVING.
Single 12": by Negus Roots Records. Dist: Jetstar

LIVESTOCK.
Album: released on Harry, Oct'85 by Harry Records. Dist: Jetstar

ROCKERS TILL THE MORNING.
Single 12": released on Nura, Oct'84 by Nura Records. Dist: Jetstarr*

TRUE TRUE LOVING.
Single 12": released on Negus Roots, Apr'81 by Negus Roots Records. Dist: Jetstar

Melody, Delroy

LIVE AND DIRECT.
Single 12": released on Sunset, Sep'84 Dist: EMI

MY LOVER.
Single 12": released on Sunset, Sep'83 Dist: EMI

POSSEE ARE YOU READY ?.
Single 12": released on Rhino, May'85 by Creole Records. Dist: PRT

SCHOOL GIRL (Melody, Delroy/Tony Zebra).
Single 12": released on Rhino, May'85 by Creole Records. Dist: PRT

Melody Four

LITTLE PICTURES.
Single 7": released on Essex, Apr'87 by Essex Records.

LOVE PLAYS SUCH FUNNY GAMES.
Tracks: / You've become habitual to me / You go to my head / How long has this been going on / I see your face before me / Harvest moon / I get along without you very well / My romance / I know it now / Secret love / Mister lucky / I'm sending you back your engagement ring / I feel romantic.
Album: released on Chabada(France), Sep'86 Dist: Essex

MELODY FOUR? SI SENOR.
Tracks: / Melody Four? Si senor / Brazil / Always in my heart / Silly song / Besame Mucho / Please stop / Taboo / Bahia / Donkey serenade,The / Begin the beguine / Perfidia.
Album: released on Chabada(France), Sep'86 Dist: Essex

Album: released on Nato(France), Dec'85 by Disques Nato. Dist: Essex

PALOMA, (LA) -LES MILLIONS D'ARLEQUIN.
Tracks: / La paloma / Les millions d'arlquin.
Notes: With: Steve Beresford/Tont Coel/Lol Coxhill/Yves Rochard.
Album: released on Chabada(France), Sep'86 Dist: Essex

TV MAIS OUI.
Album: released on Essex, Apr'87 by Essex Records.

Melody Makers

MET HER ON A RAINY DAY.
Single 7": released on EMI America, Apr'84 by EMI Records(UK). Dist: EMI

PLAY THE GAME RIGHT.
Album: released on Tuff Gong, Dec'85 by Tuff Gong Records. Dist: Jetstar

ROCK IT, BABY.
Single 7": released on EMI America, Sep'84 by EMI Records(UK). Dist: EMI

Melody, Micky

JUMBOS WE JUMBO.
Tracks: / Jumbos we Jumbo / Ungrateful girl (Troy Wonder).
Single 12": released on Taurus, Aug'86 Dist: Jetstar

UNDER ME FAT THING BOOGSIE.
Single 12": released on Jah Life, May'85 by Jah Life Records. Dist: Jetstar

Melody, Illiy

JUMB.
Tracks: / Jumb / Good good lover.
Single 12": released on Firehouse, Jun'86 Dist: Jetstar

OLDER THAN ME.
Tracks: / Older than me / Pressure me.
Single 12": released on Firehouse, May'86 Dist: Jetstar

Melon

DEEP CUT.
Tracks: / Quiet village / Uptown downtown / Hard core Hawaiian / Hawaiian break / Time enough for love / Somewhere faraway / Faraway / Pleasure before your breakfast / Funkasia / Gate of Japanesia, the.
Album: released on Epic, May'87 by CBS Records. Dist: CBS

Cassette: released on Epic, May'87 by CBS Records. Dist: CBS

Compact disc: released on Epic, May'87 by CBS Records. Dist: CBS

DEEP CUT.
Album: released on Epic, May'87 by CBS Records. Dist: CBS

Cassette: released on Epic, May'87 by CBS Records. Dist: CBS

FUNKASIA.
Tracks: / Only tonight.
Single 12": released on Epic, Feb'87 by CBS Records. Dist: CBS

GATE OF JAPANESIA.
Single 7": released on Epic, Mar'87 by CBS Records. Dist: CBS

Single 12": released on Epic, Mar'87 by CBS Records. Dist: CBS

HARDCORE HAWAIIAN.
Tracks: / Hardcore Hawaiian / Hawaiian break / Only tonight.
Single 12": released on Epic, Jul'87 by CBS Records. Dist: CBS

SERIOUS JAPAN.
Single 7": Deleted May'86.

Single 12":

WATER MELON.
Album: released on Alpha, Nov'84 by Alpha Records. Dist: Taylors, Gamut

Mel-O-Tones

BOMB SUTRA.
Album: released on Probe Plus, Mar'85 by Probe Plus Records. Dist: Probe Plus

Melson, Joe

BARBARA (A MILESTONE IN ROCK 'N' ROLL) Volume 2.
Album: released on Hickory, Sep'84 by Bear Family Records(Germany). Dist: Tonal

Melt down

MELT DOWN Various Artists (Various artists).
Album: released on Media Burn, Jul'86 by Rocks Off Record Emporium. Dist: Rough Trade, Cartel

Meltdown On Media

MELTDOWN ON MEDIA BURN Various artists (Various artists).
Album: released on Media Burn, 7 Nov'87 by Rocks Off Record Emporium. Dist: Rough Trade, Cartel

Melting Bear

IT MAKES NO DIFFERENCE.
Single 7": released on Beggars Banquet, Aug'85 by Beggars Banquet Records. Dist: WEA

Single 12": released on Beggars Banquet, Aug'85 by Beggars Banquet Records. Dist: WEA

Melton, Barry

LEVEL WITH ME (Melton, Barry (The Fish)).
Album: released on Rag Baby, Mar'81 Dist: Pinnacle, Red Lightnin'

ROBBERY.
Single 7": released on Rag Baby, Jan'82 Dist: Pinnacle, Red Lightnin'

Melvin, Brian

BRIAN MELVIN'S NIGHT FOOD.
Tracks: / Ain't nothin' but a party / Don't forget the bass / Night food / Zen turtles / For Max / Poly wanna rhythm / Primalass / Warrior, The / Continuum.
Compact disc: released on Timeless(Holland), Jan'87 Dist: Jazz Music, Jazz Horizons, Cadillac, Celtic Music

Album: released on Timeless(Holland), Nov'85 Dist: Jazz Music, Jazz Horizons, Cadillac, Celtic Music

Melvin, Harold

6 TRACK HITS (Melvin, Harold & The Bluenotes).
Extended-play record: released on Scoop 33, Sep'83 by Pickwick Records. Dist: Pickwick, PRT

Cassette: released on Scoop 33, Sep'83 by Pickwick Records. Dist: Pickwick, PRT

DON'T GIVE ME UP (Melvin, Harold & The Bluenotes).
Single 7": released on Philly World (USA), Apr'84 by Philly World Records (USA). Dist: Polygram

Single 12": released on Philly World (USA), Apr'84 by Philly World Records (USA). Dist: Polygram

DON'T LEAVE ME THIS WAY (Melvin, Harold & The Bluenotes).
Single 7": released on Philadelphia Int.(USA), May'79 Dist: Pinnacle

Single 7": released on Old Gold, Apr'83 by Old Gold Records. Dist: PRT, Counterpoint, Lightning, Jazz Music, Taylors

Single 12": released on Old Gold, 21 Nov'87 by Old Gold Records. Dist: PRT, Counterpoint, Lightning, Jazz Music, Taylors

GET OUT.
Single 7": released on Inferno, Nov'83 by Inferno Records. Dist: Inferno, Cartel, Pinnacle

GOLDEN HIGHLIGHTS OF HAROLD MELVIN.
Album: released on CBS(Import), Jun'86 by CBS Records. Dist: Counterpoint, Celtic Music, Jazz Music, Swift, Conifer

Cassette: released on CBS(Import), Jun'86 by CBS Records. Dist: Counterpoint, Celtic Music, Jazz Music, Swift, Conifer

GREATEST HITS: HAROLD MELVIN & THE BLUE NOTES (Melvin, Harold & The Bluenotes).
Album: released on Philadelphia Int.(USA), Feb'85 Dist: Pinnacle

IF YOU DON'T KNOW ME BY NOW (Melvin, Harold & The Bluenotes).
Single 7": released on Old Gold, Apr'83 by Old Gold Records. Dist: PRT, Counterpoint, Lightning, Jazz Music, Taylors

PRAYIN' (Melvin, Harold & The Bluenotes).
Tracks: / Prayin' (1986 Remix) / Prayin' (Instrumental) / Gospel (Acappela Mix).
Single 7": released on Source, May'86 by SMP Records.

Single 12": released on Source, May'86 by SMP Records.

Members

AT THE CHELSEA NIGHTCLUB.
Album: released on Virgin, Mar'84 by Virgin Records. Dist: Virgin, EMI

GOING WEST.
Single 7": released on Albion, Aug'83 by Albion Records. Dist: Spartan, Pinnacle

Single 12": released on Albion, Aug'83 by Albion Records. Dist: Spartan, Pinnacle

GOING WEST (LP).
Album: released on Albion, Aug'83 by Albion Records. Dist: Spartan, Pinnacle

WORKING GIRL.
Single 7": released on Albion, Jul'83 by Albion Records. Dist: Spartan, Pinnacle

Single 12": released on Albion, Jul'83 by Albion Records. Dist: Spartan, Pinnacle

Single 12": released on Albion, May'81 by Albion Records. Dist: Spartan, Pinnacle

Single 7": released on Albion, May'81 by Albion Records. Dist: Spartan, Pinnacle

Membranes

BACK CATALOGUE.
Album: released on Vinyl Drip, Mar'87 by Vinyl Drip Records. Dist: Backs, Cartel

CRACK HOUSE.
Album: released on Criminal Damage, Jun'85 by Criminal Damage Records. Dist: Backs, Cartel

DEATH IN TRAD ROCK.
Single 12": released on Criminal Damage, Dec'84 by Criminal Damage Records. Dist: Backs, Cartel

EVERYTHING'S BRILLIANT.
Tracks: / Everything's brilliant.
Single 7": released on In Tape, Mar'86 by In Tape Records. Dist: Red Rhino, Cartel

Single 12": released on In Tape, Mar'86 by In Tape Records. Dist: Red Rhino, Cartel

GIANT.
Album: released on Constrictor, Jun'86 by Constrictor Records. Dist: Red Rhino, Cartel

GIFT OF LIFE, THE.
Album: released on Creation, Jul'85 Dist: Rough Trade, Cartel

KENNEDY '63.
Tracks: / Kennedy '63 / Spike Milligan's tape recorder.
Single 7": released on Constrictor, Mar'87 by Constrictor Records. Dist: Red Rhino, Cartel

Album: released on Riva, May'75 Dist: PRT

MUSCLES.
Album: released on Rondelet Music & Records, May'82 Dist: Pinnacle, Cartel, Rondelet

Single 7": released on Rondelet Music & Records, May'82 Dist: Pinnacle, Cartel, Rondelet

PINSTRIPE HYPE (EP).
Single 7": released on Rondelet Music & Records, Nov'82 Dist: Pinnacle, Cartel, Rondelet

PULP BEATING 1984 AND ALL THAT.
Album: released on Criminal Damage, Feb'86 by Criminal Damage Records. Dist: Backs, Cartel

SONGS OF LOVE AND FURY.
Album: released on In Tape, Sep'86 by In Tape Records. Dist: Red Rhino, Cartel

SPIKE MILLIGAN'S TAPE (Membranes Meet Philip Boa & The Voodoo Club).
Tracks: / Spike Milligan's tape.
Single 12": released on Constrictor, Sep'86 by Constrictor Records. Dist: Red Rhino, Cartel

SPIKE MILLIGAN'S TAPE RECORDER.
Single 7": released on Criminal Damage, Jun'84 by Criminal Damage Records. Dist: Backs, Cartel

Memed My Hawk

MEMED MY HAWK Original Soundtrack.
Album: released on TER, Mar'84 Dist: Pinnacle

Memoirs Of Barry Lyndon

MEMOIRS OF BARRY LYNDON Read by Arthur Boland (Boland, Arthur).
Cassette: released on Colophone, Feb'81 by Audio-Visual Library Services. Dist: Audio-Visual Library Services

Memoirs of Sherlock...

MEMOIRS OF SHERLOCK HOLMES
(see under Conan Doyle, Sir Arthur).

Memories Are Made Of Hits

MEMORIES ARE MADE OF HITS(THE 60'S) Various 60's artists (Various artists).
Album: released on Decca, '74 by Decca Records. Dist: Polygram

MEMORIES ARE MADE OF THIS Original artists (Original artists).
Compact disc: released on Compact Collection, Sep'87 by Conifer Records. Dist: Conifer

MEMORIES ARE MADE OF THIS Various original artists (Various original artists).
Album: released on Ronco, Oct'81 by Ronco Records.

Cassette: released on Ronco, Oct'81 by Ronco Records.

Memories Of Moscow

MEMORIES OF MOSCOW Russian melodies & rhythms (Various artists).
Album: released on Accordion Record Club, '84 by Accordion Record Club. Dist: Accordion Record Club

Memories Of Osborne

MEMORIES OF OSBORNE Spoken word reminisences (Various artists).
Album: released on Saydisc, Jun'78 by Saydisc Records. Dist: Taylors, Jazz Music, Swift, Projection, Essex, Gamut, Harmonia Mundi, Celtic Music

Memories-15 Golden Hits

MEMORIES-15 GOLDEN HITS Various artists (Various artists).
Album: released on Hallmark, Mar'79 by Pickwick Records.

Cassette: released on Hallmark, Mar'79 by Pickwick Records.

Memory Of Justice Band

MASH DOWN BABYLON.
Album: released on Platinum Express, Mar'84 by Platinum Express Records. Dist: Jetstar

Memphis..

MEMPHIS.. Rock'n'roll capital of the world vol.1 (Various artists).
Album: released on White, Dec'86 by White Records. Dist: CSA

MEMPHIS-ROCK'N'ROLL CAPITAL OF THE WORLD Compilation recording (Various artists).
Album: released on White, Feb'87 by White Records. Dist: CSA

MEMPHIS-ROCK'N'ROLL CAPITAL OF THE WORLD VOL.4 (Various artists).
Album: released on White, May'87 by White Records. Dist: CSA

MEMPHIS-ROCK'N'ROLL CAPITAL OF THE WORLD VOL.5 (Various artists).
Album: released on White, May'87 by White Records. Dist: CSA

MEMPHIS BEAT Various original artists (Various original artists).
Album: released on Charly, '78 by Charly Records. Dist: Charly, Cadillac, Swift

MEMPHIS BLUES Various artists (Various artists).
Album: released on RCA(France), May'84 by RCA Records. Dist: Discovery, Silva Screen Records

Album: released on Krazy Kat(USA), Jul'85 Dist: Swift, Celtic Music, Wellards, Projection, Taylors, Charly, Hotshot, IRS

Double Album: released on RCA, Oct'85 Dist: BMG

Cassette: released on RCA. Oct'85 Dist: BMG

MEMPHIS GOLD:THE VERY BEST OF STAX Various original artists (Various original artists).
Album: released on Stax, Nov'82 by Ace Records. Dist: Pinnacle, Wellards, Swift, IMS, Polygram

Cassette: released on Stax, Nov'82 by Ace Records. Dist: Pinnacle, Wellards, Swift, IMS, Polygram

MEMPHIS HARMONICA KINGS Various artists (Lewis, Noah/Beale Street Rounders/Jed Davenport).
Album: released on Matchbox, Nov'83 Dist: Projection, Roots, Jazz Music, Celtic Music, Taylors

MEMPHIS HARMONICA KINGS 1929/30 Various artists (Various artists).
Album: released on Matchbox, Feb'84 Dist: Projection, Roots, Jazz Music, Celtic Music, Taylors

MEMPHIS HONKY TONK HILLBILLY Various artists (Various artists).
Album: released on Del Rio, Jun'86 by Ace Records. Dist: Pinnacle, Swift

MEMPHIS JAZZ FESTIVAL 1982 Various artists (Various artists).
Album: released on Jazzology, Mar'84 Dist: Jazz Music, Swift

MEMPHIS LABEL STORY (THE) (Various artists).
Album: released on Ace, Mar'87 by Ace Records. Dist: PRT, Pinnacle, Celtic Music, Cadillac, Jazz Music

MEMPHIS ROCKABILLY Various artists (Various artists).
Album: released on Ace, Mar'86 by Ace Records. Dist: PRT, Pinnacle, Celtic Music, Cadillac, Jazz Music

Album: released on Sunjay, Oct'87, CSA. Estim retail price in Oct'87 was £5.99.

MEMPHIS SHAKEDOWN Aarious artists (Various artists).
Album: released on Magpie, Apr'79 by Flyright Records. Dist: Swift, Jazz Music, Wellards, Cadillac

Memphis

YOU SUPPLY THE ROSES.
Single 7": released on Swamplands, Jan'85 Deleted '86.

Single 12": released on Swamplands, Jan'85

Memphis Blues

MEMPHIS BLUES 1927-37 (Various artists).
Album: released on HK, Sep'87 Dist: Swift

Memphis Jug Band

MEMPHIS JUG BAND 1927-34.
Tracks: / Packed my suitcase started to the train / Kansas city blues / Evergreen money blues / Coal oil blues / Peaches in the springtime / Jug band waltz / Feed your friend with a long handled spoon / I whipped my woman with a single-tree / Stonewall blues / He's in the jailhouse now / Move that thing / You got me rollin' / My love is cold / Jazzbo stomp / Tear it down bed slat and all / Fishin' in the dark / Rukus juice and chittlin' / Jug band quartette.
Notes: The Memphis Jug Band were one of the most popular and entertaining groups to perform on the infamous Beal Street in Memphis, sometimes referred to as "the Main Street of Negro America". The Memphis Jug Band performed both blues and good-time music and their recording career continued through out the Depression and re-issues of their output have been steady. This rlease fills in the gaps with some typical titles: (Mono...)
Album: released on Matchbox, Aug'86 Dist: Projection, Roots, Jazz Music, Celtic Music, Taylors

Memphis Masters

MEMPHIS MASTERS, THE.
Album: released on Ace, Mar'82 by Ace Records. Dist: PRT, Pinnacle, Celtic Music, Cadillac, Jazz Music

Memphis Minnie

HOT STUFF 1936-49.
Album: released on Magpie, Sep'87 by Flyright Records. Dist: Swift, Jazz Music, Wellards, Cadillac

WORLD OF TROUBLE.
Album: released on Flyright, Dec'82 by Flyright Records. Dist: Swift, Jazz Music, Wellards, Cadillac

Memphis Slim

20 BLUES GREATS: MEMPHIS SLIM.
Album: released on Deja Vu, Oct'86 by Deja Vu Records. Dist: Counterpoint, Record Services(Ireland), Jazz Music

BOOGIE WOOGIE PIANO.
Album: released on CBS, Feb'84 by CBS Records. Dist: CBS Deleted '87.

Cassette: released on CBS, Feb'84 by CBS Records. Dist: CBS

DIALOGUE IN BOOGIE (Memphis Slim & Philippe Lejeune).
Album: released on Happy Bird (Germany), Jul'83 Dist: Polygram, IMS

Cassette: released on Happy Bird (Germany), Jul'83 Dist: Polygram, IMS

I'LL JUST KEEP ON SINGIN' THE BLUES.
Album: released on Muse(Import), '81 Dist: Conifer, Cadillac, Cadillac, Discovery

LEGACY OF THE BLUES VOL.7.
Album: released on Sonet, '73 by Sonet Records. Dist: Jazz Music, Swift, Celtic Music, Roots, PRT, Sonet

MEMPHIS SLIM.
Album: released on Chess, Apr'87 by Charly Records. Dist: Charly, Celtic Music, Swift, Discovery, IMS, Polygram

Cassette: released on Chess, Apr'87 by Charly Records. Dist: Charly, Celtic Music, Swift, Discovery, IMS, Polygram

ROCK ME BABY.
Album: released on Black Lion, Sep'85 by Black Lion Records. Dist: Counterpoint, Jazz Music, Cadillac

ROCKIN' THE BLUES.
Album: released on Charly (R&B), Nov'81 by Charly Records. Dist: Charly, Cadillac

TRIBUTE TO BIG BILL ETC..
Album: released on Candid, Jun'86 Dist: Counterpoint, Cadillac, Jazz Music

UNISSUED 1963 BLUES FESTIVAL, THE (Memphis Slim\Sonny Boy Williamson\etc).
Album: released on Red Lightnin', Jan'87 by Red Lightnin' Records. Dist: Red Lightnin', Cadillac, Caroline, Hotshot, Lightning, Swift, Jazz Music, Projection

WILLIE'S BLUES (Memphis Slim & Willie Dixon).
Album: released on Original Blues Classics(USA), May'84

Memphis Tenorc's

BIG AS MEMPHIS.
Single 7": released on Hot Rock, Aug'80 by Hot Rock Records. Dist: Hot Rock

Men 2nd

RED TAPE.
Album: released on Antler, 21 Nov'87 by Antler Records(Belgium). Dist: Red Rhino, Cartel

Men At Play

DOCTOR JAM (IN THE FLAM).
Single 7": released on Design Communications, Sep'83 by Design Sound & Vision.

Single 12": released on Design Communications, Sep'83 by Design Sound & Vision.

Men At Work

BE GOOD JOHNNY.
Single 7": released on Epic, Feb'84 by CBS Records. Dist: CBS

Single 12": released on Epic, Feb'84 by CBS Records. Dist: CBS

Double-pack single: released on Epic, Feb'84 by CBS Records. Dist: CBS

BUSINESS AS USUAL.
Tracks: / Who can it be now / I can see it in your eyes / Down under / Underground / Helpless automaton / People just love to play with words / Be good Johnny / Touching the untouchables / Catch a star / Down by the sea / Who can it be now / I can see it in your eyes / Down under / Underground / Helpless automation / People just love to play with words / Be good Johnny / Touching the untouchables / Catch a star / Down by the sea.
Album: released on Epic, May'87 by CBS Records. Dist: CBS

Cassette: released on Epic, May'87 by CBS Records. Dist: CBS

Compact disc: released on Epic, Jan'83 by CBS Records. Dist: CBS

Album: released on Epic, Jun'82 by CBS Records. Dist: CBS

Cassette: released on Epic, Jun'82 by CBS Records. Dist: CBS

CARGO.
Tracks: / Dr Heckyll and Mr Jive / Overkill / Settle down my boy / Upstairs in my house / No sign of yesterday / It's a mistake / High wire / Blue for you / I like to / No restrictions.
Album: released on Epic, Apr'86 by CBS Records. Dist: CBS

Cassette: released on Epic, Apr'86 by CBS Records. Dist: CBS

Compact disc: released on Epic, Jan'83 by CBS Records. Dist: CBS

Album: released on Epic, Apr'83 by CBS Records. Dist: CBS

Cassette: released on Epic, Apr'83 by CBS Records. Dist: CBS

IT'S A MISTAKE.
Single 7": released on Epic, Jun'83 by CBS Records. Dist: CBS

Single 12": released on Epic, Jun'83 by CBS Records. Dist: CBS

Picture disc single: released on Epic, Jun'83 by CBS Records. Dist: CBS

LIVE IN SAN FRANCISCO.
Notes: Recorded live on stage during the Australian chart topping band's 1983 tour of America. Thirteen tracks in all, including their big hit "Down Under". Number of tracks: 13. Type of recording: Live. Total playing time: 60 minutes.
Video-cassette (VHS): released on CBS, Oct'84 by CBS Records. Dist: CBS

MARIA.
Single 7": released on Epic, Aug'85 by CBS Records. Dist: CBS

Single 12": released on Epic, Aug'85 by CBS Records. Dist: CBS

MEN AT WORK Topic sampler no.3.
Album: released on Topic, '81 by Topic Records. Dist: Jazz Music, Projection, Swift, Celtic Music, Cadillac, Ross, Duncans, Impetus

OVERKILL.
Single 7": released on Epic, Apr'83 by CBS Records. Dist: CBS

TWO HEARTS.
Tracks: / Man with two hearts / Giving up / Everything I need / Sail to you / Children on parade / Maria / Stay at home / Hard luck story / Still life / Snakes and ladders.
Compact disc: released on Epic, Sep'85 by CBS Records. Dist: CBS

Album: released on Epic, Sep'85 by CBS Records. Dist: CBS

Cassette: released on Epic, Sep'85 by CBS Records. Dist: CBS

Men From The Mountains

TREMBLING.
Single 12": released on One In Twelve, Sep'85 Dist: Backs, Cartel

Men Men

NATIVES DANCE.
Single 7": released on Gnu, Jun'84 by Gnu Records. Dist: Fast Forward, Cartel

Men O' Brass

FIREMAN'S GALOP (Men O' Brass Grand Massed Bands).
Album: released on EMI, Jun'83 by EMI Records(UK). Dist: EMI

Cassette: released on EMI, Jun'83 by EMI Records(UK). Dist: EMI

Men Of Iron

MEN OF IRON (Howard Pyle) Read by Ian Richardson.
Cassette: released on Caedmon(USA), Apr'83 by Caedmon (USA) Records. Dist: Gower, Roots

Men only

MEN ONLY Various artists (Various artists).
Album: released on Starblend, Nov'85 by Starblend Records.

Cassette: released on Starblend, Nov'85 by Starblend Records.

Men They Couldn't Hang

GHOSTS OF CABLE STREET.
Tracks: / Dream machine / Liverpool Lullaby*.
Notes: *Extra track on 12" only
Single 12": released on MCA, Apr'87 by MCA Records. Dist: Polygram

Cassette single: released on MCA, Apr'87 by MCA Records. Dist: Polygram

Single 7": released on MCA, Feb'87 by MCA Records. Dist: Polygram

GOLD RUSH.
Tracks: / Gold rush / Ghost of cable street,The / Walkin' talkin'.
Single 7": released on MCA, Jun'86 by MCA Records. Dist: Polygram

Single 12": released on MCA, Jun'86 by MCA Records. Dist: Polygram

GREEN BACK DOLLAR.
Single 7": released on Demon, Nov'85 by Demon Records. Dist: Celtic Music, Pinnacle, Jazz Music

Single 12": released on Demon, Nov'85 by Demon Records. Dist: Celtic Music, Pinnacle, Jazz Music

GREEN FIELDS OF FRANCE.
Single 7": released on Imp, Oct'84 by Demon. Dist: Pinnacle

Single 12": released on Imp, Oct'84 by Demon. Dist: Pinnacle

HOW GREEN IS THE VALLEY.
Album: released on MCA, Oct'86 by MCA Records. Dist: Polygram

Cassette: released on MCA, Oct'86 by MCA Records. Dist: Polygram

IRON MASTERS.
Single 7": released on Imp, Jun'85 by Demon. Dist: Pinnacle

Single 12": released on Imp, Jun'85 by Demon. Dist: Pinnacle

ISLAND IN THE RAIN.
Tracks: / Island in the rain / Country song / Silver dagger / Restless highway.
Single 7": released on Magnet, Oct'87 by Magnet Records. Dist: BMG

Picture disc single: released on Magnet, Oct'87 by Magnet Records. Dist: BMG

Single 12": released on Magnet, Oct'87 by Magnet Records. Dist: BMG

NIGHT OF A THOUSAND CANDLES.
Album: released on Imp, Jun'85 by Demon. Dist: Pinnacle

Cassette: released on Imp, Jun'85 by Demon. Dist: Pinnacle

SHIRT OF BLUE.
Tracks: / Shirt of blue / Johnny come home / Night to remember / Whiskey with me giro / Scarlet ribbons.
Single 7": released on MCA, Oct'86 by MCA Records. Dist: Polygram

Single 12": released on MCA, Oct'86 by MCA Records. Dist: Polygram

Men & Volts

TRAMPS IN BLOOM.
Album: released on New Rose, Mar'85 Dist: Pinnacle

Men Without Hats

ANTARCTICA.
Single 7": released on Statik, Mar'82 Dist: Rough Trade, Stage One

FOLK OF THE 80'S PART 3.
Album: released on Statik, Oct'85 Dist: Rough Trade, Stage One

Cassette: released on Statik, Oct'85 Dist: Rough Trade, Stage One

Compact disc: released on Statik, Oct'85 Dist: Rough Trade, Stage One

I'VE GOT THE MESSAGE.
Single 7": released on Statik, Dec'83 Dist: Rough Trade, Stage One

Single 12": released on Statik, Dec'83 Dist: Rough Trade, Stage One

LIVING IN CHINA.
Single 7": released on Statik, Jan'84 Dist: Rough Trade, Stage One

Single 12": released on Statik, Jan'84 Dist: Rough Trade, Stage One

POP GOES THE WORLD.
Tracks: / Pop goes the world / End of the world, The.
Single 7": released on Mercury, Nov'87 by Phonogram Records. Dist: IMS, Polygram

Single 12": released on Mercury, Nov'87 by Phonogram Records. Dist: IMS, Polygram

RHYTHM OF YOUTH.
Album: released on Statik, Oct'85 Dist: Rough Trade, Stage One

Cassette: released on Statik, Oct'85 Dist: Rough Trade, Stage One

Compact disc: released on Statik, Oct'85 Dist: Rough Trade, Stage One

SAFETY DANCE, THE.
Tracks: / Ban the game / Living in China / Great ones remember,The / I got the message / Cocoricci (Le tango des voleurs) / Safety dance,The / Ideas for walls / Things in my life / I like / Great ones remember,The (reprise).
Compact disc: released on Statik, Jan'83 Dist: Rough Trade, Stage One

SAFETY HATS.
Single 7": released on Statik, Mar'83 Dist: Rough Trade, Stage One

Single 12": released on Statik, Mar'83 Dist: Rough Trade, Stage One

---

WHERE DO THE BOYS GO?.
Single 7": released on Statik, Jun'84 Dist: Rough Trade, Stage One

Single 12": released on Statik, Jun'84 Dist: Rough Trade, Stage One

Mena, Billy

SHUT UP YER GOB.
Single 7": released on Mint, Apr'81 by Emerald Records. Dist: Ross, Solomon & Peres

Menace

GLC - R.I.P.
Album: released on Razor, May'86 by Razor. Dist: Pinnacle

YOUNG ONES, THE.
Single 7": released on Fresh, Apr'81 Dist: Jetstar

Menage

MEMORY.
Single 12": released on Carrere America (USA), Jul'83 by Polygram

Menard, D.L.

BACK DOOR, THE.
Album: Dist: Swift

CAJUN SATURDAY NIGHT.
Album: released on Demon, Feb'86 by Demon Records. Dist: Celtic Music, Pinnacle, Jazz Music

Album: released on Rounder(USA), Jan'85 Dist: Jazz Music, Projection, Swift, Celtic Music Cadillac, Ross, Duncans, Impetus

Mendelssohn

ALOHA (Mendelssohn's, Felix Hawaiian Serenaders).
Album: released on World, Oct'77 by EMI Records(UK). Dist: Conifer

---

EVERGREEN HAWAIIN STYLE (Mendelssohn's, Felix Hawaiian Serenaders).
Cassette: released on World, Feb'81 by EMI Records(UK). Dist: Conifer

Mendelssohn, Felix

GOLDEN AGE OF,THE (Mendelssohn's, Felix Hawaiian Serenaders).
Tracks: / Japanese sandman,The / Tiger rag / Oh lady be good / Goodbye blues / Sheik of Araby,The / In the mood / I got rhythm / St.Louis blues / Dinah / Crazy rhythm / Nobody's sweetheart / Cherokee / Solitude / Mood indigo / Whispering / Wabash blues.
Notes: Tracks 1,2,3,4,5: Feature Roland Peachy on the steel guitar/ Track: 16 features Harry Brooker on electric Hawaiian guitar: This compilation (P) 1981 EMI Records
Album: released on Golden Age, Jun'86 by Music For Pleasure Records. Dist: EMI

Cassette: released on Golden Age, Jun'86 by Music For Pleasure Records. Dist: EMI

Mendes Prey

WONDERLAND.
Tracks: / Wonderland / Can you believe it.
Single 7": released on Wag, Feb'86 by Wag Records. Dist: Cartel, Backs, Fast Forward, Probe, Revolver, Red Rhino

Single 12": released on Wag, Feb'86 by Wag Records. Dist: Cartel, Backs, Fast Forward, Probe, Revolver, Red Rhino

Mendes,Sergio

ALEGRIA.
Album: released on WEA, Sep'80 by WEA Records. Dist: WEA

BRAZIL 86'.
Album: released on A&M, Aug'86 by A&M Records. Dist: Polygram

Cassette: released on A&M, Aug'86 by A&M Records. Dist: Polygram

Compact disc: released on A&M, Jan'86 by A&M Records. Dist: Polygram

---

NON STOP.
Tracks: / Non stop / Flower of Bahia / Never gonna let you go.
Single 7": released on A&M, Aug'86 by A&M Records. Dist: Polygram

Single 12": released on A&M, Aug'86 by A&M Records. Dist: Polygram

---

SERGIO MENDES.
Album: released on A&M, Jul'83 by A&M Records. Dist: Polygram

Cassette: released on A&M, Jul'83 by A&M Records. Dist: Polygram

---

SERGIO MENDES & THE NEW BRAZIL 77 (Mendes,Sergio/New Brazil 77).
Album: released on Elektra, Jan'77 by WEA Records. Dist: WEA

VERY BEST OF SERGIO MENDES (Mendes Sergio & Brazill 66).
Album: released on Pickwick(A&M), May'84 by Pickwick Records. Dist: PRT

Cassette: released on Pickwick(A&M), May'84 by Pickwick Records. Dist: PRT

Mendez, Gerd Mayer

VILLAGE SONGS.
Album: released on Scarecrow, Apr'81

Mendez Prey

ON TO THE BORDERLINE/RUNNIN FOR YOU.
Single 7": released on MP, Jan'83 by MP Records. Dist: Neon

Mendoza, Lydia

LAGLORIA DE TEXAS.
Album: released on Arhoolie(USA), May'81 by Arhoolie Records. Dist: Jazz Music, Projection, Roots, Celtic Music, Cadillac, Ross, Duncans, Impetus

---

TEX-MEX BORDER MUSIC VOL 15 (LYDIA MENDOZA VOL 1).
Album: released on Folklyric(USA), Jan'79 by Arhoolie Records. Dist: Jazz Music, Projection, Roots, Celtic Music, Cadillac, Ross, Duncans, Impetus

---

TEX-MEX BORDER MUSIC VOL 16 (LYDIA MENDOZA VOL 2).
Album: released on Folklyric(USA), Jan'79 by Arhoolie Records. Dist: Jazz Music, Projection, Roots, Celtic Music, Cadillac, Ross, Duncans, Impetus

Mendoza Sisters

JUANITA MARIA.
Album: by Arhoolie Records. Dist: Jazz Music, Projection, Roots, Celtic Music, Cadillac, Ross, Duncans, Impetus

Mengalomania

FIVE FINGER SHUFFLE/PANIC STATION.
Single 7": released on Magnet, Nov'81 by Magnet Records. Dist: BMG

Single 12": released on Magnet, Nov'81 by Magnet Records. Dist: BMG

Meno,Roger

I FIND THE WAY.
Tracks: / I find the way / Do you really go.
Single 12": released on ZYX(Germany), Dec'85 by ZYX Records. Dist: Greyhound

Mensah, E.T.

ALL FOR YOU.
Album: released on Retro Afric, Oct'86, Projection, Roots, Celtic Music, Cadillac, Ross, Duncans, Impetus

Mental As Anything

FUNDAMENTAL.
Tracks: / You're so strong / Big wheel / Live it up / Surf & Mull & Sex & Fun / Good Friday / Date with destiny / Hold on / Stones of the heart / I just wanna be happy / Splashing / Bus ride.
Album: released on Epic, Apr'86 by CBS Records. Dist: CBS

Cassette: released on Epic, Apr'86 by CBS Records. Dist: CBS

LET'S GO TO PARADISE.
Tracks: / Let's go to paradise / My hands are tied.
Single 7": released on Epic, 13 Jun'87 by CBS Records. Dist: CBS

Single 12": released on Epic, 13 Jun'87 by CBS Records. Dist: CBS

Single 7": released on Epic, Jul'87 by CBS Records. Dist: CBS

LIVE IT UP.
Tracks: / Live it up / Good friday / Good Friday / Live it up.
Single 7": released on Epic, Jan'87 by CBS Records. Dist: CBS

Single 12": released on Epic, Jan'87 by CBS Records. Dist: CBS

Single 7": released on Epic, Mar'86 by CBS Records. Dist: CBS

Picture disc single: released on Epic, Mar'86 by CBS Records. Dist: CBS

Single 12": released on Epic, Mar'86 by CBS Records. Dist: CBS

MENTAL AS ANYTHING.
Album: released on Virgin, Feb'80 by Virgin Records. Dist: Virgin, EMI

MOUTH TO MOUTH.
Notes: Brand new album, Australian import.
Album: released on Pinnacle Imports, 28 Sep'87

YOU'RE SO STRONG.
Tracks: / You're so strong / Bus ride / Live it up / Good Friday / You're so strong / Take stars to your place.
Single 7": released on Epic, May'87 by CBS Records. Dist: CBS

Single 7": released on Epic, May'86 by CBS Records. Dist: CBS

Single 12": released on Epic, May'86 by CBS Records. Dist: CBS

Mental Illness

NEW PHYSICAL TREAMENTS DR W SARGENT.
Cassette: released on Seminar Cassettes, Oct'81 by Seminar Cassettes. Dist: Davidson Distribution, Eastern Educational Products Distrib., Forlaget Systime Distribution, Laser Books Ltd Distribution, MacDougall Distribution, Talktapes Distribution, Watkins Books Ltd Distribution, Norton, Jeff Distribution

Mental Maniaxe

MENTAL MANIAXE Various HM artists (Various artists).
Album: released on Ebony, Dec'83 by Ebony Records. Dist: Pinnacle, Ebony

Mental Stress

MENTAL STRESS & PHYSICAL FITNESS By Kenneth R.Pelletier (Pelletier, Kenneth R.).
Cassette: released on Psychology Today (USA), Oct'81 Dist: Seminar Cassettes

Menticide

BATHROOM IDEAS EXHIBITION EP.
Tracks: / Bathroom Ideas exhibition EP.
Single 7": released on Pink Flag, Mar'86 Dist: Rough Trade

Mentors

UP THE DOSE.
Album: released on Roadrunner(Germany), Jan'87 by Roadrunner Records (Germany). Dist: Pinnacle, Celtic Music

---

YOU AXED FOR IT.
Album: released on Roadrunner(Germany), Sep'85 by Roadrunner Records (Germany). Dist: Pinnacle, Celtic Music

Menudo

IF YOU'RE NOT HERE(BY MY SIDE).
Single 7": released on RCA, Oct'84 Dist: BMG

Menuhin, Yehudi

BRAHMS VIOLIN CONCERTO.
Video-cassette (VHS): released on PMI, Aug'87 by PMI Records. Dist: EMI*

TEA FOR TWO (see Grappelli, Stephane) (Menuhin, Yehudi & Stephane Grappelli).
TOP HAT - SONGS BY FRED ASTAIRE (Menuhin,Yehudi & Stephane Grappelli).
Tracks: / Puttin on the Ritz / Way you look tonight,The / He loves and she loves / Isn't this a lovely day (To be caught in the rain) / Piccolino,The / Alison / Change partners / Top hat, white tie and tails / They can't take that away from me / Continental,The / They all laughed / Amanda / Funny face / Carioca.
Notes: Sir Yehudi Menuhin (Violin) - Stephane Grappelli (Violin & Piano) - with Instrumental Ensemble: conducted and arranged by Nelson Riddle: (P) 1981 Original sound recording made by EMI Records Ltd: Top Hat - Songs made famous by Fred Astaire.
Album: released on CFP(Classics For Pleasure), Aug'86 by Music For Pleasure Records. Dist: EMI

Cassette: released on CFP(Classics For Pleasure), Aug'86 by Music For Pleasure Records. Dist: EMI

Menza,Don

HIP POCKET (LIVE AT CARMELOS).
Album: released on Palo Alto (Italy), Jan'84

Menzies, Ian

REUNION JAZZ REVIVAL (Menzies, Ian & His Clyde Valley Stompers).
Album: released on Country House, Jun'82 by Scotdisc Records. Dist: Taylors, Duncans, Sounds of Scotland, BGS

Cassette: released on Country House, Jun'82 by Scotdisc Records. Dist: Taylors, Duncans, Sounds of Scotland, BGS

Mephisto Waltz

MEPHISTO WALTZ.
Album: released on MLP Supporti Fonografichi, Oct'87 Dist: Cartel, Red Rhino. Estim retail price in Oct'87 was £4.99.

Merc & Monk

BABY FACE.
Single 7": released on Manhattan, May'85 by EMI Records(UK). Dist: EMI

Single 12": released on Manhattan, May'85 by EMI Records(UK). Dist: EMI

Mercenary Skank

NO MORE DANCING (EP).
Single 7": released on Criminal Damage, Oct'84 by Criminal Damage Records. Dist: Backs, Cartel

---

WORKERS GIANTS.
Single 12": released on Before The Storm, Sep'85 by Mercenary Skank Records. Dist: Backs, Cartel

Mercer, Johnny

AUDIO SCRAP BOOK.
Album: released on Magic, Jan'84 Dist: Celtic Music, Submarine, Swift, Wellards, Conifer, Jazz Music

Cassette: released on Magic, Jan'84 Dist: Celtic Music, Submarine, Swift, Wellards, Conifer, Jazz Music

---

DON'T FENCE ME IN (Mercer,Johnny & His Music Shop).
Album: released on Dance Band Days, Jun'86 by Prism Leisure Corporation PLC. Dist: Prism Leisure, Jazz Music, Taylors

Cassette: released on Dance Band Days, Jun'86 by Prism Leisure Corporation PLC. Dist: Prism Leisure, Jazz Music, Taylors

---

MUSIC SHOP.
Album: released on Artistic, Jan'84 by Submarine Records. Dist: Wellards, Swift, Jazz Music, Clyde Factors

Cassette: released on Artistic, Jan'84 by Submarine Records. Dist: Wellards, Swift, Jazz Music, Clyde Factors

Merchant

ROCK IT.
Tracks: / Rock it / Pan in danger.
Single 7": released on Hot Vinyl, Jul'86 by Hot Vinyl Records. Dist: Jetstar

Single 12": released on Hot Vinyl, Jul'86 by Hot Vinyl Records. Dist: Jetstar

Merchant sugar

TEARS OF A CLOWN (Sugar Merchant).
Tracks: / Tears of a clown / Raggamuffin.
Single 12": released on UK Bubblers, Jul'86 by Greensleeves Records. Dist: BMG, Jetstar

Mercurian

SHOT DOWN IN FLAMES.
Single 7": released on Arcadia, Jan'82 Dist: Cartel

Mercury

TOO HOT.
Single 7": released on La Fell, Feb'85 by La Fell Records. Dist: Pinnacle

Single 12": released on La Fell, Feb'85 by La Fell Records. Dist: Pinnacle

Mercury All Stars

KID ORY 1944 (Mercury All Stars Jazz Combination).
Album: released on Joy, Oct'81 by President Records. Dist: Jazz Music, Swift, President

Mercury Dance Classics

MERCURY DANCE CLASSICS various artists (Various artists).
Album: released on Mercury(USA), Oct'87 by Phonogram Records. Dist: Pinnacle

Cassette: released on Mercury(USA), Oct'87 by Phonogram Records. Dist: Pinnacle

Mercury, Freddie

BARCELONA (Mercury, Freddie & Montserrat Caballe).
Tracks: / Barcelona / Exercises in free love / Barcelona (extended version).
Single 7": released on Polydor, Oct'87 by Polydor Records. Dist: Polygram, Polydor

Single 12": released on Polydor, Oct'87 by Polydor Records. Dist: Polygram, Polydor

---

GREAT PRETENDER.
Tracks: / Great pretender(the) / Exercises in free love.
Single 7": released on Parlophone, Feb'87 by EMI Records(UK). Dist: EMI

Video-cassette (VHS): released on Picture Music International, Mar'87 by Picture Music International. Dist: EMI

Single 7": released on Parlophone, Feb'87 by EMI Records(UK). Dist: EMI

Single 7": released on Parlophone, Feb'87 by EMI Records(UK). Dist: EMI

GREAT PRETENDER, THE (VIDEO).
Video-cassette (VHS): released on PMI, '87 by PMI Records. Dist: EMI*

MR BAD GUY.
Tracks: / Lets turn it on / Made in heaven / I was born to love you / Fool'in around / Your kind of lover / Mr bad Guy / Man made paradise / There must be more to life than this / Living on my own / My Love is dangerous / Love me like there is no tomorrow.
Compact disc: released on CBS, Aug'85 by CBS Records. Dist: CBS

Album: released on CBS, Apr'85 by CBS Records. Dist: CBS

Cassette: released on CBS, Apr'85 by CBS Records. Dist: CBS

VIDEO EP.
Tracks: / I was born to love you / Made in heaven / Time / Living on my own.
Notes:
Four promo's for the Queen lead singer's solo recording-" I was born to love you"," Made in

heaven","Time" and the banned for T.V. " Living on my own". 1986 Production. Number of tracks 4 Type of recording: E.P. Total playing time : 20 minutes.

Mercury Rockabillies

MERCURY ROCKABILLIES.
Album: released on Mercury, Apr'81 by Phonogram Records. Dist: IMS, Polygram

Mercy Dee

G I FEVER.
Notes:
Retail price not advised!
Album: released on Crown Prince, Nov'85 by Mr.R&B Records. Dist: Celtic Music, Swift

Mercy Mercy

IT MUST BE HEAVEN.
Single 7": released on Ensign, Oct'84 by Ensign Records. Dist: Chrysalis, CBS

Single 12": released on Ensign, Oct'84 by Ensign Records. Dist: Chrysalis, CBS

WHAT ARE GONNA DO ABOUT IT.
Single 7": released on Ensign, Aug'85 by Ensign Records. Dist: Chrysalis, CBS

Single 12": released on Ensign, Aug'85 by Ensign Records. Dist: Chrysalis, CBS

Mercy Ray

SWOOP SWOOP ROCK ROCK.
Notes:
Track details not advised.
Album: released on Charisma, Nov'85 by Virgin Records. Dist: EMI

Cassette: released on Charisma, Nov'85 by Virgin Records. Dist: EMI

Mercyful Fate

BEGINNING, THE.
Album: released on Roadrunner, 7 Nov'87 Dist: Rough Trade, Cartel

BLACK FUNERAL.
Single 12": released on Music For Nations, Nov'83 by Music For Nations Records. Dist: Pinnacle

DON'T BREAK THE OATH.
Album: released on Music For Nations, Jul'84 by Music For Nations Records. Dist: Pinnacle

MELISSA.
Album: released on Music For Nations, Oct'83 by Music For Nations Records. Dist: Pinnacle

Merican, Mikey

CONTROL THE DANCE HALL.
Single 12": released on Unity Sound, Feb'87 Dist: Jetstar

Merlin & Percival

MERLIN & PERCIVAL (various artists) (Various artists).
Cassette: released on Anvil, Jan'81 Dist: Taylors

Merman, Ethel

MERMAN SINGS MERMAN.
Cassette: released on Decca, Apr'84 by Decca Records. Dist: Polygram

Album: released on Jasmine, Mar'85 by Jasmine Records. Dist: Counterpoint, Cadillac, Taylors, Wellards, Swift, Jazz Music

WORLD IS YOUR BALLOON, THE.
Tracks: / Little girl from Little Rock, A / Diamonds are a girls best friend / Dearie / I said my pajamas (and put on my prayers) / It's so nice to have a man around the house / If I knew you were coming I'd've baked a cake / Calico Sal / She's shimmyin' on the beach again / Hawaii / Ukulele lady / Lake song, The / Don't believe it / Once upon a nickel / Oldies / Love is the reason / World is your balloon, The / Make the man love me / You say the nicest things / Husband, A - a wife / If you catch a little cold (I'll sneeze for you).
Album: released on MCA, May'87 by MCA Records. Dist: Polygram

Cassette: released on MCA, May'87 by MCA Records. Dist: Polygram

Merran

OH CHIMERA.
Single 7": released on Siren, Aug'85 by Virgin Records. Dist: EMI

Single 12": released on Siren, Aug'85 by Virgin Records. Dist: EMI

Merrell Ray

BIG COUNTRY.
Album: released on President, Dec'80 by President Records. Dist: Spartan, Taylors, Jazz Music

Cassette: released on President, Dec'80 by President Records. Dist: Spartan, Taylors, Jazz Music

BIG JOHN WAYNE/MOVIN ON DOWN.
Single 7": released on President, Apr'81 by President Records. Dist: Spartan, Taylors, Jazz Music

BINGO COWBOYS/SEEDS.
Single 7": released on President, Sep'82 by President Records. Dist: Spartan, Taylors, Jazz Music

DISCO COUNTRY STYLE.
Album: released on President, Apr'84 by President Records. Dist: Spartan, Taylors, Jazz Music

I WILL LOVE YOU/A LITTLE WHITE LIE.
Single 7": released on Satril, Dec'83 by Satril Records. Dist: PRT

SEEDS OF LOVE.
Album: released on President, Feb'82 by President Records. Dist: Spartan, Taylors, Jazz Music

Merrick & Tibbs

CALL OF THE WILD/TIGER TIGER.
Single 7": released on CBS, Feb'83 by CBS Records. Dist: CBS

Single 12": released on CBS, Feb'83 by CBS Records. Dist: CBS

Merrill, Helen

HELEN MERRILL.
Tracks: / Don't Explain / You'd be so nice to come home to / Whats new / Falling in love with love / Yesterdays / Born to be blue / Wonderful.
Compact disc: released on Phonogram, Jan'84 by Phonogram Records. Dist: Polygram

MERRILL, HELEN\GARY PEACOCK TRIO (Merrill, Helen\Gary Peacock Trio).
Album: released on Storyville, Nov'86 by Storyville Records. Dist: Swift

ROGERS & HAMMERSTEIN ALBUM.
Tracks: / It might as well be spring / Hello young lovers / I have dreamed / People will say we're in love / Getting to know you / My lord & master / If I loved you / My favorite things / Sound of music (The).
Notes: All songs written by: Richard Rogers & Oscar Hammerstein II.
Album: released on DRG(USA), Apr'87 by DRG Records Inc.(USA). Dist: Conifer

Cassette: released on DRG(USA), Apr'87 by DRG Records Inc.(USA). Dist: Conifer

SHADE OF DIFFERENCE.
Tracks: / Never will I marry / While we're young / Lonely woman / I should care / Lady must live, A / I want a little boy / Spring can really hang you up the most / My funny valentine / Lover come back to me / Where go you go? / Where do you go?.
Album: released on Fantasy (USA), Jun'86 by Fantasy Inc USA Records. Dist: IMS, Polygram

Cassette: released on Fantasy (USA), Jun'86 by Fantasy Inc USA Records. Dist: IMS, Polygram

SHADE OF DIFFERENCE, A.
Album: released on Spotlite, Jan'83 by Spotlite Records. Dist: Cadillac, Jazz Music, Spotlite

SOMETHING SPECIAL.
Album: released on Inner City, Apr'79 Dist: Jetstar

S'POSIN.
Notes:
Mono production: with Gary Peacock Trio: Track details not advised
Album: released on Storyville, May'86 by Storyville Records. Dist: Swift

Merritt, Max

KEEPING IN TOUCH.
Album: released on Polydor, Jan'78 by Polydor Records. Dist: Polygram, Polydor

LITTLE EASIER, A (Merritt, Max & The Meteors).
Album: released on Arista, Jan'75 by Arista Records. Dist: BMG

OUT OF THE BLUE.
Album: released on Arista, Jan'76 by Arista Records. Dist: BMG

Merry Christmas

MERRY CHRISTMAS Various Artists (Various artists).
Tracks: / Silent Night / Adeste Fideles / Let it snow!Let it snow!Let it snow! / Have yourself a merry littl Christmas / I like a sleighride (jingle bells) / I'll be home for Christmas / Christmas dinner country syle / O holy night / Little drummer boy / White Christmas / O little town of bethlehem / Do you hear what I hear? / Santa Claus is comin' to town / First Noel (the) / Christmas song, The / Christmas waltz (the).

Album: released on EMI (Italy), Dec'86 by EMI Records(UK). Dist: Conifer

Cassette: released on EMI (Italy), Dec'86 by EMI Records(UK). Dist: Conifer

Compact disc: released on Entertainers, Nov'87

MERRY CHRISTMAS AND A HAPPY NEW YEAR A Various artists.
Album: released on MFP, Oct'85 by Music For Pleasure Records. Dist: EMI

Cassette: released on MFP, Oct'85 by Music For Pleasure Records. Dist: EMI

Merry Christmas Mr. Lawrence

MERRY CHRISTMAS MR. LAWRENCE
Original soundtrack (Various artists).
Compact disc: released on Virgin, Jul'86 by Virgin Records. Dist: Virgin, EMI

Merry christmas to you

MERRY CHRISTMAS TO YOU various artists (Various artists).
Album: released on Warwick, Nov'84 by Warwick Records. Dist: CBS, MSD, Taylors, Solomon & Peres

Cassette: released on Warwick, Nov'84 by Warwick Records. Dist: CBS, MSD, Taylors, Solomon & Peres

Merry Go Round

BEST OF MERRY GO ROUND.
Album: released on Rhino (USA), Jan'86 by Rhino Records (USA). Dist: Pinnacle

Merry Widow

(HIGHLIGHTS).
Album: released on Note, Oct'76 by EMI Records(UK). Dist: EMI

MERRY WIDOW Various artists (Various artists).
Album: released on Teldec, Jun'81 Dist: Pinnacle, Celtic Music

Cassette: released on Teldec, Jun'81 Dist: Pinnacle, Celtic Music

MERRY WIDOW (Various artists).
Tracks: / Merry Widow waltz / Maxim's / Vilia / Girls, girls, girls. / Merry Widow waltz / Night / Gypsy music / Can-can.
Cassette: released on CBS, Feb'87 by CBS Records. Dist: CBS

Album: released on CBS, Feb'87 by CBS Records. Dist: CBS

MERRY WIDOW (THE).
Notes: This new production was mounted by The New Sadler's Wells Opera earlier this year and starred (Eiddwen Harrhy, Alan Oke, Helen Kucharek and Glenn Winslade). It was conducted by Barry Wordsworth, who also coducted this recording. Produced for Records by Normal Newell and Engineered by John Kurlander, this recording was produced in Digital at the Olympic Sound Studios, London on June 30, 1986.
Album: released on TER, Sep'86 Dist: Pinnacle

Cassette: released on TER, Sep'86 Dist: Pinnacle

Compact disc: released on TER, Sep'86 Dist: Pinnacle

Merrybell Choir

TELL IT TO THE PEOPLE.
Album: released on Myrrh, May'85 by Word Records(UK)Ltd.. Dist: Word, CBS

Cassette: released on Myrrh, May'85 by Word Records(UK)Ltd.. Dist: Word, CBS

Mersaide

NON STOP DANCING.
Tracks: / Non stop dancing.
Single 7": released on Legal Light, Sep'87 Dist: Jetstar

Mersey Beat

MERSEY BEAT Various artists (Various artists).
Album: released on Parlophone, Oct'83 by EMI Records(UK). Dist: EMI

Cassette: released on Parlophone, Oct'83 by EMI Records(UK). Dist: EMI

Mersey Beats

BEAT AND BALLADS.
Album: released on Edsel, Oct'82 by Demon Records. Dist: Celtic Music, Pinnacle, Jazz Music

GREATEST HITS: MERSEY BEATS.
Album: by Look Records. Dist: Celtic Music, Jazz Music

I THINK OF YOU.
Single 7": released on Old Gold, Jul'82 by Old Gold Records. Dist: PRT, Counterpoint, Lightning, Jazz Music, Taylors

THIS IS MERSEYBEAT (MEDLEY).
Single 7": released on Tudor, Oct'81 Dist: Parnote, Wynd-Up

Single 12": released on Tudor, Oct'81 Dist: Parnote, Wynd-Up

MERSEYBEATS, THE.
Album: released on Fontana (Germany), Oct'87 Dist: IMS

Cassette: released on Fontana (Germany), Oct'87 Dist: IMS

Mertens, Wim

EDUCES ME.
Single 7": released on Factory, 13 Jun'87 by Factory Records. Dist: Cartel, Pinnacle

HIROSE.
Tracks: / Hirose / Noli me tangere.
Single 7": released on Les Disques Du Crepuscule(Belgium), Dec'86 by Les Disques Du Crepuscule (Belgium). Dist: Rough Trade, Pinnacle, Island, Polygram

INSTRUMENTAL SONGS.
Album: released on Les Disques Du Crepuscule(Belgium), Dec'86 by Les Disques Du Crepuscule (Belgium). Dist: Rough Trade, Pinnacle, Island, Polygram

MAN WITH NO FORTUNE, A And with a name to come.
Compact disc: released on Les Disques Du Crepuscule(Belgium), Nov'86 by Les Disques Du Crepuscule (Belgium). Dist: Rough Trade, Pinnacle, Island, Polygram

Merthyr Lewis band

WINTER CELEBRATION, A.
Album: released on Pye, Nov'79

Merton Parkas

FACE IN THE CROWD.
Cassette: released on Beggars Banquet, Oct'79 by Beggars Banquet Records. Dist: WEA

FLAT 19/BAND OF GOLD.
Single 7": released on Well Suspect, Nov'83 by Well Suspect Records. Dist: Pinnacle

YOU NEED WHEELS (5 TRACK EP).
Single 12": released on Beggars Banquet, Apr'83 by Beggars Banquet Records. Dist: WEA

Mervyn, Junior

APARTHEID.
Single 12": released on Greensleeves, May'86 by Greensleeves Records. Dist: BMG, Jetstar, Spartan

APARTHEID (LP).
Album: released on Greensleeves, Aug'86 by Greensleeves Records. Dist: BMG, Jetstar, Spartan

Mervyn Mouse

MERVYN MOUSE AT THE FAIR.
Cassette: released on Look & Listen, Nov'84 by Listen For Pleasure. Dist: EMI

MERVYN MOUSE AT THE ZOO.
Cassette: released on Look & Listen, Nov'84 by Listen For Pleasure. Dist: EMI

MERVYN MOUSE GOES CAMPING.
Cassette: released on Look & Listen, Nov'84 by Listen For Pleasure. Dist: EMI

Mesple Mady

CANTILENA ARIA (CANTILENA).
Single 7": released on EMI, Jun'85 by EMI Records(UK). Dist: EMI

Message

ASTRAL JOURNEY.
Album: released on Brian, Mar'79

MESSAGE PART 2 Compilation recording (Various artists).
Album: released on Jah Shaka, Feb'87 by Jah Shaka Records. Dist: Jetstar, Revolver, Cartel

Message People

AFRICAN PEOPLE.
Album: released on Message, Feb'87 by Greensleeves. Dist: Jetstar, BMG

Single 12": released on Music For Nations, Mar'87 by Music For Nations Records. Dist: Pinnacle

Messenger Service

GET STREETWISE.
Single 12": by Creole Records.

Messenger,Ian

LIVING IN THE NIGHT.
Tracks: / Living in the night / Love active.
Single 7": released on Warner Bros., Dec'85 by WEA Records. Dist: WEA

Messengers

GREAT INSTITUTIONS.
Single 7": released on Music Fest, Jun'84 by Chrysalis Records. Dist: Polygram

Single 12": released on Music Fest, Jun'84 by Chrysalis Records. Dist: Polygram Deleted '85.

Messina, Russ

ACCORDION IN THE MODERN MOOD.
Album: released on Accordion Record Club, '84 by Accordion Record Club. Dist: Accordion Record Club

Metal Battle

METAL BATTLE Various artists (Various artists).
Album: released on Neat, Jan'85 by Neat Records. Dist: Pinnacle, Neat

Metal Boys

SWEET MARILYN/FUGUE FOR A DARKENING.
Single 7": released on Rough Trade, Jun'79 by

Rough Trade Records. Dist: Rough Trade, Cartel

Metal Church

DARK, THE.
Tracks: / Method of your madness / Watch the children play / Over my dead body / Dark, The / Psycho / Line of death / Burial at sea / Western alliance / Ton of bricks / Start the fire.
Album: released on Elektra (USA), Nov'86 by Elektra/Asylum/Nonesuch Records. Dist: WEA, Pinnacle

Cassette: released on Elektra (USA), Nov'86 by Elektra/Asylum/Nonesuch Records. Dist: WEA, Pinnacle

Metal City

METAL CITY (Various artists).
Notes: 12 track compilation originating from NE England heavy rock label Neat Records, and three cuts apiece from Avenger, Warfare, Venom and Saracen. 1985 production.
Video-cassette (VHS): released on Polygram, Jun'86 by Polygram Records. Dist: Polygram

Video-cassette [Betamax]: released on Polygram, Jun'86 by Polygram Records. Dist: Polygram

Metal concussion

METAL CONCUSSION (Various artists).
Tracks: / Malibu beach nightmare / Trapped under ice / Black metal / War pigs / Motorhead / Back on the streets / Shake your heads / Open fire / Won't get out alive / Thunder on the tundra / Axe crazy / Never satisfied.
Album: released on Killerwatt, Jun'86 by Killerwatt Records. Dist: PRT, Kingdom Records

Cassette: released on Killerwatt, Jun'86 by Killerwatt Records. Dist: PRT, Kingdom Records

Metal Doughnut Band

LAURA NORDER.
Single 12": released on Vuggum, Apr'85 by Vuggum Records. Dist: Red Rhino, Cartel

Metal Fatigue

METAL FATIGUE Heavy metal artists (Various artists).
Album: released on Ebony, Dec'83 by Ebony Records. Dist: Pinnacle, Ebony

Metal For Muthas

METAL FOR MUTHAS various artists (Various artists).
Album: released on EMI, Jan'80 by EMI Records(UK). Dist: EMI

Album: released on Wishbone, Oct'84 by Wishbone Records. Dist: Pinnacle

METAL FOR MUTHAS-VOL.2.
Album: released on EMI, May'80 by EMI Records(UK). Dist: EMI

Metal Inferno

METAL INFERNO various artists (Various artists).
Album: released on Kastle Killers, Feb'85 Dist: Castle Communications*, Cartel

Cassette: released on Kastle Killers, Feb'85 Dist: Castle Communications*, Cartel

Metal Killers

METAL KILLERS III (Various artists).
Tracks: / White line fever / Blood guts & beer / Nothing to lose / Urban guerilla / Now comes the storm / Not for sale / Run like hell / Beerdrinkers & hellraisers / Start raisin' hell / Last flight / Bump'n'grind.
Double Album: released on Raw Power, Apr'86 by Castle Communications Records. Dist: Pinnacle

Cassette: released on Raw Power, Apr'86 by Castle Communications Records. Dist: Pinnacle

METAL KILLERS KOLLECTION (Various artists).
Tracks: / Tragedy (live) / Let them eat metal / Rock six times / Hang 'em high / Heat of the night / Eat the rich / Sabbath bloody sabbath / Boys nite out / Goin' on crazy / Friends of hell / Destroyer / Burn the Kings Road / Restless and wild / Sorcerer / I'll get you rockin' / Crazy motorcycle / Turn the hell on / Hot'n'ready / Break the chain / Heartuser / Angeline / Art & illusion / Ready as hell.
Notes: Designed: Shoot That Tiger! This compilation (c)1986 Castle Communication Plc, Unit 7, 271 Merton Road, LOndon SW18 5JS. Bar code: 5 013428 131343.
Album: released on Castle Communications, Apr'86 by Castle Communications. Dist: PRT, Pinnacle, Cartel

Cassette: released on Castle Communications, Apr'86 by Castle Communications. Dist: PRT, Pinnacle, Cartel

Album: released on Castle Communications, Nov'85 by Castle Communications. Dist: PRT, Pinnacle, Cartel

Cassette: released on Castle Communications, Nov'85 by Castle Communications. Dist: PRT, Pinnacle, Cartel

Compact disc: released on Collector Series, '86 by Castle Communications Records. Dist:

BMG

METAL KILLERS VOL 1 various artists (Various artists).
Album: released on Kastle Killers, Jan'85 Dist: Castle Communications*, Cartel

Cassette: released on Kastle Killers, Jan'85 Dist: Castle Communications*, Cartel

METAL KILLERS VOL I.I. various artists (Various artists).
Album: released on Kastle Killers, Jan'85 Dist: Castle Communications*, Cartel

Cassette: released on Kastle Killers, Jan'85 Dist: Castle Communications*, Cartel

Metal Machine

METAL MACHINE various artists (Various artists).
Album: released on Roadrunner(Germany), Dec'84 by Roadrunner Records (Germany). Dist: Pinnacle, Celtic Music

Metal Madness

METAL MADNESS (Various artists).
Album: released on New Renaissance(USA), Nov'87 Dist: Pinnacle

Cassette: released on New Renaissance(USA), Nov'87 Dist: Pinnacle

Metal Mickey

DO THE FUNKY ROBOT.
Single 7": released on Mickeypops, Oct'82 by Mickeypop Records. Dist: Spartan

IWANT TO HOLD YOUR HAND.
Single 7": released on Hollywood, Mar'83 by Hollywood Records. Dist: Pinnacle, Swift

METAL MICKEY MAGIC.
Single 7": released on Mickeypops, Oct'82 by Mickeypop Records. Dist: Spartan

METAL MICKEY THEME/FRUIT BAT RAT.
Single 7": released on Hollywood, Jan'83 by Hollywood Records. Dist: Pinnacle, Swift

PARIS MAQUIS/CLE DE CONTACT.
Single 7": released on Rough Trade, Jan'79 by Rough Trade Records. Dist: Rough Trade, Cartel

SILLYCON CHIPP.
Single 7": released on Mickeypops, Oct'82 by Mickeypop Records. Dist: Spartan

Metal Over America

METAL OVER AMERICA various artists (Various artists).
Album: released on Mausoleum, Mar'85 by Mausoleum Records. Dist: Pinnacle

Metal Plated

METAL PLATED Various heavy metal groups (Various artists).
Album: released on Ebony, Nov'83 by Ebony Records. Dist: Pinnacle, Ebony

Metal Ticket

CODE OF THE ROAD.
Album: released on EMI International, Jun'77 by EMI Records(UK). Dist: Conifer

THREE TIMES A DAY.
Album: released on EMI International, Nov'77 by EMI Records(UK). Dist: Conifer

Metal Treasures And...

METAL TREASURES & VINYL HEAVIES various artists (Various artists).
Album: released on Action Replay, Aug'84 by Action Replay Records. Dist: Celtic Music, Pinnacle

Cassette: released on Action Replay, Aug'84 by Action Replay Records. Dist: Celtic Music, Pinnacle

Metal Virgins

ANIMAL PEOPLE.
Album: released on Metal, Jun'84 Dist: Backs*, Cartel

Metal Warriors

METAL WARRIOR Various artists (Various artists).
Album: released on Metalother, Sep'87 Dist: Cartel, Revolver

METAL WARRIORS Various heavy metal artists (Various artists).
Album: released on Ebony, Dec'83 by Ebony Records. Dist: Pinnacle, Ebony

Metallergy

METALLERGY (Various artists).
Album: released on Bandit, Jun'86 by Bandit Records. Dist: PRT, Kingdom Records

Metallica

CHRIS TETLEY INTERVIEWS METALLICA.
Picture disc album: released on Music & Media, Oct'87 Dist: Spartan

CREEPING DEATH.
Tracks: / Creeping death / Am I evil / Blitzkrieg.
Single 12": released on Music For Nations, Jan'87 by Music For Nations Records. Dist: Pinnacle

Single 7": released on Music For Nations, Mar'86 by Music For Nations Records. Dist: Pinnacle

Single 12": released on Music For Nations, Nov'84 by Music For Nations Records. Dist: Pinnacle

Picture disc single: released on Music For Nations, Nov'84 by Music For Nations Records. Dist: Pinnacle

INTERVIEW PIC DISC.
Album: released on Baktabak, Sep'87 by Baktabak Records. Dist: Arabesque

JUMP IN THE FIRE.
Tracks: / Jump in the fire.
Picture disc single: released on Music For Nations, Mar'86 by Music For Nations Records. Dist: Pinnacle

Single 12": released on Music For Nations, Jan'84 by Music For Nations Records. Dist: Pinnacle

KILL 'EM ALL.
Tracks: / Hit the lights / Four horsemen, The / Motorbreath / Jump in the fire / Pulling teeth (Anesthesia) / Whiplash / Phantom Lord / No remorse / Seek and destroy / Metal militia.
Compact disc: released on Music For Nations, Apr'87 by Music For Nations Records. Dist: Pinnacle

Picture disc album: released on Music For Nations, Aug'86 by Music For Nations Records. Dist: Pinnacle

Album: released on Music For Nations, Jul'83 by Music For Nations Records. Dist: Pinnacle

MASTER OF PUPPETS.
Album: released on Music For Nations, Mar'86 by Music For Nations Records. Dist: Pinnacle

Cassette: released on Music For Nations, Mar'86 by Music For Nations Records. Dist: Pinnacle

Picture disc album: released on Music For Nations, Mar'86 by Music For Nations Records. Dist: Pinnacle

Compact disc: released on Music For Nations, Mar'86 by Music For Nations Records. Dist: Pinnacle

RIDE THE LIGHTNING.
Tracks: / Fight fire with fire / Ride the lightning / For whom the bell tolls / Fade to black / Trapped under ide / Escape / Creeping death / Call of Ktulu, The.
Picture disc album: released on Music For Nations, Sep'86 by Music For Nations Records. Dist: Pinnacle

Compact disc: by Music For Nations Records. Dist: Pinnacle

Album: released on Music For Nations, Jul'84 by Music For Nations Records. Dist: Pinnacle

Cassette: released on Music For Nations, Jul'84 by Music For Nations Records. Dist: Pinnacle

WHIPLASH.
Extended-play record: released on Megaforce(USA), Aug'87 by Megaforce Records (USA). Dist: Pinnacle

Extended-play record: released on Megaforce(USA), Aug'87 by Megaforce Records (USA). Dist: Pinnacle

Metamorphosis

GREAT BABEL GIVES BIRTH.
Album: released on Flowmotion, Jan'84 Dist: Red Rhino, Cartel

Album: released on Third Mind, Mar'84 by Third Mind Records. Dist: Backs*, Cartel*

Metal Explosion

METAL EXPLOSION.
Album: released on BBC, Sep'80 by BBC Records & Tapes. Dist: EMI

Cassette: released on BBC, Sep'80 by BBC Records & Tapes. Dist: EMI

Meteor

METEOR (Various artists).
Notes: Hillbilly bop Memphis style.

Meteors

BAD MOON RISING.
Single 7": released on Mad Pig, Sep'85 by Mad Pig Records. Dist: Pinnacle

CURSE OF THE MUTANTS.
Tracks: / Mutant rock / Insane / Scream of the mutants / When a stranger calls / Fear of the dark / Hills have eyes, the / Wild thing / Get off my cloud / Wreckin'crew / Zombie noise / Johnny remember me / Phantom of the opera / Blue sunshine / I dont worry about it / Axe attack / Rattle snake daddy.
Album: released on Dojo, Feb'85 by Castle Communications Records. Dist: Nine Mile, Cartel

DON'T TOUCH THE BANG BANG FRUIT.
Tracks: / Go Buddy go / Midnight people / Low livin' daddy / Your worst nightmare / Wildkat ways / Repo man / Don't touch the bang bang fruit / Crack me up / Shakey snakey / Psycho kat / Let's go / Revenge of El Trio Los Bastardos / Don't touch the bang bang fruit / Dateless nites / Corpse grinder.
Album: released on Anagram, Aug'87 by Cherry Red Records. Dist: Pinnacle

Cassette: released on Anagram, Aug'87 by Cherry Red Records. Dist: Pinnacle

Single 7": released on Anagram, Oct'87 by Cherry Red Records. Dist: Pinnacle

Single 12": released on Anagram, Oct'87 by Cherry Red Records. Dist: Pinnacle

FIRE FIRE.
Single 7": released on Mad Pig, Apr'85 by Mad Pig Records. Dist: Pinnacle

Single 12": released on Mad Pig, Apr'85 by Mad Pig Records. Dist: Pinnacle

GO BUDDY GO.
Tracks: / Go buddy go / Wildkat ways / You crack me up.
Single 7": released on Anagram, Jun'87 by Cherry Red Records. Dist: Pinnacle

Single 12": released on Anagram, Jun'87 by Cherry Red Records. Dist: Pinnacle

I'M JUST A DOG.
Single 7": released on Mad Pig, Oct'84 by Mad Pig Records. Dist: Pinnacle

Single 12": released on Mad Pig, Oct'84 by Mad Pig Records. Dist: Pinnacle

JOHNNY REMEMBER ME/WRECKIN.
Single 7": released on I.D., Jan'83 by I.D. Records. Dist: Revolver, Cartel

LIVE 11.
Tracks: / Torture / Sweet love on my mind / Mutant rock / Rhythm of the bell / Big Sandy / Rock house / M. Myers / Meat is meat / Lil Red Riding Hood / Voodoo rhythm / Long blond hair / Rock-bop.
Album: released on Dojo, Apr'86 by Castle Communications Records. Dist: Nine Mile, Cartel

LIVE: METEORS.
Tracks: / Wipe out / Maniac rockers from hell / Lonesome train / I ain't ready / A'int gonna bring me down / Sick things / Crazy love / When a stranger calls / Rawhide / I dont worry about it / Voodoo rhythm / Mutant rock / Graveyard stomp / Wreckin'crew / These boots were made for walking / Long blonde hair.
Album: released on Dojo, Jan'85 by Castle Communications Records. Dist: Nine Mile, Cartel

Picture disc album: released on Dojo, Sep'85 by Castle Communications Records. Dist: Nine Mile, Cartel

Album: released on Wreck, Nov'83 Dist: Indies, Cartel

Album: released on Carrere(France), Apr'84 by Carrere Records (France).

Compact disc: released on Dojo, '86 by Castle Communications Records. Dist: Nine Mile, Cartel

METEORS.
Album: released on Ace, Jul'81 by Ace Records. Dist: PRT, Pinnacle, Celtic Music, Cadillac, Jazz Music

MONKEY BREATH.
Album: released on Mad Pig, Sep'85 by Mad Pig Records. Dist: Pinnacle

MONKEYS BREATH/STAMPEDE.
Double Album: released on Cherry Red, Jul'87 by Cherry Red Records. Dist: Pinnacle

MUTANT ROCK/THE HILLS HAVE EYES.
Single 7": released on WXYZ, Aug'82 by Faulty Products. Dist: Pinnacle

NIGHT OF THE WEREWOLFS.
Album: released on Dojo, Sep'87 by Castle Communications Records. Dist: Nine Mile, Cartel

RADIOACTIVE KID/GRAVE ARD STOMP.
Single 7": released on Chiswick, Nov'81 by Chiswick Records. Dist: Pinnacle

SEWERTIME BLUES.
Cassette: released on Anagram, Nov'86 by Cherry Red Records. Dist: Pinnacle

Album: released on Anagram, Nov'86 by Cherry Red Records. Dist: Pinnacle

STAMPEDE.
Album: released on Mad Pig, Oct'84 by Mad Pig Records. Dist: Pinnacle

Album: released on Kix 4U, Sep'85 by Kix 4U Records. Dist: Charly, Pinnacle

SURF CITY.
Tracks: / Surf city.
Single 7": released on Anagram, Aug'86 by Cherry Red Records. Dist: Pinnacle

Single 12": released on Anagram, Aug'86 by Cherry Red Records. Dist: Pinnacle

TEENAGERS FROM OUTER SPACE.
Album: released on Big Beat, May'86 by Ace Records. Dist: Celtic Music, Pinnacle, Jazz Music, Projection

VOODOO RHYTHM.
Single 7": released on Chiswick, Jul'81 by Chiswick Records. Dist: Pinnacle

WRECKIN'CREW.
Tracks: / Wreckin'crew / Scream of the mutants / Hills have eyes / Mutant rock.
Notes:
Limited edition on green vinyl
Single 7": released on I.D., Sep'86 by I.D. Records. Dist: Revolver, Cartel

Album: released on I.D., Mar'84 by I.D. Records. Dist: Revolver, Cartel

Compact disc: released on Musidisc(France), Aug'87 Dist: Discovery, Swift. Estim retail price in Sep'87 was £10.68.

WRECKING CREW.
Tracks: / Wrecking crew / Johnny remember me / I dont worry about it / I dont worry about it / Wild thing.
Notes:
All tracks Licensed from Head Music Pub. Ltd.
Single 12": released on Archive 4, Aug'86 by Castle Communications Records., Cartel

Meters

GOOD OLD FUNKY MUSIC.
Album: released on Pye, May'79

HERE COMES THE METERMEN.
Tracks: / Sophisticated cissy / Here comes the Metermen / Mob, The / Fnky miracle / Ride your pony / Art / Dry spell / Thinking / Hndclapping song / Britches / Liver splach / Joog / Same old thing / 6V6 LA / Sehorns farm / Sing a simple song.
Album: released on Charly, Apr'86 by Charly Records. Dist: Charly, Cadillac, Swift

LOOK KA PY PY/TIPPI TPES.
Single 7": released on Charly, Jul'80 by Charly Records. Dist: Charly, Cadillac, Swift

STRUTTIN.
Tracks: / Tippie toes / Sophisticated cissy / Rigor mortis / Little old money maker / Look ka py py / Cissy strut / Ease back / Chicken strut / Message from the Meters, A / Ride your pony / Dry spell / Handclapping song / Liver splash / Same old thing / Sehorns Farm / Yeah your right / 9 till 5 / Pungee.
Compact disc: released on Charly, Feb'87 by Charly Records. Dist: Charly, Cadillac. Swift

Metheny, Mike

DAY IN-NIGHT OUT.
Tracks: / Like the ocean / Day in-night out / Vanity / Segment / Suadade / Olvidar / Lakeview ballad / Epilogue.
Album: released on MCA, Aug'86 by MCA Records. Dist: Polygram

Cassette: released on MCA, Aug'86 by MCA Records. Dist: Polygram

Compact disc: released on MCA, Jul'87 by MCA Records. Dist: Polygram

Metheny, Pat

80-81.
Tracks: / Goin' ahead / Two folk songs / Bat / Turn around / Open / Pretty Scattered / Every day I thank you.
Notes: Digital stereo.
Compact disc: released on ECM (Germany), Sep'84 by ECM Records. Dist: IMS, Polygram, Virgin, EMI

ABSOLUTELY LIVE.
Album: released on Platinum (W.Germany), Oct'85 Dist: Mainline

Cassette: released on Platinum (W.Germany), Oct'85 Dist: Mainline

AMERICAN GARAGE.
Tracks: / Heartland (Cross the) / Airstream / Search, The / American garage / Epic, The.
Compact disc: released on ECM (Germany), Dec'85 by ECM Records. Dist: IMS, Polygram, Virgin, EMI

Album: released on Import Music Service (IMS), Jan'80 Dist: Concord Jazz Distributions, Pablo, Polygram

ARE YOU GOING WITH ME/AU LAIT (Metheny, Pat Group).
Single 7": released on ECM, Jun'82 by ECM Records. Dist: IMS, Polygram, Virgin, EMI

AS FALLS WICHITA, SO FALLS WICHITA FALLS (Metheny, Pat & Lyle Mays).
Tracks: / As falls Wichita, so falls Wichita Falls / September 15th / It's for you / Estupenda graca.

Album: released on ECM (France), Jun'81 by ECM Records. Dist: IMS, Polygram, Virgin, EMI

Cassette: released on ECM (Germany), Jul'85 by ECM Records. Dist: IMS, Polygram, Virgin, EMI

Compact disc: released on ECM (Germany), Jul'85 by ECM Records. Dist: IMS, Polygram, Virgin, EMI

BRIGHT SIZE LIFE.
Tracks: / Bright size life / Sirabhorn / Unity village / Missori incompromised / Midwestern nights dream / Unquity road / Omaha celebration / Round trip-Broadway blues.
Compact disc: released on ECM (Germany), Dec'86 by ECM Records. Dist: IMS, Polygram, Virgin, EMI

Album: released on ECM, Jan'76 by ECM Records. Dist: IMS, Polygram, Virgin, EMI

FIRST CIRCLE (Metheny, Pat Group).
Tracks: / Forward march / Yolanda / You learn / First circle, The / If I could / Tell it all / End of the game / Mas alla (beyond) / Praise.
Album: released on ECM (Germany), Nov'84 by ECM Records. Dist: IMS, Polygram, Virgin, EMI

Compact disc: released on ECM (Germany), Nov'84 by ECM Records. Dist: IMS, Polygram, Virgin, EMI

LIVE IN CONCERT.
Album: released on Gateway, Jan'84 by Kingdom. Dist: Pinnacle

Cassette: released on Gateway, Jan'84 by Kingdom. Dist: Pinnacle

LIVE: PAT METHENY (Metheny, Pat Group Travels).
Album: released on ECM (Germany), May'83 by ECM Records. Dist: IMS, Polygram, Virgin, EMI

NEW CHAUTAUQUA.
Tracks: / New chautauqua / Country poem / Long-ago child / Fallen star / Hermitage / Sueno con Mexico / Daybreak.
Notes: Personnel: Pat Metheny-electric 6 and 12 string guitars, acoustic guitar, 15 string harp guitar, electric bass.
Album: released on ECM, May'79 by ECM Records. Dist: IMS, Polygram, Virgin, EMI

Compact disc: released on ECM (Germany), Aug'85 by ECM Records. Dist: IMS, Polygram, Virgin, EMI

OFFRAMP.
Tracks: / Barcarolles / Are you going with me? / Au lait / Eighteen / Offramp / James / Bat (the) (part 2).
Notes: Digital stereo
Compact disc: released on ECM (Germany), Sep'84 by ECM Records. Dist: IMS, Polygram, Virgin, EMI

Album: released on ECM (Germany), May'82 by ECM Records. Dist: IMS, Polygram, Virgin, EMI

PAT METHENY GROUP (Metheny, Pat Group).
Album: released on ECM, Jan'78 by ECM Records. Dist: IMS, Polygram, Virgin, EMI

REJOICING.
Tracks: / Lonely woman / Tears inside / Humpty dumpty / Blues for Pat / Rejoicing / Story from a stranger / Calling (the) / Waiting for an answer.
Notes: Personnel: Pat Metheny-guitars/Charlie Haden-bass/Billy Higgins-drums.
Album: released on ECM (Germany), Jun'84 by ECM Records. Dist: IMS, Polygram, Virgin, EMI

Compact disc: released on ECM (Germany), Jun'84 by ECM Records. Dist: IMS, Polygram, Virgin, EMI

Album: released on ECM, Jan'77 by ECM Records. Dist: IMS, Polygram, Virgin, EMI

SONG X (Metheny, Pat/Ornette Coleman).
Album: released on Geffen, May'86 by Geffen Records. Dist: WEA

Cassette: released on Geffen, May'86 by Geffen Records. Dist: WEA

STILL LIFE (TALKING) (Metheny, Pat Group).
Tracks: / Minuano / So may it secretly begin / Last train home / Talk, (It's just) / Third wind / Distance / In her family.
Album: released on Geffen, Jul'87 by Geffen Records. Dist: WEA

Cassette: released on Geffen, Jul'87 by Geffen Records. Dist: WEA

Compact disc: released on Atlantic, Jul'87 by WEA Records. Dist: WEA, Swift, Celtic Music

Compact disc: released on WEA, Oct'87 by WEA Records. Dist: WEA

TRAVELS (Metheny, Pat Group).
Tracks: / Are you going with me? / Fields, the sky (the) / Goodbye / Phase dance / Straight on red / Farmer's trust / Extradition / Goin' ahead / As falls wichita, so falls wichita falls / Travels / Song for bilbao / San Lorenzo.
Notes: Personnel: Pat Metheny-guitars, guitar synthesizer/Lly Mays-piano, synthesizers, organ, autoharp, synclavier/Steve Rodby-acoustic and electric bass, bass synthesizer/Dan Gottlieb-drums/Special guest Nana Vasconcelos-percussion, voice, berimbau.
Compact disc: released on ECM (Germany), Aug'86 by ECM Records. Dist: IMS, Polygram, Virgin, EMI

WATERCOLOURS.
Tracks: / Watercolours / Icefire / Lakes / River Quay / Sute 1 - Florida Greeting song / 11 - Legend of the fountain / Sea song.
Notes: Personnel: Pat Metheny-guitar, 12 string guitar, 15 string harp guitar/Lyle Mays-piano/Eberhard Weber-bass/Dan Gotlieb-drums.
Compact disc: released on ECM (Germany), Feb'86 by ECM Records. Dist: IMS, Polygram, Virgin, EMI

WORKS: PAT METHENY.
Tracks: / Sueno con Mexico / (Cross the) Heartland / Travels / James / It's for you / Every day (I thank you) / Goin' ahead.
Notes: Digital Stereo.
Album: released on ECM (Germany), Nov'84 by ECM Records. Dist: IMS, Polygram, Virgin, EMI

Compact disc: released on ECM (Germany), Nov'84 by ECM Records. Dist: IMS, Polygram, Virgin, EMI

Cassette: released on ECM (Germany), Nov'83 by ECM Records. Dist: IMS, Polygram, Virgin, EMI

Method

PINK PANTHER THEME/TAKING LIBERTIES.
Single 7": released on Red Lightnin', Aug'80 by Red Lightnin' Records. Dist: Red Lightnin', Cadillac, Caroline, Hotshot, Lightning, Swift, Jazz Music, Projection

Method Actors

COMMOTION/BLEEDING.
Single 12": released on Armageddon, Nov'82 by Armageddon Records. Dist: Revolver, Cartel, Pinnacle

LITTLE FIGURES.
Notes: 2 LP
Album: released on Press, Jul'86 by Compendium International Records. Dist: Music Galore

Album: released on Armageddon, Jan'82 by Armageddon Records. Dist: Revolver, Cartel, Pinnacle

LIVE IN A ROOM.
Album: released on Press, Jul'86 by Compendium International Records. Dist: Music Galore

LUXURY.
Tracks: / Beating on a drum / House on fire / Detective / Luxury / You the international language / Problem (the) / Another world / All tomorrows parties (bonus EP) / Can't act / Planet whales / Pumkin eaters / Annoymous / M R K S.
Notes: 2 LP
Album: released on Press, Jul'86 by Compendium International Records. Dist: Music Galore

Album: released on Press, May'85 by Compendium International Records. Dist: Music Galore

LUXURY PLUS.
Notes: Out takes from Luxury Sessions: Mini
Album: released on Press, Jul'86 by Compendium International Records. Dist: Music Galore

RANG-A-TANG.
Tracks: / Rang-a-tang.
Single 7": released on Press, Jul'86 by Compendium International Records. Dist: Music Galore

ROUND WORLD/E.Y.E.
Single 7": released on Armageddon, Oct'81 by Armageddon Records. Dist: Revolver, Cartel, Pinnacle

THIS IS IT.
Single 7": released on Armageddon, Jul'81 by Armageddon Records. Dist: Revolver, Cartel, Pinnacle

Methods Of Dance

METHODS OF DANCE Various artists (Various artists).
Album: released on Virgin, Nov'81 by Virgin Records. Dist: Virgin, EMI

Cassette: released on Virgin, Nov'81 by Virgin Records. Dist: Virgin, EMI

METHODS OF DANCE - VOL.2 Various artists (Various artists).
Album: released on Oval, Nov'82 by Oval Records. Dist: Projection, Pinnacle, Celtic Music

Cassette: released on Oval, Nov'82 by Oval Records. Dist: Projection, Pinnacle, Celtic Music

Metro

FUTURE IMPERFECT.
Album: released on EMI, May'80 by EMI Records(UK). Dist: EMI

Cassette: released on EMI, May'80 by EMI Records(UK). Dist: EMI

Metro, Anthony

WATERPUMPEE NEW STYLE.
Single 12": released on Stylaman, Oct'84

Metro, Peter

BOSANOVA (Metro, Peter & Lady Ann).
Single 7": released on Dynamite, Oct'83 by Dynamite Records. Dist: Jetstar

CALYPSO CALYPSO (Metro, Peter & Zu Zu).
Single 12": released on Greensleeves, Dec'83 by Greensleeves Records. Dist: BMG, Jetstar, Spartan

DEDICATED TO YOU (Metro, Peter & Friends).
Album: released on CSA, Mar'84 by CSA Records. Dist: PRT, Jetstar, Jazz Music

DON, THE.
Single 12": released on Striker Lee, Apr'85 by Striker Lee Records. Dist: Jetstar

DON'T RUN HIM DOWN.
Tracks: / Don't run him down / Don't touch the crack (cocaine).
Single 12": released on Revolutionary Sounds, Feb'87 Dist: Jetstar

FRONTLINE GET RAID.
Single 12": released on Striker Lee, Apr'85 by Striker Lee Records. Dist: Jetstar

IN THE ARMY.
Single 10": released on Dynamite, Sep'82 by Dynamite Records. Dist: Jetstar

NO PROBLEM.
Album: released on Power House, 30 May'87 by Power House Records. Dist: Jetstar

NU SELL YUSELF.
Tracks: / Nu sell yuself / Nu sell yuself (version).
Single 12": released on Greensleeves, Jul'87 by Greensleeves Records. Dist: BMG, Jetstar, Spartan

SHOULDER MOVE.
Single 12": released on Marlon Ranks, Mar'84 by Marlon Ranks Records. Dist: Jetstar

SINBAD AND METRIC SYSTEM (Metro, Peter & Captain Sinbad).
Album: released on CSA, Feb'83 by CSA Records. Dist: PRT, Jetstar, Jazz Music

TOGETHER.
Single 12": released on People Unite, Aug'87 by People Unite Records. Dist: Jetstar, Rough Trade, Cartel, Pinnacle

WARN THEM TEACH THEM (Metro, Peter & Squiddly Ranking).
Single 12": released on Greensleeves, Sep'82 by Greensleeves Records. Dist: BMG, Jetstar, Spartan

WHAT KIND OF WORLD ARE WE LIVING IN? (see Campbell, Cornell) (Metro, Peter and Cornell Campbell).

YES DADDY (Metro, Peter & Jackie Statement).
Single 12": released on Power House, May'87 by Power House Records. Dist: Jetstar

Metro Trinity

DIE YOUNG.
Single 12": released on Cafeteria, Jul'87 by Cafeteria Records. Dist: Rough Trade, Cartel

Metrophase

IN BLACK.
Single 7": released on Fresh, Apr'81 Dist: Jetstar

Metropolis

DUBLIN (Theme from liberty).
Tracks: / Dublin (Theme from liberty).
Single 7": released on Havoc House, Dec'85 by Havoc House Records.

EUROPEAN SUITE (THE).
Tracks: / Theme for liberty / London / Paris / Wien / Dublin / Athinai / Madrid.
Album: released on Havoc House, Oct'85 by Havoc House Records.

Cassette: released on Havoc House, Oct'85 by Havoc House Records.

Metropolitan Police

METROPOLITON POLICE BAND Directed by Captain C. Taylor.
Album: released on Parade, Sep'79 Dist: MSI

ON THE BEAT WITH THE METROPOLITON POLICE BAND.
Album: released on Polydor, Jul'77 by Polydor Records. Dist: Polygram, Polydor

RHAPSODY IN BLUE.
Album: released on Major Richards, Aug'78 by Major Richards Records.

Cassette: released on Major Richards, Aug'7 by Major Richards Records.

Metros
LOVE ME TOMORROW.
Single 7": released on Montivideo, Aug'81 by Montivideo Records. Dist: Montivideo

Metsers, Paul
CAUTION TO THE WIND.
Album: released on Highway, '85 by Highway Records. Dist: Jazz Music, Projection, Swift, Celtic Music, Cadillac, Ross, Duncans, Impetus

IN THE HURRICANES EYE.
Album: released on Sagem, Nov'86 Dist: Jazz Music, Projection, Swift, Celtic Music, Cadillac, Ross, Duncans, Impetus

MOMENTUM.
Album: released on Highway, '85 by Highway Records. Dist: Jazz Music, Projection, Swift, Celtic Music, Cadillac, Ross, Duncans, Impetus

PACIFIC PILGRIM.
Album: released on Sagem, Nov'86 Dist: Jazz Music, Projection, Swift, Celtic Music, Cadillac, Ross, Duncans, Impetus

Mettalica
JUMP IN THE FIRE (EP).
Cassette single: released on Music For Nations, Apr'87 by Music For Nations Records. Dist: Pinnacle

Mex
HAPPY LIFE.
Single 7": released on Lost Moments, Dec'84 Dist: Backs, Cartel

Mexican Music
MEXICAN MUSIC Various artists (Various artists).
Album: released on Unicorn, Jul'79 by Unicorn Records Ltd. Dist: Harmonia Mundi

MUSIC OF MEXICO - VOL.1.
Album: released on Arhoolie(USA), Jan'79 by Arhoolie Records. Dist: Jazz Music, Projection, Roots, Celtic Music, Cadillac, Ross, Duncans, Impetus

MUSIC OF MEXICO - VOL.2.
Album: released on Arhoolie(USA), Aug'79 by Arhoolie Records. Dist: Jazz Music, Projection, Roots, Celtic Music, Cadillac, Ross, Duncans, Impetus

Mexicano
ALONE AGAIN.
Album: released on Ice, Jan'80 by Ice Records. Dist: PRT

GODDESS OF LOVE.
Album: released on Ice, Aug'78 by Ice Records, Dist: PRT

MOVE UP STARSKY.
Album: released on Pioneer, Feb'77 by Word Records(UK) Ltd. Dist: Word, CBS

Single 7": released on Creole, Aug'83 by Creole Records. Dist: PRT

Single 7": released on Creole, Aug'83 by Creole Records. Dist: PRT

TRIAL BY TELEVISION.
Single 7": released on Stiff, Sep'80

Single 12": released on Stiff, Sep'80

Meyer, Edgar
DREAMS OF FLIGHT.
Tracks: / Webbed feet / Dreams of flight / Moderato (from Amalgamations for solo bass) / Expedition, The / For Dotsy / Andante (from Trio) / Moderato (from Trio) / Allegro Vivace (from Trio) / Life in Antartica (Is cold and lone-
Cassette: released on MCA, Jul'87 by MCA Records. Dist: Polygram

Compact disc: released on MCA, Jul'87 by MCA Records. Dist: Polygram

Album: released on MCA, Jul'87 by MCA Records. Dist: Polygram

UNFOLDING.
Tracks: / Unfolding / Cottonwood / My pet frog Fluet / After dark / Early morning.
Album: released on MCA, Jul'87 by MCA Records. Dist: Polygram

Cassette: released on MCA, Jul'87 by MCA Records. Dist: Polygram

Compact disc: released on MCA, Jul'87 by MCA Records. Dist: Polygram

Meyers, Augie
AUGIE'S BACK.
Album: released on Sonet, Mar'86 by Sonet Records. Dist: Jazz Music, Swift, Celtic Music, Roots, PRT, Sonet

AUGUST IN NEW YORK.
Album: released on Sonet, Mar'84 by Sonet Records. Dist: Jazz Music, Swift, Celtic Music, Roots, PRT, Sonet

RALLY IN LIGHTS (Meyers, Augie & Texas Shams).

Album: released on Sonet, Nov'79 by Sonet Records. Dist: Jazz Music, Swift, Celtic Music, Roots, PRT, Sonet

I'M NOT SOMEONE YOU WANT.
Single 7": released on Sonet, Apr'84 by Sonet Records. Dist: Jazz Music, Swift, Celtic Music, Roots, PRT, Sonet

JUST YOU AND ME.
Single 7": released on Sonet, May'82 by Sonet Records. Dist: Jazz Music, Swift, Celtic Music, Roots, PRT, Sonet

STILL GROWING.
Single 7": released on Sonet, May'82 by Sonet Records. Dist: Jazz Music, Swift, Celtic Music, Roots, PRT, Sonet

YOU'RE ON MY MIND.
Tracks: / You're on my mind / Peace of mind.
Single 7": released on Sonet, Apr'86 by Sonet Records. Dist: Jazz Music, Swift, Celtic Music, Roots, PRT, Sonet

Meyers, Steve
LOVE'S GONNA LAST.
Tracks: / Love's gonna last / Back alley shuffle.
Single 7": released on Pressure, Apr'86

Single 12": released on Pressure, Apr'86

Album: released on Steiner, Jul'85

Cassette: released on Steiner, Jul'85

Meynell, Anthony
HITS FROM 3000 YEARS AGO (Meynell, Anthony & Squire).
Album: released on Hi-Lo, Mar'86 by Hi-Lo Records & Tapes., Cartel

SEPTEMBER GIRLS (Meynell, Anthony & Squire).
Album: released on Hi-Lo, Jun'84 by Hi-Lo Records & Tapes., Cartel

Mezzoforte
CATCHING UP WITH MEZZOFORTE.
Album: released on Steinar (Iceland), May'83

Cassette: released on Steinar (Iceland), May'83

CRYING IN THE DARK.
Single 7": released on Suspect, Jul'82

GARDEN PARTY.
Single 7": released on Steinar, Jul'85

Single 12": released on Steinar, Jul'85

MEZZOFORTE.
Album: released on Steinar, Sep'81

MIDNIGHT SUN.
Single 7": released on Steinar (Iceland), Jan'84

Single 12": released on Steinar (Iceland), Jan'84

NO LIMIT.
Tracks: / No limit / EG blues.
Single 7": released on Funkin' Marvellous, Mar'87 Dist: Priority, BMG

Single 12": released on Funkin' Marvellous, Mar'87 Dist: Priority, BMG

NOTHING LASTS FOREVER.
Tracks: / Nothing lasts forever / Joy ride.
Single 7": released on Mezzoforte, Nov'86

Single 12": released on Mezzoforte, Nov'86

Compact disc single: released on Mezzoforte, Nov'86

OBSERVATIONS.
Tracks: / Midnight sun / Spring fever / Summer dream / Venue (The) / Rockall / Double orange juice / We're only here for the beer / Observations / Distance.
Compact disc: released on Riva, '86 Dist: PRT

Album: released on Steinar (Iceland), Feb'84

Cassette: released on Steinar (Iceland), Feb'84

RISING.
Tracks: / Check it in / Take off / Happy hour / Waves / Blizzard / Solid / Northern comfort / Fiona rising / Check it out.
Compact disc: released on Steinar. '86

Album: released on Steinar, Nov'84

Cassette: released on Steinar, Nov'84

ROCKALL.
Single 7": released on Steinar (Iceland), May'83

Single 12": released on Steinar (Iceland), May'83

Picture disc single: released on Steinar (Iceland), May'83

SAGA SO FAR, THE.
Tracks: / Midnight sun / Gazing at the clouds / Garden party / Funk suite no 1 / Sring fever / Danger, high voltage / Dreamland / Surprise / Rockall / Taking off / This is the night / Countdown.
Compact disc: released on Steiner, '86

Album: released on Steiner, Nov'85

Cassette: released on Steiner, Nov'85

SHOOTING STAR.
Single 7": released on Steinar, Jun'82

Single 12": released on Steinar, Jun'82

SPRING FEVER.
Single 7": released on Steinar, Apr'84

Single 12": released on Steinar, Apr'84

SURPRISE SURPRISE.
Tracks: / Garden party / Action man / Funk suite no.1 / Easy Jack / Fusion blues / Early party / Surprise / Gazing at the clouds / Old neighbourhood (The).
Compact disc: released on Steiner, '86

TAKE OFF.
Single 7": released on Steinar, Oct'84

Single 12": released on Steinar, Oct'84

TAKING OFF.
Single 7": released on Steinar, Mar'85

Single 12": released on Steinar, Mar'85

THIS IS THE NIGHT.
Single 7": released on Steinar, Sep'85

Single 12": released on Steinar, Sep'85

Mezzrow-Bechet
GREAT BLUES SINGERS (Mezzrow-Bechet Quintet & Septet).
Album: released on Joker, Apr'81 Dist: Counterpoint, Cadillac, Jazz Horizons, Jazz Music, Celtic Music

KING JAZZ VOL 1 (Mezzrow-Bechet Quintet & Septet).
Notes: With Sammy Price "Out of the Gallion".
Album: released on Storyville (USA), Oct'86 by Moss Music Group Records (USA). Dist: Jazz Music, Swift, Celtic Music

KING JAZZ VOL 2 (Mezzrow-Bechet Quintet & Septet).
Notes: Artists include Sammy Price 'Gone Away Blues'.
Album: released on Storyville (USA), Oct'86 by Moss Music Group Records (USA). Dist: Jazz Music, Swift, Celtic Music

KING JAZZ VOL 3 (Mezzrow-Bechet Quintet & Septet).
Notes: Artists include Sammy Price 'Gone Away Blues'.
Album: released on Storyville (USA), Oct'86 by Moss Music Group Records (USA). Dist: Jazz Music, Swift, Celtic Music

KING JAZZ VOL 4 (Mezzrow-Bechet Quintet & Septet).
Notes: Artists include Sammy Price 'Revolutionary Blues'.
Album: released on Storyville (USA), Oct'86 by Moss Music Group Records (USA). Dist: Jazz Music, Swift, Celtic Music

KING JAZZ VOL.5 (Mezzrow-Bechet Quintet & Septet).
Notes: With Sammy Price.
Album: released on Storyville, Nov'86 by Storyville Records. Dist: Swift

MEZZROW/BECHET QUINTET/SEPTET (THE) (Mezzrow-Bechet Quintet & Septet).
Notes: Mono production
Album: released on Storyville, May'86 by Storyville Records. Dist: Swift

MEZZROW-BECHET-VOLUME 2 (Mezzrow-Bechet Quintet & Septet).
Notes: MONO
Album: released on Storyville, Jun'86 by Storyville Records. Dist: Swift

OUT OF THE GALLION.
Notes: Mono production
Album: released on Storyville, May'86 by Storyville Records. Dist: Swift

REALLY THE BLUES (Mezzrow Bechet Quintet).
Album: released on Storyville (Denmark), Jul'81

M.F.G.
GIMME YOUR LOVE.
Tracks: / Gimme your love / Rock 'til you're crazy.
Single 12": released on EMI, Oct'87 by EMI Records(UK). Dist: EMI

Single 7": released on EMI, Oct'87 by EMI Records(UK). Dist: EMI

Picture disc single: released on EMI, Oct'87 by EMI Records(UK). Dist: EMI

M.F.Q.
MOONLIGHT SERENADE.
Album: released on Big Beat, Mar'87 by Ace Records. Dist: Celtic Music, Pinnacle, Jazz Music, Projection

MFSB
GAMBLE-HUFF ORCHESTRA, THE.
Album: released on Philadelphia Int.(USA), Jan'79 Dist: Pinnacle

SOUND OF PHILADELPHIA/LOVE IS THE MESSAGE.
Notes: Originally recorded in the 1970's.
Single 12": released on Philadelphia Int.(USA), Oct'87 Dist: Pinnacle

T.S.O.P.
Single 7": released on Philadelphia Int.(USA), '80 Dist: Pinnacle

MG
MG JUST FOR THE RECORD - VOL.1
Documentary (MG Just For The Record).
Album: released on West 4, Aug'80 by West 4 Records & Tapes. Dist: West 4 Records & Tapes

MGM
MGM ROCKABILLY COLLECTION Original artists (MGM Rockabilly Collection).
Album: released on MGM, Oct'77 by Polydor Records. Dist: Polygram, BMG

M.I.A.
MURDER IN A FOREIGN PLACE.
Album: released on Alternative Tentacles, Dec'84 by Alternative Tentacles Records. Dist: Rough Trade, Cartel

Miami
YOU ARE TEMPTATION.
Tracks: / You are temptation / You are temptation (instrumental)
Single 7": released on Grana, Feb'86 Dist: Spartan

Single 12": released on Grana, Feb'86 Dist: Spartan

Miami Sound Machine
BAD BOYS.
Tracks: / Bad boys / Monies.
Single 7": released on Epic, Mar'86 by CBS Records. Dist: CBS

Single 12": released on Epic, Mar'86 by CBS Records. Dist: CBS

FALLING IN LOVE.
Tracks: / Falling in love / Surrender paradise / Falling in love / Surrender paradise / Falling in love (remix) / Surrender.
Single 7": released on Epic, Nov'86 by CBS Records. Dist: CBS

Single 12": released on Epic, Jul'86 by CBS Records. Dist: CBS

Single 12": released on Epic, Aug'86 by CBS Records. Dist: CBS

PRIMITIVE LOVE.
Tracks: / Body to body / Primitive love / Words get in the way / Falling in love (uh-oh) / Conga / Mucho money / You made a fool of me / Movies / Surrender paradise.
Album: released on Epic, Jun'86 by CBS Records. Dist: CBS

Cassette: released on Epic, Jun'86 by CBS Records. Dist: CBS

Album: released on Epic, Aug'85 by CBS Records. Dist: CBS

Cassette: released on Epic, Aug'85 by CBS Records. Dist: CBS

Miami Vice
MIAMI VICE Original soundtrack (Various artists).
Tracks: / Original Miami Vice theme (the) (instrumental) / Smuggler's blues / Own the night / You belong to the city / In the air tonight / Miami Vice (instrumental) / Vice / Better be good to me / Flashback (instrumental) / Chase (instrumental) / Evan (instrumental).
Notes: Features tracks by Phil Collins/Chaka Khan/Glen Frey/Jan Hammer. From the incredibly successful BBC series.
Album: released on MCA, Jul'86 by MCA Records. Dist: Polygram

Cassette: released on MCA, Jul'86 by MCA Records. Dist: Polygram

Compact disc: released on MCA, Feb'86 by MCA Records. Dist: Polygram

Album: released on MCA-BBC, Oct'85 by MCA Records. Dist: Polygram

Cassette: released on MCA-BBC, Oct'85 by MCA Records. Dist: Polygram

MIAMI VICE II Original television soundtrack (Various artists).
Notes: Featuring Jackson browne, Phil Collins,

The Damned, jan Hammer, Steve jones, Gladys Knight and the Pips,Patti LaBelle & Bill Champlin, Roxy Music, Andy Taylor.
Compact disc: released on MCA, Feb'87 by MCA Records. Dist: Polygram

Album: released on MCA, Dec'86 by MCA Records. Dist: Polygram

Compact disc: released on MCA, Dec'86 by MCA Records. Dist: Polygram

Miamis

VAMOS A LA PLAYA.
Single 7": released on Carrere America (USA), Sep'83 by Polygram.

Single 12": released on Carrere America (USA), Sep'83 by Polygram.

Miaow

BELLE VUE.
Tracks: / Belle vue.
Single 7": released on Venus, Mar'86 by Miaow. Dist: Cartel

Single 12": released on Venus, Mar'86 by Miaow. Dist: Cartel

BREAK THE CODE.
Tracks: / Break the code / Stolen ears.
Single 7": released on Factory, 31 Oct'87 by Factory Records. Dist: Cartel, Pinnacle

WHEN IT ALL COMES DOWN.
Tracks: / When it all comes down.
Single 7": released on Factory, Feb'87 by Factory Records. Dist: Cartel, Pinnacle

Single 12": released on Factory, Feb'87 by Factory Records. Dist: Cartel, Pinnacle

Michael

MICHAEL (I'M MICHAEL).
Single 7": released on Disques Du Grand Michel, Sep'84 by December Songs Records. Dist: December Songs, Indies

SECESSION.
Tracks: / Secession / All the animals come out at night / Helter skelter.
Single 7": released on Siren, Jun'86 by Virgin Records. Dist: EMI

Single 12": released on Siren, Jun'86 by Virgin Records. Dist: EMI

Michael, Dene

HOLY CITY (Michael, Dene & Thornhill Middle School Choir).
Single 7": released on Posh, Dec'83 by Posh Records. Dist: Pinnacle

Michael & Elaine

IN LOVE.
Album: released on Bullseye, Jul'79 Dist: Bullseye Music

Michael, George

CARELESS WHISPER.
Single 12": released on Epic, Aug'84 by CBS Records. Dist: CBS

Picture disc single: released on Epic, Aug'84 by CBS Records. Dist: CBS

DIFFERENT CORNER (A).
Tracks: / Different corner (a) / Different corner (a) (instrumental).
Single 7": released on Epic, Mar'86 by CBS Records. Dist: CBS

Single 12": released on Epic, Mar'86 by CBS Records. Dist: CBS

FAITH.
Notes: **Extra tracks on compact disc and cassette only.
Single 7": released on Epic, Oct'87 by CBS Records. Dist: CBS

Single 12": released on Epic, Oct'87 by CBS Records. Dist: CBS

Cassette single: released on CBS, Oct'87 by CBS Records. Dist: CBS

Compact disc single: released on Epic, Nov'87 by CBS Records. Dist: CBS

Album: released on Epic, Nov'87 by CBS Records. Dist: CBS

Cassette: released on Epic, Nov'87 by CBS Records. Dist: CBS

Compact disc: released on Epic, Nov'87 by CBS Records. Dist: CBS

Compact disc: released on Epic, 7 Nov'87 by CBS Records. Dist: CBS

Album: released on Epic, 7 Nov'87 by CBS Records. Dist: CBS

Cassette: released on Epic, 7 Nov'87 by CBS Records. Dist: CBS

Picture disc single: released on Epic, Jul'87 by CBS Records. Dist: CBS

I KNEW YOU WERE WAITING (FOR ME) (Michael, George and Aretha Franklin).
Notes: For full information see under: Franklin, Aretha and George Michael.

I WANT YOUR SEX.
Tracks: / I want your sex / I want your sex (inst).
Single 7": released on Epic, 30 May'87 by CBS Records. Dist: CBS

Single 12": released on Epic, 30 May'87 by CBS Records. Dist: CBS

Gatefold sleeve: released on Epic, 30 May'87 by CBS Records. Dist: CBS

I WANT YOUR SEX (MONOGAMY MIX).
Tracks: / Rhythm 1 - Lust / Rhythm 2 - Brass in love / Rhythm 3 - A last request.
Compact disc single: released on Epic, 20 Jun'87 by CBS Records. Dist: CBS

Picture disc single: released on Epic, 20 Jun'87 by CBS Records. Dist: CBS

Cassette single: released on Epic, 27 Jun'87 by CBS Records. Dist: CBS

I WANT YOUR SEX (VIDEO0.
Video-cassette (VHS): released on CBS-Fox, '87 by CBS Records. Dist: CBS, Fox

Michael, Gordon

THINKING ABOUT MY GIRL.
Single 12": released on Fine Style, Aug'87 by Fine Style Records. Dist: CSA, Jetstar, Cartel

Michael John Singers

SERENADE IN SEQUENCE SING A LONG MEDLEY.
Album: released on Dansan, Jan'74 by Spartan Records. Dist: Spartan, Taylors

Michael, Ras

DISARMAMENT (Michael, Ras & The Sons of Negus).
Album: released on Trojan, '83 by Trojan Records. Dist: Jetstar

REVELATION (Michael, Ras & The Sons of Negus).
Album: released on Trojan, '83 by Trojan Records. Dist: Jetstar

TRIBUTE TO THE EMPEROR (Michael, Ras & The Sons of Negus).
Album: released on Trojan, '83 by Trojan Records. Dist: Jetstar

Michaels, Hilly

LUMIA.
Album: released on Warner Bros., Aug'81 by WEA Records. Dist: WEA

Michelle and Renato

MR. MAYBE.
Single 7": released on President, Feb'87 by President Records. Dist: Spartan, Taylors, Jazz Music

Michelow, Sybil

IN RECITAL (Michelow, Sybil & Malcolm Williamson).
Cassette: released on B'nai B'rith, Aug'85

Michener,J

TALES OF THE SOUTH PACIFIC Spoken Word.
Cassette: released on Caedmon(USA), '81 by Caedmon (USA) Records. Dist: Gower, Roots

Michigan, Papa & Smiley

DISEASES (Michigan, Papa & General Smiley).
Single 12": released on Greensleeves, Feb'82 by Greensleeves Records. Dist: BMG, Jetstar, Spartan

DOWN PRESSION (Michigan, Papa & General Smiley).
Album: released on Greensleeves, Sep'82 by Greensleeves Records. Dist: BMG, Jetstar, Spartan

GHETTO MAN (Michigan, Papa & General Smiley).
Single 12": released on Greensleeves, Feb'82 by Greensleeves Records. Dist: BMG, Jetstar, Spartan

Michigan & Smiley

REGGAE SKA.
Single 12": released on RAS(Real Authentic Sound), Jun'84 by Greensleeves Records. Dist: Greensleeves, BMG, Jetstar

SUGAR DADDY.
Album: released on RAS(Real Authentic Sound), Mar'84 by Greensleeves Records. Dist: Greensleeves, BMG, Jetstar

Single 12": released on RAS(Real Authentic Sound), Mar'84 by Greensleeves Records. Dist: Greensleeves, BMG, Jetstar

Mickey Mouse Disco

MICKEY MOUSE DISCO Various artists (Various artists).
Cassette: released on Pickwick, Nov'79 by Pickwick Records. Dist: PRT, Prism Leisure

MICKEY MOUSE DISCO / MOUSERCISE Various artists (Various artists).
Album: released on K-Tel, Oct'82 by K-Tel Records. Dist: K-Tel, Celtic Music, Terry Blood, Wynd-Up, Taylors, Pickwick, Solomon & Peres, Polygram

Cassette: released on K-Tel, Oct'82 by K-Tel Records. Dist: K-Tel, Celtic Music, Terry Blood, Wynd-Up, Taylors, Pickwick, Solomon & Peres, Polygram

Mickey & Sylvia

NEW SOUNDS.
Album: released on VIK, Jul'87 Dist: Swift

Microdisney

BIRTHDAY GIRL.
Single 7": released on Rough Trade, Sep'85 by Rough Trade Records. Dist: Rough Trade, Cartel

Single 12": released on Rough Trade, Sep'85 by Rough Trade Records. Dist: Rough Trade, Cartel

CLOCK CAME DOWN THE STAIRS, THE.
Album: released on Rough Trade, Oct'85 by Rough Trade Records. Dist: Rough Trade, Cartel

CROOKED MILE.
Album: released on Virgin, Jan'87 by Virgin Records. Dist: Virgin, EMI

Cassette: released on Virgin, Jan'87 by Virgin Records. Dist: Virgin, EMI

Compact disc: released on Virgin, Jan'87 by Virgin Records. Dist: Virgin, EMI

EVERYTHING IS FANTASTIC.
Album: released on Rough Trade, May'84 by Rough Trade Records. Dist: Rough Trade, Cartel

HELLO RASCALS.
Single 7": released on Kabuki, Sep'82 by Gareth Ryan. Dist: Rough Trade

MICRODISNEY IN THE WORLD.
Single 12": released on Rough Trade, Mar'85 by Rough Trade Records. Dist: Rough Trade, Cartel

PINK SKINNED MAN.
Single 7": released on Kabuki, May'83 by Gareth Ryan. Dist: Rough Trade

SINGER'S HAMPSTEAD HOME.
Tracks: / Singer's Hampstead home / She only gave in to her anger.
Single 7": released on Virgin, Oct'87 by Virgin Records. Dist: Virgin, EMI

TOWN TO TOWN.
Tracks: / Town to town / Little town of Ireland / Begging bowl / Horse / Loftholdingswood / Overboard / Genius / Bullwhip Road.
Single 7": released on Virgin, Jan'87 by Virgin Records. Dist: Virgin, EMI

Single 12": released on Virgin, Jan'87 by Virgin Records. Dist: Virgin, EMI

WE HATE YOU WHITE SOUTH AFRICAN BASTARDS.
Album: released on Rough Trade, Oct'84 by Rough Trade Records. Dist: Rough Trade, Cartel

Micronotz

40 FINGERS.
Album: released on Homestead, Jul'86 Dist: Rough Trade, Cartel, Shigaku

Microphone Prince

ROCK HOUSE.
Single 12": released on Still Rising (USA), Nov'87 Dist: Pinnacle

WHO'S THE CAPTAIN.
Single 7": released on Music Of Life, Apr'87 by Music Of Life Records. Dist: Pinnacle

Single 12": released on Music Of Life, Apr'87 by Music Of Life Records. Dist: Pinnacle

Micros

SOUL'N'SEX.
Album: released on Orbitone, Jul'87 by Orbitone Records. Dist: Jetstarr*

Microscopic 7

TAKE THE Z TRAIN.
Tracks: / Chinese twilight zone / Wishful thinking / Take the Z train / Mr Bradley - Mr Martin / Pack the ermines army Mary / I didn't do it / Strange thought entered my head (a).
Album: released on Press, Jul'86 by Compendium International Records. Dist: Music Galore

Microscopic Septet

TAKE THE Z-TRAIN.
Album: released on Press, Jan'85 by Compendium International Records. Dist: Music Galore

Micus, Stephan

EAST OF THE NIGHT.
Album: released on ECM (Germany), May'85 by ECM Records. Dist: IMS, Polygram, Virgin, EMI

IMPLOSIONS.
Compact disc: released on ECM (Germany), Oct'86 by ECM Records. Dist: IMS, Polygram, Virgin, EMI

Album: released on ECM, Jul'77 by ECM Records. Dist: IMS, Polygram, Virgin, EMI

KOAN.
Album: released on ECM, May'81 by ECM Records. Dist: IMS, Polygram, Virgin, EMI

LISTEN TO THE RAIN.
Album: released on Japo(ECM), Nov'83 Dist: IMS, Polygram

Cassette: released on Japo(ECM), Nov'83 Dist: IMS, Polygram

OCEAN.
Tracks: / Part 1 / Part II / Part III / Part IV.
Notes: Stephan Micus-hammered dulcimers, nay, sho, shakuhachi, Bavarian zithers, voice. With this new album 'Ocean', Stephan Micus opens a new chapter in his effort to understand music from different musical cultures. He displays a wide musical understanding, being a traveller along the borders of European and Asian cultures. Therefore, he doesn't fit into any category. Too erratic and original, he will not be swept away by te current and fashionable 'New Age' wave. His virtuosity and complex arrangement require an open minded and conscious listener.
Album: released on ECM (Germany), Jun'86 by ECM Records. Dist: IMS, Polygram, Virgin, EMI

Cassette: released on ECM (Germany), Jun'86 by ECM Records. Dist: IMS, Polygram, Virgin, EMI

Compact disc: released on ECM (Germany), Jun'86 by ECM Records. Dist: IMS, Polygram, Virgin, EMI

WINGS OVER WATER.
Album: released on Japo(ECM), Jul'82 Dist: IMS, Polygram

Midas

CAN'T STOP LOVING YOU.
Single 7": released on Small Run, Feb'83 by Small Run Records. Dist: Pinnacle

Middle East

MUSIC FROM AROUND THE WORLD VOLUME 2 THE NEAR EAST (Various artists).
Album: released on Lyrichord(USA), Oct'81 by Lyrichord Records(USA). Dist: Flexitron Ltd., Roots

Middle Of The Road

CHIRPY CHIRPY CHEEP CHEEP.
Tracks: / Chirpy chirpy cheep cheep / Tweedle Dee Twedle Dum.
Single 7": released on Old Gold, Nov'86 by Old Gold Records. Dist: PRT, Counterpoint, Lightning, Jazz Music, Taylors

Single 7": released on RCA, May'82 Dist: BMG

PARTY TIME MEDLEY.
Single 7": released on Pulsar, Jan'82 by Lismor Records. Dist: Lismor

STEAL A PIECE OF MY HEART.
Single 7": released on OK, Oct'80 Dist: Stage One

Middleton, Ian

TATTIES, MILK AND MEAL.
Notes: Cassette of poems and songs Follow up to "Tatties trou'the bree"
Cassette: released on Ross, '86 by Ross Records. Dist: Ross, Taylors, Celtic Music, Roots

TATTIES THRO' THE BREE.
Cassette: released on Ross, Dec'85 by Ross Records. Dist: Ross, Taylors, Celtic Music, Roots

Midland Radio Orchestra

BY REQUEST - BBC TOP TUNES 4.
Album: released on BBC, Sep'78 by BBC Records & Tapes. Dist: EMI

Midland Youth

STARBURST (Midland Youth Jazz Orchestra).
Album: released on Grosvenor, Jun'81 by Grosvenor Records. Dist: Taylors, Jazz Music

Midler, Bette

BEST OF BETTE.
Album: released on Atlantic, Sep'78 by WEA Records. Dist: WEA, Swift, Celtic Music

Cassette: released on Atlantic, Sep'78 by WEA Records. Dist: WEA, Swift, Celtic Music

BROKEN BLOSSOM.
Album: released on Atlantic, Jun'79 by WEA Records. Dist: WEA, Swift, Celtic Music

DIVINE.
Album: released on Atlantic, Nov'80 by WEA Records. Dist: WEA, Swift, Celtic Music

Cassette: released on Atlantic, Nov'80 by WEA Records. Dist: WEA, Swift, Celtic Music Deleted '84.

LIVE AT LAST.
Album: released on Atlantic, May'77 by W

Records. Dist: WEA, Swift, Celtic Music

MUD WILL BE FLUNG TONIGHT.
Tracks: / Taking aim / Fit or fat 'fat as I am' / Marriage, movies, Madonna and Mick / Vickie Eydie 'I'm singing Broadway' / Coping / Unfettered boob (the) / 'Otto titzling' / Why bother? / Soph.
Album: released on Atlantic, Jan'86 by WEA Records. Dist: WEA, Swift, Celtic Music

Cassette: released on Atlantic, Jan'86 by WEA Records. Dist: WEA, Swift, Celtic Music

NO FRILLS.
Tracks: / Is it love / (You're my) favourite waste of time / All I need to know / Only in Miami / Heart over head / Let me drive / My eye on you / Beast of burden / Soda and a souvenir / Come back Jimmy Dean.
Compact disc: released on Atlantic, Sep'83 by WEA Records. Dist: WEA, Swift, Celtic Music

Album: released on Atlantic, Sep'83 by WEA Records. Dist: WEA, Swift, Celtic Music

Cassette: released on Atlantic, Sep'83 by WEA Records. Dist: WEA, Swift, Celtic Music

ROSE, (THE) Original Soundtrack.
Tracks: / Whose side are you on? / Midnight in Memphis / Concert monologue / When a man loves a woman / Sold my sould o rock 'n' roll / Keep on rockin' / Love me with a feeling / Camellia / Stay with me / Homecoming / Let me call you sweetheart / Rose.
Notes: Digital stereo.
Compact disc: released on Atlantic, Jan'84 by WEA Records. Dist: WEA, Swift, Celtic Music

Cassette: released on Atlantic, Jan'80 by WEA Records. Dist: WEA, Swift, Celtic Music

Album: released on Atlantic, Jan'80 by WEA Records. Dist: WEA, Swift, Celtic Music

SONGS FOR THE NEW DEPRESSION.
Album: released on Atlantic, Dec'75 by WEA Records. Dist: WEA, Swift, Celtic Music

YOU'RE MY FAVOURITE WASTE OF TIME.
Single 7": released on Atlantic, Jan'84 by WEA Records. Dist: WEA, Swift, Celtic Music

Midnight

EASY PROMISE TO BREAK.
Tracks: / Easy promise to break / Easy promise to break (instrumental).
Single 7": released on Polo, Feb'86 by Polo Records. Dist: PRT

Single 12": released on Polo, Feb'86 by Polo Records. Dist: PRT

KING OF THE MOUNTAIN.
Tracks: / King of the mountain / Too high.
Single 7": released on Epic, Jun'87 by CBS Records. Dist: CBS

Single 12": released on Epic, Jun'87 by CBS Records. Dist: CBS

Single 7": released on Epic, Jul'87 by CBS Records. Dist: CBS

RUN WITH YOU.
Tracks: / Everything.
Single 7": released on Epic, Feb'87 by CBS Records. Dist: CBS

Single 12": released on Epic, Feb'87 by CBS Records. Dist: CBS

Midnight

COLLECTION: MIDNIGHT Brancaster Studio Orch..
Compact disc: by Object Enterprises Ltd. Dist: Jazz Music

MIDNIGHT CHRISTMAS MESS Various Artists (Various artists).
Album: released on Midnight, Dec'84 by Midnight Records. Dist: Rough Trade, Cartel

MIDNIGHT HOUR (COLLECTION OF GREAT SMOOCHERS) Various Artists (Various artists).
Album: released on K-Tel, Mar'82 by K-Tel Records. Dist: K-Tel, Celtic Music, Terry Blood, Wynd-Up, Taylors, Pickwick, Solomon & Peres, Polygram

Cassette: released on K-Tel, Mar'82 by K-Tel Records. Dist: K-Tel, Celtic Music, Terry Blood, Wynd-Up, Taylors, Pickwick, Solomon & Peres, Polygram

MIDNIGHT IN BRAZIL Various Artists (Various artists).
Album: released on Polydor, Oct'80 by Polydor Records. Dist: Polygram, Polydor

MIDNIGHT SERENADES Various Artists (Various artists).
Album: released on Sanity, Apr'85 by Sanity Records. Dist: Pinnacle, Jetstar

Midnight blue

ENJOY WITH ME.
Single 7": released on New York Connexion, Jul'83 by New York Connexion Records.

Single 12": released on New York Connexion, Jul'83 by New York Connexion Records.
Cat. no: NYCX 100

Midnight Choir

HALLELUJAH.
Extended-play record: released on Native, Sep'85 by Native Records. Dist: Red Rhino, Cartel

KISS.
Single 7": released on Golden Dawn, Nov'83 by Artery Records. Dist: Cartel

Single 12": released on Golden Dawn, Nov'83 by Artery Records. Dist: Cartel

TRUSSED BY BUDDHA.
Album: released on Probe, 21 Nov'87 Dist: Cartel

Album: released on Probe Plus, Nov'87 by Probe Plus Records. Dist: Probe Plus

WORM BELLY GRUNT.
Album: released on Native, Sep'86 by Native Records. Dist: Red Rhino, Cartel

WORMBELLYGRIN.
Album: released on Native, Jan'87 by Native Records. Dist: Red Rhino, Cartel

Midnight Cowboy

MIDNIGHT COWBOY Original Soundtrack.
Album: released on United Artists, Oct'80

Midnight Creepers

DAYTONA BLUES.
Notes: Tenor sax player: Noble 'Thin Man'Watts. Also Bob Greenlee (Root Boy Slim) Ernie Lancaster(Creepers)
Album: released on Bedrock, Mar'87 by Upright Records., Projection, Swift, Celtic Music, Cadillac, Ross, Duncans, Impetus

Midnight Express

BIEN BENIDOS.
Compact disc: released on Country House, Jun'82 by Scotdisc Records. Dist: Taylors, Duncans, Sounds of Scotland, BGS

Midnight Express

MIDNIGHT EXPRESS Original soundtrack.
Album: released on Casablanca, Apr'86 Dist: Polygram, Phonogram

Cassette: released on Casablanca, Apr'86 Dist: Polygram, Phonogram

MIDNIGHT EXPRESS Original Soundtrack
Compact disc: released on Casablanca, Apr'85 Dist: Polygram, Phonogram

Album: released on Casablanca, Nov'81 Dist: Polygram, Phonogram Deleted '86.

Cassette: released on Casablanca, Nov'81 Dist: Polygram, Phonogram Deleted '86.

Midnight movers

MIDNIGHT MOVERS Various artists (Various artists).
Album: released on Kent, Sep'86 by Kent Records. Dist: Pinnacle, Cadillac, Jazz Music

Album: released on MCA, Jul'86 by MCA Records. Dist: Polygram

Midnight Oil

10,9,8,7,6,5,4,3,2,1.
Album: released on CBS, Jun'83 by CBS Records. Dist: CBS

Cassette: released on CBS, Jun'83 by CBS Records. Dist: CBS

BEST OF BOTH WORLDS.
Single 7": released on CBS, Jul'85 by CBS Records. Dist: CBS

Single 12": released on CBS, Jul'85 by CBS Records. Dist: CBS

DIESEL AND DUST.
Album: released on CBS(Austrailia), 28 Sep'87 by CBS Records. Dist: Counterpoint, Celtic Music, Pinnacle

Album: released on CBS(Austrailia), 28 Sep'87 by CBS Records. Dist: Counterpoint, Celtic Music, Pinnacle

US FORCES.
Single 7": released on CBS, May'83 by CBS Records. Dist: CBS

Single 12": released on CBS, May'83 by CBS Records. Dist: CBS

WHEN THE GENERALS TALK.
Single 7": released on CBS, Sep'85 by CBS Records. Dist: CBS

Midnight On...

MIDNIGHT ON BOURBON STREET (Various artists).
Tracks: / Sheik of Araby / Temptation rag / Eh la bas / She's crying for me / Li'l Liza Jane / Corrine Corrina / San / Jazz it blues / That's a plenty / Won't you come home Bill Bailey / On the sunny side of the street / Mama don't allow it / Pizza pie boogie.

Album: released on Rhapsody, May'87 by President Records., Swift, Jazz Music, Wellards

Midnight Piano

MIDNIGHT PIANO Various artists (Various artists).
Notes: Cliff Jackson/Don Frye/Willie The Lion Smith.
Album: released on Classic Jazz Masters, Aug'87 by Mainline Record Company. Dist: Mainline, Swift

Midnight Star

CURIOUS.
Single 7": released on MCA, Mar'85 by MCA Records. Dist: Polygram

Single 12": released on MCA, Mar'85 by MCA Records. Dist: Polygram

ENGINE NO.9.
Tracks: / Engine No.9 / (US mix).
Single 7": released on MCA, Jan'87 by MCA Records. Dist: Polygram

Single 12": released on MCA, Jan'87 by MCA Records. Dist: Polygram

ENGINE NO.9 (EXTENDED VERSION).
Tracks: / Les Adams mega mix (Midas touch/Engine no.9/Operator) / Engine no.9 (7")
Single 12": released on MCA, Feb'87 by MCA Records. Dist: Polygram

FEELS SO GOOD.
Single 7": released on Elektra, Mar'84 by WEA Records. Dist: WEA

HEADLINES.
Tracks: / Searching for love / Headlines / Get dressed / Stay here by my side / Midas touch / Close encounter / Engine No 9 / Dead end / Headlines (extra extra mix) / Operator / Curious.
Compact disc: by MCA Records. Dist: Polygram*

Cassette: released on MCA, Jul'86 by MCA Records. Dist: Polygram

Album: released on MCA, Jul'86 by MCA Records. Dist: Polygram

Single 7": released on MCA, Jul'86 by MCA Records. Dist: Polygram

MIDAS TOUCH.
Tracks: / Midas touch (extended remix) / Midas touch (acappella).
Single 12": released on MCA, Sep'86 by MCA Records. Dist: Polygram

NO PARKING ON THE DANCE FLOOR.
Album: released on MCA, Mar'87 by MCA Records. Dist: Polygram

Cassette: released on MCA, Mar'87 by MCA Records. Dist: Polygram

PLANETARY INVASION.
Tracks: / Operator / Body snatchers / Can you stay with / Scientific love / Planetary invasion / Today my love / Let's celebrate / Curious.
Notes: Originally released in early '85.
Album: released on MCA, Dec'86 by MCA Records. Dist: Polygram

Cassette: released on MCA, Dec'86 by MCA Records. Dist: Polygram

Album: released on MCA, Jan'85 by MCA Records. Dist: Polygram

Cassette: released on MCA, Jan'85 by MCA Records. Dist: Polygram

STANDING TOGETHER.
Album: released on Solar, Jul'81 by MCA Records. Dist: Polygram*

Cassette: released on Solar, Jul'81 by MCA Records. Dist: Polygram*

WET MY WHISTLE.
Tracks: / Wet my whistle / Curious / Freak-a-zoid / Headlines (extra extra mix).
Notes: * = Extra track on 12" only.
Single 7": released on MCA, Apr'87 by MCA Records. Dist: Polygram

Single 12": released on MCA, Apr'87 by MCA Records. Dist: Polygram

Midnight String Quartet

CHRISTMAS RHAPSODIES FOR YOUNG LOVERS.
Album: released on Audio Fidelity(USA), Oct'84 by Audio Fidelity Ent.Inc.(USA).

Cassette: released on Audio Fidelity(USA), Oct'84 by Audio Fidelity Ent.Inc.(USA).

Midnight Sunrise

IN AT THE DEEP END (Midnight Sunrise & Jackie Rawe).
Tracks: / In at the deep end (Inst).
Single 7": released on Nightmare, Feb'87 by Nightmare Records. Dist: PRT

Single 12": released on Nightmare, Feb'87 by Nightmare Records. Dist: PRT

ON THE HOUSE (Midnight Sunrise & Jackie Rawe).
Tracks: / On the house / On the house (remix).
Single 7": released on Crossover, Sep'86, IMS, Polygram

Single 12": released on Crossover, Sep'86, IMS, Polygram

ON THE HOUSE REMIX (Midnight Sunrise & Jackie Rawe).
Tracks: / On the house remix.
Single 12": released on Crossover, Oct'86, IMS, Polygram

Midnite

NEVER GONNA STOP.
Single 7": released on Tivoli, Jun'83 by Tivoli Records. Dist: Unknown

Single 12": released on Tivoli, Jun'83 by Tivoli Records. Dist: Unknown

PARADISE DRIVE.
Single 7": released on Tivoli, Feb'83 by Tivoli Records. Dist: Unknown

Single 12": released on Tivoli, Feb'83 by Tivoli Records. Dist: Unknown

Midnite Follies Orchestra

JUNGLE NIGHTS IN HARLEM.
Album: released on ASV(Academy Sound & Vision), Mar'81 by Academy Sound & Vision Records. Dist: Pinnacle

Cassette: released on ASV(Academy Sound & Vision), Mar'81 by Academy Sound & Vision Records. Dist: Pinnacle

Midnite Ramblers

ALWAYS LEAVING.
Album: released on Folk Heritage, Jul'82 by Folk Heritage Records. Dist: Jazz Music, Wynd-Up, Roots, Folk Heritage

MIDNITE RAMBLERS, THE.
Album: released on Folk Heritage, Jul'82 by Folk Heritage Records. Dist: Jazz Music, Wynd-Up, Roots, Folk Heritage

ONE NIGHT STAND.
Album: released on Folk Heritage, Jul'82 by Folk Heritage Records. Dist: Jazz Music, Wynd-Up, Roots, Folk Heritage

Midniters

BEST OF THE MIDNITERS.
Album: released on Rhino (USA), Jul'84 by Rhino Records (USA). Dist: Pinnacle

Midsummer Night Fest

MIDSUMMER NIGHT FEST Folk music & dances (Various artists).
Album: released on Accordion Record Club, '84 by Accordion Record Club. Dist: Accordion Record Club

Midsummer night's dream

MIDSUMMER NIGHT'S DREAM, A Shakespeare, William (Various artists).
Notes: Read by The Old Vic Company with Robert Helpman, Moira Shearer & Stanley Holloway. Incidental music by Mendelssohn. Running time approx 2 hours. Double cassette. With this re-issue, we bring back to the Listen For Pleasure catalogue one of the most lighthearted and most popular of all Shakespeare's plays.
Double cassette: released on Listen For Pleasure, Sep'86 Dist: EMI

Midsummer Night's Sex...

MIDSUMMER NIGHT'S SEX COMEDY Soundtrack recording (Mendelssohn, Felix).
Album: released on CBS, Oct'82 by CBS Records. Dist: CBS

Cassette: released on CBS, Oct'82 by CBS Records. Dist: CBS

Midway

SET IT OUT.
Single 7": released on Personal, Nov'84 by Personal Records., Projection, Roots, Celtic Music, Cadillac, Ross, Duncans, Impetus

Single 12": released on Personal, Nov'84 by Personal Records., Projection, Roots, Celtic Music, Cadillac, Ross, Duncans, Impetus

Midway Special

MIDWAY SPECIAL, THE.
Album: released on Fountain, Jan'79 by Retrieval Records. Dist: Jazz Music, Wellards, Swift, Retrieval

Miffy & Other Stories

MIFFY & OTHER STORIES Spoken word cassette for children (Various artists).
Cassette: released on Tellastory, Dec'80 by Bartlett Bliss Productions Ltd.. Dist: PRT, Taylors, Conifer

Mighty Absalom

MIGHTY ABSALOM SINGS BATHROOM BALLADS.
Album: released on Sportsdisc, Jul'80 by Sportsdisc Records.

Mighty Baby

EGYPTIAN TOMB.
Album: released on Psycho, Nov'84 Dist: Funhouse, Rough Trade

Mighty ballistics...

GHOST TRAIN.
Tracks: / Ghost train / Spring hill Jack / Back gold.
Single 12": released on Criminal Damage, May'86 by Criminal Damage Records. Dist: Backs, Cartel

HERE COME THE BLUES.
Album: released on Criminal Damage, Jan'86 by Criminal Damage Records. Dist: Backs, Cartel

MATCHLESS TRIPLE A.
Tracks: / Matchless triple A.
Single 12": released on Criminal Damage, Jun'86 by Criminal Damage Records. Dist: Backs, Cartel

Mighty Ceasars

ACROPOLIS NOW.
Album: released on Milkshakes, Dec'86 by Milkshakes Records. Dist: Cartel, Rough Trade

BABY WHAT'S WRONG.
Tracks: / Baby what's wrong / 10 bears of the Commanchees.
Single 7": released on Empire, Feb'86 by Empire Records. Dist: Backs, Cartel

BEWARE THE IDES OF MARCH.
Album: released on Big Beat, Jan'86 by Ace Records. Dist: Celtic Music, Pinnacle, Jazz Music, Projection

CAESARS OF TRASH, THE.
Album: released on Milkshakes, Feb'86 by Milkshakes Records. Dist: Cartel, Rough Trade

LITTLE BY LITTLE.
Tracks: / Little by little / Swag (The) / I want what you got / Cyclonic.
Single 7": released on Media Burn, Feb'86 by Rocks Off Record Emporium. Dist: Rough Trade, Cartel

LIVE IN ROME.
Notes: Live album. Covers of The Pistols' 'Submission/Damned 'Neat, neat, neat' etc.
Album: released on Big Beat, Apr'87 by Ace Records. Dist: Celtic Music, Pinnacle, Jazz Music, Projection

MIGHTY CEASARS, THE.
Album: released on Milkshakes, Aug'85 by Milkshakes Records. Dist: Cartel, Rough Trade

THEE DON'T GIVE ANY DINNER TO HENRY CHINASKI.
Album: released on Hangman, Aug'87 by Revolver, Cartel. Estim retail price in Sep'87 was £5.99.

WISEBLOOD.
Album: released on Ambassador, Feb'87 by Ambassador Records. Dist: Pinnacle, Jetstar, Swift

Mighty Clouds Of Joy

BEST OF THE MIGHTY CLUDS OF JOY.
Album: released on MCA(USA), Oct'87 by MCA Records(USA). Dist: Pinnacle, Swift

CLOUDBURST.
Album: released on Myrrh, May'82 by Word Records(UK)Ltd.. Dist: Word, CBS

Cassette: released on Myrrh, May'82 by Word Records(UK)Ltd.. Dist: Word, CBS

MIRACLE MAN.
Album: released on Myrrh, May'82 by Word Records(UK)Ltd.. Dist: Word, CBS

Cassette: released on Myrrh, May'82 by Word Records(UK)Ltd.. Dist: Word, CBS

SING & SHOUT.
Album: released on Myrrh, May'84 by Word Records(UK)Ltd.. Dist: Word, CBS

Cassette: released on Myrrh, May'84 by Word Records(UK)Ltd.. Dist: Word, CBS

TRUTH IS THE POWER.
Album: released on Myrrh, May'82 by Word Records(UK)Ltd.. Dist: Word, CBS

Cassette: released on Myrrh, May'82 by Word Records(UK)Ltd.. Dist: Word, CBS

Mighty Dance

MIGHTY DANCE various artists (Various artists).
Album: released on Satril, Mar'84 by Satril Records. Dist: PRT

Mighty Diamonds

BAD BOY.
Single 7": released on Mobiliser, Nov'83 by Jetstar Records. Dist: Jetstar

BROTHER MAN.
Single 12": released on Reggae, Oct'83 by Reggae Records. Dist: Jetstar, Morpheus Distribution

CHANGES.
Album: released on Music Works, Dec'81 Dist: Jetstar

DAY IN DAY OUT.
Single 12": released on Blue Trac, Sep'85 by Blue Mountain Records. Dist: Jetstar

DEEPER ROOTS(BACK AT THE CHANNEL).
Album: released on Virgin, Aug'79 by Virgin Records. Dist: Virgin, EMI

FIGHT IT OUT THERE.
Single 12": released on Real Wax, Mar'85 Dist: Jetstar

GATES OF ZION.
Single 12": released on Greensleeves, Nov'80 by Greensleeves Records. Dist: BMG, Jetstar, Spartan

HEY GIRL.
Single 12": released on Jama, Dec'83 by Jama Records. Dist: Jetstar

I AM NOT TO BE BLAMED.
Tracks: / I am not to be blamed / I wanna love you.
Single 12": released on Rockers Plantation, Dec'86 Dist: Jetstar

IF YOU LOOKING FOR TROUBLE.
Tracks: / If you looking for trouble / Peace pipe / Satan give it / Fight, fight, fight / Make up your mind / Accept me / That's the life / Love, love come get me tonight / Cartoon living / African rootsman
Album: released on Live & Love, Sep'86 by Third World Records. Dist: Jetstar

Cassette: released on Live & Love, Sep'86 by Third World Records. Dist: Jetstar

Single 12": released on Live & Learn, Jul'86 Dist: Jetstar

I'M REALLY PICKNEY.
Single 12": released on Music Works, Dec'82 Dist: Jetstar

JUVENILE CHILD.
Tracks: / Juvenile child / Same knife (The).
Single 12": released on Revolutionary Germain, Dec'85 Dist: Jetstar

KEPT OUT.
Tracks: / Kept out.
Single 12": released on Germaine, Jun'86 by Germaine Records. Dist: Jetstar

KOUCHE VIBES.
Album: released on Burning Sounds, Nov'84 by Burning Sounds Records.

LAST DANCE.
Single 12": released on KR, Nov'82 by KR Recordings Ltd. Dist: BMG, Revolver, Cartel

Single 12": released on J.G., Sep'82 Dist: Phonogram, United Artists, Dakota

LET THE DOLLAR CIRCULATE (Mighty Diamonds & Trinity).
Single 12": released on Thunderbolt, May'82 by Magnum Music Group Ltd. Dist: PRT

LOOKING FOR TROUBLE.
Compact disc: released on Live & Learn, Nov'87 Dist: Jetstar. Estim retail price in Nov'87 was £11.99.

MARY MACK.
Single 12": released on Kingdom, Jun'84 by Kingdom Records. Dist: Kingdom. PRT

MORGAN THE PIRATE.
Single 12": released on Mobiliser, Dec'82 by Jetstar Records. Dist: Jetstar

NEVER SAY GOODBYE.
Single 12": released on Bad Gong, Oct'84 by Bad Gong Records. Dist: Jetstar

PASTAKOUCHIE.
Single 7": released on Jetstar, Jan'82 Dist: Jetstar, Stage One

PLANET EARTH.
Album: by Virgin Records. Dist: Virgin, EMI

PRETTY WOMAN.
Single 12": released on Reggae, Mar'82 by Reggae Records. Dist: Jetstar, Morpheus Distribution

REAL ENEMY.
Notes: Produced by Augustus 'Gussie' Clarke
Single 12": released on Greensleeves, Jul'87 by Greensleeves Records. Dist: BMG, Jetstar, Spartan

Cassette: released on Greensleeves, Jul'87 by Greensleeves Records. Dist: BMG, Jetstar, Spartan

RIGHT TIME.
Album: released on Shanachie (USA), Jan'84, Projection, Sterns, Celtic Music, Cadillac, Ross, Duncans, Impetus

SET ME FREE.
Single 12": released on SMJ, Aug'85 by SMJ Records. Dist: Jetstar

STAND UP TO YOUR JUDGEMENT.
Album: released on Channel 1, Jul'78 by Cha

Cha Records. Dist: Moio

STRUGGLING.
Album: released on Live & Learn, Dec'85 Dist: Jetstar

VITAL SELECTION.
Album: released on Virgin, Aug'81 by Virgin Records. Dist: Virgin, EMI

WHA DO YUH SO.
Tracks: / Wha do yuh so / Wha do yuh so (alternative version).
Single 12": released on SRI, Jul'86

WHO'S SORRY NOW.
Single 12": released on Mobiliser, Jul'83 by Jetstar Records. Dist: Jetstar

Mighty Faith

LITTLE GIRL.
Single 12": released on Fulani, Sep'84 by Fulani. Dist: Fualni-ILA

Mighty Fire

PORTRAITS.
Album: released on Asylum, May'81 by WEA Records. Dist: WEA

Mighty Flyers

FILE UNDER ROCK.
Album: released on Takoma, Apr'84 by PRT Records.

Cassette: released on Takoma, Apr'84 by PRT Records.

FROM THE START TO THE FINNISH.
Tracks: / From the start to the finnish / Where was your love / 502 / Queenie was your love / Hard work boogie / PS I love you / Somebody / Sinister woman / Blues for honey.
Album: released on Red Lightnin', Dec'86 by Red Lightnin' Records. Dist: Red Lightnin', Cadillac, Caroline, Hotshot, Jazz Music, Swift, Jazz Music, Projection

Mighty Gabby

JACK.
Single 7": released on Ice, Jul'83 by Ice Records. Dist: PRT

Single 12": released on Ice, Jul'83 by Ice Records. Dist: PRT

Single 12": released on Seara, Sep'82 by Seara Records. Dist: Jetstar

Mighty General

MY COMMANDED WIFE.
Tracks: / My commanded wife / Are you gonna run.
Single 12": released on Ragin' Lion Music, Aug'86 Dist: Jetstar

PROUD OF ME COUNTRY.
Single 12": released on Digikal, Aug'87 by Digikal Records. Dist: Jetstar, PRT, Revolver, Cartel

Mighty Grynner

STINGIN' BEES.
Single 7": released on Ensign, May'85 by Ensign Records. Dist: Chrysalis, CBS

Single 12": released on Ensign, May'85 by Ensign Records. Dist: Chrysalis, CBS

Mighty Lemon Drops

HAPPY HEAD.
Album: released on Blue Guitar, Sep'86 by Chrysalis Records. Dist: CBS

Cassette: released on Blue Guitar, Sep'86 by Chrysalis Records. Dist: CBS

LIKE AN ANGEL.
Tracks: / Like an angel.
Single 12": released on Dreamworld, Dec'85 by TV Personalities, The. Dist: Rough Trade

NIGHT TRACKS.
Tracks: / Night tracks.
Single 12": released on Night Trax, Jul'87 Dist: Pinnacle

OTHER SIDE OF YOU (THE).
Tracks: / Other side of you (The) / Uptight / Pass you by.
Single 7": released on Chrysalis, Aug'86 by Chrysalis Records. Dist: CBS

Single 12": released on Chrysalis, Aug'86 by Chrysalis Records. Dist: CBS

Mighty Maytones

BEST OF THE MAYTONES.
Album: released on Burning Sounds, Feb'83 by Burning Sounds Records.

I DON'T KNOW WHY.
Single 12": released on GG'S, Oct'83 by GG'S Records. Dist: Jetstar

MADNESS.
Album: released on Burning Sounds, Jan'77 by Burning Sounds Records.

Mighty Mighty

BUILT LIKE A CAR.
Tracks: / Built like a car / I don't need you any-

---

more / Twilight" / Love so strong".
Single 7": released on Chapter 22, 23 May'87 by Chapter 22 Records. Dist: Nine Mile, Cartel

Single 12": released on Chapter 22, 23 May'87 by Chapter 22 Records. Dist: Nine Mile, Cartel

EVERYBODY KNOW THE MONKEY.
Tracks: / Everybody knows the monkey / You're on my mind.
Single 7": released on Girlie, Apr'86 by Mighty Mighty Records., Cartel

IS THERE ANYONE OUT THERE.
Tracks: / Is there anyone out there.
Single 7": released on Girlie, Aug'86 by Mighty Mighty Records., Cartel

ONE WAY.
Tracks: / One way.
Single 7": released on Chapter 22, Oct'87 by Chapter 22 Records. Dist: Nine Mile, Cartel

Single 12": released on Chapter 22, Oct'87 by Chapter 22 Records. Dist: Nine Mile, Cartel

THROWAWAY.
Tracks: / Throwaway / Ceiling to the floor / Ghost of love.
Single 7": released on Chapter 22, Dec'86 by Chapter 22 Records. Dist: Nine Mile, Cartel

Single 12": released on Chapter 22, Dec'86 by Chapter 22 Records. Dist: Nine Mile, Cartel

Mighty Rudo

SKANK AT THE PARTY.
Single 12": released on Greensleeves, Nov'83 by Greensleeves Records. Dist: BMG, Jetstar, Spartan

Single 7": released on Jammy's, Oct'83 by Jammy's Records. Dist: Jetstar

SUNSHINE.
Single 12": released on Chartbound, Nov'83 by Chartbound Records. Dist: Jetstar

WATERHOUSE.
Single 12": released on CF, Dec'83 by CF Records. Dist: Jetstar

Mighty Seven

PUSH 1.
Single 7": released on EMI, Nov'84 by EMI Records(UK). Dist: EMI

Single 12": released on EMI, Nov'84 by EMI Records(UK). Dist: EMI

Mighty Shamrocks

CONDOR WOMAN.
Single 7": released on Independent, Sep'81 by Independent Records. Dist: Independent

Mighty Sparrow

KING OF THE WORLD.
Album: released on Dynamic, Sep'86 by Creole Records. Dist: PRT

ONLY A FOOL.
Album: released on Trojan, Sep'81 by Trojan Records. Dist: Jetstar

PEACE & LOVE.
Album: released on Trojan, Sep'81 by Trojan Records. Dist: Jetstar

SPARROW'S PARTY CLASSICS.
Album: released on Charlie's, Sep'87 by Charlie's Records. Dist: Jetstar

Mighty Wah

WEEKENDS.
Single 7": released on Beggars Banquet, Sep'84 by Beggars Banquet Records. Dist: WEA

Single 12": released on Beggars Banquet, Sep'84 by Beggars Banquet Records. Dist: WEA

WORD TO THE WISE GUY, A.
Album: released on Beggars Banquet, Jul'84 by Beggars Banquet Records. Dist: WEA

Cassette: released on Beggars Banquet, Jul'84 by Beggars Banquet Records. Dist: WEA

Mighty Wah, The

PEEL SESSION, THE.
Tracks: / Basement blues; the story of the blue / Better scream / Weekends / Yuh haan.
Single 12": released on Strange Fruit, Sep'87 by Clive Selwood. Dist: Pinnacle

Mikado

ROMANCE.
Single 7": released on Operation Twilight, Feb'83

Mike Morton Orchestra

WINDS OF WAR.
Single 7": released on M&H, Nov'83 by M&H Records.

Mike T

DO IT ANY WAY YOU WANNA.
Single 7": released on Blue Inc, Sep'81

Single 12": released on Blue Inc, Sep'81

Mike & the Mechanics

ALL I NEED IS A MIRACLE.
Tracks: / All I need is a miracle / You are the one / Call to arms (The).
Single 7": released on WEA, Apr'86 by WEA Records. Dist: WEA

Single 12": released on WEA, Apr'86 by WEA Records. Dist: WEA

MIKE AND THE MECHANICS.
Tracks: / Silent running / All I need is a miracle / Par avion / Hanging by a thread / I get the feeling / Take the reins / You are the one / Call to arms (A) / Taken in.
Album: released on WEA, Oct'85 by WEA Records. Dist: WEA

Cassette: released on WEA, Oct'85 by WEA Records. Dist: WEA

Compact disc: released on WEA, Jul'86 by WEA Records. Dist: WEA

SILENT RUNNING (on dangerous ground).
Tracks: / Silent running (on dangerous ground) / I get the feeling / Too far gone.
Single 7": released on WEA, Oct'85 by WEA Records. Dist: WEA

Single 12": released on WEA, Oct'85 by WEA Records. Dist: WEA

Mike-D And The LA Possee

I GET ROUGH.
Single 12": released on Public (USA), Nov'87 Dist: Pinnacle

Mikel Rouse

JADE TIGER (Mikel Rouse, Broken Concert).
Album: released on Les Disques Du Crepuscule(Belgium), Feb'84 by Les Disques Du Crepuscule (Belgium). Dist: Rough Trade, Pinnacle, Island, Polygram

Miker G, MC

HOLIDAY RAP (Miker G, M C/Deejay Sven).
Tracks: / Holiday rap / Holiday rap acappella / Whimsical touch / Holiday hip hop (instrumental).
Single 12": released on Debut, Aug'86 by Passion Records. Dist: PRT

Mikey, D

MY TELEPHONE (Mikey, D & The L.A. Posse).
Tracks: / My telephone / Bust a rhyme mike (vocal).
Single 7": released on 10, Apr'87 by 10 Records. Dist: Virgin, EMI*

Single 12": released on 10, Apr'87 by 10 Records. Dist: Virgin, EMI*

Miki & Griff

AT HOME WITH MIKI & GRIFF.
Album: released on Scotdisc, Aug'87 by Scotdisc Records., Duncans, Sounds of Scotland

Cassette: released on Scotdisc, Aug'87 by Scotdisc Records., Duncans, Sounds of Scotland

BEST OF MIKI AND GRIFF.
Album: released on PRT, Jun'83 by PRT Records.

Cassette: released on PRT, Jun'83 by PRT Records.

COUNTRY.
Album: released on Pye, '78

COUNTRY IS.
Album: released on Pye Special, Feb'75

ETCHINGS.
Album: released on Pye. Oct'77

GOLDEN HOUR OF MIKI AND GRIFF.
Album: by PRT Records.

Milander, Lucky

SHORTY'S GOT TO GO.
Album: released on Jukebox Lil, Apr'85 by Jukebox Lil. Dist: Swift, Celtic Music

Milburn, Amos

13 UNRELEASED MASTERS.
Album: released on Pathe Marconi (France), Sep'84 Dist: Swift

CHICKEN SHACK BOOGIE.
Album: released on Pathe Marconi (France), Apr'85 Dist: Swift

JUST ONE MORE DRINK.
Album: released on Route 66(Sweden), Jun'80 by Mr.R&B Records. Dist: Swift, Cadillac, Celtic

LET'S HAVE A PARTY.
Album: released on Pathe Marconi (France), Jul'86 Dist: Swift

Cassette: released on Pathe Marconi (France), Jul'86 Dist: Swift

LET'S ROCK AWHILE.
Album: released on Route 66(Sweden), Aug'85 by Mr.R&B Records. Dist: Swift, Cadillac, Celtic

ROCK ROCK ROCK.
Album: released on Route 66(Sweden), Aug'87 by Mr.R&B Records. Dist: Swift, Cadillac, Celtic

VICIOUS VODKA.
Album: released on Pathe Marconi (France), Apr'85 Dist: Swift

Milburn, Amos Jr.

YOU USED ME.
Album: released on Mr.R&B, Aug'87 Dist: Counterpoint, Celtic Music, Swift

Milder, Bjorn

SWING PIANO MY WAY.
Album: released on Kenneth, Mar'87 Dist: Wellards, Jazz Music

Mile End

UNCLE BILLY SE2.
Single 7": released on Toffee, Dec'85

Mile High Club

WALKING BACKWARDS.
Single 12": released on Aalto, Nov'84 by Aalto Records. Dist: Aalto Records

Miles, Barry

FUSION IS.
Album: released on RCA, Feb'79 Dist: BMG

Miles, Buddy

LIVE: BUDDY MILES (Miles, Buddy & Carlos Santana).
Album: released on CBS, Sep'84 by CBS Records. Dist: CBS

Cassette: released on CBS, Sep'84 by CBS Records. Dist: CBS

Miles, Carol

FASHION JUNKY.
Tracks: / Fashion junky(radio mix) / Fashion junky (club mix) / Fashion junky (jazz mix) / Fashion junky (dance 'crazy' mix).
Single 12": released on FM Dance, Oct'87 by FM-Revolver Records. Dist: BMG

Miles, Dick

CHEATING THE TIDE.
Album: released on Greenwich Village, Jan'85 by Sweet Folk All Records. Dist: Projection, Folksound, Lightning, Celtic Music, Wellards, Roots, Jazz Music

Miles, Dick & Sue

DUNMOW FLITCH, THE.
Album: released on Accordion Record Club, '84 by Accordion Record Club. Dist: Accordion Record Club

Miles, Graeme

EAGLE & DOVE Songs of point and protest.
Cassette: released on Folktracks, Nov'79 by Folktracks Cassettes. Dist: Folktracks, Roots

ENTERTAINERS Contemporary country song.
Cassette: released on Folktracks, Nov'79 by Folktracks Cassettes. Dist: Folktracks, Roots

HERE'S TO THE LADS Sporting songs.
Cassette: released on Folktracks, Nov'79 by Folktracks Cassettes. Dist: Folktracks, Roots

IRONMASTER, MINERS, MOULDERS, FOUNDERS.
Cassette: released on Folktracks, Nov'79 by Folktracks Cassettes. Dist: Folktracks, Roots

LYKE WAKE Primievil ballads of moors.
Cassette: released on Folktracks, Nov'79 by Folktracks Cassettes. Dist: Folktracks, Roots

RING OF IRON, THE.
Cassette: released on Folktracks, Nov'79 by Folktracks Cassettes. Dist: Folktracks, Roots

RURAL SONGS OF CLEVELAND & TEES-SIDE.
Cassette: released on Folktracks, Nov'79 by Folktracks Cassettes. Dist: Folktracks, Roots

SMOKESTACK LANO Industrial ballads.
Cassette: released on Folktracks, Nov'79 by Folktracks Cassettes. Dist: Folktracks, Roots

SONGS AND SHANTIES OF FISHER & SAILORS.
Cassette: released on Folktracks, Nov'79 by Folktracks Cassettes. Dist: Folktracks, Roots

SQUADDIES DREAM Barrackroom ballads.
Cassette: released on Folktracks, Nov'79 by Folktracks Cassettes. Dist: Folktracks, Roots

WEALDEN FOLK Ballads of Kentish folk.
Cassette: released on Folktracks, Nov'79 by Folktracks Cassettes. Dist: Folktracks, Roots

Miles, John

I NEED YOUR LOVE.
Tracks: / I need your love / Watching over me / Run.
Single 7": released on Valentino, Jun'86 by WEA Records. Dist: WEA

Single 12": released on Valentino, Jun'86 by WEA Records. Dist: WEA

MUSIC.
Single 7": released on Old Gold, Oct'83 by Old Gold Records. Dist: PRT, Counterpoint, Lightning, Jazz Music, Taylors

Single 7": released on Decca, Sep'82 by Decca Records. Dist: Polygram

Single 12": released on Decca, Sep'82 by Decca Records. Dist: Polygram

MUSIC (LP).
Album: released on Decca (Rock Echoes), Sep'82 by Decca Records. Dist: Polygram, IMS

Cassette: released on Decca (Rock Echoes), Sep'82 by Decca Records. Dist: Polygram, IMS

REBEL.
Album: released on Decca, Mar'76 by Decca Records. Dist: Polygram

RIGHT TO SING.
Single 7": released on EMI, Apr'83 by EMI Records(UK). Dist: EMI

SONG FOR YOU.
Single 7": released on EMI, Jul'83 by EMI Records(UK). Dist: EMI

STRANGER IN THE CITY.
Cassette: released on Decca, Feb'77 by Decca Records. Dist: Polygram

Album: released on Decca, Feb'77 by Decca Records. Dist: Polygram

TRANSITION.
Album: released on Valentino, Oct'85 by WEA Records. Dist: WEA

Cassette: released on Valentino, Oct'85 by WEA Records. Dist: WEA

ZARAGON.
Album: released on Decca, Mar'78 by Decca Records. Dist: Polygram

Miles, Luke'Long Gone'

COUNTRY BOY.
Album: released on Sundown, Oct'82 by Magnum Music Group Ltd. Dist: PRT

Militant Barry

GREEN VALLEY.
Album: released on Vista Sounds, '83 by Vista Sounds Records. Dist: Jetstar

Militant Dee

MEN OF TODAY.
Tracks: / Men of today / Technology.
Single 12": released on Ragin' Lion Music, May'86 Dist: Jetstar

Military Band Favourites

MILITARY BAND FAVOURITES Various military bands (Various military bands).
Cassette: released on EMI, Apr'81 by EMI Records(UK). Dist: EMI

MILITARY BANDS PLAY FAVOURITE THEMES Various Artists (Various artists).
Tracks: / Musical Joke, A / Trumpton / Mr. Benn / Flumps, The / Postman Pat / Chi mai / Chariots of fire / Thunderbirds / Noblimente (from Elgar's 1st symphony) / Squadron / Luftwaffe march / Imperial echoes / Horse Guards(Whitehall) / Knightsbridge / Mack & Mabel overture.
Album: released on Conifer, Jan'86 by Conifer Records. Dist: Conifer, Jazz Music

Cassette: released on Conifer, Jan'86 by Conifer Records. Dist: Conifer, Jazz Music

Military Bands

MUSIC FROM TIDWORTH TATTOO 1975 various military bands (Various military bands).
Album: released on Lismor, '75 by Lismor Records. Dist: Projection, Celtic Music, Taylors, Cadillac, Outlet, Roots, Ross

Military Classics

MILITARY CLASSICS various artists (Various artists).
Triple album / cassette: released on Telstar, Nov'84 by Telstar Records. Dist: BMGg*

Triple album / cassette: released on Telstar, Nov'84 by Telstar Records. Dist: BMGg*

Military Gold

MILITARY GOLD various artists (Various artists).
Album: released on Ronco, Oct'79 by Ronco Records.

Cassette: released on Ronco, Oct'79 by Ronco Records.

Military marches

MILITARY GREATS various bands (Various bands).
Triple album / cassette: released on Ronco, Nov'83 by Ronco Records.

Triple album / cassette: released on Ronco, Nov'83 by Ronco Records.

Double Album: released on Cambra, Mar'85 by Cambra Records. Dist: Celtic Music

Double cassette: released on Cambra, Mar'85 by Cambra Records. Dist: Celtic Music

MILITARY MARCHES Various Artists - the big German marches (Various artists).
Tracks: / Preubens Gloria / Parademarsch der 18er Husaren / Mussinanmarsch / Prasentiemarsch Konig Friedrich Wilhelm III von Preuben / Fehrbelliner reitermarsch / Der Koniggratzer / Fridericus-Rex-grenadiermarsch / Alte Kameraden / Regimentsgruss / Marsch aus Petersburg / Alexandermarsch / De grossen kurfursten reitermarsch / Helenenmarsch / Bayerischer defiliermarsch / Marsch des yourckschen korps / Gruss an Kiel.

MILITARY MARCHES-THE BIG GERMAN MARCHES various artists (Various artists).
Compact disc: released on Polydor (Germany), May'85 Dist: IMS-Polygram

Military marches of Sousa

MILITARY MARCHES OF SOUSA Various Bands (Various bands).
Tracks: / Stars and stripes forever / King cotton / El Capitan / National Fencibles / High school cadets / Manhattan Beach / Liberty bell / Semper fideles / Invincible eagle / Gladiator, The / Washington Post / Hands across the sea / Royal Welsh Fusiliers / Legionaires / Daughters of Texas / Gallent seventh, The / Golden Jubilee / Pride of the wolverines, The / Hail to the spirit of Liberty / Kansas wildcats / Sound off / Thunderer,The.
Cassette: released on Hour Of Pleasure, Sep'86 by Music For Pleasure Records. Dist: EMI. Estim retail price in Sep'87 was £1.99.

Military Musical Pageant

MILITARY MUSICAL PAGEANT various artists (Various military bands).
Double Album: released on Warwick, Sep'79 by Warwick Records. Dist: CBS, MSD, Taylors, Solomon & Peres

MILITARY MUSICAL PAGEANT 1981 various artists (Various military bands).
Double Album: released on Parade, Aug'81 Dist: MSD

Double cassette: released on Parade, Aug'81 Dist: MSD

MILITARY MUSICAL PAGEANT 1983 Wembley Stadium (Various military bands).
Double Album: released on Bandleader, Jul'83 by Bandleader Records. Dist: PRT, Taylors

Double cassette: released on Bandleader, Jul'83 by Bandleader Records. Dist: PRT, Taylors

Militent Red

AND THEN A VOICE.
Single 7": released on Vital, Feb'82 Dist: Fresh, Rough Trade

Milkshakes

14 RHYTHM & BEAT GREATS.
Album: released on Big Beat, Feb'83 by Ace Records. Dist: Celtic Music, Pinnacle, Jazz Music, Projection

20 ROCK'N'ROLL HITS OF THE 50'S & 60'S.
Album: released on Big Beat, Feb'84 by Ace Records. Dist: Celtic Music, Pinnacle, Jazz Music, Projection

107 TAPES Double album.
Album: released on Media Burn, Nov'86 by Rocks Off Record Emporium. Dist: Rough Trade, Cartel

AFTER SCHOOL SESSIONS.
Album: released on Upright, Aug'83 by Upright Records. Dist: Cartel, Rough Trade, Pinnacle

AMBASSADORS OF LOVE.
Single 7": released on Big Beat, Dec'84 by Ace Records. Dist: Celtic Music, Pinnacle, Jazz Music, Projection

BRAND NEW CADILLAC.
Single 7": released on Big Beat, Mar'83 by Ace Records. Dist: Celtic Music, Pinnacle, Jazz Music, Projection

LET ME LOVE YOU.
Tracks: / let me love you.
Single 7": released on Empire, Aug'86 by Empire Records. Dist: Backs, Cartel

MILKSHAKES IN GERMANY, THE.
Album: released on Wall City, Mar'84 by Wall City Records. Dist: Cartel

MILKSHAKES REVENGE, THE.
Album: released on Hangman, Jun'87 Dist: Revolver, Cartel

NOTHING CAN STOP THESE MEN.
Album: released on Milkshakes, Mar'84 by Milkshakes Records. Dist: Cartel, Rough Trade

PLEASE DON'T TELL MY BABY.
Single 7": released on Bilk-O, May'82

SOLDIER OF LOVE.
Single 7": released on Upright, Mar'83 by Upright Records. Dist: Cartel, Rough Trade, Pinnacle

TALKING 'BOUT MILKSHAKES.
Album: released on Milkshakes, Feb'86 by Milkshakes Records. Dist: Cartel, Rough Trade

THEY CAME THEY SAW THEY CONQUERED.
Album: released on Big Beat, Mar'85 by Ace Records. Dist: Celtic Music, Pinnacle, Jazz Music, Projection

THREE KNIGHTS OF TRASHE.
Album: released on Milkshakes, Dec'84 by Milkshakes Records. Dist: Cartel, Rough Trade

Millar, Gertie

OUR MISS GIBBS & other Gertie Millar successes.
Album: released on World, '73 by EMI Records(UK). Dist: Conifer

Millar, Leslie

LESLIE MILLAR.
Tracks: / Lonely / Key, The / Music of unity / Comes and goes / Eternal Flame, The / Consumociety / There is a place / Bepop and the bomb.
Album: released on Direct, '86 by Phonogram Records. Dist: Polygram

Millar, Sam

HOW DID YOU KNOW.
Tracks: / How did you know / Tropical girl.
Single 7": released on Yellow Brick Road, Sep'86

Millenium

MILLENIUM.
Album: released on Guardian, Aug'84 by Guardian Records., Pinnacle

Miller, Al

NEGRO STRING BAND MUSIC 1927-36.
Album: released on Limited Edition, Sep'87 Dist: Red Rhino, Cartel

Miller Big Band

MEMORIAL FOR GLENN MILLER, A.
Compact disc: released on Accord(France), Jun'84 Dist: Discovery

Miller, Bob

BOB MILLER & M.
Album: released on Nevis, '78

Miller, Cat

READY OR NOT.
Single 7": released on Creole, Sep'84 by Creole Records. Dist: PRT

Single 12": released on Creole, Sep'84 by Creole Records. Dist: PRT

Single 12": released on Street Level, Mar'85

Miller, Chuck

GOIN' GOIN' GONE.
Album: released on Revival, Oct'07 Dist: Lightning, Swift

Miller, Count Prince

MULE TRAIN.
Tracks: / Mule train.
Single 7": released on Mango, Nov'87 by Island Records. Dist: Polygram

Single 12": released on Mango, Nov'87 by Island Records. Dist: Polygram

Miller, C.P.

COME TO ME SOFTLY.
Tracks: / Come to me softly / It ain't no big thing.
Single 12": released on Hot Vinyl, Dec'86 by Hot Vinyl Records. Dist: Jetstar

Miller, Dale

FINGER PICKING RAGS & OTHER DELIGHTS.
Album: Dist: Sonet, Projection, Swift, Celtic Music, Cadillac, Ross, Duncans, Impetus

FINGERS DON'T FAIL ME NOW.
Album: released on Kicking Mule, Apr'80 Dist: Sonet, Projection, Swift, Celtic Music, Cadillac, Ross, Duncans, Impetus

GUITARISTS CHOICE.
Album: released on Kicking Mule, Jan'78 Dist: Sonet, Projection, Swift, Celtic Music, Cadillac, Ross, Duncans, Impetus

Miller, David

SWING AND DINE (DANCE ALL THE TIME).
Single 12": released on LGR, Feb'83 Dist: Jetstar

Miller, Eddie

LAZY MOOD FOR TWO (Miller, Eddie & Lou Stein).
Album: released on 77, Aug'79 by 77 Records. Dist: Wellards, Cadillac

SWINGING TENORS (see Freeman, Bud) (Miller, Eddie & Bud Freeman).

Miller Family

THIS THING COULD GROW.
Tracks: / This thing could grow / This thing could grow (inst).
Single 7": released on Carrere, 30 May'87 by Carrere Records(UK). Dist: PRT, Spartan

Single 12": released on Carrere, 30 May'87 by Carrere Records(UK). Dist: PRT, Spartan

Miller, Frankie

DANCING IN THE RAIN.
Tracks: / I'd lie to you for your love / Do it till we drop / That's how long my love is / How many tears can you hide / Dancing in the rain / Shakey ground / Boys and girls are doing it, The / Game of love / Gladly go blind / you're a puzzle I can't put down.
Notes: Frankie Miller-lead vocals,guitar/Brian Robertson-lead guitar/Chrissie Stewart-bass/Simon Kirke-drums
Album: released on Vertigo, Apr'86 by Phonogram Records. Dist: Polygram

Cassette: released on Vertigo, Apr'86 by Phonogram Records. Dist: Polygram

Compact disc: released on Vertigo, Apr'86 by Phonogram Records. Dist: Polygram

DARLIN'.
Tracks: / Be good to yourself.
Single 7": released on Old Gold, Feb'87 by Old Gold Records. Dist: PRT, Counterpoint, Lightning, Jazz Music, Taylors

Single 7": released on Chrysalis, Nov'81 by Chrysalis Records. Dist: CBS

DOUBLE TROUBLE.
Album: released on Chrysalis, Apr'78 by Chrysalis Records. Dist: CBS

FALLING IN LOVE.
Album: by Chrysalis Records. Dist: CBS

HEY WHERE YA GOIN'.
Album: released on CBS(USA), Sep'84 Dist: Counterpoint, Celtic Music, Jazz Music, Rollercoaster, Conifer

I'D LIE TO YOU FOR LOVE.
Tracks: / I'd lie to you for love / Dancing in the rain / Do it till we drop.
Single 7": released on Vertigo, Mar'86 by Phonogram Records. Dist: Polygram

Single 12": released on Vertigo, Mar'86 by Phonogram Records. Dist: Polygram

ROCKIN' ROLLIN' FRANKIE MILLER.
Album: released on Bear Family, Oct'83 by Bear Family Records(Germany). Dist: Celtic Music, Swift, Rollercoaster

STANDING IN THE OTHER SIDE.
Single 7": released on Good Foot, Jul'81 by Good Foot Records (USA). Dist: Pinnacle

STANDING ON THE EDGE.
Album: released on EMI (Germany), May'84 by EMI Records(UK). Dist: Conifer

Miller, Gary

JUST ANOTHER BROKEN HEART (Miller's, Gary Obsession).
Tracks: / Just another broken heart / Don't make me wait.
Notes: Gatefold Sleeve (First 5000 autographed)
Single 7": released on Plains Of Waterloo, Aug'86 Dist: Thunderbay, Spartan

Miller, Glenn

20 CLASSIC TRACKS: GLENN MILLER.
Album: released on Arena, Feb'87 by Arena Records. Dist: Spartan

Cassette: released on Arena, Feb'87 by Arena Records. Dist: Spartan

20 GREATEST HITS: GLENN MILLER.
Album: released on Astan, Nov'84 by Astan Records.

Cassette: released on Astan, Nov'84 by Astan Records.

21 GOLDEN GREATS LIVE (Miller, Glenn & His Orchestra).
Cassette: released on Magic, Jul'87 Dist: Celtic Music, Submarine, Swift, Wellards, Conifer, Jazz Music

22 GOLDEN PIECES.
Cassette: released on Submarine, Dec'86 by Submarine Records. Dist: Wellards, Conifer, Taylors

40TH ANNIVERSARY ALBUM.
Album: released on Magic, '84 Dist: Celtic Music, Submarine, Swift, Wellards, Conifer, Jazz Music

Cassette: released on Magic, '84 Dist: Celtic Music, Submarine, Swift, Wellards, Conifer, Jazz Music

1940: GLENN MILLER.
Album: released on Magic, Aug'85 Dist: Celtic Music, Submarine, Swift, Wellards, Conifer, Jazz Music

1943 BAND IN HI-FI, THE (Miller, Glenn & His Army Air Force Orchestra).
Album: released on Soundcraft, Nov'86 Dist: Jazz Music

AMERICAN PATROL (Miller, Glenn & His Orchestra).
Tracks: / Serenade in blue / Song of the volga boatman / Moonlight cocktail / Anvil chorus / Kalamazoo / Sunrise serenade / Under the double eagle / Danny boy / Chattanooga Choo Choo / American Patrol / Jeep jockey jump / Sanfu jump / Keep 'em flying / Lover / Little brown jug.
Album: released on Showcase, Apr'86 by Castle Communications Records. Dist: PRT

Cassette: released on Showcase, Apr'86 by Castle Communications Records. Dist: PRT

AMERICAN RHAPSODY.
Album: released on Swinghouse, Jun'85 Dist: Jazz Music, Swift, Wellards, Celtic Music

Cassette: released on Swinghouse, Jun'85 Dist: Jazz Music, Swift, Wellards, Celtic Music

AT THE STEEL PIER IN 1941.
Album: released on Ajaz(USA), May'84 Dist: Swift

AUTUMN SERENADE.
Album: released on Magic, '84 Dist: Celtic Music, Submarine, Swift, Wellards, Conifer, Jazz Music

Cassette: released on Magic, '84 Dist: Celtic Music, Submarine, Swift, Wellards, Conifer, Jazz Music

BBC NOVEMBER 1944 (Miller, Glenn & His Army Air Force Orchestra).
Album: released on Jasmine, May'86 by Jasmine Records. Dist: Counterpoint, Cadillac, Taylors, Wellards, Swift, Jazz Music

Cassette: released on Jasmine, May'86 by Jasmine Records. Dist: Counterpoint, Cadillac, Taylors, Wellards, Swift, Jazz Music

BEST OF GLENN MILLER.
Album: released on RCA/Camden, Jul'84 by RCA Records.

Cassette: released on RCA/Camden, Jul'84 by RCA Records.

Album: released on RCA International (USA), '84 by RCA Records. Dist: BMG

Cassette: released on RCA International (USA), '84 by RCA Records. Dist: BMG

BEST OF GLENN MILLER (CREOLE).
Cassette: released on Creole(Everest-Europa), Jul'84 by Creole Records. Dist: PRT

BEST OF GLENN MILLER VOL.1.
Album: released on CBS Cameo, Aug'85 by CBS Records. Dist: CBS

Cassette: released on CBS Cameo, Aug'85 by CBS Records. Dist: CBS

BEST OF GLENN MILLER VOL.2.
Album: released on RCA International (USA), '84 by RCA Records. Dist: BMG

Cassette: released on RCA International (USA), '84 by RCA Records. Dist: BMG

CAFE ROUGE 1941 (Miller, Glenn & His Orchestra).
Album: released on Jasmine, May'86 by Jasmine Records. Dist: Counterpoint, Cadillac, Taylors, Wellards, Swift, Jazz Music

Cassette: released on Jasmine, May'86 by Jasmine Records. Dist: Counterpoint, Cadillac, Taylors, Wellards, Swift, Jazz Music

CHESTERFIELD SHOW, LIVE Radio Playhouse, New York City 3.4.40.
Album: released on Soundcraft(Fanfare USA - Import), May'84 Dist: Jazz Music

CHESTERFIELD SHOWS 1940 Civic Theatre, Chicago 13.6.40 (Miller, Glenn & His Orchestra & Gail Reese).
Album: released on Soundcraft(USA), May'84 Dist: Jazz Music

CHESTERFIELD SHOWS, THE (Miller, Glenn & His Orchestra).
Notes: Mono. Featuring Tex Beneke\Skip Nelson\Marion Hutton\The modernaires. 1942.
Album: released on Soundcraft, Nov'86 Dist: Jazz Music

CHESTERFIELD SHOWS,THE (Miller, Glenn & His Orchestra & Gail Reese).
Album: released on Soundcraft(USA), May'84 Dist: Jazz Music

Album: released on Jasmine, Sep'85 by Jasmine Records. Dist: Counterpoint, Cadillac, Taylors, Wellards, Swift, Jazz Music

Cassette: released on Jasmine, Sep'85 by Jasmine Records. Dist: Counterpoint, Cadillac, Taylors, Wellards, Swift, Jazz Music

CHRISTMAS PROGRAMME (Miller, Glenn & His Army Air Force Orchestra).
Notes: Mono. Vocals by Johnny Desmond
Album: released on Soundcraft, Nov'86 Dist: Jazz Music

COLLECTION: GLENN MILLER.
Album: released on RCA (Germany), Jan'85 Dist: Conifer, Target

Cassette: released on RCA (Germany), Jan'85 Dist: Conifer, Target

COLLECTION: GLENN MILLER (CD).
Compact disc: by Object Enterprises Ltd. Dist: Jazz Music

COMPLETE SUNSET SERENADE PROG/LIVE, CAFE ROUGE (Miller, Glenn & His Orchestra).
Album: released on Jasmine, May'86 by Jasmine Records. Dist: Counterpoint, Cadillac, Taylors, Wellards, Swift, Jazz Music

EARLY YEARS JUNE 18,1938 PARADISE RESTAURANT NYC,THE (Miller, Glenn & His Orchestra & Gail Reese).
Album: released on Soundcraft(USA), May'84 Dist: Jazz Music

FOREVER.
Tracks: / Take the 'A' Train / Back to back / Stairway to the stars / One I Love belongs to somebody else / Song of the volga boatmen / Little man who wasn't there, The / Who's sorry now? / Runnin' wild / I want to be happy / Ding-dong, the witch is dead / Over the rainbow / You stepped out of a dream / Bugle call rag / Story of a starry night, The / When Jonny comes marching home / Adios / Skylark / Say si si / On a little street in Singapore / Ciri-biri-bin / Jingle bells / Baby me / Nearness of you / Blueberry hill / Frenesi / At last / Woodpecker song / I'll never smile again / Keep them flying / My prayer / Yours is my heart alone.
Album: released on RCA, Jul'86 Dist: BMG

Cassette: released on RCA, Jul'86 Dist: BMG

GLEN MILLER.
Album: released on Magic, Jun'86 Dist: Celtic Music, Submarine, Swift, Wellards, Conifer, Jazz Music

GLEN MILLER STORY, THE.
Compact disc: released on Compact Collection, Sep'87 by Conifer Records. Dist: Conifer

GLENN MILLER.
Tracks: / Penslyvania 6-5000.
Compact disc: released on Deja Vu, Jul'87 by Deja Vu Records. Dist: Counterpoint, Record Services(Ireland), Jazz Music

Compact disc: released on RCA, Apr'84 Dist: BMG

Album: released on Giants of Jazz, Sep'87 by Hasmick Promotions Ltd.. Dist: Counterpoint, Taylors, Wellards, Swift, Crusader, Jazz Music

GLENN MILLER, 1937 - 1942.
Tracks: / Wistful and blue / I got rhythm / Sunrise serenade / Moon love / Sold American / Glen Island special / In the mood / Johnson rag / Yes, my darling daughter / Sun Valley jump / Caribbean dipper / Here we go again.
Album: released on Joker, '87 Dist: Counterpoint, Cadillac, Jazz Horizons, Jazz Music, Celtic Music

GLENN MILLER 1940-42.
Album: released on Jasmine, Apr'87 by Jasmine Records. Dist: Counterpoint, Cadillac, Taylors, Wellards, Swift, Jazz Music

Cassette: released on Jasmine, Apr'87 by Jasmine Records. Dist: Counterpoint, Cadillac, Taylors, Wellards, Swift, Jazz Music

GLENN MILLER AIR FORCE ORCHESTRA, NOVEMBER 1944.
Album: released on Soundcraft(Fanfare USA Import), May'84 Dist: Jazz Music

GLENN MILLER AIR FORCE ORCHESTRA, JUNE 10, 1944.
Album: released on Soundcraft(Fanfare USA Import), May'84 Dist: Jazz Music

GLENN MILLER AND....., THE (Miller, Glenn & Harry James Bands, The).
Album: released on Jazz Live, Oct'86 Dist: Jazz Music, Jazz Horizons, Cadillac

GLENN MILLER ARMY AIR FORCE BAND(1943-1944),THE.
Album: released on Rarities, Apr'81 Dist: Wellards, Swift

GLENN MILLER (CD).
Tracks: / Moonlight serenade / Hallelujah / In a sentimental mood / Back to back / Jumpin' jive / In the mood / Chattanooga choo choo / Happy in love / Serenade in blue / Don't sit under the apple tree / Moonlight cocktail / Pensylvania 6-5000 / Johnson rag / St. Louis blues / My prayer / Anchors aweigh / I've got a girl in Kalamazoo / Woodpecker song, The / I know why / Medley / My melancholy baby / Moon love / Stompin' at the Savoy / Blue moon / Melancholy baby.
Compact disc: released on The Collection, Apr'87 by Object Enterprises Ltd. Dist: Jazz Music

GLENN MILLER COLLECTION, (THE).
Album: released on Deja Vu, Aug'85 by Deja Vu Records. Dist: Counterpoint, Record Services(Ireland), Jazz Music

Page 678

Cassette: released on Deja Vu, Aug'85 by Deja Vu Records. Dist: Counterpoint, Record Services(Ireland), Jazz Music

GLENN MILLER COLLECTION,THE.
Tracks: / In the mood / Moonlight serenade / Chattanooga choo choo / Pennsylvania 6-5000 / Danny boy / Indian summer / American patrol / Blueberry hill / Little brown jug / Tuxedo junction / Don't sit under the apple tree / I've got a girl in Kalamazoo / I've got a girl in Kalamazoo / That ol' black magic / String of pearls, a / Moonlight cocktail / Pavanne / Woodpecker song / Johnson rag / Sunrise serenade.
Cassette: released on Pickwick, Feb'80 by Pickwick Records. Dist: PRT, Prism Leisure

Compact disc: released on Deja Vu, Sep'87 by Deja Vu Records. Dist: Counterpoint, Record Services(Ireland), Jazz Music. Estim retail price in Sep'87 was £7.99.

GLENN MILLER & HARRY JAMES BANDS (Miller, Glenn & Harry James).
Album: released on Jazz Live, Apr'81 Dist: Jazz Music, Jazz Horizons, Cadillac

GLENN MILLER & HIS ARMY AIR FORCE ORCHESTRA 1938 (Miller, Glenn & His Army Air Force Orchestra).
Album: released on Soundcraft, Jul'86 Dist: Jazz Music

GLENN MILLER & HIS ARMY AIR FORCE ORCHESTRA 1943 (Miller, Glenn & His Army Air Force Orchestra).
Notes: MONO. Vocals: Jonny Desmond 1943
Album: released on Soundcraft(USA), Jun'86 Dist: Jazz Music

GLENN MILLER & HIS ARMY AIR FORCE ORCHESTRA 1945 (Miller, Glenn & His Army Air Force Orchestra).
Album: released on Soundcraft(USA), Jul'86 Dist: Jazz Music

GLENN MILLER & HIS ARMY AIR FORCE ORCHESTRA 1944 (Miller, Glenn & His Army Air Force Orchestra).
Album: released on Soundcraft(USA), Jun'86 Dist: Jazz Music

GLENN MILLER IN CONCERT.
Album: released on RCA, Jun'84 Dist: BMG

Cassette: released on RCA International (USA), Jun'84 by RCA Records. Dist: BMG

GLENN MILLER LEGEND, THE.
Tracks: / Moonlight serenade / Little brown jug / St. Louis blues march / Tuxedo Junction / Chattanooga choo choo / I got rhythm / Blue skies / Johnson rag / Spirit is willing, The / Running wild / Perfidia / Sliphorn jive / Stairway to the stars / A-tisket, a-tasket / Moon love / Caribbean clipper / Sweet Eloise / My blue heaven / Slow freight / Nightingale sang in Berkeley Square, A / In the mood / String of pearls, A / Pennsylvania 6-5000 / I know why / Anchors aweigh / One o'clock jump / Sunrise serenade / Don't sit under the appletree / When Johnny comes marching home / Elmer's tune / Jukebox Saturday night / Song of the Volga boatmen / Farewell blues / On a little street in Singapore / Under a blanket of blue / Hop, the / Lamplighter's serenade, The / And the angels sing / Fools rush in / Moonlight becomes you / American patrol / Starlit / Sun Valley jump / I've got a gal in Kalamazoo / Flying home / Serenade in blue / Tiger rag / Hallelujah / My melancholy baby / I want to be happy / Boulder buff / Anvil chorus / I wanna hat with cherries / Say it / Yes, my darling daughter / Dearly beloved / King Porter stomp / Adios.
Compact disc: released on RCA, Jan'87 Dist: BMG

GLENN MILLER LIVE (1939).
Album: released on Jasmine, Apr'87 by Jasmine Records. Dist: Counterpoint, Cadillac, Taylors, Wellards, Swift, Jazz Music

Cassette: released on Jasmine, Apr'87 by Jasmine Records. Dist: Counterpoint, Cadillac, Taylors, Wellards, Swift, Jazz Music

GLENN MILLER ORCHESTRA.
Album: released on Soundcraft(Fanfare USA - Import), May'84 Dist: Jazz Music

GLENN MILLER ORCHESTRA, AUGUST 30, 1941.
Album: released on Soundcraft(Fanfare USA - Import), May'84 Dist: Jazz Music

GLENN MILLER ORCHESTRA, DECEMBER 27, 1941.
Album: released on Soundcraft(Fanfare USA - Import), May'84 Dist: Jazz Music

GLENN MILLER REUNION IN CONCERT (Miller, Glenn & His Orchestra).
Notes: Conductor: Billy May
Compact disc: released on Vogue(France), Dec'85 Dist: Discovery, Jazz Music, Swift

GLENN MILLER SOUND, (THE).
Cassette: released on VFM Cassettes, Jan'85 by VFM Records., Wynd-Up

GLENN MILLER STORY, THE.
Album: released on Astan, Jun'86 by Astan Records.

GLENN MILLER STORY: VOL 1.
Album: released on RCA, Aug'85 Dist: BMG

Cassette: released on RCA, Aug'85 Dist: BMG

Album: released on RCA (Germany), '83 Dist: Conifer, Target

GLENN MILLER STORY: VOL 2.
Album: released on RCA, Aug'85 Dist: BMG

Cassette: released on RCA, Aug'85 Dist: BMG

Album: released on RCA (Germany), '83 Dist: Conifer, Target

GLENN MILLER STORY: VOL 3.
Album: released on RCA, Aug'85 Dist: BMG

Cassette: released on RCA, Aug'85 Dist: BMG

GLENN MILLER STORY: VOL 4.
Album: released on RCA, Aug'85 Dist: BMG

Cassette: released on RCA, Aug'85 Dist: BMG

GLENN MILLER & THE ARMY AIR FORCE BAND.
Tracks: / Over there / Anvil chorus / Star dust / Song of the volga boatmen / Farewell blues / They are yanks / My ideal / Mission to Moscow / Sun valley jump / Tuxedo junction / I'll be around / Poincians / I hear you screamin' / Juke box saturday night / My blue heaven / St.Louis blues march / It must be jelly / Blues in my heart / Everybody loves my baby / Alexander's ragtime band / Stompin' at the savoy / Deep purple / Don't be that way / I can't give you anything but love / Wang wang blues / Shoo-shoo baby / Way you look tonight, The / Victory polka / There'll be a hot time in the town of Berlin / Here we go again / Jeep jockey jump / Enlisted men's mess / Begin the Beguine / In the mood.
Double Album: released on Jazz Tribune, Sep'86 Dist: Discovery

Double cassette: released on Jazz Tribune, Sep'86 Dist: Discovery

Double Album: released on RCA(France), '83 by RCA Records. Dist: Discovery, Silva Screen Records

GLENN MILLER'S UPTOWN HALL GANG.
Album: released on Enquire, Apr'79

GLENN MILLER'S UPTOWN HALL GANG VOLUME 2 (Miller's, Glenn Uptown Hall Gang).
Notes: Led by Mel Powell with Peanuts Hucko/Bernie Privin & Beryl Davis.
Album: released on Esquire, Jun'86 by Titan International Productions Ltd.. Dist: Jazz Music, Cadillac Music, Swift, Wellards, Taylors

GOLDEN HOUR OF GLENN MILLER.
Album: released on Golden Hour, Oct'75 by PRT Records.

GOLDEN SERENADE.
Album: released on Swing World, '84 Dist: Jazz Music, Swift, Celtic Music

Cassette: released on Swing World, '84 Dist: Jazz Music, Swift, Celtic Music

GRAVACIOES INEDITAS.
Album: released on RCA (Brazil), Jan'84 Dist: OTC

Cassette: released on RCA (Brazil), Jan'84 Dist: OTC

GREAT GLENN MILLER, (THE).
Album: by RCA Records., Swift

HALLELUJAH.
Album: released on Magic, '84 Dist: Celtic Music, Submarine, Swift, Wellards, Conifer, Jazz Music

Cassette: released on Magic, '84 Dist: Celtic Music, Submarine, Swift, Wellards, Conifer, Jazz Music

HERE WE GO AGAIN—VOL 2 1940-41 (Miller, Glenn & His Orchestra).
Album: released on Magic, Jan'86 Dist: Celtic Music, Submarine, Swift, Wellards, Conifer, Jazz Music

HITS FROM THE GLENN MILLER STORY.
Album: released on RCA, May'76 Dist: BMG

IN 1940.
Cassette: released on Wham-Magic, Aug'85

IN A DIGITAL MOOD (Miller, Glenn & His Orchestra).
Tracks: / In the mood / Chattanooga choo choo / American patrol / String of pearls / Little brown jug / Kalamazoo / Tuxedo junction / St.Louis blues march / Pennsylvania 6-5000 / Moonlight serenade.
Notes: Digital Stereo. Also featuring: Mel Torme, Julius La Rosa & Marlen Ver Planct.
Album: released on GRP(USA), Jun'84 by GRP Records (USA). Dist: IMS, Polygram, Jazz Music

Cassette: released on GRP(USA), Jun'84 by GRP Records (USA). Dist: IMS, Polygram, Jazz

---

Music

Compact disc: released on GRP(USA), Jun'84 by GRP Records (USA). Dist: IMS, Polygram, Jazz Music

IN HOLLYWOOD.
Compact disc: released on Phonogram, Jan'87 by Phonogram Records. Dist: Polygram

IN THE MOOD (Miller, Glenn & His Orchestra).
Tracks: / In the mood / Chattanooga choo choo / American patrol / St.Louis blues march / Pennsylvania 6-5000 / Jumpin' jive / Moonlight serenade / String of pearls / Don't sit under the apple tree / I've got a gal in kalamazoo / Serenade in blue / I know why / In the mood / String of pearls.
Album: released on Topline, '86 by Charly Records.

Cassette: released on Topline, '86 by Charly Records.

Album: released on CBS, Jun'86 by CBS Records. Dist: CBS

Cassette: released on CBS(Import), Jun'86 by CBS Records. Dist: Counterpoint, Celtic Music, Jazz Music, Swift, Conifer

Single 7": released on Old Gold, Oct'86 by Old Gold Records. Dist: PRT, Counterpoint, Lightning, Jazz Music, Taylors

IN THE MOOD.
Notes: With tommy dorsey & jimmy Dorsey.
Compact disc: released on DGR (Holland), '86 by DGR (Holland) Records.

Album: released on Pathe Marconi (France), Dec'84 Dist: Swift

Cassette: released on Pathe Marconi (France), Dec'84 Dist: Swift

Album: released on Astan, Nov'84 by Astar Records.

Cassette: released on Astan, Nov'84 by Astar Records.

Single 7": released on RCA, Jan'76 Dist: BMG

KEEP ON FLYING.
Album: released on Swing World, '84 Dist: Jazz Music, Swift, Celtic Music

Cassette: released on Swing World, '84 Dist: Jazz Music, Swift, Celtic Music

LEGEND, THE.
Cassette: released on Prism, May'87 by Prism Records. Dist: Pinnacle

LEGEND, THE.
Cassette: released on Prism, May'87 by Prism Records. Dist: Pinnacle

LEGEND, THE. (Miller, Glenn & His Army Air Force Orchestra).
Album: released on Dance Band Days, Jun'86 by Prism Leisure Corporation PLC. Dist: Prism Leisure, Jazz Music, Taylors

Cassette: released on Dance Band Days, Jun'86 by Prism Leisure Corporation PLC. Dist: Prism Leisure, Jazz Music, Taylors

Compact disc: released on Prism, Oct'87 by Prism Records. Dist: Pinnacle

LEGENDARY GLENN MILLER: VOL 10.
Album: released on RCA, Mar'76 Dist: BMG

LEGENDARY GLENN MILLER: VOL 11.
Album: released on RCA, Mar'76 Dist: BMG

LEGENDARY GLENN MILLER: VOL 12.
Album: released on RCA, Mar'76 Dist: BMG

LEGENDARY GLENN MILLER: VOL 13.
Album: released on RCA, Mar'78 Dist: BMG

LEGENDARY GLENN MILLER: VOL 14.
Album: released on RCA, May'77 Dist: BMG

LEGENDARY GLENN MILLER: VOL 15.
Album: released on RCA, May'77 Dist: BMG

LEGENDARY GLENN MILLER: VOL 16.
Album: released on RCA, May'77 Dist: BMG

LEGENDARY GLENN MILLER: VOL 17.
Album: released on RCA, May'77 Dist: BMG

LIVE FROM GLEN ISLAND CASINO, JULY 24, 1939.
Album: released on Soundcraft(Fanfare USA - Import), May'84 Dist: Jazz Music

LIVE FROM THE CAFE ROUGE, NOVEMBER 6, 1940.
Album: released on Soundcraft(Fanfare USA - Import), May'84 Dist: Jazz Music

Album: released on Jasmine, Sep'85 by Jasmine Records. Dist: Counterpoint, Cadillac, Taylors, Wellards, Swift, Jazz Music

Cassette: released on Jasmine, Sep'85 by Jasmine Records. Dist: Counterpoint, Cadillac, Taylors, Wellards, Swift, Jazz Music

---

LIVE REMOTES-1938 (Miller, Glenn & His Orchestra & Gail Reese).
Notes: Mono.
Album: released on Soundcraft, Nov'86 Dist: Jazz Music

LOVE SONGS FROM THE FABULOUS FORTIES.
Album: released on Camden(RCA), Jul'87 by RCA Records., Swift

MAGIC MOMENTS.
Cassette: released on RCA, Jun'84 Dist: BMG

MEADOWBROOK 1939 LIVE.
Album: released on Jasmine, Jan'87 by Jasmine Records.' Dist: Counterpoint, Cadillac, Taylors, Wellards, Swift, Jazz Music

MEMORIAL, 1944-69.
Album: released on RCA, '84 Dist: BMG

MEMORIAL FOR GLENN MILLER, A VOL.2.
Tracks: / King's march / Tuxedo Junction / All the things you are / April in Paris / American patrol / Song of the Volga Boatmen / Night and day / Baby me / Georgia on my mind / Dream / Over the rainbow / Runnin' wild / Stormy weather / Man I love (The) / Lady is a tramp (The) / Adios / A-tisket, a-tasket.
Compact disc: released on Accord, Dec'86 Dist: Discovery

MEMORIAL FOR GLENN MILLER, A VOL.3.
Compact disc: released on Accord, Dec'86 Dist: Discovery

MEMORIAL FOR GLENN MILLER VOL.1.
Notes: Incl: In the mood, Stardust, Moonlight serenade, cheek to cheek, Laura etc.
Compact disc: released on Accord, '86 Dist: Discovery

MILLER MAGIC (Miller, Glenn & His Orchestra & Gail Reese).
Double Album: released on Cambra, '83 by Cambra Records. Dist: Celtic Music

Double cassette: released on Cambra, '83 by Cambra Records. Dist: Celtic Music

MILLION DREAMS AGO, A.
Compact disc: released on Bandstand, May'86 Dist: Swift

MOONLIGHT SERENADE (Miller, Glenn & His Orchestra).
Tracks: / Moonlight serenade / Tuxedo junction.
Single 7": released on Old Gold, Nov'86 by Old Gold Records. Dist: PRT, Counterpoint, Lightning, Jazz Music, Taylors

Single 7": released on MCA, Jul'85 by MCA Records. Dist: Polygram

Single 12": released on MCA, Jul'85 by MCA Records. Dist: Polygram

MOONLIGHT SERENADE/SUNRISE SERENADE.
Single 7": released on Lightning, '80 by Lightning Records. Dist: Jetstar

MOSTLY SWINGING.
Album: released on Nostalgia(Sweden), '82 Dist: Wellards, Jazz Music

Cassette: released on Nostalgia(Sweden), '82 Dist: Wellards, Jazz Music

ON THE AIR Volumes 1-3.
Tracks: / Slumber song(opening theme0 / Yes, my darling daughter / I don't want to set the world on fire / Song of the bayou / Nightingale sang in Berkeley Square / On the sentimental side / Mutiny in the nursery / Lamp is low / Don't wake up my heart / I,m not much on looks / My best wishes / Moonshine over Kentucky / Gentlemen needs a shave / Slumber song(closing theme) / Beat me daddy / Eight to the bar / Handful of stars / I know that you know / There I go / You've got me this way / I guess I'll have to dream the rest / Back to back / Dreamsville, Ohio / Oh baby / Do you care? / When paw was courtin' maw / This time the dream's on me / Light's out / Light's out, hold me tight / Moonlight serenade / Show boat / Why do I love you / Can't help lovin' dat man / Make believe / Ol'man river / Papa Niccolini / Moon is a silver dollar / Don't worry bout me / Hold tight / Massquerade is over / Our love / Pinball Paul / Sometime / Beer barrel polka / Starlit hour.
Triple album / cassette: released on RCA, Mar'86 BMG

Triple album / cassette: released on RCA, Mar'86 BMG

ON THE AIR.
Album: released on Queendisc(Italy), Apr'81 Dist: Celtic Music, Cadillac, Jazz Horizons

ON THE CONTINENT (Miller, Glenn & His Army Air Force Orchestra).
Notes: Mono. Directed by Ray McKinley
Album: released on Soundcraft, Nov'86 Dist: Jazz Music

ORIGINAL RECORDINGS.
Album: released on Meteor, Jun'85 by Magnum Music Group Ltd. Dist: PRT

Cassette: released on Meteor, Jun'85 by Magnum Music Group Ltd. Dist: PRT

ORIGINAL RECORDINGS BY GLENN MILLER & HIS ORCHESTRA.
Album: released on RCA/Camden, Apr'86 by RCA Records.

Cassette: released on RCA/Camden, Apr'86 by RCA Records.

ORIGINAL RECORDINGS, (THE).
Album: released on RCA, '69 Dist: BMG

ORIGINAL SESSIONS VOL2.
Album: released on Meteor, Oct'85 by Magnum Music Group Ltd. Dist: PRT

ORIGINAL SOUNDS OF THE SWING ERA VOL5.
Album: released on RCA (Germany), '83 Dist: Conifer, Target

PREVIOUSLY UNISSUED 1940-42.
Album: released on Jasmine, Jan'87 by Jasmine Records. Dist: Counterpoint, Cadillac, Taylors, Wellards, Swift, Jazz Music

REUNION IN HI-FI.
Album: released on Jasmine, Jun'83 by Jasmine Records. Dist: Counterpoint, Cadillac, Taylors, Wellards, Swift, Jazz Music

REVIVAL ORCHESTRA.
Album: released on Timeless, Oct'86 Dist: Pinnacle, Cadillac, Jazz Music

RHAPSODY IN BLUE.
Album: released on Astan, Nov'84 by Astan Records.

Cassette: released on Astan, Nov'84 by Astan Records.

SALUTE TO TRINIDAD ARMY BASE NOV.3 1941 (Miller, Glenn & His Orchestra & Gail Reese).
Album: released on Soundcraft(USA), May'84 Dist: Jazz Music

SILVER SERENADE (Miller, Glenn & His Army Air Force Orchestra).
Tracks: / Poinciana / Serenade in blue / Easter parade / Paper doll / White Christmas / Spirit is willing, The / Silent night / Blue rain / Chattanooga choo choo / St. Louis blues / My buddy / Body and soul / Songs my mother taught me / I'll never mention your name / I'll be home for Christmas / Here we go again.
Album: released on Swinghouse(Submarine), Nov'86 Dist: Jazz Music

Cassette: released on Swinghouse(Submarine), Nov'86 Dist: Jazz Music

OH! SO GOOD.
Album: released on Magic, Oct'87 Dist: Celtic Music, Submarine, Swift, Wellards, Conifer, Jazz Music

Cassette: released on Magic, Oct'87 Dist: Celtic Music, Submarine, Swift, Wellards, Conifer, Jazz Music

SOUNDTRACK.
Album: released on MCA, Jul'85 by MCA Records. Dist: Polygram

Cassette: released on MCA, Jul'85 by MCA Records. Dist: Polygram

STARDUST.
Album: released on Magic, Jan'87 Dist: Celtic Music, Submarine, Swift, Wellards, Conifer, Jazz Music

Cassette: released on Magic, Jan'87 Dist: Celtic Music, Submarine, Swift, Wellards, Conifer, Jazz Music

STORY OF A MAN AND HIS MUSIC, THE.
Compact disc: released on Delta, '86 by Delta Records. Dist: Target, Zodiac

STRING OF PEARLS.
Album: released on Astan(USA), Mar'85

STRING OF PEARLS (Miller, Glenn & His Orchestra).
Album: released on Bulldog, Mar'85 by Bulldog Records. Dist: President, Spartan, Swift, Taylors, Jazz Music

SUNSET SERENADE AUG. 1941 (Miller, Glenn & His Orchestra & Gail Reese).
Album: released on Jasmine, Sep'85 by Jasmine Records. Dist: Counterpoint, Cadillac, Taylors, Wellards, Swift, Jazz Music

Cassette: released on Jasmine, Sep'85 by Jasmine Records. Dist: Counterpoint, Cadillac, Taylors, Wellards, Swift, Jazz Music

SUSTAIN THE WINGS SHOWS 1941-42 (Miller, Glenn & His Orchestra & Gail Reese).
Album: released on Jasmine, Sep'85 by Jasmine Records. Dist: Counterpoint, Cadillac, Taylors, Wellards, Swift, Jazz Music

Cassette: released on Jasmine, Sep'85 by Jasmine Records. Dist: Counterpoint, Cadillac, Taylors, Wellards, Swift, Jazz Music

SWINGING BIG BANDS, 1939-42.
Double Album: released on Joker, '79 Dist: Counterpoint, Cadillac, Jazz Horizons, Jazz Music, Celtic Music

SWINGING BIG BANDS, 1939-42: VOL 1.
Album: released on Joker, Apr'81 Dist: Counterpoint, Cadillac, Jazz Horizons, Jazz Music, Celtic Music

SWINGING BIG BANDS, 1939-42: VOL 2.
Album: released on Joker, Apr'81 Dist: Counterpoint, Cadillac, Jazz Horizons, Jazz Music, Celtic Music

SWINGING BIG BANDS, 1939-42: VOL 3.
Album: released on Joker, Apr'81 Dist: Counterpoint, Cadillac, Jazz Horizons, Jazz Music, Celtic Music

SWINGING MR MILLER, (THE).
Double Album: released on RCA(France), Apr'84 by RCA Records. Dist: Discovery, Silva Screen Records

SWINGING SUPERSTAR ORCHESTRA, (THE).
Album: released on Up International, Apr'81

THAT OLD MILLER MAGIC.
Tracks: / In the mood / Chattanooga choo choo / St. Louis Blues / Don't sit under the apple tree(with anyone else but me) / Tuxedo junction / Little brown jug / American patrol / When Jonny comes marching home / I've got a gal in Kalamazoo / Serenade in blue / That old black amgic / King Porter stomp.
Notes: This record has been compiled from master tapes made in the 1930's and 40's. The sound quality therefore reflects the age of these recordings and recording tech-niques available at the time. This compilation (P) 1986 & (C) RCA Records Ltd. issued under exclusive licence to Music for Pleasure.
Album: released on MFP, Sep'86 by Music For Pleasure Records. Dist: EMI

Cassette: released on MFP, Sep'86 by Music For Pleasure Records. Dist: EMI

UNCLE SAM PRESENTS (Miller Direct Aatco, Capt.Glenn).
Album: released on Hep Jazz, Apr'86 by H.R. Taylor Records. Dist: Celtic Music, Cadillac, Jazz Music, Taylors, Wellards, Zodiac, Swift, Fast Forward

VERY BEST OF GLENN MILLER, (THE).
Album: released on RCA, '84 Dist: BMG

Cassette: released on RCA, '84 Dist: BMG

WEHRMACHT HOUR, THE - NOVEMBER 1944 (Miller, Major Glenn).
Notes: Mono.
Album: released on Soundcraft, Nov'86 Dist: Jazz Music

WISTFUL AND BLUE.
Album: released on Joker, Apr'81 Dist: Counterpoint, Cadillac, Jazz Horizons, Jazz Music, Celtic Music

Miller, Grant

COLDER THAN ICE.
Tracks: / Colder than ice / Red for love.
Single 12": released on ZYX(Germany), Dec'85 by ZYX Records. Dist: Greyhound

Miller, Henry

TROPIC OF CANCER.
Notes: Henry Miller was born in New York in 1891. He did a variety of jobs before taki-ng up writing full time in 1924. He moved to Paris in 1930 where he wrote Tropicof Cancer, his first 'fictionalised autobiography' about his time there as a st-ruggling artist. There is humour, 'ust and emptiness in the life of Miller's ch-aracter as he guides us through a landscape of human sensuality, sensistivity a-nd frailty.
Cassette: released on Listen For Pleasure, Feb'86 Dist: EMI

Miller, Herb

MEMORIES OF GLENN MILLER (Miller, Herb Orchestra).
Album: released on Avimus, Sep'87

MUSIC OF GLEN MILLER.
Album: released on Avimus, Sep'84

TRIBUTE TO SWING.
Album: released on Avimus, Jun'83

Cassette: released on RIM, Jun'83 by Rediffusion. Dist: Jazz Music, Pinnacle

TUXEDO JUNCTION (Miller, Herb Orchestra).
Single 7": released on Miller, Nov'81 Dist: Pinnacle

Miller, Ina

BONNIE MORVEN HILLS.
Notes: Including:*Meeting of the waters, Loch Maree Islands, Leaving Barra, Home to the Kyles etc.*
Cassette: released on Ross, '86 by Ross Records. Dist: Ross, Taylors, Celtic Music, Roots

BONNIE WEE HOOSE ON THE HILLSIDE.
Album: released on Ross, '86 by Ross Records. Dist: Ross, Taylors, Celtic Music, Roots

Cassette: by Ross Records. Dist: Ross, Taylors, Celtic Music, Roots

INA MILLER'S SONGS OF SCOTLAND.
Album: released on Ross, Aug'84 by Ross Records. Dist: Ross, Taylors, Celtic Music, Roots

Cassette: released on Ross, Aug'84 by Ross Records. Dist: Ross, Taylors, Celtic Music, Roots

MY SCOTTISH HOMELAND.
Album: released on Ross, '86 by Ross Records. Dist: Ross, Taylors, Celtic Music, Roots

Cassette: released on Ross, '86 by Ross Records. Dist: Ross, Taylors, Celtic Music, Roots

SONG OF THE MIRA.
Album: released on Ross, '86 by Ross Records. Dist: Ross, Taylors, Celtic Music, Roots

Cassette: released on Ross, Mar'85 by Ross Records. Dist: Ross, Taylors, Celtic Music, Roots

SONGS OF SCOTLAND.
Cassette: released on Ross, '86 by Ross Records. Dist: Ross, Taylors, Celtic Music, Roots

Miller, Jacob

REGGAE GREATS.
Album: released on Island, Nov'85 by Island Records. Dist: Polygram, Celtic Music

Cassette: released on Island, Nov'85 by Island Records. Dist: Polygram, Celtic Music

UNFINISHED SYMPHONY.
Album: released on Circle, Apr'84 Dist: Jazz Music

Miller, Jay

GOING TO NEW ORLEANS.
Album: released on Flyright, Jan'85 by Flyright Records. Dist: Swift, Jazz Music, Wellards, Cadillac

JAY MILLER SESSIONS VOL.16.
Album: released on Flyright, Jul'79 by Flyright Records. Dist: Swift, Jazz Music, Wellards, Cadillac

JAY MILLER STUDIO BAND 1961-63.
Album: released on Flyright, Jul'85 by Flyright Records. Dist: Swift, Jazz Music, Wellards, Cadillac

STUDIO BAND.
Album: released on Flyright, Oct'86 by Flyright Records. Dist: Swift, Jazz Music, Wellards, Cadillac

Miller, Jimmy

SIZZLIN' HOT.
Single 7": released on Backs, Mar'84 by Backs Records. Dist: Backs, Cartel

Miller, John

SAFE SWEET HOME.
Album: released on Rounder(USA), Jan'87 Dist: Jazz Music, Projection, Swift, Celtic Music, Cadillac, Ross, Duncans, Impetus

Miller, Larry

RIGHT CHAPS.
Album: released on Matinee Music, May'83 Dist: Indies, Cartel

Miller, Marcus

MARCUS MILLER.
Album: released on WEA(Import), Aug'84 by WEA Records. Dist: Swift

SUDDENLY.
Album: released on Asylum, Mar'83 by WEA Records. Dist: WEA

Miller, Max

CHEEKIE CHAPPIE.
Album: released on Philips, Nov'75 Dist: IMS-Polygram

GOLDEN AGE OF MAX MILLER.
Album: released on Golden Age, Jul'83 by Music For Pleasure Records. Dist: EMI

Cassette: released on Golden Age, Jul'83 by Music For Pleasure Records. Dist: EMI

IN THE THEATRE.
Album: released on One Up, May'75 by EMI Records(UK). Dist: EMI

Cassette: by EMI Records(UK). Dist: EMI

MAX AT THE MET PLUS TWO.
Album: released on Flashback, Nov'85 by Flashback Records/PRT Records. Dist: Mainline

Cassette: released on Flashback, Nov'85 by Flashback Records/PRT Records. Dist: Mainline

Miller, Mitch

YELLOW ROSE OF TEXAS.
Single 7": released on Impact, '80 by Ace Records. Dist: Celtic Music, Pinnacle, Swift, Cadillac

Miller O.C

HOW CAN I LOVE AGAIN/OH WHAT A FEELING.
Single 12": released on Orbitone, Dec'83 by Orbitone Records. Dist: Jetstarr*

Miller Rodney

AIRPLANE.
Album: released on Rounder(USA), Sep'85 Dist: Jazz Music, Projection, Swift, Celtic Music, Cadillac, Ross, Duncans, Impetus

Miller, Roger

BEST OF ROGER MILLER.
Album: released on Philips, Jan'78 Dist: IMS-Polygram

KING OF THE ROAD.
Single 7": released on Old Gold, Jan'85 by Old Gold Records. Dist: PRT, Counterpoint, Lightning, Jazz Music, Taylors

LITTLE GREEN APPLES.
Album: released on Contour, Jan'76 by Pickwick Records. Dist: Pickwick

MOTIVE SERIES.
Album: released on Mercury, Dec'81 by Phonogram Records. Dist: IMS, Polygram

Cassette: released on Mercury, Dec'81 by Phonogram Records. Dist: IMS, Polygram

OFF THE WALL.
Album: released on Windsong, Jan'78 by RCA Records. Dist: BMG

OLD FRIENDS (Miller Roger & Willie Nelson).
Album: released on CBS, Nov'82 by CBS Records. Dist: CBS

Cassette: released on CBS, Nov'82 by CBS Records. Dist: CBS

ROGER MILLER.
Album: released on MCA, Mar'87 by MCA Records. Dist: Polygram

Cassette: released on MCA, Mar'87 by MCA Records. Dist: Polygram

ROGER MILLER'S GREATEST HITS.
Album: released on RCA, Mar'85 Dist: BMG

Cassette: released on RCA, Mar'85 Dist: BMG

Miller, Steve

ABRACADABRA (Miller, Steve Band).
Single 7": released on Mercury, Oct'84 by Phonogram Records. Dist: IMS, Polygram

Compact disc: released on Mercury, Jan'83 by Phonogram Records. Dist: IMS, Polygram

ANTHOLOGY - STEVE MILLER.
Double Album: released on Capitol, Jan'73 by Capitol Records. Dist: EMI

ANTHOLOGY - STEVE MILLER BAND (Miller, Steve, Band).
Double Album: released on EMI (Germany), Jan'83 by EMI Records(UK). Dist: Conifer

BEST OF STEVE MILLER 1968-1973, THE.
Tracks: / Living in the USA / I love you / Don't let nobody turn you around / Seasons / Shu ba da du ma ma ma / Kow kow calqulator / Joker, The / Going to the country / My dark hour / Your saving grace / Celebration song / Space cowboy.
Album: released on Capitol, Aug'86 by Capitol Records. Dist: EMI

Cassette: released on Capitol, Aug'86 by Capitol Records. Dist: EMI

Album: released on Fame (Capitol), May'82 by Music For Pleasure Records. Dist: EMI

Cassette: released on Fame (Capitol), May'82 by Music For Pleasure Records. Dist: EMI

BOOK OF DREAMS (Miller, Steve, Band).
Album: released on Mercury, Jan'85 by Phonogram Records. Dist: IMS, Polygram

Cassette: released on Mercury, Jan'85 by Phonogram Records. Dist: IMS, Polygram

BRAVE NEW WORLD (Miller, Steve, Band).
Album: released on EMI, Feb'84 by EMI Records(UK). Dist: EMI

CHILDREN OF THE FUTURE.
Album: released on Capitol, Jan'68 by Capitol Records. Dist: EMI

CIRCLE OF LOVE (Miller, Steve, Band).
Compact disc: released on Mercury, '83 by Phonogram Records. Dist: IMS, Polygram

Album: released on Mercury(Germany), Apr'85 by Phonogram Records. Dist: IMS, Polygram

FLY LIKE AN EAGLE (Miller, Steve, Band).
Album: released on Mercury, Nov'84 by Phonogram Records. Dist: IMS, Polygram

Cassette: released on Mercury, Nov'84 by Phonogram Records. Dist: IMS, Polygram

GREATEST HITS: STEVE MILLER Decade of American Music (A), 1976-86 (Miller, Steve, Band).
Tracks: / Space intro / Fly like an eagle / Bongo bongo / Rock n' me / Jet airliner / Take the money and run / Mercury blues / Swing town / Shangri-La / Abracadabra / Italian x rays / Out of the night / Who do you love / Harmony of the spheres.
Album: released on Mercury, Jan'78 by Phonogram Records. Dist: IMS, Polygram

Cassette: released on Mercury, Jan'78 by Phonogram Records. Dist: IMS, Polygram

Album: released on Mercury, Aug'85 by Phonogram Records. Dist: IMS, Polygram

Cassette: released on Mercury, Aug'85 by Phonogram Records. Dist: IMS, Polygram

Album: released on Mercury, May'87 by Phonogram Records. Dist: IMS, Polygram

Cassette: released on Mercury, May'87 by Phonogram Records. Dist: IMS, Polygram

Compact disc: released on Mercury, May'87 by Phonogram Records. Dist: IMS, Polygram

GREATEST HITS:STEVE MILLER (CD) (Miller, Steve Band).
Tracks: / Dance dance dance / Fly like an eagle / Joker / Jet airliner / Jungle love / Rock'n'me / Serenade / Stake / Take the money and run / Swingtown / Threshold / True fire love / Winter time / Wild mountain honey.
Compact disc: released on Mercury, '83 by Phonogram Records. Dist: IMS, Polygram

I WANT TO MAKE THE WORLD TURN AROUND (Miller, Steve, Band).
Tracks: / I want to make the world turn around / Slinky.
Single 7": released on Capitol, Mar'87 by Capitol Records. Dist: EMI

Single 12": released on Capitol, Mar'87 by Capitol Records. Dist: EMI

ITALIAN X RAYS (Miller, Steve Band).
Tracks: / Radio 1&2 / Italian X Rays / Daybreak / Shangri-La / Who do you love / Harmony of the Speres 1&2 / Bongo bongo / Out of the night / Golden opportunity / Hollywood dream / One in a million.
Notes: After two years a new album from the man who brought you 'Abracadabra'. FeaturesSteve's single 'Shangri-La'. With the same band that featured on 'Abracadabra', incuding the exellent Kenny Lee Lewis on guitar, this is an album which combinesthe classic Steve Miller sound with the best modern recording technology.
Compact disc: released on Mercury, Nov'84 by Phonogram Records. Dist: IMS, Polygram

JOKER THE (Miller, Steve, Band).
Album: released on Capitol, Oct'80 by Capitol Records. Dist: EMI

Album: released on EMI, Jan'83 by EMI Records(UK). Dist: EMI

JOKER/LIVING IN THE USA C (Miller, Steve, Band).
Single 7": released on Capitol, Jan'83 by Capitol Records. Dist: EMI

JOURNEY FROM EDEN (Miller, Steve, Band).
Album: released on EMI, Feb'84 by EMI Records(UK). Dist: EMI

LIVE: STEVE MILLER (Miller, Steve Band).
Video-cassette (VHS): released on PMI, Jun'86 by PMI Records. Dist: EMI*

Video-cassette [Betamax]: released on PMI, Jun'86 by PMI Records. Dist: EMI*

LIVE VIDEO: STEVE MILLER (Miller, Steve, Band).
Notes: Inc. 'Rockin' me', 'Take the money and run', 'The joker', 'Jet air liner' etc.
Video-cassette (VHS): released on Video Collection, May'87 by Video Collection International Ltd.. Dist: Counterpoint

LIVING IN THE 20TH CENTURY (Miller, Steve, Band).
Tracks: / Nobody but you baby / I want to make the world turn around / Living in the 20th century / Maelstrom / I wanna be loved / My babe / Big boss man / Caress me baby / Ain't that lovin' you baby / Behind the barn.
Notes: Living in the 20th century is Steve Miller's 17th album and his first on the Capitol label in Britain for a number of years. The album is a collection, one side featuring new songs in the classic Steve Miller tradition of 'the Joker' and 'Abracadabra' while the other side exhibits Miller's Rock 'n' Roll roots. Three compositions by Jimmy reed are featured and the album is dedicated to Reed's memory.
Compact disc: released on EMI, Jan'87 by EMI Records(UK). Dist: EMI

Album: released on Capitol, Jan'87 by Capitol Records. Dist: EMI

Cassette: released on Capitol, Jan'87 by Capitol Records. Dist: EMI

MACHO CITY/FLY LIKE AN EAGLE.
Single 7": released on Mercury, Feb'82 by Phonogram Records. Dist: IMS, Polygram

NUMBER 5.
Album: released on Capitol, Jan'70 by Capitol Records. Dist: EMI

RECALL THE BEGINNING- A JOURNEY FROM EDEN.
Album: released on Capitol, Jan'72 by Capitol Records. Dist: EMI

ROCK LOVE.
Album: released on Capitol, Jan'71 by Capitol Records. Dist: EMI

SAILOR.
Album: released on Fame (Capitol), Nov'83 by Music For Pleasure Records. Dist: EMI

Cassette: released on Fame (Capitol), Nov'83 by Music For Pleasure Records. Dist: EMI

ST LOUIS TO FRISCO TO MEMPHIS (Miller, Steve Band & Chuck Berry).
Album: released on Karussell(Germany), Oct'82 Dist: IMS, Polygram

Cassette: released on Karussell(Germany), Oct'82 Dist: IMS, Polygram

STEVE MILLER'S BAND LIVE.
Album: released on Mercury, Apr'83 by Phonogram Records. Dist: IMS, Polygram

Cassette: released on Mercury, Apr'83 by Phonogram Records. Dist: IMS. Polygram

STORY SO FAR (Miller, Steve & Lol Coxhill).
Album: released on Caroline, Jan'74 Dist: Virgin, Island, Polygram, CBS

TAKE THE MONEY AND RUN/JOKER (LIVE) (Miller, Steve, Band).
Single 7": released on Mercury, Apr'83 by Phonogram Records. Dist: IMS, Polygram

Single 12": released on Mercury, Apr'83 by Phonogram Records. Dist: IMS. Polygram

Miller Tracy

BABY IT TAKES TWO/YOUR CONFIDENTIALLY.
Single 7": released on Peachtown, May'82 by Peachtown Records.

Miller, Vallin

HIT BACK.
Single 12": released on Governor, Nov'86 Dist: Jetstar

Miller,Ned

FROM A JACK TO A KING.
Single 7": released on Decca, Mar'82 by Decca Records. Dist: Polygram

FROM A JACK TO A KING/DO WHAT YOU DO WELL.
Single 7": released on Old Gold, Oct'83 by Old Gold Records. Dist: PRT, Counterpoint, Lightning, Jazz Music, Taylors

Millican & Nesbitt

CANADIAN SUNSET.
Album: released on Pye, Nov'76

COUNTRY ROADS.
Album: released on Pye, Sep'78

GOLDEN HOUR OF MILLICAN & NESBITT.
Album: released on Golden Hour, Sep'77 by PRT Records.

Millie

MY BOY LOLLIPOP.
Tracks: / My boy lollipop / Oh Henry.
Single 7": released on Island, Jul'87 by Island Records. Dist: Polygram, Celtic Music

Single 12": released on Island, Jul'87 by Island Records. Dist: Polygram, Celtic Music

Single 7": released on Island, Feb'80 by Island Records. Dist: Polygram, Celtic Music

SWEET WILLIAM/WINGS OF A DOVE.
Single 7": released on Island, Aug'82 by Island Records. Dist: Polygram, Celtic Music

Milligan, Spike

ADOLPH HITLER- MY PART IN HIS DOWNFALL.
Cassette: released on Columbia, Apr'81 by EMI Records(UK). Dist: EMI

AN EVENING WITH SPIKE MILLIGAN.
Album: released on MFP, Jan'78 by Music For Pleasure Records. Dist: EMI

HE'S INNOCENT OF WATERGATE (Milligan, Spike & Peter Sellers).
Album: released on Decca, Aug'74 by Decca Records. Dist: Polygram

HE'S INNOCENT OF WATERGATE (see Sellers, Peter) (Milligan, Spike & Peter Sellers).

HIMAZAS/THERE AIN'T NO MORNING.
Single 7": released on Paramount, Nov'83 by Paramount Records.

PUCKOON (Milligan, Spike & Friends).
Album: released on Columbia, Sep'80 by EMI Records(UK). Dist: EMI

SNOW GOOSE THE (Milligan, Spike & The London Symphony Orchestra).
Album: released on RCA, Jun'82 Dist: BMG

Cassette: released on RCA, Jun'82 Dist: BMG

Album: released on Big Beat, Jun'86 by Ace Records. Dist: Celtic Music, Pinnacle, Jazz Music, Projection

Cassette: released on Big Beat, Jun'86 by Ace Records. Dist: Celtic Music, Pinnacle, Jazz Music, Projection

STICKY/NONE TODAY THANK YOU.
Single 7": released on Spike, Oct'82

UNSPUN SOCKS FROM A CHICKENS LAUNDRY.
Album: released on Spike, Oct'82

Cassette: released on Spike. Oct'82

WOLVES WITHCHES AND GIANTS.
Album: released on Impression, Nov'84 Dist: CBS

Cassette: released on Impression, Nov'84 Dist: CBS

Millinder, Lucky

APOLLO JUMP (Millinder, Lucky And His Orchestra).
Album: released on Affinity, Sep'83 by Charly Records. Dist: Charly, Cadillac, Swift

LET IT ROLL AGAIN.
Album: released on Jukebox Lil, Nov'85 by Jukebox Lil. Dist: Swift, Celtic Music

LUCKY MILLINDER & HIS ORCHESTRA.
Album: released on Hindsight(USA), Sep'87 by Hindsight Records (USA). Dist: Swift, Charly, Jazz Music. Estim retail price in Sep'87 was £5.75.

Million Airs

GLENN MILLER ANNIVERSARY CONCERT.
Album: released on Decca, Mar'76 by Decca Records. Dist: Polygram

Album: released on MFP(Holland), Oct'84 by Music For Pleasure Records. Dist: Conifer

Cassette: released on MFP, Oct'84 by Music For Pleasure Records. Dist: EMI

Million Dollar Quartet

MILLION DOLLAR QUARTET.
Album: released on Sun, Sep'81 by Charly Records. Dist: Charly, Swift

Cassette: released on Sun, Sep'81 by Charly Records. Dist: Charly, Swift

MILLION DOLLAR QUARTET.
Tracks: / Peace in the valley / Just a little walk with Jesus / Walk that lonesome valley / Down by the riverside / I shall not be moved / I'm with the in crowd but oh so alone / Farther along / Blessed Jesus hold my hand / As we travel along the Jericho road / I just can't make it by myself / Little cabin on the hill / Summertime has passed and gone / I hear a sweet voice calling / And now sweetheart / You've done me wrong / Keeper of the key / Crazy arms / Don't forbid me.
Compact disc: released on Charly, Feb'87 by Charly Records. Dist: Charly, Cadillac, Swift

Million, Jeb

SECOND TIME AROUND.
Tracks: / Second time around / Welcome to love.
Single 7": released on WEA, Aug'86 by WEA Records. Dist: WEA

Single 12": released on WEA, Aug'86 by WEA Records. Dist: WEA

SPEED UP MY HEARTBEAT.
Tracks: / Speed up my heartbeat / Who send you.
Single 7": released on WEA, Oct'86 by WEA Records. Dist: WEA

Single 12": released on WEA, Oct'86 by WEA Records. Dist: WEA

Million, Max

TOO SKINNY.
Single 7": released on Anubis, Oct'85 Dist: Spartan

WALK MY WAY.
Single 7": released on Button, Jul'84 by Musical Characters Records. Dist: Spartan

Million Sellers...

MILLION SELLERS OF THE 30'S AND 40'S Various original artists (Various original artists).
Double cassette: released on Cambra, '83 by Cambra Records. Dist: Celtic Music

MILLION SELLERS OF THE 50'S Various original artists (Various original artists).
Double Album: released on Cambra, '83 by Cambra Records. Dist: Celtic Music

Double cassette: released on Cambra, '83 by Cambra Records. Dist: Celtic Music

MILLION SELLERS OF THE 50'S Various artists (Various artists).
Cassette: released on K-Tel, Aug'84 by K-Tel Records. Dist: K-Tel, Celtic Music, Terry Blood, Wynd-Up, Taylors, Pickwick, Solomon & Peres, Polygram

MILLION SELLERS OF THE FIFTIES VOL 2 Various artists (Various artists).
Tracks: / Third Man (Harry Lime theme) / Tell me why / Hold me, thrill me, kiss me / April love / P.S. I love you / Hearts of stone / Tear fell, (A) / See you later alligator / Don't forbid me / At the hop / Come go with me / Peggy Sue / Rock around the clock / More and more / Let me go, lover / Love is a many splendoured thing / Unchained melody / I hear you knocking / I'll be home / I'm yours / Tea for two cha cha / Maybe baby / Sugar time / I'm sorry / Wonderful time up there, (A) / Stranger in Paradise.
Album: released on Cambra, Sep'86 by Cambra Records. Dist: Celtic Music

Cassette: released on Cambra, Sep'86 by Cambra Records. Dist: Celtic Music

Millions Like Us

GUARANTEED FOR LIFE.
Tracks: / Guaranteed for life / Heaven help the child.
Single 7": released on Virgin, Sep'87 by Virgin Records. Dist: Virgin, EMI

Single 12": released on Virgin, Sep'87 by Virgin Records. Dist: Virgin, EMI

Millions Of Dead Chickens

CHICKEN SQWAWK.
Single 7": released on Radical, Dec'84 by Radical Records. Dist: Cartel

Millions Of Dead Cops

M.D.C..
Album: released on Alternative Tentacles, '82 by Alternative Tentacles Records. Dist: Rough Trade, Cartel

Millns Paul

TILL THE MORNING COMES.
Album: released on Mays, Jan'82 by Mays Records., Projection, Swift, Celtic Music, Cadillac, Ross, Duncans, Impetus

Mills, Alan

CANADIAN FOLK SONGS.
Cassette: released on Folktracks, Nov'79 by Folktracks Cassettes. Dist: Folktracks, Roots

Mills, Barbara

QUEEN OF FOOLS.
Single 7": released on Inferno, Aug'82 by Inferno Records. Dist: Inferno, Cartel, Pinnacle

Single 7": Dist: Backs, Cartel

Mills, Betty Lou

20 BEST LOVED GOSPEL SONGS - BETTY LOU MILLS.
Album: by Pilgrim Records. Dist: Rough Trade, Cartel

COUNTRYSTYLE.
Album: by Pilgrim Records. Dist: Rough Trade, Cartel

Mills Blue Rhythm Band

BLUE RHYTHM 1930-31.
Album: released on Hep Jazz, Sep'86 by H.R. Taylor Records. Dist: Celtic Music, Cadillac, Jazz Music, Taylors, Wellards, Zodiac, Swift, Fast Forward

MILLS BLUE RHYTHM BAND VOL. 2.
Album: released on Hep Jazz, Mar'87 by H.R. Taylor Records. Dist: Celtic Music, Cadillac, Jazz Music, Taylors, Wellards, Zodiac, Swift, Fast Forward

Mills Brothers

20 GREATEST HITS: MILLS BROTHERS.
Album: released on Nostalgia(USA), Dec'85 by Sonic Arts Corporation.

Cassette: released on Nostalgia(USA), Dec'85 by Sonic Arts Corporation.

BEST OF THE MILLS BROTHERS (CREOLE).
Cassette: released on Creole(Everest-Europa), Jul'84 by Creole Records. Dist: PRT

BEST OF THE MILLS BROTHERS (MFP).
Album: released on MFP, Apr'82 by Music For Pleasure Records. Dist: EMI

Cassette: released on MFP, Apr'82 by Music For Pleasure Records. Dist: EMI

CHRONOLOGICAL, VOLUME 2.
Album: released on JSP, Jun'86 by JSP Records. Dist: Taylors, Hotshot, Conifer, Jazz Music, Swift, Wellards

CHRONOLOGICAL, VOLUME 3.
Notes: with G.Lidberg, Robert Edman.
Album: released on JSP, Mar'87 by JSP Records. Dist: Taylors, Hotshot, Conifer, Jazz Music, Swift, Wellards

FROM THE BEGINNING VOL 1.
Album: released on JSP, May'86 by JSP Records. Dist: Taylors, Hotshot, Conifer, Jazz Music, Swift, Wellards

GOLDEN GREATS: MILLS BROTHERS.
Tracks: / Paper Doll / Glow Worm / Basin St.Blues / Nevertheless(I'm in love with you) / Till Then / Cielito Lindo / You Always Hurt the one you love / Across the alley from the Alamo / I'll be around / Rockin' chair swing / Be my life's companion / Put another chair at the table / I guess I'll get the papers and go home / Pennies from heaven / When you were sweet sixteen / Someday(you'll want me to want you) / All myself / Opus one / Please don't talk about me when I'm gone.
Notes: Another brand new collection in the 'Golden Greats' series, twenty classic hits from the legendary Mills Brothers who racked up millions of sales with such uni-que songs as 'Glow Worm','Paper Doll', 'Till Then','I'll Be Around', 'All BY My-elf' and many others. This definitive collection is a superb tribute to one of America's foremost vocal groups of the 40's.
Album: released on MCA, Feb'86 by MCA Records. Dist: Polygram

GREATEST HITS: MILLS BROTHERS.
Tracks: / Paper doll / Glow worm / Basin Street blues / Nevertheless / Till then / Lazy river / You always hurt the one you love / I'll be around / Rockin' chair / Be my life's companion.
Compact disc: released on MCA, Jul'87 by MCA Records. Dist: Polygram

MILLS BROTHERS.
Album: released on Lotus, Aug'86 Dist: Counterpoint, Jazz Music, Jazz Horizons

Cassette: released on Lotus, Aug'86 Dist: Counterpoint, Jazz Music, Jazz Horizons

MILLS BROTHERS & LOUIS ARMSTRONG, THE (Mills Brothers & Louis Armstrong).
Album: released on Giants of Jazz, Sep'87 by Hasmick Promotions Ltd.. Dist: Counterpoint, Taylors, Wellards, Swift, Crusader, Jazz Music

SWEETER THAN SUGAR.
Album: released on ASV(Academy Sound & Vision), Apr'85 by Academy Sound & Vision Records. Dist: Pinnacle

Cassette: released on ASV(Academy Sound & Vision), Apr'85 by Academy Sound & Vision Records. Dist: Pinnacle

SWEETER THAN SUGAR.
Compact disc: released on ASV(Academy Sound & Vision), Feb'87 by Academy Sound & Vision Records. Dist: Pinnacle

SWING IS THE THING.
Cassette: released on Decca, Aug'82 by Decca Records. Dist: Polygram

VERY BEST OF THE MILLS BROTHERS, THE.
Compact disc: released on DGR (Holland), '86 by DGR (Holland) Records.

Mills, Eleonore

MR. RIGHT.
Tracks: / Mr. Right / (Right mix).
Notes: Pic bag
Single 7": released on Debut, Apr'87 by Passion Records. Dist: PRT

Single 12": released on Debut, Apr'87 by Passion Records. Dist: PRT

Mills, Eric

GO YOUR WAY.
Tracks: / Go your way.
Single 12": released on Amanda, Jun'86 Dist: Jetstar

Mills, Erica

I'D RATHER GO BLIND.
Single 7": released on Code, Oct'84 by Code Records. Dist: Jetstar, EMI, Clockwork

Single 12": released on Code, Oct'84 by Code Records. Dist: Jetstar, EMI, Clockwork

Mills, Frank

KEYBOARD TRANSITIONS.
Tracks: / Heart of the city / Seascapes / Sketches of New England / Shadows of the dancer / Signs of conflict / Diamond in the rough / Island hopping / Let's not leave this way / Storm warning / Transitions and triumphs.
Compact disc: released on Capitol, Sep'87 by Capitol Records. Dist: EMI

SPECIAL CHRISTMAS A.
Album: released on Columbia, Nov'84 by EMI Records(UK). Dist: EMI

Cassette: released on Columbia, Nov'84 by EMI Records(UK). Dist: EMI

Mills, Garry

LOOK FOR A STAR.
Tracks: / Look for a star.
Single 7": released on Old Gold, Mar'87 by Old Gold Records. Dist: PRT, Counterpoint, Lightning, Jazz Music, Taylors

Mills, Irving

1928/9 VOL 1 (Mills, Irving & his Hotsy Totsy Gang).
Album: released on Retrieval, Mar'84 by Retrieval Records. Dist: Retrieval, Wellards, Swift

SOME FUN 1929-30 VOL.2 (Mills, Irving & his Hotsy Totsy Gang).
Tracks: / Some fun / Can't we get together / Sweet Savannah Sue / Ain't misbehavin' / Doin' the new low down / Harvey / March of the hoodlums / Stardust / Nobody's sweetheart / Manhattan rag / What kind of man is you? / My little honey and me / High and dry / Barbaric.
Notes: Mono.
Album: released on Fountain-Retrieval, Nov'86 by Retrieval Records. Dist: Retrieval, Swift, Wellardss*

Mills, Joan

JOLLY MACHINE THE (Mills, Joan and Michael Raven).
Album: released on Folk Heritage, Jul'82 by Folk Heritage Records. Dist: Jazz Music, Wynd-Up, Roots, Folk Heritage

Mills, John

YOUNG AT HEART.
Single 7": released on Chips, May'80

Mills & Mckenna

STRIKE IT RICH.
Tracks: / Strike it rich / Millionaire mix.
Single 7": released on BBC, Jan'86 by BBC Records & Tapes. Dist: EMI

Mills, Mick

MUSIC.
Album: released on Westwood, May'77 by Westwood Records., Pinnacle, Ross

Mills, Mrs.

ALL TIME PARTY DANCES.
Album: released on Encore, Jun'78 by EMI Records(UK). Dist: EMI

Cassette: released on Encore, Jun'78 by EMI Records(UK). Dist: EMI

AN HOUR OF MRS. MILLS.
Tracks: / Put your arms around me honey / I'm in the mood for love / Yes sir, that's my baby / Moonlight and roses / Oh, Johnny! Oh, Johnny! Oh! / Give me the moonlight, give me the girl / Winchester Cathedral / Green green grass of home / I'm nobody's baby / In the good old summertime / Tiptoe through the tulips / You are my sunshine / April showers / Down at the old bull and bush / Cruising down the river / Shine on harvest moon / I do like to be beside the seaside / Out of town / Let's all sing like the birdies sing / Good morning / Me and my shadow / My melancholy baby / Second-hand Rose / There's a blue ridge 'round my heart, Virginia / Let him go, let him tarry / I belong to Glasgow / Over the rainbow / Get out and get under the moon.
Cassette: released on Hour Of Pleasure, Sep'87 by Music For Pleasure Records. Dist: EMI. Estim retail price in Sep'87 was £1.99.

EVERYBODY'S WELCOME AT MRS MILLS PARTY.
Album: released on Retrospect, May'84 by EMI Records(UK). Dist: EMI

Cassette: released on Retrospect, May'84 by EMI Records(UK). Dist: EMI

MUSIC FOR ANYTIME.
Album: released on Savoy, Jan'87 Dist: Swift, Jazz Music, Taylors

PIANO PARTY TIME.
Album: released on MFP(Holland), Oct'84 by Music For Pleasure Records. Dist: Conifer

Cassette: released on MFP(Holland), Oct'84 by Music For Pleasure Records. Dist: Conifer

PLAYS THE ROARING TWENTIES.
Album: released on Savoy, Jan'87 Dist: Swift, Jazz Music, Taylors

Mills, Stephanie

FOR THE FIRST TIME.
Album: released on Motown, Jul'82 by Motown Records. Dist: BMG

Cassette: released on Motown, Jul'82 by Motown Records. Dist: BMG

I FEEL GOOD ALL OVER.
Tracks: / I feel good all over / Secret lady / I feel good all over (Suite) / I feel good all over / Secret lady.
Single 7": released on MCA, Oct'87 by MCA Records. Dist: Polygram

Single 12": released on MCA, 21 Nov'87 by MCA Records. Dist: Polygram

IF I WERE YOUR WOMAN.
Tracks: / I feel good all over / If I were your woman / Rush on me, A (You're puttin') / Jesse / Secret lady / Touch me now / Running for your love / Can't change my ways / I feel good all over / If I were your woman / Your puttin a rush on me / Jesse / Secret lady / Touch me now / Running for your love / Can't change my ways.
Album: released on MCA, Aug'87 by MCA Records. Dist: Polygram

Cassette: released on MCA, Aug'87 by MCA Records. Dist: Polygram

Compact disc: released on MCA, Aug'87 by MCA Records. Dist: Polygram

I'VE GOT THE CURE.
Tracks: / Medicine song / Edge of the razor / In my life / Give it half a chance / You just might need a friend / Everlasting love / Rough trade / Undercover.
Notes: Produced by George Duke and David 'Hawk' Wolinski
Compact disc: released on Club, Dec'84 by Phonogram Records. Dist: Polygram

MEDICINE SONG.
Single 12": released on Club, Aug'84 by Phonogram Records. Dist: Polygram

MERCILESS.
Album: released on Casablanca, Nov'83 Dist: Polygram, Phonogram

NEVER KNEW LOVE LIKE THIS BEFORE.
Single 7": released on Old Gold, Jan'85 by Old Gold Records. Dist: PRT, Counterpoint, Lightning, Jazz Music, Taylors

RUSH ON ME, A (YOU'RE PUTTIN').
Tracks: / Rush on me, A (You're puttin') / Rush on me, A (You're puttin') (Inst).
Single 7": released on MCA, Aug'87 by MCA Records. Dist: Polygram

Single 12": released on MCA, Aug'87 by MCA Records. Dist: Polygram

STEPHANIE MILLS.
Compact disc: released on MCA, Apr'87 by MCA Records. Dist: Polygram

Album: released on 20th Century, May'81 Dist: BMGg*, IMS-Polygram

Cassette: released on 20th Century, May'81 Dist: BMGg*, IMS-Polygram

SWEET SENSATION.
Album: released on 20th Century, Dec'80 Dist: BMGg*, IMS-Polygram

TANTALIZINGLY HOT.
Album: released on Casablanca, Jul'82 Dist: Polygram, Phonogram

Cassette: released on Casablanca, Jul'82 Dist: Polygram, Phonogram

YOU CAN'T RUN FROM MY LOVE.
Single 7": released on Phonogram, Jul'82 by Phonogram Records. Dist: Polygram

Single 12": released on Phonogram, Jul'82 by Phonogram Records. Dist: Polygram

YOU'RE PUTTIN' A RUSH ON ME.
Single 12": released on MCA(USA), Aug'87 by MCA Records(USA). Dist: Pinnacle, Swift

Mills, Warren

FLAME IN THE FIRE.
Single 7": released on Jive, Aug'86 by Zomba Productions Ltd. Dist: BMG

Single 12": released on Jive, Aug'86 by Zomba Productions Ltd. Dist: BMG

MICKIES MONKEY.
Single 7": released on Jive, Jan'84 by Zomba Productions Ltd. Dist: BMG

Single 12": released on Jive, Jan'84 by Zomba Productions Ltd. Dist: BMG

Picture disc single: released on Jive, Jan'84 by Zomba Productions Ltd. Dist: BMG

SUNSHINE.
Single 7": released on Jive, Aug'85 by Zomba Productions Ltd. Dist: BMG

Single 12": released on Jive, Jan'85 by Zomba Productions Ltd. Dist: BMG

TELL ME WHAT YOU WANT.
Tracks: / Tell me what you want / Angel eyes / Sunshine (remix).
Single 7": released on Jive, Feb'86 by Zomba Productions Ltd. Dist: BMG

Single 12": released on Jive, Feb'86 by Zomba Productions Ltd. Dist: BMG

WARREN MILLS.
Tracks: / Flame in the fire / Roxanne Roxanne / I wonder if I take you home / Sunshine / Biochemistry / Choosy girl / You thrill me / Don't tell me about your boyfriend / It's peculiar / Tell me what you want me to do.
Album: released on Jive, Nov'85 by Zomba Productions Ltd. Dist: BMG

Cassette: released on Jive, Nov'85 by Zomba Productions Ltd. Dist: BMG

Mills-Cockell, John

NEON ACCELERANDO.
Album: released on Aura, Jun'79 by Aura Records & Tapes. Dist: Pinnacle

Milly Molly Mandy

MILLY MOLLY MANDY (ADVENTURES OF...).
Cassette: released on Tellastory, Oct'79 by Bartlett Bliss Productions Ltd.. Dist: PRT, Taylors, Conifer

MILLY MOLLY MANDY STORIES (Joyce Lankester Brisley) Read by Liza Goddard.
Cassette: released on Listen For Pleasure, Sep'82 Dist: EMI

MILLY MOLLY MANDY (THE BEST OF...).
Cassette: released on Tellastory, Oct'79 by Bartlett Bliss Productions Ltd.. Dist: PRT, Taylors, Conifer

Milne, A.A.

HOUSE AT POOH CORNER.
Album: released on BBC, Jan'84 by BBC Records & Tapes. Dist: EMI

Cassette: released on BBC, Jan'84 by BBC Records & Tapes. Dist: EMI

WHEN WE WERE VERY YOUNG (Shelley, Norman).
Double cassette: released on Argo(Spokenword), Mar'84 by Decca Classics. Dist: Polygram

WINNIE THE POOH AND CHRISTOPHER ROBIN.
Cassette: released on Caedmon(USA), '84 by Caedmon (USA) Records. Dist: Gower, Roots

WINNIE THE POOH AND EEYORE.
Cassette: released on Caedmon(USA), Apr'85 by Caedmon (USA) Records. Dist: Gower, Roots

WINNIE THE POOH AND TIGGER.
Cassette: released on Caedmon(USA), Sep'82 by Caedmon (USA) Records. Dist: Gower, Roots

Milner, John

I FEEL FREE.
Single 7": released on Purple Plum, Jul'83

Milnes, Sherrill

LARGO AL FACTOTUS.
Single 7": released on Decca, Jun'79 by Decca Records. Dist: Polygram

Mils Bros

VOLUME 1 1931-33.
Album: released on Neovox, Nov'87 by Neovox Records. Dist: Jazz Music, Wellards, Worlds Records(USA)

Milsap, Ronnie

INSIDE.
Tracks: / Any day now / Inside / Carolina dreams / Wrong end of the rainbow / I love New Orleans music / He got you / Hate the lies, love the liar / Who's counting / You took her off my hands / It's just a room.
Album: released on RCA, Sep'82 Dist: BMG

Cassette: released on RCA, Sep'82 Dist: BMG

Compact disc: released on RCA, Sep'82 Dist: BMG

KEYED UP.
Album: released on RCA, May'83 Dist: BMG

Cassette: released on RCA, May'83 Dist: BMG

LOST IN THE FIFTIES TONIGHT.
Tracks: / Lost in the fifties tonight / In love / Old fashioned girl like you / I heard it through the grapevine / Don't take it tonight / How do I turn you on? / Happy, happy birthday baby / Nashville moon / I only remember the good times / Money.
Album: released on RCA, Apr'86 Dist: BMG

Cassette: released on RCA, Apr'86 Dist: BMG

MR MAILMAN.
Album: released on Phoenix, Jul'81 by Audio Fidelity Enterprises. Dist: Stage One, Gamut, Silva Screen Records, Jazz Music

ONE MORE TRY FOR LOVE.
Album: released on RCA, Jul'84 Dist: BMG

Cassette: released on RCA, Jul'84 Dist: BMG

OUT WHERE THE BRIGHT LIGHTS ARE GLOWING.
Album: released on RCA, Jun'81 Dist: BMG

Cassette: released on RCA, Jun'81 Dist: BMG

RONNIE MILSAP.
Cassette: released on Audio Fidelity(USA), Oct'84 by Audio Fidelity Ent.Inc.(USA).

SPINNING WHEEL.
Album: released on Sundown, Apr'87 by Magnum Music Group Ltd. Dist: PRT

STRANGER IN MY HOUSE.
Single 7": released on RCA, May'83 Dist: BMG

THERE GOES MY HEART.
Cassette: released on Orchid Music, Feb'82 by

Bibi. Dist: Pinnacle

Milton

LOVE IS LIKE A VILOENCE.
Single 12": released on Embryo, Jan'85 by Embryo Records. Dist: Revolver, Cartel, WEA

Milton, John

PARADISE LOST.
Cassette: released on Caedmon(USA), May'83 by Caedmon (USA) Records. Dist: Gower, Roots

Cassette: released on Argo, Apr'85 by Decca Classics. Dist: Polygram

Milton, Little

RAISE A LITTLE SAND.
Double Album: released on Red Lightnin', Dec'75 by Red Lightnin' Records. Dist: Red Lightnin', Cadillac, Caroline, Hotshot, Lightning, Swift, Jazz Music, Projection

Milton, Roy

BIG FAT MAMA (Milton, Roy and his Solid Senders).
Album: released on Jukebox Lil, Nov'85 by Jukebox Lil. Dist: Swift, Celtic Music

GRANDFATHER OF R & B.
Album: released on Jukebox Lil, Aug'87 by Jukebox Lil. Dist: Swift, Celtic Music

Milton, Ted

ODE: OH TO BE SEEN THROUGH YOUR EYES.
Single 12": released on Toeblock, Nov'85 Dist: Revolver

Milva

IMMER MEHR.
Album: released on Metronome(Italy), Aug'83 Dist: IMS, Polygram

Cassette: released on Metronome(Italy), Aug'83 Dist: IMS, Polygram

Mimi

MAN'S SO REAL.
Single 7": released on Challenge, Mar'84 by Elite Records. Dist: Pinnacle

Single 12": released on Challenge, Mar'84 by Elite Records. Dist: Pinnacle

NO MORE.
Tracks: / No more / No more (inst).
Single 12": released on Big Top, Jun'87 Dist: Cartel

TOUCH SENSITIVE.
Single 12": released on Challenge, Jun'85 by Elite Records. Dist: Pinnacle

Mimms, Garnet

ROLL WITH THE PUNCHES.
Tracks: / All about love / One woman man / Don't change your heart / Prove it to me / Truth hurts, The / There is something on my mind / Looking for you / Roll with the punches / (It won't hurt) half as much / Please send me someone to love / Only your love / I keep wanting you / Until you were gone / Anytime you want me / I'll make it up to you / Welcome home.
Album: released on Charly, Apr'86 by Charly Records. Dist: Charly, Cadillac, Swift

WARM AND SOULFUL - THE BEST OF GARNET MIMMS.
Album: released on Liberty-UA, Oct'84 by EMI Records(UK). Dist: EMI

Cassette: released on Liberty-UA, Oct'84 by EMI Records(UK). Dist: EMI

Mina

HEISSER SAND.
Tracks: / Heisser sand / Capitano / Treuer mann, (Ein) / Er liebte dieses leben / Fremdes land / Manner, madchen und pistolen / Grenzenlos / Grosste schau, (Die) / Fiesta Brasiliana / Tabu, es scheint gefahrlich zu sein, was ich tu' / Welt der verlorenen traume / Rhapsodie / Wenn du an wunder glaubst / Meine tur steht immer offen / Weisse dschunke, (Eine) / Bis zum nachsten mal.
Album: released on Bear Family, May'87 by Bear Family Records(Germany). Dist: Celtic Music, Swift, Rollercoaster

Mince, Johnny

MASTER COMES HOME, THE (Mince, Johnny & His All-Stars).
Album: released on Jazzology, Feb'87 Dist: Jazz Music, Swift

Mind Over 4

OUT HERE.
Album: released on Triple XXX (USA), Sep'87 Dist: Pinnacle

Mind over Muesli

JUST WALK AWAY.
Tracks: / Just walk away / Just walk away (inst).
Single 7": released on GFM, 20 Jun'87 by GFM Records. Dist: Fast Forward, Cartel, Cadillac, Jazz Music

Single 12": released on GFM, 20 Jun'87 by GFM Records. Dist: Fast Forward, Cartel, Cadillac, Jazz Music

Mindbenders

GROOVY KIND OF LOVE, A.
Single 7": released on Old Gold, Jul'82 by Old Gold Records. Dist: PRT, Counterpoint, Lightning, Jazz Music, Taylors

Mindel, David

DISTRICT NURSE.
Single 7": released on Savoir Faire, Mar'84 Dist: PRT

Mindless slaughter

MINDLESS SLAUGHTER Various artists (Various artists).
Album: released on Anhrefn, Sep'87 Dist: Revolver, Cartel

Mindreaders

BAN THE MINDREADER.
Album: released on Empire, Oct'87 by Empire Records. Dist: Backs, Cartel. Estim retail price in Oct'87 was £5.99.

Minelli, Liza

ACT (BROADWAY SHOW),THE.
Tracks: / Shine it on / It's the strangest thing / Bobo's / Turning / Little do they know / Arthur in the afternoon / Money tree (The) / City lights / There when I need him / Hot enough for you? / Little do they know (reprise) / My own space / Walking papers.
Compact disc: released on DRG(USA), Apr'87 by DRG Records Inc.(USA). Dist: Conifer

Miner, Tim

TIM MINER.
Album: released on Sparrow, Aug'85 by Word Records(UK)Ltd.. Dist: Word, CBS

Cassette: released on Sparrow, Aug'85 by Word Records(UK)Ltd.. Dist: Word, CBS

Minerbi, Marcello

ZORBA'S DANCE.
Single 7": released on Old Gold, Jul'82 by Old Gold Records. Dist: PRT, Counterpoint, Lightning, Jazz Music, Taylors

Miners Of Muzo

DIG DEEP FOR THE MINERS.
Album: released on Ediesta, Sep'87 by Ediesta Records. Dist: Red Rhino, Cartel

Minerva Jazz Band

PILE OF LOGS & STONE (CALLED HOME).
Album: released on Stomp Off, Oct'86 by Stomp Off Records. Dist: Jazz Music

Ming, Maurice

BUBBLING.
Single 12": released on Tracey, Oct'84 by Tracey Records. Dist: Jetstar

Ming, Sexton

OLD HORSE OF THE NATION.
Album: released on Hangman, Sep'87 Dist: Revolver, Cartel

Mingus, Charles

ABSTRACTIONS (Mingus, Charles Jazz Workshop).
Album: released on Affinity, Apr'85 by Charly Records. Dist: Charly, Cadillac, Swift

CHARLES MINGUS COLLECTION, THE.
Cassette: released on Deja Vu, Aug'85 by Deja Vu Records. Dist: Counterpoint, Record Services(Ireland), Jazz Music

CHARLES MINGUS PRESENTS CHARLES MINGUS.
Album: released on Candid, Dec'85 Dist: Counterpoint, Cadillac, Jazz Music

CONNECTION.
Album: released on Vogue(France), Sep'79 Dist: Discovery, Jazz Music, Swift

FABLES OF FAUBUS VOL 2.
Album: released on Ingo, Nov'82 Dist: Jazz Horizons, Jazz Music, Celtic Music

JAZZ WORKSHOP.
Album: released on Savoy(France), Feb'85 Dist: Discovery

MINGUS.
Album: released on Candid, Jun'86 Dist: Counterpoint, Cadillac, Jazz Music

MINGUS AND DUKE.
Album: released on Crusader Jazz Masterworks, Jun'86 Dist: Jazz Music

MINGUS AT ANTIBES.
Double Album: released on Atlantic Jazz, Dec'79 by WEA Records. Dist: WEA

MINGUS AT MONTEREY.
Compact disc: released on JVC/Fantasy(Japan), Jul'87 by Fantasy Records. Dist: Target

Double Album: released on Prestige, Dec'81 by Prestige Records (USA). Dist: BMG, Swift

MINGUS COLLECTION, THE.
Double Album: released on Vogue Jazz(France), May'83 Dist: Swift, Jazz Music

MINGUS IN EUROPE VOL 1.
Album: released on Enja(Germany), Jan'82 by Enja Records (W.Germany). Dist: Cadillac, Jazz Music

MINGUS IN EUROPE VOL 2.
Album: released on Enja(Germany), Jan'82 by Enja Records (W.Germany). Dist: Cadillac, Jazz Music

MINGUS IN STUTTGART.
Double Album: released on Unique Jazz(Import), Apr'81 Dist: Swift, Jazz Music, Jazz Horizons, Cadillac

MINGUS IN STUTTGART VOL 2.
Album: released on Unique Jazz(Import), Apr'81 Dist: Swift, Jazz Music, Jazz Horizons, Cadillac

MINGUS, MINGUS, MINGUS, MINGUS, MINGUS.
Album: released on Jasmine, Aug'82 by Jasmine Records. Dist: Counterpoint, Cadillac, Taylors, Wellards, Swift, Jazz Music

Cassette: released on Jasmine, Aug'82 by Jasmine Records. Dist: Counterpoint, Cadillac, Taylors, Wellards, Swift, Jazz Music

MINGUS OH YEAH.
Album: released on Atlantic, Jul'80 by WEA Records. Dist: WEA, Swift, Celtic Music

MINGUS PLAYS PIANO.
Album: released on Jasmine, Sep'82 by Jasmine Records. Dist: Counterpoint, Cadillac, Taylors, Wellards, Swift, Jazz Music

Cassette: released on Jasmine, Sep'82 by Jasmine Records. Dist: Counterpoint, Cadillac, Taylors, Wellards, Swift, Jazz Music

MINGUS PRESENTS MINGUS.
Album: released on Candid, Jul'87 Dist: Counterpoint, Cadillac, Jazz Music

MINGUS THREE.
Album: released on Carosello, Feb'83 Dist: Jazz Music, Jazz Horizons

NEW TIJUANA MOODS.
Tracks: / Dizzy moods / Isabel's table dance / Los mariachis(The street musicians) / Flamingo / Dizzy moods (Alternative take) / Tijuana gift shop (Alternative take) / Los mariachis (The street musicians) (Alternative take) / Flamingo (Alternative take) / Isabel's table dance-alternative take.
Album: released on RCA, Jan'87 Dist: BMG

Cassette: released on RCA, Jan'87 Dist: BMG

NEW YORK SKETCH BOOK.
Tracks: / Memories of you / East coasting / West coast ghost / Celia / Conversation / Fifty first street blues / Scenes in the city / New York sketchbook.
Notes: Track 1: Blake/Razaf. Tracks 2-9: Mingus. Including the complete 'East Coasting' session. Original Bethlehem Recordings.
Compact disc: released on Charly, Jun'86 by Charly Records. Dist: Charly, Cadillac, Swift

PARKERIANA VOL 3.
Album: released on Ingo, Nov'82 Dist: Jazz Horizons, Jazz Music, Celtic Music

PASSIONS OF A MAN.
Album: released on WEA, Sep'79 by WEA Records. Dist: WEA

PITHYCANTHROPUS ERECTUS.
Compact disc: released on Musidisc(France), Dec'85 Dist: Discovery, Swift

PRE-BIRD.
Album: released on Philips (Holland), Oct'83

REVISITED.
Tracks: / Take the 'A' train / Prayer for the passive resistance / Eclipse / Mingus Fingus No.2 / Weird nightmare / Do nothin' till you hear from me / Bemoanable lady / Half-mast inhibition.
Notes: Originally released in 1960 under the title "Pre-bird" this is one of the great Mingus large group recordings with all star line-up including Clark Terry and Marcus Belgrave trumpets, Slide Hampton and Jimmy Knepper, trombones, Eric Dolphy and Joe Farrell, saxes, Danny Richmond, drums, and others too numerous to list here. Apart from two "Ellingtonian" tracks all compositions are Mingus originals.
Compact disc: released on Verve(USA), Jun'86 by Polydor Records. Dist: Polygram

Album: released on Polydor, Jul'81 by Polydor Records. Dist: Polygram, Polydor

RIGHT NOW: LIVE AT THE JAZZ WORKSHOP.
Album:

SCENES IN THE CITY.
Album: released on Affinity, Nov'83 by Charly Records. Dist: Charly, Cadillac, Swift

STATEMENTS.
Album: released on Lotus, Sep'87 Dist: Counterpoint, Jazz Music, Jazz Horizons

STRINGS AND KEYS.
Album: released on Fantasy Inc USA, Jun'86 by Fantasy Inc USA Records. Dist: IMS, Polygram

TIJUANA MOODS.
Album: released on RCA, Feb'87 Dist: BMG

Album: released on RCA, Feb'86 Dist: BMG

Cassette: released on RCA, Feb'86 Dist: BMG

TOWN HALL CONCERT.
Compact disc: released on Carrere, Apr'87 by Carrere Records(UK). Dist: PRT, Spartan

YOUNG REBEL.
Album: released on Swingtime, Aug'86 Dist: Jazz Music, Charly, Swift, Zodiac

Mingus, Charlie

AH UM.
Album: released on CBS, May'83 by CBS Records. Dist: CBS

Cassette: released on CBS, May'83 by CBS Records. Dist: CBS

BLACK SAINT AND THE SINNER LADY, THE.
Tracks: / Solo dancer / Group and Solo dancers / Single solos and group dance / Trio and group dancers / Group dancers / Duet solo dancers.
Album: released on Jasmine, Jun'82 by Jasmine Records. Dist: Counterpoint, Cadillac, Taylors, Wellards, Swift, Jazz Music

Cassette: released on Jasmine, Jun'82 by Jasmine Records. Dist: Counterpoint, Cadillac, Taylors, Wellards, Swift, Jazz Music

Compact disc: released on MCA, '87 by MCA Records. Dist: Polygram

CHARLIE MINGUS Recorded in 1964 in Paris.
Notes: with J. Byard, C. Jordan, E. Dolphy, D. Richmond.
Album: released on Esoldun, Sep'87 by Esoldun Records. Dist: Swift

Compact disc: released on Esoldun, Sep'87 by Esoldun Records. Dist: Swift

CUMBRIA & JAZZ FUSION.
Album: released on Atlantic, Jul'78 by WEA Records. Dist: WEA, Swift, Celtic Music

EAST COASTING (Mingus, Charlie Sextet).
Album: released on Affinity, May'82 by Charly Records. Dist: Charly, Cadillac, Swift

FINAL WORKS.
Album: released on Gateway, '84 by Kingdom. Dist: Pinnacle

HOPE SO ERIC VOL 1 (Mingus, Charlie Orchestra with Eric Dolphy 1964).
Album: released on Ingo, Jul'82 Dist: Jazz Horizons, Jazz Music, Celtic Music

IN BERLIN 1970 (Mingus, Charlie Sextet).
Album: released on Beppo, Mar'77, Jazz Horizons

LIVE: CHARLIE MINGUS.
Album: released on Affinity, May'79 by Charly Records. Dist: Charly, Cadillac, Swift

LIVE IN EUROPE (Mingus, Charlie Sextet).
Album: released on Unique Jazz(Import), Apr'81 Dist: Swift, Jazz Music, Jazz Horizons, Cadillac

MINGUS QUINTET MEETS CAT ANDERSON.
Album: released on Unique Jazz(Import), Apr'81 Dist: Swift, Jazz Music, Jazz Horizons, Cadillac

PRESENTS CHARLES MINGUS.
Compact disc: released on Candid, Nov'87 Dist: Counterpoint, Cadillac, Jazz Music. Estim retail price in Nov'87 was £11.99.

STATEMENTS.
Album: released on Lotus, Apr'81 Dist: Counterpoint, Jazz Music, Jazz Horizons

Mingus Dynasty

LIVE AT MONTREUX: MINGUS DYNASTY.
Album: released on Atlantic, Mar'81 by WEA Records. Dist: WEA, Swift, Celtic Music

REINCARNATION.
Compact disc: released on Soul Note (Italy), '86 Dist: Harmonia Mundi Distributors

Miniatures

MINIATURES A sequence of 51 tiny masterpieces - various artists (Various artists).
Album: released on Pipe, '80 by Cherry Red Records. Dist: Pinnacle

Minimal compact

DEADLY WEAPONS.
Album: released on Crammed Discs, Jun'84 by Crammed Discs(Belgium). Dist: Nine Mile, Cartel

FIGURE ONE CUTS.
Album: released on Crammed Discs, May'87 by Crammed Discs(Belgium). Dist: Nine Mile, Cartel

Compact disc: released on Crammed Discs, Oct'87 by Crammed Discs(Belgium). Dist: Nine Mile, Cartel

FIGURE ONE CUTS, THE.
Album: released on Crammed Discs, Sep'87 by Crammed Discs(Belgium). Dist: Nine Mile, Cartel

IMMIGRANTS SONGS.
Notes: E.P.
Extended-play record: released on Crammed Discs, Feb'87 by Crammed Discs(Belgium). Dist: Nine Mile, Cartel

IT TAKES A LIFETIME / INTRESPECTION.
Single 7": released on Crammed Discs, May'83 by Crammed Discs(Belgium). Dist: Nine Mile, Cartel

MADE TO MEASURE VOL 1.
Album: released on Crammed Discs, Sep'84 by Crammed Discs(Belgium). Dist: Nine Mile, Cartel

MINIMAL COMPACT.
Album: released on Crammed Discs, Sep'84 by Crammed Discs(Belgium). Dist: Nine Mile, Cartel

NEXT ONE IS REAL, THE.
Album: released on Crammed Discs, Oct'84 by Crammed Discs(Belgium). Dist: Nine Mile, Cartel

Single 12": released on Crammed Discs, Oct'84 by Crammed Discs(Belgium). Dist: Nine Mile, Cartel

ONE BY ONE.
Album: released on Crammed Discs, Jul'83 by Crammed Discs(Belgium). Dist: Nine Mile, Cartel

RAGING SOULS.
Album: released on Crammed Discs, Mar'86 by Crammed Discs(Belgium). Dist: Nine Mile, Cartel

Cassette: released on Crammed Discs, Mar'86 by Crammed Discs(Belgium). Dist: Nine Mile, Cartel

SCENT OF LOVE.
Tracks: / Scent of love.
Single 7": released on Crammed Discs, Sep'87 by Crammed Discs(Belgium). Dist: Nine Mile, Cartel

Minimal Man

MINIMAL MAN.
Album: released on CD Presents, Aug'86 Dist: IMS, Polygram

SAFARI.
Compact disc: released on CD Presents, Dec'86 Dist: IMS, Polygram

SEX TEACHER.
Single 7": released on Play It Again Sam, Jan'86 Dist: Red Rhino, Cartel

SLAVE LULLABY.
Album: released on Play It Again Sam, Feb'86 Dist: Red Rhino, Cartel

Mininnya Blade

MERCHANTS IN METAL.
Album: released on Killerwatt, Oct'86 by Killerwatt Records. Dist: PRT, Kingdom Records

Minipops

ADVENTURES OF SANTA CLAUS.
Tracks: / Adventures of Santa Claus / Christmas Scenes / Ring a bell for Christmas / Rock baby Jesus.
Single 7": released on Creole, Dec'86 by Creole Records. Dist: PRT

LET'S DANCE.
Album: released on CBS, Nov'84 by CBS Records. Dist: CBS

Cassette: released on CBS, Nov'84 by CBS Records. Dist: CBS

MINIPOPS.
Album: released on Cherry Lane, Aug'85 by Cherry Lane Productions.

Cassette: released on Cherry Lane, Aug'85 by Cherry Lane Productions.

MINIPOPS.
Album: released on K-Tel, Nov'81 by K-Tel Records. Dist: K-Tel, Celtic Music, Terry Blood, Wynd-Up, Taylors, Pickwick, Solomon & Peres, Polygram

Cassette: released on K-Tel, Nov'81 by K-Tel Records. Dist: K-Tel, Celtic Music, Terry Blood, Wynd-Up, Taylors, Pickwick, Solomon & Peres, Polygram

VIDEO KILLED THE RADIO STAR / STUPID.....
Single 7": released on RCA, Nov'81 Dist: BMG

WE'RE THE MINIPOPS.
Album: released on K-Tel, Nov'82 by K-Tel Records. Dist: K-Tel, Celtic Music, Terry Blood, Wynd-Up, Taylors, Pickwick, Solomon & Peres, Polygram

Cassette: released on K-Tel, Nov'82 by K-Tel Records. Dist: K-Tel, Celtic Music, Terry Blood, Wynd-Up, Taylors, Pickwick, Solomon & Peres, Polygram

WHEN YOU WISH UPON A STAR/ WHY CAN'T WE LOVE EACH OTHER.....
Single 7": released on Bright, Jan'84 Dist: PRT

Ministry

COLD LIFE.
Single 12": released on Situation 2, Mar'82 Dist: Cartel, Pinnacle

NATURE OF LOVE.
Single 12": released on Waxtrax, Oct'85 by Jungle Records. Dist: Southern Record

TWITCH.
Tracks: / Just like you / We believe / All day remix / Angel, The / Over the shoulder / My possession / Where you at now ? / Crash and burn / Twitch (version 11).
Album: released on Sire, Apr'86

Cassette: released on Sire, Apr'86

WORK FOR LOVE.
Album: released on Arista, Sep'83 by Arista Records. Dist: BMG

Cassette: released on Arista, Sep'83 by Arista Records. Dist: BMG

Ministry of Love

BURNIN' AND LOOTIN.
Tracks: / Brothers and sisters / John y na blame rasta / Burnin' and lootin'.
Single 12": released on Midnight Music, Jun'86 by Midnight Music Records. Dist: Rough Trade, Cartel

Mink

YOU WERE THE ONE TOO LATE.
Single 12": released on Streetwave, Jul'85 Dist: BMG

Mink Deville

CABRETTA.
Album: released on Razor, Feb'87 by Razor. Dist: Pinnacle

EACH WORDS A BEAT OF MY HEART.
Single 7": released on Atlantic, Apr'84 by WEA Records. Dist: WEA, Swift, Celtic Music

Single 12": released on Atlantic, Apr'84 by WEA Records. Dist: WEA, Swift, Celtic Music

HEART OF THE CITY.
Single 7": released on Polydor, Jun'85 by Polydor Records. Dist: Polygram, Polydor

Single 12": released on Polydor, Jun'85 by Polydor Records. Dist: Polygram, Polydor

I MUST BE DREAMING.
Single 7": released on Polydor, Oct'85 by Polydor Records. Dist: Polygram, Polydor

Single 12": released on Polydor, Oct'85 by Polydor Records. Dist: Polygram, Polydor

LIVE AT THE SAVOY.
Video-cassette (VHS): released on Channel 5, '87 Dist: W.H. Smiths

MINK DEVILLE.
Tracks: / Venus of Avenue D / Little girl / One way street / Mixed up shook up girl / Gunslinger / Can't do without it / Cadillac walk / Spanish stroll / She's so tough / Party girls.
Album: by Capitol Records. Dist: EMI

RETURN TO MAGENTA.
Tracks: / Just your friends / Soul twist / 'A' train lady / Rolene / Desperate days / Guardian angel / Steady drivin' man / Easy slider / I broke that promise / Confidence to kill.
Album: released on Capitol, Jul'78 by Capitol Records. Dist: EMI

SAVOIRE FAIRE.
Tracks: / This must be the night / Train lady, A / Spanish stroll / Cadillac walk / Soul twist / Just your friends / Mixed up, shook up girl / Guardian angel / Savoir faire / Gunslinger / One way street / Mazurka / Broke that promise / Just to walk that little girl home.
Album: released on EMI (Italy), Apr'87 by EMI Records(UK). Dist: Conifer

Album: released on EMI (Italy), Apr'87 by EMI Records(UK). Dist: Conifer

Album: released on Capitol, Nov'81 by Capitol Records. Dist: EMI

Cassette: released on Capitol, Nov'81 by Capitol Records. Dist: EMI

SPANISH STROLL.
Single 7": released on EMI Golden 45's, Jul'84 by EMI Records(UK). Dist: EMI

SPORTIN' LIFE.
Tracks: / Slip away / When you walk my way / Woman's touch / Easy street / Little by little / There's no living without loving / Something beautiful dying / In the heart of the city / I must be dreaming / Italian shoes / In the heart of the city / I must be dreaming / Italian shoes / Slip away / When you walk my way / Woman's touch, A / Easy street / Little by little / There's no living (without your loving) / Something beautiful dying.
Album: released on Polydor, Jul'85 by Polydor Records. Dist: Polygram, Polydor

Cassette: released on Polydor, Jul'85 by Polydor Records. Dist: Polygram, Polydor

Compact disc: released on Polydor, Jul'85 by Polydor Records. Dist: Polygram, Polydor

WHERE ANGELS FEAR TO TREAD.
Tracks: / River of tears / Each word's a beat of my heart / Demasiado / Corazon / Lilly's daddy's cadillac / Around the corner / Pick up the pieces / Love's got a hold on me / Keep your monkey away / From my door / Are you lonely tonight / Moonlight let me down.
Album: released on Atlantic, Dec'83 by WEA Records. Dist: WEA, Swift, Celtic Music

Cassette: released on Atlantic, Dec'83 by WEA Records. Dist: WEA, Swift, Celtic Music

Minnesota rock-a-billy

MINNESOTA ROCK-A-BILLY-ROCK (Various artists).
Album: released on White Label(Holland), Feb'85 Dist: CSA

Minni, Memphis

WORLD OF TROUBLE.
Album: released on Flyright, Oct'86 by Flyright Records. Dist: Swift, Jazz Music, Wellards, Cadillac

Minnott,Echo

WHAT THE HELL.
Album: released on Jammy's, 30 May'87 by Jammy's Records. Dist: Jetstar

Minnypops

DOLPHIN SPURT.
Single 7": released on Factory, Mar'81 by Factory Records. Dist: Cartel, Pinnacle

EIN KUS.
Single 7": released on Les Temps Modernes, Jun'84 Dist: Fast Forward, Cartel

FOOTSTEPS.
Single 7": released on Pleurex, Jun'79

SECRET STORY / ISLAND.
Single 7":

SPARKS IN A DARK ROOM.
Album: released on Factory Benelux, Jul'82 by Rough Trade Records. Dist: Cartel

TIME / LIGHT.
Single 7":

Minor Classics

SIGN LANGUAGE / THIS SIDE OF PARADISE.
Single 7": released on Chiswick, Mar'82 by Chiswick Records. Dist: Pinnacle

Minor detail

MINOR DETAIL.
Album: released on Polydor, Sep'83 by Polydor Records. Dist: Polygram, Polydor

Cassette: released on Polydor, Sep'83 by Polydor Records. Dist: Polygram, Polydor

TAKE IT AGAIN.
Single 7": released on Polydor, Mar'84 by Polydor Records. Dist: Polygram, Polydor

Minott, Echo

BUBBLIN' SHE WANT.
Single 12": released on Black Joy, Oct'84 Dist: Jetstar

MY FAT MILLIE.
Single 12": released on Fu-Manchu, Jul'84 by Fu-Manchu. Dist: Jetstar

ONE MAN ONE.
Single 12": released on Twin Explosion, Mar'86 Dist: Jetstar

SHOWCASE: ECHO MINOTT ALONG WITH SLY & ROBBIE (Minott, Echo/Sly & Robbie).
Album: released on Jam Can, Mar'84 by Jam Can Records. Dist: Jetstar

SWEET DREAMS.
Single 12": released on Greensleeves, Dec'84 by Greensleeves Records. Dist: BMG, Jetstar, Spartan

WHAT THE HELL.
Tracks: / Don't touch boops / One scotch.
Single 12": released on Unity, Jul'86 by Unity Records. Dist: Jetstar

Minott, Sugar

ALL DAY & NIGHT.
Single 12": released on Burning Sounds, Aug'85 by Burning Sounds Records.

BITTER SWEET.
Album: released on Vista Sounds, '83 by Vista Sounds Records. Dist: Jetstar

Cassette: released on Vista Sounds, '83 by Vista Sounds Records. Dist: Jetstar

BOSS BOSS.
Single 12": released on Kings And Lions, May'85 by Kings And Lions Records. Dist: Jetstar

BUY OUT THE BEAR.
Single 12": released on Black Roots, Oct'83 by Black Roots Records. Dist: Jetstar

CAN YOU REMEMBER.
Single 12": released on BFM, May'83 by BFM Records. Dist: Jetstar

CHRISTMAS HOLIDAY.
Single 12": released on Tom Tom, Dec'84 by Tom Tom Records. Dist: Jetstarr*

CHRISTMAS TIME.
Single 7": released on Black Roots, Nov'82 by Black Roots Records. Dist: Jetstar

COME AGAIN.
Tracks: / Dubbing a storm.
Single 12": released on SMP, Jun'86 Dist: Jetstar

DANCE HALL SHOWCASE.
Album: released on Black Roots, Sep'83 by Black Roots Records. Dist: Jetstar

DANCEHALL WE DEH.
Single 12": released on Tads, Jun'84 by Tads Records. Dist: Jetstarr*

DEVIL'S PICKNEY.
Single 12": released on Taxi, Dec'83 by Taxi Records. Dist: Jetstar

DON'T CRY.
Single 12": released on W.O.W., Jan'85 by W.O.W. Records. Dist: Jetstar

EASY SQUEEZE.
Single 7": released on Black Roots, Jun'82 by Black Roots Records. Dist: Jetstar

Single 12": released on Black Roots, Jun'82 by Black Roots Records. Dist: Jetstar

FALSE RUMOUR.
Single 12": released on Exile, Oct'82 by Exile Records. Dist: Pinnacle

GHETTO-OLOGY.
Album: released on Trojan, '83 by Trojan Records. Dist: Jetstar

Cassette: released on Trojan, '83 by Trojan Records. Dist: Jetstar

GIMME THE TU SHUNG PENG.
Single 12": released on SMJ, Jun'85 by SMJ Records. Dist: Jetstar

GOOD THING GOING (Minott, Sugar/Desi Roots).
Single 7": released on RCA, Mar'81 Dist: BMG

Single 12": released on RCA, Mar'81 Dist: BMG

GOOD THING GOING(LP).
Album: released on RCA, Dec'81 Dist: BMG

Cassette: released on RCA, Dec'81 Dist: BMG

HARBOUR SHARK.
Single 12": released on Guidance, Apr'83 Dist: Jetstar

HEARTBREAKER.
Single 12": released on Black Roots, Feb'83 by Black Roots Records. Dist: Jetstar

HERBMAN HUSTLING.
Album: released on Black Roots, Dec'84 by Black Roots Records. Dist: Jetstar

HERBMAN HUSTLING (12").
Single 12": released on Black Roots, Dec'84 by Black Roots Records. Dist: Jetstar

HI HELLO.
Single 12": released on Wackies, May'85 by Wackies Records. Dist: Jetstar

HI HELLO HOW ARE YOU.
Single 12": released on Kings And Lions, May'85 by Kings And Lions Records. Dist: Jetstar

HIGH UP ABOVE.
Single 12": released on S&G, Jul'83 Dist: Pinnacle

HOW COULD I LET YOU GET AWAY.
Single 12": released on Thompson Sound, Mar'83 by Thompson Sound Records.

I KNOW THEM LOVE IT.
Single 12": released on Striker Lee, Jul'85 by Striker Lee Records. Dist: Jetstar

I MAN HAVE NO LUCK IN GAMBLING.
Single 12": released on Music Rock, Aug'84 by Music Rock Records. Dist: Jetstar

I REMEMBER MAMA.
Tracks: / Sound design.

Single 12": released on Sound Design Studio, Nov'85 Dist: Jetstar, Cartel

Single 7": released on Sound Design Studio, Mar'85 Dist: Jetstar, Cartel

I WANNA GIVE MY LOVE.
Single 12": released on M&M, May'84 by M&M Music Company. Dist: Jetstar

IN A DIS YAH TIME.
Single 12": released on Live & Love, Mar'82 by Third World Records. Dist: Jetstar

INDECA.
Tracks: / Indeca.
Single 12": released on Youth Promotion, Sep'87 Dist: Jetstar

IT WAS GOOD IT WAS BAD.
Single 12": released on Hitbound, Feb'85 by Hitbound Records. Dist: Jetstar

IT'S ALL IN THE GAME.
Single 7": released on Revue, Oct'86 by Creole Records. Dist: PRT

Single 12": released on Revue, Oct'86 by Creole Records. Dist: PRT

JAH LOVE IS PEOPLE.
Single 12": released on Music Works, Dec'82 Dist: Jetstar

JAMMING IN THE STREET.
Album: released on Wackies, Feb'87 by Wackies Records. Dist: Jetstar

JAMMING IN THE STREET.
Single 12": released on Black Roots, Jun'85 by Black Roots Records. Dist: Jetstar

Single 12": released on Wackies, May'84 by Wackies Records. Dist: Jetstar

JUST DON'T WANNA BE LONELY.
Single 12": released on Black Roots, Mar'84 by Black Roots Records. Dist: Jetstar

LEADER OF THE PACK, THE.
Album: released on Striker Lee, Jul'85 by Striker Lee Records. Dist: Jetstar

LEVEL VIBES.
Single 12": released on Tads, Sep'83 by Tads Records. Dist: Jetstarr*

LICK SHOT.
Single 12": released on Brand X, Oct'84 Dist: Jetstar

LOOKING FOR A HOME (EP).
Single 7": released on Future Times, Aug'82 Dist: Jetstar

LOVERS RACE.
Single 10": released on Black Roots, Dec'82 by Black Roots Records. Dist: Jetstar

LOVING YOU.
Single 12": released on EAD, May'85 by EAD Records. Dist: Jetstar

MAKE IT WITH YOU (Minott, Sugar/Carrol Thompson).
Single 12": released on Carousel, Dec'82 by Carousel Records. Dist: Spartan, Rough Trade

MEMORIES (MEDLEY).
Single 12": released on Striker Lee, Nov'85 by Striker Lee Records. Dist: Jetstar

MIND BLOWING DECISIONS.
Single 7": released on W.O.W., Jun'85 by W.O.W. Records. Dist: Jetstar

Single 12": released on W.O.W., Jun'85 by W.O.W. Records. Dist: Jetstar

MORE WE ARE TOGETHER.
Single 12": released on Black Roots, Jul'82 by Black Roots Records. Dist: Jetstar

MR. DC.
Single 12": released on KG, May'82 by Echo Records. Dist: BMD

NEVER CAN SAY GOODBYE.
Single 12": released on Carousel, Feb'83 by Carousel Records. Dist: Spartan, Rough Trade

NEW GIRLS.
Single 12": released on Black Roots, Nov'82 by Black Roots Records. Dist: Jetstar

NO WICKED.
Tracks: / No wicked.
Single 7": released on Charm, Jul'87 Dist: Jetstar

NOW THAT I'VE FOUND YOU.
Single 12": released on Scom, Dec'84 by Scom Records. Dist: Jetstar

NOW WE KNOW.
Single 12": released on Black Roots, Jun'84 by Black Roots Records. Dist: Jetstar

ROCKERS AWARD WINNERS (Minott, Sugar/Leroy Smart).
Album: released on Greensleeves, Sep'85 by Greensleeves Records. Dist: BMG, Jetstar, Spartan

RUN COME.
Single 12": released on Hawkeye, Sep'85 by Hawkeye Records. Dist: Hawkeye, Lightning (WEA) Distribution, Jetstar

RYDIM.
Album: released on Greensleeves, May'85 by Greensleeves Records. Dist: BMG, Jetstar, Spartan

SAVE YOUR LOVING FOR ME.
Tracks: / Ain't nobody moves me.
Single 12": released on Island, Mar'86 by Island Records. Dist: Polygram, Celtic Music

SEE ME YAH.
Single 12": released on Omega, Nov'85 by Omega Records. Dist: Jetstar

SO MUCH TROUBLE.
Single 12": released on Vena, Dec'84 by Vena Records. Dist: Jetstar

STICK & STONE.
Single 12": released on Crystal, Sep'85 Dist: PRT, John Goldsmith's CD Service

SUGAR AND SPICE.
Album: released on Taxi, Jul'86 by Taxi Records. Dist: Jetstar

SWEET STUFF VOLS.1 & 2.
Double Album: released on L&M, Jun'85 by L&M Records. Dist: Jetstar

TAKE A SET.
Single 12": released on Wackies, Sep'83 by Wackies Records. Dist: Jetstar

THEY HAVE TO COME WE.
Single 12": released on Striker Lee, Jun'85 by Striker Lee Records. Dist: Jetstar

TIME LONGER THAN ROPE.
Album: released on Greensleeves, Nov'85 by Greensleeves Records. Dist: BMG, Jetstar, Spartan

TOO MUCH BACKBITING.
Single 12": released on J & J, Sep'82 by J & J Records. Dist: Jetstar

TRUE, A.
Album: released on Ariwa, Oct'85 by Ariwa Records. Dist: Revolver, Cartel, Jetstar, Rough Trade

UPON THE LEVEL.
Single 12": released on African Museum, Oct'84 Dist: Jetstar

WE HAVE FI LIVE.
Single 12": released on Live & Learn, Dec'83 Dist: Jetstar

WHAT A FEELING (Minott, Sugar & Jah Son).
Tracks: / Riot inna Brixton / Candy man.
Single 12": released on CSA, Feb'86 by CSA Records. Dist: PRT, Jetstar, Jazz Music

WHO CORK THE DANCE.
Single 12": released on Kings And Lions, May'85 by Kings And Lions Records. Dist: Jetstar

WICKED A GO FEEL IT.
Album: released on Wackies, Nov'84 by Wackies Records. Dist: Jetstar

WICKED A GO FEEL IT (12").
Single 12": released on Wackies, Nov'83 by Wackies Records. Dist: Jetstar

YOU LICK ME FIRST.
Tracks: / Insert kitchen / Insert kitchen.
Single 7": released on Live & Learn, Jul'86 Dist: Jetstar

YOUR LOVE.
Single 12": released on Germaine, Nov'86 by Germaine Records. Dist: Jetstar

Mint Addicts

CHICKEN CHASING.
Tracks: / Chicken chasing.
Single 7": released on Constrictor, Oct'87 by Constrictor Records. Dist: Red Rhino, Cartel

NAKED EYES.
Album: released on Constrictor, Jun'87 by Constrictor Records. Dist: Red Rhino, Cartel

Mint Juleps

EVERY KINDA PEOPLE.
Tracks: / Every kinda people / Best of both worlds / Ain't seen nothing yet*.
Single 7": released on Stiff, May'87 by Stiff Records. Dist: EMI, Record Services(Ireland), Jazz Music

Single 12": released on Stiff, May'87 by Stiff Records. Dist: EMI, Record Services(Ireland), Jazz Music

Single 12": released on Stiff, Jun'87 by Stiff Records. Dist: EMI, Record Services(Ireland), Jazz Music

GIRL TO THE POWER OF SIX, THE.
Tracks: / Girl to the power of 6, The / Set me free.
Single 7": released on Stiff, Aug'87 by Stiff Records. Dist: EMI, Record Services(Ireland), Jazz Music

Single 12": released on Stiff, Aug'87 by Stiff Records. Dist: EMI, Record Services(Ireland), Jazz Music

ONE TIME.
Album: released on Stiff, Jul'85 by Stiff Records. Dist: EMI, Record Services(Ireland), Jazz Music

Cassette: released on Stiff, Jul'85 by Stiff Records. Dist: EMI, Record Services(Ireland), Jazz Music

ONLY LOVE CAN BREAK YOUR HEART.
Tracks: / Moving closer / Shout.
Single 7": released on Stiff, Feb'86 by Stiff Records. Dist: EMI, Record Services(Ireland), Jazz Music

Single 12": released on Stiff, Feb'86 by Stiff Records. Dist: EMI, Record Services(Ireland), Jazz Music

Minting Sisters

STRIKE COUNTRY.
Album: released on Country House, Jun'81 by Scotdisc Records. Dist: Taylors, Duncans, Sounds of Scotland, BGS

Cassette: released on Country House, Jun'81 by Scotdisc Records. Dist: Taylors, Duncans, Sounds of Scotland, BGS

Minton, Phil

AMMO (Minton, Phil & Roger Turner).
Album: released on Leo, Sep'84 Dist: Jazz Music, Wellards

Mintzer, Bob

CAMOUFLAGE (Mintzer, Bob Big Band).
Compact disc: released on DMP, '86 by DMP Records. Dist: Venture

INCREDIBLE JOURNEY (Mintzer, Bob Big Band).
Compact disc: released on DMP, '86 by DMP Records. Dist: Venture

PAPA LIPS (Mintzer, Bob Horn Man Band).
Compact disc: released on Toshiba-EMI, '86

Minutemen

3 WAY TIE (FOR LAST).
Album: released on SST, Feb'86 by SST Records. Dist: Pinnacle

DOUBLE NICKELS ON THE DIME.
Compact disc: released on SST, Oct'87 by SST Records. Dist: Pinnacle. Estim retail price in Sep'87 was £11.99.

PARANOID TIME (EP).
Single 12": released on SST, Mar'83 by SST Records. Dist: Pinnacle

PROJECT MERSH.
Album: released on SST, Jul'85 by SST Records. Dist: Pinnacle

THREE WAY TIE FOR LAST.
Compact disc: released on SST, Aug'87 by SST Records. Dist: Pinnacle

TOUR SPIEL (LIVE EP).
Single 7": released on Homestead, Apr'85 Dist: Rough Trade, Cartel, Shigaku

Miracle Legion

BACKYARD.
Tracks: / Until she talks.
Album: released on Spindrift, Nov'85 by Celtic Music. Dist: Celtic Music, Roots

Single 7":

SURPRISE SURPRISE SURPRISE.
Album: released on Rough Trade, Aug'87 by Rough Trade Records. Dist: Rough Trade, Cartel

Cassette: released on Rough Trade, Aug'87 by Rough Trade Records. Dist: Rough Trade, Cartel

Miracles

LOVE MACHINE.
Single 7": released on Motown, Oct'81 by Motown Records. Dist: BMG

Mirage

AND THE EARTH SHALL CRUMBLE.
Album: released on Razor, Feb'86 by Razor. Dist: Pinnacle

AS FROM NOW.
Single 7": released on Copasetic, Jun'82 Dist: Stage One, Jetstar

Single 12": released on Copasetic, Jun'82 Dist: Stage One, Jetstar

Single 12": released on Solid Gold, Dec'81 Dist: MCA

AVANT-GARDE AND THIRD-STREAM JAZZ.
Tracks: / Summer sequence / Clothed woman / Yesterdays / Mirage / Eclipse / Egdon Heath / Concerto for Billy the kid / Transformation / Piazza navona / Laura.
Album: released on New World(USA), Sep'86 by New World Records(USA). Dist: Conifer

DANCE MASTERS.
Tracks: / Give me the night medley / Let's groove medley / Ain't no stopping medley / Into the groove medley / Get down on it medley / Good times medley.
Album: released on Debut, Jul'86 by Passion Records. Dist: PRT

DRUGBUSTIN' MUSIC-POP MUSIC.
Single 12": released on Debut, Nov'85 by Passion Records. Dist: PRT

GET DOWN ON IT.
Single 12": released on Debut-Passion, Mar'85 by Skratch Music. Dist: PRT

GIVE ME THE NIGHT (George Benson Medley).
Single 12": released on Passion, Dec'83 by Passion Records. Dist: PRT

INTO THE GROOVE MEDLEY (Madonna medley).
Single 7": released on Debut, Oct'85 by Passion Records. Dist: PRT

Single 12": released on Debut, Oct'85 by Passion Records. Dist: PRT

JACK MIX Featuring Jack your body.
Tracks: / Jack mix (Featuring Jack your body) / Showing out / Move on out.
Single 12": released on Debut, Feb'87 by Passion Records. Dist: PRT

JACK MIX II.
Tracks: / Jack Mix 11 / Move on out.
Single 12": released on Debut, Apr'87 by Passion Records. Dist: PRT

JACK MIX III.
Notes: Feat. Living in a box/Respectable/Male stripper/Can U dance/Jack your body/Showing out/Axel F/Jackin'/Do it properly/House Nation/Under water/Let yourself go/Move on out. Yes! All your favourites transformed into one interminable jack mix!
Single 12": released on Debut, Jun'87 by Passion Records. Dist: PRT

JACK MIX IV.
Tracks: / Jack mix IV / Here it is get into it.
Single 7": released on Debut, Oct'87 by Passion Records. Dist: PRT

Single 12": released on Debut, Oct'87 by Passion Records. Dist: PRT

LET'S GROOVE (Earth Wind & Fire medley).
Single 7": released on Passion, Mar'84 by Passion Records. Dist: PRT

Single 12": released on Passion, Mar'84 by Passion Records. Dist: PRT

NO MORE NO WAR.
Single 7": released on Proto, Jul'85 by Proto Records. Dist: WEA

Single 12": released on Proto, Jul'85 by Proto Records. Dist: WEA

NOW YOU SEE IT.
Album: released on Compendium, Jul'77 by Compendium Records. Dist: Swift

SERIOUS MIX.
Notes: Inc:Serious/Keep your eye on me/What have you done for me lately/Diamons/Looking for a new love/Chicago/Chicago song/Down in one
Single 12": released on Debut, Jul'87 by Passion Records. Dist: PRT

Single 12": released on Debut, Jul'87 by Passion Records. Dist: PRT

Single 12": released on Debut-Passion, Aug'87 by Skratch Music. Dist: PRT

Mirah

MYSTERY MAN.
Single 7": released on Baskerville, Nov'83 Dist: Pinnacle

Miranda, Carmen

SOUTH AMERICAN WAY.
Album: released on MCA(Coral), Sep'82 by MCA Records. Dist: Polygram

Cassette: released on MCA(Coral), Sep'82 by MCA Records. Dist: Polygram

Mirandi, Mike

HOLIDAY.
Single 7": released on Lady London, Aug'84 by Lady London Records. Dist: M.I.S.

Miri

TRAKBAK.
Tracks: / Trakbak / Trakbak (Instrumental).
Single 7": released on Mcasso, Aug'86 Dist: Spartan

Mirk

TAK A DRAM.
Album: released on Springthyme, '83 by

Springthyme Records. Dist: Jazz Music, Projection, Swift, Celtic Music, Cadillac, Ross, Duncans, Impetus

Cassette: released on Springthyme, '83 by Springthyme Records. Dist: Jazz Music, Projection, Swift, Celtic Music, Cadillac, Ross, Duncans, Impetus

Miro Miroe

READY STEADY.
Single 7": released on CBS, Mar'83 by CBS Records. Dist: CBS

Single 12": released on CBS, Mar'83 by CBS Records. Dist: CBS

Miro, Steve

TRILEMNA.
Album: released on Glass, May'84 by Glass Records. Dist: Nine Mile, Cartel, Red Rhino, Play It Again Sam

Mirrlees Works band

SNAPSHOTS.
Album: released on Grosvenor, Jan'79 by Grosvenor Records. Dist: Taylors, Jazz Music

Mirror

REFLECTED GLORY.
Tracks: / Reflected glory.
Single 12": released on Bam Caruso, Mar'86 by Bam Caruso Records. Dist: Celtic Music, Revolver, Cartel

WE'VE GOT ALL THE TIME IN THE WORLD.
Single 7": released on Magnet, May'83 by Magnet Records. Dist: BMG

Mirror Crack'd

DANDY WALLFLOWER.
Single 7": released on Carrere, Mar'84 by Carrere Records(UK). Dist: PRT, Spartan

Single 12": released on Carrere, Mar'84 by Carrere Records(UK). Dist: PRT, Spartan

Mirror, Danny

SUSPICION (Elvis Medley) (Mirror, Danny & Jordanaires).
Single 7": released on Albion, Nov'81 by Albion Records. Dist: Spartan, Pinnacle

Mirrors

DANCE, DANCE,DANCE.
Tracks: / Dance,Dance,Dance.
Album: released on Aura, Jan'84 by Aura Records & Tapes. Dist: Pinnacle

MIRRORS, THE.
Album: released on Aura, Mar'84 by Aura Records & Tapes. Dist: Pinnacle

Mirrors Over Kiev

TAKE ME DOWN.
Tracks: / Take me down / Don't leave me.
Single 7": released on Imaginary, 31 Oct'87 by Imaginary Records. Dist: Fast Forward, Cartel

Mirza, Mahmud

CLASSICAL SITAR.
Album: released on Conifer, Jul'84 by Conifer Records. Dist: Conifer, Jazz Music

Cassette: released on MCA(USA), Sep'86 by MCA Records(USA). Dist: Pinnacle, Swift

RAG DARBARI/RAG KAFI.
Album: released on Tangent, Apr'81 by Tangent Records. Dist: Jazz Music, Projection, Swift, Celtic Music, Cadillac, Ross, Duncans, Impetus

Misacres

SO FINALLY SWEET.
Tracks: / So finally sweet.
Single 7": released on Cherry Red, Sep'86 by Cherry Red Records. Dist: Pinnacle

Mischievous Deeds

ON YOUR BIKE ARGENTINA.
Single 7": released on Firestar, May'82 Dist: Pinnacle

WISHING YOU WELL.
Single 7": released on Safari, Jul'82 by Safari Records. Dist: Pinnacle

Mi-Sex

BLUE DAY.
Single 7": released on CBS, Jun'84 by CBS Records. Dist: CBS

COMPUTER GAMES.
Single 7": released on CBS, May'83 by CBS Records. Dist: CBS

Single 12": released on CBS, May'83 by CBS Records. Dist: CBS

Misfit

MISFIT Erick & Michele (Various artists).
Album: released on Maranatha, May'82 by Word Records(UK)Ltd.. Dist: Word, CBS

Cassette: released on Maranatha, May'82 by Word Records(UK)Ltd.. Dist: Word, CBS

Misfits

BEST OF THE MISFITS.
Album: released on Revolver, Jul'86 by Revolver Records. Dist: Revolver, Cartel

BEWARE.
Single 7": released on Plan 9, Jul'81 by Armageddon Records. Dist: Spartan

DIE DIE MY DARLING.
Single 12": released on Plan 9 (USA), Nov'87 Dist: Pinnacle

EVIL LIVE.
Album: released on Caroline (USA), Sep'87 Dist: Pinnacle

MISFITS.
Tracks: / Bullet / Horror Business / Teenagers from mars / Night of the living / Where eagles dare / Vampira / Skulls / I turned into a martian / Eyes / Violent world / London Dungeon / Ghoul's night out / Halloween / Die, Die my darling / Mommy, can I go out and kill tonight?.
Notes: All songs written by Glenn Danzig:copyright G.Danzig:Produced by G.Danzig(P) OSR made by Plan 9 records/Licensed from Plan 9/Caroline Records Inc. 1986 a Revolver Records release.
Album: released on Revolver, Jul'86 by Revolver Records. Dist: Revolver, Cartel

RAIN VOICES.
Tracks: / Rain voices.
Single 7": released on Misfit, Dec'86 Dist: M.I.S.

Single 12": released on Misfit, Dec'86 Dist: M.I.S.

WOLFSBLOOD.
Album: released on Aggressive Rock Productions, Feb'84 Dist: Rough Trade, Cartel

Misha

IMAGINATION, (USE YOUR).
Single 7": released on Nu-Disk, Mar'85

Mishima

MISHIMA.
Album: released on Elektra, Nov'85 by WEA Records. Dist: WEA

Miss P

DON'T RUSH ME / IMPATIENT.
Single 12": released on Plantation, Mar'83 Dist: Jetstar

Missing Ambassador, The

MISSING AMBASSADOR, THE (Various artists).
Cassette: released on Tell-a-tale (Cassettes), Aug'84

Missing Brazilians

WARZONE.
Album: released on On-U-Sound, Mar'84 Dist: Rough Trade, Lightning, Southern Record, Spartan

Missing Persons

I CAN'T THINK ABOUT DANCING WITHOUT YOU.
Tracks: / I can't think about dancing without you / Face to face.
Single 7": released on Capitol, Aug'86 by Capitol Records. Dist: EMI

Single 12": released on Capitol, Aug'86 by Capitol Records. Dist: EMI

WORDS.
Single 7": released on Capitol, Feb'83 by Capitol Records. Dist: EMI

Single 12": released on Capitol, Feb'83 by Capitol Records. Dist: EMI

Mission

CRUSADE (VIDEO).
Notes: 10 tracks

FIRST CHAPTER, THE.
Tracks: / Over the hills and far away / Serpent's kiss / Crystal ocean,The / Dancing barefoot / Like a hurricane / Over the hills and far away / Naked and savage / Garden of delight / Wake / Like a hurricane (extended).
Album: released on Mercury, Jun'87 by Phonogram Records. Dist: IMS, Polygram

Cassette: released on Mercury, Jun'87 by Phonogram Records. Dist: IMS, Polygram

GOD'S OWN MEDICINE.
Compact disc: released on Mercury, Dec'86 by Phonogram Records. Dist: IMS, Polygram

Album: released on Mercury, Nov'86 by Phonogram Records. Dist: IMS, Polygram

Cassette: released on Mercury, Nov'86 by Phonogram Records. Dist: IMS, Polygram

LIKE A HURRICANE.
Tracks: / Like a Hurricane / Garden of delight(Double A) / Over the hills / Far away / Crystal ocean,The.
Single 7": released on Chapter 22, Jul'86 by Chapter 22 Records. Dist: Nine Mile, Cartel

Single 12": released on Chapter 22, Jul'86 by Chapter 22 Records. Dist: Nine Mile, Cartel

MISSION: INTERVIEW PICTURE DISC.
Album: released on Baktabak, Apr'87 by Baktabak Records. Dist: Arabesque

SERPENTS KISS.
Tracks: / Serpents kiss.
Single 7": released on Chapter 22, May'86 by Chapter 22 Records. Dist: Nine Mile, Cartel

Single 12": released on Chapter 22, May'86 by Chapter 22 Records. Dist: Nine Mile, Cartel

SEVERINE.
Tracks: / Severine / Tomorrow never knows / Wishing well **.
Single 7": released on Mercury, Feb'87 by Phonogram Records. Dist: IMS, Polygram

Single 12": released on Mercury, Feb'87 by Phonogram Records. Dist: IMS, Polygram

STAY WITH ME.
Tracks: / Stay with me / Blood brothers / Island in a stream.
Single 7": released on Mercury, Oct'86 by Phonogram Records. Dist: IMS, Polygram

Single 12": released on Mercury, Oct'86 by Phonogram Records. Dist: IMS, Polygram

WASTELAND.
Tracks: / Wasteland / Shelter from the storm / Dancing barefoot.
Single 7": released on Mercury, Jan'87 by Phonogram Records. Dist: IMS, Polygram

Mission Impossible

MISSION IMPOSSIBLE (Various artists).
Album: released on Power House, Jun'87 by Power House Records. Dist: Jetstar

Mission Of Burma

TERRIBLE TRUTH ABOUT BURMA,THE.
Album: released on New Rose, Jan'86 Dist: Pinnacle

Mission, The

MISSION, THE Original soundtrack.
Album: released on Virgin, Oct'86 by Virgin Records. Dist: Virgin, EMI

Cassette: released on Virgin, Oct'86 by Virgin Records. Dist: Virgin, EMI

MISSION,THE Original Soundtrack.
Compact disc: released on Virgin, Oct'86 by Virgin Records. Dist: Virgin, EMI

Mission USA

SEARCH.
Tracks: / Show a little love / Lena / Lover for life / Turn me up / Energy to burn / Ready to give my heart / Sensuous mood / Back on track.
Album: released on CBS, Nov'87 by CBS Records. Dist: CBS

Cassette: released on CBS, Nov'87 by CBS Records. Dist: CBS

SHOW A LITTLE LOVE.
Tracks: / Show a little love / Sensuous mood / Show a little love* / Senuous mood* / Sensuous mood* / Show a little love (instrumental).
Single 7": released on CBS, Oct'87 by CBS Records. Dist: CBS

Single 12": released on CBS, Oct'87 by CBS Records. Dist: CBS

Mississippi...

MISSISSIPPI DELTA BLUES (VOL.1) various artists (Various artists).
Album: released on Arhoolie(USA), May'81 by Arhoolie Records. Dist: Jazz Music, Projection, Roots, Celtic Music, Cadillac, Ross, Duncans, Impetus

MISSISSIPPI DELTA BLUES (VOL.2) various artists (Various artists).
Album: released on Arhoolie(USA), May'81 by Arhoolie Records. Dist: Jazz Music, Projection, Roots, Celtic Music, Cadillac, Ross, Duncans, Impetus

MISSISSIPPI LEGENDS Music of New Orleans (Mississippi Legends).
Triple album / cassette: released on RCA(France), '83 by RCA Records. Dist: Discovery, Silva Screen Records

MISSISSIPPI MAULERS AND OTHERS (Mississippi Maulers).
Album: released on VJM(Vintage Jazz Music), Apr'79 by Vintage Jazz Music Society(VJM). Dist: Wellards, Jazz Music, Swift, Taylors, VJM

MISSISSIPPI SHEIKS VOL 1 (1930) Various artists (Various artists).
Album: released on Matchbox, Sep'85 Dist: Projection, Roots, Jazz Music, Celtic Music, Taylors

Mississippi Blues

MISSISSIPPI BLUES (Various artists).
Album: released on HK, Sep'87 Dist: Swift

Mississippi Delta

FROM THE DELTA TO THE WASH.
Album: released on Sweet Folk All, May'81 by Sweet Folk All Records. Dist: Sweet Folk All, Projection, Celtic Music, Jazz Music, Impetus, Wellards, Festival Records

Mississippi John Hurt

SHAKE THAT THING.
Album: released on Blue Moon, Jan'86 by Magnum Music Group Ltd. Dist: PRT

Mist on the ridge

MIST ON THE RIDGE Various artists (Various artists).
Album: released on Coda, Aug'86 by Coda Records. Dist: Celtic Music, Cartel, WEA, Roots, Pinnacle

Mistaken Identity

ANSWER.
Single 12": released on Ram, Apr'85 by Ram.

Mister Murray

DOWN CAME THE RAIN.
Single 7": released on WHB, Nov'81 by WHB Records. Dist: Stage One

Mister Spaulding

SKANK IN THE DARK.
Single 12": released on Roots Rockers, Sep'85 Dist: Jetstar

Mister Steve

CHRISTMAS SONG, THE.
Single 7": released on Town & Country, Nov'83 Dist: Spartan

ONE ROAD.
Single 7": released on Albion, Jul'84 by Albion Records. Dist: Spartan, Pinnacle

Mistinguett

MISTINGUETT Various artists (Various artists).
Double Album: released on EMI (France), Jan'83 by EMI Records(UK). Dist: Conifer

Mistletoe...

GOLDEN HOUR: MISTLETOE CHILDREN'S CHOIR (Mistletoe Children's Choir).
Album: released on Audio Fidelity(USA), Oct'84 by Audio Fidelity Ent.Inc.(USA).

Cassette: released on Audio Fidelity(USA), Oct'84 by Audio Fidelity Ent.Inc.(USA).

GOLDEN HOUR: MISTLETOE ORGAN & CHIMES (Mistletoe Organ & Chimes).
Album: released on Audio Fidelity(USA), Oct'84 by Audio Fidelity Ent.Inc.(USA).

Cassette: released on Audio Fidelity(USA), Oct'84 by Audio Fidelity Ent.Inc.(USA).

GOLDEN HOUR OF CHRISTMAS CAROLS, A (Mistletoe Singers).
Album: released on Audio Fidelity(USA), Oct'84 by Audio Fidelity Ent.Inc.(USA).

Cassette: released on Audio Fidelity(USA), Oct'84 by Audio Fidelity Ent.Inc.(USA)

GOLDEN HOUR OF CHRISTMAS STORIES (Mistletoe Players).
Album: released on Audio Fidelity(USA), Oct'84 by Audio Fidelity Ent.Inc.(USA).

Cassette: released on Audio Fidelity(USA), Oct'84 by Audio Fidelity Ent.Inc.(USA).

Mistrals Daughter

MISTRALS DAUGHTER Original soundtrack.
Tracks: / Teddy's theme / Mistral's theme.
Single 7": released on Carrere, Feb'86 by Carrere Records(UK). Dist: PRT, Spartan

MISTRALS DAUGHTER, THE Original Soundtrack.
Album: released on Carrere(France), May'85 by Carrere Records (France).

Mistress Of Mellyn

MISTRESS OF MELLYN Holt, Victoria (Kendall, Felicity).
Cassette: released on Chivers Audio Books, Jan'81 by Chivers Sound & Vision. Dist: Chivers Sound & Vision

Misty In Roots

ATOMIC ENERGY/ SET ME FREE.
Single 7": released on People Unite, Dec'81 by People Unite Records. Dist: Jetstar, Rough Trade, Cartel, Pinnacle

EARTH.
Album: released on People Unite, Apr'84 by People Unite Records. Dist: Jetstar, Rough Trade, Cartel, Pinnacle

JAH JAH BLESS AFRICA.
Single 7": released on People Unite, Feb'82 by People Unite Records. Dist: Jetstar, Rough Trade, Cartel, Pinnacle

MUSI O TUNYA.
Album: released on People Unite, Mar'85 by People Unite Records. Dist: Jetstar, Rough Trade, Cartel, Pinnacle

OWN THEM CONTROL THEM.
Single 7": released on People Unite, Nov'86 by People Unite Records. Dist: Jetstar, Rough Trade, Cartel, Pinnacle

Single 12": released on People Unite, Nov'86

by People Unite Records. Dist: Jetstar, Rough Trade, Cartel, Pinnacle

PEACE AND LOVE.
Single 7": released on People, Jul'81 Dist: Trojan

Single 12": released on People, Jul'81 Dist: Trojan

POOR AND NEEDY/ FOLLOW FASHION.
Single 7": released on People Unite, Jun'83 by People Unite Records. Dist: Jetstar, Rough Trade, Cartel, Pinnacle

Single 12": released on People Unite, Jun'83 by People Unite Records. Dist: Jetstar, Rough Trade, Cartel, Pinnacle

RICH MAN/ SALVATION.
Single 12": released on People, Feb'80 Dist: Trojan

UPTOWN DOWNTOWN/ NO NEED TO....
Single 7": released on People Unite, Dec'81 by People Unite Records. Dist: Jetstar, Rough Trade, Cartel, Pinnacle

VIVA ZAPATTA.
Single 7": released on People Unite, Jan'81 by People Unite Records. Dist: Jetstar, Rough Trade, Cartel, Pinnacle

WANDERING WANDEROR.
Single 7": released on People Unite, Feb'85 by People Unite Records. Dist: Jetstar, Rough Trade, Cartel, Pinnacle

Misty Mornings

MISTY MORNINGS Various original artists (Various original artists).
Album: released on Ronco, Nov'81 by Ronco Records.

Cassette: released on Ronco, Nov'81 by Ronco Records.

Misty Water Colour..

MISTY WATER-COLOUR MEMORIES Various Orchestras (Various Orchestras).
Album: released on BBC, Jul'83 by BBC Records & Tapes. Dist: EMI

Cassette: released on BBC, Jul'83 by BBC Records & Tapes. Dist: EMI

Misunderstood

BEFORE THE DREAM FADED.
Album: released on Cherry Red, Apr'82 by Cherry Red Records. Dist: Pinnacle

CHILDREN OF THE SUN (EP).
Single 7": released on Cherry Red, Jan'81 by Cherry Red Records. Dist: Pinnacle

GOLDEN GLASS.
Album: released on Time Stood Still, Aug'84 by Cherry Red Records. Dist: Pinnacle

Single 12": released on Cherry Red, Jun'84 by Cherry Red Records. Dist: Pinnacle

SHAKE YOUR MONEY MAKER.
Single 12": released on Cherry Red, Jul'84 by Cherry Red Records. Dist: Pinnacle

Mitchell, Bill

VINTAGE PIANO VOL.3 (Mitchell, Bill/Paul Lingle).
Album: released on Euphonic, Apr'79 by Euphonic Records. Dist: Jazz Music, Swift

Mitchell, Billy

FACES.
Album: released on Optimism (Germany), Oct'87

Cassette: released on Beserkley(USA), Oct'87 by Beserkley Records. Dist: PRT. Estim retail price in Oct'87 was £6.15.

Mitchell, Blue

GRAFFITI BLUES.
Album: released on Audio Fidelity(USA), Mar'83 by Audio Fidelity Ent.Inc.(USA).

THING TO DO, THE.
Album: released on Blue Note, Oct'85 by EMI Records(UK). Dist: EMI*

Mitchell, Bobby

GONNA BE A WHEEL (Mitchell, Bobby & The Toppers).
Album: released on Mr.R&B, Aug'87 Dist: Counterpoint, Celtic Music, Swift

I'M GONNA BE A WHEEL SOMEDAY.
Album: released on Mr.R&B, Jun'80 Dist: Counterpoint, Celtic Music, Swift

Mitchell, Brenda

SIZZLIN.
Single 7": released on Ecstasy, Jul'85 by Creole Records. Dist: PRT

Single 12": released on Ecstasy, Jul'85 by Creole Records. Dist: PRT

Mitchell/ Coe Mysteries

EXILED various artists (Various artists).
Album: released on RCA, Aug'80 Dist: BMG

Cassette: released on RCA, Aug'80 Dist: BMG

Mitchell, Eddy

EDDY MITCHELL.
Album: released on RCA(France), Feb'84 by RCA Records. Dist: Discovery, Silva Screen Records

Mitchell, Geoffrey

CHRISTMAS CAROLS (Choir, Geoffrey Mitchell & English Chamber Orchestra).
Album: released on MFP, Sep'84 by Music For Pleasure Records. Dist: EMI

Cassette: released on MFP, Sep'84 by Music For Pleasure Records. Dist: EMI

JOY OF CHRISTMAS, THE.
Album: released on MFP(Holland), Sep'84 by Music For Pleasure Records. Dist: Conifer

Cassette: released on MFP(Holland), Sep'84 by Music For Pleasure Records. Dist: Conifer

Mitchell, George

30 GOLDEN GREATS (Mitchell,George Minstrels With Joe Loss Orchestra).
Album: released on EMI, Sep'80 by EMI Records(UK). Dist: EMI

Cassette: released on EMI, Sep'80 by EMI Records(UK). Dist: EMI

BLACK AND WHITE MINSTREL SHOW, THE (Mitchell,George Minstrels).
Album: released on Retrospect, Aug'84 by EMI Records(UK). Dist: EMI

Cassette: released on Retrospect, Aug'84 by EMI Records(UK). Dist: EMI

DOWN MEMORY LANE (Mitchell,George Minstrels).
Tracks: / Ring up the curtain / Ring ring de banjo / When the saints go marching in / Chicago / You made me love you / Mr Gallagher and Mr Shean / Put your arms around me honey / Down where the Swanee river flows / When the saints go marching in / While strolling through the park one day / In the good old summertime / Sweet Rosie O'Grady / I'll be your sweetheart / Little Annie Rooney / Band played on,The / Alabamy bound / Swanee / Is it true what they say about Dixie? / Carolina / Toot Toot Tootsie (Goodbye) / Old ark's a moverin,The / Along the Navajo trail / In Ole' Oklahoma / Old Dan Tucker / Country Style / Skip to my Lou / Buffalo Gal / Singin' in the rain / Together / No two people / My blue heaven / Falling in love with love / Maria from Bahia / I yi, yi ,yi ,yi,(I like you very much) / When I love I love / Bandit,The / Cielito lindo / Cuonto le Gusta / I'll si si ya in Bahia / Hard times come again no more / Gentle Annie / Way down upon the Swanee river / Tell me pretty maiden / Put on your Ta-Ta little girl / Hello!Hello! Who's your lady friend / I was a good girl until I met you / In the Twi-Twi-Twi-Light / Two little girls in blue / North and south / You're in Kentucky as sure as you're born / Yellow rose of Texas (The) / Georgia on my mind / Stars fell on Alabama / I'm going back to old Nebraska / Dixieland / Carry me back to old Virginny / Lady is a tramp (The) / In a old shanty town / Ain't we got fun / I'm sittin' high on a hill top / Big rock candy mountain / Sde by side / Widdicombe fair / Home on the range / Back in those old Kentucky days / I went down to Virginia / Sonny boy / Mockin' bird / Goin'to the county fair / Dicky bird hop / Cuckoo waltz / She was one of the early birds / When the red red robin goes / Too-White! Too-Whoo! / Chee Chee oo Chee / Lets all sing like the birdies sing / Load of hay, A / One,Two,Button your shoe / You are my sunshine / Bei mir bist du schon / Memories are made of this / Sing a song of Sunbeams / South of the border / Where or when / Frog and the mouse (The) / Long long ago / Roamin' in the Gloamin' / Let me call you Sweetheart / Meet me tonight in dreamland / Pack up your troubles / Till we meet again / Roses of Picardy.
Notes: (P)1961 & 1962 Original Soundtracks Recordings made by EMI Records Ltd. Producer Walter J.Ridley,Double Album.Long playing cassette.
Album: released on MFP, Sep'86 by Music For Pleasure Records. Dist: EMI

Cassette: released on MFP, Sep'86 by Music For Pleasure Records. Dist: EMI

SING..RODGERS & HAMMERSTEIN & RODGERS & HART (Mitchell,George Minstrels).
Album: released on MFP, Nov'82 by Music For Pleasure Records. Dist: EMI

Cassette: released on MFP, Nov'82 by Music For Pleasure Records. Dist: EMI

THIS IS THE GEORGE MITCHELL MINSTRELS (Mitchell,George Minstrels).
Album: by EMI Records(UK). Dist: EMI

Mitchell, Guy

20 GOLDEN PIECES: GUY MITCHELL.
Album: released on Bulldog, Mar'84 by Bulldog Records. Dist: President, Spartan, Swift, Taylors, Jazz Music

ALWAYS ON MY MIND.
Tracks: / Always on my mind / Wind beneath my wings.
Single 7": released on Top Hat, Aug'87 by Humber Records. Dist: PRT

GARDEN IN THE RAIN, A.
Album: released on President, Aug'85 by President Records. Dist: Spartan, Taylors, Jazz Music

Cassette: released on President, Aug'85 by President Records. Dist: Spartan, Taylors, Jazz Music

GREATEST HITS.
Double cassette: released on Warwick, 7 Nov'87 by Warwick Records. Dist: CBS, MSD, Taylors, Solomon & Peres

GREATEST HITS: GUY MITCHELL.
Album: released on Spot, Feb'83 by Pickwick Records.

Cassette: released on Spot, Feb'83 by Pickwick Records.

Cassette: released on CBS Cameo, Oct'84 by CBS Records. Dist: CBS

HIT SINGLES-1950/1960.
Double Album: released on CBS, '81 by CBS Records. Dist: CBS

Cassette: released on CBS, '81 by CBS Records. Dist: CBS

ROCKABILLY/ KNEE DEEP IN BLUES.
Single 7": released on Old Gold, Jul'82 by Old Gold Records. Dist: PRT, Counterpoint, Lightning, Jazz Music, Taylors

SINGING THE BLUES.
Album: released on Showcase, Jul'86 by Castle Communications Records. Dist: PRT

Cassette: released on Showcase, Jul'86 by Castle Communications Records. Dist: PRT

Compact disc: released on Showcase, '86 by Castle Communications Records. Dist: PRT

SINGING THE BLUES/ HEARTACHES BY THE NUMBER.
Single 7": released on Old Gold, Jul'82 by Old Gold Records. Dist: PRT, Counterpoint, Lightning, Jazz Music, Taylors

Mitchell, Joni

BLUE.
Compact disc: released on Reprise (USA), Jan'87 by WEA Records. Dist: WEA

Album: released on Reprise (USA), '72 by WEA Records. Dist: WEA

Cassette: released on Reprise (USA), '72 by WEA Records. Dist: WEA

CHINESE CAFE/ LADIES MAN.
Single 7": released on Geffen, Feb'83 by Geffen Records. Dist: WEA

CLOUDS.
Album: released on Reprise (USA), '70 by WEA Records. Dist: WEA

CLOUDS/ BLUE.
Cassette: released on Reprise (USA), Oct'82 by WEA Records. Dist: WEA

COURT AND SPARK.
Compact disc: released on Asylum, May'83 by WEA Records. Dist: WEA

Album: released on Asylum, Jun'76 by WEA Records. Dist: WEA

Cassette: released on Asylum, Jun'76 by WEA Records. Dist: WEA

COURT AND SPARK/ FOR THE ROSES.
Cassette: released on Asylum, Nov'83 by WEA Records. Dist: WEA

DOG EAT DOG.
Tracks: / Good friends / Fiction / Three great stimulants / Tax free / Smokin' / Dog eat dog / Shiny toys / Ethopia / Impossible dreamer / Lucky girl / Good friends / Fiction / Three great stimulants, The / Tax free / Smokin' / Dog eat dog / Shiny toys / Ethiopia / Impossible dreamer / Lucky girl.
Compact disc: released on Geffen, May'86 by Geffen Records. Dist: WEA

Album: released on Geffen, Oct'87 by Geffen Records. Dist: WEA

Cassette: released on Geffen, Oct'87 by Geffen Records. Dist: WEA

Compact disc: released on Geffen, Aug'87 by Geffen Records. Dist: WEA

DON JUAN'S RECKLESS DAUGHTER.
Double Album: released on Asylum, Jan'78 by WEA Records. Dist: WEA

Double cassette: released on Asylum, Jan'78 by WEA Records. Dist: WEA

FOR THE ROSES.
Album: released on Asylum, Jun'76 by WEA Records. Dist: WEA

HEJIRA.
Album: released on Asylum, Nov'76 by WEA Records. Dist: WEA

Cassette: released on Asylum, Nov'76 by WEA Records. Dist: WEA

Compact disc: released on WEA, Oct'87 by WEA Records. Dist: WEA

HISSING OF SUMMER LAWNS, THE.
Album: released on Asylum, Jun'76 by WEA Records. Dist: WEA

Cassette: released on Asylum, Jun'76 by WEA Records. Dist: WEA

JONI MITCHELL.
Album: released on Reprise (USA), '70 by WEA Records. Dist: WEA

LADIES OF THE CANYON.
Album: released on Reprise (USA), '71 by WEA Records. Dist: WEA

Cassette: released on Reprise (USA), '71 by WEA Records. Dist: WEA

MILES OF AISLES.
Double Album: released on Asylum, Jun'76 by WEA Records. Dist: WEA

Double cassette: released on Asylum, Jun'76 by WEA Records. Dist: WEA

MINGUS.
Album: released on Asylum, Jun'79 by WEA Records. Dist: WEA

SHADOWS AND LIGHT.
Double Album: released on Asylum, '80 by WEA Records. Dist: WEA

Cassette: released on Asylum, '80 by WEA Records. Dist: WEA

SHINING TOYS.
Tracks: / Shining toys / Three great stimulants.
Single 7": released on Geffen, Apr'86 by Geffen Records. Dist: WEA

Single 12": released on Geffen, Apr'86 by Geffen Records. Dist: WEA

WILD THING RUN FAST.
Tracks: / Chinese cafe / Unchained melody / Wild things run fast / Ladies man / Moon at the window / Solid love / Be cool / You're so square(Baby I don't care) / You dream flat tires / Man to Man / Underneath the streetlight / Love.
Album: released on Geffen, Sep'86 by Geffen Records. Dist: WEA

Cassette: released on Geffen, Sep'86 by Geffen Records. Dist: WEA

Mitchell, Kevin

FREE AND EASY (Traditional songs mainly from North West Ulster).
Album: released on Topic, '81 Dist: Projection

Mitchell, Kim

AKIMBO ALOGO.
Album: released on Bronze, Jun'85 by Polygram Records. Dist: Polydor

GO FOR SODA.
Single 7": released on Bronze, May'85 by Polygram Records. Dist: Polydor

Single 12": released on Bronze, May'85 by Polygram Records. Dist: Polydor

Mitchell, Les

WHISKEY (Mitchell, Les & Country Pride).
Album: released on Tank, Jun'79 by Tank Records. Dist: Jazz Music

Mitchell, Mark

EIGHTEEN YELLOW ROSES.
Album: released on Homespun(Ireland), '82 by Homespun Records. Dist: Homespun, Outlet

Cassette: released on Homespun(Ireland), '82 by Homespun Records. Dist: Homespun, Outlet

Mitchell, Neville

PREACHING LOVE.
Single 12": released on King Jam, Dec'83 by King Jam Records. Dist: Jetstar

Mitchell, Pat

UILLEANN PIPES.
Album: released on Topic, '81 Dist: Projection

Mitchell, Red

COMMUNICATION.
Album: by Sonet Records. Dist: Jazz Music, Swift, Celtic Music, Roots, PRT, Sonet

HOME COOKING (Mitchell, Red With Tommy Flanagan).
Album: released on Phontastic(Sweden), '82 Dist: Wellards, Jazz Music

HOT HOUSE (Mitchell, Red & Warne Marsh).
Album: released on Storyville, Nov'86 by Storyville Records. Dist: Swift

JAM FOR YOUR BREAD.
Tracks: / Jam for your bread / Duff / You go to my head / Where or when / Ornithology / Sec-

tion blues / East coast outpost / I'll never be the same / Will you still be mine.
Album: released on Affinity, Oct'86 by Charly Records. Dist: Charly, Cadillac, Swift

JIM HALL & RED MITCHELL (Mitchell, Red & Jim Hall).

RED MITCHELL QUARTET.
Album: released on Contemporary, Dec'81 by Contemporary Records. Dist: Pinnacle

SOFT AND WARM.
Album: released on Phontastic(Sweden), '82 Dist: Wellards, Jazz Music

WHEN I'M SINGING.
Album: released on Enja(Germany), Nov'84 by Enja Records (W.Germany). Dist: Cadillac, Jazz Music

YOU'RE ME (Mitchell, Red With Tommy Flanagan).

Mitchell, Ross

LET'S TEACH THE WORLD TO DANCE (Mitchell, Ross - Band And Singers).
Album: released on Dansan, Feb'85 by Spartan Records. Dist: Spartan, Taylors

ROSS MITCHELL & HIS BAND & SINGERS (Mitchell, Ross & His Band & Singers).
Album: released on Dance & Listen, Nov'87

ZING.
Album: released on Dansan, Aug'85 by Spartan Records. Dist: Spartan, Taylors

Mitchell, Sam

BOTTLENECK & SLIDE GUITAR.
Album: released on Kicking Mule, Jan'78 Dist: Sonet, Projection, Swift, Celtic Music, Cadillac, Ross, Duncans, Impetus

FOLLOW YOU DOWN.
Album: released on Kicking Mule, Feb'79 Dist: Sonet, Projection, Swift, Celtic Music, Cadillac, Ross, Duncans, Impetus

I GOT RHYTHM (Mitchell, Sam/ John James).

Mitchell, Sharon

HANDSOME STRANGER.
Single 12": released on Malaco, Jun'84 by Malaco Records. Dist: PRT, Charly, Celtic Music

Mitchell, Willie

CHAMPION, THE.
Single 7": released on London, Jan'76 by London Records. Dist: Polygram

EVERYTHING IS GONNA BE ALRIGHT.
Single 7": released on London, '65 by London Records. Dist: Polygram

THAT DRIVING BEAT.
Album: released on Hi, Nov'86 by Demon Records. Dist: Pinnacle, Swift

THAT DRIVING BEAT (6 TRACK EP).
Single 7": released on Spindrift, Mar'85 by Celtic Music. Dist: Celtic Music, Roots

THAT DRIVING BEAT/ MERCY.
Single 7": released on Hi-Cream, Jun'80 by Hi-Cream Records.

Mitchell,Barbara

HIGH ON LOVE.
Tracks: / Ace of my heart / High on love / Never had a love like this before / Can't help the way I feel / I need some loving / Take your time / Don't look me over.
Notes: Barbara Mitchell is a young,talented,yet seasoned perfomer who makes her solo debut on this album.She began her career at age of 16 as lead singer from the Motown group Hi Energy for 5 albums.
Album: released on Club, Jun'86 by Phonogram Records. Dist: Polygram

Cassette: released on Club, Jun'86 by Phonogram Records. Dist: Polygram

Mitchell,Eddie

HOLD ME.
Tracks: / Hold me.
Single 7": released on Mooncrest, Nov'86 by Mooncrest Records., Projection, Swift, Celtic Music, Cadillac, Ross, Duncans, Impetus

Mitchell,Graeme

FINE FETTLE (Mitchell,Graeme &His Scottish Dance Band).
Album: released on Lapwing, '85 by Lapwing Records. Dist: Projection, Celtic Music, Roots, Ross, Duncans, Graham Tosh Distribution, Sounds of Scotland

Mitchell,Roscoe

CONCERT TORONTO 4/5 OCT 1975.
Album: released on Sackville, Apr'81 Dist: Swift, Jazz Music, Jazz Horizons, Cadillac Music, Celtic Music

CONGLIPTIONS.
Album: released on Nessa, Mar'79, Swift

DUETS WITH ANTHONY BRAXTON.
Album: released on Sackville, Apr'81 Dist: Swift, Jazz Music, Jazz Horizons, Cadillac Music, Celtic Music

L.R.G - THE MAZE.
Double Album: released on Nessa, Mar'79, Swift

NONAAH.
Double Album: released on Nessa, Mar'79, Swift

OLD/ QUARTET.
Album: released on Nessa, Mar'79, Swift

ROSCOE MITCHELL SOLO SAXOPHONE CONCERTS.
Album: released on Sackville, Jul'86 Dist: Swift, Jazz Music, Jazz Horizons, Cadillac Music, Celtic Music

SOLO SAXOPHONE CONCERTS.
Album: released on Sackville, Apr'81 Dist: Swift, Jazz Music, Jazz Horizons, Cadillac Music, Celtic Music

SOUND.
Album: released on Delmark, '74, Swift, Cadillac

Mitchenko, Edvard

RUSSIAN ACCORDEON MUSIC.
Cassette: released on Melodiya(USSR), Feb'79

Mitchum, Arthur

ARRIBA TACO GRANDE/ STRANGE GOODBYE.
Single 7": released on Pastafont, Jul'82 by Pastafont Records.

Mitchum, Robert

CALYPSO.
Album: released on Capitol, Mar'84 by Capitol Records. Dist: EMI

Mitsouko, Rita

C'EST COMME CA.
Tracks: / C'est comme ca / Andy.
Single 7": released on Virgin, Mar'87 by Virgin Records. Dist: Virgin, EMI

Single 12": released on Virgin, Mar'87 by Virgin Records. Dist: Virgin, EMI

MARCIA BAILA.
Tracks: / Marcia Baila.
Single 7": released on Virgin, Jul'86 by Virgin Records. Dist: Virgin, EMI

Single 12": released on Virgin, Jul'86 by Virgin Records. Dist: Virgin, EMI

NO COMPRENDO, THE.
Single 7": released on Virgin, Jul'87 by Virgin Records. Dist: Virgin, EMI

Cassette: released on Virgin, Jul'87 by Virgin Records. Dist: Virgin, EMI

Mittoo, Jackie

NEVER CAN SAY GOODBYE/ FINGER STYLE.
Single 12": released on Carousel, May'83 by Carousel Records. Dist: Spartan, Rough Trade

ORIGINAL JACKIE MITTOO, THE.
Album: released on Third World, Apr'79 Dist: Jetstarr*

THESE EYES/ WALL STREET.
Single 7": released on Rough Trade, Aug'81 by Rough Trade Records. Dist: Rough Trade, Cartel

Single 12": released on Rough Trade, Aug'81 by Rough Trade Records. Dist: Rough Trade, Cartel

VERSION STUDIO.
Album: released on Jakki, Nov'85 Dist: Jetstar

Mitty,Walter

BRAVE NEW ENGLAND/GOOD BOYS.
Single 7": released on RCA, Jul'82 Dist: BMG

Mix blood

SKAVILLE.
Album: released on Vista Sounds, '83 by Vista Sounds Records. Dist: Jetstar

Mix it up

MICKY REFORM.
Tracks: / Close silence / 4 U my love / Cloud 9.
Single 12": released on Antworm, Feb'87 Dist: Stage One

Mixtures

PUSHBIKE SONG.
Single 7": released on Old Gold, Jul'82 by Old Gold Records. Dist: PRT, Counterpoint, Lightning, Jazz Music, Taylors

Mizarolli,John

GRANNY DID IT/MAKE UP AND LIVE.
Single 7": released on Carrere, Apr'83 by Carrere Records(UK). Dist: PRT, Spartan

MESSAGE FROM THE 5TH STONE.
Album: released on Carrere, Sep'82 by Carrere Records(UK). Dist: PRT, Spartan

Mizelle,Cyndi

THIS COULD BE THE NIGHT.
Single 7": released on Atlantic, Mar'85 by WEA Records. Dist: WEA, Swift, Celtic Music Deleted '86.

: Single 12":

Mizell,Hank

I'M READY (Mizell,Hank and his Country Rockers).
Single 7": released on Juke Box(Re-issue), Jul'85 Dist: Wynd-Up

JUNGLE ROCK.
Cassette: released on Charly, '79 by Charly Records. Dist: Charly, Cadillac, Swift

JUNGLE ROCK/BURNING EYES.
Single 7": released on Old Gold, Jul'82 by Old Gold Records. Dist: PRT, Counterpoint, Lightning, Jazz Music, Taylors

M.J.Q.

AT THE MUSIC INN WITH SONNY ROLLINS.
Album: released on Atlantic, Nov'80 by WEA Records. Dist: WEA, Swift, Celtic Music

LESTER MEETS MILES (MJQ & Jack Teagarden All Stars).
Album: released on Unique Jazz, Nov'86 Dist: Swift, Jazz Music, Jazz Horizons, Cadillac

M.Karlin & A.Williamson

TAILORS OF PONZANCE.
Album: released on Amberlee, '71 by Amberlee Records. Dist: Taylors

Mladen Franko..

PIANO ON THE ROAD (Mladen Franko Group).
Album: released on Intersound, Nov'87 by Intersound Records. Dist: Jazz Music

M + M

BLACK STATIONS.
Single (7"): released on RCA, Jul'84 by RCA Records. Dist: RCA, Roots, Swift, Wellard, Chris, I & B, Solomon & Peres Distribution

Single (7"): released on RCA, Jul'84 by RCA Records. Dist: RCA, Roots, Swift, Wellard, Chris, I & B, Solomon & Peres Distribution

COOLING THE MEDIUM.
Single (7"): released on RCA, Sep'84 by RCA Records. Dist: RCA, Roots, Swift, Wellard, Chris, I & B, Solomon & Peres Distribution

Single (12"): released on RCA, Sep'84 by RCA Records. Dist: RCA, Roots, Swift, Wellard, Chris, I & B, Solomon & Peres Distribution

MYSTERY WALK.
Album: released on RCA, Aug'84 by RCA Records. Dist: RCA, Roots, Swift, Wellard, Chris, I & B, Solomon & Peres Distribution

Cassette: released on RCA, Aug'84 by RCA Records. Dist: RCA, Roots, Swift, Wellard, Chris, I & B, Solomon & Peres Distribution

SCHOOL RAP (M + M The lady rappers).
Tracks: / Achool rap / (Not really a school fan).
Single (7"): released on Carrere, Oct'86 by Carrere Records. Dist: PRT, Spartan

Single (12"): released on Carrere, Oct'86 by Carrere Records. Dist: PRT, Spartan

SONG IN MY HEART.
Tracks: / Song in my heart / Riverine.
Single (7"): released on RCA, Oct'86 by RCA Records. Dist: RCA, Roots, Swift, Wellard, Chris, I & B, Solomon & Peres Distribution

Single (12"): released on RCA, Oct'86 by RCA Records. Dist: RCA, Roots, Swift, Wellard, Chris, I & B, Solomon & Peres Distribution

MMC

IT'S OUR THING(LET'S GET IT).
Tracks: / It's our thing(let's get it).
Single 7": released on After Sunset Music, Oct'87 by After Sunset Music Promotions. Dist: After Sunset Music Promotions

Mnemonists

BELLOWING ROOM.
Album: released on Recommended, Jun'87 by Recommended Records. Dist: Recommended, Impetus, Rough Trade

Mob

CRYING AGAIN.
Tracks: / Crying again / Youth / No doves / Gates of hell / What's going on.
Single 12": released on All The Madmen, Oct'86 by All The Madmen Records. Dist: Rough Trade, Cartel

LIVE AT LMC (Mob/Apostles).
Cassette: released on Cause For Concern, Nov'84 Dist: Cartel, Red Rhino, Fast Forward, Probe, Revolver

Album: released on Cause For Concern, Oct'87 Dist: Cartel, Red Rhino, Fast Forward, Probe, Revolver

NO DOVES FLY HERE/I HEAR YOU LAUGHING.
Single 7": released on Crass, Apr'82 by Exitstencil Music. Dist: Southern Record

Mobiles

AMOUR AMOUR/SKELETON DANCE.
Single 7": released on Rialto, Mar'82 by Rialto Records. Dist: Pinnacle

BUILD ME UP BUTTERCUP.
Single 7": released on Rialto, Mar'83 by Rialto Records. Dist: Pinnacle

DROWNING IN BERLIN.
Single 7": released on Rialto, Nov'81 by Rialto Records. Dist: Pinnacle

LOST WITHOUT YOUR LOVE.
Single 7": released on Panther, Oct'84 by MCA Records. Dist: CBS

Single 12": released on Panther, Oct'84 by MCA Records. Dist: CBS

PARTNERS IN CRIME/SNOW MAN.
Single 7": released on Rialto, Sep'82 by Rialto Records. Dist: Pinnacle

YOU'RE NOT ALONE/STRUTH.
Single 7": released on Rialto, Oct'82 by Rialto Records. Dist: Pinnacle

Mobley, Hank

ANOTHER WALKOUT.
Cassette: released on Blue Note, Sep'87 by EMI Records(UK). Dist: EMI*

ANOTHER WORKOUT.
Album: released on Blue Note, Sep'85 by EMI Records(UK). Dist: EMI*

Cassette: released on Blue Note, Sep'87 by EMI Records(UK). Dist: EMI*. Estim retail price in Sep'87 was £5.99.

DIPPIN'.
Tracks: / Dip, The / Recado bossa nova / Break through, The / Vamp, The / I see your face before me / Ballin.
Compact disc: released on Blue Note, Jun'87 by EMI Records(UK). Dist: EMI*

FAR AWAY LANDS.
Album: released on Blue Note, Apr'85 by EMI Records(UK). Dist: EMI*

HANK MOBLEY QUINTET, THE.
Tracks: / Funk in deep freeze / Funk in deep freeze (alternate take) / Wham and they're off / Wham and they're off (alternate take) / Fin de l'affaire / Startin' from scratch / Stella-wise / Bass on balls.
Compact disc: released on Blue Note, Aug'87 by EMI Records(UK). Dist: EMI*

HIGH VOLTAGE.
Tracks: / High voltage / Two and one / No more goodbyes / Advance notice / Bossa deluxe / Flirty gerty.
Notes: Bolstering hisusual quintet format with a third horn,in this case Jackie McLean Mobley adds new colours and flavours to his writing and ensamble sound.TrumpeterBlue Mitchell Completes the front line.Aside from the funky title tune,there aresuch varied fare as the soulful 'Bossa Deluxe' and the beautiful ballad 'No moregoodbyes'.
Album: released on Blue Note, Dec'85 by EMI Records(UK). Dist: EMI*

MONDAY NIGHT AT BIRDLAND.
Album: released on Vogue(France), Mar'80 Dist: Discovery, Jazz Music, Swift

ROLL CALL.
Tracks: / Roll call / My groove your move / Take your pick / Baptist beat, A / Baptist beat, A (alternate take) / More I see you, The / Breakdown, The.
Compact disc: released on Blue Note, Aug'87 by EMI Records(UK). Dist: EMI*

SOUL STATION.
Tracks: / Remember / This I dig of you / Dig dis / Split feelin's / Soul station / If I should lose you.
Notes: Produced by Alfred Lion
Compact disc: released on Manhattan, May'87 by EMI Records(UK). Dist: EMI

Album: released on Blue Note, Oct'84 by EMI Records(UK). Dist: EMI* Deleted '86.

STRAIGHT NO FILTER.
Tracks: / Straight no filter / Chain reaction / Soft impression / Third time around / Hanks waltz / Feelin's good (The).
Notes: Composed by Hank Mobley.Produced by CBS U Catalog Inc./ASCAP.Original session produced by Alfred Lion.Produced for release by Michael Cuscana.
Album: released on Manhattan, Nov'86 by EMI Records(UK). Dist: EMI

WORK OUT.
Album: released on Blue Note (USA Import), Sep'84

Moby Dick

MOBY DICK Melville,Herman (Kennedy, George).
Notes: Herman Melville's Moby Dick is one of the great American classic novels. Few authors have created one mythological character, but Melville's triumph is to have created two in one novel: Captain Ahab, the hunter and Moby Dick, the hunted. Through his narrator Ishmael we experienced a story both panoramic in

AXIS

MUSIC MASTER LABELS LIST 88

Moby Dick (continued)

scale and intimate in its study of one man's obsession. This epic adventure and psychological drama read by George Kennedy weaves an inevitable course to wards a final tragic confrontation between man and nature.
Cassette: released on Listen For Pleasure, Jul'86 Dist: EMI

WHEN THE TIME COMES.
Tracks: / When the time comes / All enough now
Single 7": released on Red House, Oct'86

Moby Grape
20 GRANITE CREEK.
LP: released on Edsel, Mar'86 by Demon Records. Dist: Celtic Music, Pinnacle, Jazz Music

Cass: released on Edsel, Mar'86 by Demon Records. Dist: Celtic Music, Pinnacle, Jazz Music

LIVE GRAPE.
LP: released on Line, Jun'87 by Line Records. Dist: Celtic Music, Rough Trade, Cartel

MOBY GRAPE.
LP: released on Edsel, Sep'84 by Demon Records. Dist: Celtic Music, Pinnacle, Jazz Music

MURDER IN MY HEART.
LP: released on Demon, Feb'86 by Demon Records. Dist: Celtic Music, Pinnacle, Jazz Music

Mock Turtles
POMONA.
Single 12": released on Imaginary, Jun'87 by Imaginary Records. Dist: Fast Forward, Cartel

Mockers
YOU'RE A MOCKER.
Single 7": released on Dead Dog, Feb'84 by Dead Dog Records. Dist: PRT

M.O.D.
U.S.A. FOR M.O.D..
LP: released on Caroline(USA), Sep'87 by Pinnacle

CD: released on Caroline(USA), Oct'87 by Pinnacle

U.S.A. OR M.O.D..
LP: released on Noise International, Sep'87 Dist: Revolver, Cartel

Model 500
SOUND OF STEREO.
Single 12": released on Metroplex(USA), Nov'87 Dist: Pinnacle

Models
OUT OF MIND OUT OF SIGHT.
Tracks: / Out of mind out of sight / Big on love / Ringing like a bell / Stormy tonight / These blues / Cold fever / Sooner in heaven / Seeing is believing / Barbados / King of kings / Out of mind out of sight / Down in the garden / Seeing is
LP: released on Geffen, Mar'86 by Geffen Records. Dist: WEA

Cass: released on Geffen, Mar'86 by Geffen Records. Dist: WEA

Single 7": released on Geffen, Mar'86 by Geffen Records. Dist: WEA

Single 12": released on Geffen, Mar'86 by Geffen Records. Dist: WEA

Moderates
EMILE.
Single 7": released on Hyped, Feb'82 Dist: Spartan

YES TO THE NEUTRON BOMB.
Single 7": released on Hyped, Apr'81 Dist: Spartan

Modern Art
DIMENSION OF NOISE.
Cass: released on Color Disc, Feb'85 by Color Disc & Tapes. Dist: Revolver, Cartel

DREAMS TO LIVE.
Single 7": released on Color Disc, Feb'85 by Color Disc & Tapes. Dist: Revolver, Cartel

STEREOLAND.
LP: released on Color Disc, Aug'87 by Color Disc & Tapes. Dist: Revolver, Cartel

Modern English
AFTER THE SNOW.
LP: released on 4AD, May'82 by 4AD Records. Dist: Rough Trade

Cass: released on 4AD, Sep'82 by 4AD Records. Dist: Rough Trade

BREAKING AWAY.
Single 7": released on 4AD, Apr'84 by 4AD Records. Dist: Rough Trade

Single 12": released on 4AD, Apr'84 by 4AD Records. Dist: Rough Trade

CHAPTER 12.
Single 7": released on 4AD, Jan'84 by 4AD Records. Dist: Rough Trade

Single 12": released on 4AD, Jan'84 by 4AD Records. Dist: Rough Trade

GATHERING DUST.
Single 7": released on 4AD, Dec'80 by 4AD Records. Dist: Rough Trade

I MELT WITH YOU.
Single 7": released on 4AD, Aug'82 by 4AD Records. Dist: Rough Trade

LIFE IN THE GLADHOUSE.
Single 7": released on 4AD, May'82 by 4AD Records. Dist: Rough Trade

MESH AND LACE.
LP: released on 4AD, '81 by 4AD Records. Dist: Rough Trade

MODERN ENGLISH.
Single 12": released on 4AD, Jun'83 by 4AD Records. Dist: Rough Trade **Media Note:** Four-track EP

RICCO CHET DAYS.
LP: released on 4AD, Feb'84 by 4AD Records. Dist: Rough Trade

Cass: released on 4AD, Feb'84 by 4AD Records. Dist: Rough Trade

SMILES AND LAUGHTER.
Single 7": released on 4AD, Aug'81 by 4AD Records. Dist: Rough Trade

SOMEONE'S CALLING.
Single 7": released on 4AD, Sep'83 by 4AD Records. Dist: Rough Trade

Single 12": released on 4AD, Sep'83 by 4AD Records. Dist: Rough Trade

---

STOP START.
Tracks: / Border, The / Ink and paper / Night train / I don't know the answer / Love breaks down / Breaking away / Greatest show, The / Love forever / Start stop - stop start
LP: released on Sire(USA), Sep'86 Dist: WEA, Pinnacle

Cass: released on Sire(USA), Sep'86 Dist: WEA, Pinnacle

Modern Eon
EUTHENICS.
Single 7": released on Inevitable, Nov'80 by Inevitable Records. Dist: Rough Trade

FICTION TALES.
LP: released on Dindisc, May'81 by Virgin Records. Dist: Virgin, EMI

Cass: released on Dindisc, May'81 by Virgin Records. Dist: Virgin, EMI

Modern heroes
MODERN HEROES Various artists (Various artists).
LP: released on TV, Sep'82

Cass: released on TV, Sep'82

Modern jazz piano album
MODERN JAZZ PIANO ALBUM.
Recording Notes: Artists include: Donald Byrd/Kenny Clarke/Max Roach/Herbie Nichols/etc... A classic double featuring legendary names recorded between 1946-1956 featuring The Be Bop Boys, Herbie Nicholls and the Kenny Clarke Quintet, to name but three
Double Album: released on Savoy Jazz, Dec'85 by RCA Records (Germany). Dist: Conifer, Discovery

Double Album: released on Savoy(France), Dec'84 Dist: Discovery

Modern Jazz Quartet
M.J.Q.

ART OF MODERN JAZZ QUARTET: AT-LANTIC YEARS.
LP: released on Atlantic, '74 by WEA Records. Dist: WEA, Swift, Celtic Music

ARTISTRY IN JAZZ Greatest hits.
CD: released on JVC/Fantasy(Japan), May'87 by Fantasy Records. Dist: Target

AT BIRDLAND: MODERN JAZZ QUARTET.
LP: released on Joker, Apr'81 Dist: Counterpoint, Cadillac, Jazz Horizons, Jazz Music, Celtic Music

AT THE OPERA HOUSE.
LP: released on Verve(USA), Oct'84 by Polydor Records. Dist: Polygram

BLUES ON BACH.
LP: released on Atlantic, Oct'74 by WEA Records. Dist: WEA, Swift, Celtic Music

COMEDY, THE.
LP: released on Atlantic, Mar'81 by WEA Records. Dist: WEA, Swift, Celtic Music

CONCORDE.
CD: released on Carrere(France), '86 by Carrere Records (France). Dist: PRT

DJANGO.
Compact disc: released on Vanguard(USA), Apr'86 Dist: IMS, Polygram

Album: released on Original Jazz Classics (USA), Jun'86 by Fantasy(USA). Dist: IMS, Polygram

---

ECHOES.
LP: released on Verve(USA), Sep'84 by Polydor Records. Dist: Polygram

Cass: released on Verve(USA), Sep'84 by Polydor Records. Dist: Polygram

LAST CONCERT, (THE).
LP: released on Atlantic, Jul'75 by WEA Records. Dist: WEA, Swift, Celtic Music

LIVE AT DONAUSCHINGEN, 1957, AND SAN REMO, 1958.
LP: released on Ingo, Feb'83 Dist: Jazz Horizons, Jazz Music, Celtic Music

LONELY WOMAN.
LP: released on Atlantic, Aug'80 by WEA Records. Dist: WEA, Swift, Celtic Music

MJQ.
LP: released on Crusader Jazz Masterworks, Apr'87 Dist: Jazz Music

Cass: released on Crusader Jazz Masterworks, Apr'87 Dist: Jazz Music

MJQ COLLECTION A Retrospective.
Tracks: / One bass hit / Queen's fancy, the / Now's the time / Django / D & E blues / Autumn in New York / Round about midnight / Delaunay's Dilemma / But not for me / Milano / La Ronde suite (piano) / La Ronde suite (bass) / La Ronde suite (vibes) / La Ronde suite (drums)
CD: released on Deja Vu, Sep'87 by Deja Vu Records. Dist: Counterpoint, Jazz Music. Estim retail price in Sep'87 was £7.99.

MODERN JAZZ QUARTET.
Tracks: / Django / Autumn in New York / Queens fancy, The / But not for me / One bass hit / Milano / Delaunay's dilemma / Nows the time / D & E blues / Round about midnight
Cass: released on Deja Vu, Nov'85 by Deja Vu Records. Dist: Counterpoint, Jazz Music

LP: released on Giants of Jazz, Sep'87 by Hasmick Promotions Ltd.. Dist: Counterpoint, Taylors, Wellard, Swift, Crusader, Jazz Music

MORE FROM THE LAST CONCERT.
LP: by WEA Records. Dist: WEA, Swift, Celtic Music

SAINT ON JAMAIS: THAT'S JAZZ, 1.
LP: released on Atlantic, Jul'76 by WEA Records. Dist: WEA, Swift, Celtic Music

SHERIFF, (THE).
LP: released on Atlantic, Oct'80 by WEA Records. Dist: WEA, Swift, Celtic Music

THREE WINDOWS.
Tracks: / Three windows / Kansas city breaks / Encounter in Cagnes / Django / Day in Dubrovnik, A (First Movement: Afternoon) / Day in Dubrovnik, A (Second Movement: Night) / Day in Dubrovnik, A (Third Movement: Morning)
LP: released on WEA, Jul'87 by WEA Records. Dist: WEA

Cass: released on WEA, Jul'87 by WEA Records. Dist: WEA

CD: released on Atlantic Jazz, Jul'87 by WEA Records. Dist: WEA

CD: released on WEA, Oct'87 by WEA Records. Dist: WEA

TOGETHER AGAIN.
LP: released on Pablo Jazz(USA), Aug'85 by Ace Records. Dist: PRT

Cass: released on Pablo Jazz(USA), Aug'85 by Ace Records. Dist: PRT

Modern Jazz Quartet (cont.)

TOPSY THIS ONE'S FOR BASIE.
Tracks: / Reunion blues / Nature boy / Topsy / D and e / Valeria / Milano / La cannet
Recording Notes: Second studio album for Pablo performances by Milt Jackson in a unique una un accompanied performance of Nature boy and John Lewis in a featured performance of a recomposed MJQ standard Milano. Also featured is a composition dedicated here to Count Basie D and D and one of the first tunes recorded by the MJQ. Personnel: Milt Jackson- vibes/ John Lewis - piano/ Percy Heathbass/ Connie Kay - drums.
LP: released on Pablo, Apr'86 by Pablo Records. Dist: Wellard, IMS, BMG, Polygram

Cass: released on Pablo, Apr'86 by Pablo Records. Dist: Wellard, IMS, BMG, Polygram

CD: released on Pablo(USA), Sep'86 by Ace Records. Dist: PRT

Modern Jazz Sextet

MODERN JAZZ SEXTET.
Album: released on Verve (USA), Nov'84 by Polydor. Dist: Polygram

Modern Jazz Society

CONCERT OF CONTEMPORARY MUSIC.
Album: released on Verve (France), Jan'85

Modern love

MODERN LOVE Various artists (Various Artists).
Album: released on K-Tel, Feb'85 by K-Tel Records. Dist: Record Merchandisers Distribution, Taylors, Terry Blood Distribution, Wynd-Up Distribution, Relay Distribution, Pickwick Distribution, Solomon & Peres Distribution, Polygram

Cassette: released on K-Tel, Feb'85 by K-Tel Records. Dist: Record Merchandisers Distribution, Taylors, Terry Blood Distribution, Wynd-Up Distribution, Relay Distribution, Pickwick Distribution, Solomon & Peres Distribution, Polygram

Modern Lovers

LIVE.
Tracks: / I'm a little airplane / Hey there little insect / egyptian reggae / I'm a little dinosaur / My little kookenhafen / south American folk song / New England / Morning of our lives, The.
Album: released on Beserkley (USA), Nov'86 by Beserkley Records. Dist: PRT

MODERN LOVERS LIVE.
Album: released on Beserkley (USA), Jan'79 by Beserkley Records. Dist: PRT

MODERN LOVERS, THE.
Tracks: / Roadrunner / Astral plane / Old world / Pablo Picasso / I'm straight / She cracked / Hospital / Someone I care about / Girl friend / Modern world.
Album: released on Beserkley (USA), Nov'86 by Beserkley Records. Dist: PRT

ORIGINAL MODERN LOVERS.
Album: released on Bomp International, Oct'81

ROCK'N'ROLL WITH THE MODERN LOVERS.
Album: released on Beserkley (USA), Jan'79 by Beserkley Records. Dist: PRT

Modern Man

CONCRETE SCHEME.
Album: released on M.A.M., Nov'80 by M.A.M. Records. Dist: T.B.C

Modern-nique

LOVE'S GONNA GET YOU.
Tracks: / Love's gonna get you / Love's gonna get you (instrumental).
Single (7"): released on 10, Sep'86 by 10 Records. Dist: Virgin, EMI

Cassette: released on 10, Sep'86 by 10 Records. Dist: Virgin, EMI

Modern rockers

MODERN ROCKERS Various artists (Various Artists).
Album: released on Warwick, Oct'82 by MSD Records. Dist: CBS

Cassette: released on Warwick, Oct'82 by MSD Records. Dist: CBS

Modern Rocketry

CUBA LIBRE.
Tracks: / Cuba libre / Homosexuality.
Single (12"): released on Greyhound, Jan'87 by Greyhound Records. Dist: PRT, Greyhound

CUBA LIBRE (REMIX).
Tracks: / Cuba libre (remix) / Homosexuality.
Notes: (Double A)
Single (12"): released on Greyhound, Nov'86

by Greyhound Records. Dist: PRT, Greyhound

HOMOSEXUALITY.
Album: released on ZYX (West Germany), Feb'86

HOMOSEXUALITY (REMIX).
Single (12"): released on ZYX (Germany), Nov'85 by ZYX Records. Dist: Greyhound

Modern rock'n'roll...

MODERN ROCK'N'ROLL AND ROCKABILLY Various artists (Various Artists).
Album: released on Ace, Nov'86 by Ace Records. Dist: Pinnacle, Swift, Hotshot, Cadillac

Modern Romance

BURN IT.
Single (7"): released on RCA, Jan'85 by RCA Records. Dist: RCA, Roots, Swift, Wellard, Chris, I & B, Solomon & Peres Distribution

Single (12"): released on RCA, Jan'85 by RCA Records. Dist: RCA, Roots, Swift, Wellard, Chris, I & B, Solomon & Peres Distribution

BY THE WAY.
Single (7"): released on WEA, Jun'82 by WEA Records. Dist: WEA

Single (12"): released on WEA, Jun'82 by WEA Records. Dist: WEA

CHERRY PINK AND APPLE BLOSSOM WHITE.
Single (7"): released on WEA, Aug'82 by WEA Records. Dist: WEA

Single (12"): released on WEA, Aug'82 by WEA Records. Dist: WEA

DON'T STOP THAT CRAZY RHYTHM.
Single (7"): released on WEA, Apr'83 by WEA Records. Dist: WEA

Single (12"): released on WEA, Apr'83 by WEA Records. Dist: WEA

Picture disc single: released on WEA, Apr'83 by WEA Records. Dist: WEA

EVERYBODY SALSA.
Single (7"): released on WEA, Jul'81 by WEA Records. Dist: WEA

HIGHLIFE.
Single (7"): released on WEA, Feb'83 by WEA Records. Dist: WEA

Single (12"): released on WEA, Feb'83 by WEA Records. Dist: WEA

MODERN ROMANCE.
Single (7"): released on WEA, Sep'80 by WEA Records. Dist: WEA

MOVE ON.
Album: released on RCA, Jan'85 by RCA Records. Dist: RCA, Roots, Swift, Wellard, Chris, I & B, Solomon & Peres Distribution

Cassette: released on RCA, Jan'85 by RCA Records. Dist: RCA, Roots, Swift, Wellard, Chris, I & B, Solomon & Peres Distribution

PARTY TONIGHT.
Album: released on Ronco, Nov'83

Cassette: released on Ronco, Nov'83

TARZAN BOY.
Single (7"): released on Carrere, Jul'85 by Carrere Records. Dist: PRT, Spartan

Single (12"): released on Carrere, Jul'85 by Carrere Records. Dist: PRT, Spartan

TONIGHT.
Single (7"): released on WEA, Mar'81 by WEA Records. Dist: WEA

Single (12"): released on WEA, Mar'81 by WEA Records. Dist: WEA

WALKING IN THE RAIN.
Single (7"): released on WEA, Jul'83 by WEA Records. Dist: WEA

Single (12"): released on WEA, Jul'83 by WEA Records. Dist: WEA Deleted '84.

Modern Soul Story

MODERN SOUL STORY Compilation recording (Various Artists).
Double Album: released on Soul Supply, Feb'87 by High Energy Records. Dist: Charly

Cassette: released on Soul Supply, Feb'87 by High Energy Records. Dist: Charly

Modern soul volume 2

MODERN SOUL VOLUME 2 (Various Artists).
Album: released on Soul Supply, 30 May'87 by High Energy Records. Dist: Charly

Modern Talk

YOU'RE MY HEART, YOU'RE MY SOUL.
Single (7"): released on Magnet, Mar'85 by Magnet Records. Dist: BMG

Single (12"): released on Magnet, Mar'85 by Magnet Records. Dist: BMG

Modern Talking

ATLANTIS IS CALLING SOS for love.
Tracks: / Atlantis is calling / You're my heart, you're my soul.
Single (7"): released on RCA, Sep'86 by RCA Records. Dist: RCA, Roots, Swift, Wellard, Chris, I & B, Solomon & Peres Distribution

Single (12"): released on RCA, Sep'86 by RCA Records. Dist: RCA, Roots, Swift, Wellard, Chris, I & B, Solomon & Peres Distribution

Picture disc single: released on RCA, Sep'86 by RCA Records. Dist: RCA, Roots, Swift, Wellard, Chris, I & B, Solomon & Peres Distribution

BROTHER LOUIE.
Tracks: / Brother Louie / Brother Louie (instrumental).
Single (7"): released on RCA, Sep'86 by RCA Records. Dist: RCA, Roots, Swift, Wellard, Chris, I & B, Solomon & Peres Distribution

Single (12"): released on RCA, Sep'86 by RCA Records. Dist: RCA, Roots, Swift, Wellard, Chris, I & B, Solomon & Peres Distribution

GIVE ME PEACE ON EARTH.
Tracks: / Give me peace on Earth / Cheri cheri lady / Just we too Mona Lisa.
Single (7"): released on RCA, Nov'86 by RCA Records. Dist: RCA, Roots, Swift, Wellard, Chris, I & B, Solomon & Peres Distribution

Single (12"): released on RCA, Nov'86 by RCA Records. Dist: RCA, Roots, Swift, Wellard, Chris, I & B, Solomon & Peres Distribution

READY FOR ROMANCE.
Tracks: / Brother Louie / Just we two (Mona Lisa) / Lady Lai / Doctor for my heart / Save me,don't break me / Cheri cheri lady / Atlantis is calling(SOS for love) / Keep love alive / Hey you / Angie's heart / Only love can break my heart / You're my heart, you're my soul.
Compact disc: released on RCA, '86 by RCA Records. Dist: RCA, Roots, Swift, Wellard, Chris, I & B, Solomon & Peres Distribution

Album: released on RCA, Oct'86 by RCA Records. Dist: RCA, Roots, Swift, Wellard, Chris, I & B, Solomon & Peres Distribution

Cassette: released on RCA, Oct'86 by RCA Records. Dist: RCA, Roots, Swift, Wellard, Chris, I & B, Solomon & Peres Distribution

YOU CAN WIN IF YOU WANT.
Single (7"): released on Magnet, Sep'85 by Magnet Records. Dist: BMG

Single (12"): released on Magnet, Sep'85 by Magnet Records. Dist: BMG

Modern Times

MODERB TIMES Original film soundtrack - Charlie Chaplin.

MODERN TIMES Various Artists (Various Artists).

MODERN TIMES Various Artists (Various Artists).
Album: released on Soul Supply, Oct'85 by High Energy Records. Dist: Charly

MODERN TIMES Original film soundtrack-Charlie Chaplin.
Album: released on EMI (Germany), '83 by EMI Records. Dist: Conifer

Modesty

NOEL.
Single (7"): released on FX, Dec'81 Dist: Spartan

Mo-Dettes

DARK PARK CREEPING.
Single (7"):

PAINT IT BLACK.
Single (7"):

STORY SO FAR, THE.
Album: released on Deram, Nov'80 by Decca Records. Dist: Polygram

Cassette: released on Deram, Oct'80 by Decca Records. Dist: Polygram

TONIGHT.
Single (7"): released on Deram, Jun'81 by Decca Records. Dist: Polygram

WHITE MICE.
Single (7"): released on Human, Jul'81 Dist: Roots, Stage One

Mods mayday 79

MODS MAYDAY 79 Various artists (Vari-

ous Artists).
Tracks: / Time for action / Let your heart dance / Don't throw your life away / Hanging in the balance / Tonight's the night / Let me be the one / B-a-b-y baby love / Midnight to six / Broadway show / All night / Love only me / Walking down the king's road / Live without her love / I'm not free / End of the night.
Album: released on Dojo, Apr'86 by Castle Communications Records. Dist: Cartel

Moebius

BLUE MOON.
Album: released on Sky (Germany), Aug'86

Moebius & Beerbohm

DOUBLE CUT.
Album: released on Sky (Germany), Sep'84

Moebius, Plank and Neumer

ZERO SET.
Album: released on Sky (Germany), Mar'84

Moerlen, Pierre

TIME IS THE KEY.
Album: released on Arista, Oct'79 by Arista Records. Dist: RCA

Moev

ALIBIS.
Single (12"): released on Ink, Sep'85 by Red Flame. Dist: Rough Trade, Cartel, Pinnacle

Moffat, Stuart

OCTOBER ISLAND.
Album: released on Dambuster, Aug'85 by Dambuster Records. Dist: Projection, Celtic Music, Roots

Moffitt, Matt

AS LITTLE AS A LOOK.
Tracks: Heathen kind / By as little as a look / Miss this night / Thursday / Overland / All that stuff / Save your worry / B.b's / Fever pitch / Ocean chimes / Light me up.
Album: released on CBS, Aug'86 by CBS Records. Dist: CBS

Cassette: released on CBS, Aug'86 by CBS Records. Dist: CBS

MISS THIS TONIGHT.
Tracks: / Miss this tonight / Save your worry.
Single (7"): released on CBS, Jun'86 by CBS Records. Dist: CBS

Single (12"): released on CBS, Sep'86 by CBS Records. Dist: CBS

Moffo, Anna

SONG FOR YOU, A.
Notes: Operetta arias.
Compact disc: released on Bridge, Apr'87 Dist: CD Centre Distribution, Pinnacle, Target

Mogodons

ZUVENBIE (Mongodons).

Single (7"): released on TD, Jul'82

Mohawks

CHAMP, THE.
Single (7"): released on Pama, Jan'87 by Pama Records. Dist: Pama, Enterprise, Jetstar

Single (12"): released on Pama, Jan'87 by Pama Records. Dist: Pama, Enterprise, Jetstar

Moho Pack

LET US TOUCH.
Tracks: / Neve stellung fun / Warpath.
Notes: *=Extra track on 12" only
Single (7"): released on Fun After All, Feb'87 Dist: Pinnacle

Moja

MEK-WE-ROCK (2 parts).
Single (7"): released on Ethnic, Jun'83 Dist: Kingdom

Moja Nya

UP RISE.
Single (12"): released on Streetwise, Jun'84 Dist: Greyhound

Mojo Jazzin Five

MOJO JAZZIN FIVE.
Album: released on Stomp Off, Jul'86 by Stomp Off Records. Dist: Jazz Music Distribution

Mojos

EVERYTHING'S ALLRIGHT.
Single (7"): released on Decca, Apr'82 by Decca Records. Dist: Polygram

WORKING.

Album: released on Edsel, Dec'82 by Demon Records. Dist: Pinnacle, Jazz Music, Projection

Mojos, Dee

IN THE SOOP.
Album: released on RVC, Jun'84

Moldgreen Junior Folk

LAST SONGS TOGETHER.
Album: released on Look, Dec'79 Dist: R. Smith & Co. Records, H.R. Taylor

Mole, Miff

MIFF MOLE'S MOLERS- 1927.
Tracks: / Alexander's ragtime band / Some sweet day / Hurricane / Davenport blues / Hot time in the old town tonight, A / Dark town strutters ball (The) / After you've gone / I ain't got nobody / One sweet letter from you / Fifty million frenchmen can't be wrong / Imagination / Feelin no pain / Original dixieland one step / My gal Sal / Honolulu blues / New twister (The).
Notes: This re-issue from one of the finest pioneers of hot jazz contains a good selection of the music which was urgently shipped to England in 1927 and released by Parlophone for the eager jazz enthusiasts. Miff was more or less responsible for the transition of the trombone's placing from a back instrument to one of the solo importance, with his virtuosity, creativity and range. Four of the tracks feature the inimitable Sophie Tucker three tug at the heart strings and one is a contemporary, wry social comment. The remainder are all by the same line up featuring Charles Elsworth Russell (known as pee wee).
Album: released on EMI Retrospect, Jul'86 by EMI Records. Dist: EMI

Cassette: released on EMI Retrospect, Jul'86 by EMI Records. Dist: EMI

MIFF MOLE'S MOLERS(1928-30) (Mole, Miff, Molers).
Album: released on Swaggie (Australia), Jan'83

MIFF MOLE'S MOLERS(1927) (Mole, Miff, Molers).
Album: released on Swaggie (Australia), Jan'83

RED & MIFF 1926-31 (Mole, Miff & Red Nichols).
Album: released on Saville, Jun'82 by Conifer Records. Dist: Conifer

Molinari, John

ACCORDION CONCERT.
Album: released on ARC (Accordion Records), '84 Dist: Accordion Record Club

ACCORDION SOLOS NO.5.
Album: released on ARC (Accordion Records), '84 Dist: Accordion Record Club

ACCORDION VARIETY CONCERT.
Album: released on ARC (Accordion Records), '84 Dist: Accordion Record Club

CLASSIC FAVOURITES.
Album: released on ARC (Accordion Records), '84 Dist: Accordion Record Club

Molineux, john

DOUCE AMERE.
Album: released on AMR, Sep'79

Molloy, Matt

CONTENTMENT IS WEALTH (Molloy, Matt & Sean Keane).
Album: released on WEA Ireland, Mar'87 by WEA Records. Dist: Celtic Distributions, Projection, I & B

Cassette: released on WEA Ireland, Mar'87 by WEA Records. Dist: Celtic Distributions, Projection, I & B

MATT MOLLOY.
Album: released on Mulligan, Sep'79 by Topic Records. Dist: Roots Distribution, Jazz Music Distribution, JSU Distribution, I & B Distribution, Projection Distribution, Wynd-Up Distribution, Celtic Distributions

MOLLOY, BRADY, PEOPLES (Molloy, Matt/ Paul Brady/ Tommy Peoples).
Tracks: / Mat peoples / Creel of turf (The).
Album: released on Mulligan (Ireland), Aug'86 by Topic Records. Dist: Roots Distribution, Jazz Music Distribution, JSU Distribution, I & B Distribution, Projection Distribution, Wynd-Up Distribution, Celtic Distributions

Cassette: released on Mulligan (Ireland), Aug'86 by Topic Records. Dist: Roots Distribution, Jazz Music Distribution, JSU Distribution, I & B Distribution, Projection Distribution, Wynd-Up Distribution, Celtic Distributions

STONY STEPS.
Album: released on Claddagh, Jul'87 by Claddagh Records. Dist: I & B, Record Services Distribution (Ireland), Roots, Topic, Impetus, Projection, CM

Molly Hatchet

BEATING THE ODDS.
Tracks: / Beating the odds / Double talker / Rambler (The) / Sailor / Dead and gone / Few and far between / Penthouse pauper / Get her back / Poison pen.
Album: released on Prix D'Ami (France), Sep'86

Cassette: released on Prix D'Ami (France), Sep'86

Album: released on Epic, Oct'80 by CBS Records. Dist: CBS

Cassette: released on Epic, Oct'80 by CBS Records. Dist: CBS

DEED IS DONE, THE.
Album: released on Epic, Jan'85 by CBS Records. Dist: CBS

Cassette: released on Epic, Jan'85 by CBS Records. Dist: CBS

DOUBLE TROUBLE LIVE.
Tracks: / Whisky man / Bounter hunter / Gator country / Flirtin with disaster / Stone in your heart / Satisfied man / Bloody reunion / Boogie no more / Freebird / Walk on the side of the angels / Walk with you / Dreams I'll never see / Edge of sundown / Fall of the peacemakers / Beatin the odds.
Double Album: released on Epic, Jan'86 by CBS Records. Dist: CBS

Double cassette: released on Epic, Jan'86 by CBS Records. Dist: CBS

NO GUTS NO GLORY.
Tracks: / What does it matter / Ain't even close / Sweet dixie / Fall of the peacemakers / what's ig gonna take / Kinda like love / Under the gun / On the prowl / Both sides.
Album: released on Epic, Feb'86 by CBS Records. Dist: CBS

Cassette: released on Epic, Feb'86 by CBS Records. Dist: CBS

Album: released on Epic, Mar'83 by CBS Records. Dist: CBS

Cassette: released on Epic, Mar'83 by CBS Records. Dist: CBS

SATISFIED MAN.
Single (7"): released on Epic, Jan'85 by CBS Records. Dist: CBS

Single (12"): released on Epic, Jan'85 by CBS Records. Dist: CBS

TAKE NO PRISONERS.
Album: released on Epic, Dec'81 by CBS Records. Dist: CBS

Cassette: released on Epic, Dec'81 by CBS Records. Dist: CBS

Moloney, Chris

GALTEE SONG.
Single (7"): released on Disc International, Aug'82

Moloney, Mick

AH-SURLEY (see Cahill, Mick) (Moloney, Mick and Eddie Cahill).

MICK MOLONEY FEATURING....
Album: released on Shanachie, Sep'79 Dist: Sterns/Triple Earth Distribution, Roots

Moloney, Peter

LOAD OF MOLONEY, A.
Album: released on Big Ben, Apr'81 by Big Ben Records. Dist: Spartan, Taylor, H.R.

Molzen, Gerty

WALK ON THE WILD SIDE.
Single (7"): released on 10, Apr'85 by 10 Records. Dist: Virgin, EMI

Moment

1,2 THEY FLY.
Single (7"): released on Diamond, Sep'85 by Revolver Records. Dist: Cartel

IN THIS TOWN.
Single (7"): released on Diamond, Apr'85 by Revolver Records. Dist: Cartel

WORK GETS DONE (THE).
Album: released on Rome, May'86 Dist: Backs, Cartel Distribution

Moments

GIRLS.
Single (7"): released on Flashback, Jan'83 by Flashback Records/PRT Records. Dist: Mainline, PRT

MOMENTS Various artists (Various Artists).
Album: released on Pye International, Nov'79

Momus

CIRCUS MAXIMUS.
Tracks: / Lucky liks St.Sebastian / Lesson of sodom (The) / John the baptist Jones / King Solomon's song and mine / Little lord obedience / Day the circus came to town (The) / Rape of Lucretia (The) / Paper wraps rock / Rules of the game of quoits.
Album: released on EL, Jan'86 by El Records. Dist: Rough Trade, Cartel, Pinnacle

MURDERERS THE HOPE OF WOMEN.
Tracks: / Murderers,the hope of women.
Single (12"): released on Creation, Mar'87 Dist: Rough Trade, Cartel

NICKY.
Tracks: / Nicky / Don't leave / See a friend in tears.
Single (12"): released on EL, Jul'86 by El Records. Dist: Rough Trade, Cartel, Pinnacle

Monae, Tia

DON'T KEEP ME WAITING (DUB MIX).
Single (7"): by Carrere Records. Dist: PRT, Spartan

Single (12"): by Carrere Records. Dist: PRT, Spartan

Mona Lisa

MONA LISA Original film soundtrack (Various Artists).
Tracks: / When I fall in love / Introduction (When I fall in love) / Story / George / Elevator attack and after / Slap your back / Mona Lisa / Kings Cross/follow Anderson / Pimp / Simone's story / Daughters of Babylon / Love duet from Madame Butterfly & Puccini.
Notes: Original score compossed and arranged by Michael Kamen. Recorded and mixed by Andy Jackson. Track (1) with orchestra conducted by Gordon Jenkins. Track (7) produced by Brian Harris/Mark Jolly. Track (14) produced by Jimmy Lindsay. Album co-ordination and compilation Simon Heyworth and Nigel Steele-Davies. (P)1986 Original Sound recordings made by Filmtrax PLC under exclusive licence to EMI Records except* (P) 1957 original sound recording made by Capitol Records Inc., ** (P) original sound recording made by Capitol Records Inc., + (P) 1958 original sound recording made by the Decca Records Co. Ltd.,***(P) 1986 City Beat Records. This comilation (P) 1986 EMI Records Ltd.
Album: released on Columbia, Sep'86 by EMI Records. Dist: EMI

Cassette: released on Columbia, Sep'86 by EMI Records. Dist: EMI

Moncur, Gracham III

EVOLUTION.
Tracks: / Air rade / Evolution / Coaster (The) / Monk in wonderland.
Notes: Grachan Moncur,Bobby Hutcherson and Tony Williams wre all brought to Blue Note as members of Jackie McLean's band. They all became driving forces in the jazz and Blue Note leaders in their own right. On trombonist-composer Grachan Moncursdebut album,he, McLean,Hutcherson and Williamsare joined by Lee Morgan and Bob Cranshaw. Moncur's marvellously appealing form of avant garde is best illustatedby his humorous, soulful melodies, such as The Coaster and Mork in wonderland.
Album: released on Blue Note, Dec'85 by EMI Records. Dist: EMI

NEW AFRICA.
Album: released on Affinity, Sep'79 by Charly Records. Dist: Charly, Cadillac

Mondo Kane

EVERLASTING LOVE.
Tracks: / Everlasting love / Everlasting love (instrumental).
Single (7"): released on Lisson, Nov'86 Dist: PRT

Single (12"): released on Lisson, Nov'86 Dist: PRT

NEW YORK AFTERNOON.
Tracks: / New York afternoon / Manhattan morning.
Single (7"): released on Lisson, Aug'86 Dist: PRT

Single (12"): released on Lisson, Aug'86 Dist: PRT

Mondo Rock

BOOM BABY BOOM.
Album: released on Polydor, Aug'87 by Polydor Records. Dist: Polygram, Polydor

Cassette: released on Polydor, Aug'87 by Polydor Records. Dist: Polygram, Polydor

Compact disc: released on Polydor, Aug'87 by Polydor Records. Dist: Polygram, Polydor

MODERN BOP, THE (New York remix).
Single (7"): released on Polydor, Jul'85 by Polydor Records. Dist: Polygram, Polydor

Single (12"): released on Polydor, Jul'85 by Polydor Records. Dist: Polygram, Polydor

PRIMITIVE LOVE RITES.
Tracks: / Primitive love rites / Under light.
Single (7"): released on Polydor, Jul'87 by Polydor Records. Dist: Polygram, Polydor

Single (12"): released on Polydor, Jul'87 by Polydor Records. Dist: Polygram, Polydor

Monese, Valerie

THIS IS VALERIE MONESE.
Album: released on Music For Pleasure (Holland), Jul'82 by EMI Records. Dist: EMI

Cassette: released on Music For Pleasure (Holland), Jul'82 by EMI Records. Dist: EMI

Money

TRUST ME.
Album: released on Heavy Metal America, Jun'84 by FM-Revolver Records. Dist: EMI

Cassette: released on Heavy Metal America, Jun'84 by FM-Revolver Records. Dist: EMI

Money Drums

HOLY MOLY.
Album: released on Fundamental, May'85 by Fundamental Records. Dist: Red Rhino, Cartel

Money, Eddie

CAN'T HOLD BACK.
Tracks: / Take me home tonight (be my baby) / One love / I wanna go back / Endless nights / One chance / We should be sleeping / Bring on the rain / I can't hold back / Stranger in a strange land / Calm before the storm.
Album: released on CBS, Nov'86 by CBS Records. Dist: CBS

Cassette: released on CBS, Nov'86 by CBS Records. Dist: CBS

Compact disc: released on CBS, May'87 by CBS Records. Dist: CBS

I WANNA GO BACK.
Tracks: / I wanna go back / Broken down Chevy.
Single (7"): released on CBS, Mar'87 by CBS Records. Dist: CBS

Single (12"): released on CBS, Mar'87 by CBS Records. Dist: CBS

PLAYING FOR KEEPS.
Album: released on CBS, Sep'80 by CBS Records. Dist: CBS

TAKE ME HOME TONIGHT.
Tracks: / Take me home tonight / Be my baby / Calm before the storm / Take me home tonight / Calm before the storm / Baby hold on.
Single (7"): released on CBS, Jan'87 by CBS Records. Dist: CBS

Single (12"): released on CBS, Nov'86 by CBS Records. Dist: CBS

WHERE'S THE PARTY?.
Album: released on CBS, Feb'84 by CBS Records. Dist: CBS

Cassette: released on CBS, Feb'84 by CBS Records. Dist: CBS

Money to Burn

MONEY TO BURN Various artists (Various Artists).
Album: released on President, Nov'85 by President Records. Dist: Taylors, Spartan

Cassette: released on President, Nov'85 by President Records. Dist: Taylors, Spartan

Money, Zoot

MR. MONEY.
Album: released on Magic Moon, Oct'80 Dist: Pinnacle

TWO OF US.
Single (7"): released on Magic Moon, Jun'82 Dist: Pinnacle

YOUR FEET'S TOO BIG.
Single (7"): released on Magic Moon, Sep'80 Dist: Pinnacle

ZOOT MONEY'S BIG ROLL BAND.
Album: released on Polydor, Nov'84 by Polydor Records. Dist: Polygram, Polydor

Cassette: released on Polydor, Nov'84 by Polydor Records. Dist: Polygram, Polydor

Monfungo

EL SALVADOR PLUS 2 (EP).
Single (7"): released on Rough Trade, Aug'82 by Rough Trade Records. Dist: Rough Trade Distribution, Cartel Distribution

Monger, Eileen

ENCHANTED VALLEY, THE (Monger, Eileen with Jim Couza).
Album: released on Saydisc, Aug'83 by Sayd-

isc Records. Dist: Essex, Harmonia Mundi, Roots, H.R. Taylor, Jazz Music, Swift, Projection, Gamut

Cassette: released on Saydisc, Aug'83 by Saydisc Records. Dist: Essex, Harmonia Mundi, Roots, H.R. Taylor, Jazz Music, Swift, Projection, Gamut

LILTING BANSHEE (THE).
Tracks: / King of the fairies / Lilting Banshee,O south wind (The) / Great high wind,The wild geese,Bonny Portmore / Ivy leaf,Limericks lamentation.(the) / Give me your hand,Niel Gow's lament / Farewell to Craigie Dhu,Fingals Cave.
Notes: Celtic harp played by Eileen Monger with Bodhran,Uilleann Pipes,Whistles & Dulcimer.
A Digital recording.
Compact disc: released on Saydisc, Mar'87 by Saydisc Records. Dist: Essex, Harmonia Mundi, Roots, H.R. Taylor, Jazz Music, Swift, Projection, Gamut

Mongolia

INSTRUMENTAL MUSIC.
Album: released on Tangent, Apr'81 Dist: Roots Distribution, Lugtons Distributors, Taylors, JSU Distribution, Spartan Distribution

VOCAL MUSIC.
Album: released on Tangent, Apr'81 Dist: Roots Distribution, Lugtons Distributors, Taylors, JSU Distribution, Spartan Distribution

Mongolie

MONGOLIE Various Artists (Various Artists).
Compact disc: by Sterns Records. Dist: Sterns/Triple Earth Distribution

Monica

HE'S THE ONE.
Single (12"): released on Rosie, May'82 by Rosie Records. Dist: PRT Distribution

Monick, Susie

MELTING POTS.
Album: released on Adelphi, May'81 by Adelphi Records. Dist: Jetstar

Monk & Bird

MONK & BIRD (A tribute to Monk & Bird).
Album: released on Tomato, Mar'79

Monkees

20 GOLDEN GREATS.
Album: released on Ronco, Oct'82

Cassette: released on Ronco, Oct'82

BEST OF THE MONKEES, (THE).
Album: released on MFP, Aug'81 by EMI Records. Dist: EMI

Cassette: released on MFP, Aug'81 by EMI Records. Dist: EMI

BIRDS, BEES AND THE MONKEES.
Album: released on Rhino (USA), Jan'86 by Rhino Records (USA).

DAYDREAM BELIEVER.
Single (7"): released on Old Gold, Jul'82 by Old Gold Records. Dist: Lightning, Jazz Music, Spartan, Counterpoint

HEAD Original soundtrack.
Album: released on Rhino (USA), Jan'86 by Rhino Records (USA).

I'M A BELIEVER.
Single (7"): released on Arista, Aug'82 by Arista Records. Dist: RCA

Single (7"): released on Old Gold, Jul'82 by Old Gold Records. Dist: Lightning, Jazz Music, Spartan, Counterpoint

INSTANT REPLAY.
Album: released on Rhino (USA), Jan'86 by Rhino Records (USA).

MONKEE FLIPS.
Album: released on Rhino (USA), Jul'84 by Rhino Records (USA).

MONKEES EP, (THE).
Single (7"): released on Arista, Feb'80 by Arista Records. Dist: RCA

MONKEES EP, VOL 2, (THE).
Single (7"): released on Arista, Jun'81 by Arista Records. Dist: RCA

MONKEES' GREATEST HITS, (THE).
Album: released on Platinum, Nov'84 by Geoffs Records.

Cassette: released on Platinum, Nov'84 by Geoffs Records.

MONKEES, (THE).
Double Album: released on Arista, Oct'81 by Arista Records. Dist: RCA

Double cassette: released on Arista, Oct'81 by Arista Records. Dist: RCA

PRESENT.
Album: released on Rhino (USA), Jan'86 by Rhino Records (USA).

SIX TRACK HITS.
Single (7"): released on Scoop 33, Mar'84 by Pickwick Records. Dist: H.R. Taylor

Cassette: released on Scoop 33, Mar'84 by Pickwick Records. Dist: H.R. Taylor

THAT WAS THEN, THIS IS NOW.
Tracks: / That was then, this is now / Monkees (theme from) / Pleasant valley sunday / Last train to Clarksville.
Single (7"): released on Arista, Sep'86 by Arista Records. Dist: RCA

Single (12"): released on Arista, Sep'86 by Arista Records. Dist: RCA

THEN & NOW-THE BEST OF THE MONKEES.
Tracks: / Then and now / Tripwire / Monkees, The (Theme from) / Last train to Clarksville / Take a giant step / I'm a believer / Stepping stone, (I'm not your) / Little bit me, a little bit you, A / Anytime, anyplace, anywhere / That was then, this is now / Girl I knew somewhere, The / Pleasant Valley Sunday / What am I doing hangin' round / Daydream believer / Valleri / Kicks.
Album: released on Arista, Oct'86 by Arista Records. Dist: RCA

Cassette: released on Arista, Oct'86 by Arista Records. Dist: RCA

Compact disc: released on Arista, Nov'86 by Arista Records. Dist: RCA

THEN AND NOW
Single (12"): released on Skysaw, Jun'87 by Skysaw Records. Dist: Red Rhino, Cartel

Monkey

MONKEY Music from the BBC television series.
Album: released on BBC, Apr'80 by BBC Records & Tapes. Dist: EMI, PRT, Pye

Monkey businesss

MONKEY BUSINESSS Various artists (Various Artists).
Album: released on Trojan, '83 by Trojan Records. Dist: PRT, Jetstar

Monkman, Francis

DWELLER ON THE THRESHOLD.
Single (7"): released on Maya, Oct'81 Dist: Spartan

MIND-BODY-SPIRIT.
Cassette: released on E.S.S.P., Dec'81 by E.S.S.P. Records. Dist: E.S.S.P.

PULU PSHU (Monkman, Francis & Jools Rathbone).
Single (7"): released on Maya, Feb'82 Dist: Spartan

Monk, Meredith

DOLMAN MUSIC.
Tracks: / Gotham lullaby / Travelling / Tale (The) / Biography / Dolman music.
Compact disc: released on ECM (Germany), Sep'86 by ECM Records. Dist: IMS, Polygram, Virgin through EMI

DOLMEN MUSIC.
Album: released on ECM (Germany), Jul'81 by ECM Records. Dist: IMS, Polygram, Virgin through EMI

DO YOU BE.
Tracks: / Scared song / I don't know / Window in 7's / Double fiesta / Do you be / Panda Chant 1 / Memory song / Panda chant 11 / Quarry lullaby / Shadow song / Astronaut Anthem / Wheel.
Notes: Personnel: Robert Een / Ching Gonzalez / Andrea Goodman / Wayne Hankin / Naaz Hosseini / Meredith Monk / Nicky Paraiso / Nurit Tilles / Johanna Arnold / John Eppler / Edmund Niemann.
Album: released on ECM (Germany), Jul'87 by ECM Records. Dist: IMS, Polygram, Virgin through EMI

Compact disc: released on ECM (Germany), Jul'87 by ECM Records. Dist: IMS, Polygram, Virgin through EMI

TURTLE DREAMS.
Album: released on ECM (Germany), Sep'83 by ECM Records. Dist: IMS, Polygram, Virgin through EMI

Monk, Rollins & Co

BRILLIANT CORNERS.
Compact disc: released on Carrere, Apr'87 by Carrere Records. Dist: PRT, Spartan

Monks

I CAN DO ANYTHING YOU LIKE.
Single (7"): released on Eagle (London), Nov'81 by Eagle Records (London). Dist: Stage One

Monk, Thelonious

1961 EUROPEAN TOUR, VOL 2.
Album: released on Ingo, '82 Dist: Jazz Horizons, Jazz Music, Celtic Music

1961 EUROPEAN TOUR, VOL 1.
Album: released on Ingo, '81 Dist: Jazz Horizons, Jazz Music, Celtic Music

ALONE IN SAN FRANCISCO.
Compact disc: released on Carrere, Apr'87 by Carrere Records. Dist: PRT, Spartan

Compact disc: released on JVC Fantasy (Japan), Nov'86

AND THE JAZZ GIANTS.
Compact disc: released on Fantasy (USA), Apr'87 by Fantasy Inc USA Records. Dist: IMS, Polygram

APRIL IN SPRING-LIVE.
Album: released on Milestone, May'84 by Ace Records. Dist: PRT

ARTISTRY IN JAZZ Greatest hits.
Compact disc: released on JVC Fantasy (Japan), May'87

BLUE MONK.
Album: released on Crusader, Apr'86 by Crusader Records. Dist: Spartan

BLUES FIVE SPOT.
Compact disc: released on Carrere, Apr'87 by Carrere Records. Dist: PRT, Spartan

Compact disc: released on Carrere, Apr'87 by Carrere Records. Dist: PRT, Spartan

BLUE SPHERE.
Album: released on Black Lion, Jul'84 by Black Lion Records. Dist: Jazz Music, Chris Wellard, Taylor, H.R., Counterpoint, Cadillac

CRISS-CROSS.
Album: released on CBS, Jan'87 by CBS Records. Dist: CBS

EPISTROPHY.
Album: released on Affinity, May'79 by Charly Records. Dist: Charly, Cadillac

GENIUS OF MODERN MUSIC VOL.1.
Cassette: released on Blue Note, Apr'87 by EMI Records. Dist: EMI

Album: released on Blue Note, Apr'87 by EMI Records. Dist: EMI

GENIUS OF MODERN MUSIC VOL.2.
Album: released on Blue Note, Apr'87 by EMI Records. Dist: EMI

Cassette: released on Blue Note, May'87 by EMI Records. Dist: EMI

GREATEST HITS:THELONIUS MONK.
Tracks: / Well, you needn't / Misteriose / Bemsha swing / Round midnight / Epistrophy / Ruby my dear / Crepuscule with Nellie / Blue monk / Straight, no chaser.
Album: released on CBS, Jul'86 by CBS Records. Dist: CBS

Cassette: released on CBS, Jul'86 by CBS Records. Dist: CBS

I MEAN YOU.
Album: released on Carrere(France), Apr'84 by Carrere Records (France). Dist: PRT

IN ACTION (Monk, Thelonius Quartet).
Album: released on Riverside (USA), Aug'84 Dist: Fantasy (USA) Distribution

Compact disc: released on Carrere, Apr'87 by Carrere Records. Dist: PRT, Spartan

IN JAPAN 1963 (Monk, Thelonious Quartet).
Compact disc: released on East Wind, '86 by East Wind Records. Dist: PRT

IN STOCKHOLM.
Album: released on Duke, Sep'86 by Melodisc Records. Dist: Jazz Horizons, Jazz Music, Celtic Music, JSU, Swift

IT'S MONK'S TIME.
Tracks: / Lulu's back in town / Memories of you / Stuffy turkey / Brake's sake / Nice work if you can get it / Shuffle boil.
Album: released on CBS, Jul'87 by CBS Records. Dist: CBS

MAN I LOVE, (THE).
Album: released on Black Lion, Apr'85 by Black Lion Records. Dist: Jazz Music, Chris Wellard, Taylor, H.R., Counterpoint, Cadillac

Cassette: released on Black Lion, Apr'85 by Black Lion Records. Dist: Jazz Music, Chris Wellard, Taylor, H.R., Counterpoint, Cadillac

MISTERIOSE.
Compact disc: released on Carrere, Apr'87 by Carrere Records. Dist: PRT, Spartan

MONK.
Album: released on CBS(I love Jazz), Aug'84 by CBS Records. Dist: CBS

MONK & COLTRANE (Monk,Thelonious with John Coltrane).
Compact disc: released on Vanguard (USA), Apr'86

Album: released on CBS(Import), Jun'86 by CBS Records. Dist: Conifer, Discovery, Swift

MONK HIMSELF.
Compact disc: released on Carrere, Apr'87 by Carrere Records. Dist: PRT, Spartan

MONK'S DREAM (Monk, Thelonious Quartet).
Album: released on CBS, Jan'87 by CBS Records. Dist: CBS

MONK'S MOODS.
Compact disc: released on Denon, Mar'85 by Denon Records. Dist: Harmonia Mundi

MONK'S MUSIC.
Compact disc: released on Carrere(USA), Dec'85 by Carrere America (USA). Dist: PRT

Compact disc: released on Vanguard (USA), Apr'86

Album: released on Riverside (USA), Feb'84 Dist: Fantasy (USA) Distribution

MONK WITH COLTRANE.
Compact disc: released on Carrere, Apr'87 by Carrere Records. Dist: PRT, Spartan

ROUND MIDNIGHT.
Album: released on Saar Giants Of Jazz (Italy), Sep'85 Dist: Mainline

Cassette: released on Saar Giants Of Jazz (Italy), Sep'85 Dist: Mainline

SOLO MONK.
Album: released on Star Jazz USA, Apr'86 by Charly Records. Dist: Charly Distribution

Cassette: released on Star Jazz USA, Apr'86 by Charly Records. Dist: Charly Distribution

SOMETHING IN BLUE.
Album: released on Black Lion, Jan'85 by Black Lion Records. Dist: Jazz Music, Chris Wellard, Taylor, H.R., Counterpoint, Cadillac

Cassette: released on Black Lion, Jan'85 by Black Lion Records. Dist: Jazz Music, Chris Wellard, Taylor, H.R., Counterpoint, Cadillac

SPHERE (Monk, Thelonious Quartet).
Album: released on Affinity, May'79 by Charly Records. Dist: Charly, Cadillac

THELONIOUS ALONE IN SAN FRANCISCO.
Album:

THELONIOUS MONK.
Album: released on Jazz Reactivation, Jul'82 Dist: PRT

Album: released on Kings Of Jazz, Apr'81 Dist: Jazz Horizons, Jazz Music, Celtic Music

THELONIOUS MONK AND HERBIE NICHOLS (Monk, Thelonious/Nichols, Herbie).
Tracks: / Brake's sake / Gallop's gallop / Shuffle boil / Nica's tempo / Who's blues / 'S'wondeful / 'S'wondeful (alternative take) / Nichols & dimes / Nichols & dimes (alternative take) / My lady gingersnap / Good story blues.
Album: released on RCA, Oct'86 by RCA Records. Dist: RCA, Roots, Swift, Wellard, Chris, I & B, Solomon & Peres Distribution

Cassette: released on RCA, Oct'86 by RCA Records. Dist: RCA, Roots, Swift, Wellard, Chris, I & B, Solomon & Peres Distribution

THELONIOUS MONK COLLECTION, (THE).
Cassette: released on Deja Vu, Aug'85 by Deja Vu Records. Dist: Counterpoint Distribution, Record Services Distribution (Ireland)

THELONIOUS MONK MEMORIAL ALBUM, (THE).
Album: released on Milestone, Jun'82 by Ace Records. Dist: PRT

THELONIOUS MONK QUARTET & OCTET IN EUROPE.
Album: released on Unique Jazz, Apr'81 Dist: Swift, Jazz Music, Jazz Horizons

THELONIOUS MONK WITH GERRY MULLIGAN (Monk, Thelonius/Gerry Mulligan).
Compact disc: released on Carrere, Apr'87 by

Page 692

Carrere Records. Dist: PRT, Spartan

THELONIUS HIMSELF.
Album:

Compact disc: released on JVC Fantasy (Japan), Nov'86

THELONIUS MONK/BUD POWELL (Monk, Thelonious/Bud Powell).
Compact disc: released on Vogue, Dec'86 Dist: Discovery, Jazz Music, PRT, Swift

THELONIUS MONK PLAYS DUKE ELLINGTON.
Compact disc: released on Carrere, Apr'87 by Carrere Records. Dist: PRT, Spartan

UNIQUE, THE.
Compact disc: released on JVC Fantasy (Japan), May'87

Compact disc: released on Carrere, Apr'87 by Carrere Records. Dist: PRT, Spartan

UNIQUE THELONIOUS MONK.
Compact disc: released on Vanguard (USA), Apr'86

Monk, T.S.

HOUSE OF MUSIC.
Album: released on Atlantic, Feb'81 by WEA Records. Dist: WEA

Monochrome Set

VOLUME! BRILLIANCE! CONTRAST!.
Album: released on Cherry Red, May'83 by Cherry Red Records. Dist: Pinnacle

CAST A LONG SHADOW.
Single (7"): released on Cherry Red, Oct'82 by Cherry Red Records. Dist: Pinnacle

COLOUR TRANSMISSION.

Tracks: / Monochrome Set (I presume), (The) / Lighter side of dating, (The) / Expresso / Puerto Rican fence climber, (The) / Tomorrow will be too long / Martians go home / Love goes down the drain / Ici les enfants / Etcetera stroll, (The) / Goodbye Joe / Strange boutique, (The) / Love zombies / Adeste fideles / 405 lines / B-I-D spells bid / RSVP / Apocalypso / Karma suture / Man with the black moustache, (The) / Weird, wild & wonderful world of Tony Potts, (The) / In love, Cancer?.
Compact disc: released on Virgin, Jun'87 by Virgin Records. Dist: EMI, Virgin Distribution

EINE SYMPHONIE DES GRAUENS.
Single (7"): released on Rough Trade, Jun'79 by Rough Trade Records. Dist: Rough Trade Distribution, Cartel Distribution

ELIGIBLE BACHELORS.
Album: released on Cherry Red, Aug'82 by Cherry Red Records. Dist: Pinnacle

FIN! Live.
Tracks: / He's Frank / Martians go home / Straits of Malacca / Sugar plum / B-I-D spells BID / Alphaville / Heaven can wait / Goodbye Joe / Strange boutique, The / Jacob's ladder / Wallflower / Apocalypso / Mr Bizzaro / I'll cry instead / Expresso / Lines / Ein symphonies des grauens / Monchrome Set, The.
Notes: All tracks produced by Bid. (P) 1986 Original soundtrack made by Cherry Red Records Ltd.
Album: released on EL, Jun'86 by El Records. Dist: Rough Trade, Cartel, Pinnacle

HE'S FRANK.
Single (7"): released on Rough Trade, Jan'79 by Rough Trade Records. Dist: Rough Trade Distribution, Cartel Distribution

Single (7"): released on Rough Trade, Jan'80 by Rough Trade Records. Dist: Rough Trade Distribution, Cartel Distribution

JET SET JUNTA.
Single (7"): released on Cherry Red, May'83 by Cherry Red Records. Dist: Pinnacle

LOST WEEKEND, THE.
Album: released on Blanco Y Negro, Jun'85 by WEA Records. Dist: WEA

Cassette: released on Blanco Y Negro, Jun'85 by WEA Records. Dist: WEA

LOVE ZOMBIES.
Album: released on Virgin, Mar'84 by Virgin Records. Dist: EMI, Virgin Distribution

MATING GAME.
Single (7"): released on Cherry Red, Jul'82 by Cherry Red Records. Dist: Pinnacle

MONOCHROME SET, THE.
Single (7"): released on Rough Trade, Sep'79 by Rough Trade Records. Dist: Rough Trade Distribution, Cartel Distribution

STRANGE BOUTIQUE.
Album: released on Virgin, Mar'84 by Virgin Records. Dist: EMI, Virgin Distribution

WALLFLOWER.
Single (7"): released on Blanco Y Negro, May'85 by WEA Records. Dist: WEA Deleted '86.

Monopoly, Tony

GOLDEN HAIRED BOY FROM THE VALLEY.
Single (12"): released on President, Jul'83 by President Records. Dist: Taylors, Spartan

Monro

SOME GIRLS.
Single (7"): released on Spellbound, Mar'87 by Spellbound Records. Dist: CBS

Single (12"): released on Spellbound, Mar'87 by Spellbound Records. Dist: CBS

Monroe

MONROE.
Album: released on Polydor, Nov'80 by Polydor Records. Dist: Polygram, Polydor

Monroe, Bill

BEST OF BILL MONROE, THE.
Tracks: / Gold rush / Blue moon of Kentucky / Close by / Memories of mother and dad / Is the blue moon still shining / Kentucky mandolin / I'm going back to old Kentucky / Footprints in the snow / Little girl and the dreadful snake / Highway of sorrow / Uncle Pen / Let me rest at the end of the journey / Blue grass twist / It's mighty dark to travel / Roane country prison / Pretty fair maiden in the garden / First wipoorwill / I live in the past / Come back to me in my dreams / Put my little shoes away.
Double Album: released on MCA, Mar'86 by MCA Records. Dist: Polygram, MCA

BLUE GRASS RAMBLES (Monroe, Bill & His Blue Grass Boys).
Album: released on Stetson, Apr'86 by Hasmick Promotions Ltd.. Dist: Counterpoint Distribution, H.R. Taylor Distribution, Swift Distribution, Chris Wellard Distribution

Cassette: released on Stetson, Apr'86 by Hasmick Promotions Ltd.. Dist: Counterpoint Distribution, H.R. Taylor Distribution, Swift Distribution, Chris Wellard Distribution

COUNTRY MUSIC HALL OF FAME.
Tracks: / Mule skinner blues / Kentucky waltz / Get up John / You'll find her name written here / Blue Moon of Kentucky / Put my little shoes on / Rocky road blues / Girl in the Blue Velvet Band / Summertime is past and gone / Footprints in the snow / Gold rush.
Album: released on MCA Import, Mar'86 by MCA Records. Dist: Polygram, IMS

FATHER OF BLUE GRASS MUSIC.
Tracks: / Six white horses / Dog house blues / Tennessee blues / No letter in the mail / Blue yodel No. 7 / Orange blossom special / Mule skinner blues / Katy Hill / I wonder if you feel the way I do / Honky tonk swing / In the pines / Back up.
Album: released on RCA, Jan'87 by RCA Records. Dist: RCA, Roots, Swift, Wellard, Chris, I & B, Solomon & Peres Distribution

Cassette: released on RCA, Jan'87 by RCA Records. Dist: RCA, Roots, Swift, Wellard, Chris, I & B, Solomon & Peres Distribution

HIGH, LONESOME SOUND OF BILL MONROE.
Tracks: / My little Georgia rose / Letter from my darlin' / Memories of mother and dad / Highway of sorrow / On the old Kentucky shores / On and on / My dying bed / Memories of you / Whitehouse blues / Sugar coated love / I'm blue, I'm lonesome / When the golden leaves begin to fall.
Album: released on MCA Import, Mar'86 by MCA Records. Dist: Polygram, IMS

KNEE-DEEP IN BLUEGRASS (Monroe, Bill & His Blue Grass Boys).
Tracks: / Cry cry darlin' / Roane country prison / Goodbye old pal / Out in the cold world / Good women's love / Come bak to me in my dreams / Lonesome road to travel / I'm sittin' on top of the world / Sally-Joe / Brand new shoes / Molly and ten brooks.
Album: released on Stetson, Nov'85 by Hasmick Promotions Ltd.. Dist: Counterpoint Distribution, H.R. Taylor Distribution, Swift Distribution, Chris Wellard Distribution

Cassette: released on Stetson, Nov'85 by Hasmick Promotions Ltd.. Dist: Counterpoint Distribution, H.R. Taylor Distribution, Swift Distribution, Chris Wellard Distribution

ORANGE BLOSSOM SPECIAL.
Album: released on Astan, Nov'84 by Astan Records. Dist: Counterpoint

Cassette: released on Astan, Nov'84 by Astan Records. Dist: Counterpoint

STARS OF THE BLUEGRASS HALL OF FAME.
Tracks: / I'm on my way back to the old home / Can't you hear me callin' / Lord, protect my soul / Golden West / Travelin' this lonesome road / I' going back to old Kentucky / I hear a sweet voice calling / Remember the cross / True life blues / Let the gates swing wide.

Album: released on MCA, Mar'86 by MCA Records. Dist: Polygram, MCA

Monroe, Marilyn

BEST OF BROADWAY.
Album:

Album: released on RCA (Germany), '83

FINE ROMANCE, A.
Notes: Double album
Double Album: released on Legends, Mar'87 Dist: Swift

GOODBYE NORMA JEAN.
Compact disc: released on Zuma, '86 by Zuma Records. Dist: CBS, PRT

Album: released on Zuma, May'87 by Zuma Records. Dist: CBS, PRT

Cassette: released on Zuma, May'87 by Zuma Records. Dist: CBS, PRT

GOODBYE PRIMADONNA.
Compact disc: released on Musidisc (France), Dec'85 Dist: Discovery Distribution, Swift Distribution

Album: released on Telefunken (Germany), Apr'84 Dist: Decca Distribution, IMS, Polygram

Album: released on Disc AZ (France), Aug'84 Dist: Discovery

Cassette: released on Disc AZ (France), Aug'84 Dist: Discovery

Double Album: released on Teldec (Germany), Sep'84 by Import Records. Dist: IMS Distribution, Polygram Distribution

Album: released on Zuma, May'85 by Zuma Records. Dist: CBS, PRT

Cassette: released on Zuma, May'85 by Zuma Records. Dist: CBS, PRT

GOODBYE PRIMADONNA.
Compact disc: released on Accord, '86 Dist: Discovery, Target

Picture disc album: Dist: Decca Distribution, IMS, Polygram

I WANNA BE LOVED BY YOU.
Compact disc: released on Solid Gold, Oct'86 Dist: MCA

Single (7"): released on United Artists, Feb'79

Single (7"): released on EMI (France), Apr'83 by EMI Records. Dist: Conifer

MARILYN MONROE.
Album: released on Lotus, Aug'86 Dist: Counterpoint

Cassette: released on Lotus, Aug'86 Dist: Counterpoint

Compact disc: released on Deja Vu, Jul'87 by Deja Vu Records. Dist: Counterpoint Distribution, Record Services Distribution (Ireland)

MARILYN MONROE COLLECTION, THE.
Album: released on Deja Vu, Aug'85 by Deja Vu Records. Dist: Counterpoint Distribution, Record Services Distribution (Ireland)

Cassette: released on Deja Vu, Aug'85 by Deja Vu Records. Dist: Counterpoint Distribution, Record Services Distribution (Ireland)

NEVER BEFORE AND NEVER AGAIN.
Tracks: / Gentlemen prefer blondes / Diamonds are a girl's best friend / Little girl from Little Rock / Ain't there anyone here for love? / When love goes wrong / Bye bye baby / Do it again / Kiss / You'd be surprised / Fine romance, A / She acts like a woman should / Heat wave / Happy birthday Mr.President.
Compact disc: released on DRG (USA), Mar'87 by DRG Records Dist: Conifer, RCA

Album: released on DRG (USA), Feb'87 by DRG Records. Dist: Conifer, RCA

Cassette: released on DRG (USA), Feb'87 by DRG Records. Dist: Conifer, RCA

RARE RECORDINGS (1948-62).
Album: Dist: Swift, Jazz Music, IMS-Polygram

REMEMBER MARILYN.
Album: released on Pye, Apr'74

SOME LIKE IT HOT Original soundtrack.
Album: released on United Artists, Mar'79

Album: released on EMI (Germany), '83 by EMI Records. Dist: Conifer

Picture disc album: released on Liberty, Nov'83 by Liberty-United. Dist: EMI

VOICE SONGS AND FILMS, THE.
Album: released on RCA (France), Oct'85 by RCA Records. Dist: Discovery

Cassette: released on RCA (France), Oct'85 by RCA Records. Dist: Discovery

WHEN I FALL IN LOVE.
Tracks: / Heatwave / Diamonds are a girl's best friend*.
Notes: *=Extra track on 12" only
Single (7"): released on Zuma, Feb'87 by Zuma Records. Dist: CBS, PRT

Picture disc single: released on Zuma, Feb'87 by Zuma Records. Dist: CBS, PRT

Single (12"): released on Zuma, Feb'87 by Zuma Records. Dist: CBS, PRT

Picture disc single: released on Zuma, Aug'87 by Zuma Records. Dist: CBS, PRT

Monroes

CHEERIO.
Single (7"): released on EMI, Nov'86 by EMI Records. Dist: EMI

FACE ANOTHER DAY.
Tracks: / Jeanette / Wish you were here / Beating of a lover's heart / Lady on 5th avenue / Cheerio / Let's go / Heaven can wait / How strong is your love? / Move in closer.
Album: released on Parlophone, Apr'86 by EMI Records. Dist: EMI

Cassette: released on Parlophone, Apr'86 by EMI Records. Dist: EMI

Compact disc: released on Parlophone, '86 by EMI Records. Dist: EMI

JEANETTE Stay with me -.
Tracks: / Jeanette / Jeanette (Stay with me) - / How strong is your love?.
Single (7"): released on Parlophone, Mar'86 by EMI Records. Dist: EMI

Single (12"): released on Parlophone, Mar'86 by EMI Records. Dist: EMI

LET'S GO.
Single (7"): released on Parlophone, Aug'85 by EMI Records. Dist: EMI

Single (12"): released on Parlophone, Aug'85 by EMI Records. Dist: EMI

SUNDAY PEOPLE.
Single (7"): by EMI Records. Dist: EMI

WISH YOU WERE HERE.
Tracks: / Wish you were here / Lady on 5th avenue.
Single (7"): released on EMI, Jun'86 by EMI Records. Dist: EMI

Single (12"): released on EMI, Jun'86 by EMI Records. Dist: EMI

Monroe, Vaughn

MONROE DOCTRINE, THE.
Album: released on Swing Era, Jul'82

Monro, Matt

16 GOLDEN CLASSICS.
Tracks: / Ev'rybody falls in love with someone / Out of sight out of mind / One I love belongs to somebody else (The) / That old feeling / Cried for you (now it's your turn to cry for me) / Cottage for sale, A / Do you ever think of me / Dancing with tears in my eyes / Gone with the wind / Memories of you / My old flame / Once in a while / You always hurt the one you love / Love me do / My house is your house (mi casa su casa) / What can i say after I say I'm sorry.
Notes: All tracks licensed from The Decca Record Co. Ltd. design: Shoot that tiger! (C)1986 Castle Communications place, Unit 7, 271 Merton Road,London SW18 5JS. Bar Code: 5\013428\920206.
Album: released on Unforgettable, Dec'86 by Castle Communications Records. Dist: Counterpoint

Cassette: released on Unforgettable, Dec'86 by Castle Communications Records. Dist: Counterpoint

BY REQUEST.
Tracks: / I will wait for you / Time after time / Wednesday's child / Music played, The / Honey on the vine / Rain sometimes / When you wish upon a star / Over the rainbow / If I never sing another song / When you became a man / Beyond the hill / You've got possibilities / Let there be love / If she walked into my life / Apple tree, The / You're sensational, My friend, my friend / When I fall in love / Look for small pleasures / I get along without you very well / I will wait for you / Time after time / Wednesday's child / Music played, The / Honey on the vine / Rain sometimes / When you wish upon a star / Over the rainbow / If I never sing another song / When you become a man / Beyond the hill / You've got possibilities / Let there be love / If she walked into my life / Apple tree, The / You're sensational / My friend, my friend / When I fall in love / Look for small pleasures / I get along without you very well.
Album: released on Capitol, Jan'87 by Capitol Records. Dist: EMI

Compact disc: released on EMI, Oct'87 by EMI Records. Dist: EMI. Estim retail price in Sep'87 was £11.99.

HEARTBREAKERS.
Tracks: / Impossible dream (The) / And you smiled / Didn't we / If I never sing another song / From Russia with love / Born free / Softly / As I leave you / Walk away / Without you / My kind of girl / Somewhere / We're gonna change the world / Speak softly, love / Why not now / Yesterday / Portrait of my love / My love and devotion / For mama / When love comes along / Gonna build a mountain.
Compact disc: released on EMI, Jan'87 by EMI Records. Dist: EMI

Album: released on EMI, Mar'80 by EMI Records. Dist: EMI

Cassette: released on EMI, Jul'80 by EMI Records. Dist: EMI

MATT MONRO.
Cassette: released on EMI, Jul'80 by EMI Records. Dist: EMI

MEMORIES.
Album: released on Decca, Apr'85 by Decca Records. Dist: Polygram

MORE HEARTBREAKERS.
Album: released on EMI, Oct'84 by EMI Records. Dist: EMI

Cassette: released on EMI, Oct'84 by EMI Records. Dist: EMI

SINGS.
Album: released on MFP, Oct'85 by EMI Records. Dist: EMI

Cassette: released on MFP, Oct'85 by EMI Records. Dist: EMI

THIS IS MATT MONRO.
Album: released on EMI, Oct'80 by EMI Records. Dist: EMI

Cassette: released on EMI, Oct'80 by EMI Records. Dist: EMI

VERY BEST OF MATT MONRO, THE.
Album: released on MFP (EMI), Sep'82 by EMI Records. Dist: EMI

Cassette: released on MFP (EMI), Sep'82 by EMI Records. Dist: EMI

Monro, Vaughn
BEST OF....
Album: released on RCA, Oct'87 by RCA Records. Dist: RCA, Roots, Swift, Wellard, Chris, I & B, Solomon & Peres Distribution. Estim retail price in Sep'87 was £3.99.

Cassette: released on RCA, Oct'87 by RCA Records. Dist: RCA, Roots, Swift, Wellard, Chris, I & B, Solomon & Peres Distribution

Monsarrat, Nicholas
CRUEL SEA, THE. Read by Robert Powell.
Cassette: released on Listen For Pleasure, May'84 by MFP Records. Dist: EMI

Monsbourgh, Lazy Ade
VINTAGE SELECTION (1950-70).
Album: released on Swaggie (Australia), Jan'83

WILD LIFE (1956-70).
Album: released on Swaggie (Australia), Jan'83

Monsieur Beaucaire
MONSIEUR BEAUCAIRE. Original 1919 cast.
Album: released on Opal, Oct'83 Dist: Pavilion Distribution

Monsoon
SHATKI (THE MEANING OF WITHIN).
Single (7"): released on Mobile Suit Corporation, May'82 Dist: Phonogram Distribution, Polygram Distribution

Single (12"): released on Mobile Suit Corporation, May'82 Dist: Phonogram Distribution, Polygram Distribution

WINGS OF THE DAWN.
Single (7"): released on Mobile Suit Corporation, May'83 Dist: Phonogram Distribution, Polygram Distribution

Single (12"): released on Mobile Suit Corporation, May'83 Dist: Phonogram Distribution, Polygram Distribution

Monstars
MONSTARS, THE.
Album: released on Aquarius, Jan'77 by President Records. Dist: President Distribution, Jazz Music, Taylors, Spartan

Monster Band
MONSTER BAND.
Notes: Monster band includes: Hugh Hopper, Elton Dean, Mike Travis, Caroffi, and/her.
Album: released on Culture Press, Dec'86 by

Vista Sounds Records. Dist: Jetstar, Rough Trade

Monster Hits Collection
MONSTER HITS COLLECTION Various artists (Various Artists).
Double Album: released on Pickwick, Jul'79 by Pickwick Records. Dist: Pickwick Distribution, Prism Leisure Distributor

Monsters Of Rock
MONSTERS OF ROCK Various artists (Various Artists).
Cassette: released on Polydor, Oct'80 by Polydor Records. Dist: Polygram, Polydor

Monster Tracks
MONSTER TRACKS Various artists (Various Artists).
Album: released on Polystar, Nov'81 Dist: Polygram

Cassette: released on Polystar, Nov'81 Dist: Polygram

Monster Walk
MONSTER WALK.
Album:

Montage
MONTAGE.
Album: released on Bam Caruso, Jan'87 by Bam Caruso Records. Dist: Rough Trade, Revolver, Cartel

WHEN I CLOSE MY EYES.
Tracks: / When I close my eyes / Where are you now?
Single (7"): released on Reekus, Aug'86 by Reekus Records. Dist: Nine Mile, Cartel

Montana
DANCE FANTASY, A.
Album: released on Atlantic, May'78 by WEA Records. Dist: WEA

Montana, Kid
SPOOKY.
Single (7"): released on Les Disques Du Crepuscule, Dec'86 Dist: Rough Trade, Pinnacle, Island, Polygram

STILL COLOUR WAITING.
Tracks: / Still colour waiting / Spooky.
Single (12"): released on Le Disques Du Crepuscule, Apr'87

Single (7"): released on Le Disques Du Crepuscule, May'87

Montana, Lee
ON THE RUN.
Album: released on Sweet Folk Country, Nov'76 Dist: Chris Wellard Distribution

YOU'RE ON MY MIND (WITH TIME ON MY HANDS).
Album: released on Sweet Folk All, May'81 by Sweet Folk All Records. Dist: Sweet Folk All, Roots, Celtic Music, Dragon, Impetus, Projection, Chris Wellard, Festival Records

Montana, Patsy
EARLY COUNTRY FAVOURITES.
Album: released on Old Homestead (USA), Mar'84

Montana Sextet
WHO NEEDS ENEMIES (WITH A FRIEND LIKE...).
Single (7"): released on Virgin, Jun'83 by Virgin Records. Dist: EMI, Virgin Distribution

Single (12"): released on Virgin, Jun'83 by Virgin Records. Dist: EMI, Virgin Distribution

Montand, Yves
HIS GREATEST HITS - VOL.2.
Album: released on CBS(France), May'85 by CBS Records. Dist: Conifer, Discovery, Swift

Cassette: released on CBS(France), May'85 by CBS Records. Dist: Conifer, Discovery, Swift

IN ENGLISH.
Album: released on Polydor (France), Jul'83 Dist: Polygram

YVES MONTAND.
Tracks: / Bicyclotte, (La) / Jazz et la java, (Le) / Chat de la voisine, (Le) / Chansonnette, (La) / Est-ce ainsi que les hommes vivent? / Je t'aime / Plus belle des mers, (La) / Amoureuse, (L') / Coucher avec elle / Port (Le) / Me souviens (La) / En sortant d'école / On l'aime / Paris at night / Quelqu'un / Page d'écriture / Jardin, (le) / Miroir brise, (Le) / Dans ma maison / Trois petites notes de musique / Il n'y plus d'apres.
Cassette: released on Philips (France), Sep'86

Montarroyos, Marcio
SAMBA SOLSTICE.
Compact disc: released on Black Sim, Jun'87

Monteith, Kelly
LETTUCE BE COOL.
Album: released on Chrysalis, Oct'84 by Chrysalis Records. Dist: CBS Deleted '86.

Cassette: released on Chrysalis, Oct'84 by Chrysalis Records. Dist: CBS

Montenegro, Hugo
BEST OF BROADWAY, THE.
Album: released on Golden Hour, Nov'77 by PRT Records. Dist: PRT

BEST OF HUGO MONTENEGRO.
Album: released on RCA International, Apr'80

Cassette: released on RCA International, Apr'80

BROADWAY MELODIES (VOL.1).
Album: released on Everest (Premier), '83 by Everest Records. Dist: Pinnacle

Cassette: released on Everest (Premier), '83 by Everest Records. Dist: Pinnacle

GOOD, THE BAD AND THE UGLY, (THE).
Tracks: / Good, the bad and the ugly, (The) / Fistful of dollars, (A).
Single (7"): released on Old Gold, Oct'86 by Old Gold Records. Dist: Lightning, Jazz Music, Spartan, Counterpoint

Single (7"): released on RCA, Jul'81 by RCA Records. Dist: RCA, Roots, Swift, Wellard, Chris, I & B, Solomon & Peres Distribution

MUSIC FROM GOOD BAD UGLY.
Album: released on RCA, '74 by RCA Records. Dist: RCA, Roots, Swift, Wellard, Chris, I & B, Solomon & Peres Distribution

PLAYS FOR LOVERS.
Cassette: released on Ampro Cassettes, Sep'81

Monte, Rey
SONGS OF SONGS.
Album: released on Conifer, Jun'86 by Conifer Records. Dist: Conifer

Monterose, J.R.
AND A LITTLE PLEASURE (Monterose, J.R. & Tommy Flanagan).
Album: released on Uptown (USA), Dec'82 by Uptown Records. Dist: Jazz Music

Montez, Chris
LET'S DANCE.
Tracks: / Let's dance / You're the one.
Single (7"): released on Old Gold, Nov'86 by Old Gold Records. Dist: Lightning, Jazz Music, Spartan, Counterpoint

Single (7"): released on Old Gold, Jul'82 by Old Gold Records. Dist: Lightning, Jazz Music, Spartan, Counterpoint

Single (7"): released on Creole Replay, Aug'84 by Creole Records. Dist: PRT, Rhino

MORE I SEE YOU, THE.
Single (7"): released on Old Gold, Jul'82 by Old Gold Records. Dist: Lightning, Jazz Music, Spartan, Counterpoint

Montgomery, Jack
DEARLY BELOVED.
Single (7"): released on Kent, Apr'85 by Ace Records. Dist: Pinnacle

Montgomery, James
SEPTEMBER MORNINGS.
Album: released on Amber, Nov'79 Dist: Nimbus Records

Montgomery, Little
TISHOMINGO BLUES.
Album: released on JSP, Mar'82 by JSP Records. Dist: Swift, Projection

Montgomery, L.M.
ANNE OF GREEN GABLES Read by Jane Jermyn.
Cassette: released on Soundings, Mar'85 Dist: Soundings

Montgomery, Marion
MARIAN MONTGOMERY ON STAGE.
Album: released on Cube, Apr'82 by Dakota Records. Dist: PRT

Cassette: released on Cube, Apr'82 by Dakota Records. Dist: PRT

PUTTIN' ON THE RITZ.

Album: released on Dakota, Feb'84 by Dakota Records. Dist: PRT

Cassette: released on Dakota, Feb'84 by Dakota Records. Dist: PRT

SUPRISE SUPRISE.
Cassette: released on Cube, Oct'81 by Dakota Records. Dist: PRT

Album: released on Cube, Oct'81 by Dakota Records. Dist: PRT

TOWN & COUNTRY.
Album: released on Cube, Apr'82 by Dakota Records. Dist: PRT

Cassette: released on Cube, Apr'82 by Dakota Records. Dist: PRT

Montgomery, Melba
DON'T LET THE GOOD TIMES FOOL YOU.
Album: released on Elektra, Aug'79 by WEA Records. Dist: WEA

MELBA MONTGOMERY.
Album: released on United Artists, Apr'78

Montgomery, Monty
BAD REPUTATION.
Tracks: / Bad reputation / Irie.
Single (12"): released on Mango, Mar'87 by Inferno Records. Dist: Inferno

Montgomery, Wes
ARTISTRY IN JAZZ Greatest hits.
Compact disc: released on JVC Fantasy (Japan), May'87

BOSS GUITAR.
Album:

BUMPIN'.
Tracks: / Tear it down / Con alma / Quiet thing / Shadow of your smile / Mi cosa / Bumpin' / Here's that rainy day / Misty.
Notes: Digital Stereo
Compact disc: released on Verve, Oct'84 by Phonogram Records. Dist: Polygram

CALIFORNIA DREAMING.
Compact disc: by Phonogram Records. Dist: Polygram

COMPACT JAZZ.
Compact disc: released on Verve, Jul'87 by Phonogram Records. Dist: Polygram

DYNAMIC DUO (Montgomery, Wes / Jimmy Smith).
Tracks: / Down by the riverside / Night train / James and Wes / 13(Death march) / Baby, it's cold outside.
Compact disc: released on Verve, Oct'84 by Phonogram Records. Dist: Polygram

ENCORES.
Album: released on Milestone, May'84 by Ace Records. Dist: PRT

FULL HOUSE.
Compact disc: released on Vanguard (USA), Apr'86

GOIN' OUT OF MY HEAD.
Tracks: / O morro nao tem vez / Boss city / Chim chim cheree / Goin' out of my head / Naptown Blues / Twisted blues / End of a love affair, The / It was a very good year / Golden earrings.
Compact disc: released on Polydor, Oct'85 by Polydor Records. Dist: Polygram, Polydor

GREATEST HITS:WES MONT-GOMERY.
Album: released on A&M, '74 by A&M Records. Dist: Polygram

IMPRESSIONS.
Album: released on Affinity, '78 by Charly Records. Dist: Charly, Cadillac

INCREDIBLE JAZZ GUITAR.
Compact disc: released on JVC Fantasy (Japan), Nov'86

Compact disc: released on Carrere, Apr'87 by Carrere Records. Dist: PRT, Spartan

LIVE AT JORGIES-LIVE RADIO-66/LIVE TELEVISION-68.
Album: released on VGM, May'86 Dist: Jazz Horizons, JSU

MIDNIGHT GUITARIST.
Notes: 1961 to 1965
Album: released on Crusader Jazz Masterworks, Jun'86 Dist: Jazz Music

MOVIN' ALONG.
Compact disc: released on Carrere, Apr'87 by Carrere Records. Dist: PRT, Spartan

Album: released on Riverside (USA), Feb'84 Dist: Fantasy (USA) Records

MOVIN' WES.
Tracks: / West coast blues / Caravan / Movin' Wes / Moca flor / Matchmaker matchmaker / Senza fine / Theodora / In and out / Born to be blue / People.
Album: released on Verve, '83 by Phonogram Records. Dist: Polygram

Cassette: released on Verve, '83 by Phonogram Records. Dist: Polygram

Compact disc: released on Verve, '83 by Phonogram Records. Dist: Polygram

Album: released on Verve, Aug'81 by Phonogram Records. Dist: Polygram

PORTRAIT OF WES.
Compact disc: released on Carrere, Apr'87 by Carrere Records. Dist: PRT, Spartan

RECORDED LIVE AT JORGIES JAZZ CLUB.
Album: released on VGM, May'86 Dist: Jazz Horizons, JSU

Album: released on VGM, Apr'81 Dist: Jazz Horizons, JSU

ROUND MIDNIGHT.
Tracks: / 4 on 6 / Girl next door, The / Mr. Walker / Here's that rainy day / 'Round midnight / Impressions.
Notes: Recorded in concert, Paris, 27 March 1965
Compact disc: released on Charly, Mar'86 by Charly Records. Dist: Charly, Cadillac

SILVER COLLECTION, THE.
Tracks: / If you could see me now / Impressions / Four on six / Unit 7 / Mellow mood / James and Wes / What's new / Misty / Portrait of Jenny / Here's that rainy day.
Compact disc: released on Verve, Nov'84 by Phonogram Records. Dist: Polygram

SOLITUDE.
Album: released on Charly, May'79 by Charly Records. Dist: Charly, Cadillac

SO MUCH GUITAR!.
Album:

Compact disc: released on Carrere, Apr'87 by Carrere Records. Dist: PRT, Spartan

TEQUILA.
Compact disc: released on Polydor, Aug'87 by Polydor Records. Dist: Polygram, Polydor

WALKMAN JAZZ.
Cassette: released on Polydor, Jun'87 by Polydor Records. Dist: Polygram, Polydor

WES MONTGOMERY.
Cassette: released on Deja Vu, Nov'85 by Deja Vu Records. Dist: Counterpoint Distribution, Record Services Distribution (Ireland)

Montollu, Tete
CATALONIAN FOLKSONGS.
Notes: Solo piano
Album: released on Timeless(import), Sep'86 Dist: Cadillac

CATALONIAN NIGHTS VOL.1.
Album: released on Steeplechase, Jun'81

LIVE AT THE KEYSTONE CORNER (Montollu, Tete/Herbie Lewis/Billy Higgins).
Album: released on Timeless(import), Sep'86 Dist: Cadillac

SECRET LOVE (Montollu, Tete Trio).
Album: released on Timeless, Apr'81

SONGS FOR LOVE.
Album: released on Enja (Germany), Jan'82 by Enja Records (W.Germany). Dist: Cadillac Music

TALK ABOUT YOU.
Album: released on Steeplechase, Apr'81

YELLOW DOLPHIN STREET.
Album: released on Timeless(import), Sep'86 Dist: Cadillac

Montoya, Carlos
FLAMENCO DIRECT VOL.1.
Album: released on Crystal Clear, Dec'80 by Crystal Records. Dist: Revolver, Cartel

FLAMENCO DIRECT VOL.2.
Album: released on Crystal Clear, Dec'80 by Crystal Records. Dist: Revolver, Cartel

Montreaux 79
MONTREAUX 79 various original artists (Various Artists).
Album: released on Rhapsody, Nov'80 by President Records. Dist: Taylors, Swift, Jazz Music, Wellard, Chris

Montreux Summit
MONTREUX SUMMIT various original jazz

artists (Various Artists).
Double Album: released on CBS, Jan'78 by CBS Records. Dist: CBS

MONTREUX SUMMIT 2 various original jazz artists (Various Artists).
Double Album: released on CBS, Sep'78 by CBS Records. Dist: CBS

Montrose
MONTROSE.
Album: by Warner Bros Records. Dist: WEA

Montrose, J.R.
......AND A LITTLE PLEASURE (Montrose, J.R.& Tommy Flanagan).
Album: released on Uptown (USA), Nov'86 by Uptown Records. Dist: Jazz Music

LIVE IN ALBANY.
Album: released on Uptown (USA), Nov'86 by Uptown Records. Dist: Jazz Music

Montrose, Ronnie
MEAN.
Album: released on Enigma, Apr'87 by Enigma Records. Dist: Rough Trade, Cartel, EMI

TERRITORY.
Compact disc: by Pacific Records (USA). Dist: Atlantic

Monty
T-T-T-TOTTENHAM.
Tracks: / T-T-T-Tottenham.
Notes: Royalties to be divided between the Jarrett/Groce & Blacklock families.
Single (7"): released on Forest, Mar'86 Dist: Jungle, Cartel

Monty M.C's
HOLIDAY RAP WITH A CAPITAL C.
Tracks: / Holiday rap with a capital C / Monty says don't scratch the B side.
Single (7"): released on Debut, Oct'86 by Skratch Music. Dist: PRT

Single (12"): released on Debut, Oct'86 by Skratch Music. Dist: PRT

Monty Python
AND THE HOLY GRAIL.
Cassette: released on Charisma, Jun'76 by Virgin Records. Dist: EMI

ANOTHER MONTY PYTHON RECORD.
Album: released on Charisma, Apr'87 by Virgin Records. Dist: EMI

Cassette: released on Charisma, Apr'87 by Virgin Records. Dist: EMI

CONTRACTUAL OBLIGATION (Monty Python's Flying Circus).
Album: released on Charisma, Apr'87 by Virgin Records. Dist: EMI

Cassette: released on Charisma, Apr'87 by Virgin Records. Dist: EMI

GALAXY SONG / EVERY SPERM.
Single (7"): released on CBS, Jun'83 by CBS Records. Dist: CBS

Single (12"): released on CBS, Jun'83 by CBS Records. Dist: CBS

INSTANT RECORD COLLECTION.
Album: released on Charisma, Apr'87 by Virgin Records. Dist: EMI

Cassette: released on Charisma, Apr'87 by Virgin Records. Dist: EMI

LIVE AT DRURY LANE (Monty Python's Flying Circus).
Album: released on Charisma, Apr'87 by Virgin Records. Dist: EMI

MATCHING TIE AND HANDKERCHIEF (Monty Python's Flying Circus).
Album: released on Charisma, Sep'83 by Virgin Records. Dist: EMI

MONTY PYTHON'S FLYING CIRCUS (Monty Python's Flying Circus).
Album: released on BBC, '74 by BBC Records & Tapes. Dist: EMI, PRT, Pye

MONTY PYTHON'S THE MEANING OF LIFE Original soundtrack (Monty Python's The Meaning Of Life).
Cassette: released on CBS, Jun'83 by CBS Records. Dist: CBS

PREVIOUS RECORD (Monty Python's Flying Circus).
Album: released on Charisma, Apr'87 by Virgin Records. Dist: EMI

SOUNDTRACK (Monty Python's Flying Circus).
Album: released on Charisma, Mar'83 by Virgin Records. Dist: EMI

Cassette: released on Charisma, Mar'83 by Virgin Records. Dist: EMI

SOUNDTRACK TO THE HOLY GRAIL (Monty Python's Flying Circus).
Album: released on Charisma, Apr'87 by Virgin Records. Dist: EMI

Cassette: released on Charisma, Apr'87 by Virgin Records. Dist: EMI

Monument To British Rock
MONUMENT TO BRITISH ROCK various artists (Various Artists).
Album: released on EMI, May'79 by EMI Records. Dist: EMI

Monyaka
GO DEH YAKA (Go to the top).
Tracks: / Go Deh Yaka (Go to the top)(1986 style) / Go Deh Yaka (Go to the top)(1986 style)(instrumental)
Single (7"): released on Boiling Point, Sep'86 by Polydor Records. Dist: Polygram

Single (12"): released on Boiling Point, Sep'86 by Polydor Records. Dist: Polygram

GO DE YAKA (GO TO THE TOP).
Single (7"): released on Polydor, Aug'83 by Polydor Records. Dist: Polygram, Polydor

Single (12"): released on Polydor, Aug'83 by Polydor Records. Dist: Polygram, Polydor

REGGAE-MATIC-FUNK.
Single (7"): released on Polydor, Nov'83 by Polydor Records. Dist: Polygram, Polydor

Single (12"): released on Polydor, Nov'83 by Polydor Records. Dist: Polygram, Polydor

ROUND THE CORNER.
Single (12"): released on Kaya, Mar'85 by Kaya Records. Dist: Jetstar

Mood
PARIS IS ONE DAY AWAY.
Single (12"): released on RCA, Apr'82 by RCA Records. Dist: RCA, Roots, Swift, Wellard, Chris, I & B, Solomon & Peres Distribution

Single (7"): released on RCA, Apr'82 by RCA Records. Dist: RCA, Roots, Swift, Wellard, Chris, I & B, Solomon & Peres Distribution

PASSION IN DARK ROOMS.
Single (7"): released on RCA, Oct'82 by RCA Records. Dist: RCA, Roots, Swift, Wellard, Chris, I & B, Solomon & Peres Distribution

Single (12"): released on RCA, Oct'82 by RCA Records. Dist: RCA, Roots, Swift, Wellard, Chris, I & B, Solomon & Peres Distribution

Mood Elevators
GEORGIE GIRL.
Single (7"): Dist: Projection, Jazz Horizons

Moodle
GIVE ME LOVE.
Single (12"): released on Port, Sep'86

HOLD ME TIGHT.
Single (12"): released on LRM, Mar'82 by Marino The Band. Dist: Spartan

LEGEND OF JUDAH CONTINUES, THE.
Double Album: released on Port Music, Sep'85

Album: released on 7 Seals, Sep'85

LOVE IS A WONDERFUL THING.
Single (12"): released on Port, Sep'85

Moodists
DISCIPLES KNOW.
Single (7"): released on Red Flame, Mar'83 by Red Flame Records. Dist: Nine Mile, Cartel

DOUBLE LIFE.
Album: released on Red Flame, Sep'85 by Red Flame Records. Dist: Nine Mile, Cartel

ENGINE SHUDDER.
Album: released on Red Flame, Jun'83 by Red Flame Records. Dist: Nine Mile, Cartel

ENOUGH LEGS TO LIVE ON.
Single (7"): released on Red Flame 10, Oct'84

Single 10": released on Red Flame, Sep'84 by Red Flame Records. Dist: Nine Mile, Cartel

GONE DEAD.
Single (7"): released on Au-Go-Go (Australia), Oct'83 by Au-Go-Go Records (Australia). Dist: Rough Trade, Cartel

HEY LITTLE GARY.
Tracks: / Hey little Gary / Someone's got to give / Somebody to love / If takes a thief
Single (7"): released on Tim, May'87 Dist:

Backs, Cartel Distribution

Single (12"): released on Tim, May'87 Dist: Backs, Cartel Distribution

JUSTICE & MONEY TOO.
Single (7"): released on Creation, Nov'85 Dist: Rough Trade, Cartel

RUNAWAY.
Single (7"): released on Red Flame 10, May'84

Single (12"): released on Red Flame 10, May'84

TAKE THE RED CARPET OUT OF TOWN.
Tracks: / Take the red carpet out of town / Jack of diamonds / Everybody don't tell her.
Single (12"): released on Tim, Sep'86 Dist: Backs, Cartel Distribution

THIRSTY'S CALLING.
Album: released on Red Flame, Apr'84 by Red Flame Records. Dist: Nine Mile, Cartel

Mood Mosaic
TOUCH OF VELVET-A STING OF BRASS.
Single (7"): released on Soul Supply, Nov'83 by High Energy Records. Dist: Charly

Moods
MOODS various original artists (Various Artists).
Double cassette: released on Cambra, '83 by Cambra Records. Dist: IDS, Conifer

Moods In Brass
MOODS IN BRASS various brass bands (Various bands).
Double cassette: released on Pickwick (Ditto series), Mar'83

Mood Six
DIFFERENCE IS..., THE.
Album: released on Psycho, Feb'85 Dist: Funhouse, Rough Trade

I SAW THE LIGHT.
Tracks: / I saw the light / Flowers and boxes / Light Music / Chase, The (Theme from).
Single (7"): released on Cherry Red, May'87 by Cherry Red Records. Dist: Pinnacle

Single (12"): released on Cherry Red, May'87 by Cherry Red Records. Dist: Pinnacle

MATTER OF..., A.
Tracks: / Contemporary Scene, (The) / Voice of reason, (The) / Eternal / Back to the day / Life that Jack built, (The) / Matter of, (A) / What have you ever done? / Love of money / Far Away / When the time comes / Perfect life, (The) / Game show.
Album: released on Cherry Red, Sep'86 by Cherry Red Records. Dist: Pinnacle

Cassette: released on Cherry Red, Sep'86 by Cherry Red Records. Dist: Pinnacle

PLASTIC FLOWERS.
Single (7"): released on Psycho, May'85 Dist: Funhouse, Rough Trade

PLASTIC FLOWERS (EP) 5-track EP.
Single (12"): released on Psycho, May'85 Dist: Funhouse, Rough Trade

WHAT HAVE YOU DONE.
Tracks: / What have you done.
Single (12"): released on Cherry Red, Aug'86 by Cherry Red Records. Dist: Pinnacle

Moody Blues
BLUE WORLD.
Single (7"): released on Threshold, Aug'83 by Threshold Records. Dist: Decca Distribution, Polygram Distribution

Single (12"): released on Threshold, Aug'83 by Threshold Records. Dist: Decca Distribution, Polygram Distribution

BOULEVARD DE LA MADELAINE.
Single (7"): released on Decca, '66 by Decca Records. Dist: Polygram

COLLECTION: MOODY BLUES.
Tracks: / Go now / Steal your heart away / Lose your money / Don't mind / Let me go / I'll go crazy / Time is on my side / It's easy child / Something you got / I've got a dream / From the bottom of my heart / Can't nobody love you / Come back / Stop / Bye bye bird / It ain't necessarily so / True story / And my baby's gone.
Compact disc: released on Collector Series, '86 by Castle Communications Records. Dist: PRT, Pinnacle, RCA, Ariola

Album: released on Castle Communications, Nov'85 by Castle Communications. Dist: Cartel, Pinnacle, Counterpoint

Cassette: released on Castle Communications, Nov'85 by Castle Communications. Dist: Cartel, Pinnacle, Counterpoint

DAYS OF FUTURE PASSED (Moody Blues/London Festival Orchestra/Peter Knight).
Notes: Digital Stereo
Compact disc: released on Threshold, '83 by Threshold Records. Dist: Decca Distribution, Polygram Distribution

Album: released on Deram, Nov'84 by Decca Records. Dist: Polygram

Cassette: released on Deram, Nov'84 by Decca Records. Dist: Polygram

EVERY GOOD BOY DESERVES FAVOURS.
Tracks: / Procession / Story in your eyes / Our guessing game / Emily's song / After you came / One more to live / Nice to be here / You can never go home / My song.
Compact disc: released on London, '86 by London Records. Dist: Polygram

Album: released on Threshold, Jul'71 by Threshold Records. Dist: Decca Distribution, Polygram Distribution

Cassette: released on Threshold, Jul'71 by Threshold Records. Dist: Decca Distribution, Polygram Distribution

FLY ME HIGH.
Single (7"): released on Decca, May'67 by Decca Records. Dist: Polygram

GO NOW.
Single (7"): released on Old Gold, Sep'85 by Old Gold Records. Dist: Lightning, Jazz Music, Spartan, Counterpoint

IN SEARCH OF THE LOST CHORD.
Tracks: / Departure / Ride my see-saw / Dr. Livingstone, I presume / House of four doors / Legend of a mind / House of four doors (part 2) / Voices in the sky / Best way to travel, The / Visions of Paradise / Actor, The / Word, The / Om.
Compact disc: released on London, '86 by London Records. Dist: Polygram

Album: released on Deram, Nov'84 by Decca Records. Dist: Polygram

Cassette: released on Deram, Nov'84 by Decca Records. Dist: Polygram

LONG DISTANCE VOYAGER.
Tracks: / Voice / Talking out of turn / Gemini dream / In my world / Meanwhile / 22,000days / Nervous / Painted smile / Reflective smile / Veteran cosmic rocker.
Compact disc: released on London, '86 by London Records. Dist: Polygram

Cassette: released on Threshold, May'81 by Threshold Records. Dist: Decca Distribution, Polygram Distribution

Album: released on Threshold, May'81 by Threshold Records. Dist: Decca Distribution, Polygram Distribution

MUSIC FOR MILLIONS.
Tracks: / I'll go crazy / Something you got / Go now / Can't nobody love you / I don't mind / I got a dream / Let me go / Thank you baby / It ain't necessarily so / True story / Bye bye bird.
Notes: 12 great trcks from the fabulous Moody Blues including their first and only No.1single 'Go Now'.
Album: released on Decca (Germany), Dec'86 by Decca Records. Dist: Polygram, IMS

Cassette: released on Decca (Germany), Dec'86 by Decca Records. Dist: Polygram, IMS

NIGHTS IN WHITE SATIN.
Single (7"): released on Old Gold, Oct'83 by Old Gold Records. Dist: Lightning, Jazz Music, Spartan, Counterpoint

Single (7"): released on Deram, '67 by Decca Records. Dist: Polygram

OCTAVE.
Tracks: / One step into the light / Day we met again, The / Steppin in a slide zone / Under moonshine / Had to fall in love / I'll be level with you / Driftwood / Top Rank Suite / I'm your man / Survival / Survival.
Album: released on Threshold, Jun'78 by Threshold Records. Dist: Decca Distribution, Polygram Distribution

Cassette: released on Threshold, Jun'78 by Threshold Records. Dist: Decca Distribution, Polygram Distribution

Compact disc: released on Threshold, Oct'86 by Threshold Records. Dist: Decca Distribution, Polygram Distribution

ON THE THRESHOLD OF A DREAM.
Tracks: / In the beginning / Lovely to see you / Dear diary / Send me no wine / To share our love / So deep within you / Never comes the day / Lazy day / Are you sitting comfortably / Dream, The / Have you heard (part 1) / Voyage, The / Have you heard (part 2).
Compact disc: released on London, '86 by London Records. Dist: Polygram

Album: released on Deram, Apr'69 by Decca Records. Dist: Polygram

Cassette: released on Deram, Apr'69 by Decca Records. Dist: Polygram Deleted '84.

OTHER SIDE OF LIFE.
Album: released on Threshold-Polydor, '86

Cassette: released on Threshold-Polydor, '86

Compact disc: released on Threshold-Polydor, '86

OTHER SIDE OF LIFE.
Tracks: / Other side of life / Nights in white satin (live) / Spirit, The.
Single (7"): released on Polydor, Oct'86 by Polydor Records. Dist: Polygram, Polydor

Single (12"): released on Polydor, Oct'86 by Polydor Records. Dist: Polygram, Polydor

PRESENT.
Compact disc: released on Three, '83 Dist: Priority Distribution, EMI

Album: released on Threshold, Sep'83 by Threshold Records. Dist: Decca Distribution, Polygram Distribution

Cassette: released on Threshold, Sep'83 by Threshold Records. Dist: Decca Distribution, Polygram Distribution Deleted '86.

QUESTION.
Single (7"): released on Old Gold, Oct'83 by Old Gold Records. Dist: Lightning, Jazz Music, Spartan, Counterpoint

QUESTION OF BALANCE, (A).
Tracks: / Question / How is it(We are here) / And the tide rushes in / Don't you feel small / Tortoise and the hare / It's up to you / Minstrel's song / Dawning is the day / Melancholy man / Balance, (The).
Compact disc: released on Threshold, Aug'86 by Threshold Records. Dist: Decca Distribution, Polygram Distribution

Album: released on Threshold, Aug'70 by Threshold Records. Dist: Decca Distribution, Polygram Distribution

Cassette: released on Threshold, Aug'70 by Threshold Records. Dist: Decca Distribution, Polygram Distribution Deleted '84.

SEVENTH SOJOURN.
Tracks: / Lost in a lost world / New horizons / For my lady / Isn't life strange! / You and me / Land of make-believe / When you're a free man / I'm just a singer(in a rock and roll band).
Notes: The next chapter in the Moody Blues success story is immortalised on CD with the release of 'Seventh Sojourn'. Unleashed on the masses in 1972, this prestige ad-dition to the Decca catalogue contains two the band's biggest selling singles: "Isn't Life Strange" and "I'm Just a Singer...."
Compact disc: released on Threshold, Sep'86 by Threshold Records. Dist: Decca Distribution, Polygram Distribution

Album: released on Threshold, Nov'72 by Threshold Records. Dist: Decca Distribution, Polygram Distribution

Cassette: released on Threshold, Nov'72 by Threshold Records. Dist: Decca Distribution, Polygram Distribution

SITTING AT THE WHEEL.
Single (7"): released on Threshold, Oct'83 by Threshold Records. Dist: Decca Distribution, Polygram Distribution

Single (12"): released on Threshold, Oct'83 by Threshold Records. Dist: Decca Distribution, Polygram Distribution

THIS IS THE MOODY BLUES.
Double Album: released on Threshold, Oct'74 by Threshold Records. Dist: Decca Distribution, Polygram Distribution

Double cassette: released on Threshold, Oct'74 by Threshold Records. Dist: Decca Distribution, Polygram Distribution

TO OUR CHILDREN'S, CHILDREN'S, CHILDREN.
Tracks: / Higher and higher / Eyes of a child / Floating / Eyes of a child II / I never thought I'd live to be a hundred / Beyond / Out and in / Gypsy / Eternity road / Candle of life / Sun is still shining / I never thought I'd live to be a million / Watching and waiting.
Compact disc: released on London, Aug'86 by London Records. Dist: Polygram

Album: released on Threshold, Nov'69 by Threshold Records. Dist: Decca Distribution, Polygram Distribution

Cassette: released on Threshold, Nov'69 by Threshold Records. Dist: Decca Distribution, Polygram Distribution

VOICES IN THE SKY.
Tracks: / Ride my see-saw / Talking out of question / Driftwood / Never comes the day / I'm just a singer (in a rock and roll band) / Gemini dream / Voice, The / After you came / Question / Veteran cosmic rocker / Isn't life strange / Nights in white satin.
Compact disc: released on Threshold, Nov'84 by Threshold Records. Dist: Decca Distribution, Polygram Distribution

Album: released on Decca, Nov'84 by Decca Records. Dist: Polygram

Cassette: released on Decca, Nov'84 by Decca Records. Dist: Polygram

VOICE, THE.
Single (7"): released on Threshold, Nov'84 by Threshold Records. Dist: Decca Distribution, Polygram Distribution

YOUR WILDEST DREAM.
Tracks: / Your wildest dream / Talkin' talkin'.
Single (7"): released on Polydor, Mar'86 by Polydor Records. Dist: Polygram, Polydor

Single (12"): released on Polydor, Mar'86 by Polydor Records. Dist: Polygram, Polydor

Moody Brothers

CARLTON MOODY & THE MOODY BROTHERS.
Tracks: / Shame on me / I tried at first not to / You turned the light on / Aunt Bea's breakdown / I'll know you're gonna cheat on me / You / You left the water running / Dreaming / Showboat gambler / Little country county fair / Start with the talking / Drive over the mountain.
Album: released on Sundown, Jul'87 by Magnum Music Group Ltd. Dist: Magnum Music Group Ltd, PRT Distribution, Spartan Distribution. Estim retail price in Aug'87 was £6.55.

COTTON EYED JOE.
Notes: Top US country act
Album: released on Sundown, Feb'86 by Magnum Music Group Ltd. Dist: Magnum Music Group Ltd, PRT Distribution, Spartan Distribution

Moody, George

I'M IN LOVE WITH A MEMORY.
Single (7"): released on Marina, Dec'82

Moody, James

BE-BOP REVISITED VOL.4 (Moody, James/Bennie Green).
Album: released on Xanadu (Import), Jan'83

EASY LIVING.
Album: released on Chess Jazz, Oct'84 by Charly Records. Dist: Charly, Swift, PRT

Cassette: released on Chess Jazz, Oct'84 by Charly Records. Dist: Charly, Swift, PRT

MOODY'S MOOD FOR LOVE.
Album: released on Dragon, Jul'87 by Dragon Records. Dist: Jazz Music, Projection, Cadillac

TENOR CONTRASTS (Moody, James/Stan Getz).
Album: released on Esquire, Apr'79 by Titan International Productions. Dist: Jazz Music, Cadillac Music, Swift, Wellard, Chris, Backs, Rough Trade, Revolver, Nine Mile

Moon, April

RECKLESS HEART.
Single (7"): released on Red Bus, Jun'84 by Red Bus Records. Dist: PRT

Moon, Derek

AT THE HAMMOND ORGAN VOL.3.
Album: by Pilgrim Records. Dist: Rough Trade, Cartel

CHRISTMAS CELEBRATION.
Album: by Pilgrim Records. Dist: Rough Trade, Cartel

DEREK MOON PLAYS FOR YOU.
Album: by Pilgrim Records. Dist: Rough Trade, Cartel

DEREK MOON PLAYS FOR YOU VOL.2.
Album: by Pilgrim Records. Dist: Rough Trade, Cartel

Moondoc, Jemel

ATHENS CONCERT, THE (Moondoc, Jemel/Quartet Muntu).
Album: released on Praxis (Greece), May'84 Dist: Mole Jazz

Moone, Jimmy

1931-1940.
Album: released on Queendisc (Import), Apr'81 Dist: Cadillac

Moone, Maggie

DEAR ANYONE.
Album: released on DJM, Jun'78 by DJM Records. Dist: CBS, Polygram

I WANNA BE LOVED BY YOU.
Album: released on Red Bus, Oct'85 by Red Bus Records. Dist: PRT

Cassette: released on Red Bus, Oct'85 by Red Bus Records. Dist: PRT

Mooney, Eddie

I BOUGHT 3 EGGS (Mooney, Eddie & The Graves).
Single (7"): released on TJM, Nov'79

Mooney, Ralph

CORN PICKIN & SLICK SLIDIN (Mooney, Ralph/ James Burton).
Album: released on Pathe MarconiEMI Europe), Jun'84

Moonglows

LOOK, ITS THE MOONGLOWS.
Album: released on Chess, Oct'87 by Charly Records. Dist: Charly, Swift, PRT, Discovery, IMS, Polygram

Cassette: released on Chess, Oct'87 by Charly Records. Dist: Charly, Swift, PRT, Discovery, IMS, Polygram

Moon, Johnny

FORWARD LOVE.
Tracks: / Forward love / Something inside of me.
Single (7"): released on Swoop, '86 Dist: Le Matt Music Distribution

OH CAROL.
Tracks: / Oh Carol / Why can't you stay.
Single (7"): released on Swoop, '67 Dist: Le Matt Music Distribution

Moonlighters

RUSH HOUR.
Album: released on Demon, Nov'83 by Demon Records. Dist: Pinnacle

Moonlighting

MOONLIGHTING (Television soundtrack album) (Various Artists).
Tracks: / Moonlighting (Theme) / Limbo rock / This old heart of mine (is weak for you) / Blue moon / I told ya I love Ya, now get out / Good lovin' / Since I fell for you / When a man loves a woman / Someone to watch over me / Stormy weather.
Album: released on MCA, Jul'87 by MCA Records. Dist: Polygram, MCA

Cassette: released on MCA, Jul'87 by MCA Records. Dist: Polygram, MCA

Moonlight Moods Orchestra

THEMES AND DREAMS.
Tracks: / Chi mai / Chariots of fire / Xanadu / Imagine / For your eyes only / Bermuda triangle / Riders in the sky / Suki yaki / Sailing / MASH / To love the lord / Bright eyes / Fantasy / Magic / Waterfalls / North star / I made it through the rain / Angel of the morning / Give us shelter / Cavatina.
Compact disc: released on Pickwick International inc, '86 by Pickwick International Inc.Records (USA). Dist: Pickwick Distribution, Taylor, H.R., PRT

Boxed set: released on Pickwick, Mar'85 by Pickwick Records. Dist: Pickwick Distribution, Prism Leisure Distribution, Luqtons

Boxed set: released on Pickwick, Mar'85 by Pickwick Records. Dist: Pickwick Distribution, Prism Leisure Distribution, Luqtons

THEMES AND DREAMS VOL.2.

Album: released on Hallmark, Sep'84 by Pickwick Records. Dist: Pickwick Distribution, PRT, Taylors

Cassette: released on Hallmark, Sep'84 by Pickwick Records. Dist: Pickwick Distribution, PRT, Taylors

Moonlight serenade

MOONLIGHT SERENADE Original artists (Original artists).
Compact disc: released on The Compact Collection, Sep'87 by Conifer Records. Dist: Conifer Distribution

Moon, Mick

FOR MY FRIENDS.
Album: released on Tank, Jun'79 by Tank Records.

Moonraker

MOONRAKER (Various Artists).
Tracks: / Moonraker (main title) / Space laser battle / Miss Goodhead meets Bond / Cable car and snake fight / Bond lured to pyramid / Flight into space / Bond arrives in Rio & boat chase / Centrifuge and Corrine put down / Bond smells a rat / Moonraker (end title).
Notes: Produced by John Barry: Music composed & conducted by John Barry: Unart Music Corp. BMI. Written by John Barry & Hal David.
Album: released on EMI (Italy), Dec'86 by EMI Records. Dist: Conifer

Album: released on EMI (Italy), Dec'86 by EMI Records. Dist: Conifer

MOONRAKER Original Soundtrack.
Album: released on EMI (France), Apr'84 by EMI Records. Dist: Conifer

Moonshine Hollow Band

GEORGIA YELLOW HAMMERS, THE.
Album: released on Rounder, Sep'79 Dist: Roots Distribution

Moontwist

SIGHT & SOUND.
Single (7"): released on Certain, Oct'85 Dist: Priority, EMI, Pinnacle

Single (12"): released on Certain, Oct'85 Dist: Priority, EMI, Pinnacle

TALKING ABOUT THE WEATHER.
Tracks: / Talking about the weather / Love in a war zone / Venus on the wing **.
Single (7"): released on London, Mar'87 by London Records. Dist: Polygram

Single (12"): released on London, Mar'87 by London Records. Dist: Polygram

Moore, Alex

PIANO BLUES.
Album: released on Arhoolie, May'81 by Arhoolie Records. Dist: Projection, Topic, Jazz Music, Swift, Roots

Album: released on Arhoolie, May'81 by Arhoolie Records. Dist: Projection, Topic, Jazz Music, Swift, Roots

Moore, Barry

TREATY STONE.
Album: released on Mulligan, Sep'78 by Topic Records. Dist: Roots Distribution, Jazz Music Distribution, JSU Distribution, I & B Distribution, Projection Distribution, Wynd-Up Distribution, Celtic Distributions

Moore, Brew

BREW MOORE & LARS SJOSTEN TRIO (Moore, Brew/Lars Sjosten Trio).
Album: released on Sonet, '74 by Sonet Records. Dist: PRT

BREW MOORE QUINTET, THE (Moore, Brew/Lars Sjosten Trio).
Album: released on Riverside (USA), Aug'84 Dist: Fantasy (USA) Distribution

DANISH BREW (Moore, Brew/Don Byas).
Album: released on Jazz Mark, Apr'83 Dist: Jazz Horizons, Jazz Music

NO MORE BREW.
Notes: Mono production: With Lars Sjosten/Stuer Nordin/F.Noren
Album: released on Storyville, May'86 by Storyville Records. Dist: Jazz Music Distribution, Swift Distribution, Chris Wellard Distribution, Counterpoint Distribution

Moore, Christy

BIKO DRUM.
Tracks: / Biko drum / Derby day.
Single (7"): released on WEA, Jul'87 by WEA Records. Dist: WEA

CHRISTY MOORE & FRIENDS (incl. Ralph McTell).
Album: released on Tara (Ireland), '82 by Tara Records. Dist: I & B Records Distribution, Record Services Distribution (Ireland), Roots Distribution

DELIRIUM TREMENS.
Single (7"): released on WEA Ireland, Aug'85 by WEA Records. Dist: Celtic Distributions, Projection, I & B

IRON BEHIND THE VELVET.
Album: released on Tara (Ireland), '82 by Tara Records. Dist: I & B Records Distribution, Record Services Distribution (Ireland), Roots Distribution

Cassette: released on Tara (Ireland), '82 by Tara Records. Dist: I & B Records Distribution, Record Services Distribution (Ireland), Roots Distribution

LIVE IN DUBLIN.
Album: released on Tara (Ireland), '82 by Tara Records. Dist: I & B Records Distribution, Record Services Distribution (Ireland), Roots Distribution

Album: released on Tara (Ireland), '82 by Tara Records. Dist: I & B Records Distribution, Record Services Distribution (Ireland), Roots Distribution

NICE 'N' EASY.
Tracks: / Bunch of thyme / Nancy Spain / Galtee mountain boy / Boys of Mullabawn / Lanigans rake / Tippin' it up to Nancy / Home by bearna / Little musgrave / Ballard of Timothy Evans / Moving on song (Go!Move!Shift!) / Sacco & Vanzetti.
Album: released on Polydor (Ireland), Aug'86 by Polydor Records. Dist: Polygram, I & B

Cassette: released on Polydor (Ireland), Aug'86 by Polydor Records. Dist: Polygram, I & B

ORDINARY MAN.
Tracks: / Ordinary man / Hard cases.
Single (7"): released on Demon, Sep'86 by Demon Records. Dist: Pinnacle

ORDINARY MEN.
Album: released on WEA Ireland, Aug'85 by WEA Records. Dist: Celtic Distributions, Projection, I & B

Cassette: released on WEA Ireland, Aug'85 by WEA Records. Dist: Celtic Distributions, Projection, I & B

PROSPEROUS.
Album: released on Tara (Ireland), '82 by Tara Records. Dist: I & B Records Distribution, Record Services Distribution (Ireland), Roots Distribution

Cassette: released on Tara (Ireland), '82 by Tara Records. Dist: I & B Records Distribution, Record Services Distribution (Ireland), Roots Distribution

RECOLLECTIONS.
Album: released on Demon, Sep'86 by Demon Records. Dist: Pinnacle

Cassette: released on Demon, Sep'86 by Demon Records. Dist: Pinnacle

RIDE ON.
Album: released on WEA Ireland, Mar'87 by WEA Records. Dist: Celtic Distributions, Projection, I & B

Cassette: released on WEA Ireland, Mar'87 by WEA Records. Dist: Celtic Distributions, Projection, I & B

Compact disc: released on WEA Ireland, Mar'87 by WEA Records. Dist: Celtic Distributions, Projection, I & B

RIDE ON (7").
Single (7"): released on WEA, Aug'84 by WEA Records. Dist: WEA

TIME HAS COME, THE.
Album: released on WEA Ireland, Mar'87 by WEA Records. Dist: Celtic Distributions, Projection, I & B

Cassette: released on WEA Ireland, Mar'87 by WEA Records. Dist: Celtic Distributions, Projection, I & B

Compact disc: released on WEA Ireland, Mar'87 by WEA Records. Dist: Celtic Distributions, Projection, I & B

UNFINISHED REVOLUTION.
Tracks: / Biko drum / Natives / Metropolitan avenue / Unfinished revolution / Other side, The / Messenger boy / On the bridge / Suffocate / Derby day / Dr. Vibes / Pair of brown eyes, A.
Compact disc: released on WEA Ireland, Jun'87 by WEA Records. Dist: Celtic Distributions, Projection, I & B

Album: released on WEA, Jun'87 by WEA Records. Dist: WEA

Cassette: released on WEA, Jun'87 by WEA Records. Dist: WEA

Moore, Dorothy

DOROTHY MOORE.
Album: released on Epic, Nov'77 by CBS Records. Dist: CBS

DOROTHY MOORE ALBUM, THE.
Cassette: released on CBS, Jan'80 by CBS Records. Dist: CBS

Album: released on CBS, Jan'80 by CBS Records. Dist: CBS

LAUGH IT OFF.
Single (7"): released on Malaco, Feb'83 by Malaco Records. Dist: Charly

MISTY BLUE.
Single (7"): released on Malaco, Jul'82 by Malaco Records. Dist: Charly

Single (7"): released on Old Gold, Oct'83 by Old Gold Records. Dist: Lightning, Jazz Music, Spartan, Counterpoint

ONCE MORE WITH FEELING.
Album: released on Epic, Apr'79 by CBS Records. Dist: CBS

Moore, Dudley

DUDLEY DOWN UNDER.
Album: released on Dakota, Dec'81 by Dakota Records. Dist: PRT

Cassette: released on Dakota, Dec'81 by Dakota Records. Dist: PRT

MUSIC OF DUDLEY MOORE.
Double Album: released on Cube, Oct'91 by Dakota Records. Dist: PRT

Double cassette: released on Cube, Oct'91 by Dakota Records. Dist: PRT

SMILIN' THROUGH (Moore, Dudley/Cleo Laine).
Album: released on CBS, Nov'82 by CBS Records. Dist: CBS

Cassette: released on CBS, Nov'82 by CBS Records. Dist: CBS

STRICTLY FOR THE BIRDS (Moore, Dudley/Cleo Laine).
Single (7"): released on CBS, Nov'82 by CBS Records. Dist: CBS

Moore, Francis

MEMORIES (Moore, Francis Orch).
Notes: Orchestral arrangements of: Never ending story, Up where we belong, To love somebody etc.
Compact disc: released on Bridge, '86 Dist: CD Centre Distribution, Pinnacle, Target

MEMORIES VOL.2 (Moore, Francis Orch).
Notes: Orchestral arrangements of: Everybody loves somebody , Rain and tears, Love hurts, Monday monday,Ruby Tuesday, Hotel California etc.
Compact disc: released on Bridge, '86 Dist: CD Centre Distribution, Pinnacle, Target

Moore, Gary

ANTHOLOGY.
Tracks: / Fanatical fascists / Don't belive a word / Spirit / Run to your mama / Women in love / Rest in peace / White Knuckles/Rock & rollin' / Back on the streets / Don't let me be misunderstood / What would you rather bee or a wasp / Dallas warhead (live) / Hurricane / Bad news / I look at you / She's got you / Parisienne walkways.
Double Album: released on Raw Power, Sep'86 Dist: Pinnacle

Double cassette: released on Raw Power, Sep'86 Dist: Pinnacle

BACK ON THE STREETS.
Album: released on MCA, Aug'81 by MCA Records. Dist: Polygram, MCA

Cassette: released on MCA, Aug'81 by MCA Records. Dist: Polygram, MCA

CORRIDORS OF POWER.
Tracks: / Don't take me for a loser / Always gonna love you / Wishing well / Gonna break my heart again / Falling in love / End of the world / Falling in love with you / Rockin' every night / Cold hearted / I can't wait until tomorrow.
Compact disc: released on Virgin, Jul'85 by Virgin Records. Dist: EMI, Virgin Distribution

Album: released on Virgin, Oct'82 by Virgin Records. Dist: EMI, Virgin Distribution

Cassette: released on Virgin, Oct'82 by Virgin Records. Dist: EMI, Virgin Distribution

DIRTY FINGERS.
Compact disc: released on Jet, Nov'86 by Jet Records. Dist: CBS

Album: released on Jet, Jun'84 by Jet Records. Dist: CBS

Cassette: released on Jet, Jun'84 by Jet Records. Dist: CBS

DON'T LET ME BE MISUNDERSTOOD.
Single (7"): released on Jet, Jun'84 by Jet Records. Dist: CBS

EMERALD AISLES.
Notes: Number of tracks: 11. Type of recording: Live. Total playing time: 67minutes
Video-cassette (VHS): released on Virgin, Jan'86 by Virgin Records. Dist: EMI, Virgin Distribution

EMPTY ROOMS.
Single (7"): released on 10, Jul'85 by 10 Records. Dist: Virgin, EMI

Single (12"): released on 10, Jul'85 by 10 Records. Dist: Virgin, EMI

FALLING IN LOVE WITH YOU.
Single (7"): released on Virgin, Feb'83 by Virgin Records. Dist: EMI, Virgin Distribution

Single (12"): released on Virgin, Feb'83 by Virgin Records. Dist: EMI, Virgin Distribution

FRIDAY ON MY MIND.
Tracks: / Friday on my mind / Reach for the sky.
Single (7"): released on 10, Apr'87 by 10 Records. Dist: Virgin, EMI

Single (12"): released on 10, Apr'87 by 10 Records. Dist: Virgin, EMI

Compact disc single: released on 10, 23 May'87 by 10 Records. Dist: Virgin, EMI

GRINDING STONE.
Album: released on CBS, Nov'85 by CBS Records. Dist: CBS

Cassette: released on CBS, Nov'85 by CBS Records. Dist: CBS

LIVE AT THE MARQUEE.
Album: released on Raw Power, Jun'87 Dist: Pinnacle

Cassette: released on Raw Power, Jun'87 Dist: Pinnacle

Compact disc: released on Raw Power, Jul'87 Dist: Pinnacle

LONER, THE.
Single (7"): released on 10, Aug'87 by 10 Records. Dist: Virgin, EMI

Single (12"): released on 10, Aug'87 by 10 Records. Dist: Virgin, EMI

NUCLEAR ATTACK.
Single (12"): released on Jet, Oct'81 by Jet Records. Dist: CBS

OUT IN THE FIELDS (see Lynott, Phil) (Moore, Gary & Phil Lynott).

OVER THE HILLS AND FAR AWAY.
Tracks: / Over the hills and far away / Crying in the shadows.
Single (7"): released on 10, Dec'86 by 10 Records. Dist: Virgin, EMI

Single (12"): released on Ten, Dec'86

Q-FORCE.
Compact disc: released on Jet, Nov'86 by Jet Records. Dist: CBS

ROCKIN' EVERY NIGHT Live in Japan.
Tracks: / Rockin' every night / Wishing well / I can't wait until tomorrow / Nuclear attack / White knuckles / Rockin' and rollin' / Back on the streets / Sunset.
Album: released on Virgin, Jun'86 by Virgin Records. Dist: EMI, Virgin Distribution

Compact disc: released on Virgin, '86 by Virgin Records. Dist: EMI, Virgin Distribution

RUN FOR COVER.
Tracks: / Out in the fields / Reach for the sky / Run for cover / Military man / Empty rooms / Nothing to lose / Once in a lifetime / All messed up / Listen to your heatbeat.
Compact disc: released on 10, Feb'86 by 10 Records. Dist: Virgin, EMI

Album: released on 10, Aug'85 by 10 Records. Dist: Virgin, EMI

VICTIMS OF THE FUTURE.
Tracks: / Murder in the skies / All I want / Hold on to love / Law of the jungle / Victims of the future / Teenage idol / Shapes of things to come / Empty rooms.
Compact disc: released on 10, Aug'85 by 10 Records. Dist: Virgin, EMI

Album: released on Ten, Feb'84

Cassette: released on Ten, Feb'84

WE WANT MOORE.
Tracks: / Murder in the skies / Shapes of things to come / Victims of the future / Cold hearted / End of the world / Back on the streets / So far away / Empty rooms / Don't take me for a loser / Rockin' and rollin'.
Double compact disc: released on 10, '86 by 10 Records. Dist: Virgin, EMI

Album: released on 10, Oct'84 by 10 Records. Dist: Virgin, EMI

Cassette: released on 10, Oct'84 by 10 Records. Dist: Virgin, EMI

WHITE KNUCKLES.
Tracks: / Nuclear attack / White knuckles/Rockin' & rollin' / Run to your mama(live) / You / Dirty fingers / Parisienne walkways(live) / Really gonna rock tonight / Hiroshima / You kissed me sweetly / Dancin' / Hot gossip / She's got you(live).
Notes: All tracks licenced from Jet Records Ltd. This compilation (C) 1985 Castle Communications Ltd, Unit 7, 271 Merton Road, London SW18 5JS
Album: released on Raw Power, Apr'86 Dist: Pinnacle

Cassette: released on Raw Power, Apr'86 Dist: Pinnacle

Compact disc: released on Raw Power, '86 Dist: Pinnacle

WILD FRONTIER.
Tracks: / Run for cover (Live).
Single (7"): released on 10, Feb'87 by 10 Records. Dist: Virgin, EMI

Single (12"): released on Ten, Feb'87

WILD FRONTIER.
Compact disc: released on 10, Feb'87 by 10 Records. Dist: Virgin, EMI

Moore, Geoffrey

SLEEP WITH ME (TONIGHT).
Tracks: / Sleep with me (tonight) / Place in your heart, A.
Single (7"): released on Hit or Miss, 20 Jun'87

Single (12"): released on Hit or Miss, 20 Jun'87

Moore, Grace

ART OF GRACE MOORE, THE.
Tracks: / Old refrain(what shall remain),The / Always / Du Barry, The / I give my heart / Ciribiribin (waltz song) / You are love / Psyche / Si mes vers avaient des ailes(If my poetry had wings) / Que deviennent les roses(What became of the roses) / Toi seule (Only you) / Phidyle / Il est doux,il est bon(He is kind,he is good).
Album: released on RCA, Jun'87 by RCA Records. Dist: RCA, Roots, Swift, Wellard, Chris, I & B, Solomon & Peres Distribution

Cassette: released on RCA, Jun'87 by RCA Records. Dist: RCA, Roots, Swift, Wellard, Chris, I & B, Solomon & Peres Distribution

WAY OF LIFE (Moore, Grace & Kay Van Cooten).
Tracks: / Way of life.
Single (12"): released on Stallion, Jun'86 Dist: Jetstar Distribution

Moore, Hamish

CAULD WIND PIPES.
Album: released on Dunkeld, Jan'85 by Dunkeld Records. Dist: Projection

Moore, Jackie

HOLDING BACK.
Single (7"): released on Satril, Apr'83 by Satril Records. Dist: PRT

Single (12"): released on Satril, Apr'83 by Satril Records. Dist: PRT

THIS TIME BABY.
Single (7"): released on CBS, Aug'84 by CBS Records. Dist: CBS

Moore, Johnny

SUNNYLAND (see under Brown,Charles) (Moore's,Johnny Three Blazers/Charles Brown).

YOUR BROKEN HEART/ SOUL OF LOVE.
Special: released on Towerbell, Oct'82 by Towerbell Records. Dist: EMI

Single (12"): released on Towerbell, Oct'82 by Towerbell Records. Dist: EMI

Moore Jon,

SHORT CUT,A (Moore,Jon & Maggie Holland).
Notes: See Holland,Maggie. For full details.

Moore, Kim

YOU'RE A FOOL/ 100 TIMES AN HOUR.
Single (7"): released on DB, Nov'80 by DB Records. Dist: Pinnacle

Moore, Marilyn

MOODY MARILYN MOORE.
Tracks: / I'm just a lucky so and so / I'll wind / If love is trouble / Is you is or is you ain't my baby? / Born to blow the blues / Lover come back to me / You're driving me crazy / Trav'lin all alone / I cried for you / Leavin'town / Trouble is a man / I got rhythm.
Notes: Licensed from Bethlehem Records
Album: released on Affinity, May'86 by Charly Records. Dist: Charly, Cadillac

Moore, Melba

DANCIN' WITH MELBA MOORE.
Album: released on Buddah, Oct'79 Dist: Swift, Jazz Music, PRT

I CAN'T BELIEVE IT (IT'S OVER).
Single (7"): released on Capitol, Oct'85 by Capitol Records. Dist: EMI

Single (12"): released on Capitol, Oct'85 by Capitol Records. Dist: EMI

LITTLE BIT MORE, A See Jackson, Freddie.

LOT OF LOVE, A.
Tracks: / There I go falling in love again / Falling / It's been so long / I'm not gonna let you go / Love the one I'm with (A lot of love) / You trip me out / Little bit more, A / Stay / When we touch (It's like fire) / Don't go away.
Notes: (P) 1986 Original sound recordings made by Capitol Records Inc.
Compact disc: released on EMI, Mar'87 by EMI Records. Dist: EMI

Album: released on Capitol, Jul'86 by Capitol Records. Dist: EMI

Cassette: released on Capitol, Jul'86 by Capitol Records. Dist: EMI

LOVE'S COMIN' AT YOU See under Bryson, Peabo - Tonight I celebrate my love....

MELBA.
Album: released on Epic, Feb'79 by CBS Records. Dist: CBS

MIND UP TONIGHT.
Single (7"): released on Capitol, Jan'83 by Capitol Records. Dist: EMI

Single (12"): released on Capitol, Jan'83 by Capitol Records. Dist: EMI

NEVER SAY NEVER.
Cassette: released on Capitol, Nov'83 by Capitol Records. Dist: EMI

PORTRAIT OF MELBA, A.
Album: released on Buddah, May'78 Dist: Swift, Jazz Music, PRT

READ MY LIPS.
Album: released on Capitol, Apr'85 by Capitol Records. Dist: EMI

Cassette: released on Capitol, Apr'85 by Capitol Records. Dist: EMI

THIS IS IT.
Single (7"): released on Flashback, Jan'83 by Flashback Records/PRT Records. Dist: Mainline, PRT

UNDERLOVE/ DON'T GO AWAY.
Single (7"): released on Capitol, Feb'83 by Capitol Records. Dist: EMI

Single (12"): released on Capitol, Feb'83 by Capitol Records. Dist: EMI

Moore, Merrill E.

20 GOLDEN PIECES OF....
Album: released on Bulldog Records, Jul'82

RED LIGHT/ HOUSE OF BLUE LIGHT.
Single (7"): released on Bulldog, Jan'80 by Bulldog Records. Dist: President Distribution, Spartan, Swift, Taylor, H.R.

Moore, Michael

TALLEST MAN IN THE WORLD, THE.
Album: released on Plant Life, Nov'81 Dist: Roots

Moore & Napier

BEST OF....
Notes: 10 tracks
Album: released on Starday, Apr'87

Cassette: released on Starday, Apr'87

LONESOME TRUCK DRIVERS.
Album: released on King (USA), Apr'87 Dist: Gusto Distribution

Cassette: released on King (USA), Apr'87 Dist: Gusto Distribution

Moore, Nicky

OTHER SIDE/ LONG TIME (Moore, Nicky Band).
Single (7"): released on Street Tunes, May'82 by Street Tunes Records. Dist: Pinnacle

SAMSON AND....
Album: released on Street Tunes, Oct'83 by Street Tunes Records. Dist: Pinnacle

Moore, Patrick

MUSIC OF PATRICK MOORE, THE Moore,Patrick.
Tracks: / Halley's comet march / Adriadne (from Theseus) / March of the Centaurs / Penguin parade / Triumphal march(entrance of Theseus) / King Neptune / Sunrise polka / Intermezzo (from Perseus & Andromeda) / Vienna clouds / Herald (The).
Notes: Track one performed by the Royal Corps. of Transport.Conducted by Major Terry Kenney. Tracks 2-10 performed by the Ever Ready Brass Band,.Guest conductor:Geoffery Brand.
Album: released on Conifer, Apr'86 by Conifer Records. Dist: Conifer

Cassette: released on Conifer, Apr'86 by Conifer Records. Dist: Conifer

Moore, Ralph

623 C STREET (Moore, Ralph Quartet).
Album: released on Criss Cross, Jul'87 Dist: Jazz Music, Jazz Horizons, Cadillac

Moore,Ray

OH MY FATHER HAD A RABBIT.
Tracks: / Oh my father had a rabbit / Oh my father had a rabbit (Instl).
Single (7"): released on Play, Oct'86 by Play Records. Dist: Spartan

Moore,R.Stevie

EVERYTHING YOU EVER WANTED TO KNOW.
Album: released on New Rose, Mar'84 Dist: Rough Trade, Cartel

GLAD MUSIC.
Album: released on New Rose, Mar'86 Dist: Rough Trade, Cartel

Moore, Sam

SOUL MAN (Moore, Sam & Lou Reed).
Tracks: / Soul man / Sweet Sarah.
Single (7"): released on A&M, Jan'87 by A&M Records. Dist: Polygram

Moore, Scotty

FIRST YEAR, (THE) (see Presley, Elvis) (Moore, Scotty/Elvis Presley/Bill Black).

Moore, Stephen

HITCHHIKERS GUIDE TO THE GALAXY.
Cassette: released on Listen For Pleasure, Nov'81 by MFP Records. Dist: EMI

Moore, Vinnie

MINDS EYE.
Tracks: / In control / Saved by a miracle / Lifeforce / Mind's eye / Jurney, The / Daydream / Hero without honour / N.N.Y. / Shadows of yesterday / Journey, the.
Compact disc: released on Roadrunner (Dutch), Apr'87 Dist: Pinnacle

Album: released on Roadrunner (Dutch), Feb'87 Dist: Pinnacle

Moose, Ade & Walker

LOUNGE AROUND.
Single (7"): released on Lost Moments, Oct'84 Dist: Backs, Cartel

Moose molten metal

MOOSE MOLTEN METAL VOLUME 1 Various artists (Various Artists).
Album: released on Heavy Metal America, Nov'85 by FM-Revolver Records. Dist: EMI

Mop And Smiff

MOP AND SMIFF Various Artists (Various Artists).
Album: released on BBC, May'85 by BBC Records & Tapes. Dist: EMI, PRT, Pye

Cassette: released on BBC, May'85 by BBC Records & Tapes. Dist: EMI, PRT, Pye

Mop & Swiff

MOP & SWIFF GO TO SCHOOL Various artists (Various Artists).
Cassette: released on Bibi, Oct'81

MOP & SWIFF IN SEARCH OF A PEDIGREE Various artists (Various Artists).
Cassette: released on Bibi, Oct'81

MOP & SWIFF ON BUNNY HILL Various artists (Various Artists).
Cassette: released on Bibi, Oct'81

MOP & SWIFF'S DAY SUNNYSEAS Various artists (Various Artists).
Cassette: released on Bibi, Oct'81

Morality Of Strikes

MORALITY OF STRIKES.
Cassette: released on International Report, Oct'81 by Seminar Cassettes. Dist: Audio-Visual Library Services, Davidson Distribution, Eastern Educational Products Distrib., Forlaget Systime Distribution, MacDougall Distribution, Talktapes Distribution, Watkins Books Ltd Distribution, Norton, Jeff Distribution

Moran, Diana

GET FIT WITH THE GREEN GODDESS.
Album: released on BBC, Jul'83 by BBC Records & Tapes. Dist: EMI, PRT, Pye

Cassette: released on BBC, Jul'83 by BBC Records & Tapes. Dist: EMI, PRT, Pye

Moran's Pit Squad, Shaun

MOTORBIKIN.
Single (7"): released on Wat, Dec'84 by Wat Records. Dist: Owlerton Speedways Distribution

Moran, Thomas

BONNY BUNCH OF ROSES O.
Cassette: released on Folktracks, Nov'79 Dist: Roots

Morath, Max

PLAY THE BEST OF SCOTT JOPLIN AND OTHER RAG CLASSICS.
Double Album: released on Vanguard (France), Jun'84

Moray Players

TASTE OF MORAY, A.
Album: released on Ross, '86 by Ross Records. Dist: Ross Distribution, Roots Distribution

Cassette: released on Ross, '86 by Ross Records. Dist: Ross Distribution, Roots Distribution

Moraz & Bruford

FLAGS.
Tracks: / Temples of joy / Split second / Karu / Impromptu too! / Flags / Machines programmed by genes / Drum also waltzes (The) / Infra dig / Way with words (A) / Everything you've heard is true.
Compact disc: released on Editions EG, May'85 by Virgin Records. Dist: EMI

Album: released on Editions EG, Apr'85 by Virgin Records. Dist: EMI

Cassette: released on Editions EG, Apr'85 by Virgin Records. Dist: EMI

MORAZ/ BRUFORD.
Album: released on Editions EG, Feb'84 by Virgin Records. Dist: EMI

Moraz, Patrick

COEXISTANCE (Moraz, Patrick & Syrinx).
Album: released on Carrere, Aug'80 by Carrere Records. Dist: PRT, Spartan

Album: released on Jungle, May'83 by Jungle Records. Dist: Jungle, Cartel

Cassette: released on Jungle, May'83 by Jungle Records. Dist: Jungle, Cartel

FUTURE MEMORIES PATRICK MORAZ LIVE ON TV.
Album: released on Jungle, May'83 by Jungle Records. Dist: Jungle, Cartel

Cassette: released on Jungle, Jun'83 by Jungle Records. Dist: Jungle, Cartel

HUMAN INTERFERENCE.
Tracks: / Light elements / Beyond binary / Cin-a-maah / Stormtroops in loops / Modular symphony (1st movement) / Goto ophioplomel / Kyushu / Stressless / Hyperwaves.
Compact disc: released on EMI, Sep'87 by EMI Records. Dist: EMI. Estim retail price in Sep'87 was £11.99.

OUT IN THE SUN.
Album: released on Charisma, Jun'77 by Virgin Records. Dist: EMI

PATRICK MORAZ.
Album: released on Charisma, Mar'76 by Virgin Records. Dist: EMI

Album: released on Charisma, '78 by Virgin Records. Dist: EMI

STORY OF: PATRICK MORAZ.
Album: released on Charisma, Sep'83 by Virgin Records. Dist: EMI

Cassette: released on Charisma, Sep'83 by Virgin Records. Dist: EMI

TIMECODE.
Album: released on Lamborghini, Nov'84 by Lamborghini Records. Dist: PRT

Cassette: released on Lamborghini, Nov'84 by Lamborghini Records. Dist: PRT

More...

MORE BALLROOM KINGS Various artists (Various Artists).
Tracks: / Beauty is as beauty does / Rag mop / Honey honey mine / Hadacol boogie / Jaw jaw yap yap yap / Waxahachie boogie woogie dishwasher boy / You played on my piano / Let me be / Idaho red / It'd surprise you / I feel the blues coming on / Child psychology / I don't think I'm gonna like it / Old Mcdonald's boogie / You can't hardly get them no more / Seven come eleven.
Notes: Address: Detour Records, P.O. Box 953, London NW2 3SW. Tel. 01-794 5223.
Album: released on Detour, Jul'87 by Detour Records. Dist: Swift, RCA, Jazz Music, Projection

MORE DEATH AND HORROR Various sound effects (More Death and Horror).
Album: released on BBC, '78 by BBC Records & Tapes. Dist: EMI, PRT, Pye

MORE (FILM) Original soundtrack (Pink Floyd).
Album: released on Columbia, '69 by EMI Records. Dist: EMI

MORE FOLK IN WORSHIP (Various Artists).
Album: by BBC Records & Tapes. Dist: EMI, PRT, Pye

MORE GRAMPIAN GEMS Various artists (Various Artists).
Album: released on Grampian, '73 by Grampian Records. Dist: Grampian, Clyde Factors Distributors, Ross

MORE HOME MADE EARLY ROCK & ROLL Various artists (Various Artists).
Album: released on White Label (Holland), Mar'84 Dist: CSA, PRT

MORE MORE MORE OF AMERICAN POP MUSIC Various artists (Various Artists).
Notes: Gary Puckett & the Union Gap, Duane Eddy, Box Tops, Kingston Trio, Del Shannon etc.

MORE-MORE-MORE-OF AMERICAN POP MUSIC Various artists (Various Artists).

Notes: Gary Pucket & Union Gap, Duane Eddy, Box Tops, Kingston Trio, Del Shannon etc.
Compact disc: released on Delta, Apr'87 by Delta Records. Dist: Target

MORE PENNSYLVANIA BOPPERS
Various artists (Various Artists).
Notes: Artists include: Gordon Sizmore & Rex Roat/Rex Zario/Nick Foley/Chuck Anthony and more.
Album: released on White Label, Oct'86 by White Label Records. Dist: Jetstar

MORE RARE ROCK (Various Artists).
Album: released on Collector (White Label Holland), Jan'85 Dist: Swift

WARHEAD.
Album: released on Atlantic, Feb'81 by WEA Records. Dist: WEA

Cassette: released on Atlantic, Feb'81 by WEA Records. Dist: WEA

More, Anthony

INDUSTRIAL DRUMS.
Single (7"): released on Parlophone, Jun'84 by EMI Records. Dist: EMI

Single (7"): released on Parlophone, Jun'84 by EMI Records. Dist: EMI

ONLY CHOICE, THE.
Album: released on Parlophone, Sep'84 by EMI Records. Dist: EMI

Cassette: released on Parlophone, Sep'84 by EMI Records. Dist: EMI

WORLD SERVICE.
Album: released on Do-It, Oct'81 by Do-It Records. Dist: Virgin, EMI

Single (12"): released on Do-It, May'82 by Do-It Records. Dist: Virgin, EMI

Album: released on Do-It, Oct'81 by Do-It Records. Dist: Virgin, EMI

WORLD SERVICE/DIVING GIRLS.
Single (12"): released on Virgin, May'82 by Virgin Records. Dist: EMI, Virgin Distribution

Morecambe & Wise

BBC TV SHOWS, THE.
Album: released on BBC, Oct'84 by BBC Records & Tapes. Dist: EMI, PRT, Pye

Cassette: released on BBC, Oct'84 by BBC Records & Tapes. Dist: EMI, PRT, Pye

IT'S MORECAMBE & WISE.
Cassette: released on BBC, Nov'76 by BBC Records & Tapes. Dist: EMI, PRT, Pye

SO WHAT DO YOU THINK OF THE SHOW SO FAR.
Album: released on BBC, Sep'75 by BBC Records & Tapes. Dist: EMI, PRT, Pye

Cassette: released on BBC, Sep'75 by BBC Records & Tapes. Dist: EMI, PRT, Pye

WEEKEND SOUNDS.
Album: by BBC Records & Tapes. Dist: EMI, PRT, Pye

More Deadly Than The Male

MORE DEADLY THAN THE MALE
Chase, James Hadley (Lankester, Barry).
Cassette: released on Soundings, Mar'85 Dist: Soundings

Morelli, Monique

CHANSONS DU QUAI DES BRUMES.
Album: released on Arion, May'79 Dist: Discovery

Cassette: released on Arion, May'79 Dist: Discovery

More Sherlock Holmes stories

MORE SHERLOCK HOLMES STORIES
(see Conan Doyle, Sir Arthur).

Moresure

ACCELERATION PROCESS.
Album: released on Madrigal (France), Nov'85 Dist: Greyhound

Moreton, Jeff

PERFECTLY ORGANISED.
Album: released on Tank, Jun'79 by Tank Records.

Morgan,Alan

TAKE THEM TO SCHOOL (Morgan,Alan & The School Band).
Tracks: / Take them to school / Take them to school (instumental).
Single (7"): released on Total Eclipse, Feb'87 Dist: Spartan

Morgan,Brett

EVERYTHING IT TAKES.
Tracks: / Everything it takes / If you want it you've got it.
Single (7"): released on Lady, Jan'86 by Relic Records. Dist: M.I.S.

Morgan,Carlton B

SUPERNORMAL THING (THE).
Single (12"): released on T.I.M., Oct'86 by T.I.M. Records. Dist: Backs, Cartel Distribution

Morgan, Dennis

SWANEE RIVER 1945 BROADCAST
(Morgan, Dennis & Al Jolson).

Morgan, Denroy

HAPPY FEELING.
Single (7"): released on Becket, Nov'82

Single (12"): released on Becket, Nov'82

HAPPY FEELING/INSTRUMENTAL VERSION.
Single (7"): released on Roulette, Nov'82 Dist: Discovery Distribution, PRT Distribution

Single (12"): released on Roulette, Nov'82 Dist: Discovery Distribution, PRT Distribution

Morgan, Derek

SEVEN LETTERS/FIRST TASTE OF LOVE.
released on Pama, Oct'82 by Pama Records. Dist: Pama, Enterprise, Jetstar

Morgan,Dermont

THANK YOU VERY MUCH MR EASTWOOD.
Tracks: / Thank you very much Mr.Eastwood(Barry McGuigan song).
Single (7"): released on Stiff, Mar'86 by Stiff Records. Dist: EMI, Record Services Distribution (Ireland)

Morgan, Derrick

CONQUERER THE.
Album: released on Vista Sounds, Mar'85 by Vista Sounds Records. Dist: Jetstar

PEOPLE DECISION.
Album: released on Third World, Jan'77 Dist: Jetstar Distribution

Morgan Fisher

GENEVA/ROLL AWAY THE STONE 79.
Single (7"): released on Pinnacle, Aug'79 by Pinnacle Records. Dist: Pinnacle

HAPPY AGAIN.
Single (7"): released on Cherry Red, Dec'84 by Cherry Red Records. Dist: Pinnacle

UN HOMME ET UNE FILLE.
Single (7"): released on Cherry Red, Sep'83 by Cherry Red Records. Dist: Pinnacle

Morgan, George

BEST OF....
Notes: 10 tracks
Album: released on Starday, Apr'87

Cassette: released on Starday, Apr'87

Morgan, Jane

DAY THE RAINS CAME, (THE).
Single (7"): released on Old Gold, Jul'82 by Old Gold Records. Dist: Lightning, Jazz Music, Spartan, Counterpoint

Morgan, Jayne

DAY THE RAINS CAME, THE.
Single (7"): released on Old Gold, Jul'82 by Old Gold Records. Dist: Lightning, Jazz Music, Spartan, Counterpoint

Morgan, Lanny

IT'S ABOUT TIME.
Album: released on Palo Alto (Italy), Jan'84

Morgan, Lee

CANDY.
Tracks: / Candy / Since I fell for you / C.T.A. / All the way / Who do you love / Personality / All at once you love her.
Compact disc: released on Manhattan-Blue Note, May'87 by EMI America Records (USA). Dist: EMI

COOKER, THE.
Album: released on Blue Note (USA), Sep'84

DELIGHTFULEE MORGAN.
Album: released on Blue Note, Apr'85 by EMI Records. Dist: EMI

EXPOOBIDENT.
Album: released on Affinity, Apr'85 by Charly Records. Dist: Charly, Cadillac

GIGOLO (THE).
Tracks: / Yes I can,no you can't / Yes I can,no you can't / Trapped / Speedball / Gigolo (The) / You go to my head.
Notes: Both Lee Morgan and Wayne Shorter are in amazingly superb form for this quintet session with Harold Mabern,Bob Cranshaw and Billy Higgins. The material ranges from the progressive 'Yes I Can,No You Can't' to Lee's soulful,rapid 'Speedball' to his superb ballard playing on 'You Go To My Head'. This is one if jazz's greatest trumpeters on peak form.
Album: released on Blue Note, Dec'85 by EMI Records. Dist: EMI

HERE'S LEE MORGAN.
Album: released on Affinity, Oct'85 by Charly Records. Dist: Charly, Cadillac

LEE MORGAN VOLUME 3.
Tracks: / Hasaan's dream / Domingo / I remember Clifford / Mesabi chant / Tip-toeing / Tiptoeing (alternate take) / With a song in my heart / With a song in my heart (alternate take) / Speak low / Speak low (alternate take) / Come rain or come shine / Sonny's crib / Sonny's crib (alternate take) / News for Lulu.
Compact disc: released on Blue Note, Aug'87 by EMI Records. Dist: EMI

ONE, TWO & FOUR (Morgan, Lee & John Coltrane).
Double Album: released on Vogue Jazz, May'83

RAJAH, THE.
Album: released on Blue Note, Apr'85 by EMI Records. Dist: EMI

Cassette: released on Blue Note, Sep'87 by EMI Records. Dist: EMI. Estim retail price in Sep'87 was £5.99.

RUMPROLLER, THE.
Tracks: / Rumproller, The / Desert moonlight / Eclipso / Edda / Lady, The / Venus de mildew.
Notes: Produced by Alfred Lion.(P) 1986 Manhattan records,a divison of Capitol Records Inc. Lee Morgan's 'The Sidewinder' was the surprise hit of 1964 when it made the pop charts and crossed over into areas in which no jazz record had gone. Blue Note wasted no time getting Lee back into the studio with a similar band that included Sidewinder holdovers Joe Henderson and Billy Higgins for a follow-up date. This time,the funky title tune was penned by another Blue Note artist Andrew Hill. Other standouts on this recording are Lee's own 'Desert Moonlight' and the Wayne Shorter Balled 'Edda'.
Album: released on Blue Note, May'86 by EMI Records. Dist: EMI

Compact disc: released on Blue Note, Sep'87 by EMI Records. Dist: EMI. Estim retail price in Sep'87 was £11.99.

SEARCH FOR THE NEW LAND.
Tracks: / Search for the new land / Joker, The / Mr Kenyatta / Melancholee / Morgan the Pirate.
Album: released on Blue Note, Sep'87 by EMI Records. Dist: EMI. Estim retail price in Sep'87 was £5.99.

SIDEWINDER.
Tracks: / Sidewinder, The / Totem pole / Gary's notebook / Boy, what a night! / Hocus-pocus.
Compact disc: released on EMI, Mar'87 by EMI Records. Dist: EMI

Album: released on Blue Note, Jul'85 by EMI Records. Dist: EMI

Cassette: released on Blue Note, Jul'85 by EMI Records. Dist: EMI

SONIC BOOM.
Album: released on Liberty-United, Jun'80 by EMI Records. Dist: EMI

VOLUME 3.
Tracks: / Hasaan's dream / Domingo.
Compact disc: released on Manhattan-Blue Note, Aug'87 by EMI America Records (USA). Dist: EMI

Morgan, Maria

ANOTHER HANDFUL OF SONGS (Morgan, Maria & Keith Field).
Album: released on President, Dec'81 by President Records. Dist: Taylors, Spartan

BEST PART OF BREAKING UP, THE.
Single (7"): released on President, Aug'85 by President Records. Dist: Taylors, Spartan

FULL CIRCLE.
Single (7"): released on President, May'80 by President Records. Dist: Taylors, Spartan

HANDFUL OF SONGS, A (Morgan, Maria & Keith Field).
Album: released on President, Dec'81 by President Records. Dist: Taylors, Spartan

RUPERT THE BEAR.
Single (7"): released on President, Sep'79 by President Records. Dist: Taylors, Spartan

Morgan, Meli'sa

DO ME BABY.
Tracks: / Fool's paradise / Heart breaking decision / Do you still love me? / I'll give it when I want it / Do me baby / Getting to know you better / Now or never / Lies.
Compact disc: released on EMI, May'87 by EMI Records. Dist: EMI

Album: released on Capitol, Mar'86 by Capitol Records. Dist: EMI

Cassette: released on Capitol, Mar'86 by Capitol Records. Dist: EMI

Single (7"): released on Capitol, Nov'85 by Capitol Records. Dist: EMI

Single (12"): released on Capitol, Nov'85 by Capitol Records. Dist: EMI

FOOLS' PARADISE.
Tracks: / Fools' paradise / Getting to know you.
Single (7"): released on Capitol, Jul'86 by Capitol Records. Dist: EMI

Single (12"): released on Capitol, Jul'86 by Capitol Records. Dist: EMI

WANTING YOU (Morgan, Meli'sa/Coffee Tea or Me).
Tracks: / Wanting you / Wanting you (radio version) / Wanting you (dub version).
Single (12"): released on Master Mix, 20 Jun'87 by PRT Records. Dist: PRT

Morgan, Portia

INFATUATION.
Single (12"): released on Afrik, May'82 by Afrik Records. Dist: Jetstar

Morgan, Robert W

CRUISIN' 1965 KHJ Los Angeles.
Cassette: released on Increase(USA), Jun'87 by Quicksilver Records (USA).

Morgan, Russ

MUSIC IN THE MORGAN MANNER
(Morgan, Russ & His Orchestra).
Notes: 1938. Mono.
Album: released on Circle(USA), Jan'87 by Jazzology Records (USA). Dist: Jazz Music, Swift, Chris Wellard

ONE NIGHT STAND.
Album: released on Joyce, Jul'82

Morgan, Sam

GET HAPPY BAND, THE.
Album: released on VJM, Aug'84 by Wellard, Chris Distribution. Dist: Wellard, Chris Distribution

Morgan,Tandy band

ACTION.
Notes: All artists royalties to West Midland Children's Hospice
Single (7"): released on FM, Feb'86 by FM-Revolver Records. Dist: EMI

Single (12"): released on FM, Feb'86 by FM-Revolver Records. Dist: EMI

Morgan, Tony

GET IT RIGHT.
Single (7"): released on Cougar, Sep'84 Dist: Pinnacle

Mori, Toshi

ABBA - THE BIG BAND (Mori, Toshi & The Blue Coats).
Album: released on Denon, Mar'82 by Denon Records. Dist: Harmonia Mundi

Moriyama, Takeo Quartet

GREEN RIVER.
Album: released on Enja (Germany), Feb'85 by Enja Records (W.Germany). Dist: Cadillac Music

Morks, Jan

PORTRAIT OF JAN MORKS.
Album: released on Phillips Holland, Mar'85

Cassette: released on Phillips Holland, Mar'85

Morley Tom

WHO BROKE THAT LOVE.
Single (7"): released on Zarjazz, Sep'85 by Virgin. Dist: EMI

Single (12"): released on Zarjazz, Sep'85 by Virgin. Dist: EMI

Morlocks

EMERGE.
Album: released on Midnight (USA), Mar'86

Mormon Tabernacle Choir

BEYOND THE BLUE HORIZON.
Album: released on CBS, Nov'80 by CBS Records. Dist: CBS

LORD'S PRAYER,THE.
Album: by CBS Records. Dist: CBS

MORMON TABERNACLE CHOIR'S GREATEST HITS.
Cassette: released on CBS, Jul'83 by CBS Records. Dist: CBS

SING SONGS OF THE BRITISH ILSES.
Album: released on CBS, Sep'81 by CBS Records. Dist: CBS

Cassette: released on CBS, Sep'81 by CBS Records. Dist: CBS

WHEN YOU WISH UPON A STAR.
Album: released on CBS, Jul'82 by CBS Records. Dist: CBS

Cassette: released on CBS, Jul'82 by CBS Records. Dist: CBS

Morning, Noon & Night

MORNING, NOON AND NIGHT various artists (Various Artists).
Triple album / cassette: released on Ronco, Nov'83

Double cassette: released on Ronco, Nov'83

Morningstar,Jackie

ALABAMA ROCKABILITY.
Single (7"): released on Spade, May'83 by Rollercoaster Records. Dist: Pinnacle, Swift

Morocco

MOROCCAN FOLK MUSIC.
Album: released on Lyrichord (USA), Oct'81 by Lyrichord Records (USA). Dist: Flexitron Distributors Ltd

MOROCCAN STREET MUSIC.
Album: released on Lyrichord (USA), Oct'81 by Lyrichord Records (USA). Dist: Flexitron Distributors Ltd

MOROCCAN SUFI MUSIC.
Album: released on Lyrichord (USA), Oct'81 by Lyrichord Records (USA). Dist: Flexitron Distributors Ltd

Cassette: released on Lyrichord (USA), Aug'82 by Lyrichord Records (USA). Dist: Flexitron Distributors Ltd

MUSIC OF MOROCCO-THE PAN ISLAMIC TRADITION.
Album: released on Lyrichord (USA), Oct'81 by Lyrichord Records (USA). Dist: Flexitron Distributors Ltd

RWAIS(THE)-MOROCCAN BERBER MUSICIANS FROM THE HIGH ATLAS.
Album: released on Lyrichord (USA), Oct'81 by Lyrichord Records (USA). Dist: Flexitron Distributors Ltd

SONGS AND RHYTHMS OF MOROCCO.
Album: released on Lyrichord (USA), Oct'81 by Lyrichord Records (USA). Dist: Flexitron Distributors Ltd

Moroder, Giorgio

CALL ME.
Single (7"): released on Chrysalis, Apr'80 by Chrysalis Records. Dist: CBS

CHROME (see Oakey, Philip) (Moroder, Giorgio & Philip Oakey).

FIRST ELECTRONIC LIVE TO DIGITAL ALBUM.
Album: released on Oasis, Aug'79 by GTO Records. Dist: CBS Distribution

NOW YOU'RE MINE (Moroder,Giorgio & Helen Terry).
Single (7"): released on Virgin, Nov'84 by Virgin Records. Dist: EMI, Virgin Distribution

Single (12"): released on Virgin, Nov'84 by Virgin Records. Dist: EMI, Virgin Distribution

PAUL'S THEME catpeople.
Single (7"): released on MCA, Jul'82 by MCA Records. Dist: Polygram, MCA

Single (12"): released on MCA, Jul'82 by MCA Records. Dist: Polygram, MCA

REACH OUT.
Single (7"): released on CBS, Aug'84 by CBS Records. Dist: CBS

TOGETHER IN ELECTRIC DREAMS (Moroder,Giorgio & Phil Oakley).
Single (7"): released on Virgin, Sep'84 by Virgin Records. Dist: EMI, Virgin Distribution

Single (12"): released on Virgin, Sep'84 by Virgin Records. Dist: EMI, Virgin Distribution

Moronic Surveyor

I SPY(FOR THE DTI).
Single (7"): released on Farse, Oct'85 by Farse Records. Dist: PRT

Single (12"): released on Farse, Oct'85 by Farse Records. Dist: PRT

Morons

MORONS FROM OUTER SPACE.
Single (7"): released on EMI, Mar'85 by EMI Records. Dist: EMI Deleted '86.

Single (12"): released on EMI, Mar'85 by EMI Records. Dist: EMI Deleted '86.

Morpeth Rant

NORTHUMBRIAN COUNTRY MUSIC.
Album: released on Topic, '81 Dist: Roots Distribution

Morricone, Ennio

BEST OF ENNIO MORRICONE.
Tracks: / For a few dollars more / Fist of dollars (A) / Sacco and venzetti / Moses the lawgiver / Metello / God with us / Once apon a time in the west / 1900 / Death rides a horse / Life's tough,isn't it? / Cirbiribin / Scetate.
Compact disc: released on RCA, Oct'84 by RCA Records. Dist: RCA, Roots, Swift, Wellard, Chris, I & B, Solomon & Peres Distribution

CHI MAI.
Single (7"): released on Old Gold, Jan'85 by Old Gold Records. Dist: Lightning, Jazz Music, Spartan, Counterpoint

Album: released on BBC, Apr'81 by BBC Records & Tapes. Dist: EMI, PRT, Pye

Cassette: released on BBC, Apr'81 by BBC Records & Tapes. Dist: EMI, PRT, Pye

FOR A FEW DOLLARS MORE.
Album: released on RCA (Germany), '83

GREATEST MOVIE THEMES.
Compact disc: released on Accord, '86 Dist: Discovery, Target

MASTERPIECES.
Album: released on RCA (Special Imports Service), Jul'84

MOSES original soundtrack.
Album: released on Pye International, Jan'77

ONCE APON A TIME IN AMERICA (SOUNDTRACK).
Notes: Digital reference
Compact disc: released on Mercury, Nov'84 by Phonogram Records. Dist: Polygram Distribution

ONCE UPON A TIME IN THE WEST.
Album: released on Deja Vu, Oct'83 by Deja Vu Records. Dist: Counterpoint Distribution, Record Services Distribution (Ireland)

Album: released on Deja Vu, Oct'83 by Deja Vu Records. Dist: Counterpoint Distribution, Record Services Distribution (Ireland)

Cassette: released on Deja Vu, Oct'83 by Deja Vu Records. Dist: Counterpoint Distribution, Record Services Distribution (Ireland)

ON EARTH AS IT IS IN HEAVEN.
Tracks: / On Earth as it is in heaven / Gabriel's obe.
Notes: 'Gabriel's Obe' is an extra track on 12" version only.
Single (7"): released on Virgin, Oct'86 by Virgin Records. Dist: EMI, Virgin Distribution

Single (12"): released on Virgin, Oct'86 by Virgin Records. Dist: EMI, Virgin Distribution

SAHARA.
Single (7"): released on Red Bus, Mar'84 by Red Bus Records. Dist: PRT

THIS IS ENNIO MORRICONE.
Album: released on EMI, May'81 by EMI Records. Dist: EMI

Cassette: released on EMI, May'81 by EMI Records. Dist: EMI

Morris, Ainsley

MY TERMS ONLY.
Single (7"): released on CBM, Mar'84 Dist: Jetstar, ILA

Morris and the Minors

STATE THE OBVIOUS EP.
Single (7"): released on Round, Feb'80 Dist: PRT, Red Rhino, Cartel

Morris, Byron

VIBRATIONS, THEMES AND SERENADES.
Album: released on EPI, Sep'79

Morris, Chris

CROSS MY PALM/SOMETHING SO RIGHT.
Single (7"): released on Tivoli, Nov'83 by Tivoli Records. Dist: Unknown

Morris Concert Band

AN HOUR OF BRASS BAND MUSIC WITH....
Tracks: / Out with the hunt / Scarborough Fair/Canticle / Shepherd's song (Bailero),The / English country garden / To a wild rose / Barwick Green (Theme from the Archers) / Greensleeves / Londonderry air / English rose (The) / Horse Guards, Whitehall (The) / Overture on famous English airs / Three dale dances / Hailstorm / Red musketeer / Fanfare polka / High spirits / Paperchase / Padstow lifeboat (The).
Cassette: released on Hour Of Pleasure, May'87 by Music For Pleasure Records. Dist: EMI. Estim retail price in Sep'87 was £1.99.

BRASS BAND MUSIC.
Cassette: released on Hour Of Pleasure, Jun'87 by Music For Pleasure Records. Dist: EMI. Estim retail price in Sep'87 was £1.99.

BRASS TRACKS.
Album: released on Meridian, Jul'78 Dist: Harmonia Mundi Distributors

MORRIS CONCERT BAND VOL.1 Director Harry Mortimer.
Album: released on Charivari, Nov'76 by Canon Records. Dist: Polygram, Jazz Music

MORRIS CONCERT BAND VOL.2 Director Harry Mortimer.
Album: released on Charivari, Nov'76 by Canon Records. Dist: Polygram, Jazz Music

Morris, David

SATURDAY NIGHT.
Single (7"): released on Becket, Aug'82

Single (12"): released on Becket, Aug'82

Morris, Dr. Desmond

MANWATCHING.
Cassette: released on Seminar Cassettes, Oct'81 by Seminar Cassettes. Dist: Davidson Distribution, Eastern Educational Products Distrib., Forlaget Systime Distribution, Laser Books Ltd Distribution, MacDougall Distribution, Talktapes Distribution, Watkins Books Ltd Distribution, Norton, Jeff Distribution

SOCCER The soccer tribe.
Cassette: released on Seminar Cassettes, Oct'81 by Seminar Cassettes. Dist: Davidson Distribution, Eastern Educational Products Distrib., Forlaget Systime Distribution, Laser Books Ltd Distribution, MacDougall Distribution, Talktapes Distribution, Watkins Books Ltd Distribution, Norton, Jeff Distribution

Morris, Gary

SECOND HAND HEART.
Tracks: / Love she found in me (The) / Velvet chains / Runaway hearts / Sweet red wine / Headed for a headache / West Texas highway and me / Roll back the rug and dance / Baby bye bye / Wind beneath my wings (The) / Second hand heart / Mama you can't give me no whippin' / Why lady why / Lasso the moon / 100% chance of rain / Second hand heart / Love she found me (The).
Album: released on Warner Bros., Mar'86 by Warner Bros Records. Dist: WEA

Cassette: released on Warner Bros., Mar'86 by Warner Bros Records. Dist: WEA

Single (7"): released on Warner Bros., Feb'86 by Warner Bros Records. Dist: WEA

TRY GETTING OVER YOU.
Tracks: / Try getting over you / Back in her arms again.
Single (7"): released on Warner Bros., Mar'86 by Warner Bros Records. Dist: WEA

Morrish, Ken

BATH WURLITZER ORGAN, THE.
Album: released on Crescent, May'77

Morris, Joe

LOW DOWN BABY.
Album: released on Juke Box Lil (Sweden), Apr'85 by Mr. R&B Records. Dist: Swift

Morris, Johnny

BEDTIME STORIES.
Album: released on BBC, Mar'87 by BBC Records & Tapes. Dist: EMI, PRT, Pye

Cassette: released on BBC, Mar'87 by BBC Records & Tapes. Dist: EMI, PRT, Pye

GEMINEE GEMINII/WILDLIFE QUIZ.
Single (7"): released on Saydisc, Jul'81 by Saydisc Records. Dist: Essex, Harmonia Mundi, Roots, H.R. Taylor, Jazz Music, Swift, Projection, Gamut

KING'S BREAKFAST, THE.
Album: released on Rubber, Jun'82 by Rubber Records. Dist: Roots Distribution, Projection Distribution, Jazz Music Distribution, Celtic Music Distribution, JSU Distribution, Spartan Distribution

Cassette: released on Rubber, Jun'82 by Rubber Records. Dist: Roots Distribution, Projection Distribution, Jazz Music Distribution, Celtic Music Distribution, JSU Distribution, Spartan Distribution

MORE BEDTIME STORIES.
Album: released on BBC, '78 by BBC Records & Tapes. Dist: EMI, PRT, Pye

Cassette: released on BBC, '78 by BBC Records & Tapes. Dist: EMI, PRT, Pye

MORE IT SNOWS / KINGS BREAKFAST.
Single (7"): released on M & W, Dec'81

Morris, Kenny

MAIN MORT, (LA).
Tracks: / La main mort.
Single (12"): released on Temple, Mar'87 by Temple Records. Dist: Roots Distribution, Folksound Distribution, Celtic Music Distribution, Projection Distribution

Morris Motors Band

MARCHING CONTRACTS.
Album: released on Polyphonic, Feb'80 by Polyphonic Records. Dist: Taylors

Morris, Naggo

FALSE RASTA / TWO TIME GIRL.
Single (12"): released on S&G, Jan'83 Dist: Pinnacle

Morris On

MORRIS ON Various Artists (Various Artists).
Tracks: / Morris call / Greensleeves / Nutting girl (The) / Old woman tossed up in a blanket / Shepherd's hey / Trunkles / Staines Morris / Lads a bunchum / Young Collins / Vandals of Hammerwich / Willow tree / Bean setting / Shooting / I'll go a list for a sailor / Princess royal / Cuckoo's nest / Morris off.
Notes: Artists:Richard Thompson,Ashley Hutchings,John Kirkpatrick,Simon Nicol,Dave Matthews,Barry Dransfield.
Album: released on Hannibal, Jun'86 by Hannibal Records. Dist: Charly, Harmonia Mundi, Projection, Celtic Music, Roots

Morrison, Alan

CORNET CASCADE.
Album: released on Look, Feb'84 Dist: R. Smith & Co. Records, H.R. Taylor

Morrison, Bruce

EYES OF SUSPICION (Morrison, Bruce & Rachel Orlane).
Single (7"): released on Compact Organisation, Aug'83 Dist: PRT

Morrison, James

PURE GENIUS OF JAMES MORRISON.
Album: released on Shanachie, Sep'79 Dist: Sterns/Triple Earth Distribution, Roots

Morrison, Junie

TECHNO-FREQS.
Single (7"): released on ZE, May'84 by Island Records. Dist: Polygram

Single (12"): released on ZE, May'84 by Island Records. Dist: Polygram

Morrison, Peter

MEMORIES.
Album: released on Lismor, Nov'81 by Lismor Records. Dist: Lismor, Roots, Celtic Music

Cassette: released on Lismor, Nov'81 by Lismor Records. Dist: Lismor, Roots, Celtic Music

SCOTLAND THE BRAVE.
Album: released on Lismor, '73 by Lismor Records. Dist: Lismor, Roots, Celtic Music

SON OF THE HOMELAND.
Album: released on Lismor, Nov'79 by Lismor Records. Dist: Lismor, Roots, Celtic Music

TOAST TO THE MUSIC OF SCOTLAND (A).
Tracks: / Toast is music / There was a lad / Roamin' in the gloamin' / Wee Deoch & Doris / Love a Lassie (I) / My love is like a red red rose / Calling me home / Man's a man / Lass I lo'v ye dearly / Bonnie lass O'Ballochmyle / Dancing in jyle / Of a the airts / Think on me / Hail Caledonia.
Album: released on Lismor, Jul'86 by Lismor Records. Dist: Lismor, Roots, Celtic Music

Cassette: released on Lismor, Jul'86 by Lismor

Records. Dist: Lismor, Roots, Celtic Music

Morrison, Tommy

HOW COME THE WEAK MAN LOOKS SO STRONG / JUST LATELY.
Single (7"): released on His Cadillac, Nov'83 by His Cadillac Records. Dist: Pinnacle

WHEN THIS PUB CLOSES.
Single (7"): released on Real, '78 Dist: WEA

Morrison, Van

ALAN WATTS BLUES.
Tracks: / Did ye get healed.
Single (7"): released on Mercury, Aug'87 by Phonogram Records. Dist: Polygram Distribution

ASTRAL WEEKS.
Compact disc: released on Warner Bros., May'87 by Warner Bros Records. Dist: WEA

BEAUTIFUL VISION.
Tracks: / Celtic ray / Northern music / Dweller on the threshold / She gives me religion / Beautiful vision / Aryan mist / Across the bridge where angels dwell / Vanlose stairway / Scandinavia / Cleaning windows.
Notes: Digital Stereo
Compact disc: released on Mercury, '83 by Phonogram Records. Dist: Polygram Distribution

Album: released on Mercury, Mar'85 by Phonogram Records. Dist: Polygram Distribution

Cassette: released on Mercury, Mar'85 by Phonogram Records. Dist: Polygram Distribution

CELTIC SWING / MR THOMAS.
Single (7"): released on Mercury, May'83 by Phonogram Records. Dist: Polygram Distribution

Single (12"): released on Mercury, May'83 by Phonogram Records. Dist: Polygram Distribution

COMMON ONE.
Album: released on Mercury, May'83 by Phonogram Records. Dist: Polygram Distribution

Cassette: released on Mercury, May'83 by Phonogram Records. Dist: Polygram Distribution

COMMON ONE, THE.
Tracks: / Haunts of ancient peace / Summertime in England / Satisfied / When heart is open / Wild honey / Spirit.
Compact disc: released on Phonogram, '86 by Phonogram Records. Dist: Polygram

CRY FOR HOME.
Single (7"): released on Mercury, Feb'83 by Phonogram Records. Dist: Polygram Distribution

Single (12"): released on Mercury, Feb'83 by Phonogram Records. Dist: Polygram Distribution

DWELLER ON THE THRESHOLD.
Single (7"): released on Mercury, Apr'84 by Phonogram Records. Dist: Polygram Distribution

HARD NOSE THE HIGHWAY.
Album: released on Warner Brothers, '71 by Warner Bros Records. Dist: WEA

HIS BAND & STREET CHOIR.
Album: released on Warner Brothers, '74 by Warner Bros Records. Dist: WEA

INARTICULATE SPEECH OF THE HEART.
Tracks: / Higher than the world / Connswater / River of time / Celtic swing / Rave on, John Donne / Inarticulate speech of the heart no.1 / Irish heartbeat / Street only knew your name, (The) / Cry for home / Inarticulate speech of the heart no.2 / September night.
Notes: Reissue of 1983 album
Album: released on Mercury, Oct'86 by Phonogram Records. Dist: Polygram Distribution

Cassette: released on Mercury, Oct'86 by Phonogram Records. Dist: Polygram Distribution

Compact disc: released on Mercury, '83 by Phonogram Records. Dist: Polygram Distribution

Album: released on Mercury, Mar'83 by Phonogram Records. Dist: Polygram Distribution

Cassette: released on Mercury, Mar'83 by Phonogram Records. Dist: Polygram Distribution

INTO THE MUSIC.
Notes: Digital stereo
Compact disc: released on Mercury, '83 by Phonogram Records. Dist: Polygram Distribution

Album: released on Mercury, May'83 by Phonogram Records. Dist: Polygram Distribution

Cassette: released on Mercury, May'83 by Phonogram Records. Dist: Polygram Distribution

IT'S TOO LATE TO STOP NOW.
Double Album: released on Warner Brothers, '74 by Warner Bros Records. Dist: WEA

LIVE AT THE GRAND OPERA HOUSE BELFAST.
Album: released on Mercury, Feb'84 by Phonogram Records. Dist: Polygram Distribution

Cassette: released on Mercury, Feb'84 by Phonogram Records. Dist: Polygram Distribution

Compact disc: by Phonogram Records. Dist: Polygram Distribution

MOONDANCE.
Tracks: / Stoned me / Moondance / Crazy love / Caravan / Into the mystic / Come running / These dreams of you / Brand new day / Everyone / Glad tidings.
Compact disc: released on WEA, Jan'86 by WEA Records. Dist: WEA

Album: released on Warner Brothers, '74 by Warner Bros Records. Dist: WEA

MOONDANCE/HIS BAND AND STREET CHOIR.
Cassette: released on Warner Brothers, Oct'82 by Warner Bros Records. Dist: WEA

NO GURU, NO METHOD, NO TEACHER.
Tracks: / Got to go back / Oh the warm feeling / Foreign window / Town called Paradise / In the garden / Tir na nog / Here comes the knight / Thanks for the information / One Irish rover / Ivory tower.
Album: released on Mercury, Jul'86 by Phonogram Records. Dist: Polygram Distribution

Cassette: released on Mercury, Jul'86 by Phonogram Records. Dist: Polygram Distribution

Compact disc: released on Mercury, Jul'86 by Phonogram Records. Dist: Polygram Distribution

PERIOD OF TRANSITION, A.
Album: released on Warner Bros., Mar'77 by Warner Bros Records. Dist: WEA

POETIC CHAMPIONS COMPOSE.
Tracks: / Spanish Steps / Mystery, The / Queen of the slipstream / I forgot that love existed / Sometimes I feel like a motherless child / Celtic Excavation / Someone like you / Alan Watts Blues / Give me my rapture / Did ye get heeled? / Allow me.
Album: released on Mercury, Sep'87 by Phonogram Records. Dist: Polygram Distribution

Cassette: released on Mercury, Sep'87 by Phonogram Records. Dist: Polygram Distribution

Compact disc: released on Mercury, Sep'87 by Phonogram Records. Dist: Polygram Distribution

SENSE OF WONDER, A.
Tracks: / Tore down a'la rimbaud / Ancient of days / Evening meditation / Master's eyes (The) / What would I do / Sense of wonder (A) / Boffyflow and Spike / If you only knew / Let the slave (Including The price of experience/A new 'man).
Notes: Lyrically, this album sees Van in an optimistic comntemplative mood. Musically, there are more up-tempo numbers than on 'Inarticulate Speech'. With two songs by other writers, two instrumentals, and two tracks featuring Van backed by the excellent Moving Hearts, it's a varied balanced record that's bound together by Van's best vocal performances in years. Digital Stereo.
Compact disc: released on Mercury, Feb'85 by Phonogram Records. Dist: Polygram Distribution

Album: released on Mercury, Feb'85 by Phonogram Records. Dist: Polygram Distribution

Cassette: released on Mercury, Feb'85 by Phonogram Records. Dist: Polygram Distribution

ST. DOMINICS PREVIEW.
Album: released on WEA, '74 by WEA Records. Dist: WEA

T.B.SHEETS.
Compact disc: released on Bellaphon, '86 by Bellaphon Records. Dist: IMS-Polygram

THEM FEATURING VAN MORRISON.
Double Album: released on Deram, '73 by Decca Records. Dist: Polygram

THIS IS WHERE I CAME IN.
Album: released on Bang, Sep'77

TUPELO HONEY.
Album: released on Warner Brothers, '74 by Warner Bros Records. Dist: WEA

VEEDON FLEECE.
Album: by Warner Bros Records. Dist: WEA

WAVELENGTH.
Cassette: released on Warner Brothers, '78 by Warner Bros Records. Dist: WEA

Album: released on Warner Brothers, '78 by Warner Bros Records. Dist: WEA

Morrissey, Bill

BILL MORRISSEY.
Album: released on Philo (USA), Apr'86

Morrissey, Dick

AFTER DARK.
Tracks: / I won't last a day without you / March on / They say it's wonderful / Pili pili / Way we were / Running out of time / Lou Grant / Change partners.
Notes: Digital stereo
Compact disc: released on Coda, Oct'84 by Coda Records. Dist: Pinnacle, Cartel, WEA, Roots

Album: released on Coda, Mar'83 by Coda Records. Dist: Pinnacle, Cartel, WEA, Roots

CAPE WRATH (Morrissey, Dick & Jim Mullen).
Album: released on Harvest, Apr'79 by EMI Records. Dist: Roots, EMI

Morrissey Mullen

BADNESS.
Tracks: / Do like you / Dragonfly / Blue tears / Stay awhile / Badness / Pass the music on / Slipstream.
Notes: Digital Stereo
Compact disc: released on Beggars Banquet, Oct'84 by Beggars Banquet Records. Dist: WEA

Album: released on Beggars Banquet, Jul'81 by Beggars Banquet Records. Dist: WEA

BLADE RUNNER.
Single (7"): released on Beggars Banquet, Nov'82 by Beggars Banquet Records. Dist: WEA

Single (12"): released on Beggars Banquet, Nov'82 by Beggars Banquet Records. Dist: WEA

COME AND GET ME.
Single (7"): released on Beggars Banquet, Feb'82 by Beggars Banquet Records. Dist: WEA

Single (12"): released on Beggars Banquet, Feb'82 by Beggars Banquet Records. Dist: WEA

IT'S ABOUT TIME.
Tracks: / Stop and look around / It's about time / Ounce of bounce / So so fine / Ol' sax and Captain Axe / Bladerunner / Why does it always happen to me? / Do I do / Above the clouds.
Notes: Digital Stereo
Compact disc: released on Beggars Banquet, Oct'84 by Beggars Banquet Records. Dist: WEA

Album: released on Beggars Banquet, Mar'83 by Beggars Banquet Records. Dist: WEA

Cassette: released on Beggars Banquet, Mar'83 by Beggars Banquet Records. Dist: WEA

LIFE ON THE WIRE.
Tracks: / Life on the wire / Takin' time / Face of a child / Come and get me / Brazil nut / Ships that pass in the night / Making waves / Running out of time.
Notes: Digital Stereo
Compact disc: released on Beggars Banquet, Oct'84 by Beggars Banquet Records. Dist: WEA

Album: released on Beggars Banquet, Mar'82 by Beggars Banquet Records. Dist: WEA

Cassette: released on Beggars Banquet, Mar'82 by Beggars Banquet Records. Dist: WEA

Single (7"): released on Beggars Banquet, Apr'82 by Beggars Banquet Records. Dist: WEA

OLD SAX AND CAPTAIN AXE.
Single (7"): released on Beggars Banquet, Jul'83 by Beggars Banquet Records. Dist: WEA

Single (12"): released on Beggars Banquet, Jul'83 by Beggars Banquet Records. Dist: WEA

SO SO FINE.
Single (7"): released on Beggars Banquet, Apr'83 by Beggars Banquet Records. Dist: WEA

STAY AWHILE.
Single (7"): released on Beggars Banquet, Sep'81 by Beggars Banquet Records. Dist: WEA

Single (12"): released on Beggars Banquet, Sep'81 by Beggars Banquet Records. Dist: WEA

THIS MUST BE THE PLACE.
Album: released on Coda, May'84 by Coda Records. Dist: Pinnacle, Cartel, WEA, Roots

Cassette: released on Coda, May'84 by Coda Records. Dist: Pinnacle, Cartel, WEA, Roots

Morris, Tom

PAST JAZZ MASTER, A 1923 - with Clarence Williams Blue Five.
Album: released on Swaggie (Australia), Jan'83

TOM MORRIS PAST JAZZ MASTERS & CLARENCE WILLIAMS (Morris, Tom Past Jazz Masters & Clarence Williams Blue Five).
Album: released on Fountain, Apr'79 by Retrieval Records. Dist: Jazz Music, Swift, VJM, Wellard, Chris, Retrieval

Morriston Orpheus Choir

AMAZING GRACE.
Notes: Musical Director: Alwyn Humphreys B.A.(Mus) L.Mus. T.C.L. Produced by Bob Barratt.
Album: released on Music For Pleasure, Jun'86 by EMI Records. Dist: EMI

Cassette: released on Music For Pleasure, Jun'86 by EMI Records. Dist: EMI

HIRAETH.
Tracks: / Cydganed pawb (Let all the world in every corner sing) / Hiraeth / Credo (from Gounod's St. Cecilia Mass) / My bonny lass she smileth / Hyder / Jesu, who didst ever guide me / Tydi a roddaist / Kalinka / I'm gonna walk / Chorus & Laura's song from Casanova / Rock-a my soul / Rose, The / Duet from the Pearl Fishers / From far inside the shrine.
Album: released on Grasmere, Aug'87 by Grasmere Records. Dist: EMI

Cassette: released on Grasmere, Aug'87 by Grasmere Records. Dist: EMI

HOW GREAT THOU ART.
Album: released on MFP, Nov'82 by EMI Records. Dist: EMI

Cassette: released on MFP, Nov'82 by EMI Records. Dist: EMI

MORRISTON ORPHEUS CHOIR, THE A digital recording.
Tracks: / Cydganed pawb (let all the world in every corner sing) / Hiraeth / Credo / Jesy, who didst ever guide me / My bonny lass she smileth / Hyder / Tydi a roddaist (Thou gavest) / I'm gonna walk / Kalinka / Rose, The / Chorus and Laura's song from 'Casanova' / Rock-a my soul / Duet from the pearl fishers: from far inside the shrine.
Notes: A Digital recording. Musical Director: Alan Humphries BA (Mus),L.Mus TCL. Recorded digitally in Wales on St. David's Day, at the Brangwyn Hall, Swansea. Organist:Alun Tregellis Williams. Pianist: Mair Wyn Jones ARCM, LGSM. Produced by Bob Barratt with Abbey Road Mobile. Engineer: Stuart Eltham. Location engineer: Graham Kirkby. Digital editing: Juliet Corp at Nova Studios.Mastered by Harry Moss at EMI's Abbey Road (London) Studios. Secretary to the choir: R. Royston Pugh, 27 Weedlands Park Drive, Cadoxton, Neath, West Glamorgan. Manufactured and distributed by EMI Records. (C) & (P) 1987. Original Sound Recordings made by Grasmere Music Ltd. Cover design: Roy Keighley. Cover photo: Worms Head, Gower, by courtesy of Wales Tourist Board.
Album: released on Grasmere, Jul'87 by Grasmere Records. Dist: EMI

Cassette: released on Grasmere, Jul'87 by Grasmere Records. Dist: EMI

MYFANWY.
Album: released on Music For Pleasure, Jul'84 by EMI Records. Dist: EMI

Cassette: released on Music For Pleasure, Jul'84 by EMI Records. Dist: EMI

SAY IT WITH MUSIC.
Album: released on Music For Pleasure, Jun'85 by EMI Records. Dist: EMI

Cassette: released on Music For Pleasure, Jun'85 by EMI Records. Dist: EMI

SING WE MERRILY.
Album: released on Note, Apr'77 by EMI Records. Dist: EMI

THIS IS WALES.
Cassette: released on EMI, May'80 by EMI Records. Dist: EMI

WE'LL KEEP A WELCOME.
Cassette: released on Note, Sep'79 by EMI Records. Dist: EMI

WE'LL KEEP A WELCOME - VOL.3.
Album: released on Lugtons Special Products, Jun'83

WE'LL KEEP A WELCOME - VOL.4.
Album: released on Lugtons Special Products, Jun'83

YOU'LL NEVER WALK ALONE.
Album: released on Grasmere, Sep'85 by Grasmere Records. Dist: EMI

Cassette: released on Grasmere, Sep'85 by Grasmere Records. Dist: EMI

Morse, Ella Mae

BARRELL HOUSE. BOOGIE AND THE BLUES.
Album: released on Pathe Marconi, Sep'84 Dist: Swift

HITS OF ELLA MAE MORSE, THE.
Compact disc: released on Capitol, Oct'84 by Capitol Records. Dist: EMI

Cassette: released on Capitol, Oct'84 by Capitol Records. Dist: EMI

MORSE CODE, THE.
Tracks: / Day in-day out / My funny valentine / Ac-cent-tchu-ate the positive / When my sugar walks down the street / Dream a little dream of me / Heart and soul / Jersey bounce / I can't get started / Baby, won't you please come home / You go to my head / Music, Maestro, please.
Notes: Orchestra conducted by the brilliant Billy May, we have here an album torch blu-es to brisk up tempo. Released originally in 1957 and still sounding as fresh astoday as then.
Album: released on Capitol T (USA), Dec'85 Dist: Conifer

SENSATIONAL.
Tracks: / Mr.Memory Maker / Put your arms around me honey / Livin' livin' livin' / Greyhound / Jump back honey / Tennessee saturday night / Sensational / Ain't that a shame / Razzle dazzle / Down in Mexico / Smake dab in the middle / I'm gone / Tain't what you do, it's the way that you do it / Seventeen.
Notes: A swing selection of tracks from "Ain't That a Shame" to "Tain't What you Do, It's the Way That You Do it", superbly delievered by one of the great ladies of the 40's and 50's.Along with her comparable contemporary, Nellie Lutcher, this lady enjoyed million selling successes in her era. Here she employs five diffe-rent orchestras including the late Nelson Riddle's.
Album: released on Capitol, Jan'86 by Capitol Records. Dist: EMI

Morse, Lee

MORSE, LEE & HER BLUE GRASS BOYS (Morse, Lee & Her Blue Grass Boys).
Notes: Featuring Goodman/Dorsey/E. Lang/etc.
Album: released on Take 2, Jun'86 Dist: Swift Distribution, Jazz Music Distribution

MORSE, LEE & HER BLUE GRASS BOYS 1925-32 (Morse, Lee & Her Blue Grass Boys).
Cassette: released on Emporium Cassettes, Jun'86 by Emporium Cassettes Records. Dist: Jazz Music

Morse, Steve Band

INTRODUCTION, THE.
Album: released on Asylum, Sep'84 by WEA Records. Dist: WEA

STAND UP.
Album: released on Elektra, Nov'84 by WEA Records. Dist: WEA

Cassette: released on Elektra, Nov'84 by WEA Records. Dist: WEA

Mortier Organ

101 KEY MORTIER DANCE ORGAN (Mortier Organ Favourites).
Cassette: released on Amberlee, Nov'81 by Amberlee Records. Dist: Amberlee Records, H.R. Taylor

FOUR COLUMNS 97 key (Mortier Show Organ).
Album: released on Joy, '74 by President Records. Dist: Jazz Music, Swift, President Distribution

SING AND DANCE WITH THE MORTIER ORGAN (Mortier Dance Organ).
Album: by Decca Records. Dist: Polygram

Mortimer, Harry

CAROLS AT CHRISTMAS (Mortimer, Harry & His All Stars).
Album: released on MFP, Dec'82 by EMI Records. Dist: EMI

Cassette: released on MFP, Dec'82 by EMI Records. Dist: EMI

MAN OF BRASS (Mortimer, Harry OBE).
Album: released on Double-Up, Aug'81 by EMI Records.

Morton, Ivan

YOU BETTER COME HOME.
Tracks: / You better come home / Sellafield rap.
Single (7"):

Morton, Jelly Roll

BEST OF JELLY ROLL MORTON.
Album: released on RCA (Germany), '83

BLACK BOTTOM STOMP.
Album: released on Saar Giants Of Jazz (Italy), Sep'85 Dist: Mainline

Cassette: released on Saar Giants Of Jazz (Italy), Sep'85 Dist: Mainline

CLIMAX RAG 1.
Album: released on Astan, Nov'84 by Astan Records. Dist: Counterpoint

Cassette: released on Astan, Nov'84 by Astan Records. Dist: Counterpoint

COMPLETE JELLY ROLL MORTON VOLS.7/8 1930-40.
Double Album: released on RCA (France), '83 by RCA Records. Dist: Discovery

COMPLETE JELLY ROLL MORTON VOLS.5/6 1929-30.
Tracks: / Wild man blues / Georgia swing / Kansas city stomps / Shoe shiner's drag / Boogaboo / Shreveport stomp / Mournful serenade / Red hot pepper / Deep creek / Pep / Seattle hunch / Frances / Freakish / Burnin' the iceberg / Courthouse bump / Pretty Lil / Sweet Aneta mine / New Orleans bump / Down my way / Try me out / Tank town bump / Sweet Peter.
Album: released on Jazz Tribune (USA), Sep'86 Dist: Discovery

Cassette: released on Jazz Tribune (USA), Sep'86 Dist: Discovery

Double Album: released on RCA (France), '83 by RCA Records. Dist: Discovery

COMPLETE JELLY ROLL MORTON VOLS.1/2 1926-27.
Tracks: / Black bottom stomp / Smoke house blues / Chant, The / Sidewalk blues.
Double Album: released on Jazz Tribune (USA), Sep'86 Dist: Discovery

Double cassette: released on Jazz Tribune (USA), Sep'86 Dist: Discovery

Double Album: released on RCA (France), '83 by RCA Records. Dist: Discovery

COMPLETE JELLY ROLL MORTON VOLS.3/4 1927-29.
Tracks: / Wild man's blues / Georgia swing / Kansas City.
Double Album: released on Jazz Tribune (USA), Sep'86 Dist: Discovery

Double cassette: released on Jazz Tribune (USA), Sep'86 Dist: Discovery

Double Album: released on RCA (France), '83 by RCA Records. Dist: Discovery

COMPLETE, VOL.5/6 (1929-30).
Tracks: / Each day / Fusy Mabel / Ponchartrain / Oil well / Load of coal / Jersey Joe / Mint julep / Turtle twist / Futuristic blues / Harmoney blues / Little Lawrence / That'll never do.
Double Album: released on Jazz Tribune, Jun'86 Dist: Discovery

Double cassette: released on Jazz Tribune, Jun'86 Dist: Discovery

COMPLETE, VOL.7/8 (1930-40).
Tracks: / High society / Gambling Jack / Oh didn't he ramble / Climax rag / Crazy chords / Ballin' the Jack / Primrose stomp / New crawley blues / Low gravy / Stokin' away / Mushmouth shuffle.
Album: released on Jazz Tribune, Jun'86 Dist: Discovery

Cassette: released on Jazz Tribune, Jun'86 Dist: Discovery

DOCTOR JAZZ.
Tracks: / Black bottom stomp / Chant / Sidewalk blues / Dead man blues / Original Jelly Roll blues / Doctor jazz / Wild man blues / Red hot pepper / Jungle blues / Pearls / Kansas city stomp / Little Lawrence.
Album: released on RCA, Jul'86 by RCA Records. Dist: RCA, Roots, Swift, Wellard, Chris, I & B, Solomon & Peres Distribution

Cassette: released on RCA, Jul'86 by RCA Records. Dist: RCA, Roots, Swift, Wellard, Chris, I & B, Solomon & Peres Distribution

GENNET PIANO SOLOS, THE 1923-24.
Album: released on Swaggie (Australia), Jan'83

HIS RED HOT PEPPERS VOL.1 (Morton, Jelly Roll & His Red Hot Peppers).
Album: released on Joker Import, Apr'81

HIS RED HOT PEPPERS & TRIOS VOL.6 (Morton, Jelly Roll & His Red Hot Peppers).
Album: released on Joker Import, Apr'81

HIS RED HOT PEPPERS & TRIOS VOL.7 (Morton, Jelly Roll & His Red Hot Peppers).
Album: released on Joker Import, Apr'81

HIS RED HOT PEPPERS VOL.4 (Morton, Jelly Roll & His Red Hot Peppers).
Album: released on Joker Import, Apr'81

HIS RED HOT PEPPERS VOL.2 (Morton, Jelly Roll & His Red Hot Peppers).
Album: released on Joker Import, Apr'81

HIS RED HOT PEPPERS VOL.3 (Morton, Jelly Roll & His Red Hot Peppers).
Album: released on Joker Import, Apr'81

HIS RED HOT PEPPERS VOL.5 (Morton, Jelly Roll & His Red Hot Peppers).
Album: released on Joker Import, Apr'81

I'M A WINNIN' BOY.
Album: released on Joy, Oct'81 by President Records. Dist: Jazz Music, Swift, President Distribution

JAZZ CLASSICS IN DIGITAL STEREO.
Tracks: / Black bottom stomp / Chant (The) / Dead man blues / Grandpa's spells / Original Jelly Roll blues / Beale Street blues / Ham and eggs / You need some loving / Kansas City stomps / Shoe shiner's drag / Deep creek / Pretty Lil / New Orleans bump / Ponchartrain / Blue blood blues / I'm alone without you.
Album: released on BBC, Oct'86 by BBC Records & Tapes. Dist: EMI, PRT, Pye

Cassette: released on BBC, Oct'86 by BBC Records & Tapes. Dist: EMI, PRT

Compact disc: released on BBC, Oct'86 by BBC Records & Tapes. Dist: EMI, PRT,

JELLY ROLL MORTON.
Album: released on Deja Vu, Jan'87 by Deja Vu Records. Dist: Counterpoint Distribution, Record Services Distribution (Ireland)

Cassette: released on Deja Vu, Jan'87 by Deja Vu Records. Dist: Counterpoint Distribution, Record Services Distribution (Ireland)

Album: released on Joker, Apr'81 Dist: Counterpoint, Mainline, Record Services Distribution (Ireland)

JELLY ROLL MORTON 1939.
Album: released on Commodore Classics, Dec'84 by Teldec Records (Germany). Dist: Conifer, IMS, Polygram

JELLY ROLL MORTON 1923-25.
Album: released on Fountain, Apr'79 by Retrieval Records. Dist: Jazz Music, Swift, VJM, Wellard, Chris, Retrieval

JELLY ROLL MORTON'S HOT SEVEN AND HOT SIX 1940.
Album: released on Commodore Classics, May'87 by Teldec Records (Germany). Dist: Conifer, IMS, Polygram

KINGS OF NEW ORLEANS JAZZ (Morton, Jelly Roll & His Red Hot Peppers).
Album: released on RCA International. Jun'81

Cassette: released on RCA International, Jun'81

LAST BAND DATES 1940.
Album: released on Commodore Classics, Sep'82 by Teldec Records (Germany). Dist: Conifer, IMS, Polygram

LIBRARY OF CONGRESS RECORDINGS VOL.2.
Album: released on Swaggie (Australia), Jan'83

LIBRARY OF CONGRESS RECORDINGS VOL.1.
Album: released on Swaggie (Australia), Jan'83

LIBRARY OF CONGRESS RECORDINGS VOL.6.
Album: released on Classic Jazz Masters, Dec'86 by Mainline Record Company. Dist: Mainline, Swift, Jazz Music

Album: released on Swaggie (Australia), Jan'83

LIBRARY OF CONGRESS RECORDINGS VOL.3.
Album: released on Swaggie (Australia), Jan'83

LIBRARY OF CONGRESS RECORDINGS VOL.5.
Album: released on Swaggie (Australia), Jan'83

LIBRARY OF CONGRESS RECORDINGS VOL.7.
Album: released on Classic Jazz Masters, Dec'86 by Mainline Record Company. Dist: Mainline, Swift, Jazz Music

Album: released on Swaggie (Australia), Jan'83

LIBRARY OF CONGRESS RECORDINGS VOL.4.
Album: released on Classic Jazz Masters, Dec'86 by Mainline Record Company. Dist: Mainline, Swift, Jazz Music

Album: released on Swaggie (Australia), Jan'83

LIBRARY OF CONGRESS RECORDINGS VOL.8.
Album: released on Classic Jazz Masters, Dec'86 by Mainline Record Company. Dist: Mainline, Swift, Jazz Music

Album: released on Swaggie (Australia), Jan'83

MISTER JELLY LORD (Morton, Jelly Roll & His New Orleans Rhythm Kings).
Album: released on Rhapsody, '74 by President Records. Dist: Taylors, Swift, Jazz Music, Wellard, Chris

NEW ORLEANS MEMORIES.
Album: released on Commodore Classics, May'87 by Teldec Records (Germany). Dist: Conifer, IMS, Polygram

Compact disc: released on Commodore Classics, May'87 by Teldec Records (Germany). Dist: Conifer, IMS, Polygram

RARITIES VOL.1.
Album: released on Rhapsody, '74 by President Records. Dist: Taylors, Swift, Jazz Music, Wellard, Chris

RARITIES VOL.2.
Notes: Mono.
Album: released on Rhapsody, Jun'86 by President Records. Dist: Taylors, Swift, Jazz Music, Wellard, Chris

SOLO PIANO SESSION 1924-1938.
Album: released on Swaggie (Australia), Jan'83

WEST END BLUES.
Notes: Collectors Edition Series. Mono recording.
Album: released on Meteor, Mar'86 by Magnum Music Group Ltd. Dist: Magnum Music Group Ltd, PRT Distribution, Spartan Distribution

Morton, Mandy Band

SEA OF STORMS.
Album: released on Polydor, Nov'80 by Polydor Records. Dist: Polygram, Polydor

Morton, Mike

CHRISTMAS CRACKERS / SANTA'S WEIN ER DINER (Morton, Mike Orchestra).
Single (7"): released on M&H, Dec'83 by M&H Records. Dist: PRT Distribution

FIDDLER ON THE GROOVE / EINE KLEINE (Morton, Mike Orchestra).
Single (7"): released on M&H, Nov'83 by M&H Records. Dist: PRT Distribution

Single (12"): released on M&H, Nov'83 by M&H Records. Dist: PRT Distribution

UNFORGETTABLE CHRISTMAS (Morton, Mike Orchestra).
Album: released on M&H, Dec'83 by M&H Records. Dist: PRT Distribution

Single (12"): released on M&H, Dec'83 by M&H Records. Dist: PRT Distribution

UNFORGETTABLE GREATS (Morton, Mike Orchestra).
Album: released on M&H, Dec'83 by M&H Records. Dist: PRT Distribution

Cassette: released on M&H, Dec'83 by M&H Records. Dist: PRT Distribution

UNFORGETTABLE SWING TIME (Morton, Mike Orchestra).
Album: released on M&H, Dec'83 by M&H Records. Dist: PRT Distribution

Cassette: released on M&H, Dec'83 by M&H Records. Dist: PRT Distribution

WINDS OF WAR LOVE THEME / BERLIN BEAT (Morton, Mike Orchestra).
Single (7"): released on M&H, Oct'83 by M&H Records. Dist: PRT Distribution

WINDS OF WAR (THEME).
Single (7"): released on Sounds Right, Jul'85 Dist: MIS-EMI Distribution

Morton, Milt

SPIRIT OF THE THING (Morton, Milt & Mandy Urban Planners).
Single (7"): released on Maze, Oct'83

Morton, Pete

FRIVOLOUS LOVE.
Album: released on Harbour Town, Jul'87

Morton, Ronnie

RONNIE & JOHNNY (Morton, Ronnie & John Pugh).
Album: released on Waterfront, Mar'84 by Waterfront Records. Dist: Rough Trade, Cartel, Projection, Roots

Mosalini

LA BORDONA (Mosalini;Beytelman;Carati ni).
Album: released on ARC (Accordion Records) '84 Dist: Accordion Record Club

Mosby, Curtis
CURTIS MOSBY BLUE BLOWERS.
Album: released on VJM, Apr'79 by VJM (UK) Records. Dist: Swift

SAL MOSCA MUSIC.
Album: released on Interplay, Aug'79 by Interplay Records. Dist: Jazz Music. Swift

Mosch, Ernst
GERMAN OOM-PAH MUSIC.
Album: released on Teldec (Germany), Jul'84 by Import Records. Dist: IMS Distribution, Polygram Distribution

Cassette: released on Teldec (Germany), Jul'84 by Import Records. Dist: IMS Distribution, Polygram Distribution

ORIGINAL EGERLANDER.
Album: released on Telefunken (Germany), Nov'83 Dist: Decca Distribution, IMS, Polygram

Cassette: released on Telefunken (Germany), Nov'83 Dist: Decca Distribution, IMS, Polygram

STAY YOUNG AT HEART (BLEIB'IM HERZEN JUNG) (Mosch, Ernst & The Original Street Musicians).
Tracks: / Bleib'im Herzen jung / Als der herrgott durch bohmen ging / Auf der ponyfarm / Seefest-walzer / Eine frau wie du / Los geht's / Musikantenball / Beim vinzenzifest / Ein ganzes leben lang / Wir sind die freunde vom sportvereinin.
Notes: You can almost see the lederhosen and feel your thighs being slapped when you listen to Ernst Mosch and his Original Street Musicians. A superb example of German Oompah.
Compact disc: released on Teldec, May'87

Cassette: released on Teldec, May'87

Album: released on Teldec, May'87

Moscow
GABRIEL.
Single (7"): released on Amazing, Jul'83 by Big Beat Records. Dist: Pinnacle, Cartel, Jungle

Moscow, Harry
STEP ON.
Cassette: released on Soulville, Feb'81 Dist: Soulville

Moses, Bob
VISIT WITH THE GREAT SPIRIT.
Album: released on Gramavision (USA), Jun'84 by Gramavision Records (USA). Dist: PRT, IMS, Polygram

Cassette: released on Gramavision (USA), Jun'84 by Gramavision Records (USA). Dist: PRT, IMS, Polygram

WHEN ELEPHANTS DREAM OF MUSIC.
Album: released on Gramavision (USA), Jul'83 by Gramavision Records (USA). Dist: PRT, IMS, Polygram

Moses, Joshua
DOMINICA INDEPENDENCE FEVER.
Single (7"): released on Shoc-Wave, Aug'80 by Uniton Records. Dist: Pinnacle

PRETTY GIRL.
Single (12"): released on Shoc-Wave, Aug'80 by Uniton Records. Dist: Pinnacle

Moses, Pablo
IN THE FUTURE.
Album: released on Mercury (USA), Nov'83 by Import Records. Dist: IMS Distribution, Polygram Distribution

Cassette: released on Mercury (USA), Nov'83 by Import Records. Dist: IMS Distribution, Polygram Distribution

SONG, A.
Album: released on Island, Apr'80 by Island Records. Dist: Polygram

TENSION.
Album: released on Mercury (France), Apr'85

Moses, Rick
IF I COULD JUST FALL IN LOVE.
Tracks: / If I could just fall in love.
Single (12"): released on Teldec (Import), Mar'86

Mosher, Jimmy
CHICK FROM CHELSEA.
Album: released on Discovery, Jun'83 Dist: PRT

Mosiah
RUMOURS OF WAR.
Single (7"): released on Big Records, Aug'79

Mosley, Snub
LIVE AT PIZZA EXPRESS.
Album: released on Pizza Express, Dec'79 by Pizza Express Records Dist: JSU, Wellard, Chris

Mosquito Coast, The
MOSQUITO COAST, THE Original Soundtrack (Jarre, Maurice).
Tracks: / Mosquito coast, The / Goodbye America (and have a nice day) / Gimme soca / Up the river / Jeronimo / Fat boy / Destruction / Storm, The / Allie's theme.
Notes: "The Mosquito Coast" was premiered in London's West End in February before H.R.H. Prince Charles and Princess Diana. The movie has been well reviewed and stars Harrison Ford and Helen Mirren. The soundtrack features original music composed and conducted by Maurice Jarre, except for "Gimme Soca" which is performed by Byron Lee and The Dragonaires.
Compact disc: released on London, Mar'87 by London Records. Dist: Polygram

Album: released on London, Mar'87 by London Records. Dist: Polygram

Cassette: released on London, Mar'87 by London Records. Dist: Polygram

Compact disc: released on London, Mar'87 by London Records. Dist: Polygram

Mosquitos
HOW COULD THEY KNOW.
Single (7"): released on Discovery, May'83 Dist: PRT

Mosquito Story
MOSQUITO STORY, THE.
Album: released on Sound Stories, Feb'80 Dist: H.R. Taylor

Moss, Anne Marie
DON'T YOU KNOW ME?.
Album: released on Stash (USA), Jul'81 Dist: Swift Distribution, Jazz Music Distribution, Jazz Horizons Distribution, Celtic Music Distribution, Cadillac, JSU Distribution, Zodiac Distribution

Moss, Buddy
GEORGIA BLUES (1930-1935).
Album: released on Travelin' Man Jul'83

Moss, Danny
DANNY MOSS QUARTET (Moss, Danny Quartet).
Album: released on Flyright, Jul'82 by Flyright Records. Dist: Krazy Kat, Swift, Jazz Music

Moss Poles
ONE SUMMER.
Tracks: / One summer / Go down / Blissful.
Single (7"): released on Idea, Jul'87 by Idea Records. Dist: Rough Trade, Cartel

Single (12"): released on Idea, Jul'87 by Idea Records. Dist: Rough Trade, Cartel

Moss, W. Stanley
I'LL MET BY MOONLIGHT.
Cassette: released on Soundings, Mar'85 Dist: Soundings

Most, Sam
FLUTE FLIGHT.
Album: released on Xanadu, Jul'82 Dist: Discovery, Jazz Horizons, Jazz Music, Swift

Mote, Danny
ROCKIN' IT OUT.
Album: released on White, Feb'87

Motels
SHAME.
Single (7"): released on Capitol, Sep'85 by Capitol Records. Dist: EMI

Single (12"): released on Capitol, Sep'85 by Capitol Records. Dist: EMI

SUDDENLY LAST SUMMER/ SOME THINGS NEVER CHANGE.
Single (7"): released on Capitol, Oct'83 by Capitol Records. Dist: EMI

Moten, Bennie
COMPLETE BENNIE MOTEN, THE (1926 - 1928) VOL.1/2.
Double Album: released on RCA (France), '83 by RCA Records. Dist: Discovery

COMPLETE BENNIE MOTEN, THE VOL.3/4 (1928/1930).
Double Album: released on RCA (France), '83 by RCA Records. Dist: Discovery

MOTEN STOMP.
Cassette: released on Submarine, Oct'86 by Submarine Records. Dist: Wellard, Chris Distribution, Conifer Distribution, H.R. Taylor Distribution

tribution

Moten, Bernie
MOTEN STOMP.
Tracks: / Thick lip stomp / Harmony blues / Kansas City shuffle / Yazoo blues / White lightnin'blues / Muscle Shoal blues / Midnight mama / Missouri wobble / Sugar / Dear heart / New Tulsa blues / Baby dear / 12th Street rag / Pass out lightly / Ding-dong blues / Moten stomp.
Album: released on Halcyon (USA), Feb'87 by Halcyon Records (USA). Dist: Jazz Music, Conifer, Taylors

Cassette: released on Halcyon (USA), Feb'87 by Halcyon Records (USA). Dist: Jazz Music, Conifer, Taylors

Mother Cube
DO THE KAMA SUTRA (Mother Cube & The Boom Tube).
Single (7"): released on Strange, Oct'85 by Strange Records. Dist: Pinnacle

Single (12"): released on Strange, Oct'85 by Strange Records. Dist: Pinnacle

YOU MAKE MY HEART GO (Mother Cube & The Boom Tube).
Single (7"): released on Strange, Oct'85 by Strange Records. Dist: Pinnacle

Single (12"): released on Strange, Oct'85 by Strange Records. Dist: Pinnacle

Mother Gong
FAIRY TALES.
Album: released on Charly, Jan'80 by Charly Records. Dist: Charly, Cadillac

ROBOT WOMAN.
Album: released on Butt, Jan'81 by Butt Records. Dist: Counterpoint

ROBOT WOMAN 2.
Album: released on Shanghai, Sep'84

ROBOT WOMAN 3.
Tracks: / It's you and me baby / Faces of woman / Desire / War / Children's song / Lady's song / Woman of streams / I'm sorry / Men cry / Solutions / Magenta part one.
Album: released on Shanghai, Dec'86

Mother Just For You
MOTHER JUST FOR YOU Various artists (Various Artists).
Album: released on Homespun(Ireland), Jan'84 by Outlet Records. Dist: Outlet

Cassette: released on Homespun(Ireland), Jan'84 by Outlet Records. Dist: Outlet

Mother Liza
MOTHER LIZA MEETS PAPPA TOLLO (Mother Liza/Pappa Tollo).
Album: released on Vista Sounds, Jan'83 by Vista Sounds Records. Dist: Jetstar

Mother Nature
BREATH OF FRESH AIR A.
Album: released on Ariwa, Mar'85 by Ariwa Records. Dist: Revolver, Cartel, Jetstar, Rough Trade

Mothers
GRAND WAZOO THE.
Album: by WEA Records. Dist: WEA

OVER NITE SENSATION.
Album: released on Discreet, Jan'73

SOUTHERN WINDS.
Album: by Warner Bros Records. Dist: WEA

SWEET HARMONY.
Album: by WEA Records. Dist: WEA

WAITRESS IN A DONUT SHOP.
Album: by WEA Records. Dist: WEA

Mothers Finest
ONE MOTHER TO ANOTHER.
Album: released on Epic, Aug'83 by CBS Records. Dist: CBS

Cassette: released on Epic, Aug'83 by CBS Records. Dist: CBS

Mothers of Invention
BURNT WEENY SANDWICH.
Album: released on Reprise, Jan'74 by WEA Records. Dist: WEA

GRAND WAZOO.
Album: released on Reprise, Jan'74 by WEA Records. Dist: WEA

JUST ANOTHER BAND FROM L.A.
Album: released on Reprise, Jan'74 by WEA Records. Dist: WEA

LIVE FILLMORE EAST JUNE 1971.
Album: released on Reprise, Jan'74 by WEA Records. Dist: WEA

WEASELS RIPPED MY FLESH.
Album: released on Reprise, Jan'74 by WEA Records. Dist: WEA

Mothers Ruin
ROAD TO RUIN.
Album: released on Moonlight, May'82 by Lithon Recording & Music Publishing.

SAY IT'S NOT TRUE/IT'S ILLOGICAL.
Single (7"): released on Spectra, May'82 by Spectra Records. Dist: Pinnacle

STREETFIGHTERS/LEAVING YOU.
Single (7"): released on Spectra, Sep'81 by Spectra Records. Dist: Pinnacle

STREETLIGHTS/TURN A CORNER.
Single (7"): released on Spectra, Jan'82 by Spectra Records. Dist: Pinnacle

Mothmen
DOES IT MATTER IRENE/PLEASE LET IT GO.
Single (7"): released on Absurd, Sep'82 by Absurd. Dist: Pinnacle, Rough Trade

ONE BLACK DOT.
Album: released on Do-It, Jan'82 by Do-It Records. Dist: Virgin, EMI

Moths
SUMMER SNOW.
Tracks: / Pimlico (the peoples show) / Maggie says / Stay / Memories / Wooden horse / Sexual suicide / Plastic christians / World turned upside down, the / Out in the rain / Years away.
Album: released on Moths, May'87

Motian, Paul
IT SHOULD'VE HAPPENED A LONG TIME AGO (Motian, Paul Trio).
Compact disc: released on ECM (Germany), Apr'85 by ECM Records. Dist: IMS, Polygram, Virgin through EMI

Album: released on ECM (Germany), Feb'85 by ECM Records. Dist: IMS, Polygram, Virgin through EMI

JACK OF CLUBS (Motian, Paul Quintet).
Compact disc: released on Soul Note (Italy), '86 Dist: Harmonia Mundi Distribution

PSALM (Motian, Paul Band).
Album: released on ECM (Germany), Jul'82 by ECM Records. Dist: IMS, Polygram, Virgin through EMI

Motion
MOTION.
Album: released on Double Dee, Jul'81

Album: released on Bluebird, Apr'85 by Bluebird Records. Dist: EMI, Jetstar

WALK ON BY.
Tracks: / Crazy deep.
Single (12"): released on Bluebird, Feb'87 by Bluebird Records. Dist: EMI, Jetstar

Motl Special
COLD DAYS HOT NIGHTS.
Single (7"): released on Carrere, Jun'85 by Carrere Records. Dist: PRT, Spartan

Single (12"): released on Carrere, Jun'85 by Carrere Records. Dist: PRT, Spartan

motivation
DON'T PLAY THAT SONG.
Single (7"): released on Rock City, Oct'84 by Brian Adams. Dist: Pinnacle

Single (12"): released on Rock City, Oct'84 by Brian Adams. Dist: Pinnacle

GIVE THE GIFT OF MUSIC/COLOR BLIND.
Single (7"): released on De-Lite, Sep'83 by Phonogram Records. Dist: Polygram

Single (12"): released on De-Lite, Sep'83 by Phonogram Records. Dist: Polygram

SO LONELY.
Single (7"): released on Rock City, Jul'84 by Brian Adams. Dist: Pinnacle

Motivators
I WISH IT WOULD RAIN.
Single (7"): released on Contraband, Jan'85 by Contraband. Dist: Pinnacle. Estim retail price in Jul'87 was £3.99.

Motley Crue
GIRLS, GIRLS, GIRLS...
Tracks: / Wild side / Girls, girls, girls. / Dancin'

on glass / Bad bad boogie / Nona / Five years dead / All in the name of rock / Sumethin' for nuthin' / All I need / Jailhouse rock (live).
Album: released on Elektra (USA), Jun'87 by Elektra/Asylum/Nonesuch Records. Dist: WEA

Cassette: released on Elektra (USA), Jun'87 by Elektra/Asylum/Nonesuch Records. Dist: WEA

Compact disc: released on Elektra (USA), Jun'87 by Elektra/Asylum/Nonesuch Records. Dist: WEA

GIRLS, GIRLS, GIRLS (SINGLE).
Tracks: / Girls, girls, girls / Sumthin' for nuthin' / Smokin' in the boys room (live)*.
Single (7"): released on Elektra (USA), Jul'87 by Elektra/Asylum/Nonesuch Records. Dist: WEA

Single (12"): released on Elektra (USA), Jul'87 by Elektra/Asylum/Nonesuch Records. Dist: WEA

INTERVIEW PICTURE DISC.
Album: released on Baktabak, Jul'87 by Baktabak Records. Dist: Arabesque

LOOKS THAT KILL.
Single (12"): released on Elektra, Jul'84 by WEA Records. Dist: WEA

MOTLEY CRUE.
Album: released on Elektra, Oct'82 by WEA Records. Dist: WEA

SHOUT AT THE DEVIL.
Tracks: / In the beggining / Shout at the devil / Looks that kill / Bastard / Knock 'em dead kid / Danger / Too young to fall in love / Helter skelter / Red hot / Ten seconds 'til love / God bless the children of the beast.
Compact disc: released on Elektra (USA), Jan'86 by Elektra/Asylum/Nonesuch Records. Dist: WEA

Album: released on Elektra, Sep'83 by WEA Records. Dist: WEA

Cassette: released on Elektra, Sep'83 by WEA Records. Dist: WEA

SMOKIN' IN THE BOYS ROOM.
Tracks: / Smokin' in the boys room / Home sweet home / Shout at the devil *.
Single (7"): released on Elektra, Aug'85 by WEA Records. Dist: WEA

Single (12"): released on Elektra, Aug'85 by WEA Records. Dist: WEA

THEATRE OF PAIN.
Tracks: / City boy blues / Fight for your rights / Use it or lose it / Smokin' in the boys room / Louder than hell / Keep your eye on the money / Home sweet home / Tonight (we need a lover) / Save our souls / Raise your hands to rock.
Compact disc: released on Elektra (USA), Jul'86 by Elektra/Asylum/Nonesuch Records. Dist: WEA

Album: released on Elektra, Jul'85 by WEA Records. Dist: WEA

Cassette: released on Elektra, Jul'85 by WEA Records. Dist: WEA

TOO YOUNG TO FALL IN LOVE (REMIX).
Single (7"): released on Elektra, Oct'84 by WEA Records. Dist: WEA

Single (12"): released on Elektra, Oct'84 by WEA Records. Dist: WEA

Motley, Frank

FRANK MOTLEY.
Album: released on Krazy Kat, Dec'86 Dist: Jazz Music, Swift, Chris Wellard, H.R. Taylor, Charly, Hotshot, IRS Distribution

FRANK MOTLEY 1951 - 1952.
Tracks: / Bow wow wow / Movin' man / Herbert's jump / That's all right / Dual trumpet blues / Hurricane lover / Diggin' / Fat man's scat / Early in the morning / Nothin' / Frank's jump / Fat man / Dual trumpet blues / Bow wow wow.
Notes: Mono.
Album: released on Krazy Kat, Oct'86 Dist: Jazz Music, Swift, Chris Wellard, H.R. Taylor, Charly, Hotshot, IRS Distribution

Motor Boys Motor

MOTOR BOYS MOTOR.
Album: released on Albion, May'82 by Albion Records. Dist: Spartan, Pinnacle

Motor City

MOTOR CITY various artists.
Album: released on Iguana, Sep'85 by Abacus. Dist: Spartan

Motor City Crew

SCRATCH BREAK (GLOVE STYLE) LETS BREAK (VOCAL) LETS.
Single (12"): released on Motown, Nov'83 by Motown Records. Dist: BMG Distribution

Motor City Eight

MOTOR CITY EIGHT various artists (Various Artists).
Album: released on Abacus, Aug'85 by Abacus. Dist: Spartan

Motor City Raiders

1-2-3-.
Single (7"): released on Magnet, Nov'84 by Magnet Records. Dist: BMG

AIN'T THAT PERCLIAR.
Single (7"): by Magnet Records. Dist: BMG

Single (12"): by Magnet Records. Dist: BMG

Motorhead

ACE OF SPADES.
Album: released on Bronze, '85 by Polygram Records. Dist: Polydor

Cassette: released on Bronze, '85 by Polygram Records. Dist: Polydor

Compact disc: released on Legacy, Aug'87 Dist: PRT. Estim retail price in Sep'87 was £9.99.

ANOTHER PERFECT DAY.
Album: released on Bronze, May'83 by Polygram Records. Dist: Polydor

Cassette: released on Bronze, May'83 by Polygram Records. Dist: Polydor

ANTHOLOGY.
Tracks: / I got mine / Jailbait / Over the top / Step down / Dirty love / Ace of spades / Hoochie coochie man / Go to hell / Heart of stone / Louie Louie / Stone dead forever / Back at the funny farm / Chase is better than the catch, The / Turn you round again / Another perfect day / Another perfect day / Capricorn / Lawman / I got mine / Jailbait.
Notes: All tarcks licensed from Bronze Records. Design: Shoot That Tiger! This compilation (C) 1985 Castle Communications PLC, 271 Merton Road, London, SW18 5JS.
Compact disc: released on Raw Power, Dec'86 Dist: Pinnacle

Album: released on Raw Power, Apr'86 Dist: Pinnacle

Cassette: released on Raw Power, Apr'86 Dist: Pinnacle

ANTHOLOGY-VOLUME1.
Compact disc: released on Legacy, '86 Dist: PRT

BEER DRINKERS AND HELL RAISERS.
Single (7"): released on Big Beat, Oct'80 by Ace Records. Dist: Projection, Pinnacle

BIRTHDAY PARTY (THE).
Notes: The legendary UK heavy metal band on stage at Hammersmith Odeon, playing 18 tracks, mostly familiar clasics from their lengthy career. 1985 production. Number of tracks: 18. Type of recording: Live. Total Playing Time: 60 minutes.
Video-cassette (VHS): released on Virgin Music, Oct'86 by Virgin Records. Dist: EMI

BOMBER.
Single (7"): released on Polydor, Dec'82 by Polydor Records. Dist: Polygram, Polydor

Single (7"): released on Bronze, Dec'82 by Polygram Records. Dist: Polydor

BOMBER (LP).
Compact disc: released on Legacy, Jul'87 Dist: PRT

BORN TO LOSE.
Tracks: / White lion fever / Leaving here / Train kept rollin' (The) / I'm your witch doctor / Lost Johnny / Keep us on the road / Vibrator / Watcher (The) / Beer drinkers and hell raisers / Motorhead / Iron horse - born to lose / City kids / Fools / On parole.
Album: released on Dojo, Apr'86 by Castle Communications Records. Dist: Cartel

Cassette: released on Dojo, Apr'86 by Castle Communications Records. Dist: Cartel

CITY KIDS.
Album: released on Platinum (W.Germany), Oct'85 Dist: Mainline

Cassette: released on Platinum (W.Germany), Oct'85 Dist: Mainline

DEAF FOREVER.
Tracks: / Deaf forever / On the road.
Single (7"): released on GWR, Jul'86 by GWR Records. Dist: RCA

Single (12"): released on GWR, Jul'86 by GWR Records. Dist: RCA

DEAF NOT BLIND.
Notes: A promo video history of the heavy matal superstars from the late 70's to date, and including their latest single 'Killed By Death'.
Video-cassette (VHS): released on Virgin, Dec'84 by Virgin Records. Dist: EMI, Virgin Distribution

IRON FIST.
Tracks: / Iron fist / Heart of stone / I'm the doctor / Go to hell / Loser / Sex & outrage / America / Shut it down / Speed freak / Grind ya down,(Don't let them) / Religion, (Don't need) / Bang to rights.
Notes: Bar code no. 5 013428 811238
Album: released on Castle Classics, Mar'87 by Castle Communications. Dist: BMG

Cassette: released on Castle Classics, Mar'87 by Castle Communications. Dist: BMG

Compact disc: released on Castle Classics, '86 by Castle Communications. Dist: BMG

LIVE IN TORONTO.
Video-cassette (VHS): released on Avatar, Oct'84 by Avatar Communications. Dist: CBS

MOTORHEAD.
Album: released on Chiswick, Sep'81 by Chiswick Records. Dist: Pinnacle

Cassette: released on Chiswick, Sep'81 by Chiswick Records. Dist: Pinnacle

MOTORHEAD/CITY KIDS (PICTURE).
Single (7"): released on Chiswick, Feb'82 by Chiswick Records. Dist: Pinnacle

NO REMORSE.
Tracks: / Ace of spades / Motorhead / Jailbait / Stay clean / Too late / Killed by death / Bomber / Iron fist / Shine / Dancing on your grave / Metropolis / Snaggletooth / Overkill / Please don't touch / Stone dead forever / like a nightmare / Emergency / Steal your face / Louie Louie / No class / Iron horse / We are the road crew / Leaving here / Locomotive.
Album: released on Castle Classics, Dec'86 by Castle Communications. Dist: BMG

Cassette: released on Castle Classics, Dec'86 by Castle Communications. Dist: BMG

Album: released on Bronze, Sep'84 by Polygram Records. Dist: Polydor

NO SLEEP TILL HAMMERSMITH.
Album: released on Bronze, Jun'81 by Polygram Records. Dist: Polydor

Cassette: released on Bronze, Jun'81 by Polygram Records. Dist: Polydor

Compact disc: released on Legacy, Aug'87 Dist: PRT. Estim retail price in Sep'87 was £9.99.

ON PAROLE.
Album: released on Fame (Liberty), May'82 by Music For Pleasure Records. Dist: EMI

Cassette: released on Fame (Liberty), May'82 by Music For Pleasure Records. Dist: EMI

ORGASMATRON.
Tracks: / Built for speed / Mean machine.
Album: released on GWR, Jul'86 by GWR Records. Dist: RCA

Cassette: released on GWR, Jul'86 by GWR Records. Dist: RCA

Compact disc: released on GWR, '86 by GWR Records. Dist: RCA

OVERKILL.
Compact disc: released on Legacy, Jul'87 Dist: PRT

RECORDED LIVE.
Album: released on Astan, Nov'84 by Astan Records. Dist: Counterpoint

Cassette: released on Astan, Nov'84 by Astan Records. Dist: Counterpoint

ROCK'N'ROLL.
Album: released on GWR, Aug'87 by GWR Records. Dist: RCA

Album: released on GWR, Aug'87 by GWR Records. Dist: RCA

WHAT'S WORDS WORTH.
Album: released on Big Beat, Mar'83 by Ace Records. Dist: Projection, Pinnacle

Cassette: released on Big Beat, Mar'83 by Ace Records. Dist: Projection, Pinnacle

Motors

GREATEST HITS: MOTORS.
Album: released on Virgin, Jul'81 by Virgin Records. Dist: EMI, Virgin Distribution

Cassette: released on Virgin, Jul'81 by Virgin Records. Dist: EMI, Virgin Distribution

Motown...

GOLDEN SOUND OF MOTOWN, THE (Various Artists).
Boxed set: released on World Records, Dec'81 Dist: Polygram

Special: released on World Records, Dec'81 Dist: Polygram

MOTOWN 20TH ANNIVERSARY ALBUM various artists (Various Artists).
Double Album: released on Motown, Oct'81 by Motown Records. Dist: BMG Distribution

Double cassette: released on Motown, Oct'81 by Motown Records. Dist: BMG Distribution

MOTOWN CRUISIN VOL 2 various artists (Various Artists).
Album: released on Motown, Sep'83 by Motown Records. Dist: BMG Distribution

MOTOWN CRUSIN VOL 1 various artists (Various Artists).
Album: released on Motown, Sep'83 by Motown Records. Dist: BMG Distribution

MOTOWN DANCE Various artists (Various Artists).
Album: released on Motown, May'85 by Motown Records. Dist: BMG Distribution

Cassette: released on Motown, May'85 by Motown Records. Dist: BMG Distribution

MOTOWN EXTRA SPECIAL various artists (Various Artists).
Album: released on Motown, Oct'81 by Motown Records. Dist: BMG Distribution

Cassette: released on Motown, Oct'81 by Motown Records. Dist: BMG Distribution

MOTOWN GIRL GROUPS Various artists (Various Artists).
Album: released on Motown, May'84 by Motown Records. Dist: BMG Distribution

Cassette: released on Motown, May'84 by Motown Records. Dist: BMG Distribution

MOTOWN LOVE SONGS Various artists (Various Artists).
Album: released on Motown, May'84 by Motown Records. Dist: BMG Distribution

Cassette: released on Motown, May'84 by Motown Records. Dist: BMG Distribution

Album: released on Motown, '82 by Motown Records. Dist: BMG Distribution

Cassette: released on Motown, '82 by Motown Records. Dist: BMG Distribution

MOTOWN LOVE SONGS Various original artists (Various original artists).

MOTOWN MALE GROUPS Various artists (Various Artists).
Album: released on Motown, Apr'84 by RCA Records. Dist: RCA Distribution

Cassette: released on Motown, Apr'84 by RCA Records. Dist: RCA Distribution

MOTOWN'S BIGGEST POP HITS Various artists (Various Artists).
Tracks: / I heard it through the grapevine / I'll be there / Upside down / Baby love / Ain't no mountain high enough / War / Fingertips (part 2) / Let's get it on / Three times a lady / Love child / I can't get next to you / I can't help myself / Tears of a clown / Keep on truckin' (part 1) / Where did our love go / A B C / Come see about me / Just my imagination (running away with me).
Compact disc: released on Motown, Mar'87 by Motown Records. Dist: BMG Distribution

MOTOWN'S BRIGHTEST STARS - THE 1960'S various artists (Various Artists).
Notes: Artists: Mary Wells, Diana Ross & The Supremes, Temptations, Marvelettes, Smokey Robinson, Jr. Walker & The All Stars, Stevie Wonder, Martha Reeves & The Vandellas, Four Tops.
Album: released on Tamla Motown, Jun'86 by Motown Records. Dist: RCA Distribution

Cassette: released on Tamla Motown, Jun'86 by Motown Records. Dist: RCA Distribution

MOTOWN SINGS THE BEATLES Varios artists (Various Artists).
Album: released on Motown, Dec'84 by RCA Records. Dist: RCA Distribution

Cassette: released on Motown, Dec'84 by RCA Records. Dist: RCA Distribution

MOTOWN SOLS STARS Various artists (Various Artists).
Album: released on Motown, Apr'84 by RCA Records. Dist: RCA Distribution

Cassette: released on Motown, Apr'84 by RCA Records. Dist: RCA Distribution

MOTOWN STORY, THE The first 25 years (Volumes 1 - 3) (Various Artists).
Tracks: / Please Mr. Postman / Baby I'm for real / Keep on truckin' / Two lovers / Dancing machine / Shop around / You've really got a hold on me / Tracks of my tears / I second that emotion / Baby baby don't cry / Super freak / Baby I need your lovin' / I can't help myself / Fingertips / I was made to love her / For once in my life / You're all I need to get by / Love machine / Three times a lady / Cruisin' / Heatwave / Dancing in the street / Nowhere to run / Let it whip / Truly / My girl / I wish it would rain / What does it take? / Let me tickle your fancy / Endless love / Where did our love go? / Stop in the name of love / Love child / Someday we'll be together / I hear a symphony / You can't hurry love / Reflections / Every little bit hurts / Can I get a witness? / Stubborn kind of fellow / How sweet it is / I heard it through the grapevine / I'm gonna make

Page 704

you love me / Intro / Bad girl / Money (that's what I want) / Shop around / Bye,bye baby / Do you love me / Way you do the things you do, The / My guy / Shotgun / Stop! In the name of love / I'll be doggone / This old heart of mine (is weak for you) / Beauty is only skin deep / What becomes of the brokenhearted / Reach out I'll be there / Jimmy Mack / Cloud nine / I heard it through the grapevine / I'm gonna make you love me / My whole world ended (the moment you left me) / I want you back / Up the ladder to the roof / Signed, sealed, delivered I'm yours / War / Ain't no mountain high enough / I'll be there / What's going on / Ben / Just my imagination (running away with me) / You are the sunshine of my life / Papa was a rollin' stone / Neither one of us (wants to be the first to say goodbye) / Let's get it on / Don't leave me this way / Sir Duke / Upside down / With you I'm born again / Being with you / All night long (all night) / Somebody's watching me / Rhythm of the night / In my house / Say you, say me / Do you know where you're going to.
Notes: 3 compact discs.
Compact disc: released on Motown, Feb'87 by Motown Records. Dist: BMG Distribution

MOTOWN STORY - THE FIRST 25 YEARS Various artists (Various Artists).
Boxed set: released on Motown, Nov'83 by RCA Records. Dist: RCA Distribution

Cassette: released on Motown, Nov'83 by RCA Records. Dist: RCA Distribution

MOTOWN TRACKIN' (Various Artists).
Tracks: / You're what's missing in my life / Our hearts (will always shine) / Fall in love / Gotta find a woman / Trust me / Coolin' out / You're all I need to survive / Ain't nobody straight in L.A. / To the last drop / Everyday love / Dark side of the world / No one there / Date with the rain / Lovin' fever.
Notes: Artists include: G.C. Cameron/Ozone/Bobby King/Platinum Hook/Jean Carn/Dennis Edwards/Teena Marie/Ronnie McNeir/Miracles/Warp 9/Dazz Band/Marvin Gaye/Martha Reeves/Eddie Kendricks/High Energy.
Cassette: released on Motown, Jan'87 by Motown Records. Dist: BMG Distribution

Album: released on Motown, Oct'86 by Motown Records. Dist: BMG Distribution

SEVENTIES, THE Motown Time Capsule (Various Artists).
Video-cassette (VHS): released on CIC Video, May'87 by CBS Records. Dist: CBS, Pickwick Distribution

SING MOTOWN SUPERSTARS (Various Artists).
Album: released on Motown, Sep'83 by RCA Records. Dist: RCA Distribution

Cassette: released on Motown, Sep'83 by RCA Records. Dist: RCA Distribution

SIXTIES, THE Motown Time Capsule (Various Artists).
Video-cassette (VHS): released on CIC Video, Mar'87 by CBS Records. Dist: CBS, Pickwick Distribution

Motown chartbusters

MOTOWN CHARTBUSTERS (Various Artists).
Album: released on Telstar, Nov'86 by Telstar Records. Dist: RCA Distribution

Cassette: released on Telstar, Nov'86 by Telstar Records. Dist: RCA Distribution

Album: released on Motown, Oct'81 by Motown Records. Dist: BMG Distribution

MOTOWN CHARTBUSTERS 80 various artists (Various Artists).
Album: released on Motown, Oct'81 by Motown Records. Dist: BMG Distribution

Cassette: released on Motown, Oct'81 by Motown Records. Dist: BMG Distribution

MOTOWN CHARTBUSTERS VOL.1 Various artists (Various Artists).
Cassette: released on Motown, Oct'81 by Motown Records. Dist: BMG Distribution

MOTOWN CHARTBUSTERS VOL.2 Various artists (Various Artists).
Album: released on Motown, Oct'81 by Motown Records. Dist: BMG Distribution

Cassette: released on Motown, Oct'81 by Motown Records. Dist: BMG Distribution

MOTOWN CHARTBUSTERS VOL.3 Various artists (Various Artists).
Album: released on Motown, Oct'81 by Motown Records. Dist: BMG Distribution

Cassette: released on Motown, Oct'81 by Motown Records. Dist: BMG Distribution

MOTOWN CHARTBUSTERS VOL.4 Various artists (Various Artists).
Album: released on Motown, Oct'81 by Motown Records. Dist: BMG Distribution

Cassette: released on Motown, Oct'81 by Motown Records. Dist: BMG Distribution

MOTOWN CHARTBUSTERS VOL.5 Various artists (Various Artists).
Album: released on Motown, Oct'81 by Motown Records. Dist: BMG Distribution

Cassette: released on Motown, Oct'81 by Motown Records. Dist: BMG Distribution

MOTOWN CHARTBUSTERS VOL.6 Various artists (Various Artists).
Album: released on Motown, Oct'81 by Motown Records. Dist: BMG Distribution

Cassette: released on Motown, Oct'81 by Motown Records. Dist: BMG Distribution

MOTOWN CHARTBUSTERS VOL.7 Various artists (Various Artists).
Album: released on Motown, Oct'81 by Motown Records. Dist: BMG Distribution

Cassette: released on Motown, Oct'81 by Motown Records. Dist: BMG Distribution

MOTOWN CHARTBUSTERS VOL.8 Various artists (Various Artists).
Album: released on Motown, Oct'81 by Motown Records. Dist: BMG Distribution

Cassette: released on Motown, Oct'81 by Motown Records. Dist: BMG Distribution

MOTOWN CHARTBUSTERS VOL.9 Various artists (Various Artists).
Album: released on Motown, Oct'81 by Motown Records. Dist: BMG Distribution

Cassette: released on Motown, Oct'81 by Motown Records. Dist: BMG Distribution

MOTOWN CHARTBUSTERS VOL.10 Various artists (Various Artists).
Album: released on Motown, Oct'81 by Motown Records. Dist: BMG Distribution

Cassette: released on Motown, Oct'81 by Motown Records. Dist: BMG Distribution

Motown hits of gold

MOTOWN HITS OF GOLD VOL.1 Various Artists (Various Artists).
Album: released on Motown, Oct'85 by Motown Records. Dist: BMG Distribution

MOTOWN HITS OF GOLD VOL.2 Various Artists (Various Artists).
Album: released on Motown, Oct'85 by Motown Records. Dist: BMG Distribution

MOTOWN HITS OF GOLD VOL.3 Various Artists (Various Artists).
Album: released on Motown, Oct'85 by Motown Records. Dist: BMG Distribution

Cassette: released on Motown, Oct'85 by Motown Records. Dist: BMG Distribution

MOTOWN HITS OF GOLD VOL.4 Various Artists (Various Artists).
Album: released on Motown, Oct'85 by Motown Records. Dist: BMG Distribution

Cassette: released on Motown, Oct'85 by Motown Records. Dist: BMG Distribution

MOTOWN HITS OF GOLD VOL.5 Various Artists (Various Artists).
Album: released on Motown, Oct'85 by Motown Records. Dist: BMG Distribution

Cassette: released on Motown, Oct'85 by Motown Records. Dist: BMG Distribution

Album: released on Motown, Oct'85 by Motown Records. Dist: BMG Distribution

Cassette: released on Motown, Oct'85 by Motown Records. Dist: BMG Distribution

MOTOWN HITS OF GOLD VOL.6 Various Artists (Various Artists).
Album: released on Motown, Oct'85 by Motown Records. Dist: BMG Distribution

Cassette: released on Motown, Oct'85 by Motown Records. Dist: BMG Distribution

MOTOWN HITS OF GOLD VOL.7 Various Artists (Various Artists).
Album: released on Motown, Oct'85 by Motown Records. Dist: BMG Distribution

Cassette: released on Motown, Oct'85 by Motown Records. Dist: BMG Distribution

MOTOWN HITS OF GOLD VOL.8 Various Artists (Various Artists).
Album: released on Motown, Oct'85 by Motown Records. Dist: BMG Distribution

Cassette: released on Motown, Oct'85 by Motown Records. Dist: BMG Distribution

Motown Magic

MORE MOTOWN MAGIC (Various Artists).
Album: released on MFP, Sep'81 by EMI Records. Dist: EMI

Cassette: released on MFP, Sep'81 by EMI Records. Dist: EMI

MORE MOTOWN MAGIC Various artists (Various Artists).
Album: released on MFP, Sep'81 by EMI Records. Dist: EMI

Cassette: released on MFP, Sep'81 by EMI Records. Dist: EMI

MORE MOTOWN MAGIC VOL.2 Various artists (Various Artists).
Cassette: released on MFP, Sep'81 by EMI Records. Dist: EMI

Cassette: released on MFP, Sep'81 by EMI Records. Dist: EMI

MORE MOTOWN MAGIC VOL 2 Various original artists (Various Artists).
Album: released on MFP, Sep'81 by EMI Records. Dist: EMI

Cassette: released on MFP, Sep'81 by EMI Records. Dist: EMI

Motto, Denise

DOING IT PROPERLY IS XTC (Motto, Denise & Scobby Swift...).
Tracks: / Doing it properly is XTC / I.M.N.X.T.C. (2 mixes).
Notes: Full artist title: Denise Motto, Scobby Swift, 2 Brummies, a Cockney and a Mancunian. Can this record be for real!
Single (12"): released on Kool Kat, Jul'87 by Kool Kat Records. Dist: PRT

IMNXTC (JACK YOUR BODY TO THE BEAT).
Tracks: / Imnxtc(Jack your body to the beat) / Imnxtc(Ext. vocal version) / Imnxtc(Inst. version) / Imnxtc(Dub mix) / Imnxtc(Scratch mix(radio edit)).
Single (12"): released on Kool Kat, Mar'87 by Kool Kat Records. Dist: PRT

Mott The Hoople

ALL THE WAY FROM MEMPHIS.
Album: released on Hallmark, Mar'81 by Pickwick Records. Dist: Pickwick Distribution, PRT, Taylors

Cassette: released on Hallelujah Sounds, Mar'81 Dist: Nine Mile, Rough Trade, Cartel

ALL THE YOUNG DUDES.
Single (7"): released on CBS, Jul'84 by CBS Records. Dist: CBS

ALL THE YOUNG DUDES/ROLL AWAY THE...
Single (7"): released on Old Gold, Apr'83 by Old Gold Records. Dist: Lightning, Jazz Music, Spartan, Counterpoint

BEST OF Rock 'n' roll queen.
Album: released on Island, Sep'86 by Island Records. Dist: Polygram

Cassette: released on Island, Sep'86 by Island Records. Dist: Polygram

BRAIN CAPERS.
Album: released on Island, '74 by Island Records. Dist: Polygram

GREATEST HITS: MOTT THE HOOPLE.
Album: released on CBS, Jun'81 by CBS Records. Dist: CBS

Cassette: released on CBS, Jun'81 by CBS Records. Dist: CBS

Mouldy Five

VOLUME 1.
Notes: Mono. Featuring Sammy Rimington.
Album: released on GHB, Jun'86 Dist: Jazz Music, Swift

Moule,Ken

AS TIME GOES BY.
Album: released on BBC, Sep'75 by BBC Records & Tapes. Dist: EMI, PRT, Pye

Moulin Rouge

MOULIN ROUGE Musical (Various Artists).
Notes: Zsa ZSa Gabor in a lavish musical set in the naughty nineties.
Video-cassette (VHS): released on Video Collection, May'87 by Video Collection International Ltd.. Dist: Counterpoint

MY BABY HOLDS THE KEY/BLUER THAN...
Single (7"): released on Polo, Sep'83 by Polo Records. Dist: PRT

Single (12"): released on Polo, Sep'83 by Polo Records. Dist: PRT

Mountain

GO FOR YOUR LIFE.
Compact disc: released on Bellaphon, '86 by Bellaphon Records. Dist: IMS-Polygram

Mountaineers

MAGIC BOOTS/FOREIGN TONGUE.
Single (7"): released on Swift, Jun'82 Dist: Swift Distribution

Single (12"): released on Swift, Jun'82 Dist: Swift Distribution

Mountain Top

MOUNTAIN TOP Comhaltas tour 1976 (Various Artists).
Album: released on Comhaltas, Jun'79 Dist: Celtic Music, Jazz Music

Mountbatten,Lord

LIFE AND TIMES OF LORD MOUNTBATTEN,THE.
Triple album / cassette: released on Pye, Oct'79

Mounten,Liberty

I'M JUST A CHILD AGAIN.
Single (7"): released on Climber, Nov'85 by Climber Records. Dist: PRT

Mounting..

MOUNTING EXCITMENT various artists (Various Artists).
Album: released on K-Tel, Sep'80 by K-Tel Records. Dist: Record Merchandisers Distribution, Taylors, Terry Blood Distribution, Wynd-Up Distribution, Relay Distribution, Pickwick Distribution, Solomon & Peres Distribution, Polygram

Mourant,Norman

IT'S HARD TO LIVE ON DREAMS.
Album: released on Folk Heritage, Jul'82 by Folk Heritage Records. Dist: Roots, Wynd-Up Distribution, Jazz Music, Folk Heritage

Mournblade

EIN HELDENTRAUM a heros dream.
Single (12"): released on Vanishing Tower, Dec'85

TIME'S RUNNING OUT.
Album: released on Flicknife, Jun'85 by Flicknife Records. Dist: Spartan

Mournin' Blues

MOURNIN'BLUES/ACCENT ON THE BOBCATS* Various artists (Various Artists).
Cassette: released on Affinity, Sep'86 by Charly Records. Dist: Charly, Cadillac

Mouse, John

TRICKSTER.
Tracks: / Trickster / Lyrical brain.
Single (12"): released on Magnificent Master Blaster, Sep'86 Dist: Jetstar

Mouskouri, Nana

ALONE.
Tracks: / Recuerdos / I have a dream / Only love / Come on blue / Photographs / All my trials / My rainbow race / Alone / Place in my heart, A / Seeing is believing / Queen of hearts (The) / Amazing grace.
Notes: Beautiful ballads, swinging country - tinged songs, timeless traditional songs. The classic blend of old and new which has sold so many Nana Mouskouri albums in the past.
Album: released on Philips, Feb'86 Dist: IMS-Polygram

Cassette: released on Philips, Feb'86 Dist: IMS-Polygram

Compact disc: released on Philips, Feb'86 Dist: IMS-Polygram

ATHENS Ein Griechisches album.
Tracks: / Fidaki / Psarapoula / Nafti yero-nafti / Ximeroni / Ta kronia ekina / Samiotisa / Athina / Yalo yalo / To kalotaxida poulia / Aide to malono / I amygdalia.
Compact disc: released on E.G., '84 by Virgin Records. Dist: Virgin, EMI

ATHENS-EIN GRIECHISCHES ALBUM.
Compact disc: released on Fontana Import, '84 by Phonogram Records. Dist: Polygram

BALLADES.
Album: released on Philips (Europe), Mar'83

Cassette: released on Philips (Europe), Mar'83

FARBEN Colours.
Tracks: / Gut, wieder hier zu sein / Ich lieb' im traume / De colores / Adieu Marleen / Mein wider garten / La bella piccolino isola / Geh nicht zu den soldaten / Spuren im sand / Nino / Mauen aus schweigen / Bilder / Amazing grace.
Compact disc: released on Fontana Import, '84 by Phonogram Records. Dist: Polygram

Compact disc: released on Fontana Import, '84 by Phonogram Records. Dist: Polygram

I HAVE A DREAM.
Tracks: / I have a dream / Recuerdos / Wite rose of Athens (the) / White rose of Athens (The) / Bridge over troubled waters.
Single (7"): released on Philips, Feb'86 Dist: IMS-Polygram

Single (12"): released on Philips, Feb'86 Dist: IMS-Polygram

LIVE AT THE HERODES HATTICUS THEATRE.
Notes: Concert by Nana Mouskouri from the Herodes Hatticus Theatre Athens 1984. Double album and cassette.
Album: released on Philips, Apr'86 Dist: IMS-Polygram

Cassette: released on Philips, Apr'86 Dist: IMS-Polygram

NANA.
Tracks: / Johnny / Half a crown / Just a ribbon / If you love me / Love we never knew / I love my man / Ballinderry / I gave my love a cherry / He didn't know me / Tiny sparrow / My kind of man.
Notes: Digital Stereo.
Compact disc: released on Mercury, Sep'84 by Phonogram Records. Dist: Polygram Distribution

NANA MOUSKOURI.
Tracks: / Solitaire / Keeping the love alive / Apples won't grow / How can I be sure / Maybe this time / Do I ever cross your mind / When the lovin' goes out of the lovin' / Endlessly / Even a fool would let go / Think it over.
Notes: Digital stereo.
Compact disc:

Album:

Cassette:

Compact disc:

NA NA NA.
Album: released on Flashback, Oct'85 by PRT Records. Dist: PRT

Cassette: released on Flashback, Oct'85 by PRT Records. Dist: PRT

ONLY LOVE.
Tracks: / Only love / White rose of Athens (The) / Bridge over troubled water.
Single (7"): released on Philips, Feb'86 Dist: IMS-Polygram

Single (12"): released on Philips, Feb'86 Dist: IMS-Polygram

Single (7"): released on Carrere, Oct'85 by Carrere Records. Dist: PRT, Spartan

Single (12"): released on Carrere, Oct'85 by Carrere Records. Dist: PRT, Spartan

PASSPORT.
Album: released on Philips, Oct'83 Dist: IMS-Polygram

Cassette: released on Philips, Oct'83 Dist: IMS-Polygram

SONG FOR LIBERTY.
Tracks: / Daydreams / Guests / Till all the rivers run dry / Droom droom / Bad old days / On my way to town / Song for Liberty / Loving him was easier / Rose / Every grain of sand / Sweet music man / To Potami.
Compact disc: released on Fontana Import, '84 by Phonogram Records. Dist: Polygram

SONG FOR LIBERTY.
Album: released on Philips (Europe), Aug'82

Cassette: released on Philips (Europe), Aug'82

Compact disc: released on Philips (Europe), Aug'82

SONGS FROM HER T.V. SERIES.
Cassette: released on Philips, Sep'80 Dist: IMS-Polygram

SPOTLIGHT ON.
Double Album: released on Fontana, Sep'74 by Phonogram Records. Dist: Polygram

WHY WORRY?.
Tracks: / Why worry? / Yesterday / Sweet surrender / Rose (The) / Song for liberty / Missing / Love me tender / Only love / Time in a bottle / Every grain of sand / Why worry / Song for liberty.
Notes: A brand new album, featuring the new single, Mark Knopfler's 'Why Worry' and the No. 2 hit 'Only Eyes', plus songs by Tim Rice and Vangelis, Lennon and McCartney, Elvis, John Denver and more.
Album: released on Philips, Oct'86 Dist: IMS-Polygram

Cassette: released on Philips, Oct'86 Dist: IMS-Polygram

Compact disc: released on Philips, Oct'86 Dist: IMS-Polygram

Single (7"): released on Philips, Oct'86 Dist: IMS-Polygram

Moustaki, Georges

GEORGES MOUSTAKI.
Tracks: / Pornographie / L'ambassadeur / Sanforneiro / Si cet amour / Pour un ami / Lazy blues / L'aede / Dans la maison ou je suis ne / En regardant ton corps / L'instrument de malheur / Femmes - fleurs - fruits / Pau de chuva.
Compact disc: released on Polydor (France), Apr'85 Dist: Polygram

Album: released on Polydor (France), May'81 Dist: Polygram

Cassette: released on Polydor (France), May'81 Dist: Polygram

Compact disc: released on Polydor (France), May'81 Dist: Polygram

LE METEQUE.
Album: released on Polydor-Heciodor, Sep'84

Cassette: released on Polydor-Heciodor, Sep'84

MOUSTAKI.
Album: released on Polydor (France), Feb'85 Dist: Polygram

Cassette: released on Polydor (France), Feb'85 Dist: Polygram

Compact disc: released on Polydor (France), Feb'85 Dist: Polygram

TROUBADOR.
Album: released on Polydor, Apr'78 by Polydor Records. Dist: Polygram, Polydor

Mouth

OOH AH YEAH OOH.
Single (7"): released on Recreational, Jan'82 by Revolver Records. Dist: Rough Trade

TO WHOM IT MAY CONCERN.
Single (7"): released on Sheet, Jun'82 Dist: Rough Trade

WHO'S HOT/CATCH A CAB.
Single (7"): released on Y, May'82

Single 10": released on Y, May'82

Mouzon, Alphonse

BABY COME BACK.
Album: released on MPS Jazz, May'81

BACK TO JAZZ (Mouzon, Alphonse band).
Album: released on L & R (Germany), Dec'86

BY ALL MEANS (see Hancock, Herbie) (Mouzon, Alphonse & Herbie Hancock).

BY ALL MEANS.
Tracks: / Do I have to? / Space invaders / Next time we love (The) / Jogger (The) / By all means.
Compact disc: released on Verve, Apr'84 by Phonogram Records. Dist: Polygram

BY ALL MEANS (SINGLE).
Single (7"): released on Excaliber, Jul'87 by Red Bus Records. Dist: PRT

Single (12"): released on Excaliber, Jul'87 by Red Bus Records. Dist: PRT

IN SEARCH OF A DREAM.
Album: released on MPS Jazz, May'81

MORNING SUN.
Album: released on London, Nov'81 by London Records. Dist: Polygram

STEP INTO THE FUNK.
Album: released on Polydor (Germany), Jul'82 Dist: IMS-Polygram

Move

BLACKBERRY WAY/BRONTOSAURUS.
Single (7"): released on Old Gold, Jul'82 by Old Gold Records. Dist: Lightning, Jazz Music, Spartan, Counterpoint

BLACKBERRY WAY/I CAN HEAR THE GRASS GROW.
Single (7"): released on Dakota, Sep'82 by Dakota Records. Dist: PRT

COLLECTION: MOVE.
Tracks: / Night of fear / I can hear the grass grow / Wave your flag and stop the train / Flowers in the rain / Fire brigade / Wild tiger woman / Blackberry way / Curly / Brontosaurus / So you wanna be a rock and roll star / Something else / It'll be me / Sunshine help me / When Alice comes back to the farm / Zing went the strings of my heart / Cherry blossom clinic revisited / Hello Susie / Kilroy was here / Last thing on my mind (The) / Lemon tree (Here we go round the) / Fields of people / Don't make my baby blue / Yellow rainbow / Walk upon the water.
Compact disc: released on Collector Series, '86 by Castle Communications Records. Dist: PRT, Pinnacle, RCA, Ariola

FLOWERS IN THE RAIN/BRONTOSAURUS.
Single (7"): released on Old Gold, Aug'82 by Old Gold Records. Dist: Lightning, Jazz Music, Spartan, Counterpoint

FLOWERS IN THE RAIN/FIRE BRIGADE.
Single (7"): released on Old Gold, Jul'82 by Old Gold Records. Dist: Lightning, Jazz Music, Spartan, Counterpoint

I CAN HEAR THE GRASS GROW.
Tracks: / I can hear the grass grow / Flowers in the rain / Fire brigade / Blackberry way.
Notes: Written by Roy Wood. Published by Westminster Music. Licensed from C-Era Music.
Single (12"): released on Archive 4, Sep'86 by Castle Communications Records. Dist: Nine Mile, Cartel

MOVE COLLECTION(THE).
Tracks: / Night of fear / I can hear the grass grow / Wave your flag and stop the train / Flowers in the rain / Fire brigade / Wild tiger woman / Blackberry way / Curly / Brontosaurus / So you wanna be a rock and roll star / Something else / It'll be me / Sunshine help me / When Alice comes back to the farm / Zing went the strings of my heart / Cherry blossom clinic revisited / Hello Susie / Kilroy was here / Last thing on my mind(The) / (Here we go round)the lemon tree / Field's of people / Don't make my baby blue / Yellow rainbow / Walk upon the water.
Double Album: released on Collectors, Apr'86 by Castle Communications Records. Dist: PRT, Pinnacle, Jazz Music

Double cassette: released on Collectors, Apr'86 by Castle Communications Records. Dist: PRT, Pinnacle, Jazz Music

MOVE SHINES ON, THE.
Album: released on Harvest, Sep'79 by EMI Records. Dist: Roots, EMI

NIGHT OF FEAR/FIRE BRIGADE.
Single (7"): released on Dakota, Aug'82 by Dakota Records. Dist: PRT

NIGHT OF FEAR/I CAN HEAR THE GRASS GROW.
Single (7"): released on Dakota, Jul'82 by Dakota Records. Dist: PRT

OFF THE RECORD WITH THE MOVE.
Double Album: released on Sierra, Nov'84 by Sierra Records. Dist: WEA

Cassette: released on Sierra, Nov'84 by Sierra Records. Dist: WEA

PLATINUM COLLECTION.
Double Album: released on Cube (Platinum coll), Oct'81

Double cassette: released on Cube (Platinum coll), Oct'81

SHAZAM.
Album: released on Cube, '82 by Dakota Records. Dist: PRT

Move closer

MOVE CLOSER (Various Artists).
Tracks: / I knew you were waiting for me / Sometimes / Is this love? / Give me the reason / Rain (The) / When love comes calling / Shake you down / Caravan of love / Take my breath away / On my own / No more the fool / Through the barricades / Why does a man have to be strong / Holding back the years / Move closer / Frozen heart*.
Notes: *=Extra track on compact disc only.
Album: released on CBS, Mar'87 by CBS Records. Dist: CBS

Cassette: released on CBS, Mar'87 by CBS Records. Dist: CBS

Compact disc: released on CBS, Mar'87 by CBS Records. Dist: CBS

Move Into Soul

MOVE INTO SOUL EP (Various Artists).
Single (12"): released on Move, Sep'85 by Charly Records. Dist: Charly Distribution, Fast Forward Distribution, Cartel Distribution

MOVE INTO SOUL PART 3 Various artists (Various Artists).
Album: released on Move, Jan'86 by Charly Records. Dist: Charly Distribution, Fast Forward Distribution, Cartel Distribution

MOVE INTO SOUL PART 4 Various artists (Various Artists).
Notes: Artists include: Miss Louisitine/Oscar Parry/Willie Clayton.
Album: released on Move, Feb'86 by Charly Records. Dist: Charly Distribution, Fast Forward Distribution, Cartel Distribution

MOVE INTO SOUL PART 6 Various artists (Various Artists).
Album: released on Move, Apr'86 by Charly Records. Dist: Charly Distribution, Fast Forward Distribution, Cartel Distribution

MOVE INTO SOUL PART 2 various artists (Various Artists).
Album: released on Move, Nov'85 by Charly Records. Dist: Charly Distribution, Fast Forward Distribution, Cartel Distribution

Movement

MAGIC (Movement feat. Lee Genesis).
Tracks: / Magic / Magic (7" version) / Magic (dub).
Single (7"): released on Debut, May'87 by Skratch Music. Dist: PRT

Mover, Bob

IN THE TRUE TRADITION.
Album: released on Xanadu (Import), Jul'82

Movie...

MOVIE BUSTERS (Various Artists).
Album: released on Emerald, Nov'84 by Emerald Records. Dist: Ross, PRT, Solomon & Peres Distribution

Cassette: released on Emerald, Nov'84 by Emerald Records. Dist: Ross, PRT, Solomon & Peres Distribution

MOVIE COLLECTION Various artists (Various Artists).
Notes: Artists include: Gene Kelly/Judy Garland/Fred Astaire/Al Jolson/Ginger Rogers/Marilyn Monroe/etc.
Album: released on Deja Vu, May'86 by Deja Vu Records. Dist: Counterpoint Distribution, Record Services Distribution (Ireland)

Cassette: released on Deja Vu, May'86 by Deja Vu Records. Dist: Counterpoint Distribution, Record Services Distribution (Ireland)

MOVIE THEMES (Various Artists).
Cassette: released on Ideal(Tapes), Jul'84 Dist: EMI

MOVIE WONDERLAND (Various Artists).
Cassette: released on Bravo, Feb'80 by Pickwick Records. Dist: Lugtons

Movie Land

POSTCARD OF NEW YORK.
Tracks: / Postcard of New York / Dreamtime.
Single (7"): released on RCA, Jun'86 by RCA Records. Dist: RCA, Roots, Swift, Wellard, Chris, I & B, Solomon & Peres Distribution

Single (12"): released on RCA, Jun'86 by RCA Records. Dist: RCA, Roots, Swift, Wellard, Chris, I & B, Solomon & Peres Distribution

Movies

MOTOR, MOTOR, MOTOR.
Album: released on RCA, Aug'81 by RCA Records. Dist: RCA, Roots, Swift, Wellard, Chris, I & B, Solomon & Peres Distribution

Cassette: released on RCA, Aug'81 by RCA Records. Dist: RCA, Roots, Swift, Wellard, Chris, I & B, Solomon & Peres Distribution

Movie Stars

NO TIME TO KILL.
Single (7"): released on Lancaster, Oct'82 by Lancaster Records. Dist: PRT

Movietone

NEXT TIME ALONG.
Album: released on Minder, Jul'83

Moving Fingers

DOUBLE VISION.
Single (7"): released on French, Mar'82 by French Records. Dist: Stage One

EVERYTHING CHANGES.
Single (7"): released on Sonet, Jul'87 by Sonet Records. Dist: PRT

FINAL WORD OF HISTORY.
Tracks: / Final word of history / Love is.
Single (7"): released on Sonet, Sep'86 by Sonet Records. Dist: PRT

KAREN.
Tracks: / Karen / Chlorophyll.
Single (7"): released on Sonet, Mar'86 by Sonet Records. Dist: PRT

LOCKED ONTO LOVE.
Single (12"): released on KSV, Feb'85 by Kingsley Sound & Vision. Dist: Kingsley Sound & Vision Distribution

NATURAL SELECTION.
Tracks: / Final word of history (The) / Karen / Everything changes / Heartlands / Sink like a stone / Rome lies burning / Dreamtime / Subway and the stars / Chlorophyll (in my eyes) / Lock up your heart / Natural selection.
Album: released on Sonet, Jan'87 by Sonet Records. Dist: PRT

ROME LIES BURNING.
Tracks: / Rome lies burning / Heartland.
Single (7"): released on Sonet, May'87 by Sonet Records. Dist: PRT

SINK LIKE A STONE.
Single (7"): released on Sonet, May'85 by Sonet Records. Dist: PRT

SUBWAY AND THE STARS.
Tracks: / Subway and the stars / Lock up your heart.
Single (7"): released on Sonet, Nov'86 by

Sonet Records. Dist: PRT

Moving Hearts

2-1 FREDDIE.
Single (7"): released on 51%, May'83 by 51% Records. Dist: Spartan

DARK END OF THE STREET.
Album: released on 51%, Sep'84 by 51% Records. Dist: Spartan

LET SOMEBODY KNOW.
Single (7"): released on WEA, Sep'82 by WEA Records. Dist: WEA

LIVE HEARTS.
Album: released on WEA, Sep'84 by WEA Records. Dist: WEA

MOVING HEARTS.
Album: released on WEA Ireland, Mar'87 by WEA Records. Dist: Celtic Distributions, Projection, I & B

Cassette: released on WEA Ireland, Mar'87 by WEA Records. Dist: Celtic Distributions, Projection, I & B

Compact disc: released on WEA Ireland, Mar'87 by WEA Records. Dist: Celtic Distributions, Projection, I & B

MOVING HEARTS.
Album: released on WEA, Apr'82 by WEA Records. Dist: WEA

Cassette: released on WEA, Apr'82 by WEA Records. Dist: WEA

MOVING HEARTS/DARK END OF THE STREET.
Double cassette: released on WEA, Jun'85 by WEA Records. Dist: WEA

STORM, THE.
Album: released on Tara (Ireland), Aug'85 by Tara Records. Dist: I & B Records Distribution, Record Services Distribution (Ireland), Roots Distribution

Cassette: released on Tara (Ireland), Aug'85 by Tara Records. Dist: I & B Records Distribution, Record Services Distribution (Ireland), Roots Distribution

Moving On Up

MOVING ON UP (Various Artists).
Album: released on Kent (MCA), Mar'84 by Ace Records. Dist: Pinnacle

Moving Pictures

PARTY NIGHT.
Single (7"): released on Runaway, Jul'82

WHAT ABOUT ME.
Single (7"): released on Epic, Dec'82 by CBS Records. Dist: CBS

Mowatt, Judy

BLACK WOMAN.
Album: released on Island, Nov'80 by Island Records. Dist: Polygram

Album: released on Ashandan, Apr'85 Dist: Jetstar

LOVE IS OVERDUE.
Notes: Produced by Dexter Wansal. Also features a version of the Otis Redding classic "Try a little tenderness"
Album: released on Greensleeves, Jul'87 by Greensleeves Records. Dist: BMG, Jetstar, Spartan

Cassette: released on Greensleeves, Jul'87 by Greensleeves Records. Dist: BMG, Jetstar, Spartan

Compact disc: released on Greensleeves, Jul'87 by Greensleeves Records. Dist: BMG, Jetstar, Spartan

Music for the world

ONLY A WOMAN.
Album: released on Greensleeves, Sep'82 by Greensleeves Records. Dist: BMG, Jetstar, Spartan

WORKING WONDERS.
Album: released on Shanachie, Aug'85 Dist: Sterns/Triple Earth Distribution, Roots

Mowrey,Irvin

CONTINENTAL DRIFT.
Album: released on Initial, Sep'81 by Initial Records. Dist: Pinnacle

QUEEN OF MAYBE/FAT CITY.
Single (7"): released on Initial, '80 by Initial Records. Dist: Pinnacle

Moxham,Steve

LOVE AT FIRST SIGHT/LIGHT AIRCRAFT.
Single (7"): released on Rough Trade, Aug'82 by Rough Trade Records. Dist: Rough Trade Distribution, Cartel Distribution

Mox Nix

MOX NIX.
Album: released on Eva-Lolita, Jul'86 Dist: Pinnacle

Moyet, Alison

ALF f.
Tracks: / Love resurrection / Honey for the bees / For you only / Invisible / Steal me blind / All cried out / Money mile / Twisting the knife / Where hides sleep.
Notes: Digital Stereo.
Compact disc: released on CBS, Mar'85 by CBS Records. Dist: CBS

Album: released on CBS, Nov'84 by CBS Records. Dist: CBS

Cassette: released on CBS, Nov'84 by CBS Records. Dist: CBS

ALL CRIED OUT.
Single (7"): released on CBS, Sep'84 by CBS Records. Dist: CBS Deleted '86.

Single (12"): released on CBS, Sep'84 by CBS Records. Dist: CBS Deleted '85.

INVISIBLE.
Single (7"): released on CBS, Dec'84 by CBS Records. Dist: CBS

IS THIS LOVE.
Tracks: / Is this love / Blow wind blow.
Single (7"): released on CBS, Nov'86 by CBS Records. Dist: CBS

LOVE RESSURECTION.
Single (7"): released on CBS, Jun'84 by CBS Records. Dist: CBS

Single (12"): released on CBS, Jun'84 by CBS Records. Dist: CBS Deleted '85.

ORDINARY GIRL.
Tracks: / Ordinary girl / Palm of your hand.
Single (7"): released on CBS, 23 May'87 by CBS Records. Dist: CBS

Single (12"): released on CBS, 23 May'87 by CBS Records. Dist: CBS

RAINDANCING.
Tracks: / Weak in the presence of beauty / Ordinary girl / You got me wrong / Without you / Sleep like breathing / Is this love? / Blow wind blow / Glorious love / When I say (no giveaway) / Stay.
Album: released on CBS, Apr'87 by CBS Records. Dist: CBS

Cassette: released on CBS, Apr'87 by CBS Records. Dist: CBS

Compact disc: released on CBS, Apr'87 by CBS Records. Dist: CBS

Compact disc: by CBS Records. Dist: CBS

THAT OLD DEVIL CALLED LOVE.
Single (7"): released on CBS, Mar'85 by CBS Records. Dist: CBS Deleted '86.

Single (12"): released on CBS, Mar'85 by CBS Records. Dist: CBS Deleted '86.

THAT OLE DEVIL CALLED LOVE.
Single (7"): released on CBS, Mar'85 by CBS Records. Dist: CBS Deleted '86.

WEAK IN THE PRESENCE OF BEAUTY.
Tracks: / To work on you / Take my imagination to bed*.
Notes: *=Extra track on 12" only
Single (7"): released on CBS, Feb'87 by CBS Records. Dist: CBS

Single (12"): released on CBS, Feb'87 by CBS Records. Dist: CBS

Mozart's Greatest Hits

MOZART'S GREATEST HITS (Various Artists).
Cassette: released on CBS, Jul'83 by CBS Records. Dist: CBS

Mr Able

LITTLE BIT OFF, A.
Cassette: released on Klub, Apr'79

NOTHING LEFT TO SAY BUT GOODBYE.
Single (7"): released on Igus, Dec'82 by Klub. Dist: PRT, Musac Distribution Ltd (Scotland)

Mr.Amir

LINES OF LOVE.
Tracks: / Lines of love.
Single (12"): released on Pink Pop, Feb'87 Dist: Red Rhino, Cartel

REASONS TO LIVE/ OH NO OPPRESSOR.
Single (7"): released on Probe Plus, Nov'83 by Probe Plus Records. Dist: Probe Plus Distribution

Mra Sleeping Figures

HANDFUL OF HEART.
Single (7"): released on Kapac, Mar'83 by Kapac Records. Dist: Rough Trade

Mr. Barleywine

OPEN DOOR (Mr. Barleywine & The B.W. Band).
Single (7"): released on Top Dog, Jan'85 by Top Dog Records. Dist: Jetstar Distribution

Mr. Bloe

GROOVIN' WITH MR. BLOE/ SINFUL.
Single (7"): released on Old Gold, Jul'82 by Old Gold Records. Dist: Lightning, Jazz Music, Spartan, Counterpoint

Mr. Burns

WHEN I'M ASLEEP/ 3RD DEGREE BURNS.
Single (7"): released on Korova, Aug'80 Dist: WEA

Mr. Cinders

MR. CINDERS London cast (London Cast).
Album: released on TER, Sep'83 Dist: Pinnacle
Cat. no: **TER 1069**
Cassette: released on TER, Sep'83 Dist: Pinnacle

Mr. Floods Party

COMPARED TO WHAT.
Single (7"): released on Bulldog, May'78 by Bulldog Records. Dist: President Distribution, Spartan, Swift, Taylor, H.R.

Mr Lee

I CAN'T FORGET.
Single (7"): released on Breakout, Aug'87 by A&M Records. Dist: Polygram

Single (12"): released on Breakout, Aug'87 by A&M Records. Dist: Polygram

THIS GIRL IS MY LOVER.
Tracks: / This girl is my lover / Miss Mavis.
Single (12"): released on Unity Sound, Feb'86 Dist: Jetstar

Mr Men

COUNT TO TEN WITH MR MEN Read by Arthur Lowe and Roy Castle (Lowe, Arthur & Roy Castle).
Cassette: released on Tempo Storytime, May'84

MR. MEN (Lowe, Arthur).
Album: released on BBC, '78 by BBC Records & Tapes. Dist: EMI, PRT, Pye

MR.MEN RIDE AGAIN, THE.
Album: released on Ingot, Dec'82 by Ingot Records. Dist: PRT

Cassette: released on Ingot, Dec'82 by Ingot Records. Dist: PRT

MR MEN SONGS (Lowe, Arthur).
Album: by BBC Records & Tapes. Dist: EMI, PRT, Pye

MR. MEN STORIES VOL.2 (Lowe, Arthur).
Album: released on BBC, Oct'80 by BBC Records & Tapes. Dist: EMI, PRT, Pye

Cassette: released on BBC, Oct'80 by BBC Records & Tapes. Dist: EMI, PRT, Pye

MR. MEN STORIES VOL.3 (Lowe, Arthur).
Album: released on BBC, Oct'82 by BBC Records & Tapes. Dist: EMI, PRT, Pye

Cassette: released on BBC, Oct'82 by BBC Records & Tapes. Dist: EMI, PRT, Pye

PARTY TIME WITH MR MEN.
Album: released on Stylus, Nov'85 Dist: Pinnacle, Terry Blood Distribution, Stylus Distribution

Cassette: released on Stylus, Nov'85 Dist: Pinnacle, Terry Blood Distribution, Stylus Distribution

RETURN OF THE MR. MEN, THE (Lowe, Arthur).
Album: released on Ingot, Dec'82 by Ingot Records. Dist: PRT

Cassette: released on Ingot, Dec'82 by Ingot Records. Dist: PRT

Mr Mertha

WONDER.
Tracks: / Wonder.
Single (12"): released on Fundamental, Sep'86 by Fundamental Records. Dist: Red Rhino, Cartel

Mr Mister

BROKEN WINGS.
Single (7"): released on RCA, Jul'85 by RCA Records. Dist: RCA, Roots, Swift, Wellard, Chris, I & B, Solomon & Peres Distribution

Single (12"): released on RCA, Jul'85 by RCA Records. Dist: RCA, Roots, Swift, Wellard, Chris, I & B, Solomon & Peres Distribution

HUNTERS OF THE NIGHT.
Single (7"): released on RCA, Apr'84 by RCA Records. Dist: RCA, Roots, Swift, Wellard, Chris, I & B, Solomon & Peres Distribution

Single (12"): released on RCA, Apr'84 by RCA Records. Dist: RCA, Roots, Swift, Wellard, Chris, I & B, Solomon & Peres Distribution

IS IT LOVE?.
Tracks: / Is it love? / 32 / Is it love? - dance mix / Is it love (Dub mix).
Single (7"): released on RCA, Apr'86 by RCA Records. Dist: RCA, Roots, Swift, Wellard, Chris, I & B, Solomon & Peres Distribution

Single (12"): released on RCA, Apr'86 by RCA Records. Dist: RCA, Roots, Swift, Wellard, Chris, I & B, Solomon & Peres Distribution

I WEAR THE FACE.
Tracks: / Hunters of the night / Code of love / Partners in crime / 32 / Runaway / Talk the talk / I'll let you drive / I get lost sometimes / I wear the face / Life goes on.
Compact disc: released on RCA, Nov'86 by RCA Records. Dist: RCA, Roots, Swift, Wellard, Chris, I & B, Solomon & Peres Distribution

Album: released on RCA, May'86 by RCA Records. Dist: RCA, Roots, Swift, Wellard, Chris, I & B, Solomon & Peres Distribution

Cassette: released on RCA, May'86 by RCA Records. Dist: RCA, Roots, Swift, Wellard, Chris, I & B, Solomon & Peres Distribution

KYRIE.
Tracks: / Kyrie - edited version / Kyrie - full version / Hunters of the night.
Single (7"): released on RCA, Feb'86 by RCA Records. Dist: RCA, Roots, Swift, Wellard, Chris, I & B, Solomon & Peres Distribution

Single (12"): released on RCA, Feb'86 by RCA Records. Dist: RCA, Roots, Swift, Wellard, Chris, I & B, Solomon & Peres Distribution

WELCOME TO THE REAL WORLD.
Tracks: / Is it love / Broken wings / Kyrie / Uniform of youth / Welcome to the real world / Tangent tears / Run to her / Into my own hands / Don't slow down / Black-white.
Album: released on RCA, Nov'85 by RCA Records. Dist: RCA, Roots, Swift, Wellard, Chris, I & B, Solomon & Peres Distribution

Cassette: released on RCA, Nov'85 by RCA Records. Dist: RCA, Roots, Swift, Wellard, Chris, I & B, Solomon & Peres Distribution

Compact disc: released on RCA, Apr'86 by RCA Records. Dist: RCA, Roots, Swift, Wellard, Chris, I & B, Solomon & Peres Distribution

Mr & Mrs Yellowman

WHERE IS SANTA CLAUS.
Single (12"): released on Greensleeves, Nov'85 by Greensleeves Records. Dist: BMG, Jetstar, Spartan

Mr. Palmer

MIXED ME PROPERLY.
Single (12"): released on Sweetcorn, Apr'85 by Sweetcorn Records. Dist: Jetstar

RIBIBONSCAN.
Single (12"): released on Melody, Sep'84 by Melody Records. Dist: Jetstar Distribution

Mrs.Green

MRS.GREEN.
Tracks: / No time for penance / Happy now / Visions of you / Hurry / Another cold morning / East of Eden / I should care / Already gone / Start again / Tuesday.
Album: released on Beserkley (USA), Jun'87 by Beserkley Records. Dist: PRT

Mr. Slob's Spring...

MR. SLOB'S SPRING CLEANING COLLECTION Various artists (Various Artists).
Cassette: released on Slob, Feb'84 by Slob Records. Dist: Falling A Distribution

Mr. Smith

TWO VERY SIMILAR VIEWS OF....
Album: released on Sweet Folk, May'81 Dist: Roots Distribution

Mr Snowman

MR SNOWMAN (Mr Snowman & The Brimpton Horrors).
Single (7"): released on Solid, Dec'83 by Solid Records. Dist: Graduate, Spartan

Mr Spalding

ROCKY ROAD.
Tracks: / Rocky road / Rocky dub.

Single (12"): released on Rocky Road, Jun'86 Dist: Jetstar Distribution

Mr. T

I'M FALLING IN LOVE WITH YOU.
Album: released on Poor Millionaires, Apr'86 Dist: Red Rhino, Cartel

MSO

MUSIC MAN.
Single (7"): released on Mainstreet, Aug'81 Dist: Stage One

Single (12"): released on Mainstreet, Aug'81 Dist: Stage One

Mtoto, Mungu

GHETTO CHILDREN.
Single (12"): released on Ghetto Tears, Dec'84 by Ghetto Tears Records. Dist: Jetstar

M.T Quarter

CRUCIAL LOVER.
Single (12"): released on Illuminated, Apr'85 by IKF Records. Dist: Pinnacle, Cartel, Jetstar

Mtume

BREATHLESS.
Tracks: / Breathless / Theme from the theatre of the mind.
Single (7"): released on Epic, May'86 by CBS Records. Dist: CBS

Single (12"): released on Epic, May'86 by CBS Records. Dist: CBS

IN SEARCH OF THE RAINBOW SEEKERS.
Album: released on Epic, Jan'81 by CBS Records. Dist: CBS

JUICY FRUIT.
Tracks: / Juicy friut / Prime time / Just be good to me / Weekend girl.
Single (12"): released on Old Gold, Feb'86 by Old Gold Records. Dist: Lightning, Jazz Music, Spartan, Counterpoint

Album: released on Epic, Jun'83 by CBS Records. Dist: CBS

Cassette: released on Epic, Jun'83 by CBS Records. Dist: CBS Deleted May'85.

JUICY FRUIT (PART 1).
Single (7"): released on Epic, May'83 by CBS Records. Dist: CBS

Single (12"): released on Epic, May'83 by CBS Records. Dist: CBS

MTUME.
Compact disc: released on Epic, May'87 by CBS Records. Dist: CBS

THEATER OF THE MIND.
Tracks: / Theme from theater of the mind / P.O.P. generation / Breathless / I don't believe you heard me / Body & soul (take me) / New face Deli / I'd rather be with you / Deep freez (rap-a-song) / Deep freez (tree's thing).
Album: released on Epic, Jun'86 by CBS Records. Dist: CBS

Cassette: released on Epic, Jun'86 by CBS Records. Dist: CBS

YOU ME AND HE.
Album: released on Epic, Sep'84 by CBS Records. Dist: CBS

Cassette: released on Epic, Sep'84 by CBS Records. Dist: CBS

MTV Collection

VIDEO MUSIC AWARDS (Various Artists).
Video-cassette (VHS): released on WEA, May'87 by WEA Records. Dist: WEA

Much to do about nothing

MUCH ADO ABOUT NOTHING Shakespeare, William.
Double cassette: released on Argo (Spokenword), Jul'82 by Decca Records. Dist: Polygram

Muckle Sangs

SCOTTISH TRADITIONS VOL.5.
Double Album: released on Tangent, Apr'81 by Tangent Records. Dist: Roots Records Distribution, Impetus Distribution, H.R. Taylor Distribution, Jazz Music Distribution, JSU Distribution, Projection Distribution, Gordon Duncan Distribution, Ross Records Distribution

Muckram Wakes

DUCHESS OF HAMILTON'S RANT, (THE).
Album: released on Leader, May'81 Dist: Jazz Music, Projection

MAP OF DERBYSHIRE, A.
Album: released on Leader, May'81 Dist: Jazz Music, Projection

WARBLES JANGLES AND REEDS.
Album: released on Highway, May'81 by Highway Records. Dist: Roots, Projection, Ross

Mud

LONELY THIS CHRISTMAS.
Single (7"): released on RAK, Nov'85 by RAK. Dist: EMI

Single (12"): released on RAK, Nov'85 by RAK. Dist: EMI

MUD.
Album: released on Runaway (France), Apr'83

TIGER FEET.
Single (7"): released on Rak Replay, Jan'77

Muddy Waters

WE THREE KINGS.
Album: released on Syndicate Chapter, Sep'82 Dist: JSU Distribution, Projection Distribution, Red Lightnin' Distribution, Swift Distribution

Mudguards

MUDGUARDS.
Album: released on Only A Revolution, Jul'84 by Only A Revolution Records., Rough Trade Distribution, Cartel Distribution, Jungle Distribution

WESTERN CULTURAL NOISE.
Album: released on Only A Revolution, Dec'84 by Only A Revolution Records., Rough Trade Distribution, Cartel Distribution, Jungle Distribution

Mudy, Jimmy

GROOVIN' HIGH.
Album: released on Hep, Apr'79 by H.R. Taylor Records. Dist: Jazz Music, Cadillac Music, JSU, Taylors, Wellard, Chris, Zodiac, Swift, Fast Forward

Muerte, (La)

SERIALIST MYSTERY.
Single (12"): released on Red Rhino, Oct'84 by Red Rhino Records. Dist: Red Rhino, Cartel

Mugshots

TOO OLD FOR FAIRY TALES.
Single (7"): released on Lancaster, Oct'82 by Lancaster Records. Dist: PRT

Muhammad, Idris

BOOGIE TO THE TOP.
Album: released on CTI, May'78 by Polydor Records. Dist: IMS, Polygram

Muir, Frank

SUPER WHAT-A-MESS.
Tracks: / Super What-a-mess / rince What-a-mess / What-a-mess the good / What-a-mess goes to school / What-a-mess at the seaside / What-a-mess and the cat next door.
Notes: Playing time approx. 1 hour. Read and written by Frank Muir.
Cassette: released on Tellastory, Dec'86 by Bartlett Bliss Productions. Dist: PRT Distribution, Hayward Promotions Distribution, H.R. Taylor Distribution

WHAT-A-MESS.
Tracks: / What-a-mess / What-a-mess (continued).
Cassette: released on Tellastory, Dec'86 by Bartlett Bliss Productions. Dist: PRT Distribution, Hayward Promotions Distribution, H.R. Taylor Distribution

Muldaur, Maria

ANY OLD TIME.
Album: released on Reprise, May'74 by WEA Records. Dist: WEA

LIVE IN LONDON.
Album: released on Spindrift, May'86 Dist: Roots

SWEET & LOW.
Album: released on Spindrift, Jun'84

Cassette: released on Spindrift, Jun'84

THERE IS ALOVE.
Album: released on Myrrh, May'82 by Word Records. Dist: Word Distribution

Cassette: released on Myrrh, May'82 by Word Records. Dist: Word Distribution

Mulerman, Vadim

FOLK SONG RECITAL.
Cassette: released on Melodiya (USSR), Feb'79 Dist: T.B.C Distribution

Muleskinner

MULESKINNER (Various Artists).
Notes: Muleskinner is the collective title for:Pete Rowan (Earth Opera) Richard Green(Sea Train) Clarence White(The Byrds)
Album: released on Edsel, Mar'87 by Demon Records. Dist: Pinnacle, Jazz Music, Projection

Mulgrew, John

FIDDLE TUNES.
Cassette: released on Outlet (Ireland), Feb'79

Mulhaire Celi Band

MULHAIRE CELI BAND, (THE).
Album: released on Harp(Ireland), May'80 by Pickwick Records. Dist: Taylors

Mullen, Jim

THUMBS UP.
Tracks: / Blue Montreaux / Fall / As if you read my mind / Crepescule / Thumbs up / Herbal scent / Friends / Beauty & The Beast.
Notes: Digital Stereo recording.
Compact disc: released on Coda, Oct'84 by Coda Records. Dist: Pinnacle, Cartel, WEA, Roots

Muller,Egon

GO GO GO MAN GO/LET'S DANCE THE ROCK 'N' ROLL.
Single (7"): released on President, Nov'83 by President Records. Dist: Taylors, Spartan

Muller-Steger, Gila

LOVERS, THE.
Tracks: / Lovers, The / Together.
Single (7"): released on First Time/Fugore, Jun'87 by First Time Records. Dist: First Time Records

Muller, Werner

INTERCONTINENTAL SOUVENIRS (Muller, Werner & His Orchester).
Tracks: / Massachusetts / One rainy night in Tokyo / In a little spanish town / Spanish harlem / Blue Hawaii / Istanbul / Nights are long in Hamburg, the / Brazil / Arrivederci, Roma / Foggy day in London Town / I love Paris / Sayonara / Espana / Hawaiin war chant / Viva Las Vegas / Zambesi.
Compact disc: released on Teldec, May'87

Mullican, Moon

GREATEST HITS:MOON MULLICAN.
Album: released on Starday, Apr'87

Cassette: released on Starday, Apr'87

SEVEN NIGHTS TO ROCK.
Album: released on Western Swing, Mar'82

SWEET ROCKIN' MUSIC.
Album: released on Charly, Feb'84 by Charly Records. Dist: Charly, Cadillac

Mulligan, Gerry

BEST OF, THE Walkman & compact jazz series.
Cassette: released on Verve, May'87 by Phonogram Records. Dist: Polygram

Compact disc: released on Mercury, Jul'87 by Phonogram Records. Dist: Polygram Distribution

BLUES IN TIME (Mulligan,Gerry & Paul Desmond).
Album: released on Verve (USA), Mar'84 by Polydor. Dist: Polygram

COMPACT JAZZ.
Tracks: / Lady is a tramp,The / Westwood walk.
Compact disc: released on Phonogram, Jul'87 by Phonogram Records. Dist: Polygram

Cassette: released on Phonogram, Jul'87 by Phonogram Records. Dist: Polygram

CONCERT IN JAZZ,A.
Album: released on Verve (USA), May'83 by Polydor. Dist: Polygram

FABULOUS GERRY MULLIGAN QUARTET,THE.
Double Album: released on Vogue, Oct'74

FABULOUS (THE) (Mulligan, Gerry Quartet).
Tracks: / May be wrong / Five brothers / Gold rush / Lullaby of the leavds / Makin' whoopee / Laura / Soft shoes / Nearness of you (The) / Limelight / Come out wherever you are / Love me or leave me / Bernie's tune / Walkin' shoes (The) / Moonlight in Vermont / Lady is a tramp (The) / Bark for Barkdale.
Compact disc: released on Vogue, '86 Dist: Discovery, Jazz Music, PRT, Swift

GERRY MULLIGAN.
Cassette: released on Deja Vu, Nov'85 by Deja Vu Records. Dist: Counterpoint Distribution, Record Services Distribution (Ireland)

Album: released on Kings Of Jazz, '81 Dist: Jazz Horizons, Jazz Music, Celtic Music

Album: released on Jazz Reactivation, Jul'82 Dist: PRT

HOLIDAY WITH MULLIGAN (Mulligan,Gerry & Judy Holiday).
Album: released on DRG (USA), Aug'84 by DRG Records. Dist: Conifer, RCA

Cassette: released on DRG (USA), Aug'84 by DRG Records. Dist: Conifer, RCA

JERU.
Tracks: / Get out of town / Here I'll stay / Inside impromptu / Blue boy / You've come home / Lonely town / Capricious.
Album: released on CBS, Jul'86 by CBS Records. Dist: CBS

Cassette: released on CBS, Jul'86 by CBS Records. Dist: CBS

LA MENACE O soundtrack.
Double Album: released on DRG (USA), Jul'83 by DRG Records. Dist: Conifer, RCA

LIONEL HAMPTON PRESENTS.
Album: released on Gateway, '84 by Kingdom. Dist: Pinnacle

LIONEL HAMPTON PRESENTS GERRY MULLIGAN.
Tracks: / Apple core / Song for Johnny Hodges / Blight of the fumble bee / Gerry meets Hamp / Blues for Gerry / Line for Lyons.
Compact disc: released on Kingdom Records, Jun'87 by Kingdom Records. Dist: Kingdom Records

LITTLE BIG HORN.
Tracks: / Under a star / Sun on stairs / Another kind of Sunday / Bright angel falls / I never was a young man / Little Big Horn.
Notes: Digital stereo.
Compact disc: released on GRP (USA), Aug'84 by GRP Records (USA). Dist: IMS, Polygram

LITTLE BIG HORN.
Album: released on Gramavision (USA), Jun'84 by Gramavison Records (USA). Dist: PRT, IMS, Polygram

Cassette: released on Gramavision (USA), Jun'84 by Gramavison Records (USA). Dist: PRT, IMS, Polygram

Compact disc: released on Gramavision (USA), Jun'84 by Gramavison Records (USA). Dist: PRT, IMS, Polygram

LIVE IN STOCKHOLM-MAY 1957 (Mulligan, Gerry Quartet).
Album: released on Ingo, Apr'81 Dist: Jazz Horizons, Jazz Music, Celtic Music

LIVE IN STOCKHOLM VOL 2.
Album: released on Ingo, '81 Dist: Jazz Horizons, Jazz Music, Celtic Music

MEETS BEN WEBSTER.
Album: released on Verve (USA), May'84 by Polydor. Dist: Polygram

MEETS JOHNNY HODGES.
Album: released on Verve (USA), Mar'82 by Polydor. Dist: Polygram

MULLIGAN-BAKER.
Album: released on Prestige (USA), May'84

MY FUNNY VALENTINE.
Album: released on CBS, '84 by CBS Records. Dist: CBS

Cassette: released on CBS, '84 by CBS Records. Dist: CBS

NIGHT LIGHTS.
Tracks: / Morning of the carnival / Prelude in E minor / Night lights / Festive minor / Tell me when / In the wee small hours of the morning.
Notes: Digital Stereo.
Compact disc: released on Mercury Jazz Masters, Aug'84

Album: released on Mercury Jazz Masters, Dec'83

Cassette: released on Mercury Jazz Masters, Dec'83

PARIS 1954/L.A. 1953 (Mulligan, Gerry Quartet).
Compact disc: released on Vogue, Jul'87 Dist: Discovery, Jazz Music, PRT, Swift

PLEYEL CONCERT.
Tracks: / I may be wrong / Gold rush / Makin' whoopee / Laura / Soft shoes / Nearness of you (The) / Love me or leave me / Bernie's tune / Walkin' shoes / Moonlight in Vermont / Lady is a tramp (The) / Bark for Barkdale.
Compact disc: released on Vogue (France), Jun'84 Dist: Discovery, Jazz Music, PRT, Swift

Compact disc: released on Vogue (France), Jun'84 Dist: Discovery, Jazz Music, PRT, Swift

SILVER COLLECTION, THE.
Compact disc: by Phonogram Records. Dist: Polygram

SOFT LIGHTS AND SWEET MUSIC (Mulligan, Gerry & Scott Hamilton).

Tracks: / Soft lights and sweet music / Gone / Do you know what I use? / I've just seen her / Noblesse / Ghosts / Port of Baltimore blues.
Notes: Personnel: Gerry Mulligan:baritone sax/Scott Hamilton:tenor sax/Mike Renzi:piano/Jay Leonhart:bass/Grady Tate:drums.
Compact disc: released on Concord Jazz(USA), Jan'87 by Concord Jazz Records (USA). Dist: IMS, Polygram

Album: released on Concord Jazz(USA), Jul'86 by Concord Jazz Records (USA). Dist: IMS, Polygram

Cassette: released on Concord Jazz(USA), Jul'86 by Concord Jazz Records (USA). Dist: IMS, Polygram

SUMMIT.
Album: released on Carosello, Feb'83 Dist: Jazz Music, Jazz Horizons

THELONIUS MONK WITH GERRY MULLIGAN (see Monk, Thelonius) (Mulligan, Gerry/Thelonius Monk).

TIMES GETTING TOUGHER THAN TOUGH (Mulligan,Gerry,Jimmy Witherspoon,Ben Webster).
Album: released on Joker, Apr'81 Dist: Cadillac, Zodiac Distribution, Jazz Horizons, Jazz Music, JSU, Celtic Music

WALK ON THE WATER (Mulligan, Gerry & His Orchestra).
Tracks: / For an unfinished woman / Song for strayhorn / 42nd and Broadway / Angelica / Across the track blues / I'm getting sentimental over you.
Album: released on DRG (USA), Mar'87 by DRG Records. Dist: Conifer, RCA

Cassette: released on DRG (USA), Mar'87 by DRG Records. Dist: Conifer, RCA

Compact disc: released on DRG (USA), Mar'87 by DRG Records. Dist: Conifer, RCA

WALK ON THE WATER.
Album: released on DRG (USA), May'83 by DRG Records. Dist: Conifer, RCA

Cassette: released on DRG (USA), May'83 by DRG Records. Dist: Conifer, RCA

WHAT IS THERE TO SAY? (Mulligan, Gerry Quartet).
Tracks: / What is there to say / Just in time / News from blueport / Festive minor / My funny valentine / As catch can / Blueport / Utter chaos.
Album: released on Avan-Guard, Sep'86 by Vanguard Records. Dist: Conifer, Discovery

Multicoloured Shades
2000 LIGHT YEARS FROM HOME.
Single (12"): released on ABC, Aug'87 Dist: CBS, Pinnacle

HOUSE OF WAX.
Album: released on Hybrid, Feb'86 by Statik Records. Dist: Pinnacle

TEEN SEX TRANSFUSION.
Tracks: / Teen sex transfusion / Roses / Miss Terry shade.
Single (7"): released on Situation 2, Nov'86 Dist: Cartel, Pinnacle

Single (12"): released on Situation 2, Nov'86 Dist: Cartel, Pinnacle

Multicoloured world
BOLERO FOR PEACE.
Single (7"): released on Oblivion, Jun'82 Dist: Projection

Multi-national firms
MULTI-NATIONAL FIRMS (Tokyo,Paris,Africa,London).
Cassette: released on International Report, Oct'81 by Seminar Cassettes. Dist: Audio-Visual Library Services, Davidson Distribution, Eastern Educational Products Distrib., Forlaget Systime Distribution, MacDougall Distribution, Talktapes Distribution, Watkins Books Ltd Distribution, Norton, Jeff Distribution

Multi story
BREAKING NEW GROUND.
Single (7"): released on Heavy Metal, Sep'85 by FM-Revolver Records. Dist: EMI

CARRIE.
Single (7"): released on FM, Apr'85 by FM-Revolver Records. Dist: EMI

EAST/WEST.
Album: released on FM, Apr'85 by FM-Revolver Records. Dist: EMI

Cassette: released on FM, Apr'85 by FM-Revolver Records. Dist: EMI

THROUGH YOUR EYES.
Tracks: / Hold back the night / All out of love / Through your eyes / Rub it off / Heart of mine / Hot seat / Further than now / Spirit of love / Turn me onto.
Album: released on See For Miles, Aug'87 by

See For Miles Records. Dist: Pinnacle

Cassette: released on See For Miles, Aug'87 by See For Miles Records. Dist: Pinnacle

Multivizion
WORK TO LIVE DON'T LIVE TO WORK.
Single (7"): released on Situation 2, Jul'81 Dist: Cartel, Pinnacle

Single (12"): released on Situation 2, Jul'81 Dist: Cartel, Pinnacle

Mummy Calls
BEAUTY HAS HER WAY.
Tracks: / Beauty has her way / Messages on your door.
Single (7"): released on Geffen, Feb'86 by Geffen Records. Dist: WEA, CBS

Single (12"): released on Geffen, Feb'86 by Geffen Records. Dist: WEA, CBS

LET'S GO.
Tracks: / Let's go / Jane I'll kiss you in the desert.
Single (7"): released on Geffen, Apr'86 by Geffen Records. Dist: WEA, CBS

Single (12"): released on Geffen, Apr'86 by Geffen Records. Dist: WEA, CBS

MARY I SWEAR.
Single (7"): released on Mummy Calls, Nov'83 by Backs. Dist: Cartel Distribution

Munch Bunch
MUNCH BUNCH STORIES & SONGS Read by John Noakes, Ben Purves & Lesley Judd.
Album: released on Super Tempo, May'84 by Multiple Sounds Records. Dist: Multiple Sound Distributors

MUNCH BUNCH STORIES VOL.1 Read by Matthew Kelly.
Cassette: released on Tempo Storytime, May'84

MUNCH BUNCH STORIES VOL.2 Read by Matthew Kelly.
Cassette: released on Tempo Storytime, May'84

RORY RHUBARB & THE.... Read by Nigel Pegram.
Cassette: released on Tempo, May'84 by Warwick Records. Dist: Multiple Sound Distributors

SALLY STRAWBERRY & THE ..... Read by Nigel Pegram.
Cassette: released on Tempo, May'84 by Warwick Records. Dist: Multiple Sound Distributors

SCRUFF GOOSEBERRY & THE.... Read by Nigel Pegram.
Cassette: released on Tempo, May'84 by Warwick Records. Dist: Multiple Sound Distributors

SPUD AND THE....... Read by Nigel Pegram.
Cassette:

Munch, D.J.
PARTY ROCK.
Tracks: / Party rock.
Single (12"): released on FM Dance, Jul'87 by FM-Revolver Records. Dist: BMG, RCA, Ariola

Mundell, Hugh
AFRICA MUST BE FREE BY 1983.
Album: released on Greensleeves, Jun'86 by Greensleeves Records. Dist: BMG, Jetstar, Spartan

BLACK MAN FOUNDATION.
Album: released on Shanachie, Jun'85 Dist: Sterns/Triple Earth Distribution. Roots

MUNDELL.
Album: released on Greensleeves, May'82 by Greensleeves Records. Dist: BMG, Jetstar, Spartan

Mundy, Jimmy
GROOVIN' HIGH (see Wilson, Gerald) (Mundy,Jimmy/Gerald Wilson/Wilbert Baranco).

Mungo Jerry
100 MINUTES OF.....
Cassette: released on PRT (100 Minute Series), Nov'82

BABY JUMP.
Single (7"): released on Old Gold, Jul'82 by Old Gold Records. Dist: Lightning, Jazz Music, Spartan, Counterpoint

GOLDEN HOUR PRESENTS MUNGO JERRY'S GREATEST HITS.
Album: released on Golden Hour, Nov'74 by PRT Records. Dist: PRT

GREATEST HITS: MUNGO JERRY.
Album: released on Astan, Nov'84 by Astan Records. Dist: Counterpoint

Cassette: released on Astan, Nov'84 by Astan Records. Dist: Counterpoint

IN THE SUMMERTIME.
Single (7"): released on Illegal, Jul'87 by Faulty Products Records. Dist: Pinnacle, Lightning, Cartel

Single (7"): released on Flashback, Apr'79 by Flashback Records/PRT Records. Dist: Mainline, PRT

Single (7"): released on Old Gold, Apr'83 by Old Gold Records. Dist: Lightning, Jazz Music, Spartan, Counterpoint

Album: released on Flashback, Oct'85 by Flashback Records/PRT Records. Dist: Mainline, PRT

Cassette: released on Flashback, Oct'85 by Flashback Records/PRT Records. Dist: Mainline, PRT

IN THE SUMMERTIME (Mungo Jerry And The Brothers Grimm).
Tracks: / Got a job.
Single (7"): released on Illegal, Aug'87 by Faulty Products Records. Dist: Pinnacle, Lightning, Cartel

MUNGO'S SUMMER FUN PACKAGE (EP).
Single (7"): released on Scratch, Aug'82

SIX A SIDE.
Cassette: released on Astan, Nov'84 by Astan Records. Dist: Counterpoint

SOUL PARTY.
Cassette: released on Autograph, Apr'85 Dist: Record Services Distribution (Ireland)

SUNSHINE REGGAE.
Single (7"): released on Orbit, Jun'85 by Orbit Records. Dist: PRT Distribution

THERE GOES MY HEART AGAIN.
Single (7"): released on Mach 1, Jun'83 by Mach 1 Records. Dist: PRT

Munich Philharmonic
ANASTASIA.
Album: released on Silva Screen, 30 May'87 by Silva Screen Records. Dist: Silva Screen, PRT

Cassette: released on Silva Screen, 30 May'87 by Silva Screen Records. Dist: Silva Screen, PRT

Munroe, Caroline
PUMP ME UP.
Single (7"): released on Numa, Apr'85 by Numa Records. Dist: PRT Distribution

Single (12"):

Munro, Lee
STEREO HEADPHONES (I'VE GOT).
Tracks: / Stereo headphones (I've got) / Give me your love.
Single (7"): released on Numa, Jan'87 by Numa Records. Dist: PRT Distribution

Munrow, David
GREENSLEEVES (Munrow, David & Early Music C.L.).
Album: released on H.M.V., Jun'77 by EMI Records. Dist: EMI

GREENSLEEVES TO A GROUND Early music.
Cassette: released on H.M.V., Jun'77 by EMI Records. Dist: EMI

Munsey, Adrian
MAIN THEME.
Single (7"): released on Armageddon, May'81 by Armageddon Records. Dist: Revolver, Cartel, Pinnacle

Muppet Babies
MUPPET BABIES Various artists (Various Artists).
Notes: This programme is on your screens every Saturday morning. The original and lively music on the album is heavily featured throughout the serial.
Album: released on BBC, Oct'86 by BBC Records & Tapes. Dist: EMI, PRT, Pye

Cassette: released on BBC, Oct'86 by BBC Records & Tapes. Dist: EMI, PRT, Pye

Muppets
HALFWAY DOWN THE STAIRS.
Single (7"): released on PRT, May'77 by PRT Records. Dist: PRT

GREATEST HITS: MUNGO JERRY.
Album: released on Astan, Nov'84 by Astan Records. Dist: Counterpoint

MUPPET SHOW-2, THE.
Album:

MUPPET SHOW MUSIC ALBUM, THE.
Album: released on Pye, Nov'79

Cassette: released on PRT, Nov'79 by PRT Records. Dist: PRT

MUPPET SHOW MUSIC HALL.
Single (7"): released on Import Music Service (IMS), Sep'80 Dist: Concord Jazz Distributions, Pablo, Polygram

MUPPET SHOW, THE.
Album: released on Pye, Jun'77

Cassette: released on PRT, Jun'77 by PRT Records. Dist: PRT

Murder in the Cathedral
MURDER IN THE CATHEDRAL (T.S. Eliot & The Royal Shakespear Co.).
Cassette: released on Argo (Spokenword), Jul'82 by Decca Records. Dist: Polygram

Murder in the Mews
MURDER IN THE MEWS Agatha Christie (Nigel Hawthorne).
Cassette: released on Listen For Pleasure, Mar'84 by MFP Records. Dist: EMI

Murdoch, Allstair
FIELDS OF ATHENRY.
Notes: Incl:"Nancy Spain", "Molly darlin", "Danny boy","You are my sunshine" etc.
Cassette: released on Ross, '86 by Ross Records. Dist: Ross Distribution, Roots Distribution

ON THAT BEAUTIFUL SHORE.
Album: released on Ross, '86 by Ross Records. Dist: Ross Distribution, Roots Distribution

Cassette: released on Ross, '86 by Ross Records. Dist: Ross Distribution, Roots Distribution

Murdock, Shirley
AS WE LAY.
Tracks: / As we lay (remix) / Danger zone.
Single (7"): released on Elektra (USA), Mar'87 by Elektra/Asylum/Nonesuch Records. Dist: WEA

Single (12"): released on Elektra (USA), Mar'87 by Elektra/Asylum/Nonesuch Records. Dist: WEA

NO MORE.
Tracks: / No more / One I need (The) / Truth or dare.
Single (7"): released on Elektra (USA), Aug'86 by Elektra/Asylum/Nonesuch Records. Dist: WEA

Single (12"): released on Elektra (USA), Aug'86 by Elektra/Asylum/Nonesuch Records. Dist: WEA

SHIRLEY MURDOCK.
Tracks: / Be free / No more / Go on without you / Truth or dare / Danger zone / Teaser / As we lay / One I need (The) / Tribute.
Album: released on Elektra (USA), Mar'86 by Elektra/Asylum/Nonesuch Records. Dist: WEA

TRUTH OR DARE.
Tracks: / Truth or dare / Go on without you.
Single (7"): released on Elektra (USA), Feb'86 by Elektra/Asylum/Nonesuch Records. Dist: WEA

Single (12"): released on Elektra (USA), Feb'86 by Elektra/Asylum/Nonesuch Records. Dist: WEA

Mur, Mona
JESZCZE POLSKE.
Single (12"): released on Supermax, Sep'81

Murphy, Delia
SPINNING WHEEL (Murphy, Delia The Legendary).
Tracks: / Spinning wheel (The) / If I were a blackbird / I was told by my aunt / I wish that I never was wed / Roving journeyman (The) / Boston burglar (The) / Thank you ma'am says Dan / Three lovely lassies / Down by the glenside / Moonshiner (The) / Croppy bar (The) / Goodbye Mike (and goodbye Pat) / Nora Creina.
Notes: The legendary Delia Murphy, the queen of Connemara, died in 1971 but her indomitable spirit lives on through her hit songs: 'The Spinning Wheel', 'If I Were A Blackbird', 'Coortin' In The Kitchen', et al. The incessant demand for British record buyers for these timeless, nostalgic Irish ballads has led to the release of this classic collection on Grasmere Records.
Album: released on Grasmere, Nov'86 by Grasmere Records. Dist: EMI

Cassette: released on Grasmere, Nov'86 by Grasmere Records. Dist: EMI

Murphy, Eddie
EDDIE MURPHY.
Album: released on CBS, Dec'82 by CBS Records. Dist: CBS

HOW COULD IT BE.
Tracks: / How could it be / Con confused.
Single (7"): released on CBS, Apr'86 by CBS Records. Dist: CBS

Album: released on CBS, Nov'85 by CBS Records. Dist: CBS

Cassette: released on CBS, Nov'85 by CBS Records. Dist: CBS

PARTY ALL THE TIME.
Tracks: / Party all the time.
Single (7"): released on CBS, Dec'85 by CBS Records. Dist: CBS

Single (12"): released on CBS, Dec'85 by CBS Records. Dist: CBS

Murphy, Elliot

TEXAS.
Tracks: / Texas / Out for the killing.
Single (7"): released on Closer (France), Mar'86 Dist: Nine Mile, Cartel

Single (12"): released on Closer (France), Mar'86 Dist: Nine Mile, Cartel

Murphy, Mark

ARTISTRY OF MARK MURPHY, THE.
Album: released on Muse, Dec'82 by Peerless Records. Dist: Lugtons Distributors

BOP FOR KEROUAC.
Tracks: / Be-Bop lives (boplicity) / Goodbye porkpie hat / Parker's mood / You better go now / You've proven your point (bongo beep) / Bad and the beautiful / Down St Thomas way / Ballad of the sad young man.
Cassette: released on Muse (USA), Feb'87 by Muse Records (USA). Dist: Conifer Distribution, Jazz Music Distribution

BRAZIL SONG.
Tracks: / Desafinado / Two kites / Island, The / Bolero de sata / She / Someone to light up my life / Nothing will be as it was tomorrow / Outubro / bridges.
Cassette: released on Muse (USA), Feb'87 by Muse Records (USA). Dist: Conifer Distribution, Jazz Music Distribution

BRIDGING A GAP.
Album: released on Muse, Apr'81 by Peerless Records. Dist: Lugtons Distributors

MARK 11.
Album: released on Muse, Apr'81 by Peerless Records. Dist: Lugtons Distributors

MARK MURPHY.
Album: released on Muse, Apr'81 by Peerless Records. Dist: Lugtons Distributors

SATISFACTION GUARANTEED.
Album: released on Muse, Apr'81 by Peerless Records. Dist: Lugtons Distributors

SINGS NAT'S CHOICE VOLUMES 1 & 2.
Tracks: / Nature boy\Calypso blues / Love letters\Serenata / Oh you crazy moon / 'Tis autumn / I keep going back to Joe's / Tangerine / Lush life / Never let me go / These foolish things / Prtrait of Jenny\Ruby / For all we know / Maybe you'll be there / Blue gardenia / Don't let your eyes go shopping / More than you know / Look out for love / End of a love affair.
Compact disc: released on Muse (USA), Feb'87 by Muse Records (USA). Dist: Conifer Distribution, Jazz Music Distribution

SINGS THE NAT KING COLE SONG-BOOK.
Tracks: / Nature boy / Calypso blues / Love letters / Serenata / Oh you crazy moon / 'Tis autumn / I keep going back to Joe's / Tangerine / Lush life / Until the real thing comes along / Baby, baby all the time / Never let me go / These foolish things.
Album: released on Muse (USA), Aug'86 by Muse Records (USA). Dist: Conifer Distribution, Jazz Music Distribution

STOLEN MOMENTS.
Album: released on Muse, Apr'81 by Peerless Records. Dist: Lugtons Distributors

Murphy, Mike

DREAM OF EVERYDAY HOUSEWIFE, THE.
Album: released on Harp(Ireland), May'80 by Pickwick Records. Dist: Taylors

Murphy, Noel

MURPHY AND THE BRICKS.
Tracks: / Murphy and the bricks / From Clare to here.
Single (7"): released on Murphy's, Mar'87

NOEL MURPHY PERFORMS.
Album: released on Plant Life, Nov'81 Dist: Roots

Murphy, Peter

BLUE HEART.
Tracks: / Blue heart / Canvas beauty.
Single (7"): released on Beggars Banquet, Jun'86 by Beggars Banquet Records. Dist: WEA

Single (7"): released on Beggars Banquet, Jun'86 by Beggars Banquet Records. Dist: WEA

FINAL SOLUTION, THE.
Single (7"): released on Beggars Banquet, Nov'85 by Beggars Banquet Records. Dist: WEA

Single (12"): released on Beggars Banquet, Nov'85 by Beggars Banquet Records. Dist: WEA

INTERVIEW DISC.
Single (12"): released on Beggars Banquet, Dec'86 by Beggars Banquet Records. Dist: WEA

SHOULD THE WORLD FAIL TO FALL APART.
Tracks: / Should the world fail to fall apart (version two) / Canvas beauty / Light pours out of me,The / Confessions / Should the world fail to fall apart / Never man / God sends / Blue heart / Answer is clear,The / Final solution / Jemal.
Compact disc: released on Beggars Banquet, Dec'86 by Beggars Banquet Records. Dist: WEA

Single (12"): released on Beggars Banquet, Jan'87 by Beggars Banquet Records. Dist: WEA

Album: released on Beggars Banquet, Jul'86 by Beggars Banquet Records. Dist: WEA

Cassette: released on Beggars Banquet, Jul'86 by Beggars Banquet Records. Dist: WEA

TALE OF THE TONGUE.
Tracks: / Tale of the tongue / Should the world fail to fall apart.
Single (7"): released on Beggars Banquet, Oct'86 by Beggars Banquet Records. Dist: WEA

Single (12"): released on Beggars Banquet, Oct'86 by Beggars Banquet Records. Dist: WEA

Murphy,Rose

OLD TIME IRISH FIDDLE AND ACCORDION.
Album: released on Topic, '81 Dist: Roots Distribution

ROSE MURPHY.
Album: released on Audiophile, Jun'86 by Jazzology Records (USA). Dist: Jazz Music, Swift

Murphy, Turk

FAVOURITES (Murphy, Turk, Jazz Band).
Compact disc: released on London, Apr'87 by London Records. Dist: Polygram

IN CONCERT VOLUME 1. (Murphy,Turk & His San Francisco Jazz Band).
Album: released on GHB, Jun'86 Dist: Jazz Music, Swift

IN CONCERT VOLUME 2. (Murphy,Turk & His San Francisco Jazz Band).
Album: released on GHB, Jun'86 Dist: Jazz Music, Swift

IN CONCERT VOLUME 3. (Murphy,Turk & His San Francisco Jazz Band).
Album: released on GBH, Jun'86 by GBH Records. Dist: Jazz Music, Swift

LIVE AT EASY STREET VOL.1 (Murphy,Turk & His San Francisco Jazz Band).
Album: released on Dawn Club, Jun'79 Dist: Cadillac, Swift, JSU

LIVE AT EASY STREET VOL.3 (Murphy,Turk & His San Francisco Jazz Band).
Album: released on Dawn Club, Jun'79 Dist: Cadillac, Swift, JSU

LIVE AT EASY STREET VOL.2 (Murphy,Turk & His San Francisco Jazz Band).
Album: released on Dawn Club, Jun'79 Dist: Cadillac, Swift, JSU

LIVE AT EASY STREET (Murphy, Turk San Fransisco Jazz Band).
Album: released on Dawn Club, Dec'86 Dist: Cadillac, Swift, JSU

LIVE AT EASY STREET (II) (Murphy, Turk San Fransisco Jazz Band).
Album: released on Dawn Club, Dec'86 Dist: Cadillac, Swift, JSU

LIVE AT EASY STREET (III) (Murphy, Turk San Fransisco Jazz Band).
Album: released on Dawn Club, Dec'86 Dist: Cadillac, Swift, JSU

Murphy, Walter

DANCE TO THEMES FROM E.T..
Single (7"): released on MCA, Nov'82 by MCA Records. Dist: Polygram, MCA

DISCOSYMPHONY.
Album: released on New York International, Nov'79

MOSTLY MOZART.
Single (7"): released on New York, Feb'80 by New York Records. Dist: Jetstar

Murrain,Marie

HOW CAN LOVE BE SO CRUEL.
Tracks: / How can love be so cruel.
Single (12"): released on Body Music, Mar'86 by Body Music Records. Dist: Jetstar

Single (12"): released on Body Music, Jan'83 by Body Music Records. Dist: Jetstar

Murray, Anne

ANNE MURAY.
Tracks: / Talk it over in the morning / You've got a friend / Cotton Jenny.
Album: released on Music For Pleasure (Holland), Jan'86 by EMI Records. Dist: EMI

Cassette: released on Music For Pleasure (Holland), Jan'86 by EMI Records. Dist: EMI

ANN MURRAY'S COUNTRY HITS.
Tracks: / Cotton Jenny / He still thinks I care / Son of a rotten gambler / Walk right back / Lucky me / Blessed are the believers / It's all I can do / Another sleepless night / Hey baby / Somebody's always saying goodbye / Little good news, A / Just another woman in love / Nobody loves me like you do / Time don't run out on me / I don't think I'm ready for you.
Compact disc: released on Capitol, Apr'87 by Capitol Records. Dist: EMI

BOTH SIDES NOW.
Tracks: / It's all over / For baby / Last thing on my mind / Both sides now / Paths of victory / All the time / Some birds / Buffalo in the park.
Album: released on Showcase, Apr'86 Dist: Counterpoint

Cassette: released on Showcase, Apr'86 Dist: Counterpoint

Album: released on Astan, Nov'84 by Astan Records. Dist: Counterpoint

Cassette: released on Astan, Nov'84 by Astan Records. Dist: Counterpoint

CHRISTMAS WISHES.
Tracks: / Winter wonderland / Silver bells / Little drummer boy, the / I'll be home for Christmas / Christmas wishes / Loy to the world / Away in a manger / O holy night / Go tell it on the mountain / Silent night.
Compact disc: released on Capitol, Dec'86 by Capitol Records. Dist: EMI

COUNTRY HITS.
Compact disc: released on Capitol, Mar'87 by Capitol Records. Dist: EMI

HARMONY.
Tracks: / Are you still in love with me / Anyone can do the heartbreak / Great divide, The / Tonight (I want to be in love) / Perfect strangers / Give me your love / It happens all the time / Harmony / Natural love / Without you / Are you still in love with me / Anyone can do the heartbreak / Great divide, The / Tonight (I want to be in love) / Perfect strangers / Give me your love / It happens all the time / Harmony / Natural love / Without you.
Compact disc: released on Capitol, Jun'87 by Capitol Records. Dist: EMI

Album: released on Capitol, Aug'87 by Capitol Records. Dist: EMI

Cassette: released on Capitol, Aug'87 by Capitol Records. Dist: EMI

Album: released on Capitol, Aug'87 by Capitol Records. Dist: EMI

Cassette: released on Capitol, Aug'87 by Capitol Records. Dist: EMI

HEART OVER MIND.
Tracks: / Once you've had it / Time don't run out on me / I don't think I'm ready for you / Let your heart do the talking / You haven't heard the last of me / Nobody loves me like you do / I should know by now / Love you out of your mind / Take good care of my heart / Our love.
Compact disc: released on Capitol, Jul'85 by Capitol Records. Dist: EMI

LITTLE GOOD NEWS.
Single (7"): released on Capitol, Oct'83 by Capitol Records. Dist: EMI

NOBODY LOVES ME LIKE YOU DO (Murray, Anne & Dave Loggins).
Single (7"): released on Capitol, Oct'84 by Capitol Records. Dist: EMI

NOW AND FOREVER.
Tracks: / Now and forever (you and me) / I don't wanna spend another night without you.
Single (7"): released on Capitol, Mar'86 by Capitol Records. Dist: EMI

SNOWBIRD.
Tracks: / Snowbird / Fire and rain / Break my mind / Just bidin' my time / Put your hand in the hand / Running / Musical friends / Get together / I'll be your baby tonight.
Notes: Canada's queen of country music - Anne Murray comes to Music For Pleasure with the classic album 'Snowbird'. Released on the Fame label as part of the origi- nal launch list this LP is now given a further lease of life with the increase in the market place of country music in general. Featured tracks included her biggest hit 'Snowbird', also James Taylor's 'Fire and Rain' the semi gospel 'PutYour Hand In The Hand' and her superb version of Bob Dylan's 'I'll Be Your Baby Tonight'.
Album: released on Music For Pleasure, Feb'86 by EMI Records. Dist: EMI

Cassette: released on Music For Pleasure, Feb'86 by EMI Records. Dist: EMI

Single (7"): released on Capitol, '80 by Capitol Records. Dist: EMI

Cassette: released on Fame (Capitol), May'82 by Music For Pleasure Records. Dist: EMI

SOMEBODY'S WAITING.
Cassette: released on Capitol, May'80 by Capitol Records. Dist: EMI

SOMETHING TO TALK ABOUT.
Tracks: / Now and forever (you and me) / Who's leaving who / My life's a dance / Call us fools / On and on / Heartaches / Reach for me / When you're gone / You never know / Cotcha.
Notes: Anne Murray's new album features three songs produced by Keith Diamond who had such a success in 1985 with his work on Billy Ocean's album "Suddenly".
Album: released on Capitol, Apr'86 by Capitol Records. Dist: EMI

Cassette: released on Capitol, Apr'86 by Capitol Records. Dist: EMI

SONGMAKERS ALMANAC (Murray, Anne & Graham Johnson).
Album: released on Hyperion, Nov'86 by Hyperion Records. Dist: Taylors, PRT, Gamut

SONGS OF THE HEART.
Tracks: / You needed me / Hold me tight / That's why I love you / I just fall in love again / You've got me to hold on to / Broken hearted me / Fallin' in love (fallin' apart) / I'm happy just to dance with you / Come to me / Take good care of my heart / More we try (The) / You havn't heard the last of me / Heart stealer / Let your heart do the talking / Once you've had it.
Compact disc: released on Capitol, Apr'87 by Capitol Records. Dist: EMI

TOGETHER (see Campbell, Glen) (Murray, Anne & Glen Campbell).
Album: released on Music For Pleasure (Holland), Jan'85 by EMI Records. Dist: EMI
Cat. no: **MFP 41 5689 1**

VERY BEST OF ANNE MURRAY.
Album: released on Capitol, Sep'81 by Capitol Records. Dist: EMI

Cassette: released on Capitol, Sep'81 by Capitol Records. Dist: EMI

YOU NEEDED ME.
Single (7"): released on Capitol, Sep'78 by Capitol Records. Dist: EMI

Murray, Arthur

ARTHUR MURRAY SWINGS FOX TROTS (Murray, Arthur/Anthony, Ray & His Orchestra).
Tracks: / Poor butterfly / Froggy day, A / On the sunny side of the street / This year's kisses / I can't beleive that you're in love with me / Can't get out of this mood / You stepped out of this dream / You're the cream in my coffee / I've never been in love before / (Gang that sang, The) Heart of my heart / let's get lost / Love walked in.
Notes: A different tempo from best selling artist Ray Anthony - famed for the dream dancing albums. Not to be confused with the LP "Fox Trots", this selection of well-known tunes has only been previously available in the UK as an abridged 10" version. Arrangements courtesy of one of the masters, Billy May, include "On The Sunny Side Of The Street", "You're The Cream In My Coffee" and "Love Walked In". Like the Stan Kenton album, this is perfect for dance enthusiasts and nostalgia listeners alike. [EMI release sheet, May 1987]
Album: released on Capitol, May'87 by Capitol Records. Dist: EMI

Cassette: released on Capitol, May'87 by Capitol Records. Dist: EMI

Murray, Bert

ON THE FIDDLE.
Notes: 23 tracks ranging from Birlin' Reels to Slow Airs played by Bert Murray of Aberdeen.
Cassette: released on Ross, '86 by Ross Records. Dist: Ross Distribution, Roots Distribution

Murray, David

CHILDREN.
Compact disc: released on Black Saint (Italy), '86 Dist: Target, Jazz Music, Harmonia Mundi

CONCEPTUAL SAXOPHONE.
Album: released on Cadillac, Jul'87 by Cadillac Records. Dist: Cadillac

Page 710

Album: released on Cadillac, '78 by Cadillac Records. Dist: Cadillac

FLOWERS FOR ALBERT.
Album: released on India Navigation, Jul'78 by India Navigation Records. Dist: Cadillac, Projection, Swift

HOME (Murray, David Octet).
Tracks: / Home / Santa Barbara and Crenshaw / Follies / Choctaw blues / Last of the hipmen / 3-D family.
Compact disc: released on Black Saint (Italy), Apr'87 Dist: Target, Jazz Music, Harmonia Mundi

Compact disc: released on Black Saint, Sep'85 Dist: Projection, IMS, Polygram, Chris Wellard, Harmonia Mundi, Swift

INTERBOOGIEOLOGY Various Artists (Various Artists).
Album: released on Black Saint Import, Jul'78

LET THE GREAT BIG WORLD KEEP TURNING.
Tracks: / let the great big world keep tuning / Let the great big world keep turning (Instrumental).
Single (7"): released on Pectcode, Nov'85 Dist: Spartan

LIVE AT SWEET BASIL VOL.2 (Murray, David Big Band).
Compact disc: released on Black Saint (Italy), '86 Dist: Target, Jazz Music, Harmonia Mundi

LIVE AT SWEET BASIL VOL.1 (Murray, David Big Band).
Compact disc: released on Black Saint (Italy), '86 Dist: Target, Jazz Music, Harmonia Mundi

Album: released on Black Saint, May'85 Dist: Projection, IMS, Polygram, Chris Wellard, Harmonia Mundi, Swift

LIVE AT "SWEET BASIL" VOL.2 (Murray, David Big Band).
Compact disc: released on Black Saint (Italy), Apr'87 Dist: Target, Jazz Music, Harmonia Mundi

LIVE AT SWEET BASIL VOL.1 (Murray, David Big Band).

LIVE AT "SWEET BASIL" VOL.1 (Murray, David Big Band).
Compact disc: released on Black Saint (Italy), Apr'87 Dist: Target, Jazz Music, Harmonia Mundi

LONDON CONCERT, THE Live at Collegiate Theatre.
Double Album: released on Cadillac, Jul'87 by Cadillac Records. Dist: Cadillac

LOW CLASS CONSPIRACY.
Album: released on Adelphi, May'81 by Adelphi Records. Dist: Jetstar

MING (Murray, David Octet).
Tracks: / Fast life, The / Hill, The / Ming / Jasvan / Dewey's circle.
Compact disc: released on Black Saint, Sep'85 Dist: Projection, IMS, Polygram, Chris Wellard, Harmonia Mundi, Swift

Album: released on Black Saint, Sep'85 Dist: Projection, IMS, Polygram, Chris Wellard, Harmonia Mundi, Swift

MORNING SONG (Murray, David Quartet).
Compact disc: released on Black Saint (Italy), Apr'87 Dist: Target, Jazz Music, Harmonia Mundi

MORNING SONG (Murray, David Octet).
Tracks: / Morning song / Body and soul / Light blue frolic / Jitterbug waltz / Off season / Duet.
Compact disc: released on Black Saint, Sep'85 Dist: Projection, IMS, Polygram, Chris Wellard, Harmonia Mundi, Swift

MURRAY'S STEPS (Murray, David Octet).
Compact disc: released on Black Saint (Italy), '86 Dist: Target, Jazz Music, Harmonia Mundi

ORGANIC SAXAPHONE.
Album: released on Natural Organic Import, Jan'80

PENTHOUSE JAZZ VOL.1.
Album: released on Circle Import, May'78 Dist: Projection

SOLOMON'S SONS (Murray, David & James Newton).
Album: released on Circle Import, May'78 Dist: Projection

SUR-REAL SAXOPHONE.
Album: released on Horo, '78 Dist: Cadillac Music

Murray, Gwen

ALL MY RICHES.
Album: released on Dove, May'79 by Dove Records. Dist: Jetstar

Murray, Pauline

HOLOCAUST (Murray, Pauline & Storm).
Single (7"): released on Polestar, Oct'84 by Polestar Records. Dist: Red Rhino, Cartel

Single (12"): released on Polestar, Oct'84 by Polestar Records. Dist: Red Rhino, Cartel

HONG KONG.
Tracks: / Hong Kong.
Single (12"): released on Polestar, Feb'87 by Polestar Records. Dist: Red Rhino, Cartel

NEW AGE (Murray, Pauline & Storm).
Tracks: / New age / Body music.
Single (7"): released on Polestar, Oct'86 by Polestar Records. Dist: Red Rhino, Cartel

Single (12"): released on Polestar, Oct'86 by Polestar Records. Dist: Red Rhino, Cartel

PAULINE MURRAY & THE INVISIBLE GIRLS (Murray, Pauline & the Invisible Girls).
Album: released on Dreamland, Sep'80 by RSO. Dist: Polygram

Murray, Ruby

BEST OF RUBY MURRAY, THE.
Album: released on One Up, Jun'75 by EMI Records.

Cassette: released on One Up, Jun'75 by EMI Records.

Murray, Sonny

LIVE AT MOERS FESTIVAL.
Album: released on Moers Music, Jan'80 Dist: Cadillac, JSU Distribution, Projection Distribution

Murray, Sunny

AN EVEN BREAK.
Album: released on Affinity, Aug'79 by Charly Records. Dist: Charly, Cadillac

APPLE CORES.
Album: released on Philly-Jazz, Sep'79

Murrell, Kris

CHERRY PIE.
Single (7"): released on Birdland Records, Mar'85 by Birdland Records. Dist: RCA

WHO'S WITH YOU.
Single (7"): released on Survival, Sep'85 by Survival Records. Dist: Backs, Cartel Distribution

Murrin,Jelly Belly

BACK FROM L.A..
Tracks: / Back from L.A. (Swed Mix) / (Pinner Mix) / Murrin rap (Jacko Mix).
Single (7"): released on Greyhound, Apr'86 by Greyhound Records. Dist: PRT, Greyhound

Murvin,Junior

BAD MAN POSSE.
Album: released on Dread At The Controls, Nov'82 Dist: Dub Vendor, Virgin Records, EMI

Single (12"): released on Dread At The Controls, Jul'82 Dist: Dub Vendor, Virgin Records, EMI

MUGGERS IN THE STREET.
Album: released on Greensleeves, Sep'84 by Greensleeves Records. Dist: BMG, Jetstar, Spartan

POLICE & THIEVES.
Album: released on Island, Mar'77 by Island Records. Dist: Polygram

Single (7"): released on Island, Jul'81 by Island Records. Dist: Polygram

POLICE & THIEVES (Murvin,Junior, Jah Lion, Glen Dacasta & Upsetters).
Single (12"): released on Island, Apr'80 by Island Records. Dist: Polygram

Muscle Shoals Horns

BORN TO GET DOWN.
Album: released on Bang, Feb'77 Dist: Red Rhino, Cartel

Muse All Stars

BUDDY TATE AND THE MUSE ALL STARS (see under Tate, Buddy).

Musette

MUSIQUE EN ENVASION.
Cassette: released on Polydor (France), Apr'84 Dist: Polygram

Musettorama

MUSETTORAMA Various artists (Various Artists).
Tracks: / La valse de radio montmarte / Cajouleuse / La valse du populo / Musettorama / Ca marche / Poesia / Super favourite / Resto paso / Sambatina / Nocturnal ballade / El feo / La marche de L'A.C.Vitry le Francois.
Notes: (Cassette & Music Book) Artists include: Lacarnge/Trichot/Ferrai/Elicrisio.

Music...

MUSICAL HIGHLIGHTS FROM PHILARMONIC 1979 Various artists (Various Artists).
Album: released on United Artists, Dec'79

MUSICAL VIEW OF IRELAND Various artists (Various Artists).
Album: released on Stoic, Mar'84 by Stoic Records. Dist: Spartan Distribution

Cassette: released on Stoic, Mar'84 by Stoic Records. Dist: Spartan Distribution

MUSICAL WORLD OF RICHARD RODGERS Various artists (Various Artists).
Double Album: released on CBS, Jul'80 by CBS Records. Dist: CBS

MUSIC BY SOUND IN BRASS HANDBELLS (Various Artists).
Cassette: released on Saydisc, May'79 by Saydisc Records. Dist: Essex, Harmonia Mundi, Roots, H.R. Taylor, Jazz Music, Swift, Projection, Gamut

MUSIC CITY SOUL (SUN RECORDINGS) Various artists (Various Artists).
Album: released on Charly, Jun'76 by Charly Records. Dist: Charly, Cadillac

MUSIC IMPROVISATION COMPANY 1968-1971 Various Artists (Various Artists).
Album: released on Incus, Feb'77 Dist: Jazz Music, Cadillac

MUSIC IN TRANSIT Various artists (Various Artists).
Cassette: released on Temple, Jul'86 by Temple Records. Dist: Roots Distribution, Folksound Distribution, Celtic Music Distribution, Projection Distribution

MUSIC MAN, THE Original Cast (Various Artists).
Tracks: / Overture & rock island / Iowa stubborn / Ya got trouble / Piano lesson / Goodnight my someone / Seventy six trombones / Sincere / Sadder-but-wiser girl for me, The / Pick-a-little, take-a-little & goodnight ladies / Marian the librian / My white knight / Wells Fargo wagon / It's you / Shipoopi / Lida Rose & will I ever tell you / Gary, Indiana / Till there was you / Finale.
Compact disc: released on EMI, Jul'87 by EMI Records. Dist: EMI

MUSIC, NOISE, SOUND & BEAT Various Artists (Various Artists).
Cassette: released on Music For Midgets, Nov'84 Dist: Backs, Cartel Distribution

MUSIC & RHYTHM Various Artists (Various Artists).
Album: released on WEA, Jul'82 by WEA Records. Dist: WEA

Cassette: released on WEA, Jul'82 by WEA Records. Dist: WEA

MUSIC & SOUND LIBRARY VOLS.1&2 Various sound effects (Music & Sound Library).
Double Album: released on PRT, Nov'85 by PRT Records. Dist: PRT

MUSIC THAT MATTERS Mercury Country (Various Artists).
Tracks: / I'll go steppin' too / Amazing Grace / Waitin' for the sun to shine / Old violin / Do you mind if I step into your dreams / She's the trip that I've been on / These shoes / Hard baby to rock / Walk the way the wind blows / Down at the Mall / Everybody needs love on a Saturday night / That's what her memory is for / Winners / Love is the way.
Notes: By way of a UK introduction, this excellent compilation by Tony Byworth highlig-hts the success of Mercury in the USA as a country label. Most of the tracks have not been released in the UK before and will be of great interest to all fans of Country music. This album is a UK only release.
Album: released on Mercury, May'87 by Phonogram Records. Dist: Polygram Distribution

Cassette: released on Mercury, May'87 by Phonogram Records. Dist: Polygram Distribution

MUSIC TO REMEMBER Various Artists (Various Artists).
Cassette: released on Ditto, Aug'84 by Pickwick Records. Dist: H.R. Taylor

MUSIC YOU KNOW & LOVE Various Artists (Various Artists).
Cassette: released on Aim (Budget Cassettes), Feb'83

Music Academy

RINGING THE BELL.
Single (7"): released on Record Shack, Mar'85 by Record Shack Records. Dist: PRT

Single (12"): released on Record Shack Mar'85 by Record Shack Records. Dist: PRT

Music after Midnight

MUSIC AFTER MIDNIGHT PART 1 Various Artists (Various Artists).
Album: released on Mercury (Holland), Jul'85 by Phonogram Records. Dist: Polygram Distribution

Cassette: released on Mercury (Holland), Jul'85 by Phonogram Records. Dist: Polygram Distribution

MUSIC AFTER MIDNIGHT PART 2 Various Artists (Various Artists).
Album: released on Mercury (Holland), Jul'85 by Phonogram Records. Dist: Polygram Distribution

Cassette: released on Mercury (Holland), Jul'85 by Phonogram Records. Dist: Polygram Distribution

Musical Youth

DIFFERENT STYLE.
Album: released on MCA, Oct'83 by MCA Records. Dist: Polygram, MCA Deleted '87

Cassette: released on MCA, Oct'83 by MCA Records. Dist: Polygram, MCA

PASS THE DUTCHIE.
Tracks: / Pass the Dutchie / Never gonna give you up.
Single (7"): released on Old Gold, Apr'86 by Old Gold Records. Dist: Lightning, Jazz Music, Spartan, Counterpoint

POLITICAL / GENERAL.
Single (7"): released on 021, Oct'82 by 021 Records. Dist: Spartan

SHE'S TROUBLE.
Single (7"): released on MCA, Apr'84 by MCA Records. Dist: Polygram, MCA

Single (12"): released on MCA, Apr'84 by MCA Records. Dist: Polygram, MCA

SIXTEEN / STRICTLY VIBES.
Single (7"): released on MCA, Jan'84 by MCA Records. Dist: Polygram, MCA

Single (12"): released on MCA, Jan'84 by MCA Records. Dist: Polygram, MCA

Picture disc single: released on MCA, Jan'84 by MCA Records. Dist: Polygram, MCA

YOUTH OF TODAY.
Album: released on MCA, Nov'82 by MCA Records. Dist: Polygram, MCA Deleted '87

Cassette: released on MCA, Nov'82 by MCA Records. Dist: Polygram, MCA

Music emporium

MUSIC EMPORIUM.
Album: released on Psycho, Sep'83 Dist: Funhouse, Rough Trade

Music for...

MUSIC FOR ACCORDION ORCHESTRA NO 6 Various artists (Various Artists).
Album: released on ARC (Accordion Records), May'84 Dist: Accordion Record Club

MUSIC FOR ACCORDION ORCHESTRA NO. 5 Various artists (Various Artists).
Album: released on ARC (Accordion Records), May'84 Dist: Accordion Record Club

MUSIC FOR ALL Various artists (Various Artists).
Notes: Artists include: Allun Davies/Brian Sharp/Byron Jones, Llandudno.
Album: released on Grosvenor, May'86 by Grosvenor Records. Dist: Taylors

MUSIC FOR NATIONS SINGLES ALBUM (Various Artists).
Album: released on Music For Nations, Dec'86 by Music For Nations Records. Dist: Pinnacle

Cassette: released on Music For Nations, Dec'86 by Music For Nations Records. Dist: Pinnacle

MUSIC FOR ROYAL OCCASIONS Various artists (Various Artists).
Cassette: released on Argo, May'77 by Decca Records. Dist: Polygram

MUSIC FOR ROYAL WEDDINGS Various artists (Various Artists).
Album: released on CBS, Jul'81 by CBS Records. Dist: CBS

Cassette: released on CBS, Jul'81 by CBS Records. Dist: CBS

MUSIC FOR THE MAGIC LANTERN (BARREL ORGANS ETC) (Various Artists).
Cassette: released on Saydisc, Jan'81 by Saydisc Records. Dist: Essex, Harmonia Mundi, Roots, H.R. Taylor, Jazz Music, Swift, Projection, Gamut

MUSIC FOR THE MIRACLE Various artists (Various Artists).

Tracks: / Heart and soul / Run to you / Out of touch / Running with the night / Careless whisper / Smooth operator / Cover me / I'm so excited / She bop / Everybody wants to rule the world / Can't fight this feeling / Everytime you go away.
Album: released on Epic, Jun'86 by CBS Records. Dist: CBS

Cassette: released on Epic, Jun'86 by CBS Records. Dist: CBS

MUSIC FOR THE SEASONS Various orchestras (Various Artists).
Special: released on Ronco, Apr'82

Special: released on Ronco, Apr'82

Music for Aborigines

SITTING ON A BISCUIT TIN.
Tracks: / Sitting on a biscuit tin / Faith / Ragbone man.
Single (12"): released on Spartan, 30 May'87 by Spartan Records. Dist: Spartan

Music for Pleasure

BLACKLANDS.
Album: released on Whirlpool, Aug'85 by Whirlpool Records. Dist: Cartel

CHROME HIT CORROSION.
Single (12"): released on Whirlpool, May'84 by Whirlpool Records. Dist: Cartel

DARK CRASH / URBAN POISON / BLACK.
Single (7"): released on Polydor, Jun'83 by Polydor Records. Dist: Polygram, Polydor

Single (12"): released on Polydor, Jun'83 by Polydor Records. Dist: Polygram, Polydor

DISCONNECTION / WHIPLASH CARESS.
Single (7"): released on Whirlpool, Jan'84 by Whirlpool Records. Dist: Cartel

INTO THE RAIN.
Album: released on Polydor, Aug'82 by Polydor Records. Dist: Polygram, Polydor

Cassette: released on Polydor, Aug'82 by Polydor Records. Dist: Polygram, Polydor

LIGHT / MALEFICE.
Single (7"): released on Polydor, Oct'82 by Polydor Records. Dist: Polygram, Polydor

LIGHT / NOSTALGIA.
Single (12"): released on Polydor, Oct'82 by Polydor Records. Dist: Polygram, Polydor

TIME.
Single (7"): released on Polydor, Jan'83 by Polydor Records. Dist: Polygram, Polydor

Single (12"): released on Polydor, Jan'83 by Polydor Records. Dist: Polygram, Polydor

Music from...

MUSIC FROM BURUNDI Various Artists (Various Artists).
Album: released on Albatross(Italy), Jul'84

MUSIC FROM GREAT AUSTRALIAN FILMS Various artists (Various Artists).
Album: released on DRG (USA), Jun'83 by DRG Records. Dist: Conifer, RCA

MUSIC FROM GREAT ROYAL OCCASIONS Various artists (Various Artists).
Album: released on BBC, May'83 by BBC Records & Tapes. Dist: EMI, PRT, Pye

Cassette: released on BBC, May'83 by BBC Records & Tapes. Dist: EMI, PRT, Pye

MUSIC FROM ST.CLEMENT DANES (THE CHOIR,ORGAN,BELLS & CHIMES) Various artists (Various Artists).
Tracks: / Psalm twenty three / How shall I fitly meet thee / O magnum mysterium / Stille nacht / I saw three ships / When to the temple Mary went / Adoramus to Jesu Christe / Ye now are sorrowful / This youful Eastertide / Coelos ascendit hodie / Let the bright seraphim / Greater love / Oranges & Lemons / Bells of St.Clements,The / Toccata in b minor.
Notes: St.Clements Church is world famous in connection with the 'Oranges & Lemons' nursery rhyme and its bells chime out the tune every three hours. Standing in the middle of the busy Strand, the Church was rebuilt after war damage and reco-nsecrated in the presence of Her Majesty The Queen in 1958 as the Central Churchof the Royal Air Force. The Church is well-known for the high standard of the musical tradition, which has been maintained since the reopening by the same Director of Music, Martindale Sidwell with a small choir of eight professional singers. This cassette release is more than just a sound souvenir of an historicChurch but a true experience featuring a fine choir and organ plus the superb trumpet playing of John Wilbraham. It is recorded in Ambisonic stereo to repro-duce a lovely acoustic.
Cassette: released on Saydisc, Jun'86 by Saydisc Records. Dist: Essex, Harmonia Mundi, Roots, H.R. Taylor, Jazz Music, Swift, Projection, Gamut

MUSIC FROM STREETS OF FIRE (Music from Streets of Fire).
Notes: With the film imminent in cinemas, this EP contains three of its song sequences,plus a behind-the-scenes look at the production in the making. Number of tracks: 3. Type of recording: EP. Total playing time: '26 minutes.
Video-cassette (VHS): released on CIC Video, Sep'84 by CBS Records. Dist: CBS, Pickwick Distribution

MUSIC FROM THE 11TH WORLD PENTECOSTAL CONFERENCE (PRAISE 31) Various Artists (Various Artists).
Album: by Pilgrim Records. Dist: Rough Trade, Cartel

MUSIC FROM THE BILL CROSBY SHOW Various artists (Various Artists).
Tracks: / Resthatherian / Camille / Love in its proper place / Poppin' / Kitchen jazz / Clair (Phylicia) / Huxtable kids, The / Outstretched hands (Gloria) / Look at this / House full of love,A.
Album: released on CBS, Mar'86 by CBS Records. Dist: CBS

Cassette: released on CBS, Mar'86 by CBS Records. Dist: CBS

MUSIC FROM THE COTTON CLUB Various artists (Various Artists).
Album: released on Astan, Jun'86 by Astan Records. Dist: Counterpoint

Cassette: released on Astan, Jun'86 by Astan Records. Dist: Counterpoint

MUSIC FROM THE PASOLINI FILMS Original soundtrack (Various Artists).
Album: released on General Music (France), May'85 by General Music Records (France). Dist: Studio Import & Export Distribution, Silva Screen

MUSIC FROM THE WESTERN ISLES - SCOTTISH TRADITION VOLUME 2 Various Artists (Various Artists).
Album: released on Tangent, Apr'81 Dist: Roots Distribution, Lugtons Distributors, Taylors, JSU Distribution, Spartan Distribution

MUSIC FROM UTOPIA Various artists (Various Artists).
Tracks: / Old Fulham fertility / Irden / Gravity's angel / East wind / Naturliche liebe / Constellation (part 1) / Kommunikation hipp-ipp / Conditioning / Speed display / High on tech / Eh-ei-joa / Happy Grenada / Expedition extra / Cielouvert / Ganna plasmid / Silicon valley / Interne 1 / Morgen und ein spaziergang / Tique-taque / Annabella / Exotic defiler / Later bagatelles 1 & 2 / Hotel reform / Pujaparwata / Selig, die-grerchtigkeit willen - tolgt werden.
Notes: A fascinating collection featuring artists such as Laurie Anderson, Yello and Howard Jones, to name but three. The theme is computers, futuristic holograms and a time beyond this century, expressed by various computer keyboard 'wizards'Side Four = Bob Moog's contribution to the Erdenklang Premiere.
Album: released on Teldec (Germany), Nov'85 by Import Records. Dist: IMS Distribution, Polygram Distribution

Album: released on Erdenklang (Germany), Aug'85

PRISONER, THE (Various Artists).
Compact disc single: released on Bam Caruso, '86 by Bam Caruso Records. Dist: Rough Trade, Revolver, Cartel

WHO PAYS THE FERRYMAN (Various Artists).
Album: released on BBC, May'78 by BBC Records & Tapes. Dist: EMI, PRT, Pye

Cassette: released on BBC, May'78 by BBC Records & Tapes. Dist: EMI, PRT, Pye

WICKED LADY (Various Artists).
Album: released on Atlantic, Jun'83 by WEA Records. Dist: WEA

Music from a Small Planet

LOVE SACRIFICE.
Single (12"): released on Safari, Jul'84 by Safari Records. Dist: Pinnacle

Music Goes Round...

GOLDEN YEARS OF TIN PAN ALLEY,THE.
Tracks: / Stormy weather / How deep is the ocean / Heartaches / All of me / Blue moon / Ghost of a chance / Shoe shine boy / Music goes round and around,The / Untill the real thing comes along / When my dreamboat comes home / Once in a while / Undecided / Heart and soul / Tain't what you do (it's the way that cha do it).
Notes: Full title: The golden years of Tin Pan Alley 1930-1939.
Album: released on New World (USA), Sep'86 by New World Records (USA). Dist: Conifer

Music Hall

MUSIC HALL (TOP OF THE BILL) Various artists (Various Artists).
Double Album: released on World, Apr'74 Dist: Jetstar

MUSIC HALL TO VARIETY VOL 1 (MATINEE) Various artists (Various Artists).
Album: released on World, '70 Dist: Jetstar

MUSIC HALL TO VARIETY VOL 2 (FIRST HOUSE) Various artists (Various Artists).
Album: released on World, '70 Dist: Jetstar

MUSIC HALL TO VARIETY VOL 3 (SECOND HOUSE) Various artists (Various Artists).
Album: released on World, '70 Dist: Jetstar

Musichini, Alain

PRINCE DE L'ACCORDEON.
Album: released on Accordion Record Club, Jul'86 by Accordion Record Club Records. Dist: Accordion Record Club

Musicians for Mission

HEART CRY.
Notes: Musicians For Mission, based in Amsterdam Holland, is a ministry of Youth With aMission. This album presents some of the music ministries of Musicians for Mis-sions, featuring songs by a band called Judah, husband and wife team Dale and Sue Trullinger, and soloists Karen Lafferty and Darren Smith.
Album: released on Word, Apr'86 by Word Records. Dist: Word Distribution, CBS

Cassette: released on Word, Apr'86 by Word Records. Dist: Word Distribution, CBS

Musicians of Bremen

MUSICIANS OF BREMEN, THE Various artists (Various Artists).
Cassette: released on Pickwick (Ladybird), '83

Music Machine

12 SUPER HITS (Various Artists).
Cassette: released on Bibi, Sep'80

BEST OF.....
Album: released on Rhino (USA), Feb'85 by Rhino Records (USA).

MUSIC MACHINE Various Artists (Various Artists).
Double cassette: released on Pickwick, Mar'83 by Pickwick Records. Dist: Pickwick Distribution, Prism Leisure Distribution, Lugtons

TURN ON THE MUSIC MACHINE.
Album: released on Big Beat, Jul'83 by Ace Records. Dist: Projection, Pinnacle

Music of....

MUSIC OF THE MILITARY Various artists (Various Artists).
Tracks: / Royal Air Force march past / Cavalry of the Steppes / Light of foot / Blaze away / Amazing Grace / Men of Harlech & God bless the Prince of Wales / Aces high / Anchors aweigh / Battle of Britain / Old comrades / Cronation March / Lochanside / Green hills of Tyrol, The / Dambusters, The / Washington post, The / Sons of the brave / National Emblem / Battle of the Somme / Dagshai hills / Argyll & Sutherland Highlanders' entry into crater,The / Under the double eagle / Australian march / Redetzky / 633 Squadron / Flower of Scotland, The / Famous British marches / British Grenadiers, The / Lillibulero / All through the night / Highland Laddie / Rule Britannia / Bonnie Ann / Athol cummers / Sheepwife, The / Macleod of Mull / Semper fidelis / Those magnificent men in their flying machines.
Notes: Featuring seven will known Military Bands: H.M.Royal Marines/Central Band of the Royal Air Force/The Royal Hussars/Royal Corps of Transport/The Pipes & Drumsof the 1st Battalion Scots Guards/The Pipes & Drums of the 1st Battalion The Argyll & Sutherland Highlanders/The Southern Band of the Royal Air Force. 26 tracks in all which include such popular and loved military tunes including 'Cavalry of The Steppes','Blaze Away','Amazing Grace','The Dambusters','The Washington Post','633 Squadron','Anchors Aweigh','Ace High' and many more. As we have only one Military album in the catalogue this being MFP 1015 Royal Mari-nes-'On Parade' the time is right to introduce a second Military album.
Double Album: released on Music For Pleasure, Apr'86 by EMI Records. Dist: EMI

Cassette: released on Music For Pleasure, Apr'86 by EMI Records. Dist: EMI

MUSIC OF THE STREET Various Mechanical Street Instruments (Various Artists).
Album: released on Saydisc, Nov'83 by Saydisc Records. Dist: Essex, Harmonia Mundi, Roots, H.R. Taylor, Jazz Music, Swift, Projection, Gamut

Cassette: released on Saydisc, Nov'83 by Saydisc Records. Dist: Essex, Harmonia Mundi, Roots, H.R. Taylor, Jazz Music, Swift, Projection, Gamut

MUSIC OF THE STREETS (Various Artists).
Notes: Mechanical street entertainment street piano, cylinder piano, organette.
Compact disc: released on Saydisc, Jun'87 by Saydisc Records. Dist: Essex, Harmonia Mundi, Roots, H.R. Taylor, Jazz Music, Swift, Projection, Gamut

MUSIC OF THE TATAR PEOPLE Various Artists (Various Artists).
Album: released on Tangent, Apr'78 by Tangent Records. Dist: Roots Records Distribution, Impetus Distribution, H.R. Taylor Distribution, Jazz Music Distribution, JSU Distribution, Projection Distribution, Gordon Duncan Distribution, Ross Records Distribution

MUSIC OF TORVILLE & DEAN 2 Various Artists (Various Artists).
Single (7"): released on Safari, Jul'85 by Safari Records. Dist: Pinnacle

Music of Yugoslavia

FOLK MUSIC OF YUGOSLAVIA Collected & edited by Wolf Dietrich.
Album: released on Topic, Sep'81 by Topic Records. Dist: JSU Distribution, Projection Distribution, Jazz Music Distribution

Music on the move

MUSIC ON THE MOVE (20 BIG BAND & JAZZ GREATS) Various Artists (Various Artists).
Cassette: released on RCA International, Jun'81

MUSIC ON THE MOVE (20 COUNTRY GREATS) Various Artists (Various Artists).
Cassette: released on RCA International, Jun'81

MUSIC ON THE MOVE (20 EASY LISTENING FAVOURITES) Various Artists (Various Artists).
Cassette: released on RCA International, Jun'81

MUSIC ON THE MOVE (20 LADIES & GENTLEMEN OF SONG) Various Artists (Various Artists).
Cassette: released on RCA International, Jun'81

MUSIC ON THE MOVE (20 ORIGINAL POP HITS) Various Artists (Various Artists).
Cassette: released on RCA International, Jun'81

Musique de film

MUSIQUE DE FILM (FILM MUSIC) Various artists (Various Artists).
Triple album / cassette: released on Pathe MarconiFrance), Jan'85

Musique Zen

MUSIQUE ZEN Various artists (Various Artists).
Album: released on Auvidis (France), Feb'85 Dist: Discovery

Cassette: released on Auvidis (France), Feb'85 Dist: Discovery

Muskrats

INSIGHT.
Album: released on Sweet Folk and Country, '78 Dist: Chris Wellard Distribution

MUSKRATS, THE.
Album: released on SRT, May'76 by SRT Records. Dist: Pinnacle, Solomon & Peres Distribution, SRT Distribution, H.R. Taylor Distribution, PRT Distribution

Muslimgauze

BUDDHIST ON FIRE.
Album: released on Recluse, Jul'85 by Backs Records. Dist: Cartel

FLAJELATA.
Album: released on Limited, Feb'86 Dist: Red Rhino, Cartel

HAJJ.
Album: released on Limited, Sep'86 Dist: Red Rhino, Cartel

HUNTING OUT WITH AN ARIEL EYE.
Album: released on Limited Edition, Jul'84 by Aardvark. Dist: Red Rhino Records, Cartel

Musselwhite, Charlie

CURTAIN CALL.
Album: released on Red Lightnin', Nov'82 by Red Lightnin' Records. Dist: Roots, Swift, Jazz Music, JSU, Pinnacle, Cartel, Wynd-Up Distribution

GOIN' BACK DOWN SOUTH.
Compact disc: released on Arhoolie, May'81 by Arhoolie Records. Dist: Projection, Topic, Jazz Music, Swift, Roots

HARMONICA ACCORDING TO CHARLIE MUSSELWHITE, THE.
Album: released on Kicking Mule, Feb'79 by Sonet. Dist: Roots, PRT-Pye Distribution

MELLOW DEE.
Tracks: / Hey Miss Bessie / Need my baby / I'll get a break / Peach orchard mama / Ask me nice / Come back baby / Coming home baby / Baby please don't go / Lotsa poppa / Steady on your trail / Can't you see what you're doing to me / Christo redemptor (slight return).
Album: released on Crosscut, Sep'86 by IMS-Polygram Records. Dist: IMS, Polygram, Rollercoaster Distribution

MEMPHIS TENNESSEE.
Album: released on Crosscut, Nov'84 Dist: Rollercoaster Distribution, Swift

TAKIN' MY TIME.
Album: released on Arhoolie, May'81 by Arhoolie Records. Dist: Projection, Topic, Jazz Music, Swift, Roots

Mussolini, Boots Quartet
LITTLE MAN.
Album: released on Affinity, Jul'81 by Charly Records. Dist: Charly, Cadillac

Mussolini, Romano
JAZZ ALBUM.
Album: released on Bang bang (Import), Apr'83

Musso, Vido
ONE NIGHT STAND.
Album: released on Joyce, Jul'82

Mustang
I DON'T WANT TO CRY.
Album: released on Look, '79 Dist: R. Smith & Co. Records, H.R. Taylor

Mustard, Doc
NUCLEAR BOOGIE.
Single (7"): released on Joy, May'84 by President Records. Dist: Jazz Music, Swift, President Distribution

Muta Baruka
HARD TIME LOVE / NAH I GIVE UP.
Single (12"): released on Hightide, Jun'82 Dist: Jetstar

MYSTERY UNFOLDS,THE.
Tracks: / Leaders speak / Dub poem / Revolutionary words / My great shun / Old cut bruk / Bun dung Babylon / Mystery unfolds / Dis poem / Famine injection / Eyes of liberty / Walkin' on gravel / Voice.
Album: released on Shanachie, Oct'86 Dist: Sterns/Triple Earth Distribution, Roots
Compact disc: released on Shanachie, Aug'87

OUT CRY.
Album: released on Shanachie, Oct'84

Mutant Disco
MUTANT DISCO Various artists (Various Artists).
Album: released on ZE, May'81 on Island Records. Dist: Polygram

Mutant Rockers
CLASSICAL SCRATCH.
Single (7"): released on Beggars Banquet, Jan'85 by Beggars Banquet Records. Dist: WEA Deleted '86.
Single (12"): released on Beggars Banquet, Jan'85 by Beggars Banquet Records. Dist: WEA

Mutants
BOSS MAN.
Single (7"): released on Rox, '78 by Rox Records. Dist: Spartan Distribution

HARD TIMES.
Single (7"): released on Rox, '79 by Rox Records. Dist: Spartan Distribution

Mutiny!
MUTINY!... Original London cast.
Album: released on Telstar, Oct'85 by Telstar Records. Dist: RCA Distribution
Cassette: released on Telstar, Oct'85 by Telstar Records. Dist: RCA Distribution

MUTINY featuring David Essex (Various Artists).
Album: released on Mercury, Oct'83 by Phonogram Records. Dist: Polygram Distribution
Cassette: released on Mercury, Oct'83 by Phonogram Records. Dist: Polygram Distribution

Mwab
IS MICHAEL BUM AN APPLE / ANGUS YUNG.
Single (7"): released on Mwab, Jan'84

Mwana Wambele
MWANA WAMBELE.
Album: released on Orchid, Jan'85 Dist: Impetus Distribution, Orchid

Mwendo Dawa
STRAIGHT LINES.
Album: released on Move, Feb'86 by Charly Records. Dist: Charly Distribution, Fast Forward Distribution, Cartel Distribution

MWRT Sound
BAD BEHAVIOR / UNRULY PICKNEY.
Single (12"): released on MWRT, Dec'82 by Music Works. Dist: Jetstar Distribution

My...
MY BOOK OF PETS Various artists (Various Artists).
Cassette: released on Invicta, Jul'84 by Audio-Visual Productions. Dist: Spartan

MY BOOK OF WORDS Various artists (Various Artists).
Cassette: released on Invicta, Jul'84 by Audio-Visual Productions. Dist: Spartan

MY FRIEND THE PROFESSOR Andrews, Lucilla (Wallace, Jean).
Double cassette: released on Soundings, Mar'85 Dist: Soundings

MY ONE AND ONLY Original cast recording (Various Artists).
Album: released on Atlantic, Dec'83 by WEA Records. Dist: WEA
Cassette: released on Atlantic, Dec'83 by WEA Records. Dist: WEA Deleted '85.

Myami, George
WE'RE HAVIN' A PARTY / THE FIRST TIME.
Single (7"): released on Passion, Feb'84 by Skratch Records. Dist: PRT
Single (12"): released on Passion, Feb'84 by Skratch Records. Dist: PRT

My baby's arm
HUNG IN THE PLAYGROUND.
Tracks: / Primitive kind (The).
Single (7"): released on Kasper, Feb'87 by Stiff, EMI

My Bloody Valentine
MY BLOODY VALENTINE.
Tracks: / My Bloody valentine (EP).
Single (12"): released on Fever, Mar'86 by Fever Records. Dist: Red Rhino, Cartel

NEW RECORD BY, A.
Tracks: / New record by, A.
Single (12"): released on Kaleidoscope, Sep'86

SUNNY SUNDAE SMILE.
Tracks: / Sunny sundae smile.
Single (12"): released on Lazy, Mar'87 Dist: Rough Trade, Cartel

My Brilliant Career
MESSAGE OF LOVE.
Single (12"): released on Dingbat, Oct'84 Dist: ILA

My Captains
FALL / CONVERSE.
Single (7"): released on 4AD, Aug'81 by 4AD Records. Dist: Rough Trade

Mycron
MARCH OF THE SPACE INVADERS.
Single (7"): released on Multi Media Tapes, Dec'82 by Multi Media Tapes Records. Dist: Stage One Distribution, Conifer Distribution, H.R. Taylor Distribution, Pinnacle

Myers, Alicia
APPRECIATION.
Single (7"): released on MCA, Mar'85 by MCA Records. Dist: CBS
Single (12"): released on MCA, Mar'85 by MCA Records. Dist: CBS

YOU GET THE BEST FROM ME.
Single (7"): released on MCA, Aug'84 by MCA Records. Dist: Polygram, MCA

Myers, Amina Claudine
SALUTES BESSIE SMITH.
Album: released on Leo, Sep'84 Dist: Recommended

SONG FOR MOTHER E.
Album: released on Leo, Sep'84 Dist: Recommended

Myers, Louis
I'M A SOUTHERN MAN.
Single (7"): released on Advent, Apr'79 Dist: Celtic Music, Projection, Swift

WAILING THE BLUES.
Album: released on JSP, Jan'84 by JSP Records. Dist: Swift, Projection

Myers, Sam
MY LOVE IS HERE TO STAY (Myers,Sam & Anson Funderburgh).
Album:

Myers, Stanley
DIANA/THE HUNTRESS.
Single (7"): released on BBC, Jan'84 by BBC Records & Tapes. Dist: EMI, PRT, Pye

My Fair Lady
MY FAIR LADY Original Soundtrack (Various Artists).
Notes: Artists incl: Marni Nixon, Rex Harrison,Wilfred Hyde-White, Stanley Holloway, Jeremy Brett.
Compact disc: released on CBS, Dec'85 by CBS Records. Dist: CBS

MY FAIR LADY Original film soundtrack.
Album: released on CBS, Jun'81 by CBS Records. Dist: CBS
Cassette: released on CBS, Jun'81 by CBS Records. Dist: CBS

MY FAIR LADY Original London cast.
Album: released on CBS Cameo, Aug'85 by CBS Records. Dist: CBS
Cassette: released on CBS Cameo, Aug'85 by CBS Records. Dist: CBS

My Mine
HYPNOTIC TANGO.
Single (7"): released on Sonet, Jun'84 by Sonet Records. Dist: PRT

Mynk
GET UP AND DANCE (DANCE WITH ME).
Single (12"): released on Cricket International, May'82 by Cricket International Records. Dist: Stage One

Myrick, Gary
GARY MYRICK AND THE FIGURES (Myrick, Gary & the Figures).
Album: released on Epic, Oct'80 by CBS Records. Dist: CBS

Mystere Five
SHAKE SOME ACTION/NO MESSAGE.
Single (7"): released on Flicknife, Apr'80 by Flicknife Records. Dist: Spartan

Mysteries....
MYSTERIES.... Various artists.
Album: released on Coda, Feb'85 by Coda Records. Dist: Pinnacle, Cartel, WEA, Roots
Cassette: released on Coda, Feb'85 by Coda Records. Dist: Pinnacle, Cartel, WEA, Roots

Mysteriods
SANTA CLAUS IS COMING TO TOWN.
Single (7"): released on Superville, Nov'81 Dist: Pinnacle

Mysterious, William
SECURITY OF NOISE/ALRIGHT.
Single (7"): released on Mezzanine, Apr'82 by Indies International. Dist: Spartan

Mystery Boys
LOUIE LOUIE/SIXY MINUTES.
Single (7"): released on President, Nov'82 by President Records. Dist: Taylors, Spartan

Mystery Girls
ASH IN DRAG/FIRE MONSTERS.
Single (7"): released on A&M, Jan'84 by A&M Records. Dist: Polygram
Single (12"): released on A&M, Jan'84 by A&M Records. Dist: Polygram

Mystery Guests
SPARROW THAT ATE NEW YORK.
Single (7"): released on Boys Own, Jul'81 Dist: Rough Trade

Mystery of Edwin Drood
MYSTERY OF EDWIN DROOD Original soundtrack.
Compact disc: by Polydor Records. Dist: Polygram, Polydor
Album: released on Polydor, Aug'86 by Polydor Records. Dist: Polygram, Polydor
Cassette: released on Polydor, Aug'86 by Poly-

---

dor Records. Dist: Polygram, Polydor

Mystic Angels
CHEATING IN THE NEXT ROOM.
Single (12"): released on S&D, Nov'82

Mystic Feat
SPECIAL LOVING/DUB (Mystic Feat, Robin & the Brown Tits).
Single (12"): released on Ariwa, Aug'82 by Ariwa Records. Dist: Revolver, Cartel, Jetstar, Rough Trade

Mystic Harmony
LIVING IN THE COUNTRY.
Single (12"): released on Clouds, Aug'84 by Clouds Records. Dist: Jetstar

NIGHT OVER EGYPT/OUT IN LONDON.
Single (12"): released on Clouds, May'83 by Clouds Records. Dist: Jetstar

PHONE LINE.
Single (12"): released on SS, Sep'81 by SS Records. Dist: Bullet Distribution, Fresh Distribution, Inferno Distribution, Red Rhino Distribution, Rough Trade Distribution

STAY WITH ME.
Single (12"): released on SS, Mar'82 by SS Records. Dist: Bullet Distribution, Fresh Distribution, Inferno Distribution, Red Rhino Distribution, Rough Trade Distribution

SWEET FEELINGS.
Single (12"): released on SS, May'82 by SS Records. Dist: Bullet Distribution, Fresh Distribution, Inferno Distribution, Red Rhino Distribution, Rough Trade Distribution

Mystic Merlin
MYSTIC MERLIN.
Album: released on Capitol, Jun'80 by Capitol Records. Dist: EMI

Mystic Moods Orchestra
ANOTHER STORMY NIGHT.
Compact disc: released on Mobile Fidelity, '86 by Mobile Fidelity Records.

COSMIC FORCE.
Album: released on Mobile Fidelity Sd. Lab., Jun'79 by Mobile Fidelity Records.

EMOTIONS.
Album: released on Mobile Fidelity Sd. Lab., Jun'79 by Mobile Fidelity Records.

Mystic Radics
NATIONWIDE.
Single (12"): released on Water Mount, Sep'84 Dist: ILA, Jetstar

Mystic Revelations...
DRUMMER BOY.
Tracks: / Drummer boy / Drummer boy (Version).
Single (12"): released on Star Apple, Dec'86

Mystics
COMPLETE MYSTICS, (THE).
Album: released on Ace, Nov'85 by Ace Records. Dist: Pinnacle, Swift, Hotshot, Cadillac

Mystral
PUSHING BACK THE HAND OF TIME (Mystral. Featuring Kevin Power).
Tracks: / Pushing back the hands of time / Twilight / Radio mix.
Single (7"): released on Citybeat, Mar'86 Dist: WEA
Single (12"): released on Citybeat, Mar'86 Dist: WEA

PUSHING BACK THE HANDS OF TIME (Mystral, featuring Kevin Power).
Single (12"): released on T-Mac, Jan'86 by T-Mac Records. Dist: PRT Distribution

Mythra
DEATH AND DESTINY.
Single (7"): released on Guardian, Oct'82 by Guardian Records. Dist: Jazz Music, Pinnacle

Myths
MYTHS VOL.2 Various Artists (Various Artists).
Notes: Includes: SPK, Hula,Etc.
Album: released on Sub Rosa, Dec'85 by Sub Rosa Records. Dist: Red Rhino Distribution, Cartel Distribution

Myths of mental illness
MYTHS OF MENTAL ILLNESS Szasz, Thomas S. (Szasz, Thomas S.).
Cassette: released on Psychology Today, Oct'81

Myton, Cedric
FACE THE MUSIC (Myton, Cedric & The Congos).
Album: released on Go Feet, Oct'81 by Arista Records. Dist: RCA

N

Nabney, Joe
HE LIFTED ME.
Cassette: released on Outlet (Praise), Jul'84

HIDING IN THE SHADOW OF THE ROCK.
Album: by Pilgrim Records. Dist: Rough Trade, Cartel

WALKING IN THE KING'S HIGHWAY.
Album: by Pilgrim Records. Dist: Rough Trade, Cartel

Na Casaidigh
FEAD AN IOLAIR.
Album: released on Gael-Linn (Ireland), Feb'86 by Gael Linn Records. Dist: Roots, Projection, Celtic Music, Jazz Music

Cassette: released on Gael-Linn (Ireland), Feb'86 by Gael Linn Records. Dist: Roots, Projection, Celtic Music, Jazz Music

Nadens, The
FOX ON THE RUN.
Album: released on Nadens, Mar'83

Nadjma
HABIBI.
Album: released on Crammed UK, Sep'84 Dist: Rough Trade, Nine Mile, Cartel

RAPTURE IN BAGHDAD.
Album: released on Crammed Discs, Oct'84 Dist: Rough Trade, Nine Mile, Cartel

Naffi
D'Y HEAR ME/FREDDIE'S FEVER (Naffi/Sandwich).
Single (7"): released on Naffi Productions, Oct'81 Dist: Rough Trade

Naffis
SLICE TWO/SLICE ONE.
Single (7"): released on Relentless, Oct'82 by Relentless Records. Dist: Cartel

Na Fill
CHANTER'S TUNE.
Album: released on Harp(Ireland), Feb'82 by Pickwick Records. Dist: Taylors

Cassette: released on Harp(Ireland), Feb'82 by Pickwick Records. Dist: Taylors

Nagle, Ron
BAD RICE.
Album: released on Edsel, Nov'86 by Demon Records. Dist: Pinnacle, Jazz Music, Projection

Nail, Jimmy
LOVE DON'T LIVE HERE ANYMORE.
Single (7"): released on Virgin, Mar'85 by Virgin Records. Dist: EMI, Virgin Distribution

Single (12"): released on Virgin, Mar'85 by Virgin Records. Dist: EMI, Virgin Distribution

TAKE IT OR LEAVE IT.
Album: released on Virgin, Nov'86 by Virgin Records. Dist: EMI, Virgin Distribution

Cassette: released on Virgin, Nov'86 by Virgin Records. Dist: EMI, Virgin Distribution

Compact disc: released on Virgin, Feb'87 by Virgin Records. Dist: EMI, Virgin Distribution

THAT'S THE WAY LOVE IS.
Tracks: / That's the way love is / Way out west, The.
Single (7"): released on Virgin, Oct'86 by Virgin Records. Dist: EMI, Virgin Distribution

Single (12"): released on Virgin, Oct'86 by Virgin Records. Dist: EMI, Virgin Distribution

Nails
MOOD SWING.
Album: released on RCA, Dec'84 by RCA Records. Dist: RCA, Roots, Swift, Wellard, Chris, I & B, Solomon & Peres Distribution

Cassette: released on RCA, Dec'84 by RCA Records. Dist: RCA, Roots, Swift, Wellard, Chris, I & B, Solomon & Peres Distribution

Naima
YOU NEVER HAD A LOVE LIKE MINE.
Single (7"): released on Ten, Mar'85

Single (12"): released on Ten, Mar'85

Naimro, Jean C
EN BALATE.
Compact disc: by Sterns. Dist: Sterns, Triple Earth

Nairobi
SOUL MAKOSSA (2 PARTS).
Single (7"): released on London, Nov'82 by London Records. Dist: Polygram

Single (12"): released on London, Nov'82 by London Records. Dist: Polygram

Naive, Steve
KEYBOARD JUNGLE (Steve Naive).
Notes:
Track details Not advised
Compact disc: released on Demon, '86 by Demon Records. Dist: Pinnacle

Najee
NAJEE'S THEME.
Tracks: / Feel so good to me / Feel so good to me / Najee's theme / For the love of you / Can't hide love / We're still family / Sweet love / Betcha don't know / What you do to me / Mysterious.
Notes: Produced by Charles Elgart, Najee and Rahni Song
Compact disc: released on EMI America, Mar'87 by EMI Records. Dist: EMI

Album: released on EMI America, Jan'87 by EMI Records. Dist: EMI

Cassette: released on EMI, Jan'87 by EMI Records. Dist: EMI

Najma
QAREEB.
Album: released on Triple Earth, Jul'87 by Sterns Records. Dist: Sterns/Triple Earth Distribution

Cassette: released on Triple Earth, Jul'87 by Sterns Records. Dist: Sterns/Triple Earth Distribution

Nakanishi, Toshiriro
TOSHIRIRO NAKANISHI (Toshiriro nakanishi).
Tracks: / Silent romance / Falling Star / Smile / Limelight.
Compact disc: released on Denon, May'86 by Denon Records. Dist: Harmonia Mundi

Naked Eyes
IN THE NAME OF LOVE.
Single (7"): released on Parlophone, Aug'84 by EMI Records. Dist: EMI

VOICES IN MY HEAD/SWEET POISON.
Single (7"): released on EMI, Jan'83 by EMI Records. Dist: EMI

Naked In Paris
CAZA/NO NO HEY HEY.
Single (7"): released on VM, Jul'83 by VM Records. Dist: PRT

Naked Lunch
MAKE BELIEVE.

RABIES/SLIPPING AGAIN.
Single (7"): released on Ramkup, May'81 Dist: Pinnacle

YOU TIE ME DOWN.
Single (7"): released on Plezure, Apr'84 by Plezure Records. Dist: Pinnacle

Naked Ray Gun
ALL RISE.
Album: released on Homestead, May'86 Dist: Rough Trade, Cartel, Shigaku

Naked Reagan
THROB THROB.
Album: released on Homestead, Mar'85 Dist: Rough Trade, Cartel, Shigaku

Naked & The Dead
NAKED & THE DEAD Mailer, Norman
Cassette: released on Caedmon(USA), '84 by Caedmon (USA) Records. Dist: Gower, Taylors, Discovery

NAKED & THE DEAD BY NORMAN MAILER Read by Norman Mailer.
Cassette: released on Caedmon(USA), '84 by Caedmon (USA) Records. Dist: Gower, Taylors, Discovery

Naked voice
DREAM HOUSE.
Single (7"): released on Lambs To The Slaughter, Sep'85 by Prism Records. Dist: Pinnacle, Red Rhino, Cartel

FORGOTTEN FRONTIERS.
Album: released on Prism LTSS, Jan'87

Name Of The Rose
NAME OF THE ROSE Original soundtrack.
Album: released on First Night, Jan'87 by Safari Records. Dist: Pinnacle

Cassette: released on First Night, Jan'87 by Safari Records. Dist: Pinnacle

Names
NIGHTSHIFT/I WISH I COULD SPEAK.
Single (7"): released on Factory, Jan'81 by Factory Records. Dist: Cartel, Pinnacle

POSTCARDS/CALCUTTA.
Single (7"): released on Factory, Feb'82 by Factory Records. Dist: Cartel, Pinnacle

Namyslowski, Zbigniew
AIR CONDITION.
Album: released on Affinity, Feb'82 by Charly Records. Dist: Charly, Cadillac

Nana
NANA (EXCERPT) BY EMILE ZOLA.
Cassette: released on Caedmon(USA), '82 by Caedmon (USA) Records. Dist: Gower, Taylors, Discovery

Nance, Ray
JUST SITTIN' & A ROCKIN' (see Gonsalves,Paul & Ray Nance) (Nance, Ray & Paul Gonsalves).

RAY NANCE QUARTET & SEXTET (Nance, Ray-Quartet &Sextet).
Album: released on Unique Jazz, Nov'86 Dist: Swift, Jazz Music, Jazz Horizons

Nancy Boys
I LIKE I LIKE I LIKE/DO YOU WANNA TOUCH.
Single (7"): released on Rola, Apr'83 by Rola Records. Dist: Roots Distribution, JSU Distribution, Spartan Distribution

Nanssen, Wolf
GUITAR TALES.
Album: released on Intersound, Dec'86 by Intersound Records. Dist: Jazz Music

Nan Tuck Five
NAN TUCK'S AXE.
Extended-play record: released on Brickyard, Sep'83 Dist: Pinnacle

RAINWATER RELICS.
Album: released on Brickyard, Oct'84 Dist: Pinnacle

Naomi
HEATWAVE.
Single (7"): released on Rosie, May'82 by Rosie Records. Dist: PRT Distribution

Napalm Death
SCUM.
Album: released on Earache, Jun'87 by Earache Records. Dist: Revolver, Cartel

Napalm Stars
FICTION.
Single (7"): released on Stranded, Jun'85 by Stranded Records. Dist: Fast Distribution, Cartel Distribution

WORK HARD.
Single (7"): released on Stranded, Jul'85 by Stranded Records. Dist: Fast Distribution, Cartel Distribution

Naples, Angelo
NEAPOLITAN MANDOLINES (Naples, Angelo Petisi Ensemble).
Album: released on Arion, May'79 Dist: Discovery

Napolean, Phil Red
BAILEY'S LUCKY SEVEN.
Album: released on Queendisc (Import), May'83 Dist: Cadillac

Napoleon
NAPOLEON-SOUNDTRACK ALBUM.
Album: released on Chrysalis, May'83 by Chrysalis Records. Dist: CBS

Cassette: released on Chrysalis, May'83 by Chrysalis Records. Dist: CBS

NAPOLEON (TELL-A-TALE).
Cassette: released on Pickwick (Tell-a-tale), Mar'84 by Pickwick Records. Dist: Pickwick Distribution

Napoleon of Nottinghill
NAPOLEON OF NOTTINGHILL, THE BY G.K. CHESTERTON Read by Paul Scofield.
Double cassette: released on Argo (Spokenword), Oct'83 by Decca Records. Dist: Polygram

Napoleon, Phil
1946-49 (Napoleon,Phil/Frank Signorelli).
Tracks: / Alabama Blues / Blue Danube / Margie / Stationary Woman / My Man O'War / Save it pretty mama.
Mono Recording
Album: released on Harlequin, Jun'86 by Harlequin Records. Dist: Swift, Jazz Music, Wellard, Chris, IRS, Taylor, H.R.

Napoleon XIV
THEY'RE COMING TO TAKE ME AWAY.
Album: released on Rhino (USA), Jan'86 by Rhino Records (USA).

Single (7"): released on Old Gold, '85 by Old Gold Records. Dist: Lightning, Jazz Music, Spartan, Counterpoint

Nappe, Nell
JULY.
Compact disc: by Pacific Records (USA). Dist: Atlantic

Napper, Tom
TRIPPING UPSTAIRS (Napper, Tom & Alistair Russel).
Album: released on Celtic Music, Jan'79 by Celtic Music Distribution. Dist: Celtic Music, Jazz Music, Projection, Roots

Naptali, Raymond
ANY RIDDIM.
Single (12"): released on Patmans studio, Aug'85

DIRTY RAT/ABC.
Single (12"): released on Sir George, Oct'82 by Sir George Records. Dist: Jetstar, Pinnacle

LOVE TRAP (see Campbell, Cornell) (Naptali, Raymond & Cornell Campbell).

TROUBLE POSSEE.
Album: released on CSA, Dec'82 by CSA Records. Dist: PRT, Jetstar

Naptl, Karin
BAD BAD BOY.
Single (12"): released on RCR, Jun'85 by RCR Records. Dist: Jetstar

Narayan, Pandit Ram
RAGA PURIA KALYAN.
Album: released on Amigo, Sep'79 Dist: Red Rhino, Cartel

Nardinl, Peter
IS THERE ANYBODY OUT THERE (Peter Nardini).
Notes:
Track details not advised
Album: released on Temple, Jan'86 by Temple Records. Dist: Roots Distribution, Folksound Distribution, Celtic Music Distribution, Projection Distribution

Cassette: released on Temple, Jan'86 by Temple Records. Dist: Roots Distribution, Folksound Distribution, Celtic Music Distribution, Projection Distribution

THINK YOU'RE GREAT.
Single (7"): released on Kettle, Dec'81 Dist: JSU, Folksound, Celtic Music, MK

WE JUST MIGHT WIN/STOP IT I LIKE IT.
Single (7"): released on Kettle, May'82 Dist: JSU, Folksound, Celtic Music, MK

Nariz, Wazmo
THINGS AREN'T RIGHT.
Album: released on Illegal, Jan'80 by Faulty Products Records. Dist: Pinnacle, Lightning, Cartel

Nascimento, Milton
ENCONTROS E DESPEDIDAS (Meetings & Farewells).
Tracks: / Threshold of colours / Love affair / Nights in the country / Sea of our love / Southern Tear / Race / Meetings and farewells / Who asked for me / Morning star, The / Radio Expierience.
Notes:
Featuring Pat Metheney
Compact disc: released on IMS, Oct'86 by Polydor Records. Dist: IMS. Polygram

MEETINGS AND FAREWELLS.
Tracks: / Threshold of colours / Love affair / Nights in the country / Sea of our love / Southern Tear / Race / Meetings and farewells / Who asked for me / Morning Star, The / Glass and cut / Radio Expierience.
Notes:
Milton nascimento is one of Brazil's most popular temporary Contemporary musicians. Fusing traditional Brazilian music with contemporary Jazz, he commands great respect from botyh Musicians in his homeland and in America. An indication of this is shown in the special guests featured on this album - Pat Metheney and Herbert Laws. Milton will play in the U.K. for his first and only appearance on July 11th at hammer-smith odeon-london.
The Album 'Audiophile is pressing.
Album: released on Polydor (USA), Jun'86

Cassette: released on Polydor (USA), Jun'86

SHIP OF LOVERS.
Tracks: / Gypsy cloud / Thought / Two of us, The / Southern tear / In praise of Mariama / Indian love / Ship of lovers / Afternoon / At the dance.
Notes: Milton Nascimento and his band featuring guest saxophonist Wayne Shorter. Recorded in 1986 for Verve. Personnel: Milton Nascimento - vocals, acoustic guitar / Ricardo Silveira - electric guitar / Luiz Avellar - keyboards / Nico Assumpcao - electric bass.
Compact disc: released on Verve (USA), Jul'87 by Polydor. Dist: Polygram

TRAVESSIA.

Nash, Billy
COME ON.
Tracks: / Come on / Mikey's Rap.
Single (7"): released on Laurel, Jul'86 by Laurel Records. Dist: RCA

JUST WANNA BE LOVED.
Notes: 5 track EP.
Extended-play record: released on Laurel, Feb'87 by Laurel Records. Dist: RCA

Nash, Cody
LONG RIDE HOME.
Album: released on Folk Heritage, Jul'82 by Folk Heritage Records. Dist: Roots, Wynd-Up Distribution, Jazz Music, Folk Heritage

Nash, Dick
NASHVILLE (see Sims, Zoot) (Nash, Dick & Zoot Sims).

Nash, Graham
INNOCENT EYES.
Tracks: / See You in prague / Keep away from em' / Innocent Eyes / Chippin' away / Over the wall / Don't listen to the rumours / Sad Eyes / New Day / Glass and steel / I got a Rock.
Album: released on Atlantic, May'86 by WEA Records. Dist: WEA

Cassette: released on Atlantic, May'86 by WEA Records. Dist: WEA

Nash, Johnny
GOLDEN HIGHLIGHTS OF.
Notes:
No Track details advised
Album: released on CBS(import), Jun'86 by CBS Records. Dist: Conifer, Discovery, Swift

Cassette: released on CBS(import), Jun'86 by CBS Records. Dist: Conifer, Discovery, Swift

HERE AGAIN.
Compact disc: released on London, '86 by London Records. Dist: Polygram

HOLD ME TIGHT.
Single (7"): released on Old Gold, Jul'84 by Old Gold Records. Dist: Lightning, Jazz Music, Spartan, Counterpoint

I CAN SEE CLEARLY NOW.
Album: released on CBS, '74 by CBS Records. Dist: CBS

Single (7"): released on CBS, May'82 by CBS Records. Dist: CBS

JOHNNY NASH.
Cassette: released on Ditto, Jan'85 by Pickwick Records. Dist: H.R. Taylor

JOHNNY NASH ALBUM, (THE).
Cassette: released on CBS, Jan'80 by CBS Records. Dist: CBS

ROCK ME BABY.
Single (7"): released on Sierra, Oct'85 by Sierra Records. Dist: WEA

Single (12"): released on Sierra, Oct'85 by Sierra Records. Dist: WEA

SIX TRACK HITS.
Extended-play record: released on Scoop 33, Sep'83 by Pickwick Records. Dist: H.R. Taylor

Cassette: released on Scoop 33, Sep'83 by Pickwick Records. Dist: H.R. Taylor

STIR IT UP.
Album: released on Hallmark, Mar'81 by Pickwick Records. Dist: Pickwick Distribution, PRT, Taylors

Cassette: released on Hallmark, Mar'81 by Pickwick Records. Dist: Pickwick Distribution, PRT, Taylors

TEARS ON MY PILLOW.
Album: by CBS Records. Dist: CBS
Cat. no: 69148
Single (7"): released on CBS, May'82 by CBS Records. Dist: CBS

Single (7"): released on Old Gold, Jul'82 by Old Gold Records. Dist: Lightning, Jazz Music, Spartan, Counterpoint

Nash, Ogden
OGDEN NASH SONGBOOK.
Boxed set: released on Caedmon(USA), May'80 by Caedmon (USA) Records. Dist: Gower, Taylors, Discovery

Nash, Paul
JAZZ COMPOSER'S ENSEMBLE, (A).
Album: released on Revelation, Apr'81

Nash, Terry
TERRY NASH COUNTRY.
Album: released on Country House, Jun'81 by BGS Productions Ltd. Dist: Taylor, H.R., Record Merchandisers Distribution, Pinnacle, Sounds of Scotland Records

Cassette: released on Country House, Jun'81 by BGS Productions Ltd. Dist: Taylor, H.R., Record Merchandisers Distribution, Pinnacle, Sounds of Scotland Records

Nash the Slash
19TH NERVOUS BREAKDOWN.
Single (7"): released on Dindisc, Mar'81 by Virgin Records. Dist: Virgin, EMI

AMERICAN BAND-AGES.
Album: released on Heavy Metal America, Jul'85 by FM-Revolver Records. Dist: EMI

AND YOU THOUGHT YOU WERE NORMAL.
Album: released on Shanghai, Sep'84

CHILDREN OF THE NIGHT.
Single (7"): released on Dindisc, Jan'81 by Virgin Records. Dist: Virgin, EMI

DEAD MAN'S CURVE.
Single (7"): released on Dindisc, Jan'81 by Virgin Records. Dist: Virgin, EMI

NOVEL ROMANCE.
Single (7"): released on Dindisc, Jul'81 by Virgin Records. Dist: Virgin, EMI

Nashville...
ABBA - OUR WAY (Nashville Train).
Album: released on Buffalo (UK), Jan'80

ALL-TIME COUNTRY & WSETERN HITS: VOL 3 (Nashville Cats).
Cassette: released on Bibi, Jan'83

BEAUTIFUL COUNTRY MUSIC: VOL 1 (Nashville All-Stars Country Band).
Cassette: released on Bibi, Jan'82

BEAUTIFUL COUNTRY MUSIC: VOL 2 (Nashville All-Stars Country Band).
Cassette: released on Bibi, Jan'82

COWBOYS AND CLOWNS (Nashville Cats).
Cassette: released on Bibi, Jan'82

MY NATIVE HOME (Nashville Bluegrass Band).
Album: released on Rounder (USA), Sep'85 Dist: Mike's Country Music Room Distribution, Jazz Music Distribution, Swift Distribution, Roots Records Distribution, Projection Distribution, Topic Distribution

NASHVILLE COUNTRY ROCK, VOL 3: STEPPIN' OUT TONIGHT Various artists (Various Artists).
Album: released on Redita (Holland). Jun'85

NASHVILLE COUNTRY ROCK, VOL 4: CRAZY ABOUT THE BOOGIE Various artists (Various Artists).
Album: released on Redita (Holland). Jun'85

NASHVILLE JUMPS Various artists (Various Artists).
Album: released on Krazy Kat (USA), May'84

NASHVILLE R&B, VOL ONE 1951-56 Various artists (Various Artists).
Notes:
Track details not advised.
Album: released on Krazy Kat (USA), Nov'95

NASHVILLE WEST Various artists (Various Artists).
Album: released on Sierra, Jan'79

SUPERPICKIN' (Nashville Superpickers).
Album: released on Sundown, Jan'84 by Magnum Music Group Ltd. Dist: Magnum Music Group Ltd, PRT Distribution, Spartan Distribution

Nashville Sound Orchestra
WESTERN MOVIE THEMES.
Tracks: / Good, the bad and the ugly, The / Shenandoah / Magnificent seven / Rawhide.
Notes: These tracks and more.
Compact disc: released on Bridge, '86 Dist: CD Centre Distribution, Pinnacle, Target

WESTERN MOVIE THEMES.
Album: released on Bridge, Jun'87 Dist: CD Centre Distribution, Pinnacle, Target

WESTERN MOVIE THEMES.
Notes:
Starr Marketing Services Ltd. 90 Queens Rd, Twickenham, Middlesex. TW1 4ET. TEL:01 891 6 4 8 7

Nashville Teens
LIVE AT THE RED HOUSE.
Album: released on Shanghai, Sep'84

MIDNIGHT.
Single (7"): released on Butt, Mar'82 by Butt Records. Dist: Counterpoint

TOBACCO ROAD.
Single (7"): released on Butt, Feb'84 by Butt Records. Dist: Counterpoint

Single (7"): released on Import Music Service (IMS), '80 Dist: Concord Jazz Distributions, Pablo, Polygram

Single (7"): released on EMI Golden 45's, Feb'85 by EMI Records. Dist: EMI

Nasmak
PLASTER.
Single (7"): released on Aura, Jun'83 by Hollywood Nites Distribution. Dist: Pinnacle

Nasser, Jimmy
EXPRESSLY ELLINGTON (Nasser, Jimmy Combo).
Album: released on Spotlite, Jan'80 by Spotlite Records. Dist: Cadillac, Jazz Music, Spotlite

Nasty Facts
DRIVE MY CAR.
Single (7"): released on 5th Column, Dec'82 by Graduate Records. Dist: Pinnacle

Nasty Savage
INDULGENCE.
Album: released on Roadrunner (Dutch), Mar'87 Dist: Pinnacle

NASTY SAVAGE.
Album: released on Roadrunner (Dutch), Sep'85 Dist: Pinnacle

NO MORE (REMIX BY FROGGY).
Tracks: / No more / Heartbreak.
Single (7"): released on Columbia, Jul'87 by EMI Records. Dist: EMI

Single (12"): released on Columbia, Jul'87 by EMI Records. Dist: EMI

Natalie, Ann
DOCTOR GAMES.
Single (7"): released on Spellbound, Sep'84 by Spellbound Records. Dist: CBS

Natasha
BOOM BOOM BOOM/I CASUALLY.
Single (7"): released on Towerbell, Aug'82 by Towerbell Records. Dist: EMI

Picture disc single: released on Towerbell, Aug'82 by Towerbell Records. Dist: EMI

DON'T WALK AWAY.
Album: released on Towerbell, Apr'85 by Towerbell Records. Dist: EMI

Cassette: released on Towerbell, Apr'85 by Towerbell Records. Dist: EMI

Single (7"): released on Towerbell, May'85 by Towerbell Records. Dist: EMI

HOME LANDS.
Single (7"): released on Towerbell, Mar'84 by Towerbell Records. Dist: EMI

Single (12"): released on Towerbell, Mar'84 by Towerbell Records. Dist: EMI

I CAN'T HOLD ON/TONIGHT.
Single (7"): released on Towerbell, Jan'83 by Towerbell Records. Dist: EMI

Single (12"): released on Towerbell, Mar'84 by Towerbell Records. Dist: EMI

IKO IKO.
Single (7"): released on Towerbell, May'82 by Towerbell Records. Dist: EMI

Single (12"): released on Towerbell, May'82 by Towerbell Records. Dist: EMI

I WANT YOU TO BE MY BABY.
Single (7"): released on Towerbell, Oct'83 by Towerbell Records. Dist: EMI

Single (12"): released on Towerbell, Oct'83 by Towerbell Records. Dist: EMI

PATA PATA/TEASE.
Single (7"): released on Towerbell, Oct'82 by Towerbell Records. Dist: EMI

STAY WITH ME.
Single (7"): released on Towerbell, Jun'84 by Towerbell Records. Dist: EMI

Single (12"): released on Towerbell, Jun'84 by Towerbell Records. Dist: EMI

STRANGEST FEELING/MAYBE.
Single (7"): released on Towerbell, Oct'81 by Towerbell Records. Dist: EMI

Natashe

BABY LOVE.
Single (7"): released on Mass Media Music, Feb'82

Nathaniel the Grublet

NATHANIEL THE GRUBLET Various artists (Various Artists).
Album: released on Birdwing, May'82 by Word Records. Dist: Word Distribution

Cassette: released on Birdwing, May'82 by Word Records. Dist: Word Distribution

Nathanson, Roy

BROKEN NIGHT (Nathanson, Roy & Curtis Fowlkes & Jazz).
Album: released on Crepescule, Jun'87 by Island Records. Dist: Polygram, Pinnacle

Nation

WONDATIME.
Single (12"): released on Sweet Release, Nov'85 Dist: Revolver Distribution

National...

COLONEL BOGEY ON PARADE (National Band of New Zealand).
Album: released on Viking, Jun'78 Dist: Harmonia Mundi Distributors

Cassette: released on Viking, Jun'78 Dist: Harmonia Mundi Distributors

DANCABILITY (National Euphoria).
Single (7"): released on Amidisque, Dec'83 by Amidisque Records. Dist: RCA, Pinnacle

KICK ME HARD (National Rhythm & Blues Quartet).
Album: released on Rounder, Sep'79 Dist: Roots Distribution

NATIONAL ANTHEMS Various artists (Various Artists).
Album: released on Score (France), Aug'84

Cassette: released on Score (France), Aug'84

NATIONAL BRASS BAND GALA FESTIVAL CONCERT, 1981 Various bands (Various bands).
Album: released on Polyphonic, Nov'81 by Polyphonic Records. Dist: Taylors

Cassette: released on Polyphonic, Nov'81 by Polyphonic Records. Dist: Taylors

NATIONAL BRASS BAND FESTIVAL, 1979 Various bands (Various bands).
Album: released on Chandos, Aug'81 by Chandos Records. Dist: Harmonia Mundi, Taylors

Cassette: released on Chandos, Aug'81 by Chandos Records. Dist: Harmonia Mundi, Taylors

NATIONAL DOWNHOME BLUES FESTIVAL VOL 3 (Various Artists).
Notes: with Snooky Pryor/Homesick James/Piano Red etc.
Album: released on Southland, Mar'87

NATIONAL DOWNHOME BLUES FESTIVAL VOL. 4 (Various Artists).
Notes: with Booker T. Laury/Doctor Ross/L. Johnson etc.
Album: released on Southland, Mar'87

NATIONAL DOWNHOME BLUES FESTIVAL VOL 1 (Various Artists).
Notes: with Lonnie Pitchford/Precious Bryant etc
Album: released on Southland, Mar'87

NATIONAL DOWNHOME BLUES FESTIVAL VOL.2 (Various Artists).
Notes: with Sunnyland Slim/T. Burt/F. Edwards etc.
Album: released on Southland, Mar'87

NATIONAL FESTIVAL OF POPULAR SCOTTISH MUSIC Various artists (Various Artists).
Double Album: released on Klub, Jul'82

NATIONAL WAKE (National Wake).
Album: released on WEA, Feb'82 by WEA Records. Dist: WEA

SPECTACULAR BRASS (National Band of New Zealand).
Album: released on Viking, Jul'78 Dist: Harmonia Mundi Distributors

THIS IS NEW ZEALAND (National Band of New Zealand).
Album: released on Viking, '78 Dist: Harmonia Mundi Distributors

National Health

DD AL CODE.
Album: released on Lounging, Mar'83 by Lounging Records. Dist: Revolver. Cartel

NATIONAL HEALTH.
Album: released on Affinity, Feb'78 by Charly Records. Dist: Charly, Cadillac

NATIONAL HEALTH OF QUEUES AND CURES.
Album: released on Charly, '78 by Charly Records. Dist: Charly, Cadillac

National Lampoon

ANIMAL HOUSE.
Album: released on MCA, Mar'79 by MCA Records. Dist: Polygram, MCA

Compact disc: released on MCA, Aug'87 by MCA Records. Dist: Polygram, MCA

NATIONAL LAMPOON'S ANIMAL HOUSE Original soundtrack (Various Artists).
Tracks: / Faber College theme / Louie, Louie / Twistin' the night away / Tossin' and turnin' / Shama lama ding dong / Hey Paula / Animal house / Money (that's what I want) / Let's dance / Dream girl / Wonderful world (what a) / Shout / Faber College theme - reprise.
Compact disc: released on MCA, Jun'87 by MCA Records. Dist: Polygram, MCA

THAT'S NOT FUNNY, THAT'S SICK.
Album: released on Radar, Mar'78 by WEA Music Ltd. Dist: WEA, PRT

National Pastime

IT'S ALL A GAME.
Single (7"): released on Spellbound, Feb'85 by Spellbound Records. Dist: CBS

Single (12"): released on Spellbound, Feb'85 by Spellbound Records. Dist: CBS

LUNACY.
Single (7"): released on Spellbound, May'84 by Spellbound Records. Dist: CBS

Single (12"): released on Spellbound, May'84 by Spellbound Records. Dist: CBS

National Philharmonic

BEN HUR (Miklos Rosza).
Album: released on Phase 4, Jul'77

BOHEME, (LA)/MADAME BUTTERFLY.
Double Album: released on Horatio Nelson, Nov'85 Dist: PRT

Cassette: released on Horatio Nelson, Nov'85 Dist: PRT

CLASSIC SCORES FROM HUMPHREY BOGART FILMS.
Notes: NPO conducted by Charles Gerhardt.
Album: released on RCA (Italy), May'85

Cassette: released on RCA (Italy), May'85

CLOSE ENCOUNTERS.....
Album: released on Damont, Apr'78 by WEA Records. Dist: WEA

CLOSE ENCOUNTERS OF 3RD KIND.
Cassette: released on Damont, Apr'78 by WEA Records. Dist: WEA

GOLDEN OVERTURES.
Compact disc: released on Reflection, '86 Dist: Taylor, H.R., MSD

GOLDEN OVERTURES.
Triple album / cassette: released on Warwick, Nov'80 Dist: Multiple Sound Distributors

Triple album / cassette: released on Warwick, Nov'80 Dist: Multiple Sound Distributors

HIGHLIGHTS FROM HYMNS TRIUMPHANT.
Album: released on Birdwing, May'82 by Word Records. Dist: Word Distribution

Cassette: released on Birdwing, May'82 by Word Records. Dist: Word Distribution

JESUS OF NARZARETH TV film score.
Album: released on Pye International, Mar'79

RETURN OF THE JEDI.
Compact disc: released on RCA, May'83 by RCA Records. Dist: RCA, Roots, Swift, Wellard, Chris, I & B, Solomon & Peres Distribution

Album: released on RCA, Aug'83 by RCA Records. Dist: RCA, Roots, Swift, Wellard, Chris, I & B, Solomon & Peres Distribution

Cassette: released on RCA, Aug'83 by RCA Records. Dist: RCA, Roots, Swift, Wellard, Chris, I & B, Solomon & Peres Distribution

SUNSET BOULEVARD Classic film scores of Franz Waxman.
Tracks: / Prince Valiant / To have and have not / Peyton Place / Place in the sun / Bride of Frankenstein / Two Mrs carrolls / Sunset Boulevard / Mr Skeffington / Objective Burma / Rebecca / Philadelphia story / Old acquaintance / Taras bulba.
Compact disc: released on RCA, Jul'86 by RCA Records. Dist: RCA, Roots, Swift, Wellard, Chris, I & B, Solomon & Peres Distribution

National Youth Jazz...

11 PLUS National Youth Jazz Orchestra live at LWT.
Tracks: / NYJO / Spaghetti junction / Good to be there / Marianne / Wait and see / 11 plus / Who-wray / Yesterday's blues today / Legs eleven / Threshing machine, The / Full house / NYJO reprise.
Album: released on RCA, '76 by RCA Records. Dist: RCA, Roots, Swift, Wellard, Chris, I & B, Solomon & Peres Distribution

11 PLUS NYJO LIVE AT L.W.T..
Album: released on Nyjo, '83

BORN AGAIN.
Tracks: / Sweetheat of Sigmund Freud / Infinity promenade / I'm gonna go fishin' / Contours / Topsy / Short stop / Walk don't run / Viva puente / Boar jibu / Manteca / Un poco loco / Jazz waltz.
Cassette: released on Nyjo, '83 by Nyjo Records. Dist: IMS Distribution

CONCRETE COWS.
Tracks: / Concrete cows / Dear John / John's Jape / Airedale Sunset / Robbers of Vissenburg / Dialectics / Lady Di / Dynamo.
Notes:
New Album from the world famous NYJO with John Dankworth as soloist and composer on three main titles.
Album: released on Nyjo, Apr'86 by Nyjo Records. Dist: IMS Distribution

FULL SCORE.
Tracks: / Luton hoo / Waltz for Duke / Waiting for Morgan / London / Full score / Bud / Midnight newsroom / Lady can tell, A / Sea beaver, The.
Album: released on Nyjo, '85 by Nyjo Records. Dist: IMS Distribution

Album: released on Nyjo, May'85

Cassette: released on Nyjo, May'85

IN CAMRA.
Album: released on Nyjo, Feb'77

LONDON.
Single (7"): released on Nyjo, Jul'85

MARY ROSE.
Album: released on Nyjo, Oct'79

NYJO DOWN UNDER.

Tracks: / Australian opener / Okay with Jay / Schedule D / Barrio / Groover, The / Question time / Out of sight, out of mind / Blenkinsop's blues / As if I cared / Getting down to it / Gynaecology / To set before a queen / Cobwebs / Song to sing by, A / Amazing grace / Tubbs lives / Fox fur / Paying my tax.
Double Album: released on Nyjo, '80 by Nyjo Records. Dist: IMS Distribution

PLAYING TURKEY.
Tracks: / Istanbul now / Jack of Hart's / Round Robin / Leaving here / And Henry guards the door / Looking back / Three for Tay / Turkish delight.
Album: released on Nyjo, '83 by Nyjo Records. Dist: IMS Distribution

RETURN TRIP.
Album: by RCA Records. Dist: RCA, Roots, Swift, Wellard, Chris, I & B, Solomon & Peres Distribution

SHERWOOD FOREST SUITE, THE.
Tracks: / Fanfare for Robin / Robin's epitaph / Sherwood Forest / All clad in Lincoln green / Lincoln green / She is called Maid Marion / Maid Marion / Sheriff's song / Sheriff of Nottingham, The / Mrs A'Dales's diary / Minstrel's lay, The / Serving the bishop / Bishop's move / Robin and Marion / Outlaws / Robin's epitaph - reprise / Last arrow, The.
Album: released on Nyjo, '77 by Nyjo Records. Dist: IMS Distribution

TO RUSSIA WITH JAZZ.
Tracks: / Buffle off to shuffalo / Cruisin' / I wasn't looking for a love affair / Ballad for Bing / Y.H.B. / Blues two / Cannonball / With you in mind / Parkinson's law / Half-man / Where is the music / Bristol cream / Home brew / Sneaky Pete / As long as there are summers / Summer sands / Black velvet / Girl can't grumble, A / Almost home / To Russia with jazz.
Double Album: released on Nyjo, '78

WHY DON'T THEY WRITE SONGS LIKE THIS ANYMORE.
Tracks: / Why don't they write songs like this anymore / I'll wait here / Too much, too soon / Don't try and argue with me / When I'm with you / Girl can't grumble, A / Don't go to her / No flowers by request / Wait and see / Rich man / I said there'd be thunder / Accident prone.
Album: released on Nyjo, '82 by Nyjo Records. Dist: IMS Distribution

WITH AN OPEN MIND.
Tracks: / Cheese'n'Carrots / Revenge of the Amoebae / With an open mind / Remembrance for Jim / Aardvark / Syrup of Phiggs / Fly to me / Midnight oil / Going Dutch.
Notes:
Released on occasion of the Band's 21st anniversary and featuring nine new compositions.
Album: released on NYJO, Oct'86

Cassette: released on Nyjo, Oct'86 by Nyjo Records. Dist: IMS Distribution

Native Europe

SEARCHING FOR AN ORCHESTRATION.
Album: by Red Rhino Records. Dist: Red Rhino, Cartel

Native Hipsters

LARRY'S COMING BACK.
Single (7"): released on Plattekop, Jul'83 by Volume Records. Dist: Cartel

TENDERLY HURT ME.
Single (7"): released on Illuminated Glass, Feb'82 by IKF Records. Dist: Stage One

THERE GOES CONCORDE AGAIN.
Single (7"): released on Heater, Oct'80 by Volume. Dist: Pinnacle

Natives

HERE IS THE NEWS.
Single (7"): released on Fearless, Jul'84 by Fearless Records. Dist: Spartan, Cartel

Native Tongue

HISTORY.
Single (7"): released on Squanderlust, Jul'84 Dist: Backs, Cartel Distribution

Natoli, Joseph

ACCORDION MASTERWORKS (Natoli, Joseph & Richard Romiti).
Album: released on ARC (Accordion Records), Jan'84 Dist: Accordion Record Club

Natty Papa

DON'T KNOW WHY I LOVE YOU.
Single (12"): released on Natural Sounds, Mar'85 by Natural Sounds Records. Dist: Jetstar

Natural Beauty

YOU WANNA BE LOVED/TOOSHOOPENG (SUPERMAN Z& JESSE).
Single (12"): released on Must Dance, Dec'83 by Must Dance Records. Dist: Jetstar Distribution

Natural, Clive

JUICY WATER MELON.
Tracks: / Juicy Water Melon / Juicy water melon (Version).
Single (12"): released on W.I.R.L., Sep'86 Dist: Jetstar

Natural Ites

BLACK ROSES.
Single (12"): released on Realistic, Jul'84 by Realistic Records. Dist: Jetstar

LATELY.
Single (12"): released on Realistic, Nov'86 by Realistic Records. Dist: Jetstar

LION INNA JUNGLE.
Single (7"): released on CSA, Apr'85 by CSA Records. Dist: PRT, Jetstar

Single (12"): released on CSA, Apr'85 by CSA Records. Dist: PRT, Jetstar

PICTURE ON THE WALL.
Tracks: / Picture on the wall / Jah works mamma.
Single (7"): released on CSA, Jun'86 by CSA Records. Dist: PRT, Jetstar

Single (12"): released on CSA, Jun'86 by CSA Records. Dist: PRT, Jetstar

PICTURE ON THE WALL/JAH WORKS MAMMA.
Single (12"): released on Realistic, Apr'83 by Realistic Records. Dist: Jetstar

PICTURE ON THE WALL.
Single (7"): released on CSA, Jul'85 by CSA Records. Dist: PRT, Jetstar

Single (12"): released on CSA, Jul'85 by CSA Records. Dist: PRT, Jetstar

PICTURE ON THE WALL (Natural Ites And The Realistics).
Album: released on CSA, May'85 by CSA Records. Dist: PRT, Jetstar

Cassette: released on CSA, May'85 by CSA Records. Dist: PRT, Jetstar

Natural Life
NATURAL LIFE (DIRECT CUT).
Album: released on Nautilus, Aug'78 by Cambra Sound.

Natural Mystic
GROOVE ROCKING.
Album: released on Starlight, Mar'85 by Starlight Records. Dist: Jetstar Distribution

Single (12"): released on Starlight, Jun'84 by Starlight Records. Dist: Jetstar Distribution

LITTLE BIT MAYBE, A.
Tracks: / Little Bit Maybe, A / Little bit maybe, A (dub version).
Single (12"): released on Starlight, Jan'86 by Starlight Records. Dist: Jetstar Distribution

Natural Mystics
TILL I KISS YOU (see Barker, Dave & Natural Mystics) (Natural Mystics & Dave Barker).

Natural Mystique
GENERALS/IN THIS TIME.
Single (7"): released on Dune, May'82

Natural Roots
KNOW YOURSELF/AIN'T GOT NO MONEY.
Single (12"): released on Fasim, Aug'82 Dist: Kingsley Sound & Vision

NATURAL ROOTS.
Album: released on Fasim, Feb'84 Dist: Kingsley Sound & Vision

Naturals
FUNKY RASTA (YA EDIT).
Tracks: / Funky rasta (ya edit) / Organ jam.
Single (7"): released on Cool Tempo, Jan'87 by Chrysalis Records. Dist: CBS

Single (12"): released on Cool Tempo, Jan'87 by Chrysalis Records. Dist: CBS

Natural Scientists
SEE THROUGH YOU/LIAR.
Single (7"): released on Dental, Apr'85 by Dental Records. Dist: Pinnacle

Natural Touch
COLLECTORS ITEM.
Album: released on NK Music, Dec'85 by Sound City. Dist: Jetstar, Pinnacle

GIMME GOOD LOVING/INSTRUMENTAL.
Single (12"): released on Neville King, Dec'83 by Neville King Records. Dist: Jetstar

HOLD ME TIGHT.
Single (12"): released on NK, May'85

LETS GET IT ON/GET IT OFF.
Single (12"): released on NK, Nov'83

LIVIN IT UP.
Single (12"): released on Neville King, Dec'84 by Neville King Records. Dist: Jetstar

THAT FUNNY FEELING.
Single (12"): released on MK, Mar'84

YOU MAKE ME FEEL SO RIGHT.
Single (12"): released on MK, Aug'84

Nature Lovers
BEGINNING TO END.
Album: released on Ink, Feb'85 by Red Flame. Dist: Rough Trade, Cartel, Pinnacle

Nature's Creation
FREAK UNIQUE.
Tracks: / Freak unique.
Single (12"): released on Capitol City, Mar'86 Dist: Greyhound

LET'S FIRE IT UP.
Tracks: / Let's fire it up (instrumental).
Single (12"): released on Sound Makers, Mar'86 Dist: Greyhound

Nat West Jazz Band
HOOKED ON DIXIE.
Album: released on NWJB, Jun'82

Cassette: released on NWJB, Jun'82

YOU CAN BANK ON US.
Album: released on Nat West Bank, May'87

Cassette: released on Nat West Bank, May'87

Naughtiest Girl...
ALL THE NAKED HEROES (Naughtiest

Girl Was Monitor).
Single (7"): released on Aardvark, Nov 80 by Aardvark. Dist: Aardvark

FRONT/NO SENSATION (Naughtiest Girl Was Monitor).
Single (7"): released on Illumination, Sep'81 by IKF Records. Dist: Stage One

IS ALL I NEED (Naughtiest Girl Was Monitor).
Single (7"): released on Dining Out, Feb'82 by Dining Out Records. Dist: IKF Independent

NAUGHTIEST GIRL IN THE SCHOOL
Blyton, Enid (Various Artists).
Album: released on Enid Blyton, Dec'77 Dist: Polygram

Naughty Thoughts
ALL OR NOTHING/WEEKDAYS.
Single (7"): released on Maestro, Jun'82 by Maestro Records.

Navah
WELCOME TO THE NIGHT/ONLY TIME.
Single (7"): released on RCA, May'83 by RCA Records. Dist: RCA, Roots, Swift, Wellard, Chris, I & B, Solomon & Peres Distribution

Navarro, Fats
FABULOUS FATS NAVARRO VOL 2 THE.
Album: released on Blue Note, Jul'85 by EMI Records. Dist: EMI

FABULOUS FATS NAVARRO VOL ONE THE.
Album: released on Blue Note, Apr'85 by EMI Records. Dist: EMI

FAST GIRL THE SAVOY SESSION.
Album: released on Savoy (USA), Mar'85 by Arista Records. Dist: Polygram, Swift

FATS AND TADD AT ROOGT (1948) 2.
Album: released on Beppo, Jun'76

FATS & TADD AT ROOST (1948) 1.
Album: released on Beppo, Jun'76

MOVE (Navarro, Fats/Bud Powell/Charlie Parker).

SATURDAY NIGHT SWING (Navarro, Fats & Allen Eager).
Album: released on G.I., Nov'76 by G.I. Records. Dist: G.I. Records

Nazareth
20 GREATEST HITS.
Album: released on Sahara, Jun'85

Cassette: released on Sahara, Jun'85

2XS.
Album: released on Nems International, Feb'83

BROKEN DOWN ANGEL/HAIR OF THE DOG.
Single (7"): released on Import Music Service (IMS), Jan'80 Dist: Concord Jazz Distributions, Pablo, Polygram

CATCH THE.
Album: released on Vertigo, Sep'84 by Phonogram Records. Dist: Polygram

Cassette: released on Vertigo, Sep'84 by Phonogram Records. Dist: Polygram

CLOSE ENOUGH FOR ROCK AND ROLL.
Album: released on Sahara, May'85

DREAM ON/JUICY LUCY.
Single (7"): released on Nems, Jun'83 Dist: Castle Communications Records, Pinnacle Records

DRESSED TO KILL.
Single (7"): released on Nems, Mar'81 Dist: Castle Communications Records, Pinnacle Records

EXCERSIZES.
Album: released on Sahara, May'85

EXPECT NO MERCY.
Album: released on Sahara, May'85

FULL CIRCLE THE.
Single (7"): released on Nems, Feb'81 Dist: Castle Communications Records, Pinnacle Records

GAMES/YOU LOVE ANOTHER.
Single (7"): released on Nems, Jan'83 Dist: Castle Communications Records, Pinnacle Records

GREATEST HITS: NAZARETH.
Album: released on Mercury, Jul'81 by Phonogram Records. Dist: Polygram Distribution

Album: released on Nems, Oct'82 Dist: Castle Communications Records, Pinnacle Records

Cassette: released on Nems, Oct'82 Dist: Castle Communications Records, Pinnacle Records

HAIR OF THE DOG.
Album: released on Sahara, May'85

LOUD N PROUD.
Album: released on Sahara, May'85

LOVE HURTS (4 TRACK PICTURE DISC EP).
Single (7"): released on Nems, Jan'83 Dist: Castle Communications Records, Pinnacle Records

LOVE LEADS TO MADNESS.
Single (7"): released on Nems, Jul'82 Dist: Castle Communications Records, Pinnacle Records

MORNING DEW/JUICY LUCY.
Single (7"): released on Nems, Aug'81 Dist: Castle Communications Records, Pinnacle Records

NAZARETH.
Album: released on Mountain, Apr'80 Dist: Mike's Country Music Room Distribution

NO MEAN CITY.
Album: released on Sahara, May'85

PLAY THE GAME.
Album: released on Sahara, May'85

RAMPANT.
Album: released on Mountain, Apr'80 Dist: Mike's Country Music Room Distribution

RAZAMANAZ.
Album: released on Nems, Oct'82 Dist: Castle Communications Records, Pinnacle Records

Cassette: released on Nems, Oct'82 Dist: Castle Communications Records, Pinnacle Records

Album: released on Philips (Germany), Apr'85

RUBY TUESDAY.
Single (7"): released on Vertigo, Sep'84 by Phonogram Records. Dist: Polygram

Single (12"): released on Vertigo, Sep'84 by Phonogram Records. Dist: Polygram

SNAZ.
Compact disc: released on Castle Classics, Jul'87 by Castle Communications. Dist: BMG

Album: released on Nems, Sep'81 Dist: Castle Communications Records, Pinnacle Records

SOUND ELIXIR.
Album: released on Sahara, May'85

Nazz
BEST OF.
Album: released on Rhino (USA), Feb'85 by Rhino Records (USA).

Cassette: released on Rhino (USA), Feb'85 by Rhino Records (USA).

Nazz Nasko
NO MORE.
Tracks: / No more / Heartbreak.
Single (7"): released on Columbia, Feb'87 by EMI Records. Dist: EMI

Single (12"): released on Columbia, Feb'87 by EMI Records. Dist: EMI

N'Dour, Youssou
NELSON MANDELA.
Album: released on Earthworks, Apr'86 by Earthworks Records. Dist: Earthworks Distributors, Rough Trade, Cartel, Projection

RUBBER BAND MAN.
Tracks: / Rubber band man / Nelson Mandela.
Single (12"): released on Rough Trade, Mar'86 by Rough Trade Records. Dist: Rough Trade Distribution, Cartel Distribution

Near Holly
JOURNEYS.
Album: released on Redwood, Apr'84 Dist: WRPM

Cassette: released on Redwood, Apr'84 Dist: WRPM

Nearly Normal
BEDTIME/DIE BABY DIE.
Single (7"): released on Insurrection, May'82 Dist: Cartel

Neary, Paddy
HIGHLANDER SOUVENIR THE.
Album: released on ARC (Accordion Records), Jan'84 Dist: Accordion Record Club

HIGHLANDERS SOUVENIR.
Album: released on Stebelin, Sep'83 Dist: H.R. Taylor Distribution

HIGHLAND SOUVENIR.
Tracks: / 6/8 March / Strip the willow / Lara's theme / Turkey in the straw / Whistler & his dog / road to isles med / Bunch of thyme / Skyeboat / Greenhills of Tyrol / Tourist selection / Scottish waltzes / Film themes / Dark Island / Granni's hie landhame / Scotch.
Album: released on Accordion Record Club, Jul'86 by Accordion Record Club Records. Dist: Accordion Record Club

HIGH LEVELS OF.
Album: released on Stebelin, Sep'83 Dist: H.R. Taylor Distribution

HIGH LEVELS OF PADDY NEARY THE.
Album: released on ARC (Accordion Records), Jan'84 Dist: Accordion Record Club

SOUNDS LIKE ACCORDION.
Album: released on Country House, Aug'80 by BGS Productions Ltd. Dist: Taylor, H.R., Record Merchandisers Distribution, Pinnacle, Sounds of Scotland Records

Cassette: released on Country House, Aug'80 by BGS Productions Ltd. Dist: Taylor, H.R., Record Merchandisers Distribution, Pinnacle, Sounds of Scotland Records

Neasdon Connection
(4 TRACK EP WITH VAL BENNETT HARRY J).
Single (7"): released on Trojan, Jan'81 by Trojan Records. Dist: PRT, Jetstar

Necessaries
EVENT HORIZON.
Album: released on Sire, Feb'82

Necklace of raindrops
NECKLACE OF RAINDROPS Aiken, Joan (Aiken, Joan).
Cassette: released on Caedmon(USA), Sep'82 by Caedmon (USA) Records. Dist: Gower, Taylors, Discovery

Necros
TANGLED UP.
Album: released on Enigma, Jun'87 by Enigma Records. Dist: Rough Trade, Cartel, EMI

Nederlands Akkordeon...
AKKORDEON IN CONCERT.
Album: released on ARC (Accordion Records), '84 Dist: Accordion Record Club

Needs, Lyndon
COOL SCHOOL DAYS.
Album: released on Magnum, Mar'83 by Bulldog Records. Dist: Spartan

Neegan, Josephine
FIFTY ODD YEARS (see also Powers Jimmy (Neegan, Josephine & Jimmy Powers).

Neely, Bill
BLACKLAND FARM BOY.
Album: released on Arhoolie, May'81 by Arhoolie Records. Dist: Projection, Topic, Jazz Music, Swift, Roots

Neep, Rod
HEADING FOR THE SUN.
Album: released on Folk Heritage, Jul'82 by Folk Heritage Records. Dist: Roots, Wynd-Up Distribution, Jazz Music, Folk Heritage

Negatives
ELECTRIC WALTZ/ MONEY TALK.
Single (7"): released on Aardvark, Nov'80 by Aardvark. Dist: Aardvark

Negative Trend
WE DON'T PLAY WE RIOT.
Single (7"): released on Subterranean, Dec'84 by Subterranean Records. Dist: Rough Trade Distribution

Negazione/Declino
MUCCHIO MCLVAGGIO.
Album: released on Children Of The Revolution, Feb'86 by Revolver Records. Dist: Revolver, Cartel

Negro, J Walter
COST OF LIVING (2 PARTS).
Single (12"): released on Albion, May'83 by Al-

bion Records. Dist: Spartan, Pinnacle

SHOOT THE PUMP (Negro, J Walter & Loose Jointz).
Single (7"): released on Island, Dec'81 by Island Records. Dist: Polygram

Single (12"): released on Island, Dec'81 by Island Records. Dist: Polygram

Negus, Peter

I WON'T BE AROUND/DUB VERSION.
78 rpm record: released on Progressive, Jul'82 by Progressive Records. Dist: Jetstar

PLACE IN THE SUN/DUSTY ROAD (Negus, Peter & Waterhouse).
Single (12"): released on Progressive, Aug'82 by Progressive Records. Dist: Jetstar

Neighborhoods

REPTILE MEN.
Album: released on Emergo, Jun'87 by Roadrunner Records (Germany). Dist: Pinnacle

Neighbourhood Rhythms

NEIGHBOURHOOD RHYTHMS various artists (Various Artists).
Album: released on Rhino/Freeway, Mar'85

Neighbour Hoods

REPTILE MEN,THE.
Album: released on Emergo, 30 May'87 by Roadrunner Records (Germany). Dist: Pinnacle

Neighbours

WHOLE IN YOUR LIFE.
Single (7"): released on Closer (France), Mar'86 Dist: Nine Mile, Cartel

Neighbours & Lovers

NEIGHBOURS & LOVERS Original Cast recording (Various Artists).
Tracks: / Isn't it amazing / I love you, I really do / You must understand / Who cares what people think / Wouldn't it be wonderful / Yes I love him / Bitter-sweet anguish / If only / Yes it's true / It's a fantasy / What does he see (when he looks at me) / Don't ask me why / I feel sorry for her (being married to him!) / Top of the tree, (I'm going to the) / It's New Year's Eve! / George & Dragon, The / Everyone needs to be needed (finale).
Cassette: released on Sagittarius, Mar'87 by Sagittarius Records. Dist: Sagittarius Distribution

Neil

HOLE IN MY SHOE.
Picture disc single: released on WEA, Jun'84 by WEA Records. Dist: WEA

NEIL'S HEAVY CONCEPT ALBUM.
Album: released on WEA, Nov'84 by WEA Records. Dist: WEA

Cassette: released on WEA, Nov'84 by WEA Records. Dist: WEA

Neil, Fred

VERY BEST OF FRED NEIL.
Tracks: / That's the bag I'm in / Badi-da / Farethewell / Merry go round / Felicity / Everybody's talkin' / Everything happens / Sweet cocaine / Green rocky road / Cynicrustpetefredjohnraga / Please send me someone to love / Fools are a long time coming / Dolphins, The / I've got a secret (didn't we shake sugaree).
Album: released on See For Miles, Nov'86 by See For Miles Records. Dist: Pinnacle

Neilson, Chris

LADY FROM VIRGINIA.
Album: released on Music World, Jan'77

Nelwood, Gerry

SHARE MY DREAM.
Notes: With Joe Beck, Jay Leonhart.
Compact disc: released on DMP, '86 by DMP Records. Dist: Venture

Nekroplis

LIVE.
Cassette: released on Liksvider, Nov'84 by Liksvider. Dist: Falling A Distribution, Cartel

Nelken, Laurie

AUDIO BOOK (THE).
Cassette: released on Nicrodisc, Feb'84 Dist: Disco System Records

Nelly International...

KENYA PARTOUT, VOL.5.
Album: released on Playasound, '74 Dist: Conifer, Discovery

Nelson

MIH LOVER.
Tracks: / We like it.
Single (12"): released on Bumble Bee, Nov'86 by CSA Records. Dist: PRT, Jetstar, CSA

TELL A TALE.
Cassette: released on Pickwick, Mar'84 by Pickwick Records. Dist: Pickwick Distribution, Prism Leisure Distribution,

Nelson, Big Pete

DO IT!.
Tracks: / As time goes by.
Single (7"): released on Debut, Jun'86 by Skratch Music. Dist: PRT

Nelson, Bill

ACCELERATION.
Single (7"): released on Cocteau, Aug'84 by Cocteau Records. Dist: Pinnacle, IDS

Picture disc single: released on Cocteau, Jun'85 by Cocteau Records. Dist: Pinnacle, IDS

BE BOP DELUXE.
Single (12"): released on Cocteau, Jul'85 by Cocteau Records. Dist: Pinnacle, IDS

BROND (THEME FROM) (Nelson, Bill & Daryl Runswick).
Single (12"): released on Cocteau, May'87 by Cocteau Records. Dist: Pinnacle, IDS

CHAMBER OF DREAMS.
Tracks: / Blazing memory of innuendo, The / Into the luminous future / Dip in the swimming / Reactor / Tomorrowland (the threshold of 1947) / Listening to lizards / Endless torsion / My sublime perversion / Eros in autumn / Sleeplessness / Latest skyline, The / train of thought / Parks and fountains clouds and trees / Golden bough / Forever Orpheus / In Arcadia / Sentimental / Autumn fires / Wild blue yonder.
Notes: Music from the Invisibility Exhibition.
Album: released on Cocteau, Jul'86 by Cocteau Records. Dist: Pinnacle, IDS

CHIMERA.
Album: released on Mercury, May'83 by Phonogram Records. Dist: Polygram Distribution

Cassette: released on Mercury, May'83 by Phonogram Records. Dist: Polygram Distribution

DAS KABINETTE (THE CABINET OF DR CALIGAR).
Album: released on Cocteau, Nov'81 by Cocteau Records. Dist: Pinnacle, IDS

DAS KABINET (THE CABINET OF DR CALIGARI.....&).
Tracks: / Asylum, The / Waltz / Fairground, The / Doctor Caligari / Cesare the somnambulist / Murder / Funeral (The) / Somnambulist and the children (The) / Children (The) / Caligari disciplines Cesare / Caligari opens the cabinet / Jane discovers Cesare / Attempted murder of Jane (The) / Dream dance of Jane and the somnambulist (The) / Escape over the rooftops / Unmasking (The) / Shot (The) / Cabinet closes (The) / Overture / Family (The) / Sisters & sedan chairs / In the forest of storms / Castle (The) / Gates (The) / Corridor (The) / Great hall (The) / Dreams (the merchant sleeps) / Dreams (the merchant sleeps) / Rose and the beast (the) / Magnificent (the white horse) / Beauty enters the castle / Door (The) / Mirror (The) / Candelabra and the gargoyles / Beauty and the beast / Transition no.1 / Transition No.2 / Gift (The) / Garden (The) / Transition No.3 / Transition No.4 / Tragedy (The) / Transition No.5 / Enchanted glove (The) / Tears as diamonds (The gift reverses) / Beast in solitude (The) / Return of magnificent / Transition No.6 (The journey) / Pavillion of Diana (The) / Transformation no.1 / Transformation No.2 / Final curtain (The).
Notes: Full title: "das kabinet (the cabinet of Dr Caligari & La belle et la bete (beauty and the beast
Double album and cassette. Instrumental.
Album: released on Cocteau, Jan'85 by Cocteau Records. Dist: Pinnacle, IDS

EROS ARRIVING/HAUNTING IN MY HEAD (DOUBLE PACK).
Single (7"): released on Mercury, Apr'82 by Phonogram Records. Dist: Polygram Distribution

Single (7"): released on Mercury, Apr'82 by Phonogram Records. Dist: Polygram Distribution

FLAMING DESIRE/THE PASSION.
Single (7"): released on Mercury, Jul'82 by Phonogram Records. Dist: Polygram Distribution

Single (12"): released on Mercury, Jul'82 by Phonogram Records. Dist: Polygram Distribution

GETTING THE HOLY GHOST ACROSS.
Tracks: / Suvasini / Contemplation / Theology / Wildest dreams / Lost in your mystery / Rise like a fountain / Age of reason / Hidden flame / Because of you / Pansophia / Living for the spangled moment / Word for word / Illusions of you / Heart and soul / Finks and stooges of the spirit.
Album: released on Portrait, Apr'86 by CBS Records. Dist: CBS

Cassette: released on Portrait, Apr'86 by CBS Records. Dist: CBS

LIVING FOR THE SPANGLED MOMENT.
Album: released on Portrait (USA), Sep'86 Dist: CBS

LOVE THAT WHIRLS.
Tracks: / Empire of the senses / Hope for the heat beat / Waiting for voices / Eros arriving / Bride of christ in autumn, The / When your dream of perfect beauty comes true / Flaming desire / Portrait of Jan with flowers / Crystal excalator in the place god department store / Echo in her eyes / October man, The / Flesh / He and see LP were brothers.
Compact disc: released on Cocteau, Jul'86 by Cocteau Records. Dist: Pinnacle, IDS

LOVE THAT WHIRLS, THE.
Double Album: released on Mercury, Jun'82 by Phonogram Records. Dist: Polygram Distribution

Cassette: released on Mercury, Jun'82 by Phonogram Records. Dist: Polygram Distribution

MAP OF DREAMS.
Tracks: / Legions of the endless night / Spinning creatures / At the gates of the singing garden / Heavenly message number one / Heavenly message number three / Fellini's picnic / Dark angel / Infernal regions / Dance of the fragrant woman / Alchemy of ecstacy (The) / Aphrodite adorned / Wheel of fortune and the hand of fate (The) / Forked tongues, mixed blessings / Another tricky mission for the celestial pilot / Water of life (transfiguration).
Album: released on Cocteau, Jan'87 by Cocteau Records. Dist: Pinnacle, IDS

Cassette: released on Cocteau, Jan'87 by Cocteau Records. Dist: Pinnacle, IDS

NORTHERN DREAM.
Album: released on Butt, Aug'86 by Butt Records. Dist: Counterpoint

PERMANENT FLAME.
Single (7"): released on Cocteau, Jul'85 by Cocteau Records. Dist: Pinnacle, IDS

QUIT DREAMING AND GET ON THE BEAM.
Tracks: / Banal / Living in my limousine / Vertical games / Disposable / False alarms / Decline and fall / Life runs out like sand / Kind of loving, A / Do you dream in colour / UHF / Youth of nations on fire / Quit dreaming and get on the beam / Annunication / Ritual echo, The / Sleep / Near east / Emak Bakia / Endless orchard / My intricate image / Heat in the room / Another willingly opened window / Vanashing parade / Glass fish (for the final aquarium) / Cubical domes / Ashes of roses / Shadow garden, The / Opium / White sound.
Compact disc: released on Cocteau, Jul'86 by Cocteau Records. Dist: Pinnacle, IDS

Double Album: released on Mercury, May'81 by Phonogram Records. Dist: Polygram Distribution

Cassette: released on Mercury, May'81 by Phonogram Records. Dist: Polygram Distribution

RED NOISE.
Single (12"): released on Cocteau, Jul'85 by Cocteau Records. Dist: Pinnacle, IDS

REVOLT INTO STYLE/STAY YOUNG/FURNITURE MUSIC (Nelson, Bill with red noise).

SAVAGE GESTURES FOR CHARMS SAKE.
Tracks: / Man in the rexine suit (The) / Watching my dreamboat go down in flames / Meat room (The) / Another happy thought (carved forever in your cortex) / Portrait of jan with Moon and stars.
Notes: Instrumental mini-album.
Album: released on Cocteau, Feb'85 by Cocteau Records. Dist: Pinnacle, IDS

SOUNDING THE RITUAL ECHO.
Tracks: / Annunciation / Ritual echo (The) / Sleep / Near East / Emak bakia / My intricate image / Endless orchids / Heat in the room (The) / Another willingly opened window / Vanishing parades / Glass fish (for the final aquarium) / Cubical domes / Ashes of roses / Shadow garden (opium) (The).
Album: released on Cocteau, Jun'85 by Cocteau Records. Dist: Pinnacle, IDS

SOUND ON SOUND (Nelson, Bill Red Noise).
Album: released on Cocteau, Nov'85 by Cocteau Records. Dist: Pinnacle, IDS

Cassette: released on Cocteau, Nov'85 by Cocteau Records. Dist: Pinnacle, IDS

SUMMER OF GOD'S PIANO.
Tracks: / Antennae two / (N.B.C. 97293) / Sleep of Hollywood (the) / Celestial bridegroom (The) / Under the red arch / Orient pearl / Sacrament / Falling blossoms / Difficulty of being (The) / Zanoni / Chinese nightingale (The) / Soon september (another enchantment) / Rural shires / Perfidio incanto / Lost years (The) / Charm of transit (The) / Night thoughts (twilight radio) / Wysteria / Swing / Snowfall / Real of dusk / over ocean.
Notes: Instrumental.
Album: released on Cocteau, Oct'86 by Cocteau Records. Dist: Pinnacle, IDS

Cassette: released on Cocteau, Oct'86 by Cocteau Records. Dist: Pinnacle, IDS

TOUCH AND GLOW/DANCING IN THE WIND/LOVE WITHOUT FEAR.
Single (7"): released on Cocteau, Aug'83 by Cocteau Records. Dist: Pinnacle, IDS

TRIAL BY ITIMACY.
Boxed set: released on Cocteau, Jan'85 by Cocteau Records. Dist: Pinnacle, IDS

TWOFOLD ASPECT OF EVERYTHING (THE).
Tracks: / Acceleration (remix) / White sound / Living in my limousine (remix) / Flesh / Eros arriving (single version) / Hope for heartbeat (remix) / Passion (The) / Ideal homes / Instantly yours / Atom man loves Radium girl / Mr Magnetism himself / Burning question (The) / Haunting in my head / He and sleep were brothers / Connie buys a kodak / Be my dynamo / Touch and glow / Love without fear / Dada guitare / Turn to fiction / Rooms with brittle views / Love in the abstract / Head facts from the fiction department / Hers is a lush situation / When the birds return / All my wives were Iron.

Notes: Double album\compilation.
Album: released on Cocteau, Feb'85 by Cocteau Records. Dist: Pinnacle, IDS

WILDEST DREAMS.
Single (7"): released on Portrait, Mar'86 by CBS Records. Dist: CBS

Single (12"): released on Portrait, Mar'86 by CBS Records. Dist: CBS

Nelson, Erick

FLOW RIVER FLOW.
Album: released on Maranatha, May'79

Nelson, Jackie

BOY WITH A FUTURE.
Tracks: / Midnight in heaven.
Single (7"): released on August (USA), Oct'86 Dist: Taylors

DEAREST MOTHER MINE.
Single (7"): released on Country House, Sep'84 by BGS Productions Ltd. Dist: Taylor, H.R., Record Merchandisers Distribution, Pinnacle, Sounds of Scotland Records

FOOL SUCH AS I.
Single (7"):

WALKING TALKING DOLLY/SILENT NIGHT.
Single (7"):

WITH LOVE.
Album: released on Country House, Sep'84 by BGS Productions Ltd. Dist: Taylor, H.R., Record Merchandisers Distribution, Pinnacle, Sounds of Scotland Records

Cassette:

Nelson, Jimmy

WATCH THAT ACTION! (Nelson, Jimmy 'T-99').
Album: released on Ace, Oct'87 by Ace Records. Dist: Pinnacle, Swift, Hotshot, Cadillac. Estim retail price in Sep'87 was £6.49.

Nelson, Larry

TOO MUCH GROUND.
Single (7"): released on Artic, May'84

Nelson, Louis

EVERYBODY'S TALKING 'BOUT THE....
Album: released on GHB, Jun'86 Dist: Jazz Music, Swift

LOUIS NELSON BIG FOUR VOL.1.
Album: released on GHB, Jul'87 Dist: Jazz Music, Swift

LOUIS NELSON BIG FOUR VOL.2.
Album: released on GHB, Jul'87 Dist: Jazz Music, Swift

LOUIS NELSON'S NEW ORLEANS BAND (Nelson, Louis & New Orleans Band).
Cassette: released on Nola, May'87 Dist: JSU, Jazz Music, Cadillac, Chris Wellard

Album: released on Nola, Apr'79 Dist: JSU, Jazz Music, Cadillac, Chris Wellard

SKATER'S WALTZ (Nelson, Louis/Barry Martin's Serenaders).
Album: released on 504, Sep'86 by 504 Records. Dist: Chris Wellard, Jazz Music

Cassette: released on 504, Sep'86 by 504 Records. Dist: Chris Wellard, Jazz Music

Nelson, Oliver

BLUES & THE ABSTRACT TRUTH.
Tracks: / Stolen moments / Hoe down / Cascades / Yearnin' / Butch and butch / Teenie's blues.
Compact disc: released on MCA, Apr'87 by MCA Records. Dist: Polygram, MCA

HAPPENINGS (Nelson, Oliver-Hank Jones).
Album: released on Jasmine, Mar'83 by Jasmine Records. Dist: Counterpoint, Lugtons, Taylor, H.R., Wellard, Chris, Swift, Cadillac

MEET OLIVER NELSON.
Album:

MORE BLUES AND THE ABSTRACT TRUTH.
Album: released on Jasmine, Jun'82 by Jasmine Records. Dist: Counterpoint, Lugtons, Taylor, H.R., Wellard, Chris, Swift, Cadillac

Cassette: released on Jasmine, Jun'82 by Jasmine Records. Dist: Counterpoint, Lugtons, Taylor, H.R., Wellard, Chris, Swift, Cadillac

SCREAMIN' THE BLUES.
Album: released on New Jazz (USA), Feb'84 by Fantasy Records. Dist: RCA

STRAIGHT AHEAD (Nelson, Oliver/Eric Dolphy).
Album: released on New Jazz (USA), Aug'84 by Fantasy Records. Dist: RCA

Nelson, Ozzie

BROADCASTING FROM CHICAGO'S.... (Nelson, Ozzie & His Orchestra).
Album: released on Aircheck (USA), Oct'86 Dist: Swift, Jazz Music

OZZIE NELSON & HIS ORCHESTRA (Nelson, Ozzie & His Orchestra).
Album: released on Bandstand, Jul'82 Dist: Swift

Nelson, Pat

MORE THAN MEETS THE EYE.
Album: released on Sweerfolk & Country, Dec'77

Nelson, Pete

EVERYBODY'S MAKING IT BIG BUT ME.
Album: released on Sweet Folk All, May'81 by Sweet Folk All Records. Dist: Sweet Folk All, Roots, Celtic Music, Dragon, Impetus, Projection, Chris Wellard, Festival Records

I REMEMBER ELVIS.
Album: released on Tank, Jun'79 by Tank Records.

Nelson, Phyllis

CHEMICAL REACTION.
Tracks: / Stop don't do this to me.
Single (7"): released on Carrere, Oct'86 by Carrere Records. Dist: PRT, Spartan

Single (12"): released on Carrere, Oct'86 by Carrere Records. Dist: PRT, Spartan

I LIKE YOU.
Single (7"): released on Carrere, Jul'86 by Carrere Records. Dist: PRT, Spartan

Single (12"): released on Carrere, Jul'86 by Carrere Records. Dist: PRT, Spartan

MOVE CLOSER.
Single (7"): released on Carrere, Feb'85 by Carrere Records. Dist: PRT, Spartan

Single (12"): released on Carrere, Feb'85 by Carrere Records. Dist: PRT, Spartan

MOVE CLOSER.
Album: released on Carrere, Feb'85 by Carrere Records. Dist: PRT, Spartan

Cassette: released on Carrere, Feb'85 by Carrere Records. Dist: PRT, Spartan

STOP DON'T DO THIS TO ME.
Single (12"): released on Carrere America (USA), Jul'83 by Polygram.

Nelson, Red

1935-36 RECORDINGS (RED NELSON & OTHERS).
Album: released on Magpie, Feb'79 Dist: Projection

Nelson, Rick

BEST OF....
Tracks: / Stood up / Waitin' in school / Be bop baby / Never be anyone else but you / Lonesome town / Poor little fool / It's late / Hello Mary Lou / Young world / Believe what you say / Just a little too much / I'ts up to you / Teenage idol / Young emotions / Travelin' man.
Compact disc: released on EMI America, Apr'87 by EMI Records. Dist: EMI

COUNTRY FEVER, BRIGHT LIGHTS AND COUNTRY MUSIC.
Tracks: / Salty dog / Truck drivin' man / You just can't quit / Louisiana man / Welcome to my world / Kentucky means paradise / Here I am / Bright lights and country music / Hello walls / No vacancy / I'm a fool to care / Congratulations / Night train to Memphis / Take a city bride / Funny how time slips away / Bridge washed out (The) / Alone / Big Chief Buffalo Nickel / Mystery train / Things you gave to me / Take these chains from my heart / Lonesome whistle blow (I heard that) / Walkin' down the line / You win again.
Album: released on See For Miles, Mar'87 by See For Miles Records. Dist: Pinnacle

GOLDEN GREATS: RICK NELSON.
Tracks: / Garden party / Fools rush in / Gypsy woman / She belongs to me / Mystery train / Since I don't have you / Take these chains from my heart / Legend in my time, A / For you / Very thought of you, The / String along / I got a woman / Reason to believe / It doesn't matter anymore / I think it's gonna rain today / Funny how time slips away.
Notes: His astounding career tragically cut short recently, rick Nelson will be remembered for a host of great records begining in the 50's, with more than fifty chart entries to his credit and millions of record sales behind time he was truly one of rock'n'rolls superstars. His "Golden Greats" collection is a superb new compilation featuring the very best of Rick Nelson's MCA recordings. Featuring his 1972 worldwide smash 'Garden Party' the album brims over with classic Rick Nelson bound to delight his enormous U.K. following.
Album: released on MCA, Feb'86 by MCA Records. Dist: Polygram, MCA

Cassette: released on MCA, Feb'86 by MCA Records. Dist: Polygram, MCA

INTAKES.
Album: released on Epic, Nov'77 by CBS Records. Dist: CBS

IT'S LATE.
Single (7"): released on Imperial (USA), '80 Dist: United Artists

NEVER BE ANYONE ELSE BUT YOU.
Single (7"): released on Imperial (USA), '80 Dist: United Artists

PLAYING TO WIN.
Album: released on Capitol, '81 by Capitol Records. Dist: EMI

RICK NELSON The best of.
Compact disc: released on EMI America, '87 by EMI Records. Dist: EMI

ROCKIN' ROCK.
Album: released on MCA, Sep'79 by EMI Records. Dist: EMI

STRING ALONG WITH RICK.
Album: released on Charly, Jul'84 by Charly Records. Dist: Charly, Cadillac

Nelson, Ricky

20 ROCK 'N' ROLL HITS.
Album: released on EMI (Germany), '83 by EMI Records. Dist: Conifer

BEST OF RICKY NELSON, THE.
Album: released on Liberty, Oct'85 by Liberty-United. Dist: EMI

Cassette: released on Liberty, Oct'85 by Liberty-United. Dist: EMI

GREATEST HITS:RICKY NELSON.
Album: released on Rhino (USA), Jan'86 by Rhino Records (USA).

Picture disc album: released on Rhino (USA), Jan'86 by Rhino Records (USA).

HELLO MARY LOU.
Single (7"): released on United Artists, Oct'80

Single (7"): released on EMI Golden 45's, Jul'84 by EMI Records. Dist: EMI

MORE SONGS BY RICKY.
Tracks: / I'm not afraid / Baby won't you please come home / Here I go again / I'd climb the highest mountain / Make believe / Ain't nothin'but love / When your lover has gon / Proving my love / Hey pretty baby / Time after time / I'm all through with you / Again.
Album: released on EMI-Liberty (Holland), Sep'86 by EMI Records. Dist: Conifer

RICKY.
Album: released on Liberty (France), '83

RICKY IS 21.
Album: released on EMI (France), '83 by EMI Records. Dist: Conifer

RICKY NELSON.
Album: released on Liberty (France), '83

RICKY SINGS AGAIN.
Album: released on EMI (France), '83 by EMI Records. Dist: Conifer

ROCKIN' WITH RICKY.
Album: released on Ace(Liberty), Jan'84 by Ace Records. Dist: Pinnacle, Swift, Hotshot

SINGLES ALBUM (1958-1963), THE.
Album: released on Fame (Liberty), Nov'82 by Music For Pleasure Records. Dist: EMI

Cassette: released on Fame (Liberty), Nov'82 by Music For Pleasure Records. Dist: EMI

SONGS BY RICKY.
Album: released on EMI (France), '83 by EMI Records. Dist: Conifer

Nelson, Sandy

20 ROCK 'N' ROLL HITS.
Album: released on EMI (Germany), '83 by EMI Records. Dist: Conifer

LET THERE BE DRUMS.
Single (7"): released on Imperial, '80 by K-Tel Records. Dist: K-Tel, Taylors, Polygram

VERY BEST OF SANDY NELSON, THE.
Album: released on Sun Set, Feb'78 by Sun Set Records. Dist: Jetstar Distribution

Nelson, Shara

LOVE HITS YOU.
Single (12"): released on Disco Tex, Oct'82 by Disco Tex Records. Dist: Jetstar

Nelson, Sharon

AIMING AT YOUR HEART (Nelson, Sharon & The Circuit).
Single (12"): released on On-U-Sound, Dec'83 Dist: Rough Trade Distribution, Lightning

Nelson, Tony

OVERNIGHT SENSATION (Nelson, Tony, Cool Country).
Album: released on Westwood, Nov'77 by Westwood Records. Dist: Jazz Music, H.R. Taylor, JSU, Pinnacle, Ross Records

Nelson, Tracy

DOIN' IT MY WAY.
Album: released on Adelphi(USA), '81 by Adelphi Records (USA). Dist: Projection, Swift

Nelson, Vicki

ONLY A FOOL.
Single (7"): released on Lunar, Jan'82 by Lunar. Dist: Record Services Distribution (Ireland), DJM, CBS

Nelson, Willie

18 GREAT SONGS.
Album: released on Design, May'84 by Breakaway Records. Dist: PRT, Stage One

Cassette: released on Design, May'84 by Breakaway Records. Dist: PRT, Stage One

20 GOLDEN CLASSICS.
Album: released on Astan, Nov'84 by Astan Records. Dist: Counterpoint

Cassette: released on Astan, Nov'84 by Astan Records. Dist: Counterpoint

Compact disc: released on The Compact Collection, Sep'87 by Conifer Records. Dist: Conifer Distribution

20 GOLDEN HITS.
Compact disc: released on Spectrum, Oct'86 Dist: ACD

20 OF THE BEST.
Album: released on RCA International, '84

Cassette: released on RCA International, '84

20 OUTLAW REUNION HITS (Nelson, Willie & Waylon Jennings).

ALWAYS ON MY MIND.
Single (7"): released on CBS, May'84 by CBS Records. Dist: CBS

Album: released on CBS, Apr'82 by CBS Records. Dist: CBS

Cassette: released on CBS, Apr'82 by CBS Records. Dist: CBS

Album: released on RCA, Jul'85 by RCA Records. Dist: RCA, Roots, Swift, Wellard, Chris, I & B, Solomon & Peres Distribution

Cassette: released on RCA, Jul'85 by RCA Records. Dist: RCA, Roots, Swift, Wellard, Chris, I & B, Solomon & Peres Distribution

Single (7"): released on RCA, Jul'85 by RCA Records. Dist: RCA, Roots, Swift, Wellard, Chris, I & B, Solomon & Peres Distribution

Single (12"): released on RCA, Jul'85 by RCA Records. Dist: RCA, Roots, Swift, Wellard, Chris, I & B, Solomon & Peres Distribution

AT THE COUNTRY STORE.
Album: released on Starblend Country Store, Aug'86 by Starblend Records. Dist: PRT Distribution

Cassette: released on Starblend Country Store, Aug'86 by Starblend Records. Dist: PRT Distribution

BEAUTIFUL TEXAS 1836-1986.
Tracks: / Dallas / San Antonio / Streets of Laredo / Who put all my ex's in Texas / Hill country theme (The) / Waltz across Texas / San Antonio Rose / Travis letter / Remember the Alamo / Texas in my soul / There's a little bit of everything in Texas / Beautiful Texas / San Antonio Rose (2) / Home in San Antone.
Album: released on Bear Family, Nov'86 by Bear Family Records. Dist: Rollercoaster Distribution, Swift

BEST OF WILLIE NELSON, THE.
Album: released on EMI (Germany), '83 by EMI Records. Dist: Conifer

BLUE SKIES.
Album: released on CBS, Sep'81 by CBS Records. Dist: CBS Deleted '86.

Cassette: released on CBS, Sep'81 by CBS Records. Dist: CBS

CITY OF NEW ORLEANS.
Single (7"): released on CBS, Jan'85 by CBS Records. Dist: CBS

Album: released on CBS, Nov'84 by CBS Records. Dist: CBS

Cassette: released on CBS, Nov'84 by CBS Records. Dist: CBS

CLASSIC WILLIE NELSON.
Album: released on Music For Pleasure, Jan'83 by EMI Records. Dist: EMI

Cassette: released on Music For Pleasure, Jan'83 by EMI Records. Dist: EMI

COUNTRY FAVOURITES.
Tracks: / Columbus stockade blues / Seasons of my heart / I'd trade all of my tomorrows (for just one yesterday) / My window faces the south / Go on home / Fraulein / San Antonio rose / I love hyou because / Don't you ever get tired (of hurting me) / Home in San Antone / Heartaches byh the number / Making believe.
Album: released on RCA, Jan'87 by RCA Records. Dist: RCA, Roots, Swift, Wellard, Chris, I & B, Solomon & Peres Distribution

Cassette: released on RCA, Jan'87 by RCA Records. Dist: RCA, Roots, Swift, Wellard, Chris, I & B, Solomon & Peres Distribution

COUNTRY WILLIE.
Tracks: / Country Willie / River boy / Darkness on the face of the Earth / Mr record man / Night life / I'll walk alone / Take me as I am (or let me go) / Tomorrow night / Take my word / Home motel / Blue must be the colour of the blues / Feed it a memory / Three days / One step beyond / Undo the right / Right or wrong / Columbus stockade blues / Part where I cry,The / Where my house lives / There goes a man.
Notes: Original sound recordings made by Liberty Records, a division of capitol RecordsInc. This compilation (P) 1987 EMI Records Ltd.
Album: released on Liberty (USA), May'87 Dist: United Artists

Cassette: released on Liberty (USA), May'87 Dist: United Artists

CRY.
Single (7"): released on CBS, Oct'84 by CBS Records. Dist: CBS

FAMILY BIBLE.
Album: released on MCA, Mar'86 by MCA Records. Dist: Polygram, MCA

GEORGIA ON MY MIND.
Album: released on Hallmark, Sep'84 by Pickwick Records. Dist: Pickwick Distribution, PRT, Taylors

Cassette: released on Hallmark, Sep'84 by Pickwick Records. Dist: Pickwick Distribution, PRT, Taylors

GREATEST HITS: WILLIE NELSON.
Double Album: released on CBS, Jan'82 by CBS Records. Dist: CBS

Double cassette: released on CBS, Jan'82 by CBS Records. Dist: CBS

HALF NELSON.
Album: released on CBS, Oct'85 by CBS Records. Dist: CBS

Cassette: released on CBS, Oct'85 by CBS Records. Dist: CBS

HELP ME MAKE IT THROUGH THE NIGHT.
Album: released on RCA, Nov'84 by RCA Records. Dist: RCA, Roots, Swift, Wellard, Chris, I & B, Solomon & Peres Distribution

Cassette: released on RCA, Nov'84 by RCA Records. Dist: RCA, Roots, Swift, Wellard, Chris, I & B, Solomon & Peres Distribution

HISTORIC RE-ISSUE.
Compact disc: released on Bridge, Oct'86 Dist: CD Centre Distribution, Pinnacle, Target

HOME IS WHERE YOU'RE HAPPY.
Tracks: / Building heartaches / Slow down / Old world / Healing hands of time / And so will you my love / Things to remember / One step beyond / If you can't undo the right undo the wrong / Home is where you're happy / Moment isn't very long, A / Some other time / Blame it on the times / Shelter of my arms / End of an understanding / Will y... ...ber mine / Everything but you / I hope so.
Album: released on Showcase, Apr'86 Dist: Counterpoint

Cassette: released on Showcase, Apr'86 Dist: Counterpoint

ISLAND IN THE SEA.
Tracks: / Island in the sea / Wake me when it's over / Little things / Last thing on my mind, The / There is no easy way (but there is a way) / Nobody there but me / Cols November wind / Women who love too much / All in the name of love / Sky train.
Album: released on CBS, Aug'87 by CBS Records. Dist: CBS

Cassette: released on CBS, Aug'87 by CBS Records. Dist: CBS

JUST TO SATISFY YOU (see Jennings, Waylon) (Nelson, Willie & Waylon Jennings).

LEGEND BEGINS, THE.
Album: released on Allegiance, Apr'84 by PRT Records. Dist: PRT

Cassette: released on Allegiance, Apr'84 by PRT Records. Dist: PRT

LONGHORN JAMBOUREE, THE (Nelson, Willie & Friends).
Album: released on Charly, Jan'77 by Charly Records. Dist: Charly, Cadillac

LOVE SONGS.
Tracks: / To all the girls I've loved before / Blue skies / Let it be me / Tenderly / Harbour lights / Mona Lisa / To each his own / Over the rainbow / Seven Spanish angels / Georgia on my mind / Bridge over troubled water / Without a song / Unchained melody / That lucky old sun / In my Mother's eyes / Always on my mind.
Compact disc: released on CBS, May'87 by CBS Records. Dist: CBS

Album: released on Arena, Feb'87 by Arena Records. Dist: Spartan

Cassette: released on Arena, Feb'87 by Arena Records. Dist: Spartan

NIGHT LIFE.
Album: released on Premier, '84 by Premier Records. Dist: CBS

Cassette: released on Premier, '84 by Premier Records. Dist: CBS

OFF THE RECORD WITH....
Album: released on Sierra, Aug'87 by Sierra Records. Dist: WEA. Estim retail price in Sep'87 was £4.99.

Cassette: released on Sierra, Aug'87 by Sierra Records. Dist: WEA. Estim retail price in Sep'87 was £4.99.

OLD FRIENDS (Nelson, Willie & Waylon Jennings).
Album: released on Hallmark, Jul'87 by Pickwick Records. Dist: Pickwick Distribution, PRT, Taylors

Cassette: released on Hallmark, Jul'87 by Pickwick Records. Dist: Pickwick Distribution, PRT, Taylors

OUTLAW REUNION.
Album: released on Sundown, Sep'83 by Magnum Music Group Ltd. Dist: Magnum Music Group Ltd, PRT Distribution, Spartan Distribution

OUTLAW REUNION - VOL.2 (Nelson, Willie & Waylon Jennings).
Album: released on Sundown, Apr'84 by Magnum Music Group Ltd. Dist: Magnum Music Group Ltd, PRT Distribution, Spartan Distribution

OUTLAWS (Nelson, Willie & Allan Coe).
Tracks: / What a way to live / Misery mansion / Rainy day blues / Night life / Man with the blues / Storm has just begun / Got you on my mind / These days / Mississippi woman / Why you been gone so long / Mary Magdelene / West Virginia man.
Album: released on Topline, '86 by Charly Records. Dist: Charly Distribution

Cassette: released on Topline, '86 by Charly Records. Dist: Charly Distribution

OUTLAWS' REUNION (see Jennings, Waylon) (Nelson, Willie & Waylon Jennings).

OUTLAWS' REUNION: VOL 2 (see Jennings, Waylon) (Nelson, Willie & Waylon Jennings).

POCHO AND LEFTY With Merle Haggard.
Album: released on Epic, Feb'83 by CBS Records. Dist: CBS Deleted '87.

Cassette: released on Epic, Feb'83 by CBS Records. Dist: CBS

PORTRAIT IN MUSIC.
Album: released on Premier, Jun'85 by Premier Records. Dist: CBS

Cassette: released on Premier, Jun'85 by Premier Records. Dist: CBS

PROMISELAND.
Tracks: / Living in the promised land / I'm not trying to forget you / Here in my heart / I've got the craziest feeling / No place but Texas / You're only in my arms (to cry on my shoulder) / Pass it on / Do you ever think of me / Old fashioned love / Basin street blues / Bach minuet in G.
Album: released on CBS, Apr'86 by CBS Records. Dist: CBS

Cassette: released on CBS, Apr'86 by CBS Records. Dist: CBS

SLOW DOWN OLD WORLD.
Album: released on Sundown, Apr'84 by Magnum Music Group Ltd. Dist: Magnum Music Group Ltd, PRT Distribution, Spartan Distribution

SONG FOR YOU, A.
Album: released on Hallmark, Aug'83 by Pickwick Records. Dist: Pickwick Distribution, PRT, Taylors

Cassette: released on Hallmark, Aug'83 by Pickwick Records. Dist: Pickwick Distribution, PRT, Taylors

SOUND IN YOUR MIND.
Cassette: released on CBS, Feb'83 by CBS Records. Dist: CBS

STARDUST.
Cassette: released on CBS, Jun'78 by CBS Records. Dist: CBS

TAKE IT TO THE LIMIT (Nelson, Willie & Waylon Jennings).
Album: released on CBS, Sep'83 by CBS Records. Dist: CBS

Cassette: released on CBS, Sep'83 by CBS Records. Dist: CBS

TAKE IT TO THE LIMIT (see Jennings, Waylon) (Nelson, Willie & Waylon Jennings).

THERE'LL BE NO MORE TEARDROPS TONIGHT.
Album: released on United Artists, Mar'79

THEY ALL WENT TO MEXICO (Nelson, Willie & Carlos Santana).
Single (7"): released on CBS, May'83 by CBS Records. Dist: CBS

TO ALL THE GIRLS I'VE LOVED BEFORE (Nelson, Willie & Julio Iglesias).
Single (7"): released on CBS, Mar'84 by CBS Records. Dist: CBS

TOUCH ME.
Album: released on Liberty-UA, Aug'85

Cassette: released on Liberty-UA, Aug'85

TROUBLEMAKER.
Tracks: / Uncloudy day / When the roll is called up yonder / Wispering hope / There is a fountain / Will the circle be unbroken / Troublemaker / In the garden / Where the soul never dies / Sweet bye and bye / Shall we gather / Precious memories.
Album: released on CBS, Mar'86 by CBS Records. Dist: CBS

Cassette: released on CBS, Mar'86 by CBS Records. Dist: CBS

UNCHAINED MELODY.
Single (7"): released on CBS, May'83 by CBS Records. Dist: CBS

WAYLON & WILLIE (Nelson, Willie & Waylon Jennings).
Notes: For full information see under: Jennings, Waylon & Willie Nelson

WILD & WILLIE.
Album: released on Allegiance, Apr'84 by PRT Records. Dist: PRT

Cassette: released on Allegiance, Apr'84 by PRT Records. Dist: PRT

WILLIE NELSON I love country.
Tracks: / No tomorrow sight / New way to cry, A / I'll stay around / Broken promises / Lets pretend / Take it to the limit / Angel eyes / I'm movin' on / Faded love / Old friends / Jim, I wore a tie today / I gotta get drunk / Reasons to quit / Seven Spanish angels / Loving you was easier (than anything I'll ever do again) / Show me yours (and I'll show you mine) / They all went to Mexico / Hello walls / There stands the glass / Heartbreak Hotel.
Notes: These tracks and more.
Compact disc: released on Bridge, '86 Dist: CD Centre Distribution, Pinnacle, Target

Album: released on CBS, Mar'87 by CBS Records. Dist: CBS

Cassette: released on CBS, Mar'87 by CBS Records. Dist: CBS

Cassette: released on Audio Fidelity, Oct'84 Dist: PRT

WILLIE NELSON AND BAND (Nelson, Willie, Yesterday's Wine).
Album: released on RCA International, Apr'80

Cassette: released on RCA International, Apr'80

WILLIE NELSON & JOHNNY LEE (Nelson, Willie & Johnny Lee).
Album: released on Astan, Nov'84 by Astan Records. Dist: Counterpoint

Cassette: released on Astan, Nov'84 by Astan Records. Dist: Counterpoint

WINNING HAND, THE With Kris Kristofferson, Dolly Parton & Brenda Lee.
Double Album: released on Monument, Jan'83 by CBS Records. Dist: CBS Distribution

Double cassette: released on Monument, Jan'83 by CBS Records. Dist: CBS Distribution Deleted '85.

WITHOUT A SONG.
Album: released on CBS, Mar'85 by CBS Records. Dist: CBS

Cassette: released on CBS, Mar'85 by CBS Records. Dist: CBS

WORLD OF WILLIE NELSON, THE.
Tracks: / Will you remember mine / Some other time / I hope so / Is there something on your mind / Broken promises / Blame it on the times / Face of a fighter / Shelter of your arms / End of understanding / Home is where you're are happy / And so will you my love / Waiting time / Everything but you / Happiness lives next door / No tomorrow in sight / Right from wrong / Go away / I'll stay around.
Notes: Licensed from Philip H.A.Bailey (PHAB).(P) & (C) Warwick Records. A Warwick Leisure Product. Made & Printed in the U.K.
Album: released on Warwick Reflections, Jun'86 by Warwick Records.

Cassette: released on Warwick Reflections, Jun'86 by Warwick Records.

Nemasheva, Galina

RUSSIAN POPULAR SONGS.
Cassette: released on Melodiya (USSR), Feb'79 Dist: T.B.C Distribution

Nena

99 RED BALLONS.
Single (7"): released on Epic, Jan'84 by CBS Records. Dist: CBS

?/ICH LIEBE DICHT.
Single (7"): released on Epic, Jul'84 by CBS Records. Dist: CBS

Single (12"): released on Epic, Jul'84 by CBS Records. Dist: CBS

IT'S ALL IN THE GAME.
Tracks: / Utopia / It's all in the game / Young as you / Are you awake? / Woman on fire / Warning signs / Let's humanize / Anyplace, anywhere, anytime / You don't know what love is / Auf Wiedersehn.
Album: released on Epic, Feb'86 by CBS Records. Dist: CBS

Cassette: released on Epic, Feb'86 by CBS Records. Dist: CBS

JUST A DREAM.
Single (7"): released on Epic, Mar'83 by CBS Records. Dist: CBS

Single (7"): released on Epic, Apr'84 by CBS Records. Dist: CBS

Picture disc single: released on Epic, Apr'84 by CBS Records. Dist: CBS

Single (12"): released on Epic, Apr'84 by CBS Records. Dist: CBS

NENA.
Cassette: released on Epic, Mar'84 by CBS Records. Dist: CBS

Nenad

MARIE'S THE NAME OF HIS LATEST FLAME.
Single (7"): released on Camab, Jul'82 Dist: PRT

Neo Arya

ENTIRE L'AMOUR AT LA HAINE.
Album: released on Play It Again Sam, Jun'84 Dist: Red Rhino, Cartel

Neon Barbs

BREAK YOUR CHAINS.
Single (7"): released on Logic Step, Jul'81

Neon Blondes

MIRROR FREAK.
Single (7"): released on 4 Series, Nov'81

Neon Hearts

POPULAR MUSIC (Neon Judgement).
Album: released on Satril, May'79 by Satril Records. Dist: PRT

Neon Judgement

MAFU CAGE.
Album: released on Play It Again Sam, May'86 Dist: Red Rhino, Cartel

TOMORROW IN THE PAPERS.
Single (12"): released on Play It Again Sam, Nov'85 Dist: Red Rhino, Cartel

VOODOO NIPPLEFIELD.
Single (7"): released on Play It Again Sam, May'86 Dist: Red Rhino, Cartel

Neon Leon

LAS PALMAS.
Single (7"): released on Tansing, Feb'83 by Tansing Records. Dist: Pinnacle

Neon Rome, A

NEW HEROIN.
Album: released on New Rose, Jun'87 Dist: Rough Trade, Cartel

Neon Tetra

TIGHTROPE.
Single (7"): released on Deeda, Aug'82

Nerious, Joseph

SENSI CRISIS.
Single (12"): released on Fashion, Jun'85 by Fashion Records. Dist: PRT, Jetstar

Nero, Peter

SOLID GOLD PIANO.
Cassette: released on RCA, '84 by RCA Records. Dist: RCA, Roots, Swift, Wellard, Chris, I & B, Solomon & Peres Distribution

WIZ, THE (Direct cut 45).

Album: released on Crystal, Aug'78 by Crystal Records. Dist: Jetstar, Revolver, Cartel

Nerve

I'LL GIVE YOU UP.
Single (7"): released on Future Earth, Jul'83 by Future Earth Records. Dist: Red Rhino, Cartel

LITTLE BIT OF JAZZ.
Tracks: / Little bit of jazz / It only takes a minute.
Single (7"): released on Sedition, 20 Jun'87 Dist: PRT

LITTLE BIT OF JAZZ, A.
Tracks: / Little bit of jazz, A / It only takes a minute.
Single (12"): released on Sedition, May'87 Dist: PRT

STUNNING GOOD...FUTURE MAKERS.
Album: released on Eva-Lolita, Dec'85 Dist: Pinnacle

WELCOME TO YOUR T.V..
Single (12"): released on D.M.D., Apr'86 by D.M.D Records. Dist: Jetstar

Nerve senta

NERVE SENTA.
Album: released on Superville, Dec'81 Dist: Pinnacle

Nervex

REBECCA.
Single (7"): released on Lost Moments, Feb'85 Dist: Backs, Cartel

Nervous Choir

HOLD EVERYTHING.
Album: released on Choir Cuts, Nov'86 Dist: Fast Forward, Cartel

Nervous Germans

DESOLATION ZONE.
Album: released on Rondelet, Jun'82 Dist: Spartan Distribution

Cassette: released on Rondelet, Jun'82 Dist: Spartan Distribution

SUMMER OF LOVE.
Album: released on Vertigo, Dec'83 by Phonogram Records. Dist: Polygram

THESE BOOTS ARE MADE FOR WALKING.
Single (7"): released on Rondelet, May'82 Dist: Spartan Distribution

Nervous, Joseph
MOVE ON UP.
Single (12"): released on Fine Style, Aug'87 by Fine Style Records. Dist: Revolver, Jetstar, PRT, Cartel

Nervous Norvous
TRANSFUSION.
Album: released on Ace, Feb'85 by Ace Records. Dist: Pinnacle, Swift, Hotshot, Cadillac

Nervus Rex
NERVUS REX.
Album: released on Dreamland, Aug'80 by RSO. Dist: Polygram

Nesmith, Michael
BEST OF MIKE NESMITH.
Album: released on RCA, Aug'76 by RCA Records. Dist: RCA, Roots, Swift, Wellard, Chris, I & B, Solomon & Peres Distribution

Netto, Loz
FADEAWAY.
Single (7"): released on 21 Records, Jul'83 by Polydor Records. Dist: Polydor

Single (12"): released on 21 Records, Jul'83 by Polydor Records. Dist: Polydor

LOZ NETTO.
Tracks: / Walking in the dark / We touch / Dance to the music / No reaction / Silent movie / Fat city / Do what you want / One night out / Substitute.
Album: released on Atlantic, Jul'86 by WEA Records. Dist: WEA

WE TOUCH.
Tracks: / Do what you want.
Single (7"): released on Atlantic, Aug'86 by WEA Records. Dist: WEA

Single (12"): released on Atlantic, Aug'86 by WEA Records. Dist: WEA

YOU ARE RHYTHM.
Single (7"): released on 21 Records, May'84 by Polydor Records. Dist: Polydor

Neu
BLACK FOREST GATEAU.
Album: released on Cherry Red, Nov'82 by Cherry Red Records. Dist: Pinnacle

Neuronium
HERITAGE.
Album: released on Jive Electro, Sep'84 by Zomba Records. Dist: RCA

Cassette: released on Jive Electro, Sep'84 by Zomba Records. Dist: RCA

Neurotic Arseholes
LIVE WIERD SYSTEMS.
Album: released on Wierd Systems, Apr'87

Neurotics
KICK STARTING A BACKFIRING NATION.
Album: released on Jungle, Sep'86 by Jungle Records. Dist: Jungle, Cartel

Double cassette: released on Jungle, Sep'86 by Jungle Records. Dist: Jungle, Cartel

LIVING WITH UNEMPLOYEMENT.
Tracks: / Living with unemployement / Airstrip 1 / My death / Oh no / Mindless violence / Porky the poet / Peter Campbell.
Single (7"): released on Jungle, Jun'86 by Jungle Records. Dist: Jungle, Cartel

Single (12"): released on Jungle, Jun'86 by Jungle Records. Dist: Jungle, Cartel

REPERCUSSIONS.
Album: released on Jungle, May'85 by Jungle Records. Dist: Jungle, Cartel

Neverending Story
NEVERENDING STORY Original motion picture Soundtrack.
Album: released on EMI, Mar'85 by EMI Records. Dist: EMI

Cassette: released on EMI, Mar'85 by EMI Records. Dist: EMI

Never Forget...
NEVER FORGET YOUR WELSH VOL.1 Various artists (Various Artists).
Album: released on Black Mountain, '82 by Black Mountain Records.

Never Mind The Jacksons..
NEVER MIND THE JACK-SONS...HERE'S THE POLLOCKS Various artists (Various Artists).
Single (12"): released on Abstract, Mar'85 by Abstract. Dist: Pinnacle

Never Never
AMERICANA.
Single (7"): released on Round, Feb'87 by PRT, Red Rhino, Cartel

Neves, Castro
Pedro Paulo, Castro Neves & Michel Legrand

Neville, Aaron
HUMDINGER.
Tracks: / Over you / I'm waitin' at the station / Every day / Sweet little mama / Let's live / Humdinger / Wrong number [I'm sorry, goodbye] / Reality / How many times / Don't cry / Get out of my life / I found another love / How could I help but love you / Show me the way.
Album: released on Stateside, Sep'86 Dist: EMI

Cassette: released on Stateside, Sep'86 Dist: EMI

MAKE ME STRONG.
Tracks: / Struttin' on Sunday / Hercules / Make me strong / All these things / Baby I'm a want you / Performance / Mojo Hannah / Greatest love (The) / One fine day / Tell it like it is / Cry me a river / Been so wrong / Speak to me / Wild flower / Feelings / Nadie / For the good times / She's on my mind.
Notes: Licensed from Charly Records International APS.   This CD P 1987   Charly Holdings   Inc. This CD C 1987 Charly Records Ltd.
Compact disc: released on Charly, Feb'87 by Charly Records. Dist: Charly, Cadillac

Cassette: released on Charly, Sep'86 by Charly Records. Dist: Charly, Cadillac

ORCHID IN THE STORM.
Album: released on Demon, Apr'86 by Demon Records. Dist: Pinnacle

TELL IT LIKE IT IS.
Single (7"): released on Charly, Jul'80 by Charly Records. Dist: Charly, Cadillac

Neville, Art
MARDI GRAS ROCK AND ROLL.
Album: released on Ace, Nov'86 by Ace Records. Dist: Pinnacle, Swift, Hotshot, Cadillac

MARDI GRAS ROCK 'N' ROLL.
Tracks: / Zing zing / Oooh-whee baby / Bella Mae / I'm a fool to care / Cha dooky-do / Back home to me / What's going on / Old time Rock n'n Roll / Rocking Pneumonia & The Boogie Woogie / Bring it on home baby / Dummy / Let's rock / Arabian love call / Please listen to my song / Whiffenpoof song.
Notes: Mono.
Album: released on Ace, Nov'86 by Ace Records. Dist: Pinnacle, Swift, Hotshot, Cadillac

Neville Brothers
FIYO ON THE BAYOU.
Album: released on Demon, Jul'86 by Demon Records. Dist: Pinnacle

Cassette: released on Demon, Jul'86 by Demon Records. Dist: Pinnacle

NEVILLISATION.
Tracks: / Fever / Woman's gotta have it / Mojo Hannah / Tell it like it is / Why you wanna hurt my heart / Fear, hate, envy, jealousy / Caravan / Big chief / Africa.
Compact disc: released on Demon, Nov'86 by Demon Records. Dist: Pinnacle

NEVILLIZATION.
Album: released on Demon, Sep'84 by Demon Records. Dist: Pinnacle

Nevil, Robbie
C'EST LA VIE.
Tracks: / C'est la vie / Time waits for no-one.
Single (7"): released on Manhattan, Nov'86 by President Records. Dist: Jazz Music, Swift, Taylors, Chris Wellard

Single (12"): released on Manhattan, Dec'86 by President Records. Dist: Jazz Music, Swift, Taylors, Chris Wellard

Compact disc: released on Manhattan, Jun'87 by EMI Records. Dist: EMI

C'EST LA VIE (EXT. REMIX).
Tracks: / C'est la vie (ext remix) / Time waits for

no-one.
Notes: Side A extended remix by Michael Braver.
Single (12"): released on Manhattan, Dec'86 by President Records. Dist: Jazz Music, Swift, Taylors, Chris Wellard

DOMINOES.
Tracks: / Dom dom domino dub / C'est la vie".
Single (7"): released on Manhattan, Mar'87 by President Records. Dist: Jazz Music, Swift, Taylors, Chris Wellard

Single (12"): released on Manhattan, Mar'87 by President Records. Dist: Jazz Music, Swift, Taylors, Chris Wellard

DOMINOES (EXT VOCAL MIX).
Tracks: / Dominoes (ext vocal mix) / C'est la vie (Steve Street mix) / Dominoes / Dom dom domino dub) / Dominoes (Dance mix).
Double-pack single: released on Manhattan, Apr'87 by EMI Records. Dist: EMI

Compact disc single: released on Manhattan, 23 May'87 by EMI Records. Dist: EMI

ROBBIE NEVIL.
Tracks: / Just a little closer / Dominoes / Limousines / Back to you / C'est la vie / Wot's it to ya / Walk your talk / Simple life / Neighbors / Look who's alone tonight.
Compact disc: released on Manhattan, Feb'87 by President Records. Dist: Jazz Music, Swift, Taylors, Chris Wellard

Album: released on Manhattan, Nov'86 by EMI Records. Dist: EMI

Cassette: released on Manhattan, Nov'86 by EMI Records. Dist: EMI

WHAT'S IT TO YA.
Tracks: / What's it to ya / What's it to ya (remix).
Single (7"): released on Manhattan, 20 Jun'87 by EMI Records. Dist: EMI

Single (12"): released on Manhattan, 20 Jun'87 by EMI Records. Dist: EMI

WOT'S IT TO YA? (EXT TO YA REMIX).
Tracks: / Wot's it to ya / C'est la vie (Steve Street mix) / Dominoes (Ext).
Cassette single: released on Manhattan, Jul'87 by EMI Records. Dist: EMI

WOT'S IT TO YA (RUSTY'S 12" DANCE MIX).
Tracks: / Wot's it to ya (Rusty's 12" dance mix) / Wot's it to ya (Dub to ya mix) / Wot's it to ya (To ya remix).
Single (12"): released on Manhattan, Jul'87 by EMI Records. Dist: EMI

New Accoustic Sampler
NEW ACCOUSTIC SAMPLER Various artists (Various Artists).
Album: released on Ambient Sound, Apr'85

New age
ALL THE MONKEYS AREN'T IN THE ZOO.
Album: released on Dining Out, Jan'83 by Dining Out Records. Dist: IKF, Independent

JANE FONDA.
Single (7"): released on Dining Out, Sep'81 by Dining Out Records. Dist: IKF, Independent

LIVING FOR NOW (EP).
Single (12"): released on Dining Out, Feb'82 by Dining Out Records. Dist: IKF, Independent

New age music
NEW AGE MUSIC Various artists (Various Artists).
Double Album: released on Innovative Communication, Apr'86 by Innovative Communication Records. Dist: Pickwick Distribution

New Age Steppers
MY LOVE.
Single (12"): released on Statik, Jul'81 Dist: Rough Trade Distribution, Stage One Distribution

NEW AGE STEPPERS.
Album: released on Statik, Oct'85 Dist: Rough Trade Distribution, Stage One Distribution

New Air
LIVE AT MONTREAL INT. JAZZ FESTIVAL.
Compact disc: released on Black Saint (Italy), '86 Dist: Target, Jazz Music, Harmonia Mundi

LIVE AT MONTREAL INTERNATIONAL JAZZ FESTIVAL.
Album: released on Black Saint, May'85 Dist: Projection, IMS, Polygram, Chris Wellard, Harmonia Mundi, Swift

New amalgam
ANOTHER TIME.
Album: released on Vinyl, Feb'77

New American Orchestra
MUSIC FROM BLADE RUNNER.
Album: released on Full Moon, Sep'82 by Epic. Dist: CBS

Cassette: released on Full Moon, Sep'82 by Epic. Dist: CBS

New Anatomy
INNER CITY UNIT.
Album: released on Demi Monde, Jan'85 Dist: Charly

New Apartment
CATCH 22.
Single (7"): released on Demon, Jul'81 by Demon Records. Dist: Pinnacle

Newart Bob
BOB NEW ART.
Cassette: released on Pickwick, Sep'80 by Pickwick Records. Dist: Pickwick Distribution, Prism Leisure Distribution, Luutons

MASTERS.
Album: released on Warner Brothers, Jan'74 by Warner Bros Records. Dist: WEA

New Art Ensemble
SEEKING.
Album: released on Revelation, Apr'81

New Asia
NEW ASIA.
Album: released on Situation 2, Apr'82 Dist: Cartel, Pinnacle

New Band
HAPPY NEW YEAR.
Single (7"): released on RPM, Feb'85 by RPM Records. Dist: PRT Distribution

New Batchalors
NOW AND THEN.
Album: released on CBS, Mar'85 by CBS Records. Dist: CBS

Cassette: released on CBS, Mar'85 by CBS Records. Dist: CBS Deleted '87.

New Beats
BREAD AND BUTTER.
Tracks: / Bread and butter / Every thing's alright.
Single (7"): released on WEA, Jun'87 by WEA Records. Dist: WEA

Single (12"): released on WEA, Jun'87 by WEA Records. Dist: WEA

RUN BABY RUN.
Single (7"): released on Inferno, Aug'82 by Inferno Records. Dist: Inferno, Cartel, Pinnacle

Newberry, Booker
LOVE TOWN (Newberry, Booker III).
Album: released on Polydor (Germany), Sep 84 by IMS-Polygram

Album: released on Malaco, Nov'84 by Malaco Records. Dist: Charly

Cassette: released on Malaco, Nov'84 by Malaco Records. Dist: Charly

SHADOWS.
Single (7"): released on Malaco, Oct'84 by Malaco Records. Dist: Charly

Single (12"): released on Malaco, Oct'84 by Malaco Records. Dist: Charly

TAKE A PIECE OF ME.
Tracks: / Take a piece of me.
Single (7"): released on Omni, Apr'86 Dist: Pinnacle

Single (12"): released on Omni, Apr'86 Dist: Pinnacle

Newbery, Mickey
SWEET MEMORIES.
Tracks: / American trilogy (An) / Good morning, dear / If you ever get to Houston / She even woke me up to say Goodbye / Dizzy Lizzy / Sweet memories / Remember the good / Snshine / Future's not what it used to be, (The) / How I love them old songs.
Album: released on MCA Import, Mar'86 by MCA Records. Dist: Polygram, IMS

New Black Eagle...
NEW BLACK EAGLE JAZZ BAND (New Black Eagle Jazz Band).
Album: released on GHB, Oct'86 Dist: Jazz Music, Swift

New Bluebloods

NEW BLUEBLOODS Various Artists (Various Artists).
Album: released on Sonet, Mar'87 by Sonet Records. Dist: PRT

Newborn, Phineas

LOOK OUT PHINEAS BACK.
Album: released on Pablo (USA), Jan'82 by Pablo Records (USA). Dist: Wellard, Chris, IMS-Polygram, BMG

Cassette: released on Pablo (USA), Jan'82 by Pablo Records (USA). Dist: Wellard, Chris, IMS-Polygram, BMG

Newborn, Phineas Jr.

FABULOUS PHINEAS.
Album: released on RCA (France), Jan'83 by RCA Records. Dist: Discovery

HARLEM BLUES.
Notes: With Ray Brown and Elvin Jones
Compact disc: released on JVC Fantasy (Japan), '86

NEWBORN PIANO.
Album: released on Vogue Jazz (France), May'83

New Christs

DETRITUS EP.
Tracks: / Born out of time / No next time / Like a curse / Sun God.
Extended-play record: released on What Goes On, Feb'87 Dist: Rough Trade, Cartel, Shigaku

New City Jazzmen

ANOTHER MAN DONE GONE.

Album: released on Flyright, Mar'79 by Flyright Records. Dist: Krazy Kat, Swift, Jazz Music

GOING TO TOWN.
Album: released on Flyright, Aug'79 by Flyright Records. Dist: Krazy Kat, Swift, Jazz Music

TO BE COLLECTED.
Album: released on Flyright, Mar'79 by Flyright Records. Dist: Krazv Kat, Swift, Jazz Music

Newcleus

COMPUTER AGE.
Single (7"): released on Sunny View, Sep'84 by Sunny View Records. Dist: PRT Distribution

Single (12"): released on Sunny View, Sep'84 by Sunny View Records. Dist: PRT Distribution

JAM ON IT.
Single (7"): released on Sunny View, Apr'84 by Sunny View Records. Dist: PRT Distribution

Single (12"): released on Sunny View, Apr'84 by Sunny View Records. Dist: PRT Distribution

JAM ON REVENGE.
Album: released on Sunny View, Aug'84 by Sunny View Records. Dist: PRT Distribution

Cassette: released on Sunny View, Aug'84 by Sunny View Records. Dist: PRT Distribution

JAM ON REVENGE (THE WIKKI WIKKI SONG).
Single (7"): released on Becket, Aug'83

Single (12"): released on Becket, Aug'83

New Creation Singers

SWEETER THAN HONEY.
Album: released on Birdwing, May'82 by Word Records. Dist: Word Distribution

Cassette: released on Birdwing, May'82 by Word Records. Dist: Word Distribution

New Delta Jazzmen '76

NEW DELTA JAZZMEN, THE.
Album: released on VJM, Apr'79 by VJM (UK) Records. Dist: Swift

New Edition

ALL FOR LOVE.
Tracks: / Count me in / Little bit of love, A / Sweet thing / With you all the way / Let's be friends / Kick back / Tonight's your night / Whispers in bed / Who do you trust / School / All for love.
Album: released on MCA, Jun'86 by MCA Records. Dist: Polygram, MCA

Cassette: released on MCA, Jun'86 by MCA Records. Dist: Polygram, MCA

CALL IT NOW.
Single (7"): released on MCA, Oct'84 by MCA Records. Dist: CBS

Single (12"): released on MCA, Oct'84 by MCA Records. Dist: CBS

CANDY GIRL.
Album: released on Streetwise, Aug'83 Dist: Greyhound Deleted '87.

Cassette: released on Streetwise, Aug'83 Dist: Greyhound

Single (7"): released on London, Apr'83 by London Records. Dist: Polygram

Single (12"): released on London, Apr'83 by London Records. Dist: Polygram

COOL IT NOW.
Single (7"): released on MCA, Apr'85 by MCA Records. Dist: CBS

Single (12"): released on MCA, Apr'85 by MCA Records. Dist: CBS

EARTH ANGEL.
Tracks: / Million to one, A / Duke of Earl / Hey there lonely girl / Thousand miles away / What's your name / Tears on my pillow / Blue moon / Since I don't have you / Bring back the memories.
Album: released on MCA, Feb'87 by MCA Records. Dist: Polygram, MCA

Cassette: released on MCA, Feb'87 by MCA Records. Dist: Polygram, MCA

EARTH ANGEL (SINGLE).
Tracks: / Earth angel / With you all the way.
Single (7"): released on MCA, Nov'86 by MCA Records. Dist: Polygram, MCA

Single (12"): released on MCA, Nov'86 by MCA Records. Dist: Polygram, MCA

IS THIS THE END.
Single (7"): released on London, Oct'83 by London Records. Dist: Polygram

Single (12"): released on London, Oct'83 by London Records. Dist: Polygram

LITTLE BIT OF LOVE, A (IS ALL IT TAKES).
Tracks: / Little bit of love, A (is all it takes) / Sneakin' around / Little bit of love, A / Little bit of love, A (Inst).
Single (7"): released on MCA, Feb'86 by MCA Records. Dist: Polygram, MCA

Single (12"): released on MCA, Feb'86 by MCA Records. Dist: Polygram, MCA

MR TELEPHONE MAN.
Single (7"): released on MCA, Feb'85 by MCA Records. Dist: CBS

Single (12"): released on MCA, Feb'85 by MCA Records. Dist: CBS

NEW EDITION.
Compact disc: by MCA Records. Dist: Polygram, MCA

Album: released on MCA, Nov'84 by MCA Records. Dist: CBS

Cassette: released on MCA, Nov'84 by MCA Records. Dist: CBS

POPCORN LOVE.
Single (7"): released on London, Aug'83 by London Records. Dist: Polygram

Single (12"): released on London, Aug'83 by London Records. Dist: Polygram
Cat. no: **LONX 31**

SEASIDE SPECIAL.
Album: by CBS Records. Dist: CBS

New Electric Warriors

NEW ELECTRIC WARRIORS Various artists (Various Artists).
Album: released on Logo, Sep'80 by Logo Records. Dist: Roots, BMG

Newell Martin

WHEN THE FIRE BURNS DREAMS/AMATEUR PARANOIC.

Cassette single: released on Matol, Jan'84 by Matol Records. Dist: Falling A Distribution

YOUNG JOBLESS/SYLVIE IN TOWN.
Single (7"): released on Offstreet, May'83 by Offstreet Records. Dist: EMI, Pinnacle

Newell, Norman

WHEN I FALL IN LOVE.
Tracks: / Love story ("Where do I begin") / Something.

Newely Anthony

WHY/ANYTHING YOU WANNA DO.
Single (7"): released on Decca-Originals, Apr'82 by Decca Records. Dist: Polygram, IMS

New England Conservatory

MORE SCOTT JOPLIN RAGS.
Album: released on London, Jul'74 by London Records. Dist: Polygram

RED BACK BOOK, SCOTT JOPLIN RAGS.
Album: released on H.M.V., May'83 by EMI Records. Dist: EMI

Cassette: released on H.M.V., May'83 by EMI Records. Dist: EMI

New Experience

PROVE IT TO ME.
Single (7"): released on Boiling Point, Jul'85 by Polydor Records. Dist: Polygram

Single (12"): released on Boiling Point, Jul'85 by Polydor Records. Dist: Polygram

New Generation...

VOLUME 1 (New Generation Cuban All Stars).
Tracks: / Guaracha para los dedos / Cancion de Jose Lazardo / Chango chango / Montuno de monte afuera / Punto neutro / Siglo li de nuestra era.
Notes: Full title:*New Generation Cuban All Stars-Volume1*
Album: released on Messidor (Germany), Jan'87 Dist: IMS Distribution, Polygram

VOLUME2 (New Generation Cuban All Stars).
Tracks: / Elegua soyu / Songo blue / Siglo I A N. E. / Yemaya asesu / Danzon para las estrellas marinas / Tormenta Africana.
Notes: Full title:*New Generation Cuban All Stars-Volume2*
Album: released on Messidor (Germany), Jan'87 Dist: IMS Distribution, Polygram

New Gladiators

NEW GLADIATORS Various artists (Various Artists).
Tracks: / Fortuna-back to back / Get out / I shall return / Autoblast / High school / Heavy Christmas / Come one, come all / Heavy metal shuffle / Party all night / All fired up / I need your love / Without you.
Album: released on Epic, Apr'86 by CBS Records. Dist: CBS

Cassette: released on Epic, Apr'86 by CBS Records. Dist: CBS

New Grass Revival

BARREN COUNTRY.
Album: released on Flying Fish (USA), May'79 by Flying Fish Records (USA). Dist: Roots, Projection

NEW GRASS REVIVAL.
Tracks: / What you do to me / Love someone like me / Lonely rider / Sweet release / How many hearts / In the middle of the night / Saw you runnin' / Ain't that peculiar / Seven by seven.
Notes: New Grass Revival has always had a reputation for being in tune with a rainbow spectrum of music. Individually, and collectively the band have been lifelong innovators, incorporating elements of Country, Jazz, Rock, Blues, Reggae and Gospelinto their repetoire. With their debut album on EMI Records, Titled simply, *New grass revival*, the group is aiming for its widest audience ever. Its producedby Garth Fundis, who is well known for his association with Don Williams. [EMI release sheet, April 87]
Album: released on EMI America, Apr'87 by EMI Records. Dist: EMI

Cassette: released on EMI America, Apr'87 by EMI Records. Dist: EMI

NEW GRASS REVIVAL.
Album: released on EMI America, Apr'87 by EMI Records. Dist: EMI

Cassette: released on EMI America, Apr'87 by EMI Records. Dist: EMI

ON THE BOULEVARD.
Album: released on Sugarhill (USA), Mar'85 by PRT Records. Dist: PRT Distribution

STORM IS OVER, THE.
Album: released on Flying Fish (USA), Feb'79 by Flying Fish Records (USA). Dist: Roots, Projection

TOO LATE TO TURN BACK.
Album: released on Sonet, Aug'78 by Sonet Records. Dist: PRT

New Guinea

GIZRA AND BINE PEOPLE, THE.
Album: released on Lyrichord (Import), May'83

New Guys On The Block

ON THE DANCE FLOOR.
Single (7"): released on Sugar Hill USA, Jun'83 by MCA Records. Dist: Roots Distribution, Mike's Country Music Room Distribution, Projection Distribution, PRT Distribution

Single (12"): released on Sugar Hill USA, Jun'83 by MCA Records. Dist: Roots Distribution, Mike's Country Music Room Distribution, Projection Distribution, PRT Distribution

New Harlem Funk

ASK THE BOSS.
Single (7"): released on Greyhound, Oct'84 by Greyhound Records. Dist: PRT, Greyhound

Single (12"): released on Greyhound, Oct'84 by Greyhound Records. Dist: PRT, Greyhound

Newhart, Bob

BEST OF BOB NEWHART.
Album: released on Warner Brothers, Jan'74 by Warner Bros Records. Dist: WEA

New Hawaiians

HAWAIIAN PARADISE.
Album: released on Dansan, Nov'79 by Spartan Records. Dist: Spartan

Cassette: released on Dansan, Apr'80 by Spartan Records. Dist: Spartan

HAWAIIANS IN SEQUENCE.
Album: released on Dansan, Feb'79 by Spartan Records. Dist: Spartan

New Hebrides String Band

PARADE.
Album: released on Viking, Nov'77 Dist: Harmonia Mundi Distributors

New High Level Ranters

NEW HIGH LEVEL RANTERS, THE.
Album: released on Topic, '82 by Topic Records. Dist: JSU Distribution, Projection Distribution, Jazz Music Distribution

New Hope Singers

NEW HOPE SINGERS.
Album: by Pilgrim Records. Dist: Rough Trade, Cartel

New Horizon

SOMETIMES ALLELUIA.
Album: by Pilgrim Records. Dist: Rough Trade, Cartel

WALK ON.
Single (7"): released on Red Bus, Oct'81 by Red Bus Records. Dist: PRT

New Hot Club Quartet

I REMEMBER DJANGO.
Album: released on Black Lion, '79 by Black Lion Records. Dist: Jazz Music, Chris Wellard, Taylor, H.R., Counterpoint, Cadillac

New Jersey Connection

LOVE DON'T COME EASY.
Single (7"): released on Nite Life, Nov'82

Single (12"): released on Nite Life, Nov'82

New Jersey Mass choir

DONALD.
Tracks: / Donald / I want to know what love is / Jesus is right on.
Single (7"): released on Prelude, Nov'86 Dist: CBS

Single (12"): released on Prelude, Nov'86 Dist: CBS
Cat. no: **ZT 41030**

I WANT TO KNOW WHAT LOVE IS.
Single (7"): released on Prelude, Jan'85 Dist: CBS

Single (12"): released on Prelude, Jan'85 Dist: CBS

LOOK UP AND LIVE.
Notes: The choir is directed by Donnie Harper who also writes and sings lead vocals on a number of tracks.
Album: released on Light, May'87 by Mainline Record Company. Dist: Mainline

Cassette: released on Light, May'87 by Mainline Record Company. Dist: Mainline

Newley, Anthony

ANTHONY NEWELY "MR PERSONALITY".
Album: released on Decca, Apr'85 by Decca Records. Dist: Polygram

SINGER AND HIS SONGS THE.
Album: released on United Artists, Apr'78

STOP THE WORLD (ORIGINAL CAST).
Album: released on Decca, Jan'61 by Decca Records. Dist: Polygram

New London Chorale

UNTO US A CHILD IS BORN.
Single (7"): released on RCA, Dec'82 by RCA Records. Dist: RCA, Roots, Swift, Wellard, Chris, I & B, Solomon & Peres Distribution

YOUNG MESSIAH.
Tracks: / Comfort ye / Every valley / Who shall abide? / O thou that tellest / Unto us a child is born / He shall feed his flock / How beautiful are the feet / He was Despised / Hallelujah / I know that my redeemer liveth / Finale.
Compact disc: released on RCA, '86 by RCA Records. Dist: RCA, Roots, Swift, Wellard, Chris, I & B, Solomon & Peres Distribution

Album: released on RCA International, '84

Cassette: released on RCA International, '84

New Look At Psychologists

NEW LOOK AT PSYCHOLOGISTS By Liam Hudson.
Cassette: released on Psychology Today (USA), Oct'81

New Lost City Ramblers

20TH ANNIVERSARY CONCERT.
Album: released on Flying Fish (USA), Feb'87 by Flying Fish Records (USA). Dist: Roots, Projection

TWENTY YEARS.
Album: released on Flying Fish (USA), May'79 by Flying Fish Records (USA). Dist: Roots, Projection

New LSO

MAGIC OF STRAUSS.
Cassette: released on Bravo, Feb'80 by Pickwick Records. Dist: Lugtons

Newman, Bob

HANGOVER BOOGIE.
Album: released on Bear Family, Nov'84 by Bear Family Records. Dist: Rollercoaster Distribution, Swift

Newman, Chris

CHRIS NEWMAN 2.
Album: released on Coast, Jul'83 by Coast Records. Dist: Phonogram, Polygram

Newman, Colin

A - Z.
Album: released on Beggars Banquet, Oct'80 by Beggars Banquet Records. Dist: WEA

COMMERCIAL SUCCESS.
Album: released on Crammed Discs, Oct'86 Dist: Rough Trade, Nine Mile, Cartel

FEIGNED HEARING.
Tracks: / Feigned hearing.
Single (7"): released on Crammed Discs, Oct'86 Dist: Rough Trade, Nine Mile, Cartel

NOTTO.
Album: released on 4AD, Jan'82 by 4AD Records. Dist: Rough Trade

RESURGENCE.
Album: released on Muse (Import), Jan'81

WE MEAN WE STARTS/NOT TOO (REMIX).
Single (7"): released on 4AD, May'82 by 4AD Records. Dist: Rough Trade

Newman, David 'Fathead'

STILL HARD TIMES.
Album: released on Muse, Nov'82 Dist: JSU Distribution, Jazz Horizons Distribution, Jazz Music Distribution, Celtic Music Distribution

WIDE OPEN SPACES.
Album:

Newman, Gary

Biographical Details: see under Numan, Gary

STORMTROOPER IN DRAG (see Gardiner, Paul) (Newman, Gary with Paul Gardiner).

Newman, Jimmy

1949-1952 (Newman, Jimmy & Al Terry).
Album: released on Flyright, Jun'81 by Flyright Records. Dist: Krazy Kat, Swift, Jazz Music

PROGRESSIVE CC.
Album: released on Charly, Nov'77 by Charly Records. Dist: Charly, Cadillac

Newman, Jimmy C.

ALLIGATOR MAN.
Album: released on Charly, Jan'84 by Charly Records. Dist: Charly, Cadillac

CAJUN AND COUNTRY TOO.
Album:

CAJUN COUNTRY.
Tracks: / Sugar bee / Alons a lafayette / Cajun man can, (A) / Sweet Suzannah / Alligator man / Diggy liggy lo / Louisiana Saturday night / Jole blon / Cry, cry darling / Big Mamou / Hippie ti you / Grand chenier.
Album: released on Topline, '86 by Charly Records. Dist: Charly Distribution

Cassette: released on Topline, '86 by Charly Records. Dist: Charly Distribution

Album: released on RCA International (USA), Jan'82 by RCA Records. Dist: RCA

CAJUN COUNTRY CLASSICS.
Tracks: / Alligator man / Tribodeaux & his Cajun band / Jambalaya (on the Bayou) / Jole Blon / Boo-Dan / Diggy Liggy Lo / Big Mamou / Louisiana saturday night / Cajun man can, A / Big Bayou / Colinda / Basile Waltz / Daydreamin' / Lache pas la Patate / Happy Cajun, The / Sugar bee.
Cassette: released on Charly, Sep'86 by Charly Records. Dist: Charly, Cadillac

Album: released on Charly, Nov'81 by Charly Records. Dist: Charly, Cadillac

FOLK SONGS OF THE BAYOU COUNTRY.
Album: released on Stetson, Apr'86 by Hasmick Promotions Ltd.. Dist: Counterpoint Distribution, H.R. Taylor Distribution, Swift Distribution, Chris Wellard Distribution

HAPPY CAJUN THE.
Album: released on Charly, Mar'80 by Charly Records. Dist: Charly, Cadillac

JIMMY C. NEWMAN & CAJUN COUNTRY (Newman, Jimmy C./Cajun Country).
Album: released on MCA Import, Mar'86 by MCA Records. Dist: Polygram, IMS

LOUISIANA SATURDAY NIGHT.
Tracks: / Diggy liggy lo / Happy Cajun (The) / More happy cajun (The) / Sugar bee / Jambalaya (on the bayou) / Alligator man / Louisiana Saturday night / Hippy ti yo / Jole Blon / Thibodeaux & his cajun band / Boo-dan / Corrine Corrina / Alons a lafayette / Big bayou / Sweet Suzannah / Big Texas / Cajun man can, A / Big mamou / Colinda / Daydreamin' / Lache pas la patate / Basile Waltz / Grand chenier.
Notes: Original Plantation recordings. Licensed from Charly Records International APS.This CD P 1987 Charly Holdings Inc. This CD C 1987 Charly Records Ltd.
Compact disc: released on Charly, Apr'87 by Charly Records. Dist: Charly, Cadillac

WILD N CAJUN.

Album: released on RCA, Sep'84 by RCA Records. Dist: RCA, Roots, Swift, Wellard, Chris, I & B, Solomon & Peres Distribution

Cassette: released on RCA, Sep'84 by RCA Records. Dist: RCA, Roots, Swift, Wellard, Chris, I & B, Solomon & Peres Distribution

Newman, Joe

HANGIN OUT (Newman, Joe & Joe Wilder).
Album: released on Concord Jazz(USA), Feb'85 by Concord Jazz Records (USA). Dist: IMS, Polygram

HAPPY CATS THE (Newman, Joe Sextet).
Album: released on Jasmine, Feb'83 by Jasmine Records. Dist: Counterpoint, Lugtons, Taylor, H.R., Wellard, Chris, Swift, Cadillac

SHINY STOCKINGS.
Album: released on Honeydew, Oct'79 Dist: Swift, JSU

SIMILAR SOULS.
Double Album: released on Vogue Jazz (France), May'83

WAY DOWN BLUES.
Album: released on Honeydew, Oct'79 Dist: Swift, JSU

Newman, Randy

BEST OF RANDY NEWMAN.
Compact disc: released on Atlantic, Jul'87 by WEA Records. Dist: WEA

BLUES, THE (Newman, Randy/Paul Simon).
Single (7"): released on Warner Bros., Jan'83 by Warner Bros Records. Dist: WEA

Single (12"): released on Warner Bros., Jan'83 by Warner Bros Records. Dist: WEA

BORN AGAIN.
Album: released on Warner Brothers, Sep'79 by WEA Records. Dist: WEA

Cassette: released on Warner Brothers, Sep'79 by WEA Records. Dist: WEA

I LOVE L.A..
Tracks: / I love L.A. / Song for the dead.
Single (7"): released on Warner Bros., 23 May'87 by Warner Bros Records. Dist: WEA

LITTLE CRIMINALS.
Cassette: released on Warner Bros., Nov'77 by Warner Bros Records. Dist: WEA

Album: released on Warner Bros., Nov'77 by Warner Bros Records. Dist: WEA

LONELY AT THE TOP Best of Randy Newman.
Tracks: / Love story / Living without you / I think it's going to rain today / Mama told me not to come / Sail away / Simon Smith and the amazing dancing bear / Political science / Gods' song (That's why I love mankind) / Rednecks / Birmingham / Louisiana 1927 / Marie / Baltimore / Jolly coppers of parade / Rider in the rain / Short people / I love L.A. / Lonely at the top / My life is good / In Germany before the war / Christmas in Capetown / My old Kentucky home.
Album: released on WEA, Jun'87 by WEA Records. Dist: WEA

Cassette: released on WEA, Jun'87 by WEA Records. Dist: WEA

Compact disc: released on WEA, Jun'87 by WEA Records. Dist: WEA

RANDY NEWMAN: LIVE.
Album: released on Reprise, '74 by WEA Records. Dist: WEA

TROUBLE IN PARADISE.
Album: released on Warner Bros., Jan'83 by Warner Bros Records. Dist: WEA

Cassette: released on Warner Bros., Jan'83 by Warner Bros Records. Dist: WEA

Compact disc: released on Warner Bros., Jan'83 by Warner Bros Records. Dist: WEA

TWELVE SONGS.
Album: released on Reprise, '74 by WEA Records. Dist: WEA

Newman, Richard

POETRY.
Album: released on Christabel, Apr'86 by Gerard Management. Dist: Projection

POETRY POLITICS & THE ART OF THE ACOUSTIC GUITAR.
Album: released on Christabel, Nov'85 by Gerard Management. Dist: Projection

Newman, Thunderclap

SOMETHING IN THE AIR.
Single (7"): released on Track, '74 by Polydor Records. Dist: Polygram

Newmantics

TEARS OF CLOWN.
Single (7"): released on Music International, Aug'82 by Music International Records. Dist: Pinnacle

Single (12"): released on Music International, Aug'82 by Music International Records. Dist: Pinnacle

Newman, Tom

ASPECT.
Album: released on Coda Landscape, Feb'86 by Coda Records. Dist: WEA

Cassette: released on Coda Landscape, Feb'86 by Coda Records. Dist: WEA

ASPECTS.
Compact disc: released on Coda, '86 by Coda Records. Dist: Pinnacle, Cartel, WEA, Roots

BAYOU MOON.
Album: released on Coda Landscape, Jan'86 by Coda Records. Dist: WEA

Cassette: released on Coda Landscape, Jan'86 by Coda Records. Dist: WEA

Compact disc: released on Coda Landscape, Feb'86 by Coda Records. Dist: WEA

New Mayfair Dance Orch.

HARMONY HEAVEN.
Album: released on Saville, Dec'83 by Conifer Records. Dist: Conifer

New Mexborough...

NEW MEXBOROUGH ENGLISH CONCERTINA QUARTET (New Mexborough English Concertina Quartet).
Album: released on Plant Life, Jul'85 Dist: Roots

New Model

CHILEAN WARNING.
Single (7"): released on Mr.Clean, Sep'83 Dist: Pinnacle

New Model Army

51ST STATE.
Tracks: / 51st State / Ten commandments / Liberal Education (A) / No rest / No man's land.
Single (7"): released on EMI, Oct'86 by EMI Records. Dist: EMI

Double-pack single: released on EMI, Nov'86 by EMI Records. Dist: EMI

BETTER THAN THEM.
Single (7"): released on EMI, Jul'85 by EMI Records. Dist: EMI

Double-pack single: released on EMI, Jul'85 by EMI Records. Dist: EMI

Single (12"): released on EMI, Jul'85 by EMI Records. Dist: EMI

BITTER SWEET.
Single (7"): released on Quiet, May'83 by Quiet Records. Dist: Nine Mile, Cartel

BITTERSWEET.
Tracks: / Bittersweet / Betcha / Tension.
Single (7"): released on Quiet, Jan'86 by Quiet Records. Dist: Nine Mile, Cartel

BRAVE NEW WORLD.
Single (7"): released on EMI, Nov'85 by EMI Records. Dist: EMI

Single (12"): released on EMI, Nov'85 by EMI Records. Dist: EMI

Double-pack single: released on EMI, Nov'85 by EMI Records. Dist: EMI

GHOST OF CAIN.
Tracks: / Hunt, The / Lights go out / 51st State / All of this / Poison Street / Western dream / Love songs / Heroes / Balled / Master race.
Notes: Composers Sullivan/Heaton except "51st State" (Cartwright/NMA) and "Heroes", "Balled" & "Master Race" (Sullivan).
Album: released on EMI, Sep'86 by EMI Records. Dist: EMI

Cassette: released on EMI, Sep'86 by EMI Records. Dist: EMI

GHOST OF CAIN (THE).
Tracks: / Hunt (The) / Lights go out / 51st state / All of this / Poison Street / Western dream / Love songs / Heroes / Ballad / Master race.
Compact disc: released on EMI, Apr'87 by EMI Records. Dist: EMI

Compact disc: released on EMI, May'87 by EMI Records. Dist: EMI

GREAT EXPECTATIONS.
Single (7"): released on Abstract, Nov'83 by Abstract. Dist: Pinnacle

LIVE 21.04.85.
Video-cassette (VHS): released on PMI, Jun'86 by PMI Records. Dist: EMI

NO REST.
Single (7"): released on EMI, Apr'85 by EMI Records. Dist: EMI

Single (12"): released on EMI, Apr'85 by EMI Records. Dist: EMI

Cassette: released on EMI, May'85 by EMI Records. Dist: EMI

POISON STREET.
Tracks: / Courage / All of this (Live at The Ritz, New York)* / My country (Live at Coventry Poly).
Notes: *=Extra tracks in double pack only
Single (7"): released on EMI, Feb'87 by EMI Records. Dist: EMI

Single (12"): released on EMI, Feb'87 by EMI Records. Dist: EMI

Double-pack single: released on EMI, Feb'87 by EMI Records. Dist: EMI

PRICE, THE.
Single (7"): released on Abstract, Oct'84 by Abstract. Dist: Pinnacle

Single (12"): released on Abstract, Oct'84 by Abstract. Dist: Pinnacle

VENGEANCE.
Cassette: released on Abstract, Nov'85 by Abstract. Dist: Pinnacle

Album: released on Abstract, Nov'85 by Abstract. Dist: Pinnacle

VENGEANCE - THE INDEPENDENT STORY.
Notes: C.D compilation,featuring all the tracks recorded by N.M.A. on independent labels (Abstract & Quiet).18 tracks in total,including the material from the 'Bittersweet','Great Expectations','Price',singles and the 'Vengeance' album.
Compact disc: released on Abstract, Jun'87 by Abstract. Dist: Pinnacle

New Music

NEW MUSIC: SECOND WAVE Various artists (Various Artists).
Album: released on Savoy (USA), Mar'85 by Arista Records. Dist: Polygram, Swift

New Musik

FROM A TO B.

Album: released on GTO, May'80 by GTO Records. Dist: CBS

New Number Two

NEW NUMBER TWO.
Single (12"): released on Lightbeat, Aug'82 by Lightbeat Records. Dist: Pinnacle

New Optimism

NEW OPTIMISM Various artists (Various Artists).
Album: released on Situation 2, Jun'84 Dist: Cartel, Pinnacle

Cassette: released on Situation 2, Jun'84 Dist: Cartel, Pinnacle

New Order

BIZZARE LOVE TRIANGLE.
Tracks: / Bizzare love triangle.
Single (7"): released on Factory, Nov'86 by Factory Records. Dist: Cartel, Pinnacle

Single (12"): released on Factory, Nov'86 by Factory Records. Dist: Cartel, Pinnacle

BLUE MONDAY.
Single (12"): released on Factory, Mar'83 by Factory Records. Dist: Cartel, Pinnacle

BROTHERHOOD.
Album: released on Factory, Sep'86 by Factory Records. Dist: Cartel, Pinnacle

Cassette: released on Factory, Sep'86 by Factory Records. Dist: Cartel, Pinnacle

Compact disc: released on Factory, '86 by Factory Records. Dist: Cartel, Pinnacle

CEREMONY.
Single (7"): released on Factory, Mar'81 by Factory Records. Dist: Cartel, Pinnacle

CONFUSION.
Single (7"): released on Factory, Jul'83 by Factory Records. Dist: Cartel, Pinnacle

Single (12"): released on Factory, Jul'83 by Factory Records. Dist: Cartel, Pinnacle

EVERYTHING GONE GREEN.
Single (7"): released on Factory, Sep'81 by Factory Records. Dist: Cartel, Pinnacle

INTERVIEW PICTURE DISC.
Album: released on Baktabak, May'87 by Baktabak Records. Dist: Arabesque

LOW LIFE.
Compact disc: by Factory Records. Dist: Cartel, Pinnacle

Album: released on Factory, May'85 by Factory Records. Dist: Cartel, Pinnacle

Cassette: released on Factory, May'85 by Factory Records. Dist: Cartel, Pinnacle

MOVEMENT.
Tracks: / Dreams never end / Truth / Senses / Chosen time / Him, The / I.C.B. / Doubts even here / Denial.
Album: released on Factory, Nov'86 by Factory Records. Dist: Cartel, Pinnacle

Cassette: released on Factory, Nov'86 by Factory Records. Dist: Cartel, Pinnacle

Compact disc: released on Factory, '86 by Factory Records. Dist: Cartel, Pinnacle

MURDER.
Single (12"): released on Factory Benelux, Jun'84 by Rough Trade Records. Dist: Cartel

PEEL SESSION 1.6.82.
Tracks: / Session (1st June 1982) turn the heater on / We all stand / Too late / 5.8.6.
Single (12"): released on Strange Fruit, 30 May'87 by Clive Selwood. Dist: Pinnacle

PERFECT KISS.
Single (7"): released on Factory, Nov'85 by Factory Records. Dist: Cartel, Pinnacle

Single (12"): released on Factory, Nov'85 by Factory Records. Dist: Cartel, Pinnacle

POWER, CORRUPTION AND LIES.
Cassette: released on Factory, Dec'86 by Factory Records. Dist: Cartel, Pinnacle

POWER CORRUPTION AND LIES.
Tracks: / Your silent face / Ecstacy / Leave me alone / Age of consent / We all stand / Village, The / 5-8-6.
Compact disc: released on Factory, '86 by Factory Records. Dist: Cartel, Pinnacle

Cassette: released on Factory, May'83 by Factory Records. Dist: Cartel, Pinnacle

Cassette: released on Factory, Nov'84 by Factory Records. Dist: Cartel, Pinnacle

PUMPED FULL OF DRUGS.

Video-cassette (VHS): released on Icon, Oct'86 by Icon Records. Dist: IKF, Cartel

SHELLSHOCK.
Tracks: / Shellshock.
Single (7"): released on Factory, Mar'86 by Factory Records. Dist: Cartel, Pinnacle

Single (12"): released on Factory, Mar'86 by Factory Records. Dist: Cartel, Pinnacle

STATE OF THE NATION.
Tracks: / State of the Nation.
Single (7"): released on Factory, Aug'86 by Factory Records. Dist: Cartel, Pinnacle

SUB-CULTURE.
Single (7"): released on Factory, Nov'85 by Factory Records. Dist: Cartel, Pinnacle

Single (12"): released on Factory, Nov'85 by Factory Records. Dist: Cartel, Pinnacle

SUBSTANCE.
Album: released on Factory, Aug'87 by Factory Records. Dist: Cartel, Pinnacle

Cassette: released on Factory, Aug'87 by Factory Records. Dist: Cartel, Pinnacle

Compact disc: released on Factory, Aug'87 by Factory Records. Dist: Cartel, Pinnacle

TARAS SCHEVENKO.
Video-cassette (VHS): released on Factory, Jan'84 by Factory Records. Dist: Cartel, Pinnacle

TEMPTATION.
Single (7"): released on Factory, May'82 by Factory Records. Dist: Cartel, Pinnacle

Single (12"): released on Factory, May'82 by Factory Records. Dist: Cartel, Pinnacle

THIEVES LIKE US.
Single (12"): released on Factory, May'84 by Factory Records. Dist: Cartel, Pinnacle

TRUE FAITH.
Tracks: / True faith / 1963.
Single (7"): released on Factory, Jul'87 by Factory Records. Dist: Cartel, Pinnacle

Single (12"): released on Factory, Jul'87 by Factory Records. Dist: Cartel, Pinnacle

Single (12"): released on Factory, Aug'87 by Factory Records. Dist: Cartel, Pinnacle

New Orleanians

MIDWAY DANCE ORCHESTRA AND OTHERS, THE.
Album: released on VJM, Apr'79 by VJM (UK) Records. Dist: Swift

New Orleans...

1925/26 (New Orleans Owls).
Album: released on VJM, '74 by Wellard, Chris Distribution. Dist: Wellard, Chris Distribution

ALGIERS STRUT (New Orleans Joymakers).
Album: released on Sonet, '74 by Sonet Records. Dist: PRT

AT PRESERVATION HALL (New Orleans Rascals of Osaka, Japan).
Album: released on Stomp Off, Sep'86 by Stomp Off Records. Dist: Jazz Music Distribution

LOST DREAMS (New Orleans Vocal Groups).
Album: released on Stateside, Apr'87 Dist: EMI

Cassette: released on Stateside, Apr'87 Dist: EMI

MISTER JELLY LORD (New Orleans Rhythm Kings).
Album: released on Rhapsody, Oct'81 by President Records. Dist: Taylors, Swift, Jazz Music, Wellard, Chris

NEAR THE CROSS (New Orleans Gospel).
Album: released on Nola, Apr'79 Dist: JSU, Jazz Music, Cadillac, Chris Wellard

NEW ORLEANS Various artists (Various Artists).
Album: by Sonet Records. Dist: PRT

NEW ORLEANS 1924-1925 Various artists (Various Artists).
Tracks: / Panama / Nobody knows blues / Southern woman blues / Seawall special blues / Swing, The / Frankie & Johnny / Pianoflage / Black but sweet oh God / My heart-breakin' gal / Cross word mama / I never knew what a gal could do / Original Tuxedo rag / Careless love / Black rag.
Album: released on Rhapsody, Apr'87 by President Records. Dist: Taylors, Swift, Jazz Music, Wellard, Chris

NEW ORLEANS BANDS 1924-28 Various artists (Various Artists).

Cassette: released on Neovox, Jan'82 by Neovox Records. Dist: VJM Records, Jazz Music, JSU, Chris Wellard

NEW ORLEANS DIXIELAND EXPRESS Various artists (Various Artists).
Notes: Artists include: Emile Christian/J.Capraro/Almerico
Album: released on GHB, Sep'86 Dist: Jazz Music, Swift

NEW ORLEANS GOSPEL QUARTETS (Various Artists).
Album: released on Heritage, Mar'87 by Heritage Records. Dist: Chart

NEW ORLEANS GOSPEL QUARTETS 1947-1956 Various artists (Various Artists).
Album: released on Heritage, Jul'85 by Heritage Records. Dist: Chart

NEW ORLEANS HORNS (Various Artists).
Double Album: released on Document, Jul'87

NEW ORLEANS IN THE TWENTIES Various artists (Various Artists).
Album: released on VJM, Mar'83 by Wellard, Chris Distribution. Dist: Wellard, Chris Distribution

NEW ORLEANS JAZZ FESTIVAL Various artists (Various Artists).
Album: released on Sonet, Jun'80 by Sonet Records. Dist: PRT

NEW ORLEANS JAZZ PARTY Various artists (Various Artists).
Album: released on Rarities, Apr'81

NEW ORLEANS MASTERS VOL.1 Various artists (Various Artists).
Album: released on Swinghouse, '84 Dist: Jazz Music Distribution, Swift Distribution, Chris Wellard Distribution

Cassette: released on Swinghouse, '84 Dist: Jazz Music Distribution, Swift Distribution, Chris Wellard Distribution

NEW ORLEANS OWLS/HALFWAY HOUSE ORCHESTRA VOL.2 (New Orleans Owls/Halfway House Orchestra).
Album: released on VJM, Apr'79 by Wellard, Chris Distribution. Dist: Wellard, Chris Distribution

NEW ORLEANS RAGTIME ORCHESTRA (New Orleans Ragtime Orchestra).
Album: released on Arhoolie, Jul'87 by Arhoolie Records. Dist: Projection, Topic, Jazz Music, Swift, Roots

Album: released on Arhoolie, May'81 by Arhoolie Records. Dist: Projection, Topic, Jazz Music, Swift, Roots
Cat. no: **ARHOOLIE 1058**
Album: released on Sonet, '74 by Sonet Records. Dist: PRT

NEW ORLEANS RASCALS (New Orleans Rascals).
Album: released on Stomp Off, Jun'86 by Stomp Off Records. Dist: Jazz Music Distribution

NEW ORLEANS RHYTHM & BLUES OFFICIAL ANNIVERSARY LP - VOL.1 Various artists (Various Artists).
Album: released on Sonet, Aug'85 by Sonet Records. Dist: PRT

NEW ORLEANS ROCK'N'ROLL various artists (Various Artists).
Album: released on Rarin', Apr'79 Dist: Swift

NEW ORLEANS RYTHYM KINGS 1934/5 (New Orleans Rythym Kings 1934/5).
Notes: Wingy Manone/G. Brunies/N. Lamare/etc.
Cassette: released on Holmia Cassettes, Jun'86 Dist: Jazz Music, Wellard, Chris

NEW ORLEANS STOMP various artists (Various Artists).
Album: released on VJM, Dec'84 by Wellard, Chris Distribution. Dist: Wellard, Chris Distribution

NEW ORLEANS TEA PARTY various artists (Various Artists).
Album: released on Nola, Apr'79 Dist: JSU, Jazz Music, Cadillac, Chris Wellard

NEW ORLEANS VOL.2 Various artists (Various Artists).
Album: released on Ace, Oct'86 by Ace Records. Dist: Pinnacle, Swift, Hotshot, Cadillac

NEW ORLEANS VOLUME 2 Various artists (Various Artists).
Notes: Artists include: Lil Millet/Art Neville/Big Boy Myles/Robert Parker/Ernie K Doe/Etc.
Album: released on Ace, Oct'86 by Ace Records. Dist: Pinnacle, Swift, Hotshot, Cadillac

NEW ORLEANS VOLUME 1 Various artists (Various Artists).
Tracks: / Eternity / I want you / Bouncing the boogie / Do you really love me baby / I need your love / Say baby / Heavy sugar / I s everything alright / Who's ben fooling you / Hopeless love / Mr Bumps / My dreams are in vain / Got a Gal in Nashville / Long lost stranger / Looked at the moon / Preachin' & teachin'.
Album: released on Ace, May'86 by Ace Records. Dist: Pinnacle, Swift, Hotshot, Cadillac

RECORDED 1923 (New Orleans Rhythm Kings).
Album: released on Joker, Apr'81 Dist: Counterpoint, Mainline, Record Services Distribution (Ireland)

WAY DOWN YONDER (New Orleans All Stars 1966).
Album: released on Nola, Apr'79 Dist: JSU, Jazz Music, Cadillac, Chris Wellard

New Orleans Jazz

AT THE KITTY HALLS.
Album: released on Arhoolie, May'81 by Arhoolie Records. Dist: Projection, Topic, Jazz Music, Swift, Roots

NEW ORLEANS JAZZ (Various Artists).
Notes: with Punch Miller/Kid Thomas/B. & DeDe Pierce etc.
Album: released on Arhoolie, Jan'87 by Arhoolie Records. Dist: Projection, Topic, Jazz Music, Swift, Roots

NEW ORLEANS JAZZ SERENADERS VOL.1 (New Orleans Jazz Serenaders).
Album: released on GHB, Jul'87 Dist: Jazz Music, Swift

NEW ORLEANS JAZZ SERENADERS VOL.2 (New Orleans Jazz Serenaders).
Album: Dist: Jazz Music, Swift

PUD BROWN'S TENOR FOR TWO.
Album: released on Pud Brown, Jul'79

New Ovation

COUNTRY FAVOURITES.
Album: released on Neptune, Jul'80 by Lismor. Dist: Spartan

Cassette: released on Neptune, Jul'80 by Lismor. Dist: Spartan

NEW OVATION.
Cassette: released on Neptune, Jan'79 by Lismor. Dist: Spartan

Album: released on Neptune, Jan'79 by Lismor. Dist: Spartan

New Philharmonic...

BODY TALK (New Philharmonic Orchestra).
Single (7"): released on Red Bus, Jun'84 by Red Bus Records. Dist: PRT

Single (12"): released on Red Bus, Jun'84 by Red Bus Records. Dist: PRT

Newport All Stars

NEWPORT ALL STARS Various Artists (Various Artists).
Album: released on Black Lion, Jan'85 by Black Lion Records. Dist: Jazz Music, Chris Wellard, Taylor, H.R., Counterpoint, Cadillac

Newport Jazz Festival...

NEWPORT JAZZ FESTIVAL ALL STARS.
Double Album: released on Concord Jazz(USA), Feb'85 by Concord Jazz Records (USA). Dist: IMS, Polygram

Newport,Kim

I NEED A LOVER.
Single (7"): released on Sunset, Feb'82 Dist: EMI

Newport Male Voice Choir

LOVE ME TENDER.
Album: released on Polydor, Mar'78 by Polydor Records. Dist: Polygram, Polydor

New Race

FIRST & THE LAST, THE.
Album: released on Statik, Jun'83 Dist: Rough Trade Distribution, Stage One Distribution

New Reflections Orchestra

BEST OF BEAUTIFUL MUSIC.
Tracks: / That old Devil called love / I should have known better / Crying / Chi Mai / Pie Jesu / Flower Duet (From Lakme) / Eastenders, Theme from / Careless Whisper / I just called to say I love you / Hello / Could it be I'm falling in love / Being with you / Thornbirds, Theme from / Move closer / Arthur's theme / Hard to say I'm sorry / Deer Hunter, Theme from / One more night / Hill Street Blues, Theme from / I want to know what love is.
Notes: Licenced from Coombe Music International (P) & (C) Warwick Records. A Warwick Leisure Product. Made and printed in th U.k. Bar code 5 012106 22003.
Album: released on Warwick Reflections,

Page 724

Jun'86 by Warwick Records.

Cassette: released on Warwick Reflections, Jun'86 by Warwick Records.

New Reformation...

BEGINNINGS (New Reformation Dixieland Band).
Album: released on IMF Electronics, Dec'80 by Unicorn Records Ltd. Dist: Unicorn

New Riders Of The...

MARIN COUNTY LINE (New Riders Of The Purple Sage).
Album: released on MCA, Feb'78 by MCA Records. Dist: Polygram, MCA

News

AUDIO VIDEO.
Single (7"): released on KA, Sep'81

HOLE IN MY SHOE.
Single (7"): released on KA, Nov'82

WORLD WITHOUT LOVE.
Single (7"): released on KA, Oct'81

New Sadler's Wells Cast

COUNTESS MARITZA.
Compact disc: Dist: Pinnacle

COUNT OF LUXEMBOURG.
Compact disc: Dist: Pinnacle

New Seekers

15 GREAT HITS.
Album: released on Orbit, Nov'83 by Orbit Records. Dist: PRT Distribution

Cassette: released on Orbit, Nov'83 by Orbit Records. Dist: PRT Distribution

BEST OF..., THE.
Album: released on Contour, May'85 by Pickwick Records. Dist: Pickwick Distribution, PRT

Cassette: released on Contour, May'85 by Pickwick Records. Dist: Pickwick Distribution, PRT

LET THE BELLS RING OUT FOREVER.
Single (7"): released on Tom Cat, Nov'85 Dist: RCA Distribution

MOTIVE SERIES.
Album: released on Polydor (Germany), Dec'81 Dist: IMS-Polygram

Cassette: released on Polydor (Germany), Dec'81 Dist: IMS-Polygram

News From Babel

LETTERS FROM HOME.
Album: released on Recommended, May'86 by Recommended Records. Dist: Recommended, Impetus, Rough Trade

New Sister Theatre, The

NEW SISTER THEATRE, THE Andrews, Lucilla (Jermyn, Jane).
Double cassette: released on Soundings, Mar'85 Dist: Soundings

New Squadronaires

IN THE MOOD.
Tracks: / April in Paris / Body and soul / Kid from red bank / Tangerine / Harlem Nocturne / Fever / Moonlight serenade / One o'clock jump / Doin' basies thing / In the mood / Lil' darlin' / Begin the beguine / You made me love you / American patrol / Woodchoppers ball.
Album: released on CBS, May'86 by CBS Records. Dist: CBS

Cassette: released on CBS, May'86 by CBS Records. Dist: CBS

New Statesman

I WALK IN THE LIGHT / LOW LIFE.
Single (7"): released on Underground Music, Mar'82 Dist: Pinnacle

Newton Family

DON QUIXOTE.
Single (7"): released on White Dove, Nov'81 by White Dove Records. Dist: Pinnacle

Newton,Isaac

HISTORY MAKERS 1642 - 1727.
Cassette: released on History Makers, Apr'82 by Ivan Berg. Dist: Pinnacle

Newton, James

AFRICAN FLOWER, (THE).
Tracks: / Black and Tan fantasy / Virgin jungle / Strange feeling / Fleurette africaine (the African flower) / Cottontail / Sophisticated lady / Passion flower.
Compact disc: released on Blue Note, Oct'86 by EMI Records. Dist: EMI

AXUM.
Album: released on ECM (Germany), Mar'82 by ECM Records. Dist: IMS, Polygram, Virgin through EMI

BINU (Newton,James,Quartet).
Album: released on Circle, May'79 Dist: Jazz Music

ECHO CANYON.
Album: released on Celestial Harmonies, May'87 by TM Records. Dist: PRT

Cassette: released on Celestial Harmonies, May'87 by TM Records. Dist: PRT

Compact disc: released on Celestial Harmonies, May'87 by TM Records. Dist: PRT

Album: released on Celestial Harmonies, Feb'85 by TM Records. Dist: PRT

FLUTES (Newton, James & Sam Rivers).
Album: released on Circle, Jul'78 Dist: Jazz Music

JAMES NEWTON.
Album: released on India Navigation, May'79 by India Navigation Records. Dist: Cadillac, Projection, Swift

Compact disc single: released on Gramavision (USA), Jul'83 by Gramavision Records (USA). Dist: PRT, IMS, Polygram

LUELLA.
Album: released on Gramavision (USA), Jun'84 by Gramavision Records (USA). Dist: PRT, IMS, Polygram

Cassette: released on Gramavision (USA), Jun'84 by Gramavision Records (USA). Dist: PRT, IMS, Polygram

PORTRAITS.
Album: released on India Navigation, Oct'84 by India Navigation Records. Dist: Cadillac, Projection, Swift

ROMANCE AND REVOLUTION.
Tracks: / Forever Charles / Meditations of integration / Peace / Evening leans towards you / Forever Charles / Meditations of integration / Tenderly / Peace / Evening leans toward you, The.
Notes: Flautist James Newton's first Blue Note album 'African Flower' a tribute to Duke Ellington and Billy Strayhorn, was met with universal critical acclaim and voted No.1 Record of the year in 1986 Down Beat International Critics Poll. With his latest release Newton has organised a celebrated octet of some of the most vital and innovative musicians in New York including trombonists Steve Turre and Robin Eubanks, vibist Jay Hoggard and pianist Geri Allen. His intricate and beautiful arrangements are executed with soul and precision. His 'Forever Charles' is a complex but irresistable piece with one of his finest flute solos to date and a tune that should earn him expanded airplay. The album's program ranges from a cool, relaxed groove on Ornette Coleman's 'Peace' to the complicated but organic hirdles of Mingus''Meaditation on integration'.This innovative album is a dazzling triumph that speaks of both romance and revolution. A major step forward for a major new artist.
Album: released on Blue Note, Mar'87 by EMI Records. Dist: EMI

Newton-John, Olivia

COME ON OVER.
Album: released on EMI, May'76 by EMI Records. Dist: EMI

Cassette: released on EMI, May'76 by EMI Records. Dist: EMI

DON'T STOP BELIEVIN'.
Album: released on EMI, Nov'76 by EMI Records. Dist: EMI

FIRST IMPRESSIONS.
Tracks: / If not for you / Banks of the Ohio / Love song / Winterwood / Everything I own / What is life / Take me home country roads / Amoureuse / Let me be there / Changes / Music makes my day / If you love me (let me know).
Notes: Repackaged. Sleeve notes: Roger St. Pierre
Album: released on Music For Pleasure, Feb'86 by EMI Records. Dist: EMI

Cassette: released on Music For Pleasure, Feb'86 by EMI Records. Dist: EMI

GREATEST HITS: OLIVIA NEWTON-JOHN.
Album: released on EMI, Oct'82 by EMI Records. Dist: EMI

Cassette: released on EMI, Oct'82 by EMI Records. Dist: EMI

I HONESTLY LOVE YOU.
Single (7"): released on EMI, Jan'83 by EMI Records. Dist: EMI

Single (12"): released on EMI, Jan'83 by EMI Records. Dist: EMI

LIVE.
Notes: Live recording. Total playing time 90 minutes.
Video-cassette (VHS): released on Channel 5, Jun'86 Dist: W.H. Smiths

OLIVIA NEWTON-JOHN'S GREATEST HITS.
Album: released on EMI, Nov'77 by EMI Records. Dist: EMI

OLIVIA'S GREATEST HITS.
Notes: Digital Audio.
Compact disc: released on EMI, Apr'84 by EMI Records. Dist: EMI

PHYSICAL.
Tracks: / Landslide / Strangers touch / Make a move on me / Falling / Love make me strong / Physical / Silvery rain / Carried away / Recovery / Promise, (The) (The dolphin song).
Video-cassette (VHS): released on PMI, Jun'86 by PMI Records. Dist: EMI

Video-cassette [Betamax]: released on PMI, Jun'86 by PMI Records. Dist: EMI

Album: released on EMI, Oct'81 by EMI Records. Dist: EMI

Cassette: released on EMI, Oct'81 by EMI Records. Dist: EMI

Single (7"): released on EMI, Sep'81 by EMI Records. Dist: EMI

SOUL KISS (ALBUM).
Tracks: / Toughen up / Soul kiss / Queen of the publication / Emotional tangle / Culture shock / Moth to a flame / Overnight observation / You were great, how was I? / Driving music / Right moment, (The) / Electric.
Notes: Track 'Electric' is only on cassette and CD, not on album.
Album: released on Mercury, Feb'86 by Phonogram Records. Dist: Polygram Distribution

Cassette: released on Mercury, Feb'86 by Phonogram Records. Dist: Polygram Distribution

Compact disc: released on Mercury, Feb'86 by Phonogram Records. Dist: Polygram Distribution

SOUL KISS (SINGLE).
Tracks: / Soul kiss / Electric.
Single (7"): released on Mercury, Feb'86 by Phonogram Records. Dist: Polygram Distribution

Single (12"): released on Mercury, Feb'86 by Phonogram Records. Dist: Polygram Distribution

SOUL KISS VIDEO SINGLES.
Notes: Playing time 20 minutes Promo videos for five tracks from 'Soul kiss' plus interview footage - and......it says here 'a very sexy sleeve'!!!
Video-cassette (VHS): released on Polygram, Sep'86 by Polygram Records. Dist: Polygram

TIED UP.
Single (7"): released on EMI, Mar'83 by EMI Records. Dist: EMI

TOTALLY HOT.
Album: released on EMI, Jan'78 by EMI Records. Dist: EMI

Cassette: released on EMI, Jan'78 by EMI Records. Dist: EMI

TWIST OF FATE.
Single (7"): released on EMI, Oct'83 by EMI Records. Dist: EMI

TWIST OF FATE (VIDEO).
Notes: 4 tracks with John Travolta inc. 'Take a chance' & 'Twist of fate'
Video-cassette (VHS): released on Video Collection, May'87 by Video Collection International Ltd.. Dist: Counterpoint

VIDEO EP.
Tracks: / Desparate times (Livin' in-) / Shakin' you / Take a chance / Twist of fate.
Notes: Duration: 15 minutes
Video-cassette (VHS): released on PMI, Jan'84 by PMI Records. Dist: EMI

Video-cassette [Betamax]: released on PMI, Jan'84 by PMI Records. Dist: EMI

Newton, Juice

CAN'T WAIT ALL NIGHT.
Album: released on RCA, Oct'84 by RCA Records. Dist: RCA, Roots, Swift, Wellard, Chris, I & B, Solomon & Peres Distribution

Cassette: released on RCA, Oct'84 by RCA Records. Dist: RCA, Roots, Swift, Wellard, Chris, I & B, Solomon & Peres Distribution

Compact disc: released on RCA, Oct'84 by RCA Records. Dist: RCA, Roots, Swift, Wellard, Chris, I & B, Solomon & Peres Distribution

Single (7"): released on RCA, Sep'84 by RCA Records. Dist: RCA, Roots, Swift, Wellard, Chris, I & B, Solomon & Peres Distribution

COLLECTION: JUICE NEWTON.
Album: released on EMI (Germany), Jan'83 by EMI Records. Dist: Conifer

COME TO ME (Newton, Juice & Silver Spur).
Album: released on Fame (Capitol), May'82 by Music For Pleasure Records. Dist: EMI

Cassette: released on Fame (Capitol), May'82 by Music For Pleasure Records. Dist: EMI

DIRTY LOOKS.
Single (7"): released on Capitol, Nov'83 by Capitol Records. Dist: EMI

HEART OF THE NIGHT.
Single (7"): released on Capitol, Feb'83 by Capitol Records. Dist: EMI

JUICE.
Cassette: released on Capitol, Jun'81 by Capitol Records. Dist: EMI

LOVE'S BEEN A LITTLE BIT HARD ON ME.
Single (7"): released on Capitol, May'82 by Capitol Records. Dist: EMI

WELL KEPT SECRET.
Album: released on Capitol, Jan'78 by Capitol Records. Dist: EMI

Newton,William

SET UP,THE.
Cassette: released on Soundings, May'85 Dist: Soundings

Newtown Neurotics

BEGGARS CAN BE CHOOSERS.
Album: released on Razor, Sep'83 by Razor. Dist: Pinnacle

BLITZKRIEG BOP.
Single (7"): released on Razor, Aug'83 by Razor. Dist: Pinnacle

KICK OUT THE TORIES.
Single (7"): released on CNT, May'82 Dist: Rough Trade, Cartel

LICENCING HOURS.
Single (7"): released on CNT, Dec'82 Dist: Rough Trade, Cartel

SUZI.
Single (7"): released on No Wonder, Nov'84 Dist: Pinnacle

Single (12"): released on No Wonder, Nov'84 Dist: Pinnacle

WHEN THE OIL RUNS OUT.
Single (7"): released on No Wonder, Oct'84 Dist: Pinnacle

Newtrament

LONDON BRIDGE IS FALLING DOWN.
Single (7"): released on Jive, Jul'83 by Zomba Records. Dist: RCA, PRT, CBS

Single (12"): released on Jive, Jul'83 by Zomba Records. Dist: RCA, PRT, CBS

New Vaudeville Band

6 TRACK HITS.
Single (7"): released on Scoop 33, Aug'84 by Pickwick Records. Dist: H.R. Taylor

Cassette: released on Scoop 33, Aug'84 by Pickwick Records. Dist: H.R. Taylor

LIVE VAUDEVILLE.
Album: released on SRT, Oct'77 by SRT Records. Dist: Pinnacle, Solomon & Peres Distribution, SRT Distribution, H.R. Taylor Distribution, PRT Distribution

TAP YOUR FEET.
Album: released on Cambra, Apr'85 by Cambra Records. Dist: IDS, Conifer

Cassette: released on Cambra, Apr'85 by Cambra Records. Dist: IDS, Conifer

New Victory Band

ONE MORE DANCE & THEN.
Album: released on Topic, '81 by Topic Records. Dist: JSU Distribution, Projection Distribution, Jazz Music Distribution

New Voices from Scotland

NEW VOICES FROM SCOTLAND Various artists (Various Artists).
Album: released on Topic, '74 by Topic Records. Dist: JSU Distribution, Projection Distribution, Jazz Music Distribution

New Walk

PRESSURE POINT.
Single (7"): released on Web, Nov'83 by Web Records. Dist: ILA, PRT, Web

JSU Distribution, Zodiac Distribution

Records. Dist: Pinnacle

New Wave

NEW WAVE Various artists (Various Artists).
Album: released on Vertigo, Jul'77 by Phonogram Records. Dist: Polygram

New World

I TALK TO MY CAR.
Single (7"): released on Slipped Discs, Oct'83 by Slipped Discs Records. Dist: PRT, Self Distribution

New World Philharmonic

ACE OF THEMES, VOLUME TWO.
Album: released on Red Bus, Jun'84 by Red Bus Records. Dist: PRT

Cassette: released on Red Bus, Jun'84 by Red Bus Records. Dist: PRT

FAMOUS THEMES.
Tracks: / Reilly, Ace of spies / Terms of endearment / Thorn Birds (The) / No matter what happens / Hill Street Blues / Up where we belong / Bolero / Body talk / Only he has the power to move me / Dynasty / Almost paradise / Memory / Seduction(The) / Sometimes.
Notes: Conducted by Iain Sutherland and Alyn Ainsworth.
Compact disc: released on Red Bus, '86 by Red Bus Records. Dist: PRT

THEME FROM DYNASTY.
Single (7"): released on Red Bus, Sep'84 by Red Bus Records. Dist: PRT

New York...

ABOUT TIME (New York Gong).
Album: released on Charly, Apr'80 by Charly Records. Dist: Charly, Cadillac

GATHERING, THE (New York Community Choir).
Album: released on Myrrh, May'82 by Word Records. Dist: Word Distribution

Cassette: released on Myrrh, May'82 by Word Records. Dist: Word Distribution

HOOKED ON YOU (New York Sensation).
Tracks: / Hooked on you / Hooked on you (Dub).
Single (7"): released on 10, Aug'86 by 10 Records. Dist: Virgin, EMI

Single (12"): released on 10, Aug'86 by 10 Records. Dist: Virgin, EMI

HOTHOUSE ORGAN (New York Pig Funkers).
Tracks: / Hothouse organ / Tomato grosso.
Single (12"): released on Pasta Spectacular, Jan'87 Dist: Fast Forward, Cartel

HOT ON THE CLUE (New York Express).
Album: released on WEA, Nov'82 by WEA Records. Dist: WEA

NEW YORK CITY LA BEAT (New York City La Beat).
Album: released on Streetsounds, Aug'85

NEW YORK CITY SOUL Various artists (Various Artists).
Album: released on Kent, Aug'85 by Ace Records. Dist: Pinnacle

NEW YORK NOTABLES Various artists (Various Artists).
Album: released on Moonshine (Holland), May'85 Dist: Projection Distribution

NEW YORK QUARTET & IMAMU AMIRI BARAKA (New York Quartet/Imamu Amiri Baraka).
Album: released on ESP, '73 by ESP Records. Dist: Jazz Horizons, Jazz Music

NEW YORK R 'N' B Various artists (Various Artists).
Album: released on Magpie, Jul'79 Dist: Projection

NEW YORK SAXOPHONE QUARTET (New York Saxophone Quartet).
Album: released on Stash (Import), '81 Dist: Swift Distribution, Jazz Music Distribution, Jazz Horizons Distribution, Celtic Music Distribution, Cadillac, JSU Distribution, Zodiac Distribution

NEW YORK THRASH Various Artists (Various Artists).
Cassette: released on Reach Out International, '83 Dist: Red Rhino, Cartel

SET IT OFF (New York Spice).
Single (12"): released on Champion, Oct'85 by Champion Records. Dist: RCA

THREE THOUSAND MILES FROM HOME (New York Port Authority).
Album: released on Invictus, Sep'77 by CBS Records. Dist: CBS

New York Dolls

LIPSTICK KILLERS.
Cassette: released on Reach Out Int, '83

NEW YORK DOLLS, (THE).
Tracks: / Babylon / Bad detective / Bad girl / Chatterbox / Don't start me talkin' / Frankenstein / Human being / It's too late / Jet boy / Lonely planet boy / Looking for a kiss / Personality crisis / Pills / Private world / Puss 'n' boots / Showdown / Stranded in the jungle / Subway train / Trash / Vietnamese baby / Who are the mystery girls?.
Album: released on Mercury, Apr'86 by Phonogram Records. Dist: Polygram Distribution

Cassette: released on Mercury, Apr'86 by Phonogram Records. Dist: Polygram Distribution

PERSONALITY CRISIS.
Single (12"): released on Kamera, Sep'82

PERSONALITY CRISIS EP LOOKING FOR A KISS.
Tracks: / Personality crisis EP looking for a kiss / Subway train / Bad girl.
Single (12"): released on Kamera, Feb'86

PILLS.
Single (7"): released on Fan Club, Oct'84 by New Rose. Dist: Rough Trade, Cartel, Pinnacle

RED PATENT LEATHER.
Album: released on Fan Club, Sep'84 by New Rose. Dist: Rough Trade, Cartel, Pinnacle

Single (7"): released on Fan Club, Sep'84 by New Rose. Dist: Rough Trade, Cartel, Pinnacle

TOO MUCH TOO SOON.
Album: released on Mercury, May'81 by Import Records. Dist: IMS-Polygram Distribution

New York Jazz Quartet

BLUES FOR SARKA.
Album: released on Enja (Germany), Jan'82 by Enja Records (W.Germany). Dist: Cadillac Music

OASIS.
Album: released on Enja (Germany), Jan'82 by Enja Records (W.Germany). Dist: Cadillac Music

SONG OF BLACK NIGHT.
Album: released on Sonet, Aug'78 by Sonet Records. Dist: PRT

SURGE.
Album: released on Enja (Germany), Jan'82 by Enja Records (W.Germany). Dist: Cadillac Music

New York New Wave

MAX'S KANSAS CITY.
Album: by CBS Records. Dist: CBS

MAX'S KANSAS CITY: VOL 2.
Album: by CBS Records. Dist: CBS

New York New York

NEW YORK EXPERIENCE, (THE).
Single (12"): released on Beat Culture, Sep'85

NEW YORK NEW YORK Original motion picture score (Volume 1) (Various Artists).
Tracks: / Main title / You brought a new kind of love to me / Flip the dip / V.J.Stomp / Opus number one / Once in a while / You are my lucky star / Game over / It's a wonderful world / Man I love, (The) / Hazoy / Just you, just me.
Notes: Burns, Ralph: Arranger, conductor & album producer.
Cassette: released on Liberty - EMI, Sep'86

NEW YORK NEW YORK Original film soundtrack.
Double Album: released on EMI (Holland), Jun'84 by EMI Records. Dist: Conifer

Compact disc: released on EMI America, Aug'87 by EMI Records. Dist: EMI. Estim retail price in Sep'87 was £11.99.

NEW YORK NEW YORK Original Motion Picture Score (Volume 2) (Various Artists).
Tracks: / There goes the ball game / Blue Moon / Don't be that way / Happy endings / But the world goes round / New York New York (Theme from) / New York New York (Theme from) / New York New York (Theme from) (Orchestral reprise) / Honeysuckle Rose / Once again right away.
Notes: Burns, Ralph: Arranger, conductor, album producer. Track 4(Happy Endings) was originally recorded for the film but deleted during final editing.
Cassette: released on Liberty - EMI, Sep'86

ROGER WILSON SAID.
Single (7"): released on Urchin, Nov'83

SOUNDS OF THE BIG APPLE.
Album: released on Stash, '79 Dist: Swift Distribution, Jazz Music Distribution, Jazz Horizons Distribution, Celtic Music Distribution, Cadillac,

TBA.
Album: released on Izuma, Jan'85 Dist: Backs, Cartel

New York Philharmonic

WORLD'S 25 GREATEST MARCHES, (THE).
Album: released on CBS, Jul'82 by CBS Records. Dist: CBS

New York Skyy

FROM THE LEFT SIDE.
Tracks: / Givin' it (to you) / Love attack / Non-stop / Song song / Big fun / Love illogical / Tell her you care / Jelousitis / Rock it.
Notes: Producer/Arranger: Randy Muller & Solomon Roberts for Alligator Bit Him Product-ion.
Album: released on Capitol, May'86 by Capitol Records. Dist: EMI

Cassette: released on Capitol, May'86 by Capitol Records. Dist: EMI

GIVIN' IT To you.
Tracks: / Givin' it (to you) / Givin' it (to you) (Dub remix).
Single (12"): released on Capitol, May'86 by Capitol Records. Dist: EMI

GREATEST HITS:NEW YORK SKYY.
Album: released on Streetsounds, Jan'87

Cassette: released on Streetsounds, Jan'87

Compact disc: released on Streetsounds, Jan'87

NON-STOP.
Tracks: / Non-stop / Tell her you care.
Single (7"): released on Capitol, Sep'86 by Capitol Records. Dist: EMI

Single (12"): released on Capitol, Sep'86 by Capitol Records. Dist: EMI

SKYYLIGHT.
Album: released on Epic, Aug'83 by CBS Records. Dist: CBS

Cassette: released on Epic, Aug'83 by CBS Records. Dist: CBS

SKYYPORT.
Album: released on Excaliber, Feb'81 by Red Bus Records. Dist: PRT

New Zealand

AUSTRALIAN TOUR (New Zealand National Youth Jazz Band).
Album: released on Viking, Nov'79 Dist: Harmonia Mundi Distributors

BRASS TO GO (New Zealand Army Band).
Album: released on One Up, Mar'78 by EMI Records.

CONDUCTED BY PETER GODFREY (New Zealand, National Youth Choir of).
Album: released on Tartar (New Zealand), '84

Cassette: released on Tartar (New Zealand), '84

NEW ZEALAND SINGS (New Zealand Maori Chorale).
Album: released on Viking, Jan'80 Dist: Harmonia Mundi Distributors

ORIGINAL JAZZ COMPOSERS BY N.Z.S (New Zealand Jazz Orchestra).
Album: released on Kiwi-Pacific (New Zealand), '84 Dist: Flexitron Distributors Ltd

Cassette: released on Kiwi-Pacific (New Zealand), '84 Dist: Flexitron Distributors Ltd

SONGS OF NEW ZEALAND (New Zealand Maori Chorale).
Album: released on Viking, Jul'79 Dist: Harmonia Mundi Distributors

Cassette: released on Viking, Jul'79 Dist: Harmonia Mundi Distributors

TRIUMPH BRASS (New Zealand, National Band of).
Album: released on Viking, Feb'79 Dist: Harmonia Mundi Distributors

TWENTY GOLDEN MAORI SONGS.
Album: released on Viking, Nov'77 Dist: Harmonia Mundi Distributors

Next

NEXT.
Album: released on Epic, Jun'78 by CBS Records. Dist: CBS

Next Step

CRUSHED BY THE CRISIS.
Single (7"): released on Trial, Oct'84 by Trial

Next Up

NEXT UP Various Artist (Various Artists).
Cassette: released on Bomb Alley, Oct'85 Dist: Red Rhino, Cartel

Nexus

NIGHTRIDING.
Notes: with Daniele Cavallanti/Tiziano Tononi/Glen Ferris
Album: released on Red, Jan'87 Dist: Projection, Jazz Horizons

Niagara, Joe

CRUISIN' 1957 WIBG Philadelphia.
Cassette: released on Increase(USA), Jun'87 by Quicksilver Records (USA).

Niah,George

SWEETA JAMAICA.
Single (12"): released on Freedom Sounds, Nov'81 by Freedom Sounds Records. Dist: Jetstar

WALKING IN THE RAIN.
Single (12"): released on Future Times, Jul'82 Dist: Jetstar

Nica's dream

NICA'S DREAM Various Artists (small jazz groups of the 50s and early 60s (Various Artists).
Tracks: / Woody'n you / Donna Lee / Nica's dream / Blues march / Now's the time / War gewessen / Original Faubus fables.
Album: released on New World (USA), Aug'86 by New World Records (USA). Dist: Conifer

Nicci

CAN'T GET CLOSE TO YOU.
Tracks: / Can't get close to you / Close to who?.
Single (7"): released on Debut, Feb'86 by Skratch Music. Dist: PRT

RESPECT.
Single (7"): released on Sedition, May'87 Dist: PRT

Single (12"): released on Sedition, May'87 Dist: PRT

SO IN LOVE.
Single (7"): released on Debut, Aug'85 by Skratch Music. Dist: PRT

Single (12"): released on Debut, Aug'85 by Skratch Music. Dist: PRT

Single (7"): released on Boiling Point, Oct'85 by Polydor Records. Dist: Polygram

Single (12"): released on Boiling Point, Oct'85 by Polydor Records. Dist: Polygram

Nice

20TH ANNIVERSARY, THE.
Album: released on Seal, Aug'87 by In-Market Ltd.. Dist: Revolver, Cartel. Estim retail price in Sep'87 was £4.99.

Cassette: released on Seal, Aug'87 by In-Market Ltd.. Dist: Revolver, Cartel. Estim retail price in Sep'87 was £4.99.

AMERICA.
Single (7"): released on Immediate, Dec'82 by Castle Communications. Dist: Cartel

AMOENI REDIVIVI.
Album: released on Immediate, Mar'76 by Castle Communications. Dist: Cartel

ARS LONGA VITA BREVIS.
Compact disc: released on Castle Classics, '86 by Castle Communications. Dist: BMG

COLLECTION: NICE.
Tracks: / America / Happy Freuds / Cry of Eugene, (The) / Thoughts of Emerlist Darjack, (The) / ondo / Daddy, where did I come from? / Little Arabella / Intermezzo from Ravelia / Hang on to a dream / Diamond hard apples of the moon, (The) / Angel of Death / Ars longa vita brevis suite.
Album: released on Castle Communications, Nov'85 by Castle Communications. Dist: Cartel, Pinnacle, Counterpoint

Cassette: released on Castle Communications, Nov'85 by Castle Communications. Dist: Cartel, Pinnacle, Counterpoint

COLLECTION: NICE (CD).

Compact disc: released on Castle Collectors, Oct'86 by Castle Communications Records. Dist: Pinnacle

ELEGY.
Album: released on Charisma, Sep'83 by Virgin Records. Dist: EMI

Cassette: released on Charisma, Sep'83 by Virgin Records. Dist: EMI

FIVE BRIDGES SUITE.
Cassette: released on Charisma, Mar'83 by Virgin Records. Dist: EMI

Nice and Wild

DIAMOND GIRL.
Tracks: / EMU 2.
Single (7"): released on Atlantic, May'87 by WEA Records. Dist: WEA

Single (7"): released on Atlantic, May'87 by WEA Records. Dist: WEA

ENERGY LOVE AND UNITY.
Tracks: / Obsession/Money can't buy you love. / Dangerous in the dark / Oh baby / Diamond girl / Energy, love and unity / Hazel eyes / If you can feel it / Hey y'all we're nice and wild.
Album: released on Atlantic, Jun'87 by WEA Records. Dist: WEA

Cassette: released on Atlantic, Jun'87 by WEA Records. Dist: WEA

Nice Men

SENILE YOUTH.
Single (7"): released on Demon, Apr'82 by Demon Records. Dist: Pinnacle

Nice 'n' easy

NICE 'N' EASY Various Artists (Various Artists).
Album: released on Philips, Nov'85 Dist: IMS-Polygram

Cassette: released on Philips, Nov'85 Dist: IMS-Polygram

Nicholas, Albert

ALBERT NICHOLAS QUARTET.
Album: released on Delmark, '74 Dist: Projection, Swift, Cadillac

NICHOLAS, ALBERT/JOHN DEFFERARY JAZZTET (Nicholas, Albert/John Defferary Jazztet).
Notes: Monophonic recording.
Album: released on GHB, Jun'86 Dist: Jazz Music, Swift

THIS IS JAZZ VOL.2.
Album: released on Storyville, May'86 by Storyville Records. Dist: Jazz Music Distribution, Swift Distribution, Chris Wellard Distribution, Counterpoint Distribution

TRADITIONAL JAZZ 2.
Album: released on Import Music Service (IMS), Dec'83 Dist: Concord Jazz Distributions, Pablo, Polygram

Nicholas, Nick

50 SWINGING HONKY TONK FAVOURITES.
Double Album: released on Pickwick-Five-O, May'77

HONKY TONK FAVOURITES.
Cassette: released on Ditto, Mar'86 by Pickwick Records. Dist: H.R. Taylor

Nicholas Nickleby

NICHOLAS NICKLEBY Dickens, Charles (Rees, Roger).
Cassette: released on Caedmon(USA), Sep'82 by Caedmon (USA) Records. Dist: Gower, Taylors, Discovery

Double cassette: released on Argo (Spokenword), Nov'82 by Decca Records. Dist: Polygram

NICHOLAS NICKLEBY Original cast soundtrack.
Album: released on That's Entertainment, Apr'83 by That's Entertainment Records. Dist: Pinnacle, PRT

Nicholas, Paul

HOUSE OF ROCK.
Single (7"): released on Flying, Oct'83 by Flying Records. Dist: DMS

Single (12"): released on Flying, Oct'83 by Flying Records. Dist: DMS

JUST GOOD FRIENDS.
Tracks: / Just good friends / You don't bring me flowers / I'm not in love / Air that I breathe / Boy's in love, (The) / Made it through the rain / You light up my life / Sometimes when we touch / If you leave now / Always a woman to me / Lady in red / All because of love / Fool (if you think it's over) / Don't wanna go home alone.
Compact disc: released on K-Tel, Nov'86 by K-Tel Records. Dist: Record Merchandisers Distribution, Taylors, Terry Blood Distribution, Wynd-Up Distribution, Relay Distribution, Pickwick Distribution, Solomon & Peres Distribution, Polygram

Album: released on K-Tel, Oct'86 by K-Tel Records. Dist: Record Merchandisers Distribution, Taylors, Terry Blood Distribution, Wynd-Up Distribution, Relay Distribution, Pickwick Distribution, Solomon & Peres Distribution, Polygram

Cassette: released on K-Tel, Oct'86 by K-Tel Records. Dist: Record Merchandisers Distribution, Taylors, Terry Blood Distribution, Wynd-Up Distribution, Relay Distribution, Pickwick Distribution, Solomon & Peres Distribution, Polygram

Single (7"): released on Flying, Dec'84 by Flying Records. Dist: DMS

LEAST OF MY TROUBLES.
Single (7"): released on MCA, Jan'84 by MCA Records. Dist: CBS

PAUL NICHOLAS.
Album: released on RSO, Apr'77

Nicholl, Derek

PATRON.
Single (7"): released on Clubland, Oct'82 by Clubland Records. Dist: EMI, Pinnacle

Nicholl, Phil

ONE WAY.
Single (7"): released on Mont Music, Dec'82

Nichols, Herbie

HERBIE NICHOLS TRIO.
Album: released on Blue Note (USA Import), Sep'84

OUT OF THE SHADOW.
Album: released on Affinity, May'82 by Charly Records. Dist: Charly, Cadillac

Nichols, Loring "Red"

SYNCOPATED CHAMBER MUSIC.
Album: released on Audiophile, Jan'87 by Jazzology Records (USA). Dist: Jazz Music, Swift

Nicholson, Eann

OVER THE ORD (Nicholson,Eann & Wick dance band).
Notes: Mail order address: Accordion Record Club, 146 Birmingham Road, Kidderminster, Worcs. DY10 2SI. Tel. 0562 - 746105.

Nicholson, Hugh

LOVE, YOU MADE A FOOL OF ME.
Single (7"): released on Zuma, Jan'85 by Zuma Records. Dist: CBS, PRT

Nicholson, Lea

CONCERTINA RECORD,(THE).
Album: released on Kicking Mule, Aug'80 by Sonet. Dist: Roots, PRT-Pye Distribution

HORSEMUSIC.
Album: released on Leader, '81 Dist: Jazz Music, Projection

Nicholson, Roger

DULCIMER PLAYERS, (THE).
Album: released on Trailer, '81 Dist: Jazz Music, Celtic Music, JSU

NONESUCH FOR DULCIMER.
Album: released on Leader, '81 Dist: Jazz Music, Projection

TIMES AND TRADITION FOR DULCIMER.
Album: Dist: Jazz Music, Projection

Nichols, Red

1925 - 1928 (Nichols, Red & Sam Lanin's Orchestra).
Album: released on Broadway, Apr'79 Dist: Jetstar

CLASS OF 39 Radio transcriptions (Nichols, Red & His Five Pennies).
Album: released on Blue Lantern, Apr'79 Dist: Swift

FEELIN' NO PAIN.
Tracks: / Japanese Sandman / China boy / After you've gone / Sally, won't you come back? / Feelin' no pain / Wash board blues / Bugle call rag / Eccentric / Ida, sweet as apple cider / Smiles / Buddy's habits / Indiana / That's no bargain / Avalon / Boneyard shuffle / Riverboat shuffle / Sheik of Araby.
Album: released on Affinity, Mar'87 by Charly Records. Dist: Charly, Cadillac

RED & BEN (Nichols, Red & Ben Pollack).
Album: released on Broadway, Apr'79 Dist: Jetstar

RED & MIFF, 1926-31 (Nichols, Red & Miff Mole).
Album: released on Saville, Jun'82 Dist: Swift, Chris Wellard, Jazz Music, H.R. Taylor

RED NICHOLS: VOL 2.
Album: released on Classic Jazz Masters, Aug'79 by Mainline Record Company. Dist: Mainline, Swift, Jazz Music

RHYTHM OF THE DAY (Nichols, Red & His Five Pennies).
Compact disc: released on ASV, Feb'87 by Academy Sound & Vision Records. Dist: Pinnacle

Album: released on ASV, Nov'83 by Academy Sound & Vision Records. Dist: Pinnacle

Cassette: released on ASV, Nov'83 by Academy Sound & Vision Records. Dist: Pinnacle

SONGWRITERS FOR THE STARS 3 (Nichols, Roger & Bruce Roberts).
Album: released on Polydor (Norway), Oct'83

VOL' 4.
Album: released on Classic Jazz Masters, Oct'86 by Mainline Record Company. Dist: Mainline, Swift, Jazz Music

VOLUME 1.
Album: released on Swaggie, Sep'86 Dist: Jazz Music Distribution

VOLUME 2.
Album: released on Swaggie, Sep'86 Dist: Jazz Music Distribution

Nicht at...

NICHT AT THE BOTHY (Various Artists).
Notes: With Bobby Colgan, Jim Johnstone and His Band, The McCalmans, Jimmy Fletcher andPibroch MacKenzie.
Cassette: released on Ross, '86 by Ross Records. Dist: Ross Distribution, Roots Distribution

Nick & Elaine

LOOK AND LIVE.
Album: released on Key, May'79 by Key Records. Dist: Spartan

Nick & Nock

HELPERS OF SANTA CLAUS.
Single (7"): released on Custard Pie, Nov'86 Dist: DMS, RCA

Nick O Teen

SMOKE THAT CIGARETTE.
Single (7"): released on White Rose, '79 by White Rose Records. Dist: Lightning

Nicks & Buckingham

BUCKINGHAM NICKS.
Album: released on Polydor, Jun'81 by Polydor Records. Dist: Polygram, Polydor

Nicks, Stevie

BELLA DONNA.
Tracks: / Bella Donna / Kind of woman / Stop draggin' my heart around / Think about it / After the glitter fades / Edge of seventeen / How still my love / Leather and lace / Highway man (The).
Compact disc: released on WEA, '84 by WEA Records. Dist: WEA

Album: released on WEA, Jul'81 by WEA Records. Dist: WEA

Compact disc: released on WEA, Jan'84 by WEA Records. Dist: WEA

HAS ANYONE EVER WRITTEN ANYTHING FOR YOU.
Tracks: / Has anyone ever written anything for you / I can't wait / No spoken word.
Single (7"): released on EMI, Aug'86 by EMI Records. Dist: EMI

Single (12"): released on EMI, Aug'86 by EMI Records. Dist: EMI

I CAN'T WAIT.
Tracks: / I can't wait / Rock a little.
Notes: Video: A survey of the solo work of Fleetwood Mac's lead singer, with promos for six US hit single tracks like 'If Anyone Falls' and the recent 'I Can't Wait'. 1986 compilation. Number of tracks: 6. Type of recording: EP. Total playing time: 26 minutes.
Single (7"): released on Parlophone, Jan'86 by EMI Records. Dist: EMI

Single (12"): released on Parlophone, Jan'86 by EMI Records. Dist: EMI

Video-cassette (VHS): released on RCA, Jun'86 by RCA Records. Dist: RCA, Roots, Swift, Wellard, Chris, I & B, Solomon & Peres Distribution

NIGHT BIRD.
Single (7"): released on WEA International, Jan'84 by WEA Records. Dist: WEA

ROCK A LITTLE.
Tracks: / I can't wait / Rock a little / Sister honey / I sing for the things / Imperial hotel / Some become strangers / Talk to me / Nightmare (The) / If I were you / No spoken word / Has anyone ever written anything for you.
Notes: One of the world's finest singer/songwriters with her first album for Parlophone. 'Rock A Little' is Stevie Nicks third solo album following 'Belladonna' and "Wild Heart'.
Album: released on Parlophone, Jan'86 by EMI Records. Dist: EMI

Cassette: released on Parlophone, Jan'86 by EMI Records. Dist: EMI

Compact disc: released on Parlophone, Mar'86 by EMI Records. Dist: EMI

TALK TO ME.
Tracks: / Talk to me / One more big time rock 'n' roll star / Imperial hotel.
Single (7"): released on Parlophone, Mar'86 by EMI Records. Dist: EMI

Single (12"): released on Parlophone, Mar'86 by EMI Records. Dist: EMI

WILD HEART.
Tracks: / Stand back / I will run to you / Nothing ever changes / Sable on blond / Beauty and the beast / Wild heart / If anyone talks / Gate and garden / Night bird / Enchanted.
Compact disc: released on WEA, '84 by WEA Records. Dist: WEA

Album: released on WEA International, Jul'83 by WEA Records. Dist: WEA

Cassette: released on WEA International, Jul'83 by WEA Records. Dist: WEA

Nico

BEHIND THE IRON CURTAIN.
Tracks: / All Saints Night from a Polish motorway / One more chance / Frozen warnings / Song of the lonely girl (The) / Win a few / Konig / Purple lips / All tomorrow's parties / Fearfully in danger / End (The) / My funny valentine / 60-40 / Tananoori / Janitor of lunacy / My heart is empty / Femme fatale / All saints night from a polish motorway / One more chance / Frozen warnings / Song of the lonely girl (Tha) / Win a few / Konig / Purple lips / All tomorrow's parties / Fearfully in danger / End (The) / My funny valentine / 60/40 / Tananoori / Janitor of lunacy / My heart is empty / Femme fatale.
Compact disc: released on PRT, '86 by PRT Records. Dist: PRT

Album: released on Dojo, Apr'86 by Castle Communications Records. Dist: Cartel

Cassette: released on Dojo, Apr'86 by Castle Communications Records. Dist: Cartel

BLUE ANGEL, THE.
Tracks: / Femme fatale / All tomorrows parties / I'll keep it with mine / Chelsea girls / Janitor of lunacy / Heroes / One more chance / Sixty forty / Waiting for the man / End, The.
Album: released on Aura, Jan'86 by Hollywood Nites Distribution. Dist: Pinnacle

Cassette: released on Aura, Jan'86 by Hollywood Nites Distribution. Dist: Pinnacle

Compact disc: released on Aura, Jan'86 by Hollywood Nites Distribution. Dist: Pinnacle

CAMERA OBSCURA.
Album: released on Beggars Banquet, Aug'85 by Beggars Banquet Records. Dist: WEA

Cassette: released on Beggars Banquet, Aug'85 by Beggars Banquet Records. Dist: WEA

CHELSEA GIRL.
Album: released on Polydor, '74 by Polydor Records. Dist: Polygram, Polydor

DESERT SHORE.
Album: released on Reprise, '74 by WEA Records. Dist: WEA

DO OR DIE.
Cassette: released on Reach Out International, '83 Dist: Red Rhino, Cartel

DRAMA OF EXILE.
Album: released on Aura, Jul'81 by Hollywood Nites Distribution. Dist: Pinnacle

HEROES.
Single (7"): released on Aura, Jun'83 by Hollywood Nites Distribution. Dist: Pinnacle

I'M NOT SAYING.
Single (7"): released on Immediate, May'82 by Castle Communications. Dist: Cartel

LIVE.
Single (12"): released on Archive 4, Feb'87 by Castle Communications Records. Dist: Nine Mile, Cartel

MY FUNNY VALENTINE.
Single (7"): released on Beggars Banquet, Jun'85 by Beggars Banquet Records. Dist: WEA Deleted '86.

Single (12"): released on Beggars Banquet, Jun'85 by Beggars Banquet Records. Dist: WEA

SAETA.
Single (7"): released on Flicknife, Sep'81 by Flicknife Records. Dist: Spartan

WAITING FOR THE MAN.
Single (7"): released on Aura, Oct'85 by Hollywood Nites Distribution. Dist: Pinnacle

Nicodemus
BONE CONNECTION.
Single (7"): released on Greensleeves, Feb'82 by Greensleeves Records. Dist: BMG, Jetstar, Spartan

DJ CLASH - NICODEMUS V TOYAN (Nicodemus/Toyan).
Album: released on Greensleeves, Feb'82 by Greensleeves Records. Dist: BMG, Jetstar, Spartan

GUN MAN CONNECTION.
Single (12"): released on Cha-Cha, Dec'81 by Cha Cha. Dist: Jetstar

Nicole
DON'T YOU WANT MY LOVE.
Tracks: / Don't you want my love / Shy boy.
Single (7"): released on Portrait, Feb'86 by CBS Records. Dist: CBS

Single (12"): released on Portrait, Feb'86 by CBS Records. Dist: CBS

HORSE CALLS.
Tracks: / Horse calls / It happens every night.
Single (7"): released on Portrait, Oct'86 by CBS Records. Dist: CBS

NEW YORK EYES (Nicole/Timmy Thomas).
Notes: New York Eyes remix on 12" version only, also sticker with 12".
Single (7"): released on Portrait, Dec'85 by CBS Records. Dist: CBS

Single (12"): released on Portrait, Dec'85 by CBS Records. Dist: CBS

WHAT ABOUT ME.
Tracks: / What about me / New York eyes(with Timmy Thomas) / Housecalls / What about me / Always and forever / Why you take my love / Ordinary girl / Shy boy / It happens every night / New York eyes(Remix).
Album: released on Portrait, Feb'86 by CBS Records. Dist: CBS

Cassette: released on Portrait, Feb'86 by CBS Records. Dist: CBS

Single (7"): released on Portrait, Jun'86 by CBS Records. Dist: CBS

Single (12"): released on Portrait, Jun'86 by CBS Records. Dist: CBS

Nicol, Hector
BRAVO JULIET.
Album: released on Klub, Mar'84

Cassette: released on Klub, Mar'84

COP OF THE NORTH.
Album: released on Klub, Nov'79

Cassette: released on Klub, Nov'79

GOLDEN YEARS OF, (THE).
Album: released on Klub, Nov'85

Cassette: released on Klub, Nov'85

HOBO SEXUAL, (THE).
Album: released on Klub, Nov'80

Cassette: released on Klub, Nov'80

I'M A COUNTRY MEMBER (brand x).
Album: released on Klub, Nov'82

Cassette: released on Klub, Nov'82

LADY & THE CHAMP, (THE).
Album: released on Klub, May'79

LAFFIN ROOM ONLY.
Album: released on Klub, May'79

QUEEN OF THE ROAD.
Album:

SCOTCH & FULL OF IT.
Album: released on Klub, May'79

Nicol, James
LAST ROSE OF SUMMER.
Album: released on Lismor, Sep'83 by Lismor Records. Dist: Lismor, Roots, Celtic Music

Cassette: released on Lismor, Sep'83 by Lismor Records. Dist: Lismor, Roots, Celtic Music

SCOTLAND AGAIN.
Tracks: / Bonnie lass o'tyvie / Barnyards of delgaty / Anniversary song / Scotland again / Answer me / Old house / Annie Laurie / Mary of Argyll / Cara mia / Gentle maiden / Bonnie lass o'ballochmyle / Lassie who loves me still.

Album: released on Lismor, Jul'86 by Lismor Records. Dist: Lismor, Roots, Celtic Music

Cassette: released on Lismor, Jul'86 by Lismor Records. Dist: Lismor, Roots, Celtic Music

Nicol, Jean
MEET ME AT THE SAVOY.
Boxed set: released on Soundings, Mar'85 Dist: Soundings

Nicoll, Helen
MEG'S EGGS (Nicoll,Helen & Jan Piekowski).
Cassette: released on Cover to Cover, Sep'86 by Cover to Cover Cassettes. Dist: Conifer

Nicol, Simon
BEFORE YOUR TIME.
Tracks: / Over the Lancashire hills / Caught a whisper / Deserter, The / Insult to injury / From a distance / Live not where I love / Before your time/Merry Sherwood rangers / Rosemary's sister.
Album: released on Woodworm, Aug'87 by Woodworm Records. Dist: Projection, Celtic Music

CLOSE TO THE WIND (Nicol, Simon/Dave Swarbrick).
Album: released on Woodworm, Aug'84 by Charly Records. Dist: Charly

Nicols, Maggie
NICOLS 'N' NU (see Nu/Maggie Nicols) (Nicols,Maggie/Nu).

Nicolson, Eann
HIGHLAND JOURNEY, A (Nicolson, Eann & The Wick Scottish Dance Band).
Album: released on Ross, '86 by Ross Records. Dist: Ross Distribution, Roots Distribution

Cassette: released on Ross, '86 by Ross Records. Dist: Ross Distribution, Roots Distribution

OVER THE ORD (Nicolson, Eann & The Wick Scottish Dance Band).
Album: released on Ross, '86 by Ross Records. Dist: Ross Distribution, Roots Distribution

Cassette: released on Ross, '86 by Ross Records. Dist: Ross Distribution, Roots Distribution

Niehaus, Lennie
OCTET, NO.2, (THE).
Album: released on Contemporary, Apr'86 by Contemporary Records. Dist: Pinnacle

Nielsen, Chris
LET ME DOWN EASY.
Album: released on Emerald, Jun'78 by Emerald Records. Dist: Ross, PRT, Solomon & Peres Distribution

Nielsson, Carol
ELEVEN O'CLOCK IN MY LIFE.
Single (7"): released on Safari, Jul'84 by Safari Records. Dist: Pinnacle

Nieve, Steve
KEYBOARD JUNGLE.
Album: released on Demon, Nov'83 by Demon Records. Dist: Pinnacle

Night
LONG DISTANCE.
Album: released on Elektra Asylum, Nov'80 by Elektra/Asylum/Nonesuch Records. Dist: WEA

NIGHT.
Album: released on Elektra Asylum, Nov'79 by Elektra/Asylum/Nonesuch Records. Dist: WEA

Night at...
NIGHT AT BIRDLAND various artists (Various Artists).
Double Album: released on Vogue Jazz (France), May'83

NIGHT AT THE AULD MEAL MILL, A (Various Artists).
Notes: John Mearns and others.
Album: released on Ross, '86 by Ross Records. Dist: Ross Distribution, Roots Distribution

Cassette: released on Ross, '86 by Ross Records. Dist: Ross Distribution, Roots Distribution

NIGHT AT THE AULD MEAL MILL (Various Artists).
Notes: Vocals from John Mearns, Graham Geddes, George Duffus, Ina Miller. Music from Graham Geddes and His Band and Gordon Pattullo.
Cassette: released on Ross, '86 by Ross Records. Dist: Ross Distribution, Roots Distribution

Album: released on Ross, Dec'84 by Ross Records. Dist: Ross Distribution, Roots Distribution

---

Cat. no: WGR 076
Cassette: released on Ross, Dec'84 by Ross Records. Dist: Ross Distribution, Roots Distribution

NIGHT AT THE AULD MEAL MILL-1985, A (Various Artists).
Notes: With Robbie Shepherd, John Mearns, Ina Miller, Argo Cameron, Colin Campbell, Graham Geddes & his Scottish Dance Band.

NIGHT AT THE AULD MEAL MILL 1985, A Various Artists (Various Artists).
Album: released on Ross, Dec'85 by Ross Records. Dist: Ross Distribution, Roots Distribution

Cassette: released on Ross, Dec'85 by Ross Records. Dist: Ross Distribution, Roots Distribution

NIGHT AT THE PROMS various orchestras (Various Orchestras).
Double cassette: released on Ditto Cassettes, Sep'83

Night Beat
NIGHT BEAT Various Artists (Various Artists).
Album: released on Stylus, Aug'85 Dist: Pinnacle, Terry Blood Distribution, Stylus Distribution

Cassette: released on Stylus, Aug'85 Dist: Pinnacle, Terry Blood Distribution, Stylus Distribution

NIGHT BEAT II Various Artists (Various Artists).
Tracks: / Alice I want you just for me / If you're ready (Come go with me) / I'll be good / Girls are more fun / In your car / Mated / Zapped by love / Say I'm your number one / When the going get's tough the tough get going / Baby love / Oh Sheila-Ready for the world-Trapped / Your personal touch / Theme from Shaft / Knock on wood / Single life / I miss you / Cherish / Could it be I'm falling in love / Do what you do / I'll be your friend / Sunshine / Round and around / She's strange / Inspector Gadget / Just for money / We are the team / Dynasty rap / King heroin (Don't mess with heroin) / African breez.
Album: released on Stylus, Feb'86 Dist: Pinnacle, Terry Blood Distribution, Stylus Distribution

Cassette: released on Stylus, Feb'86 Dist: Pinnacle, Terry Blood Distribution, Stylus Distribution

Nightcaps
WINE WINE WINE.
Album: released on Charly, Apr'80 by Charly Records. Dist: Charly, Cadillac

Nightcatchers
I CAN'T BELIEVE.
Single (7"): released on RCA, Jun'85 by RCA Records. Dist: RCA, Roots, Swift, Wellard, Chris, I & B, Solomon & Peres Distribution

Single (12"): released on RCA, Jun'85 by RCA Records. Dist: RCA, Roots, Swift, Wellard, Chris, I & B, Solomon & Peres Distribution

Night & Day U.S.A.
NIGHT & DAY U.S.A. various artists (Various Artists).
Album: released on Sevilla, Nov'82 by President Records. Dist: Jazz Music, Swift

Nightdoctor
JUST ENOUGH/HIT & MISS AFFAIR.
Single (7"): released on Race, Feb'82

Night Flight
GROWING UP.
Single (7"): released on Iguana, Aug'84 by Iguana Records. Dist: ILA, Grapevine

Night Force
HOLD THE NIGHT.
Single (7"): released on Carrere America (USA), Jul'83 by Polygram.

Single (12"): released on Carrere America (USA), Jul'83 by Polygram.

Nighthawk, Robert
BLUES IN D NATURAL (Nighthawk, Robert/Elmore James).
Album: released on Red Lightnin', Apr'79 by Red Lightnin' Records. Dist: Roots, Swift, Jazz Music, JSU, Pinnacle, Cartel, Wynd-Up Distribution

Nighthawks
FULL HOUSE.
Album: released on Adelphi, May'81 by Adelphi Records. Dist: Jetstar

HARD LIVING.
Album: released on Rounder Europa, Jul'86

JACKS & KINGS
Album: released on Adelphi, May'81 by Adelphi Records. Dist: Jetstar

LIVE.
Album: released on Adelphi, May'79 by Adelphi Records. Dist: Jetstar

LIVE IN EUROPE.
Album: released on Crosscut, Aug'87 Dist: Rollercoaster Distribution, Swift

OPEN ALL NIGHT.
Album: released on Adelphi, May'81 by Adelphi Records. Dist: Jetstar

ROCK'N'ROLL.
Album: released on Rounder (USA), Jan'84 by Mike's Country Music Room Distribution, Jazz Music Distribution, Swift Distribution, Roots Records Distribution, Projection Distribution, Topic Distribution

SIDE POCKET SHOT.
Album: released on Adelphi, May'81 by Adelphi Records. Dist: Jetstar

Night In Cologne
JUST A WHISPER (IN THE AIR).
Single (7"): released on LD, Jan'85 by LD Records. Dist: Rough Trade, Cartel

Nightingale
NIGHTINGALE (Dotrice, Michele).
Cassette: released on Listen Productions, Nov'84 Dist: H.R. Taylor, Hayward Promotions Distribution

ORIGINAL LONDON CAST.
Album: released on That's Entertainment, Apr'83 by That's Entertainment Records. Dist: Pinnacle, PRT

Cassette: released on That's Entertainment, Apr'83 by That's Entertainment Records. Dist: Pinnacle, PRT

Nightingale, Maxine
BITTERSWEET.
Album: released on Liberty, Feb'81 by Liberty-United. Dist: EMI

LOVE HIT ME.
Album: released on United Artists, May'77

Cassette: released on United Artists, May'77

RIGHT BACK WHERE WE STARTED FROM.
Tracks: / Love hit me.
Single (7"): released on Old Gold, Mar'87 by Old Gold Records. Dist: Lightning, Jazz Music, Spartan, Counterpoint

Album: released on United Artists (USA), May'76 by EMI Records. Dist: EMI, Swift, Solomon & Peres Distribution

Nightingale, Pamela
I'LL NEVER FALL IN LOVE AGAIN.
Single (7"): released on Carrere, Mar'85 by Carrere Records. Dist: PRT, Spartan

Single (12"): released on Carrere, Mar'85 by Carrere Records. Dist: PRT, Spartan

Nightingales
4 PIECE SESSION.
Extended-play record: released on Cherry Red, Jul'82 by Cherry Red Records. Dist: Pinnacle

CAKEHOLE/URBAN OSPREYS.
Single (7"): released on Cherry Red, Feb'83 by Cherry Red Records. Dist: Pinnacle

CRAFTY FAG/HOW TO AGE.
Single (7"): released on Ink, Nov'83 by Red Flame. Dist: Rough Trade, Cartel, Pinnacle

CRUNCH, (THE).
Extended-play record: released on Vindaloo, May'84 by Vindaloo Records. Dist: WEA, Cartel

HYSTERICS.
Album: released on Ink, Nov'83 by Red Flame. Dist: Rough Trade, Cartel, Pinnacle

IDIOT STRENGTH/SECONDS.
Single (7"): released on Rough Trade, Apr'81 by Rough Trade Records. Dist: Rough Trade Distribution, Cartel Distribution

IN THE GOOD OLD COUNTRY WAYS.
Album: released on Vindaloo, Apr'86 by Vindaloo Records. Dist: WEA, Cartel

IT'S A CRACKER.
Single (7"): released on Vindaloo, Jan'85 by Vindaloo Records. Dist: WEA, Cartel

JUST THE JOB.
Album: released on Vindaloo, Sep'84 by Vin-

Page 728

PARAFFIN BRAIN.
Single (7"): released on Cherry Red, Apr'82 by Cherry Red Records. Dist: Pinnacle

PIGS ON PURPOSE.
Album: released on Cherry Red, Nov'82 by Cherry Red Records. Dist: Pinnacle

USE YOUR LOAF (EP).
Single (7"): released on Cherry Red, Feb'82 by Cherry Red Records. Dist: Pinnacle

WHAT A CARRY ON.
Single (12"): released on Vindaloo, Sep'85 by Vindaloo Records. Dist: WEA, Cartel

Night Life
NIGHT LIFE various artists (Various Artists).
Double Album: released on Starblend, Nov'83 by Starblend Records. Dist: PRT Distribution

Double cassette: released on Starblend, Nov'83 by Starblend Records. Dist: PRT Distribution

Nightmare
CHILDREN OF THE NIGHT.
Tracks: / Kung fu, karate and tai kwando / Doctor voodoo / Children of the night / Boogi bogi man / I wanna be a monster in a movie / Drac's back / Young dead heroes / Fly angel fly / Evolution / Video nasties / Schitzo psycho homicidal maniac / Cellar, The / Witch woman / Dance of death.
Album: released on Zarg, Mar'87 by Le Matt Music

I WANNA BE A MONSTER IN A MOVIE.
Tracks: / I wanna be a monster in a movie / Boogi bogi man.
Single (7"): released on Swoop, '86 Dist: Le Matt Music Distribution

I WANNA BE A SHOT.
Tracks: / I wanna be shot.
Single (7"): released on PVK, '87

Single (7"): released on PVK, Nov'83

NEW ORLEANS.
Tracks: / New Orleans / Drac's back.
Single (7"): released on Swoop, '85 Dist: Le Matt Music Distribution

Single (7"): released on Swoop, Jan'83 Dist: Le Matt Music Distribution

POWER OF THE UNIVERSE.
Album: released on Ebony, Apr'85 by Ebony Records. Dist: Pinnacle, Ebony

RUTH ELLIS.
Single (7"): released on PVK, Mar'85

SIDE POCKET SHOT.

Nightmares
NIGHTMARES-POEM TO TROUBLE YOUR SLEEP Prelutsky, Jack (Prelutsky, Jack).
Cassette: released on Caedmon(USA), Aug'83 by Caedmon (USA) Records. Dist: Gower, Taylors, Discovery

Nightmares In Wonderland
NIGHTMARES IN WONDERLAND Various artists (Various Artists).
Album: released on Bam Caruso, Mar'87 by Bam Caruso Records. Dist: Rough Trade, Revolver, Cartel

Night moods orchestra
NIGHT MOODS.
Notes: Double Album,double cassette
Album: released on Avon, Jul'86 by Avon Records. Dist: Counterpoint

Cassette: released on Avon, Jul'86 by Avon Records. Dist: Counterpoint

Night Moves
NIGHT MOVES various artists (Various Artists).
Album: released on K-Tel, Sep'84 by K-Tel Records. Dist: Record Merchandisers Distribution, Taylors, Terry Blood Distribution, Wynd-Up Distribution, Relay Distribution, Pickwick Distribution, Solomon & Peres Distribution, Polygram

Cassette: released on K-Tel, Sep'84 by K-Tel Records. Dist: Record Merchandisers Distribution, Taylors, Terry Blood Distribution, Wynd-Up Distribution, Relay Distribution, Pickwick Distribution, Solomon & Peres Distribution, Polygram

TRANSDANCE.
Single (7"): released on GC, May'83 by GC Recordings. Dist: DMS, RCA

Single (12"): released on GC, May'83 by GC Recordings. Dist: DMS, RCA

Single (12"): released on GC, Dec'84 by GC

Night Movies
NIGHT MOVIES various artists (Various Artists).
Album: released on K-Tel, Nov'79 by K-Tel Records. Dist: Record Merchandisers Distribution, Taylors, Terry Blood Distribution, Wynd-Up Distribution, Relay Distribution, Pickwick Distribution, Solomon & Peres Distribution, Polygram

Night Music
NIGHT MUSIC Various artists (Various Artists).
Compact disc: released on Coda Records. Dist: Pinnacle, Cartel, WEA, Roots

Album: released on Coda, Jul'84 by Coda Records. Dist: Pinnacle, Cartel, WEA, Roots

Cassette: released on Coda, Jul'84 by Coda Records. Dist: Pinnacle, Cartel, WEA, Roots

Night Of...
NIGHT OF LATIN SOUNDS various artists (Various Artists).
Cassette: released on AIM (Budget Cassettes), Feb'83

NIGHT OF THE COMET Various artists (Various Artists).
Album: released on Chord, Feb'87 by Chord Records. Dist: Charly

Cassette: released on Chord, Feb'87 by Chord Records. Dist: Charly

NIGHT OF THE COMET Original Soundtrack (Night of the Comet).
Notes: Includes free 7" single
Album: released on Chord, May'86 by Chord Records. Dist: Charly

NIGHT OF THE WOLF Pemberton, Victor (Price, Vincent & Coral Browne).
Cassette: released on BBC, May'84 by BBC Records & Tapes. Dist: EMI, PRT, Pye

Night People
WE LOVE BULLDOG BOGGY.
Single (7"): released on PRT, Mar'82 by PRT Records. Dist: PRT

Nightranger
BIG LIFE.
Tracks: / Big life / Color of your smile / Love is standing near / Rain comes crashing down / Secret of my success / Carry on / Better let it go / I know tonight / Hearts away.
Album: released on MCA, Apr'87 by MCA Records. Dist: Polygram, MCA

Cassette: released on MCA, Apr'87 by MCA Records. Dist: Polygram, MCA

Compact disc: released on MCA, Apr'87 by MCA Records. Dist: Polygram, MCA

COLOUR OF YOUR SMILE.
Tracks: / Colour of your smile / Girls will like it / When you close your eyes (live) / Don't tell me you love me (live).
Notes: *Extra track on 12"only
Single (7"): released on MCA, Apr'87 by MCA Records. Dist: Polygram, MCA

Single (12"): released on MCA, Apr'87 by MCA Records. Dist: Polygram, MCA

DAWN PATROL.
Album: released on Epic, Mar'83 by CBS Records. Dist: CBS

Cassette: released on Epic, Mar'83 by CBS Records. Dist: CBS

DON'T TELL ME YOU LOVE ME.
Single (7"): released on Epic, Mar'83 by CBS Records. Dist: CBS

MIDNIGHT MADNESS.
Album: released on MCA, Jul'84 by MCA Records. Dist: Polygram, MCA

Cassette: released on MCA, Jul'84 by MCA Records. Dist: Polygram, MCA

Compact disc: released on MCA, Jul'84 by MCA Records. Dist: Polygram, MCA

Album: released on Epic, Jan'84 by CBS Records. Dist: CBS

Cassette: released on Epic, Jan'84 by CBS Records. Dist: CBS

NIGHT RANGER.
Compact disc: by MCA Records. Dist: Polygram, MCA

SECRET OF MY SUCCESS, THE.
Tracks: / Secret of my success, The / Carry on / Sister Christian (live)*.
Single (7"): released on MCA, 20 Jun'87 by MCA Records. Dist: Polygram, MCA

Single (12"): released on MCA, 20 Jun'87 by

SEVEN WISHES.
Album: released on MCA, Jun'85 by MCA Records. Dist: Polygram, MCA

Cassette: released on MCA, Jun'85 by MCA Records. Dist: Polygram, MCA

SISTER CHRISTIAN.
Single (7"): released on MCA, Jun'84 by MCA Records. Dist: Polygram, MCA

Night Sky, The
NIGHT SKY, THE A laymans guide to astronomy (Moore, Patrick).
Cassette: released on Audiocord Cassettes, May'83

Night Time Flyer
OUT WITH A VENGEANCE.
Single (7"): released on Red Eye, Sep'80

Nightwing
BARREL OF PAIN.
Single (7"): released on Ovation, Jul'80 by Gull Records. Dist: PRT Distribution

NIGHT OF MYSTERY.
Single (7"): released on Gull, Feb'84 by Gull Records. Dist: Pinnacle

NIGHT OF THE MYSTERY ALIVE ALIVE.
Album: released on Gull, Jun'85 by Gull Records. Dist: Pinnacle

STAND UP AND BE COUNTED.
Album: released on Gull, Jul'85 by Gull Records. Dist: Pinnacle

STRANGERS ARE WELCOME.
Double-pack single: released on Gull, Jun'85 by Gull Records. Dist: Pinnacle

TREADING WATER.
Single (7"): released on Gull, Jun'85 by Gull Records. Dist: Pinnacle

Nihilism Spasm Band
1X - X = X.
Album: released on United Dairies, Oct'85 Dist: Rough Trade, Indies

Niles, Tessa
PRESIDENT'S GIRL, (THE).
Single (7"): released on Rainbow, Nov'85 Dist: I & B, CBS

TOUGH GIRLS.
Tracks: / Tough girls (Part 2) / Directable JJT / Bowling family mix (The) / Play by Harold Punter (A).
Notes: 'A play by Harold Punter' is only available on 12" version.
Single (7"): released on Rainbow, May'86 Dist: I & B, CBS

Single (12"): released on Rainbow, May'86 Dist: I & B, CBS

Nile, Willie
GOLDEN DOWN.
Album: released on Arista, Apr'81 by Arista Records. Dist: RCA

WILLIE NILE.
Album: released on Arista, May'80 by Arista Records. Dist: RCA

Nils flacke pa bredden
NILS FLACKE PA BREDDEN Various artists (Various Artists).
Album: released on ARC (Accordion Records), '84 Dist: Accordion Record Club

Nilsson
AERIAL BALLET.
Album: released on Victor, '74

AERIAL PANDEMONIUM BALLET.
Album: released on Victor, '73

DUIT ON MON DEI.
Album: released on Victor, Mar'75

HARRY AND....
Album: released on K-Tel, Oct'79 by K-Tel Records. Dist: Record Merchandisers Distribution, Taylors, Terry Blood Distribution, Wynd-Up Distribution, Relay Distribution, Pickwick Distribution, Solomon & Peres Distribution, Polygram

KNNILLSSONN.
Album: released on RCA, Jul'77 by RCA Records. Dist: RCA, Roots, Swift, Wellard, Chris, I & B, Solomon & Peres Distribution

NIGHT AFTER NIGHT.
Album: released on Polydor, Sep'79 by Poly-

NILSSON Greatest Hits.
Tracks: / Everybody's talkin' / 1941 / I guess the Lord must be in New York City / Me and my arrows / Spaceman / Kojak Columbo / Who's done it / Coconut / Without you / Love story / Remember Christmas / Without her / Makin' whoopee / As time goes by / You made me love you / All I think about is you.
Notes: Digital Stereo

NILSSON SINGS NEWMAN.
Album: released on RCA, Sep'77 by RCA Records. Dist: RCA, Roots, Swift, Wellard, Chris, I & B, Solomon & Peres Distribution

PANDEMONIUM SHADOW.
Album: released on Victor, '74

WITHOUT YOU.
Tracks: / Without you / Everybody's talking.
Single (7"): released on Old Gold, Oct'86 by Old Gold Records. Dist: Lightning, Jazz Music, Spartan, Counterpoint

Single (7"): released on RCA Golden Grooves, Jul'81 by RCA Records. Dist: RCA

Nilsson, Harry
ALL FOR YOUR LOVE.
Cassette: released on Orchid Music, Feb'82 by Bibi. Dist: Pinnacle

FLASH HARRY.
Album: released on Mercury, Sep'80 by Phonogram Records. Dist: Polygram Distribution

GREATEST HITS:HARRY NILSSON.
Album: released on RCA (Germany), '83

Album: released on RCA International (USA), '84 by RCA Records. Dist: RCA

Cassette: released on RCA International, '84

Compact disc: released on RCA, '84 by RCA Records. Dist: RCA, Roots, Swift, Wellard, Chris, I & B, Solomon & Peres Distribution

LITTLE TOUCH OF SCHMILSSON IN THE NIGHT.
Tracks: / For me and my gal / It had to be you / Lazy moon / Always / Makin' whoopee / You made me love you / Lullaby in ragtime / I wonder who's kissing her now / What'll I do? / Nevertheless / This is all I ask / As time goes by.
Album: released on RCA International (USA), Nov'84 by RCA Records. Dist: RCA

Cassette: released on RCA International (USA), '84 by RCA Records. Dist: RCA

Compact disc: released on RCA, Jan'83 by RCA Records. Dist: RCA, Roots, Swift, Wellard, Chris, I & B, Solomon & Peres Distribution

NILSSON SCHMILSSON.
Tracks: / Gotta get up / Driving along / Early in the morning / Moonbeam song (The) / Down / Without you / Let the good times roll / Jump into the fire / I'll never leave you.
Notes: Produced by Richard Perry.
Album: released on Fame, Sep'86 by Music For Pleasure Records. Dist: EMI

Cassette: released on Fame, Sep'86 by Music For Pleasure Records. Dist: EMI

Compact disc: by RCA Records. Dist: RCA, Roots, Swift, Wellard, Chris, I & B, Solomon & Peres Distribution

Album: released on RCA International (USA), Nov'84 by RCA Records. Dist: RCA

Cassette: released on RCA International, Nov'84

Nimmons, Phil
ATLANTIC SUITE (THE).
Album: released on Sackville, Jul'86 Dist: JSU, Jazz Music, Jazz Horizons, Cadillac Music, Celtic Music, Swift

NINE PLUS SIX.
Album: released on Sackville, Apr'81 Dist: JSU, Jazz Music, Jazz Horizons, Cadillac Music, Celtic Music, Swift

Nina
GOLDEN HOUR PRESENTS NINA.
Album: released on Golden Hour, Apr'78 by PRT Records. Dist: PRT

Nine and a half weeks
9 1/2 WEEKS Various artists (Various Artists).
Tracks: / I do what I do / Best is yet to come, The / Slave to love / Black on black / Eurasian eyes / You can leave your hat on / Bread and butter / This city never sleeps / Cannes / Let it go.
Album: released on Capitol, Mar'86 by Capitol Records. Dist: EMI

Cassette: released on Capitol, Mar'86 by Capitol Records. Dist: EMI

Nine Below Zero

AIN'T COMIN' BACK.
Single (7"): released on A&M, Apr'81 by A&M Records. Dist: Polygram

DON'T POINT YOUR FINGER.
Album: released on A&M, Feb'81 by A&M Records. Dist: Polygram

Cassette: released on A&M, Feb'81 by A&M Records. Dist: Polygram

HELEN.
Single (7"): released on A&M, Jun'81 by A&M Records. Dist: Polygram

LIVE AT THE MARQUEE.
Tracks: / Tore down / Straighten her out / Homework / I can't help myself / Can I get a witness / Ridin' on the L&N / I can't quit baby / Stop your naggin' / Hootchie cootchie coo / Wooly bully / Got my mojo working / Pack fair and square / Watch yourself / Swing job.
Album: released on A&M, Nov'85 by A&M Records. Dist: Polygram

Cassette: released on A&M, Nov'85 by A&M Records. Dist: Polygram

THIRD DEGREE.
Cassette: released on A&M, Mar'82 by A&M Records. Dist: Polygram

Album: released on A&M, Mar'82 by A&M Records. Dist: Polygram

THREE TIMES CAUGHT.
Single (7"): released on A&M, Mar'81 by A&M Records. Dist: Polygram

WHY DON'T YOU TRY ME TONIGHT?.
Single (7"): released on A&M, Oct'81 by A&M Records. Dist: Polygram

Nine Eleven

ALL OF ME FOR ALL OF YOU.
Single (7"): released on RCA, Jun'85 by RCA Records. Dist: RCA, Roots, Swift, Wellard, Chris, I & B, Solomon & Peres Distribution

Single (12"): released on RCA, Jun'85 by RCA Records. Dist: RCA, Roots, Swift, Wellard, Chris, I & B, Solomon & Peres Distribution

Nine Nine Nine

13TH FLOOR MADNESS.
Album: released on Albion, Nov'83 by Albion Records. Dist: Spartan, Pinnacle

Cassette: released on Albion, Nov'83 by Albion Records. Dist: Spartan, Pinnacle

Single (7"): released on Albion, Oct'83 by Albion Records. Dist: Spartan, Pinnacle

Single (12"): released on Albion, Oct'83 by Albion Records. Dist: Spartan, Pinnacle

999.
Notes: Debut studio album, originally released 1978, now available again.
Album: released on Fan Club, Jun'87 by New Rose. Dist: Rough Trade, Cartel, Pinnacle

999 SINGLES ALBUM.
Album: released on United Artists, Jun'80

FACE TO FACE.
Album: released on Labritain, Mar'85 by Albion Records.

FOUND OUT TOO LATE.
Single (7"): released on Radar, Sep'79 by WEA Music Ltd. Dist: WEA, PRT

GREATEST HITS: 999.
Album: released on Albion, Mar'84 by Albion Records. Dist: Spartan, Pinnacle

Cassette: released on Albion, Mar'84 by Albion Records. Dist: Spartan, Pinnacle

HOMICIDE.
Single (7"): released on UA, '78 Dist: EMI

IN CASE OF EMERGENCY.
Tracks: / Homicide / Nasty nasty / Public enemy no. 1 / Silent anger / Emergency / High energy plan / Lil' Red Riding Hood / Me and my desire / Obsessed / Feelin' alright with the crew / Break it up / Titanic (my over) reaction.
Album: released on Dojo, Sep'86 by Castle Communications Records. Dist: Cartel

INDIAN RESERVATION.
Single (7"): released on Albion, Nov'81 by Albion Records. Dist: Spartan, Pinnacle

LUST, POWER & MONEY.
Notes: Recorded in London live in concert. Including 'I'm Alive','Homicide','Nasty Nasty','Emergency' and lots more. Cassette has four extra tracks.
Album: released on ABC, Jun'87 by ABC Dist: CBS, Pinnacle

Cassette: released on ABC, Jun'87 by ABC Dist: CBS, Pinnacle

OBSESSED.
Single (7"): released on Albion, Apr'78 by Albion Records. Dist: Spartan, Pinnacle

RED RIDING HOOD.
Single (7"): released on Albion, Jun'81 by Albion Records. Dist: Spartan, Pinnacle

SEPARATES.
Notes: Collector's reissue of the second 999 album, now very collectable.
Album: released on Fan Club, Jan'87 by New Rose. Dist: Rough Trade, Cartel, Pinnacle

WILD SUN.
Single (7"): released on Albion, Jun'82 by Albion Records. Dist: Spartan, Pinnacle

Single (12"): released on Albion, Jun'82 by Albion Records. Dist: Spartan, Pinnacle

Nine O Nine Section

CLASSICAL JACK.
Single (12"): released on Nine O Nine, Aug'87 by Creole Records. Dist: Rhino, PRT

Nine Out Of Ten Cats

SOUND OF MUSIC.
Single (12"): released on Slaughter, Nov'84

Nine, Sadie

LET'S WORK IT OUT.
Single (7"): released on Record Shack, Feb'87 by Record Shack Records. Dist: PRT

Single (12"): released on Record Shack, Feb'87 by Record Shack Records. Dist: PRT

Nineteen Eighty-Five

1985 MASTER MEGAHITS VOL 2 Various artists (Various Artists).
Album: released on Jammy's, May'85 by Jammy's Records. Dist: Jetstar

Nineteen Eighty-Four

1984 George Orwell (Jacobi, Derek).
Double cassette: released on Listen For Pleasure, Jan'84 by MFP Records. Dist: EMI

Nineteen Eighty-Three

1983 BRASS BAND FESTIVAL Various bands (Various bands).
Album: released on Chandos, Dec'83 by Chandos Records. Dist: Harmonia Mundi, Taylors

Cassette: released on Chandos, Dec'83 by Chandos Records. Dist: Harmonia Mundi, Taylors

1983 EDINBURGH MILITARY TATTOO Various bands (Various bands).
Album: released on Ross Records, Jan'84

1983 R & B JAMBOREE Various artists (Various Artists).
Album: released on Ace, Nov'83 by Ace Records. Dist: Pinnacle, Swift, Hotshot, Cadillac

Nineteen Forty Four...

1944 REVISITED (Various Artists).
Notes: Jim Robinson, S. Rimmington, B. Bissonnette.
Album: released on GHB, Mar'87 Dist: Jazz Music, Swift

Nineteen nineteen

CAGED / AFTER THE FALL.
Single (7"): released on Red Rhino, Jun'82 by Red Rhino Records. Dist: Red Rhino, Cartel

CRY WOLF / STORM / DREAM.
Single (7"): released on Abstract, Sep'83 by Abstract. Dist: Pinnacle

Single (12"): released on Abstract, Sep'83 by Abstract. Dist: Pinnacle

EARTHSONG EP, THE.
Single (12"): released on Abuse, Jul'84 by Revolver

MACHINE.
Album: released on Red Rhino, '84 by Red Rhino Records. Dist: Red Rhino, Cartel

REPULSION / TEAR DOWN THESE WALLS.
Single (7"): released on Red Rhino, Oct'82 by Red Rhino Records. Dist: Red Rhino, Cartel

Nineteen Ten...

SIMON SAYS (Nineteen Ten Fruitgum Co).
Single (7"): released on Old Gold, Apr'83 by Old Gold Records. Dist: Lightning, Jazz Music, Spartan, Counterpoint

Nineteenth Century...

19TH CENTURY AMERICAN BALLROOM MUSIC Featuring the Smithonian Social Orchestra and Quadrille band (Smithonian Social Orchestra).
Album:

Nineteen Twenty-Eight

1928 Various artists (Various Artists).
Album: released on RCA, Oct'84 by RCA Records. Dist: RCA, Roots, Swift, Wellard, Chris, I & B, Solomon & Peres Distribution

Cassette: released on RCA, Oct'84 by RCA Records. Dist: RCA, Roots, Swift, Chris, I & B, Solomon & Peres Distribution

Nineteen twenty's

1920'S FLAPPER PARTY Various artists (Various Artists).
Album: released on Halcyon, Dec'82 by Halcyon Records. Dist: Jazz Music

Nineteen Twenty-Seven

1927 Various artists (Various Artists).
Album: released on RCA, Oct'84 by RCA Records. Dist: RCA, Roots, Swift, Wellard, Chris, I & B, Solomon & Peres Distribution

Cassette: released on RCA, Oct'84 by RCA Records. Dist: RCA, Roots, Swift, Wellard, Chris, I & B, Solomon & Peres Distribution

Nineteen Twenty-Six

1926 Various artists (Various Artists).
Album: released on RCA, Oct'84 by RCA Records. Dist: RCA, Roots, Swift, Wellard, Chris, I & B, Solomon & Peres Distribution

Cassette: released on RCA, Oct'84 by RCA Records. Dist: RCA, Roots, Swift, Wellard, Chris, I & B, Solomon & Peres Distribution

Ninety...

FIRE OVER YONDER (Ninety Degrees Inclusive).
Album: released on Ice, '78 by Ice Records. Dist: RCA

Ninety minutes...

NINETY MINUTES OF SUSPENSE McConnell, Jean (McConnell, Jean).
Cassette: released on Soundings, Feb'85 Dist: Soundings

Ninety Three...

DOGS BLOOD RISING (Ninety Three Current Ninety Three).
Album: released on Laylah Antirecords, Feb'85 Dist: Rough Trade, Cartel

Nipple Erectors

BOPS, BABES, BOOZE AND BOVVER.
Album: released on Big Beat, Oct'87 by Ace Records. Dist: Projection, Pinnacle. Estim retail price in Sep'87 was £3.99.

Nips

ALL THE TIME IN THE WORLD.
Single (7"): released on Soho, 79

GABIELLE.
Single (7"): released on Soho, Nov'79

HAPPY SONG.
Single (7"): released on Burning Rome, Oct'81 Dist: CBS

Nirvana

BLACK AND WHITE OR COLOUR.
Single (7"): released on Zilch, Feb'82 by Zilch Records. Dist: Stage One

BLACK FLOWER (7").
Tracks: / Black flower / Save my soul.
Single (7"): released on Bam Caruso, Apr'87 by Bam Caruso Records. Dist: Rough Trade, Revolver, Cartel

BLACK FLOWER (LP).
Album: released on Bam Caruso, May'87 by Bam Caruso Records. Dist: Rough Trade, Revolver, Cartel

Nirvana Devils

SECRET AGENT GIRL.
Single (7"): released on Exile, Sep'85 by Exile Records. Dist: Pinnacle

SOME FOREIGN SHORE.
Single (7"): released on Exile, Apr'85 by Exile Records. Dist: Pinnacle

TWISTED TALES EP.
Tracks: / Twisted tales EP.
Single 10": released on Exile, May'86 by Exile Records. Dist: Pinnacle

Nistico, Sal

EAST OF ISAR (Nistico, Sal/Benny Bailey).
Album: released on Ego, Oct'79 by Ego Records. Dist: Jazz Services Unlimited Dist. (JSU), Cadillac Music

JUST FOR FUN.
Album: released on Ego, Oct'79 by Ego Records. Dist: Jazz Services Unlimited Dist. (JSU), Cadillac Music

NEO/NISTICO.
Album: released on Beehive (USA), Dec'79 by Cadillac Records. Dist: JSU

Nita Rita & Ruby

ROCK LOVE.
Album: released on Bear Family, Nov'85 by Bear Family Records. Dist: Rollercoaster Distribution, Swift

Nite Blues...

CARIBBEAN CARNIVAL (Nite Blues Steel Band).
Album: released on Golden Hour, May'76 by PRT Records. Dist: PRT

CARNIVAL TIME (Nite Blues Steel Band).
Album: released on Vista Sounds, Sep'84 by Vista Sounds Records. Dist: Jetstar

Nitecaps

GO TO THE LINE.
Album: released on Sire, Apr'83

Nitro Deluxe

THIS BRUTAL HOUSE.
Tracks: / This brutal house / This brutal house (Dub).
Single (7"): released on Cool Tempo, Jan'87 by Chrysalis Records. Dist: CBS

Single (12"): released on Cool Tempo, Jan'87 by Chrysalis Records. Dist: CBS

Nits

NESCIO.
Single (7"): released on Epic, May'83 by CBS Records. Dist: CBS

Nitty Gritty

BORDERLINE/007.
Tracks: / Borderline/007 / In Africa.
Single (12"): released on Uptempo, Jul'86 by Uptempo Records. Dist: Jetstar Distribution

CREATOR.
Tracks: / Creator / Love fever (Junior Brammer).
Single (12"): released on SMJ, Jul'86 by SMJ Records. Dist: Jetstar

GIMME SOME OF YOU SOMETHING.
Single (12"): released on Greensleeves, Nov'85 by Greensleeves Records. Dist: BMG, Jetstar, Spartan

HOG IN A MINTY.
Single (12"): released on Greensleeves, Aug'85 by Greensleeves Records. Dist: BMG, Jetstar, Spartan

LICK HIM, KILL HIM.
Single (12"): released on Bowl, Nov'86 by Jetstar

LICK HIM KILL HIM.
Single (12"): released on Bowl, Nov'86 by Jetstar

LOVING FEELING.
Single (12"): released on Twin Explosion, Mar'86 by Jetstar

MAN IN A HOUSE.
Tracks: / Man in a house / False Alarm.
Single (12"): released on Greensleeves, Apr'86 by Greensleeves Records. Dist: BMG, Jetstar, Spartan

MUSICAL CONFRONTATION (Nitty Gritty & King Kong).
Album: released on Jammy's, Jun'86 by Jammy's Records. Dist: Jetstar

ORIGINAL BANGA RANG.
Tracks: / Original banga rang / Original banga rang (Version).
Single (12"): released on Jammy's, Jul'86 by Jammy's Records. Dist: Jetstar

SO THEM COME SO THEY GO.
Single (12"): released on Live & Love, Feb'87 by Third World Records. Dist: Jetstar

SWEET REGGAE MUSIC.
Tracks: / Sweet reggae music.
Single (12"): released on Unity Sound, Dec'85 Dist: Jetstar

TURBO CHARGED.
Notes: Nitty Gritty is one of the two biggest Jamaican artists of the past few months, (along with Tenor Saw). Unlike most exciting new artists on the reggae scene, Nitty Gritty has been far more selective in the recordings he has made. After ten very successful singles he now has his debut album released by Greensleeves.

The album, entitled 'Tirbo Charged' was produced by Prince Jammy and includes 'Hog In A Minty' and the high riding 'Gimme Some Of Your Something'.
Album: released on Greensleeves, Jan'86 by Greensleeves Records. Dist: BMG, Jetstar, Spartan

USED TO BE MY LOVER.
Tracks: / Used to be my lover / Used to be my dubber.
Single (12"): released on Uptempo, Mar'86 by Uptempo Records. Dist: Jetstar Distribution

Nitty Gritty Dirt Band

20 YEARS OF DIRT.
Album: released on Warner Bros., Aug'87 by Warner Bros Records. Dist: WEA

Cassette: released on Warner Bros., Aug'87 by Warner Bros Records. Dist: WEA

AT THE COUNTRY STORE.
Album: released on Country Store, Apr'87 by Starblend Records. Dist: PRT, Prism Leisure Corporation Records

Cassette: released on Country Store, Apr'87 by Starblend Records. Dist: PRT, Prism Leisure Corporation Records

BEST OF NITTY GRITTY DIRT BAND (THE).
Tracks: / Buy for me the rain / Mr. Bojangles / Some of Shelly's blues / House at Pooh Corner / Cosmic cowboy (part 1) / Honky tonk blues / Collegiana / An American dream / Dream (All I have to do is) / Fire in the sky / Make a little magic / In for the night / Bayou jubilee/Sally was a goodun / Battle of New Orleans / Jambalaya (on the Bayou).
Compact disc: released on EMI, Apr'87 by EMI Records. Dist: EMI

BEST OF THE NITTY GRITTY DIRT BAND, THE.
Compact disc: released on EMI, Aug'87 by EMI Records. Dist: EMI

EARLY DIRT 1967-70.
Tracks: / Buy for me the rain / Euphoria / Holding / Song for Julia / Dismal swamp / It's raining here in Long Beach / Shadow dream song / Truly right / Tide of love / Collegians / Mournin' blues / These days / Some of Shelley's blues / Rave on / Mr. Bohangles / House at Pooh Corner / Living without you.
Album: released on Decal, Jun'86 by Charly Records. Dist: Charly

Cassette: released on Decal, Jun'86 by Charly Records. Dist: Charly

UNCLE CHARLIE AND HIS DOG TEDDY.
Tracks: / Some of Shelley's blues / Rave on / Livin without you / Uncle Charlie / Mr Bojangles / Clinch mountain / Back step / Propinquity / Cure (The) / Opus 36 / Clementi (John) / Chicken reel / Travellin' mood / Billy in the low / Swanee river / Randy Lynn rag / Santa Rosa / Prodigal's return / Yukon railroad / House at Pooh Corner.
Album: released on EMI (Italy), Feb'87 by EMI Records. Dist: Conifer

Cassette: released on EMI (Italy), Feb'87 by EMI Records. Dist: Conifer

LET YOUR BODY LEARN.
Tracks: / Let your body learn / Let your body learn (inst version) / Get clean.
Single (7"): released on Mute, Apr'87 Dist: Spartan Distribution, Rough Trade Distribution, Cartel Distribution

Single (12"): released on Mute, Apr'87 Dist: Spartan Distribution, Rough Trade Distribution, Cartel Distribution

Single (7"): released on Power Of Voice Communications, May'86 Dist: Backs, Cartel

MURDEROUS.
Tracks: / Murderous / Fitness to purpose.
Single (7"): released on Mute, Nov'86 Dist: Spartan Distribution, Rough Trade Distribution, Cartel Distribution

THAT TOTAL AGE.
Compact disc: released on Mute, May'87 Dist: Spartan Distribution, Rough Trade Distribution, Cartel Distribution

Album: released on Mute, May'87 Dist: Spartan Distribution, Rough Trade Distribution, Cartel Distribution

Double-pack single: released on Mute, May'87 Dist: Spartan Distribution, Rough Trade Distribution, Cartel Distribution

WARSAW GHETTO.
Tracks: / Warsaw ghetto / Warsaw ghetto (dub mix) / Warsaw ghetto (rap mix) / So bright so strong.
Single (12"): released on Power Of Voice, Mar'86

Single (12"): released on Power Of Voice, Oct'85

Nitzsche, Jack

T. GILES CRIPPLEGATE.
Album: released on Initial, 9 Aug'1 by Initial Records. Dist: Pinnacle

ENCHANTED ORCHESTRA, (THE) (Niven, David/National Philharmonic Orchestra).
Album: released on Maiden, Oct'79 by Maiden Records. Dist: Spartan

Cassette: released on Maiden, Oct'79 by Maiden Records. Dist: Spartan
Cat. no: **MRC 116**

Niven, Kristina

MAMMY BLUE.
Tracks: / Mammy blue / Wait until tomorrow.
Single (7"): released on Amidisque, Aug'86 by Amidisque Records. Dist: RCA, Pinnacle

Nkomo, Pablo

WICKED MURDERER.
Single (12"): released on Sun Set, Sep'84 by Sun Set Records. Dist: Jetstar Distribution

NME C86

NME C86 Various artists (Various Artists).
Album: released on Rough Trade, Nov'86 by Rough Trade Records. Dist: Rough Trade Distribution, Cartel Distribution

Cassette: released on Rough Trade, Nov'86 by Rough Trade Records. Dist: Rough Trade Distribution, Cartel Distribution

No..

NO INTRODUCTION NECESSARY various artists (Various Artists).
Album: released on Thunderbolt, Apr'84 by Magnum Music Group Ltd. Dist: Magnum Music Group Ltd, PRT Distribution, Spartan Distribution

NO NUKES various artists (Various Artists).
Double Album: released on Elektra, Dec'79 by WEA Records. Dist: WEA

No. 4 Joystreet

WATCH THE WORLD.
Single (7"): released on Golden Pathway, Sep'86 Dist: Revolver, Cartel

Noack, Eddie

GENTLEMEN PREFER BLONDES.
Album: released on Del Rio, Oct'85 by Ace Records. Dist: Pinnacle, Swift, Counterpoint

Noah House...

MURDER (Noah House Of Dread).
Single (12"): released on On-U-Sound, Jun'82 Dist: Rough Trade Distribution, Lightning

Noah Noah

UTOPIA.
Single (7"): released on Exclusive, Jul'85 Dist: Jetstar

Single (12"): released on Exclusive, Jul'85 Dist: Jetstar

Noakes, Rab

RAB NOAKES.
Album: released on MCA, Apr'81 by MCA Records. Dist: Polygram, MCA

UNDER THE RAIN.
Album: released on Black Crow, Mar'84 by Mawson & Wareham Records. Dist: Projection

Cassette: released on Black Crow, Mar'84 by Mawson & Wareham Records. Dist: Projection

Noble, George

GEORGE NOBLE & OTHERS-1935-36 RECORDINGS.
Album: released on Magpie, Feb'79 Dist: Projection

Noble, Kara

ALL I WANT (IS TO SEE YOU SMILE).
Single (7"): released on Towerbell, Oct'82 by Towerbell Records. Dist: EMI

MUMMY.
Single (7"): released on Town & Country, May'82 Dist: Spartan

Noble, Ray

DINNER MUSIC (Noble, Ray & His Orchestra).
Album: released on Golden Era, Jul'82 by Import Records. Dist: Wellard. Chris, Swift

GOODNIGHT SWEETHEART (Noble, Ray & His Orchestra).
Album: released on Joy, Apr'83 by President Records. Dist: Jazz Music, Swift, President Distribution

HMV SESSIONS, THE (Noble, Ray, Orchestra/Al Bowlly).
Album: released on EMI, Mar'84 by EMI Records. Dist: EMI

Cassette: released on EMI, Mar'84 by EMI Records. Dist: EMI

MY SONG GOES ROUND THE WORLD* (Noble, Ray & Al Bowlly).
Notes: Mono. For full information see under: Bowlly, Al.

NOTABLE NOBLE.
Album: released on EMI Retrospect, Apr'85 by EMI Records. Dist: EMI

Cassette: released on EMI Retrospect, Apr'85 by EMI Records. Dist: EMI

OVER ON THE SUNNY SIDE (Noble, Ray & His Orchestra).
Album: released on Old Bean, Apr'86 Dist: Jazz Music

Cassette: released on Old Bean, Apr'86 Dist: Jazz Music

RAY NOBLE/AL BOWLLY, NO.1 (Noble, Ray & His Orchestra).
Album: released on Monmouth, Mar'79

RAY NOBLE/AL BOWLLY, NO.2 (Noble, Ray & His Orchestra).
Album: released on Monmouth, Mar'79

RAY NOBLE/AL BOWLLY, NO.6 (Noble, Ray & His Orchestra).
Album: released on Monmouth, Mar'79

RAY NOBLE ENCORES (Noble, Ray & His Orchestra).
Album: released on Monmouth, Mar'79

RAY NOBLE & HIS ORCHESTRA (Noble, Ray & His Orchestra).
Album: released on Halcyon, May'84 by Halcyon Records. Dist: Jazz Music

RAY NOBLE & JOE HAYMES 1935.
Album: released on Aircheck, Apr'79

RAY NOBLE & JOE HAYMES 1935 (see Haymes,Joe & Ray Noble) (Noble, Ray & Joe Haymes).

RAY NOBLE ORCHESTRA 1935-6 (VOLUME 2) (Noble, Ray & His Orchestra).
Album: released on London, Jul'78 by London Records. Dist: Polygram

RAY NOBLE'S ENCORES, VOL.3.
Album: released on Monmouth, May'79

RAY NOBLE'S ENCORES, VOL.6 (Noble, Ray & His Orchestra).
Album: released on Monmouth, May'79

RAY NOBLE'S ENCORES, VOL.1 (Noble, Ray & His Orchestra).
Album: released on Monmouth, May'79

Album: released on Monmouth, May'79

RAY NOBLE'S ENCORES, VOL.2 (Noble, Ray & His Orchestra).

RAY NOBLE'S ENCORES, VOL.4 (Noble, Ray & His Orchestra).
Album: released on Monmouth, May'79

RAY NOBLE'S ENCORES, VOL.5 (Noble, Ray & His Orchestra).
Album: released on Monmouth, May'79

WE DANCED ALL NIGHT (Noble, Ray & His Orchestra).
Album: released on RCA, Oct'84 by RCA Records. Dist: RCA, Roots, Swift, Wellard, Chris, I & B, Solomon & Peres Distribution

Cassette: released on RCA, Oct'84 by RCA Records. Dist: RCA, Roots, Swift, Wellard, Chris, I & B, Solomon & Peres Distribution

Nocera

SUMMERTIME SUMMERTIME.
Tracks: / Summertime summertime / Summertime summertime - hard summer dub.
Single (7"): released on Fourth & Broadway, Oct'86 by Island Records. Dist: Polygram, EMI

Single (12"): released on Fourth & Broadway, Oct'86 by Island Records. Dist: Polygram, EMI

No Choice

SADIST DREAM.
Extended-play record: released on Riot City, Feb'83 by Riot City Records. Dist: Revolver

Nock, Mike

IN OUT AND AROUND (Nock, Mike Quartet).
Notes: Featuring: Mike Brecker/G. Mraz/Al Foster.
Album: released on Timeless, Sep'86

ONDAS.
Tracks: / Forgotten love / Ondas / Visionary / Land of the long white cloud / Doors.
Notes: Personnel: Mike Nock - piano/Eddie Gomez - bass/Jon Christensen - drums.
Compact disc: released on ECM (Germany), Aug'86 by ECM Records. Dist: IMS, Polygram, Virgin through EMI

PIANO SOLOS.
Album: released on Timeless, Apr'81

TALISMAN.
Album: released on Enja (Germany), Jan'82 by Enja Records (W.Germany). Dist: Cadillac Music

No Comment

IN MY MIND.
Single (7"): released on Spectrum & Spectrum, Mar'82

No Corridor

SOFT TARGET.
Tracks: / Soft target / Last time.
Single (7"): released on A.1, May'86 by A.1 Records. Dist: PRT

No Cover

TWO HUNDRED VOICES.
Single (7"): released on Northeast Music, Jul'83 by Northeast Music Records. Dist: Northeast Music Distribution, Pinnacle

Nocturnal Emissions

BEFEHLOSNOTSTAND.
Album: released on Sterile, '84 Dist: Red Rhino Distribution, Cartel Distribution

CHAOS.
Album: released on Cause For Concern, Aug'84 Dist: Cartel

DROWNING IN A SEA OF BLISS.
Album: released on Sterile, '84 Dist: Red Rhino Distribution, Cartel Distribution

NOCTURNAL EMISSIONS Various artists (Various Artists).
Cassette: released on Touch, Sep'86 by Touch Records. Dist: Rough Trade, Cartel

NO SACRIFICE.
Single (12"): released on Sterile, Sep'84 Dist: Red Rhino Distribution, Cartel Distribution

SHAKE THOSE CHAINS Rattle those cages.
Tracks: / Shake those chains rattle those cages.
Album: released on Sterile, Jan'86 Dist: Red Rhino Distribution, Cartel Distribution

Cassette: released on Sterile, Jan'86 Dist: Red Rhino Distribution, Cartel Distribution

SONGS OF LOVE AND REVOLUTION.
Album: released on Sterile, Jun'85 Dist: Red Rhino Distribution, Cartel Distribution

TISSUE OF LIES.
Album: released on Sterile, '84 Dist: Red Rhino Distribution, Cartel Distribution

Noddy...

NODDY AND THE MAGIC BOOTS (Bryer, Denise).
Cassette: released on Tempo, Aug'84 by Warwick Records. Dist: Multiple Sound Distributors

NODDY HAS AN ADVENTURE By Enid Blyton (Noddy Has An Adventure).
Album: released on Golden Wand, Nov'82 Dist: Taylors

Cassette: released on Golden Wand, Nov'82 Dist: Taylors

NODDY MAKES EVERYONE CROSS (Bryer, Denise).
Cassette: released on Tempo, Aug'84 by Warwick Records. Dist: Multiple Sound Distributors

NODDY'S BIG BALLOON (Bryer, Denise).
Cassette: released on Tempo, Aug'84 by Warwick Records. Dist: Multiple Sound Distributors

NODDY STORIES By Enid Blyton (Briers, Richard).
Cassette: released on Pickwick Talking Books, '83

NODDY'S UNLUCKY DAY (Bryer, Denise).
Cassette: released on Tempo, Aug'84 by Warwick Records. Dist: Multiple Sound Distributors

No Deposit

MOUNTAIN LAKE.
Single (7"): released on Shockwave, Jul'80

Nod & Friends

DAD.
Single (7"): released on Red Rhino, Oct'82 by Red Rhino Records. Dist: Red Rhino, Cartel

No Dice
NO DICE.
Album: released on EMI, Nov'77 by EMI Records. Dist: EMI

ONE MORE NIGHT.
Single (7"): released on Seara, Sep'82 by Seara Records. Dist: Jetstar

Noel
IS THERE MORE TO LIFE THAN DANCING.
Album: by Virgin Records. Dist: EMI, Virgin Distribution

Noel And Gertie
NOEL AND GERTIE Original London cast.
Album: released on That's Entertainment, Jan'87 by That's Entertainment Records. Dist: Pinnacle, PRT

Cassette: released on That's Entertainment, Jan'87 by That's Entertainment Records. Dist: Pinnacle, PRT

No Entiendes
NO ENTIENDES Live at the ICA (Various Artists).
Album: released on Antilles, Nov'86 by Island Records. Dist: Polygram

No Excuses
NO EXCUSES Original TV sountrack.
Album: released on CBS, Apr'83 by CBS Records. Dist: CBS Deleted '85.
Cat. no: **CBS 70234**
Cassette: released on CBS, Jun'83 by CBS Records. Dist: CBS

No Exit
CASABLANCAN NIGHT.
Single (7"): released on Slug, Oct'83 by Slug Records. Dist: Indies

No Hat Moon
I LOVE TODAY.
Tracks: / I love today / It's only the rain.
Single (7"): released on Towerbell, Apr'86 by Towerbell Records. Dist: EMI

WON'T YOU DANCE WITH ME.
Single (7"): released on Towerbell, Nov'85 by Towerbell Records. Dist: EMI

Nohumaneye
WET YOUR LIPS/OWNERS LOSE A PACKAGE.
Single (7"): released on Rhodium, Oct'82

No Idea
RUSSIAN ROULETTE.
Single (7"): released on Paro, Mar'83 by Paro Records. Dist: Spartan

Noise Boyz
BOYZ-GO SCRATCH.
Tracks: / Boyz-go scratch / Lean Street.
Single (12"): released on Citybeat, Sep'86 Dist: WEA

NO WAY BACK.
Tracks: / No way back / No way back (alt. dance mix).
Single (12"): released on Citybeat, 20 Jun'87 Dist: WEA

Noiseworks
NO LIES.
Tracks: / No lies / Learning to swim.
Single (7"): released on Epic, May'87 by CBS Records. Dist: CBS

Single (7"): released on Epic, Aug'87 by CBS Records. Dist: CBS

Single (12"): released on Epic, Aug'87 by CBS Records. Dist: CBS

No Jaz
SIX FLIGHTS OF STAIRS.
Single (7"): released on Fleeced, Aug'84 by Fleeced. Dist: ILA

Nola
LOVE STRIKER.
Single (7"): released on Chantel, Dec'83 by Chantel Records. Dist: Faulty

Nolan, Dennis
PILLOW TALK.
Tracks: / Pillow talk / Killer thriller.
Single (7"): released on Blakarmix, Jul'87 by Blakarmix Records. Dist: Jetstar

Nolan, Jerry
TAKE A CHANCE WITH ME.
Single (7"): released on Tansing, Feb'83 by

Page 732

Tansing Records. Dist: Pinnacle

Nolans
6 TRACK HITS.
Extended-play record: released on Scoop 33, Mar'84 by Pickwick Records. Dist: H.R. Taylor

Cassette: released on Scoop 33, Mar'84 by Pickwick Records. Dist: H.R. Taylor

GIRLS JUST WANNA HAVE FUN.
Album: released on Towerbell, Nov'84 by Towerbell Records. Dist: EMI

Cassette: released on Towerbell, Nov'84 by Towerbell Records. Dist: EMI

GOODBYE NOTHING TO SAY.
Single (7"): released on Towerbell, Jun'85 by Towerbell Records. Dist: EMI

Single (12"): released on Towerbell, Jun'85 by Towerbell Records. Dist: EMI

GREATEST ORIGINAL HITS 4 Track EP.
Single (7"): released on Epic, Mar'83 by CBS Records. Dist: CBS

HARMONY.
Album: released on Premier, '84 by Premier Records. Dist: CBS

Cassette: released on Premier, '84 by Premier Records. Dist: CBS

I'M IN THE MOOD FOR DANCING.
Album: released on Hallmark, Apr'83 by Pickwick Records. Dist: Pickwick Distribution, PRT, Taylors

Cassette: released on Hallmark, Apr'83 by Pickwick Records. Dist: Pickwick Distribution, PRT, Taylors

LET'S SPEND THE NIGHT TOGETHER.
Tracks: / Let's spend the night together / When I fall in love.
Single (7"): released on Spartan, Mar'86 by Spartan Records. Dist: Spartan

LOVE SONGS.
Album: released on Pickwick, May'85 by Pickwick Records. Dist: Pickwick Distribution, Prism Leisure Distribution, Lugtons

Cassette: released on Pickwick, May'85 by Pickwick Records. Dist: Pickwick Distribution, Prism Leisure Distribution, Lugtons

NOLANS.
Album: released on Nevis, Jun'83 Dist: H.R. Taylor

TIMES GONE BY.
Album: released on Spartan, Nov'85 by Spartan Records. Dist: Spartan

Cassette: released on Spartan, Nov'85 by Spartan Records. Dist: Spartan

Nolan Sisters
BEST OF THE NOLAN SISTERS, THE (VOL.1).
Album: released on Pickwick, May'79 by Pickwick Records. Dist: Pickwick Distribution, Prism Leisure Distribution, Lugtons

BEST OF THE NOLAN SISTERS, THE (VOL.2).
Album: released on Pickwick, May'79 by Pickwick Records. Dist: Pickwick Distribution, Prism Leisure Distribution, Lugtons

NOLAN SISTERS.
Album: released on Epic, Jun'81 by CBS Records. Dist: CBS Deleted '85.

Cassette: released on Epic, Jun'81 by CBS Records. Dist: CBS

NOLAN SISTERS COLLECTION, THE.
Double Album: released on Pickwick, Jul'80 by Pickwick Records. Dist: Pickwick Distribution, Prism Leisure Distribution, Lugtons

Cassette: released on Pickwick, Jul'80 by Pickwick Records. Dist: Pickwick Distribution, Prism Leisure Distribution, Lugtons

NOLAN SISTERS, THE.
Album: released on CBS, Oct'79 by CBS Records. Dist: CBS

Nolen & Crossley
READY OR NOT.
Single (7"): released on Motown, Apr'82 by Motown Records. Dist: BMG Distribution

Single (12"): released on Motown, Apr'82 by Motown Records. Dist: BMG Distribution

Nomad, Naz
GIVE DADDY THE KNIFE CINDY (Nomad, Naz & The Nightmares).
Album: released on Big Beat, Feb'84 by Ace Records. Dist: Projection, Pinnacle

---

I HAD TOO MUCH TO DREAM (LAST NIGHT) (Nomad, Naz & The Nightmares).
Single (7"): released on Ace, Mar'84 by Ace Records. Dist: Pinnacle, Swift, Hotshot, Cadillac

Nomad Pop!
DIGNITY.
Tracks: / Dignity / Best man.
Notes: 01 208 1686
Single (7"): released on Redhouse, May'86

Nomads
16 FOREVER.
Tracks: / 16 forever / Come on / You're gonna miss me.
Single (12"): released on Wire, 23 May'87 Dist: Nine Mile, Cartel

HARDWARE.
Album: released on Wire, May'87 Dist: Nine Mile, Cartel

OUTBURST.
Album: released on Goes On, Dec'84 by Goes On Records. Dist: Rough Trade, Cartel

SHE PAYS THE RENT.
Single (7"): released on Wire, Nov'85 Dist: Nine Mile, Cartel

SOMETHING BAD.
Single (7"): released on Soul Supply, May'85 by High Energy Records. Dist: Charly

STAGGER IN THE SNOW.
Album: released on Fools Rush, Nov'84 Dist: Rough Trade, Cartel

No Man's Band
HEY JOE.
Single (7"): released on Energy, Jul'82 by Energy Records. Dist: Jazz Music

No Man's Land
SPLASH.
Tracks: / Splash / Building a road.
Single (7"): released on Future Earth, Oct'86 by Future Earth Records. Dist: Red Rhino, Cartel

No mercy
NO MERCY Original soundtrack (Silvestri, Alan).
Album: released on Silva Screen, May'87 by Silva Screen Records. Dist: Silva Screen, PRT

Cassette: released on Silva Screen, May'87 by Silva Screen Records. Dist: Silva Screen, PRT

Nomi, Klaus
DING DONG THE WITCH IS DEAD.
Single (7"): released on RCA, Oct'82 by RCA Records. Dist: RCA, Roots, Swift, Wellard, Chris, I & B, Solomon & Peres Distribution

ENCORE, NOMI'S BEST.
Album: released on RCA (France), Jun'84 by RCA Records. Dist: Discovery

KLAUS NOMI.
Album: released on RCA, '84 by RCA Records. Dist: RCA, Roots, Swift, Wellard, Chris, I & B, Solomon & Peres Distribution

Cassette: released on RCA, '84 by RCA Records. Dist: RCA, Roots, Swift, Wellard, Chris, I & B, Solomon & Peres Distribution

LIGHTNING STRIKES.
Single (7"): released on RCA, Jan'82 by RCA Records. Dist: RCA, Roots, Swift, Wellard, Chris, I & B, Solomon & Peres Distribution

SIMPLE MAN.
Album: released on RCA, '84 by RCA Records. Dist: RCA, Roots, Swift, Wellard, Chris, I & B, Solomon & Peres Distribution

Cassette: released on RCA, '84 by RCA Records. Dist: RCA, Roots, Swift, Wellard, Chris, I & B, Solomon & Peres Distribution

Non
BLOOD AND FAME.
Compact disc: released on Mute, Jan'87 Dist: Spartan Distribution, Rough Trade Distribution, Cartel Distribution

Album: released on Mute, Nov'86 Dist: Spartan Distribution, Rough Trade Distribution, Cartel Distribution

OUT OUT OUT.
Single (7"): released on Mute, Jan'82 Dist: Spartan Distribution, Rough Trade Distribution, Cartel Distribution

PHYSICAL EVIDENCE.
Album: released on Mute, Apr'84 Dist: Spartan Distribution, Rough Trade Distribution, Cartel Distribution

---

Cassette: released on Mute, Sep'82 Dist: Spartan Distribution, Rough Trade Distribution, Cartel Distribution

None So Blind
MY FAVOURITE EYES.

Non Fiction
NO FICTION.
Album: released on Demon, Sep'86 by Demon Records. Dist: Pinnacle

No No Nanette
NO NO NANETTE Original London cast (Various Artists).
Album: released on World, '73 Dist: Jetstar

No,No,No,No,No...
NO,NO,NO,NO,NO NOT MY GIRL Various Artists.
Notes: 16 classic Northern Soul dance tracks from....The Platters,Tommy Hunt, Lavern Baker, Judy Clay,Betty Moorer,The Gentlemen Four,Otis Leavill,Young Holt Unlimited,Bobby Martin,Johnny Howard,Candy And The Kisses,Sandy Waddy etc.
Album: released on Kent, Jun'87 by Ace Records. Dist: Pinnacle

Non Stop..
NON STOP DANCE PARTY various artists (Various Session Artists).
Cassette: released on AIM (Budget Cassettes), Feb'83

NON STOP ELECTRICTIY various artists (Various Artists).
Album: released on Passion, Feb'85 by Skratch Records. Dist: PRT

NON STOP NURSERY RHYMES (2) various artists (Various Artists).
Album: released on Cherry Lane, Aug'85 by Cherry Lane Productions. Dist: PRT

Cassette: released on Cherry Lane, Aug'85 by Cherry Lane Productions. Dist: PRT

NON STOP NURSERY RHYMES various artists (Various Artists).
Album: released on Cherry Lane, Aug'85 by Cherry Lane Productions. Dist: PRT

Cassette: released on Cherry Lane, Aug'85 by Cherry Lane Productions. Dist: PRT

NON STOP PASSION,VOL.1 various artists (Various Artists).
Album: released on Passion, Jan'85 by Skratch Records. Dist: PRT

NON STOP TIJUANA 100 Party hits from the man with the golden horn (Non Stop Tijuana).
Album: released on Ronco, Nov'83

Cassette: released on Ronco, Nov'83

NONSTOP XMAS 20 various artists (Various Session Artists).
Album: released on Spiral, Oct'81 by President Records. Dist: Jazz Music

Nookes, George
FREEDOM BLUES.
Single (12"): released on Oak Sound, Sep'83

ROCKING TIMES.
Single (12"): released on Hitbound, Oct'83 by Hitbound Records. Dist: Jetstar

Nooks, George
BE YOUR LOVER.
Single (12"): released on Moa Anbessa, Dec'85 by Moa Anbessa Records. Dist: Jetstar Distribution

TIME FOR LOVE.
Single (7"): released on J.B., Oct'82 Dist: Warren, Mojo Distribution, Jetstar, Lightning, Arawak, Soundoff

TODAY.
Album: released on Jinty's, Sep'84 by Jinty's Records. Dist: Jetstar

Noone, Jimmie
1941 His Quartet-recorded live at Yes Ye Club, Chicago.
Album: released on Swaggie (Australia) Jan'83

APEX CLUB BLUES.
Tracks: / Apex blues / New Orleans hop sco blues / Blues my naughty sweety gives to me Keystone blues / Four or five times / Bump it Way down yonder in New Orleans / Every eve ning / My monday date / I know that you know Body & soul / Sweet Lorraine / Sweet Georg Brown / King Joe / Sweet Joe / Oh! Sister, ai that ho?.
Album: released on Affinity, Jun'86 by Char Records. Dist: Charly, Cadillac

JIMMIE NOONE (1936-41).
Album: released on Swaggie (Australia), Jan'83

JIMMIE NOONE'S APEX CLUB ORCHESTRA VOL. 3 1929 (Noone, Jimmie Apex club orchestra).
Notes: Mono.
Album: released on Swaggie, Mar'87 Dist: Jazz Music Distribution

JIMMIE NOONE'S APEX CLUB ORCHESTRA VOL. 4 1929-1930 (Noone, Jimmie Apex club orchestra).
Notes: Mono
Album: released on Swaggie, Mar'87 Dist: Jazz Music Distribution

JIMMIE NOONE, VOL.1.
Album: released on Classic Jazz Masters, Aug'79 by Mainline Record Company. Dist: Mainline, Swift, Jazz Music

Noone, Jimmy

1931-40.
Album: released on Queen-Disc, '79 Dist: Celtic Music, JSU, Jazz Horizons, Jazz Music

KINGS OF NEW ORLEANS (Noone, Jimmy/Johnson, Bunk).
Album: released on Avenue, Oct'86 Dist: Swift, Jazz Music

Album: released on Jazz Bird, '82 Dist: Cassion (Melandy)

KINGS OF NEW ORLEANS (Noone, Jimmy & Bunk Johnson).
Cassette: released on Jazz Bird, '82 Dist: Cassion (Melandy)

MERCURY THEATRE, L.A., BROADCASTS (see Ory, Kid) (Noone, Jimmy & Kid Ory).

VOLUME 1.
Album: released on Swaggie, Sep'86 Dist: Jazz Music Distribution

VOLUME 2.
Album: released on Swaggie, Sep'86 Dist: Jazz Music Distribution

No Other Name

DEATH INTO LIFE.
Notes: Daylight Records, Daylight Co. (Distribution) Ltd, 2. Dorset Place, New Street, Honiton, Devon EX14 8AB.
Album: released on Daylight, '86 by Daylight Records. Dist: Daylight

Cassette: released on Daylight, '86 by Daylight Records. Dist: Daylight

NO OTHER NAME.
Notes: Daylight Records, The Daylight (Distribution) Ltd, 2 Dorset Place, New Street, Honiton, Devon. EX14 8AB.
Album: released on Daylight, '86 by Daylight Records. Dist: Daylight

Cassette: released on Daylight, '86 by Daylight Records. Dist: Daylight

No Quarter

SURVIVORS.
Single (12"): released on Reel, Nov'83 Dist: Backs

Norah Lofts

MADSELINE (Rosalind Lloyd).
Cassette: released on Colophone Audio Visual, Sep'81 by Audio-Visual Library Services. Dist: Audio-Visual Library Services

Norfolk & Good

KRISTMAS KRACKER.
Single (7"): released on Gipsy, Dec'81 by Gipsy Records. Dist: PRT

Norfolk Jubilee Quartet

927-1938.
lbum: released on Heritage, Jan'86 by Heritage Records. Dist: Chart

Noris, Gunter

986.
racks: / Hibiskus / Jasmin / Amaryllis / Narssen / Iris / Akelei / Nelken / Lilien / Margeriten Rosen / Kam-Elien / Tulpen.
lbum: released on Teldec (Germany), Nov'85 y Import Records. Dist: IMS Distribution, Polyram Distribution

assette: released on Teldec (Germany), ov'85 by Import Records. Dist: IMS Distribuon, Polygram Distribution

ELLA ITALIA (Noris, Gunter & His Orchesa).
racks: / Mamma mia / Made in Italy / Sharazan Tu, soltanto tu / Felicita / Ciao, ciao bambina / ome prima / Volare / Santa Lucia / Torna a surnto / Oh Marie / Capri-fischer / Azzuro / Vivi / rividerci Claire.

Compact disc: released on Teldec, Jul'87

DANCE RECORD '84 (Noris, Gunter Big Band).
Album: released on Teldec (Germany), Sep'84 by Import Records. Dist: IMS Distribution, Polygram Distribution

Cassette: released on Teldec (Germany), Sep'84 by Import Records. Dist: IMS Distribution, Polygram Distribution

DANCE RECORD OF THE YEAR '87 (Noris, Gunter Big Band, String & Chorus).
Tracks: / Saxy cha cha / Harmonica romantica / Tropic trumpets / Jiving guitar / Lonesome trumpet / Rock 'n' roll piano / Ballroom memories / Valse pour mandoline / El bandoneon / Waltzing violins / Golden velvet / Swing in harmony.
Compact disc: released on Teldec, Jul'87

Cassette: released on Teldec, Jul'87

Album: released on Teldec, Jul'87

DANCE RECORD OF THE YEAR '85 (Noris, Gunter Big Band).
Tracks: / Rubin cha cha / Topas-rumba / Smaragd-samba / Jade-jive / Granat-paso doble / Tigerauge - rock / Turkis-fox / Diamant - waltz / Saphir - tango / Aquamarin - walzer / Opal - slow / Amethyst - quick.
Compact disc: released on Teldec, Jul'87

Album: released on Teldec, Jul'87

DANCE RECORD OF THE YEAR '86 (Noris, Gunter Big Band, String & Chorus).
Tracks: / Hibiskus - cha cha / Jasmin - rumba / Amaryllis - samba / Narzissen - jive / Iris - blues / Akelei - rock / Nelken - fox / Lilien - walzer / Margeriten - tango / Rosen - walzer / Kamelien - slow / Tulphen - quick.
Compact disc: released on Teldec, Jul'87

Album: released on Teldec, Jul'87

DANCING THROUGH THE YEAR 1982.
Album: released on Dansan, Oct'81 by Spartan Records. Dist: Spartan

FESTIVAL TROPICAL Famous Latin-American dances (Noris, Gunter Big Band).
Tracks: / Samba d'orphee / Brazil / Tristezza / Amor, amor / Canavelito / Ay, ay, ay / Kingston town / Banana boat / Soul limbo / El Cumbanchero / Adios Muchachos / Moliendo cafe / El condor pasa / Todos los Domingos / Mexican hat-dance / Adelita / La Bamba.
Album: released on Teldec (Germany), Nov'85 by Import Records. Dist: IMS Distribution, Polygram Distribution

Compact disc: released on Teldec (Germany), Aug'86 by Import Records. Dist: IMS Distribution, Polygram Distribution

Cassette: released on Teldec, Jul'87

NORIS, GUNTER.
Tracks: / Saxy cha cha / Harmonica romantica / tropic trumpets / Jiving guitar / Lonesome trumpet / Rock 'n' roll piani / Ballroom melodies / Valse pour mandoline / El Bandoneon / Waltzing violins / Golden velvet / Swing in harmony.
Album: released on Teldec (Germany), Sep'86 by Import Records. Dist: IMS Distribution, Polygram Distribution

PETTICOAT AND BUBBLEGUM Dance to the 50's and 60's.
Tracks: / Elvis Presley medley / Beatles medley / Twist medley / Bert Kaempfert medley / Glen Miller medley / Bubblegum medley / Singalong medley / Rock'n'roll medley / Cha-cha medley / Oldie medley / Whistling medley / Boogie woogie medley / Harry belafonte medley / Bye bye tunes.
Compact disc: released on Teldec, Jul'87

Cassette: released on Teldec, Jul'87

Album: released on Teldec, Jul'87

PIANO BAR.
Album: released on Teldec (Germany), Jul'85 by Import Records. Dist: IMS Distribution, Polygram Distribution

SALUTES '81.
Album: released on Dansan, Mar'81 by Spartan Records. Dist: Spartan

STEP IN GUNTER NORIS PIANO BAR.
Tracks: / Fascination / Autumn leaves / Memory / Romantic rendezvous / La vie en rose / Chanson d'amour / Entertainer, The / As time goes by / Moon river / Summertime / Bilitis / Dankeschon.
Compact disc: released on Teldec, Jul'87

Cassette: released on Teldec, Jul'87

Album: released on Teldec, Jul'87

TANZPLATTE 1985.
Album: released on Teldec (Import), Sep'84

TANZPLATTE DES JAHRES, DIE (Noris, Gunter & Seine Big Band).
Tracks: / Rubin (Cha cha) / Topas (Rumba) / Smaragd (Samba) / Jade (Jive) / Granat (Paso Doble) / Tigerauge rock (Rock 'n roll) / Turkis fox (Foxtrot) / Diamant waltz (Langsmer Waltz) / Saphir (Tango) / Aquamarin (Waltzer) / Opal slow (Longsamer-foxtrot) / Amethyst (Quickstep).
Compact disc: released on Teldec (Germany), Aug'86 by Import Records. Dist: IMS Distribution, Polygram Distribution

TANZPLATTE DES JAHRES '86, DIE.
Album: released on Teldec (Germany), Sep'85 by Import Records. Dist: IMS Distribution, Polygram Distribution

WORLD IS DANCING, THE Greatest musical hits.
Tracks: / I could have danced all night / If I were a rich man / Memory / Mack the knife / Summertime / You're the one that I want / Edelweiss / Don't cry for me Argentina / Springtime in Paris / Mame / Cabaret.
Compact disc: released on Teldec, May'87

Cassette: released on Teldec, May'87

Album: released on Teldec (Germany), Apr'86 by Import Records. Dist: IMS Distribution, Polygram Distribution

Norlanders

BREAKING THROUGH.
Cassette: released on Ross, Jul'87 by Ross Records. Dist: Ross Distribution, Roots Distribution

Norma

LIFE IS THE REASON.
Single (7"): released on ERC, Nov'83 by ERC Records. Dist: PRT

Single (12"): released on ERC, Nov'83 by ERC Records. Dist: PRT

Norma Jean

MEGA STAR HIT ONE.
Single (7"): released on Uptown, Aug'87 by Uptown Records. Dist: PRT, Cartel

Single (12"): released on Uptown, Aug'87 by Uptown Records. Dist: PRT, Cartel

Normal

LIVE AT WEST RUNTON (Normal & Robert Rental).
Album: released on Rough Trade, '84 by Rough Trade Records. Dist: Rough Trade Distribution, Cartel Distribution

TVOD.
Single (7"): released on Mute, Nov'79 Dist: Spartan Distribution, Rough Trade Distribution, Cartel Distribution

Normal, Henry

OSTRICH MAN.
Album: released on Native, Mar'87 by Native Records. Dist: Red Rhino, Cartel

Norman, Chris

LOVE IS A BATTLEFIELD.
Single (7"): released on RCA, Jan'84 by RCA Records. Dist: RCA, Roots, Swift, Wellard, Chris, I & B, Solomon & Peres Distribution

MIDNIGHT LADY.
Tracks: / Midnight lady / Woman.
Single (7"): released on Arista, Aug'86 by Arista Records. Dist: RCA

Single (12"): released on Arista, Aug'86 by Arista Records. Dist: RCA

MY GIRL AND ME.
Single (7"): released on RCA, Aug'84 by RCA Records. Dist: RCA, Roots, Swift, Wellard, Chris, I & B, Solomon & Peres Distribution

Norman, Gene

GENE NORMAN'S JUST JAZZ CONCERTS.
Boxed set: released on Vogue, Oct'80

Norman, Jessye

60 MINUTES OF MUSIC.
Tracks: / I couldn't hear nobody pray / My, Lord, what a morning / Do Lawd, oh do Lawd / There's a man going round / Ev'ry time I feel de spirit / There is a balm in Gilead / Gospel train / Great day / Mary had a baby / Soon ah will be done / Give me Jesus / Ave Maria / Holy city / Amazing grace / Greensleeves / Let us break bread / I wonder if I wonder / Sweet little Jesus boy.
Notes: Popular spirituals
Cassette: released on Phillips France, Jul'86

SPIRITUALS & SACRED SONGS.
Album: released on Philips, Jun'85 Dist: IMS-Polygram

Cassette: released on Philips, Jun'85 Dist: IMS-Polygram

WITH A SONG IN MY HEART.
Compact disc: Dist: IMS-Polygram

Compact disc: released on Philips, Jun'85 Dist: IMS-Polygram

Norman, Larry

FRIENDS ON TOUR (Norman, Larry/Alwyn Wall/Barratt Band).
Album: released on Chapel Lane, Dec'83 Dist: RCA

Cassette: released on Chapel Lane, Dec'83 Dist: RCA

SOMETHING NEW UNDER THE SUN.
Album: released on Chapel Lane, Dec'83 Dist: RCA

Cassette: released on Chapel Lane, Dec'83 Dist: RCA

UPON THIS ROCK.
Album: released on Dove, May'79 by Dove Records. Dist: Jetstar

Norman, Neil

GREATEST SCIENCE FICTION HITS (Norman, Neil & his Orchestra).
Album: released on PRT, Jan'82 by PRT Records. Dist: PRT

GREATEST SCIENCE FICTION HITS: VOL 2 (Norman, Neil & his Orchestra).
Album: released on PRT, Mar'84 by PRT Records. Dist: PRT

Cassette: released on PRT, Mar'84 by PRT Records. Dist: PRT

INDIANA JONES AND THE TEMPLE OF DOOM (Norman, Neil & his Orchestra).
Single (7"): released on PRT, Aug'84 by PRT Records. Dist: PRT

SOUND OF THE UNIVERSE (Norman, Neil & his Orch.).
Notes: Music from "Return of the Jedi", "Star Wars", "Star Trek", "E.T.", "Battlestar Galactica", "2001", "Radar" etc.
Compact disc: released on Delta, '86 by Delta Records. Dist: Target

Normil Hawaiians

BEAT GOES ON, (THE).
Single (7"): released on Dining Out, Jun'81 by Dining Out Records. Dist: IKF, Independent

MORE WEALTH THAN MONEY.
Album: released on Illuminated, Jan'83 by IKF Records. Dist: Pinnacle, Cartel, Jetstar

STILL OBEDIENT.
Single (7"): released on Illuminated, Nov'81 by IKF Records. Dist: Pinnacle, Cartel, Jetstar

WHAT'S GOING ON?.
Album: released on Illuminated, May'84 by IKF Records. Dist: Pinnacle, Cartel, Jetstar

Norris, John

JOHN NORRIS PLAYS BALDWIN FANTASIA ORGAN.
Album: released on Grosvenor, '75 by Grosvenor Records. Dist: Taylors

Norris, Walter

DRIFTING.
Album: released on Enja (Germany), Jan'82 by Enja Records (W.Germany). Dist: Cadillac Music

STEPPING ON CRACKS.
Album: released on Progressive, Nov'82 by Progressive Records. Dist: Jetstar

SYNCHRONICITY.
Album: released on Enja (Germany), Jan'82 by Enja Records (W.Germany). Dist: Cadillac Music

WINTER ROSE.
Album: released on Enja (Germany), Jan'82 by Enja Records (W.Germany). Dist: Cadillac Music

North by Northeast

NORTH BY NORTHEAST Various artists (Various Artists).
Album: released on MWM, Jun'82 by Mawson & Wareham. Dist: Spartan Distribution, Jazz Music Distribution, JSU Distribution

North by Northwest

NORTH BY NORTHWEST Original film score.
Compact disc: released on TER, Nov'84 Dist: Pinnacle

North Carolina Boys

NORTH CAROLINA BOYS Various artists (Various Artists).
Album: released on Leader, Jun'86 Dist: Jazz Music, Projection

North, Christopher

STRAY.
Single (7"): released on North Corporation, Nov'86

North country rants...

NORTH COUNTRY RANTS & REELS Border folk dances by traditional players (Various Artists).
Cassette: released on Folktracks, Nov'79 by Folktracks Cassettes. Dist: Folktracks

Northern floorshakers

NORTHERN FLOORSHAKERS Various artists (Various Artists).
Album: released on Kent (MCA), Nov'83 by Ace Records. Dist: Pinnacle

Northern Island...

NORTHERN ISLAND WORLD CHAMPION PIPE BANDS Various artists (Various Artists).
Tracks: / Scotland the brave / Mairi's Wedding / I love a lassie / No awa tae bide awa / Police Tattoo 1976 / Minnie Hynd / Old tasty / Rose among the heather / High road to Linton / Jock Wilson's ball / Schiehallion / 51st Highlands division / Rowan tree / Meeting of waters / Loch Rannoch / Louden's bonnie woods / Orange & Blue / Magersfontein / Auld house / Lee Rig / Lilliecrankie / Cock of the north / Glendaurel Highlanders / Bonawe Highlanders / Green hills of Tyrol / Battle's o'er / City of Hastings / Waters of Kylesku / London's bonnie woods & braes / Orange & Blue / Castle Kennedy / Archie McKinlay / Black Isle / Banks of the Lossie / Flowers of the forest / Within a mile of Edinburgh town / Black watch polka / Highland whiskey / Shetland fiddler / Willie Roy's looming house / Blackthorn stick / Black Isle / Abide with me / Jesus love of my soul / Work for the night is coming.
Cassette: released on Homespun(Ireland), May'86 by Outlet Records. Dist: Outlet

Northern lights

TRIBUTE TO ABBA, A.
Cassette: released on Kingfisher, Nov'81 Dist: PRT

Northern sky

TAKE IT ON TRUST.
Single (7"): released on Rebound, Oct'85 by Rebound Records. Dist: Terry Blood Distribution

Northern Soul

HURTING.
Tracks: / Hurting / My baby ain't no play thing / In the pocket* / Assorted tracks*.
Single (7"): released on Kool Kat, 23 May'87 by Kool Kat Records. Dist: PRT

Single (12"): released on Kool Kat, 23 May'87 by Kool Kat Records. Dist: PRT

Northern soul story

NORTHERN SOUL STORY-VOLUME2 (Various Artists).
Double Album: released on Soul Supply, Jan'87 by High Energy Records. Dist: Charly

Cassette: released on Soul Supply, Jan'87 by High Energy Records. Dist: Charly

NORTHERN SOUL STORY VOL.1 Various artists (Various Artists).
Tracks: / I'm gonna get you / Stick by me baby / Come on and live / Sugar pie honey / Day my heart stood still / Goose pimples / Breakdown / Cross my heart / Lady love / Don't wanna face the truth / I'm where it's at / I didn't want to cry / Mind in a bind / I know what to do to satisfy you / Your wish is my command / Lonely lover / Girl across the street (The) / Another day / Love's such a funny thing / Love time / Love's like a quicksand / I love my baby / Heave is in your arms / Don't bring me down / Baby that's a groove / We must be doing something right / There's nothing else to say / There's that mountain / You got it / Never never (will I fall in love) / Job opening / Wash and wear love.
Notes: Double album.
Album: released on Soul Supply, Jan'87 by High Energy Records. Dist: Charly

Cassette: released on Soul Supply, Jan'87 by High Energy Records. Dist: Charly

NORTHERN SOUL STORY VOL.3 Various artists (Various Artists).
Album: released on Soul Supply, Feb'87 by High Energy Records. Dist: Charly

Cassette: released on Soul Supply, Feb'87 by High Energy Records. Dist: Charly

NORTHERN SOUL STORY PART 4 (Various Artists).
Album: released on Soul Supply, 30 May'87 by High Energy Records. Dist: Charly

Northern Tracks

BEST OF NORTHERN TRACKS, (THE).
Album: released on Spark, May'74 by Spark Records. Dist: PRT

North, Hugo

WOLFGANG JACOBI (North, Hugo, Saabrucken Madrigal Choir).
Tracks: / Impromtu / Scherzo / Franzosische / Piange Maria / Ich spring an diesm ringe / Es ist ein schnee gefallen / Bet't Kinder, Bet't / Tanz / Choral / Kinderspiele in Ascoli.
Notes: Retail price given by ARC excluding P & P (via Mail Order) is 7.35 . Mail order distribution address: Accordian Record Club, 146 Birmingham Road, Kidderminster, Worcs, DY10 2SL. Tel: 0562 746105
Album: released on Accordion Record Club, Jul'86 by Accordion Record Club Records. Dist: Accordion Record Club

North, Ian

NEO.
Album: released on Aura, Oct'79 by Hollywood Nites Distribution. Dist: Pinnacle

North India

NORTH INDIA Music from the shrines of Ajmer & Mundra (Various Artists).
Album: released on Tangent, Apr'81 Dist: Roots Distribution, Lugtons Distributors, Taylors, JSU Distribution, Spartan Distribution

North London Community...

ETERNALLY GRATEFUL Bible Week highlights.
Album: released on Word, Dec'84 by Word Records. Dist: Word Distribution, CBS

Cassette: released on Word, Dec'84 by Word Records. Dist: Word Distribution, CBS

North, Nicky

JAMES BOND 21ST ANNIVERSARY (North, Nicky Orchestra).
Album: released on VCL, Jul'83 by Elecstar Records. Dist: PRT

North Sea Gas

FROM FIELDS A'FAR.
Album: released on MK, Oct'84
Cat. no: **MK 2**
Cassette: released on MK, Oct'84

North shore accordion...

CONCERT USA.
Album: released on ARC (Accordion Records), May'84 Dist: Accordion Record Club

North star band

NORTH STAR BAND.
Album: released on Adelphi(USA), May'81 by Adelphi Records (USA). Dist: Projection, Swift

Northumbria...

CUT AND DRY DOLLY (FOLK MUSIC) (Northumbrian small pipes).
Album: released on Topic, May'76

NORTHUMBRIAN PIPES Various artists (Various Artists).
Album: released on Topic, May'74 by Polygram Records.

North West Ten

YOU'VE GOT ALL NIGHT.
Single (7"): released on Ensign, Jun'85 by Ensign Records. Dist: CBS Distribution

Single (12"): released on Ensign, Jun'85 by Ensign Records. Dist: CBS Distribution

No Rules

NO RULES Various artists (Various Artists).
Tracks: / Time bomb city / Cold love / City brave / Poison pen letters / Shout and scream / Time of our lives / Duty unto death / Khmer Rouge / Religion / Electronic church / No compromise / Conscience prayer / No rules / Slow death.
Album: released on Conifer, Jan'87 by Conifer Records. Dist: Conifer

Norvo, 'Red'

1983 (Norvo, Red & His Orchestra).
Notes: With: Mildred Bailey/Terry Allen
Album: released on Circle(USA), Jun'86 by Jazzology Records (USA). Dist: Jazz Music, Swift, Chris Wellard

MISTER SWING.
Album: released on Swinghouse, May'84 Dist: Jazz Music Distribution, Swift Distribution, Chris Wellard Distribution

RED NORVO'S FABULOUS JAM SESSION.
Album: released on Spotlite, May'83 by Spotlite Records. Dist: Cadillac, Jazz Music, Spotlite

RED NORVO'S SWINGING BANDS.
Album: released on Rarities (Import), Apr'81

SWING THAT MUSIC (see Braff, Ruby) (Norvo, Red & Ruby Braff).

TOWN HALL CONCERT 1945 (Norvo, Red & His Orchestra).
Album: released on Commodore Classics, '87 by Teldec Records (Germany). Dist: Conifer, IMS, Polygram

TOWN HALL CONCERT 1 (Norvo, Red & His Orchestra).
Album: released on London, May'74 by London Records. Dist: Polygram

Norway

TALES FROM.....
Cassette: released on Anvil, Apr'80 Dist: Anvil

Norwood

I CAN'T LET YOU GO.
Tracks: / I can't let you go / Don't let love / Should have been us together / Lady in love / I can't live without you / Give it up / Feels so good / Glad I found you / Come back my lover.
Single (7"): released on MCA, Apr'87 by MCA Records. Dist: Polygram, MCA

Single (12"): released on MCA, Apr'87 by MCA Records. Dist: Polygram, MCA

Album: released on MCA, May'87 by MCA Records. Dist: Polygram, MCA

Cassette: released on MCA, May'87 by MCA Records. Dist: Polygram, MCA

SHOULD HAVE BEEN US TOGETHER.
Single (7"): released on MCA, Aug'87 by MCA Records. Dist: Polygram, MCA

Norwood B

AN EVENING WITH NORWOOD B.
Album:

YOUR ON THE ONE (YOU ON THE MONEY).
Single (7"):

Single (12"):

Norwood builder

NORWOOD BUILDER Various artists (Various Artists).
Cassette: released on Anvil, Jan'81 Dist: Anvil

Nose Flutes

LEARNING TO SPRAY WITH CATARRH.
Single (12"): released on Reflex, Nov'85

LEG FULL OF ALCOHOL.
Single (12"): released on Ron Johnson, Feb'87 by Ron Johnson Records. Dist: Nine Mile Distribution, Cartel Distribution

RAVERS, THE.
Tracks: / Ravers, The.
Single (12"): released on Ron Johnson, Mar'87 by Ron Johnson Records. Dist: Nine Mile Distribution, Cartel Distribution

SEVERAL YOUNG MEN IGNITE HARDBOARD STUMP.
Tracks: / Perfect cockney hard-on / Romance takes control / Dreamboat / Bullet enters Brad / This is my home / Lumbo/The harmony of dogs / Holiday time / Past promise broken in previous life / Why is everyone a man / Sugar buch, The / Cowboy factory.
Notes: Composer: The Nose Flutes. Published by Flex Music (C) 1986
Album: released on Reflex, Jun'86

No Sovereign

SHOWDOWN.
Tracks: / Showdown / Know love so well.
Single (7"): released on Geffen, Apr'87 by Geffen Records. Dist: WEA, CBS

Single (12"): released on Geffen, Apr'87 by Geffen Records. Dist: WEA, CBS

Nostalgic...

NOSTALGIC MEMORIES Various artists (Various Artists).
Album: released on Note, Aug'80 by EMI Records. Dist: EMI

Cassette: released on Note, Aug'80 by EMI Records. Dist: EMI

NOSTALGIC MEMORIES VOL.2 Various artists (Various Artists).
Cassette: released on Note, Jun'81 by EMI Records. Dist: EMI

NOSTALGIC TRIP TO THE STARS VOL.1 Various artists (Various Artists).
Album: released on Monmouth, Jun'79

NOSTALGIC TRIP TO THE STARS VOL.2 Various artists (Various Artists).
Album: released on Monmouth, Jun'79

Notch, Kenny

RING UP MY NUMBER.
Tracks: / Ring up my number / Ring up my number (Version).
Single (12"): released on Unity Sound, Dec'86 Dist: Jetstar

Notch, Trevor

BIP BIP BIP BIP BOP BOP BOP.
Tracks: / Bip bip bip bip bop bop bop / Just cool.
Single (7"): released on Island, Feb'86 by Island Records. Dist: Polygram

FAMILY COURT.
Single (12"): released on Sound Disc, Feb'87 Dist: Jetstar

Not drowning waving

SING SING.
Album: released on Rampant, Nov'86

Nothing But Happiness

COULDN'T MAKE YOU MINE.
Tracks: / Couldn't make you mine / Narcotics day.
Single (12"): released on Remorse, Jun'86 by Remorse Records. Dist: Revolver, Cartel

DETOUR.
Album: released on Remorse, Mar'87 by Remorse Records. Dist: Revolver, Cartel

NARCOTICS DAY.
Tracks: / Narcotics day.
Single (12"): released on Remorse, Nov'86 by Remorse Records. Dist: Revolver, Cartel

Nothing In Common

NOTHING IN COMMON Original soundtrack (Various Artists).
Tracks: / Nothing in common / Burning of the heart / If it wasn't love / Over the weekend / Loving strangers / Until you say you love me / Don't forget to dance / No one's gonna love you / 7 summers / Instrumental theme.
Album: released on Arista, Mar'87 by Arista Records. Dist: RCA

Cassette: released on Arista, Mar'87 by Arista Records. Dist: RCA

Not just beat music

NOT JUST BEAT MUSIC 1965-70 Various artists (Various Artists).
Album: released on See For Miles, Oct'82 by Charly Records. Dist: Spartan

Not just Mandela

NOT JUST MANDELA Various artists (Various Artists).
Album: released on Davy Lamp, Nov'86 Dist: Jungle, Cartel

Not Quite Jerusalem

NOT QUITE JERUSALEM Original soundtrack (Rondo Veneziano).
Album: released on Fanfare, Apr'85 by Ferroway/Fanfare Records. Dist: PRT

Cassette: released on Fanfare, Apr'85 by Ferroway/Fanfare Records. Dist: PRT

No Trend

HEART OF DARKNESS (No Trend with Lydia Lunch).
Single (12"): released on Widowspeak, Oct'85 Dist: Rough Trade

WHEN DEATH WON'T SOLVE YOUR PROBLEM.
Album: released on Widowspeak, Feb'86 Dist: Rough Trade

Notsensibles

I AM THE BISHOP.
Single (7"): released on Snotty Snail, May'81 Dist: Rough Trade

I THOUGHT YOU WERE DEAD.
Single (7"): released on Snotty Snail, Aug'80 Dist: Rough Trade

MARGARET THATCHER.
Single (7"): released on Snotty Snail, May'8[illegible] Dist: Rough Trade

Not the nine o'clock news

AYATOLLAH SONG.
Single (7"): released on BBC, Dec'80 by BB[illegible] Records & Tapes. Dist: EMI, PRT, Pye

NOT THE DOUBLE ALBUM.
Album: released on BBC, Oct'84 by BBC Re[illegible]ords & Tapes. Dist: EMI, PRT, Pye

Cassette: released on BBC, Oct'84 by BB[illegible] Records & Tapes. Dist: EMI, PRT, Pye

NOT THE NINE O'CLOCK NEWS Origin[illegible] cast.
Album: released on BBC, Oct'80 by BBC Re[illegible]ords & Tapes. Dist: EMI, PRT, Pye

Cassette: released on BBC, Oct'80 by BB[illegible]

Records & Tapes. Dist: EMI, PRT, Pye

NOT THE NINE O'CLOCK NEWS (HEDGEHOG SANDWICH) Various artists (Various Artists).
Album: released on BBC, Oct'81 by BBC Records & Tapes. Dist: EMI, PRT, Pye

Cassette: released on BBC, Oct'81 by BBC Records & Tapes. Dist: EMI, PRT, Pye

NOT THE NINE O'CLOCK NEWS: THE MEMORY KINDA LINGERS Original cast.
Double Album: released on BBC, Oct'82 by BBC Records & Tapes. Dist: EMI, PRT, Pye

Double cassette: released on BBC, Oct'82 by BBC Records & Tapes. Dist: EMI, PRT, Pye

Not the US...

NOT THE US PRESIDENTIAL PRESS.... Various artists (Various Artists).
Single (7"): released on BBC, Oct'84 by BBC Records & Tapes. Dist: EMI, PRT, Pye

Notts alliance

CHEERFUL 'ORN, (THE).
Album: released on Tradition, Aug'76

Nourse, Everett

MEMORIES OF THE FABULOUS FOX Wurlitzer Organ (Nourse, Everett/Tony James).

MEMORIES OF THE FABULOUS FOX VOL.2 Wurlitzer Organ (Nourse, Everett/Tony James).

Nova

VIMANA.
Album: released on Arista, Nov'76 by Arista Records. Dist: RCA

WINGS OF LOVE.
Album: released on Arista, Oct'77 by Arista Records. Dist: RCA

Nova, Aldo

HOLD BACK THE NIGHT.
Single (7"): released on Portrait, Jan'84 by CBS Records. Dist: CBS

Single (12"): released on Portrait, Jan'84 by CBS Records. Dist: CBS

Double-pack single: released on Portrait, Jan'84 by CBS Records. Dist: CBS

SUBJECT.
Cassette: released on Portrait, Nov'83 by CBS Records. Dist: CBS

Album: released on Portrait, Nov'83 by CBS Records. Dist: CBS

TWITCH.
Album: released on Portrait, Nov'85 by CBS Records. Dist: CBS

Cassette: released on Portrait, Nov'85 by CBS Records. Dist: CBS

Nova Casper

TURNED ON TO YOU.
Tracks: / Turned on to you / Turned on to you (Inst.).
Single (7"): released on Bluebird, Jul'86 by Bluebird Records. Dist: EMI, Jetstar

Single (12"): released on Bluebird, Jul'86 by Bluebird Records. Dist: EMI, Jetstar

Novak, Sean

THIS IS YOUR CAPTAIN.
Single (7"): released on Priority, Sep'84 by Priority Records. Dist: RCA

Single (12"): released on Priority, Sep'84 by Priority Records. Dist: RCA

Novalis

BANISHED BRIDGE.
Album: released on Logo, '79 by Logo Records. Dist: Roots, BMG

BRANDUNG.
Album: released on Logo, '79 by Logo Records. Dist: Roots, BMG

KONZERTE.
Album: released on Logo, '79 by Logo Records. Dist: Roots, BMG

NOVALIS.
Album: released on Brain, Jan'78

SOMMERABEND.
Album: released on Logo, '79 by Logo Records. Dist: Roots, BMG

VIELLEICHT BIST DU EIN CLOWN.
Album: released on Brain, Mar'79

Nova, Nancy

LIFELINE.
Single (7"): released on EMI, Aug'83 by EMI Records. Dist: EMI

Album: by A&M Records. Dist: Polygram

Nova, Paul

FAMOUS BOYS.
Single (7"): released on Exhibit One, Jul'83 Dist: Pinnacle

TREES WITHOUT LEAVES.
Album: released on Exhibit One, Apr'84 Dist: Pinnacle

Nova Vaga Album

NOVA VAGA ALBUM various artists (Various Artists).
Album: released on Warm, Jul'79 Dist: EMI

Novelle, Jay

IF THIS AIN'T LOVE.
Single (7"): released on Club, Aug'84 by Phonogram Records. Dist: Polygram

Single (12"): released on Club, Aug'84 by Phonogram Records. Dist: Polygram

Novello, Ivor

DANCING YEARS (THE).
Album: Dist: Polygram

Novelty...

NOVELTY GUITAR INSTRUMENTALS various artists (Various Artists).
Album: released on Sonet, '74 by Sonet Records. Dist: PRT

Novick, Billy

NEW PENNY WHISTLE ALBUM.
Album: released on Innisfree(USA), May'79 by Green Linnet (USA). Dist: Projection

Novik,Bridget

DANUBE (Novik,Bridget & M).
Single (7"): released on Stiff, Jun'82 by Stiff Records. Dist: EMI, Record Services Distribution (Ireland)

Single (12"): released on Stiff, Jun'82 by Stiff Records. Dist: EMI, Record Services Distribution (Ireland)

WEDDING DANCE.
Single (7"): released on Stiff, Oct'82 by Stiff Records. Dist: EMI, Record Services Distribution (Ireland)

Single (12"): released on Stiff, Oct'82 by Stiff Records. Dist: EMI, Record Services Distribution (Ireland)

Novo

EXTREMIX (INSTRUMENTAL).
Single (7"): released on Carrere, Apr'84 by Carrere Records. Dist: PRT, Spartan

Single (12"): released on Carrere, Apr'84 by Carrere Records. Dist: PRT, Spartan

Novocento

MOVIN' ON.
Single (7"): released on WEA, Jan'85 by WEA Records. Dist: WEA

Now

DEVELOPMENT CORPORATIONS.
Single (7"): released on Ultimate, Jun'81 by Ultimate Records. Dist: Spartan

NOW 8 VIDEO (Various Artists).
Tracks: / Notorious / Suburbia / Forever live and die / Sometimes / Don't leave me this way / showing out (get fresh at the weekend) / Venus / Step right up / Break out / Think for a minute / Ghost train (waiting for the) / Anything / One great thing / All fall down / In the army now / Don't forget me when I'm gone / Warriors of the wasteland / You keep me hanging on / I wanna wake up with you.
Notes: 19 tracks. Total playin time: 80 minutes approx.
Video-cassette (VHS): released on PMI, Dec'86 by PMI Records. Dist: EMI

NOW - THE CHRISTMAS ALBUM Various artists (Various Artists).
Tracks: / Do they know it's Christmas / I wish it could be Christmas everyday / Merry Xmas everybody / Last Christmas / Step into Christmas / Il Dulce jubilo / Another Rock 'n' Roll Christmas / Wonderful Christmas time / Blue Christmas / Happy Xmas (war is over) / I believe in Father Christmas / Spaceman came travelling, A / Stop the cavalry / Little Saint Nick / Thank God it's Christmas / Lonely this Christmas / When a child is born / White Christmas / Spaceman came travelling, A.
Album: released on Virgin, Nov'86 by Virgin Records. Dist: EMI, Virgin Distribution

Cassette: released on Virgin, Nov'86 by Virgin Records. Dist: EMI, Virgin Distribution

Compact disc: released on Virgin, Nov'86 by Virgin Records. Dist: EMI, Virgin Distribution

NOW - THE CHRISTMAS COMPACT DISC Various artists (Various Artists).

NOW...VOL.1 (VIDEO) (Various Artists).
Notes: With Phil Collins, Duran Duran, UB 40 etc. etc.
Video-cassette (VHS): released on Video Collection, May'87 by Video Collection International Ltd.. Dist: Counterpoint

NOW...VOL.2 (VIDEO) (Various Artists).
Notes: With Nik Kershaw, Big Country, Status Quo etc.
Video-cassette (VHS): released on Video Collection, May'87 by Video Collection International Ltd.. Dist: Counterpoint

NOW...VOL.3 (VIDEO) (Various Artists).
Notes: With Simple Minds, Madness, Talk Talk etc.
Video-cassette (VHS): released on Video Collection, May'87 by Video Collection International Ltd.. Dist: Counterpoint

Now And Then

NOW AND THEN VOL. 1 Various artists (Various Artists).
Album: released on King Jammy's, Jul'87

No Way Jose

TEQUILA.
Single (7"): released on Fourth & Broadway, Aug'85 by Island Records. Dist: Polygram, EMI

Picture disc single: released on Fourth & Broadway, Aug'85 by Island Records. Dist: Polygram, EMI

Single (12"): released on Fourth & Broadway, Aug'85 by Island Records. Dist: Polygram, EMI

Now Creative Arts...

NOW CREATIVE ARTS JAZZ ENSEMBLE Various artists (Various Artists).
Album: released on Arhoolie, May'81 by Arhoolie Records. Dist: Projection, Topic, Jazz Music, Swift, Roots

Now Dance!

NOW DANCE! Various artists (Various Artists).
Double Album: released on Virgin-EMI, Jun'85 by EMI Records. Dist: EMI

Double cassette: released on Virgin-EMI, Jun'85 by EMI Records. Dist: EMI

Now-Dance 86

NOW-DANCE 86 Various artists (Various Artists).
Tracks: / Pull up to the bumper / So macho / Hit that perfect beat / I can prove it / I wanna wake up with you / Chain reaction / We don't have to / Don't leave me this way / Can't wait another minute / midas touch / Ain't nothin' goin' on but the rent / love can't turn around / Rumours / All and all / Mine all mine / Who's zoomin' who? / Heaven must be missing an angel / Don't waste my time / breaking away.
Notes: Over two hours of smash hits. adouble album of extended 12" mixes.
Double Album: released on Virgin, Oct'86 by Virgin Records. Dist: EMI, Virgin Distribution

Double cassette: released on Virgin, Oct'86 by Virgin Records. Dist: EMI, Virgin Distribution

Now That's What...

NOW THAT'S WHAT I CALL MUSIC VOL 8 Various artists (Various Artists).
Tracks: / Showing out (get fresh at the weekend) / We don't have to / Step right up / What have you done for me lately / Human / I wanna wake up with you / Dont give up / Think for a minute / Ghost train (Waiting for the) / In the army now / Stuck with you / One great thing / Greetings to the new brunette / Die in your arms (I just) / You keep me hanging on / Calling all the heroes / Waterloo / French kissing in the USA / I didn't mean to turn you on / Wizard (The) / Close to you (They long to be) / Every loser wins / Forever live and die / Notorious / Suburbia / Walk this way / Don't leave me this way / Breakout / Higher love / Live and die (forever) / In too deep / Word up / I'm not perfect (but I'm perfect for you).
Double Album: released on Virgin, Nov'86 by Virgin Records. Dist: EMI, Virgin Distribution

Double cassette: released on Virgin, Nov'86 by Virgin Records. Dist: EMI, Virgin Distribution

Compact disc: by EMI Records. Dist: EMI

NOW THAT'S WHAT I CALL MUSIC 86 Various artists (Various Artists).
Tracks: / Kind of magic, A / Absolute beginners / Sledgehammer / West end girls / Lessons in love / Don't leave me this way / Chain reaction / We don't have to / Ain't nothin' goin' on but the rent / Sing our own song / Everybody wants to rule the world / In the army now / Died in your arms (I just) / On my own / I wanna wake up with you.
Compact disc: released on EMI, Nov'86 by EMI Records. Dist: EMI

NOW THAT'S WHAT I CALL MUSIC VOL 9 Various artists (Various Artists).
Tracks: / Reet Petite / Live it up / Right Thing, The / Sometimes / C'est La Vie / You Sexy Thing / It doesn't have to be this way / Caravan of love / Everything I own / Rat In Mi Kitchen / Big Fun / Stay out of my life / Heartache / Trick of the night / Take my breath away / Great Pretender / Stand by me / Down to Earth / So Cold the Night / Jack your body / I Love My Radio / Loving you is sweeter than ever / Manhattan Skyline / Sonic Boom Boy / Livin' on a prayer / Land of confusion / Final Countdown / Over the hills / Cross the bridge / Hymn to her.
Double Album: released on EMI, Mar'87 by EMI Records. Dist: EMI

Double cassette: released on EMI, Mar'87 by EMI Records. Dist: EMI

Compact disc: released on Virgin-EMI, Apr'87 by EMI Records. Dist: EMI

NOW THAT'S WHAT I CALL MUSIC VIDEO 1 Various artists (Various Artists).
Video-cassette (VHS): released on EMI-Virgin, Jun'86 by EMI Records. Dist: EMI

Video-cassette [Betamax]: released on EMI-Virgin, Jun'86 by EMI Records. Dist: EMI

NOW THAT'S WHAT I CALL MUSIC VIDEO 2 Various artists (Various Artists).
Video-cassette (VHS): released on EMI-Virgin, Jun'86 by EMI Records. Dist: EMI

Video-cassette [Betamax]: released on EMI-Virgin, Jun'86 by EMI Records. Dist: EMI

NOW THAT'S WHAT I CALL MUSIC VIDEO 5 Various artists (Various Artists).
Notes: Artists include:Duran Duran/Phil Collins/Elton John/Millie Jackson
Video-cassette (VHS): released on EMI-Virgin, Jun'86 by EMI Records. Dist: EMI

Video-cassette [Betamax]: released on EMI-Virgin, Jun'86 by EMI Records. Dist: EMI

NOW THAT'S WHAT I CALL MUSIC VIDEO 3 Various artists (Various Artists).
Video-cassette (VHS): released on EMI-Virgin, Jun'86 by EMI Records. Dist: EMI

Video-cassette [Betamax]: released on EMI-Virgin, Jun'86 by EMI Records. Dist: EMI

NOW THAT'S WHAT I CALL MUSIC VIDEO 4 Various artists (Various Artists).
Notes: Artists include: Queen/Culture Club/UB40/Limahl/Tina Turner. Number of tracks: 20. Type of recording:Compilation. Total playing time: 85 minutes.
Video-cassette (VHS): released on EMI-Virgin, Jun'86 by EMI Records. Dist: EMI

Video-cassette [Betamax]: released on EMI-Virgin, Jun'86 by EMI Records. Dist: EMI

NOW THAT'S WHAT I CALL MUSIC VIDEO 6 Various artists (Various Artists).
Notes: Number of tracks: 19. Type of recording: Compilation. Total playing time: 77 minutes.
Video-cassette (VHS): released on EMI-Virgin, Jun'86 by EMI Records. Dist: EMI

Video-cassette [Betamax]: released on EMI-Virgin, Jun'86 by EMI Records. Dist: EMI

NOW THAT'S WHAT I CALL MUSIC VIDEO 7 Various artists (Various Artists).
Video-cassette (VHS): released on PMI, Nov'86 by PMI Records. Dist: EMI

Video-cassette [Betamax]: released on PMI, Nov'86 by PMI Records. Dist: EMI

NOW THAT'S WHAT I CALL MUSIC VIDEO 8 Various artists (Various Artists).
Notes: 20 top chart hits on video. Number of tracks:20.
Video-cassette (VHS): released on PMI, Nov'86 by PMI Records. Dist: EMI

Video-cassette [Betamax]: released on PMI, Nov'86 by PMI Records. Dist: EMI

NOW THAT'S WHAT I CALL MUSIC VOL 7 Various artists (Various Artists).
Tracks: / Sledgehammer / Sing our own song / Let's go all the way / Lessons in love / Opportunities(Lets make lots of money) / Sinful / Camouflage / Paranoimia / Lady in red (The) / Absolute beginners / Invisible touch / All the things she said / Happy hour / Look away / Brilliant mind / Call of the wild / Edge of heaven (The) / My favourite waste of time / Too good to be forgotten / Spirit in the sky / New beginning (Mamba Seyra) / Hunting high and low (Remix) / Holding back the years / When the going gets tough the tough get going / Set me free / I can't wait / (Bang Zoom)Let's go go / Amityville / Headlines / You and me tonight / On my own.
Notes: Double album and double cassette.
Double Album: released on Virgin-EMI, Aug'86 by EMI Records. Dist: EMI

Double cassette: released on Virgin-EMI, Aug'86 by EMI Records. Dist: EMI

NOW THAT'S WHAT I CALL MUSIC VOL 6 Various artists (Various Artists).
Double Album: released on EMI-Virgin,

Nov'85 by EMI Records. Dist: EMI

Double cassette: released on EMI-Virgin, Nov'85 by EMI Records. Dist: EMI

NOW THAT'S WHAT I CALL MUSIC Various artists (Various Artists).
Double Album: released on Virgin-EMI, Nov'83 by EMI Records. Dist: EMI

Double cassette: released on Virgin-EMI, Nov'83 by EMI Records. Dist: EMI

NOW THAT'S WHAT I CALL MUSIC VOL 2 Various artists (Various Artists).
Double Album: released on EMI, Apr'84 by EMI Records. Dist: EMI

Double cassette: released on EMI, Apr'84 by EMI Records. Dist: EMI

NOW THAT'S WHAT I CALL MUSIC VOL 3 Various artists (Various Artists).
Double Album: released on EMI-Virgin, Aug'84 by EMI Records. Dist: EMI

Double cassette: released on EMI-Virgin, Aug'84 by EMI Records. Dist: EMI

NOW THAT'S WHAT I CALL MUSIC VOL 4 Various artists (Various Artists).
Compact disc: by EMI Records. Dist: EMI

Double Album: released on EMI-Virgin, Nov'84 by EMI Records. Dist: EMI

Double cassette: released on EMI-Virgin, Nov'84 by EMI Records. Dist: EMI

NOW THAT'S WHAT I CALL MUSIC VOL 5 Various artists (Various Artists).
Double Album: released on EMI-Virgin, Aug'85 by EMI Records. Dist: EMI

Double cassette: released on EMI-Virgin, Aug'85 by EMI Records. Dist: EMI

NOW...VOL.9 (Various Artists).
Notes: Released on Virgin/PVG for under #10

Now - The Summer Album

NOW-THE SUMMER ALBUM Various artists (Various Artists).
Tracks: / Groovin' / Summer breeze / Do it again / Lovely day / Dreadlock holiday / Girl from Ipanema (The) / Summer (The first time) / Summer holiday / California girls / Summertime blues / Sunny afternoon / Under the boardwalk / California dreamin' / San Francisco(Be sure to wear some flowers in your hair) / All you need is love / Sun goes go down (Living it up) / Walking on sunshine / Give it up / Fantastic day / Island girl / Echo beach / Summer fun / Here comes the sun / Day I met Marie (The) / In the summertime / Daydream / Daydream believer / Here comes summer.
Notes: Double album and cassette
Album: released on EMI-Virgin, Jul'86 by EMI Records. Dist: EMI

Cassette: released on EMI-Virgin, Jul'86 by EMI Records. Dist: EMI

No Zion Band

FREEDOM CITY.
Single (12"): released on Freedom City, Nov'82 by Freedom City. Dist: Pinnacle

NRBQ

ALL HOPPED UP.
Album: released on Rounder, May'79 Dist: Roots Distribution

KICK ME HARD.
Album: released on Rounder, May'79 Dist: Roots Distribution

TAP DANCING BATS.
Album: released on Demon, Mar'86 by Demon Records. Dist: Pinnacle

Cassette: released on Demon, Mar'86 by Demon Records. Dist: Pinnacle

TAP DANCING BATS(ROCK).
Album: released on Rounder (USA), Jan'84 Dist: Mike's Country Music Room Distribution, Jazz Music Distribution, Swift Distribution, Roots Records Distribution, Projection Distribution, Topic Distribution

Nu

NICOLS 'N' NU (Nu/Maggie Nicols).
Album: released on Leo, Oct'85 Dist: Recommended

Nuance

TAKE A CHANCE (Nuance feat.Vikki Love).
Single (12"): released on Fourth & Broadway, Apr'84 by Island Records. Dist: Polygram, EMI

Nuclear Assault

BRAIN DEATH.
Tracks: / Brain death / final flight / Demolition.
Single (12"): released on Under One Flag, Jan'87 Dist: Pinnacle

GAME OVER.
Tracks: / LSD / Cold steel / Betrayal / Radiation sickness / Hang the Pope / After the holocaust / Mr Softee theme / Stranded in Hell / Nuclear war / My America / Vengeance / Brain death.
Album: released on Under One Flag, Nov'86 Dist: Pinnacle

Compact disc: released on Under One Flag, Aug'87 Dist: Pinnacle

PLAGUE, THE.
Album: released on Under One Flag, Jul'87 Dist: Pinnacle

Cassette: released on Under One Flag, Sep'87 Dist: Pinnacle. Estim retail price in Sep'87 was £4.10.

Nuclear Socketts

PLAY LOUD.
Single (7"): released on Subversive, Jul'81 Dist: Backs, Cartel Distribution

Nucleus

WE'LL TALK ABOUT IT LATER.
Album: released on Vertigo, Jan'70 by Phonogram Records. Dist: Polygram

Nude

MODERN JAZZ.
Album: released on Cleopatra, Dec'86 by Musicland Records. Dist: Rough Trade, Cartel

Nugent, Ted

ANTHOLOGY.
Tracks: / Flesh and blood / Weekend warriors / Workin' hard, playin' hard / Snakeskin cowboys / Motor city madness / Scream dream / Come and get it / Smoke screen / Stormtroopin' / Stranglehold / Cat scratch fever / Dog eat dog / Turn it up / Hard as nails / Death by misadventure / State of shock / Where have you been all my life / I love you so I told you a lie / Out of control / Live it up.
Double Album: released on Raw Power, Sep'86 Dist: Pinnacle

Double cassette: released on Raw Power, Sep'86 Dist: Pinnacle

CALL OF THE WILD & TOOTH FANG (Nugent, Ted & Amboy Dukes).
Double Album: released on Discreet, Feb'77

CAT SCRATCH FEVER.
Album: released on Epic, Jun'77 by CBS Records. Dist: CBS

Cassette: released on Epic, Jun'77 by CBS Records. Dist: CBS

FREE FOR ALL.
Album: released on Epic, Jan'84 by CBS Records. Dist: CBS

Cassette: released on Epic, Jan'84 by CBS Records. Dist: CBS

INTENSITIES-(IN 10 CITIES).
Album: released on Epic, Apr'81 by CBS Records. Dist: CBS

Cassette: released on Epic, Apr'81 by CBS Records. Dist: CBS

JOURNEYS AND MIGRATIONS.
Double Album: released on Mainstream, Feb'83

LITTLE MISS DANGEROUS.
Tracks: / High heels in motion / Strangers / Little miss dangerous / Savage dancer / Crazy ladies / When your body talks / My little red book / take me away / Angry young man / Painkiller.
Compact disc: released on WEA, Nov'86 by WEA Records. Dist: WEA

Album: released on WEA, Nov'86 by WEA Records. Dist: WEA

Cassette: released on WEA, Nov'86 by WEA Records. Dist: WEA

MARRIAGE & ON THE ROCKS (Nugent, Ted & Amboy Dukes).
Double Album: released on Polydor, Jun'77 by Polydor Records. Dist: Polygram, Polydor

STATE OF SHOCK.
Album: released on Epic, Jun'79 by CBS Records. Dist: CBS

Cassette: released on Epic, Jun'79 by CBS Records. Dist: CBS

TIED UP IN LOVE.
Single (7"): released on Atlantic, Feb'84 by WEA Records. Dist: WEA

WEEKEND WARRIORS.
Album: released on Epic, Jan'78 by CBS Records. Dist: CBS

Nuggets

NUGGETS VOL.5 POP PART 3 various artists (Various Artists).
Album: released on Rhino (USA), Jan'86 by Rhino Records (USA).

NUGGETS VOL.6 POP PART 2 Various Artists (Various Artists).
Album: released on Rhino (USA), Jan'86 by Rhino Records (USA).

NUGGETS VOL.7 EARLY SAN FRANSISCO Various artists (Various Artists).
Album: released on Rhino (USA), Jan'86 by Rhino Records (USA).

NUGGETS - VOLUME 1 (THE HITS) Various Artists (Various Artists).
Album: released on Rhino (USA), Jan'85 by Rhino Records (USA).

NUGGETS - VOLUME 2 (PUNK) Various Artists (Various Artists).
Album: released on Rhino (USA), Jan'85 by Rhino Records (USA).

NUGGETS - VOLUME 3 (POP) Various Artists (Various Artists).
Album: released on Rhino (USA), Jan'85 by Rhino Records (USA).

NUGGETS - VOLUME 4 (POP PART 2) Various Artists (Various Artists).
Album: released on Rhino (USA), Jan'85 by Rhino Records (USA).

NUGGETS VOLUME 5 Pop part 3 (Various Artists).
Album: released on Rhino (USA), Jan'86 by Rhino Records (USA).

Numan, Gary

1978/79 (Numan,Gary & Tubeway Army).
Cassette: released on Beggars Banquet, Apr'85 by Beggars Banquet Records. Dist: WEA

1978/79 VOL.2.
Single (12"): released on Beggars Banquet, Mar'85 by Beggars Banquet Records. Dist: WEA

1978/79 VOL.3 6-track EP.
Single (12"): released on Beggars Banquet, Feb'85 by Beggars Banquet Records. Dist: WEA

ARE FRIENDS ELECTRIC.
Single (7"): released on Numa, Apr'85 by Numa Records. Dist: PRT Distribution

Single (12"): released on Numa, Apr'85 by Numa Records. Dist: PRT Distribution

ASSASSIN.
Album: released on Beggars Banquet, Aug'82 by Beggars Banquet Records. Dist: WEA

BERSERKER.
Album: released on Numa, Nov'84 by Numa Records. Dist: PRT Distribution

Cassette: released on Numa, Nov'84 by Numa Records. Dist: PRT Distribution

Single (7"): released on Numa, Oct'84 by Numa Records. Dist: PRT Distribution

Single (12"): released on Numa, Oct'84 by Numa Records. Dist: PRT Distribution

BERSERKER TOUR.
Notes: Number of tracks: 11. Type of recording: Live. Total playing time: 58 minutes.
Video-cassette (VHS): released on Peppermint, Jan'86

BERSERKER TOUR, THE (VIDEO).
Notes: Gary camps it up in white leather and blue make-up . All your favourites are here!
Video-cassette (VHS): released on Video Collection, May'87 by Video Collection International Ltd.. Dist: Counterpoint

CALL OUT THE DOGS.
Single (7"): released on Numa, Sep'85 by Numa Records. Dist: PRT Distribution

Single (12"): released on Numa, Sep'85 by Numa Records. Dist: PRT Distribution

CARS.
Single (7"): released on Beggars Banquet, Aug'79 by Beggars Banquet Records. Dist: WEA

CARS (E REG MODEL).
Tracks: / Are "friends" electric? / I die, you die / We are glass / Cars (E reg model) (Ext.) / Motorway mix.
Single (7"): released on Beggars Banquet, Aug'87 by Beggars Banquet Records. Dist: WEA

Single (12"): released on Beggars Banquet, Aug'87 by Beggars Banquet Records. Dist: WEA

CHANGE YOUR MIND (see Sharpe,Bill/Gary Numan) (Numan, Gary/Bill Sharpe).

FURY (THE).
Tracks: / Call out the dogs / This disease / Your fascination / Miracles / Pleasure skin / Creatures / Tricks / God only knows / I still remember.
Compact disc: released on Numa, '86 by Numa Records. Dist: PRT Distribution

FURY,THE.
Album: released on Numa, Oct'85 by Numa Records. Dist: PRT Distribution

Cassette: released on Numa, Oct'85 by Numa Records. Dist: PRT Distribution

Picture disc album: released on Numa, Oct'85 by Numa Records. Dist: PRT Distribution

I CAN'T STOP.
Tracks: / I can't stop / Faces.
Picture disc single: released on Numa, Jun'86 by Numa Records. Dist: PRT Distribution

Picture disc single: released on Numa, Jun'86 by Numa Records. Dist: PRT Distribution

Single (7"): released on Numa, Jun'86 by Numa Records. Dist: PRT Distribution

Single 10": released on Numa, Jun'86 by Numa Records. Dist: PRT Distribution

Single (12"): released on Numa, Jun'86 by Numa Records. Dist: PRT Distribution

I DIE - YOU DIE.
Single (7"): released on Beggars Banquet, Aug'80 by Beggars Banquet Records. Dist: WEA

I STILL REMEMBER.
Tracks: / I still remember / Puppets.
Notes: All royalties to RSPCA.
Single (7"): released on Numa, Dec'86 by Numa Records. Dist: PRT Distribution

Single (12"): released on Numa, Dec'86 by Numa Records. Dist: PRT Distribution

Single (7"): released on Numa, Nov'86 by Numa Records. Dist: PRT Distribution

LOVE NEEDS NO DISGUISE.
Single (7"): released on Beggars Banquet, Nov'81 by Beggars Banquet Records. Dist: WEA

Single (12"): released on Beggars Banquet, Nov'81 by Beggars Banquet Records. Dist: WEA

MIRACLES.
Single (7"): released on Numa, Nov'85 by Numa Records. Dist: PRT Distribution

Single (12"): released on Numa, Nov'85 by Numa Records. Dist: PRT Distribution

MUSIC FOR CHAMELEONS.
Single (7"): released on Beggars Banquet, Mar'82 by Beggars Banquet Records. Dist: WEA

Single (12"): released on Beggars Banquet, Mar'82 by Beggars Banquet Records. Dist: WEA

MY DYING MACHINE.
Single (7"): released on Numa, Dec'84 by Numa Records. Dist: PRT Distribution

Single (12"): released on Numa, Dec'84 by Numa Records. Dist: PRT Distribution

NEW MAN NUMAN (THE BEST OF GARY NUMAN).
Album: released on TV, Nov'82

Cassette: released on TV, Nov'82

NUMA RECORDS YEAR 1 (Numan, Gary/Various).
Notes: Album shrinkwrapped with Italian Import single 'My Dying Machine'. Cassette includes extra track 'My Dying Machine'.
Album: released on Numa, Mar'86 by Numa Records. Dist: PRT Distribution

Cassette: released on Numa, Mar'86 by Numa Records. Dist: PRT Distribution

PLAN,THE.
Album: released on Beggars Banquet, Mar'85 by Beggars Banquet Records. Dist: WEA

Cassette: released on Beggars Banquet, Mar'85 by Beggars Banquet Records. Dist: WEA

Picture disc album: released on Beggars Banquet, Mar'85 by Beggars Banquet Records. Dist: WEA

PLEASURE PRINCIPLE.
Cassette: released on Beggars Banquet, Sep'79 by Beggars Banquet Records. Dist: WEA

RADIOHEART (Numan, Gary with Radio Heart).
Single (7"): released on GFM, Mar'87 by GFM Records. Dist: Fast Forward, Cartel, PRT, Projection

RADIO HEART (PICTURE DISC)
(Numan, Gary with Radio Heart).
Tracks: / Radio heart / Radio heart (Instrumental).
Single (7"): released on GFM, Mar'87 by GFM Records. Dist: Fast Forward, Cartel, PRT, Projection
Single (12"): released on GFM, Mar'87 by GFM Records. Dist: Fast Forward, Cartel, PRT, Projection

REPLICAS.
Cassette: released on Beggars Banquet, Oct'82 by Beggars Banquet Records. Dist: WEA

SISTER SUPRISE.
Single (7"): released on Beggars Banquet, Oct'83 by Beggars Banquet Records. Dist: WEA
Single (12"): released on Beggars Banquet, Oct'83 by Beggars Banquet Records. Dist: WEA

STRANGE CHARM.
Compact disc: released on Numa, '86 by Numa Records. Dist: PRT Distribution
Album: released on Numa, Nov'86 by Numa Records. Dist: PRT Distribution
Cassette: released on Numa, Nov'86 by Numa Records. Dist: PRT Distribution

TELEKON.
Album: released on Beggars Banquet, Sep'80 by Beggars Banquet Records. Dist: WEA
Cassette: released on Beggars Banquet, Sep'80 by Beggars Banquet Records. Dist: WEA

THAT'S TOO BAD (Numan,Gary & Tubeway Army).
Single (7"): released on Beggars Banquet, Apr'83 by Beggars Banquet Records. Dist: WEA

THIS IS LOVE.
Tracks: / This is love / Survival.
Single (7"): released on Numa, Apr'86 by Numa Records. Dist: PRT Distribution
Picture disc single: released on Numa, Apr'86 by Numa Records. Dist: PRT Distribution
Single (12"): released on Numa, Apr'86 by Numa Records. Dist: PRT Distribution
Single (12"): released on Numa, Apr'86 by Numa Records. Dist: PRT Distribution

THIS WRECKAGE.
Single (7"): released on Beggars Banquet, Nov'80 by Beggars Banquet Records. Dist: WEA

WARRIORS.
Picture disc single: released on Beggars Banquet, Sep'83 by Beggars Banquet Records. Dist: WEA
Single (7"): released on Beggars Banquet, Aug'83 by Beggars Banquet Records. Dist: WEA

WE ARE GLASS.
Single (7"): released on Beggars Banquet, May'80 by Beggars Banquet Records. Dist: WEA

WE TAKE MYSTERY.
Single (7"): released on Beggars Banquet, May'82 by Beggars Banquet Records. Dist: WEA
Single (12"): released on Beggars Banquet, May'82 by Beggars Banquet Records. Dist: WEA

WHITE BOYS AND HEROES.
Single (7"): released on Beggars Banquet, Aug'82 by Beggars Banquet Records. Dist: WEA
Single (12"): released on Beggars Banquet, Aug'82 by Beggars Banquet Records. Dist: WEA

WHITE NOISE.
Album: released on Numa, Apr'85 by Numa Records. Dist: PRT Distribution
Cassette: released on Numa, Apr'85 by Numa Records. Dist: PRT Distribution

YOUR FASCINATION.
Single (7"): released on Numa, Aug'85 by Numa Records. Dist: PRT Distribution
Picture disc single: released on Numa, Aug'85 by Numa Records. Dist: PRT Distribution
Single (12"): released on Numa, Aug'85 by Numa Records. Dist: PRT Distribution

Picture disc single: released on Numa, Aug'85 by Numa Records. Dist: PRT Distribution

Numarx
RHYMES SO DEF.
Tracks: / Rhymes so def / Rhymes so def (ext mix).
Single (12"): released on Bluebird, Apr'87 by Bluebird Records. Dist: EMI, Jetstar

Number Four Joy Street
NFJS (THE).
Tracks: / NFJS (The).
Single (7"): released on Golden Pathway, Aug'86 Dist: Revolver, Cartel

Number & Nature Songs...
NUMBER & NATURE SONGS & RHYMES sung by children (Various Artists).
Album: released on Macdonald, '79

Number One Hits
NUMBER ONE HITS VOL.2 various artists (Various Artists).
Cassette: released on Autograph, Apr'85 Dist: Record Services Distribution (Ireland)

Numbers
I DON'T KNOW.
Single (7"): released on RCA, Jan'82 by RCA Records. Dist: RCA, Roots, Swift, Wellard, Chris, I & B, Solomon & Peres Distribution
NUMBERS, THE.
Album: released on RCA, Mar'82 by RCA Records. Dist: RCA, Roots, Swift, Wellard, Chris, I & B, Solomon & Peres Distribution

Numero Uno
TORA TORA TORA.
Single (7"): released on Starblend, Mar'85 by Starblend Records. Dist: PRT Distribution

Nunn, Bobby
DON'T KNOCK IT.
Single (7"): released on Motown, Jan'84 by RCA Records. Dist: RCA Distribution
Single (12"): released on Motown, Jan'84 by RCA Records. Dist: RCA Distribution
PRIVATE PARTY.
Album: released on Motown, Jul'84 by RCA Records. Dist: RCA Distribution

Nuns
SUN IS GOING TO GET TO ME, THE.
Single (12"): released on Hive, May'87 Dist: PRT

Nunsense
NUNSENSE Original Broadway Cast (Various Artists).
Tracks: / Nunsense is habit-forming / Difficult transition, A / Benedicte/Biggest ain't best / Playing second fiddle / So you want to be a Nun / Turn up the spotlight / Lilacs bring back memories / Tackle that temptation with a time-step / Growing up Catholic / Drive-in / I could've gone to Nashville / Holier than thou / Finale.
Album: released on DRG (USA), Apr'87 by DRG Records. Dist: Conifer, RCA
Cassette: released on DRG (USA), Apr'87 by DRG Records. Dist: Conifer, RCA
NUNSENSE - ORIGINAL LONDON CAST (Various Artists).
Album: released on That's Entertainment, Jun'87 by That's Entertainment Records. Dist: Pinnacle, PRT
Cassette: released on That's Entertainment, Jun'87 by That's Entertainment Records. Dist: Pinnacle, PRT

Nuns Of Stanbrook Abbey
WELLSPRINGS.
Notes: The nuns of Stanbrook Abbey sing and read favourite psalms (chiefly in English) with psaltery, recorder, guitar and organ accompaniment. This release is designed to bring comfort and inspiration and is recorded in the glorious acoustic of Stanbrook Abbey.
Album: released on Saydisc, Oct'86 by Saydisc Records. Dist: Essex, Harmonia Mundi, Roots, H.R. Taylor, Jazz Music, Swift, Projection, Gamut
Cassette: released on Saydisc, Oct'86 by Saydisc Records. Dist: Essex, Harmonia Mundi, Roots, H.R. Taylor, Jazz Music, Swift, Projection, Gamut

Nuptown Corporation Band
DISCO CHRISTMAS.
Single (7"): released on Springsong, Dec'82 by Springsong Records. Dist: Unknown

Nuremberg Symphony...
CLASSIC MOKLOS ROZSA, THE.
Compact disc: released on TER, Aug'87 Dist: Pinnacle

Nurnberger Accordion...
MUSIC FOR ACCORDION ORCHESTRA NO.1.
Album: released on ARC (Accordion Records), '84 Dist: Accordion Record Club
MUSIC FOR ACCORDION ORCHESTRA NO.7.
Album: released on ARC (Accordion Records), '84 Dist: Accordion Record Club

Nu Romance Crew
TONIGHT.
Tracks: / Tonight / Tonight (sax version).
Single (7"): released on EMI, May'87 by EMI Records. Dist: EMI
Single (12"): released on EMI, May'87 by EMI Records. Dist: EMI

Nursery Rhymes
MY 40 FAVOUTITE NURSERY RHYMES
Various artists (Various Artists).
Album: released on MFP, Oct'85 by EMI Records. Dist: EMI
Cassette: released on MFP, Oct'85 by EMI Records. Dist: EMI
NURSERY RHYMES various artists (Various Artists).
Cassette: released on Audiocord Cassettes, May'83
Album: released on Multi Media Tapes, Apr'82 by Multi Media Tapes Records. Dist: Stage One Distribution, Conifer Distribution, H.R. Taylor Distribution, Pinnacle
Cassette: released on Multi Media Tapes, Apr'82 by Multi Media Tapes Records. Dist: Stage One Distribution, Conifer Distribution, H.R. Taylor Distribution, Pinnacle
NURSERY RHYMES (VIDEO) (Various Artists).
Notes: Released on Longman/Screen Legends
WALLY WHYTON'S GOLDEN HOUR OF NURSERY RHYMES (Whyton, Wally).
Album: released on Golden Hour, '74 by PRT Records. Dist: PRT

Nurse With Wound
AUTOMATING Volume 1.
Album: released on United Dairies, May'86 Dist: Rough Trade, Indies
BRAINED BY FALLING MASONRY.
Single (12"): released on Layla, Dec'84 by Layla Records. Dist: Rough Trade, Cartel
HOMOTOPY FOR MARIE.
Album: released on United Dairies, Jul'85 Dist: Rough Trade, Indies
LIVE AT BAR MALDOROR.
Album: released on White, Jan'85
MISSING SENSE Rasa (Nurse With Wound/Organum).
Album: released on Third Mind, Jun'86 by Third Mind Records. Dist: Backs, Cartel Distribution
MISSING SENSE Rasa (Nurse With Wound/Organum).
Album: released on United Dairies, Jul'86 Dist: Rough Trade, Indies
OSTRANENIE 1913.
Album: released on Third Mind, Feb'84 by Third Mind Records. Dist: Backs, Cartel Distribution
SPIRAL INSANA.
Album: released on Torso, Nov'86 by Torso Records. Dist: Rough Trade. Cartel, EMI
SYLVIE & BABS HIGH-THIGH COMPANION.
Album: released on Layla, Sep'85 by Layla Records. Dist: Rough Trade, Cartel
TERMITE QUEEN,THE.
Tracks: / Termite queen,The.
Single (7"): released on Crystal, Mar'87 by Crystal Records. Dist: Jetstar, Revolver, Cartel

Nu Shooz
I CAN'T WAIT.
Tracks: / I can't wait / Make your mind up.
Single (7"): released on Atlantic, May'86 by WEA Records. Dist: WEA
POINT OF NO RETURN (THE).
Tracks: / Pont of no return (The) / Going through the motions.
Single (7"): released on Atlantic, Jul'86 by WEA Records. Dist: WEA

Single (12"): released on Atlantic, Jul'86 by WEA Records. Dist: WEA
POOLSIDE.
Tracks: / Lost your number / I can't wait / Don't let me be the one / Goin' thru' the motions / You put me in a trance / Point of no return / Secret message / Don't you be afraid.
Album: released on Atlantic, Jul'86 by WEA Records. Dist: WEA
Cassette: released on Atlantic, Jul'86 by WEA Records. Dist: WEA
Compact disc: released on Atlantic, Jul'86 by WEA Records. Dist: WEA

Nusrac Fateh All Khan
BEST OF... Volume 1.
Album: released on Womad, Mar'86 by Womad Records. Dist: Revolver, Cartel

Nutcracker Suite
NIGHT BEFORE CHRISTMAS, THE.
Album: released on Audio Fidelity, Oct'84 Dist: PRT
Cassette: released on Audio Fidelity, Oct'84 Dist: PRT

Nutmeg
AND IN ENGLAND THEY'RE GOING MENTAL.
Tracks: / And in England they're going mental / You're the only one / Walking in the rain.
Single (12"): released on Molesworth, May'87 Dist: Backs

Nutshell
BEGIN AGAIN.
Album: released on Myrrh, May'82 by Word Records. Dist: Word Distribution
Cassette: released on Myrrh, May'82 by Word Records. Dist: Word Distribution
BELIEVE IT OR NOT.
Album: released on Myrrh, May'82 by Word Records. Dist: Word Distribution
Cassette: released on Myrrh, May'82 by Word Records. Dist: Word Distribution
BEST OF NUTSHELL.
Album: released on Myrrh, May'82 by Word Records. Dist: Word Distribution
Cassette: released on Myrrh, May'82 by Word Records. Dist: Word Distribution
FLYAWAY.
Cassette: released on Myrrh, May'82 by Word Records. Dist: Word Distribution
Album: released on Myrrh, May'82 by Word Records. Dist: Word Distribution
IN YOUR EYES.
Album: released on Myrrh, May'82 by Word Records. Dist: Word Distribution
Cassette: released on Myrrh, May'82 by Word Records. Dist: Word Distribution

Nutwood Pals
RUPERT.
Single (7"): released on Rose, Oct'83

NV
IT'S ALRIGHT.
Single (12"): released on Sire, Jan'84

N.W.Ten
COOL COOL LOVING.
Single (12"): released on Pro, Dec'81

Nya
FEEL IT.
Tracks: / Feel it / Five star version.
Single (12"): released on Fivestar, May'86 Dist: Jetstar

Nyah Fearties
TASTY HEIDFU', A.
Album: released on L.Y.T., Feb'87 by L.Y.T. Records. Dist: Revolver, Cartel
TASTY HEIDFU, A.
Tracks: / Red roller / Glen Ashdale falls / Theme fae the barn / Lugton calling / Rantin' Robbie / When the wind blows cold / Bludgeon man / Apathy / Hallelujah!.
Album: released on L.Y.T., 26 Feb'87 by L.Y.T. Records. Dist: Revolver, Cartel

Nyam Nyam
ARCHITECT.
Single (12"): released on Situation 2, Mar'85 Dist: Cartel, Pinnacle

BENEATH RELIGIONS WINGS.
Album: released on Situation 2, Jun'84 Dist:
Cartel, Pinnacle

NYJO

**WHY DON'T THEY WRITE SONGS LIKE
THIS ANYMORE.**
Single (7"): released on SRT, Oct'83 by SRT
Records. Dist: Pinnacle, Solomon & Peres Distribution, SRT Distribution, H.R. Taylor Distribution, PRT Distribution

Nylon, Judy
CARLOTTA.

PAL JUDY.
Album: released on On-U-Sound, May'82 Dist:
Rough Trade Distribution, Lightning

Nylon Juice
NYLON JUICE various artists.
Album: released on I.R.S. (Independent Record Syndicate), Dec'84 by I.R.S.. Dist: MCA

Nylons
KISS HIM GOODBYE.
Tracks: / Kiss him goodbye / It's what they call
magic.
Single (7"): released on A&M, Jul'87 by A&M
Records. Dist: Polygram

Single (12"): released on A&M, Jul'87 by A&M
Records. Dist: Polygram

MILLION WAYS.
Single (7"): released on Attic, Sep'82 Dist: Pinnacle

NYLONS, THE.
Album: released on Attic, Jul'82 Dist: Pinnacle

Cassette: released on Attic, Jul'82 Dist: Pinnacle

PRINCE OF DARKNESS.
Single (7"): released on Attic, Mar'83 Dist: Pinnacle

Nyman, Michael
AND DO THEY DO\ZOO CAPRICES.
Album: released on That's Entertainment,
Dec'86 by That's Entertainment Records. Dist:
Pinnacle, PRT

Cassette: released on That's Entertainment,
Dec'86 by That's Entertainment Records. Dist:
Pinnacle, PRT

DECAY MUSIC.
Tracks: / One hundred / Bell set No.1.
Album: released on Editions EG, Jan'87 by Virgin Records. Dist: EMI

Album: released on Obscure, Apr'78 by Polydor Records. Dist: Polygram Distribution

DRAUGHTSMAN'S CONTRACT, THE.
Album: released on Charisma, Jan'83 by Virgin Records. Dist: EMI

IN RE DON GIOVANNI.
Single (7"): released on Piano, Feb'82 Dist:
Recommended

KISS AND OTHER MOVEMENTS (THE).
Cassette: released on Editions EG, Jan'87 by
Virgin Records. Dist: EMI

Album: released on Editions EG, Jan'87 by Virgin Records. Dist: EMI

MICHAEL NYMAN.
Album: released on Sheet, Mar'82 Dist: Rough
Trade

Nyro, Laura
IMPRESSIONS.
Album: released on CBS, Dec'80 by CBS Records. Dist: CBS

Cassette: released on CBS, Dec'80 by CBS
Records. Dist: CBS

Oak
WELCOME TO OUR FAIR.
Album: released on Topic, '81 Dist: Roots Distribution

Oakband Sound
OAKBAND SOUND.
Album: released on Scotdisc, Jul'85 Dist: Clyde Factors Distributors

Cassette: released on Scotdisc, Jul'85 Dist: Clyde Factors Distributors

Oakenshield
ACROSS THE NARROW SEAS.
Album: released on Acorn, Feb'85 Dist: Folksound, Jazz Music

Oakey, Philip
CHROME (Oakey, Philip & Giorgio Moroder).
Compact disc: by Virgin Records. Dist: EMI, Virgin Distribution

Album: released on Virgin, Jul'85 by Virgin Records. Dist: EMI, Virgin Distribution

Cassette: released on Virgin, Jul'85 by Virgin Records. Dist: EMI, Virgin Distribution

Oakie Boogie
OAKIE BOOGIE Capitol Country Vol. 2 (Various Artists).
Tracks: / Freight train boogie / My gal Gertie / I'm gettin' rid of you / Alone with you / Wait a little younger / I've got five dollars and its Saturday night / Red hen boogie / Stand up sit down shut your mouth / You're there / When I found you / I've had enough / Go ahead on / Country junction / Hambone / Fatback Louisiana USA.
Album: released on Charly, Jun'86 by Charly Records. Dist: Charly, Cadillac

Cassette: released on Charly, Jun'86 by Charly Records. Dist: Charly, Cadillac

Oakland blues
OAKLAND BLUES Various artists (Various Artists).
Album: released on Arhoolie, May'81 by Arhoolie Records. Dist: Projection, Topic, Jazz Music, Swift, Roots

Oakley, Glenroy
IF IT AIN'T ONE THING IT'S ANOTHER.
Single (12") : released on Exclusive, Nov'82 Dist: Jetstar

THERE'S NO ME WITHOUT YOU.
Single (12") : released on Exclusive, Oct'82 Dist: Jetstar

Oak Ridge Boys
20 COUNTRY GOSPEL CLASSICS.
Album: released on Astan, Nov'84 by Astan Records. Dist: Counterpoint

Cassette: released on Astan, Nov'84 by Astan Records. Dist: Counterpoint

AMERICAN MADE.
Album: released on MCA Import, Mar'86 by MCA Records. Dist: Polygram, IMS

DELIVER.
Album: released on MCA, Mar'84 by MCA Records. Dist: CBS

Cassette: released on MCA, Mar'84 by MCA Records. Dist: CBS

FANCY FREE.
Album: released on MCA, Jul'81 by MCA Records. Dist: CBS

Cassette: released on MCA, Jul'81 by MCA Records. Dist: CBS

GLORY TRAIN.
Album: released on Sundown, Dec'84 by Magnum Music Group Ltd. Dist: Magnum Music Group Ltd, PRT Distribution, Spartan Distribution

GREATEST HITS:OAKRIDGE BOYS-1 Volume 1.
Tracks: / You're the one / I'll be true to you / Trying to love two women / Cryin' again / Dream on / Leaving Louisiana in the broad daylight / Heart of mine / Come on in / Sail away / Y'all come back saloon / Elvira / Ozark mountain jubilee / Love song / Fancy free / Everyday / Beautiful you / Thank God for kids / American made / Make my life with you / I guess it never hurts to hurt sometimes.
Album: released on MCA Import, Mar'86 by MCA Records. Dist: Polygram, IMS

Album: released on MCA Import, Mar'86 by MCA Records. Dist: Polygram, IMS

Compact discs: released on MCA, '86 by MCA Records. Dist: Polygram, IMS

I GUESS IT NEVER HURTS SOMETIMES.
Single (7") : released on MCA, Mar'84 by MCA Records. Dist: CBS

SEASONS.
Tracks: / Seasons / What are you doing in my dream? / Bed-time / Hidin' place / Don't break the code / Juliet / You made a rock of a rolling stone / Take a step (yesterday waltz) / What you do to me / Everybody wins.
Compact disc: released on MCA, Feb'87 by MCA Records. Dist: Polygram, MCA

SEASONS.
Tracks: / Seasons / What are you doing in my dream / Bedtime / Don't bread the code / Juliet / You made a rock of a rolling stone / Take a step (Yesterday waltz) / What you do to me / Everybody wins.
Notes: The 'Seasons' album includes three songs written by John Hall, known for his work with the group Orleans. One of those songs, written with John's partner in Orleans Larry Hoppen is the first single. 'Juliet'. A long-time Oakridge Boys songwriter, Jimbeau Hinson, contributes the title track 'Seasons', which he wrote with Jack Williams, and also the album's closer, 'Everbody Wins'. On that tune, Hinson and Williams were joined by Oak Duane Allen as a co-writer.A song written by MCA's Ray Stevens, Hidin Place' is also included. The first Oakridge boys album to be digitally recorded. Seasons was produced by the man who has produced all the Oaks' ABC/MCA albums, Ron Chancey.
Album: released on MCA, Mar'86 by MCA Records. Dist: Polygram, MCA

Cassette: released on MCA, Mar'86 by MCA Records. Dist: Polygram, MCA

SENSATIONAL.
Album: released on Starday, Apr'87

Cassette: released on Starday, Apr'87

STEP ON OUT.
Album: released on MCA, May'85 by MCA Records. Dist: CBS

Cassette: released on MCA, May'85 by MCA Records. Dist: CBS

THANK GOD FOR KIDS.
Single (7") : released on MCA, Nov'84 by MCA Records. Dist: CBS

TOGETHER.
Album: released on MCA, May'80 by MCA Records. Dist: CBS

WHERE THE FAST LANE ENDS.
Tracks: / Love has a mind of its own / Is there any way for us to say goodbye / Where the fast lane ends / It takes a little rain to make love grow / Looking for love / Little late to say goodbye (A) / Rainbow at midnight / This crazy love / Little love can go a long, long way (A) / Whatever it takes.
Album: released on MCA, Apr'87 by MCA Records. Dist: Polygram, MCA

Cassette: released on MCA, Apr'87 by MCA Records. Dist: Polygram, MCA

WHERE THE FAST LANE ENDS.
Album: released on MCA, Apr'87 by MCA Records. Dist: Polygram, MCA

Cassette: released on MCA, Apr'87 by MCA Records. Dist: Polygram, MCA

Y'ALL COME BACK SALOON.
Album: released on ABC, '78 Dist: CBS, Pinnacle

YOU'LL NEVER WALK ALONE.
Tracks: / I know / Wonderful saviour / Without God / Old country church, The / I'll wake up on the other side / Dear Jesus, abide with me / Christian way, The / Hide thou me / I asked the lord / Farther along / Day of rejoicing / Lead me to cavary / River of life / You'll never walk alone / One of these mornings / When I lay my burdens down / At the roll call / Time has made a change in me.
Album: released on Showcase, Apr'86 Dist: Counterpoint

Cassette: released on Showcase, Apr'86 Dist: Counterpoint

Oakville Tune Wranglers
HEADIN' HOME.
Single (7") : released on Shark, Aug'87 by Shark records.

Oasis
CHRISTMAS REGGAE TIME.
Single (7") : released on Oasis, Dec'85 by GTO Records. Dist: CBS Distribution

OASIS.
Notes: Digital Stereo.
Compact disc: released on WEA, Jul'84 by WEA Records. Dist: WEA

Album: released on WEA International, Apr'84 by WEA Records. Dist: WEA

Cassette: released on WEA International, Apr'84 by WEA Records. Dist: WEA

Compact disc: released on WEA, Jul'84 by WEA Records. Dist: WEA

PROMISED LAND.
Album: released on Dove, May'79 by Dove Records. Dist: Jetstar

SMILE FOR THE SUN.
Album: released on Dove, May'79 by Dove Records. Dist: Jetstar

Oates, John
Along the red ledge

Beauty on a back street

BIG BAM BOOM (Oates, John & Daryl Hall).
Album: released on RCA, Sep'84 by RCA Records. Dist: RCA, Roots, Swift, Wellard, Chris, I & B, Solomon & Peres Distribution

BIGGER THAN BOTH OF US (Oates, John & Daryl Hall).

Daryl Hall & John Oates

Daryl Hall & John Oates

Family man

I can't go for that

Kiss on my list

Live at the Apollo

Live time

Method of modern love

Nite at the Apollo live, A

No goodbyes

One on one

Out of touch

Past times behind

PROVIDER, THE (Oates, John & Daryl Hall).

Really smokin'

Say it isn't so

She's gone

Whole Oats

X-static

Your Imagination

Oattes Van Schaik
LIMIT, THE.
Album: released on Portrait, Apr'85 by CBS Records. Dist: CBS

Cassette: released on Portrait, Apr'85 by CBS Records. Dist: CBS

O Band
WITHIN REACH.
Album: released on Liberty - EMI, Feb'84

O'Banion, John
JOHN O'BANION.
Album: released on Elektra Asylum, Jun'81 by Elektra/Asylum/Nonesuch Records. Dist: WEA

Cassette: released on Elektra Asylum, Jun'81 by Elektra/Asylum/Nonesuch Records. Dist: WEA

Oberanmmergau Passion...
OBERAMMERGAU PASSION PLAY 1980.
Album: released on Import Music Service (IMS), Mar'81 Dist: Concord Jazz Distributions, Pablo, Polygram

OBERAMMERGAU PASSION PLAY various artists (Various Artists).
Album: released on Polydor (Germany), Apr'85 Dist: IMS-Polygram

Cassette: released on Polydor (Germany), Apr'85 Dist: IMS-Polygram

Obey, Ebenezer
JE KA JO (Obey, Chief Ebenezer).
Album: released on Virgin, Nov'83 by Virgin Records. Dist: EMI, Virgin Distribution Deleted '85.

Cassette: released on Virgin, Nov'83 by Virgin Records. Dist: EMI, Virgin Distribution

MILIKI PLUS (Obey, Chief Ebenezer).
Album: released on Virgin, Dec'83 by Virgin Records. Dist: EMI, Virgin Distribution

Cassette: released on Virgin, Dec'83 by Virgin Records. Dist: EMI, Virgin Distribution

SECURITY.
Album: released on Obey (Africa), Aug'85

SOLUTION Nigeria.
Tracks: / Gbebe mi / Olupese / Ma kuku sise / Oluwa ni mo gbojule / To ba nwa ire / Ibi aiye feni di / O dowa oluwa / Kaiye ma bere pe olorun mi da / Di ro mo / Wai.
Notes: The master of juju innovation bounces back with a jazz/blues flavour and clean-cut sound in music for a new era. "...a passionate rush of the most refined jujumusic" (Echoes)"
Album: released on Sterns, Sep'86 by Sterns Records. Dist: Sterns/Triple Earth Distribution

Oboade
KPANLOGO PARTY With Mustapha Tettey Addy.
Album: released on Tangent, Apr'81 Dist: Roots Distribution, Lugtons Distributors, Taylors, JSU Distribution, Spartan Distribution

O, Bobby
GIVING IT UP.
Single (7") : released on Design Communications, Dec'83

O'Brien, Dermot
20 GREATEST HITS.
Album: released on Platinum, Sep'84 by Geoffs Records.

Cassette: released on Platinum, Sep'84 by Geoffs Records.

ACCORDIAN SOUNDS , THE.
Cassette: released on AIM (Budget Cassettes), Feb'83

ACCORDION SOUNDS.
Album: released on ARC (Accordion Records), '84 Dist: Accordion Record Club

CEILI TIME IN IRELAND.
Tracks: / Reels / Drunken piper etc. / Jigs / Lannigan's ball / Waltz / Hornpipes / Showmans fancy / March / Wearin' the green / Set dances / Bonnie Kate / Waltzs / Gentle mother etc. / Irish washerwoman etc..
Album: released on Accordion Record Club, Jul'86 by Accordion Record Club Records. Dist: Accordion Record Club

DANCING FINGERS.
Album: released on ARC (Accordion Records), '84 Dist: Accordion Record Club

DERMOTT O'BRIEN.
Album: released on Arrival, '84 by Arrival. Dist: Revolver, Cartel

FAREWELL TO GALWAY.
Album: released on ARC (Accordion Records), '84 Dist: Accordion Record Club

HIMSELF.
Cassette: released on AIM (Budget Cassettes), Feb'83

LAUGHING ACCORDION, TE.
Album: released on ARC (Accordion Records), '84 Dist: Accordion Record Club

MERRY PLOUGHBOY, THE.
Album: released on ARC (Accordion Records), '84 Dist: Accordion Record Club

OULD CLADDAUGH RING, THE.
Album: released on ARC (Accordion Records), '84 Dist: Accordion Record Club

ROVING BOY.
Album: released on ARC (Accordion Records), '84 Dist: Accordion Record Club

SONGS OF IRELAND.
Album: released on Stoic, Mar'84 by Stoic Records. Dist: Spartan Distribution

Cassette: released on Stoic, Mar'84 by Stoic Records. Dist: Spartan Distribution

SONGS OF IRELAND, HIS 20 FAVOURITES.
Tracks: / Ould cladd ring / Merry ploughboy / Cliffs O Dunoon / Fiddler's green / Boys of Killybegs / Home boy home / Slieve na mon / 3 leaf shamrock / Galway shawl / Spancil hill / Nora Turfman from Ardee / Rocks of Bawn / Carrifergus / As I roved / Mslieve gallion.
Album: released on Accordion Record Club, Jul'86 by Accordion Record Club Records. Dist: Accordion Record Club

SONGS OF IRELAND,VOL.3.
Album: released on ARC (Accordion Records), '84 Dist: Accordion Record Club

THREE DIMENSIONS.
Album: released on ARC (Accordion Records), '84 Dist: Accordion Record Club

TRIBUTE TO SCOTLAND.
Album: released on ARC (Accordion Records), '84 Dist: Accordion Record Club

WHAT'S GOING TO HAPPEN TO US.
Single (7"): released on Ritz, Aug'82 by Outlet Records. Dist: Outlet, Prism Leisure Distribution, Record Services Distribution (Ireland), Roots

O'Brien, Hod

BITS AND PIECES.
Album: released on Uptown (USA), Nov'86 by Uptown Records. Dist: Jazz Music

O'Brien, Michael

ACTION MAN/SEVEN QUID A WEEK.
Single (7"): released on Zilch, Apr'82 by Zilch Records. Dist: Stage One

DREAMS OF IRELAND.
Album: released on Western Songs, Mar'86

Cassette: released on Western Songs, Mar'86

ZYLOPHONE JET/HONEY.
Single (7"): released on Zilch, Nov'81 by Zilch Records. Dist: Stage One

O'Brien, Stuart

LIVE TO BE OLD.
Tracks: / Live to be old / Live to be old (Instrumental).
Single (7"): released on AGR, Feb'86 by AGR Records. Dist: PRT

O'Bryan

I'M FREAKY/DOIN' ALRIGHT.
Single (7"): released on Capitol, Apr'83 by Capitol Records. Dist: EMI

Single (7"): released on Capitol, Apr'83 by Capitol Records. Dist: EMI

Obscur, Clair

SMURF IN THE GULAG.
Tracks: / Smurf in the gulag / La ballade de genes heureux.
Single (12"): released on Cathexis, Oct'86 Dist: Fast Forward, Cartel

Obscured By Degrees

I'M DYING.
Single (7"): released on KA, Mar'82

Obus

PODEROSO COMOEL TRUENO.
Album: released on Mausoleum, Oct'84 by Mausoleum Records. Dist: Pinnacle

O' Canainn, Tomas

BEAL NA TRA.
Album: released on Outlet, Dec'82 by Outlet Records. Dist: Outlet Distribution

Cassette: released on Outlet, Dec'82 by Outlet Records. Dist: Outlet Distribution

Ocasek,Ric

BEATITUDE.
Tracks: / Jimmy Jimmy / Something to grab for / Prove / I can't wait / Connect up to me / Quick one,A / Out of control / Take a walk / Sneak attack / Time bomb.
Album: released on Geffen, Sep'86 by Geffen Records. Dist: WEA, CBS

Cassette: released on Geffen, Sep'86 by Geffen Records. Dist: WEA, CBS

EMOTION IN MOTION.
Tracks: / Emotion in motion / P.F.J. / Step by step.
Single (7"): released on Geffen, Oct'86 by Geffen Records. Dist: WEA, CBS

Single (12"): released on Geffen, Oct'86 by Geffen Records. Dist: WEA, CBS

THIS SIDE OF PARADISE.
Tracks: / Keep on laughin' / True to you / Emotion in motion / Look in your eyes / Coming for you / Mystery / True love / P.F.J. / Hello darkness / This side of paradise.
Album: released on Geffen, Oct'86 by Geffen Records. Dist: WEA, CBS

Cassette: released on Geffen, Oct'86 by Geffen Records. Dist: WEA, CBS

Compact disc: released on Geffen, Oct'86 by Geffen Records. Dist: WEA, CBS

O'Casey, Sean

GREEN CROW CAWS, THE.
Album: released on EMI, Mar'80 by EMI Records. Dist: EMI

Occult Chemistry

OCCULT CHEMISTRY.
Single (7"): released on Dining Out, Jun'81 by Dining Out Records. Dist: IKF, Independent

Ocean

LIFE IS GOOD.
Single (7"): released on New Stars, Dec'84 by New Stars Records. Dist: ILA

OCEAN.
Album: released on Import Music Service (IMS), Sep'81 Dist: Concord Jazz Distributions, Pablo, Polygram

Ocean, Billy

6 TRACK HITS.
Extended-play record: released on Scoop 33, Sep'83 by Pickwick Records. Dist: H.R. Taylor

Cassette: released on Scoop 33, Sep'83 by Pickwick Records. Dist: H.R. Taylor

BILLY OCEAN.
Album: released on Epic, Jan'85 by CBS Records. Dist: CBS

Cassette: released on Epic, Jan'85 by CBS Records. Dist: CBS

BITTERSWEET.
Tracks: / Bitter sweet / Bittersweet (inst.).
Single (7"): released on Jive, Sep'86 by Zomba Records. Dist: RCA, PRT, CBS

Single (7"): released on Jive, Oct'86 by Zomba Records. Dist: RCA, PRT, CBS

Single (12"): released on Jive, Oct'86 by Zomba Records. Dist: RCA, PRT, CBS

CARIBBEAN QUEEN.
Single (7"): released on Jive, Sep'84 by Zomba Records. Dist: RCA, PRT, CBS

Single (12"): released on Jive, Sep'84 by Zomba Records. Dist: RCA, PRT, CBS Deleted '87.

CARIBBEAN QUEEN (UK 12" VERSION).
Cassette: released on Jive, Oct'84 by Zomba Records. Dist: RCA, PRT, CBS

EUROPEAN QUEEN (NO MORE LOVE ON THE RUN) 12".
Single (12"): released on Jive, Jun'84 by Zomba Records. Dist: RCA, PRT, CBS

EUROPEAN QUEEN (NO MORE LOVE ON THE RUN).
Single (7"): released on Jive, May'84 by Zomba Records. Dist: RCA, PRT, CBS

Single (12"): released on Jive, May'84 by Zomba Records. Dist: RCA, PRT, CBS

IN MOTION.
Tracks: / On the run / Emotions in motion / Whose little girl are you / Love really hurts / Black as he's painted / Wild beautiful women / What's gonna happen / Light up the world / On the run / On the run (hold on brother) / Emotions in motion / Love really hurts / Whose little girl are you / Black as he's painted / Wild beautiful women / What's gonna happen / Light up the world / On the run (extended remix long).
Album: released on Music For Pleasure, Oct'86 by EMI Records. Dist: EMI

Cassette: released on Music For Pleasure, Oct'86 by EMI Records. Dist: EMI

Compact disc: released on The Collection, Apr'87 by Object Enterprises Ltd. Dist: Counterpoint Distribution

INNER FEELINGS.
Tracks: / Calypso funkin / Rock-a-bye baby / No matter what / Dance with me / I can't stop / Tryin' to get through / Mind games / Was it you / Inner feelings.
Album: released on Epic, Jun'86 by CBS Records. Dist: CBS

Cassette: released on Epic, Jun'86 by CBS Records. Dist: CBS

LOVE IS FOREVER.
Tracks: / Love is forever / Suddenly / Loverboy.
Single (7"): released on Jive, Dec'86 by Zomba Records. Dist: RCA, PRT, CBS

Single (12"): released on Jive, Dec'86 by Zomba Records. Dist: RCA, PRT, CBS

LOVER BOY.
Single (7"): released on Jive, Jan'85 by Zomba Records. Dist: RCA, PRT, CBS

Picture disc single: released on Jive, Jan'85 by Zomba Records. Dist: RCA, PRT, CBS

LOVE REALLY HURTS/RED LIGHT.
Single (7"): released on Old Gold, Jul'82 by Old Gold Records. Dist: Lightning, Jazz Music, Spartan, Counterpoint

LOVE REALLY HURTS WITHOUT YOU (CUPID MIX).
Tracks: / Love really hurts without you (cupid mix) / Love really hurts...(Dub mix) / (86' 7" mix).
Single (12"): released on Supreme, Nov'86 by Supreme Records. Dist: PRT Distribution

LOVE REALLY HURTS WITHOUT YOU.
Tracks: / Love really hurts without you (1986 mix) / Love really hurts without you (inst.).
Single (7"): released on Supreme, Nov'86 by Supreme Records. Dist: PRT Distribution

Single (12"): released on Supreme, Nov'86 by Supreme Records. Dist: PRT Distribution

LOVE ZONE.
Tracks: / When the going gets though, the though get going / Love zone / Without you / There'll be sad songs (to make you cry) / Bittersweet / It's never too late to try / Showdown / Promise me / Love is forever / Love zone / Love zone (Instrumental mix).
Album: released on Jive, Jun'86 by Zomba Records. Dist: RCA, PRT, CBS

Cassette: released on Jive, Jun'86 by Zomba Records. Dist: RCA, PRT, CBS

Compact disc: released on Jive, Aug'86 by Zomba Records. Dist: RCA, PRT, CBS

Single (7"): released on Jive, Jul'86 by Zomba Records. Dist: RCA, PRT, CBS

Single (12"): released on Jive, Jul'86 by Zomba Records. Dist: RCA, PRT, CBS

MYSTERY LADY.
Single (7"): released on Jive, Jan'85 by Zomba Records. Dist: RCA, PRT, CBS Deleted '1.

Single (12"): released on Jive, Aug'85 by Zomba Records. Dist: RCA, PRT, CBS

Cassette: released on Jive, Aug'85 by Zomba Records. Dist: RCA, PRT, CBS

NIGHTS (FEEL LIKE GETTING DOWN).
Tracks: / Are you ready / Don't say stop / Whatever turns you on / Another day won't matter / nights (feel like getting down) / Who's gonna rock you / Stay the night / Everlasting love / Taking chances.
Album: released on Epic, Apr'86 by CBS Records. Dist: CBS

Cassette: released on Epic, Apr'86 by CBS Records. Dist: CBS

SUDDENLY.
Compact disc: by Zomba Records. Dist: RCA, PRT, CBS

Album: released on Jive, Aug'84 by Zomba Records. Dist: RCA, PRT, CBS

Cassette: released on Jive, Aug'84 by Zomba Records. Dist: RCA, PRT, CBS

SUDDENLY (SINGLE).
Single (12"): released on Jive, May'85 by Zomba Records. Dist: RCA, PRT, CBS

THERE'LL BE SAD SONGS (TO MAKE YOU CRY).
Tracks: / There'll be sad songs (to make you cry) / If I should lose you.
Single (7"): released on Jive, Apr'86 by Zomba Records. Dist: RCA, PRT, CBS

Single (12"): released on Jive, Apr'86 by Zomba Records. Dist: RCA, PRT, CBS

WHEN THE GOING GETS TOUGH, THE TOUGH GET GOING.
Tracks: / When the going gets though, the though get going.
Single (7"): released on Jive, Jan'86 by Zomba Records. Dist: RCA, PRT, CBS

Single (12"): released on Jive, Jan'86 by Zomba Records. Dist: RCA, PRT, CBS

Picture disc single: released on Jive, Jan'86 by Zomba Records. Dist: RCA, PRT, CBS

Single (12"): released on Jive, Jan'86 by Zomba Records. Dist: RCA, PRT, CBS

Double-pack single: released on Jive, Jun'86 by Zomba Records. Dist: RCA, PRT, CBS

Oceans

PACIFIC DREAMING/GOOD GUY BAD GUY.
Single (7"): released on Record Shack, Mar'82 by Record Shack Records. Dist: PRT

Oceans Eleven

THIS SPORTING LIFE.
Single (12"): released on Compact Organisation, Jun'85 Dist: PRT

Ochs, Phil

GREATEST HITS:PHIL OCHS.
Album: released on Edsel, Jun'86 by Demon Records. Dist: Pinnacle, Jazz Music, Projection

O'Connell, Helen

GREEN EYES.
Tracks: / Star eyes / Not mine / Tangerine / Green eyes / Yours / When the sun comes out / Al of me / Jim / Amapola / Time was / Embraceable you / Brazil.
Album: released on RCA, Jun'87 by RCA Records. Dist: RCA, Roots, Swift, Wellard, Chris, I & B, Solomon & Peres Distribution

Cassette: released on RCA, Jun'87 by RCA Records. Dist: RCA, Roots, Swift, Wellard, Chris, I & B, Solomon & Peres Distribution

SINGS GREAT SONGS IN HIGH STYLE.
Album: released on Audiophile, Jul'87 by Jazzology Records (USA). Dist: Jazz Music, Swift

O'Connell, Maura

JUST IN TIME.
Tracks: / Scholar, The / If you love me / Feet of a dancer / Isle of Malachy, The / New Orleans / Water is wide, The / Leaving Neidin / Crazy dreams / Loves old sweet song / Another morning / I will / Just in time.
Notes: New album from Irish singer Maura O'Connell. Recorded in Nashville, it includes songs written by,among others, Thom Moore, Charlie McGettigan and Jimmy McCarthyGuitarist Albert Lee plays on the album, as do Jerry Douglas, Mark O'Conner and Bela Fleck, Who also produced the album.
Album: released on Polydor, Jan'87 by Polydor Records. Dist: Polygram, Polydor

Cassette: released on Polydor, Jan'87 by Polydor Records. Dist: Polygram, Polydor

O'Connor, Cavan

DOWN MEMORY LANE.
Album: released on President, Jul'84 by President Records. Dist: Taylors, Spartan

IN THE STILL OF THE NIGHT.
Tracks: / One alone / Where the river shannon flows / Round the bend of the road / My wild Irish rose / Pretty girl is like a melody, A / I'll take you home again Kathleen / Starlight serenade / When I leave the world behind / Desert song, The / Rose of Tralee, The / Shannon river / Let us live for tonight / Kathleen Mavoureen / Daybreak / Bantry Bay / My Irish song of songs / There's a blue haze on the mountains / I hear your voice / White cliffs of Dover / Little town in the ould County Down / God will remember / Old oak tree, The / Mountains o'mourne, The / When evening comes / Two heads against the moon / When April comes again / Mother Machree / At the close of a long long day / Goodnight (I'm only a strolling vagabond)..... / In the still of the night / Singing a vagabond song / Fool with a dream, A.
Notes: This is a double album and a double cassette.
Double Album: released on Decca (London), Mar'87 by Decca Records. Dist: Polygram, IMS

Cassette: released on Decca (London), Mar'87 by Decca Records. Dist: Polygram, IMS

O'Connor, Des

ANYTIME.
Tracks: / When you're smiling / Everybody's talkin' / Raindrops keep fallin' on my head / For the good times / You always hurt the one you love / Carless hands / One, two three o' leary / Your cheatin' heart / Didn't we / I pretend / Dream a little dream of me / With love / Anytime / Dick-a-dum-dum / Tip of my fingers, The / I'll go on hoping / Loneliness / Something / All I need is you / Heartaches / Try to remember / Red roses for a blue lady / My thanks to you.
Cassette: released on Hour Of Pleasure, Oct'86 by Music For Pleasure Records. Dist: EMI

CHRISTMAS WITH......
Album: released on Pickwick, Oct'79 by Pickwick Records. Dist: Pickwick Distribution, Prism Leisure Distribution, Lugtons

Cassette: released on Pickwick, Oct'79 by Pickwick Records. Dist: Pickwick Distribution, Prism Leisure Distribution, Lugtons

DES....
Cassette: released on Ideal(Tapes), Apr'80 Dist: EMI

DES O'CONNOR COLLECTION.
Double Album: released on Pickwick, Aug'78 by Pickwick Records. Dist: Pickwick Distribution, Prism Leisure Distribution, Lugtons

DES O'CONNOR NOW.
Album: released on Telstar, Nov'84 by Telstar Records. Dist: RCA Distribution

Cassette: released on Telstar, Nov'84 by Telstar Records. Dist: RCA Distribution

DES O'CONNOR REMEMBER ROMANCE.
Album: released on Warwick, Nov'80 bv Warwick Records. Dist: Pinnacle

GOLDEN HITS: DES O'CONNOR.
Double Album: released on Music for Pleasure, Feb'83 by EMI Records. Dist: MFP Distribution

Double cassette: released on Music for Pleasure, Feb'83 by EMI Records. Dist: MFP Distribution

GREAT SONGS, THE.
Album: released on Telstar, Nov'85 by Telstar Records. Dist: RCA Distribution

Cassette: released on Telstar, Nov'85 by Telstar Records. Dist: RCA Distribution

SKYE BOAT SONG (O'Connor, Des & Roger Wittaker).

WITH FEELINGS.
Album: released on Hallmark, Jan'79 by Pickwick Records. Dist: Pickwick Distribution, PRT, Taylors

Cassette: released on Hallmark, Jan'79 by Pickwick Records. Dist: Pickwick Distribution, PRT, Taylors

O'Connor, Hazel

BREAKING GLASS.
Album: released on A&M, Aug'80 by A&M Records. Dist: Polygram

Cassette: released on A&M, Aug'80 by A&M Records. Dist: Polygram

COVER PLUS.
Album: released on Albion, Sep'81 by Albion Records. Dist: Spartan, Pinnacle

Cassette: released on Albion, Sep'81 by Albion Records. Dist: Spartan, Pinnacle

Single (7"): released on Albion, Jul'81 by Albion Records. Dist: Spartan, Pinnacle

Single (12"): released on Albion, Jul'81 by Albion Records. Dist: Spartan, Pinnacle

D-DAYS.
Single (7"): released on Albion, Mar'81 by Albion Records. Dist: Spartan, Pinnacle

Single (12"): released on Albion, Mar'81 by Albion Records. Dist: Spartan, Pinnacle

Cassette: released on Albion, Mar'81 by Albion Records. Dist: Spartan, Pinnacle

DON'T TOUCH ME.
Single (7"): released on RCA, Jan'84 by RCA Records. Dist: RCA, Roots, Swift, Wellard, Chris, I & B, Solomon & Peres Distribution

Single (12"): released on RCA, Jan'84 by RCA Records. Dist: RCA, Roots, Swift, Wellard, Chris, I & B, Solomon & Peres Distribution

Picture disc single: released on RCA, Jan'84 by RCA Records. Dist: RCA, Roots, Swift, Wellard, Chris, I & B, Solomon & Peres Distribution

FIGHTING BACK (O'Connor, Hazel And The Arts Freedom Singers).
Tracks: / Fighting back / Reach.
Single (7"): released on BBC, Jul'86 by BBC Records & Tapes. Dist: EMI, PRT, Pye

Single (12"): released on BBC, Jul'86 by BBC Records & Tapes. Dist: EMI, PRT, Pye

GLASS HOUSES.
Album: released on Albion, Apr'80 by Albion Records. Dist: Spartan, Pinnacle

HANGING AROUND.
Single (7"): released on Albion, Sep'81 by Albion Records. Dist: Spartan, Pinnacle

JUST GOOD FRIENDS.
Single (7"): released on RCA, Jun'84 by RCA Records. Dist: RCA, Roots, Swift, Wellard, Chris, I & B, Solomon & Peres Distribution

Single (12"): released on RCA, Jun'84 by RCA Records. Dist: RCA, Roots, Swift, Wellard, Chris, I & B, Solomon & Peres Distribution

PUSH AND SHOVE (O'Connor, Hazel & Chris Thompson).
Single (12"): released on Greenpeace, Jun'85 Dist: Towerbell, EMI

Single (7"): released on Greenpeace, Jun'85 Dist: Towerbell, EMI

SMILE.
Album: released on RCA, Sep'84 by RCA Records. Dist: RCA, Roots, Swift, Wellard, Chris, I & B, Solomon & Peres Distribution

Cassette: released on RCA, Sep'84 by RCA Records. Dist: RCA, Roots, Swift, Wellard, Chris, I & B, Solomon & Peres Distribution

SONS AND LOVERS.
Album: released on Albion, Oct'80 by Albion Records. Dist: Spartan, Pinnacle

THAT'S LIFE.
Single (7"): released on Albion, Apr'82 by Albion Records. Dist: Spartan, Pinnacle

TIME.
Single (7"): released on Albion, Nov'80 by Albion Records. Dist: Spartan, Pinnacle

Single (12"): released on Albion, Dec'80 by Albion Records. Dist: Spartan, Pinnacle

TODAY COULD BE SO GOOD.
Tracks: / Today could be so good / We tried.
Single (7"): released on Red Bus, Mar'86 by Red Bus Records. Dist: PRT

WILL YOU?.
Single (7"): released on A&M, May'81 by A&M Records. Dist: Polygram

WILL YOU.
Single (7"): released on Old Gold, Sep'85 by Old Gold Records. Dist: Lightning, Jazz Music, Spartan, Counterpoint

O'Connor, Karen

GIRL IN THE UNIFORM.
Single (7"): released on Legacy, May'83 Dist: PRT

O'Connor, Mark

FALSE DAWN.
Album: released on Rounder (USA), Jan'84 Dist: Mike's Country Music Room Distribution, Jazz Music Distribution, Swift Distribution, Roots Records Distribution, Projection Distribution, Topic Distribution

O'Connor, Tom

FESTIVAL SONG.
Single (7"): released on Mayfield, Apr'84 by Mayfield Records. Dist: PRT

Octavia

2 THE LIMIT.
Tracks: / 2 the limit / 2 the limit (instrumental).
Single (7"): released on Cool Tempo, Sep'86 by Chrysalis Records. Dist: CBS

Single (12"): released on Cool Tempo, Sep'86 by Chrysalis Records. Dist: CBS

October 9

SIREN, THE.
Tracks: / Siren, The / Is this the end.
Single (7"): released on Gold Direction, Feb'86 by Gold Direction Records. Dist: M.I.S., EMI

October, Gene

DON'T QUIT.
Single (7"): released on Slipped Discs, Jan'84 by Slipped Discs Records. Dist: PRT, Self Distribution

SUFFERING IN THE LAND.
Single (7"): released on Illegal, Jan'83 by Faulty Products Records. Dist: Pinnacle, Lightning, Cartel

Octopus

AN OCEAN OF ROCKS.
Album: released on Sky, '78 by President Records.

Octopussy

OCTOPUSSY Original motion picture soundtrack (Various Artists).
Album: released on A&M, Jun'83 by A&M Records. Dist: Polygram

Cassette: released on A&M, Jun'83 by A&M Records. Dist: Polygram

O'Cuthbert, Martin

CELEBRATE OR DEGENERATE.
Extended-play record: released on Esoteric, Nov'83 by Esoteric Records. Dist: Rough Trade, Independent

FOR ALIEN EARS.
Album: released on Esoteric, '80 by Esoteric Records. Dist: Rough Trade, Independent

NAVIGATOR THROUGH NOWHERE.
Single (7"): released on Esoteric, Jul'81 by Esoteric Records. Dist: Rough Trade, Independent

OH GOD.
Tracks: / Oh God.
Single (7"): released on Esoteric, '85 by Esoteric Records. Dist: Rough Trade, Independent

SERENE MACHINES.
Single (7"): released on Esoteric, Jul'81 by Esoteric Records. Dist: Rough Trade, Independent

SONGS FOR SQUARE PEGS.
Extended-play record: released on Esoteric, Jul'81 by Esoteric Records. Dist: Rough Trade, Independent

VOCAL VIGILANTE.
Single (7"): released on Esoteric, Jul'81 by Esoteric Records. Dist: Rough Trade, Independent

O'Day, Anita

ANITA SINGS THE MOST.
Tracks: / S'wonderful / They can't take that away from me / Old devil moon / Love me or leave me / We'll be together again / Stella by starlight / Taking a chance on love / Them there eyes / I've got the world on a string / You turned the tables on me / Bewitched, bothered and bewildered.
Notes: Anita O'Day singing eleven great standards with accompaniment from Oscar Peterson, Herb Ellis, Ray Brown and John Poole. Recorded January 1957 and digitally remastered directly from the original mono master tape.
Compact disc: released on Verve (USA), Oct'86 by Polydor. Dist: Polygram

LIVE AT RONNIE SCOTT'S.
Notes: Anita O'Day confirms in the second of the programmes her reputation as being probably the finest ever white jazz singer. In a set full of classic songs - 'S'Marvellous', 'On Green Dolphin Street', 'My Funny Valentine', 'It Don't Mean A Thing' and more, she exudes the style and class first seen in the milestone film 'Jazz On A Summers Day'.
Compact disc: released on Heron, Jun'87

SINGS THE WINNERS.
Album: released on Verve (America), Mar'82

TRAVELIN' LIGHT.
Album: released on Verve (USA), Mar'83 by Polydor. Dist: Polygram

O'Day, Pat

CRUISIN' 1966 KJR Seattle.
Cassette: released on Increase(USA), Jun'87 by Quicksilver Records (USA).

Odd

LAST TIME I SAW YOU.
Single (7"): released on OK, Apr'84 Dist: Stage One Distribution

Odds

DREAD IN MY BED.
Single (7"): released on JSO, Jul'81 Deleted '81.

Odd Socks

MEN OF THE MOMENT.
Album: released on Sweet Folk Country, Dec'77 Dist: Chris Wellard Distribution

Odetta

IT'S IMPOSSIBLE.
Album: released on Four Leaf Clover, '78 Dist: Jazz Music, Swift

ODETTA AND THE BLUES.
Album: released on Prestige, Jun'84 by Prestige Records (USA). Dist: RCA JSU, Swift

O.D.J.B. Re-Visited

O.D.J.B. RE-VISITED.
Album: released on Rarities, Apr'81

O'Domhnaill, Michael

NIGHTNOISE (see Oskay, Bill).

O'Donnell, Al

AL O'DONNELL.
Album: released on Leader, '81 Dist: Jazz Music, Projection

AL O'DONNELL 2.
Album: released on Trailer, '81 Dist: Jazz Music, Celtic Music, JSU

O'Donnell, Conal

SONGS IN IRISH GAELIC (& OTHERS).
Cassette: released on Folktracks, Nov'79 by Folktracks Cassettes. Dist: Folktracks

O'Donnell, Daniel

I NEED YOU.
Tracks: / Sing an old Irish song / I need you / From a jack to a king / Lovely rose of Clare / Stand beside me / Irish eyes / Dear old Galway town / Three leaf shamrock / Veil of white lace / Kickin' each others hearts around / Madals for mothers / Wedding bells / Snowflake / Your friendly Irish way / Lough Melvin's rocky shore / I love you because.
Album: released on Ritz, Nov'86 by Outlet Records. Dist: Outlet, Prism Leisure Distribution, Record Services Distribution (Ireland), Roots

Cassette: released on Ritz, Nov'86 by Outlet Records. Dist: Outlet, Prism Leisure Distribution, Record Services Distribution (Ireland), Roots

Compact disc: released on Ritz, Jun'87 by Outlet Records. Dist: Outlet, Prism Leisure Distribution, Record Services Distribution (Ireland), Roots

I NEED YOU (SINGLE).
Tracks: / I need you / Your friendly irish way.
Single (7"): released on Ritz, Jan'87 by Outlet Records. Dist: Outlet, Prism Leisure Distribution, Record Services Distribution (Ireland), Roots

TAKE GOOD CARE OF HER.
Tracks: / Take good care of her / I wonder where you are tonight / Summertime in Ireland / My side of the road.
Single (7"): released on Ritz, Jul'87 by Outlet Records. Dist: Outlet, Prism Leisure Distribution, Record Services Distribution (Ireland), Roots

Cassette single: released on Ritz, Jul'87 by Outlet Records. Dist: Outlet, Prism Leisure Distribution, Record Services Distribution (Ireland), Roots

TWO SIDES OF DANIEL O'DONNELL, THE.
Album: released on Ritz, Nov'85 by Outlet Records. Dist: Outlet, Prism Leisure Distribution, Record Services Distribution (Ireland). Roots

Cassette: released on Ritz, Nov'85 by Outlet Records. Dist: Outlet, Prism Leisure Distribution, Record Services Distribution (Ireland), Roots

VEIL OF WHITE LACE, A.
Tracks: / Veil of white lace, A / Your friendly Irish way.
Single (7"): released on Ritz, Oct'86 by Outlet Records. Dist: Outlet, Prism Leisure Distribution, Record Services Distribution (Ireland), Roots

O'Donnell, Triona

TRIONA O'DONNELL.
Album: released on Gael-Linn (Ireland), '76 by Gael Linn Records. Dist: Roots, Projection, Celtic Music, Jazz Music

O'Dowd, Barry
IRISH MEMORIES.
Tracks: Galway bay / That old Irish mother of mine / Gypsy, The / Dear little shamrock, The / Macushla / Mickey / Dear old Donegal / Last rose of summer, The / My girl's an Irish girl / If you ever go back to Ireland / Kelly / Come back to Erin / Mother Macree / Star of the County Down / How are things in Glocca Mora / I'll take you home again Kathleen.
Notes: A Harbour reading. Licensed from Image Records Pty.Ltd. (Chappell)(MCP5)Music Group.
Album: released on Emerald (Ireland), Oct'84 by Emerald Records. Dist: I & B, Ross, PRT

Ods Band
RED ARROWS THEME - FLY.
Single (7"): released on BBC, Aug'81 by BBC Records & Tapes. Dist: EMI, PRT, Pye

Odysseus The Wanderer
ODYSSEUS THE WANDERER (Various Artists).
Cassette: released on Anvil, Jan'81 Dist: Anvil

Odyssey
BEST OF ODYSSEY.
Album: released on RCA, Dec'81 by RCA Records. Dist: RCA, Roots, Swift, Wellard, Chris, I & B, Solomon & Peres Distribution

Cassette: released on RCA, Dec'81 by RCA Records. Dist: RCA, Roots, Swift, Wellard, Chris, I & B, Solomon & Peres Distribution

EASY COME EASY GO.
Single (7"): released on RCA, Oct'82 by RCA Records. Dist: RCA, Roots, Swift, Wellard, Chris, I & B, Solomon & Peres Distribution

Single (12"): released on RCA, Oct'82 by RCA Records. Dist: RCA, Roots, Swift, Wellard, Chris, I & B, Solomon & Peres Distribution

GREATEST HITS: ODYSSEY.
Album: released on Stylus, Aug'87 Dist: Pinnacle, Terry Blood Distribution, Stylus Distribution

HANG TOGETHER.
Album: released on RCA, Sep'81 by RCA Records. Dist: RCA, Roots, Swift, Wellard, Chris, I & B, Solomon & Peres Distribution

Cassette: released on RCA, Sep'81 by RCA Records. Dist: RCA, Roots, Swift, Wellard, Chris, I & B, Solomon & Peres Distribution

HAPPY TOGETHER.
Cassette: released on RCA, Jun'82 by RCA Records. Dist: RCA, Roots, Swift, Wellard, Chris, I & B, Solomon & Peres Distribution

HOLLYWOOD PARTY NIGHT.
Album: by RCA Records. Dist: RCA, Roots, Swift, Wellard, Chris, I & B, Solomon & Peres Distribution

I GOT THE MELODY.
Album: released on RCA, May'81 by RCA Records. Dist: RCA, Roots, Swift, Wellard, Chris, I & B, Solomon & Peres Distribution

Cassette: released on RCA, May'81 by RCA Records. Dist: RCA, Roots, Swift, Wellard, Chris, I & B, Solomon & Peres Distribution

Cassette: released on RCA, May'81 by RCA Records. Dist: RCA, Roots, Swift, Wellard, Chris, I & B, Solomon & Peres Distribution

I KNOW IT.
Single (7"): released on Mirror-Priority, Jul'85 by Priority Records. Dist: Priority Distribution

Single (12"): released on Mirror-Priority, Jul'85 by Priority Records. Dist: Priority Distribution

INSIDE OUT.
Single (12"): released on RCA, May'82 by RCA Records. Dist: RCA, Roots, Swift, Wellard, Chris, I & B, Solomon & Peres Distribution Deleted '85.

MAGIC MOMENTS.
Cassette: released on RCA, Jun'84 by RCA Records. Dist: RCA, Roots, Swift, Wellard, Chris, I & B, Solomon & Peres Distribution

MAGIC TOUCH OF ODYSSEY.
Album: released on Telstar, Nov'82 by Telstar Records. Dist: RCA Distribution

Cassette: released on Telstar, Nov'82 by Telstar Records. Dist: RCA Distribution

MAGIC TOUCH (REMIX).
Single (7"): released on RCA, Aug'82 by RCA Records. Dist: RCA, Roots, Swift, Wellard, Chris, I & B, Solomon & Peres Distribution

Single (12"): released on RCA, Aug'82 by RCA Records. Dist: RCA, Roots, Swift, Wellard, Chris, I & B, Solomon & Peres Distribution

NATIVE NEW YORKER.
Single (7"): released on RCA, Jul'81 by RCA Records. Dist: RCA, Roots, Swift, Wellard,

---

Chris, I & B, Solomon & Peres Distribution

ODYSSEY.
Cassette: released on RCA, May'83 by RCA Records. Dist: RCA, Roots, Swift, Wellard, Chris, I & B, Solomon & Peres Distribution

PIPING JOURNEY, A.
Album: released on Mannick Music, Aug'87 Dist: Ross

Ofarim, Esther & Abi
CINDERELLA ROCKEFELLER
Single (7"): released on Old Gold, Jan'85 by Old Gold Records. Dist: Lightning, Jazz Music, Spartan, Counterpoint

O.F.B.
SATURDAY NIGHTS AND SUNDAY MORNINGS (O.F.B. (Our Favourite Band).
Album: released on New Rose, Jun'87 Dist: Rough Trade, Cartel

Single (7"): released on DJM, Sep'78 by DJM Records. Dist: CBS, Polygram

Off
ELECTRICA SALSA.
Tracks: Electrica salsa / Electrica salsa (inst).
Single (7"): released on Sonet, May'87 by Sonet Records. Dist: PRT

Single (12"): released on Sonet, May'87 by Sonet Records. Dist: PRT

Offerings Of Isca
OFFERINGS OF ISCA (Various Artists).
Album: released on Micro, Jul'85 by Micro Records. Dist: Micro

Office Boy
GIMME A BREAK.
Single (7"): released on REL, Jul'81 Dist: Roots

HOW CAN I.
Single (7"): released on Holyrood, Nov'82 by Holyrood Records. Dist: Pinnacle

WITH A WOMAN LIKE YOU.
Single (7"): released on Holyrood, Jul'83 by Holyrood Records. Dist: Pinnacle

Officer and a Gentleman
OFFICER AND A GENTLEMAN, AN
Original soundtrack (Various Artists).
Album: released on Island, Jan'83 by Island Records. Dist: Polygram

Cassette: released on Island, Jan'83 by Island Records. Dist: Polygram

Officers & Gentlemen
THAT'S LIFE AND LOVE.
Single (7"): released on G.A.P., Jun'85 by G.A.P. Records. Dist: Revolver, Cartel

Official...
OFFICIAL GUIDE TO CB RADIO (Various Artists).
Cassette: released on Stage One, Mar'81 by Stage One Records. Dist: Stage One Distribution

OFFICIAL MUSIC - MEXICO '86 (Various Artists).
Album: released on Meteor, Jun'86 by Magnum Music Group Ltd. Dist: Magnum Music Group Ltd, PRT Distribution, Spartan Distribution

OFFICIAL MUSIC OF THE 1984 GAMES (Various Artists).
Album: released on CBS, Jul'84 by CBS Records. Dist: CBS

Cassette: released on CBS, Jul'84 by CBS Records. Dist: CBS

Offspring
NOT A SAD SONG.
Single (7"): released on Offspring Promotions, Sep'84 by Offspring Promotions Records. Dist: Offspring Promotions Ltd. Distribution

Off The Record With...
OFF THE RECORD...COUNTRY CLASSICS Various artists (Various Artists).
Album: released on Sierra, Aug'87 by Sierra Records. Dist: WEA. Estim retail price in Sep'87 was £4.99.

Cassette: released on Sierra, Aug'87 by Sierra Records. Dist: WEA. Estim retail price in Sep'87 was £4.99.

OFF THE RECORD WITH...THEMES Various artists (Various Artists).
Album: released on Sierra, Aug'87 by Sierra Records. Dist: WEA. Estim retail price in Sep'87 was £4.99.

Cassette: released on Sierra, Aug'87 by Sierra Records. Dist: WEA. Estim retail price in Sep'87 was £4.99.

Off To California
OFF TO CALIFORNIA Traditional Irish music in San Francisco (Various Artists).
Album: released on Advent, Apr'79 Dist: Celtic Music, Projection, Swift

O'Flaherty, Tyrone
PARTY TING.
Single (12"): released on Sunburn, Jul'83 by Orbitone Records. Dist: Jetstar Distribution

O'Flynn, Liam
BRENDAN VOYAGE, THE (O'Flynn, Liam & Orchestra).
Album: released on Tara (Ireland), '82 by Tara Records. Dist: I & B Records Distribution, Record Services Distribution (Ireland), Roots Distribution

Cassette: released on Tara (Ireland), '82 by Tara Records. Dist: I & B Records Distribution, Record Services Distribution (Ireland), Roots Distribution

Ofra Haza
GABI.
Tracks: / Gabi (remix).
Single (7"): released on Ace, Jun'86 by Ace Records. Dist: Pinnacle, Swift, Hotshot, Cadillac

Ofwerman, Rune
BAD BOYS FROM BRAZIL (Ofwerman, Rune Trio).
Album: released on Amigo, Jul'87 Dist: Red Rhino, Cartel

Ogden, Nigel
IT'S A MUSICAL WORLD.
Album: released on Amberlee, Jun'82 by Amberlee Records. Dist: Amberlee Records, H.R. Taylor

Ogerman
CITYSCAPE (Ogerman & Brecker).
Album: released on WEA (Import). Jul'83

Oggy
CLOG DANCE.
Single (7"): released on Taurus, Oct'82 Dist: Jetstar

O Give Thanks ..
O GIVE THANKS TO THE LORD various religious artists (Various Artists).
Album: released on Saydisc, Sep'85 by Saydisc Records. Dist: Essex, Harmonia Mundi, Roots, H.R. Taylor, Jazz Music, Swift, Projection, Gamut

Cassette: released on Saydisc, Sep'85 by Saydisc Records. Dist: Essex, Harmonia Mundi, Roots, H.R. Taylor, Jazz Music, Swift, Projection, Gamut

O'Halloran Brothers
MEN OF THE ISLAND, THE Irish traditional music and song.
Album: released on Topic, '81 by Topic Records. Dist: JSU Distribution, Projection Distribution, Jazz Music Distribution

O'Hara, Mary
AT THE ROYAL FESTIVAL HALL.
Album: released on Chrysalis, Dec'77 by Chrysalis Records. Dist: CBS

Cassette: released on Chrysalis, Dec'77 by Chrysalis Records. Dist: CBS

Album: released on MFP, Oct'84 by EMI Records. Dist: EMI

Cassette: released on MFP, Oct'84 by EMI Records. Dist: EMI

COLOURS.
Album: released on Images, Nov'81 by MSD Records. Dist: PRT

Cassette: released on Images, Nov'81 by MSD Records. Dist: PRT

FOCUS ON MARY O'HARA.
Cassette: released on Decca, May'78 by Decca Records. Dist: Polygram

IN HARMONY ALBUM.
Album: by Chrysalis Records. Dist: CBS

LAST ROSE OF SUMMER.
Album: released on Premier, May'85 by Premier Records. Dist: CBS

Cassette: released on Premier, May'85 by Premier Records. Dist: CBS

MARY O'HARA.
Cassette: released on Pickwick, Sep'80 by Pickwick Records. Dist: Pickwick Distribution, Prism Leisure Distribution, Lugtons

Album: released on Hallmark, Feb'82 by Pickwick Records. Dist: Pickwick Distribution, PRT, Taylors

Cassette: released on Hallmark, Feb'82 by Pickwick Records. Dist: Pickwick Distribution, PRT, Taylors

MARY O'HARA LIVE IN NEW YORK.
Album: released on Valentine, '84 by Valentine Records. Dist: PRT

Cassette: released on Valentine, '84 by Valentine Records. Dist: PRT

MESSENGER.
Single (7"): released on Valentine, Apr'85 by Valentine Records. Dist: PRT

MUSIC SPEAKS LOUDER THAN WORDS.
Album: released on Pickwick, Sep'80 by Pickwick Records. Dist: Pickwick Distribution, Prism Leisure Distribution, Lugtons

ROSE.
Single (7"): released on Images, Nov'81 by MSD Records. Dist: PRT

SCALLYWAG GANG (8 CANINE RASCALS) (Read by Mary O'Hara).
Cassette: released on Tempo Storytime, Oct'82

SCENT OF ROSES, THE.
Album: released on Chrysalis, Oct'80 by Chrysalis Records. Dist: CBS

Cassette: released on Chrysalis, Oct'80 by Chrysalis Records. Dist: CBS

SONG FOR IRELAND, A.
Album: released on Valentine, Apr'83 by Valentine Records. Dist: PRT

Cassette: released on Valentine, Apr'83 by Valentine Records. Dist: PRT

SPREAD A LITTLE HAPPINESS.
Album: released on Telstar, Aug'85 by Telstar Records. Dist: RCA Distribution

Cassette: released on Telstar, Aug'85 by Telstar Records. Dist: RCA Distribution

TRANQUILITY 20 SONGS OF LIFE.
Album: released on Warwick, Oct'79 by MSD Records. Dist: CBS

O'Hare, Pat
TRAVELLING MAN.
Single (7"): released on Pax, May'82 by Pax Records. Dist: Red Rhino, Cartel

Oh Boy
OH BOY.
Album:

OH BOY Jack Good's TV Show (Various Artists).
Album: released on Nut, Jul'78 by EMI Records. Dist: EMI

Oh Happy Days
OH HAPPY DAYS.
Album: released on Lotus, '78

Ohio Express
YUMMY YUMMY YUMMY.
Single (7"): released on Buddah, Feb'75 Dist: Swift, Jazz Music, PRT

Single (7"): released on Old Gold, Apr'83 by Old Gold Records. Dist: Lightning, Jazz Music, Spartan, Counterpoint

Ohio Players
FIRE.
Album: released on Mercury, Jan'75 by Phonogram Records. Dist: Polygram Distribution

Single (7"): released on Mercury (USA Import), '80

FOLLOW ME.
Single (7"): released on Air, Mar'85 by Chrysalis Records. Dist: Polygram

Single (12"): released on Air, Mar'85 by Chrysalis Records. Dist: Polygram

GOLD.
Album: released on Mercury (USA), Aug'87 by Import Records. Dist: IMS Distribution, Polygram Distribution

Cassette: released on Mercury (USA), Aug'87 by Import Records. Dist: IMS Distribution, Polygram Distribution

GRADUATION.
Album: released on Air City (USA), Mar'85 Dist: PRT

Cassette: released on Air City (USA), Mar'85 Dist: PRT

OHIO PLAYERS.
Album: released on Capitol(USA), '77 by Capitol (USA) Records. Dist: EMI

TENDERNESS.
Album: released on Epic, May'81 by CBS Records. Dist: CBS

Ohno, Eri

EASY TO LOVE.
Compact disc: by Denon Records. Dist: Harmonia Mundi

ERI MY DEAR.
Compact disc: by Denon Records. Dist: Harmonia Mundi

Oh Praise Ye the Lord

OH PRAISE YE THE LORD (Various Artists).
Album: released on Abbey, Nov'79 by Abbey. Dist: PRT, Taylors, Gamut

Ohrensausen

OHRENSAUSEN (Various Artists).
Notes: Includes Nurse With Wound, Coil etc.
Album: released on Dom, Jun'86 Dist: Red Rhino, Cartel

Oh Romeo

ONCE IS NOT ENOUGH.
Single (12"): released on Personal, Oct'84 by Personal Records. Dist: PRT

SAVING MYSELF (FOR THE ONE I LOVE).
Single (12"): released on ZYX (Germany), Nov'85 by ZYX Records. Dist: Greyhound

Oh What A Lovely War

OH WHAT A LOVELY WAR (ORIGINAL 1914-18 RECORDINGS) (Various Artists).
Album: released on World, '69 Dist: Jetstar

OH WHAT A LOVELY WAR Original London Cast (Various Artists).
Album: released on That's Entertainment, Apr'83 by That's Entertainment Records. Dist: Pinnacle, PRT

Cassette: released on That's Entertainment, Apr'83 by That's Entertainment Records. Dist: Pinnacle, PRT

Oi

OI (Various Artists).
Album: released on Zonophone, Oct'80 by EMI Records. Dist: EMI

OI - CHARTBUSTER VOL.1 Various artists (Various Artists).
Album: released on Link, Feb'87 Dist: DMS, RCA

OI OF SEX, THE (Various Artists).
Album: released on Syndicate, Aug'84

OI THAT'S YER LOT (Various Artists).
Album: released on Secret, Sep'82 by Secret Records. Dist: EMI

Cassette: released on Secret, Sep'82 by Secret Records. Dist: EMI

OI-THE RESURRECTION (Various Artists).
Album: released on Link, Nov'86 Dist: DMS, RCA

Oil A world Crisis

OIL A WORLD CRISIS Beirut, Washington, London.
Cassette: released on International Report, Oct'81 by Seminar Cassettes. Dist: Audio-Visual Library Services, Davidson Distribution, Eastern Educational Products Distrib., Forlaget Systime Distribution, MacDougall Distribution, Talktapes Distribution, Watkins Books Ltd Distribution, Norton, Jeff Distribution

Oi Polloi

RESIST THE ATOMIC MANACE.
Tracks: / Resist the atomic manace.
Single (7"): released on Endangered Musik, May'86 by Endangered Musik Records. Dist: Revolver

SKINS AND PUNKS VOLUME 2 (Oi Polloi\Betrayed).
Album: released on Oi!, Jan'87 Dist: Revolver Distribution

UNITE AND WIN.
Album: released on Oi!, Oct'87 Dist: Revolver Distribution. Estim retail price in Sep'87 was 4.99.

Oisin

BEALOIDEAS.
Album: released on Tara (Ireland), '82 by Tara Records. Dist: I & B Records Distribution, Record Services Distribution (Ireland), Roots Distribution

Cassette: released on Tara (Ireland), '82 by Tara Records. Dist: I & B Records Distribution, Record Services Distribution (Ireland), Roots Distribution

OISIN.
Album: released on Tara (Ireland), '82 by Tara Records. Dist: I & B Records Distribution, Record Services Distribution (Ireland), Roots Distribution

Cassette: released on Tara (Ireland), '82 by Tara Records. Dist: I & B Records Distribution, Record Services Distribution (Ireland), Roots Distribution

OVER THE MOOR TO MAGGIE.
Album: released on Tara (Ireland), '82 by Tara Records. Dist: I & B Records Distribution, Record Services Distribution (Ireland), Roots Distribution

Cassette: released on Tara (Ireland), '82 by Tara Records. Dist: I & B Records Distribution, Record Services Distribution (Ireland), Roots Distribution

O'Jays

COLLECTOR'S ITEMS Greatest hits.
Album: released on Philadelphia International, Nov'82 by CBS Records. Dist: CBS

Cassette: released on Philadelphia International, Nov'82 by CBS Records. Dist: CBS

EXTRAORDINARY GIRL.
Single (7"): released on Philadelphia International, Apr'84 by CBS Records. Dist: CBS

Single (12"): released on Philadelphia International, Apr'84 by CBS Records. Dist: CBS

Album: released on Chess, Oct'84 by Charly Records. Dist: Charly, Swift, PRT, Discovery, IMS, Polygram

GREATEST HITS: O'JAYS.
Album: released on Philadelphia International, Jun'84 by CBS Records. Dist: CBS

Cassette: released on Philadelphia International, Jun'84 by CBS Records. Dist: CBS

IDENTIFY YOURSELF.
Album: released on Philadelphia, Sep'79

Cassette: released on Philadelphia, Sep'79

I LOVE MUSIC.
Single (7"): released on Philadelphia, Apr'82

JUST ANOTHER LONELY NIGHT.
Single (7"): released on Philadelphia International, Sep'85 by CBS Records. Dist: CBS

Single (12"): released on Philadelphia International, Sep'85 by CBS Records. Dist: CBS

LET ME TOUCH YOU.
Tracks: / Don't take your love away / Lovin' you / True love never dies / Still missing / I just want somebody to love me / Let me touch you / Undercover lover / No lies to cloud my eyes / Don't let the dream get away / Cause I want you back again / Don't take your love away / Lovin' you / True love never dies / Still missing / I just want somebody to love me / Let me touch you / Undercover lover / No lies to cloud my eyes / Don't let the dream get away / Cause I want you back again.
Album: released on Manhattan, Jul'87 by EMI Records. Dist: EMI

Cassette: released on Manhattan, Jul'87 by EMI Records. Dist: EMI

Compact disc: released on Philadelphia, Jul'87

Compact disc: released on Philadelphia, Jul'87

LOVE AND MORE.
Album: released on Philadelphia International, Jul'84 by CBS Records. Dist: CBS

Cassette: released on Philadelphia International, Jul'84 by CBS Records. Dist: CBS

LOVE TRAIN.
Tracks: / Love train / I love music.
Single (7"): released on Portrait, May'86 by CBS Records. Dist: CBS

Single (7"): released on Old Gold, Apr'83 by Old Gold Records. Dist: Lightning, Jazz Music, Spartan, Counterpoint

Extended-play record: released on Scoop, Oct'84

Cassette: released on Scoop, Oct'84

MESSAGE IN THE MUSIC.
Album: released on Philadelphia International, Sep'76 by CBS Records. Dist: CBS

MY FAVOURITE PERSON.
Tracks: / Summer fling.
Single (12"): released on Epic, Aug'87 by CBS Records. Dist: CBS

O'JAYS 4 track cassette EP.
Cassette: released on Philadelphia International, Aug'82 by CBS Records. Dist: CBS

PEACE.
Album: released on Phoenix, Jul'81 by Audio Fidelity Enterprises. Dist: Stage One, Lugtons

SUMMER FLING.
Single (7"): released on Philadelphia International, Jul'84 by CBS Records. Dist: CBS

WHEN WILL I SEE YOU AGAIN.
Album: released on Philadelphia International, Sep'83 by CBS Records. Dist: CBS

Cassette: released on Philadelphia International, Sep'83 by CBS Records. Dist: CBS

WORKING ON YOUR CASE.
Album: released on Stateside, Mar'85 Dist: EMI

Cassette: released on Stateside, Mar'85 Dist: EMI

YEAR 2000, THE.
Album: released on Philadelphia International, Oct'80 by CBS Records. Dist: CBS

Cassette: released on Philadelphia International, Oct'80 by CBS Records. Dist: CBS

O'Jays, The

LET ME TOUCH YOU.
Compact disc: released on EMI, Aug'87 by EMI Records. Dist: EMI

O'Kanes

OH DARLING.
Tracks: / Oh darling / When I found you.
Single (7"): released on CBS, Apr'87 by CBS Records. Dist: CBS

O'KANES (THE).
Tracks: / Oh darlin' (why don't you care for me no more) / Just lovin' you / Daddies need to grow up too / Can't stop my heart from loving you / Bluegrass blues / Oh lonesome you / When we're gone' long gone / That's alright mama / Gonna walk that line / When I found you.
Compact disc: released on CBS, May'87 by CBS Records. Dist: CBS

Album: released on CBS, Mar'87 by CBS Records. Dist: CBS

Cassette: released on CBS, Mar'87 by CBS Records. Dist: CBS

Okay Temiz Trio

TURKISH FOLK JAZZ.
Album: by Sonet Records. Dist: PRT

O'Keefe, Danny

DAY TO DAY, THE.
Album: released on Coldwater(Germany), Aug'85

Okeh...

OKEH CHICAGO BLUES (Various Artists).
Album: released on Epic, May'82 by CBS Records. Dist: CBS

Cassette: released on Epic, May'82 by CBS Records. Dist: CBS

OKEH RHYTHM AND BLUES (Various Artists).
Album: released on Epic, May'82 by CBS Records. Dist: CBS

Cassette: released on Epic, May'82 by CBS Records. Dist: CBS

OKEH SOUL (Various Artists).
Album: released on Epic, May'82 by CBS Records. Dist: CBS

Cassette: released on Epic, May'82 by CBS Records. Dist: CBS

OKEH WESTERN SWING (Various Artists).
Album: released on Epic, '84 by CBS Records. Dist: CBS

Cassette: released on Epic, '84 by CBS Records. Dist: CBS

Okin, Earl

EARL OKIN HIMSELF.
Album: released on Whoopee, '82 by Whoopee Records. Dist: Whoopee Records, Waterfront Records, Jazz Music, JSU, Chris

Cassette: released on Whoopee, '82 by Whoopee Records. Dist: Whoopee Records, Waterfront Records, Jazz Music, JSU, Chris

EARL'S CAUGHT.
Album: released on Waterfront, Sep'86 by Waterfront Records. Dist: Rough Trade, Cartel, Projection, Roots

MR OKIN COMES TO TOWN.
Album: released on Folkland, Sep'79 Dist: Projection

Okines, Ken

CLOSE RELATIONS (Okines, Ken/Sue Ashby).
Album: released on Burlington, Oct'86 by Plant Life Records. Dist: Jazz Music, Celtic Music, Clyde Factors Distributors, I.R.S., Projection, Wellard, Chris, Roots

Oklahoma

OKLAHOMA Original film soundtrack (Various Artists).
Tracks: / Overture / Oh, what a beautiful mornin' / Surrey with the fringe on top / Kansas City / I can't say no / Many a new day / People will say we're in love / Poor Jud is dead / Out of my dreams / Farmer and the cowman (The) / All er nothing / Oklahoma.
Compact disc: released on Capitol, Apr'87 by Capitol Records. Dist: EMI

Album: released on Capitol, '59 by Capitol Records. Dist: EMI

Album: released on Stiff, Nov'80 by Stiff Records. Dist: EMI, Record Services Distribution (Ireland)

Cassette: released on Stiff, Nov'80 by Stiff Records. Dist: EMI, Record Services Distribution (Ireland)

OKLAHOMA-ORIGINAL CAST (Various Artists).
Album: released on World Records, Feb'81 Dist: Polygram

Album: released on MCA, Mar'82 by MCA Records. Dist: CBS

Cassette: released on MCA, Mar'82 by MCA Records. Dist: CBS

Okossun, Sonny

MOTHER AND CHILD (Okossun, Sonny Ozziddi).
Single (12"): released on OTI, Nov'82

WHICH WAY NIGERIA.
Album: released on Jive Alive, Oct'84 Dist: Jungle

O.K.s

DESIRE.
Album: released on Line, Apr'87

Oku, Keichi

SUNSET TINT.
Notes: New Age Music for piano, violin, harp and flute.
Compact disc: released on Denon, May'86 by Denon Records. Dist: Harmonia Mundi

Oku, Onuara

WI A COME.
Single (12"): released on Heartbeat, Jul'85 Dist: Revolver, Pinnacle

Old...

OLD COUNTRY BLUES (Various Artists).
Album: released on Flyright, Apr'79 by Flyright Records. Dist: Krazy Kat, Swift, Jazz Music

OLD COUNTRY MUSIC IN A NEW LAND Various artists (Various Artists).
Tracks: / Sedliacky Zabavny Czardas (The farmer's diversion Czardas) / Malenky Barabanshtchik (The little drummer-boy) / Kassaka Polka (Cossack Polka) / Zalim te Momce (I saw you, lad) / Stack-O-Barley / Tailor's Thimble / El Coco-Cancion (The Coconut Song) / La Piedera / I tickled 'em / Jeuns Gens Campagnard (Young men from the country) / La Valse de Bon Baurche (Valse du Bambocheur) / Pastorale / Yar Ounenal (I love you) / Sayf Lahziq (Your sword has pierced me) / Siteiako (Dance of Siteia) / Kuomet Sokis (When you dance) / Red haired lass, The.
Album: released on New World (USA), Apr'87 by New World Records (USA). Dist: Conifer

OLD GOLD'N'JUKEBOX (Various Artists).
Cassette: released on RCA, Mar'79 by RCA Records. Dist: RCA, Roots, Swift, Wellard, Chris, I & B, Solomon & Peres Distribution

OLD MUSIC BOX WALTZ MELODIES Swiss music boxes - Bornand collection (Old Music Box...).
Album: released on Bornard Music Box Co.(USA), Nov'80

Cassette: released on Bornard Music Box Co.(USA), Nov'80

OLD SONGS (Old Songs).

Album: released on Greenwich Village, Jan'85 by Sweet Folk All Records. Dist: Roots, Projection, Lightning, Celtic Music, Wellard, Chris

Old And New Dreams

PLAYING.
Tracks: / Happy house / Mopti / New dream / Rushour / Broken shadows / Playing.
Notes: Personnel: Don Cherry - trumpet, piano/Dewey Redman - tenor sax, musette/Charlie Hayden - bass/Ed Blackwell - drums.
Compact disc: released on ECM (Germany), Jun'86 by ECM Records. Dist: IMS, Polygram, Virgin through EMI

Oldfield, Mike

BOXED SET.
Album: released on Virgin, '85 by Virgin Records. Dist: EMI, Virgin Distribution

Cassette: released on Virgin, '85 by Virgin Records. Dist: EMI, Virgin Distribution

COMPLETE MIKE OLDFIELD (THE).
Compact disc: by Virgin Records. Dist: EMI, Virgin Distribution

Album: released on Virgin, Oct'85 by Virgin Records. Dist: EMI, Virgin Distribution

Cassette: released o.. Virgin, Oct'85 by Virgin Records. Dist: EMI, Virgin Distribution

CRISES.
Compact disc: released on Virgin, '83 by Virgin Records. Dist: EMI, Virgin Distribution

DISCOVERY.
Compact disc: by Virgin Records. Dist: EMI, Virgin Distribution

Album: released on Virgin, Jun'84 by Virgin Records. Dist: EMI, Virgin Distribution

Cassette: released on Virgin, Jun'84 by Virgin Records. Dist: EMI, Virgin Distribution

EXPOSED.
Notes: Double compact disc.
Compact disc: released on Virgin, Jul'86 by Virgin Records. Dist: EMI, Virgin Distribution

Album: released on Virgin, '76 by Virgin Records. Dist: EMI, Virgin Distribution

FIVE MILES OUT.
Compact disc: released on Virgin, '83 by Virgin Records. Dist: EMI, Virgin Distribution

Album: released on Virgin, Mar'82 by Virgin Records. Dist: EMI, Virgin Distribution

Cassette: released on Virgin, Mar'82 by Virgin Records. Dist: EMI, Virgin Distribution

HERGEST RIDGE.
Album: released on Virgin, Aug'74 by Virgin Records. Dist: EMI, Virgin Distribution

Album: released on Virgin, Apr'86 by Virgin Records. Dist: EMI, Virgin Distribution

Cassette: released on Virgin, Apr'86 by Virgin Records. Dist: EMI, Virgin Distribution

Compact disc: released on Virgin, Apr'86 by Virgin Records. Dist: EMI, Virgin Distribution

Compact disc: released on Virgin, Aug'74 by Virgin Records. Dist: EMI, Virgin Distribution

INCANTATIONS.
Tracks: / Incantations Parts 1-4 / Guilty.
Double compact disc: released on Virgin, Jul'86 by Virgin Records. Dist: EMI, Virgin Distribution

Double Album: released on Virgin, '78 by Virgin Records. Dist: EMI, Virgin Distribution

Cassette: released on Virgin, '78 by Virgin Records. Dist: EMI, Virgin Distribution

IN HIGH PLACES.
Tracks: / In high places / Poison arrows.
Single (7"): released on Virgin, May'87 by Virgin Records. Dist: EM' ,irgin Distribution

Single (12"): releaseu on Virgin, May'87 by Virgin Records. Dist: EMI, Virgin Distribution

KILLING FIELDS (THE).
Single (7"): released on Virgin, Nov'84 by Virgin Records. Dist: EMI, Virgin Distribution Deleted '85.

Single (12"): released on Virgin, Nov'84 by Virgin Records. Dist: EMI, Virgin Distribution

Album: released on Virgin, Nov'84 by Virgin Records. Dist: EMI, Virgin Distribution

Cassette: released on Virgin, Nov'84 by Virgin Records. Dist: EMI, Virgin Distribution

Compact disc: released on Virgin, Nov'84 by Virgin Records. Dist: EMI, Virgin Distribution

MOONLIGHT SHADOW/RITE OF MAN.
Single (7"): released on Virgin, Jun'83 by Virgin Records. Dist: EMI, Virgin Distribution

Picture disc single: released on Virgin, Jun'83 by Virgin Records. Dist: EMI, Virgin Distribution Deleted '84.

Single (12"): released on Virgin, Jun'83 by Virgin Records. Dist: EMI, Virgin Distribution

OMMADAWN.
Album: released on Virgin, Nov'75 by Virgin Records. Dist: EMI, Virgin Distribution

Cassette: released on Virgin, Nov'75 by Virgin Records. Dist: EMI, Virgin Distribution

Compact disc: released on Virgin, Nov'75 by Virgin Records. Dist: EMI, Virgin Distribution

ORCHESTRAL TUBULAR BELLS.
Compact disc: released on Virgin, Jul'87 by Virgin Records. Dist: EMI, Virgin Distribution

PICTURES IN THE DARK.
Single (7"): released on Virgin, Nov'85 by Virgin Records. Dist: EMI, Virgin Distribution Deleted '86.

Single (12"): released on Virgin, Nov'85 by Virgin Records. Dist: EMI, Virgin Distribution Deleted '86.

PLATINUM.
Album: released on Cube (Platinum coll), Oct'81

Album: released on Virgin, Nov'79 by Virgin Records. Dist: EMI, Virgin Distribution

Cassette: released on Virgin, Nov'79 by Virgin Records. Dist: EMI, Virgin Distribution

Compact disc: released on Virgin, Nov'79 by Virgin Records. Dist: EMI, Virgin Distribution

QE2.
Album: released on Virgin, Oct'80 by Virgin Records. Dist: EMI, Virgin Distribution

Cassette: released on Virgin, Oct'80 by Virgin Records. Dist: EMI, Virgin Distribution

Compact disc: released on Virgin, Oct'80 by Virgin Records. Dist: EMI, Virgin Distribution

SHINE.
Tracks: / Shine / Past, The.
Single (7"): released on Virgin, Apr'86 by Virgin Records. Dist: EMI, Virgin Distribution

Single (12"): released on Virgin, Apr'86 by Virgin Records. Dist: EMI, Virgin Distribution

TUBULAR BELLS.
Notes: Tubular bells parts 1 & 2.
Album: released on Virgin, '73 by Virgin Records. Dist: EMI, Virgin Distribution

Picture disc album: released on Virgin, '78 by Virgin Records. Dist: EMI, Virgin Distribution

Compact disc: released on Virgin, '83 by Virgin Records. Dist: EMI, Virgin Distribution

Oldfield, Sally

ANTHOLOGY.
Compact disc: released on Legacy, '86 Dist: PRT

CELEBRATION.
Tracks: / Mandala / Morning of my life / Woman of the night / Celebration / Blue water / My damsel heart / Love is everywhere.
Album: released on Castle Classics, Apr'86 by Castle Communications. Dist: BMG

Cassette: released on Castle Classics, Apr'86 by Castle Communications. Dist: BMG

Compact disc: released on Castle Classics, '86 by Castle Communications. Dist: BMG

COLLECTION: SALLY OLDFIELD.
Tracks: / Mirrors / Water bearer / Path with a heart / River of my childhood / Sons of the free / Mandala / Sun in my eyes / My damsel heart / Easy / Song of the lamp / You set my gypsy blood free / Woman of the night / Answering you / Love of a lifetime / Song of the healer / Morning of my life / Meet me in Verona / Celebration / Weaver / Love is everywhere.
Compact disc: released on Collector Series, '86 by Castle Communications Records. Dist: PRT, Pinnacle, RCA, Ariola

Album: released on Castle Communications, Feb'86 by Castle Communications. Dist: Cartel, Pinnacle, Counterpoint

Cassette: released on Castle Communications, Feb'86 by Castle Communications. Dist: Cartel, Pinnacle, Counterpoint

EASY.
Tracks: / Sun is in my eyes / You set my gypsy blood free / Answering you / Boulevard song / Easy / Sons of the free / Hide and seek / First born of the earth / Man of storm.
Album: released on Castle Classics, Apr'86 by Castle Communications. Dist: BMG

Cassette: released on Castle Classics, Apr'86 by Castle Communications. Dist: BMG

PEKKA POHJOLA (Oldfield, Sally & Mike).
Album: released on Bellaphon, '82 by Bellaphon Records. Dist: IMS-Polygram

STRANGE DAY IN BERLIN.
Album: released on Bronze, Oct'83 by Polygram Records. Dist: Polydor Deleted '85.

Cassette: released on Bronze, Oct'83 by Polygram Records. Dist: Polydor

WATER BEARER.
Tracks: / Water bearer / Songs of the quendi / Mirrors / Weaver / Mirrors / Night of the hunger's moon / Child of Allah / Song of the bow / Fire and honey / Song of the healer.
Album: released on Castle Classics, Apr'86 by Castle Communications. Dist: BMG

Oldfield, Terry

IN SEARCH OF THE TROJAN WARS.
Album: released on BBC, Mar'85 by BBC Records & Tapes. Dist: EMI, PRT, Pye

Cassette: released on BBC, Mar'85 by BBC Records & Tapes. Dist: EMI, PRT, Pye

MAIN THEM FROM JOHN SILVER'S TREASURE ISLAND (Oldfield, Terry & Tom McGuinness).
Tracks: / John Silver's return to Treasure Island (main theme) / Isabella / Island of dreams.
Single (7"): released on Towerbell, Jul'86 by Towerbell Records. Dist: EMI

Old Gold Decades

OLD GOLD DECADES (1) (Various Artists).
Cassette: released on Old Gold, Sep'85 by Old Gold Records. Dist: Lightning, Jazz Music, Spartan, Counterpoint

OLD GOLD DECADES (10) (Various Artists).
Cassette: released on Old Gold, Sep'85 by Old Gold Records. Dist: Lightning, Jazz Music, Spartan, Counterpoint

OLD GOLD DECADES (11) (Various Artists).
Tracks: / All I have to do is dream / To know him is to love him / Donna / Born too late / Tammy.
Extended-play record: released on Old Gold, May'86 by Old Gold Records. Dist: Lightning, Jazz Music, Spartan, Counterpoint

OLD GOLD DECADES (12) (Various Artists).
Tracks: / Girl can't help it, The / Great balls of fire / Ain't that a shame / Be bop a lula / Rave on.
Extended-play record: released on Old Gold, May'86 by Old Gold Records. Dist: Lightning, Jazz Music, Spartan, Counterpoint

OLD GOLD DECADES (13) (Various Artists).
Tracks: / Tom Dooley / Sixteen tons / Love letters in the sand / When / Whole lotta woman.
Extended-play record: released on Old Gold, May'86 by Old Gold Records. Dist: Lightning, Jazz Music, Spartan, Counterpoint

OLD GOLD DECADES (14) (Various Artists).
Tracks: / Sailor / Sealed with a kiss / Run to him / Rhythm of the rain / Soldier boy.
Extended-play record: released on Old Gold, May'86 by Old Gold Records. Dist: Lightning, Jazz Music, Spartan, Counterpoint

OLD GOLD DECADES (15) (Various Artists).
Tracks: / Poetry in motion / Locomotion, The / Let's dance / He's so fine.
Extended-play record: released on Old Gold, May'86 by Old Gold Records. Dist: Lightning, Jazz Music, Spartan, Counterpoint

OLD GOLD DECADES (17) (Various Artists).
Tracks: / How do you do it / Do you want to know a secret / I'm into something good / Hippy hippy shake / I'm alive.
Extended-play record: released on Old Gold, May'86 by Old Gold Records. Dist: Lightning, Jazz Music, Spartan, Counterpoint

OLD GOLD DECADES (18) (Various Artists).
Tracks: / She's not there / For your love / All or nothing / Out of time / Go now.
Extended-play record: released on Old Gold, May'86 by Old Gold Records. Dist: Lightning, Jazz Music, Spartan, Counterpoint

OLD GOLD DECADES (19) (Various Artists).
Extended-play record: released on Old Gold, May'86 by Old Gold Records. Dist: Lightning, Jazz Music, Spartan, Counterpoint

OLD GOLD DECADES (2) (Various Artists).
Cassette: released on Old Gold, Sep'85 by Old Gold Records. Dist: Lightning, Jazz Music, Spartan, Counterpoint

OLD GOLD DECADES (20) (Various Artists).
Tracks: / From a jack to a king / Green green grass of home / Release me / She wears my ring / Honey.
Extended-play record: released on Old Gold, May'86 by Old Gold Records. Dist: Lightning, Jazz Music, Spartan, Counterpoint

OLD GOLD DECADES (21) (Various Artists).
Tracks: / Where do you go to my lovely / Nights in white satin / Whiter shade of pale / Sloop John B / Pretty flamingo.
Notes: 5 track EP.
Cassette: released on Old Gold, May'86 by Old Gold Records. Dist: Lightning, Jazz Music, Spartan, Counterpoint

OLD GOLD DECADES (22) (Various Artists).
Tracks: / I'm a believer / Sugar sugar / Sweet talkin' guy / Baby, now that I've found you / Half as nice (If paradise is).
Notes: 5 track EP.
Cassette: released on Old Gold, May'86 by Old Gold Records. Dist: Lightning, Jazz Music, Spartan, Counterpoint

OLD GOLD DECADES (23) (Various Artists).
Tracks: / You're my best friend / Don't it make your brown eyes blue / Blanket on the ground / I recall a gypsy woman / Lucille.
Notes: 5 track EP.
Cassette: released on Old Homestead, May'86 Dist: Mike's Country Music Room Distribution, Swift Distribution

OLD GOLD DECADES (24) (Various Artists).
Tracks: / Mississippi / Love is in the air / Seasons in the sun / All by myself / Billy don't be a hero.
Notes: 5 track EP.
Cassette: released on Old Gold, May'86 by Old Gold Records. Dist: Lightning, Jazz Music, Spartan, Counterpoint

OLD GOLD DECADES (25) (Various Artists).
Tracks: / When I'm dead and gone / I hear you knockin' / Spirit in the sky / Lady Eleanor / Ride a white swan.
Notes: 5 track EP.
Cassette: released on Old Gold, May'86 by Old Gold Records. Dist: Lightning, Jazz Music, Spartan, Counterpoint

OLD GOLD DECADES (3) (Various Artists).
Cassette: released on Old Gold, Sep'85 by Old Gold Records. Dist: Lightning, Jazz Music, Spartan, Counterpoint

OLD GOLD DECADES (4) (Various Artists).
Cassette: released on Old Gold, Sep'85 by Old Gold Records. Dist: Lightning, Jazz Music, Spartan, Counterpoint

OLD GOLD DECADES (5) (Various Artists).
Cassette: released on Old Gold, Sep'85 by Old Gold Records. Dist: Lightning, Jazz Music, Spartan, Counterpoint

OLD GOLD DECADES (6) (Various Artists).
Cassette: released on Old Gold, Sep'85 by Old Gold Records. Dist: Lightning, Jazz Music, Spartan, Counterpoint

OLD GOLD DECADES (7) (Various Artists).
Cassette: released on Old Gold, Sep'85 by Old Gold Records. Dist: Lightning, Jazz Music, Spartan, Counterpoint

OLD GOLD DECADES (8) (Various Artists).
Cassette: released on Old Gold, Sep'85 by Old Gold Records. Dist: Lightning, Jazz Music, Spartan, Counterpoint

OLD GOLD DECADES (9) (Various Artists).
Cassette: released on Old Gold, Sep'85 by Old Gold Records. Dist: Lightning, Jazz Music, Spartan, Counterpoint

Old Grey Whistle Test

OLD GREY WHISTLE TEST TAKE 2 (Various Artists).
Double Album: released on Beeb, Jan'77 by BBC Records. Dist: PRT

Oldham, Andrew

RARITIES (Oldham, Andrew 'Orchestra & Chorus').
Album: released on See For Miles, Dec'84 by See For Miles Records. Dist: Pinnacle

ROLLING STONES SONGBOOK,THE (Oldham, Andrew 'Orchestra & Chorus').
Album: released on Decca, Feb'85 by Decca Records. Dist: Polygram

Oldham Tinkers

BEST O'T' BUNCH.
Album: released on Topic, '81 Dist: Roots Distribution

FOR OLD TIMES SAKE.
Album: released on Topic, '81 Dist: Roots Distribution

OLDHAMS BURNING SANDS.
Album: released on Topic, '81 Dist: Roots Distribution

SIT THEE DOWN.
Album: released on Topic, '81 Dist: Roots Distribution

THAT LANCASHIRE BAND.
Album: released on Topic, '81 Dist: Roots Distribution

Oldies But Goldies

OLDIES BUT GOLDIES 1 various artists (Various Artists).
Album: released on Teldec, May'82

Cassette: released on Teldec, May'82

OLDIES BUT GOLDIES 2 various artists (Various Artists).
Album: released on Teldec, May'82

Cassette: released on Teldec, May'82

Oldies But Goodies

OLDIES BUT GOODIES-DOO WOP STYLE various artists (Various Artists).
Tracks: / Blue moon / Smokey places / Jerk (The) / Those oldies but goodies / Earth angel / Since I don't have you / Love potion no.9 / La la la la la / Lovers island / Come go with me / Needles and pins / Diamonds and pearls.
Album: released on Topline, Jan'87 by Charly Records. Dist: Charly Distribution

Cassette: released on Topline, Jan'87 by Charly Records. Dist: Charly Distribution

OLDIES BUT GOODIES (Various Artists).
Notes: soul and blues compilation with Eddie Floydd, Ike and Tina Turner, Llord Price, Sam Cooke, Lee Dorsey etc.
Compact disc: released on Bridge, '86 Dist: CD Centre Distribution, Pinnacle, Target

OLDIES BUT GOODIES VOL.2 (Various Artists).
Notes: Ike & Tina Turner, Lee dorsey, Chuck berry, Little Richard, Gladys knight & the Pips etc.
Compact disc: released on Bridge, '86 Dist: CD Centre Distribution, Pinnacle, Target

Oldimers, Jenaer

MIT BANJO UND TUBA.
Album: released on Amiga, Jun'79

Old MacDonald Had A Farm

OLD MACDONALD HAD A FARM (Various Artists).
Cassette: released on Storyteller, Jun'86

Old Man

SACK.
Single (7"): released on Black Lagoon, May'85 by Black Lagoon Records. Dist: Red Rhino, Cartel

Old Man Of Lochnagar

OLD MAN OF LOCHNAGAR (THE) Original cast recording (Various Artists).
Album: released on First Night, Nov'86 by Safari Records. Dist: Pinnacle

Old & New Dreams

PLAYING.
Album: released on ECM, Nov'81 by ECM Records. Dist: IMS, Polygram, Virgin through EMI

Old People Are Mad

TRUST.
Single (7"): released on Wrinkley, Feb'85

Old Swan Band

GAMESTERS,PICKPOCKETS AND HARLOTS.
Album: released on Dingles, '83 by Dingles Records. Dist: Projection

NO REELS.
Album: released on Freereed, Sep'79 by Topic Records. Dist: JSU

OLD SWAN BAND.
Album: released on Freereed, Oct'80 by Topic Records. Dist: JSU

Old Time...

OLD TIME JAZZBAND (Old Time Jazzband).

Notes: Reine Rimon with New Orleansians.
Album: released on 504, Feb'87 by 504 Records. Dist: Chris Wellard, Jazz Music

OLDTIME JAZZ FOREVER (Various Artists).
Album: released on Wam, May'87

OLD TIME ROCK 'N' ROLL Various artists (Old Time Rock 'n' Roll).
Tracks: / Old time rock 'n' roll / Snake and the bookworm (The) / I ain't gonna be your lowdown dog no more / Silly Willy / Real wild child / Baby I'm bugged / Dangerous doll / Like wow / Knock knock / Short hair and turtle necked sweater / Pucker paint / You were mean baby / Box of candy and a piece of fruit / Livin' high / I'm glad I waited so long / Doodlebug.
Album: released on Charly, Apr'86 by Charly Records. Dist: Charly, Cadillac

OLD TOWN BLUES VOL.1 (Various Artists).
Album: released on Ace, Jun'86 by Ace Records. Dist: Pinnacle, Swift, Hotshot, Cadillac
Cat. no: CH 180

Old Vic Company

ROMEO AND JULIET W. Shakespear.
Cassette: released on Listen For Pleasure, Oct'80 by MFP Records. Dist: EMI

O'Leary,Johnny

MUSIC FOR THE COMPLETE POLKA SET.
Album: released on Topic, '81 Dist: Roots Distribution

O'Leary, Kim

PUT THE PIECES BACK.
Tracks: / Put the pieces back / Kids downtown, The.
Single (7"): released on Motown, Jun'87 by Motown Records. Dist: BMG Distribution

Single (12"): released on Motown, Jun'87 by Motown Records. Dist: BMG Distribution

O'Leary, Tony

ROAD TO HELL.
Single (7"): released on Blue Stack, Jun'84 by Blue Stack Records. Dist: ILA

Olenn, Johnny

JUST ROLLIN' WITH JOHNNY OLENN.
Album: released on Ace, Sep'82 by Ace Records. Dist: Pinnacle, Swift, Hotshot, Cadillac

Ole Ole

CONSPIRACY.
Single (7"): released on CBS, Aug'84 by CBS Records. Dist: CBS

Single (12"): released on CBS, Aug'84 by CBS Records. Dist: CBS

Ole Tennessee country

OLE TENNESSEE COUNTRY (Various Artists).
Tracks: / Feelin' low / Laughin' and jokin' / Round and round / My destiny / Baby doll / Believe me / When you stop lovin' me / Easy to love / Down on the border / Goin' crazy / Poor boy / This train / Pink wedding gown / Satisfied with me.
Notes: Original Sun Recordings. Licensed from Charly Records International APS. This compilation (P) 1986 Charly Holdings Inc. (C) Charly records Ltd.
Album: released on Sun, '86 by Charly Records. Dist: Charly Distribution

Oliver

OLIVER Original cast (Various Artists).
Cassette: released on Decca, '79 by Decca Records. Dist: Polygram

OLIVER Original film soundtrack.
Album: released on RCA, '84 by RCA Records. Dist: RCA, Roots, Swift, Wellard, Chris, I & B, Solomon & Peres Distribution

Cassette: released on RCA, '84 by RCA Records. Dist: RCA, Roots, Swift, Wellard, Chris, I & B, Solomon & Peres Distribution

OLIVER Original London cast.
Album: released on That's Entertainment, Apr'83 by That's Entertainment Records. Dist: Pinnacle, PRT

Cassette: released on That's Entertainment, Apr'83 by That's Entertainment Records. Dist: Pinnacle, PRT

Oliver, Gene

TRIBUTE TO NEIL DIAMOND,A.
Cassette: released on Kingfisher, Nov'81 Dist: PRT

Oliver, James

WHAT WE SAY WITH OUR EYES.
Single (7"): released on Ritz, Apr'85 by Ritz Records. Dist: Spartan

---

Oliver, King

1923 (Oliver, King & His Creole Jazz Band).
Album: released on Swaggie (Australia), Jan'83

31.3.23 (Oliver, King & His Creole Jazz Band).
Album: released on Joker, Apr'81 Dist: Counterpoint, Mainline, Record Services Distribution (Ireland)

CHIMES BLUES.
Album: released on Saar Giants Of Jazz (Italy), Sep'85 Dist: Mainline

Cassette: released on Saar Giants Of Jazz (Italy), Sep'85 Dist: Mainline

FAREWELL BLUES (1926-7).
Album: released on Joker Import, Apr'81

FRANKIE & JOHNNY (1926-7).
Album: released on Joker Import, Apr'81

GENNETT SIDES OF APRIL & OCTOBER,1923,THE (Oliver, King & His Creole Jazz Band).
Album: released on Rhapsody, Oct'81 by President Records. Dist: Taylors, Swift, Jazz Music, Wellard, Chris

HOMETOWN BLUES.
Tracks: / Kiss me sweet / Construction gang / Hometown blues / Sorrow Valley blues / Empty bed blues part one / Empty bed blues part two / You're such a cruel papa to me / My diff'rent kind of man / My handy man / Organ grinder blues / I'm busy and you can't come in / Jasnine / In the bottle blues / What do you want me to do / Blue blood blues.
Album: released on Rhapsody, Mar'87 by President Records. Dist: Taylors, Swift, Jazz Music, Wellard, Chris

I'M CRAZY 'BOUT MY BABY (1930-31).
Album: released on Joker Import, Apr'81

KING OLIVER.
Album: released on Deja Vu, Jan'87 by Deja Vu Records. Dist: Counterpoint, Record Services Distribution

Cassette: released on Deja Vu, Jan'87 by Deja Vu Records. Dist: Counterpoint, Record Services Distribution (Ireland)

KING OLIVER AND HIS ORCHESTRA (Oliver, King & his Orchestra).
Double Album: released on RCA (France), '83 by RCA Records. Dist: Discovery

KING OLIVER & HIS ORCHESTRA 1929-30.
Tracks: / West end blues / I've got that thing / Call of the freaks / Trumpet's prayer / Freakish light blues / Can I tell you / My good man Sam / What you want me to do / Sweet like this / Too late / I'm lonesome, sweetheart / I want you just myself / I can't stop loving you / Everybody does it in Hawaii / Frankie and Johnny / New Orleans shout / St James Infirmary / I must have it / Rhythm club stomp (curwhip glide) / You're just my type / Echo / Boogie woogie / Mule face blues / Struggle bunny / Don't you think I love you / Olga / Shake it and break it / Stingaree blues / What's the use of living without you / You were only passing time with me / Nelson stomp / Stealing.
Notes: Double album. Double cassette. Mono.
Album: released on Jazz Tribune (USA), Sep'86 Dist: Discovery

Cassette: released on Jazz Tribune (USA), Sep'86 Dist: Discovery

KING OLIVER VOL..
Album: released on Classic Jazz Masters, Oct'86 by Mainline Record Company. Dist: Mainline, Swift, Jazz Music

OKEY SESSIONS,THE (Oliver, King & His Creole Jazz Band).
Album: released on EMI Retrospect, Jun'85 by EMI Records. Dist: EMI

Cassette: released on EMI Retrospect, Jun'85 by EMI Records. Dist: EMI

SNAG IT (1926-7).
Album: released on Joker Import, Apr'81

SWEET LIKE THIS.
Tracks: / West end blues / I've got that thing / Call of the freaks / Trumpet's prayer / Freakish light blues / Can I tell you / My good man Sam / What you want me to do? / Sweet like this / Too late / I'm lonesome, sweetheart / I want you just myself / Everybody does it in Hawaii / Frankie & Johnny / St. James' infirmary / When you're smiling.
Album: released on Halcyon (USA), Feb'87 by Halcyon Records (USA). Dist: Jazz Music, Conifer, Taylors

Cassette: released on Halcyon (USA), Feb'87 by Halcyon Records (USA). Dist: Jazz Music, Conifer, Taylors

WEST END BLUES 1929.
Album: released on Joker Import, Apr'81

Oliver, Laurence

THEME FROM TIME.
Single (7"): released on EMI, Nov'85 by EMI Records. Dist: EMI

Single 10": released on EMI, Nov'85 by EMI Records. Dist: EMI

Oliver, Sy

JULY 7TH 1960 & OCTOBER 18TH 1962.
Album: released on Jazz Vault, Oct'80 Dist: Jazz Music, JSU, Taylor, H.R.

SENTIMENTAL SY.
Album: released on Jasmine, Oct'84 by Jasmine Records. Dist: Counterpoint, Lugtons, Taylor, H.R., Wellard, Chris. Swift, Cadillac

Oliver, Valerie

GET THE MONEY.
Single (12"): released on I.R.S.(Independent Record Syndicate), Oct'83 by I.R.S.. Dist: MCA

Olivier, Jim

CAJUN MUSIC FOR EVERYONE.
Album:

I LOVE CAJUN MUSIC.
Album:

LA MUSIQUE DE JIM OLIVIER.
Album:

LET's KEEP IT CAJUN.
Album:

SINGS THE CAJUN WAY.
Album:

Olsson, Ingemar

I FEEL FREE.
Album: released on Day Spring, Aug'85 by Word Records. Dist: Word Distribution, CBS

Cassette: released on Day Spring, Aug'85 by Word Records. Dist: Word Distribution, CBS

Olsson, Kai

CRAZY LOVE.
Album: released on Chrysalis, Sep'79 by Chrysalis Records. Dist: CBS

Olsson, Kvintetten

LATT PA SNE Also featuring The Olsson Quintet.
Album: released on Phontastic, '82 Dist: Wellard, Chris

Olton, Mike

FAVOURITE FLAVOURS.
Tracks: / Favourite flavours / Love's a gamble.
Album: released on UK Sunshine Records, Nov'86 by UK Sunshine Records. Dist: PRT

Single (12"): released on UK Sunshine Records, Nov'86 by UK Sunshine Records. Dist: PRT

Olympia Brass Band

NOLA SINGLES ALBUM.
Notes: with Jim Duggan, Lee Allen
Cassette: released on Nola, Mar'87 Dist: JSU, Jazz Music, Cadillac, Chris Wellard

OLYMPIA BRASS BAND.
Album: released on Nola, Sep'79 Dist: JSU, Jazz Music, Cadillac, Chris Wellard

Olympic Orchestra

REILLY - ACE OF SPIES.
Single (7"): released on Red Bus, Sep'83 by Red Bus Records. Dist: PRT

Olympic Rock

OLYMPIC ROCK Don Radar, Jack Earls, Leon James & others.
Album: released on Dial (Holland), Apr'79 Dist: Swift

Olympic Runners

KEEP IT UP.
Album: released on RCA, Mar'78 by RCA Records. Dist: RCA, Roots, Swift, Wellard, Chris, I & B, Solomon & Peres Distribution
Cat. no: PL 25124

PUTTING IT ON YA.
Album: released on Polydor, '78 by Polydor Records. Dist: Polygram, Polydor

Olympics

DOIN' THE HULLY GULLY.
Album: released on Ace, Aug'82 by Ace Records. Dist: Pinnacle, Swift, Hotshot, Cadillac

OLYMPICS MEET THE MARATHON's, THE.

Album: released on Ace, Jan'85 by Ace Records. Dist: Pinnacle, Swift, Hotshot, Cadillac

Olympic Sideburns

OLYMPIC SIDEBURNS.
Single (12"): released on New Rose, Aug'85 Dist: Rough Trade, Cartel

OLYMPIC SIDEBURNS (LP).
Album: released on New Rose, May'85 Dist: Rough Trade, Cartel

Olympic Smiles

SOMETHING'S PUSHING ME.
Single (7"): released on Slipped Discs, Aug'84 by Slipped Discs Records. Dist: PRT, Self Distribution

Om

CEREBUS.
Album: released on Japo, Feb'82 by ECM (Germany). Dist: IMS, Polygram

OM (Om with Dom Um Roamoa).
Album: released on Japo, Jan'78 by ECM (Germany). Dist: IMS, Polygram

RAUTIONAHA.
Album: released on ECM, Apr'77 by ECM Records. Dist: IMS, Polygram, Virgin through EMI

Omar

GET IT OUT OF YOUR SYSTEM.
Tracks: / Get it out of your system / Get it out of your system (instrumental).
Single (12"): released on Kongo, Aug'86 by Kongo Records. Dist: Jetstar

MR POSTMAN.
Single (12"): released on Kongo, May'85 by Kongo Records. Dist: Jetstar

Omari

AFTER LOVING YOU.
Single (12"): released on Beau-Jolly, Feb'84 by Nouveau Records. Dist: PRT

Single (12"): released on Recent Future, Nov'85 by Recent Future. Dist: PRT

Omartian, Michael

ADAM AGAIN.
Album: released on Myrrh, May'82 by Word Records. Dist: Word Distribution

Cassette: released on Myrrh, May'82 by Word Records. Dist: Word Distribution

BUILDER, THE (Omartian, Michael & Stormie).
Album: released on Myrrh, May'82 by Word Records. Dist: Word Distribution

Cassette: released on Myrrh, May'82 by Word Records. Dist: Word Distribution

CONVERSATIONS.
Tracks: / Homelands / Soldier (The) / Rest is now (The) / Feast (The) / Right at the start / Desert (The) / Call (The) / Rest (The).
Notes: Although Michael Omartian is best known as one of the most successful producers in the general market for his work with such artists as Christopher Cross, DonnaSummer, Rod Stewart and Peter Cetera, he now invites you to trace his musical life in his first album on Reunion Records called "Conversations". Michael Composed and arranged all the scores, played most of the instruments and produced the album.The piano base is orchestrated using various synthesizers and percussion. Conversations is a 1980's instrumental masterpiece.
Album: released on Reunion, Jan'87

Cassette: released on Reunion, Jan'87

SEASONS OF THE SOUL.
Album: released on Myrrh, May'82 by Word Records. Dist: Word Distribution

Cassette: released on Myrrh, May'82 by Word Records. Dist: Word Distribution

WHITE HORSE.
Album: released on Myrrh, May'82 by Word Records. Dist: Word Distribution

Cassette: released on Myrrh, May'82 by Word Records. Dist: Word Distribution

O.M.D.

Orchestral Manoeuvres in The Dark

ARCHITECTURE & MORALITY (Orchestral Manoeuvres In The Dark).
Album: released on Dindisc, Dec'81 by Virgin Records. Dist: Virgin, EMI

Cassette: released on Dindisc, Dec'81 by Virgin Records. Dist: Virgin, EMI

Compact disc: released on Dindisc, Dec'81 by Virgin Records. Dist: Virgin, EMI

CRUSH (Orchestral Manoeuvres In The Dark).
Compact disc: by Virgin Records. Dist: EMI, Virgin Distribution

Album: released on Virgin, Jun'85 by Virgin Records. Dist: EMI, Virgin Distribution

Cassette: released on Virgin, Jun'85 by Virgin Records. Dist: EMI, Virgin Distribution

DAZZLE SHIPS (Orchestral Manoeuvres In The Dark).
Tracks: / Radio Prague / Genetic engineering / ABC auto indistry / Telegraph / This is Helena / International dazzle ships / Romance of the telescope / Silent running / Radio waves / Time zones / Of all the things we've made.
Album: released on Virgin, Mar'83 by Virgin Records. Dist: EMI, Virgin Distribution

Cassette: released on Virgin, Mar'83 by Virgin Records. Dist: EMI, Virgin Distribution

Compact disc: released on Virgin, Mar'83 by Virgin Records. Dist: EMI, Virgin Distribution

Single (7"): released on Virgin, Mar'84 by Virgin Records. Dist: EMI, Virgin Distribution

Single (12"): released on Virgin, Mar'84 by Virgin Records. Dist: EMI, Virgin Distribution

ELECTRICITY (Orchestral Manoeuvres In The Dark).
Single (7"): released on Dindisc, Apr'80 by Virgin Records. Dist: Virgin, EMI

IF YOU LEAVE (Orchestral Manoeuvres In The Dark).
Tracks: / If you leave / 88 seconds Greensboro.
Single (7"): released on Virgin, Apr'86 by Virgin Records. Dist: EMI, Virgin Distribution

Single (12"): released on Virgin, Apr'86 by Virgin Records. Dist: EMI, Virgin Distribution

JUNK CULTURE (Orchestral Manoeuvres In The Dark).
Compact disc: by Virgin Records. Dist: EMI, Virgin Distribution

Album: released on Virgin, May'84 by Virgin Records. Dist: EMI, Virgin Distribution

Cassette: released on Virgin, May'84 by Virgin Records. Dist: EMI, Virgin Distribution

LA FEMME ACCIDENT (Orchestral Manoeuvres In The Dark).
Single (7"): released on Virgin, Oct'85 by Virgin Records. Dist: EMI, Virgin Distribution Deleted '86.

Single (12"): released on Virgin, Oct'85 by Virgin Records. Dist: EMI, Virgin Distribution Deleted '86.

LIVE AND DIE (FOREVER) (Orchestral Manoeuvres In The Dark).
Tracks: / Live and die (forever) / This town.
Single (7"): released on Virgin, Aug'86 by Virgin Records. Dist: EMI, Virgin Distribution

Single (12"): released on Virgin, Aug'86 by Virgin Records. Dist: EMI, Virgin Distribution

NEVER TURN AWAY (Orchestral Manoeuvres In The Dark).
Single (7"): released on Virgin, Oct'84 by Virgin Records. Dist: EMI, Virgin Distribution

Single (12"): released on Virgin, Oct'84 by Virgin Records. Dist: EMI, Virgin Distribution

ORCHESTRAL MANOEUVRES IN THE DARK (Orchestral Manoeuvres In The Dark).
Compact disc: released on 10, Jul'87 by 10 Records. Dist: Virgin, EMI

Album: released on Dindisc, Aug'84 by Virgin Records. Dist: Virgin, EMI

ORGANISATION (Orchestral Manoeuvres In The Dark).
Tracks: / Onolagay / Second thought / VCL X1 / Motion and heart / Statues / Misunderstanding, The / More I see you / Promise / Stanlow.
Compact disc: released on 10, Jul'87 by 10 Records. Dist: Virgin, EMI

Album: released on Dindisc, Oct'80 by Virgin Records. Dist: Virgin, EMI

Cassette: released on Dindisc, Oct'80 by Virgin Records. Dist: Virgin, EMI

PACIFIC AGE (Orchestral Manoeuvres In The Dark).
Compact disc: released on Virgin, Oct'86 by Virgin Records. Dist: EMI, Virgin Distribution

Album: released on Virgin, Sep'86 by Virgin Records. Dist: EMI, Virgin Distribution

Cassette: released on Virgin, Sep'86 by Virgin Records. Dist: EMI, Virgin Distribution

SECRET (Orchestral Manoeuvres In The Dark).
Single (7"): released on Virgin, Jul'85 by Virgin Records. Dist: EMI, Virgin Distribution

Single (12"): released on Virgin, Jul'85 by Virgin Records. Dist: EMI, Virgin Distribution

SHAME (Orchestral Manoeuvres In The Dark).
Tracks: / Shame / Goddess of love.
Compact disc single: released on Virgin, May'87 by Virgin Records. Dist: EMI, Virgin Distribution

Single (7"): released on Virgin, Apr'87 by Virgin Records. Dist: EMI, Virgin Distribution

Single (12"): released on Virgin, Apr'87 by Virgin Records. Dist: EMI, Virgin Distribution

SO IN LOVE WITH YOU (Orchestral Manoeuvres In The Dark).
Single (7"): released on Virgin, May'85 by Virgin Records. Dist: EMI, Virgin Distribution Deleted '86.

Single (12"): released on Virgin, May'85 by Virgin Records. Dist: EMI, Virgin Distribution

TALKING LOUD AND CLEAR (Orchestral Manoeuvres In The Dark).
Single (7"): released on Virgin, Jun'84 by Virgin Records. Dist: EMI, Virgin Distribution

Single (12"): released on Virgin, Jun'84 by Virgin Records. Dist: EMI, Virgin Distribution

TESLA GIRLS (Orchestral Manoeuvres In The Dark).
Single (7"): released on Virgin, Aug'84 by Virgin Records. Dist: EMI, Virgin Distribution Deleted '86.

Single (12"): released on Virgin, Aug'84 by Virgin Records. Dist: EMI, Virgin Distribution

WE LOVE YOU (Orchestral Manoeuvres In The Dark).
Single (7"): released on Virgin, Nov'86 by Virgin Records. Dist: EMI, Virgin Distribution

Single (12"): released on Virgin, Nov'86 by Virgin Records. Dist: EMI, Virgin Distribution

Omega

GAMBLER.
Cassette: released on Vision, Feb'85 Dist: Vision

GOD LOVES TO ROCK AND ROLL.
Cassette: released on Vision, Dec'84 Dist: Vision

PROPHET, THE.
Album: released on Rock Machine, Mar'85 by Razor Records. Dist: Pinnacle

Omega Theatre

ROBOTS MACHINES AND SILICON DREAMS.
Single (7"): released on Sunny, Nov'82 by Sunny Records. Dist: PRT Distribution

Omega Tribe

ANGRY SONGS.
Single (7"): released on Crass, Jun'83 by Exitstencil Music. Dist: Rough Trade, Cartel

IT'S A HARD LIFE.
Single (7"): released on Corpus Christi, Sep'84 by Exitstencil Music. Dist: Cartel

Single (12"): released on Corpus Christi, Sep'84 by Exitstencil Music. Dist: Cartel

LIVE AT THE CLARENDON.
Cassette: released on 96 Tapes, Mar'85 by 96 Tapes Records. Dist: Rough Trade, Cartel

NO LOVE LOST.
Album: released on Corpus Christi, '83 by Exitstencil Music. Dist: Cartel

Omen

BATTLE CRY.
Album: released on Music For Nations, Sep'84 by Music For Nations Records. Dist: Pinnacle

NIGHTMARES.
Album: released on Roadrunner (Dutch), Jun'86 Dist: Pinnacle

WARNING OF DANGER.
Album: released on Roadrunner (Dutch), Nov'85 Dist: Pinnacle

Omnibus Big Band

MEMORIES OF YOU (Omnibus Big Band & Putte Wickman).
Album: released on Dragon, Jul'87 by Dragon Records. Dist: Jazz Music, Projection, Cadillac

Once Bitten

ONCE BITTEN (Various Artists).
Album: released on Red Door, Feb'84 by Red Door Records. Dist: Red Door

Once Upon A Time

ONCE UPON A TIME & HAPPY EVER AFTER (Various Artists).
Album: released on Ronco, Dec'81

Cassette: released on Ronco, Dec'81

ONCE UPON A TIME IN AMERICA Original soundtrack.
Compact disc: by Phonogram Records. Dist: Polygram

One...

ONE GIANT LEAP Various artists (Various Artists).
Album: released on 101 International, Mar'84

ONE NIGHT WITH BLUE NOTE - VOLUME 1 Various artists (Various Artists).
Album: released on Blue Note, Aug'85 by EMI Records. Dist: EMI

ONE NIGHT WITH BLUE NOTE - VOLUME 2 Various artists (Various Artists).
Album: released on Blue Note, Aug'85 by EMI Records. Dist: EMI

ONE NIGHT WITH BLUE NOTE - VOLUME 3 Various artists (Various Artists).

ONE NIGHT WITH BLUE NOTE - VOLUME 4 Various artists (Various Artists).
Album: released on Blue Note, Aug'85 by EMI Records. Dist: EMI

Album: released on Blue Note, Aug'85 by EMI Records. Dist: EMI

ONE OF EACH Various artists (Various Artists).
Album: released on Dixie, Apr'79 Dist: Jazz Music, JSU

ONE POUND NINETY NINE Various artists (Various Artists).
Album: released on Beggars Banquet, Oct'85 by Beggars Banquet Records. Dist: WEA

Cassette: released on Beggars Banquet, Oct'85 by Beggars Banquet Records. Dist: WEA

ONE TRACK MIND Various artists (Various Artists).
Album: released on Red Lightnin', Apr'82 by Red Lightnin' Records. Dist: Roots, Swift, Jazz Music, JSU, Pinnacle, Cartel, Wynd-Up Distribution

O'Neal, Alexander

ALEXANDER O'NEAL.
Tracks: / Broken heart can mend, A / Broken heart can mend, A / If you were here tonight / Do you wanna like I do / Look at us now / Innocent\Alex 99\What's missing / You were meant to be my lady (not my girl).
Notes: Includes free remix album.
Album: released on Tabu, Nov'86 by CBS Records. Dist: CBS Distribution

Cassette: released on Tabu, Nov'86 by CBS Records. Dist: CBS Distribution

Cassette: released on CBS, May'85 by CBS Records. Dist: CBS

BROKEN HEART CAN'T MEND.
Tracks: / Broken heart can't mend, A / If you were here tonight.
Single (7"): released on Tabu, Mar'86 by CBS Records. Dist: CBS Distribution

Single (12"): released on Tabu, Mar'86 by CBS Records. Dist: CBS Distribution

FAKE.
Tracks: / Fake / Look at us now.
Single (7"): released on Tabu, 23 May'87 by CBS Records. Dist: CBS Distribution

Single (12"): released on Tabu, 23 May'87 by CBS Records. Dist: CBS Distribution

FAKE (EXT VERSION).
Tracks: / Fake (ext version) / Fake (patty mix) / Fake (acappella) / Fake (inst).
Cassette single: released on Tabu, Jun'87 by CBS Records. Dist: CBS Distribution

HEARSAY.
Tracks: / To make you love me (what can I say) / Hearsay / Lovers, The / Fake / Criticize / Never knew love like this / Sunshine / Crying overtime / When the party's over / What can I say to make you love me / Hearsay / Lovers, The / Fake / Criticize / Never knew love like this / Sunshine / Crying overtime / When the party's over.
Album: released on Tabu, Jul'87 by CBS Records. Dist: CBS Distribution

Cassette: released on Tabu, Jul'87 by CBS Records. Dist: CBS Distribution

Compact disc: released on Tabu, Sep'87 by CBS Records. Dist: CBS Distribution

IF YOU WERE HERE TONIGHT.
Tracks: / If you were here tonight / If you were here tonight (remix) / Soft version.
Single (7"): released on Tabu, Feb'86 by CBS Records. Dist: CBS Distribution

Single (12"): released on Tabu, Feb'86 by CBS Records. Dist: CBS Distribution

WHAT'S MISSING.
Tracks: / What's missing / Do you wanna.
Single (7"): released on Tabu, May'86 by CBS Records. Dist: CBS Distribution

Single (12"): released on Tabu, May'86 by CBS Records. Dist: CBS Distribution

YOU WERE MEANT TO BE MY LADY.
Single (7"): released on Tabu, Aug'86 by CBS Records. Dist: CBS Distribution

Single (12"): released on Tabu, Aug'86 by CBS Records. Dist: CBS Distribution

O'Neal, Johnny

COMING OUT.
Album: released on Concord Jazz(USA), Nov'83 by Concord Jazz Records (USA). Dist: IMS, Polygram

One-A-Way

SUFFERER.
Single (12"): released on Route, Oct'84 by Route Records. Dist: Jetstar Distribution

One Away Style

ONE AWAY STYLE Various artists (Various Artists).
Album: released on Top Rank, Mar'85 by Top Rank Records. Dist: Jetstar Distribution

One Blood

BE THANKFUL.
Single (12"): released on Sound City, Feb'82 by Sound City Records. Dist: Jetstar

Single (12"): released on Sound City, Aug'84 by Sound City Records. Dist: Jetstar

CHANGED MAN,(I'M A).
Tracks: / Changed man,(I'm a) / Romance, (It's a).
Single (12"): released on Level Vibes, Feb'86 by Level Vibes Records. Dist: Jetstar

CHRISTMAS PRESENT, THE.
Tracks: / Christmas present, The / Don't have to fight.
Single (12"): released on Level Vibes, Dec'86 by Level Vibes Records. Dist: Jetstar

DON'T STOP LOVIN'.
Tracks: / Don't stop lovin' / When i'm with you.
Single (12"): released on Level Vibes, Jun'86 by Level Vibes Records. Dist: Jetstar

GET IN TOUCH.
Single (7"): released on Sound City, Feb'84 by Sound City Records. Dist: Jetstar

Single (12"): released on Sound City, Feb'84 by Sound City Records. Dist: Jetstar

I CAN MAKE YOU HAPPY.
Single (12"): released on Neville King, Jan'83 by Neville King Records. Dist: Jetstar

I'M YOUR FOOL.
Single (12"): released on Neville King, Apr'82 by Neville King Records. Dist: Jetstar

MY LOVE DON'T COME EASY.
Tracks: / At the dance.
Single (12"): released on King's Records Label, Dec'86

ONE BLOOD IN LOVE.
Album: released on NK Music, Dec'83 by Sound City. Dist: Jetstar, Pinnacle

RUNNING AROUND.
Single (7"): released on Sound City, Mar'85 by Sound City Records. Dist: Jetstar

Single (12"): released on Sound City, Mar'85 by Sound City Records. Dist: Jetstar

SHOW SOME LOVE.
Single (12"): released on NK, Oct'81

SUPER SHOWCASE.
Album: released on NK Music, Dec'83 by Sound City. Dist: Jetstar, Pinnacle

YOU'RE WORTH IT.
Single (12"): released on Neville King, Sep'82 by Neville King Records. Dist: Jetstar

One By One

I KEPT MY PROMISE.
Single (7"): released on Discovery, Mar'85 Dist: PRT

One Destiny

NO REGRETS.
Tracks: / We've found love.
Notes: Featuring Dennis Gregory.
Single (12"): released on UK Bubblers, Dec'86 by Greensleeves Records. Dist: RCA, Jetstar

One Force

CRUISIN'.
Single (12"): released on After Lord, May'82

One From The Heart

ONE FROM THE HEART Original soundtrack.
Album: released on CBS, Feb'83 by CBS Records. Dist: CBS

One Gang Logic

ALIENATE.
Single (7"): released on Stark, Oct'79 Dist: Rough Trade Distribution

One Hit Wonders

ONE HIT WONDERS OF THE 50'S Various artists (Various Artists).
Tracks: / Zambesi / Buona sera / Unchained melody / Wayward wind, The / Man with the golden arm (main title) / Say you're mine again / Vaya con dios / Portuguese washerwomen / Happy whistler / This ole house / Mad passionate love / Arrivederci darling / Poppa piccolino / He's got the whole world in his hands / Bad penny blues / Pickin' a chicken / Pub with no beer / Happy wanderer, The (Der frohliche wanderer).
Album: released on MFP, Sep'87 by EMI Records. Dist: EMI

Cassette: released on MFP, Sep'87 by EMI Records. Dist: EMI

One Hundred...

100 COMEDY INSERTS VOL 2 Various Artists (Various Artists).
Album: released on East Anglian Productions, '81 by East Anglian Productions. Dist: Lightning
Cat. no: **EAP 1006 SLP**
Cassette: released on East Anglian Productions, '81 by East Anglian Productions. Dist: Lightning

100 COMEDY INSERTS VOL 3 Various Artists (Various Artists).
Album: released on East Anglian Productions, '81 by East Anglian Productions. Dist: Lightning

Cassette: released on East Anglian Productions, '81 by East Anglian Productions. Dist: Lightning

100 DANCING PARTY FAVOURITES Various artists (Various Artists).
Cassette: released on Trid, Nov'85

Cassette: released on MFP (Trio), Oct'85

100 DEEJAY INSERTS VOL 1 Various Artists (Various Artists).
Album: released on East Anglian Productions, '77 by East Anglian Productions. Dist: Lightning

Cassette: released on East Anglian Productions, '77 by East Anglian Productions. Dist: Lightning

100 DISCOTHEQUE JINGLES VOL 4 Various Artists (Various Artists).
Album: released on East Anglian Productions, '81 by East Anglian Productions. Dist: Lightning

Cassette: released on East Anglian Productions, '81 by East Anglian Productions. Dist: Lightning

100 DISCOTHEQUE JINGLES VOL 3 Various Artists (Various Artists).
Album: released on East Anglian Productions, '81 by East Anglian Productions. Dist: Lightning

Cassette: released on East Anglian Productions, '81 by East Anglian Productions. Dist: Lightning

100 DISCOTHEQUE JINGLES VOL 2 Various Artists (Various Artists).
Album: released on East Anglian Productions, '77 by East Anglian Productions. Dist: Lightning

Cassette:

100 DISCOTHEQUE JINGLES VOL 1 Various artists (Various Artists).
Album: released on East Anglian Productions, '76 by East Anglian Productions. Dist: Lightning

Cassette: released on East Anglian Productions, '76 by East Anglian Productions. Dist: Lightning

100 MINUTES OF STRINGS AND THINGS Various artists (Various Artists).
Cassette: released on PRT, Nov'85 by PRT Records. Dist: PRT

100 SONOVOX JINGLES Various Artists (Various Artists).
Album: released on East Anglian Productions, '77 by East Anglian Productions. Dist: Lightning

Cassette: released on East Anglian Productions, '77 by East Anglian Productions. Dist: Lightning

ALLO (One Hundred & Twenty Three).
Single (7"): released on JSO, Jul'81

One Hundred And Fifty...

150 MOTOWN HITS OF GOLD various artists (Various Artists).
Album: released on Motown, Oct'85 by RCA Records. Dist: RCA Distribution

Cassette: released on Motown, Oct'85 by RCA Records. Dist: RCA Distribution

One Hundred And One...

AROUND THE WORLD VOL 1.
Album: released on Avon, Jul'86 by Avon Records. Dist: Counterpoint

Cassette: released on Avon, Jul'86 by Avon Records. Dist: Counterpoint

BOLERO.
Album: released on Avon, Nov'84 by Avon Records. Dist: Counterpoint

Cassette: released on Avon, Nov'84 by Avon Records. Dist: Counterpoint

CLASSIC OVERTURES.
Album: released on Avon, Nov'84 by Avon Records. Dist: Counterpoint

Cassette: released on Avon, Nov'84 by Avon Records. Dist: Counterpoint

CLASSICS UP TO DATE.
Album: released on Avon, Nov'84 by Avon Records. Dist: Counterpoint

Cassette: released on Avon, Nov'84 by Avon Records. Dist: Counterpoint

GREAT AMERICAN COMPOSERS, (THE).
Album: released on Avon, Jul'86 by Avon Records. Dist: Counterpoint

Cassette: released on Avon, Jul'86 by Avon Records. Dist: Counterpoint

GREAT INSTRUMENTALS.
Album: released on Avon, Nov'84 by Avon Records. Dist: Counterpoint

Cassette: released on Avon, Nov'84 by Avon Records. Dist: Counterpoint

GYPSY.
Album: released on Avon, Nov'84 by Avon Records. Dist: Counterpoint

Cassette: released on Avon, Nov'84 by Avon Records. Dist: Counterpoint

HAWAIIAN PARADISE.
Album: released on Avon, Nov'84 by Avon Records. Dist: Counterpoint

Cassette: released on Avon, Nov'84 by Avon Records. Dist: Counterpoint

INSTRUMENTAL COLLECTION.
Triple album / cassette: released on Ronco, Nov'83

Triple album / cassette: released on Ronco, Nov'83

JOURNEY INTO SPACE.
Album: released on Avon, Jul'86 by Avon Records. Dist: Counterpoint

Cassette: released on Avon, Jul'86 by Avon Records. Dist: Counterpoint

MAGIC OF THE WALTZ.
Album: released on Avon, Nov'84 by Avon Records. Dist: Counterpoint

Cassette: released on Avon, Nov'84 by Avon Records. Dist: Counterpoint

MORNING, NOON AND NIGHT.
Triple album / cassette: released on Ronco, Nov'83

Double cassette: released on Ronco, Nov'83

NIGHTS IN VIENNA.
Album: released on Avon, Nov'84 by Avon Records. Dist: Counterpoint

Cassette: released on Avon, Nov'84 by Avon Records. Dist: Counterpoint

ROMANTIC PIANO MUSIC.
Album: released on Avon, Nov'84 by Avon Records. Dist: Counterpoint

Cassette: released on Avon, Nov'84 by Avon Records. Dist: Counterpoint

ROMANTIC YEARS, (THE).
Album: released on CJMO, Jan'78 Dist: Jazz Music, Spartan, Taylors

SHOWSTOPPERS.
Album: released on Avon, Nov'84 by Avon Records. Dist: Counterpoint

Cassette: released on Avon, Nov'84 by Avon Records. Dist: Counterpoint

SONGS OF PRAISE.
Album: released on Avon, Nov'84 by Avon Records. Dist: Counterpoint

Cassette: released on Avon, Nov'84 by Avon Records. Dist: Counterpoint

SOUL OF GREECE.
Album: released on Avon, Nov'84 by Avon Records. Dist: Counterpoint

Cassette: released on Avon, Nov'84 by Avon Records. Dist: Counterpoint

SOUL OF ISRAEL.
Album: released on Avon, Nov'84 by Avon Records. Dist: Counterpoint

Cassette: released on Avon, Nov'84 by Avon Records. Dist: Counterpoint

SOUL OF RUSSIA.
Album: released on Avon, Nov'84 by Avon Records. Dist: Counterpoint

Cassette: released on Avon, Nov'84 by Avon Records. Dist: Counterpoint

SOUL OF SPAIN.
Album: released on Avon, Jul'86 by Avon Records. Dist: Counterpoint

Cassette: released on Avon, Jul'86 by Avon Records. Dist: Counterpoint

SOUTH OF THE BORDER.
Album: released on Avon, Nov'84 by Avon Records. Dist: Counterpoint

Cassette: released on Avon, Nov'84 by Avon Records. Dist: Counterpoint

TCHAIKOVSKY BALLET.
Album: released on Avon, Nov'84 by Avon Records. Dist: Counterpoint

Cassette: released on Avon, Nov'84 by Avon Records. Dist: Counterpoint

THEMES ROMANTIC.
Album: released on Avon, Nov'84 by Avon Records. Dist: Counterpoint

Cassette: released on Avon, Nov'84 by Avon Records. Dist: Counterpoint

THEMES SPECTACULAR.
Album: released on Avon, Nov'84 by Avon Records. Dist: Counterpoint

Cassette: released on Avon, Nov'84 by Avon Records. Dist: Counterpoint

One Hundred Minutes

100 MINUTES OF BIG BAND MEDLEYS Various Artists (Various Artists).
Cassette: released on PRT, Nov'85 by PRT Records. Dist: PRT

100 MINUTES OF BLUES Various Artists (Various Artists).
Cassette: released on PRT (100 Minute Series), Nov'83

100 MINUTES OF BRASS BANDS Various Artists (Various Artists).
Cassette: released on PRT, Nov'85 by PRT Records. Dist: PRT

100 MINUTES OF DANCE PARTY HITS Various Artists (Various Artists).
Cassette: released on PRT (100 Minute Series), Nov'82

100 MINUTES OF .. DISCO DANCE Various Artists (Various Artists).
Cassette: released on PRT (100 Minute Series), Nov'83 Deleted '1.

100 MINUTES OF .. EASY LISTENING,INSTRUMENTAL Various Artists (Various Artists).
Cassette: released on PRT (100 Minute Series), Nov'83

100 MINUTES OF LOVE SONGS Various Artists (Various Artists).
Cassette: released on PRT (100 Minute Series), Nov'82

100 MINUTES OF ..POPULAR CLASSICS Various Artists (Various Artists).
Cassette: released on PRT (100 Minute Series), Nov'83

100 MINUTES OF SCOTTISH FAVOURITES Various artists (Various Artists).
Cassette: released on PRT (100 Minute Series), Nov'82

100 MINUTES OF...SCOTTISH Various Artists (Various Artists).
Cassette: released on PRT (100 Minute Series), Nov'83

100 MINUTES OF SOUL GREATS Various Artists (Various Artists).
Cassette: released on PRT (100 Minute Series), Nov'82

100 MINUTES OF TRAD JAZZ Various Artists.
Cassette: released on PRT, Nov'85 by PRT Records. Dist: PRT

One Hundred & One...

101 DALMATIONS Various Artists (Various Artists).
Album: released on Disneyland, Dec'78 by Disneyland-Vista Records (USA). Dist: BBC Records & Tapes, Rainbow Communications Ltd(Distribution)

Album: released on Disney, Oct'84 by BBC Records & Tapes. Dist: BBC Records & Tapes, PRT

Cassette: released on Disney, Oct'84 by BBC Records & Tapes. Dist: BBC Records & Tapes, PRT

101 DALMATIONS (Rogers, Anton).
Cassette: released on Whinfrey Strachan, Jan'85 Dist: Whinfrey Strachan

OFF THE CUFF (One Hundred & One Club).
Album: released on 101 Club, Jul'81

One Hundred Percent

GREEN FOR GO.
Single (7"): released on Backstop, Apr'82

One Hundred Proof

SOMEBODYS BEEN SLEEPING IN MY BED (One Hundred Proof(Aged in soul)).
Single (7"): released on HDH(Holland/Dozier/Holland), May'84 by Demon Records. Dist: Pinnacle

One Hundredth...

BOUNCY BOUNCY (One Hundredth Monkey Effect).
Single (7"): released on Wooltown, Sep'85 by Wooltown Records. Dist: M.I.S.

O'Neil, Dyer

ROBBERY.
Single (7"): released on Cha-Cha, Dec'82 by Cha Cha. Dist: Jetstar

O'Neil, John

ELIZABETH.
Single (7"): released on August (USA), May'85 Dist: Taylors

O'Neill, Aura

WITCHERY WOODS.
Single (7"): released on Uncanny, Jul'84 by Uncanny Records. Dist: Cartel, Rough Trade

O'Neill, Dennis

DENNIS O'NEILL.
Album: released on BBC, Jul'87 by BBC Records & Tapes. Dist: EMI, PRT, Pye

Cassette: released on BBC, Jul'87 by BBC Records & Tapes. Dist: EMI, PRT, Pye

O'Neill, Jonjo

I STILL LOVE HER.
Single (7"): released on OBM, Mar'81

O'Neill, Sarah

SHORES OF LOUGHNEAGH (O'Neill, Sarah & George Hanna).
Album: released on Topic, Aug'78 by Polygram Records.

O'Neill, Sean

CITY BY THE LAGAN SIDE (O'Neill, Sean & Tara Folk Group).
Single (7"): released on Homespun(Ireland), Mar'84 by Outlet Records. Dist: Outlet

One Last Fight

MENAGE A TROIS.
Tracks: / Menage a trois.
Single (12"): released on Skysaw, Jun'86 by Skysaw Records. Dist: Red Rhino, Cartel

One Love

SOUNDS JAMAICA.
Cassette: released on Chevron, Nov'84 Dist: Multiple Sound Distributors

One Million Fuzz Guitars

MENS HEARTS.
Single (7"): released on Monsters In Orbit, May'83 Dist: Rough Trade Distribution

ONE MILLION FUZZ GUITARS.
Single (7"): released on Monsters In Orbit, Jan'82 Dist: Rough Trade Distribution

One Minit At A Time

ONE MINIT AT A TIME Various artists (Various Artists).
Tracks: / Well / Lot of love, A / Take me / I'm gonna do all I can(To do right by my man) / Girls from Texas, The / Working on your case / Party in the woods / Funky Broadway / Gonna get that boat / I wanna be free / Give me your love / I know you know I know / Hunk of funk, A / I can't stand the pain / Shing a-ling.
Notes: A compilation of the best artists from the New Orleans Minit label.Classic 60's r'n'b & soul from such artists as Bobby Womack & Ike & Tina Turner.
Album: released on Stateside, Apr'86 Dist: EMI

Cassette: released on Stateside, Apr'86 Dist: EMI

Oneness

EVERYBODY LOVES A BEAUTIFUL WOMAN.
Single (12"): released on Fantasy, Oct'85 by RCA Records. Dist: RCA, Jetstar

Oneness Of Juju

ELECTRIC JUJU NATION.
Album: released on Move, Apr'86 by Charly Records. Dist: Charly Distribution, Fast Forward Distribution, Cartel Distribution

EVERYWAY BUT LOOSE.
Single (7"): released on Buddah, Apr'82 Dist: Swift, Jazz Music, PRT

Single (12"): released on Buddah, Apr'82 Dist: Swift, Jazz Music, PRT

One Night With...

ONE NIGHT WITH BLUE NOTE VOL.1 Various artists (Various Artists).
Notes: Part of a celebratory concert held on behalf of the Blue Note Jazz label in New York,by many of its most renowned artists.Icludes Herbie Hancock,Stanley Jordan And Art B.Stereo hi-fi sound.Total playing time: 60 minutes.
Video-cassette (VHS): released on PMI, Jun'86 by PMI Records. Dist: EMI

Video-cassette [Betamax]: released on PMI, Jun'86 by PMI Records. Dist: EMI

ONE NIGHT WITH BLUE NOTE VOL.2 Various artists (Various Artists).
Video-cassette (VHS): released on PMI, Jun'86 by PMI Records. Dist: EMI

One o'clock Gang

CLOSE YOUR EYES(AND THINK OF ENGLAND).
Single (7"): released on Arista, Mar'85 by Arista Records. Dist: RCA

Single (12"): released on Arista, Mar'85 by Arista Records. Dist: RCA

ONE O'CLOCK GANG.
Album: released on Arista, May'85 by Arista Records. Dist: RCA

Cassette: released on Arista, May'85 by Arista Records. Dist: RCA

TRIGGER HAPPY.
Single (7"): released on Arista, May'85 by Arista Records. Dist: RCA

Single (12"): released on Arista, May'85 by Arista Records. Dist: RCA

One Of You

DON'T BE DESPERATE.
Single (7"): released on Scarab, Oct'82 Dist: Recommended

One-O-One'ers

KEY'S TO YOUR HEART.
Single (7"): released on Big Beat, Aug'83 by Ace Records. Dist: Projection, Pinnacle

SWEET REVENGE.
Single (7"): released on Big Beat, Jan'81 by Ace Records. Dist: Projection, Pinnacle

One Plus One

AUTUMN LEAVES.
Single (7"): released on R & B, Nov'82 by Red Bus. Dist: PRT

IVY ROOM , (THE).
Album: released on Homestead, Jun'86 Dist: Rough Trade, Cartel, Shigaku

One Plus Two

ONCE IN A BLUE MOON.
Album: released on Homestead, Sep'86 Dist: Rough Trade, Cartel, Shigaku

One Syntax One

FEEL NO TOUCH.
Single (7"): released on Proteus, Mar'84

One The Juggler

ARE YOU THE ONE.
Single (7"): released on Regard, Jan'84

Single (12"): released on Regard, Jan'84

DAMAGE IS DONE.
Single (7"): released on Regard, Jul'83

Single (12"): released on Regard, Jul'83

DJANGO'S COMING.
Single (7"): released on Regard, Sep'83

Single (12"): released on Regard, Sep'83

HOURS AND HOURS.
Single (7"): released on RCA, Apr'85 by RCA Records. Dist: RCA, Roots, Swift, Wellard, Chris, I & B, Solomon & Peres Distribution

Single (12"): released on RCA, Apr'85 by RCA Records. Dist: RCA, Roots, Swift, Wellard, Chris, I & B, Solomon & Peres Distribution

IT HURT'S.
Single (7"): released on Regard, Aug'84

Single (12"): released on Regard, Aug'84

NEARLY A SIN.
Album: released on RCA, Apr'84 by RCA Records. Dist: RCA, Roots, Swift, Wellard, Chris, I & B, Solomon & Peres Distribution

Cassette: released on RCA, Apr'84 by RCA Records. Dist: RCA, Roots, Swift, Wellard, Chris, I & B, Solomon & Peres Distribution

PASSION KILLER.
Single (7"): released on Regard, Jan'83

Single (12"): released on Regard, Jan'83

SOME STRANGE FASHION.
Album: released on RCA, Apr'85 by RCA Records. Dist: RCA, Roots, Swift, Wellard, Chris, I & B, Solomon & Peres Distribution

One Thousand...

GOD BLESS THE PRINCE OF WALES (One Thousand English Voices).
Album: released on Chandos, Aug'84 by Chandos Records. Dist: Harmonia Mundi, Taylors

Cassette: released on Chandos, Aug'84 by Chandos Records. Dist: Harmonia Mundi, Taylors

UNGRATEFUL BASTARD (One thousand violins).
Tracks: / I remember when everyone used to ride bikes.
Single (7"): released on Constrictor, Feb'87 Dist: Rough Trade, Red Rhino, Cartel

One Thousand Mexicans

ART OF LOVE.
Single (7"): released on Whaam, Sep'83 Dist: Pinnacle

CHINESE WHISPERS.
Cassette: released on Cracknorm, Apr'83 by Cracknorm Records. Dist: Rough Trade

CRIMINAL.
Single (7"): released on Play It Again Sam, May'85 Dist: Red Rhino, Cartel

DANCE LIKE AMMUNITION.
Album: released on Fire, Mar'85 by Twist and Shout Music. Dist: Nine Mile, Rough Trade, Cartel

DIVING FOR PEARLS.
Single (12"): released on Fire, Nov'84 by Twist and Shout Music. Dist: Nine Mile, Rough Trade, Cartel

LAST POP SONG/CHINESE WHISPERS.
Single (7"): released on Abstract, Jan'84 by Abstract. Dist: Pinnacle

Single (12"): released on Abstract, Jan'84 by Abstract. Dist: Pinnacle

UNDER CONSTRUCTIONS.
Single (12"): released on Abstract, Jul'84 by Abstract. Dist: Pinnacle

One thousand violins

HALYCON DAYS.
Single (12"): released on Dreamworld, Jul'85 by TV Personalities, The. Dist: Rough Trade

PLEASE DON'T SAND BLAST MY HOUSE.
Tracks: / Please don't sand blast my house / Time I broke down / Though it poured the next day I never noticed the rain* / You ungrateful bastard*.
Notes: *= Extra tracks on 12" only.
Single (7"): released on Dreamworld, Oct'86 by TV Personalities, The. Dist: Rough Trade

Single (12"): released on Dreamworld, Oct'86 by TV Personalities, The. Dist: Rough Trade

One Thousand Welsh Male

Group

ALL OF US ONE.
Album: released on BBC, Jan'79 by BBC Records & Tapes. Dist: EMI, PRT, Pye

Cassette: released on BBC, Jan'79 by BBC Records & Tapes. Dist: EMI, PRT, Pye

AT THE ROYAL ALBERT HALL 1980.
Album: released on Black Mountain, Jul'80 by Black Mountain Records.

AT THE ROYAL ALBERT HALL 1979.
Album: released on Black Mountain, Jun'79 by Black Mountain Records.

AT THE ROYAL ALBERT HALL 1982.
Album: released on Black Mountain, Jan'82 by Black Mountain Records.

COMRADES IN SONG.
Notes: An all digital recording live from the Albert Hall. Featuring the following choirs: Abu Bekr Shrine Chanters, Brymbo Male Voice Choir, Cambrian Male Voice Choir, Cardiff Athletic Club Male Voice Choir, Cor Meibion Caron, Felling Male Voice Choir, Gralia Male Choir, Llantrisant Male Choir, London Welsh Male Voice Choir, Morriston Rugby Football Club Choir, Cor Ceibion Mynydd Mawr, Onllwyn Welfare Male Voice Choir, Cor Meibion Pennybontfawr, Porthcawl Male Choir. Tenth Festival of One Thousand Male Voices.
Album: released on BBC, Feb'87 by BBC Records & Tapes. Dist: EMI, PRT, Pye

Cassette: released on BBC, Feb'87 by BBC Records & Tapes. Dist: EMI, PRT, Pye

RIDE THE CHARRIOT.
Album: released on BBC, Feb'85 by BBC Records & Tapes. Dist: EMI, PRT, Pye

Cassette: released on BBC, Feb'85 by BBC Records & Tapes. Dist: EMI, PRT, Pye

SOUND AN ALARM.
Album: released on BBC, Jan'79 by BBC Records & Tapes. Dist: EMI, PRT, Pye

Cassette: released on BBC, Jan'79 by BBC Records & Tapes. Dist: EMI, PRT, Pye

STOUTHEARTED MEN.
Album: released on BBC, Mar'83 by BBC Records & Tapes. Dist: EMI, PRT, Pye

Cassette: released on BBC, Mar'83 by BBC Records & Tapes. Dist: EMI, PRT, Pye

WE'LL KEEP A WELCOME.
Album: released on Lugtons Special Products, Jun'83

One To One

ANGEL IN MY POCKETS.
Tracks: / Angel in my pockets / Where's the answer.
Single (7"): released on Bonaire, Jun'86 Dist: RCA, Ariola

Single (12"): released on Bonaire, Jun'86 Dist: RCA, Ariola

FORWARD YOUR EMOTIONS.
Tracks: / Don't call it Lore / Angel in my pocket / Hearts & diamonds / Where's the answer / Forward your emotions / There was a time / Black on white / Love is blind / Boys will be boys / Tell me straight.
Album:

Cassette: released on Bonaire, May'86 Dist: RCA, Ariola

THERE WAS A TIME.
Single (7"): released on Bonaire, Oct'85 Dist: RCA, Ariola

Single (12"): released on Bonaire, Oct'85 Dist: RCA, Ariola

One Touch

DON'T THROW AWAY YOUR LOVE.
Tracks: / Don't throw your love away.
Single (7"): released on Sierra, Feb'86 by Sierra Records. Dist: WEA

Single (12"): released on Sierra, Feb'86 by Sierra Records. Dist: WEA

One Way

AL HUDSON.
Single (7"): released on MCA, Feb'82 by MCA Records. Dist: CBS

Single (12"): released on MCA, Feb'82 by MCA Records. Dist: CBS

DON'T THINK ABOUT IT.
Tracks: / Don't think about it / Don't think about it (bass appella).
Single (7"): released on MCA, Jun'87 by MCA Records. Dist: Polygram, MCA

Single (12"): released on MCA, Jun'87 by MCA Records. Dist: Polygram, MCA

IX.
Tracks: / Don't think about it / Who does she think she is / You better quit / You better quit / Stary eyes / Starry eyes / Whammy / Set it out / Stole my heart / I can't help myself / Oh girl.
Album: released on MCA, Nov'86 by MCA Records. Dist: Polygram, MCA

Cassette: released on MCA, Nov'86 by MCA Records. Dist: Polygram, MCA

LADY YOU ARE.
Single (7"): released on MCA, Apr'84 by MCA Records. Dist: CBS

Single (12"): released on MCA, Apr'84 by MCA Records. Dist: CBS

LET'S TALK.
Single (7"): released on MCA, Jun'85 by MCA Records. Dist: CBS

Single (12"): released on MCA, Jun'85 by MCA Records. Dist: CBS

LOVE IS ONE WAY.
Album: released on MCA, Feb'81 by MCA Records. Dist: CBS

MR GROOVE.
Single (7"): released on MCA, Jun'84 by MCA Records. Dist: CBS

Single (12"): released on MCA, Jun'84 by MCA Records. Dist: CBS Deleted '87

WHO'S FOOLING WHO?.
Album: released on MCA, Mar'82 by MCA Records. Dist: CBS

Cassette: released on MCA, Mar'82 by MCA Records. Dist: CBS

WRAP YOUR BODY.
Album: released on MCA, Jul'85 by MCA Records. Dist: CBS

Cassette: released on MCA, Jul'85 by MCA Records. Dist: CBS

YOU BETTER QUIT.
Tracks: / You better quit / Oh girl.
Single (7"): released on MCA, Apr'87 by MCA Records. Dist: Polygram. MCA

Single (12"): released on MCA, Apr'87 by MCA Records. Dist: Polygram, MCA

One Way System

CUM ON FEEL THE NOIZE.
Single (7"): released on Anagram, Jul'83 by Cherry Red Records. Dist: Pinnacle

JERUSALEM.
Single (7"): released on Anagram, Dec'82 by Cherry Red Records. Dist: Pinnacle

JUST ANOTHER HERO.
Single (7"): released on Anagram, Aug'82 by Cherry Red Records. Dist: Pinnacle

MIRACLES IN THE RAIN.
Album: released on Anagram, Jun'85 by Cherry Red Records. Dist: Pinnacle

STAB THE JUDGE.
Single (7"): released on Lightbeat, Jun'82 by Lightbeat Records. Dist: Pinnacle

THIS IS THE AGE.
Single (7"): released on Anagram, Sep'83 by Cherry Red Records. Dist: Pinnacle

VISIONS OF ANGELS.
Single (7"): released on Anagram, Mar'84 by Cherry Red Records. Dist: Pinnacle

Single (12"): released on Anagram, Mar'84 by Cherry Red Records. Dist: Pinnacle

WRITING ON THE WALL.
Album: released on Anagram, Sep'83 by Cherry Red Records. Dist: Pinnacle

One Way Ticket

TIME IS RIGHT.
Album: released on President, Apr'79 by President Records. Dist: Taylors, Spartan

On Her Majesty's...

ON HER MAJESTY'S SECRET SERVICE.
Album:

Onidis, Nicky

BABY I LOVE YOU.
Single (7"): released on Carrere, Jan'83 by Carrere Records. Dist: PRT Spartan

Onlookers

YOU AND I.
Single (7"): released on Demon, Mar'82 by Demon Records. Dist: Pinnacle

Only After Dark

GHOSTS OF ROMANCE.
Single (7"): released on Disclexia, Apr'82 Dist: Pinnacle

Only Alternative

AS FATE WOULD HAVE IT - THE ONLY ALTERNATIVE.
Album: released on Midnight Music, Sep'85 by Midnight Music Records. Dist: Rough Trade Distribution, Cartel Distribution

Only Connect

KHAN.
Tracks: / Khan / Bop / Catharsis.
Single (12"): released on Only Connect, Mar'86 by Only Connect Records. Dist: Revolver Distribution

Only Lonely

TEENAGE LOVE.
Tracks: / Teenage love / Rainbow.
Single (7"): released on Sierra, Aug'86 by Sierra Records. Dist: WEA

Single (12"): released on Sierra, Aug'86 by Sierra Records. Dist: WEA

Only Ones

ALONE IN THE NIGHT.
Tracks: / Why don't you kill yourself / Another girl another planet / From here to eternity / Strange mouth / Fools / Out there in the night / Me and my shadow / Flaming torch / Trouble in the world / Imortal story / Deadly nightshade / You've got to pay / Big sleep / My way out of here.
Album: released on Dojo, Sep'86 by Castle Communications Records. Dist: Cartel

ONLY ONES, THE.
Cassette: released on CBS, May'78 by CBS Records. Dist: CBS Deleted '81.

REMAINS.
Album: released on Closer (France), Jun'84 Dist: Nine Mile, Cartel

Ono, Seigen

SEIGEN.
Notes: L.O.E. Entertainment Ltd. 159, Broadhurst Gardens, London NW6 3AU. Tel: 01-328 6100/6215/6228.
Album: released on Pan East, Jul'86 by L.O.E. Records. Dist: Nine Mile, PRT, Cartel

Cassette: released on Pan East, Jul'86 by L.O.E. Records. Dist: Nine Mile. PRT, Cartel

Compact disc: released on Pan East, Jul'86 by L.O.E. Records. Dist: Nine Mile, PRT, Cartel

Ono, Yoko

MY MAN.
Single (7"): released on Polydor, Dec'82 by Polydor Records. Dist: Polygram, Polydor

SEASON OF GLASS.
Album: released on Geffen, Jun'81 by Geffen Records. Dist: WEA, CBS

Cassette: released on Geffen, Jun'81 by Geffen Records. Dist: WEA. CBS

STARPEACE.
Tracks: / Hell in paradise / I love all of me / Children power / Rainbow revolution / King of the zoo / Remember raven / Cape clear / Sky people / You and I / It's gonna rain (living on tiptoe) / Starpeace / I love you, Earth.
Cassette: released on Polydor, Nov'85 by Polydor Records. Dist: Polygram. Polydor

Album: released on Polydor, Nov'85 by Polydor Records. Dist: Polygram Polydor

Compact disc: released on Polydor, Dec'85 by Polydor Records. Dist: Polygram Polydor

Onslaught

FORCE, THE.
Album: released on Under One Flag, Apr'86 Dist: Pinnacle

Cassette: released on Under One Flag, Sep'87 Dist: Pinnacle. Estim retail price in Sep'87 was £5.99.

POWER FROM HELL.
Album: released on Under One Flag, Mar'87 Dist: Pinnacle

Album: released on Children Of The Revolution, Jun'85 by Revolver Records. Dist: Revolver, Cartel

On stage at...

ON STAGE AT THE GRAND OLE OPRY (Various Artists).
Album: released on Stetson, Jun'86 by Hasmick Promotions Ltd.. Dist: Counterpoint Distribution, H.R. Taylor Distribution, Swift Distribution, Chris Wellard Distribution

Cassette: released on Stetson, Jun'86 by Hasmick Promotions Ltd.. Dist: Counterpoint Distribution, H.R. Taylor Distribution, Swift Distribution, Chris Wellard Distribution

On The...

ON THE AIR 60 years of BBC theme music (Various Artists).
Album: released on BBC, Oct'82 by BBC Records & Tapes. Dist: EMI. PRT. Pye

Cassette: released on BBC, Oct'82 by BBC Records & Tapes. Dist: EMI, PRT, Pye

ON THE DOTTED LINE (HERE) Various artists (Various Artists).
Tracks: / Redbury joy town / Round and round / Motorcycle rain / Sorrow floats / In our song / Murder of your smile / Plastic horse / Crazyhead / Parallax avenue / Tolerance / Everything I ever wanted / Hunger, The / Dallas blues.
Album: released on EMI, May'87 by EMI Records. Dist: EMI

Cassette: released on EMI, May'87 by EMI Records. Dist: EMI

ON THE DOTTED LINE (THERE) Various artists (Various Artists).
Tracks: / What you have / Again & again / Roger / Falling over December / I bet she's gonna go / Gunning the works / Chime / Beat box baby / Same old game / Wish away / E-lollipop / Area brothers / Snake eyes / Confusion reigns / Stoned and bruised.
Notes: On The Dotted Line (There) is the second of two LP's recorded live at ICA Rock Week. Jan 26-31 1987.
Album: released on EMI, Jul'87 by EMI Records. Dist: EMI

Cassette: released on EMI, Jul'87 by EMI Records. Dist: EMI

ON THE HALLS (Various Artists).
Double Album: released on World, Jun'77 Dist: Jetstar

ON THE ROAD AGAIN Rock's new frontiers 1966/1970 (Various Artists).
Album: released on Capitol, Nov'81 by Capitol Records. Dist: EMI

Cassette: released on Capitol, Nov'81 by Capitol Records. Dist: EMI

ON THE ROCKS (On The Rocks).
Album: released on TPL, Mar'84 Dist: PRT

ON THE SOUL SIDE (On The Soul Side).
Album: released on Kent, Sep'83 by Ace Records. Dist: Pinnacle

ON THE SPOT VOL.2 (Various Artists).
Album: released on Elite, Jan'84 Dist: PRT

ON THE TOWN Broadway cast (Various Artists).
Album: released on CBS Cameo, Jul'83 by CBS Records. Dist: CBS

Cassette: released on CBS Cameo, Jul'83 by CBS Records. Dist: CBS

ON THE UPBEAT Various artists (Various Artists).
Tracks: / Serious / Fake / No lies / See me / Thigh ride / Shake you down / Happy / After loving you / Rain, The / My favourite person.
Album: released on Epic, Jul'87 by CBS Records. Dist: CBS

Cassette: released on Epic, Jul'87 by CBS Records. Dist: CBS

Album: released on Kent, Aug'84 by Ace Records. Dist: Pinnacle

On The House

GIVE ME BACK THE LOVE.
Single (7"): released on Serious, Jun'87 by Serious Records. Dist: PRT

Single (12"): released on Serious, Jun'87 by Serious Records. Dist: PRT

On The Waterfront

KIDS ARE ALRIGHT, THE.
Tracks: / Kids are alright, The / Never surrender / Far from the madding crowd / Mrs Harrington.
Single (7"): by Sierra Records. Dist: WEA

Onuora, Oku

I A TELL.
Single (12"): released on Kuya, Apr'82

PRESSURE DROP.
Album: released on Blue Moon, Nov'84 Dist: Magnum Music Group Ltd. PRT. Spartan

Onward International

FOOT IN THE DOOR.
Single (12"): released on Paladin, Dec'83 by Paladin Records. Dist: Rough Trade. Pinnacle

Ony

GIVE IT TO THEM.
Single (7"): released on HR, Sep'84 by HR Records. Dist: ILA

Onyeka

TRINA FOUR (HIGHLAND TOWN).
Single (7"): released on Mother Africa, Feb'85 Dist: Cartel Distribution, Stern's Distribution, Rough Trade Distribution

Single (12"): released on Mother Africa, Feb'85 Dist: Cartel Distribution, Stern's Distribution, Rough Trade Distribution

On Your Toes

ON YOUR TOES Various artists (Various Artists).
Compact disc: Dist: Pinnacle

Album: released on That's Entertainment, Jul'83 by That's Entertainment Records. Dist: Pinnacle, PRT

Cassette: released on That's Entertainment, Jul'83 by That's Entertainment Records. Dist: Pinnacle, PRT

Compact disc: released on That's Entertainment, Jul'83 by That's Entertainment Records. Dist: Pinnacle, PRT

Ooh Poo Pah Doo

OOH POO PAH DOO Early sixties soul 1960/1965 (Various Artists).
Album: released on Capitol, Nov'81 by Capitol Records. Dist: EMI

Cassette: released on Capitol, Nov'81 by Capitol Records. Dist: EMI

Oo Pop A Dah

OO POP A DAH.
Album: released on Affinity, Aug'85 by Charly Records. Dist: Charly, Cadillac

Opal

NORTHERN LINE.
Tracks: / Northern line / Empty bottles / Soul giver.
Single (12"): released on One Big Guitar, Jan'86 by One Big Guitar Records. Dist: Revolver Distribution, Cartel Distribution Pinnacle

Open Mind

OPEN MIND.
Album: released on Antar, Apr'86 by Bam Caruso Records. Dist: Rough Trade, Revolver

Open mind surgery

OPEN MIND SURGERY (Various Artists).
Album: released on Bluurg, Dec'86 by Bluurg Records. Dist: Rough Trade, Nine Mile

Open Space

WE CALL IT CHRISTMAS.
Single (7"): released on Open Space, Dec'83 by Open Space Records. Dist: Pinnacle

Open Top Cars...

OPEN TOP CARS AND GIRLS IN T-SHIRTS (Various Artists).
Album: released on Telstar, Aug'85 by Telstar. Records. Dist: RCA Distribution

Cassette: released on Telstar, Aug'85 by Telstar Records. Dist: RCA Distribution

Opera For Africa

OPERA FOR AFRICA (Various Artists).
Tracks: / Andrea Chenier / Carmen / Norma / Requiem / Cats / Showboat / West side story / La Traviata / La donna del lago / Un ballo in mashera / Magic flute, The / Nabucco.
Notes: The project "Opera for Africa" was conceived by Jose Carreras and is a contribution from world famous Opera Singers and musicians to the starving people of Africa. On 2nd December 1985, BBC Television broadcast excerpts from a video "Opera for Africa" resulting in immediate interest from the public on the availability of a commercial recording.
Album: released on Polygram Austria, Jun'86 by Polygram Records. Dist: Polygram

Cassette: released on Polygram Austria, Jun'86 by Polygram Records. Dist: Polygram

Operating Theatre

MISS MAUGER.
Album: released on Kabuki, Nov'83 by Gareth Ryan. Dist: Rough Trade

QUEEN OF NO HEARTS.
Tracks: / Queen of no hearts / Spring is coming with a strawberry in the mouth / Part of my make-up * / Atlanteon * / Satonosa *.
Single (7"): released on Mother, Apr'86 Dist: Island Distribution

Single (12"): released on Mother, Apr'86 Dist: Island Distribution

Operators' Special

OPERATORS' SPECIAL (Various Artists).
Album: released on Topic, Aug'79 by Polygram Records.

Ophelia Ragtime Orchestra

ECHOES FROM THE SNOWBALL CLUB.
Album: released on Stomp Off, Sep'86 by Stomp Off Records. Dist: Jazz Music Distribution

O.P.M.

MOVE THAT BODY.
Single (7"): released on Ram, Jun'83 by Ram. Dist: PRT

Single (12"): released on Ram, Jun'83 by Ram. Dist: PRT

Oppenheimer, Andie

NEW MEXICO.
Cassette single: released on JTN, Sep'83

Opposition

5 MINUTES.
Single (7"): released on Charisma, Jun'85 by Virgin Records. Dist: EMI

EMPIRE DAYS.
Album: released on Charisma, Oct'85 by Virgin Records. Dist: EMI

Cassette: released on Charisma, Oct'85 by Virgin Records. Dist: EMI

INNOCENT.
Single (7"): released on Charisma, Jul'84 by Virgin Records. Dist: EMI

Single (12"): released on Charisma, Jul'84 by Virgin Records. Dist: EMI

INTIMACY.
Album: released on Charisma, Jun'83 by Virgin Records. Dist: EMI

Cassette: released on Charisma, Jun'83 by Virgin Records. Dist: EMI

MY ROOM IS WHITE 4 track EP.
Single (12"): released on Charisma, Apr'83 by Virgin Records. Dist: EMI

PROMISES.
Album: released on Charisma, Mar'84 by Virgin Records. Dist: EMI

Cassette: released on Charisma, Mar'84 by Virgin Records. Dist: EMI

SOMEONE TO TALK TO.
Single (7"): released on Virgin, Sep'85 by Virgin Records. Dist: EMI, Virgin Distribution

Single (12"): released on Virgin, Sep'85 by Virgin Records. Dist: EMI, Virgin Distribution

STRANDED.
Single (7"): released on Virgin, Mar'84 by Virgin Records. Dist: EMI, Virgin Distribution

Single (12"): released on Virgin, Mar'84 by Virgin Records. Dist: EMI, Virgin Distribution

Oppressed

FATAL BLOW.
Album: released on Skinhead, Mar'85 by Skinhead Records. Dist: Cartel Distribution

NEVER SAY DIE EP.
Single (7"): released on Firm, Aug'83 Dist: Cartel, Revolver

O, O, MUSIC.
Album: released on Oppressed, Dec'84

WORK TOGETHER.
Single (7"): released on Jungle, Dec'83 by Jungle Records. Dist: Jungle, Cartel

Opry time in Tennessee

OPRY TIME IN TENNESSEE (Various Artists).
Album: released on Starday, Apr'87

Cassette: released on Starday, Apr'87

Optimists

MULL OF KINTYRE.
Single (7"): released on Armageddon, Jul'81 by Armageddon Records. Dist: Revolver, Cartel, Pinnacle

Opus

FLYIN' HIGH.
Single (7"): released on Polydor, Aug'85 by Polydor Records. Dist: Polygram, Polydor

Single (12"): released on Polydor, Aug'85 by Polydor Records. Dist: Polygram, Polydor

LIVE IS LIFE.
Tracks: / Opusspocus / Positive / No job / Opposition / Again and again / Double bubbles / Live is life / Flyin' high / Follow me / Eleven / Keep your mind / Last note, The.
Compact disc: released on Polydor, Aug'85 by Polydor Records. Dist: Polygram, Polydor

Album: released on Polydor, Aug'85 by Polydor Records. Dist: Polygram, Polydor Deleted '86.

Album: released on Polydor, Aug'85 by Polydor Records. Dist: Polygram, Polydor

OPUS ELEVEN.
Album: released on Teldec (Germany), Sep'85 by Import Records. Dist: IMS Distribution, Polygram Distribution

Oral

SEX.
Album: released on Conquest, Sep'85 Dist: Stage One

Orall, Robert Ellis

FIXATION.
Album: released on Why-Fi, Jun'81 by Why-Fi Records. Dist: RCA, Indies

Cassette: released on Why-Fi, Jun'81 by Why-Fi Records. Dist: RCA, Indies

I COULDN'T SAY NO / NEXT TIME.
Single (7"): released on Why-Fi, Feb'83 by Why-Fi Records. Dist: RCA, Indies

Orange

MADBRINGER.
Album: released on TRB (Yugoslavia), Jun'84 Dist: IMS, Polygram

Orange Juice

BRIDGE.
Single (7"): released on Polydor, Jan'84 by Polydor Records. Dist: Polygram, Polydor

Single (12"): released on Polydor, Jan'84 by Polydor Records. Dist: Polygram, Polydor

FLESH OF MY FLESH.
Single (7"): released on Polydor, May'83 by Polydor Records. Dist: Polygram, Polydor

Single (12"): released on Polydor, May'83 by Polydor Records. Dist: Polygram, Polydor

IN A NUTSHELL.
Album: released on Polydor, Jun'85 by Polydor Records. Dist: Polygram, Polydor

Cassette: released on Polydor, Jun'85 by Polydor Records. Dist: Polygram, Polydor

ORANGE JUICE.
Tracks: / Lean period / I guess I'm just a little too sensitive / Burning desire / Scaremonger / Artisan / What presence / Out for the count / Get while the gettings good / All that ever mattered / Salon fishing in New York.
Album: released on Polydor, Aug'86 by Polydor Records. Dist: Polygram Polydor

Cassette: released on Polydor, Aug'86 by Polydor Records. Dist: Polygram, Polydor

RIP IT UP.
Double-pack single: released on Polydor, Feb'83 by Polydor Records. Dist: Polygram, Polydor

RIP IT UP (LP).
Album: released on Polydor, Oct'82 by Polydor Records. Dist: Polygram, Polydor

Cassette: released on Polydor, Oct'82 by Polydor Records. Dist: Polygram, Polydor Deleted '87.

TEXAS FEVER.
Album: released on Polydor, Feb'84 by Polydor Records. Dist: Polygram, Polydor

Cassette: released on Polydor, Feb'84 by Polydor Records. Dist: Polygram, Polydor Deleted '85.

WHAT PRESENCE.
Single (7"): released on Polydor, Jun'84 by Polydor Records. Dist: Polygram, Polydor

Single (7"): released on Polydor, Apr'84 by Polydor Records. Dist: Polygram, Polydor

Single (12"): released on Polydor, Apr'84 by Polydor Records. Dist: Polygram, Polydor

YOU CAN'T HIDE YOUR LOVE FOREVER.
Album: released on Polydor, Feb'82 by Polydor Records. Dist: Polygram, Polydor

Cassette: released on Polydor, Feb'82 by Polydor Records. Dist: Polygram, Polydor

Orbidoig

NOCTURNAL OPERATION.
Single (7"): released on Situation 2, Dec'81 Dist: Cartel, Pinnacle

Orbison, Roy

ALL-TIME GREATEST HITS.
Double Album: released on Monument, '73 by CBS Records. Dist: CBS Distribution

ALMOST EIGHTEEN.
Single (7"): released on Bear Family, Sep'82 by Bear Family Records. Dist: Rollercoaster Distribution, Swift

...AT ROCK HOUSE.
Album: released on Charly, Feb'81 by Charly Records. Dist: Charly, Cadillac

BIG O COUNTRY.
Album: released on Decca, Aug'83 by Decca Records. Dist: Polygram

Cassette: released on Decca, Aug'83 by Decca Records. Dist: Polygram

BIG 'O', THE.
Cassette: released on Charly, Jan'82 by Charly Records. Dist: Charly Cadillac

Album: released on Charly, Oct'85 by Charly Records. Dist: Charly, Cadillac

BIG O, THE.
Album: released on Magnum Force, Jun'86 by Magnum Music Group Ltd. Dist: Magnum Music Group Ltd, PRT, Spartan

CRYING.
Single (7"): released on Monument, '80 by CBS Records. Dist: CBS Distribution

EXCITING SOUND OF ROY ORBISON.
Album: released on Ember, '74 by Bulldog Records. Dist: President Distribution, Spartan, Swift, Taylor, H.R.

FOCUS ON.
Double Album: released on Decca, Jul'76 by Decca Records. Dist: Polygram

GO GO GO.
Tracks: / Go go go / Ooby dooby / Tryin to get you / You're my baby / Rockhouse / Domino / Devil doll / Sweet and easy to love / Cause of it all (The) / Mean little mama / You're gonna cry / Problem child / True love goodbye, A / Fools hall of fame / I like love / Chicken hearted / It's too late / This kind of love / I never knew / You tell me / I give up / Lovestruck / Clown (The) / Claudette.
Notes: Original Sun Records recordings. Licensed from Charly Records International APS.
Compact disc: released on Charly, Oct'86 by Charly Records. Dist: Charly, Cadillac

GOLDEN DAYS.
Album: released on Monument, Aug'81 by CBS Records. Dist: CBS Distribution

Cassette: released on Monument, Aug'81 by CBS Records. Dist: CBS Distribution

GREATEST HITS: ROY ORBISON.
Album: released on Monument, '74 by CBS Records. Dist: CBS Distribution

IN DREAMS.
Single (7"): released on Virgin, May'87 by Virgin Records. Dist: EMI, Virgin Distribution

Single (7"): released on Monument, May'82 by CBS Records. Dist: CBS Distribution

IN DREAMS (LP).
Album: released on Virgin, Jun'87 by Virgin Records. Dist: EMI, Virgin Distribution

Cassette: released on Virgin, Jun'87 by Virgin Records. Dist: EMI, Virgin Distribution

Compact disc: released on Virgin, Apr'87 by Virgin Records. Dist: EMI, Virgin Distribution

OH PRETTY WOMAN.
Single (7"): released on Monument, '80 by CBS Records. Dist: CBS Distribution

ONLY THE LONELY.
Picture disc album: released on Astan, Dec'85 by Astan Records. Dist: Counterpoint

ONLY THE LONELY (SINGLE).
Single (7"): released on Monument, Jan'80 by CBS Records. Dist: CBS Distribution

OTHER SIDE (THE).
Album: released on Musketeer, Jan'87

ROY ORBISON COLLECTION.
Tracks: / Tryin' to get to you / Ooby dooby / Go go go / You're my baby / Rock house / Domino / Sweet and easy to love / Devil doll / Cause of it all, The / Fools hall of fame / True love goodbye / Chicken hearted / I like love / Mean little mama / Problem child / This kind of love / It's too late / I never knew / You're gonna cry / One more time / Love struck / Clown / Claudette.
Album: released on Castle Classics, Sep'86 by Castle Communications. Dist: BMG

Cassette: released on Castle Classics, Sep'86 by Castle Communications. Dist: BMG

ROY ORBISON & SONNY JAMES (Orbison, Roy & Sonny James).
Tracks: / Almost eighteen / Bug, The / I'll never tell / Jolie / Paper boy / Sweet and innocent / Seems to me / Apache / Magnetism / Young love / No Lana / The legend of the brown mountain light / Listen to my heart / Hey little ducky / Innocent angel / Broken wings / Day's not over yet, The / Dance her by me (one more time) / Time's running backwards for me.
Compact disc: released on Bear Family, Jul'87 by Bear Family Records. Dist: Rollercoaster Distribution, Swift. Estim retail price in Aug'87 was £13.50.

Album: released on Bear Family (Rollercoaster), Aug'87. Estim retail price in Aug'87 was £13.50.

RUNNING SCARED.
Single (7"): released on Monument, Jan'80 by CBS Records. Dist: CBS Distribution

SEEMS TO ME.
Single (7"): released on Bear Family, Feb'82 by Bear Family Records. Dist: Rollercoaster Distribution, Swift

SUN YEARS, THE.
Album: released on Charly, Jul'84 by Charly Records. Dist: Charly, Cadillac

WILD HEARTS Time.
Single (7"): released on ZTT, Jun'85 by Island Records. Dist: Polygram

Double-pack single: released on ZTT, Jun'85 by Island Records. Dist: Polygram

Single (12"): released on ZTT, Jun'85 by Island Records. Dist: Polygram Deleted '87.

Orbit

BEAT GOES ON.
Single (7"): released on Arista, Jan'83 by Arista Records. Dist: RCA

Single (12"): released on Arista, Jan'83 by Arista Records. Dist: RCA

FEEL LIKE JUMPIN'.
Tracks: / Feel like jumpin' / Blue Street.
Single (7"): released on MCA, 23 May'87 by MCA Records. Dist: Polygram, MCA

Single (12"): released on MCA, 23 May'87 by MCA Records. Dist: Polygram, MCA

ORBIT.
Tracks: / Love my way / Fool to myself / Heartbroken highway / Escape to Mexico / Rider in black / Swamp dog / Feel like jumping / Blue Street / Cluny Ann / Night runs forever, (The) / Cry one more tear.
Album: released on I.R.S.(Independent Record Syndicate), Apr'87 by I.R.S.. Dist: MCA

Cassette: released on I.R.S.(Independent Record Syndicate), Apr'87 by I.R.S. Dist: MCA

Compact disc: released on MCA, Jun'87 by MCA Records. Dist: Polygram, MCA

Orbitone Allstars

THIS LOVE OF MINE (PART 2).
Single (12"): released on Orbitone, Jan'85 by Orbitone Records. Dist: Jetstar Distribution

Orbit, William

LOVE MY WAY.
Single (7"): released on MCA, Aug'87 by MCA Records. Dist: Polygram, MCA

Single (12"): released on MCA, Aug'87 by MCA Records. Dist: Polygram, MCA

Orchard

SECRET, A.
Single (7"): released on Swan, Apr'85 Dist: Global Records Distribution

Orchestra Arcana

ICONOGRAPHY.
Tracks: / Christ via wires / Clock conscious / Clock conscious / Eastern eltric / Search and listen / News from nowhere / One man's fetish is another man's faith / Right then left / Iconography / Gods speak (The) / Life class / Altar natives / Sex, psyche, etcetera.
Album: released on Cocteau, Nov'86 by Cocteau Records. Dist: Pinnacle, IDS

Cassette: released on Cocteau, Nov'86 by Cocteau Records. Dist: Pinnacle, IDS

SEX PSYCHE.
Single (12"): released on Cocteau, May'85 by Cocteau Records. Dist: Pinnacle, IDS

Orchestra Des Hauses...

MUSIC FOR ACCORDION ORCHESTRA NO.4.
Tracks: / Pastorale Francaise / Kompositionen fur akkordeon orchestra.

Album: released on Accordion Record Club, Jul'86 by Accordion Record Club Records. Dist: Accordion Record Club

Orchestra Makassy

MAMBO BADO.
Single (7"): released on Virgin, Sep'82 by Virgin Records. Dist: EMI, Virgin Distribution

Single (12"): released on Virgin, Sep'82 by Virgin Records. Dist: EMI, Virgin Distribution

Orchestra Manhattan

DIGITAL BROADWAY.
Tracks: / Something's coming / Send in the clowns / Putting it together / Pretty women / Johanna / Perfect strangers / Memory / One night in Bangkok / I loves you Porgy / Where am I going / I know him so well / I'm losing me mind / At the ballet/One.
Compact disc: released on Manhattan, Oct'86 by EMI Records. Dist: EMI

Orchestra Suisse Romand

INTERMEZZO.
Single (7"): released on Polydor, Mar'84 by Polydor Records. Dist: Polygram, Polydor

Orchestra Virunga

MALAKO.
Album: released on Earthworks (Kenya), Jul'84 by Earthworks Records. Dist: Earthworks Distributors, Rough Trade, Cartel, Projection

Orchestre Jazira

HAPPY DAY (CELEBRATION).
Single (7"): released on Beggars Banquet, Jul'84 by Beggars Banquet Records. Dist: WEA

Single (12"): released on Beggars Banquet, Jul'84 by Beggars Banquet Records. Dist: WEA Deleted '87.

LOVE.
Single (7"): released on Earthworks, Sep'82 by Earthworks Records. Dist: Earthworks Distributors, Rough Trade, Cartel, Projection

NOMADIC ACTIVITIES.
Album: released on Beggars Banquet, Sep'84 by Beggars Banquet Records. Dist: WEA

Cassette: released on Beggars Banquet, Sep'84 by Beggars Banquet Records. Dist: WEA

SAKABO.
Single (7"): released on Beggars Banquet, Jan'84 by Beggars Banquet Records. Dist: WEA

Single (12"): released on Beggars Banquet, Jan'84 by Beggars Banquet Records. Dist: WEA Deleted '87.

Orchestre Victoria

SANS PREAVIS.
Album: released on Vercky's (Zaire), Jul'84 Dist: Earthworks Distributors, Rough Trade

Ordinary Man

I CAN'T BELIEVE IT'S COME TO THIS.
Tracks: / I can't believe it's come to this / Goodbye America.
Single (7"): released on EMI, Jul'87 by EMI Records. Dist: EMI

Single (12"): released on EMI, Jul'87 by EMI Records. Dist: EMI

Ore

YOUR TIME WILL COME.
Single (7"): released on Bandit Records, Sep'82 by Bandit Records. Dist: Pinnacle, Kingdom

Oregon

CROSSING.
Compact disc: by ECM Records. Dist: IMS, Polygram, Virgin through EMI

Album: released on ECM (Germany), Jul'85 by ECM Records. Dist: IMS, Polygram, Virgin through EMI

OREGON.
Album: released on ECM (Germany), Oct'83 by ECM Records. Dist: IMS, Polygram, Virgin through EMI

Compact disc: released on ECM (Germany), Oct'83 by ECM Records. Dist: IMS, Polygram, Virgin through EMI

OUT OF THE WOODS.
Album: released on Elektra, '78 by WEA Records. Dist: WEA

Oreo Moon

WALK DON'T SCREAM.
Album: released on Sonet, Jul'83 by Sonet Records. Dist: PRT

Organ Boogie Woogie

ORGAN BOOGIE WOOGIE (Various Artists).
Album: released on CBS(I love Jazz), Aug'84 by CBS Records. Dist: CBS

Cassette: released on CBS(I love Jazz), Aug'84 by CBS Records. Dist: CBS

Organist Entertains You

ORGANIST ENTERTAINS YOU (Various Artists).
Album: released on Decca, Jan'83 by Decca Records. Dist: Polygram

Cassette: released on Decca, Jan'83 by Decca Records. Dist: Polygram

Organum

IN EXTREMIS.
Album: released on Antirecords, Dec'85 Dist: Rough Trade, Cartel

SUBMISSION.
Album: released on United Dairies, Jun'87 Dist: Rough Trade, Indies

Oriental Wind

BAZAAR.
Album: released on Sonet, Sep'81 by Sonet Records. Dist: PRT

CHILA CHILA.
Album: released on Sonet, Jan'80 by Sonet Records. Dist: PRT

SANKIRNA (Oriental Wind & The Karnataka College Of Percussion).
Album: released on Sonet, Jun'85 by Sonet Records. Dist: PRT

Original...

ORIGINAL CLASSICS: DOO WOP HITS (Various Artists).
Album: released on Vogue (France), Oct'85 Dist: Discovery, Jazz Music, PRT, Swift

Cassette: released on Vogue (France), Oct'85 Dist: Discovery, Jazz Music, PRT, Swift

ORIGINAL EARLY ROCK INSTRUMENTALS (Various Artists).
Album: released on White label (Germany), Apr'85

ORIGINAL MIXED UP KID (Various Artists).
Single (7"): released on Fried Egg, Jul'81 by Fried Egg Records. Dist: Rough Trade, Cartel

ORIGINAL MUSIC FOR ACCORDION NO.3 (Various Artists).
Album: released on ARC (Accordion Records), '84 Dist: Accordion Record Club

ORIGINAL REGGAE HITS (Various Artists).
Album: released on Wild Flower, Jun'84 by Wild Flower Records. Dist: Jetstar

ORIGINAL RHYTHM'N'BLUES (Various Artists).
Album: released on Chess (France), Oct'85 by Charly Records. Dist: Charly, Swift, PRT

Cassette: released on Chess (France), Oct'85 by Charly Records. Dist: Charly, Swift, PRT

ORIGINAL RHYTHM'N'BLUES 1948-52 (Various Artists).
Album: released on Arbee, Jul'85

ORIGINAL ROCKABILLY COLLECTION (Various Artists).
Album: released on MGM (USA), Oct'83 by Polydor. Dist: Polygram, Swift

Cassette: released on MGM (USA), Oct'83 by Polydor. Dist: Polygram, Swift

ORIGINAL ROCK'N'ROLL CLASSICS (Various Artists).
Album: released on Chess (France), Oct'85 by Charly Records. Dist: Charly, Swift, PRT

Cassette: released on Chess (France), Oct'85 by Charly Records. Dist: Charly, Swift, PRT

ORIGINALS (Various Artists).
Notes: Artists include Smokey Robinson & The Miracles, Marvin Gaye, Sam Cooke, Stevie Wonder, Martha Reeves & The Vandellas, Gene Chandler, Eddie Floyd. Double album and cassette.

Album: released on Towerbell, Jul'86 by Towerbell Records. Dist: EMI

Cassette: released on Towerbell, Jul'86 by Towerbell Records. Dist: EMI

ORIGINAL SOUND OF THE TWENTIES (Various Artists).
Tracks: / Blue room, The / St Louis blues / Varsity drag / Alexander's ragtime band / Black and blue / Am I blue/Can't help lovin' dat man / Bill / Man I love / Nobody's sweetheart / Rhythm king / Someone to watch over me / Home on the range / Can't we be friends.
Notes: Mono.
Album: released on CBS, Mar'86 by CBS Records. Dist: CBS

Cassette: released on CBS, Mar'86 by CBS Records. Dist: CBS

ORIGINAL STALAG 17-18 AND 19 (Various Artists).
Album: released on Techniques, Sep'85 Dist: Jetstar Distribution

ORIGINAL TOP HITS (VOL.4) (Various Artists).
Tracks: / Blue world / Nightmares / Sporcati / Where did we go wrong / That's the way / Love to love / No news / To hell with him / Vamos a la playa / Maybe one day / Turn to me / Magic touch / Just one more kiss / Tango / Danger games / Downtown rock 'n' roll discotheque / Number one contender.
Cassette: released on Teldec (Germany), Jun'86 by Import Records. Dist: IMS Distribution, Polygram Distribution

ORIGINAL TRINIDAD TROPICANA STEEL BAND (Original Trinidad Tropicana Steel Band).
Album: released on Polydor, Aug'83 by Polydor Records. Dist: Polygram, Polydor

Cassette: released on Polydor, Aug'83 by Polydor Records. Dist: Polygram, Polydor

ORIGINAL USA FOLK BLUES FESTIVAL Various artists (Various Artists).
Compact disc: by Polydor Records. Dist: Polygram, Polydor

Original 5 Blind Boys

PRECIOUS MEMORIES.
Album: released on MCA (USA), Jun'84

Original Animals

BEFORE WE WERE SO RUDELY......
Album: released on Barn, '77 by Barn Records. Dist: RCA

Original Camelia Jazz...

ORIGINAL CAMELIA JAZZ BAND.
Album: released on New Orleans, Sep'86 Dist: Swift, Zodiac Distribution, Jazz Music, JSU

Original Dixieland...

1943.
Notes: Mono.
Album: released on GHB, Jun'86 Dist: Jazz Music, Swift

DIXIELAND.
Notes: Including: When the saints go marching in, C.C.Rider, Tell it to the mountains etc.
Compact disc: released on Delta, '86 by Delta Records. Dist: Target

ORIGINAL DIXIELAND JAZZ.
Album: released on Fountain, Apr'79 by Retrieval Records. Dist: Jazz Music, Swift, VJM, Wellard, Chris, Retrieval

ORIGINAL DIXIELAND JAZZ BAND REVISITED.
Album: released on Rarities, Apr'79

SENSATION.
Album: released on ASV Living Era, May'83 by ASV Records. Dist: PRT

Cassette: released on ASV Living Era, May'83 by ASV Records. Dist: PRT

Original East

SHORES OF LAKE PLACID.
Album: released on Zoo, Feb'82

Original Glenn Miller,The

GLEN MILLER STORY, THE.
Compact disc: released on The Compact Collection, Sep'87 by Conifer Records. Dist: Conifer Distribution

Original Jazz Hounds

ORIGINAL JAZZ HOUNDS & GULF COAST 7.
Album: released on VJM, Apr'79 by VJM (UK) Records. Dist: Swift

Original Oldies

ORIGINAL OLDIES (1) 6 track EP (Various Artists).
Extended-play record: released on Original Oldies, Nov'84 Dist: PRT Distribution

ORIGINAL OLDIES (10) 6 track EP (Various Artists).
Extended-play record: released on Original Oldies, Nov'84 Dist: PRT Distribution

ORIGINAL OLDIES (11) 6 track EP (Various Artists).
Extended-play record: released on Original Oldies, Nov'84 Dist: PRT Distribution

ORIGINAL OLDIES (12) 6 track EP (Various Artists).
Extended-play record: released on Original Oldies, Nov'84 Dist: PRT Distribution

ORIGINAL OLDIES (13) 6 track EP (Various Artists).
Extended-play record: released on Original Oldies, Nov'84 Dist: PRT Distribution

ORIGINAL OLDIES (14) 6 track EP (Various Artists).
Extended-play record: released on Original Oldies, Nov'84 Dist: PRT Distribution

ORIGINAL OLDIES (15) 6 track EP (Various Artists).
Extended-play record: released on Original Oldies, Nov'84 Dist: PRT Distribution

ORIGINAL OLDIES (16) 6 track EP (Various Artists).
Extended-play record: released on Original Oldies, Nov'84 Dist: PRT Distribution

ORIGINAL OLDIES (17) 6 track EP (Various Artists).
Extended-play record: released on Original Oldies, Nov'84 Dist: PRT Distribution

ORIGINAL OLDIES (18) 6 track EP (Various Artists).
Extended-play record: released on Original Oldies, Nov'84 Dist: PRT Distribution

ORIGINAL OLDIES (19) 6 track EP (Various Artists).
Extended-play record: released on Original Oldies, Nov'84 Dist: PRT Distribution

ORIGINAL OLDIES (2) 6 track EP (Various Artists).
Extended-play record: released on Original Oldies, Nov'84 Dist: PRT Distribution

ORIGINAL OLDIES (20) 6 track EP (Various Artists).
Extended-play record: released on Original Oldies, Nov'84 Dist: PRT Distribution

ORIGINAL OLDIES (21) 6 track EP (Various Artists).
Extended-play record: released on Original Oldies, Nov'84 Dist: PRT Distribution

ORIGINAL OLDIES (22) 6 track EP (Various Artists).
Extended-play record: released on Original Oldies, Nov'84 Dist: PRT Distribution

ORIGINAL OLDIES (23) 6 track EP (Various Artists).
Extended-play record: released on Original Oldies, Nov'84 Dist: PRT Distribution

ORIGINAL OLDIES (24) 6 track EP (Various Artists).
Extended-play record: released on Original Oldies, Nov'84 Dist: PRT Distribution

ORIGINAL OLDIES (25) 6 track EP (Various Artists).
Extended-play record: released on Original Oldies, Nov'84 Dist: PRT Distribution

ORIGINAL OLDIES (26) 6 track EP (Various Artists).
Extended-play record: released on Original Oldies, Nov'84 Dist: PRT Distribution

ORIGINAL OLDIES (27) 6 track EP (Various Artists).
Extended-play record: released on Original Oldies, Nov'84 Dist: PRT Distribution

ORIGINAL OLDIES (28) 6 track EP (Various Artists).
Extended-play record: released on Original Oldies, Nov'84 Dist: PRT Distribution

ORIGINAL OLDIES (29) 6 track EP (Various Artists).
Extended-play record: released on Original Oldies, Nov'84 Dist: PRT Distribution

ORIGINAL OLDIES (3) 6 track EP (Various Artists).
Extended-play record: released on Original Oldies, Nov'84 Dist: PRT Distribution

ORIGINAL OLDIES (30) 6 track EP (Various Artists).
Extended-play record: released on Original Oldies, Nov'84 Dist: PRT Distribution

ORIGINAL OLDIES (31) 6 track EP (Various Artists).
Extended-play record: released on Original Oldies, Nov'84 Dist: PRT Distribution

ORIGINAL OLDIES (32) 6 track EP (Various Artists).
Extended-play record: released on Original Oldies, Nov'84 Dist: PRT Distribution

ORIGINAL OLDIES (4) 6 track EP (Various Artists).
Extended-play record: released on Original Oldies, Nov'84 Dist: PRT Distribution

ORIGINAL OLDIES (5) 6 track EP (Various Artists).
Extended-play record: released on Original Oldies, Nov'84 Dist: PRT Distribution

ORIGINAL OLDIES (6) 6 track EP (Various Artists).
Extended-play record: released on Original Oldies, Nov'84 Dist: PRT Distribution

ORIGINAL OLDIES (7) 6 track EP (Various Artists).
Extended-play record: released on Original Oldies, Nov'84 Dist: PRT Distribution

ORIGINAL OLDIES (8) 6 track EP (Various Artists).
Extended-play record: released on Original Oldies, Nov'84 Dist: PRT Distribution

ORIGINAL OLDIES (9) 6 track EP (Various Artists).
Extended-play record: released on Original Oldies, Nov'84 Dist: PRT Distribution

Original Pistols

LIVE.
Tracks: / Anarchy in the UK / I wanna be me / I'm a lazy sod / Dolls (New York) / Don't give me no lip, child / Substitute / Liar / No feelings / No fun / Pretty vacant / Problems.
Album: released on Fame, May'86 by Music For Pleasure Records. Dist: EMI

Cassette: released on Fame, May'86 by Music For Pleasure Records. Dist: EMI

LIVE.
Album: released on Receiver, Jul'85 by Receiver Records. Dist: Pinnacle

Cassette: released on Receiver, Jul'85 by Receiver Records. Dist: Pinnacle

Original Red Box

NEVER TRUST YOUR SOUL.
Single (7"): released on Polo, Jul'84 by Polo Records. Dist: PRT

Single (12"): released on Polo, Jul'84 by Polo Records. Dist: PRT

Original Salty Dogs

DOWN IN HONKY TONKY TOWN.
Album: released on Stomp Off, Mar'87 by Stomp Off Records. Dist: Jazz Music Distribution

Original Sin

SHADOW, THE.
Single (12"): released on Original Sin, May'84 by Original Sin Records. Dist: Cartel Distribution

SIN WILL FIND YOU OUT.
Album: released on Roadrunner (Dutch), Oct'86 Dist: Pinnacle

Original Tornadoes

TELSTAR.
Single (7"): released on SRT, Jan'79 by SRT Records. Dist: Pinnacle, Solomon & Peres Distribution, SRT Distribution, H.R. Taylor Distribution, PRT Distribution

Original Wailers

MUSIC LESSON.
Tracks: / Music lesson / Nice time.
Single (7"): released on Tuff Gong, Mar'86 by Tuff Gong Records. Dist: Jetstar

Single (12"): released on Tuff Gong, Mar'86 by Tuff Gong Records. Dist: Jetstar

Orioles

JUMP CHILDREN 16 tracks recorded 1953-56 (Orioles/Moonglows/Flamingos).
Album: released on Charly, Aug'83 by Charly Records. Dist: Charly, Cadillac

Orion

INSANE IN ANOTHER WORLD.
Single (7"): released on Lost Moment, Jul'84

MEN FROM WHITEHALL, THE.
Single (7"): released on County Cat, Jan'85 by County Cat Records. Dist: M.I.S.

REBORN.
Album: released on Charly, Apr'80 by Charly Records. Dist: Charly, Cadillac

Orion the Hunter

ORION THE HUNTER.
Album: released on Portrait, Jul'84 by CBS Records. Dist: CBS Deleted '87.

Cassette: released on Portrait, Jul'84 by CBS Records. Dist: CBS Deleted '86.

SO YOU RAN.
Single (7"): released on Portrait, Jul'84 by CBS Records. Dist: CBS

Single (12"): released on Portrait, Jul'84 by CBS Records. Dist: CBS

Or-Kestral-Line

CRAZY ROMANCE.
Single (7"): released on Riviere, Jan'85 by Riviere Records. Dist: M.I.S.

Ork,Gene Roland

BAND THAT NEVER WAS,THE.
Album: released on Spotlite, Jan'80 by Spotlite Records. Dist: Cadillac, Jazz Music, Spotlite

Orkney Strathspey...

ORKNEY FIDDLE MUSIC.
Tracks: / Signature tune of The Orkney Strathspey & Reel Soc. / 2/4 march / Jig / Waltz / Reel / Polka / March / Reel / Polka / Slow air and march / March / Polka.
Album: released on MFP, Jun'86 by EMI Records. Dist: EMI

Cassette: released on MFP, Jun'86 by EMI Records. Dist: EMI

Double Album: released on One Up, Nov'76 by EMI Records.

Orlando

ORLANDO (THE MARMALADE CAT) (Orlando (The Marmalade Cat)).
Tracks: / Orlando keeps a dog / Orlando buys a cottage.
Cassette: released on Tellastory, Dec'86 by Bartlett Bliss Productions. Dist: PRT Distribution, Hayward Promotions Distribution, H.R. Taylor Distribution

Cassette: released on Tellastory, Oct'79 by Bartlett Bliss Productions. Dist: PRT Distribution, Hayward Promotions Distribution, H.R. Taylor Distribution

Orlando, Johnny

LET'S GIVE LOVE A TRY.
Tracks: / Let's give love a try / Let's give love a try (Inst).
Single (12"): released on Orbitone, Nov'86 by Orbitone Records. Dist: Jetstar Distribution

LOOKING BACK ON MY LIFE.
Single (12"): released on Orbitone, Nov'85 by Orbitone Records. Dist: Jetstar Distribution

TELL ME WHEN.
Tracks: / Tell me when / In and out (Inst).
Single (12"): released on Orbitone, May'86 by Orbitone Records. Dist: Jetstar Distribution

Orlando,Tony

BLESS YOU/HALFWAY TO PARADISE.
Single (7"): released on Old Gold (Reissue), Jul'82

O'Rourke,Jim

JIM O'ROURKE AR HOELION WYTH.
Album: released on Loco Records, '84 by Loco Records. Dist: Loco Records

Orphan

JULIE ISN'T JULIE IN THE BATH.
Tracks: / Julie isn't Julie in the bath / Time-bombs.
Single (7"): released on Brilliant, Jul'87 by PVK. Dist: Spartan

Single (7"): released on Brilliant, Apr'84 by PVK. Dist: Spartan

LOVE ON THE LICHFIELD LINE.
Tracks: / Love on the Lichfield line / Ambition.
Single (7"): released on Swoop, '85 Dist: Le Matt Music Distribution

NERVOUS.
Tracks: / Nervous / Little England.
Notes: Le Matt Music 0789 750474/0494 36301
Single (7"): released on Swoop, Sep'86 Dist: Le Matt Music Distribution

Single (7"): released on Swoop, Aug'85 Dist: Le Matt Music Distribution

PHOBIAS.
Tracks: / Phobias / Nervous / I don't want it like that / Time bombs / R.S.V.P.U. / Dream boat / Julie isn't Julie in the bath / Mouth to mouth / 7 teen / Ambition / Little England / Love on the Lichfield line.
Album: released on PVK, May'87

Album: released on PVK, Apr'85

R.S.V.P.U..
Tracks: / R.S.V.P.U. / Mouth to mouth.

R.S.V.P.U. / MOUTH TO MOUTH.
Single (7"): released on Swoop, Oct'82 Dist: Le Matt Music Distribution

Orpheon Celesta

ORPHEON CELESTA VOLUME 2.
Album: released on Stomp Off, Jun'86 by Stomp Off Records. Dist: Jazz Music Distribution

Orpheus

PSYCHOTRONIC SOUND.
Cassette: released on Complex(R.A.P.), Mar'85 Dist: Complex (R.A.P.), Red Rhino, Cartel

Orr, Benjamin

LACE (THE).
Tracks: / Too hot to stop / In circles / Stay the night / Skyline / When you're gone / Spinning / Hold on / Lace (The) / That's the way / This time around.
Album: released on Elektra (USA), Nov'86 by Elektra/Asylum/Nonesuch Records. Dist: WEA

Cassette: released on Elektra (USA), Nov'86 by Elektra/Asylum/Nonesuch Records. Dist: WEA

STAY THE NIGHT.
Tracks: / Stay the night / That's the way.
Single (7"): released on Elektra (USA), Jan'87 by Elektra/Asylum/Nonesuch Records. Dist: WEA

Single (12"): released on Elektra (USA), Jan'87 by Elektra/Asylum/Nonesuch Records. Dist: WEA

Orson Family

BALL AND CHAIN / YOU SHAKE MY SOUL.
Single (7"): released on Orson, Jul'83 by Orson Records. Dist: Rough Trade Distribution

BUGLES GUITARS AND AMPJETAMINES.
Album: released on Criminal Damage, May'85 by Criminal Damage Records. Dist: Backs, Cartel

HEARTBEAT / YOU SHAKE MY SOUL.
Single (7"): released on Orson, Jun'83 by Orson Records. Dist: Rough Trade Distribution

RIVER OF DESIRE, THE.
Album: released on New Rose, Oct'83 Dist: Rough Trade, Cartel

SWEETEST EMBRACE.
Single (7"): released on Orson Enterprises, Oct'84 by Orson Family. Dist: Cartel Distribution

Ortega, Anthony

NEW DANCE.
Album: released on Revelation (USA), Apr'81 Dist: Jazz Music, Jazz Horizons, Swift

PERMUTATIONS.
Album: released on Revelation (USA), Apr'81 Dist: Jazz Music, Jazz Horizons, Swift

Ortiz, Pertico

IN TRADITION.
Album: released on Messidor (Germany), May'87 Dist: IMS Distribution, Polygram

Orwell, George

ANIMAL FARM.
Cassette: released on Listen For Pleasure, Oct'84 by MFP Records. Dist: EMI

Ory, Kid

1944 - 1945 (Ory, Kid & His Creole Jazz Band).
Notes: Mono.
Album: released on Folklyric (USA), Oct'86 by Arhoolie Records. Dist: Topic, Projection

1954.
Album: released on Hot Society, Dec'82 Dist: Jazz Music, Chris Wellard

AT THE JAZZBAND BALL Live in concert (Ory, Kid & His Creole Jazz Band).
Tracks: / Panama rag / At the jazzband ball / Peoria / Basin Street blues / St James Infirmary blues / Wolverine blues / Savoy blues / Tin roof blues / That's a plenty / Aunt Hagar blues.
Album: released on Rhapsody, Jan'87 by President Records. Dist: Taylors, Swift, Jazz Music, Wellard, Chris

KID ORY FAVOURITES.
Compact disc: released on London, Apr'87 by London Records. Dist: Polygram

KID ORY & HIS CREOLE JAZZBAND.
Album: released on Rhapsody, Mar'87 by President Records. Dist: Taylors, Swift, Jazz Music, Wellard, Chris

KID ORY MEETS RED ALLEN (Ory, Kid & Red Allen).
Album: released on Verve (Import), Oct'82

KID ORY PLAYS THE BLUES.
Album: released on Storyville (USA), Aug'83 by Moss Music Group Records (USA). Dist: Discovery Distribution, Jazz Music Distribution, Swift Distribution, Chris Wellard Distribution, JSU Distribution, Celtic Music Distribution

KID ORY'S CREOLE BAND.
Album: released on Queendisc (Import), '81 Dist: Cadillac

KID ORY'S CREOLE JAZZ BAND.
Album: released on Good Time Jazz (USA), Sep'81 by Good Time Jazz Records (USA). Dist: Polygram

KID ORY'S CREOLE JAZZ BAND 1955.
Album: released on Contemporary, Apr'82 by Good Time Jazz Records (USA). Dist: IMS, Polygram

LIVE AT CLUB HANGOVER VOL.1 (Ory, Kid & His Creole Jazz Band).

LIVE AT CLUB HANGOVER VOL.4 (Ory, Kid & His Creole Jazz Band).
Album: released on Dawn Club, Jun'79 Dist: Cadillac, Swift, JSU

LIVE AT CLUB HANGOVER VOL.3 (Ory, Kid & His Creole Jazz Band).
Album: released on Dawn Club, Jun'79 Dist: Cadillac, Swift, JSU

LIVE AT CLUB HANGOVER VOL.2 (Ory, Kid & His Creole Jazz Band).
Album: released on Dawn Club, Jun'79 Dist: Cadillac, Swift, JSU

Album: released on Dawn Club, Jun'79 Dist: Cadillac, Swift, JSU

MERCURY THEATRE, L.A., BROADCASTS (Ory, Kid & Jimmy Noone).
Album: released on Joker (Import), Apr'81

NEW ORLEANS (Ory, Kid & His Creole Jazz Band).
Album: released on CBS, May'83 by CBS Records. Dist: CBS

Cassette: released on CBS, May'83 by CBS Records. Dist: CBS

NEW ORLEANS JUBILEE (Ory, Kid & His Creole Jazz Band).
Tracks: / Fanfare / Maryland / Milenberg joys / Muskrat ramble / 12th street rag / Eh la bas / Blues for Jimmy Noone / St Louis blues / Tiger rag.
Compact disc: released on Vogue, '86 Dist: Discovery, Jazz Music, PRT, Swift

PLAYS THE BLUES.
Album: released on Storyville, Mar'87 by Storyville Records. Dist: Jazz Music Distribution, Swift Distribution, Chris Wellard Distribution, Counterpoint Distribution

RED ALLEN MEETS KID ORY (see Allen, Red meets Kid Ory) (Ory, Kid meets Red Allen).

SONG OF THE WANDERER.
Album: released on Verve, May'82 by Phonogram Records. Dist: Polygram

THIS KID'S THE GREATEST (Ory, Kid & His Creole Jazz Band).
Album: released on Contemporary (USA), Nov'83 Dist: Fantasy (USA) Distribution

WE'VE GOT RHYTHM (Ory, Kid & Red Allen).
Album: released on Verve (America), Jun'81

Osborne, Brian

AE FOND KISS.
Album: released on Tradition, Aug'76 Dist: JSU, Cassion Distribution, Celtic Music, Jazz Music, Projection, Roots Records

Cassette: released on Tradition, Aug'76 Dist: JSU, Cassion Distribution, Celtic Music, Jazz Music, Projection, Roots Records

Osborne Brothers

VOICES IN BLUEGRASS.
Tracks: / Take this hammer / Cotton fields / Me and my old banjo / Pathway of teardrops / Kentucky / Bluegrass express / This heart of mine / Cuckoo bird / Don't ever look at me / Charlie Cotton / Bugle on the banjo / Salty dog blues.
Album: released on Stetson, Nov'85 by Hasmick Promotions Ltd.. Dist: Counterpoint Distribution, H.R. Taylor Distribution, Swift Distribution, Chris Wellard Distribution

Cassette: released on Stetson, Nov'85 by Hasmick Promotions Ltd.. Dist: Counterpoint Distribution, H.R. Taylor Distribution, Swift Distribution, Chris Wellard Distribution

Osborne, Jeffrey

BORDERLINE, (THE).
Single (7"): released on A&M, Jan'85 by A&M Records. Dist: Polygram

Single (12"): released on A&M, Jan'85 by A&M Records. Dist: Polygram

DON'T STOP.
Compact disc: by A&M Records. Dist: Polygram

Album: released on A&M, Oct'84 by A&M Records. Dist: Polygram

Cassette: released on A&M, Oct'84 by A&M Records. Dist: Polygram

Single (7"): released on A&M, Oct'84 by A&M Records. Dist: Polygram

Single (12"): released on A&M, Oct'84 by A&M Records. Dist: Polygram

EMOTIONAL.
Tracks: / We belong to love / You should be mine / Soweto / In your eyes / Room with a view / Emotional / Second chance / Love's not ready / Who would have guessed / Come midnight.
Notes: 18 months in the making, 'Emotional' features the finest collection of songs yeton a Jeffrey Osborne album, including compositions by Jeffrey himself, Rod Temperton, Michael Masser, and showcasing the songwriting/production work oflong-time Osborne associate and hit maker George Duke (producer of all Jeffrey'sprevious hits). Other producers involved in this album are: Richard Perry (The Cars, Barbra Streisand etc.), Rod Temperton (writer of several tracks on MichaelJackson's 'Thriller' album) and Michael Masser (wrote Whitney Houston's 'Saving all my love for you). Ranging in tone from the instantly commercial pop/dance title track, through the classic ballad strains of 'You should be mine' (the newand first single to be taken from the album), to the political and contemporary track 'Soweto',the album features, in all, 10 superb songs.
Album: released on A&M, Jun'86 by A&M Records. Dist: Polygram

Cassette: released on A&M, Jun'86 by A&M Records. Dist: Polygram

Compact disc: released on A&M, Jun'86 by A&M Records. Dist: Polygram

JEFFREY OSBORNE.
Tracks: / New love / Eenie meenie / I really don't need no light / On the wings of love / Ready for your love / Who you talkin' to / You were made to love / Ain't nothin' missin' baby / Congratulations.
Album: released on A&M, Nov'85 by A&M Records. Dist: Polygram

Cassette: released on A&M, Nov'85 by A&M Records. Dist: Polygram

ON THE WINGS OF LOVE.
Single (7"): released on Funk America, Jan'83 by A&M Records. Dist: CBS

Single (12"): released on Funk America, Jan'83 by A&M Records. Dist: CBS

Single (7"): released on A&M, Jun'84 by A&M Records. Dist: Polygram

Single (12"): released on A&M, Jun'84 by A&M Records. Dist: Polygram Deleted '85.

ROCK ME, ROCK ME.
Album: released on Top Rank, Sep'86

ROOM WITH A VIEW.
Tracks: / Room with a view / Power, The.
Single (7"): released on A&M, Sep'86 by A&M Records. Dist: Polygram

Single (12"): released on A&M, Sep'86 by A&M Records. Dist: Polygram

SOWETO.
Tracks: / Soweto / Plain love.
Single (7"): released on A&M, Jul'86 by A&M Records. Dist: Polygram

Single (12"): released on A&M, Jul'86 by A&M Records. Dist: Polygram

STAY WITH ME TONIGHT.
Album: released on A&M, Aug'83 by A&M Records. Dist: Polygram

Cassette: released on A&M, Aug'83 by A&M Records. Dist: Polygram

Compact disc: released on A&M, Aug'83 by A&M Records. Dist: Polygram

Single (7"): released on A&M, Oct'83 by A&M Records. Dist: Polygram

Single (12"): released on A&M, Oct'83 by A&M Records. Dist: Polygram

YOU SHOULD BE MINE.
Tracks: / You should be mine / Eenie / Stay with me tonight *.
Single (7"): released on A&M, May'86 by A&M Records. Dist: Polygram

Single (12"): released on A&M, May'86 by A&M Records. Dist: Polygram

Osborne, Leroy

AIN'T NOTHING STRONGER THAN LOVE.
Single (7"): released on Excaliber, Jun'84 by Red Bus Records. Dist: PRT

Single (12"): released on Excaliber, Jun'84 by Red Bus Records. Dist: PRT

Osborne, Tony

NICE AND EASY LISTENING.
Cassette: released on AIM (Budget Cassettes), Feb'83

Osborne, Will

1936 (Osborne, Will & His Orchestra).
Album: released on Hindsight(USA), Mar'84 by Hindsight Records (USA). Dist: Swift, Charly

HALLELUJAH (Osborne, Will & His Orchestra).
Album: released on Golden Era, Jul'82 by Import Records. Dist: Wellard, Chris, Swift

Osbourne Brothers

SOME THINGS I WANT TO SING ABOUT.
Album: released on Sugarhill (USA), Mar'85 by PRT Records. Dist: PRT Distribution

Osbourne, Johnny

BABY I LOVE YOU.
Tracks: / Baby I love you / Gwan black hot summer.
Single (12"): released on Vibes & Vibes, Nov'86 by Vibes & Vibes Records. Dist: Jetstar

BABY LOVE.
Single (12"): released on Tads, May'84 by Tads Records. Dist: Jetstar Distribution

BACK OFF.
Single (12"): released on Greensleeves, May'81 by Greensleeves Records. Dist: BMG, Jetstar, Spartan

BEDTIME STORY.
Single (12"): released on D-Music, Jul'83 by D-Music Records. Dist: Jetstar

BRING THE SENSI COME.
Album: released on Midnight Rock, Oct'85 Dist: Jetstar Distribution, Kingdom Distribution

BRING YOUR DAUGHTER.
Single (12"): released on Tads, Dec'84 by Tads Records. Dist: Jetstar Distribution

CAN'T LEAVE JAH.
Single (12"): released on Black Joy, Aug'82 Dist: Jetstar

COME IN A DANCE.
Single (12"): released on Music Tab, Mar'85 by Music Tab Records. Dist: Jetstar Distribution

CROSS BREED.
Single (12"): released on D-Music, Jun'84 by D-Music Records. Dist: Jetstar

DANCING TIME.
Album: released on Londisc, Aug'84 by Londisc Records.

DO IT AGAIN.
Single (12"): released on Plantation, May'82 Dist: Jetstar

DON'T BITE THE HAND (Osbourne, Johnny & Aswad).
Single 10": released on Simba, Feb'83 by Simba Records. Dist: Jetstar

DON'T YOU KNOW THAT I LOVE YOU?.
Single (12"): released on D-Music, May'84 by D-Music Records. Dist: Jetstar

DUB PLATE PLAYING.
Single (12"): released on Greensleeves, Nov'86 by Greensleeves Records. Dist: BMG, Jetstar, Spartan

FALLY LOVER.
Album: released on Greensleeves, Nov'80 by Greensleeves Records. Dist: BMG, Jetstar, Spartan

FOR THE LONGEST TIME.
Single (12"): released on Tads, Jul'84 by Tads Records. Dist: Jetstar Distribution

GET CRACKING.
Single (12"): released on Londisc, Mar'84 by Londisc Records.

GROOVING.
Single (12"): released on Dancefloor, Jul'84 by Dancefloor Records. Dist: Vista Sounds Records, Jetstar

HERE I COME AGAIN.
Single (12"): released on Foundation, Dec'83 by Foundation Records, The. Dist: Jetstar

HILL AND GULLEY.
Single (12"): released on Moodies, Aug'87 Dist: Jetstar

I DON'T WANT TO BE LONELY.
Single (12"): released on Hawkeye, Sep'85 by Hawkeye Records. Dist: Hawkeye, Lightning (WEA) Distribution, Jetstar, PRT

IF JAH DIDN'T LOVE YOU.
Single (12"): released on Rockers Forever, May'85 Dist: Jetstar Distribution

IF YOU LOVE DE RUB-A-DUB SAY FORWARD.
Single (12"): released on Selection, Dec'83 by Selection Records. Dist: Jetstar

IN THE AREA.
Single (12"): released on Greensleeves, Dec'84 by Greensleeves Records. Dist: BMG, Jetstar, Spartan

JOHNNY OSBOURNE.
Album: released on Lix, Nov'84 by Lix Records. Dist: Jetstar

LEND ME A CHOPPER (Osbourne, Johnny & Pappa Tullo).
Single (12"): released on Starlight, Feb'83 by Starlight Records. Dist: Jetstar Distribution

MICHAEL PALMER MEETS JOHNNY OSBOURNE (Osbourne, Johnny & Michael Palmer).
Album: released on Vibes & Vibes, Nov'84 by Vibes & Vibes Records. Dist: Jetstar

NO SOUND LIKE WE.
Single (12"): released on Greensleeves, Nov'85 by Greensleeves Records. Dist: BMG, Jetstar, Spartan

ONE MORE RUB-A-DUB.
Single (12"): released on Tads, Jun'83 by Tads Records. Dist: Jetstar Distribution

ONE RUB-A-DUB FOR THE ROAD.
Single (12"): released on Top Rank, Mar'85

ORIGINAL REWIND, (THE).
Single (12"): released on Unity Sound, Apr'85 Dist: Jetstar

PUT IT BY NUMBER 1.
Single (12"): released on Unity, Jul'85 by Unity Records. Dist: Jetstar

QUASAI.
Single (12"): released on Cha-Cha, Dec'83 by Cha Cha. Dist: Jetstar

REALITY.
Album: released on Selection, Jan'85 by Selection Records. Dist: Jetstar

REGGAE ON BROADWAY.
Single (12"): released on Black Music, Nov'82 by Black Music Records. Dist: Jetstar

Album: released on Vista Sounds, Feb'84 by Vista Sounds Records. Dist: Jetstar

REWIND.
Single (12"): released on Jammy's, Sep'84 by Jammy's Records. Dist: Jetstar

ROCK-A-DUB.
Single (12"): released on Germaine, Oct'85 by Germaine Records. Dist: Jetstar

ROCK AND COME ON YA (Osbourne, Johnny & Pappa Tullo).
Single (12"): released on Black Joy, Jul'82 Dist: Jetstar

RUBADUB SOLDIER.
Album: released on Jammy's, Jul'85 by Jammy's Records. Dist: Jetstar

SHOW ME YOUR SIGN.
Tracks: / Show me your sign / Six for a nine.
Single (12"): released on Unity Sounds, Aug'86

T.K.O..
Single (12"): released on Roots Radical, May'83 by Roots Radical Records. Dist: Jetstar Distribution

TROUBLEMAKER.
Single (12"): released on Greensleeves, Nov'83 by Greensleeves Records. Dist: BMG, Jetstar, Spartan

UHURU IN DUB/OSBOURNE IN DUB (see Black Uhuru) (Osbourne, Johnny & Black Uhuru).

UPFRONT LOVER.
Single (7"): released on Top Rank, Oct'83

WATER PUMPING.
Album: released on Greensleeves, Jan'84 by Greensleeves Records. Dist: BMG, Jetstar, Spartan

Single (12"): released on CF, Aug'83 by CF Records. Dist: Jetstar

WIPE OUT APARTHEID.
Tracks: / Wipe out apartheid / Wipe out apartheid (version).
Single (12"): released on Top Rank, Feb'86

YO YO.
Single (12"): released on Oak Sound, Oct'82

Osbourne, Ozzy

BARK AT THE MOON.
Album: released on Epic, Dec'83 by CBS Records. Dist: CBS

Cassette: released on Epic, Dec'83 by CBS Records. Dist: CBS

BARK AT THE MOON.
Tracks: / Rock 'n' roll rebel / Bark at the moon / You're no different / Now you see it (now you don't) / Forever / So tired / Waiting for darkness / Spiders.
Album: released on Epic, Apr'86 by CBS Records. Dist: CBS

Cassette: released on Epic, Apr'86 by CBS Records. Dist: CBS

BLIZZARD OF OZ.
Compact disc:

CRAZY TRAIN.
Single (7"): released on Epic, 20 Jun'87 by CBS Records. Dist: CBS

Single (12"): released on Epic, 20 Jun'87 by CBS Records. Dist: CBS

DIARY OF A MADMAN.
Compact disc: released on Jet, May'87 by Jet Records. Dist: CBS

Album: released on Jet, Nov'81 by Jet Records. Dist: CBS

Cassette: released on Jet, Nov'81 by Jet Records. Dist: CBS

INTERVIEW PICTURE DISC.
Album: released on Baktabak, Jul'87 by Baktabak Records. Dist: Arabesque

SHOT IN THE DARK.
Tracks: / Shot in the dark / Rock 'n' roll rebel.
Single (7"): released on Epic, Jan'86 by CBS Records. Dist: CBS

Single (7"): released on Epic, Jan'86 by CBS Records. Dist: CBS

Single (12"): released on Epic, Jan'86 by CBS Records. Dist: CBS

SO TIRED.
Double-pack single: released on CBS, Mar'84 by CBS Records. Dist: CBS

Single (12"): released on CBS, Mar'84 by CBS Records. Dist: CBS

Single (7"): released on Epic, Jun'84 by CBS Records. Dist: CBS

Single (12"): released on Epic, Jun'84 by CBS Records. Dist: CBS

TALK OF THE DEVIL.
Tracks: / Sympton of the Universe / Snow blind / Black sabbath / Fairies wear boots / War pigs / Wizard, The / N.I.B / Sweatleaf / Never say die / Sabbath bloody sabbath / Iron man / Children of the grave / Paranoid.
Double Album: released on Jet, Nov'82 by Jet Records. Dist: CBS

Double cassette: released on Jet, Nov'82 by Jet Records. Dist: CBS

Album: released on Epic, Sep'87 by CBS Records. Dist: CBS

Cassette: released on Epic, Sep'87 by CBS Records. Dist: CBS

TRIBUTE.
Tracks: / I don't know / Crazy train / Believer / Mr.Crowley / Flying high again / Revelation (mother earth) / Steal away (the night) / Suicide solution / Iron man / Children of the grave / Paranoid / Goodbye to romance / No bone movies / Dee / Randy Rhoads studio outtakes.
Album: released on Epic, May'87 by CBS Records. Dist: CBS

Cassette: released on Epic, May'87 by CBS Records. Dist: CBS

TRIBUTE.
Compact disc: released on Epic, Jun'87 by CBS Records. Dist: CBS

ULTIMATE OZZY, THE.
Video-cassette (VHS): released on Virgin Video, May'87 by Virgin Records. Dist: EMI

ULTIMATE SIN.
Tracks: / Ultimate sin / Secret loser / Never know why / Thank God for the bomb / Never / Lightning strikes / Killer of giants / Fool like you / Shot in the dark.
Album: released on Epic, Feb'86 by CBS Records. Dist: CBS

Album: released on Epic, Feb'86 by CBS Records. Dist: CBS

Picture disc album: released on Epic, Aug'86 by CBS Records. Dist: CBS

Compact disc: released on CBS, Jul'86 by CBS Records. Dist: CBS

ULTIMATE SIN (SINGLE).
Tracks: / Ultimate sin / Lightning strikes (double).
Single (7"): released on Epic, Jul'86 by CBS Records. Dist: CBS

Oshama

HIGHWAY.
Single (12"): released on Smokey, Aug'82 Dist: Jetstar

O'Shamrock, Barney

IRISH ACCORDION, THE.
Tracks: / Slievenamon / Old flames / Doonaree / Rose of Tralee / Rose of Mooncoin / Wild colonial boy / Irish American medley / How to buy Killarney / Maggie / Fields of Athenry / Galway bay / Molly Malone / Bunch of thyme / Danny boy / Hanniganm's hooley.
Notes: Mail order address: Accodion Record Club, 146, Birmingham Road, Kidderminster, Worcs. DY10 2SL. Tel: 0562 746105.
Album: released on Accordion Record Club, Jul'86 by Accordion Record Club Records. Dist: Accordion Record Club

Cassette: released on Accordion Record Club, Jul'86 by Accordion Record Club Records. Dist: Accordion Record Club

Osibisa

BEST OF OSIBISA, (THE).
Album: released on MCA, Jul'82 by MCA Records. Dist: Polygram, MCA

Cassette: released on MCA, Jul'82 by MCA Records. Dist: Polygram, MCA

LIVE AT THE MARQUEE, 1983.
Album: released on Premier, '84 by Premier Records. Dist: CBS

Cassette: released on Premier, '84 by Premier Records. Dist: CBS

MYSTIC ENERGY.
Album: released on Calibre, Jan'81 by Calibre Records. Dist: PRT

Cassette: released on Calibre, Jan'81 by Calibre Records. Dist: PRT

OSIBISA UNLEASHED.
Album: released on Magnet, Jul'83 by Magnet Records. Dist: BMG

Cassette: released on Magnet, Jul'83 by Magnet Records. Dist: BMG

RAGHUPATI REGHAVA RAJA RAM.
Single (7"): released on AVM, Mar'83 Dist: PRT

WOOLY BULLY.
Single (7"): released on Sierra, Aug'85 by Sierra Records. Dist: WEA

Single (12"): released on Sierra, Aug'85 by Sierra Records. Dist: WEA

Osiris

WAR ON THE BULLS.
Single (12"): released on Cherry Red, Jun'86 by Cherry Red Records. Dist: Pinnacle

WAR ON THE BULLSHIT.
Album: released on Cherry Red, Nov'86 by Cherry Red Records. Dist: Pinnacle

Oskay, Bill

NIGHTNOISE (Oskay, Bill & Michael O'Domhnaill).
Album: released on Windham Hill (Germany), Dec'84

Osman, Sophie

WITH ALL MY HEART.
Tracks: / With all my heart / Come on (Charlie Brown).
Single (12"): released on Fresh, Nov'86 Dist: Jetstar

WITH ALL MY HEART (7").
Tracks: / With all my heart / Heavy heart.
Single (7"): released on Fresh, May'86 Dist: Jetstar

Osmond Brothers

I THINK ABOUT YOUR LOVIN'.
Single (7"): released on Range, Mar'85 Dist: PRT, Jetstar

TODAY.
Album: released on Range, Mar'85 Dist: PRT, Jetstar

Osmond, Marie

I ONLY WANTED YOU.
Tracks: / Cry just a little / I only wanted you / You're still new to me / Making magic / I know the feeling / Your love carries me away / We're gonna need a love song / New love / More than dancing / Everybody's crazy 'bout me baby.
Compact disc: released on Capitol, Feb'87 by Capitol Records. Dist: EMI

Album: released on Capitol, Oct'86 by Capitol Records. Dist: EMI

Cassette: released on Capitol, Oct'86 by Capitol Records. Dist: EMI

THERE'S NO STOPPING YOUR HEART.
Tracks: / There's no stopping your heart / Needing a night like this / Read my lips / Best of you / I'll be faithful to you / Meet me in Montana / That old devil moon / Love will find it's way to you / Until I fall in love again / Blue sky / Shinin'.
Notes: First UK solo album since Osmonds in early 70's. Contains US Country No.1 hit with Dan Seals 'Meet me in Montana'.
Album: by Capitol Records. Dist: EMI Deleted Feb'86.

Cassette: released on Capitol, Feb'86 by Capitol Records. Dist: EMI

THERE'S NO STOPPING YOUR HEART (7").
Tracks: / There's no stopping your heart / Love will find its way to you.
Single (7"): released on Capitol, Feb'86 by Capitol Records. Dist: EMI

Osmonds

OSMONDS' GREATEST HITS.
Cassette: released on Bravo, Feb'80 by Pickwick Records. Dist: Lugtons

Double Album: released on Polydor, Jan'78 by Polydor Records. Dist: Polygram, Polydor

Ossian

BORDERS.
Album: released on Iona, Jan'85 Dist: Folksound, Jazz Music, JSU, Swift, Celtic Music

Cassette: released on Iona, Jan'85 Dist: Folksound, Jazz Music, JSU, Swift, Celtic Music

OSSIAN.
Album: released on Springthyme, Oct'6 by Springthyme Records. Dist: Jazz Music Distribution, Projection Distribution, Roots Distribution

Cassette: released on Springthyme, Oct'6 by Springthyme Records. Dist: Jazz Music Distribution, Projection Distribution, Roots Distribution

Album: released on Springthyme, '83 by Springthyme Records. Dist: Folksound Distribution

Cassette: released on Springthyme, '83 by Springthyme Records. Dist: Folksound Distribution

SEAL SONG.
Album: released on Iona, Jul'81 Dist: Folksound, Jazz Music, JSU, Swift, Celtic Music

ST KILDA WEDDING.
Album: released on Iona, Apr'79 Dist: Folksound, Jazz Music, JSU, Swift, Celtic Music

Ossie, Count

MAN FROM HIGHER HEIGHTS (Ossie, Count & The Rasta Family).
Album: released on Vista Sounds, Jul'84 by Vista Sounds Records. Dist: Jetstar

Osterman Weekend

OSTERMAN WEEKEND Original soundtrack recording.
Album: released on TER, Mar'84 Dist: Pinnacle

Ostrogoth

DON'T POINT YOUR FINGER.
Album: released on Mausoleum, Jul'85 by Mausoleum Records. Dist: Pinnacle

ECSTASY AND DANGER.
Cassette: released on Mausoleum, May'84 by Mausoleum Records. Dist: Pinnacle

Album: released on Mausoleum, Mar'84 by Mausoleum Records. Dist: Pinnacle

FULL MOONS EYES.
Single (12"): released on Mausoleum, Aug'84 by Mausoleum Records. Dist: Pinnacle

Ostroushko, Peter

SLUZ DUZ MUSIC.
Album: released on Rounder (USA), Jul'85 Dist: Mike's Country Music Room Distribution, Jazz Music Distribution, Swift Distribution, Roots Records Distribution, Projection Distribution, Topic Distribution

Osu

LIGHT UP MY FIRE.
Single (7"): released on Shaka, Aug'84 by Shaka Records. Dist: Jetstar

O'Suilleabhain, Michael

DOLPHIN WAY, THE.
Album: released on Venture, Jul'87 Dist: Revolver, Cartel

Cassette: released on Venture, Jul'87 Dist: Revolver, Cartel

O'Sullevan, Peter

PETER O'SULLEVAN TALKS TUFF.
Album: released on Charisma, May'83 by Virgin Records. Dist: EMI

Cassette: released on Charisma, May'83 by Virgin Records. Dist: EMI

O'sullivan, Bernard & ...

CLARE CONCERTINAS.
Album: released on Free Reed, '81 by Free Reed Records. Dist: Roots, Projection, Hobgoblin Records, Oblivion

IRISH TRADITIONAL MUSIC OF COUNTY.
Album: released on Free Reed, '81 by Free Reed Records. Dist: Roots, Projection, Hobgoblin Records, Oblivion

O'Sullivan, Gilbert

16 GOLDEN CLASSICS.
Tracks: / Nothing rhymed / Matrimony / We will / No matter how I try / Alone again (naturally) / Clair / Get down / Ooh baby / Friend of mine, A / They've only themselves to blame / Where peaceful waters flow / Happiness is me and you / Why oh why oh why / I don't love you but I think I like you / Miss my love today / What's in a kiss.
Notes: All tracks licensed from Gilbert O'Sullivan: Design by Shoot that Tiger! (C) 1986 Castle Communications Place, Unit 7, 271, Merton Road, London SW18 5JS Bar code: 5\013428\920046.
Album: released on Unforgettable, Dec'86 by Castle Communications Records. Dist: Counterpoint

Cassette: released on Unforgettable, Dec'86 by Castle Communications Records. Dist: Counterpoint

Compact disc: released on Unforgettable, '86 by Castle Communications Records. Dist: Counterpoint

20 GOLDEN GREATS.
Album: released on K-Tel, Sep'81 by K-Tel Records. Dist: Record Merchandisers Distribution, Taylors, Terry Blood Distribution, Wynd-Up Distribution, Relay Distribution, Pickwick Distribution, Solomon & Peres Distribution, Polygram

Cassette: released on K-Tel, Sep'81 by K-Tel Records. Dist: Record Merchandisers Distribution, Taylors, Terry Blood Distribution, Wynd-Up Distribution, Relay Distribution, Pickwick Distribution, Solomon & Peres Distribution, Polygram

20 GOLDEN PIECES OF GILBERT O'SULLIVAN.
Album: released on Bulldog, Oct'85 by Bulldog Records. Dist: President Distribution, Spartan, Swift, Taylor, H.R.

Cassette: released on Bulldog, Oct'85 by Bulldog Records. Dist: President Distribution, Spartan, Swift, Taylor, H.R.

20 OF THE VERY BEST.
Album: released on Hallmark, Sep'81 by Pickwick Records. Dist: Pickwick Distribution, PRT, Taylors

Cassette: released on Hallmark, Sep'81 by Pickwick Records. Dist: Pickwick Distribution, PRT, Taylors

CLAIRE/ALONE AGAIN.
Single (7"): released on Old Gold, Jul'82 by Old Gold Records. Dist: Lightning, Jazz Music, Spartan, Counterpoint

COLLECTION: GILBERT O'SULLIVAN.
Notes: Double LP.
Album: released on Network, Nov'85 by Epic. Dist: PRT, CBS

Cassette: released on Network, Nov'85 by Epic. Dist: PRT, CBS

GET DOWN/NOTHING RHYMED.
Single (7"): released on Old Gold, Jul'82 by Old Gold Records. Dist: Lightning, Jazz Music, Spartan, Counterpoint

GILBERT O'SULLIVAN.
Double cassette: released on Cambra, Jan'82 by Cambra Records. Dist: IDS, Conifer

GILBERT O'SULLIVAN GREATEST HITS.
Album: released on M.A.M., Nov'76 by M.A.M. Records. Dist: T.B.C

I LOVE IT BUT/HELP IS ON THE WAY.
Single (7"): released on CBS, Nov'80 by CBS Records. Dist: CBS

OFF CENTRE.
Album: released on CBS, Nov'80 by CBS Records. Dist: CBS

Cassette:

SPOTLIGHT ON GILBERT O'SULLIVAN.
Double Album: released on PRT, '80 by PRT Records. Dist: PRT

Double cassette: released on PRT, '80 by PRT Records. Dist: PRT

VERY BEST OF GILBERT O'SULLIVAN, THE.
Album: released on Hallmark, Sep'84 by Pickwick Records. Dist: Pickwick Distribution, PRT, Taylors

Cassette: released on Hallmark, Sep'84 by Pickwick Records. Dist: Pickwick Distribution, PRT, Taylors

OTB

OUT OF THE BLUE.
Tracks: / RH factor / Eastern love village / Output / Reunited / Git in there / Blue Hughes / OTB.
Notes: OTB is a group of young players, who are already astounding audiences and critics with their expertise. Directly as a result of the Blue Note tradition of bringing together outstanding instrumentalists in an ensemble form, they delivera highly effective debut album which contains all original material and reinterprets the jazz basics that is their grounding in a new and very exciting way.
Album: released on Blue Note, Dec'85 by EMI Records. Dist: EMI

Cassette: released on Blue Note, Dec'85 by EMI Records. Dist: EMI

Othermothers

NO PLACE LIKE HOME.
Album: released on Spindrift, Nov'85 Dist: Roots

Other Ones

HOLIDAY.
Tracks: / Holiday / Another holiday / Jackson".
Single (12"): released on Virgin, Jul'87 by Virgin Records. Dist: EMI, Virgin Distribution

Single (12"): released on Virgin, Jul'87 by Virgin Records. Dist: EMI, Virgin Distribution

OTHER ONES.
Tracks: / Another holiday / Stay with me / We are what we are / Losing it / Moments / He's a man / All the love / All day all night / Makes me higher / Stranger.
Album: released on Virgin, Feb'87 by Virgin Records. Dist: EMI, Virgin Distribution

Cassette: released on Virgin, Feb'87 by Virgin Records. Dist: EMI, Virgin Distribution

Compact disc: released on Virgin, Feb'87 by Virgin Records. Dist: EMI, Virgin Distribution

WE ARE WHAT WE ARE.
Tracks: / We are what we are / Dark ages.
Single (7"): released on Virgin, Jan'87 by Virgin Records. Dist: EMI, Virgin Distribution

Single (12"): released on Virgin, Jan'87 by Virgin Records. Dist: EMI, Virgin Distribution

Other People

HAVE A NICE DAY.
Single (7"): released on Arcadia, Dec'84 Dist: Cartel

Single (12"): released on Arcadia, Dec'84 Dist: Cartel

Other Reggae Superstars

OTHER REGGAE SUPERSTARS, THE Various artists (Various Artists).
Album: released on Vista Sounds, '83 by Vista Sounds Records. Dist: Jetstar

Other side of Nashville

OTHER SIDE OF NASHVILLE (Various Artists).
Notes: Artists include: Kenny Rogers, Johnny Cash, Kris Kristofferson, Emmylou Harris, Willie Nelson, Charlie Daniels, Hank Williams Jr, Carl Perkins, Bobby Bare, Rattlesnake Annie, Charlie McCoy, Ricky Skaggs, Gail Davies, Terri Gibbs, Donny Quails, Porter Waggoner, and introducing Owen Davis. A fascinating look inside Nashville as seen through the eyes of the stars who've made it one the greatest centres of the music world. The music makers who've shaped the Nashville sounds, talking frankly about their own livesbehind the scenes - breaking in, life on the road, how the music's changing and what it takes to make it in Nashville. The other side of Nashville is jam packedwith original concert footage. Willie Nelson performing "Always on my mind", Johnny Cash's "Fulsom prison blues", Emmy-

Page 754

lou Harris with Springsteen's "racing in the streets",Kenny Rogers "The gambler", "Will the circle be unbroken" by Charlie Daniels and many more.
In rare footage, Bob Dylan and Johnny Cash record together, Carl (The father of rock 'n' roll) Perkins belts out "Blue suede shoes" and Hank Williams Sr shows you why he became a legend in his own time. The music that's touched the lives of millions - all or part of over 37 great songs, and the truestories behind the sounds. You'll find it all on The Other Side Of Nashville. Total playing time: 112 minutes.
Video-cassette (VHS): released on MGM Sep'86 Dist: Polygram Distribution, Swift Distribution

Video-cassette [Betamax]: released on MGM, Sep'86 Dist: Polygram Distribution, Swift Distribution

Otis, Byron
BRING BACK MY BABY.
Single (12"): released on Ital, Mar'82 Dist: Pinnacle

MISSING YOUR LOVE.
Album: released on Clarendon Sounds, Jun'86 by Clarendon Sounds. Dist: Jetstar

SO YOU SAY.
Single (12"): released on Shashanane, '82

Otis & Carla
TRAMP/OOH OTIS OOH CARLA.
Single (12"): released on Atlantic, Apr'80 by WEA Records. Dist: WEA

Otis, Johnny
GREAT RHYTHM AND BLUES VOL 3.
Album: released on Bulldog, Jul'82 by Bulldog Records. Dist: President Distribution, Spartan, Swift, Taylor, H.R.

INTO THE EIGHTIES.
Tracks: / Rock and roll wedding / Stand by me / Love (makes me do foolish things) / Hit that jive, jack rollin' / Do it again, baby / In the still of the night / Hide away / Will you love me tomorrow / Soothe me baby / When something is wrong with my baby / I found you / Fine and mellow / I'm gonna leave these women alone.
Album: released on Charly, May'86 by Charly Records. Dist: Charly, Cadillac

JOHNNY OTIS SHOW, THE.
Album: released on Capitol (France), '83 by Capitol Records. Dist: Conifer

MA, HE'S MAKING EYES AT ME (Otis, Johnny Show).
Tracks: / Ma, he's making eyes at me / Fever.
Notes: Also contains:"Fever" by Peggy Lee
Single (12"): released on Old Gold, Apr'87 by Old Gold Records. Dist: Lightning, Jazz Music, Spartan, Counterpoint

NEW JOHNNY OTIS SHOW, THE.
Album: released on Alligator, Feb'82 Dist: Jetstar

ORIGINAL JOHNNY OTIS SHOW, THE.
Album: released on Savoy, Mar'85

ORIGINAL JOHNNY OTIS VOL 2, THE.
Album:

REASON WHY/SECRET AGENT.
Single (7"): released on Sonet, Jun'83 by Sonet Records. Dist: PRT

ROCK AND ROLL HIT PARADE.
Album: released on Flyright (USA), Oct'79 by Flyright Records. Dist: Swift, Jazz Music, Wellard, Chris, Cadillac

ROCK'N'ROLL REVUE.
Tracks: / Shake it Lucy baby / Willie and the hand jive / Bye bye baby / Light still shines (The) / Tell me so / Telephone baby / Mumblin' music / Good golly / Ma, he's makin' eyes at me / Crazy country hop / Hum ding a ling / You just kissed me goodbye / In the dark / Can't you hear me callin' / Castin' my spell.
Album: released on Charly, Mar'82 by Charly Records. Dist: Charly, Cadillac

SNATCH AND THE POONTANGS.
Album: released on Snatch, Oct'86 by Charly Records. Dist: Charly

Otitis
FOUR O'CLOCK ROCK/THAILAND.
Single (7"): released on Sonet, Jan'83 by Sonet Records. Dist: PRT

NEANDERTHAL MAN/BOY.
Single (7"): released on Sonet, Dec'83 by Sonet Records. Dist: PRT

NEXT TIME.
Single (7"): released on Sonet, Nov'83 by Sonet Records. Dist: PRT

Otito
TRUTH, (THE) (see Ade, King Sunny) (Otito/King Sunny Ade).

O'Toole, Shameless
ALBERT & MARY/FOREVER(STU STEVENS).
Single (7"): released on Crazy Viking, Aug'83 by Crazy Vikings Records. Dist: Pinnacle

Ottawa
CRAZY MUSIC/SHALALA SONG.
Single (7"): released on Carrere, Mar'83 by Carrere Records. Dist: PRT, Spartan

Single (12"): released on Carrere, Mar'83 by Carrere Records. Dist: PRT, Spartan

D.I.S.C.O/HANDS UP.
Single (7"): released on Carrere, Mar'85 by Carrere Records. Dist: PRT, Spartan

Single (12"): released on Carrere, Mar'85 by Carrere Records. Dist: PRT, Spartan

D.I.S.C.O./YOU'RE OK.
Single (7"): released on Carrere, Sep'80 by Carrere Records. Dist: PRT, Spartan

Single (12"): released on Carrere, Sep'80 by Carrere Records. Dist: PRT, Spartan

OTTAWAN.
Album: released on Carrere, Oct'80 by Carrere Records. Dist: PRT, Spartan

OTTAWAN(4TRACK EP).
Cassette: released on Carrere, May'83 by Carrere Records. Dist: PRT, Spartan

Otte, Hans
DAS BUCH DER KLANGE.
Compact disc: released on Kuckuck (Germany), '86

Otters
OTTERS FIRST SONG COLLECTION.
Tracks: / Hallo there hi / One cat, two cats / Another alphabet song / Keep on dancing / Excuse me, please / We met on sunday / Yellow banana / Barn dance / London bridge / I like food / Seasons / In my room / What's that thing / Pets / Otter rag / Barn dance (reprise).
Notes: Lyrics: David Stoll and Michael Hinton. Music: David Stoll. A tape of original songs for foreign learners of English, particularly children. The tape is sold accompanied by a workbook.
Cassette: released on Otter Sound, Oct'85

Otto's chemical lounge
SPILLOVER.
Album: released on Homestead, Jul'85 Dist: Rough Trade, Cartel, Shigaku

Ottowan
HANDS UP.
Single (7"): released on Carrere, Aug'81 by Carrere Records. Dist: PRT, Spartan

Single (12"): released on Carrere, Aug'81 by Carrere Records. Dist: PRT, Spartan

OTTAWAN'S GREATEST HITS.
Album: released on Carrere, Nov'81 by Carrere Records. Dist: PRT, Spartan

Cassette: released on Carrere, Nov'81 by Carrere Records. Dist: PRT, Spartan

Otway, John
ALL BALLS AND NO WILLY.
Album: released on Empire, Jul'82 by Empire Records. Dist: Backs, Cartel, Jetstar

DEEP AND MEANINGLESS (Otway, John & Wild Billy Barrett).
Album: released on Polydor, May'78 by Polydor Records. Dist: Polygram, Polydor

GONE WITH THE BIN OR THE BEST OF OTWAY AND BARRETT (Otway, John & Willy Barrett).
Album: released on Polydor, Aug'81 by Polydor Records. Dist: Polygram, Polydor

Cassette: released on Polydor, Aug'81 by Polydor Records. Dist: Polygram, Polydor

GREATEST HITS:JOHN OTWAY.
Album:

Cassette:

GREATEST HITS: JOHN OTWAY.
Cassette: released on Strikeback, Aug'87 by Strikeback Records. Dist: Rough Trade

GREEN GREEN GRASS OF HOME.
Single (7"): released on Stiff, Oct'80 by Stiff Records. Dist: EMI, Record Services Distribution

HEAD BUTTS.
Single (7"): released on Empire, Aug'82 by Empire Records. Dist: Backs, Cartel, Jetstar

IN DREAMS.
Single (7"): released on Empire, Oct'82 by Empire Records. Dist: Backs, Cartel, Jetstar

pire Records. Dist: Backs, Cartel, Jetstar

JOHN OTWAY & WILD WILLY BARRETT (Otway, John & Wild Billy Barrett).
Album: released on Polydor, Aug'77 by Polydor Records. Dist: Polygram, Polydor

MASS COMMUNICATION.
Single (7"): released on Empire, May'83 by Empire Records. Dist: Backs, Cartel, Jetstar

MIDDLE OF WINTER.
Single (7"): released on Strikeback, Dec'84 by Strikeback Records. Dist: Rough Trade
Cat. no: SBR 1

NEW JERUSALEM.
Tracks: / New Jerusalem / Tyger, The.
Single (7"): released on WEA, Nov'86 by WEA Records. Dist: WEA

TURNING POINT.
Single (7"): released on Stiff, Apr'81 by Stiff Records. Dist: EMI, Record Services Distribution (Ireland)

WAY AND BAR (Otway, John & Wild Billy Barrett).
Notes: Featuring Lol Coxhill.
Album: released on Polydor, Oct'86 by Polydor Records. Dist: Polygram, Polydor

WHERE DID I GO RIGHT.
Album: released on Polydor, Apr'79 by Polydor Records. Dist: Polygram, Polydor

WHOOPS APOCALYPSE.
Tracks: / Losing.
Single (7"): released on WEA, Mar'87 by WEA Records. Dist: WEA

Single (12"): released on WEA, Mar'87 by WEA Records. Dist: WEA

O-Two-One
POP SONG.
Single (7"): released on UK Pop, Sep'82

Ouba
BEST IS YET TO COME.
Tracks: / Best is yet to come, The / Storm before the calm.
Single (7"): released on Capitol, May'86 by Capitol Records. Dist: EMI

Oui
IS THAT ALL THERE IS.
Single (7"): released on Jet, Sep'83 by Jet Records. Dist: CBS

Our Daughters Wedding
AUTO MUSIC.
Single (7"): released on EMI, Aug'82 by EMI Records. Dist: EMI

Single (12"): released on EMI, Aug'82 by EMI Records. Dist: EMI

Our folk heritage
OUR FOLK HERITAGE Various artists (Various Artists).
Album: released on Leader, '81 Dist: Jazz Music, Projection

Our Heroes
NOW THE SCARS ARE HEALING.
Single (12"): released on Icon, Oct'84 by Icon Records. Dist: IKF, Cartel

Our Kate
OUR KATE Cookson, Catherine (Blakiston, Caroline).
Double cassette: released on Listen For Pleasure, '83 by MFP Records. Dist: EMI

Our man in Tokyo
SET UP.
Single (7"): released on Shakev Joe, May'82

Our tune
OUR TUNE (Various Artists).
Tracks: / Sad songs / Romeo & Juliet / Sub ain't gonna shine anymore / I will survive / Look of love, The / Can't give you anything / Slave to love / I'm not in love / Head over heels / Cherish / You've lost that lovin' feeling / I guess that's why they call it the blues / How deep is your love / Nights in white satin / Leaving me now / Jealous guy.
Album: released on Polydor, Oct'86 by Polydor Records. Dist: Polygram, Polydor

Cassette: released on Polydor, Oct'86 by Polydor Records. Dist: Polygram, Polydor

Compact disc: released on Polydor, Oct'86 by Polydor Records. Dist: Polygram, Polydor

Ousley, Harold
SWEET DOUBLE HIPNESS.
Single (7"): released on Muse, May'82 by Peerless Records. Dist: Lugtons Distributors

Out
BETTER THE DEVIL.
Single (7"): released on Cargo, Jul'81 Dist: Rough Trade

TOUGH ENOUGH.
Single (12"): released on Illuminated, Feb'85 by IKF Records. Dist: Pinnacle, Cartel, Jetstar

WHO IS INNOCENT.
Single (7"): released on Rabid, Sep'82 by Rabid Records. Dist: Pinnacle, Rough Trade

Outbar
AWAY FROM THE HEART.
Tracks: / Away from the heart / Gate gate.
Single (7"): released on EMI, Sep'86 by EMI Records. Dist: EMI

Single (12"): released on EMI, Sep'86 by EMI Records. Dist: EMI

WHEN THE BAD MEN COME (HAKI-BO SADO-BO).
Tracks: / When the bad men come (Haki-bo sado-bo) / When the bad men come etc. (Inst).
Single (7"): released on EMI, May'86 by EMI Records. Dist: EMI

Single (12"): released on EMI, May'86 by EMI Records. Dist: EMI

Out Bar Squeek
AWAY FROM THE HEAT.
Single (7"): released on EMI, Sep'84 by EMI Records. Dist: EMI

Single (12"): released on EMI, Sep'84 by EMI Records. Dist: EMI

DISCO EDDIE.
Single (7"): released on EMI, Jun'84 by EMI Records. Dist: EMI

Single (12"): released on EMI, Jun'84 by EMI Records. Dist: EMI

Outcasts
1969.
Single (7"): released on New Rose, Jul'85 Dist: Rough Trade, Cartel

ANGEL FACE/GANGLAND WARFARE.
Single (7"): released on Outcasts only, Jun'82

BLOOD AND THUNDER.
Album: released on Abstract, Jan'83 by Abstract. Dist: Pinnacle

JUST ANOTHER TEENAGE REBEL.
Single (7"): released on Good Vibration, Aug'79 by Good Vibrations Records. Dist: Pinnacle, Rough Trade

NOWHERE LEFT TO RUN/RUNNINGS OVER.
Single (7"): released on Abstract, Jun'83 by Abstract. Dist: Pinnacle

Single (12"): released on Abstract, Jun'83 by Abstract. Dist: Pinnacle

NOWHERE LEFT TO RUN/RUNNINGS OVER/RUBY.
Single (7"): released on Anagram, Sep'83 by Cherry Red Records. Dist: Pinnacle

Single (12"): released on Anagram, Sep'83 by Cherry Red Records. Dist: Pinnacle

SELF CONCIOUS OVER YOU.
Single (7"): released on Good Vibration, Nov'79 by Good Vibrations Records. Dist: Pinnacle, Rough Trade

SEVEN DEADLY SINS.
Single (7"): released on New Rose, Aug'84 Dist: Rough Trade, Cartel

Album: released on New Rose, Aug'84 Dist: Rough Trade, Cartel

Outcasts Only
PROGRAMME LOVE.
Single (7"): released on Outcast, Nov'81

Outer Limits
CHASE, (THE).
Single (7"): released on SD, Sep'84 by SD Records. Dist: Backs, Cartel

CRUISIN'.
Single (12"): released on Sir George, Jul'85 by Sir George Records. Dist: Jetstar, Pinnacle

EDGE OF TIME.
Single (12"): released on Dog Rock, Jul'85 by Dog Rock Records. Dist: Backs, Cartel

Outfield
ALL THE LOVE IN THE WORLD (II).
Tracks: / All the love in the world / Mystery man.

Single (7"): released on CBS, Sep'86 by CBS Records. Dist: CBS

ALL THE LOVE IN THE WORLD.
Tracks: / All the love in the world / Taking my chance.
Single (7"): released on CBS, Aug'86 by CBS Records. Dist: CBS

Single (12"): released on CBS, Aug'86 by CBS Records. Dist: CBS

BANGIN'.
Tracks: / Somewhere in America / Bangin' on my heart / No surrender / Moving target / Long way home / Playground / Alone with you / Main attraction / Better than nothing / Since you've been gone.
Album: released on CBS, Sep'87 by CBS Records. Dist: CBS

Cassette: released on CBS, Sep'87 by CBS Records. Dist: CBS

Compact disc: released on CBS, Sep'87 by CBS Records. Dist: CBS

PLAY DEEP.
Tracks: / Say it isn't so / Your love / I don't need her / Everytime you cry / 61 seconds / Mystery man / All the love in the world / Talk to me / Taking my chances / Nervous alibi.
Album: released on CBS, Nov'86 by CBS Records. Dist: CBS

Cassette: released on CBS, Nov'86 by CBS Records. Dist: CBS

Compact disc: released on CBS, Nov'86 by CBS Records. Dist: CBS

SINCE YOU'VE BEEN GONE.
Tracks: / Since you've been gone / Better than nothing.
Single (7"): released on CBS, Jul'87 by CBS Records. Dist: CBS

Single (12"): released on CBS, Jul'87 by CBS Records. Dist: CBS

YOUR LOVE.
Tracks: / Your love / 61 seconds / Mystery man.
Single (7"): released on CBS, Apr'86 by CBS Records. Dist: CBS

Single (12"): released on CBS, May'86 by CBS Records. Dist: CBS

Outland

OUTLAND Original film soundtrack.
Album: released on Warner Brothers, Jul'81 by Warner Bros Records. Dist: WEA

Outlaw Blues

OUTLAW BLUES Music from the film soundtrack.
Album: released on Capitol, Nov'77 by Capitol Records. Dist: EMI

Outlaws

BRING IT BACK ALIVE.
Double Album: released on Arista, Apr'78 by Arista Records. Dist: RCA

HURRY SUNDOWN.
Album: released on Arista, May'77 by Arista Records. Dist: RCA

IN THE EYE OF THE STORM.
Album: released on Arista, Jan'80 by Arista Records. Dist: RCA

LADY IN WAITING.
Album: released on Arista, May'76 by Arista Records. Dist: RCA

LOS HOMBRES MALO.
Album: released on Arista (USA), Jun'82

ON THE RUN AGAIN.
Tracks: / Ghost riders in the sky / Green grass and high tides / There goes another love song / You are the show / Stick around for Rock 'n' Roll / Stick around for Rock 'n' Roll / I can't stop loving you / Devil's Road / Real good feelin', A / Breaker-breaker / Lover boy / Foxtail Lily.
Notes: All tracks from RCA\Ariola Ltd. (C) 1986\castle Communications Place, Unit 7, 271, merton Road London SW18 5JS: Bar Code 5\013428\140284.
Album: released on Raw Power, Dec'86 Dist: Pinnacle

Cassette: released on Raw Power, Dec'86 Dist: Pinnacle

OUTLAWS.
Compact disc: by RCA Records. Dist: RCA, Roots, Swift, Wellard, Chris, I & B, Solomon & Peres Distribution

Album: by Arista Records. Dist: RCA

Compact disc: released on RCA, Sep'85 by RCA Records. Dist: RCA, Roots, Swift, Wellard, Chris, I & B, Solomon & Peres Distribution

PLAYING TO WIN.
Album: released on Arista, '78 by Arista Records. Dist: RCA

SOLDIERS OF FORTUNE.
Tracks: / One last ride / Soldiers of fortune / Night cries (The) / Outlaw (The) / Cold harbour / Whatcha don't do / Just the way I like it / Saved by the bell / Lady luck / Racin' for the red light.
Album: released on Epic, Feb'87 by CBS Records. Dist: CBS

Cassette: released on Epic, Feb'87 by CBS Records. Dist: CBS

Out now

OUT NOW: 28 HOT HITS Various artists (Various Artists).
Album: released on Chrysalis-MCA, May'85 by Chrysalis Records. Dist: CBS

Cassette: released on Chrysalis-MCA, May'85 by Chrysalis Records. Dist: CBS

OUT NOW: VOL 2 Various artists (Various Artists).
Album: released on Chrysalis-MCA, Oct'85 by Chrysalis Records. Dist: CBS

Cassette: released on Chrysalis-MCA, Oct'85 by Chrysalis Records. Dist: CBS

Outnumbered

HOLDING THE GRENADE TO LONG.
Album: released on Homestead, Jun'86 Dist: Rough Trade, Cartel, Shigaku

WHY ARE ALL THE GOOD PEOPLE GOING CRAZY?.
Album: released on Homestead, May'85 Dist: Rough Trade, Cartel, Shigaku

Out Of Africa

OUT OF AFRICA (Blixen, Karen).
Notes: Read by Geraldine James. Another major film this year was'Out of Africa' featuring Meryl Streep & Robert Redford.This delightful story was taken from the book of the same name by Karen Blixen.'Out of Africa' is the autobiographical story of Karen Blixen's time in Africa managing a coffee plantation.
Double cassette: released on Listen For Pleasure, Nov'86 by MFP Records. Dist: EMI

OUT OF AFRICA Original soundtrack (Various Artists).
Tracks: / I had a farm in Africa (main title) / I'm better at hello (Karen's theme I) / Have you got a story for me / Concerto for clarinet in A (K 622) / Safari / Karen's journey / Siyawe / Flying over Africa / I had a compass from Denys (Karen's theme II) / Alone on the farm / Let the rest of the world go by / If I know a song from Africa (Karen's theme III) / You are Karen (end theme).
Notes: John Barry's music for Sidney Pollack's "Out of Africa" is as timelessand hauntingly beautiful as the Kenyan landscapes that dominate this film based on the famed novels of Izak Dinesen and this Danish writer's life on an African coffee plantation in the early part of the century. Starring Meryl Streep and Robert Redford in the major roles. John Barry's emotive score is complimented bythe brilliant vocal peformances of Melissa Manchester and Al Jarreau in the song"The music of goodbye", the album's musical highlight.
Album: released on MCA, Mar'86 by MCA Records. Dist: Polygram, MCA

Cassette: released on MCA, Mar'86 by MCA Records. Dist: Polygram, MCA

Compact disc: released on MCA, '86 by MCA Records. Dist: Polygram, MCA

Out Of Bad Luck

OUT OF BAD LUCK (Various Artists).
Tracks: / Out of bad luck / Every night about this time / Blue light boogie / It's like heaven to me / Honky tonk / I swing 'em the way I feel / I feel so good / Heavy heart beat / Good things / Too many cooks / Crossroads / My baby's sweet / Ouch / I'd rather fight than switch.
Album: released on Flyright, Oct'86 by Flyright Records. Dist: Krazy Kat, Swift, Jazz Music

Out of the blue

HOW MUCH IS THAT DOGGY IN THE WINDOW.
Single (7"): released on PRT, Nov'82 by PRT Records. Dist: PRT

INSIDE TRACK.
Tracks: / Inside track / Cherry Pickens / Hot house / E force / Nathan Jones / Isolation / Elevation.
Compact disc: released on EMI, Mar'87 by EMI Records. Dist: EMI

LIVE AT MT.FUJI.
Tracks: / Parisian thoroughfare, A / Blue pearl / Nathan Jones / Elevation / OTB.
Album: released on Manhattan-Blue Note, Jul'87 by EMI America Records (USA). Dist: EMI

OUT OF THE BLUE Various artists (Various Artists).
Tracks: / I'll make the living if you make the loving worthwhile / It's cool / L.A. nights / Oh darlin' / Share my love with you / I'll never love the same way twice / Rose of Sharon / One more time.
Album: released on Ambient Sound, Apr'85

Album: released on Bluebird, Sep'87 by Bluebird Records. Dist: EMI, Jetstar

Out Of The Box

OUT OF THE BOX (Various Artists).
Notes: Artists include: Billy Ocean, Warren Mills, Hugh Masekela.
Album: released on Jive, Nov'85 by Zomba Records. Dist: RCA, PRT, CBS

Cassette: released on Jive, Nov'85 by Zomba Records. Dist: RCA, PRT, CBS

Out of the unknown

OUT OF THE UNKNOWN.
Album: released on Peninsula, Feb'84 by Prism Records. Dist: Various Distribution

Out of this world

OUT OF THIS WORLD.
Album: by BBC Records & Tapes. Dist: EMI, PRT, Pye

Out on the floor tonight

OUT ON THE FLOOR TONIGHT Various artists (Various Artists).
Album: released on Inferno, Apr'80 by Inferno Records. Dist: Inferno, Cartel, Pinnacle

Outram, Ken

PLAYS THE HAMMOND COMMODORE.
Album: released on Grosvenor, Jul'86 by Grosvenor Records. Dist: Taylors

Outside Edge

HEARTBEAT AWAY.
Tracks: / Heartbeat away / Out of my head / Soldier boy.
Single (7"): released on 10, Mar'86 by 10 Records. Dist: Virgin, EMI

Single (12"): released on 10, Mar'86 by 10 Records. Dist: Virgin, EMI

RUNNING HOT.
Album: released on 10, May'86 by 10 Records. Dist: Virgin, EMI

Cassette: released on 10, May'86 by 10 Records. Dist: Virgin, EMI

Outsider - 20 years on

OUTSIDER - 20 YEARS ON Wilson, Colin (Wilson, Colin).
Cassette: released on Seminar Cassettes, Oct'81 by Seminar Cassettes. Dist: Davidson Distribution, Eastern Educational Products Distrib., Forlaget Systime Distribution, Laser Books Ltd Distribution, MacDougall Distribution, Talktapes Distribution, Watkins Books Ltd Distribution, Norton, Jeff Distribution

Outsiders

THAT CAR.
Single (7"): released on Impact, Aug'82 by Ace Records. Dist: Rough Trade, Pinnacle, Swift, Backs, Counterpoint, Jungle, Hotshot, Cartel

Outskirts

DOWN.
Tracks: / Down.
Extended-play record: released on Glass, May'86 by Glass Records. Dist: Nine Mile, Rough Trade, Red Rhino, Play It Again Sam

HEAVEN'S ON THE MOVE.
Album: released on Glass, Sep'85 by Glass Records. Dist: Nine Mile, Rough Trade, Red Rhino, Play It Again Sam

TOO BAD.
Tracks: / Too bad.
Single (7"): released on Glass, Mar'86 by Glass Records. Dist: Nine Mile, Rough Trade, Red Rhino, Play It Again Sam

Outta Place

WE'RE THE OUTTA PLACE.
Album: released on Midnight, Nov'84

Out west at Berkeley

OUT WEST AT BERKELEY Various artists (Various Artists).
Album: released on Arhoolie, May'81 by Arhoolie Records. Dist: Projection, Topic, Jazz Music, Swift, Roots

Ova

OUT OF BOUNDS.
Tracks: / Self-defence / Madness of a memory / Helium ballon / Walking in mercury / Nuclear madness / We can share our visions / Rainbowomon / Bloodstream / Auto-Erotic blues / Full moonlight Dance / Either gives in / Neither gives in.
Album: released on Stroppy Cow, '82 by stroppy cow records. Dist: WRPM Distribution

OVA.
Tracks: / I can see the dream / Rock 'n' Roll fever / Woman at the crossroads / Little girls / Voci 01 Donne / Lesbian fighting song / Offer that decision / Woman behind bars / Early in the evening.
Album: released on Stroppy Cow, '78 by stroppy cow records. Dist: WRPM Distribution

POSSIBILITIES.
Tracks: / Moving inside / Tidal dream / Possibilities / Travelling spirit / Granny song / Language for lovers / Far beyond the dawn / Happy drumming / Earthquake.
Album: released on Stroppy Cow, '84 by stroppy cow records. Dist: WRPM Distribution

Album: released on Stroppy Cow, May'85 Dist: Rough Trade Distribution, Cartel Distribution, WRPM Distribution

Ovaltineys

HAPPY DAYS ARE HERE AGAIN.
Single (7"): released on CJMO, Oct'80 Dist: Jazz Music, Spartan, Taylors

OVALTINEYS SING YOUR ALL-TIME FAVOURITES.
Album: released on CJMO, Nov'80 Dist: Jazz Music, Spartan, Taylors

Ovation

LOVE WILL GROW AGAIN.
Single (7"): released on Small Run, May'83 by Small Run Records. Dist: Pinnacle

OVATION Best of Andrew Lloyd Webber, The (Various Artists).
Tracks: / Don't cry for me Argentina / Another suitcase in another hall / I don't know how to love him / Take that look off your face / Tell me on a Sunday / King Herods sona / One more angel in heaven / Pumping iron / Starlight expres / Pie Jesu / Old deuteronomy / Introduction: variations.
Compact disc: released on K-Tel, Nov'86 by K-Tel Records. Dist: Record Merchandisers Distribution, Taylors, Terry Blood Distribution, Wynd-Up Distribution, Relay Distribution, Pickwick Distribution, Solomon & Peres Distribution, Polygram

OVATION: THE BEST OF ANDREW LLOYD WEBBER Various artists (Various Artists).
Album: released on K-Tel, Nov'85 by K-Tel Records. Dist: Record Merchandisers Distribution, Taylors, Terry Blood Distribution, Wynd-Up Distribution, Relay Distribution, Pickwick Distribution, Solomon & Peres Distribution, Polygram

Cassette: released on K-Tel, Nov'85 by K-Tel Records. Dist: Record Merchandisers Distribution, Taylors, Terry Blood Distribution, Wynd-Up Distribution, Relay Distribution, Pickwick Distribution, Solomon & Peres Distribution, Polygram

Ovationz

FOREVER LOVE.
Single (7"): released on Dread At The Controls, Feb'82 Dist: Dub Vendor, Virgin Records, EMI

SECRET ADMIRER.
Single (12"): released on Live & Love, Apr'82 by Third World Records. Dist: Jetstar

Overcoming shyness

OVERCOMING SHYNESS Zimbardo,Philip.
Cassette: released on Psychology Today, Oct'81

Overdraft

SAVE YOUR LOVE.
Single (7"): released on Pay, Aug'85 by Pay Records. Dist: Spartan

Single (12"): released on Pay, Aug'85 by Pay Records. Dist: Spartan

Overkill

FEEL THE FIRE.
Album: released on Noise, Feb'86 by Dorane. Dist: Revolver, Cartel

TAKING OVER.
Tracks: / Deny the cross / Wrecking crew / Fear his name / Use your head / Fatal if swallowed / Powersurge / In union we stand / Electro-violence / Overkill II.
Album: released on Atlantic, Apr'87 by WEA Records. Dist: WEA

Cassette: released on Atlantic, Apr'87 by WEA Records. Dist: WEA

TRIUMPH OF WILL.
Album: released on SST, Sep'85 by SST Records. Dist: Pinnacle

Overlanders

MICHELLE.
Single (7"): released on Old Gold, Jul'82 by Old Gold Records. Dist: Lightning, Jazz Music, Spartan, Counterpoint

Overload
OVERLOAD Various artists (Various Artists).
Album: released on Ronco, Jun'82

Cassette: released on Ronco, Jun'82

Overstreet, Rev Louis
REV LOUIS OVERSTREET, HIS GUITAR & CONGREGATION.
Album: released on Arhoolie, May'81 by Arhoolie Records. Dist: Projection, Topic, Jazz Music, Swift, Roots

Over the Brooklyn Bridge
OVER THE BROOKLYN BRIDGE Original film soundtrack (Various Artists).
Album: released on Red Bus, Mar'84 by Red Bus Records. Dist: PRT

Cassette: released on Red Bus, Mar'84 by Red Bus Records. Dist: PRT

Over The Top
OVER THE TOP Original soundtrack (Various Artists).
Tracks: / Winner takes it all / In this country / Take it higher / All I need is you / Bad nite / Meet me half way / Gypsy soul / Fight, The / Mind over matter / I will be strong.
Album: released on CBS, Apr'87 by CBS Records. Dist: CBS

Cassette: released on CBS, Apr'87 by CBS Records. Dist: CBS

Overtone
OVERTONE 1 - THE MODERN ALBUM Various artists (Various Artists).
Album: released on Overtone, Jun'84

OVERTONE 2 - THE PROGRESSIVE ALBUM Various artists (Various Artists).
Album: released on Overtone, Jun'84

OVERTONE 3 - THE ROCK ALBUM Various artists (Various Artists).
Album: released on Overtone, Jun'84

Oville, Helena
AMOUREUX BLUER THAN BLUE.
Single (12"): released on Fid Def, Oct'82 Dist: Jetstar

'Owdham 'Edge
'OWDHAM 'EDGE Song and verse from Lancashire (Various Artists).
Album: released on Topic, '81 by Topic Records. Dist: JSU Distribution, Projection Distribution, Jazz Music Distribution

Owen, Beti Mary
GOOD TIDINGS.
Album: released on Seren, Jun'83 by Seren Records. Dist: Sain, Seren

Cassette: released on Seren, Jun'83 by Seren Records. Dist: Sain, Seren

OUR SONG IS JESUS.
Album: released on Seren, Jun'83 by Seren Records. Dist: Sain, Seren

Cassette: released on Seren, Jun'83 by Seren Records. Dist: Sain, Seren

SONGS WE LOVE.
Album: released on Seren, Jun'83 by Seren Records. Dist: Sain, Seren

Cassette: released on Seren, Jun'83 by Seren Records. Dist: Sain, Seren

WELSH FOLK SONGS AND THE LIKE.
Album: released on Seren, Jun'83 by Seren Records. Dist: Sain, Seren

Cassette: released on Seren, Jun'83 by Seren Records. Dist: Sain, Seren

Owen, Bill
COMPO'S GONE AND LOST HIS WELLIES.
Single (7"): released on Look, Feb'83 Dist: R. Smith & Co. Records, H.R. Taylor

NORA BATTY'S STOCKINGS (see also Kathy Staff) (Owen, Bill & Kathy Staff).
Single (7"): released on AVM, Mar'83 Dist: PRT

Owen, Dilys
SOPHY.
Cassette: released on Soundings, Feb'85 Dist: Soundings

Owen, Jack
YOUNG OWEN.
Album: released on Dingles, '83 by Dingle's Records. Dist: Projection

Owens, Buck
12 GREAT NUMBER 1 COUNTRY HITS.
Album: released on MFP, Mar'78 by EMI Records. Dist: EMI

BUCK OWENS.
Cassette: released on Audio Fidelity, Oct'84 Dist: PRT

CRYING TIME / I'VE GOT A TIGER BY THE.
Single (7"): released on Capitol(USA), '80 by Capitol (USA) Records. Dist: EMI

Owens-Collins, Jamie
LOVE EYES.
Album: released on Light USA, May'82 by Lexicon Music. Dist: Word Distribution

Cassette: released on Light USA, May'82 by Lexicon Music. Dist: Word Distribution

STRAIGHT AHEAD.
Album: released on Sparrow, May'82 by Word Records. Dist: Spartan

Cassette: released on Sparrow, May'82 by Word Records. Dist: Spartan

Owens, Jamie
GROWING PAINS.
Album: released on Light USA, May'82 by Lexicon Music. Dist: Word Distribution

Cassette: released on Light USA, May'82 by Lexicon Music. Dist: Word Distribution

LAUGHTER IN YOUR SOUL.
Album: released on Light USA, May'82 by Lexicon Music. Dist: Word Distribution

Cassette: released on Light USA, May'82 by Lexicon Music. Dist: Word Distribution

Owens, Jimmy & Carol
COME TOGETHER (see also Pat Boone) (Owens, Jimmy & Carol & Pat Boone).
Album: released on Light USA, May'82 by Lexicon Music. Dist: Word Distribution

Cassette: released on Light USA, May'82 by Lexicon Music. Dist: Word Distribution

COME TOGETHER AGAIN.
Notes: As a follow on to "Come Together", this is a musical about worship and commitment. In the tradition of "Come Together" and "If My people", "Come Together Again" is a joyful musical experience involving the choir and the congregation, led by Pat Boone as the minister/narrator, and featuring solos by Terry Talbot, Anne Herring and Jamie Owens-Collins.
Album: released on Oak, Sep'86 by Oak Records. Dist: Spartan Distribution, Pinnacle

Cassette: released on Oak, Sep'86 by Oak Records. Dist: Spartan Distribution, Pinnacle

GLORY OF CHRISTMAS, THE.
Album: released on Light USA, May'82 by Lexicon Music. Dist: Word Distribution

Cassette: released on Light USA, May'82 by Lexicon Music. Dist: Word Distribution

IF MY PEOPLE.
Album: released on Light USA, May'82 by Lexicon Music. Dist: Word Distribution

Cassette: released on Light USA, May'82 by Lexicon Music. Dist: Word Distribution

VICTOR, THE.
Album: released on Oak, Feb'85 by Oak Records. Dist: Spartan Distribution, Pinnacle

Cassette: released on Oak, Feb'85 by Oak Records. Dist: Spartan Distribution, Pinnacle

O'Williams, Wendy
IT'S MY LIFE.
Single (7"): released on Music For Nations, May'84 by Music For Nations Records. Dist: Pinnacle

Single (12"): released on Music For Nations, May'84 by Music For Nations Records. Dist: Pinnacle

KOMMANDER OF CHAOS.
Album: released on Zebra, Feb'86 by Cherry Red Records. Dist: Pinnacle

MAGGOTS (O'Williams, Wendy/Plasmatics).
Album: released on GWR, Mar'87 by GWR Records. Dist: RCA

W.O.W.
Album: released on Music For Nations, Jul'84 by Music For Nations Records. Dist: Pinnacle

Owl who was afraid...
OWL WHO WAS AFRAID OF THE DARK, THE Tomlinson, Jill (Lipman, Maureen).

Cassette: released on Cover to Cover, Sep'86 by Cover to Cover Cassettes. Dist: Conifer

Owusu, Steve
NEGATIVE REALITY.
Single (12"): released on Trinity House, Jan'85 by Trinity House. Dist: M.I.S.

Oxala, Nezinho de
NEZINHO DE OXALA.
Album: released on Philips Import, '78

Ox-Bow Incident
OX-BOW INCIDENT (Fonda, Henry).
Cassette: released on Caedmon(USA), May'80 by Caedmon (USA) Records. Dist: Gower, Taylors, Discovery

Oxford, Jumpin' George
CRUISIN' 1955 KSAN San Francisco.
Cassette: released on Increase(USA), Jun'87 by Quicksilver Records (USA).

Oxford Sound
FIRST CUT.
Album: released on Waterfall, Mar'84 by Waterfall Records. Dist: Revolver, Cartel

Oxford, Vernon
20 OF THE BEST.
Album: released on RCA, Mar'84 by RCA Records. Dist: RCA, Roots, Swift, Wellard, Chris, I & B, Solomon & Peres Distribution

Cassette: released on RCA, Mar'84 by RCA Records. Dist: RCA, Roots, Swift, Wellard, Chris, I & B, Solomon & Peres Distribution

IF I HAD MY WIFE TO LOVE OVER.
Album: released on Rounder, May'79

KEEPIN' IT COUNTRY.
Album: released on Sundown, Apr'85 by Magnum Music Group Ltd. Dist: Magnum Music Group Ltd, PRT Distribution, Spartan Distribution

TRIBUTE TO HANK WILLIAMS, A.
Album: released on Meteor, Mar'78 by Magnum Force Music. Dist: CBS Distribution

Oxley, Dave
BALLAD OF THE BLACK COUNTRY.
Album: released on Broadside, Jun'81 by Broadside Records. Dist: Celtic Distributions, H.R. Taylor, Jazz Music, Projection, Jazz Services Unlimited Dist. (JSU)

Cassette: released on Broadside, Jun'81 by Broadside Records. Dist: Celtic Distributions, H.R. Taylor, Jazz Music, Projection, Jazz Services Unlimited Dist. (JSU)

HARVEST (see Raven, Jon/Nigel Jones/Dave Oxley) (Oxley, Dave/Nigel Jones/Jon Raven).

Oxley, Louie
GO GO GADGET.
Tracks: / Go go gadget / Go go gadget (not so long version).
Single (7"): released on Cool Tempo, Apr'86 by Chrysalis Records. Dist: CBS

Single (12"): released on Cool Tempo, Apr'86 by Chrysalis Records. Dist: CBS

Oxley, Tony
SECOND ALBUM.
Album: released on Incus, Nov'76 Dist: Jazz Music, Cadillac

SONG FOR SOMEONE (see also D Bailey, E Parker) (Oxley, Tony, D Bailey, E Parker).
Album: released on Incus, Nov'76 Dist: Jazz Music, Cadillac

TONY OXLEY.
Album: released on Incus, Nov'76 Dist: Jazz Music, Cadillac

Oxo
OXO.
Album: released on Geffen, Aug'83 by Geffen Records. Dist: WEA, CBS

Cassette: released on Geffen, Aug'83 by Geffen Records. Dist: WEA, CBS

WHIRLY GIRLS / IN THE STARS.
Single (7"): released on Geffen, Mar'83 by Geffen Records. Dist: WEA, CBS

Oxtot, Dick
DICK OXTOT'S GOLDEN AGE JAZZ BAND (Oxtot's, Dick Golden Age Jazz Band).
Album: released on Arhoolie, May'81 by Arhoolie Records. Dist: Projection, Topic, Jazz Music, Swift, Roots

DOWN IN HONKY TONKY TOWN (Oxtot's, Dick Golden Age Jazz Band).
Album: released on Arhoolie, May'81 by Arhoolie Records. Dist: Projection, Topic, Jazz Music, Swift, Roots

Oxy & The Morons
WORK / THE GOOD LIFE.
Single (7"): released on Music for the deaf, Apr'82

Oye Listen
OYE LISTEN! COMPACTO CALIENTE various artists (Various Artists).
Compact disc: released on Globestyle, Aug'87 by Ace Records. Dist: Projection

OYE LISTEN (Various Artists).
Album: released on Globestyle, Jan'87 by Ace Records. Dist: Projection

Compact disc: released on Globestyle, Aug'87 by Ace Records. Dist: Projection. Estim retail price in Sep'87 was £11.99.

Oyster Band
20 GOLDEN TIE SLACKENERS.
Album: released on Pukka, Feb'85 Dist: Roots, JSU, Projection

ENGLISH ROCK AND ROLL THE EARLY YEARS (1800-1850).
Album: released on Pukka Records, '82

HAL-AN-TOW.
Tracks: / Hal-an-tow / Ashes to ashes.
Single (7"): released on Cooking Vinyl, Oct'86 Dist: Nine Mile, Cartel, Red Rhino

LIBERTY HALL.
Album: released on Pukka, May'85 Dist: Roots, JSU, Projection

Cassette: released on Pukka, May'85 Dist: Roots, JSU, Projection

STEP OUTSIDE.
Album: released on Cooking Vinyl, Oct'86 Dist: Nine Mile, Cartel, Red Rhino

WIDE BLUE YONDER.
Album: released on Cooking Vinyl, Aug'87 Dist: Nine Mile, Cartel, Red Rhino. Estim retail price in Sep'87 was £5.99.

Cassette: released on Cooking Vinyl, Aug'87 Dist: Nine Mile, Cartel, Red Rhino. Estim retail price in Sep'87 was £5.99.

Oyster Ceilidh Band
JACK'S ALIVE.
Album: released on Dingles, '83 by Dingle's Records. Dist: Projection

Oyuki Conjugate
SCENE IN MIRAGE.
Album: released on A.Mission, Feb'85 Dist: Red Rhino, Cartel

SCENE IN MIRAGE/SOUNDTRACKS.
Album: released on Final Image, Feb'86 Dist: Red Rhino, Cartel

Ozila
OZILA 2001.
Album: released on Pye International, Jun'78

Ozo
LISTEN TO THE BUDDAH.
Album: released on DJM, Nov'76 by DJM Records. Dist: CBS, Polygram

Single (7"): released on Sphinx, Feb'84 by Sphinx Records. Dist: Stage One Records

Single (12"): released on Sphinx, Feb'84 by Sphinx Records. Dist: Stage One Records

MUSEUM OF MANKIND.
Album: released on DJM, Jan'78 by DJM Records. Dist: CBS, Polygram

Cassette: released on DJM, Jan'78 by DJM Records. Dist: CBS, Polygram Deleted '80.

SKINTIGHT (NO ROOM TO MOVE UP).
Single (7"): released on Sphinx, Aug'82 by Sphinx Records. Dist: Stage One Records

Single (12"): released on Sphinx, Aug'82 by Sphinx Records. Dist: Stage One Records

SPIRITS OF AFRICA.
Album: released on Sphinx, Feb'84 by Sphinx Records. Dist: Stage One Records

WHY WASTE (ZAINAB) / DREAMING.
Single (7"): released on Mother Africa, Feb'85 Dist: Cartel Distribution, Stern's Distribution, Rough Trade Distribution

Single (12"): released on Mother Africa, Feb'85 Dist: Cartel Distribution, Stern's Distribution, Rough Trade Distribution

Ozone

DO WHAT'CHA WANNA DO / COME ON IN.
Single (7"): released on Motown, Apr'82 by RCA Records. Dist: RCA Distribution

Single (12"): released on Motown, Apr'82 by RCA Records. Dist: RCA Distribution

GIGOLETTE.
Single (7"): released on Motown, Nov'81 by RCA Records. Dist: RCA Distribution

Single (12"): released on Motown, Nov'81 by RCA Records. Dist: RCA Distribution

WALK ON / THIS IS FUNKIN INSANE.
Single (7"): released on Motown, Oct'81 by RCA Records. Dist: RCA Distribution

Ozone, Makoto

AFTER.
Tracks: / Yellow fever / If you knew sushi / After / Merry go round / Katos revenge / Waltz for Ronko / Improvisation.
Album: released on CBS, Jul'86 by CBS Records. Dist: CBS

Cassette: released on CBS, Jul'86 by CBS Records. Dist: CBS

MAKOTO OZONE.

Album: released on CBS, Dec'94 by CBS Records. Dist: CBS

Cassette: released on CBS, Dec'94 by CBS Records. Dist: CBS

Ozz II

ASSASSIN, THE.
Album: released on Zebra, Jan'84 by Cherry Red Records. Dist: Pinnacle

P

Pablo All Stars
PABLO ALL STARS JAM.
Album: released on Pablo, '82 by Pablo Records. Dist: Wellard, Chris, IMS-Polygram, BMG

Cassette: released on Pablo, '82 by Pablo Records. Dist: Wellard, Chris, IMS-Polygram, BMG

Pablo, Augustus
AFRICA MUST BE FREE BY 1983 DUB.
Album: released on Greensleeves, Oct'86 by Greensleeves Records. Dist: BMG, Jetstar, Spartan

EARTHS RIGHTFUL RULER.
Album: released on Message, Jun'85 by Message Records. Dist: Making Waves

EASTERN PROMISE.
Tracks: / Eastern promise (Dub) / Suki Yaki / Eastern promise (Version).
Single (12"): released on Island, Jan'87 by Island Records. Dist: Polygram

EAST OF THE RIVER NILE.
Album: released on Message, Jun'85 by Message Records. Dist: Making Waves

ITAL DUB.
Album: released on Trojan, '83 by Trojan Records. Dist: PRT, Jetstar

KING TUBBY MEETS ROCKERS.
Album: released on Message, Jun'85 by Message Records. Dist: Making Waves

ORIGINAL ROCKERS.
Album: released on Greensleeves, Nov'79 by Greensleeves Records. Dist: BMG, Jetstar, Spartan

PABLE MEETS MR. BASIE.
Single (7"): released on Rough Trade, Jan'79 by Rough Trade Records. Dist: Rough Trade Distribution, Cartel Distribution

RISING SUN.
Notes: This is the first Pablo material released by Greensleeves for six years. His previous albums 'Original Rockers', released in 1979, is one of Greensleeves most successful albums of their catalogue. The new album features ten new tracks all is self produced and arranged. The musicians playing on the LP are are as follows: Bass-Chris Meridith, Boogsie from Jamalla. Drum-Sly Dunbar, Noel Alphonso of Jamalla, Basil 'Benbow' Creary. Lead guitar-Earl 'Chinna' Smith, Gibby Morrison. Rhythm Guitar-Clive Jeffray, Fazal Prendergast. Percussion- Menolek, Shacka, Jango. All keyboard instruments played by Augustus Pablo.
Album: released on Greensleeves, Jan'86 by Greensleeves Records. Dist: BMG, Jetstar, Spartan

ROCKERS COMES EAST.
Album: released on Greensleeves, Aug'87 by Greensleeves Records. Dist: BMG, Jetstar, Spartan

Cassette: released on Greensleeves, Aug'87 by Greensleeves Records. Dist: BMG, Jetstar, Spartan

SUKIYAKI.
Tracks: / Sukiyaki / Easter promise / Sukiyaki (Dub).
Single (12"): released on Mango, Nov'86 by Inferno Records. Dist: Inferno

THRILLER.
Album: released on Vista Sounds, '83 by Vista Sounds Records. Dist: Jetstar

Cassette: released on Vista Sounds, '83 by Vista Sounds Records. Dist: Jetstar

Pablo Cruise
PABLO CRUISE.
Album: by A&M Records. Dist: Polygram

PLACE IN THE SUN, A.
Album: by A&M Records. Dist: Polygram

REFLECTOR.

Album: released on A&M, Jul'81 by A&M Records. Dist: Polygram

WORLDS AWAY.
Album: released on A&M Records. Dist: Polygram

Pace, Papa
JAMMING/MODELLER.
Single (12"): released on Fashion, Jul'83 by Fashion Records. Dist: PRT, Jetstar

Pacific 1860
PACIFIC 1860 Original London cast.
Album: released on That's Entertainment, Apr'83 by That's Entertainment Records. Dist: Pinnacle, PRT

Cassette: released on That's Entertainment, Apr'83 by That's Entertainment Records. Dist: Pinnacle, PRT

Pacific Ethno Techno
C'MON A MY HOUSE.
Single (7"): released on Dakota, Aug'83 by Dakota Records. Dist: PRT

Pack
LONG LIVE THE PAST.
Single (7"): released on Cyclops, Apr'82

MUCHOS GRACIAS/LIMELIGHT.
Single (7"): released on Escape, Aug'81

NUMBER 12.
Single (7"): released on Rough Trade, Nov'79 by Rough Trade Records. Dist: Rough Trade Distribution, Cartel Distribution

Packin' up my blues
PACKIN' UP MY BLUES (BLUES FROM THE DEEP SOUTH) Various artists (Various Artists).
Album: released on Muskadine, Apr'79 Dist: Swift Distribution

Packman
I'M A PACKMAN/PLAY IT AGAIN SAM.
Single (12"): released on Malaco, Nov'83 by Malaco Records. Dist: Charly

Packmen's blue record
PACKMEN'S BLUE RECORD various artists (Various Artists).
Album: released on Fellside, Apr'81 by Fellside Records. Dist: Roots, Jazz Music, Celtic Music, Projection

Pac Man
ADVENTURES OF PAC MAN, THE (Pac Man- The adventures of).
Cassette: released on Pickwick Talking Books, Mar'84

Pad Anthony
NUFF NICENESS.
Album: released on Jammy's, Jul'85 by Jammy's Records. Dist: Jetstar

Padden, Bernard
MASS MOVEMENT/CAREER ADVICE.
Single (7"): released on Dancing Sideways, Nov'83 by Dancing Sideways Records. Dist: Pinnacle

Paddington...
BEAROBICS/EVERLASTING TOFFEE (Paddington bear).
Single (7"): released on Nouveau, Aug'83

PADDINGTON ABROAD (NARRATOR BERNARD CRIBBINS).
Cassette: released on Pinnacle, '79 by Pinnacle Records. Dist: Pinnacle

PADDINGTON AT LARGE(NARRATOR BERNARD CRIBBENS).

Cassette: released on Pinnacle, '79 by Pinnacle Records. Dist: Pinnacle

PADDINGTON BEAR VOL 2 (NARRATOR BERNARD CRIBBINS).
Cassette: released on Pinnacle, '79 by Pinnacle Records. Dist: Pinnacle

PADDINGTON GOES TO TOWN(NARRATOR BERNARD CRIBBENS).
Cassette: released on Pinnacle, '79 by Pinnacle Records. Dist: Pinnacle

PADDINGTON HELPS OUT(NARRATOR BERNARD CRIBBINS).
Cassette: released on Pinnacle, '79 by Pinnacle Records. Dist: Pinnacle

PADDINGTON MARCHES ON(NARRATOR LESLIE CROWTHER).
Cassette: released on Pinnacle, '79 by Pinnacle Records. Dist: Pinnacle

PADDINGTON'S GOLDEN RECORD (Paddington bear).
Album: released on Audiotrax, Nov'84 by Audiotrax. Dist: PRT

Cassette: released on Audiotrax, Nov'84 by Audiotrax. Dist: PRT

SONGS OF PADDINGTON, THE (Paddington bear).
Album: released on Spot, May'84 by Pickwick Records. Dist: H.R. Taylor.

Cassette: released on Spot, May'84 by Pickwick Records. Dist: H.R. Taylor.

Paddy
MY ROCKA ROCKA GOOCHI GOOCHI WOMAN YEH/BLUE WATERS (Paddy & the pineapples).
Single (7"): released on Little Acorns, Dec'83 by Little Acorns Records. Dist: Pinnacle

Paddy in the smoke
PADDY IN THE SMOKE various artists (Various Artists).
Album: released on Topic, '81 Dist: Roots Distribution

Paddy's Dream
OLD FRIENDS.
Tracks: / Galtee mountain boy.
Single (7"): released on Homespun(Ireland), Jul'86 by Outlet Records. Dist: Outlet

Padlock
PADLOCK various artists (Various Artists).
Album: released on Garage, May'85 by Island Records. Dist: Island Records, Polygram

Cassette: released on Garage, May'85 by Island Records. Dist: Island Records, Polygram

Pagan Ritual
PAGAN DANCE.
Single (7"): released on Backs, Mar'84 by Backs Records. Dist: Backs, Cartel

Page Boys
YOU'RE MY KIND OF GIRL.
Single (7"): released on Whaam, Sep'83 Dist: Pinnacle

Page, Cleo
I LOVE TO EAT IT.
Single (7"): released on JSP, Jan'79 by JSP Records. Dist: Swift, Projection

LEAVING MISSISSIPPI.
Album: released on JSP, Apr'79 by JSP Records. Dist: Swift, Projection

Page, Elizabeth
PLAYING THE RECORDER.
Album: released on Music For Pleasure (Holland), Jul'84 by EMI Records. Dist: EMI

Album: released on Music For Pleasure (Holland), Jul'84 by EMI Records. Dist: EMI

Page, Hot Lips
SWING STREET (Page, Hot Lips and His Orchestra with Jonah Jones & Orch.).
Album: released on Commodore Classics, Feb'84 by Teldec Records (Germany). Dist: Conifer, IMS, Polygram

SWING STREET SHOWCASE (see Jones, Jonah) (Page, Hot Lips/Jonah Jones).

Page, Ian and Bop
UNITY STREET.
Single (7"): released on Parlophone, Aug'84 by EMI Records. Dist: EMI

Page, Jim
HOT TIMES.
Album: released on Whid-Isle, Sep'79 Dist: Coast

SHOT OF THE USUAL,A.
Album: released on Whid-Isle, May'79 Dist: Coast

VISIONS IN MY VIEW.
Album: released on Flying Fish (USA), Jun'86 by Flying Fish Records (USA). Dist: Roots, Projection

Page, Jimmy
JAM SESSION (Page, Jimmy, Sonny Boy Williamson & Brian Auger).
Album: released on Charly, Jan'82 by Charly Records. Dist: Charly, Cadillac

JAM SESSIONS (see Auger, Brian) (Page, Jimmy/Brian Auger/Sonny Boy Williamson).

NO INTRODUCTION NECESSARY (Page,Jimmy & Friends).
Album: released on Thunderbolt, Sep'84 by Magnum Music Group Ltd. Dist: Magnum Music Group Ltd, PRT Distribution, Spartan Distribution

Cassette: released on Thunderbolt, Sep'84 by Magnum Music Group Ltd. Dist: Magnum Music Group Ltd, PRT Distribution, Spartan Distribution

Compact disc: released on Thunderbolt, Sep'84 by Magnum Music Group Ltd. Dist: Magnum Music Group Ltd, PRT Distribution, Spartan Distribution

SMOKE AND FIRE.
Tracks: / Wailing sounds / 'Cause i love you / Flashing lights / Gutty guitar / Would you believe / Smoke and fire / Thumping beat / Union Jack Car / One for you baby / L-O-N-D-O-N / Brightest lights / Baby come back.
Compact disc: released on Thunderbolt, '86 by Magnum Music Group Ltd. Dist: Magnum Music Group Ltd, PRT Distribution, Spartan Distribution

Album: released on Thunderbolt, May'85 by Magnum Music Group Ltd. Dist: Magnum Music Group Ltd, PRT Distribution, Spartan Distribution

WHATEVER HAPPENED TO 1214 A.D. (Page, Jimmy with Roy Harper).
Album: released on Beggars Banquet, Feb'85 by Beggars Banquet Records. Dist: WEA

Cassette: released on Beggars Banquet, Feb'85 by Beggars Banquet Records. Dist: WEA

Page, Larry
STAY AWHILE (Page,Larry Orchestra).
Single (7"): released on Page One, Oct'82 by Page, Larry. Dist: PRT, Spartan

Page, Patti
BEST OF.
Cassette: released on Creole (Everest-Europa), Jul'84 by Creole Records. Dist: PRT, Rhino

HOW MUCH IS THAT DOGGIE IN THE WINDOW.
Single (7"): released on Old Gold, Jan'85 by Old Gold Records. Dist: Lightning, Jazz Music, Spartan, Counterpoint

Page, Stu

HONEYSUCKLE DREAMING (Page, Stu/Remuda).
Cassette: released on Sylvantone, Jul'86 Dist: Outlet Distribution, Sylvantone Distribution

Pagoda

FINDERS KEEPERS.
Single (7"): released on Chrysalis, Jun'83 by Chrysalis Records. Dist: CBS

Pahinui, Gabby

GABBY PAHINUI HAWAIIAN BAND.
Album: released on Edsel, Jul'87 by Demon Records. Dist: Pinnacle, Jazz Music, Projection

Paice Ashton Lord

MALICE IN WONDERLAND.
Album: released on Polydor, Nov'80 by Polydor Records. Dist: Polygram, Polydor

Paich,Marty Big Band

NEW YORK SCENE,THE.
Album: released on Discovery(Trend USA), Oct'82

Paige, Elaine

AVE MARIA.
Single (7"): released on WEA, Dec'82 by WEA Records. Dist: WEA

BARRIER (Paige, Elaine with Peter Oliver).
Double Album: released on Euro Disk, Aug'78 Dist: Polygram

CHRISTMAS.
Tracks: / Walking in the air / Peace on Earth / Father Christmas eyes / Ave Maria / Wishin' on a star / Santa Claus is comin' to town / Coventry carol / Coldest night of the year / Light of the stable / I believe in Father Christmas / Winters tale, A / Thirty two feet and eight little tails / Winters tale, A.
Album: released on WEA, Nov'86 by WEA Records. Dist: WEA

Cassette: released on WEA, Nov'86 by WEA Records. Dist: WEA

Compact disc: released on WEA, Nov'86 by WEA Records. Dist: WEA

CINEMA.
Tracks: / Windmills of your mind / Out here on my own / Prisoner / Sometimes / Theme from Mahogany / Up where we belong / Unchanged melody / Bright eyes / Alfie / Missing / Way we were (The) / Rose.
Album: released on WEA, Nov'86 by WEA Records. Dist: WEA

Cassette: released on WEA, Nov'86 by WEA Records. Dist: WEA

Compact disc: released on K-Tel, Oct'86 by K-Tel Records. Dist: Record Merchandisers Distribution, Taylors, Terry Blood Distribution, Wynd-Up Distribution, Relay Distribution, Pickwick Distribution, Solomon & Peres Distribution, Polygram

Album: released on K-Tel, Oct'84 by K-Tel Records. Dist: Record Merchandisers Distribution, Taylors, Terry Blood Distribution, Wynd-Up Distribution, Relay Distribution, Pickwick Distribution, Solomon & Peres Distribution, Polygram

Cassette: released on K-Tel, Oct'84 by K-Tel Records. Dist: Record Merchandisers Distribution, Taylors, Terry Blood Distribution, Wynd-Up Distribution, Relay Distribution, Pickwick Distribution, Solomon & Peres Distribution, Polygram

Compact disc: released on K-Tel, Oct'84 by K-Tel Records. Dist: Record Merchandisers Distribution, Taylors, Terry Blood Distribution, Wynd-Up Distribution, Relay Distribution, Pickwick Distribution, Solomon & Peres Distribution, Polygram

ELAINE PAIGE.
Album: released on WEA, Nov'81 by WEA Records. Dist: WEA

Cassette: released on WEA, Nov'81 by WEA Records. Dist: WEA

FOR YOU.
Tracks: / For you / Don't cry for me Argentina*.
Single (7"): released on WEA, Jan'86 by WEA Records. Dist: WEA

Single (12"): released on WEA, Jan'86 by WEA Records. Dist: WEA

HEAVEN HELP MY HEART.
Tracks: / Heaven help my heart / Argument / Russian and Molokov* / Where i want to be*.
Single (7"): released on RCA, Sep'86 by RCA Records. Dist: RCA, Roots, Swift, Wellard, Chris, I & B, Solomon & Peres Distribution

Single (12"): released on RCA, Sep'86 by RCA Records. Dist: RCA, Roots, Swift, Wellard, Chris, I & B, Solomon & Peres Distribution

ISLAND.
Tracks: / We're only flesh and blood.
Single (7"): released on Inspiration, Jun'86 Dist: Spartan

LIKE AN IMAGE PASSING BY (Paige, Elaine/Finola Hughes).
Single (7"): released on Epic, Jan'84 by CBS Records. Dist: CBS

LOVE HURTS.
Tracks: / Love Hurts / Sorry seems to be the hardest word / This is where i came in / All things considered / Mac Arthur Park / For you / My man and me / Without you / Apply tree, The / Shaking you / I know him so well.
Compact disc: released on WEA, Oct'85 by WEA Records. Dist: WEA

Album: released on WEA, Oct'85 by WEA Records. Dist: WEA

Cassette: released on WEA, Oct'85 by WEA Records. Dist: WEA

MEMORY.
Single (7"): released on Polydor, May'81 by Polydor Records. Dist: Polygram, Polydor

NOBODIES SIDE.
Tracks: / Embassy lament / World chess champions, The*.
Single (7"): released on RCA, Apr'86 by RCA Records. Dist: RCA, Roots, Swift, Wellard, Chris, I & B, Solomon & Peres Distribution

Single (12"): released on RCA, Apr'86 by RCA Records. Dist: RCA, Roots, Swift, Wellard, Chris, I & B, Solomon & Peres Distribution

NOBODY'S SIDE.
Single (7"): released on RCA, Oct'84 by RCA Records. Dist: RCA, Roots, Swift, Wellard, Chris, I & B, Solomon & Peres Distribution

Single (12"): released on RCA, Oct'84 by RCA Records. Dist: RCA, Roots, Swift, Wellard, Chris, I & B, Solomon & Peres Distribution

RUNNING BACK FOR MORE.
Single (7"): released on WEA, Jan'84 by WEA Records. Dist: WEA

SITTING PRETTY.
Album: released on Music For Pleasure, Mar'85

Cassette: released on Music For Pleasure, Mar'85

STAGES.
Album: released on WEA, Nov'86 by WEA Records. Dist: WEA

Cassette: released on WEA, Nov'86 by WEA Records. Dist: WEA

Compact disc: by K-Tel Records. Dist: Record Merchandisers Distribution, Taylors, Terry Blood Distribution, Wynd-Up Distribution, Relay Distribution, Pickwick Distribution, Solomon & Peres Distribution, Polygram

Album: released on K-Tel, Nov'83 by K-Tel Records. Dist: Record Merchandisers Distribution, Taylors, Terry Blood Distribution, Wynd-Up Distribution, Relay Distribution, Pickwick Distribution, Solomon & Peres Distribution, Polygram

Cassette: released on K-Tel, Nov'83 by K-Tel Records. Dist: Record Merchandisers Distribution, Taylors, Terry Blood Distribution, Wynd-Up Distribution, Relay Distribution, Pickwick Distribution, Solomon & Peres Distribution, Polygram

TONIGHT IS THE NIGHT.
Single (7"): released on Avatar, Mar'85 by Avatar Communications. Dist: CBS

WALKING IN THE AIR.
Tracks: / Thirty two feet and eight little tails.
Single (7"): released on WEA, Nov'86 by WEA Records. Dist: WEA

WINDMILLS OF MY MIND.
Single (7"): released on WEA, Jan'85 by WEA Records. Dist: WEA

Pain

PAIN.
Album: released on Noise, Jun'86 by Dorane. Dist: Revolver, Cartel

Pain Famine

LIQUID LIGHT.
Single (7"): released on AV, Sep'86 by Priority Records. Dist: EMI

Pain Famine, The

STARVISION.
Tracks: / Vanity Fayre.
Single (7"): released on AV, Apr'86 by Priority Records. Dist: EMI

Painted Word

INDEPENDENCE DAY.
Tracks: / Letter from Jackie / State of mind*.
Single (7"): released on Mother, Jun'86 Dist: Island Distribution

Single (12"): released on Mother, Jun'86 Dist: Island Distribution

Paint Your Wagon

PAINT YOUR WAGON Original Film Soundtrack.
Album: released on ABC, Apr'82 Dist: CBS, Pinnacle

Cassette: released on ABC, Apr'82 Dist: CBS, Pinnacle

PAINT YOUR WAGON Original London cast.
Album: released on That's Entertainment, Apr'83 by That's Entertainment Records. Dist: Pinnacle, PRT

Cassette: released on That's Entertainment, Apr'83 by That's Entertainment Records. Dist: Pinnacle, PRT

Paisley Abbey

GREAT ORGAN MUSIC (Paisley Abbey, Organ of).
Album: by Lismor Records. Dist: Lismor, Roots, Celtic Music

IN QUIRES & PLACES NO. 24 (Paisley Abbey Choir).
Album: released on Abbey, Jan'78 by Abbey. Dist: PRT, Taylors, Gamut

WORLD OF SACRED MUSIC,THE (Paisley Abbey Choir).
Album: by Decca Records. Dist: Polygram

Paisley,Ronnie,Band

SMOKING MIRROR.
Album: released on Pye, Jan'78

Paisleys

COSMIC MIND AT PLAY.
Album: released on Psycho, Sep'83 Dist: Funhouse, Rough Trade

Paiton, Tony

TRUST ME BABY.
Tracks: / Love.
Single (7"): released on Gipsy, Jul'86 by Gipsy Records. Dist: PRT

Pajah,Paulette

COZ YOU LOVE ME BABY.
Single (7"): released on Raiders, Aug'84 Dist: Jetstar

Pajama Game

PAJAMA GAME Original London cast.
Album: released on That's Entertainment, Apr'83 by That's Entertainment Records. Dist: Pinnacle, PRT

Album: released on That's Entertainment, Apr'83 by That's Entertainment Records. Dist: Pinnacle, PRT

Pal

TALK WE DON'T.
Tracks: / Talk we don't (inst) / Talk we don't (club mix)* / Tribal Mix Inst.* / Safari Mix* / Jungletalk mix*.
Single (7"): released on Motown, Mar'86 by Motown Records. Dist: BMG Distribution

Single (12"): released on Motown, Mar'86 by Motown Records. Dist: BMG Distribution

TRUTH FOR THE MOVEMENT.
Tracks: / Man about town (new boy / Like it / Her husband / On the edge / Everbody's nasty / Panic / Talk we don't, spellbound / Strange dreams / Checkin' u out.
Album: released on Motown, Jul'86 by Motown Records. Dist: BMG Distribution

Palace Of Light

BEING THERE AND TRAVELLING OUTWARD.
Album: released on Bam Caruso, Jul'87 by Bam Caruso Records. Dist: Rough Trade, Revolver, Cartel

CITY OF GOLD.
Tracks: / City of gold.
Single (12"): released on Bam Caruso, Mar'87 by Bam Caruso Records. Dist: Rough Trade, Revolver, Cartel

Palais Schaumburg

BEAT OF TWO.
Single (7"): released on Mercury, Apr'84 by Phonogram Records. Dist: Polygram Distribution

HOCKEY.
Single (7"): released on Mercury, Aug'83 by Phonogram Records. Dist: Polygram Distribution

Single (12"): released on Mercury, Aug'83 by Phonogram Records. Dist: Polygram Distribution

WIR BAUNEN EINE NEUE STADT.
Single (7"): released on Kamera, Jun'82

Pale Fountains

ACROSS THE KITCHEN TABLE.
Single (7"): released on Virgin, Jun'85 by Virgin Records. Dist: EMI, Virgin Distribution

DON'T LET YOUR LOVE START A WAR.
Single (7"): released on Virgin, Mar'84 by Virgin Records. Dist: EMI, Virgin Distribution

Single (12"): released on Virgin, Mar'84 by Virgin Records. Dist: EMI, Virgin Distribution

FROM ACROSS THE KITCHEN TABLE.
Tracks: / Shelter / Stole the love / Jean's not happening / Bicycle thieves / Limit / 27 Ways to get back home / Bruised arcade / These are the things / It's only hard / ...From across the kitchen table / Hey / September sting.
Album: released on Virgin, Apr'86 by Virgin Records. Dist: EMI, Virgin Distribution

Cassette: released on Virgin, Apr'86 by Virgin Records. Dist: EMI, Virgin Distribution

FROM ACROSS THE KITCHENTABLE.
Album: released on Virgin, Feb'85 by Virgin Records. Dist: EMI, Virgin Distribution

Cassette: released on Virgin, Feb'85 by Virgin Records. Dist: EMI, Virgin Distribution

JEAN'S NOT HAPPENING.
Single (12"): released on Virgin, Dec'84 by Virgin Records. Dist: EMI, Virgin Distribution

PACIFIC STREET.
Album: released on Virgin, Feb'84 by Virgin Records. Dist: EMI, Virgin Distribution

Cassette: released on Virgin, Feb'84 by Virgin Records. Dist: EMI, Virgin Distribution

SOMETHING ON MY MIND.
Single (7"): released on Operation, Jul'82

UNLESS.
Single (7"): released on Virgin, Jan'84 by Virgin Records. Dist: EMI, Virgin Distribution

Pale Red Competitor

FUTURE LOST.
Single (7"): released on Revolver, Mar'84 by Revolver Records. Dist: Revolver, Cartel

Palermo,Ed Orchestra

ED PALERMO ORCHESTRA.
Album: released on Vile Heifer, May'83 Dist: Jazz Horizons Distribution

Paley,Tom

WHO'S GOING TO SHOE (Paley,Tom & P.Seeger).
Album: released on Topic, Jan'74 by Polygram Records.

Palin,Michael

MOWGLI'S BROTHERS.
Cassette: released on Listen Productions, Nov'84 Dist: H.R. Taylor, Hayward Promotions Distribution

Palladin,Patti

SIAMESE LOVERS.
Single (12"): released on Love Corporation, Feb'83

Pallas

ARRIVE ALIVE.
Album: released on Cool King, Feb'83 Dist: Pinnacle

EYES IN THE NIGHT (ARIVE ALIVE).
Picture disc single: released on EMI, Feb'84 by EMI Records. Dist: EMI

PARIS IS BURNING.
Single (7"): released on Cool King, Apr'83 Dist: Pinnacle

Single (12"): released on Cool King, Apr'83 Dist: Pinnacle

SENTINEL,THE.
Album: released on Harvest, Feb'84 by EMI Records. Dist: Roots, EMI

Cassette: released on Harvest, Feb'84 by EMI Records. Dist: Roots, EMI

STRANGERS.
Single (7"): released on Harvest, Apr'85 by EMI Records. Dist: Roots, EMI

Single (12"): released on Harvest, Apr'85 by EMI Records. Dist: Roots, EMI

Picture disc single: released on Harvest, Apr'85 by EMI Records. Dist: Roots, EMI

THROWING STONES AT THE WINDOW.
Tracks: / Cut and run / Crown of thorns*.
Single (7"): released on Harvest, Jan'86 by EMI Records. Dist: Roots, EMI

Single (12"): released on Harvest, Jan'86 by EMI Records. Dist: Roots, EMI

WEDGE, THE.
Tracks: / Dance through the fire / Throwing stones at the wind / Win or lose / Executioner (Bernie Goetz a gun) / Million miles away, A (imagination) / Ratracing / Just a memory.
Notes: Musically, this, the second album from Pallas, sees a more straightfoward rock approach than previously. Produced by Mick Glossop whose credits this year include The Waterboys, Van Morrison and X-Mal Deutschland.
Album: released on Harvest, Feb'86 by EMI Records. Dist: Roots, EMI

Cassette: released on Harvest, Feb'86 by EMI Records. Dist: Roots, EMI

WIN OR LOSE.
Tracks: / Just a memory.
Single (7"): released on EMI, Apr'86 by EMI Records. Dist: EMI

Single (12"): released on EMI, Apr'86 by EMI Records. Dist: EMI

Pallas, Laura

CRY TO THE WIND.
Single (7"): released on MDM-Siren, Aug'86, Virgin, EMI

Single (12"): released on MDM-Siren, Aug'86, Virgin, EMI

EMERGENCY.
Single (7"): released on Record Shack, Mar'84 by Record Shack Records. Dist: PRT

Single (12"): released on Record Shack, Mar'84 by Record Shack Records. Dist: PRT

HANDS OFF.
Single (7"): released on Record Shack, Oct'84

Single (12"): released on Record Shack, Oct'84

IN THE NIGHT.
Single (12"): released on Solo, Nov'82 by Solo Records. Dist: PRT

SKING IN THE SNOW (Pallas,Laura & The Reputations).
Single (7"): released on Record Shack, Nov'83

Single (12"): released on Record Shack, Nov'83

SWEET CONFUSION.
Single (7"): released on MDM, Apr'86 Dist: Siren, Virgin, EMI

Palm Beach Orchestra

PLAY GLENN MILLER (BIG BAND VOLUME 1).
Cassette: released on Bi Bi(Budget Cassettes), Jan'83

Palm Court...

DOWN PEACOCK VALLEY (Palm Court Theatre Orchestra).
Album: released on Chandos, Aug'84 by Chandos Records. Dist: Harmonia Mundi, Taylors

Cassette: released on Chandos, Aug'84 by Chandos Records. Dist: Harmonia Mundi, Taylors

PICNIC PARTY, THE (Palm Court Theatre Orchestra).
Compact disc: released on Chandos, Mar'87 by Chandos Records. Dist: Harmonia Mundi, Taylors

Album: released on Chandos, Aug'84 by Chandos Records. Dist: Harmonia Mundi, Taylors

Cassette: released on Chandos, Aug'84 by Chandos Records. Dist: Harmonia Mundi, Taylors

PUTTIN' ON THE RITZ (Palm Court Theatre Orchestra).
Tracks: / Puttin' on the ritz / It must be true / Tot toot tootsie / Sheik of Araby, The / Let's get friendly / Honeymoon lane / Happy feet / Oh! what a night / Roll along covered wagon / Ain't misbehavin' / She's a Latin from Manhattan / Horatio Nicholls' Californian Serenade / Loving you / Tiger rag.
Notes: A sparkling selection of arrangements from 20s and 30s dance orchestra repertoire brilliantly created by The Palm Court Theatre Orchestra. Winners of a Grand Prix du Disque for 'The Picnic Party'.
Album: released on Chandos, Oct'86 by Chandos Records. Dist: Harmonia Mundi, Taylors

Cassette: released on Chandos, Oct'86 by Chandos Records. Dist: Harmonia Mundi, Taylors

SECOND SERENADE (Palm Court Trio).
Album: released on Response, Feb'81 by Priority Records. Dist: BMG

SERENADE (Palm Court Trio).
Album: released on Response, Feb'81 by Priority Records. Dist: BMG

VINTAGE PARADE (CHILDHOOD MEMORIES) (Palm Court Theatre Orchestra).
Album: released on Chandos, Apr'84 by Chandos Records. Dist: Harmonia Mundi, Taylors

Cassette: released on Chandos, Apr'84 by Chandos Records. Dist: Harmonia Mundi, Taylors

Palmer, Barry

HOUSE OF THE RISING SUN.
Single (7"): released on Starblend, '87 by Starblend Records. Dist: PRT Distribution

Single (12"): released on Starblend, Feb'87 by Starblend Records. Dist: PRT Distribution

WHEN ONE DOOR CLOSES.
Single (7"): released on Venom, Mar'85 Dist: Pinnacle

Single (12"): released on Venom, Mar'85 Dist: Pinnacle

WITHOUT AIM.
Album: released on Starblend, Feb'85 by Starblend Records. Dist: PRT Distribution

Cassette: released on Starblend, Feb'85 by Starblend Records. Dist: PRT Distribution

Palmer, David

MAGIC GUITAR SOUND.
Tracks: / Apache / Amapola / Johnny guitar / Karrella / Malaguena / Wheels.
Compact disc: released on Bridge, '86 Dist: CD Centre Distribution, Pinnacle, Target

MUSIC OF GENESIS, THE (Palmer, David/LSO).
Album: released on RCA, Aug'87 by RCA Records. Dist: RCA, Roots, Swift, Wellard, Chris, I & B, Solomon & Peres Distribution

Cassette: released on RCA, Aug'87 by RCA Records. Dist: RCA, Roots, Swift, Wellard, Chris, I & B, Solomon & Peres Distribution

Palmer Dog

DON'T SMOKE THE SEED.
Single (12"): released on Hitbound, Oct'83 by Hitbound Records. Dist: Jetstar

Single (12"): released on Jedi, Jun'84 Dist: Jetstar

Palmer, Michael

ANGELLA.
Album: released on Vista Sounds, Oct'84 by Vista Sounds Records. Dist: Jetstar

BUS STOP.
Single (12"):

DONE WITH IT.
Single (12"):

DOUBLE TROUBLE.
Album: released on Greensleeves, Feb'85 by Greensleeves Records. Dist: BMG, Jetstar, Spartan

GHETTO DANCE (Palmer, Michael & Jim Brown).
Single (12"): released on Greensleeves, Nov'83 by Greensleeves Records. Dist: BMG, Jetstar, Spartan

GHETTO LIVING.
Album: released on Bebo's Music, Jul'85

GUN SHOT AUUST.
Single (12"):

HAPPY MERRY CHRISTMAS.
Single (12"): released on Greensleeves, Dec'83 by Greensleeves Records. Dist: BMG, Jetstar, Spartan

I'M STILL DANCING.
Single (12"): released on Greensleeves, Mar'84 by Greensleeves Records. Dist: BMG, Jetstar, Spartan

JAIL HOUSE ROCK.
Single (12"): released on Londisc, Apr'85 by Londisc Records.

JUBIE ROCK.
Single (12"): released on Londisc, Dec'84 by Londisc Records.

LICK SHOT.
Cassette: released on Sonic Sounds, Sep'84 by Sonic Sound Records. Dist: Jetstar

Single (12"):

MICHAEL PALMER MEETS KELLY RANKS (Palmer, Michael & Kelly Ranks).
Album: released on Dancefloor, Dec'84 by Dancefloor Records. Dist: Vista Sounds Records, Jetstar

MICHAEL PALMER MEETS JOHNNY OSBOURNE (see Osbourne, Johnny) (Palmer, Michael & Johnny Osbourne).

MY NIGHT.
Single (12"): released on Up Tempo, Oct'84 by Up Tempo Records. Dist: Jetstar

NO TIME FOR ME.
Single (12"): released on Rockers Forever, Jul'85 Dist: Jetstar Distribution

ONE MORE YOUTH GET SHOT.
Single (12"): released on Scom, May'85 by Scom Records. Dist: Jetstar

PULL IT UP NOW.
Album: released on Greensleeves, Jul'85 by Greensleeves Records. Dist: BMG, Jetstar, Spartan

Single (12"): released on Greensleeves, May'85 by Greensleeves Records. Dist: BMG, Jetstar, Spartan

SHE HAS FE GET IT.
Single (12"): released on Vibes, Jan'85 Dist: Vibes

SHE NO READY YET.
Single (12"): released on Jammy's, Oct'84 by Jammy's Records. Dist: Jetstar

SHOWCASE - I'M STILL DANCING.
Album: released on Sonic Sounds, Aug'84 by Sonic Sound Records. Dist: Jetstar

SHOW ME YOUR COMPANY.
Single (12"): released on Vena, Dec'84 by Vena Records. Dist: Jetstar

STAR PERFORMER.
Album: released on Tonos, Jul'84 by Tonos Records. Dist: Jetstar Distribution

SWEET DADDY.
Album: released on World Enterprise, Jul'86 Dist: Jetstar

Palmer, Mr.

CLICK CLICK.
Tracks: / See ninja deh.
Single (12"): released on Sweetcorn, Jun'86 by Sweetcorn Records. Dist: Jetstar

TELEVISION.
Single (12"): released on Mab, Dec'85 by Mab Records. Dist: Jetstar

Palmer, Poli

HUMAN ERROR.
Notes: Formerly of the legendary band Family, this is an album which explores he full potential of the Fairlight Music Computer with various musical accompaniments courtesy of the likes of Mel Collins and Boz Burrell. Written, engineered and produced by Poli Palmer himself.
Album: released on Teldec (Germany), Dec'86 by Import Records. Dist: IMS Distribution, Polygram Distribution

Palmer, Robert

ADDICTED TO LOVE.
Tracks: / Remember to remeber / You are in my system*.
Single (7"): released on Island, Apr'86 by Island Records. Dist: Polygram

Single (12"): released on Island, Apr'86 by Island Records. Dist: Polygram

CLUES.
Tracks: / Looking for clues / Sulky girl / Johnny & Mary / What do you care / I dream of wires / Woke up laughing / Not a second time / Found you now.
Album: released on Island, Jan'87 by Island Records. Dist: Polygram

Cassette: released on Island, Jan'87 by Island Records. Dist: Polygram

Compact disc: released on Island, Jan'87 by Island Records. Dist: Polygram

DISCIPLINE OF LOVE.
Tracks: / Dance for me / Addicted to love / Remember to remember / Wake up laughing.
Single (7"): released on Island, Oct'86 by Island Records. Dist: Polygram

Single (12"): released on Island, Oct'86 by Island Records. Dist: Polygram

Single (12"): released on Island, Oct'86 by Island Records. Dist: Polygram

DOUBLE FUN.
Tracks: / Every kinda people / Best of both worlds / Where can it go / Night people / Love can run faster / You overwhelm me / You really got me / Your gonna get whats coming.
Album: released on Island, Jan'87 by Island Records. Dist: Polygram

Cassette: released on Island, Jan'87 by Island Records. Dist: Polygram

EARLY YEARS, THE (Palmer, Robert with The Alan Bown).
Tracks: / My friend / Strange little friend / Perfect day / Children of the night / Gypsy girl / Elope / All I can do / Still as stone / Prisoner, The / Kick me out / Wrong idea.
Album: released on C5, Jul'87 by See For Miles Records. Dist: Counterpoint

I DIDN'T MEAN TO TURN YOU ON.
Tracks: / Get it through your heart / Back in arms / Johnny and Mary / Trick bag (live) / No not much (live).
Single (7"): released on Island, Jul'86 by Island Records. Dist: Polygram

Single (12"): released on Island, Jul'86 by Island Records. Dist: Polygram

Single (7"): released on Island, Jan'86 by Island Records. Dist: Polygram

Single (12"): released on Island, Jan'86 by Island Records. Dist: Polygram

Double-pack single: released on Island, Jan'86 by Island Records. Dist: Polygram

JOHNNY & MARY / WHAT'S IT TAKE.
Single (7"): released on Island, Aug'80 by Island Records. Dist: Polygram

PRESSURE DROP.
Tracks: / Give me an inch girl / Work to make it work / Back in my arms / Riverboat / Pressure drop / Here with you tonight / Trouble / Fine time / Which of us is the fool.
Album: released on Island, Jan'87 by Island Records. Dist: Polygram

Cassette: released on Island, Jan'87 by Island Records. Dist: Polygram

Compact disc: released on Island, Apr'87 by Island Records. Dist: Polygram

PRIDE.
Tracks: / Pride / Deadline / Want you more / Dance for me / You are in my system / It's not difficult / Say you will / You can have it (take my heart) / What you waiting for / Silver gun.
Album: released on Island, Jan'87 by Island Records. Dist: Polygram

Cassette: released on Island, Jan'87 by Island Records. Dist: Polygram

Compact disc: released on Island, Jan'87 by Island Records. Dist: Polygram

RIPTIDE.
Compact disc: by Island Records. Dist: Polygram

Album: released on Island, Nov'85 by Island Records. Dist: Polygram

Cassette: released on Island, Nov'85 by Island Records. Dist: Polygram

Single (7"): released on Island, Nov'85 by Island Records. Dist: Polygram

Single (12"): released on Island, Nov'85 by Island Records. Dist: Polygram

Double-pack single: released on Island, Nov'85 by Island Records. Dist: Polygram

SECRETS.
Tracks: / Bad case of lovin' you / Too good to be true / Can we still be friends / In walks love again / Mean 'ol' world / Love stop / Jealous / Under suspicion / Woman you're wonderful / What's it take / Remember to remember.
Album: released on Island, Jan'87 by Island Records. Dist: Polygram

Cassette: released on Island, Jan'87 by Island Records. Dist: Polygram

SNEAKIN' SALLY THROUGH THE ALLEY.
Tracks: / Sailing shoes / Hey Julia / Sneakin' Sally through the alley / Get outside / How much fun / From a whisper to a scream / Through it all there's you.
Compact disc: released on Island, Jan'87 by Island Records. Dist: Polygram

SOME PEOPLE CAN DO WHAT THEY LIKE.
Album: released on Island, Jan'78 by Island Records. Dist: Polygram

Cassette: released on Island, Jun'81 by Island Records. Dist: Polygram

Palmer, Sinclair
GROWING UP TOO YOUNG / ALMOST GROWN.
Single (7"): released on Carrere America (USA), Nov'83 by Polygram.

Single (12"): released on Carrere America (USA), Nov'83 by Polygram.

Palmer, Teddy
NOBODY LOVES LIKE AN IRISHMAN.
Single (7"):

Palmer, Triston
CAN'T EXPLAIN.
Single (12"): released on World Enterprise, Aug'84 Dist: Jetstar

DANCEHALL FAN.
Single (12"): released on Black Solidarity, Sep'84 by Black Solidarity Records. Dist: Jetstar

DREAM OF ME.
Single (12"): released on Oak Sound, Dec'84

ENTERTAINMENT.
Single (12"): released on Greensleeves, Aug'81 by Greensleeves Records. Dist: BMG, Jetstar, Spartan

HOW CAN A MAN BE HAPPY.
Single (12"): released on Attack, Mar'81 by Trojan Records. Dist: Trojan, Pinnacle, Red Rhino

I'M LEAVING.
Single (12"): released on Sharp Axe, Nov'83 by Sharp Axe Records. Dist: Jetstar

IT'S NOT WHAT YOU SAY.
Single (12"): released on Londisc, Sep'83 by Londisc Records.

JOKER SMOKER.
Album: released on Greensleeves, Sep'82 by Greensleeves Records. Dist: BMG, Jetstar, Spartan

Single (12"): released on Greensleeves, Jul'82 by Greensleeves Records. Dist: BMG, Jetstar, Spartan

MR FALSE PREACHER (Palmer, Triston & Nica Smart).
Single (12"): released on Greensleeves, Feb'82 by Greensleeves Records. Dist: BMG, Jetstar, Spartan

NO SHOT, NO FIRE.
Single (12"): released on Greensleeves, Aug'83 by Greensleeves Records. Dist: BMG, Jetstar, Spartan

ON THE ATTACK.
Album: released on Blue Mountain, May'86 Dist: Jetstar

RAVING.
Single (12"): released on Midnight Rock, Feb'82 Dist: Jetstar Distribution, Kingdom Distribution

REGGAE '85 (Palmer, Triston & Al Campbell).
Notes: For full details see under Al Campbell.

SETTLE DOWN.
Single(12"): released on Trojan, Apr'83 by Trojan Records. Dist: PRT, Jetstar

SETTLE DOWN GIRL.
Album: released on Trojan, Jun'83 by Trojan Records. Dist: PRT, Jetstar

SHOW CASE.
Album: released on Vista Sounds, '83 by Vista Sounds Records. Dist: Jetstar

TOUCH ME, TAKE ME.
Album: released on Vista Sounds, '83 by Vista Sounds Records. Dist: Jetstar

Cassette: released on Vista Sounds, '83 by Vista Sounds Records. Dist: Jetstar

TRASH AND READY.
Single (12"): released on Blue Trac, Jan'85 by Blue Mountain Records. Dist: Jetstar

TRISTON PALMER MEETS EARLY B (Palmer, Triston & Early B).
Album: released on Fantasticar, May'85 Dist: Jetstar

UPTOWN GIRL.
Single (12"): released on High Music, Sep'84 by High Music Records. Dist: Jetstar

WOMAN WOMAN.
Single (12"): released on Rusty International, Mar'83 by Rusty International Records. Dist: Jetstar Distribution

Palmer, Trudi
ANYTHING CAN HAPPEN.
Single (7"): released on Thunderbay, Apr'83 Dist: Spartan Distribution

FOOL WITH A BOTTLE.
Single (7"): released on Thunderbay, Apr'83 Dist: Spartan Distribution

WHEEL OF LIFE.
Single (7"): released on Thunderbay, Apr'83 Dist: Spartan Distribution

Palmer, Wayne
COME SEE ME YA.
Tracks: / Suzie.
Single (12"): released on Firm, May'86 by Firm Records. Dist: Jetstar

Palmvist, Claes
RAGTIME GUITAR DUETS (Palmvist, Claes & L.Johansson).
Album: released on Kicking Mule, Feb'77 by Sonet. Dist: Roots, PRT-Pye Distribution

Palookas
CLEAR DAY.
Single (12"): released on Prophet, Jul'85 by Prophet Records. Dist: Pinnacle

Pam Parsnip..
PAM PARSNIP & LAWRENCE LEMON various artists (Various Artists).
Cassette: released on Tell-a-tale (Cassettes), '84

Pamplemousse
SWEET MAGIC.
Album: released on AVI (USA), Feb'79 by A.V.I. Records. Dist: Target, PRT

Panache
HEROES.
Single (7"): released on Mach 1, May'84 by Mach 1 Records. Dist: PRT

HEROES/LUCINDA.
Single (7"): released on Mach 1, Jun'83 by Mach 1 Records. Dist: PRT

HOW CAN I BE SURE/MAYFAIR.
Single (7"): released on KJ Music, Aug'82

I WANNA DANCE/CRAZY FOR YOU LOVE.
Single (7"): released on Mach 1, Jan'83 by Mach 1 Records. Dist: PRT

Panama
IF YOU'RE LEAVING NOW/ALL NIGHT LONG.
Single (7"): released on Jive, Sep'82 by Zomba Records. Dist: RCA, PRT, CBS

WILL YOU LOVE ME TOMORROW.
Single (7"): released on Jive, Mar'82 by Zomba Records. Dist: RCA, PRT, CBS

Single (12"): released on Jive, Mar'82 by Zomba Records. Dist: RCA, PRT, CBS

Pan Assembly
GOODBYE MY LOVE.
Tracks: / Mr Magic.
Single (7"): released on Carotte, Mar'86 Dist: Jetstar

Panatella, Slim
SLIM PANATELLA AND THE MELLOW VIRGINIANS (Panatella, Slim & The Mellow Virginians).
Cassette: released on Acoustics, Jul'87 by Acoustics Records. Dist: Cartel

Pancoute & trinity
IF LOVING JAH IS WRONG.
Single (12"): released on September, Jan'83 by September Records. Dist: Jetstar

Pandemonium
HOLE IN THE SKY.
Single (7"): released on Roadrunner (Dutch), Nov'85 Dist: Pinnacle

Pandora
MARIANNE/GAELS SONG.
Single (7"): released on Oscar, Aug'82 Dist: Pinnacle

Pandoras
STOP PRETENDING.
Album: released on Rhino (USA), May'86 by Rhino Records (USA).

Pandy, Darryl
ANIMAL MAGNETISM.
Tracks: / Animal magnetism (inst) / Tearing up the house (Remix).
Single (7"): released on Nightmare, Oct'86 by Nightmare Records. Dist: PRT

Single (12"): released on Nightmare, Oct'86 by Nightmare Records. Dist: PRT

I PUT MY LOVE ON THE LINE.
Single (7"): released on Nightmare, 23 May'87 by Nightmare Records. Dist: PRT

Panic
SHE'S NOT THERE.
Single (7"): released on PRT, Jan'83 by PRT Records. Dist: PRT

Single (12"): released on PRT, Jan'83 by PRT Records. Dist: PRT

TICKET TO THE TROPICS.
Single (7"): released on PRT, Jun'83 by PRT Records. Dist: PRT

Single (12"): released on PRT, Jun'83 by PRT Records. Dist: PRT

Panic Brothers
IN THE RED.
Tracks: / Bivouac / No news / I made a mess on a dirty weekend / Rapp man / Almost as blue as Hank Williams / In debt / Later than you think / I'm broke in evironment but my heart / Late night picture show / I've forgotten what it is that I was drinking to forget.
Album: released on Special Delivery, Jun'87 Dist: Nine Mile, Cartel

Panic Stations
DEM BONES/MINE BONES.
Single (7"): released on Crash, May'83 by Satril Records. Dist: PRT

Panit Pran Nath
RAGAS OF MORNING AND NIGHT.
Compact disc: released on Gramavision (USA), '86 by Gramavision Records (USA). Dist: PRT, IMS, Polygram

Panorama
DREAM HOME/REVISITED.
Single (7"): released on Kamera, Jun'82

Pan Pipes
TRANQUILITY.
Album: released on Cambra, Feb'85 by Cambra Records. Dist: IDS, Conifer

Cassette: released on Cambra, Feb'85 by Cambra Records. Dist: IDS, Conifer

Pan pipes play love songs
PAN PIPES PLAY LOVE SONGS (Various Artists).
Tracks: / If you leave me now / Something / Do you know where you're going to / Feelings / I'm stone in love with you / Unchained melody / She's out of my life / Softly as I leave you / First time ever I saw your face / Endless love / True love ways / Light my fire / Why can't it wait till morning / Godfather, The (love theme from).
Album: released on Conifer, May'87 by Conifer Records. Dist: Conifer

Cassette: released on Conifer, May'87 by Conifer Records. Dist: Conifer

Panther Burns
BEHIND THE MAGNOLIA CURTAIN.
Album: released on Rough Trade, '84 by Rough Trade Records. Dist: Rough Trade Distribution, Cartel Distribution

BLOW YOUR TOP.
Single (12"): released on Rough Trade, Nov'82 by Rough Trade Records. Dist: Rough Trade Distribution, Cartel Distribution

TRAIN KEPT A ROLLIN'.
Single (12"): released on Rough Trade, Oct'81 by Rough Trade Records. Dist: Rough Trade Distribution, Cartel Distribution

Pantry, John
EMPTY-HANDED.
Album: released on Dove, May'79 by Dove Records. Dist: Jetstar

Panza Division
WE'LL ROCK THE WORLD/STANDIND ON...
Single (7"): released on Panza Trax, Apr'82

Panzer
SALVESE QUIEN PUEDA.
Album: released on Mausoleum, Aug'84 by Mausoleum Records. Dist: Pinnacle

Paolo, Frankie
QUE PASA?MANANA!.
Single (7"): released on Sonet, Jun'85 by Sonet Records. Dist: PRT

Single (12"): released on Sonet, Jun'85 by Sonet Records. Dist: PRT

Papa Bemsle
DANCING FEVER.
Single (12"): released on Music Rock, Mav'85

SETTLEMENT.
Single (12"): released on Creole, May'85 by Creole Records. Dist: Rhino, PRT

Papa Biggie
UNDER THE PLANE WING.
Single (12"): released on Taxi, Sep'84 by Taxi Records. Dist: Jetstar Distribution

Papadimitriou,Sakis
PIANO PLAYS.
Album: released on Leo, Sep'84 Dist: Recommended

Papa Face
GIRLS/DANCE PON DE CORNER.
Single (12"): released on Fashion, Sep'82 by Fashion Records. Dist: PRT, Jetstar

IN A JAMAICA STYLE/FORWARD STYLE.
Single (12"): released on Top Notch, Feb'82

WE'RE BUBBLING HOT.
Single (12"): released on Fashion, Sep'84 by Fashion Records. Dist: PRT, Jetstar

Papa Levi
BIG'N'BROAD.
Single (7"): released on Island, Oct'84 by Island Records. Dist: Polygram

Single (12"): released on Island, Oct'84 by Island Records. Dist: Polygram

Papa Peacock
PAPA PEACOCK various artists (Various Artists).
Cassette: released on Anvil, Jan'81 Dist: Anvil

Papa's New Faith
SHINE.
Single (12"): released on Garage, Jul'87 by Island Records. Dist: Island Records, Polyoram

Papathanassiou, Vangelis
IGNACIO.
Album: released on Egg, Nov'79 by Red Rhino, Cartel

Paper Boats In Puddles
PAPER BOATS IN PUDDLES Brighton Compilation (Various Artists).
Album: released on Hang Ten Yeah!, Jul'87

Paper Dolls
SOMETHING HERE IN MY HEART.
Single (7"): released on Flashback, Jan'83 by Flashback Records/PRT Records. Dist: Mainline, PRT

Single (7"): released on Old Gold, Jan'85 by Old Gold Records. Dist: Lightning, Jazz Music, Spartan, Counterpoint

Paper Garden
PRESENTS THE PAPER GARDEN.
Album: released on Antar, Mar'86 by Bam Caruso Records. Dist: Rough Trade, Revolver

Paper Lace
BILLY DON'T BE A HERO.
Single (7"): released on Old Gold, Jul'82 by Old Gold Records. Dist: Lightning, Jazz Music, Spartan, Counterpoint

PAPER LACE COLLECTION.
Cassette: released on Pickwick, Feb'80 by Pickwick Records. Dist: Pickwick Distribution, Prism Leisure Distribution, Lugtons

Double Album: released on Pickwick, Jul'76 by Pickwick Records. Dist: Pickwick Distribution, Prism Leisure Distribution, Lugtons

Papers
B.M.X BANDITS.
Single (7"): released on Creole, Jun'84 by Creole Records. Dist: Rhino, PRT

REGGAE ON THE RADIO.
Single (7"): released on Radioactive, Aug'81

Paperwate
MEMORIES DE PLAISER.
Album: released on Tank, Dec'77 by Tank Records.

Papetti, Fausto
AMBIENCE SAX.
Double Album: released on Vogue (France), Dec'84 Dist: Discovery, Jazz Music, PRT, Swift

Cassette: released on Vogue (France), Dec'84 Dist: Discovery, Jazz Music, PRT, Swift

J'AIME LE BAL.
Album: released on Vogue (France), Dec'84 Dist: Discovery, Jazz Music, PRT, Swift

Cassette: released on Vogue (France), Dec'84 Dist: Discovery, Jazz Music, PRT, Swift

MEDLEY IN SAX.
Album: released on Vogue (France), Mar'84 Dist: Discovery, Jazz Music, PRT, Swift

Cassette: released on Vogue (France), Mar'84 Dist: Discovery, Jazz Music, PRT, Swift

MY ONE & ONLY LOVE.
Compact disc: released on Vogue (France), Jun'84 Dist: Discovery, Jazz Music, PRT, Swift

Papparazzi
DON'T STAY ALL NIGHT.
Single (7"): released on MCA, May'84 by MCA Records. Dist: Polygram, MCA

Single (12"): released on MCA, May'84 by MCA Records. Dist: Polygram, MCA

Parable
ILLUSTRATIONS.
Album: released on Maranatha, May'79

MORE THAN WORD.
Album: released on Maranatha, May'79

Parachute Club
LOVE IS FIRE.
Tracks: / Love is fire / Zeljo Mojo / Love is fire / Waves.
Single (7"): released on RCA, Mar'87 by RCA Records. Dist: RCA, Roots, Swift, Wellard, Chris, I & B, Solomon & Peres Distribution

Single (12"): released on RCA, Mar'87 by RCA Records. Dist: RCA, Roots, Swift, Wellard, Chris, I & B, Solomon & Peres Distribution

PARACHUTE CLUB, (THE).
Album: released on Magnet, Dec'84 by Magnet Records. Dist: BMG

Cassette: released on Magnet, Dec'84 by Magnet Records. Dist: BMG

RISE UP.
Single (7"): released on Magnet, Jul'85 by Magnet Records. Dist: BMG

Single (12"): released on Magnet, Jul'85 by Magnet Records. Dist: BMG

SMALL VICTORIES.
Tracks: / Tearing the veil / Love is fire / Secret heart(wild zone) / Walk to the rhythm of your heartbeat / Love & compassion / Small victories / Journey, The / Cheat the prophecy / Waves.
Album: released on RCA, Jun'87 by RCA Records. Dist: RCA, Roots, Swift, Wellard, Chris, I & B, Solomon & Peres Distribution

Cassette: released on RCA, Jun'87 by RCA Records. Dist: RCA, Roots, Swift, Wellard, Chris, I & B, Solomon & Peres Distribution

Parachute Regiment
AIRBORNE SALUTE.
Album: released on Bandleader (Military), May'83

Cassette: released on Bandleader (Military), May'83

GET FIGHTING FIT WITH TWO PARA.
Album: released on WEA, Jan'83 by WEA Records. Dist: WEA

Cassette: released on WEA, Jan'83 by WEA Records. Dist: WEA

MASSED BANDS.
Album: released on Parade, Oct'80 Dist: MSD

MASSED BANDS OF THE PARACHUTE REGIMENT.
Cassette: released on Parade, Oct'80 Dist: MSD

PARACHUTE REGIMENT, 2ND BATTALION.
Album: released on Music Masters, May'82 by Music Masters Records. Dist: Taylors

PEGASUS.
Album: released on Bandleader, Jun'83 by Bandleader Records. Dist: PRT

TAKE IT EASY.
Album: released on Major Richards, Oct'77 by Major Richards Records. Dist: Taylors

Parade Ground
DUAL PERSPECTIVE.
Single (12"): released on Play It Again Sam, 20 Jan'87 Dist: Red Rhino, Cartel

Parade Vol 2
PARADE VOL 2 Original Soundtrack.
Album: by Pickwick Records. Dist: Pickwick Distribution, Prism Leisure Distribution, Lugtons

Paradine Express
HUNGRY FOR YOUR LOVE.
Tracks: / Hungry for your love.
Single (7"): released on Parasound, Oct'86

Single (12"): released on Parasound, Oct'86

Paradise
HEARTSTRINGS.
Single (7"): released on Priority, Jul'85 by Priority Records. Dist: RCA

Single (12"): released on Priority, Jul'85 by Priority Records. Dist: RCA

LOVE IS THE ANSWER.
Album: released on Priority, Nov'83 by Priority Records. Dist: RCA

Cassette: released on Priority, Nov'83 by Priority Records. Dist: RCA

LOVE IS THE ANSWER (SINGLE).
Single (7"): released on Priority, Nov'83 by Priority Records. Dist: RCA

Single (12"): released on Priority, Nov'83 by Priority Records. Dist: RCA

ONE MIND TWO HEARTS.
Single (7"): released on Priority, Aug'83 by Priority Records. Dist: RCA

Single (12"): released on Priority, Aug'83 by Priority Records. Dist: RCA

Paradise, Leesha
WAITING.
Single (7"): released on EMI, Mar'83 by EMI Records. Dist: EMI

Single (12"): released on EMI, Mar'83 by EMI Records. Dist: EMI

Paradise Postponed
SIR MICHAEL HORDERN.
Notes: For full information see: Hordern, Sir Michael

Paradise, Sal
SLOW PASSION.
Single (7"): released on Abstract, Mar'82 by Abstract. Dist: Pinnacle

THERE IS A UNIVERSE.
Single (7"): released on Arista, Mar'84 by Arista Records. Dist: RCA

Single (12"): released on Arista, Mar'84 by Arista Records. Dist: RCA

Paradox
WE CAN'T LET MAGGIE GO.
Tracks: / We can't let Maggie go / Cabinet shuffle.
Single (7"): released on Gipsy, Jun'87 by Gipsy Records. Dist: RCA

Paragon Brass Band
LIVE ON THE STREETS OF ROUEN.
Album: released on GHB, Jun'86 Dist: Jazz Music, Swift

Paragonne
ASPECTS OF.....
Album: released on MMC, Sep'85 by MMC Records. Dist: PRT Distribution, Pinnacle

Paragons
MODELING CROWD.
Single (12"): released on Starlight, Jul'82 by Starlight Records. Dist: Jetstar Distribution

NOW.
Album: released on Starlite, Oct'82 Dist: Swift Distribution, PRT Distribution

ON THE BEACH.
Album: released on Treasure Isle, Feb'86 by Treasure Isle Records. Dist: Jetstar

---

PARAGONS.
Album: released on Island, Jul'81 by Island Records. Dist: Polygram Deleted '84.

Cassette: released on Island, Jul'81 by Island Records. Dist: Polygram

Parallel
WORKING.
Single (7"): released on Swagman, Sep'84 Dist: Pinnacle

Paramedics Squad
MOVEMENT IN TIME.
Single (7"): released on Gargoyle, Aug'82 Dist: Fresh

Paramor, Norrie
BEST OF NORRIE PARAMOR, (THE).
Album: released on BBC, Aug'84 by BBC Records & Tapes. Dist: EMI, PRT, Pye

Cassette: released on BBC, Aug'84 by BBC Records & Tapes. Dist: EMI, PRT, Pye

BY REQUEST (Paramor, Norrie Orchestra).
Cassette: released on BBC, '79 by BBC Records & Tapes. Dist: EMI, PRT, Pye

CLASSICAL RHYTHM (Paramor, Norrie Orchestra).
Album: released on Pye, Mar'79

RAGTIME (Paramor, Norrie/Big Ben Banjo Band).
Album: released on Flashback, Nov'85 by Flashback Records/PRT Records. Dist: Mainline, PRT

Cassette: released on Flashback, Nov'85 by Flashback Records/PRT Records. Dist: Mainline, PRT

THANK YOU FOR THE MUSIC.
Album: released on BBC, Nov'79 by BBC Records & Tapes. Dist: EMI, PRT, Pye

Cassette: released on BBC, Nov'79 by BBC Records & Tapes. Dist: EMI, PRT, Pye

Paramount
PARAMOUNT VOL 2 Various Artists (Various Artists).
Album: released on Magpie, Jul'82 Dist: Projection

Paramounts
WHITER SHADES OF R & B.
Album: released on Edsel, Apr'83 by Demon Records. Dist: Pinnacle, Jazz Music, Projection

Paranoia
DEAD MAN'S DREAMS.
Single (7"): released on Rot, Mar'84 by Rot Records. Dist: Red Rhino Through Cartel Distributions

SHATTERED GLASS.
Album: released on Rot, Jun'84 by Rot Records. Dist: Red Rhino Through Cartel Distributions

SHATTERED GLASS (SINGLE).
Single (7"): released on Rot, Jul'84 by Rot Records. Dist: Red Rhino Through Cartel Distributions

Paranoia you can dance to
PARANOIA YOU CAN DANCE TO Various Artists (Various Artists).
Notes: Artists include: Dickies, Misfits
Album: released on Weird System, Apr'86 Dist: Revolver

Paranoid visions
ROBOT HAS RUN AMOK.
Tracks: / Robot has run amok (EP).
Extended-play record: released on All The Madmen, Oct'86 by All The Madmen Records. Dist: Rough Trade, Cartel

Parasite
PARASITE.
Album: released on Music For Nations, Feb'85 by Music For Nations Records. Dist: Pinnacle

Parchman, Kenny
TREAT ME RIGHT.
Single (7"): released on Bison Bop (USA), Jan'85

Parchment
REHEARSAL FOR A REUNION.
Album: by Pilgrim Records. Dist: Rough Trade, Cartel

Pardon, Walter
BRIGHT GOLDEN STORE.
Album: released on Home Made, Nov'84 by

Home Made Records. Dist: Roots, Celtic Music

COUNTRY LIFE, (A).
Album: released on Topic, '82 by Topic Records. Dist: JSU Distribution, Projection Distribution, Jazz Music Distribution

OUR SIDE OF THE BAULK.
Double Album: released on Leader, '81 Dist: Jazz Music, Projection

PROPER SORT, (A).
Double Album: released on Leader, '81 Dist: Jazz Music, Projection

Parenti's Liberty...
MIDWAY DANCE ORCHESTRA & OTHERS, (THE) (Parenti's Liberty Syncopators).
Album: released on VJM, Apr'79 by VJM (UK) Records. Dist: Swift

Parenti, Tony
FINAL BAR (Parenti, Tony & His Jazz Stars).
Album: released on Jazzology, Jun'86 Dist: Jazz Music, Swift

FROM THE LATE 1920'S (Parham, Tiny and His Musicians).
Album: released on Folklyric (USA), Oct'86 by Arhoolie Records. Dist: Topic, Projection

WNYC JAZZ FESTIVAL (Parenti, T./Clarence Williams/Albert Nicholas).
Notes: For full information see : Williams, Clarence/Albert Nicholas/T.Parenti

Paris
ANOTHER SAD AFFAIR.
Single (7"): released on RCA, Jul'83 by RCA Records. Dist: RCA, Roots, Swift, Wellard, Chris, I & B, Solomon & Peres Distribution

CENSORED.
Single (7"): released on RCA, Jan'83 by RCA Records. Dist: RCA, Roots, Swift, Wellard, Chris, I & B, Solomon & Peres Distribution

Single (12"): released on RCA, Jan'83 by RCA Records. Dist: RCA, Roots, Swift, Wellard, Chris, I & B, Solomon & Peres Distribution

HAVE YOU EVER BEEN IN LOVE.
Single (7"): released on RCA, Mar'82 by RCA Records. Dist: RCA, Roots, Swift, Wellard, Chris, I & B, Solomon & Peres Distribution

I CHOOSE YOU.
Tracks: / I choose you / Punkin' funkin'.
Single (7"): released on Bluebird, 20 Jun'87 by Bluebird Records. Dist: EMI, Jetstar

Single (12"): released on Bluebird, 20 Jun'87 by Bluebird Records. Dist: EMI, Jetstar

Single (7"): released on Bluebird, Oct'84 by Bluebird Records. Dist: EMI, Jetstar

Single (12"): released on Bluebird, Oct'84 by Bluebird Records. Dist: EMI, Jetstar

NO GETTING OVER YOU.
Single (7"): released on RCA, Apr'82 by RCA Records. Dist: RCA, Roots, Swift, Wellard, Chris, I & B, Solomon & Peres Distribution

Paris France Transit
CHILD.
Single (7"): released on Vogue, Mar'83 Dist: Discovery, Jazz Music, PRT, Swift

Single (12"): released on Vogue, Mar'83 Dist: Discovery, Jazz Music, PRT, Swift

PARIS FRANCE TRANSIT.
Album: released on Vogue (France), Apr'83 Dist: Discovery, Jazz Music, PRT, Swift

Cassette: released on Vogue (France), Apr'83 Dist: Discovery, Jazz Music, PRT, Swift

Paris Reunion Band
FRENCH COOKING.
Compact disc: released on Sonet, Jul'87 by Sonet Records. Dist: PRT

PARIS REUNION BAND Various artists (Various Artists).
Notes: Artists include: Kenny Clarke/Johnny Griffin/Slide Hampton.
Album: released on Sonet, Jun'86 by Sonet Records. Dist: PRT

Paris, Ryan
DOLCE VITA.
Single (7"): released on Carrere America (USA), Sep'83 by Polygram.

Single (12"): released on Carrere America (USA), Sep'83 by Polygram.

FALL IN LOVE.
Single (7"): released on Carrere America (USA), Jan'84 by Polygram.

Single (12"): released on Carrere America (USA), Jan'84 by Polygram.

Paris Sisters

I LOVE HOW YOU LOVE ME.
Single (7"): released on Old Gold, Oct'83 by Old Gold Records. Dist: Lightning, Jazz Music, Spartan, Counterpoint

Paris, Texas

PARIS, TEXAS Original Soundtrack.
Album: released on Warner Bros., Feb'85 by Warner Bros Records. Dist: WEA

Cassette: released on Warner Bros., Feb'85 by Warner Bros Records. Dist: WEA

Paris, Twila

SAME GIRL.
Tracks: / Prince of peace / Running to the rescue / Let no man take your crown / Send me / Same girl / I feel it / Bonded together / Holy is the lord / Praise and worship medley.
Album:

Cassette:

Park

KICKING STONES.
Single (7"): released on C&D, Apr'83 by Phonogram Records. Dist: Polygram

PUTTING ON HER MAKEUP.
Single (7"): released on C&D, Oct'83 by Phonogram Records. Dist: Polygram

SINGER, (THE).
Single (7"): released on C&D, Aug'83 by Phonogram Records. Dist: Polygram

Single (12"): released on C&D, Aug'83 by Phonogram Records. Dist: Polygram

Park, Andy

SILK STOCKINGS.
Single (7"): released on Blue Hat, Sep'83 by Blue Hat Records. Dist: Blue Hat

Park Avenue

LOOKING FOR NUMBER ONE.
Single (7"): released on Offstreet, Jul'81 by Offstreet Records. Dist: EMI, Pinnacle

Parker, Belinda

DON'T MAKE WAVES.
Single (12"): released on B.B. Music, Nov'84 by B.B. Music Records. Dist: Jetstar

DREAM LOVER.
Single (12"): released on B.B. Music, Mar'85 by B.B. Music Records. Dist: Jetstar

GYPSY LOVE.
Single (12"): released on Sunburn, Mar'83 by Orbitone Records. Dist: Jetstar Distribution

HOLD TIGHT.
Single (12"): released on Whiplash, Apr'84 by Whiplash Records. Dist: Amanda Records Distribution

RED RED WINE.
Single (12"): released on Sunburn, Oct'83 by Orbitone Records. Dist: Jetstar Distribution

Parker, Billie Jean

TRUTH ABOUT BONNIE & CLYDE, THE.
Album: released on RCA, Oct'84 by RCA Records. Dist: RCA, Roots, Swift, Wellard, Chris, I & B, Solomon & Peres Distribution

Cassette: released on RCA, Oct'84 by RCA Records. Dist: RCA, Roots, Swift, Wellard, Chris, I & B, Solomon & Peres Distribution

Parker, Cecil

CHIRPIN.
Album: released on EMI, Dec'80 by EMI Records. Dist: EMI

Parker, Charlie

1947-1948.
Album: released on Musidisc (France), Aug'83 Dist: Discovery Distribution, Swift Distribution

ANTHOLOGY.
Triple album / cassette: released on Musidisc (France), Jun'84 Dist: Discovery Distribution, Swift Distribution

ANTHROPOLOGY.
Album: released on Spotlite, '83 by Spotlite Records. Dist: Cadillac, Jazz Music, Spotlite

APARTMENT SESSIONS.
Album: released on Spotlite, '83 by Spotlite Records. Dist: Cadillac, Jazz Music, Spotlite

AT THE PERSHING BALLROOM.
Album: released on Zim, Apr'81 Dist: JSU, Jazz Horizons, Jazz Music, Swift

BIRD AT THE ROOST.
Album: released on Savoy (USA), Mar'85 by Arista Records. Dist: Polygram, Swift

BIRD FLIES DEEP, THE Charlie Parker in live performance.
Tracks: / Move / Ornithology / Out of nowhere / Hot house / How high the moon / Bebop / Scrapple for the apple / Street beat / 'Round midnight / Koko / Groovin' high.
Album: released on Atlantis, Apr'87 by Charly Records. Dist: Charly

Cassette: released on Atlantis, Apr'87 by Charly Records. Dist: Charly

BIRD IN PARIS.
Album: released on Spotlite, '83 by Spotlite Records. Dist: Cadillac, Jazz Music, Spotlite

BIRD IS FREE.
Album: released on Rhapsody, Feb'82 by President Records. Dist: Taylors, Swift, Jazz Music, Wellard, Chris

BIRD ON TENOR 1943.
Album: released on Stash, Jun'86 Dist: Swift Distribution, Jazz Music Distribution, Jazz Horizons Distribution, Celtic Music Distribution, Cadillac, JSU Distribution, Zodiac Distribution

BIRD ON VERVE VOL.1.
Album: released on Verve (USA), Mar'84 by Polydor. Dist: Polygram

BIRD ON VERVE VOL 2.
Album: released on Verve (USA), Mar'84 by Polydor. Dist: Polygram

BIRD ON VERVE VOL 3.
Album: released on Verve (USA), Mar'84 by Polydor. Dist: Polygram

BIRD ON VERVE VOL 4.
:

BIRD ON VERVE VOL 5.
Album: released on Verve (USA), Apr'84 by Polydor. Dist: Polygram

BIRD ON VERVE VOL 6.
Album: released on Verve (USA), Apr'84 by Polydor. Dist: Polygram

BIRD ON VERVE VOL 7.
Album: released on Verve (USA), Apr'84 by Polydor. Dist: Polygram

BIRD ON VERVE VOL 8.
Album: released on Verve (USA), Apr'84 by Polydor. Dist: Polygram

BIRDS & FATS (Parker, Charlie Quintet).
Album: released on Jazz Live, Apr'81

BIRDS & FATS - VOL.2 (Parker, Charlie & Fats Navarro Quintet).
Album: released on Jazz Live, Apr'81

BIRD SONG.
Album: released on Star Jazz USA, Apr'86 by Charly Records. Dist: Charly Distribution

Cassette: released on Star Jazz USA, Apr'86 by Charly Records. Dist: Charly Distribution

BIRD SYMBOLS.
Album: released on Rhapsody, Nov'80 by President Records. Dist: Taylors, Swift, Jazz Music, Wellard, Chris

BIRD, THE.
Album: released on Astan, Nov'84 by Astan Records. Dist: Counterpoint

Cassette: released on Astan, Nov'84 by Astan Records. Dist: Counterpoint

BIRD, THE SAVOY RECORDINGS, THE MASTER TAKES.
Album:

CHALRIE PARKER, VOL.2.
Album: Dist: PRT

CHARLIE PARKER.
Cassette: released on Audio Fidelity, Oct'84 Dist: PRT

Album: released on Queen-Disc, Apr'81 Dist: Celtic Music, JSU, Jazz Horizons, Jazz Music

Album: released on Queen-Disc, Apr'81 Dist: Celtic Music, JSU, Jazz Horizons, Jazz Music

Double Album: released on Prestige, Jul'75 by Prestige Records (USA). Dist: RCA, JSU, Swift

Album: released on Jazz Live, Apr'81

CHARLIE PARKER AT STORYVILLE.
Tracks: / Moose on the mooche / I'll walk alone / Ornithology / Out of nowhere / Now's the time / Don't blame me / Dancing on the ceiling / Cool blues / Groovin' high.
Notes: Previously unreleased recordings of the legendary sax player, recorded in two sessions for radio broadcast in 1953. Of all the great figures in jazz, Charlie 'Bird' Parker's work remains undoubtedly the most influential - his life the most written about.
Album: released on Blue Note, Dec'85 by EMI Records. Dist: EMI

CHARLIE PARKER COLLECTION, THE.
Album: released on Deja Vu, Aug'85 by Deja Vu Records. Dist: Counterpoint Distribution, Record Services Distribution (Ireland)

Cassette: released on Deja Vu, Aug'85 by Deja Vu Records. Dist: Counterpoint Distribution, Record Services Distribution (Ireland)

CHARLIE PARKER & DIZZY GILLESPIE (Parker, Charlie & Dizzy Gillespie).
Album: released on Jazz Reactivation, Jan'82 Dist: PRT

Album: released on EMI Europe, Jun'84 by EMI Records. Dist: Conifer

Cassette: released on EMI Europe, Jun'84 by EMI Records. Dist: Conifer

CHARLIE PARKER IN SWEDEN.
Double Album: released on Spotlite, '83 by Spotlite Records. Dist: Cadillac, Jazz Music, Spotlite

CHARLIE PARKER & MILES DAVIS (see also Miles Davis) (Parker, Charlie & Miles Davis).
Album: released on Chase Music, Nov'84 by Chase Records. Dist: PRT

Cassette: released on Chase Music, Nov'84 by Chase Records. Dist: PRT

CHARLIE PARKER, VOL. 1.
Album: released on Jazz Reactivation, Jan'82 Dist: PRT

CHARLIE PARKER WITH THE ORCHESTRA.
Album: released on Elektra(Musician), Mar'82 by WEA Records. Dist: WEA

CHOICE BIRD (Parker/Charles).
Album: released on Jazz Bird, '82 Dist: Cassion (Melandy)

Cassette: released on Jazz Bird, '82 Dist: Cassion (Melandy)

COLE PORTER SONGBOOK, THE.
Album: released on Verve, Aug'85 by Phonogram Records. Dist: Polygram

COMPLETE ROYAL ROOST PERFORMANCES, VOL. 3 The Savoy Years.
Tracks: / Deedle - 1 / Deedle - 2 / Cheryl- 1 / Half-nelson / Night in Tunisia / Scrapple from the apple / What's this? / Anthropology / Hurry home / Royal Roost bop (all the things you are) / Cheryl - 2 / Slow boat to China / Chasin' the bird.
Album: released on RCA, Oct'86 by RCA Records. Dist: RCA, Roots, Swift, Wellard, Chris, I & B, Solomon & Peres Distribution

Cassette: released on RCA, Oct'86 by RCA Records. Dist: RCA, Roots, Swift, Wellard, Chris, I & B, Solomon & Peres Distribution

COMPLETE ROYAL ROOST PERFORMANCES, VOL. 2 Bird at the roost.
Tracks: / How high the moon / Scrapple from the apple - 1 / Be-bop - 1 / Hot house / Oop bop sh'bam / Scrapple from the apple - 2 / Scrapple from the apple - 3 / Scrapple from the apple - 4 / Salt peanuts - 1 / Salt peanuts - 2 / Salt peanuts - 3 / Groovin' high - 1 / Groovin' high - 2 / Barbados - 1 / Barbados - 2 / Confirmation / Bebop - 2.
Double cassette: released on RCA, Jan'87 by RCA Records. Dist: RCA, Roots, Swift, Wellard, Chris, I & B, Solomon & Peres Distribution

COMPLETE SAVOY SESSIONS VOLUME 3(THE).
Tracks: / Donna Lee / Chasing the bird / Cheryl / Buzzy / Milestones / Little Willie leaps.
Album: released on RCA, Nov'85 by RCA Records. Dist: RCA, Roots, Swift, Wellard, Chris, I & B, Solomon & Peres Distribution

Cassette: released on RCA, Nov'85 by RCA Records. Dist: RCA, Roots, Swift, Wellard, Chris, I & B, Solomon & Peres Distribution

COMPLETE SAVOY SESSION, VOLUME 2.
Album: released on RCA, Oct'85 by RCA Records. Dist: RCA, Roots, Swift, Wellard, Chris, I & B, Solomon & Peres Distribution

Cassette: released on RCA, Oct'85 by RCA Records. Dist: RCA, Roots, Swift, Wellard, Chris, I & B, Solomon & Peres Distribution

COMPLETE SAVOY SESSIONS VOL. 1.
Tracks: / Tiny's tempo / I'll always love you just the same / Romance without finance / Red cross / Billie's bounce / Warming up a riff.
Album: released on Savoy (France), Feb'85

COMPLETE SAVOY SESSIONS.
Album:

COMPLETE SAVOY SESSIONS, VOL 5 (1948).
Tracks: / Parker's mood (Takes 3 & 4) / Parker's mood (Take 5) / Perhaps (Take 1) / Perhaps (Takes 2 & 3) / Perhaps (Takes 4, 5, & 6) / Perhaps (Take 7) / Marmaduke (Takes 1, 2, & 3) / Marmaduke (Takes 4 & 5) / Marmaduke (Takes 6, 7, 8 & 9) / Marmaduke (Takes 10, 11, & 12) / Steeplechase (Takes 1 & 2) / Merry go round (Take 1) / Merry go round (Take 2) / Parker's mood (Takes 1 & 2).
Album: released on RCA, Jan'87 by RCA Records. Dist: RCA, Roots, Swift, Wellard, Chris, I & B, Solomon & Peres Distribution

Cassette: released on RCA, Jan'87 by RCA Records. Dist: RCA, Roots, Swift, Wellard, Chris, I & B, Solomon & Peres Distribution

COMPLETE SAVOY SESSIONS VOLUME 4.
Tracks: / Half Nelson / Sippin' at bell's / Another hair-do / Bluebird / Klaunstance / Bird gets the worm / Barbados / Ah leu cha / Constellation.
Album: released on Savoy, Jul'86

Cassette: released on Savoy, Jul'86

CONCERT MASSEY HALL TORONTO (MAY 15, 1953) (see also Dizzy Gillespie) (Parker, Charlie & Dizzy Gillespie).
Album: released on Joker, Apr'84 Dist: Counterpoint, Mainline, Record Services Distribution (Ireland)

COOL BLUES.
Album: released on Jazz Live, Apr'81

DIAL 6 LP BOX SET The stupendous Charlie Parker dial masters Vol 1.
Boxed set: released on Spotlite, '83 by Spotlite Records. Dist: Cadillac, Jazz Music, Spotlite

DIAL 7 LP BOX SET The stupendous Charlie Parker dial masters Vol 2.
Boxed set: released on Spotlite, '83 by Spotlite Records. Dist: Cadillac, Jazz Music, Spotlite

DIAL MASTERS VOL 1.
Album: released on Spotlite, '83 by Spotlite Records. Dist: Cadillac, Jazz Music, Spotlite

DIAL MASTERS VOL 2.
Album: released on Spotlite, '83 by Spotlite Records. Dist: Cadillac, Jazz Music, Spotlite

DIAL MASTERS VOL 3.
Album: released on Spotlite, '83 by Spotlite Records. Dist: Cadillac, Jazz Music, Spotlite

DIAL MASTERS VOL 4.
Album: released on Spotlite, '83 by Spotlite Records. Dist: Cadillac, Jazz Music, Spotlite

DIAL MASTERS VOL 5.
Album: released on Spotlite, '83 by Spotlite Records. Dist: Cadillac, Jazz Music, Spotlite

DIAL MASTERS VOL 6.
Album: released on Spotlite, '83 by Spotlite Records. Dist: Cadillac, Jazz Music, Spotlite

DIAL MATERIAL.
Album: released on Joker (Import), Apr'81

DIAL MATERIAL VOL 1.
Album: released on Up International, Apr'81

DIAL MATERIAL VOL 2.
Album: released on Up International, Apr'81

DIAL MATERIAL VOL 3.
Album: released on Up International, Apr'81

ENCORES.
Album:

ENCORES VOL 2.
Album:

EVERY BIT OF IT.
Double Album: released on Spotlite, '83 by Spotlite Records. Dist: Cadillac, Jazz Music, Spotlite

FRAGMENTS.
Album: released on Audio Fidelity, Sep'84 Dist: PRT

HALLELUJAH (Parker, Charlie & Dizzy Gillespie).
Album: released on Kings Of Jazz, Apr'81 Dist: Jazz Horizons, Jazz Music, Celtic Music

HAPPY BIRD, THE.
Album: released on Rhapsody, Mar'81 by President Records. Dist: Taylors, Swift, Jazz Music, Wellard, Chris

IN SWEDEN.
Notes: Recorded 1950
Compact disc: released on Storyville, Jun'87 by Storyville Records. Dist: Jazz Music Distribution, Swift Distribution, Chris Wellard Distribution, Counterpoint Distribution

IN SWEDEN 1950.
Album: released on Storyville, Jun'86 by Sto-

Page 764

ryville Records. Dist: Jazz Music Distribution, Swift Distribution, Chris Wellard Distribution, Counterpoint Distribution

IT HAPPENED ONE NIGHT (Parker, Charlie / Dizzy Gillespie / Ella Fitzgrald).
Album: released on Natural Organic Import, Apr'81

LIVE AT THE CAFE SOCIETY.
Album: released on Audio Fidelity, Sep'84 Dist: PRT

LIVE AT THE ROCKLAND PALACE.
Album: released on Audio Fidelity, Aug'84 Dist: PRT

Cassette: released on Audio Fidelity, Aug'84 Dist: PRT

LULLABY IN RHYTHM.
Album: released on Spotlite, '83 by Spotlite Records. Dist: Cadillac, Jazz Music, Spotlite

MAGNIFICENT BIRD.
Album: released on Meteor, Sep'85 by Magnum Music Group Ltd. Dist: Magnum Music Group Ltd, PRT Distribution, Spartan Distribution

MILES DAVIS, DIZZY GILLESPIE & CHARLIE PARKER (see Davis, Miles) (Parker, Charlie/Miles Davis/Dizzy Gillespie).

Miles of jazz

MOVE (Parker, Charlie/Fats Navarro/Bud Powell).
Album: released on Kings Of Jazz, Apr'81 Dist: Jazz Horizons, Jazz Music, Celtic Music

NEW BIRD.
Album: released on Phoenix, Apr'81 by Audio Fidelity Enterprises. Dist: Stage One, Lugtons

NEW BIRD, VOL 2.
Album: released on Phoenix, Apr'81 by Audio Fidelity Enterprises. Dist: Stage One, Lugtons

NOW'S THE TIME.
Compact disc: by Polydor Records. Dist: Polygram, Polydor

Album: released on Verve, May'82 by Phonogram Records. Dist: Polygram

Compact disc: released on Verve, May'82 by Phonogram Records. Dist: Polygram

ONCE THERE WAS BIRD.
Album: released on Rhapsody, Nov'80 by President Records. Dist: Taylors, Swift, Jazz Music, Wellard, Chris

ONE NIGHT IN CHICAGO.
Album:

SAVOY MASTER TAKES.
Tracks: / Tinyms tempo / Red cross / Warming up a riff / Billie's bounce / Now's the time / Thriving on a riff / Koko / Donna Lee / Chasin' the bird / Milestones / Little willie leaps / Half Nelson / Sippin' at bells / Another hair-do / Bluebird / Klaunstance / Bird gets the worm / Barbados / Ah-leu cha / Constellation / Parker's mood / Perhaps / Marmaduke / Steeple chase / Merry-go-round.
Compact disc: released on RCA, Mar'86 by RCA Records. Dist: RCA, Roots, Swift, Wellard, Chris, I & B, Solomon & Peres Distribution

VOLUME 2 (Parker, Charlie/Miles Davis/Dizzy Gillespie).
Album: released on Jazz Reactivation, Jul'83 Dist: PRT

YARDBIRD - DC - 53.
Album: released on VGM, Apr'83 Dist: Jazz Horizons, JSU

YARDBIRD IN LOTUS LAND.
Album: released on Spotlite, '83 by Spotlite Records. Dist: Cadillac, Jazz Music, Spotlite

Parker, Evan

AT THE UNITY THEATRE (Parker, Evan & Paul Lytton).
Album: released on Incus, Nov'76 Dist: Jazz Music, Cadillac

COLLECTIVE CALLS (URBAN) (Parker, Evan & Paul Lytton).
Album: released on Incus, Nov'76 Dist: Jazz Music, Cadillac

LONGEST NIGHT, VOL 1 (see Stevens, John) (Parker, Evan & John Stevens).

LONGEST NIGHT,VOL.1 (Parker, Evan & John Stevens).
Single (7"): released on Ogun, Feb'78 Dist: Jazz Music, JSU, Cadillac. Estim retail price in Jul'87 was £3.48.

LONGEST NIGHT, VOL 2 (see Stevens, John) (Parker, Evan & John Stevens).

SAXOPHONE SOLOS.
Album: released on Incus, Nov'76 Dist: Jazz Music, Cadillac

SECOND EVAN PARKER SOLO A1.
Album: released on Incus, '78 Dist: Jazz Music, Cadillac

TOPOGRAPHY OF THE LUNGS (Parker, Evan & Derek Bailey).
Album: released on Incus, Nov'76 Dist: Jazz Music, Cadillac

Parker,Graham

ANOTHER GREY AREA.
Album: released on RCA, Mar'82 by RCA Records. Dist: RCA, Roots, Swift, Wellard, Chris, I & B, Solomon & Peres Distribution

ANY TROUBLE.
Album: released on Stiff, Jun'80 by Stiff Records. Dist: EMI, Record Services Distribution (Ireland)

BEST OF GRAHAM PARKER AND THE RUMOUR, THE.
Album: released on Vertigo, May'82 by Phonogram Records. Dist: Polygram

Cassette: released on Vertigo, May'82 by Phonogram Records. Dist: Polygram

IT DON'T MEAN A THING IF IT AIN'T GOT THAT SWING (Parker,Graham & the Rumours).
Album: released on Philips, May'84 Dist: IMS-Polygram

Cassette: released on Philips, May'84 Dist: IMS-Polygram

LIFE GETS BETTER.
Single (7"): released on RCA, Jul'83 by RCA Records. Dist: RCA, Roots, Swift, Wellard, Chris, I & B, Solomon & Peres Distribution

Single (12"): released on RCA, Jul'83 by RCA Records. Dist: RCA, Roots, Swift, Wellard, Chris, I & B, Solomon & Peres Distribution

LOVE WITHOUT GREED y.
Single (7"): released on Stiff, Jun'80 by Stiff Records. Dist: EMI, Record Services Distribution (Ireland)

NO MORE EXCUSES.
Single (7"): released on RCA, Jul'82 by RCA Records. Dist: RCA, Roots, Swift, Wellard, Chris, I & B, Solomon & Peres Distribution

REAL MACAW, THE.
Album: released on RCA, Sep'83 by RCA Records. Dist: RCA, Roots, Swift, Wellard, Chris, I & B, Solomon & Peres Distribution

Cassette: released on RCA, Sep'83 by RCA Records. Dist: RCA, Roots, Swift, Wellard, Chris, I & B, Solomon & Peres Distribution

STEADY NERVES (Parker,Graham & The Shot).
Tracks: / Break them down / Might rivers / Lunatic fringe / Wake up(next to you) / When you do that to me / weekend's too short / Take everything back / Black lincoln continental / Canned laughter / Everyone's hand is on the switch / Locked into grgeen.
Notes: Digital stereo recording.
Compact disc: released on Elektra (USA), Apr'85 by Elektra/Asylum/Nonesuch Records. Dist: WEA

Album: released on Elektra, Apr'85 by WEA Records. Dist: WEA

Single (12"): released on Elektra, Apr'85 by WEA Records. Dist: WEA Deleted '86.

UP ESCALATOR, THE.
Album: released on Stiff, Apr'80 by Stiff Records. Dist: EMI, Record Services Distribution (Ireland)

Cassette: released on Stiff, Apr'80 by Stiff Records. Dist: EMI, Record Services Distribution (Ireland)

YOU CAN'T TAKE LOVE FOR GRANTED.
Single (7"): released on RCA, Oct'83 by RCA Records. Dist: RCA, Roots, Swift, Wellard, Chris, I & B, Solomon & Peres Distribution

Parker, Greg

BLACK DOG.
Tracks: / Future perfect.
Single (7"): released on Mec, Nov'86

Single (12"): released on Mec, Nov'86

Parker, Johnny

BOOGIE WOOGIE.
Album: released on Dawn Club, Dec'86 Dist: Cadillac, Swift, JSU

JOHNNY PARKER'S BOOGIE WOOGIE TRIO.
Album: released on Dawn (USA), May'84 by Dawn Records (USA). Dist: VJM

JOHNNY PARKER TRIO (Parker, Johnny Trio).
Album: released on Dawn Club, May'79 Dist: Cadillac, Swift, JSU

Parker, Junior

BAREFOOT, ROCK, (THE) (see Bland, Bobby) (Parker, Junior & Bobby Bland).

LEGENDARY SUN PERFORMERS, THE (Parker, Junior & Billy 'Red' Love).
Album: released on Charly, Nov'77 by Charly Records. Dist: Charly, Cadillac

Parker, Ken

GLINT OF GOLD, A.
Album: released on Pisces, May'86 Dist: Jetstar

GOD BLESS OUR LOVE.
Single (12"): released on Pama, Dec'82 by Pama Records. Dist: Pama, Enterprise, Jetstar

JIMMY BROWN.
Tracks: / Holy holy medley.
Single (12"): released on Time, Jan'87 Dist: Jetstar Distribution

THREE BELLS.
Single (12"): released on Clouds, Jan'84 by Clouds Records. Dist: Jetstar

Parker, Kim

SOMETIMES I'M BLUE.
Compact disc: released on Soul Note (Italy), '86 Dist: Harmonia Mundi Distributors

Parker, Knocky

EIGHT ON EIGHTY-EIGHT - VOL.15.
Album: released on Euphonic, Apr'79 by Euphonic Records. Dist: Jazz Music, Swift

FROM CAKEWALK TO RAGTIME.
Notes: With:Bill Coffman/R.Rhodes.Mono recording.
Album: released on Jazzology, Jun'86 Dist: Jazz Music, Swift

Parker, Leo

LET ME TELL YOU 'BOUT IT.
Album: released on Blue Note (USA Import), Sep'84

ROLLIN' WITH LEO.
Tracks: / Lion's roar (The) / Bad girl / Rollin' with Leo / Music hall beat / Jumpin' Leo / Stuffy / Talkin' the blues / Mad lad returns / Daphne.
Album: released on Blue Note, Jul'86 by EMI Records. Dist: EMI

Parker, Little Junior

I WANNA RAMBLE.
Album: released on Ace, Feb'82 by Ace Records. Dist: Pinnacle, Swift, Hotshot, Cadillac

Parker, Louis

IS THAT YOU.
Single (7"): released on Red Bus, Sep'85 by Red Bus Records. Dist: PRT

Parker, Paul

DESIRE.
Single (7"): released on Technique, Mar'84 by Technique. Dist: CBS

Single (12"): released on Technique, Mar'84 by Technique. Dist: CBS

Parker, Pop

JUST ASK NICK AYLING.
Tracks: / Just ask Nick Ayling.
Single (7"): released on Goldeb Pathway, Sep'86 Dist: Revolver, Cartel

Parker, Ray Jnr.

GHOSTBUSTERS.
Single (7"): released on Arista, Nov'84 by Arista Records. Dist: RCA

Single (12"): released on Arista, Nov'84 by Arista Records. Dist: RCA

Special: released on Arista, Nov'84 by Arista Records. Dist: RCA

Special: released on Arista, Nov'84 by Arista Records. Dist: RCA

GIRLS ARE MORE FUN.
Tracks: / Girls are more fun / I'm in love / Ghost busters.
Single (12"): released on Arista, Dec'85 by Arista Records. Dist: RCA

Single (7"): released on Arista, Nov'85 by Arista Records. Dist: RCA

OTHER WOMAN, THE.
Album: released on Arista, May'82 by Arista Records. Dist: RCA

Cassette: released on Arista, May'82 by Arista Records. Dist: RCA

SEX AND THE SINGLE MAN.
Album: released on Arista, Oct'85 by Arista Records. Dist: RCA

Cassette: released on Arista, Oct'85 by Arista Records. Dist: RCA

VERY BEST OF RAY PARKER JNR..
Album: released on Arista, Dec'82 by Arista Records. Dist: RCA

Cassette: released on Arista, Dec'82 by Arista Records. Dist: RCA

WOMAN NEEDS LOVE, A (Parker, Ray Jnr.& Raydio).
Album: released on Arista, Apr'81 by Arista Records. Dist: RCA

WOMAN OUT OF CONTROL.
Album: released on Arista, Nov'83 by Arista Records. Dist: RCA

Cassette: released on Arista, Nov'83 by Arista Records. Dist: RCA

YOU CAN'T CHANGE THAT/BAD BOY.
Single (7"): released on Arista, Feb'83 by Arista Records. Dist: RCA

Single (12"): released on Arista, Feb'83 by Arista Records. Dist: RCA

Parker, Robert

BARE FOOTIN'.
Tracks: / Bare Footin' / Duke of earl.
Single (7"): released on Important, Aug'86 Dist: EMI

BAREFOOTIN'.
Tracks: / Barefootin' / Let's go baby (where the action is).
Single (7"): released on Charly, Jul'87 by Charly Records. Dist: Charly, Cadillac

Single (12"): released on Charly, Jul'87 by Charly Records. Dist: Charly, Cadillac

BAREFOOTIN.
Single (7"): released on Creole, Aug'84 by Creole Records. Dist: Rhino, PRT

BAREFOOTIN/TROPICAL.
Single (7"): released on Charly, Jul'80 by Charly Records. Dist: Charly, Cadillac

Parker, Shan Lee

WORK IT OUT.
Single (7"): released on VP, Jun'84 by VP Records. Dist: Pinnacle

FUGITIVE FROM BROKEN DREAMS.
Tracks: / Fugitive from broken dreams.
Single (7"): released on Garden Isle, Jan'86 Dist: Maingrove Enterprises Distribution

GOOD TIME TONIGHT.
Album: released on President, Apr'83 by President Records. Dist: Taylors, Spartan

I'LL TAKE YOU THERE AGAIN.
Album: released on Garden Isle, Jan'86 Dist: Maingrove Enterprises Distribution

MONTANA SKIES.
Single (7"): released on Garden Isle, Jun'85 Dist: Maingrove Enterprises Distribution

SUSQUEHANNA RIVER VALLEY SONG.
Single (7"): released on President, Apr'83 by President Records. Dist: Taylors, Spartan

WHITE LINES NORTH.
Single (7"): released on Garden Isle, Mar'85 Dist: Maingrove Enterprises Distribution

Parkes, Clarence

RUN UP AND DOWN IN THE DARK.
Single (12"): released on Rola, Aug'82 by Rola Records. Dist: Roots Distribution, JSU Distribution, Spartan Distribution

TAKE A MIRICLE/VERSION (PIC DISC).
Single (7"): released on Roller, Aug'82

Parkins, Molly

PURPLE PASSES.
Cassette: released on Response, May'81 by Priority Records. Dist: BMG

Parkinson, Michael

BEER IS BEST/TWO HEADS ARE BETTER THAN ONE.
Single (7"): released on Paramount, Nov'83 by Paramount Records. Dist: PRT

PARKINSON MEETS THE GOONS.
Album: released on BBC, Nov'76 by BBC Records & Tapes. Dist: EMI, PRT, Pye

Parkinson, Philip

CONTROL THEM/TAKE US HOME.
Single (12"): released on Twinkle, Sep'83 by Twinkle Records. Dist: Jetstar

Parkinson, Robin

TWO STORIES FROM BUTTON MOON.
Cassette: released on Red Bus, Aug'85 by Red Bus Records. Dist: PRT

Park, Lloyd

BABY HANG UP THE PHONE.
Tracks: / Baby hang up the phone / 18 with the bullet.
Single (7"): released on Classy, Apr'86 Dist: PRT

Park Mains School

SOUNDS OF PARK MAINS HIGH, THE (Park Mains School - Erskine).
Album:

Parkside Shivers

PARKSIDE SHIVERS various artists (Various Artists).
Album: released on Leeds Independent, Jan'85 by Revolver Records. Dist: Cartel

Parkside Steelworks

PARKSIDE STEELWORKS Various artists (Various Artists).
Album: released on Leeds Independent, Jun'85 by Revolver Records. Dist: Cartel

Park, Simon Orchestra

EYE LEVEL.
Tracks: / Eye level / Floral dance, The.
Single (7"): released on Old Gold, Apr'86 by Old Gold Records. Dist: Lightning, Jazz Music, Spartan, Counterpoint

Parks, Lloyd

HELLO.
Single (12"): released on Tads, Jul'84 by Tads Records. Dist: Jetstar Distribution

NO WAR IN THE DANCE/ROCK.
Single (12"): released on Plantation, Aug'82 Dist: Jetstar

Parks, Van Dyke

CLANG OF THE YANKEE REAPER.
Album: released on Edsel, Nov'86 by Demon Records. Dist: Pinnacle, Jazz Music, Projection

DISCOVER AMREICA.
Album: released on Edsel, Nov'86 by Demon Records. Dist: Pinnacle, Jazz Music, Projection

SONG CYCLE.
Album: released on Edsel, Nov'86 by Demon Records. Dist: Pinnacle, Jazz Music, Projection

Parlan, Horace

BLUE PARLAN (Parlen, Horace Trio).
Album: released on Steeplechase, Sep'79

HAPPY FRAME OF MIND.
Tracks: / Home is africa / Tune for Richard, A / Back from the gig / Dexi / Kucheza blues / Happy frame of mind.
Notes: In the late fifties and sixties Horace Parlan was not only a frequent Blue Note recording artists,but also one of the label's busiest 'house' pianists,recordingwith Lou Donaldson,Stanley Turrentine,Dexter Gordon, and many others.This sextetdate with tenor saxophonist Booker Ervin and guitarist Grant Green offers a brilliant selection of tunes including Ronnie Boykin's "Home is Africa" and Randy Westons' "Kucheza Blues"
Album: released on Blue Note, Jul'86 by EMI Records. Dist: EMI

MUSICALLY YOURS.
Album: released on Steeplechase, May'81

PANNONICA (Parlen, Horace Trio).
Album: released on Enja (Germany), Feb'85 by Enja Records (W.Germany). Dist: Cadillac Music

SANDRA JEAN (Parlan, Horace/Don Pender).
Notes: see under Don Pender.

TROUBLE IN MIND (Parlan, Horace & Archie Shepp).
Album: released on Steeplechase(USA), Sep'81

US THREE.
Album: released on Blue Note (USA), Sep'84

Parliament

GLORYHALLASTOOPID.
Album: released on Casablanca, Jan'80 Dist: Polygram, Phonogram

I CALL MY BABY PUSSYCAT.
Single (7"): released on HDH(Holland/Dozier/Holland), Dec'84 by Demon Records. Dist: Pinnacle

MOTHERSHIP CONNECTION.
Album: released on Casablanca, Aug'87 Dist: Polygram, Phonogram

Cassette: released on Casablanca, Aug'87 Dist: Polygram, Phonogram

TROMBIPULATION.
Album: released on Casablanca, Apr'81 Dist: Polygram, Phonogram

UNCUT FUNK-THE BOMB The best of Parliament.
Tracks: / P-Funk(wants to get funked) / Give up the Funk(Tear the roof off the sucker) / Up for the down stroke / Chocolate city / Big bang theory,The / Flashlight / Gloryhallastoopid (Pin the tail on the Funk) / Aqua boogie (A Psycholiphadisco-betabioaquadoloop).
Album: released on Club, Sep'86 by Phonogram Records. Dist: Polygram

Cassette: released on Club, Sep'86 by Phonogram Records. Dist: Polygram

Parma, Edward Jnr

KING KONG IN HONG KONG.
Single (7"): released on Code, Sep'82 by Code Records. Dist: Jetstar, EMI

Parnell, Jack

50 BIG BAND FAVOURITES (Parnell, Jack & His Orchestra/Joe Loss & His Orchestra).
Cassette: released on Trio, Nov'84 by MFP. Dist: EMI

BIG HAND STEREO SPECTACULAR (Parnell, Jack & His Orchestra/Joe Loss & His Orchestra).
Double Album: released on MFP, Sep'81 by EMI Records. Dist: EMI

Double cassette: released on MFP, Sep'81 by EMI Records. Dist: EMI

PORTRAIT OF CHARLIE GILBRAITH.
Album: released on Plant Life, Aug'77 Dist: Roots

Parrish, Dean

I'M ON MY WAY + 2 TRS V/A.
Single (7"): released on RK, Feb'78

Parrish, Mick

WELCOME BACK TO MICK PARRISH.
Album: released on Jin, Feb'79 by Priority Records. Dist: EMI

Parr, John

JOHN PARR.
Compact disc: by London Records. Dist: Polygram

Album: released on London, Oct'85 by London Records. Dist: Polygram

Cassette: released on London, Oct'85 by London Records. Dist: Polygram

NAUGHTY NAUGHTY.
Tracks: / Naughty naughty / Revenge / Everything they said was true.
Single (7"): released on London, Jan'86 by London Records. Dist: Polygram

Single (12"): released on London, Jan'86 by London Records. Dist: Polygram

RUNNING THE ENDLESS MILE.
Album: released on London, Oct'86 by London Records. Dist: Polygram

Cassette: released on London, Oct'86 by London Records. Dist: Polygram

Compact disc: released on London, Dec'86 by London Records. Dist: Polygram

TWO HEARTS.
Tracks: / Two hearts / Two hearts(Version) / Somebody stole my thunder.
Single (7"): released on London, Sep'86 by London Records. Dist: Polygram

Single (12"): released on London, Sep'86 by London Records. Dist: Polygram

Parrots

PHOTOGRAPHY SONG/HOME SWEET HOME.
Single (12"): released on Attrix, Aug'80 Dist: Pinnacle, Rough Trade

Parr, Sheila

LONDON REVUE HIGHLIGHTS (Parr, Sheila & The National Philharmonic Orchestra).
Album: released on Crescendo, Sep'85 by Crescendo Records. Dist: Pinnacle

Cassette: released on Crescendo, Sep'85 by Crescendo Records. Dist: Pinnacle

Parry, Bernie

'A' TO 'Z' OF LONDON.
Single (7"): released on Celtic Music, Oct'81 by Celtic Music Distribution. Dist: Celtic Music, Jazz Music, Projection, Roots

SAILING TO THE MOON.
Album: released on Free Reed, Jan'87 by Free Reed Records. Dist: Roots, Projection, Hobgoblin Records, Oblivion

Parry, Big John

MARIA/ROMEO.
Single (7"): released on Lady London, Dec'83 by Joanne Barrett.

Parry, Harry

PARRY OPUS (Parry, Harry & His Radio Rhythm Club Sextet).
Album: released on EMI Retrospect, Oct'84 by EMI Records. Dist: EMI Deleted '86.

Cassette: released on EMI Retrospect, Oct'84 by EMI Records. Dist: EMI Deleted '86.

Parsons, Alan

I ROBOT.
Album: released on Arista, Jul'77 by Arista Records. Dist: RCA

Cassette: released on Arista, Jul'77 by Arista Records. Dist: RCA

PYRAMID.
Album: released on Voyager, May'78

Cassette: released on Voyager, May'78

TALES OF MYSTERY & IMAGINATION (EDGER ALLEN POE).
Album: released on Charisma, Jun'76 by Virgin Records. Dist: EMI

Cassette: released on Charisma, Nov'82 by Virgin Records. Dist: EMI

Parsons, Alan Project

AMMONIA AVENUE.
Album: released on Arista, Feb'84 by Arista Records. Dist: RCA

Cassette: released on Arista, Feb'84 by Arista Records. Dist: RCA

Compact disc: released on Arista, Feb'84 by Arista Records. Dist: RCA

AMONIA AVENUE.
Tracks: / Prime time / Let me go home / One god reason / Since the last goodbye / Don't answer me / Dancing on a high wire / You don't believe / Pipeline / Amonia avenue.
Compact disc: released on Arista, Mar'84 by Arista Records. Dist: RCA

Tracks: / I wouldn't like to be like you / Eye in the sky / Games people play / Time / Pyromania / You don't believe / Lucifer / Damned if I do / Pyschobabble / Don't let it show / Can't take it with you / Old and wise.
Compact disc: released on Arista, Feb'87 by Arista Records. Dist: RCA

BEST OF ALAN PARSONS PROJECT THE.
Album: released on Arista, Oct'83 by Arista Records. Dist: RCA

Cassette: released on Arista, Oct'83 by Arista Records. Dist: RCA

DON'T ANSWER ME.
Single (7"): released on Arista, Feb'84 by Arista Records. Dist: RCA

Single (12"): released on Arista, Feb'84 by Arista Records. Dist: RCA

Picture disc single: released on Arista, Feb'84 by Arista Records. Dist: RCA

EVE.
Tracks: / Lucifer / You lie down with the dogs / I'd rather be a man / You won't be there / Winding me up / Damned if I do / Don't hold back / Secret garden / If I could change your mind.
Compact disc: released on Arista, Feb'87 by Arista Records. Dist: RCA

Album: released on Fame (Arista), Jul'83 by Music For Pleasure Records. Dist: EMI

Cassette: released on Fame (Arista), Jul'83 by Music For Pleasure Records. Dist: EMI

EVE IN THE SKY.
Album: released on Arista, May'82 by Arista Records. Dist: RCA

Cassette: released on Arista, May'82 by Arista Records. Dist: RCA

Compact disc: released on Arista, Jan'83 by Arista Records. Dist: RCA

EVE IN THE SKY/GEMINI.
Single (7"): released on Arista, May'82 by Arista Records. Dist: RCA

EYE IN THE SKY.
Compact disc: released on Arista, May'83 by Arista Records. Dist: RCA

GAUDI.
Tracks: / La sagrada familia / Too late / Closer to heaven / Standing on higher ground / Money talks / Inside looking out / Paseo de gracia.
Album: released on Arista, Jan'87 by Arista Records. Dist: RCA

Cassette: released on Arista, Jan'87 by Arista Records. Dist: RCA

Compact disc: released on Arista, Feb'87 by Arista Records. Dist: RCA

I ROBOT.
Notes: Starr marketing services Ltd,90 Queens Road,Twickenham,Middlesex.TW1 4ET. TEL:01-891 6487
Compact disc: released on Mobile Fidelity, Oct'86 by Mobile Fidelity Records.

I, ROBOT (ARISTA C.D.).
Tracks: / I wouldn't want to be like you / Some other time / Breakdown / Don't let it show / Voice (The) / Nucleus / Day after day / Total eclipse / Genesis / I, robot.
Compact disc: released on Arista, Feb'87 by Arista Records. Dist: RCA

LETS TALK ABOUT ME.
Single (7"): released on Arista, Jan'85 by Arista Records. Dist: RCA

Single (12"): released on Arista, Jan'85 by Arista Records. Dist: RCA

OLD AND WISE/CHILDREN OF THE MOON.
Single (7"): released on Arista, Nov'82 by Arista Records. Dist: RCA

PRIME TIME.
Single (7"): released on Arista, Jun'84 by Arista Records. Dist: RCA

Single (12"): released on Arista, Jun'84 by Arista Records. Dist: RCA

PYRAMID.
Tracks: / Voyager / What goes up... / Eagle will rise again (The) / One more river / Can't take it with you / In the lap of the Gods / Pyramania / Hyper-gamma-spaces / Shadow of a lonely man.
Compact disc: released on Arista, Feb'87 by Arista Records. Dist: RCA

STEREOTOMY.
Tracks: / Stereotomy / Urbania(Instrumental).
Notes: Produced by Alan Parsons.Features guest vocalists John Miles,Chris Rainbow,Gary Brooker(Procul Harum).Also features the Philharmonia Orchestra.
Album: released on Arista, Dec'85 by Arista Records. Dist: RCA

Cassette: released on Arista, Dec'85 by Arista Records. Dist: RCA

Compact disc: released on Arista, Dec'85 by Arista Records. Dist: RCA

Single (7"): released on Arista, Mar'86 by Arista Records. Dist: RCA

Single (12"): released on Arista, Mar'86 by Arista Records. Dist: RCA

TURN OF A FRIENDLY CARD.
Tracks: / Turn of a friendly card / Gold bug (The) / Time / Games people play / I don't wanna go home / Nothing left to lose / May be a price to pay.
Compact disc: released on Arista, Feb'87 by Arista Records. Dist: RCA

Album: released on Arista, Oct'80 by Arista Records. Dist: RCA

VULTURE CULTURE.
Tracks: / Let's talk about me / Seperate lives / Days are numbers (The traveller) / Sooner or later / Vulture Culture / Hawkeye / Somebody out there / Same old song (The).
Album: released on Arista, Feb'85 by Arista Records. Dist: RCA

Cassette: released on Arista, Feb'85 by Arista Records. Dist: RCA

Compact disc: released on Arista, Feb'85 by Arista Records. Dist: RCA

Parsons & Babel Steve

HOWLING THE.
Single (7"): released on Filmtrax, Oct'85 by Filmtrax Records. Dist: BMG

Parsons, Gene

GENE PARSONS.
Album: released on Sierra, May'79 by Sierra Records. Dist: WEA

Parsons, Gram

EARLY YEARS 1963-65 (THE).
Album: released on Sierra (USA), Feb'84 by

Sierra Records (USA).

EARLY YEARS THE.
Album: released on Sundown, May'84 by Magnum Music Group Ltd. Dist: Magnum Music Group Ltd, PRT Distribution, Spartan Distribution

Cassette: released on Sundown, May'84 by Magnum Music Group Ltd. Dist: Magnum Music Group Ltd, PRT Distribution, Spartan Distribution

G.P.
Album: released on Reprise, Apr'76 by WEA Records. Dist: WEA

GRAM PARSONS.
Album: released on Shiloh, May'79

Album: released on Warner Brothers, Jun'82 by Warner Bros Records. Dist: WEA

Cassette: released on Warner Brothers, Jun'82 by Warner Bros Records. Dist: WEA

GRIEVOUS ANGEL.
Album: released on Reprise, Jun'74 by WEA Records. Dist: WEA

LIVE (Parsons, Gram/Emmylou Harris).
Album: released on Sundown, Nov'83 by Magnum Music Group Ltd. Dist: Magnum Music Group Ltd, PRT Distribution, Spartan Distribution

LIVE 1973 (Parsons, Gram/Emmylou Harris).
Cassette: released on Sundown, Aug'85 by Magnum Music Group Ltd. Dist: Magnum Music Group Ltd, PRT Distribution, Spartan Distribution

Album: released on Repertoire, Apr'82 Dist: JSU, PRT, Spartan

LIVE 73 (Parsons, Gram & Fallen Angels).
Album: released on Sierra (USA), Feb'84 by Sierra Records (USA).

LUXURY LINER.
Album: released on Shiloh, Mar'79

MELODIES.
Album: released on Sundown, May'84 by Magnum Music Group Ltd. Dist: Magnum Music Group Ltd, PRT Distribution, Spartan Distribution

Cassette: released on Sundown, May'84 by Magnum Music Group Ltd. Dist: Magnum Music Group Ltd, PRT Distribution, Spartan Distribution

SNEAKY PETE KLENIOW.
Album: released on Shiloh, Mar'79

WITH EMMYLOU HARRIS (Parsons, Gram & Fallen Angels).
Single (7"): released on Sierra (USA), Feb'83 by Sierra Records (USA).

Part, Arvo

ARBOS.
Tracks: / Arbos / An den Wassern zu Babel / ari Intervallo / De Profundis / Es sang vor langen Jahren / Summa / Stabat Mater.
Notes: Features the Brass Ensemble of the Staatsorchester Stuttgart, conducted by Dennis Russell Davies, violinist Gidon Kremer, Vladimir Mendelssohn on viola, Thomas Demenga on cello and the Hilliard Ensemble. Features the Brass Ensemble of the Staatsorchester Stuttgart, conducted by Dennis Russell Davies, violinist Gidon Kremer, Vladimir Mendelssohn on viola, Thomas Demenga on cello and the Hilliard Ensemble.
Compact disc: released on ECM (Germany), Jul'87 by ECM Records. Dist: IMS, Polygram, Virgin through EMI

Album: released on ECM (Germany), Jul'87 by ECM Records. Dist: IMS, Polygram, Virgin through EMI

Partisans

YEARS OF HELL (EP).
Single (7"): released on No Future, Jun'82 by No Future Records. Dist: Pinnacle, Rough Trade, Cartel

BLIND AMBITION/COME CLEAN/CHANGE.
Single (7"): released on Cloak And Dagger, '83 by Dorane Ltd.

PARTISANS THE.
Album: released on No Future, Mar'83 by No Future Records. Dist: Pinnacle, Rough Trade, Cartel

POLICE STORY.
Single (7"): released on No Future, Jul'82 by No Future Records. Dist: Pinnacle, Rough Trade, Cartel

HE WAS RIGHT THE.
Album: released on Cloak And Dagger, Jun'84 by Dorane Ltd.

Partners In Crime

ACLES.
Single (7"): released on Epic, Jan'85 by CBS Records. Dist: CBS

Parton, Dolly

9 TO 5 AND ODD JOBS.
Album: released on RCA, Sep'81 by RCA Records. Dist: RCA, Roots, Swift, Wellard, Chris, I & B, Solomon & Peres Distribution

Cassette: released on RCA, Sep'81 by RCA Records. Dist: RCA, Roots, Swift, Wellard, Chris, I & B, Solomon & Peres Distribution

BURLAP AND SATIN.
Album: released on RCA, Jan'84 by RCA Records. Dist: RCA, Roots, Swift, Wellard, Chris, I & B, Solomon & Peres Distribution

Cassette: released on RCA, Jan'84 by RCA Records. Dist: RCA, Roots, Swift, Wellard, Chris, I & B, Solomon & Peres Distribution

CHRISTMAS WITHOUT YOU (Parton, Dolly & Kenny Rogers).
Single (7"): released on RCA, Nov'84 by RCA Records. Dist: RCA, Roots, Swift, Wellard, Chris, I & B, Solomon & Peres Distribution

DOLLY PARTON.
Album: released on Camden(RCA), Apr'78 by RCA Records. Dist: Pickwick Distribution, Taylors, Swift

Album: released on RCA Camden, Mar'82 by RCA Records. Dist: Pickwick Distribution, Taylor, H.R.

Cassette: released on RCA Camden, Mar'82 by RCA Records. Dist: Pickwick Distribution, Taylor, H.R.

DOLLY PARTON COLLECTION, THE.
Double Album: released on Pickwick, Apr'79 by Pickwick Records. Dist: Pickwick Distribution, Prism Leisure Distribution, Lugtons

Double Album: released on Monument, May'82 by CBS Records. Dist: CBS Distribution

Double cassette: released on Monument, May'82 by CBS Records. Dist: CBS Distribution

DOLLY PARTON STORY, THE.
Cassette: released on Pickwick, Dec'79 by Pickwick Records. Dist: Pickwick Distribution, Prism Leisure Distribution, Lugtons

Album: released on Embassy, Sep'77 by CBS Records. Dist: CBS

GREAT DOLLY PARTON VOL.1, THE.
Album: released on Camden(RCA), Apr'79 by RCA Records. Dist: Pickwick Distribution, Taylors, Swift

GREAT DOLLY PARTON, THE.
Album: released on Pickwick, Feb'80 by Pickwick Records. Dist: Pickwick Distribution, Prism Leisure Distribution, Lugtons

Album: released on Camden(RCA), Apr'80 by RCA Records. Dist: Pickwick Distribution, Taylors, Swift

GREATEST HITS:DOLLY PARTON.
Tracks: / 9 To 5 / But you know I love you / Heartbreak express / Old flames can't hold a candle to you / Applejack / Me and little Andy / Here you come again / Hard candy Christmas / Two doors down / It's all wrong,but it's all right / Don't I ever cross your mind / I will always love you.
Notes: Digital stereo recording.
Album: released on RCA, Mar'84 by RCA Records. Dist: RCA, Roots, Swift, Wellard, Chris, I & B, Solomon & Peres Distribution

Cassette: released on RCA, Mar'84 by RCA Records. Dist: RCA, Roots, Swift, Wellard, Chris, I & B, Solomon & Peres Distribution

Compact disc: released on RCA, Mar'84 by RCA Records. Dist: RCA, Roots, Swift, Wellard, Chris, I & B, Solomon & Peres Distribution

GREAT PRETENDER.
Tracks: / Save the last dance for me / I walk the line / Turn,Turn,Turn(To everything there is a season) / Downtown / We had it all / She don't love you (like I love you) / We'll sing in the sunshine / I can't help myself(Sugar pie,honey bunch) / Elusive butterfly / Great pretender(The).
Compact disc: released on RCA, Sep'84 by RCA Records. Dist: RCA, Roots, Swift, Wellard, Chris, I & B, Solomon & Peres Distribution

Album: released on RCA, Aug'84 by RCA Records. Dist: RCA, Roots, Swift, Wellard, Chris, I & B, Solomon & Peres Distribution

Cassette: released on RCA, Aug'84 by RCA Records. Dist: RCA, Roots, Swift, Wellard, Chris, I & B, Solomon & Peres Distribution

HEARTBREAK EXPRESS.
Album: released on RCA, Jan'84 by RCA Records. Dist: RCA, Roots, Swift, Wellard, Chris, I & B, Solomon & Peres Distribution

Cassette: released on RCA, Jan'84 by RCA Records. Dist: RCA, Roots, Swift, Wellard, Chris, I & B, Solomon & Peres Distribution

HITS OF DOLLY PARTON.
Album: released on RCA, Jan'84 by RCA Records. Dist: RCA, Roots, Swift, Wellard, Chris, I & B, Solomon & Peres Distribution

Cassette: released on RCA, Jan'84 by RCA Records. Dist: RCA, Roots, Swift, Wellard, Chris, I & B, Solomon & Peres Distribution

IN THE GOOD OLD DAYS When times were bad.
Tracks: / Don't let it trouble your mind / He's a go getter / In the good old days (when times were bad) / It's my time / Harper Valley PTA / Little bird / Mine / Carroll county accident, The / Fresh out of forgiveness / Mama say a prayer / Always the first time / D-I-V-O-R-C-E.
Album: released on RCA, Jan'87 by RCA Records. Dist: RCA, Roots, Swift, Wellard, Chris, I & B, Solomon & Peres Distribution

Cassette: released on RCA, Jan'87 by RCA Records. Dist: RCA, Roots, Swift, Wellard, Chris, I & B, Solomon & Peres Distribution

I WILL ALWAYS LOVE YOU/DO I EVER.
Single (7"): released on RCA, Nov'82 by RCA Records. Dist: RCA, Roots, Swift, Wellard, Chris, I & B, Solomon & Peres Distribution

I WILL ALWAYS LOVE YOU.
Tracks: / Love is like a butterfly / If I cross your mind / My eyes can only see you / Take me back / Blackie,Kentucky / Gettin' happy / You're the one that taught me / Once upon a memory / Sacred memories.
Single (7"): released on Old Gold, Jan'87 by Old Gold Records. Dist: Lightning, Jazz Music, Spartan, Counterpoint

JOLENE.
Tracks: / Jolene / Bargain store (The).
Single (7"): released on Old Gold, Oct'86 by Old Gold Records. Dist: Lightning, Jazz Music, Spartan, Counterpoint

JOLENE/LOVE IS LIKE A BUTTERFLY.
Single (7"): released on RCA, Apr'76 by RCA Records. Dist: RCA, Roots, Swift, Wellard, Chris, I & B, Solomon & Peres Distribution

JUST BECAUSE I'M A WOMAN.
Tracks: / You're gonna be sorry / I felt this way at home / False eye lashes / I'll oil wells love you / Only way out (The)(is to walk over me) / Little bit slow to catch on / Bridge (The) / Love and learn / I'm running out of love / Just because I'm a woman / Baby sister / Try being lonely.
Album: released on RCA, Mar'86 by RCA Records. Dist: RCA, Roots, Swift, Wellard, Chris, I & B, Solomon & Peres Distribution

Cassette: released on RCA, Mar'86 by RCA Records. Dist: RCA, Roots, Swift, Wellard, Chris, I & B, Solomon & Peres Distribution

LOVE IS LIKE A BUTTERFLY.
Tracks: / Love is like a butterfly.
Notes: Produced Bob Ferguson.(P) 1974 & (C) original sound recordings owned by RCA records Ltd. issued under exclusive licence to Music For Pleasure.
Album: released on MFP, Sep'86 by EMI Records. Dist: EMI

Cassette: released on MFP, Sep'86 by EMI Records. Dist: EMI

Album: released on RCA Camden, Apr'81 by RCA Records. Dist: Pickwick Distribution, Taylor, H.R.

Cassette: released on RCA Camden, Apr'81 by RCA Records. Dist: Pickwick Distribution, Taylor, H.R.

MAGIC MOMENTS WITH DOLLY PARTON.
Cassette: released on RCA, May'85 by RCA Records. Dist: RCA, Roots, Swift, Wellard, Chris, I & B, Solomon & Peres Distribution

ONCE UPON A CHRISTMAS (Parton, Dolly & Kenny Rogers).
Album: released on RCA, Dec'84 by RCA Records. Dist: RCA, Roots, Swift, Wellard, Chris, I & B, Solomon & Peres Distribution

Cassette: released on RCA, Dec'84 by RCA Records. Dist: RCA, Roots, Swift, Wellard, Chris, I & B, Solomon & Peres Distribution

POTENTIAL NEW BOYFRIEND.
Single (7"): released on RCA, May'83 by RCA Records. Dist: RCA, Roots, Swift, Wellard, Chris, I & B, Solomon & Peres Distribution

REAL LOVE.
Tracks: / Think about love / Tie our love / We got too much / It's such a heartache / Don't call it love / Real love / I can't be true / I hope you're never happy / Once in every blue moon / Come back to me.
Album: released on RCA, Mar'85 by RCA Records. Dist: RCA, Roots, Swift, Wellard, Chris, I & B, Solomon & Peres Distribution

Cassette: released on RCA, Mar'85 by RCA Records. Dist: RCA, Roots, Swift, Wellard, Chris, I & B, Solomon & Peres Distribution

Compact disc: released on RCA, Mar'86 by RCA Records. Dist: RCA, Roots, Swift, Wellard, Chris, I & B, Solomon & Peres Distribution

RHINESTONE Film Soundtrack.
Album: released on RCA, Aug'84 by RCA Records. Dist: RCA, Roots, Swift, Wellard, Chris, I & B, Solomon & Peres Distribution

Cassette: released on RCA, Aug'84 by RCA Records. Dist: RCA, Roots, Swift, Wellard, Chris, I & B, Solomon & Peres Distribution

SAVE THE LAST DANCE FOR ME.
Single (7"): released on RCA, Jan'84 by RCA Records. Dist: RCA, Roots, Swift, Wellard, Chris, I & B, Solomon & Peres Distribution

Album: released on Camden(RCA), Jul'87 by RCA Records. Dist: Pickwick Distribution, Taylors, Swift

Cassette: released on Camden(RCA), Jul'87 by RCA Records. Dist: Pickwick Distribution, Taylors, Swift

THINK ABOUT LOVE.
Single (7"): released on RCA, Apr'85 by RCA Records. Dist: RCA, Roots, Swift, Wellard, Chris, I & B, Solomon & Peres Distribution

TRIO, THE (Parton, Dolly/Linda Rondstadt/Emmylou Harris).
Album: released on WEA, Mar'87 by WEA Records. Dist: WEA

Cassette: released on WEA, Mar'87 by WEA Records. Dist: WEA

Compact disc: released on WEA, Mar'87 by WEA Records. Dist: WEA

VERY BEST OF DOLLY PARTON, THE.
Album: released on RCA, '84 by RCA Records. Dist: RCA, Roots, Swift, Wellard, Chris, I & B, Solomon & Peres Distribution

Cassette: released on RCA, '84 by RCA Records. Dist: RCA, Roots, Swift, Wellard, Chris, I & B, Solomon & Peres Distribution

WINNING HAND With Kris Kristofferson, Willie Nelson and Brenda Lee.
Album: released on Monument, Jan'83 by CBS Records. Dist: CBS Distribution

YOU ARE.
Album: released on RCA International, Oct'80

Cassette: released on RCA International, Oct'80

Parton, Stella

COUNTRY SWEET.
Album: released on Elektra, Jan'78 by WEA Records. Dist: WEA

I WANT TO HOLD YOU....
Album:

STELLA PARTON.
Album: released on Elektra, May'78 by WEA Records. Dist: WEA

Partridge, Andy

TAKE AWAY.
Album: released on Virgin, Feb'80 by Virgin Records. Dist: EMI, Virgin Distribution

Party

CHRISTMAS CRACKERS.
Single (7"): released on Rox, Dec'81 by Rox Records. Dist: Spartan Distribution

Party at hanging rock

PARTY AT HANGING ROCK Various artists (Various Artists).
Notes: Artistes include:Stupidity/Dynamic Hepnotics.
Album: released on Countdown, Apr'86 by Stiff Records. Dist: EMI, Swift

Cassette: released on Countdown, Apr'86 by Stiff Records. Dist: EMI, Swift

Party Classics

PARTY CLASSICS Various artists (Various Artists).
Triple album / cassette: released on Telstar, Nov'84 by Telstar Records. Dist: RCA Distribution

Triple album / cassette: released on Telstar, Nov'84 by Telstar Records. Dist: RCA Distribution

Party Day

GLASSHOUSE.
Album: released on Party Day, May'85 by Party Day Records. Dist: Red Rhino, Cartel

GLASSHOUSE (EP).
Single (12"): released on Rouska, Nov'85 Dist: Red Rhino Distribution, Cartel Distribution

ROW THE BOAT ASHORE.
Single (7"): released on Party Day, Aug'83 by Party Day Records. Dist: Red Rhino, Cartel

SIMPLICITY.
Album: released on Party Day, May'86 by Party Day Records. Dist: Red Rhino, Cartel

SPIDER, THE.
Single (7"): by Party Day Records. Dist: Red Rhino, Cartel

Party Fever

PARTY FEVER Various Original artists (Various Artists).
Album: released on TV, Nov'82

Cassette: released on TV, Nov'82

Party, party

PARTY, PARTY Various artists (Various Artists).
Video-cassette (VHS): released on A&M, Dec'86 by A&M Records. Dist: Polygram

PARTY PARTY Various artists (Various Artists).
Album: released on Hallmark, Sep'84 by Pickwick Records. Dist: Pickwick Distribution, PRT, Taylors

Cassette: released on Hallmark, Sep'84 by Pickwick Records. Dist: Pickwick Distribution, PRT, Taylors

Party People

SUPERMAN SYMSONIC DANCE.
Single (12"): released on Hi-Hut, Aug'87 by Hi Hat. Dist: Rough Trade, Cartel

Party Pooping Punk...

PARTY POOPING PUNK PROVOCATION Various artists (Various Artists).
Album: released on Xcentric Noise, May'85 by Xcentric Noise Records & Tapes Records. Dist: Cartel

Party Poppers

SING-ALONG CHRISTMAS PARTY.
Tracks: / White Christmas / I saw mommy kissing Santa Claus / Let it snow, let it snow, let it snow / Frosty the snowman / Happy holiday / That's what I'd like for Christmas / When Santa got stuck up the chimney / It's the most wonderful time of the year / We three kings / Jingle bells / Good King Wenceslas / Kings' horses, The / Santa Claus is coming to town / Rudolph the red-nosed reindeer / Holiday season, The / Mary's boy child / When a child is born / Silent night / Deck the halls / Stop the cavalry / Have yourself a merry little Christmas / Christmas song, The / Do you hear what I hear / Christmas dream (a little early this year) / Little donkey / Winter wonderland / It's beginning to look like Christmas / I saw three ships / All I want for Christmas (is my two front teeth) / Silver bells / Sleigh ride / Joy to the world / I wish it could be Christmas every day / Merry Christmas everybody / We wish you a merry Christmas / Auld lang syne.
Album: released on MFP, Sep'87 by EMI Records. Dist: EMI

Cassette: released on MFP, Sep'87 by EMI Records. Dist: EMI

Party's Begun

KISS THE BLADE.
Single (12"): released on Incision, Feb'85 by Incision Records. Dist: M.I.S., Revolver

Party Sing-Along

PARTY SING-ALONG Various artists (Various Artists).
Album: released on Hallmark, Oct'79 by Pickwick Records. Dist: Pickwick Distribution, PRT, Taylors

Cassette: released on Bravo, Feb'80 by Pickwick Records. Dist: Lugtons

Party time with...

PARTY TIME WITH THE MISTER MEN Original Cast (Party time with the Mister Men).
Notes: Music From the Show.
Album: released on Stylus, Nov'85 Dist: Pinnacle, Terry Blood Distribution, Stylus Distribution

Cassette: released on Stylus, Nov'85 Dist: Pinnacle, Terry Blood Distribution, Stylus Distribution

Parvez, Shahid

INTRODUCING.... (Parvez, Shahid & Zakir Hussain).
Album: released on Music (India), Jun'84 Dist: Triple Earth Distributions

Pasadena Roof Orchestra

ANTHOLOGY.
Album: released on Transatlantic, Apr'78 by Logo Records. Dist: Roots Distribution, RCA Distribution

C'MON ALONG AND LISTEN.
Tracks: / Don't be that way / Honey pie / I'm on the crest of a wave / Duke steps out (The) / Show must go on(The) / She's a latin from manhattan / Josephine baker / Introducing Josephine Charleston / What is this thing called love / Sing,Sing,Sing / As time goes by / Skokiaan / Lullaby of Broadway (The).
Notes: Arr.by Keith Nichols. Produced by Rolf Enoch.
Album: released on Conifer, May'86 by Conifer Records. Dist: Conifer

Cassette: released on Conifer, May'86 by Conifer Records. Dist: Conifer

EVERYTHIN STOPS FOR TEA.
Album: released on Cambra, Apr'84 by Cambra Records. Dist: IDS, Conifer

Cassette: released on Cambra, Apr'84 by Cambra Records. Dist: IDS, Conifer

FIFTEEN YEARS ON.
Tracks: / I can't dance / Yes yes(my baby said yes) / You took advantage of me / Varsity drag / Very thought of you, The / Casa loma stomp / Pasadena / Lambeth walk / Solitude / I heard / Don't bring Lulu * / Ain't she sweet * / Five foot two,eyes of blue* / Charleston* / Here's to the next time.
Compact disc: released on P.R.O., May'87 Dist: Jetstar

Album: released on Pasadena Roof Orchestra, Mar'85 Dist: IMS, Polygram

Cassette: released on Pasadena Roof Orchestra, Mar'85 Dist: IMS, Polygram

GOOD NEWS.
Tracks: / Good news / Vo do do de o blues / Stormy weather (keeps rainin' all the time) / My canary has circles under his eyes / Choo-choo / Three little words / Home / Everything stops for tea / Pasadena / Sugarfoot stomp / Sing Holly, Go whistle, hey hey / Georgia / That's my weakness now / King's horses / Mooche, The / Here's to the next time.
Notes: Limited edition.
Album: released on Transatlantic, Jul'87 by Transatlantic Records. Dist: IMS-Polygram

HAPPY FEET.
Tracks: / Happy feet / Nightingale sang, A / I got rhythm / Georgia on my mind / Cotton Club stomp / Crazy 'bout my baby / Sleepy time / Oh Donna Clara / Wikki waki / Just squeeze me / Du schon.
Album: released on Pasadena Roof Orchestra, Feb'87 Dist: IMS, Polygram

Cassette: released on Pasadena Roof Orchestra, Feb'87 Dist: IMS, Polygram

ISN'T IT ROMANTIC.
Tracks: / Isn't it romantic / I won't dance / I've told every little star / Cheek to cheek / Hey Miss Moonlight / Singing in the rain / Whispering / I'll see you again / Dream a little dream of me / Creole love call / Soft shoe shuffle blues / Sunday.
Album: released on Transatlantic, Jul'87 by Transatlantic Records. Dist: IMS-Polygram

NIGHT OUT.
Album: released on CBS, Apr'79 by CBS Records. Dist: CBS

Cassette: released on CBS, Apr'79 by CBS Records. Dist: CBS

ON TOUR.
Tracks: / Black bottom / Top hat white tie and tails / East St. Louis toodle-oo / Mississippi mud / Blue skies / Ball and chain / It don't mean a thing (if it ain't got that swing) / Bye bye blackbird / Clarinet marmalade / Meadow lark / Temptation rag / Nagasaki / Pasadena.
Album: released on Transatlantic, Jul'87 by Transatlantic Records. Dist: IMS-Polygram

PASADENA ROOF ORCHESTRA, THE.
Tracks: / Pasadena / It doesn't mean a thing / Isn't it romantic / Nagasaki / Singin' in the rain / Everything stops for tea / Mississippi mud / Cheek to cheek / Dream a little dream of me / Creole love call / Don't be that way / Sing,sing,sing / Shokiaan / Come on baby.
Notes: Issued from the Transatlantic catalogue. Limited edition.
Compact disc: released on P.R.O., May'87 Dist: Jetstar

PASADENA ROOF ORCHESTRA.
Tracks: / Paddlin' Madelin' home / You've got me crying again / Wo-ba-ly walk / Love in bloom / Me and Jane in a plane / Savoy Christmas medley / Nagasaki / Muddy water / Varsity rag / Can't we be friends / Eccentric / Charleston / Come on baby.
Notes: Limited edition.
Album: released on Transatlantic, Jul'87 by Transatlantic Records. Dist: IMS-Polygram

PASADENA ROOF ORCHESTRA.
Album: released on Cambra, Feb'85 by Cambra Records. Dist: IDS, Conifer

Cassette: released on Cambra, Feb'85 by Cambra Records. Dist: IDS, Conifer

PUTTIN' ON THE RITZ.
Album: released on Spot, Feb'83 by Pickwick Records. Dist: H.R. Taylor, Lugtons

Cassette: released on Spot, Feb'83 by Pickwick Records. Dist: H.R. Taylor, Lugtons

TALKING PICTURE, A.
Cassette: released on CBS, Jun'78 by CBS Records. Dist: CBS

WAY WE GET IT TOGETHER.
Single (7"): released on That's Entertainment, May'82 by That's Entertainment Records. Dist: Pinnacle, PRT

Pascoe, Freddy

TAKE IT.
Album: released on Bullseye, Jul'79 Dist: Bullseye Music

Pasha

NOW WE ARE FRIENDS.
Single (7"): released on Floating World, Dec'83 by Indiet Records. Dist: Pinnacle

Pask, Morgan

OVERKILL (Theme from The Bill).
Single (7"): released on Columbia, Jan'85 by EMI Records. Dist: EMI

Passage

DEGENERATES.
Album: released on Cherry Red, Jun'82 by Cherry Red Records. Dist: Pinnacle

ENFLAME.
Album: released on Cherry Red, Mar'83 by Cherry Red Records. Dist: Pinnacle

Cassette: released on Cherry Red, Mar'83 by Cherry Red Records. Dist: Pinnacle

FOR ALL AND DONE.
Album: released on Virgin, Jun'81 by Virgin Records. Dist: EMI, Virgin Distribution

Album: released on Virgin, Jun'81 by Virgin Records. Dist: EMI, Virgin Distribution

TABOOS.
Single (12"): released on Cherry Red, Nov'81 by Cherry Red Records. Dist: Pinnacle

THROUGH THE PASSAGE.
Album: released on Cherry Red, Nov'83 by Cherry Red Records. Dist: Pinnacle

Album: released on Cherry Red, Nov'83 by Cherry Red Records. Dist: Pinnacle

WAVE.
Single (7"): released on Cherry Red, Oct'82 by Cherry Red Records. Dist: Pinnacle

Single (12"): released on Cherry Red, Oct'82 by Cherry Red Records. Dist: Pinnacle

XOYO.
Single (7"): released on Cherry Red, Apr'82 by Cherry Red Records. Dist: Pinnacle

Single (12"): released on Cherry Red, Jun'82 by Cherry Red Records. Dist: Pinnacle

Passage to India, A

PASSAGE TO INDIA, A Original motion picture soundtrack.
Album: released on EMI, Mar'85 by EMI Records. Dist: EMI

Cassette: released on EMI, Mar'85 by EMI Records. Dist: EMI

PASSAGE TO INDIA, A See Forster, E.M. (Spoken Word).

Passion

SUNSET & VINE(THE VERY FIRST TIME).
Tracks: / Sunset & vine(The very first time) / La pornographique.
Single (7"): released on Wag, Feb'86 by Wag Records. Dist: Priority/EMI Distribution

Single (12"): released on Wag, Feb'86 by Wag Records. Dist: Priority/EMI Distribution

Passion All Stars

PASSION MEDLEY.
Single (12"): released on Passion, Feb'85 by Skratch Records. Dist: PRT

Passionate Friends

TIME BANDITS.
Single (7"): released on T.Toons, Apr'83

Passion Day

MALE SLUTS.
Single (7"): released on Red Energy Dynamo, Feb'84 by Red Energy Dynamo Records. Dist: Red Rhino, Cartel

PURITAN LEFT, THE.
Cassette: released on Red Energy Dynamo, Mar'84 by Red Energy Dynamo Records. Dist: Red Rhino, Cartel

PassionelI

OUR PROMISE.
Album: released on Enigma, Nov'85 by Enigma Records. Dist: Rough Trade, Cartel, EMI

Passion Fodder

FAT TUESDAY.
Tracks: / Luz Blabca / St.Helens / Heart hunters / Mardi gras / Sin poetry / In the echo / Not waltz away / In the moodswing / Hard work / As you dig your hole / Extra extra / I.O.U. / So this is love / My world is empty without you / I want it to be real / Dream, The / Move.
Album: released on Beggars Banquet, Jul'87 by Beggars Banquet Records. Dist: WEA

Cassette: released on Beggars Banquet, Jul'87 by Beggars Banquet Records. Dist: WEA

Compact disc: released on Beggars Banquet, Jul'87 by Beggars Banquet Records. Dist: WEA

HARD WORDS FROM A SOFT MOUTH.
Album: released on Upright, Mar'87 by Upright Records. Dist: Cartel, Rough Trade

LUZ BLANCA.
Tracks: / Luz Blanca / Tomorrow is a long time / Dirt* / God couldn't fight his way out of a wet brown bag*.
Single (7"): released on Beggars Banquet, Jul'87 by Beggars Banquet Records. Dist: WEA

Single (12"): released on Beggars Banquet, Jul'87 by Beggars Banquet Records. Dist: WEA

Passion Play

UNKNOWN HEIGHT.
Cassette: released on Vision, Aug'86 Dist: Vision

Passion Puppets

BEYOND THE TALE.
Single (7"): released on Stiff, May'84 by Stiff Records. Dist: EMI, Record Services Distribution (Ireland)

Single (12"): released on Stiff, May'84 by Stiff Records. Dist: EMI, Record Services Distribution (Ireland)

Album: released on Stiff, Mar'84 by Stiff Records. Dist: EMI, Record Services Distribution (Ireland)

Cassette: released on Stiff, Mar'84 by Stiff Records. Dist: EMI, Record Services Distribution (Ireland)

LIKE DUST.
Single (7"): released on Stiff, Jul'83 by Stiff Records. Dist: EMI, Record Services Distribution (Ireland)

Single (12"): released on Stiff, Jul'83 by Stiff Records. Dist: EMI, Record Services Distribution (Ireland)

VOICES.
Single (7"): released on Stiff, Sep'83 by Stiff Records. Dist: EMI, Record Services Distribution (Ireland)

Single (12"): released on Stiff, Sep'83 by Stiff Records. Dist: EMI, Record Services Distribution (Ireland)

Passions

PASSION PLAYS.
Album: released on Polydor, Feb'85 by Polydor Records. Dist: Polygram, Polydor

PASSIONS, THE.
Album: released on Fiction, May'80 by Fictio Records. Dist: Polygram

THIRTY THOUSAND FEET OVER CHINA.
Album: released on Polydor, Sep'81 by Polydor Records. Dist: Polygram, Polydor

Cassette: released on Polydor, Sep'81 by Polydor Records. Dist: Polygram, Polydor

Passion Spent

SOMEONE TO TALK TO.
Tracks: / Wildlife.
Notes: Tel: 0482 571745
Single (12"): released on Paragon, Feb'87 by Paragon Records. Dist: Paragon

Passion tracking

PASSION TRACKING VOLUME IV Various artists (Various Artists).
Tracks: / Eat you up / Don't let the flame die / Reincarnation (coming back for love)(US M / Fighter, The / Midnight lover (US Mix) / Are y ready for love / Timebomb / Feels like love / F me up.
Notes: Track 1, Side 1 and Track 3, Side 2 P duced by Les Hunt for AVM Productions. Tra 2, Side 1 and Tracks 2,4 & 5, Side 2 produc by Nigel Stock and John Dav-ie Track 3, Side 1 Produced by Paul Crossley a Terry Owen. Track 4, Side 1 P duced and arranged by Simon Soussa Track 1, Side 2 Produced by Paul Cros ley/Terry Owen/Bobby Summerfield/Pep Cotummacio.

Album: released on Passion, Apr'86 by Skratch Records. Dist: PRT

PASSION TRACKING VOLUME 1 Various artists (Various Artists).
Album: released on Passion, Dec'83 by Skratch Records. Dist: PRT

PASSION TRACKING VOLUME 2 Various artists (Various Artists).
Album: released on Passion, May'84 by Skratch Records. Dist: PRT

Cassette: released on Passion, May'84 by Skratch Records. Dist: PRT

PASSION TRACKING VOLUME 3 Various artists (Various Artists).
Album: released on Passion, Jul'85 by Skratch Records. Dist: PRT

Pass, Joe

A SALLE PLEYEL (Pass, Joe & Peterson, Oscar).
Double Album: released on Pablo, '82 by Pablo Records. Dist: Wellard, Chris, IMS-Polygram, BMG

Cassette: released on Pablo, '82 by Pablo Records. Dist: Wellard, Chris, IMS-Polygram, BMG

AT THE MONTREUX JAZZ FESTIVAL 1975.
Album: released on Pablo, '82 by Pablo Records. Dist: Wellard, Chris, IMS-Polygram, BMG

BEST OF, THE.
Album: released on Pablo Jazz (USA), Oct'84 by United Artists. Dist: Swift

BIG THREE, THE (Pass, Joe, Milt Jackson, Ray Brown).
Album: released on Pablo (USA), '82 by Pablo Records (USA). Dist: Wellard, Chris, IMS-Polygram, BMG

assette: released on Pablo (USA), '82 by ablo Records (USA). Dist: Wellard, Chris, MS-Polygram, BMG

LUES FOR TWO (see Sims, Zoot) (Pass, oe & Zoot Sims).

HECKMATE (Pass, Joe/Jimmy Rowles).
bum: released on Pablo, '82 by Pablo Records. Dist: Wellard, Chris, IMS-Polygram, BMG

assette: released on Pablo, '82 by Pablo Records. Dist: Wellard, Chris, IMS-Polygram, BMG

HOPS (Pass, Joe and Niels Pederson).
bum: released on Pablo, '82 by Pablo Records. Dist: Wellard, Chris, IMS-Polygram, BMG

ssette: released on Pablo, '82 by Pablo Records. Dist: Wellard, Chris, IMS-Polygram, BMG

GITAL III AT MONTREUX (Pass, /Ella Fitzgerald/Count Basie).
otes: See also under Ella Fitzgerald and unt Basie.
mpact disc: released on Pablo (USA), '87 by Pablo Records (USA). Dist: Wellard, ris, IMS-Polygram, BMG

IMIOUS (Pass, Joe Trio).
mpact disc: released on Pablo (USA), '87 by Pablo Records (USA). Dist: Wellard, is, IMS-Polygram, BMG

ZGERALD AND PASS....AGAIN ss, Joe and Ella Fitzgerald).
um: released on Pablo, '82 by Pablo Rec. Dist: Wellard, Chris, IMS-Polygram, BMG

sette: released on Pablo, '82 by Pablo Rec. Dist: Wellard, Chris, IMS-Polygram, BMG

ERCONTINENTAL.
um: released on Memoir, Oct'85 by Memoir ords. Dist: PRT Distribution

sette: released on Memoir, Oct'85 by Mem-ecords. Dist: PRT Distribution

, GEORGE, & JOE (Pass, Joe Loves hwin).
m: released on Pablo, Jul'82 by Pablo ords. Dist: Wellard, Chris, IMS-Polygram,

ette: released on Pablo, Jul'82 by Pablo rds. Dist: Wellard, Chris, IMS-Polygram,

MEMBER CHARLIE PARKER.
n: released on Pablo, '82 by Pablo Rec-Dist: Wellard, Chris, IMS-Polygram, BMG

ette: released on Pablo, '82 by Pablo Rec-Dist: Wellard, Chris, IMS-Polygram, BMG

PASS.
n: released on Pablo, '82 by Pablo Rec-Dist: Wellard, Chris, IMS-Polygram, BMG

tte: released on Pablo, '82 by Pablo Rec-Dist: Wellard, Chris, IMS-Polygram, BMG

AT DONTE'S (Pass, Joe Trio).
act disc: released on Pablo (USA), Apr'87 by Pablo Records (USA). Dist: Wellard, Chris, IMS-Polygram, BMG

Cassette: released on Pablo, '82 by Pablo Records. Dist: Wellard, Chris, IMS-Polygram, BMG

LIVE AT LONG BEACH CITY COLLEGE.
Album: released on Pablo (USA), Sep'84 by Pablo Records (USA). Dist: Wellard, Chris, IMS-Polygram, BMG

Cassette: released on Pablo (USA), Sep'84 by Pablo Records (USA). Dist: Wellard, Chris, IMS-Polygram, BMG

LIVE IN COPENHAGEN (see Grappelli, Stephane) (Pass, Joe /Stephane Grappelli).

LIVE IN THE NETHERLANDS (80) (see Thielemans, Toots) (Pass, Joe/Toots Thielemans).

LOVES GERSHWIN.
Compact disc: released on Pablo (USA), May'86 by Pablo Records (USA). Dist: Wellard, Chris, IMS-Polygram, BMG

NORTHSEA NIGHTS (Pass, Joe and Niels Pederson).
Album: released on Pablo, '82 by Pablo Records. Dist: Wellard, Chris, IMS-Polygram, BMG

Cassette: released on Pablo, '82 by Pablo Records. Dist: Wellard, Chris, IMS-Polygram, BMG

PARIS CONCERT, THE (Pass, Joe, Oscar Peterson, Niels Pederson).
Double Album: released on Pablo (USA), '82 by Pablo Records (USA). Dist: Wellard, Chris, IMS-Polygram, BMG

Double cassette: released on Pablo (USA), '82 by Pablo Records (USA). Dist: Wellard, Chris, IMS-Polygram, BMG

PORGY AND BESS (Pass, Joe & Peterson, Oscar).
Album: released on Pablo, '82 by Pablo Records. Dist: Wellard, Chris, IMS-Polygram, BMG

Cassette: released on Pablo, '82 by Pablo Records. Dist: Wellard, Chris, IMS-Polygram, BMG

PORTRAITS OF DUKE ELLINGTON.
Compact disc: released on Pablo (USA), May'86 by Pablo Records (USA). Dist: Wellard, Chris, IMS-Polygram, BMG

Album: released on Pablo (USA), '82 by Pablo Records (USA). Dist: Wellard, Chris, IMS-Polygram, BMG

Cassette: released on Pablo (USA), '82 by Pablo Records (USA). Dist: Wellard, Chris, IMS-Polygram, BMG

STONE JAM, THE.
Album: released on Memoir, Aug'87 by Memoir Records. Dist: PRT Distribution

Album: released on Memoir, Aug'87 by Memoir Records. Dist: PRT Distribution

TAKE LOVE EASY (Pass, Joe and Ella Fitzgerald).
Album: released on Pablo (USA), '82 by Pablo Records (USA). Dist: Wellard, Chris, IMS-Polygram, BMG

Cassette: released on Pablo (USA), '82 by Pablo Records (USA). Dist: Wellard, Chris, IMS-Polygram, BMG

TIVOLI GARDENS, COPENHAGEN (Pass, Joe/Stephane Grappelli/Niels Pedersen).
Album: released on Pablo (USA), '82 by Pablo Records (USA). Dist: Wellard, Chris, IMS-Polygram, BMG

Cassette: released on Pablo (USA), '82 by Pablo Records (USA). Dist: Wellard, Chris, IMS-Polygram, BMG

TUDO BEM! (Pass, Joe and Paulingo Da Costa).
Album: released on Pablo (USA), '82 by Pablo Records (USA). Dist: Wellard, Chris, IMS-Polygram, BMG

Cassette: released on Pablo (USA), '82 by Pablo Records (USA). Dist: Wellard, Chris, IMS-Polygram, BMG

TWO FOR THE ROAD (Pass, Joe\Herb Ellis).
Notes: For full info. see under: Ellis, Herb.
Album: released on Pablo (USA), '82 by Pablo Records (USA). Dist: Wellard, Chris, IMS-Polygram, BMG

Cassette: released on Pablo (USA), '82 by Pablo Records (USA). Dist: Wellard, Chris, IMS-Polygram, BMG

VIRTUOSO.
Album: released on Pablo (USA), '82 by Pablo Records (USA). Dist: Wellard, Chris, IMS-Polygram, BMG

Cassette: released on Pablo (USA), '82 by Pablo Records (USA). Dist: Wellard, Chris, IMS-Polygram, BMG

VIRTUOSO NO.2.
Album: released on Pablo (USA), '82 by Pablo Records (USA). Dist: Wellard, Chris, IMS-Polygram, BMG

Cassette: released on Pablo (USA), '82 by Pablo Records (USA). Dist: Wellard, Chris, IMS-Polygram, BMG

VIRTUOSO NO.3.
Album: released on Pablo (USA), '82 by Pablo Records (USA). Dist: Wellard, Chris, IMS-Polygram, BMG

Cassette: released on Pablo (USA), '82 by Pablo Records (USA). Dist: Wellard, Chris, IMS-Polygram, BMG

VIRTUOSO NO.4.
Album: released on Pablo, May'83 by Pablo Records. Dist: Wellard, Chris, IMS-Polygram, BMG

Cassette: released on Pablo, May'83 by Pablo Records. Dist: Wellard, Chris, IMS-Polygram, BMG

WE'LL BE TOGETHER AGAIN (Pass, Joe/J J Johnson).
Notes: See also under J J Johnson.
Compact disc: released on Pablo (USA), Apr'87 by Pablo Records (USA). Dist: Wellard, Chris, IMS-Polygram, BMG

Album: released on Pablo (USA), Mar'85 by Pablo Records (USA). Dist: Wellard, Chris, IMS-Polygram, BMG

Cassette: released on Pablo (USA), Mar'85 by Pablo Records (USA). Dist: Wellard, Chris, IMS-Polygram, BMG

WHITESTONE.
Tracks: / Light in your eyes / Shuffle city / Estate / Daquilo que eu sei / Whitestone / Lovin' eyes / Amancer / I can't help it / Tarde / Fleeting moments.
Notes: Personnel includes:John Pisano-rhythm guitar/Don Grusin-keyboards/Harvey Mason-drums/Abraham Laboriel & nathan East-bass/Paulinho Da Costa-percussion/Armando Compean-vocalist on'Lovin'Eyes'.
Compact disc: released on Pablo Jazz (USA), Apr'86 by United Artists. Dist: Swift

Album: released on Pablo Jazz (USA), Aug'85 by United Artists. Dist: Swift

Cassette: released on Pablo Jazz (USA), Aug'85 by United Artists. Dist: Swift

Passmore Sisters

DANCE THE HOUSE DOWN.
Single (7"): released on Sharp, Nov'85 by Sharp Records. Dist: Red Rhino, Cartel

EVERY CHILD IN HEAVEN.
Single (7"): released on Sharp, Jun'87 by Sharp Records. Dist: Red Rhino, Cartel

Single (12"): released on Sharp, Jun'87 by Sharp Records. Dist: Red Rhino, Cartel

VIOLENT BLUE.
Tracks: / Violent blue.
Single (12"): released on Sharp, Aug'86 by Sharp Records. Dist: Red Rhino, Cartel

Passport

ATARAXIA.
Album: released on Atlantic, May'78 by WEA Records. Dist: WEA

CROSS COLLATERAL.
Album: released on WEA, Apr'75 by WEA Records. Dist: WEA

INFINITY MACHINE.
Album: released on Atlantic, Jun'76 by WEA Records. Dist: WEA

NEW MOON.
Single (7"): released on WEA, Dec'82 by WEA Records. Dist: WEA

Pass The Time

PASS THE TIME An Anthology of Donegal fiddling.
Album: released on Topic, '81 Dist: Roots Distribution

Pastels

CRAWL BABIES.
Tracks: / Crawl babies.
Single (7"): released on Glass, Mar'87 by Glass Records. Dist: Nine Mile, Rough Trade, Red Rhino, Play It Again Sam

Single (12"): released on Glass, Mar'87 by Glass Records. Dist: Nine Mile, Rough Trade, Red Rhino, Play It Again Sam

HEAVENS ABOVE.
Single (7"): released on Whamm, Oct'82 Dist: Pinnacle

Single (7"): released on Villa, Mar'85 Dist: Fast Forward, Cartel

I'M ALRIGHT WITH YOU.
Single (12"): released on Creation, Nov'85 Dist: Rough Trade, Cartel

I WONDER WHY.
Single (7"): released on Rough Trade, Oct'83 by Rough Trade Records. Dist: Rough Trade Distribution, Cartel Distribution

MILLION TEARS, A.
Single (12"): released on Creation, Oct'84 Dist: Rough Trade, Cartel

SOMETHING'S GOING ON.
Single (7"): released on Rough Trade, Mar'84 by Rough Trade Records. Dist: Rough Trade Distribution, Cartel Distribution

TRUCK TRAIN TRACTOR.
Tracks: / Truck train tractor / Breaking lines / Truck train tractor (2).
Single (7"): released on Glass, Jun'86 by Glass Records. Dist: Nine Mile, Rough Trade, Red Rhino, Play It Again Sam

Single (12"): released on Glass, Jun'86 by Glass Records. Dist: Nine Mile, Rough Trade, Red Rhino, Play It Again Sam

UP FOR A BIT WITH THE PASTELS.
Album: released on Glass, Feb'87 by Glass Records. Dist: Nine Mile, Rough Trade, Red Rhino, Play It Again Sam

Pastiche

WHERE DID THAT SOUL GO.
Single (7"): released on Inferno, Nov'83 by Inferno Records. Dist: Inferno, Cartel, Pinnacle

Single (12"): released on Inferno, Nov'83 by Inferno Records. Dist: Inferno, Cartel, Pinnacle

Pastorius, Jaco

TRILOGUE-LIVE (Pastorius, Jaco/Danielson/Mangelsdorff).

Pastor, Tony

MR. PASTOR GOES TO TOWN.
Album: released on Swing House, '84 Dist: Jazz Music Distribution, Swift Distribution, Chris Wellard Distribution

RADIO DISCS OF ...LATE 1940'S, THE.
Album: released on Joyce, Jul'82

Pastourelle

PASTOURELLE various artists (Various Artists).
Album: released on Red Seal, Jul'82 by RCA Records. Dist: RCA

Cassette: released on Red Seal, Jul'82 by RCA Records. Dist: RCA

Patches

DON'T THINK TWICE.
Album: released on Country House, Feb'83 by BGS Productions Ltd. Dist: Taylor, H.R., Record Merchandisers Distribution, Pinnacle, Sounds of Scotland Records

Cassette: released on Country House, Feb'83 by BGS Productions Ltd. Dist: Taylor, H.R., Record Merchandisers Distribution, Pinnacle, Sounds of Scotland Records

Patchwork

INTRAMENTO.
Album: released on Cobra, May'79 by Cobra Records. Dist: Projection, EMI

Patea Maori Club

POI-E.
Single (7"): released on Sonet, Feb'85 by Sonet Records. Dist: PRT

Paterson, P.

VIEW FROM THE HILL.
Album: released on Zara, Jun'84 by Zara Records. Dist: Rough Trade

Paterson, Rod

TWO HATS.
Tracks: / Bleacher Lass O' Kelvinhaugh / My funny valentine / Everytime we say goodbye / Willie Wassle / My Nannie / Pierre le Bateau / Wong joke again / I do it for your love / Steggie.
Album: released on Greentrax, Feb'87 by Greentrax Records. Dist: Projection, CM, Gordon Duncan Distribution, Rough Trade, Nine Mile, Cartel

Cassette: released on Greentrax, Mar'87 by Greentrax Records. Dist: Projection, CM, Gordon Duncan Distribution, Rough Trade, Nine Mile, Cartel

Patillo, Leon

DANCE CHILDREN DANCE.
Album: released on Marantha Music, May'82

Album: released on Marantha Music, May'82

DON'T GIVE IN.
Album: released on Myrrh, May'82 by Word Records. Dist: Word Distribution

Cassette: released on Myrrh, May'82 by Word Records. Dist: Word Distribution

LOVE AROUND THE WORLD.
Notes: The latest album from this charismatic performer made to coincide with visits Leon intends to make in many parts of the world.
Album: released on Myrrh, Feb'86 by Word Records. Dist: Word Distribution

Cassette: released on Myrrh, Feb'86 by Word Records. Dist: Word Distribution

SKY'S THE LIMIT, THE.
Album: released on Myrrh, Jun'84 by Word Records. Dist: Word Distribution

Cassette: released on Myrrh, Jun'84 by Word Records. Dist: Word Distribution

Patinkin, Mandy
YOUNGER THAN SPRINGTIME (Patinkin, Mandy/London Symphony Orchestra).
Tracks: / Younger than springtime / I'm gonna wash that man right out-a my hair.
Single (7"): released on CBS, Oct'86 by CBS Records. Dist: CBS

Pato
ALLO TOSH.
Single (12"): released on Don Christie, Feb'85 by Don Christie Records. Dist: Jetstar

Patrick
IMMIGRANT.
Single (7"): released on Patrick, Apr'85 Dist: Red Rhino

Patrick Andy
SHUTDOWN VOLUME 7 also see Smith Wayne (Patrick Andy & Wayne Smith).
Album: released on Empire (reggae), Oct'84 Dist: Jetstar

Patrick, Bobby
DALLAS.
Single (7"): released on Monza, Mar'80 Dist: Pinnacle

Patrick, Keith
NIGHT TO REMEMBER, A.
Single (7"): released on In Recordings, Dec'86 Dist: RCA, DMS

Single (12"): released on In Recordings, Dec'86 Dist: RCA, DMS

Patrick Pear...
PATRICK PEAR & COLIN CUCUMBER Various artists (Various Artists).
Cassette: released on Tell-A-tale (Cassettes), '84

Patrick, Rikki
CLEAR THE WAY.
Single (12"): released on CBS, Jan'85 by CBS Records. Dist: CBS

I NEVER THOUGHT IT WOULD COME TO THIS.
Single (7"): released on CBS, Jun'84 by CBS Records. Dist: CBS

NIGHT MOVES.
Tracks: / Night moves / Night moves (remix) / Break point.
Single (7"): released on DMC, Mar'87 Dist: Red Rhino, Cartel

Single (12"): released on DMC, Mar'87 Dist: Red Rhino, Cartel

Single (7"): released on CBS, Mar'84 by CBS Records. Dist: CBS

Single (12"): released on CBS, Mar'84 by CBS Records. Dist: CBS

Patriots/Chicaynes
PHAROAH'S   LAND/SECOND THOUGHTS.
Notes: Split album.
Album: released on Bam Caruso, Mar'87 by Bam Caruso Records. Dist: Rough Trade, Revolver, Cartel

Patris
LOVE OASIS.
Single (12"): released on MDM-Siren, Nov'85, Virgin, EMI

Pat's Big Band
SWING IT AGAIN, PAT.
Album: released on Spectrum (Swiss), Jan'85

Patten, Brian
POEMS AND SONGS.
Album: released on Tangent, Apr'81 Dist: Roots Distribution, Lugtons Distributors, Taylors, JSU Distribution, Spartan Distribution

Patterns
PART 2 - THE BISHOPS'S IN THE FRIDGE.
Single (7"): released on Heater, Aug'80 by Volume. Dist: Pinnacle

Patterns in Peru
THIS IS THE NIGHT.
Tracks: / This is the night / Playing games.
Single (7"): released on WEA, Feb'86 by WEA Records. Dist: WEA

Single (12"): released on WEA, Feb'86 by WEA Records. Dist: WEA

Patterson, Bobby
BOBBY PATTERSON.
Cassette: released on Bullseye, Jan'79 Dist: Bullseye Music

Patterson, Don
MOVIN' UP.
Album: released on Muse, Apr'81 by Peerless Records. Dist: Lugtons Distributors

Patterson, Frank
AT CHRISTMAS.
Tracks: Little drummer boy, The / White Christmas / O holy night / Jingle bells / Silent night / Adeste Fidels / Joy to the world / When a child is born / O little town of Bethlehem / Mary's boy child / Scarlet ribbons / Nazareth.
Notes: 12 popular Christmas songs from Irish tenor Frank Patterson, Goethe Institute Choir and the Irish Promenade Orchestra.
Album: released on Philips, Dec'85 Dist: IMS-Polygram

Cassette: released on Philips, Dec'85 Dist: IMS-Polygram

FAVOURITE TENOR ARIAS.
Album: released on IMS(Import), Mar'84 by Polydor Records. Dist: IMS, Polygram

Cassette: released on IMS(Import), Mar'84 by Polydor Records. Dist: IMS, Polygram

GOLDEN VOICE OF FRANK PATTERSON.
Tracks: / O sole mio / Can't help falling in love / Cara mia / Try to remember / Be my love / True love / Impossible dream (The) / Perhaps love / Granada / Memory (cats) / You'll never walk alone / Vaja con dios / Twelfth of never (The) / You needed me / Moon river / Galway Bay / I'll take you home again, Kathleen / How great thou art.
Notes: This commercial album from Ireland's favourite tenor is now available on compactdisc. A generous selection of 19 songs ranging from light classical, popular   and contemporary standards and irish ballads.
Album: released on Polydor (Ireland), Apr'87 by Polydor Records. Dist: Polygram, I & B

Compact disc: released on Polydor (Ireland), Apr'87 by Polydor Records. Dist: Polygram, I & B

Cassette: released on Philips (Ireland), Aug'86

JOHN MCCORMACK FAVOURITES.
Album: released on Mercury, Dec'81 by Import Records. Dist: IMS-Polygram Distribution

Cassette: released on Mercury, Dec'81 by Import Records. Dist: IMS-Polygram Distribution

PEACE AND JOY.
Album: released on Import Music Service (IMS), Mar'81 Dist: Concord Jazz Distributions, Pablo, Polygram

ROSE OF TRALEE, THE.
Album: released on Philips (Ireland), Sep'85 Dist: IMS-Polygram

Cassette: released on Philips (Ireland), Sep'85 Dist: IMS-Polygram

Patterson, Sir Les
12 INCHES OF LES.
Album: released on Towerbell, Oct'85 by Towerbell Records. Dist: EMI

Cassette: released on Towerbell, Oct'85 by Towerbell Records. Dist: EMI

Patterson, Ottilie
CARELESS LOVE/GEORGIA GRIND.
Single (7"): released on Fat Hen, Nov'82 by Fat Hen Records. Dist: Pinnacle

MADAME BLUES AND DOCTOR JAZZ.
Album: released on Black Lion, Jul'84 by Black Lion Records. Dist: Jazz Music, Chris Wellard, Taylor, H.R., Counterpoint, Cadillac

Pattersons
PATTERSONS FROM DONGAL THE.
Album: released on Harp(Ireland), Jul'80 by Pickwick Records. Dist: Taylors

Cassette: released on Harp(Ireland), Jul'80 by Pickwick Records. Dist: Taylors

GIVE HER ONE FOR CHRISTMAS.
Single (7"): released on Towerbell, Dec'85 by Towerbell Records. Dist: EMI

Single (12"): released on Towerbell, Dec'85 by Towerbell Records. Dist: EMI

Patterson, Uncle John
PLAINS GEORGIA ROCK.
Album: released on Arhoolie, May'81 by Arhoolie Records. Dist: Projection, Topic, Jazz Music, Swift, Roots

Pattinson, James
FLIGHT TO THE SEA.
Cassette: released on Soundings, Mar'85 Dist: Soundings

Patti, Sandi
MORNING LIKE THIS.
Notes: Recently signed to Word Records, this is Sandi's first album on the Word label.
Album: released on Word, Apr'86 by Word Records. Dist: Word Distribution, CBS

Cassette: released on Word, Apr'86 by Word Records. Dist: Word Distribution, CBS

Patti & The Dep Band
BIKO.
Tracks: / Biko / Try me.
Single (7"): released on Important, Aug'86 Dist: EMI

Single (12"): released on Important, Aug'86 Dist: EMI

Patto
BLACK AND WHITE.
Single (12"): released on Teldec, Aug'84

Patton, John
BLUE JOHN.
Tracks: / Hot sauce / Bermuda clay house / Dem dirty dues / Country girl / Nicety / Blue John.
Notes: All tracks 1 - 6 CBS Unart Catalogue Inc:
Album: released on Manhattan-Blue Note, Jul'86 by EMI America Records (USA). Dist: EMI

SOUL CONNECTION.
Album: released on Nilva (Switzerland), Apr'84

Pattullo, Gordon
ACCORDION FAVOURITES.
Cassette: released on Ross, '86 by Ross Records. Dist: Ross Distribution, Roots Distribution

Album: released on Accordion Record Club, Jul'86 by Accordion Record Club Records. Dist: Accordion Record Club

Album: released on Ross, May'86 by Ross Records. Dist: Ross Distribution, Roots Distribution

Album: released on Ross, May'86 by Ross Records. Dist: Ross Distribution, Roots Distribution

GORDON FOR YOU A.
Album: released on One Up, Aug'76 by EMI Records. Dist: EMI

NORTHLANDS - A SELECTION OF SCOTTISH MUSIC, THE.
Album: released on One Up, Apr'78 by EMI

SCOTCH ON THE BOX.
Notes: 15 track accordion album - Broon's Reel, Gaelic Waltz, Bothy Ballads medley etc.
Album: released on Ross, Dec'86 by Ross Records. Dist: Ross Distribution, Roots Distribution

Cassette: released on Ross, Dec'86 by Ross Records. Dist: Ross Distribution, Roots Distribution

Patty
RED LIGHT.
Tracks: / Red light / Red light (Instrumental).
Single (7"): released on Spartan, May'86 by Spartan Records. Dist: Spartan

Single (12"): released on Spartan, May'86 by Spartan Records. Dist: Spartan

Paula
BEE BOP DANCING.

Single (12"): released on Rock'n'Groove, Sep'85 by Rock'n'Groove Records. Dist: Jetstar Distribution

DYNAMIC.
Single (7"): released on Rhino, Sep'85 by Creole Records. Dist: PRT, Rhino

JAZZY.
Single (12"): released on Rock'n'Groove, Nov'84 by Rock'n'Groove Records. Dist: Jetstar Distribution

Paul, Andrew
CRAZY.
Tracks: / Crazy / What the police can do.
Single (12"): released on Fashion, Aug'86 by Fashion Records. Dist: PRT, Jetstar

HUSTLE THEM A HUSTLE.
Single (12"): released on Fashion, Nov'85 by Fashion Records. Dist: PRT, Jetstar

SOUND BOY BURIAL (Paul, Andrew & Mikey General).
Notes: For full information see: General, Mikey & Andrew Paul
Single (12"): released on Fashion, Aug'86 by Fashion Records. Dist: PRT, Jetstar

WHAT POLICE CAN DO.
Tracks: / What police can do / Crazy.
Single (12"): released on Digikal, Mar'86 by Digikal Records. Dist: Revolver

WHO'S GONNA MAKE THE DANCE RAM.
Single (12"): released on Fashion, Jun'85 by Fashion Records. Dist: PRT, Jetstar

Paul, Andy
BUILD ME UP BUTTERCUP.
Tracks: / Build me up buttercup / I believe.
Single (7"): released on Face, 20 Jun'87 by Face Records & Music. Dist: T.One Records

HEARTBREAK SITUATION.
Single (7"): released on Sticky, Jun'83

Paulas Country
WELCOME.
Album: released on Tank, Dec'77 by Tank Records.

Paul, Billy
6 TRACK HITS.
Single (7"): released on Scoop, Sep'83

Cassette: released on Scoop, Sep'83

BILLY PAUL'S GREATEST HITS.
Album: released on Philadelphia International, Jul'83 by CBS Records. Dist: CBS

Cassette: released on Philadelphia International, Jul'83 by CBS Records. Dist: CBS

BRING THE FAMILY BACK.
Single (12"): released on Streetwave, Sep'1 by Streetwave Records. Dist: PRT Distribution

LATELY.
Tracks: / Fire in her love / Sexual therapy / Lately / I search no more / I only have eyes for you / Hot date / Get down to lovin' / Let me in / Me and you / On a clear day / Lately / I search more.
Album: released on Total Experience, Sep by Phonogram. Dist: Polygram

Cassette: released on Total Experience, Sep'85 by Phonogram. Dist: Polygram

Single (7"): released on RCA, Jan'86 by RCA Records. Dist: RCA, Roots, Swift, Wellard, Chris, I & B, Solomon & Peres Distribution

Single (12"): released on RCA, Jan'86 by RCA Records. Dist: RCA, Roots, Swift, Wellard, Chris, I & B, Solomon & Peres Distribution

ME & MRS JONES/LETS MAKE A BABY.
Single (7"): released on Old Gold, Apr'83 by Old Gold Records. Dist: Lightning, Jazz Music, Spartan, Counterpoint

ONLY THE STRONG SURVIVE.
Album: released on Philadelphia, Dec'77

SEXUAL THERAPY.
Single (7"): released on Total Experience, Sep'85 by Phonogram. Dist: Polygram

Single (12"): released on Total Experience, Sep'85 by Phonogram. Dist: Polygram

WHEN LOVE IS NEW.
Album: released on Philadelphia, Jan'76

Paul, Chris
EXPANSIONS 86'.

Tracks: / Expansions 86' (expand your mind) / Broadway Boulevard.
Single (7"): released on Fourth & Broadway, May'86 by Island Records. Dist: Polygram, EMI

Single (12"): released on Fourth & Broadway, May'86 by Island Records. Dist: Polygram, EMI

Tracks: / Expansions '86 (expand your mind)(Remix) / Expansions '86 / Broadway boulevard.
Single (12"): released on Fourth & Broadway, Jul'86 by Island Records. Dist: Polygram, EMI

Paulette

MY ONLY LOVE/DUB VERSION.
Single (7"): released on Solomonic, Nov'82 by Solomonic Records. Dist: Jetstar, Pinnacle

Paul, Eugene

SENTIMENTAL REASON.
Album: released on World International, Jul'84 Dist: Jetstar

THERE'S AN ISLAND.
Single (12"): released on Hot Vinyl, Dec'84 by Hot Vinyl Records. Dist: Jetstar

Paul, Frankie

AFRICAN PRINCESS.
Album: released on Ethnic, Jul'84 Dist: Kingdom

Single (12"): released on Ethnic, Jun'84 Dist: Kingdom

ALESHA.
Single (12"): released on Power House, Dec'86 by Power House Records. Dist: Jetstar

BEGINNING THE.
Single (7"): released on Scom, Dec'84 by Scom Records. Dist: Jetstar

BE MY LADY.
Album: released on Joe Gibbs, Nov'84 by Joe Gibbs Records. Dist: Jetstar

BROKEN HEART REFUGE (Paul, Frankie/Rob Taylor).
Single (12"): released on High Power, Sep'85 by High Power Records. Dist: Jetstar

CHATTE CHATTE.
Single (12"): released on Blue Trac, Oct'84 by Blue Mountain Records. Dist: Jetstar

CLOSER I GET TO YOU.
Single (12"): released on Greensleeves, Jun'85 by Greensleeves Records. Dist: BMG, Jetstar, Spartan

DO GOOD.
Single (12"): released on Greensleeves, Nov'84 by Greensleeves Records. Dist: BMG, Jetstar, Spartan

DOUBLE TROUBLE.
Album: released on Greensleeves, Feb'85 by Greensleeves Records. Dist: BMG, Jetstar, Spartan

EAGLES FEATHER.
Single (12"): released on SMP, Dec'86 Dist: Jetstar, PRT

ELISHA.
Album: released on Power House, Jun'87 by Power House Records. Dist: Jetstar

FIRE DEDE A MUS MUS TAIL.
Single (12"): released on Blacker Dread, Aug'84

FOOLS FIGHTING.
Single (12"): released on Greensleeves, Sep'85 by Greensleeves Records. Dist: BMG, Jetstar, Spartan

FOREIGN MIND.
Single (12"): released on Greensleeves, Sep'84 by Greensleeves Records. Dist: BMG, Jetstar, Spartan

GUN SHOT.
Tracks: / Gun shot / Gun shot (version).
Single (12"): released on Skengdom, Jun'87 by Skengdom Records. Dist: Jetstar

Single (12"): released on Sweatbox, Jun'87 by Sweatbox Records. Dist: Rough Trade, Cartel

HARDER THAN THE REST.
Single (12"):

I AM YOUR LOVER.
Tracks: / Baby come on.
Single (12"): released on Fingers, Jan'87 Dist: Jetstar

INFERIORITY COMPLEX.
Single (12"): released on Blue Mountain, Aug'85 Dist: Jetstar

IT'S YOU I LOVE.

Single (12"): released on Londisc, Aug'84 by Londisc Records.

JUST BE MY LADY (Paul, Frankie & U Mike).
Single (12"): released on Real Wax, Jun'84

KEEP ON DANCING.
Tracks: / Keep on dancing / Dancing dub.
Single (12"): released on Greensleeves, Feb'86 by Greensleeves Records. Dist: BMG, Jetstar, Spartan

KICK UP RUMPUS.
Single (12"): released on Power House, May'87 by Power House Records. Dist: Jetstar

MIDNIGHT RAVER.
Single (12"): released on Hornpipe, Jun'85 by Hornpipe Records. Dist: Jetstar

NO TOUCH NO STYLEE.
Single (12"): released on Black Address, Oct'85 Dist: Jetstar

PASS ME THE SCALE.
Tracks: / Pass me the scale / Island rock (Top Rank Players).
Single (12"): released on Top Rank, Jan'86

Single (12"): released on Top Rank, Oct'84

PASS THE TU-SHENG PENG.
Album: released on Greensleeves, Nov'84 by Greensleeves Records. Dist: BMG, Jetstar, Spartan

RICH AND POOR.
Album: released on Classic, Oct'86 Dist: Jetstar

RIDE ON.
Single (12"): released on Top Rank, Mar'85

RIDE THE RHYTHM.
Single (12"): released on Time, Dec'84 Dist: Jetstar Distribution

SHINING STAR.
Single (12"): released on Tonas, Jul'85 Dist: Jetstar Distribution

SHOWDOWN VOLUME 1 (Paul, Frankie & Little John).

SHOWDOWN VOLUME 6 (Paul, Frankie & Little John).
Album: released on Empire, Jun'84 by Empire Records. Dist: Backs, Cartel, Jetstar

SOUTH AFRICA.
Single (12"): released on Fu-Manchu, Oct'84 by Fu-Manchu. Dist: Jetstar

STRANGE FEELING.
Album: released on Technique (Import), Jul'84 by Technique (Import). Dist: Jetstar Distribution

STRICTLY REGGAE MUSIC.
Album: released on Londisc, Nov'84 by Londisc Records.

THRILLER.
Single (12"): released on Ranking Joe, May'85 by Ranking Joe Records. Dist: Jetstar

TIDAL WAVE.
Album: released on Greensleeves, Apr'85 by Greensleeves Records. Dist: BMG, Jetstar, Spartan

Cassette: released on Greensleeves, Apr'85 by Greensleeves Records. Dist: BMG, Jetstar, Spartan

Single (12"): released on Greensleeves, Mar'85 by Greensleeves Records. Dist: BMG, Jetstar, Spartan

YOU'RE SO GOOD TO ME.
Tracks: / You're so good to me / Bald head, treat your woman good (Little Kirk).
Single (12"): released on Technique, Nov'86 by Technique. Dist: CBS

Paulin, Tom

CORONET SOLOS.
Album: released on Look, Feb'84 Dist: R. Smith & Co. Records, H.R. Taylor

Paul, Les

ALL TIME GREATEST HITS (Paul, Les and Mary Ford).
Album: released on EMI (Holland), Jan'83 by EMI Records. Dist: Conifer

CHESTER & LESTER (Paul, Les & Chet Atkins).
Album: released on RCA, Jan'77 by RCA Records. Dist: RCA, Roots, Swift, Wellard, Chris, I & B, Solomon & Peres Distribution

FEEDBACK (1944-1945) (Paul, Les & His Trio).
Notes: Mono
Album: released on Circle(USA), Dec'86 by Jazzology Records (USA). Dist: Jazz Music, Swift, Chris Wellard

HOW HIGH THE MOON/VAYA CON DIOS (Paul, Les and Mary Ford).
Single (7"): released on Capitol, Feb'83 by Capitol Records. Dist: EMI

Single 10": released on Capitol, Feb'83 by Capitol Records. Dist: EMI

LES PAUL & MARY FORD (Paul, Les & Mary Ford).
Tracks: / Johnny is the boy for me / Tennessee Waltz / Mockin' bird hill / Mr.Sandman.
Album: released on Music For Pleasure (Holland), Jan'86 by EMI Records. Dist: EMI

Cassette: released on Music For Pleasure (Holland), Jan'86 by EMI Records. Dist: EMI

NEW SOUND VOLUME II, THE (Paul, Les & Mary Ford).
Tracks: / In the good old summer time / Three little words / Lonesome road, The / Chicken reel / I'm confessin' (That I love you) / Carioca / I can't give you anything but love / Just one more chance / I'm forever blowing bubbles / Moon of Manakoora, The / Don'cha hear them bells / La rosita.
Notes: Here we bring you the nostalgic 'New Sound' of the 50's by the duo who enjoyed million selling hits in their era. As ever, the album features the multi-track vocal and guitar effects which the couple pioneered and which are so popular today.
Album: released on Capitol, Dec'85 by Capitol Records. Dist: EMI

Cassette: released on Capitol, Dec'85 by Capitol Records. Dist: EMI

VERY BEST OF LES PAUL AND MARY FORD (Paul, Les and Mary Ford).
Album: released on Music For Pleasure, Apr'83 by EMI Records. Dist: EMI

Cassette: released on Music For Pleasure, Apr'83 by EMI Records. Dist: EMI

Paul, Lyn

ECHOES OF LOVE/YOU NEVER TOLD ME IT LOVE HURTS.
Single (7"): released on Crash, Jul'83 by Satril Records. Dist: PRT

MAKE THE NIGHT.
Single (7"): released on Mute, Apr'84 Dist: Spartan Distribution, Rough Trade Distribution, Cartel Distribution

Single (7"): released on Mute, Sep'84 Dist: Spartan Distribution, Rough Trade Distribution, Cartel Distribution

Paul, Owen

AS IT IS.
Tracks: / Pleased to meet you / Smebody's angel / My favourite waste of time / Sonny / Just another day / One world / Only for the young (remix) / Prime time / Pharaoh / Bring me back that spark / Pleased to meet you / Somebody's angel / My favourite waste of time / Sonny / Just another day / One world / Only for the young (Remix) / Prime time / Paraoh / Bring me back that spark.
Compact disc: released on Epic, Apr'87 by CBS Records. Dist: CBS

Album: released on Epic, Nov'86 by CBS Records. Dist: CBS

Cassette: released on Epic, Nov'86 by CBS Records. Dist: CBS

BRING ME BACK THAT SPARK.
Tracks: / Bring me back that spark / Feeling, A / Feeling, A.
Single (7"): released on Epic, Mar'87 by CBS Records. Dist: CBS

Single (12"): released on Epic, Mar'87 by CBS Records. Dist: CBS

MY FAVOURITE WASTE OF TIME.
Tracks: / My favourite waste of time / Just another day.
Single (7"): released on Epic, May'86 by CBS Records. Dist: CBS

Single (12"): released on Epic, May'86 by CBS Records. Dist: CBS

ONE WORLD.
Tracks: / One world / Please to meet you.
Single (7"): released on Epic, Oct'86 by CBS Records. Dist: CBS

Single (12"): released on Epic, Oct'86 by CBS Records. Dist: CBS

ONLY FOR THE YOUNG.
Tracks: / Only for the young / Another homeland.
Single (7"): released on Epic, Jan'86 by CBS Records. Dist: CBS

Single (12"): released on Epic, Jan'86 by CBS Records. Dist: CBS

PLEASED TO MEET YOU.
Tracks: / Pleased to meet you / Sunny.
Single (7"): released on Epic, Sep'86 by CBS Records. Dist: CBS

Single (12"): released on Epic, Sep'86 by CBS Records. Dist: CBS

Paul & Paula

HEY PAULA.

Paul, PK

JUMPED THE GUN/PICKING UP THE PIECES.
Single (7"): released on Pastafont, Jul'82 by Pastafont Records.

Paul & Sharon

TAKE THE TIME.
Album: by Pilgrim Records. Dist: Rough Trade, Cartel

Pauly, Danielle

FLEUR DU JURA.
Tracks: / Reve gourmand / L'Epatante / Ballade matinale / Delice Catalan / Rapide digitale / Rapide digitale / Carte postale / Ballade Vosgienne / Clin D'Oeil / File Indienne / Piccolo rag / Fleur du jura / Exotic samba.
Notes: French style accordion playing.
Album: released on Saydisc, Mar'87 by Saydisc Records. Dist: Essex, Harmonia Mundi, Roots, H.R. Taylor, Jazz Music, Swift, Projection, Gamut

LEUR DU JURA (FRENCH ACCORDION MUSIC).
Tracks: / Reve gourman / L'Epatante / Ballade matinale / Delice catalan / Rapide digitale / Carte postale / Ballade vosgienne / Clin D'Oeil / File indienne / Piccolo rag / Fleur du jura / Exoctic samba.
Notes: Danielle Pauly is one of France's up and coming stars of the Accordion. This her first LP, has been widely acclaimed by the experts and hers is a name to watch for the future. Some imaginative band accompaniments assist her:
Album: released on Saydisc, Sep'86 by Saydisc Records. Dist: Essex, Harmonia Mundi, Roots, H.R. Taylor, Jazz Music, Swift, Projection, Gamut

Cassette: released on Saydisc, Sep'86 by Saydisc Records. Dist: Essex, Harmonia Mundi, Roots, H.R. Taylor, Jazz Music, Swift, Projection, Gamut

Pauvros, Jean-Francois

GRAND AMOUR, (LE).
Tracks: / Cri de coeur / Juste un peu de brume / Other side,The / Los paranoidos / Philippine / Chante nix / Alors / Arithmetique amoureuse / Pas decales soixante-deux.
Notes: With: Arto Lindsay/Ted Milton/Terry Day.
Album: released on Nato (France), Sep'86 by Disques Nato. Dist: Essex Record Distributors Ltd.

Pavane

LIKE ODYSSEUS.
Cassette: released on Fragile, Jun'85 by Fragile Records. Dist: Cartel

Pavarotti, Luciano

60 MINUTES OF MUSIC.
Tracks: / Vesti la giubba / Celeste aida / O mes amis....pour mon ame / E Lucevan le stelle / Che gelida manina / Di quella pira / Panis angelicus / Una furtiva lagrima / O Fede negar potessi....Quando sere al placido / Questa o quella / La donna e mobile / Cielo e mar / Nessun Dorma / Che faro senza euridice.
Notes: Popular tenor arias.
Cassette: released on Decca (France), Jul'86 by Decca Records. Dist: Discovery

AVE MARIA/O COME ALL YE FAITHFUL.
Single (7"): released on Decca, Oct'80 by Decca Records. Dist: Polygram

IF I WERE IN LOVE/NONE SHALL SLEEP.
Single (7"): released on Decca, Feb'83 by Decca Records. Dist: Polygram

MAMMA Popular Italian Songs.
Album: released on Decca, Jul'84 by Decca Records. Dist: Polygram

Cassette: released on Decca, Jul'84 by Decca Records. Dist: Polygram

PAVAROTTI COLLECTION, THE.
Album: released on Decca (France), Jul'87 by Decca Records. Dist: Discovery

Cassette: released on Decca (France), Jul'87 by Decca Records. Dist: Discovery

PAVAROTTI COLLECTION.
Album: released on Stylus, Jul'86 Dist: Pinnacle, Terry Blood Distribution, Stylus Distribution

Cassette: released on Stylus, Jul'86 Dist: Pinnacle, Terry Blood Distribution, Stylus Distribution

Compact disc: released on Stylus, Jul'86 Dist: Pinnacle, Terry Blood Distribution, Stylus Distribution

PAVAROTTI FAVOURITES.
Notes: A collection recorded between 1968 and 1983. This selction came about through a French TV show "Les Airs du Grand Echiquier" on which Pavarotti sang all these songs.
Compact disc: released on Polygram, Jul'87 by Polygram Records. Dist: Polygram

Album: released on Polygram, Jul'87 by Polygram Records. Dist: Polygram

Cassette: released on Polygram, Jul'87 by Polygram Records. Dist: Polygram

ROYAL GALA CONCERT (VIDEO) At The Albert Hall.
Notes: Released on Channel 5 Video

Pavillion percy

CRICKET EP CRICKET IN THE JUNGLE THE.
Single (7"): released on Pavilloned in Splendour, Jul'83 Dist: Rough Trade

GOWER POWER.
Single (7"): released on Dead Good, Jun'84

Pavlov's Dog

AT THE SOUND OF THE BELL.
Album: released on CBS, Apr'76 by CBS Records. Dist: CBS

PAMPERED MENIAL.
Album: released on CBS, Oct'75 by CBS Records. Dist: CBS

Paxton,Tom

BAD OLD DAY'S.
Single (7"): released on Cherry Lane, Nov'85 by Cherry Lane Productions. Dist: PRT

COMPLEAT TOM PLAXTON THE.
Album: released on Elektra, Nov'76 by WEA Records. Dist: WEA

Cassette: released on Elektra, Jan'74 by WEA Records. Dist: WEA

EVEN A GRAY DAY.
Album: released on Sundown, Feb'86 by Magnum Music Group Ltd. Dist: Magnum Music Group Ltd, PRT Distribution, Spartan Distribution

HEROES.
Album: released on Vanguard, Jan'79 by PRT Records. Dist: PRT

IN THE ORCHARD.
Album: released on Cherry Lane, Jul'85 by Cherry Lane Productions. Dist: PRT

Cassette: released on Cherry Lane, Jul'85 by Cherry Lane Productions. Dist: PRT

MARVELOUS TOY & OTHER GALLIMAUFRY THE.
Album: released on Pip, Mar'84 by PRT Records. Dist: PRT

Cassette: released on Pip, Mar'84 by PRT Records. Dist: PRT

ONE MILLION LAWYERS AND OTHER DISASTERS.
Album: released on Flying Fish (USA), Apr'86 by Flying Fish Records (USA). Dist: Roots, Projection

PAXTON REPORT THE.
Album: released on Evolution, Dec'81 Dist: RCA, Folksound

Cassette: released on Evolution, Dec'81 Dist: RCA, Folksound

Paxton, Tony

TONY PAXTON IN CONCERT.
Album: released on Cherry Lane, Oct'84 by Cherry Lane Productions. Dist: PRT

Cassette: released on Cherry Lane, Oct'84 by Cherry Lane Productions. Dist: PRT

Paycheck, Johnny

BACK ON THE JOB.
Album: released on Astan, Nov'84 by Astan Records. Dist: Counterpoint

Cassette: released on Astan, Nov'84 by Astan Records. Dist: Counterpoint

BIGGEST HITS.
Cassette: released on Epic, Mar'83 by CBS Records. Dist: CBS

HONKY TONK AND SLOW MUSIC.
Album: released on Sundown, Apr'87 by Magnum Music Group Ltd. Dist: Magnum Music Group Ltd, PRT Distribution, Spartan Distribution

I DON'T NEED TO KNOW THAT RIGHT NOW.
Album: released on Allegiance, Apr'84 by PRT Records. Dist: PRT

Cassette: released on Allegiance, Apr'84 by PRT Records. Dist: PRT

JOHNNY PAYCHECK.
Cassette: released on Audio Fidelity, Oct'84 Dist: PRT

JUKEBOX CHARLIE.
Album: released on President, May'81 by President Records. Dist: Taylors, Spartan

Payere

PEYERE Various artists (Various Artists).
Cassette: released on Peyere, Feb'86 by Peyere Records. Dist: Pinnacle

Pay It All Back

PAY IT ALL BACK-VOL.1 various artists (Various Artists).
Album: released on Onyx, Nov'84 by Relic. Dist: Swift

Payne, Cecil

BIRD GETS THE WORM.
Album: released on Muse, Apr'81 by Peerless Records. Dist: Lugtons Distributors

BRIGHT MOMENTS.
Album: released on Spotlite, '83 by Spotlite Records. Dist: Cadillac, Jazz Music, Spotlite

BROOKFIELD ANDANTE.
Album: released on Spotlite, '83 by Spotlite Records. Dist: Cadillac, Jazz Music, Spotlite

PAYNE, TERRY, GREEN - THE CONNECTION (Payne, Cecil/Clark Terry & Bennie Green).
Album: released on Jazz Reactivation, Jan'82 Dist: PRT

Payne, Cy

CHEEK TO CHEEK (Payne, Cy Band).
Album: released on Fox, Feb'85 by Fox Records. Dist: Jazz Music

LATIN MAGIC OF CY PAYNE.
Album: released on Maestro, Jan'87 by Maestro Records.

Payne, Devin

EXCUSE ME.
Album: released on Polydor, May'81 by Polydor Records. Dist: Polygram, Polydor

Payne, Freda

BANDS OF GOLD.
Album: released on HDH(Holland/Dozier/Holland), Apr'84 by Demon Records. Dist: Pinnacle

Single (7"): released on HDH(Holland/Dozier/Holland), Mar'84 by Demon Records. Dist: Pinnacle

Payne, Jack

GOLDEN AGE OF JACK PAYNE THE.
Album: released on Golden Age, Jul'85 by Music For Pleasure Records. Dist: EMI

IMPERIAL DAYS THE.
Album: released on Joy, Jun'83 by President Records. Dist: Jazz Music, Swift, President Distribution

JACK PAYNE.
Album: released on World, '70 Dist: Jetstar

RADIO NIGHTS, 1928-31 (Payne, Jack & His BBC Dance Orch.).
Album: released on Saville, Apr'83 by Conifer Records. Dist: Conifer

Cassette: released on Saville, Jan'86 by Conifer Records. Dist: Conifer

RHYTHMATITIS.
Tracks: / Yes Sir! That's my baby / Sally's come back / Out of the dawn / Sweet Sue, just you / Little dicky bird told me so,A / I faw down an' go boom / Blondy / When it's Springtime in the rockies / Moochi,The / My baby just cares for me / If I could be with you (one hour tonight) / Lady of Spain / River, stay 'way from my door / Miss Elizabeth Brown / Lazy day / When the moon comes over the mountain / Rhythmatitis / Guilty / Love letters in the sand / Hot coffee.
Notes: (A) F.Day & Hunter Ltd/EMI: (B) Lawrence Wright: (C) Keith Prowse Music/EMI: (D)Campbell Connelly & Co.Ltd: (E) Leonard Gould & Bolttler/MCPS: (F) United Part- nership Ltd: (G) L.Wright: (H) P'Maurice Music/EMI: (I) B.Feldman & Co.Ltd/EMI: (J) United Partnership: *= Vocal: Jack Payne - + Vocals Jack Payne, Bob Busby, Bob Manning(tracks 1 - 10) / Vocal:Billy Scott - Coomber. Above 18 Titles by Jack Payne & The BBC Dance Orchestra: (tracks 11 - 20)

Album: released on EMI Retrospect, Jul'86 by EMI Records. Dist: EMI

Cassette: released on EMI Retrospect, Jul'86 by EMI Records. Dist: EMI

Payne, John

FLY AWAY/COMING HOME.
Single (7"): released on Arrival, Dec'83 by Arrival. Dist: Revolver, Cartel

GONNA GIVE HER ALL THE LOVE I'VE GOT.
Single (7"): released on Arrival, Mar'84 by Arrival. Dist: Revolver, Cartel

RAZOR'S EDGE THE (Payne, John Band).
Album: released on Freedom, Feb'79 by Logo Records. Dist: RCA, Discovery, Wellard. Chris

Payne, Mike

ONCE IN A WHILE (Payne, Mike & Humphrey Littleton).
Album: released on Black Lion, Jun'78 by Black Lion Records. Dist: Jazz Music, Chris Wellard, Taylor, H.R., Counterpoint, Cadillac

Payne, Scherrie

CHASING ME INTO SOMEONE ELSE'S ARMS.
Single (12"): released on Nightmare Gold, Feb'87 Dist: PRT

I'M NOT IN LOVE/GIRL YOU'RE IN LOVE.
Single (7"): released on Record Shack, Dec'82 by Record Shack Records. Dist: PRT

Payolas

JUKE BOX/TNT.
Single (7"): released on Illegal, Feb'81 by Faulty Products Records. Dist: Pinnacle, Lightning, Cartel

Payton, Walter

NEW ORLEANS MUSIC OF WALTER PAYTON, THE.
Cassette: released on Nola, May'87 Dist: JSU, Jazz Music, Cadillac, Chris Wellard

Paz

ALWAYS THERE.
Tracks: / Right moment,The / Always there / Big shot,The / Angels delight / For art / I can see you / You've got something / Be natural / Hold back / Always there.
Album: released on Coda, Mar'86 by Coda Records. Dist: Pinnacle, Cartel, WEA, Roots

Cassette: released on Coda, Mar'86 by Coda Records. Dist: Pinnacle, Cartel, WEA, Roots

Single (7"): released on Coda, Mar'86 by Coda Records. Dist: Pinnacle, Cartel. WEA, Roots

Single (12"): released on Coda, Mar'86 by Coda Records. Dist: Pinnacle, Cartel, WEA, Roots

KANDEEN LOVE SONGS.
Album: released on Spotlite-Jazz, Jan'83 by Spotlite Records. Dist: Cadillac, Jazz Music, Spotlite

LOOK INSIDE.
Album: released on Paladin, Dec'83 by Paladin Records. Dist: Rough Trade, Pinnacle

Cassette: released on Paladin, Dec'83 by Paladin Records. Dist: Rough Trade, Pinnacle

Album: released on Coda, Oct'85 by Coda Records. Dist: Pinnacle, Cartel, WEA, Roots

PAZ ARE BACK.
Album: released on Spotlite, '83 by Spotlite Records. Dist: Cadillac, Jazz Music, Spotlite

Peabody, Dave

AMERICANA.
Album: released on Waterfront, May'87 by Waterfront Records. Dist: Rough Trade, Cartel, Projection, Roots

PAYDAY.
Album: released on Waterfront, Mar'84 by Waterfront Records. Dist: Rough Trade, Cartel, Projection, Roots

Peace Band

WISHES.
Single (7"): released on Southbank-GLC, May'84 by Southbank-GLC Records. Dist: Rough Trade

P.E.A.C.E. Compilation

P.E.A.C.E. COMPILATION Various artists (Various Artists).
Album: released on Radical, Mar'85 by Radical Records. Dist: Cartel

Peaceful Revolution

PEACEFUL REVOLUTION By Laurens Van Der Post.
Cassette: released on Seminar Cassettes, Oct'81 by Seminar Cassettes. Dist: Davidson Distribution, Eastern Educational Products Distrib., Forlaget Systime Distribution, Laser Books Ltd Distribution, MacDougall Distribution, Talktapes Distribution, Watkins Books Ltd Distribution, Norton, Jeff Distribution

Peace In The Valley

PEACE IN THE VALLEY 22 religious favourites.
Album: released on Ronco, Nov'79

Cassette: released on Ronco, Nov'79

Peach, Dixie

GET UP AND SKANK (Peach, Dixie & The Off Beat Posse).
Tracks: / Get up and skank / Skank with me.
Single (12"): released on YND, May'87

LOVE IS A THING.
Tracks: / Love is a thing.
Single (12"): released on Jah Tubbys, Nov'86 by Jah Tubbys Records. Dist: Jetstar

PURE WORRIES.
Single (12"): released on Jah Tubbys, Jul'85 by Jah Tubbys Records. Dist: Jetstar

SLAUGHTER (Peach, Dixie & The Off Beat Posse).
Tracks: / Slaughter / Slaughter mix.
Single (12"): released on Jah Tubbys, Jul'86 by Jah Tubbys Records. Dist: Jetstar

SPIN SPIN.
Single (12"): released on Jah Tubbys, Dec'85 by Jah Tubbys Records. Dist: Jetstar

Peaches

FOR THE LOVE OF YOU.
Single (12"): released on Peaches, Apr'85 by Peaches Records. Dist: Jetstar

SWEET TALK.
Single (12"): released on Starlite, May'83 Dist: Swift Distribution, PRT Distribution

WHY.
Single (12"): released on Peaches, Sep'83 by Peaches Records. Dist: Jetstar

YOUR LOVE IS KING.
Single (12"): released on Arena, May'84 by Arena Records. Dist: Spartan

Peaches & Herb

REUNITED.
Single (7"): released on Old Gold, Jul'84 by Old Gold Records. Dist: Lightning, Jazz Music, Spartan, Counterpoint

SAYIN' SOMETHING.
Album: released on Polydor (Germany), Feb'82 Dist: IMS-Polygram

WELL WORTH THE WAIT.
Album: released on Polydor, Sep'80 by Polydor Records. Dist: Polygram, Polydor

Peacock

DON'T BE CRUEL.
Single (7"): released on Aura, May'78 by Hollywood Nites Distribution. Dist: Pinnacle

Peacock, Annette

BEEN IN THE STREETS TOO LONG.
Album: released on Ironic, May'83 by Ironic Records. Dist: IMS, Polygram, Cartel, Indies, Cadillac

I HAVE NO FEELINGS.
Tracks: / Nothing ever was, anyway / Butterflie / I'm not perfect / I have no feelings / Cynic,The / Carousel,The / You've left me / Sincereless / Freefall / This almost spring / Feeling's free,The / Personal revolution,A / Not enough.
Notes: Annette's third album on Ironic records the previous two were 'SkySkating and Beer In The Streets Too Long' both of which sold well Annette is one of todaysleading contemporar music composers/ musicians with a large cul following. 'I Have No Feelings' is something of an event and will be eagerly received by critics and fans alike Personnel: Anette Peacock - all music and words, all vocals and instruments, arrangements and programming /Roger Turner - percussion and paiste cymbals/Benj-amin Allen sound/ Alfrede Benje - cover painting
Album: released on Ironic, Feb'86 by Ironi Records. Dist: IMS, Polygram, Cartel, Indies Cadillac

I'M THE ONE.
Tracks: / I'm the one / Seven days / Pony / Bee and gone / Blood / One way / Love me tender Gesture without plot / Did you hear me mommy
Album: released on RCA, Jul'86 by RCA Records. Dist: RCA, Roots, Swift, Wellard, Chris, & B, Solomon & Peres Distribution

Cassette: released on RCA, Jul'86 by RC Records. Dist: RCA, Roots, Swift, Wellar Chris, I & B, Solomon & Peres Distribution

LOVE'S OUT TO LUNCH.
Single (7"): released on Aura, Nov'82 by Ho lywood Nites Distribution. Dist: Pinnacle

PERFECT RELEASE.
Album: released on Aura, Oct'79 by Hollywood Nites Distribution. Dist: Pinnacle

SKY-SKATING.
Album: released on Iron, Aug'82 by IMS Records. Dist: IMS, Polygram

Single (7"): released on Ironic, Dec'81 by Ironic Records. Dist: IMS, Polygram, Cartel, Indies, Cadillac

X-DREAMS.
Album: released on Aura, Jul'79 by Hollywood Nites Distribution. Dist: Pinnacle

Peacock, Charlie
LIE DOWN IN THE GRASS.
Album: released on Word, Feb'85 by Word Records. Dist: Word Distribution, CBS

Cassette: released on Word, Feb'85 by Word Records. Dist: Word Distribution, CBS

Peacock, Gary
DECEMBER POEMS.
Album: released on ECM, Mar'79 by ECM Records. Dist: IMS, Polygram, Virgin through EMI

SHIFT IN THE WIND.
Tracks: / So green / Fractions / Last first / Shift in the wind centers / Caverns beneath the zoth / Valentine.
Compact disc: released on ECM (Germany), Aug'86 by ECM Records. Dist: IMS, Polygram, Virgin through EMI

Album: released on ECM, Apr'81 by ECM Records. Dist: IMS, Polygram, Virgin through EMI

TALES OF... (Peacock, Gary, K. Jarrett & J. DeJohnette).
Album: released on ECM, Aug'77 by ECM Records. Dist: IMS, Polygram, Virgin through EMI

TALES OF ANOTHER.
Tracks: / Vignette / Tone field / Major / Trilogy / Trilogy II / Trilogy III.
Compact disc: released on ECM (Germany), Feb'86 by ECM Records. Dist: IMS, Polygram, Virgin through EMI

Cassette: released on ECM (Germany), Jul'85 by ECM Records. Dist: IMS, Polygram, Virgin through EMI

VOICES FROM THE PAST - PARADIGM.
Album: released on ECM, May'82 by ECM Records. Dist: IMS, Polygram, Virgin through EMI

Peak
EBONDAZZAR.
Album: released on Innovative Communication, Jan'85 by Innovative Communication Records. Dist: Pickwick Distribution

Peak Folk
PEAK FOLK, THE.
Album: released on Folk Heritage, Jul'82 by Folk Heritage Records. Dist: Roots, Wynd-Up Distribution, Jazz Music, Folk Heritage

Peanuts Hucko
TRIBUTE TO BENNY GOODMAN (Peanuts Hucko / Butterfield / Erstrand).
Album: released on Timeless, Sep'86

Pearce, Alison
LAND OF HEART'S DESIRE.
Album: released on Meriklan, Apr'78 Dist: Harmonia Mundi Distributors

Pearce, Monty
MAGIC MOMENTS (Pearce, Monty & His Musicians).
Album: released on Dansan, Jun'84 by Spartan Records Dist: Spartan

Pearce, Paulette
LIVE AND LEARN.
Single (12"): released on Small Acts, Oct'84 by Small Acts Records. Dist: Jetstar

Pearce-Pickering
1975-76 (Pearce-Pickering Barrelhouse Jazz Band).
Album: released on Swaggie (Australia), Jan'83

FLANAGAN'S SHENANIGANS (1971-72) (Pearce-Pickering Ragtime Five).
Album: released on Swaggie (Australia), Jan'83

'IN LIZZIE DAYS (1970-71) (Pearce-Pickering Ragtime Five).
Album: released on Swaggie (Australia), Jan'83

Pearl Harbour
DON'T FOLLOW ME I'M LOST TOO (Pearl Harbour & The Explosions).
Album: released on Warner Brothers, Jan'81 by WEA Records. Dist: WEA

HULA LOVE.
Single (7"): released on Island, Jul'84 by Island Records. Dist: Polygram

Single (12"): released on Island, Jul'84 by Island Records. Dist: Polygram Deleted '85.

PEARLS GALORE.
Album: released on Island, Feb'85 by Island Records. Dist: Polygram

Pearls Before Swine
BEST OF.
Double Album: released on Adelphi(USA), May'81 by Adelphi Records (USA). Dist: Projection, Swift

Pearson, Buster
YOU KEEP ME HANGIN' ON.
Single (12"): released on Pavillion, Mar'82

Pearson, Duke
WAHOO.
Tracks: / Amanda / Bedouin / Farewell Machelle / Wahoo / Esp / Fly little bird fly.
Album: released on Manhattan, Nov'86 by EMI Records. Dist: EMI

Pearson, Johnny
SLEEPY SHORES.
Single (7"): released on Old Gold (Reissue), Jul'82

Pearson, Keith
BABY YOU'VE FALLEN IN LOVE AGAIN.
Single (7"): released on Mix, Jun'84

KEITH PEARSON RIGHT HAND BAND (Pearson, Keith Right Hand Band).
Notes: Band consists of: Keith banjo/guitar; Dave Arbus fiddle/saxophone- formerly of East of Eden and Fiddlers Dram; plus Paul and David Craswell. Songs written by Keith (1978 Melody Maker winner) plus much sparkling banjo and fiddle work in humerous bluegrass songs from Kentucky.
Album: released on Eron, Sep'86 by Eron Records. Dist: Eron Records

Cassette: released on Eron, Sep'86 by Eron Records. Dist: Eron Records

Pearson, Maureen
HANDSOME.
Single (12"): released on Jammy's, Sep'84 by Jammy's Records. Dist: Jetstar

RAIN OR SHINE.
Tracks: / Rain or shine (Inst).
Single (12"): released on Virgo, Nov'86

SOULFUL LOVER BABY.
Single (7"): released on Echo, Mar'82 by Vista Sounds. Dist: Jazz Music

Pears, Peter
FOLK SONGS (Pears, Peter & Benjamin Britten).
Album: released on Decca, Jun'84 by Decca Records. Dist: Polygram

Cassette: released on Decca, Jun'84 by Decca Records. Dist: Polygram

Peasants All
BROADSIDE ON.
Album: released on Plant Life, Nov'81

COUNTRIE FAIRE (Peasants All & Benjamin Luxton).
Album: released on Plant Life, Nov'81

HANDFUL OF PLEASANT DELITES, A.
Album: released on Plant Life, Nov'81

Pebbles
DO IT.
Single (12"): released on Sapphire, Feb'84 by Sapphire Records. Dist: Jetstar

Pedersen, Niels
CHOPS (Pedersen, Niels & Joe Pass).
Album: released on Pablo (USA), '82 by Pablo Records (USA). Dist: Wellard, Chris, IMS-Polygram, BMG

Cassette: released on Pablo (USA), '82 by Pablo Records (USA). Dist: Wellard, Chris, IMS-Polygram, BMG

ETERNAL TRAVELLER, THE.
Album: released on Pablo Jazz (USA), Aug'85 by United Artists. Dist: Swift

Cassette: released on Pablo Jazz (USA), Aug'85 by United Artists. Dist: Swift

NORTHSEA NIGHTS (Pedersen, Niels & Joe Pass).
Album: released on Pablo (USA), '82 by Pablo Records (USA). Dist: Wellard, Chris, IMS-Polygram, BMG

Cassette: released on Pablo (USA), '82 by Pablo Records (USA). Dist: Wellard, Chris, IMS-Polygram, BMG

PARIS CONCERT, THE (Pedersen, Niels, Oscar Peterson & Joe Pass).
Double Album: released on Pablo (USA), '82 by Pablo Records (USA). Dist: Wellard, Chris, IMS-Polygram, BMG

Cassette: released on Pablo (USA), '82 by Pablo Records (USA). Dist: Wellard, Chris, IMS-Polygram, BMG

PEDERSON, NIELS, OSCAR PETERSON, JOE PASS (Pedersen, Niels, Oscar Peterson & Joe Pass).
Notes: For full information see under Peterson, Oscar, Niels Pederson, Joe Pass

TIVOLI GARDENS, COPENHAGEN (Pedersen, Niels, Stephane Grappelli & Joe Pass).
Album: released on Pablo (USA), '82 by Pablo Records (USA). Dist: Wellard, Chris, IMS-Polygram, BMG

Cassette: released on Pablo (USA), '82 by Pablo Records (USA). Dist: Wellard, Chris, IMS-Polygram, BMG

VIKING, THE.
Album: released on Pablo Jazz (USA), Oct'84 by United Artists. Dist: Swift

VIKING (THE) (Pederson, Neils H.O.).
Compact disc: released on Pablo (USA), Apr'87 by Pablo Records (USA). Dist: Wellard, Chris, IMS-Polygram, BMG

Pedro Pepper
PEDRO PEPPER & THE CHERRY TWINS Various artists (Various Artists).
Cassette: released on Tell-a-tale (Cassettes), '84

Pee Bee Squad
RUGGED AND MEAN BUTCH AND ON-SCREEN.
Single (7"): released on Project, Sep'85 by Marvin Howell. Dist: Polygram

Single (12"): released on Project, Sep'85 by Marvin Howell. Dist: Polygram

SCARS AND STRIPES.
Tracks: / Scars and stripes / DJ talking the blues (part 2) / Main event mix.
Single (7"): released on Legacy, Apr'86 Dist: PRT

Single (12"): released on Legacy, Apr'86 Dist: PRT

Peebles, Ann
I CAN'T STAND THE RAIN.
Album: released on London, '74 by London Records. Dist: Polygram

Single (7"): released on Hi, Mar'85 by Demon Records. Dist: Pinnacle

Single (12"): released on Hi, Mar'85 by Demon Records. Dist: Pinnacle

TEAR YOUR PLAYHOUSE DOWN.
Cassette: released on Hi(UK), Mar'86 by London Records. Dist: Polygram

Peech Boys
DON'T MAKE ME WAIT.
Single (7"): released on TMT Productions, Oct'82

Single (12"): released on TMT Productions, Oct'82

LIFE IS SOMETHING SPECIAL.
Album: released on Island, Sep'83 by Island Records. Dist: Polygram

Cassette: released on Island, Sep'83 by Island Records. Dist: Polygram Deleted '85.

Peek, Kevin
GUITAR JUNCTION.
Album: released on Intersound, Mar'80 by Intersound Records. Dist: Jazz Music

LIFE AND OTHER GAMES.
Album: released on Ariola, May'82 Dist: RCA, Ariola

Cassette: released on Ariola, May'82 Dist: RCA, Ariola

Peek, Paul
ROCK-A-ROUND.
Tracks: / Rock-a-round (The) / Sweet skinny Jenny / Olds-mo-William / Gee but I miss that girl.
Single (12"): released on Rollercoaster, Aug'86 by Rollercoaster Records. Dist: Swift Distribution, Rollercoaster Distribution

Peelers
BANISH MISFORTUNE.
Album: released on Barlev, Jan'80

Cassette: released on Barlev. Jan'80

DODGER, THE.
Single (7"): released on Etude, Sep'84 by Etude Records. Dist: Spartan

JOHN O'DREAMS.
Single (7"): released on After Hours, Jun'83 Dist: CBS

WIND IN THE WILLOWS.
Single (7"): released on Masquerade, Nov'82

Peep show
SETTING ME UP.
Single (7"): released on Boff, Jan'85 Dist: M.I.S.

Peer Gynt
BACK SEAT.
Album: released on Neat, Jul'87 by Neat Records. Dist: Pinnacle, Neat

Peers, Donald
DONALD PEERS COLLECTION, (THE).
Album: released on Encore, Jun'78 by EMI Records. Dist: EMI

PEERS, DONALD.
Notes: Full information see under Starlight Serenades

WORLD OF..., (THE).
Cassette: released on Decca, May'74 by Decca Records. Dist: Polygram

Peg
PEG Original cast (Various Artists).
Album: released on TER. Mar'84

Cassette: released on TER, Mar'84

Pegasus the winged horse
PEGASUS THE WINGED HORSE Various artists (Various Artists).
Cassette: released on Tellastory, Oct'79 by Bartlett Bliss Productions. Dist: PRT Distribution, Hayward Promotions Distribution, H.R. Taylor Distribution

Pegg, Bob & Carole
COMPLETE MR FOX, (THE).
Album: released on Transatlantic, May'79 by Transatlantic Records. Dist: IMS-Polygram

HE CAME FROM THE MOUNTAINS.
Album: released on Leader, Jun'86 Dist: Jazz Music, Projection

Pegg, Dave
COCKTAIL COWBOY.
Single (7"): released on Projection, Sep'83

COCKTAIL COWBOY GOES IT ALONE, (THE).
Album: released on Woodworm, Aug'84 by Woodworm Records. Dist: Projection, Celtic Music

Peggy Sue
DYNAMITE COUNTRY.
Album: released on Meteor, Jun'78 by Magnum Force Music. Dist: CBS Distribution

Peggy Sue got married
PEGGY SUE GOT MARRIED Original soundtrack (Various Artists).
Album: released on TER, Mar'87 Dist: Pinnacle

Cassette: released on TER, Mar'87 Dist: Pinnacle

Pegler, Tony
AS REQUESTED (THE LOWRY CONTILLION ORGAN).
Album: released on Grosvenor, Oct'82 by Grosvenor Records. Dist: Taylors

CORONADO CASCADE (PLAYING THE CORONADO CASCADE 297).
Album: released on Grosvenor, Jun'81 by Grosvenor Records. Dist: Taylors

Peking man
ROOM THAT ECHOES.
Tracks: Room that echoes (round and around) / Vision high.
Single (7"): released on Epic, Feb'87 by CBS Records. Dist: CBS

Single (12"): released on Epic, Feb'87 by CBS Records. Dist: CBS

Pellay, Alan
DEMONIC FORCES.
Single (7"): released on ON-U, May'81

Pellay, Lana
PISTOL IN MY POCKET.
Tracks: / Pistol in my pocket / Pistol in my pocket (Instrumental) / Dirty Harry.
Single (7"): released on Sublime, Feb'86 by Sublime Records. Dist: PRT Distribution

Single (12"): released on Sublime, Feb'86 by Sublime Records. Dist: PRT Distribution

Pell, Chris Orchestra
50 HIT SOUNDS OF BIG BANDS.
Double Album: released on Pickwick, May'77

BIG BAND FAVOURITES.
Double cassette: released on Pickwick (Ditto series), Jul'82

Pemberton, Victor
NIGHT OF THE WOLF.
Cassette: released on BBC, May'84 by BBC Records & Tapes. Dist: EMI, PRT, P;ne

Pembroke Male Choir
PEMBROKE MALE VOICE CHOIR.
Album: released on Black Mountain, Mar'80 by Black Mountain Records.

Pena, Paco
ART OF FLAMENCO GUITAR, (THE).
Album: released on Gold Crown, Sep'79 by Decca Records. Dist: Polygram

FLAMENCO VIVO.
Album: released on Cord, Sep'86 by M.I.S., PRT

LIVE IN LONDON (GUITAR).
Album: released on Decca, Jul'79 by Decca Records. Dist: Polygram

LIVE IN MUNICH.
Album: released on Cord, Oct'86 by M.I.S., PRT

Album: released on Flamenco Vivo, Mar'85 by Flamenco Vivo Records. Dist: M.I.S.

PACO PENA FLAMENCO COMPANY LIVE AT SADLERS WELLS, (THE).
Album: released on Decca, Jan'80 by Decca Records. Dist: Polygram

Pencils
IF YOU REALLY WANNA HURT SOMEBODY.
Single (7"): released on Next Records. Sep'82

PICTURES OF PARIS.
Single (7"): released on Next, Apr'83 by Next Records. Dist: Chris Wellard Distribution

WATCHING THE TEARS.
Single (7"): released on Next Records, Jul'82

Pendarvis, Tracy
BISON POP.
Album: released on Bear Family (USA Import), Oct'81

Pender, Don
SANDRA JEAN (Pender, Don/Horace Parlan).
Notes: With Jesper Lundgaard/Ed Thigpen/Finn Ziegler.
Album: released on Sandra, Jan'87

Pendergrass, Teddy
GREATEST HITS: TEDDY PENDERGRASS.
Album: released on Philadelphia International, Jun'84 by CBS Records. Dist: CBS

HEAVEN ONLY KNOWS.
Cassette: released on Philadelphia International, Dec'83 by CBS Records. Dist: CBS

HOLD ME.
Tracks: / Hold me / Love.
Single (7"): released on Elektra (USA), Jan'86 by Elektra/Asylum/Nonesuch Records. Dist: WEA

IT'S TIME FOR LOVE.
Album: released on Philadelphia International, Oct'81 by CBS Records. Dist: CBS

LIFE IS A SONG WORTH SINGING.
Album: released on Philadelphia International, Apr'83 by CBS Records. Dist: CBS

LOVE LANGUAGE.
Tracks: / In my time / So sad the song / Hot love / Stay with me / Hold me / You're my choice tonight / Love / This time is yours.
Album: released on Asylum, Jul'86 by WEA Records. Dist: WEA

Cassette: released on Asylum, Jul'86 by WEA Records. Dist: WEA

Compact disc: released on Asylum, Jul'86 by WEA Records. Dist: WEA

READY FOR TEDDY.
Album: released on Philadelphia International, Apr'81 by CBS Records. Dist: CBS

Cassette: released on Philadelphia International, Apr'81 by CBS Records. Dist: CBS

TEDDY.
Cassette: released on Philadelphia, Aug'79

TEDDY PENDERGRASS.
Album: released on Philadelphia International, Mar'82 by CBS Records. Dist: CBS

THIS ONE'S FOR YOU.
Cassette: released on Philadelphia International, Aug'82 by CBS Records. Dist: CBS

WORKING IT BACK.
Tracks: / Love 4/2 / One of us fell in love / Never felt like dancing / Closer / Lovely colour blue / Want you back in my life / Working it back / Reach out and touch.
Compact disc: released on Elektra (USA), Jul'86 by Elektra/Asylum/Nonesuch Records. Dist: WEA

Album: released on Elektra, Nov'85 by WEA Records. Dist: WEA

Cassette: released on Elektra, Nov'85 by WEA Records. Dist: WEA

Pender, Mike
IT'S OVER.
Tracks: / It's over / Brothers and sisters.
Single (7"): released on Sierra, Jun'86 by Sierra Records. Dist: WEA

Single (12"): released on Sierra, Jun'86 by Sierra Records. Dist: WEA

Pendragon
9.15 LIVE.
Album: released on Awareness, Dec'86 by Awareness. Dist: EMI

Cassette: released on Awareness, Dec'86 by Awareness. Dist: EMI

FIRE IN HARMONY.
Album: released on Elusive, Mar'85 by All Round Productions Company Records. Dist: EMI

FLY HIGH FALL FAR.
Album: released on Elusive, Nov'84 by All Round Productions Company Records. Dist: EMI

JEWEL.
Album: released on Awareness, Nov'86 by Awareness. Dist: EMI

Cassette: released on Awareness, Nov'86 by Awareness. Dist: EMI

Album: released on Elusive, Aug'85 by All Round Productions Company Records. Dist: EMI

JEWEL/FLY HIGH FALL FAR.
Cassette: released on Awareness, Dec'86 by Awareness. Dist: EMI

RED SHOES.
Tracks: / Searching / Contact*.
Notes: *=Extra track on 12" only
Single (7"): released on Awareness, Feb'87 by Awareness. Dist: EMI

Single (12"): released on Awareness, Feb'87 by Awareness. Dist: EMI

Pendulum
JINGLES.
Single (7"): released on Monarch, Nov'82 by Chart Records. Dist: Pinnacle

WHITE CONFETTI.
Single (7"): released on Monarch, Oct'82 by Chart Records. Dist: Pinnacle

Pendyrus Male Choir
FAVOURITE HYMNS.

Album: released on Word, May'82 by Word Records. Dist: Word Distribution, CBS

Cassette: released on Word, May'82 by Word Records. Dist: Word Distrib tion, CBS

SHEEP MAY SAFELY GRAZE.
Album: released on Word, May'82 by Word Records. Dist: Word Distribution, CBS

Cassette: released on Word, May'82 by Word Records. Dist: Word Distribution, CBS

Penetration
MOVING TARGETS.
Album: released on Virgin, Mar'84 by Virgin Records. Dist: EMI, Virgin Distribution

Penfold, Jim
DREAM ON.
Single (7"): released on Water, Oct'85 Dist: MIS-EMI Distribution

Penfold, Rebecca
SWEET PROMROSES & FAMILY (DEVON).
Cassette: released on Folktracks, Nov'79 by Folktracks Cassettes. Dist: Folktracks

Penguin Cafe Orchestra
BROADCASTING FROM HOME.
Tracks: / Music for a found harmonium / Prelude and yodel / More milk / Ship dip / White mischief / In the back of a taxi / Music by numbers / Another one from the colonies / Air / Heartwind / Isle of view (music for helicopter pilots) / Now nothing.
Album: released on Editions EG, Jan'87 by Virgin Records. Dist: EMI

Cassette: released on Editions EG, Jan'87 by Virgin Records. Dist: EMI

Compact disc: released on Editions EG, Jan'87 by Virgin Records. Dist: EM'

DRT.
Tracks: / DRT / Air a danser / Air.
Single (7"): released on Virgin, May'87 by Virgin Records. Dist: EMI, Virgin Distribution

Single (12"): released on Virgin, May'87 by Virgin Records. Dist: EMI, Virgin Distribution

MUSIC FOR A SOUND HARMONIAN.
Tracks: / Music for a sound harmonian / In the back of a taxi/ Bean fields / Penguin cafe single.
Single (7"): released on E.G., Mar'87 by Virgin Records. Dist: Virgin, EMI

Single (12"): released on E.G., Mar'87 by Virgin Records. Dist: Virgin, EMI

MUSIC FROM THE PENGUIN CAFE.
Tracks: / Chartered flight / Hugebaby / Penguin Cafe single / Sound of someone you love who's going away ... / Zopf / Coronation / From the Colonies / Giles Farnaby's dream / In a Sydney motel / Pigs / Surface tension.
Compact disc: released on Editions EG, Jun'87 by Virgin Records. Dist: EMI

Album: by Virgin Records. Dist: EMI

PENGUIN CAFE ORCHESTRA MINI ALBUM, (THE).
Album: released on E.G., Jul'83 by Virgin Records. Dist: Virgin, EMI

Cassette: released on E.G., Jul'83 by Virgin Records. Dist: Virgin, EMI

PENGUIN CAFE ORCHESTRA.
Tracks: / Air a dancer / Yodel 1&2 / Telephone and rubber band / Cutting branches for a temporary shelter / Pythagoras' trousers / Number 1-4 / Salt bean tumble / Paul's dance / Ecstacy of dancing fleas / Walk don't run / Flux / Walk don't run / Flux / Simon's dream / Harmonic necklace / Steady state.
Album: released on Editions EG, Jan'87 by Virgin Records. Dist: EMI

SIGNS OF LIFE.
Album: released on E.G., Mar'87 by Virgin Records. Dist: Virgin, EMI

Cassette: released on E.G., Mar'87 by Virgin Records. Dist: Virgin, EMI

Penguins
EARTH ANGEL.
Tracks: / Don't do it / Promises, promises, promises / She's gone, gone, gone / Okey ook / Walkin down Broadway / Hey senorita / Cool baby cool / Ice / Jingle jangle / Christmas prayer, A / Earth angel / It only happens with you / Be mine / My troubles are note at an end / Love will make your mind go wild / Dealer of dreams / Will Earth angel (2).
Album: released on Bear Family, Sep'86 by Bear Family Records. Dist: Rollercoaster Distribution, Swift

Pennies from heaven
LOVE IS GOOD FOR ANYTHING.

Single (7"): released on Warner Brothers, Jun'82 by WEA Records. Dist: WEA

MORE PENNIES FROM HEAVEN (Various Artists).
Album: released on World Records, May'78 Dist: Polygram

PENNIES FROM HEAVEN (GOLDEN AGE) Various artists (Various Artists).
Album: released on Golden Age, Jul'83 by Music For Pleasure Records. Dist: EMI

Cassette: released on Golden Age, Jul'83 by Music For Pleasure Records. Dist: EMI

PENNIES FROM HEAVEN Various artists (Various Artists).
Double Album: released on Decca. May'78

Penning, Les
SHOULD HAVE BEEN FOREVER.
Single (7"): released on Plant Life, Dec'83

WILLOW FAIR.
Single (7"): released on Plant Life, Jun'83

Pennington, Barbara
ALL AMERICAN BOY.
Single (7"): released on Record Shack, Sep'84

Single (12"): released on Record Shack, Sep'84

DON'T STOP THE WORLD.
Single (7"): released on Nightmare, Feb'87 by Nightmare Records. Dist: PRT

Single (12"): by Nightmare Records. Dist: PRT

FAN THE FLAME.
Single (7"): released on Record Shack, Mar'85
Cat. no: SOHO 37
Single (12"): released on Record Shack, Mar'85

MIDNIGHT RIDE.
Album: released on United Artists, Mar'78

ON A CROWDED STREET.
Single (7"): released on Record Shack, Aug'85 by Record Shack Records. Dist: PRT

Single (12"): released on Record Shack, Aug'85 by Record Shack Records. Dist: PRT

Single (12"): released on Record Shack, Aug'85 by Record Shack Records. Dist: PRT

OUT OF THE DARKEST NIGHT.
Album: released on Record Shack, Aug'85 by Record Shack Records. Dist: PRT

Cassette: released on Record Shack, Aug'85 by Record Shack Records. Dist: PRT

WAYDOWN DEEP IN MY SOUL.
Single (7"): released on Record Shack, Jan'85 by Record Shack Records. Dist: PRT

Single (12"): released on Record Shack, Jan'85 by Record Shack Records. Dist: PRT

Penny Arcade
CALLIN' YOU.
Tracks: / Callin' you / Midnight train.
Single (7"): released on Brilliant, Jul'87 by PVK. Dist: Spartan

I DO LOVE YOU.
Tracks: / I do love you / London lights.
Single (7"): released on PVK, '86

RADIO STATION.
Tracks: / Radio station / Alright on the night.
Single (7"): released on PVK, '86

Penny, Dave
IN FOR A PENNY.
Album: released on EMI, Apr'84 by EMI Records. Dist: EMI

Penny, Hank
ROMPIN' STOMPIN' SINGIN' SWINGIN
Album: released on Bear Family (RCA), Sep'8

TOBACCO STATE SWING (Penny, Hank & His Radio Cowboys).
Album: released on Rambler, Jul'81 Dist: Sw

Penny serenade
PENNY SERENADE Various artists (Various Artists).
Album: released on Halcyon, Dec'82 by Halcyon Records. Dist: Jazz Music

Album: released on Joy, Feb'84 by President Records. Dist: Jazz Music, Swift, President Distribution

Penny & The Rims

JUMP AND JERK.
Single (7"): released on Electro, Jan'81 Dist: Pinnacle

Pennywhistlers

PENNYWHISTLERS Various artists (Various Artists).
Album: released on Nonesuch Explorer (USA), Jul'84

Pens Guns and Riffs

PENS GUNS AND RIFFS Various artists (Various Artists).
Album: released on Compact Organisation, Jun'85 Dist: PRT

Pentagram

DAY OF RECKONING.
Album: released on Homestead, Jun'87 Dist: Rough Trade, Cartel, Shigaku

PENTAGRAM.
Album: released on Pentagram, Jul'85 by Pentagram Records. Dist: Rough Trade

Pentangle

BASKET OF LIGHT.
Album: released on Transatlantic, Oct'81 by Transatlantic Records. Dist: IMS-Polygram

Cassette: released on Transatlantic, Oct'81 by Transatlantic Records. Dist: IMS-Polygram

Tracks: / Light flight / Once I had a sweetheart / Springtime promises / Lyke-wyke dirge / Train song / Hunting song / Sally go round the roses / Cuckoo, The / House carpenter.
Compact disc: released on Transatlantic, Jul'87 by Transatlantic Records. Dist: IMS-Polygram

ESSENTIAL PENTANGLE, THE (VOL. 1).
Tracks: / Once I had a sweetheart / Hear my call / Hole in the coal / Omie wise / Waltz / Trees they do grow high, The / Sweet child / Woman like you, A / Reflection / Will the circle be unbroken / Watch the stars / Helping hand / Goodbye pork pie hat / When I was in my prime.
Notes: Personnel: John Renbourn - guitar, vocals / Bert Jansch - guitar, vocals / Jacqui McShee - vocals / Terry Cox - drums / Danny Thompson - double bass.
Compact disc: released on Transatlantic, Jul'87 by Transatlantic Records. Dist: IMS-Polygram

ESSENTIAL PENTANGLE, THE (VOL. 2).
Tracks: / Pentangling / Bruton town / Shake shake mama / Let no man steal your thyme / Soho / Cruel sister / Bells / Wedding dress / I've got a feeling / Three part thing / Rain and snow / Way behind the sun / When I get home / Time has come, The / When I was in my prime.
Compact disc: released on Transatlantic, Sep'87 by Transatlantic Records. Dist: IMS-Polygram

OPEN THE DOOR.
Album: released on Spindrift, Jun'85

PENTANGLE - AT THEIR BEST.
Album: released on Cambra, '83 by Cambra Records. Dist: IDS, Conifer

Cassette: released on Cambra, '83 by Cambra Records. Dist: IDS, Conifer

PENTANGLING.
Album: released on Transatlantic, May'81 by Transatlantic Records. Dist: IMS-Polygram

Cassette: released on Transatlantic, May'81 by Transatlantic Records. Dist: IMS-Polygram

Pentecostal Praise

GENERAL CONFERENCE.
Album: by Pilgrim Records. Dist: Rough Trade, Cartel

Penthouse

LOVE SYMPHONY ORCHESTRA, THE.
Album: released on Miracle, Mar'79 by Gull Records. Dist: PRT Distribution

Penumbrah

HOW GOOD IT IS.
Single (12"): released on Jah Observers, Dec'83 by Jah Observers Records. Dist: Ruff Lion Distribution

People

MUSICAL MAN.
Single (7"): released on Race, May'81

People, Animals And...

PEOPLE, ANIMALS AND OTHER MONSTERS Jack Prelutsky (Prelutsky, Jack).
Cassette: released on Caedmon(USA), Sep'82 by Caedmon (USA) Records. Dist: Gower, Taylors, Discovery

People In Control

WHEN IT'S WAR.
Single (7"): released on Crammed, Apr'83 Dist: Rough Trade, Nine Mile, Cartel

People in progress

THIS IS MY SONG.
Tracks: / This is my song (Part 1) / This is my song (Part 2).
Single (7"): released on Polydor, Nov'86 by Polydor Records. Dist: Polygram, Polydor

Single (12"): released on Polydor, Nov'86 by Polydor Records. Dist: Polygram, Polydor

People like us

DELIVERANCE (People like us featuring Cindy Dickinson).
Tracks: / Deliverance / Deliverance(Instrumental).
Single (12"): released on Passion, Nov'86 by Skratch Records. Dist: PRT

MIDNIGHT LOVER.
Tracks: / Midnight lovers / Midnight lovers (Instrumental).
Single (12"): released on Passion, Feb'86 by Skratch Records. Dist: PRT

REINCARNATION (COMING BACK FOR LOVE).
Single (7"): released on Passion, Aug'85 by Skratch Records. Dist: PRT

Single (12"): released on Passion, Aug'85 by Skratch Records. Dist: PRT

People Of The World Band

PEOPLE OF THE WORLD.
Single (12"): released on Carousel, Feb'83 by Carousel Records. Dist: Spartan, Rough Trade

People's Carol

PEOPLE'S CAROL Various artists (Various Artists).
Album: released on Leader, '81 Dist: Jazz Music, Projection

Peoples Choice

DO IT (ANYWAY YOU WANNA).
Single (7"): released on Old Gold, Sep'85 by Old Gold Records. Dist: Lightning, Jazz Music, Spartan, Counterpoint

WE GOT THE RHYTHM.
Album: released on Philadelphia International, Jul'76 by CBS Records. Dist: CBS

People's concert...

PEOPLE'S CONCERT FOR KAMPUCHEA Various artists (Various Artists).
Album: released on Atlantic, Nov'80 by WEA Records. Dist: WEA

Peoples, Tommy

IRONMAN, THE (Peoples, Tommy With Daithi Sproule).
Album: released on Shanachie, Jun'85

Molloy, Brady, Peoples

People unite band

BROTHERS AND SISTERS.
Tracks: / Brothers and sisters / Zabandis.
Single (12"): released on People Unite, Mar'86 by People Unite Records. Dist: Jetstar, Rough Trade, Cartel, Pinnacle, Nine Mile

People unite in progress

PEOPLE UNITE IN PROGRESS Various artists (Various Artists).
Album: released on People Unite, Apr'84 by People Unite Records. Dist: Jetstar, Rough Trade, Cartel, Pinnacle, Nine Mile

Pepito, Don

A ERA DE OURO (Pepito, Don Y Su Ritmo Tropical).
Album: released on Philips, '76 Dist: IMS-Polygram

Pepper and Maureen

WINDSONG.
Single (12"): released on Holly Cone, Dec'82 by Ariwa Records. Dist: Jetstar, Rough Trade

Pepper, Art

ARTISTRY IN JAZZ Greatest hits.
Compact disc: released on JVC Fantasy (Japan), May'87

ART PEPPER.
Album: released on Deja Vu, Jan'87 by Deja Vu Records. Dist: Counterpoint Distribution, Record Services Distribution (Ireland)

Cassette: released on Deja Vu, Jan'87 by Deja Vu Records. Dist: Counterpoint Distribution, Record Services Distribution (Ireland)

ART PEPPER MEETS THE RHYTHM SECTION.
Compact disc: released on Contemporary, Jun'87 by Contemporary Records. Dist: Pinnacle

Compact disc: released on Contemporary, Jun'87 by Contemporary Records. Dist: Pinnacle

Compact disc: released on Contemporary, Jun'87 by Contemporary Records. Dist: Pinnacle

Album: released on Boplicity, Jun'85 by Boplicity Records. Dist: Ace Records, Pinnacle

ART PEPPER WITH WARNE MARSH (Pepper, Art/Warne Marsh).
Compact disc: released on JVC Fantasy (Japan), May'87

AT THE VILLAGE VANGUARD VOL 4.
Compact disc: released on Carrere, Apr'87 by Carrere Records. Dist: PRT, Spartan

BALLADS BY FOUR.
Compact disc: released on Fantasy (USA), Nov'86 by Fantasy Inc USA Records. Dist: IMS, Polygram

BLUES FOR THE FISHERMAN.
Compact disc: released on Mole, Mar'86 by Mole Records. Dist: Mole Music Co., Spartan Distribution

Album: released on Mole, Apr'81 by Mole Records. Dist: Mole Music Co., Spartan Distribution

BLUES FOR THE FISHERMEN.

DISCOVERIES (Pepper, Art/7 others).
Tracks: / Chili pepper / Susie the poodle / Everything happens to me / Tickle toe / Nutmeg / Cinnamon / What's new / Thyme time / Straight life / Art's oregano / Way you look tonight.
Notes: Other artists: Russ Freman(piano) Bob Whitlock(bass) Bobby White(drums) Jack Montrose(tenor sax) Claude Williamson(piano) Monte Ludwig(bass) Larry Bunker(drums)
Album: released on Savoy Jazz, Dec'85 by RCA Records (Germany). Dist: Conifer

DISCOVERIES, THE SAVOY SESSIONS.
Album:

DISCOVERY.
Album: released on RCA, Oct'85 by RCA Records. Dist: RCA, Roots, Swift, Wellard, Chris, I & B, Solomon & Peres Distribution

Album: released on RCA, Oct'85 by RCA Records. Dist: RCA, Roots, Swift, Wellard, Chris, I & B, Solomon & Peres Distribution

FRIDAY NIGHT AT THE VILLAGE VANGUARD.
Album: released on Contemporary Jazz, Jul'81

GETTIN' TOGETHER (Pepper,Art/Conte Candoli).
Compact disc: released on JVC Fantasy (Japan), May'87

GETTIN' TOGETHER.
Album: released on Contemporary, May'86 by Contemporary Records. Dist: Pinnacle

GOIN' HOME.
Notes: With George Cables-piano
Compact disc: released on JVC Fantasy (Japan), '86

INTENSITY.
Compact disc: released on JVC Fantasy, Jul'87 Dist: Target

Album: released on Contemporary (Boplicity), Oct'85 Dist: Pinnacle

LIVING LEGEND (Pepper, Art/Hampton Hawes/Shelley Manne).
Compact disc: released on JVC Fantasy (Japan), May'87

LIVING LEGEND.
Tracks: / Orphelia / Here's that rainy day / What Laurie likes / Mr Yohe / Lost life / Samba mom-mom.
Album: released on Contemporary, Jan'86 by Contemporary Records. Dist: Pinnacle

MEETS THE RHYTHM SECTION.
Album: released on Boplicity, Jun'85 by Boplicity Records. Dist: Ace Records, Pinnacle

Notes: With Red Garland, Paul Chambers & Philly Joe Jones
Compact disc: released on JVC Fantasy (Japan), '86

Compact disc: released on Boplicity, Jul'87 by Boplicity Records. Dist: Ace Records, Pinnacle

MODERN JAZZ CLASSICS (Pepper, Art + Eleven).
Compact disc: released on JVC Fantasy (Japan), May'87

MODERN JAZZ CLASSICS (Pepper, Art + Eleven).
Compact disc: released on Mobile Fidelity, Oct'86 by Mobile Fidelity Records.

MORE FOR LES.
Album: released on Contemporary, Jun'86 by Contemporary Records. Dist: Pinnacle

NO LIMIT (Pepper, Art/George Cables/Tony Dumas).
Compact disc: released on JVC Fantasy (Japan), May'87

NO LIMIT.
Album: released on Contemporary, Mar'86 by Contemporary Records. Dist: Pinnacle

Compact disc: released on Boplicity, Jul'87 by Boplicity Records. Dist: Ace Records, Pinnacle

OMEGA ALPHA.
Album: released on Liberty, Mar'81 by Liberty-United. Dist: EMI

PLUS ELEVEN.
Album: released on Boplicity, Aug'85 by Boplicity Records. Dist: Ace Records, Pinnacle

Compact disc: released on Contemporary, Aug'87 by Contemporary Records. Dist: Pinnacle

POPO (Pepper, Art & Shorty Rogers).
Album: released on Xanadu, Jul'82 Dist: Discovery, Jazz Horizons, Jazz Music, Swift

PORTRAIT OF ART PEPPER.
Album: released on Contemporary, Sep'86 by Contemporary Records. Dist: Pinnacle

REDISCOVERIES.
Tracks: / Chili pepper (Take 3) / Suzy the poodle (Take 3) / Everything happens to me (Take 2) / Nutmeg (Take 6) / Cinnamon / What's new / Thyme time / Straight line / Art's oregano / Chili pepper (Take 5) / Suzy the poodle (Take 5) / Everything happens to me (Take 3) / Everything happens to me (Take 6) / Nutmeg (Take 7).
Album: released on RCA, Nov'86 by RCA Records. Dist: RCA, Roots, Swift, Wellard, Chris, I & B, Solomon & Peres Distribution

Cassette: released on RCA, Nov'86 by RCA Records. Dist: RCA, Roots, Swift, Wellard, Chris, I & B, Solomon & Peres Distribution

ROADGAME.
Album: released on Galaxy, Aug'82 by Galaxy Records. Dist: RCA, Red Lightnin' Distribution, Discovery, Swift

SATURDAY NIGHT AT THE VILLAGE VANGUARD.
Album: released on Contemporary, Dec'81 by Contemporary Records. Dist: Pinnacle

SMACK UP.
Album: released on Contemporary, Nov'86 by Contemporary Records. Dist: Pinnacle

STRAIGHT LIFE.
Tracks: / Straight life / Chili pepper / Cinnamon / Tickle toe / Suzy the poodle / Everything happens to me / Nutmeg / Deep purple / What's new / Thyme time / Art's oregano / Way you look tonight, The / Straight life.
Compact disc: released on Carrere(France), '86 by Carrere Records (France). Dist: PRT

Compact disc: released on RCA, Jan'87 by RCA Records. Dist: RCA, Roots, Swift, Wellard, Chris, I & B, Solomon & Peres Distribution

Compact disc: released on Carrere, Apr'87 by Carrere Records. Dist: PRT, Spartan
Cat. no: 98175
Album: released on Galaxy, Jan'80 by Galaxy Records. Dist: RCA, Red Lightnin' Distribution, Discovery, Swift

TODAY.
Album: released on Galaxy (USA), May'84 by Prestige Records. Dist: RCA

TRIP, (THE) (Pepper, Art/George Cables/Elvin Jones).
Compact disc: released on JVC Fantasy (Japan), May'87

TRIP, (THE).
Album: released on Contemporary, Nov'86 by Contemporary Records. Dist: Pinnacle

TRUE BLUES featuring Milcho Leviev Quartet.
Album: released on Mole Jazz, Aug'81 by Mole Jazz Records. Dist: Mole Jazz Distributors

WAY IT WAS, THE.
Notes: Side one of this album is a previously unissued session that Art Pepper recordedin 1957 with Warne Marse on tenor. Side two is three outtakes from the sessions that have ended up on the three previous Contemporary Pepper albums.
Album: released on Contemporary, May'87 by Contemporary Records. Dist: Pinnacle

WINTER MOON.
Tracks: / Our song / Here's that rainy day / That's love / Winter moon / When the sun comes out / Blues in the night / Prisoner, (The) (Love theme from 'Eyes of Laura Mars').
Compact disc: released on Fantasy (USA), Nov'86 by Fantasy Inc USA Records. Dist: IMS, Polygram

Peppermint Harris

SITTIN' IN WITH HISTORICAL RECORDINGS.
Album: released on Lunar 2, Apr'79

Peppers

PEPPER BOX.
Single (7"): released on Import Music Service (IMS), '80 Dist: Concord Jazz Distributions, Pablo, Polygram

Pepper's Lounge Chicago

PEPPER'S LOUNGE ,CHICAGO VOL.2 various artists (Various Artists).
Album: released on Rarities, May'79

Peppers,Nancy

FIRST NIGHT.
Single (7"): released on Sounds Right, Nov'85 Dist: MIS-EMI Distribution

Peppertree,Ricky

BABY IT'S NICE TO SEE YOU.
Single (7"): released on Mekaliteit, Feb'82 by Mekaliteit Music Records. Dist: Jetstar Distribution, Third World Distribution

Pepsi & Shirlie

GOODBYE STRANGER.
Single (7"): released on Polydor, May'87 by Polydor Records. Dist: Polygram, Polydor

Single (12"): released on Polydor, May'87 by Polydor Records. Dist: Polygram, Polydor

HEARTACHE.
Single (7"): released on Polydor, Jan'87 by Polydor Records. Dist: Polygram, Polydor

Single (12"): released on Polydor, Jan'87 by Polydor Records. Dist: Polygram, Polydor

Percival,Norman

FIGHTER PILOT/VALLEY WELSH.
Single (7"): released on Splash, Jan'83 by Splash Records. Dist: CBS

Percival Pea..

PERCIVAL PEA & POLLY POMEGRANATE various artists (Various Artists).
Cassette: released on Tell-a-tale (Cassettes), '84

Percussions of Africa

PERCUSSIONS OF AFRICA Various Artists (Various Artists).
Tracks: / Ceremonia de mariage(Percussions Diolas) / Mil Pile, (Le) / Lutte Senegalaise, (La) (Percussions diolas).
Compact disc: released on Sunset (France), Aug'86 Dist: IMS-Polygram Distribution

Percy

PERCY Original soundtrack (Kinks).
Tracks: / God's children / Lola / Way love used to be (The) / Completely / Running round town / Moments / Animals in the zoo / Just friends / Whip lady / Dreams / Helga / Willesden Green / End titles.
Compact disc: released on PRT, '86 by PRT Records. Dist: PRT

Album: released on Euphonic, Apr'79 by Euphonic Records. Dist: Jazz Music, Swift

Perennial divide

BURN DOWN.
Single (12"): released on Sweatbox, Oct'86 by Sweatbox Records. Dist: Rough Trade, Cartel

PURGE.
Album: released on Sweatbox, Sep'86 by Sweatbox Records. Dist: Rough Trade, Cartel

Pere Ubu

ARCHIVAL COLLECTION, (AN) (Pere Ubu/Terminal Tower).
Album: released on Rough Trade, Nov'85 by Rough Trade Records. Dist: Rough Trade Distribution, Cartel Distribution

NEW PICNIC TIME.
Album: released on Chrysalis, Sep'79 by Chrysalis Records. Dist: CBS

Perfect

PERFECT Original soundtrack.
Album: released on Arista, Aug'85 by Arista Records. Dist: RCA

Cassette: released on Arista, Aug'85 by Arista Records. Dist: RCA

Perfect Beat

PERFECT BEAT various artists (Various Artists).
Album: released on Polydor, Dec'84 by Polydor Records. Dist: Polygram, Polydor

Cassette: released on Polydor, Dec'84 by Polydor Records. Dist: Polygram, Polydor

Perfect,Christine

CHRISTINE PERFECT.
Album: released on CBS, '84 by CBS Records. Dist: CBS

Cassette: released on CBS, '84 by CBS Records. Dist: CBS

ALBATROSS (Perfect,Cristine & Fleetwood Mac).
Album: released on Embassy, Aug'77 by CBS Records. Dist: CBS

Cassette: released on Embassy, Aug'77 by CBS Records. Dist: CBS

Perfect Crime

I FEEL LIKE AN ESKIMO/NO DRUMS.
Single (7"): released on MCA, Jan'84 by MCA Records. Dist: Polygram, MCA

Single (12"): released on MCA, Jan'84 by MCA Records. Dist: Polygram, MCA

Perfect Daze

BUBBLEGUM.
Special: released on Vinyl Solution, Mar'87 Dist: Pinnacle

Perfect End

SWEET DREAM/NATURAL CAUSES.
Single (7"): released on Hellfire disc, Apr'82 Dist: Rough Trade

Perfect Fit, (A)

IF YOU ONLY KNEW.
Tracks: / If you only knew / Heartbreaking.
Single (12"): released on Move, Sep'86 by Charly Records. Dist: Charly Distribution, Fast Forward Distribution, Cartel Distribution

Perfect Match

PERFECT MATCH.
Album: released on Country House, Nov'81 by BGS Productions Ltd. Dist: Taylor, H.R., Record Merchandisers Distribution, Pinnacle, Sounds of Scotland Records

Cassette: released on Country House, Nov'81 by BGS Productions Ltd. Dist: Taylor, H.R., Record Merchandisers Distribution, Pinnacle, Sounds of Scotland Records

Perfect Strangers

LOVE THAT TURNED AWAY/15 MINUTES.
Single (7"): released on Best, Jun'83 by Best Records. Dist: Stage One

Perfect Vision

DEMONSTRATION.
Cassette: released on Peeved, Feb'84 by Peeved Records. Dist: Peeved, Cartel, Backs

DREAMSHIP.
Single (12"): released on Backs, Feb'85 by Backs Records. Dist: Backs, Cartel

OUR BROKEN CROWN (EP).
Single (7"): released on Leave It Art, Sep'84 by Leave It Art Records. Dist: Cartel

THIS HOOK.
Single (12"): released on Perfect Vision, Jul'84 Dist: Backs, Cartel

TONGUES OUT.
Album: released on Backs, Mar'86 by Backs Records. Dist: Backs, Cartel

Perfect world

HAVE A GOOD LOOK.
Album:

Perfect Zebras

ANOTHER LOVE STORY.
Single (7"): released on Focus, Oct'82 by Virgin. Dist: EMI

MIXING WITH WILDLIFE.
Album: released on Focus, Aug'82 by Virgin. Dist: EMI

RUNNING WITH ZEBRAS.
Single (7"): released on Focus, May'82 by Virgin. Dist: EMI

Single (12"): released on Focus, May'82 by Virgin. Dist: EMI

TOUCHING MY HEART AGAIN.
Single (7"): released on Focus, Jul'82 by Virgin. Dist: EMI

Single (12"): released on Focus, Jul'82 by Virgin. Dist: EMI

Performance

WISH I WAS FREE AGAIN.
Tracks: / Wish I was free again / Free again.
Single (7"): released on Clay, Mar'86 by Clay Records. Dist: Pinnacle

Performing Ferrets

FERRETABLE THING, THE.
Cassette: released on Dead Happy, '82 by Dead Happy Records. Dist: Mason's Music Distributors/Wholesalers, Rough Trade

PERFORMING FERRETS(EP).
Single (7"): released on Dead Happy, Nov'82 by Dead Happy Records. Dist: Mason's Music Distributors/Wholesalers, Rough Trade

Perfumed Garden

PERFUMED GARDEN, THE (1) various artists (Various Artists).
Album: released on Psycho, Sep'83 Dist: Funhouse, Rough Trade

PERFUMED GARDEN, THE (2) various artists (Various Artists).
Album: released on Psycho, Sep'83 Dist: Funhouse, Rough Trade

Perils of Plastic

RING A DING RING.
Tracks: / Ring a Ding Ring / Debile Matin.
Single (7"): released on WEA, May'86 by WEA Records. Dist: WEA

Single (12"): released on WEA, May'86 by WEA Records. Dist: WEA

WOMANHOOD.
Tracks: / Womanhood / Moth Music.
Single (7"): released on WEA, Sep'86 by WEA Records. Dist: WEA

Single (12"): released on WEA, Sep'86 by WEA Records. Dist: WEA

Perishers

PERISHERS SING, THE.
Album: released on Response, Feb'81 by Priority Records. Dist: BMG

Perkins, Bill

WEST COAST CONFERENCE (Perkins, Bill/Paul Chambers/Philly Joe Jones).
Album: released on Affinity, Jan'81 by Charly Records. Dist: Charly, Cadillac

Perkins, Carl

20 GOLDEN PIECES OF CARL PERKINS.
Album: released on Bulldog, Nov'83 by Bulldog Records. Dist: President Distribution, Spartan, Swift, Taylor, H.R.

BLUE SUEDE SHOES.
Single (7"): released on USA Import, '80

BOPPIN' THE BLUES.
Album: released on Topline, Nov'84 by Charly Records. Dist: Charly Distribution

Cassette: released on Topline, Nov'84 by Charly Records. Dist: Charly Distribution

CARL PERKINS.
Tracks: / Matchbox / If I had 'a known / Green green grass of home / Texas woman / Signs.
Notes: Carl Perkins returns to the recording studo by route of Record producer billy Strange and MCA/DOT Records.
Album: released on MCA, Mar'86 by MCA Records. Dist: Polygram, MCA

Cassette: released on MCA, Mar'86 by MCA Records. Dist: Polygram, MCA

CARL PERKINS ROCK'N'ROLL PARTY, THE.
Album: released on Warwick, Nov'84 by Warwick Records. Dist: Pinnacle

Cassette: released on Warwick, Nov'84 by Warwick Records. Dist: Pinnacle

CLASS OF 55 (Perkins, Carl/Jerry lee Lewis/ Roy Orbison/ Johnnny Cash.).
Notes: No track details advised
Compact disc: released on American Smash, Aug'86 by Phonogram Records. Dist: Polygram

DANCE ALBUM.
Tracks: / Blue suede shoes / Movie magg / Sure to fall / Gone gone gone / Honey don't / Only you / All mama's children / Tennessee / Wrong yo yo / Everybody's trying to be my baby / Matchbox / Your true love / Boppin' the blues.
Notes: Licensed from Charly International APS. This CD (P) 1987 Charly Holdings Inc. (C) 1987 Charly Records Ltd.
Compact disc: released on Topline, Apr'87 by Charly Records. Dist: Charly Distribution

DISCIPLINE IN BLUE SUEDE SHOES.
Album: released on Astan, Nov'84 by Astan Records. Dist: Counterpoint

Cassette: released on Astan, Nov'84 by Astan Records. Dist: Counterpoint

DIXIE FRIED.
Tracks: / Honey don't / Boppin' the blues / Blue suede shoes / Put your cat clothes on / Dixie fried / Matchbox / Pink pedal pushers / Thats right / I'm sorry I'm not sorry / Roll over beethoven / Glad all over / Right string baby but the wrong yoyo / Everybody's trying to be my baby / Gone gone gone / Lend me your comb / All mama's children / Sweet hearts or strangers / Your true love / Movie Magg / Tennessee / Sure to gall / Honky tonk gal / Turn around / Let the juke box keep on playing.
Compact disc: released on Charly, Mar'86 by Charly Records. Dist: Charly, Cadillac

GOIN' BACK TO MEMPHIS.
Notes: Track details not advised

Album: released on Magnum Force, Feb'86 by Magnum Music Group Ltd. Dist: Magnum Music Group Ltd, PRT, Spartan

Album: released on Magnum Force, Feb'86 by Magnum Music Group Ltd. Dist: Magnum Music Group Ltd, PRT, Spartan

HEART AND SOUL OF CARL PERKINS, THE.
Album: released on Allegiance, Apr'84 by PRT Records. Dist: PRT

Cassette: released on Allegiance, Apr'84 by PRT Records. Dist: PRT

INTRODUCING.....
Album: released on Boplicity, Sep'84 by Boplicity Records. Dist: Ace Records, Pinnacle

MAN & THE LEGEND, THE.
Notes: No track details advised
Album: released on Magnum, Oct'86 by Bulldog Records. Dist: Spartan

ORIGINAL CARL PERKINS, THE.
Album: released on Charly, Feb'78 by Charly Records. Dist: Charly, Cadillac

ROCKABILLY SESSION, A (Perkins, Carl & Friends).
Notes: A live Jam in London between the Rockabilly Legend and a band featuring the likes of Eric Clapton, george Harrison and Ringo Starr. 1985 Production. Playing time: 60 Minutes
Video-cassette (VHS): released on Virgin, May'86 by Virgin Records. Dist: EMI, Virgin Distribution

ROCKIN' GUITARMAN.
Album: released on Charly, Feb'78 by Charly Records. Dist: Charly, Cadillac

ROCKIN' THE HOUSE DOWN.
Double Album: released on Network, Nov'85 by Epic. Dist: PRT, CBS

Double cassette: released on Network, Nov'85 by Epic. Dist: PRT, CBS

SONGS IN CARL PERKINS ALBUM.
Album: released on Charly, Jul'81 by Charly Records. Dist: Charly, Cadillac

SUN YEARS, THE.
Triple album / cassette: released on Sun, Mar'82 by Charly Records. Dist: Charly Distribution

SURVIVORS, THE (Perkins, Carl/Johnny Cash/Jerry Lee Lewis).
Album: released on CBS, May'82 by CBS Records. Dist: CBS

Cassette: released on CBS, May'82 by CBS Records. Dist: CBS

SWEETER THAN CANDY.
Album: released on Astan, Nov'84 by Astan Records. Dist: Counterpoint

Cassette: released on Astan, Nov'84 by Astan Records. Dist: Counterpoint

TRIO PLUS (see Lewis, Jerry Lee/Charlie Rich/Carl Perkins) (Perkins, Carl/Jerry Lee Lewis/Charlie Rich)).

TURN AROUND.
Album: released on Culture Press, Sep'85 by Vista Sounds Records. Dist: Jetstar, Rough Trade

UP THROUGH THE YEARS '1954-1957'.
Tracks: / Honky tonk gal / Movie magg / Turn around / Gone,gone,gone / Let the jukebox keep on playing / You can't make love to someone / Blue suede shoes / Honey don't / Tennessee / Boppin' the blues / All mama's children / Everybody's trying to be my baby / Dixie fried / I'm sorry I'm not sorry / You can do no wrong /

Matchbox / Your true love / Put your cat clothes on / Only you / Pink pedal pushers / That's right / Lend me your comb / Glad all over / Right string baby(But wrong yo yo).
Compact disc: released on Bear Family, Nov'86 by Bear Family Records. Dist: Rollercoaster Distribution, Swift

Perkins, Jonathan

BELIEVE IN ME (Perkins, Jonathan 'Silver Spurs').
Single (7"): released on Checkmount, Feb'85 Dist: Spartan

I'LL LAY MY SILVER SPURS.
Single (7"): released on RCA, Sep'83 by RCA Records. Dist: RCA, Roots, Swift, Wellard, Chris, I & B, Solomon & Peres Distribution

Single (12"): released on RCA, Sep'83 by RCA Records. Dist: RCA, Roots, Swift, Wellard, Chris, I & B, Solomon & Peres Distribution

Perkins, Laura Lee

GONNA ROCK MY BABY TONIGHT.
Single (7"): released on Detour, Feb'83 by Detour Records. Dist: Swift, RCA, Jazz Music, Projection

Perkins, Pinetop

BOOGIE WOOGIE KING.
Compact disc: released on Black & Blue (France), '86 Dist: Swift, Target, Discovery

CHICAGO BOOGIE BLUES PIANO MAN (Pinetop Perkins).
Notes: Track details not advised
Album: released on JSP, Sep'86 by JSP Records. Dist: Swift, Projection

Perks, Katie

COLD STONE.
Single (7"): released on Plastic Head, Nov'83 Dist: Pinnacle, Rough Trade, Cartel

HAT MUSIC.
Album: released on Plas, Jun'85

SHINE THE LIGHT.
Tracks: / Shine the light / Cut the rope / Beauty / Rambling shambling man / Golden city / Let it rain / Angel says / Blues, The / Naming of the game, The / Shake hands / Floating world, The.
Album: released on Plastic Head, 5 Jul'87 Dist: Pinnacle, Rough Trade, Cartel

Album: released on Plastic Head, Aug'87 Dist: Pinnacle, Rough Trade, Cartel

Pernell Lovers

BLACK IS THE BEST.
Single (12"): released on Export, Jun'82 by Import Records. Dist: Jetstar

Perrenial Divide

PURGE.
Album: released on Sweatbox, Jun'87 by Sweatbox Records. Dist: Rough Trade, Cartel

Perrett, Peter

BABY'S GOT A GUN (Perrett, Peter & Only Ones).
Single (7"): released on Vengeance, Jan'83 Dist: Pinnacle

Perri

CELEBRATE.
Album: released on MCA, Nov'86 by MCA Records. Dist: Polygram, MCA

Cassette: released on MCA, Nov'86 by MCA Records. Dist: Polygram, MCA

Perrier, Cher

I WANNA DANCE.
Single (7"): released on Musik, Feb'87 Dist: PRT Distribution, MIS-EMI Distribution

Single (12"): released on Musik, Feb'87 Dist: PRT Distribution, MIS-EMI Distribution

Single (12"): released on Music UK, Nov'86 Dist: PRT Distribution

I WANNA DANCE (Cher Perrier).
Tracks: / I Wanna Dance, (Side A on 12" and 7") / I wanna Dance (Side B on 12" and 7").
Single (7"): released on Music UK, Nov'86 Dist: PRT Distribution

Perri, Lorna

JUST A MEMORY.
Single (12"): released on Ital, May'83 Dist: Pinnacle

Perry, Eden

CHRISTMAS ELVIS PRESLEY STYLE.
Cassette: released on Chevron, Nov'84 Dist: Multiple Sound Distributors

Perry, Frank

BALANCE.
Album: released on Incus, Nov'76 Dist: Jazz Music, Cadillac

Perry, Joe Project

ONCE A ROCKER,ALWAYS A ROCKER.
Album: released on MCA, Jan'84 by MCA Records. Dist: Polygram, MCA

Cassette: released on MCA, Jan'84 by MCA Records. Dist: Polygram, MCA

Perry, King

KING PERRY 1947-54.
Album: released on Krazy Kat, Jan'87 Dist: Jazz Music, Swift, Chris Wellard, H.R. Taylor, Charly, Hotshot, IRS Distribution

Perry, Lee

ALL THINGS ARE POSSIBLE (Perry, Lee 'Scratch').
Tracks: / All things are possible / Sexy lady.
Single (7"): released on Trojan, Sep'86 by Trojan Records. Dist: PRT, Jetstar

BATTLE OF ARMAGIDEON Millionaire Liquadator (Lee 'Scratch' Perry and the Upsetters).
Notes: After 12 years (Double seven: 1974) Mr Lee Scratch Perry returns to Trojan For his Finest album for years. Recorded in London between Nov 85 and March 86 ,'Scratch' produced and mixed His latest masterpiece...
Album: released on Trojan, May'86 by Trojan Records. Dist: PRT, Jetstar

Cassette: released on Trojan, May'86 by Trojan Records. Dist: PRT, Jetstar

BEST OF LEE PERRY & THE UPSETTERS VOL.2 (Perry, Lee 'Scratch' And the Upsetters).
Album: released on Pama, Feb'84 by Pama Records. Dist: Pama, Enterprise, Jetstar

BLACK ARK, VOL.2.
Album: released on Black Ark, Mar'84

HEART OF THE ARK (Perry, Lee 'Scratch').
Album: released on Seven Leaves, Oct'82 by Seven Leaves Records. Dist: Jetstar

MEGATON DUB 2.
Album: released on Seven Leaves, Sep'84 by Seven Leaves Records. Dist: Jetstar

MERRY CHRISTMAS, HAPPY NEW YEAR.
Tracks: / Perry Christmas(The)(dub mix) / I am a mad man * / Mad men dub wise * / Merry christmas, Happy New Year / Return of Django / All things are Possible / Happy Birthday.
Single (7"): released on Trojan, Dec'86 by Trojan Records. Dist: PRT, Jetstar

Single (12"): released on Trojan, Dec'86 by Trojan Records. Dist: PRT, Jetstar

MERRY CHRISTMAS, HAPPY NEW YEAR (Lee Perry).
Single (7"): released on Trojan, Dec'85 by Trojan Records. Dist: PRT, Jetstar

Single (12"): released on Trojan, Dec'85 by Trojan Records. Dist: PRT, Jetstar

MYSTIC MIRACLE STAR (Perry, Lee & The Majestics).
Album: released on Heartbeat, Aug'85 Dist: Revolver, Pinnacle

REGGAE GREATS Various artists produced by Lee Perry (Various Artists).
Album: released on Island, Nov'85 by Island Records. Dist: Polygram

Cassette: released on Island, Nov'85 by Island Records. Dist: Polygram

REVOLUTION DUB.
Album: released on Cactus, '79 by Creole Records. Dist: CBS

SCRATCH.
Album: released on On-U-Sound, May'87 Dist: Rough Trade Distribution, Lightning

Cassette: released on On-U-Sound, May'87 Dist: Rough Trade Distribution, Lightning

SOME OF THE BEST (Perry, Lee 'Scratch' And the Upsetters).
Notes: Track details not advised
Album: released on Heartbeat, Jul'86 Dist: Revolver, Pinnacle

Album: released on Heartbeat, Jul'87 Dist: Revolver, Pinnacle

UPSETTER BOX SET, THE (Perry, Lee 'Scratch').
Triple album / cassette: released on Upsetter, Jul'85

Perry, Lee 'Scratch'

TIME BOOM X DE DEVIL DEAD.
Tracks: / S.D.I. / Blinkers / Jungle / De devil dead / Music & Science lovers / Kiss the champion / Allergic to lies / Time conquer.
Album: released on Syncopate, Sep'87 by EMI Records. Dist: EMI. Estim retail price in Sep'87 was £5.99.

Cassette: released on Syncopate, Sep'87 by EMI Records. Dist: EMI. Estim retail price in Sep'87 was £5.99.

Perry, Roy

MANCUNIAN WAY, THE (Perry, Roy /Ronnie Wood).
Album: released on Deroy, Jun'81 by Deroy Records. Dist: Jazz Music, Swift

Perry, Steve

FOOLISH HEART.
Single (7"): released on CBS, Feb'85 by CBS Records. Dist: CBS

SHE'S MINE.
Single (7"): released on CBS, Aug'84 by CBS Records. Dist: CBS

STREET TALK.
Album: released on CBS, Jul'84 by CBS Records. Dist: CBS

Cassette: released on CBS, Jul'84 by CBS Records. Dist: CBS

Persian Flowers

SOMEBODY ELSE'S SIN.
Single (7"): released on Fourth Dimension, Mar'84 by Backs. Dist: Cartel

Persian Gulf

TRAILER, THE.
Tracks: / Trailer(E.P.), The.
Notes: E.P. disc.
Single (12"): released on T.I.M., Oct'86 by T.I.M. Records. Dist: Backs, Cartel Distribution

Persian Risk

RIDIN' HIGH.
Single (7"): released on Neat, Mar'83 by Neat Records. Dist: Pinnacle, Neat

RISE UP.
Notes: Track details not advised
Album: released on Razor, May'86 by Razor. Dist: Pinnacle

Persian Rug

PERSIAN RUG Unusual patterns in jazz (Various Artists).
Tracks: / Willow Tree / Sippi / Thou Swell / Persian Rug / Mediterranean Blues / Hallelujah / Zulu Wail / You dont Like It, Not Much / Junk Man / Your guess is as good as mine / Hula girl / Keka / That lovin Hula / Baby, oh where can you be / Do Something / Always in all ways / It's a great life / My Silent Love / Hummin' to myself.
Notes: Mono recording
Album: released on VJM, Jul'86 by Wellard, Chris Distribution. Dist: Wellard, Chris Distribution

Persian Rugs

BURNING PASSION PAIN.
Single (7"): released on Phoenix, Mar'82 by Audio Fidelity Enterprises. Dist: Stage One, Lugtons

DROWNING POOL.
Album: released on Phoenix, May'83 by Audio Fidelity Enterprises. Dist: Stage One, Lugtons

SHE SAID.
Single (7"): released on Plus One, Jan'84 by Plus One Records. Dist: Cartel

Single (12"): released on Plus One, Jan'84 by Plus One Records. Dist: Cartel

Persion Risk

TOO DIFFERENT, TWO PEOPLE.
Single (12"): released on Zebra, Jul'84 by Cherry Red Records. Dist: Pinnacle

Persip, Charlie

SUPERBAND (Persip, Charlie & Gerry LcFurns).
Album: released on Stash (Import), '81 Dist: Swift Distribution, Jazz Music Distribution, Jazz Horizons Distribution, Celtic Music Distribution, Cadillac, JSU Distribution, Zodiac Distribution

Persistant Gods

ASH GARDEN EP.
Single (7"): released on Alternative, Feb'82 Dist: PRT

COME INTO THE ASH GARDEN.
Single (7"): released on Alternative, Apr'82 Dist: PRT

Personal Column

SAME OLD SITUATION.
Single (7"): released on Convenience (USA), Jul'83 Dist: Rough Trade, Interdisc

STRICTLY CONFIDENTIAL.
Single (7"): released on Stiff, Apr'84 by Stiff Records. Dist: EMI, Record Services Distribution (Ireland)

Personality..

PERSONALITY CRISIS various artists (Various Artists).
Album: released on Action Replay, Aug'84 by Action Replay Records. Dist: PRT

Cassette: released on Action Replay, Aug'84 by Action Replay Records. Dist: PRT

Personality Crisis

PERSONALITY CRISIS(VARIOUS ARTISTS) (Various Artists).
Notes: Track details not advised
Album: released on Action Replay, Nov'85 by Action Replay Records. Dist: PRT

Cassette: released on Action Replay, Nov'85 by Action Replay Records. Dist: PRT

Person, Houston

BIG HORN, THE.
Album: released on Muse, Apr'81 by Peerless Records. Dist: Lugtons Distributors

HEAVY JUICE.
Album: released on Muse, Nov'82 by Peerless Records. Dist: Lugtons Distributors

NEARNESS OF YOU, THE.
Album: released on Muse, Apr'81 by Peerless Records. Dist: Lugtons Distributors

STOLEN SWEETS.
Album: released on Muse, Apr'81 by Peerless Records. Dist: Lugtons Distributors

SUSPICIONS.
Album: released on Muse, '81 by Peerless Records. Dist: Lugtons Distributors

Person To Person

HIGH TIME.
Single (7"): released on Epic, May'85 by CBS Records. Dist: CBS

REPUTATION.
Single (7"): released on Epic, Jan'85 by CBS Records. Dist: CBS

Single (12"): released on Epic, Jan'85 by CBS Records. Dist: CBS

STRONGER THAN REASON.
Album: released on Epic, Jul'85 by CBS Records. Dist: CBS

Cassette: released on Epic, Jul'85 by CBS Records. Dist: CBS

Perspectives..

PERSPECTIVES AND DISTORTION various artists (Various Artists).
Album: released on Cherry Red, Oct'81 by Cherry Red Records. Dist: Pinnacle

Perspico Acumine

PERFECT ACTION, A (Perspico Acumine (Holdings)).
Tracks: / Pre match tension / Robinson Moxon / Thin man from Orpington / Sir Derek, The Retford Prince / Thin Man Reprise / Lubo(visor Crunch) / I.T.Man Preview / Sow Coda / Movement (Off the perch throuh the air) / Colchester Express, The / Son of Ivanhoe / Twelfth just man, The.
Notes: All written by McDonough-Jones except * McDonough-Jones/C.O'sullivan, ** McDonough-Jones/Keefe. Publishers: El/Complete Music Ltd.
Album: released on EL, Jun'86 by El Records. Dist: Rough Trade, Cartel, Pinnacle

Persuasions

CHIRPIN.
Album: released on Elektra, May'77 by WEA Records. Dist: WEA

COMIN' AT YA.
Album: released on Flying Fish (USA), Sep'79 by Flying Fish Records (USA). Dist: Roots, Projection

I WOKE UP IN LOVE THIS MORNING.
Single (7"): released on Demon, Apr'85 by Demon Records. Dist: Pinnacle

NO FRILLS.
Album: released on Rounder (USA), Jul'84 Dist: Mike's Country Music Room Distribution, Jazz Music Distribution, Swift Distribution, Roots Records Distribution, Projection Distribution, Topic Distribution

Album: released on Demon, Apr'85 by Demon

Records. Dist: Pinnacle

Pertwee, John

JOHNY TOMORROW.
Cassette: released on VFM Cassettes, Jan'85

Pertwee, Jon

NEVER EVER TALK TO A STRANGER
Worzel's warning.
Tracks: / Never ever talk to a stranger / Worzel's world.
Single (7"): released on Splash, Mar'87 by Splash Records. Dist: CBS

SING THE BEATLES WHEN I'M 64 (Pertwee, Jon & Friends).
Single (7"): released on Flightstream, Apr'84 by Flightstream Records. Dist: Taylor, H.R.

SPOTTYMAN SONG.
Single (7"): released on Rainbow, Jan'84 Dist: I & B, CBS

WHO IS THE DOCTOR.
Single (7"): released on Safari, Jun'85 by Safari Records. Dist: Pinnacle

WORZEL GUMMIDGE (see Waterhouse, Keith and Willis Hall).
Tracks: / Scarecrow hop / Tea party (The) / Saucy Nancy (The) / Worzel's 'ansome 'ead / Fair old pullover (A) / Little learning (A) / Worzel's nephew / Trial or Worzel (The) / Worzel gives a lecture / Worzel's wedding.
Double cassette: released on Cover to Cover, Nov'86 by Cover to Cover Cassettes. Dist: Conifer

Cassette: released on Cover to Cover, Nov'86 by Cover to Cover Cassettes. Dist: Conifer

Double cassette: released on Cover to Cover, Nov'86 by Cover to Cover Cassettes. Dist: Conifer

Cassette: released on Cover to Cover, Nov'86 by Cover to Cover Cassettes. Dist: Conifer

Double cassette: released on Cover to Cover, Nov'86 by Cover to Cover Cassettes. Dist: Conifer

WORZEL GUMMIDGE SINGS.
Album: released on Decca, Oct'80 by Decca Records. Dist: Polygram

Cassette: released on Decca, Oct'80 by Decca Records. Dist: Polygram

Peru

PERU Various Artists (Various Artists).
Compact disc: by Sterns Records. Dist: Sterns/Triple Earth Distribution

Peruna Jazzmen

VOLUME 2 (PERUNA JAZZMEN).
Notes: Track details not advised
Album: released on Stomp Off, Jun'86 by Stomp Off Records. Dist: Jazz Music Distribution

VOLUME 3 (PERUNA JAZZMEN).
Notes: Tracks not advised
Album: released on Stomp Off, Jun'86 by Stomp Off Records. Dist: Jazz Music Distribution

Peryglus, Eirin

BRONSON.
Single (7"): released on Welsh Celtic and Worldwide, May'87

Pestalozzi Int'...

IMAGINE (Pestalozzi Int' Childrens Choir).
Single (7"): released on Contact, Dec'81 by RK Records. Dist: PRT

Pestalozzi School

SONGS OF JOY.
Album: released on K-Tel, Nov'81 by K-Tel Records. Dist: Record Merchandisers Distribution, Taylors, Terry Blood Distribution, Wynd-Up Distribution, Relay Distribution, Pickwick Distribution, Solomon & Peres Distribution, Polygram

Cassette: released on K-Tel, Nov'81 by K-Tel Records. Dist: Record Merchandisers Distribution, Taylors, Terry Blood Distribution, Wynd-Up Distribution, Relay Distribution, Pickwick Distribution, Solomon & Peres Distribution, Polygram

Petards

BURNING RAINBOWS.
Album: released on Bear Family, Oct'82 by Bear Family Records. Dist: Rollercoaster Distribution, Swift

GOLDEN GLASS.
Album: released on Bear Family, Oct'82 by Bear Family Records. Dist: Rollercoaster Distribution, Swift

HITSHOCK.
Album: released on Liberty (USA), Feb'82 Dist: United Artists

PETARDS, THE.
Album: released on Liberty (USA), Feb'82 Dist: United Artists

Petchersky, Alma

SPANISH PIANO MUSIC.
Album: released on Academy Sound & Vision, Apr'84 by Academy Sound & Vision Records. Dist: Pinnacle

Cassette: released on Academy Sound & Vision, Jun'84 by Academy Sound & Vision Records. Dist: Pinnacle

Peter & Gordon

BEST OF PETER & GORDON, THE.
Tracks: / True love ways / Five hundred miles / My litle girl's gone / Lady Godiva / My little girl's gone / I go to pieces / Nobody I know / I don't want to see you again / World without love / Woman / Let it be me / Lucille / Crying in the rain / Hurtin' is loving / To know you is to love you / Someone ain't right / You've had better times / Baby, I'm yours / Exodus song / High Noon (Do not forsake me).
Album: released on C5, Jul'87 by See For Miles Records. Dist: Counterpoint

Album: released on EMI (Holland), '83 by EMI Records. Dist: Conifer

HITS AND MORE.
Tracks: / World without love / Nobody I know / I don't want to see you again / I go to pieces / True love ways / To know you is to love you / Let it be me / Crying in the rain / Baby I'm yours / There's no living without your loving / Lady Godiva / Knight in rusty armour / Sunday for tea / Lucille / Leave my woman alone.
Notes: When it was announced that this duo would be making their record debut with a sofar unreleased song from their prolific pens of John Lennon and Paul McCartney, Peter and Gorden were 90% certain of a hit record. That first single 'A World Without Love' was their biggest hit topping both the British and American chartsin the summer of 1964. They were by no means without talent, but it was Pete's Aquaintance with McCartney which gave them a short cut of fame and fortune. Thisalbum incudes the dozen hits Peter and Gorden chalked up in their glory years and also features their rendition of four Everly Brothers' tracks.
Album: released on EMI, Jan'86 by EMI Records. Dist: EMI

Cassette: released on EMI, Jan'86 by EMI Records. Dist: EMI

WORLD WITHOUT LOVE.
Album: released on See For Miles, Mar'82 by See For Miles Records. Dist: Pinnacle

Single (7"): released on EMI (Holland), Jul'84 by EMI Records. Dist: Conifer

Single (7"): released on Old Gold, Oct'83 by Old Gold Records. Dist: Lightning, Jazz Music, Spartan, Counterpoint

Peter Pan

PETER PAN Barrie, J.M (Craig, Wendy).
Cassette: released on Listen For Pleasure, Nov'81 by MFP Records. Dist: EMI

PETER PAN Various artists (Various Artists).
Cassette: released on Tell-A-tale (Cassettes), Oct'84

PETER PAN AND CINDERELLA Various artists (Various Artists).
Album: released on BBC, Oct'85 by BBC Records & Tapes. Dist: EMI, PRT, Pye

Cassette: released on BBC, Oct'85 by BBC Records & Tapes. Dist: EMI, PRT, Pye

Peter, Paul & Mary

LEAVING ON A JET PLANE.
Single (7"): released on Warner Bros. (USA Import), May'80 by WEA Records. Dist: WEA

PUFF THE MAGIC DRAGON.
Single (7"): released on Warner Brothers, Jul'81 by WEA Records. Dist: WEA

REUNION.
Album: released on Warner Brothers, May'78 by Warner Bros Records. Dist: WEA

TEN YEARS TOGETHER.
Album: released on Warner Brothers, May'74 by WEA Records. Dist: WEA

Peter Potato...

PETER POTATO & ALICE APPLE Various artists (Various Artists).
Cassette: released on Tell-A-tale (Cassettes), Oct'84

Peters, Chris

LOVE INSURANCE.
Tracks: / Love insurance.
Single (7"): released on Titanic, Jul'86 Dist: Essex Record Distributors Ltd.

PHANTOM OF THE BASSLINE, THE.
Single (12"): released on Nine O Nine, Aug'87 by Creole Records. Dist: Rhino, PRT

Peters, Chriss

CAUGHT IN THE ACT.
Single (7"): released on Ecstasy, Jul'85 by Creole Records. Dist: CBS

Single (12"): released on Ecstasy, Jul'85 by Creole Records. Dist: CBS

Album: released on Titania, Oct'87 by Creole Records. Dist: PRT

LOVE TRAP.
Tracks: / Love Trap (Megamix) / Caught in the act(remix).
Single (12"): released on Titania, Jan'87 by Creole Records. Dist: PRT

Peters, Eddie

JOCK MIX 2.
Single (12"): released on Rhino, Aug'87 by Creole Records. Dist: PRT, Rhino

Petersen, Herb

LONESOME FEELING.
Album: released on Sugarhill (USA), May'84 by PRT Records. Dist: PRT Distribution

Peters & Lee

ALL I EVER NEED IS YOU.
Album: released on Spot, Sep'85 by Pickwick Records. Dist: H.R. Taylor, Lugtons

Cassette: released on Spot, Sep'85 by Pickwick Records. Dist: H.R. Taylor, Lugtons

FAMILIAR FEELINGS.
Tracks: / Familiar feelings / Guess you'll never know.
Single (7"): released on A.1, Oct'86 by A.1 Records. Dist: PRT

FAVOURITES.
Album: released on Philips, Sep'75 Dist: IMS-Polygram

SMILE.
Album: released on Philips, Dec'77 Dist: IMS-Polygram

WELCOME HOME.
Single (7"): released on Old Gold (Reissue), Jul'82

YESTERDAY AND TODAY.
Double Album: released on Cambra, May'83 by Cambra Records. Dist: IDS, Conifer

Double cassette: released on Cambra, May'83 by Cambra Records. Dist: IDS, Conifer

Peters, Lennie

KEY LARGO.
Single (7"): released on Relax, Nov'85 Dist: CBS

WHY ME.
Single (7"): released on Lifestyle, Dec'82 by Zomba Records. Dist: CBS, PRT, RCA

Peters,Mike

DJANGO'S MUSIC (Peters,Mike/Bob Wilberg/Birelli Lagrene).
Notes: Track details not advised
Album: released on Stash (US), Dec'85 Dist: Swift Distribution, Jazz Music Distribution, Jazz Horizons Distribution, Celtic Music Distribution, Cadillac, JSU Distribution, Zodiac Distribution

Peterson, Colleen

TAKIN' MY BOOTS OFF.
Album: released on Capitol, Jan'79 by Capitol Records. Dist: EMI

Peterson, John

NIGHT OF MIRACLES.
Album: by Pilgrim Records. Dist: Rough Trade, Cartel

Peterson, Lal & Mike

BRIGHT PHOEBUS.
Album: released on Highway, Aug'85 by Highway Records. Dist: Roots, Projection, Ross

Peterson, Marvin

ANGELS OF ATLANTA, THE (Peterson, Marvin 'Hannibal').
Album: released on Enja (Germany), Jan'82 by Enja Records (W.Germany). Dist: Cadillac Music

HANNIBAL IN ANTIBES (Peterson, Marvin 'Hannibal').
Album: released on Enja (Germany), Jan'82 by Enja Records (W.Germany). Dist: Cadillac Music

POEM SONG (Peterson, Marvin 'Hannibal').
Album: released on Mole, Jul'83 by Mole Records. Dist: Mole Music Co., Spartan Distribution

Peterson, Oscar

ACTION.
Album: released on MPS Jazz, May'81

AIN'T BUT A FEW OF US (see Jackson, Milt) (Peterson, Oscar/ Milt Jackson/ Grady Tate/ Ray Brown).
Album: released on Pablo, Sep'82 by Pablo Records. Dist: Wellard, Chris, IMS-Polygram, BMG

Cassette: released on Pablo, Sep'82 by Pablo Records. Dist: Wellard, Chris, IMS-Polygram, BMG

Alone together

AN EVENING AT THE HOLLYWOOD BOWL (Peterson, Oscar & Ella Fitzgerald).
Double Album: released on Import Music Service (IMS), '82 Dist: Concord Jazz Distributions, Pablo, Polygram

ANOTHER DAY (Peterson, Oscar Trio).
Tracks: / Blues for Martha / I'm old fashioned / All the things you are / Too close for comfort / Jamfs are coming, The / It never entered my mind / Carolina shout.
Notes: Recorded November 1970
Compact disc: released on MPS Jazz, May'87

Album: released on MPS Jazz, May'81

AT THE MONTREUX JAZZ FESTIVAL 1975 (Peterson, Oscar Big Six).
Album: released on Pablo (USA), '82 by Pablo Records (USA). Dist: Wellard, Chris, IMS-Polygram, BMG

Cassette: released on Pablo (USA), '82 by Pablo Records (USA). Dist: Wellard, Chris, IMS-Polygram, BMG

AT THE OPERA HOUSE (see Modern Jazz Quartet) (Peterson, Oscar Trio & Modern Jazz Quartet).

BEST OF, THE Walkman jazz series.
Cassette: released on Verve, May'87 by Phonogram Records. Dist: Polygram

BIG SIX AT MONTREUX.
Tracks: / Au priveve / Here's that rainy day / Poor butterfly / Reunion blues.
Notes: Personnel: Oscar Peterson-Piano/Milt Jackson-Vibes/Joe Pass-Guitar/Toots Thilemans-harmonica/Niels Pederson-Bass/Louis Bellson-Drums
Compact disc: released on Pablo Jazz (USA), Apr'86 by United Artists. Dist: Swift

BUSTIN' OUT WITH THE ALL STAR BAND.
Compact disc: released on Polydor, Oct'86 by Polydor Records. Dist: Polygram, Polydor

CARIOCA.
Album: released on Happy Bird (Germany), Jun'83 Dist: Polygram, IMS

Cassette: released on Happy Bird (Germany), Jun'83 Dist: Polygram, IMS

COLE PORTER SONGBOOK (THE).
Compact disc: released on Polydor, Nov'86 by Polydor Records. Dist: Polygram, Polydor

COMPACT JAZZ.
Tracks: / Let's fall in love / Mack the knife.
Compact disc: released on Phonogram, Jul'87 by Phonogram Records. Dist: Polygram

Cassette: released on Phonogram, Jul'87 by Phonogram Records. Dist: Polygram

DIGITAL AT MONTREUX.
Notes: Recorded July 1979
Compact disc: released on Pablo (USA), May'86 by Pablo Records (USA). Dist: Wellard, Chris, IMS-Polygram, BMG

Album: released on Pablo (USA), '82 by Pablo Records (USA). Dist: Wellard, Chris, IMS-Polygram, BMG

Cassette: released on Pablo (USA), '82 by Pablo Records (USA). Dist: Wellard, Chris, IMS-Polygram, BMG

FIORELLO.
Album: released on Verve (France), Jun'84

FREEDOM SONG (Peterson, Oscar Big 4).
Album: released on Pablo, Mar'83 by Pablo Records. Dist: Wellard, Chris, IMS-Polygram, BMG

Cassette: released on Pablo, Mar'83 by Pablo Records. Dist: Wellard, Chris, IMS-Polygram, BMG

GIANTS, THE (Peterson, Oscar/Joe Pass/Ray Brown).

GIRL TALK.
Album: released on MPS Jazz, May'81

GOOD LIFE (THE).
Compact disc: released on Pablo (USA), Apr'87 by Pablo Records (USA). Dist: Wellard, Chris, IMS-Polygram, BMG

Album: released on Pablo (USA), Dec'84 by Pablo Records (USA). Dist: Wellard, Chris, IMS-Polygram, BMG

Cassette: released on Pablo (USA), Dec'84 by Pablo Records (USA). Dist: Wellard, Chris, IMS-Polygram, BMG

GREAT CONNECTION (Peterson, Oscar Trio).
Tracks: / Younger than springtime / Where do we go from here / Smile / Soft winds / Just squeeze me / On the trail / Wheatland.
Notes: Recorded October 1971
Compact disc: released on MPS Jazz, May'87

Album: released on MPS Jazz, May'81

HARK (Peterson, Oscar Quartet/Buddy De Franco).
Notes: Full details under Budde De Franco.

HELLO HERBIE (Peterson, Oscar & Herb Ellis).
Album: released on MPS Jazz, May'81

HISTORY OF AN ARTIST VOL.2.
Compact disc: released on Pablo (USA), Apr'87 by Pablo Records (USA). Dist: Wellard, Chris, IMS-Polygram, BMG

HISTORY OF AN ARTIST, THE.
Album: released on Pablo (USA), '82 by Pablo Records (USA). Dist: Wellard, Chris, IMS-Polygram, BMG

Cassette: released on Pablo (USA), '82 by Pablo Records (USA). Dist: Wellard, Chris, IMS-Polygram, BMG

IF YOU COULD SEE ME NOW (Peterson, Oscar Four).
Tracks: / Weird blues / If I should lose you / On Danish shore / L'impossible / If you could see me now / Limehouse blues.
Notes: Following Oscar Peterson's sellout concert at London's Festival Hall last month, we have a superb new offering from the regular Oscar Peterson Trio plus Joe Pass. Featuring two original compositions from Oscar and Niels-Henning Orsted Pedersen, one from Miles Davis and three popular standards of which "If I should Lose You" and "If You Could See Me Now" are the highlights. Personnel: Oscar Peterson - piano/Niels-Henning Orsted Pedersen-bass/Martin Drew-drums/Joe Pass-guitar.
Album: released on Pablo (USA), Jul'86 by Pablo Records (USA). Dist: Wellard, Chris, IMS-Polygram, BMG

Cassette: released on Pablo (USA), Jul'86 by Pablo Records (USA). Dist: Wellard, Chris, IMS-Polygram, BMG

Compact disc: released on Pablo (USA), Feb'87 by Pablo Records (USA). Dist: Wellard, Chris, IMS-Polygram, BMG

IN CONCERT.
Album: released on Polydor (Holland), Apr'84

IN RUSSIA.
Album: released on Pablo (USA), '82 by Pablo Records (USA). Dist: Wellard, Chris, IMS-Polygram, BMG

Cassette: released on Pablo (USA), '82 by Pablo Records (USA). Dist: Wellard, Chris, IMS-Polygram, BMG

JAZZ PORTRAIT OF FRANK SINATRA, A.
Tracks: / You make me feel so young / Come dance with me / Learnin' the blues / Witchcraft / (Love is) The tender trap / Saturday night (Is the lonliest night of the week) / Just in time / It happened in Monterey / I get a Kick out of you / All of me / irth of the Blues / How about you.
Compact disc: released on Verve, Sep'85 by Phonogram Records. Dist: Polygram

JOUSTS (Peterson, Oscar & The Trumpet Kings).
Album: released on Pablo (USA), '82 by Pablo Records (USA). Dist: Wellard, Chris, IMS-Polygram, BMG

Cassette: released on Pablo (USA), '82 by Pablo Records (USA). Dist: Wellard, Chris, IMS-Polygram, BMG

LIVE AT THE NORTH SEA JAZZ FESTIVAL 1980.
Album: released on Pablo (USA), '82 by Pablo Records (USA). Dist: Wellard, Chris, IMS-Polygram, BMG

Cassette: released on Pablo (USA), '82 by Pablo Records (USA). Dist: Wellard, Chris, IMS-Polygram, BMG

LOUIS ARMSTRONG MEETS OSCAR PETERSON The Silver Collection (Peterson, Oscar & Louis Armstrong).
Compact disc: by Phonogram Records. Dist: Polygram

MASTERS OF JAZZ.
Album: released on RCA (Germany), '83

MEETS DIZZY GILLESPIE.
Tracks: / Caravan / Mozambique / Autumn leaves / Close your eyes / Blues for bird / Dizzy atmosphere / Alone together / Cone alma.
Notes: Personnel: Oscar Peterson/Dizzy Gillespie
Compact disc: released on Pablo (USA), Jul'86 by Pablo Records (USA). Dist: Wellard, Chris, IMS-Polygram, BMG

MELLOW MOOD.
Album: released on MPS Jazz, May'81

MOTIONS AND EMOTIONS.
Album: released on MPS (Germany), Sep'84 Dist: IMS-Polygram Distribution, Parnote Distribution (Formerly MDC)

Album: released on MPS Jazz, May'81

MY FAVOURITE INSTRUMENT.
Album: released on MPS Jazz, May'81

NIGERIAN MARKET PLACE.
Album: released on Pablo, '82 by Pablo Records. Dist: Wellard, Chris, IMS-Polygram, BMG

Cassette: released on Pablo, '82 by Pablo Records. Dist: Wellard, Chris, IMS-Polygram, BMG

NIGHT CHILD (Peterson, Oscar Quartet).
Album: released on Pablo (USA), '82 by Pablo Records (USA). Dist: Wellard, Chris, IMS-Polygram, BMG

Cassette: released on Pablo (USA), '82 by Pablo Records (USA). Dist: Wellard, Chris, IMS-Polygram, BMG

NIGHT RIDER (Peterson, Oscar & Count Basie).
Album: released on Pablo (USA), '82 by Pablo Records (USA). Dist: Wellard, Chris, IMS-Polygram, BMG

Cassette: released on Pablo (USA), '82 by Pablo Records (USA). Dist: Wellard, Chris, IMS-Polygram, BMG

NIGHT TRAIN.
Tracks: / Night Train / C jam blues / Georgia on my mind / Bag's groove / Moten swing / Easy does it / Honeydripper, The / Things ain't what they used to be / I got it bad and that ain't good / Band call / Hymn to freedom.
Compact disc: released on Verve, Sep'84 by Phonogram Records. Dist: Polygram

OSCAR PETERSON.
Cassette: released on Deja Vu, Nov'85 by Deja Vu Records. Dist: Counterpoint Distribution, Record Services Distribution (Ireland)

Album: released on Kings Of Jazz, '81 Dist: Jazz Horizons, Jazz Music, Celtic Music

OSCAR PETERSON AND ROY ELDRIDGE (Peterson, Oscar & Roy Eldridge).
Album: released on Pablo (USA), '82 by Pablo Records (USA). Dist: Wellard, Chris, IMS-Polygram, BMG

Cassette: released on Pablo (USA), '82 by Pablo Records (USA). Dist: Wellard, Chris, IMS-Polygram, BMG

OSCAR PETERSON AND CLARK TERRY (Peterson, Oscar & Clark Terry).
Album: released on Pablo (USA), '82 by Pablo Records (USA). Dist: Wellard, Chris, IMS-Polygram, BMG

Cassette: released on Pablo (USA), '82 by Pablo Records (USA). Dist: Wellard, Chris, IMS-Polygram, BMG

OSCAR PETERSON AND DIZZY GILLESPIE (Peterson, Oscar & Dizzy Gillespie).
Album: released on Pablo (USA), '82 by Pablo Records (USA). Dist: Wellard, Chris, IMS-Polygram, BMG

Cassette:

OSCAR PETERSON-IN CONCERT.
Double Album: released on Verve, Jan'76 by Phonogram Records. Dist: Polygram

OSCAR PETERSON JAM.
Album: released on Pablo (USA), '82 by Pablo Records (USA). Dist: Wellard, Chris, IMS-Polygram, BMG

Cassette: released on Pablo (USA), '82 by Pablo Records (USA). Dist: Wellard, Chris, IMS-Polygram, BMG

OSCAR PETERSON & STEPHANE GRAPPELLI (Peterson, Oscar & Stephane Grappelli).
Album: released on Music Disc (France), Apr'84 Dist: IMS-Polygram Distribution

OSCAR PETERSON & THE BASSISTS.
Album: released on Pablo (USA), '82 by Pablo Records (USA). Dist: Wellard, Chris, IMS-Polygram, BMG

Cassette: released on Pablo (USA), '82 by Pablo Records (USA). Dist: Wellard, Chris, IMS-Polygram, BMG

OSCAR PETERSON TRIO WITH CLARK TERRY (Peterson, Oscar Trio with Clark Terry).
Album: released on Mercury Jazz Masters, Dec'83

PARIS CONCERT, THE (Peterson, Oscar/Joe Pass/Niels Pedersen).
Double Album: released on Pablo (USA), '82 by Pablo Records (USA). Dist: Wellard, Chris, IMS-Polygram, BMG

Double cassette: released on Pablo (USA), '82 by Pablo Records (USA). Dist: Wellard, Chris, IMS-Polygram, BMG

PLUS ONE-CLARK TERRY (Peterson, Oscar Trio).
Tracks: / Jim / Blues for Smedley / Roundalay / Mumbles / Mack the knife / They didn't believe me / Sqeaky's blues / I want a little girl / Incoherant blues.
Notes: Emarcy productions recorded in August 1964. Personnel: Oscar Peterson-piano/Ray Brown-bass/Thigpen-drums/lark Terry-trumpet, flugelhorn, vocal
Compact disc: released on Emarcy(USA), Apr'85 by Emarcy Records(USA). Dist: Polygram

PORGY AND BESS (Peterson, Oscar & Joe Pass).
Album: released on Pablo (USA), '82 by Pablo Records (USA). Dist: Wellard, Chris, IMS-Polygram, BMG

Tracks: / Summertime / Bess, you is my woman / My man's gone now / It ain't necessarily so / I got plenty o' nuttin' / Oh, Bess oh where's my Bess / They pass by singin' / There's a boat dat's leavin' for New York / Strawberry woman.
Notes: Oscar Peterson-Clavichord/Joe Pass-Acoustic guitar
Compact disc: released on Pablo Jazz (USA), Apr'86 by United Artists. Dist: Swift

REUNION BLUES (Peterson, Oscar & Milt Jackson).
Tracks: / Satisfaction / Dream of you / Someday my Prince will come / Time for love, A / Reunion blues / When I fall in love / Red top.
Compact disc: released on Verve, Jul'84 by Phonogram Records. Dist: Polygram

Album: released on MPS Jazz, May'81

ROMANCE.
Album: released on Polydor, Mar'82 by Polydor Records. Dist: Polygram, Polydor

ROYAL WEDDING SUITE, A.
Album: released on Pablo (USA), '82 by Pablo Records (USA). Dist: Wellard, Chris, IMS-Polygram, BMG

Cassette: released on Pablo (USA), '82 by Pablo Records (USA). Dist: Wellard, Chris, IMS-Polygram, BMG

SALLE PLEYE, A (Peterson, Oscar & Joe Pass).
Album: released on Pablo (USA), '82 by Pablo Records (USA). Dist: Wellard, Chris, IMS-Polygram, BMG

Cassette: released on Pablo (USA), '82 by Pablo Records (USA). Dist: Wellard, Chris, IMS-Polygram, BMG

SATCH' AND 'JOSH (Peterson, Oscar & Count Basie).
Album: released on Pablo (USA), '82 by Pablo Records (USA). Dist: Wellard, Chris, IMS-Polygram, BMG

SATCH AND JOSH AGAIN (Peterson, Oscar & Count Basie).
Album: released on Pablo (USA), '82 by Pablo Records (USA). Dist: Wellard, Chris, IMS-Polygram, BMG

Cassette: released on Pablo (USA), '82 by Pablo Records (USA). Dist: Wellard, Chris, IMS-Polygram, BMG

SATCH & JOSH (Peterson, Oscar & Count Basie).
Compact disc: by Pablo Records (USA). Dist: Wellard, Chris, IMS-Polygram, BMG
Cat. no: J33J 20013
Compact disc: released on Pablo (USA), May'86 by Pablo Records (USA). Dist: Wellard, Chris, IMS-Polygram, BMG

SILENT PARTNER.
Album: released on Pablo (USA), '82 by Pablo Records (USA). Dist: Wellard, Chris, IMS-Polygram, BMG

Cassette: released on Pablo (USA), '82 by Pablo Records (USA). Dist: Wellard, Chris, IMS-Polygram, BMG

SILVER COLLECTION, THE.
Tracks: / My foolish heart / Round midnight / Someday my Prince will come / Come Sunday / Nightingale / My ship / Sleeping bee / Portrait of Jenny / Goodbye / Con alma / Maidens of Cadiz / My heart stood still / Woody 'n' you.
Compact disc: released on Verve, Nov'84 by Phonogram Records. Dist: Polygram

SKOL (Peterson, Oscar & Stephane Grappelli & Mickey Roker).
Album: released on Pablo, Sep'82 by Pablo Records. Dist: Wellard, Chris, IMS-Polygram, BMG

Cassette: released on Pablo, Sep'82 by Pablo Records. Dist: Wellard, Chris, IMS-Polygram, BMG

TRACKS.
Album: released on MPS Jazz, May'81

TRAVELIN' ON.
Album: released on MPS Jazz, '81

TRIBUTE TO MY FRIENDS, A.
Album: released on Pablo (USA), May'84 by Pablo Records (USA). Dist: Wellard, Chris, IMS-Polygram, BMG

Cassette: released on Pablo (USA), May'84 by Pablo Records (USA). Dist: Wellard, Chris, IMS-Polygram, BMG

TRIO IN TRANSITION.
Double Album: released on Mercury (USA), Oct'83 by Import Records. Dist: IMS Distribution, Polygram Distribution

TRIO LIVE FROM CHICAGO, THE.
Album: released on Verve (USA), Sep'84 by Polydor. Dist: Polygram

Album: released on Verve (USA), Sep'84 by Polydor. Dist: Polygram

TRIO, THE.
Compact disc: released on Polydor, Feb'87 by Polydor Records. Dist: Polygram, Polydor

Album: released on Pablo, '82 by Pablo Records. Dist: Wellard, Chris, IMS-Polygram, BMG

Album: released on Pablo, '82 by Pablo Records. Dist: Wellard, Chris, IMS-Polygram, BMG

TRIO, THE.
Tracks: / Blues Etude / Chicago blues / Easy listening blues / Come sunday / Secret love.
Notes: Personnel: Oscar Peterson/Niels Pedersen/Joe Pass
Compact disc: released on Pablo (USA), Jul'86 by Pablo Records (USA). Dist: Wellard, Chris, IMS-Polygram, BMG

TRISTEZA ON PIANO.
Tracks: / Tristeza / Nightingale / Porgy / Triste / You stepped out of a dream / Watch what happens / Down here on the ground / Fly me to the moon.
Compact disc: released on Pablo, May'84 by Pablo Records. Dist: Wellard, Chris, IMS-Polygram, BMG

Album: released on MPS Jazz, May'81

TRUMPET SUMMIT MEETS THE OSCAR PETERSON BIG FOUR (Peterson, Oscar Big 4).
Album: released on Pablo (USA), '82 by Pablo Records (USA). Dist: Wellard, Chris, IMS-Polygram, BMG

Cassette: released on Pablo (USA), '82 by Pablo Records (USA). Dist: Wellard, Chris, IMS-Polygram, BMG

TWO OF THE FEW (Peterson, Oscar & Milt Jackson).
Album: released on Pablo, May'83 by Pablo Records. Dist: Wellard, Chris, IMS-Polygram, BMG

Cassette: released on Pablo, May'83 by Pablo Records. Dist: Wellard, Chris, IMS-Polygram, BMG

Very tall

WALKING ON THE LINE.
Album: released on MPS Jazz, May'81

WAY I REALLY PLAY, THE.
Album: released on MPS Jazz, May'81

WE GET REQUESTS.
Tracks: / Quiet nights of quiet stars / Days of wine and roses / My one and only love / People / Have you met Miss Jones / You look good to me / Girl from Ipanema / D and E blues / Time and again / Goodbye JD.
Compact disc: released on Verve, '83 by Phonogram Records. Dist: Polygram

WEST SIDE STORY.
Tracks: / Something's coming / Somewhere / Jet song / Tonight / Maria / I feel pretty / Reprise.
Compact disc: released on Verve, Oct'84 by Phonogram Records. Dist: Polygram

YESSIR THAT'S MY BABY (Peterson, Oscar & Count Basie).
Notes: Full details under Count basie.
Compact disc: released on Pablo (USA), Apr'87 by Pablo Records (USA). Dist: Wellard, Chris, IMS-Polygram, BMG

Album: released on Pablo (USA), Dec'86 by Pablo Records (USA). Dist: Wellard, Chris, IMS-Polygram, BMG

Cassette: released on Pablo (USA), Dec'86 by Pablo Records (USA). Dist: Wellard, Chris, IMS-Polygram, BMG

Peterson, Ray

ALL HIS HITS.
Tracks: / Corrine Corrina / I'm gone / Doggone it / I'm tired / Shirley Purly / Is it wrong / Promises / Patricia / Fever / Tell Laura I love her / Tell Tommy I miss him (Skeeter Davis) / Give us your blessing / The wonder of you / Missing you / We're old enough to cry / Teenage heartache / Come and get it / Be my girl.
Album: released on Bear Family, Jul'87 by Bear Family Records. Dist: Rollercoaster Distribution, Swift. Estim retail price in Aug'87 was £8.99.

Peters Sisters

TERRIFIC PETERS SISTERS, THE.
Album: released on Capitol(USA), Mar'84 by Capitol (USA) Records. Dist: EMI

Peter the Great

PETER THE GREAT (Original TV soundtrack) (Various Artists).
Album: released on Silva Screen, Nov'86 by Silva Screen Records. Dist: Silva Screen, PRT

Cassette: released on Silva Screen, Nov'86 by Silva Screen Records. Dist: Silva Screen, PRT

Compact disc: released on Silva Productions, '86

Peter & the Test....

3 X 45 (Peter & the Test Tube babies).
Album: released on Trapper, Oct'85 Dist: Pinnacle, Rough Trade

ANOTHER NOISY PUNK ROCK LP (Peter & the Test Tube babies).
Album: released on Hairy Pie, May'85 Dist: Red Rhino, Cartel

BANNED FROM THE PUB (Peter & the Test Tube babies).
Single (7"): released on No Future, Jul'82 by No Future Records. Dist: Pinnacle, Rough Trade, Cartel

JINX (Peter & the Test Tube babies).
Single (7"): released on Trapper, Mar'85 Dist: Pinnacle, Rough Trade

Single (12"): released on Trapper, Mar'85 Dist: Pinnacle, Rough Trade

JOURNEY TO THE CENTRE OF... (Peter & the Test Tube babies).

KEYS TO THE CITY (Peter & the Test Tube babies).
Tracks: / Keys to the city / Keith Moon / Work hard.
Single (7"): released on Hairy Pie, Jun'86 Dist: Red Rhino, Cartel

Single (12"): released on Hairy Pie, Jun'86 Dist: Red Rhino, Cartel

LOUD BLARING PUNK ROCK LP (Peter & the Test Tube babies).
Album: released on Hairy Pie, Jul'85 Dist: Red Rhino, Cartel

MATING SOUNDS OF THE SOUTH AMERICAN FROG, (THE) (Peter & the Test Tube babies).
Album: released on Trapper, Nov'83 Dist: Pinnacle, Rough Trade

PISSED AND PROUD (Peter & the Test Tube babies).
Cassette: released on No Future, Dec'83 by No Future Records. Dist: Pinnacle, Rough Trade, Cartel

PRESSED FOR CASH (Peter & the Test Tube babies).
Single (12"): released on Trapper, Mar'85 Dist: Pinnacle, Rough Trade

ROTTING IN THE FART SACK (Peter & the Test Tube babies).
Single (12"): released on Metal Knob, May'85 Dist: Jungle Distribution, Cartel Distribution

ROTTING IN THE FART SACK EP (Peter & the Test Tube babies).
Single (12"): released on Jungle, Jul'85 by Jungle Records. Dist: Jungle, Cartel

RUN LIKE HELL (Peter & the Test Tube babies).
Single (7"): released on No Future, Jul'82 by No Future Records. Dist: Pinnacle, Rough Trade, Cartel

SOBERPHOBIA (Peter & the Test Tube babies).
Album: released on Dojo, Feb'87 by Castle Communications Records. Dist: Cartel

WHIMPEEZ (Peter & the Test Tube babies).
Single (7"): released on Trapper, Dec'85 Dist: Pinnacle, Rough Trade

ZOMBIE CREEPING FLESH (Peter & the Test Tube babies).
Single (7"): released on Trapper, Mar'85 Dist: Pinnacle, Rough Trade

Peter Ustinov

MOUSE AND HIS CHILD.
Album: released on Caedmon(USA), Jan'78 by Caedmon (USA) Records. Dist: Gower, Taylors, Discovery

Cassette: released on Caedmon(USA), Jan'78 by Caedmon (USA) Records. Dist: Gower, Taylors, Discovery

Pete's Dragon

PETE'S DRAGON Original Soundtrack.
Album: released on Capitol, '78 by Capitol Records. Dist: EMI

PETE'S DRAGON various artists (Various Artists).
Extended-play record: released on Disneyland, Dec'82 Dist: EMI

Cassette: released on Disneyland, Dec'82 Dist: EMI

Pet Hate

BAD PUBLICITY.
Album: released on Heavy Metal, Dec'85 by FM-Revolver Records. Dist: EMI

Album: released on Heavy Metal, Dec'84 by FM-Revolver Records. Dist: EMI

Cassette: released on Heavy Metal, Dec'84 by FM-Revolver Records. Dist: EMI

BLOWN OUT AGAIN.
Single (12"): released on Trapper, Mar'84 Dist: Pinnacle, Rough Trade

BRIDE WORE RED, THE.
Album: released on Heavy Metal, Apr'84 by FM-Revolver Records. Dist: EMI

Cassette: released on Heavy Metal, Apr'84 by FM-Revolver Records. Dist: EMI

GIRLS GROW UP TOO FAST.
Single (7"): released on Fobik, Apr'85 Dist: Indies

ROLL AWAY THE STONE.
Single (12"): released on FM, Jul'84 by FM-Revolver Records. Dist: EMI

Petit Cheval

ONCE IN A LIFETIME.
Single (7"): released on WEA, Feb'86 by WEA Records. Dist: WEA

Petitjean, Dave

CAJUN CAPERS.
Album:

CAJUN HUMOR.
Album:

HUMOR FROM CAJUN COUNTRY.
Album:

MY FRANS.
Album:

REAL AND FUNNY CAJUN, A.
Album:

Petra

BACK TO THE STREET.
Notes: "Back to the Street" represents a shift in musical development,a new vocalist, two new producers and a revitalised rock sound.Their eigth studio album,Petra's sound now relies heavily on Bob Hartman's guitar rhythms;the'live'feel of the rhythm section,Mark Kelly & Louie Weaver;& the voice of new Petra member John Schlitt.John Lawry's keyboard touches add subtley to the overall sound.With the aid of John & Dino Elefante,"Back to the Street" is perhaps the best culminationand expression of Petra's talents to date.
Album: released on Word, Jan'87 by Word Records. Dist: Word Distribution, CBS

Cassette: released on Word, Jan'87 by Word Records. Dist: Word Distribution, CBS

CAPTURED IN SPACE AND TIME.
Notes: Captured in Time and Space Chronicles the band's "Beat the System" tour, Featuring no less than seven tracks from "Beat the System", three medleys and a few instrumental breaks. One can speak of Petra without considering the effect they've had on the Christian music scene. Nowhere is it more evident than here as Petra gives the audience what it wants while educating and proclaiming the gospel. Petra's performance on Captured in Time and Space is professional, and personable, making music palatable to a variety of tastes, moderating the rock 'n' roll but still capturing the feel and energy of a live perfomance.
Album: released on Word, Aug'86 by Word Records. Dist: Word Distribution, CBS

Cassette: released on Word, Aug'86 by Word Records. Dist: Word Distribution, CBS

Petrie, Anne

PERSONALITIES / FORECAST FOR 1982.
Single (7"): released on Stars, Nov'81

Petrol Emotion

BIG DECISION (Petrol Emotion, The).
Tracks: / Big decision / Souldeep.
Single (7"): released on Polydor, Mar'87 by Polydor Records. Dist: Polygram, Polydor

Single (12"): released on Polydor, Mar'87 by Polydor Records. Dist: Polygram, Polydor

Petrol & Pollution

PETROL & POLLUTION Coventry,Brussels,New York (An International report).
Cassette: released on International Report, Oct'81 by Seminar Cassettes. Dist: Audio-Visual Library Services, Davidson Distribution, Eastern Educational Products Distrib., Forlaget Systime Distribution, MacDougall Distribution, Talktapes Distribution, Watkins Books Ltd Distribution, Norton, Jeff Distribution

Petrov, A

RUSSIAN SONGS-SONGS & INSTRUMENTAL PIECES.
Cassette: released on Melodiya (USSR), Feb'79 Dist: T.B.C Distribution

Petrucciani, Michel

100 HEARTS.
Album: released on George Wein Concord Jazz (USA), Apr'84 by Concord Jazz Records (USA). Dist: IMS, Polygram

LIVE AT THE VILLAGE VANGUARD.
Album: released on George Wein Concord Jazz (USA), May'85 by Concord Jazz Records (USA). Dist: IMS, Polygram

POWER OF THREE.
Tracks: / Limbo / Careful / Morning blues / Waltz new / Beautiful love / In a sentimental mood / Bimini.
Notes: At the age of 23, Michel Petrucciani is already well on his way to becoming a major force in jazz piano. With this album, recorded live at the 1986 Montreaux Jazz Festival in Switzerland, Michel has taken a giant step forward. This recording took place midway through a European tour by Petrucciani and the legendary jazz guitarist Jim Hall. By Montreaux, they had developed a deep empathy and a wonderful programme of Hall originals and standard tunes. In Montreaux, they intersected with a very special guest: saxophonist Wayne Shorter. The three had previously met on the tour trail in Toronto and Copenhagen to prepare for this night. Shorter joins the duo for his own "Limbo" made famous by Miles Davis, Jim Hall's "SRO", a powerful calypso dedicated to Sonny Rollins and Michel's soulful "Morning Blues". It was a special night indeed and it was captured by Blue Note Records.
Album: released on Blue Note, Mar'87 by EMI Records. Dist: EMI

Pet Shop Boys

ACTUALLY.
Tracks: / One more chance / Shopping / Rent / Hit music / What have I done to deserve this? / It couldn't happen here / It's a sin / I want to wake up / Heart / King's Cross.
Compact disc: released on Parlophone, Sep'87 by EMI Records. Dist: EMI

Album: released on Parlophone, Sep'87 by EMI Records. Dist: EMI

Cassette: released on Parlophone, Sep'87 by EMI Records. Dist: EMI

DISCO.
Tracks: / In the night / Suburbia / Opportunities / Paninaro / Love comes quickly / West End Girls.
Notes: (P)by:Pet Shop Boys/Julian Mendleson/J.J.Jexzalli&Nicholas Frome(London) & Ron Dean Miller(NY)/Stephen Hague: Remixes:Arthur Baker/Julian Mendleson: tracks 1-6 Cage Music Ltd/10 Music Ltd:
Cassette: released on EMI, Nov'86 by EMI Records. Dist: EMI

Compact disc: released on EMI, Dec'86 by EMI Records. Dist: EMI

Album: released on Parlophone, Nov'86 by EMI Records. Dist: EMI

IT'S A SIN.
Tracks: / It's a sin / You know where you went wrong / It's a sin (disco mix)*.
Single (7"): released on Parlophone, 13 Jun'87 by EMI Records. Dist: EMI

Single (12"): released on Parlophone, 13 Jun'87 by EMI Records. Dist: EMI

Cassette single: released on Parlophone, 13 Jun'87 by EMI Records. Dist: EMI

Compact disc single: released on Parlophone, Jul'87 by EMI Records. Dist: EMI

IT'S A SIN (REMIX).
Tracks: / I's a sin (remix) / You know where you went wrong (rough mix).
Single (12"): released on Parlophone, Jul'87 by EMI Records. Dist: EMI

LOVE COMES QUICKLY.
Tracks: / Love comes Quickly / Thats My Impression / Love comes quickly (Dance Mix 12" Only). / That's my impression (disco Mix 12" Only).
Single (7"): released on Parlophone, Mar'86 by EMI Records. Dist: EMI

Single (12"): released on Parlophone, Mar'86 by EMI Records. Dist: EMI

OPPERTUNITIES.
Tracks: / opportunities (Lets make lots of money) / Was that what it was.
Single (7"): released on Parlophone, May'86 by EMI Records. Dist: EMI

Single (12"): released on Parlophone, May'86 by EMI Records. Dist: EMI

OPPORTUNITIES (LET'S MAKE LOTS OF MONEY).
Single (7"): released on Parlophone, Jun'85 by EMI Records. Dist: EMI

Single (7"): released on Parlophone, Jun'85 by EMI Records. Dist: EMI

PLEASE.
Tracks: / Two divide by zero / West End Girls / Opportunities (Lets make lots of money / Love comes quickly / Suburbia / Tonight is forever / Violence / I want a lover / Later tonight / Why dont we live together.
Notes: Includes the hit single "west End Girls"(Full length version 'love comes Quickl ', and are-recorded version of Opportunities, their stunning first single. The inner sleeve features 98 colour and black and white picturestelling the history of the group. the cassette package includes select trannies from the inner bag on an extended inlay.
Album: released on Parlophone, Mar'86 by EMI Records. Dist: EMI

Cassette: released on Parlophone, Mar'86 by EMI Records. Dist: EMI

Compact disc: released on Parlophone, Jul'86 by EMI Records. Dist: EMI

SUBURBIA.
Tracks: / Suburbia / Jack the lad / Love comes quickly / Paninaro.
Single (7"): released on Parlophone, Sep'86 by EMI Records. Dist: EMI

Single (12"): released on Parlophone, Sep'86 by EMI Records. Dist: EMI

Double-pack single: released on Parlophone, Sep'86 by EMI Records. Dist: EMI

TELEVISION.
Tracks: / Opportunities / West End girls / Love Comes Quickly / Suburbia / Paninaro.
Notes: A collection of videoes from all the singles on the million selling"Please" album linked together by excerpts from the Boys on TV all over the world. Includes the little seen early version of"Opportunities" and the never before seen Milanese mini epic "Paninaro". No.of tracks: 6 : Total playing time: 30 minutes approx.
Video-cassette (VHS): released on PMI, Dec'86 by PMI Records. Dist: EMI

Video-cassette [Betamax]: released on PMI, Nov'86 by PMI Records. Dist: EMI

WEST END GIRLS.
Tracks: / West End girls / West End dub / Man could get arrested, A.
Single (12"): released on Parlophone, Jan'86 by EMI Records. Dist: EMI

Single (7"): released on Paro, Oct'85 by Paro Records. Dist: Spartan

Single (12"): released on Paro, Oct'85 by Paro Records. Dist: Spartan

Picture disc single: released on Parlophone, Dec'85 by EMI Records. Dist: EMI

Single 10": released on Parlophone, Dec'85 by EMI Records. Dist: EMI

Single (12"): released on Parlophone, Dec'85 by EMI Records. Dist: EMI

WHAT HAVE I DONE TO DESERVE THIS? (Pet Shop Boys & Dusty Springfield).
Tracks: / What have I done to deserve this? (Shep Pettibone mix) / What have I done to deserve this? / New life, A.
Cassette single: released on Parlophone, Aug'87 by EMI Records. Dist: EMI

Single (12"): released on Parlophone, Aug'87 by EMI Records. Dist: EMI

Single (7"): released on Parlophone, Aug'87 by EMI Records. Dist: EMI

Pets Of Friction

CAREER IN THE MORNING.
Single (7"): released on Turning Purple, Dec'82

Page 780

Pettiford, Oscar

BLUES BROTHERS.
Album: released on Black Lion, Apr'85 by Black Lion Records. Dist: Jazz Music, Chris Wellard, Taylor, H.R., Counterpoint, Cadillac

BOHEMIA AFTER DARK.
Album: released on Affinity, Apr'84 by Charly Records. Dist: Charly, Cadillac

IN HIGH FI.
Album: released on Jasmine, Feb'84 by Jasmine Records. Dist: Counterpoint, Lugtons, Taylor, H.R., Wellard, Chris, Swift, Cadillac

LEGENDARY OSCAR PETTIFORD, THE.
Album: released on Black Lion, Sep'85 by Black Lion Records. Dist: Jazz Music, Chris Wellard, Taylor, H.R., Counterpoint, Cadillac

OSCAR RIDES AGAIN (Pettiford, Oscar-Quintet & Nonet).
Tracks: / Sextet / Golden touch / Cable car / Trictatism / Edge of love / Oscar rides again / Jack the bear / Tamalpais / Swing t'll the girls come home / Mood indigo / Chuckles / Time on my hands.
Album: released on Affinity, Sep'86 by Charly Records. Dist: Charly, Cadillac

Petty, Tom

CHANGE OF HEART (Petty, Tom & The Heartbreakers).
Single (7"): released on MCA, Apr'83 by MCA Records. Dist: Polygram, MCA

DAMN THE TORPEDOES (Petty, Tom & The Heartbreakers).
Album: released on Backstreet, Oct'79

DAMN THE TORPEDOS.
Tracks: / Refugee / Here comes the girl / Even the losers / Shadow of a doubt / Century city / Don't do me like that / You tell me / What are you doin' in my life? / Louisiana rain.
Notes: All tracks written by Tom Petty except "Refugee" & "Here comes the girl" written by Tom Petty and Mike Campbell. All tracks By Virgin Music (Publishers) Ltd. (P) 1979 Backstreet Records, a division of MCA Records Inc.
Compact disc: released on MCA, Dec'84 by MCA Records. Dist: Polygram, MCA

HARD PROMISES.
Tracks: / Waiting, The / Woman in love (It's not me) / Nightwatchman / Something big / Kings road / Letting you go / Thing about you / Insider / Criminal kind / You can still change your mind.
Notes: One of rock's greatest superstars whose talents remain undiminished and it showson this album! An exciting mid-line prospect. Produced by Tom Petty & Jimmy Iovine. Engineered by Shelly Yakus.
Album: released on MCA, May'86 by MCA Records. Dist: Polygram, MCA

Cassette: released on MCA, May'86 by MCA Records. Dist: Polygram, MCA

Compact disc: released on MCA, Sep'86 by MCA Records. Dist: Polygram, MCA

HARD PROMISES/DAMN THE TORPEDOES.
Double cassette: released on MCA, Sep'84 by MCA Records. Dist: Polygram, MCA

JAMMIN' ME.
Tracks: / Jammin' me / Let me up (I've had enough) / Make that collection.
Single (7"): released on MCA, Apr'87 by MCA Records. Dist: Polygram, MCA

Single (12"): released on MCA, Apr'87 by MCA Records. Dist: Polygram, MCA

LET ME UP (I'VE HAD ENOUGH) (Petty, Tom & The Heartbreakers).
Tracks: / Jammin' me / Runaway trains / Damage you've done (The) / It'll all work out / My life/your world / Think about me / All mixed up / Self-made man (A) / Ain't love strange / How many more days / Let me up (I've had enough).
Album: released on MCA, Apr'87 by MCA Records. Dist: Polygram, MCA

Cassette: released on MCA, Apr'87 by MCA Records. Dist: Polygram, MCA

Compact disc: released on MCA, Apr'87 by MCA Records. Dist: Polygram, MCA

LONG AFTER DARK (Petty, Tom & The Heartbreakers).
Tracks: / One story town, A / You got lucky / Deliver me / Change of heart / Finding out / We stand a chance / Straight into darkness / Same old you, The / Between two worlds / Wasted life, A.
Compact disc: by MCA Records. Dist: Polygram, MCA

Album: released on MCA, May'86 by MCA Records. Dist: Polygram, MCA

Compact disc: released on MCA, Sep'86 by MCA Records. Dist: Polygram, MCA

PACK UP THE PLANTATION-LIVE (Petty, Tom & The Heartbreakers).
Notes: The essential live double album from one of the biggest acts in American rock! Tom Petty has always had a strong following in this country and his profile here has undoubtedly been significantly raised in recent months after his appearence on Live Aid and Farm Aid.
Double Album: released on MCA, Dec'85 by MCA Records. Dist: Polygram, MCA

Double cassette: released on MCA, Dec'85 by MCA Records. Dist: Polygram, MCA

Video-cassette (VHS): released on Virgin, May'86 by Virgin Records. Dist: EMI, Virgin Distribution

REFUGEE (Petty, Tom & The Heartbreakers).
Tracks: / Refugee / Don't do me like that / Here comes the girl / Waiting, The.
Single (12"): released on MCA, Apr'86 by MCA Records. Dist: Polygram, MCA

SOUTHERN ACCENTS.
Tracks: / Rebels / It ain't nothin' to me / Don't come around here no more / Southern accents / Make it better (forget about me) / Spike / Dogs on the run / Mary's new car / Best of everything, The.
Compact disc: released on MCA, '86 by MCA Records. Dist: Polygram, MCA

Album: released on MCA, Apr'85 by MCA Records. Dist: Polygram, MCA

Cassette: released on MCA, Apr'85 by MCA Records. Dist: Polygram, MCA

SO YOU WANT TO BE A ROCK 'N' ROLL STAR (Petty, Tom & The Heartbreakers).
Tracks: / So you want to be a rock 'n' roll star / American girl / Spike.
Single (7"): released on MCA, Feb'86 by MCA Records. Dist: Polygram, MCA

Single (12"): released on MCA, Feb'86 by MCA Records. Dist: Polygram, MCA

TOM PETTY AND THE HEARTBREAKERS (Petty, Tom & The Heartbreakers).
Tracks: / Rockin' around (with you) / Breakdown / Hometown blues / Wild one (The) / Forever / Anything that's rock 'n' roll / Strangered in the night / Fooled again (I don't like it) / Mystery man / Luna / American girl.
Compact disc: released on MCA, '87 by MCA Records. Dist: Polygram, MCA

TOM PETTY & THE HEARTBREAKERS.
Compact disc: released on MCA, Jul'87 by MCA Records. Dist: Polygram, MCA

Compact disc: released on MCA, Jul'87 by MCA Records. Dist: Polygram, MCA

Peyer

FOURTH REICH (EP).
Single (12"): released on Shout, Oct'82 by Shout Records. Dist: Rough Trade, Cartel

Peyr

AS ABOVE....
Album: released on Shout, May'82 by Shout Records. Dist: Rough Trade, Cartel

Peyton, Craig

BE THANKFUL FOR WHAT YOU GOT.
Single (12"): released on Elite, Jun'83 Dist: PRT

Pezband

LAUGHING IN THE DARK.
Album: released on Radar, May'78 by WEA Music Ltd. Dist: WEA, PRT

Pfeifer, Diane

DIANE PFEIFER.
Album: released on Capitol, Nov'80 by Capitol Records. Dist: EMI

PFM

COOK.
Album: released on Manticore, Jan'75 by Atlantic Records. Dist: WEA

ENIGMATIC OCEAN.
Album: by WEA Records. Dist: WEA

IMAGINARY VOYAGE.
Album: by WEA Records. Dist: WEA

JET LAG.
Album: released on Manticore, Jul'77 by Atlantic Records. Dist: WEA

PHOTOS OF GHOSTS.
Album: by Atlantic Records. Dist: WEA

WORLD BECAME THE WORLD, THE.
Album: released on Manticore, '74 by Atlantic Records. Dist: WEA

P.funk

P.FUNK Various artists (Various Artists).
Album: released on Streetsounds, Jul'86

Cassette: released on Streetsounds, Jul'86

P.G.Wodehouse

MULLINER'S BUCK U UPPO (Various Artists).
Cassette: released on Talking Tape Company, '84 by Talking Tape Company Records.

Phantasm

PHANTASM Original soundtrack.
Album: released on Gem, Feb'80 by Gem Records. Dist: RCA

Phantom

LAZY FASCIST.
Single (7"): released on Cool Ghoul, Jul'83 by Cool Ghoul Records. Dist: Rough Trade, Cool Ghoul

LOVE ME.
Single (7"): released on DJ Jamboree, Mar'85 Dist: Tonal Distribution

Phantom of the opera

PHANTOM OF THE OPERA (THE) Original London Cast.
Double Album: released on Polydor, Feb'87 by Polydor Records. Dist: Polygram, Polydor

Cassette: released on Polydor, Feb'87 by Polydor Records. Dist: Polygram, Polydor

Compact disc: released on Polydor, Feb'87 by Polydor Records. Dist: Polygram, Polydor

Compact disc: released on Polydor, Feb'87 by Polydor Records. Dist: Polygram, Polydor

Phantom Of The Park, The

PHANTOM OF THE PARK, THE (Kiss).
Notes: Full length thriller featuring performances by Kiss.
Video-cassette (VHS): released on IVS, Apr'87

Phantom, Rocker

MEN WITHOUT SHAME (Phantom, Rocker & Flick).
Single (7"): released on EMI America, Nov'85 by EMI Records. Dist: EMI

Single (12"): released on EMI America, Nov'85 by EMI Records. Dist: EMI

MY MISTAKE (Phantom, Rocker and Slick).
Tracks: / My mistake / Runnin' from the hounds.
Single (7"): released on EMI America, Mar'86 by EMI Records. Dist: EMI

PHANTOM, ROCKER AND SLICK (Phantom, Rocker and Slick).
Tracks: / What you want / My mistake / Hollywood distractions / No regrets / Well kept secret / Men without shame / Runnin' from the hounds / Time is on my hands / Sing for the supper / Lonely actions.
Notes: Slim Jim Phantom, Lee Rocker and Earl Slick combine to form one of the most exciting new rock bands this year, Drummer Phantom and Bassist Rocker were together the rhythm section of the Stray Cats, while guitarist Slick's work with David Bowie on the serious Moonlight tour and with John Waite on his recent worldwide tour has earned him great visibility and respect. Phantom, Rocker & Slick are out to break down the traditional limitations of playing within a single style. As a result they emerge not only as highly skilled players but also as innovative and challenging writers. The album is produced by Steve Thompson and Michael Barbiero, who have worked on sveral of David Bowie's singles, including the recent No.1 with Mick Jagger, "Dancing in the Street" and kieth Richard lends a little of his gitar wizardry to the album.
Album: released on EMI America, Dec'85 by EMI Records. Dist: EMI

Cassette: released on EMI America, Dec'85 by EMI Records. Dist: EMI

Phantom Tollbooth

PHANTOM TOLLBOOTH, THE Juster, Norman (Carroll, Pat).
Cassette: released on Caedmon(USA), Apr'83 by Caedmon (USA) Records. Dist: Gower, Taylors, Discovery

PHANTOM TOLLBOOTH.
Album: released on Homestead, Sep'86 Dist: Rough Trade, Cartel, Shigaku

VALLEY OF THE GWANGI.
Tracks: / Valley of the Gwangi.
Single (7"): released on Homestead, Sep'86 Dist: Rough Trade, Cartel, Shigaku

VALLEY OF THE GWANGI.
Tracks: / Flip Your Lid / Wailing Ultimate(the).
Single (7"): released on Homestead, Dec'86 Dist: Rough Trade, Cartel, Shigaku

Pharaohs

BLUE EYGPT.
Album: released on Nervous, Feb'86 by Nervous Records. Dist: Nervous, Rough Trade

BROKEN HEART, CRYING EYES.
Tracks: / Broken heart, crying eyes.
Single (7"): released on Ace, Aug'86 by Ace Records. Dist: Pinnacle, Swift, Hotshot, Cadillac

VIGILANTE.
Tracks: / Vigilante / Cleopatra / You're on your own / Pharaohs to cowboys.
Single (12"): released on Nervous, Jun'87 by Nervous Records. Dist: Nervous, Rough Trade

Phar Lap...

PHAR LAP - HEART OF A NATION Original soundtrack (Various Artists).
Album: released on EMI, Apr'85 by EMI Records. Dist: EMI

Cassette: released on EMI, Apr'85 by EMI Records. Dist: EMI

Phase 111 Mod Bands

PHASE 111 MOD BANDS (Various Artists).
Notes: Featuring: Manual Scan, City Motors, The Pictures, XL.
Single (7"): released on Unicorn, 23 May'87 Dist: Nine Mile, Cartel

Phase 2

ROXY.
Single (7"): released on Celluloid, May'83 by Charly Records. Dist: Charly

Phase III Project

FOUR-BANK INTERNATIONAL EP.
Tracks: / Naked City / Look In Your Eyes (The) / Jobs For The Boys / Love Someone.
Single (7"): released on Unicorn, Jan'87 Dist: Nine Mile, Cartel

Phasslayne

CUT IT UP.
Album: released on Neat, '85 by Neat Records. Dist: Pinnacle, Neat

P.Hawkins

TUBBY THE TUBA.
Album: released on Castle, '74 by Castle Records. Dist: Pinnacle

PhD

I DIDN'T KNOW.
Single (7"): released on WEA International, Mar'83 by WEA Records. Dist: WEA

Single (12"): released on WEA International, Apr'83 by WEA Records. Dist: WEA

I WON'T LET YOU DOWN.
Single (7"): released on WEA, Feb'82 by WEA Records. Dist: WEA

Philadelphia Int...

LET'S CLEAN UP THE GHETTO (Philadelphia International All Stars).
Single (12"): released on Streetwave, Jul'85 by Streetwave Records. Dist: PRT Distribution

Phenomena

DANCE WITH THE DEVIL.
Single (7"): released on Bronze, Jun'85 by Polygram Records. Dist: Polydor

Single (12"): released on Bronze, Jun'85 by Polygram Records. Dist: Polydor

PHENOMENA Various artists (Various Artists).
Album: released on Bronze, Jun'85 by Polygram Records. Dist: Polydor

Cassette: released on Bronze, Jun'85 by Polygram Records. Dist: Polydor

Philadelphia...

PHILADELPHIA CLASSICS Harious artists (Various Artists).
Double Album: released on Philadelphia International, Feb'78 by CBS Records. Dist: CBS

PHILADELPHIA STORY (THE) Various artists (Various Artists).
Notes: 14 LP Box Set or 9 Cassette Box Set.
Album: released on Streetsounds, Nov'86

Cassette: released on Streetsounds, Nov'86

Philco Radio...

PHILCO RADIO TIME Two complete broadcasts (Philco Radio Broadcasts).
Album: released on Totem, Jun'79 Dist: Jazz Music, Projection, Swift

Philharmonia Orc.

ORIGINAL SOUNDTRACK - CHAMPIONS (Philharmonia Orchestra).
Album: released on Island, Mar'84 by Island Records. Dist: Polygram

Cassette: released on Island, Mar'84 by Island Records. Dist: Polygram

Philippe, Louis

APPOINTMENT WITH VENUS.
Tracks: / La pluie fait des claquettes / Man down the stairs / When I'm an astronaut / We live on an island / Orchard, The / Heaven is above me / Rescue the Titanic / Touch of evil / Ballad of Sophie Sololl / Angelica my love / I will / Exporado tales / Apertivo / Fires rise and die / La pluie fait des claquettes.
Album: released on EL, Jul'86 by El Records. Dist: Rough Trade, Cartel, Pinnacle

LIKE NOBODY DO.
Tracks: / Like nobody do / Twangy twangy.
Single (7"): released on EL-Cherry Red, Jul'86 by Cherry Red Records. Dist: Pinnacle

METHODE DE POUR LA FLUTE.
Album: released on Crepescule, Dec'86 by Island Records. Dist: Polygram, Pinnacle

PLUIE FAIT DES CLAQUETTES, (LA).
Tracks: / La pluie fait des claquettes / Touch of evil / You're missing someone / Sirens call.
Single (12"): released on EL-Cherry Red, Apr'86 by Cherry Red Records. Dist: Pinnacle

RED ROSES & RED NOSES.
Tracks: / Red roses & red noses / La pluie fait des claquettes / Touch of evil / If you're missing somebody / Sirens call.
Single (12"): released on EL, Jul'86 by El Records. Dist: Rough Trade, Cartel, Pinnacle

YOU MARY YOU.
Tracks: / You Mary you / With and without you / Little pad* / Blue roofs of Ispahan*.
Single (7"): released on EL, Mar'87 by El Records. Dist: Rough Trade, Cartel, Pinnacle

Single (12"): released on EL, Mar'87 by El Records. Dist: Rough Trade, Cartel, Pinnacle

Philippine Gong Music

PHILIPPINE GONG MUSIC FROM LANAO.
Album: released on Lyrichord (USA), Oct'81 by Lyrichord Records (USA). Dist: Flexitron Distributors Ltd

PHILIPPINE GONG MUSIC FROM LANOA VOL.2.
Album: released on Lyrichord (USA), Oct'81 by Lyrichord Records (USA). Dist: Flexitron Distributors Ltd

Philips, Anthony

1984.
Album: released on RCA, Jun'81 by RCA Records. Dist: RCA, Roots, Swift, Wellard, Chris, I & B, Solomon & Peres Distribution

Cassette: released on RCA, Jun'81 by RCA Records. Dist: RCA, Roots, Swift, Wellard, Chris, I & B, Solomon & Peres Distribution

ANTIQUES.
Album: released on RCA International (USA), Oct'82 by RCA Records. Dist: RCA

Cassette: released on RCA International (USA), Oct'82 by RCA Records. Dist: RCA

GEESE & THE GHOST, THE.
Album: released on Hit & Run Music, Mar'77 Dist: Virgin

HARVEST OF THE HEART.
Album: released on Cherry Red, Sep'85 by Cherry Red Records. Dist: Pinnacle

Philips, Glen

ELEVATOR.
Album: released on SST, Aug'87 by SST Records. Dist: Pinnacle

Philips, Paul

SINCERELY.
Album: released on Igus, Jul'87 by Klub. Dist: PRT, Musac Distribution Ltd (Scotland)

Cassette: released on Igus, Jul'87 by Klub. Dist: PRT, Musac Distribution Ltd (Scotland)

Phil & John

LONELY DANCER.
Album: released on Word, Aug'87 by Word Records. Dist: Word Distribution, CBS

Cassette: released on Word, Aug'87 by Word Records. Dist: Word Distribution, CBS

Phill & Company

TRA LA LA.
Single (7"): released on Sonet, Apr'85 by Sonet Records. Dist: PRT

Phillinganes, Greg

BEHIND THE MASK.
Single (7"): released on Planet, Mar'85 Dist: WEA

Single (12"): released on Planet, Mar'85 Dist: WEA

PULSE.
Tracks: / Behind the mask / Won't be long now / Playin' with fire / I have dreamed / Come as you are / Lazy Nina / Signals / Countdown to love / Shake it.
Album: released on RCA, Jan'87 by RCA Records. Dist: RCA, Roots, Swift, Wellard, Chris, I & B, Solomon & Peres Distribution

Cassette: released on RCA, Jan'87 by RCA Records. Dist: RCA, Roots, Swift, Wellard, Chris, I & B, Solomon & Peres Distribution

Album: released on Planet, Mar'85 Dist: WEA

Cassette: released on Planet, Mar'85 Dist: WEA

SIGNIFICANT GAINS.
Album: released on Elektra Asylum, Jul'81 by Elektra/Asylum/Nonesuch Records. Dist: WEA

Phillipe, Brun

1930-38.
Album: released on Pathe MarconiFrance), Sep'84

Phillip & His...

TELL ME WHAT IS THE BANE OF YOUR LIFE (Phillip & His Foetus Vibrations).
Single (7"): released on Self Immolation, Jan'82 Dist: Rough Trade

Phillips, Anthony

INVISIBLE MEN.
Album: released on Street Tunes, Mar'84 by Street Tunes Records. Dist: Pinnacle

Cassette: released on Street Tunes, Mar'84 by Street Tunes Records. Dist: Pinnacle

SALLY.
Single (12"): released on Street Tunes, Feb'84 by Street Tunes Records. Dist: Pinnacle

WISE AFTER THE EVENT.
Album: released on Arista, May'78 by Arista Records. Dist: RCA

Phillips, Arlene

KEEP IN SHAPE SYSTEM.
Album: released on Ferroway Records, Aug'82 Dist: PRT

Cassette: released on Ferroway Records, Aug'82 Dist: PRT

KEEP IN SHAPE, VOL.2.
Album: released on Ferroway Records, Nov'83 Dist: PRT

Cassette: released on Ferroway Records, Nov'83 Dist: PRT

Phillips, Barre

CALL ME WHEN YOU GET THERE.
Album: released on ECM (Germany), Feb'84 by ECM Records. Dist: IMS, Polygram, Virgin through EMI

MOUNTAINSCAPES.
Album: released on ECM, Sep'76 by ECM Records. Dist: IMS, Polygram, Virgin through EMI

MUSIC BY.
Album: released on ECM, May'81 by ECM Records. Dist: IMS, Polygram, Virgin through EMI

THREE DAY MOON.
Album: released on ECM, '78 by ECM Records. Dist: IMS, Polygram, Virgin through EMI

Phillips, Brewer

WHOLE LOTTA BLUES.
Album: released on JSP, Jan'83 by JSP Records. Dist: Swift, Projection

Phillips, Bryars

IRMA.
Album: by Polydor Records. Dist: Polygram Distribution

Phillips, Dave

BEST OF ROCKS.
Album: released on Rockhouse, Sep'86 by Rockhouse Records. Dist: Swift Distribution, Charly Distribution

DAVE PHILLIPS.
Album: released on Rockhouse, Mar'85 Dist: Pinnacle

Picture disc album: released on Rockhouse, Jan'85 by Rockhouse Records. Dist: Swift Distribution, Charly Distribution

NEXT STOP.
Single (7"): released on Rockhouse, Mar'84 by Rockhouse Records. Dist: Swift Distribution, Charly Distribution

UNDERSTATEMENTS.
Album: released on Kix 4 U (Holland), Sep'85 by Kix 4 U Records(Holland). Dist: Pinnacle

WILD YOUTH (Phillips, Dave & Hot Road Gang).
Album: released on Rockhouse(USA), Nov'82

Phillips, Edwin

LIFE ON EARTH.
Tracks: / Life on Earth.
Single (7"): released on T-Mac, Jan'86 by T-Mac Records. Dist: PRT Distribution

Single (12"): released on T-Mac, Dec'85 by T-Mac Records. Dist: PRT Distribution

Phillips, Ester

WAY TO SAY GOODBYE.
Compact disc: released on Muse (USA), Feb'87 by Muse Records (USA). Dist: Conifer Distribution, Jazz Music Distribution

Phillips, Esther

COMPLETE SAVOY RECORDINGS (Phillips, Little Esther).
Double Album: released on Savoy, Jan'87

Album:

ESTHER PHILLIPS.
Album: released on Kudu, Apr'78 Dist: IMS-Polygram

GOOD BLACK IS HARD TO CRACK.
Album: released on Mercury, Apr'81 by Phonogram Records. Dist: Polygram Distribution

HERE'S ESTHER-ARE YOU READY.
Album: released on Mercury, Sep'79 by Phonogram Records. Dist: Polygram Distribution

WAY TO SAY GOODBYE, A.
Tracks: / It's All In The Game / Mama Said / Goin' In Circles / Nowhere To Run / We Are Through / FaFaFa (Sad Song) / Mr. Bojangles / Shake This Off / Way To Say Goodbye, A / Way to say goodbye, A.
Cassette: released on Muse (USA), Feb'87 by Muse Records (USA). Dist: Conifer Distribution, Jazz Music Distribution

WHAT A DIFF'RENCE A DAY MAKES.
Album: released on CTI (Musidisc France), Jul'85 by Polydor Records. Dist: IMS, Polygram

Cassette: released on CTI (Musidisc France), Jul'85 by Polydor Records. Dist: IMS, Polygram

Phillips, Gene

VOLUME 1 (Phillips, Gene & His Rhythm Aces).
Tracks: / Hey lawdy mama / Short haired ugly woman / I could make you love me / Slippin' and slidin' / Honey chile / Gene jumps the blues / Superstitious woman / I've been fooled before / I wonder what the poor folks are doing / Getting down wrong / Boogie everywhere / Gene's guitar blues / Women, women, women / It's a lonely world / Hey now / Honky tonk train (take one) / Honky tonk train (take two).
Double Album: released on Ace, Mar'86 by Ace Records. Dist: Pinnacle, Swift, Hotshot, Cadillac

Phillips, Ken

ANGELINA.
Single (7"): released on Dakota, Mar'84 by Dakota Records. Dist: PRT

Phillips, Leslie

BLACK AND WHITE IN A GREY WORLD.
Notes: Fastmovinhardhittinstraightalkinnomessin Leslie! The lady is here again. For those of you who missed her debut album 'Beyond Saturday Night' or her follow up 'Dancing With Danger', or even her dynamic debut at Greenbelt 85 main stage, now's your chance to hear what all the fuss is about. Her voice has the edge of a Cindi Lauper and the heart of a Bonnie Tyler. Her songs give it a perfect platform - the sound is thoroughly 1980s if not 1990s and her lyrics have the kind of concerned relevance that Steve Taylor would be proud of. Leslie's straight talking is an inspiration in days of relative morality and situational ethics, where absolute Biblical standards are frowned upon.
Album: released on Myrrh, Jan'86 by Word Records. Dist: Word Distribution

Cassette: released on Myrrh, Jan'86 by Word Records. Dist: Word Distribution

DANCING WITH DANGER.
Album: released on Myrrh, Sep'85 by Word Records. Dist: Word Distribution

Cassette: released on Myrrh, Sep'85 by Word Records. Dist: Word Distribution

TURNING, THE.
Tracks: / River of love / Love is not lost / Turning, The / Libera me / Carry you / Beating heart / Expectation / Down / Answer - don't come easy / God is watching you.
Album: released on Myrrh, Jul'87 by Word Records. Dist: Word Distribution

Cassette: released on Myrrh, Jul'87 by Word Records. Dist: Word Distribution

Phillips, Noel

YOUTHMAN.
Single (12"): released on KG, Apr'82

Phillips, Sid

GOODY, GOODY.
Album: released on President, '83 by President Records. Dist: Taylors, Spartan

Cassette: released on President, '83 by President Records. Dist: Taylors, Spartan

STARDUST.
Album: released on Halcyon, Apr'85 by Halcyon Records. Dist: Jazz Music

Phillips, Utah

ALL USED UP & A SCRAPE BOOK.
Album: released on Philo, Sep'79 Dist: Roots

CAPITAN, EL.
Album: released on Philo, May'79 Dist: Roots

WE HAVE FED YOU ALL THESE YEARS.
Album: released on Philo (USA), Apr'85

Phillips, West

I'M JUST A SUCKER FOR A PRETTY FACE.
Single (12"): released on Trans Q, Mar'84 by Sound Records. Dist: Pinnacle

TELL ME.
Single (12"): released on Kool Kat, Aug'87 by Kool Kat Records. Dist: PRT

Philly Cream

NO TIME LIKE NOW.
Album: released on Wmot, Nov'80

Phil Spector

PHIL SPECTOR 1974/1979 Various artists (Various Artists).
Album: released on Phil Spector Int., Nov'79

PHIL SPECTOR: EARLY PRODUCTIONS '58-'61 Various artists (Various Artists).
Album: released on Rhino (USA), Jul'84 by Rhino Records (USA).

PHIL SPECTOR - ECHOES OF THE 60'S Various artists (Various Artists).
Album: released on Philadelphia, Oct'77

Phoenix

IN FULL VIEW.
Album: released on Charisma, Feb'80 by Virgin Records. Dist: EMI

Phontastic Dixieland Band

DIXIE DISC (From Basin Street to Louisiana).
Album: released on Phontastic (Sweden), '82 by Wellard, Chris Distribution. Dist: Wellard, Chris Distribution

Phorphazade

AAH YOU ARE AS LIGHT AS A FEATHER.
Single (12"): released on Crackle & Corkette, May'85 Dist: Revolver, Cartel

Photofit

ANOTHER ALIAS.
Single (7"): released on Raffia, Nov'83 Dist: Spartan

Photoglo, Jim

FOOL IN LOVE WITH YOU.
Album: released on 20th Century, Aug'81 Dist: RCA, IMS-Polygram

Cassette: released on 20th Century, Aug'81 Dist: RCA, IMS-Polygram

Photos

THERE'S ALWAYS WORK.
Single (7"): released on Rialto, Apr'83 by Rialto Records. Dist: Pinnacle

Single (12"): released on Rialto, Apr'83 by Rialto Records. Dist: Pinnacle

Phranc

AMAZON.
Single (7"): released on Stiff, Nov'85 by Stiff Records. Dist: EMI, Record Services Distribution (Ireland)

Single (12"): released on Stiff, Nov'85 by Stiff Records. Dist: EMI, Record Services Distribution (Ireland)

FOLKSINGER.
Album: released on Stiff, Jan'86 by Stiff Records. Dist: EMI, Record Services Distribution (Ireland)

Album: released on Rhino (USA), Jan'86 by Rhino Records (USA).

LONESOME DEATH OF HAPPIE CARROLL.
Tracks: / Lonesome death of Happie Carroll / El Salvador.
Single (7"): released on Stiff, Mar'86 by Stiff Records. Dist: EMI, Record Services Distribution (Ireland)

Physical Blue

DAY OF GLORY.
Tracks: / Day of glory / Day of glory (instrumental).
Single (7"): released on MTG, Apr'86 Dist: MIS-EMI Distribution

Piacentini, Paul

OUT OF MY BOX.
Album: released on Acting School Again, Jul'85 Dist: Fast Forward, Cartel

Piaf, Edith

25 GREATEST HITS.
Album: released on EMI (Double-up), '73 by EMI Records. Dist: EMI

BEST OF VOL.1.
Tracks: / L'accordeoniste / C'etait une histoire / C'est toujours la meme histoire / Le disque use / Le petit monsieur triste / De l'autre cote de la rue / Mon legionnaire / C'etait un jour de fete / C'est lui que mon coeur a choisi / Entre saint-queen et clingnancourt / C'est un monsieur tres distinque / Ding din dan.
Notes: Compilation offering the very best of Paif's material. Recorded between 1936 and 1943. All original versions.
Album: released on Philips (France), Aug'86

Cassette: released on Philips (France), Aug'86

BEST OF VOL.2.
Tracks: / Y a pas d' printemps / Elle frequentait la rue pigalle / Mon amant de la coloniale / L'Julie jolie / Un jeune homme chantait / Fais-moi valser / J'entends la sirene / Le vagabond / L'entranger / Va danser / Tout fout le camp.
Notes: Compilation offering the very best of Piaf's material. Recorded between 1936 and 1943. All original versions.
Album: released on Philips (France), Aug'86

Cassette: Deleted Aug'86.

BOBINO 1963 - LES AMANTS.
Album: released on EMI (France), '83 by EMI Records. Dist: Conifer

COMPLETE PIAF.
Boxed set: released on EMI (France), '83 by EMI Records. Dist: Conifer

DE BRAVO LE CLOWN A J'M'EN FOUS PAS MAL.
Album: released on EMI (France), '83 by EMI Records. Dist: Conifer

DE L'ACCORDEONISTE A MILORD (VOL.2).
Tracks: / Les amants de venise / Johnny tu n'es pas un ange / Un etranger / C'est a Hambourg / Je hais les dimanches / C'est l'amour / Les amants des Paris / Pour moir tout seule / Le chevalier de Paris / L'homme au piano / C'est un gars / Bravo pour le clown.
Album: released on EMI (Italy), Sep'86 by EMI Records. Dist: Conifer

Cassette: released on EMI (Italy), Sep'86 by EMI Records. Dist: Conifer

Album: released on EMI (Italy), Sep'86 by EMI Records. Dist: Conifer

DE L'ACCORDEONISTE A MILORD.
Tracks: / L'accordeoniste / La vie en rose / Je sais comment / Mon dieul / Toi tu l'entends pas / Hymne a l'amour / Non, je ne regrette rien / Le trois cloches / Milord / La foule / A quoi ca sert l'amour / Con theo sarapo / Le droit d'aimer.
Album: released on EMI (France), '83 by EMI Records. Dist: Conifer

DISQUE D'OR (COLLECTION) VOL 2.
Album: released on EMI (France), '83 by EMI Records. Dist: Conifer

DISQUE D'OR (COLLECTION) VOL 1.
Album: released on EMI (France), '83 by EMI Records. Dist: Conifer

DROIT D'AIMER.
Album: released on EMI (France), '83 by EMI Records. Dist: Conifer

EDITH ET MARCEL.
Album: released on EMI (Double-up), May'83 by EMI Records. Dist: EMI

Cassette: released on EMI (Double-up), May'83 by EMI Records. Dist: EMI

EDITH PIAF.
Cassette: released on EMI, Jul'80 by EMI Records. Dist: EMI

EDITH PIAF - 60 MINUTES OF MUSIC.
Tracks: / Mon legionnaire / Les momes de la cloche / Je n'en connais pas la fin / La fanion de la legion / Les marins ca fait des voyages / Il riait / Madeleine Qu'avait du coeur / Embrasse-moi / Mon coeur est au coin d'une rue / L'Accordioniste / La Java en mnineur / Y'avait du soleil / Dans un bouge du vieux port / Ou sont-ils mes petits copains / Un monsieur me suit dans la rue / Les deux rengaines / On danse sur ma chanson.
Notes: Superb value on chrome tape. 60 minutes of Piaf's most popular songs including "L'Accordioniste" and " Mon Legionairre".
Cassette:

EDITH PIAF (83).
Album: released on EMI (France), '83 by EMI Records. Dist: Conifer

EDITH PIAF COLLECTION.
Album: released on Deja Vu, Jul'86 by Deja Vu Records. Dist: Counterpoint Distribution, Record Services Distribution (Ireland)

Cassette: released on Deja Vu, Jul'86 by Deja Vu Records. Dist: Counterpoint Distribution, Record Services Distribution (Ireland)

Compact disc: released on Deja Vu, Jul'87 by Deja Vu Records. Dist: Counterpoint Distribution, Record Services Distribution (Ireland)

EDITH PIAF (EMI FRANCE).
Album: released on EMI (France), Apr'83 by EMI Records. Dist: Conifer

Cassette: released on EMI (France), Apr'83 by EMI Records. Dist: Conifer

ENREGISTREMENTS ORIGINAUX.
Tracks: / La vien en rose / Bal dans ma rue / Bal dans ma rue / Je hais les dimanches / Padam...padam / Bravo pour le clown / Johnny, tu n'es pas un ange / Heureuse / Mea culpa / Serenade du pave / Un grand amour qui s'acheve / L'accordioniste / Le amants d'un jour / Marie la Francaise / La foule / Je sais comment / Le neiges de Finlande / Milord.
Compact disc: released on Pathe Marconi, Apr'87 Dist: Swift

GREATEST HITS:EDITH PIAF.
Album: released on Astan, Dec'85 by Astan Records. Dist: Counterpoint

HER LEGENDARY LIVE RECORDINGS.
Album: released on Columbia, Sep'79 by EMI Records. Dist: EMI

I REGRET NOTHING.
Album: released on Columbia, '71 by EMI Records. Dist: EMI

JE VOUS AIME Original cast recording.
Album: released on Pye, Jun'77

MON LEGIONNAIRE.
Album: released on Philips (France), Sep'84

Cassette: released on Philips (France), Sep'84

NON JE NE REGRETTE RIEN/NO REGRETS.
Single (7"): released on EMI, Oct'76 by EMI Records. Dist: EMI

OLYMPIA 1955/56.
Album: released on Encore, Mar'80 by EMI Records. Dist: EMI

OLYMPIA 1961 - NON, JE NE REGRETTE RIEN.
Album: released on EMI (France), '83 by EMI Records. Dist: Conifer

PIAF ALBUM, THE.
Album: released on EMI, Nov'83 by EMI Records. Dist: EMI

Cassette: released on EMI, Nov'83 by EMI Records. Dist: EMI

TWENTY FRENCH HIT SINGLES.
Album: released on Columbia, Mar'79 by EMI Records. Dist: EMI

VERY BEST OF EDITH PIAF.
Album: released on EMI, Aug'76 by EMI Records. Dist: EMI

Cassette: released on EMI, Aug'76 by EMI Records. Dist: EMI

VOLUME 3.
Tracks: / La Giyalante / Tes Beau' Tu Sais / Les Croix / Cri Du Colur / Padam Padam / C'est Un Homme Terribi / Exodus / Mea Culpa / Je Me Souviens D'une Chanson / Et Pourtant / Le Da Ira / Mon Manece A Mor.
Album: released on EMI (Italy), Dec'86 by EMI Records. Dist: Conifer

Cassette: released on EMI (Italy), Dec'86 by EMI Records. Dist: Conifer

VOLUME 4.
Tracks: / Mariagr / Qu'as Tu Tait John / Notre Dame De Parie / Monsieur et Madam / Pout Pourrt / Misericorde / Toi Qua Sais / Unde Dame / C'est Mer Vulletre / Sous Te Ciel De Paris.
Album: released on EMI (Italy), Dec'86 by EMI Records. Dist: Conifer

Cassette: released on EMI (Italy), Dec'86 by EMI Records. Dist: Conifer

Piano Blues

PIANO BLUES LEGENDS (Piano Blues Legends).
Album: released on JSP, Jun'83 by JSP Records. Dist: Swift, Projection

PIANO BLUES VOL.1 Paramount 1929-30 (Various Artists).
Album: released on Magpie, Sep'77 Dist: Projection

PIANO BLUES VOL.12 (Various Artists).
Album: released on Magpie, Oct'79 Dist: Projection

PIANO BLUES VOL.21 Unissued boogie 1938-1945 (Various Artists).
Album: released on Magpie, Jul'84 Dist: Projection

PIANO BLUES VOL.5 Hot Box.
Album: released on Magpie, Jul'78 Dist: Projection

Piano Jazz

PIANO JAZZ Boogie woogie pianists 1928-30 (Various Artists).
Album: released on Swaggie (Australia), Jan'83

Pianola Jazz

PIANOLA JAZZ (Various Artists).
Cassette: released on Saydisc, Jun'82 by Saydisc Records. Dist: Essex, Harmonia Mundi, Roots, H.R. Taylor, Jazz Music, Swift, Projection, Gamut

Pianola Ragtime

PIANOLA RAGTIME (Piano rolls 1895-1916) (Various Artists).
Album: released on Saydisc, Nov'82 by Saydisc Records. Dist: Essex, Harmonia Mundi, Roots, H.R. Taylor, Jazz Music, Swift, Projection, Gamut

Cassette: released on Saydisc, Nov'82 by Saydisc Records. Dist: Essex, Harmonia Mundi, Roots, H.R. Taylor, Jazz Music, Swift, Projection, Gamut

Piano Magic

PIANO MAGIC Over 80 rhapsodies of piano masterpieces (Various Artists).
Boxed set: released on Ronco, Nov'83

Cassette: released on Ronco, Nov'83

Piano Portraits

PIANO PORTRAITS.VOLUME ONE. Various artists (Various Artists).
Tracks: / You've got to be mordenistic / Pearls (The) / Early morning blues / Kacyee feeling / Time Square blues / Passionette / Nobody knows when you're down & out / Beautiful love / I've got my love to keep / I'm sober now / King porter stomp / What is this thing called love / Hot & bothered / Mr.Freddie blues / Morning air / Dive bomber.
Album: released on Affinity, Apr'86 by Charly Records. Dist: Charly, Cadillac

PIANO PORTRAITS.VOLUME 2 Various artists (Various Artists).
Notes: Artists:Pete Johnson,Mary Lou Williams,Johnny Guarnieri,Slim Gaillard,Cleo Brown,Count Basie,Ralph Sutton w.Eddie Condon's Band,Art Tatum. MONO.
Album: released on Affinity, Jul'86 by Charly Records. Dist: Charly, Cadillac

PIANO PORTRAITS VOLUME 3 Various artists (Various Artists).
Album: released on Affinity, Mar'87 by Charly Records. Dist: Charly, Cadillac

Piano Ragtime

PIANO RAGTIME OF THE 20'S & 30'S (Various Artists).
Album: released on Herwin, Feb'79 Dist: Jazz Music

Piano Red

AIN'T GOING TO BE YOUR LOW DOWN DOG NO MORE.
Album: released on Black Lion, Jul'87 by Black Lion Records. Dist: Jazz Music, Chris Wellard, Taylor, H.R., Counterpoint, Cadillac

DR. FEELGOOD.
Album: released on Black Lion, May'79 by Black Lion Records. Dist: Jazz Music, Chris Wellard, Taylor, H.R., Counterpoint, Cadillac

DR. FEELGOOD ALONE.
Album: released on Arhoolie, May'81 by Arhoolie Records. Dist: Projection, Topic, Jazz Music, Swift, Roots

ORIGINAL DR.FEELGOOD (THE).
Album: released on JSP, May'86 by JSP Records. Dist: Swift, Projection

BE A FOOL FOR YOU.
Single (7"): released on Plaza Plastic Co, Feb'81

Piano slim

MEAN WOMAN BLUES.
Album: released on Swingmaster, May'86 Dist: Jazz Music Distribution

Piano Solo

PIANO SOLO (Various Artists).
Tracks: / Laura / When I fall in love / Lady in red / Way we were, The / Smoke gets in your eyes / Love is a many splendoured thing / Moon river / Love story / Another suitcase, anither hall / Folks who live on the hill / Over the rainbow / Umbrellas of Cherbourg / Smile / Softly as I leave you / My way / Lara's theme / Feelings / One more night / As time goes by / Song for Guy / New York, New York.
Compact disc: released on The Collection, Apr'87 by Object Enterprises Ltd. Dist: Counterpoint Distribution

Piano & Swing

PIANO AND SWING (1935-1938).
Album: released on Pathe MarconiFrance), Sep'84

Piazolla, Astor

LIVE IN WEIN.
Album: released on Messidor (Germany), May'87 Dist: IMS Distribution, Polygram

Piazza,Rod

HARPBURN.
Album: released on Making Waves, Aug'86 by Making Waves Records.

Piazzola, Astor

LIVE IN VIENNA.
Tracks: / Fracanapa / Verano Porteno / Caliente / Decarisimo / Libertango / Revirado / Invierno porteno / Adios Nanina.
Album: released on Messidor (Germany), Jul'87 Dist: IMS Distribution, Polygram

Compact disc: released on Messidor (Germany), Jul'87 Dist: IMS Distribution, Polygram

Album: released on Messidor (Germany), Jul'87 Dist: IMS Distribution, Polygram

Picante, Salsa

AND SOMETIMES VOICES (see Fischer, Clare) (Picante, Salsa & Clare Fischer).

Picassos (the)

PICASSOS (THE).
Album: released on Technical, Nov'86 Dist: Stage One Distribution

Piccadilly Hotel Bands

PICCADILLY REVELS BANDS.
Album: released on World, Aug'77 Dist: Jetstar

Piccadilly nights

PICCADILLY NIGHTS(BRITISH DANCE BANDS OF THE 1920'S) Various bands (Various bands).
Tracks: / That girl over there / Swing on the gait / It's a million to one you're in love / What'll you do? / Make my cot where the cot cot cotton grows / How long has this been going on? / Miss Annabelle Lee / Lila / That's my weakness / Sunny skies / Matilda / Saskatchewan / Virginia(There's a blue ridge 'round my heart) / 's wonderful / Crazy rhythm / I'm a one-man girl / Spread a little happiness / Out of the dawn / Ida(Sweet as apple cider) / I don't know why I do it(but I do).
Notes: Mono.
Album: released on Halcyon (USA), Mar'86 by Halcyon Records (USA). Dist: Jazz Music, Conifer, Taylors

Pickens, Slim

FIDDLIN' FOOL, THE.
Album: released on Westwood, '82 by Westwood Records. Dist: Jazz Music, H.R. Taylor, JSU, Pinnacle, Ross Records

Pickett, Bobby 'Boris'

MONSTER MASH.
Single (7"): released on Decca, Feb'82 by Decca Records. Dist: Polygram

Single (7"): released on Old Gold, Oct'83 by Old Gold Records. Dist: Lightning, Jazz Music, Spartan, Counterpoint

Pickett, Charlie
ROUTE 33.
Album:

Pickett, Dan
1949 - COUNTRY BLUES.
Album: released on Krazy Kat (USA), Apr'87

Pickett, Lenny
LENNY PICKETT & THE BORNEO HORNS.
Album: released on Hannibal, Jul'87 by Hannibal Records. Dist: Charly, Harmonia Mundi, Projection, Celtic Music, Roots

Pickett, Phil
DESTINY.
Single (7"): released on MCA, Jul'84 by MCA Records. Dist: Polygram, MCA

Single (12"): released on MCA, Jul'84 by MCA Records. Dist: Polygram. MCA Deleted '85.

FAREWELL TO BERLIN.
Single (7"): released on BBC, Jul'83 by BBC Records & Tapes. Dist: EMI, PRT, Pye

Pickett, Wilson
BEST OF WILSON PICKETT.
Compact disc: released on Atlantic, Jul'87 by WEA Records. Dist: WEA

Album: released on Atlantic, Apr'82 by WEA Records. Dist: WEA

Cassette: by WEA Records. Dist: WEA Deleted Jul'84.

RIGHT TRACK, THE.
Album: released on EMI America, Mar'81 by EMI Records. Dist: EMI

Picketywitch
THAT SAME OLD FEELING.
Single (7"): released on Old Gold, Jan'85 by Old Gold Records. Dist: Lightning, Jazz Music, Spartan, Counterpoint

Pickford, Gary & Friends
WHY? (THE SONG).
Single (12"): released on Spartan, Dec'86 by Spartan Records. Dist: Spartan

WHY (THE SONG).
Tracks: / Why (The song) / Story, The.
Single (7"): released on Spartan, Nov'86 by Spartan Records. Dist: Spartan

Pickles, Lion John
WHAT'S THE MATTER WITH THE WORLD.
Single (7"): released on Future Earth, Oct'83 by Future Earth Records. Dist: Red Rhino, Cartel

Pick & The Malt Shovel
PICK & THE MALT SHOVEL (Various Artists).
Album: released on Tradition, Aug'76 Dist: JSU, Cassion Distribution, Celtic Music, Jazz Music, Projection, Roots

Pickwick Papers
PICKWICK PAPERS (Orchard, Julian).
Cassette: released on Pinnacle, '79 by Pinnacle Records. Dist: Pinnacle

Picky Picnic
HA HA TARACHINE.
Album: released on Atatak, Mar'86 by Atatak Records. Dist: Rough Trade, Cartel

DOORS ARE OPEN, THE.
Tracks: / Human outro / Eternal / Doors are open, the / East river / Success / We need protection / Little lady / Intro of human / Human / Clockwork blue / Heaven / All I need.
Album: released on Portrait, May'87 by CBS Records. Dist: CBS

Cassette: released on Portrait, May'87 by CBS Records. Dist: CBS

Compact disc: released on Portrait, May'87 by CBS Records. Dist: CBS

EAST RIVER.
Tracks: / East River / Clockwork blue.
Single (7"): released on Portrait, Jun'86 by CBS Records. Dist: CBS

Single (12"): released on Portrait, Jun'86 by CBS Records. Dist: CBS

SUCCESS.
Tracks: / Success / I wanna be.
Single (7"): released on Portrait, Mar'87 by CBS Records. Dist: CBS

Single (12"): released on Portrait, Mar'87 by

CBS Records. Dist: CBS

WE NEED PROTECTION.
Tracks: / We need protection / We need protection (Inst.) / We need protection (Mother mix) / Little lady.
Notes: 'We need protection' and 'Little lady' available on 12" version only.
Single (7"): released on Portrait, Feb'86 by CBS Records. Dist: CBS

Single (7"): released on Portrait, Feb'86 by CBS Records. Dist: CBS

Single (12"): released on Portrait, Feb'86 by CBS Records. Dist: CBS

Picnic Boys
WHITE HOTEL.
Single (7"): released on Challet, Nov'82 Dist: ILA

Picture
DIAMOND DREAMER.
Album: released on Back Door (Holland), Dec'83

ETERNAL DARK.
Album: released on Carrere America (USA), Jul'85 by Polygram

Album: released on Carrere America (USA), Jul'85 by Polygram.

HEAVY METAL EARS.
Album:

NIGHT HUNTER.
Album: released on Carrere America (USA), Jul'83 by Polygram

Cassette: released on Carrere America (USA), Jul'83 by Polygram.

TRAITOR.
Album: released on Mercury (Holland), Oct'85 by Phonogram Records. Dist: Polygram Distribution

Picture Frame Seduction
GOOD ENOUGH (FOR ME).
Single (7"): released on Soso, Jun'84 by Soso Records. Dist: Cartel

Picture Music
PICTURE MUSIC COMPILATION (Various Artists).
Video-cassette (VHS): released on PMI, Jun'86 by PMI Records. Dist: EMI

Video-cassette [Betamax]: released on PMI, Jun'86 by PMI Records. Dist: EMI

PICTURE MUSIC INSTRUMENTAL VOL.4 various artists (Various Artists).
Picture disc album: released on Sky (Germany), Oct'85

Pictures
PICTURES.
Album: released on E.G., Jul'83 by Virgin Records. Dist: Virgin, Soti

Pictures In A Dark Room
ANIMALS IN MUSIC, SPIDERS IN PIANOS.
Single (7"): released on Zone To Zone, '83 by Zone To Zone Records. Dist: Pinnacle

LOVE IS FIRE.
Single (7"): released on Zone To Zone, '83 by Zone To Zone Records. Dist: Pinnacle

Pictures In The Dark Room
VOLUNTEERS.
Single (7"): released on Tube, Jun'82 by Tony Hatch. Dist: Pinnacle

Pictures Like This
NIGHT VENDETTA.
Single (7"): released on T.W., Apr'83 by T.W. Records. Dist: Cartel

Pictures of Innocence
NO ONE CRYING.
Tracks: / No one crying / Love and war.
Single (7"): released on Little Prince, Oct'84 Dist: Probe, Cartel

Piece Of Steak
PIECE OF STEAK, A (Bryce, James).
Cassette: released on Colophone Audio Visual, Feb'81 by Audio-Visual Library Services. Dist: Audio-Visual Library Services

Pieces
COULD IT BE YOU (see Jones, Vivian) (Pieces/Vivian Jones).

PIECES.

WINNERS.
Single (7"): released on Pieces, Oct'83

Pieces Of A Dream
JOYRIDE.
Tracks: / Save some time for me / Say la la / I can give you want you want / Joyride / Love of my life / Careless whisper / Outside in / Winning streak / Sunshine.
Notes: Produced by Lenny White and Maurice White for Kalimba Productions.
Album: released on Manhattan, Aug'86 by President Records. Dist: Jazz Music, Swift, Taylors, Chris Wellard

Cassette: released on Manhattan, Aug'86 by President Records. Dist: Jazz Music, Swift, Taylors, Chris Wellard

PIECES OF A DREAM.
Album: released on WEA (Import), Jul'83

SAY LA LA.
Tracks: / Say la la / Outside in.
Single (7"): released on Manhattan, Jul'86 by EMI Records. Dist: EMI

Single (12"): released on Manhattan, Jul'86 by EMI Records. Dist: EMI

WARM WEATHER.
Single (7"): released on Elektra, Sep'82 by WEA Records. Dist: WEA

Single (12"): released on Elektra, Sep'82 by WEA Records. Dist: WEA

Pied Piper
PIED PIPER story tape (Various Artists).
Cassette: released on Tellastory, Oct'79 by Bartlett Bliss Productions. Dist: PRT Distribution, Hayward Promotions Distribution, H.R. Taylor Distribution

Pied Piper Of Hamelin
PIED PIPER OF HAMELIN & OTHER FAMOUS POEMS various artists (Various Artists).
Cassette: released on Tellastory, Jul'82 by Bartlett Bliss Productions. Dist: PRT Distribution, Hayward Promotions Distribution, H.R. Taylor Distribution

Compact disc: released on Statik, Oct'85 Dist: Rough Trade Distribution, Stage One Distribution

Pierce, Nat
1948-1950 (Pierce, Nat Orchestra).
Album: released on Zim, Apr'81 Dist: JSU, Jazz Horizons, Jazz Music, Swift

5400 NORTH (Pierce, Nat Quintet).
Album: released on Hep, Apr'81 by H.R. Taylor Records. Dist: Jazz Music, Cadillac Music, JSU, Taylors, Wellard, Chris, Zodiac, Swift, Fast Forward

BALLAD OF JAZZ STREET, (THE) (Pierce, Nat Orchestra).
Album: released on Hep, Feb'81 by H.R. Taylor Records. Dist: Jazz Music, Cadillac Music, JSU, Taylors, Wellard, Chris, Zodiac, Swift, Fast Forward

BOSTON BUSTOUT.
Album: released on Hep, Apr'81 by H.R. Taylor Records. Dist: Jazz Music, Cadillac Music, JSU, Taylors, Wellard, Chris, Zodiac, Swift, Fast Forward

Pierce, Webb
GREAT SONGS OF WEBB PIERCE, (THE).
Album: released on Bulldog Records, Jul'82

I AIN'T NEVER.
Album: released on Charly, Jul'84 by Charly Records. Dist: Charly, Cadillac

WEBB!.
Album: released on Stetson, Sep'86 by Hasmick Promotions Ltd.. Dist: Counterpoint Distribution, H.R. Taylor Distribution, Swift Distribution, Chris Wellard Distribution

Cassette: released on Stetson, Sep'86 by Hasmick Promotions Ltd.. Dist: Counterpoint Distribution, H.R. Taylor Distribution, Swift Distribution, Chris Wellard Distribution

CROSS COUNTRY.
Tracks: / Heartaches by the number / You are my life / Cry cry darlin' / Waterloo / Free of the blues / I'm letting you go / Take time / Someday you'll call my name / All my love / Crazy wild dreams / I'm falling in love with you / I close my eyes.
Album: released on Stetson, Nov'85 by Hasmick Promotions Ltd.. Dist: Counterpoint Distribution, H.R. Taylor Distribution, Swift Distribution, Chris Wellard Distribution

---

Album: released on United Artists, Nov'79

Cassette: released on Stetson, Nov'86 by Hasmick Promotions Ltd.. Dist: Counterpoint Distribution, H.R. Taylor Distribution, Swift Distribution, Chris Wellard Distribution

Pierre, Marie
LOVE AFFAIR.
Album: released on Trojan, '83 by Trojan Records. Dist: PRT, Jetstar

WALK AWAY.
Single (7"): released on Trojan, Apr'82 by Trojan Records. Dist: PRT, Jetstar

Single (12"): released on Trojan, Apr'82 by Trojan Records. Dist: PRT, Jetstar

Pigalle, Anne
PIED PIPER OF HAMELIN/UGLY DUCKLING various artists (Various Artists).
Extended-play record: released on Mr.Pickwick, Aug'83 Dist: H.R. Taylor Distribution

Pied Pipers
GOOD DEAL MACNEAL 1944-1946.
Notes: MONO.
Album: released on Hep, Sep'86 by H.R. Taylor Records. Dist: Jazz Music, Cadillac Music, JSU, Taylors, Wellard, Chris, Zodiac, Swift, Fast Forward

Pie'n'Ears
CUSTARD PIE SONG.
Single (7"): released on Towerbell, Nov'81 by Towerbell Records. Dist: EMI

Pienkowski, Jan
MEG ON THE MOON (Pienkowski, Jan & Helen Nicoll).

MEG'S EGGS (Pienkowski, Jan & Helen Nicoll).

Pierce, Billie & DeDe
NEW ORLEANS MUSIC.
Album: released on Arhoolie, Jan'87 by Arhoolie Records. Dist: Projection, Topic, Jazz Music, Swift, Roots

Album: released on Arhoolie, May'81 by Arhoolie Records. Dist: Projection, Topic, Jazz Music, Swift, Roots

Pierce, Billy
WILLIAM THE CONQUEROR.
Compact disc: released on Sunnyside (USA), Feb'87 Dist: Mole Jazz Distribution, Conifer Distribution

Pierce, Billy Quartet
WILLIAM THE CONQUEROR.
Tracks: / Blue nostalgia / Pannonica / Color blind / Over the edge / William the Conqueror / Sudan blue / We'll be together / Nature folk-song.
Album: released on Sunnyside (USA), Feb'86 Dist: Mole Jazz Distribution, Conifer Distribution

Pierce, Jeffrey Lee
FLAMINGO (EP).
:

LOVE & DESPERATION.
Single (7"): released on Statik, Aug'85 Dist: Rough Trade Distribution, Stage One Distribution

Single (12"): released on Statik, Aug'85 Dist: Rough Trade Distribution, Stage One Distribution

WILDWEED.
Tracks: / Sensitivity / Hey Juana / Love Circus / Wildweed / Midnight promise (The) / Fertility Goddess (The) / Open The Door / Osiris / Portrait Of The Sticks In Hell / Chris & Maggie meet blind Willie McTell at... / Love & Desperation (Long & Short Versions) / Sex Killer / Cleopatra Dreams On / From Temptation To You.
Compact disc: released on Statik, Dec'86 Dist: Rough Trade Distribution, Stage One Distribution

Album: released on Statik, Oct'85 Dist: Rough Trade Distribution, Stage One Distribution

Cassette: released on Statik, Oct'85 Dist: Rough Trade Distribution, Stage One Distribution

EVERYTHING COULD BE SO PERFECT.
Album: released on ZTT, Oct'85 by Island Records. Dist: Polygram

Cassette: released on ZTT, Oct'85 by Island Records. Dist: Polygram

HE STRANGER.
Single (7"): released on ZTT, Apr'85 by Island Records. Dist: Polygram

Single (12"): released on ZTT, Apr'85 by Island Records. Dist: Polygram

---

WHY DOES IT HAVE TO BE THIS WAY.
Single (7"): released on ZTT, Nov'85 by Island Records. Dist: Polygram

Single (12"): released on ZTT, Nov'85 by Island Records. Dist: Polygram

Pig Bag
BIG BEAN, (THE).
Single (7"): released on Y, Jun'82

DR HECKLE & MR JIVE.
Album: released on Y, Mar'82

GETTING UP.
Single (7"): released on Y, Jan'81

Single (12"): released on Y, Feb'82

HIT THE 'O' DECK.
Single (7"): released on Y, Feb'83

Single (12"): released on Y, Feb'83

LEND AN EAR.
Album: released on Y, Feb'83

Cassette: released on Y, Feb'83

PAPA'S GOT A BRAND NEW PIG BAG.
Single (7"): released on Y, Mar'82

Single (12"): released on Y, Mar'82

PIG BAG - LIVE.
Album: released on Y, Jun'83

Cassette: released on Y, Jun'83

SUNNY DAY.
Single (7"): released on Y, Oct'81

Pig bros
BLUBBERHOUSE EP, THE.
Single (12"): released on Vinyl Drip, Nov'85 Dist: Backs, Cartel

CHEAP LIFE.
Tracks: / Cheap life / In doubt / Bad attitude / Bad attitude.
Single (12"): released on Backs, Sep'86 by Backs Records. Dist: Backs, Cartel

Pig, Clive
ONE NIGHT IN GREECE WITH AN AMERICAN.
Single (12"): released on Pig Enterprises, May'85 Dist: Rough Trade, Cartel

TIME TO GET TOUGH.
Album: released on Waldo's, Sep'83 by Waldo's Records. Dist: Pinnacle

Pigeon, Fred
BONNY BREAST, THE.
Cassette: released on Folktracks, Nov'79 by Folktracks Cassettes. Dist: Folktracks

Pigg, Billy
BORDER MINSTREL, THE.
Album: released on Leader, '81 Dist: Jazz Music, Projection

Piggleswick Folk
PIG .N THE MIDDLE.
Album: released on Acorn, Jun'79 Dist: Folksound, Jazz Music

Pig, Martin
LOVELY RITA.
Single (7"): released on R. Trade, Jun'83 by Rough Trade Records. Dist: Rough Trade Distribution

Pigor Och Drangar
PIGOR OCH DRANGAR.
Album: released on Phontastic (Sweden), '82 by Wellard, Chris Distribution. Dist: Wellard, Chris Distribution

Pigwig
PIGWIG.
Cassette: released on Look & Listen, Nov'84 by Listen For Pleasure. Dist: EMI

PIGWIG AND THE PIRATES.
Cassette: released on Look & Listen, Nov'84 by Listen For Pleasure. Dist: EMI

Pike, Dave
DAVE PIKE,VIBES WITH CEDAR WALTON TRIO.
Album: released on Criss Cross, Jul'86 Dist: Jazz Music, Jazz Horizons, Cadillac

LET THE MINSTRELS PLAY ON.
Album: released on Muse, Apr'81 by Peerless Records. Dist: Lugtons Distributors

PIKE'S GROOVE (Pike, Dave/Cedar Walton Trio.)
Album: released on Criss Cross Jazz, Jan'87 Dist: Jazz Music, Jazz Horizons

TIMES OUT OF MIND.
Album: released on Muse, Apr'81 by Peerless Records. Dist: Lugtons Distributors

PIL
FLOWERS OF ROMANCE.
Album: released on Virgin, Mar'84 by Virgin Records. Dist: EMI, Virgin Distribution

Cassette: released on Virgin, Mar'84 by Virgin Records. Dist: EMI, Virgin Distribution

PARIS IN THE SPRING.
Album: released on Virgin, Mar'84 by Virgin Records. Dist: EMI, Virgin Distribution

Cassette: released on Virgin, Mar'84 by Virgin Records. Dist: EMI, Virgin Distribution

SEATTLE.
Single (7"): released on Virgin, Aug'87 by Virgin Records. Dist: EMI, Virgin Distribution

Single (12"): released on Virgin, Aug'87 by Virgin Records. Dist: EMI, Virgin Distribution

Cassette single: released on Virgin, Aug'87 by Virgin Records. Dist: EMI, Virgin Distribution

THIS IS NOT A LOVE SONG.
Single (7"): released on Virgin, Aug'83 by Virgin Records. Dist: EMI, Virgin Distribution

Single (12"): released on Virgin, Aug'83 by Virgin Records. Dist: EMI, Virgin Distribution

THIS IS WHAT YOU WANT..THIS IS WHAT YOU GET.
Album: released on Virgin, Jul'84 by Virgin Records. Dist: EMI, Virgin Distribution

Pilditch, Colin
TAKE A HAND.
Single (7"): released on Thunderbay, Jan'83 Dist: Spartan Distribution

Piledriver
METAL INQUISITION.
Album: released on Roadrunner (Dutch), Sep'85 Dist: Pinnacle

STAY UGLY.
Album: released on Roadrunner (Dutch), Jul'86 Dist: Pinnacle

Pilgrim
PILGRIM (Various Artists).
Album: released on Tara (Ireland), Mar'84 by Tara Records. Dist: I & B Records Distribution, Record Services Distribution (Ireland), Roots Distribution

Pilgrim, Billy
THEY ARE COMING TO GET US.
Single (7"): released on Zone To Zone, '83 by Zone To Zone Records. Dist: Pinnacle

Pilgrim Jubilee
OLD SHIP OF ZION.
Album: released on MCA (USA). Jun'84

Pilkington,Foster
IN THE TOWN OF FORGOTTEN TALENT.
Tracks: / In the town of forgotten talent / Last tango.
Single (7"): released on Rockin' Horse, Mar'86 by Arista Records. Dist: RCA Distribution

Single (12"): released on Rockin' Horse, Mar'86 by Arista Records. Dist: RCA Distribution

LISTENING LAND.
Tracks: / Listening land / Art of being shy (The).
Single (7"): released on Rockin' Horse, Jul'86 by Arista Records. Dist: RCA Distribution

Single (12"): released on Rockin' Horse, Jul'86 by Arista Records. Dist: RCA Distribution

Pillar, Michele
LOOK WHO LOVES YOU NOW.
Album: released on Birdwing, Feb'85 by Word Records. Dist: Word Distribution

Cassette: released on Birdwing, Feb'85 by Word Records. Dist: Word Distribution

Pillow, Ray
ONE TOO MANY MEMORIES.
Album: released on Allegiance, Apr'84 by PRT Records. Dist: PRT

Cassette: released on Allegiance, Apr'84 by PRT Records. Dist: PRT

Pillows & Prayers
PILLOWS & PRAYERS (A Cherry Red compilation 1982-3).
Album: released on Cherry Red, Nov'82 by Cherry Red Records. Dist: Pinnacle

Album: released on Cherry Red, Mar'83 by Cherry Red Records. Dist: Pinnacle

Pilot
BEST OF PILOT.
Album: released on EMI, Oct'80 by EMI Records. Dist: EMI

JANUARY.
Tracks: / January / Magic.
Notes: Also contains:"Magic" by Pilot
Single (7"): released on Old Gold, Apr'87 by Old Gold Records. Dist: Lightning, Jazz Music, Spartan, Counterpoint

Pilot Error
PILOT ERROR.
Cassette: released on Cockpit, Apr'84 Dist: Vibes

Piltdown Men
PILTDOWN RIDES AGAIN.
Tracks: / Piltdown rides again / Macdonalds cave.
Single (7"): released on Old Gold, Mar'87 by Old Gold Records. Dist: Lightning, Jazz Music, Spartan, Counterpoint

Pincher
AGONY.
Single (12"): released on Live & Love, Feb'87 by Third World Records. Dist: Jetstar

Pinchers
ABRACADABRA.
Tracks: / Abracadabra / Trouble and problem.
Single (12"): released on Blue Trac, Jun'86 by Blue Mountain Records. Dist: Jetstar

GOT TO BE ME.
Album: released on Live & Love, May'87 by Third World Records. Dist: Jetstar

LIFT IT UP AGAIN.
Album: released on Vienna, Jun'87

ROUGH NECK.
Tracks: / Rough neck / Rough neck (version).
Single (12"): released on Revelationary Sound, Jun'87 by Revelationary Sound Records. Dist: Jetstar

SIT DOWN PON IT.
Tracks: / Sit down pon it / Sit down pon it (version).
Single (12"): released on Live & Love, Mar'87 by Third World Records. Dist: Jetstar

Pineapple Party
WALK AWAY.
Single (7"): released on Anubis, May'85 by Spartan

Pine,Courtney
CHILDREN OF THE GHETTO.
Tracks: / Children of the ghetto / E.F.P. / When,where,how and why / Children of the ghetto / E.S.P. / Courtney Pine talks to Robert Elms (Part 1).
Single (7"): released on Island, Oct'86 by Island Records. Dist: Polygram

Single (12"): released on Island, Oct'86 by Island Records. Dist: Polygram

Cassette single: released on Island, Nov'86 by Island Records. Dist: Polygram

JOURNEY TO THE URGE WITHIN.
Compact disc: released on Island, Nov'86 by Island Records. Dist: Polygram

JOURNEY TO THE URGE WITHIN.
Tracks: / Mis-interpret / I believe / Peace / Delores / As we would say / Children of the ghetto / When,where,how and why / C.G.C. / Seen / Sunday song.
Album: released on Island, Oct'86 by Island Records. Dist: Polygram

Cassette: released on Island, Oct'86 by Island Records. Dist: Polygram

Compact disc: released on Island, Oct'86 by Island Records. Dist: Polygram

Pinewood
HEARTACHE & PROMISES.
Album: released on Folk Heritage, Jul'82 by Folk Heritage Records. Dist: Roots, Wynd-Up Distribution, Jazz Music, Folk Heritage

Pinhas, Richard
CHRONOLYSE.
Album: released on Cobra, May'79 by Cobra Records. Dist: Projection, EMI

RHIZOSPERE.
Album: released on Cobra, Sep'79 by Cobra Records. Dist: Projection, EMI

Pink
SOUL FIGHT.
Tracks: / Soul fight / Ramon night / Jin Taiho-shizukiyo.
Single (7"): released on Rime, Nov'86 Dist: DMS-RCA

Single (12"): released on Rime, Nov'86 Dist: DMS-RCA

Album: released on Making Waves, Aug'86 by Making Waves Records.

Pink and Black
SOMETIMES I WISH.
Single (12"): released on Illuminated, Feb'85 by IKF Records. Dist: Pinnacle, Cartel, Jetstar

Pinkees
DANGER GAMES.
Single (7"): released on Creole, Aug'82 by Creole Records. Dist: Rhino, PRT

GONNA BE LONELY AGAIN.
Single (7"): released on Creole, May'82 by Creole Records. Dist: Rhino, PRT

HOLDING ME TIGHT.
: released on Creole, Nov'82 by Creole Records. Dist: Rhino, PRT

I'LL BE THERE.
Single (7"): released on Creole, Feb'83 by Creole Records. Dist: Rhino, PRT

PINKEES, THE.
Album: released on Creole, Nov'82 by Creole Records. Dist: Rhino, PRT

Cassette: released on Creole, Nov'82 by Creole Records. Dist: Rhino, PRT

Pinkertons Assorted...
MIRROR.
Single (7"): released on Old Gold, Oct'83 by Old Gold Records. Dist: Lightning, Jazz Music, Spartan, Counterpoint

MIRROR MIRROR.
Single (7"): released on Decca, Apr'82 by Decca Records. Dist: Polygram

Pink Fairies
LIVE AT THE ROUNDHOUSE.
Album: released on Big Beat, Jul'82 by Ace Records. Dist: Projection, Pinnacle

NEVER NEVER LAND.
Album: released on Polydor, '74 by Polydor Records. Dist: Polygram, Polydor

PREVIOUSLY UNRELEASED.
Album: released on Big Beat, Oct'84 by Ace Records. Dist: Projection, Pinnacle

WHAT A BUNCH OF SWEETIES.
Album: released on Polydor, '74 by Polydor Records. Dist: Polygram, Polydor

Pink Flamingos
HIT THE DECK.
Single (12"): released on Prophet, Jul'85 by Prophet Records. Dist: Pinnacle

Pink Floyd
ANIMALS.
Tracks: / Pigs on the wing (Part One) / Dogs / Pigs (Three different ones) / Sheep / Pigs in the wing (Part two).
Compact disc: released on Harvest, Jul'86 by EMI Records. Dist: Roots, EMI

ANOTHER BRICK IN THE WALL.
Single (7"): released on Harvest, Nov'79 by EMI Records. Dist: Roots, EMI

ATOM HEART MOTHER.
Tracks: / Rise and shine / Sunny side up / Morning glory / Remergence / Father's shout / Breast milky / Mother fore / Funky dung / Mind your throats please / If / Summer 68 / Fat old sun / Alan's psychedelic breakfast.
Compact disc: released on EMI, Mar'87 by EMI Records. Dist: Roots, EMI

COLLECTION OF DANCE SONGS (A).
Tracks: / One of these days / Money / Money / Shine on you crazy diamond / Wish you were here / Another brick in the wall Part 2.
Notes: A unique compilation of the 'hits' of Pink Floyd. Every track a classic including 'Money'(Originally from 'Dark Side Of The Moon'),'Sheep'(from'Animals'),'Shine On You Crazy Diamond'(from 'Wish You Were Here') and 'Another Brick In The Wall',their only No.1 single in almost 20 years. This is,in effect,a greatest hits package.
Album: released on Fame, Nov'85 by Music For Pleasure Records. Dist: EMI

Cassette: released on Fame, Nov'85 by Music For Pleasure Records. Dist: EMI

DARK SIDE OF THE MOON.
Tracks: / Speak to me / Breath in the air / On the run / Time / Time / Great gig in the sky (The) / Money / Us and them / Any colour you like / Brain damage / Eclipse.
Album: released on Harvest, Apr'73 by EMI Records. Dist: Roots, EMI

Cassette: released on Harvest, Apr'73 by EMI Records. Dist: Roots, EMI

Compact disc: released on Harvest, Apr'73 by EMI Records. Dist: Roots, EMI

FINAL CUT.
Tracks: / Postwar dream / Your possible / One of the few / Hero's return / Gunner's dream / Paranoid eyes / Get your filthy hands off my desert / Fletcher memorial home / Southampton dock / Final cut / Not now John / Two suns in the desert.
Compact disc: released on Harvest, '86 by EMI Records. Dist: Roots, EMI

FINAL CUT, THE (VIDEO).
Notes: Inc. 'Not now John', 'The gunner's dream'
Video-cassette (VHS): released on Video Collection, May'87 by Video Collection International Ltd.. Dist: Counterpoint

FREE FOUR.
Single (7"): released on Lightning, '80 by Lightning Records. Dist: Jetstar

LEARNING TO FLY.
Tracks: / Learning to fly (Edited version) / One slip (Edited version) / Terminal frost (Album version) / Terminal frost (Dyol Version) / Learning to fly.
Compact disc: released on EMI, Aug'87 by EMI Records. Dist: EMI

MASTERS OF ROCK VOL.1.
Album: released on EMI (Germany), '83 by EMI Records. Dist: Conifer

MEDDLE.
Tracks: / One of these days / Pillow of winds (A) / Fearless (interpolating) / You'll never walk alone / San Tropez.
Notes: Originally released in November 1971
Album: released on Harvest, '85 by EMI Records. Dist: Roots, EMI

Cassette: released on Harvest, '85 by EMI Records. Dist: Roots, EMI

Compact disc: released on Harvest, '85 by EMI Records. Dist: Roots, EMI

MOMENTARY LAPSE OF REASON, A.
Tracks: / Signs of life / Learning to fly / Dogs of war, The / One slip / On the turning away / Yet another movie / Round and around / New machine, A (part 1) / Terminal frost / New machine (part 2) / Sorrow / Yet another movie / Round and around / New machine part 1, A / Terminal frost / New machine part 2, A / Sorrow / Signs of life / Leaning to fly / Dogs of war, The / One slip / On the turning away.
Compact disc: released on EMI, Sep'87 by EMI Records. Dist: EMI. Estim retail price in Sep'87 was £11.99.

Album: released on EMI, 7 Sep'87 by EMI Records. Dist: EMI

Cassette: released on EMI, 7 Sep'87 by EMI Records. Dist: EMI

MONEY.
Single (7"): released on EMI (France), Apr'83 by EMI Records. Dist: Conifer

MORE.
Tracks: / Cirrus minor / Nile song, The / Crying song / Up the Khyber / Green is the colour / Cymbaline / Party sequence / Party sequence / Main theme / Ibiza bar / More blues / Quicksilver / Spanish piece, A / Dramatic theme.
Compact disc: released on EMI, Mar'87 by EMI Records. Dist: EMI

NICE PAIR, A.
Album: released on Harvest, Dec'73 by EMI Records. Dist: Roots, EMI

Cassette: released on Harvest, Dec'73 by EMI Records. Dist: Roots, EMI

NOT NOW JOHN.
Single (7"): released on Harvest, May'83 by EMI Records. Dist: Roots, EMI

Single (12"): released on Harvest, May'83 by EMI Records. Dist: Roots, EMI

OBSCURED BY CLOUDS.
Tracks: / Obscured by clouds / When you're in / Burning bridges / Gold it's in the, The / Wots...uh the deal / Mudmen / Childhood's end / Free four / Stay / Absolutely curtains.
Compact disc: released on EMI, Mar'87 by EMI Records. Dist: EMI

ONE OF THESE DAYS.
Single (7"): by Lightning Records. Dist: Jetstar

PINK FLOYD: INTERVIEW PICTURE DISC.
Album: released on Baktabak, Apr'87 by Baktabak Records. Dist: Arabesque

PIPER AT THE GATES OF DAWN.
Album: released on Fame (Columbia), May'83 by Music For Pleasure Records. Dist: EMI

Cassette: released on Fame (Columbia), May'83 by Music For Pleasure Records. Dist: EMI

POINT ME AT THE SKY.
Single (7"): released on Lightning, '80 by Lightning Records. Dist: Jetstar

RELICS.
Album: released on MFP, Jan'79 by EMI Records. Dist: EMI

Cassette: released on MFP, Jan'79 by EMI Records. Dist: EMI

SAUCERFUL OF SECRETS, A.
Tracks: / Let there be more light / Remember a day / Set the controls for the heart of the sun / Corporal Clegg / Saucerful of secrets (A) / Seesaw.
Compact disc: released on EMI, Jan'87 by EMI Records. Dist: EMI

Album: released on Fame, Aug'86 by Music For Pleasure Records. Dist: EMI

Cassette: released on Fame, Aug'86 by Music For Pleasure Records. Dist: EMI

Album: released on Liberty, Jun'85 by Liberty-United. Dist: EMI

Cassette: released on Liberty, Jun'85 by Liberty-United. Dist: EMI

SHINE ON YOU CRAZY DIAMOND.
Single (7"): released on Lightning, '80 by Lightning Records. Dist: Jetstar

UMMAGUMMA.
Tracks: / Astronomy domine / Careful with that axe, Eugene / Set the controls for the heart of the sun / Saucerful of secrets, A / Sysyphus (parts 1-4) / Grantchester meadows / Several species of small furry animals gathered together... / Narrow way, The / Grand Vizier's garden party, The.
Compact disc: released on EMI, Mar'87 by EMI Records. Dist: EMI

VIDEO EP.
Video-cassette (VHS): released on PMI, '86 by PMI Records. Dist: EMI

Video-cassette [Betamax]: released on PMI, '86 by PMI Records. Dist: EMI

WALL (THE).
Tracks: / In The Flesh / Thin Ice (the) / Another Brick In the Wall / Happiest Days of Our Lives / Another Brick In the Wall Part 2 / Mother / Goodbye Blue Sky / Empty Spaces / Young Lust / One Of My Turns / Don't Leave Me Now / Another Brick In the Wall Part 3 / Goodbye Cruel World / Hey You! / Is There Anybody Out There? / Nobody Home / Comfortably Numb / Show Must Go On (The) / In The Flesh / Run Like Hell / Waiting For The Worms / Stop! / Trial (The) / Outside The Wall.
Double Album: released on Harvest, Dec'79 by EMI Records. Dist: Roots, EMI

Cassette: released on Harvest, Dec'79 by EMI Records. Dist: Roots, EMI

Compact disc: by EMI Records. Dist: Roots, EMI

WHEN THE TIGERS BROKE FREE.
Single (7"): released on Harvest, Jul'82 by EMI Records. Dist: Roots, EMI

WISH YOU WERE HERE.
Tracks: / Shine on you crazy diamond (Parts 1-9) / Welcome to the machine / Have a cigar / Wish you were here.
Album: released on Harvest, '75 by EMI Records. Dist: Roots, EMI

Cassette: released on Harvest, '75 by EMI Records. Dist: Roots, EMI

Compact disc: released on Harvest, '75 by EMI Records. Dist: Roots, EMI

Pink grease

PINK GREASE Various artists (Various Artists).
Album: released on Ensign, Mar'79 by Ensign Records. Dist: CBS Distribution

Pinkie & His Band

BURN THE CITADEL DOWN.
Extended-play record: released on Fluffy, Mar'85 by Fluffy. Dist: Revolver, Cartel

Pink Industry

LOW TECHNOLOGY.
Album: released on Zulu, Mar'83 by Zulu Records. Dist: Rough Trade

NEW BEGINNINGS.
Album: released on Zulu, Jun'85 by Zulu Records. Dist: Rough Trade

WHAT I WOULDN'T GIVE.
Single (7"): released on Zulu, Jun'85 by Zulu Records. Dist: Rough Trade

WHO TOLD YOU YOU WERE NAKED.
Album: released on Zulu, Oct'83 by Zulu Records. Dist: Rough Trade

Pinkney, Bill

LIVE (BILL PINKNEY) (Pinkney, Bill & The Original Drifters).
Album: released on Bulldog, Sep'82 by Bulldog Records. Dist: President Distribution, Spartan, Swift, Taylor, H.R.

Cassette: released on Bulldog, Nov'82 by Bulldog Records. Dist: President Distribution, Spartan, Swift, Taylor, H.R.

Pinkney, Fayette

ONE DEGREE.
Album: released on Chopper, Jul'79 by Chopper Records. Dist: Polygram

Pink Panther

PINK PANTHER - HENRY MANCINI Original Soundtrack.
Album: released on RCA (France), Apr'84 by RCA Records. Dist: Discovery

Cassette: released on RCA (France), Apr'84 by RCA Records. Dist: Discovery

Pink Peg Slacks

BELTING OUT A TUNA.
Album: released on Half Cut, '86 Dist: Red Rhino, Cartel

DRIPPING My love for you.
Single (7"): released on Black Fish, Mar'84 by Black Fish Records. Dist: Red Rhino, Cartel

SELF PITYING.
Single (7"): released on Half Cut, Jan'85 Dist: Red Rhino, Cartel

SOUND OF THE MEANWOOD VALLEY.
Single (12"): released on Half Cut, Jan'87 Dist: Red Rhino, Cartel

Pink Project

DISCO PROJECT MEDLEY.
Single (7"): released on Baby, Feb'83 by New Rose Records. Dist: Cartel

Single (12"): released on Baby, Feb'83 by New Rose Records. Dist: Cartel

Pink Rhythm

INDIA.
Single (7"): released on Beggars Banquet, Sep'85 by Beggars Banquet Records. Dist: WEA

Single (12"): released on Beggars Banquet, Sep'85 by Beggars Banquet Records. Dist: WEA

Pink Umbrellas

RASPBERRY RAINBOWS.
Single (7"): released on Ready Steady Go, Apr'83

Pinnock, Delroy

I DON'T KNOW WHY.
Single (7"): released on Solid Groove, Nov'81 Dist: Jetstar, Pinnacle

Pinnock, Dennis

IN AND OUT OF LOVE.
Tracks: / In and out of love dub disco.
Single (12"): released on Disco Tex, Feb'87 by Disco Tex Records. Dist: Jetstar

Pinocchio

PINOCCHIO (Various Artists).
Album: released on Disney, Oct'84 by BBC Records & Tapes. Dist: BBC Records & Tapes, PRT

Album: released on Disneyland, Dec'82 by WEA Records. Dist: WEA

Cassette: released on Disneyland, Dec'82 by WEA Records. Dist: WEA

Album: released on Disneyland, Dec'82 by WEA Records. Dist: WEA

Picture disc album: released on Disneyland, Dec'82 by WEA Records. Dist: WEA

Cassette: released on Pickwick (Tell-a-tale), '83 by Pickwick Records. Dist: Pickwick Distribution

WHEN YOU WISH UPON A STAR.
Tracks: / When you wish upon a star / I've got no strings.
Single (7"): released on BBC, '86 by BBC Records & Tapes. Dist: EMI, PRT, Pye

Pinochio

C.COLLODI.
Notes: For full information see under "Collodi,C"

Pinpoint

WAKING UP TO MORNING.
Single (7"): released on Albion, Sep'80 by Albion Records. Dist: Spartan, Pinnacle

YO YO.
Single (7"): released on Albion, Jan'81 by Albion Records. Dist: Spartan, Pinnacle

Pinter, Harold

NO MAN'S LAND various artists (Various Artists).
Cassette: released on Caedmon(USA), Apr'83 by Caedmon (USA) Records. Dist: Gower, Taylors, Discovery

Pintev, Stefan

MORNING SUN.
Tracks: / Morning sun / Let there be some love.
Single (7"): released on Memoir, '86 by Memoir Records. Dist: PRT Distribution

Pioneers

LONG SHOT KICK THE BUCKET.
Single (7"): released on Old Gold, Apr'83 by Old Gold Records. Dist: Lightning, Jazz Music, Spartan, Counterpoint

PUSHER MAN.
Album: released on Trojan, Sep'81 by Trojan Records. Dist: PRT, Jetstar

REGGAE FOR LOVERS.
Album: released on Vista Sounds, Mar'84 by Vista Sounds Records. Dist: Jetstar

REGGAE FOR LOVERS VOL.1.
Album: released on Vista Sounds, '83 by Vista Sounds Records. Dist: Jetstar

REGGAE IN LONDON CITY.
Tracks: / Reggae in London city / My woman.
Single (7"): released on Trojan, '86 by Trojan Records. Dist: PRT, Jetstar

Single (12"): released on Trojan, '86 by Trojan Records. Dist: PRT, Jetstar

ROCK MY SOUL.
Single (7"): released on Creole, Apr'85 by Creole Records. Dist: Rhino, PRT

WHAT A FEELING.
Album: released on Pioneer International, May'85 by Pioneer International Records. Dist: Jetstar

Pioneers of French Jazz

PIONEERS OF FRENCH JAZZ 1906-31 (Various Artists).
Album: released on Pathe MarconiFrance), Sep'84

Pipe Dreams

QUICK SILVER.
Single (7"): released on Design Communications, Nov'83

Single (12"): released on Design Communications, Nov'83

Pipes...

CEILIDH LINES (Pipes & Drums:1st Bn. Queen's Own Highlanders).
Tracks: / Monte Catarelto / Murdo Mackenzie of Blughasary / Banks of the Skiach, THe / Balmoral highlanders, The / Atholl cummers, The / Brown haired maiden, The / Cutting bracken / Spirits of Old Pulteney, The / Modder river / Bridge of bogie / Kissing reel, The / O'rourkes / Black mill, The / Swallows tail, The / Raigmore / Single petre, The / Alex Robertson's limp / Shona's jig / Lads from Glendale, The / Shawbost is dear to me / Leaving Barra / Kiss me sweetheart / Old favourite, The / One horned cow / Gudgeon of Morris's motorcar, The / Four courts, The / Lillie Long-Wades welcome to Inverness / Eighth army, The / An Eileen Ard / Macphail of Bunnessan / Hills of Kintail / Redcoat, The / Yesterhouse / Gravel walk, The / Rakish paddy / Scarce o'tatties / Rabs loon / Ceilidh lines / Robertson's lament / Kyly Alexander / Weaver, The / Paddy be easy / Foxhunter, The / Angelena's lullaby / Wee man from South Uist, The / Hi ho hirum / Kiwi, The / Cromdale hornpipe, The / Dick Gossips / Maid beyond the bar, The.
Album: released on Grasmere, Aug'87 by Grasmere Records. Dist: EMI

Cassette: released on Grasmere, Aug'87 by Grasmere Records. Dist: EMI

PIPES & DRUMS OF SCOTLAND (Various Artists).
Album: released on Lochshore, Apr'85 by Klub Records. Dist: PRT

Cassette: released on Lochshore, Apr'85 by Klub Records. Dist: PRT

PIPES & STRINGS OF SCOTLAND (Various Artists).
Compact disc: released on Scotdisc, Dec'86 Dist: Clyde Factors Distributors

PIPES & STRINGS OF SCOTLAND.VOL.2. Various artists (Various Artists).
Album: released on Country House, '85 by BGS Productions Ltd. Dist: Taylor, H.R., Record Merchandisers Distribution, Pinnacle, Sounds of Scotland Records

Cassette: released on Country House, '85 by BGS Productions Ltd. Dist: Taylor, H.R., Record Merchandisers Distribution, Pinnacle, Sounds of Scotland Records

Pipe, Spoon, Pot & Jug

PIPE, SPOON, POT & JUG 14 jazz vocals (Various Artists).
Album: released on Stash (Import), Apr'81 Dist: Swift Distribution, Jazz Music Distribution, Jazz Horizons Distribution, Celtic Music Distribution, Cadillac, JSU Distribution, Zodiac Distribution

Pipkins

GIMME DAT DING.
Single (7"):

Pippanannakim

CASTLES IN THE AIR.
Single (7"): released on Dakota, Jun'84 by Dakota Records. Dist: PRT

Pips

AT LAST...THE PIPS.
Album: released on Casablanca, Jan'78 Dist: Polygram, Phonogram

CALLIN'.
Album: released on Casablanca, '78 Dist: Polygram, Phonogram

Piranhas

PIRANHAS.
Album: released on Sire, '80

ZAMBESE.
Single (7"): released on Dakota, Sep'82 by Dakota Records. Dist: PRT

Pirate Movie

PIRATE MOVIE (Various Artists).
Album: released on Polydor, Jan'83 by Polydor Records. Dist: Polygram, Polydor

Cassette: released on Polydor, Jan'83 by Polydor Records. Dist: Polygram, Polydor

Pirates

FISTFUL OF DUBLOONS, A.
Album: released on Edsel, Jun'81 by Demon Records. Dist: Pinnacle, Jazz Music, Projection

PETER GUNN EP.
Single (7"): released on Charly, Aug'82 by Charly Records. Dist: Charly, Cadillac

PIRATES Original Soundtrack (Polanski,Roman).
Compact disc: released on SPI Milan (France), Nov'86 Dist: Silva Screen

SKULL WARS.
Album: released on Warner Bros., Apr'78 by Warner Bros Records. Dist: WEA

Cassette: released on Warner Bros., Apr'78 by Warner Bros Records. Dist: WEA

Pirates of Penzance

PIRATES OF PENZANCE Gilbert & Sullivan (Various Artists).
Double Album: released on Decca, '68 by Decca Records. Dist: Polygram

PIRATES OF PENZANCE - BROADWAY CAST (Various Artists).
Album: released on Elektra Asylum, Jul'81 by Elektra/Asylum/Nonesuch Records. Dist: WEA

Pirates (Roman Polanski)

PIRATES (ROMAN POLANSKI) Original soundtrack (Philippe Sarde).
Tracks: / Pirates / Sauves mais captifs / Linares se meurt / Mutinerie a bord / C'ptain red maitre du galion / Red,la grenouille et le requin / Dolores (Theme D,Amour') / Don alfonso s'evade / Red,la grenouille,le tronde,boomako et le boa / C'ptain red's empare du tresor tandis....... / Red et la grenouille voguent vers de nouvelles aventures.
Notes: From Roman Polanski's latest film starring Walter Matthau.
Album: released on Milan France, '86

Cassette: released on Milan France, '86

Compact disc: released on Milan France, '86

Pirchner,Werner

EU.
Tracks: / Sonate vom rauhen leben / Streichquartett fur blaserquintett / Good news from the Ziller family / Kammer-symphonie 'Soiree Tyrolienne' / Do you know emperor Joe / Two war & peace choirs / Kleine mes um 'c' fur den lieben gott / Solo sonata for bass-vibes.
Notes: In 1981 Austrian vibraphonist and composer Werner Pirchner decided to devote most of his time to composition,writing primarily for classical concert musicians. His works have seen many performances in Austria and 'Eu' is the first recording of his written work. Werner Pirchner's music stubbornly evades traditonal categories and because it is written with humour in mind is best exemplified to Gerard Hoffnung. What distinguishes Pirchner from Hoffnung is Hoffnung's almost exclusive use of other people's material while Pirchner integrates borrowed phrases into his compositions. Double album or Compact Disc.
Album: released on ECM (Germany), '86 by ECM Records. Dist: IMS, Polygram, Virgin through EMI

Compact disc: released on ECM (Germany), '86 by ECM Records. Dist: IMS, Polygram, Virgin through EMI

Pisces

PISCES.
Album: released on Leader, '81 Dist: Jazz Music, Projection

Pistol for two/Hazard

PISTOL FOR TWO/HAZARD Read by Christopher Cazanove (Heyer, Georgette).
Cassette: released on Pickwick Talking Books, '83

Pitney, Gene

20 GOLDEN PIECES OF GENE PITNEY.
Album: released on Bulldog, Oct'82 by Bulldog Records. Dist: President Distribution, Spartan, Swift, Taylor, H.R.

Cassette: released on Bulldog, Oct'82 by Bulldog Records. Dist: President Distribution, Spartan, Swift, Taylor, H.R.

20 GREATEST HITS.
Compact disc: released on Spectrum, '86 Dist: ACD

22 GREATEST HITS,THE.
Tracks: / Louisiana mama / Only love can break my heart / (Man who shot,The)liberty valance / It hurts to be in love / I'm gonna be strong / Half-heaven heartache / Mecca / Town without pity / Last chance to turn around / Every breath I take / Just a smile / Twenty four hours from tulsa / True love never runs smooth / Backstage / Looking through the eyes of love / I must be seeing things / Princess in rags / (I wanna) love my life away / Yesterday's hero / She let her hair down / If I didn't have a dime / She's a heartbreaker.
Compact disc: released on Bescol, Jul'87 Dist: Target

24 HOURS FROM TULSA.
Tracks: / 24 hours from Tulsa / Mecca / Every breath I take / I'm gonna be strong / Town without pity / (I wanna) love my life away / Only love can break a heart / Man who shot liberty valance (The) / It hurts to be in love / Looking through the eyes of love / Somethings gotta hold of my heart / Backstage (I'm lonely).
Album: released on Topline, '86 by Charly Records. Dist: Charly Distribution

Cassette: released on Topline, '86 by Charly Records. Dist: Charly Distribution

Single (7"): released on Old Gold, Apr'83 by Old Gold Records. Dist: Lightning, Jazz Music, Spartan, Counterpoint

6 TRACK HITS.
Extended-play record: released on Scoop 33, Sep'83 by Pickwick Records. Dist: H.R. Taylor

ANTHOLOGY 1961-1968.
Double Album: released on Rhino (USA), Feb'85 by Rhino Records (USA).

BEST OF GENE PITNEY.
Cassette: released on Creole (Everest-Europa), Jul'84 by Creole Records. Dist: PRT, Rhino

GENE PITNEY.
Album: released on Dakota (Countdown series), Oct'82 by Dakota Records. Dist: PRT

Cassette: released on Dakota (Countdown series), Oct'82 by Dakota Records. Dist: PRT

GENE PITNEY (CASSETTE).
Cassette: released on Audio Fidelity, Oct'84 Dist: PRT

GENE PITNEY COLLECTION, THE.
Double Album: released on Pickwick, Mar'76 by Pickwick Records. Dist: Pickwick Distribution, Prism Leisure Distribution, Lugtons

Cassette: released on Pickwick, Mar'76 by Pickwick Records. Dist: Pickwick Distribution, Prism Leisure Distribution, Lugtons

GENE PITNEY COLLECTION VOL.2.
Double Album: released on Pickwick, Jul'77 by Pickwick Records. Dist: Pickwick Distribution, Prism Leisure Distribution, Lugtons

Cassette: released on Pickwick, Jul'77 by Pickwick Records. Dist: Pickwick Distribution, Prism Leisure Distribution, Lugtons

GREATEST HITS OF ALL TIME.
Album: released on Phoenix, Oct'82 by Audio Fidelity Enterprises. Dist: Stage One, Lugtons

HALF HEAVEN-HALF HEARTACHE.
Double Album: released on Cambra, '83 by Cambra Records. Dist: IDS, Conifer

Double cassette: released on Cambra, '83 by Cambra Records. Dist: IDS, Conifer

HITS OF GENE PITNEY, THE.
Album: released on Spot, Jun'85 by Pickwick Records. Dist: H.R. Taylor, Lugtons

Cassette: released on Spot, Jun'85 by Pickwick Records. Dist: H.R. Taylor, Lugtons

I'M GONNA BE STRONG.
Single (7"): released on Dakota, Aug'82 by Dakota Records. Dist: PRT

LOVE MY LIFE AWAY.
Cassette: released on Orchid Music, Feb'82 by Bibi. Dist: Pinnacle

PROFILE.
Album:

Cassette:

SOMETHING'S GOTTEN HOLD OF MY HEART.
Double cassette: released on Pickwick, Mar'83 by Pickwick Records. Dist: Pickwick Distribution, Prism Leisure Distribution, Lugtons

VERY BEST OF GENE PITNEY, THE.
Album: released on Impact, Jun'85 by Ace Records. Dist: Rough Trade, Pinnacle, Swift, Backs, Counterpoint, Jungle, Hotshot, Cartel

Pitre, Austin

BACK TO THE BAYOU.
Album: released on Sonet, Jun'80 by Sonet Records. Dist: PRT

EVANGALINE PLAYBOYS.
Album:

Pittman, Barbara

TEXAS BOOGIE.
Album: released on Magnum Force, Jun'87 by Magnum Music Group Ltd. Dist: Magnum Music Group Ltd, PRT, Spartan

Pizzarelli, Bucky

2 X 7 = PIZZARELLI.
Album: released on Stash, Apr'81 Dist: Swift Distribution, Jazz Music Distribution, Jazz Horizons Distribution, Celtic Music Distribution, Cadillac, JSU Distribution, Zodiac Distribution

BUCKY PLAYS BIX.
Album: released on Monmouth, Mar'79

BUCKY'S BUNCH.
Album: released on Monmouth, Mar'79

CAFE PIERRE TRIO, THE.
Album: released on Retrospect, Jan'87 by World Records.

DIALOGUE.
Album: released on Sonet, Jun'80 by Sonet Records. Dist: PRT

GREEN GUITAR BLUES.
Album: released on Monmouth, Mar'79

SWINGING SEVENS (Pizzarelli,Bucky & John).
Album: released on Stash, '86 Dist: Swift Distribution, Jazz Music Distribution, Jazz Horizons Distribution, Celtic Music Distribution, Cadillac, JSU Distribution, Zodiac Distribution

P King

HEY ROSALYN.
Single (7"): released on Red Bus, May'83 by Red Bus Records. Dist: PRT

Placebo

ENGLAND'S TRANCE.
Album: released on Aura, Jun'82 by Hollywood Nites Distribution. Dist: Pinnacle

PAYING HOMAGE.
Single (7"): released on Aura, Mar'82 by Hollywood Nites Distribution. Dist: Pinnacle

POPPY DANCE.
Single (7"): released on Aura, Jun'82 by Hollywood Nites Distribution. Dist: Pinnacle

Places In The Heart

PLACES IN THE HEART Original soundtrack (Various Artists).
Album: released on SPI Milan, Apr'85 Dist: Silva Screen

Plague Of Fools

FOOLS ALL DAY.
Single (12"): released on Partizan Pestilenti, Mar'85 Dist: Fast Forward, Cartel

HEART OF HEART.
Single (12"): released on Partizan Pestilenti, Aug'85 Dist: Fast Forward, Cartel

Plaidy, Jean

SIXTH WIFE, THE Read by Marie Palmer.
Cassette: released on Soundings, Mar'85 Dist: Soundings

Plain Characters

INVISIBLE YEARNINGS.
Album: released on Abstract, Aug'83 by Abstract. Dist: Pinnacle

MENIAL TASKS.
Single (7"): released on Abstract, Nov'81 by Abstract. Dist: Pinnacle

Plain Clothes

MAXI TAXI.
Single (12"): released on Charlie's, Dec'84 by Charlie's Records. Dist: Jetstar

Plain Jane

ONE LOOK.
Single (7"): released on Avatar, Aug'81 by Avatar Communications. Dist: CBS

Plains Indians

POW WOW SONGS.
Tracks: / Slow war dance songs / Contest songs for straight dancers / Contest songs for fancy dancers / Round dance / Sioux flag song / Grass dance theme song / Grass dance song / War dance song / Slow war dance, Vietnam song / War dance songs - flag parade.
Notes: This album offers ceremonial and social music of Indians from the Great Plains. Although the styles of singing and drumming vary greatly in different regions and among different tribes, the forms of music are similar, enabaling musicians from many tribes to perform together. Most of the music here is intertribal singing of what are now the Southern Plains Indians, primarily from Oklahoma; part of side two adds the intertribal music of the Northern Plains Indians. The setting for the music is the powwow, a general gathering, usually several days in length, that includes feasting, giveaways, arts-and-crafts sales, raffles, and the honoring of special guests and veterans. The powwow itself has been transplanted to the cities, where an estimated half of the nation's Indians now live. Each powwow club, composed of Indian community members, takes the year long responsibility of planning and raising money for this annual event. The need for prize money, gas money, and food for singers and dancers; fees for a master of ceremonies; and rental of public-address systems demands a complex volunteer organization. [New World Records release sheet, May '87]
Album: released on New World (USA), May'87 by New World Records (USA). Dist: Conifer

Plan 9

ANYTIME, ANYPLACE, ANYWHERE.
Album: released on Enigma, Dec'86 by Enigma Records. Dist: Rough Trade, Cartel, EMI

KEEP YOUR COOL.
Album: released on Enigma, '86 by Enigma Records. Dist: Rough Trade, Cartel, EMI

PLAN 9.
Album: released on New Rose, Nov'84 Dist: Rough Trade, Cartel

Plan B

I DON'T KNOW.
Single (7"): released on Racket, Sep'84 Dist: Rough Trade

Planer,Nigel

ROUGH WITH THE SMOOTH.
Tracks: / Rough with the smooth / Nicholas Craig and Max.
Single (7"): released on Columbia, '86 by EMI Records. Dist: EMI

Planet Earth

PLANET EARTH.
Album: released on Pye, Apr'78

Planet Gong

LIVE - FLOATING ANARCHY.
Album: released on Charly, Apr'78 by Charly Records. Dist: Charly, Cadillac

Planet Of The Elves

PLANET OF THE ELVES, THE.
Cassette: released on Tell-A-Tale, '84 by Pickwick Records. Dist: Spartan-Taylors Distribution

Planet Of The Hoojibs

PLANET OF THE HOOJIBS (Various Artists).
Album: released on Disneyland, Jul'83 by Disneyland-Vista Records (USA). Dist: BBC Records & Tapes, Rainbow Communications Ltd(Distribution)

Cassette: released on Disneyland, Jul'83 by Disneyland-Vista Records (USA). Dist: BBC Records & Tapes, Rainbow Communications Ltd(Distribution)

Planet,P

PINK PROJECT.
Album: released on MCA, Feb'85 by MCA Records. Dist: Polygram, MCA

Cassette: released on MCA, Feb'85 by MCA Records. Dist: Polygram, MCA

PLANET P.
Album: released on Geffen, May'83 by Geffen Records. Dist: WEA, CBS

Cassette: released on Geffen, May'83 by Geffen Records. Dist: WEA, CBS

PLANT P.
Tracks: / Static / King for a day / I won't wake up / Top of the world / Armageddon / Why me? / Power tools / Send it in a letter / Adam and eve / Only you and me.
Album: released on Geffen, '86 by Geffen Records. Dist: WEA, CBS

Cassette: released on Geffen, '86 by Geffen Records. Dist: WEA, CBS

WHY ME.
Single (7"): released on Geffen, May'83 by Geffen Records. Dist: WEA, CBS

Single (12"): released on Geffen, May'83 by Geffen Records. Dist: WEA, CBS

Planet Patrol

PLAY AT YOUR OWN RISK.
Single (7"): released on 21 Records, Nov'82 by Polydor Records. Dist: Polydor

Single (12"): released on 21 Records, Nov'82 by Polydor Records. Dist: Polydor Deleted '85.

Planets

GOONHILLY DOWN.
Album: released on Rialto, Nov'79 by Rialto Records. Dist: Pinnacle

Cassette: released on Rialto, Nov'79 by Rialto Records. Dist: Pinnacle

SPOT.
Album: released on Rialto, Oct'80 by Rialto Records. Dist: Pinnacle

Cassette: released on Rialto, Oct'80 by Rialto Records. Dist: Pinnacle

Planning By Numbers

LIVING NEON/KINETIC.
Single (7"): released on Beggars Banquet, Dec'82 by Beggars Banquet Records. Dist: WEA

Plant, Richard

BETTER BE SANE.
Album: released on Tradition, Aug'76 Dist: JSU, Cassion Distribution, Celtic Music, Jazz Music, Projection, Roots Records

Plant, Robert

24K.
Album: released on Thunderbolt, Sep'83 by Magnum Music Group Ltd. Dist: Magnum Music Group Ltd, PRT Distribution, Spartan Distribution

BIG LOG.
Single (7"): released on WEA, Jul'83 by WEA Records. Dist: WEA

Single (12"): released on WEA, Jul'83 by WEA Records. Dist: WEA

BURNING DOWN ONE SIDE/MOONLIGHT.
Single (7"): released on Swan Song USA, Sep'82 by Atlantic Records. Dist: WEA Distribution, Atlantic Distribution

Single (12"): released on Swan Song USA, Sep'82 by Atlantic Records. Dist: WEA Distribution, Atlantic Distribution

IN THE MOOD.
Single (7"): released on Es Paranza (USA), Nov'83 by Atlantic Records. Dist: Polygram, Atlantic

Single (12"): released on Es Paranza (USA), Jan'84 by Atlantic Records. Dist: Polygram, Atlantic

LITTLE BY LITTLE.
Single (7"): released on Es Paranza (USA), Aug'85 by Atlantic Records. Dist: Polygram, Atlantic

Single (12"): released on Es Paranza (USA), Aug'85 by Atlantic Records. Dist: Polygram, Atlantic

PICTURES AT ELEVEN.
Tracks: / Burning down one side / Moonlight in Samosa / Pledge pin / Slow dancer / Worse than Detroit / Fat lip / Like I've never been gone / Mystery title.
Compact disc: released on Swansong, '86

Album: released on Swan Song USA, Jul'82 by Atlantic Records. Dist: WEA Distribution, Atlantic Distribution

Cassette: released on Swan Song USA, Jul'82 by Atlantic Records. Dist: WEA Distribution, Atlantic Distribution

PINK AND BLACK.
Single (7"): released on Es Paranza (USA), May'85 by Atlantic Records. Dist: Polygram, Atlantic

Single (12"): released on Es Paranza (USA), May'85 by Atlantic Records. Dist: Polygram, Atlantic

PRINCIPAL OF MOMENTS.
Tracks: / Other arms / In the mood / Messin' with the mekon / Wreckless love / Through with the two step / Horizontal departure / Big log / Stranger here than over there.
Notes: Digital Stereo
Compact disc: released on Es Paranza (USA), '83 by Atlantic Records. Dist: Polygram, Atlantic

Album: released on Es Paranza (USA), Jul'83 by Atlantic Records. Dist: Polygram, Atlantic

Cassette: released on Es Paranza (USA), Jul'83 by Atlantic Records. Dist: Polygram, Atlantic

SHAKEN 'N' STIRRED.
Tracks: / Hip to hoo / Kallalou / Too loud / Trouble your money / Pink and black / Little by little / Doo doo a do do / Easily lead / Sixes and sevens.
Compact disc: released on Es Paranza (USA), '85 by Atlantic Records. Dist: Polygram, Atlantic

Album: released on Es Paranza (USA), Jun'85 by Atlantic Records. Dist: Polygram, Atlantic

Cassette: released on Es Paranza (USA), Jun'85 by Atlantic Records. Dist: Polygram, Atlantic

Planxty

AFTER THE BREAK.
Album: released on Tara (Ireland), '82 by Tara Records. Dist: I & B Records Distribution, Record Services Distribution (Ireland), Roots Distribution

Cassette: released on Tara (Ireland), '82 by Tara Records. Dist: I & B Records Distribution, Record Services Distribution (Ireland), Roots Distribution

ARIS.
Album: released on Polydor, Sep'84 by Polydor Records. Dist: Polygram, Polydor

Cassette: released on Polydor, Sep'84 by Polydor Records. Dist: Polygram, Polydor

PLANXTY ARIS.
Tracks: / Kid on the mountain(The).An phis fhliuch / Arthur McBride / Old torn petticoat.Dublin reel.Wind that shakes the barley. / Yarmouth town / Johnny Cope / Only our rivers / Dogs among the bushes(The). Jenny's wedding / Cliffs of Dooneen / Si bheag si mhor / Fisherman's lilt.Cronin's hornpipe / Well below the valley(The).
Album: released on Polydor (Ireland), '86 by Polydor Records. Dist: Polygram, I & B

Cassette: released on Polydor (Ireland), '86 by Polydor Records. Dist: Polygram, I & B

WOMAN I LOVED SO WELL, THE.
Album: released on Tara (Ireland), '82 by Tara Records. Dist: I & B Records Distribution, Record Services Distribution (Ireland), Roots Distribution

Cassette: released on Tara (Ireland), '82 by Tara Records. Dist: I & B Records Distribution, Record Services Distribution (Ireland), Roots Distribution

WORDS AND MUSIC.
Album: released on WEA Ireland, Mar'87 by WEA Records. Dist: Celtic Distributions, Projection, I & B

Cassette: released on WEA Ireland, Mar'87 by WEA Records. Dist: Celtic Distributions, Projection, I & B

Plasmatics

BUTCHER BABY.
Single (7"): released on Stiff, Jun'80 by Stiff Records. Dist: EMI, Record Services Distribution (Ireland)

Single (12"): released on Stiff, Jun'80 by Stiff Records. Dist: EMI, Record Services Distribution (Ireland)

COUP D'ETAT.
Album: released on Revolver, '86 by Revolver Records. Dist: Revolver, Cartel

Cassette: released on Revolver, '86 by Revolver Records. Dist: Revolver, Cartel

MAGGOTS Original soundtrack (Plasmatics/Wendy O'Williams).
Notes: Full details see under O'WILLIAMS, Wendy

MONKEY SUIT/SQUIRM.
Single (7"): released on Stiff, Sep'80 by Stiff Records. Dist: EMI, Record Services Distribution (Ireland)

NEW HOPE FOR THE WRETCHED.
Album: released on Stiff, Sep'80 by Stiff Records. Dist: EMI, Record Services Distribution (Ireland)

Plastic Fles

SENSE OF TIME/MILLIONS JUST LIKE YOU.
Single (7"): released on Y Finto, Oct'82

Plasticland

EUPHORIC TRAPDOOR BLUES.
Single (7"): released on Scadillac (USA), Mar'84 by Scadillac Records (USA). Dist: Rough Trade, Cartel

PLASTIC LAND.
Album: released on Bam Caruso, '85 by Bam Caruso Records. Dist: Rough Trade, Revolver, Cartel

SALON.
Album: released on Enigma, Jun'87 by Enigma Records. Dist: Rough Trade, Cartel, EMI

Album: released on Pink Dust (USA), Aug'87 Dist: Enigma

Plastic Ono Band

LIVE PEACE IN TORONTO.
Album: released on Parlophone, '70 by EMI Records. Dist: EMI

POWER TO THE PEOPLE.
Single (7"): released on Apple, '80 Dist: EMI

Plastic Surgery

TORMENT.
Tracks: / Surgery Looks Nice (At a Price).
Single (7"): released on Watch Out!, Jan'87

Plata, Manitas De

BEST OF MANITAS DE PLATA.
Album: released on Vanguard, '73 by PRT Records. Dist: PRT

SAGA OF MANITAS, THE.
Album: released on CBS(France), Aug'84 by CBS Records. Dist: Conifer, Discovery, Swift

Cassette: released on CBS(France), Aug'84 by CBS Records. Dist: Conifer, Discovery, Swift

Plath, Sylvia

READING HER POETRY.
Album: released on Caedmon(USA), Jan'78 by Caedmon (USA) Records. Dist: Gower, Taylors, Discovery

Cassette: released on Caedmon(USA), Jan'78 by Caedmon (USA) Records. Dist: Gower, Taylors, Discovery

Platinum Album

PLATINUM ALBUM (Various Artists).
Album: released on K-Tel, Sep'81 by K-Tel Records. Dist: Record Merchandisers Distribution, Taylors, Terry Blood Distribution, Wynd-Up Distribution, Relay Distribution, Pickwick Distribution, Solomon & Peres Distribution, Polygram

Cassette: released on K-Tel, Sep'81 by K-Tel Records. Dist: Record Merchandisers Distribution, Taylors, Terry Blood Distribution, Wynd-Up Distribution, Relay Distribution, Pickwick Distribution, Solomon & Peres Distribution, Polygram

Platinum Blonde

ALIEN SHORES.
Album: released on Epic, Nov'85 by CBS Records. Dist: CBS

Cassette: released on Epic, Nov'85 by CBS Records. Dist: CBS

DOESN'T REALLY MATTER.
Single (7"): released on Epic, Jul'84 by CBS Records. Dist: CBS

Platinum Dance Orchestra

STRICT TEMPO 64 great dance melodies.
Album: released on Platinum, Sep'84 by Geoffs Records.

Cassette: released on Platinum, Sep'84 by Geoffs Records.

Platinum High School

PLATINUM HIGH SCHOOL.
Album: released on Magnum Force, Jan'83 by Magnum Music Group Ltd. Dist: Magnum Music Group Ltd, PRT, Spartan

Platoon

'PLATOON' AND SONGS FROM THE ERA (Original motion picture soundtrack) (Various Artists).
Tracks: / Village,The. Adagio for strings / Tracks of my tears, The / Okie from Muskokie / Hello, I love you / White rabbit / Barnes shoots Elias / Respect / (Sittin' on) The dock of the bay / When a man loves a woman / Groovin' / Adagio for strings.
Album: released on Atlantic, Jun'87 by WEA Records. Dist: WEA

Cassette: released on Atlantic, Jun'87 by WEA Records. Dist: WEA

Compact disc: released on Atlantic, Jun'87 by WEA Records. Dist: WEA

Platters

20 GOLDEN PIECES.
Album: released on Astan, Nov'84 by Astan Records. Dist: Counterpoint

Cassette: released on Astan, Nov'84 by Astan Records. Dist: Counterpoint

20 GOLDEN PIECES OF THE PLATTERS.
Album: released on Bulldog, Feb'84 by Bulldog Records. Dist: President Distribution, Spartan, Swift, Taylor, H.R.

20 GREATEST HITS.
Album: released on Mercury, Dec'83 by Phonogram Records. Dist: Polygram Distribution

Cassette: released on Mercury, Dec'83 by Phonogram Records. Dist: Polygram Distribution

20 GREATEST HITS, THE.
Tracks: / My prayer / Smoke gets in your eyes / Great pretender,The / Twilight time / (You've got)the magic touch / And you(and you alone) / Harbour lights / I'm sorry / If I had you / How beautiful our love / With this ring / I love you 1000 times / Red sails in the sunset / Washed ashore(on a lonely island in the sun) / Sweet sweet lovin' / Doesn't it ring a bell / Unchained melody / Devri / One in a million / Pledging my love.
Compact disc: released on Bescol, May'87 Dist: Target

6 TRACK HITS.
Single (7"): released on Scoop 33, Sep'83 by Pickwick Records. Dist: H.R. Taylor

Cassette: released on Scoop 33, Sep'83 by Pickwick Records. Dist: H.R. Taylor

BEST OF THE PLATTERS.
Cassette: released on Creole, Jul'84 by Creole Records. Dist: Rhino, PRT

COLLECTION: PLATTERS.
Album: released on Deja Vu, '86 by Deja Vu Records. Dist: Counterpoint Distribution, Record Services Distribution (Ireland)

Cassette: released on Deja Vu, '86 by Deja Vu Records. Dist: Counterpoint Distribution, Record Services Distribution (Ireland)

EARLY YEARS, THE.
Album: released on Bulldog Records, Jul'82

ENCORE OF GOLDEN HITS.
Album: released on Mercury, Oct'80 by Phonogram Records. Dist: Polygram Distribution

Cassette: released on Mercury, Oct'80 by Phonogram Records. Dist: Polygram Distribution

GOLDEN HIT COLLECTION.
Cassette: released on Pickwick (Ditto series), Jul'82

GOLDEN HITS: PLATTERS.
Album: released on Phoenix, Oct'82 by Audio Fidelity Enterprises. Dist: Stage One, Lugtons

GOLDENS HITS (THE).
Compact disc: released on Mercury, '86 by Phonogram Records. Dist: Polygram Distribution

GREAT PRETENDER.

Tracks: / My prayer / Great pretender / Smoke gets in your eyes / Harbour lights / Only you / Pledging my love / I'll be home / Red sails in the sunset / With this ring / Twilight time / I'm sorry / If I had you.
Album: released on Magnum Force, Apr'87 by Magnum Music Group Ltd. Dist: Magnum Music Group Ltd, PRT, Spartan

Album: released on Mercury (USA), Nov'81 by Import Records. Dist: IMS Distribution, Polygram Distribution

Cassette: released on Mercury (USA), Nov'81 by Import Records. Dist: IMS Distribution, Polygram Distribution

Album: released on Topline, Jul'85 by Charly Records. Dist: Charly Distribution

Cassette: released on Topline, Jul'85 by Charly Records. Dist: Charly Distribution

JUKE BOX GIANTS.
Album: released on Audio Fidelity, May'82 Dist: PRT

MORE I SEE YOU, THE.
Album: released on Spot, '83 by Pickwick Records. Dist: H.R. Taylor, Lugtons

Cassette: released on Spot, Feb'83 by Pickwick Records. Dist: H.R. Taylor, Lugtons

MUSIC FOR THE MILLIONS.
Album: released on Phonogram (Holland), May'84 Dist: IMS-Polygram

Cassette: released on Phonogram (Holland), May'84 Dist: IMS-Polygram

Album:

Cassette:

ONLY YOU.
Cassette: released on Bravo, Feb'80 by Pickwick Records. Dist: Lugtons

Album: released on Karussell (Import), Apr'82

Cassette: released on Karussell (Import), Apr'82

Single (7"): released on Mercury, '80 by Phonogram Records. Dist: Polygram Distribution

Single (7"): released on Old Gold, Jan'85 by Old Gold Records. Dist: Lightning, Jazz Music, Spartan, Counterpoint

PLATTERAMA.
Cassette: released on Mercury, Sep'82 by Phonogram Records. Dist: Polygram Distribution

PLATTERS.
Album: released on Dakota (Countdown series), Oct'82 by Dakota Records. Dist: PRT

Cassette: released on Dakota (Countdown series), Oct'82 by Dakota Records. Dist: PRT

PLATTERS COLLECTION, THE.
Album: released on Pickwick, Mar'76 by Pickwick Records. Dist: Pickwick Distribution, Prism Leisure Distribution, Lugtons

Cassette: released on Pickwick, Feb'80 by Pickwick Records. Dist: Pickwick Distribution, Prism Leisure Distribution, Lugtons

PLATTERS, THE.
Cassette: released on Audio Fidelity, Oct'84 Dist: PRT. Estim retail price in Jul'87 was £3.48.

SMOKE GETS IN YOUR EYES.
Single (7"): released on Mercury, '80 by Phonogram Records. Dist: Polygram Distribution

Single (7"): released on Old Gold, Jan'85 by Old Gold Records. Dist: Lightning, Jazz Music, Spartan, Counterpoint

Play

CHASING THE SUN.
Single (12"): released on Survival, Oct'82 by Survival Records. Dist: Backs, Cartel Distribution

IN MY MIND.
Single (7"): released on Survival, Jun'84 by Survival Records. Dist: Backs, Cartel Distribution

Single (12"): released on Survival, Jun'84 by Survival Records. Dist: Backs, Cartel Distribution

PLAY ANOTHER BEFORE YOU GO Various Music Hall Artists (Various Artists).
Album: released on Topic, Nov'86 Dist: Roots Distribution

PLAY AWAY Various artists (Various Artists).
Album: released on BBC, Oct'76 by BBC Records & Tapes. Dist: EMI, PRT, Pye

Cassette: released on BBC, Oct'76 by BBC Records & Tapes. Dist: EMI, PRT, Pye

PLAY LISTEN AND LEARN WITH RONALD MCDONALD Various artists (Various Artists).
Album: released on Spot, May'84 by Pickwick Records. Dist: H.R. Taylor, Lugtons

Cassette: released on Spot, May'84 by Pickwick Records. Dist: H.R. Taylor, Lugtons

PLAY NEW ROSE FOR ME (Various Artists).
Notes: Double album
Double Album: released on New Rose, Jan'87 Dist: Rough Trade, Cartel

PLAY ON Songs from Playschool - Various artists (Various Artists).
Album: released on BBC, '78 by BBC Records & Tapes. Dist: EMI, PRT, Pye

Cassette: released on BBC, '78 by BBC Records & Tapes. Dist: EMI, PRT, Pye

PLAY THOSE OLDIES MR. D.J. - VOL.5 All night worker (Various Artists).
Album: released on Mercury (USA Import), Jun'82

Cassette: released on Mercury (USA Import), Jun'82

PLAY THOSE OLDIES MR. D.J. - VOL.3 Brokenhearted melody (Various Artists).
Album: released on Mercury (USA Import), Jun'82

Cassette: released on Mercury (USA Import), Jun'82

PLAY THOSE OLDIES MR. D.J. - VOL.1 Giddy up a ding dong (Various Artists).
Album: released on Mercury (USA Import), Jun'82

Cassette: released on Mercury (USA Import), Jun'82

PLAY THOSE OLDIES MR. D.J. - VOL.2 Whole lotta shakin' goin' on (Various Artists).
Album: released on Mercury (USA Import), Jun'82

Cassette: released on Mercury (USA Import), Jun'82

PLAY THOSE OLDIES MR. D.J. - VOL.4 Twistin' the night away (Various Artists).
Album: released on Mercury (USA Import), Jun'82

Cassette: released on Mercury (USA Import), Jun'82

RED MOVIES.
Album: released on Survival, Feb'85 by Survival Records. Dist: Backs, Cartel Distribution

YOU DON'T LOOK THE SAME.
Single (7"): released on Survival, Aug'83 by Survival Records. Dist: Backs, Cartel Distribution

Single (12"): released on Survival, Aug'83 by Survival Records. Dist: Backs, Cartel Distribution

Playbox

LIZ & THE SANDPIPERS.
Cassette: released on MacMillan, Oct'81

Playboy Jazz Festival

PLAYBOY JAZZ FESTIVAL various artists (Various Artists).
Double Album: released on Elektra, Apr'84 by WEA Records. Dist: WEA

Playboys

LIVE.
Album: released on Tank, Jun'79 by Tank Records.

MADE IN THE COUNTRY.
Album: released on Tank, Jun'79 by Tank Records.

Play Dead

BREAK.
Single (7"): released on Clay, Apr'84 by Clay Records. Dist: Pinnacle

Single (12"): released on Clay, Apr'84 by Clay Records. Dist: Pinnacle

BURNING DOWN.
Tracks: / Burning down.
Single (12"): released on Tanz, Apr'86 Dist: Red Rhino Distribution, Cartel Distribution

CAUGHT FROM BEHIND.
Tracks: / Break / Last degree / Solace / Shine / Isabel / Sin of sins / Torn on desire / This side of heaven / Sacroscanct / Tenant (The).
Notes: Tracks 1, 2: (University of London, England, 22nd Feb 1985)/3,4: (Le Saint, Paris, France 10th Dec 1984)/5: (The Metropole, West Berlin Germany 15th Oct 1984)/6, 7: Fri-son, Friboug, Switzerland 20th Sept 1984)/8, 9, 10: (Rock City, Nottingham, England 27th Feb 1985).

Album: released on Dojo, Aug'86 by Castle Communications Records. Dist: Cartel

COMPANY OF JUSTICE.
Album: released on Tanz, Nov'85 Dist: Red Rhino Distribution, Cartel Distribution

CONSPIRACY.
Single (7"): released on Clay, Oct'84 by Clay Records. Dist: Pinnacle

Single (12"): released on Clay, Oct'84 by Clay Records. Dist: Pinnacle

FINAL EPITAPH - LIVE.
Album: released on Jungle, Mar'87 by Jungle Records. Dist: Jungle, Cartel

FIRST FLOWER, THE.
Cassette: released on Jungle, Jul'84 by Jungle Records. Dist: Jungle, Cartel

IN THE BEGINNING.
Tracks: / In the beginning / 1981 singles (The) / Poison takes a hold / Introduction / TV eye / Final epitaph.
Single (12"): released on Jungle, Feb'86 by Jungle Records. Dist: Jungle, Cartel

INTO THE FIRE.
Album: released on Clay, May'85 by Clay Records. Dist: Pinnacle

ISABEL.
Single (7"): released on Clay, May'84 by Clay Records. Dist: Pinnacle

Single (12"): released on Clay, May'84 by Clay Records. Dist: Pinnacle

POISON TAKES A HOLD.
Single (7"): released on Fresh, Jan'84 Dist: Jetstar

PROPAGANDA.
Single (7"): released on Jungle, Nov'82 by Jungle Records. Dist: Jungle, Cartel

Single (12"): released on Jungle, Sep'84 by Jungle Records. Dist: Jungle, Cartel

SACROSANCT.
Single (7"): released on Clay, Feb'85 by Clay Records. Dist: Pinnacle

Single (12"): released on Clay, Feb'85 by Clay Records. Dist: Pinnacle

SHINE.
Single (7"): released on Situation 2, Sep'83 Dist: Cartel, Pinnacle

Single (12"): released on Situation 2, Sep'83 Dist: Cartel, Pinnacle

SINGLES 82'-85' (THE).
Album: released on Clay, Jul'86 by Clay Records. Dist: Pinnacle

THIS SIDE OF HEAVEN.
Single (12"): released on Tanz, Sep'85 Dist: Red Rhino Distribution, Cartel Distribution

T.V. EYE.
Single (7"): released on Fresh, Jan'84 Dist: Jetstar

Player

AM I A DREAMER.
Tracks: / Am I a dreamer / I'll never forget you / I'll cry for you tonight.
Single (7"): released on Rainbow, Apr'86 Dist: I & B, CBS

Single (12"): released on Rainbow, Apr'86 Dist: I & B, CBS

DANGER ZONE.
Album: released on RSO, Mar'79

PLAYER.
Album: released on RSO, Jan'78

ROOM WITH A VIEW.
Album: released on Casablanca, Sep'80 Dist: Polygram, Phonogram

Playford, John

JOHN PLAYFORD'S POPULAR TUNES.
Tracks: / Greenwood / Hearts ease / Excuse me / Lady catherine Ogle / Scotchmans dance, The / In the Northern lass / Never love thee more / Miller's jig / Granadees march, The / Saraband by Mr.Simon Ives / Lady Hatton's almaine / Prince Robbert Masco / Prince Rupert's march / Daphne / Lilli Burlerlo / Parthenia / Corant la chabott / Jocobella / Paul's steeple / Lady Nevils delight, The / Whisk, The / New rigaudon, A / Italian rant, An / Buzer castle / Childgrove / Mr.Lane's minuet / Up with ailey / Cheshire rounds / Hunt the squirrell.
Notes: Popular tunes and dances on original instruments from the publications of John Playford 1623-1686 - The Dancing Master, Musicks Hand-maide etc. played on archcittern, lute, mandore, harpsichord, renaissance and baroque recorders, lyra viol, bass viol, hurdy-gurdy, flageolets, baroque violin and regal by The Broadside Band. Digital recording, Direct Metal Mastering (LP), Chrome tape (cassette).

Album: released on Amon Ra, Mar'87 by Saydisc Records. Dist: H.R. Taylor, Gamut, PRT, Jazz Music, Essex Record Distributors Ltd., Projection, Swift

Cassette: released on Amon Ra, Mar'87 by Saydisc Records. Dist: H.R. Taylor, Gamut, PRT, Jazz Music, Essex Record Distributors Ltd., Projection, Swift

Compact disc: released on Amon Ra, Mar'87 by Saydisc Records. Dist: H.R. Taylor, Gamut, PRT, Jazz Music, Essex Record Distributors Ltd., Projection, Swift

Playgroup Favourites

PLAYGROUP FAVOURITES (Various Artists).
Tracks: / Grand Old Duke Of York / Oranges & Lemons / John Browns Baby / Head, shoulders, knees & toes / Music Man / Pop Goes The Weasel / All Creatures / London Bridge Is Falling Down / One, two, three, four, five / Wheels on the bus (The) / Cat goes fiddle I fee (The) / Have you ever noticed your nose / Oranges and lemons / One finger, one thumb / Millie millipede / John Brown's baby / Teddy bear / Ostrich (The) / Little rabbit (A) / An elephant / Smile please! / Head, shoulders, knees and toes / Music man (The) / Ring a ring a roses / I jump out of bed / Someone's in the kitchen with Dinah / Peter hammers with one hammer / Pop goes the weasel / This old man / If you're happy and you know it / Here we go gathering nuts in May / Grandma and grandad / Billy Bumble / Cherry stone (The) / All creatures / Before you cross the road / London Bridge is falling down.
Cassette: released on Music For Pleasure, Oct'86 by EMI Records. Dist: EMI

Album: released on Music For Pleasure, Oct'86 by EMI Records. Dist: EMI

Playing At Trains

PLAYING AT TRAINS.
Album: released on Idea, Jun'87 by Idea Records. Dist: Rough Trade, Cartel

WORLD WITHOUT LOVE, A.
Single (7"): released on Idea, May'87 by Idea Records. Dist: Rough Trade, Cartel

Cassette: released on See For Miles, Mar'82 by See For Miles Records. Dist: Pinnacle

Single (7"): released on Import Music Service (IMS), '80 Dist: Concord Jazz Distributions, Pablo, Polygram

Playing For Keeps

PLAYING FOR KEEPS Various artists.
Tracks: / Life to life / It's not over / Distant drums / It's gettin' hot / Think we're gonna maake it / We said hello goodbye / Here to stay / Say the word / Make a wish / Stand by me.
Video-cassette (VHS): released on Guild Home Video, Jun'87 by Guild Records. Dist: Gold & Sons

Album: released on Parlophone, Oct'86 by EMI Records. Dist: EMI

Cassette: released on Parlophone, Oct'86 by EMI Records. Dist: EMI

Playmates

LONG SWEET DREAMS.
Album: released on What Goes On, Jul'86 Dist: Rough Trade, Cartel, Shigaku

WASTED YEARS.
Tracks: / Wasted years.
Single (7"): released on What Goes On, Jun'86 Dist: Rough Trade, Cartel, Shigaku

Playn Jayn

5 GOOD EVILS.
Album: released on ABC, Jul'85 Dist: CBS, Pinnacle

FRIDAY THE 13TH AT THE MARQUEE CLUB.
Album: released on A&M, Aug'84 by A&M Records. Dist: Polygram

I LOVE YOU LIKE I LOVE MYSELF.
Single (7"): released on ABC, Aug'85 Dist: CBS, Pinnacle

Single (12"): released on ABC, Aug'85 Dist: CBS, Pinnacle

JULIETTE.
Single (7"): released on A&M, Mar'85 by A&M Records. Dist: Polygram

Single (12"): released on A&M, Mar'85 by A&M Records. Dist: Polygram

Playschool

BANG ON A DRUM (Playschool & Play Away).
Album: by BBC Records & Tapes. Dist: EMI, PRT, Pye

HELLO Various artists (Various Artists).
Album: released on BBC, Oct'81 by BBC Records & Tapes. Dist: EMI, PRT, Pye

Cassette: released on BBC, Oct'81 by BBC Records & Tapes. Dist: EMI, PRT, Pye

PLAYSCHOOL - STORIES.
Album: released on Roundabout, '74 by Roundabout Records. Dist: ILA Distribution

SING A SONG OF PLAYSCHOOL.
Album: by BBC Records & Tapes. Dist: EMI, PRT, Pye

Cassette: released on BBC, '79 by BBC Records & Tapes. Dist: EMI, PRT, Pye

Playtime

CHILDREN'S SONGS PLAYED BY KENNY DREW/MADS VINDING.
Album: released on Metronome, Sep'86 Dist: Jazz Music Distribution, Jazz Horizons

Plaza

DON'T LOOK BACK.
Tracks: / Don't look back.
Single (7"): released on Record Shack, Jul'86 by Record Shack Records. Dist: PRT

Single (12"): released on Record Shack, Jul'86 by Record Shack Records. Dist: PRT

Single (7"): released on Record Shack, Nov'85 by Record Shack Records. Dist: PRT

Single (12"): released on Record Shack, Nov'85 by Record Shack Records. Dist: PRT

MOVING ON.
Single (7"): released on Record Shack, Jul'85 by Record Shack Records. Dist: PRT

Single (12"): released on Record Shack, Jul'85 by Record Shack Records. Dist: PRT

Plaza, Martin

CONCRETE AND CLAY.
Tracks: / Concrete and clay / New shoes / I could be so good / Concrete & clay / New suit.
Single (7"): released on Epic, Jul'86 by CBS Records. Dist: CBS

Single (12"): released on Epic, Jul'86 by CBS Records. Dist: CBS

PLAZA SUITE.
Tracks: / Pit stop / I could be so good / Concrete and clay / Out the door / Best foot forward / Miss you like mad / Chalk and cheese / Use me all over / Rollerina / Bats and balls.
Album: released on Epic, Aug'86 by CBS Records. Dist: CBS

Cassette: released on Epic, Aug'86 by CBS Records. Dist: CBS

Please, Peter

UFFINGTON.
Album: released on Plant Life, Nov'83

Please Y'self Skiffle...

DON'T GIMME NON O' THAT COYOTE.
Single (7"): released on Green Fringe, Feb'85 by Green Fringe Records. Dist: ILA

SKIFFLE PARTY.
Single (7"): released on Green Fringe, Feb'84 by Green Fringe Records. Dist: ILA

SURFIN' UK.
Single (7"): released on Green Fringe, Aug'84 by Green Fringe Records. Dist: II A

Pleasurama

COME DANCE WITH ME.
Single (7"): released on Sedition, May'85 Dist: PRT

Single (12"): released on Sedition, May'85 Dist: PRT

MAGGIE.
Tracks: / Maggie / Forever amber.
Single (7"): released on DMC, May'87 Dist: Red Rhino, Cartel

TEMPTATION.
Tracks: / Temptation / Stop the world / Modern times.
Single (7"): released on Sedition, Oct'86 Dist: PRT

Single (12"): released on Sedition, Oct'86 Dist: PRT

Pleasure Crew

I COULD BE SO GOOD FOR YOU.
Single (12"): released on Factory, Jun'87 by Factory Records. Dist: Cartel, Pinnacle

Pleasureheads

DON'T FAKE IT.
Tracks: / Don't fake it.
Single (7"): released on Molesworth, Jul'86 Dist: Backs

Pleasure Pump

FANTASISE ME.
Single (7"): released on Serious, Jun'87 by Serious Records. Dist: PRT

Single (12"): released on Serious, Jun'87 by Serious Records. Dist: PRT

Pleasures and treasures

PLEASURES AND TREASURES (A KALEIDOSCOPE OF SOUND) Various artists (Various Artists).
Tracks: / March by Mr Handel / Mira O Norma / Jean's real / Lezghinka (best of brass) / Prelude to the suite in E / Collette / John come kiss me now / Music from compline / Le coucou / Whistling Rufus (sound in brass bells) / Limerick's lamentation - give me your hand / La quinte estampie real / I've got a lovely bunch of coconuts (barrel organ) / Love at the fair / Miss Annabelle Lee / Scherzo (from the 'Spring' sonata) / Wibbly wobbly walk (The) / Jenny Lind medley / Turkish rondo / O sancitissima / Reve gourmand / Sportive litte trifler.
Notes: 21st Anniversary sampler: 21 track sampler of Saydisc and Amon Ra releases to clelebrate our 21st Anniversary in October. An hour-long kaleidoscopic tour of what Saydisc is all about and a marvellous introduction to our catalogue.
Album: released on Saydisc, Sep'86 by Saydisc Records. Dist: Essex, Harmonia Mundi, Roots, H.R. Taylor, Jazz Music, Swift, Projection, Gamut

Cassette: released on Saydisc, Sep'86 by Saydisc Records. Dist: Essex, Harmonia Mundi, Roots, H.R. Taylor, Jazz Music, Swift, Projection, Gamut

Compact disc: released on Saydisc, Sep'86 by Saydisc Records. Dist: Essex, Harmonia Mundi, Roots, H.R. Taylor, Jazz Music, Swift, Projection, Gamut

Pleasure starts here

PLEASURE STARTS HERE Various artists (Various Artists).
Album: released on Plezure, Apr'84 by Plezure Records. Dist: Pinnacle

Pleasure & The Beast

DR. SEX.
Single (7"): released on Carrere America (USA), May'83 by Polygram.

Single (12"): released on Carrere America (USA), May'83 by Polygram.

GOD'S EMPTY CHAIR.
Single (12"): released on Carrere, Jun'84 by Carrere Records. Dist: PRT, Spartan

Pleasure Zone

ALL THE KINGS HORSES.
Single (7"): released on Carrere, Mar'84 by Carrere Records. Dist: PRT, Spartan

Single (12"): released on Carrere, Mar'84 by Carrere Records. Dist: PRT, Spartan

Plimsouls

EVERYWHERE AT ONCE.
Album: released on Geffen, Sep'83 by Geffen Records. Dist: WEA, CBS

MILLION MILES AWAY.
Single (7"): released on Bomp International, May'82

P Lion

HAPPY CHILDREN.
Single (7"): released on Carrere, Oct'84 by Carrere Records. Dist: PRT, Spartan

Single (12"): released on Carrere, Oct'84 by Carrere Records. Dist: PRT, Spartan

Plod

LAUGHING POLICEMAN.
Single (7"): released on MFP, Oct'83 by EMI Records. Dist: EMI

Plow

PLOW Various artists (Various Artists).
Album: released on Organik, Apr'85 Dist: Rough Trade Distribution, Cartel Distribution

Plum

TOO MUCH AIN'T ENOUGH (FAT IS BACK).
Single (7"): released on Stiff, Mar'83

Single (12"): released on Stiff, Mar'83

Plum And Youth

I GOT YOU BABE.
Single (7"): released on Checkmount, Oct'84 Dist: Spartan

Plummer, Paul

LOVE REVOLUTION.
Tracks: / Love revolution / Love revolution (instrumental).
Single (12"): released on New Jerusalem, Apr'86 Dist: Jetstar

Pluto

I MAN BITTER.
Single (7"): released on KR, May'82 by KR Recordings Ltd. Dist: RCA, Revolver, Cartel

Single (12"): released on KR, May'82 by KR Recordings Ltd. Dist: RCA, Revolver, Cartel

OUVERTURE.
Cassette: released on Strawberry, Jul'83 Dist: Pinnacle

RAM GOAT LIVER.
Single (7"): released on Trojan, Apr'82 by Trojan Records. Dist: PRT, Jetstar

Single (12"): released on Trojan, Apr'82 by Trojan Records. Dist: PRT, Jetstar

YOUR HONOUR.
Single (7"): released on KR, Jan'82 by KR Recordings Ltd. Dist: RCA, Revolver, Cartel

Single (12"): released on KR, Jan'82 by KR Recordings Ltd. Dist: RCA, Revolver, Cartel

Plytas, Nick

HOT SEGAS (EP) (Plytas, Nick & Anne Pigalle).
Single 10": released on Illuminated, Oct'82 by IKF Records. Dist: Pinnacle, Cartel, Jetstar

P'O

WHILST CLIMBING THIEVES VIE FOR POSITION.
Album: released on Court, Jan'83 by Court Records. Dist: Cartel

Poacher

POACHER.
Album: released on RK, Sep'78

SUZY LOVES YOU NO MORE.
Single (7"): released on Ritz, Nov'83 by Ritz Records. Dist: Spartan

YOU ARE NO ANGEL.
Tracks: / You are no angel.
Single (7"): released on Ritz, Mar'86 by Outlet Records. Dist: Outlet, Prism Leisure Distribution, Record Services Distribution (Ireland), Roots

Single (7"): released on Ritz, Nov'82 by Ritz Records. Dist: Spartan

Poacher, Cyril

BROOMFIELD WAGER, THE.
Album: released on Topic, '81 by Topic Records. Dist: JSU Distribution, Projection Distribution, Jazz Music Distribution

Pocket Change

RANDOM AXIS.
Compact disc: by Pacific Records (USA). Dist: Atlantic

Pocket Rockets

VIDEO KID KO.
Tracks: / Video Kid KO / Rock socket.
Single (7"): released on MCA, May'87 by MCA Records. Dist: Polygram, MCA

Single (12"): released on MCA, May'87 by MCA Records. Dist: Polygram, MCA

Poco

FROM THE INSIDE.
Album: released on Epic, '74 by CBS Records. Dist: CBS

LEGEND.
Cassette: released on ABC, '78 Dist: CBS, Pinnacle

PICKING UP THE PIECES.
Album: released on Edsel, Feb'86 by Demon Records. Dist: Pinnacle, Jazz Music, Projection

SONGS OF RICHIE FURAY.
Album: released on CBS, Mar'80 by CBS Records. Dist: CBS

Cassette: released on CBS, Mar'80 by CBS Records. Dist: CBS

Podmore, J. F.

KITCHENETTE (Podmore, J. F. & Peter Hope).
Notes: For full details see under Peter Hope.

Podmore,Jonathan S.

DRY HIP ROTATION.
Notes: For full information see under:Hope,Peter/Jonathan S.Podmore.

Poeme Electronique

ECHOES FADE.
Single (7"): released on Carrere America (USA), Mar'82 by Polygram.

Poems & Pints

ANOTHER ROUND OF POEMS & PINTS.
Album: by EMI Records. Dist: EMI

Poetry Olympics

POETRY OLYMPICS VOL 1 Various artists (Various Artists).
Album: released on All Round Productions, Mar'82 Dist: Pinnacle

Pogues

GOOD, THE BAD AND THE UGLY, THE.
Tracks: / Good, the bad and the ugly, The / Rak at the gates of hell.
Single (7"): released on Hell, Jun'87 Dist: Red Rhino, Cartel

Single (12"): released on Hell, Jun'87 Dist: Red Rhino, Cartel

HAUNTED.
Tracks: / Haunted / Junk theme / Hot dogs with everything.
Single (7"): released on MCA, Aug'86 by MCA Records. Dist: Polygram, MCA

Single (12"): released on MCA, Aug'86 by MCA Records. Dist: Polygram, MCA

IRISH ROVER, THE (Pogues, The & The Dubliners).
Tracks: / Irish rover, The / Rave ould mountain dew, The / Dubliners fancy, The*.
Single (7"): released on Stiff, Mar'87 by Stiff Records. Dist: EMI, Record Services Distribution (Ireland)

Single (12"): released on Stiff, Mar'87 by Stiff Records. Dist: EMI, Record Services Distribution (Ireland)

POGUETRY IN MOTION EP; LONDON GIRL.
Tracks: / Poguetry in motion ep; London girl / Body of an American (The) / Rainy night (A) / Planxy / Noel / Hill.
Single (7"): released on Stiff, Feb'86 by Stiff Records. Dist: EMI, Record Services Distribution (Ireland)

Single (12"): released on Stiff, Feb'86 by Stiff Records. Dist: EMI, Record Services Distribution (Ireland)

RED ROSES FOR ME.
Tracks: / Transmetropolitan / Battle of Brisbane, The / Auld triangle, The / Waxie's dargle / Boys from the county hell / Sea shanty / Dark streets of London / Streams of whiskey / Poor Paddy / Dingle regatta / Greenland whale fisheries / Down in the ground where the dead men go / Kitty.
Compact disc: released on Stiff, May'87 by Stiff Records. Dist: EMI, Record Services Distribution (Ireland)

Point 3 FM

PICKS ME UP (YOUR LOVE).
Tracks: / Picks me up (your love) / Picks me up (your love)(remix).
Single (12"): released on Hardcore, 30 May'87 by Hardcore Records. Dist: PRT

Pointer Sisters

BACK IN MY ARMS AGAIN.
Tracks: / Back in my arms again / Dance electric / Dare me (remix).
Single (7"): released on RCA, May'86 by RCA Records. Dist: RCA, Roots, Swift, Wellard, Chris, I & B, Solomon & Peres Distribution

Single (12"): released on RCA, May'86 by RCA Records. Dist: RCA, Roots, Swift, Wellard, Chris, I & B, Solomon & Peres Distribution

BE THERE From Beverly Hills cop II.
Tracks: / Be there / Be there (Acappella) / Be there (Ext. Version).
Single (7"): released on MCA, Jun'87 by MCA Records. Dist: Polygram, MCA

Single (12"): released on MCA, Jun'87 by MCA Records. Dist: Polygram, MCA

BREAK OUT.
Tracks: / Jump (for my love) / Automatic / I'm so excited / I need you / Dance electric / Neutron dance / Easy persuasion / Baby come and get it / Telegraph your love / Operator.
Album: released on Planet, Oct'84 Dist: WEA

Cassette: released on Planet, Oct'84 Dist: WEA

Compact disc: released on Planet, Oct'84 Dist: WEA

CONTACT.
Tracks: / Twist my arm / Hey you / Pound, pound, pound / Back in my arms / Burn down the night / Bodies and souls / Contact / Dare me / Freedom.

Compact disc: released on RCA, '86 by RCA Records. Dist: RCA, Roots, Swift, Wellard, Chris, I & B, Solomon & Peres Distribution

FREEDOM.
Single (7"): released on RCA, Nov'85 by RCA Records. Dist: RCA, Roots, Swift, Wellard, Chris, I & B, Solomon & Peres Distribution

Single (12"): released on RCA, Nov'85 by RCA Records. Dist: RCA, Roots, Swift, Wellard, Chris, I & B, Solomon & Peres Distribution

GOLDMINE.
Tracks: / Sexual Power.
Single (7"): released on Planet, Nov'86 Dist: WEA

Single (12"): released on Planet, Nov'86 Dist: WEA

HEART TO HEART.
Single (7"): released on Planet, Sep'82 Dist: WEA

Single (12"): released on Planet, Sep'82 Dist: WEA

HE'S SO SHY.
Single (7"): released on Planet, Nov'82 Dist: WEA

HOT TOGETHER.
Tracks: / My life / Mercury rising / Goldmine / Say the word / Hot together / Sexual power / Set me free / Tast / Eyes don't lie.
Album: released on RCA, Jan'87 by RCA Records. Dist: RCA, Roots, Swift, Wellard, Chris, I & B, Solomon & Peres Distribution

Cassette: released on RCA, Jan'87 by RCA Records. Dist: RCA, Roots, Swift, Wellard, Chris, I & B, Solomon & Peres Distribution

Compact disc: released on RCA, Jan'87 by RCA Records. Dist: RCA, Roots, Swift, Wellard, Chris, I & B, Solomon & Peres Distribution

I'M SO EXCITED.
Single (7"): released on Planet, Oct'84 Dist: WEA

Single (12"): released on Planet, Oct'84 Dist: WEA

I NEED YOU.
Single (7"): released on Planet, Aug'84 Dist: WEA

Single (12"): released on Planet, Aug'84 Dist: WEA

JUMP (for my love).
Single (7"): released on Planet, Jun'84 Dist: WEA

Single (12"): released on Planet, Jun'84 Dist: WEA

NEUTRON DANCE.
Single (7"): released on Planet, Dec'84 Dist: WEA

Single (12"): released on Planet, Dec'84 Dist: WEA

POINTER SISTERS.
Tracks: / Twist my arm / Hey you / Pound pound pound / Back in my arms / Burn down the night / Bodies and souls / Contact / Dare me / Freedom.
Compact disc: released on Planet, Nov'85 Dist: WEA

PRIORITY.
Cassette: released on Planet, Sep'79 Dist: WEA

Album: released on Planet, Aug'79 Dist: WEA

RETROSPECT.
Album: released on MCA, Dec'81 by MCA Records. Dist: Polygram, MCA

Cassette: released on MCA, Dec'81 by MCA Records. Dist: Polygram, MCA

SAVE THIS NIGHT/SPECIAL THINGS.
Single (7"): released on Planet, Nov'80 Dist: WEA

SLOW HAND.
Single (7"): released on Planet, Jul'81 Dist: WEA

SO EXCITED.
Notes: The hitmaking US girl group with the promos for seven singles, including the well-known 'DARE ME' and 'JUMP (FOR MY LOVE)' 1986 compilation. Total playing time 30 minutes.
Video-cassette (VHS): released on RCA, Jun'86 by RCA Records. Dist: RCA, Roots, Swift, Wellard, Chris, I & B, Solomon & Peres Distribution

Album: released on RCA, Aug'82 by RCA Records. Dist: RCA, Roots, Swift, Wellard, Chris, I & B, Solomon & Peres Distribution

Cassette: released on RCA, Aug'82 by RCA Records. Dist: RCA, Roots, Swift, Wellard, Chris, I & B, Solomon & Peres Distribution

SPECIAL THINGS.
Album: released on Planet, Sep'80 Dist: WEA

Cassette: released on Planet, Sep'80 Dist: WEA

Album: released on RCA, Oct'85 by RCA Records. Dist: RCA, Roots, Swift, Wellard, Chris, I & B, Solomon & Peres Distribution

Cassette: released on RCA, Oct'85 by RCA Records. Dist: RCA, Roots, Swift, Wellard, Chris, I & B, Solomon & Peres Distribution

WHO DO YOU LOVE/WE TURNED UP.
Single (7"): released on Planet, Jan'80 Dist: WEA

Point of honour, (The)

POINT OF HONOUR, (THE) Maugham, Somerset (Burden, Hugh).
Cassette: released on Talking Tape, '84

Poison

CRY TOUGH.
Single (7"): released on Music For Nations, Aug'87 by Music For Nations Records. Dist: Pinnacle

Single (12"): released on Music For Nations, Aug'87 by Music For Nations Records. Dist: Pinnacle

INTERVIEW PICTURE DISC.
Album: released on Baktabak, Jun'87 by Baktabak Records. Dist: Arabesque

LOOK WHAT THE CAT DRAGGED IN.
Tracks: / Cry tough / I want action / I won't forget you / Play dirty / Look what the cat dragged in / Talk dirty to me / Want some, need some / Blame it on you / No.1 bad boy / Let me go to the show.
Cassette: released on MFN, Apr'87 by Music For Nations Records. Dist: Pinnacle

Album: released on Music For Nations, Oct'86 by Music For Nations Records. Dist: Pinnacle

Picture disc single: released on Music For Nations, Oct'86 by Music For Nations Records. Dist: Pinnacle

TALK DIRTY TO ME.
Tracks: / Talk dirty to me / Want some, need some / Poison interview.
Single (7"): released on Music For Nations, May'87 by Music For Nations Records. Dist: Pinnacle

Single (12"): released on Music For Nations, May'87 by Music For Nations Records. Dist: Pinnacle

Picture disc single: released on MFN, May'87 by Music For Nations Records. Dist: Pinnacle

Poison Girls

7 YEAR SCRATCH.
Album: released on Xntrix, Mar'84

ALL SYSTEMS GO.
Single (7"): released on Crass, Oct'81 by Exitstencil Music. Dist: Rough Trade, Cartel

ARE YOU HAPPY NOW.
Single (7"): released on Illuminated, Mar'85 by IKF Records. Dist: Pinnacle. Cartel, Jetstar

Single (12"): released on Illuminated, Mar'85 by IKF Records. Dist: Pinnacle. Cartel, Jetstar

ARE YOU HAPPY NOW (REMIX).
Single (12"): by IKF Records. Dist: Pinnacle, Cartel, Jetstar

CHAPPOQUIDICK BRIDGE.
Album: released on Crass, Oct'81 by Exitstencil Music. Dist: Rough Trade, Cartel

(I'M NOT A)REAL WOMAN.
Single (7"): released on X Centrix, Nov'84

Single (12"): released on X Centrix, Nov'84

ONE GOOD REASON.
Single (7"): released on Illuminated, Mar'85 by IKF Records. Dist: Pinnacle, Cartel, Jetstar

PERSONS UNKNOWN (Poison Girls/Crass).
Single (7"): released on Crass, Oct'81 by Exitstencil Music. Dist: Rough Trade, Cartel

PRICE OF GRAIN,THE.
Single (12"): released on Upright, Nov'85 by Upright Records. Dist: Cartel. Rough Trade

SONGS OF PRAISE.
Album: released on Antrix, Jun'85

WHERE'S THE PLEASURE.
Album: released on Xntrix, Nov'82

Poison No.9

LAY ALL YOUR LOVE ON ME.
Single (12"): released on Boy, Jan'87 Dist: Pinnacle

Polanski,Roman

PIRATES (OST).
Notes: For full information see under "Pirates" Original Soundtrack (Roman Polanski)

Polecats

CULT HEROES.
Album: released on Nervous, Jul'84 by Nervous Records. Dist: Nervous, Rough Trade

MAKE A CIRCUIT WITH ME/JUVENILE.
Single (7"): released on Mercury, Jan'83 by Phonogram Records. Dist: Polygram Distribution

Single (12"): released on Mercury, Jan'83 by Phonogram Records. Dist: Polygram Distribution

Police

AROUND THE WORLD.
Video-cassette (VHS): released on Thorn-Emi, Jan'84

CAN'T STAND LOSING YOU/DEAD END JOB.
Single (7"): released on A&M, Jan'84 by A&M Records. Dist: Polygram

DE DO DO DO DE DA DA DA/A SERMON.
Single (7"): released on A&M, Nov'80 by A&M Records. Dist: Polygram

DON'T STAND SO CLOSE TO ME/FRIENDS.
Single (7"): released on A&M, Sep'80 by A&M Records. Dist: Polygram

DON'T STAND SO CLOSE TO ME.
Tracks: / Don't stand so close to me / Don't stand so close to me (live).
Single (7"): released on A&M, Oct'86 by A&M Records. Dist: Polygram

Single (12"): released on A&M, Oct'86 by A&M Records. Dist: Polygram

EVERY BREATH YOU TAKE/MURDER BY NUMBERS.
Single (7"): released on A&M, Jun'83 by A&M Records. Dist: Polygram

Picture disc single: released on A&M, Jun'83 by A&M Records. Dist: Polygram

EVERY BREATH YOU TAKE - THE VIDEOS.
Notes: Compilation of 15 clips telling the story of the Police's career through their string of hit singles. Includes the 'new' version of 'DON'T STAND SO CLOSE TO ME'. 1986 compilation. Total playing time 60 minutes.
Video-cassette (VHS): released on A&M, Nov'86 by A&M Records. Dist: Polygram

EVERY BREATH YOU TAKE- THE ALBUM.
Tracks: / Roxanne / Can't Stand Losing You / Message In A Bottle / Walking On The Moon / Don't Stand So Close To Me '86 / De Do Do Do De Da Da Da / Every Little Thing She Does Is Magic / Invisible Sun / Spirits In The Material World / Every Breath You Take / King Of Pain / Wrapped Around Your Finger / So Lonely **.
Notes: Twelve songs,five number 1's,ten Top10 hits.Twelve classics.The definitive albumfrom one of the most successful recording acts of all time.
Album: released on A&M, Oct'86 by A&M Records. Dist: Polygram

Cassette: released on A&M, Oct'86 by A&M Records. Dist: Polygram

Compact disc: released on A&M, Oct'86 by A&M Records. Dist: Polygram

EVERY LITTLE THING SHE DOES IS MAGIC.
Single (7"): released on A&M, Oct'81 by A&M Records. Dist: Polygram

FALL OUT.
Single (7"): released on Illegal, Oct'77 by Faulty Products Records. Dist: Pinnacle, Lightning, Cartel

GHOST IN THE MACHINE.
Tracks: / Spirit in the material world / Every little thing she does is magic / Invisible sun / Hungry for you / Demolition man / Too much information / Rehumanise yourself / One world (not three) / Omega man / Secret journey / Darkness.
Notes: The Police were voted best band of the year and 'ZENYATTA MONDATTA' best album of the year in the combined BBC Television and Daily Mirror Pop Awards - the biggest national poll in Britain. They were runners up in every other category except best female vocalist. They also received awards for best British single and best British album from Capital Radio, the biggest commercial radio station in the country. But the most important objective measure of their success is their sale of records. Two years ago they were almost unknown, today the Police have sold over twelve million albums worldwide. They have Gold and Platinum status in Australia, Belgium, Canada, France, Germany, Holland, Italy, New Zealand, Portugal, Spain, United Kingdom and the USA. The result - The Police are established as perhaps the only band with true world wide status in the 1980's. "Ghost in the machine was recorded in Monserrat during July 1981.
Compact disc: released on A&M, '83 by A&M Records. Dist: Polygram

Album: released on A&M, Oct'81 by A&M Records. Dist: Polygram

Cassette: released on A&M, Oct'81 by A&M Records. Dist: Polygram

KING OF PAIN.
Single (7"): released on A&M, Jan'84 by A&M Records. Dist: Polygram

Single (12"): released on A&M, Jan'84 by A&M Records. Dist: Polygram Deleted '85.

MESSAGE IN A BOTTLE.
Single (7"): released on A&M, Sep'79 by A&M Records. Dist: Polygram

OUTLANDOS D'AMOUR.
Tracks: / Next to you / So lonely / Hole in my life / Roxanne / Peanuts / Can't stand losing you / Truth hits everybody / Born in the 50's / Be my girl - Sally / Masoko Tango.
Album: released on A&M, '78 by A&M Records. Dist: Polygram

Cassette: released on A&M, '78 by A&M Records. Dist: Polygram

Compact disc: released on A&M, '78 by A&M Records. Dist: Polygram

REGGATTA DE BLANC.
Tracks: / Message in a bottle / Reggatta de blanc / It's alright for you / Bring on the night / Deathwish / Walking on the moon / On any other day / Bed's too big without you, The / Contact / Does everybody stare / No time this time.
Album: released on A&M, Sep'79 by A&M Records. Dist: Polygram

Cassette: released on A&M, Sep'79 by A&M Records. Dist: Polygram

Compact disc: released on A&M, Sep'79 by A&M Records. Dist: Polygram

ROXANNE.
Tracks: / Synchronicity 11.
Single (7"): released on A&M, Nov'86 by A&M Records. Dist: Polygram

Single (7"): released on A&M, Mar'79 by A&M Records. Dist: Polygram

SO LONELY.
Single (7"): released on A&M, '78 by A&M Records. Dist: Polygram

SPIRITS IN THE MATERIAL WORLD.
Single (7"): released on A&M, Dec'81 by A&M Records. Dist: Polygram

SYNCHRONICITY.
Tracks: / Synchronicity 1 / Walking in your footsteps / Oh my God / Mother / Miss Gradenko / Synchronicity 2 / Every breath you take / King of pain / Wrapped around your finger / Tea in the Sahara.
Notes: Digital stereo
Compact disc: released on A&M, '83 by A&M Records. Dist: Polygram

Album: released on A&M, Jun'83 by A&M Records. Dist: Polygram

Cassette: released on A&M, Jun'83 by A&M Records. Dist: Polygram

SYNCHRONICITY CONCERT.
Notes: Music from the 'Synchronicity' album plus most of the band's greatest hits filmed live on by Godley and Creme. Total playing time 76 minutes.
Video-cassette (VHS): released on A&M Sound Pictures, Sep'84 by A&M Records. Dist: PVG

ZENYATTA MONDATTA.
Tracks: / Don't stand so close to me / Driven to tears / When the world is running down / Canary in a coal mine / Voices inside my head / Bombs away / De do do do, de da da da / Behind my camel / Man in a suitcase / Shadows in the rain / Other way of stopping (The).
Notes: 'Zenyatta' features the smash hits 'Don't Stand So Close To Me' and 'De Do Do Do, De Da Da Da' also included 'Driven to Tears', spotlighted by Sting at the Live Aid Concert in front of millions of viewers.
Album: released on A&M, Sep'86 by A&M Records. Dist: Polygram

Cassette: released on A&M, Sep'86 by A&M Records. Dist: Polygram

Compact disc: released on A&M, Sep'86 by A&M Records. Dist: Polygram

Album: released on A&M, Oct'80 by A&M Records. Dist: Polygram

Police Academy

POLICE ACADEMY FOUR 'CITIZENS ON PATROL' Original soundtrack (Various Artists).
Tracks: / Rock the house / It's time to move / Dancin' up a storm / Let's go to heaven in my car / High flyers, The (Police Academy theme) / Citizens on patrol / Rescue me / I like my body / Winning streak / Shoot for the top.
Album: released on Motown, Jul'87 by Motown Records. Dist: BMG Distribution

Cassette: released on Motown, Jul'87 by Motown Records. Dist: BMG Distribution

Politburo

EUPHORIA.
Tracks: / Euphoria.
Single (12"): released on Skysaw, Jun'86 by Skysaw Records. Dist: Red Rhino, Cartel

RADIO/MONEY.
Single (7"): released on Avatar, Aug'81 by Avatar Communications. Dist: CBS

Politians

HOLDING ON MY HAND.
Single (7"): released on Edible, Nov'84 by Edible Records. Dist: Pinnacle

Political Asylum

WINTER.
Single (7"): released on Children Of The Revolution, Apr'85 by Revolver Records. Dist: Revolver, Cartel

Polka..

POLKA'S GREATEST HITS various artists (Various Artists).
Album: released on ARC (Accordion Records), '84 Dist: Accordion Record Club

Polka Dots

OH ROSEMARY/DON'T LOVE ME AT ALL.
Single (7"): released on RCA, Apr'82 by RCA Records. Dist: RCA, Roots, Swift, Wellard, Chris, I & B, Solomon & Peres Distribution

Polkement Grorud Pipe...

FROM CELTIC ROOTS.
Notes: Tracks include hornpipes/Irish airs/Irish reels/marches etc.
Album: released on Lismor, Jul'86 by Lismor Records. Dist: Lismor, Roots, Celtic Music

Cassette: released on Lismor, Jul'86 by Lismor Records. Dist: Lismor, Roots, Celtic Music

Pollack,Ben

BEN POLLACK & HIS ORCHESTRA 1933/4.
Album: released on VJM, Apr'79 by Wellard, Chris Distribution. Dist: Wellard, Chris Distribution

FUTURISTIC RHYTHM (Pollack,Ben and his Park Central Orchestra).
Album: released on Saville, Apr'83 by Conifer Records. Dist: Conifer

IN LOS ANGELES 1937.
Album: released on Jazz Archives, Jan'80 by Jazz Archives Records. Dist: Jazz Music

RED AND BEN (Pollack, Ben & Red Nichols).
Album: released on Broadway, Apr'79 Dist: Jetstar

RED & BEN (see Nichols, Red) (Pollack, Ben & Red Nichols).

Pollard,Chuck

CHUCK POLLARD AND OTHERS.
Album: released on Jin, Feb'79 by Priority Records. Dist: EMI

Pollard, Su

COME TO ME (I am woman).
Tracks: / You don't really want me.
Single (7"): released on Rainbow, Feb'87 Dist: I & B, CBS

COME TO ME(IRON WOMAN).
Single (7"): released on Rainbow, Aug'85 Dist: I & B, CBS

STARTING TOGETHER.
Tracks: / Starting together / Good news.
Single (7"): released on Rainbow, Jan'86 Dist: I & B, CBS

SU.
Tracks: / Starting together / Perhaps love / You never done it like that / Once you lose your heart / Falling for you / Lies (la la lies) / You've lost that loving feeling / Wives will always be the last to know / Band of gold / Never thought I'd be losing you / Come to me I am a woman.
Album: released on K-Tel, Oct'86 by K-Tel Records. Dist: Record Merchandisers Distribution, Taylors, Terry Blood Distribution, Wynd-Up Distribution, Relay Distribution, Pickwick Distribution, Solomon & Peres Distribution, Polygram

Cassette: released on K-Tel, Oct'86 by K-Tel Records. Dist: Record Merchandisers Distribution, Taylors, Terry Blood Distribution, Wynd-Up Distribution, Relay Distribution, Pickwick Distribution, Solomon & Peres Distribution, Polygram

WIVES WILL ALWAYS BE THE LAST TO KNOW.
Tracks: / Wives will always be the last to know / Too late.
Single (7"): released on Rainbow, Oct'86 Dist: I & B, CBS

YOU'VE LOST THAT LOVING FEELING.
Tracks: / You've lost that loving feeling / Too late rainbow.
Single (7"): released on Rainbow, Jul'86 Dist: I & B, CBS

Single (12"): released on Rainbow, Jul'86 Dist: I & B, CBS

Pollard Tommy

SPIKE ROBINSON/TOMMY POLLARD'S DOWNBEAT FIVE/VICTOR FELDMAN See Robinson,Spike (Tommy Pollard's Downbeat Five/Victor Feldman/Spike Robinson).

Polo Praxis

MUSIC FOR FIREWORKS.
Album: released on Scarface, May'86 by Scarface Records. Dist: Cartel

Polyrock

NO LOVE'S LOST.
Cassette: released on Raw, Nov'86 by Raw Records. Dist: Spartan

Polystyrene

GODS AND GODDESSES.
Tracks: / Gods and goddesses (EP) / Trick of the witch / Paratma / Big boy, bog toy / Sacred temple.
Single (7"): released on Awesome, Aug'86 by Awesome Records. Dist: Rough Trade, Cartel

Single (12"): released on Awesome, Aug'86 by Awesome Records. Dist: Rough Trade, Cartel

TRANSLUCENCE.
Album: released on United Artists, Nov'80

Poni-Tails

BORN TOO LATE.
Single (7"): released on Old Gold, Jul'82 by Old Gold Records. Dist: Lightning, Jazz Music, Spartan, Counterpoint

Ponomareva, Valentina

FORTUNE TELLER.
Album: released on Leo, Oct'85 Dist: Recommended

Ponsar, Serge

I WANT MONEY.
Single (7"): released on WEA International, Nov'83 by WEA Records. Dist: WEA

Single (12"): released on WEA International, Nov'83 by WEA Records. Dist: WEA

OUT IN THE NIGHT.
Single (7"): released on WEA International, Jul'83 by WEA Records. Dist: WEA

Single (12"): released on WEA International, Jul'83 by WEA Records. Dist: WEA

Pontarddulais Male Choir

SOFTLY AS I LEAVE YOU.
Album: released on Grasmere, Oct'85 by Grasmere Records. Dist: EMI

Cassette: released on Grasmere, Oct'85 by Grasmere Records. Dist: EMI

Pontiac Brothers

DOLL HUT.
Album: released on Fountain Of Youth, Dec'85 Dist: Rough Trade, Cartel

FIESTA EN LA BIBLIOTECA.
Album: released on Shigaku, Nov'86

Ponty, Jean Luc

FABLES.
Tracks: / Infinite pursuit / Elephants in love / Radioactive legacy / Cats tales / Perpetual rondo / In the kingdom of peace / Plastic idols.
Album: released on Atlantic, Jan'86 by WEA Records. Dist: WEA

Cassette: released on Atlantic, Jan'86 by WEA Records. Dist: WEA

INDIVIDUAL CHOICE.
Tracks: / Computer incantations for world peace / Far from the beaten paths / In spiritual love / Eulogy to Oscar Romero / Nostalgia / Individual choice / In spite of all.
Notes: Digital stereo
Album: released on Polydor, Apr'84 by Polydor Records. Dist: Polygram, Polydor Deleted '85.

Compact disc: released on Polydor, Apr'84 by Polydor Records. Dist: Polygram, Polydor

JAZZ FIRST (Ponty, Jean Luc/Cleo Laine).
Tracks: / King Kong / Idiot bastard son / Twenty small cigars / How would you like to have a head like that / Music for electric violin and low budget orchestra / America drinks and goes home.
Cassette: released on Timeless Treasures, Jul'86 Dist: Counterpoint Distribution

Album: released on EMI (Italy), Sep'86 by EMI Records. Dist: Conifer

Cassette: released on EMI (Italy), Sep'86 by EMI Records. Dist: Conifer

KING KONG.
Tracks: / King Kong / Idiot bastard son / Twenty small cigars / How would you like to have a head like that / Music for elec.violin & low budget orchestra / America drinks & goes home / King kong / Idiot bastard son / Twenty small cigars / How would you like to have a head like that / Music for electric violin and low budget orchestra / America drinks and goes home.
Notes: Produced by Richard Brock Arranged by Frank Zappa
Album: released on Liberty, Jun'87 by Liberty-United. Dist: EMI

Cassette: released on Liberty, Jun'87 by Liberty-United. Dist: EMI

OPEN MIND.
Tracks: / Open mind / Solitude / Watching birds / Modern times blue / Orbital encounters / Intuition.
Notes: Digital stereo
Album: released on Polydor, Nov'84 by Polydor Records. Dist: Polygram, Polydor Deleted '85.

Cassette: released on Polydor, Nov'84 by Polydor Records. Dist: Polygram, Polydor

Compact disc: released on Polydor, Nov'84 by Polydor Records. Dist: Polygram, Polydor

SONATA EROTICA.
Album: released on Affinity, May'85 by Charly Records. Dist: Charly, Cadillac

Album: released on Atmosphere, Sep'79 by E.S.S.P..

UPON THE WINGS OF MUSIC.
Album: released on Atlantic, Aug'75 by WEA Records. Dist: WEA

Ponzel, Peter

PRISM.
Album: released on Vinyl, Mar'79

Pooh song book, (The)

POOH SONG BOOK, (THE) Milne, A.A. (Channing, Carol).
Cassette: released on Caedmon(USA), Aug'83 by Caedmon (USA) Records. Dist: Gower, Taylors, Discovery

Pookah Makes Three

LUCKY LUCKY LUCKY.
Single (7"): released on 10, Feb'84 by 10 Records. Dist: Virgin, EMI

Single (12"): released on 10, Feb'84 by 10 Records. Dist: Virgin, EMI Deleted '86.

TAKE IT BACK.
Single (7"): released on 10, Sep'84 by 10 Records. Dist: Virgin, EMI

Single (12"): released on 10, Sep'84 by 10 Records. Dist: Virgin, EMI Deleted '86.

WAVING A FLAME.
Single (7"): released on 10, Mar'85 by 10 Records. Dist: Virgin, EMI

Pookiesnackenburger

AS ADVERTISED ON TV.
Album: released on Talkback, Apr'85

Cassette: released on Talkback, Apr'85

JUST ONE CORNETTO.
Single (7"): released on Stiff, Jan'82 by Stiff Records. Dist: EMI, Record Services Distribution (Ireland)

Poole, Brian

DO YOU LOVE ME? (Poole, Brian & Tramline).
Single (7"): released on Outlook, Apr'83 by Brian Poole. Dist: Spartan Distribution

DO YOU LOVE ME? (Poole, Brian & the Tremeloes).
Single (7"): released on Old Gold, Oct'83 by Old Gold Records. Dist: Lightning, Jazz Music, Spartan, Counterpoint

GREATEST HITS: BRIAN POOLE
Album: released on BPCV, Jan'85 Dist: M.I.S.

Cassette: released on Autograph, Apr'85 Dist: Record Services Distribution (Ireland)

REMEMBERING BRIAN POOLE & THE TREMELOES (Poole, Brian & the Tremeloes).
Album: released on Decca, Apr'77 by Decca Records. Dist: Polygram

SOMEONE SOMEONE (Poole, Brian (Black Cat)).
Single (7"): released on Sumatra, Nov'83 by Sumatra Records. Dist: Pinnacle

TWIST AND SHOUT (Poole, Brian & the Tremeloes).
Album: released on Spot, May'86 by Pickwick Records. Dist: H.R. Taylor, Lugtons

Cassette: released on Spot, May'86 by Pickwick Records. Dist: H.R. Taylor, Lugtons

Single (7"): released on Decca, Oct'80 by Decca Records. Dist: Polygram

Album: released on Decca, May'82 by Decca Records. Dist: Polygram Deleted '84.

Cassette: released on Decca, May'82 by Decca Records. Dist: Polygram

Pool Sharks

FINAL ADJUSTMENTS.
Album: released on Strike, 30 May'87 by Strike Records. Dist: Fresh Distribution, Rough Trade Distribution, Strike Distribution

Poorboys

MOVE BABY MOVE.
Single (7"): released on Ace, Nov'82 by Ace Records. Dist: Pinnacle, Swift, Hotshot, Cadillac

POORBOY SHUFFLE.
Tracks: / Poorboy shuffle / Waterfront girls / Wolfman moan.
Single (7"): released on El Panzon, Jan'86 by El Panzon Records. Dist: Rough Trade

Poor Howard

MAYBE TOMORROW.
Single (7"): released on Self Drive, Apr'84 Dist: Red Rhino, Cartel

Poorsah

GO RIGHT UP IN DEY.
Single (7"): released on Trindisc, Mar'84 by Trindisc Records. Dist: Jetstar, Pinnacle, Rough Trade, Cartel

Poors of reign

CHERISH.
Tracks: / Cherish.
Single (7"): released on Low Type, Aug'86 Dist: Red Rhino

Poovey, Groovey Joe

YESTERDAY & TODAY.
Album: released on Dee-Jay Jambouree, May'86

Poovey, Groovy Joe

LIFE'S AMBITION.
Single (7"): released on Rollin, Jun'80

Pop

HEARTS AND KNIVES.
Album: released on Rhino (USA), Feb'85 by Rhino Records (USA).

POP BRASS (Various Artists).
Album: released on Decca, Nov'80 by Decca Records. Dist: Polygram

Pop Black

BLACK AND WHITE RAG.
Single (7"): released on Weasel, May'80 by Weasel Records. Dist: Spartan

Pop Concert

SOUND SENSATIONS.
Album: released on Tempo, '79 by Warwick Records. Dist: Multiple Sound Distributors

Pope, Dave

BEST OF DAVE POPE.
Album: released on Myrrh, May'82 by Word Records. Dist: Word Distribution

Cassette: released on Myrrh, May'82 by Word Records. Dist: Word Distribution

SAIL AWAY.
Album: released on Myrrh, May'82 by Word Records. Dist: Word Distribution

Cassette: released on Myrrh, May'82 by Word Records. Dist: Word Distribution

TASTE AND SEE.
Album: released on Myrrh, Apr'85 by Word Records. Dist: Word Distribution

Cassette: released on Myrrh, Apr'85 by Word Records. Dist: Word Distribution

Pope, Jana

I'M LOSING YOU (REMIX).
Tracks: / You won't believe it.
Single (7"): released on Polydor, Feb'87 by Polydor Records. Dist: Polygram, Polydor

Single (12"): released on Polydor, Feb'87 by Polydor Records. Dist: Polygram, Polydor

Pope John Paul II

LIVERPOOL 30TH MAY 1982.
Album: released on Alpha, Aug'82 by Alpha Records. Dist: H.R. Taylor, Gamut

Cassette: released on Alpha, Oct'82 by Alpha Records. Dist: H.R. Taylor, Gamut

PILGRIM POPE, THE.
Album: released on BBC, Jun'82 by BBC Records & Tapes. Dist: EMI, PRT, Pye

Cassette: released on BBC, Jun'82 by BBC Records & Tapes. Dist: EMI, PRT, Pye

RECORDED SOUVENIR OF THE HISTORIC VISIT OF HIS HOLINESS, A (England, May 28th 1982 - June 2nd 1982).
Album: released on Ronco, Apr'82

Pope, Tim

I WANT TO BE A TREE.
Single (7"): released on Fiction, Jun'84 by Fiction Records. Dist: Polygram

Single (12"): released on Fiction, Jun'84 by Fiction Records. Dist: Polygram

Pop explosion

POP EXPLOSION! Various original artists (Various original artists).
Tracks: / Still I'm sad / I can never go home anymore / Folsom prison blues / Johnny B. Goode / Cry for a shadow / Lucille / Matchbox / Why / Iko-Iko / Evil hearted you / It's in his kiss / Everybody's trying to be my baby / High school confidential / Shapes of things / Give him a great big kiss / Lawdy Miss Clawdy / Harper valley PTA / Heartful of sould / Ya ya / Girl most likely (The) / Whole lotta shakin' goin' on (A) / Raunchy / For your love.
Album: released on Cambra, Sep'86 by Cambra Records. Dist: IDS, Conifer

Cassette: released on Cambra, Sep'86 by Cambra Records. Dist: IDS, Conifer

POP EXPLOSION VOL.1 Various artists (Various Artists).
Album: released on Cambra, Aug'83 by Cambra Records. Dist: IDS, Conifer

Cassette: released on Cambra, Aug'83 by Cambra Records. Dist: IDS, Conifer

Pop Explosion (Vol 2)

POP EXPLOSION (VOL 2) Various artists (Various Artists).
Album: released on Cambra, Aug'83 by Cambra Records. Dist: IDS, Conifer

Cassette: released on Cambra, Aug'83 by Cambra Records. Dist: IDS, Conifer

Popeye

POPEYE Original motion picture soundtrack.
Album: released on Epic, Apr'81 by CBS Records. Dist: CBS

Pop Group

HOW MUCH LONGER.
Album: released on Rough Trade, Mar'80 by Rough Trade Records. Dist: Rough Trade Distribution, Cartel Distribution

WE ARE TIME.
Album: released on Rough Trade, Aug'84 by Rough Trade Records. Dist: Rough Trade Distribution, Cartel Distribution

Pop Guitar...

POP GUITAR EXTRAVAGANZA (Various Artists).
Double cassette: released on Pickwick, '83 by Pickwick Records. Dist: Pickwick Distribution, Prism Leisure Distribution, Lugtons

Pop Hits...

POP HITS OF THE EARLY 60'S (Various Artists).
Album: released on Old Gold, Jun'85 by Old Gold Records. Dist: Lightning, Jazz Music, Spartan, Counterpoint

Cassette: released on Old Gold, Jun'85 by Old Gold Records. Dist: Lightning, Jazz Music, Spartan, Counterpoint

POP HITS OF THE MID-LATE 50'S (Various Artists).
Tracks: / Love Letters In The Sand / Just Walking In The Rain / Young Love / Sixteen Tons / Banana Boat Song / Fever / Patricia / Coma Prima / Tom Dooley / Freight Train / Lollipop / I Love You Baby / Smoke Gets In Your Eyes / Broken Hearted Melody.
Notes: They reflect the variety of musical styles prevelant in the mid 50's.From skiffle to folk,cha-cha,country ,ballads and pop,all these memorable songs transcendedthe changing musical emphasis brought about by the emergence of rock'n'roll.
Digital audio tape: released on Old Gold, Nov'86 by Old Gold Records. Dist: Lightning, Jazz Music, Spartan, Counterpoint

Cassette: released on Old Gold, Nov'86 by Old Gold Records. Dist: Lightning, Jazz Music, Spartan, Counterpoint

Pop Icons

SAME OLD STORY.
Tracks: / Same old story / Devil and the deep blue sea.
Single (7"): released on Vital spark, Jan'86 Dist: Vital Spark Records

Pop, Iggy

BLAH BLAH BLAH.
Album: released on A&M, Sep'86 by A&M Records. Dist: Polygram

Cassette: released on A&M, Sep'86 by A&M Records. Dist: Polygram

Compact disc: released on A&M, Oct'86 by A&M Records. Dist: Polygram

CHOICE CUTS.
Album: released on RCA (Germany), Sep'84

CRY FOR LOVE.
Tracks: / Cry for love / Winners and losers.
Single (7"): released on A&M, Oct'86 by A&M Records. Dist: Polygram

Single (12"): released on A&M, Oct'86 by A&M Records. Dist: Polygram

FIRE GIRL.
Tracks: / Fire girl / Blah-blah-blah (live).
Single (7"): released on A&M, Apr'87 by A&M Records. Dist: Polygram

Single (12"): released on A&M, Apr'87 by A&M Records. Dist: Polygram

ISOLATION.
Tracks: / Isolation / Hideaway / Fire girl (remix)*.
Single (7"): released on A&M, Jun'87 by A&M Records. Dist: Polygram

Single (12"): released on A&M, Jun'87 by A&M Records. Dist: Polygram

LUST FOR LIFE.
Album: released on RCA International, '84

Cassette: released on RCA International, '84

PARTY.
Tracks: / Pleasure / Rock and roll party / Eggs on plate / Sincerity / Houston is hot tonight / Pumpin' for Jill / Happy man / Bang bang / Sea of love / Time won't let me.
Album: released on Arista, Jan'87 by Arista Records. Dist: RCA

Cassette: released on Arista, Jan'87 by Arista Records. Dist: RCA

Album: released on Arista, Jun'81 by Arista Records. Dist: RCA

PASSENGER, THE.
Single (7"): released on RCA, May'82 by RCA Records. Dist: RCA, Roots, Swift, Wellard, Chris, I & B, Solomon & Peres Distribution

SHADES.
Tracks: / Baby it cant fall / Cry for love*.
Notes: *=Extra track on 12" only
Single (7"): released on A&M, Feb'87 by A&M Records. Dist: Polygram

Single (12"): released on A&M, Feb'87 by A&M Records. Dist: Polygram

TV EYE (1977 LIVE).
Album: released on RCA (Germany), Apr'83

WILD CHILD.
Tracks: / Little Miss Emperor.
Single (7"): released on A&M, Nov'86 by A&M Records. Dist: Polygram

Single (12"): released on A&M, Nov'86 by A&M Records. Dist: Polygram

ZOMBIE BIRDHOUSE.
Album:

Cassette: released on Animal, Sep'82 by Chrysalis Records. Dist: Polygram Deleted '85.

Pop Invitation...

POP INVITATION TO THE CLASSICAL MUSIC VOL.2 (Various Artists).
Album: released on Demon, Mar'82 by Demon Records. Dist: Pinnacle

POP INVITATION TO THE CLASSICAL MUSIC (Various Artists).
Album: released on Denon, Mar'82

Pop Machine

SING AND PLAY ABBA.
Cassette: released on Bravo, Feb'80 by Pickwick Records. Dist: Lugtons

Popman and the...

JUST LIKE A WOMAN (Popman and the raging bull).
Tracks: / Just like a woman / Casual aquaintance.
Single (12"): released on MCA, Aug'86 by MCA Records. Dist: Polygram, MCA

Pop Masters

POP MASTERS, THE.
Album: released on Jazz Live (Import), Apr'81

Poppie Nongena

POPPIE NONGENA Original Cast Recording.
Notes: Traditional harmony singing from the award-winning play depicting the true storyof a South African woman and her family.
Album: released on Hannibal, Jan'87 by Hannibal Records. Dist: Charly, Harmonia Mundi, Projection, Celtic Music, Roots

POPPIE NONGENA Cast album (Various artists) (Various Artists).
Album: released on Hannibal, '84 by Hannibal Records. Dist: Charly, Harmonia Mundi, Projection, Celtic Music, Roots

Popples

THERE'S A PAIN IN MY HEART.
Single (7"): released on Inferno, '79 by Inferno Records. Dist: Inferno, Cartel, Pinnacle

Poppin, Keith

ENVIOUS.
Tracks: / Envious.
Single (12"): released on Unknown, Jun'86

Poppy

POPPY Royal Shakespeare Company's stage production (Various Artists).
Album: released on WEA, Nov'82 by WEA Records. Dist: WEA

Cassette: released on WEA, Nov'82 by WEA Records. Dist: WEA

Poppy, Andrew

32 FRAMES FOR ORCHESTRA.
Tracks: / 32 frames for orchestra / Impossible (The).
Single (12"): released on ZTT, Sep'86 by Island Records. Dist: Polygram

ALPHABED A mystery dance.
Tracks: / 45 is / Goodbye Mr.G / Amusement, The.
Notes: Engineered by Dave Meegan. All songs written by Andrew Poppy.
Album: released on ZTT, Jun'87 by Island Records. Dist: Polygram

Cassette: released on ZTT, Jun'87 by Island Records. Dist: Polygram

AMUSEMENT, THE.
Tracks: / Amusement, The / Listening in / Kink konk presto* / East fragment / Kink konk adagio.
Single (7"): released on ZTT, Feb'87 by Island Records. Dist: Polygram

Single (12"): released on ZTT, Feb'87 by Island Records. Dist: Polygram

BEATING OF WINGS (THE).
Tracks: / Object is a hungry wolf (The) / 32 frames for orchestra / Listening in / Cadenza.
Album: released on ZTT, Oct'85 by Island Records. Dist: Polygram

Cassette: released on ZTT, Oct'85 by Island Records. Dist: Polygram

Compact disc: released on ZTT, Oct'85 by Island Records. Dist: Polygram

Poppy Family

WHICH WAY YOU GOIN' BILLY.
Single (7"): released on Decca, '69 by Decca Records. Dist: Polygram

Poppy Fields

ALIEN.
Single (12"): released on Illuminated, Feb'85 by IKF Records. Dist: Pinnacle, Cartel, Jetstar

Pop Rivits

POP RIVETS GREATEST HITS.
Album: released on Ace, May'80 by Ace Records. Dist: Pinnacle, Swift, Hotshot, Cadillac

Pop/Rock Group Hits

POP/ROCK GROUP HITS OF THE MID 60'S ~ (Various Artists).
Tracks: / Here Comes the Night / Needles & Pins / You Really Got Me / She's Not There / Do Wah Diddy Diddy / I'm Alive / Go Now / Hippy Hippy Shake / House Of The Rising Sun / All or nothing / Here comes the night / Heart Full Of Soul / Tobacco Road / I Can't Explain / I Feel Free.
Notes: They reflect the energy,variety and innovation that echoed around the world fromBritish groups during the mid 60's,much of which provided the inspiration for later generations of rock acts.
Album: released on Old Gold, Nov'86 by Old Gold Records. Dist: Lightning, Jazz Music, Spartan, Counterpoint

Cassette: released on Old Gold, Nov'86 by Old Gold Records. Dist: Lightning, Jazz Music, Spartan, Counterpoint

Pop-Rock Symphonia

Tracks: / Mickey / Take it away / Girl crazy / Fantasy island / Head over heels / Jive talkin' / Come on Eileen / Super trouper / Hi fidelity / I could be so good for you / I will survive / Modern girl / Nine to five (morning train) / Can't smile without you / Arthur's theme / Begin the beguine / Copacobana / One of us / Hill Street Blues / Fame / Hands up / Staying alive / Just another broken heart / If I should love again / I write the songs.
Notes: Double album, double cassette.
Album: released on Cambra, Sep'86 by Cambra Records. Dist: IDS, Conifer

Cassette: released on Cambra, Sep'86 by Cambra Records. Dist: IDS, Conifer

Pops, Charlie

DON'T TEASE THE ANIMALS.
Single (7"): released on JSO, May'82

Pop Sike Pipe Dreams

POP SIKE PIPE DREAMS (Various Artists).
Album: released on Bam Caruso, Mar'87 by Bam Caruso Records. Dist: Rough Trade, Revolver, Cartel

Pop Sixties

POP SIXTIES (Various Artists).
Notes: Including The Hollies, Beach Boys.
Album: released on Trax Baby Boomer Classics, Apr'87

Cassette: released on Trax Baby Boomer Classics, Apr'87

Pop & The Beagle

NAME THAT TUNE.
Single (7"): released on Venture, Mar'80 Dist: Revolver, Cartel

Popticians

MOBILE HOME.
Single (7"): released on Off The Kerb, Jun'84 by Off The Kerb Records. Dist: Rough Trade Distribution, Cartel Distribution

Poptones

WOODEN HEART.
Single (7"): released on Square, Nov'80

Popular Christmas Carols

POPULAR CHRISTMAS CAROLS (Choir Of St. Mary, Warwick).
Album: released on Abbey, Nov'83 by Abbey. Dist: PRT, Taylors, Gamut

Cassette: released on Abbey, Nov'83 by Abbey. Dist: PRT, Taylors, Gamut

Popular Front

BIG BANG, THE.
Cassette: released on Sounds Of Suburbia, Apr'85

FALLING OUT.
Single (7"): released on Midnight Music, 23 May'87 by Midnight Music Records. Dist: Rough Trade Distribution, Cartel Distribution

HEARTBEAT OF LAUGHING, A.
Album: released on Midnight Music, Oct'86 by Midnight Music Records. Dist: Rough Trade Distribution, Cartel Distribution

LIBERTE+EGALITE+DANSABILITE.
Tracks: / Liberte+egalite+dansabilite (EP) / Did

the earth move? / Listening (A) / Buffet of forbidden fruit (A) / La position soixante-huit.
Single (7"): released on Midnight Music, Jun'86 by Midnight Music Records. Dist: Rough Trade Distribution, Cartel Distribution

Popular History Of Signs
BODY AND SOUL.
Single (7"): released on Jungle, Oct'84 by Jungle Records. Dist: Jungle, Cartel

Single (12"): released on Jungle, Oct'84 by Jungle Records. Dist: Jungle, Cartel

COMRADES.
Album: released on Jungle, Jan'85 by Jungle Records. Dist: Jungle, Cartel

DANCING WITH IDEAS.
Single (12"): released on Melodia, Oct'82 Dist: Rough Trade Distribution

HOUSE.
Single (12"): released on Jungle, Mar'84 by Jungle Records. Dist: Jungle, Cartel

IF SHE WAS A CAR.
Single (12"): released on Jungle, Sep'83 by Jungle Records. Dist: Jungle, Cartel

LADDERJACK.
Single (12"): released on Waxtrax, Dec'84 by Jungle Records. Dist: PRT

Popular roots (Reggae)
POPULAR ROOTS (REGGAE) Various artists (Various Artists).
Notes: Double album
Album: released on Virgin, Nov'85 by Virgin Records. Dist: EMI, Virgin Distribution

Cassette: released on Virgin, Nov'85 by Virgin Records. Dist: EMI, Virgin Distribution

Popul Vuh
AGAPE AGAPE.
Album: released on Uniton (Norway), Apr'85 Dist: Cartel

BRUDER DES SCHATTENS SOHNE DES LICHTS.
Album: released on Brain Import, Jan'79

MUSIC FROM COEUR DE VERRE.
Album: released on Egg, Nov'79 by Barclay Records. Dist: Logo, RCA, Discovery

MUSIC FROM NOSFERATU.
Album: released on Egg, Nov'79 by Barclay Records. Dist: Logo, RCA, Discovery

SPIRIT OF PEACE.
Album: released on Uniton (Norway), May'86 Dist: Cartel

Cassette: released on Uniton (Norway), May'86 Dist: Cartel

Pop wallpaper
OVER YOUR SHOULDER.
Single (12"): released on Spark, Aug'84 by Spark Records. Dist: PRT

STRAWBERRY LETTER 23.
Tracks: Strawberry letter 23 / Nothing can call me back.
Single (12"): released on Rosebud, Apr'86 Dist: Fast Forward Distributors

Pop Will Eat Itself
IMAGES ON GUITAR.
Album: released on MPS Jazz, May'81

LOVE MISSILE F1-11.
Tracks: / Love missile F1-11 / Orgone accumulator / Everything that rises" / Like an angel".
Single (7"): released on Chapter 22, 23 May'87 by Chapter 22 Records. Dist: Nine Mile, Cartel

Single (12"): released on Chapter 22, 23 May'87 by Chapter 22 Records. Dist: Nine Mile, Cartel

LOVE MISSILE F1-11 (REMIX).
Tracks: / Love missile F1-11 (remix) / Everything that rises (remix) / Orgone accumulator / Like an angel.
Single (12"): released on Chapter 22, Jun'87 by Chapter 22 Records. Dist: Nine Mile, Cartel

POPPIECOCK.
Notes: 5 track EP
Single (7"): released on Chapter 22, Nov'86 by Chapter 22 Records. Dist: Nine Mile, Cartel

Single (12"): released on Chapter 22, Nov'86 by Chapter 22 Records. Dist: Nine Mile, Cartel

SWEET SWEET PIE.
Tracks: / Devil Inside / Runaround.
Single (7"): released on Chapter 22, Jan'87 by Chapter 22 Records. Dist: Nine Mile, Cartel

Single (12"): released on Chapter 22, Jan'87 by Chapter 22 Records. Dist: Nine Mile, Cartel

Porgy & Bess
PORGY AND BESS REVISITED Various artists (Various Artists).
Album: released on Ace, Oct'86 by Ace Records. Dist: Pinnacle, Swift, Hotshot, Cadillac

PORGY & BESS Original cast.
Album: released on MCA, Mar'82 by MCA Records. Dist: CBS

Cassette: released on MCA, Mar'82 by MCA Records. Dist: CBS

PORGY & BESS Original soundtrack.
Album: released on CBS(Holland), Jun'84 by CBS Records. Dist: Discovery

PORGY & BESS Various artists (Various Artists).
Boxed set: released on Decca, Apr'76 by Decca Records. Dist: Polygram

Pork dukes
PIG IN A POKE.
Album: released on Butt, Mar'82 by Butt Records. Dist: Counterpoint

PIG OUT OF HELL.
Tracks: / Devil driver / House of the rising sun / Three men in an army truck / My mother / Gin sin / Let's spend the night together / I'm a guitar / Day tripper / Do you love me / Marxist ceninist feminist / Stop / Around and around.
Album: released on Shanghai, Aug'86

Porky's
PORKY'S Original soundtrack.
Album: released on Polydor, Aug'82 by Polydor Records. Dist: Polygram, Polydor

Cassette: released on Polydor, Aug'82 by Polydor Records. Dist: Polygram, Polydor

Porky's revenge
PORKY'S REVENGE Original soundtrack.
Album: released on CBS, Jul'85 by CBS Records. Dist: CBS

Cassette: released on CBS, Jul'85 by CBS Records. Dist: CBS

Porres, Nannie
SANGER MED SONJA.
Notes: With Sonja Akkesson, P Ortman etc
Album: released on Dragon, Jun'86 by Dragon Records. Dist: Jazz Music, Projection, Cadillac

Porridge people
EXTENSION 38 (EP).
Single (7"): released on Oat, May'83 by Oat Records. Dist: Cartel Distribution

Porter-Brown, Reginald
REGINALD PORTER-BROWN.
Notes: Reginald Porter-Brown in Australia, Wurlitzer 2-10, Town Hall, Sydney.
Album: released on Deroy, May'86 by Deroy Records. Dist: Jazz Music, Swift

Album: released on Deroy, May'86 by Deroy Records. Dist: Jazz Music, Swift

Porter, Cole
DREAM DANCING (Porter, Cole/Ella Fitzgerald).
Album: released on Pablo (USA), May'82 by Pablo Records (USA). Dist: Wellard, Chris, IMS-Polygram, BMG

Cassette: released on Pablo (USA), May'82 by Pablo Records (USA). Dist: Wellard, Chris, IMS-Polygram, BMG

IN LONDON.
Double Album: released on World, Sep'74 Dist: Jetstar

MEYER DAVIS PLAYS COLE PORTER.
Album: released on Monmouth, Mar'79

Porter, Eddie Ray
WHEN THE MORNING FALLS.
Album: released on New Rose, Jul'87 Dist: Rough Trade, Cartel

Porter, Hugh
LITTLE LOVE, A (Porter, Hugh/Dean Frazer).
Single (12"): released on Reggae, May'85 by Reggae Records. Dist: Jetstar, Morpheus Distribution

WOMAN (FEELING THE FEELING).
Single (12"): released on Intense, Dec'83 by Intense Records. Dist: PRT, Kingdom

Porter, Jerry
DON'T BOTHER ME.
Notes: Blues 1966
Album: released on Mirror, Sep'86 by Priority Records. Dist: Priority Distribution

Porthos, Pablo
PABLO PABLO.
Album: released on Globestyle, Nov'85 by Ace Records. Dist: Projection

Portion Control
ASSAULT.
Cassette: released on For All And None, Nov'86 Dist: Backs

GO TALK.
Single (12"): released on Illuminated, Mar'85 by IKF Records. Dist: Pinnacle, Cartel, Jetstar

GREAT DIVIDE, (THE).
Single (7"): released on Rhythmic, Jul'85 by Rhythmic Records. Dist: Havoc Distribution

Single (12"): released on Rhythmic, Jul'85 by Rhythmic Records. Dist: Havoc Distribution

HIT THE PULSE.
Album: released on In Phaze, Nov'83 by In Phaze Records. Dist: Rough Trade

PSYCHO BOD SAVES THE WORLD.
Album: released on Deadman's Curve, Nov'86 by Dave Henderson

PURGE.
Single (12"): released on DMC, Aug'86 Dist: Red Rhino, Cartel

RAISE THE PULSE.
Single (12"): released on Illuminated, Mar'85 by IKF Records. Dist: Pinnacle, Cartel .Jetstar

ROUGH JUSTICE.
Single (12"): released on Illuminated, Mar'84 by IKF Records. Dist: Pinnacle, Cartel, Jetstar

SIMULATE SENSUAL.
Album: released on In Phaze, Jun'84 by In Phaze Records. Dist: Rough Trade

STEP FORWARD.
Album: released on Illuminated, Oct'84 by IKF Records. Dist: Pinnacle, Cartel, Jetstar

SURFACE TO BE SEEN (EP).
Single (12"): released on In Phaze, Mar'82 by In Phaze Records. Dist: Rough Trade

Portland Bill & A.....
PORTLAND BILL & A..... (Rossington,Norman).
Cassette: released on Tempo, Aug'84 Dist: MSD Distribution

Portland Bill's busy day
PORTLAND BILL'S BUSY DAY (Rossington,Norman).
Cassette: released on Tempo, Aug'84 Dist: MSD Distribution

Portland Bill's message
PORTLAND BILL'S IMPORTANT MESSAGE (Rossington,Norman).
Cassette: released on Tempo, Aug'84 Dist: MSD Distribution

Portland Bill & the storm
PORTLAND BILL & THE STORM (Rossington,Norman).
Cassette: released on Tempo, Aug'84 Dist: MSD Distribution

Portland stone
PORTLAND STONE QUARRIES WORK CHANTS.
Cassette: released on Folktracks, Nov'79 by Folktracks Cassettes. Dist: Folktracks

Portnoy, Gary
CHEERS THEME.
Single (7"): released on Starblend, Jan'84 by Starblend Records. Dist: PRT Distribution

Port-O-Spain
PHYSICAL CONTACT.
Single (7"): released on Vista Sounds, Jul'83 by Vista Sounds Records. Dist: Jetstar

Portsmouth Sinfonia
20 CLASSIC ROCK CLASSIC.
Album: released on Philips, Aug'79 Dist: IMS-Polygram

Portway Peddlars
IN GREENWOOD SHADES.
Album:

Posey, Sandy
SINGLE GIRL.
Tracks: / Single girl / Born a woman.
Single (7"): released on Old Gold, Mar'86 by Old Gold Records. Dist: Lightning, Jazz Music, Spartan, Counterpoint

VERY BEST OF SANDY POSEY.
Album: released on MGM, Mar'84 Dist: Polygram Distribution, Swift Distribution

Cassette: released on MGM, Mar'84 Dist: Polygram Distribution, Swift Distribution Deleted May'87.

Posh
LETTER TO LINDA.
Single (7"): released on Marathon, Aug'81 by Marathon Records. Dist: PRT

SAND IN MY FACE.
Single (7"): released on Marathon, Aug'83 by Marathon Records. Dist: PRT

Posh Hits
GOD BLESS AMERICA Posh hits Vol.1 (Various Artists).
Album: released on Fall Out, May'85 Dist: Swift, Red Rhino, Cartel

Posion No. 9
LAY ALL YOUR LOVE ON ME.
Tracks: / Lay all your love on me.
Single (7"): released on Boy, Mar'87 Dist: Pinnacle

Position Alpha
CREDA.
Album: released on Dragon, Jul'87 by Dragon Records. Dist: Jazz Music, Projection. Cadillac

GREAT SOUND OF SOUND, THE.
Notes: Double Album.
Double Album: released on Dragon, Feb'87 by Dragon Records. Dist: Jazz Music, Projection, Cadillac

Positive force
WE GOT THE FUNK.
Tracks: / We got the funk / Rappers delight (Sugarhill gang).
Single (12"): released on Streetwave, Dec'85 by Streetwave Records. Dist: PRT Distribution

Positive noise
CHANGE OF HEART.
Album: released on Statik, Jul'82 Dist: Rough Trade Distribution, Stage One Distribution

DISTANT FIRES.
Album: released on Statik, Jun'85 Dist: Rough Trade Distribution, Stage One Distribution

Single (7"): released on Statik, Jun'85 Dist: Rough Trade Distribution, Stage One Distribution

Single (12"): released on Statik, Jun'85 Dist: Rough Trade Distribution, Stage One Distribution

GET UP AND GO.
Single (7"): released on Statik, Sep'82 Dist: Rough Trade Distribution, Stage One Distribution

Single (12"): released on Statik, Sep'82 Dist: Rough Trade Distribution, Stage One Distribution

HEART OF DARKNESS.
Album: released on Stage One, May'81 by Stage One Records. Dist: Stage One Distribution

MILLION MILES AWAY.
Single (7"): released on Statik, Aug'84 Dist: Rough Trade Distribution, Stage One Distribution

Single (12"): released on Statik, Aug'84 Dist: Rough Trade Distribution, Stage One Distribution

WHEN THE LIGHTNING STRIKES.
Single (7"): released on Statik, Sep'83 Dist: Rough Trade Distribution, Stage One Distribution

Single (12"): released on Statik, Sep'83 Dist: Rough Trade Distribution, Stage One Distribution

Posit, Jean Pierre
SANTA MONICA.
Single (7"): released on Ferroway, Mar'84 Dist: PRT

Single (12"): released on Ferroway, Mar'84 Dist: PRT

Posit, John Pierre
FLUTE D'AMOUR.
Album: released on Ferroway, Mar'84 Dist: PRT

Cassette: released on Ferroway, Mar'84 Dist: PRT

Posse, George

SMILE (see Adekile, Toyin) (Posse, George/Toyin Adekile).

TOUCH A FOUR LEAF CLOVER.
Single (12"): released on Sir George, Sep'84 by Sir George Records. Dist: Jetstar, Pinnacle

Possessed

BEYOND THE GATES.
Tracks: / Heretic / Tribulation / March To Die / Phantasm / No Will To Live / Beyond The Gates / Beast of the Apocalypse / Seance / Restless Dead / Dog Fight.
Album: released on Under One Flag, Nov'86 Dist: Pinnacle

Compact disc: released on Under One Flag, Aug'87 Dist: Pinnacle

EYES OF HORROR, THE.
Album: released on Under One Flag, Jun'87 Dist: Pinnacle

SEVEN CHURCHES.
Album: released on Road Runner, Dec'85

Possession

THIN WHITE ARMS.
Album: released on A.Mission, Jul'84 Dist: Red Rhino, Cartel

Postman Pat

POSTMAN PAT (SONGS AND DANCES FROM THE BBC TV SERIES) (Barrie, Ken).
Album:

Cassette:

POSTMAN PAT STORIES John Cunliffe (Cunliffe, John).
Notes: For full information see under "Cunliffe,John".

Post, Mike

A TEAM, (THE).
Album: released on RCA, Nov'84 by RCA Records. Dist: RCA, Roots, Swift, Wellard, Chris, I & B, Solomon & Peres Distribution

Cassette: released on RCA, Nov'84 by RCA Records. Dist: RCA, Roots, Swift, Wellard, Chris, I & B, Solomon & Peres Distribution

HILL STREET BLUES.
Single (7"): released on Elektra, Nov'85 by WEA Records. Dist: WEA

Picture disc single: released on Elektra, Nov'85 by WEA Records. Dist: WEA

Single (7"): released on Old Gold, Sep'85 by Old Gold Records. Dist: Lightning, Jazz Music, Spartan, Counterpoint

HILL STREET BLUES-ORIGINAL TV SCORE.
Album: released on Indiana, Aug'85 Dist: PRT

Cassette: released on Indiana, Aug'85 Dist: PRT

MAGNUM P.I..
Single (7"): released on Elektra, Apr'82 by WEA Records. Dist: WEA

THEME FROM THE A-TEAM.
Single (7"): released on RCA, Sep'84 by RCA Records. Dist: RCA, Roots, Swift, Wellard, Chris, I & B, Solomon & Peres Distribution

Post Mortem

AGAINST ALL ODDS (EP).
Single (7"): released on Flowmotion, Aug'84 Dist: Red Rhino, Cartel

CORONER'S OFFICE.
lbum: released on New Renaissance (USA), ug'87

OST MORTEM (EP).
ingle (7"): released on Lightbeat, May'83 by ightbeat Records. Dist: Pinnacle

Post War Nudes

O NOW.
ingle (7"): released on Virgin, Jan'83

Potamus

HAMBERPOT.
bum: released on Bead (Import), Feb'77

Potato 5

KA DANGER.
acks: / Dead Boring (DUB).
otes: Self-20 Porchester Terrace,W.2., one:01-723-5435
ngle (7"): released on Drolltone, Jan'87 by olltone Records. Dist: Drolltone Records

WESTERN SPECIAL.
Tracks: / Big City.
Single (7"): released on Gaz's, Jan'87 by Gaz's Records. Dist: Backs, Cartel

WESTERN SPECIAL.
Tracks: / Western special / Big city.
Single (7"): released on Gaz's Rockin' Records, Mar'86 Dist: Stiff Records, EMI

Potato Five

SPIN YOUR HEAD.
Single (12"): released on Gaz's Rockin' Records, Nov'85 Dist: Stiff Records, EMI

Potential Threat

BRAINWASHED.
Single (7"): released on Children Of The Revolution, Apr'85 by Revolver Records. Dist: Revolver, Cartel

WHAT'S SO GREAT ABOUT BRITAIN (EP).
Single (7"): released on Out Of Town, Jun'82

Pot, Spoon, Pipe & Jug

POT SPOON PIPE & JUG Various artists (Various Artists).
Album: released on Stash, Jan'79 Dist: Swift Distribution, Jazz Music Distribution, Jazz Horizons Distribution, Celtic Music Distribution, Cadillac, JSU Distribution, Zodiac Distribution

POT SPOON PIPE & JUG(14 JAZZ VOCALS & REFFER SOONGS).
Album: released on Stash, Sep'79 Dist: Swift Distribution, Jazz Music Distribution, Jazz Horizons Distribution, Celtic Music Distribution, Cadillac, JSU Distribution, Zodiac Distribution

Potter, Beatrix

BEATRIX POTTER STORIES VOL 1 Potter, Beatrix (Leigh, Vivien).
Tracks: / Tale of Peter Rabbit, The / Tale of Benjamin Bunny, The / Tale of the Flopsy bunnies / Tale of Mrs. Tiggy Winkle.
Cassette: released on EMI (Starline), Nov'83 by EMI Records. Dist: EMI

BEATRIX POTTER STORIES VOL 2 Potter, Beatrix (Leigh, Vivien).
Tracks: / Tale of Jemima Puddle - Duck, The / Tale of Squirrel Nutkin, The / Tale of Johnny Town-Mouse, The.
Cassette: released on EMI (Starline), Nov'83 by EMI Records. Dist: EMI

TAILOR OF GLOUCESTER(THE).
Tracks: / Tailor of Gloucester / Tale of Mrs. Tittlemouse / Tale of Mr.Tod.
Notes: Contains 2 other stories
Cassette: released on Tellastory, Dec'86 by Bartlett Bliss Productions. Dist: PRT Distribution, Hayward Promotions Distribution, H.R. Taylor Distribution

TALE OF BENJAMIN BUNNY.
Cassette: released on Tellastory, Aug'81 by Bartlett Bliss Productions. Dist: PRT Distribution, Hayward Promotions Distribution, H.R. Taylor Distribution

TALE OF JEMIMA PUDDLE-DUCK (THE) & MANY MORE.
Tracks: / Tale of Jemima Puddle-Duck / Tale of Samuel Whiskers or the Roly-Poly Pudding / Tale of Samuel Whiskers the Roly-Poly Pudding (cont.) / Tale of the Pie & the Patty Pan.
Notes: Approx. playing time 1hour
Cassette: released on Tellastory, Dec'86 by Bartlett Bliss Productions. Dist: PRT Distribution, Hayward Promotions Distribution, H.R. Taylor Distribution

TALE OF LITTLE PIG ROBINSON.
Cassette: released on Tellastory, Aug'81 by Bartlett Bliss Productions. Dist: PRT Distribution, Hayward Promotions Distribution, H.R. Taylor Distribution

TALE OF PETER RABBIT, THE.
Tracks: / Tale of the Flopsy Bunnies / Tale of Mrs.Tiggywinkle / Appley Dapply's Nursery Rhymes / Tale of Two Bad Mice / Tale of Mr Jeremy Fisher / Tale of Ginger & Pickles.
Notes: Contains 6 other stories
Cassette: by Bartlett Bliss Productions. Dist: PRT Distribution, Hayward Promotions Distribution, H.R. Taylor Distribution Deleted Dec'86.

TALE OF PETER RABBIT & OTHER STORIES.
Album: released on Tellastory, Aug'81 by Bartlett Bliss Productions. Dist: PRT Distribution, Hayward Promotions Distribution, H.R. Taylor Distribution

TALE OF TOM KITTEN, THE.
Tracks: / Cecily Parsley's Nursery Rhymes / Tale of Timmy Tiptoes / Tale of Johnny Town-Mouse / Tale of Squirrel Nutkin.
Notes: Contains 4 other stories
Cassette: released on Tellastory, Dec'86 by Bartlett Bliss Productions. Dist: PRT Distribution, Hayward Promotions Distribution, H.R. Taylor Distribution

TALE OF TUPPENNY.
Tracks: / Sly old cat, The / Tale of the Faithful Dove / Tale of the Faithful Dove (cont.).
Notes: Contains 3 other stories
Cassette: released on Tellastory, Dec'86 by Bartlett Bliss Productions. Dist: PRT Distribution, Hayward Promotions Distribution, H.R. Taylor Distribution

YOURS AFFECTIONATELY PETER RABBIT.
Tracks: / Peter Rabbit's Correspondence / Squirrel Nutkin's Correspondence / Lucinda Doll's Correspondence / Mrs. Tiggywinkle's Correspondence / Correspondence Concerning Jeremy Fisher / Mr. Alderman PT Tortoise,s Invitations / Ribby's Invitation / Mr.Samuel Whisker's Correspondence / Sally Henny Penny's Invitations / Rebeccah Puddleduck's Correspondence / Bird's Correspondence, The / Flopsy Bunnies Correspondence.
Notes: Miniature letters by Beatrix Potter
Cassette: released on Tellastory, Dec'86 by Bartlett Bliss Productions. Dist: PRT Distribution, Hayward Promotions Distribution, H.R. Taylor Distribution

Potter, Dennis

SINGING DETECTIVE (THE).
Notes: From the same creator as 'Pennies from Heaven' - Dennis Potter. Songs from the 1940's including original hits by artists such as Bing Crosby, The Andrew Sisters, Vera Lynn etc. Mono
Album: released on BBC, Oct'86 by BBC Records & Tapes. Dist: EMI, PRT, Pye

Cassette: released on BBC, Oct'86 by BBC Records & Tapes. Dist: EMI, PRT, Pye

Potter, Don

OVER THE RAINBOW.
Notes: Jazz Vocalist
Album: released on Mirror, Sep'86 by Priority Records. Dist: Priority Distribution

Potter, Nic

DOLPHINS.
Single (7"): released on Butt, Mar'82 by Butt Records. Dist: Counterpoint

LONG HELLO 2.
Album: released on Butt, Mar'82 by Butt Records. Dist: Counterpoint

SKETCHES IN SOUND.
Album: released on Zomart, Jun'86 Dist: Pinnacle

Potter, Nick

MOUNTAIN MUSIC.
Album: released on Zomart, Jul'84 Dist: Pinnacle

Cassette: released on Zomart, Jul'84 Dist: Pinnacle

Potts, Mick

MICK POTTS & THE GATEWAY JAZZ BAND Featuring George Chisholm.
Album: released on Fellside (Cumbria), May'83 by Fellside Records. Dist: Roots, Projection, CM, Jazz Music

Pourcel, Franck

CLASSICAL IN DIGITAL(VOL.3).
Album: released on EMI (France), Apr'83 by EMI Records. Dist: Conifer

Cassette: released on EMI (France), Apr'83 by EMI Records. Dist: Conifer

DIGITAL AROUND THE WORLD.
Album: released on EMI (France), May'83 by EMI Records. Dist: Conifer

EDITH AND POURCEL.
Album: released on EMI (France), May'83 by EMI Records. Dist: Conifer

Cassette: released on EMI (France), May'83 by EMI Records. Dist: Conifer

FILM MUSIC.
Album: released on EMI (France), May'83 by EMI Records. Dist: Conifer

FRANCK POURCEL.
Tracks: / Grease (you're the one that I want) / Singing in the rain / Copacabana / Turbo rhapsody / Tico tico / Recontre du troisieme type (Close Encounters of the 3rd kind / Lay all your love on me / Saturday night fever (Manhattan skyline) / Rodmarton parade / I will survive / Race, The (La course) / Concorde / Putting on the ritz / C'est magnifique / Super trouper / Star wars (theme original du film).
Compact disc: released on Pathe Marconi, Apr'87 Dist: Swift

HITS CLASSIQUES, (LES).
Tracks: / La danza / Badinerie / Bolero / Danse horgroise No 5 / Carmina bura burana (No 1 'O fortuna') / Marche turque / La moldau / Allegro du concerto en re minueur / Marche de Radetsky / Theme du lac des cygnes / Carmen (air du toreador) / Valse No 6 en re majeur, OP 64 / Aida 'Marche triomphale' (trompettes) / Marche hongroise de 'La damnation de faust' / Can-Can / Aagio pour cordes et orgue.
Album: released on Pathe Marconi, Aug'86 Dist: Swift

Cassette: released on Pathe Marconi, Aug'86 Dist: Swift

LA FEMME ROMANTIQUE.
Album: released on EMI (France), May'83 by EMI Records. Dist: Conifer

NEW SOUND TANGOS.
Album: released on EMI (France), May'83 by EMI Records. Dist: Conifer

NOSTALGIA MOOD.
Tracks: / Cry me a river / Puting on the Ritz / Flamingo / Tweedle Dee / Fascination / Mona Lisa / All of me / Answer me my love / In a nostalgia mood / I'm getting sentimental over you / I love you / September in the rain / Unforgetable.
Notes: Digital audio
Compact disc: released on EMI, Apr'84 by EMI Records. Dist: EMI

Pourcel, Frank

CLASSICAL FAVOURITES IN DIGITAL.
Album: released on Studio 2, Mar'80

FRANCK POURCEL & ORCHESTRA (Pourcel, Frank & His Orchestra).
Cassette: released on Ideal(Tapes), Feb'81 Dist: EMI

FRANK POURCEL PLAYS ABBA.
Album: released on EMI, Feb'79 by EMI Records. Dist: EMI

IN A NOSTALGIA MOOD.
Album: released on Marconi (Import), Apr'84

Cassette: released on Marconi (Import), Apr'84

THIS IS DIGITAL RECORDING (Pourcel, Frank & Manuel).
Cassette: released on EMI, May'80 by EMI Records. Dist: EMI

Poussez

LEAVE THAT BOY ALONE.
Album: released on Vanguard, Aug'80 by PRT Records. Dist: PRT

POUSSEZ.
Album: released on Vanguard, Apr'79 by PRT Records. Dist: PRT

Cassette: released on Vanguard, Apr'79 by PRT Records. Dist: PRT

Powell, Andrew

LUCIFER (AND MAMA GAMMA).
Single (7"): released on EMI, Jul'83 by EMI Records. Dist: EMI

PLAYS THE BEST OF THE ALAN PARSONS PROJECT (Powell, Andrew/Philharmonic Orchestra (The)).
Notes: Andrew Powell has played an important part in contributing to the vast international sales and success of the Alan Parsons Project. This album, of which he is immensely proud, features such well-known musicians as Max Middleton, Ian Bairnson, David Paton and Mike Moran, as well as one of the country's finest orchestras.
Compact disc: released on EMI, '83 by EMI Records. Dist: EMI

Compact disc: released on Mobile Fidelity, Oct'86 by Mobile Fidelity Records.

Powell, Baden

APAIXONADO.
Album: released on MPS Jazz, May'81

CANTO ON GUITAR.
Album: released on MPS Jazz, Jun'81

ESTUDOS.
Album: released on MPS Jazz, May'81

MELANCOLIE.
Compact disc: released on Accord (France), '86 Dist: Discovery, Target

POEMA ON GUITAR.
Album: released on MPS Jazz, May'81

TRISTEZA ON GUITAR.
Tracks: / Tristeza / Canto de zango / Round about midnight / Sarava / Canto de ossanha / Manha de carnaval / Invencao em 71-2 / Das rosas / Som do carnaval / Astronauta.
Compact disc: released on Verve, Apr'84 by Phonogram Records. Dist: Polygram

Album: released on MPS Jazz, May'81

Powell, Bud

ALTERNATIVE TAKES.
Album: released on Blue Note, Sep'85 by EMI Records. Dist: EMI

AMAZING BUD POWELL THE.
Album: released on Blue Note, Oct'84 by EMI Records. Dist: EMI

AMAZING BUD POWELL VOL.3, THE.
Cassette: released on Blue Note, Apr'87 by EMI Records. Dist: EMI

Album: released on Blue Note, Apr'87 by EMI Records. Dist: EMI

AMAZING BUD POWELL THE (VOL 2).
Album: released on Blue Note, Jul'85 by EMI Records. Dist: EMI

AMAZING BUD POWELL THE (VOL 1).
Album: released on Blue Note, May'85 by EMI Records. Dist: EMI

AMAZING BUD POWELL VOL 3, THE.
Tracks: / Some soul / Blue pearl / Frantic fancies / Bud on Bach / Keepin' in the groove / Idaho / Don't blame me / Moose the mooche.
Notes: For his first full length Blue Note album, Bud Powell uses his regular drummer, Art Taylor and Miles Davis' bassist, Paul Chambers. They play several unique Powell originals including the lovely 'Blue Pearl'. On the second half of the session, virtuoso trombonist, Curtis Fuller joins them for three extended jazz standards including a rousing 'Moose The Mooche'. One of this disc's highlights is the astonishing and self explanatory solo piano performance 'Bud on Bach'.

AT THE BLUE NOTE CAFE PARIS 1961.
Album: released on ESP, Apr'81 by ESP Records. Dist: Jazz Horizons, Jazz Music

AT THE GOLDEN CIRCLE VOL 4.
Album: released on Steeplechase, Apr'81

AUTUMN SESSION 1953.
Album: released on Base, Apr'83 Dist: Jazz Horizons

BEST YEARS THE.
Album: released on Vogue, May'78 Dist: Discovery, Jazz Music, PRT, Swift

BOUNCING WITH BUD (Powell, Bud Trio).
Album: released on Storyville, Nov'86 by Storyville Records. Dist: Jazz Music Distribution, Swift Distribution, Chris Wellard Distribution, Counterpoint Distribution

BUD POWELL.
Album: released on Kings Of Jazz, Jan'81 Dist: Jazz Horizons, Jazz Music, Celtic Music

BUD POWELL & THELONIOUS MONK (Powell, Bud & Thelonious Monk).
Compact disc: released on Vogue, '86 Dist: Discovery, Jazz Music, PRT, Swift

BUD POWELL VOL 2.
Album: released on Jazz Reactivation, May'83 Dist: PRT

BUD: THE AMAZING BUD POWELL VOL.3.
Cassette: released on Blue Note, May'87 by EMI Records. Dist: EMI

GENIUS OF BUD POWELL THE.
Album: released on Verve (France), Feb'84

IN EUROPE.
Notes: With Kenny Clarke, Johnny Griffin and P Michelot.
Album: released on Duke, Jun'86 by Melodisc Records. Dist: Jazz Horizons, Jazz Music, Celtic Music, JSU, Swift

INVISIBLE CAGE THE.
Album: released on Black Lion, Jan'85 by Black Lion Records. Dist: Jazz Music, Chris Wellard, Taylor, H.R., Counterpoint, Cadillac

LIVE AT BIRDLAND.
Album: released on Queen-Disc, Apr'81 Dist: Celtic Music, JSU, Jazz Horizons, Jazz Music

ORNITHOLOGY.
Notes: 'Ornithology' Trio Performances from Birdland 1953
Album: released on Jazz Live, Oct'86

Album: released on Jazz Live, Apr'81

PARIS-NEW YORK.
Tracks: / Someone to watch over me.
Compact disc: released on Vogue (France), May'85 Dist: Discovery, Jazz Music, PRT, Swift

PORTRAIT OF LONIOUS.
Album: released on Jazz Odyssey, Mar'81

SCENE CHANGES, (THE).
Tracks: / Cleopatra's dream / Duid deed / Down with it / Danceland / Borderick / Crossin' the channel / Gettin' there / Scene changes, The / Comin' up (alternate take).
Notes: All titles: Composed by Bud Powell. Published by Planetary Nom (Ldn) Ltd.
Compact disc: released on Blue Note, Jun'87 by EMI Records. Dist: EMI

SPRING SESSIONS 1953.
Album: released on Base, Apr'83 Dist: Jazz Horizons

SUMMER SESSIONS 1953.
Album: released on Base, Apr'83 Dist: Jazz Horizons

SWINGIN WITH BUD.
Album: released on RCA (France), Jan'83 by RCA Records. Dist: Discovery

TIME WAITS.
Tracks: / Buster rides again / Sub city / Time waits / Marmalade / Monopoly / John's abbey / Dry soul / Sub city (alternate take) / John's abbey (alternate take).
Compact disc: released on Blue Note, Aug'87 by EMI Records. Dist: EMI

Powell, Cozy

DANCE WITH THE DEVIL.
Single (7"): released on EMI Golden 45's, Jul'84 by EMI Records. Dist: EMI

OCTOPUSS.
Cassette: released on Polydor, Apr'83 by Polydor Records. Dist: Polygram, Polydor

OVER THE TOP.
Album: released on Fame (Ariola), Jan'83 by Music For Pleasure Records. Dist: EMI

Cassette: released on Fame (Ariola), Jan'83 by Music For Pleasure Records. Dist: EMI

Powell, Dick

LULLABY OF BROADWAY.
Album: released on ASV, Dec'86 by Academy Sound & Vision Records. Dist: Pinnacle

LULLABY OF BROADWAY.
Tracks: / Lullaby of broadway / I'm sitting high on a hilltop / I'm goin' shoppin' with you / Lulu's back in town / Words are in my heart (The) / Don't give up the ship / Down sunshine lane / Pop goes your heart / Happiness ahead / Rose in her heart (The) / Mr & Mrs is the name / Flirtation walk / Don't say goodnight / Wonder bar / Thanks a million / I've got a pocket full of sunshine.
Notes: Star of the unforgettable Busby Berkeley musicals, Dick Powell recreated the atmosphere of glamour with this collection of his original movie hits from the early Thirties. Powell himself enjoyed a long and varied career in Hollywood on both sides of the camera, bu the extravaganzas which spawned these these songs created his international fame. Amoung the films represented are 'Gold Diggers of 1935', 'Flirtation Walk' and 'Broadway Gondolier'.
Album: released on American Recollections, Sep'86 by London Records. Dist: Polygram

Cassette: released on American Recollections, Sep'86 by London Records. Dist: Polygram

Powell, Mel

BOUQUET (Powell, Mel Trio).
Album: released on Vogue Jazz (France), May'83

PIANO FORTE (Powell, Mel & His Uptown Hall Gang).
Album: released on Nostalgia, May'86 Dist: Jazz Music, Counterpoint

WORLD IS WAITING 1942-46 see Buskin, Joe (Powell, Mel & Joe Buskin).
Album: released on Commodore Classics, Sep'82 by Teldec Records (Germany). Dist: Conifer, IMS, Polygram

WORLD IS WAITING, THE (Powell, Mel & His Orchestra/Joe Bushkin Sextet/Bill Harris).
Album: released on Commodore Classics, May'87 by Teldec Records (Germany). Dist: Conifer, IMS, Polygram

Powell, Patsy

FOR THE GOOD TIMES (Powell, Patsy & The Goodtimers).
Album: released on Folk Heritage, Jul'82 by Folk Heritage Records. Dist: Roots, Wynd-Up Distribution, Jazz Music, Folk Heritage

THANK YOU FOR LOVING ME.
Album: released on Folk Heritage, Jul'82 by Folk Heritage Records. Dist: Roots, Wynd-Up Distribution, Jazz Music, Folk Heritage

THAT'S WHAT THE WORLD NEEDS (Powell, Patsy & The Goodtimers).
Album: released on Folk Heritage, Jul'82 by Folk Heritage Records. Dist: Roots, Wynd-Up Distribution, Jazz Music, Folk Heritage

Powell, Peter

KEEP FIT AND DANCE.
Album: released on K-Tel, Feb'82 by K-Tel Records. Dist: Record Merchandisers Distribution, Taylors, Terry Blood Distribution, Wynd-Up Distribution, Relay Distribution, Pickwick Distribution, Solomon & Peres Distribution, Polygram

Cassette: released on K-Tel, Feb'82 by K-Tel Records. Dist: Record Merchandisers Distribution, Taylors, Terry Blood Distribution, Wynd-Up Distribution, Relay Distribution, Pickwick Distribution, Solomon & Peres Distribution, Polygram

Powell, Picker

DANCING FEELING.
Tracks: / Dancing feeling / Dancing feeling (version).
Single (12"): released on Sunjam, Jul'86 Dist: Jetstar Distribution

Powell, Shezwae

ACT OF WAR.
Single (7"): released on Nightmare, Feb'87 by Nightmare Records. Dist: PRT

Single (12"): released on Nightmare, Feb'87 by Nightmare Records. Dist: PRT

BACK TRACK.
Tracks: / Back track / Back track (inst).
Single (7"): released on Nightmare, 13 Jun'87 by Nightmare Records. Dist: PRT

Single (12"): released on Nightmare, 13 Jun'87 by Nightmare Records. Dist: PRT

Power

GROOVIN/HOT.
Single (7"): released on Malaco, Jun'82 by Malaco Records. Dist: Charly

PLAY IT AGAIN SAM/INSTRUMENTAL.
Single (7"): released on Malaco, Oct'81 by Malaco Records. Dist: Charly

Single (12"): released on Malaco, Oct'81 by Malaco Records. Dist: Charly

POWER.
Album: released on Malaco, Jul'82 by Malaco Records. Dist: Charly

SEVENTEEN.
Tracks: / Seventeen / In a world (reach out) / US remix / Acappella mix.
Single (7"): released on Arista, Aug'86 by Arista Records. Dist: RCA

Single (12"): released on Arista, Aug'86 by Arista Records. Dist: RCA

SOUL IN MY SHOES.
Tracks: / Soul in my shoes / Sad boy / Soul in my shoes (dance mix).
Single (7"): released on Arista, Jan'86 by Arista Records. Dist: RCA

Single (12"): released on Arista, Jan'86 by Arista Records. Dist: RCA

TRY A LITTLE TENDERNESS.
Tracks: / Try a little tenderness / In a world.
Single (7"): released on Arista, Oct'86 by Arista Records. Dist: RCA

Single (12"): released on Arista, Oct'86 by Arista Records. Dist: RCA

WORK HARD.
Tracks: / Work hard / Work hard (soul party mix) / Callous love.
Single (7"): released on Arista, Mar'86 by Arista Records. Dist: RCA

Single (12"): released on Arista, Mar'86 by Arista Records. Dist: RCA

Single (12"): released on Arista, May'86 by Arista Records. Dist: RCA

Single (7"): released on Arista, Aug'85 by Arista Records. Dist: RCA

Single (12"): released on Arista, Aug'85 by Arista Records. Dist: RCA

Power,Duffy

MARY OPEN THE DOOR.
Album: released on Razor, Dec'86 by Razor. Dist: Pinnacle

Power Farm

WHICH WAY USA/GLASS.
Single (7"): released on Boob, Nov'83

Power Heddy

I DON'T BELIEVE IT.
Single (7"): released on Sandos, May'85

Powerhouse

POWERHOUSE.
Album: released on Ambush, Jun'86 Dist: PRT

POWERHOUSE PRESENTS STRICTLY LIVESTOCK Various artists (Various Artists).
Album: released on Greensleeves, May'85 by Greensleeves Records. Dist: BMG, Jetstar, Spartan

POWERHOUSE REPRESENTS FINAL MISSION Various artists (Various Artists).
Album: released on Power House, Aug'86 by Power House Records. Dist: Jetstar

Power Jam

POWER JAM 85 various artists (Various Artists).
Album: released on Tommy Boy, Aug'85 by Warner Brothers. Dist: WEA Distribution

Power Jimmy

FIFTY ODD YEARS (Power Jimmy & Josephine Neegan).
Album: released on Tompo, Jun'85 by Tompo Records.

IRISH FIDDLE PLAYER.
Album: released on Topic, Jan'81 Dist: Roots Distribution

IRISH MUSIC FROM THE FAVOURITE also see Tony ledwith.
Album: released on Leader, Jan'81 Dist: Jazz Music, Projection

Powerline

WATCHING YOU/INSTRUMENTAL VERSION.
Single (7"): released on PLR, Jul'82

Single (12"): released on PLR, Jul'82

YOU'RE THE GIRL (2 PARTS).
Single (7"): released on Plant Life, Apr'83 Dist: Roots

Power of Love (The)

POWER OF LOVE (Various Artists).
Album: released on West Five, Oct'86 Dist: PRT

Cassette: released on West Five, Oct'86 Dist: PRT

POWER OF LOVE (THE) Various artists (Various Artists).
Notes: Artists include Jennifer Rush, Billy Ocean etc. Double LP and cassette.
Album: released on Capitol, Dec'85 by Capitol Records. Dist: EMI

Cassette: released on Capitol, Dec'85 by Capitol Records. Dist: EMI

Power Pack Orchestra

CRIMEBUSTERS.
Tracks: / Cagney & Lacey / Miami Vice / Sarecrow & Mrs King / Gentle Touch (The) / Hunter / Miss Marple / Remington Steele / Hart to Hart / Mike Hammer Theme / Highway Patrol / Airwolf / Crazy like a fox / Murder She Wrote / Magnum / Juliet Bravo / Sweeney (The) / Fall Guy (The) / Chineses Detective (The) / Bill (The) (Overkill) / Z Cars.
Notes: 1986 riginal Sound Recordings made by Gordon Lorenz Productions Limited.
Album: released on Music For Pleasure, Sep'86 by EMI Records. Dist: EMI

Cassette: released on Music For Pleasure, Sep'86 by EMI Records. Dist: EMI

MUSIC OF ANDREW LLOYD WEBBER
Tracks: / Jesus Christ superstar / Phantom o the opera / Tell me on a Sunday / Starlight ex press / Mr. Mistoffelees / Music of the night Take that look off your face / Another suitcase in another hall / I don't know how to love Him Any dream will do / Don't cry for me Argentina Old Deuteronomy / All I ask of you.
Album: released on MFP, Sep'87 by EMI Rec ords. Dist: EMI

Cassette: released on MFP, Sep'87 by EM Records. Dist: EMI

SOAPS.
Tracks: / Soap / Coronation Street / Eastende / Dynasty / Crossroads / Knots Landing / Sor & Daughters / Colbys (The) / Brookside / Wa tons (The) / Dallas / Emmerdale Farm / Falco Crest / Alice / Albion Market / Hotel / Take th High Road / St Elsewhere / Sullivans (The) Barwick Green (The Archers).
Notes: Producer/Arranger - Gordon Lorenz.
Album: released on Music For Pleasur Aug'86 by EMI Records. Dist: EMI

Cassette: released on Music For Pleasur Aug'86 by EMI Records Dist: EMI

TOP T.V. THEMES.
Tracks: / Eastenders / Cagney and Lacey / D nasty / Miss Marple / Hill Street Blues / Dalla Bergerac / Crossroads / St. Elsewhere / Soa Juliet Bravo / Colbys, The / Cronation Stree Bill, The (Overkill) / Brookside / Hart to Ha Sons and Daughters / Knots Landing / Remir ton Steele / Falcon Crest / Emmerdale Farr Hotel / Scarecrow and Mrs King / Dukes of Ha zard - Good Ol' Boys / Waltons, The / Ger touch, The.
Compact disc: released on MFP, Jul'87 by E Records. Dist: EMI

Powers, Chris

CHRIS POWERS & HIS ORCH. (Powe Chris & His Orchestra).
Notes: Mono.
Album: released on Circle(USA), Jan'87 Jazzology Records (USA). Dist: Jazz Mu Swift, Chris Wellard

Powers, Johnny
ROCK ROCK ROCK.
Album: released on Rollercoaster, Jun'85 by Rollercoaster Records. Dist: Swift Distribution, Rollercoaster Distribution

Power Station
COMMUNICATION.
Single (7"): released on Parlophone, Oct'85 by EMI Records. Dist: EMI

Single (12"): released on Parlophone, Oct'85 by EMI Records. Dist: EMI

GET IT ON.
Single (7"): released on Parlophone, Apr'85 by EMI Records. Dist: EMI

Single (12"): released on Parlophone, Apr'85 by EMI Records. Dist: EMI

POWER STATION (THE).
Tracks: / Some Like It Hot / Murderess / Lonely Tonight / Communication / Get it on (Bang a gong) / Go To Zero / Harvest for the world / Still in your heart.
Notes: The Power Station is a marriage of four major talents with impeccable track records. The distinctive vocal style of Robert Palmer coupled with Duran Duran's bassist John Taylor, lead guitarist Andy Taylor and 'Serious Moonlight Tour' drummer Tony Thompson. Produced by the mastermind behind Chuck Bernard Edwards. Jhon Taylor met Robert Palmer in Birmingham 3 years ago, following Duran Duran's 1984 US tour and after a meeting with Bernard Edwards the project was confirmed. The Power Station album was recorded at the studio of the same name in New York late last year. The album features brand new compositions by Robert Palmer and John and Andy Taylor plus 2 classic tracks - T Rex's 'Get it On' and the Isley Brothers' 'Harvest for the world'. Original full catalogue numbers: EJ 2402971 (LP), EJ 240297 (CS)
Album: released on Parlophone, Apr'85 by EMI Records. Dist: EMI

Cassette: released on Parlophone, Apr'85 by EMI Records. Dist: EMI

Compact disc: released on Parlophone, Apr'85 by EMI Records. Dist: EMI

SOME LIKE IT HOT.
Picture disc: released on Parlophone, Apr'85 by EMI Records. Dist: EMI

Picture disc: released on Parlophone, Mar'85 by EMI Records. Dist: EMI

Single (7"): released on Parlophone, Feb'85 by EMI Records. Dist: EMI

Single (12"): released on Parlophone, Feb'85 by EMI Records. Dist: EMI

VIDEO EP.
Notes: Number of tracks: 3. Type of recording: EP. Total playing time 30 minutes.
Video-cassette (VHS): released on PMI, Jun'86 by PMI Records. Dist: EMI

Video-cassette [Betamax]: released on PMI, Jun'86 by PMI Records. Dist: EMI

Power Supply
LATIN COOKING/ALL RIGHT BY ME.
Cassette single: released on Rapture, Feb'83 Dist: PRT

Powers, Will
ADVENTURES IN SUCESS/DUB.
Single (7"): released on Island, Jan'84 by Island Records. Dist: Polygram

DANCING FOR MENTAL HEALTH.
Album: released on Island, Oct'83 by Island Records. Dist: Polygram

Cassette: released on Island, Oct'83 by Island Records. Dist: Polygram

Power & The Majesty
SOUND EFFECTS.
Notes: Double compact disc
Compact disc: released on Mobile Fidelity Sound, Dec'85 by Mobile Fidelity Records.

Power to Dream
BODIES GONE.
Single (12"): released on Illuminated, Feb'85 by IKF Records. Dist: Pinnacle, Cartel, Jetstar

FAITH HEALER.
Single (12"): released on Illuminated, Mar'85 by IKF Records. Dist: Pinnacle, Cartel, Jetstar

FRANTIC.
Tracks: / Frantic.
Single (7"): released on Illuminated, Oct'86 by IKF Records. Dist: Pinnacle, Cartel, Jetstar

Single (12"): released on Illuminated, Oct'86 by IKF Records. Dist: Pinnacle, Cartel, Jetstar

Powley, Kim
VAMPIRES FROM OUTERSPACE.
Album: released on Line, Jun'87

Powrie, Ian
LEGENDS OF SCOTLAND (Powrie, Ian Band).
Tracks: / St Johnstoun reel / Lass of Patie's mill / Dr Robertson's reel Margaret-Anne Robertson / Lochaber gathering (The) / Tam Bain's lum / Stool of repentance / David Ross / Irish washerwoman (The) / Bandboys / Bonnie lass o'bon accord / Tushker (The) / St Ann's / Callum Donaldson / Dancing the baby / Gloomy winter / Silver city waltz / Old maid in a garret / Flower of the queen (The) / Merry boys of Greenland / Willfijord / Leveneep head.
Cassette: released on Lochshore, Aug'86 by Klub Records. Dist: PRT

P.O.X.
VOODOO POWER.
Album: released on Rockhouse, Oct'86 by Rockhouse Records. Dist: Swift Distribution, Charly Distribution

Pozo Seco Singers
POZO SECO SINGERS (Pozo Seco Singers feat. Don Williams).
Tracks: / Take my hand for a while / There's never a time / Where do I go from here / On her way to being a woman / Follow me to Louisville / Spend some time with me / There's always something there to remind me / Ruby Tuesday / Storybook children / Coming apart / Tears'.
Compact disc: released on Pickwick, Apr'86 by Pickwick Records. Dist: Pickwick Distribution, Prism Leisure Distribution, Lugtons

PEREZ PRADO.
Album: released on Bright Orange, Apr'79 Dist: Swift

Praeger, Lou
ON THE SUNNY SIDE OF THE STREET (Praeger, Lou & His Orchestra).
Album: released on President, Jan'83 by President Records. Dist: Taylors, Spartan

Cassette: released on President, Jan'83 by President Records. Dist: Taylors, Spartan

Praise Album
PRAISE ALBUM Various artists (Various Artists).
Album: released on Maranatha Music, May'82

Cassette: released on Maranatha Music, May'82

Praise II
PRAISE II Various artists (Various Artists).
Album: released on Maranatha Music, May'82

Cassette: released on Maranatha Music, May'82

Praise IV
IN HIS TIME.
Album: released on Maranatha Music, May'82

Cassette: released on Maranatha Music, May'82

Praise Strings
PRAISE STRINGS 1 Various artists (Various Artists).
Album: released on Maranatha Music, May'82

Cassette: released on Maranatha Music, May'82

PRAISE STRINGS 2 Various artists (Various Artists).
Album: released on Maranatha Music, May'82

Cassette: released on Maranatha Music, May'82

PRAISE STRINGS 3 Various artists (Various Artists).
Album: released on Maranatha Music, May'82

Cassette: released on Maranatha Music May'82

PRAISE STRINGS 4 Various artists (Various Artists).
Album: released on Maranatha Music, May'82

Cassette: released on Maranatha Music, May'82

PRAISE STRINGS 5 Various artists (Various Artists).
Album: released on Maranatha Music, May'82

Cassette: released on Maranatha Music, May'82

PRAISE STRINGS 7 Various artists (Various Artists).
Album: released on Maranatha, Jun'85

Cassette: released on Maranatha, Jun'85

Praise The Lord...
PRAISE THE LORD AND PASS THE AMMUNITION Various artists (Various Artists).
Tracks: / Let's all be Americans now / When the Lusitania went down / I didn't raise my boy to be a soldier / Over there / Hello, central give me no man's land / There's a vacant chair in every home tonight / I've got a captain working for me now / My dream of the big parade / Defuehrer's face / He's 1-A in the army and he's 1-A in my heart / Stalin wasn't stallin' (a modern spiritual) / We did it before and we can do it again / I left my heart at the stage door canteen / Goodbye, mama (I'm off to Yokohama) / No love, no nothin' / Praise the lord and pass the ammunition / My guy's come back.
Notes: Songs of World Wars 1 & 2. Mono.
Album: released on New World (USA), Jul'86 by New World Records (USA). Dist: Conifer

Praise V
IT'S TIME TO PRAISE THE LORD.
Album: released on Marantha, Jun'81 Dist: Kingsway Distribution, Pilgrim, Word Distribution

Cassette: released on Marantha, Jun'81 Dist: Kingsway Distribution, Pilgrim, Word Distribution

Pram
BLACK SHEEP.
Tracks: / Black sheep / Classic quotes.
Single (7"): released on Unknown. Mar'86

Prams
DON'T DROP ANY BOMBS ON ME.
Single (7"): released on Wabbit, Aug'81 by Wabbit Records. Dist: Pinnacle

WHAT'S THE TIME MR WOLF.
Album: released on Wabbit, Oct'81 by Wabbit Records. Dist: Pinnacle

Pra Sylvio de
SOUVENIRS FOR YOU.
Album: released on ARC (Accordion Records), Jan'84 by ARC. Dist: Accordion Record Club

Prats
GENERAL DAVIS/ALLIANCE.
Single (7"): released on Rough Trade, Nov'81 by Rough Trade Records. Dist: Rough Trade Distribution, Cartel Distribution

Pratt Andy
CARRY YOU/MODERN POLICE.
Single (7"): released on Lamborghini, Aug'83 by Lamborghini Records. Dist: PRT

Pratt, Graham & Eileen
HIEROGLYPHICS.
Album: released on Plant Life, Jun'85

MAGIC PEAR TREE, THE.
Cassette: released on Folktracks, Nov'79 by Folktracks Cassettes. Dist: Folktracks

TO FRIEND AND FOE.
Album: released on Dingles, '83 by Dingle's Records. Dist: Projection

Pratt & McClain
HAPPY DAYS.
Single (7"): released on Reprise, Oct'77 by WEA Records. Dist: WEA

Pravda
LESSON ONE.
Cassette: released on Shrewd Corporation, Jul'85 Dist: Revolver, Cartel

Praying Mantis
TIME TELLS NO LIES.
Album: released on Arista, Apr'81 by Arista Records. Dist: RCA

Preacher Jack
ROCK'N'ROLL.
Album: released on Sonet, Jun'80 by Sonet Records. Dist: PRT

Precinct
DON'T GO.
Single (7"): released on Calibre, Jun'85 by Calibre Records. Dist: PRT
Cat. no: CAB 204

Single (12"): released on Calibre, Jun'85 by Calibre Records. Dist: PRT
Cat. no: CABL 204

SHINING STAIR.
Single (7"): released on Passion, Aug'84 by Skratch Records. Dist: PRT
Cat. no: PASH 32

Single (12"): released on Passion, Aug'84 by Skratch Records. Dist: PRT
Cat. no: PASH 32 12

Precious
TABOO.
Single (7"): released on Passion, May'84 by Skratch Records. Dist: PRT
Cat. no: PASH 1228

Precious Little
LET'S TOUCH DANCE.
Single (7"): released on Speed, Sep'83
Cat. no: SPEED 16

ON AND ON SONG/ON AND ON AND ON.
Single (7"): released on KA, Nov'82
Cat. no: KA 14

ON N ON SONG/DO IT YOURSELF.
Single (7"): released on Precious, Sep'82 by Precious Records. Dist: CBS, Polygram
Cat. no: AVE 4

Precious Metal
RIGHT HERE, RIGHT NOW.
Tracks: / This girl / Right here, right now / Bad guys / Pretty boy / Emily / Shakin' / Girls nite out / You do something special / Cheesecake / Rembering old times.
Notes: Debut album from American heavy rock/metal band Precious Metal. Described as a femal Cheap Trick or a Go-Go's with dirt, they have received good press both here and in the States.
Album: released on Mercury (USA), Apr'86 by import Records. Dist: IMS Distribution, Polygram Distribution
Cat. no: 8261461

Precious Moments
PRECIOUS MOMENTS Various artists (Various Artists).
Album: released on Impression, Oct'83 Dist: CBS
Cat. no: LPIMP 3

Cassette: released on Impression, Oct'83 Dist: CBS
Cat. no: TCIMP 3

Predator
PREDATOR.
Album: released on Road Runner, Apr'86
Cat. no: RR 9714

Prediction
AFTER THIS DANCE IS THROUGH.
Single (12"): released on White, Feb'85
Cat. no: ADET 801

PRETTY LADY/DUB THAT LADY.
Single (12"): released on Prediction, Mar'83
Cat. no: PTN 001

THROUGH IT ALL.
Single (12"): released on Sanity, Oct'84 by Sanity Records. Dist: Projection
Cat. no: ES 001

WAY WE WERE/DUB VERSION.
Single (12"): released on Student, Mar'82
Cat. no: STUDENT 008

WONDERLAND.
Single (7"): released on Adelphi(USA), Oct'85 by Adelphi Records (USA). Dist: Projection, Swift
Cat. no: ADET 003

Prefab Sprout
COULDN'T BEAR TO BE SPECIAL.
Single (7"): released on Kitchenware, Mar'84 by Kitchenware Records. Dist: Cartel, CBS, Polygram, RCA-Ariola Distribution
Cat. no: SK 10

Single (12"): released on Kitchenware, Mar'84 by Kitchenware Records. Dist: Cartel, CBS, Polygram, RCA-Ariola Distribution
Cat. no: SK 1012

DEVIL HAS ALL THE BEST TUNES (THE).
Tracks: / Devil has all the best tunes (The).
Single (7"): released on Kitchenware, Jun'86 by Kitchenware Records. Dist: Cartel, CBS, Polygram, RCA-Ariola Distribution
Cat. no: SK 8

DEVIL HAS ALL THE BEST TUNES, THE.
Single (7"): released on Kitchenware, Oct'83 by Kitchenware Records. Dist: Cartel, CBS, Polygram, RCA-Ariola Distribution
Cat. no: SK 7

DON'T SING/GREEN ISAAC LL/HE'LL HAVE TO GO.
Single (7"): released on Kitchenware, Jan'84 by Kitchenware Records. Dist: Cartel, CBS, Polygram, RCA-Ariola Distribution
Cat. no: SK 9

Single (12"): released on Kitchenware, Jan'84 by Kitchenware Records. Dist: Cartel, CBS, Polygram, RCA-Ariola Distribution
Cat. no: SK 912

JOHNNY JOHNNY.
Tracks: / Johnny Johnny / Wigs.
Single (7"): released on Kitchenware, Jan'86 by Kitchenware Records. Dist: Cartel, CBS, Polygram, RCA-Ariola Distribution

Single (12"): released on Kitchenware, Jan'86 by Kitchenware Records. Dist: Cartel, CBS, Polygram, RCA-Ariola Distribution

LIONS IN MY GARDEN/RADIO LOVE/DEVIL HAS ALL THE BEST TUNE/.
Single (12"): released on Kitchenware, Dec'83 by Kitchenware Records. Dist: Cartel, CBS, Polygram, RCA-Ariola Distribution

LIONS IN MY OWN GARDEN/RADIO LOVE.
Single (7"): released on Candle, Aug'82 Dist: Cartel

STEVE MCQUEEN.
Tracks: / Faron young / Bonny / Apetite / When love breaks down / Goodbye Lucille / Hallelujah / Moving the river / Horsin' around / Desire as / Blueberry pies / When the angels.
Album: released on Kitchenware, Jun'85 by Kitchenware Records. Dist: Cartel, CBS, Polygram, RCA-Ariola Distribution

Cassette: released on Kitchenware, Jun'85 by Kitchenware Records. Dist: Cartel, CBS, Polygram, RCA-Ariola Distribution

Compact disc: released on Kitchenware, Jun'85 by Kitchenware Records. Dist: Cartel, CBS, Polygram, RCA-Ariola Distribution

SWOON.
Album: released on Kitchenware, Feb'84 by Kitchenware Records. Dist: Cartel, CBS, Polygram, RCA-Ariola Distribution

Cassette: released on Kitchenware, Feb'84 by Kitchenware Records. Dist: Cartel, CBS, Polygram, RCA-Ariola Distribution

Preface

AMERICAN YOUTH.
Single (7"): released on Bumtickler, Sep'82

NOTHING SURPRISES ME ANYMORE.
Single (7"): released on Bumtickler, Mar'83

Prefects

GOING THROUGH THE MOTIONS.
Single (7"): released on Rough Trade, Jul'80 by Rough Trade Records. Dist: Rough Trade Distribution, Cartel Distribution

LOVE IS ALL AROUND.
Single (7"): released on Variety, Dec'82 by Variety Records. Dist: PRT

PEEL SESSION 8.1.79.

YOUNG WORLD.
Single (7"): released on Rag Baby, Oct'81 Dist: Pinnacle, Red Lightnin' Distribution

Preiss, Byron

VAMPIRE STATE BUILDING & THE CRYING COMPUTOR.
Cassette: released on Caedmon(USA), Sep'85 by Caedmon (USA) Records. Dist: Gower, Taylors, Discovery

Prelude

AFTER THE GOLDRUSH.
Single (7"): released on After Hours, Apr'82 Dist: CBS

CITY TONIGHT.
Single (7"): released on After Hours, Oct'82 Dist: CBS

FREEDOM.
Single (7"): released on Black Crow, Aug'83 by Mawson & Wareham Records. Dist: Projection

ONLY THE LONELY.
Single (7"): released on After Hours, Jul'82 Dist: CBS

P.R.E.L.U.D.E..
Album: released on After Hours, Dec'82 Dist: CBS

Cassette: released on After Hours, Dec'82 Dist: CBS

PRELUDES GREATEST HITS - VOL.I & II Various artists (Various Artists).
Double Album: released on Prelude, Apr'83 Dist: CBS

Double cassette: released on Prelude, Apr'83 Dist: CBS

SILENT NIGHT.
Single (7"): released on After Hours, Nov'82 Dist: CBS

Premi

MEIN TERI HOGAYEE.
Tracks: / Palley Punjeban walley / Saun mahiney / Mein teri hogayee / Tere lakh de hularey / Yaar mere di chaal / Kagara swadey menoon haniaan / Ban mohrni / Chaa muklavey da / Aj mein peenia / Aj di mehfil.
Notes: Music composed by Kuljit Singh Bhamra. Multitone Records Ltd/Savera, Unit 24, Vernon Building, Westbourne St., High Wycome, Bucks. Tel: 0494 25441
Album: released on Multitone Records/Savera, Jun'86 by Multitone Records/Savera. Dist: Multitone Records/Savera

Cassette: released on Multitone Records/Savera, Jun'86 by Multitone Records/Savera. Dist: Multitone Records/Savera

Premiere Accordian Band

GO COUNTRY & WESTERN.
Tracks: / Catch me if you can / Jambalaya / Crystal chandeliers / Help me make it through the night / Old rugged cross (the) / One day at a time / Good bad & the ugly (the) / Ghostriders in the sky / Bonanza / Dixie / Today I started loving you / I can't help it if I'm still in love with you / Laura / Mull of Kintyre / Wabash cannonball / Wreck of the old 97 / Casey Jones / Turkey in the straw / Green green grass of home / Release me / Cryin' time / Maggie / Tiny bubbles / Send me the pillow (that you dream on) / I won't forget you / It's four in the morning / There goes my everything / Sea of heartbreak.
Album: released on Scotdisc, Dec'86 Dist: Clyde Factors Distributors

Cassette: released on Scotdisc, Dec'86 Dist: Clyde Factors Distributors

Premiere Classe

POUPEE FLASH.
Single (7"): released on Carrere America (USA), Feb'83 by Polygram.

Single (12"): released on Carrere America (USA), Feb'83 by Polygram.

Pren, Ceffyl

COLLASANT EU GWAED.
Single (7"): released on Anthem, May'84 by Anthem. Dist: ILA

Prentiss, Lee

SWEETHEARTS.
Tracks: / Sweethearts / U + Me (The Einstein song) / Love this way.
Single (7"): released on Funkin' Marvellous, May'87 Dist: Priority, RCA, Ariola

Single (12"): released on Funkin' Marvellous, May'87 Dist: Priority, RCA, Ariola

Cassette single: released on Funkin' Marvellous, May'87 Dist: Priority, RCA, Ariola

U + ME (The Einstein song).
Tracks: / U + me (Special New York dance mix) / U + me (Ext. club version) / U + me (Einstein dub mix).
Single (12"): released on Funkin' Marvellous, Mar'87 Dist: Priority, RCA, Ariola

Prento, Gussie

RAW RUB A DUB INNA FASHION.
Album: released on Top Notch, Nov'85

Presage

PRODUCT 1: LOCOMOTION.
Tracks: / S.O.S..
Single (7"): released on Presage, Dec'86 Dist: Spartan

Single (12"): released on Presage, Dec'86 Dist: Spartan

Presencer, Alain

SINGING BOWLS OF TIBET.
Tracks: / Invocation / Bowl voices / Shepherd's song / Lullaby / Bon-po chant / Lamentation / Symphony of the bowls.
Notes: Tibetologist Alain Presencer creates strange and mystical sounds from ancient singing bowls made of precious metals and from a thighbone trumpet, bell cymbol and gong.
Compact disc: released on Saydisc, Mar'87 by Saydisc Records. Dist: Essex, Harmonia Mundi, Roots, H.R. Taylor, Jazz Music, Swift, Projection, Gamut

Album: released on Saydisc, Nov'81 by Saydisc Records. Dist: Essex, Harmonia Mundi, Roots, H.R. Taylor, Jazz Music, Swift, Projection, Gamut

Cassette: released on Saydisc, Nov'81 by Saydisc Records. Dist: Essex, Harmonia Mundi, Roots, H.R. Taylor, Jazz Music, Swift, Projection, Gamut

Present

DANCE AWAY.
Single (7"): released on Plezure, Dec'84 by Plezure Records. Dist: Pinnacle

Presenting The Posse

PRESENTING THE POSSE VOLUME III (Various Artists).
Album: released on Uptempo, Oct'86 by Uptempo Records. Dist: Jetstar Distribution

PRESENTING THE POSSE Various artists (Various Artists).
Album: released on Up Tempo, Mar'84 by Up Tempo Records. Dist: Jetstar

PRESENTING THE POSSE - VOL.2 Various artists (Various Artists).
Album: released on Up Tempo, Jun'85 by Up Tempo Records. Dist: Jetstar

Present Laughter

PRESENT LAUGHTER Coward, Noel (Scofield, Paul/Fenella Fielding/Margoles/Routledge).
Cassette: released on Talking Tape Company, '84 by Talking Tape Company Records.

Preservation Of...

PRESERVATION OF SWEDISHNESS Various artists (Various Artists).
Album: released on ARC (Accordion Records), '84 Dist: Accordion Record Club

President

EUROPEAN SUMMER.
Tracks: / European summer pt.1 / European summer pt.2.
Single (7"): released on Rekords UK, Jul'87 by Rekords Records UK. Dist: PRT

President Reagan...

FROM THIS TO THAT (President Reagan is Clever).
Tracks: / From this to that.
Single (12"): released on Hyena, Jun'86 Dist: Backs, Cartel

Presidents Men

OUT IN THE OPEN.
Single (7"): released on Oily, Jul'81 by Oily Records. Dist: Fast Distribution

REASONS FOR LEAVING.
Single (7"): released on Oily, Mar'81 by Oily Records. Dist: Fast Distribution

Presidentti, Tasavallan

LAMBERTLAND.
Album: released on Sonet, '73 by Sonet Records. Dist: PRT

MILKY WAY MOSES.
Album: by Sonet Records. Dist: PRT

Presley, Elvis

20 GOLDEN HITS VOL. 2.

20 GOLDEN HITS VOL. 3.
Cassette: released on Astan, Jun'86 by Astan Records. Dist: Counterpoint

20 GREATEST HITS - VOL.2.
Album: released on RCA International, '84

Cassette: released on RCA International, '84

20 GREATEST HITS - VOL.1.
Album: released on RCA International, '84

Cassette: released on RCA International, '84

32 FILM HITS.
Tracks: / Fun in Acapulco / Mexico / Marguerita / Bossa Nova baby / Blue Hawaii / Can't help falling in love / Rock-a-hula baby / Ku-u-I-po / King Creole / Hard headed woman / Trouble / Dixieland rock / Frankie and Johnny / Please don't stop loving me / Easy come, easy go / Sing you children / Tonight's all right for love / Frankfurt special / Wooden heart / G.I. blues / Blue suede shoes / Doin' the best I can / Dog's life, A / Charro / Roustabout / Little Egypt / Poison ivy league / Girls! girls! girls! / Where do you come from / Return to sender / Follow that dream / Angel.
Compact disc: released on RCA (S.I.S.), Oct'84

Double Album: released on RCA (S.I.S.), Aug'84

Cassette: released on RCA (S.I.S.), Aug'84

32 FILM HITS VOLUME 2.
Tracks: / Change of habit / Fun in Aapulco / Roustabout / Blue Hawaii / Easy come easy go / King Creole / G.I. blues / Follow that dream / It happened at the World's Fair / Jailhouse rock.
Double Album: released on RCA (Germany), Jul'85

Compact disc: released on RCA (Germany), Jul'85

50TH ANNIVERSARY.
Single (12"): released on RCA International, Jan'85

68 COMEBACK SPECIAL.
Video-cassette (VHS): released on Virgin, Jan'86 by Virgin Records. Dist: EMI, Virgin Distribution

96 HITS OF THE KING.
Notes: 6 LP Box Set
Album: released on RCA (Germany), Dec'86

AIN'T THAT LOVING YOU BABY.
Tracks: / ain't that loving you baby / Bossa nova baby / Rocka hula.
Single (7"): released on RCA, Mar'87 by RCA Records. Dist: RCA, Roots, Swift, Wellard, Chris, I & B, Solomon & Peres Distribution

Single (12"): released on RCA, Mar'87 by RCA Records. Dist: RCA, Roots, Swift, Wellard, Chris, I & B, Solomon & Peres Distribution

AIN'T THAT LOVING YOU BABY (DOUBLE A).
Single (7"): released on RCA, Apr'87 by RCA Records. Dist: RCA, Roots, Swift, Wellard, Chris, I & B, Solomon & Peres Distribution

Single (12"): released on RCA, Apr'87 by RCA Records. Dist: RCA, Roots, Swift, Wellard, Chris, I & B, Solomon & Peres Distribution

ALL SHOOK UP.
Single (7"): released on RCA, May'77 by RCA Records. Dist: RCA, Roots, Swift, Wellard, Chris, I & B, Solomon & Peres Distribution

ALL TIME GREATEST HITS, THE.
Album: released on RCA, Aug'87

Cassette: released on RCA, Aug'87

ALOHA FROM HAWAII (via satellite).
Tracks: / What now my love / Fever / Welcome to my world / Suspicious minds / See see rider / Burning loveysomething loving you / Hound dog / I'll remember you / Long tall Sally / Whole lotta shakin' goin' on / American trilogy / Big hunk o' love / Can't help falling in love / Burning love / Something / You gave me a mountain / Steamroller blues / My way / Love me / Johnny B Goode / It's over / Blue suede shoes / I'm so lonesome I could cry / I can't stop loving you / Hound dog.
Compact disc: released on RCA, Nov'85 by RCA Records. Dist: RCA, Roots, Swift, Wellard, Chris, I & B, Solomon & Peres Distribution

Album: released on RCA, Nov'85 by RCA Records. Dist: RCA, Roots, Swift, Wellard, Chris, I & B, Solomon & Peres Distribution

Video-cassette (VHS): released on Virgin, Feb'86 by Virgin Records. Dist: EMI, Virgin Distribution

Cassette: released on RCA, '84 by RCA Records. Dist: RCA, Roots, Swift, Wellard, Chris, I & B, Solomon & Peres Distribution

ALWAYS ON MY MIND.
Tracks: / Separate ways / Don't cry daddy / M[illegible] boy / I miss you / Bitter they are / Solitaire / Hu[illegible] / Pieces of my life / It's midnight / I've lost you / Unchained melody / You gave me a fountain
Compact disc: released on RCA, '86 by RCA Records. Dist: RCA, Roots, Swift, Wellard, Chris, I & B, Solomon & Peres Distribution

AN AMERICAN TRILOGY.
Tracks: / An American trilogy / Until it's time [illegible] you to go.
Single (7"): released on Old Gold, Oct'86 Old Gold Records. Dist: Lightning, Jazz Music, Spartan, Counterpoint

Single (7"): released on RCA, Jul'81 by RCA Records. Dist: RCA, Roots, Swift, Wellard, Chris, I & B, Solomon & Peres Distribution

ANYTHING THAT'S PART OF YOU.
Single (7"): released on RCA, May'77 by RCA Records. Dist: RCA, Roots, Swift, Wellard, Chris, I & B, Solomon & Peres Distribution

ARE YOU LONESOME TONIGHT.
Tracks: / Are you lonesome tonight / Wood[en] heart.
Single (7"): released on Old Gold, Apr'87 Old Gold Records. Dist: Lightning, Jazz Music, Spartan, Counterpoint

Album: released on RCA Camden, Mar'8[illegible] RCA Records. Dist: Pickwick Distribution, Taylor, H.R.

Cassette: released on RCA Camden, Ma[illegible] by RCA Records. Dist: Pickwick Distribution, Taylor, H.R.

Single (7"): released on RCA, Feb'82 by RCA Records. Dist: RCA, Roots, Swift, Wellard, Chris, I & B, Solomon & Peres Distribution

ARE YOU SINCERE.
Single (7"): released on RCA, '80 by RCA Records. Dist: RCA, Roots, Swift, Wellard, Chris, I & B, Solomon & Peres Distribution

BABY I DON'T CARE.
Single (7"): released on RCA, Apr'83 by RCA Records. Dist: RCA, Roots, Swift, Wellard, Chris, I & B, Solomon & Peres Distribution

Single (12"): released on RCA, Apr'83 by RCA Records. Dist: RCA, Roots, Swift, Wellard, Chris, I & B, Solomon & Peres Distribution

BALLADS.
Tracks: / Can't help falling in love / In the ghetto / Moody blues / Suspicion / Are you lonesome tonight / Girl of my best friend (The) / Don't / Wooden heart / It's now or never / Wonder of you (The) / There goes my everything / Crying in the chapel / My boy / It's only me / Don't cry daddy / Hawaiian wedding song / Suspician minds / My way.
Compact disc: released on Telstar, '86 by Telstar Records. Dist: RCA Distribution

BALLADS.
Album: released on Telstar, Oct'85 by Telstar Records. Dist: RCA Distribution

Cassette: released on Telstar, Oct'85 by Telstar Records. Dist: RCA Distribution

BEST OF ELVIS,THE.
Album: released on RCA (Germany), Apr'84

BLUE HAWAII Original Soundtrack.
Album: released on RCA International, '84

Cassette: released on RCA International. '84

Single (7"): released on RCA, '80 by RCA Records. Dist: RCA, Roots, Swift, Wellard, Chris, I & B, Solomon & Peres Distribution

BLUE MOON.
Tracks: / Blue moon / I don't care if the sun don't shine.
Single (7"): released on Old Gold, Oct'86 by Old Gold Records. Dist: Lightning, Jazz Music, Spartan, Counterpoint

Single (7"): released on RCA, '80 by RCA Records. Dist: RCA, Roots, Swift, Wellard, Chris, I & B, Solomon & Peres Distribution

BLUE RHYTHMS.
Album: released on Preimer, '84

Cassette: released on Preimer, '84

BLUE RIVER.
Single (7"): released on RCA, '75 by RCA Records. Dist: RCA, Roots, Swift, Wellard, Chris, I & B, Solomon & Peres Distribution

BLUE SUEDE SHOES.
Cassette: released on Astan, Jun'86 by Astan Records. Dist: Counterpoint

Single (7"): released on RCA, '75 by RCA Records. Dist: RCA, Roots, Swift, Wellard, Chris, I & B, Solomon & Peres Distribution

Single (7"): released on RCA, '75 by RCA Records. Dist: RCA, Roots, Swift, Wellard, Chris, I & B, Solomon & Peres Distribution

BOSSA NOVA BABY.
Single (7"): released on RCA, '80 by RCA Records. Dist: RCA, Roots, Swift, Wellard, Chris, I & B, Solomon & Peres Distribution

BURNING LOVE.
Single (7"): released on RCA, '80 by RCA Records. Dist: RCA, Roots, Swift, Wellard, Chris, I & B, Solomon & Peres Distribution

CALIFORNIA HOLIDAY Film Soundtrack.
Album: released on RCA International, '80

Cassette: released on RCA International, Aug'80

CAN'T HELP FALLING IN LOVE.
Single (7"): released on RCA, May'77 by RCA Records. Dist: RCA, Roots, Swift, Wellard, Chris, I & B, Solomon & Peres Distribution

CAN'T HELP FALLING IN LOVE EP.
Single (7"): released on RCA, Dec'83 by RCA Records. Dist: RCA, Roots, Swift, Wellard, Chris, I & B, Solomon & Peres Distribution

CAN'T HELP FALLING IN LOVE AND OTHER GREAT MOVIE HITS.
Album: released on RCA Camden, Apr'83 by RCA Records. Dist: Pickwick Distribution, Taylor, H.R.

Cassette: released on RCA Camden, Apr'83 by RCA Records. Dist: Pickwick Distribution, Taylor, H.R.

CHRISTMAS ALBUM.
Album: released on RCA, Oct'85 by RCA Records. Dist: RCA, Roots, Swift, Wellard, Chris, I & B, Solomon & Peres Distribution

CLAMBAKE Film Soundtrack.
Album: released on RCA International. '84

Cassette: released on RCA International, '84

COLLECTION: ELVIS PRESLEY VOL.4.
Tracks: / Guitar man / US male / If I can dream / In the ghetto / Suspicious minds / Don't cry daddy / Wonder of you, The / An American trilogy / Burning love / Always on my mind / It's only love.
Compact disc: released on RCA, Feb'85 by RCA Records. Dist: RCA, Roots, Swift, Wellard, Chris, I & B, Solomon & Peres Distribution

COLLECTION: ELVIS PRESLEY VOL.3.
Tracks: / ooden heart / Surrender / Wild in the country / Can't help falling in love / Rock-a-hula baby / His latest flame / Follow that dream / Good luck charm / Se's not you / Return to sender.
Compact disc: released on RCA, Feb'85 by RCA Records. Dist: RCA, Roots, Swift, Wellard, Chris, I & B, Solomon & Peres Distribution

COLLECTION: ELVIS PRESLEY VOL.2.
Tracks: / Teddy bear / Party / Jailhouse rock / Don't / Wear my ring around your neck / I got stung / It's now or never / Stuck on you / Girl of my best friend, The / Mess of blues, A / Are you lonesome tonight / Big hunk o' love, A / Fool such as I, A / My wish came true.
Compact disc: released on RCA, '86 by RCA Records. Dist: RCA, Roots, Swift, Wellard, Chris, I & B, Solomon & Peres Distribution

COLLECTION: ELVIS PRESLEY VOL.1.
Tracks: / That's alright / Heartbreak hotel / I was the one / Blue suede shoes / My baby left me / Hound dog / Don't be cruel / Peace in the valley / One night / Loving you / I want you / I want you I need you I love you / Love me tender / Love me / All shook up / That's when your heartaches begin.
Compact disc: released on RCA, '86 by RCA Records. Dist: RCA, Roots, Swift, Wellard, Chris, I & B, Solomon & Peres Distribution

COLLECTOR'S GOLD.
Single (7"): released on RCA, Oct'82 by RCA Records. Dist: RCA, Roots, Swift, Wellard, Chris, I & B, Solomon & Peres Distribution

COMPLETE BONUS SONGS,THE.
Album: released on RCA (S.I.S.), Aug'84

Cassette: released on RCA (S.I.S.), Aug'84

COMPLETE SINGLES,THE (11 BOX SET).
Boxed set: released on RCA (Japan), Sep'85

COMPLETE SUN SESSIONS, THE.
Double Album: released on RCA Victor, Jul'87

CONFIDENTIALLY ELVIS.
Notes: Double album, four interviews.
Double Album: released on Arena, Feb'87 by Arena Records. Dist: Spartan

Cassette: released on Arena, Feb'87 by Arena Records. Dist: Spartan

CRYING IN THE CHAPEL.
Single (7"): released on RCA, May'77 by RCA Records. Dist: RCA, Roots, Swift, Wellard, Chris, I & B, Solomon & Peres Distribution

DANNY BOY.
Single (7"): released on RCA, '80 by RCA Records. Dist: RCA, Roots, Swift, Wellard, Chris, I & B, Solomon & Peres Distribution

DATE WITH ELVIS, A.
Album: released on RCA, '84 by RCA Records. Dist: RCA, Roots, Swift, Wellard, Chris, I & B, Solomon & Peres Distribution

Cassette: released on RCA, '84 by RCA Records. Dist: RCA, Roots, Swift, Wellard, Chris, I & B, Solomon & Peres Distribution

DEVIL IN DISGUISE.
Single (7"): released on RCA, May'77 by RCA Records. Dist: RCA, Roots, Swift, Wellard, Chris, I & B, Solomon & Peres Distribution

DON'T.
Single (7"): released on RCA, '80 by RCA Records. Dist: RCA, Roots, Swift, Wellard, Chris, I & B, Solomon & Peres Distribution

DON'T BE CRUEL.
Single (7"): released on RCA, Jun'78 by RCA Records. Dist: RCA, Roots, Swift, Wellard, Chris, I & B, Solomon & Peres Distribution

DON'T CRY DADDY.
Single (7"): released on RCA, '80 by RCA Records. Dist: RCA, Roots, Swift, Wellard, Chris, I & B, Solomon & Peres Distribution

DOUBLE DYNAMITE COLLECTION.
Double Album: released on RCA Camden, Jan'80 by RCA Records. Dist: Pickwick Distribution, Taylor, H.R.

Double cassette: released on RCA Camden, Jan'80 by RCA Records. Dist: Pickwick Distribution, Taylor, H.R.

DOUBLE DYNAMITE VOL.1.
Album: released on RCA Camden, Jan'80 by RCA Records. Dist: Pickwick Distribution, Taylor, H.R.

Cassette: released on RCA Camden, Jan'80 by RCA Records. Dist: Pickwick Distribution, Taylor, H.R.

DOUBLE DYNAMITE VOL.2.
Album: released on RCA Camden, Jan'80 by RCA Records. Dist: Pickwick Distribution, Taylor, H.R.

Cassette: released on RCA Camden, Jan'80 by RCA Records. Dist: Pickwick Distribution, Taylor, H.R.

EASY COME EASY GO.
Album: released on Camden(RCA), '75 by RCA Records. Dist: Pickwick Distribution, Taylors, Swift

Cassette: released on Camden(RCA), '75 by RCA Records. Dist: Pickwick Distribution, Taylors, Swift

ELVIS.
Tracks: / Rip it up / Love me / When my blue moon turns to gold again / Long tall Sally / First in line / Paralysed / So glad you're mine / Old Shep / Ready teddy / Anyplace in paradise / How's the world treating you / How do you think I fee.
Notes: Digital stereo
Compact disc: released on RCA, Dec'84 by RCA Records. Dist: RCA, Roots, Swift, Wellard, Chris, I & B, Solomon & Peres Distribution

Cassette: released on RCA, Aug'71 by RCA Records. Dist: RCA, Roots, Swift, Wellard, Chris, I & B, Solomon & Peres Distribution

Album: released on RCA Camden, Jan'81 by RCA Records. Dist: Pickwick Distribution, Taylor, H.R.

Cassette: released on RCA Camden, Jan'81 by RCA Records. Dist: Pickwick Distribution, Taylor, H.R.

Album: released on RCA (Germany), '83

ELVIS CHRISTMAS ALBUM.
Album: released on RCA Camden, Oct'79 by RCA Records. Dist: Pickwick Distribution, Taylor, H.R.

Cassette: released on RCA Camden, Oct'79 by RCA Records. Dist: Pickwick Distribution, Taylor, H.R.

Album: released on RCA, '84 by RCA Records. Dist: RCA, Roots, Swift, Wellard, Chris, I & B, Solomon & Peres Distribution

Cassette: released on RCA, '84 by RCA Records. Dist: RCA, Roots, Swift, Wellard, Chris, I & B, Solomon & Peres Distribution

ELVIS EP COLLECTION NO.2.
Single (7"): released on RCA, Oct'82 by RCA Records. Dist: RCA, Roots, Swift, Wellard, Chris, I & B, Solomon & Peres Distribution

ELVIS FOREVER.
Album: released on RCA (Germany), '83

ELVIS FOREVER-96 HITS.
Album: released on RCA, Aug'87 by RCA Records. Dist: RCA, Roots, Swift, Wellard, Chris, I & B, Solomon & Peres Distribution

Cassette: released on RCA, Aug'87 by RCA Records. Dist: RCA, Roots, Swift, Wellard, Chris, I & B, Solomon & Peres Distribution

ELVIS FOREVER VOL.2.
Double Album: released on RCA (Germany), '83

ELVIS FOREVER VOLUME 4.
Album: released on RCA (Germany), Dec'86

ELVIS FOR EVERYONE.
Album: released on RCA, '84 by RCA Records. Dist: RCA, Roots, Swift, Wellard, Chris, I & B, Solomon & Peres Distribution

Cassette: released on RCA, '84 by RCA Records. Dist: RCA, Roots, Swift, Wellard, Chris, I & B, Solomon & Peres Distribution

ELVIS GOLDEN RECORDS VOL.5.
Album: released on RCA, Mar'85 by RCA Records. Dist: RCA, Roots, Swift, Wellard, Chris, I & B, Solomon & Peres Distribution

Cassette: released on RCA, Mar'85 by RCA Records. Dist: RCA, Roots, Swift, Wellard, Chris, I & B, Solomon & Peres Distribution

ELVIS' GOLD RECORDS - VOL.5.
Tracks: / Suspicious minds / Kentucky rain / In the ghetto / Clean up your own backyard / If I can dream / Burning love / If you talk in your sleep / For the heart / Moody blue / Way down.
Compact disc: released on RCA, '86 by RCA Records. Dist: RCA, Roots, Swift, Wellard, Chris, I & B, Solomon & Peres Distribution

ELVIS' GOLD RECORDS - VOL.1.
Tracks: / Hound dog / Loving you / All shook up / Heartbreak hotel / Teddy bear / Jailhouse rock / Love me tender / Treat me nice / Anyway you want me (that's how I will be) / I want you, I need you, I love you.
Compact disc: released on RCA, '86 by RCA Records. Dist: RCA, Roots, Swift, Wellard, Chris, I & B, Solomon & Peres Distribution

ELVIS IN CONCERT.
Double Album: released on RCA, Oct'77 by RCA Records. Dist: RCA, Roots, Swift, Wellard, Chris, I & B, Solomon & Peres Distribution

Double cassette: released on RCA, Oct'77 by RCA Records. Dist: RCA, Roots, Swift, Wellard, Chris, I & B, Solomon & Peres Distribution

ELVIS IN DEMAND.
Album: released on RCA, Sep'81 by RCA Records. Dist: RCA, Roots, Swift, Wellard, Chris, I & B, Solomon & Peres Distribution

Cassette: released on RCA, Sep'81 by RCA Records. Dist: RCA, Roots, Swift, Wellard, Chris, I & B, Solomon & Peres Distribution

ELVIS IN GERMANY.
Album: released on RCA (S.I.S.), Aug'84

Cassette: released on RCA (S.I.S.), Aug'84

ELVIS IN HOLLYWOOD.
Album: released on Premier, '84 by Premier Records. Dist: CBS

Cassette: released on Premier, '84 by Premier Records. Dist: CBS

ELVIS IN MEMPHIS live on stage.
Album: released on Victor, Aug'74

ELVIS IS BACK.
Album: released on RCA, '84 by RCA Records. Dist: RCA, Roots, Swift, Wellard, Chris, I & B, Solomon & Peres Distribution

Cassette: released on RCA, '84 by RCA Records. Dist: RCA, Roots, Swift, Wellard, Chris, I & B, Solomon & Peres Distribution

ELVIS LIVE AT MADISON SQUARE GARDEN.
Album: released on Victor, '74

Cassette: released on Victor, '74

ELVIS LOVE SONGS.
Album: released on K-Tel, Oct'79 by K-Tel Records. Dist: Record Merchandisers Distribution, Taylors, Terry Blood Distribution, Wynd-Up Distribution, Relay Distribution, Pickwick Distribution, Solomon & Peres Distribution, Polygram

Cassette: released on K-Tel, Oct'79 by K-Tel Records. Dist: Record Merchandisers Distribution, Taylors, Terry Blood Distribution, Wynd-Up Distribution, Relay Distribution, Pickwick Distribution, Solomon & Peres Distribution, Polygram

ELVIS (MEDLEY).
Single (7"): released on RCA, Jan'85 by RCA Records. Dist: RCA, Roots, Swift, Wellard, Chris, I & B, Solomon & Peres Distribution

ELVIS NBC SPECIAL Original Soundtrack.
Album: released on RCA, '84 by RCA Records. Dist: RCA, Roots, Swift, Wellard, Chris, I & B, Solomon & Peres Distribution

Cassette: released on RCA, '84 by RCA Records. Dist: RCA, Roots, Swift, Wellard, Chris, I & B, Solomon & Peres Distribution

ELVIS ON TOUR.
Video-cassette (VHS): released on MGM, Jan'84 Dist: Polygram Distribution, Swift Distribution

ELVIS PRESLEY.
Tracks: / Blue suede shoes / I'm counting on you / I got a woman / One sided love affair / I love you because / Just because / Tutti frutti / Tryin' to get you / I'm gonna sit right down and cry / I'll never let you go / Bluer moon / Money honey.
Album: released on RCA, Mar'85 by RCA Records. Dist: RCA, Roots, Swift, Wellard, Chris, I & B, Solomon & Peres Distribution

Cassette: released on RCA, Mar'85 by RCA Records. Dist: RCA, Roots, Swift, Wellard, Chris, I & B, Solomon & Peres Distribution

Compact disc: released on RCA, Mar'85 by RCA Records. Dist: RCA, Roots, Swift, Wellard, Chris, I & B, Solomon & Peres Distribution

Double Album: released on RCA, Oct'79 by RCA Records. Dist: RCA, Roots, Swift, Wellard, Chris, I & B, Solomon & Peres Distribution

Album: released on RCA (Germany), '83

ELVIS PRESLEY COLLECTION VOL.2.
Double Album: released on Pickwick, Jun'78 by Pickwick Records. Dist: Pickwick Distribution, Prism Leisure Distribution, Lugtons

Double cassette: released on Pickwick, Jun'78 by Pickwick Records. Dist: Pickwick Distribution, Prism Leisure Distribution, Lugtons

ELVIS PRESLEY COLLECTION VOL.3.
Double Album: released on Pickwick, Apr'79 by Pickwick Records. Dist: Pickwick Distribution, Prism Leisure Distribution, Lugtons

Double cassette: released on Pickwick, Apr'79 by Pickwick Records. Dist: Pickwick Distribution, Prism Leisure Distribution, Lugtons

ELVIS PRESLEY COLLECTION.
Double Album: released on Pickwick, Jul'76 by Pickwick Records. Dist: Pickwick Distribution, Prism Leisure Distribution, Lugtons

Double cassette: released on Pickwick, Jul'76 by Pickwick Records. Dist: Pickwick Distribution, Prism Leisure Distribution, Lugtons

ELVIS PRESLEY EP (4 track cassette EP).
Cassette: released on RCA, May'83 by RCA Records. Dist: RCA, Roots, Swift, Wellard, Chris, I & B, Solomon & Peres Distribution

Single (7"): released on RCA, Feb'81 by RCA Records. Dist: RCA, Roots, Swift, Wellard, Chris, I & B, Solomon & Peres Distribution

ELVIS PRESLEY SINGS LEIBER & STOLLER.
Album: released on RCA, '84 by RCA Records. Dist: RCA, Roots, Swift, Wellard, Chris, I & B, Solomon & Peres Distribution

Cassette: released on RCA, '84 by RCA Records. Dist: RCA, Roots, Swift, Wellard, Chris, I & B, Solomon & Peres Distribution

ELVIS PRESLEY SUN COLLECTION.
Album: released on RCA, Mar'79 by RCA Records. Dist: RCA, Roots, Swift, Wellard, Chris, I & B, Solomon & Peres Distribution

Cassette: released on RCA, Mar'79 by RCA Records. Dist: RCA, Roots, Swift, Wellard, Chris, I & B, Solomon & Peres Distribution

ELVIS SAILS.
Single (7"): released on RCA, '76 by RCA Records. Dist: RCA, Roots, Swift, Wellard, Chris, I & B, Solomon & Peres Distribution

ELVIS,SCOTTY & BILL.
Album: released on Virgin, Nov'79 by Virgin Records. Dist: EMI, Virgin Distribution

Album: released on Topline, Jun'85 by Charly Records. Dist: Charly Distribution

Cassette: released on Topline, Jun'85 by Charly Records. Dist: Charly Distribution

ELVIS'S GOLDEN RECORDS VOL.3.
Album: released on RCA International, Sep'81

Cassette: released on RCA International, Sep'81

ELVIS'S GOLDEN RECORDS VOL.2.
Album: released on RCA, Jan'84 by RCA Records. Dist: RCA, Roots, Swift, Wellard, Chris, I & B, Solomon & Peres Distribution

Cassette: released on RCA, Jan'84 by RCA Records. Dist: RCA, Roots, Swift, Wellard, Chris, I & B, Solomon & Peres Distribution

ELVIS'S GOLDEN RECORDS VOL.1.
Album: released on RCA, Jan'84 by RCA Records. Dist: RCA, Roots, Swift, Wellard, Chris, I & B, Solomon & Peres Distribution

Cassette: released on RCA, Jan'84 by RCA Records. Dist: RCA, Roots, Swift, Wellard, Chris, I & B, Solomon & Peres Distribution

ELVIS'S GOLDEN RECORDS VOL.4.
Album: released on RCA International, Jan'84

Cassette: released on RCA International, Jan'84

ELVIS SINGS HITS FROM HIS MOVIES.
Album: released on RCA/Camden, Jan'72

Cassette: released on RCA/Camden, Jan'72

ELVIS SINGS THE WONDERFUL WORLD OF CHRISTMAS.
Album: released on RCA, Nov'79 by RCA Records. Dist: RCA, Roots, Swift, Wellard, Chris, I & B, Solomon & Peres Distribution

Cassette: released on RCA, Nov'79 by RCA Records. Dist: RCA, Roots, Swift, Wellard, Chris, I & B, Solomon & Peres Distribution

ELVIS TAPES.
Notes: Mid-priced reissue. Pre-army interview with Elvis Presley.
Album: released on Redwood, Apr'87 Dist: WRPM

Album: released on Ace, Mar'79 by Ace Records. Dist: Pinnacle, Swift, Hotshot, Cadillac

ELVIS THE PELVIS 50th anniversary album.
Tracks: / Tutti frutti / Money honey / Tryin' to get to you / Mystery train / Mystery train / Heartbreak hotel / I got a woman / TGreat me nice / One sided love affair / Don't be cruel / Shake,rattle and roll / I want you, I need you, I love you / Good rockin' tonight / Lawdy Miss Clawdy / I'm gonna sit right down and cry / I was the one / I want to be free / Ready teddy / Blue moon of Kentucky / Baby let's play house / Long tall Sally / I'm left, your right, she's gone / How do you think I feel / I love you because / Blue suede shoes / When my blue moon turns to gold again / Young and beautiful.
Notes: This is the collection of all the best Elvis, from his 'Pelvis' period when fansswooned and the authorities protested as Elvis gyrated on T.V. and stage to boththe delight and horror of first a nation and soon the world.
Double Album: released on RCA (Germany), Nov'85

Double cassette: released on RCA (Germany), Nov'85

ELVIS-THE ULTIMATE PERFORMANCE.
Album: released on K-Tel, Nov'81 by K-Tel Records. Dist: Record Merchandisers Distribution, Taylors, Terry Blood Distribution, Wynd-Up Distribution, Relay Distribution, Pickwick Distribution, Solomon & Peres Distribution, Polygram

Cassette: released on K-Tel, Nov'81 by K-Tel Records. Dist: Record Merchandisers Distribution, Taylors, Terry Blood Distribution, Wynd-Up Distribution, Relay Distribution, Pickwick Distribution, Solomon & Peres Distribution, Polygram

ESSENTIAL ELVIS.
Tracks: / Teddy bear / Loving you - 2 / Loving you - 3 / Mean woman blues / Got a lot o'livin' to do / Party / Lonesome cowboy / Jailhouse rock / Treat me nice / Young and beautiful / Don't leave me now / I want to be free / Baby I don't care / Jailhouse rock - 2 / Got a lot o'livin' to do - 2 / Love me tender (with the Jordanaires) / Loving you - 4 / Loving you - 5 / Mean woman blues - 2 / Treat me nice - 2 / Love me tender / Let me / Poor boy / Poor boy / We're gonna move / Loving you / Party / Hot dog.
Album: released on RCA, Dec'86 by RCA Records. Dist: RCA, Roots, Swift, Wellard, Chris, I & B, Solomon & Peres Distribution

Cassette: released on RCA, Dec'86 by RCA Records. Dist: RCA, Roots, Swift, Wellard, Chris, I & B, Solomon & Peres Distribution

Compact disc: released on RCA, Jan'87 by RCA Records. Dist: RCA, Roots, Swift, Wellard, Chris, I & B, Solomon & Peres Distribution

FILM HITS 50th anniversary album.
Boxed set: released on RCA (Germany), Nov'85

FIRST LIVE RECORDINGS.
Album: released on RCA, Jul'84 by RCA Records. Dist: RCA, Roots, Swift, Wellard, Chris, I & B, Solomon & Peres Distribution

Cassette: released on RCA, Jul'84 by RCA Records. Dist: RCA, Roots, Swift, Wellard, Chris, I & B, Solomon & Peres Distribution

FIRST TEN YEARS,THE.
Album: released on RCA/Camden, Sep'84

Cassette: released on RCA/Camden, Sep'84

FIRST YEAR, (THE) (Presley, Elvis/Bill Black/Scotty Moore).
Album: released on Charly, '83 by Charly Records. Dist: Charly, Cadillac

FLAMING STAR.
Album: released on RCA/Camden, Jan'80

Cassette: released on RCA/Camden, Jan'80

FLAMING STAR (EP).
Single (7"): released on RCA, Oct'82 by RCA Records. Dist: RCA, Roots, Swift, Wellard, Chris, I & B, Solomon & Peres Distribution

FLIPHITS.
Cassette: released on RCA, Jul'83 by RCA Records. Dist: RCA, Roots, Swift, Wellard, Chris, I & B, Solomon & Peres Distribution

FOLLOW THAT DREAM.
Single (7"): released on RCA, Feb'82 by RCA Records. Dist: RCA, Roots, Swift, Wellard, Chris, I & B, Solomon & Peres Distribution

FOOL SUCH AS I, A.
Single (7"): released on RCA, May'77 by RCA Records. Dist: RCA, Roots, Swift, Wellard, Chris, I & B, Solomon & Peres Distribution

FOREVER.
Tracks: / My baby left me / Heartbreak hotel / I got stung / Hound dog / Teddy bear / Love me tender / Guitar man / In the Ghetto / Suspicious minds / Don't / One night / Stuck on you / Surrender / Wooden heart / All shook up.
Double Album: released on RCA, Jul'86 by RCA Records. Dist: RCA, Roots, Swift, Wellard, Chris, I & B, Solomon & Peres Distribution

Double cassette: released on RCA, Jul'86 by RCA Records. Dist: RCA, Roots, Swift, Wellard, Chris, I & B, Solomon & Peres Distribution

FRANKIE AND JOHNNY.
Single (7"): released on RCA, Jan'80 by RCA Records. Dist: RCA, Roots, Swift, Wellard, Chris, I & B, Solomon & Peres Distribution

FRANKIE & JOHNNY.
Album: released on RCA International, Jan'84

Cassette: released on RCA International, Jan'84

FROM MEMPHIS TO VEGAS.
Album: released on RCA International, Jan'84

G.I.BLUES Film Soundtrack.
Album: released on RCA International, Jan'84

Cassette: released on RCA International, Jan'84

G.I. BLUES ALTERNATE TAKE.
Single (7"): released on RCA, Feb'82 by RCA Records. Dist: RCA, Roots, Swift, Wellard, Chris, I & B, Solomon & Peres Distribution

GIRL HAPPY Film Soundtrack.
Album: released on RCA International, Nov'84

Cassette: released on RCA International, Nov'84

GIRL OF MY BEST FRIEND.
Single (7"): released on RCA Golden Grooves, Jul'81 by RCA Records. Dist: RCA

GIRLS! GIRLS! GIRLS!.
Album: released on RCA/Camden, Sep'86

Cassette: released on RCA/Camden, Sep'86

Album: released on RCA International, Jan'84
Cat. no: **NL 89048**

Cassette: released on RCA International, Jan'84

GOLDEN CELEBRATION.
Album: released on RCA, Oct'84 by RCA Records. Dist: RCA, Roots, Swift, Wellard, Chris, I & B, Solomon & Peres Distribution

Cassette: released on RCA, Oct'84 by RCA Records. Dist: RCA, Roots, Swift, Wellard, Chris, I & B, Solomon & Peres Distribution

GOLD RECORDS VOLUME 2.
Tracks: / Big hunk o' love / My wish came true / Fool such as I, A / I need your love tonight / Don't / I beg of you / Santa bring my baby back to me / Party / Paralyzed / One night / I got stung / King Creole / Wear my ring around your neck / Doncha' think it's time.
Album: released on RCA, Nov'84 by RCA Records. Dist: RCA, Roots, Swift, Wellard, Chris, I & B, Solomon & Peres Distribution

Cassette: released on RCA, Nov'84 by RCA Records. Dist: RCA, Roots, Swift, Wellard, Chris, I & B, Solomon & Peres Distribution

Compact disc: released on RCA, Nov'84 by RCA Records. Dist: RCA, Roots, Swift, Wellard, Chris, I & B, Solomon & Peres Distribution

GOOD LUCK CHARM.
Single (7"): released on RCA, May'77 by RCA Records. Dist: RCA, Roots, Swift, Wellard, Chris, I & B, Solomon & Peres Distribution

GOOD ROCKIN TONIGHT.
Single (7"): released on RCA Golden Grooves, Oct'81 by RCA Records. Dist: RCA

GOOD TIMES.
Album: released on RCA (Germany), Dec'86

GREEN GREEN GRASS OF HOME.
Single (7"): released on RCA, May'84 by RCA Records. Dist: RCA, Roots, Swift, Wellard, Chris, I & B, Solomon & Peres Distribution

GUITAR MAN.
Single (7"): released on RCA, Feb'81 by RCA Records. Dist: RCA, Roots, Swift, Wellard, Chris, I & B, Solomon & Peres Distribution

HARD HEADED WOMAN.
Single (7"): released on RCA, Jan'80 by RCA Records. Dist: RCA, Roots, Swift, Wellard, Chris, I & B, Solomon & Peres Distribution

HAREM HOLIDAY Film Soundtrack.
Album: released on RCA International, Jan'84

Cassette: released on RCA International, Jan'84

HEARTBREAK HOTEL.
Tracks: / Heartbreak Hotel / All shook up.
Single (7"): released on Old Gold, Apr'87 by Old Gold Records. Dist: Lightning, Jazz Music, Spartan, Counterpoint

Album: released on RCA/Camden, Sep'81

Cassette: released on RCA/Camden, Sep'81

Album: released on Platinum (W.Germany), Oct'85 Dist: Mainline

Cassette: released on Platinum (W.Germany), Oct'85 Dist: Mainline

Single (7"): released on RCA, May'77 by RCA Records. Dist: RCA, Roots, Swift, Wellard, Chris, I & B, Solomon & Peres Distribution

Single (7"): released on RCA, Feb'82 by RCA Records. Dist: RCA, Roots, Swift, Wellard, Chris, I & B, Solomon & Peres Distribution

HIS HAND IN MINE.
Album: released on RCA International, Jan'84

Cassette: released on RCA International, Jan'84

HIS LATEST FLAME.
Tracks: / His latest flame / Girl of my best friend.
Single (7"): released on Old Gold, Oct'86 by Old Gold Records. Dist: Lightning, Jazz Music, Spartan, Counterpoint

Single (7"): released on RCA, May'77 by RCA Records. Dist: RCA, Roots, Swift, Wellard, Chris, I & B, Solomon & Peres Distribution

HITS OF THE 70'S.
Album: released on Victor, Dec'74

Cassette: released on Victor, Dec'74

HOUND DOG.
Cassette: released on Astan, Aug'86 by Astan Records. Dist: Counterpoint

HOUND DOG.
Tracks: / Hound dog / Don't be cruel.
Single (7"): released on Old Gold, Apr'87 by Old Gold Records. Dist: Lightning, Jazz Music, Spartan, Counterpoint

HOW GREAT THOU ART.
Album: released on RCA International, Jan'84

Cassette: released on RCA International, Jan'84

I CAN HELP.
Album: released on RCA, Mar'84 by RCA Records. Dist: RCA, Roots, Swift, Wellard, Chris, I & B, Solomon & Peres Distribution

Cassette: released on RCA, Mar'84 by RCA Records. Dist: RCA, Roots, Swift, Wellard, Chris, I & B, Solomon & Peres Distribution

Single (7"): released on RCA, Nov'83 by RCA Records. Dist: RCA, Roots, Swift, Wellard, Chris, I & B, Solomon & Peres Distribution

I DON'T CARE IF THE SUN DON'T SHINE.
Single (7"): released on RCA, Jan'80 by RCA Records. Dist: RCA, Roots, Swift, Wellard, Chris, I & B, Solomon & Peres Distribution

IF EVERY DAY WAS LIKE CHRISTMAS.
Single (7"): released on RCA Golden Grooves, Nov'81 by RCA Records. Dist: RCA

IF I CAN DREAM.
Single (7"): released on RCA, Jan'80 by RCA Records. Dist: RCA, Roots, Swift, Wellard, Chris, I & B, Solomon & Peres Distribution

I GOT A WOMAN.
Cassette: released on Astan, Aug'86 by Astan Records. Dist: Counterpoint

I GOT LUCKY.
Album: released on RCA/Camden, Nov'75

Cassette: released on RCA/Camden, Nov'75

I GOT STUNG.
Single (7"): released on RCA, May'77 by RCA Records. Dist: RCA, Roots, Swift, Wellard, Chris, I & B, Solomon & Peres Distribution

I JUST CAN'T HELP BELIEVIN.
Single (7"): released on RCA Golden Grooves, Jul'81 by RCA Records. Dist: RCA

I'M 10,000 YEARS OLD, ELVIS COUNTRY.
Album: released on RCA International, Jan'84

Cassette: released on RCA International, Jan'84

IMAGES.
Album: released on Cambra, Mar'85 by Cambra Records. Dist: IDS, Conifer

Album: released on Cambra, Mar'85 by Cambra Records. Dist: IDS, Conifer

I'M LEAVIN.
Single (7"): released on RCA, Jan'80 by RC Records. Dist: RCA, Roots, Swift, Wellard Chris, I & B, Solomon & Peres Distribution

IN CONCERT.
Video-cassette (VHS): released on Mountain Films, Jan'86 Dist: Gold & Sons Distribution

I NEED YOUR LOVE TONIGHT.
Single (7"): released on RCA, May'77 by RC Records. Dist: RCA, Roots, Swift, Wellard Chris, I & B, Solomon & Peres Distribution

I NEED YOU SO.
Single (7"): released on RCA, Oct'82 by RC Records. Dist: RCA, Roots, Swift, Wellard Chris, I & B, Solomon & Peres Distribution

INSPIRATION.
Album: released on K-Tel, Oct'80 by K-T Records. Dist: Record Merchandisers Distribu tion, Taylors, Terry Blood Distribution, Wynd-U Distribution, Relay Distribution, Pickwick Dis tribution, Solomon & Peres Distribution, Pol gram

Cassette: released on K-Tel, Oct'80 by K-T Records. Dist: Record Merchandisers Distrib tion, Taylors, Terry Blood Distribution, Wynd-U Distribution, Relay Distribution, Pickwick Di

tribution, Solomon & Peres Distribution, Polygram

IN THE BEGINNING.
Album: released on Topline, Nov'84 by Charly Records. Dist: Charly Distribution

Cassette: released on Topline, Nov'84 by Charly Records. Dist: Charly Distribution

IN THE GHETTO.
Tracks: / In the ghetto / Suspicious minds.
Single (7"): released on Old Gold, Oct'86 by Old Gold Records. Dist: Lightning, Jazz Music, Spartan, Counterpoint

Single (7"): released on RCA, Jan'75 by RCA Records. Dist: RCA, Roots, Swift, Wellard, Chris, I & B, Solomon & Peres Distribution

IT HAPPENED AT THE WORLD'S FAIR.
Album: released on RCA International, Nov'84

Cassette: released on RCA International, Nov'84

IT'S NOW OR NEVER.
Album: released on RCA/Camden, Sep'81

Cassette: released on RCA/Camden, Sep'81

Single (7"): released on RCA, May'77 by RCA Records. Dist: RCA, Roots, Swift, Wellard, Chris, I & B, Solomon & Peres Distribution

Single (7"): released on RCA, Dec'83 by RCA Records. Dist: RCA, Roots, Swift, Wellard, Chris, I & B, Solomon & Peres Distribution

IT WON'T SEEM LIKE CHRISTMAS WITHOUT YOU.
Album: released on RCA International, Nov'84

Cassette: released on RCA International, Nov'84

Single (7"): released on RCA, Nov'79 by RCA Records. Dist: RCA, Roots, Swift, Wellard, Chris, I & B, Solomon & Peres Distribution

I'VE LOST YOU.
Single (7"): released on RCA, Jan'80 by RCA Records. Dist: RCA, Roots, Swift, Wellard, Chris, I & B, Solomon & Peres Distribution

I WANT YOU, I NEED YOU, I LOVE YOU.
Single (7"): released on RCA, Jan'80 by RCA Records. Dist: RCA, Roots, Swift, Wellard, Chris, I & B, Solomon & Peres Distribution

JAILHOUSE ROCK (VIDEO).
Notes: Released on MGM/UA/Screen Legends

JANIS AND ELVIS.
Album: released on RCA (France), May'85 by RCA Records. Dist: Discovery

KENTUCKY RAIN.
Single (7"): released on RCA, Jan'80 by RCA Records. Dist: RCA, Roots, Swift, Wellard, Chris, I & B, Solomon & Peres Distribution

KID GALAHAD.
Single (7"): released on RCA, Feb'82 by RCA Records. Dist: RCA, Roots, Swift, Wellard, Chris, I & B, Solomon & Peres Distribution

KID GALAHAD AND EASY COME EASY GO.
Album: released on RCA (Germany), Apr'83

Cassette: released on RCA (Germany), Apr'83

KING.
Album: released on RCA/Camden, Jan'80

Cassette: released on RCA/Camden, Jan'80

KING CREOLE.
Tracks: / Was war das alles ohne dich / Gaucho gaucho.
Cassette: released on Astan, Aug'86 by Astan Records. Dist: Counterpoint

Album: released on RCA International, Jan'84

Cassette: released on RCA International, Jan'84

Single (7"): released on RCA, Feb'82 by RCA Records. Dist: RCA, Roots, Swift, Wellard, Chris, I & B, Solomon & Peres Distribution

KING CREOLE VOL.2.
Single (7"): released on RCA, Oct'82 by RCA Records. Dist: RCA, Roots, Swift, Wellard, Chris, I & B, Solomon & Peres Distribution

KISSIN' COUSINS.
Album: released on RCA/Camden, Sep'86

Cassette: released on RCA/Camden, Sep'86

Album: released on RCA International, Nov'84

Cassette: released on RCA International, Nov'84

Single (7"): released on RCA, Jan'80 by RCA Records. Dist: RCA, Roots, Swift, Wellard, Chris, I & B, Solomon & Peres Distribution

LAST FAREWELL,THE.
Single (7"): released on RCA, Oct'84 by RCA Records. Dist: RCA, Roots, Swift, Wellard, Chris, I & B, Solomon & Peres Distribution

LEGENDARY PERFORMANCE VOL.4.
Album: released on RCA, Nov'83 by RCA Records. Dist: RCA, Roots, Swift, Wellard, Chris, I & B, Solomon & Peres Distribution

Cassette: released on RCA, Nov'83 by RCA Records. Dist: RCA, Roots, Swift, Wellard, Chris, I & B, Solomon & Peres Distribution

LEGENDARY PERFORMER VOL.2, A.
Album: released on RCA, Oct'77 by RCA Records. Dist: RCA, Roots, Swift, Wellard, Chris, I & B, Solomon & Peres Distribution

Cassette: released on RCA, Oct'77 by RCA Records. Dist: RCA, Roots, Swift, Wellard, Chris, I & B, Solomon & Peres Distribution

LEGENDARY PERFORMER VOL.1.
Album: released on RCA, Oct'77 by RCA Records. Dist: RCA, Roots, Swift, Wellard, Chris, I & B, Solomon & Peres Distribution

Cassette: released on RCA, Oct'77 by RCA Records. Dist: RCA, Roots, Swift, Wellard, Chris, I & B, Solomon & Peres Distribution

LEGEND, THE.
Tracks: / Heartbreak hotel / Blue suede shoes / Hound dog / Teddy bear / Jailhouse rock / King Creole / Fool such as I, A / My wish came true / Girl of my best friend / Wooden heart / Rock-a-hula baby / Return to sender / Devil in disguise / Such a night / Love letter / US male / Rags to riches / It's only love.
Compact disc: released on RCA, '84 by RCA Records. Dist: RCA, Roots, Swift, Wellard, Chris, I & B, Solomon & Peres Distribution

Album: released on RCA/Camden, Nov'83

Cassette: released on RCA/Camden, Nov'83

LEGEND, THE '68-'70.
Boxed set: released on RCA Australia, Apr'86

LIVE IN CHILE.
Album: released on RCA (Import), Aug'86

LOVE IN LAS VEGAS.
Single (7"): released on RCA, Oct'82 by RCA Records. Dist: RCA, Roots, Swift, Wellard, Chris, I & B, Solomon & Peres Distribution

LOVE LETTERS.
Single (7"): released on RCA, Jan'80 by RCA Records. Dist: RCA, Roots, Swift, Wellard, Chris, I & B, Solomon & Peres Distribution

LOVE ME TENDER.
Tracks: / Love me tender / Teddy bear.
Single (7"): released on Old Gold, Oct'86 by Old Gold Records. Dist: Lightning, Jazz Music, Spartan, Counterpoint

Album: released on RCA (Germany), Jul'85

Single (7"): released on RCA, Feb'82 by RCA Records. Dist: RCA, Roots, Swift, Wellard, Chris, I & B, Solomon & Peres Distribution

LOVE SONGS.
Album: released on RCA/Camden, Aug'83

Cassette: released on RCA/Camden, Aug'83

LOVIN ARMS.
Single (7"): released on RCA, Apr'81 by RCA Records. Dist: RCA, Roots, Swift, Wellard, Chris, I & B, Solomon & Peres Distribution

LOVING YOU.
Album: released on RCA International, Jan'84

Cassette: released on RCA International, Jan'84

Album: released on RCA (Germany), May'84

Single (7"): released on RCA, Jan'80 by RCA Records. Dist: RCA, Roots, Swift, Wellard, Chris, I & B, Solomon & Peres Distribution

Single (7"): released on RCA, Feb'82 by RCA Records. Dist: RCA, Roots, Swift, Wellard, Chris, I & B, Solomon & Peres Distribution

MAGIC MOMENTS.
Cassette: released on RCA, Jun'84 by RCA Records. Dist: RCA, Roots, Swift, Wellard, Chris, I & B, Solomon & Peres Distribution

MEMORIES'.
Single (7"): released on RCA, Jan'80 by RCA Records. Dist: RCA, Roots, Swift, Wellard, Chris, I & B, Solomon & Peres Distribution

MEMPHIS DECADES, THE.
Double Album: released on RCA Victor, Jul'87

MOODY BLUES.
Album: released on RCA, Sep'81 by RCA Records. Dist: RCA, Roots, Swift, Wellard, Chris, I & B, Solomon & Peres Distribution

Cassette: released on RCA, Sep'81 by RCA Records. Dist: RCA, Roots, Swift, Wellard, Chris, I & B, Solomon & Peres Distribution

Single (7"): released on RCA Golden Grooves, May'82 by RCA Records. Dist: RCA

MY BABY LEFT ME.
Single (7"): released on RCA, Jan'80 by RCA Records. Dist: RCA, Roots, Swift, Wellard, Chris, I & B, Solomon & Peres Distribution

MYSTERY TRAIN.
Single (7"): released on RCA, Jan'80 by RCA Records. Dist: RCA, Roots, Swift, Wellard, Chris, I & B, Solomon & Peres Distribution

OLD SHEP.
Single (7"): released on RCA, Jan'79 by RCA Records. Dist: RCA, Roots, Swift, Wellard, Chris, I & B, Solomon & Peres Distribution

ONE NIGHT.
Single (7"): released on RCA, Jan'80 by RCA Records. Dist: RCA, Roots, Swift, Wellard, Chris, I & B, Solomon & Peres Distribution

ONE NIGHT WITH YOU.
Video-cassette (VHS): released on Virgin, '86 by Virgin Records. Dist: EMI, Virgin Distribution

PARADISE HAWAIIAN STYLE Film Soundtrack.
Album: released on RCA International, Jan'84

Cassette: released on RCA International, Jan'84

PARTY.
Tracks: / Party / Got a lot o' livin' to do.
Single (7"): released on Old Gold, Oct'86 by Old Gold Records. Dist: Lightning, Jazz Music, Spartan, Counterpoint

PEACE IN THE VALLEY.
Single (7"): released on RCA, Oct'82 by RCA Records. Dist: RCA, Roots, Swift, Wellard, Chris, I & B, Solomon & Peres Distribution

PICTURES OF ELVIS.
Album: released on RCA International, Apr'80

Cassette: released on RCA International, Apr'80

PICTURES OF ELVIS (II).
Picture disc album: released on RCA (Import), Feb'83

PLEASE DON'T STOP LOVING ME.
Album: released on RCA/Camden, Jan'79

Cassette: released on RCA/Camden, Jan'79

POT LUCK.
Album: released on RCA International, Jan'84

Cassette: released on RCA International, Jan'84

PROMISED LAND.
Single (7"): released on RCA, Jan'80 by RCA Records. Dist: RCA, Roots, Swift, Wellard, Chris, I & B, Solomon & Peres Distribution

RAGS TO RICHES.
Single (7"): released on RCA, Jan'80 by RCA Records. Dist: RCA, Roots, Swift, Wellard, Chris, I & B, Solomon & Peres Distribution

RARE ELVIS (VOL. 1).
Tracks: / Early mornin' rain / Hawaiian wedding song / Ku-u-I-po / No more / It's only love / Come what may / I'm yours / First time ever I saw your face / Patch it up / Don't cry daddy / High-heel sneakers / Lover doll / Doncha' think it's time / Sound of your cry / Elvis Presley interviews.
Compact disc: released on RCA, Jul'86 by RCA Records. Dist: RCA, Roots, Swift, Wellard, Chris, I & B, Solomon & Peres Distribution

Album: released on RCA, Mar'85 by RCA Records. Dist: RCA, Roots, Swift, Wellard, Chris, I & B, Solomon & Peres Distribution

Cassette: released on RCA, Mar'85 by RCA Records. Dist: RCA, Roots, Swift, Wellard, Chris, I & B, Solomon & Peres Distribution

RARE ELVIS VOL.2.
Album: released on RCA, Mar'85 by RCA Records. Dist: RCA, Roots, Swift, Wellard, Chris, I & B, Solomon & Peres Distribution

Cassette: released on RCA, Mar'85 by RCA Records. Dist: RCA, Roots, Swift, Wellard, Chris, I & B, Solomon & Peres Distribution

RARE ELVIS VOL.3.
Album: released on RCA, Mar'85 by RCA Records. Dist: RCA, Roots, Swift, Wellard, Chris, I & B, Solomon & Peres Distribution

Cassette: released on RCA, Mar'85 by RCA Records. Dist: RCA, Roots, Swift, Wellard, Chris, I & B, Solomon & Peres Distribution

READY TEDDY.
Cassette: released on Astan, Aug'86 by Astan Records. Dist: Counterpoint

REAL ELVIS.
Single (7"): released on RCA, Feb'82 by RCA Records. Dist: RCA, Roots, Swift, Wellard, Chris, I & B, Solomon & Peres Distribution

RECONSIDER BABY.
Tracks: / Reconsider baby / Tomorrow night / So glad you're mine / When it rains, it really pours / My baby left me / Ain't that loving you baby / I feel so bad / Down in the alley / Hi-heel sneakers / Stranger in my own home town / Merry Christmas baby.
Compact disc: released on RCA, Nov'85 by RCA Records. Dist: RCA, Roots, Swift, Wellard, Chris, I & B, Solomon & Peres Distribution

Album: released on RCA, May'85 by RCA Records. Dist: RCA, Roots, Swift, Wellard, Chris, I & B, Solomon & Peres Distribution

Cassette: released on RCA, May'85 by RCA Records. Dist: RCA, Roots, Swift, Wellard, Chris, I & B, Solomon & Peres Distribution

RETURN OF THE ROCKER (THE).
Album: released on RCA (Germany), Dec'86

RETURN TO SENDER.
Album: released on RCA/Camden, Jan'81

Cassette: released on RCA/Camden, Jan'81

Single (7"): released on RCA, May'77 by RCA Records. Dist: RCA, Roots, Swift, Wellard, Chris, I & B, Solomon & Peres Distribution

ROCK A-HULA BABY.
Single (7"): released on RCA, May'77 by RCA Records. Dist: RCA, Roots, Swift, Wellard, Chris, I & B, Solomon & Peres Distribution

ROCKER.
Tracks: / Blue suede shoes / Tutti frutti / Lawdy Miss Clawdy / I got a woman / Money honey / Jailhouse rock / Ready teddy / Rip it up / Shake rattle & roll / Long tall Sally / Hound dog / Baby I don't care.
Album: released on RCA, Mar'85 by RCA Records. Dist: RCA, Roots, Swift, Wellard, Chris, I & B, Solomon & Peres Distribution

Cassette: released on RCA, Mar'85 by RCA Records. Dist: RCA, Roots, Swift, Wellard, Chris, I & B, Solomon & Peres Distribution

Compact disc: released on RCA, Mar'85 by RCA Records. Dist: RCA, Roots, Swift, Wellard, Chris, I & B, Solomon & Peres Distribution

ROCK HITS, THE.
Album: released on RCA/Camden, Apr'86

Cassette: released on RCA/Camden, Apr'86

ROCK'N'ROLL.
Album: released on RCA, Jan'84 by RCA Records. Dist: RCA, Roots, Swift, Wellard, Chris, I & B, Solomon & Peres Distribution

Cassette: released on RCA, Jan'84 by RCA Records. Dist: RCA, Roots, Swift, Wellard, Chris, I & B, Solomon & Peres Distribution

ROCK'N'ROLL NO.2.
Album: released on RCA International, Jan'84

Cassette: released on RCA International, Jan'84

ROCK'N'ROLL REBEL (20 rock 'n' roll originals).
Album: released on K-Tel, Jun'82 by K-Tel Records. Dist: Record Merchandisers Distribution, Taylors, Terry Blood Distribution, Wynd-Up Distribution, Relay Distribution, Pickwick Distribution, Solomon & Peres Distribution, Polygram

Cassette: released on K-Tel, Jun'82 by K-Tel Records. Dist: Record Merchandisers Distribution, Taylors, Terry Blood Distribution, Wynd-Up Distribution, Relay Distribution, Pickwick Distribution, Solomon & Peres Distribution, Polygram

ROMANTIC ELVIS-20 LOVE SONGS.
Album: released on RCA, Jan'84 by RCA Records. Dist: RCA, Roots, Swift, Wellard, Chris, I & B, Solomon & Peres Distribution

Cassette: released on RCA, Jan'84 by RCA Records. Dist: RCA, Roots, Swift, Wellard, Chris, I & B, Solomon & Peres Distribution

ROUSTABOUT Film Sountrack.
Album: released on RCA International, Jan'84

Cassette: released on RCA International, Jan'84

SANTA CLAUS IS BACK IN TOWN.
Single (7"): released on RCA, Nov'80 by RCA Records. Dist: RCA, Roots, Swift, Wellard, Chris, I & B, Solomon & Peres Distribution

SEPARATE WAYS.
Album: released on RCA/Camden, Jan'73

Cassette: released on RCA/Camden, Jan'73

SHAKE RATTLE AND ROLL.
Single (7"): released on RCA, Oct'82 by RCA Records. Dist: RCA, Roots, Swift, Wellard,

Chris, I & B, Solomon & Peres Distribution

SHE'S NOT YOU.
Single (7"): released on RCA, May'77 by RCA Records. Dist: RCA, Roots, Swift, Wellard, Chris, I & B, Solomon & Peres Distribution

SINGS MORT SHUMAN.
Album: released on RCA (Germany), Jul'85

SINGS WORLD HITS.
Album: released on RCA (Germany), Jan'85

Cassette: released on RCA (Germany), Jan'85

SOMETHING FOR EVERYBODY.
Album: released on RCA International, Jan'84

Cassette: released on RCA International, Jan'84

SOUND OF YOU CRY.
Single (7"): released on RCA, Jun'82 by RCA Records. Dist: RCA, Roots, Swift, Wellard, Chris, I & B, Solomon & Peres Distribution

SPEEDWAY Film Soundtrack.
Album: released on RCA International, Jan'84

Cassette: released on RCA International, Jan'84

STUCK ON YOU.
Single (7"): released on RCA, Jan'80 by RCA Records. Dist: RCA, Roots, Swift, Wellard, Chris, I & B, Solomon & Peres Distribution

SUCH A NIGHT.
Single (7"): released on RCA, Feb'82 by RCA Records. Dist: RCA, Roots, Swift, Wellard, Chris, I & B, Solomon & Peres Distribution

SURRENDER.
Single (7"): released on RCA, May'77 by RCA Records. Dist: RCA, Roots, Swift, Wellard, Chris, I & B, Solomon & Peres Distribution

SUSPICION.
Single (7"): released on RCA, Nov'76 by RCA Records. Dist: RCA, Roots, Swift, Wellard, Chris, I & B, Solomon & Peres Distribution

SUSPICIOUS MINDS.
Album: released on RCA/Camden, Mar'82

Cassette: released on RCA/Camden, Mar'82

Single (7"): released on RCA, Jan'80 by RCA Records. Dist: RCA, Roots, Swift, Wellard, Chris, I & B, Solomon & Peres Distribution

TELL ME WHY.
Single (7"): released on RCA, Jan'80 by RCA Records. Dist: RCA, Roots, Swift, Wellard, Chris, I & B, Solomon & Peres Distribution

THAT'S ALL RIGHT MAMA.
Single (7"): released on RCA Golden Grooves, Aug'81 by RCA Records. Dist: RCA

THAT'S THE WAY IT IS.
Video-cassette (VHS): released on MGM, Nov'86 Dist: Polygram Distribution, Swift Distribution

Album: released on RCA International, Jan'84

Cassette: released on RCA International, Jan'84

THIS IS ELVIS.
Video-cassette (VHS): released on Warner, Dec'84 by Warner Bros Records. Dist: WEA

TOUCH OF GOLD - VOL.1.
Single (7"): released on RCA, Oct'82 by RCA Records. Dist: RCA, Roots, Swift, Wellard, Chris, I & B, Solomon & Peres Distribution

TOUCH OF GOLD - VOL.2.
Single (7"): released on RCA, Oct'82 by RCA Records. Dist: RCA, Roots, Swift, Wellard, Chris, I & B, Solomon & Peres Distribution

TOUCH OF GOLD - VOL.3.
Single (7"): released on RCA, Oct'82 by RCA Records. Dist: RCA, Roots, Swift, Wellard, Chris, I & B, Solomon & Peres Distribution

UNCHAINED MELODY.
Single (7"): released on RCA (USA Import), '80

UNTIL IT'S TIME FOR YOU TO GO.
Single (7"): released on RCA (USA Import), '80

U.S. MALE.
Album: released on RCA Camden, Jun'75 by RCA Records. Dist: Pickwick Distribution, Taylor, H.R.

Cassette: released on RCA Camden, Jun'75 by RCA Records. Dist: Pickwick Distribution, Taylor, H.R.

Single (7"): released on RCA (USA Import), '80

VIVA LAS VEGAS.
Single (7"): released on RCA (USA Import), '80

WAY DOWN.
Single (7"): released on RCA, Jul'77 by RCA Records. Dist: RCA, Roots, Swift, Wellard, Chris, I & B, Solomon & Peres Distribution

WEAR MY RING AROUND YOUR NECK.
Single (7"): released on RCA (USA Import). '80

WELCOME TO MY WORLD.
Album: released on RCA, Sep'81 by RCA Records. Dist: RCA, Roots, Swift, Wellard, Chris, I & B, Solomon & Peres Distribution

Cassette: released on RCA, Sep'81 by RCA Records. Dist: RCA, Roots, Swift, Wellard, Chris, I & B, Solomon & Peres Distribution

WILD IN THE COUNTRY.
Tracks: / Wild in the country / I feel so bad.
Single (7"): released on Old Gold, Apr'87 by Old Gold Records. Dist: Lightning, Jazz Music, Spartan, Counterpoint

WONDERFUL WORLD OF ELVIS.
Double Album: released on RCA Camden, Jan'81 by RCA Records. Dist: Pickwick Distribution, Taylor, H.R.

Double cassette: released on RCA Camden, Jan'81 by RCA Records. Dist: Pickwick Distribution, Taylor, H.R.

WOODEN HEART.
Single (7"): released on RCA, May'77 by RCA Records. Dist: RCA, Roots, Swift, Wellard, Chris, I & B, Solomon & Peres Distribution

WORLD WIDE 50 GOLD AWARD HITS - VOL.2.
Boxed set: released on RCA, Aug'71 by RCA Records. Dist: RCA, Roots, Swift, Wellard, Chris, I & B, Solomon & Peres Distribution

YOU DON'T HAVE TO SAY YOU LOVE ME.
Single (7"): released on RCA (USA Import), '80

YOU'LL NEVER WALK ALONE.
Album: released on RCA Camden, '71 by RCA Records. Dist: Pickwick Distribution, Taylor, H.R.

Cassette: released on RCA Camden, '71 by RCA Records. Dist: Pickwick Distribution, Taylor, H.R.

YOU'RE A HEARTBREAKER.
Single (7"): released on RCA (USA Import). '80

PEARLY KING OF ROCK'N'ROLL.
Album: released on Playground, Sep'87 by Playground Records. Dist: Playground

COLD TURKEY.
Single (7"): released on S.P.E., Dec'84 by Sid Presley Experience. Dist: Rough Trade, Cartel

HUP TWO THREE FOUR.
Single (7"): released on I.D., May'84 by I.D. Records. Dist: Revolver, Cartel

Single (12"): released on I.D., May'84 by I.D. Records. Dist: Revolver, Cartel

BALLETTA, LA.
Single (7"): released on EMI, Mar'83 by EMI Records. Dist: EMI

51ST STATE.
Single (12"): released on Admiralty, Mar'85 by Probe Records. Dist: Cartel

JAMES WHERE ARE YOU NOW?.
Single (12"): released on Admiralty, Nov'85 by Probe Records. Dist: Cartel

IN THE HEAT OF THE NIGHT.
Tracks: / In the heat of the night / Invisible (remix).
Single (7"): released on Offshore, Jul'87 Dist: Probe Plus Distribution, Cartel

Single (12"): released on Offshore, Jul'87 Dist: Probe Plus Distribution, Cartel

INVISIBLE.
Tracks: / Invisible / Streetwise girl.
Single (7"): released on Offshore, Aug'86 Dist: Probe Plus Distribution, Cartel

Single (12"): released on Offshore, Aug'86 Dist: Probe Plus Distribution, Cartel

PRESSURE.
Single (12"): released on Anagram, May'83 by Cherry Red Records. Dist: Pinnacle

YOU TALK WE TALK.

Single (7"): released on Anagram, Nov'82 by Cherry Red Records. Dist: Pinnacle

LIVE IN SHEFFIELD 19TH JANUARY 1982.
Album: released on Paradox, Mar'82 Dist: Virgin

FROM HERE TO ETERNITY.
Single (7"): released on Noose, Jun'83 by Noose Records. Dist: Probe-Cartel Distribution

MELLOW MOODS.
Tracks: / Mellow moods / I need your love.
Single (7"): released on Hardback, Nov'86 by Streetwave Records. Dist: PRT, Priority, DMS, RCA

Single (12"): released on Hardback, Nov'86 by Streetwave Records. Dist: PRT, Priority, DMS, RCA

Single (7"): released on Viceroy, Aug'85 by Viceroy Records. Dist: PRT

Single (12"): released on Viceroy, Aug'85 by Viceroy Records. Dist: PRT

CHEATIN'.
Album: released on Atlantic (Import), Nov'83

ROOTS.
Notes: Artists include: Pepper Adams, Tommy Flanagan, E. Jones, etc.
Album: released on Original Jazz Classics (USA), Jun'86 Dist: Fantasy (USA) Distribution, Chris Wellard Distribution, IMS-Polygram Distribution

PRESTIGE BLUES SWINGERS Various Artists (Various Artists).
Album: released on Fantasy Inc USA, Jun'86 by Fantasy Inc USA Records. Dist: IMS, Polygram

SAY YOU KNOW.
Single (7"): released on Rebound, Jan'84 by Rebound Records. Dist: Terry Blood Distribution

AND DANCE.
Single (12"): released on ERC, Jun'84 by ERC Records. Dist: PRT

BEHOLD.
Album: released on Myrrh, May'82 by Word Records. Dist: Word Distribution

Cassette: released on Myrrh, May'82 by Word Records. Dist: Word Distribution

BILLY PRESTON.
Cassette: released on Ditto, Jan'85 by Pickwick Records. Dist: H.R. Taylor

BILLY PRESTON & SYREETA (Preston, Billy & Syreeta).
Album: released on Motown, Oct'81 by RCA Records. Dist: RCA Distribution

Cassette: released on Motown, Oct'81 by RCA Records. Dist: RCA Distribution

BILLY'S BAG.
Tracks: / Billy's bag / Steady gettin' it / Let me know / Soul meeting / Octopus, The / Slippin' and slidin' / Low down / I am coming through / My girl / Shotgun / Stop in the name of love / Can't you hear my heartbeat / Downtown / Eight days a week / King of the road / If I had a hammer.
Album: released on Topline, Feb'87 by Charly Records. Dist: Charly Distribution

Cassette: released on Topline, Feb'87 by Charly Records. Dist: Charly Distribution

Compact disc: released on Charly, Jun'87 by Charly Records. Dist: Charly, Cadillac

Single (7"): released on Old Gold (Reissue), Jul'82

CHANGE IS GONNA COME, A.
Single (7"): released on Motown, Oct'81 by RCA Records. Dist: RCA Distribution

FAST BREAK (Preston, Billy & Syreeta).
Album: released on Motown, Oct'81 by RCA Records. Dist: RCA Distribution

GO FOR IT (Preston, Billy & Syreeta).
Single (7"): released on Motown, Oct'81 by RCA Records. Dist: RCA Distribution

HOPE.

Single (7"): released on Motown, Oct'81 by RCA Records. Dist: RCA Distribution

Single (12"): released on Motown, Oct'81 by RCA Records. Dist: RCA Distribution

I'M NEVER GONNA SAY GOODBYE.
Single (7"): released on Motown, Oct'82 by RCA Records. Dist: RCA Distribution

IT WILL COME IN TIME (Preston, Billy & Syreeta).
Single (7"): released on Motown, Oct'81 by RCA Records. Dist: RCA Distribution

LATE AT NIGHT.
Album: released on Motown, Oct'81 by RCA Records. Dist: RCA Distribution

Cassette: released on Motown, Oct'81 by RCA Records. Dist: RCA Distribution

NEW WAY TO SAY I LOVE YOU (Preston, Billy & Syreeta).
Single (7"): released on Motown, Feb'83 by RCA Records. Dist: RCA Distribution

Single (12"): released on Motown, Feb'83 by RCA Records. Dist: RCA Distribution

ONE MORE TIME FOR LOVE (Preston, Billy & Syreeta).
Single (7"): released on Motown, Oct'81 by RCA Records. Dist: RCA Distribution

PLEASE STAY (Preston, Billy & Syreeta).
Single (7"): released on Motown, Oct'81 by RCA Records. Dist: RCA Distribution

PRESSIN ON.
Album: released on Motown, Nov'82 by RCA Records. Dist: RCA Distribution

Cassette: released on Motown, Nov'82 by RCA Records. Dist: RCA Distribution

WAY I AM, THE.
Album: released on Motown, Oct'81 by RCA Records. Dist: RCA Distribution

Cassette: released on Motown, Oct'81 by RCA Records. Dist: RCA Distribution

WITH YOU I'M BORN AGAIN (Preston, Billy & Syreeta).
Single (7"): released on Motown, Mar'83 by RCA Records. Dist: RCA Distribution

SACRE BLUES.
Album: released on Rag Baby, Mar'81 Dist: Pinnacle, Red Lightnin' Distribution

DALEY.
Single (7"): released on Dux, Aug'84 by Dux Records. Dist: Spartan

JIMMY PRESTON 1949-1950.
Tracks: / Swingin' in the groove / They call me the champ / I'm lonesome / Hang out tonight / Potato Salad / Oh Mr. Possum / Hey everybody / Hey everybody (alternative take) / Early morning blues / Hay Ride / Estellina bim bam / Credit blues / Swingin' in / Going away.
Notes: Monophonic recording.
Album: released on Krazy Kat, Oct'86 Dist: Jazz Music, Swift, Chris Wellard, H.R. Taylor, Charly, Hotshot, IRS Distribution

RUNNING BEAR.
Single (7"): released on Mercury, '80 by Phonogram Records. Dist: Polygram Distribution

Single (7"): released on Old Gold, Jan'85 by Old Gold Records. Dist: Lightning, Jazz Music, Spartan, Counterpoint

I WON'T SEND ROSES.
Single (7"): released on ABC, Nov'82 by CBS, Pinnacle

BRASS IN POCKET.
Single (7"): released on Real, Nov'79 by WEA

DON'T GET ME WRONG.
Tracks: / Don't get me wrong / Dance.
Single (7"): released on WEA, Sep'86 by WEA Records. Dist: WEA

Single (12"): released on WEA, Sep'86 by WEA Records. Dist: WEA

GET CLOSE.
Tracks: / My baby / When I change my life / Light of the moon / Dance / Tradition of love / Don't get me wrong / I remember you / How much did you get for your soul? / Chill factor / Hymn to her / Room full of mirrors.

Album: released on WEA, Oct'86 by WEA Records. Dist: WEA

Cassette: released on WEA, Oct'86 by WEA Records. Dist: WEA

Compact disc: released on WEA, Oct'86 by WEA Records. Dist: WEA

HYMN TO HER.
Tracks: / Room Full of Mirrors.
Single (7"): released on Real, Nov'86 Dist: WEA

Single (12"): released on Real, Nov'86 Dist: WEA

INTERVIEW PICTURE DISC.
Picture disc album: released on Baktabak, May'87 by Baktabak Records. Dist: Arabesque

LEARNING TO CRAWL.
Tracks: / Middle of the road / Back on the chain gang / Time the avenger / Show me / Watching the clothes / Thumbelina / My city was gone / Thin line between love and hate / I hurt you / 2,000 miles.
Notes: Digital Stereo
Compact disc: released on Real, Jul'84 Dist: WEA

Album: released on Real, Jan'84 Dist: WEA

Cassette: released on Real, Jan'84 Dist: WEA

MIDDLE OF THE ROAD.
Single (7"): released on Real, Feb'84 Dist: WEA

Single (12"): released on Real, Feb'84 Dist: WEA

MY BABY.
Tracks: / My baby / Tradition of love (remix).
Single (7"): released on Real, Mar'87 Dist: WEA

Single (12"): released on Real, Mar'87 Dist: WEA

PRETENDERS.
Album: released on Real, Jan'80 Dist: WEA

Compact disc: released on Real, '83 Dist: WEA

PRETENDERS 2.
Compact disc: released on WEA, Nov'86 by WEA Records. Dist: WEA

Album: released on Real, Aug'81 Dist: WEA

Cassette: released on Real, Aug'81 Dist: WEA

PRETENDERS, THE.
Tracks: / Precious / Phone call, The / Up to the neck / Tattooed love / Space invader / Wait, (The) / Stop your sobbin' / Kid / Private life / Lovers of today / Brass in pocket / Mystery achievement.
Notes: Digital Stereo.
Compact disc: released on Real, '83 Dist: WEA

Pretenders For 007

IF THERE WAS A MAN.
Single (7"): released on WEA, Aug'87 by WEA Records. Dist: WEA

Single (12"): released on WEA, Aug'87 by WEA Records. Dist: WEA

Pretty In Pink

PRETTY IN PINK (Various Artists).
Notes: US teen-culture love story featuring music by the Psychedelic Furs and others.
Video-cassette (VHS): released on CIC Video, Apr'87 by CBS Records. Dist: CBS, Pickwick Distribution

Video-cassette [Betamax]: released on CIC Video, Apr'87 by CBS Records. Dist: CBS, Pickwick Distribution

PRETTY IN PINK Various Artists (Various Artists).
Tracks: / Left of centre / Get to know ya / Do wot you do / Pretty in pink / Shell shock / Round round / Wouldn't it be good / Bring on the dancing horses / Please, please let me get what I want.
Album: released on A&M, Jul'86 by A&M Records. Dist: Polygram

Cassette: released on A&M, Jul'86 by A&M Records. Dist: Polygram

Pretty Maids

FUTURE WORLD.
Tracks: / Future world / Loud'n'proud / Love games / Yellow rain / Rodeo / We came to rock / Needles in the dark / Eye of the storm / Long way to go.
Album: released on Epic, May'87 by CBS Records. Dist: CBS

Cassette: released on Epic, May'87 by CBS Records. Dist: CBS

LOVE GAMES.
Tracks: / Love games / Needles in the dark / Yellow rain.
Single (7"): released on Epic, May'87 by CBS Records. Dist: CBS

Single (12"): released on Epic, May'87 by CBS Records. Dist: CBS

PRETTY MAIDS.
Album: released on Bullet, Oct'83 Dist: Bullet Distribution

RED HOT AND HEAVY.
Album: released on Epic, Jun'85 by CBS Records. Dist: CBS

Cassette: released on Epic, Jun'85 by CBS Records. Dist: CBS

Pretty Ricky Boo-ski

IT'S MINE.
Tracks: / It's mine.
Single (12"): released on Cherry Red, Apr'86 by Cherry Red Records. Dist: Pinnacle

Pretty Things

1967-1971.
Tracks: / Defecting Grey / Mr. Evasion / Talkin' / About the good times / Walking through my dreams / Private Sorrow (A phase in the life of S.F.Sorrow) / Balloon burning (A phase in the life of S.F.Sorrow) / Good Mr. Square / Blue serge blues / October 26 / Cold stone / Summertime / Circus mind / Stone hearted mama.
Album: released on See For Miles, Mar'82 by See For Miles Records. Dist: Pinnacle

Cassette: released on See For Miles, Mar'82 by See For Miles Records. Dist: Pinnacle

CLOSED RESTAURANT BLUES.
Album: released on Bam Caruso, Feb'87 by Bam Caruso Records. Dist: Rough Trade, Revolver, Cartel

CRIES FROM THE MIDNIGHT CIRCUS.
Tracks: / S F Sorrow is born / Journey, (The) / I see you / Well of destiny / Old man going / Cries from the midnight circus / Grass / She's a lover / What's the use / Cold stone / October 26 / Stone-hearted mama.
Album: released on Harvest, Apr'86 by EMI Records. Dist: Roots, EMI

Cassette: released on Harvest, Apr'86 by EMI Records. Dist: Roots, EMI

CROSS TALK.
Album: released on WEA, Aug'80 by WEA Records. Dist: WEA

DON'T BRING ME DOWN.
Single (7"): released on Old Gold, Jul'82 by Old Gold Records. Dist: Lightning, Jazz Music, Spartan, Counterpoint

GET A BUSS.
Album: released on Edsel, Jun'84 by Demon Records. Dist: Pinnacle, Jazz Music, Projection

GET THE PICTURE.
Album: released on Fontana, Mar'84 by Phonogram Records. Dist: Polygram

LET ME HEAR THE CHOIR SING.
Album: released on Edsel, Sep'84 by Demon Records. Dist: Pinnacle, Jazz Music, Projection

LIVE AT HEARTBREAK HOTEL.
Album: released on Big Beat, Aug'84 by Ace Records. Dist: Projection, Pinnacle

PRETTY THINGS, THE.
Album: released on Fontana (Europe), Apr'84 by Phonogram Records. Dist: Polygram

S.F. SORROW & PARACHUTE.
Double Album: released on Harvest, Jun'75 by EMI Records. Dist: Roots, EMI

Previn, Andre

DIFFERENT KIND OF BLUES, A.
Album: released on H.M.V., Oct'80 by EMI Records. Dist: EMI

Cassette: released on H.M.V., Oct'80 by EMI Records. Dist: EMI

DUET (see Day, Doris) (Previn, Andre & Doris Day).

EASY WINNERS (Previn, Andre/Itzhak Perlman).
Tracks: / Ragtime dance / Bethena / Easy winners / Magnetic rag / Strenuous life / Entertainer / Elite syncopations / Solace / Pineapple rag / Sugarcane rag.
Compact disc: released on EMI, May'86 by EMI Records. Dist: EMI

GENIUS OF ANDRE PREVIN, THE.
Album: released on Allegiance, Jul'84 by PRT Records. Dist: PRT

Cassette: released on Allegiance, Jul'84 by PRT Records. Dist: PRT

GIGI.
Album: released on Contemporary, Sep'82 by Good Time Jazz Records (USA). Dist: IMS, Polygram

PAL JOEY.
Album: released on Contemporary Jazz, Dec'81

PLAYS FATS WALLER.
Album: released on Orchid, Feb'82 Dist: Impetus Distribution, Orchid

PLAYS "MY FAIR LADY" Dave Brubeck play "West Side Story".
Album: released on CBS, May'83 by CBS Records. Dist: CBS

Cassette: released on CBS, May'83 by CBS Records. Dist: CBS

PREVIN AT SUNSET.
Album: released on Black Lion, Jan'85 by Black Lion Records. Dist: Jazz Music, Chris Wellard, Taylor, H.R., Counterpoint, Cadillac

Previn, Dory

DORY AND ANDRE PREVIN.
Album: released on DRG (USA), Aug'83 by DRG Records. Dist: Conifer, RCA

DORY PREVIN.
Album: released on Warner Brothers, Oct'74 by Warner Bros Records. Dist: WEA

MARY C.BROWN & THE HOLLYWOOD SIGN.
Notes: Singer/songwriter once married to conductor Andre Previn. Recorded seven albums for U.A. & Warner Bros. during 1970's of which majority now deleted and very collectable. Released in original gatefold sleeve.
Album: released on Beat Goes On, Mar'87 Dist: Pinnacle

MYTHICAL KINGS AND IGUANAS.
Album: released on Greenlight-Capitol, Jun'81 by Capitol Records. Dist: EMI

WE'RE CHILDREN OF COINCIDENCE & HARPO MARX.
Album: released on WEA, '82 by WEA Records. Dist: WEA Deleted '82.

Cassette: released on WEA, '82 by WEA Records. Dist: WEA Deleted '82.

Previn, Lovely

FROM A TO B.
Single (7"): released on Secret, Jun'81 by Secret Records. Dist: EMI

I'LL NEVER GET OVER YOU.
Single (7"): released on Secret, Jul'82 by Secret Records. Dist: EMI

SHATTERPROOF.
Album: released on Secret, Feb'83 by Secret Records. Dist: EMI

WASTED LOVE.
Single (7"): released on Secret, Jul'82 by Secret Records. Dist: EMI

WASTED, THE.
Single (12"): released on Secret, Aug'82 by Secret Records. Dist: EMI

Prevost,Eddie

HANDSCAPES (Prevost,Eddie/Marcio Mattos/Akemi Kuniyoshi-Kuhn).
Notes: For full information see under:Kuniyoshi-Kuhn,Akemi/Marcio Mattos/etc.

NOW HERE THIS THEN (Prevost, Eddie Band).
Album: released on Spotlite-Jazz, '83 by Spotlite Records. Dist: Cadillac, Jazz Music, Spotlite

Prewitt, James

YOU'RE INSATIABLE.
Tracks: / You're insatiable.
Single (12"): released on Move, Jul'86 by Charly Records. Dist: Charly Distribution, Fast Forward Distribution, Cartel Distribution

Prey, Herman

PORTRAIT.
Album: released on Teldec (Germany), Jul'82 by Import Records. Dist: IMS Distribution, Polygram Distribution

Cassette: released on Teldec (Germany), Jul'82 by Import Records. Dist: IMS Distribution, Polygram Distribution

Price, Alan

16 GOLDEN CLASSICS.
Tracks: / Simon Smith & the amazing dancing bear / Cherie / Don't stop the carnival / If I could / Slow down / Shame / People are talking / Angel eyes / Jarrow song / Don't slam that door / Nobody can / Too much / Jump children / Mama divine / Please / I'll put a spell on you.
Notes: All tracks licensed from Jarrow Productions Ltd/Trojan Records: Design: Shoot That Tiger! (c) 1986/Castle Communications Place,Unit 7,271 MertonRoad,London S W 1 8 5 J S .
Bar code: 5/013428/920114:
Album: released on Unforgettable, Dec'86 by Castle Communications Records. Dist: Counterpoint

ALAN PRICE COLLECTION, THE.
Tracks: / Simon Smith & the amazing dancing bear / In times like these / Too many people / Falling in love again / I put a spell on you / Barefootin' / Barefootin' / O lucky man / House that Jack built, The / Don't stop the carnival / Poor people / Tickle me / My old Kentucky home / Hi lili hi lo / Trimdon Grange explosion, The / Shame.
Album: released on Music For Pleasure (Holland), Jun'86 by EMI Records. Dist: EMI

Cassette: released on Music For Pleasure (Holland), Jun'86 by EMI Records. Dist: EMI

BEAT OUT DAT RHYTHM ON A DRUM.
Single (7"): released on Key, Dec'80 by Key Records. Dist: Spartan

BEST OF ALAN PRICE.
Album: released on Action Replay, Nov'85 by Action Replay Records. Dist: PRT

Cassette: released on Action Replay, Nov'85 by Action Replay Records. Dist: PRT

Album: released on Action Replay, Aug'84 by Action Replay Records. Dist: PRT

Cassette: released on Action Replay, Aug'84 by Action Replay Records. Dist: PRT

CLAIR DE LUNE.
Single (7"): released on Safari, Jun'84 by Safari Records. Dist: Pinnacle

FOCUS ON.
Album: released on Decca, Oct'86 by Decca Records. Dist: Polygram

GEORDIE ROOTS & BRANCHES.
Album: released on MWM, May'83 by Mawson & Wareham. Dist: Spartan Distribution, Jazz Music Distribution, JSU Distribution

Cassette: released on MWM, May'83 by Mawson & Wareham. Dist: Spartan Distribution, Jazz Music Distribution, JSU Distribution

JARROW MARCH'86(THE MINI LP).
Album: released on Mooncrest, Nov'86 by Mooncrest Records. Dist: PRT Distribution

JARROW SONG '86.
Tracks: / Between today & yesterday.
Single (7"): released on Mooncrest, Nov'86 by Mooncrest Records. Dist: PRT Distribution

JARROW SONG, (THE).
Single (7"): released on Old Gold, Jul'82 by Old Gold Records. Dist: Lightning, Jazz Music, Spartan, Counterpoint

JUST FOR YOU.
Single (7"): released on Jet, May'78 by Jet Records. Dist: CBS

LOVE IS A MIRACLE.
Single (7"): released on Key, Aug'81 by Key Records. Dist: Spartan

PAPERS.
Tracks: / Papers / Frozen moments.
Single (7"): released on Trojan, Mar'86 by Trojan Records. Dist: PRT, Jetstar

PROFILE.
Album: released on Decca (Teldec), May'83 by Decca Records. Dist: Polygram, IMS

Cassette: released on Decca (Teldec), May'83 by Decca Records. Dist: Polygram, IMS

ROCK'N'ROLL NIGHT AT THE ROYAL COURT.
Album: released on Key, Jan'81 by Key Records. Dist: Spartan

SIMON SMITH AND HIS AMAZING DANCING BEAR (Price, Alan Set).
Tracks: / Simon Smith and his amazing dancing bear / I put a spell on you.
Single (7"): released on Old Gold, May'86 by Old Gold Records. Dist: Lightning, Jazz Music, Spartan, Counterpoint

TOGETHER (Price, Alan & Georgie Fame).
Album: released on CBS, Sep'84 by CBS Records. Dist: CBS

Cassette: released on CBS, Sep'84 by CBS Records. Dist: CBS

TRAVELLIN' MAN.
Album: released on Trojan, May'86 by Trojan Records. Dist: PRT, Jetstar

Cassette: released on Trojan, May'86 by Trojan Records. Dist: PRT, Jetstar

WORLD OF ALAN PRICE, (THE).
Album: released on World of Learning, '70 by

World Of Learning Records. Dist: World Of Learning

Price, Bill

FINE OLD YORKSHIRE GENTLEMAN, (THE).
Album: released on Folk Heritage, Jul'82 by Folk Heritage Records. Dist: Roots, Wynd-Up Distribution, Jazz Music, Folk Heritage

Price, David

ACCORDION MAGIC.
Tracks: / Delilah / Memory / Tijuana taxi / Autumn leave / Whiter shade of pale / I'll wait for you / Spanish eyes / Guantanamera / Charade / Chanson d'amour / Windmills of your mind / March post / La vie en rose / Girl from Ipanema / So nice / Petite fleur / If / She.
Notes: Retail price is given by ARC excluding P & P (via mail order) is 4.50. Mail order distribution address: Accordion Record Club, 146 Birmingham Road, Kidderminster, Worcs DY10 2SL. Tel:0562-746105.
Cassette: released on Accordion Record Club, Jul'86 by Accordion Record Club Records. Dist: Accordion Record Club

Price, Lloyd

JUKE BOX GIANTS.
Album: released on Audio Fidelity, May'82 Dist: PRT

LAWDY MISS CLAWDY.
Album: released on Ace, Jan'85 by Ace Records. Dist: Pinnacle, Swift, Hotshot, Cadillac

MR. PERSONALITY REVISITED.
Album: released on Charly(R&B), Jun'83 by Charly Records. Dist: Charly, Cadillac

STAGGERLEE.
Single (7"): released on Dakota, Aug'82 by Dakota Records. Dist: PRT

Single (7"): released on Creole Replay, Aug'84 by Creole Records. Dist: PRT, Rhino

Price, Malcolm

AND THEN WE ALL GOT UP.....
Album: released on Sweet Folk and Country, Dec'77 Dist: Chris Wellard Distribution

BOURGEOIS BLUES, (THE).
Album: released on Waterfront, Mar'84 by Waterfront Records. Dist: Rough Trade, Cartel, Projection, Roots

IN AN OLD DUTCH HOUSE.
Album: released on Stoof, Jan'78 Dist: Roots Distribution

Price, Ray

HONKY TONK YEARS 1951-53, THE.
Album: released on Rounder (USA), Apr'86 Dist: Mike's Country Music Room Distribution, Jazz Music Distribution, Swift Distribution, Roots Records Distribution, Projection Distribution, Topic Distribution

Price, Ronnie

DANCING PIANO, THE.
Album: released on Maestro, Jul'86 by Maestro Records.

Price, Sam

PLAY IT AGAIN SAM.
Album: released on Whiskey, Women and (Sweden), Jan'85 Dist: Swift

RIB JOINT.
Double Album:

SINGING WITH SAMMY.
Album: released on Bluetime, Aug'86 by Charly Records. Dist: Charly

Price, Sammy

BARRELHOUSE & BLUES.
Album: released on Black Lion, Apr'85 by Black Lion Records. Dist: Jazz Music, Chris Wellard, Taylor, H.R., Counterpoint, Cadillac

BLUES ON MY MIND.
Album: released on Black Lion, Aug'78 by Black Lion Records. Dist: Jazz Music, Chris Wellard, Taylor, H.R., Counterpoint, Cadillac

KING JAZZ VOLUME 5 (Price,Sammy & Mezzrow-Bechet Quintet Septet).
Notes: For full information see under:Mezzrow-Bechet Quintet Septet

ORIGINAL PIANO SOLO.
Album: released on Joker, Apr'81 Dist: Cadillac, Zodiac Distribution, Jazz Horizons, Jazz Music, JSU, Celtic Music

PIANO SOLOS.
Album: released on Joker, Apr'81 Dist: Cadillac, Zodiac Distribution, Jazz Horizons, Jazz Music, JSU, Celtic Music

ROCKIN' BOOGIE.
Album: released on Black & Blue (France), Jan'85 Dist: Swift, Target, Discovery

SWEET SUBSTITUTE.
Album: released on Sackville, Jul'86 Dist: JSU, Jazz Music, Jazz Horizons, Cadillac Music, Celtic Music, Swift

Price, Wilson

FORWARD & TYAKE.
Single (12"): released on Castro Brown, Feb'82 Dist: Jetstar

Price & Wright

COME ON DOWN.
Single (7"): released on Young Blood, Jul'85 by Young Blood Records. Dist: Pinnacle

Prick up your ears

PRICK UP YOUR EARS Original soundtrack (Myers, Stanley).
Album: released on Silva Screen, May'87 by Silva Screen Records. Dist: Silva Screen, PRT

Cassette: released on Silva Screen, May'87 by Silva Screen Records. Dist: Silva Screen, PRT

Pride

WHAT'S LOVE.
Single (7"): released on Pride Productions, Mar'85 Dist: Fast Forward, Cartel

Pride and Prejudice

PRIDE AND PREJUDICE Austen, Jane (Sutcliffe, Irene).
Boxed set: released on Cover to Cover, Jun'85 by Cover to Cover Cassettes. Dist: Conifer

Pride, Charley

20 OF THE BEST.
Tracks: / All I have to offer you is me / Wonder could I live there anymore / I can't believe that you've stopped loving me / I'd rather love you / I'm just me / It's gonna take a little bit longer / Amazing love / Then who am I / Hope you're feelin' me (like I'm feelin' you) / My eyes can only see as far as you / She's just an old love turned memory / Someone loves you honey / Where do I put her memory / You're my Jamaica / Honky tonk blues / You win again / Never been so loved (in all my life) / You're so good when you're bad / Why baby why / Night games.
Album: released on RCA, Mar'86 by RCA Records. Dist: RCA, Roots, Swift, Wellard, Chris, I & B, Solomon & Peres Distribution

Cassette: released on RCA, Mar'86 by RCA Records. Dist: RCA, Roots, Swift, Wellard, Chris, I & B, Solomon & Peres Distribution

BEST OF CHARLEY PRIDE.
Cassette: released on RCA, Sep'77 by RCA Records. Dist: RCA, Roots, Swift, Wellard, Chris, I & B, Solomon & Peres Distribution

BEST OF VOLUME 2.
Cassette: released on RCA, Jan'77 by RCA Records. Dist: RCA, Roots, Swift, Wellard, Chris, I & B, Solomon & Peres Distribution

CHARLEY PRIDE COLLECTION, (THE).
Double Album: released on Pickwick, Apr'79 by Pickwick Records. Dist: Pickwick Distribution, Prism Leisure Distribution, Lugtons

Cassette: released on Pickwick, Jul'80 by Pickwick Records. Dist: Pickwick Distribution, Prism Leisure Distribution, Lugtons

CHARLEY PRIDE GOLDEN COLLECTION, (THE).
Album: released on K-Tel, Jan'80 by K-Tel Records. Dist: Record Merchandisers Distribution, Taylors, Terry Blood Distribution, Wynd-Up Distribution, Relay Distribution, Pickwick Distribution, Solomon & Peres Distribution, Polygram

CHARLEY SINGS EVERYBODY'S CHOICE.
Album: released on RCA, Jun'84 by RCA Records. Dist: RCA, Roots, Swift, Wellard, Chris, I & B, Solomon & Peres Distribution

Cassette: released on RCA, Jun'84 by RCA Records. Dist: RCA, Roots, Swift, Wellard, Chris, I & B, Solomon & Peres Distribution

Cassette: released on RCA, Jun'84 by RCA Records. Dist: RCA, Roots, Swift, Wellard, Chris, I & B, Solomon & Peres Distribution

Album: released on RCA, Jun'84 by RCA Records. Dist: RCA, Roots, Swift, Wellard, Chris, I & B, Solomon & Peres Distribution

EVERY HEART SHOULD HAVE ONE.
Single (7"): released on RCA, Mar'84 by RCA Records. Dist: RCA, Roots, Swift, Wellard, Chris, I & B, Solomon & Peres Distribution

GREATEST HITS: CHARLY PRIDE VOL.2.
Album: released on RCA, Jul'85 by RCA Records. Dist: RCA, Roots, Swift, Wellard, Chris, I & B, Solomon & Peres Distribution

Cassette: released on RCA, Jul'85 by RCA Records. Dist: RCA, Roots, Swift, Wellard, Chris, I & B, Solomon & Peres Distribution

IN CONCERT.
Album: released on RCA (Germany), '83

IN PERSON.
Album: released on RCA International, Jul'80

Cassette: released on RCA International, Jul'80

Cassette: released on RCA International, Jul'80

Album: released on RCA International, Jul'80

MAGIC MOMENTS WITH CHARLEY PRIDE.
Cassette: released on RCA, May'85 by RCA Records. Dist: RCA, Roots, Swift, Wellard, Chris, I & B, Solomon & Peres Distribution

NIGHT GAMES.
Tracks: / Draw the line / Love on a blue rainy day / Late show, The / Night games / Down in Louisiana / Ev'ry heart should have one / Thanks for wakin' me up this mornin' / Lovin' it up (livin' it down) / Just can't leave that woman alone / I could let her get close to me.
Album: released on RCA, Oct'83 by RCA Records. Dist: RCA, Roots, Swift, Wellard, Chris, I & B, Solomon & Peres Distribution

Cassette: released on RCA, Oct'83 by RCA Records. Dist: RCA, Roots, Swift, Wellard, Chris, I & B, Solomon & Peres Distribution

Compact disc: released on RCA, Oct'83 by RCA Records. Dist: RCA, Roots, Swift, Wellard, Chris, I & B, Solomon & Peres Distribution

POWER OF LOVE.
Album: released on RCA, Aug'84 by RCA Records. Dist: RCA, Roots, Swift, Wellard, Chris, I & B, Solomon & Peres Distribution

Cassette: released on RCA, Aug'84 by RCA Records. Dist: RCA, Roots, Swift, Wellard, Chris, I & B, Solomon & Peres Distribution

ROLL ON MISSISSIPPI.
Album: released on RCA, Apr'81 by RCA Records. Dist: RCA, Roots, Swift, Wellard, Chris, I & B, Solomon & Peres Distribution

Cassette: released on RCA, Apr'81 by RCA Records. Dist: RCA, Roots, Swift, Wellard, Chris, I & B, Solomon & Peres Distribution

SONGS OF PRIDE.
Cassette: released on RCA, Mar'78 by RCA Records. Dist: RCA, Roots, Swift, Wellard, Chris, I & B, Solomon & Peres Distribution

THAT'S MY WAY.
Album: released on RCA Camden, Mar'85 by RCA Records. Dist: Pickwick Distribution, Taylor, H.R.

Cassette: released on RCA Camden, Mar'85 by RCA Records. Dist: Pickwick Distribution, Taylor, H.R.

VERY BEST OF CHARLEY PRIDE, (THE).
Album: released on RCA, Jul'81 by RCA Records. Dist: RCA, Roots, Swift, Wellard, Chris, I & B, Solomon & Peres Distribution

Cassette: released on RCA, Jul'81 by RCA Records. Dist: RCA, Roots, Swift, Wellard, Chris, I & B, Solomon & Peres Distribution

Cassette: released on RCA, Jul'81 by RCA Records. Dist: RCA, Roots, Swift, Wellard, Chris, I & B, Solomon & Peres Distribution

Album: released on RCA, Jul'81 by RCA Records. Dist: RCA, Roots, Swift, Wellard, Chris, I & B, Solomon & Peres Distribution

YOU'RE MY JAMAICA.
Album: released on RCA, Dec'79 by RCA Records. Dist: RCA, Roots, Swift, Wellard, Chris, I & B, Solomon & Peres Distribution

Cassette: released on RCA, Dec'79 by RCA Records. Dist: RCA, Roots, Swift, Wellard, Chris, I & B, Solomon & Peres Distribution

Pride, Charlie

AFTER ALL THIS TIME.
Album: released on Ritz, Apr'87 by Outlet Records. Dist: Outlet, Prism Leisure Distribution, Record Services Distribution (Ireland), Roots

Cassette: released on Ritz, Apr'87 by Outlet Records. Dist: Outlet, Prism Leisure Distribution, Record Services Distribution (Ireland), Roots

AT THE COUNTRY STORE.
Album: released on Starblend Country Store, Aug'86 by Starblend Records. Dist: PRT Distribution

Cassette: released on Starblend Country Store, Aug'86 by Starblend Records. Dist: PRT Distribution

HAVE I GOT SOME BLUES FOR YOU.
Tracks: / Have I got some blues for you / Even knowin'.
Single (7"): released on Ritz, 30 May'87 by Outlet Records. Dist: Outlet, Prism Leisure Distribution, Record Services Distribution (Ireland), Roots

Pride of London Big Band

GEE WHIZ.
Album: released on Intersound, Jul'87 by Intersound Records. Dist: Jazz Music

Pride of Nashville

COUNTRY SYMPHONY.
Single (7"): released on Thumbs Up, Jan'81 Dist: Spartan Distribution

Pride of the Cross

TOMMY'S BLUE VALENTINE.
Single (7"): released on Big Beat, Apr'85 by Ace Records. Dist: Projection, Pinnacle

Single (12"): released on Big Beat, Apr'85 by Ace Records. Dist: Projection, Pinnacle

Pride & prejudice

PRIDE & PREJUDICE (See Johnson, Celia) (Austen, Jane).
Cassette: released on MFP, Oct'85 by EMI Records. Dist: EMI

Priest, Maxi

CRAZY LOVER.
Tracks: / Crazy lover / Pretty little girl.
Single (7"): released on 10, Oct'86 by 10 Records. Dist: Virgin, EMI

Single (12"): released on 10, Oct'86 by 10 Records. Dist: Virgin, EMI

DANCIN' MOOD.
Single (7"): released on 10, Jul'85 by 10 Records. Dist: Virgin, EMI

Single (12"): released on 10, Jul'85 by 10 Records. Dist: Virgin, EMI

INTENTIONS.
Album: released on 10, Nov'86 by 10 Records. Dist: Virgin, EMI

Cassette: released on 10, Nov'86 by 10 Records. Dist: Virgin, EMI

IN THE SPRINGTIME.
Tracks: / In the springtime / Bubble (we are go bubble) / Should I (roots mix).
Single (7"): released on 10, Jun'86 by 10 Records. Dist: Virgin, EMI

Single (12"): released on 10, Jun'86 by 10 Records. Dist: Virgin, EMI

LET ME KNOW.
Tracks: / Let me know / I dream.
Single (7"): released on 10, Mar'87 by 10 Records. Dist: Virgin, EMI

Single (12"): released on 10, Mar'87 by 10 Records. Dist: Virgin, EMI

STROLLING ON.
Tracks: / Strolling on / Dancing mood / Strolling on (2).
Single (7"): released on 10, Mar'86 by 10 Records. Dist: Virgin, EMI

Single (12"): released on 10, Mar'86 by 10 Records. Dist: Virgin, EMI

THROW MY CORN (Priest, Maxi/Caution).
Single (12"): released on Level Vibes, May'84 by Level Vibes Records. Dist: Jetstar

WOMAN IN YOU.
Tracks: / Woman in you / Problems / Must be a way* / I dream (live)*.
Single (7"): released on 10, Jun'87 by 10 Records. Dist: Virgin, EMI

Single (12"): released on 10, Jun'87 by 10 Records. Dist: Virgin, EMI

YOU'RE SAFE.
Tracks: / Should I / Hey little girl / Dancin' mood / Sensi / Caution / Stand up and fight.
Compact disc: released on 10, '86 by 10 Records. Dist: Virgin, EMI

Priest of love

PRIEST OF LOVE Original Soundtrack.
Album: released on That's Entertainment, Feb'82 by That's Entertainment Records. Dist: Pinnacle, PRT

Prima Dona

PRIMA DONA.
Album: released on Cobra, May'79 by Cobra Records. Dist: Projection, EMI

Primadonna

FLASHING ON THE FLOOR.

Single (12"): released on ZYX (Germany), Dec'85 by ZYX Records. Dist: Greyhound

Prima, Louis

BEST OF LOUIS PRIMA, THE.
Tracks: / Buona sera / Angelina / Oh Marie / Hey boy.
Album: released on Music For Pleasure (Holland), '86 by EMI Records. Dist: EMI

Cassette: released on Music For Pleasure (Holland), '86 by EMI Records. Dist: EMI

BUONA SERA.
Single (7"): released on EMI (Holland), Jul'84 by EMI Records. Dist: Conifer

HEY BOY, HEY GIRL (Prima, Louis and Keely Smith).
Tracks: / Hey boy, Hey girl / Banana split for my baby, A / You are my love / Fever / Oh Marie / Lazy river / Nitey-nite / When the saints go marching in / Autumn leaves.
Album: released on Capitol T (USA), Nov'85 Dist: Conifer

JUMP, JIVE AN' WAIL.
Tracks: / Jump jive an' wail / Medley: Just a gigolo / Oh Marie / You rascal you (I'll be glad when you're dead) / Buona sera / I've got the world on a string / Pennies from heaven / Medley: Zooma zooma / Medley: I ain't got nobody / Medley: Don't worry 'bout me / Medley: I'm in the mood for love / Medley: Them there eyes / Medley: Honeysuckle Rose / Ya gotta see baby tonight / Fee fie foo / Jump, jive an' wail / Gigolo / I ain't got nobody / Oh Marie / (I'll be glad when you're dead) you rascal you / Buona sera / I've got the world on a string / Pennies from heaven / Angelinda / Zooma zooma / Don't worry bout me / I'm in the mood for love / Them there eyes / Honeysuckle rose / Ya gotta see baby tonight / Fee fie foo.
Cassette: released on Charly, Sep'86 by Charly Records. Dist: Charly, Cadillac

Album: released on Charly, Apr'86 by Charly Records. Dist: Charly, Cadillac

JUST A GIGOLO.
Single (7"): released on EMI (France), Apr'83 by EMI Records. Dist: Conifer

PLAY IT PRETTY FOR THE PEOPLE (Prima, Louis/his big Band).
Album: released on Golden Era, Jul'82 by Import Records. Dist: Wellard, Chris, Swift

REMEMBER.
Album: released on Magic(UK), Apr'85

STRICTLY PRIMA (Prima, Louis with Sam Butera & The Witnesses).
Tracks: / If you were the only girl in the world / Judy / 5 months, 2 weeks, 2 days / That's my home / Sing, sing, sing / Gotta see baby tonight / Felicia no capacia / Moonglow / Bourbon street blues / Fie fie foo.
Notes: A collectors album, featuring Louis Prima with Sam Butera and the Witnesses bringing you an excellent selection of tracks in a style heralding their succesful US nightclub act of the 60's.
Album: released on Capitol, Dec'85 by Capitol Records. Dist: EMI

Cassette: released on Capitol, Dec'85 by Capitol Records. Dist: EMI

WILDEST SHOW AT TAHOE, (THE) (Prima, Louis and Keely Smith).
Album: released on Capitol, Oct'84 by Capitol Records. Dist: EMI

Cassette: released on Capitol, Oct'84 by Capitol Records. Dist: EMI

WILDEST, (THE).
Album: released on Pathe MarconiFrance), Jan'85

Cassette: released on Pathe MarconiFrance), Jan'85

Primal Scream

ALL FALL DOWN.
Single (7"): released on Creation, May'85 Dist: Rough Trade, Cartel

CRYSTAL CRESCENT.
Tracks: / Crystal crescent / Velocity girl / Sirea X.
Single (7"): released on Creation, May'86 Dist: Rough Trade, Cartel

Single (12"): released on Creation, May'86 Dist: Rough Trade, Cartel

GENTLE TUESDAY.
Tracks: / Gentle tuesday / Black star carnival.
Single (7"): released on WEA, 13 Jun'87 by WEA Records. Dist: WEA

Single (12"): released on WEA, 13 Jun'87 by WEA Records. Dist: WEA

PRIMAL SCREAM.
Tracks: / Imperial / Gentle Tuesday / Silent spring / Rock / Country / I love you / Leaves / Tomorrow ends today / Aftermath / Sunshine right / What's the matter?.

Album: released on WEA, Aug'87 by WEA Records. Dist: WEA

Cassette: released on WEA, Aug'87 by WEA Records. Dist: WEA

Primary

RADIO SILENCE.
Single (7"): released on Peeved, May'84 by Peeved Records. Dist: Peeved, Cartel, Backs

Primary Industry

AT GUNPOINT.
Tracks: / At gunpoint / Perversion.
Single (7"): released on Niss, Feb'86 Dist: Rough Trade, Cartel

CICATRICE.
Single (12"): released on Sweatbox, Nov'85 by Sweatbox Records. Dist: Rough Trade, Cartel

HEART OF GLASS.
Single (12"): released on Sweatbox, Aug'87 by Sweatbox Records. Dist: Rough Trade, Cartel

ULTRAMARINE.
Album: released on Sweatbox, Oct'86 by Sweatbox Records. Dist: Rough Trade, Cartel

Prima Tanz Musik

PRIMA TANZ MUSIK Various Artists (Various Artists).
Special: released on Polydor, Jun'82 by Polydor Records. Dist: Polygram, Polydor

Cassette: released on Polydor, Jun'82 by Polydor Records. Dist: Polygram, Polydor

Prime Design

TIME DESIGN.
Notes: Composition by Ornette Coleman for four string instruments in honour of Buckminster Fuller. The Gregory Gelman Ensemble: Larrisa Blitz/Alex Deych/ Matthew Meister/Denardo Coleman.
Album: released on Caravan Of Dreams (USA), Apr'87 by Caravan Of Dreams Records (USA). Dist: IMS, Polygram

Prime Movers

DARK WESTERN NIGHT.
Tracks: / Dark western night / Lost in your world / Museum.
Single (7"): released on Island, Mar'86 by Island Records. Dist: Polygram

Single (12"): released on Island, Mar'86 by Island Records. Dist: Polygram

MATTERS OF TIME (Prime Movers, Boston).
Album: released on Closer (France), Mar'86 Dist: Nine Mile, Cartel

ON THE TRAIL.
Tracks: / On the trail / Strong as I am.
Single (7"): released on Island, Jan'86 by Island Records. Dist: Polygram

Single (12"): released on Island, Jan'86 by Island Records. Dist: Polygram

Primetime

BABY CONFESS IT.
Tracks: / Guilty / What's that you slipped into my wine / I bet 'cha / Sex-o-logical / Confess it baby / Baby don't break my back / Come into my love life / Give me a chance / Remote control.
Album: released on RCA, Nov'85 by RCA Records. Dist: RCA, Roots, Swift, Wellard, Chris, I & B, Solomon & Peres Distribution

Cassette: released on RCA, Nov'85 by RCA Records. Dist: RCA, Roots, Swift, Wellard, Chris, I & B, Solomon & Peres Distribution

PRIME TIME Various artists (Various Artists).
Notes: Featuring Hugh Lawson, Ben Riley, Bob Cranshaw.
Album: released on Storyville, May'86 by Storyville Records. Dist: Jazz Music Distribution, Swift Distribution, Chris Wellard Distribution, Counterpoint Distribution

Primevals

HEYA.
Single (7"): released on New Rose, Jul'87 Dist: Rough Trade, Cartel

Single (12"): released on New Rose, Jul'87 Dist: Rough Trade, Cartel

SOUND HOLE.
Album: released on New Rose, Mar'86 Dist: Rough Trade, Cartel

Primitives

REALLY STUPID.
Tracks: / Really stupid / We found a way to the sun / Were the wind blows.
Single (7"): released on Lazy, Oct'86 Dist: Rough Trade, Cartel

STOP KILLING ME.
Tracks: / Buzz, buzz, buzz. / Laughing up my sleeve*.
Notes: *=Extra track on 12" only
Single (7"): released on Lazy, Feb'87 Dist: Rough Trade, Cartel

Single (12"): released on Lazy, Feb'87 Dist: Rough Trade, Cartel

THRU THE FLOWERS.
Tracks: / Thru the flowers.
Single (12"): released on Lazy, May'86 Dist: Rough Trade, Cartel

Single (7"): released on Lazy, Aug'87 Dist: Rough Trade, Cartel

Single (7"): released on Lazy, Aug'87 Dist: Rough Trade, Cartel

Single (12"): released on Lazy, Aug'87 Dist: Rough Trade, Cartel

Primitons

DON'T GO AWAY.
Tracks: / Something on my mind / Come what may.
Single (12"): released on What Goes On, Dec'86 Dist: Rough Trade, Cartel, Shigaku

Single (12"): released on What Goes On, Feb'87 Dist: Rough Trade, Cartel, Shigaku

HAPPY ALL THE TIME.
Album: released on What Goes On, Apr'87 Dist: Rough Trade, Cartel, Shigaku

Prince

1999.
Tracks: / 1999 / Little red corvette / Delirious / Let's pretend were married / D.M.S.R. / Automatic / Something in the water / Free / Lady cab driver / All the critics love you in New York / International Lover.
Double Album: released on Warner Brothers, Nov'84 by Warner Bros Records. Dist: WEA

Double cassette: released on Warner Brothers, Nov'84 by Warner Bros Records. Dist: WEA

Double compact disc: released on Warner Brothers, Nov'84 by Warner Bros Records. Dist: WEA

ANOTHERLOVEHOLENYOHEAD (Prince & The Revolution).
Tracks: / Anotherloveholenyohead / I wanna be your lover.
Single (7"): released on Paisley Park (usa), Oct'86 by WEA Records. Dist: WEA

Single (12"): released on Paisley Park (usa), Oct'86 by WEA Records. Dist: WEA

AROUND THE WORLD IN A DAY.
Tracks: / Around the world in a day / Paisley Park / Condition of the heart / Rasberry beret / Tamborine / America / Pop life / Ladder (The) / Temptation.
Compact disc: released on Warner Bros., May'85 by Warner Bros Records. Dist: WEA

CONTROVERSY.
Tracks: / Private joy / Ronnie talk to Russia / Let's work / Annie Christian / Jack u off / Sexuality / Controversy / Do my baby.
Notes: Digital stereo.
Compact disc: released on Warner Bros., '84 by Warner Bros Records. Dist: WEA

DIRTY MIND.
Tracks: / Dirty mind / When you were mine / Do it all night / Gotta broken heart again / Uptown / Head / Sister / Party up.
Compact disc: released on Warner Bros., Jan'86 by Warner Bros Records. Dist: WEA

DOUBLE LIVE (Prince & The Revolution).
Notes: Type of recording: Double cassette package. Total playing time: 60 minutes each.
Video-cassette (VHS): released on Polygram, Jan'86 by Polygram Records. Dist: Polygram

FOR YOU.
Tracks: / For you / In love / Soft and wet / Crazy you / Just as long as we're together / Baby / My love is forever / So blue / I'm yours.
Notes: Recorded in 1978, this album has never before been released in the UK.
Album: released on Warner Bros., Sep'86 by Warner Bros Records. Dist: WEA

Cassette: released on Warner Bros., Sep'86 by Warner Bros Records. Dist: WEA

Cassette: released on Warner Bros., Sep'86 by Warner Bros Records. Dist: WEA

GIRLS AND BOYS (Prince and the Revolution).
Tracks: / Girls and Boys / Under the cherry moon / She's always in my hair / 17 days / Erotic city.
Double-pack single: released on Paisley Park (usa), Aug'86 by WEA Records. Dist: WEA

Double-pack single: released on Paisley Park (usa), Aug'86 by WEA Records. Dist: WEA

IF I WAS YOUR GIRLFRIEND.
Tracks: / If I was your girlfriend / Shock Adelica.
Single (7"): released on Paisley Park (usa), Jun'87 by WEA Records. Dist: WEA

Single (12"): released on Paisley Park (usa), Jun'87 by WEA Records. Dist: WEA

INTERVIEW PICTURE DISC.
Album: released on Baktabak, Oct'87 by Baktabak Records. Dist: Arabesque. Estim retail price in Sep'87 was £4.91.

KISS (Prince and the Revolution).
Tracks: / Kiss / Love or money.
Single (7"): released on Paisley Park (usa), Feb'86 by WEA Records. Dist: WEA

Single (12"): released on Paisley Park (usa), Feb'86 by WEA Records. Dist: WEA

MOUNTAINS (Prince and the Revolution).
Tracks: / Mountains / Alexa de Paris.
Single (7"): released on Warner Brothers, May'86 by Warner Bros Records. Dist: WEA

Single (12"): released on Warner Brothers, May'86 by Warner Bros Records. Dist: WEA

PARADE (Prince and the Revolution).
Tracks: / Christopher Tracey's parade / New position / I wonder u / Under the cherry moon / Girls and boys / Life can be so nice / Venus de Milo / Mountains / Do u lie / Kiss / Anotherloverholenyohead / Smetimes it snows in April.
Album: released on Warner Brothers, Apr'86 by Warner Bros Records. Dist: WEA

Cassette: released on Warner Brothers, Apr'86 by Warner Bros Records. Dist: WEA

Compact disc: released on Warner Brothers, Apr'86 by Warner Bros Records. Dist: WEA

PURPLE RAIN From Motion Picture (Prince and the Revolution).
Tracks: / Let's go crazy / Take me with U / Beuatiful ones / Computer blue / Darling Nikki / When doves cry / I would die 4 U / Baby I'm a star / Purple rain.
Compact disc: released on Warner Brothers, Aug'84 by Warner Bros Records. Dist: WEA

SIGN OF THE TIMES.
Tracks: / Sign of the times / La la la la he he he he / Play in the sunshine / Housequake / Ballad of Dorothy Parker / It / Starfish and coffee / Slow love / Hot thing / Forever in my life / U got the look / If I was your girlfriend / Strange relationship / I could never take the place of your man / Cross, The / It's gonna be a beautiful night / Adore.
Single (7"): released on Paisley Park (usa), Feb'87 by WEA Records. Dist: WEA

Single (12"): released on Paisley Park (usa), Feb'87 by WEA Records. Dist: WEA

Double Album: released on Paisley Park (usa), Apr'87 by WEA Records. Dist: WEA

Double cassette: released on Paisley Park (usa), Apr'87 by WEA Records. Dist: WEA

Double compact disc: released on Paisley Park (usa), Apr'87 by WEA Records. Dist: WEA

U GOT THE LOOK.
Single (7"): released on Warner Brothers, Aug'87 by Warner Bros Records. Dist: WEA

Single (12"): released on Warner Brothers, Aug'87 by Warner Bros Records. Dist: WEA

Prince Buster

AL CAPONE.
Tracks: / One step beyond.
Single (7"): released on Spartan, Feb'87 by Spartan Records. Dist: Spartan

Single (12"): released on Spartan, Feb'87 by Spartan Records. Dist: Spartan

Prince Charles

CAN'T STOP LOVING YOU (Prince Charles & The City Beat Band).
Single (12"): released on Carrere, Apr'87 by Carrere Records. Dist: PRT, Spartan

WE CAN MAKE IT HAPPEN (Prince Charles & The City Beat Band).
Tracks: / We can make it happen / Chaka beat / We can make it happen (vocal mix) / Radio live / Saxxy licks.
Single (7"): released on PRT, Mar'86 by PRT Records. Dist: PRT

Single (12"): released on PRT, Mar'86 by PRT Records. Dist: PRT

Picture disc single: released on PRT, Mar'86 by PRT Records. Dist: PRT

Prince Hammer

DANCE HALL STYLE.
Single (12"): released on Progressive, Jul'84 by Progressive Records. Dist: Jetstar

VENGEANCE.
Album: released on Melinda, Mar'85 by Melinda Records. Dist: Jetstar Distribution

Prince, Ian

MASTER OF THE GAME.
Single (7"): released on Virgin, Apr'87 by Virgin Records. Dist: EMI, Virgin Distribution

Single (12"): released on Virgin, Apr'87 by Virgin Records. Dist: EMI, Virgin Distribution

TOO MUCH TOO SOON.
Single (7"): released on London, Aug'83 by London Records. Dist: Polygram

Single (12"): released on London, Aug'83 by London Records. Dist: Polygram

Prince Jammy

CMPUTERISED DUB.
Album: released on Greensleeves, Feb'86 by Greensleeves Records. Dist: BMG, Jetstar, Spartan

DUB WAR, VOL.1.
Album: released on Vista Sounds, Mar'85 by Vista Sounds Records. Dist: Jetstar

KAMIKAZI DUB.
Album: released on Trojan, Sep'81 by Trojan Records. Dist: PRT, Jetstar

OSBOURNE IN DUB.
Album: released on CSA, Dec'83 by CSA Records. Dist: PRT, Jetstar

PRINCE JAMMY PRESENTS VOL.3 (Various Artists).
Album: released on Live & Love, Apr'87 by Third World Records. Dist: Jetstar

PRINCE JAMMY PRESNTS VOL.1 Various artists (Various Artists).
Album: released on World Enterprise, Jul'86 Dist: Jetstar

SUPERSTARS HIT PARADE.
Album: released on Greensleeves, May'86 by Greensleeves Records. Dist: BMG, Jetstar, Spartan

UHURU IN DUB.
Album: released on CSA, '83 by CSA Records. Dist: PRT, Jetstar

Prince JJ

I BELIEVE.
Single (7"): released on JSO, Nov'81

Prince Junior & Mannings

FREE MANDELA!.
Tracks: / Free Mandela (Version).
Single (12"): released on Metrosound, Nov'86 by Metrosound Records. Dist: Jetstar Distribution

Prince Lessa Lassan

DJALENGA.
Single (12"): released on Swahili, Aug'83 by Albion. Dist: Spartan Distribution

Prince Lincoln

I MAN FEEL IT.
Single (12"): released on MSR, Jun'83 by Midland Sound Recordings. Dist: Jetstar Distribution

ROOTS MAN BLUES (Prince Lincoln & Royal Rasses).
Album: released on Target, Oct'83 by Target Records. Dist: Spartan Distribution

Single (12"): released on Target, Mar'84 by Target Records. Dist: Spartan Distribution

Prince, Michael

DANCE YOUR LOVE AWAY.
Tracks: / Dance your love away.
Single (12"): released on Bolts, Feb'86 by Bolts Records. Dist: PRT, Pinnacle

Prince of the City

PRINCE OF THE CITY Original motion picture sountrack.
Album: released on That's Entertainment, Dec'81 by That's Entertainment Records. Dist: Pinnacle, PRT

Prince of Wales...

YORKIES ON TOUR, THE (Prince of Wales Yorkshire Regiment).
Album: released on Music Masters, Jun'81 by Music Masters Records. Dist: Taylors

Prince Oliver

RUNAWAY GIRL.
Single (12"): released on Ariwa, Mar'85 by Ariwa Records. Dist: Revolver, Cartel, Jetstar, Rough Trade

Prince Phalms

I LOVE YOUR STYLE.
Single (12"): released on Tropical Sunset, Jun'85 by Tropical Sunset Records. Dist: Jetstar

Prince Philip Mitchell

DEVASTATION.
Album: released on Ichiban, Aug'87 by Ichiban Records. Dist: PRT

Cassette: released on Ichiban, Aug'87 by Ichiban Records. Dist: PRT

Prince, Roland

COLOUR VISIONS.
Album: released on Vanguard, Jan'77 by PRT Records. Dist: PRT

Princess

AFTER THE LOVE HAS GO GO GONE.
Tracks: / After the love has go go gone / After the dub has gone.
Single (7"): released on Supreme, Jan'86 by Supreme Records. Dist: PRT Distribution

Single (7"): released on Supreme, Oct'85 by Supreme Records. Dist: PRT Distribution

Single (12"): released on Supreme, Oct'85 by Supreme Records. Dist: PRT Distribution

Double-pack single: released on Supreme, Oct'85 by Supreme Records. Dist: PRT Distribution

Single (12"): released on Supreme, Oct'85 by Supreme Records. Dist: PRT Distribution

I'LL KEEP ON LOVING YOU.
Tracks: / I'll keep on loving you / I'll keep on loving you (instrumental) / Say dub it / Cheeses DJ / Keep on scratching mix / Chad's scratch mix.
Notes: 7" shrinkwrapped together with SUPE 105 and SUPE 103. 12" gatefold sleeve.
Single (7"): released on Supreme, Apr'86 by Supreme Records. Dist: PRT Distribution

Single (12"): released on Supreme, Apr'86 by Supreme Records. Dist: PRT Distribution

Single (7"): released on Supreme, Apr'86 by Supreme Records. Dist: PRT Distribution

Single (12"): released on Supreme, Apr'86 by Supreme Records. Dist: PRT Distribution

Single (12"): released on Supreme, May'86 by Supreme Records. Dist: PRT Distribution

Picture disc single: released on Supreme, May'86 by Supreme Records. Dist: PRT Distribution

IN THE HEAT OF A PASSIONATE MOMENT.
Tracks: / In the heat of a passionate moment / I'll keep loving you.
Single (7"): released on Supreme, Sep'86 by Supreme Records. Dist: PRT Distribution

Single (12"): released on Supreme, Sep'86 by Supreme Records. Dist: PRT Distribution

PRINCESS.
Tracks: / In the heat of a passionate moment / I'll keep on loving you / After the love has gone / Say I'm your number one / If it makes you feel good / Tell me tomorrow / Anytimes the right time / Just a teaze.
Notes: Cassette and CD also includes remixes.
Album: released on Supreme, Jul'86 by Supreme Records. Dist: PRT Distribution

Cassette: released on Supreme, Jul'86 by Supreme Records. Dist: PRT Distribution

Compact disc: released on Supreme, Jul'86 by Supreme Records. Dist: PRT Distribution

PRINCESS AND THE FROG, THE various artists (Various Artists).
Cassette: released on Pickwick (Ladybird), '83

PRINCESS AND THE PEA, THE Tell-a-tale-series (Various Artists).
Cassette: released on Pickwick (Ladybird), '83

RED HOT.
Tracks: / Red hot / Programmed to love you / Red hot (Ext.Mix) / Red hot (Dub Mix) / Red hot (Inferno Mix).
Single (7"): released on Polydor, May'87 by Polydor Records. Dist: Polygram, Polydor

Single (12"): released on Polydor, 30 May'87 by Polydor Records. Dist: Polygram, Polydor

Single (12"): released on Polydor, May'87 by Polydor Records. Dist: Polygram, Polydor

SAY I'M YOUR NUMBER ONE.
Single (7"): released on Supreme, Jul'85 by Supreme Records. Dist: PRT Distribution

Single (12"): released on Supreme, Jul'85 by Supreme Records. Dist: PRT Distribution

Single (12"): released on Supreme, Jul'85 by Supreme Records. Dist: PRT Distribution

Single (12"): released on Supreme, Jul'85 by Supreme Records. Dist: PRT Distribution

TELL ME TOMORROW.
Single (7"): released on Supreme, Jun'86 by Supreme Records. Dist: PRT Distribution

Single (12"): released on Supreme, Jun'86 by Supreme Records. Dist: PRT Distribution

Princess Ida

PRINCESS IDA Gilbert & Sullivan (Various Artists).

Princess On...

PRINCESS ON THE PEA/THE THREE MUSICIANS (Fullerton, Fiona).
Cassette: released on Listen Productions, Nov'84 Dist: H.R. Taylor, Hayward Promotions Distribution

Princess Snowdrop

PRINCESS SNOWDROP Various artists (Various Artists).
Tracks: / What a wonderful world we live in / You're welcome / Handful of flowers, A / Poor little moon / Always together.
Notes: Artists include: Dover Children and backed by popular dance band 'Tangent'. A good story with super songs cleverly arranged. Profits for the International Year of the Child. Eron Records, 27, Balmoral Road, Kingsdown, Deal, Kent CT14 8BX.
Album: released on Eron, Sep'85 by Eron Records. Dist: Eron Records

Cassette: released on Eron, Sep'85 by Eron Records. Dist: Eron Records

Princess & the Goblin

PRINCESS AND THE GOBLIN MacDonald, G.
Cassette: released on Colophone Audio Visual, Sep'81 by Audio-Visual Library Services. Dist: Audio-Visual Library Services

Princess Tinymeat

ANGELS IN PAIN.
Single (7"): released on Rough Trade, Apr'87 by Rough Trade Records. Dist: Rough Trade Distribution, Cartel Distribution

Single (12"): released on Rough Trade, Apr'87 by Rough Trade Records. Dist: Rough Trade Distribution, Cartel Distribution

BUN IN THE OVEN, A.
Tracks: / Bun in the oven, A / Wigs on the green.
Single (7"): released on Rough Trade, Jan'86 by Rough Trade Records. Dist: Rough Trade Distribution, Cartel Distribution

SLOBLANDS.
Single (12"): released on Rough Trade, Mar'85 by Rough Trade Records. Dist: Rough Trade Distribution, Cartel Distribution

Princess UFO

HI-FLYER.
Single (7"): released on Young Blood, Jan'85 by Young Blood Records. Dist: Pinnacle

LILI MARLENE.
Single (7"): released on Young Blood, Nov'84 by Young Blood Records. Dist: Pinnacle

Single (12"): released on Young Blood, Nov'84 by Young Blood Records. Dist: Pinnacle

Picture disc single: released on Young Blood, Nov'84 by Young Blood Records. Dist: Pinnacle

Prince, Steve

SHOULD HAVE BEEN YOU.
Single (12"): released on Pyramid, Nov'83 Dist: Jetstar

Princes' Trust

PRINCE'S TRUST 10TH ANNIVERSARY BIRTHDAY PARTY Various artists (Various Artists).
Notes: Recorded highlights of the magical Prince's Trust 10th Anniversary concert at Wembley, which John Blake of the Daily Mirror described as "the greatest gathering of pop megastars in one place since 'Live Aid'" From the wonderful opening track "Money for nothing" by Dire Straits with Sting, through songs of the calibre of Suzanne Vega's "Marlene on the wall",Rod Stewart's "Sailing" and Elton John's "I'm still standing",and ending with Paul McCartney's show-stopping "Get back",this truly an exceptional release. The L.P.features a limited edition free Paul McCartney 7" single, while the cassette and C.D. feature one bonus McCartney track.
Album: released on A&M, Apr'87 by A&M Records. Dist: Polygram

Cassette: released on A&M, Apr'87 by A&M Records. Dist: Polygram

Compact disc: released on A&M, Apr'87 by A&M Records. Dist: Polygram

PRINCES TRUST COLLECTION Various artists (Various Artists).
Notes: The Prince's Trust was formed in 1976 by His Royal Highness The Prince of Wales when with his support hundreds of volunteers throughout the United Kingdom came together to carry out the work of the Trust and support the young people who applied for assistance. Since 1976 many of the artists have donated the proceeds from concerts and some of these artists have come together to donate one track each which have been put together on this double album, from which all royalties are being donated to The Prince's Trust. The album features such artists as Genesis, Paul Young, Eric Clapton, Spandau Ballet, Duran Duran, Dire Straits and Bill Wyman. Several of the tracks are specially recorded 12 inch versions and Status Quo have donated the live version of Rockin' All Over The World. Since the formation of the Trust many young people who have suffered from some disadvantage in life have been helped but with the rise in unemployement there are many more young people who need the help that the Trust can provide. We hope that with the sale of this album that money from the royalties donated will go towards funds t hat will help with the continuation of the Trust.
Album: released on Telstar, Dec'85 by Telstar Records. Dist: RCA Distribution

Cassette: released on Telstar, Dec'85 by Telstar Records. Dist: RCA Distribution

PRINCES' TRUST, THE various artists (Various Artists).
Tracks: / Running in the family / If I was / Behind the mask / You've lost that lovin' feelin' / Stand by me / Misfit / Wonderful tonight / Don't look down / Invisible / Through the barricades / So strong / Run to you / Saturday night's alright (for fighting) / It's the same old song / I can't help myself / Reach out-I'll be there / Your song / Wanderer, The / While my guitar gently weeps / Here comes the sun / With a little help from my friends / God save The Queen.
Notes: Double album, with material recorded over two night at the Wembley Arena concertincluding exclusive versions of Dion's 'The Wanderer' performed by Dave Edmunds and Bryan Adams, a classic version of the Righteous Brothers' hit 'You've Lost That Lovin' Feelin' ' by top stars Phil Collins and Paul Young, who also performa medley of Four Tops' classics. Ringo Starr performs The Beatles' Sergeant Pepper favourite 'With A Little Help From My Friends'.
Album: released on A&M, Aug'87 by A&M Records. Dist: Polygram

Cassette: released on A&M, Aug'87 by A&M Records. Dist: Polygram

Compact disc: released on A&M, Aug'87 by A&M Records. Dist: Polygram

Album: released on A&M, Aug'87 by A&M Records. Dist: Polygram

Cassette: released on A&M, Aug'87 by A&M Records. Dist: Polygram

Principato, Tom

SMOKIN'.
Album: released on Emergo, Jul'87 by Roadrunner Records (Germany). Dist: Pinnacle

Principle

THIS IS NOT A SONG BY TALKING HEADS.
Tracks: / This is not a song by Talking Heads / Nursery crime / I can tell.
Single (12"): released on Principle, May'87

Principle, Jamie

WAITING ON MY ANGEL.
Tracks: / Waiting on my angel.
Single (12"): released on ZYX (Germany), Dec'85 by ZYX Records. Dist: Greyhound

Prine, John

BRUISED ORANGE.
Album: released on Asylum, Aug'78 by WEA Records. Dist: WEA

DIAMONDS IN THE ROUGH.
Album: released on Atlantic, '74 by WEA Records. Dist: WEA

GERMAN AFTERNOONS.
Compact disc: released on Demon, Aug'87 by Demon Records. Dist: Pinnacle
Cat. no: **FIENDCD 103**
Album: released on Demon, Aug'87 by Demon Records. Dist: Pinnacle

PINK CADILLAC.
Album: released on Elektra Asylum, Oct'79 by Elektra/Asylum/Nonesuch Records. Dist: WEA

SWEET REVENGE.
Album: released on Atlantic, '74 by WEA Records. Dist: WEA

Prinknash Abbey...

MUSIC FROM PRINKNASH ABBEY (Prinknash Abbey Monks).
Album: released on Saydisc, Apr'82 by Saydisc Records. Dist: Essex, Harmonia Mundi, Roots, H.R. Taylor, Jazz Music, Swift, Projection, Gamut

Cassette: released on Saydisc, Apr'82 by Saydisc Records. Dist: Essex, Harmonia

Mundi, Roots, H.R. Taylor, Jazz Music, Swift, Projection, Gamut

Prior, Maddy

DEEP IN THE DARKEST NIGHT.
Tracks: / Deep in the darkest night / Western movies.
Single (7"): released on Making Waves, Jan'86 by Making Waves Records.

Single (7"): released on RCA, Nov'83 by RCA Records. Dist: RCA, Roots, Swift, Wellard, Chris, I & B, Solomon & Peres Distribution

FACE TO FACE (Prior, Maddy Band).
Single (7"): released on Plant Life, Oct'82 Dist: Roots

GOING FOR GLORY (Prior, Maddy & The Answers).
Album: released on Spindrift, Oct'83 Dist: Roots

HOOKED ON WINNING (Prior, Maddy Band).
Album: released on Plant Life, May'82 Dist: Roots

SILLY SISTERS (Prior, Maddy & June Tabor).
Album: released on Chrysalis, Mar'76 by Chrysalis Records. Dist: CBS

STOOKIE.
Single (7"):

SUMMER SOLSTICE (see Hart, Tim) (Prior, Maddy; Hart, Tim).

TAPESTRY OF CAROLS, A (Prior, Maddy & The Carnival Band).
Compact disc: released on Saydisc, Sep'87 by Saydisc Records. Dist: Essex, Harmonia Mundi, Roots, H.R. Taylor, Jazz Music, Swift, Projection, Gamut

Cassette: released on Saydisc, Sep'87 by Saydisc Records. Dist: Essex, Harmonia Mundi, Roots, H.R. Taylor, Jazz Music, Swift, Projection, Gamut

Album: released on Saydisc, Sep'87 by Saydisc Records. Dist: Essex, Harmonia Mundi, Roots, H.R. Taylor, Jazz Music, Swift, Projection, Gamut

WOMAN IN THE WINGS.
Cassette: released on Chrysalis, May'78 by Chrysalis Records. Dist: CBS

Prior, Snooky

SHAKE YOUR BOOGIE.
Album: released on Big Bear, Oct'86 by Big Bear Records. Dist: Big Bear, Swift

Prism

ARMEGEDDON.
Album: by Capitol Records. Dist: EMI

YOUNG AND RESTLESS.
Album: released on Capitol, Jul'80 by Capitol Records. Dist: EMI

Prisonaires

FIVE BEATS BEHIND BARS.
Album: by Charly Records. Dist: Charly, Cadillac

Prisoners

ELECTRIC FIT.
Single (7"): released on Ace, Aug'84 by Ace Records. Dist: Pinnacle, Swift, Hotshot, Cadillac

HURRICANE.
Single (7"): released on Big Beat, Nov'83 by Ace Records. Dist: Projection, Pinnacle

IN FROM THE COLD.
Tracks: / More that I teach you,The / Wish the rain / Find and seek / Mourn my health / Ain't no telling / Lesser evil,The / All you gotta do is say / Be on your way / I know how to please you / Deceiveng eye / Come closer / In from the cold.
Notes: All Copyright Control except "Intersong" Copyright Control/Plagent Visions. (P) 1986 Countdown Records. Licensed by Stiff Records. Produced by Troy Tate. Special thanks to Russell Wilkins. Special Pict. Sleeve.
Album: released on Stiff, May'86 by Stiff Records. Dist: EMI, Record Services Distribution (Ireland)

LAST FOURFATHERS, THE.
Album: released on Own Up, Jun'85 Dist: Rough Trade Distribution, Cartel Distribution

LAST NIGHT AT THE MIC CLUB,THE.
Album: released on Empire, Jan'86 by Empire Records. Dist: Backs, Cartel, Jetstar

TASTE OF PINK, A.
Album: released on Own, Mar'85 Dist: MIS-EMI Distribution

WHENEVER I'M GONE.
Tracks: / Whenever I'm gone / Promised land / Gravedigger.
Single (7"): released on Countdown, Mar'86 by Stiff Records. Dist: EMI, Swift

Single (12"): released on Countdown, Mar'86 by Stiff Records. Dist: EMI, Swift

WISERMISERDEMELZA.
Album: released on Big Beat, Nov'83 by Ace Records. Dist: Projection, Pinnacle

Prison Work Songs

PRISON WORK SONGS various artists (Various Artists).
Album: released on Arhoolie, May'81 by Arhoolie Records. Dist: Projection, Topic, Jazz Music, Swift, Roots

Pritchard,Bill

BILL PRITCHARD.
Album: released on Third Mind, 30 May'87 by Third Mind Records. Dist: Backs, Cartel Distribution

Pritchard, Chris

SWEET ROTHIE VALE (Pritchard, Chris & Terry Taylor).
Cassette: released on Ross, '86 by Ross Records. Dist: Ross Distribution, Roots Distribution

Private Collection

IT'S HOPELESS.
Single (7"): released on Gallery, Jul'82 by Lightning Records. Dist: Lightning, WEA

Private Eye

I CRY FOR YOU.
Single (7"): released on Spider, Oct'83 Dist: Outlet

PRIVATE EYE GOLDEN SATIRICALS various artists (Various Artists).
Album: released on Springtime, Nov'81 by Springtime Records. Dist: Island Distribution, Polygram Distribution

Cassette: released on Springtime, Nov'81 by Springtime Records. Dist: Island Distribution, Polygram Distribution

Private I.D

COLD COLD SWEAT.
Single (7"): released on War, Oct'84 by War Records. Dist: PRT

Single (12"): released on War, Oct'84 by War Records. Dist: PRT

Private Is

DO I WORRY.
Single (12"): released on Dub Vendor, Aug'81 by Fashion Records. Dist: Fashion Records

Private,Jo

DU SWING AU MUSETTE.
Tracks: / La Marseillaise / Mains de velours / Love for sale / Caravane gitane / Montagne St.Genevieve / Undecided / Mister 'B' / Romanella / Poinciana / Swing-Charleston / Confessin' / Douce ambiance.
Album: released on Accordion Record Club, Jul'86 by Accordion Record Club Records. Dist: Accordion Record Club

Private Joy

COOLIN' OUT.
Tracks: / Coolin' out / Coolin' out (inst).
Single (12"): released on Champion, 20 Jun'87 by Champion Records. Dist: RCA

Private Lives

BECAUSE YOU'RE YOUNG.
Single (12"): released on Chrysalis, Feb'82 by Chrysalis Records. Dist: CBS

Single (7"): released on Chrysalis, Feb'82 by Chrysalis Records. Dist: CBS

PREJUDICE AND PRIDE.
Album: released on EMI, Jul'84 by EMI Records. Dist: EMI

Cassette: released on EMI, Jul'84 by EMI Records. Dist: EMI

PRIVATE LIVES Coward, Noel (Various Artists).
Cassette: released on Talking Tape, '84

Private Party

CHANGE.
Single (7"): released on Button, Nov'83 by Musical Characters Records. Dist: Spartan

IT TEARS ME UP.
Single (7"): released on Shoestring, May'85 by Shoestring Records. Dist: Shoestring

Private Popsicle

PRIVATE POPSICLE Original soundtrack (Various original artists).
Album: released on CBS, Jul'83 by CBS Records. Dist: CBS Deleted '85.

Cassette: released on CBS, Jul'83 by CBS Records. Dist: CBS

Private Possession

PRIVATE LIVES Coward, Noel (Scofield, Paul/Fenella Fielding/Margoles/Routledge).
Cassette: released on Talking Tape, '84

THIS TIME.
Tracks: / This time / Rap.
Notes: Featuring Hunter Hayes.
Single (12"): released on Fourth & Broadway, Nov'86 by Island Records. Dist: Polygram, EMI

Privates

ASHAMED TO BE WHITE.
Single (7"): released on Dune, May'82

Private Sector

LIKE A TON OF BRICKS (IT'S HIT ME).
Single (12"): released on Food For Thought, Jun'83 by Food For Thought Records. Dist: Pinnacle

Privates On...

PRIVATES ON PARADE Original London cast (Privates On Parade).
Album: released on EMI, Apr'78 by EMI Records. Dist: EMI

Private Tabby

JAILHOUSE.
Tracks: / Jailhouse / If you leave me (Double A).
Single (12"): released on Trojan, Sep'86 by Trojan Records. Dist: PRT, Jetstar

Private View

WALLS.
Single (7"): released on New Label, Jun'84 by New Label.

Prize Guys

THATS WHAT I CALL LOVIN.
Single (7"): released on Castle, Aug'81 by Castle Records. Dist: Pinnacle

Pro Arte Orc

BOX OF DELIGHTS.
Single (7"): released on BBC, Dec'84 by BBC Records & Tapes. Dist: EMI, PRT, Pye

Pro Arte Orchestra

TRIBUTE TO ERIC COATES.
Album: released on PRT, Mar'86 by PRT Records. Dist: PRT

Cassette: released on PRT, Mar'86 by PRT Records. Dist: PRT

Problemist

NINE TIMES SANITY.
Album: released on Sordide Sentimental (France), Dec'84 Dist: Cartel

Pro Bow Trio

STRING VIBRATIONS (Pro Bow Trio,+ Richard Carr).
Notes: see under: Carr,Richard + Pro Bow Trio

Probst,Marianne

RUDOLPH WURTHNER ERFOLGE (Probst,Marianne & Ensemble).
Tracks: / La Campanella - solo / Carmen-fantasie - solo / Variation uber russische volkslied - solo / Ouverture uber zwei finnische themen - orch. / Variationen uber 'komm lieber mai' - orch..
Album: released on Accordion Record Club, Jul'86 by Accordion Record Club Records. Dist: Accordion Record Club

Proby, P.J.

AT HIS VERY BEST.
Tracks: / When love has passed you by / I'm coming home / Give me time / Turn her away / Why baby why / I've got my eyes on you / I apologise baby / Somewhere / That means a lot / Maria / Rain on snow / My prayer / To make a big man cry / I can't make it alone / What's wrong with my world / Day Lorraine came down,The / Today I killed a man I didn't know / Zing! went the strings of my heart.
Notes: Original Sound Recording made by Liberty Records, a division of Capitol Records Inc. This compilation P.1986 by See For Miles Records Ltd. A Colin Miles Com- pilation.
Album: released on See For Miles, Jul'86 by See For Miles Records. Dist: Pinnacle

CLOWN SHOES.
Tracks: / She's helping me get over you / Handsome guy / Memories of you / Cinderella's fool / Ain't gonna kiss ya / In a moment / What did I do to you / Like all the times before / Hold me / Tonight / Clown shoes / Place for girls like you, A / Life you offered me, The / Maria / Somewhere / I apologise / Niki Hoeky / Hold me.
Album: released on Meteor, Jul'87 by Magnum Music Group Ltd. Dist: Magnum Music Group Ltd, PRT Distribution, Spartan Distribution. Estim retail price in Aug'87 was £5.49

HOLD ME.
Single (7"): released on Decca, Apr'81 by Decca Records. Dist: Polygram

LEGENDARY P.J. AT HIS VERY BEST, THE , VOL11.
Tracks: / Rockin' pneumonia & the boogie woogie flu / Masquerade is over / I'll go crazy / You don't love me no more / Just call and I'll be there / Cuttin' in / Hold me / Together / Nicki hoeky / Honey hush / Butterfly high / She's looking good / You can't come home again (if you leave me now) / Pretty girls everywhere / Hold what you've got / Sweet summer wine / That's the tune / Work with me Annie / Mary Hopkins.
Album: released on See For Miles, Feb'87 by See For Miles Records. Dist: Pinnacle

LOVE WILL TEAR US APART.
Single (7"): released on Savoy, Nov'85

Single (12"): released on Savoy, Nov'85

SOMEWHERE.
Album: released on Liberty, Jul'85 by Liberty-United. Dist: EMI

Cassette: released on Liberty, Jul'85 by Liberty-United. Dist: EMI

Single (7"): released on Juke Box, Mar'82

TAINTED LOVE.
Single (7"): released on Savoy, Oct'85

Pro Cantione Antiqua

MEDIEVEAL CHRISTMAS, A.
Compact disc: released on Hallmark, '86 by Pickwick Records. Dist: Pickwick Distribution, PRT, Taylors

Proce,David

ELKAVOX ORCHESTRA, THE.
Tracks: / They long to be close / For all we know / Somewhere my love / More / Many splendoured thing / Hungarian dance no.5 / Can can / Funiculi / One day in your life / Hello Dolly / Bye bye blues / Born free / Michelle / Yesterday / Spanish eyes.
Cassette: released on Accordion Record Club, Jul'86 by Accordion Record Club Records. Dist: Accordion Record Club

Proclaimers

THIS IS THE STORY.
Tracks: / Throw the 'r' away / Over and done with / Misty blue / Part that really matters, the / (I'm gonna) burn your playhouse down / Letter from America / Sky takes the soul / It broke my heart / First attack, the / Make my heart fly / Beautiful truth / Joyful Kilmarnock blues, the.
Notes: Produced by John Williams
Album: released on Chrysalis, Apr'87 by Chrysalis Records. Dist: CBS

Cassette: released on Chrysalis, Apr'87 by Chrysalis Records. Dist: CBS

THROW THE R AWAY.
Tracks: / Throw the R away / Train went past the window, A / Long gone lonesome (live)* / I can't be myself (live)*.
Single (7"): released on Chrysalis, 23 May'87 by Chrysalis Records. Dist: CBS

Single (12"): released on Chrysalis, 23 May'87 by Chrysalis Records. Dist: CBS

Procol Harum

EXOTIC BIRDS & FRUIT.
Album: released on Chrysalis, '74 by Chrysalis Records. Dist: CBS

Cassette: released on Chrysalis, '74 by Chrysalis Records. Dist: CBS

GREATEST HITS: PROCUL HARUM.
Album: released on Plato Tapes, Oct'85 by Plato Tapes. Dist: Plato Tapes

Cassette: released on Platinum (W.Germany), Oct'85 Dist: Mainline

HOMBURG.
Single (7"): released on Cube, Aug'82 by Dakota Records. Dist: PRT

OFF THE RECORD WITH PROCOL HARUM.
Album: released on Sierra, Nov'84 by Sierra Records. Dist: WEA

Cassette: released on Sierra, Nov'84 by Sierra Records. Dist: WEA

PLATINUM COLLECTION.
Album: released on Cube (Platinum coll), Oct'81

Cassette: released on Cube (Platinum coll), Oct'81

PROCOL HARUM.

Album: released on Impact, Apr'82 by Ace Records. Dist: Rough Trade, Pinnacle, Swift, Backs, Counterpoint, Jungle, Hotshot. Cartel

Cassette: released on Impact, Apr'82 by Ace Records. Dist: Rough Trade, Pinnacle, Swift, Backs, Counterpoint, Jungle, Hotshot, Cartel

Album: released on Dakota (Countdown series), Oct'82 by Dakota Records. Dist: PRT

Cassette: released on Dakota (Countdown series), Oct'82 by Dakota Records. Dist: PRT

PROCOL HARUM COLLECTION.
Tracks: / Whiter shade of pale / Homburg / Too much between us / Salty dog.A / Devil came from Kansas, The / Whaling stories / Good Captain Clack / All this and more / Quite rightly so / Shine on brightly / Grand Hotel / Bringing home the baco / Toujours l'amour / Broken barricades / Power failure / Conquistador (Live) / Nothing but the truth / Butterfly Boys / Pandora's box / Simple sister.
Notes: All tracks Licensed from Chrysalis Records Ltd. Design: Shoot that Tiger!. This compilation (C) 1985 Castle Communications Ltd.Unit 7,271 Merton Road, London. SW18 5JS. Bar Code: 5013428 131206. (Double Album/Double Cassette)
Album: released on Collectors, Apr'86 by Castle Communications Records. Dist: PRT, Pinnacle, Jazz Music

Cassette: released on Collectors, Apr'86 by Castle Communications Records. Dist: PRT, Pinnacle, Jazz Music

SHINE ON BRIGHTLY.
Album: released on Cube, Oct'81 by Dakota Records. Dist: PRT

Cassette: released on Cube, Oct'81 by Dakota Records. Dist: PRT

Album: released on Cube, Oct'81 by Dakota Records. Dist: PRT

Cassette: released on Cube, Oct'81 by Dakota Records. Dist: PRT

WHITER SHADE OF PALE, A.
Album: released on Sierra, May'85 by Sierra Records. Dist: WEA

Cassette: released on Sierra, May'85 by Sierra Records. Dist: WEA

Album: released on Cube, Oct'81 by Dakota Records. Dist: PRT

Cassette: released on Cube, Oct'81 by Dakota Records. Dist: PRT

Single (7"): released on Old Gold, Jul'82 by Old Gold Records. Dist: Lightning, Jazz Music, Spartan, Counterpoint

Single (7"): released on Cube, Aug'82 by Dakota Records. Dist: PRT

Single (12"): released on Cube, Aug'82 by Dakota Records. Dist: PRT

CONQUISTADOR.
Tracks: / Pandora's box.
Single (7"): released on Old Gold, Feb'87 by Old Gold Records. Dist: Lightning, Jazz Music, Spartan, Counterpoint

SALTY DOG, A.
Compact disc: released on Mobile Fidelity, '86 by Mobile Fidelity Records.

Album: released on Sierra, May'85 by Sierra Records. Dist: WEA

Cassette: released on Sierra, May'85 by Sierra Records. Dist: WEA

Producers
RADIO.
Single (7"): released on Hobo, Jul'79 by Hobo Records. Dist: Hobo

WALK RIGHT BACK.
Single (7"): released on Magic, Nov'80 Dist: Jazz Music, Submarine, Swift, Chris Wellard, Conifer

Producers, The
PRODUCERS, THE Original motion picture soundtrack.
Album: released on RCA International (USA), Mar'81 by RCA Records. Dist: RCA

Cassette: released on RCA International (USA), Mar'81 by RCA Records. Dist: RCA

Product
STYLE WARS.
Single (7"): released on Clay, Jul'81 by Clay Records. Dist: Pinnacle

Product, Clive
HONEST IT'S PRODUCT 5 Track EP.
Single (7"): released on Nuclear, Mar'82 by Nu-

clear Records.

STRETCHING ARMS AND LEGS (Product, Clive & Gary Williams).
Album: released on Nuclear, Feb'85 by Nuclear Records.

VILLAGE TOURS START HERE.
Album: released on Nuclear, Aug'83 by Nuclear Records.

Production House
COMING ROUND.
Single (12"): released on Production House, Jun'85 Dist: Bluebird, Revolver, Cartel

Product Of Reason
MAN OF YOUR DREAMS.
Single (7"): released on TER, Mar'83 Dist: Pinnacle

Profane,Benny
WHERE IS PIG.
Tracks: / Where is pig.
Single (12"): released on Sub Pop, May'86 Dist: Pinnacle

Professionals
I DIDN'T SEE IT COMING.
Album: released on Virgin, Nov'81 by Virgin Records. Dist: EMI, Virgin Distribution

Cassette: released on Virgin, Nov'81 by Virgin Records. Dist: EMI, Virgin Distribution

Professor Lee
FREEDOM TO BANDAGE.
Single (12"): released on Serious, Nov'85 by Serious Records. Dist: PRT

Professor Longhair
COMPLETE LONDON CONCERT, THE.
Compact disc: released on JSP, Jul'87 by JSP Records. Dist: Swift, Projection

CRAWFISH FIESTA.
Album: released on Sonet, Jun'80 by Sonet Records. Dist: PRT

HOUSEPARTY NEW ORLEANS STYLE The lost sessions 1971-72.
Notes: Previously unreleased studio recordings.
Album: released on Rounder Europa, May'87

LIVE ON THE QUEEN MARY.
Tracks: / Tell me pretty baby / Mess around / Every day I have the blues / Tipitina / I'm movin' on / Mardi Gras in New Orleans / Cry to me / Gone so long / Stagger Lee.
Notes: The greatest New Orleans piano player ever - the man who influenced them all - from Fats Domino and Dr John to Allen Toussaint. This album, recorded by Paul McCartney in 1978 features 'Fess' running through hits such as 'Tipitina' and 'Mardi Gras in New Orleans'. With the increase in popularity of New Orleans music via visits by Dr.John and the Neville Brothers, this makes a timely re-issue.
Album: released on Stateside, Mar'86 Dist: EMI

Cassette: released on Stateside, Mar'86 Dist: EMI

LONDON CONCERT, THE.
Album: released on JSP, Mar'84 by JSP Records. Dist: Swift, Projection

MARDI GRAS IN NEW ORLEANS.
Album: released on Nighthawk, Jan'87 by Faulty Products Records. Dist: Pinnacle, Swift

Album: released on Krazy Kat, Dec'82 Dist: Jazz Music, Swift, Chris Wellard, H.R. Taylor, Charly, Hotshot, IRS Distribution

Professor Nut
CRISIS.
Single (12"): released on Gorgon, Oct'84 by Gorgon Records. Dist: Jetstar

Proffitt, Frank
NORTH CAROLINA SONGS AND BALLADS.
Album: released on Topic, '81 Dist: Roots Distribution

Progoganda For Frankie
MEDLEY WITH RELAX.
Tracks: / Medley with relax / Dee Jay.
Single (12"): released on Record Shack, Jul'86 by Record Shack Records. Dist: PRT

Single (12"): released on Record Shack, Jul'86 by Record Shack Records. Dist: PRT

Progressive Records
PROGRESSIVE RECORDS ALL STAR TRUMPET SPECTACULAR various artists (Various Artists).

Album: released on Projection, Sep'79

PROGRESSIVE RECORDS ALL STAR TRUMPET SPECTACULAR, VOL.2 various artists (Various Artists).
Album: released on Progressive, Nov'82 by Progressive Records. Dist: Jetstar

Project
PROJECT 1 (Various Artists).
Album: released on Product Korps, Jun'87

Project 4
LIFE AFTER LIVE.
Single (7"): released on Never, Jan'82 Dist: Rough Trade

Project Future
RAY-GUN-OMICS.
Single (7"): released on Capitol, Aug'83 by Capitol Records. Dist: EMI

Single (12"): released on Capitol, Aug'83 by Capitol Records. Dist: EMI

Projection
DON'T FAKE MY LOVE.
Tracks: / Don't fake my love.
Single (7"): released on Elite, Sep'86 Dist: PRT

LOVESTRUCK.
Tracks: / Lovestruck(wireless mix) / Dumbstruck.
Single (12"): released on Elite, Dec'86 Dist: PRT

TURN YOUR LOVE (RIGHT AROUND).
Tracks: / Turn your love (right around) / Hardrock soul remix / Allstars (Remix).
Single (12"): released on Elite, Mar'86 Dist: PRT

Projection Brothers
CRYSTAL EYES.
Single (7"): released on Flying, Jul'83 by Flying Records. Dist: DMS

Project One
PLAY PLAY GIRL.
Single (12"): released on Sea View, Aug'85 by Sea View Records. Dist: Jetstar

Proletariat
INDIFFERENCE.
Album: released on Homestead, Sep'86 Dist: Rough Trade, Cartel, Shinaku

Cassette: released on Homestead, Aug'86 Dist: Rough Trade, Cartel, Shinaku

MARKETPLACE.
Tracks: / Marketplace.
Single (7"): released on Homestead, Aug'86 Dist: Rough Trade, Cartel, Shinaku

Promenaders
PROMENADERS, THE.
Album: released on Y, Oct'82

Promise
AWAY AWAY.
Single (12"): released on Inner Vision, Oct'84 by CBS Records. Dist: CBS

Promises
I SEE NO REASON.
Single (12"): released on Jama, Apr'82 by Jama Records.

Promises,Promises
CAN YOU TAKE THE RISK.
Tracks: / an you take the risk? (Monty) / Empty rooms and echos (Monty).
Single (7"): released on Fend For Yourself, Sep'86 by Fend For Yourself Records. Dist: Probe Plus Distribution, Cartel

SHUT OUT THE LIGHT.
Tracks: / Shut out the light (Monty) / Apocalypse of fashion (Monty).
Single (7"): released on Fend For Yourself, Sep'86 by Fend For Yourself Records. Dist: Probe Plus Distribution, Cartel

Propaganda
DOCTOR MABUSE.
Single (7"): released on Island, Mar'84 by Island Records. Dist: Polygram

Single (12"): released on Island, Mar'84 by Island Records. Dist: Polygram

DUEL.
Single (7"): released on ZTT, Apr'85 by Island Records. Dist: Polygram

Single (12"): released on ZTT, Apr'85 by Island Records. Dist: Polygram

Single (7"): released on ZTT, May'85 by Island Records. Dist: Polygram

Cassette: released on ZTT, May'85 by Island Records. Dist: Polygram

NINE LIVES OF DR. MABUSE EP.
Cassette single: released on ZTT, May'84 by Island Records. Dist: Polygram

P MACHINERY.
Single (7"): released on ZTT, Nov'85 by Island Records. Dist: Polygram

P.MACHINERY (BETA MIX).
Single (12"): released on ZTT, Aug'85 by Island Records. Dist: Polygram

SECRET WISH,A.
Tracks: / Dream within a dream / Murder of love,The / Jewel Duel / P-Machinery / Power force push drive / Dr-Mabuse (The first love) / Sorry for laughing.
Notes: Produced by: Steve Lipson; and featuring (Michael Mertens, Suzanne Freytag, Claudia Brucken and Ralf Dorper) "Without Love, Beauty and Danger It Would Al- most Be Easy To Live"-"A Secret Wish"-"Chasing After Passing Visions").
Album: released on ZTT, Jul'85 by Island Records. Dist: Polygram

Cassette: released on ZTT, Jul'85 by Island Records. Dist: Polygram

Compact disc: released on ZTT, Jul'85 by Island Records. Dist: Polygram

WISHFUL THINKING (DISTURB DANCES).
Album: released on ZTT, Nov'85 by Island Records. Dist: Polygram

Cassette: released on ZTT, Nov'85 by Island Records. Dist: Polygram

Propellors
DAMBUSTERS.
Single (7"): released on Carve Up, Mar'81 Dist: Jazz Music, Red Lightnin' Distribution, Rough Trade, Pinnacle

Proper Little Madams
PROPER LITTLE MADAMS.
Album: released on Starward, Oct'82 Dist: Roots Distribution, Red Sky Distribution, Celtic Music Distribution, Projection Distribution

Prophet, Michael
BOOM HIM UP NOW.
Single (12"): released on Greensleeves, May'82 by Greensleeves Records. Dist: BMG, Jetstar, Spartan

BUBBLE DOWN BUBBLE DOWN.
Single (12"): released on Greensleeves, Mar'85 by Greensleeves Records. Dist: BMG, Jetstar, Spartan

CEASE FIRE.
Album: released on Move, May'85 by Charly Records. Dist: Charly Distribution, Fast Forward Distribution, Cartel Distribution

Single (12"): released on Live & Learn, Jun'85 Dist: Jetstar

COME ON LOVE ME TONIGHT (Prophet, Michael & Aswad).
Single (12"): released on Simba, Mar'83 by Simba Records. Dist: Jetstar

COME ON OVER.
Single (12"): released on C & E, May'87 Dist: Jetstar

GIRLS A FI MI.
Tracks: / Girls a fi mi / Girls a fi mi (Version) (Techniques Posse).
Single (12"): released on Techniques, Oct'86 Dist: Jetstar Distribution

HERE COMES THE BRIDE.
Single (12"): released on Greensleeves, Feb'82 by Greensleeves Records. Dist: BMG, Jetstar, Spartan

Single (12"): released on Greensleeves, Mar'82 by Greensleeves Records. Dist: BMG, Jetstar Spartan

JANE.
Single (12"): released on Impact, Dec'85 by Ace Records. Dist: Rough Trade, Pinnacle, Swift, Backs, Counterpoint, Jungle, Hotshot Cartel

JOINT FAVOURITES (Prophet,Michael & Half Pint).
Album: released on Greensleeves, Feb'86 by Greensleeves Records. Dist: BMG, Jetstar, Spartan

JUST TALKING.

Single (12"): released on Greensleeves, Nov'82 by Greensleeves Records. Dist: BMG, Jetstar, Spartan

LOVE IS AN EARTHLY THING.
Album: released on CSA, May'83 by CSA Records. Dist: PRT, Jetstar

MICHAEL PROPHET.
Album: released on Greensleeves, Dec'81 by Greensleeves Records. Dist: BMG, Jetstar, Spartan

RICH AND POOR.
Single (12"): released on Thunderbolt, Oct'84 by Magnum Music Group Ltd. Dist: Magnum Music Group Ltd, PRT Distribution, Spartan Distribution

RICH MAN POOR MAN.
Single (12"): released on CSA, Apr'83 by CSA Records. Dist: PRT, Jetstar

RIGHTEOUS ARE THE CONQUEROR.
Album: released on Greensleeves, Nov'80 by Greensleeves Records. Dist: BMG, Jetstar, Spartan

ROCK ME BABY.
Single (7"): released on WLN, Sep'82

SERIOUS REASONING.
Album: released on Island, Mar'80 by Island Records. Dist: Polygram

SETTLE YOU FER SETTLE.
Tracks: / Settle you fer settle / Accept me live (The Mighty Diamonds).
Single (12"): released on Live & Learn, May'86 Dist: Jetstar

WEY U A DO OVER DEY.
Single (12"): released on Kings Of Jazz, May'85 Dist: Jazz Horizons, Jazz Music, Celtic Music

Prophets

BACK TO THE BURNER.
Single (7"): released on Hypothetical, Oct'81 by Initial Records. Dist: Pinnacle

Prospect Of..

PROSPECT OF SCOTLAND Topic sampler no.5 (Various Artists).
Album: released on Topic, '81 Dist: Roots Distribution

Prospects

PROSPECTS Original Soundtrack.
Album: released on Red Bus, Mar'86 by Red Bus Records. Dist: PRT

Cassette: released on Red Bus, Mar'86 by Red Bus Records. Dist: PRT

Prosser, Alan

ROYAL DAVID'S CITY (Prosser, Alan & Canterbury Saints).
Single (7"): released on Phantom, Dec'81 by Mean Records. Dist: Pinnacle

Protagonist

28 NEIN.
Single (12"): released on Snak, Oct'85 by Snak Records. Dist: Rough Trade, Cartel

Protagonist 28-Nein

CONTENT TO WRITE IN I DINE WEATHERCRAFT.
Album: released on Magnet, Dec'85 by Magnet Records. Dist: BMG

Protection

AN EGG IS BREAKING OPEN.
Album: released on Touch, Aug'87 by Touch Records. Dist: Rough Trade, Cartel

Protector

MASS FANTASY.
Single (12"): released on Charlie's, Dec'84 by Charlie's Records. Dist: Jetstar

Protest

VINYL OVERLOAD EP.
Single (7"): released on Xcentric Noise, Nov'83 by Xcentric Noise Records & Tapes Records. Dist: Cartel

Protocol

THERE'S NO HOLDING BACK.
Tracks: / Lonely man, A.
Single (7"): released on Hit The Deck, Aug'87 by Hit The Deck Records. Dist: PRT

Proton Plus

PAY UP (Proton Plus/ Phil Fearon).
Single (12"): released on Yew Wood, Apr'84 by Sound Recordings Records. Dist: Pinnacle

Prototypes

PROTOTYPES various artists (Various Artists).
Album: released on Blue Print, Jan'80 Dist: PRT

Proudlove

MIDAS TOUCH.
Single (7"): released on KRP, Nov'83 by High Energy Records. Dist: PRT

Proud, Malcolm

HARPSICHORD PLAYS.
Compact disc: released on Claddagh, Oct'85 by Claddagh Records. Dist: I & B, Record Services Distribution (Ireland), Roots, Topic, Impetus, Projection, CM

Prowizorka Dzezz Bed

MOON LIGHTING.
Album: released on Timeless, Oct'86

Prowlers

LIVING OUTSIDE THE LAW.
Album: released on Unamerican Activities, Mar'87 by Hotshot Records. Dist: Cartel, Projection, Red Rhino, Hotshot

Proysen, Alf

MRS. PEPPERPOT STORIES (Patricia Gallimore).
Tracks: / Mrs.Pepperpot tries to please her husband / Mrs.Pepperpot minds the baby / Mrs.Pepperpot's penny watchman / Mrs.Pepperpot & the moose / Mrs.Pepperpot finds hidden treasure / Mr.Pepperpot.
Notes: Stories read by Patricia Gallimore
Cassette: released on Tellastory, Dec'86 by Bartlett Bliss Productions. Dist: PRT Distribution, Hayward Promotions Distribution, H.R. Taylor Distribution

Pruett, Jeanne

JEANNE PRUETT.
Album: released on MCA, Mar'87 by MCA Records. Dist: Polygram, MCA

Cassette: released on MCA, Mar'87 by MCA Records. Dist: Polygram, MCA

Prussia's Glory

PRUSSIA'S GLORY: MILITARY BRASS BAND MUSIC various artists (Various Artists).
Album: released on Teldec (Germany), Sep'84 by Import Records. Dist: IMS Distribution, Polygram Distribution

Cassette: released on Teldec (Germany), Sep'84 by Import Records. Dist: IMS Distribution, Polygram Distribution

Pruvot, Michel

DEL DUCASS AU BAL MUSETTE VOL.2 (Pruvot,Michel et ses Picards).
Tracks: / Trumpet echo / Banda,A / Rendesvous au the dansant / Melodie d'amore / Jolis quartiers de Paris / Vive campeurs / Les refraines tricolores / Si la valse m'etait chantee / Maria la Portuguaise / Radio Montmarte / Mediteranee March.
Album: released on Accordion Record Club, Jul'86 by Accordion Record Club Records. Dist: Accordion Record Club

DEL DUCCASS AU BAL MUSETTE.
Tracks: / Rosi Rosita / Chanson des becs sales / Faut pas craquer / Azur / Depart en piste / Rendezvous au the dansant / Si tu reviens danser ce soir / Du sacre coeur a la grande bleue / Melodia d'amore / Accordeon a la carte.
Album: released on Accordion Record Club, Jul'86 by Accordion Record Club Records. Dist: Accordion Record Club

RECORD MUSETTE.
Tracks: / Train d'enfer / Les guinguettes / Clap clap sand / Pedrillo / La java du loto / Buvons un coup marins pecheurs / Le fana du Charleston / Record musette / Et ca repart / Variations auvergnates / Tango des cocus / March des mineurs / Moulin rouge,etc..
Album: released on Accordion Record Club, Jul'86 by Accordion Record Club Records. Dist: Accordion Record Club

Pryde, Jimmy

PIPE DREAMS.
Cassette: released on Ross, '86 by Ross Records. Dist: Ross Distribution, Roots Distribution

Album: released on Polydor, Dec'76 by Polydor Records. Dist: Polygram, Polydor

Pryor, Richard

JO JO DANCER, YOUR LIFE IS CALLING (Pryor, Richard With Various Artists).
Tracks: / Baby Jo Jo / My destiny / For the love of money / Off the cliff / Into the past / I heard it through the grapevine / White kids/black kids / Heckler, The / What's going on / Michelle / Mighty love / In the upper room / Theme for mother / Bass behavior / Burn ward / I'm back / Shotgun.
Notes: Original Soundtrack.
Album: released on Warner Brothers, Aug'86 by Warner Bros Records. Dist: WEA

Cassette: released on Warner Brothers, Aug'86 by Warner Bros Records. Dist: WEA

LIVE IN CONCERT-WANTED.
Double Album: released on WEA, Apr'80 by WEA Records. Dist: WEA

Prysock, Arthur

ROCKIN' GOOD WAY, A.
Tracks: / Baby (you've got what it takes) / I want to thank you, girl / Bloodshot eyes / Teach me tonight / Every morning baby / Passing strangers / Next time you see me / Rockin' good way,A.
Notes: One of America's great vocalists, warm-voiced and in the Billy Eckstine and Brook Benton mould. During his long career spanning more than 35 years he reco-rded many fine albums, some of which were issued on Verve, including one with Count Basie. Personnel: Arthur Prysock - vocals/ The Red Prysock - teno sax/ Lloyd Wilson - keyboards/ Ralph Caldwell - guitar/ Ralph Hamperian - bass/ Don Williams - drums/ Betty Joplin - vocals.
Album: released on Fantasy (USA), Feb'86 by Fantasy Inc USA Records. Dist: IMS, Polygram

Psalms Alive

PSALMS ALIVE III Various Artists (Various Artists).
Tracks: / Those who sow in tears / Break into songs of joy / My soul waits / Bless the Lord, my soul / Clap your hands / I take refuge in the Lord / There's a longing in my heart / To every generation / Teach me thy way / Give glory to the Lord.
Notes: Producer/Composers: Tom Howard & Bill Batstone Classic psalms set to new music.
Album: released on Maranatha!, Jul'86 Dist: Kingsway Music, Pilgrim, Word Distribution

Cassette: released on Maranatha!, Jul'86 Dist: Kingsway Music, Pilgrim, Word Distribution

PSALMS ALIVE INSTRUMENTAL various artists (Various Artists).
Album: released on Maranatha, Mar'84

Cassette: released on Maranatha, Mar'84

Psalty Singalongathon

PSALTY SINGALONGATHON Best of kids praise (Various Artists).
Album: released on Maranatha, Dec'84

Pseudo Echo

AUTUMNAL PARK.
Album: released on EMI, Apr'85 by EMI Records. Dist: EMI

Cassette: released on EMI, Apr'85 by EMI Records. Dist: EMI

FUNKY TOWN.
Tracks: / Funky town / Lies are nothing.
Single (7"): released on RCA, Jul'87 by RCA Records. Dist: RCA, Roots, Swift, Wellard, Chris, I & B, Solomon & Peres Distribution

Single (12"): released on RCA, Jul'87 by RCA Records. Dist: RCA, Roots, Swift, Wellard, Chris, I & B, Solomon & Peres Distribution

LOVE AND ADVENTURE (All tied up).
Tracks: / Love and adventure(all tied up).
Single (7"): released on EMI, May'86 by EMI Records. Dist: EMI

Cassette: released on EMI, May'86 by EMI Records. Dist: EMI

Pseudo Elektronixx

ROTE GEFAHR 5 Track EP.
Single (12"): released on Rocky Road, Dec'83 Dist: Jetstar Distribution

P.S. Personal

SHOOT ME DOWN.
Single (7"): released on New World, Aug'83 by President Records. Dist: Swift, Spartan

Psyche

INSOMNIA THEATRE.
Album: released on New Rose, Jan'86 Dist: Rough Trade, Cartel

NEVER LAUGH.
Single (7"): released on Burning Bing, Jun'83 Dist: Pinnacle

PRISONER OF DESIRE.
Single (12"): released on New Rose, Aug'87 Dist: Rough Trade, Cartel

UNVEILING THE SECRET.
Compact disc: released on New Rose, Mar'87 Dist: Rough Trade, Cartel

UNVEILLING THE SECRET.
Single (12"): released on New Rose, 13 Jun'87 Dist: Rough Trade, Cartel

Psychedelic

PSYCHEDELIC SMASHES various artists (Various Artists).
Album: released on Cambra, May'85 by Cambra Records. Dist: IDS, Conifer

Cassette: released on Cambra, May'85 by Cambra Records. Dist: IDS, Conifer

PSYCHEDELIC SNARL (THE) various artists (Various Artists).
Album: released on Bam Caruso, Feb'87 by Bam Caruso Records. Dist: Rough Trade, Revolver, Cartel

PSYCHEDELIC TRIP 1966-1969 various artists (Various Artists).
Tracks: / Muffin man / Anniversary(of love) / Shades of orange / Iceman / Run & hide / Come on back / Vacuum cleaner / Love / Saynia / Romeo & Juliet / Magician / Beeside / Fathers name is dad / I'm not your stepping stone / Red sky at night / Tales of Flossie Fillet / Created by Clive / Baked jam roll in your eye / In your tower / Leave me here 23rd.
Album: released on See For Miles, Apr'86 by See For Miles Records. Dist: Pinnacle

Psychedelic Furs

12" TAPE, THE.
Tracks: / Pretty in pink / Love my way / Heaven / Heartbeat / Ghost in you, (The).
Cassette: released on CBS, Sep'86 by CBS Records. Dist: CBS

ANGELS DON'T CRY.
Tracks: / No release / We love you / Pretty in pink / Love my way.
Single (7"): released on CBS, Jan'87 by CBS Records. Dist: CBS

Single (7"): released on CBS, Jan'87 by CBS Records. Dist: CBS

Double-pack single: released on CBS, Jan'87 by CBS Records. Dist: CBS

FOREVER NOW.
Tracks: / President Gas / Love my way / Run and run / Merry-go-round / Danger / You and I / No easy street / Shadow*.
Notes: Track 'Shadow' is on Cassette only, NOT on Album.
Album: released on CBS, Apr'86 by CBS Records. Dist: CBS

Cassette: released on CBS, Apr'86 by CBS Records. Dist: CBS

Album: released on CBS, Sep'82 by CBS Records. Dist: CBS

Cassette: released on CBS, Sep'82 by CBS Records. Dist: CBS

GHOST IN YOU.
Single (7"): released on CBS, May'84 by CBS Records. Dist: CBS

Single (12"): released on CBS, May'84 by CBS Records. Dist: CBS

Picture disc single: released on CBS, May'84 by CBS Records. Dist: CBS

GREATEST ORIGINAL HITSZZ 4 Track EP.
Single (7"): released on CBS, Mar'83 by CBS Records. Dist: CBS

HEARTBREAK BEATS.
Tracks: / Heartbreak beats / New Dream.
Single (7"): released on CBS, Oct'86 by CBS Records. Dist: CBS

Single (12"): released on CBS, Oct'86 by CBS Records. Dist: CBS

HEAVEN.
Single (7"): released on CBS, Mar'84 by CBS Records. Dist: CBS

Single (12"): released on CBS, Mar'84 by CBS Records. Dist: CBS

MIDNIGHT TO MIDNIGHT.
Tracks: / Heartbreak beat / Shock / Shadow in my heart / Angels don't cry / Midnight to midnight / One more word / Torture / All of the law / Pretty in pink / No release*.
Album: released on CBS, Feb'87 by CBS Records. Dist: CBS

Cassette: released on CBS, Feb'87 by CBS Records. Dist: CBS

Notes: Extra track on cassette release only ****No Release"
Compact disc: released on CBS, Jan'87 by CBS Records. Dist: CBS

MIRROR MOVES.
Tracks: / Ghost in You / Here come cowboys / Heaven / Heartbeat / My time / Like a stranger / Alice's house / Only a game / Highwire days.
Album: released on CBS, Jan'87 by CBS Records. Dist: CBS

Cassette: released on CBS, Jan'87 by CBS Records. Dist: CBS

Album: released on CBS, May'84 by CBS Records. Dist: CBS

Cassette: released on CBS, May'84 by CBS Records. Dist: CBS

PRETTY IN PINK.
Tracks: / Pretty in pink / Love my way.
Single (7"): released on CBS, Jul'86 by CBS Records. Dist: CBS

Single (12"): released on CBS, Jul'86 by CBS Records. Dist: CBS

PSYCHEDELIC FURS.
Album: released on CBS, Mar'83 by CBS Records. Dist: CBS

Cassette: released on CBS, Mar'83 by CBS Records. Dist: CBS

PSYCHEDELIC FURS (4 TRACK CASSETTE EP).
Cassette: released on CBS, Dec'82 by CBS Records. Dist: CBS

TALK, TALK, TALK.
Album: released on CBS, Nov'84 by CBS Records. Dist: CBS

Cassette: released on CBS, Nov'84 by CBS Records. Dist: CBS

Psychic TV

DREAMS LESS SWEET.
Album: released on CBS, Oct'83 by CBS Records. Dist: CBS

Cassette: released on CBS, Oct'83 by CBS Records. Dist: CBS

GODSTAR (Psychic TV/Angels of Light).
Tracks: / Godstar / Godstar B.J. Mix.
Single (7"): released on Temple, Mar'86 by Temple Records. Dist: Roots Distribution, Folksound Distribution, Celtic Music Distribution, Projection Distribution

Single (12"): released on Temple, Mar'86 by Temple Records. Dist: Roots Distribution, Folksound Distribution, Celtic Music Distribution, Projection Distribution

JUST DRIFTING.
Single (7"): released on Some Bizarre, Dec'82 by Virgin Records. Dist: EMI, CBS, Polygram

Single (12"): released on Some Bizarre, Dec'82 by Virgin Records. Dist: EMI, CBS, Polygram

LIVE EN SUISSE.
Album: released on Temple, Jul'87 by Temple Records. Dist: Roots Distribution, Folksound Distribution, Celtic Music Distribution, Projection Distribution

LIVE IN HEAVEN.
Album: released on Temple, Mar'87 by Temple Records. Dist: Roots Distribution, Folksound Distribution, Celtic Music Distribution, Projection Distribution

LIVE IN REYJAVIK.
Album: released on Temple, Jun'87 by Temple Records. Dist: Roots Distribution, Folksound Distribution, Celtic Music Distribution, Projection Distribution

LIVE IN TOKYO 1986.
Album: released on Temple, Dec'86 by Temple Records. Dist: Roots Distribution, Folksound Distribution, Celtic Music Distribution, Projection Distribution

MAGICK DEFENDS ITSELF.
Tracks: / Magick defends itself.
Single (12"): released on Temple, Mar'87 by Temple Records. Dist: Roots Distribution, Folksound Distribution, Celtic Music Distribution, Projection Distribution

MOUTH OF THE NIGHT.
Album: released on Temple, Nov'85 by Temple Records. Dist: Roots Distribution, Folksound Distribution, Celtic Music Distribution, Projection Distribution

Picture disc album: released on Temple, Nov'85 by Temple Records. Dist: Roots Distribution, Folksound Distribution, Celtic Music Distribution, Projection Distribution

Cassette: released on Temple, Nov'85 by Temple Records. Dist: Roots Distribution, Folksound Distribution, Celtic Music Distribution, Projection Distribution

NEW YORK SCUM HATERS.
Album: released on Temple, Dec'84 by Temple Records. Dist: Roots Distribution, Folksound Distribution, Celtic Music Distribution, Projection Distribution

PAGAN DAY.
Album: released on Temple, Mar'87 by Temple Records. Dist: Roots Distribution, Folksound Distribution, Celtic Music Distribution, Projection Distribution

Album: released on Temple, Dec'84 by Temple Records. Dist: Roots Distribution, Folksound Distribution, Celtic Music Distribution, Projection Distribution

ROMAN P.
Tracks: / Roman P / Good vibrations.
Notes: Double A side.
Single (7"): released on Temple, Sep'86 by Temple Records. Dist: Roots Distribution, Folksound Distribution, Celtic Music Distribution, Projection Distribution

Single (7"): released on Sordid Sentimental, Jun'84 Dist: Cartel

THEMES.
Album: released on Temple Arcadia, Jul'85 Dist: Rough Trade Distribution

UNCLEAN.
Single (12"): released on Temple, Aug'84 by Temple Records. Dist: Rough Trade Distribution, Cartel Distribution

Psycho-attack over Europe

2ND PSYCHO-ATTACK OVER EUROPE (Various Artists).
Album: released on Kix 4 U, Jul'87 by Kix 4u Records. Dist: Pinnacle

PSYCHO-ATTACK OVER EUROPE Various Artists (Various Artists).
Album: released on Rockhouse, Dec'85 by Rockhouse Records. Dist: Swift Distribution, Charly Distribution

Psycho III

PSYCHO III ORIGINAL SOUNDTRACK (Various Artists).
Album: released on MCA, Oct'86 by MCA Records. Dist: Polygram, MCA

Cassette: released on MCA, Oct'86 by MCA Records. Dist: Polygram, MCA

Psycho Surgeon

GIVE A MAN A BADGE.
Tracks: / Give a man a badge / Diagnosis.
Single (7"): released on Flexible Response, Oct'86 Dist: Red Rhino, Cartel

Psychosurgery

CASE AGAINST IT.
Cassette: released on Seminar Cassettes, Oct'81

Psychotic Reactions

PSYCHOTIC REACTIONS Early American Rock Groups (Various Artists).
Tracks: / Psychotic reaction / Bend me,shape me / Kind of a drag / Time won't let me / Like to get to know you / One toe over the line / In a gadda da vida / Liar,Liar / Mercy,mercy,mercy / Let it all hang out / Incense & peppermints / They're gonna get you.
Album: released on Topline, Jan'87 by Charly Records. Dist: Charly Distribution

Cassette: released on Topline, Jan'87 by Charly Records. Dist: Charly Distribution

Psyclones

ANOTHER BRIDGE.
Album: released on DMC, Jul'87 Dist: Red Rhino, Cartel

Psycon

MAKE YOURSELF SCARCE.
Single (7"): released on Interdisc, Sep'84 by Interdisc Records. Dist: Island, EMI

Single (12"): released on Interdisc, Sep'84 by Interdisc Records. Dist: Island, EMI

Psycons

RUN TO THE STRANGER.
Tracks: / Run to the stranger.
Single (7"): released on Crystal, Apr'86 by Crystal Records. Dist: Jetstar, Revolver, Cartel

Psylons

ALL THE THINGS WE NEED.
Single (7"): released on Iron Lung, Jun'87 by Iron Lung Records. Dist: Revolver, Cartel

MOCKERY OF DECLINE, THE.
Tracks: / Mockery of decline, (The) / Clear Sky.
Single (7"): released on E-Type, Aug'86 by E-Type Records. Dist: Revolver, Cartel

Public Disgrace

TOXTETH.
Single (7"): released on Probe, May'82

Public Enemy

PUBLIC ENEMY NO.1.
Tracks: / Public enemy no.1 / Timebomb / Son of public enemy.
Single (7"): released on Def Jam (USA), Mar'87 by CBS Records. Dist: CBS

Single (12"): released on Def Jam (USA), Mar'87 by CBS Records. Dist: CBS

YO, BUM RUSH THE SHOW.
Tracks: / You're gonna get yours / Sophisticated bitch / Miuzi weighs a ton / Timebomb / Too much posse / Rightstarter (message to a black man) / Public Enemy No. 1 / M.P.E. / Yo! bum rush the show / Raise the roof / Megablast / Terminator X speaks with his hands.
Album: released on Def Jam (USA), Apr'87 by CBS Records. Dist: CBS

Cassette: released on Def Jam (USA), Apr'87 by CBS Records. Dist: CBS

YOU'RE GONNA GET YOURS.
Tracks: / You're gonna get yours / Miuzi weighs a ton.
Single (7"): released on Def Jam (USA), 20 Jun'87 by CBS Records. Dist: CBS

Single (12"): released on Def Jam (USA), 20 Jun'87 by CBS Records. Dist: CBS

Public Heirs

RUN FOXY RUN.
Tracks: / Run foxy run / Stomping in the pit.
Single (7"): released on Quiet, 23 May'87 by Quiet Records. Dist: Nine Mile, Cartel

WHAT'S GOING ON?.
Tracks: / What's going on?.
Single (12"): released on Quiet, Jun'86 by Quiet Records. Dist: Nine Mile, Cartel

Public Image Ltd

ALBUM/CASSETTE/COMPACT DISC.
Album: released on Virgin, Feb'86 by Virgin Records. Dist: EMI, Virgin Distribution

Cassette: released on Virgin, Feb'86 by Virgin Records. Dist: EMI, Virgin Distribution

Compact disc: released on Virgin, Feb'86 by Virgin Records. Dist: EMI, Virgin Distribution

HOME.
Tracks: / Home / Round.
Single (7"): released on Virgin, Apr'86 by Virgin Records. Dist: EMI, Virgin Distribution

Single (12"): released on Virgin, Apr'86 by Virgin Records. Dist: EMI, Virgin Distribution

LIVE.
Video-cassette (VHS): released on Virgin, Jan'84 by Virgin Records. Dist: EMI, Virgin Distribution

LIVE IN TOKYO.
Tracks: / Annalisa / Religion / Low life / Flowers of Romance / Death Disco / Solitaire / Love song (This is not a-) / Bad life / Banging the door / Under the house.
Compact disc: released on Virgin, '86 by Virgin Records. Dist: EMI, Virgin Distribution

Double Album: released on Virgin, Sep'83 by Virgin Records. Dist: EMI, Virgin Distribution

Double cassette: released on Virgin, Sep'83 by Virgin Records. Dist: EMI, Virgin Distribution

NATIONAL SERVICE.
Album: released on Illuminated, Nov'85 by IKF Records. Dist: Pinnacle, Cartel, Jetstar

PUBLIC IMAGE.
Tracks: / Theme / Religion 1 / Religion 2 / Annalisa / Fodderstompt / Low life / Public image / Attack.
Album: released on Virgin, Apr'86 by Virgin Records. Dist: EMI, Virgin Distribution

Cassette: released on Virgin, Apr'86 by Virgin Records. Dist: EMI, Virgin Distribution

Compact disc: released on Virgin, Oct'86 by Virgin Records. Dist: EMI, Virgin Distribution

Album: released on Virgin, Sep'78 by Virgin Records. Dist: EMI, Virgin Distribution

Cassette: released on Virgin, Sep'78 by Virgin Records. Dist: EMI, Virgin Distribution

Single (7"): released on Virgin, Sep'78 by Virgin Records. Dist: EMI, Virgin Distribution

SECOND EDITION.
Compact disc: released on Virgin, Dec'86 by Virgin Records. Dist: EMI, Virgin Distribution

Triple album / cassette: released on Virgin, Feb'80 by Virgin Records. Dist: EMI, Virgin Distribution

SINGLE.
Single (7"): released on Virgin, Jan'86 by Virgin Records. Dist: EMI, Virgin Distribution

Single (12"): released on Virgin, Jan'86 by Virgin Records. Dist: EMI, Virgin Distribution

Public, Joe

WHAT I WANT.
Single (7"): released on Knocked Back, Dec'83 by Knocked Back Records.

Pub Singer, The

I SINK THEM MY WAY.
Tracks: / I sink them my way / Rock on the Rocks.
Single (7"): released on PRT, Jul'86 by PRT Records. Dist: PRT

Single (12"): released on PRT, Jul'86 by PRT Records. Dist: PRT

Puckett, Gary

YOUNG GIRL (Puckett, Gary & The Union Gap).
Single (7"): released on CBS, May'68 by CBS Records. Dist: CBS

Single (7"): released on Old Gold (Reissue), Apr'83

Puente, Tito

EL REY (Puente, Tito & his Latin ensemble).
Album: released on Concord Jazz Picante(USA), Oct'84 Dist: IMS, Polygram

Cassette: released on Concord Jazz Picante(USA), Oct'84 Dist: IMS, Polygram

EL REY.
Tracks: / Oye como va / Autumn leaves / Ran kan kan / Rainfall / Giant steps / Linda Chicana / Medley: Stella by starlight / Delirio / Equinox / El rey del timbal.
Notes: Tito Puente and his Latin Ensemble.
Compact disc: released on Concord Jazz(USA), Jan'87 by Concord Jazz Records (USA). Dist: IMS, Polygram

MAMBO DIABLO (Puente, Tito & his Latin ensemble).
Tracks: / Mambo diablo / Take five / Lush life / Pick yourself up / Lullaby of Birdland / No pienses asi / China / Eastern joy dance.
Notes: Tito Puente - timbales, vibes, percussion Sonny Bravo - piano Jimmy Frisaura - valve trombone, trumpet, flugelhorn Ray Gonzalez - trumpet, flugelhorn George Shearing - piano ("special guest") Jose Madera - congas, percussion Mario Rivera - tenor & soprano saxophone, flute Bobby Rodriguez - bass Johnny 'Dandy' Rodriguez - bongos, percussion
Album: released on Concord Jazz(USA), Dec'85 by Concord Jazz Records (USA). Dist: IMS, Polygram

Compact disc: released on Concord Jazz(USA), Sep'86 by Concord Jazz Records (USA). Dist: IMS, Polygram

ON BROADWAY (Puente, Tito & his Latin ensemble).
Album: released on Concord Jazz, Apr'83 by Concord Jazz Records (USA). Dist: IMS, Polygram

Cassette: released on Concord Jazz, Apr'83 by Concord Jazz Records (USA). Dist: IMS, Polygram

PUENTE NOW.
Album: released on Vogue (France), Aug'84 Dist: Discovery, Jazz Music, PRT, Swift

SENSACION.
Tracks: / Fiesta a la king / Guajira for cal / 'Round Midnight / Que sensacion / Jordu / Cantigo en la distancia / Morning / Spain.
Notes: Tito Puente - timbales, vibes, percussion Sonny Bravo - piano Jimmy Frisaura - valve trombone, trumpet, flugelhorn Ray Gonzalez - trumpet, flugelhorn Jose Madera - congas, percussion Madero Rivera - tenor & soprano saxophone, alto flute, flute, piccolo Bobby Rodriquez - bass Johnny 'Dandy' Rodriquez - bongos, percussion Terry Gibbs - vibes (special guest)
Compact disc: released on Jazz (USA), Apr'87

Album: released on Concord Jazz(USA), Aug'86 by Concord Jazz Records (USA). Dist: IMS, Polygram

Cassette: released on Concord Jazz(USA), Aug'86 by Concord Jazz Records (USA). Dist: IMS, Polygram

Puff, Tony

I'LL HAVE TO GET YOU.
Single (12"): released on GG'S, Jul'84 by GG'S Records. Dist: Jetstar

Pugh-Taylor Project

PUGH-TAYLOR PROJECT (THE).
Notes: With Jim Pugh, Dave Taylor, George Young, Gerry Newood, Lew Del Gratts.
Compact disc: released on DMP, '86 by DMP Records. Dist: Venture

Puka, Karoly

VICTORIOUS PRIMAS (Puka, Karoly and His Gypsy Band).
Tracks: / That's no news to me / There were two pearls in the village / You may you may you may / Wind won't blow, the dorozsma windmill won't turn (The) / Listen you brown-haired girl / There's a little house on the hilltop.
Notes: Karoly Puka was born in 1963. As a

child he already scored great success with the Hungarian Rajko Band in several countries of Europe and America. In 1984 he won first prize at the contest organised for young Gypsy primases. He often participates at concert tours with his band in the great cities of West-Europe. [Confer release sheet, May '87]
Compact disc: released on Hungaraton(Hungary), May'87 Dist: Conifer

Pukwana, Dudu
LIFE IN BRACKNELL & WILLISAU (Pukwana, Dudu & John Stevens).
Tracks: / Hug pine (Bambelela) / Mahlomole (Lament) / Lafente (Ntabeni - In the mountains) / Baganga / Freely / Funk them up to Erika / Ziyekeleni(Let them be) / Big (pine)apple / Zama khwalo(Try again).
Album: released on Jika, Feb'84 Dist: Cadillac

RADEBE-THEY SHOOT TO KILL (Pukwana, Dudu & John Stevens).
Album: released on Affinity, Aug'87 by Charly Records. Dist: Charly, Cadillac

THEY SHOOT TO KILL (Pukwana, Dudu & John Stevens).
Tracks: / Mbizo Radebe Pt. 1 / Mbizo Radebe Pt.2.
Notes: Recorded at The Glass Trap, Southall, Middlesex, January 14 1987. Engineer - Chaz Rowden. Assistant Engineer - Alan Heaton. Front cover painting "Johnny last summer" by John Stevens. Photo of John and Dudu by Jo Smith. Photo of Johnny Dyani by Martin Butner. This album is a dedication to the loving member of Johnny Mbizo Dyani. Licensed from Charly Records International APS P 1987 Charly Holdings Inc. C 1987 Charly Records Ltd.
Album: released on Affinity, Jul'87 by Charly Records. Dist: Charly, Cadillac

ZILA 86 (Pukwana, Dudu & Zila).
Tracks: / Madodana (the young ones) / Hamba (Go away) / Mra / Khali / Harare / Nonceba (Merciful) / Nompongo (Ace) / Let's get together / August one (Ntulukazi).
Album: released on Jika, Aug'86 Dist: Cadillac

Puleo, Johnny
JOHNNY PULEO.
Cassette: released on Audio Fidelity, Oct'84 Dist: PRT

Pullen, Don
CAPRICORN RISING.
Album: released on Black Saint Import. Jul'78

HEALING FORCE.
Album: released on Black Saint, Mar'77 Dist: Projection, IMS, Polygram, Chris Wellard, Harmonia Mundi, Swift

LIFE LINE (Pullen, Don Quartet).
Cassette: released on Timeless. Oct'86

MONTREUX CONCERT.
Album: released on Atlantic, Jul'78 by WEA Records. Dist: WEA

PLAYS MONK.
Album: released on King (USA), Apr'76 Dist: Gusto Distribution

RESOLUTION (Pullen, Don/H. Bluiett).
Album: released on Black Saint Import, Jul'78

SIXTH SENSE THE (Pullen, Don Quintet).
Compact disc: released on Black Saint (Italy), '86 Dist: Target, Jazz Music, Harmonia Mundi

SOLO PIANO ALBUM.
Album: released on Sackville, Jul'86 Dist: JSU, Jazz Music, Jazz Horizons, Cadillac Music, Celtic Music, Swift

SONG EVERLASTING (Pullen, Don & Adams, George Quartet).
Tracks: / Another reason to celebrate * / Sunwatchers / Serenade for Sarah / 1529 Gunr Street / Warm up / Sing me a song everlasting
Notes: * Extra track on CD only.
Compact disc: released on Blue Note, Aug'87 by EMI Records. Dist: EMI
Album: released on Manhattan-Blue Note, Aug'87 by EMI America Records (USA). Dist: EMI

WARRIORS.
Album: released on Black Saint Import. Jul'78

Pullens, Vern
VERN PULLENS.
Album: released on Rockhouse, Mar'85 Dist: Pinnacle

Pullen, Whitey
RINKIN' WINE.
Single (7"): released on Rollin' Rock (USA Import). Jun'80

LET'S ALL GO WILD.
Single (7"): released on Rollin' Rock (USA Import), Jun'80

Pulling Faces
DANCE OF GHOSTS.
Album: released on WEA Ireland, Jul'87 by WEA Records. Dist: Celtic Distributions, Projection, I & B

Cassette: released on WEA Ireland, Jul'87 by WEA Records. Dist: Celtic Distributions, Projection, I & B

Pullins, Leroy
I'M A NUT (The Original).
Tracks: / I'm a nut / Knee deep / Out in the Smokehouse taking a bath / Tatersville auxiliar sewing circle, (The) / Meter maid / What's his name / I love you drops / Swimming at the bottom of the pool / I done you wrong song / Tickled pink / Okeefenokee / Billy Roy and Jackson Sam / Yellow / S tree towers / World what have I done.
Notes: Original Kapp Recordings
Album: released on Bear Family, Mar'86 by Bear Family Records. Dist: Rollercoaster Distribution, Swift

Single (7"): released on MCA (USA Import). May'80

Pulp
DOGS ARE EVERYWHERE.
Tracks: / Dogs are everywhere.
Single (7"): released on Fire, Jun'86 by Twist and Shout Music. Dist: Nine Mile, Rough Trade, Cartel

EVERYBODY'S PROBLEM.
Single (7"): released on Red Rhino, Sep'83 by Indies Records. Dist: Cartel Distribution

FREAKS.
Album: released on Fire, May'87 by Twist and Shout Music. Dist: Nine Mile, Rough Trade, Cartel

IT.
Album: released on Red Rhino, May'84 by Red Rhino Records. Dist: Red Rhino, Cartel

LITTLE GIRL WITH BLUE EYES.
Single (12"): released on Dec'85 by Twist and Shout Music. Dist: Nine Mile, Rough Trade, Cartel

MASTER OF THE UNIVERSE.
Tracks: / Master of the universe.
Single (7"): released on Fire, Mar'87 by Twist and Shout Music. Dist: Nine Mile, Rough Trade, Cartel

Single (12"): released on Fire, Mar'87 by Twist and Shout Music. Dist: Nine Mile, Rough Trade, Cartel

MASTERS OF THE UNIVERSE.
Single (12"): released on Fire, 30 May'87 by Twist and Shout Music. Dist: Nine Mile, Rough Trade, Cartel

MY LIGHTHOUSE.
Single (7"): released on Red Rhino, May'83 by Red Rhino Records. Dist: Red Rhino, Cartel

THEY SUFFOCATE AT NIGHT.
Tracks: / Tunnel.
Single (7"): released on Fire, Jan'87 by Twist and Shout Music. Dist: Nine Mile, Rough Trade, Cartel

Single (12"): released on Fire, Jan'87 by Twist and Shout Music. Dist: Nine Mile, Rough Trade, Cartel

Pulsallama
QUI QUI.
Single (7"): released on Y, Mar'83

Single (12"): released on Y, Mar'83

UNGAWA PART 2.
Single (7"): released on Y, Jul'82
Cat. no: Y 25
Single (12"): released on Y, Jul'82

Pulse 8
PULSE 8 Various Artists (Various Artists).
Album: released on Survival, Feb'86 by Survival Records. Dist: Backs, Cartel Distribution

Cassette: released on Survival, Feb'86 by Survival Records. Dist: Backs, Cartel Distribution

Punk...
VARIOUS PUNK BANDS Various artists (Various Artists).
Tracks: / Time bomb city / Shout and scream / Duty unto death / No compromise / Khemer rouge / Cold love / No rules / City brave / Conscience prayer / Religion / Time of our lives / Electronik church / Poison pen letter / Slow death.
Album: released on Conifer, Apr'86 by Conifer Records. Dist: Conifer

Cassette: released on Conifer, Apr'86 by Conifer Records. Dist: Conifer

Punk Lives Let's Slam
PUNK LIVES LET SLAM (Various Artists).
Album: released on Slam, Nov'86

Punters Choir
WORLD CUP SPECIAL, (THE).
Single (7"): released on Scotdisc, May'86 Dist: Clyde Factors Distributors

Pure Energy
LOVE GAME.
Tracks: / Love game / Love game (Remix) / Love game (Original mix).
Single (12"): released on ZYX (Germany), Mar'86 by ZYX Records. Dist: Greyhound

Pure Glass
DON'T TAKE YOUR LOVE.
Single (7"): released on R4, May'85 by R & R. Dist: EMI

Single (12"): released on R4, May'85 by R & R. Dist: EMI

MATTER OF TIME.
Tracks: / Matter of time (Ext. Edit.) / Flip the lid
Single (7"): released on Legend, Feb'87 by Legend Records. Dist: EMI, Legend Distribution, Island

Single (12"): released on Legend, Jan'87 by Legend Records. Dist: EMI, Legend Distribution, Island

Pure Gold
PURE GOLD VOL.1 various artists (Various Artists).
Album: released on Success, Feb'85 Dist: Counterpoint Distribution

Pure Overkill
PURE OVERKILL various artists (Various Artists).
Album: released on Guardian, Aug'84 by Guardian Records. Dist: Jazz Music, Pinnacle

Pure Prairie League
PURE PRAIRIE COLLECTION.
Album: released on RCA International (USA) Oct'81 by RCA Records. Dist: RCA

Cassette: released on RCA International (USA), Oct'81 by RCA Records. Dist: RCA

SOMETHING IN THE NIGHT.
Album: released on Casablanca, Jun'81 Dist: Polygram, Phonogram

Cassette: released on Casablanca, Jun'81 Dist: Polygram, Phonogram

Pure Silk
BLUES AWAY.
Tracks: / Blues away / Blues away (Instrumental).
Single (12"): released on Raiders, Aug'86 Dist: Jetstar

IT AIN'T EASY (Pure Silk / P. Tajah).
Single (12"): released on Sir George, Nov'86 by Sir George Records. Dist: Jetstar, Pinnacle

LADY IN RED.
Tracks: / Lady in red / Electronic.
Single (7"): released on Champion, Aug'86 by Champion Records. Dist: RCA

Single (12"): released on Champion, Aug'86 by Champion Records. Dist: RCA

Pure Soul
PURE SOUL various artists (Various Artists).
Album: released on Kent, Apr'84 by Ace Records. Dist: Pinnacle

Pure Vision
COSMOPOLITAN.
Single (7"): released on LBA-Gipsy, Jul'85 by Gipsy Records. Dist: CBS

Purify, James & Bobby
SHAKE A TAIL FEATHER.
Single (7"): released on Neil Rushton, Mar'83 by Inferno. Dist: Pinnacle

Purim, Flora
LOVE REBORN.
Compact disc: released on Fantasy (USA), Nov'86 by Fantasy Inc USA Records. Dist: IMS, Polygram

Purim, Flora & Airto
HUMBLE PEOPLE.
Album: released on George Wein Concord Jazz (USA), Sep'86 by Concord Jazz (USA). Dist: IMS, Polygram

Cassette: released on George Wein Concord Jazz (USA), Sep'85 by Concord Jazz (USA). Dist: IMS, Polygram

MAGICIANS (THE).
Tracks: / Sweet baby blues / Garimpo / Esquinas / Bird of paradise / Magicians, The / Jennifer / Jump / Two minutes of peace / Love reborn.
Notes: Frequent visitors to the UK,Flora Purim & husband Airto Moreira,with a programmeof unique & exciting latin-American pop music.Anchored by Latin,Bossa Nova and African dance rhythms,steeped in Brazilian blues & richly textured with synthesisers.Supported by 20 musicians including the very special guests,Kenny Loggins & George Duke.
Album: released on Crosscut, Nov'86 by IMS-Polygram Records. Dist: IMS, Polygram, Rollercoaster Distribution

Cassette: released on Crosscut, Nov'86 by IMS-Polygram Records. Dist: IMS, Polygram, Rollercoaster Distribution

Compact disc: released on Crosscut, Nov'86 by IMS-Polygram Records. Dist: IMS, Polygram, Rollercoaster Distribution

Purple Cow & Goops
PURPLE COW & GOOPS G. Burgess (Channing, Carol).
Cassette: released on Caedmon(USA), Oct'81 by Caedmon (USA) Records. Dist: Gower, Taylors, Discovery

Purple Gang
GRANNY TAKES A TRIP.
Album: released on Razor, Nov'86 by Razor. Dist: Pinnacle

Purple Hearts
BEAT THAT.
Album: released on Fiction, May'80 by Fiction Records. Dist: Polygram

MY LIFE'S A JIGSAW.
Single (7"): released on Safari, '81 by Safari Records. Dist: Pinnacle

POP-ISH FRENZY.
Album: released on Razor, Jul'86 by Razor. Dist: Pinnacle

PURPLE HEARTS FROM PASTURES GONE various artists (Various Artists).
Album: released on PRT, Feb'84 by PRT Records. Dist: PRT

Cassette: released on PRT, Feb'84 by PRT Records. Dist: PRT

SCOOBY DOO.
Single (7"): released on Roadrunner (Dutch), Jul'82 Dist: Pinnacle

Purpleman
LEVEL VIBES PUMPING.
Single (7"): released on Jammy's, Oct'83 by Jammy's Records. Dist: Jetstar

PURPLEMAN SAVES PAPPPA TOLLO IN A DANCE HALL STYLE.
Album: released on Vista Sounds, '83 by Vista Sounds Records. Dist: Jetstar

Purple Things
DEEP IN THE MIND OF THE PURPLE THINGS.
Single (12"): released on Media Burn, Dec'85 by Rocks Off Record Emporium. Dist: Rough Trade Distribution, Cartel Distribution

KING SNAKE.
Single (7"): released on Absolutely Free, Aug'87 Dist: Red Rhino, Cartel

OUT OF THE DEEP.
Tracks: / Out of the deep.
Single (12"): released on Media Burn, May'86 by Rocks Off Record Emporium. Dist: Rough Trade Distribution, Cartel Distribution

Pursey, James T.
IF ONLY BEFORE.
Single (12"): Dist: Stage One

Pursey, Jimmy
IMAGINATION CAMOUFLAGE.
Album: released on Polydor, Oct'80 by Polydor Records. Dist: Polygram, Polydor

ZAP POW.
Tracks: / Zap pow.
Single (7"): released on Videocat, Sep'86 Dist: DMS-RCA

Single (12"): released on Videocat, Sep'86 Dist: DMS-RCA

Pursuit
PURSUIT Original film soundtrack (Various Artists).
Album: released on Polydor, Nov'81 by Poly-

dor Records. Dist: Polygram, Polydor

Cassette: released on Polydor, Nov'81 by Polydor Records. Dist: Polygram, Polydor

Purveyors of taste
PURVEYORS OF TASTE Creation compilation, A (Various Artists).
Notes: Includes Felt, Primal Scream, Bodines.
Album: released on Creation, Jun'86 Dist: Rough Trade, Cartel

Purvis, Geoff
BORDER FIDDLER, THE (Purvis, Geoff & The Border Country Dance Band).
Album: released on Fellside (Cumbria), '83 by Fellside Records. Dist: Roots, Projection, CM, Jazz Music

Purvis, Pam
HEART SONG (Purvis, Pam / Bob Ackerman).
Album: released on Blackhawk, Aug'86 by Blackhawk Records (USA). Dist: IMS-Polygram

Push
MIDNIGHT.
Single (7"): released on Excaliber, May'83 by Red Bus Records. Dist: PRT

Single (12"): released on Excaliber, May'83 by Red Bus Records. Dist: PRT

MY HEART.
Single (7"): released on Excaliber, Oct'82 by Red Bus Records. Dist: PRT

Single (12"): released on Excaliber, Oct'82 by Red Bus Records. Dist: PRT

Push Button Pleasure
LAST DISSONANCE, THE.
Album: released on Hamster, Jun'87 by Hamster Records And Tapes. Dist: Backs, Cartel

PUSHBUTTON PLEASURE various artists (Various Artists).
Cassette: released on Hamster, Nov'83 by Hamster Records And Tapes. Dist: Backs, Cartel

VAST DIFFERENCE, THE.
Album: released on Hamster, Mar'85 by Hamster Records And Tapes. Dist: Backs, Cartel

Pushtwangers
PUSHTWANGERS.
Album: released on Vinyl Mania, Nov'84 Dist: Rough Trade, Cartel

Puss In Boots
PUSS IN BOOTS various artists.
Cassette: released on Anvil, Jan'81 Dist: Anvil

Album: released on Pickwick (Ladybird), Feb'83

PUSS IN BOOTS & JACK & THE BEANSTALK.
Cassette: released on Tellastory, Jan'87 by Bartlett Bliss Productions. Dist: PRT Distribution, Hayward Promotions Distribution, H.R. Taylor Distribution

PUSS IN BOOTS & OTHER STORIES
For children aged 3-7 (Various Artists).
Cassette: released on VFM Cassettes, Jul'85

Pussycat
MISSISSIPPI.
Tracks: / Smile / Mississippi.
Single (7"): released on Old Gold, Mar'87 by Old Gold Records. Dist: Lightning, Jazz Music, Spartan, Counterpoint

Single (7"): released on European Import, '80 Dist: Conifer

Put On Your Dancing Shoes
PUT ON YOUR DANCING SHOES various artists (Various Artists).
Album: released on Capitol, Sep'85 by Capitol Records. Dist: EMI

Cassette: released on Capitol, Sep'85 by Capitol Records. Dist: EMI

Putrone, Patrick
DIAMONDS ARE A BOY'S BEST FRIEND.
Single (7"): released on Ideal Music, Aug'85 by Ideal Music Records. Dist: Ideal Music

Putsch
SOLIDARITY.
Single (7"): released on Pip, Mar'82 by PRT

Records. Dist: PRT

Puzzle
I LOVE FUNKIN'.
Single (7"): released on Steinar, Aug'84

Single (12"): released on Steinar, Aug'84

Pyewackett
7 TO MIDNIGHT.
Album: released on Familiar, '85 by Familiar Records. Dist: Projection

MAN IN THE MOON DRINKS CLARET, THE.
Album: released on Familiar, Sep'84 by Familiar Records. Dist: Projection

PYEWACKETT.
Album: released on Dingles, '83 by Dingles Records. Dist: Projection

THIS CRAZY PARADISE.
Album: released on Familiar, Jan'87 by Familiar Records. Dist: Projection

Pyjama Sutra
ALL HARD WORK.
Single (7"): released on Plastic Head, Aug'85 Dist: Pinnacle, Rough Trade, Cartel

KILLING TIME.
Album: released on Plastic Head, Nov'85 Dist: Pinnacle, Rough Trade, Cartel

TEN SECOND TAN.
Tracks: / Ten second tan / When killed time / Song of sixpence, A.
Single (12"): released on Plastic Head, Nov'86 Dist: Pinnacle, Rough Trade, Cartel

Pylon
BEEP.
Single (7"): released on DB, Jul'86 by DB Records. Dist: Pinnacle

CHOMP.
Tracks: / K / Yo-Yo / Beep / Italian movie theme / Crazy / -Train / Buzz / No clocks / Reptiles / Spider / Gyrate / Altitude.
Album: released on DB, Jul'86 by DB Records. Dist: Pinnacle

Cassette: released on DB, Jul'86 by DB Records. Dist: Pinnacle

COOL.
Single 10": released on Armageddon, Feb'81 by Armageddon Records. Dist: Revolver, Cartel, Pinnacle

CRAZY.
Single (7"): released on DB, Jul'86 by DB Records. Dist: Pinnacle

GYRATE.
Album: released on Armageddon, Sep'83 by Armageddon Records. Dist: Revolver, Cartel, Pinnacle

Pyne, Mick
ALONE TOGETHER (piano/cornet duets).
Album: released on Spotlite, '83 by Spotlite Records. Dist: Cadillac, Jazz Music, Spotlite

Pyrolator
WUNDERLAND.
Album: released on Atatak, Jun'84 by Atatak Records. Dist: Rough Trade, Cartel

Python Lee Jackson
IN A BROKEN DREAM.
Single (7"): released on Bold Reprieve, Jul'87 by Bold Reprieve Records. Dist: Pinnacle

Single (12"): released on Bold Reprieve, Jul'87 by Bold Reprieve Records. Dist: Pinnacle

Single (7"): released on Young Blood, Jul'80 by Young Blood Records. Dist: Pinnacle

Single (12"): released on Young Blood, Jul'80 by Young Blood Records. Dist: Pinnacle

Pzazz
LOOK INSIDE.
Album: released on Paladin, Dec'83 by Paladin Records. Dist: Rough Trade, Pinnacle

SKY TRAIN.
Single (7"): released on Magenta, Jul'80 Dist: Windham Hill

SWITCH, THE.
Single (7"): released on Keytone, Nov'83

Single (12"): released on Keytone, Nov'83

Q

PLAYBACK.
Single 7": released on Cocteau, Oct'82 by Cocteau Records. Dist: Pinnacle

VOICE OF Q.
Single 7": released on Philly World(USA), Oct'82 by Philly World(USA). Dist: Polygram

Single 12": released on Philly World(USA), Oct'82 by Philly World(USA). Dist: Polygram

Q, Stacey
TWO OF HEARTS.
Single 7": released on Atlantic, Jan'87 by WEA Records. Dist: WEA, Swift, Celtic Music

Single 12": released on Atlantic, Jan'87 by WEA Records. Dist: WEA, Swift, Celtic Music

WE CONNECT.
Single 7": released on Atlantic, Jun'87 by WEA Records. Dist: WEA, Swift, Celtic Music

Single 12": released on Atlantic, Jun'87 by WEA Records. Dist: WEA, Swift, Celtic Music

Q5
MIRROR CRACKS, THE/ STEEL THE LIGHT.
Compact disc: released on Music For Nations, Records. Dist: Pinnacle

STEEL THE LIGHT.
Single 12": released on Music For Nations, May'86 by Music For Nations Records. Dist: Pinnacle

STEEL THE NIGHT.
Cassette: released on Music For Nations, Mar'85 by Music For Nations Records. Dist: Pinnacle

Compact disc: released on Music For Nations, Mar'85 by Music For Nations Records. Dist: Pinnacle

WHEN THE MIRROR CRACKS.
Album: released on Music For Nations, Sep'86 by Music For Nations Records. Dist: Pinnacle

Cassette: released on Music For Nations, Sep'86 by Music For Nations Records. Dist: Pinnacle

Q.A.X.
DOES ME GOOD.
Single 7": released on Vinyl Beat, Jan'84 by Vinyl Beat Records.

QCD
QCD (Various artists).
Compact disc: released on Virgin, Dec'86 by Virgin Records. Dist: Virgin, EMI

Q.E.D.
CAN'T WAIT TO GET ON THE BEACH.
Single 7": released on Climber, Jul'86 by Climber Records. Dist: PRT

SANTA'S GOING TO MISS ME.
Single 7": released on Dingles, Nov'87 by Dingles Records. Dist: Projection, Celtic Music, Roots, Spartan **Media Note:** Picture Bag.

YUPPIE SONG.
Single 7": released on Dingles, 30 May'87 by Dingles Records. Dist: Projection, Celtic Music, Roots, Spartan

Q-Pid with Nikki D
MY LATIN LOVER.
Single 7": released on Rhythm King, Oct'86 by Mute. Dist: Rough Trade, Cartel

Single 12": released on Rhythm King, Oct'86 by Mute. Dist: Rough Trade, Cartel

Q-Tips
Q-Tips (Q-Tips featuring Paul Young).
Recording Notes: Produced by Bob Sargeant.
Album: released on MFP, Sep'86 by Music For Pleasure Records. Dist: EMI

Cassette: released on MFP, Sep'86 by Music For Pleasure Records. Dist: EMI

Quando Quango
PIGS AND BATTLESHIPS.
Album: released on Factory, Nov'85 by Factory Records. Dist: Pinnacle

Cassette: released on Factory, Nov'85 by Factory Records. Dist: Pinnacle

Quarterflash
QUARTERFLASH.
Album: released on Geffen, Sep'86 by Geffen Records. Dist: WEA

Cassette: released on Geffen, Sep'86 by Geffen Records. Dist: WEA

Compact disc: released on Geffen, '83 by Geffen Records. Dist: WEA

TAKE ANOTHER PICTURE.
Album: released on Geffen, Sep'86 by Geffen Records. Dist: WEA

Cassette: released on Geffen, Sep'86 by Geffen Records. Dist: WEA

Quartet, Adam
SONG EVERLASTING (Quartet, Adam/Don Pullen).
Album: released on Blue Note, Aug'87 by EMI Records(UK). Dist: EMI

Quatro, Suzi
LOST IN HIS ARMS.
Single 7": released on First Night, Sep'86 by Safari Records. Dist: Pinnacle

SATURDAY NIGHT SPECIAL.
Album: released on Biff, Oct'87 by Blaylock Management Ltd.. Dist: Revolver, Cartel. Estim retail price in Oct'87 was £5.99.

WILD THING.
Single 7": released on PRT, Nov'86 by PRT Records.

Single 12": released on PRT, Nov'86 by PRT Records.

Quay, Judy
GOOD AS GOLD (Quay, Judy / Francke Thore).
Recording Notes: Official Sport Aid disc
Single 7": released on Musik, May'86, EMI, M.I.S.

Quebec, Ike
BLUE AND SENTIMENTAL.
Album: released on Blue Note, Mar'86 by EMI Records(UK). Dist: EMI

Cassette: released on Blue Note, Mar'86 by EMI Records(UK). Dist: EMI

EASY LIVING.
Recording Notes: * Extra tracks on CD only: B.G.'s groove two; I.Q. shuffle.
Album: released on Manhattan, Aug'87 by EMI Records(UK). Dist: EMI

Compact disc: released on Blue Note, Aug'87 by EMI Records(UK). Dist: EMI

Queen
ANOTHER ONE BITES THE DUST.
Single 7": released on EMI, Sep'80 by EMI Records(UK). Dist: EMI

Single 7": released on EMI, Nov'75 by EMI Records(UK). Dist: EMI

COMPLETE WORKS.
Recording Notes: A high quality 14 record box set by one of the world's biggest selling acts. This set contains all of Queen's recorded output from 'Queen' which came onto the scene in 1973, through to the platinum selling 'The Works'. In addition to their album output, the set contains a bonus album containing 7 tracks which have never appeared on Queen albums. All albums have been digitally re-mastered by Queen and have been cut using the Direct Metal Mastering process for the best sound quality on record yet. The records will be sleeved in specially designed 'Complete Works' design. The set will also contain a full colour 12" 12" booklet containing: New pictures of the band. 12" 12" colour reproduction of all the original sleeve designs from the albums included in the box set. Complete album and singles discography stating chart performance; gold and platinum awards achieved for both the U.K. and U.S. as well as worldwide release information. A separate booklet containing: A complete tour itinerary listing the first dates when the band was formed through to the present day. A complete list of Queen's massive equipment inventory which is taken on the road. Previously unpublished contract riders detailing the various items for the band and road crew in their dressing room at every Queen concert. Features exclusive map of the world showing the extent of Queen's success, both in recording and in concert. All this is boxed in a high finished box covered in leather-look material with the title embossed in gold. 'The Complete Works consists of the following albums: Queen/Queen II/Sheer Heart Attack/A Night at the Opera/News of the World/Jazz/Live Killers/The Game/Flash Gorden/Hot Space/The Works. Bonus album containing the following tracks: Sole Brother/Human Body/I Go Crazy/See What a Fool/Thank God It's Christmas/One Vision/Blurred Version.
Boxed set: released on EMI, Dec'85 by EMI Records(UK). Dist: EMI **Media Note:** 14 LP set

CRAZY LITTLE THING CALLED LOVE.
Video-cassette (VHS): released on Gold Rushes, Mar'87 by Video Collection International Ltd.. **Media Note:** Video single

DAY AT THE RACES, A.
Album: released on EMI, '85 by EMI Records(UK). Dist: EMI

Cassette: released on EMI, '85 by EMI Records(UK). Dist: EMI

Compact disc: released on EMI, '85 by EMI Records(UK). Dist: EMI

Compact disc: released on EMI, Nov'86 by EMI Records(UK). Dist: EMI

FLASH GORDON Original soundtrack by Queen.
Compact disc: released on EMI, Dec'86 by EMI Records(UK). Dist: EMI

Album: released on EMI, '85 by EMI Records(UK). Dist: EMI

Cassette: released on EMI, '85 by EMI Records(UK). Dist: EMI

FRIENDS WILL BE FRIENDS.
Single 7": released on EMI, Jun'86 by EMI Records(UK). Dist: EMI

Single 12": released on EMI, Jun'86 by EMI Records(UK). Dist: EMI

Picture disc single: released on EMI, Jun'86 by EMI Records(UK). Dist: EMI

GAME, THE.
Compact disc: released on EMI, '86 by EMI Records(UK). Dist: EMI

Album: released on EMI, '85 by EMI Records(UK). Dist: EMI

Cassette: released on EMI, '85 by EMI Records(UK). Dist: EMI

GOOD OLD-FASHIONED LOVER BOY / DEATH ON TWO LEGS.
Single 7": released on EMI, May'77 by EMI

Records(UK). Dist: EMI

GREATEST FLIX.
Recording Notes: 17 tracks
Video-cassette (VHS): released on PMI, Jun'86 by PMI Records. Dist: EMIa*

Video-cassette (Betamax): released on PMI, Jun'86 by PMI Records. Dist: EMIa*

GREATEST HITS: QUEEN.
Compact disc: released on EMI, Sep'84 by EMI Records(UK). Dist: EMI

Album: released on EMI, Oct'84 by EMI Records(UK). Dist: EMI

Cassette: released on EMI, Oct'84 by EMI Records(UK). Dist: EMI

HAMMER TO FALL.
Single 7": released on EMI, Sep'84 by EMI Records(UK). Dist: EMI

Single 12": released on EMI, Sep'84 by EMI Records(UK). Dist: EMI

HOT SPACE.
Compact disc: released on EMI, Dec'86 by EMI Records(UK). Dist: EMI

Album: released on EMI, '85 by EMI Records(UK). Dist: EMI

Cassette: released on EMI, '85 by EMI Records(UK). Dist: EMI

I WANT TO BREAK FREE.
Single 7": released on EMI, Apr'84 by EMI Records(UK). Dist: EMI

Single 12": released on EMI, Apr'84 by EMI Records(UK). Dist: EMI

INTERVIEW PICTURE DISC.
Album: released on Baktabak, Jul'87 by Baktabak Records. Dist: Arabesque

IT'S A HARD LIFE.
Single 7": released on EMI, Jul'84 by EMI Records(UK). Dist: EMI

Single 12": released on EMI, Jul'84 by EMI Records(UK). Dist: EMI

Picture disc single: released on EMI, Jul'84 by EMI Records(UK). Dist: EMI

JAZZ.
Compact disc: released on EMI, Dec'86 by EMI Records(UK). Dist: EMI

Album: released on EMI, '85 by EMI Records(UK). Dist: EMI

Cassette: released on EMI, '85 by EMI Records(UK). Dist: EMI

KILLER QUEEN.
Cassette: released on EMI(Import), '80 by EMI Records(UK). Dist: Conifer

KIND OF MAGIC, A.
Album: released on EMI, Jun'86 by EMI Records(UK). Dist: EMI

Cassette: released on EMI, Jun'86 by EMI Records(UK). Dist: EMI

Compact disc: released on EMI, Jun'86 by EMI Records(UK). Dist: EMI

Single 7": released on EMI, Mar'86 by EMI Records(UK). Dist: EMI

Single 12": released on EMI, Mar'86 by EMI Records(UK). Dist: EMI

Picture disc single: released on EMI, Mar'86 by EMI Records(UK). Dist: EMI **Media Note:** 12" picture disc single

LAS PALABRAS DE AMOUR / COOL CAT.
Single 7": released on EMI, Jun'82 by EMI Records(UK). Dist: EMI

LIVE IN BUDAPEST.
Recording Notes: A unique film of Queen performing the largest ever concert in Eastern Europe before a capacity 80,000 audience at the Nepstadium in Budapest, during their "Magic Tour". Number of tracks is 22. Live recording. Total playing time is approx 90 minutes.
Video-cassette (VHS): released on Picture Music International, Feb'87 by Picture Music International. Dist: EMI

LIVE IN RIO.
Recording Notes: Just that, plus some backstage footage and interviews. Includes nearly all the hit singles, sixteen songs in all, from a band that specialises in spectacularly good entertainment. Hi fi sound.
Video-cassette (VHS): released on PMI, Jun'86 by PMI Records. Dist: EMIa*

Video-cassette [Betamax]: released on PMI, Jun'86 by PMI Records. Dist: EMIa*

LIVE KILLERS.
Compact disc: released on EMI, Dec'86 by EMI Records(UK). Dist: EMI

Double Album: released on EMI, '85 by EMI Records(UK). Dist: EMI

Cassette: released on EMI, '85 by EMI Records(UK). Dist: EMI

LIVE MAGIC.
Compact disc: released on EMI, Jan'87 by EMI Records(UK). Dist: EMI

NEWS OF THE WORLD.
Compact disc: released on EMI, '86 by EMI Records(UK). Dist: EMI

Cassette: released on EMI, '85 by EMI Records(UK). Dist: EMI

Album: released on EMI, '85 by EMI Records(UK). Dist: EMI

NIGHT AT THE OPERA, A.
Album: released on EMI, '85 by EMI Records(UK). Dist: EMI

Cassette: released on EMI, '85 by EMI Records(UK). Dist: EMI

Compact disc: released on EMI, Nov'86 by EMI Records(UK). Dist: EMI

ONE VISION.
Single 7": released on EMI, Nov'85 by EMI Records(UK). Dist: EMI

Single 12": released on EMI, Nov'85 by EMI Records(UK). Dist: EMI

QUEEN.
Compact disc: released on EMI, Nov'86 by EMI Records(UK). Dist: EMI

Album: released on Fame (EMI), Sep'82 by Music For Pleasure Records. Dist: EMI

Cassette: released on Fame (EMI), Sep'82 by Music For Pleasure Records. Dist: EMI

QUEEN LL.
Compact disc: released on EMI, Nov'86 by EMI Records(UK). Dist: EMI

Album: released on Fame (EMI), Apr'84 by Music For Pleasure Records. Dist: EMI

Cassette: released on Fame (EMI), Apr'84 by Music For Pleasure Records. Dist: EMI

RADIO GA GA.
Single 7": released on EMI, Jan'84 by EMI Records(UK). Dist: EMI

Single 12": released on EMI, Jan'84 by EMI Records(UK). Dist: EMI

SHEER HEART ATTACK.
Compact disc: released on EMI, Nov'86 by EMI Records(UK). Dist: EMI

Album: released on EMI, '85 by EMI Records(UK). Dist: EMI

Cassette: released on EMI, '85 by EMI Records(UK). Dist: EMI

Compact disc: released on EMI, '85 by EMI Records(UK). Dist: EMI

SOMEBODY TO LOVE.
Single 7": released on EMI, '80 by EMI Records(UK). Dist: EMI

SOUL BROTHER.
Single 12": released on EMI(Germany), Jul'84 by EMI Records(UK). Dist: Pinnacle

THANK GOD IT'S CHRISTMAS.
Single 7": released on EMI, Nov'84 by EMI Records(UK). Dist: EMI

Single 12": released on EMI, Nov'84 by EMI Records(UK). Dist: EMI

UNDER PRESSURE / SOUL BROTHER (see also David Bowie) (Queen & David Bowie).
Single 7": released on EMI, Nov'81 by EMI Records(UK). Dist: EMI

VIDEO SINGLE.
Video-cassette (VHS): released on Gold Rushes, '87 by Video Collection International Ltd..

WE ARE THE CHAMPIONS / WE WILL ROCK YOU.
Single 7": released on EMI, Oct'77 by EMI Records(UK). Dist: EMI

WE WILL ROCK YOU.
Recording Notes: Queen filmed live on stage in 1982, running through a repertoire of classics like "Bohemain Rhapsody", "Killer Queen" and 'Another One Bites The Dust"
Video-cassette (VHS): released on Peppermint Music, Sep'84 Dist: Peppermint Music **Media Note:** Number of tracks: 20. Type of recording: Live. Total playing time: 90 minutes.

WE WILL ROCK YOU (VIDEO).
Video-cassette (VHS): released on Video Collection, May'87 by Video Collection International Ltd.. Dist: Counterpoint **Media Note:** 90 minutes

WHO WANTS TO LIVE FOREVER.
Recording Notes: Video single coupling Queen's new single promo with that for previous release "A Kind of Magic", both using footage from Highlander in which they feature.
Video-cassette (VHS): released on PMI, Oct'86 by PMI Records. Dist: EMIa* **Media Note:** Numberof tracks: 2.

Single 7": released on EMI, Sep'86 by EMI Records(UK). Dist: EMI

Single 12": released on EMI, Sep'86 by EMI Records(UK). Dist: EMI

WORKS EP, THE.
Recording Notes: PMI are pleased to announce the release of Queen's first ever video EP, The Works. The video features tracks which appear on the group's platinum selling album "The Works"."Radio Ga Ga" and "I Want to Break Free" have maintained Queen's reputaion for making sensational video clips, a reputation that started with "Bohemain Rhapsody" in 1975. Both tracks are incuded an this new EP. There will be major promotion and publicity for the Video LP upon it's release and a major press advertising campaign will be staged.
Video-cassette (VHS): released on PMI, Nov'84 by PMI Records. Dist: EMIa* **Media Note:** Number of tracks: 3. Type of recording: EP. Total playing time: 22 minutes.

Video-cassette [Betamax]: released on PMI, Nov'84 by PMI Records. Dist: EMIa* **Media Note:** Number of tracks: 3. Type of recording: EP. Total playing time: 22 minutes.

Video-cassette (VHS): released on PMI, Aug'87 by PMI Records. Dist: EMIa*

WORKS, THE.
Compact disc: released on EMI, Apr'84 by EMI Records(UK). Dist: EMI

Album: released on EMI, Mar'84 by EMI Records(UK). Dist: EMI

Cassette: released on EMI, Mar'84 by EMI Records(UK). Dist: EMI

YOU'RE MY BEST FRIEND.
Single 7": released on EMI Golden 45's, Mar'84 by EMI Records(UK). Dist: EMI

Single 7": released on EMI(Import), '80 by EMI Records(UK). Dist: Conifer

Queen Ida

CAUGHT IN THE ACT (Queen Ida and Her Zydeco Band).
Album: released on Sonet, Feb'86 by Sonet Records. Dist: Jazz Music, Swift, Celtic Music, Roots, PRT, Sonet

Queen Sylvia

MIDNIGHT BABY.
Album: released on L&R, Aug'87 Dist: Celtic Music, Swift

Queensland Irish...

QUEENSLAND IRISH... (Queensland Irish and Association Pipe Band).
Recording Notes: Full title of album: "Queensland Irish Association Pipe Band". Australia's first grade one pipe band in great form. Has nice Irish tune selection and, of course "Waltzing Matilda".
Album: released on Lismor, May'86 by Lismor Records. Dist: Projection, Celtic Music, Taylors, Cadillac, Outlet, Roots, Ross

Cassette: released on Lismor, May'86 by Lismor Records. Dist: Projection, Celtic Music, Taylors, Cadillac, Outlet, Roots, Ross

Queensryche

GONNA GET CLOSE TO YOU.
Single 7": released on EMI, Aug'86 by EMI Records(UK). Dist: EMI

Double-pack single: released on EMI, Aug'86 by EMI Records(UK). Dist: EMI

LIVE IN TOKYO.
Video-cassette (VHS): released on PMI, Jun'86 by PMI Records. Dist: EMIa* **Media Note:** Type of rcording: Live

Video-cassette [Betamax]: released on PMI, Jun'86 by PMI Records. Dist: EMIa* **Media Note:** Type of rcording: Live

RAGE FOR ORDER.
Compact disc: released on EMI, Jan'87 by EMI Records(UK). Dist: EMI

Album: released on EMI America, Jul'86 by EMI Records(UK). Dist: EMI

Cassette: released on EMI America, Jul'86 by EMI Records(UK). Dist: EMI

WARNING, THE.
Compact disc: released on EMI, Mar'87 by EMI Records(UK). Dist: EMI

Quest for Life

BABY DON'T STOP ME.
Single 7": released on MDM, Jun'86 Dist: Siren, Virgin, EMI

Single 12": released on MDM, Jun'86 Dist: Siren, Virgin, EMI

Questionaires

LOOK OUT.
Single 7": released on Shark, Jan'87 by Shark Records., Projection, Swift, Celtic Music, Cadillac, Ross, Duncans, Impetus

Queue Dance

NOT THE ONE FOR ME.
Single 12": released on Pylon, May'87

Quick

BED OF NAILS.
Single 7": released on A&M, Mar'86 by A&M Records. Dist: Polygram

Single 12": released on A&M, Mar'86 by A&M Records. Dist: Polygram

I NEEDED YOU.
Single 7": released on A&M, Feb'87 by A&M Records. Dist: Polygram

Single 12": released on A&M, Feb'87 by A&M Records. Dist: Polygram

WAH WAH.
Recording Notes: The debut A&M album from the British duo, Colin Campsie and George McFarlane, Colin and George wre most recently in the charts as producers for Haywoode's hit single "Roses", on which they played virtually all the instruments. They also produced a further four tracks (writing one) on her new LP. Produced by: Phil Thornally.
Album: released on A&M, Oct'86 by A&M Records. Dist: Polygram

Cassette: released on A&M, Oct'86 by A&M Records. Dist: Polygram

Compact disc: released on A&M, Oct'86 by A&M Records. Dist: Polygram

WE CAN LEARN FROM THIS.
Single 7": released on A&M, Jul'86 by A&M Records. Dist: Polygram

Single 12": released on A&M, Jul'86 by A&M Records. Dist: Polygram

Quick neat job, A

QUICK NEAT JOB, A Various artists (Various artists).
Recording Notes: Artists include: Anna Domino/Paul Haig/Cheyne.
Album: released on Les Disques Du Crepuscule(Belgium), Feb'86 by Les Disques Du Crepuscule (Belgium). Dist: Rough Trade, Pinnacle, Island, Polygram

Cassette: released on Les Disques Du Crepuscule(Belgium), Feb'86 by Les Disques Du Crepuscule (Belgium). Dist: Rough Trade, Pinnacle, Island, Polygram

Quicksilver

QUICKSILVER Original soundtrack.
Album: released on Atlantic, Sep'86 by WEA Records. Dist: WEA, Swift, Celtic Music

Cassette: released on Atlantic, Sep'86 by WEA Records. Dist: WEA, Swift, Celtic Music

Quicksilver Messenger...

1ST LP.
Album: released on Demon, Jul'86 by Demon Records. Dist: Celtic Music, Pinnacle, Jazz Music

Compact disc: released on Edsel, '86 by Demon Records. Dist: Celtic Music, Pinnacle, Jazz Music

SHADY GROVE.
Album: released on Edsel, Feb'87 by Demon Records. Dist: Celtic Music, Pinnacle, Jazz Music

ULTIMATE JOURNEY.
Album: released on See For Miles, Feb'86 by See For Miles Records. Dist: Pinnacle

Quiet riot

METAL HEALTH.
Album: released on Epic, Jan'87 by CBS Records. Dist: CBS

Cassette: released on Epic, Jan'87 by CBS Records. Dist: CBS

QR III.
Album: released on Epic, Aug'86 by CBS Records. Dist: CBS

Cassette: released on Epic, Aug'86 by CBS Records. Dist: CBS

QUIET RIOT 3.
Compact disc: released on Epic, Oct'86 by CBS Records. Dist: CBS

WILD AND THE YOUNG.
Single 7": released on Epic, Sep'86 by CBS Records. Dist: CBS

Single 12": released on Epic, Sep'86 by CBS Records. Dist: CBS

WILD, YOUNG AND CRAZEE.
Album: released on Raw Power, May'87 by Castle Communications Records. Dist: Pinnacle

Cassette: released on Raw Power, May'87 by Castle Communications Records. Dist: Pinnacle

Quiet Sun

MAINSTREAM.
Album: released on Editions EG, Jan'87 by Virgin Records. Dist: EMI

Quine, Robert

BASIC (Quine, Robert & Fred Maher).
Album: released on Editions EG, Jan'87 by Virgin Records. Dist: EMI

Quinichette, Paul

KID FROM DENVER, THE.
Album: released on Fresh Sounds, 7 Nov'87 by Charly Records. Dist: Charly

Quinn, Brendan

BRENDAN QUINN COLLECTION.
Album: released on Emerald, Nov'87 by Emerald Records. Dist: PRT, Solomon & Peres, Ross

Cassette: released on Emerald, Nov'87 by Emerald Records. Dist: PRT, Solomon & Peres, Ross

CAN'T HOLD BACK THE YEARS.
Single 7": released on Ritz, Aug'86 by Outlet Records. Dist: Outlet, Spartan, Record Services(Ireland), Roots, Prism, Celtic Music, Solomon & Peres

HUSTLER.
Single 7": released on Ritz, Jan'87 by Outlet Records. Dist: Outlet, Spartan, Record Services(Ireland), Roots, Prism, Celtic Music, Solomon & Peres

IRISH HEARTBEAT.
Single 7": released on Ritz, Jan'86 by Outlet Records. Dist: Outlet, Spartan, Record Services(Ireland), Roots, Prism, Celtic Music, Solomon & Peres

JUST AN ORDINARY MAN.
Album: released on Ritz, Nov'86 by Outlet Records. Dist: Outlet, Spartan, Record Services(Ireland), Roots, Prism, Celtic Music, Solomon & Peres

Cassette: released on Ritz, Nov'86 by Outlet Records. Dist: Outlet, Spartan, Record Services(Ireland), Roots, Prism, Celtic Music, Solomon & Peres

Quinn, Freddy

1956-1965.
Compact disc: released on Bear Family, Jul'87 by Bear Family Records(Germany). Dist: Celtic Music, Swift, Rollercoaster. Estim retail price in Aug'87 was £13.50.

EDITION 1: HEIMWEH... DORT WO DIE BLUMEN BLUH'N.
Album: released on Bear Family, May'87 by Bear Family Records(Germany). Dist: Celtic Music, Swift, Rollercoaster

EDITION 2: HAVE I TOLD YOU LATELY THAT I LOVE YOU.
Album: released on Bear Family, May'87 by Bear Family Records(Germany). Dist: Celtic Music, Swift, Rollercoaster

EDITION 3: DIE GITARRE UND DAS MEER.
Album: released on Bear Family, May'87 by Bear Family Records(Germany). Dist: Celtic Music, Swift, Rollercoaster

EDITION 4: WEIT IST DER WEG.
Album: released on Bear Family, May'87 by Bear Family Records(Germany). Dist: Celtic Music, Swift, Rollercoaster

EDITION 5: SEUL AU MONDE.
Album: released on Bear Family, May'87 by Bear Family Records(Germany). Dist: Celtic Music, Swift, Rollercoaster

Quinn, Paul

ONE DAY (see Clarke, Vince) (Quinn, Paul & Vince Clarke).

Quiver full of arrows

QUIVER FULL OF ARROWS Archer, Jeffrey (Scofield, Paul).
Double cassette: released on Listen Productions, Nov'84, Hayward Promotions

Quo Vadis

QUO VADIS Original soundtrack.
Compact disc: released on London, '86 London Records. Dist: Polygram

Album: released on General Music (France), '86 by General Music Records (France).

R

Rabbit Action
RABBIT ACTION various artists (Various Artists).
Album: released on Sun, Apr'85 by Charly Records. Dist: Charly Distribution

Rabbitt, Eddie
EVERY WHICH WAY BUT LOOSE.
Single (7"): released on Elektra, Jan'79 by WEA Records. Dist: WEA

RABBIT TRAX.
Tracks: / Threw it away / Singing in the subway / Tis moment / World without love / Gotta have you / Repetitive regret / Both to each other / When we make love / Letter from home.
Album: released on RCA, Jun'86 by RCA Records. Dist: RCA, Roots, Swift, Wellard, Chris, I & B, Solomon & Peres Distribution

Cassette: released on RCA, Jun'86 by RCA Records. Dist: RCA, Roots, Swift, Wellard, Chris, I & B, Solomon & Peres Distribution

STEP BY STEP.
Tracks: / Early in the mornin' / Bring back the sunshine / Skip-a-beat / Dim dim the lights / Rivers / Step by step / Someone could lose a heart tonght / I don't know where to start / Nobody loves me like my baby / My only wish.
Compact disc: released on Mercury, '83 by Phonogram Records. Dist: Polygram Distribution

Racer X
STREET LETHAL (Racer X, with Paul Gilbert).
Album: released on Roadrunner (Dutch), Sep'86 Dist: Pinnacle

Rachet, Don
SWEET ROSIE.
Tracks: / Sweet Rosie / Sweet Rosie (version).
Single (12"): released on Startime, Jun'87 by Startime Records. Dist: Jetstar Distribution

Racing cars
THEY SHOOT HORSES DON'T THEY.
Tracks: / They shoot horses don't they / Gonna capture your heart.
Notes: Double 'A' side
Single (7"): released on Old Gold, Apr'87 by Old Gold Records. Dist: Lightning, Jazz Music, Spartan, Counterpoint

Radar Blues
RADAR BLUES (Various Artists).
Album: released on King (USA), Apr'87 Dist: Gusto Distribution

Cassette: released on King (USA), Apr'87 Dist: Gusto Distribution

Radar, Don
WALLFLOWER (Radar, Don Quintet).
Compact disc: released on Discovery (USA), Dec'86 by Discovery Records. Dist: Swift, Flexitron-Audio, Jazz Music

Radford, Phil
TELL ME.
Tracks: / Tell me / Smiling moon.
Single (7"): released on Excaliber, Aug'86 by Red Bus Records. Dist: PRT

Single (12"): released on Excaliber, Aug'86 by Red Bus Records. Dist: PRT

Radiators from Space
BUYING GOLD IN HEAVEN.
Album: released on Hotwire (Ireland), May'86 Dist: Rough Trade, Cartel

RADIATORS FROM SPACE.
Album: released on WEA Ireland, Jul'87 by WEA Records. Dist: Celtic Distributions, Projection, I & B

Cassette: released on WEA Ireland, Jul'87 by WEA Records. Dist: Celtic Distributions, Projection, I & B

Radical Dance
SURVIVE THE DAY.
Tracks: / Survive the day.
Single (7"): released on Bite Back, Sep'86 Dist: Backs, Cartel

Radicals
RUMTREE.
Tracks: / Rumtree / Radics in dub.
Single (12"): released on Blue Trac, Jun'86 by Blue Mountain Records. Dist: Jetstar

Radio Active
RADIO ACTIVE (Various Artists).
Notes: Artists include UK Subs, Fallen Angels, Action Pact.
Boxed set: released on Fall Out, Sep'86 Dist: Swift, Red Rhino, Cartel

Radio active box set
RADIO ACTIVE BOX SET (Various Artists).
Single (7"): released on Fall Out, Dec'86 Dist: Swift, Red Rhino, Cartel

Radio Days
RADIO DAYS Soundtrack selections (Various Artists).
Tracks: / Frenesi / Donkey serenade, The / You & I / Remeber Pearl Harbour / That old feeling / White cliffs of Dover, The / Goodbye / I'm gettin' sentimental over you / American patrol / Take the'A' train / One, two,three kick.
Album: released on RCA, Jun'87 by RCA Records. Dist: RCA, Roots, Swift, Wellard, Chris, I & B, Solomon & Peres Distribution

Cassette: released on RCA, Jun'87 by RCA Records. Dist: RCA, Roots, Swift, Wellard, Chris, I & B, Solomon & Peres Distribution

Compact disc: released on RCA, Jun'87 by RCA Records. Dist: RCA, Roots, Swift, Wellard, Chris, I & B, Solomon & Peres Distribution

Radio Earth
DISTANT LAND (BA-DO-BOMB-BOMB).
Tracks: / Distant land (ba-do-bomb-bomb) / Race.
Single (12"): released on WEA, May'87 by WEA Records. Dist: WEA

Single (7"): released on WEA, May'87 by WEA Records. Dist: WEA

NEVER TO MAKE YOU CRY.
Single (7"): released on WEA, Aug'87 by WEA Records. Dist: WEA

Single (12"): released on WEA, Aug'87 by WEA Records. Dist: WEA

Single (7"): released on Priority, Aug'87 by Priority Records. Dist: RCA

Single (12"): released on Priority, Aug'87 by Priority Records. Dist: RCA

Radio Favourites
RADIO FAVOURITES - COUNTRY VOLUME 1 (Various Artists).
Album: released on Ritz, Jan'86 by Outlet Records. Dist: Outlet, Prism Leisure Distribution, Record Services Distribution (Ireland), Roots Cat. no: RITZ SP 411
Cassette: released on Ritz, Jan'86 by Outlet Records. Dist: Outlet, Prism Leisure Distribution, Record Services Distribution (Ireland), Roots

RADIO FAVOURITES - IRISH FOLK VOLUME 3 (Various Artists).
Album: released on Ritz, Jan'86 by Outlet Records. Dist: Outlet, Prism Leisure Distribution, Record Services Distribution (Ireland), Roots Cat. no: RITZ SP 413
Cassette: released on Ritz, Jan'86 by Outlet Records. Dist: Outlet, Prism Leisure Distribution, Record Services Distribution (Ireland), Roots

Radio Freedom
RADIO FREEDOM (Commentary & Music) (Various Artists).
Notes: Royalties to Radio Freedom
Album: released on Rounder Europa, Jul'86

Radio Heart
LONDON TIMES (Radio Heart / Gary Numan).
Tracks: / London Times / Rumour.
Single (7"): released on GFM, 23 May'87 by GFM Records. Dist: Fast Forward, Cartel, PRT, Projection

Single (12"): released on GFM, 23 May'87 by GFM Records. Dist: Fast Forward, Cartel, PRT, Projection

Picture disc single: released on GFM, Jun'87 by GFM Records. Dist: Fast Forward, Cartel, PRT, Projection

Picture disc single: released on GFM, Jun'87 by GFM Records. Dist: Fast Forward, Cartel, PRT, Projection

RADIO HEART (Radio Heart / Gary Numan).
Tracks: / Radio Heart / Mistasax version2.
Single (7"): released on GFM, Apr'87 by GFM Records. Dist: Fast Forward, Cartel, PRT, Projection
Single (12"): released on GFM, Apr'87 by GFM Records. Dist: Fast Forward, Cartel, PRT, Projection

Raeburn, Boyd
1943 - 1948 (Raeburn, Boyd & His Musicians).
Album: released on First Heard, Jul'77 by Submarine Records. Dist: Conifer, Taylors

BOYD RAEBURN 1945.
Album: released on Aircheck, Apr'79

GEP BOYDS (Raeburn, Boyd & His Orchestra).
Album: released on Golden Era, Jul'82 by Import Records. Dist: Wellard, Chris, Swift

JEWELS.
Double Album:

MEMPHIS IN JUNE.
Album: released on Hep, Apr'81 by H.R. Taylor Records. Dist: Jazz Music, Cadillac Music, JSU, Taylors, Wellard, Chris, Zodiac, Swift, Fast Forward

ON THE AIR VOLUME 1 (Raeburn, Boyd Orchestra).
Album: released on Hep, Apr'81 by H.R. Taylor Records. Dist: Jazz Music, Cadillac Music, JSU, Taylors, Wellard, Chris, Zodiac, Swift, Fast Forward

ON THE AIR VOLUME 2 (Raeburn, Boyd Orchestra).
Album: released on Hep, Apr'81 by H.R. Taylor Records. Dist: Jazz Music, Cadillac Music, JSU, Taylors, Wellard, Chris, Zodiac, Swift, Fast Forward

RHYTHMS BY RAEBURN (Raeburn, Boyd & His Orchestra).
Album: released on Aircheck, Jan'78

Rae, Dashiell
SONG WITHOUT WORDS.
Album: released on Coda, Jan'86 by Coda Records. Dist: Pinnacle, Cartel, WEA, Roots

Cassette: released on Coda, Jan'86 by Coda Records. Dist: Pinnacle, Cartel, WEA, Roots

Compact disc: released on Coda Landscape, Feb'86 by Coda Records. Dist: WEA

Rae, Jamie
SHE'S THE ONE.
Single (7"): released on CBS, Jun'84 by CBS Records. Dist: CBS

Rae, Jesse
IT'S JUST THE DOG IN ME.
Single (12"): released on Supreme International Editions, Dec'84 Dist: Rough Trade Distribution, Cartel Distribution

THISTLE, THE.
Tracks: / Inside-out / That kind o' girl / Houdini / Don't give up / Friend-ship / Thistle, The / Be yer sel / Rusha / Over the sea / Scotland the brave/Idio-syn-crazy.
Album: released on WEA, Aug'87 by WEA Records. Dist: WEA

Cassette: released on WEA, Aug'87 by WEA Records. Dist: WEA

Rae, Jessie
THAT KIND O'GIRL.
Single (7"): released on WEA, Jul'87 by WEA Records. Dist: WEA

Single (12"): released on WEA, Jul'87 by WEA Records. Dist: WEA

Raemon
PRIVATE JOY.
Single (7"): released on T-Mac, Oct'85 by T-Mac Records. Dist: PRT Distribution

R.A.F.
CHANGE YOUR MIND.
Single (7"): released on Carrere, Jan'85 by Carrere Records. Dist: PRT, Spartan

Single (12"): released on Carrere, Jan'85 by Carrere Records. Dist: PRT, Spartan

RAF TUNES OF GLORY Various artists (Various Artists).
Cassette: released on AIM (Budget Cassettes), Feb'83

RESTLESS SPIRIT.
Tracks: / Dream boy / Only the heart can tell / Steal your love / Faces in the windshield / Woman like you / Stranger in the mirror / We can only dream / It's only love / Reprise: restless spirit.
Album: released on Aura, Oct'86 by Hollywood Nites Distribution. Dist: Pinnacle

Cassette: released on Aura, Oct'86 by Hollywood Nites Distribution. Dist: Pinnacle

SELF CONTROL PART 1.
Single (7"): released on Carrere, May'84 by Carrere Records. Dist: PRT. Soartan

Single (12"): released on Carrere, May'84 by Carrere Records. Dist: PRT, Spartan

WOMAN LIKE YOU.
Tracks: / Woman like you / It's only love.
Single (7"): released on Aura, Nov'86 by Hollywood Nites Distribution. Dist: Pinnacle

RAF Band of Germany
KEEPERS OF THE PEACE.
Album: released on Bandleader, '84 by Bandleader Records. Dist: PRT

Cassette: released on Bandleader, '84 by Bandleader Records. Dist: PRT

RAF Central Band
BEST OF THE CENTRAL BAND OF THE RAF.
Album: released on One Up, Mar'79 by EMI Records.

BEST OF THE RAF CENTRAL BAND.
Album: released on One Up, Jul'75 by EMI Records.

CAVALRY OF THE CLOUDS AND OTHER MARCHES.
Album: released on H.M.V., Nov'83 by EMI Records. Dist: EMI

Cassette: released on H.M.V., Nov'83 by EMI Records. Dist: EMI

DIAMONDS IN THE SKY.
Album: released on EMI, '78 by EMI Records. Dist: EMI

I COULD HAVE DANCED ALL NIGHT.
Album: released on Dansan, Oct'81 by Spartan Records. Dist: Spartan

MARCHING WITH THE RAF.
Album: released on One Up, Jan'78 by EMI Records.

RAF CENTRAL BAND.
Album: released on EMI, Oct'83 by EMI Records. Dist: EMI

Cassette: released on EMI, Oct'83 by EMI Records. Dist: EMI

Rafferty, Gerry

BAKER STREET.
Single (7"): released on EMI (France), Apr'83 by EMI Records. Dist: Conifer

Single (7"): released on United Artists, Feb'78

BAKER STREET (VIDEO).
Tracks: / Baker Street / Bring it all home.
Notes: Video single.
Video-cassette (VHS): released on Gold Rushes, Mar'87 by Video Collection International Ltd.. Dist: Counterpoint

CAN I HAVE MY MONEY BACK.
Cassette: released on Autograph, Apr'85 Dist: Record Services Distribution (Ireland)

Album: released on Transatlantic, Sep'81 by Logo Records. Dist: Roots Distribution, RCA Distribution

Cassette: released on Transatlantic, Sep'81 by Logo Records. Dist: Roots Distribution, RCA Distribution

CHANGE OF HEART/ GOOD INTENTIONS.
Single (7"): released on United Artists, Nov'82

CITY TO CITY.
Tracks: / Ark, The / Baker street / Right down the line / City to city / Sealin' time / Mattie's rag / Whatever's written in your heart / Home and dry / [illegible] / Island / Waiting for the day.
Notes: This record must stand amongst the Top 10 all time classic albums. The lead track 'Baker Street' made no.3 in 1978 and stayed in the charts for 15 weeks. The album made no.6 in 1978 and stayed in the charts for 37 weeks! Tracks from this album are continually played on the radio, in particular 'Right Down The Line', 'Stealin Time', 'Whatever's In Your Heart' and of course, the classic ' Baker Street'.
Album: released on Fame (United Artists), Mar'85 by Music For Pleasure Records. Dist: EMI

Cassette: released on Fame (United Artists), Mar'85 by Music For Pleasure Records. Dist: EMI

Compact disc: released on Fame (United Artists), Mar'85 by Music For Pleasure Records. Dist: EMI

EARLY COLLECTION.
Tracks: / Look over the hill & far away / Patrick / Rick rack / Her father didn't like me anyway / Please sing a song for us / Blood & glory / Coconut tree / Steam boat row / Shoeshine boy / All the best people do it / Song for Simon / Keep it to yourself / Can I have my money back? / New street blues / Didn't I / Don't count me out / Make you break you / To each & everyone / Mary Skeffington / Half a chance / Where I belong.
Compact disc: released on Transatlantic, Jul'87 by Transatlantic Records. Dist: IMS-Polygram

FIRST CHAPTER, THE.
Album: released on Cambra, Mar'85 by Cambra Records. Dist: IDS, Conifer

Cassette: released on Cambra, Mar'85 by Cambra Records. Dist. IDS, Conifer

NIGHT OWL.
Tracks: / Days gone down / Night owl / Way that you do it, The / Get it right next time / Take the money and run / Why won't you talk to me / Get it right next time / Take the money and run / Family tree / Already gone / Tourist, The / It's gonna be a long night.
Album: released on Fame, Jul'86 by Music For Pleasure Records. Dist: EMI

Cassette: released on Fame, Jul'86 by Music For Pleasure Records. Dist: EMI

Album: released on United Artists, '85

Cassette: released on United Artists, '85

SLEEPWALKING.
Tracks: / Standing at the gates / Good intentions / Change of heart, A / On the way / Sleepwalking / Cat and mouse / Right moment, The / As wise as a serpent.
Compact disc: released on EMI, May'87 by EMI Records. Dist: EMI

Album: released on Liberty, Aug'86 by Liberty-United. Dist: EMI

Cassette: released on Liberty, Aug'86 by Liberty-United. Dist: EMI

Compact disc: released on EMI, '87 by EMI Records. Dist: EMI

Compact disc: released on I.R.S.(Independent Record Syndicate), '87 by I.R.S.. Dist: MCA

Album: released on Fame (United Artists), Sep'84 by Music For Pleasure Records. Dist: EMI

Cassette: released on Fame (United Artists), Sep'84 by Music For Pleasure Records. Dist: EMI

SLEEPWALKING/ WHEN I REST.
Single (7"): released on Liberty, Aug'82 by Liberty-United. Dist: EMI

SNAKES AND LADDERS.
Tracks: / Royal mile / I was a boy scout / Welcome to Hollywood / Wastin' away / Look at the moon / Bring it all home / Garden of England, The / Johnny's song / Didn't I / Syncopatin' Sandy / Cafe le cabotin / Don't close the door.
Compact disc: released on EMI, May'87 by EMI Records. Dist: EMI

Compact disc: released on EMI, '87 by EMI Records. Dist: EMI

SNAKES & LADDERS.
Cassette: released on Liberty, Mar'80 by Liberty-United. Dist: EMI

Raffles

RAFFLES VOL.1 (Elder, Micheal).
Cassette: released on Colophone Audio Visual, Feb'81 by Audio-Visual Library Services. Dist: Audio-Visual Library Services

RAFFLES VOL.2 (Elder, Micheal).
Cassette: released on Colophone, Feb'81 by Audio-Visual Library Services. Dist: Audio-Visual Library Services

TURNED INTO THE EVERLY'S.
Single (7"): released on Paro, Oct'82 by Paro Records. Dist: Spartan

Raful Neal

LOUISIANA LEGEND.
Album: released on Blue Horizon, Oct'87 by Ace Records. Dist: Pinnacle. Estim retail price in Sep'87 was £5.67.

Rage

EXECUTION GUARANTEED.
Album: released on Noise, Jun'87 by Dorane. Dist: Revolver, Cartel

LOOKING FOR YOU.
Tracks: / Looking for you / Come on now / Great balls of fire / Hallelujah I love her so.
Single (12"): released on Diamond, May'86 by Revolver Records. Dist: Cartel

Single (7"): released on ERC, Aug'87 by ERC Records. Dist: PRT

NEVER BEFORE.
Single (7"): released on Carrere, Oct'83 by Carrere Records. Dist: PRT, Spartan

NICE 'N' DIRTY.
Album: released on Carrere, Jun'82 by Carrere Records. Dist: PRT, Spartan

Cassette: released on Carrere, Jun'82 by Carrere Records. Dist: PRT, Spartan

OUT OF CONTROL.
Cassette: released on Carrere, Mar'81 by Carrere Records. Dist: PRT, Spartan

Album: released on Carrere, Mar'81 by Carrere Records. Dist: PRT, Spartan

REIGN OF FEAR.
Album: released on Noise, Jun'86 by Dorane. Dist: Revolver, Cartel

RUN FOR THE NIGHT.
Album: released on Carrere, Oct'83 by Carrere Records. Dist: PRT, Spartan

Cassette: released on Carrere, Oct'83 by Carrere Records. Dist: PRT, Spartan

WOMAN.
Single (7"): released on Carrere America (USA), Jul'82 by Polygram.

Ragged Heroes

RAGGED HERO ANNUAL.
Album: released on Celtic Music, Mar'84 by Celtic Music Distribution. Dist: Celtic Music, Jazz Music, Projection, Roots

Ragged Reggie

FALLING DOWN THE HOLE / BRIDGETOWN.....
Single (7"): released on ESR, Jan'83 by ESR Records. Dist: ESR, Pinnacle

Raggerty

BORROWED TIME.
Album: released on Sweet Folk and Country, Dec'77 Dist: Chris Wellard Distribution

Raging Sun

RAGING SUN Various artists (Various Artists).
Album: released on Rouska, Sep'85 Dist: Red Rhino Distribution, Cartel Distribution

Ragland, Lou

TRAVEL ALONE / DIDN'T I TELL YOU.
Single (7"): released on Inferno Soul Club, Dec'83 by Inferno Records. Dist: Inferno, Cartel, Pinnacle

Rags & Ritches

SESSIONS / YOUR LOVING.
Single (12"): released on Oak Sound, Nov'82

Ragtime Banjo Commision

RAGTIME BANJO COMMISION, THE.
Album: released on GHB, Jul'87 Dist: Jazz Music, Swift

Ragtime Blues Guitar

RAGTIME BLUES GUITAR (1928-30) Various artists (Various Artists).
Album: released on Matchbox (Bluesmaster), Nov'82

Ragtime Cakewalks

I'LL DANCE TILL DE SUN BREAKS THROUGH.
Album: released on Saydisc, Aug'83 by Saydisc Records. Dist: Essex, Harmonia Mundi, Roots, H.R. Taylor, Jazz Music, Swift, Projection, Gamut

Cassette: released on Saydisc, Aug'83 by Saydisc Records. Dist: Essex, Harmonia Mundi, Roots, H.R. Taylor, Jazz Music, Swift, Projection, Gamut

Ragtime Charlie

AN EVENING WITH RAGTIME CHARLIE AND SISTER KATE (Ragtime Charlie & Sister Kate).
Album: released on Broadway, Feb'79 Dist: Jetstar

Ragtime Memories

RAGTIME MEMORIES Various artists (Various Artists).
Album: released on VJM, Mar'83 by Wellard, Chris Distribution. Dist: Wellard, Chris Distribution

Rah Band

ACROSS THE BAY.
Tracks: / Jammin' on the byte / Take some Thyme.
Single (7"): released on RCA, Jan'87 by RCA Records. Dist: RCA, Roots, Swift, Wellard, Chris, I & B, Solomon & Peres Distribution

Single (12"): released on RCA, Jan'87 by RCA Records. Dist: RCA, Roots, Swift, Wellard, Chris, I & B, Solomon & Peres Distribution

ARE YOU SATISFIED (FUNKA NOVA).
Single (7"): released on RCA, Dec'84 by RCA Records. Dist: RCA, Roots, Swift, Wellard, Chris, I & B, Solomon & Peres Distribution

Single (12"): released on RCA, Dec'84 by RCA Records. Dist: RCA, Roots, Swift, Wellard, Chris, I & B, Solomon & Peres Distribution

CLOUDS ACROSS THE MOON.
Single (7"): released on RCA, Mar'85 by RCA Records. Dist: RCA, Roots, Swift, Wellard, Chris, I & B, Solomon & Peres Distribution

Single (12"): released on RCA, Mar'85 by RCA Records. Dist: RCA, Roots, Swift, Wellard, Chris, I & B, Solomon & Peres Distribution

CRUNCH & BEYOND, (THE).
Album: released on Ebony, Jun'78 by Ebony Records. Dist: Pinnacle, Ebony

CRUNCH, (THE).
Single (7"): released on RCA, Nov'85 by RCA Records. Dist: RCA, Roots, Swift, Wellard, Chris, I & B, Solomon & Peres Distribution

Single (12"): released on RCA, Nov'85 by RCA Records. Dist: RCA, Roots, Swift, Wellard, Chris, I & B, Solomon & Peres Distribution

MESSAGES FROM THE STARS.
Single (7"): released on T.M.T., Jul'83 by T.M.T. Records. Dist: Unknown

Single (12"): released on T.M.T., Jul'83 by T.M.T. Records. Dist: Unknown

MYSTERY.
Album: released on RCA, Mar'85 by RCA Records. Dist: RCA, Roots, Swift, Wellard, Chris, I & B, Solomon & Peres Distribution

PAST PRESENT AND FUTURE.
Album: released on RCA, Oct'85 by RCA Records. Dist: RCA, Roots, Swift, Wellard, Chris, I & B, Solomon & Peres Distribution

Cassette: released on RCA, Oct'85 by RCA Records. Dist: RCA, Roots, Swift, Wellard, Chris, I & B, Solomon & Peres Distribution

PERFUMED GARDEN / FUNK ME DOWN.
Single (7"): released on KR, Apr'82 by KR Recordings Ltd. Dist: RCA, Revolver, Cartel

Single (12"): released on KR, Apr'82 by KR Recordings Ltd. Dist: RCA, Revolver. Cartel

QUESTIONS (WHAT YOU GONNA DO).
Single (7"): released on Sound Recordings, Nov'83

Single (12"): released on Sound Recordings, Nov'83

RUN FOR THE SUN.
Tracks: / Run for the sun / Life after love.
Single (7"): released on RCA, Jul'87 by RCA Records. Dist: RCA, Roots, Swift, Wellard, Chris, I & B, Solomon & Peres Distribution

Single (12"): released on RCA, Jul'87 by RCA Records. Dist: RCA, Roots, Swift, Wellard, Chris, I & B, Solomon & Peres Distribution

SAM THE SAMBA MAN.
Single (7"): released on T.M.T., Apr'83 by T.M.T. Records. Dist: Unknown

Single (12"): released on T.M.T., Apr'83 by T.M.T. Records. Dist: Unknown

Single (7"): released on Sound, Jun'84 Dist: CBS

Single (12"): released on Sound, Jun'84 Dist: CBS

SORRY DOESN'T MAKE IT ANYMORE.
Single (7"): released on RCA, Jun'85 by RCA Records. Dist: RCA, Roots, Swift, Wellard, Chris, I & B, Solomon & Peres Distribution

Single (12"): released on RCA, Jun'85 by RCA Records. Dist: RCA, Roots, Swift, Wellard, Chris, I & B, Solomon & Peres Distribution

SWEET FORBIDDEN.
Tracks: / Sweet forbidden / Perfect stranger.
Single (7"): released on RCA, Jun'86 by RCA Records. Dist: RCA, Roots, Swift, Wellard, Chris, I & B, Solomon & Peres Distribution

Single (12"): released on RCA, Jun'86 by RCA Records. Dist: RCA, Roots, Swift, Wellard, Chris, I & B, Solomon & Peres Distribution

TEARS & RAIN.
Single (7"): released on KR, Jul'82 by KR Recordings Ltd. Dist: RCA, Revolver, Cartel

Single (12"): released on KR, Jul'82 by KR Recordings Ltd. Dist: RCA, Revolver, Cartel

UPPER CUTS.
Album: released on Sound Recordings, Apr'84

WHAT'LL BECOME OF THE CHILDREN.
Single (7"): released on RCA, Sep'85 by RCA Records. Dist: RCA, Roots, Swift, Wellard, Chris, I & B, Solomon & Peres Distribution

Single (12"): released on RCA, Sep'85 by RCA Records. Dist: RCA, Roots, Swift, Wellard, Chris, I & B, Solomon & Peres Distribution

Rahim, Emanuel K.

TOTAL SUBMISSION.

Album: released on Muse, Apr'81 Dist: JSU Distribution, Jazz Horizons Distribution, Jazz Music Distribution, Celtic Music Distribution

Raices Incas

FLAUTUS ANDINAS.
Album: released on RCA (Brazil), Aug'83

MUSIC FROM THE ANDES.
Tracks: / Casarjeta / Mariposa / An oranzas / Patajaliphapi / Waca waca / Kacharpari / Peregrino / Buscando / Es un lisura / Peregrinacion / Los carnavales / La diablada / Huayruro / E condo pasa.
Album: released on RCA, Aug'86 by RCA Records. Dist: RCA, Roots, Swift, Wellard, Chris, I & B, Solomon & Peres Distribution

Cassette: released on RCA, Aug'86 by RCA Records. Dist: RCA, Roots, Swift, Wellard, Chris, I & B, Solomon & Peres Distribution

Rald

HIGH NOON.
Single (12"): released on Nervous, Nov'85 by Nervous Records. Dist: Nervous, Rough Trad

Raiders

TWO COLD POTATOES AND A BOTTLE OF WINE.
Tracks: / Two cold potatoes and a bottle of wine.
Single (12"): released on Lost Moment, May'86

Raiders of...

RAIDERS OF THE LOST ARK Original motion picture soundtrack (Various Artists).
Tracks: / Raiders of the lost ark / Flight from Peru / Map room (The) / Dawn / Basket game (The) / Well of souls (The) / Desert chase / Marion's theme / Miracle of the ark (The) / Raiders march (The).
Notes: Digital stereo.
Compact disc: released on Polydor, Aug'84 by Polydor Records. Dist: Polygram, Polydor

Album: released on CBS, Aug'81 by CBS Records. Dist: CBS

Cassette: released on CBS, Aug'81 by CBS Records. Dist: CBS

RAIDERS OF THE LOST DUB Various artists (Various Artists).
Album: released on Island, Jan'82 by Island Records. Dist: Polygram

RAIDERS OF THE POP CHARTS Various artists (Various Artists).
Double Album: released on Ronco, Dec'82

Rail, D

PETROL SUNSET.
Single (12"): released on Survival, Sep'85 by Survival Records. Dist: Backs, Cartel Distribution

Railway

CLIMAX.
Album: released on Roadrunner (Dutch), Jul'87 Dist: Pinnacle

RAILWAY.
Album: released on Roadrunner (Germany), Jan'85 Dist: Rough Trade, Cartel

Railway 11

RAILWAY 11.
Album: released on Road Runner, Feb'86

Railway Children

BRIGHTER.
Single (7"): released on Factory, Feb'87 by Factory Records. Dist: Cartel, Pinnacle

Single (12"): released on Factory, Feb'87 by Factory Records. Dist: Cartel, Pinnacle

GENTLE SOUND.
Tracks: / Gentle sound.
Single (7"): released on Factory, Sep'86 by Factory Records. Dist: Cartel, Pinnacle

REUNION WILDERNESS.
Tracks: / Gentle sound / Content / Another town / Railroad side / Brighter / Listen on / First notebook / Careful / Hands of freedom.
Notes: Mini CD.
Compact disc: released on Factory, Mar'87 by Factory Records. Dist: Cartel, Pinnacle

Railway Stories

RAILWAY STORIES (1) Reverend W. Awdry (Rushton, Willie).
Double cassette: released on Argo (Spoken-word), Jul'82 by Decca Records. Dist: Polygram

RAILWAY STORIES (2) Reverend W. Awdry (Rushton, Willie).
Double cassette: released on Argo (Spoken-word), Nov'83 by Decca Records. Dist: Polygram

RAILWAY STORIES (3) Reverend W. Awdry (Rushton, Willie).
Double cassette: released on Argo (Spoken-word), Nov'83 by Decca Records. Dist: Polygram

Rain

ONCE.
Single (7"): released on Jive Alive, Jun'85 Dist: Jungle

Rainbow

BENT OUT OF SHAPE.
Tracks: / Stranded / Can't let you go / Fool for the night / Fire dance / Anybody there / Desperate heart / Street of dreams / Drinking with the devil / Snowman / Make your move.
Notes: Digital stereo.
Compact disc: released on Polydor, '83 by Polydor Records. Dist: Polygram, Polydor

BEST OF RAINBOW.
Tracks: / All night long / Man on the silver / Can't happen here / Lost in Hollywood / Since you've been gone / Stargazer / Catch the rainbow / Kill the king / Sixteenth century greensleeves / I surrender / Long live rock 'n' roll / Eyes of the world / Starstruck / Light in the black, A / Mistreated.
Compact disc: released on Polydor, '83 by Polydor Records. Dist: Polygram, Polydor

BEST OF RAINBOW, THE.
Double Album: released on Polydor, Oct'81 by Polydor Records. Dist: Polygram, Polydor

Double cassette: released on Polydor, Oct'81 by Polydor Records. Dist: Polygram, Polydor

BLACKMORE'S RAINBOW.
Compact disc: by Polydor Records. Dist: Polygram, Polydor

DIFFICULT TO CURE.
Tracks: / I surrender / Spotlight kid / No release / Magic / Vielleicht das nachster zeit / Can't happen here / Freedom fighter / Midtown tunnel vision / Difficult to cure.
Album: released on Polydor, Aug'84 by Polydor Records. Dist: Polygram, Polydor

Cassette: released on Polydor, Aug'84 by Polydor Records. Dist: Polygram, Polydor

Compact disc: released on Polydor, Aug'84 by Polydor Records. Dist: Polygram, Polydor

Double cassette: released on Polydor, Feb'83 by Polydor Records. Dist: Polygram, Polydor

DOWN TO EARTH.
Tracks: / All night long / Eyes of the world / No time to lose / Makin' love / Since you been gone / Love's no friend / Danger zone / Lost in Hollywood.
Compact disc: released on Polydor, Dec'86 by Polydor Records. Dist: Polygram, Polydor

Double cassette: released on Polydor, Feb'83 by Polydor Records. Dist: Polygram, Polydor

Album: released on Polydor, Apr'84 by Polydor Records. Dist: Polygram, Polydor

Cassette: released on Polydor, Apr'84 by Polydor Records. Dist: Polygram, Polydor

FINAL CUT (THE).
Notes: Compilation of hit tracks and live performances from the heavy rock legends' Japanese tour, and including familiar numbers like 'All Night Long'. 1985 production. Type of recording: Compilation. Total playing time: 60 minutes.
Video-cassette (VHS): released on Polygram, Jun'86 by Polygram Records. Dist: Polygram

Video-cassette [Betamax]: released on Polygram, Jun'86 by Polygram Records. Dist: Polygram

FINYL VINYL.
Tracks: / Spotlight kid / I surrender / Miss mistreated / Jealous lover / Can't happen here / Tearin' out my heart / Since you've been gone / Bad girl / Difficult to cure / Stone cold / Power man on the silver mountain / Long live rock 'n' roll / Weiss heim.
Album: released on Polydor, Feb'86 by Polydor Records. Dist: Polygram, Polydor

Cassette: released on Polydor, Feb'86 by Polydor Records. Dist: Polygram, Polydor

Compact disc: released on Polydor, Feb'86 by Polydor Records. Dist: Polygram, Polydor

LONG LIVE ROCK 'N' ROLL.
Single (7"): released on Oyster, Aug'83 by Oyster Records. Dist: Polygram Distribution Cat. no: **SPELP 34**
Cassette: released on Oyster, Aug'83 by Oyster Records. Dist: Polygram Distribution

ON STAGE.
Tracks: / Over the Rainbow / Kill the king / Man on the silver mountain / Blues / Starstruck / Catch the Rainbow / Mistreated / 16th century Greensleeves / Still I'm sad.
Compact disc: released on Polydor, Nov'86 by Polydor Records. Dist: Polygram, Polydor

RISING.
Tracks: / Tarot woman / Run with the wolf / Starstruck / Do you close your eyes / Stargazer / Light in the black.
Compact disc: released on Polydor, Nov'86 by Polydor Records. Dist: Polygram, Polydor

STRAIGHT BETWEEN THE EYES.
Tracks: / Death alley driver / Stone cold / Bring on the night / Tite squeeze / Tearin' out my heart / Power / Miss mistreated / Rock fever / Eyes on fire.
Compact disc: released on Polydor, '83 by Polydor Records. Dist: Polygram, Polydor

Rainbow Brite

RAINBOW BRITE Various artists (Various Artists).
Album: released on BBC, Aug'85 by BBC Records & Tapes. Dist: EMI, PRT, Pye

Cassette: released on BBC, Aug'85 by BBC Records & Tapes. Dist: EMI, PRT, Pye

Rainbow, Chris

BODY MUSIC.
Video-cassette (VHS): released on PMI, Jun'86 by PMI Records. Dist: EMI

Video-cassette [Betamax]: released on PMI, Jun'86 by PMI Records. Dist: EMI

Rainbow Cottage

I'M ALIVE/ FANTASY/ LET ME IN.
Single (7"): released on Castle, Aug'81 by Castle Records. Dist: Pinnacle

Rainbow People

LIVING IN A DREAM WORLD (Rainbow People & Tammy St. John).
Single (7"): released on Casino Classics, Nov'79 by RK Records. Dist: PRT

Rainbow Remiped...

TAHITI SYNDROME, THE (Rainbow Remiped Dance Band).
Album: released on Banana, Sep'81 Dist: Pinnacle, Fresh

Rainbow Rhymes

RAINBOW RHYMES TV Cast (TV Cast).
Album: released on Red Bus, Oct'84 by Red Bus Records. Dist: PRT

Cassette: released on Red Bus, Oct'84 by Red Bus Records. Dist: PRT

Rainbow Songtime

RAINBOW SONGTIME Various artists (Various Artists).
Album: released on Tempo, Jul'80 by Warwick Records. Dist: Multiple Sound Distributors

Cassette: released on Tempo, Jul'80 by Warwick Records. Dist: Multiple Sound Distributors

Rainbow, Tucker

JAH IS COMING.
Tracks: / Jah is coming / Hard to be.
Single (12"): released on Melody, Jun'86 by Melody Records. Dist: Jetstar Distribution

Rainbow Valley

DO IT FOR THE CHILDREN.
Single (7"): released on Half Moon, Sep'82 by Rondelet Music And Records. Dist: Spartan

Single (12"): released on Half Moon, Sep'82 by Rondelet Music And Records. Dist: Spartan

Raincoats

ANIMAL RHAPSODY/ NO ONE'S LITTLE WOMAN/ HONEY MAD WOMAN.
Single (12"): released on Rough Trade, Nov'83 by Rough Trade Records. Dist: Rough Trade Distribution, Cartel Distribution

FIARYTALE IN THE SUPERMARKET.
Single (7"): released on Rough Trade, Jan'79 by Rough Trade Records. Dist: Rough Trade Distribution, Cartel Distribution

KITCHEN TAPES, THE.
Cassette: released on Reach Out Int, '83

MOVING.
Tracks: / Overheard / Animal rhapsody / Dreaming in the past / Body, the / Honey mad woman / Dance of hopping mad / I saw a hill / Rainstorm.
Album: released on Rough Trade, Feb'84 by Rough Trade Records. Dist: Rough Trade Distribution, Cartel Distribution. Estim retail price in Sep'87 was £4.99.

ODY SHAPE.
Album: released on Rough Trade, Jun'81 by Rough Trade Records. Dist: Rough Trade Distribution, Cartel Distribution

RAINCOATS, THE.
Album: released on Rough Trade, Jan'79 by Rough Trade Records. Dist: Rough Trade Distribution, Cartel Distribution

RUNNING AWAY/ NO ONES LITTLE GIRL.
Single (7"): released on Rough Trade, Jul'82 by Rough Trade Records. Dist: Rough Trade Distribution, Cartel Distribution

Raindrops On...

RAINDROPS ON BANANA LEAVES Various artists (Various Artists).
Album: released on Womad, Jun'84 by Womad Records. Dist: Revolver, Cartel

Rainer & Das Combo

BAREFOOT ROCK WITH....
Album: released on Spindrift, May'86 Dist: Roots

Rainer, J.E.

J.E. RAINER & HIS MOUNTAINEERS.
Album: released on Arhoolie, May'81 by Arhoolie Records. Dist: Projection, Topic, Jazz Music, Swift, Roots

Rainey, Ma

COMPLETE RECORDINGS - VOL.1.
Album: released on VJM, Aug'79 by Wellard, Chris Distribution. Dist: Wellard, Chris Distribution

MA RAINEY'S BLACK BOTTOM.
Album: released on Yazoo(USA), May'86

VOLUME 2 August 1924 - July 1925.
Tracks: / Shave 'em dry blues / Farewell Daddy blues / Booze and blues / Toad frog blues / Jealous hearted blues / See see rider blues / Jelly bean blues / Countin' the blues / Cell bound blues / Army camp harmony blues / Explaining the blues / Louisiana hoo doo blues / Goodbye daddy blues / Rough and tumble blues / Night time blues.
Notes: Mono recording.
Album: released on VJM, Jul'86 by Wellard, Chris Distribution. Dist: Wellard, Chris Distribution

Rain Gods

IN SOME WAKING HOUR.
Album: released on Thin Sliced, Apr'86 by Thin Sliced Records. Dist: Rough Trade Distribution, Cartel Distribution

Rainmakers

DOWN STREAM.
Tracks: / Down stream / Carpenter's son / Drinking on the job.
Single (7"): released on Mercury, May'87 by Phonogram Records. Dist: Polygram Distribution

Single (12"): released on Mercury, May'87 by Phonogram Records. Dist: Polygram Distribution

LET MY PEOPLE GO.
Tracks: / Nobody knew / Kissing time*.
Single (7"): released on Mercury, Jan'87 by Phonogram Records. Dist: Polygram Distribution

Single (12"): released on Mercury, Jan'87 by Phonogram Records. Dist: Polygram Distribution

RAINMAKERS.
Tracks: / Rockin' at the T-Dance / Downstream / Let my people go-go / Doomsville / Big fat blonde / Long gone long / One that got away (The) / Government cheese / Drinkin' on the job / Nobody knows / Information / Drinkin' on the job / Information.
Notes: A fine debut album packed with great songs played with fire and energy. Produced by Terry Manning, whose previous work includes ZZ Top's 'Eliminator' album.
Album: released on Mercury, May'87 by Phonogram Records. Dist: Polygram Distribution

Cassette: released on Mercury, May'87 by Phonogram Records. Dist: Polygram Distribution

Compact disc: released on Mercury, May'87 by Phonogram Records. Dist: Polygram Distribution

Album: released on Mercury, Oct'86 by Phonogram Records. Dist: Polygram Distribution

Cassette: released on Mercury, Oct'86 by Phonogram Records. Dist: Polygram Distribution

Rain Parade

BEYOND THE SUNSET.
Album: released on Island, Jun'85 by Island Records. Dist: Polygram

Cassette: released on Island, Jun'85 by Island Records. Dist: Polygram Deleted '87.

CRASHING DREAM.
Album: released on Island, Nov'85 by Island Records. Dist: Polygram Deleted '87

Cassette: released on Island, Nov'85 by Island Records. Dist: Polygram

EMERGENCY THIRD RAIL POWER TRIP.
Album: released on Enigma (USA), '83 Dist: Funhouse

YOU ARE MY FRIEND.
Single (7"):

Rain & Tears

I HAD A FRIEND.
Tracks: / I had a friend / Music has a way.
Single (7"): released on MCA, Oct'86 by MCA Records. Dist: Polygram, MCA

Single (12"): released on MCA, Oct'86 by MCA Records. Dist: Polygram, MCA

Rainwater, Marvin

ESPECIALLY FOR YOU.
Album: released on Westwood, '82 by Westwood Records. Dist: Jazz Music, H.R. Taylor, JSU, Pinnacle, Ross Records

HENRYETTA....
Single (7"): released on Sonet, Apr'81 by Sonet Records. Dist: PRT

I DIG YOU BABY/ DANCE ME DADDY.
Single (7"): released on MGM, '80 Dist: Polygram Distribution, Swift Distribution

ROCKIN' ROLLIN' RAINWATER.
Album: released on Bear Family, Sep'84 by Bear Family Records. Dist: Rollercoaster Distribution, Swift

WHOLE LOTTA WOMAN.
Single (7"): released on Old Gold, Jul'84 by Old Gold Records. Dist: Lightning, Jazz Music, Spartan, Counterpoint

WITH A HEART WITH A BEAT.
Album: released on Bear Family, Mar'84 by Bear Family Records. Dist: Rollercoaster Distribution, Swift

Rainy Day
PAINTING PICTURES.
Single (7"): released on EMI, Mar'84 by EMI Records. Dist: EMI

RAINY DAY.
Album: released on Rough Trade, Apr'84 by Rough Trade Records. Dist: Rough Trade Distribution, Cartel Distribution

Rainy, Jimmy Trio
JIMMY RAINY TRIO.
Notes: Artists include: Tommy Flanagan/George Mraz.
Album: released on Criss Cross, Jul'86 Dist: Jazz Music, Jazz Horizons. Cadillac

Raising Arizona
RAISING ARIZONA/BLOOD SIMPLE
Original soundtrack (Raising Arizona/Blood Simple).
Album: released on TER, Aug'87 Dist: Pinnacle

Cassette: released on TER, Aug'87 Dist: Pinnacle

Raising Cane
SILENCE.
Single (12"): released on Arcane, Aug'87 Dist: Backs, Cartel

Raitt, Bonnie
GIVE IT UP.
Album: released on Warner Brothers, Jun'76 by Warner Bros Records. Dist: WEA

GLOW, THE.
Album: released on Warner Brothers, Oct'79 by Warner Bros Records. Dist: WEA

ME AND THE BOYS/ KEEP THIS HEART.
Single (7"): released on Warner Bros., Apr'82 by Warner Bros Records. Dist: WEA

NINE LIVES.
Tracks: / No way to treat a lady / Runnin' back to me / Who but a fool / Crime of passion / All day, all night / Stand up to the night / Excited / Frezin' (for a little human love) / True love is hard to find / Angel.
Album: released on Warner Bros., Sep'86 by Warner Bros Records. Dist: WEA

Cassette: released on Warner Bros., Sep'86 by Warner Bros Records. Dist: WEA

STREETLIGHTS.
Album: released on Warner Bros., Nov'74 by Warner Bros Records. Dist: WEA

SWEET FORGIVENESS.
Album: released on Warner Bros., Apr'77 by Warner Bros Records. Dist: WEA

Rajan
TIME.
Single (12"): released on St.James, Jan'85

Raj Quartet
WHOOPS, WHAT A PALAVER.
Notes: Introducing Lord Clifton.
Single (12"): released on EL, Mar'87 by El Records. Dist: Rough Trade, Cartel, Pinnacle

Rakes
RAKES, THE.
Double Album: released on Leader, '81 Dist: Jazz Music, Projection

Rakim & Eric B.
PAID IN FULL.
Notes: Singles are included ('Dope remixes' of 'Eric B. is President' and 'My melody') plus the title track.
Album: released on 4th & Broadway (USA), Aug'87

Ralls, Tony
LIFE.
Notes: Daylight Records, The Daylight Record Co. (Distribution) Ltd, 2, Dorset Place, New Street, Honiton, Devon EX14 8AB.
Album: released on Daylight, '86 by Daylight Records. Dist: Daylight

Cassette: released on Daylight, '86 by Daylight Records. Dist: Daylight

Ralph before '84
RALPH BEFORE '84, VOL 1 Various artists (Various Artists).
Album: released on Korova, Jan'85 Dist: WEA

Ralph, Sheryl Lee
IN THE EVENING.
Single (7"): released on Arista, Jan'85 by Arista Records. Dist: RCA

Single (12"): released on Arista, Jan'85 by Arista Records. Dist: RCA

Ralphs, Mick
TAKE THIS.
Album: released on Razor, Jun'85 by Razor. Dist: Pinnacle

Ramblers
PLAIN AND SIMPLE LIFE.
Single (7"): released on Smile, Sep'81 by Smile Records. Dist: Spartan

SONG FOR MOTHER/ LET THERE BE PEACE FOR CHILDREN.
Single (7"): released on EMI, Oct'83 by EMI Records. Dist: EMI

SPARROW, THE / LOLLIPOPS & SKIPPING ROPE.
Single (7"): released on Decca, Sep'79 by Decca Records. Dist: Polygram

Ramblin Rod
I CAN DO THE MOLLY DANCE.
Single (7"): released on New Leaf, Mar'84 by New Leaf Records. Dist: Backs, Cartel

Ramblin' Thomas
RAMBLIN' THOMAS (1928-32).
Album: released on Matchbox, Nov'83 by Saydisc Records. Dist: Roots, Projection, Jazz Music, JSU, Celtic Music

Rambo
RAMBO Original Soundtrack.
Album: released on TER, Sep'85 Dist: Pinnacle

Cassette: released on TER, Sep'85 Dist: Pinnacle

Ramirez, Ram
RAMPANT RAM.
Album: released on Swaggie (Australia), Jan'83

Ramirez, Ramon Orchestra
PLUS BEAUX TANGOS DU MONDE, (LES).
Compact disc: released on Vogue, '86 Dist: Discovery, Jazz Music, PRT, Swift

Ram Jam
BLACK BETTY.
Single (7"): released on Old Gold, Jul'82 by Old Gold Records. Dist: Lightning, Jazz Music, Spartan, Counterpoint

Single (7"): released on CBS, Jul'84 by CBS Records. Dist: CBS

Ram Jam Band
FREETOWN/ DO WHAT.
Single (7"): released on White Line, Sep'81 by White Line Records. Dist: Pinnacle

Ramming Speed
WHEN YOU WALK IN THE ROOM.
Single (12"): released on Proto, Apr'84 by Proto Records. Dist: WEA

Ramm, Ken
DRAGON.
Album: released on Rag Baby, Mar'82 Dist: Pinnacle, Red Lightnin' Distribution

Ramones
ANIMAL BOY.
Tracks: / Somebody put something in my drink / Animal boy / Love kills / Ape man hop / She belongs to me / Crummy stuff / Bonzo goes to Bitburg / Metal hell / Eat that rat / Freak of nature / Hair of the dog / Something to believe in.
Album: released on Beggars Banquet, Jul'86 by Beggars Banquet Records. Dist: WEA

Cassette: released on Beggars Banquet, Jul'86 by Beggars Banquet Records. Dist: WEA
Cat. no: BEGC70

BONZO GOES TO BITBURG.
Single (7"): released on Beggars Banquet, Jun'85 by Beggars Banquet Records. Dist: WEA

Single (12"): released on Beggars Banquet, Jun'85 by Beggars Banquet Records. Dist: WEA

CHASING THE NIGHT/ HOWLING AT THE MOON.
Double-pack single: released on Beggars Banquet, Mar'85 by Beggars Banquet Records. Dist: WEA

Single (12"): released on Beggars Banquet, Mar'85 by Beggars Banquet Records. Dist: WEA

CRUMMY STUFF.
Tracks: / Crummy stuff / She belongs to me / I don't want to live the life.
Single (7"): released on Beggars Banquet, Jul'86 by Beggars Banquet Records. Dist: WFA

END OF THE CENTURY.
Album: released on Sire, Jan'80

Cassette: released on Sire, Jan'80

HOWLING AT THE MOON (SHA LA LA).
Single (7"): released on Beggars Banquet, Jan'85 by Beggars Banquet Records. Dist: WEA

Single (12"): released on Beggars Banquet, Jan'85 by Beggars Banquet Records. Dist: WEA

IT'S ALIVE.
Album: released on Sire, Jun'79

Cassette: released on Sire, Jun'79

LEAVE HOME.
Album: released on Sire, Sep'78

PLEASANT DREAMS.
Album: released on Sire, Jul'81

Cassette: released on Sire, Jul'81

ROAD TO RUIN.
Album: released on Sire, Sep'78

ROCKET TO RUSSIA.
Album: released on Sire, Sep'78

Cassette: released on Sire, Sep'78

SOMETHING TO BELIEVE IN.
Tracks: / Something to believe in / Somebody put something in my drink / Can't say anything nice.
Single (7"): released on Beggars Banquet, May'86 by Beggars Banquet Records. Dist: WEA

Single (12"): released on Beggars Banquet, May'86 by Beggars Banquet Records. Dist: WEA

TIME HAS COME TODAY.
Single (7"): released on Sire, Jun'83

Single (12"): released on Sire, Jun'83

TO TOUGH TO DIE.
Album: released on Beggars Banquet, Jan'85 by Beggars Banquet Records. Dist: WEA

Cassette: released on Beggars Banquet, Jan'85 by Beggars Banquet Records. Dist: WEA

Rampal, Jean Pierre
SCOTT JOPLIN.
Album: released on CBS, May'83 by CBS Records. Dist: CBS

Cassette: released on CBS, May'83 by CBS Records. Dist: CBS

Ram Ram Kino
TANTRIC ADVANTAGE 1.5.
Single (12"): released on Temple, Dec'85 by Temple Records. Dist: Roots Distribution, Folksound Distribution, Celtic Music Distribution, Projection Distribution

Ramrods
GHOST RIDERS IN THE SKY.
Single (7"): released on USA Import, '80

Ramsby, Walter
MORNING SONG.
Album: released on Sonet, Aug'78 by Sonet Records. Dist: PRT

Ram & Tan
MARKET PLACE.
Single (12"): released on Hyphen, Aug'84 by Hyphen Records. Dist: Jetstar

Ranch
PUT YOUR LOVE IN ME.
Single (7"): released on Sedition, Mar'85 Dist: PRT

Single (12"): released on Sedition, Mar'85 Dist: PRT

Ranch, Martini
HOW CAN THE LABOURING MAN FIND TIME FOR SELF-CULTURE.
Tracks: / How can the labouring man find time for self-culture / Back at the ranch / Fallen, idols.
Single (7"): released on Warner Bros., Jul'86 by Warner Bros Records. Dist: WEA

Single (12"): released on Warner Bros., Jul'86 by Warner Bros Records. Dist: WEA

Randall, Alan
HOOKED ON FORMBY.
Tracks: / Mystic Vibes.
Single (7"): released on Superb, Dec'86

WORLD OF ALAN RANDALL, THE.
Album: released on Decca, Mar'77 by Decca Records. Dist: Polygram

Randall, Freddy
FREDDY RANDALL.
Album: released on Dormouse, May'86 by Dormouse Records. Dist: Swift

FREDDY RANDALL & HIS BAND (Randall, Freddy & His Band).
Album: released on Dormouse, Jun'86 by Dormouse Records. Dist: Swift

SOMETHING BORROWED, SOMETHING BLUE.
Album: released on Alamo, Apr'78 Dist: Jazz Music

Randell, Helen
COUNTRY CLASS.
Album: released on Country House, Sep'79 by BGS Productions Ltd. Dist: Taylor, H.R., Record Merchandisers Distribution, Pinnacle, Sounds of Scotland Records

Cassette: released on Country House, Sep'79 by BGS Productions Ltd. Dist: Taylor, H.R., Record Merchandisers Distribution, Pinnacle, Sounds of Scotland Records

SOMEBODY STOLE MY HAPPY SONGS.
Album: released on Country House, Sep'79 by BGS Productions Ltd. Dist: Taylor, H.R., Record Merchandisers Distribution, Pinnacle, Sounds of Scotland Records

SWEETEST THING, (THE).
Single (7"): released on August (USA), Oct'85 Dist: Taylors

Randell, Lynne
STRANGER IN MY ARMS.
Single (7"): released on Neil Rushden (Import), Mar'83

Randells
MARTIAN HOP.
Single (7"): released on USA Import, '80

SING COUNTRY.
Cassette: released on Kingfisher, Nov'81 Dist: PRT

Randi, Don
NEW BABY (Randi, Don & The Quest Jazz Sextet).
Album: released on Sheffield Lab, Oct'82

Randle, Alan
EEH BAH GUM GIVE IT SOME CLOG.
Single (12"): released on Legacy, Jul'85 Dist: PRT

Randolph, Barbara
I GOT A FEELING.
Single (7"): released on Motown, Oct'81 by Motown Records. Dist: BMG Distribution

Random, Eric
DOW CHEMICAL COMPANY.
Single (7"): released on New Hormones, Jul'81 by New Hormones Records.

FLOOD.
Single (12"): released on Double Vision, Oct'84 by Double Vision Records. Dist: Rough Trade, Cartel

ISHMAEL (Random, Eric & The Bedlamites).
Tracks: / Demolition man / Done it again.
Album: released on Fon, Dec'86 by Fon Records. Dist: Rough Trade, Red Rhino, Cartel

MAD AS MANKIND (Random, Eric & The Bedlamites).
Single (12"): released on Double Vision Nov'84 by Double Vision Records. Dist: Rough Trade, Cartel

THAT'S WHAT I LIKE ABOUT ME.
Single (12"): released on New Hormones Jul'81 by New Hormones Records.

TIME SPLICE (Random, Eric & The Bedlamites).
Album: released on Double Vision, Feb'85 by Double Vision Records. Dist: Rough Trade, Cartel

Raney, Sue

FLIGHT OF FANCY.
Compact disc: released on Discovery (USA), Dec'86 by Discovery Records (USA). Dist: Swift, Flexitron-Audio, Jazz Music

RIDIN' HIGH (Raney, Sue with The Bob Florence Group).
Tracks: / How's that for openers / This happy madness / Stardust / Baseballs / I let a song go out of my heart / Pure imagination / Tea for two / Ridin' high / Body and soul / No more blues.
Notes: Sue Raney-vocals/Bob Florence-keyboards/Bob Magnusson-bass/Nick Ceroli-drums/Carmen Fanzone-flugelhorn
Compact disc: released on Discovery (USA), Sep'86 by Discovery Records (USA). Dist: Swift, Flexitron-Audio, Jazz Music

Raney, Wayne

MORE HOT BOOGIE.
Tracks: / Why don't you haul off and love me (one more time) / Gone with the eind this morning / I ain't nothing but a tom cat, kitten / Powerful love / Falling / I want a home in Dixie / I've done sold my soul / Lonesome wind blues / Roosters are crowing (The) / Pardon my whiskers / I'd feel like a millionaire / Gonna row my boat / I'm really needin' you / When they let the hammer down / Old fashioned matrimony in mind / No one's crying but me.
Album: released on Charly, Jan'87 by Charly Records. Dist: Charly, Cadillac

REAL HOT BOOGIE.
Tracks: / Jack and Jill Boogie / Lost John Boogie / Real hot boogie / Catfish baby / Bootleg boogie / I was there / You better treat your man right / Adam / I had my fingers crossed / If you've got the money I've got the time / Heads or tails I win / Blues at my door / I'm on my way / Undertaking daddy / Real good feeling / Beating around the bush.
Notes: All tracks side one W. Raney. Ridgetop Music except "If You Got The Money I've Got The Time" Southern Music. Licenced from Dave Travis. This compilation: (P) Charly Records Ltd. (C) 1986 Charly Records Ltd.
Album: released on Charly, Apr'86 by Charly Records. Dist: Charly, Cadillac

Rank and File

SUNDOWN.
Cassette: released on Slash, Jan'87 by London Records. Dist: Polygram

Album: released on Slash, Jan'87 by London Records. Dist: Polygram

Cassette: released on Slash, Jan'87 by London Records. Dist: Polygram

Rankine, Alan

LAST BULLET.
Single (7"): released on Les Disques Du Crepuscule, Dec'86 Dist: Rough Trade, Pinnacle, Island, Polygram

SANDMAN.
Tracks: / Sandman.
Single (7"): released on Himalaya, Sep'86 by Himalaya Records. Dist: Rough Trade, Cartel

Single (12"): released on Himalaya, Sep'86 by Himalaya Records. Dist: Rough Trade, Cartel

SHE LOVES ME NOT.
Album: released on Virgin, Oct'87 by Virgin Records. Dist: EMI, Virgin Distribution

Album: released on Virgin, Oct'87 by Virgin Records. Dist: EMI, Virgin Distribution

WORLD BEGINS TO LOOK HER AGE.
Album: released on Les Disques Du Crepuscule, Nov'86 Dist: Rough Trade, Pinnacle, Island, Polygram

Single (7"): released on Virgin, Aug'87 by Virgin Records. Dist: EMI, Virgin Distribution

Single (12"): released on Virgin, Aug'87 by Virgin Records Dist: EMI, Virgin Distribution

Ranking, Ann

SLICE OF ENGLISH TOAST, A.
Album: released on Ariwa, May'86 by Ariwa Records. Dist: Revolver, Cartel, Jetstar, Rough Trade

Ranking, Luxley

REGGAE FEVER.
Tracks: / Reggae Fever / Warm and easy.
Single (12"): released on King Jam, Jul'86 by King Jam Records. Dist: Jetstar

Ranking Peter

JAH STANDING OVER ME / ISLAND IN THE.....
Single (12"): released on Silver Camel, Sep'82 Dist: Jetstar, Rough Trade

Ranking Predigas

MURDERER.
Single (12"): released on Tads, Sep'83 by Tads Records. Dist: Jetstar Distribution

Ranking, Ricky

DIGITAL ROCK.
Tracks: / Digital rock / Digital rock (dub version).
Single (12"): released on Conqueror, Apr'86 Dist: Jetstar

Ranking Superstar

HOT ME HOT.
Single (12"): released on Roots Rockers, Mar'82

Ranking Tiny

DANCE STYLE.
Single (12"): released on TCD Music, Dec'81

OLD TIME RELIGION.
Single (12"): released on TCD Music, Jan'82

Ranking, Tippa

FEEL IT FOR THEM (Ranking, Tippa (original)).
Tracks: / Feel it for them / One time selector.
Single (12"): released on Virgo Stomach, Sep'86 by Virgo Stomach Records. Dist: Jetstar

Ranking Toyan

PANTS AND BLOUSES.
Single (12"): released on Grim Bim, Jul'82 by Grim Bim Records. Dist: Jetstar

TROD ALONG.
Single (12"): released on Black Roots, Feb'82 by Black Roots Records. Dist: Jetstar

Ranking Tranny

VAN MAN.
Single (7"): released on Top Rank, Oct'83

Ranking Trevor

IRON LADY Maggie May.
Single (12"): released on Trojan, Jun'83 by Trojan Records. Dist: PRT, Jetstar

Ranks, Andrew

MASSIVE SKANK.
Single (12"): released on Wackies, Dec'83 by Wackies Records. Dist: Jetstar

Ranks, Goldie

KILL UP A SOUND.
Single (12"): released on Roots Connection, Nov'85 Dist: Jetstar

Ranks, Junie

CRY SEE ME BOOPS.
Tracks: / Cry see me boops / Cry see me boops (Version).
Single (12"): released on Technique, Aug'86 by Technique. Dist: CBS

Ranks, Oliver

85 SHACK.
Single (12"): released on High Power, Jul'85 by High Power Records. Dist: Jetstar

Raped

PHILES AND SMILES.
Album: released on Iguana, Sep'84 by Iguana Records. Dist: ILA, Grapevine

PRETTY PAEDOPHILES (EP).
Single (7"): released on Parole, Sep'82 by Parole Records. Dist: Cartel, Rough Trade, Faulty Products

Rap Graffiti

RAP GRAFFITI (Various Artists).
Album: released on Charly, Jul'85 by Charly Records. Dist: Charly, Cadillac

Cassette: released on Charly, Jul'85 by Charly Records. Dist: Charly, Cadillac

Rapheal, Jean

LE TEMPS DU TANGO (Acc/Song).
Tracks: / Temps du tango, Le / Adios pampa mia / Non je ne veux pas revior tes yeux / Chemin de ta maison / J'ai pleure sur tes pas / Tango de marilou / Plus beau tango du monde, Le / Paloma, La / Partir un jour / Serenade a violetta etc..
Notes: Mail order distribution address: Accordian Music Club, 146 Birmingham Road, Kidderminster, Worcs. DY10 2SL. Tel: 0562-746105. Retail price given by ARC excluding P & P (via mail order) is 5.95
Album: released on Accordion Record Club, Jul'86 by Accordion Record Club Records. Dist: Accordion Record Club

Rapid Dance

FRAGMENTS OF YOUTH.
Single (7"): released on Resolute, Jul'82 by Resolute Records. Dist: Cartel

Rapids

RAID, THE.
Tracks: / Raid, The / Silver bullet / High noon / Eighties girl.
Single (12"): released on Nervous, Dec'85 by Nervous Records. Dist: Nervous, Rough Trade

TURNING POINT.
Album: released on Nervous, Dec'85 by Nervous Records. Dist: Nervous, Rough Trade

Rapiers

1961.
Album: released on Off-Beat, Jun'87 by Off-Beat Records. Dist: Jetstar Distribution

CLOSING THEME, THE.
Tracks: / Closing, The / Still I cry.
Single (7"): released on Off-Beat, Feb'86 by Off-Beat Records. Dist: Jetstar Distribution

RAPIERS 1961, THE.
Album: released on Big Beat, Jun'87 by Ace Records. Dist: Projection, Pinnacle

STRAIGHT TO THE POINT.
Album: released on Off-Beat, Aug'85 by Off-Beat Records. Dist: Jetstar Distribution

Rap It up

RAP IT UP Various artists (Various Artists).
Tracks: / Message, The / Planet rock / Magic's wand / Mr. D.J. / Rapper's delight / (Nothing serious) Just buggin' / White lines (don't don't do it) / Fat boys are back, The / Rock box / Breaks, The.
Album: released on K-Tel, Jun'86 by K-Tel Records. Dist: Record Merchandisers Distribution, Taylors, Terry Blood Distribution, Wynd-Up Distribution, Relay Distribution, Pickwick Distribution, Solomon & Peres Distribution, Polygram

Cassette: released on K-Tel, Jun'86 by K-Tel Records. Dist: Record Merchandisers Distribution, Taylors, Terry Blood Distribution, Wynd-Up Distribution, Relay Distribution, Pickwick Distribution, Solomon & Peres Distribution, Polygram

Rapologists

KIDS RAP.

Single (7"): released on Billy Boy, Jun'84 by Bluebird Records. Dist: PRT

Single (12"): released on Billy Boy, Jun'84 by Bluebird Records. Dist: PRT

Rapone, Al

LET'S HAVE A ZYDECO PARTY (Rapone, Al & The Zydeco Express).
Album: released on JSP, Jul'85 by JSP Records. Dist: Swift, Projection

Rapped Uptight

RAPPED UPTIGHT (Various Artists).
Album: released on Sugarhill, Dec'82 by PRT Records. Dist: PRT Distribution

Cassette: released on Sugarhill, Dec'82 by PRT Records. Dist: PRT Distribution

RAPPED UPTIGHT VOL.2 (Various Artists).
Album: released on Sugarhill (USA), Feb'84 by PRT Records. Dist: PRT Distribution

Cassette: released on Sugarhill (USA), Feb'84 by PRT Records. Dist: PRT Distribution

Rappin'

RAPPIN' (Various Artists).
Album: released on Atlantic, Oct'85 by WEA Records. Dist: WEA

Cassette: released on Atlantic, Oct'85 by WEA Records. Dist: WEA

Rappin' Reverend

I AIN'T INTO THAT.
Tracks: / I ain't into that / Original rap.
Single (7"): released on Cool Tempo, 30 May'87 by Chrysalis Records. Dist: CBS

Single (12"): released on Cool Tempo, 30 May'87 by Chrysalis Records. Dist: CBS

Rap: The next generation

RAP: THE NEXT GENERATION Various artists (Various Artists).
Notes: The follow-up to DEG BEATS 1 featuring Derek, C.J. Mackintosh, Thrash Pack, Asher D.
Album: released on Music Of Life, Sep'87 Dist: Streetwave. Estim retail price in Sep'87 was £5.99.

Rap Tracks

RAP TRACKS (Various Artists).
Album: released on Virgin, Mar'82 by Virgin Records. Dist: EMI, Virgin Distribution

Rare...

RARE Various artists (Various Artists).
Album: released on RCA, Aug'87 by RCA Records. Dist: RCA, Roots, Swift, Wellard, Chris, I & B, Solomon & Peres Distribution

Cassette: released on RCA, Aug'87 by RCA Records. Dist: RCA, Roots, Swift, Wellard, Chris, I & B, Solomon & Peres Distribution

RARE BLUES Aarious artists (Various Artists).
Album: released on Takoma, Mar'81 by PRT Records. Dist: PRT Distribution

RARE GROOVES Various artists (Various Artists).
Album: released on Jam Today, May'87 Dist: PRT, Jetstar

Cassette: released on Jam Today, May'87 Dist: PRT, Jetstar

RARE HOT MUSIC IN BRITAIN 1927-31 various artists (Various Artists).
Cassette: released on Neovox, Jan'82 by Neovox Records. Dist: VJM Records, Jazz Music, JSU, Chris Wellard

RARE SOUL UNCOVERED Carious artists (Various Artists).
Album: released on Charly(R&B), May'84 by Charly Records. Dist: Charly, Cadillac

Cassette: released on Charly(R&B), May'84 by Charly Records. Dist: Charly, Cadillac

RARE SOUL UNCOVERED VOL.2 Various artists (Various Artists).
Tracks: / Lonely for you baby / I'm your love man / Don't ever leave me / Nothing worse than being alone / Unwanted love / Gonna take a journey / What can a man do / Night the angels cried, The / Touch me, hold me, kiss me / I'd think it over / Being without you / You're gonna need me / I keep tryin' / I'm a teardrop / Running for my life / 'Til I get it right / Sweet and easy / Make up your mind.
Album: released on Charly, '86 by Charly Records. Dist: Charly, Cadillac

Cassette: released on Charly, '86 by Charly Records. Dist: Charly, Cadillac

RARE STUFF, (THE) various original artists (Various original artists).
Album: released on Harvest, Apr'79 by EMI Records. Dist: Roots, EMI

Rarebell, Herman

HERMAN ZE GERMAN.
Album: released on FM, Mar'87 by FM-Revolver Records. Dist: EMI

Cassette: released on FM, Mar'87 by FM-Revolver Records. Dist: EMI

Rare Bird

SYMPATHY.
Album: released on Charisma, Sep'83 by Virgin Records. Dist: EMI

Cassette: released on Charisma, Sep'83 by Virgin Records. Dist: EMI

SYMPATHY (7").
Single (7"): released on Old Gold, Jul'82 by Old Gold Records. Dist: Lightning, Jazz Music, Spartan, Counterpoint

Rare Earth

GET READY.
Album: released on Motown, Oct'81 by RCA Records. Dist: RCA Distribution

Rare Moods

DANCIN' THRO THE NIGHT.
Tracks: / Dancin' thro the night / Dancin' thro the night (dub).
Single (7"): released on Creole, Mar'86 by Creole Records. Dist: Rhino, PRT

Single (12"): released on Creole, Mar'86 by Creole Records. Dist: Rhino, PRT

I'VE GOT LOVE.
Tracks: / I've got love.
Single (7"): released on AGR, Sep'86 by AGR Records. Dist: PRT

Single (12"): released on AGR, Sep'86 by AGR Records. Dist: PRT

I'VE GOT LOVE.
Tracks: / I've got love / Closer to your love.
Single (7"): released on AGR, Jul'86 by AGR Records. Dist: PRT

Single (12"): released on AGR, Jul'86 by AGR Records. Dist: PRT

Rare Rockabilly

RARE ROCKABILLY VOL.2 Various artists (Various Artists).
Tracks: / Mama don't you think I know ? / Ten little women / Cool it baby / Shake baby shake / Here comes the night / All by myself / See you later Alligator / Behave, be quiet, or be gone / Flip flop and fly / Rock it on down to my house / Tennessee rock'n'roll / Crazy crazy lovin' / Corrine Corrina / Wee Willy Brown / Crazy chicken / Is that all to the ball, Mr Hall? / She wanna rock / Don't go baby / Hypnotised.
Cassette: released on MCA, Nov'86 by MCA Records. Dist: Polygram, MCA

Album: released on MCA, '83 by MCA Records. Dist: Polygram, MCA

RARE ROCKABILLY VOL.3 Various artists (Various Artists).
Tracks: / Lorraine / It would be a dog-gone lie / Everybody's tryin' to be my baby / Moon's rock / Teenage love is a misery / Don't stop me now / Move on / You gotta move / Juke joint Johnny / Way out there / Cheat on me baby / I wanna bop / Schoolhouse rock / Knock knock rattle / Crazy little guitar man / Pan American boogie / Sputnick / Baby's gone / Hey Ruby / Let's go downtown.
Cassette: released on MCA, Nov'86 by MCA Records. Dist: Polygram, MCA

Album: released on MCA, '83 by MCA Records. Dist: Polygram, MCA

RARE ROCKABILLY VOL.4 Various artists (Various Artists).
Tracks: / Tennessee Toddy / Baby don't leave me / Uncle John's bongos / Jenny Lee / One and only / Rockabilly boogie / Come back to me / Touch of loving / Crazy Bullfrog / You've got me where I wanna be / Rock around the world / Rock-a-boogie Lou / Got a lot of rhythm in my soul / Be my bride / Show me how / You played on my piano / California blues (blue yodel no.4) / Falling in love / It hurts the one who loves you / All nite boogie.
Cassette: released on MCA, Nov'86 by MCA Records. Dist: Polygram, MCA

Album: released on MCA, '83 by MCA Records. Dist: Polygram, MCA

RARE ROCKABILLY VOL.1 various artists (Various Artists).
Tracks: / Cast iron arm / Be bop baby / Sweet love on my mind / Hot rock / Rock'n'roll Ruby / Wild wild women / Tryin' to get to you / Alligator come across / Crazy baby / Barking up the wrong tree / Make like a rock and roll / Morse code / Bird dog / Ruby pearl / Teenage boogie / Whole lotta shakin' / Diggin' the boogie / Offbeat boogie / Shakin' the blues.
Album: released on MCA, '83 by MCA Records. Dist: Polygram, MCA

Cassette: released on MCA, '83 by MCA Records. Dist: Polygram, MCA

Rare Rocking Girls

MORE RARE ROCKIN' GIRLS (Various Artists).
Album: released on White, Feb'87

RARE ROCKING GIRLS (Various Artists).
Album: released on White, Jul'87

Rare silk

NEW WEAVE.
Tracks: / New York afternoon / Red clay / You know it's wrong / Lush life / Joy! (I can recall) Spain / Sugar / Happying / DC farewell.
Compact disc: released on Polydor (Germany), Nov'86 Dist: IMS-Polygram

Rarest Rockabilly &...

RAREST ROCKABILLY & HILLBILLY BOOGIE various artists (Various Artists).
Album: released on Ace, Feb'82 by Ace Records. Dist: Pinnacle, Swift, Hotshot, Cadillac

Rarin' Rockabillies

RARIN' ROCKABILLIES various artists (Various Artists).
Album: released on Rarin', Apr'79 Dist: Swift

Ras Allah

SHOWCASE.
Album: released on Vista Sounds, Sep'84 by Vista Sounds Records. Dist: Jetstar

Ras christmas album

RAS CHRISTMAS ALBUM Various artists (Various Artists).
Tracks: / Night before christmas / We wish you a merry christmas / Jingle bells / Joy to the world / O come all ye faithful / Feliz Navidad / Little drummer boy / 12 days of Christmas, The / Silent night.
Album: released on Ras, Nov'86 by Real Authentic Sound. Dist: Greensleeves Records, RCA, Jetstar

Rasheda

PSALM 61.
Tracks: / Psalm 61 / Psalm 61 (version).
Single (12"): released on Shaka, Jul'87 by Shaka Records. Dist: Jetstar

Ras Iley

SPRING GARDEN ON FIRE.
Album: released on Rohit, Feb'87

Rasmussen, Peter

DANISH JAZZ VOL.5 1943 -44.
Album: released on Storyville, Jul'82 by Storyville Records. Dist: Jazz Music Distribution, Swift Distribution, Chris Wellard Distribution, Counterpoint Distribution

Raspberries

OVERNIGHT SENSATION Very best of The Raspberries.
Tracks: / Overnight sensation / Go all the way / Let's pretend / Driving around / On the beach / Ecstasy / I reach for the light / All through the night / I wanna be with you / Cruisin' music / Tonight / I don't know what I want / Rose coloured glasses / Waiting / Starting over.
Album: released on Zap, Jul'87 Dist: Revolver, Cartel

Rasses

EXPERIENCE.
Album: released on United Artists, Sep'79

NATURAL WILD.
Album: released on Ballistic, Jul'80 by Ballistic Records. Dist: EMI, Mojo Distribution

Rasses Band

HARDER NA RASS.
Album: by Liberty-United. Dist: EMI

Rasta Have Ambition

RASTA HAVE AMBITION various artists (Various Artists).
Album: released on Third World, Jan'79 Dist: Jetstar Distribution

Ratcliff, John

KERRY GIRL.
Single (7"): released on OGP, Jan'84 Dist: Pinnacle

Single (12"): released on OGP, Jan'84 Dist: Pinnacle

Cassette single: released on OGP, Jan'84 Dist: Pinnacle

Rathbone, Jools

PULU PSHU (see Monkman, Francis) (Rathbone, Jools & Francis Monkman).

Rational Emotive Therapy

RATIONAL EMOTIVE THERAPY by Albert Ellis (Ellis, Albert).
Cassette: released on Psychology Today (USA), Oct'81

Rational & Intuitive

RATIONAL & THE INTUITIVE BRAIN (Ornstein, Rbt./D.Galin).
Cassette: released on Seminar Cassettes, Oct'81 by Seminar Cassettes. Dist: Davidson Distribution, Eastern Educational Products Distrib., Forlaget Systime Distribution, Laser Books Ltd Distribution, MacDougall Distribution, Talktapes Distribution, Watkins Books Ltd Distribution, Norton, Jeff Distribution

Ratlers

I DON'T WANT YOU.
Single (7"): released on Lost Moment, Jul'84

SCARE ME TO DEATH.
Album: released on Lost Moment, Oct'84

Rat Patrol

LAST OFFENSIVE.
Single (7"): released on Si Jenn, Dec'83 by Si Jenn Records. Dist: Si Jenn Distribution

Rat Race

RAT RACE Dick Francis (Ogilvy, Ian).
Cassette: released on Chivers Audio Books, Apr'81 by Chivers Sound & Vision. Dist: Chivers Sound & Vision

Rat, Roland

LIVING LEGEND.
Tracks: / Living legend / Living legend (TV theme).
Single (7"): released on Rodent, Sep'86 by Magnet. Dist: RCA Distribution

Single (12"): released on Rodent, Sep'86 by Magnet. Dist: RCA Distribution

LIVING LEGEND - THE ALBUM.
Notes: This album includes the signature tune "Living Legend" and other music featured in the current series.
Album: released on BBC, Oct'86 by BBC Records & Tapes. Dist: EMI, PRT, Pye

Cassette: released on BBC, Oct'86 by BBC Records & Tapes. Dist: EMI, PRT, Pye

Ratt

DANCIN' UNDER COVER.
Tracks: / Dance / Body talk / Take a chance / Looking for love / Seventh avenue / Drive me crazy / Slip of the lip / One good lover / Enough is enough / It doesn't matter.
Album: released on Atlantic, Oct'86 by WEA Records. Dist: WEA

Cassette: released on Atlantic, Oct'86 by WEA Records. Dist: WEA

Compact disc: released on Atlantic, Oct'86 by WEA Records. Dist: WEA

INVASION OF YOUR PRIVACY.
Tracks: / You're in love / Never use love / Lay it down / Give it all / Closer to my heart / Between the eyes / What you give me is what you get / Gome me on the line / You should know by now / Dangerous but worth the risk.
Album: released on Atlantic, Jun'85 by WEA Records. Dist: WEA

Cassette: released on Atlantic, Jun'85 by WEA Records. Dist: WEA

Compact disc: released on Atlantic, Jun'85 by WEA Records. Dist: WEA

OUT OF THE CELLAR.
Album: released on Atlantic, Apr'84 by WEA Records. Dist: WEA

Cassette: released on Atlantic, Apr'84 by WEA Records. Dist: WEA

RATT.
Tracks: / Sweet cheater / You think you're tough / U got it / Tell the world / Back for more / Walking the dog.
Album: released on Time Coast, Sep'86

Cassette: released on Time Coast, Sep'86

Album: released on Music For Nations, Jun'83 by Music For Nations Records. Dist: Pinnacle

ROUND AND AROUND.
Single (7"): released on Atlantic, Sep'84 by WEA Records. Dist: WEA

VIDEO, (THE).
Video-cassette (VHS): released on Atlantic, Jun'86 by WEA Records. Dist: WEA

Video-cassette [Betamax]: released on Atlantic, Jun'86 by WEA Records. Dist: WEA

YOU'RE IN LOVE.
Tracks: / You're in love / Between the eyes.
Single (7"): released on Atlantic, Jan'86 by WEA Records. Dist: WEA

Rattlers

I DON'T WANT YOU.
Single (7"): released on Lost Moment, Jun'85

Rattlers N.Y.C.

RATTLED.
Album: released on PVC, May'86 Dist: Pacific

Rattles

WITCH, THE.
Single (7"): released on Decca-Originals, Mar'82 by Decca Records. Dist: Polygram, IMS

Single (7"): released on Old Gold, Sep'85 by Old Gold Records. Dist: Lightning, Jazz Music, Spartan, Counterpoint

Rattlesnake Annie

COUNTRY LIVIN'.
Album: released on Rattlesnake, Apr'86

RATTLESNAKE ANNIE.
Tracks: / Funky country livin' / Sixteen tons / Country music hall of pain / Somewhere south of Macon / Goodbye to a river / Outskirts of town / Callin' your bluff / Long black limousine / Been waitin' that long / Lonesome on'ry and mean.
Album: released on CBS, Jul'87 by CBS Records. Dist: CBS

Cassette: released on CBS, Jul'87 by CBS Records. Dist: CBS

TENNESSEE WALTZ.
Single (7"):

Rauber, Francois

CIRCUS MUSIC.
Album: released on Auvidis (France), May'85 Dist: Discovery

Cassette: released on Auvidis (France), May'85 Dist: Discovery

Rauch

PUT YOUR LOVE IN ME.
Single (7"): released on Sedition, Feb'85 Dist: PRT

Single (12"): released on Sedition, Feb'85 Dist: PRT

Raunchy Rockabilly

RAUNCHY ROCKABILLY Sun sounds special-various original artists (Various original artists).
Album: released on Charly, '78 by Charly Records. Dist: Charly, Cadillac

Rava

STRING BAND.
Album: released on Soul Note, May'85 Dist: Harmonia Mundi Distributors

Rava, Enrico

IL GIRO DEL GIORNO IN 80.
Album: released on Black Saint, Jul'78 Dist: Projection, IMS, Polygram, Chris Wellard, Harmonia Mundi, Swift

OPENING NIGHT (Rava, Enrico Quartet).
Album: released on ECM (Germany), Jul'82 by ECM Records. Dist: IMS, Polygram, Virgin through EMI

Ravage

WRECKING BALL.
Album: released on Roadrunner (Dutch), Jan'87 Dist: Pinnacle

Ravan, Genya

URBAN DESIRE.
Album: released on Twentieth Century, '78 by Twentieth Century Records. Dist: BMG, IMS-Polygram

Rave From the Grave

RAVE FROM THE GRAVE VOL.1 Transfusion (Various Artists).
Album: released on Union Pacific, Apr'79 Dist: Swift, Jazz Music, Red Lightnin' Distribution

RAVE FROM THE GRAVE VOL.2 Loose Ends (Various Artists).
Album: released on Union Pacific, Apr'79 Dist: Swift, Jazz Music, Red Lightnin' Distribution

Raven

ALL FOR ONE.

Tracks: / Take control / Mind over metal / Sledgehammer rock / All for one / Run silent, run deep / Hung drawn & quartered / Break the chain / Take it away / Seek & destroy / Athletic rock.
Album: released on Neat, '85 by Neat Records. Dist: Pinnacle, Neat

Cassette: released on Neat, '85 by Neat Records. Dist: Pinnacle, Neat

Compact disc: released on Neat, '85 by Neat Records. Dist: Pinnacle, Neat

BORN TO BE WILD.
Single (7"): released on Neat, Aug'83 by Neat Records. Dist: Pinnacle, Neat

Single (12"): released on Neat, Aug'83 by Neat Records. Dist: Pinnacle, Neat

Picture disc single: released on Neat, Aug'83 by Neat Records. Dist: Pinnacle, Neat

BREAK THE CHAIN.
Tracks: / Break the chain.
Single (12"): released on Neat, Jun'86 by Neat Records. Dist: Pinnacle, Neat

CRASH BANG WALLOP (EP).
Single (12"): released on Neat, Oct'82 by Neat Records. Dist: Pinnacle, Neat

Single (7"): released on Neat, May'83 by Neat Records. Dist: Pinnacle, Neat

DEVILS CARRION, THE.
Tracks: / Hard ride / Bring the hammer down / Inquisitor / All for one / Hellraiser / Action (Medley) / Live at the inferno / Crash, bang, wallop / Ballad of Marshall Stack / Crazy world / Crazy world / Rock until you drop / Don't need your money / Hell patrol / Rock hard / Faster than the speed of light / Wiped out / Break the chain / Read all about it / Firepower / Firepower / Athletic rock / Run silent, run deep.
Double Album: released on Raw Power, Apr'86 Dist: Pinnacle

Cassette: released on Raw Power, Apr'86 Dist: Pinnacle

DON'T NEED YOUR MONEY.
Single (7"): released on Neat, Aug'80 by Neat Records. Dist: Pinnacle, Neat

GIMME SOME LOVIN'.
Tracks: / Gimme some lovin' / One on.
Single (7"): released on Atlantic, Feb'86 by WEA Records. Dist: WEA

HARD RIDE.
Single (7"): released on Neat, Nov'81 by Neat Records. Dist: Pinnacle, Neat

LIFE'S A BITCH.
Tracks: / Savage and the hungry, The / Pick your window / Life's a bitch / Never forgive / Iron league / On the wings of an eagle / Overload / You're a liar / Fuel to the fire / Only the strong survive / Juggernaut / Playing with the razor / Finger on the trigger *.
Album: released on Atlantic, Apr'87 by WEA Records. Dist: WEA

Cassette: released on Atlantic, Apr'87 by WEA Records. Dist: WEA

LIVING AT THE INFERNO.
Double Album: released on Neat, May'85 by Neat Records. Dist: Pinnacle, Neat

PACK IS BACK, THE.
Tracks: / Pack is back, (The) / Gimme some lovin' / Screamin' down the house / Young blood / Hyperactive / Rock dogs / Don't let it die / Get into your car / All I want / Nightmare ride.
Album: released on Atlantic, Mar'86 by WEA Records. Dist: WEA

Cassette: released on Atlantic, Mar'86 by WEA Records. Dist: WEA

ROCK UNTIL YOU DROP.
Album: released on Neat, May'85 by Neat Records. Dist: Pinnacle, Neat

Picture disc album: released on Neat, May'85 by Neat Records. Dist: Pinnacle, Neat

WIPED OUT.
Album: released on Neat, May'85 by Neat Records. Dist: Pinnacle, Neat

Raven, Jon

BALLAD OF THE BLACK COUNTRY.
Album: released on Broadside, Jun'81 by Broadside Records. Dist: Celtic Distributions, H.R. Taylor, Jazz Music, Projection, Jazz Services Unlimited Dist. (JSU)

Cassette: released on Broadside, Jun'81 by Broadside Records. Dist: Celtic Distributions, H.R. Taylor, Jazz Music, Projection, Jazz Services Unlimited Dist. (JSU)

ENGLISH CANALS.
Album: released on Broadside, Jun'81 by Broadside Records. Dist: Celtic Distributions, H.R. Taylor, Jazz Music, Projection, Jazz Services Unlimited Dist. (JSU)

Cassette: released on Broadside, Jun'81 by Broadside Records. Dist: Celtic Distributions, H.R. Taylor, Jazz Music, Projection, Jazz Services Unlimited Dist. (JSU)

HARVEST (Raven, Jon/Nigel Jones/Dave Oxley).
Album: released on Broadside, Jun'81 by Broadside Records. Dist: Celtic Distributions, H.R. Taylor, Jazz Music, Projection, Jazz Services Unlimited Dist. (JSU)

Cassette: released on Broadside, Jun'81 by Broadside Records. Dist: Celtic Distributions, H.R. Taylor, Jazz Music, Projection, Jazz Services Unlimited Dist. (JSU)

SONGS OF A CHANGING WORLD (Raven, Jon/Nic Jones/Tony Rose).
Album: released on Leader, '81 Dist: Jazz Music, Projection

STEAM BALLADS.
Album: released on Broadside, Jun'81 by Broadside Records. Dist: Celtic Distributions, H.R. Taylor, Jazz Music, Projection, Jazz Services Unlimited Dist. (JSU)

Cassette: released on Broadside, Jun'81 by Broadside Records. Dist: Celtic Distributions, H.R. Taylor, Jazz Music, Projection, Jazz Services Unlimited Dist. (JSU)

Raven, Marsha

CATCH ME(I'M FALLING IN LOVE).
Single (7"): released on Passion, Mar'85 by Skratch Records. Dist: PRT

Single (12"): released on Passion, Mar'85 by Skratch Records. Dist: PRT

DOCTOR DJ.
Single (12"): released on Record Shack, Oct'84 by Record Shack Records. Dist: PRT

FALSE ALARM.
Single (7"): released on Passion, Jun'84 by Skratch Records. Dist: PRT

Single (12"): released on Passion, Jun'84 by Skratch Records. Dist: PRT

I LIKE PLASTIC.
Single (7"): released on Red Bus, May'82 by Red Bus Records. Dist: PRT

Single (12"): released on Red Bus, May'82 by Red Bus Records. Dist: PRT

STRANGER IN DISGUISE.
Single (7"): released on Record Shack, May'85 by Record Shack Records. Dist: PRT

Single (12"): released on Record Shack, May'85 by Record Shack Records. Dist: PRT

YOU MAKE ME FEEL LIKE LOVING YOU.
Single (7"): released on Big Boy, May'83 by Big Boy Records. Dist: Pinnacle

Single (12"): released on Big Boy, May'83 by Big Boy Records. Dist: Pinnacle

Raven, Michael

GYPSY- A VARIETY OF GUITAR MUSIC.
Album: by Decca Records. Dist: Polygram

JOLLY MACHINE, THE (Raven, Michael/Joan Mills).
Album: released on Folk Heritage, Jul'82 by Folk Heritage Records. Dist: Roots, Wynd-Up Distribution, Jazz Music, Folk Heritage

MISCELLANY OF GUITAR MUSIC, A.
Album: released on Broadside, Jun'81 by Broadside Records. Dist: Celtic Distributions, H.R. Taylor, Jazz Music, Projection, Jazz Services Unlimited Dist. (JSU)

Cassette: released on Broadside, Jun'81 by Broadside Records. Dist: Celtic Distributions, H.R. Taylor, Jazz Music, Projection, Jazz Services Unlimited Dist. (JSU)

Ravenna & The Magnetics

FEELS SO GOOD.
Single (7"): released on Rondelet, Dec'81 Dist: Spartan Distribution

ROCKABILLY FOOLS.
Album: released on Rondelet, Apr'81 Dist: Spartan Distribution

TENNESSEE & TEXAS.
Album: released on Rondelet, Nov'81 Dist: Spartan Distribution

Ravens

GREATEST VOCAL GROUP OF THEM ALL.
Double Album:

RAVEN COUNTRY.
Album: released on Outlet, Jun'79 by Outlet Records. Dist: Outlet Distribution

Cassette: released on Outlet, Jun'79 by Outlet Records. Dist: Outlet Distribution

Ravenscroft Partnership

HOLD ON (THIS IS CLIVE'S SONG).
Tracks: / Hold on.
Notes: All royalties to 'Search 88' fund.
Single (7"): released on Columbia, Jul'87 by EMI Records. Dist: EMI

Single (12"): released on Columbia, Jul'87 by EMI Records. Dist: EMI

Ravenscroft, Raf

LIFELINE.
Single (7"): released on Nems, Nov'81 Dist: Castle Communications Records, Pinnacle Records

MAXINE.
Single (7"): released on Solid, Jul'85 by Solid Records. Dist: Graduate, Spartan

Single (12"): released on Solid, Jul'85 by Solid Records. Dist: Graduate, Spartan

Rave On

RAVE ON various artists (Various Artists).
Album: released on Mooncrest, '83 by Mooncrest Records. Dist: PRT Distribution

Ravers Rock

RAVERS ROCK VOL.1 various artists (Various Artists).
Album: released on Vista Sounds, '83 by Vista Sounds Records. Dist: Jetstar

RAVERS ROCK VOL.2 various artists (Various Artists).
Album: released on Vista Sounds, Feb'84 by Vista Sounds Records. Dist: Jetstar

Rave-ups

TOWN AND COUNTRY.
Album: released on Demon, Nov'85 by Demon Records. Dist: Pinnacle

Cassette: released on Demon, Nov'85 by Demon Records. Dist: Pinnacle

Ravin' Auto

GRAB BAG.
Cassette: released on El Flasho, Nov'84 by El Flasho Records. Dist: Falling A Distribution

Raw Cuts

RAW CUTS 2 - SWEDISH GARAGE BANDS Various Artists (Various Artists).
Album: released on Criminal Damage, May'86 by Criminal Damage Records. Dist: Backs, Cartel

RAW CUTS 3 - GERMAN UNDERGROUND (Various Artists).
Album: released on Satellite, Jun'87 by Satellite Records. Dist: Stage One

RAW CUTS-A BEGINNERS GUIDE TO GARAGE FRENCH various artists (Various Artists).
Album: released on Criminal Damage, Aug'85 by Criminal Damage Records. Dist: Backs, Cartel

Raw cut vol 4 - Australian nitro

RAW CUT VOL 4 - AUSTRALIAN NITRO Various artists (Various Artists).
Album: released on Satellite, Aug'87 by Satellite Records. Dist: Stage One

Raw Deal

LONE WOLF.
Single (7"): released on Neat, Nov'81 by Neat Records. Dist: Pinnacle, Neat

Rawe Deal

HEARTBEAT.
Single (7"): released on Passion, Aug'85 by Skratch Records. Dist: PRT

Single (12"): released on Passion, Aug'85 by Skratch Records. Dist: PRT

Rawe, Jackie

I BELIEVE IN DREAMS.
Single (7"): released on Fanfare, Jul'85 by Ferroway/Fanfare Records. Dist: PRT

Single (12"): released on Fanfare, Jul'85 by Ferroway/Fanfare Records. Dist: PRT

Rawes, Peter

WHY SHOULD I ASK HER TO STAY?.
Tracks: / Why should I ask her to stay / Shark (Theme from -) / Forever (Theme from -).
Single (7"): released on Official, Jan'86 by Official Records. Dist: Revolver Distribution, Cartel Distribution

Raw Herbs

OLD JOE.
Tracks: / Old Joe.
Special: released on Medium Cool, Nov'86 Dist: Red Rhino Distribution, Cartel Distribution

Raw-Ho

BE ME.
Tracks: / Be me / Pay the mother.
Notes: Limited edition of 500 pic bag plus sticker.
Single (7"): released on Roarecords, Jan'86 Dist: Backs, Cartel

SUMMER.
Single (7"): released on Roarecords, Jul'84 Dist: Backs, Cartel

Rawicz/Landauer

MAGIC PIANOS OF RAWICZ & LANDAUER, (THE).
Cassette: released on Ditto, Mar'86 by Pickwick Records. Dist: H.R. Taylor

Rawle, Len

LEN RAWLE GOES NORTH.
Double Album: released on Acorn, Jun'79 Dist: Folksound, Jazz Music

Rawls, Lou

ARE YOU WITH ME?.
Tracks: / Are you with me / Are you with me (Instrumental).
Single (7"): released on Epic, Mar'86 by CBS Records. Dist: CBS

Single (12"): released on Epic, Mar'86 by CBS Records. Dist: CBS

BEST OF LOU RAWLS, THE.
Album: released on Capitol, Apr'79 by Capitol Records. Dist: EMI

Album: released on Music For Pleasure (Holland), '86 by EMI Records. Dist: EMI

Cassette: released on Music For Pleasure (Holland), '86 by EMI Records. Dist: EMI

CLASSIC SOUL.
Notes: First UK Release
Album: released on Blue Moon, Apr'86 Dist: Magnum Music Group Ltd, PRT, Spartan

LET ME BE GOOD TO YOU.
Album: released on Philadelphia International, Jul'79 by CBS Records. Dist: CBS

LOVE ALL YOUR BLUES AWAY.
Tracks: / Change your mind / Are you with me / Love all your blues away / Stop me from starting this feeling / Learn to love again / Willow weep for me / We'll be together again / Way you look tonight, The / It never entered my mind.
Album: released on Epic, Apr'86 by CBS Records. Dist: CBS

Cassette: released on Epic, Apr'86 by CBS Records. Dist: CBS

SHADES OF BLUE.
Album: released on Philadelphia International, Apr'81 by CBS Records. Dist: CBS

Cassette: released on Philadelphia International, Apr'81 by CBS Records. Dist: CBS

SOUL SERENADE.
Album: released on Stateside, Aug'85 Dist: EMI

Cassette: released on Stateside, Aug'85 Dist: EMI

STOP ME FROM STARTING THIS FEELING.
Tracks: / Stop me from starting this feeling / Love all your blues away / See you when I get there* / Natural man*.
Single (7"): released on Epic, Jun'86 by CBS Records. Dist: CBS

Single (12"): released on Epic, Jun'86 by CBS Records. Dist: CBS

STORMY MONDAY (see also Les McCann Limited) (Rawls, Lou & Les McCann Limited).
Album: released on See For Miles, Jun'85

UNMISTAKABLY LOU.
Album: released on Philadelphia International, May'77 by CBS Records. Dist: CBS

YOU'LL NEVER FIND ANOTHER LOVE LIKE MINE.
Single (7"): released on Old Gold, Sep'85 by Old Gold Records. Dist: Lightning, Jazz Music, Spartan, Counterpoint

Raw Power

SCREAMS FROM THE GUTTER.
Album: released on Toxic Shock, Nov'85 Dist: Cartel

Raw Silk

DO IT TO THE MUSIC.
Single (7"): released on KR, Sep'82 by KR Recordings Ltd. Dist: RCA, Revolver, Cartel

Single (12"): released on KR, Sep'82 by KR Recordings Ltd. Dist: RCA, Revolver, Cartel

Raww

DON'T YOU TRY IT.
Tracks: / Don't you try it / Don't you try it (Dub version).
Single (12"): released on Debut, Oct'86 by Skratch Music. Dist: PRT

Ray, Alan

ALAN RAY'S INTERNATIONAL ALBUM.
Album: released on Westwood, '82 by Westwood Records. Dist: Jazz Music, H.R. Taylor, JSU, Pinnacle, Ross Records

Rayband

MAKES YOU WANNA DANCE.
Single (7"): released on Buffalo (UK), Jun'85

Ray, Barbara

WALKING TALKING DOLLY.
Tracks: / Walking talking dolly / Wild mountain thyme.
Single (7"): released on August (USA), Dec'85 Dist: Taylors

Raybeats

GUITAR BEAT.
Album: released on Don't Fall Off The Mountain, Jul'81 by Don't Fall Off The Mountain Records. Dist: Pinnacle, Rough Trade, Nine Mile, Indies

Single (7"): released on Don't Fall Off The Mountain, Jun'81 by Don't Fall Off The Mountain Records. Dist: Pinnacle, Rough Trade, Nine Mile, Indies

HOLIDAY INN SPAIN.
Single (7"): released on Don't Fall Off The Mountain, Aug'81 by Don't Fall Off The Mountain Records. Dist: Pinnacle, Rough Trade, Nine Mile, Indies

IT'S ONLY A MOVIE.
Album: released on Shanachie, Feb'84

ROPING WILD BEARS / SEARCHING.
Single (12"): released on Don't Fall Off The Mountain, Jan'81 by Don't Fall Off The Mountain Records. Dist: Pinnacle, Rough Trade, Nine Mile, Indies

Ray, Bobby

COUNTRY WAY, THE.
Album: released on Tank, Dec'77 by Tank Records.

SOMETHING IN THE AYRE.
Album: released on Tank, Jun'79 by Tank Records.

Ray, Danny

HOW 'BOUT US / BACK IN MY ARMS
(see also Shirley James) (Ray, Danny & Shirley James).
Single (12"): released on Black Jack, Apr'83 Dist: Jetstar, Spartan

PLAYBOY / FIRE REDDER THAN RED.
Single (12"): released on Black Jack, Jan'81 Dist: Jetstar, Spartan

SPRING AGAIN.
Single (12"): released on Black Jack, Apr'82 Dist: Jetstar, Spartan

WHY DON'T YOU SPEND THE NIGHT
(featuring Shirley James).
Album: released on Black Jack, Dec'84 Dist: Jetstar, Spartan

Ray, David

STRIKES.
Single (7"): released on Rollin' Rock, Jun'80

Raydio

ROCK ON.
Album: released on Arista, Aug'79 by Arista Records. Dist: RCA

TWO PLACES AT THE SAME TIME.
Album: released on Arista, May'80 by Arista Records. Dist: RCA

Rayemon

PRIVATE JOY.
Single (12"): released on T-Mac, Nov'85 by T-Mac Records. Dist: PRT Distribution

Raye, Sol

COME HOME LOVE.
Album: released on Calendar, Mar'77 Dist: Polygram

Ray, Fay

FAMILY AFFAIRS.
Single (7"): released on Surrey Sound, Jan'81 Dist: Pinnacle

WAITING FOR THE HEATWAVE / I WISH.
Single (7"): released on WEA, Apr'82 by WEA Records. Dist: WEA

Ray, Goodman & Brown

LL.
Album: released on Mercury (Import), Mar'81

RAY, GOODMAN & BROWN.
Album: released on Mercury, Mar'80 by Phonogram Records. Dist: Polygram Distribution

STAY.
Album: released on Mercury (Import), Apr'82

TAKE IT TO THE LIMIT.
Tracks: / Take it to the limit / Baby, let's wake love tonight / Good love / Celebrate your love / Why must I wait / Waiting for Dawn / We've got tonight / Someone's missing your love.
Album: released on EMI America, Dec'86 by EMI Records. Dist: EMI

Cassette: released on EMI America, Dec'86 by EMI Records. Dist: EMI

Compact disc: released on EMI America, Jul'87 by EMI Records. Dist: EMI

Ray, Harry

IT'S GOOD TO BE HOME.
Album: released on Sugarhill (USA), Apr'83 by PRT Records. Dist: PRT Distribution

Cassette: released on Sugarhill (USA), Apr'83 by PRT Records. Dist: PRT Distribution

LOVE IS A GAME / SWEET BABY.
Single (7"): released on Sugarhill, Feb'83 by PRT Records. Dist: PRT Distribution

Single (12"): released on Sugarhill, Feb'83 by PRT Records. Dist: PRT Distribution

Ray, James

MEXICO SUNDOWN BLUES (Ray, James & the Performance).
Tracks: / Mexico sundown blues.
Single (12"): released on Merciful Release, Jul'86 by Sisterhood Records. Dist: WEA

TEXAS (Ray, James & the Performance).
Single (7"): released on Merciful Release, 20 Jun'87 by Sisterhood Records. Dist: WEA

Single (12"): released on Merciful Release, 20 Jun'87 by Sisterhood Records. Dist: WEA

Ray, Jamey

PRETTY ONE.
Single (7"): released on Stiff, Feb'85 by Stiff Records. Dist: EMI, Record Services Distribution (Ireland)

Single (12"): released on Stiff, Feb'85 by Stiff Records. Dist: EMI, Record Services Distribution (Ireland)

Ray, Johnnie

AN AMERICAN LEGEND.
Album: released on Embassy, Feb'79 by CBS Records. Dist: CBS

Cassette: released on Embassy, Feb'79 by CBS Records. Dist: CBS

BEST OF JOHNNIE RAY, (THE).
Album: released on Spot, Feb'83 by Pickwick Records. Dist: H.R. Taylor, Lugtons

Cassette: released on Spot, Feb'83 by Pickwick Records. Dist: H.R. Taylor, Lugtons

YES TONIGHT JOSEPHINE.
Single (7"): released on Old Gold, Jul'82 by Old Gold Records. Dist: Lightning, Jazz Music, Spartan, Counterpoint

Ray, Johnny

HIS TOP HITS.
Cassette: released on Timeless Treasures, Aug'86 Dist: Counterpoint Distribution

Ray, Mercy

SHE'LL BE HOME LATER TONIGHT.
Single (7"): released on Charisma, Oct'85 by Virgin Records. Dist: EMI

Single (12"): released on Charisma, Oct'85 by Virgin Records. Dist: EMI

Raymond & Claudia

IS IT ALWAYS GONNA BE LIKE THIS.
Single (12"): released on JB Music, Nov'82

Raymonde

RAYMONDE.
Tracks: / Raymonde / These boots are made for walking.
Single (7"): released on Desire, Mar'86 by Desire Records. Dist: Pinnacle

Single (12"): released on Desire, Mar'86 by Desire Records. Dist: Pinnacle

Ray O'Sunshine

HAPPY PARTY TIME.
Single (7"): released on A.1, Mar'83 by A.1 Records. Dist: PRT

Raze

JACK THE GROOVE.
Tracks: / Jack the groove / Bonus beats / Oh song" / Jump in your dance"
Notes: Two tracks on 12" version only, NOT on 7"
Single (7"): released on Champion, Oct'86 by Champion Records. Dist: RCA

Single (12"): released on Champion, Oct'86 by Champion Records. Dist: RCA

LET THE MUSIC MOVE U.
Tracks: / Jack the groove.
Single (7"): released on Champion, Feb'87 by Champion Records. Dist: RCA

Tracks: / Get down / Control me".
Single (7"): released on Champion, Jan'87 by Champion Records. Dist: RCA

Single (12"): released on Champion, Jan'87 by Champion Records. Dist: RCA

Razor

EVIL INVADORS.
Album: released on Road Runner, Dec'85

EXECUTIONER'S SONG.
Album: released on Roadrunner (Dutch), Jun'85 Dist: Pinnacle

MALICIOUS INTENT.
Album: released on Roadrunner (Dutch), Aug'86 Dist: Pinnacle

Razorcuts

I HEARD YOU THE FIRST TIME.
Single (7"): released on Flying Nun, Jun'87 Dist: Rough Trade, Cartel

Single (12"): released on Flying Nun, Jul'87 Dist: Rough Trade, Cartel

I'LL STILL BE THERE.

Tracks: / I'll still be there / Big pink cake.
Single (7"): released on Subway, May'86 Dist: Revolver Distribution, Spartan Distribution

SORRY TO EMBARASS YOU.

Tracks: / Sorry to embarass you.
Single (7"): released on Subway, Nov'86 Dist: Revolver Distribution, Spartan Distribution

Single (12"): released on Subway, Nov'86 Dist: Revolver Distribution, Spartan Distribution

Razz

ALRIGHT TONIGHT.
Single (7"): released on Lady London, May'85 by Joanne Barrett.

WHEN YOU FALL IN LOVE.
Single (7"): released on Lady London, Jan'85 by Joanne Barrett.

R&B...

R&B AND BOOGIE WOOGIE Various artists (Various Artists).
Tracks: / Caldonia / Oh Boy! That's where my money goes / Down the road a-piece / Loumel's boogie / Hamp boogie woogie, The / Kansas city boogie / Four months, three weeks, two days & one hour blues / St Louis blues / Chicago blues / Sx wheel chaser / I ain't mad at you / Why don't you do it right? / Jam boogie.
Album: released on Swinghouse(Submarine), Nov'85

Cassette: released on Swinghouse(Submarine), Nov'85

R&B BOOGIE WOOGIE VOL.1 various artists (Various Artists).
Album: released on Swinghouse, '84 Dist: Jazz Music Distribution, Swift Distribution, Chris Wellard Distribution

Cassette: released on Swinghouse, '84 Dist: Jazz Music Distribution, Swift Distribution, Chris Wellard Distribution

R&B BOOGIE WOOGIE VOL.2 Harious artists (Various Artists).
Cassette: released on Swing House (UK), Apr'85

Album: released on Swing House (UK), Apr'85

R&B BOOGIE WOOGIE VOL.3 various artists (Various Artists).
Album: released on Swing House (UK), '84

R&B SCENE VOLUME 2 (1963-1969)
Various artists (Various Artists).
Tracks: / Hound dog / Feelin' blue / Boom boom / I'm gonna move to the outskirts of town / Anytime at all / Heart of stone / Breakdown blues / Can I get a witness / Hoochie coochie man / Talkin' about you / Hurt me if you will / I feel so blue / Dancing in the street / Baby what you want me to do / Not fade away / Stu-Ball / I can only give you everything.
Notes: Recordings courtesy of the Decca Records Co. Ltd. This compilation (P) 1986 by See For Miles Records Ltd. (C) 1986. See For Miles Records Ltd.; A Colin Miles compilation.
Album: released on See For Miles, Jul'86 by See For Miles Records. Dist: Pinnacle

R&B VOLTS FROM THE VJ VAULTS
various artists (Various Artists).
Album: released on Charly(R&B), Oct'85 by Charly Records. Dist: Charly Distribution

Album: released on Red Lightnin', Jul'85 by Red Lightnin' Records. Dist: Roots, Swift, Jazz Music, JSU, Pinnacle, Cartel, Wynd-Up Distribution

RB Method

QUANTUM HOP.
Single (12"): released on Survival, Apr'85 by Survival Records. Dist: Backs, Cartel Distribution

RB's

EXPLAIN / LET ME FEEL IT.
Single (7"): released on Phoenix, Nov'80 by John Mayer and Robert Bell. Dist: Spartan, Pinnacle

URUGUAY / TIME.
Single (7"): released on Hansa, Apr'82 by Hansa Records. Dist: Polygram

Single (12"): released on Hansa, Apr'82 by Hansa Records. Dist: Polygram

R.Cajun

BAYOU- RHYTHMS.
Album: released on Moonraker, Oct'84, Projection Distribution

Cassette: released on Moonraker, Oct'84, Projection Distribution

JAMBALAYA (GRAND TEXAS).
Single (7"): released on Moonraker, Sep'84, Projection Distribution

R & D

IN BERLIN.
Single (7"): released on Sonet, Nov'84 by Sonet Records. Dist: PRT

Single (12"): released on Sonet, Nov'84 by Sonet Records. Dist: PRT

Reach for the Sky

REACH FOR THE SKY Brickhill, Paul (Britton, Tony).
Cassette: released on Listen For Pleasure, May'84 by MFP Records. Dist: EMI

Rea, Chris

ACE OF HEARTS (SPECIAL MIX).
Single (7"): released on Magnet, Nov'85 by Magnet Records. Dist: BMG

Single (12"): released on Magnet, Nov'85 by Magnet Records. Dist: BMG

Cassette single: released on Magnet, Nov'85 by Magnet Records. Dist: BMG

BOMBOLLINI.
Single (7"): released on Magnet, May'84 by Magnet Records. Dist: BMG

Single (12"): released on Magnet, May'84 by Magnet Records. Dist: BMG

CHRIS REA.
Tracks: / Loving you / If you choose to go / Guitar street / Do you still dream? / Every beat of my heart / Goodbye little Columbus / One sweet tender touch / Do it for your love / Just want to be with you / Runaway / When you know your love has died.
Notes: Written by Chris Rea. Produced by Jon Kelly & Chris Rea. Published by Magnet Music Ltd.
Compact disc: released on Magnet, Dec'85 by Magnet Records. Dist: BMG

Album: released on Magnet, '83 by Magnet Records. Dist: BMG

Cassette: released on Magnet, '83 by Magnet Records. Dist: BMG

DANCING WITH STRANGERS.
Tracks: / Joys of Christmas / I can't dance to that / Windy town / Gonna buy a hat / Curse of the traveller / Let's dance / Que sera / Josie's tune / Loving you again / That girl of mine / September blue / I don't care anymore" / Donahue's broken wheel" / Danielle's breakfast".
Notes: * Extra track on CD only.
Album: released on Magnet, Sep'87 by Magnet Records. Dist: BMG

Cassette: released on Magnet, Sep'87 by Magnet Records. Dist: BMG

Compact disc: released on Magnet, Sep'87 by Magnet Records. Dist: BMG

DELTICS.
Tracks: / Twisted wheel / Things lovers should do, The / Dance (don't think) / Raincoat and a rose / Cenotaph-Letter from Amsterdam / Deltics / Diamonds / She gave it away / Don't want your best friend / No qualifications / Seabird.
Notes: Written by Chris Rea. Produced by Gus Dudgeon. Published by Magnet Music Ltd.
Compact disc: released on Magnet, Dec'85 by Magnet Records. Dist: BMG

Album: released on Magnet, '83 by Magnet Records. Dist: BMG

Cassette: released on Magnet, '83 by Magnet Records. Dist: BMG

DRIVING HOME FOR CHRISTMAS.
Tracks: / Hello friend.
Single (7"): released on Magnet, Dec'86 by Magnet Records. Dist: BMG

HELLO FRIEND.
Tracks: / Hello friend / Driving home for Christmas / It's all gone (recorded live at Montreaux) / Steel river.
Double-pack single: released on Magnet, Nov'86 by Magnet Records. Dist: BMG

Single (12"): released on Magnet, Nov'86 by Magnet Records. Dist: BMG

Tracks: / Driving home for christmas.
Single (7"): released on Magnet, Nov'86 by Magnet Records. Dist: BMG

I DON'T KNOW WHAT IT IS BUT I LOVE IT / MYSTERY MAN.
Single (7"): released on Magnet, Feb'84 by Magnet Records. Dist: BMG

Single (12"): released on Magnet, Feb'84 by Magnet Records. Dist: BMG

IT'S ALL GONE.
Tracks: / It's all gone / Bless them all / Crack that mold / Look out for me / Let's dance.
Single (7"): released on Magnet, Mar'86 by Magnet Records. Dist: BMG

Single (12"): released on Magnet, Mar'86 by Magnet Records. Dist: BMG

Cassette single: released on Magnet, Mar'86 by Magnet Records. Dist: BMG

JOSEPHINE.
Single (7"): released on Magnet, Jun'85 by Magnet Records. Dist: BMG

Single (12"): released on Magnet, Jun'85 by Magnet Records. Dist: BMG

LET'S DANCE.
Tracks: / Let's dance / I don't care anymore / Let's dance (12" Special mix) / Josephine (Extended French Re-record).
Single (7"): released on Magnet, May'87 by Magnet Records. Dist: BMG

Single (12"): released on Magnet, May'87 by Magnet Records. Dist: BMG

Compact disc single: released on Magnet, Mar'87 by Magnet Records. Dist: BMG

Cassette single: released on Magnet, Mar'87 by Magnet Records. Dist: BMG

LOVE'S STRANGE WAYS / SMILE.
Single (7"): released on Magnet, Jul'83 by Magnet Records. Dist: BMG

LOVING YOU AGAIN.
Single (7"): released on Magnet, Aug'87 by Magnet Records. Dist: BMG

Single (12"): released on Magnet, Aug'87 by Magnet Records. Dist: BMG

ON THE BEACH.
Tracks: / On the beach / One golden rule (Live) / Midnight (Live).
Double-pack single: released on Magnet, May'86 by Magnet Records. Dist: BMG

Single (12"): released on Magnet, May'86 by Magnet Records. Dist: BMG

ON THE BEACH.
Tracks: / On the beach / Little Blondi plaits / Giverney / Lucky day / Just passing through / It's all gone / Hello friend / Two roads / Light of hope / Auf immerund ewig / Bless them all / Freeway / Crack that mould.
Notes: Produced by Chris Rea/Dave Richards. Published by Magnet Music Ltd.
Album: released on Magnet, Apr'86 by Magnet Records. Dist: BMG

Cassette: released on Magnet, Apr'86 by Magnet Records. Dist: BMG

Compact disc: released on Magnet, Apr'86 by Magnet Records. Dist: BMG

SHAMROCK DIARIES.
Tracks: / Steel river / Stainsby girls / Chisel hill / Josephine / One golden rule / All summer long / Stone / Shamrock diaries / Love turns to lies / Hired gun.
Compact disc: released on Magnet, Jun'86 by Magnet Records. Dist: BMG

Album: released on Magnet, May'85 by Magnet Records. Dist: BMG

Cassette: released on Magnet, May'85 by Magnet Records. Dist: BMG

STAINSBY GIRLS.
Single (7"): released on Magnet, Mar'85 by Magnet Records. Dist: BMG

Single (12"): released on Magnet, Mar'85 by Magnet Records. Dist: BMG

Cassette: released on Magnet, Mar'85 by Magnet Records. Dist: BMG

TENNIS.
Tracks: / Tennis / Sweet kiss / Since I don't see you anymore / Dancing girls / No work today / Everytime I see you smile / For ever and ever / Good news / Friends across the water / Distant summers / Only with you / Stick it.
Compact disc: released on Magnet, Dec'85 by Magnet Records. Dist: BMG

Album: released on Magnet, '83 by Magnet Records. Dist: BMG

Cassette: released on Magnet, '83 by Magnet Records. Dist: BMG

TOUCHE D'AMOUR.
Single (7"): released on Magnet, Jul'84 by Magnet Records. Dist: BMG

Single (12"): released on Magnet, Jul'84 by Magnet Records. Dist: BMG

WATER SIGN.
Tracks: / Nothing's happening by the sea / Deep water / Candles / Love's strange ways / Texas / Let it loose / I can hear your heartbeat / Midnight blue / Hey you / Out of darkness.
Compact disc: released on Magnet, Dec'85 by Magnet Records. Dist: BMG

Album: released on Magnet, May'83 by Magnet Records. Dist: BMG

Cassette: released on Magnet, May'83 by Magnet Records. Dist: BMG

WHATEVER HAPPENED TO BENNY SANTINI?.
Tracks: / Whatever happened to Benny Santini? / Closer you get (The) / Because of you / Dancing with Charlie / Bows and bangles / Fool (if you think it's over) / Three angles / Just one of those days / Standing in your doorway / Fires of spring.
Compact disc: released on Magnet, Dec'85 by Magnet Records. Dist: BMG

Album: released on Magnet, '83 by Magnet Records. Dist: BMG

Cassette: released on Magnet, '83 by Magnet Records. Dist: BMG

WIRED TO THE MOON.
Tracks: / Bombollini / Touche d'amour / Shine Shine Shine / Wired to the moon / Reasons / I dont know what it is but I love it / Ace of hearts / Holding out / Winning.
Compact disc: released on Magnet, Dec'85 by Magnet Records. Dist: BMG

Reaction

MAKE UP YOUR MIND.
Tracks: / 4 x 4.
Single (7"): released on Waterloo Sunset, Feb'87 by Waterloo Sunset Records. Dist: MIS-EMI Distribution, Back-

Reaction, Junior C

BETTER MUST COME.
Tracks: / Better must come / Better must come (Dub version).
Single (7"): released on Cool Tempo, Mar'86 by Chrysalis Records. Dist: CBS

Single (12"): released on Cool Tempo, Mar'86 by Chrysalis Records. Dist: CBS

IF IT DON'T FIT DON'T FORCE IT.
Tracks: / If it don't fit don't force it / I am.

Single (7"): released on Chrysalis, Sep'86 by Chrysalis Records. Dist: CBS

Single (12"): released on Chrysalis, Sep'86 by Chrysalis Records. Dist: CBS

Reactions

CRACKED MARBLE.
Single (12"): released on Homestead, Dec'86 Dist: Rough Trade, Cartel, Shigaku

Album: released on Homestead, Oct'86 Dist: Rough Trade, Cartel, Shigaku

Read:All:Over

HARD TO LOVE.
Single (7"): released on Station, Jun'85 Dist: Probe Distribution, Cartel Distribution

Read, Cheese

CAJUN HOUSE PARTY.
Album: released on Arhoolie, May'81 by Arhoolie Records. Dist: Projection, Topic, Jazz Music, Swift, Roots

Read, Darryl

NO SOUL THROUGH MIDNIGHT.
Tracks: / (No place,soul kitchen) / Through my eyes / Midnight rendezvous.
Single (12"): released on Aim, Nov'86 Dist: H.R. Taylor

Reading, Bertice

BERTICE.
Album: released on That's Entertainment, Feb'84 by That's Entertainment Records. Dist: Pinnacle, PRT

Cassette: released on That's Entertainment, Feb'84 by That's Entertainment Records. Dist: Pinnacle, PRT

YOU'RE GONNA SUFFER.
Tracks: / You're gonna suffer / Nightmare (Dub mix).
Single (12"): released on Sublime, Oct'86 by Sublime Records. Dist: PRT Distribution

Reading Festival

READING FESTIVAL '82 various artists (Various Artists).
: released on Mean, Jan'83 by Mean Records. Dist: Spartan

Readings From The Bible

READINGS FROM THE BIBLE -THE AUTHORISED VERSION various artists (Various Artists).
Double cassette: released on Argo (Spokenword), Nov'83 by Decca Records. Dist: Polygram

Read, John Dawson

I AM WITH YOU MARY.
Single (7"): released on Open Space, Jun'84 by Open Space Records. Dist: Pinnacle

Read, Martin Wyndham

ANDY'S GONE.
Notes: Martin Wyndham Read Dave & Toni Arthur Nic Jones
Album: released on Broadside, Jun'81 by Broadside Records. Dist: Celtic Distributions, H.R. Taylor, Jazz Music, Projection, Jazz Services Unlimited Dist. (JSU)

Cassette: released on Broadside, Jun'81 by Broadside Records. Dist: Celtic Distributions, H.R. Taylor, Jazz Music, Projection, Jazz Services Unlimited Dist. (JSU)

Read, Mike

TELL ME I'M WRONG.
Single (7"): released on MCA, Apr'84 by MCA Records. Dist: Polygram, MCA

Single (12"): released on MCA, Apr'84 by MCA Records. Dist: Polygram, MCA

Ready For The World

LONG TIME COMING.
Notes: This is the second LP from the young Michigan group who had a U.S.No.1 with 'Oh Sheila' and sold over a million albums in the States too. As before, all songs were written and produced by the band themselves.
Album: released on MCA, Dec'86 by MCA Records. Dist: Polygram, MCA

Cassette: released on MCA, Dec'86 by MCA Records. Dist: Polygram, MCA

LOVE YOU DOWN.
Tracks: / Human toy.
Single (7"): released on MCA, Feb'87 by MCA Records. Dist: Polygram, MCA

Single (12"): released on MCA, Feb'87 by MCA Records. Dist: Polygram, MCA

MARY GOES ROUND.
Tracks: / Mary goes round / It's all a game.
Single (7"): released on MCA, 23 May'87 by MCA Records. Dist: Polygram, MCA

OH SHEILA.
Tracks: / Oh Sheila / I'm the one who loves you / Side over.
Single (7"): released on MCA, May'86 by MCA Records. Dist: Polygram, MCA

Single (12"): released on MCA, May'86 by MCA Records. Dist: Polygram, MCA

Single (7"): released on MCA, Sep'85 by MCA Records. Dist: Polygram, MCA

Single (12"): released on MCA, Sep'85 by MCA Records. Dist: Polygram, MCA

READY FOR THE WORLD.
Album: released on MCA, Nov'85 by MCA Records. Dist: Polygram, MCA

Cassette: released on MCA, Nov'85 by MCA Records. Dist: Polygram, MCA

Ready Steady...

READY STEADY WIN....PLUS Various Artists (Various Artists).
Tracks: / Hide 'n seek / I'll miss you / Bo street runner / Did you ever hear the sound / Lonely one, A.
Album: released on See For Miles, Aug'87 by See For Miles Records. Dist: Pinnacle. Estim retail price in Sep'87 was £5.67.

Ready Steady Go!

READY STEADY GO! Volume 1.
Video-cassette (VHS): released on PMI, Jun'86 by PMI Records. Dist: EMI

Video-cassette [Betamax]: released on PMI, Jun'86 by PMI Records. Dist: EMI

READY STEADY GO! VOLUME 2.
Video-cassette (VHS): released on PMI, Jun'86 by PMI Records. Dist: EMI

Video-cassette [Betamax]: released on PMI, Jun'86 by PMI Records. Dist: EMI

Reagan, Ronald

ON RADIO.
Album: released on IMS(Import), Mar'82 by Polydor Records. Dist: IMS, Polygram

WIT & WISDOM, THE.
Album: released on Magic, Dec'80 Dist: Jazz Music, Submarine, Swift, Chris Wellard, Conifer

Rea, Jesse

HOU-DI-NI.
Tracks: / Hou-di-ni / Idio-syn-crazy.
Single (7"): released on WEA, Apr'87 by WEA Records. Dist: WEA

Single (12"): released on WEA, Apr'87 by WEA Records. Dist: WEA

Rea, John

IRISH MUSIC ON THE HAMMER DULCIMER.
Album: released on Topic, '81 by Topic Records. Dist: JSU Distribution, Projection Distribution, Jazz Music Distribution

Real Ale & Thunder Band

AT VESPERS.
Album: released on Halcyon (USA), Apr'85 by Halcyon Records (USA). Dist: Jazz Music, Conifer, Taylors

REAL ALE & THUNDER BAND AT VESPERS.
Album: released on Halcyon, Apr'85 by Halcyon Records. Dist: Jazz Music

Real Blend

GOLDEN MEMORIES.
Album: released on Klub, May'85

Cassette: released on Klub, May'85

WHITE CHRISTMAS.
Album: released on Klub, Nov'85

Cassette: released on Klub, Nov'85

Realistics

FEELIN' FINE/DISCO INSTRUMENTAL.
Single (7"): released on Spinach, May'82

Single (12"): released on Spinach, May'82

JAMAICA YOU'VE LOST YOUR MAKER.
Single (7"): released on 101, Aug'81 Dist: Spartan

Reality

BLIND TO THE TRUTH (EP).
Single (7"): released on Subversive, Dec'82 Dist: Backs, Cartel Distribution

STAND UP AND BE COUNTED.
Single (7"): released on Romantic, Oct'81 Dist: MCA Distribution

Single (12"): released on Romantic, Oct'81 Dist: MCA Distribution

WHO KILLED THE GOLDEN GOOSE.
Single (7"): released on Fight Back, Jun'84 by Fight Back Records. Dist: Jungle, Cartel

Reality Band

STEP INTO MY LIFE.
Single (7"): released on Record Shack, Oct'80 by Record Shack Records. Dist: PRT

Reality Control

REPRODUCTION OF HATE/ SUNNY OUTLOOK/ ANOTHER SURPRISE.
Single (7"): released on Volume, Oct'83 by Volume Records. Dist: Pinnacle

Real Life

CATCH ME I'M FALLING.
Single (7"): released on MCA, Apr'84 by MCA Records. Dist: Polygram, MCA

Single (12"): released on MCA, Apr'84 by MCA Records. Dist: Polygram, MCA

FACE TO FACE.
Tracks: / Face to face / Flame / Face to face(Insrtumental).
Single (7"): released on MCA, Jan'86 by MCA Records. Dist: Polygram, MCA

Single (12"): released on MCA, Jan'86 by MCA Records. Dist: Polygram, MCA

Really Free Band

JESUS OUR LOVE.
Cassette: released on Plankton, Nov'85 by Plankton Records. Dist: Cantio (Sweden)

REVERENCE.
Cassette: released on Plankton, Mar'85 by Plankton Records. Dist: Cantio (Sweden)

Really Rosie

REALLY ROSIE Maurice Sendak (King, Carole).
Cassette: released on Caedmon(USA), '82 by Caedmon (USA) Records. Dist: Gower, Taylors, Discovery

Real Macarbe

ALICE IS DRESSED IN GREY.
Tracks: / Alice is dressed in grey.
Single (7"): released on Dacarpo, Oct'86 Dist: Pinnacle

EMOTION.
Tracks: / Emotion / Dance (The).
Single (7"): released on Push, Dec'85 Dist: Red Rhino, Cartel

Single (12"): released on Push, Dec'85 Dist: Red Rhino, Cartel

WHITE HORSES(REMIX).
Tracks: / White horses(Remix) / Call (The).
Single (12"): released on Push, Dec'85 Dist: Red Rhino, Cartel

Real Rockin' Now
REAL ROCKIN' NOW Rockabilly (Various Artists).
Album: released on White Label (Holland), Feb'85 Dist: CSA, PRT

Real Rock Instrumentals
REAL ROCK INSTRUMENTALS Various artists (Various Artists).
Notes: Artists include:The Rel-Yeas,Treblemakers,The Shadows Five,Jerry & Reggie.
Album: released on White, Oct'86

Real Roxanne
LET'S GO-GO (BANG ZOOM) (Real Roxanne with Hitman Howie Tee).
Tracks: / (Bang Zoom) Let's go-go / Howie teed off.
Single (7"): released on Cool Tempo, Jun'86 by Chrysalis Records. Dist: CBS

Single (12"): released on Cool Tempo, Jun'86 by Chrysalis Records. Dist: CBS

Real Sounds
HARARE.
Album:

WALK FOR THE WORLD.
Tracks: / Walk for the world / Dynamos vs Tornados*.
Notes: Guests: Desmond Dekker & The London Community Gospel Choir
Single (7"): released on Cooking Vinyl, 23 May'87 Dist: Nine Mile, Cartel, Red Rhino

Single (12"): released on Cooking Vinyl, 23 May'87 Dist: Nine Mile, Cartel, Red Rhino

WENDE ZACKO.
Album: released on Cooking Vinyl, Jun'87 Dist: Nine Mile, Cartel, Red Rhino

Cassette: released on Cooking Vinyl, Jun'87 Dist: Nine Mile, Cartel, Red Rhino

Real Thing
100 MINUTES.
Cassette: released on PRT, Jun'82 by PRT Records. Dist: PRT

BEST OF THE REAL THING (THE).
Tracks: / You to me are everything(Remix) / Rainin' through my sunshine / She's got a groovy freak / (We've gotta take it to the)Second stage / You'll never know what you're missing / Can you feel the force? / Can't get by without you(Remix) / Won't you step into our world? / Love takes tears / Whenever you want my love / Children of the Ghetto / Whatcha say watcha do.
Album: released on West 5, Aug'86 Dist: PRT

Cassette: released on West 5, Aug'86 Dist: PRT

Compact disc: released on West 5, Aug'86 Dist: PRT

CAN'T GET BY WITHOUT YOU.
Tracks: / Can't get by without you / Can't get by without you(The 2nd decade remix) / She's a groovy freak / You'll never know what you're missing.
Single (7"): released on PRT, May'86 by PRT Records. Dist: PRT

Single (12"): released on PRT, May'86 by PRT Records. Dist: PRT

CAN YOU FEEL THE FORCE (INST).
Single (12"): released on Pye, May'79

CAN YOU FEEL THE FORCE.
Tracks: / Can you feel the force(1986 Mix) / Love's such a wonderful thing / Lightning strikes.
Single (7"): released on PRT, Aug'86 by PRT Records. Dist: PRT

Single (12"): released on PRT, Aug'86 by PRT Records. Dist: PRT

CAN YOU FEEL THE FORCE (LP).
Album: released on Pye, Feb'79

GREATEST HITS: REAL THING.
Album: released on K-Tel, May'80 by K-Tel Records. Dist: Record Merchandisers Distribution, Taylors, Terry Blood Distribution, Wynd-Up Distribution, Relay Distribution, Pickwick Distribution, Solomon & Peres Distribution, Polygram

HARD TIMES.
Tracks: / Children of the ghetto / Mystique*.
Notes: * = Extra track on 12" only
Single (7"): released on Jive, Feb'87 by Zomba Records. Dist: RCA, PRT, CBS

Single (12"): released on Jive, Feb'87 by Zomba Records. Dist: RCA, PRT, CBS

I BELIEVE IN YOU/YOUR MY....
Single (7"): released on Calibre, Jun'81 by Calibre Records. Dist: PRT

Single (12"): released on Calibre, Jun'81 by Calibre Records. Dist: PRT

LOVE TAKES TEARS/GOING FOR THE....
Single (7"): released on Calibre, Jan'82 by Calibre Records. Dist: PRT

Single (12"): released on Calibre, Jan'82 by Calibre Records. Dist: PRT

REAL THING, THE.
Album: released on Pye, Oct'76

SHE'S A GROOVY FREAK/IT'S THE REAL THING.
Single (7"): released on Calibre, Nov'80 by Calibre Records. Dist: PRT

Single (12"): released on Calibre, Nov'80 by Calibre Records. Dist: PRT

STRAIGHT TO THE HEART.
Tracks: / Straight to the heart / Mystique.
Single (7"): released on Zomba, Oct'86 Dist: BMG

Single (12"): released on Zomba, Oct'86 Dist: BMG

YOU TO ME ARE EVERYTHING/CAN'T GET.
Single (7"): released on Old Gold, Apr'83 by Old Gold Records. Dist: Lightning, Jazz Music, Spartan, Counterpoint

YOU TO ME ARE EVERYTHING.
Tracks: / You to me are everything / You to me are everything(decade remix '76-78) / Foot tappin / Children of the Ghetto (remix)
Single (7"): released on PRT, Feb'86 by PRT Records. Dist: PRT

Single (12"): released on PRT, Feb'86 by PRT Records. Dist: PRT

Real To Reel
MR & MRS/NOT THE ONE.
Single (7"): released on Red Shadow, Feb'81 Dist: Pinnacle

Reasonable Strollers
TOOLS FOR AFRICA/ SMILE/ NO WASTING.
Single (7"): released on Robust, Mar'82

Reasonable, Wooly
YOU'RE THE ONLY ONE.
Tracks: / You're the only one / You're the only one (Instrumental).
Single (7"): released on Club, Mar'87 by Phonogram Records. Dist: Polygram

Single (12"): released on Club, Mar'87 by Phonogram Records. Dist: Polygram

Reaves, Giles
WUNJO.
Tracks: / Wunjo (Joy) / Sowelu (Wholeness) / Uruz (Strength) / Eithwaz / Eihwaz (Defense)/Kano (Opening) / Odin (The Unknowable).
Album: released on MCA, Jul'87 by MCA Records. Dist: Polygram, MCA

Cassette: released on MCA, Jul'87 by MCA Records. Dist: Polygram, MCA

Compact disc: released on MCA, Jul'87 by MCA Records. Dist: Polygram, MCA

Reavy, Ed
IRISH FIDDLER.
Album: released on Rounder, Sep'79

Rebb, Johnny
COME ON LET'S GO.
Album: released on Rebel (Australia), Feb'84 Dist: Swift

Rebecca
REBECCA Du Maurier, Daphne (Bloom, Claire).
Double cassette: released on Listen For Pleasure, '83 by MFP Records. Dist: EMI

Rebecca Of...
REBECCA OF SUNNYBROOK FARM (Harris, Julie).
Picture disc album: released on Caedmon(USA), Feb'81 by Caedmon (USA) Records. Dist: Gower, Taylors, Discovery

Rebekka Frame
HAYSTACKS.
Tracks: / Sensative boys / Stray away / Haystacks / Speak in rhymes / Jelous of youth / False prophet.
Album: released on Revolver, Jul'86 by Revolver Records. Dist: Revolver, Cartel

---

Rebel
VALENTINO.
Tracks: / Valentino / Lonely traveller.
Single (7"): released on Flying Pig, Sep'86 by Flying Pig Records. Dist: Flying Pig

Rebel Christening
TRIBAL EYE.
Single (12"): released on Clay, Aug'85 by Clay Records. Dist: Pinnacle

Rebel Kind
REBEL KIND (Various Artists).
Album: released on Lolita, Feb'84 by Lolita Records. Dist: Rough Trade, Cartel

Rebel Music
REBEL MUSIC (Various Artists).
Album: released on Trojan, '83 by Trojan Records. Dist: PRT, Jetstar

Rebel Rock
REBEL ROCK (Various Artists).
Album: released on Third World, Jan'79 Dist: Jetstar Distribution

Rebel Rockabilly
REBEL ROCKABILLY (Various Artists).
Album: released on Charly, Jul'81 by Charly Records. Dist: Charly, Cadillac

Rebel Rock Quality
REBEL ROCK QUALITY Various artists (Various Artists).
Album: released on Konnexion, Feb'86 Dist: Roots, Pinnacle

Rebel Songs Of Ireland
REBEL SONGS OF IRELAND (Various Artists).
Album: released on Shamrock (Ireland), Oct'75 Dist: I & B, EMI (Ireland), Swift, Chris Wellard, Solomon & Peres Distribution, Jazz Music

Rebel Teng
REBEL TENG Various artists (Various Artists).
Album: released on Techniques, Nov'85 Dist: Jetstar Distribution

Rebirth
GUILTY.
Single (12"): released on Roots Radical, Oct'84 by Roots Radical Records. Dist: Jetstar Distribution

Rebirth Jazz Band
HERE TO STAY (Rebirth Jazz Band of New Orleans).
Album: released on Arhoolie, Jul'87 by Arhoolie Records. Dist: Projection, Topic, Jazz Music, Swift, Roots

REBIRTH JAZZ BAND OF NEW ORLEANS.
Album: released on Arhoolie, Mar'85 by Arhoolie Records. Dist: Projection, Topic, Jazz Music, Swift, Roots

Rebroff, Ivan
IVAN REBROFF.
Album: released on CBS, '74 by CBS Records. Dist: CBS

SOMEWHERE MY LOVE Ivan Rebroff sings in English.
Album: released on CBS, '74 by CBS Records. Dist: CBS

TAIGA TRAUME.
Album: released on CBS(Holland), Mar'84 by CBS Records. Dist: Discovery

Cassette: released on CBS(Holland), Mar'84 by CBS Records. Dist: Discovery

Recipe
HOME'S OVER.
Tracks: / Home's over / Outboard.
Single (12"): released on Emertial-Survival, Feb'86 Dist: Backs, Cartel

Reckless
HEART OF STEEL.
Picture disc album: released on Heavy Metal, Aug'85 by FM-Revolver Records. Dist: EMI

Cassette: released on Heavy Metal, Aug'85 by FM-Revolver Records. Dist: EMI

Album: released on Heavy Metal America, Jan'85 by FM-Revolver Records. Dist: EMI

Album: released on Heavy Metal America, Jan'85 by FM-Revolver Records. Dist: EMI

HOT 'N' READY.
Single (7"): released on FM, Aug'85 by FM-Revolver Records. Dist: EMI

NITTY GRITTY.
Tracks: / Nitty gritty / Deadly game.
Single (12"): released on Valentino, Mar'87

NO FRILLS.
Tracks: / Nitty gritty / Wild in the streets / Deadly game / Voices in the night / Crazy over you / Breakin' up / Night after night / Railroad alley / Eye for an eye / Holdin' on.
Album: released on Valentino, Apr'86

Cassette: released on Valentino, Apr'86

RECKLESS.
Album: released on EMI, Mar'81 by EMI Records. Dist: EMI

Recognitions
BIM BAM BOM.
Single (7"): released on Blue Train, Feb'85 by Checkmount Distribution. Dist: Spartan

FIRST DANCE.
Single (7"): released on Blue Train, Mar'84 by Checkmount Distribution. Dist: Spartan

TOO MUCH FICTION/ SMOKEY JOES.
Single (7"): released on Ryme Time, May'81 by Lismor Records. Dist: Lismor Distribution, Pinnacle

Recoil
RECOIL 1&2.
Album: released on Mute, Aug'86 Dist: Spartan Distribution, Rough Trade Distribution, Cartel Distribution

Recommended...
RECOMMENDED SAMPLER Various artists (Various Artists).
Notes: Artists include Robert Wyatt and Art Bears.
Album: released on Recommended, Sep'86 by Recommended Records. Dist: Recommended, Impetus, Rough Trade

VARIOUS RECOMMENDED ARTISTS various artists (Various Artists).
Single (7"): released on Recommended, Jun'82 by Recommended Records. Dist: Recommended, Impetus, Rough Trade

Record City
RECORD CITY Music from the original soundtrack.
Album: released on Polydor, Mar'78 by Polydor Records. Dist: Polygram, Polydor

Record collector
RECORD COLLECTOR, VOL 1 Various artists (Various Artists).
Album: released on Destiny, May'80 Dist: Destiny Records. Dist: Red Rhino, Cartel

Record City
RECORDIAU PRIOD
MADOG Y MORWR.
Single (7"): released on Recordiau Priod, May'84

Record Players
MONEY WORRIES.
Single (7"): released on Wreckord, May'84 by Wreckord Records. Dist: Independant, ILA

Records
MUSIC ON BOTH SIDES.
Album: released on Virgin, Mar'82 by Virgin Records. Dist: EMI, Virgin Distribution

RECORDS WAS CHEAP TO MAKE THEN various artists (Various Artists).
Album: released on Red Lightnin', Sep'82 by Red Lightnin' Records. Dist: Roots, Swift, Jazz Music, JSU, Pinnacle, Cartel, Wynd-Up Distribution

SHADES IN BED.
Album: by Virgin Records. Dist: EMI, Virgin Distribution

Record Shack Presents
RECORD SHACK PRESENTS THE MIXES Various artists (Various Artists).
Album: released on Record Shack, Aug'86 by Record Shack Records. Dist: PRT

Cassette: released on Record Shack, Aug'86 by Record Shack Records. Dist: PRT

RECORD SHACK PRESENTS VOLUME THREE MIXES.
Tracks: / High Energy / Second best / He's a saint,He's a sinner / Manpower / So many men,so little time / Caught in the act / I'm caught living on my own / Boys come to town(The) / Fan the flame / On a crowded street / Out of the darkest night.
Album: released on Record Shack, Sep'86 by Record Shack Records. Dist: PRT

Cassette: released on Record Shack, Sep'86 by Record Shack Records. Dist: PRT

RECORD SHACK PRESENTS...VOL.1
(Various Artists).
Album: released on Record Shack, Sep'84 by Record Shack Records. Dist: PRT

Cassette: released on Record Shack, Sep'84 by Record Shack Records. Dist: PRT

RECORD SHACK PRESENTS...VOL.2
(Various Artists).
Album: released on Record Shack, Oct'85 by Record Shack Records. Dist: PRT

Cassette: released on Record Shack, Oct'85 by Record Shack Records. Dist: PRT

Rectonob
SPANK THAT LOBSTER.
Cassette: released on Falling A, Nov'84 by Falling A Records. Dist: Falling A Distribution

Rector, Red
ANOTHER HAPPY DAY (Rector, Red & Bill Clifton).
Album: released on Breakdown, Jan'77

ARE YOU FROM DIXIE? (see Clifton, Bill) (Rector, Red & Bill Clifton).

RED RECTOR & FRIENDS.
Album: released on Revonah, Jun'79

Album: released on Revonah, Jun'79

Red
CRACK.
Album: released on Lost Moment, Mar'87

DANCING.
Single (7"): released on RGM, May'84 by RGM Records. Dist: Pinnacle

I CAN FLY.
Single (7"): released on Lost Moment, Apr'85

Single (12"): released on Lost Moment, Apr'85

IN MOTION.
Album: released on RGM, Jan'84 by RGM Records. Dist: Pinnacle

LET HER GO.
Single (7"): released on RGM, Jan'84 by RGM Records. Dist: Pinnacle

Single (12"): released on RGM, Jan'84 by RGM Records. Dist: Pinnacle

NAOMI.
Single (12"): released on RGM, Jan'84 by RGM Records. Dist: Pinnacle

PROMISES SAIL AWAY.
Tracks: / Promises sail away.
Single (7"): released on Lost Moment, Apr'86

RED.
Album: released on Jigsaw, Nov'84 Dist: Roots, Pinnacle, Projection

THOSE WHO TRY.
Single (7"): released on Lost Moments, Apr'87 Dist: Backs, Cartel

Single (12"): released on Lost Moments, Apr'87 Dist: Backs, Cartel

Red Alert
CITY EVASION.
Single (7"): released on No Future, Jan'83 by No Future Records. Dist: Pinnacle, Rough Trade, Cartel

IN BRITAIN (EP).
Single (7"): released on No Future, Jul'82 by No Future Records. Dist: Pinnacle, Rough Trade, Cartel

TAKE NO PRISONERS.
Single (7"): released on No Future, Jul'82 by No Future Records. Dist: Pinnacle, Rough Trade, Cartel

THERE'S A GUITAR BURNING (EP) (6-track EP).
Single (12"): released on No Future, Dec'83 by No Future Records. Dist: Pinnacle, Rough Trade, Cartel

WE'VE GOT THE POWER.
Album: released on No Future, Jun'83 by No Future Records. Dist: Pinnacle, Rough Trade, Cartel

Red Army Ensemble
TRADITIONAL RUSSIAN SONGS VOL.1.
Album: released on Melodiya (USSR), May'78 Dist: T.B.C Distribution

TRADITIONAL RUSSIAN SONGS VOL.2.
Album: released on Melodiya (USSR), May'78 Dist: T.B.C Distribution

TRADITIONAL RUSSIAN SONGS VOL.3.
Album: released on Melodiya (USSR), May'78 Dist: T.B.C Distribution

Red Assassin
RISE (EP).
Single (7"): released on R.A.S, Oct'84 by Greensleeves Records. Dist: RCA

Red Bamboo
DANCE OF LOVE.
Tracks: / Dance of love / On the line.
Single (7"): released on EMI, Jul'86 by EMI Records. Dist: EMI

Single (12"): released on EMI, Jul'86 by EMI Records. Dist: EMI

Red Beans & Rice
LIVE AT THE DUBLIN CASTLE.
Album: released on Ace, Jun'83 by Ace Records. Dist: Pinnacle, Swift, Hotshot Cadillac

Red Beards From Texas
GUDBUY T'JANE.
Tracks: / Gudbuy T'Jane.
Single (7"): released on Receiver, Nov'86 by Receiver Records. Dist: Pinnacle

I DIDN'T KNOW I LOVED YOU Till I saw you rock'n'roll.
Tracks: I didn't know I loved you / Rockin' and boppin'.
Single (7"): released on Receiver, Jul'87 by Receiver Records. Dist: Pinnacle

I SAW HER STANDING THERE.
Tracks: I saw her standing there / Poker with the boys.
Single (7"): released on Receiver, May'86 by Receiver Records. Dist: Pinnacle

Red Beat
DREAM.
Single (12"): released on Red Beat, Feb'82

SURVIVAL.
Single (7"): released on Red Beat, Jun'81

Red Bird Story, The
RED BIRD STORY, THE Various artists (Various Artists).
Tracks: / Chapel of love / I wanna love him so bad / People say / Remember(Walking in the sand) / Goodnight baby / Leader of the pack / Gee baby gee / Iko Iko / Give him a great big kiss / Gee the moon is shining bright / I can never go home anymore / Boy from New York City / Give us your blessing / He ain't no angel / Past present & future / I'm just a down home girl / Down home girl / I hurt on the other side / Something you got / Bad as they come / Let the good times roll / Come on baby / Fever / Go now / Bossa nova baby / My heart said(The bossa nova) / I can't let go / Take me for a little while / Standing by / I don't think my baby's coming back / New Yorks a lonely town / I know it's alright.
Notes: Original Red Bird Group Recordings.Licensed from Charly International APs.This compilation (P)1987 Charly Holdings Inc. (C)1987 Charly Records Ltd.
Double Album: released on Charly, May'87 by Charly Records. Dist: Charly, Cadillac

Double cassette: released on Charly, May'87 by Charly Records. Dist: Charly, Cadillac

Redbone
WITCH QUEEN OF NEW ORLEANS.
Single (7"): released on Epic, Jan'80 by CBS Records. Dist: CBS

Redbone, Leon
RED TO BLUE.
Album: released on August (USA), Apr'86 Dist: Taylors

Red Box
CHENKO.
Tracks: / Chenko / R in A / Ain't got no.
Single (7"): released on WEA, Jan'86 by WEA Records. Dist: WEA

Single (12"): released on WEA, Jan'86 by WEA Records. Dist: WEA

CHENKO (TENKO-LO).
Tracks: / Chenko / Speeches / Heart of the sun (slash and burn)*.
Single (7"): released on WEA, Jul'87 by WEA Records. Dist: WEA

Single (12"): released on WEA, Jul'87 by WEA Records. Dist: WEA

CHENKO/VALLEY.
Single (7"): released on Cherry Red, Jan'84 by Cherry Red Records. Dist: Pinnacle

Single (12"): released on Cherry Red, Jan'84 by Cherry Red Records. Dist: Pinnacle

CIRCLE & THE SQUARE.
Tracks: / For America / Heart of the sun / Billy's line / Bantu / Living in domes / Lean on me / Chenko / Saskatchewan / Leaders in the seventh heaven / Walk walk / Amen.
Album: released on WEA, Nov'86 by WEA Records. Dist: WEA

Cassette: released on WEA, Nov'86 by WEA Records. Dist: WEA

Compact disc: released on WEA, Nov'86 by WEA Records. Dist: WEA

FOR AMERICA.
Tracks: / For America / R'n'a / Ain't got no.
Single (7"): released on WEA, Oct'86 by WEA Records. Dist: WEA

Single (12"): released on WEA, Oct'86 by WEA Records. Dist: WEA

HEART OF THE SUN.
Tracks: / Enjoy (solid gold easy amex) / Lean on me*.
Single (7"): released on WEA, Jan'87 by WEA Records. Dist: WEA

Single (12"): released on WEA, Jan'87 by WEA Records. Dist: WEA

LEAN ON ME.
Single (7"): released on Sire, Aug'85

Single (12"): released on Sire, Aug'85

SASKATCHEWAN.
Single (7"): released on WEA, Dec'84 by WEA Records. Dist: WEA

Single (12"): released on WEA, Dec'84 by WEA Records. Dist: WEA

Redbridge Brass
REDBRIDGE PHENOMENON.
Album: released on Grosvenor, Jan'74 by Grosvenor Records. Dist: Taylors

Redcap James
PLAYS BROADWAY & UHURU.
Album: released on Afroboom, Mar'86 Dist: Sterns, Triple Earth

Red Clay Ramblers
CHUCKIN' THE FRIZZ.
Album: released on Flying Fish (USA), Sep'79 by Flying Fish Records (USA). Dist: Roots, Projection

Red Cloud
DOUBLE TALK/I WANT TO BE FREE.
Single (7"): released on Dancefloor, Jun'83 by Dancefloor Records. Dist: Vista Sounds Records, Jetstar

Single (12"): released on Dancefloor, Jun'83 by Dancefloor Records. Dist: Vista Sounds Records, Jetstar

RED CLOUD IN DUB.
Album: released on Vista Sounds, '83 by Vista Sounds Records. Dist: Jetstar

WHEN A MAN LOVES A WOMAN.
Single (7"): released on Echo, Mar'82 by Vista Sounds. Dist: Jazz Music

Single (12"): released on Echo, Mar'82 by Vista Sounds. Dist: Jazz Music

Red Crayola
BLACK SNAKES.
Album: released on Pure Freude, Sep'83 Dist: Swift

GOD BLESS THE RED CRAYOLA AND ALL WHO SAIL IN IT.
Album: released on Radar, Jun'79 by WEA Music Ltd. Dist: WEA, PRT

PARABLE OF ARABLE LAND.
Album: released on Radar, '78 by WEA Music Ltd. Dist: WEA, PRT

SOLDIER TALK.
Album: released on Radar, Mar'79 by WEA Music Ltd. Dist: WEA, PRT

Redder Than Red
REDDER THAN RED various artists (Various Artists).
Album: released on Chanan-Jah, Aug'84 by Chanan-Jah Records. Dist: Jetstar

Redd, Freddie
CONNECTION, THE.
Album: released on Blue Note (USA), Sep'84

STRAIGHT AHEAD.
Album: released on Interplay, Sep'79 by Interplay Records. Dist: Jazz Music, Swift

UNDER PARIS SKIES.
Album: released on Futura Swing Imports, Jul'77 Dist: JSU

Redd Holt Unlimited
I SHOT THE SHERIFF.
Single (7"): released on Charly, Jul'80 by Charly Records. Dist: Charly, Cadillac

Redding,George
GIVE ME YOUR BODY.
Single (7"): released on Solida, Oct'85

Single (12"): released on Solida, Oct'85

I WISH/LET'S GIVE LOVE A TRY.
Single (7"): released on Major, Nov'81 by Major Records. Dist: Pinnacle

Redding, Jacqui
TICKLE ON THE TUM (Redding, Jacqui & Ralph McTell).
Notes: For full information see under: McTell, Ralph

Redding, Otis
BEST OF.
Compact disc: released on Atlantic, Mar'87 by WEA Records. Dist: WEA

BEST OF OTIS REDDING,THE.
Double Album: by WEA Records. Dist: WEA

Album: released on Atlantic, Jul'84 by WEA Records. Dist: WEA

Cassette: released on Atlantic, Jul'84 by WEA Records. Dist: WEA

Cassette: released on Atlantic, '74 by WEA Records. Dist: WEA

COME TO ME.
Album: released on Charly(R&B), Apr'84 by Charly Records. Dist: Charly, Cadillac

Cassette: released on Charly(R&B), Apr'84 by Charly Records. Dist: Charly, Cadillac

DOCK OF THE BAY The definitive collection.
Tracks: / Shake / Mr.Pitiful / Respect / Love man / Satisfaction (I can't get no) / I can't turn you loose / Hard to handle / Fa-fa-fa-fa-fa (sad song) / My girl / I've been loving you too long / Try a little tenderness / My lover's prayer / That's how strong my love is / Pain in my heart / Change is gonna come, A / Dock of the bay / Cigarettes and coffee / These arms of mine / Tramp.
Album: released on Atlantic, Jul'87 by WEA Records. Dist: WEA

Cassette: released on Atlantic, Jul'87 by WEA Records. Dist: WEA

Compact disc: released on Atlantic, Jul'87 by WEA Records. Dist: WEA

Single (7"): released on Atlantic, '74 by WEA Records. Dist: WEA

DOCK OF THE BAY,THE (THE DEFINITIVE COLLECTION).
Album: released on Atlantic, 30 May'87 by WEA Records. Dist: WEA

Cassette: released on Atlantic, 30 May'87 by WEA Records. Dist: WEA

HISTORY OF OTIS REDDING.
Album: released on Atlantic, '74 by WEA Records. Dist: WEA

Cassette: released on Atlantic, '74 by WEA Records. Dist: WEA

I CAN'T TURN YOU LOOSE.
Single (12"): released on Atlantic, Apr'80 by WEA Records. Dist: WEA

LOVE MAN.
Album: released on Atlantic, '74 by WEA Records. Dist: WEA

MY GIRL.
Single (7"): released on Atlantic, '80 by WEA Records. Dist: WEA

Single (7"): released on Atlantic, Mar'84 by WEA Records. Dist: WEA

OTIS BLUE.
Album: released on Atco, Dec'83 by Atlantic Records. Dist: WEA

Cassette: released on Atco, Dec'83 by Atlantic Records. Dist: WEA

PURE OTIS.
Album: released on Atlantic, Jul'79 by WEA Records. Dist: WEA

READY STEADY GO SPECIAL, A.
Video-cassette (VHS): released on PMI, Sep'84 by PMI Records. Dist: EMI

Video-cassette [Betamax]: released on PMI, Sep'84 by PMI Records. Dist: EMI

(SITTING ON THE)DOCK OF THE BAY.
Single (7"): released on Atlantic, Oct'84 by WEA Records. Dist: WEA

Single (7"): released on Old Gold, Jan'85 by Old Gold Records. Dist: Lightning, Jazz Music, Spartan, Counterpoint

READY STEADY GO! SPECIAL, A.
Video-cassette (VHS): released on PMI, Aug'87 by PMI Records. Dist: EMI

TRY A LITTLE TENDERNESS.
Tracks: / Try a little tenderness / I've been loving you too long / Hard to handle.
Notes: Pic bag
Single (7"): released on Atlantic, May'87 by WEA Records. Dist: WEA

Single (12"): released on Atlantic, May'87 by WEA Records. Dist: WEA

Reddings

AWAKENING,THE.
Album: released on Epic, Mar'81 by CBS Records. Dist: CBS

PARASITE.
Single (7"): released on Boiling Point, Jul'85 by Polydor Records. Dist: Polygram

Single (12"): released on Boiling Point, Jul'85 by Polydor Records. Dist: Polygram

Redd Kross

NEUROTICA.
Tracks: / Neurotica / Play my song / Frosted flake / Janus, Jeanie and George Harrison / Love is you / Peach kelli pop / McKenzie / Ballad of a love doll / What they say / Ghandi is dead (I'm the cartoon man) / Beautiful bye byes.
Album: released on Big Time, Sep'87 by Mainline Record Company. Dist: Mainline. Estim retail price in Sep'87 was £6.29.

Cassette: released on Big Time, Sep'87 by Mainline Record Company. Dist: Mainline. Estim retail price in Sep'87 was £6.29.

Red Dragon

HOL A FRESH.
Single (12"): released on Technics, 20 Jun'87 by Technics Records. Dist: Jetstar Distribution

Redds and the Boys

MOVIN' AND GROOVIN'.
Single (7"): released on Washington Gogo, Feb'85

Single (12"): released on Washington Gogo, Feb'85

PUT YOUR RIGHT HAND IN THE AIR.
Single (7"): released on London, Jun'85 by London Records. Dist: Polygram

Redd, Sharon

BEAT THE STREET.
Album: released on Prelude, Oct'84 Dist: CBS

Cassette: released on Prelude, Oct'84 Dist: CBS

SHARON REDD.
Album: released on Epic, Apr'81 by CBS Records. Dist: CBS

Cassette: released on Epic, Apr'81 by CBS Records. Dist: CBS

TAKIN' A CHANCE ON LOVE.
Single (7"): released on Prelude, Mar'83 Dist: CBS

Single (12"): released on Prelude, Mar'83 Dist: CBS

THAT'S FUNK.
Album: released on Teldec (Germany), Apr'84 by Import Records. Dist: IMS Distribution, Polygram Distribution

YOU'RE A WINNER.
Single (7"): released on Prelude, Jan'84 Dist: CBS

Single (12"): released on Prelude, Jan'84 Dist: CBS

Reddy, Helen

ANGIE BABY.
Single (7"): released on Capitol, '80 by Capitol Records. Dist: EMI

BEST OF HELEN REDDY.
Album: released on Capitol, Jan'76 by Capitol Records. Dist: EMI

Cassette: released on Capitol, Jan'76 by Capitol Records. Dist: EMI

HELEN REDDY'S GREATEST HITS And More.
Tracks: / I am woman / I don't know how to love him / Leave me alone (Ruby red dress) / Delta dawn / You and me against the world / Angie baby / Emotion / Keep on singing / Peaceful / Ain't no way to treat a lady / Somewhere in the night / I can't hear you no more / You're my world / Happy girls (The) / Make love to me.
Compact disc: released on Capitol, Apr'87 by Capitol Records. Dist: EMI

I AM WOMAN.
Tracks: / Peaceful / I am woman / This masquerade / I didn't mean to love you / Where is my friend / And I love you so / What would they say / Where is the love / Hit the road Jack / Last blues song (The).
Notes: For the first time on Music For Pleasure with an album previosly released on the Fame label we present Helen Reddy. I am woman features not only the title track which many people regard as the theme song for the femininst movement, but also many other great tunes including another of her hits Peaceful, Don McLean's And I Love You so and the Ray Charles classic Hit The Road Jack.
Album: released on Music For Pleasure, Feb'86 by EMI Records. Dist: EMI

Cassette: released on Music For Pleasure, Feb'86 by EMI Records. Dist: EMI

I CAN'T SAY GOODBYE TO YOU/SAVE ME...
Single (7"): released on MCA, Sep'81 by MCA Records. Dist: Polygram, MCA

LIVE IN LONDON.
Double Album: released on Capitol, Jan'79 by Capitol Records. Dist: EMI

LOOKS LIKE LOVE/YESTERDAY CAN'T...
Single (7"): released on MCA, Feb'83 by MCA Records. Dist: Polygram, MCA

REDDY.
Album: released on Capitol, Aug'79 by Capitol Records. Dist: EMI

TAKE WHAT YOU FIND.
Album: released on Capitol, May'80 by Capitol Records. Dist: EMI

WE'LL SING IN THE SUNSHINE.
Album: released on Capitol, Jul'78 by Capitol Records. Dist: EMI

Redell, Teddy

TEDDY REDELL SOUND.
Album: released on White, Dec'86

Red Funk 'N' Green

LOUISIANA RED 'N' SUGAR BLUE.
Album: released on Black Panther, Apr'79 by Black Panther Records. Dist: Pinnacle, Swift

Red, Georgie

GET IN TOUCH.
Tracks: / Get in touch (inst) / Night time (is the right time).
Single (7"): released on WEA Int, Feb'87

Red Guitars

AMERICA AND ME.
Tracks: / America and me / Marianna.
Single (7"): released on Virgin, May'86 by Virgin Records. Dist: EMI, Virgin Distribution

Single (12"): released on Virgin, May'86 by Virgin Records. Dist: EMI, Virgin Distribution

BE WITH ME.
Single (7"): released on One Way, Mar'85 Dist: Red Rhino Distribution

Single (12"): released on One Way, Mar'85 Dist: Red Rhino Distribution

BLUE CARAVAN.
Tracks: / Blue caravan / Suspicion & fear.
Single (7"): released on Virgin, Oct'86 by Virgin Records. Dist: EMI, Virgin Distribution

Single (12"): released on Virgin, Oct'86 by Virgin Records. Dist: EMI, Virgin Distribution

FACT/LIVE (GUYS).
Single (7"): released on Self Drive, Nov'83 Dist: Red Rhino, Cartel

GOOD TECHNOLOGY.
Single (7"): released on Self Drive, May'84 Dist: Red Rhino, Cartel

Single (12"): released on Self Drive, May'84 Dist: Red Rhino, Cartel

GOOD TECHNOLOGY/FACT/PARIS FRANCE.
Single (12"): released on Self Drive, Jan'84 Dist: Red Rhino, Cartel

GOOD TECHNOLOGY/HEARTBEAT GO.
Single (7"): released on Self Drive, Jun'83 Dist: Red Rhino, Cartel

MARIMBA JIVE.
Single (7"): released on Self Drive, Sep'84 Dist: Red Rhino, Cartel

Single (12"): released on Self Drive, Sep'84 Dist: Red Rhino, Cartel

NATIONAL AVENUE.
Tracks: / National avenue / King and country / Things I want.
Single (7"): released on Virgin, Feb'86 by Virgin Records. Dist: EMI, Virgin Distribution

Single (12"): released on Virgin, Feb'86 by Virgin Records. Dist: EMI, Virgin Distribution

SLOW TO FADE.
Tracks: / Remote control / Dive / Astronomy / Cloak and dagger / Shaken not stirred / Crocodile tears / Sting in the tail / Marimba / Slow to fade.
Compact disc: released on Self Drive, Nov'86 Dist: Red Rhino, Cartel

STEELTOWN.
Single (7"): released on Self Drive, Jun'84 Dist: Red Rhino, Cartel

Single (12"): released on Self Drive, Jun'84 Dist: Red Rhino, Cartel

TALES OF THE EXPECTED.
Tracks: / Be with me / Suspicion and fear / Love and understanding / House of love / Storyville / Trains on time / Marianne / Baby's got a gun / Sweet water ranch / National Avenue.
Album: released on Virgin, Jul'86 by Virgin Records. Dist: EMI, Virgin Distribution

Cassette: released on Virgin, Jul'86 by Virgin Records. Dist: EMI, Virgin Distribution

Compact disc: released on Virgin, Jul'87 by Virgin Records. Dist: EMI, Virgin Distribution

Red Gun

IF YOU DON'T FIGHT YOU LOSE.
Album: released on CBS, Jul'85 by CBS Records. Dist: CBS

Cassette: released on CBS, Jul'85 by CBS Records. Dist: CBS

I WAS ONLY NINETEEN.
Single (7"): released on CBS, Jun'85 by CBS Records. Dist: CBS

Red Hackle Pipers

BLEND OF RED HACKLE.
Album: released on Great Bands, Oct'81 by Decca Records. Dist: Polygram, Solomon & Peres Distribution

Cassette: released on Great Bands, Oct'81 by Decca Records. Dist: Polygram, Solomon & Peres Distribution

PRIDE O' SCOTLAND.
Album: released on RCA International (USA), '84 by RCA Records. Dist: RCA

Cassette: released on RCA International (USA), '84 by RCA Records. Dist: RCA

Red Heads

RED HEADS, SIX HOTTENTOTS & LANIN'S ARCADIANS.
Album: released on Fountain, Apr'79 by Retrieval Records. Dist: Jazz Music, Swift, VJM, Wellard, Chris, Retrieval

WE THREE.
Album: released on Fountain, Sep'79 by Retrieval Records. Dist: Jazz Music, Swift, VJM, Wellard, Chris, Retrieval

Red Hot Max

LONESOME ROCKER.
Album: released on Rockhouse, May'83 by Rockhouse Records. Dist: Swift Distribution, Charly Distribution

Red Hot 'n' Blue

RED HOT 'N' BLUE (Various Artists).
Album: released on Charly, Sep'83 by Charly Records. Dist: Charly, Cadillac

WAIT'N'SEE.
Album: released on Northwood, Jan'86 by Northwood Records. Dist: Backs-Cartel

Red Hot Rockabilly

RED HOT ROCKABILLY VOL.2 (Various Artists).
Tracks: / 49 women / One way ticket / Jackson dog / Satellite hop / Roll over Beethoven / You don't mean to make me cry / Clickety clack / Go go heart / Rock on Mabel / Puppy love / Tore up / Move over Rover.
Album: released on Magnum Force, Jul'87 by Magnum Music Group Ltd. Dist: Magnum Music Group Ltd, PRT, Spartan

RED HOT ROCKABILLY.
Album: released on Magnum Force, Feb'85 by Magnum Music Group Ltd. Dist: Magnum Music Group Ltd, PRT, Spartan

Red Letter Day

RELEASED EMOTIONS.
Single (12"): released on Quiet, Aug'86 by Quiet Records. Dist: Nine Mile, Cartel

TAKE ME IN YOUR ARMS.
Tracks: / Take me in your arms / Moving on
Single (7"): released on Quiet, Jul'87 by Quiet Records. Dist: Nine Mile, Cartel

WHEREVER YOU MAY RUN.
Tracks: / Wherever you may run / Susie's bombed out tonite.
Single (7"): released on Last Generation, Mar'86

Red Lipstique

DRAC'S BACK.
Single (7"): released on Magnet, Mar'82 by Magnet Records. Dist: BMG

Single (12"): released on Magnet, Mar'82 by Magnet Records. Dist: BMG

OSCAR WILDE/MORE GDM.
Single (7"): released on Charly, Feb'83 by Charly Records. Dist: Charly, Cadillac

Single (12"): released on Charly, Feb'83 by Charly Records. Dist: Charly, Cadillac

SHAME SHAME SHAME/SPECIAL NEW YORK MIX.
Single (7"): released on Disco Int, Oct'83

Single (12"): released on Disco Int, Oct'83

Red London

STEN GUNS IN SUNDERLAND (EP) / THIS IS ENGLAND.
Single (7"): released on Razor, Jul'83 by Razor. Dist: Pinnacle

Red Lorry Yellow Lorry

BEATING MY HEAD.
Single (7"): released on Red Rhino, Sep'82 by Red Rhino Records. Dist: Red Rhino, Cartel

CHANCE.
Single (7"): released on Red Rhino, Mar'85 by Red Rhino Records. Dist: Red Rhino, Cartel

Single (12"): released on Red Rhino, Mar'85 by Red Rhino Records. Dist: Red Rhino, Cartel

CUT DOWN.
Tracks: / Cut down / Running fever / Pushed me.
Single (7"): released on Red Rhino, Oct'86 by Red Rhino Records. Dist: Red Rhino, Cartel

Single (12"): released on Red Rhino, Oct'86 by Red Rhino Records. Dist: Red Rhino, Cartel

HE'S RED / SEE THE FIRE.
Single (7"): released on Red Rhino, Oct'83 by Red Rhino Records. Dist: Red Rhino, Cartel

HOLLOW EYES.
Single (7"): released on Red Rhino, Oct'84 by Red Rhino Records. Dist: Red Rhino, Cartel

Single (12"): released on Red Rhino, Oct'84 by Red Rhino Records. Dist: Red Rhino, Cartel

MONKEYS ON JUICE.
Single (7"): released on Red Rhino, Jun'84 by Red Rhino Records. Dist: Red Rhino, Cartel

Single (12"): released on Red Rhino, Jun'84 by Red Rhino Records. Dist: Red Rhino, Cartel

PAINT YOUR WAGON.
Album: released on Red Rhino, Mar'86 by Red Rhino Records. Dist: Red Rhino, Cartel

Cassette: released on Red Rhino, Mar'86 by Red Rhino Records. Dist: Red Rhino, Cartel

Compact disc: released on Red Rhino, Oct'8[illegible] by Red Rhino Records. Dist: Red Rhino, Cartel

REVOLT INTO STYLE (EP).
Single (12"): released on Cocteau, Feb'83 by Cocteau Records. Dist: Pinnacle, IDS

SPINNING ROUND.
Single (7"): released on Red Rhino, Sep'85 by Red Rhino Records. Dist: Red Rhino, Cartel

Single (12"): released on Red Rhino, Sep'85 by Red Rhino Records. Dist: Red Rhino, Cartel

TAKE IT ALL / HAPPY.
Single (7"): released on Red Rhino, Apr'83 by Red Rhino Records. Dist: Red Rhino, Cartel

TALK ABOUT THE WEATHER.
Album: released on Red Rhino, Jan'85 by Red Rhino Records. Dist: Red Rhino, Cartel

THIS TODAY.
Single (7"): released on Red Rhino, Mar'84 by Red Rhino Records. Dist: Red Rhino, Cartel

WALKING ON YOUR HANDS.
Tracks: / Walking on your hands.
Single (7"): released on Red Rhino, May'86 by Red Rhino Records. Dist: Red Rhino, Cartel

Single (12"): released on Red Rhino, May'86 by Red Rhino Records. Dist: Red Rhino, Cartel

Redman and Blackwell
IN WILLISAU.
Album: released on Black Saint, May'85 Dist: Projection, IMS, Polygram, Chris Wellard, Harmonia Mundi, Swift

Redman, Dewey Quartet
STRUGGLE CONTINUES, THE.
Album: released on ECM (Germany), Mar'83 by ECM Records. Dist: IMS, Polygram, Virgin through EMI

Redman, Don
1932-1936 REDMAN'S RED BOOK (Redman, Don & his orchestra).
Album: released on Collectors Must, Dec'86 Dist: Jazz Music

DOIN' THE NEW LOWDOWN (Redman, Don & his Orchestra).
Album: released on Hep, Dec'84 by H.R. Taylor Records. Dist: Jazz Music, Cadillac Music, JSU, Taylors, Wellard, Chris, Zodiac, Swift, Fast Forward

EVE OF DESTRUCTION.
Single (7"): released on CBS, Jan'85 by CBS Records. Dist: CBS

GOOD AS GOLD.
Album: released on CBS, Jul'83 by CBS Records. Dist: CBS

: released on CBS, Jul'83 by CBS Records. Dist: CBS

Redrose, Anthony
BANG AROUND.
Tracks: / Bang around / Elegant lover.
Single (7"): released on Firehouse, Apr'86 Dist: Jetstar

CANTA.
Tracks: / Canta / Up Lender.
Single (12"): released on Firehouse, Apr'86 Dist: Jetstar

CAN'T KNOCK ME.
Tracks: / Can't knock me / Gwan talk.
Single (12"): released on Firehouse, Apr'86 Dist: Jetstar

FRAID A PRISON.
Tracks: / Fraid a prison / Josephine.
Single (12"): released on Toughest, Jun'86 Dist: Jetstar

LAUNCH AND ATTACK.
Tracks: / Launch and attack / Visit (The).
Single (12"): released on Aces Music, Oct'86 Dist: Jetstar

ME NO WANT NO BOOPS.
Tracks: / Me no want no boops / No call me no boops.
Single (12"): released on Firehouse, Jul'86 Dist: Jetstar

SOUND BOY GET NERVOUS.
Tracks: / Sound boy get nervous / Love me country.
Single (12"): released on BP International, Jul'86 Dist: Jetstar

TEMPO.
Single (12"): released on Firehouse, Nov'85 Dist: Jetstar

Red Roseland Cornpickers
VOLUME 1.
Album: released on Stomp Off, Jul'86 by Stomp Off Records. Dist: Jazz Music Distribution

VOLUME 2.
Album: released on Stomp Off, Jun'86 by Stomp Off Records. Dist: Jazz Music Distribution

Reds
DANGER/DO YOU PLAY THE GAME.
Single (7"): released on Kingdom, Oct'81 by Kingdom Records. Dist: Kingdom

STRONGER SILENCE.
Album: released on Kingdom, Oct'81 by Kingdom Records. Dist: Kingdom

Red Shark
SOUR MASH (Red Shark / Strange Men With Guns).
Tracks: / Sour mash.
Single (7"): released on Bite Back, Jun'86 Dist: Backs, Cartel

Red Shift
BACK IN THE RED.
Album: released on Backshift, Jul'87 Dist: Roots, Projection

Red Shoes
ALL FALL DOWN.
Single (7"): released on Stepping Out, Nov'85

BY THE TIME IT GETS DARK.
Tracks: / By the time it gets dark / Her song / Room with a view.
Single (7"): released on Mooncrest, May'87 by Mooncrest Records. Dist: PRT Distribution

Redskins
BRING IT DOWN (THIS INSANE THING).
Single (7"): released on Decca, Jun'85 by Decca Records. Dist: Polygram

Single (12"): released on Decca, Jun'85 by Decca Records. Dist: Polygram

IT CAN BE DONE.
Tracks: / It can be done / K.o.k.o / Let's make it work / Plateful of hate, A.
Single (7"): released on Decca, May'86 by Decca Records. Dist: Polygram

Single 10": released on Decca, May'86 by Decca Records. Dist: Polygram

KEEP ON KEEPING ON.
Single (7"): released on Decca, Oct'84 by Decca Records. Dist: Polygram

Single (12"): released on Decca, Oct'84 by Decca Records. Dist: Polygram

KICK OVER THE STATUES.
Single (7"): released on Abstract Dance, Nov'85 Dist: Priority, RCA

LEAN ON ME / UNIONIZE.
Single (7"): released on CNT, Jul'83 Dist: Rough Trade, Cartel

Single (12"): released on CNT, Jul'83 Dist: Rough Trade, Cartel

LEV BRONSTEIN / THE PEASANT ARMY.
Single (7"): released on CNT, Jul'82 Dist: Rough Trade, Cartel

NEITHER WASHINGTON NOR MOSCOW.
Album: released on Decca, Mar'86 by Decca Records. Dist: Polygram

Cassette: released on Decca, Mar'86 by Decca Records. Dist: Polygram

PEEL SESSIONS 9.10.82.
Single (12"): released on Strange Fruit, Jun'87 by Clive Selwood. Dist: Pinnacle

POWER IS YOURS (THE).
Tracks: / Power is yours, The / 99 (and a half) won't do / Take 3 / Take your goods and buy them.
Single (7"): released on London, Feb'86 by London Records. Dist: Polygram

Single (12"): released on London, Feb'86 by London Records. Dist: Polygram

Double-pack single: released on London, Feb'86 by London Records. Dist: Polygram

Red, Snowy
LONG RUN.
Single (7"): released on Soundworks, Mar'84 by Rough Trade Records. Dist: Cartel

Red Sonja
RED SONJA Original soundtrack.
Album: released on JMP (W.Germany), Jan'86 Dist: Silva Screen Distribution

Red, Sonny
OUT OF THE BLUE.
Album: released on Blue Note (USA), Sep'84

Red Star Belgrade
MAD DOGS AND ENGLISHMEN.
Single (7"): released on Stagecoach, Apr'82

Red Sun
CINDERELLA ROCKAFELLA.
Single (7"): released on Oliver D, Feb'81 by Spartan Records. Dist: Spartan

Red, Tampa
YOU CAN'T GET THAT STUFF NO MORE.
Album: released on Oldie Blues, Sep'79 Dist: Cadillac, Projection Distribution, Celtic Music Distribution, JSU Distribution, Swift Distribution

Red Turns To
DEEP SLEEP.
Single (12"): released on Factory, May'85 by Factory Records. Dist: Cartel, Pinnacle

Redundants
ON YER BIKE/MY BABY'S GONE.
Single (7"): released on Leo, May'82 Dist: Jazz Music, Chris Wellard

Red Wave
RED WAVE Various artists (Various Artists).
Tracks: / Ashes / Tonight / Thirst, The / Saw a night / Films / City / Streetcar headed east / Experimentor / Doctor boogie / Juice squeezer / Metamorphoses / If you think / No telephone / Paper flowers.
Album: released on Big Time, Sep'87 by Mainline Record Company. Dist: Mainline. Estimtail price in Sep'87 was £6.29.

Cassette: released on Big Time, Sep'87 by Mainline Record Company. Dist: Mainline. Estim retail price in Sep'87 was £6.29.

Redway, Mike
COME ON HOME.
Tracks: / Come on home / Georgie Sunday.
Single (7"): for sale

DON'T WANNA BE FAMOUS/BLUE SUNRISE.
Single (7"): released on Go Ahead, Sep'82 by Go Ahead Records. Dist: Go Ahead

MORRIS MINOR/HAPPY BIRTHDAY TO YOU.
Single (7"): released on Button, Nov'81 by Musical Characters Records. Dist: Spartan

MY KINDA MUSIC.
Album: released on Go Ahead, Feb'83 by Go Ahead Records. Dist: Go Ahead

Cassette: released on Go Ahead, Feb'83 by Go Ahead Records. Dist: Go Ahead

OUR ANNIVERSARY OF LOVE.
Tracks: / Our anniversary of love / Someday the loving will be.
Single (7"): released on Aveca, Jun'86 Dist: Spartan

ROCK AND ROLL YOU'RE BEAUTIFUL.
Tracks: / What are you like love.
Single (7"): released on Aveca, Jan'87 Dist: Spartan

Single (12"): released on Go Ahead, Jan'82 by Go Ahead Records. Dist: Go Ahead

SHOW IS OVER.
Single (7"): released on Go Ahead, May'83 by Go Ahead Records. Dist: Go Ahead

WHAT ARE YOU LIKE LOVE/HEAVEN ONLY KNOWS.
Single (7"): released on Go Ahead, Aug'83 by Go Ahead Records. Dist: Go Ahead

Reece, Colin
WELL KEPT SECRETS.
Album: released on Dambuster, Oct'85 by Dambuster Records. Dist: Projection, Celtic Music, Roots

Reece, Dizzy
BLOWIN' AWAY (Reece, Dizzy & Ted Curson).
Album: released on Interplay, Aug'79 by Interplay Records. Dist: Jazz Music, Swift

MANHATTAN PROJECT.
Album: released on Beehive (USA), Dec'79 by Cadillac Records. Dist: JSU

POSSESSION, EXORCISM, PEACE.
Album: released on Honeydew, Oct'79 Dist: Swift, JSU

PROGRESS REPORT.
Album: released on Jasmine, Mar'83 by Jasmine Records. Dist: Counterpoint, Lugtons, Taylor, H.R., Wellard, Chris, Swift, Cadillac

Reed, Al
I AM FED UP WITH THIS MUSIC.
Single (12"): released on Ice Cube, Mar'82 Dist: Jetstar

Reed, B Mitchell
CRUISIN' 1963 WMCA New York.
Cassette: released on Increase(USA), Jun'87 by Quicksilver Records (USA).

Reed, Jerry
20 OF THE BEST.
Album: released on RCA International, Jul'82

Cassette: released on RCA International, Jul'82

Reed, Jimmy
12 GREATEST HITS.
Tracks: / Sun is shining, The / Honest I do / Down in Virginia / Baby what you want me to do / Found love / Hush hush / Bright lights big city / Close together / Big boss man / Ay shucks hush your mouth / Good lover / Shame shame shame.
Album: released on Topline, May'87 by Charly Records. Dist: Charly Distribution

Cassette: released on Topline, May'87 by Charly Records. Dist: Charly Distribution

BIG BOSS BLUES.
Tracks: / You don't have to go / I ain't got you / Ain't that loving you baby / Can't stand to see you go / You got me dizzy / Honest I do / Down in Virginia / I'm gonna get my baby / I wanna be loved / Going to New York / Take out some insurance / Baby, what you want me to do / Hush hush / Found love / Big boss man / I'm a love you / Bright lights, big city / Aw shucks, hush your mouth / Good lover / Too much / I'll change my style / Shame, shame, shame.
Compact disc: released on Charly, Mar'86 by Charly Records. Dist: Charly, Cadillac

BOOGIE IN THE DARK.
Album: released on Blue Moon, Feb'84 by Magnum Music Group Ltd, PRT, Spartan

COLD CHILLS 1967-1970.
Album: released on Krazy Kat, Jan'85 Dist: Jazz Music, Swift, Chris Wellard, H.R. Taylor, Charly, Hotshot, IRS Distribution

HIGH AND LONESOME.
Album: released on Charly, Mar'81 by Charly Records. Dist: Charly, Cadillac

I'M THE MAN(DOWN THERE).
Album: released on Charly(R&B), Jun'85 by Charly Records. Dist: Charly, Cadillac

ROCKIN' WITH REED.
Tracks: / I found my baby / Shoot my baby / Roll & rhumba / You upset my mind / Pretty thing / Rockin' with Reed / She don't want me no more / Come on baby / I don't go for that / When you left me / Do the thing / Little rain / Signals of love / Sun is shining (The) / Caress me baby / Laughing at the blues / Baby what's wrong / Left handed woman / I'm going upside your head.
Notes: All compositions by Jimmy Reed unless otherwise stated. All songs published by Tristan Music Ltd.
Compact disc: released on Charly, Apr'87 by Charly Records. Dist: Charly, Cadillac

SHAME SHAME SHAME Vol 1.
Album: released on Krazy Kat, Jan'84 Dist: Jazz Music, Swift, Chris Wellard, H.R. Taylor, Charly, Hotshot, IRS Distribution

SHAME SHAME SHAME/BIG BOSS MAN.
Single (7"): released on Charly, Jul'80 by Charly Records. Dist: Charly, Cadillac

UPSIDE YOUR HEAD.
Album: released on Charly(R&B), '85 by Charly Records. Dist: Charly, Cadillac

Cassette: released on Charly(R&B), '85 by Charly Records. Dist: Charly, Cadillac

Reed, Junior
RUBBA DUBBING.
Single (7"): released on Black Roots, Sep'84 by Black Roots Records. Dist: Jetstar

THANKS & PRAISE.
Single (12"): released on W.O.W., Jan'85 by W.O.W. Records. Dist: Jetstar

Reed, Les
MAN OF ACTION (Reed, Les, Orchestra).
Single (7"): released on European Import, '80 Dist: Conifer

Reed, Lou
BELLS, THE.
Album: released on Arista, Oct'79 by Arista Records. Dist: RCA

BERLIN.
Tracks: / Berlin / Lady day / Men of good fortune / Caroline says / How do you think it feels / On Jim / Caroline says || / Kids (The) / Bed (The) / Sad songs.
Album: released on RCA, Jun'86 by RCA Records. Dist: RCA, Roots, Swift, Wellard, Chris, I & B, Solomon & Peres Distribution

Cassette: released on RCA, Jun'86 by RCA Records. Dist: RCA, Roots, Swift, Wellard, Chris, I & B, Solomon & Peres Distribution

Compact disc: released on RCA, Jun'86 by RCA Records. Dist: RCA, Roots, Swift, Wellard, Chris, I & B, Solomon & Peres Distribution

BLUE MASK/WALK ON THE WILD SIDE.
Single (12"): released on RCA, Dec'83 by RCA Records. Dist: RCA, Roots, Swift, Wellard, Chris, I & B, Solomon & Peres Distribution

COFFRET OR.
Album: released on RCA (Special Imports Service), Jul'84

CONEY ISLAND BABY.
Album: released on RCA International, '84

Cassette: released on RCA International, Mar'81

CONEY ISLAND BABY.
Tracks: / Crazy feeling / Charley's girl / She's my best friend / Kicks / Gift / Oooh baby / Nobody's business / Coney island baby.
Compact disc: released on RCA, Dec'86 by RCA Records. Dist: RCA, Roots, Swift, Wellard, Chris, I & B, Solomon & Peres Distribution

GROWING UP IN PUBLIC.
Album: released on Arista, May'80 by Arista Records. Dist: RCA

I CAN'T STAND IT.
Album: released on RCA (Germany), Jul'83

Cassette: released on RCA (Germany), Jul'83

I LOVE YOU SUZANNE.
Single (7"): released on RCA, May'84 by RCA Records. Dist: RCA, Roots, Swift, Wellard, Chris, I & B, Solomon & Peres Distribution

Single (12"): released on RCA, May'84 by RCA Records. Dist: RCA, Roots, Swift, Wellard, Chris, I & B, Solomon & Peres Distribution

LEGENDARY HEARTS.
Tracks: / Legendary hearts / Don't talk to me about work / Make up mind / Martial law / Last shot (The) / Turn out the light / Pow wow / Betrayed / Bottoming out / Home of the brave / Rooftop garden.
Album: released on RCA, Oct'86 by RCA Records. Dist: RCA, Roots, Swift, Wellard, Chris, I & B, Solomon & Peres Distribution

Cassette: released on RCA, Oct'86 by RCA Records. Dist: RCA, Roots, Swift, Wellard, Chris, I & B, Solomon & Peres Distribution

Album: released on RCA, Mar'83 by RCA Records. Dist: RCA, Roots, Swift, Wellard, Chris, I & B, Solomon & Peres Distribution

Cassette: released on RCA, Mar'83 by RCA Records. Dist: RCA, Roots, Swift, Wellard, Chris, I & B, Solomon & Peres Distribution

LIVE.
Tracks: / Walk on the wild side / I'm waiting for the man / Vicious / Oh Jim / Satellite of love / Sad song.
Compact disc: released on RCA, Mar'87 by RCA Records. Dist: RCA, Roots, Swift, Wellard, Chris, I & B, Solomon & Peres Distribution

Album: released on RCA International, '84

Cassette: released on RCA International, '84

LIVE IN ITALY.
Album: released on RCA, Jan'84 by RCA Records. Dist: RCA, Roots, Swift, Wellard, Chris, I & B, Solomon & Peres Distribution

Cassette: released on RCA, Jan'84 by RCA Records. Dist: RCA, Roots, Swift, Wellard, Chris, I & B, Solomon & Peres Distribution

LOU REED.
Album: released on RCA (Germany), '83

LOU REED & VELVET UNDERGROUND.
Album: released on Polydor, '74 by Polydor Records. Dist: Polygram, Polydor

MAGIC MOMENTS.
Cassette: released on RCA, May'86 by RCA Records. Dist: RCA, Roots, Swift, Wellard, Chris, I & B, Solomon & Peres Distribution

MISTRIAL.
Tracks: / Mistrial / No money down / Outside / Don't hurt a woman / Video violence / Spit it out / Original wrapper / Mama's got a lover / I remember you / Tell it to your heart.
Album: released on RCA, Apr'86 by RCA Records. Dist: RCA, Roots, Swift, Wellard, Chris, I & B, Solomon & Peres Distribution

Cassette: released on RCA, Apr'86 by RCA Records. Dist: RCA, Roots, Swift, Wellard, Chris, I & B, Solomon & Peres Distribution

Compact disc: released on RCA, Apr'86 by RCA Records. Dist: RCA, Roots, Swift, Wellard, Chris, I & B, Solomon & Peres Distribution

NEW SENSATION.
Tracks: / I love you Suzanne / Endlessly jealous / My red joystick / Turn to me / New sensations / Doin the things that we want to / What becomes a legend most / Fly into the sun / My friend George / High in the city / Down at the arcade.
Compact disc: released on RCA, Jul'86 by RCA Records. Dist: RCA, Roots, Swift, Wellard, Chris, I & B, Solomon & Peres Distribution

Album: released on RCA, Apr'84 by RCA Records. Dist: RCA, Roots, Swift, Wellard, Chris, I & B, Solomon & Peres Distribution

Cassette: released on RCA, Apr'84 by RCA Records. Dist: RCA, Roots, Swift, Wellard, Chris, I & B, Solomon & Peres Distribution

NEW YORK SUPERSTAR.
Tracks: / Walk on the wild side / Vicious / Charley's girl / Berlin / Lady day / Gift, A / Intro to sweet Jane / Sweet Jane / Caroline says / Billy / Goodnight ladies.
Album: released on Fame, Sep'86 by Music For Pleasure Records. Dist: EMI

Cassette: released on Fame, Sep'86 by Music For Pleasure Records. Dist: EMI

Album: released on RCA (Germany), '83

NO MONEY DOWN.
Tracks: / No money down / Don't hurt a woman / No money down (ext. version) / No money down (Dub version).
Single (7"): released on RCA, Jun'86 by RCA Records. Dist: RCA, Roots, Swift, Wellard, Chris, I & B, Solomon & Peres Distribution

Single (12"): released on RCA, Jun'86 by RCA Records. Dist: RCA, Roots, Swift, Wellard, Chris, I & B, Solomon & Peres Distribution

Single (12"): released on RCA (Germany), Sep'86

ROCK AND ROLL DIARY 1967-1980.
Double Album: released on Arista, Dec'80 by Arista Records. Dist: RCA

ROCK AND ROLL HEART.
Album: released on Arista, Nov'76 by Arista Records. Dist: RCA

ROCK GALAXY.
Album: released on RCA (Germany), '83

ROCK'N'ROLL ANIMAL.
Tracks: / Intro- sweet Jane / White light- White heat / Heroin / Lady day / Rock'n' roll.
Album: released on RCA, Jun'86 by RCA Records. Dist: RCA, Roots, Swift, Wellard, Chris, I & B, Solomon & Peres Distribution

Cassette: released on RCA, Jun'86 by RCA Records. Dist: RCA, Roots, Swift, Wellard, Chris, I & B, Solomon & Peres Distribution

Compact disc: released on RCA, Jun'86 by RCA Records. Dist: RCA, Roots, Swift, Wellard, Chris, I & B, Solomon & Peres Distribution

SALLY CAN'T DANCE.
Tracks: / Ride, Sally, ride / Animal language / Baby face / NY stars / Kill your sons / Billy / Sally can't dance / Ennui.
Compact disc: released on RCA, Mar'87 by RCA Records. Dist: RCA, Roots, Swift, Wellard, Chris, I & B, Solomon & Peres Distribution

SEPTEMBER SONG.
Single (7"): released on A&M, Oct'85 by A&M Records. Dist: Polygram

SOUL MAN (Reed, Lou & Sam Moore).
Notes: For full information see: Moore, Sam & Lou Reed.

STREET HASSLE.
Album: released on Arista, Apr'78 by Arista Records. Dist: RCA

TAKE NO PRISONERS.
Album: released on RCA (Special Imports Service), Jul'84

TRANSFORMER.
Tracks: / Vicious / Andy's chest / Perfect day / Hangin around / Walk on the wild side / Make up / Satelite of love / Wagon wheel / New York telephone conversation / I'm so free / Goodnight ladies.
Compact disc: released on RCA, Jan'83 by RCA Records. Dist: RCA, Roots, Swift, Wellard, Chris, I & B, Solomon & Peres Distribution

Album: released on RCA International (USA), '84 by RCA Records. Dist: RCA

Cassette: released on RCA International (USA), '84 by RCA Records. Dist: RCA

Compact disc: released on RCA International (USA), '84 by RCA Records. Dist: RCA

Album: released on RCA International (USA), '84 by RCA Records. Dist: RCA

WALK ON THE WILD SIDE Best of Lou Reed.
Tracks: / Satellite of love / Wild child / I love you / How do you think it feels? / New York telephone conversation / Walk on the wild side / Sweet Jane / White light/White heat / Sally can't dance / Nowhere at all / Coney Island baby / Walk on the wild side / Vicious.
Compact disc: released on RCA, Mar'87 by RCA Records. Dist: RCA, Roots, Swift, Wellard, Chris, I & B, Solomon & Peres Distribution

Single (7"): released on Old Gold, Oct'86 by Old Gold Records. Dist: Lightning, Jazz Music, Spartan, Counterpoint

Single (7"): released on RCA Golden Grooves, Aug'81 by RCA Records. Dist: RCA

WITH THE VELVET UNDERGROUND 1969.
Album: released on Mercury, Apr'79 by Phonogram Records. Dist: Polygram Distribution

Reed, Marc

ONE BODY.
Tracks: / One body / Remix.
Single (7"): released on 20/20, May'86 Dist: Jetstar

Single (12"): released on 20/20, May'86 Dist: Jetstar

Reed, Mike

CHARLIE NOT SO GOOD.
Album: released on CSA, Dec'86 by CSA Records. Dist: PRT, Jetstar

Reed, Waymon

46TH & 8TH.
Album: released on Artists House, May'81 Dist: JSU, Swift

Reedy, Winston

AMBITION.
Single (12"): released on DEP International, Sep'85 by DEP International Records. Dist: Virgin Records, EMI

BABY LOVE.
Single (12"): released on Inner Light, Oct'84 by Inner Light Records. Dist: Jetstar

BEING WITH YOU.
Single (7"): released on P.R.O., Nov'81 Dist: Jetstar

Single (12"): released on P.R.O., Nov'81 Dist: Jetstar

CROSSOVER.
Album: released on DEP International, Mar'85 by DEP International Records. Dist: Virgin Records, EMI

Cassette: released on DEP International, Mar'85 by DEP International Records. Dist: Virgin Records, EMI

DAUGHTER OF ZION.
Single (12"): released on S&G, Mar'82 Dist: Pinnacle

DIM THE LIGHT.
Album: released on Inner Light, Oct'83 by Inner Light Records. Dist: Jetstar

DIM THE LIGHT/SHOWER OF RAIN.
Single (7"): released on Carousel, Feb'3 by Carousel Records. Dist: Spartan, Rough Trade

EVERY DAY I WRITE THE BOOK.
Tracks: / Every day I write the book.
Single (7"): released on Priority, Aug'86 by Priority Records. Dist: RCA

Single (12"): released on Priority, Aug'86 by Priority Records. Dist: RCA

MOI EMMA OH/LEND ME.
Single (12"): released on Inner Light, Aug'83 by Inner Light Records. Dist: Jetstar

PARADISE IN YOUR EYES.
Single (12"): released on Dasala, Aug'82

PERSONALLY SPEAKING.
Single (12"): released on Inner Light, May'84 by Inner Light Records. Dist: Jetstar

REGGAE MAN (Reedy, Winston & Tom Hain).
Tracks: / Reggae man / Everyday I write the book.
Single (7"): released on IRS, Mar'87 Dist: Polygram

Single (12"): released on IRS, Mar'87 Dist: Polygram

Single (12"): released on Priority, Jul'87 by Priority Records. Dist: RCA

SUPERSTAR.
Single (7"): released on DEP International, Mar'85 by DEP International Records. Dist: Virgin Records, EMI

Single (12"): released on DEP International, Mar'85 by DEP International Records. Dist: Virgin Records, EMI

Reefer Madness

REEFER MADNESS.
Album: released on Stash (Import), Apr'81 Dist: Swift Distribution, Jazz Music Distribution, Jazz Horizons Distribution, Celtic Music Distribution, Cadillac, JSU Distribution, Zodiac Distribution

Reefer Songs

REEFER SONGS (Various Artists).
Cassette: released on Stash (US), Mar'85 Dist: Swift Distribution, Jazz Music Distribution, Jazz Horizons Distribution, Celtic Music Distribution, Cadillac, JSU Distribution, Zodiac Distribution

Album: released on Stash (Import), Apr'81 Dist: Swift Distribution, Jazz Music Distribution, Jazz Horizons Distribution, Celtic Music Distribution, Cadillac, JSU Distribution, Zodiac Distribution

Reego & Yvonne

PATTERNS/RISE ABOVE THE CLOUD.
Single (7"): released on Medical, Aug'82 Dist: Pinnacle

Reel To Reel

LOVE ME LIKE THIS.
Single (7"): released on Arista, Apr'84 by Arista Records. Dist: RCA

Single (12"): released on Arista, Apr'84 by Arista Records. Dist: RCA

Reese, Della

3 GREAT GIRLS (see 3 Great Girls) (Reese, Della/Ann-Margaret/Kitty Kallen).

CLASSIC DELLA.
Album: released on RCA International (USA), Oct'80 by RCA Records. Dist: RCA

Cassette: released on RCA International (USA), Oct'80 by RCA Records. Dist: RCA

DELLA.
Album: released on Deja Vu, Oct'83 by Deja Vu Records. Dist: Counterpoint Distribution, Record Services Distribution (Ireland)

Cassette: released on Deja Vu, Oct'83 by Deja Vu Records. Dist: Counterpoint Distribution, Record Services Distribution (Ireland)

DELLA DELLA CHA-CHA-CHA.
Tracks: / Diamonds are a girl's best friend / Come on...a my house / Why don't you do right / My heart belongs to daddy / Let's do it / Whatever Lola wants / Daddy / Tea for two / Always true to you in my fashion / It's so nice to have a man around the house / There's a small hotel / Love for sale.
Album: released on RCA, Jun'87 by RCA Records. Dist: RCA, Roots, Swift, Wellard, Chris, I & B, Solomon & Peres Distribution

Cassette: released on RCA, Jun'87 by RCA Records. Dist: RCA, Roots, Swift, Wellard, Chris, I & B, Solomon & Peres Distribution

I LIKE IT LIKE DAT.
Album: released on Jasmine, Mar'84 by Jasmine Records. Dist: Counterpoint, Lugtons, Taylor, H.R., Wellard, Chris, Swift, Cadillac

SURE LIKE LOVIN' YOU.
Album: released on President, May'85 by President Records. Dist: Taylors, Spartan

Reeve, Douglas

PACK UP YOUR TROUBLES.
Album: released on Acorn, Jun'79 Dist: Folksound, Jazz Music

PERFECT COMBINATION.
Album: released on Grosvenor, Jun'81 by Grosvenor Records. Dist: Taylors

SAY IT WITH MUSIC.
Album: released on Grosvenor, Sep'83 by Grosvenor Records. Dist: Taylors

Reeves, Chris

DINING AT DZERZHINSKY'S.
Single (7"): released on Y, Jun'82

Single (12"): released on Y, Jun'82

Reeves, Dianne

FOR EVERY HEART.
Album: released on Palo Alto (USA), Jan'85 by Palo Alto Records. Dist: Conifer

WELCOME TO MY LOVE.
Cassette: released on Palo Alto (USA), Jul'86 by Palo Alto Records. Dist: Conifer

Album: released on Palo Alto (Italy), Jan'84

Reeves, James

SIMPLE PIP.
Cassette: released on Talking Tape Company, '84 by Talking Tape Company Records.

Reeves, Jim

12 SONGS FOR CHRISTMAS.
Album: released on Pickwick, Oct'79 by Pickwick Records. Dist: Pickwick Distribution, Prism Leisure Distribution, Lugtons

Cassette: released on RCA Camden, Oct'79 by RCA Records. Dist: Pickwick Distribution, Taylor, H.R.

20 OF THE BEST.
Tracks: / I won't come in while he's there / Storm (The) / I heard a heart break last night / That's when I see the blues(In your pretty brow

Page 828

eyes) / When you're gone / When two worlds collide / Nobody's fool / Angels don't lie / Gypsy feel / Writing's on the wall (The) / Missing you / Am I that easy to forget / I'd fight the world / It's nothin' to me / Little ole dime / You're the only good thing(That's happened to me) / Don't let me cross over / Oh,how I miss you tonight / Take me In your arms and hold me / Have you ever been lonely(Have you ever been blue?).
Album: released on RCA, Mar'86 by RCA Records. Dist: RCA, Roots, Swift, Wellard, Chris, I & B, Solomon & Peres Distribution

Cassette: released on RCA, Mar'86 by RCA Records. Dist: RCA, Roots, Swift, Wellard, Chris, I & B, Solomon & Peres Distribution

ABBOTT RECORDINGS VOL 1, THE.
Album: released on RCA International, Aug'82

Cassette: released on RCA International, Aug'82

ABBOTT RECORDINGS VOL 2, THE.
Album: released on RCA International, '84

Cassette: released on RCA International, '84

ADIOS AMIGO/GUILTY.
Single (7"): released on RCA (USA Import), '80

AT THE COUNTRY STORE.
Album: released on Starblend Country Store, Aug'86 by Starblend Records. Dist: PRT Distribution

Cassette: released on Starblend Country Store, Aug'86 by Starblend Records. Dist: PRT Distribution

BEST OF JIM REEVES, THE.
Album: released on RCA International, Nov'84

Cassette: released on RCA International, Nov'84

BIMBO.
Album: released on RCA/Camden, '70

COUNTRY SIDE OF JIM REEVES.
Album: released on RCA/Camden, '69

DISTANT DRUMS.
Tracks: / Distant drums / I won't forget you.
Single (7"): released on Old Gold, Oct'86 by Old Gold Records. Dist: Lightning, Jazz Music, Spartan, Counterpoint

FABULOUS JIM REEVES, THE.
Double Album: released on Cambra, '83 by Cambra Records. Dist: IDS, Conifer

Double cassette: released on Cambra, '83 by Cambra Records. Dist: IDS, Conifer

FOREVER.
Tracks: / Make the world go away / Deep dark water / Welcome to my world / One dozen roses / Hawaiian wedding song (The) / Penny Candy / Fall walls / I won't forget you / Wreck of the number nine (The) / Missing you / Bimbo / When you are gone / Angels don't lie / According to my heart / Missing angel / Auf wiederseh'n sweetheart / Memories are made of this / Guilty / Have I told you lately that I love you / Distant drums / Gypsy feet / Storm (The) / Scarlet ribbons / But you love me daddy / He'll have to go / Roses are red / Is it really over / Blizzard (The) / Am I losing you / Mexican Joe / You're the only good thing(that's happened to me) / Crying in my sleep.
Album: released on RCA, Jul'86 by RCA Records. Dist: RCA, Roots, Swift, Wellard, Chris, I & B, Solomon & Peres Distribution

Cassette: released on RCA, Jul'86 by RCA Records. Dist: RCA, Roots, Swift, Wellard, Chris, I & B, Solomon & Peres Distribution

OUR WALLS/BIMBO.
Single (7"): released on RCA (USA Import), '80

GENTLEMAN JIM.
Album: released on Victor/RCA (USA), '74 by RCA Records. Dist: RCA

GIRLS I HAVE KNOWN.
Tracks: / Marie / Mona Lisa / My Juanita / Charmaine / Margie / Anna Marie / Sweet Sue, just you / Linda / Ramona / Maria Elena / My Mary / Goodnight Irene.
Album: released on RCA, Jan'87 by RCA Records. Dist: RCA, Roots, Swift, Wellard, Chris, I & B, Solomon & Peres Distribution

Cassette: released on RCA, Jan'87 by RCA Records. Dist: RCA, Roots, Swift, Wellard, Chris, I & B, Solomon & Peres Distribution

GOD BE WITH YOU.
Album: released on RCA/Camden, '71

GOLDEN RECORDS.
Album: released on RCA (S.I.S.), Aug'84

Cassette: released on RCA (S.I.S.), Aug'84

Album: by RCA Records. Dist: Pickwick Distribution, Taylors, Swift

GOOD 'N' COUNTRY.
Album: released on RCA/Camden, '70

GREATEST HITS: JIM REEVES (Reeves, Jim/ Patsy Cline).
Album: released on RCA, Mar'82 by RCA Records. Dist: RCA, Roots, Swift, Wellard, Chris, I & B, Solomon & Peres Distribution

Cassette: released on RCA, Mar'82 by RCA Records. Dist: RCA, Roots, Swift, Wellard, Chris, I & B, Solomon & Peres Distribution

HAVE I TOLD YOU LATELY.
Album: released on RCA Camden, '69 by RCA Records. Dist: Pickwick Distribution, Taylor, H.R.

HE'LL HAVE TO GO.
Single (7"): released on RCA (USA Import), '80

HIS BEST LOVED SONGS.
Album: released on Camden(RCA), Jul'87 by RCA Records. Dist: Pickwick Distribution, Taylors, Swift

I'LL ALWAYS LOVE YOU.
Album: released on Camden(RCA), Apr'78 by RCA Records. Dist: Pickwick Distribution, Taylors, Swift

I LOVE YOU BECAUSE.
Tracks: / I love you because / He'll have to go.
Single (7"): released on Old Gold, Oct'86 by Old Gold Records. Dist: Lightning, Jazz Music, Spartan, Counterpoint

JIM REEVES COLLECTION VOL 2.
Double Album: released on Pickwick, Feb'78 by Pickwick Records. Dist: Pickwick Distribution, Prism Leisure Distribution, Lugtons

Cassette: released on Pickwick, Jul'80 by Pickwick Records. Dist: Pickwick Distribution, Prism Leisure Distribution, Lugtons

JIM REEVES COLLECTION.
Double Album: released on Pickwick, Mar'76 by Pickwick Records. Dist: Pickwick Distribution, Prism Leisure Distribution, Lugtons

Cassette: released on Pickwick, Dec'79 by Pickwick Records. Dist: Pickwick Distribution, Prism Leisure Distribution, Lugtons

MAGIC MOMENTS.
Cassette: released on RCA, Jun'84 by RCA Records. Dist: RCA, Roots, Swift, Wellard, Chris, I & B, Solomon & Peres Distribution

OLD TIGE.
Album: released on RCA/Camden, Jul'86

Cassette: released on RCA/Camden, Jul'86

REMEMBERING (Reeves, Jim/ Patsy Cline).
Notes: For full information see under Cline, Patsy / Jim Reeves

SONGS FROM THE HEART.
Album: released on RCA Camden, Jul'84 by RCA Records. Dist: Pickwick Distribution, Taylor, H.R.

Cassette: released on RCA Camden, Jul'84 by RCA Records. Dist: Pickwick Distribution, Taylor, H.R.

SONGS OF LOVE.
Album: released on RCA, Mar'78 by RCA Records. Dist: RCA, Roots, Swift, Wellard, Chris, I & B, Solomon & Peres Distribution

SONGS TO WARM THE HEART.
Album: released on RCA Camden, '72 by RCA Records. Dist: Pickwick Distribution, Taylor, H.R.

THERE'S ALWAYS ME.
Album: released on RCA, Apr'81 by RCA Records. Dist: RCA, Roots, Swift, Wellard, Chris, I & B, Solomon & Peres Distribution

TOUCH OF SADNESS, A.
Album: released on Victor/RCA (USA), '74 by RCA Records. Dist: RCA

TOUCH OF VELVET, A.
Tracks: / Have you ever been lonely / There's always me / Just walking in the rain / Be honest with me / I fall to pieces / It's no sin / Welcome to my world / Am I that easy to forget / Blue skies / All dressed up and lonely / Wild rose / I'm a fool to care.
Album: released on MFP, Sep'86 by EMI Records. Dist: EMI

Cassette: released on MFP, Sep'86 by EMI Records. Dist: EMI

VERY BEST OF JIM REEVES, THE.
Album: released on RCA, Nov'84 by RCA Records. Dist: RCA, Roots, Swift, Wellard, Chris, I & B, Solomon & Peres Distribution

Cassette:

Cassette: released on RCA, Nov'84 by RCA Records. Dist: RCA, Roots, Swift, Wellard, Chris, I & B, Solomon & Peres Distribution

VERY SPECIAL LOVE SONGS.
Album: released on Premier, May'85 by Premier Records. Dist: CBS

Cassette: released on Premier, May'85 by Premier Records. Dist: CBS

WELCOME TO MY WORLD.
Tracks: / Welcome to my world / Adios amigo.
Single (7"): released on Old Gold, Nov'86 by Old Gold Records. Dist: Lightning, Jazz Music, Spartan, Counterpoint

Album: released on RCA Camden, Aug'75 by RCA Records. Dist: Pickwick Distribution, Taylor, H.R.

WELCOME TO MY WORLD / I WON'T.....
Single (7"): released on RCA Golden Grooves, Oct'81 by RCA Records. Dist: RCA

WE THANK THEE.
Album: released on RCA Camden, '72 by RCA Records. Dist: Pickwick Distribution, Taylor, H.R.

Reeves, Martha

4 TRACK CASSETTE EP (Reeves, Martha & The Vandellas).
Cassette: released on Motown, May'83 by RCA Records. Dist: RCA Distribution

ANTHOLOGY (Reeves, Martha & The Vandellas).
Album: released on Motown, Sep'82 by RCA Records. Dist: RCA Distribution

Cassette: released on Motown, Sep'82 by RCA Records. Dist: RCA Distribution

COMPACT COMMAND PERFORMANCES 24 greatest hits (Reeves, Martha & The Vandellas).
Tracks: / Come and get these memories / Heatwave / Quicksand / In my lonely room / Dancing in the street / Nowhere to run / You've been in love too long / My baby loves me / I'm ready for love / Jimmy Mack / Love bug leave my heart alone / Honey chile / I can't dance to that music you're playin' / Honey love / I gotta let you go / I gotta let you go / Bless you / Love like yours, A (don't come knocking everyday) / Live wire / Wild one / Motoring / Motoring / Love (makes me do foolish things) / Third finger, left hand / I promise to wait my love / Sweet darlin' / Love like yours,A (don't come knocking everyday).
Compact disc: released on Motown, Mar'87 by Motown Records. Dist: BMG Distribution

HEATWAVE (Reeves, Martha & The Vandellas).
Album: released on Motown, Oct'81 by RCA Records. Dist: RCA Distribution

Cassette: released on Motown, Oct'81 by RCA Records. Dist: RCA Distribution

Single (7"): released on Motown, Oct'81 by RCA Records. Dist: RCA Distribution

JIMMY MACK (Reeves, Martha & The Vandellas).
Tracks: / Jimmy Mack / Dancing in the street / Medley / My guy.
Single (7"): released on Creole Classics, Mar'87 by Creole Records. Dist: PRT, Rhino

Single (12"): released on Creole Classics, Mar'87 by Creole Records. Dist: PRT, Rhino

JIMMY MACK / THIRD FINGER LEFT HAND.
Single (7"): released on Motown, Mar'80 by Motown Records. Dist: BMG Distribution

MARTHA REEVES (Reeves, Martha & The Vandellas).
Tracks: / Jimmy Mack / Quick sand / Heatwave / Dancing in the street / Nowhere to run / Spooky / In the midnight hour / It's the same old song / I want you back / I say a little prayer / Come see about me / Get ready / I heard it through the grapevine / Gotta see Jane.
Compact disc: released on The Collection, Apr'87 by Object Enterprises Ltd. Dist: Counterpoint Distribution

Reeves, Reuben 'River'

RIVER BOYS 1929.
Album: released on Fountain-Retrieval, Jul'87 by Retrieval Records. Dist: Retrieval, VJM, Swift, Jazz Music, Wellard, Chris

Reflections

FOUR COUNTRIES.
Single (7"): released on Cherry Red, Dec'81 by Cherry Red Records. Dist: Pinnacle

JUST LIKE ROMEO AND JULIET.
Single (7"): released on Motown (Re-issue), Oct'81

REFLECTIONS Various artists (Various Artists).
Album: released on CBS, Oct'82 by CBS Records. Dist: CBS

Cassette: released on CBS, Oct'82 by CBS Records. Dist: CBS

SEARCHING.
Single (7"): released on Cherry Red, Jan'84 by Cherry Red Records. Dist: Pinnacle

SLUGS & TOADS.
Album: released on Cherry Red, Nov'81 by Cherry Red Records. Dist: Pinnacle

Reflections A.O.B

ONLY IN MY DREAMS.
Tracks: / Only in my dreams.
Single (12"): released on Keep It, Oct'86 Dist: Backs-Cartel

Reflections in Brass

REFLECTIONS IN BRASS VOL 3 Various artists (Various Artists).
Album: released on Polyphonic, Nov'85 by Polyphonic Records. Dist: Taylors

Cassette: released on Polyphonic, Nov'85 by Polyphonic Records. Dist: Taylors

REFLECTIONS IN BRASS VOL 1 Various artists (Various Artists).
Album: released on Polyphonic, Sep'80 by Polyphonic Records. Dist: Taylors

Cassette: released on Polyphonic, Mar'81 by Polyphonic Records. Dist: Taylors

REFLECTIONS IN BRASS VOL 2 Various artists (Various Artists).
Album: released on Polyphonic, Nov'81 by Polyphonic Records. Dist: Taylors

Cassette: released on Polyphonic, Nov'81 by Polyphonic Records. Dist: Taylors

Reflections in Guitar

TIME FOR JOY, A.
Notes: Tracks include Bach's Jesus,Joy of man's desiring,Rejoice in the lord always,The joy of the lord is my strength plus others. Features Guitarists Steve Erquiaga and Wayne Brazil,both renowned session and stage musicians,accompanied by Frank Martin(Synthesizers)and Kenneth Nash(percu-ssion).
Album: released on Maranatha Music, May'86

Cassette: released on Maranatha Music, May'86

Reflex Compilation, A

REFLEX COMPILATION, A Various artists (Various Artists).
Album: released on Reflex, Jun'85

Refugee

I'M NOT LIKE YOU / WHEN I WAS YOUNG.
Single (7"): released on New World, Oct'81 by President Records. Dist: Swift, Spartan

Regal, Norace

STRUGGLE.
Single (12"): released on Sirron Music, May'84 by Sirron Music Records. Dist: Jetstar

Regal Slip

BANDSTAND.
Album: released on Dingles, '83 by Dingle's Records. Dist: Projection

Regan, Joan

UNCHAINED MELODIES Four stars of the 50's (Regan, Joan/Jimmy Young/Lita Roza/ Dickie Valentine).
Notes: For full details see under Jimmy Young.

Reggae...

ALLSTAR REGGAE (Reggae Allstars).
Single (7"): released on Spitfire, Oct'81

Single (12"): released on Spitfire, Oct'81

DAY 1 BEST OF THE REGGAE SUNSPLASH Various artists (Various Artists).
Album: released on Vista Sounds, Feb'84 by Vista Sounds Records. Dist: Jetstar

REGGAE 14 Various artists (Various Artists).
Album: released on Starlight, Mar'84 by Starlight Records. Dist: Jetstar Distribution

REGGAE CHARTBUSTERS Various artists (Various Artists).
Single (7"): released on Scoop, Jun'84

Cassette: released on Scoop, Jun'84

REGGAE CHRISTMAS Various artists (Various Artists).
Album: released on RAS, Nov'85

REGGAE CLASSICS Various artists (Various Artists).
Single (7"): released on Trojan, Nov'83 by Trojan Records. Dist: PRT, Jetstar

Single (12"): released on Trojan, Nov'83 by Trojan Records. Dist: PRT, Jetstar

REGGAE COLLECTION Various artists (Various Artists).
Album: released on Shanghai, Aug'86

REGGAE CONFUSION BOOPS Various artists (Various Artists).
Album: released on World Enterprise, Jul'86 Dist: Jetstar

REGGAE DANCE PARTY (Various Artists).
Album: released on R.A.S, 30 May'87 by Greensleeves Records. Dist: RCA

REGGAE GOLD Various artists (Various Artists).
Album: released on Goldrush, Jan'85 by Goldrush Records. Dist: Jetstar

REGGAE INVASION VOL.1 (Various Artists).
Album: released on W&B, Nov'86

REGGAE, REGGAE, REGGAE (Various Artists).
Album: released on Receiver, Feb'87 by Receiver Records. Dist: Pinnacle

REGGAE REPLAY Barious artists (Various Artists).
Tracks: / Liquidator / Soul shakedown party / Love of the common people / Crying over you / Red Red wine / Skinhead moonstomp / Dollar in the teeth / Double barrel / Train to Skaville / Suzanne beware of the Devil / Israelites / Monkey Man / Many rivers to cross.
Album: released on Action Replay, Apr'86 by Action Replay Records. Dist: PRT

Cassette: released on Action Replay, Apr'86 by Action Replay Records. Dist: PRT

REGGAE ROCKERS Various artists (Various Artists).
Album: released on Black Joy, Mar'84 Dist: Jetstar

REGGAE SHOWCASE VOL.1 (Various Artists).
Album: released on Munich, Oct'86 Dist: Celtic Music Distribution, Swift Distribution, Jetstar Distribution

Compact disc: released on Munich, Oct'86 Dist: Celtic Music Distribution, Swift Distribution, Jetstar Distribution

REGGAE STAR JAM VOL.1 Various artists (Various Artists).
Album: released on Reggae City, Mar'86 by Reggae City Records. Dist: Jetstar

REGGAE STARS 1 Various artists (Various Artists).
Album: released on World Enterprise, Dec'84 Dist: Jetstar

REGGAE STARS EXPLOSION, VOL 1 Various artists (Various Artists).
Album: released on Kingdom, Aug'85 by Kingdom Records. Dist: Kingdom

REGGAE STEADY GO 1 Various artists (Various Artists).
Tracks: / I want to wake up with you / Police officer / Am I the same girl / Man in a house / Rub a dub soldier / Wet look crazy / Cherish / Come back Charlie / Girlie girlie / Monday morning feeling / No good girl / As if I didn't know / Dreaming of a little island / What one dance can do / Dynamic / Kool & Deadly / Side show / Everything I own / You can get it if you really want / Impossible Love / Young gifted & black / Ire feelings / Help me make it through the night / Double Barrel / Liquidator / Israelites / Mad about you / Hurt so good / Love of the common people / Wonderful world,beautiful people / Midnight rider / Tree ring circus.
Notes: Double album
Album: released on Rhino, '86 by Creole Records. Dist: PRT, Rhino

Album: released on Rhino, '86 by Creole Records. Dist: PRT, Rhino

Cassette: released on Rhino, '86 by Creole Records. Dist: PRT, Rhino

REGGAE SWEET AND SMOOTH Various artists (Various Artists).
Album: released on Tackle, Mar'78

REGGAE TREASURE Various artists (Various Artists).
Album: released on Chinless, '83 by Chinless Productions. Dist: Music Galore, Spartan

Reggae George

EVERYBODY BALLING.
Single (12"): released on Sky Juice, Jan'84 by Sky Juice Records. Dist: Jetstar

FIGHT ON MY OWN.
Album: released on Sky Juice, Jul'84 by Sky Juice Records. Dist: Jetstar

MIX UP.
Album: released on Trojan, '83 by Trojan Records. Dist: PRT, Jetstar

THREE TIMES A LADY.
Single (12"): released on Lion Kingdom, Jan'84 by Lion Kingdom Records. Dist: Jetstar, Pinnacle

THREE WICKED MEN.
Single (12"): released on Yvonne's Special, Sep'82

YOU'LL NEVER KNOW.
Single (12"): released on Greensleeves, Jan'83 by Greensleeves Records. Dist: BMG, Jetstar, Spartan

Reggae Hits

REGGAE HITS (Various Artists).
Tracks: / I wanna wake up with you / Girlie girlie / Side show / Midnight rider / Rub a dub soldier / Israelites / Love Trilogy / Everything I own / Cherry oh baby / You can get it if you really want / Lazy body / All I have to do is dream / It mek / All in the game / You're everthing to me.
Notes: Many thanks to Creole Records and Trojan Records for making this compilation possible.
This compilation (P) & (C) 1987 K-Tel International.
Compact disc: released on K-Tel, Jun'87 by K-Tel Records. Dist: Record Merchandisers Distribution, Taylors, Terry Blood Distribution, Wynd-Up Distribution, Relay Distribution, Pickwick Distribution, Solomon & Peres Distribution, Polygram

REGGAE HITS OF THE 80'S (Various Artists).
Album: released on Blue Moon, Jan'87 Dist: Magnum Music Group Ltd, PRT, Spartan

Album: released on Blue Moon, Jan'87 Dist: Magnum Music Group Ltd, PRT, Spartan

REGGAE HITS VOL 1 Various artists (Various Artists).
Album: released on Jetstar, Feb'85 Dist: Jetstar, Stage One

Cassette: released on Jetstar, Feb'85 Dist: Jetstar, Stage One

REGGAE HITS VOL 2 Various artists (Various Artists).
Album: released on Jetstar, Oct'85 Dist: Jetstar, Stage One

Cassette: released on Jetstar, Oct'85 Dist: Jetstar, Stage One

REGGAE HITS VOL 3 Various artists (Various Artists).
Compact disc: released on Jetstar, Mar'87 Dist: Jetstar, Stage One

Album: released on Jetstar, Oct'86 Dist: Jetstar, Stage One

Cassette: released on Jetstar, Oct'86 Dist: Jetstar, Stage One

Reggae Nomix

REGGAE NOMIX.
Album: released on Clay, Oct'84 by Clay Records. Dist: Pinnacle

REGGAE RECIPE Various original artists (Various Artists).
Album: released on MFP, Mar'81 by EMI Records. Dist: EMI

Reggae Regular

BLACK STARLINER.
Single (12"): released on Greensleeves, Jun'78 by Greensleeves Records. Dist: BMG, Jetstar, Spartan

GHETTO ROCK.
Album: released on Greensleeves, Mar'84 by Greensleeves Records. Dist: BMG, Jetstar, Spartan

Single (12"): released on Greensleeves, Mar'84 by Greensleeves Records. Dist: BMG, Jetstar, Spartan

HOUSE PARTY (Reggae Regular & Clint Eastwood).
Single (12"): released on Greensleeves, Feb'82 by Greensleeves Records. Dist: BMG, Jetstar, Spartan

Reggae Superstars

CRUCIAL COLLECTION.
Album: released on Vista Sounds, May'83 by Vista Sounds Records. Dist: Jetstar

Regimental Band...

SILVER SERENADE (Regimental Band 16th/5th The Queen's Royal Lancers).
Tracks: / Silver serenade / Victory salute / Tchaike on parade.
Single (7"): released on Help The Aged, '86 Dist: Spartan

Regina

BABY LOVE.
Tracks: / Baby love / Baby love (inst).
Single (7"): released on Funkin' Marvellous, '86 Dist: Priority, RCA, Ariola

Single (12"): released on Funkin' Marvellous, '86 Dist: Priority, RCA, Ariola

Single (12"): released on Funkin' Marvellous, '86 Dist: Priority, RCA, Ariola

Picture disc single: released on Funkin' Marvellous, '86 Dist: Priority, RCA, Ariola

Regina Sings Opera

REGINA SINGS OPERA (Regina music box-Bornand Collection) (Regina Music Box).
Album: released on Bornard Music Box Co.(USA), Nov'80

Cassette: released on Bornard Music Box Co.(USA), Nov'80

Regist, Ronnie

TIME TO PLAY.
Single (7"): released on Oscar, Aug'84 Dist: Pinnacle

Single (12"): released on Oscar, Aug'84 Dist: Pinnacle

Regular Music

REGULAR MUSIC.
Album: released on Rough Trade, Jun'85 by Rough Trade Records. Dist: Rough Trade Distribution, Cartel Distribution

Reichman, Joe

PAGLIACCI OF THE PIANO (Reichman, Joe & His Orchestra).
Notes: Mono. 1941-1942.
Album: released on Circle(USA), Jan'87 by Jazzology Records (USA). Dist: Jazz Music, Swift, Chris Wellard

Reich, Steve

DESERT MUSIC (THE).
Notes: Performed by Steve Reich and Musicians with chorus members of the Brooklyn Philharmonic. Conducted by Michael Tilson Thomas.
Album: released on Elektra (USA), '86 by Elektra/Asylum/Nonesuch Records. Dist: WEA

Compact disc: released on Elektra (USA), '86 by Elektra/Asylum/Nonesuch Records. Dist: WEA

FOUR ORGANS-PHASE PATTERNS.
Album: released on Shandar, Mar'78

MUSIC FOR 18 MUSICIANS.
Compact disc: released on ECM (Germany), '84 by ECM Records. Dist: IMS, Polygram, Virgin through EMI

Album: released on ECM, '78 by ECM Records. Dist: IMS, Polygram, Virgin through EMI

OCTET,MUSIC FOR A LARGE ENSEMBLE.
Tracks: / Music for a large ensemble / Violin Phase / Octet.
Compact disc: released on ECM (Germany), '85 by ECM Records. Dist: IMS, Polygram, Virgin through EMI

SEXTET - 'SIX MARIMBAS'.
Album: released on Nonesuch, Jan'87

Cassette: released on Nonesuch, Jan'87

Compact disc: released on Nonesuch, Jan'87

TEHILLIM.
Tracks: / Parts I & II / Parts III & IV.
Compact disc: released on ECM (Germany), '86 by ECM Records. Dist: IMS, Polygram, Virgin through EMI

Album: released on ECM (Germany), Oct'82 by ECM Records. Dist: IMS, Polygram, Virgin through EMI

Reid, Alan

SIDETRACKS (Reid, Alan/ Brian McNeill).
Album: released on Topic, Jun'81 by Topic Records. Dist: JSU Distribution, Projection Distribution, Jazz Music Distribution

Reid, Duke

GOLDEN HITS: DUKE REID.
Album: released on Treasure Isle, May'80 by Treasure Isle Records. Dist: Jetstar

Reid, Jim

I SAW THE WILD GEESE.
Album: released on Springthyme, '86 by Springthyme Records. Dist: Jazz Music Distribution, Projection Distribution, Roots Distribution

Cassette: released on Springthyme, '86 by Springthyme Records. Dist: Jazz Music Distribution, Projection Distribution, Roots Distribution

Reid, Jimmy

ARE YOU READY.
Album: released on Londisc, Apr'85 by Londisc Records.

Reid, Junior

BACK TO BACK (Reid, Junior/Leroy Smart).
Album: released on Volcano, Mar'85 by Volcano Records. Dist: Jetstar

BANK CLERK.
Single (12"): released on Rusty International, Mar'85 by Rusty International Records. Dist: Jetstar Distribution

BOOM SHACK A LACK.
Album: released on Greensleeves, Feb'85 by Greensleeves Records. Dist: BMG, Jetstar, Spartan

BOOM SHACK-A-LACK-LACK.
Single (12"): released on Greensleeves, Nov'84 by Greensleeves Records. Dist: BMG, Jetstar, Spartan

CHANTING.
Single (12"): released on Unknown, Nov'85

FIREHOUSE CLASH (Reid, Junior & Don Carlos).

JAILHOUSE.
Single (12"): released on KG, Apr'82

MOVIE STAR.
Single (12"): released on Dove, Mar'84 by Dove Records. Dist: Jetstar

ORIGINAL FOREIGN MIND.
Album: released on Black Roots, Apr'85 by Black Roots Records. Dist: Jetstar

ORIGINAL FOREIGN MIND, THE.
Single (12"): released on Black Roots, Feb'85 by Black Roots Records. Dist: Jetstar

PALAVING STREET.
Single (12"): released on Chartbound, Dec'83 by Chartbound Records. Dist: Jetstar

POOR MAN TRANSPORTATION.
Single (12"): released on Rockers Forever, Mar'85 Dist: Jetstar Distribution

RUB-A-DUBBING.
Single (12"): released on Black Roots, Nov'84 by Black Roots Records. Dist: Jetstar

SHACKA LACK.
Single (12"): released on Jammy's, Oct'84 by Jammy's Records. Dist: Jetstar

TURN THE RADIO ON.
Tracks: / Turn the radio on / Sufferation.
Single (12"): released on Hard Rock, '86 Dist: Jetstar

TWO OF A KIND (Reid, Junior & Teasy).
Album: released on Wambesi, '86 by Wambesi records. Dist: Jetstar

WHAT YOU KNOW.
Single (12"): released on Black Roots, Jan'84 by Black Roots Records. Dist: Jetstar

Reid, Mike

GOLDEN HOUR PRESENTS MIKE REID.
Album: released on Golden Hour, Jun'79 by PRT Records. Dist: PRT

PATIENTS LAMENT(BED PAN SONG).
Single (7"): released on Pel, Nov'80

Reid, Neil

MOTHER OF MINE.
Single (7"): released on Old Gold, Sep'85 by Old Gold Records. Dist: Lightning, Jazz Music, Spartan, Counterpoint

Reid, Richard

HOW DOES IT FEEL.
Single (7"): released on Solid Groove, Nov'8 Dist: Jetstar, Pinnacle

Single (12"): released on Solid Groove, Nov'8 Dist: Jetstar, Pinnacle

Reid, Roy

WHAP'N'BAP.
Album: released on Virgin, Jun'80 by Virg Records. Dist: EMI, Virgin Distribution

Reid, Rufus

SEVEN MINDS (Reid, Rufus Trio).
Tracks: / Seven minds / Along came Betty / Yo make me smile / Tones for Joan's bones / Stru tin' about.
Album: released on Sunnyside (USA), '86 Di Mole Jazz Distribution, Conifer Distribution

TOO MARVELLOUS FOR WORDS (s Carter, Joe) (Reid, Rufus/Joe Carter).

Reid, Sandra

DON'T LET IT GO.
Tracks: / Don't let it go / Rave on.
Single (12"): released on Sir George, '86 by George Records. Dist: Jetstar, Pinnacle

DON'T TELL ME TELL HER.
Single (12"): released on Sir George, Sep'83 by Sir George Records. Dist: Jetstar, Pinnacle

FEELS SO GOOD.
Single (7"): released on Sir George, Apr'84 by Sir George Records. Dist: Jetstar, Pinnacle

IF DREAMS WERE REAL.
Album: released on Sir George, Oct'83 by Sir George Records. Dist: Jetstar, Pinnacle

IN A LIE.
Single (12"): released on Sir George, Sep'85 by Sir George Records. Dist: Jetstar, Pinnacle

LOOK IN YOUR EYES.
Single (12"): released on Sir George, Nov'82 by Sir George Records. Dist: Jetstar, Pinnacle

LOVE EACH OTHER.
Single (12"): released on Sir George, May'85 by Sir George Records. Dist: Jetstar, Pinnacle

MAKE ME LOVE THE RAIN.
Single (12"): released on Sir George, Mar'84 by Sir George Records. Dist: Jetstar, Pinnacle

OOH BOY.
Single (7"): released on Sir George, Jul'82 by Sir George Records. Dist: Jetstar, Pinnacle

Single (12"): released on Sir George, Jul'82 by Sir George Records. Dist: Jetstar, Pinnacle

WE BELONG TOGETHER.
Single (12"): released on Sir George, Nov'84 by Sir George Records. Dist: Jetstar, Pinnacle

Reid, Terry

HAND DON'T FIT THE GLOVE, (THE).
Album: released on See For Miles, Jun'85

Reilly - ace of themes

REILLY - ACE OF THEMES Various Artists (Various Artists).
Album: released on Red Bus, Nov'83 by Red Bus Records. Dist: PRT

Cassette: released on Red Bus, Nov'83 by Red Bus Records. Dist: PRT

Reilly, John

BONNY GREEN TREE, (THE).
Album: released on Topic, '81 by Topic Records. Dist: JSU Distribution, Projection Distribution, Jazz Music Distribution

Reilly, Maggie

AS TEARS GO BY.
Single (7"): released on Arista, Apr'84 by Arista Records. Dist: RCA

Single (12"): released on Arista, Apr'84 by Arista Records. Dist: RCA

Reilly, Paddy

FIELDS OF ATHENRY.
Album: released on Ritz, Nov'84 by Ritz Records. Dist: Spartan

Cassette: released on Ritz, Nov'84 by Ritz Records. Dist: Spartan

Album: released on Dolphin (Ireland), Jun'85 by Dolphin Records. Dist: I & B, Jazz Music, EMI (Ireland), Celtic Music

FIELDS OF ATHENRY, (THE).
Single (7"): released on Ritz, Oct'84 by Ritz Records. Dist: Spartan

LIFE OF PADDY REILLY, (THE).
Album: released on Dolphin, Nov'76

PADDY REILLY AT HOME.
Album: released on Dolphin, Nov'76

TOWN I LOVED SO WELL, (THE).
Album: released on Dolphin, Nov'76

Reilly, Peter

IRISH TINKER BALLADS.
Cassette: released on Folktracks, Nov'79 by Folktracks Cassettes. Dist: Folktracks

Reilly, Tommy

SERENADE (Reilly, Tommy/St. Martin-in-the-Field Chamber Ensemble).
Compact disc: released on Chandos, '86 by Chandos Records. Dist: Harmonia Mundi, Taylors

Reilly, Vinny

ANOTHER SETTING.
Cassette: released on Factory, Nov'86 by Factory Records. Dist: Cartel, Pinnacle

Cassette: released on Factory, Nov'84 by Factory Records. Dist: Cartel, Pinnacle

RETURN OF THE DURUTTI COLUMN.
Album: released on Factory, Apr'80 by Factory Records. Dist: Cartel, Pinnacle

TWO TRIANGLES.
Single (12"):

Reincarnate

TAKE IT OR LEAVE IT.
Single (7"): released on Zipp, Feb'83 Dist: Professional Tapes

Reinhardt, Django

50TH ANNIVERSARY CONCERT (Reinhardt, Django & Stephane Grappelli).
Album: released on Vogue, Oct'84 Dist: Discovery, Jazz Music, PRT, Swift

CRAZY RHYTHM.
Tracks: / How high the moon / Fine and dandy / Yesterdays / Lover / Apple honey / Manoir de mes reves / Dream of you / Crazy rhythm.
Album: released on Topline, '86 by Charly Records. Dist: Charly Distribution

Cassette: released on Topline, '86 by Charly Records. Dist: Charly Distribution

Album: released on Topline, Jul'85 by Charly Records. Dist: Charly Distribution

Cassette: released on Topline, Jul'85 by Charly Records. Dist: Charly Distribution

DJANGO.
Album: released on CBS(Blue Diamond), Jun'85 by CBS Records. Dist: CBS Deleted '87.

Cassette: released on CBS(Blue Diamond), Jun'85 by CBS Records. Dist: CBS

Boxed set: released on Charly, Oct'87 by Charly Records. Dist: Charly, Cadillac

DJANGO ET COMPAGNIE.
Album: released on Polydor (France), Oct'82 Dist: Polygram

DJANGOLOGIE, VOL 1.
Album: released on EMI (France), '83 by EMI Records. Dist: Conifer

DJANGOLOGIE, VOL 10.
Album: released on EMI (France), '83 by EMI Records. Dist: Conifer

DJANGOLOGIE, VOL 11.
Album: released on EMI (France), '83 by EMI Records. Dist: Conifer

DJANGOLOGIE, VOL 12.
Album: released on EMI (France), '83 by EMI Records. Dist: Conifer

DJANGOLOGIE, VOL 13.
Album: released on EMI (France), '83 by EMI Records. Dist: Conifer

DJANGOLOGIE, VOL 14.
Album: released on EMI (France), '83 by EMI Records. Dist: Conifer

DJANGOLOGIE, VOL 15.
Album: released on EMI (France), '83 by EMI Records. Dist: Conifer

DJANGOLOGIE, VOL 16.
Album: released on EMI (France), '83 by EMI Records. Dist: Conifer

DJANGOLOGIE, VOL 17.
Album: released on EMI (France), '83 by EMI Records. Dist: Conifer

DJANGOLOGIE, VOL 18.
Album: released on EMI (France), '83 by EMI Records. Dist: Conifer

DJANGOLOGIE, VOL 19.
Album: released on EMI (France), '83 by EMI Records. Dist: Conifer

DJANGOLOGIE, VOL 2.
Album: released on EMI (France), '83 by EMI Records. Dist: Conifer

DJANGOLOGIE, VOL 20.
Album: released on EMI (France), '83 by EMI Records. Dist: Conifer

DJANGOLOGIE, VOL 3.
Album: released on EMI (France), '83 by EMI Records. Dist: Conifer

DJANGOLOGIE, VOL 4.
Album: released on EMI (France), '83 by EMI Records. Dist: Conifer

DJANGOLOGIE, VOL 5.
Album: released on EMI (France), '83 by EMI Records. Dist: Conifer

DJANGOLOGIE, VOL 6.
Album: released on EMI (France), '83 by EMI Records. Dist: Conifer

DJANGOLOGIE, VOL 7.
Album: released on EMI (France), '83 by EMI Records. Dist: Conifer

DJANGOLOGIE, VOL 8.
Album: released on EMI (France), '83 by EMI Records. Dist: Conifer

DJANGOLOGIE, VOL 9.
Album: released on EMI (France), '83 by EMI Records. Dist: Conifer

DJANGO REINHARDT.
Album: released on Pathe Marconi, Jan'85 Dist: Swift

Cassette: released on Pathe Marconi, Jan'85 Dist: Swift

Boxed set: released on World Records, Dec'81 Dist: Polygram

Boxed set: released on World Records, Dec'81 Dist: Polygram

DJANGO REINHARDT (1936-37).
Album: released on Swaggie (Australia), Jan'83

DJANGO REINHARDT COLLECTION (THE).
Album: released on Deja Vu, '86 by Deja Vu Records. Dist: Counterpoint Distribution, Record Services Distribution (Ireland)

Cassette: released on Deja Vu, '86 by Deja Vu Records. Dist: Counterpoint Distribution, Record Services Distribution (Ireland)

DJANGO REINHARDT/HOT CLUB DE FRANCE.
Album: released on Music Disc (France), Jan'85 Dist: IMS-Polygram Distribution

DJANGO REINHARDT & QUINTET OF HOT CLUB OF FRANCE (1937) (Reinhardt, Django & Quintet of Hot Club of France).
Album: released on Swaggie (Australia), Jan'83

DJANGO REINHARDT & QUINTET OF HOT CLUB OF FRANCE (1946-47) (Reinhardt, Django & Quintet of Hot Club of France).
Album: released on Swaggie (Australia), Jan'83

DJANGO REINHARDT & QUINTET OF HOT CLUB OF FRANCE (1936-37) (Reinhardt, Django & Quintet of Hot Club of France).
Album: released on Swaggie (Australia), Jan'83

DJANGO REINHARDT/SIDNEY BECHET (Reinhardt, Django/Sidney Bechet).
Compact disc: released on Vogue, Dec'86 Dist: Discovery, Jazz Music, PRT, Swift

DJANGO REINHARDT/STEPHANE GRAPPELLI (Reinhardt, Django/Stephane Grappelli).
Compact disc: released on Vogue, Dec'86 Dist: Discovery, Jazz Music, PRT, Swift

DJANGO REINHARDT, VOL 1.
Album: released on Jazz Reactivation, Jan'82 Dist: PRT

DJANGO REINHARDT WITH STEPHANE GRAPELLI (1947-49) (Reinhardt, Django & Stephane Grappelli).
Album: released on Swaggie (Australia), Jan'83

DJANGO RHYTHM.
Album: released on Swaggie (Australia), Jan'83

DJANGO'S CASTLE.
Tracks: / Minor swing / Manoir de mes reve (Django's castle) / Saw star (I) / Nuages / Swing guitars / Artillerie lourde / Djangologie / Daphne / After you've gone / Swing 42 / Bricktop / Honeysuckle rose.
Album: released on RCA, '86 by RCA Records. Dist: RCA, Roots, Swift, Wellard, Chris, I & B, Solomon & Peres Distribution

Cassette: released on RCA, '86 by RCA Records. Dist: RCA, Roots, Swift, Wellard, Chris, I & B, Solomon & Peres Distribution

DJANGO SWING.
Album: released on Swaggie (Australia), Jan'83

DOUBLE ALBUM.
Tracks: / Ma reguliere / Par correspondance / Rosetta / Limehouse blues / Nagasaki / Charleston / Charleston / Runnin' wild / Improvisation / Honeysuckle rose / Eddie's blues / Bill Coleman blues / Minors swing.
Album: released on Pathe Marconi, Jun'87 Dist: Swift

Cassette: released on Pathe Marconi, Jun'87 Dist: Swift

ENREGISTREMENTS ORIGINAUX.
Tracks: / Improvisation / Honeysuckle rose / Eddie's blues / Bill Coleman blues / Minor's swing / Swingin' with Django / Christmas swing / I got rhythm / Younger generation / Tears / Swing 41 / Nuages / Les yeux noirs / La cigale et la fourmi / Belleville / Welcome (2e partie) / Ol' man river / Sweet Georgia Brown / Just a gigalo / Manoir de mes reves.
Compact disc: released on Pathe Marconi, Apr'87 Dist: Swift

ET LE QUINTETTE DU 'HOT CLUB DE FRACE'.
Tracks: / Ma reguliere / Par correspondance / Rossetta / Lime house blues / Nagasaki / Charleston / Runnin' wild / Improvisation / Honeysuckle rose / Eddie's blues / Bill Coleman blues / Swingin' with Django / Minor's swing / Bolero / Christmas swing / I got rhythm / Younger generation / Tears / Swing 41 / Nuages / Les yeux noirs / La cigale et la fouirmi / Belleville / Welcome / Ol'man river / Just a Gigolo / Manoir de mes reves.
Album: released on Pathe Marconi/EMI (France), Dec'86 Dist: Swift

GOT RHYTHM (I).
Notes: Collectors Edition series. Top session musicians.
Album: released on Meteor, '86 by Magnum Music Group Ltd. Dist: Magnum Music Group Ltd, PRT Distribution, Spartan Distribution

INDISPENSABLE DJANGO REINHARDT (1949-50).
Tracks: / Minor swing / Beyond the sea (la Mer) / World is waiting for sunrise (The) / Django's castle (Manoir de mes reves) / Dream of you / Menilmontant / It's only a paper moon / Saw stars (I) / Nuages / Swing guitars / All the things you are / A-tisket, a-tasket / September song / Heavy artillery (Artillerie lourde) / Improvisation of Tchaikovsky's 'pathetique' andante / Djangology / Daphne / I'll never be the same / Marie / Jersy bounce / Surrender dear (I) / Hallelluyah / Anniversary song / After you've gone / Swing 42 / Stormy weather / Brick top / Lover man(Oh,where can you be?) / Got rhythm (I) / Honeysuckle rose / St.Louis blues.
Notes: Double album. Double cassette. Mono.
Album: released on Jazz Tribune (USA), '86 Dist: Discovery

Cassette: released on Jazz Tribune (USA), '86 Dist: Discovery

PARIS 1945' DJANGO REINHARDT.
Tracks: / If dreams come true / Stompin' at the Savoy / Hallelujah / How high the moon / Hommage a Fats Waller / Hommage a Debussy / After you've gone / Shoemaker's apron / China boy / Sugar / Don't blame me / Poor Miss Black.
Album: released on Avan-Guard (Australia), Dec'86 by Avan-Guard Records (Australia). Dist: Conifer, Discovery

RHYTHM IS OUR BUSINESS (Reinhardt, Django & Stephane Grappelli).
Album: released on Decca, Nov'82 by Decca Records. Dist: Polygram

Cassette: released on Decca, Nov'82 by Decca Records. Dist: Polygram

STRUTTIN' OUT (Reinhardt, Django & Stephane Grappelli).
Album: released on Decca, Jul'84 by Decca Records. Dist: Polygram

STRUTTIN' OUT (see Grappelli, Stephane) (Reinhardt, Django/Stephane Grappelli).

TOGETHER (Reinhardt, Django/Stephane Grappelli/Eddie South).
Album: released on Pathe Marconi, Dec'84 Dist: Swift

Cassette: released on Pathe Marconi, Dec'84 Dist: Swift

Reininger, Blaine

BYZANTIUM.
Album: released on Crepescule, Apr'87 by Island Records. Dist: Polygram, Pinnacle

COLORADO SUITE (Reininger, Blaine/Mikel Rouse).
Album: released on Made To Measure, Oct'84 by Made To Measure Records. Dist: Pinnacle

LIVE IN BRUSSELS.
Compact disc: released on Le Disques Du Crepuscule, Jan'87

PARIS EN AUTOMNE (Reininger, Blaine/Alain Goutier).
Album: released on Les Disques Du Crepuscule, Aug'85 Dist: Rough Trade, Pinnacle, Island, Polygram

Rein, Paul

HOLD BACK YOUR LOVE.

Tracks: / Hold back you love / Ce mej en chans.
Single (12"): released on ZYX (Germany), '85 by ZYX Records. Dist: Greyhound

Rei, Panta

PANTA REI.
Album: released on Dragon, Jul'87 by Dragon Records. Dist: Jazz Music, Projection, Cadillac

Reja Bumu

REJA BUMU.
Single (12"): released on Eon, Aug'82

Rejects

BACK TO THE START.
Single (7"): released on FM, Mar'85 by FM-Revolver Records. Dist: EMI

QUIET STORM.
Album: released on Heavy Metal, Nov'84 by FM-Revolver Records. Dist: EMI

Cassette: released on Heavy Metal, Nov'84 by FM-Revolver Records. Dist: EMI

Album: released on Heavy Metal, Apr'85 by FM-Revolver Records. Dist: EMI

Relations

BIG MANS SHOES.
Tracks: / Big mans shoes.
Single (7"): released on Hush, '86 Dist: Pinnacle

BRAINWASHED & BLOWDRIED.
Tracks: / Brainwashed & blowdried / Come home (Tell us everything).
Single (7"): released on Hush, '86 Dist: Pinnacle

Relative band

RELATIVE BAND '85.
Album: released on Hot, '86 by Hot Records. Dist: Rough Trade, Cartel

Relativity

GATHERING PACE.
Tracks: / Blackwell court / Gathering pace / Rose catha na mumhan / Miss Tara Macadam / Ma theid tu un aonaigh / Siun ni dhuibhir / When she sleeps / Monday morning reel, The / Ceol Anna.
Album: released on WEA, Aug'87 by WEA Records. Dist: WEA

Cassette: released on WEA, Aug'87 by WEA Records. Dist: WEA

Relaxing sounds

RELAXING SOUNDS Various sound effects.
Album: released on BBC, Aug'79 by BBC Records & Tapes. Dist: EMI, PRT, Pye

Cassette: released on BBC, Aug'79 by BBC Records & Tapes. Dist: EMI, PRT, Pye

Release

IT'S NOT FAIR.
Single (7"): released on EMI, Jul'84 by EMI Records. Dist: EMI

Single (12"): released on EMI, Jul'84 by EMI Records. Dist: EMI

Release the Bats

UNACCEPTABLE BEHAVIOUR.
Single (7"): released on Belfry, Apr'85 Dist: Red Rhino, Cartel

Relief

WE ARE THE WORLD.
Single (12"): released on Dough Boy, Jul'85

Religious...

RELIGIOUS AS HELL (Various Artists).
Album: released on Hell, Nov'86 Dist: Red Rhino, Cartel

RELIGIOUS GOLD Various Artists (Various Artists).
Boxed set: released on Effects Gold, Nov'80 by Ronco Records. Dist: Ronco Records

Cassette: released on Effects Gold, Nov'80 by Ronco Records. Dist: Ronco Records

RELIGIOUS MUSIC OF INDIA Various Artists (Various Artists).
Album: released on EMI (India), Apr'84 by EMI Records. Dist: Conifer, Sterns, Triple Earth

Religious Overdose

25 MINUTES.
Single (7"): released on Glass, Sep'82 by Glass Records. Dist: Nine Mile, Rough Trade, Red Rhino, Play It Again Sam

GIRL WITH THE DISAPPEARING HEAD.
Single (12"): released on Glass, Jun'82 by Glass Records. Dist: Nine Mile, Rough Trade, Red Rhino, Play It Again Sam

IN THIS CENTURY.
Single (12"): released on Glass, Apr'82 by Glass Records. Dist: Nine Mile, Rough Trade, Red Rhino, Play It Again Sam

I SAID GO.
Single (7"): released on Glass, Sep'81 by Glass Records. Dist: Nine Mile, Rough Trade, Red Rhino, Play It Again Sam

Reluctant Stereotypes

LABEL, (THE).
Album: released on WEA, Oct'80 by WEA Records. Dist: WEA

Cassette: released on WEA, Jan'81 by WEA Records. Dist: WEA

ROUNDS, (THE).
Single (7"): released on Oval, May'82 by Oval Records. Dist: Pinnacle

R.E.M.

CAN'T GET THERE FROM HERE.
Single (7"): released on I.R.S.(Independent Record Syndicate), Jul'85 by I.R.S.. Dist: MCA

Single (12"): released on I.R.S.(Independent Record Syndicate), Jul'85 by I.R.S.. Dist: MCA

CHRONIC TOWN.
Album: released on IRS (Holland), Feb'85 Dist: Polygram

DEAD LETTER OFFICE.
Tracks: / Crazy / There she goes again / Burning down / Voice of Harold / Burning hell / White Tornado / Toys in the attic / Windout / Ages of you / Pale blue eyes / Rotary ten / Bandwagon / Femme fatale / Walters theme / King of the road.
Notes: R.E.M.'s "Dead Letter Office" packs 15 tracks of unbridled energy into one fascinating L P
A definative must for the R.E.M.fan, with new mixes of "Ages Of You" and "Burning Down",plus a never before releassed version of "White Tornado". Also included: exclusive live versions of three Lou Reed/Velvet Underground classics "Pale Blue Eyes","There She Goes Again"and "Femme Fatale". For C.D. buyers, there is an added bonus: along with the 15 L.P.tracks, the C.D. includes R.E.M's "Chronic Town" E.P.,never before released on this format.
Album: released on IRS, May'87 Dist: Polygram

Cassette: released on IRS, May'87 Dist: Polygram

Compact disc: released on IRS, May'87 Dist: Polygram

FABLES OF RECONSTRUCTION.
Album: released on I.R.S.(Independent Record Syndicate), May'85 by I.R.S.. Dist: MCA

Cassette: released on I.R.S.(Independent Record Syndicate), May'85 by I.R.S.. Dist: MCA

FABLES OF THE RECONSTRUCTION.
Tracks: / Feeling gravity's pull / Maps and legends / Driver 8 / Life and how to live it / Old man Kensey / Can't get there from here / Green grow the rushes / Kohoutek / Auctioneer (another engine) / Good advices / Wendell Gee.
Compact disc: released on MCA, Apr'87 by MCA Records. Dist: Polygram, MCA

FALL ON ME.
Tracks: / Fall on me / Rotary ten / Toys in the attic.
Single (7"): released on I.R.S.(Independent Record Syndicate), '86 by I.R.S.. Dist: MCA

Single (12"): released on I.R.S.(Independent Record Syndicate), '86 by I.R.S.. Dist: MCA

INTERVIEW PICTURE DISC.
Album: released on Baktabak, Oct'87 by Baktabak Records. Dist: Arabesque. Estim retail price in Sep'87 was £4.91.

LIFE'S RICH PAGEANT.
Compact disc: released on IRS, Nov'86 Dist: Polygram

LIFES RICH PAGEANT.
Notes: The single "Fall On Me" taken from this album. Their last album released in 1985,"Fables Of Reconstruction" reached No.35 in the national LP charts.
Album: released on IRS, '86 Dist: Polygram

Cassette: released on IRS, '86 Dist: Polygram

MURMUR.
Tracks: / Radio free Europe / Pilgrimage / Laughing / Talk about the passion / Moral kiosk / Perfect circle / Catapult / Sitting still / 9-9 / Shaking through / We walk / West of the fields.
Notes: Re-issue: Rolling Stone Magazine wrote of the album:"Its twelve tunes embody all the best virtues of classic pop-concise,artful arrangements,subtle hooks and a perfectly modulated small-combo sound.
Album: released on I.R.S.(Independent Record Syndicate), '86 by I.R.S.. Dist: MCA

Cassette: released on IRS, '86 Dist: Polygram

RECKONING.
Album: released on I.R.S.(Independent Record Syndicate), Apr'84 by I.R.S.. Dist: MCA

Cassette: released on I.R.S.(Independent Record Syndicate), Apr'84 by I.R.S.. Dist: MCA

SUPERMAN.
Tracks: / Superman / White tornado / Femme fatale.
Notes: Femme fatale is an extra track available only on 12" version.
Single (7"): released on IRS, Mar'87 Dist: Polygram

Single (12"): released on IRS, Mar'87 Dist: Polygram

TALK ABOUT THE PASSION.
Single (12"): released on I.R.S.(Independent Record Syndicate), Nov'83 by I.R.S.. Dist: MCA

WENDELL GEE.
Single (7"): released on I.R.S.(Independent Record Syndicate), Oct'85 by I.R.S.. Dist: MCA

Double-pack single: released on I.R.S.(Independent Record Syndicate), Oct'85 by I.R.S.. Dist: MCA

Single (12"): released on I.R.S.(Independent Record Syndicate), Oct'85 by I.R.S.. Dist: MCA

Rema

GERMAINE.
Tracks: / Germaine.
Single (7"): released on Gas, '86 by Gas Records. Dist: Pinnacle

Rema Rema

WHEEL IN THE ROSES.
Tracks: / Wheel in the roses.
Single (12"): released on 4AD, '86 by 4AD Records. Dist: Rough Trade

Remayns

WHY.
Single (7"): released on Bam Caruso, Aug'85 by Bam Caruso Records. Dist: Rough Trade, Revolver, Cartel

Remember....

REMEMBER....A COLLECTION OF POP MEMORIES VOLUME 1 Various Artists (Various Artists).
Double Album: released on Cambra, Aug'83 by Cambra Records. Dist: IDS, Conifer

Double cassette: released on Cambra, Aug'83 by Cambra Records. Dist: IDS, Conifer

REMEMBER THEN Various artists (Various Artists).
Compact disc: released on Pickwick, '86 by Pickwick Records. Dist: Pickwick Distribution, Prism Leisure Distribution, Lugtons

REMEMBER THESE Various Artists (Various Artists).
Album: released on Sonus, Mar'84 by Sonus Records. Dist: Spartan

Cassette: released on Sonus, Mar'84 by Sonus Records. Dist: Spartan

REMEMBER....VOLUME 2 Various Artists (Various Artists).
Double Album: released on Cambra, May'85 by Cambra Records. Dist: IDS, Conifer

Double cassette: released on Cambra, May'85 by Cambra Records. Dist: IDS, Conifer

REMEMBER WHEN Various Artists (Various Artists).
Album: released on Everest (Premier), Sep'83 by Everest Records. Dist: Pinnacle

Cassette: released on Everest (Premier), Sep'83 by Everest Records. Dist: Pinnacle

REMEMBER WHEN (MEMORIES OF 50S & 60S) Various Artists (Various Artists).
Double Album: released on Pickwick, Jun'81 by Pickwick Records. Dist: Pickwick Distribution, Prism Leisure Distribution, Lugtons

Cassette: released on Pickwick, Jun'81 by Pickwick Records. Dist: Pickwick Distribution, Prism Leisure Distribution, Lugtons

Remipeds

REMIPEDS.
Album: released on Rialto, Sep'82 by Rialto Records. Dist: Pinnacle

Re-mixture

RE-MIXTURE Various Artists (Various Artists).
Cassette: released on Champagne, Mar'81 by DJM Records.

Remler, Emily

CATWALK.
Notes: Emily Remler - guitar
John D'Earth - trumpet
Eddie Gomez - bass
Bob Moses - drums
Album: released on Concord Jazz(USA), Apr'85 by Concord Jazz Records (USA). Dist: IMS, Polygram

TAKE TWO (Remler, Emily Quartet).
Notes: Emily Remler - guitar
James Williams - piano
Don Thompson - bass
Terry Clarke - drums

Album: released on Concord Jazz(USA), Nov'82 by Concord Jazz Records (USA). Dist: IMS, Polygram

TOGETHER (Remler, Emily & Larry Coryell).
Notes: For full information see under: Coryell, Larry & Emily Remler.
Album: released on Concord Jazz(USA), Dec'85 by Concord Jazz Records (USA). Dist: IMS, Polygram

Cassette: released on Concord Jazz(USA), Dec'85 by Concord Jazz Records (USA). Dist: IMS, Polygram

TRANSITIONS.
Notes: Emily Remler - guitar
John D'Earth - trumpet
Eddie Gomez - bass
Bob Moses - drums
Album: released on Concord Jazz(USA), Apr'84 by Concord Jazz Records (USA). Dist: IMS, Polygram

Remmler, Stephan

I DON'T GO TO USA.
Tracks: / I don't go to USA / Kine sterne in Athen (Janet in Sankt Katreine) / Die zeit ohne stimmer".
Single (7"): released on Mercury, Jul'87 by Phonogram Records. Dist: Polygram Distribution

Single (12"): released on Mercury, Jul'87 by Phonogram Records. Dist: Polygram Distribution

Remote

FEELS SO GOOD.
Tracks: / Feels so good / Feels so good (remix).
Single (12"): released on FM Dance, Jul'87 by FM-Revolver Records. Dist: BMG, RCA, Ariola

Remote start

AUTOMATED MAN.
Single (7"): released on Jigsaw, Mar'82 Dist: Roots, Pinnacle, Projection

Remue, Charles

CHARLES REMUE & THE NEW STOMPER ORCHESTRA 1927.
Album: released on Retrieval, Apr'79 by Retrieval Records. Dist: Retrieval, VJM, Swift, Record Sales(Chris Wellard), Jazz Music

Renaissance

AZURE D'OR.
Cassette: released on Warner Brothers, May'79 by WEA Records. Dist: WEA

BACK HOME ONCE AGAIN.
Single (7"): released on Warner Brothers, Sep'77 by WEA Records. Dist: WEA

BONJOUR SWANSONG.
Single (7"): released on Illegal, Jan'82 by Faulty Products Records. Dist: Pinnacle, Lightning, Cartel

CAMERA CAMERA.
Album: released on Illegal, Sep'81 by Faulty Products Records. Dist: Pinnacle, Lightning, Cartel

FAIRIES LIVING AT THE BOTTOM OF MY.....
Single (7"): released on Illegal, Sep'81 by Faulty Products Records. Dist: Pinnacle, Lightning, Cartel

LIVE AT CARNEGIE HALL.
Album: released on RCA (Germany), '83

NORTHERN LIGHTS.
Single (7"): released on Warner Brothers, May'78 by WEA Records. Dist: WEA

NOVELLA.
Cassette: released on Warner Brothers, Aug'77 by WEA Records. Dist: WEA

ROCK GALAXY.
Album: released on RCA (Germany), '83

SCHEREZADE.
Album: released on RCA (Germany), '83
Cat. no: **26 21554**

SONG FOR ALL SEASONS, (A).
Album: released on Warner Brothers, Mar'78 by WEA Records. Dist: WEA

Cassette: released on Warner Brothers, Mar'78 by WEA Records. Dist: WEA

TIME LINE.
Album: released on I.R.S.(Independent Record Syndicate), Apr'83 by I.R.S.. Dist: MCA

TURN OF THE CARDS.
Album: released on RCA (Germany), '83

Renaissance group of....

MUSIC OF LIGHT & SHADOW.
Album: released on Alpha, Aug'82 by Alpha Records. Dist: H.R. Taylor, Gamut

Cassette: released on Alpha, Aug'82 by Alpha Records. Dist: H.R. Taylor, Gamut

Renaissance Players

MEMORIES OF ENGLISH MINSTRELSY.
Album: released on Viking, Jan'80 Dist: Harmonia Mundi Distributors

Renaldo, Lee

FROM HERE TO ETERNITY.
Single (12"): released on Blast First, Jul'87 by Sonic Youth Records. Dist: Rough Trade, Nine Mile, Red Rhino, Cartel

Renaldo & The Loaf

ARABIC YODELLING.
Album: released on Ralph, May'83 Dist: Recommended, Rough Trade

ELBOW IS TABOO.
Album: released on Some Bizarre, May'87 by Virgin Records. Dist: EMI, CBS, Polygram

HAMBU HODO.
Tracks: / He loves us all.
Single (12"): released on Some Bizzare, Jan'87 by Charisma Records. Dist: EMI, CBS, Polygram

Single (7"): released on Hollywood, Nov'86 by Hollywood Records. Dist: Pinnacle

Single (12"): released on Hollywood, Nov'86 by Hollywood Records. Dist: Pinnacle

HAMBU HODO (LP).
Album: released on Ross, Dec'86 by Ross Records. Dist: Ross Distribution, Roots Distribution

Cassette: released on Ross, Dec'86 by Ross Records. Dist: Ross Distribution, Roots Distribution

OLLEH OLLEH ROTCOD.
Album: released on Rotcod, '85 Dist: Rough Trade Distribution, Cartel Distribution

SONGS FOR SWINGING LARVAE.
Album: released on Do-It, '81 by Do-It Records. Dist: Virgin, EMI

Rena Rama

RENA RAMA.
Album: released on Dragon, Jul'87 by Dragon Records. Dist: Jazz Music, Projection, Cadillac

Renate

NICOLEOS.
Single (7"): released on Cambridge, Oct'81 Dist: PRT

Renato

FUNICULI FUNICULA.
Tracks: / Funiculi funicula / He loves us all.
Single (7"): released on Hollywood, Nov'86 by Hollywood Records. Dist: Pinnacle

Single (12"): released on Hollywood, Nov'86 by Hollywood Records. Dist: Pinnacle

SAVE YOUR LOVE.
Album: released on Lifestyle, Dec'82 by Zomba Records. Dist: CBS, PRT, RCA

Cassette: released on Lifestyle, Dec'82 by Zomba Records. Dist: CBS, PRT, RCA

SHE WEARS MY RING.
Single (7"): released on Lifestyle, Jan'83 by Zomba Records. Dist: CBS, PRT, RCA

Renbourne, John

Biographical Details: see also under Grossman, Stefan.

JOHN RENBOURN & BERT JANSCH (Renbourne, John/Bert Jansch).
Double Album: released on Cambra, May'85 by Cambra Records. Dist: IDS, Conifer

Double cassette: released on Cambra, May'85 by Cambra Records. Dist: IDS, Conifer

NINE MAIDENS.
Album: released on Spindrift, '86 Dist: Roots

Renbourn, John

BLACK BALLON, THE.
Album: released on Zu Zazz, Jul'87 by Charly Records. Dist: Charly

ENCHANTED GARDEN (Renbourn, John Group).
Album: released on Transat, Feb'80

ESSENTIAL COLLECTION, THE (VOL. 2) Moon shines bright.
Tracks: / Gypsy dance/Jews dance / Lady nothinge's toye puffe / Lady & the unicorn, The / Lady goes to church / Trees they do grow high, The / Watermill / Moon shines bright, The / My Johny was a shoemaker / Alman / Melancholy galliard / Pelican, The / Three pieces by O'Carolan / Morgana part 1 & 2 / Earl of Salisbury / English dance / Pavane/Tourdion.
Compact disc: released on Transatlantic, Sep'87 by Transatlantic Records. Dist: IMS-Polygram

ESSENTIAL COLLECTION, THE (VOL 1) The Soho years.
Tracks: / Judy / Candy man / Lost lover blues / East wind / Nobody's fault but mine / Wildest pig in captivity, The / I know my babe / After the dance / No exit / Lord Franklin / Cuckoo, The / Another Monday / Country blues / Waltz / White House blues / My dear boy / Hermit, The / Buffalo skinners / Sweet potato / Kokomo blues / So clear.
Compact disc: released on Transatlantic, Jul'87 by Transatlantic Records. Dist: IMS-Polygram

ESSENTIAL JOHN RENBOURN-VOL.1-THE SOHO YEARS, THE.
Tracks: / Kakomo Blues.

JOHN RENBOURN & STEFAN GROSSMAN (Renbourn, John & Stefan Grossman).

LADY AND THE UNICORN, THE.
Tracks: / Lady and the unicorn, The.

LADY & THE UNICORN, THE.
Tracks: / Trotto / Saltarello / Lamento di tristan / La rotta / Veri floris / Triple ballade / Bransie gay / Bransie de bourgogne / Alman / Melancholy galliard / Sarabande / Lady & the unicorn, The / My Johnny was a shoemaker / Westron wynde / Scarborough fair.
Compact disc: released on Transatlantic, Jul'87 by Transatlantic Records. Dist: IMS-Polygram

LIVE.....IN CONCERT (Renbourn, John & Stefan Grossman).
Double Album: released on Spindrift, Aug'85

Rendall, Ruby

NEVER LOOK BACK.
Notes: 11 modern country tracks from Scotland's no.1 Female country vocalist.
Album: released on Ross, '86 by Ross Records. Dist: Ross Distribution, Roots Distribution

Cassette: released on Ross, '86 by Ross Records. Dist: Ross Distribution, Roots Distribution

STRAIGHT FROM THE HEART.
Album: released on Ross, '86 by Ross Records. Dist: Ross Distribution, Roots Distribution

Cassette: released on Ross, '86 by Ross Records. Dist: Ross Distribution, Roots Distribution

Rendell, Don

EARTH MUSIC (Rendell, Don Nine).
Album: released on Spotlite, '83 by Spotlite Records. Dist: Cadillac, Jazz Music, Spotlite

JUST MUSIC (Rendell, Don Five).
Album: released on Spotlite, '83 by Spotlite Records. Dist: Cadillac, Jazz Music, Spotlite

LIVE AT THE AVGARDE GALLERY (Rendell, Don/Joe Palin Trio).
Album: released on Spotlite, '83 by Spotlite Records. Dist: Cadillac, Jazz Music, Spotlite

SET 2 (Rendell, Don Five).
Album: released on Spotlite, '83 by Spotlite Records. Dist: Cadillac, Jazz Music, Spotlite

Rendez Vous

YOU LOOK SO BEAUTIFUL TONIGHT.
Single (7"): released on Red Diamond, May'85 by Red Diamond Records. Dist: Red Diamond

Rene & Angela

BANGING THE BOOGIE.
Single (7"): released on Capitol, May'83 by Capitol Records. Dist: EMI

Single (12"): released on Capitol, May'83 by Capitol Records. Dist: EMI

SECRET RENDEZVOUS.
Single (7"): released on Champion, Oct'85 by Champion Records. Dist: RCA

Single (12"): released on Champion, Oct'85 by Champion Records. Dist: RCA

STREET CALLED DESIRE.
Tracks: / Save your love (For-1) / I'll be good / No How-No Way / You don't have to cry / Street called desire / Your smile / Who's foolin' who / Drive my love.
Album: released on Club, '85 by Phonogram Records. Dist: Polygram

Cassette: released on Club, '85 by Phonogram Records. Dist: Polygram

Compact disc: released on Club, '85 by Phonogram Records. Dist: Polygram

WALL TO WALL.
Tracks: / Wall to wall / Just friends / Secret rendezvous / Wanna be close to you / Love you more (I) / Love's alright / Imaginary playmates / Come my way.
Notes: Here is the duo's second album for Capitol from 1981,which contains the dancefloor classic 'Secret rendezvous'. An exciting up-beat funk album which sounds just as fresh today.
Album: released on Capitol, '85 by Capitol Records. Dist: EMI

Cassette: released on Capitol, '85 by Capitol Records. Dist: EMI

YOUR SMILE.
Tracks: / Your smile / Your smile (Inst.) / Secret rendevous'86.
Single (7"): released on Club, '86 by Phonogram Records. Dist: Polygram

Single (12"): released on Club, '86 by Phonogram Records. Dist: Polygram

Renee & Renato

JESUS LOVES US ALL.
Single (7"): released on Hollywood, Nov'83 by Hollywood Records. Dist: Pinnacle

JUST ONE......
Album: released on Hollywood, Jul'83 by Hollywood Records. Dist: Pinnacle

Cassette: released on Hollywood, Jul'83 by Hollywood Records. Dist: Pinnacle

JUST ONE MORE KISS.
Single (7"): released on Hollywood, Oct'85 by Hollywood Records. Dist: Pinnacle

LITTLE BITTA ME, A.
Single (7"): released on Hollywood, Oct'83 by Hollywood Records. Dist: Pinnacle

ONLY YOU.
Single (7"): released on Hollywood, May'84 by Hollywood Records. Dist: Pinnacle

SAVE YOUR LOVE.
Single (7"): released on Hollywood, Sep'82 by Hollywood Records. Dist: Pinnacle

Renegade Soundwave

KRAY TWINS.
Single (7"): released on Rhythm King, May'87 Dist: Rough Trade, Cartel

Single (12"): released on Rhythm King, May'87 Dist: Rough Trade, Cartel

Rene & Yvette

JE T'AIME (ALLO ALLO).
Tracks: / Rene DMC.
Single (7"): released on Sedition, Nov'86 Dist: PRT

Single (12"): released on Sedition, Nov'86 Dist: PRT

Reno, Don

FASTEST FIVE STRINGS ALIVE.
Album: released on King (USA), Apr'87 Dist: Gusto Distribution

Cassette: released on King (USA), Apr'87 Dist: Gusto Distribution

Reno, Johnny

FULL BLOWN (Reno, Johnny and The Sax Maniacs).
Album: released on Rounder (USA), Dec'85 Dist: Mike's Country Music Room Distribution, Jazz Music Distribution, Swift Distribution, Roots Records Distribution, Projection Distribution, Topic Distribution

Cassette: released on Rounder (USA), Dec'85 Dist: Mike's Country Music Room Distribution, Jazz Music Distribution, Swift Distribution, Roots Records Distribution, Projection Distribution, Topic Distribution

Reno, Mike

ALMOST PARADISE (Reno, Mike & Anne Wilson).
Single (7"): released on CBS, Jun'84 by CBS Records. Dist: CBS

Reno & Smiley

16 GREATEST HITS.
Album: released on Starday, Apr'87

Cassette: released on Starday, Apr'87

20 BLUEGRASS SPECIALS.
Album: released on Starday, Apr'87

Cassette: released on Starday, Apr'87

BEST OF....
Notes: 10 tracks
Album: released on Starday, Apr'87

Cassette: released on Starday, Apr'87

COUNTRY SINGING AND INSTRUMENTALS.
Album: released on King (USA), Apr'87 Dist: Gusto Distribution

Cassette: released on King (USA), Apr'87 Dist: Gusto Distribution

COUNTRY SONGS.
Album: released on King (USA), Apr'87 Dist: Gusto Distribution

on King (USA), Apr'87 Dist:

LAST TIME TOGETHER.
Album: released on Starday, Apr'87

Cassette: released on Starday, Apr'87

WORLD'S BEST FIVE STRING BANJO.
Album: released on King (USA), Apr'87 Dist: Gusto Distribution

Cassette: released on King (USA), Apr'87 Dist: Gusto Distribution

Rental, Robert

DOUBLE HEART.
Single (7"): released on Mute, Oct'80 Dist: Spartan Distribution, Rough Trade Distribution, Cartel Distribution

LIVE AT WEST RUNTON (see Normal) (Rental, Robert & Normal).

Rentals

I'VE GOT A CRUSH ON YOU.
Single (7"): released on Beggars Banquet, Jan'80 by Beggars Banquet Records. Dist: WEA

Rentaracket

MANIAC.
Single (7"): released on Killing For Pleasure, '86 Dist: Red Rhino, Cartel

Rent Party

AIN'T MISBEHAVIN'.
Tracks: / Ain't misbehavin' / Somebody turned the lights out / Liquor store / Barking jump.
Single (7"): released on Waterfront, '86 by Waterfront Records. Dist: Rough Trade, Cartel, Projection, Roots

Single (12"): released on Waterfront, '86 by Waterfront Records. Dist: Rough Trade, Cartel, Projection, Roots

HONEY BEE.
Single (7"): released on Waterfront, Feb'84 by Waterfront Records. Dist: Rough Trade, Cartel, Projection, Roots

HONK THAT SAXAPHONE.
Album: released on Waterfront, Apr'85 by Waterfront Records. Dist: Rough Trade, Cartel, Projection, Roots

RENT PARTY.
Single (7"): released on Projection, Sep'83

WALK THAT MESS.
Single (7"): released on Waterfront, Aug'84 by Waterfront Records. Dist: Rough Trade, Cartel, Projection, Roots

Rent Party Revellers

SHAKE THAT THING.
Album: released on GHB, Jul'87 Dist: Jazz Music, Swift

REO Speedwagon

6 TRACK HITS.
Extended-play record: released on Scoop 33, Aug'84 by Pickwick Records. Dist: H.R. Taylor

Cassette: released on Scoop 33, Aug'84 by Pickwick Records. Dist: H.R. Taylor

BEST FOOT FORWARD.
Album: released on Epic, Nov'85 by CBS Records. Dist: CBS

Cassette: released on Epic, Nov'85 by CBS Records. Dist: CBS

GOOD TROUBLE.
Tracks: / Keep the fire burnin' / Sweet time / Girl with the heart of gold / Every now and then / I'll follow you / Key (The) / Back in my heart again / Let's be-bop / Stillness of the night / Good trouble.
Album: released on Epic, '86 by CBS Records. Dist: CBS

HI INFIDELITY.
Album: released on Epic, Nov'84 by CBS Records. Dist: CBS

Cassette: released on Epic, Nov'84 by CBS Records. Dist: CBS

Cassette: released on Epic, Apr'81 by CBS Records. Dist: CBS

KEY, THE.
Single (7"): released on Epic, Oct'82 by CBS Records. Dist: CBS

LIFE AS WE KNOW IT.
Tracks: / New way to love / Thatain't love / In my dreams / One too many girlfriends / Variety tonight / Screams and whispers / Can't get you out of my heart / Over the edge / Accidents can happen / Tired of getting nowhere.
Album: released on Epic, Apr'87 by CBS Rec-

ords. Dist: CBS

Cassette: released on Epic, Apr'87 by CBS Records. Dist: CBS

Compact disc: released on CBS, May'87 by CBS Records. Dist: CBS

LIVE(YOU GET WHAT YOU PLAY).
Double Album: released on Epic, Aug'77 by CBS Records. Dist: CBS

NINE LIVES.
Album: released on Epic, Aug'79 by CBS Records. Dist: CBS

REO GRANDE.
Compact disc: released on Epic, May'87 by CBS Records. Dist: CBS

SWEET TIME.
Single (7"): released on Epic, Sep'82 by CBS Records. Dist: CBS

THAT AIN'T LOVE.
Tracks: / That ain't love / Accidents can happen.
Single (7"): released on Epic, Mar'87 by CBS Records. Dist: CBS

WHEELS ARE TURNIN'.
Tracks: / I do wanna know / One lonely night / Thru the window / Rock 'n' roll star / Live every moment / Can't fight this feeling / Gotta feel more / Break his spell / Wheels are turnin'.
Album: released on Epic, '84 by CBS Records. Dist: CBS

Cassette: released on Epic, '84 by CBS Records. Dist: CBS

Compact disc: released on Epic, '84 by CBS Records. Dist: CBS

YOU GET WHAT YOU PLAY FOR.
Album: by CBS Records Dist: CBS

PANIC.
Single (7"): released on Neil Rushton, Mar'83 by Inferno. Dist: Pinnacle

WILL TO WIN.
Single (12"): released on Red Flame, Dec'82 by Red Flame Records. Dist: Nine Mile, Cartel

ALEX CHILTON.
Tracks: Alex Chilton / Election day / Nightclub jitters* / Route 66*.
Single (7"): released on Sire, Jun'87

Single (12"): released on Sire, Jun'87

BOINK.
Album: released on Glass, '86 by Glass Records. Dist: Nine Mile, Rough Trade, Red Rhino, Play It Again Sam

Cassette: released on Glass, '86 by Glass Records. Dist: Nine Mile, Rough Trade, Red Rhino, Play It Again Sam

KISS ME ON THE BUS.
Tracks: / Kiss me on the bus / Little mascara.
Single (7"): released on Sire '86

LET IT BE.
Album: released on Zippo, Oct'84

PLEASED TO MEET ME.
Tracks: / I.O.U. / Alex Chilton / I don't know / Valentine / Shooting dirty pool / Red red wine / Skyway / Can't hardly wait.
Album: released on Warner Bros., May'87 by Warner Bros Records. Dist: WEA

Cassette: released on Warner Bros., May'87 by Warner Bros Records. Dist: WEA

SWINGIN'PARTY.
Single (7"): released on Warner Bros., '86 by Warner Bros Records. Dist: WEA

TIM.
Album: released on Sire, Nov'85

REPO MAN Original soundtrack (Various Artists).
Album: released on MCA, Jun'84 by MCA Records. Dist: Polygram, MCA

Cassette: released on MCA, Jun'84 by MCA Records. Dist: Polygram, MCA

SOUTH PACIFIC.
Album: released on Reprise, Aug'81 by WEA Records. Dist: WEA

LETTERS HOME.
Single (7"): released on Observation, Sep'82

REPRO 80.
Single (7"): released on Observation, Oct'81

SETTLEMENT.
Single (12"): released on Fashion, Sep'84 by Fashion Records. Dist: PRT, Jetstar

NOISES.
Single (7"): released on Volume, Mar'83 by Volume Records. Dist: Pinnacle

REPTILES FOR TEA EP.
Single (7"): released on Volume, Jul'83 by Volume Records. Dist: Pinnacle

AFTER THE PLAGUE.
Single (7"): released on New Rose, Mar'87 Dist: Rough Trade, Cartel

Double-pack single: released on New Rose, 13 Jun'87 Dist: Rough Trade, Cartel

NAKED IN THE WILDERNESS.
Album: released on New Rose, '86 Dist: Rough Trade, Cartel

NIGHT AFTER NIGHT.
Tracks: / Night after night / Half way to heaven.
Single (7"): released on Blue Hat, Jun'87 by Blue Hat Records. Dist: Blue Hat

JAB AND MOVE.
Single (7"): released on Bridgehouse, Apr'80 Dist: Pinnacle

MY SPIES.
Single (12"): released on Oval, Apr'83 Dist: Projection

ONE CHANCE.
Single (7"): released on Oval, Apr'84 Dist: Projection

Single (12"):

1984.
Album: released on Mega (Supermusic), Feb'84 by Pinnacle Records. Dist: Pinnacle

CASA FORTE.
Single (12"): released on Passion, Dec'84 by Skratch Records. Dist: PRT

RE QUARTERLY LP MAGAZINE Various Artists (Various Artists).
Album: released on Recommended, Sep'86 by Recommended Records. Dist: Recommended, Impetus, Rough Trade

RE QUARTERLY NO.3 Various Artists (Various Artists).
Notes: Includes Robert Wyatt, Cassiber. With free magazine.
Album: released on Recommended, Jun'86 by Recommended Records. Dist: Recommended, Impetus, Rough Trade

RE QUARTERLY NO.4 Various artists (Various Artists).
Album: released on Recommended, Dec'86 by Recommended Records. Dist: Recommended, Impetus, Rough Trade

RE RECORDS QUARTERLY NO.1 Various Artists (Various Artists).
Notes: includes fanzine.
Album: released on Recommended, Mar'86 by Recommended Records. Dist: Recommended, Impetus, Rough Trade

RE RECORDS QUARTERLY NO.2 Various Artists (Various Artists).
Album: released on Recommended, Mar'86 by Recommended Records. Dist: Recommended, Impetus, Rough Trade

REQUIEM Various artists (Various Artists).
Album: released on EMI, Mar'85 by EMI Records. Dist: EMI

Cassette: released on EMI, Mar'85 by EMI Records. Dist: EMI

RESCUERS Various artists (Various Artists).
Extended-play record: Dist: EMI

Cassette: released on Disneyland, Dec'82 Dist: EMI

13TH ANNIVERSARY SHOW Live in Japan.
Album: released on Torso, '86 by Torso Records. Dist: Rough Trade, Cartel, EMI

COMMERCIAL ALBUM.
Album: released on Charisma, Oct'80 by Virgin Records. Dist: EMI

ESKIMO.
Compact disc: released on Torso, Jul'87 by Torso Records. Dist: Rough Trade, Cartel, EMI

HIT THE ROAD.
Single (7"): released on Torso, 30 May'87 by Torso Records. Dist: Rough Trade, Cartel, EMI

Single (12"): released on Torso, 30 May'87 by Torso Records. Dist: Rough Trade, Cartel, EMI

INTERMISSION-LIGHTS OUT.
Single (12"): released on London, Jun'83 by London Records. Dist: Polygram

KAW-LIGA.
Single (7"): released on Torso, Dec'86 by Torso Records. Dist: Rough Trade, Cartel, EMI

Single (12"): released on Torso, Dec'86 by Torso Records. Dist: Rough Trade, Cartel, EMI

LIVE IN HOLLAND.
Compact disc: released on Torso, Jul'87 by Torso Records. Dist: Rough Trade, Cartel, EMI

NIBBLES (Residents & Snakefinger).
Album: released on Virgin, Aug'79 by Virgin Records. Dist: EMI, Virgin Distribution

PAL TV LP.
Album: released on Double Vision, Sep'85 by Double Vision Records. Dist: Rough Trade, Cartel

RALPH BEFORE '84 VOLUME 1.
Album: released on Korova, Oct'84 Dist: WEA

Cassette: released on Korova, Oct'84 Dist: WEA

RALPH BEFORE '84 VOLUME 2.
Album: released on Korova, Jan'85 D'+ WEA

SNAKE.
Album: released on Torso, May'87 by Torso Records. Dist: Rough Trade, Cartel, EMI

STARS AND HANK FOREVER.
Album: released on Torso, Nov'86 by Torso Records. Dist: Rough Trade, Cartel, EMI

TITLE IN LIMBO (Residents & Renaldo & The Loaf).
Album: released on New Ralph, Jan'84 by New Ralph Records. Dist: Rough Trade

TUNES OF TWO CITIES, THE.
Album: released on Ralph (USA), May'82 by Ralph Records (USA). Dist: Recommended

VILENESS FATS.
Album: released on Ralph, Dec'84 Dist: Recommended, Rough Trade

IS THIS WHAT ENGLAND IS?.
Single (7"): released on Timebox, 13 Jun'87 by Timebox records. Dist: Pinnacle

Single (12"): released on Timebox, 13 Jun'87 by Timebox records. Dist: Pinnacle

NOWHERE TO PLAY EP.
Single (7"): released on Riot City, Dec'82 by Riot City Records. Dist: Revolver

THOROUGHBRED MEN.
Album: released on Rot, Nov'84 by Rot Records. Dist: Red Rhino Through Cartel Distribution

VIVA LA RESISTANCE.
Single (7"): released on Red Rhino, Mar'84 by Red Rhino Records. Dist: Red Rhino, Cartel

SOMEBODY HELP ME.
Single (7"): released on Stagecoach, Feb'81

RESSURECTION (THE) (Various Artists).
Notes: O.I.D. = Oasis Independent Distribution
Album: released on Link, Feb'87 Dist: DMS, RCA

CARNIVAL.
Single (7"): released on Shooting Star, Apr'80

SHAPE I'M IN.
Single (7"): released on RCA Golden Grooves, Aug'81 by RCA Records. Dist: RCA

SHAPE I'M IN (THE).
Tracks: / Shape I'm in (The) / Makin' love.
Single (7"): released on Old Gold, '86 by Old Gold Records. Dist: Lightning, Jazz Music, Spartan, Counterpoint

SHAPE I'M IN, THE.
Single (7"): released on Bear Family, Mar'85 by Bear Family Records. Dist: Rollercoaster Distribution, Swift

AFTER MIDNIGHT.
Album: released on ABC, '86 Dist: CBS, Pinnacle

Cassette: released on ABC, '86 Dist: CBS, Pinnacle

DO YOU FEEL RESTLESS ?.
Album: released on Nervous, Jul'84 by Nervous Records. Dist: Nervous, Rough Trade

EARLY YEARS.
Album: released on Nervous, Dec'86 by Nervous Records. Dist: Nervous, Rough Trade

EDGE ON YOU.
Single (7"): released on Nervous, Oct'83 by Nervous Records. Dist: Nervous, Rough Trade

ICE COLD.
Single (12"): released on ABC, Apr'87 Dist: CBS, Pinnacle

Single (7"): released on ABC, Apr'87 Dist: CBS, Pinnacle

JUST A FRIEND.
Tracks: / Just a friend / Girl invisible (The).
Single (7"): released on ABC, Aug'86 Dist: CBS, Pinnacle

MR. BLUES.
Single (7"): released on Big Beat, Jan'85 by Ace Records. Dist: Projection, Pinnacle

SOMEBODY TOLD ME.
Tracks: / Somebody told me / How can I find you / Deep (The).
Single (7"): released on ABC, May'86 Dist: CBS, Pinnacle

Single (12"): released on ABC, May'86 Dist: CBS, Pinnacle

VANISH WITHOUT A TRACE.
Single (7"): released on ABC, May'85 Dist: CBS, Pinnacle

Single (12"): released on ABC, May'85 Dist: CBS, Pinnacle

WE ROCK THE NATION.
Album: released on Powerstation Records, Jul'86 by Powerstation Records. Dist: Pinnacle

WHY DON'T YOU.....JUST ROCK!.
Album: released on Nervous, Jul'84 by Nervous Records. Dist: Nervous, Rough Trade

LOVE TO MEET YOU.
Single (7"): released on Pop Aural, May'81 Dist: Fresh, Rough Trade, Swift, Spartan, Virgin

ACTION EP.
Single (7"): released on Restriction, May'84 by Restriction Records. Dist: Cartel

RESTAURANT AT THE END OF THE UNIVERSE Douglas Adams (Stephen moore).
Double cassette: released on Listen For Pleasure, Apr'83 by MFP Records. Dist: EMI

COLOURS.
Album: released on Light, May'82 by Mainline Record Company. Dist: Mainline

Cassette: released on Light, May'82 by Mainline Record Company. Dist: Mainline

DMZ.
Album: by Mainline Record Company. Dist: Mainline

LIVE BOOTLEG.

Album: released on Birdson, Apr'84 by Word Records. Dist: Word Distribution, Spartan

Cassette: released on Birdson, Apr'84 by Word Records. Dist: Word Distribution, Spartan

MOMMY DON'T LOVE DADDY ANY-MORE.
Album: released on Light, May'82 by Mainline Record Company. Dist: Mainline

Cassette: released on Light, May'82 by Mainline Record Company. Dist: Mainline

Return Journey...

RETURN JOURNEY TO SWANSEA Various artists (Various Artists).
Album: released on Caedmon(USA), May'80 by Caedmon (USA) Records. Dist: Gower, Taylors, Discovery

Cassette: released on Caedmon(USA), May'80 by Caedmon (USA) Records. Dist: Gower, Taylors, Discovery

Return Of...

RETURN OF JAZZ FOR ABSOLUTE BEGINNERS (Various Artists).
Tracks: / Your feet's too big / Boogie woogie man / Conga brava / Pick-a-rib (Part 1) / Subtle slough / Whoa babe / I got it bad (and that ain't good) / Scat song, The / Rock it for me / Bach goes to town / Crawl, The / Riffin' at 24th St / Night in Tunisia / Solitude.
Album: released on RCA, Jan'87 by RCA Records. Dist: RCA, Roots, Swift, Wellard, Chris, I & B, Solomon & Peres Distribution

Cassette: released on RCA, Jan'87 by RCA Records. Dist: RCA, Roots, Swift, Wellard, Chris, I & B, Solomon & Peres Distribution

RETURN OF ROCKAPHILLY Various artists (Various Artists).
Album: released on Rollercoaster, Sep'84 by Rollercoaster Records. Dist: Swift Distribution, Rollercoaster Distribution

RETURN OF THE JEDI Various artists (Various Artists).
Album: released on Disneyland, Jul'83 by WEA Records. Dist: WEA

Cassette: released on Disneyland, Jul'83 by WEA Records. Dist: WEA

RETURN OF THE JEDI The Ewoks join the fight (Various Artists).
Album: released on Disneyland, Jul'83 by WEA Records. Dist: WEA

Cassette: released on Disneyland, Jul'83 by WEA Records. Dist: WEA

RETURN OF THE JEDI Original soundtrack (Return of the Jedi).
Compact disc: released on RSO, May'83

RETURN OF THE JEDI Star Wars 3 (Return of the Jedi).
Album: released on Polydor, May'83 by Polydor Records. Dist: Polygram, Polydor

Cassette: released on Polydor, May'83 by Polydor Records. Dist: Polygram, Polydor

RETURN OF THE LIVING DEAD Various artists (Various Artists).
Album: released on Big Beat, Jun'85 by Ace Records. Dist: Projection, Pinnacle

Cassette: released on Big Beat, Jun'85 by Ace Records. Dist: Projection, Pinnacle

RETURN OF THE NATIVE Hardy, Thomas (Richardson, Lee).
Cassette: released on Caedmon(USA), '84 by Caedmon (USA) Records. Dist: Gower, Taylors, Discovery

Cassette: released on Cover to Cover, Jun'85 by Cover to Cover Cassettes. Dist: Conifer

RETURN OF THE SOLDIER Original soundtrack (Return Of The Soldier).
Album: released on That's Entertainment, Apr'83 by That's Entertainment Records. Dist: Pinnacle, PRT

Return of Sherlock Holmes

RETURN OF SHERLOCK HOLMES, THE (see under Conan Doyle, Sir Arthur).

Return To Oasis

RETURN TO OASIS An anthology of poetry from the Second World War.
Cassette: released on Talking Tape Company, '84 by Talking Tape Company Records.

Reuben

DON'T RUSH ME.
Tracks: / Don't rush me / Don't rush me (Dub rush).
Single (12"): released on Blakarmix, Jul'86 by Blakarmix Records. Dist: Jetstar

Reubens, Jack

BOXING.
Tracks: / Boxing / Heavyweight champion.
Single (12"): released on Shuttle, Aug'86 Dist: RCA

Reunion

BE BORN AGAIN.
Album: released on Pilgrim Records. Dist: Rough Trade, Cartel

REUNION Peking Opera.
Album: released on Lyrichord (USA), Oct'81 by Lyrichord Records (USA). Dist: Flexitron Distributors Ltd

Revelation

BOOK OF REVELATION.
Album: released on Burning Sounds, Mar'79 by Ross, Bill/Burning Sounds Records. Dist: PRT

CRAZY FOR YOU.
Single (12"): released on Kingdom, Aug'85 by Kingdom Records. Dist: Kingdom

THAT GIRL.
Single (12"): released on Kingdom, Dec'81 by Kingdom Records. Dist: Kingdom

TONIGHT.
Single (7"): released on Kingdom, Feb'81 by Kingdom Records. Dist: Kingdom

Single (12"): released on Kingdom, Feb'81 by Kingdom Records. Dist: Kingdom

VARIATION ON A THEME.
Album: released on Burning Sounds, Sep'79 by Ross, Bill/Burning Sounds Records. Dist: PRT

Revell, Graeme

INSECT MUSICIANS, THE.
Album: released on Musique Brut, Jul'87

Revenge Of...

BLOOD ON THE CATS/REVENGE OF THE KILLER PUSSIES (see Blood on the cats).

REVENGE OF KILLER PUSSIES Various artists (Various Artists).
Album: released on Anagram, Sep'84 by Cherry Red Records. Dist: Pinnacle

Cassette: released on Anagram, Sep'84 by Cherry Red Records. Dist: Pinnacle

REVENGE OF THE PINK PANTHER Original soundtrack (Revenge Of Pink Panther).
Album: released on United Artists, Jul'78

REVENGE OF THE SLENG TENG Various artists (Various Artists).
Notes: Catalogue number unknown.
Album: released on Youth Promotion, Dec'85 Dist: Jetstar

REVENGE OF THE UNDERDOG Various artists (Various Artists).
Album: released on Situation 2, Feb'82 Dist: Cartel, Pinnacle

Reverb Brothers

AIN'T SO SORRY.
Single (7"): released on Spectacle, Jun'84

SOMEONE'S SELLING OF THE COUNTRY.
Tracks: / Someone's selling of the country / Big thing(The) / Far away aint so sorry.
Single (7"): released on RCA, Jul'86 by RCA Records. Dist: RCA, Roots, Swift, Wellard, Chris, I & B, Solomon & Peres Distribution

Single (12"): released on RCA, Jul'86 by RCA Records. Dist: RCA, Roots, Swift, Wellard, Chris, I & B, Solomon & Peres Distribution

YOU'RE THE ONLY ONE.
Single (7"): released on RCA, Oct'85 by RCA Records. Dist: RCA, Roots, Swift, Wellard, Chris, I & B, Solomon & Peres Distribution

Single (12"): released on RCA, Oct'85 by RCA Records. Dist: RCA, Roots, Swift, Wellard, Chris, I & B, Solomon & Peres Distribution

Reverend Sunshine

TONIGHT.
Single (12"): released on DATC, Oct'82 by DATC Records. Dist: Rough Trade

Revere, Paul

KICKS (Revere, Paul & Raiders).
Album: released on Edsel, Jan'84 by Demon Records. Dist: Pinnacle, Jazz Music, Projection

PAUL REVERE AND THE RAIDERS (Revere, Paul and the Raiders).
Cassette: released on Timeless Treasures,

Jul'86 Dist: Counterpoint Distribution

Revie, Kim

COMING ALIVE TONIGHT.
Single (7"): released on Pavillion, Jun'82

DREAMS IN THE NIGHT.
Single (7"): released on Mystery, Dec'83 by Mystery Records. Dist: CBS Distribution

Revillos

BITTEN BY A LOVE BUG.
Single (7"): released on EMI, Oct'83 by EMI Records. Dist: EMI

Single (12"): released on EMI, Oct'83 by EMI Records. Dist: EMI

BONGO BRAIN.
Single (7"): released on Superville, Feb'82 Dist: Pinnacle

HUNGRY FOR LOVE.
Single (7"): released on Dindisc, Aug'80 by Virgin Records. Dist: Virgin, EMI

MONSTER MAN.
Single (7"): released on Superville, Aug'81 Dist: Pinnacle

MOTORBIKE BEAT.
Single (7"): released on Dindisc, Jan'80 by Virgin Records. Dist: Virgin, EMI

REV UP.
Album: released on Virgin, Mar'84 by Virgin Records. Dist: EMI, Virgin Distribution

SCUBA SCUBA.
Single (7"): released on Dindisc, Apr'80 by Virgin Records. Dist: Virgin, EMI

TELL HIM.
Single (7"): released on Aura, Nov'82 by Hollywood Nites Distribution. Dist: Pinnacle

WHERE'S THE BOY FOR ME.
Single (7"): released on Dindisc, Sep'79 by Virgin Records. Dist: Virgin, EMI

Revival

FLY THROUGH THE COUNTRY.
Album: released on Flying Fish (USA), Feb'79 by Flying Fish Records (USA). Dist: Roots, Projection

Revival London Cast

PAL JOEY.
Album: released on That's Entertainment, Apr'83 by That's Entertainment Records. Dist: Pinnacle, PRT

Cassette: released on That's Entertainment, Apr'83 by That's Entertainment Records. Dist: Pinnacle, PRT

Revival Time Choir

20 BEST LOVED CAROLS - VOL.2.
Album: by Pilgrim Records. Dist: Rough Trade, Cartel

HAPPY REVIVAL TIME CHRISTMAS, A.
Album: by Pilgrim Records. Dist: Rough Trade, Cartel

HE'S THE ONE.
Album: by Pilgrim Records. Dist: Rough Trade, Cartel

IT'S REVIVAL TIME.
Album: by Pilgrim Records. Dist: Rough Trade, Cartel

IT'S REVIVAL TIME (ALBUM 3).
Album: by Pilgrim Records. Dist: Rough Trade, Cartel

IT'S REVIVAL TIME (ALBUM 2).
Album: by Pilgrim Records. Dist: Rough Trade, Cartel

SHOW A LITTLE BIT OF LOVE AND KINDNESS.
Album: by Pilgrim Records. Dist: Rough Trade, Cartel

Rev, Martin

CLOUDS OF GLORY.
Album: released on New Rose, Mar'85 Dist Rough Trade, Cartel

Revolting Cocks

NO DEVOTION.
Tracks: / No devotion / Attack ships / On Fire.
Single (12"): released on Beauty & The Beast, Feb'86 Dist: Pinnacle

YOU OFTEN FORGET.
Single (12"): released on Waxtrax, Feb'87 by Jungle Records. Dist: PRT

Revolutionaries

BLACK ASH DUB.
Album: released on Trojan, '83 by Trojan Records. Dist: PRT, Jetstar

CINDERELLA.
Single (7"): released on Dart, Jul'83 by President Records. Dist: Jazz Music, Swift

GOLDMINE DUB.
Album: released on Greensleeves, Apr'79 by Greensleeves Records. Dist: BMG, Jetstar, Spartan

NEGREA LOVE DUB.
Album: released on Trojan, '83 by Trojan Records. Dist: PRT, Jetstar

OUTLAW DUB.
Album: released on Trojan, Jan'86 by Trojan Records. Dist: PRT, Jetstar

REVOLUTIONARIES SOUNDS - VOL.2.
Album: released on Ballistic, Jun'79 by Ballistic Records. Dist: EMI, Mojo Distribution

Revolutionary Ensemble

MANHATTAN CYCLES.
Album: released on India Navigation, '78 by India Navigation Records. Dist: Cadillac, Projection, Swift

PEOPLES REPUBLIC, THE.
Album: released on Horizon, Jul'76 by A&M Records. Dist: CBS

REVOLUTIONARY ENSEMBLE.
Album: released on Uni/Base, Apr'81 Dist: Jazz Music, Jazz Horizons

Revolver

MAYHEM.
Single (7"): released on Riot City, Sep'83 by Riot City Records. Dist: Revolver

NORTHERN SONGS.
Album: released on Rox, Dec'79 by Rox Records. Dist: Spartan Distribution

ONE AND ONE IS TWO.
Single (7"): released on Rox, Dec'79 by Rox Records. Dist: Spartan Distribution

Revolving Paint Dream

FLOWERS ARE IN THE SKY.
Single (7"): released on Creation, Feb'84 Dist: Rough Trade, Cartel

OFF TO HEAVEN.
Cassette: released on Creation, Jun'87 Dist: Rough Trade, Cartel

Revox Cadets

TONY GOES TO TOKYO.
Single (7"): released on Cocteau, Dec'81 by Cocteau Records. Dist: Pinnacle, IDS

Revulsion

EVER GET THE FEELING OF UTTER REVULSION.
Single (12"): released on Radical Change, Apr'85 by Backs Records. Dist: Backs, Cartel

Reward

IT MUST BE LOVE.
Single (7"): released on Impression, Jul'84 Dist: CBS

Single (12"): released on Impression, Jul'84 Dist: CBS

STRANGERS THIS TIME.
Single (7"): released on Impression, Jan'85 Dist: CBS

Single (12"): released on Impression, Jan'85 Dist: CBS

Reward, Live From Jamaica

REWARD, LIVE FROM JAMAICA Various artists (Various Artists).
Album: released on Vista Sounds, Mar'85 by Vista Sounds Records. Dist: Jetstar

Rey, Alvino

1940/1 - VOL.3 (Rey, Alvino & His Orchestra).
Album: released on Hindsight(USA), Mar'84 by Hindsight Records (USA). Dist: Swift, Charly

Rey, David

WHAT DO YOU DO WITH YOUR LIFE.
Tracks: / What do you do with your life / No one's hero.
Single (7"): released on Absoloot, 30 Apr'87

Reyes, Walfredo De Los

ECUE.
Album: released on Pablo (USA), '82 by Pablo Records (USA). Dist: Wellard, Chris, IMS-Polygram, BMG

Cassette: released on Pablo (USA), '82 by Pablo Records (USA). Dist: Wellard, Chris, IMS-Polygram, BMG

Rey, Monte

GOLDEN AGE OF MONTE REY.
Album: released on Golden Age, Jun'87 by Music For Pleasure Records. Dist: EMI

GOLDEN AGE OF..., THE.
Tracks: / So deep is the night / When our dreams grow old / World is waiting for the sunrise, The / Love's last word is spoken / Darling / Song of the rose, The ("Tango Des Roses") / O lonely moon (Cielito Lindo) / My serenade / Love is a song / Kiss in the night, A (Anoche Te Bese) / Sweetheart, we'll never grow old / Stars in your eyes / Carmelita / My lovely world and you / Stars will remember, The / Rose I bring you, The.
Cassette: released on Golden Age, Jun'87 by Music For Pleasure Records. Dist: EMI

SONG OF SONGS.
Tracks: / Smoke gets in your eyes / Can I forget you / World is mine tonight(The) / Yira Yira / Without a song / Love is mine / Vida mia / My heart will never sing / Beyond the blue horizon / I surrender dear / Song of songs / Love I give you my all / Donde / Shine through my dreams / In my little red book / O maiden, my maiden / Balloons / Rose of tralee (The).
Notes: Musicians:Monte Ray,Sidney Torch,Ceraldo & his Gaucho Tango Orch,Geraldo & His Orch. & The Ovaltineys,The Radio Times. Mono recording.
Album: released on Happy Days, May'86 by Conifer Records. Dist: Conifer

Reynard

FRESH FROM THE EARTH.
Album: by Pilgrim Records. Dist: Rough Trade, Cartel

Reynolds, Ambrose

GREATEST HITS: AMBROSE REYNOLDS.
Album: released on Zulu, Oct'83 by Zulu Records. Dist: Rough Trade

Reynolds, Barry

I SCARE MYSELF.
Single (7"): released on Island, Aug'82 by Island Records. Dist: Polygram

Reynolds, Debbie

DEBBIE.
Album: released on Jasmine, Oct'85 by Jasmine Records. Dist: PRT

TAMMY.
Single (7"): released on Old Gold (Reissue), Jul'82

Reynolds, Judy

ENDLESS SLEEP.
Single (7"): released on Old Gold (Reissue), Jul'82

Reynolds, L.J.

TELL ME YOU WILL.
Album: released on Fantasy, Aug'87 by RCA Records. Dist: RCA, Jetstar

TELL ME YOU WILL.
Album: released on Fantasy, Aug'87 by RCA Records. Dist: RCA, Jetstar

WEIGH ALL THE FACTS.
Single (7"): released on Club, Jun'84 by Phonogram Records. Dist: Polygram

Single (12"): released on Club, Jun'84 by Phonogram Records. Dist: Polygram

Reynolds, Ray

SHANK.
Single (12"): released on Darace, Sep'82

Rezanova, Svetlana

RUSSIAN POPULAR SONGS.
Cassette: released on Melodiya (USSR), Feb'79 Dist: T.B.C Distribution

Rez Band

BETWEEN HEAVEN AND HELL.
Notes: What can you say about Rez Band that hasn't already been said ?Made for metalmenthis power-drenched battle music.It's been nearly eight years sinfce the Resurr-ection Band unleashed their first album 'Awaiting Your Reply'Now with the rele- ase of their eighth LP,the powerful,challenging group of five is delivering most thought-provoking,hardest rocking album to date.'On our last studio album, "Hostage" they say 'we did everything from dance music to heavy metal.This time we went back to straight-ahead rock 'n' roll-no drum machines,no synths'
Album: released on Birdwing, Jan'86 by Word Records. Dist: Word Distribution

Cassette: released on Birdwing, Jan'86 by Word Records. Dist: Word Distribution

HOSTAGE.
Album: released on Birdwing, Mar'84 by Word Records. Dist: Word Distribution

Cassette: released on Birdwing, Mar'84 by Word Records. Dist: Word Distribution

Rezillos

CAN'T STAND THE REZILLOS.
Album: released on Sire, Jul'78

Cassette: released on Sire, Jul'78

COLD WARS.
Single (7"): released on Sire, Apr'79

DESTINATION VENUS.
Single (7"): released on Sire, '78

I CAN'T STAND MY BABY.
Single (7"): released on Sensible, Jul'79

MISSION ACCOMPLISHED BUT THE BEAT GOES ON.
Cassette: released on Sire, Apr'79

TOP OF THE POPS.
Cassette: released on Sire, Apr'81

Single (7"): released on Sire, Jul'78

RFB

REVERENCE.
Cassette: released on Plankton, Aug'85 by Plankton Records. Dist: Cantio (Sweden)

Rhead Brothers

BLACK SHAHEEN.
Album: released on EMI, Feb'79 by EMI Records. Dist: EMI

Rhenyard's Grin

ROUSKA.
Album: released on Concorde, Mar'87 Dist: Red Rhino, Cartel

Rhiannon

BIRDS OF RHIANNON (THE).
Tracks: / TWA corbies / Rince Briotanach(Gavotten ar menez) / Galloping trots / Lovely Joan / Will ye go to Flanders / Apples in winter / Fhir a bhata / Spanish ladies.
Album: released on Fellside, May'85 by Fellside Records. Dist: Roots, Jazz Music, Celtic Music, Projection

Rhiannon Tomos

DWED Y GWIR.
Album: released on Sain, '85 by Sain Records. Dist: Projection, Sain

Rhine Heart

STUCK BETWEEN A ROCK.
Single (7"): released on Brain Stir, Mar'85

Rhino Teen Magazine

RHINO TEEN MAGAZINE Various artists (Various Artists).
Album: released on Rhino (USA), Jul'84 by Rhino Records (USA).

Rhoda

BOILER, THE (Rhoda & Special A.K.A.).
Single (7"): released on 2-Tone, Jan'82 by Chrysalis Records. Dist: Polygram

Rhoden, Donna

DON'T YOU.
Single (12"): released on Ital, Oct'82 Dist: Pinnacle

I'M FALLING IN LOVE.
Single (12"): released on Ital, Mar'82 Dist: Pinnacle

SHY GIRL.
Single (12"): released on Solid Gold, Sep'81 Dist: MCA

WARM AND TENDER LOVE.
Single (12"): released on Ital, Jan'84 Dist: Pinnacle

WE ARE IN LOVE.
Single (12"): released on Ital, May'83 Dist: Pinnacle

Rhoden, Pat

STOP.
Single (7"): released on Jama, Jul'82 by Jama Records.

Single (12"): released on Jama, Jul'82 by Jama Records.

Rhodes, Abigail

TOGETHER AGAIN.
Single (7"): released on Klub, Oct'79

Rhodes, Emitt

FRESH AS A DAISY.
Tracks: / With my face on the floor / Somebody made for me / She's such a beauty / Long time no see / Lullaby / Fresh as a daisy / Live till you die / Promises I've made / You take the dark out of the night / You should be ashamed / Ever find yourself running / You must have / Blue horizon / Only lovers decide / Love will stone you / Better side of life / Mirror / Really wanted you.
Album: released on See For Miles, Jul'86 by See For Miles Records. Dist: Pinnacle

Rhodes, Roy

COUNTRY HEARTBREAK.
Album: released on Country House, Jun'81 by BGS Productions Ltd. Dist: Taylor, H.R., Record Merchandisers Distribution, Pinnacle, Sounds of Scotland Records

Cassette: released on Country House, Jun'81 by BGS Productions Ltd. Dist: Taylor, H.R., Record Merchandisers Distribution, Pinnacle, Sounds of Scotland Records

COUNTRY SIDE OF ROY RHODES (THE).
Notes: Tracks include: Walk tall/Banks of the Ohio/Wedding bells/Picture of you.
Cassette: released on Ross, '86 by Ross Records. Dist: Ross Distribution, Roots Distribution

Rhodes, Sonny

I DON'T WANT MY BLUES COLOURED.
Album: released on Amigo, Sep'79 Dist: Red Rhino, Cartel

Rhone, Joan

TRY ME.
Single (12"): released on Dancebeat, Aug'81 by Dancebeat Records. Dist: Jetstar

Rhos Male Voice Choir

COR MEIBION ORFFIWS Y RHOS.
Album: by Decca Records. Dist: Polygram

GREAT OPERA CHORUSES.
Album: released on Decca, Jul'83 by Decca Records. Dist: Polygram

Cassette: released on Decca, Jul'83 by Decca Records. Dist: Polygram

JIM REEVES - WE THANK THEE.
Album: released on Decca, Apr'78 by Decca Records. Dist: Polygram

RHOS MALE VOICE CHOIR.
Album: by PRT Records. Dist: PRT

SING JIM REEVES FAVOURITES.
Album: released on Spot, May'86 by Pickwick Records. Dist: H.R. Taylor, Lugtons

Cassette: released on Spot, May'86 by Pickwick Records. Dist: H.R. Taylor, Lugtons

Rhyme & Rhythm

RHYME & RHYTHM A collection of poetry & song for children.
Cassette: released on Argo, Mar'84 by Decca Records. Dist: Polygram

Rhymes To Remember

RHYMES TO REMEMBER Various artists (Various Artists).
Album: released on Kiddicraft, Jun'82 by MacDonald Educational Records. Dist: H.R. Taylor

Cassette: released on Kiddicraft, Jun'82 by MacDonald Educational Records. Dist: H.R. Taylor

Rhythm...

RHYTHM & BLUES & BOOGIE WOOGIE Various artists (Various Artists).
Album: released on Swing House (UK), Feb'84

RHYTHM & BLUES HOUSEPARTY Various artists (Various Artists).
Tracks: / Let the doorbell ring / I'll never let you go(Boo-hoo-hoo) / Stranded in the jungle / Harbour lights / Who's been foolin' you / Chop Chop / Hey fine mama / How long she's been gone / Ay la bas / Pretty soon-Young Jessie / Great pretender (The) / These golden rings / Hole in the wall / Drag race / W-O-M-A-N / Ooh-Bop-She-Bop / Come on little children / Every time I hear that mellow saxophone (I wanna rock).
Album: released on Ace, Sep'86 by Ace Records. Dist: Pinnacle, Swift, Hotshot, Cadillac

Cassette: released on Ace, Sep'86 by Ace Records. Dist: Pinnacle, Swift, Hotshot, Cadillac

Compact disc: released on Ace, Jul'86 by Ace Records. Dist: Pinnacle, Swift, Hotshot, Cadillac

RHYTHM & BOOZE - VOL.2 Various artists (Various Artists).
Album: released on Lunar 2, Apr'79

RHYTHM IN RHYTHM & BLUES, THE 1951-62 (Various Artists).
Album: released on Stateside, Jul'87 Dist: EMI

Cassette: released on Stateside, Jul'87 Dist: EMI

RHYTHM IN SOUL Various artists (Various Artists).
Cassette: released on Autograph, Apr'85 Dist: Record Services Distribution (Ireland)

RHYTHM IN SOUL - VOL.2 Various artists (Various Artists).
Cassette: released on Autograph, Apr'85 Dist: Record Services Distribution (Ireland)

RHYTHM 'N' BLUES AT IT'S BEST Various artists (Various Artists).

Double Album: released on Cambra, Aug'83 by Cambra Records. Dist: IDS, Conifer

Cassette: released on Cambra, Aug'83 by Cambra Records. Dist: IDS, Conifer

RHYTHM 'N' BLUES IN THE '40'S AND 50'S Various artists (Various Artists).
Album: released on Arbee, Jun'85

RHYTHM OF THE NIGHT (Various Artists).
Tracks: / Single life / Freeway of love / Nightshift / If you were here tonight / Gotta get you home tonight / Treat her like a lady / Love can't turn around / Pull up to the bumper / Finest (The) / Mine all mine / Cherish / Your love is king / Ain't nothing going on but the rent / Rhythm of the night.
Album: released on K-Tel, Feb'87 by K-Tel Records. Dist: Record Merchandisers Distribution, Taylors, Terry Blood Distribution, Wynd-Up Distribution, Relay Distribution, Pickwick Distribution, Solomon & Peres Distribution, Polygram

Cassette: released on K-Tel, Feb'87 by K-Tel Records. Dist: Record Merchandisers Distribution, Taylors, Terry Blood Distribution, Wynd-Up Distribution, Relay Distribution, Pickwick Distribution, Solomon & Peres Distribution, Polygram

Compact disc: released on K-Tel, Feb'87 by K-Tel Records. Dist: Record Merchandisers Distribution, Taylors, Terry Blood Distribution, Wynd-Up Distribution, Relay Distribution, Pickwick Distribution, Solomon & Peres Distribution, Polygram

RHYTHM PIANISTS Various artists (Various Artists).
Album: released on World, Aug'79 Dist: Jetstar

RHYTHM QUARTETS IN THE 30'S Various artists (Various Artists).
Album: released on Clanka Lanka, Jun'85 by Mr. R&B Records. Dist: Swift

RHYTHM & ROCK Best of Chess, Checker, Cadet - Various artists (Various Artists).
Album: released on Chess, Apr'81 by Charly Records. Dist: Charly, Swift, PRT, Discovery, IMS, Polygram

RHYTHMS OF RESITANCE Various artists (Various Artists).
Album: released on Virgin, Mar'84 by Virgin Records. Dist: EMI, Virgin Distribution

Rhythmakers 1932

RHYTHMAKERS 1932 Various artists (Various Artists).
Album: released on VJM, Jun'83 by Wellard, Chris Distribution. Dist: Wellard, Chris Distribution

Rhythm & Faith

TIME TO RUN.
Single (12"): released on Future, Nov'83 Dist: Pinnacle

Rhythm Hawks

NO CHANCE.
Single (7"): released on Hot Rock, Apr'81 by Hot Rock Records. Dist: Hot Rock

ZODIAC.
Single (7"): released on Hot Rock, Jul'80 by Hot Rock Records. Dist: Hot Rock

Rhythm Kings

SETTING FIRE TO MY HEART.
Album: released on Magnet, Dec'85 by Magnet Records. Dist: BMG

Page 836

Rhythm Method

DIANA.
Single (7"): released on Watteau, Jul'81 by Armageddon Records. Dist: Stage One

Rhythm Of Life

SOON.
Single (12"): released on Rhythm of Life, Jan'82

Single (7"): released on Rhythm of Life. Jan'82

UNCLE SAM.
Single (7"): released on Rational, Apr'82 Dist: Lightning

Rhythm On The Radio

WITCHES BREW.
Single (7"): released on Oval, Jan'80 by Oval Records. Dist: Pinnacle

Rhythm Party

NOW I KNOW YOUR HERE.
Single (7"): released on Sly, Sep'84 by Sly Records. Dist: Revolver, Cartel

Rhythm Tendencies

COME BACK.
Single (7"): released on Dakota, Mar'83 by Dakota Records. Dist: PRT

Single (12"): released on Dakota, Mar'83 by Dakota Records. Dist: PRT

Ria

NICE GUYS.
Single (7"): released on Dead Dog, Jun'84 by Dead Dog Records. Dist: PRT

Ria, Nikki

JUST AS I THOUGHT.
Single (7"): released on PRT, May'83 by PRT Records. Dist: PRT

Rias Orchestra

BABYLON A.M.C. (Rias Orchestra, The/Helmuth Brandenburg).

Ricchi & Poveri

NO.1S, MADE IN ITALY, THE.
Album: released on Ibach (France), May'84 Dist: Studio Imports

Cassette: released on Ibach (France), May'84 Dist: Studio Imports

Riccs, Glen

KEEP ON SEARCHING.
Single (12"): released on Jetstar, Dec'84 Dist: Jetstar, Stage One

LOVELY LADY.
Single (12"): released on Diamond C, Jul'83 by Diamond C Records. Dist: Jetstar

THIS CHRISTMAS.
Single (12"): released on Intense, Dec'83 by Intense Records. Dist: PRT, Kingdom

Rice, Boyd

EASY LISTENING FOR THE HARD OF HEARING.
Album: released on Mute, Nov'84 Dist: Spartan Distribution, Rough Trade Distribution, Cartel Distribution

EASY LISTENING FOR THE HARD OF HEARING (Rice, Boyd & Frank Tovey).

Rice/Lloyd Webber

70'S SHOWS Limited edition.
Album: released on MCA, Oct'81 by MCA Records. Dist: Polygram, MCA

PERFORMANCE Best of Tim Rice & Andrew Lloyd Webber, The (Rice, Tim & Andrew Lloyd Webber).
Tracks: / Jesus Christ Superstar / I dont know how to love him / Oh what a circus / Close every door to me / Another suitcase in another hall / High flying adored / Pity the child / Don't cry for me Argentina / Memory / Mr Mistoffelees / One night in Bangkok / Least of my troubles, The / Take that look off your face / I am the Starlight / Running back for more / I know him so well.
Notes: As the title of this Album indicates we have selected what we believe to be the best songs from the Musicals of Tim and Andrew. Many of these tracks have been specially recorded and feature such artists as David Essex, Judy Collins and Helen Terry. Along with these special recordings there are a couple of originals by Elaine Paige taken from the Shows Evita and Cats. the Album includes songs from such shows as Jesus Christ Superstar, Starlight Express and Chessmany of which have been box office hits in the West End.
Album: released on Telstar, Dec'85 by Telstar Records. Dist: RCA Distribution

Cassette: released on Telstar, Dec'85 by Telstar Records. Dist: RCA Distribution

Rice, Tony

CALIFORNIA AUTUMN.
Album: released on Sundown, Jun'87 by Magnum Music Group Ltd. Dist: Magnum Music Group Ltd, PRT Distribution, Spartan Distribution

COLD ON THE SHOULDER.
Compact disc: released on Rounder (USA), Dec'86 Dist: Mike's Country Music Room Distribution, Jazz Music Distribution, Swift Distribution, Roots Records Distribution, Projection Distribution, Topic Distribution

MANZANITA.
Album: released on Rounder, Aug'79

RICKY SCAGGS.
Album: released on Rounder, Sep'79

Richard, Belton

AT HIS BEST.
Album:

BELTON RICHARD - VOLUME 2.
Album:

GOOD 'N' CAJUN.
Album:

LOUISIANA CAJUN MUSIC.
Album:

MODERN SOUNDS IN CAJUN MUSIC.
Album: released on Swallow, Feb'79

MODERN SOUNDS OF CAJUN MUSIC-VOL.2.
Album: released on Swallow, Feb'79

Richard, Cliff

20 ROCK 'N' ROLL HITS.
Album: released on EMI (Germany), '83 by EMI Records. Dist: Conifer

ALADDIN AND HIS WONDERFUL LAMP.
Album: released on EMI (Holland), '83 by EMI Records. Dist: Conifer

ALL I ASK OF YOU (Richard, Cliff & Sarah Brightman).
Tracks: / All I ask of you / Phantom of the opera overture (Act II) / Only you.
Single (7"): released on Polydor, Sep'86 by Polydor Records. Dist: Polygram, Polydor

Single (12"): released on Polydor, Sep'86 by Polydor Records. Dist: Polygram, Polydor

ALWAYS GUARANTEED.
Tracks: / One night / Once upon a time / Some people / Forever / Two hearts / Under your spell / This time now / My pretty one / Remember me / Always guaranteed / One night / Once upon a time / Some people / Forever / Two hearts / Under your spell / This time now / Pretty one / Remember me / Always guaranteed.
Album: released on EMI, Sep'87 by EMI Records. Dist: EMI

Cassette: released on EMI, Sep'87 by EMI Records. Dist: EMI

Compact disc: released on EMI, Sep'87 by EMI Records. Dist: EMI

AT THE LONDON PALLADIUM (Richard, Cliff & The Shadows).
Notes: 22 tracks on this live recording playing approx:52 minutes.
Video-cassette (VHS): released on Video Music Collection, Jun'86

BABY YOU'RE DYNAMITE.
Single (7"): released on EMI, Mar'84 by EMI Records. Dist: EMI

BEST OF CLIFF RICHARD, THE.
Compact disc: released on Maybellene, May'87

BORN TO ROCK 'N' ROLL.
Tracks: / Born to rock 'n' roll / law of the universe.
Single (7"): released on EMI, May'86 by EMI Records. Dist: EMI

Single (12"): released on EMI, May'86 by EMI Records. Dist: EMI

CAROL SINGERS (EP).
Single (12"): released on EMI (Holland), '83 by EMI Records. Dist: Conifer

CARRIE.
Single (12"): released on EMI (Germany), '83 by EMI Records. Dist: Conifer

CINDERELLA.
Album: released on EMI (Holland), '83 by EMI Records. Dist: Conifer

CLIFF.
Tracks: / Apron strings / My babe / Down the line / I got a feeling / Jet black / Baby I don't care / Donna / Move it / Ready Teddy / Too much / Don't bug me baby / Driftin' / That'll be the day / Be-bop-a-lula / Danny / Whole lotta shakin' goin' on.
Compact disc: released on EMI, Oct'87 by EMI Records. Dist: EMI. Estim retail price in Sep'87 was £11.99.

CLIFF AND THE SHADOWS (Richard, Cliff & The Shadows).
Album: released on EMI, Jul'84 by EMI Records. Dist: EMI

Cassette: released on EMI, Jul'84 by EMI Records. Dist: EMI

CLIFF IN THE 60'S.
Album: released on Music For Pleasure (Holland), May'84 by EMI Records. Dist: EMI

Cassette: released on Music For Pleasure (Holland), May'84 by EMI Records. Dist: EMI

CLIFF IS 21 TODAY.
Album: released on EMI (Holland), Jan'85 by EMI Records. Dist: Conifer

CLIFF RICHARD.
Tracks: / I could easily fall (In love with you) / Gee Whizz it's you / Travelin' light / Unchained melody / Beat out that rhythm on a drum / Blueberry hill / Got a funny feeling / Spanish harlem / It's no secret / We say yeh / Day by day / Dancin' shoes / Blue turns to grey / Voice in the wilderness, A / When my dreamboat comes home / D in love / So I've been told / Fire and rain (LIVE) / With the eyes of a child / Good news / Sing a song of freedom / Mr.Businessman (LIVE).
Cassette: released on Hour Of Pleasure, May'86 by Music For Pleasure Records. Dist: EMI

Boxed set: released on EEC Import (Limited Edition), Dec'82 Dist: IMS, Polygram

CLIFF RICHARD BOX SET.
Boxed set: released on EMI (Belgium), '83 by EMI Records. Dist: Conifer

CLIFF RICHARD LIVE.
Album: released on MFP, Oct'76 by EMI Records. Dist: EMI

Cassette: released on MFP, Oct'76 by EMI Records. Dist: EMI

CLIFF RICHARD LOVE SONGS.
Tracks: / Miss you nights / Constantly / Up in the world / Carrie / Voice in the wilderness, A / Twelfth of never, The / I could easily fall (in love with you) / Day I met Marie, A / Can't take the hurt anymore / Little in love, A / Minute you're gone, The / Visions / When two worlds drift apart / Next time, The / It's all in the game / Don't talk to him / When the girl in your arms is the girl in your heart / Theme for a dream / Fall in love with you / We don't talk anymore.
Compact disc: by EMI Records. Dist: EMI. Estim retail price in Sep'87 was £11.99.

CLIFF RICHARD'S 40 GOLDEN GREATS.
Double Album: released on EMI, Oct'77 by EMI Records. Dist: EMI

Double cassette: released on EMI, Oct'77 by EMI Records. Dist: EMI

CLIFF RICHARD SONGBOOK, (THE).
Boxed set: released on World Records, '81 Dist: Polygram

Boxed set: released on World Records, '81 Dist: Polygram

CLIFF RICHARD STORY, VOL 1 : CLIFF.
Album: released on EMI (Holland), '83 by EMI Records. Dist: Conifer

CLIFF RICHARD STORY, VOL 2 : CLIFF SINGS.
Album: released on EMI (Holland), '83 by EMI Records. Dist: Conifer

CLIFF RICHARD & THE SHADOWS (Richard, Cliff & The Shadows).
Album: released on EMI (Holland), '83 by EMI Records. Dist: Conifer

CLIFF'S HIT ALBUM.
Album: released on Columbia, Aug'71 by EMI Records. Dist: EMI

CONGRATULATIONS.
Single (7"): released on Columbia, Feb'82 by EMI Records. Dist: EMI

DADDY'S HOME.
Single (7"): released on EMI, Nov'81 by EMI Records. Dist: EMI

DEVIL WOMAN.
Single (7"): released on EMI, Feb'82 by EMI Records. Dist: EMI

DREAM (EP) (Richard, Cliff & The Shadows).
Single (12"): released on EMI (Holland), '82 by EMI Records. Dist: Conifer

DRESSED FOR THE OCCASION (Richard, Cliff & The Philharmonic Orchestra).
Album: released on EMI, May'83 by EMI Records. Dist: EMI

Cassette: released on EMI, May'83 by EMI Records. Dist: EMI

DRIFTING (EP) (Richard, Cliff & Sheila Walsh).
Single (7"): released on DJM, May'83 by DJM Records. Dist: CBS, Polygram

Single (12"): released on DJM, May'83 by DJM Records. Dist: CBS, Polygram

ESTABLISHED 1958.
Album: released on Columbia, Oct'68 by EMI Records. Dist: EMI

EXPRESSO BONGO (EP) (Richard, Cliff & The Shadows).
Single (12"): released on EMI (Holland), '83 by EMI Records. Dist: Conifer

FINDERS KEEPERS.
Album: released on EMI (Holland), '83 by EMI Records. Dist: Conifer

GUARANTEE, THE.
Tracks: / One night / Forever / My pretty one / Remember me / Once upon a time / Some people / Two hearts / Always guaranteed / This time now / Under your spell.
Album: released on EMI, Sep'87 by EMI Records. Dist: EMI

Cassette: released on EMI, Sep'87 by EMI Records. Dist: EMI

HIGH CLASS BABY.
Single (7"): released on Columbia, '80 by EMI Records. Dist: EMI

HOLIDAY CARNIVAL (EP).
Single (12"): released on EMI (Holland), '82 by EMI Records. Dist: Conifer

HYMNS AND INSPIRATIONAL SONGS.
Tracks: / What a friend we have in Jesus / High ground / King of love my shepherd is (The) / All glory laud and honour / When I survey the wondrous cross / Just a closer walk / Take my hand / Amazing grace / Lord's my shepherd(The) / It is no secret / May the good lord.
Notes: A substantial paragraph written by Cliff on each song gives this album a person-al touch.
Album: released on Word, May'86 by Word Records. Dist: Word Distribution, CBS

Cassette: released on Word, May'86 by Word Records. Dist: Word Distribution, CBS

I LOVE YOU.
Album: released on Music For Pleasure, May'86 by EMI Records. Dist: EMI

Cassette: released on Music For Pleasure, May'86 by EMI Records. Dist: EMI

I'M NEARLY FAMOUS.
Album: released on Fame (EMI), May'82 by Music For Pleasure Records. Dist: EMI

Cassette: released on Fame (EMI), May'82 by Music For Pleasure Records. Dist: EMI

I'M NO HERO.
Tracks: / Take another look / Anything I can do / Little in love, A / Here(so doggone blue) / Give a litle bit more / In the night / I'm no hero / Dreamin' / Heart will break, A / Everyman.
Notes: (P) 1980 Original sound recording made by EMI Records Ltd.
Album: released on Fame, May'86 by Music For Pleasure Records. Dist: EMI

Cassette: released on Fame, May'86 by Music For Pleasure Records. Dist: EMI

IT'S IN EVERY ONE OF US.
Single (7"): released on EMI, Nov'85 by EMI Records. Dist: EMI

Single (12"): released on EMI, Nov'85 by EMI Records. Dist: EMI

LISTEN TO CLIFF.
Double Album: released on MFP, Sep'81 by EMI Records. Dist: EMI

Double cassette: released on MFP, Sep'81 by EMI Records. Dist: EMI

LITTLE TOWN.
Single (7"): released on EMI, Nov'82 by EMI Records. Dist: EMI

LIVING DOLL (Richard, Cliff & The Young ones).
Tracks: / Living doll / (All the flowers are)Happy / Disco Funk get up,get down (go to the lavatory mix).
Single (7"): released on WEA, Mar'86 by WEA Records. Dist: WEA

Single (12"): released on WEA, Mar'86 by WEA Records. Dist: WEA

LIVING DOLL.
Single (7"): released on Columbia, Feb'82 by

EMI Records. Dist: EMI

LIVIN' LOVIN' DOLL.
Single (7"): released on Columbia, '80 by EMI Records. Dist: EMI

LOVE SONGS.
Album: released on EMI, Jun'81 by EMI Records. Dist: EMI

Cassette: released on EMI, Jun'81 by EMI Records. Dist: EMI

ME AND MY SHADOWS (Richard, Cliff & The Shadows).
Album: released on EMI (Holland), '83 by EMI Records. Dist: Conifer

MEAN STREAK.
Single (7"): released on Columbia, '80 by EMI Records. Dist: EMI

MISS YOU NIGHTS.
Single (7"): released on EMI, Feb'82 by EMI Records. Dist: EMI

MOVE IT.
Single (7"): released on Columbia, Feb'82 by EMI Records. Dist: EMI

MY PRETTY ONE.
Tracks: / My pretty one / Love ya / Under the gun.
Single (7"): released on EMI, Jun'87 by EMI Records. Dist: EMI

Single (12"): released on EMI, Jun'87 by EMI Records. Dist: EMI

Single (7"): released on EMI, Jun'87 by EMI Records. Dist: EMI

Single (12"): released on EMI, Jun'87 by EMI Records. Dist: EMI

NEXT TIME.
Single (7"): released on Columbia, Feb'82 by EMI Records. Dist: EMI

NOW YOU SEE ME, NOW YOU DON'T.
Album: released on EMI, '85 by EMI Records. Dist: EMI

Cassette: released on EMI, '85 by EMI Records. Dist: EMI

PLEASE DON'T TEASE.
Single (7"): released on Columbia, Feb'82 by EMI Records. Dist: EMI

ROCK CONNECTION, (THE).
Album: released on EMI, Nov'84 by EMI Records. Dist: EMI

Cassette: released on EMI, Nov'84 by EMI Records. Dist: EMI

ROCK IN AUSTRALIA.
Tracks: / I'm nearly famous / Wired for sound / Learning how to rock and roll / Dreamin' / Donna / Only way out, The / Love stealer / Miss you nights / Shooting from the hand / Devil woman / Lucille / Under the gun / Where you are / Lovers and friends/ Ocean deep / Theif in the night / Living doll / Summer holiday / Bachelor boy / We don't talk.
Notes: The first ever solo live video release from Cliff. Filmed during the Australian leg of the Worldwide rock connection tour in front of a 12,000 capacity audience in the Entertainment Centre, Sydney. The spectacular show ranges from the latest in laser light effects through to just cliff, on stage with his acoustic guitar. 10 cameras and 2 Luma cranes filmed this award winning spectacular which features all Cliff's hit songs and more.
Video-cassette (VHS): released on PMI, Dec'86 by PMI Records. Dist: EMI

Video-cassette (Betamax): released on PMI, Dec'86 by PMI Records. Dist: EMI

ROCK'N'ROLL JUVENILE.
Album: released on EMI, Sep'79 by EMI Records. Dist: EMI

Cassette: released on EMI, Sep'79 by EMI Records. Dist: EMI

ROCK ON WITH.
Tracks: / Move it / High class baby / My feet hit the ground / Mean Streak / Living doll / Apron strings / Travelin' light / Dynamite / Willie and the hand jive / Voice in the wilderness, A / Please don't tease / Theme for a dream / It'll be me / We say yeah / Do you want to dance.
Album: released on EMI Europe, Sep'86 by EMI Records. Dist: Conifer

Cassette: released on EMI Europe, Sep'86 by EMI Records. Dist: Conifer

ROCK ON WITH CLIFF.
Album: released on MFP, Feb'80 by EMI Records. Dist: EMI

Cassette: released on MFP, Feb'80 by EMI Records. Dist: EMI

ROCK ON WITH CLIFF RICHARD.
Notes: Tracks include Living doll, Do you want to dance, Move it.

Album: released on Music For Pleasure, May'86 by EMI Records. Dist: EMI

Cassette: released on Music For Pleasure, May'86 by EMI Records. Dist: EMI

SEINE GROSSEN ERFOLGE.
Album: released on EMI (Germany), '83 by EMI Records. Dist: EMI

SERIOUS CHARGE (EP) (Richard, Cliff & The Drifters).
Single (12"): released on EMI (Holland), '83 by EMI Records. Dist: Conifer

SHE MEANS NOTHING TO ME (see Everly, Phil) (Richard, Cliff & Phil Everly).

SHOOTING FROM THE HEART.
Picture disc single: released on EMI, Nov'84 by EMI Records. Dist: EMI

SILVER.
Tracks: / Silver's home tonight / Hold on / Never say die (give a little bit more) / Front page / Ocean deep / Locked inside your prison / Please don't fall in love / Baby you're dynamite / Golden days are over(The) / Love stealer.
Album: released on EMI, Oct'83 by EMI Records. Dist: EMI

Compact disc: released on EMI, Oct'83 by EMI Records. Dist: EMI

SMALL CORNERS.
Album: released on MFP, Nov'81 by EMI Records. Dist: EMI

Cassette: released on MFP, Nov'81 by EMI Records. Dist: EMI

SOME PEOPLE.
Single (7"): released on EMI, Aug'87 by EMI Records. Dist: EMI

Gatefold sleeve: released on EMI, Aug'87 by EMI Records. Dist: EMI

Single (12"): released on EMI, Aug'87 by EMI Records. Dist: EMI

STARS OF ROCK AND ROLL (Richard, Cliff & The Shadows).
Album: released on EMI (Holland), '83 by EMI Records. Dist: Conifer

SUMMER HOLIDAY.
Album: released on EMI (Holland), '83 by EMI Records. Dist: Conifer

Single (7"): released on Columbia, Feb'82 by EMI Records. Dist: EMI

SUMMER HOLIDAY (Richard, Cliff & The Shadows).
Album: released on EMI, Apr'83 by EMI Records. Dist: EMI

Cassette: released on EMI, Apr'83 by EMI Records. Dist: EMI

SUPERGOLD (Richard, Cliff & The Shadows).
Double Album: released on EMI (Germany), '83 by EMI Records. Dist: Conifer

THANK YOU VERY MUCH... (Richard, Cliff & The Shadows).
Album: released on Music For Pleasure (Holland), Oct'84 by EMI Records. Dist: Conifer

Cassette: released on Music For Pleasure (Holland), Oct'84 by EMI Records. Dist: Conifer

Album: released on EMI (Holland), '83 by EMI Records. Dist: Conifer

THANK YOU VERY MUCH.
Video-cassette (VHS): released on Thorn-Emi, Jan'84

THANK YOU VERY MUCH (Richard, Cliff & The Shadows).
Video-cassette (VHS): released on PMI, Jun'86 by PMI Records. Dist: EMI

Video-cassette [Betamax]:

THANK YOU VERY MUCH (VIDEO) (Richard, Cliff & The Shadows).
Notes: At the London Palladium
Video-cassette (VHS): released on Video Collection, May'87 by Video Collection International Ltd.. Dist: Counterpoint

THUNDERBIRDS (EP).
Single (12"): released on EMI (Holland), '83 by EMI Records. Dist: Conifer

TOGETHER.
Notes: Live footage from the sell-out reunion concerts at the NEC in Birmingham,this July,packaged with no less than 24 former hits.
Video-cassette (VHS): released on PMI, Dec'84 by PMI Records. Dist: EMI

Video-cassette (VHS): released on PMI,

Dec'84 by PMI Records. Dist: EMI

Video-cassette [Betamax]: released on PMI, Dec'84 by PMI Records. Dist: EMI

TRAVELLIN' LIGHT.
Single (7"): released on Columbia, Feb'82 by EMI Records. Dist: EMI

TWO A PENNY.
Album: released on EMI (Holland), '83 by EMI Records. Dist: Conifer

TWO TO THE POWER (Richard, Cliff & Janet Jackson).
Single (7"): released on A&M, Sep'84 by A&M Records. Dist: Polygram

Single (12"): released on A&M, Sep'84 by A&M Records. Dist: Polygram

VIDEO CONNECTION.
Video-cassette (VHS): released on Thorn-Emi, Jan'84

VIDEO CONNECTION (THE).
Video-cassette (VHS): released on PMI, Jun'86 by PMI Records. Dist: EMI

Video-cassette [Betamax]: released on PMI, Jun'86 by PMI Records. Dist: EMI

WALKING IN THE LIGHT.
Album: released on Myrrh, May'85 by Word Records. Dist: Word Distribution

Cassette: released on Myrrh, May'85 by Word Records. Dist: Word Distribution

WE DON'T TALK ANYMORE (VIDEO).
Tracks: / We don't talk anymore / Miss you nights.
Notes: Video single.
Video-cassette (VHS): released on Gold Rushes, Mar'87 by Video Collection International Ltd.. Dist: Counterpoint

WE DON'T TALK ANYMORE.
Single (7"): released on EMI, Feb'82 by EMI Records. Dist: EMI

Single (12"): released on EMI (Germany), '83 by EMI Records. Dist: Conifer

WE'RE LOST ERRE.
Album: released on EMI (Holland), '83 by EMI Records. Dist: Conifer

WHEN IN FRANCE.
Album: released on EMI (Holland), '83 by EMI Records. Dist: Conifer

WHEN IN GERMANY, VOL 2.
Album: released on EMI (Holland), '83 by EMI Records. Dist: Conifer

WHEN IN GERMANY, VOL 1.
Album: released on EMI (Holland), '83 by EMI Records. Dist: Conifer

WHEN IN ROME.
Album: released on EMI (Holland), '83 by EMI Records. Dist: Conifer

WHEN IN ROME & WHEN IN SPAIN.
Double Album: released on EMI, Aug'83 by EMI Records. Dist: Conifer

Double cassette: released on EMI, Aug'83 by EMI Records. Dist: Conifer

WHEN IN SPAIN.
Album: released on EMI (Holland), '83 by EMI Records. Dist: Conifer

WIND ME UP (LET ME GO).
Single (7"): released on Columbia, Feb'82 by EMI Records. Dist: EMI

WIRED FOR SOUND.
Tracks: / Wired for sound / Once in a while / Better than I know myself / Oh no don't let me go / Cos I love that rock 'n' roll / Broken doll / Lost in a lonely world / Summer rain / Young love / Say you don't mind / Daddy's home.
Album: released on Fame, Oct'86 by Music For Pleasure Records. Dist: EMI

Cassette: released on Fame, Oct'86 by Music For Pleasure Records. Dist: EMI

Single (7"): released on EMI, Aug'81 by EMI Records. Dist: EMI

Album: released on EMI, '85 by EMI Records. Dist: EMI

Cassette: released on EMI, '85 by EMI Records. Dist: EMI

WONDERFUL LIFE.
Album: released on EMI (Holland), '83 by EMI Records. Dist: Conifer

YOUNG ONES.
Album: released on EMI (Holland), '83 by EMI Records. Dist: Conifer

Single (7"): released on Columbia, Feb'82 by

EMI Records. Dist: EMI

YOUNG ONES, (THE) (Richard, Cliff & The Shadows).
Album: released on EMI, Apr'83 by EMI Records. Dist: EMI

Cassette: released on EMI, Apr'83 by EMI Records. Dist: EMI

RICHARD & MAUREEN.
Album: released on Klub, May'80

Cassette: released on Klub, May'80

BEAUTIFUL TO ME.
Single (7"): released on Peach River, Sep'81 by Peach River Records. Dist: PRT

CATHY COME HOME.
Single (7"): released on Peach River, Jul'82 by Peach River Records. Dist: PRT

WHISKEY SUNDOWN.
Album: released on RCA, Jun'78 by RCA Records. Dist: RCA, Roots, Swift, Wellard, Chris, I & B, Solomon & Peres Distribution

SUPER BAD.
Single (12"): released on Sunset, Jul'83 by EMI

GOFF RICHARDS & BURNISHED BRASS (Richards, Goff & Burnished Brass).
Tracks: / Stop the cavalry / Busy doing nothing / Shadow of your smile / Putting on the Ritz / Change Partners / Someone to watch over me / Let yourself go / Tritsch Tratsch Polka / Doin' the Racoon / My cherie amour / Spread a little happiness / One day / Get out of your lazy bed / Sweet & Low / Super Trouper.
Album: released on Polyphonic, Apr'86 by Polyphonic Records. Dist: Taylors

Cassette: released on Polyphonic, Apr'86 by Polyphonic Records. Dist: Taylors

GOLDEN FLUTE, (THE).
Cassette: released on Kingfisher, Nov'81 by PRT

AIJALON (Richards, Johnny & his Orchestra).

AQUI HABLA ESPANOL.
Album: released on Jazz Reactivation, Jul'82 Dist: PRT

ARRANGERS TOUCH, (THE).
Double Album: released on Vogue Jazz (France), May'83

Double cassette: released on Vogue Jazz (France), May'83

SOMETHING ELSE (Richards, Johnny & his Orchestra).
Tracks: / Waltz anyone? / For all we know / Dimples / Band aside / Turn about / Burrito Borracho / Long ago & far away / Aijalon.
Notes: Mono recording.
Album: released on Affinity, Jul'86 by Charly Records. Dist: Charly, Cadillac

WALK SOFTLY-RUN WILD (Richards, Johnny & his Orchestra).
Album: released on Jasmine, May'83 by Jasmine Records. Dist: Counterpoint, Lugtons, Taylor, H.R., Wellard, Chris, Swift, Cadillac

HARPS & HORNPIPES.
Cassette: released on Folktracks, Nov'79 by Folktracks Cassettes. Dist: Folktracks

ART OF NANSI RICHARDS, (THE).
Album: released on Qualiton, May'73

JOYOUS VOICE OF NANSI RICHARDS, (THE).
Album: by Decca Records. Dist: Polygram

SONGS OF PRAISE.
Album: released on Quatiton, Mar'76

MUSIC TO WATCH GIRLS BY.
Single (7"): released on Legacy, Nov'84 by PRT

Richards, Noel

DANGER LINE (THE).
Album: released on Praise, Oct'86 Dist: Outlet

Cassette: released on Praise, Oct'86 Dist: Outlet

RECORDING LINE(THE).
Album: released on Praise, Oct'86 Dist: Outlet

Richardson, Betty

STOREY BOOK CHILDREN See under Soul, Junior.

Richardson,I

TALES OF HOFFMAN (Councillor Krespel).
Cassette: released on Caedmon(USA), Oct'81 by Caedmon (USA) Records. Dist: Gower, Taylors, Discovery

Richardson, Ian

TALES OF KING ARTHUR Spoken Word.
Cassette: released on Caedmon(USA), Oct'79 by Caedmon (USA) Records. Dist: Gower, Taylors, Discovery

Richardson John

MAHATMA GANDHI KNEW/B.P.U.
Single (7"): released on Loose, May'83 by Loose Records. Dist: Nine Mile, Cartel
Cat. no: **SE 1**
Picture disc single: released on Loose, May'83 by Loose Records. Dist: Nine Mile, Cartel

Richards, Paul

MYRIAD SOUNDS OF PAUL RICHARDS.
Album: released on Grosvenor, Jan'87 by Grosvenor Records. Dist: Taylors

Richards, Reuben

I FOUND LOVE.
Tracks: / I found love(inst).
Single (12"): released on Orbitone, Nov'86 by Orbitone Records. Dist: Jetstar Distribution

Richards, Roy

POWER OF LOVE.
Single (12"): released on Salamo, Sep'82 by Aitken, Laurel Records. Dist: Pinnacle

Richards, Sam

ENGLISH FOLKSINGER, (THE) (Richards, Sam/Tish Stubbs).
Album: released on Logo, Jul'79 by Logo Records. Dist: Roots, BMG

Richards, Trevor

TREVOR RICHARDS NEW ORLEANS TRIO, THE (Richards, Trevor New Orleans Trio).
Album: released on Wam, May'87

Richard, Wendy

COME OUTSIDE (Richard, Wendy & Mike Sarne).
Tracks: / Give it a try.
Single (7"): released on WEA, Nov'86 by WEA Records. Dist: WEA

Single (12"): released on WEA, Nov'86 by WEA Records. Dist: WEA

Rich, Buddy

1947/48.
Album: released on Hep, Apr'81 by H.R. Taylor Records. Dist: Jazz Music, Cadillac Music, IRS, Taylors, Wellard, Chris, Zodiac, Swift, Fast Forward

BUDDY RICH AT RONNIE SCOTTS.
Album: released on RCA, May'84

Cassette: released on RCA, May'84

BUDDY RICH BAND (Rich, Buddy Band).
Tracks: / Never can say goodbye / Fantasy / Listen here goes funky / Slo-funk / Good news / Hullah witch.
Album: released on MCA, Jul'87 by MCA Records. Dist: Polygram, MCA

Cassette: released on MCA, Jul'87 by MCA Records. Dist: Polygram, MCA

BUDDY RICH & HIS GREATEST BAND (1946-7).
Album: released on First Heard, Jul'77 by Submarine Records. Dist: Conifer, Taylors

COOL BREEZE.
Album: released on Astan (USA), Mar'85

EXCITING BUDDY RICH JAZZ SPECIAL, (THE).
Album: released on RCA (Germany), May'83

GREAT MOMENTS-1946.
Album: released on Golden Era, Jul'82 by Import Records. Dist: Wellard, Chris, Swift

IN LONDON.
Album: released on RCA (France), May'83 by RCA Records. Dist: Discovery

JAZZ OFF THE AIR (VOL.5).
Album: released on Spotlite, May'83 by Spotlite Records. Dist: Cadillac, Jazz Music, Spotlite

KEEP THE CUSTOMER SATISFIED (Rich, Buddy Big band).
Tracks: / Keep the customer satisfied / Long days journey / Midnight cowboy / He quit me / Everybody's talkin' / Tears and joys / Celebration.
Album: released on Liberty, Oct'86 by Liberty-United. Dist: EMI

Cassette: released on Liberty, Oct'86 by Liberty-United. Dist: EMI

KEEP THE CUSTOMER SATISFIED (Rich band, Buddy).
Tracks: / Groovin'hard / Juicer is wild (The) / Winning the west.
Album: released on Capitol, Oct'86 by Capitol Records. Dist: EMI

Cassette: released on Capitol, Oct'86 by Capitol Records. Dist: EMI

LIONEL HAMPTON PRESENTS BUDDY RICH.
Tracks: / Moment's notice / Second tune / Buddy's Cherokee / Take the 'A' train / Ill never be the same.
Compact disc: released on Kingdom Records, Jun'87 by Kingdom Records. Dist: Kingdom Records

Album: released on Gateway, Sep'83 by Kingdom. Dist: Pinnacle

MAN FROM PLANET JAZZ, (THE).
Album: released on PRT, Jan'81

RICH AND FAMOUS.
Album: released on Meteor, Nov'86 by Magnum Music Group Ltd. Dist: Magnum Music Group Ltd, PRT Distribution, Spartan Distribution

Cassette: released on Meteor, Nov'86 by Magnum Music Group Ltd. Dist: Magnum Music Group Ltd, PRT Distribution, Spartan Distribution

RICH RIOT (Rich, Buddy & his Orchestra).
Tracks: / Theme quiet riot / Day by Day / Nellie's nightmare / Great moments / Goof and I, the / Man could be such a wonderful thing, A / Daily double / Just a sittin and a rockin / Rags to riches / Little handicap, A / Man could be such a wonderful thing, A (second version) / Quiet riot encore.
Album: released on First Heard, May'87 by Submarine Records. Dist: Conifer, Taylors

Cassette: released on First Heard, May'87 by Submarine Records. Dist: Conifer, Taylors

RICH RIOT.
Album: released on First Heard, May'84 by Submarine Records. Dist: Conifer, Taylors

Cassette: released on First Heard, May'84 by Submarine Records. Dist: Conifer, Taylors

THIS ONES FOR BASIE.
Tracks: / Blue and sentimental / Down for double / Jump for me / Blues for Basie / Jumpin' at the woodside / Ain't it the truth / Shorty George / 9.20 Special.
Compact disc: released on Polydor, Nov'86 by Polydor Records. Dist: Polygram, Polydor

TOGETHER AGAIN-FOR THE FIRST TIME.
Album: by RCA Records. Dist: RCA, Roots, Swift, Wellard, Chris, I & B, Solomon & Peres Distribution

Rich, Charlie

CHARLIE RICH I love country.
Tracks: / Big boss man / River stay 'way from my door / Big Jack / Mountain dew / She loved everybrody but me / Let me go my merry way / Ol' man river / Grass is always greener, The / Ways of a woman in love, The / Why, oh why / Rosanna / Are you still my baby / Behind closed doors / Most beautiful girl (The) / Daddy don't you walk so fast / My elusive dreams / I love my friend / Sunday kind of woman, A / Papa was a good man / Spanish eyes / Very special love song, A / Rollin' with the flow / Life has it's little up's and downs / Every time you touch me (I get high) / Since I fell for you / On my knees / Somebody wrote that song for me / That's the way a cowboy rocks and rolls.
Album: released on RCA, Jan'87 by RCA Records. Dist: RCA, Roots, Swift, Wellard, Chris, I & B, Solomon & Peres Distribution

Cassette: released on RCA, Jan'87 by RCA Records. Dist: RCA, Roots, Swift, Wellard, Chris, I & B, Solomon & Peres Distribution

Album: released on I Love Country, Sep'86 Dist: Counterpoint

Album: released on Epic, Mar'87 by CBS Records. Dist: CBS

Cassette: released on Epic, Mar'87 by CBS Records. Dist: CBS

DON'T PUT NO HEADSTONE ON MY GRAVE.
Album: released on Zu Zazz, Mar'87 by Charly Records. Dist: Charly

FOOL STRIKES AGAIN, (THE).
Album: released on United Artists, Mar'79

GREATEST HITS:CHARLIE RICH.
Cassette: released on Epic, Jul'76 by CBS Records. Dist: CBS

Cassette: released on Epic, Feb'85 by CBS Records. Dist: CBS

LONELY WEEKENDS.
Cassette: released on Bravo, Feb'80 by Pickwick Records. Dist: Lugtons

MOST BEAUTIFUL GIRL IN THE WORLD, (THE).
Single (7"): released on Old Gold (Reissue), Jul'82

MY ELUSIVE DREAMS.
Album: released on Premier, Feb'87 by Premier Records. Dist: CBS

Cassette: released on Premier, Feb'87 by Premier Records. Dist: CBS

NOBODY BUT YOU.
Album: released on Liberty-United, Mar'80 by EMI Records. Dist: EMI

ONCE A DRIFTER.
Album: released on Elektra Asylum, Oct'80 by Elektra/Asylum/Nonesuch Records. Dist: WEA

ORIGINAL CHARLIE RICH, (THE).
Album: released on Charly, Oct'76 by Charly Records. Dist: Charly, Cadillac

ORIGINAL HITS AND MIDNIGHT DEMOS.
Tracks: / Whirlwind / Philadelphia baby / Rebound / Big man / Lonely weekends / Everything I do is wrong / Schooldays / Ascap / Gonna be waitin' / Stay / Who will the next fool be / Caught in the middle / It's too late / Just a little bit sweet / Midnight blues / Easy money / Sittin' and thinkin' / I finally found out / I need your love / There's another place I can't go / Little woman friend of mine / Ain't it a shame / Everything I do is wrong / Thanks a log / My baby done left me / There won't be anymore / Juicehead baby / Everyday / Charlie's boogie / You made a hit / Now everybody knows / Baby I need you / Stop thief / Too many tears / Ways of a woman / Sittin' and Thinkin' (2) / Popcorn polly.
Double Album: released on Charly, Dec'85 by Charly Records. Dist: Charly, Cadillac

REBOUND.
Tracks: / Rebound / Whirlwind / Break up / Philadelphia baby / Big man / Everything I do is wrong / Lonely weekends / You never know about love / School days / There won't be anymore / Juanita / Little woman friend of mine / C.C. rider / Easy money / Gonna be waitin' / There's another place I can't go / Who will the next fool be / Sittin' and thinkin' / Midnight blues / Unchained melody / You finally found out / Stay / My baby done left me / Charlie's boogie.
Compact disc: released on Charly, Feb'87 by Charly Records. Dist: Charly, Cadillac

ROLLIN' WITH THE FLOW.
Album: released on Epic, Nov'77 by CBS Records. Dist: CBS

SONGS OF LOVE.
Album: released on Pickwick, Feb'80 by Pickwick Records. Dist: Pickwick Distribution, Prism Leisure Distribution, Lugtons

Cassette: released on Pickwick, Feb'80 by Pickwick Records. Dist: Pickwick Distribution, Prism Leisure Distribution, Lugtons

Rich, Denise

SWEET PAIN OF LOVE.
Tracks: / Do you wanna dance / Sweet pain of love / Frankie / Too good for you / Show her / We walked away from love a love affair / Do ya wanna dance / Silent majority / Years go by so qiuckly (The) / Talking love / Wind in my soul.
Single (7"): released on Foundry, Feb'87 by Foundry Records. Dist: Virgin, EMI
Cat. no: **FOUND 4**
Single (12"): released on Foundry, Feb'87 by Foundry Records. Dist: Virgin, EMI

Album: released on MCA, Jun'86 by MCA Records. Dist: Polygram, MCA

Cassette: released on MCA, Jun'86 by MCA Records. Dist: Polygram, MCA

WE WALKED AWAY FROM A LOVE AFFAIR.
Tracks: / We walked away from a love affair / Win in my soul.
Single (7"): released on MCA, May'86 by MCA Records. Dist: Polygram, MCA

Single (12"): released on MCA, May'86 by MCA Records. Dist: Polygram, MCA

Richenel

DANCE AROUND THE WORLD.
Single (7"): released on CBS, 13 Jun'87 by CBS Records. Dist: CBS

Single (12"): released on CBS, 13 Jun'87 by CBS Records. Dist: CBS

L'ESCLAVE ENDORM.
Tracks: / L'Esclave endorm.
Single (12"): released on 4AD, Mar'86 by 4AD Records. Dist: Rough Trade

YEAR HAS MANY DAYS, A.
Tracks: / Dance around the world / Don't save your love / Temptation / Secret wish / Higher ground / Tell me / 50/50 (makes 100%) / Don't fear / Take it to the max / Can't give it up.
Album: released on CBS, Aug'87 by CBS Records. Dist: CBS

Cassette: released on CBS, Aug'87 by CBS Records. Dist: CBS

Richey Paul

DEVIL INSIDE/JEDIDIAH JONES.
Single (7"): released on Pinnacle, Jul'83 by Pinnacle Records. Dist: Pinnacle

DEVIL INSIDE THE.
Album: released on Parliament, Sep'84 by Parliament Records. Dist: Spartan Distribution

Rich, Freddie

FREDDIE RICH ON THE AIR-VOL.1.
Album: released on Aircheck, Apr'79

FREDDIE RICH ON THE AIR-VOL.2.
Album: released on Aircheck, Apr'79

Richie

BE YOUR OWN WOMAN.
Single (12"): released on Challenge, Aug'84 by Elite Records. Dist: Pinnacle

TRYING IT ON/HOT AND STICKY MIX.
Single (12"): released on Challenge, Dec'83 by Elite Records. Dist: Pinnacle

Richie, Lionel

ALL NIGHT LONG.
Video-cassette (VHS): released on RCA/Columbia, Jan'86

Single (7"): released on Motown, Sep'83 by Motown Records. Dist: BMG Distribution

BALLERINA GIRL.
Tracks: / Deep river woman / Dancing on the ceiling*.
Single (7"): released on Motown, Dec'86 by Motown Records. Dist: BMG Distribution

Single (12"): released on Motown, Dec'86 by Motown Records. Dist: BMG Distribution

CAN'T SLOW DOWN.
Tracks: / All night long / Stuck on you / Penny lover / Hello / Love will find a way / Running with the night / Only one (The) / Can't slow down.
Album: released on Motown, Oct'83 by Motown Records. Dist: BMG Distribution

Cassette: released on Motown, Oct'83 by Motown Records. Dist: BMG Distribution

Compact disc: released on Motown, Oct'83 by Motown Records. Dist: BMG Distribution

DANCING ON THE CEILING.
Tracks: / Dancing on the ceiling / Sela / Ballerina girl / Don't stop / Deep river woman / Love will conquer all / Tonight will be alright / Say you, say me / Night train (Smooth alligator) / Dancing on the ceiling / Love will find a way.
Album: released on Motown, Jan'87 by Motown Records. Dist: BMG Distribution

Cassette: released on Motown, Jan'87 by Motown Records. Dist: BMG Distribution

Compact disc: released on Motown, Jan'87 by Motown Records. Dist: BMG Distribution

Single (7"): released on RCA, Jul'86 by RCA Records. Dist: RCA, Roots, Swift, Wellard, Chris, I & B, Solomon & Peres Distribution

Single (12"): released on RCA, Jul'86 by RCA Records. Dist: RCA, Roots, Swift, Wellard, Chris, I & B, Solomon & Peres Distribution

ENDLESS LOVE (Richie, Lionel & Diana Ross).
Single (7"): released on Motown, Oct'81 by Motown Records. Dist: BMG Distribution

HELLO.
Single (7"): released on RCA, Mar'84 by RCA Records. Dist: RCA, Roots, Swift, Wellard, Chris, I & B, Solomon & Peres Distribution

Single (12"): released on RCA, Mar'84 by RCA Records. Dist: RCA, Roots, Swift, Wellard, Chris, I & B, Solomon & Peres Distribution

LIONEL RICHIE.
Tracks: / Serves you right / Wanding stranger / Tell me / My love / Round and round / Truly / You are / You mean more to me / Just put some love in your heart.
Album: released on Motown, Nov'82 by Motown Records. Dist: BMG Distribution

Cassette: released on Motown, Nov'82 by Motown Records. Dist: BMG Distribution

Compact disc: released on Motown, Nov'82 by Motown Records. Dist: BMG Distribution

LOVE WILL CONQUER ALL.
Tracks: / Love will conquer all / Only one(The) / Love will conquer all (remix) / Love will conquer all (Ext.remix) / Love will conquer all (Radio edit) / Love will conquer all (Inst).
Single (7"): released on Motown, Sep'86 by Motown Records. Dist: BMG Distribution

Single (12"): released on Motown, Sep'86 by Motown Records. Dist: BMG Distribution

Single (12"): released on Motown, Oct'86 by Motown Records. Dist: BMG Distribution

MY LOVE/ROUND AND ROUND.
Single (7"): released on Motown, Apr'83 by Motown Records. Dist: BMG Distribution

Single (12"): released on Motown, Apr'83 by Motown Records. Dist: BMG Distribution

PENNY LOVER.
Single (7"): released on Motown, Oct'84 by Motown Records. Dist: BMG Distribution

Single (12"): released on Motown, Oct'84 by Motown Records. Dist: BMG Distribution

ROCKIN AND ROMANCE.
Album: released on Rough Trade, Jun'85 by Rough Trade Records. Dist: Rough Trade Distribution, Cartel Distribution

RUNNING WITH THE NIGHT/ALL NIGHT LONG.
Single (7"): released on Motown, Nov'83 by Motown Records. Dist: BMG Distribution

Single (12"): released on Motown, Nov'83 by Motown Records. Dist: BMG Distribution

SAY YOU SAY ME.
Single (7"): released on Motown, Nov'85 by Motown Records. Dist: BMG Distribution

Single (12"): released on Motown, Nov'85 by Motown Records. Dist: BMG Distribution

SELA.
Tracks: / Sela / Serves you right.
Single (7"): released on Motown, Mar'87 by Motown Records. Dist: BMG Distribution

Single (12"): by Motown Records. Dist: BMG Distribution

TRULY/JUST PUT SOME LOVE IN YOUR......
Single (7"): released on Motown, Nov'82 by Motown Records. Dist: BMG Distribution

Single (7"): released on Motown, Jan'83 by Motown Records. Dist: BMG Distribution

Single (12"): released on Motown, Jan'83 by Motown Records. Dist: BMG Distribution

Richie, Pearl

ONE DAY YOU'LL COME.
Tracks: / One day you'll come / Radio show (The) / Sloane Army;Kensington war cry.
Notes: Distributor:Splinter Records,33 Regents Park Road London NW1 7TL.
Single (7"): released on Splinter, Mar'86 Dist: Splinter

Richie & The Lowdowners

HAVE A NICE DAY.
Single (7"): released on Rosie, Sep'84 by Rosie Records. Dist: PRT Distribution

Rich Kids

GHOSTS OF PRINCES TOWERS.
Album: released on Fame (EMI), Nov'83 by Music For Pleasure Records. Dist: EMI

Cassette: released on Fame (EMI), Nov'83 by Music For Pleasure Records. Dist: EMI

Rich, Lisa

TOUCH OF THE RARE (Rich, Lisa with Clare Fischer).
Compact disc: released on Trend, Dec'86 by Discovery Records. Dist: Flexitron Distributors Ltd, Swift

Richman, Jonathan

BACK IN YOUR LIFE (Richman, Jonathan & The modern lovers).
Tracks: / Abdul and Cleopatra / (She's gonna) respect me / Lover please / Affection / Buzz buzz buzz / Back in your life / Party in the woods tonight / My love is a flower (just beggining to bloom) / I'm natures mosquito / Emaline / Lydia / I hear you calling me.
Album: released on Beserkley (USA), Nov'86 by Beserkley Records. Dist: PRT

EYPTIAN REGGAE/MORNING OF OUR LIVES.
Single (7"): released on Old Gold, Jul'82 by Old Gold Records. Dist: Lightning, Jazz Music, Spartan, Counterpoint

I'M JUST BEGINNING TO LIVE.
Single (7"): released on Rough Trade, Aug'85 by Rough Trade Records. Dist: Rough Trade Distribution, Cartel Distribution

Single (12"): released on Rough Trade, Aug'85 by Rough Trade Records. Dist: Rough Trade Distribution, Cartel Distribution

IT'S TIME FOR JONATHAN RICHMAN &..... (Richman, Jonathan & The modern lovers).
Album: released on Rough Trade, Feb'86 by Rough Trade Records. Dist: Rough Trade Distribution, Cartel Distribution

Cassette: released on Rough Trade, Feb'86 by Rough Trade Records. Dist: Rough Trade Distribution, Cartel Distribution

JOHNATHAN RICHMAN SONGBOOK.
Album: released on Beserkley (USA), Jan'80 by Beserkley Records. Dist: PRT

JONATHAN RICHMAN AND THE MODERN LOVERS.
Compact disc: released on Beserkley (USA), Nov'86 by Beserkley Records. Dist: PRT

Compact disc: released on Beserkley (USA), Nov'86 by Beserkley Records. Dist: PRT

JONATHAN SINGS (Richman, Jonathan & The modern lovers).
Album: released on Rough Trade, '84 by Rough Trade Records. Dist: Rough Trade Distribution, Cartel Distribution

Cassette: released on Rough Trade, '84 by Rough Trade Records. Dist: Rough Trade Distribution, Cartel Distribution

J. RICHMAN AND THE MODERN LOVERS (Richman, Jonathan & The modern lovers).
Tracks: / Rockin' / Shopping centre / Back in the U.S.A. / Important in your life / New England / Lonely financial zone / Hiddear / Abominable snowman in the market / Hey there little insect / Here comes the Martian Martians / Springtime / Amazing Grace.
Album: released on Beserkley (USA), Nov'86 by Beserkley Records. Dist: PRT

MODERN LOVERS.
Album: released on Beserkley (USA), Nov'86 by Beserkley Records. Dist: PRT

MODERN LOVERS LIVE.
Album: released on Beserkley (USA), Nov'86 by Beserkley Records. Dist: PRT

ROAD RUNNER ONCE/ROAD RUNNER TWICE.
Single (7"): released on Old Gold, Jul'82 by Old Gold Records. Dist: Lightning, Jazz Music, Spartan, Counterpoint

ROCK'N'ROLL WITH MODERN LOVERS (Richman, Jonathan & The modern lovers).
Tracks: / Sweeping wind (Kwa ti feng) / Ice cream man / Rockin' rockin' / Leprechauns / Summer morning / Afternoon / Fly into the mystery / South American folk song / Roller coaster by the sea / Dodge veg-o-matic / Egyptian reggae / Coomyah / Wheels on the bus / Angels watching me.
Album: released on Beserkley (USA), Nov'86 by Beserkley Records. Dist: PRT

THAT SUMMER FEELING (Richman, Jonathan & The modern lovers).
Single (7"): released on Rough Trade, May'85 by Rough Trade Records. Dist: Rough Trade Distribution, Cartel Distribution

Single (12"): released on Rough Trade, May'85 by Rough Trade Records. Dist: Rough Trade Distribution, Cartel Distribution

Richman Richie

HARRY RICHMAN & SOPHIE TUCKER.
Album: released on Monmouth, Mar'79

Rich mix

I'VE GOT THE LOVE.
Single (7"): released on Satril, Aug'83 by Satril Records. Dist: PRT

Single (12"): released on Satril, Aug'83 by Satril Records. Dist: PRT

Richmond Danny

LAST MINGUS BAND PLAYS CHARLES MINGUS.
Album: released on Timeless, Jan'81

FROM A SEAT IN THE STALLS.
Album: released on Acorn, Jun'79 Dist: Folksound, Jazz Music

NOSTALGIA IN RHYTHM.
Album: released on Grosvenor, Jun'81 by Grosvenor Records. Dist: Taylors

Rich, Ritchie

CHECK IT OUT!.
Tracks: / Check it out / Scratch it out.
Notes: G/Self-98 Fulham Place Road,London-01 741 0543.
Single (12"): released on Spin-Off's, Jun'86 Dist: Spin-Off

Rickets, Glen

FOUND A LOVE.
Album: released on Scorpio, May'86 by Scorpio Records. Dist: Jetstar

JUST CAN'T GET OVER YOU.
Album: released on Paradise, Jan'87 Dist: Jetstar, JSU, WEA

Rick & Lisa

WHEN YOU GONNA.
Single (7"): released on RCA, May'87 by RCA Records. Dist: RCA, Roots, Swift, Wellard, Chris, I & B, Solomon & Peres Distribution

Single (12"): released on RCA, May'87 by RCA Records. Dist: RCA, Roots, Swift, Wellard, Chris, I & B, Solomon & Peres Distribution

Ricky

BANG BANG BANG.
Tracks: / Bang Bang Bang / Bang Bang Bang(who's on the phone).
Single (7"): released on A&M, Jun'86 by A&M Records. Dist: Polygram

Single (12"): released on A&M, Jun'86 by A&M Records. Dist: Polygram

Ricky & The Mutations

THATCHER RAP/ CRISIS.
Single (12"): released on Cool Ghoul, Jul'83 by Cool Ghoul Records. Dist: Rough Trade, Cool Ghoul

Rico

THAT MAN IS FORWARD.
Album: released on Two-Tone, Mar'81 by Chrysalis Records. Dist: H.R. Taylor

Cassette: released on Two-Tone, Mar'81 by Chrysalis Records. Dist: H.R. Taylor

Ricochets

MADE IN THE SHADE.
Album: released on Nervous, Jul'84 by Nervous Records. Dist: Nervous, Rough Trade

Ric Tic Live Revue

RIC TIC LIVE REVUE Various artists (Various Artists).
Single (12"): released on Inferno, Mar'84 by Inferno Records. Dist: Inferno, Cartel, Pinnacle

Riddim Force

HOW SWEET IT IS TO BE LOVED.
Album: released on Pioneer International, Nov'85 by Pioneer International Records. Dist: Jetstar

Riddle, Nelson

101 STRINGS.
Compact disc: released on Vogue, May'87 Dist: Discovery, Jazz Music, PRT, Swift

BEST IS YET TO COME (THE) (Riddle, Nelson/Ella Fitzgerald).
Notes: Full details under Ella Fitzgerald.

CAN CAN (Riddle, Nelson And His Orchestra).
Album: released on Capitol, Feb'84 by Capitol Records. Dist: EMI

Cassette: released on Capitol, Feb'84 by Capitol Records. Dist: EMI

HEY LET YOURSELF GO.
Album: released on Pathe Marconi, Mar'85 Dist: Swift

Cassette: released on Pathe MarconiFrance), Mar'85

JOY OF LIVING, THE (Riddle, Nelson And His Orchestra).
Album: released on Capitol, Jul'85 by Capitol Records. Dist: EMI

Cassette: released on Capitol, Jul'85 by Capitol Records. Dist: EMI

LOOK OF LOVE, THE (Riddle, Nelson And His Orchestra).
Album: released on Bulldog, Jun'82 by Bulldog Records. Dist: President Distribution, Spartan, Swift, Taylor, H.R.

Cassette: released on Bulldog, Jun'82 by Bulldog Records. Dist: President Distribution, Spartan, Swift, Taylor, H.R.

ROMANCE, FIRE AND FANCY (Riddle, Nelson & his orchestra).
Album: released on Intersound, Dec'86 by Intersound Records. Dist: Jazz Music

SILVER COLLECTION, THE.
Tracks: / My life / My sweet lord / Dao Paulo / Close to you / My one and only love / Lamento / When the world was young / Naomi / Just a little lovin' / Changing colours / Born happy / Night of love / Uptown dance / Time and space / Dedication / Volcano's daughter / Romantic places / It's your turn / Rachel / Greenwich village.
Compact disc: released on Polydor, Feb'85 by Polydor Records. Dist: Polygram, Polydor

WONDERFUL NAT KING COLE SONGS(THE).
Tracks: / Too young / It's only a paper moon / Nature boy / Walkin' my baby back home / Mona Lisa / Night Lights / Dance Ballerina dance / Sweet Lorraine / Ramblin' Rose.
Album: released on CBS, Mar'86 by CBS Records. Dist: CBS

Cassette: released on CBS, Mar'86 by CBS Records. Dist: CBS

Riders In the sky

NEW TRIALS.
Compact disc: released on Rounder (USA), Dec'86 Dist: Mike's Country Music Room Distribution, Jazz Music Distribution, Swift Distribution, Roots Records Distribution, Projection Distribution, Topic Distribution

SADDLE PALS.
Album: released on Rounder (USA), Sep'85 Dist: Mike's Country Music Room Distribution, Jazz Music Distribution, Swift Distribution, Roots Records Distribution, Projection Distribution, Topic Distribution

WEEDS IN WATER.
Album: released on Rounder (USA), Jan'84 Dist: Mike's Country Music Room Distribution, Jazz Music Distribution, Swift Distribution, Roots Records Distribution, Projection Distribution, Topic Distribution

Ride The Chariot

NINTH FESTIVAL 100 WELSH MALE VOICES.
Album: released on BBC, Feb'85 by BBC Records & Tapes. Dist: EMI, PRT, Pye

Cassette: released on BBC, Feb'85 by BBC Records & Tapes. Dist: EMI, PRT, Pye

Ride The Rhythm

RIDE THE RHYTHM Various artists (Various Artists).
Album: released on Top Rank, Apr'85

Ridgway, Stan

BIG HEAT.
Single (7"): released on Illegal, Apr'85 by Faulty Products Records. Dist: Pinnacle, Lightning, Cartel

Single (12"): released on Illegal, Apr'85 by Faulty Products Records. Dist: Pinnacle, Lightning, Cartel

BIG HEAT (THE).
Tracks: / Pick it up (and put it in your pocket) / Can't stop the show / Pile driver / Walkin' home alone / Drive she said / Twisted / Camouflage / Big heat (The) / Salesman.
Notes: Former Wall of Voodoo frontman.Brilliant debut solo album from a unique songwriter.
Compact disc: by Faulty Products Records. Dist: Pinnacle, Lightning, Cartel

Album: released on I.R.S.(Independent Record Syndicate), May'86 by I.R.S.. Dist: MCA

Cassette: released on I.R.S.(Independent Record Syndicate), May'86 by I.R.S.. Dist: MCA

Single (7"): released on I.R.S.(Independent Record Syndicate), Sep'86 by I.R.S.. Dist: MCA

Single (12"): released on I.R.S.(Independent Record Syndicate), Sep'86 by I.R.S.. Dist: MCA

CAMOUFLAGE.
Tracks: / Camouflage / Rio greyhound / Stormy side of town / Infatuation / All right now / Some guys have all the luck / Can we still be friends / Bad for you / Heart is on the line / Camouflage / Trouble.
Single (7"): released on I.R.S.(Independent Record Syndicate), Jun'86 by I.R.S.. Dist: MCA

Single (12"): released on I.R.S.(Independent Record Syndicate), Jun'86 by I.R.S.. Dist: MCA

WALKING HOME ALONE.
Notes: "=Extra track on 12" only
Single (12"): released on I.R.S.(Independent

Record Syndicate), Feb'87 by I.R.S.. Dist: MCA

Single (7"): released on I.R.S.(Independent Record Syndicate), Feb'87 by I.R.S.. Dist: MCA

Ridim Force

NOTHING BUT LOVE SONGS.
Album: released on Tom Tom, Sep'85 by Tom Tom Records. Dist: Jetstar Distribution

Ridin' In Rhythm

RIDIN' IN RHYTHM Various original artists (Various original artists).
Double Album: released on World Records, Feb'77 Dist: Polygram

Ridin' the riff

RIDIN' THE RIFF Various artists (Various Artists).
Tracks: / Big Bob's boogie / Ridin'the riff / Tom,Dick & Harry / Tina's canteen / 125th street,New York / Tan skin lad / Buttermilk and beans / Please Mr.Jive / Hi Ho / I need my baby / I ain't mad no more / Come home baby / Tra la la / Anything but love / I wanna go steady / Baby don't cry.
Album: released on Charly, Aug'86 by Charly Records. Dist: Charly, Cadillac

Rieman Kurt

ELECTRONIC NIGHTWORKS.
Album: released on Innovative Communication, Jan'85 by Innovative Communication Records. Dist: Pickwick Distribution

Riethmuller, Heinrich

TWO IN A GREAT CITY Well-known evergreens.
Tracks: / Kauf dir einen luftballon / Glaube mir / Tulpen aus Amsterdam / Es leuchten die stern / Nimm uns mit, Kapitan / Vor meinem vaterhaus steht eine linde / Goodbye Jonny / So ein tag / Abends in der taverne / Zwei in einer grossen stadt / Bel ami / Auf der Reeperbahn nachts um halb eins etc.
Notes: Heinrich Riethmuller on the great wurlitzer organ, Berlin. "Two In A Great City" is one of 14 well-known evergreens played by Heinrich Reithmuller on the gigantic wurlitzer housed in the berlin musical instrument museum.
Album: released on Teldec, May'87

Riff Raff

VINYL FUTURES.
Album: released on Acto, Jul'81 by WEA Records. Dist: WEA

Rifkin Joshua

SCOTT JOPLIN.
Album: by EMI Records. Dist: EMI

Rift, Zoogz

LOOSER THAN CLAMS.
Album: released on SST, Aug'87 by SST Records. Dist: Pinnacle

Album: released on SST, Aug'87 by SST Records. Dist: Pinnacle

Album: released on SST, Aug'87 by SST Records. Dist: Pinnacle

Rigadoon

SAE FRESH & FAIR.
Tracks: / Reels / Medley / Moulin rouge / Moon river / Jigs / Five foot two/modern Millie / Reels / Jigs / March/Strathspey / Carillon / Hayfield twostep / Bulgarian folk tunes / Flight of the bumble bee / Reels.
Album: released on Accordion Record Club, Jul'86 by Accordion Record Club Records. Dist: Accordion Record Club

TARTEN LASSIES THE.
Album: released on Lochshore, Jun'83 by Klub Records. Dist: PRT

Cassette: released on Lochshore, Jun'83 by Klub Records. Dist: PRT

Rigby,Eleanor

I WANT TO SLEEP WITH YOU.
Single (7"): released on Waterloo Sunset, Apr'85 by Waterloo Sunset Records. Dist: MIS-EMI Distribution, Backs

KISS ME QUICKLY IT'S CHRISTMAS.
Tracks: / Kiss me quickly it's Christmas / Mad Christmas.
Single (7"): released on Waterloo Sunset, Nov'86 by Waterloo Sunset Records. Dist: MIS EMI Distribution, Backs

TAKE ANOTHER SHOT AT MY HEART.
Single (7"): released on Waterloo Sunset, Jun'85 by Waterloo Sunset Records. Dist: MIS-EMI Distribution, Backs

Rigg Michael

ANGEL/WATCHA GONNA DO NOW.
Single (7"): released on Rooster, Jul'83 by Rooster Records. Dist: PRT Distribution

DON'T YOU BELIEVE IT/HOLD ON.
Single (7"): released on Rooster, Oct'83 by Rooster Records. Dist: PRT Distribution

TONIGHT/YOU LIGHT UP MY LIFE.
Single (7"): released on Rooster, Jan'83 by Rooster Records. Dist: PRT Distribution

Right Back...

RIGHT BACK WHERE WE STARTED FROM Various artists (Various Artists).
Album: released on Kent, May'85 by Ace Records. Dist: Pinnacle

Righteous Brothers

GREATEST HITS:RIGHTEOUS BROTHERS.
Tracks: / You've lost that lovin' feelin' / White cliffs of Dover / For sentimental reasons / Georgia on my mind / You'll never walk alone / Just once in my life / Unchained Melody / See that girl / Ebb tide / Guess who / Hung on you / Great pretender.
Album: released on MGM, Nov'83 Dist: Polygram Distribution, Swift Distribution

Cassette: released on MGM, Nov'83 Dist: Polygram Distribution, Swift Distribution

Compact disc: released on MGM, Nov'83 Dist: Polygram Distribution, Swift Distribution

YOU'VE LOST THAT LOVING FEELING.
Tracks: / Unchained melody.
Single (7"): released on Old Gold, Jan'87 by Old Gold Records. Dist: Lightning, Jazz Music, Spartan, Counterpoint

YOU'VE LOST THAT LOVIN FEELING.
Single (7"): released on Phil Spector International, Nov'77

Rikki

BAD MONKEY.
Single (7"): released on OK, Mar'85 Dist: Stage One Distribution

Single (12"): released on OK, Mar'85 Dist: Stage One Distribution

HEAVEN AND HELL/CAN'T STOP DANCING.
Single (7"): released on OK, Nov'82 Dist: Stage One Distribution

ONLY THE LIGHT.
Tracks: / Only the light / You came into my life.
Notes: UK Eurovision entry
Single (12"): released on OK, Apr'87 Dist: Stage One Distribution

Single (7"): released on OK, Apr'87 Dist: Stage One Distribution

SEVEN DAYS A WEEK.
Single (7"): released on OK, Oct'85 Dist: Stage One Distribution

Single (12"): released on OK, Oct'85 Dist: Stage One Distribution

SMILE FOR ME.
Single (7"): released on OK, Apr'84 Dist: Stage One Distribution

Riley

IMPROVISATIONS ARE FOREVER NOW (Riley/Wachsmann/Guy).
Album: released on Vinyl, Mar'79

Riley, Billy

ROCK WITH ME BABY.
Compact disc: released on Charly, Jan'87 by Charly Records. Dist: Charly, Cadillac

Riley, Billy Lee

BLUE MONDAY/GOOD OLD ROCK N ROLL.
Single (7"): released on Rollercoaster, Mar'79 by Rollercoaster Records. Dist: Swift Distribution, Rollercoaster Distribution

LEGENDARY SUN PERFORMERS THE.
Album: released on Charly, Nov'77 by Charly Records. Dist: Charly, Cadillac

RED HOT RILEY (Riley, Billy Lee And The Little Green Men).
Album: released on Charly, Oct'85 by Charly Records. Dist: Charly, Cadillac

SUN SOUNDS SPECIAL.
Album: released on Charly, Jan'78 by Charly Records. Dist: Charly, Cadillac

Riley Doug

DREAMS.
Album: released on PMR, Oct'79

FOR FOUR ON TWO TWO.
Album: released on Charly, Feb'84 by Charly Records. Dist: Charly, Cadillac

IN FOCUS (Riley Howard/Keith Tippett).
Album: released on Affinity, May'85 by Charly Records. Dist: Charly, Cadillac

INTERWINE (MUSIC OF 2 PIANOS).
Album: released on Mosiac, Aug'77

OTHER SIDE THE (SOLO PIANO).
Album: released on Spotlite, Jan'83 by Spotlite Records. Dist: Cadillac, Jazz Music, Spotlite

SYNOPSIS.
Album: released on Incus, Nov'76 Dist: Jazz Music, Cadillac

TORONTO CONCERT.
Album: released on Vinyl, Mar'79

Riley, Jeannie C

GIRL FROM TEXAS, THE.
Album: released on President, Jun'81 by President Records. Dist: Taylors, Spartan

HARPER VALLEY PTA.
Tracks: / Harper valley PTA / Yearbooks and yesterdays / Things go better with love / Country girl / Grneration gap,The / Back side of Dallas,The / Girl most likely,The / Duty not desire / He made a woman out of me / Help me make it through the night / Macom Georgia ban girl / Will the real Jesus please stand up.
Album: released on Topline, May'86 by Charly Records. Dist: Charly Distribution

Cassette: released on Topline, May'86 by Charly Records. Dist: Charly Distribution

JEANNIE C.RILEY.
Album: released on Spot, May'86 by Pickwick Records. Dist: H.R. Taylor, Lugtons

Cassette: released on Spot, May'86 by Pickwick Records. Dist: H.R. Taylor, Lugtons

Riley, Jimmy

EVERYBODY NEEDS MONEY.
Single (12"): released on Full Moon, Sep'84 by Epic. Dist: CBS

EVERYTIME YOU GO AWAY.
Single (12"): released on Germain Revolutionary, Nov'85 Dist: Jetstar

HEY LOVE.
Single 10": released on Taxi, Jul'82 by Island Records. Dist: EMI

HOT SUMMER.
Single (12"): released on Blue Trac, Oct'84 by Blue Mountain Records. Dist: Jetstar

ROCKIN' DOLLY.
Single (12"): released on Taxi, Apr'85 by Taxi Records. Dist: Jetstar Distribution

TELL THE YOUTHS THE TRUTH.
Album: released on Trojan, Sep'81

WORLD FOR EVERYONE.
Album: released on Blue Mountain, Nov'85 Dist: Jetstar

Riley, Marc

BABY'S ON FIRE (Riley, Marc & The Creepers).
Tracks: / Baby's on fire.
Single (7"): released on In Tape, Apr'86 by In Tape Records. Dist: Red Rhino, Cartel

Single (12"): released on In Tape, Apr'86 by In Tape Records. Dist: Red Rhino, Cartel

CREEPING AT MAIDA VALE (EP).
Single (7"): released on In Tape, Feb'84 by In Tape Records. Dist: Red Rhino, Cartel

CULL.
Album: released on In Tape, Apr'84 by In Tape Records. Dist: Red Rhino, Cartel

FANCY MEETING GOD.
Album: released on In Tape, Mar'85 by In Tape Records. Dist: Red Rhino, Cartel

FAVOURITE SISTER.
Single (7"): released on In Tape, Jul'83 by In Tape Records. Dist: Red Rhino, Cartel

FOUR A'S AT MAIDA VALE (Riley, Marc & The Creepers).
Single (7"): released on In Tape, Oct'85 by In Tape Records. Dist: Red Rhino, Cartel

Single (12"): released on In Tape, Oct'85 by In Tape Records. Dist: Red Rhino, Cartel

GROSS CUT (Riley, Marc & The Creepers).
Album: released on In Tape, Jun'84 by In Tape Records. Dist: Red Rhino, Cartel

JUMPER CLOWN.
Single (7"): released on In Tape, Oct'83 by In Tape Records. Dist: Red Rhino, Cartel

POLLYSTIFF.
Single (7"): released on In Tape, May'84 by In Tape Records. Dist: Red Rhino, Cartel

SHADOW FIGURE (Riley, Marc & The Creepers).
Single (12"): released on In Tape, Sep'84 by In Tape Records. Dist: Red Rhino, Cartel

WARTS AND ALL - LIVE IN AMSTERDAM (Riley, Marc & The Creepers).
Single 10": released on In Tape, Nov'85 by In Tape Records. Dist: Red Rhino, Cartel

Riley, Teddy

HONKY TONK TOWN (Riley, Teddy Band).
Cassette: released on Nola, May'87 Dist: JSU, Jazz Music, Cadillac, Chris Wellard

HONKY TONK TOWN '79.
Album: released on 504, Sep'86 by 504 Records. Dist: Chris Wellard, Jazz Music

Cassette: released on 504, Sep'86 by 504 Records. Dist: Chris Wellard, Jazz Music

Album: released on Nola, Jul'82 Dist: JSU, Jazz Music, Cadillac, Chris Wellard

Riley, Terry

CADENZA ON THE NIGHT PLAIN (Riley, Terry & The Kronos Quartet).
Compact disc: released on Gramavision (USA), Jan'86 by Gramavison Records (USA). Dist: PRT, IMS, Polygram

HARP OF NEW ALBION.
Notes: Double album and cassette.
Album: released on Celestial Harmonies, May'87 by TM Records. Dist: PRT

Cassette: released on Celestial Harmonies, May'87 by TM Records. Dist: PRT

Double compact disc: released on Celestial Harmonies, May'87 by TM Records. Dist: PRT

PERSIAN SURGERY DERVISHES.
Double Album: released on Shandar Import, Mar'78

SONGS FOR THE TEN VOICES OF THE TWO PROPHETS.
Album: released on Kuckuck (Germany), May'84

Rimarimba

CHICAGO DEATH EXCRETION GEOMETRY.
Album: released on Hamster, Jun'87 by Hamster Records And Tapes. Dist: Backs, Cartel

Rimington, Sammy

Biographical Details: see under Bobby McDonald.

GEORGE LEWIS CLASSICS.
Album: released on GHB, Mar'87 Dist: Jazz Music, Swift

Rimmington, Sammy

ONLY A LOOK.
Album: released on Dawn Club, May'79 Dist: Cadillac, Swift, JSU

REED ALL ABOUT IT (Rimmington, Sammy/Ian Wheeler Band).
Album: released on Hefty Jazz, Sep'79 Dist: JSU, Swift, Wellard, Chris, Jazz Music, Cadillac Music

Rimshots

7654321 (BLOW YOUR WHISTLE).
Single (7"): released on Flashback (reissue), Jan'83 Dist: PRT

AT NIGHT.
Single (7"): released on Spectro, Oct'81

I WAS WRONG.
Single (7"): released on Shoc-Wave, Jul'80 by Uniton Records. Dist: Pinnacle

Rinder, Laurin

SEVEN DEADLY SINS (Rinder, Laurin/Michael Lewis).
Album: released on Pye International, May'78

Ringer, Jim

ANY OLD WIND THAT BLOWS.
Album: released on Philo, May'79 by Philo Records (USA). Dist: Mike's Country Music Room Distribution, Swift, Roots, Projection, Topic

GOOD TO GET HOME.
Album: released on Philo, May'79 by Philo Records (USA). Dist: Mike's Country Music Room Distribution, Swift, Roots, Projection, Topic

Ringers

NO NO NO.
Single (7"): released on Magic Moon, Jun'81
Dist: Pinnacle

Ringing

CAPRICE.
Single (7"): released on Pink, Sep'84 by Pink
Records. Dist: Rough Trade

Ringing clear

RINGING CLEAR (THE ART OF HAND-BELL RINGING) Various artists (Various Artists).
Album: released on Saydisc, Nov'82 by Saydisc Records. Dist: Essex, Harmonia Mundi,
Roots, H.R. Taylor, Jazz Music, Swift, Projection, Gamut

Cassette: released on Saydisc, Nov'82 by
Saydisc Records. Dist: Essex, Harmonia
Mundi, Roots, H.R. Taylor, Jazz Music, Swift,
Projection, Gamut

Ringo

DUB AND LEF.
Single (7"): released on Musical Ambassador, Aug'82

ONE O'CLOCK ROCK.
Single (12"): released on Black Roots, Apr'83
by Black Roots Records. Dist: Jetstar

Ring of bright water

RING OF BRIGHT WATER Maxwell, Gavin
(Timothy, Christopher).
Cassette: released on Listen For Pleasure,
Feb'81 by EMI Records. Dist: MFP

Ringo, Johnny

ASHER SENATOR V JOHNNY RINGO
(see Senator, Asher) (Ringo, Johnny & Asher
Senator).

Rini, Anthony Galla

IN CONCERT.
Album: released on ARC (Accordion Records),
May'84 Dist: Accordion Record Club

Rink

RINK,THE Original Broadway Cast (Various
Artists).
Notes: Music by John Kander, Lyrics by Fred
Ebb. Starring two of Broadway's Great Stars;Liza Minnelli and Chita Rivera. Nominated for 5
Tony Awards with Chita Rivera winning the Best Actress award. Kander and Ebb wrote amongst
others, the music Cabaret.
Compact disc: released on That's Entertainment, Oct'84 by That's Entertainment Records.
Dist: Pinnacle, PRT

Album: released on That's Entertainment,
Sep'84 by That's Entertainment Records. Dist:
Pinnacle, PRT

Cassette: released on That's Entertainment,
Sep'84 by That's Entertainment Records. Dist:
Pinnacle, PRT

Compact disc: released on That's Entertainment, Sep'84 by That's Entertainment Records.
Dist: Pinnacle, PRT

Rin Tin Tin

SHAKE IT.
Single (7"): released on Irrepressable, Oct'85
by Irrepressable. Dist: CBS

Single (12"): released on Irrepressable, Oct'85
by Irrepressable. Dist: CBS

Rio

ATLANTIC RADIO.
Tracks: / Atlantic radio.
Single (7"): released on Music For Nations,
Jul'86 by Music For Nations Records. Dist: Pinnacle

Single (12"): released on Music For Nations,
Jul'86 by Music For Nations Records. Dist: Pinnacle

BORDERLAND.
Album: released on Music For Nations, Sep'85
by Music For Nations Records. Dist: Pinnacle

Cassette: released on Music For Nations,
Sep'85 by Music For Nations Records. Dist: Pinnacle

I DON'T WANNA BE THE FOOL.
Single (7"): released on Music For Nations,
Sep'85 by Music For Nations Records. Dist: Pinnacle

Single (12"): released on Music For Nations,
Sep'85 by Music For Nations Records. Dist: Pinnacle

SEX CRIMES.
Tracks: / Pay for love / Under pressure / Atlantic radio / Highschool rock / Guilty / When the
walls come down / Danger zone / Sex crimes /
Dirty movies / Bad blood.

Album: released on Music For Nations, Sep'86
by Music For Nations Records. Dist: Pinnacle

Rio, Bob

TASTE OF COUNTRY, A.
Album: released on Sweet Folk All, May'81 by
Sweet Folk All Records. Dist: Sweet Folk All,
Roots, Celtic Music, Dragon, Impetus, Projection, Chris Wellard, Festival Records

Rio, James

SKA REGGAE.
Single (7"): released on Carib Jems, Sep'82 by
Carib Jems. Dist: Spartan, Jetstar

Riopelli, Jerry

LIVIN' THE LIFE.
Tracks: / Livin' the life / Naomi's song / Shoulder
to the wheel / Blues on my table / Doodlay doo
/ Silly old gigolo / Roll with the feelin' / Take a
chance / River on the run / Hey old friend / Me
and the fox / Valentine / Cryin' out loud / Talk to
me / Walkin' on water / Steppin' out.
Album: released on See For Miles, Jun'86 by
See For Miles Records. Dist: Pinnacle

Rios, Waldo De Los

**GREATEST HITS: WALDO DE LOS
RIOS.**
Album: released on Carrere(France), May'84
by Carrere Records (France). Dist: PRT

Cassette: released on Carrere(France),
May'84 by Carrere Records (France). Dist: PRT

SINFONIAS.
Album: released on Carrere(France), May'84
by Carrere Records (France). Dist: PRT

Cassette: released on Carrere(France),
May'84 by Carrere Records (France). Dist: PRT

SYMPHONIES FOR 70'S.
Album: released on Warner Bros., May'75 by
Warner Bros Records. Dist: WEA

Riot Clone

BLOOD ON YOUR HANDS.
Extended-play record: released on Riot
Clone, Dec'84 by Riot Clone Records. Dist: Cartel, Rough Trade

DESTROY THE MYTH OF MUSICAL DE-STRUCTION.
Single (7"): released on Riot Clone, Dec'82 by
Riot Clone Records. Dist: Cartel, Rough Trade

THERE'S NO GOVT LIKE NO GOVT..
Single (7"): released on Riot Clone, Apr'82 by
Riot Clone Records. Dist: Cartel, Rough Trade

Rio & The Robots

FIND A GOAL.
Single (7"): released on Tuff, Nov'81

Riot of Colour

SKINK.
Single (12"): released on Dreamworld, Mar'87
by TV Personalities, The. Dist: Rough Trade

Riotous Assembly

RIOTOUS ASSEMBLY various artists
(Various Artists).
Album: released on Riot City, Jun'82 by Riot
City Records. Dist: Revolver

Riot Rockers

BRAND NEW CADILLAC.
Single (7"): released on Humber, Jun'81 by
Humber Records. Dist: Humber

RIOT ROCKER, THE.
Album: released on Charly, '78 by Charly Records. Dist: Charly, Cadillac

Riot Squad

DON'T BE DENIED (EP).
Single (7"): released on Rondelet, Jun'83 Dist:
Spartan Distribution

FUCK THE TORIES.
Single (7"): released on Rondelet, Aug'82 Dist:
Spartan Distribution

I'M OK FUCK YOU.
Single (7"): released on Rot, Sep'83 by Rot
Records. Dist: Red Rhino Through Cartel Distributions

NO POTENTIAL THREAT.
Album: released on Rot, Mar'85 by Rot Records. Dist: Red Rhino Through Cartel Distributions

RIOT IN THE CITY.
Single (7"): released on Rondelet, Sep'82 Dist:
Spartan Distribution

THERE AIN'T NO SOLUTION.
Single (7"): released on Rot, Jan'84 by Rot
Records. Dist: Red Rhino Through Cartel Dis-

tributions

TOTAL ONSLAUGHT.
Single (7"): released on the, Aug'82

WHY DO YOU MAKE ME WAIT (Riot
Squad & Matumbi).
Single (12"): released on Extinguish, Mar'82
Dist: Jetstar

Ripcord

DEFIANCE OF POWER.
Album: released on Manic Ears, Jun'87

Riperton, Minnie

LOVE LIVES FOREVER.
Album: released on Capitol, Oct'80 by Capitol
Records. Dist: EMI

LOVING YOU.
Tracks: / Loving you / Inside my love.
Notes: Also contains:"Inside my love" by Minnie Riperton.
Single (7"): released on Old Gold, Apr'87 by
Old Gold Records. Dist: Lightning, Jazz Music,
Spartan, Counterpoint

Single (7"): released on Epic, '80 by CBS Records. Dist: CBS

MINNIE.
Album: released on Fame (Capitol), May'82 by
Music For Pleasure Records. Dist: EMI

Cassette: released on Fame (Capitol), May'82
by Music For Pleasure Records. Dist: EMI

MINNIE RIPERTON, THE BEST OF.
Album: released on Capitol, Dec'81 by Capitol
Records. Dist: EMI

Cassette: released on Capitol, Dec'81 by Capitol Records. Dist: EMI

STAY IN LOVE.
Album: released on Epic, Mar'77 by CBS Records. Dist: CBS

Rip it up...

RIP IT UP, ROCK'N'ROLL (Various Artists).
Compact disc: released on K-Tel, '86 by K-Tel
Records. Dist: Record Merchandisers Distribution, Taylors, Terry Blood Distribution, Wynd-Up
Distribution, Relay Distribution, Pickwick Distribution, Solomon & Peres Distribution, Polygram

Ripley, Duane

**REVENGE OF THE 50 FOOT KILLER
GO GO GIRLS** (Ripley, Duane and The Go
Go Set).
Tracks: / Revenge of the 50 foot killer go go
girls.
Single (7"): released on Barbarella, Feb'86
Dist: Rough Trade

Ripley Wayfarers

GENTLEMEN OF HIGH RENOWN.
Album: released on Tradition, Aug'76 Dist:
JSU, Cassion Distribution, Celtic Music, Jazz
Music, Projection, Roots Records

Rippingtons

MOONLIGHTING.
Compact disc: by Pacific Records (USA). Dist:
Atlantic

Rippon, Angela

BABAR THE ELEPHANT.
Album: released on Enigma, Nov'79 by Enigma Records. Dist: Rough Trade, Cartel, EMI

READS VICTORIA PLUM STORIES.
Cassette: released on Philips, Apr'81 Dist:
IMS-Polygram

STORIES FROM THE BALLET.
Album: by BBC Records & Tapes. Dist: EMI,
PRT, Pye

Cassette: released on BBC, '79 by BBC Records & Tapes. Dist: EMI, PRT, Pye

Rip Rig & Panic

YOU'RE MY KIND OF CLIMATE.
Single (7"): released on Virgin, Jun'82 by Virgin Records. Dist: EMI, Virgin Distribution

Rip Stip And.....

**MONTH IN BOHEMIA IS WORTH TWO
IN THE BUSH,A.**
Album: released on Disposable, Nov'85 by
Fast Forward Records. Dist: Fast Forward, Cartel

Risan

EASTERN PALACE.
Single (7"): released on Saffron, Nov'82

Risca male voice choir

SING LENNON & MCCARTNEY.
Album: released on Black Marketing, '82 PRT,
Pinnacle

SOUND OF WALES.
Album: released on ASV, Aug'81 by Academy
Sound & Vision Records. Dist: Pinnacle

Cassette: released on ASV, Aug'81 by Academy Sound & Vision Records. Dist: Pinnacle

Rising fire

YOU LIED.
Single (12"): released on Cha-Cha, Jan'82 by
Cha Cha. Dist: Jetstar

Risky Business

JAMMIN' TO NEW ORLEANS.
Tracks: / Jammin' to New Orleans / Jammin' to
New Orleans (club mix) / Jammin' to New Orleans (alternate mix) / Jammin' to New Orleans
(radio edit).
Single (12"): released on Kool Kat, Apr'87 by
Kool Kat Records. Dist: PRT

RISKY BUSINESS Original soundtrack
(Various Artists).
Compact disc: released on Virgin, May'87 by
Virgin Records. Dist: EMI, Virgin Distribution

Album: released on Virgin, Feb'84 by Virgin
Records. Dist: EMI, Virgin Distribution

Cassette: released on Virgin, Feb'84 by Virgin
Records. Dist: EMI, Virgin Distribution

RISKY BUSINESS various artists (Various
Artists).

Ritchie Family

AMERICAN GENERATION.
Album: released on Mercury, Mar'79 by Phonogram Records. Dist: Polygram Distribution

RITCHIE FAMILY.
Album: released on Mercury, Sep'79 by Phonogram Records. Dist: Polygram Distribution

Ritchie & Houseowners

HAVE A NICE DAY.
Single (7"): released on Fliptone, Feb'82 by
Spartan

Ritchie, Jean

NONE BUT ONE.
Album: released on Sire, Feb'79

Ritchie, Lynn

LOVE IS BAD FOR YOUR HEALTH.
Single (7"): released on Abstract, Apr'82 by Abstract. Dist: Pinnacle

Ritchie & the Lowdowners

HAVE A NICE DAY.
Single (7"): released on Rosie, Sep'82 by
Rosie Records. Dist: PRT Distribution

Ritenour, Lee

AMERICAN FLYERS original soundtrack
(Ritenour, Lee & Greg Mathieson).
Notes: For full information see: RITENOUR,
Lee & Greg Mathieson.

AMERICAN FLYERS (O.S.T.) (Ritenour,
Lee and Greg Mathieson).
Tracks: / American flyers / Travelling music /
Brand new day / Gone ridin' / Bad moon rising /
Brothers theme (part 1) / 'J' factor (The) / Theme
from American flyers / Breakaway / Brothers
theme (part 2) / Treadmill / Epilogue (Third
race).
Album: released on GRP (USA), Nov'86 by
GRP Records (USA). Dist: IMS, Polygram

Cassette: released on GRP (USA), Nov'86 by
GRP Records (USA). Dist: IMS, Polygram

EARTH RUN.
Tracks: / Soaring / Earth run / If I'm dreamin'
(don't wake me) / Watercolours / Sauce,The /
Butterfly / Sanctuary / Water from the moon.
Notes: Lee Ritenour's first solo album for GRP
since his highly successful collaborati-ve venture, 'Harlequin' with Dave Grusin. 'Earth Run
is markedly the immense virtuosity and intense
electric range of composition and arrangements
that has made 'Captain Fingers' one of the
world's most renowned guitarists. Lee
Grusin- keyboards/ Larry Williaims and Don
Grusin - synthesizers/ Harvey Mason
drums/Tom Scott - lyrican/ Abraham Laboriel
bass; the cast goes on and on includingon the
only track 'If I'm Dreamin'(Don't Wake Me)' vocals by Phil Perry, MauriceWhite and Tomm
Funderburk.
Album: released on GRP (USA), Aug'86 b
GRP Records (USA). Dist: IMS, Polygram

Cassette: released on GRP (USA), Aug'86 b
GRP Records (USA). Dist: IMS, Polygram

Compact disc: released on GRP (USA), Aug'86 by GRP Records (USA). Dist: IMS, Polygram

FRIENDSHIP.
Album: released on JVC, Nov'79 Dist: Target

GENTLE THOUGHTS.
Album: released on JVC, Apr'78 Dist: Target

HARLEQUIN for full information see under:Grusin, Dave & Lee Ritenour.

HARLEQUIN (Ritenour, Lee & Dave Grusin).
Notes: For full information see under; Grusin,Dave & Lee Ritenour.
Compact disc: released on GRP (USA), Jul'85 by GRP Records (USA). Dist: IMS, Polygram

Album: released on GRP (USA), Jul'85 by GRP Records (USA). Dist: IMS, Polygram

IS IT YOU.
Single (7"): released on Elektra Asylum, Jun'81 by Elektra/Asylum/Nonesuch Records. Dist: WEA

Single (12"): released on Elektra Asylum, Jun'81 by Elektra/Asylum/Nonesuch Records. Dist: WEA

MR. BRIEFCASE.
Single (7"): released on Elektra Asylum, Apr'81 by Elektra/Asylum/Nonesuch Records. Dist: WEA

Single (12"): released on Elektra Asylum, Apr'81 by Elektra/Asylum/Nonesuch Records. Dist: WEA

RIO.
Tracks: / Rainbow / San Juan sunset / Rio funk / It happens every day / Ipanema sol / Simplicidad / Little bit of this and a little bit of that,A.
Compact disc: released on GRP (USA), Sep'85 by GRP Records (USA). Dist: IMS, Polygram

Compact disc: released on Elektra(Musician), Jul'84 by WEA Records. Dist: WEA

Album: released on GRP (USA), Sep'85 by GRP Records (USA). Dist: IMS, Polygram

Compact disc: released on GRP (USA), Sep'85 by GRP Records (USA). Dist: IMS, Polygram

Compact disc: released on Elektra(Musician), Jul'84 by WEA Records. Dist: WEA

RIT.
Album: released on Elektra Asylum, Apr'81 by Elektra/Asylum/Nonesuch Records. Dist: WEA

SUGARLOAF EXPRESS.
Single (7"): released on Elite, Jul'84 Dist: PRT

SUGARLOAF EXPRESS (Ritenour, Lee & Kazumi Watanbe).
Single (12"): released on Elite(Inner City), Oct'82 Dist: Rough Trade, Cartel

Rites Of Spring

SPRING.
Album: released on Dischord, Nov'85 Dist: Rough Trade, Cartel

Ritter, Tex

HIGH NOON.
Album: released on Bear Family, Dec'83 by Bear Family Records. Dist: Rollercoaster Distribution, Swift

LADY KILLIN' COWBOY.
Tracks: / Sam Hall / Get along little doggies / Thirty three years in prison / Lady killin' cowboy / I'm a do right cowboy / Bill the bar fly / Nobody's darling but mine / My brown eyed Texas rose / Take me back to my boots and saddle / Oregon trail,The / Answer to nobody's darling but mine / Melody from the sky,A / Hills of old Wyomin',The / We'll rest at the end of the trail.
Picture disc album: released on Bear Family, Jul'86 by Bear Family Records. Dist: Rollercoaster Distribution, Swift

SINGIN' IN THE SADDLE.
Tracks: / High wide and handsome / Headin' for the Rio Grande / Out on the lone praire / Arizona days / My sweet Chiquita / Jailhouse lament / (I'm) hittin' the trail (for home) / I'm a natural born cowboy / Ride, ride, ride / Ridin' down, the trail of Albuquerque / Sing cowboy sing / Down the Colorado trail / When it's lamplighting time in the valley / Singin' in the saddle / Sundown on the prairie / Ai viva tequila.
Notes: All titles recorded in Los Angeles: Produced By: Richard Weize:
Picture disc album: released on Bear Family, Jul'86 by Bear Family Records. Dist: Rollercoaster Distribution, Swift

SONGS FROM THE WESTERN SCREEN.
Album: released on Stetson, Jul'87 by Hasmick Promotions Ltd.. Dist: Counterpoint Distribution, H.R. Taylor Distribution, Swift Distribution, Chris Wellard Distribution

Cassette: released on Stetson, Jul'87 by Hasmick Promotions Ltd.. Dist: Counterpoint Distribution, H.R. Taylor Distribution, Swift Distribution, Chris Wellard Distribution

STREETS OF LAREDO.
Album: released on Bulldog, Jul'82 by Bulldog Records. Dist: President Distribution, Spartan, Swift, Taylor, H.R.

Cassette: released on Bulldog, Jul'82 by Bulldog Records. Dist: President Distribution, Spartan, Swift, Taylor, H.R.

Ritual

KANGEROO COURT/BRIDGES.
Single (12"): released on Red Flame, Mar'83 by Red Flame Records. Dist: Nine Mile, Cartel

MIND DISEASE/NINE.
Single (7"): released on Red Flame, Oct'82 by Red Flame Records. Dist: Nine Mile, Cartel

Ritz Radio Favourites

RITZ RADIO FAVOURITES (VOLUME 1 - COUNTRY) Various Artists (Various Artists).
Album: released on Ritz, Nov'85 by Outlet Records. Dist: Outlet, Prism Leisure Distribution, Record Services Distribution (Ireland), Roots

Cassette: released on Ritz, Nov'85 by Outlet Records. Dist: Outlet, Prism Leisure Distribution, Record Services Distribution (Ireland), Roots

RITZ RADIO FAVOURITES (VOLUME 2 - EASY LISTENING) Various Artists (Various Artists).
Album: released on Ritz, Nov'85 by Outlet Records. Dist: Outlet, Prism Leisure Distribution, Record Services Distribution (Ireland), Roots

Cassette: released on Ritz, Nov'85 by Outlet Records. Dist: Outlet, Prism Leisure Distribution, Record Services Distribution (Ireland), Roots

RITZ RADIO FAVOURITES (VOLUME 3 - IRISH FOLK) Various Artists (Various Artists).
Album: released on Ritz, Nov'85 by Outlet Records. Dist: Outlet, Prism Leisure Distribution, Record Services Distribution (Ireland), Roots

Cassette: released on Ritz, Nov'85 by Outlet Records. Dist: Outlet, Prism Leisure Distribution, Record Services Distribution (Ireland), Roots

Rivals

FUTURE RIGHTS/FLOWERS.
Single (7"): released on Ace, Feb'80 by Ace Records. Dist: Pinnacle, Swift, Hotshot, Cadillac

HERE COMES THE NIGHT.
Single (7"): released on Dead Good, May'80

Riverboat Shuffle

RIVERBOAT SHUFFLE Various artists (Various Artists).
Double Album: released on Black Lion-Intercord, '82

River Boys

MY ROOF COMES TUMBLING DOWN.
Album: released on Sillicone, Aug'86

Rivers Ben Lee

SUNSHINE ON THE SNOW.
Album: released on Tank, Sep'79 by Tank Records.

Rivers Deke

RETURN TO SENDER (ELVIS MEDLY).
Single (7"): released on Ace, Sep'81 by Ace Records. Dist: Pinnacle, Swift, Hotshot, Cadillac

Riverside Jazz Band

IN AT THE DEEP END.
Album: released on Burlington, Oct'86 by Plant Life Records. Dist: Jazz Music, Celtic Music, Clyde Factors Distributors, I.R.S., Projection, Wellard, Chris, Roots

Riverside, Maros

FOLK MUSIC FROM LORINCREVE.
Tracks: / Oreges/Oldish Csarda / Gyors/Fast Csardas / Szapora/ Quick(Hategana) / Duljon le a Botfalvi var./Let the castle in Botfalva fall / Megyek az uton lefele/ I walk along the road / Edesanyam, mondanek en valamit/ Mother, I would tell you / Invirtita / Haidau / Pontozos oreges csarda/ Marking slow lad's dance / Szabad madar vagy te, babam/ You are a free bird / Kek ibolya, ha leszakitanalak/ Blue violet / Pontozo I./ Marking lad's dance I / Kek ibolya, ha leszakitanalak/ Blue violet / Falu vegen van egy valyu/ There is a trough / En istenem, teremtom/Oh, my god, good lord / Pontozo II./ Marking lad's dance II..
Album: released on Hungaraton(Hungary), May'87 Dist: Conifer

Riverside Trio

FLAT BROKE.
Album: released on Northwood, Jan'86 by Northwood Records. Dist: Backs-Cartel

Rivers, Jimmy

BRISBANE BOP 1961-64 (Rivers, Jimmy & The Cherokees).
Album: released on Western (USA), Feb'84 by Arhoolie Records. Dist: Projection, Topic

Rivers Joan

CAN WE TALK.
Album: released on Geffen, Nov'83 by Geffen Records. Dist: WEA, CBS

Cassette: released on Geffen, Nov'83 by Geffen Records. Dist: WEA, CBS

Rivers, Johnny

BEST OF....
Tracks: / Maybelline / Seventh son (The) / Muddy water / Memphis / Mountain of love / Poor side of town / Where have all the flowers gone / Baby I need your lovin' / Tracks of my tears / Secret agent man / Midnight srecial / Smmer rain / Look to your soul / Rockin' pneumonia / Blue suede shoes.

BEST OF JOHNNY RIVERS, THE.
Tracks: / Maybelline / Seventh son, The / I washed my hands in muddy water / Memphis / Mountain of love / Poor side of town / Where have all the flowers gone / Baby I need your lovin' / Tracks of my tears / Secret agent man / Midnight special / Summer rain / Look to your soul / Rockin' pneumonia & boogie woogie flu / Blue suede shoes.
Notes: P 1987 EMI America Records, a division of Capitol Records Inc.
Compact disc: released on EMI America, Apr'87 by EMI Records. Dist: EMI

Rivers of Delight

RIVERS OF DELIGHT American folk hymns (American Folk Hymns).
Album: released on Nonsuch, Nov'79

Rivers, Sam

DIMENSIONS & EXTENTIONS.
Tracks: / Precis / Paean / Effusive Melange / Involution / Afflatus / Helix.
Notes: All tracks composed by Sam Rivers: All tracks published by: CBS Unart Catalog Inc./BMI
Album: released on Manhattan-Blue Note, Jul'86 by EMI America Records (USA). Dist: EMI

TUBA TRIO VOL 1 (see also J Daley, W Smith) (Rivers, Sam & J Daley & W Smith).
Album: released on Circle, May'78 Dist: Jazz Music

TUBA TRIO VOL 2 (see also J Daley, W Smith) (Rivers, Sam & J Daley & W Smith).
Album: released on Circle, May'78 Dist: Jazz Music

TUBA TRIO VOL 3 (see also J Daley, W Smith) (Rivers, Sam & J Daley & W Smith).

Rivers, Sam & Dave Holland

RIVERS & HOLLAND VOL 2.
Album: released on Impro-arts, Jul'78 Dist: Projection

Riviera

NOTHING TO HIDE/EMOTION.
Single (7"): released on Jungle, Jun'83 by Jungle Records. Dist: Jungle, Cartel

RIVIERA.
Album: released on Jungle, May'83 by Jungle Records. Dist: Jungle, Cartel

Rizma

I'M ON MY WAY.
Single (7"): released on Zone, Mar'84

RMO

BEYOND THE LIMIT.
Album: released on Logo, Jan'79 by Logo Records. Dist: Roots, BMG

GARUDA.
Album: released on Logo, Jan'79 by Logo Records. Dist: Roots, BMG

GET THE BALL.
Album: released on Logo, Jan'79 by Logo Records. Dist: Roots, BMG

Album: released on MMC, Nov'83 by MMC Records. Dist: PRT Distribution, Pinnacle

RMS

CENTENNIAL PARK.
Tracks: / Broadway rundown / Tootin' back / After all these years / Truck Centennial park / Hoover the duvet / First love / Juma the last / Memories of Crete.
Compact disc: released on MMC, Jan'86 by MMC Records. Dist: PRT Distribution, Pinnacle

RnB from Joe Davies

RNB FROM JOE DAVIES 1952-53 various artists (Various Artists).
Album: released on Krazy Kat, Sep'85 Dist: Jazz Music, Swift, Chris Wellard, H.R. Taylor, Charly, Hotshot, IRS Distribution

R'N'B houseparty

R'N'B HOUSEPARTY Various artists (Various Artists).
Album: released on Ace, Sep'86 by Ace Records. Dist: Pinnacle, Swift, Hotshot, Cadillac

Cassette: released on Ace, Sep'86 by Ace Records. Dist: Pinnacle, Swift, Hotshot, Cadillac

Roach, Dave

RUNNING WITH THE RIVER.
Tracks: / Running with the river / Move it / Innocent child / Love is / Back to back / Hot line / Rocketta / Every morning / Letter.
Album: released on Coda, Mar'84 by Coda Records. Dist: Pinnacle, Cartel, WEA, Roots

Cassette: released on Coda, Mar'84 by Coda Records. Dist: Pinnacle, Cartel, WEA, Roots

Compact disc: released on Coda, Mar'84 by Coda Records. Dist: Pinnacle, Cartel, WEA, Roots

Roach, David

TALKING CITY.
Compact disc: released on Coda, Mar'85 by Coda Records. Dist: Pinnacle, Cartel, WEA, Roots

TALKING CITY THE.
Album: released on Coda, Apr'85 by Coda Records. Dist: Pinnacle, Cartel, WEA, Roots

Cassette: released on Coda, Apr'85 by Coda Records. Dist: Pinnacle, Cartel, WEA, Roots

Roach, Hal

BEST OF IRISH HUMOUR.
Album: released on Cabaret, Jun'84 by Cabaret. Dist: Spartan

Cassette: released on Cabaret, Jun'84 by Cabaret. Dist: Spartan

WE IRISH TALK LIKE THAT.
Album: released on Evergreen, Jun'84

Cassette: released on Evergreen, Jun'84

WRITE IT DOWN.
Album: released on Evergreen, Jun'84

Cassette: released on Evergreen, Jun'84

Roach, Max

AT BASIN STREET (Roach, Max and Clifford Brown).
Album: released on Mercury, Dec'83 by Phonogram Records. Dist: Polygram Distribution

BIRTH AND REBIRTH (Roach, Max & Anthony Braxton).
Compact disc: released on Black Saint (Italy), '86 Dist: Target, Jazz Music, Harmonia Mundi

CONVERSATIONS.
Album: released on Milestone, Dec'81 by Ace Records. Dist: PRT

DRUMMIN THE BLUES (Roach Max/Stan Levy).
Album: released on EMI (France), Jan'85 by EMI Records. Dist: Conifer

EASY WINNERS (Roach, Max Double Quartet).
Compact disc: released on Soul Note (Italy), '86 Dist: Harmonia Mundi Distributors

FORCE (see Shepp, Archie) (Roach, Max & Archie Shepp).

FREEDOM NOW SUITE.
Album: released on Amigo, Oct'79 Dist: Red Rhino, Cartel

GRAZ CONCERT 1963 (see also Sonny Rollins Trio) (Roach, Max Quintet & Sonny Rollins Trio).
Album: released on Jazz Connoisseur, Apr'79 Dist: Jazz Horizons, Jazz Music, Swift, Wellard, Chris

HISTORIC CONCERTS (see also Cecil Taylor) (Roach, Max & Cecil Taylor).
Album: released on Soul Note, May'85 Dist: Projection, Celtic Music, Chris Wellard

IN CONCERT (Roach, Max and Clifford Brown).
Tracks: / Jor-du / I can't get started / I get a kick out of you / Parisian thoroughfare / All god's chillun got rhythm / Tenderly / Sunset eyes / Clifford's axe.
Compact disc: released on Vogue, Jan'86 Dist: Discovery, Jazz Music, PRT, Swift

IN THE LIGHT (Roach, Max Quartet).
Compact disc: released on Soul Note (Italy), '86 Dist: Harmonia Mundi Distributors

IT'S TIME.
Album: released on Impulse, Oct'85 by Impulse Records. Dist: MCA, Polygram

LONG AS YOU'RE LIVING.
Album: released on Enja (Germany), Nov'84 by Enja Records (W.Germany). Dist: Cadillac Music

MAX ROACH AGAIN.
Double Album: released on Affinity, Aug'79 by Charly Records. Dist: Charly, Cadillac

PERCUSSION DISCUSSION (see also Art Blakey) (Roach, Max & Art Blakey).

PICTURES IN A FRAME (Roach, Max Quartet).
Compact disc: released on Soul Note (Italy), '86 Dist: Harmonia Mundi Distributors

SCOTT FREE.
Album: released on Soul Note (USA), Aug'85 Dist: Harmonia Mundi Distributors

SCOTT FREE (Roach, Max Quartet).
Compact disc: released on Soul Note (Italy), '86 Dist: Harmonia Mundi Distributors

SOUND AS A ROACH (see also Abbey Lincoln) (Roach, Max & Abbey Lincoln).

SOUNDS AS A ROACH (Roach, Max & Abbey Lincoln).
Album: released on Lotus, Sep'86 Dist: Counterpoint

SURVIVORS.
Tracks: / Survivors / Third eye,The / Billy the kid / Jasme / Drum also waltzes,The / Sassy Max (self portrait) / Smoke that thunders,The.
Notes: Recorded 19,20,21 October 1984 at Vanguard Studios, New York. Personnel: Max Roach - multiple percussion set/ String Quartet - Guillermo Figueroa - 1st violin/ Donald Bauch - 2nd violin/ Louise Schulman - viola/ Christopher Finckel - cello.
Album: released on Soul Note, May'85 Dist: Harmonia Mundi Distributors

Compact disc: released on Soul Note, May'85 Dist: Harmonia Mundi Distributors

WE INSIST.
Album: released on Candid, Jul'87 Dist: Counterpoint, Cadillac

Roadie

ROADIE Original soundtrack (Various Artists).
Double Album: released on WEA, Jun'80 by WEA Records. Dist: WEA

Cassette: released on Warner Brothers, Jun'80 by Warner Bros Records. Dist: WEA

Road to Heaven

ROAD TO HEAVEN Various artists (Various Artists).
Album: released on Saydisc, Sep'82 by Saydisc Records. Dist: Essex, Harmonia Mundi, Roots, H.R. Taylor, Jazz Music, Swift, Projection, Gamut

Road works ahead

NIGHT AND DAY.
Album: released on Trend (USA), Jan'84 by Discovery Records. Dist: Flexitron Distributors Ltd, Swift

Cassette: released on Trend (USA), Jan'84 by Discovery Records. Dist: Flexitron Distributors Ltd, Swift

Roald Dahl Soundbook

ROALD DAHL SOUNDBOOK (Dahl, Roald).
Boxed set: released on Caedmon(USA), Sep'80 by Caedmon (USA) Records. Dist: Gower, Taylors, Discovery

Roar

ROAR Original motion picture soundtrack.
Album: released on GT, May'82 by GT Records. Dist: Spartan

Cassette: released on GT, May'82 by GT Records. Dist: Spartan

Roaring 20's

ROARING 20'S, THE Various artists (Various Artists).
Album: released on Saydisc, Nov'84 by Saydisc Records. Dist: Essex, Harmonia Mundi, Roots, H.R. Taylor, Jazz Music, Swift, Projection, Gamut

Cassette: released on Saydisc, Nov'84 by Saydisc Records. Dist: Essex, Harmonia Mundi, Roots, H.R. Taylor, Jazz Music, Swift, Projection, Gamut

Roaring Jelly

CHRISTMAS IN AUSTRALIA.
Single (7"): released on Ideal, Nov'80 by Topic. Dist: Projection, Wynd-Up Distribution

IN THE ROAR.
Album: released on Topic, Jun'81 Dist: Roots Distribution

ROARING JELLY'S GOLDEN GRATES.
Album: released on Free Reed, Jan'87 by Free Reed Records. Dist: Roots, Projection, Hobgoblin Records, Oblivion

ROARING JELLY'S GREATEST GRATES.
Album: released on Free Reed, Sep'79 by Free Reed Records. Dist: Roots, Projection, Hobgoblin Records, Oblivion

Roaring Seven Jazz Band

ROARING SEVEN JAZZ BAND.
Album: released on Stomp Off, Jun'86 by Stomp Off Records. Dist: Jazz Music Distribution

Roar Sound

SHARE.
Single (7"): released on Roar, Jun'85 Dist: Priority, EMI

Single (12"): released on Roar, Jun'85 Dist: Priority, EMI

Robbins, Hargus 'Pig'

PIG IN A POKE.
Album: released on Elektra, Mar'78 by WEA Records. Dist: WEA

Robbins, Kate

KATE ROBBINS.
Album: released on RCA, Oct'81 by RCA Records. Dist: RCA, Roots, Swift, Wellard, Chris, I & B, Solomon & Peres Distribution

Cassette: released on RCA, Oct'81 by RCA Records. Dist: RCA, Roots, Swift, Wellard, Chris, I & B, Solomon & Peres Distribution

REAL ME THE/PHOTO FIT.
Single (7"): released on RCA, Jan'83 by RCA Records. Dist: RCA, Roots, Swift, Wellard, Chris, I & B, Solomon & Peres Distribution

THAT FIRST LOVE.
Single (7"): released on Bright, Mar'84

Robbins, Marty

AFTER MIDNIGHT.
Album: released on Hallmark, Sep'86 by Pickwick Records. Dist: Pickwick Distribution, PRT, Taylors

Cassette: released on Hallmark, Sep'86 by Pickwick Records. Dist: Pickwick Distribution, PRT, Taylors

ALL ROUND COWBOY.
Album: released on Hallmark, Aug'85 by Pickwick Records. Dist: Pickwick Distribution, PRT, Taylors

Cassette: released on Hallmark, Aug'85 by Pickwick Records. Dist: Pickwick Distribution, PRT, Taylors

BIGGEST HITS.
Album: released on CBS, Mar'83 by CBS Records. Dist: CBS

Cassette: released on CBS, Mar'83 by CBS Records. Dist: CBS

BORDER TOWN AFFAIR.
Album: by CBS Records. Dist: CBS

BY THE TIME I GET TO PHOENIX.
Album: released on Hallmark, Apr'79 by Pickwick Records. Dist: Pickwick Distribution, PRT, Taylors

Cassette: released on Hallmark, Apr'79 by Pickwick Records. Dist: Pickwick Distribution, PRT, Taylors

DON'T LET ME TOUCH YOU.
Album: released on CBS, Dec'77 by CBS Records. Dist: CBS

DOUBLE-BARRELLED MARTY ROBBINS, THE.
Double Album: released on CBS, Aug'75 by CBS Records. Dist: CBS

Cassette: released on CBS, Aug'75 by CBS Records. Dist: CBS

EL PASO.
Album: released on Hallmark, Jan'71 by Pickwick Records. Dist: Pickwick Distribution, PRT, Taylors

FASTEST GUN AROUND, THE.
Album: released on Hallmark, Nov'75 by Pickwick Records. Dist: Pickwick Distribution, PRT, Taylors

GREAT YEARS, THE.
Album: released on Hallmark, Mar'87 by Pickwick Records. Dist: Pickwick Distribution, PRT, Taylors

Cassette: released on Hallmark, Mar'87 by Pickwick Records. Dist: Pickwick Distribution, PRT, Taylors
Cat. no: **HSC 3208**

HAWAII'S CALLING ME.
Album: released on Bear Family, Dec'83 by Bear Family Records. Dist: Rollercoaster Distribution, Swift

IN THE WILDEST PART 1.
Album: released on Bear Family, Nov'85 by Bear Family Records. Dist: Rollercoaster Distribution, Swift

IN THE WILD WEST PART 4.
Album: released on Bear Family, Nov'85 by Bear Family Records. Dist: Rollercoaster Distribution, Swift

IN THE WILD WEST PART 2.
Album: released on Bear Family, Jul'84 by Bear Family Records. Dist: Rollercoaster Distribution, Swift

IN THE WILD WEST PART 3.
Album: released on Bear Family, Nov'85 by Bear Family Records. Dist: Rollercoaster Distribution, Swift

IN THE WILD WEST PART 5.
Album: released on Bear Family, Nov'85 by Bear Family Records. Dist: Rollercoaster Distribution, Swift

JUST ME AND MY GUITAR.
Album: released on Bear Family, Sep'84 by Bear Family Records. Dist: Rollercoaster Distribution, Swift

LIFETIME OF SONG A (1951-1982).
Cassette: released on CBS, Feb'84 by CBS Records. Dist: CBS

LONG LONG AGO.
Album: released on CBS, Mar'85 by CBS Records. Dist: CBS

Cassette: released on CBS, Mar'85 by CBS Records. Dist: CBS

MARTY ROBBINS I love country.
Tracks: / Some memories just won't die / My woman, my woman, my wife / Good hearted woman / Air that I breathe (The) / My elusive dream / Oh my papa / She's made of faith / I'm just here to get my baby out of jail / El Paso City / Sometimes when we touch / Return to me / Among my souveniers / 18 yellow roses / Don't let me touch you / Honky tonk man / Performer (The).
Album: released on CBS, Mar'87 by CBS Records. Dist: CBS

Cassette: by CBS Records. Dist: CBS

Album: released on Hallmark, Jan'70 by Pickwick Records. Dist: Pickwick Distribution, PRT, Taylors

Double cassette: released on Pickwick, Jan'83 by Pickwick Records. Dist: Pickwick Distribution, Prism Leisure Distribution, Lugtons

Album: released on Spot, Feb'83 by Pickwick Records. Dist: H.R. Taylor, Lugtons

Cassette: released on Spot, Feb'83 by Pickwick Records. Dist: H.R. Taylor, Lugtons

Cassette: released on Ditto, Jan'85 by Pickwick Records. Dist: H.R. Taylor

MARTY ROBBINS COLLECTIO THE.
Cassette: released on Pickwick, Dec'79 by Pickwick Records. Dist: Pickwick Distribution, Prism Leisure Distribution, Lugtons

MARTY ROBBINS COLLECTION.
Double Album: released on Pickwick, Mar'76 by Pickwick Records. Dist: Pickwick Distribution, Prism Leisure Distribution, Lugtons

MARTY ROBBINS FILES VOL 5 1958/1959/1962, THE.
Album: released on Bear Family, Nov'84 by Bear Family Records. Dist: Rollercoaster Distribution, Swift

MARTY ROBBINS FILES VOL 2 1953-1954, THE.
Album: released on Bear Family, Sep'84 by Bear Family Records. Dist: Rollercoaster Distribution, Swift

MARTY ROBBINS FILES VOL 4 1957-1958, THE.
Album: released on Crosscut, Nov'84

MARTY ROBBINS FILES VOL 3 1954-1956, THE.
Album: released on Bear Family, Sep'84 by Bear Family Records. Dist: Rollercoaster Distribution, Swift

PERFORMER, THE.
Album: released on CBS, Apr'79 by CBS Records. Dist: CBS

Cassette: released on CBS, Apr'79 by CBS Records. Dist: CBS

PIECES OF YOUR HEART.
Album: released on Bear Family, Nov'85 by Bear Family Records. Dist: Rollercoaster Distribution, Swift

ROCKIN' ROLLIN' ROBBINS VOL.3.
Album: released on Bear Family, Nov'85 by Bear Family Records. Dist: Rollercoaster Distribution, Swift

ROCKIN ROLLIN ROBBINS VOL 2 (THE RAY CONNIFF RECORDING).
Album: released on Bear Family, Sep'84 by Bear Family Records. Dist: Rollercoaster Distribution, Swift

ROCKIN ROLLIN ROBBINS.
Album: released on Bear Family (CBS), Sep'84

SOME MEMORIES JUST WON'T DIE.
Cassette: released on Spot, Apr'86 by Pickwick Records. Dist: H.R. Taylor, Lugtons

SONG OF THE ISLANDS.
Album: released on Bear Family (Rollercoaster), Oct'83

TWENTIETH CENTURY DRIFTER.
Tracks: / Twentieth century drifter / This much a man / Love me / Don't you think / Crawling on my knees / Walking piece of heaven / Man and a train,A / Two gun daddy / It takes faith / Life.
Album: released on MCA Import, Mar'86 by MCA Records. Dist: Polygram, IMS

WITH LOVE MARTY ROBBINS.
Album: released on CBS, Aug'80 by CBS Records. Dist: CBS

Cassette: released on CBS, Aug'80 by CBS Records. Dist: CBS

Robbinson Teddy

BEST OF.
Cassette: released on Tellastory, Oct'79 by Bartlett Bliss Productions. Dist: PRT Distribution, Hayward Promotions Distribution, H.R. Taylor Distribution

Robbins, Rockie

I'VE GOT YOUR NUMBER.
Single (7"): released on MCA, Jul'85 by MCA Records. Dist: Polygram, MCA

Single (12"): released on MCA, Jul'85 by MCA Records. Dist: Polygram, MCA

WE BELONG TOGETHER.
Single (7"): released on MCA, Apr'85 by MCA Records. Dist: Polygram, MCA

Single (12"): released on MCA, Apr'85 by MCA Records. Dist: Polygram, MCA

Robechaux, Joe

1933 (Robechaux, Joe and his New Orleans boys).
Album: released on Classic Jazz Masters, Dec'86 by Mainline Record Company. Dist: Mainline, Swift, Jazz Music

JOE ROBECHAUX AND HIS NEW ORLEANS BOYS (Robechaux, Joe and his New Orleans boys).

Album: released on Folklyric (USA), Dec'86 by Arhoolie Records. Dist: Topic, Projection

Robert Burns Songbook

ROBERT BURNS SONGBOOK Various original Scottish artists (Various Artists).

Robert & Elizabeth

ROBERT & ELIZABETH Original London cast.
Album: released on Encore, Apr'80 by EMI Records. Dist: EMI

Robert & Johnny

WE BELONG TOGETHER.
Album: released on Ace, Apr'86 by Ace Records. Dist: Pinnacle, Swift, Hotshot, Cadillac

Robert, Moja-Rappa

UPTOWN ROCK (GHETTO MAN SOUNDS).
Single (12"): released on Ethnic, Dec'83 Dist: Kingdom

Robert Raspberry...

ROBERT RASPBERRY & GRACE GRAPE Various artists (Various Artists).
Cassette: released on Tell-a-tale (Cassettes), Oct'84

Roberts, Alan

CALEDONIA (Roberts, Alan & Dougie Maclean).
Album: released on Plant Life, Nov'81 Dist: Roots

Roberts, Al'Jnr.

I WISH I WAS IN LA.
Single (7"): released on Red Hot, Feb'80 Dist: Swift

ROCKABILLY.
Album: released on Frog, Jan'80 by Frog Records. Dist: Lightning, Superdisc Distribution, Swift

ROCKABILLY GUITAR MAN.
Album: released on Frog, Apr'80 by Frog Records. Dist: Lightning, Superdisc Distribution, Swift

Roberts, Andy

FROM TIME TO TIME.
Album: released on Big Ben, Apr'85 by Big Ben Records. Dist: Spartan, Taylor, H.R.

LOOSE CONNECTIONS.
Album: released on Virgin, Apr'85 by Virgin Records. Dist: EMI, Virgin Distribution

Roberts, Bob

BREEZE FOR A BARGEMAN.
Album: released on Solent, Aug'84 by Solent Records.

SONGS FROM THE SAILING BARGES.
Album: released on Topic, '81 by Topic Records. Dist: JSU Distribution, Projection Distribution, Jazz Music Distribution

STORMY WEATHER, BOYS.
Cassette: released on Folktracks, Nov'79 by Folktracks Cassettes. Dist: Folktracks

Roberts, Bruce

BRUCE ROBERTS.
Album: released on Elektra, Feb'78 by WEA Records. Dist: WEA

SONGWRITERS FOR THE STARS 3 (see Nichols, Roger) (Roberts, Bruce & Roger Nichols).
Album: released on Polydor (Norway), Oct'83

Roberts, Charlie

BLOWIN' MY MIND.
Tracks: / Blowin' my mind / Blowin' my mind (inst).
Single (7"): released on Arista, Jul'87 by Arista Records. Dist: RCA

Single (12"): released on Arista, Jul'87 by Arista Records. Dist: RCA

BLOWIN' MY MIND WITH YOUR BODY.
Single (7"): released on Affair, Feb'87 Dist: DMS, RCA

Single (12"): released on Affair, Feb'87 Dist: DMS, RCA

Roberts, David

BOYS IN AUTUMN.
Single (7"): released on WEA, Mar'83 by WEA Records. Dist: WEA

RAGS (Roberts, David Thomas).
Album: released on Stomp Off, Jun'86 by Stomp Off Records. Dist: Jazz Music Distribution

Roberts, Eric

NEXT IN LINE.
Single (7"): released on Electricity, Jun'84 by Electricity Records. Dist: PRT

Single (12"): released on Electricity, Jun'84 by Electricity Records. Dist: PRT

Robert Service Story

ROBERT SERVICE STORY Read by John Cairney (Cairney, John).
Album: released on REL, Oct'79 Dist: Roots

Roberts, Howard

GOOD PICKINS.
Album: released on Verve (France), Jun'83

Roberts, Isabel

I JUST FALL IN LOVE.
Tracks: / Ijust fall in love / Ijust fall in love (version).
Single (12"): released on Hot Vinyl, Jun'87 by Hot Vinyl Records. Dist: Jetstar

Roberts, Isobel

RHYTHM OF YOUR LOVE.
Tracks: / Rhythm of your love / Rhythm of your love (Instrumental).
Single (12"): released on Hot Vinyl, Mar'86 by Hot Vinyl Records. Dist: Jetstar

Roberts, Joy

LOVE ME INSIDE.
Single (12"): released on Love Linch, Apr'82 Dist: Jetstar

Roberts, Judy

OTHER WORLD, THE.
Album: released on Inner City, Sep'80 Dist: Jetstar

Roberts, Julie

AIN'T YOU HAD ENOUGH LOVE.
Single (7"): released on Bluebird, Oct'85 by Bluebird Records. Dist: EMI, Jetstar

Single (12"): released on Bluebird, Oct'85 by Bluebird Records. Dist: EMI, Jetstar

I DON'T WANNA LOSE YOU.
Single (7"): released on Bluebird, Aug'84 by Bluebird Records. Dist: EMI, Jetstar

Single (12"): released on Bluebird, Aug'84 by Bluebird Records. Dist: EMI, Jetstar

IT'S BEEN A LONG LONG TIME.
Single (7"): released on Bluebird, Jul'83 by Bluebird Records. Dist: EMI, Jetstar

Single (12"): released on Bluebird, Jul'83 by Bluebird Records. Dist: EMI, Jetstar

Roberts, Juliette

MORE THAN ONE NIGHT.
Tracks: / More than one night / More than one night (Instrumental).
Single (7"): released on Bluebird, Jun'86 by Bluebird Records. Dist: EMI, Jetstar

Single (12"): released on Bluebird, Jun'86 by Bluebird Records. Dist: EMI, Jetstar

Roberts, Kenny

INDIAN LOVE CALL.
Album: released on Starday, Apr'87

Cassette: released on Starday, Apr'87

Roberts, Lloyd

BABY HANG UP THE PHONE.
Single (12"): released on Nice And Cool, Jul'85 Dist: Jetstar

Roberts, Luckey

HARLEM PIANO (Roberts, Luckey & Willie 'The Lion' Smith).
Album: released on Good Time Jazz (USA), Jul'81 by Good Time Jazz Records (USA). Dist: Polygram

Roberts, Malcolm

WANDERER (Roberts, Malcolm & Billy Fury 'Dave Berry).
Single (7"): released on Dakota, Mar'83 by Dakota Records. Dist: PRT

Robertson, B.A.

BANG BANG.
Single (7"): released on Elektra Asylum, Jun'79 by Elektra/Asylum/Nonesuch Records. Dist: WEA

CEUD MILE FAILTE (A HUNDRED THOUSAND WELCOMES).
Tracks: / Ceud mile failte (A hundred thousand welcomes) / BBC TR Commonwealth Games theme,The / See you in Auckland.
Single (7"): released on BBC, Jul'86 by BBC Records & Tapes. Dist: EMI, PRT, Pye

Single (12"): released on BBC, Jul'86 by BBC Records & Tapes. Dist: EMI, PRT, Pye

DOT DOT DOT.
Single (7"): released on Elektra Asylum, Jul'82 by Elektra/Asylum/Nonesuch Records. Dist: WEA

I AM A SEEKER.
Single (7"): released on Epic, Dec'83 by CBS Records. Dist: CBS

NOW AND THEN.
Single (7"): released on After Hours, Mar'83 Dist: CBS

ONE PLUS ONE.
Single (7"): released on Asylum, Feb'82 by WEA Records. Dist: WEA

Robertson, Deby

SWEETA JAMAICA.
Single (12"): released on Freedom, Nov'81 by Logo Records. Dist: RCA, Discovery, Wellard, Chris

Robertson, Eric

PIANO MAGIC.
Album: released on K-Tel, Apr'83 by K-Tel Records. Dist: Record Merchandisers Distribution, Taylors, Terry Blood Distribution, Wynd-Up Distribution, Relay Distribution, Pickwick Distribution, Solomon & Peres Distribution, Polygram

Cassette: released on K-Tel, Apr'83 by K-Tel Records. Dist: Record Merchandisers Distribution, Taylors, Terry Blood Distribution, Wynd-Up Distribution, Relay Distribution, Pickwick Distribution, Solomon & Peres Distribution, Polygram

Robertson, Jackie

PRETTY BLUE EYES.
Single (12"): released on Dancebeat, Jan'84 by Dancebeat Records. Dist: Jetstar

Robertson, Jeannie

JEANNIE ROBERTSON.
Album: released on Topic, '81 Dist: Roots Distribution

UP THE DEE AND DOWN THE DON.
Album: released on Lismor, '84 by Lismor Records. Dist: Lismor, Roots, Celtic Music

Cassette: released on Lismor, '84 by Lismor Records. Dist: Lismor, Roots, Celtic Music

WHAT A VOICE.
Cassette: released on Folktracks, Nov'79 by Folktracks Cassettes. Dist: Folktracks

Robertson, Liz

SOMEBODY'S GIRL.
Album: released on VIP, Dec'84 Dist: Jetstar Distribution

Cassette: released on VIP, Dec'84 Dist: Jetstar Distribution

Robertson/Oliff

HOO HA RAH.
Single (7"): released on Noga, Mar'84 Dist: Noga, MSA Distribution

Robertson, Paul

OLD FRIENDS,NEW FRIENDS.
Album: released on Palo Alto (Italy), Jan'84

SONG IS YOU, THE.
Album: released on Palo Alto (Italy), Jan'84

Roberts, Paddy

WORLD OF PADDY ROBERTS.
Album: released on World of Learning, '69 by World Of Learning Records. Dist: World Of Learning

Roberts, Papa

GANJA TRAFFICKING.
Single 10": released on Spiderman, Sep'82

Roberts, Paul

BACK TO ENGLAND.
Tracks: / Back to England / Good life,The.
Single (7"): released on Sonet, Feb'86 by Sonet Records. Dist: PRT

CITY WITHOUT WALLS.
Album: released on Sonet, Nov'85 by Sonet Records. Dist: PRT

HAND OF FATE.
Tracks: / Night starvation.
Single (7"): released on Sonet, Jan'87 by Sonet Records. Dist: PRT

ON STAGE AT THE PARK.
Tracks: / I want to be happy / I hear music / Murder on the Orient Express / Let's go live in the country / Pied piper,The / I know him so well / That olde' devil called love / Serenade to a Japanese tea bag / When I'm 64/ 'One' / Things we did last summer,The / Dad's army theme / Upstairs downstairs / Alley cat song,The / Tales of the unexpected / Jolly Coppersmith,The / World is waiting for the sunrise,The/ Bye bye blues / Blow the wind southerly/ Skye boat song / Hot canary,The/butterflies in the rain/the parrot / Walking in the air/ Aira's theme / I'm chambre separee/ boulevard de Paris / I feel pretty / somewhere / Tonight / Run rabbit run.
Album: released on Sounds Ultimate, Nov'86 Dist: PRT, H.R. Taylor

ON YOUR TOES.
Tracks: / I want to be happy / Happy talk / Let's face the music and dance / I'm putting all my eggs in one basket / Spoonful of sugar, A / Supercalifragilisticexpialidocious / On your toes / Honey bun / Small Hotel / Out of my dreams / This nearly was mine / Tammy / An affair to remember / Rain in Spain,The / Younger than Springtime / I have dreamed / I can't get started / Life upon the wicked stage / Blue room / Hey look me over/Pass me by. / Wedding of the painted doll,The.
Album: released on Sounds Ultimate, May'87 Dist: PRT, H.R. Taylor

RAILROAD TO THE SEA.
Single (7"): released on Sonet, Oct'85 by Sonet Records. Dist: PRT

WORKING FOR THE GOODTIMES.
Tracks: / Working for the goodtimes / Away too long.
Single (7"): released on Sonet, Aug'87 by Sonet Records. Dist: PRT

Single (12"): released on Sonet, Aug'87 by Sonet Records. Dist: PRT

Roberts, Steve

AS TEARS GO BY.
Single (7"): released on Exploited, Jun'82 Dist: Red Rhino, Cartel

DO YOU KNOW WHO I AM.
Album: released on Exploited, Jun'82 Dist: Red Rhino, Cartel

Roberts, Wendy

I WANT YOU BACK.
Single (7"): released on PRT, Aug'85 by PRT Records. Dist: PRT

Single (12"): released on PRT, Aug'85 by PRT Records. Dist: PRT

Robeson, Paul

BEST OF PAUL ROBESON, THE.
Album: released on Note, Nov'79 by EMI Records. Dist: EMI

Cassette: released on EMI, Nov'79 by EMI Records. Dist: EMI

ESSENTIAL, THE.
Double Album: released on Vanguard (USA), Nov'83

GOLDEN AGE OF PAUL ROBESON, THE.
Album: released on Golden Age, Jul'83 by Music For Pleasure Records. Dist: EMI

Cassette: released on Golden Age, Jul'83 by Music For Pleasure Records. Dist: EMI

GREEN PASTURES.
Tracks: / St. Louis blues / Rockin' chair / Mary had a baby, yes lord / Love song / All god's chillun got wings / Banjo song / Bear the burden / When it's sleepy time down south / Killing song / High water / Lazy bones / Carry me back to green pastures / Congo lullaby / Shortnin' bread / Snowball / Fat li'l feller with his mammy's eyes / Canoe song / River stay away from my door.
Notes: ASV's "Living Era" series, now with 47 titles, continues to bring the past to life. One of the most successful issues has been "Lonesome Road" by Paul Robeson(ZC\AJA 5027), and a new compilation from this beloved singer is sure of a warm reception. Paul Robeson (1898-1976) was blessed with a great bass voice of enveloping richness and earthy resonance, and his majestic presence made hearinghim sing, especially spirituals, such a memorable experience. "Green pastures" presents 18 of his most famous recordings, dating from the years of his vocal prime, 1930-35. The range is wide, from Hoagy Carmichael's "Rockin' chair" and "Lazy bones" to all four songs featured in the film "Saunders of the river", to spirituals such as "Mary had a baby, yes lord"- all presented with sincerity andfeeling.
Cassette: released on ASV Living Era, Jun'87 by ASV Records. Dist: PRT

Album: released on ASV Living Era, Jun'87 by ASV Records. Dist: PRT

LONESOME ROAD.
Album: released on Academy Sound & Vision, Feb'84 by Academy Sound & Vision Records. Dist: Pinnacle

Cassette: released on Academy Sound & Vision, Feb'84 by Academy Sound & Vision Records. Dist: Pinnacle

PAUL ROBESON.
Album: released on Deja Vu, Jan'87 by Deja Vu Records. Dist: Counterpoint Distribution, Record Services Distribution (Ireland)

Cassette: released on Deja Vu, Jan'87 by Deja Vu Records. Dist: Counterpoint Distribution, Record Services Distribution (Ireland)

PAUL ROBESON SINGS 'OL' MAN RIVER' AND OTHER FAVOURITES.
Tracks: / Ol' man river / Roll away, clouds / Lonesome road, the / Got the south in my soul / Hush-a-bye lullaby / Around the bend of the road / Carry me back to green pastures / Blue prelude / Wagon wheels / So shy / St. Louis blues / Little man, you've had a busy day / I ain't lazy, I'm just dreaming / Shenandoah / All through the night / Solitude / Song of the volga boatmen / Dear old southland / Perfect day, A.
Compact disc: released on H.M.V., May'87 by EMI Records. Dist: EMI

...SINGS 'OL' MAN RIVER' AND OTHER FAVOURITES.
Album: released on EMI Retrospect, Oct'85 by

EMI Records. Dist: EMI

Cassette: released on EMI Retrospect, Oct'85 by EMI Records. Dist: EMI

SONGS OF FREE MEN.
Album: released on CBS(Masterworks), Feb'85 by CBS Records. Dist: CBS

Cassette: released on CBS(Masterworks), Feb'85 by CBS Records. Dist: CBS

Robillard, Duke

DUKE ROBILLARD (Robillard, Duke & The Pleasure Kings).
Album: released on Demon, '84 by Demon Records. Dist: Pinnacle

SWING.
Album: released on Rounder Europa, Mav'87

TOO HOT TO HANDLE (Robillard, Duke & The Pleasure Kings).
Album: released on Demon, Mar'85 by Demon Records. Dist: Pinnacle

Robin Hood

ROBIN HOOD.
Tracks: / Robin Hood (continued).
Cassette: released on Tellastory, Dec'86 by Bartlett Bliss Productions. Dist: PRT Distribution, Hayward Promotions Distribution, H.R. Taylor Distribution

ROBIN HOOD (Jarvis, Martin).
Cassette: released on Pinnacle, '79 by Pinnacle Records. Dist: Pinnacle

ROBIN HOOD (Woolf, Gabriel & David Brierly).
Cassette: released on Squirrel, Nov'81

ROBIN HOOD (Hyde, Anthony).
Cassette: released on Tellastory, Mar'82 by Bartlett Bliss Productions. Dist: PRT Distribution, Hayward Promotions Distribution, H.R. Taylor Distribution

ROBIN HOOD Various artists (Various Artists).
Album: released on BBC, Oct'85 by BBC Records & Tapes. Dist: EMI, PRT, Pye

Cassette: released on BBC, Oct'85 by BBC Records & Tapes. Dist: EMI, PRT, Pye

ROBIN HOOD & OTHER FAVOURITE STORIES FOR CHILDREN Various artists (Various Artists).
Cassette: released on VFM, Jul'85 by VFM Records. Dist: Taylors, Wynd-Up Distribution

Robins, Butch

FRAGMENTS OF MY IMAGINATION.
Album: released on Rounder, May'79 Dist: Roots Distribution

Robins, Cantor Stephen

CANTOR STEPHEN ROBINS.
Cassette: released on B'nai B'rith, Aug'85

Robinsn, Lloyd

CANDY GIRL.
Single 10": released on Pama, Nov'82 by Pama Records. Dist: Pama, Enterprise, Jetstar

Robinson, Banjo Ikey

1929-35 - BLUES, SKIFFLE & JAZZ.
Album: released on Document, Jul'87

Robinson Crusoe

ROBINSON CRUSOE (Richardson, Ian).
Album: released on Caedmon(USA), Jul'78 by Caedmon (USA) Records. Dist: Gower, Taylors, Discovery

ROBINSON CRUSOE (Duncan, Frank).
Cassette: released on Pinnacle, '79 by Pinnacle Records. Dist: Pinnacle

ROBINSON CRUSOE (Norgate, Clifford).
Cassette: released on Squirrel, Nov'81

ROBINSON CRUSOE & OTHER FAVOURITE STORIES FOR CHILDREN Various artists (Various Artists).
Cassette: released on VFM, Jul'85 by VFM Records. Dist: Taylors, Wynd-Up Distribution

Robinson, Dave

GIVE THANKS.
Single (12"): released on Iyah Bingi, Jun'84 by Iyah Bingi Records. Dist: Jetstar, Kingdom, Iyah Bingi

Robinson, Dutch

HAPPY.
Single (7"): released on Epic, Feb'85 by CBS Records. Dist: CBS

Robinson, Fenton

BLUES IN PROGRESS.
Album: released on Black Magic (Holland), Aug'84

I HEAR SOME BLUES DOWNSTAIRS.
Album: by Sonet Records. Dist: PRT

MELLOW FELLOW.
Tracks: / Somebody loan me a dime / Little turch / Leave you in the arms (of your other man) / Let me come on home / She's a wiggler / Laughin cryin blues / I wanna ooh / I fell in love one time / Sky is crying / Getaway, The / Sideman / Mellow fellow.
Album: released on Charly, Jan'87 by Charly Records. Dist: Charly, Cadillac

SOMEBODY LOAN ME A DIME.
Album: released on Sonet, Aug'76 by Sonet Records. Dist: PRT

Robinson, Floyd

MAKIN' LOVE.
Tracks: / Makin' love / Shape I'm in,The.
Single (7"): released on Old Gold, Oct'86 by Old Gold Records. Dist: Lightning, Jazz Music, Spartan, Counterpoint

Robinson, Geoff

TAKE ME BACK/ HOT STUFF.
Single (7"): released on PVK, Jul'81

Robinson, Jackie

SANTA ISN'T COMING TO BRIXTON TOWN.
Tracks: / Santa isn't coming to Brixton town / Santa isn't coming to Brixton town (Dub).
Single (12"): released on Reel Grande, Jan'86 Dist: Jetstar

Robinson, James

CAN WE DO IT AGAIN.
Tracks: / Can we do it again / You're the one I've been dreaming of.
Single (7"): released on Tabu, Jul'87 by CBS Records. Dist: CBS Distribution

Single (12"): released on Tabu, Jul'87 by CBS Records. Dist: CBS Distribution

GUILTY.
Tracks: / Can we do it again / Guilty / Pretend / Feel like going on / Seems so long / Lord's prayer, The / Kind of love, A / Just what I've been missing / When you'll be mine / You're the one I've been dreaming of.
Album: released on Tabu (USA), Aug'87 Dist: CBS Distribution

Album: released on Tabu, Sep'87 by CBS Records. Dist: CBS Distribution

Robinson, Jim

JIM ROBINSON WITH.....
Album: released on Smokey Mary, Apr'79 Dist: Swift

Robinson, Joan

BEST OF TEDDY ROBINSON, THE.
Tracks: / Teddy Robinson goes to hospital / Teddy Robinson's night out / Teddy Robinson is put in a book.
Notes: For full information see under ROBINSON, Joan.
Cassette: released on Tellastory, Dec'86 by Bartlett Bliss Productions. Dist: PRT Distribution, Hayward Promotions Distribution, H.R. Taylor Distribution

Robinson, Kieth

WORLD NEEDS LOVE, THE (Robinson, Kieth & some mates).
Album: released on Waiting-In-Vain, Oct'82 by Waiting-In-Vain Records. Dist: December Songs, Independents Distribution

Robinson, L.C.

UPS AND DOWNS.
Album: released on Arhoolie, May'81 by Arhoolie Records. Dist: Projection, Topic, Jazz Music, Swift, Roots

Robinson, Lloyd

HAPPY TO BE WITH YOU.
Tracks: / Happy to be with you / Happy to be with you (Version).
Single (12"): released on Jah Tubbys, Feb'86 by Jah Tubbys Records. Dist: Jetstar

MIDAS TOUCH.
Tracks: / Midas touch / Midas touchings.
Single (12"): released on Paradise, Apr'86 Dist: Jetstar, JSU, WEA

Robinson, Mark

PRETTY JANE (Robinson, Martell).
Single (7"): released on Bison Bop (USA), Jan'85

Robinson, Michael

DON'T GIRLS GET LONELY.
Single (7"): released on DJM, Jul'84 by DJM Records. Dist: CBS, Polygram

Robinson, Nambo

SANITY (Robinson, Roscoe).
Album: released on Sanity, Sep'84 by Sanity Records. Dist: Pinnacle, Jetstar

Robinson, Paul

COME ON SISTER.
Single (12"): released on King & City, May'82 Dist: Jetstar

Robinson, Sandra

SENSI FOR SALE.
Single (12"): released on Trojan, Nov'85 by Trojan Records. Dist: PRT, Jetstar

Robinson's Jacinto...

ROBINSON'S JACINTO BALLROOM ORCHESTRA.
Album: released on GHB, Jun'86 Dist: Jazz Music, Swift

Robinson, Smokey

18 GREATEST HITS (Robinson, Smokey And The Miracles).
Tracks: / Shop around / You've really got a hold on me / I'll try something new / Depend on me / Mickey's monkey / Tracks of my tears / Going to a go-go / I second that emotion / If you can want / Baby, baby, don't cry / Doggone right / Tears of a clown / I don't blame you at all / Baby come close / Baby that's backatcha / Quiet storm / Cruisin / Being with you.
Compact disc: released on Motown, May'84 by Motown Records. Dist: BMG Distribution

Compact disc: released on Motown, May'84 by Motown Records. Dist: BMG Distribution
Cat. no: **TCD 06071 TD**

22 GREATEST HITS II-COMPACT COMMAND PERFORMANCES.
Compact disc: by Motown Records. Dist: BMG Distribution

2 CLASSIC ALBUMS: GOING TO A GO-GO/..... (Robinson, Smokey And The Miracles).
Tracks: / Tracks of my tears,The / Going to a go-go / Ooo baby baby / My girl has gone / In case you need love / Choosey beggar / Since you won my heart / From head to toe / All that's good / My baby changes like the weather / Let me have some / Fork in the road,A/ The tears of a clown / Soulful shack,The / Love I saw in you was just a mirage,The / My love for you / I'm on the outside (looking in) / Don't think it's me / My love is your love (forever) / More love / After you put back the pieces / It's a good feeling / You must be love / Dancing's alright / Tears of a clown,The.
Notes: Full title: 2 Classic albums: Going to a go-go/ The tears of a clown.
Compact disc: released on Motown, Oct'86 by Motown Records. Dist: BMG Distribution

AND I DON'T LOVE YOU.
Single (7"): released on Motown, Jun'84 by RCA Records. Dist: RCA Distribution

Single (12"): released on Motown, Jun'84 by RCA Records. Dist: RCA Distribution

ANTHOLOGY Volumes 1 & 2 (Robinson, Smokey And The Miracles).
Tracks: / Got a job / Bad girl / Way over there / Depend on me, (You can) / Shop around / Who's lovin' you / What's so good about goodbye / I'll try something new / I've been good to you / You've really got a hold on me / Love she can count on, A / Mickey's monkey / I gotta dance to keep from crying / I like it like that / That's what love is made of / Come on do the jerk / Ooo baby baby / Tracks of my tears, The / My girl has gone / Choosey beggar / Going to a go-go / I'm the one you need / Save me / Love I saw in you was just a mirage, The / More love / I second that emotion / If you can want / Yester-love / Special occasion / Baby baby don't cry / Doggone right / Here I go again / Abraham, Martin and John / Darling dear / Point it out / Who's gonna take the blame / Tears of a clown, The / I don't blame you at all / Satisfaction / We've come too far to end it now / I can't stand to see you cry / Crazy about the la la la / Do it baby / Don't cha love it / Love machine.
Double compact disc: released on Motown, Jan'87 by Motown Records. Dist: BMG Distribution

Double compact disc: released on Motown, 20 Jun'87 by Motown Records. Dist: BMG Distribution

Album: released on Motown, Sep'82 by RCA Records. Dist: RCA Distribution

Cassette: released on Motown, Sep'82 by RCA Records. Dist: RCA Distribution

BEING WITH YOU.
Album: released on Motown, Apr'85 by RCA Records. Dist: RCA Distribution

Cassette: released on Motown, Apr'85 by RCA Records. Dist: RCA Distribution

Single (7"): released on Motown, Apr'85 by RCA Records. Dist: RCA Distribution

BLAME IT ON LOVE Greatest hits.
Album: released on Motown, Oct'83 by RCA Records. Dist: RCA Distribution

Cassette: released on Motown, Oct'83 by RCA Records. Dist: RCA Distribution

Single (7"): released on Motown, Aug'83 by RCA Records. Dist: RCA Distribution

COMPACT COMMAND PERFORMANCES VOL. 2 (Robinson, Smokey And The Miracles).
Tracks: / Bad girl / What's so good about goodbye? / Way over there / Love you can count on, A / I gotta dance to keep from crying / I like it like that / That's what love is made of / Come on do the jerk / Ooo baby baby / Choosey beggar / My girl has gone / Love I saw in your eyes was just a mirage (The) / More love / I'm the one you need / Yester love / Secial occasion / Here I go again / Abraham, Martin and John / Point it out / We've come too far to end it now / Do it baby / Love machine / Love you can count on, A.
Compact disc: released on Motown, Mar'87 by Motown Records. Dist: BMG Distribution

CRUISIN/THE HUMAN SONG.
Single (7"): released on Motown, Oct'81 by Motown Records. Dist: BMG Distribution

CRUISIN/THE ONLY GAME IN TOWN.
Single (7"): released on Motown, Aug'82 by Motown Records. Dist: BMG Distribution

Single (12"): released on Motown, Aug'82 by Motown Records. Dist: BMG Distribution

ESSAR.
Album: released on Motown, Jul'84 by Motown Records. Dist: BMG Distribution

Cassette: released on Motown, Jul'84 by Motown Records. Dist: BMG Distribution

GOING TO A GO-GO/THE TEARS OF A CLOWN 2 Classic albums (Robinson, Smokey And The Miracles).
Tracks: / Tracks of my tears, The / Going to a go-go / Ooo baby baby / My girl has gone / In case you need love / Choosey beggar / Since you won my heart / From head to toe / All that's good / My baby changes like the weather / Let me have some / Fork in the road, A / Soulful shack, The / Love I saw in you was just a mirage, The / My love for you / I'm on the outside (looking in) / Don't think it's me / My love is your love (forever) / More love / After you put back the pieces I'll still have a broken heart / It's a good feeling / You must be love / Dancing's alright / Tears of a clown, The.
Compact disc: released on Motown, Jan'87 by Motown Records. Dist: BMG Distribution

GOING TO GO GO (Robinson, Smokey And The Miracles).
Single (7"): released on Motown, Oct'81 by Motown Records. Dist: BMG Distribution

GREATEST SONGS.
Compact disc: by Motown Records. Dist: BMG Distribution

HEAVY ON THE PRIDE(LIGHT OF LOVE).
Single (7"): released on Motown, Oct'81 by Motown Records. Dist: BMG Distribution

HOLD ON TO YOUR LOVE.
Tracks: / Hold on to your love / Train of tought.
Single (7"): released on Motown, Jan'86 by Motown Records. Dist: BMG Distribution

Single (12"): released on Motown, Jan'86 by Motown Records. Dist: BMG Distribution

HOT SMOKEY.
Album: released on Motown, Jan'82 by Motown Records. Dist: BMG Distribution

Cassette: released on Motown, Jan'82 by Motown Records. Dist: BMG Distribution

I DON'T BLAME YOU AT ALL (Robinson, Smokey And The Miracles).
Single (7"): released on Motown, Mar'83 by Motown Records. Dist: BMG Distribution

I MADE LOVE TO YOU A THOUSAND TIMES.
Single (7"): released on Motown, Feb'83 by Motown Records. Dist: BMG Distribution

I'M THE ONE (Robinson, Smokey And The Miracles).
Single (7"): released on Motown, Oct'81 by RCA Records. Dist: RCA Distribution

JUST TO SEE HER.
Tracks: / Just to see her / I'm gonna love you like there's no tomorrow / You've really got a hold on me / That's what love is made of / Ooh baby baby.
Notes: There are three extra tracks on 12" version all by Smokey Robinson and The Miracles.
Single (7"): released on Motown, Feb'87 by Motown Records. Dist: BMG Distribution

Single (12"): released on Motown, Feb'87 by

Motown Records. Dist: BMG Distribution

Single (7"): released on Motown, 13 Jun'87 by Motown Records. Dist: BMG Distribution

Single (12"): released on Motown, 13 Jun'87 by Motown Records. Dist: BMG Distribution

LET ME BE THE CLOCK/TRAVELIN THROUGH.
Single (7"): released on Motown, Oct'81 by Motown Records. Dist: BMG Distribution

OLD FASHIONED LOVE/DESTINY.
Single (7"): released on Motown, May'82 by Motown Records. Dist: BMG Distribution

Single (12"): released on Motown, May'82 by Motown Records. Dist: BMG Distribution

ONE HEARTBEAT.
Tracks: / Just to see her / One heartbeat / It's time to stop shoppin' around / Why do happy memories hurt so bad / You don't know what it's like / What's too much / Love bought us here tonight / Love don't give no reason / Keep me.
Album: released on Motown, Jan'87 by Motown Records. Dist: BMG Distribution

Cassette: released on Motown, Jan'87 by Motown Records. Dist: BMG Distribution

Compact disc: released on Motown, Jan'87 by Motown Records. Dist: BMG Distribution

PURE SMOKEY.
Album: released on Motown, Mar'82 by Motown Records. Dist: BMG Distribution

Cassette: released on Motown, Mar'82 by Motown Records. Dist: BMG Distribution

QUIET STORM, A.
Album: released on Motown, Mar'82 by RCA Records. Dist: RCA Distribution

Cassette: released on Motown, Mar'82 by RCA Records. Dist: RCA Distribution

SLEEPLESS NIGHTS.
Tracks: / Sleepless nights / Close encounters of the first kind / Mickey's monkey / I got a dance to keep from crying / Some people (will do anything for love) / Sleepless nithts / Because of you / Te quiero como si no hubiera un manana / Hold on to your love / Photograph in my mind / No time to stop believing / Wishful thinking / Hanging on by a thread.
Single (7"): released on Motown, May'86 by Motown Records. Dist: BMG Distribution

Single (12"): released on Motown, May'86 by Motown Records. Dist: BMG Distribution

SMOKE SIGNALS.
Tracks: / Some people (will do anything for love) / Sleepless nights / Because of you (it's the best it's ever been) / Be kind to the growing mind / Te quiero como si no hubiera un manana / Hold on to your love / Photograph in my mind / No time to stop believing / Wishful thinking / Hanging on by a thread.
Compact disc: released on Motown, Jan'87 by Motown Records. Dist: BMG Distribution

Album: released on Motown Ace, Mar'86

Cassette: released on Motown Ace, Mar'86

Compact disc: released on Motown, Jan'86 by Motown Records. Dist: BMG Distribution

SMOKEY.
Album: released on Motown, Oct'81 by Motown Records. Dist: BMG Distribution

Album: released on Motown, Oct'81 by Motown Records. Dist: BMG Distribution

Cassette: released on Motown, Oct'81 by Motown Records. Dist: BMG Distribution

SMOKEY ROBINSON AND THE MIRACLES (Robinson, Smokey And The Miracles).
Cassette: released on Motown, May'83 by Motown Records. Dist: BMG Distribution

SMOKEY ROBINSON STORY THE.
Album: released on K-Tel, Jun'83 by K-Tel Records. Dist: Record Merchandisers Distribution, Taylors, Terry Blood Distribution, Wynd-Up Distribution, Relay Distribution, Pickwick Distribution, Solomon & Peres Distribution, Polygram

Cassette: released on K-Tel, Jun'83 by K-Tel Records. Dist: Record Merchandisers Distribution, Taylors, Terry Blood Distribution, Wynd-Up Distribution, Relay Distribution, Pickwick Distribution, Solomon & Peres Distribution, Polygram

TEARS OF A CLOWN (Robinson, Smokey And The Miracles).
Album: released on Motown, Jun'82 by Motown Records. Dist: BMG Distribution

Cassette: released on Motown, Jun'82 by Motown Records. Dist: BMG Distribution

TEARS OF A CLOWN, THE (Robinson, Smokey And The Miracles).
Album: released on Motown, Oct'81 by Motown Records. Dist: BMG Distribution

Cassette: released on Motown, Oct'81 by Motown Records. Dist: BMG Distribution

TEARS OF A CLOWN/ TRACKS OF MY TEARS (Robinson, Smokey And The Miracles).
Single (7"): released on Motown, Jun'83 by Motown Records. Dist: BMG Distribution

TELL ME TOMORROW/PART 2.
Single (7"): released on Motown, Feb'82 by Motown Records. Dist: BMG Distribution

Single (12"): released on Motown, Feb'82 by Motown Records. Dist: BMG Distribution

TOUCH THE SKY.
Album: released on Motown, Mar'83 by Motown Records. Dist: BMG Distribution

Cassette: released on Motown, Mar'83 by Motown Records. Dist: BMG Distribution

TOUCH THE SKY/ALL MY LIFE'S A LIE.
Single (7"): released on Motown, May'83 by Motown Records. Dist: BMG Distribution

TRACKS OF MY TEARS (Robinson, Smokey And The Miracles).
Single (7"): released on Motown, Oct'81 by Motown Records. Dist: BMG Distribution

TRACKS OF MY TEARS, THE (Robinson, Smokey And The Miracles).
Tracks: / Tracks of my tears / I second that emotion / Going to a go-go* / Shop around*.
Single (7"): released on Motown, 23 May'87 by Motown Records. Dist: BMG Distribution

Single (12"): released on Motown, 23 May'87 by Motown Records. Dist: BMG Distribution

WARM THOUGHTS.
Album: released on Motown, Oct'81 by Motown Records. Dist: BMG Distribution

WHERE THERE'S SMOKE.
Album: released on Motown, Oct'81 by Motown Records. Dist: BMG Distribution

Cassette: released on Motown, Oct'81 by Motown Records. Dist: BMG Distribution

YES IT'S YOU LADY.
Album: released on Motown, Mar'82 by Motown Records. Dist: BMG Distribution

Cassette: released on Motown, Mar'82 by Motown Records. Dist: BMG Distribution

YOU ARE FOREVER/I HEAR THE....
Single (7"): released on Motown, Oct'81 by Motown Records. Dist: BMG Distribution

Robinson, Spike

AT CHESTERS VOL.2 (Robinson, Spike/Eddie Thompson Trio).
Album: released on Hep, Jan'87 by H.R. Taylor Records. Dist: Jazz Music, Cadillac Music, JSU, Taylors, Wellard, Chris, Zodiac, Swift, Fast Forward

MUSIC OF HARRY WARREN (Robinson, Spike Quartet).
Album: released on Discovery, Jun'83 Dist: PRT

SPIKE ROBINSON/TOMMY POLLARD'S DOWNBEAT FIVE/VICTOR FELDMAN (Robinson,Spike/Tommy Pollard's Downbeat Five/Victor Feldman).
Album: released on Esquire, Jun'86 by Titan International Productions. Dist: Jazz Music, Cadillac Music, Swift, Wellard, Chris, Backs, Rough Trade, Revolver, Nine Mile

Robinson,Sugar Chile

GO BOY GO.
Album: released on Oldie Blues (Holland), Dec'84

JUNIOR JUMP.
Tracks: / Go boy go / Say little girl / Bases were loaded / Sticks and stones / Whop whop / Yancey special / I'll eat my spinach / Caldonia / Numbers boogie / Frustration boogie / Lazy boys boogie / Bounding ball boogie / After school blues / Christmas boogie.
Album: released on Charly, Jun'86 by Charly Records. Dist: Charly, Cadillac

Robinson, Tom

2.4.6.8 MOTORWAY/DON'T TAKE NO FOR AN ANSWER.
Single (7"): released on Old Gold (Reissue), Oct'83

2.4.6.8 MOTORWAY/I SHALL BE RELEASED.
Single (7"): released on EMI, Oct'77 by EMI Records. Dist: EMI

ATMOSPHERICS (5 TRACK EP).
Single (12"): released on Panic, Feb'83 by Tom Robinson.

BACK IN THE OLD COUNTRY.
Single (7"): released on Castaway, Jun'84 by RCA Records. Dist: RCA

Single (12"): released on Castaway, Jun'84 by RCA Records. Dist: RCA

CABARET '79.
Album: released on Teldec (Germany), Apr'84 by Import Records. Dist: IMS Distribution, Polygram Distribution

Album: released on Panic, Nov'82 by Tom Robinson.

FEELS SO GOOD.
Tracks: / Northern rain / You tattoed me / Change.
Single (7"): released on Castaway, Jan'87 by RCA Records. Dist: RCA

HOPE AND GLORY.
Album: released on Castaway, Sep'84 by RCA Records. Dist: RCA

Cassette: released on Castaway, Sep'84 by RCA Records. Dist: RCA

LISTEN TO THE RADIO:ATMOSPHERICS.
Single (7"): released on Panic, Nov'83 by Tom Robinson.

Single (12"): released on Panic, Nov'83 by Tom Robinson.

LIVE- MIDNIGHT AT THE FRINGE (Robinson, Tom and Crew).
Tracks: / Atmospherics / Night time, The / Cabin boy / Surabaya Johnny / Bonfire / Back in the old country / Old friend / War baby / Never gonna fall in love (again) / Blond & blue.
Album: released on Dojo, Mar'87 by Castle Communications Records. Dist: Cartel

Compact disc: released on Dojo, '86 by Castle Communications Records. Dist: Cartel

NORTH BY NORTHWEST.
Compact disc: released on Castle Classics, '86 by Castle Communications. Dist: BMG

NOW MARTIN'S GONE.
Single (7"): released on Panic, Jul'82 by Tom Robinson.

Single (12"): released on Panic, Jul'82 by Tom Robinson.

POWER IN THE DARKNESS.
Album: released on EMI, Aug'83 by EMI Records. Dist: EMI

Cassette: released on EMI, Aug'83 by EMI Records. Dist: EMI Deleted May'87.

PRISON.
Single (7"): released on Castaway, May'85 by RCA Records. Dist: RCA

Single (12"): released on Castaway, May'85 by RCA Records. Dist: RCA

REAL THING,THE.
Tracks: / Real thing,The / Wedding,The / (It ain't nothing like) the real thing.
Single (7"): released on RCA, Jun'86 by RCA Records. Dist: RCA, Roots, Swift, Wellard, Chris, I & B, Solomon & Peres Distribution

Single (12"): released on RCA, Jun'86 by RCA Records. Dist: RCA, Roots, Swift, Wellard, Chris, I & B, Solomon & Peres Distribution

RIKKI DON'T LOSE THAT NUMBER.
Single (7"): released on Castaway, Aug'84 by RCA Records. Dist: RCA

Single (12"): released on Castaway, Aug'84 by RCA Records. Dist: RCA

SECTOR 27.
Cassette: released on EMI, Jul'80 by EMI Records. Dist: EMI

Album: released on EMI, Jul'80 by EMI Records. Dist: EMI

SPAIN.
Tracks: / Spain / Drive all night / Nothing like the real thing.
Single (7"): released on RCA, May'87 by RCA Records. Dist: RCA, Roots, Swift, Wellard, Chris, I & B, Solomon & Peres Distribution

Single (12"): released on RCA, May'87 by RCA Records. Dist: RCA, Roots, Swift, Wellard, Chris, I & B, Solomon & Peres Distribution

STILL LOVING YOU.
Tracks: / Feel so good /hurt so bad / Nothing like the real thing / Still loving you / Take me home again / You tattooed me / Drive all night / Living in a love town / Spain / This little romance / Wedding / Still loving you / Saturday disco,The.
Album: released on RCA, Aug'86 by RCA Records. Dist: RCA, Roots, Swift, Wellard, Chris, I & B, Solomon & Peres Distribution

Cassette: released on RCA, Aug'86 by RCA Records. Dist: RCA, Roots, Swift, Wellard, Chris, I & B, Solomon & Peres Distribution

Compact disc: released on RCA, Aug'86 by RCA Records. Dist: RCA, Roots, Swift, Wellard, Chris, I & B, Solomon & Peres Distribution

Single (7"): released on Castaway, Aug'86 by RCA Records. Dist: RCA

Single (12"): released on Castaway, Aug'86 by RCA Records. Dist: RCA

TANGO AN DER WAND.
Single (7"): released on IMS, Dec'81 by Polydor Records. Dist: IMS, Polygram

TRB TWO.
Album: released on EMI, Aug'83 by EMI Records. Dist: EMI

Cassette: released on EMI, Aug'83 by EMI Records. Dist: EMI Deleted May'87.

WAR BABY/HELL YES /MARTIN GONE.
Single (7"): released on Panic, Jun'83 by Tom Robinson.

Single (12"): released on Panic, Jun'83 by Tom Robinson.

Robinson, Vicki Sue

MOVIN' ON.
Album: released on RCA, Oct'79 by RCA Records. Dist: RCA, Roots, Swift, Wellard, Chris, I & B, Solomon & Peres Distribution

NEVER GONNA LET YOU GO.
Album: released on RCA, Jul'76 by RCA Records. Dist: RCA, Roots, Swift, Wellard, Chris, I & B, Solomon & Peres Distribution

Robinson,Vikki Su

TURN THE BEAT AROUND.
Tracks: / Turn the beat around / Rock the boat.
Single (7"): released on Old Gold, Nov'86 by Old Gold Records. Dist: Lightning, Jazz Music, Spartan, Counterpoint

Robin & The Mad Professor

MYSTIC LOVING.
Single (12"): released on Ariwa, Jul'82 by Ariwa Records. Dist: Revolver, Cartel, Jetstar, Rough Trade

Robles, Marisa

NARNIA SUITE, (THE) Inspired by the chronicles of narnia by C.S Lewis.
Album: released on ASV, Nov'81 by Academy Sound & Vision Records. Dist: Pinnacle

Cassette: released on ASV, Nov'81 by Academy Sound & Vision Records. Dist: Pinnacle

Robot

DISCOMEDY A.
Album: released on Pye, Jun'78

Robotiks

MAN & MACHINE.
Album: released on Ariwa, Jun'85 by Ariwa Records. Dist: Revolver, Cartel, Jetstar, Rough Trade

MY COMPUTER'S ACTING STRANGE.
Album: released on Ariwa, May'86 by Ariwa Records. Dist: Revolver, Cartel, Jetstar, Rough Trade

Robotman & Friends

I WANNA BE YOUR ROBOTMAN.
Tracks: / I wanna be your Robotman / Hi tech heart touch.
Single (7"): released on Columbia, Feb'86 by EMI Records. Dist: EMI

Robots of dawn

ISAAC ASIMOV.
Cassette: released on Caedmon(USA), Jan'84 by Caedmon (USA) Records. Dist: Gower, Taylors, Discovery

ROBOTS OF DAWN, THE Asimov, Isaac (Asimov, Isaac).
Cassette: released on Caedmon(USA), '84 by Caedmon (USA) Records. Dist: Gower, Taylors, Discovery

Robson Carolyn

BANKS OF TYNE.
Album: released on Dingles, Jan'83 by Dingles Records. Dist: Projection

Rocca, John

EXTRA EXTRA.
Album: released on Citybeat, Jul'87 Dist: WEA

Cassette: released on Citybeat, Jul'87 Dist: WEA

Compact disc: released on Citybeat, Jul'87 Dist: WEA

I WANT IT TO BE REAL.
Tracks: / I want it to be real / Club vocal mix / I want it to be real (club vocal) / Basement beats / Farley's hot house piano mix / I want it to be real (Alternate dance mix).
Single (7"): released on Citybeat, Mar'87 Dist: WEA

Single (12"): released on Citybeat, Mar'87 Dist: WEA

ONCE UPON A TIME.
Album: released on Beggars Banquet, Nov'84 by Beggars Banquet Records. Dist: WEA

Cassette: released on Beggars Banquet, Nov'84 by Beggars Banquet Records. Dist: WEA

Rocha, Sebastiao

BRAZIL 99.
Album: released on Sunset (France), Sep'84 Dist: IMS-Polygram Distribution

Rochdale Band

CRUSADERS.
Album: released on Grosvenor, Jun'77 by Grosvenor Records. Dist: Taylors

Rochdale Fairies

THREE GREEN BOTTLES.
Single (7"): released on SNT, Dec'83 by SNT Records. Dist: ILA, SNT

Rochdale Wilsons Band

BRASS BAND ON THE MARCH.
Album: released on Parade, Oct'80 Dist: MSD

Cassette: released on Parade, Oct'80 Dist: MSD

Roche, Betty

TAKE THE A TRAIN.
Album: released on Affinity, Jul'87 by Charly Records. Dist: Charly, Cadillac

Roche, David

ALL IRELAND CHAMPION BUTTON ACCORDION.
Album: released on Greenwich Village, Jun'81 by Sweet Folk All Records. Dist: Roots, Projection, Lightning, Celtic Music, Wellard, Chris

Rochee & the Sarnos

SARNO FEVER.
Single (7"): released on Kay-Y, Mar'84 by Kay-Y Records. Dist: Rough Trade

---

UNDERSTANDING SARNOS.
Album: released on Nervous, Aug'85 by Nervous Records. Dist: Nervous, Rough Trade

---

WHISTLE WRIGGLE.
Single (7"): released on Nervous, Jun'85 by Nervous Records. Dist: Nervous, Rough Trade

Rochelle

MY MAGIC MAN.
Tracks: / My magic man / Machine gun dub.
Single (7"): released on Warner Bros., Jan'86 by Warner Bros Records. Dist: WEA

Single (12"): released on Warner Bros., Jan'86 by Warner Bros Records. Dist: WEA

Roches

KEEP ON DOING.
Album: released on Warner Brothers, Oct'82 by WEA Records. Dist: WEA

Cassette: released on Warner Brothers, Oct'82 by WEA Records. Dist: WEA

LOSING TRUE.
Single (7"): released on Warner Brothers, Nov'82 by WEA Records. Dist: WEA

ROCHES, THE.
Album: released on WEA, Sep'79 by WEA Records. Dist: WEA

Rochester

VEASLEY BAND.
Album: released on Gramavision (USA), Dec'85 by Gramavison Records (USA). Dist: PRT, IMS, Polygram

Rock...

ROCK EXPRESS Various original artists (Various Artists).
Album: released on Bulldog Records, '82

ROCK FROM THE CAROLINAS (Various Artists).
Album: released on White Label, Feb'87 by White Label Records. Dist: Jetstar

---

ROCK FURY Various Artists (Various Artists).
Tracks: / Radar love / Boys are back in town,The / Freebird / Cat scratch fever / Hold your head up / What you're propsing / Career of evil / Hit me with your best shot (live) / Funk no.48 / Spaceman / Natural born boogie.
Album: released on Raw Power, Apr'86 Dist: Pinnacle

Cassette: released on Raw Power, Apr'86 Dist: Pinnacle

ROCK GIANTS (Various Artists).
Compact disc: released on Delta, '86 by Delta Records. Dist: Target

---

ROCK HEROES (Various Artists).
Album: released on Pickwick, Sep'79 by Pickwick Records. Dist: Pickwick Distribution, Prism Leisure Distribution, Lugtons

Cassette: released on Pickwick, Sep'79 by Pickwick Records. Dist: Pickwick Distribution, Prism Leisure Distribution, Lugtons

---

ROCK HOUSE (Various Artists).
Album: released on Ronco, Oct'81

Cassette: released on Ronco, Oct'81

ROCK LEGENDS Various artists (Various Artists).
Album: released on Telstar, Oct'86 by Telstar Records. Dist: RCA Distribution

Album: released on Telstar, Oct'86 by Telstar Records. Dist: RCA Distribution

Cassette: released on Pickwick, Sep'80 by Pickwick Records. Dist: Pickwick Distribution, Prism Leisure Distribution, Lugtons

Album: released on Pickwick, Sep'80 by Pickwick Records. Dist: Pickwick Distribution, Prism Leisure Distribution, Lugtons

---

ROCK MACHINE Various Artists (Various Artists).
Album: released on Action Replay, Nov'85 by Action Replay Records. Dist: PRT

Cassette: released on Action Replay, Nov'85 by Action Replay Records. Dist: PRT

ROCK MACHINE...STILL TURNS YOU ON (Various Artists).
Album: released on Epic, May'83 by CBS Records. Dist: CBS

Cassette: released on Epic, May'83 by CBS Records. Dist: CBS

ROCK ME ALL NIGHT LONG Various Artists (Various Artists).
Notes: Full title: Rock Me All Night Long-J.D. Miller Series Vol.41.
Album: released on Flyright, Nov'85 by Flyright Records. Dist: Krazy Kat, Swift, Jazz Music

---

ROCK-ON-ROLL-ON (Various Artists).
Album: released on White Label (Holland), Mar'84 Dist: CSA, PRT

ROCK ON THROUGH THE SIXTIES (Various Artists).
Album: released on MFP, Feb'80 by EMI Records. Dist: EMI

ROCK PRETTY (Various Artists).
Album: released on Heavy Metal, Jan'85 by FM-Revolver Records. Dist: EMI

Album: released on Heavy Metal, Jan'85 by FM-Revolver Records. Dist: EMI
Cat. no: **HMR LP 25 (Pink Vinyl)**

ROCK REVIVAL various artists (Various Artists).
Double Album: released on K-Tel, Feb'79 by K-Tel Records. Dist: Record Merchandisers Distribution, Taylors, Terry Blood Distribution, Wynd-Up Distribution, Relay Distribution, Pickwick Distribution, Solomon & Peres Distribution, Polygram

---

ROCK SHOP various artists (Various Artists).
Album: released on Hallmark, Mar'82 by Pickwick Records. Dist: Pickwick Distribution, PRT, Taylors

Cassette: released on Hallmark, Mar'82 by Pickwick Records. Dist: Pickwick Distribution, PRT, Taylors

---

ROCK SOCK THE BOOGIE various artists (Various Artists).
Album: released on Charly, Sep'84 by Charly Records. Dist: Charly, Cadillac

---

ROCK SUPERSTARS VOL 1 various artists (Various Artists).
Album: released on Pickwick, May'79 by Pickwick Records. Dist: Pickwick Distribution, Prism Leisure Distribution, Lugtons

Cassette: released on Pickwick, May'79 by Pickwick Records. Dist: Pickwick Distribution, Prism Leisure Distribution, Lugtons

---

ROCK THE FLAG various artists (Various Artists).
Album: released on Magnum Force, May'83 by Magnum Music Group Ltd. Dist: Magnum Music Group Ltd, PRT, Spartan

Rockabilly...

ROCKABILLY Various artists (Various Artists).

Album: released on Mercury (USA), Nov'81 by Import Records. Dist: IMS Distribution, Polygram Distribution

Cassette: released on Mercury (USA), Nov'81 by Import Records. Dist: IMS Distribution, Polygram Distribution

---

ROCKABILLY BASH Various artists (Various Artists).
Album: released on Bopallacious, Jun'85 Dist: Swift

ROCK-A-BILLY BLUES Harious Artists (Various Artists).
Tracks: / Blues at midnight / Hey Slim / Bottle to the baby / Drinkin' scotch / Pop and mamma / You can't make love to somebody / Crawdad hole / They can't keep me from you / Fool for lovin' you,A / Hey Jim / Uh babe / Go ahead baby / Slow down / Sign on the dotted line.
Album: released on Sun, May'86 by Charly Records. Dist: Charly Distribution

---

ROCK A BILLY BOPPIN' Various artists (Various Artists).
Album: released on White, Jul'87

ROCKABILLY BOP VOL.1 (Various Artists).
Tracks: / Look kat / Little jewel / Hard hearted girl / Rocky road blues / Flat top box / Got rockin' on my mind / Got the best of me / Hey Mr. Poter / Rocket on the moon / Curfew cop / Robinson Crusoe bop / Hey doll baby / Cloud 13 / Rockin' Rochester.
Album: released on Esoldun, Dec'86 by Esoldun Records. Dist: Swift

---

ROCKABILLY BOP VOL.2 (Various Artists).
Tracks: / Alley cat / Jelly roll rock / Teenage ball / Night club r'n'roll / Come to your Tommy now / Dig me a crazy record / Gee whiz Liz / Saturday night party / Pretty Kitty / Big Sandy / Rattle shakin' mama / That big old moon / Rockin' with r'n'b / Calypso boogie.
Album: released on Esoldun, Dec'86 by Esoldun Records. Dist: Swift

---

ROCKABILLY BOP VOL.3 (Various Artists).
Tracks: / Cat all night / It's night / Juke box Johnnie / Pretty woman blues / How about me? / Cat daddy / 21 carpenters / Let's all go wild / Drinkin' wine / Walk me back home / Moonshine liquor / Tuscaloosa Lucy / Tight slacks / I dreamed I was Elvis.
Album: released on Esoldun, Dec'86 by Esoldun Records. Dist: Swift

---

ROCKABILLY CRAZY Various original artists (Various original artists).
Album: released on Charly, Feb'82 by Charly Records. Dist: Charly, Cadillac

---

ROCKABILLY FEVER Various original artists (Various original artists).
Album: released on Charly, Feb'82 by Charly Records. Dist: Charly, Cadillac

---

ROCKABILLY FROM TENNESSEE Various artists (Various Artists).
Album: released on White Label, Jul'79 by White Label Records. Dist: Jetstar

---

ROCKABILLY FROM TENNESSEE VOL.2 Various artists (Various Artists).
Album: released on White Label, Jul'79 by White Label Records. Dist: Jetstar

---

ROCKABILLY GREATEST HITS Various Artists (Various Artists).
Album: released on Astan, Nov'84 by Astan Records. Dist: Counterpoint

Album: released on Astan, Nov'84 by Astan Records. Dist: Counterpoint

---

ROCKABILLY JAMBOREE Various artists (Various Artists).
Album: released on Charly, Sep'81 by Charly Records. Dist: Charly, Cadillac

---

ROCK-A-BILLY LEGENDS Various session artists (Various Session Artists).
Cassette: released on AIM (Budget Cassettes), Sep'83

ROCKABILLY PARTY Various artists (Various Artists).
Album: released on Ace, Jul'79 by Ace Records. Dist: Pinnacle, Swift, Hotshot, Cadillac

---

ROCKABILLY PSYCHOSIS & THE GARAGE DISEASE Various artists (Various Artists).
Album: released on Big Beat, Jun'84 by Ace Records. Dist: Projection, Pinnacle

---

ROCKABILLY PSYCHOSIS Various artists (Various Artists).
Cassette: released on Big Beat, Jan'85 by Ace Records. Dist: Projection, Pinnacle

---

ROCKABILLY REBELS Various artists (Various Artists).
Album: released on Hallmark, Jul'84 by Pickwick Records. Dist: Pickwick Distribution, PRT, Taylors

Cassette: released on Hallmark, Jul'84 by Pickwick Records. Dist: Pickwick Distribution, PRT, Taylors

Album: released on Cambra, Apr'85 by Cambra Records. Dist: IDS, Conifer

Cassette: released on Cambra, Apr'85 by Cambra Records. Dist: IDS, Conifer

---

ROCKABILLY RULES U.K. Original various artists (Various Artists).
Album: released on Charly, Apr'78 by Charly Records. Dist: Charly, Cadillac

---

ROCKABILLY SHAKEOUT - NUMBER 1 Carious Artists (Various Artists).
Album: released on Ace, Nov'86 by Ace Records. Dist: Pinnacle, Swift, Hotshot, Cadillac

Cassette: released on Ace, Nov'86 by Ace Records. Dist: Pinnacle, Swift, Hotshot, Cadillac

---

ROCK-A-BILLY TIME (Various Artists).
Notes: The best of Linn & Kliff.
Album: released on White, Apr'87

ROCKABILLY TUNES Various artists (Various Artists).
Album: released on Sun, Apr'85 by Charly Records. Dist: Charly Distribution

---

ROCK-A-BILLY WORLD Carious Artists (Various Artists).
Album: released on White, Oct'86

Rockabilly Rebels

REBELS TILL THE END.
Album: released on JSP, Apr'82 by JSP Records. Dist: Swift, Projection

Rockabilly Rebs.

BOPPIN' BULLFROG/ RAGBONES.
Single (7"): released on Small Run, May'83 by Small Run Records. Dist: Pinnacle

Rock along ....

ROCK ALONG .... Various artists (Various Artists).
Album: released on White Label (Holland), Jun'85 Dist: CSA, PRT

Rock and Hyde

DIRTY WATER.
Tracks: / Dirty water (single) / Dirty water (version 1) / Dirty water (dance version) / Middle of the night / Dirty Water (version 2) / Dirty Water (version 3).
Double-pack single: released on EMI, Mar'87 by EMI Records. Dist: EMI

Single (7"): released on EMI, Mar'87 by EMI Records. Dist: EMI

Single (12"): released on EMI, Mar'87 by EMI Records. Dist: EMI

UNDER THE VOLCANO.
Tracks: / Dirty water / I will / Blind, the deaf and the lame (The) / Knocking on closed doors / What children say / Talk to me / Middle of the night / There is always someone tougher / It's always raining / Blind, the deaf, and the lame, The / Oh Ruby.
Notes: *Under the volcano* is the debut album from Bob Rock and Paul Hyde known as *Rock and Hyde*. This ten track album is without doubt one of the most strongest debut albums recorded in recent years. The tracks show a depth of talent one would normally associate with an established act. The album has several hit singles on it plus a couple of potential *classics*. The album has been produced by Bruce Fairbarn whose credits include Blue Oyster Cult, right through to his most recent number one single and album from Bon Jovi; incidentlly, it should be noted that Bob Rock himself has mixed and engineered hits for Donna Summer and Bon Jovi. [EMI release sheet, April 87].
Album: released on EMI, Apr'87 by EMI Records. Dist: EMI

Cassette: released on EMI America, Apr'87 by EMI Records. Dist: EMI

Compact disc: released on EMI America, Apr'87 by EMI Records. Dist: EMI

Compact disc: released on EMI, May'87 by EMI Records. Dist: EMI

Rock and rhythm

ROCK AND RHYTHM Various artists (Various Artists).
Album: released on White Label, Jul'79 by White Label Records. Dist: Jetstar

Rock and roll...

ROCK AND ROLL AT THE CAPITOL TOWER (VOL 3) Various artists (Various original artists).
Album: released on EMI (France), Jun'83 by EMI Records. Dist: Conifer

Page 848

ROCK AND ROLL AT THE CAPITOL TOWER (VOL 1) Various original artists (Various original artists).
Album: released on EMI (France), Jun'83 by EMI Records. Dist: Conifer

ROCK AND ROLL AT THE CAPITOL TOWER (VOL 2) Various original artists (Various original artists).
Album: released on EMI (France), Jun'83 by EMI Records. Dist: Conifer

ROCK AND ROLL CLASSICS Original artists (Various Artists).
Cassette: released on PRT, Jun'82 by PRT Records. Dist: PRT

ROCK AND ROLL DANCE PARTY Various session artists (Various session artists).
Cassette: released on Aim, Feb'83 Dist: H.R. Taylor

ROCK AND ROLL PILLS Various Artists (Various Artists).
Tracks: / Wild woman / Bop pills / Fire engine red / Sonny boy / Watch that stuff / Sentimental fool / Tootsie / Slow rock and roll / I won't be rockin' tonight / Red velvet / Welcome to the club / Rock 'n' roll cinnamon tree / Call me anything but call me / Voice of a fool.
Album: released on Sun, May'86 by Charly Records. Dist: Charly Distribution

ROCK AND ROLL RADIO 1956 Various artists (Various Artists).
Album: released on Radiola, Apr'79 Dist: Jazz Music, Swift

ROCK AND ROLL' (THE EARLY DAYS) Various Artists (Various Artists).
Tracks: / Sh Boom / Good rockin' Tonight / Hound dog / I'm your Hoochie Coochie man / Shake, rattle and roll / Rock around the clock (we're gonna) / That's all right / Blue sued shoes / Maybelline / Bo diddley / Tutti frutti / Great balls of fire.
Notes: Just look at these names! A classic compilation of the greats of Rock 'n' Roll, from the 1954 'Sh Boom' by the Chords (Life could be a dream.....) to Jerry Lee Lewis's Great Balls Of Fire' - his 1957 No.1 hit, and all that happened in betw-een....this album has them all!.
Album: released on RCA (Germany), Nov'85

Cassette: released on RCA (Germany), Nov'85

Rock anthems

ROCK ANTHEMS Various artists (Various Artists).
Album: released on K-Tel, Nov'85 by K-Tel Records. Dist: Record Merchandisers Distribution, Taylors, Terry Blood Distribution, Wynd-Up Distribution, Relay Distribution, Pickwick Distribution, Solomon & Peres Distribution, Polygram

Cassette: released on K-Tel, Nov'85 by K-Tel Records. Dist: Record Merchandisers Distribution, Taylors, Terry Blood Distribution, Wynd-Up Distribution, Relay Distribution, Pickwick Distribution, Solomon & Peres Distribution, Polygram

ROCK ANTHEMS II Various Artists (Various Artists).
Tracks: / Walk on the wilde side / Don't fear the reaper / Hot blooded / Black Betty / Radar Love / School's out / All along the watchtower / Badge / White light, white heat / For your love / Here comes the night / Nutbush city limits / Fire / Layla / One & one is one / Spanish stroll / Mocking-bird / In a broken dream / Paranoid / Silver machine / Rock 'n' roll star / American woman / We gotta get outta this place / Hi ho silver lining.
Album: released on K-Tel, Nov'86 by K-Tel Records. Dist: Record Merchandisers Distribution, Taylors, Terry Blood Distribution, Wynd-Up Distribution, Relay Distribution, Pickwick Distribution, Solomon & Peres Distribution, Polygram

Cassette: released on K-Tel, Nov'86 by K-Tel Records. Dist: Record Merchandisers Distribution, Taylors, Terry Blood Distribution, Wynd-Up Distribution, Relay Distribution, Pickwick Distribution, Solomon & Peres Distribution, Polygram

Rockaphilly

ROCKAPHILLY - PHILADELPHIA ROCK 'N' ROLL Various artists (Various Artists).
Album: released on Rollercoaster, Sep'84 by Rollercoaster Records. Dist: Swift Distribution, Rollercoaster Distribution

Rock around the clock

ROCK AROUND THE CLOCK Various artists (Various Artists).
Album: released on Premier, '84 by Premier Records. Dist: CBS

Cassette: released on Premier, '84 by Premier Records. Dist: CBS

Rock Around The Dock

ROCK AROUND THE DOCK (VIDEO) (Various Artists).
Notes: Released by Granada Video

Rock bop boogie

ROCK BOP BOOGIE Various artists (Various Artists).
Album: released on Sun, Apr'85 by Charly Records. Dist: Charly Distribution

Rock cocktail

ROCK COCKTAIL.
Video-cassette (VHS): released on CBS, Oct'84 by CBS Records. Dist: CBS

Rock, Dickie

DICKIE.
Album: released on Solo, Jan'76 by Solo Records. Dist: PRT

DICKIE ROCK IN STYLE.
Album: released on Solo, Jan'78 by Solo Records. Dist: PRT

TILL.
Album: released on Harp(Ireland), Jul'80 by Pickwick Records. Dist: Taylors

Cassette: released on Harp(Ireland), Jul'80 by Pickwick Records. Dist: Taylors

Rockers

ROCKERS Film soundtrack.
Album: released on Island, Sep'79 by Island Records. Dist: Polygram

ROCKERS ALL STAR EXPLOSION Various artists (Various Artists).
Album: released on Alligator, Mar'85 Dist: Jetstar

ROCKERS AWARDS WINNERS (Various Artists).
Album: released on Greensleeves, Sep'85 by Greensleeves Records. Dist: BMG, Jetstar, Spartan

Rockers Galore

SARGEANT PEPPER.
Single (7"): released on Jive, Jul'87 by Zomba Records. Dist: RCA, PRT, CBS

Single (12"): released on Jive, Jul'87 by Zomba Records. Dist: RCA, PRT, CBS

Rockers Revenge

HARDER THEY COME.
Single (7"): released on London, Jan'83 by London Records. Dist: Polygram

Single (12"): released on London, Jan'83 by London Records. Dist: Polygram

WALKIN' ON SUNSHINE.
Single (7"): released on London, Jul'82 by London Records. Dist: Polygram

Single (12"): released on London, Jul'82 by London Records. Dist: Polygram

Rocket

I WANT TO KNOW/ IT KEEPS ME....
Single (7"): released on Virgin, Nov'82 by Virgin Records. Dist: EMI, Virgin Distribution

Single (12"): released on Virgin, Nov'82 by Virgin Records. Dist: EMI, Virgin Distribution

Rocket 88

ROCKET 88.
Album: released on Atlantic, Mar'81 by WEA Records. Dist: WEA

Rockets

LOVE TRANSFUSION.
Album: released on RCA, Jun'78 by RCA Records. Dist: RCA, Roots, Swift, Wellard, Chris, I & B, Solomon & Peres Distribution

NO BALLADS.
Album: released on RSO, May'80

TURN UP THE RADIO.
Album: released on RSO, Aug'79

Rockfella

ROCKAFELLA Various artists (Various Artists).
Album: released on Stage Two, Apr'81 by Penthouse Records. Dist: Pinnacle

Rockfile 11

ROCKFILE 11 Various artists (Various Artists).
Album: released on Magnum Force, Apr'83 by Magnum Music Group Ltd. Dist: Magnum Music Group Ltd, PRT, Spartan

Rock Follies

ROCK FOLLIES.
Album: released on Polydor, Feb'77 by Polydor Records. Dist: Polygram, Polydor

ROCK FOLLIES OF 1977.
Album: released on Polydor, Jun'77 by Polydor Records. Dist: Polygram, Polydor

Rock Goddess

HELL HATH NO FURY.
Cassette: released on A&M, Oct'83 by A&M Records. Dist: Polygram

MY ANGEL/ IN THE HEAT OF THE NIGHT.
Single (7"): released on A&M, Feb'83 by A&M Records. Dist: Polygram

Single (12"): released on A&M, Feb'83 by A&M Records. Dist: Polygram

ROCK GODDESS.
Album: released on A&M, Mar'83 by A&M Records. Dist: Polygram

Cassette: released on A&M, Mar'83 by A&M Records. Dist: Polygram

Rockies

STOP WASTING YOUR TIME.
Single (7"): released on 10, Oct'84 by 10 Records. Dist: Virgin, EMI

Rockin'...

ROCKIN' 50'S Various artists (Various Artists).
Album: released on Magnum Force, Jan'87 by Magnum Music Group Ltd. Dist: Magnum Music Group Ltd, PRT, Spartan

ROCKIN' AGAIN AT THE 2 1'S Various artists (Various Artists).
Album: released on Ace, Sep'83 by Ace Records. Dist: Pinnacle, Swift, Hotshot, Cadillac

ROCKIN' AND BOPPIN' (Various Artists).
Tracks: / Dis a itty bit / Makin' love with... / Rock on baby / Cool baby / Rhythm guitar / Boppin guitar / I'm out / Batman / Sweet rockin' mama / Chicken rock / Yeah, Yeah, My baby / My minds make up / Funny feeling / Long legged Linda.
Album: released on Esoldun, Dec'86 by Esoldun Records. Dist: Swift

ROCKIN' AND ROLLIN' Various artists (Various Artists).
Cassette: released on Ditto Cassettes, Sep'83

ROCKIN' AT THE HOP VOL.1 Harious artists (Various Artists).
Cassette: released on VFM Cassettes, Jan'85

ROCKIN' AT THE HOP VOL.2 Various artists (Various Artists).
Cassette: released on VFM Cassettes, Jan'85
Cat. no: **VCA 095**

ROCKIN' CHRISTMAS THE 50'S Various artists (Various Artists).
Album: released on Rhino (USA), Feb'85 by Rhino Records (USA).

ROCKIN' COUNTRY SIDES Various artists (Various Artists).
Album: released on Sun, Aug'85 by Charly Records. Dist: Charly Distribution

ROCKIN' IN LOUISIANA VOL. 3 Various artists (Various Artists).
Album: released on White, Jul'87

ROCKIN' IN LOUISIANA VOL. 1 Various artists (Various Artists).
Album: released on White, Jul'87

ROCKIN' IN RHYTHM Various artists (Various Artists).
Album: released on Affinity, Jun'86 by Charly Records. Dist: Charly, Cadillac

ROCKIN' ON TOP Various artists (Various Artists).
Album: released on Goldband, Sep'84 by Charly Records. Dist: Charly

ROCKIN' RHYTHMS Various artists (Various Artists).
Cassette: released on K-Tel Goldmasters, Aug'84 by K-Tel Records. Dist: K-Tel

ROCKIN' THIS JOINT TONITE Various artists (Various Artists).
Album: released on JSP, Jan'82 by JSP Records. Dist: Swift, Projection

Rockin' Berries

HE'S IN TOWN/ POOR MAN'S SON.
Single (7"): released on Flashback, Apr'79 by Flashback Records/PRT Records. Dist: Mainline, PRT

Rockin' Date ...

ROCKIN' DATE WITH SOUTH LOUISIANA STARS Various artists (Various Artists).
Album: Dist: Swift

Rockin' Dopsie

BIG BAD ZYDECO (Rockin' Dopsie & His Cajun Twisters).
Album: released on Sonet, Nov'80 by Sonet Records. Dist: PRT

CROWN PRINCE OF ZYDECO.
Album: released on Sonet, Mar'87 by Sonet Records. Dist: PRT

DOING THE ZYDECO (Rockin' Dopsie And The Twisters).
Album: released on Sonet, Jul'77 by Sonet Records. Dist: PRT

FRENCH STYLE (Rockin' Dopsie & His Cajun Twisters).
Album: released on Sonet, Feb'82 by Sonet Records. Dist: PRT

HOLD ON (Rockin' Dopsie & His Cajun Twisters).
Album: released on Sonet, Sep'79 by Sonet Records. Dist: PRT

ROCKIN' WITH DUPSEE.
Tracks: / Woman I don't want your troubles / Things I used to do / Night and day / You told me baby / Ma Negresse / She's my little girl / Rockin' with Dupsee / Don't you want a man like me / Oh Negresse / Dupsee shuffle / Don't let the green grass fool you.
Album: released on Flyright, Oct'86 by Flyright Records. Dist: Krazy Kat, Swift, Jazz Music

ZY-DE-BLUE (Rockin' Dopsie And The Twisters).
Album: released on Sonet, Aug'78 by Sonet Records. Dist: PRT

Rockin' Dupree

ROCKIN' WITH.
Album: released on Flyright, May'83 by Flyright Records. Dist: Krazy Kat, Swift, Jazz Music

Rocking..

ROCKING DATE WITH SOUTH LOUISIANA,A various artists (Various Artists).
Album: released on Jin, Feb'79 Dist: Swift

ROCKING FIFTIES (Various Artists).
Notes: Including Eddie Cochran, Chuck Berry.
Album: released on Trax Baby Boomer Classics, Apr'87

Cassette: released on Trax Baby Boomer Classics, Apr'87

ROCKING FROM HOLLYWOOD TO GRONINGEN various artists (Various Artists).
Album: released on Dial, Apr'79

ROCKING MASTERS (Various Artists).
Album: released on White, Apr'87

ROCKING SIXTIES (Various Artists).
Notes: Including The Who, T.Rex
Album: released on Trax Baby Boomer Classics, Apr'87

Cassette: released on Trax Baby Boomer Classics, Apr'87

ROCKING WON'T STOP Various Artists (Various Artists).
Album: released on Lost Moment, Jun'86

Rockin' Jimmy

BY THE LIGHT OF THE MOON (Rockin'Jimmy And The Brothers Of Night).
Album: released on Sonet, Mar'81 by Sonet Records. Dist: PRT

ROCKIN' ALL NITE (Rockin'Jimmy And The Brothers Of Night).
Single (7"): released on Sonet, May'83 by Sonet Records. Dist: PRT

ROCKIN' JIMMY AND THE BROTHERS OF NIGHT (Rockin'Jimmy And The Brothers Of Night).
Album: released on Sonet, Jun'86 by Sonet Records. Dist: PRT

Rockin' Johnny

ALL THE TIME EP.
Single (7"): released on Nervous, Apr'80 by Nervous Records. Dist: Nervous, Rough Trade

MEETS THE FEDS.
Single (7"): released on Nervous, Jun'81 by Nervous Records. Dist: Nervous, Rough Trade

Rockin' Louie

IT WILL STAND (Rockin' Louie & Mama Jammers).
Album: released on Charly, Apr'80 by Charly Records. Dist: Charly, Cadillac

Rockin' Renegades

TEENAGER IN LOVE/ ROCKIN' CHAIR.
Single (7"): released on Zone To Zone, Nov'83 by Zone To Zone Records. Dist: Pinnacle

Rockin' Robin

PLAY THAT FUNKY MUSIC.
Single (12"): released on Debut, Apr'85 by Skratch Music. Dist: PRT

Rockin' Rollin'...

ROCKIN' ROLLIN' COUNTRY STYLE Various artists (Various Artists).
Album: released on Sun, May'85 by Charly Records. Dist: Charly Distribution

ROCKIN' ROLLIN' HIGH SCHOOL VOL.3 Various artists (Various Artists).
Album: released on Bear Family, Sep'84 by Bear Family Records. Dist: Rollercoaster Distribution, Swift

ROCKIN' ROLLIN' HIGH SCHOOL VOL.4 Various artists (Various Artists).
Album: released on Bear Family, Sep'84 by Bear Family Records. Dist: Rollercoaster Distribution, Swift

ROCKIN' ROLLIN' HIGH SCHOOL VOL.5 Harious artists (Various Artists).
Album: released on Bear Family, Sep'84 by Bear Family Records. Dist: Rollercoaster Distribution, Swift

ROCKIN' ROLLIN' HIGH SCHOOL VOL.6 Various artists (Various Artists).
Album: released on Bear Family, Sep'84 by Bear Family Records. Dist: Rollercoaster Distribution, Swift

ROCKIN' ROLLIN' HIGH SCHOOL VOL.7 Various artists (Various Artists).
Album: released on Bear Family, Sep'84 by Bear Family Records. Dist: Rollercoaster Distribution, Swift

Rockin'Sidney

BOOGIE BLUES 'N' ZYDECO.
Album: released on Maison De Soul (USA), Mar'84 Dist: Swift

Album: released on Krazy Kat, Jun'85 Dist: Jazz Music, Swift, Chris Wellard, H.R. Taylor, Charly, Hotshot, IRS Distribution

GIVE ME A GOOD TIME WOMAN.
Album: Dist: Swift

LOUISIANA CREOLE MAN/GOOD TIME.
Single (7"): released on Bally Hoo (USA), Dec'82 Dist: Swift

MY TOOT TOOT.
Album: released on Ace, Mar'86 by Ace Records. Dist: Pinnacle, Swift, Hotshot, Cadillac

Single (7"): released on Ace, Sep'85 by Ace Records. Dist: Pinnacle, Swift, Hotshot, Cadillac

MY ZYDECO SHOES Got the zydeco blues.
Album: Dist: Swift

PLAY JOLI BLON FOR ME.
Single (7"): released on Bally Hoo (USA), Nov'82 Dist: Swift

SCOOP,THE/I'M NOT GONNA SPEND...
Single (7"): released on Bally Hoo (USA), Dec'82 Dist: Swift

SHOW ME WHERE IT ITCHES/WET EYES.
Single (7"): released on Bally Hoo (USA), Dec'82 Dist: Swift

THEY CALL ME ROCKIN'.
Album: released on Flyright, Jun'85 by Flyright Records. Dist: Krazy Kat, Swift, Jazz Music

Rockit

RED CADILLAC & A BLACK MOUSTACHE.
Single (7"): released on Revolver, Jun'81 by Revolver Records. Dist: Revolver, Cartel

ROCK IT VOL 1 Various artists (Various Artists).
Album: released on Rockhouse, Sep'84 by Rockhouse Records. Dist: Swift Distribution, Charly Distribution

ROCK IT VOL 2 Various artists (Various Artists).
Album: released on Rockhouse, Jul'85 by Rockhouse Records. Dist: Swift Distribution, Charly Distribution

Rock It Baby Rock It

ROCK IT BABY ROCK IT Original Soundtrack (Various Artists).
Notes: Featuring: Johnny Carroll/Rosco Gordon/Preacher Smith/Etc. MONO.
Album: released on Rhino (USA), Jan'86 by Rhino Records (USA).

Rockleodeon

MUSIC MUSIC MUSIC/I GOT HITCHED.
Single (7"): released on Technical, Jun'82 Dist: Stage One Distribution

Rock'n'Roll

I JUST WANNA RAP.
Single (7"): released on Magnetic Dance, Aug'87 by Magnetic Dance Records. Dist: BMG

Single (12"): released on Magnetic Dance, Aug'87 by Magnetic Dance Records. Dist: BMG

ROCK'N'ROLL 16 classic hits (Various Artists).
Album: released on Everest (Premier), '83 by Everest Records. Dist: Pinnacle

Cassette: released on Everest (Premier), '83 by Everest Records. Dist: Pinnacle

ROCK'N'ROLL BEAT Various Artists (Various Artists).
Tracks: / Do baby do / Me and my baby / Mickey Lee / Oh baby what can I do / On the corner of the street / All by myself / Plant you know / Jump and shout / Big boy blue / Girls girls girls / Rock and roll beat / Rock me mama / My baby's cheatin / Eennie meenie mo.
Album: released on Flyright, Oct'86 by Flyright Records. Dist: Krazy Kat, Swift, Jazz Music

ROCK'N'ROLL COLLECTION Various Artists (Various Artists).
Notes: Artists include: Bill Haley/Jerry Lee Lewis/Little Richard/Carl Perkins/Chuck Berry/Etc.
Album: released on Deja Vu, May'86 by Deja Vu Records. Dist: Counterpoint Distribution, Record Services Distribution (Ireland)

Cassette: released on Deja Vu, May'86 by Deja Vu Records. Dist: Counterpoint Distribution, Record Services Distribution (Ireland)

ROCK'N'ROLL GIANTS (Various Artists).
Cassette: released on Gold Label, Apr'81 by White Dove. Dist: Pinnacle

ROCK'N'ROLL GIRLS (Various Artists).
Album: released on White, Jul'87

ROCK'N'ROLL HITS VOL 1 (Various Artists).
Album: released on Polygram (France), Sep'85

Cassette: released on Polygram (France), Sep'85

ROCK'N'ROLL HITS VOL 2 Various artists (Various Artists).
Album: released on Polygram (France), Sep'85

Cassette: released on Polygram (France), Sep'85

ROCK'N'ROLLING BRITAIN Various artists (Various Artists).
Album: released on Decca, Apr'85 by Decca Records. Dist: Polygram

ROCK'N'ROLL IS HERE TO STAY Various artists (Various Artists).
Notes: 17 original tracks by Duane Eddy, Sam the Sham, Johnny & the Hurricanes, B.Bumble etc.
Compact disc: released on Delta, Apr'87 by Delta Records. Dist: Target

ROCK'N'ROLL IS STILL ALIVE Various artists (Various Artists).
Album: released on Charly, Oct'76 by Charly Records. Dist: Charly, Cadillac

ROCK'N'ROLL MAMAS Various artists (Various Artists).
Album: released on Charly(R&B), Dec'84 by Charly Records. Dist: Charly, Cadillac

ROCK'N'ROLL PARTY (Various Artists).
Cassette: released on AIM (Budget Cassettes), Feb'83

ROCK'N'ROLL PARTY 1957-1962 (Various Artists).
Tracks: / Motorbiene (Motorcycle) / Buona Sera / My happiness* / Ein Engel ohine fliguel (I can see an angel walking)* / Lippenstift am jacket (lipstick on my collar) / Oh eh oh ah ah (witch doctor)* / Plitsch pltasch (splish splash)* / Speedy Gonzales / Rock a hula baby* / Fur gabi tu ich alles* / Fraulein / Norman / Ja,heut nacht,Josephine(yes,tonight Josephine) / Kuba rock (I don't you just know it)* / Wundrbares madchen (catch a falling star) / Oh,das war schon (oh lonesome me)* / Lollipop* / Due farbe der liebe (a white sports coat) / Zahn Hag (Oliver Twist) / Japanisches absciedslied.
Compact disc: released on Bear Family, Nov'86 by Bear Family Records. Dist: Rollercoaster Distribution, Swift

ROCK'N'ROLL PARTY MIT TED HEROLD UND ANDEREN TEIL 4 (Various Artists).
Album: released on Bear Family, Sep'84 by Bear Family Records. Dist: Rollercoaster Distribution, Swift

ROCK'N'ROLL PARTY MIT TED HEROLD UND ANDEREN TEIL 3 (Various Artists).
Album: released on Bear Family, Sep'84 by Bear Family Records. Dist: Rollercoaster Distribution, Swift

ROCK'N'ROLL PARTY VOL 5 (Various Artists).
Album: released on Ace, Nov'85 by Ace Records. Dist: Pinnacle, Swift, Hotshot, Cadillac

ROCK'N'ROLL PARTY VOL.6 (Various Artists).
Notes: Artists: Big Boy Myles & Shaw-Wee, Chimes, Crowns, Marvin & Johnny, Gene PillipsJoe Liggins, Arthur Lee Maye & The Crowns, Rod Bernard, Roddy Jackson,Glen Barber,Bob Gaddy, Titans, Jerry Byrne, Don & Dewey, Chuch Higgins.
Album: released on Ace, Jun'86 by Ace Records. Dist: Pinnacle, Swift, Hotshot, Cadillac

ROCK'N'ROLL PARTY VOL 7 (Various Artists).
Album: released on Ace, Jun'87 by Ace Records. Dist: Pinnacle, Swift, Hotshot, Cadillac

ROCK'N'ROLL STORY VOL.1 (Various Artists).
Album: released on Timewind (Germany), Jun'83

ROCK'N'ROLL STORY VOL.3 (Various Artists).
Album: released on Happy Bird (Germany), Aug'83 Dist: Polygram, IMS

Cassette: released on Happy Bird (Germany), Aug'83 Dist: Polygram, IMS

ROCK'N'ROLL STORY VOL.2 (Various Artists).
Album: released on Timewind (Germany), Jun'83

ROCK'N'ROLL SUPERSTARS (Various Artists).
Album: released on Pickwick (Ditto series), Jul'82

ROCK'N'ROLL SURVIVAL SHOW (Rock 'N' Roll Survival Show).
Album: released on Bullseye, Apr'75 Dist: Bullseye Music

ROCK'N'ROLL VOL.1 (Various Artists).
Tracks: / Lucille / Long tall Sally / Blue suede shoes / Honey don't / Be bop a lula / Say mama / Blueberry Hill / I'm gonna be a wheel someday / Maybelline / Reelin' and rockin' / Sheila / Maybe baby / Jungle rock / Silver wings / Get up and get out / Sooting gallery / Rockabilly baby / Crazy little teddy girl / Hey you guys / Maybe that's why I care.
Compact disc: released on The Collection, Apr'87 by Object Enterprises Ltd. Dist: Counterpoint Distribution

Rock'n'Roll Greats

MORE ROCK'N'ROLL GREATS (Various Artists).
Double cassette: released on Pickwick (Ditto series), Jul'82

MORE ROCK 'N' ROLL GREATS various artists (Various Artists).
Cassette: released on Pickwick, Jul'82 by Pickwick Records. Dist: Pickwick Distribution, Prism Leisure Distribution, Lugtons

ROCK'N'ROLL GREATS (Various Artists).
Cassette: released on Pickwick (Ditto series), Jul'82

ROCK'N'ROLL GREATS VOL.1 Various Artists (Various Artists).
Tracks: / Tutti Frutti / That'll be the day / Blueberry hill / Take good care of my baby / Walk don't run / Say mama / Bird dog / Sweet little sixteen / Somethin' else / (We're gonna)Rock around the clock / I'm walkin' / Oh boy / Don't ever change / Why do fools fall in love / Be-bop-a-lula / Summertime blues / You're sixteen, you're beautiful(and you're mine) / Rubber ball.
Notes: Chuck Berry, Little Richard, The Everly Brothers - for the first time on the Music For Pleasure label - Rock 'n' Roll Greats! A superb 18 track compilation of Rock 'n' Roll blockbusters - including "Sweet Little Sixteen". "Bird Dog", "Walk Don't Run", "Tutti Frutti", "Summertime Blues", and many more. A fabulous sleeve sets the tone for this Great Rock 'n' Roll album and cassette.
Album: released on Music For Pleasure (Holland), Apr'86 by EMI Records. Dist: EMI

Cassette: released on Music For Pleasure (Holland), Apr'86 by EMI Records. Dist: EMI

ROCK'N'ROLL GREATS VOL.1 Do you wanna dance (Various Artists).
Album: released on Everest (Premier), '83 by Everest Records. Dist: Pinnacle

Cassette: released on Everest (Premier), '83 by Everest Records. Dist: Pinnacle

ROCK'N'ROLL GREATS VOL.2 Various Artists (Various Artists).
Tracks: / C'mon everybody / Ain't that a shame / Willie and the hand jive / Memphis Tennessee / Dreamin' / Red river rock / Git it / I'm not a juvenile delinquent / Whole lotta shakin' goin' on / At the hop / Great balls of fire / Peggy Sue / Claudette / Three steps to heaven / Blue monday / Blue jean hop / Johnny B.Goode / Good golly Miss Molly.
Notes: Volume 2 of Rock 'n' Roll Greats. 18 more terrific tracks from Jerry Lee Lewis,Johnny & The Hurricanes, Chuck Berry, Johnny Otis, Frankie Lymon, Buddy Holly, etc. With tracks licensed from all over the world, this is Rock 'n' Roll at its best.
Album: released on Music For Pleasure (Holland), Apr'86 by EMI Records. Dist: EMI

Cassette: released on Music For Pleasure (Holland), Apr'86 by EMI Records. Dist: EMI

Rock'n'Roll Years

ROCK'N'ROLL YEARS (1964-1967) Various artists (Various Artists).
Tracks: / Tobacco road / I'm in to something good / You really got me / House of the rising sun / Anyone who had a heart / Leader of the pack / Go now / Here comes the night / Little things / My generation / River deep, mountain high / Keep on running / Sun ain't gonna shine anymore, The / Good vibrations / I can't let go / Dedicated to the one I love / Whiter shade of pale / I'm a believer / San Francisco / All you need is love.
Notes: Compilation from the BBC1 TV series. Artists include: The Animals, Herman's Hermits, the Moody Blues, The Who, Spencer Davis Group, The Hillies, Ike and Tina Turner, The Mamas & Papas, Procol Harum and The Beatles.
Album: released on BBC, 15 Jun'87 by BBC Records & Tapes. Dist: EMI, PRT, Pye

Cassette: released on BBC, 15 Jun'87 by BBC Records & Tapes. Dist: EMI, PRT, Pye

ROCK'N'ROLL YEARS (1968-1971) Various artists (Various Artists).
Tracks: / This wheel's on fire / Fire / Crossroads / Knights in white satin / Voodoo chile / Pinball Wizard / I'm the urban spaceman / Going up the country / I'd rather go blind / Games people play / Instant Karma / Rag mama rag / Black night / Witches promise / All right now / My sweet lord / Your song / Get it on / Malt & barley blues / Maggie may.
Notes: Compilation from the BBC1 TV series. Artists include: Cream, Jimi Hendrix, Canned Heat, The Who, Jethro Tull, Lennon,Ono Band, Free, Deep Purple, George Harrison, T.Rex, Elton John and Rod Stewart.
Album: released on BBC, 15 Jun'87 by BBC Records & Tapes. Dist: EMI, PRT, Pye

Cassette: released on BBC, 15 Jun'87 by BBC Records & Tapes. Dist: EMI, PRT, Pye

ROCK'N'ROLL YEARS (1956-1959) Various artists (Various Artists).
Tracks: / Rock around the clock / Rock Island Line / Great pretender / Be-bop-a-lula / Ain't that a shame / Tutti frutti / 6-5 Special / Diana / That'll be the day / Singing the blues / Great balls of fire / At the hop / When / Summertime blues / All I have to do is dream / Donna / Lipstick on your collar / Here comes the summer / Livin' doll / Teenager in love.
Notes: Compilation from the BBC1 TV series. Artists include: Bill Haley, Gene Vincent, Little Richard, Buddy Holly, Jerry Lee Lewis, The Everly Brothers, Eddie Cochran and Cliff Richard & The Shadows.
Album: released on BBC, 15 Jun'87 by BBC Records & Tapes. Dist: EMI, PRT, Pye

Cassette: released on BBC, 15 Jun'87 by BBC Records & Tapes. Dist: EMI. PRT, Pye

ROCK'N'ROLL YEARS (1960-1963) Various artists (Various Artists).
Tracks: / What do you want / Apache / Ain't misbehavin' / Good timin' / On the rebound / Runaway / Johnny remember me / Walkin' back to happiness / Runaround Sue / Take good care of my baby / Let's dance / Nut rocker / Twisting the night away / Locomotion, The / How do you do it / Surf city / Do you want to know a secret / Sugar and spice / She loves you.
Notes: Artists include: Adam Faith, Johnny Kidd and The Pirates, Del Shannon, Dion and the Belmonts, Bobby Vee, Sam Cooke, The Searchers and the Beatles.
Album: released on BBC, 15 Jun'87 by BBC Records & Tapes. Dist: EMI, PRT, Pye

Cassette: released on BBC, 15 Jun'87 by BBC Records & Tapes. Dist: EMI, PRT, Pye

Rock-olas

LANGUAGE OF LOVE/EYES OF BLUE.
Single (7"): released on Rocket, Mar'82 by Phonogram Records. Dist: Polygram Distribution

Rockpile

SECONDS OF PLEASURE.
Gatefold sleeve: released on Demon, Nov'85 by Demon Records. Dist: Pinnacle

Cassette: released on F-Beat, Oct'80 by F-Beat Records. Dist: RCA, Pinnacle

Album: released on Demon, Jun'84 by Demon Records. Dist: Pinnacle

Rock, Pretty Baby

PRETTY BABY Music from the film (Various Artists).
Album: released on Jasmine, Aug'83 by Jas-

mine Records. Dist: Counterpoint, Lugtons, Taylor, H.R., Wellard, Chris, Swift, Cadillac

Rock revolution

ROCK REVOLUTION, THE Various Artists (Various Artists).
Notes: Compilation of material by artists who came to fame in the new wave of the late 70's and early 80's, like Ian Drury, Kate Bush, Bob Marley, The Sex Pistols. Number of tracks: Type of recording: Compilation. Total playing time: 60 minutes.
Video-cassette (VHS): released on Peppermint Music, Sep'84 Dist: Peppermint Music

ROCK REVOLUTION VOL 1 various artists (Various Artists).
Album: released on Hallmark, Nov'77 by Pickwick Records. Dist: Pickwick Distribution, PRT, Taylors

Cassette: released on Hallmark, Nov'77 by Pickwick Records. Dist: Pickwick Distribution, PRT, Taylors

ROCK REVOLUTION VOL 2 various artists (Various Artists).
Album: released on Pickwick, May'79 by Pickwick Records. Dist: Pickwick Distribution, Prism Leisure Distribution, Lugtons

Cassette: released on Pickwick, May'79 by Pickwick Records. Dist: Pickwick Distribution, Prism Leisure Distribution, Lugtons

Rock Rock Rock

ROCK ROCK ROCK (Various Artists).
Album: released on Chess, Apr'87 by Charly Records. Dist: Charly, Swift, PRT, Discovery, IMS, Polygram

Cassette: released on Chess, Apr'87 by Charly Records. Dist: Charly, Swift, PRT, Discovery, IMS, Polygram

Album: released on White, Jul'79

ROCK ROCK ROCK various artists (Various Artists).

Rock & roll...

ROCK & ROLL GOLD Various artists (Various Artists).
Album: released on Cambra, May'85 by Cambra Records. Dist: IDS, Conifer

Cassette: released on Cambra, May'85 by Cambra Records. Dist: IDS, Conifer

ROCK & ROLL LEGENDS RECORDED LIVE IN LONDON (Various Artists).
Album: released on Harvest, Apr'78 by EMI Records. Dist: Roots, EMI

ROCK & ROLLS GIRLS Various artists (Various Artists).
Album: released on White Label (Holland), Feb'84 Dist: CSA, PRT

Rock & Roll Circus

AT LAST.
Album: released on Loco Records, Apr'84 by Loco Records. Dist: Loco Records

Rocksnax

ROCKSNAX various artists (Various Artists).
Album: released on Guardian, Aug'84 by Guardian Records. Dist: Jazz Music, Pinnacle

Rocksteady...

ROCK STEADY YEARS various artists (Various Artists).
Album: released on Island, May'80 by Island Records. Dist: Polygram

ROCKSTEADY YEARS various artists (Various Artists).
Cassette: released on Island, May'80 by Island Records. Dist: Polygram

Rocksteady Crew

HEY YOU THE ROCK STEADY CREW.
Single (7"): released on Charisma, Sep'83 by Virgin Records. Dist: EMI

Single (12"): released on Charisma, Sep'83 by Virgin Records. Dist: EMI

READY FOR BATTLE.
Album: released on Charisma, May'84 by Virgin Records. Dist: EMI

Cassette: released on Charisma, May'84 by Virgin Records. Dist: EMI

Rockwell

CAPTURED.
Album: released on Motown, Mar'85 by Motown Records. Dist: BMG Distribution

Cassette: released on Motown, Mar'85 by Motown Records. Dist: BMG Distribution

CARME.
Tracks: / Carme / Carme (Inst.) / Somebody's watching me.
Single (7"): released on RCA, Jul'86 by RCA Records. Dist: RCA, Roots, Swift, Wellard, Chris, I & B, Solomon & Peres Distribution

Single (12"): released on RCA, Jul'86 by RCA Records. Dist: RCA, Roots, Swift, Wellard, Chris, I & B, Solomon & Peres Distribution

GENIE,THE.
Tracks: / That's nasty / Carme / Baby on the corner / Grown-up / Nervous condition / Concentration / Man from mars,The / Genie of love.
Album: released on Motown, Jul'86 by Motown Records. Dist: BMG Distribution

Cassette: released on Motown, Jul'86 by Motown Records. Dist: BMG Distribution

HE'S A COBRA.
Single (7"): released on Motown, Mar'85 by Motown Records. Dist: BMG Distribution Deleted '1.

Single (12"): released on Motown, Mar'85 by Motown Records. Dist: BMG Distribution

OBSCENE PHONE CALLER.
Single (7"): released on Motown, Mar'84 by Motown Records. Dist: BMG Distribution

Single (12"): released on Motown, Mar'84 by Motown Records. Dist: BMG Distribution

PEEPING TOM.
Single (7"):

Single (12"):

SOMEBODY'S WATCHING ME.
Album: released on Motown, Feb'84 by Motown Records. Dist: BMG Distribution

Cassette: released on Motown, Feb'84 by Motown Records. Dist: BMG Distribution

Single (7"): released on Motown, Jan'84 by Motown Records. Dist: BMG Distribution

Single (12"): released on Motown, Jan'84 by Motown Records. Dist: BMG Distribution

TAXMAN.
Single (7"): released on Motown, Jul'84 by Motown Records. Dist: BMG Distribution

Single (12"): released on Motown, Jul'84 by Motown Records. Dist: BMG Distribution

Rocky

ROCKY Original Soundtrack (Various Artists).
Tracks: / Gonna fly now (theme from Rocky) / Philadelphia morning / Going the distance / Reflections / Marine's hymn/yankie doodle / Take you back / First date / You take my heart away / Fanfare for Rocky / Butkus / Alone in the ring / Final bell, the / Rocky's reward.
Compact disc: released on EMI, May'87 by EMI Records. Dist: EMI

ROCKY Original Film Soundtrack.
Cassette: released on United Artists, Apr'77

ROCKY II Original Film Soundtrack (Rocky II).
Album: released on Liberty-United, Apr'80 by EMI Records. Dist: EMI

ROCKY III Original Film Soundtrack (Rocky III).
Tracks: / Eye of the tiger / Take you back (Tough Gym) / Pushin' / Reflections / Mickey / Take you back / Decision / Gonna fly now / Adrian / Conquest.
Album: released on Liberty-United, Aug'82 by EMI Records. Dist: EMI

Cassette: released on Liberty-United, Aug'82 by EMI Records. Dist: EMI

Compact disc: released on Liberty, Jun'87 by Liberty-United. Dist: EMI

ROCKY IV Original Film Soundtrack (Rocky IV).

Album: released on Scotti Brothers (USA), Dec'85 by Scotti Brothers Records. Dist: Polydor

Cassette: released on Scotti Brothers (USA), Dec'85 by Scotti Brothers Records. Dist: Polydor

Rocky Horror...

ROCKY HORROR DISCO SHOW various artists (Various Artists).
Single (12"): released on ZYX (Germany), Nov'85 by ZYX Records. Dist: Greyhound

ROCKY HORROR PICTURE SHOW Original soundtrack (Various Artists).
Album: released on Pacific, Jul'86 by Pacific Records (USA). Dist: Atlantic

Cassette: released on Pacific, Jul'86 by Pacific Records (USA). Dist: Atlantic

Compact disc: released on Pacific, Jan'86 by Pacific Records (USA). Dist: Atlantic

ROCKY HORROR PICTURE SHOW Original soundtrack (Various Artists).
Compact disc: by Pacific Records (USA). Dist: Atlantic

ROCKY HORROR SHOW - ORIGINAL LONDON CAST (Rocky Horror Show).
Album: released on Dojo, May'87 by Castle Communications Records. Dist: Cartel

ROCKY HORROR STAGE SHOW Original Roxy Cast (Various Artists).
Compact disc: by Pacific Records (USA). Dist: Atlantic

Rocky IV

FAN FARE.
Tracks: / Fan fare.
Single (12"): released on O.B.G., May'86 Dist: Pinnacle

ROCKY IV Original soundtrack (Various Artists).
Notes: Artists: Survivor, John Cafferty, Kenny Loggins & Gladys Knight, Vince Di Cola, James Brown, Robert Tepper, Go West, Touch.
Compact disc: released on Scotti Brothers (USA), Jul'86 by Scotti Brothers Records. Dist: Polydor

Rocky M

DISCO LADY.
Tracks: / Disco lady (special DJ mix) / Disco lady (inst.).
Single (12"): released on Conifer, May'86 by Conifer Records. Dist: Conifer

Rocky Mountain..

ROCKY MOUNTAIN HIGH various artists (Various Artists).
Cassette: released on VFM Cassettes, Jan'85

Rocky Roads

AVALON.
Album: released on Lismor, Jul'86 by Lismor Records. Dist: Lismor, Roots, Celtic Music

Rockytops

LIFE CAN BE BEAUTIFUL.
Album: released on Fellside (Cumbria), '83 by Fellside Records. Dist: Roots, Projection, CM, Jazz Music

Rocky Valley

FESTIVAL SONG.
Tracks: / Festival song / National garden festival theme / Festival song (inst. version).
Single (7"): released on Valentine, Jun'86 by Valentine Records. Dist: PRT

Roco

HELLO HELLO/SARA.
Single (7"): released on Straight 8, Jul'83

Rod

JUST KEEP ON WALKING.
Single (7"): released on Creole, Mar'83 by Creole Records. Dist: Rhino, PRT

Single (12"): released on Creole, Mar'83 by Creole Records. Dist: Rhino, PRT

Rodedelius, Hans- Joachim

GESCHENK DES AUGENBLICKS.
Album: released on Polydor, Jul'84 by Polydor Records. Dist: Polygram, Polydor

Roden, Jess

STONE CHASER.
Album: released on Island, Oct'79 by Island Records. Dist: Polygram

Roden,Shirley

IS THIS GOODBYE/I THINK I'LL DISAPPEAR.
Single (7"): released on Nouveau, Nov'83

Rodgers, Dick

ENTERS THE POLKA HALL OF FAME.
Double Album: released on ARC (Accordion Records), '84 Dist: Accordion Record Club

Rodgers, Frank

CHILDHOOD HEROES.
Single (7"): released on Pulsar, May'82 by Lismor Records. Dist: Lismor

Rodgers & Hart In London

RODGERS & HART IN LONDON various artists (Various Artists).
Album: released on World, Sep'73 Dist: Jetstar

Rodgers, Jimmie

20 OF THE BEST.
Album: released on RCA, Mar'84 by RCA Records. Dist: RCA, Roots, Swift, Wellard, Chris, I & B, Solomon & Peres Distribution

Cassette: released on RCA, Mar'84 by RCA Records. Dist: RCA, Roots, Swift, Wellard, Chris, I & B, Solomon & Peres Distribution

NEVER NO MO' BLUES.
Tracks: / Never no mo' blues / Daddy and home / Blue yodel No. 4 (California blues) / Waiting for a train / You and my old guitar / Prairie lullaby / Blue yodel no. 6 / Dear old sunny south by the sea / Jimmie's mean mama blues / Pistol packin' papa / Old pal of my heart / My little lady.
Album: released on RCA, Jan'87 by RCA Records. Dist: RCA, Roots, Swift, Wellard, Chris, I & B, Solomon & Peres Distribution

Cassette: released on RCA, Jan'87 by RCA Records. Dist: RCA, Roots, Swift, Wellard, Chris, I & B, Solomon & Peres Distribution

TRAIN WHISTLE BLUES.
Tracks: / Jimmmie's mean mamma blues / Southern cannonball,The / Jimmie the kid / Travellin' blues / Mystery of no.5',The / Memphis yodel / Blue yodel no.4 (California blues) / Hobo Bill's last ride / Waiting for a train / Ben Dewberryt's final run / My rough and rowdy ways / Blue yodel no.7 (Anniversary blue yodel) / Brakeman's blues,The (Yodelling the blues away) / Let me be your side track / Hobo's meditation,The / Train whistle blues.
Notes: Jimmie Rodgers....a fellow with a guitar who sang about the sort of things that would strike response from country and city dwellers alike - remains to this daythe original yodelling white blues singer from the southern railroads. He was aunique artist whose brilliant career was cut cruelly short by tuberculosis and he died at only thirtey-six years of age. The disc boasts a superb sleeve, inc-luding an informative sleeve note - as quoted from above - from Capitol Radio's Brian Rust. Mono....
Album: released on Living Era, Dec'86 by ASV. Dist: PRT

Album: released on ASV Living Era, Jun'86 by ASV Records. Dist: PRT

Cassette: released on ASV Living Era, Jun'86 by ASV Records. Dist: PRT

Rodgers, Jimmy

ENGLISH COUNTRY GARDEN.
Single (7"): released on Flashback, Jan'83 by Flashback Records/PRT Records. Dist: Mainline, PRT

Rodgers, Nile

LAND OF THE GOOD GROOVE.
Single (7"): released on Mirage, Apr'83 Dist: Pinnacle

Single (12"): released on Mirage, Apr'83 Dist: Pinnacle

YUM YUM.
Single (7"): released on Mirage, May'83 Dist: Pinnacle

Single (12"): released on Mirage, May'83 Dist: Pinnacle

Rodgers, Paul

CUT LOOSE.
Album: released on Atlantic, Nov'83 by WEA Records. Dist: WEA

Cassette: released on Atlantic, Nov'83 by WEA Records. Dist: WEA

CUT LOOSE(7").
Single (7"): released on Atlantic, Nov'84 by WEA Records. Dist: WEA

Rodgers, Richard

BOYS FROM SYRACUSE, THE (Rodgers,Richard & Lorenz Hart).
Album: released on DRG (USA), Jul'79 by DRG Records. Dist: Conifer, RCA

IT'S SMOOTH,IT'S SMART-IT'S RODGERS,IT'S HART (Rodgers,Richard & Lorenz Hart).
Album: released on Monmouth, Mar'79

NO STRINGS.
Album: released on DRG (USA), Jul'79 by DRG Records. Dist: Conifer, RCA

RICHARD RODGERS & N.Y. PHILHARMONIC (Rodgers, Richard/N.Y.Philharmonic).
Album: released on CBS, May'80 by CBS Records. Dist: CBS

Rod,Jane & Freddy

HAPPY CHRISTMAS.
Single (7"): released on Video, Dec'81

Rodney, Red

3 R'S, THE (Rodney, Red/Richie Cole/Ricky Ford).
Album: released on Muse, Dec'82 by Peerless Records. Dist: Lugtons Distributors

BIRD LIVES.
Album: released on Muse, May'81 by Peerless Records. Dist: Lugtons Distributors

HOME FREE.
Album: released on Muse, May'81 by Peerless Records. Dist: Lugtons Distributors

LIVE AT THE VILLAGE VANGUARD featuring Ira Sullivan.
Album: released on Muse, May'81 by Peerless Records. Dist: Lugtons Distributors

MODERN MUSIC FROM CHICAGO (Rodney,Red Quintet).
Album: released on Original Jazz Classics (USA), Jun'86 Dist: Fantasy (USA) Distribution, Chris Wellard Distribution, IMS-Polygram Distribution

RED RODNEY.
Album: released on Jazz Reactivation, Jul'82 Dist: PRT

RED TORNADO.
Album: released on Muse, May'81 by Peerless Records. Dist: Lugtons Distributors

RED,WHITE & BLUES.
Album: released on Muse, Apr'81 by Peerless Records. Dist: Lugtons Distributors

SUPERBOP.
Album: released on Muse, Apr'81 by Peerless Records. Dist: Lugtons Distributors

WITH THE BEBOP PRESERVATION SOCIETY.
Album: released on Spotlite, '83 by Spotlite Records. Dist: Cadillac, Jazz Music, Spotlite

YARD'S PAD.
Album: released on Sonet, Mar'87 by Sonet Records. Dist: PRT

Rodrigue, Gene

BAYOU CAJUN MUSIC OF GENE RODRIGUE.
Album:

Rodrigues, Amalia

BEST OF: AMALIA RODRIGUES.
Album: released on EMI (Holland), '83 by EMI Records. Dist: Conifer

GOSTAVA DE SER QUEM ERA.
Album: released on EMI (France), '83 by EMI Records. Dist: Conifer

Rodriguez, Antonia

LA BAMBA.
Single (7"): released on Magnet, Sep'81 by Magnet Records. Dist: BMG

Single (12"): released on Magnet, Sep'81 by Magnet Records. Dist: BMG

Rodriguez, Maria

TREMENDA, (LA).
Album: released on World Circuit, Apr'87 by Taurus Records. Dist: Sterns/Triple Earth Distribution

Rodrigue, Gene

BAYOU CAJUN MUSIC OF GENE RODRIQUE, THE.
Album: released on Swallow, Jun'87

Rods

HEAVIER THAN THOU.
Tracks: / Heavier than thou / Make me a beleiver / Angels never run / Crossfire / I'm gonna rock / She' trouble / Born to rock / Chains of love / Communication breakdown / Fool for your love / Cold sweat and love.
Album: released on Zebra, Jan'87 by Cherry Red Records. Dist: Pinnacle

LET THEM EAT METAL.
Album: released on Music For Nations, Jul'84 by Music For Nations Records. Dist: Pinnacle

POWER LOVER.
Single (7"): released on Arista, Mar'82 by Arista Records. Dist: RCA

Single (12"): released on Arista, Feb'82 by Arista Records. Dist: RCA

RODS LIVE, THE.
Album: released on Music For Nations, Jan'84 by Music For Nations Records. Dist: Pinnacle

Cassette: released on Music For Nations, Jan'84 by Music For Nations Records. Dist: Pinnacle

RODS, THE.
Album: released on Arista, Sep'81 by Arista Records. Dist: RCA

YOU KEEP ME HANGING ON.
Picture disc single: released on Arista, May'82 by Arista Records. Dist: RCA

Rodway, Steve

KEEP ON WALKING.
Single (7"): released on Record Shack, Jun'85 by Record Shack Records. Dist: PRT

Single (12"): released on Record Shack, Jun'85 by Record Shack Records. Dist: PRT

Rodwell, Bryan

PROJECTED SOUNDS OF BRYAN RODWELL, THE.
Album: released on Polyphonic, Feb'85 by Polyphonic Records. Dist: Taylors

Cassette: released on Polyphonic, Feb'85 by Polyphonic Records. Dist: Taylors

PURELY FOR PLEASURE (Eminent F 225 Organ).
Album: released on Grosvenor, Aug'82 by Grosvenor Records. Dist: Taylors

Roedelius

AUF LEISEN SOHLEN.
Album: released on Sky (Germany), Sep'84

DURCH DIE WUSTE.
Album: released on Sky, '78 by President Records.

Roedelius, Eno M.

AFTER THE HEAT.
Album: released on Sky, May'79 by President Records.

Roedelius, Hans Joachim

GESCHENK DES AUGENBLICKS.
Tracks: / Gesckenk des Augenblicks (gift of the moment) / Adieu Quichotte / Troubadour / Kleine blume irgendwo (little flower somewhere) / Ohn' unterlass (continuously) / Gefundene zeit (time regained) / Sehnsucht ich will dich lassen (to be free and yearning) / Das sanfte (mellowness) / Tag fur tag (day by day) / Zu fussen der berge am ufer des sees / Wurzeln des glucks (roots of joy).
Album: released on Editions EG, Jan'87 by Virgin Records. Dist: EMI

Album: released on Monmouth, Mar'79

MONENTE SELICI.
Album: released on Venture, Jul'87 Dist: Revolver, Cartel

Cassette: released on Venture, Jul'87 Dist: Revolver, Cartel

Roe, Tommy

GOLDEN GREATS: TOMMY ROE.
Album: released on MCA, Oct'85 by MCA Records. Dist: Polygram, MCA

Cassette: released on MCA, Oct'85 by MCA Records. Dist: Polygram MCA

SHEILA.
Single (7"): released on Old Gold, Jul'82 by Old Gold Records. Dist: Lightning, Jazz Music, Spartan, Counterpoint

Rogers, Billie

ONE NIGHT STAND...WOMENS LIB IN 1944.
Album: released on Joyce, Jul'82

Rogers, Evan

PRIVATE JOY.
Single (7"): released on RCA International, Jul'85

Single (12"): released on RCA International, Jul'85

SECRET LOVE.
Single (12"): released on RCA, Feb'84 by RCA Records. Dist: RCA, Roots, Swift, Wellard, Chris, I & B, Solomon & Peres Distribution

STAY HERE WITH ME.
Single (7"): released on RCA, May'84 by RCA Records. Dist: RCA, Roots, Swift, Wellard, Chris, I & B, Solomon & Peres Distribution

Single (12"): released on RCA, May'84 by RCA Records. Dist: RCA, Roots, Swift, Wellard, Chris, I & B, Solomon & Peres Distribution

Rogers, Ginger

COLLECTION: GINGER ROGERS.
Album: released on Deja Vu, May'86 by Deja Vu Records. Dist: Counterpoint Distribution, Record Services Distribution (Ireland)

Cassette: released on Deja Vu, May'86 by Deja Vu Records. Dist: Counterpoint Distribution, Record Services Distribution (Ireland)

Album: released on Chess, Oct'86 by Charly Records. Dist: Charly, Swift, PRT, Discovery, IMS, Polygram

MISS GINGER ROGERS.
Album: released on EMI, '78 by EMI Records. Dist: EMI

Rogers, Helen

CANDIDATE FOR LOVE.
Single (12"): released on Justice, Sep'84 Dist: Pinnacle

WHAT'S LOVE GO TO DO WITH IT.
Single (12"): released on Hot Rod, Sep'84 by Hot Rod Records. Dist: Jetstar

Rogers, Jimmy

CHESS MASTERS...JIMMY ROGERS.
Double Album: released on Chess(USA), Apr'82 by Sugar Hill (USA). Dist: PRT, Swift

CHICAGO BLUES (Rogers, Jimmy & Left Hand Frank).
Album: released on JSP, Jan'82 by JSP Records. Dist: Swift, Projection

DIRTY DOZENS (Rogers, Jimmy & Left Hand Frank).
Album: released on JSP, May'85 by JSP Records. Dist: Swift, Projection

FEELIN' GOOD.
Album: released on Murray Brothers (USA), May'84 Dist: Swift Distribution

LIVE (Rogers, Jimmy & Left Hand Frank).
Album: released on JSP, Mar'82 by JSP Records. Dist: Swift, Projection

Rogers, Julie

WEDDING, THE.
Single (7"): released on Old Gold (Reissue), Jul'82

Rogers, Kenny

20 GOLDEN HITS.
Album: released on Masters (Holland), Jan'87

25 GREATEST HITS.
Tracks: / Lucille / Lady / Love lifted me / We've got tonight / Scarlet fever / Love or something like it / She believes in me / Ruby don't take your love to town / Don't fall in love with a dreamer / You were a good friend / Gambler, The / Through the years / Daytime friends / You decorated my life / Till I can make it on my own / Reuben James / Coward of the county / I don't need you / Something's burning / Love will turn you around / Abraham,Martin & John / Precious memories / Love is what we make it / Green green grass of home / Desperado / Sweet music man.
Double compact disc: released on Liberty, Apr'87 by Liberty-United. Dist: EMI

ALL MY LIFE.
Single (7"): released on United Artists, Apr'83

AT THE COUNTRY STORE.
Album: released on Country Store, Apr'87 by Starblend Records. Dist: PRT, Prism Leisure Corporation Records

Cassette: released on Country Store, Apr'87 by Starblend Records. Dist: PRT, Prism Leisure Corporation Records

BEST OF KENNY ROGERS.
Album: released on Breakaway, Mar'84 Dist: PRT, Stage One

CHRISTMAS.
Tracks: / Christmas everyday / Kentucky homemade Christmas / Carol of the bells / Kids / Sweet little Jesus boy / Christmas is my favourite time of the year / White Christmas / My favourite things / O' holy night / When a child is born.
Album: released on Liberty, Dec'85 by Liberty-United. Dist: EMI

Cassette: released on Liberty, Dec'85 by Liberty-United. Dist: EMI

Album: released on MFP, Sep'87 by EMI Records. Dist: EMI

Cassette: released on MFP, Sep'87 by EMI Records. Dist: EMI

CHRISTMAS WITHOUT YOU (Rogers, Kenny & Dolly Parton).
Single (7"): released on RCA, Nov'84 by RCA Records. Dist: RCA, Roots, Swift, Wellard, Chris, I & B, Solomon & Peres Distribution

CLASSICS (Rogers, Kenny & Dotty West).
Album: released on MFP, Jan'83 by EMI Records. Dist: EMI

Cassette: released on MFP, Jan'83 by EMI Records. Dist: EMI

COLLECTION: KENNY ROGERS (THE).
Album: released on EMI (Holland), '83 by EMI Records. Dist: Conifer

Album: released on Castle Communications, Nov'85 by Castle Communications. Dist: Cartel, Pinnacle, Counterpoint

Cassette: released on Castle Communications, Nov'85 by Castle Communications. Dist: Cartel, Pinnacle, Counterpoint

Compact disc: released on Spectrum, Oct'86 Dist: ACD

COWARD OF THE COUNTY.
Single (7"): released on United Artists, Jan'80

Single (7"): released on Liberty, Sep'85 by Liberty-United. Dist: EMI

DON'T FALL IN LOVE WITH A DREAMER (Rogers, Kenny with Kim Carnes).
Single (7"): released on EMI America, Oct'85 by EMI Records. Dist: EMI

DUETS.
Compact disc: released on EMI America, Mar'87 by EMI Records. Dist: EMI

EVERY TIME TWO FOOLS COLLIDE (Rogers, Kenny & Dotty West).
Album: released on United Artists, Apr'78

EYES THAT SEE IN THE DARK.
Tracks: / This woman / You and I / Buried treasure / Islands in the stream / Living with you / Evening star / Hold me / Midsummer night / I will always love you / Eyes that see in the dark.
Compact disc: released on RCA, Jan'84 by RCA Records. Dist: RCA, Roots, Swift, Wellard, Chris, I & B, Solomon & Peres Distribution

Album: released on RCA, Aug'83 by RCA Records. Dist: RCA, Roots, Swift, Wellard, Chris, I & B, Solomon & Peres Distribution

Cassette: released on RCA, Aug'83 by RCA Records. Dist: RCA, Roots, Swift, Wellard, Chris, I & B, Solomon & Peres Distribution

Single (7"): released on RCA, Sep'83 by RCA Records. Dist: RCA, Roots, Swift, Wellard, Chris, I & B, Solomon & Peres Distribution

FOR THE GOOD TIMES (Rogers, Kenny & The First Edition).
Album: released on Arena, Feb'87 by Arena Records. Dist: Spartan

Cassette: released on Arena, Feb'87 by Arena Records. Dist: Spartan

GAMBLER,THE.
Album: released on United Artists, Feb'79 Deleted '87.

Cassette: released on United Artists, Feb'79 Deleted '87.

Single (7"): released on United Artists, Mar'85

GIDEON.
Album: released on United Artists, May'80

GOLDEN GREATS: KENNY ROGERS (Rogers, Kenny & The First Edition).
Album: released on MCA, Oct'85 by MCA Records. Dist: Polygram, MCA

Cassette: released on MCA, Oct'85 by MCA Records. Dist: Polygram. MCA

GREATEST HITS:KENNY ROGERS.
Tracks: / Gambler,The / Lady / Don't fall in love with a dreamer / Ruby don't take your love to town / She believes in me / Coward of the county / Lucille / You decorated my life / Rueben James / Love the world away / Every time two fools collide / Long arm of the law,The.
Compact disc: released on Liberty-UA, Jan'84

HEART OF THE MATTER.
Tracks: / Don't wanna have to worry / You made me feel love / Morning desire / Heart of the matter / Don't look in my eyes / Best of me / Tomb of the unknown love / People in love / I can't believe your eyes / Our perfect song.
Album: released on RCA, Nov'85 by RCA Records. Dist: RCA, Roots, Swift, Wellard, Chris, I & B, Solomon & Peres Distribution

Cassette: released on RCA, Nov'85 by RCA Records. Dist: RCA, Roots, Swift, Wellard, Chris, I & B, Solomon & Peres Distribution

Compact disc: released on RCA, May'86 by RCA Records. Dist: RCA, Roots, Swift, Wellard, Chris, I & B, Solomon & Peres Distribution

ISLANDS IN THE STREAM (see also Dolly Parton) (Rogers, Kenny & Dolly Parton).
Single (7"): released on RCA, Nov'83 by RCA Records. Dist: RCA, Roots, Swift, Wellard, Chris, I & B, Solomon & Peres Distribution

KENNY ROGERS.
Compact disc: released on Intertape, Jul'87 Dist: Target

KENNY ROGERS SINGLES ALBUM,THE.
Album: released on United Artists, Sep'79

Cassette: released on United Artists, Sep'79

KENNY ROGERS STORY,THE.
Album: released on Liberty, Jul'85 by Liberty-United. Dist: EMI

Cassette: released on Liberty, Jul'85 by Liberty-United. Dist: EMI

LADY (Rogers,Kenny with Kim Carnes & Dottie West).
Album: released on Liberty-United, Feb'81 by EMI Records. Dist: EMI

Cassette: released on Liberty-United, Feb'81 by EMI Records. Dist: EMI

LOVE WILL TURN YOU AROUND.
Single (7"): released on United Artists, Jul'82

LUCILLE.
Tracks: / Laura / I wasn't man enough / Mother country / Why don't we go somewhere and love / Green green grass of home / Till I get it right / Lucille / Son of Hickory Holler's tramp / Lay down beside me / uttin' in overtime at home / While I play the fiddle / Laura (What's he got that I ain't got) / I wasn't man enough / Mother country music / Why don't we go somewhere and love / Green green grass of home / Till I get it right / Lucille / Son of Hickory Holler's tramp,The / Lay down beside me / Puttin' in overtime at home / While I play the fiddle.
Album: released on MFP, Oct'86 by EMI Records. Dist: EMI

Cassette: released on MFP, Oct'86 by EMI Records. Dist: EMI

Album: released on Music For Pleasure, Sep'86 by EMI Records. Dist: EMI

Cassette: released on Music For Pleasure, Sep'86 by EMI Records. Dist: EMI

Single (7"): released on United Artists, Apr'77

MORNING DESIRE.
Single (7"): released on RCA, Oct'85 by RCA Records. Dist: RCA, Roots, Swift, Wellard, Chris, I & B, Solomon & Peres Distribution

Single (12"): released on RCA, Oct'85 by RCA Records. Dist: RCA, Roots, Swift, Wellard, Chris, I & B, Solomon & Peres Distribution

RUBY DON'T TAKE YOUR LOVE TO TOWN.
Tracks: / Ticket to nowhere / Conditions (Just dropped in) / She even woke me up to say goodbye / My Washington woman / Run thru your mind / Sleep comes easy / After all (I live my life) / For the good times / Something burning / Hurry up. Love / Trying just as hard / Ruby don't take your love to town / Heed the call / we all got to help each other / Poem for my little lady / Where does Rosie go / Sunshine / Ruben James / Loser / Church without a name.
Album: released on Showcase, Apr'86 Dist: Counterpoint

Cassette: released on Showcase, Apr'86 Dist: Counterpoint

Album: released on MFP, Apr'81 by EMI Records. Dist: EMI

Cassette: released on Music For Pleasure, Apr'81

Single (7"): released on EMI Golden 45's, Mar'84 by EMI Records. Dist: EMI

SHARE YOUR LOVE.
Album: released on Liberty, Aug'81 by Liberty-United. Dist: EMI Deleted '87.

Cassette: released on Liberty, Aug'81 by Liberty-United. Dist: EMI Deleted '87.

SOMETHING BURNING.
Album: released on Premier, '84 by Premier Records. Dist: CBS

SOMETHING BURNING (Rogers, Kenny & The First Edition).
Single (7"): released on Reprise, May'80 by WEA Records. Dist: WEA

SUNSHINE.
Compact disc: released on Bellaphon, '86 by Bellaphon Records. Dist: IMS-Polygram

THEY DON'T MAKE 'EM LIKE THEY USED TO.
Tracks: / This love we share / If I could hold on to love / You're my love / Time for love / They don't make them like they used to / Life is good, love is better / Just thje thought of losing you / Anything at all / After all this time / Twenty years ago.
Album: released on RCA, 1 May'87 by RCA Records. Dist: RCA, Roots, Swift, Wellard, Chris, I & B, Solomon & Peres Distribution

Cassette: released on RCA, 1 May'87 by RCA Records. Dist: RCA, Roots, Swift, Wellard, Chris, I & B, Solomon & Peres Distribution

Compact disc: released on RCA, Mar'87 by RCA Records. Dist: RCA, Roots, Swift, Wellard, Chris, I & B, Solomon & Peres Distribution

THIS WOMAN/HOLD ME.
Single (7"): released on RCA (America), Jan'84

WE'VE GOT TONIGHT.
Album: released on Liberty, Mar'83 by Liberty-United. Dist: EMI

WHAT ABOUT ME.
Tracks: / Didn't we / Somebody took my love / Crazy / Stranger / Heart to heart / What about me / Night goes on / Dream dancin' / Two hearts one love / I don't want to know why.
Album: released on RCA, Oct'84 by RCA Records. Dist: RCA, Roots, Swift, Wellard, Chris, I & B, Solomon & Peres Distribution

Cassette: released on RCA, Oct'84 by RCA Records. Dist: RCA, Roots, Swift, Wellard, Chris, I & B, Solomon & Peres Distribution

Compact disc: released on RCA, Oct'84 by RCA Records. Dist: RCA, Roots, Swift, Wellard, Chris, I & B, Solomon & Peres Distribution

Rogers/Maucerl

GHOST TOWN/SLAUGHTER ON 10TH AVENUE.
Album: released on That's Entertainment, Dec'86 by That's Entertainment Records. Dist: Pinnacle, PRT

Cassette: released on That's Entertainment, Dec'86 by That's Entertainment Records. Dist: Pinnacle, PRT

Rogers,Mick

BRING BACK THE NIGHT.
Tracks: / Bring back the night / Too late.
Single (7"): released on Trojan, Feb'86 by Trojan Records. Dist: PRT, Jetstar

Rogers,Nile

STATE OF MIND.
Tracks: / State of mind / Stayed out of light.
Single (12"): released on Warner Bros., Jan'86 by Warner Bros Records. Dist: WEA

Rogers, Richard

MARY MARTIN SINGS, RICHARD ROGERS PLAYS (see Martin, Mary) (Rogers, Richard & Mary Martin).

Rogers, Ron

DON'T PLAY WITH MY EMOTIONS.
Album: released on ZE, Aug'82 by Island Records. Dist: Polygram

Rogers,Roy

GOOD LIFE (Rogers,Roy/Dale Evans).
Album: by Word Records. Dist: Word Distribution, CBS

KING OF THE COWBOYS.
Album: released on Bear Family, Dec'83 by Bear Family Records. Dist: Rollercoaster Distribution, Swift

ROLL ON TEXAS MOON.
Tracks: / Gay ranchero, A / Yellow rose of Texas / Don't fence me in / Gay ranchero, A / Roll on Texas moon / I met a miss in Texas / On the old Spanish trail / May the good Lord take a likin' to ya(& Dale Evans) / San Fernando Valley / I'm a rollin' / Little hula honey / California Rose / Home in Oklahoma / Rock me to sleep in my saddle / Old fashioned cowboy / There's a cloud to the valley of sunshine / Along the Navajo Trail.
Notes: Deluxe gatefold cover. Original RCA Victor recordings. Album picture disc.
Album: released on Bear Family, Nov'86 by Bear Family Records. Dist: Rollercoaster Distribution, Swift

Rogers,Sally

LOVE WILL GIDE US.
Album: released on Flying Fish (USA), Apr'86 by Flying Fish Records (USA). Dist: Roots, Projection

Rogers, Shorty

BACK AGAIN- LIVE AT THE CONCORDE CLUB.
Album: released on Concept, Feb'85 Dist: Jazz Music, Swift, Chris Wellard, Polygram

BLUES EXPRESS.
Album: released on RCA (France), Feb'85 by RCA Records. Dist: Discovery

COLLABORATION (Rogers,Shorty/Andre Previn).
Album: released on RCA (France), Nov'84 by RCA Records. Dist: Discovery

GREATEST HITS:SHORTY ROGERS.
Tracks: / Short stop / Blues for Brando / Goof & I / Sweetheart of Sigmund Freud / Gigi.../ Martian's lullaby / Doggin' around / Morpo / Bunny / Blues express / Tickletow / Red dog play.
Album: released on RCA, Jul'86 by RCA Records. Dist: RCA, Roots, Swift, Wellard, Chris, I & B, Solomon & Peres Distribution

Cassette: released on RCA, Jul'86 by RCA Records. Dist: RCA, Roots, Swift, Wellard, Chris, I & B, Solomon & Peres Distribution

JAZZ WALTZ (Rogers,Shorty Big Band).
Album: released on Discovery(Trend USA), Oct'82

LIVE FROM THE RENDEZVOUS BALLROOM 1953 (Rogers,Shorty Big Band).
Album: released on Scarecrow, Apr'81 Dist: Jazz Music

MARTIANS STAY AT HOME.
Album: released on Atlantic, Jun'80 by WEA Records. Dist: WEA

MODERN SOUND (Rogers,Shorty & Gerry Mulligan).
Tracks: / Pop / Didi / Four mothers / Over the rainbow / Apropos / Sam and the lady / Westwood walk / Ballad / Walking shoes / Rocker / Taking a chance on love / Flash / Simbah / Ontet.
Album: released on Affinity, Aug'86 by Charly Records. Dist: Charly, Cadillac

RETURN TO RIO (Rogers,Shorty & His Giants).
Album: released on Discovery (USA), Apr'84 by Discovery Records (USA). Dist: Swift, Flexitron-Audio, Jazz Music

SHORTY ROGERS BIG BAND-LIVE 1935 (Rogers,Shorty Big Band).
Album: released on Scarecrow, Jan'80 Dist: Jazz Music

SHORTY ROGERS & HIS GIANTS VOL.1 (Rogers,Shorty & His Giants).
Album: released on RCA (France), '83 by RCA Records. Dist: Discovery

WEST COAST JAZZ.
Album: released on Atlantic, Jul'76 by WEA Records. Dist: WEA

YESTERDAY,TODAY & FOREVER.
Album: released on Concord Jazz(USA), Oct'83 by Concord Jazz Records (USA). Dist: IMS, Polygram

Rogers, Sydney

MIRACLE WORKER.
Album: released on Ethnic, Apr'80 Dist: Kingdom

TIPPIN' IN.
Album: released on Ethnic, Apr'80 Dist: Kingdom

Rogue

FALLEN ANGELS.
Album: released on Epic, Jan'76 by CBS Records. Dist: CBS

LET IT GO.
Album: released on Epic, May'77 by CBS Records. Dist: CBS

Rogue Male

ALL OVER YOU.
Single (12"): released on Music For Nations, May'85 by Music For Nations Records. Dist: Pinnacle

ANIMAL MAN.
Tracks: / Progress / L.U.S.T. / Take no shit / You're on fire / Real me,The / Animal man,The / Belfast / Job centre / Low rider / Passing,The.
Album: released on Music For Nations, Jul'86 by Music For Nations Records. Dist: Pinnacle

BELFAST.
Tracks: / Belfast / Rough tough (pretty too) / Take no shit.
Single (12"): released on Music For Nations, Jul'86 by Music For Nations Records. Dist: Pinnacle

FIRST VISIT.
Album: released on Music For Nations, May'85 by Music For Nations Records. Dist: Pinnacle

Roicoco

WEEKEND AT TAHITTI (Roicoco & His Music Of The Isles).
Album: released on Deere (France), Sep'84 Dist: Studio Imports

Cassette: released on Deere (France), Sep'84 Dist: Studio Imports

Roldinger, Adelhard

SCHATTSEITE.
Album: released on ECM (Germany), Oct'82 by ECM Records. Dist: IMS, Polygram, Virgin through EMI

Rokko, Red

GUM GUM TREE, THE.
Single (7"): released on Frame Up, Sep'84 by Frame Up Records. Dist: M.I.S.

Rokoca

I'LL BE THERE.
Single (7"): released on PRT, Mar'85 by PRT Records. Dist: PRT

Roland

DEATH OF GLORY.
Tracks: / Death or glory / Great Edwardian air raid,The / Beau Brummel / Curious case of Richard Fielding,The.
Single (12"): released on Aftermath, Jul'86 by Aftermath Records. Dist: Cartel

PARADISE.
Single (7"): released on Master Discs, Sep'84 by Master Discs Records & Tapes. Dist: Master Discs

STORMY NIGHT (Roland with Sounds Inc.).
Single (12"): released on Plantation, Jan'82 Dist: Jetstar

Roland, Gene

BAND THAT NEVER WAS, THE (Roland, Gene Orchestra with Charlie Parker).
Album: released on Spotlite, '83 by Spotlite Records. Dist: Cadillac, Jazz Music, Spotlite

Roland, Ken

TWO SIDES OF KEN ROLAND.
Album: released on Nevis, '75 Dist: H.R. Taylor

Roland, Paul

BLADES OF BATTENBURG (EP) (4 track EP).
Single (12"): released on Aftermatch, Aug'83 by Aftermath Records. Dist: Jetstar

BURNT ORCHIDS.
Album: released on Aftermath, Aug'85 by Aftermath Records. Dist: Cartel

DANSE MACABRE.
Album: released on Bam Caruso, Apr'87 by Bam Caruso Records. Dist: Rough Trade, Revolver, Cartel

DOCTOR STRANGE.
Single (7"): released on Aristocrat, Jul'82 by Lithon Recording & Music Publishing.

GABRIELLE.
Tracks: / Gabrielle / Berlin / Sword and sorcery.
Extended-play record: released on Aftermath, 23 May'87 by Aftermath Records. Dist: Cartel

Roland Rat

ALBUM OF THE CASSETTE, THE.
Cassette: released on Rodent, Nov'84 by Magnet. Dist: RCA Distribution

CASSETTE OF THE ALBUM, THE.
Album: released on Rodent, Nov'84 by Magnet. Dist: RCA Distribution

LOVE ME TENDER.
Single (7"): released on Rodent, Mar'84 by Magnet. Dist: RCA Distribution

Single (12"): released on Rodent, Mar'84 by Magnet. Dist: RCA Distribution

NUMBER ONE RAT FAN (Roland Rat Superstar).
Single (7"): released on Rodent, Jan'85 by Magnet. Dist: RCA Distribution

Single (12"): released on Rodent, Jan'85 by Magnet. Dist: RCA Distribution

Picture disc single: released on Rodent, Jan'85 by Magnet. Dist: RCA Distribution

RAT RAPPING.
Single (7"): released on Rodent, Nov'83 by Magnet. Dist: RCA Distribution

Single (12"): released on Rodent, Nov'83 by Magnet. Dist: RCA Distribution

SUMMER HOLIDAY (Roland Rat /Kevin Gerbil).
Single (7"): released on Rodent, Jul'84 by Magnet. Dist: RCA Distribution

Rolands

BELINDA.
Single 10": released on Pama, Aug'82 by Pama Records. Dist: Pama, Enterprise, Jetstar

Rolfe,Nigel

AFRICAN FLOWER.
Tracks: / African flower / P.W. Botha's funeral march.
Single (7"): released on Reekus, Sep'86 by Reekus Records. Dist: Nine Mile, Cartel

Single (12"): released on Reekus, Sep'86 by Reekus Records. Dist: Nine Mile, Cartel

ISLAND STORIES.
Album: released on Reekus, Oct'86 by Reekus Records. Dist: Nine Mile, Cartel

Cassette: released on Reekus, Oct'86 by Reekus Records. Dist: Nine Mile, Cartel

Rolie, Gregg

GREGG ROLIE.
Album: released on CBS, Oct'85 by CBS Records. Dist: CBS

Cassette: released on CBS, Oct'85 by CBS Records. Dist: CBS Deleted '87.

Roll Along Prairie Moon

ROLL ALONG PRAIRIE MOON various original artists (Various original artists).
Album: released on World, '78 Dist: Jetstar

Cassette: released on World. '78 Dist: Jetstar

Rollens, Audley

ALL I WANT.
Single (12"): released on Wackies, Dec'83 by Wackies Records. Dist: Jetstar

ROLE MODE.
Album: released on Wackies, Apr'84 by Wackies Records. Dist: Jetstar

Rollercoaster Rockers

ROLLERCOASTER ROCKERS VOL.1 various artists (Various Artists).
Album: released on Rollercoaster, May'85 by Rollercoaster Records. Dist: Swift Distribution, Rollercoaster Distribution

Roller Disco

NON STOP CHRISTMAS DISCO (Roller Disco Orchestra).
Double Album: released on Pickwick, Oct'79 by Pickwick Records. Dist: Pickwick Distribution, Prism Leisure Distribution, Lugtons

ROLLER DISCO various session artists.
Cassette: released on AIM (Budget Cassettes), Feb'83

Rolling Stones

12 X 5.
Album: released on Decca, Aug'84 by Decca Records. Dist: Polygram

Cassette: released on Decca, Aug'84 by Decca Records. Dist: Polygram

Compact disc: released on Decca, Aug'84 by Decca Records. Dist: Polygram

12 X 5.
Tracks: / Around & around / Confessin' the blues / Empty heart / Time is on my side / Good times, bad times / It's all over now / 2120 south Michigan Avenue / Under the boardwalk / Congratulations / Grown up wrong / If you need me / Susie Q.
Compact disc: released on London, Nov'84 by London Records. Dist: Polygram

1965/70.
Album: released on Decca (Import), Feb'83 by Decca Records. Dist: Polygram, IMS

Cassette: released on Decca (Import), Feb'83 by Decca Records. Dist: Polygram, IMS

19TH NERVOUS BREAKDOWN.
Single (7"): released on Decca(re-issue), Mar'82 by Decca Records. Dist: Polygram, IMS

AFTERMATH.
Tracks: / Mother's little helper / Stupid girl / Lady Jane / Under my thumb / Doncha brother me / Goin' home / Flight 505 / High and dry / Out of time / It's not easy / I am waiting / Take it or leave it / Think / What to do.
Album: released on Decca, May'85 by Decca Records. Dist: Polygram

Compact disc: released on Decca, May'85 by Decca Records. Dist: Polygram

ANGIE.
Single (7"): released on Rolling Stones, '74 Dist: EMI, WEA Distribution

Single (7"): released on EMI (France), Apr'83 by EMI Records. Dist: Conifer

AT THEIR SATANIC MAJESTIES REQUEST.
Tracks: / Sing this all together / Citadel / In another land A.2,ooo man / Sing this all together (see what happens) / She's a rainbow / Lantern,The / Gomper / 2,000 light years from home / On with the show ..A Bill Wyman.
Compact disc: released on London, Feb'86 by London Records. Dist: Polygram

BEGGARS BANQUET.
Tracks: / Sympathy for the devil / No expectations / Dear Doctor / Parachute woman / Jigsaw puzzle / Street fighting man / Prodigal son / Stray cat blues / Factory girl / Salt of the earth.
Compact disc: released on Decca, Jan'83 by Decca Records. Dist: Polygram

BETWEEN THE BUTTONS.
Tracks: / Let's spend the night together / Yesterday's paper / Ruby Tuesday / Connection / She smiled sweetly / Cool calm and collected / All sold out / My obsession / Who's been sleeping here / Complicated / Miss Amanda Jones / Something happened to me yesterday.
Compact disc: released on Decca, Jul'85 by Decca Records. Dist: Polygram

BETWEEN THE SHEETS.
Album: released on Decca, Apr'85 by Decca Records. Dist: Polygram

BIG HITS HIGH TIDE & GREEN GRASS.
Album: released on Decca, '66 by Decca Records. Dist: Polygram

Cassette: released on Decca, '66 by Decca Records. Dist: Polygram

BLACK & BLUE.
Tracks: / Hot stuff / Hand of fate / Cherry oh baby / Memory motel / Hey Negrita / Melody / Fool to cry / Crazy mama.
Compact disc: released on CBS, Dec'86 by CBS Records. Dist: CBS

BROWN SUGAR.
Picture disc single: released on Rolling Stones, Jul'84 Dist: EMI, WEA Distribution

Single (7"): released on Rolling Stones, Jun'84 Dist: EMI, WEA Distribution

Single (7"): released on Rolling Stones, Nov'76 Dist: EMI, WEA Distribution

COME ON.
Single (7"): released on Decca(re-issue), Mar'82 by Decca Records. Dist: Polygram, IMS

DECEMBER'S CHILDREN.
Album: released on Import Music Service (IMS), Mar'81 Dist: Concord Jazz Distributions, Pablo, Polygram

DIRTY WORK.
Tracks: / One hit / Fight / Harlem shuffle / Hold back / Too rude / Winning ugly / Back to zero / Dirty work / Had it with you / Sleep tonight.
Album: released on CBS, May'86 by CBS Records. Dist: CBS

Cassette: released on CBS, May'86 by CBS Records. Dist: CBS

Compact disc: released on CBS, May'86 by CBS Records. Dist: CBS

EMOTIONAL RESCUE.
Single (7"): released on Rolling Stones, Jun'80 Dist: EMI, WEA Distribution

EMOTIONAL RESCUE.
Tracks: / Summer romance / Send it to me / Let me go / Indian girl / Where the boys go / Down in the hole / Emotional rescue / She's so cold / All about you.
Compact disc: released on CBS, Dec'86 by CBS Records. Dist: CBS

EXILE ON MAIN STREET.
Tracks: / Soul survivor / Rocks off / Rip this joint / Shake Your Hips / Casino boogie / Tumbling dice / Sweet Virginia / Torn & frayed / Sweet black angel / Loving cup / Happy / Turd on the run / Ventilator blues / I just want to see his face / Let it loose / All down the line / Stop breaking down / Shine a light / Rocks off / Rip this joint / Shake your hips / Casino boogie / Tumbling dice / Sweet Virgina / Torn and frayed / Sweet black angel / Loving cup / Happy / Turd on the run / Ventilator blues / I just want to see his face / Let it loose / All down the line / Stop breaking down / Shine a light / Soul survivor.
Compact disc: released on CBS, Dec'86 by CBS Records. Dist: CBS

Album: released on CBS, Sep'87 by CBS Records. Dist: CBS

Cassette: released on CBS, Sep'87 by CBS Records. Dist: CBS

FOOL TO CRY.
Single (7"): released on Rolling Stones, May'76 Dist: EMI, WEA Distribution

GET OFF MY CLOUD.
Single (7"): released on Decca(re-issue), Mar'82 by Decca Records. Dist: Polygram, IMS

GIMME SHELTER.
Album: released on Decca, '71 by Decca Records. Dist: Polygram

Cassette: released on Decca, '71 by Decca Records. Dist: Polygram

GOATS HEAD SOUP.
Tracks: / Dancing with Mr.D / 100 years ago / Coming down again / Doo doo doo doo(Heartbraker) / Angie / Angie / Silver train / Hide your love / Winter / Can you hear the music / Star star.
Compact disc: released on CBS, Dec'86 by CBS Records. Dist: CBS

GOING TO A GO-GO.
Single (7"): released on Rolling Stones, Jun'82 Dist: EMI, WEA Distribution

HARLEM SHUFFLE.
Tracks: / Harlem shuffle,The / Had it with you / Harlem shuffle (New York Mix) / Harlem shuffle (London Mix).
Single (7"): released on CBS, Mar'86 by CBS Records. Dist: CBS

Single (12"): released on CBS, Mar'86 by CBS Records. Dist: CBS

Single (12"): released on CBS, Mar'86 by CBS Records. Dist: CBS

HAVE YOU SEEN YOUR MOTHER BABY.
Single (7"): released on Decca(re-issue), Mar'82 by Decca Records. Dist: Polygram, IMS

HONKY TONK WOMEN.
Single (7"): released on Decca-Originals, May'82 by Decca Records. Dist: Polygram, IMS

HOT ROCK.
Compact disc: released on Decca, Jan'83 by Decca Records. Dist: Polygram

HOT ROCKS 1.
Tracks: / Time is on my side / Heart of stone / Play with fire / I can't get no satisfaction / As tears go by / Get off of my cloud / Mother's little helper / 19th nervous breakdown / Paint it black / Under my thumb / Ruby Tuesday / Let's spend the night together.
Compact disc: released on London, Aug'85 by London Records. Dist: Polygram
Cat. no: **820 141-2**

HOT ROCKS 2.
Tracks: / Jumpin' Jack Flash / Sympathy for the devil / Street fighting man / Gimme shelter / You can't always get what you want / Honky tonky woman / Midnight rambler / Brown sugar / Wild horses.
Compact disc: released on London, Aug'85 by London Records. Dist: Polygram

I CAN'T GET NO SATISFACTION.
Album: released on Decca (Holland), Feb'84 by Decca Records. Dist: Polygram, IMS

Cassette: released on Decca (Holland), Feb'84 by Decca Records. Dist: Polygram, IMS

IN CONCERT:ROLLING STONES.
Double Album: released on Telefunken (Germany), Dec'81 Dist: Decca Distribution, IMS, Polygram

Double cassette: released on Telefunken (Germany), Dec'81 Dist: Decca Distribution, IMS, Polygram

IT'S ALL OVER NOW.
Single (7"): released on Decca(re-issue), Mar'82 by Decca Records. Dist: Polygram, IMS

IT'S ONLY ROCK'N'ROLL.
Single (7"): released on Rolling Stones, '74 Dist: EMI, WEA Distribution

IT'S ONLY ROCK'N'ROLL.
Tracks: / If you can't rock me / Ain't too proud to beg / It's only rock'n'roll / Till the next goodbye / Luxury / Time waits for no one / Dance little sister / If you really want to be my friend / Short & curlies / Fingerprint file.
Compact disc: released on CBS, Dec'86 by CBS Records. Dist: CBS

I WANNA BE YOUR MAN.
Single (7"): released on Decca(re-issue), Mar'82 by Decca Records. Dist: Polygram, IMS

JUMPING JACK FLASH.
Tracks: / Jumping Jack Flash / Child of the man / Sympathy for the devil.
Single (12"): released on Decca, May'87 by Decca Records. Dist: Polygram

Single (7"): released on Decca, May'87 by Decca Records. Dist: Polygram

Single (7"): released on Decca(re-issue), Mar'82 by Decca Records. Dist: Polygram, IMS

LAST TIME.
Single (7"): released on Decca(re-issue), Mar'82 by Decca Records. Dist: Polygram, IMS

LET IT BLEED.
Tracks: / Gimmi shelter / Love in vain / Country honk / Live with me / Let it bleed / Midnight rambler / You got the silver / Monkey man / You can't always get what you want.
Compact disc: released on London, Feb'86 by London Records. Dist: Polygram

Album: released on Decca, '70 by Decca Records. Dist: Polygram

Cassette: released on Decca, '70 by Decca Records. Dist: Polygram

LET'S SPEND THE NIGHT TOGETHER.
Single (7"): released on Rolling Stones, May'83 Dist: EMI, WEA Distribution

LETS SPEND THE NIGHT TOGETHER/RUBY TUESDAY.
Single (7"): released on Decca-Originals, May'82 by Decca Records. Dist: Polygram, IMS

LITTLE RED ROOSTER.
Single (7"): released on Decca(re-issue), '64 by Decca Records. Dist: Polygram, IMS

LOVE YOU LIVE.
Tracks: / Fanfare for the common man / Honky tonk woman / If you can't rock me / Get off my cloud / Happy / Hot stuff / Star star / Tumbling dice / Fingerprint file / You gotta move / You can't always get what you want / Mannish boy / Crackin' up / Little red rooster / Around and around / It's only rock 'n' roll / Brown sugar / Jumping Jack Flash / Sympathy for the devil.
Compact disc: released on CBS, Dec'86 by CBS Records. Dist: CBS

Album: released on CBS, Sep'87 by CBS Records. Dist: CBS

Cassette: released on CBS, Sep'87 by CBS Records. Dist: CBS

MADE IN THE SHADE.
Tracks: / Dancing with Mr. D / 100 years ago / Coming down again / Doo doo doo doo (Heartbreaker) / Angie / Silver train / Hide your love / Can you hear the magic? / Winter / Star star.
Compact disc: released on CBS, Dec'86 by CBS Records. Dist: CBS

MISS YOU.
Single (12"): released on EMI Europe, Sep'84 by EMI Records. Dist: Conifer

MUSIC FOR THE MILLIONS.
Album: released on Polydor (Holland), Jul'83

Cassette: released on Polydor (Holland), Jul'83

NOT FADE AWAY/LITTLE BY LITTLE.
Single (7"): released on Decca-Originals, May'82 by Decca Records. Dist: Polygram, IMS

ONE HIT TO THE BODY.
Tracks: / One hit to the body / Fight.
Single (7"): released on Rolling Stones, May'86 Dist: EMI, WEA Distribution

Single (12"): released on Rolling Stones, May'86 Dist: EMI, WEA Distribution

OUT OF OUR HEADS.
Tracks: / She said 'yeah' / Mercy mercy / Hitch hike / That's how strong my love is / Good times / Gotta get away / Talkin bout you / Cry to me / Oh baby / Heart of stone / Under assistant west coast promotion man,The / I'm free.
Compact disc: released on Decca, Nov'84 by Decca Records. Dist: Polygram

Album: released on Decca, Aug'84 by Decca Records. Dist: Polygram

Cassette: released on Decca, Aug'84 by Decca Records. Dist: Polygram

PAINT IT BLACK.
Single (7"): released on Decca(re-issue), Mar'82 by Decca Records. Dist: Polygram, IMS

PRECIOUS STONES.
Picture disc album: released on Astan, Dec'85 by Astan Records. Dist: Counterpoint

RESPECTABLE.
Single (7"): released on EMI, Sep'78 by EMI Records. Dist: EMI

REWIND.
Tracks: / Brown sugar / Undercover of the night / Start me up / Tumbling dice / It's only rock 'n'roll (but I like it) / She's so cold / Miss you / Beast of burden / Fool to cry / Waiting on a friend / Angie / Respectable.
Notes: Cassette also includes : Hang fire/Emotional rescue
Compact disc: released on CBS, Dec'86 by CBS Records. Dist: CBS

ROLLED GOLD.
Double Album: released on Decca, Nov'75 by Decca Records. Dist: Polygram

Double cassette: released on Decca, Nov'75 by Decca Records. Dist: Polygram

ROLLING STONES.
Tracks: / Route 66 / I just want to make love to you / Honest I do / I need you baby / Now i've got a witness / Little by little / I'm a king bee / Carol / Tell me (you're coming back) / Can I get a witness / You can make it if you try / Walking the dog.
Compact disc: released on London, '85 by London Records. Dist: Polygram

Album: released on Decca, Jul'84 by Decca Records. Dist: Polygram

Cassette: released on Decca, Jul'84 by Decca Records. Dist: Polygram

Compact disc: released on Decca, Jul'84 by Decca Records. Dist: Polygram

ROLLING STONES (EP).
Single (7"): released on Decca, Dec'83 by Decca Records. Dist: Polygram

Single (12"): released on Decca, Dec'83 by Decca Records. Dist: Polygram

ROLLING STONES,THE VOL 2.
Album: released on Decca, '65 by Decca Records. Dist: Polygram

Cassette: released on Decca, '65 by Decca Records. Dist: Polygram

SATISFACTION.
Single (7"): released on Decca(re-issue), Mar'82 by Decca Records. Dist: Polygram, IMS

SHE'S SO COLD/SEND IT TO ME.
Single (7"): released on Rollin' Rock, Sep'80

SHE WAS HOT/I THINK I'M GOING MAD.
Single (7"): released on Rolling Stones, Jan'84 Dist: EMI, WEA Distribution

Single (12"): released on Rolling Stones, Jan'84 Dist: EMI, WEA Distribution

SLOW ROLLERS.
Album: released on Decca, Sep'81 by Decca Records. Dist: Polygram

Cassette: released on Decca, Sep'81 by Decca Records. Dist: Polygram

SOLID ROCK.
Album: released on Decca, Oct'80 by Decca Records. Dist: Polygram

Cassette: released on Decca, Oct'82 by Decca Records. Dist: Polygram

SOME GIRLS.
Tracks: / Miss you / When the whip comes down / Just my imagination / Some girls / Lies / Faraway eyes / Respectable / Before they make me run / Beast of burden / Shattered / Some girls / Princess.
Compact disc: released on CBS, Dec'86 by CBS Records. Dist: CBS

Album: released on CBS, Sep'87 by CBS Records. Dist: CBS

Cassette: released on CBS, Sep'87 by CBS Records. Dist: CBS

START ME UP/NO USE IN CRYING.
Single (7"): released on Rolling Stones, Aug'81 Dist: EMI, WEA Distribution

STICKY FINGERS.
Tracks: / Brown sugar / Sway / Wild horses / Can't hear me knocking? / You gotta move / Bitch / I got the blues / Sister morphine / Dead flowers / Moonlight mile.
Compact disc: released on CBS, Dec'86 by CBS Records. Dist: CBS

STILL LIFE American Concert 1981.
Tracks: / Under my thumb / Let's spend the night together / Shattered / Twenty flight rock / Going to a go-go / Let me go / Time is on my side / Just my imagination / Start me up / Satisfaction.
Compact disc: released on CBS, Dec'86 by CBS Records. Dist: CBS

STONES STORY VOL.1.
Double Album: released on Decca (Import), Sep'82 by Decca Records. Dist: Polygram, IMS

Double cassette: released on Decca (Import), Sep'82 by Decca Records. Dist: Polygram, IMS

STONES STORY VOL.2.
Double Album: released on Decca (Import), Sep'82 by Decca Records. Dist: Polygram, IMS

Double cassette: released on Decca (Import), Sep'82 by Decca Records. Dist: Polygram, IMS

STONES STORY VOL.3.
Double cassette: released on Decca (Import), Sep'82 by Decca Records. Dist: Polygram, IMS

Double Album: released on Decca (Import), Sep'82 by Decca Records. Dist: Polygram, IMS

STORY OF THE STONES,THE.
Album: released on K-Tel, Nov'82 by K-Tel Records. Dist: Record Merchandisers Distribution, Taylors, Terry Blood Distribution, Wynd-Up Distribution, Relay Distribution, Pickwick Distribution, Solomon & Peres Distribution, Polygram

Cassette: released on K-Tel, Nov'82 by K-Tel Records. Dist: Record Merchandisers Distribution, Taylors, Terry Blood Distribution, Wynd-Up Distribution, Relay Distribution, Pickwick Distribution, Solomon & Peres Distribution, Polygram

STREET FIGHTING MAN/SURPRISE/EVERBODY NEEDS.
Single (7"): released on Decca, Mar'82 by Decca Records. Dist: Polygram

SUCKING IN THE SEVENTIES.
Tracks: / Shattered / Everything is turning to gold / Hot stuff / Time waits for no-one / Fool to cry / Mannish boy / When the whip comes down / If I was a dancer / Crazy Mama / Beast of burden.
Compact disc: released on CBS, Dec'86 by CBS Records. Dist: CBS

TATTOO YOU.
Tracks: / Start me up / Hang fire / Slave / Little T.A. / Black limousine / No use in crying / Neighbours / Worried about you / Tops / Heaven / Waiting for a friend.
Compact disc: released on CBS, Dec'86 by CBS Records. Dist: CBS

THEIR SATANIC MAJASTIES REQUEST.
Album: released on Decca, Dec'67 by Decca Records. Dist: Polygram

TIME IS ON MY SIDE/20 FLIGHT ROCK.
Single (7"): released on Rolling Stones, Sep'82 Dist: EMI, WEA Distribution

Single (12"): released on Rolling Stones, Sep'82 Dist: EMI, WEA Distribution

TUMBLING DICE.
Single (7"): released on Rolling Stones, '80 Dist: EMI, WEA Distribution

TWENTY SUPER HITS.
Album: released on Telefunken, Feb'79

UNDER COVER.
Tracks: / Too much blood / Pretty beat up / Too tough / All the way down / It must be hell / Undercover of the night / She was hot / Tie you up (The pain of love) / Wanna hold you / Feel on baby.
Compact disc: released on CBS, Dec'86 by CBS Records. Dist: CBS

Compact disc: released on Rolling Stones, Mar'84 Dist: EMI, WEA Distribution

Album: released on Rolling Stones, Nov'83 Dist: EMI, WEA Distribution

Cassette: released on Rolling Stones, Nov'83 Dist: EMI, WEA Distribution

UNDERCOVER OF THE NIGHT/ALL THE WAY DOWN/FEEL ON BABY.
Single (7"): released on Rolling Stones, Oct'83 Dist: EMI, WEA Distribution

Single (12"): released on Rolling Stones, Oct'83 Dist: EMI, WEA Distribution

VIDEO REWIND.
Video-cassette (VHS): released on Vestron, Jan'86

WAITING ON A FRIEND.
Single (7"): released on Rolling Stones, Nov'81 Dist: EMI, WEA Distribution

WE LOVE YOU/DANDELION.
Single (7"): released on Decca, Mar'82 by Decca Records. Dist: Polygram

Rolling Thunder

LONESOME.
Album: released on Hell's Kitchen, Feb'86 Dist: Red Rhino, Cartel

Rollins, Audrey

ALL I WANT.
Single (12"): released on Wackies, Dec'83 by Wackies Records. Dist: Jetstar

Rollins, Henry

HOT ANIMAL MACHINE.
Album: released on Fundamental, Aug'87 by Fundamental Records. Dist: Red Rhino, Cartel

Rollins, Sonny

ALTERNATE TAKES.
Album: released on Contemporary, Nov'86 by Contemporary Records. Dist: Pinnacle

ALTERNATIVE ROLLINS, THE With Herbie Hancok, Ron Carter, Jim Hall etc..
Double Album: released on RCA (France), '83 by RCA Records. Dist: Discovery

ARTISTRY IN JAZZ Greatest hits.
Compact disc: released on JVC Fantasy (Japan), May'87

BRASS TRIO.
Tracks: / Who cares / Love is a simple thing / Grand street / Far out east / What's my name? / If you were the only girl in the world / Manhattan / Body and soul.
Compact disc: released on Verve, Apr'84 by Phonogram Records. Dist: Polygram

Album: released on Verve (USA), Apr'83 by Polydor. Dist: Polygram

CONTEMPORARY LEADERS.
Compact disc: released on Boplicity, Jul'87 by Boplicity Records. Dist: Ace Records, Pinnacle

EAST BROADWAY RUN DOWN.
Album: released on Jasmine, Mar'83 by Jasmine Records. Dist: Counterpoint, Lugtons, Taylor, H.R., Wellard, Chris, Swift, Cadillac

ESSENTIAL, THE.
Compact disc: released on Fantasy (USA), Apr'87 by Fantasy Inc USA Records. Dist: IMS, Polygram

FREEDOM SUITE.
Compact disc: released on Vanguard (USA), Apr'86

IN STOCKHOLM 1959 (Rollins, Sonny Trio).
Album: released on Dragon, Jun'86 by Dragon Records. Dist: Jazz Music, Projection, Cadillac

Album: released on Dragon, Jan'85 by Dragon Records. Dist: Jazz Music, Projection, Cadillac

IN SWEDEN 1959.
Album: released on Ingo, Jul'83 Dist: Jazz Horizons, Jazz Music, Celtic Music

ISLAND LADY.
Album: released on Lotus, Apr'81

LIVE IN EUROPE.
Album: released on Unique Jazz (Import), Apr'81

LIVE IN JAPAN.
Album: released on G.I., Apr'78 by G.I. Records. Dist: G.I. Records

MASTERS OF JAZZ.
Album: released on RCA (Germany), '83

NEWK'S TIME.
Album: released on Blue Note (USA Import), Sep'84 Deleted '87.

NIGHT AT THE VILLAGE VANGUARD VOL.1.
Tracks: / Night in Tunisia, A / I've got you under my skin / Softly as in a morning sunrise / Four / Woody 'n' you / Old devil moon.
Notes: P 1986 Manhattan Records,a division of Capitol Records Inc. Tenor saxophonist Sonny Rollins was at the height of his considerable creative powers in the mid fifties. This daring session is one of the finest examples from the period. HereRollins takes the bandstand with only Wilbur Ware's bass and Elvin Jones' drums behind, Two of his best known compositions 'Striver's Row' and 'Sonnymoon For Two' made their debut here. Rollins' interpretations of standard have been his trademark andhis performances of 'Old Devil Moon' and 'Softly As In A Morning Sunrise' on this set are masterful.
Cassette: released on Blue Note, Apr'87 by EMI Records. Dist: EMI

Album: released on Blue Note, Apr'87 by EMI Records. Dist: EMI

Compact disc: released on Manhattan-Blue Note, May'87 by EMI America Records (USA). Dist: EMI

NIGHT AT THE VILLAGE VANGUARD VOL.2.
Tracks: / What is thing called love / Softly as in a morning sunrise(take 2) / Sonnymoon for two / I can't get started / I'll remember April / Get happy / Strivers row / All the things you are / Get happy(short version).
Compact disc: released on Manhattan-Blue Note, May'87 by EMI America Records (USA). Dist: EMI

Cassette: released on Blue Note, May'87 by EMI Records. Dist: EMI

NO PROBLEM.
Album: released on Milestone, Jul'82 by Ace Records. Dist: PRT

ON IMPULSE.
Album: released on Jasmine, Jun'82 by Jasmine Records. Dist: Counterpoint, Lugtons, Taylor, H.R., Wellard, Chris, Swift, Cadillac

Cassette: released on Jasmine, Jun'82 by Jasmine Records. Dist: Counterpoint, Lugtons, Taylor, H.R., Wellard, Chris, Swift, Cadillac

ON IMPULSE.
Tracks: / On green dolphin street / Everything happens to me / Hold 'em Joe / Blue room / Three little words.
Compact disc: released on Impulse, Feb'87 by Impulse Records. Dist: MCA, Polygram

PLUS ELEVEN.
Compact disc: released on Boplicity, Jul'87 by Boplicity Records. Dist: Ace Records, Pinnacle

PLUS FOUR.
Compact disc: released on Vanguard (USA), Apr'86

QUARTET (THE).
Tracks: / God bless the child / John S. / You do something to me / Where are you / Without a song / Bridge, The / If ever I would leave you / Brownskin girl / Don't stop the carnival / Night has a thousand eyes, The / My ship / Love letters / Long ago (and far away).
Album: released on RCA, Feb'87 by RCA Records. Dist: RCA, Roots, Swift, Wellard, Chris, I & B, Solomon & Peres Distribution

Cassette: released on RCA, Feb'87 by RCA Records. Dist: RCA, Roots, Swift, Wellard, Chris, I & B, Solomon & Peres Distribution

ROLLINS PLAYS FOR BIRD (Rollins, Sonny Quintet).
Album:

SAXOPHONE COLOSSUS.
Compact disc: released on Vanguard (USA), Apr'86

Compact disc: released on Carrere, Apr'87 by Carrere Records. Dist: PRT, Spartan

SOLO ALBUM (THE).
Tracks: / Soloscope (Part 1) / Sonny Rollins - Tenor saxophone / Soloscope (Part 2).
Notes: Sonny Rollins has been a major force in jazz since 1957 when he won the Down Beat critics poll as New Star. One critic wrote 'No other jazzman approaches him insustaining the creativity and aesthetic balance of solo work ... Rollins has performed entire concerts by himself in brilliant style as if he were accompanied by a huge orchestra'. This new album was recorded live in New Yorkon 19th July 1985 and features a Sonny Rollins original extended composition titled 'Soloscope'.
Compact disc: released on JVC Fantasy (Japan), '86

Album: released on Fantasy (USA), Feb'86 by Fantasy Inc USA Records. Dist: IMS, Polygram

Compact disc: released on Carrere, Apr'87 by Carrere Records. Dist: PRT, Spartan

SONNY ROLLINS (IN EUROPE).
Album: released on Unique Jazz, '81 Dist: Swift, Jazz Music, Jazz Horizons

SONNY ROLLINS PLUS FOUR.
Compact disc: released on JVC Fantasy (Japan), '86

Album:

SONNY ROLLINS & THE CONTEMPARY LEADERS PLUS.
Compact disc: released on Contemporary, Jun'87 by Contemporary Records. Dist: Pinnacle

Album: released on Contemporary, Apr'86 by Contemporary Records. Dist: Pinnacle

SONNY ROLLINS VOL.2.
Cassette: released on Blue Note, Apr'87 by EMI Records. Dist: EMI

Album: released on Blue Note, Apr'87 by EMI Records. Dist: EMI

SOUND OF SONNY, THE.
Album: released on Gateway, Nov'79 by Kingdom. Dist: Pinnacle

STUTTGART 1963 CONCERT.
Album: released on Jazz Connoisseur (Italy), Jul'81 Dist: Jazz Horizons, Jazz Music, Swift, Wellard, Chris

SUNNY DAYS, STARRY NIGHTS.
Tracks: / Mava mava / I'm old fashioned / Wynton / Tell me you love me / I'll see you again / Klauea.
Notes: Personnel: Sonny Rollins-tenor sax/Clifton Anderson-trombone/Mark Soskin-keyboards/Russel Blake-electric bass/Tommy Campbell-drums.
Compact disc: released on Fantasy (USA), Jan'87 by Fantasy Inc USA Records. Dist: IMS, Polygram

Compact disc: released on Carrere, Apr'87 by Carrere Records. Dist: PRT, Spartan

TENOR MADNESS.
Compact disc: released on JVC Fantasy (Japan), May'87

TOUR DE FORCE.
Album: released on Prestige (USA), Aug'84

VOLUME ONE.
Tracks: / Decision / Bluenote / How are things on Glocca / Plain Jane / Sonn phere.
Album: released on Blue Note, May'85 by EMI Records. Dist: EMI

Cassette: released on Blue Note, May'85 by EMI Records. Dist: EMI

VOLUME TWO.
Album: released on Blue Note, Jul'85 by EMI Records. Dist: EMI

WAY OUT WEST.
Compact disc: released on Mobile Fidelity, '86 by Mobile Fidelity Records.

Compact disc: released on Carrere, Apr'87 by Carrere Records. Dist: PRT, Spartan

Compact disc: released on Boplicity, Jul'87 by Boplicity Records. Dist: Ace Records, Pinnacle

Album: released on Boplicity, Aug'85 by Boplicity Records. Dist: Ace Records, Pinnacle

WAY OUT WEST PLUS.
Compact disc: released on Contemporary, Jun'87 by Contemporary Records. Dist: Pinnacle

Rollin' The Rock

ROLLIN' THE ROCK VOL.1 various artists (Various Artists).
Album: released on Rollin' Rock, Jun'80

ROLLIN' THE ROCK VOL.2 various artists (Various Artists).
Album: released on Rollin' Rock, Jun'80

ROLLIN' THE ROCK VOL.3 various artists (Various Artists).
Album: released on Rollin' Rock, Jun'80

Rollin'Thunder

HOWL.
Tracks: / Atlantic to Pacific / B.A.R.B. / Pink and greens / Goin' south / Bloodstained legends / Shadow fall / Immortal soul / Street of lost causes / Once.
Album: released on Flicknife, Apr'87 by Flicknife Records. Dist: Spartan

HOWL.
Album: released on Flicknife, Mar'87 by Flicknife Records. Dist: Spartan

Roll Over Beethoven

ROLL OVER BEETHOVEN various artists (Various Artists).
Album: released on Telebell, Apr'85 by Towerbell Records. Dist: EMI

Cassette: released on Telebell, Apr'85 by Towerbell Records. Dist: EMI

Rollright, Craig

YOUNG GIRL WITH CHINESE EYES.
Single (7"): released on A Record Company, Jul'84 by A Record company. Dist: CBS

Roll Ups

BLACKMAIL.
Single (7"): released on Bridgehouse, Jan'80 Dist: Pinnacle

Roly Poly

LUMPY LUMP LUMP.
Single (7"): released on Crash, May'83 by Satril Records. Dist: PRT

Romance Of The Movies

ROMANCE OF THE MOVIES Various artists (Various Artists).
Album: released on Spot, Sep'84 by Pickwick Records. Dist: H.R. Taylor, Lugtons

Cassette: released on Spot, Sep'84 by Pickwick Records. Dist: H.R. Taylor, Lugtons

Romancers

ROMANCERS (Saki) read by Hugh Burden (Romancers & Others).
Cassette: released on Talking Tape Company, Aug'81 by Talking Tape Company Records.

Romanelli

CONNECTING FLIGHT.
Single (7"): released on 21 Records, Jul'82 by Polydor Records. Dist: Polydor

Single (12"): released on 21 Records, Jul'82 by Polydor Records. Dist: Polydor

Roman Grey

LOOK ME IN THE EYES.
Single (7"): released on Food For Thought, Apr'83 by Food For Thought Records. Dist: Pinnacle

SHAKEDOWN.
Single (12"): released on Food For Thought, Jun'84 by Food For Thought Records. Dist: Pinnacle

Roman Holiday

COOKIN' ON THE ROOF.
Album: released on Jive, Oct'83 by Zomba Records. Dist: RCA, PRT, CBS

Cassette: released on Jive, Oct'83 by Zomba Records. Dist: RCA, PRT, CBS

DON'T TRY TO STOP IT.
Single (7"): released on Jive, Jun'83 by Zomba Records. Dist: RCA, PRT, CBS

Single (12"): released on Jive, Jun'83 by Zomba Records. Dist: RCA, PRT, CBS

FIRE ME UP.
Single (7"): released on Jive, Aug'84 by Zomba Records. Dist: RCA, PRT, CBS

Single (12"): released on Jive, Aug'84 by Zomba Records. Dist: RCA. PRT, CBS

MOTOR MANIA.
Single (7"): released on Jive, Sep'83 by Zomba Records. Dist: RCA, PRT, CBS

Single (12"): released on Jive, Sep'83 by Zomba Records. Dist: RCA, PRT, CBS

ONE FOOT BACK IN YOUR DOOR.
Single (7"): released on Jive, Feb'85 by Zomba Records. Dist: RCA, PRT, CBS

Single (12"): released on Jive, Feb'85 by Zomba Records. Dist: RCA, PRT, CBS

STAND BY.
Double-pack single: released on Jive, Jan'83 by Zomba Records. Dist: RCA, PRT, CBS

Single (7"): released on Jive, Mar'83 by Zomba Records. Dist: RCA, PRT, CBS

Single (12"): released on Jive, Mar'83 by Zomba Records. Dist: RCA, PRT, CBS

TOUCH TOO MUCH.
Single (7"): released on Jive, May'85 by Zomba Records. Dist: RCA, PRT, CBS

Single (12"): released on Jive, May'85 by Zomba Records. Dist: RCA, PRT, CBS

Romanian Virtuosi

CONCERT DES VIRTUOSES ROUMAINS.
Album: released on Cellier, Mar'79 Dist: Conifer

Roman, Johnny

BUONA SERA.
Single (7"): released on Crazy Viking, Jul'83 by Crazy Vikings Records. Dist: Pinnacle

KING OF ROCK 'N' ROLL.
Single (7"): released on Young Blood, Aug'87 by Young Blood Records. Dist: Pinnacle

Single (12"): released on Young Blood, Aug'87 by Young Blood Records. Dist: Pinnacle

Romans

LAST DAYS AT THE RANGE.
Album: released on Enigma, Nov'86 by Enigma Records. Dist: Rough Trade, Cartel, EMI

Romantic...

ROMANTIC CLARINET FOR LOVERS Various artists (Various Artists).
Tracks: / Stranger on the shore / Sentimental journey / Alley cat / In San Francisco (I left my heart) / Let's put out the lights / Here's that rainy day / You don't know how much you can suffer / Forbidden games / LO.V.E. / Love walked in / Night lights / I'll walk alone / Easy living / Last spring that old feeling / Memories of you / Lonesome.
Compact disc: released on Phonogram Import, '84

ROMANTIC GUITAR FOR LOVERS Various artists (Various Artists).
Tracks: / Your song / Once upon a time in the west / Do you know where you're going to? (Mahogany theme) / If / How insensitive / Alone at last / Emmanuelle / Don't cry for me Argentina / Aranjuez / Sing along junk / Summertime / Body and soul / Autumn leaves / I sing to the moon / Who can I turn to? / Here there and everywhere.
Compact disc: released on Phonogram Import, '84

ROMANTIC NIGHTS 20 Romantic reggae songs (Various Artists).
Notes: Artists include: Dennis Brown,Chalice,Errol Dunkley,John Holt,Gregory Isaacs etc
Compact disc: released on Sound-CSA, May'87

ROMANTIC NIGHTS (20 SONGS FOR LOVERS) Various artists (Various Artists).
Tracks: / Funny feeling / How could I let you get away / Betcha by golly wow / Vaya con dios / My devotion / My time / What a feeling / You move me / True love / I never knew love / Aware of your love / Nice time / Shine eye gal / It's you gal / No time to lose / My love / Sticky wicket / Peek-a-boo / I'm in the mood / Girl is mine, The.
Album: released on CSA, Dec'86 by CSA Records. Dist: PRT, Jetstar

Single (7"): released on CSA, Nov'86 by CSA Records. Dist: PRT, Jetstar

Compact disc: released on CSA, Jun'87 by CSA Records. Dist: PRT, Jetstar

ROMANTIC PIANO FOR LOVERS Various artists (Various Artists).
Tracks: / Ballade pour Adeline / Love story / Meditation / Desafinado / Corcovado / La comparsa / End, The / Imaginary landscapes / Just a simple love song / La chanson des vieux amants / Chanson pour Milan / Sunrise serenade / Strangers in the night / Forgotten dreams / Moonglow / Windmills of your mind, The.
Compact disc: released on Phonogram Import, '84

ROMANTIC POP SONGS FOR LOVERS Various artists (Various Artists).
Tracks: / Do that to me one more time / Princess / Dreamland / All my life, all my love / Stay with me till dawn / Memories / Killing me softly with his song / Tooralooralooraloo-Is it old and is it new / You and I / Gone are the days / I'm falling out of love / Joanna / Pirate / Miss you nights.
Compact disc: released on Phonogram, Apr'85 by Phonogram Records. Dist: Polygram

ROMANTIC SAX FOR LOVERS Various artists (Various Artists).
Tracks: / Three times a lady / Don't it make my brown eyes blue / You needed me / When I need you / Shadow of your smile, The / Second time around, The / PS I love you / Solitude / Woman in love / Abrazame / Are you lonesome tonight? / Broken promises / My man / Once I loved / Yesterdays / If / Harlem Nocturne / How insensitive.
Compact disc: released on Polydor Int., Nov'85

ROMANTIC TANGOS FROM BUENOS ARIES Various artists (Various Artists).
Album: released on CBS(France), May'85 by CBS Records. Dist: Conifer, Discovery, Swift

Cassette: released on CBS(France), May'85 by CBS Records. Dist: Conifer, Discovery, Swift

ROMANTIC THEMES (Various Artists).
Compact disc: released on K-Tel, May'87 by K-Tel Records. Dist: Record Merchandisers Distribution, Taylors, Terry Blood Distribution, Wynd-Up Distribution, Relay Distribution, Pickwick Distribution, Solomon & Peres Distribution, Polygram

ROMANTIC YEARS, THE All time greats from famous musicals.
Album: released on CJMO, Sep'79 Dist: Jazz Music, Spartan, Taylors

Romantics

NATIONAL BREAKOUT.
Album: released on Epic, Feb'81 by CBS Records. Dist: CBS

TALKING IN YOUR SLEEP.
Single (12"): released on Epic, Jan'84 by CBS Records. Dist: CBS

TOP OF THE WORLD.
Single (7"): released on Towerbell, Sep'82 by Towerbell Records. Dist: EMI

Romantique Orchestra

MEMORIES.
Double Album: released on Cambra, Feb'85 by Cambra Records. Dist: IDS, Conifer

Double cassette: released on Cambra, Feb'85 by Cambra Records. Dist: IDS, Conifer

Romany Tales

ROMANY TALES Various artists (Various Artists).
Cassette: released on Anvil, Jan'81 Dist: Anvil

Rome

SYMPATHY.
Tracks: / Sympathy / Listen to your heart.
Single (7"): released on Network, Oct'86 by Epic. Dist: PRT, CBS

Romeo and Juliet

LOVE THEME.
Single (7"): released on Stiff, Nov'85 by Stiff Records. Dist: EMI, Record Services Distribution (Ireland)

ROMEO AND JULIET Shakespeare, William (Various Artists).
Notes: Shakespeare's Romeo & Juliet is a romantic tragedy which takes place in 14th century Verona, and tells the story of two young lovers caught up in a deadly feud between their families, the Montagues and the Capulets - ending with the tragic suicides of both lovers. Performed superbly by a cast which includes famous actors and acresses such as Alan Badel, Claire Bloom, Peter Finch, AtheneSeyler and the Old Vic Company. Running time: 2 hrs. 30 mins. approx.
Cassette: released on LFP, Jun'87

Romeo, Jennifer

I'M NOT GUILTY.
Tracks: / I'm not guilty / Medley connection.
Single (12"): released on Pioneer International, Oct'86 by Pioneer International Records. Dist: Jetstar

YOU CAN WAKE UP WITH ME.
Tracks: / You can wake up with me / One life to live.
Single (12"): released on Pioneer International, Aug'86 by Pioneer International Records. Dist: Jetstar

Romeo, Max

I LOVE MY MUSIC.
Album: released on Solid Groove, '82 Dist: Jetstar, Pinnacle

OWEN GRAY MEETS MAX ROMEO (see Gray, Owen) (Romeo, Max & Owen Gray).

WAR INA BABYLON.
Album: released on Island, Aug'76 by Island Records. Dist: Polygram

WET DREAM.
Single (7"): released on Old Gold, Jul'82 by Old Gold Records. Dist: Lightning, Jazz Music, Spartan, Counterpoint

Romeo & Rose

EBONY AND IVORY.
Single (12"): released on Seara, Apr'82 by Seara Records. Dist: Jetstar

Romeo Void

GIRL IN TROUBLE (IS A TEMPORY THING), A.
Single (7"): released on 415, Oct'84 by CBS Records. Dist: CBS

SAY NO.
Single (7"): released on CBS, Jan'85 by CBS Records. Dist: CBS

Single (12"): released on CBS, Jan'85 by CBS Records. Dist: CBS

Romero, Celedonio

PROGRAM OF SPANISH GUITAR MUSIC, A (Romero, Celedonio & His Son Celin Romero).
Album: released on Contemporary (USA), Nov'83 Dist: Fantasy (USA) Distribution

Romero, Pepe

FLAMENCO.
Tracks: / Noche en malaga / Seguiri yas / Medias Granadinas.
Album: released on Contemporary(Import), May'83 Dist: IMS, Polygram

Rome, Toney

ROCK THIS WAY.
Single (7"): released on Rhythm King, Feb'87 Dist: Rough Trade, Cartel

Single (12"): released on Rhythm King, Feb'87 Dist: Rough Trade, Cartel

Ronalde, Ronnie

HAPPY WHISTLER, THE.
Album: released on World Records, Feb'81 Dist: Polygram

Cassette: released on World Records, Feb'81 Dist: Polygram

Rondelle, Gordon

AUTUMN LEAVE.
Single (7"): released on Igloo, Sep'85 by Igloo Records. Dist: M.I.S., EMI

Rondo, Jean

YOU WANT I TO BELIEVE A LIE.
Single (12"): released on R & H, Dec'82

Rondo, Johnny

LAS BICICLETAS.
Single (7"): released on Chiltern Sound, '78 by Chiltern Sound Records. Dist: JSU, Lightning, Pinnacle

Rondo Rondo

HELLO WORDS/MISSING PERSONS.
Single (7"): released on Scoff, Sep'81 Dist: Rough Trade, Cartel

Rondo Veneziano

GENIUS OF VENICE.
Compact disc: released on Fanfare, Nov'86 by Ferroway/Fanfare Records. Dist: PRT

Album: released on Ferroway, 11 Aug'4 Dist: PRT

Cassette: released on Ferroway, 11 Aug'4 Dist: PRT

LA SERENISSIMA.
Single (7"): released on Ferroway, Jun'84 Dist: PRT

LOVE THEME FROM "NOT QUITE JERUSALEM".
Single (7"): released on Fanfare, Mar'85 by Ferroway/Fanfare Records. Dist: PRT

ODDISEA.
Compact disc: released on Fanfare, Nov'86 by Ferroway/Fanfare Records. Dist: PRT

ODISSEA.
Single (7"): released on Fanfare, Oct'85 by Ferroway/Fanfare Records. Dist: PRT

SAN MARCO.
Single (7"): released on Ferroway, Oct'84 Dist: PRT

SINFONIA PER UN ADDIO.
Single (7"): released on Ferroway, Nov'83 Dist: PRT

Single (12"): released on Ferroway, Nov'83 Dist: PRT

VENICE.
Single (7"): released on Ferroway, Jan'84 Dist:

VENICE IN PERIL.
Compact disc: released on Fanfare, Nov'86 by Ferroway/Fanfare Records. Dist: PRT

VENICE IN PERIL.
Album: released on Ferroway, Oct'83 Dist: PRT

Cassette: released on Ferroway, Oct'83 Dist: PRT. Estim retail price in Jul'87 was £3.99.

Ronettes
BE MY BABY.
Single (7"): released on Phil Spector International, '80

FROSTY THE SNOWMAN.
Single (7"): released on Phil Spector, Dec'82

RONETTES SING THEIR GREATEST HITS.
Album: released on Phil Spector, Sep'75

Roni
CLEAN UP.
Single (12"): released on Love Shark, Jul'85

Ronk, Dave Von
YOUR BASIC.
Album: released on Sonet, Jun'82 by Sonet Records. Dist: PRT

Ron Levy's Wild Kingdom
RON LEVY'S WILD KINGDOM.
Album: released on Demon, Jan'87 by Demon Records. Dist: Pinnacle

Ronmar Accordion...
SOUNDS ACCORDION (Ronmar Accordion Orchestra).
Tracks: / Thunderer march, The / Bonanza two-step / Carnival of Venice / Sea shanty fantasy / Clarinet polka / Sorgenfrei / Carmen vorspiel / Cole Porter medley / Mrs Mary Printy / Ische suite / Dambuster's march.
Cassette: released on Accordion Record Club, Jul'86 by Accordion Record Club Records. Dist: Accordion Record Club

Ronmar Concert Orchestra
ROCK'N'ROMANCE.
Album: released on ARC (Accordion Records), '86 Dist: Accordion Record Club

Cassette: released on Arc, Aug'87 Dist: Arc

Ronnie Can You Hear Me?
VROOM FOR ROMANCE.
Single (7"): released on Ronnie, Jun'85 Dist: Backs, Cartel Distribution

Ronnie & Carl
DOWN BY THE RIVER.
Album: by Pilgrim Records. Dist: Rough Trade, Cartel

Ronnie & The Jitters
ROLL OVER.
Album: released on Nervous, Jul'84 by Nervous Records. Dist: Nervous, Rough Trade

Ronnie & The Ralders
THROUGH THE MIDDLE OF THE HOUSE.
Single (7"): released on Da Doo Ron Ron, Jun'85 by Da Doo Ron Ron Records. Dist: PRT

Ronnie & Yurl
SATELLITE ZAP.
Single (12"): released on Zap International, Jun'85 Dist: PRT

Ronson, Mick
BILLY PORTER.
Single (7"): released on RCA Golden Grooves, May'82 by RCA Records. Dist: RCA

Ronstadt, Linda
BACK IN THE USA.
Single (7"): released on Atlantic, '79 by WEA Records. Dist: WEA

DON'T CRY NOW.
Album: released on Asylum, '74 by WEA Records. Dist: WEA

FOR SENTIMENTAL REASONS.
Tracks: / When you wish upon a star / Bewitched / You go to my head / But not for me / My funny valentine / I get along without you very well / Am I blue / I love you for sentimental reasons / Straighten up and fly right / Little girl blue / Round midnight.
Album: released on Asylum, Sep'86 by WEA Records. Dist: WEA

Cassette: released on Asylum, Sep'86 by WEA Records. Dist: WEA

Compact disc: released on Asylum, Sep'86 by WEA Records. Dist: WEA

GET CLOSER.
Tracks: / Get closer / Moon is a harsh mistress, The / I knew you when / Easy for you to say / People gonna talk / Talk to me of Mendocino / I think it's gonna work out fine / Mr. Radio / Lies / Tell him / Sometimes you can't win / My blue tears.
Compact disc: released on Asylum, '84 by WEA Records. Dist: WEA

Single (7"): released on Asylum, Nov'82 by WEA Records. Dist: WEA

Album: released on Asylum, Oct'82 by WEA Records. Dist: WEA

Cassette: released on Asylum, Oct'82 by WEA Records. Dist: WEA

GREATEST HITS:LINDA RONSTADT.
Tracks: / You're no good / Silver threads and golden / Desperado / Love is a rose / That'll be the day / Long long time / Different drum / When will I be loved / Love has no pride / Heat wave / It doesn't matter anymore / Tracks of my tears.
Compact disc: released on Asylum, '83 by WEA Records. Dist: WEA

Album: released on Asylum, Jan'77 by WEA Records. Dist: WEA

Cassette: released on Asylum, Jan'77 by WEA Records. Dist: WEA

GREATEST HITS: LINDA RONSTADT VOL.2.
Tracks: / It's so easy / I can't let go / Hurt so bad / Blue Bayou / How do I make you / Back in the USA / Ooh baby baby / Poor poor pitiful me / Tumbling dice / Just one look / Someone to lay down beside me.
Compact disc: released on Asylum, '83 by WEA Records. Dist: WEA

Album: released on Asylum, Nov'80 by WEA Records. Dist: WEA

Cassette: released on Asylum, Nov'80 by WEA Records. Dist: WEA

HEART LIKE A WHEEL.
Tracks: / You're no good / It doesn't matter anymore / Faithless love / Dark end of the street, The / Heart is like a wheel / When will I be loved / I can't help it (if I'm still in love with you) / Keep me from blowing away / You can close your eyes.
Notes: Strings arranged and conducted by Gregory Rose. Produced by Peter Asher.
Album: released on EMI (Italy), Dec'86 by EMI Records. Dist: Conifer

Cassette: released on EMI (Italy), Dec'86 by EMI Records. Dist: Conifer

Album: released on EMI (Germany), '83 by EMI Records. Dist: Conifer

I KNEW YOU WHEN.
Single (7"): released on Elektra, Jan'83 by WEA Records. Dist: WEA

Single (12"): released on Elektra, Jan'83 by WEA Records. Dist: WEA

LINDA RONSTADT.
Album: released on Fame (Capitol), May'82 by Music For Pleasure Records. Dist: EMI

Cassette: released on Fame (Capitol), May'82 by Music For Pleasure Records. Dist: EMI

LINDA RONSTADT & FRIENDS.
Album: released on EMI (Holland), Jan'85 by EMI Records. Dist: Conifer

LUSH LIFE.
Tracks: / When I fall in love / Skylark / It never entered my mind / Mean to me / When your lover has gone / I'm a fool to want you / You took advantage of me / Sophisticated lady / Can't we be friends / My old flame / Falling in love again / Lush life.
Album: released on Asylum, Nov'84 by WEA Records. Dist: WEA

Cassette: released on Asylum, Nov'84 by WEA Records. Dist: WEA

Compact disc: by WEA Records. Dist: WEA

RETROSPECTIVE.
Double Album: released on EMI (Holland), Aug'84 by EMI Records. Dist: Conifer

SIMPLE DREAMS.
Compact disc: released on Asylum, Jan'87 by WEA Records. Dist: WEA

TELL HIM.
Single (7"): released on Elektra, Mar'83 by WEA Records. Dist: WEA

Single (12"): released on Elektra, Apr'83 by WEA Records. Dist: WEA

TWO ORIGINALS OF LINDA RONSTADT.

Double Album: released on EMI (Germany), '83 by EMI Records. Dist: Conifer

WHAT'S NEW.
Tracks: / What's new? / I've a crush on you / Guess I'll hang my tears out to dry / Crazy he calls me / Someone to watch over me / I don't stand a ghost of a chance with you / What'll I do? / Lover man (oh where can you be) / Goodbye.
Compact disc: released on Asylum, '83 by WEA Records. Dist: WEA

Video-cassette (VHS): released on Vestron, Oct'84

Album: released on Asylum, Sep'83 by WEA Records. Dist: WEA

Cassette: released on Asylum, Sep'83 by WEA Records. Dist: WEA

Compact disc: released on Asylum, '83 by WEA Records. Dist: WEA

WHAT'S NEW /LUSH LIFE/FOR SENTIMENTAL REASON.
Album: released on Asylum, Nov'86 by WEA Records. Dist: WEA

Cassette: released on Asylum, Nov'86 by WEA Records. Dist: WEA

Compact disc: released on Asylum, Nov'86 by WEA Records. Dist: WEA

Roogalator
PLAY IT BY EAR.
Album: released on Do it, Jan'77

Rooke, Fred
BALLADS OF BAWLENBRO, VOL 1.
Cassette: released on Folktracks, Nov'79 by Folktracks Cassettes. Dist: Folktracks

BALLADS OF BAWLENBRO, VOL 2.
Cassette: released on Folktracks, Nov'79 by Folktracks Cassettes. Dist: Folktracks

RABBIT PIE: NEW NORFOLK FOLK SONGS.
Cassette: released on Folktracks, Nov'79 by Folktracks Cassettes. Dist: Folktracks

Room
100 YEARS.
Single (7"): released on Red Flame, Dec'82

CLEAR.
Album: released on Red Flame, Nov'83

IN EVIL HOUR.
Album: released on Red Flame, Nov'84

Cassette: released on Red Flame, Nov'84

IN SICKNESS AND HEALTH.
Single (7"): released on Box, Jul'81 Dist: Rough Trade

JACKPOT JACK.
Single (12"): released on Red Flame, Mar'85

NEW DREAMS FOR OLD.
Single (7"): released on Red Flame, Jun'84

Single (12"): released on Red Flame, Jun'84

THINGS HAVE LEARNT TO WALK THAT SHOULD....
Single (7"): released on Red Flame, May'82

Room 101
ONE BY ONE.
Single (7"): released on Norwood, Nov'83 by Norwood Records.

Single (7"): released on Red Bus, May'85 by Red Bus Records. Dist: PRT

Single (12"): released on Red Bus, May'85 by Red Bus Records. Dist: PRT

TOKYO NIGHTS.
Single (7"): released on Norwood, Mar'84 by Norwood Records.

Roomful of Blues
DRESSED UP TO GET MESSED UP.
Album: released on Demon, Jan'85 Dist: Jazz Music, Projection

HOT LITTLE MAMA.
Album: released on Ace, May'81 by Ace Records. Dist: Pinnacle, Swift, Hotshot, Cadillac

LIVE AT LUPO'S HEARTBREAK HOTEL.
Album: released on Border Europa, May'87

Room of one's own, (A)
ROOM OF ONE'S OWN, (A) Woolf, Virginia (Bloom, Claire).

Cassette: released on Caedmon(USA), Aug'83 by Caedmon (USA) Records. Dist: Gower, Taylors, Discovery

Room, The
NEMESIS.
Album: released on Red Flame, Mar'86 by Red Flame Records. Dist: Nine Mile, Cartel

Room With A View, A
ROOM WITH A VIEW, A Original soundtrack (Various Artists).
Tracks: / O mio babbino caro / Pensione Bertolini (The) / Lucy, Charlotte and Miss Lavish see the city / In the piazza signora / Embankment (The) / Phaeton and Persephone / Hi il bel sogno di doretta / Storm (The) / Home and the betrothal / Sacred lake (The) / Allan sisters (The) / In the National Gallery / Windy corner / Habenera / Broken engagement (The) / Return to Florence / End titles.
Notes: Music composed by Richard Robbins.
Compact disc: released on DRG (USA), Apr'87 by DRG Records. Dist: Conifer, RCA

Rooney, Jim
COLLECTION: JIM ROONEY (Rooney, Jim & Bill Keith).
Album: released on Waterfront, Mar'84 by Waterfront Records. Dist: Rough Trade, Cartel, Projection, Roots

READY FOR THE TIMES TO GET BETTER.
Album: released on Appaloosa, May'81 Dist: Roots, Folksound, JSU, Projection, Celtic Music, Chris Wellard

Root Boy Slim
DON'T LET THIS HAPPEN TO YOU.
Album: released on Bedrock, Nov'86 by Upright Records. Dist: Pinnacle

ROOT 1 (Root Boy Slim & The Sex Change Band).
Album: released on Illegal, Jul'79 by Faulty Products Records. Dist: Pinnacle, Lightning, Cartel

ZOOM (Root Boy Slim & The Sex Change Band).
Album: released on Illegal, Jul'79 by Faulty Products Records. Dist: Pinnacle, Lightning, Cartel

Rootin' and tootin'
ROOTIN' AND TOOTIN' Various artists (Various Artists).
Album: released on Charly(R&B), Jun'85 by Charly Records. Dist: Charly, Cadillac

Roots
AFRICAN IMAGE.
Album: released on Gramavision (USA), Jun'84 by Gramavison Records (USA). Dist: PRT, IMS, Polygram

Cassette: released on Gramavision (USA), Jun'84 by Gramavison Records (USA). Dist: PRT, IMS, Polygram

ROOTS REGGAE/REGGAE ROCK Various artists (Various Artists).
Double Album: released on Telstar, Nov'83 by Telstar Records. Dist: RCA Distribution

Double cassette: released on Telstar, Nov'83 by Telstar Records. Dist: RCA Distribution

ROOTS ROCK REGGAE Carious artists (Various Artists).
Album: released on Cactus, May'78 by Creole Records. Dist: CBS

ROOTS ROCK REGGAE, VOL 2 Various artists (Various Artists).
Album: released on Savannah, '78 Dist: CBS

Roots Foundation
HERE COMES THE SUN.
Single (7"): released on Lagos International, Aug'81

Roots, Junior
LOSING YOU.
Single (12"): released on Exile, Aug'82 by Exile Records. Dist: Pinnacle

Roots, Levi
IT A FI BUM.
Single (7"): released on Conqueror, Nov'84 Dist: Jetstar

SHOULDER MOVE.
Single (12"): released on Scom, Aug'84 by Scom Records. Dist: Jetstar

Roots of..
ROOTS OF AMERICAN'S MUSIC Various artists (Various Artists).
Double Album: released on Arhoolie, May'81 by Arhoolie Records. Dist: Projection, Topic, Jazz Music, Swift, Roots

ROOTS OF INFLATION Bonn, N.York, London, Buenos Aires (Roots of inflation).
Cassette: released on International Report, Oct'81 by Seminar Cassettes. Dist: Audio-Visual Library Services, Davidson Distribution, Eastern Educational Products Distrib., Forlaget Systime Distribution, MacDougall Distribution, Talktapes Distribution, Watkins Books Ltd Distribution, Norton, Jeff Distribution

ROOTS OF ROCK Various artists (Various Artists).
Album: released on Yazoo, May'79 Dist: Swift, Projection

ROOTS OF ROCK & ROLL Various artists (Various Artists).
Album:

ROOTS OF THE BLUES (Various Artists).
Tracks: / Louisiana / Field song from Senegal / Po' boy blues / Katie left Memphis / Berta berta / Old original blues / Jim and John / Emmaline, take your time / Buttermilk / Mama Lucy / I'm gonna live, anyhow till I die / No more my lord / Lining hymn and prayer / Death comes a creepin' in my room / Church house moan / Beggin the blues / Rolled and tumbled / Goin' down to the races / You gotta cut that out.
Album: released on New World (USA), Mar'87 by New World Records (USA). Dist: Conifer

Roots, Puddy
KING DISCOTHEQUE.
Single (12"): released on Greensleeves, Nov'84 by Greensleeves Records. Dist: BMG, Jetstar, Spartan

Roots Radics
FREELANCE.
Tracks: / Earsay / Rainbow / I'm not a king / Too much fuss / Party time / Everywhere Natty go / Dance with me / Midnight / Mash it up / Reggae on Broadway.
Compact disc: released on Kingdom Records, Jan'87 by Kingdom Records. Dist: Kingdom Records

Album: released on Kingdom, Feb'85 by Kingdom Records. Dist: Kingdom

I'M NOT A KING.
Single (7"): released on Kingdom, Feb'85 by Kingdom Records. Dist: Kingdom

RADICAL DUB SESSION.
Album: released on Solid Groove, Feb'82 Dist: Jetstar, Pinnacle

SCIENTIST AND JAMMY STRIKE BACK.
Album: released on Trojan, '83 by Trojan Records. Dist: PRT, Jetstar

Roots Rebel
GIVE THANKS.
Single (12"): released on Off-Beat, Oct'82 by Off-Beat Records. Dist: Jetstar Distribution

Roots Rockers
REGGAE MASTERPIECES.
Album: released on Vista Sounds, '83 by Vista Sounds Records. Dist: Jetstar

Cassette: released on Vista Sounds, '83 by Vista Sounds Records. Dist: Jetstar

REGGAE MASTERPIECES, VOL 2.
Album: released on Vista Sounds, May'84 by Vista Sounds Records. Dist: Jetstar

ROOTS ROCKERS Various artists (Various Artists).
Album: released on Action Replay, Nov'85 by Action Replay Records. Dist: PRT

Cassette: released on Action Replay, Nov'85 by Action Replay Records. Dist: PRT

Roots to Roots
SOUL TO SOUL, VOL 1.
Album: released on Vista Sounds, Sep'84 by Vista Sounds Records. Dist: Jetstar

SOUL TO SOUL, VOL 2.
Album: released on Vista Sounds, Sep'84 by Vista Sounds Records. Dist: Jetstar

Ropejump, Vic
MCENROE.
Single (7"): released on Surrey Sound, Jul'81 Dist: Pinnacle

Roques, Andre
CA C'EST DE L'ACCORDEON.
Tracks: / Chantons sarlot / Miss Karting / Sabor ami / Bal du Samedi soir / A la canaro / Don Pepito / Les filles du Quercy / Brise cadurciennne / Douce reverie / L'auberge des routiers / Je ne veux plus revoir tes yeux / Senor Manuello / Notre Quercy.
Album: released on Accordion Record Club, Jul'86 by Accordion Record Club Records. Dist: Accordion Record Club

---

day made / Breeze and I (The) / Corcovado / In a little Spanish town / La cumparsita / El rancho grande / Solamente una vez / Abia / Brazil / Amapola / Delicado / Perfidia / Felicidade / Cumania / Peanut vendor (The).
Compact disc: released on London, Mar'87 by London Records. Dist: Polygram

LATIN MELODIES OLD AND NEW.
Tracks: / La cucaracha / One note samba / Girl from Ipanema, The / Valencia / Blame it on the bossa nova / La paloma / La golondrina / Mexico / Mexico / Meditation / Spanish gipsy dance / Jet flight / Vaya con dios.
Compact disc: released on London, Jul'87 by London Records. Dist: Polygram

LATIN SONG & DANCE MEN (Ros, Edmundo & Victor Sylvester Orch).
Album: released on Pye, Feb'80

MUSIC FOR THE MILLIONS.
Album:

Cassette:

ROS REMEMBERS.
Cassette: released on Decca, '74 by Decca Records. Dist: Polygram

STRINGS LATINO.
Compact disc: released on Decca, Sep'85 by Decca Records. Dist: Polygram

THIS IS MY WORLD.
Album: released on Decca, '72 by Decca Records. Dist: Polygram

Rose, Dr. Don
CRUISIN' 1967 WOXI Atlanta.
Cassette: released on Increase(USA), Jun'87 by Quicksilver Records (USA).

Rose, George
BILLY BUDD.
Cassette: released on Caedmon(USA), '81 by Caedmon (USA) Records. Dist: Gower, Taylors, Discovery

Rosehips
ROOM IN YOUR HEART.
Tracks: / Room in your heart.
Single (7"): released on Subway, Mar'87 Dist: Revolver Distribution, Spartan Distribution

Single (12"): released on Subway, Mar'87 Dist: Revolver Distribution, Spartan Distribution

Rose, John
FORWARD OF SHORT LEG.
Album: released on Dossier, Jun'87 Dist: Red Rhino, Cartel

Rose, Judy
GIRL NOBODY KNOWS.
Album: released on Westwood, '78 by Westwood Records. Dist: Jazz Music, H.R. Taylor, JSU, Pinnacle, Ross Records

Roselli, Jimmy
LET ME SING AND I'M HAPPY.
Album: released on M & R, Apr'87

Cassette: released on M & R, Apr'87

Album: released on M & R, Apr'87

Cassette: released on M & R, Apr'87

MORE I SEE IN YOU,(THE).
Album: released on First Night, Nov'86 by Safari Records. Dist: Pinnacle

Cassette: released on First Night, Nov'86 by Safari Records. Dist: Pinnacle

ROCK A BYE YOUR BABY.
Album: released on M & R, Apr'87

Cassette: released on M & R, Apr'87

SALOON SONGS.
Album: released on M & R, Apr'87

Cassette: released on M & R, Apr'87

SALOON SONGS VOL2.
Album: released on M & R, Apr'87

Cassette: released on M & R, Apr'87

SALOON SONGS VOL4.
Album: released on M & R, Apr'87

Cassette: released on M & R, Apr'87

SAY IT ISN'T SO.
Tracks: / Addio amor.
Single (7"): released on First Night, Nov'86 by Safari Records. Dist: Pinnacle

WHEN MY OLD WEDDING RING WAS NEW.
Album: released on A.1, '83 by A.1 Records.

QUERCY, (LE) (Roques, Andre & His Orchestra).
Tracks: / Quercy mon beau pays / Vin de cahors / Filles de montbaudan / Quercy querele / Bourree querycynoise / La capaleto / Mon canal du midi / Grand pere / Auvergne et Quercy / Aio de rosta / Chez la mere Antoine / A pas legers / Polka pique.
Album: released on Accordion Record Club, Jul'86 by Accordion Record Club Records. Dist: Accordion Record Club

Cassette: released on Accordion Record Club, Jul'86 by Accordion Record Club Records. Dist: Accordion Record Club

Rori
WILD GIRL.
Tracks: / Wild girl / Wild girls.
Single (7"): released on WEA, Dec'86 by WEA Records. Dist: WEA

Rosanne
THIS IS THE NIGHT.
Single (7"): released on Futura, Aug'85 by Futura. Dist: Jetstar, EMI

Single (12"): released on Futura, Aug'85 by Futura. Dist: Jetstar, EMI

THIS IS THE NIGHT/THEME FROM DALLAS.
Single (12"): released on ACA, Sep'85 Dist: Jetstar

Rosbif
TRADITIONAL DANCE MSIC FROM S. FRANCE.
Album: released on Railfort, Feb'85 by Railfort.

Rose
KITES.
Tracks: / Voodoo.
Single (7"): released on Ratpack, Nov'86 by Ratpack. Dist: Spartan

ROSE,THE Original Film Soundtrack.
Album: released on Atlantic, Jan'80 by WEA Records. Dist: WEA

Cassette: released on Atlantic, Jan'80 by WEA Records. Dist: WEA

Compact disc: released on Atlantic, Jan'84 by WEA Records. Dist: WEA

Rose, Avis
WOMAN IN LOVE/RANKIN' BOGART.
Single (12"): released on Real Wax, Oct'82

Rose Brothers
EVERYTHING'S COMING UP ROSES.
Album: released on Malaco, Feb'87 by Malaco Records. Dist: Charly

WALL TO WALL FREAKS.
Tracks: / Wall to wall (inst).
Single (7"): released on Affair, Nov'86 Dist: DMS, RCA

Single (12"): released on Affair, Nov'86 Dist: DMS, RCA

Rosebury,Arthur
ARTHUR ROSEBURY AND HIS KIT-CAT DANCE BAND (Rosebury,Arthur and his Kit-cat dance band).
Album: released on World Records, Mar'79 Dist: Polygram

Rose, David
STRIPPER, THE.
Single (7"): released on Old Gold, Jul'84 by Old Gold Records. Dist: Lightning, Jazz Music, Spartan, Counterpoint

VERY THOUGHT OF YOU.
Album: released on Memoir, Nov'84 by Memoir Records. Dist: PRT Distribution

Cassette: released on Memoir, Nov'84 by Memoir Records. Dist: PRT Distribution

Ros, Edmundo
DANCE AGAIN.
Album: released on Decca, '63 by Decca Records. Dist: Polygram

EDMUNDO ROS TODAY.
Album: released on Decca, Mar'78 by Decca Records. Dist: Polygram

LATIN FAVOURITES.
Album: released on Decca (Gold Crown), Nov'79 by Decca Records. Dist: Polygram, IMS

LATIN MAGIC (Ros, Edmundo & His Orchestra).
Tracks: / Mas que nada / What a difference a

Dist: PRT

Cassette: released on A.1, '83 by A.1 Records. Dist: PRT

WHEN YOUR OLD WEDDING RING WAS NEW.
Single (7"): released on A.1, Nov'82 by A.1 Records. Dist: PRT

Rose Marie
ALL THE LOVE (IN ALL THE WORLD).
Single (7"): released on A.1, Oct'85 by A.1 Records. Dist: PRT

Single (12"): released on A.1, Dec'85 by A.1 Records. Dist: PRT

IF I HAD MY LIFE TO LIVE OVER.
Single (7"): released on A.1, Apr'85 by A.1 Records. Dist: PRT

I'M COMING HOME.
Tracks: / I'm coming home.
Single (7"): released on A.1, Nov'86 by A.1 Records. Dist: PRT

Single (12"): released on A.1, Nov'86 by A.1 Records. Dist: PRT

LET THE REST OF THE WORLD PASS BY.
Single (7"): released on A.1, Oct'84 by A.1 Records. Dist: PRT

LOOKING FOR LOVE.
Album: released on A.1, Jul'84 by A.1 Records. Dist: PRT

Cassette: released on A.1, Jul'84 by A.1 Records. Dist: PRT

SO LUCKY.
Tracks: / So lucky / Is it too late.
Single (7"): released on A.1, May'86 by A.1 Records. Dist: PRT

TEARDROPS AND ROMANCE.
Album: released on A.1, Oct'86 by A.1 Records. Dist: PRT

Cassette: released on A.1, Oct'86 by A.1 Records. Dist: PRT

Rosemary
SHOOBY DOOBY DOO.
Single (12"): released on M & R. May'83

WISHING ON A STAR/WAY WE WERE.
Single (12"): released on Negus Roots, Feb'83 by Negus Roots Records. Dist: Jetstar

Rosemary,Althea
MY BABY JUST CARES FOR ME.
Single (12"): released on SS Music, Mar'82

TONIGHT IS THE NIGHT/YOU'RE UNIQUE.
Single (12"): released on SS Music, Jul'82

Rosemary's Children
KINGS AND PRINCES.
Tracks: / Kings and princes / Visiting a house / W.W. 1 / Round and round / Lighthouse song.
Album: released on Cherry Red, Jun'87 by Cherry Red Records. Dist: Pinnacle

SOUTHERN FIELDS.
Tracks: / Southern fields / Alice, (Whatever happened to)?.
Single (7"): released on EL, Jul'86 by El Records. Dist: Rough Trade, Cartel, Pinnacle

Rose, Michael
BOGUS BADGE.
Single (12"): released on Germaine, Nov'85 by Germaine Records. Dist: Jetstar

GUESS WHO'S COMING TO DINNER/DUB VERSION.
Single (7"): released on Oval, May'82 Dist: Projection

Rose,Mike
SOUL AND SAX.
Album: released on Orbitone, 30 May'87 by Orbitone Records. Dist: Jetstar Distribution

Rosenbaum,Art
FIVE STRING BANJO.
Album: released on Kick Mule, '74

Rosenman,Leonard
MUSIC FROM THE FILMS OF JAMES DEAN (Rosenman,Leonard & His Orchestra).
Album: released on Sunset, Mar'79 Dist: EMI

Rosen,Michael
MINERS STRIKE RAP,THE.
Single (7"): released on Pit, Feb'85 by Pit Rec

ords. Dist: M.I.S.

Rosenthal & Old dog

INDIAN SUMMER.
Album: released on Flying Fish (USA), May'79 by Flying Fish Records (USA). Dist: Roots, Projection

Rose of Avalanche

ALWAYS THERE.
Tracks: / Always there / Waiting for the sun / Majesty / Mainline man.
Notes: Mainline man is an extra track only available on 12" remix limited edition.
Single (12"): released on Fire, Mar'87 by Twist and Shout Music. Dist: Nine Mile, Rough Trade, Cartel

Single (7"): released on Fire, Feb'87 by Twist and Shout Music. Dist: Nine Mile, Rough Trade, Cartel

Single (12"): released on Fire, Feb'87 by Twist and Shout Music. Dist: Nine Mile, Rough Trade, Cartel

FIRST AVALANCHE.
Album: released on Fire, Mar'87 by Twist and Shout Music. Dist: Nine Mile, Rough Trade, Cartel

GODDESS.
Single (12"): released on Leeds Independent, Sep'85 by Revolver Records. Dist: Cartel

LA RAIN.
Single (7"): released on Lil, May'85 Dist: Red Rhino, Cartel

Single (12"): released on Lil, May'85 Dist: Red Rhino, Cartel

TOO MANY CASTLES IN THE SKY.
Tracks: / Too many castles in the sky / Dizzy Miss Lizzy / Assassin / Velveteen / Who cares / Just like yesterday / Too many castles in the sky / Assassin / Dizzy Miss Lizzy.
Extended-play record: released on Fire, May'87 by Twist and Shout Music. Dist: Nine Mile, Rough Trade, Cartel

Single (7"): released on Fire, May'86 by Twist and Shout Music. Dist: Nine Mile, Rough Trade, Cartel

Single (12"): released on Fire, May'86 by Twist and Shout Music. Dist: Nine Mile, Rough Trade, Cartel

VELVETEEN.
Tracks: / Velveteen / Who cares / Just like yesterday.
Single (7"): released on Fire, Sep'86 by Twist and Shout Music. Dist: Nine Mile, Rough Trade, Cartel

Cassette: released on Fire, Sep'86 by Twist and Shout Music. Dist: Nine Mile, Rough Trade, Cartel

Rose Of Romance Orch

TARA'S THEME.
Single (7"): released on BBC, Dec'81 by BBC Records & Tapes. Dist: EMI, PRT, Pye

WHITER SHADE OF PALE/KEEPSAKE.
Single (7"): released on Moon, Sep'82 by Moon Records. Dist: PRT Distribution

Rose Of Sharon

SINCE JESUS PASSED BY.
Album: by Pilgrim Records. Dist: Rough Trade, Cartel

Rose Of Victory

SUFFRAGETTE CITY/OVERDRIVE.
Single (7"): released on No Future, Jul'83 by No Future Records. Dist: Pinnacle, Rough Trade, Cartel

Rose, Patrick

I WANNA GET NEXT TO YOU.
Tracks: / I wanna get next to you / I don't wanna bealone.
Single (12"): released on Sea View, Aug'86 by Sea View Records. Dist: Jetstar

YOU ARE MY LADY (Rose, Patrick & Davina Wright).
Tracks: / You are my lady / You are my lady (version).
Single (12"): released on Sea View, Dec'85 by Sea View Records. Dist: Jetstar

Rose, Pete

PETE ROSE JAZZ BAND.
Album: released on Foldback, Nov'82 by Foldback Records. Dist: Lugtons

Rose Royce

BEST LOVE.
Single (7"): released on Epic, Apr'82 by CBS Records. Dist: CBS

CAR WASH/I WANNA GET NEXT TO YOU.
Single (7"): released on Old Gold, Apr'83 by Old Gold Records. Dist: Lightning, Jazz Music, Spartan, Counterpoint

GOLDEN TOUCH.
Album: released on Warner Brothers, Jan'81 by Warner Bros Records. Dist: WEA

Cassette: released on Warner Brothers, Jan'81 by Warner Bros Records. Dist: WEA

GOLDEN TOUCH/HELP YOURSELF.
Single (7"): released on Whitfield, Feb'81 Dist: WEA

Single (12"): released on Whitfield, Feb'81 Dist: WEA

GREATEST HITS: ROSE ROYCE.
Album: released on Whitfield, Feb'80 Dist: WEA

Cassette: released on Whitfield, Feb'80 Dist: WEA

I'M IN LOVE.
Single (7"): released on Warner Bros., Jan'79 by Warner Bros Records. Dist: WEA

IN FULL BLOOM.
Album: released on Whitfield, Aug'77 Dist: WEA

Cassette: released on Whitfield, Aug'77 Dist: WEA

I WONDER WHERE YOU ARE TONIGHT.
Single (7"): released on Whitfield, Aug'79 Dist: WEA

LONELY ROAD.
Single (7"): released on Carrere, Aug'87 by Carrere Records. Dist: PRT, Spartan

Single (12"): released on Carrere, Aug'87 by Carrere Records. Dist: PRT, Spartan

LOVE DON'T LIVE HERE ANYMORE.
Single (7"): released on Whitfield, Sep'78 Dist: WEA

OOH BOY/WHAT YOU BEEN WAITIN' FOR...
Single (7"): released on Whitfield, Feb'80 Dist: WEA

POP YOU FINGERS.
Single (12"): released on Warner Bros., Nov'80 by Warner Bros Records. Dist: WEA

RAINBOW CONNECTION IV.
Album: released on Whitfield, Aug'79 Dist: WEA

Cassette: released on Whitfield, Aug'79 Dist: WEA

SHOW MUST GO ON,THE.
Album: released on Streetwave, May'85 by Streetwave Records. Dist: PRT Distribution

Cassette: released on Streetwave, May'85 by Streetwave Records. Dist: PRT Distribution

STRONGER THAN EVER.
Album: released on Epic, Apr'82 by CBS Records. Dist: CBS

Cassette: released on Epic, Apr'82 by CBS Records. Dist: CBS

WISHING ON A STAR.
Single (7"): released on Warner Bros., Jan'78 by Warner Bros Records. Dist: WEA

Single (7"): released on Old Gold, Sep'85 by Old Gold Records. Dist: Lightning, Jazz Music, Spartan, Counterpoint

Rose, Samantha

GO AWAY LITTLE GIRL/YOU'LL NEVER GET...
Single (12"): released on Third World, May'82 Dist: Jetstar Distribution

IN PERSON.
Album: released on Empire, Jan'79 by Empire Records. Dist: Backs, Cartel, Jetstar

TOGETHER IN LOVE.
Album: released on World International, Nov'86 Dist: Jetstar

Rose Tattoo

ASSAULT AND BATTERY.
Album: released on Carrere, Sep'81 by Carrere Records. Dist: PRT, Spartan

Cassette: released on Carrere, Sep'81 by Carrere Records. Dist: PRT, Spartan

BEATS FROM A SINGLE DRUM.
Compact disc: by Pacific Records (USA). Dist: Atlantic

IT'S GONNA WORK ITSELF OUT.
Single (7"): released on Carrere, Mar'83 by Carrere Records. Dist: PRT, Spartan

ROCK'N'ROLL OUTLAW.
Album: released on Carrere, Apr'81 by Carrere Records. Dist: PRT, Spartan

Cassette: released on Carrere, Apr'81 by Carrere Records. Dist: PRT, Spartan

SCARRED FOR LIFE.
Album: released on Carrere, Nov'82 by Carrere Records. Dist: PRT, Spartan

Cassette: released on Carrere, Nov'82 by Carrere Records. Dist: PRT, Spartan

Rose, Tony

ON THE BANK OF GREEN WILLOW.
Album: released on Leader, '81 Dist: Jazz Music, Projection

POOR FELLOWS.
Album: released on Dingles, '82 by Dingles Records. Dist: Projection

SONGS OF A CHANGING WORLD (see Raven, Jon/Nic Jones/Tony Rose) (Rose, Tony/Nic Jones/Jon Raven).

STEAM BALLARDS.
Album: released on Broadside, Jun'81 by Broadside Records. Dist: Celtic Distributions, H.R. Taylor, Jazz Music, Projection, Jazz Services Unlimited Dist. (JSU)

Cassette: released on Broadside, Jun'81 by Broadside Records. Dist: Celtic Distributions, H.R. Taylor, Jazz Music, Projection, Jazz Services Unlimited Dist. (JSU)

UNDER THE GREENWOOD TREE.
Album: released on Leader, '81 Dist: Jazz Music, Projection

YOUNG HUNTING.
Album: released on Leader, '81 Dist: Jazz Music, Projection

Rosetta stone

HIDING FROM LOVE.
Single (7"): released on Limo, Jan'81 Dist: PRT

REMEMBER.
Single (7"): released on Limo, May'81 Dist: PRT

STRAIGHT FROM THE HEART/TOO BAD.
Single (7"): released on Sire, Nov'82

WATCH OUT I'M BACK.
Single (7"): released on Limo, Sep'81 Dist: PRT

Rose, Wally

YERBA BUENA DAYS (Rose, Wally/Lu Watters/Benny Strickler).
Album: released on Dawn Club, Dec'86 Dist: Cadillac, Swift, JSU

Rosie and the Originals

ANGEL BABY.
Single (7"): released on Revival, Jul'82 Dist: Lightning, Swift

Rosolino, Frank

Biographical Details: See under Sims, Zoot and...

FRANKLY SPEAKING (Rosolino,Frank,Quintet).
Album: released on Affinity, Dec'81 by Charly Records. Dist: Charly, Cadillac

FRANK ROSOLINO SEXTET (Rosolino,Frank,Sextet).
Album: released on Affinity, Apr'81 by Charly Records. Dist: Charly, Cadillac

THINKING ABOUT YOU.
Notes: Artists also include: Ed Bickert/Don Thompson/T.Clarke.
Album: released on Sackville, Jul'86 Dist: JSU, Jazz Music, Jazz Horizons, Cadillac Music, Celtic Music, Swift

Ros, Patrick

SEND ME YOUR TEARS/WHEN YOU'RE LONELY.
Single (7"): released on Magic, Feb'84 Dist: Jazz Music, Submarine, Swift, Chris Wellard, Conifer

SONG OF LOVE/ONLY THE HEART.
Single (7"): released on Magic, Sep'83 Dist: Jazz Music, Submarine, Swift, Chris Wellard, Conifer

SPECIAL FEELINGS.
Album: released on Magic, Dec'83 Dist: Jazz Music, Submarine, Swift, Chris Wellard, Conifer

Cassette: released on Magic, Dec'83 Dist: Jazz Music, Submarine, Swift, Chris Wellard, Conifer

Ross, Andy, Orchestra

ANDY ROSS ORCHESTRA PLAY BILL & BOBBIE FAVOURITES,THE.
Album: released on Dansan, '78 by Spartan Records. Dist: Spartan

COME DANCE TO BILL AND BOBBY IRVINES.
Cassette: released on Dansan, Apr'80 by Spartan Records. Dist: Spartan

DANCE PARTY.
Album: released on Dansan, Jul'82 by Spartan Records. Dist: Spartan

IT'S KNEES UP TIME.JOIN IN AND SING WITH ANDY ROSS AND PALS.
Album: by CBS Records. Dist: CBS

SING 'N' SWING.
Album: released on Pye, Sep'78

Ross, Annie

LIKE SOMEONE IN LOVE (Ross,Annie with Johnny spence & his Orchestra).
Album: released on Bulldog, Jul'83 by Bulldog Records. Dist: President Distribution, Spartan, Swift, Taylor, H.R.

Ross, Billy

MISTY MOUNTAIN (see Jackson, Billy) (Ross, Billy & Billy Jackson).

Ross, David

POET'S GOLD.
Cassette: released on Caedmon(USA), '84 by Caedmon (USA) Records. Dist: Gower, Taylors, Discovery

Ross, Diana

14 GREATEST HITS.
Tracks: / Reach out & touch / Somebody's hand / Ain't no mountain high enough / Remember me / Reach out, I'll be there / Good morning heartache / Touch me in the morning / Last time I saw him / Theme from mahogany / Love hangover / I'm coming out / Upside down / It's my turn / Endless love.
Compact disc: released on Motown, May'86 by Motown Records. Dist: BMG Distribution

20 GOLDEN GREATS.
Album: released on Motown, Oct'81 by RCA Records. Dist: RCA Distribution

Cassette: released on Motown, Oct'81 by RCA Records. Dist: RCA Distribution

20 GREATEST HITS (Ross, Diana & The Supremes).
Tracks: / When the lovelight starts to shine through his eyes / Where did our love go / Baby love / Come see about me / My world is empty without you / Stop in the name of love / Back in my arms again / I hear a symphony / You can't hurry love / Love is like an itching in my heart / You keep me hangin on / Love is here now you're gone / Reflections / Love child / I'll try something new / I'm gonna make you love me / Someday we'll be together / Ladder to the roof (The) / Stoned love / Nathan Jones.
Compact disc: released on Motown, May'86 by Motown Records. Dist: BMG Distribution

25TH ANNIVERSARY (Ross, Diana & The Supremes).
Tracks: / Where did our love go / Come see about me / Stop in the name of love / Back in my arms again / You can't hurry love / Love is here and now you're gone / Happening, The / Someday we'll be together / I'm gonna make you love me / When the lovelight starts shining through his eyes / Nothing but heartaches / My world is empty without you / Love is like an itching in my heart / I'm livin' in shame / Forever came today / Some things you never get used to / Composer, The / No matter what sign you are / Blue room, The / Manhattan / Who can I turn to (when nobody needs me) / Someday my prince will come / Sleep walk / Treat me nice John Henry / Come on and see me / It's all your fault / Ooowee baby / Come on boy / Heigh-ho / Those D.J. shows / Sincerely / Surfer boy / Beach ball / Heaven must have sent you / Just a little misunderstanding / Coca-Cola commercial (1) / Coca-Cola commercial (2) / Supremes - interview / Baby love / I hear a symphony / Reflections / You keep me hangin on / Love child / In and out of love / If I ruled the world / When you wish upon a star / Are you sure love is the name of this game / Penny pincher / Send me no flowers / We couldn't get along without you.
Double compact disc: released on Motown, Mar'87 by Motown Records. Dist: BMG Distribution

Album: released on Tamla Motown, Jul'86 by Motown Records. Dist: RCA Distribution

Cassette: released on Tamla Motown, Jul'86 by Motown Records. Dist: RCA Distribution

2 CLASSIC ALBUMS: DIANA/ BOSS (THE).
Tracks: / Upside down / Tenderness / Friend to friend / I'm coming out / Have fun (again) / My old piano / Now that you're gone / Give up / No one gets the prize / I ain't been licked / All for one / Boss (The) / Once in the morning / It's my house / Sparkle / I'm in the world.

Compact disc: released on Motown, Oct'86 by Motown Records. Dist: BMG Distribution

2 CLASSIC ALBUMS : GREATEST HITS (Ross, Diana, Marvin Gaye, Tammi Terrell).

AIN'T NO MOUNTAIN HIGH ENOUGH (Ross, Diana & The Supremes).
Tracks: / Ain't no mountain high enough / It's my house / Boss (The) / Remember me.
Single (7"): released on Tamla Motown, Jul'86 by Motown Records. Dist: RCA Distribution

Single (12"): released on Tamla Motown, Jul'86 by Motown Records. Dist: RCA Distribution

AIN'T NO MOUNTAIN HIGH ENOUGH/SURRENDER 2 Classic albums.
Tracks: / Reach out and touch (somebody's hand) / Now that there's you / Ain't no mountain high enough / Something on my mind / I wouldn't change the man he is / Keep an eye / Where there was darkness / Can't wait until tomorrow / Dark side of the world / Surrender / I can't give back the love I feel for you / Remember me / And if you see him / Reach out I'll be there / Didn't you know (you'd have to cry sometime) / Simple thing like cry, A / Did you read the morning paper? / I'll settle for you / I'm a winner / All the befores.
Compact disc: released on Motown, Jul'87 by Motown Records. Dist: BMG Distribution

ALL OF MY LIFE/A SIMPLE THING LIKE LOVE.
Single (7"): released on Motown (Re-issue), Oct'81

ALL OF YOU.
Single (7"): released on CBS, Jun'84 by CBS Records. Dist: CBS

ALL THE GREAT HITS.
Album: released on Motown, Dec'81 by Motown Records. Dist: BMG Distribution

Cassette: released on Motown, Dec'81 by Motown Records. Dist: BMG Distribution

ALL THE GREAT LOVE SONGS.
Tracks: / I'm still waiting / My man / All of my life / Love me / After you / All night lover / Sparkle / It's my turn / Cryin in my heart out for you / Endless love.
Compact disc: released on Motown, Oct'86 by Motown Records. Dist: BMG Distribution

AN EVENING WITH....
Album: released on Motown, Oct'81 by Motown Records. Dist: BMG Distribution

Cassette: released on Motown, Oct'81 by Motown Records. Dist: BMG Distribution

AN EVENING WITH DIANA ROSS.
Album: released on Motown, Aug'85 by Motown Records. Dist: BMG Distribution

Cassette: released on Motown, Aug'85 by Motown Records. Dist: BMG Distribution

ANTHOLOGY Volumes 1 & 2 (Ross, Diana & The Supremes).
Tracks: / Your heart belongs to me / Let me go the right way / Breathtaking guy, A / When the lovelight starts shining through his eyes / Standing at the crossroads of love / Run, run, run / Where did our love go / Baby love / Ask any girl / Come see about me / Stop! in the name of love / Back in my arms again / Nothing but heartaches / I hear a symphony / My world is empty without you / Love is like an itching in my heart / You can't hurry love / You keep me hanging on / Love is here and now you're gone / Happening, The / Hard day's night, A / Funny how times slips away / You send me / Falling in love with love / I'm the greatest star / Reflections / In and out of love / Forever came today / Some things you never get used to / Love child / I'm gonna make you love me / I'm livin' in shame / Composer, The / I'll try something new / Young folks, The / No matter what sign you are / I'm livin' in shame / Someday we'll be together / Up the ladder to the roof / Everybody's got the right to love / Stoned love / Nathan Jones / Floy joy / Touch / Automatically sunshine / Your wonderful sweet, sweet love / I guess I'll miss the man / Bad weather / It's all been said before / I'm gonna let my heart do the walking / Reflections / In & out of love / Love child / Composer / Young folks / Stoned love / Nathan Jones / Bad weather / Floy joy / Touch / Run run run / Baby love / Ask any girl / Stop in the name of love / I hear a symphony / You keep me hangin on / You send me / I'm the greatest star.
Compact disc: released on Motown, Oct'86 by Motown Records. Dist: BMG Distribution

AT THE COPA (Ross, Diana & The Supremes).
Album: released on Motown, Mar'82 by Motown Records. Dist: BMG Distribution

Cassette: released on Motown, Mar'82 by Motown Records. Dist: BMG Distribution

BABY IT'S ME.
Album: released on Motown, Jun'83 by Motown Records. Dist: BMG Distribution

Cassette: released on Motown, Jun'83 by Motown Records. Dist: BMG Distribution

BABY LOVE/STOP IN THE NAME OF LOVE (Ross, Diana & The Supremes).
Single (7"): released on Motown, Oct'81 by Motown Records. Dist: BMG Distribution

BOSS, THE.
Album: released on Motown, Mar'82 by RCA Records. Dist: RCA Distribution

Cassette: released on Motown, Mar'82 by RCA Records. Dist: RCA Distribution

Single (7"): released on Motown, Oct'81 by RCA Records. Dist: RCA Distribution

CAPTURED LIVE ON STAGE (Ross, Diana & The Supremes).
Tracks: / T.C.B. / Medley (1) / Medley (2) / Monologue - Diana Ross (1) / Love is here and now you're gone / I'm gonna make you love me / Monologue - Mary Wilson / Can't take my eyes off you / Monologue - Diana Ross & Mary Wilson / Reflections / My man / Didn't we / It's alright with me / Big spender / Falling in love with love / Love child / Dialogue - Diana Ross / Aquarius/Let the sun shine in (The flesh failures) / Monologue - Diana Ross (2) / Impossible dream, The / Monologue - Diana Ross (3) / Someday we'll we together / Closing dialogue - Diana Ross & the Supremes.

CHAIN REACTION.
Tracks: / Chain reaction / More and more / Chain reaction (Special dance remix) / Chain reaction (Single version).
Single (7"): released on Capitol, Jan'86 by Capitol Records. Dist: EMI

Single (12"): released on Capitol, Jan'86 by Capitol Records. Dist: EMI

COMPACT COMMAND PERFORMANCES 20 greatest hits (Ross, Diana & The Supremes).
Tracks: / When the lovelight starts shining through his eyes / Where did our love go / Baby love / My world is empty without you / Stop! in the name of love / Back in my arms again / I hear a symphony / You can't hurry love / Love is like an itching in my heart / You keep me hangin' on / Love is here and now you're gone / Reflections / Love child / I'll try someting new / I'm gonna make you love me / Someday we'll be together / Up the ladder to the roof / Stoned love / Nathan Jones.
Compact disc: released on Motown, '86 by Motown Records. Dist: BMG Distribution

COMPACT COMMAND PERFORMANCE (Ross, Diana & The Supremes).
Tracks: / When the lovelight starts shining through his eyes / Where did our love go / Baby love / Come see about me / My world is empty without you / Stop in the name of love / Back in my arms again / I hear a symphony / You can't hurry love / Love is like an itching in my heart / You keep me hangin on / Love is here now your gone / Reflections / Love child / I'll try something new / I'm gonna make you love me / Someday we'll be together / Up the ladder to the roof / Stoned love / Nathan Jones.
Compact disc: released on Motown, Oct'86 by Motown Records. Dist: BMG Distribution

CREAM OF THE CROP/LET THE SUNSHINE IN (Ross, Diana & The Supremes).
Compact disc: released on Motown, Feb'87 by Motown Records. Dist: BMG Distribution

CRYIN' MY HEART OUT FOR YOU.
Single (7"): released on Motown, Oct'81 by Motown Records. Dist: BMG Distribution

DIANA.
Tracks: / Upside down / Tenderness / Friend to friend / I'm coming out / Have fun (again) / My old piano / Now that you're gone / Give up.
Album: released on Motown, Oct'81 by Motown Records. Dist: BMG Distribution

Cassette: released on Motown, Oct'81 by Motown Records. Dist: BMG Distribution

DIANA & MARVIN (See Gaye, Marvin) (Ross, Diana & Marvin Gaye).

DIANA, MICHAEL... (Ross, Diana/Michael Jackson/Gladys Knight/Stevie Wonder).
Album: released on Priority, Nov'86 by Priority Records. Dist: RCA

Cassette: released on Priority, Nov'86 by Priority Records. Dist: RCA

Compact disc: released on Priority, Nov'86 by Priority Records. Dist: RCA

DIANA ROSS.
Album: released on Motown, Oct'81 by Motown Records. Dist: BMG Distribution

Cassette: released on Motown, Oct'81 by Motown Records. Dist: BMG Distribution

Cassette: released on Motown, May'83 by RCA Records. Dist: RCA Distribution

DIANA ROSS (ORIGINALLY 1970).
Album: released on Motown, Oct'81 by Motown Records. Dist: BMG Distribution

Cassette: released on Motown, Oct'81 by Motown Records. Dist: BMG Distribution

DIANA ROSS & THE SUPREMES WITH THE TEMPTATIONS (Ross, Diana & The Supremes).
Album: released on Motown, Oct'82 by Motown Records. Dist: BMG Distribution

Cassette: released on Motown, Oct'82 by Motown Records. Dist: BMG Distribution

Boxed set: released on World Records, '81 Dist: Polygram

Boxed set: released on World Records, '81 Dist: Polygram

DIANA ROSS & THE SUPREMES JOIN THE TEMPTATIONS (Ross, Diana, The Supremes & The Temptations).
Album: released on Motown, Oct'81 by RCA Records. Dist: RCA Distribution

Cassette: released on Motown, Oct'81 by RCA Records. Dist: RCA Distribution

DIANA ROSS & THE SUPREMES - 20 GOLDEN GREATS (Ross, Diana & The Supremes).
Album: released on Motown, Oct'81 by RCA Records. Dist: RCA Distribution

Cassette: released on Motown, Oct'81 by RCA Records. Dist: RCA Distribution

DIANA'S DUETS.
Album: released on Motown, Mar'82 by RCA Records. Dist: RCA Distribution

Cassette: released on Motown, Mar'82 by RCA Records. Dist: RCA Distribution

DIANA/THE BOSS 2 Classic albums.
Tracks: / Upside down / Tenderness / Friend to friend / I'm coming out / Have fun (again) / My old piano / Now that you're gone / Give up / No one gets the prize / I ain't been licked / All for one / Boss, The / Once in the morning / It's my house / Sparkle / I'm in the world.
Compact disc: released on Motown, Jan'87 by Motown Records. Dist: BMG Distribution

DIANA (TV SPECIAL).
Album: released on Motown, Mar'82 by Motown Records. Dist: BMG Distribution

Cassette: released on Motown, Mar'82 by Motown Records. Dist: BMG Distribution

DIRTY LOOKS.
Tracks: / Dirty looks / So close.
Single (7"): released on EMI, 23 May'87 by EMI Records. Dist: EMI

Single (12"): released on EMI, 23 May'87 by EMI Records. Dist: EMI

DIRTY LOOKS (REMIX).
Tracks: / Dirty looks / Dirty looks (bonus beat) / Dirty looks (inst).
Single (12"): released on EMI, Jun'87 by EMI Records. Dist: EMI

DO YOU KNOW WHERE YOU'RE GOING TO?.
Single (7"): released on Motown, Oct'81 by RCA Records. Dist: RCA Distribution

DYNAMIC DIANA (Ross, Diana & The Supremes).
Album: released on Motown, '82 by Motown Records. Dist: BMG Distribution

Cassette: released on Motown, '82 by Motown Records. Dist: BMG Distribution

EARLY YEARS 1961-1964 (Ross, Diana & The Supremes).
Album: released on Motown, Oct'81 by RCA Records. Dist: RCA Distribution

Cassette: released on Motown, Oct'81 by RCA Records. Dist: RCA Distribution

EATEN ALIVE.
Tracks: / Eaten alive / Oh teacher / Experience / Chain reaction / More and more / I'm watching you / Love on the line / I love being in love with you / Crime of passion / Don't give up on each other / Eaten alive (Extended remix).

ENDLESS LOVE (Ross, Diana & Lionel Richie).
Single (7"): released on Motown, Oct'81 by RCA Records. Dist: RCA Distribution

EVERYTHING IS EVERYTHING.
Album: released on Motown, '82 by RCA Records. Dist: RCA Distribution

Cassette: released on Motown, '82 by RCA Records. Dist: RCA Distribution

EXPERIENCE.
Tracks: / Experience / Oh teacher.
Single (7"): released on Capitol, Apr'86 by Capitol Records. Dist: EMI

Single (12"): released on Capitol, Apr'86 by Capitol Records. Dist: EMI

GETTIN' READY FOR LOVE.
Single (7"): released on Motown, Oct'81 by RCA Records. Dist: RCA Distribution

GREATEST HITS: DIANA ROSS VOL.1 & 2 2 Classic albums (Ross, Diana & The Supremes).
Tracks: / When the lovelight starts shining through his eyes / Where did our love go / Ask any girl / Baby love / Run, run, run / Stop in the name of love / Back in my arms again / Come see about me / Nothing but heartaches / Everything is good about you / I hear a symphony / Love is here and now you're gone / My world is empty without you / Whisper you love me boy / Happening, The / You keep me hangin' on / You can't hurry love / Standing at the crossroads of love / Love is like an itching in my heart / There's no stopping us now.
Compact disc: released on Motown, Nov'86 by Motown Records. Dist: BMG Distribution

GREATEST HITS: DIANA ROSS VOL.2.
Album: released on Motown, Oct'81 by RCA Records. Dist: RCA Distribution

Cassette: released on Motown, Oct'81 by RCA Records. Dist: RCA Distribution

GREATEST HITS:DIANA ROSS.
Tracks: / Remember me / Didn't you know (you'd have to cry sometime) / Doobedood'ndoobe, doobedood'ndoobe, doobedood'ndoo / Surrender / And if you see him / Ain't no mountain high enough / How about you / Reach out and touch (somebody's hand) / These things will keep me loving you / Reach out I'll be there / Close to you, (They long to be) / I'm still waiting.
Album: released on Motown, Oct'81 by RCA Records. Dist: RCA Distribution

Cassette: released on Motown, Oct'81 by RCA Records. Dist: RCA Distribution

GREATEST HITS: DIANA ROSS VOL.1.
Album: released on Tamla Motown, Oct'86 by Motown Records. Dist: RCA Distribution

Cassette: released on Tamla Motown, Oct'86 by Motown Records. Dist: RCA Distribution

I HEAR A SYMPHONY (Ross, Diana & The Supremes).
Album: released on Motown, Oct'81 by RCA Records. Dist: RCA Distribution

Cassette: released on Motown, Oct'81 by RCA Records. Dist: RCA Distribution

I'M COMING OUT.
Single (7"): released on Motown, Oct'81 by RCA Records. Dist: RCA Distribution

Single (12"): released on Motown, Oct'81 by RCA Records. Dist: RCA Distribution

I'M GONNA MAKE YOU LOVE ME (Ross, Diana, The Supremes, The Temptations & Marvin Gaye).
Single (7"): released on Motown, Apr'85 by RCA Records. Dist: RCA Distribution

Single (12"): released on Motown, Apr'85 by RCA Records. Dist: RCA Distribution

Single (7"): released on Motown (Re-issue), Oct'81

I'M STILL WAITING.
Album: released on Motown, Mar'82 by RCA Records. Dist: RCA Distribution

Cassette: released on Motown, Mar'82 by RCA Records. Dist: RCA Distribution

Album: released on Motown, Apr'84 by RCA Records. Dist: RCA Distribution

Cassette: released on Motown, Apr'84 by RCA Records. Dist: RCA Distribution

Single (7"): released on Motown, Mar'83 by RCA Records. Dist: RCA Distribution

IT'S MY HOUSE.
Single (7"): released on Motown, Oct'81 by RCA Records. Dist: RCA Distribution

Single (12"): released on Motown, Oct'81 by RCA Records. Dist: RCA Distribution

IT'S MY TURN.
Single (7"): released on Motown, Oct'81 by RCA Records. Dist: RCA Distribution

IT'S NEVER TOO LATE.
Single (7"): released on Capitol, Jul'82 by Capitol Records. Dist: EMI

Single (12"): released on Capitol, Jul'82 by Capitol Records. Dist: EMI

LADY SINGS THE BLUES.
Compact disc: released on Motown, Jul'86 by Motown Records. Dist: BMG Distribution

Double Album: released on Motown, Oct'81 by RCA Records. Dist: RCA Distribution

Double cassette: released on Motown, Oct'81 by RCA Records. Dist: RCA Distribution

LAST TIME I SAW HIM.
Album: released on Motown, Aug'82 by RCA Records. Dist: RCA Distribution

Cassette: released on Motown, Aug'82 by RCA Records. Dist: RCA Distribution

LET THE SUN SHINE IN/CREAM OF THE CROP 2 Classic albums (Ross, Diana & The Supremes).
Tracks: / Composer, The / Everyday people / No matter what sign you are / Hey Western Union man / What becomes of the broken-hearted / I'm livin' in shame / Aquarius (medley) / Let the sun shine in (the flesh failures) (medley) / Let the music play / With a child's heart / Discover me (and you'll discover love) / Will this be the day / I'm so glad I got somebody (like you around) / Someday we'll be together / Can't you see it's me / You gave me love / Hey Jude / Young folks, The / Shadows of society / Loving you is better than ever / When it's to the top (still I won't stop giving you love) / Till Johnny comes / Blowin' in the wind / Beginning of the end, The.
Compact disc: released on Motown, Dec'86 by Motown Records. Dist: BMG Distribution

LIVE AT CAESAR'S PALACE.
Album: released on Motown, Oct'81 by RCA Records. Dist: RCA Distribution

Cassette: released on Motown, Oct'81 by RCA Records. Dist: RCA Distribution

LOVE CHILD (Ross, Diana & The Supremes).
Album: released on Motown, Aug'82 by RCA Records. Dist: RCA Distribution

Cassette: released on Motown, Aug'82 by RCA Records. Dist: RCA Distribution

LOVE CHILD/SUPREMES A GO GO 2 Classic albums (Ross, Diana & The Supremes).
Tracks: / Love child / Keep an eye / How long has that evening train been gone / Does your Mama know about me / Honey bee (keep on stingin me) / Some things you never get used to / He's my sunny boy / You've been so wonderful to me / Chains of love (Don't break these) / You ain't livin' till you're lovin' / I'll set you free / Can't shake it loose / Love is like an itching in my heart / This old heart of mine (is weak for you) / You can't hurry love / Shake me, wake me (when it's over) / Baby I need your loving / These boots are made for walking / I can't help myself / Get ready / Put yourself in my place / Money (that's what I want) / Come and get these memories / Hang on Sloopy.
Compact disc: released on Motown, Nov'86 by Motown Records. Dist: BMG Distribution

LOVE HANGOVER.
Single (7"): released on Motown, Oct'81 by RCA Records. Dist: RCA Distribution

Single (7"): released on Motown, Apr'85 by RCA Records. Dist: RCA Distribution

Single (12"): released on Motown, Apr'85 by RCA Records. Dist: RCA Distribution

LOVE IS HERE AND NOW YOU'RE GONE (Ross, Diana & The Supremes).
Single (7"): released on Motown (Re-issue), Mar'83

LOVE SONGS.
Album: released on K-Tel, Nov'82 by K-Tel Records. Dist: Record Merchandisers Distribution, Taylors, Terry Blood Distribution, Wynd-Up Distribution, Relay Distribution, Pickwick Distribution, Solomon & Peres Distribution, Polygram

Cassette: released on K-Tel, Nov'82 by K-Tel Records. Dist: Record Merchandisers Distribution, Taylors, Terry Blood Distribution, Wynd-Up Distribution, Relay Distribution, Pickwick Distribution, Solomon & Peres Distribution, Polygram

MAHOGANY.
Album: released on Motown, Nov'82 by RCA Records. Dist: RCA Distribution

Cassette: released on Motown, Nov'82 by RCA Records. Dist: RCA Distribution

MERRY CHRISTMAS (Ross, Diana & The Supremes).
Album: released on Motown, Nov'82 by RCA Records. Dist: RCA Distribution

Cassette: released on Motown, Nov'82 by RCA Records. Dist: RCA Distribution

MISSING YOU.
Single (7"): released on Capitol, Dec'84 by Capitol Records. Dist: EMI

Single (12"): released on Capitol, Mar'85 by Capitol Records. Dist: EMI

MORE HITS BY THE SUPREMES (Ross, Diana & The Supremes).
Album: released on Motown, Oct'81 by RCA Records. Dist: RCA Distribution

Cassette: released on Motown, Oct'81 by RCA Records. Dist: RCA Distribution

MOTOWN SPECIAL (Ross, Diana & The Supremes).
Album: released on Motown, Oct'81 by RCA Records. Dist: RCA Distribution

Cassette: released on Motown, Oct'81 by RCA Records. Dist: RCA Distribution

MUSCLES.
Single (7"): released on Capitol, Oct'82 by Capitol Records. Dist: EMI

Single (12"): released on Capitol, Oct'82 by Capitol Records. Dist: EMI

MY OLD PIANO.
Single (7"): released on Motown, Oct'81 by RCA Records. Dist: RCA Distribution

Single (7"): released on Motown, Apr'85 by RCA Records. Dist: RCA Distribution

Single (12"): released on Motown, Apr'85 by RCA Records. Dist: RCA Distribution

NO ONE GETS THE PRIZE.
Single (7"): released on Motown, Oct'81 by RCA Records. Dist: RCA Distribution

OLD FUNKY ROLLS.
Single (7"): released on Motown, Aug'82 by RCA Records. Dist: RCA Distribution

Single (12"): released on Motown, Aug'82 by RCA Records. Dist: RCA Distribution

ONE MORE CHANCE.
Single (7"): released on Motown, Oct'81 by RCA Records. Dist: RCA Distribution

PIECES OF ICE.
Single (7"): released on Capitol, Jun'83 by Capitol Records. Dist: EMI

Single (12"): released on Capitol, Jun'83 by Capitol Records. Dist: EMI

Double Album: released on Telstar, Jan'84 by Telstar Records. Dist: RCA Distribution

Cassette: released on Telstar, Jan'84 by Telstar Records. Dist: RCA Distribution

PORTRAIT.
Tracks: / Where did our love go / Baby love / Stop in the name of love / You can't hurry love / You keep me hangin on / Happening (The) / Reflections / Love child / I'm gonna make you love me / I second that emotion / Someday we'll be together / Doobedood'n doobe doobedood'n doobe / Ain't no mountain high enough / Remember me / Surrender / Love hangover / I'm still waiting / Reach out and touch / All of my life / Sorry doesn't always make it right / Theme from mahogany- Do you know where your going to / Touch me in the morning / Upside down / It's my house / Boss (The) / My old piano / I'm coming out / It's my turn / Endless love.
Album: released on Telstar, Apr'86 by Telstar Records. Dist: RCA Distribution

Double cassette: released on Telstar, Apr'86 by Telstar Records. Dist: RCA Distribution

PORTRAIT VOL 2.
Compact disc: released on Telstar, Jul'86 by Telstar Records. Dist: RCA Distribution

PROTRAIT VOL. 1.
: released on Telstar, Jul'86 by Telstar Records. Dist: RCA Distribution

REACH AND TOUCH (SOMEBODY'S HAND).
Single (7"): released on Motown, Jul'84 by RCA Records. Dist: RCA Distribution

RED HOT RHYTHM 'N' BLUES.
Tracks: / Dirty looks / Stranger in paradise / Shine / Shockwaves / Selfish one / Mr. Lee / Tell mama / There goes my baby / Summertime / Cross my heart / It's hard for me to say / Tell me again.
Notes: This album has been produced by Tom Dowd who is famous for his work with Chicago, Eric Clapton and Rod Stewart. Diana has been joined on this album by some of the world's finest players, like drummers Steve Ferrone and Steve Gadd; guitarist-Eric Gale; bass player-Nathan East; keyboard players-Greg Phillingaines and Richard Tee. [EMI release sheet, May 1987]
Compact disc: released on EMI, May'87 by EMI Records. Dist: EMI

Album: released on EMI, May'87 by EMI Records. Dist: EMI

Cassette: released on EMI, May'87 by EMI Records. Dist: EMI

Compact disc: released on EMI, May'87 by EMI Records. Dist: EMI

REFLECTIONS (Ross, Diana & The Supremes).
Album: released on Motown, Mar'85 by RCA Records. Dist: RCA Distribution

Cassette: released on Motown, Mar'85 by RCA Records. Dist: RCA Distribution

Single (7"): released on Motown, Oct'81 by Motown Records. Dist: BMG Distribution

REMEMBER ME.
Single (7"): released on Motown, Oct'81 by Motown Records. Dist: BMG Distribution

SILK ELECTRIC.
Tracks: / Muscles / So close / Still in love / Fool for your love / Turn me over / Who / Loves lies / In your arms / Anywhere you run to / I am me.
Notes: This is the second album Diana Ross recorded for Capitol after almost 20 years with Motown as a Supreme and a solo artist. Contains the single "Muscles" which charted as did the album which stayed in the charts in the for 3 months. The sleeve features a portrait of Diana Ross by Andy Warhol. Re-issued in June '87.
Album: released on Fame, Jun'87 by Music For Pleasure Records. Dist: EMI

Cassette: released on Fame, Jun'87 by Music For Pleasure Records. Dist: EMI

Album: released on Capitol, Oct'82 by Capitol Records. Dist: EMI

Cassette: released on Capitol, Oct'82 by Capitol Records. Dist: EMI

SO CLOSE.
Single (7"): released on Capitol, Jan'83 by Capitol Records. Dist: EMI

Single (12"): released on Capitol, Jan'83 by Capitol Records. Dist: EMI

SOMEDAY WE'LL BE TOGETHER (Ross, Diana & The Supremes).
Single (7"): released on Motown, Oct'81 by Motown Records. Dist: BMG Distribution

STOP LOOK LISTEN TO YOUR HEART (Ross, Diana & Marvin Gaye).
Single (7"): released on Motown, Oct'81 by Motown Records. Dist: BMG Distribution

SUPREMES A GO GO (Ross, Diana & The Supremes).
Album: released on Motown, Oct'81 by Motown Records. Dist: BMG Distribution

Cassette: released on Motown, Oct'81 by Motown Records. Dist: BMG Distribution

SUPREMES MEDLEY (Ross, Diana & The Supremes).
Single (7"): released on Motown, Oct'81 by RCA Records. Dist: RCA Distribution

Single (12"): released on Motown, Oct'81 by RCA Records. Dist: RCA Distribution

SUPREMES SING MOTOWN (Ross, Diana & The Supremes).
Album: released on Motown, Oct'81 by Motown Records. Dist: BMG Distribution

Cassette: released on Motown, Oct'81 by Motown Records. Dist: BMG Distribution

SWEPT AWAY.
Tracks: / Missing you / Touch by touch / Rescue me / It's your move / Swept away / Telephone / Nobody makes me crazy like you do / All of you / We are the children of the world / Forever love.
Notes: A new album from Diana Ross, the title track is co-written and produced by Daryl Hall. The album includse the duet All Of You with Julio Iglesias. Other songs include cover versions of the hit for Fontella Bass Rescue Me It's Your Move by America and Bob Dylan's Forever Young. Bernard Edwards of Chichas co- written and produced a song for Diana and Lionel Ritchie has contributeda ballad reputed to be dedicated to Marvin Gaye.
Album: released on Capitol, Oct'86 by Capitol Records. Dist: EMI

Cassette: released on Capitol, Oct'86 by Capitol Records. Dist: EMI

Compact disc: released on Capitol, Oct'86 by Capitol Records. Dist: EMI

T.C.B. - THE ORIGINAL SOUNDTRACK (Ross, Diana & The Supremes with The Temptations).
Album: released on Motown, Mar'82 by RCA Records. Dist: RCA Distribution

Cassette: released on Motown, Mar'82 by RCA Records. Dist: RCA Distribution

TENDERNESS.
Single (7"): released on Motown, Dec'81 by RCA Records. Dist: RCA Distribution

Single (12"): released on Motown, Dec'81 by RCA Records. Dist: RCA Distribution

TO LOVE AGAIN.
Album: released on Motown, Oct'81 by RCA Records. Dist: RCA Distribution

Cassette: released on Motown, Oct'81 by RCA Records. Dist: RCA Distribution

TOUCH ME IN THE MORNING/BABY IT'S ME 2 Classic albums.
Tracks: / Touch me in the morning / All of my life / We need you / Leave a little room / I won't last a day without you / Little girl blue / My baby (my baby my own) / Imagine / Brown baby (medley) / Save the children (medley) / Gettin' ready for love / You got it / Baby it's me / Too shy to say / Your love is so good for me / Top of the world / All night lover / Confide in me / Same love that made me laugh, The / Come in from the rain.
Compact disc: released on Motown, Dec'86 by Motown Records. Dist: BMG Distribution

Compact disc: released on Motown, Dec'86 by Motown Records. Dist: BMG Distribution

TOUCH ME IN THE MORNING.
Album: released on Motown, Oct'81 by RCA Records. Dist: RCA Distribution

Cassette: released on Motown, Oct'81 by RCA Records. Dist: RCA Distribution

Album: released on Motown, May'84 by RCA Records. Dist: RCA Distribution

Cassette: released on Motown, May'84 by RCA Records. Dist: RCA Distribution

Single (7"): released on Motown, Oct'81 by Motown Records. Dist: BMG Distribution

UP FRONT.
Single (7"): released on Capitol, Oct'83 by Capitol Records. Dist: EMI

Single (12"): released on Capitol, Oct'83 by Capitol Records. Dist: EMI

VERY BEST OF DIANA ROSS.
Double Album: released on Motown, Dec'83 by RCA Records. Dist: RCA Distribution

Double cassette: released on Motown, Dec'83 by RCA Records. Dist: RCA Distribution

VISIONS OF DIANA ROSS.
Video-cassette (VHS): released on PMI, Jun'86 by PMI Records. Dist: EMI

Video-cassette [Betamax]: released on PMI, Jun'86 by PMI Records. Dist: EMI

WE REMEMBER SAM COOKE (Ross, Diana & The Supremes).
Album: released on Motown, May'86 by Motown Records. Dist: BMG Distribution

Cassette: released on Motown, May'86 by Motown Records. Dist: BMG Distribution

WHAT YOU GAVE ME.
Single (7"): released on Motown, Oct'81 by RCA Records. Dist: RCA Distribution

WHERE DID OUR LOVE GO (Ross, Diana & The Supremes).
Single (7"): released on Motown, Oct'81 by Motown Records. Dist: BMG Distribution

Album: released on Capitol, Oct'81 by Capitol Records. Dist: EMI

Cassette: released on Capitol, Oct'81 by Capitol Records. Dist: EMI

Single (7"): released on Capitol, Oct'81 by Capitol Records. Dist: EMI

WHERE DID OUR LOVE GO/I HEAR A SYMPHONY 2 Classic albums (Ross, Diana & The Supremes).
Tracks: / Where did our love go / Run, run, run / Baby love / When the lovelight starts shining through his eyes / Come see about me / Long gone lover / I'm giving you your freedom / Breath taking guy, A / He means the world to me / Standing at the crossroads of love / Your kiss of fire / Ask any girl / Stranger in paradise / Stranger in paradise / Yesterday / I hear a symphony / Unchained melody / With a song in my heart / Without a song / My world is empty without you / Lover's concerto, A / Any girl in love (knows what I'm going through) / Wonderful, wonderful / Everything is good about you / He's all I got.
Compact disc: released on Motown, Dec'86 by Motown Records. Dist: BMG Distribution

WHY DO FOOLS FALL IN LOVE.
Tracks: / Why do fools fall in love / Sweet surrender / Mirror mirror / Endless love / It's never too late / Think I'm in love / Sweet nothings / Two can make it / Work that body / Why do fools fall in love / Sweet surrender / Mirror mirror / Endless love / It's never too late / Think I'm in love / Sweet nothin's / Two can make it / Work that body.
Compact disc: released on Capitol, Mar'86 by Capitol Records. Dist: EMI

Cassette: released on Fame, Sep'87 by Music For Pleasure Records. Dist: EMI. Estim retail price in Sep'87 was £3.49.

Album: released on Fame, Sep'87 by Music For Pleasure Records. Dist: EMI. Estim retail price in Sep'87 was £3.49.

YOU ARE EVERYTHING (Ross, Diana & Marvin Gaye).
Single (7"): released on Motown (Re-issue), May'82

Single (7"): released on Motown, Apr'85 by RCA Records. Dist: RCA Distribution

Single (12"): released on Motown, Apr'85 by RCA Records. Dist: RCA Distribution

YOU CAN'T HURRY LOVE (Ross, Diana & The Supremes).
Single (7"): released on Motown (Re-issue), Oct'81

YOU KEEP ME HANGIN ON (Ross, Diana & The Supremes).

Tracks: / You keep me hangin on / Come see about me / I hear a symphony / Your love is like an itching in my heart.
Single (7"): released on Motown, Apr'86 by Motown Records. Dist: BMG Distribution

Single (12"): released on Motown, Apr'86 by Motown Records. Dist: BMG Distribution

Ross, Doctor
HARMONICA BLUES, THE (Ross, Doctor/ Sonny Boy Williams/ Sonny Terry).

Ross, Drew
BALLAD OF JR / MIDNIGHT IN DALLAS.
Single (7"): released on Hot Rod, Jun'80 by Hot Rod Records. Dist: Jetstar

Rosselli, Jimmy
WHEN YOUR WEDDING RING WAS NEW.
Tracks: / When your wedding ring was new / Say it isn't so / Addio amor.
Single (7"): released on First Night, 23 May'87 by Safari Records. Dist: Pinnacle

Single (12"): released on First Night, 23 May'87 by Safari Records. Dist: Pinnacle

Cassette single: released on First Night, 30 May'87 by Safari Records. Dist: Pinnacle

Rosselson, Leon
BRINGING THE NEWS FROM NOWHERE.
Album: released on Fuse, May'86 by Fuse Records. Dist: Projection

FOR THE GOOD OF THE NATION.
Album: released on Fuse, May'86 by Fuse Records. Dist: Projection

PALACES OF GOLD.
Album: released on Fuse, May'86 by Fuse Records. Dist: Projection

TEMPORARY LOSS OF VISION.
Album: released on Fuse, May'86 by Fuse Records. Dist: Projection

THAT'S NOT THE WAY IT'S GOT TO BE (Rosselson, Leon/Roy Bailey).
Album: released on Fuse, May'86 by Fuse Records. Dist: Projection

WORD IS ... (THE) (see Carthy, Martin) (Rosselson, Leon & Martin Carthy).

Rossendale Male Voice
VALLEY OF SONG, THE.
Album: released on Chandos, Aug'84 by Chandos Records. Dist: Harmonia Mundi, Taylors

Cassette: released on Chandos, Aug'84 by Chandos Records. Dist: Harmonia Mundi, Taylors

Rosser & Davies
FRIENDS.
Single (7"): released on Lifestyle, Aug'87 by Zomba Records. Dist: CBS, PRT, RCA

Single (12"): released on Lifestyle, Aug'87 by Zomba Records. Dist: CBS, PRT, RCA

Rosser, Simon
BY CHANCE IT WAS (Rosser, Simon & Keith Dignum).
Album: released on Dingles, '83 by Dingles Records. Dist: Projection

Rossi, Francis
MODERN ROMANCE (Rossi, Francis & Bernard Frost).
Single (7"): released on Vertigo, Apr'85 by Phonogram Records. Dist: Polygram

Rossi, Manuel
CLASSICAL DREAMS.
Notes: A superb popular classical collection. Selections from Dvorak/Tschaikowsky and Handel performed in an easy-on-the ear fashion, making very pleasant listening.
Album: released on Teldec (Germany), Dec'85 by Import Records. Dist: IMS Distribution, Polygram Distribution

Cassette: released on Teldec (Germany), Dec'85 by Import Records. Dist: IMS Distribution, Polygram Distribution

Rossington Collins Band
ANYTIME, ANYPLACE, ANYWHERE.
Tracks: / Prime time / Three times as bad / Don't misunderstand me / One good man / Opportunity / Getaway / Winners & losers / Misery loves company / Sometimes you can put it out.
Album: released on MCA, Jun'87 by MCA Records. Dist: Polygram, MCA

Cassette: released on MCA, Jun'87 by MCA Records. Dist: Polygram, MCA

Rossiter, Leonard
RISING DAMP.
Single (7"): released on Chips, Jan'80 by PRT. Dist: PRT

Rossi, Tino
DISQUE D'OR.
Album: released on EMI (France), '83 by EMI Records. Dist: Conifer

DOUBLE ALBUM.
Tracks: / O Corse Ile d'amour / Vieni vieni / J'ai reve d'une fleur / L'amour est une etoile / Chanson pour Nina / J'aime les femmes, c'est ma folie / Marinella / Tchi-tchi / Bella Ragazzina / Loin des guitares / Tarentelle / Ecoutez les mandolines / Seranade de Lena / Laissez-moi vous aimer / Pescadore / Quand on est marinier / Tant qu'il y aura des etoiles / Tango d'un soir / Chanson pour ma brune / Mia piccolina / Apres toi je n'aurai plus d'amour / Credo / Rien qu'un chant d'amour / Je vous aime sans espoir.
Album: released on Pathe Marconi, Apr'87 Dist: Swift

Double cassette: released on Pathe Marconi, Apr'87 Dist: Swift

TINO ROSSI.
Album: released on Pathe Marconi(France), May'87

Cassette: released on Pathe Marconi(France), May'87

Ross, Jimmy
NEW YORK TO MOSCOW.
Single (7"): released on Trance, Sep'84

Single (12"): released on Trance, Sep'84

Ross, Lian
FANTASSY.
Single (12"): released on ZYX (Germany), Nov'85 by ZYX Records. Dist: Greyhound

FANTASY.
Tracks: / Fantasy / Remix / Say you'll never / Saturday night.
Single (12"): released on Greyhound, Nov'86 by Greyhound Records. Dist: PRT, Greyhound

IT'S UP TO YOU.
Tracks: / It's up to you / Love call mix.
Single (12"): released on Conifer, May'86 by Conifer Records. Dist: Conifer

SAY YOU'LL NEVER.
Tracks: / Say you'll never / D.j alternative mix.
Single (12"): released on ZYX (Germany), Dec'85 by ZYX Records. Dist: Greyhound

Ross, Lindsay...
GREAT SCOTTISH DANCE BANDS VOL 1 (Ross, Lindsay & His Scottish Dance Band).
Album: released on Polydor, Dec'76 by Polydor Records. Dist: Polygram, Polydor

LINDSAY ROSS AND HIS SCOTTISH DANCE BAND (Ross, Lindsay & His Scottish Dance Band).
Album: released on Ross, '86 by Ross Records. Dist: Ross Distribution, Roots Distribution

Cassette: released on Ross, '86 by Ross Records. Dist: Ross Distribution, Roots Distribution

LINDSAY ROSS AND HIS BAND (Ross, Lindsay & his Band).
Cassette: released on Accordion Record Club, Jul'86 by Accordion Record Club Records. Dist: Accordion Record Club

Rosslyn Mountain Boys
ROSSLYN MOUNTAIN BOYS.
Album: released on Adolphi, May'81 by Adelphi Records. Dist: Jetstar

Rosso, Nini
IL SILENZIO.
Single (7"): released on Old Gold, Jul'82 by Old Gold Records. Dist: Lightning, Jazz Music, Spartan, Counterpoint

Ross, Steven
THEN THERE WAS YOU.
Single (7"): released on Arista, Jul'85 by Arista Records. Dist: RCA

Single (12"): released on Arista, Jul'85 by Arista Records. Dist: RCA

Ross, T.T.
HE IS MINE.
Tracks: / He is mine / He is mine (Instrumental version).
Single (12"): released on Dione, Apr'86 Dist: Jetstar

LAST DATE.
Single (12"): released on Cima, Oct'84 by Cima Records. Dist: Jetstar

Rostal & Schaefer
MELODIES WITH MEMORIES.
Album: released on EMI, Dec'75 by EMI Records. Dist: EMI

WITH RON GOODWIN & THE ROYAL LIVERPOOL PHILHARMONIC ORCH..
Album: released on Parlophone, Jun'79 by EMI Records. Dist: EMI

Rosy Vista
YOU BETTER BELIEVE IT.
Notes: Mini LP.
Album: released on Noise, Feb'86 by Dorane. Dist: Revolver, Cartel

Rota, Nino
NINO ROTA MOVIES (THE).
Tracks: / Godfather (The) / Taming of the shrew, (The) / La dolce vita / Rocco and his brothers / Napoli millionaria / Romeo and Juliet / War and peace / Il gattopardo / Amarcord / La strada / Le notti di cabiria / Giulietta degli spiriti / I Vitelloni / Otto e mezzo.
Notes: 14 tracks of some of the most beautiful music ever written for movie soundtracks, including 'The Godfather', 'War And Peace' and 'Romeo And Juliet'. Orchestra conducted by Carlo Savina.
Compact disc: released on Polydor (Germany), May'85 Dist: IMS-Polygram

Roth, Arlen
PAINT JOB.
Album: released on Breaking, May'84

Roth, David Lee
CRAZY FROM THE HEAT.
Album: released on Warner Bros., Feb'85 by Warner Bros Records. Dist: WEA

Cassette: released on Warner Bros., Feb'85 by Warner Bros Records. Dist: WEA

EAT 'EM AND SMILE.
Tracks: / Yankee rose / Shyboy / I'm easy / Ladies' nite in Buffalo? / Goin' crazy / Tobacco Road / Elephant gun / Big trouble / Bump and grind / That's life.
Album: released on Warner Bros., Aug'86 by Warner Bros Records. Dist: WEA

Cassette: released on Warner Bros., Aug'86 by Warner Bros Records. Dist: WEA

Compact disc: released on Warner Bros., Aug'86 by Warner Bros Records. Dist: WEA

JUST A GIGOLO (MEDLEY).
Single (7"): released on Warner Bros., Apr'85 by Warner Bros Records. Dist: WEA

YANKEE ROSE.
Tracks: / Yankee rose / Shyboy / Easy Street.
Single (7"): released on Warner Bros., Jul'86 by Warner Bros Records. Dist: WEA

Single (12"): released on Warner Bros., Jul'86 by Warner Bros Records. Dist: WEA

Rother, Michael
SUSSHERZ UND TIEFENSCHARFE.
Album: released on Polydor (Germany), Aug'85 Dist: IMS-Polygram

Roth, Philip
ZUCKERMAN BOUND.
Cassette: released on Caedmon(USA), Sep'85 by Caedmon (USA) Records. Dist: Gower, Taylors, Discovery

Roth, Uli John
BEYOND THE ASTRAL SKIES (Roth, Uli John & Electric Sun).
Album: released on EMI, Jan'85 by EMI Records. Dist: EMI

Cassette: released on EMI, Jan'85 by EMI Records. Dist: EMI

NIGHT THE MASTER COMES (Roth, Uli John & Electric Sun).
Single (7"): released on EMI, Jan'85 by EMI Records. Dist: EMI

Rot In Hell
ROT IN HELL (77) (Various Artists).
Album: released on Rot, Apr'85 by Rot Records. Dist: Red Rhino Through Cartel Distributions

Rot, Jan
COUNTING SHEEP.
Single (7"): released on WEA, Sep'82 by WEA Records. Dist: WEA

Rouen
HOLD ME.
Tracks: / Hold me / No better place / Follow me.
Single (7"): released on E.G., Sep'86 by Virgin Records. Dist: Virgin, EMI

Rostal & Schaefer
MELODIES WITH MEMORIES.

Single (12"): released on E.G., Sep'86 by Virgin Records. Dist: Virgin, EMI

LET IT ALL OUT.
Tracks: / Too close to the edge / All the way back home'.
Single (7"): released on E.G., Jan'87 by Virgin Records. Dist: Virgin, EMI

Single (12"): released on E.G., Jan'87 by Virgin Records. Dist: Virgin, EMI

ORDINARY LIFE.
Single (7"): released on Island, Jun'85 by Island Records. Dist: Polygram

Single (12"): released on Island, Jun'85 by Island Records. Dist: Polygram Deleted '87.

YOUNG FOR A DAY (7").
Tracks: / Young for a day / Take me back home.
Single (7"): released on Kick, Jun'86 by Mike Collier. Dist: Pinnacle

YOUNG FOR A DAY (LP).
Album: released on E.G., May'87 by Virgin Records. Dist: Virgin, EMI

Cassette: released on E.G., May'87 by Virgin Records. Dist: Virgin, EMI

Compact disc: released on Virgin, May'87 by Virgin Records. Dist: EMI, Virgin Distribution

Rough Cutt
WANTS YOU.
Tracks: / Rock the USA / Bad reputation / Don't settle for less / Hot'n'heavy / Take a chance / We like it loud / Double trouble / You wanna be a star / Let em' talk / Night cries out, The.
Album: released on Warner Brothers, Nov'86 by Warner Bros Records. Dist: WEA

Cassette: released on Warner Brothers, Nov'86 by Warner Bros Records. Dist: WEA

Rough dried blues
ROUGH DRIED BLUES (Various Artists).
Tracks: / Bowlegged woman-knock kneed man / I don't know / Count the days I'm gone / What you're looking for / High cost of living / I can't understand / Raining in my heart / Lonesome as can be / I've been up the mountain / I found something better / Rough dried woman part1 / Food stamp blues parts 1&2 / Stoop down / Go on help yourself.
Album: released on Charly, Jan'87 by Charly Records. Dist: Charly, Cadillac

Rough Road
ROUGH ROAD Various original reggae artists (Various Artists).
Album: released on Burning Sounds, Jan'79 by Ross, Bill/Burning Sounds Records. Dist: PRT

Rough Trade
CRIMES OF PASSION.
Single (7"): released on FM, Oct'85 by FM-Revolver Records. Dist: EMI

Single (12"): released on FM, Oct'85 by FM-Revolver Records. Dist: EMI

O TEMPORA! O mores!.
Album: released on FM-Revolver, Mar'86 by FM-Revolver Records. Dist: BMG (RCA/Ariola), Pathe Marconi, Polygram

ROUGHEST TRADE.
Tracks: / Crimes of passion / All touch / Lie back and do everything / Weapons / Birds of a feather / Grade B movie / Baptism of fire / High school confidential (sexual outlaw) / Shaking the foundations / Territorial / America bad and beautiful.
Compact disc: released on FM-Revolver, '86 by FM-Revolver Records. Dist: BMG (RCA/Ariola), Pathe Marconi, Polygram

Album: released on Heavy Metal, Sep'85 by FM-Revolver Records. Dist: EMI

Album: released on Heavy Metal, Sep'85 by FM-Revolver Records. Dist: EMI

SHAKING THE FOUNDATIONS.
Album: released on CBS, May'83 by CBS Records. Dist: CBS

Cassette: released on CBS, May'83 by CBS Records. Dist: CBS

Rough with the smooth
ROUGH WITH THE SMOOTH Various artists (Various Artists).
Album: released on Crepescule, Dec'86 by Island Records. Dist: Polygram. Pinnacle

Roulette Rock'N'Roll
ROULETTE ROCK'N'ROLL COLLECTION (Various Artists).
Album: released on Pye International, May' ...

Roulettes
RUSS, BOB, PETE & MOD.
Album: released on Edsel, Aug'83 by Demon Records. Dist: Pinnacle, Jazz Music, Projection

Round At Calum's
ROUND AT CALUM'S   Various artists (Various Artists).
Cassette: released on Highlander, Jun'86 Dist: PRT

Round-A-Way-Wrong
BOY.
Single (7"): released on Wrong, Dec'84 by Wrong Records. Dist: Wrong

Rounder Folk
ROUNDER FOLK VOLUME 1 Various artists (Various Artists).
Album: released on Rounder (USA), Dec'85 Dist: Mike's Country Music Room Distribution, Jazz Music Distribution, Swift Distribution, Roots Records Distribution, Projection Distribution, Topic Distribution

Cassette: released on Rounder (USA), Dec'85 Dist: Mike's Country Music Room Distribution, Jazz Music Distribution, Swift Distribution, Roots Records Distribution, Projection Distribution, Topic Distribution

[C]assette: released on Rounder (USA), Dec'85 [Di]st: Mike's Country Music Room Distribution, Jazz Music Distribution, Swift Distribution, [R]oots Records Distribution, Projection Distribution, Topic Distribution

[Al]bum: released on Rounder (USA), Dec'85 [Di]st: Mike's Country Music Room Distribution, Jazz Music Distribution, Swift Distribution, [R]oots Records Distribution, Projection Distribution, Topic Distribution

Round Midnight
ROUND MIDNIGHT   Original soundtrack (Various Artists).
[Tra]cks: / Round midnight / Body and soul / Be-[b]opper's nightmare / Fair weather / Una noche [de] Francis / Peacocks (The) / How long has [it] been going on? / Rhythm-a-ning / Still time / [Ti]vnuit aux champselysees / Chan's song.
Compact disc: released on CBS, Nov'89 by [C]BS Records. Dist: CBS
                    Cat. no: CBS CD 70300
[Alb]um: released on CBS, Nov'86 by CBS Records. Dist: CBS

[Ca]ssette: released on CBS, Nov'86 by CBS [Re]cords. Dist: CBS

Round The Horne
[BE]ST OF ROUND THE HORNE (Various [Arti]sts).
[Alb]um: by BBC Records & Tapes. Dist: EMI, [PRT,] Pye

[Ca]ssette: released on BBC, '79 by BBC Rec-[ord]s & Tapes. Dist: EMI, PRT, Pye

[MO]RE OF THE BEST (Various Artists).
[Alb]um: released on BBC, Oct'76 by BBC Rec-[ord]s & Tapes. Dist: EMI, PRT, Pye

[ROU]ND THE HORNE VOL.2 (Various Artists).
[Alb]um: released on BBC, Oct'76 by BBC [Rec]ords & Tapes. Dist: EMI, PRT, Pye

[ROU]ND THE HORNE VOL.3 (Various Artists).
[Alb]um: released on BBC, Oct'77 by BBC Rec-[ord]s & Tapes. Dist: EMI, PRT, Pye

[Ca]ssette: released on BBC, Oct'77 by BBC [reco]rds & Tapes. Dist: EMI, PRT, Pye

Roundtown Boys
[MEA]DHEADS AND SUCKERS.
[Album]: released on Swallow, Feb'79

Rouse
[NOI]SE IS ON (THE) (Rouse, Charlie/Paul [Moti]chette).
[Albu]m: released on Affinity, Jul'86 by Charly [Reco]rds. Dist: Charly, Cadillac

[TW]ENTS NOTICE (Rouse, Charlie Quar-[tet])
[Albu]m: released on Storyville, Nov'86 by Sto-[ryvil]le Records. Dist: Jazz Music Distribution, [Swift] Distribution, Chris Wellard Distribution, [Counter]point Distribution

Rousseau, Charles
[WAN]T YOUR LOVE RIGHT NOW.
[Single] (7"): released on Dancefloor, May'83 by [Danc]floor Records. Dist: Vista Sounds Records-[cord]star

[Single] (12"): released on Dancefloor, May'83 by [Dance]floor Records. Dist: Vista Sounds Records-[cord]star

Roussos, Demis
[WOR]LD HITS.
[? Al]bum: released on Philips (Germany).

[? ca]ssette: released on Philips (Germany), [Jul]'82

DEMIS.
Tracks: / Lament / We're shining / Take me sailing / Song without end / Song for the free / Gypsy lady / Need to forget / Race to the end / Where are they now?
Compact disc: released on Polydor, '83 by Polydor Records. Dist: Polygram, Polydor

Album: released on Polydor, Mar'82 by Polydor Records. Dist: Polygram, Polydor

Cassette: released on Polydor, Mar'82 by Polydor Records. Dist: Polygram, Polydor

Compact disc: released on Polydor, Mar'82 by Polydor Records. Dist: Polygram, Polydor

DEMIS ROUSSOS.
Double Album:

Double cassette:

FOLLOW ME.
Single (7"): released on Polydor, Sep'82 by Polydor Records. Dist: Polygram, Polydor

FOR EVER AND EVER.
Album: released on Philips, Aug'83 Dist: IMS-Polygram

Cassette: released on Philips, Aug'83 Dist: IMS-Polygram

Single (7"): released on Old Gold, Jan'85 by Old Gold Records. Dist: Lightning, Jazz Music, Spartan, Counterpoint

GREATEST HITS:DEMIS ROUSSOS.
Tracks: / We shall dance / My reason / Forever and ever / Goodbye my love goodbye / My friend the wind / Velvet morning / Lovely lady of Arcadia / Someday somewhere / My only fascination / Sing an ode to love / Perdoname / From souvenirs to souvenirs / Happy to be an island in the sun / Mourir aupres de mon amour / Ainsi soitil / Lost in love.
Compact disc: released on Philips Import, '84

Album: released on Arcade Music Gala, Apr'86 Dist: Stage One

Cassette: released on Arcade Music Gala, Apr'86 Dist: Stage One

HAPPY TO BE.
Album: released on Philips, Mar'76 Dist: IMS-Polygram

JAY.
Single (7"): released on Polydor, Jun'83 by Polydor Records. Dist: Polygram, Polydor

LOVE ME TENDER.
Single (7"): released on Starblend, Nov'84 by Starblend Records. Dist: PRT Distribution

MAGIC.
Album: released on Contour, Sep'81 by Pickwick Records. Dist: Pickwick Distribution, PRT

Cassette: released on Contour, Sep'81 by Pickwick Records. Dist: Pickwick Distribution, PRT

MUSIC OF DEMIS ROUSSOS VOL.1 1974/75.
Cassette: released on Philips, Feb'81 Dist: IMS-Polygram

RAIN AND TEARS.
Tracks: / Rain and tears / Summer wine.
Single (7"): released on Apollo Music Int., May'87

Single (12"): released on Apollo Music Int., May'87

REFLECTION.
Album: released on Starblend, Nov'84 by Starblend Records. Dist: PRT Distribution

Cassette: released on Starblend, Nov'84 by Starblend Records. Dist: PRT Distribution

SOUVENIRS.
Album: released on Philips, Mar'75 Dist: IMS-Polygram

SUMMER IN HER EYES.
Tracks: / Summer in her eyes / I miss you.
Single (7"): released on Jive, Sep'86 by Zomba Records. Dist: RCA, PRT, CBS

Single (12"): released on Jive, Sep'86 by Zomba Records. Dist: RCA, PRT, CBS

Routers
LET'S GO.
Single (7"): released on Warner Bros., Jul'81 by Warner Bros Records. Dist: WEA

Routledge, Keith
WORSHIP HIS MAJESTY.
Notes: Instrumental praise and worship.
Album: released on Spirit of Praise, May'86

Rovers
NO MORE BREAD AND BUTTER.
Album: released on Attic, Jul'82 Dist: Pinnacle

ROVERS, THE.
Album: released on Attic, Jan'82 Dist: Pinnacle

Rowan, Chris & Lorin
LIVIN' THE LIFE.
Album: released on Appaloosa, Feb'81 Dist: Roots, Folksound, JSU, Projection, Celtic Music, Chris Wellard

Rowan, Keith & Rooney
ROWAN, KEITH & ROONEY.
Album: released on Waterfront, Aug'85 by Waterfront Records. Dist: Rough Trade, Cartel, Projection, Roots

Rowan, Neil
AMAZING SOUNDS OF NEIL ROWAN (THE).
Tracks: / Horse of the year theme / Loch Lomond / Nothern lights / Westering home / Toccata / Erinskay love song / Sky boat song / Quando quando / Chatanooga choo choo / American patrol / In the mood / Dark island / I've got rhythm.
Notes: mail order distribution address: Accordion Record Club, 146 Birmingham Road, Kidderminster, Worcs. DY10 2SL. Tel: 00562 - 746105.
Cassette: released on Accordion Record Club, Jul'86 by Accordion Record Club Records. Dist: Accordion Record Club

NEIL ROWAN.
Cassette: released on ARC (Accordion Records), '84 Dist: Accordion Record Club

Rowan, Peter
FIRST WHIPPERWILL (THE).
Album: released on Sugarhill (USA), May'86 by PRT Records. Dist: PRT Distribution

REVELRY.
Album: released on Waterfront, Mar'84 by Waterfront Records. Dist: Rough Trade, Cartel, Projection, Roots

T FOR TEXAS.
Cassette: released on Waterfront, Jun'86 by Waterfront Records. Dist: Rough Trade, Cartel, Projection, Roots

Single (12"): released on Waterfront, Apr'85 by Waterfront Records. Dist: Rough Trade, Cartel, Projection, Roots

WITH THE RED HOT PICKERS.
Album: released on Spindrift, Jun'84 Dist: Roots

Cassette: released on Spindrift, Jun'84 Dist: Roots

Rowan, Peter & Tex Logan
RIVALRY.
Album: released on Waterfront, Mar'86 by Waterfront Records. Dist: Rough Trade, Cartel, Projection, Roots

Rowe, Gwen
WOMAN NEEDS TO BELONG TO A GOOD MAN, A.
Single (12"): released on WE, Jun'84 by We Records. Dist: Jetstar

Rowe, Keith
GROOVY SITUATION.
Single (12"): released on Seven Leaves, Jun'84 by Seven Leaves Records. Dist: Jetstar

Rowen, Peter
PETER ROWEN.
Album: released on Flying Fish (USA), May'79 by Flying Fish Records (USA). Dist: Roots, Projection

Rowe, Xenia
REACHING FOR THE BEST.
Single (12"): released on Crystal City, Oct'84 by Crystal City Records. Dist: Crystal City Records

Rowland, Kevin & D.M.R.
CELTIC SOUL BROTHERS (Rowland, Kevin & Dexy's Midnight Runners).
Single (7"): released on Mercury, Mar'83 by Phonogram Records. Dist: Polygram Distribution

Single (12"): released on Mercury, Mar'83 by Phonogram Records. Dist: Polygram Distribution

LET'S GET THIS STRAIGHT (Rowland, Kevin & Dexy's Midnight Runners).
Single (7"): released on Mercury, Nov'82 by Phonogram Records. Dist: Polygram Distribution

Single (12"): released on Mercury, Nov'82 by Phonogram Records. Dist: Polygram Distribution

---

Rowles, Jimmy
CHECKMATE (see Pass,Joe) (Rowles, Jimmy/Joe Pass).
Compact disc: released on Pablo (USA), May'86 by Pablo Records (USA). Dist: Wellard, Chris, IMS-Polygram, BMG

IF I'M LUCKY (Rowles, Jimmy & Zoot Sims).
Album: released on Pablo (USA), '82 by Pablo Records (USA). Dist: Wellard, Chris, IMS-Polygram, BMG

Cassette: released on Pablo (USA), '82 by Pablo Records (USA). Dist: Wellard, Chris, IMS-Polygram, BMG

ISFAHAN.
Album: released on Sonet, Jan'79 by Sonet Records. Dist: PRT

MUSIC'S THE ONLY THING ON MY MIND (Rowles, Jimmy & George Mraz).
Album: released on Progressive (Import), '81

WARM TENOR (Rowles, Jimmy & Zoot Sims).
Album: released on Pablo (USA), '82 by Pablo Records (USA). Dist: Wellard, Chris, IMS-Polygram, BMG

Cassette: released on Pablo (USA), '82 by Pablo Records (USA). Dist: Wellard, Chris, IMS-Polygram, BMG

Rowles, John
IF I ONLY HAD TIME.
Single (7"): released on Old Gold, Jul'82 by Old Gold Records. Dist: Lightning, Jazz Music, Spartan, Counterpoint

Rowles, Stacy
TELL IT LIKE IT IS.
Album: released on Concord Jazz, Oct'84 by Concord Jazz Records (USA). Dist: IMS, Polygram

Rowsome, Leo
CLASSICS OF IRISH PIPING VOL.1.
Album: released on Topic, '81 Dist: Roots Distribution

CLASSICS OF IRISH PIPING VOL.3.
Album: released on Topic, '81 Dist: Roots Distribution

Rox
HOT LOVE IN THE CITY.
Single (7"): released on Teentees, Aug'82

KRAZY KUTS.
Single (12"): released on Music For Nations, Sep'83 by Music For Nations Records. Dist: Pinnacle

VIOLENT BREED.
Album: released on Music For Nations, Oct'83 by Music For Nations Records. Dist: Pinnacle

Rox, Angie
ARE YOU WAITING.
Single (7"): released on Surrey Sound, Dec'80 Dist: Pinnacle

Roxon Roadshow
MOTORWAY QUEEN.
Single (7"): released on Roxon, Apr'82 by Roxon Records. Dist: Pinnacle

Roxy, London WC2
ROXY, LONDON WC2 (JAN-APR 77) Various artists (Various Artists).
Tracks: / Runaway / Boston babies / Freedom / Lowdown / 1.2.X.U. / Bored teenagers / Hard loving man / Don't need it / Oh bondage, up yours / Breakdown / Love battery.
Album: released on Harvest, Jan'87 by EMI Records. Dist: Roots, EMI

Cassette: released on Harvest, Jan'87 by EMI Records. Dist: Roots, EMI

Roxy Music
Group

ATLANTIC YEARS (THE) 1973-1980.
Tracks: / Dance away / Angel eyes / Over you / Love is the drug / Oh yeah / Ain't that so / My only love / In the midnight hour / Still falls the rain / Do the Strand.
Compact disc: released on E.G., '83 by Virgin Records. Dist: Virgin, EMI

Album: released on E.G., Nov'83 by Virgin Records. Dist: Virgin, EMI

Cassette: released on E.G., Nov'83 by Virgin Records. Dist: Virgin, EMI

AVALON.
Tracks: / More than this / Space between / India / While my heart is still beating / Main thing / Take a chance with me / Avalon / To turn you on / True to life / Tara.

Page 863

Notes: Compact disc in digital stereo.
Album: released on E.G., Jan'87 by Virgin Records. Dist: Virgin, EMI

Cassette: released on E.G., Jan'87 by Virgin Records. Dist: Virgin, EMI

Compact disc: released on E.G., Jan'87 by Virgin Records. Dist: Virgin, EMI

Compact disc: released on E.G., '83 by Virgin Records. Dist: Virgin, EMI

Album: released on E.G., May'82 by Virgin Records. Dist: Virgin, EMI

Cassette: released on E.G., May'82 by Virgin Records. Dist: Virgin, EMI

COUNTRY LIFE.
Tracks: / Thrill of it all / Three and nine / All I want is you / Out of the blue / If it takes all night / Bitter sweet / Triptych / Casonova / Really good time, A / Prairie Rose.
Album: released on E.G., Jan'87 by Virgin Records. Dist: Virgin, EMI

Cassette: released on E.G., Jan'87 by Virgin Records. Dist: Virgin, EMI

Compact disc: released on E.G., Jan'87 by Virgin Records. Dist: Virgin, EMI

Album: released on Polydor, Feb'77 by Polydor Records. Dist: Polygram, Polydor

Cassette: released on Polydor, Feb'77 by Polydor Records. Dist: Polygram, Polydor

Compact disc: released on Polydor, Feb'77 by Polydor Records. Dist: Polygram, Polydor

DANCE AWAY.
Single (7"): released on Island, '80 by Island Records. Dist: Polygram

DO THE STRAND.
Single (7"): released on Polydor, Jan'78 by Polydor Records. Dist: Polygram, Polydor

FIRST SEVEN ALBUMS, THE.
Boxed set: released on E.G., Nov'81 by Virgin Records. Dist: Virgin, EMI

Boxed set: released on E.G., Nov'81 by Virgin Records. Dist: Virgin, EMI

FLESH AND BLOOD.
Tracks: / In the midnight hour / Oh yeah / Same old scene / Flesh and blood / My only love / Over you / Eight miles high / Rain,rain,rain / Running wild / No strange delight.
Notes: Compact disc in digital stereo.
Album: released on E.G., Jan'87 by Virgin Records. Dist: Virgin, EMI

Cassette: released on E.G., Jan'87 by Virgin Records. Dist: Virgin, EMI

Compact disc: released on E.G., Jan'87 by Virgin Records. Dist: Virgin, EMI

Compact disc: released on E.G., '83 by Virgin Records. Dist: Virgin, EMI

Album: released on Polydor, '81 by Polydor Records. Dist: Polygram, Polydor

Cassette: released on Polydor, '81 by Polydor Records. Dist: Polygram, Polydor

FOR YOUR PLEASURE.
Tracks: / Do the Strand / Beauty Queen / Strictly confidential / Editions of you / In every dream home a heartache / Bogus man / Grey lagoons / For your pleasure.
Album: released on E.G., Jan'87 by Virgin Records. Dist: Virgin, EMI

Cassette: released on E.G., Jan'87 by Virgin Records. Dist: Virgin, EMI

Compact disc: released on E.G., Jan'87 by Virgin Records. Dist: Virgin, EMI

Album: released on Polydor, Feb'77 by Polydor Records. Dist: Polygram, Polydor

Cassette: released on Polydor, Feb'77 by Polydor Records. Dist: Polygram, Polydor

Compact disc: released on Polydor, Feb'77 by Polydor Records. Dist: Polygram, Polydor

GREATEST HITS:ROXY MUSIC.
Tracks: / Virginia plain / Do the Strand / All I want is you / Out of the blue / Pyjamarama / Editions of you / Love is the drug / Mother of pearl / Song for Europe, A / Thrill of it all / Street life.
Compact disc: released on E.G., Jan'87 by Virgin Records. Dist: Virgin, EMI

HIGH ROAD (THE).
Notes: Number of tracks: 14. Type of recording: Live. Total playing time: 75 minutes.
Video-cassette (VHS): released on Channel 5, Apr'86 Dist: W.H. Smiths

Album: released on E.G., Mar'83 by Virgin Records. Dist: Virgin, EMI

Cassette: released on E.G., Mar'83 by Virgin Records. Dist: Virgin, EMI

MANIFESTO.
Tracks: / Ain't that so / Angel eyes / Cry cry cry / Dance away / Manifesto / My little girl / Spin me round / Still falls the rain / Trash / Stronger through the years.
Album: released on E.G., Jan'87 by Virgin Records. Dist: Virgin, EMI

Cassette: released on E.G., Jan'87 by Virgin Records. Dist: Virgin, EMI

Compact disc: released on E.G., Jan'87 by Virgin Records. Dist: Virgin, EMI

Compact disc: released on E.G., '83 by Virgin Records. Dist: Virgin, EMI

Album: released on Polydor, Mar'79 by Polydor Records. Dist: Polygram, Polydor

Cassette: released on Polydor, Mar'79 by Polydor Records. Dist: Polygram, Polydor

MORE THAN THIS.
Single (7"): released on E.G., Mar'82 by Virgin Records. Dist: Virgin, EMI

OH YEAH.
Single (7"): released on Polydor, Jul'80 by Polydor Records. Dist: Polygram, Polydor

OVER YOU.
Single (7"): released on Polydor, May'80 by Polydor Records. Dist: Polygram, Polydor

ROXY MUSIC.
Tracks: / Bitters end / Bob / Chance meeting / If there is something / Ladytron / Remake remodel / 2HB / Would you beleive? / Virginia plain / Bitters end.
Album: released on E.G., Jan'87 by Virgin Records. Dist: Virgin, EMI

Cassette: released on E.G., Jan'87 by Virgin Records. Dist: Virgin, EMI

Compact disc: released on E.G., Jan'87 by Virgin Records. Dist: Virgin, EMI

Compact disc: released on Polydor, Jun'84 by Polydor Records. Dist: Polygram, Polydor

Album: released on Polydor, Feb'77 by Polydor Records. Dist: Polygram, Polydor

Cassette: released on Polydor, Feb'77 by Polydor Records. Dist: Polygram, Polydor

SIREN.
Tracks: / Love is the drug / End of the line / Sentimental fool / Whirl wind / She sells / Could it happen to me / Both ends burning / Nightingale / Just another high.
Album: released on E.G., Jan'87 by Virgin Records. Dist: Virgin, EMI

Cassette: released on E.G., Jan'87 by Virgin Records. Dist: Virgin, EMI

Compact disc: released on E.G., Jan'87 by Virgin Records. Dist: Virgin, EMI

Compact disc: released on Polydor, Jul'84 by Polydor Records. Dist: Polygram. Polydor

Album: released on Polydor, Feb'77 by Polydor Records. Dist: Polygram, Polydor

Cassette: released on Polydor, Feb'77 by Polydor Records. Dist: Polygram, Polydor

STRANDED.
Tracks: / Street life / Just like you / Amazon / Psalm / Serenade / Song for Europe, A / Mother of pearl / Sunset.
Album: released on E.G., Jan'87 by Virgin Records. Dist: Virgin, EMI

Cassette: released on E.G., Jan'87 by Virgin Records. Dist: Virgin, EMI

Compact disc: released on E.G., Jan'87 by Virgin Records. Dist: Virgin, EMI

Album: released on Polydor, Feb'77 by Polydor Records. Dist: Polygram, Polvdor

Cassette: released on Polydor, Feb'77 by Polydor Records. Dist: Polygram, Polydor

Compact disc: released on Polydor, Feb'77 by Polydor Records. Dist: Polygram, Polydor

VIRGINIA PLAIN.
Single (7"): released on Polydor, Oct'77 by Polydor Records. Dist: Polygram, Polydor

VIVA ROXY MUSIC.
Tracks: / Out of the blue / Pyjamarama / Bogus man / Chance meeting / Both ends burning / If there is something / In every dream home a heartache / Do the Strand / Love is the drug / End of the line / Sentimental / Whirlwind / She sells / Could it happen to me / Both ends burning / Nightingale / Just another high.
Compact disc: released on E.G., Jan'87 by Virgin Records. Dist: Virgin, EMI

VIVA ROXY MUSIC.
Album: released on Polydor, Feb'77 by Polydor Records. Dist: Polygram, Polydor

Cassette: released on Polydor, Feb'77 by Polydor Records. Dist: Polygram, Polydor

Royal...

BAND OF THE JUNIOR LEDERS REGIMENT (Royal Armoured Corps).
Album: released on Music Masters, Jul'83 by Music Masters Records. Dist: Taylors

Cassette: released on Music Masters, Jul'83 by Music Masters Records. Dist: Taylors

BIG BAND SOUNDS (Royal Artillery Mounted Band).
Album: released on Note, Sep'77 by EMI Records. Dist: EMI

CALL FOR THE GUNS (Royal Artillery Band).
Album: released on Bandleader, Feb'86 by Bandleader Records. Dist: PRT

Cassette: released on Bandleader, Feb'86 by Bandleader Records. Dist: PRT

DIGITAL MARCHING STRINGS (Royal Artillery Orchestra).
Tracks: / Royal Artillery Show March / Marching strings / Stars and Stripes forever / Skye boat song / Knots Landing / El Capitan / March of the toys / 76 trombones / Semper fidelis / Trap (The) / Entry of the boyards / Marching folk / Allies (The) / Ob la di, ob la da / Winged serpent (The).
Compact disc: released on Bandleader, '86 by Bandleader Records. Dist: PRT

DREAM DOMINION (Royal Family).
Single (12"): released on Factory, Feb'82 by Factory Records. Dist: Cartel, Pinnacle

FIJI BRASS (Royal Fiji Military Forces Band).
Album: released on Viking, Jun'78 Dist: Harmonia Mundi Distributors

HAPPY MUSIC (Royal Artillery Mounted Band).
Album: released on Lismor, Nov'76 by Lismor Records. Dist: Lismor, Roots, Celtic Music

HOMEWARD BOUND FOR CHRISTMAS (Royal Eltham Scouts).
Single (7"): released on Empire, Dec'85 by Empire Records. Dist: Backs, Cartel, Jetstar

HUCKLEBUCK, THE (Royal Showband).
Single (7"): released on H.M.V., Feb'81 by EMI Records. Dist: EMI

IN CONCERT (Royal Regiment Of Fusiliers Band Of The 1st Battalion).
Album: released on Music Masters, Mar'82 by Music Masters Records. Dist: Taylors

LAND OF SUGAR (Royal Crescent Mob).
Album: released on Play It Again Sam, Nov'86 Dist: Red Rhino, Cartel

MARCHING WITH THE GUNNERS (Royal Artillery Mounted Band).
Album: released on Note, Aug'80 by EMI Records. Dist: EMI

MUSICAL DRIVE (Royal Horse Artillery King's Troop).
Album: released on Major Richards, Oct'77 by Major Richards Records. Dist: Taylors

MUSIC BY THE REGIMENT BAND,BUGLES,PIPES & DRUMS (Royal Irish Rangers).
Album: released on Music Masters, Jun'81 by Music Masters Records. Dist: Taylors

PETER PAN (Royal Shakespeare Cast).
Album: released on Dakota, Dec'83 by Dakota Records. Dist: PRT

PROUD HERITAGE (Royal Highland Fusiliers).
Notes: A well packaged Military Band album. Mostly pipe band but 'Flower Of Scotland' and 'The Highland Cathedral' and two regiment pieces have brass.
Album: released on Lismor, May'86 by Lismor Records. Dist: Lismor, Roots, Celtic Music

Cassette: released on Lismor, May'86 by Lismor Records. Dist: Lismor, Roots, Celtic Music

QUEENS LIFE GUARD, THE The band and trumpeters of the Blues & Royals (Royal Horse Guards & 1st Dragoon).

RIGHT OF THE LINE (Royal Scots Reg. Band & Pipes & Drums).
Cassette: released on Ross, '86 by Ross Records. Dist: Ross Distribution, Roots Distribution

ROYAL ARTILLERY MOUNTED BAND (Royal Artillery Mounted Band).
Album: released on Bandleader, '84 by Bandleader Records. Dist: PRT

Cassette: released on Bandleader, '84 by Bandleader Records. Dist: PRT

ROYAL BRITISH LEGION BAND Conducted by Jeremy F.Royle (Royal British Legion Band).
Album: released on Music Masters, Jun'81 by Music Masters Records. Dist: Taylors

ROYAL FAMILY ALBUM (Royal Family Album).
Notes: A new double album on the Royal Family from 1924 to the present day. It includes both historical highlights and many informal and humerous moments.
Double Album: released on BBC, May'86 by BBC Records & Tapes. Dist: EMI, PRT, Pye

Cassette: released on BBC, May'86 by BBC Records & Tapes. Dist: EMI, PRT, Pye

ROYAL HAMPSHIRE REGIMENT 1ST BATTALION (Royal Hampshire Regiment).
Album: released on Music Masters, Feb'80 by Music Masters Records. Dist: Taylors

RULE BRITTANIA (Royal Anglian regiment, 1st Battalion Band).
Album: released on Music Masters, Jan'80 by Music Masters Records. Dist: Taylors

SHORT SHORTS (Royal Teens).
Single (7"): released on Revival, Jul'82 Dist: Lightning, Swift

SOUNDS OF CEREMONY (Royal Army Ordance Corps Staff Band).
Album: released on Music Masters, Mar'82 by Music Masters Records. Dist: Taylors

TRIBUTE TO BRAVERY (Royal Regimen of Wales Regimental Band & Choir).
Album: released on Major Richards, Aug'79 by Major Richards Records. Dist: Taylors

TRIBUTE TO HAROLD WALTERS (Royal Army Corps Staff Band).
Album: released on Major Richards Militar Records, Nov'82 by Major Richards Records Dist: Taylors

VOICE OF GUNS (Royal Artillery Alan brooke Band).
Album: released on Parade, Oct'80 Dist: MSD

Cassette: released on Parade, Oct'80 Dist MSD

Royal Air Force

BIG BAND SPECTACULAR (Royal A Force Squadronaires).
Album: released on Bandleader, Jun'87 b Bandleader Records. Dist: PRT

Cassette: released on Bandleader, Jun'87 b Bandleader Records. Dist: PRT

FESTIVAL OF MUSIC '86 (Royal Air For Massed Bands).
Album: released on Polyphonic, Mar'87 Polyphonic Records. Dist: Taylors

Cassette: released on Polyphonic, Mar'87 Polyphonic Records. Dist: Taylors

ROYAL AIRFORCE.
Album: released on Eva-Lolita, Nov'85 D Pinnacle

STRIKE UP THE BAND (Royal Air Fo Central Band).
Compact disc: by EMI Records. Dist: EMI

Roy, Alan

FORGOTTEN DREAMS.
Album: released on Neptune, Jul'81 by Lism Dist: Spartan

Cassette: released on Neptune, Jul'81 by mor. Dist: Spartan

Royal Cash

RADIOACTIVITY.
Single (12"): released on Buddah, Dec'83 Swift, Jazz Music, PRT

Royal Corps...

BANDSTAND (Royal Corps of Trans Band).
Album: released on Bandleader, '84 by dleader Records. Dist: PRT

Cassette: released on Bandleader, '84 by dleader Records. Dist: PRT

GILBERT AND SULLIVAN ON PARA (Royal Corps of Transport Band).
Album: released on Bandleader, '84 by dleader Records. Dist: PRT

Cassette: released on Bandleader, '84 by dleader Records. Dist: PRT

ICE TIME (Royal Corps of Signals).
Album: released on BBC, Jan'79 by BBC ords & Tapes. Dist: EMI, PRT, Pye

Cassette: released on BBC, Jan'79 by Records & Tapes. Dist: EMI, PRT, Pye

MUSIC FROM THE HORSE OF YEAR SHOW (Royal Corps of Trar Band).
Album: released on Bandleader, Nov' Bandleader Records. Dist: PRT

Cassette: released on Bandleader, Nov'81 by Bandleader Records. Dist: PRT

SALUTE TO ABBA (Royal Corps of Transport Band).
Album: released on Parade, Jan'81 Dist: MSD

Cassette: released on Parade, Jan'81 Dist: MSD

SOUSA THE MARCH KING (Royal Corps of Transport Band).
Album: released on Major Richards, Jul'80 by Major Richards Records. Dist: Taylors

WAIT FOR THE WAGON (Royal Corps of Transport Band).
Album: released on Major Richards, Jun'79 by Major Richards Records. Dist: Taylors

WINTER SPORTS (Royal Corps Signals Concert Band).
Album: released on BBC, Apr'77 by BBC Records & Tapes. Dist: EMI, PRT, Pye

Royal Doulton Band

BRASS ARIA.
Album: released on Top Brass, Apr'77 by PRT Records. Dist: PRT Distribution

BRASS BAND COUNTRY.
Album: released on Bandleader, Jun'82 by Bandleader Records. Dist: PRT

Cassette: released on Bandleader, Jun'82 by Bandleader Records. Dist: PRT

BRASS SHOWCASE.
Cassette: released on Parade, Oct'80 Dist: MSD

Album: released on Parade, Oct'80 Dist: MSD

CHRISTMAS CELEBRATION FOR BRASS BAND.
Album: released on Bandleader, '82 by Bandleader Records. Dist: PRT

Cassette: released on Bandleader, '82 by Bandleader Records. Dist: PRT

CLAYHANGER.
Album:

IMAGES IN BRASS.
Album: released on Bandleader, Sep'84 by Bandleader Records. Dist: PRT

Cassette: released on Bandleader, Sep'84 by Bandleader Records. Dist: PRT

STANDARD OF ST GEORGE.
Album: released on Top Brass, Apr'78 by PRT Records. Dist: PRT Distribution

Royal Engineers Band

ENGINEER EVERYWHERE.
Album: released on Bandleader, Feb'86 by Bandleader Records. Dist: PRT

Cassette: released on Bandleader, Feb'86 by Bandleader Records. Dist: PRT

GOLDEN HOUR OF NATIONAL ANTHEMS AND INTERNATIONAL MARCHES.
Album: released on Golden Hour, Oct'75 by PRT Records. Dist: PRT

...QUE.
Album: released on Music Masters, Jun'82 by Music Masters Records. Dist: Taylors
Cat. no: **MM 0585**

Royal Family and The Poor

...E.
Album: released on Recloose, Oct'86

PROJECT (THE).
Album: released on Factory, Apr'86 by Factory Records. Dist: Cartel, Pinnacle

WE LOVE THE MOON.
Tracks: / We love the moon.
Single (7"): released on Factory, Jan'86 by Factory Records. Dist: Cartel, Pinnacle

Royal green jackets

ROYAL GREEN JACKETS 2ND BATTALION BAND & BUGLES Under the direction of bandmaster WOI C.R.Donaldson.
Album: released on Music Masters, Mar'83 by Music Masters Records. Dist: Taylors

ROYAL GREEN JACKETS 3RD BATTALION BAND & BUGLES.
Album: released on Music Masters, Apr'83 by Music Masters Records. Dist: Taylors

Cassette: released on Music Masters, Apr'83 by Music Masters Records. Dist: Taylors

Royal Guardsmen

SNOOPY AND HIS FRIENDS THE ROYAL GUARDSMEN.
Album: released on Audio Fidelity, Oct'84 Dist: PRT

Cassette: released on Audio Fidelity, Oct'84 Dist: PRT

SNOOPY VERSUS THE RED DRAGON.
Single (7"): released on RCA, Oct'81 by RCA Records. Dist: RCA, Roots, Swift, Wellard, Chris, I & B, Solomon & Peres Distribution

Royal Hussars...

13TH & 18TH REGIMENTS (Royal Hussars Regiment Band).
Album: released on Grosvenor, '74 by Grosvenor Records. Dist: Taylors

HO' WAY THE LADS 15th/19th King's (Royal Hussars Regiment Band).
Album: released on Music Masters, Sep'81 by Music Masters Records. Dist: Taylors

LILLY WHITES, THE 13th & 18th regiments (Royal Hussars Regiment Band).
Cassette: released on Grosvenor, '74 by Grosvenor Records. Dist: Taylors

Album: released on Grosvenor, '74 by Grosvenor Records. Dist: Taylors

ROYAL HUSSARS 13th/18th Queen Mary's Own (Royal Hussars Regiment Band).
Album: released on Music Masters, Sep'81 by Music Masters Records. Dist: Taylors

Royalle Delite

I'LL COME WHEN YOU CALL.
Tracks: / I'll come when you call / Radio cut.
Single (12"): released on Streetwise, Aug'86 Dist: Greyhound

SPEND A LITTLE TIME WITH ME.
Tracks: / Send a little time with me.
Single (7"): released on Streetwise, Dec'85 Dist: Greyhound

Single (12"): released on Streetwise, Dec'85 Dist: Greyhound

Cassette: released on Streetwise, Dec'85 Dist: Greyhound

Picture disc single: released on Streetwise, Dec'85 Dist: Greyhound

Royal Marines...

AND THE BAND PLAYED ON... (Royal Marines Commando Forces Band).
Album: released on EMI, May'83 by EMI Records. Dist: EMI

Cassette: released on EMI, May'83 by EMI Records. Dist: EMI

BAND OF H.M. ROYAL MARINES (Royal Marines, Band of H.M.).
Compact disc: released on K-Tel, '86 by K-Tel Records. Dist: Record Merchandisers Distribution, Taylors, Terry Blood Distribution, Wynd-Up Distribution, Relay Distribution, Pickwick Distribution, Solomon & Peres Distribution, Polygram

BEST OF THE ROYAL MARINES, THE (Royal Marines Band).
Album: released on Polydor, Nov'82 by Polydor Records. Dist: Polygram, Polydor

Cassette: released on Polydor, Nov'82 by Polydor Records. Dist: Polygram, Polydor

GRAND NIGHT FOR SINGING, A (Royal Marines Band).
Album: released on EMI, Apr'76 by EMI Records. Dist: EMI

HANDS ACROSS THE SEA (Royal Marines Band).
Album: released on EMI, Dec'84 by EMI Records. Dist: EMI

Cassette: released on EMI, Dec'84 by EMI Records. Dist: EMI

HERE COMES THE BAND (Royal Marines Band).
Album: released on H.M.V., Mar'83 by EMI Records. Dist: EMI

LAST FAREWELL, THE (Royal Marines Band).
Cassette: released on BBC, Apr'79 by BBC Records & Tapes. Dist: EMI, PRT, Pye

MARCHING WITH THE MARINES (Royal Marines Band).
Cassette: released on EMI, Sep'73 by EMI Records. Dist: EMI

MEN OF ACTION (Royal Marines Band).
Album: released on Bandleader, Aug'85 by Bandleader Records. Dist: PRT

Cassette: released on Bandleader, Aug'85 by Bandleader Records. Dist: PRT

OLD COMRADES - NEW COMRADES (Royal Marines Band).
Album: released on Grasmere, Sep'84 by Grasmere Records. Dist: EMI

Cassette: released on Grasmere, Sep'84 by Grasmere Records. Dist: EMI

ON PARADE (Royal Marines Band).
Double Album: released on MFP, Apr'81 by EMI Records. Dist: EMI

Cassette: released on MFP, Apr'81 by EMI Records. Dist: EMI

PLYMOUTH'S OWN (Royal Marines Commando Forces Band).
Album: released on Grasmere, Mar'85 by Grasmere Records. Dist: EMI

Cassette: released on Grasmere, Mar'85 by Grasmere Records. Dist: EMI

SOMETHING DIFFERENT (Royal Marines Band).
Album: released on Foldback, Nov'80 by Foldback Records. Dist: Lugtons

Cassette: released on Foldback, Nov'80 by Foldback Records. Dist: Lugtons

SOUSA MARCHES-VOLUME 2 (Royal Marines Band).
Tracks: / Hands across the sea / Royal Welsh Fusiliers, The / Legionaires, The / Daughters of Texas / Gallant seventh, The / Golden jubilee / Pride of the wolverines / Hail to the spirit of liberty / From Maine to Oregon / Diplomat, The / Powhatan's daughter / Kansas wildcats / Sound off / Thunderer, The.
Notes: Band of H.M.Royal Marines (Royal Marines School of Music). Conducted by Lt. Col.G.A.C.Hoskins MVO, LRAM, RM. (Principal Director of Music, Royal Marines).
Compact disc: released on H.M.V., Jun'87 by EMI Records. Dist: EMI

STARS AND STRIPES FOREVER (Royal Marines Band).
Tracks: / King Cotton / Gladiator / Belle of Chicago / Semper fidelis / Invincible eagle / Manhattan beach / Liberty bell / El captain / Washington post / Crusador / Black troop / Fairest of the fair / High school cadet / Stars and stripes forever.
Compact disc: released on EMI, '86 by EMI Records. Dist: EMI

STARS AND STRIPES FOREVER (Royal Marines, Band of H.M.).
Album: released on H.M.V., Oct'83 by EMI Records. Dist: EMI

Cassette: released on H.M.V., Oct'83 by EMI Records. Dist: EMI

THIS IS THE ROYAL MARINES BAND (Royal Marines Band).
Album: released on EMI, Jul'80 by EMI Records. Dist: EMI

Cassette: released on EMI, Jul'80 by EMI Records. Dist: EMI

VERY BEST OF THE BAND OF HM ROYAL MARINES, THE (Royal Marines Band).
Album: released on EMI (Studio 2), Nov'77 by EMI Records. Dist: EMI

Cassette: released on EMI (Studio 2), Nov'77 by EMI Records. Dist: EMI

VERY BEST OF THE ROYAL MARINES BAND (Royal Marines Band).
Tracks: / Colonel Bogey / Standard of St. Georde (The) / Great little army (The) / El Abanico / National Emblem / Anchors Aweigh / Semper Fidelis / Cockleshell heroes / Espana / Life on the ocean wave (A) / Warship / On the square / This guy's in love with you / Sutherland's lar theme / Shadow of your smile (The) / Troika / Eye level / What the world needs now is love / On the track / When the saints go marching in.
Notes: First half conducted by Lieut. Col. Sir F. Vivian Dunn, KCVO, OBE, FRAM, RM. Second half conducted by Lieut. Col. Paul Neville, MVO, OBE, FRAM, RM.
Album: released on MFP, May'87 by EMI Records. Dist: EMI

Cassette: released on MFP, May'87 by EMI Records. Dist: EMI

Royal Military...

KNELLER HALL 1857-1982 (Royal Military School of Music).
Album: released on Polyphonic, Jun'83 by Polyphonic Records. Dist: Taylors

KNELLER HALL IN CONCERT (Royal Military School of Music).
Album: released on Polyphonic, Jun'87 by Polyphonic Records. Dist: Taylors

Cassette: released on Polyphonic, Jun'87 by Polyphonic Records. Dist: Taylors

MILITARY MUSIC THROUGH THE AGES (Royal Military School of Music).
Album: released on Bandleader, Jun'82 by Bandleader Records. Dist: PRT

Cassette: released on Bandleader, Jun'82 by Bandleader Records. Dist: PRT

ROYAL MILITARY SPECTACULAR Various artists (Various Artists).
Album: released on Unicorn, Jun'82 Dist: Nine Mile, Cartel

SANDHURST (Royal Military Band Corps).
Album: released on Bandleader (Military), Apr'83

Cassette: released on Bandleader (Military), Aug'83

SOVEREIGNS BANNER, THE (Royal Military Band Corps).
Album: released on Major Richards, Aug'79 by Major Richards Records. Dist: Taylors

Royal Naval....

20 FAVOURITE HYMNS (Royal Naval College Choir/Congregation).
Compact disc: released on Abbey, '86 by Abbey. Dist: PRT, Taylors, Gamut

Royal Philharmonic...

ACADEMY AWARDS.
Tracks: / Lawrence of Arabia / Chim chim cheree / Raindrops keep falling on my head / Somewhere my love / Let it be / Shaft / Lapis lazuli / If ever I would leave you / My love / Here's that rainy day / Charade / Bridge over troubled water / Something's coming / Way we were (The) / MacArthur Park.
Notes: Conducted by Vic L.wis

ACADEMY WINNERS.
Tracks: / Lawrence of Arabia / Chim chim cheree / Rindrops keep fallin' on my head / Somewhere my love / Let it be / Shaft / Lapis lazuli / If ever I would leave you / My love / Here's that rainy day / Charade / Bridge over troubled water / Somethings coming / Way we were (The) / MacArthur Park.
Notes: Conducted by Vic Lewis.
Compact disc: released on PRT, '86 by PRT Records. Dist: PRT

ARRESTED.
Album: released on Starblend, Nov'86 by Starblend Records. Dist: PRT Distribution

Cassette: released on Starblend, Nov'86 by Starblend Records. Dist: PRT Distribution

AS TIME GOES BY.
Compact disc: released on Telstar, Jul'87 by Telstar Records. Dist: RCA Distribution

AS TIME GOES BY.
Album: released on Telstar, May'85 by Telstar Records. Dist: RCA Distribution

Cassette: released on Telstar, May'85 by Telstar Records. Dist: RCA Distribution

BEATLES MEDLEY.
Single (7"): released on Evolution, Apr'83 Dist: RCA, Folksound

BEST OF BRITISH Love theme.
Tracks: / Best of British (love theme) / Best of British (main theme).
Single (7"): released on RCA, 13 Jun'87 by RCA Records. Dist: RCA, Roots, Swift, Wellard, Chris, I & B, Solomon & Peres Distribution

BEST OF HOOKED ON CLASSICS.
Album: released on K-Tel, Dec'83 by K-Tel Records. Dist: Record Merchandisers Distribution, Taylors, Terry Blood Distribution, Wynd-Up Distribution, Relay Distribution, Pickwick Distribution, Solomon & Peres Distribution, Polygram

Cassette: released on K-Tel, Dec'83 by K-Tel Records. Dist: Record Merchandisers Distribution, Taylors, Terry Blood Distribution, Wynd-Up Distribution, Relay Distribution, Pickwick Distribution, Solomon & Peres Distribution, Polygram

BEST OF HOOKED ON CLASSICS.
Compact disc: released on K-Tel, Nov'86 by K-Tel Records. Dist: Record Merchandisers Distribution, Taylors, Terry Blood Distribution, Wynd-Up Distribution, Relay Distribution, Pickwick Distribution, Solomon & Peres Distribution, Polygram

BY THE SLEEPY LAGOON And other Eric Coates favourites.
Tracks: / By the sleepy lagoon / From meadow to Mayfair / Springtime in Angus / Dam busters, The / Saxo-Rhapsody / Three bears, The / London suite / London again suite / Cinderella (Phantasy).
Album: released on EMI (Miles Of Music), Nov'83 by EMI Records. Dist: EMI

CAN'T STOP THE CLASSICS.
Compact disc: released on K-Tel, Nov'86 by K-Tel Records. Dist: Record Merchandisers Distribution, Taylors, Terry Blood Distribution, Wynd-Up Distribution, Relay Distribution, Pickwick Distribution, Solomon & Peres Distribution, Polygram

CHAMPIONS THEME.
Single (7"): released on Safari, Mar'84 by Safari Records. Dist: Pinnacle

CHRISTMAS CAROUSEL.
Single (7"): released on PRT, Dec'82 by PRT Records. Dist: PRT

Single (12"): released on PRT, Dec'82 by PRT Records. Dist: PRT

CLASSICAL GOLD.
Double Album: released on Ronco, Sep'78

CLASSICS OF LOVE.
Tracks: / Three times a lady / If you leave me now / Up where we belong / You don't bring me flowers / Imagine / Weekend in New England / Miss you nights / One day I'll fly away / Memory / With you I'm born again / One day in your life / Sun ain't gonna shine anymore.
Album: released on MFP, Jun'87 by EMI Records. Dist: EMI

Cassette: released on MFP, Jun'87 by EMI Records. Dist: EMI

CLASSIC THEMES.
Album: released on Nouveau Music, '83 Dist: PRT Distribution

Cassette: released on Nouveau Music, '83 Dist: PRT Distribution

CLASSIC THEMES.
Album: released on Nouveau Music, '83 Dist: PRT Distribution

Cassette: released on Nouveau Music, '83 Dist: PRT Distribution

COLOURS.
Album: released on RCA, Mar'78 by RCA Records. Dist: RCA, Roots, Swift, Wellard, Chris, I & B, Solomon & Peres Distribution

EVENING WITH RPO ON THEIR 50TH ANNIVERSARY.
Boxed set: released on Mont Music, Apr'83

Boxed set: released on Mont Music, Apr'83

GREAT HITS FROM HOOKED ON CLASSICS.
Album: released on Hallmark, Sep'84 by Pickwick Records. Dist: Pickwick Distribution, PRT, Taylors

Cassette: released on Hallmark, Sep'84 by Pickwick Records. Dist: Pickwick Distribution, PRT, Taylors

GREAT LOVE SONGS OF JULIO.
Album: released on CBS, Jul'84 by CBS Records. Dist: CBS

Cassette: released on CBS, Jul'84 by CBS Records. Dist: CBS

HAPPY VALLEY.
Single (7"): released on Nouveau, Jul'83

HOOKED ON A CAN CAN.
Single (7"): released on RCA, Oct'81 by RCA Records. Dist: RCA, Roots, Swift, Wellard, Chris, I & B, Solomon & Peres Distribution

Single (12"): released on RCA, Oct'81 by RCA Records. Dist: RCA, Roots, Swift, Wellard, Chris, I & B, Solomon & Peres Distribution

HOOKED ON AMERICA.
Single (7"): released on RCA, Oct'82 by RCA Records. Dist: RCA, Roots, Swift, Wellard, Chris, I & B, Solomon & Peres Distribution

HOOKED ON CHRISTMAS.
Single (7"): released on PRT, Dec'81 by PRT Records. Dist: PRT

Single (12"): released on PRT, Dec'81 by PRT Records. Dist: PRT

Single (7"): released on K-Tel, Dec'83 by K-Tel Records. Dist: Record Merchandisers Distribution, Taylors, Terry Blood Distribution, Wynd-Up Distribution, Relay Distribution, Pickwick Distribution, Solomon & Peres Distribution, Polygram

HOOKED ON CLASSICS 3.
Album: released on K-Tel, Mar'83 by K-Tel Records. Dist: Record Merchandisers Distribution, Taylors, Terry Blood Distribution, Wynd-Up Distribution, Relay Distribution, Pickwick Distribution, Solomon & Peres Distribution, Polygram

Cassette: released on K-Tel, Mar'83 by K-Tel Records. Dist: Record Merchandisers Distribution, Taylors, Terry Blood Distribution, Wynd-Up Distribution, Relay Distribution, Pickwick Distribution, Solomon & Peres Distribution, Polygram

HOOKED ON CLASSICS 2.
Album: released on K-Tel, Jul'82 by K-Tel Records. Dist: Record Merchandisers Distribution, Taylors, Terry Blood Distribution, Wynd-Up Distribution, Relay Distribution, Pickwick Distribution, Solomon & Peres Distribution, Polygram

Cassette: released on K-Tel, Jul'82 by K-Tel Records. Dist: Record Merchandisers Distribution, Taylors, Terry Blood Distribution, Wynd-Up Distribution, Relay Distribution, Pickwick Distribution, Solomon & Peres Distribution, Polygram

HOOKED ON CLASSICS.
Album: released on K-Tel, Sep'81 by K-Tel Records. Dist: Record Merchandisers Distribution, Taylors, Terry Blood Distribution, Wynd-Up Distribution, Relay Distribution, Pickwick Distribution, Solomon & Peres Distribution, Polygram

Cassette: released on K-Tel, Sep'81 by K-Tel Records. Dist: Record Merchandisers Distribution, Taylors, Terry Blood Distribution, Wynd-Up Distribution, Relay Distribution, Pickwick Distribution, Solomon & Peres Distribution, Polygram

Single (7"): released on RCA, Jul'81 by RCA Records. Dist: RCA, Roots, Swift, Wellard, Chris, I & B, Solomon & Peres Distribution

Single (12"): released on RCA, Jul'81 by RCA Records. Dist: RCA, Roots, Swift, Wellard, Chris, I & B, Solomon & Peres Distribution

HOOKED ON RODGERS & HAMMERSTEIN.
Single (7"): released on K-Tel, Aug'83 by K-Tel Records. Dist: Record Merchandisers Distribution, Taylors, Terry Blood Distribution, Wynd-Up Distribution, Relay Distribution, Pickwick Distribution, Solomon & Peres Distribution, Polygram

HOOKED ON SCOTLAND THE BRAVE.
Single (7"): released on K-Tel, Apr'83 by K-Tel Records. Dist: Record Merchandisers Distribution, Taylors, Terry Blood Distribution, Wynd-Up Distribution, Relay Distribution, Pickwick Distribution, Solomon & Peres Distribution, Polygram

IF YOU KNEW SOUSA.
Single (7"): released on RCA, Jul'82 by RCA Records. Dist: RCA, Roots, Swift, Wellard, Chris, I & B, Solomon & Peres Distribution

Single (12"): released on RCA, Jul'82 by RCA Records. Dist: RCA, Roots, Swift, Wellard, Chris, I & B, Solomon & Peres Distribution

ISLAND IN THE SUN.
Album: released on Cherry Lane, Jul'85 by Cherry Lane Productions. Dist: PRT

Cassette: released on Cherry Lane, Jul'85 by Cherry Lane Productions. Dist: PRT

ISLAND IN THE SUN.
Album: released on Cherry Lane, May'84 by Cherry Lane Productions. Dist: PRT

Cassette: released on Cherry Lane, May'84 by Cherry Lane Productions. Dist: PRT

JOURNEY THROUGH THE CLASSICS.
Tracks: / Also sprach zarathustra / Journry through the classics / Hooked on romance / Viva Vivaldi / Dance of the furies / Scotland the brave / Journey through the classics part 2 / Journey through America / Hooked on marching / Symphony on the sea / Hooked on Rogers and Hammerstein.
Compact disc: released on K-Tel, Nov'86 by K-Tel Records. Dist: Record Merchandisers Distribution, Taylors, Terry Blood Distribution, Wynd-Up Distribution, Relay Distribution, Pickwick Distribution, Solomon & Peres Distribution, Polygram

LOVE CAME FOR ME.
Single (7"): released on Cherry Lane, Jun'84 by Cherry Lane Productions. Dist: PRT

LOVE CLASSICS.
Tracks: / More than words can say / Weekend in New England / Fanfare / Miss you nights / One day I'll fly away / Memory / With you I'm born again / One day in your life / Sun ain't gonna shine anymore (The) / Three times a lady / If you leave me now / Up where we belong / You don't bring me flowers / Imagine.
Compact disc: released on Nouveau Music, '86 Dist: PRT Distribution

Album: released on Nouveau Music, May'83 Dist: PRT Distribution

Cassette: released on Nouveau Music, May'83 Dist: PRT Distribution

LOVE CLASSICS.
Album: released on Nouveau Music, '83 Dist: PRT Distribution

Cassette: released on Nouveau Music, '83 Dist: PRT Distribution

MOUNTBATTEN.
Album: released on TER, Apr'86 Dist: Pinnacle

Cassette: released on TER, Apr'86 Dist: Pinnacle

ON SCREEN.
Compact disc: released on K-Tel, Nov'86 by K-Tel Records. Dist: Record Merchandisers Distribution, Taylors, Terry Blood Distribution, Wynd-Up Distribution, Relay Distribution, Pickwick Distribution, Solomon & Peres Distribution, Polygram

ORCHESTRAL TUBULAR BELLS.
Album: released on Virgin, Jan'75 by Virgin Records. Dist: EMI, Virgin Distribution

RPO PLAYS THE QUEEN COLLECTION.
Album: released on Music For Pleasure, Sep'84

Cassette: released on Music For Pleasure, Sep'84

SONGS OF JOHN DENVER.
Album: released on Cherry Lane, Jul'85 by Cherry Lane Productions. Dist: PRT

Cassette: released on Cherry Lane, Jul'85 by Cherry Lane Productions. Dist: PRT

STAR TREK VOL.1.
Compact disc: released on Silva Productions, '86

STAR TREK VOL.2.
Compact disc: released on Silva Productions, '86

SUPERSTAR SYMPHONY.
Cassette: released on Cambra, '83 by Cambra Records. Dist: IDS, Conifer

TEMPEST.
Single (7"): released on Nouveau, Jun'83

WALKING ON THE MOON.
Single (7"): released on RCA, Feb'83 by RCA Records. Dist: RCA, Roots, Swift, Wellard, Chris, I & B, Solomon & Peres Distribution

WILTSHIRE RADIO ENTERTAINER.
Single (7"): released on Wiltshire Radio, Nov'82 Dist: Wiltshire Radio Distribution

WORLD CUP GRANDSTAND.
Single (7"): released on BBC, Jun'82 by BBC Records & Tapes. Dist: EMI, PRT, Pye

Royal Rasses

WALL FLOWER.
Single (7"): released on Rhino-Creole, Nov'86

WALL FLOWER.
Tracks: / Wall flower / Rising up to love.
Single (7"): released on Rhino, Aug'86 by Creole Records. Dist: PRT, Rhino

Royal Romance

ROYAL ROMANCE Various artists (Various Artists).
Album: released on Ronco, May'81

Cassette: released on Ronco, May'81

Royals

MAN WHO WOULD BE KING.
Single (7"): released on Dakota, Dec'84 by Dakota Records. Dist: PRT

MOVING ON.
Album: released on Kingdom, Sep'83 by Kingdom Records. Dist: Kingdom

PICK UP THE PIECES.
Single (12"): released on Studio One, Sep'84 Dist: Jetstar

ROYALS COLLECTION.
Album: released on Trojan, Nov'83 by Trojan Records. Dist: PRT, Jetstar

STRANGE WORLD.
Single (12"): released on Kingdom, Jun'81 by Kingdom Records. Dist: Kingdom

Royal Scots Dragoon...

AMAZING GRACE.
Tracks: / Amazing grace / Little donkey.
Single (7"): released on Old Gold, Nov'86 by Old Gold Records. Dist: Lightning, Jazz Music, Spartan, Counterpoint

Single (7"): released on RCA Golden Grooves, Oct'81 by RCA Records. Dist: RCA

AMAZING GRACE.
Album: released on Camden(RCA), Feb'77 by RCA Records. Dist: Pickwick Distribution, Taylors, Swift

AMAZING SOUND OF..., THE.
Album: released on RCA, '84 by RCA Records. Dist: RCA, Roots, Swift, Wellard, Chris, I & B, Solomon & Peres Distribution

Cassette: released on RCA, '84 by RCA Records. Dist: RCA, Roots, Swift, Wellard, Chris, I & B, Solomon & Peres Distribution

FAREWELL TO THE GREYS.
Album: released on RCA International, '84

Cassette: released on RCA International, '84

GOLDEN SOUNDS OF THE ROYAL SCOTS DRAGOON GUARDS.
Album: released on RCA, '84 by RCA Records. Dist: RCA, Roots, Swift, Wellard, Chris, I & B, Solomon & Peres Distribution

Cassette: released on RCA, '84 by RCA Records. Dist: RCA, Roots, Swift, Wellard, Chris, I & B, Solomon & Peres Distribution

LEGENDARY AMAZING GRACE, THE.
Album:

MAGIC MOMENTS.
Cassette: released on RCA, May'86 by RCA Records. Dist: RCA, Roots, Swift, Wellard, Chris, I & B, Solomon & Peres Distribution

ROYAL SCOTS DRAGOON GUARDS.
Album: released on Deutsche A Ustrophon (Germany), Jun'83

Cassette: released on Deutsche A Ustrophon (Germany), Jun'83

Cassette: released on Autograph, Apr'85 Dist: Record Services Distribution (Ireland)

SPOTLIGHT ON THE ROYAL SCOTS.
Double Album: released on PRT, Oct'84 by PRT Records. Dist: PRT

Double cassette: released on PRT, Oct'84 by PRT Records. Dist: PRT

Royal Tounament

ROYAL TOURNAMENT 1978 various original bands (Various Artists).
Album: released on Columbia, Jul'78 by EMI Records. Dist: EMI

ROYAL TOURNAMENT 1980 Centenary special various bands (Centenary special various bands).
Album: released on Note, Jul'80 by EMI Records. Dist: EMI

ROYAL TOURNAMENT 1983-MUSICAL HIGHLIGHTS Various artists (Various Artists).
Album: released on Polydor, Jul'83 by Polydor Records. Dist: Polygram, Polydor

Cassette: released on Polydor, Jul'83 by Polydor Records. Dist: Polygram, Polydor

Roy, Alvin

JAZZ IN PARK ROYAL (Roy, Alvin St Sound).
Album: released on Zodiac, May'81 Dist: Ja Music

Royal Wedding

ROYAL WEDDING In the good old summ time (Various Artists).
Tracks: / Too late now / Ev'ry night at seve Happiest day of my life (The) / I left my hat Haiti / You're all the world to me / How could y believe me when I said I loved you... / I do care / Meet me tonight in dreamland / Pay th barber shop chord / Last night when we w young / Put your arms around me honey / Me Christmas.
Album: released on CBS, Feb'87 by CBS R ords. Dist: CBS

Cassette: released on CBS, Feb'87 by C Records. Dist: CBS

ROYAL WEDDING (H.R.H. The Prince drew and Miss Sarah Ferguson).
Notes: The marriage ceremony and music corded from Westminster abbey.
Album: released on BBC, Aug'86 by BBC R ords & Tapes. Dist: EMI, PRT, Pye

Cassette: released on BBC, Aug'86 by B Records & Tapes. Dist: EMI, PRT. Pve

ROYAL WEDDING Official BBC albu the royal wedding ceremony (Official Album Of The Royal Wedding Ceremony).
Album: released on BBC, Jul'81 by BBC ords & Tapes. Dist: EMI, PRT, Pye

Roy, Barbara

GONNA PUT UP A FIGHT.
Tracks: / Gonna put up a fight / Gotta see tonight.
Single (7"): released on RCA, Mar'87 by Records. Dist: RCA, Roots, Swift, We Chris, I & B, Solomon & Peres Distribution

Single (12"): released on RCA, Mar'87 by Records. Dist: RCA, Roots, Swift, We Chris, I & B, Solomon & Peres Distributio

GOT TO SEE YOU TONIGHT.
Tracks: / Got to see you tonight.
Single (7"): released on RCA, Aug'86 by Records. Dist: RCA, Roots, Swift, W Chris, I & B, Solomon & Peres Distributio

Single (12"): released on RCA, Aug'86 by Records. Dist: RCA, Roots, Swift, W Chris, I & B, Solomon & Peres Distributio

WALKING TALKING DOLLY.
Tracks: / Wild mountain.
Single (7"): released on August (USA), Dist: Taylors

Roy C

SHOTGUN WEDDING.
Single (7"): released on Decca-Ori Mar'82 by Decca Records. Dist: Polygra
Cat. no: F

Single (7"): released on Old Gold, Oc Old Gold Records. Dist: Lightning, Jazz Spartan, Counterpoint

Ro Yeah Yeah
I HOPE AND PREY.
Single (7"): released on Chrysalis, Aug'85 by Chrysalis Records. Dist: CBS

Single (12"): released on Chrysalis, Aug'85 by Chrysalis Records. Dist: CBS

Roy, Harry
ARE YOU LISTENING? (Roy, Harry & His Orchestra).
Double Album: released on World, Nov'73 Dist: Jetstar

GOLDEN AGE OF HARRY ROY & HIS ORCHESTRA, (THE) (Roy, Harry & His Orchestra).
Album: released on Golden Age, Jul'83 by Music For Pleasure Records. Dist: EMI

Cassette: released on Golden Age, Jul'83 by Music For Pleasure Records. Dist: EMI

HARRY ROY & HIS ORCHESTRA (Roy, Harry & His Orchestra).
Tracks: / Truckin' on down / No moon, no stars, just you / London on a rainy night / Troublesome trumpet / Smoke gets in you eyes / Beat o'my heart (The) / Gertie the girl with the gong / Object of my affection (The) / Cowboy in Manhattan / Let's have a jubilee / Louisiana lullaby / We're gonna have smooth sailing / Love and a dime / Words are in my heart (The) / My hat's on the side of my head / Was in the mood (I) / Hurricane Harry / Stars over Devon / You've got me crying again / Swingly little thingy.
Notes: Produced and transferred by Colin Brown. MONO
Album: released on Old Bean, '86 Dist: Jazz Music

Cassette: released on Old Bean, '86 Dist: Jazz Music

RAGGIN' THE RAGS (Roy, Harry & The Hotcha Boys).
Album: released on Joy, Nov'82 by President Records. Dist: Jazz Music, Swift, President Distribution

THERE GOES THAT SONG AGAIN (Roy, Harry & His Band).
Album: released on President, '83 by President Records. Dist: Taylors, Spartan

Cassette: released on President, '84 by President Records. Dist: Taylors, Spartan

Roys
KICKED OFF THE TRAIN.
Album: released on Stiff, '86 by Stiff Records. Dist: EMI, Record Services Distribution (Ireland)

Royston
I'VE BEEN LOVING YOU SO LONG.
Album: released on Folk Heritage, Jul'82 by Folk Heritage Records. Dist: Roots, Wynd-Up Distribution, Jazz Music, Folk Heritage

LONG DISTANCE LOVE.
Single (7"): released on VM, Oct'83 by VM Records. Dist: PRT

Roy, William
WHEN I SING ALONE.
Notes: William Roy - piano/vocal. J. Loehrke - bass. Double album.
Double Album: released on Audiophile, Feb'87 by Jazzology Records (USA). Dist: Jazz Music, Swift

Roza, Lita
LOVE SONGS FOR NIGHT PEOPLE.
Album: released on Bulldog, Aug'83 by Bulldog Records. Dist: President Distribution, Spartan, Swift, Taylor, H.R.

UNCHAINED MELODIES Four stars of the 50's (Roza, Lita/ Dickie Valentine/Joan Regan/Jimmy Young).
Notes: For full details see under Jimmy Young.

YOU'RE DRIVING ME CRAZY (Roza, Lita with Billy Munn's All Stars).
Album: released on President, Dec'83 by President Records. Dist: Taylors, Spartan

Cassette: released on President, Jan'84 by President Records. Dist: Taylors, Spartan

Rozsa, Miklos
BEN HUR.
Tracks: / Fanfare to Prelude / Star of Bethlehem and adoration of the Magi / Friendship / Burning desert (The) / Arrius / Rowing of the galley slaves / Parade of the charioteers / Mother's love (The) / Return to Judea / Ring for freedom / Lepers search for freedom (The) / Christ / Procession to Calvary / Miracle and finale.
Compact disc: released on London, '86 by London Records. Dist: Polygram

PIC FILM SCORES.
Album: released on Cloud Nine, Dec'86 by Cloud Nine Records. Dist: Silva Screen, Harmonia Mundi

IMMORTAL FILM MUSIC OF MIKLOS ROZSA.
Album: released on Memoir, Nov'84 by Memoir Records. Dist: PRT Distribution

Cassette: released on Memoir, Nov'84 by Memoir Records. Dist: PRT Distribution

Ruadh, Calum
SCOTTISH TRADITION VOLUME 7.
Album: released on Tangent, Apr'81 Dist: Roots Distribution, Lugtons Distributors, Taylors, JSU Distribution, Spartan Distribution

Rubalcaba, Gonzalo
LIVE IN HAVANA.
Notes: 23 year old Gonzalo Rubalcaba, the Cuban piano wizzard, with his band Gonzalito recorded live in Havana, Cuba. Gonzalo appeared at the Ronnie Scott Afro-Cuban Festival. Personnel: Gonzalo Rubalcaba-keyboards/Manuel Varela-sax/Larazo Cruz-trumpet, flugelhorn/Felipe Cabrera-bass, fagott/Horacio Hernandez-drums/Roberto Vizciano- percussion.
Album: released on Messidor (Germany), Jan'87 Dist: IMS Distribution, Polygram

LOVE IN HAVANA VOL.2.
Album: released on Messidor (Germany), May'87 Dist: IMS Distribution, Polygram

Rubber Rodeo
ANYWHERE WITH YOU.
Single (7"): released on EAT, Aug'84 by Phonogram Records. Dist: Polygram

Single (12"): released on EAT, Aug'84 by Phonogram Records. Dist: Polygram

HARDEST THING.
Single (7"): released on EAT, Jun'84 by Phonogram Records. Dist: Polygram

Single (12"): released on EAT, Jun'84 by Phonogram Records. Dist: Polygram

SCENIC VIEWS.
Album: released on EAT, Aug'84 by Phonogram Records. Dist: Polygram

Cassette: released on EAT, Aug'84 by Phonogram Records. Dist: Polygram

Rubber Yahoo
RUBBER YAHOO.
Single (7"): released on Off The Cuff, Jul'85 Dist: Fast Forward Distribution, Cartel Distribution

Rubble dub-Mc's Choice
RUBBLE DUB-MC'S CHOICE Various artists (Various Artists).
Album: released on Fashion, '86 by Fashion Records. Dist: PRT, Jetstar

Rubella Ballet
42%.
Single (12"): by Jungle Records. Dist: Jungle, Cartel

ARTIC FLOWERS.
Tracks: / Artic flowers.
Single (7"): released on Dayglo, '86 by Dayglo Records. Dist: Red Rhino, Cartel

BALLET BAG.
Cassette: released on Xntrix, '86

Cassette: released on Xntrix, '86

Cassette: released on X Centrix, Sep'85

BALLET DANCE, (THE).
Single (7"): released on Xntrix, Sep'82

MONEY TALKS.
Single (12"): released on Ubiquitous Dayglo, Mar'85 by Nine Mile Records. Dist: Cartel

Ruben Blades
MOVE ON(MUEVETE) (Ruben Blades y seis del solar).
Single (7"): released on Elektra (USA), '86 by Elektra/Asylum/Nonesuch Records. Dist: WEA

Rubettes
DON'T COME CRYING.
Single (7"): released on V-Tone, Feb'82 by Relic. Dist: Swift

IMPACT.
Album: released on Impact, Apr'82 by Ace Records. Dist: Rough Trade, Pinnacle, Swift, Backs, Counterpoint, Jungle, Hotshot, Cartel

Cassette: released on Impact, Apr'82 by Ace Records. Dist: Rough Trade, Pinnacle, Swift, Backs, Counterpoint, Jungle, Hotshot, Cartel

ROCKIN'RUBETTES PARTY 45.
Single (7"): released on Polydor, Aug'81 by Polydor Records. Dist: Polygram, Polydor

SUGAR BABY I LOVE YOU.
Single (7"): released on Old Gold, Jul'82 by Old Gold Records. Dist: Lightning, Jazz Music, Spartan, Counterpoint

Rubey Forde
SPEED OF LIGHT.
Single (12"): released on Ram, Aug'85 by Ram. Dist: PRT

Rubies, Jack
BE WITH YOU.
Single (12"): released on Idea, 30 May'87 by Idea Records. Dist: Rough Trade, Cartel

WITCH HUNT IN LOTUS LAND.
Album: released on Criminal Damage, Jun'86 by Criminal Damage Records. Dist: Backs, Cartel

Rubinoos
BACK TO THE DRAWING BOARD.
Album: released on Beserkley (USA), Oct'79 by Beserkley Records. Dist: PRT

RUBINOOS IN WAX.
Album: released on Beserkley (USA), Feb'79 by Beserkley Records. Dist: PRT

Rubovia
RUBOVIA Various artists (Various Artists).
Album: released on BBC, Jul'77 by BBC Records & Tapes. Dist: EMI, PRT, Pye

Ruby & The Romantics
OUR DAY WILL COME.
Album: released on Charly, Sep'84 by Charly Records. Dist: Charly, Cadillac

Rudder, David
BAHIA GIRL (Rudder, David & Charlie's Roots).
Tracks: / Bahia girl / Outta hand.
Single (7"): released on London, '86 by London Records. Dist: Polygram

Single (12"): released on London, '86 by London Records. Dist: Polygram

Ruddigore
RUDDIGORE (D'Oyly Carte Opera Company).
Double Album: released on Decca, '62 by Decca Records. Dist: Polygram

RUDDIGORE G&S Festival chorus & orchestra (G&S Festival Chorus & Orchestra).
Double Album: released on PRT, Oct'84 by PRT Records. Dist: PRT

Double cassette: released on PRT, Oct'84 by PRT Records. Dist: PRT

Rudd, Rosswell
REGENERATION (Russ, Rosswell /Steve Lacy).
Notes: With Misha Mengelberg, Kent Carter, Han Bennink
Compact disc: released on Soul Note (Italy), '86 Dist: Harmonia Mundi Distributors

Single (12"):

Rudd, Roswell
INSIDE JOB.
Album: released on Freedom, Mar'79 by Logo Records. Dist: RCA, Discovery, Wellard, Chris

Rudi
BIG TIME.
Single (12"): released on Good Vibration, Sep'79 by Good Vibrations Records. Dist: Pinnacle, Rough Trade

CRIMSON.
Single (7"): released on Jamming, Feb'82

I SPY.
Single (7"): released on Good Vibration, Aug'79 by Good Vibrations Records. Dist: Pinnacle, Rough Trade

WHEN I WAS DEAD.
Single (7"): released on Jamming, Oct'81

Rudie, Jennifer
FOREVER LOVING YOU.
Single (12"): released on Ruff Cut, Mar'84 by Ruff Cut Records. Dist: Jetstar Distribution

Rudi Mental
PLAIN TALK.
Single (7"): released on Slime, Dec'81

Rudimentary Peni
DEATH CHURCH.
Album: released on Corpus Christi, Sep'83 by Exitstencil Music. Dist: Cartel

FARCE.
Single (7"): released on Crass, Jul'82 by Exitstencil Music. Dist: Rough Trade, Cartel

RUDIMENTARY PENI.
Single (7"):

Rudi & Mona
AEROBIC AFFAIR.
Single (7"): released on Cambra, Nov'83 by Cambra Records. Dist: IDS, Conifer

Rudy & Rhonda
AEROBIC AFFAIR (Rudy & Rhonda & Sweat Band).
Single (7"): released on Cambra, Mar'84 by Cambra Records. Dist: IDS, Conifer

Rudy & Sketto
EVERY NIGHT.
Single (12"): released on Pama, Jan'84 by Pama Records. Dist: Pama, Enterprise, Jetstar

Rudy & Valentinos
SWAMP STOMP.
Single (7"): released on Towerbell, Jul'84 by Towerbell Records. Dist: EMI

Single (12"): released on Towerbell, Jul'84 by Towerbell Records. Dist: EMI

Rue De Remarx
ONE WAY TRIP.
Single (7"): released on Underground Music, Jan'82 Dist: Pinnacle

Ruefrex
CAPITAL LETTERS.
Single (7"): released on Kabuki, Apr'83 by Gareth Ryan. Dist: Rough Trade

FLOWERS FOR ALL OCCASIONS.
Album:

IN THE TRAPS.
Tracks: / In the traps / Leader of the last resort / In the tracks(inst).
Single (7"): released on Kasper, '86 Dist: Stiff, EMI

Single (12"): released on Kasper, '86 Dist: Stiff, EMI

PAIN IN MIND.
Single (7"): released on One By One, Aug'84 Dist: Red Rhino, Cartel

WILD COLONIAL BOY.
Tracks: / Wild colonial boy / Even in the dark hours.
Single (7"): released on Kasper, '86 Dist: Stiff, EMI

Single (12"): released on Kasper, '86 Dist: Stiff, EMI

Single (7"): released on Kasper, Aug'85 Dist: Stiff, EMI

Rufaro
RUFARO.
Album: by Pilgrim Records. Dist: Rough Trade, Cartel

Ruffelle, Francis
HE'S MY HERO.
Tracks: / He's my hero / Love's not for me.
Single (7"): released on RCA, '86 by RCA Records. Dist: RCA, Roots, Swift, Wellard, Chris, I & B, Solomon & Peres Distribution

Single (12"): released on RCA, '86 by RCA Records. Dist: RCA, Roots, Swift, Wellard, Chris, I & B, Solomon & Peres Distribution

ON MY OWN.
Tracks: / On my own / Finale / Do you hear the people sing / One day more / Prologue.
Single (7"): released on First Night, '86 by Safari Records. Dist: Pinnacle

Cassette: released on First Night, '86 by Safari Records. Dist: Pinnacle

Ruffin, Bruce
JUST A PRECAUTION.
Single (7"): released on Slick, May'83 by Slick Records. Dist: Pinnacle

Ruffin, David
WALK AWAY FROM LOVE.
Single (7"): released on Motown, Oct'81 by Motown Records. Dist: BMG Distribution

Ruffin, Jimmy
20 GOLDEN CLASSICS.
Album: released on Motown, Oct'81 by RCA Records. Dist: RCA Distribution

Cassette: released on Motown, Oct'81 by RCA Records. Dist: RCA Distribution

EASY JUST TO SAY (I LOVE YOU).
Tracks: / Esy to say I love you / You never have time (for me) / Easy just to say (I love you) / You never have time (for me) / Easy just to say (I love you) (Ext. club mix) / Easy just to say (I love you) (Eeesay mix).
Single (7"): released on Polydor, Jun'87 by Polydor Records. Dist: Polygram, Polydor

Single (12"): released on Polydor, Jun'87 by Polydor Records. Dist: Polygram, Polydor

FAREWELL IS A LONELY SOUND.
Single (7"): released on Motown, Oct'81 by Motown Records. Dist: BMG Distribution

GONNA GIVE HER ALL THE LOVE I'VE GOT.
Single (7"): released on Motown, Apr'85 by RCA Records. Dist: RCA Distribution

Single (12"): released on Motown, Apr'85 by RCA Records. Dist: RCA Distribution

I'LL SAY FOREVER MY LOVE.
Single (7"): released on Motown, Oct'81 by Motown Records. Dist: BMG Distribution

I'M GONNA LOVE YOU FOREVER (Ruffin, Jimmy & Jackson Moore).
Single (7"): released on ERC, Jun'84 by ERC Records. Dist: PRT

Single (12"): released on ERC, Jun'84 by ERC Records. Dist: PRT

I'VE PASSED THIS WAY BEFORE.
Single (7"): released on Motown, Oct'81 by Motown Records. Dist: BMG Distribution

JIMMY RUFFIN.
Cassette: released on Motown, May'83 by RCA Records. Dist: RCA Distribution

WHAT BECOMES OF THE BROKEN-HEARTED.
Single (7"): released on Motown, Oct'81 by Motown Records. Dist: BMG Distribution

YOUNG HEART.
Single (7"): released on ERC, Mar'85 by ERC Records. Dist: PRT

Single (12"): released on ERC, Mar'85 by ERC Records. Dist: PRT

Rufty Tufty

RUFTY TUFTY Various artists (Various Artists).
Cassette: released on Anvil, Jan'81 Dist: Anvil

Rufus

AIN'T NOBODY (Rufus & Chaka Khan).
Single (7"): released on Warner Brothers, Mar'84 by WEA Records. Dist: WEA

Single (12"): released on Warner Brothers, Mar'84 by WEA Records. Dist: WEA

DO YOU LOVE WHAT YOU FEEL (Rufus & Chaka Khan).
Single (7"): released on MCA, Jun'84 by MCA Records. Dist: CBS

Single (12"): released on MCA, Jun'84 by MCA Records. Dist: CBS

TAKE IT TO THE TOP.
Single (7"): released on Warner Brothers, Mar'83 by WEA Records. Dist: WEA

Single (12"): released on Warner Brothers, Mar'83 by WEA Records. Dist: WEA

Rugby Songs

RUGBY SONGS Various artists (Various Artists).
Album: released on Sportsdisc, Nov'82 by Sportsdisc Records. Dist: H.R. Taylor, MIS-EMI Distribution

Rugg, Louisa

ICARUS (see Cripps,Geoff/Louisa Rugg) (Rugg, Louisa/Geoff Cripps).

Ruhland, Paul

Biographical Details: see under - Forrest Westbrook.

Ruiz, Hilton

FANTASIA.
Album: released on Denon, Mar'82

Rumblefish

TUG BOAT LINE.
Single (7"): released on Pink, Mar'87 by Pink Records. Dist: Rough Trade

Single (12"): released on Pink, Mar'87 by Pink Records. Dist: Rough Trade

Rumillajta

CITY OF STONE.
Album: released on Tumi, Jul'87 Dist: ILA

Album: released on Tumi, Apr'84 Dist: ILA

HOJA DE COCA.
Album: released on Tumi, Jul'87 Dist: ILA

Album: released on Tumi, Feb'85 Dist: ILA

Cassette: released on Tumi, Feb'85 Dist: ILA

PACHAMAMA.
Album: released on Tumi, Jul'87 Dist: ILA

Rummel,Jack

BACK TO RAGTIME.
Album: released on Stomp Off, '86 by Stomp Off Records. Dist: Jazz Music Distribution

Rumpelstiltskin

RUMPELSTILTSKIN (Ogilvy, Ian).
Cassette: released on Listen Productions, Nov'84 Dist: H.R. Taylor, Hayward Promotions Distribution

Rumpole of the Bailey

RUMPOLE OF THE BAILEY By John Mortimer (Mckern, Leo).
Double cassette: released on Listen For Pleasure, '83 by EMI Records. Dist: MFP

Rumsey, Howard

MUSIC FOR LIGHTHOUSEKEEPING (Rumsey, Howard, Lighthouse All Stars).
Album: released on Contemporary, Dec'81 by Good Time Jazz Records (USA). Dist: IMS, Polygram

Runaways

AND NOW...THE RUNAWAYS.
Album: released on Wayward, Jul'79

Cassette: released on Cherry Red, Jul'79 by Cherry Red Records. Dist: Pinnacle

FLAMING SCHOOLGIRLS (Runaways & Cherie Currie).
Album: released on Cherry Red, '82 by Cherry Red Records. Dist: Pinnacle

LIVE IN JAPAN.
Album: released on Mercury (Import), Oct'82

QUEENS OF NOISE.
Album: released on Mercury, Feb'77 by Phonogram Records. Dist: Polygram Distribution

RUNAWAYS, THE.
Album: released on Mercury, Sep'82 by Phonogram Records. Dist: Polygram Distribution

Cassette: released on Mercury, Sep'82 by Phonogram Records. Dist: Polygram Distribution

WAITIN' FOR THE NIGHT.
Album: released on Mercury, Dec'77 by Phonogram Records. Dist: Polygram Distribution

Runaway Train

RUNAWAY TRAIN Original soundtrack (Various Artists).
Tracks: / Jailbreak / Moving on / Destination unknown / Clear the tracks / Reflections / Runaway train / Prison memories / Yellow rose of Texas(The) / Collision course / Past,present,future? / Red for danger / Gloria / End of the line.
Notes: The track on side two "Gloria" is Vivaldi's "Gloria" in "D" (second movement) arranged by Alfredo Casella and performed by the USSR Academic Russian Choir and the Moscow Conservatorie Students Orchestra,conducted by Alexander Aveshnikov. Subtly augmented and mixed with electronics,this section of the soundtrack is causing a great deal of interest resulting in a number of requests for information on the piece and its' availability on record.
Album: released on IMS(Import), '86 by Polydor Records. Dist: IMS, Polygram

Cassette: released on IMS(Import), '86 by Polydor Records. Dist: IMS, Polygram

Compact disc: released on IMS(Import), '86 by Polydor Records. Dist: IMS, Polygram

Rundgren, Todd

ADVENTURES IN UTOPIA.
Album: released on Bearsville (USA), Nov'80 by Warner Bros Records. Dist: WEA

BACK TO THE BARS.
Double Album: released on Bearsville (USA), '78 by Warner Bros Records. Dist: WEA

BANG THE DRUM ALL DAY.
Single (7"): released on Lamborghini, Jun'83 by Lamborghini Records. Dist: PRT

CAPPELLA, A.
Album: released on Warner Brothers, Nov'85 by WEA Records. Dist: WEA

Cassette: released on Warner Brothers, Nov'85 by WEA Records. Dist: WEA

EVER POPULAR TORTURED ARTIST EFFECT, THE.
Album: released on Lamborghini, Aug'83 by Lamborghini Records. Dist: PRT

Cassette: released on Lamborghini, Aug'83 by Lamborghini Records. Dist: PRT

FAITHFUL.
Album: released on Bearsville (USA), Apr'76 by Warner Bros Records. Dist: WEA

HEALING.
Album: released on Bearsville (USA), Dec'81 by Warner Bros Records. Dist: WEA

Cassette: released on Bearsville (USA), Dec'81 by Warner Bros Records. Dist: WEA

INITIATION, THE.
Album: released on Bearsville (USA), Jun'75 by Warner Bros Records. Dist: WEA

MATED (Rundgren, Todd, Utopia).
Single (7"): released on Food For Thought, Jun'85 by Food For Thought Records. Dist: Pinnacle

P.O.V (Rundgren, Todd, Utopia).
Album: released on Food For Thought, Jun'85 by Food For Thought Records. Dist: Pinnacle

SOMETHING TO FALL BACK ON.
Tracks: / Something to fall back on / Lock jaw / Something to fall back on (Dance mix).
Single (7"): released on Warner Bros., '86 by Warner Bros Records. Dist: WEA

Single (12"): released on Warner Bros., '86 by Warner Bros Records. Dist: WEA

SWING TO THE RIGHT (Rundgren, Todd, Utopia).
Album: released on Bearsville (USA), Jun'82 by Warner Bros Records. Dist: WEA

Cassette: released on Bearsville (USA), Jun'82 by Warner Bros Records. Dist: WEA

TIME HEALS.
Single (7"): released on Bearsville (USA), Nov'82 by Warner Bros Records. Dist: WEA

UTOPIA OOPS WRONG PLANET.
Album: by Warner Bros Records. Dist: WEA

Rundle, Bob

BUTTON & BLOWS Wind instrumentals.
Cassette: released on Folktracks, Nov'79 by Folktracks Cassettes. Dist: Folktracks

Run D.M.C.

IT'S TRICKY.
Single (7"): released on London, 23 May'87 by London Records. Dist: Polygram

Single (12"): released on London, 23 May'87 by London Records. Dist: Polygram

IT'S TRICKY (REMIX).
Tracks: / It's tricky (remix) / Proud to be black / Uptempo * / It's tricky(scratchapella) / Tricky reprise *.
Single (7"): released on London, May'87 by London Records. Dist: Polygram

Single (12"): released on London, May'87 by London Records. Dist: Polygram

KING OF ROCK.
Tracks: / King of rock (cut-up) / Rock box / Jay's game / Jam-master Jay / You talk too much.
Single (12"): released on Fourth & Broadway, '86 by Island Records. Dist: Polygram, EMI

KING OF ROCK.
Tracks: / King of rock / Jam master Jay / You talk too much.
Single (7"): released on Fourth & Broadway, '86 by Island Records. Dist: Polygram, EMI

Single (12"): released on Fourth & Broadway, '86 by Island Records. Dist: Polygram, EMI

Album: released on Fourth & Broadway, Feb'85 by Island Records. Dist: Polygram, EMI

Cassette: released on Fourth & Broadway, Feb'85 by Island Records. Dist: Polygram, EMI

Picture disc album: released on Fourth & Broadway, Feb'85 by Island Records. Dist: Polygram, EMI

Single (7"): released on Fourth & Broadway, Mar'85 by Island Records. Dist: Polygram, EMI

Single (12"): released on Fourth & Broadway, Mar'85 by Island Records. Dist: Polygram, EMI

MY ADIDAS.
Tracks: / My Adidas / Peter Pan (Inst).
Single (7"): released on London, '86 by London Records. Dist: Polygram

Single (12"): released on London, '86 by London Records. Dist: Polygram

RAISING HELL.
Compact disc: released on Profile, Nov'86 by Profile Records (USA).

RAISING HELL.
Tracks: / Peter Piper / It's tricky / My Adidas / Walk this way / Is it live / Perfection / Hit it run / Raising hell / You be illin' / Dumb girl / Son of Byford / Proud to be black.
Album: released on London, '86 by London Records. Dist: Polygram

Cassette: released on London, '86 by London Records. Dist: Polygram

ROCK BOX.
Single (7"): released on Fourth & Broadway, Jul'84 by Island Records. Dist: Polygram, EMI

Single (12"): released on Fourth & Broadway, Jul'84 by Island Records. Dist: Polygram, EMI Deleted '87.

RUN D.M.C..
Album: released on Fourth & Broadway, May'85 by Island Records. Dist: Polygram, EMI

Cassette: released on Fourth & Broadway, May'85 by Island Records. Dist: Polygram, EMI

WALK THIS WAY.
Tracks: / Walk this way / Walk this way (Inst.) / My Adidas.
Single (7"): released on London, '86 by London Records. Dist: Polygram

Single (12"): released on London, '86 by London Records. Dist: Polygram

YOU BE ILLIN'.
Tracks: / Hit it Run.
Single (7"): released on London, Jan'87 by London Records. Dist: Polygram

Single (12"): released on London, Jan'87 by London Records. Dist: Polygram

YOU TALK TOO MUCH.
Single (7"): released on Fourth & Broadway, Apr'85 by Island Records. Dist: Polygram, EM

Single (12"): released on Fourth & Broadway, Apr'85 by Island Records. Dist: Polygram, EMI

Runestaff

DO IT!.
Single (7"): released on FM, Oct'85 by FM-Revolver Records. Dist: EMI

ROAD TO RUIN.
Single (7"): released on FM, Mar'85 by FM-Revolver Records. Dist: EMI

RUNESTAFF.
Album: released on Heavy Metal Worldwide, Feb'85 by FM-Revolver Records. Dist: EMI

Cassette: released on Heavy Metal Worldwide Feb'85 by FM-Revolver Records. Dist: EMI

Running Dogs

PRESENT TENSE.
Single (7"): released on Shooting Star, Mar'8

Running scared

RUNNING SCARED Original soundtrack.
Compact disc: by MCA Records. Dist: Polygram, MCA

RUNNING SCARED Original soundtrack (Various Artists).
Notes: Great new soundtrack album from the movie starring Gregory Hines and Bill Crysta Album features 'Sweet Freedom' by Michae McDonald. Also included are potential hits b Kylmaxx,Kim Wilde,New Edition,Patti LaBell and Ready For the World. Also features two ex cellent tracks by Rod Temperton,who has writ ten and co-produced most features of th album.
Album: released on MCA, '86 by MCA Rec ords. Dist: Polygram, MCA

Cassette: released on MCA, '86 by MCA Rec ords. Dist: Polygram, MCA

Running Wild

BRANDED AND EXILED.
Album:

GATES TO PURGATORY.
Album:

UNDER JOLLY ROGER.
Album:

Runnin' Wild

RUNNIN' WILD Original sounds of the Jaz Age (Various Artists).
Album: released on ASV Living Era, Jan'83 b ASV Records. Dist: PRT

Cassette: released on ASV Living Era, Jan'8 by ASV Records. Dist: PRT

Run Rig

DANCE CALLED AMERICA.
Single (7"): released on Simple, Aug'84 b

Simple Records. Dist: EMI
Cat. no: **SIM 4**
Single (12"): released on Simple, Aug'84 by Simple Records. Dist: EMI

HEARTLAND.
Album: released on Ridge, Feb'86 Dist: Roots, Wynd-Up Distribution, MK, Celtic Music, Projection

Cassette: released on Ridge, Feb'86 Dist: Roots, Wynd-Up Distribution, MK, Celtic Music, Projection

HIGHLAND CONNECTION.
Album: released on Ridge, Sep'84 Dist: Roots, Wynd-Up Distribution, MK, Celtic Music, Projection

HIGHLAND CONNECTION, THE.
Album: released on Ridge, Feb'86 Dist: Roots, Wynd-Up Distribution, MK, Celtic Music, Projection

LOCH LOMOND.
Single (7"): released on Run Rig, Dec'82

PLAY GAELIC.
Album: released on Neptune, Sep'84 by Lismor. Dist: Spartan

Cassette: released on Neptune, Apr'78 by Lismor. Dist: Spartan

RECOVERY.
Album: released on Ridge, Feb'86 Dist: Roots, Wynd-Up Distribution, MK, Celtic Music, Projection

RECOVERY.
Album: released on Ridge, Sep'84 Dist: Roots, Wynd-Up Distribution, MK, Celtic Music, Projection

SKYE.
Single (7"): released on Simple, Nov'84 by Simple Records. Dist: EMI

Runswick, Daryl

SKY CRYING RAIN.
Single (7"): released on BBC, May'81 by BBC Records & Tapes. Dist: EMI, PRT.

Rupert Bear

RUPERT BEAR (Nutwood Chums).
Album: released on Animated Expressions, Nov'86

Cassette: released on Animated Expressions, Nov'86

RUPERT BEAR AND THE LONELY BIRD (Bennett, Judy).
Cassette: released on Tempo, Aug'84 by Warwick Records. Dist: Multiple Sound Distributors

RUPERT BEAR AND THE YOUNG DRAGON (Bennett, Judy).
Cassette: released on Tempo, Aug'84 by Warwick Records. Dist: Multiple Sound Distributors

RUPERT BEAR AND THE MUDDLED MAGIC (Bennett, Judy).
Cassette: released on Tempo, Aug'84 by Warwick Records. Dist: Multiple Sound Distributors

RUPERT BEAR AND THE HIDDEN LAKE (Bennett, Judy).
Cassette: released on Tempo, Aug'84 by Warwick Records. Dist: Multiple Sound Distributors

RUPERT BEAR - STORIES FROM THE 1982 ANNUAL.
Cassette: released on Pickwick Talking Books, Mar'84

SINGS A GOLDEN HOUR OF NURSERY RHYMES.
Album: released on Spot, Feb'83 by Pickwick Records. Dist: H.R. Taylor,

Cassette: released on Spot, Feb'83 by Pickwick Records. Dist: H.R. Taylor,

Rupert & Rupettes

SLOAN RAP.
Single (7"): released on Works, May'83 Dist: PRT

Rural Tension

WAITING ROOM.
Single (7"): released on Rural Tension, Apr'82 Dist: Backs, Cartel Distribution

Rusca, Mario

RECREATIONS (Rusca, Mario, Group).
Album: released on Jump, Apr'81 Dist: Jazz Music, Jazz Horizons

Rush

2112.
Compact disc: released on Mercury, Apr'87 by Phonogram Records. Dist: Polygram Distribution

Album: released on Mercury, Jan'85 by Phonogram Records. Dist: Polygram Distribution

Cassette: released on Mercury, Jan'85 by Phonogram Records. Dist: Polygram Distribution

ALL THE WORLD'S A STAGE.
Compact disc: released on Mercury, Apr'87 by Phonogram Records. Dist: Polygram Distribution

Double Album: released on Mercury, Sep'84 by Phonogram Records. Dist: Polygram Distribution

Double cassette: released on Mercury, Sep'84 by Phonogram Records. Dist: Polygram Distribution

BODY ELECTRIC, THE.
Single (7"): released on Vertigo, Apr'84 by Phonogram Records. Dist: Polygram

Single 10": released on Vertigo, Apr'84 by Phonogram Records. Dist: Polygram

CARESS OF STEEL.
Compact disc: released on Mercury, Apr'87 by Phonogram Records. Dist: Polygram Distribution

Album: released on Mercury, Jun'83 by Phonogram Records. Dist: Polygram Distribution

Cassette: released on Mercury, Jun'83 by Phonogram Records. Dist: Polygram Distribution

EXIT....STAGE LEFT.
Compact disc: released on Mercury, Apr'87 by Phonogram Records. Dist: Polygram Distribution

EXIT STAGE LEFT.
Double Album: released on Mercury, Nov'81 by Phonogram Records. Dist: Polygram Distribution

Double cassette: released on Mercury, Nov'81 by Phonogram Records. Dist: Polygram Distribution

FAREWELL TO KINGS.
Compact disc: released on Mercury, Apr'87 by Phonogram Records. Dist: Polygram Distribution

FAREWELL TO KINGS, A.
Album: released on Phonogram, Apr'86 by Phonogram Records. Dist: Polygram

Cassette: released on Phonogram, Apr'86 by Phonogram Records. Dist: Polygram

FLY BY NIGHT.
Compact disc: released on Mercury, Apr'87 by Phonogram Records. Dist: Polygram Distribution

Album: released on Mercury, Jun'83 by Phonogram Records. Dist: Polygram Distribution

Cassette: released on Mercury, Jun'83 by Phonogram Records. Dist: Polygram Distribution

GRACE UNDER PRESSURE TOUR.
Notes: A live performance from the canadian trio of Pomp rockers, including most of their hits either in medley or complete form. 1984 production. Live recording. total duration 60 minutes.
Single (7"): released on Phonogram, Feb'86 by Phonogram Records. Dist: Polygram
Cat. no: **Rush 13**
Single (12"):

GRACE UNDER PRESSURE.
Tracks: / Distant early warning / After image / Red sector.A. / An enemy within / Body electric / Kid gloves / Red lenses / Between the wheels.
Notes: A superb new album from the best rock band in the world! 8 magnificent new tracks coproduced by rush with Peter henderson. Featuring more guitar than recent releases, this album sees Rush back at their magnificent best.
Video-cassette (VHS): released on Polygram, Jun'86 by Polygram Records. Dist: Polygram

Video-cassette [Betamax]: released on Polygram, Jun'86 by Polygram Records. Dist: Polygram

Album: released on Phonogram, Apr'84 by Phonogram Records. Dist: Polygram

Cassette: released on Phonogram, Apr'84 by Phonogram Records. Dist: Polygram

Compact disc: released on Phonogram, Apr'84 by Phonogram Records. Dist: Polygram

HEMISPHERES.
Compact disc: released on Mercury, Apr'87 by Phonogram Records. Dist: Polygram Distribution

Compact disc: released on Mercury, Apr'87 by Phonogram Records. Dist: Polygram Distribution

Album: released on Gramavision (USA), Feb'84 by Gramavison Records (USA). Dist: PRT, IMS, Polygram

Album: released on Mercury, '78 by Phonogram Records. Dist: Polygram Distribution

Cassette: released on Mercury, '78 by Phonogram Records. Dist: Polygram Distribution

MANHATTAN PROJECT.
Tracks: / Manhattan project:*.
Single (7"): released on Vertigo, Feb'86 by Phonogram Records. Dist: Polygram

Single (12"): released on Vertigo, Feb'86 by Phonogram Records. Dist: Polygram

MOVING PICTURES.
Compact disc: released on Phonogram, '83 by Phonogram Records. Dist: Polygram

Album: released on Mercury, Feb'82 by Phonogram Records. Dist: Polygram Distribution

Cassette: released on Mercury, Feb'81 by Phonogram Records. Dist: Polygram Distribution

NEW WORLD MAN.
Single (7"): released on Mercury, Jun'83 by Phonogram Records. Dist: Polygram Distribution

Picture disc single: released on Mercury, Jun'83 by Phonogram Records. Dist: Polygram Distribution

Single (12"): released on Mercury, Jun'83 by Phonogram Records. Dist: Polygram Distribution

PERMANENT WAVES.
Album: released on Mercury, Jan'80 by Phonogram Records. Dist: Polygram Distribution

Cassette: released on Mercury, Jan'80 by Phonogram Records. Dist: Polygram Distribution

POWER WINDOWS.
Tracks: / Big money, The / Grand design / Manhattan Project / Manhattan Project / Marathon / Territories / Middletown dreams / Emotion detector / Mystic rhythms.
Compact disc: released on Vertigo, Nov'85 by Phonogram Records. Dist: Polygram

Album: released on Vertigo, Nov'85 by Phonogram Records. Dist: Polygram

Cassette: released on Vertigo, Nov'85 by Phonogram Records. Dist: Polygram

RUSH.
Compact disc: released on Mercury, Apr'87 by Phonogram Records. Dist: Polygram Distribution

Album: released on Mercury, Jun'83 by Phonogram Records. Dist: Polygram Distribution

Cassette: released on Mercury, Jun'83 by Phonogram Records. Dist: Polygram Distribution

RUSH ARCHIVES.
Triple album / cassette: released on Mercury, May'78 by Phonogram Records. Dist: Polygram Distribution

Cassette: released on Mercury, Jun'78 by Phonogram Records. Dist: Polygram Distribution

RUSH THROUGH TIME.
Album: released on Mercury, Sep'81 by Phonogram Records. Dist: Polygram Distribution

Cassette: released on Mercury, Sep'81 by Phonogram Records. Dist: Polygram Distribution

SIGNALS.
Compact disc: released on Mercury, '83 by Phonogram Records. Dist: Polygram Distribution

Album: released on Mercury, Sep'82 by Phonogram Records. Dist: Polygram Distribution

Cassette: released on Mercury, Sep'82 by Phonogram Records. Dist: Polygram Distribution

TOM SAWYER (LIVE).
Single (7"): released on Mercury, Oct'81 by Phonogram Records. Dist: Polygram Distribution

Single (12"): released on Mercury, Oct'81 by Phonogram Records. Dist: Polygram Distribution

VITAL SIGNS.
Single (7"): released on Mercury, Mar'81 by Phonogram Records. Dist: Polygram Distribution

Single (12"): released on Mercury, Mar'81 by Phonogram Records. Dist: Polygram Distribution

Rush, Barbara

CRUSIN' (Rush, Barbara & Dave Barker).
Single (12"):

MODERATION (Rush, Barbara & Cecillia Huston).
Single (12"): released on Terminal, Mar'85 by Terminal. Dist: Jetstar Distribution

RIGHT TIME (Rush, Barbara & Cecillia Huston).
Single (12"):

Rushen, Patrice

BREAKING ALL THE RULES.
Compact disc: released on Arista, Dec'86 by Arista Records. Dist: RCA

DON'T BLAME ME.
Single (7"): released on Elektra, Jun'81 by WEA Records. Dist: WEA

Single (12"): released on Elektra, Jun'81 by WEA Records. Dist: WEA

FORGET ME NOT.
Single (7"): released on Elektra, Apr'82 by WEA Records. Dist: WEA

Single (12"): released on Elektra, Apr'82 by WEA Records. Dist: WEA

I WAS TIRED OF BEING ALONE.
Single (7"): released on Elektra, Jun'82 by WEA Records. Dist: WEA

Single (12"): released on Elektra, Jun'82 by WEA Records. Dist: WEA

LOOK UP.
Single (7"): released on Elektra, Apr'81 by WEA Records. Dist: WEA

Single (12"): released on Elektra, Apr'81 by WEA Records. Dist: WEA

NEVER GONNA GIVE YOU UP.
Single (7"): released on Elektra, Nov'80 by WEA Records. Dist: WEA

Single (12"): released on Elektra, Nov'80 by WEA Records. Dist: WEA

NOW.
Album: released on Elektra, Jul'84 by WEA Records. Dist: WEA Deleted '87.

Cassette: released on Elektra, Jul'84 by WEA Records. Dist: WEA

WATCH OUT!.
Tracks: / Watch out! / Breakin' all the rules / Long time coming / All my love / Somewhere / Anything can happen / Burnin' / Till she's out of your mind / Come back to me / Tender lovin'.
Album: released on Arista, Jan'87 by Arista Records. Dist: RCA

Cassette: released on Arista, Jan'87 by Arista Records. Dist: RCA

Compact disc: released on Arista, Jan'87 by Arista Records. Dist: RCA

WATCH OUT (OBSERVATION MIX).
Tracks: / Watch out (observation mix) / Watch out (ext mix) / Over the phone.
Single (12"): released on Arista, Apr'87 by Arista Records. Dist: RCA

Rush, Heather

SOMEBODY (IS TAKING YOUR LOVE AWAY).
Single (7"): released on President, Jun'85 by President Records. Dist: Taylors, Spartan

Single (12"): released on President, Jun'85 by President Records. Dist: Taylors, Spartan

Rushing, Jimmy

BLUESWAY SESSIONS, THE.
Tracks: / Baby don't tell on me / Berkely campus blues / Blues in the dark / Everyday I have the blues / Evil blues / Keep the faith baby / Sent for you yesterday (Here you come today) / I left my baby / Sonny boy blues / Bad loser / You can't run around / Tell me I'm not too late / Crying blues / Undecided blues / Take me back baby / We remember Pres.
Double Album: released on Charly, Sep'86 by Charly Records. Dist: Charly, Cadillac

BLUES YEARS.
Tracks: / Baby don't tell me / Berkeley campus blues / Blues in the dark / Everyday I have the blues / Evil blues / Keep the faith baby / Sent for you yesterday / I left my baby / Sonny boy blues / Bad loser / You can't run around / Tell me I'm not too late / You can't run around / Tell me I'm not too late / Crying Blues / Undecided blues / Take me back baby / We remember pres.
Album: released on Charly, Oct'86 by Charly Records. Dist: Charly, Cadillac

ESSENTIAL JIMMY RUSHING, THE.
Double Album: released on Vogue Jazz (France), May'83

GOOD MOURNIN' BLUES (Rushing, Jimmy & The Count Basie Band).
Album: released on Affinity, Nov'85 by Charly Records. Dist: Charly, Cadillac

Rush, Jennifer

DESTINY.
Tracks: / Destiny / Right time has come now.
Single (7"): released on CBS, Apr'86 by CBS

Records. Dist: CBS

Single (12"): released on CBS, Apr'86 by CBS Records. Dist: CBS

Single (7"): released on CBS, Apr'86 by CBS Records. Dist: CBS

Picture disc single: released on CBS, Apr'86 by CBS Records. Dist: CBS

HEART OVER MIND.
Tracks: / I come undone / Down to you / Heqrtover mind / Serch the sky / Flames of Paradise / Love of a stranger / Heart wars / Stronghold / Sidekick / Call myname.
Album: released on CBS, Apr'87 by CBS Records. Dist: CBS

Cassette: released on CBS, Apr'87 by CBS Records. Dist: CBS

Compact disc: released on CBS, Apr'87 by CBS Records. Dist: CBS

I COME UNDONE.
Tracks: / I come undone / Search for the sky.
Single (7"): released on CBS, Feb'87 by CBS Records. Dist: CBS

Single (12"): released on CBS, Feb'87 by CBS Records. Dist: CBS

JENNIFER RUSH.
Tracks: / Madonna's eyes / 25 lovers / Come give me your hand / Nobody move / Never gonna turn back again / Ring of ice / Into my dreams / I see a shadow (not a fantasy) / Surrender / Power of love, The.
Compact disc: released on CBS, Dec'85 by CBS Records. Dist: CBS

Album: released on CBS, Nov'85 by CBS Records. Dist: CBS

Cassette: released on CBS, Nov'85 by CBS Records. Dist: CBS

MADONNA'S EYES.
Tracks: / Madonna's eyes / Surrender.
Single (7"): released on CBS, Feb'86 by CBS Records. Dist: CBS

Single (12"): released on CBS, Feb'86 by CBS Records. Dist: CBS

MOVIN'.
Tracks: / Destiny / Live wire / Silent killer / Automatic / If you're ever gonna lose my love / Ave Maria (survivors of a different kind) / Testify with my heart / Yester-me, yester-you, yesterday / Right time has mow come, The / Hero of a fool.
Album: released on CBS, Apr'86 by CBS Records. Dist: CBS

Cassette: released on CBS, Apr'86 by CBS Records. Dist: CBS

Compact disc: released on CBS, '86 by CBS Records. Dist: CBS

POWER OF LOVE.
Single (7"): released on CBS, Nov'86 by CBS Records. Dist: CBS

Single (12"): released on CBS, Nov'86 by CBS Records. Dist: CBS

POWER OF LOVE.
Single (7"): released on CBS, May'85 by CBS Records. Dist: CBS

Rush, Otis

CLASSIC RECORDINGS, THE.
Album: released on Charly(R&B), Oct'85 by Charly Records. Dist: Charly, Cadillac

CLASSIC RECORDINGS.
Tracks: / All your love / Three times a fool / She's a good 'un / It takes time / Double trouble / My love will never die / My baby is a good 'un / Checking on my baby / Jump sister Bessie / I can't quit you baby / If you were mine / Groaning the blues / Keep on loving me baby / Sit down baby / Love that woman / Violent love.
Album: released on Charly, Jul'86 by Charly Records. Dist: Charly, Cadillac

Cassette: released on Charly, Jul'86 by Charly Records. Dist: Charly, Cadillac

FINAL TAKES & OTHERS, THE (Rush, Otis & Buddy Guy).
Album: released on Flyright, May'84 by Flyright Records. Dist: Krazy Kat, Swift, Jazz Music

FINAL TAKES, THE (Rush, Otis & Buddy Guy).
Album: released on Flyright, Oct'86 by Flyright Records. Dist: Krazy Kat, Swift, Jazz Music

OTIS RUSH.
Tracks: / Double trouble / Jump sister Bessie / She's a good 'un (Take A) / Checking on my baby / Sit down baby / Love that woman / Keep on lovin'g me baby (Take B) / Keep on loving me baby (Take A0 / My baby is a good 'un / If you were mine / I can't quit you baby / All your love / Groaning the blues / It takes time / Violent love / Three times a fool / My love will never die / She's a good 'un (Take B).
Album: released on Flyright, Jul'86 by Flyright Records. Dist: Krazy Kat, Swift, Jazz Music

RIGHT PLACE, WRONG TIME.
Album: released on Edsel, Mar'87 by Demon Records. Dist: Pinnacle, Jazz Music, Projection

Album: released on Bullfrog, Apr'79 Dist: Swift

TROUBLES TROUBLES.
Album: released on Sonet, Aug'78 by Sonet Records. Dist: PRT

Rush, Tom

LATE NIGHT RADIO.
Album: released on Nightlight, Aug'85 Dist: Projection

Rushton, William

TALE OF ALE, THE.
Double Album: released on Freereed, Nov'77 by Topic Records. Dist: JSU

TALE OF ALE,THE (Rushton, William & Various Artists).
Double Album: released on Free Reed, '77 by Free Reed Records. Dist: Roots, Projection, Hobgoblin Records, Oblivion

Russanti

CARRY THE CAN.
Single (7"): released on Mach 1, Jun'83 by Mach 1 Records. Dist: PRT

IT HAPPENED THEN.
Single (7"): released on Mach 1, Jan'83 by Mach 1 Records. Dist: PRT

Russco

FACE THE WORLDS Folksongs for today.
Cassette: released on Folktracks, Nov'79 by Folktracks Cassettes. Dist: Folktracks

Russ, Eddie

ZAIUS.
Single (12"): released on Impact, Aug'82 by Ace Records. Dist: Rough Trade, Pinnacle, Swift, Backs, Counterpoint, Jungle, Hotshot, Cartel

Russell, Arthur

INSTRUMENTALS.
Album: released on Les Disques Du Crepuscule, May'84 Dist: Rough Trade, Pinnacle, Island, Polygram

LETS GO SWIMMING.
Tracks: / Lets go swimming.
Single (12"): released on Rough Trade, Sep'86 by Rough Trade Records. Dist: Rough Trade Distribution, Cartel Distribution

WORLD OF ECHO.
Album: released on Rough Trade, Apr'87 by Rough Trade Records. Dist: Rough Trade Distribution, Cartel Distribution

Russell, Brenda

TWO EYES.
Single (7"): released on Warner Brothers, Jul'83 by WEA Records. Dist: WEA

Russell & Brown

CAN'T GET YOU OUT OF MY MIND.
Single (7"): released on Creole, Nov'83 by Creole Records. Dist: Rhino, PRT

Russell, Dan

LET SLEEPING DOGS LIE.
Single (12"): released on Dove, Dec'84 by Dove Records. Dist: Jetstar

TENNIS SHOES (Russell, Dan & The Sweat Band).
Tracks: / Tennis shoes (new mix) / Tennis shoes (back spin).
Single (7"): released on Tembo, Jun'86 by Tembo (Canada). Dist: IMS Distribution, Polygram Distribution

Single (12"): released on Tembo, Jun'86 by Tembo (Canada). Dist: IMS Distribution, Polygram Distribution

Single (7"): released on Tembo, Jun'85 by Tembo (Canada). Dist: IMS Distribution, Polygram Distribution

Single (12"): released on Tembo, Jun'85 by Tembo (Canada). Dist: IMS Distribution, Polygram Distribution

Russell, Devon

CARELESS WHISPER.
Tracks: / Careless whisper / Careful whisper.
Single (12"): released on Uptempo, Jun'86 by Uptempo Records. Dist: Jetstar Distribution

COME-A-ME GIRL.
Single (12"): released on Ethnic, Jul'83 Dist: Kingdom

PRISON LIFE.
Album: released on Tamboki Wambesi, Sep'86

VISION OF LOVE.
Single (12"): released on Jedi, Feb'85 Dist: Jetstar

Russell Family

RUSSELL FAMILY OF DOOLIN, CO. CLARE, THE.
Album: released on Topic, '81 Dist: Roots Distribution

Russell, George

AFRICAN GAME, THE.
Tracks: / Organic life on earth begins- Event I / Paleolithic game- Event II / Consciousness- Event III / Survival game- Event IV / Human sensing of unity with great nature- Event V / African Empires- Event VI / Cartesian man- Event VII / Mega-minimalist age- Event VIII / Future, The- Event IX / Event I: Organic life on earth begins / Event II: The Paleolithic game / Event III: Consciousness / Event IV: The survival game / Event V: The human sensing of unity wiht great nature / Event VI: African Empires / Event VII: Cartesian man / Event VIII: The mega-minimalist age / Event IX: The future.
Notes: George Russell Has been on the leading edge of jazz since the 1940's as a composer and theorist. His compositions have been performed by Dixxle Gillespie's big band, Charlie Parker, John Coltrane, Miles Davis, and others.'The African Game' is a ten movement, rythmically-charged work performed by a twenty-six piece prchestra.
Album: released on Blue Note, Dec'85 by EMI Records. Dist: EMI

Cassette: released on Blue Note, Dec'85 by EMI Records. Dist: EMI

Compact disc: released on Blue Note, Sep'87 by EMI Records. Dist: EMI. Estim retail price in Sep'87 was £11.99.

ELECTRONIC SONATA FOR SOULS LOVED BY NATURE - 1968.
Album: released on Soul Note, May'85 Dist: Projection, Celtic Music, Chris Wellard

JAZZ IN THE SPACE AGE (Russell, George & His Orchestra).
Tracks: / Chromatic Universe-Part 1 / Dimensions / Chromatic Universe-Part 2 / Lydiot, The / Waltz from outer space / Chromatic Universe-Part 3.
Notes: All tracks George Russell/ all Tracks (P) Russ Hix Pub. Co.(MCPS): Bill Evans plays piano: Licenced from MCA Records Inc: This compilation (P) 1986 Charly Records Ltd (C) 1986 Charly Records Ltd:
Album: released on Affinity, Jun'86 by Charly Records. Dist: Charly, Cadillac

LIVE IN AN AMERICAN TIME SPIRAL (Russell, George New York Band).
Compact disc: released on Soul Note (Italy), '86 Dist: Harmonia Mundi Distributors

NEW YORK BIG BAND.
Compact disc: released on Soul Note (Italy), '86 Dist: Harmonia Mundi Distributors

SO WHAT.
Tracks: / So what / Rhymes / War gewesen / Time spiral.
Compact disc: released on EMI, Mar'87 by EMI Records. Dist: EMI

Album: released on Blue Note, Dec'86 by EMI Records. Dist: EMI

STRATUSPHUNK (Russell, George Sextet).
Album:

TRIP TO PRILLARGURI (Russell, George Sextet).
Album: released on Soul Note, Jul'82 Dist: Harmonia Mundi Distributors

Russell, Johnny

MR. ENTERTAINER.
Tracks: / Nobody touches my baby / Our marriage was a failure / Someday I'll sober up / Too late to turn back now / She goes walking through my mind / Over Georgia / She burnt the little roadside tavern down / Finer things in life / Queen of my heart / Remembering / Some kind of a woman / Leona / I'm staying / Your fool / This man and woman thing / What a price.
Album: released on RCA, Jan'87 by RCA Records. Dist: RCA, Roots, Swift, Wellard, Chris, I & B, Solomon & Peres Distribution

Cassette: released on RCA, Jan'87 by RCA Records. Dist: RCA, Roots, Swift, Wellard, Chris, I & B, Solomon & Peres Distribution

Russell, Leon

AMERICANA.
Album: released on Warner Brothers, '78 by WEA Records. Dist: WEA

LIVE ALBUM, THE (Russell, Leon & New Grass Revival).
Album: released on Warner Brothers, Mar'81 by Warner Bros Records. Dist: WEA

Russell, Luis

1926-30 (Russell, Luis & His Orchestra).
Album: released on VJM, Dec'84 by Wellard, Chris Distribution. Dist: Wellard, Chris Distribution

1930-1934.
Tracks: / Give me your telephone number / Higginbotham blues / Muggin' lightly / Panama / High tension / I got rhythm / Saratoga drag / Ease on down / Honey, that reminds me / You rascal, you / Goin' to town / Say the word / Freakish blues / Darktown strutters ball, The / My blue heaven / Ghost of the freaks / Hokus pokus / Primitive / Ol' man river.
Notes: Classic recordings by one of the hottest groups in the history of jazz. Chronological, of course. Featuring: Red Allen, J.C. Higginbotham, Charlie Holmes, Pops Foster, Albert Nicholas, Dickie Wells, Rex Stewart, Etc.
Album: released on VJM, Apr'86 by Wellard, Chris Distribution. Dist: Wellard, Chris Distribution

Russell, Micho

TRADITIONAL MUSIC OF COUNTY CLARE.
Album: released on Freereed, Sep'79 by Topic Records. Dist: JSU

Russell, Pee Wee

COLLEGE CONCERT, THE (Russell, Pee Wee & Red Allen).
Album: released on Jasmine, Mar'85 by Jasmine Records. Dist: Counterpoint, Lugtons, Taylor, H.R., Wellard, Chris, Swift, Cadillac

HOT LICOURICE (Russell, Pee Wee & His Rhythm Cats).
Album: released on Honeydew, Oct'79 Dist Swift, JSU

INDIVIDUALISM OF..., THE.
Double Album:

JAM SESSION IN SWINGVILLE (Russell, Pee Wee & Coleman Hawkins).
Double Album: released on Prestige, Apr'76 by Prestige Records (USA). Dist: RCA, JSU Swift

MUGGSY SPANIER AND PEE WEE RUSSELL (see Spanier, Muggsy) (Russell, Pee Wee/Muggsy Spanier).
Notes: With Bob Haggart/G Wettling etc.

OVER THE RAINBOW.
Album: released on Xanadu, Jan'83 Dist: Discovery, Jazz Horizons, Jazz Music, Swift

PEE WEE RUSSELL AND THE RHYTHM CATS.
Album: released on Shoestring, Apr'81 by Shoestring Records. Dist: Shoestring

PIED PIPER OF JAZZ, (THE).
Album: released on Commodore Classics, May'87 by Teldec Records (Germany). Dist: Conifer, IMS, Polygram

PIED PIPER OF JAZZ THREE DEUCES AND HOT FOUR, THE.
Album: released on Teldec (Germany), Sep'8 by Import Records. Dist: IMS Distribution, Polygram Distribution

Russell, Tom

HEART ON A SLEEVE.
Tracks: / One and one / Heart on a sleeve / Blinded by the light of love / Touch of grey, A / Wild hearts / St Olav's gate / Gallo de cielo / Mandarin oranges / Cropduster / Canadia whiskey / Chinese silver / Bowl of red, A.
Compact disc: released on Bear Family, Aug'86 by Bear Family Records. Dist: Rolle coaster Distribution, Swift

Russia

MOSCOW RADIO RUSSIAN FOLK INSTRUMENTS.
Album: released on Melodiya (USSR), May'7 Dist: T.B.C Distribution

NORTHERN RUSSIAN FOLK CHORU FOLK SONGS.
Album: released on Melodiya (USSR), May' Dist: T.B.C Distribution

OMSK STATE RUSSIAN FOLK CHOI FOLK SONGS.
Album: released on Melodiya (USSR), May' Dist: T.B.C Distribution

OSIPOV RUSSIAN FOLK ORCHESTR VOL.1 Traditional Music.
Album: released on Melodiya (USSR), May' Dist: T.B.C Distribution

OSIPOV RUSSIAN FOLK ORCHESTR VOL.2 Traditional Music.
Album: released on Melodiya (USSR), May' Dist: T.B.C Distribution

PYATNITSKY STATE RUSSIAN FOL CHOIR (VOLUME 4).
Album: released on Melodiya (USSR), May' Dist: T.B.C Distribution

PYATNITSKY STATE RUSSIAN FOL CHOIR(VOLUME 2).
Album: released on Melodiya (USSR), May' Dist: T.B.C Distribution

PYATNITSKY STATE RUSSIAN FOLK CHOIR (VOLUME 3).
Album: released on Melodiya (USSR), May'78 Dist: T.B.C Distribution

PYATNITSKY STATE RUSSIAN FOLK CHOIR VOL.1.
Album: released on Melodiya (USSR), May'78 Dist: T.B.C Distribution

Russian...

AKVARELLI & TCHARIVINI GITARY (Russian Jazz Groups).
Cassette: released on Melodiya (USSR), Dist: T.B.C Distribution

COME INTO MY ROOM (Russian Roulette).
Single (7"): released on Red Bus, Jan'84 by Red Bus Records. Dist: PRT

FOLKSONGS (Russian Balalaika).
Album: released on Melodiya (USSR), May'78 Dist: T.B.C Distribution

FROM OLD RUSSIA (Russian Dance Music).
Cassette: released on Melodiya (USSR), Feb'79 Dist: T.B.C Distribution

IVANOV KRAMSKOY (Russian guitar music).
Cassette: released on Melodiya (USSR), Feb'79 Dist: T.B.C Distribution

LIGHT JAZZ (Russian Radio Ensemble).
Cassette: released on Melodiya (USSR), Feb'79 Dist: T.B.C Distribution

MERRY MELODIES (Russian Popular Music).
Cassette: released on Melodiya (USSR), Feb'79 Dist: T.B.C Distribution

PETRUSHKA (Russian Vocal Quartet).
Cassette: released on Melodiya (USSR), Feb'79 Dist: T.B.C Distribution

RUSSIAN (see Language courses).

RUSSIAN ACCORDEON MUSIC (Russian Accordeon).
Cassette: released on Melodiya (USSR), Feb'79 Dist: T.B.C Distribution

RUSSIAN DANCE MUSIC (Russian Dance Music).
Cassette: released on Melodiya (USSR), Feb'79 Dist: T.B.C Distribution

RUSSIAN OLD MARCHES & WALTZES (Russian marches/waltzes).
Cassette: released on Melodiya (USSR), Feb'79 Dist: T.B.C Distribution

RUSSIAN ROMANCES (ORCHESTRAL MUSIC) (Russian Romances).
Cassette: released on Melodiya (USSR), Feb'79 Dist: T.B.C Distribution

SKALDS (Russian Ensemble).
Cassette: released on Melodiya (USSR), Feb'79 Dist: T.B.C Distribution

SPRING VOICES (Russian Popular Music).
Cassette: released on Melodiya (USSR), Feb'79 Dist: T.B.C Distribution

TOP MELODY '72 (Russian Orchestra).
Cassette: released on Melodiya (USSR), Feb'79 Dist: T.B.C Distribution

WING GROUP-HELMUT ORUSAAR (Russian Jazz Group).
Cassette: released on Melodiya (USSR), Feb'79 Dist: T.B.C Distribution

Russian Folk...

ALEXSANDROU SONG AND DANCE ENSEMBLE (Russian Folk Songs).
Cassette: released on Melodiya (USSR), Feb'79 Dist: T.B.C Distribution

DANCES & FOLK DANCES BY RUSSIAN COMP. (Russian Folk Songs).
Cassette: released on Melodiya (USSR), Feb'79 Dist: T.B.C Distribution

ESTONIAN FOLK MUSIC (Russian Folk Songs).
Cassette: released on Melodiya (USSR), Feb'79 Dist: T.B.C Distribution

FESTIVAL OF RUSSIAN FOLK SONGS USSR Russian chorus conducted by Alexander Sveshnikov (Russian Folk Songs).
Album: released on H.M.V., May'74 by EMI Records. Dist: EMI

OLD RUSSIAN FOLK SONGS (Russian Folk Songs).
Cassette: released on Melodiya (USSR), Feb'79 Dist: T.B.C Distribution

PIATNITSKY STATE ACADEMIC FOLK CHORUS (Russian Folk Songs).
Cassette: released on Melodiya (USSR), Feb'79 Dist: T.B.C Distribution

---

RUSSIAN FOLK FESTIVAL, A (Russian Folk Festival).
Album: by EMI Records. Dist: EMI

RUSSIAN FOLK INSTRUMENTS ENSEMBLE Traditional Music (Russian Folk Ensemble).
Album: released on Melodiya (USSR), May'78 Dist: T.B.C Distribution

SONGS OF TOURISTS (Russian Folk Songs).
Cassette: released on Melodiya (USSR), Feb'79 Dist: T.B.C Distribution

UKRAINIAN FOLK SONGS (Russian Folk Songs).
Cassette: released on Melodiya (USSR), Feb'79 Dist: T.B.C Distribution

Russian Orthodox Music

RUSSIAN ORTHODOX CHURCH MUSIC (VOLUME 1) Various artists (Various Artists).
Album: released on Ikon (USSR), Aug'78 by Five Records. Dist: Ikon

RUSSIAN ORTHODOX CHURCH MUSIC (VOLUME 2) Various artists (Various Artists).
Album: released on Ikon (USSR), Aug'78 by Five Records. Dist: Ikon

RUSSIAN ORTHODOX CHURCH MUSIC (VOLUME 4) Various artists (Various Artists).
Album: released on Ikon (USSR), Aug'78 by Five Records. Dist: Ikon

RUSSIAN ORTHODOX CHURCH MUSIC (VOLUME 5) Various artists (Various Artists).
Album: released on Ikon (USSR), Aug'78 by Five Records. Dist: Ikon

RUSSIAN ORTHODOX CHURCH MUSIC (VOLUME 6) Various artists (Various Artists).
Album: released on Ikon (USSR), Aug'78 by Five Records. Dist: Ikon

TRIO ROMEN.
Cassette: released on Melodiya (USSR), Feb'79 Dist: T.B.C Distribution

Russo, Mike

HIS GUITAR AND PIANO.
Album: released on Arhoolie, May'81 by Arhoolie Records. Dist: Projection, Topic, Jazz Music, Swift, Roots

Rusty Dusty

RUSTY DUSTY Various artists (Various Artists).
Album: released on Wild Flower, Jun'84 by Wild Flower Records. Dist: Jetstar

Rusty Parts

DON'T YOU WISH YOU WERE.
Album: released on Sweet Folk & Country, May'77 Dist: Chris Wellard Distribution

Rutherford, Michael

SATISFACTION.
Single (12"): released on Rudy T, Aug'82

SMALL CREEPS DAY.
Album: released on Charisma, Oct'86 by Virgin Records. Dist: EMI

Rutherford, Mike

ACTING VERY STRANGE.
Single (7"): released on WEA, Oct'82 by WEA Records. Dist: WEA

Single (12"): released on WEA, Oct'82 by WEA Records. Dist: WEA

HALFWAY THERE.
Single (7"): released on WEA, Aug'82 by WEA Records. Dist: WEA

HIDEAWAY.
Single (7"): released on WEA, Jan'83 by WEA Records. Dist: WEA

MIKE & THE MECHANICS.
Album: released on WEA International, Oct'85 by WEA Records. Dist: WEA

Cassette: released on WEA International, Oct'85 by WEA Records. Dist: WEA

Rutherford, Paul

ISKRA 1903 (Rutherford, Paul/Derek Bailey/Barry Guy).
Double Album: released on Incus, Nov'76 Dist: Jazz Music, Cadillac

LIVE MOERS (SOLO TROMBONE 1976).
Album: released on Ring (Import), Jul'78

NEUPH.
Album: released on Sweet Folk All, May'81 by Sweet Folk All Records. Dist: Sweet Folk All, Roots, Celtic Music, Dragon, Impetus, Projection, Chris Wellard, Festival Records

---

Ruthless people

RUTHLESS PEOPLE Original soundtrack (Various Artists).
Tracks: / Ruthless people / Give me the reason / Modern woman / Wherever I lay my hat (that's my home) / No say in it / Waiting to see you / Dance champion / Neighbourhood Watch / Stand on it / Don't you want my love.
Album: released on Epic, Nov'86 by CBS Records. Dist: CBS

Cassette: released on Epic, Nov'86 by CBS Records. Dist: CBS

Compact disc: released on Epic, Nov'86 by CBS Records. Dist: CBS

Rutles

RUTLES, (THE).
Album: released on Warner Brothers, Mar'78 by WEA Records. Dist: WEA

Cassette: released on Warner Brothers, Mar'78 by WEA Records. Dist: WEA

Ruts

BABYLON BURNING (RUTS 4 TRACK EP).
Single (12"): released on Virgin, Apr'83

GRIN AND BEAR IT.
Album: released on Virgin, Mar'84 by Virgin Records. Dist: EMI, Virgin Distribution

IN A RUT.
Single (7"): released on Spartan, Jun'79 by Spartan Records. Dist: Spartan

LIVE.
Tracks: / Sus / Dope for guns / It was cold / In a rut / Society / Jah war / Babylon's burning / You're just a / Love song / Criminal mind / Demolition dancing.
Album: released on Dojo, Mar'87 by Castle Communications Records. Dist: Cartel

PEEL SESSION 21.5.79.

PEEL SESSION 27.11.78.
Single (12"): released on Strange Fruit, Jun'87 by Clive Selwood. Dist: Pinnacle

WEAK HEART.
Single (12"): released on Bohemian, Mar'83 Dist: Spartan

YOU'VE GOTTA GET OUT OF IT.
Compact disc: released on Virgin, '87 by Virgin Records. Dist: EMI, Virgin Distribution

Ruts D.C

ANIMAL NOW.
Album: released on Virgin, May'81

RHYTHM COLLISION.
Album: released on Bohemian, Jul'82 Dist: Spartan

STEPPING BONDAGE.
Single (7"): released on Bohemian, Mar'83 Dist: Spartan

WHATEVER WE DO.
Single (7"): released on Bohemian, Jul'82 Dist: Spartan

RVT Ljubljana big band

INVITATION TO DANCE.
Album: released on Dansan, Sep'86 by Spartan Records. Dist: Spartan

Ryan, Barry

ELOISE.
Album: released on Polydor (Import), Apr'82

Cassette: released on Polydor (Import), Apr'82

Single (7"): released on Old Gold, Jul'84 by Old Gold Records. Dist: Lightning, Jazz Music, Spartan, Counterpoint

Ryan, Bill

MIDNIGHT IN THE MORNING.
Album: released on Harp(Ireland), Jul'81 by Pickwick Records. Dist: Taylors

Ryan, Jimmy

COMMODORE CLASSICS (Ryan, Jimmy/Edmond Hall/Wilbur De Paris).
Album: released on Commodore, Mar'83 Dist: Swift

Ryan, Lloyd

JUNGLE ANTHEM (Ryan, Lloyd Express).
Single (7"): released on Playback, Nov'79 by Playback Records. Dist: Pinnacle

LET THERE BE DRUMS (Ryan, Lloyd Express).
Single (7"): released on Playback, Jan'84 by Playback Records. Dist: Pinnacle

NEW DIRECTION (Ryan, Lloyd Jazz Four).
Album: released on Playback, May'87 by Playback Records. Dist: Pinnacle

NEW DIRECTIONS (Ryan, Lloyd Jazz Four).
Album: released on Playback, Jul'87 by Play-

---

back Records. Dist: Pinnacle

Ryan, Mick

FAIR WAS THE CITY (Ryan, Mick/Jon Burge).
Album: released on Trailer, Sep'81 Dist: Jazz Music, Celtic Music, JSU

Ryan, Pat

LEABOY'S LASSIE.
Album: released on Folk Heritage, Jul'82 by Folk Heritage Records. Dist: Roots, Wynd-Up Distribution, Jazz Music, Folk Heritage

Ryan, Ron

AH YOU GOT YOUR EARS ON.
Single (7"): released on Buffalo (UK), Sep'82

NASSINGTON FLYER (see Duffy Brothers)

Ryans, Jimmy

JIMMY RYANS & THE UPTOWN CAFE SOCIETY... (Ryans, Jimmy, Deparis Brothers, Edmond Hall).
Tracks: / I've found a new baby / I've found a new baby - Alternative choice / (What did I do to be so) black and blue / (What did I do to be so) black and blue - Alternative choice / Change of key boogie / Change o' key boogie - Alternative choice / Sheik of Araby, The / Sheik of Araby, The - Alternative choice / Man I love, The / Man I love, The - Alternative choice / Downtown cafe boogie / Downtown cafe boogie - Alternative choice / Uptown cafe blues / Coquette.
Notes: Full title: Jimmy Ryans & The Uptown Cafe Society/Deparis Brothers & Edmond Hall-Sextet.
Album: released on Commodore Classics, Nov'85 by Teldec Records. Dist: Conifer, IMS, Polygram

Ryan & The Texolets

JOE TEX.
Single (7"): released on Prairie Dust, Oct'82 by Prairie Dust Records.

Rydell, Bobby

WILD ONE.
Tracks: / Dream lover / Stagger Lee / This magic moment / Tossin' and turnin' (all night) / Wild one / Wildwood days / Forget him / Then you can tell me goodbye / Kissin' time U.S.A. / Volare.
Notes: Licenced fron Acplause Records Inc.
Album: released on President, Sep'86 by President Records. Dist: Taylors, Spartan

Ryder

RUNNER IN THE NIGHT.
Tracks: / Runner in the night.
Notes: Eurovision entry
Single (7"): released on 10, Apr'86 by 10 Records. Dist: Virgin, EMI

Ryder, Mark

WRAP MY ARMS AROUND YOU.
Single (7"): released on PRT, Sep'85 by PRT Records. Dist: PRT

Ryder, Mitch

NEVER KICK A SLEEPING DOG.
Album: released on Towerbell, Oct'83

Cassette: released on Towerbell, Oct'83

WHEELS OF STEEL (Ryder, Mitch & The Detroit Wheels).
Album: released on PRT, Apr'83 by PRT Records. Dist: PRT

Cassette: released on PRT, Apr'83 by PRT Records. Dist: PRT

WHEN YOU WERE MINE.
Single (7"): released on Towerbell, Nov'83

Rye Whiskey Road Band

I DREAMED OF HIGHWAYS.
Album: released on Folk Heritage, Jul'82 by Folk Heritage Records. Dist: Roots, Wynd-Up Distribution, Jazz Music, Folk Heritage

RUNNING KID, (THE).
Album: released on Folk Heritage, Jul'82 by Folk Heritage Records. Dist: Roots, Wynd-Up Distribution, Jazz Music, Folk Heritage

Rypdal

AFRIC POPPERBIRD (Rypdal/Garbarek/Anderson).
Album: released on ECM (Germany), May'74 by ECM Records. Dist: IMS, Polygram, Virgin through EMI

SART (Rypdal/Stenson/Garbarek).
Album: released on ECM (Germany), May'74 by ECM Records. Dist: IMS, Polygram, Virgin through EMI

TERJE RYPDAL (Rypdal/Finti/Garbarek).
Album: released on ECM (Germany), May'74 by ECM Records. Dist: IMS, Polygram, Virgin through EMI

Rypdal, Terje

AFTER THE RAIN.
Album: released on ECM (Germany), Dec'76 by ECM Records. Dist: IMS, Polygram, Virgin through EMI

S

SA 55
COMPROMISE / LOVE IS BLIND.
Single (7"): released on 1966, Jul'82 by 1966
Records. Dist: Cartel

Saatchi, Phil
LITTLE IN LOVE.
Tracks: / Little in love / When we dream.
Single (7"): released on A&M, Apr'87 by A&M
Records. Dist: Polygram

Single (12"): released on A&M, Apr'87 by A&M
Records. Dist: Polygram

POOR MAN'S PARADISE.
Tracks: / Poor man's paradise / You should be
mine / Cancel my subscriptions.
Single (7"): released on A&M, Mar'86 by A&M
Records. Dist: Polygram

STRIPPED.
Tracks: / Little In Love / When We Dream / King
of another country / Build a bridge / Love is a
mission / No one gonna love you (like I do) /
Wheel of fortune / Poor man's paradise / White
flag / People of the New World.
Notes: This ten collection which includes Phil's
'A Little In Love', combines soulful vocals and
superbly structured songs to maximum effect.
Album: released on A&M, Apr'87 by A&M Records. Dist: Polygram

Cassette: released on A&M, Apr'87 by A&M
Records. Dist: Polygram

Compact disc: released on A&M, Apr'87 by
A&M Records. Dist: Polygram

WHEEL OF FORTUNE.
Tracks: / Wheel of fortune / Contradictions /
White.
Notes: no text.
Single (7"): released on A&M, Jan'87 by A&M
Records. Dist: Polygram

Single (12"): released on A&M, Jan'87 by A&M
Records. Dist: Polygram

Sabastian, John
IN A CARE BEAR FAMILY.
Single (7"): released on Cherry Lane, Jul'85 by
Cherry Lane Productions. Dist: PRT

Sabastians Men
HORIZON.
Single (7"): released on Horizon 5, Aug'84 by
Horizon 5 Records. Dist: Cartel

Sablon, Jean
1933/1936.
Album: released on World Records, Jun'80
Dist: Polygram

JEAN SABLON.
Double Album: released on EMI (France), '83
by EMI Records. Dist: Conifer

Sabotage
FIGHT FOR THE ROCK.
Album: released on Atlantic, May'86 by WEA
Records. Dist: WEA

Cassette: released on Atlantic, May'86 by WEA
Records. Dist: WEA

Sabre
MIRACLE MAN / ON THE LOOSE.
Single (7"): released on Neat, Jun'83 by Neat
Records. Dist: Pinnacle, Neat

Sabu
**ANGELINE / SHAKE RATTLE AND
ROLL.**
Single (7"): released on FM, Oct'85 by FM-Re-
volver Records. Dist: EMI

HEARTBREAK.
Album: released on Heavy Metal America,
Oct'85 by FM-Revolver Records. Dist: EMI

Sacbe
AZTLAN.
Album: released on Trend (USA), Aug'83 by
Discovery Records. Dist: Flexitron Distributors
Ltd, Swift

STREET CORNER.
Album: released on Discovery, Jun'83 Dist:
PRT

Sacchi, Robert
JUNGLE QUEEN / CASABLANCA.
Single (7"): released on Splash, Oct'82 by
Splash Records. Dist: CBS

Single (12"): released on Splash, Oct'82 by
Splash Records. Dist: CBS

Sacharine Trust
WORLDBROKEN.
Album: released on SST, Apr'86 by SST Rec-
ords. Dist: Pinnacle

Sacred Allen
LEGENDS.
Single (7"): released on Neon, Mar'84 by Neon
Records. Dist: Neon, Pinnacle

Sacred Cowboys
SACRED COWBOYS.
Album: released on New Rose, Nov'84 Dist:
Rough Trade, Cartel

Sacred Denial
NORTH OF THE ORDER.
Album: released on Forefront (USA), Aug'87

Sacred Heart School
HURDY GURDY MAN (Girls of Sacred
Heart School).
Single (7"): released on Tin Pan Alley Music,
Jan'81

Sacred Rite
IS NOTHING SACRED.
Album: released on Megaton, Nov'86 by Mega-
ton Records. Dist: Rough Trade Distribution,
Cartel Distribution

RITUAL, THE.
Album: released on Megaton, Aug'86 by Mega-
ton Records. Dist: Rough Trade Distribution,
Cartel Distribution

Compact disc: released on Megaton, Aug'86
by Megaton Records. Dist: Rough Trade Distribution, Cartel Distribution

Sacrifice
DREAMING OF YOUR LOVE.
Single (7"): released on S&G, Oct'81 Dist: Pin-
nacle

TORMENT IN FIRE.
Album: released on Roadrunner (Dutch),
Oct'86 Dist: Pinnacle

Sacrilege
WITHIN THE PROPHECY.
Album: released on Under One Flag, Aug'87
Dist: Pinnacle

Sad Among Strangers
TAKING OFF THE BREAKS.
Tracks: / Taking off the breaks. / I Salamander.
Single (7"): released on Broken Hill, Oct'86 by
Carrere Records-Broken Hill (USA). Dist: PRT

Single (12"): released on Broken Hill, Oct'86 by
Carrere Records-Broken Hill (USA). Dist: PRT

Sadane
ONE WAY LOVE AFFAIR.
Album: released on Warner Brothers, May'81
by WEA Records. Dist: WEA

Single (7"): released on Warner Brothers,
Jun'81 by WEA Records. Dist: WEA

Single (12"): released on Warner Brothers,
Jun'81 by WEA Records. Dist: WEA

Sadane, Mark
EXCITING.
Album: released on Warner Brothers, Nov'82
by WEA Records. Dist: WEA

Sad Cafe
EVERY DAY HURTS.
Tracks: / Every day hurts / My oh boy.
Single (7"): released on Old Gold, Nov'86 by
Old Gold Records. Dist: Lightning, Jazz Music,
Spartan, Counterpoint

FACADES.
Album: released on RCA, Sep'81 by RCA Rec-
ords. Dist: RCA, Roots, Swift, Wellard, Chris, I
& B, Solomon & Peres Distribution

Cassette: released on RCA, Sep'81 by RCA
Records. Dist: RCA, Roots, Swift, Wellard,
Chris, I & B, Solomon & Peres Distribution

FANX-TA-RA.
Album: released on RCA International, Sep'81

Cassette: released on RCA International,
Sep'81

FOLLOW YOU ANYWHERE / NO 9.
Single (7"): released on Polydor, Feb'82 by
Polydor Records. Dist: Polygram, Polydor

MISPLACED IDEALS.
Album: released on RCA International, Sep'81

Cassette: released on RCA International,
Sep'81

ONLY LOVE.
Tracks: / Only love (special remix) / China
seize.
Single (7"): released on Legacy, Jan'86 Dist:
PRT

POLITICS OF EXISTING, THE.
Album: released on Legacy, Feb'86 Dist: PRT

Cassette: released on Legacy, Feb'86 Dist:
PRT

REFUGEES.
Single (7"): released on Legacy, Oct'85 Dist:
PRT

Single (12"): released on Legacy, Oct'85 Dist:
PRT

SAD CAFE.
Notes: Having gained a colossal following in the
USA, the English band Sad Cafe have repeated
this fantastic success on the European scene.
Seen here playing their own unique brand of
music at London's Victoria Palace, Sad Cafe
confirm their reputation for giving the ultimate in
'live' performances.   Type of
recording: Live. Total playing time: 52 minutes.
Video-cassette (VHS): released on VCL,
Sep'86 by Elecstar Records. Dist: PRT

Sade
Biographical Details: Sade's full name is
Helen Folasade Adu; she was born 16 January
1960, in Ibada, Nigeria. Her mother was British
and her father a Nigerian teacher at Ibadan
University. She came to the UK in 1963. She
was influenced by singers like Peggy Lee, Julie
London and Astrud Gilberto; She studied
fashion design but switched to music, joining a
Latin-funk group called Ariva in 1981, which
evolved into Pride and hired saxophonist Stuart
Matthewman (born in 1961), who recruited bassist Paul Denman (born in 1959); Pride changed
his name to Sade (name of both singer and
group, pronounced Sha-day, abbreviation of
Folasade), added pianist Andre Hale (born in
1963); other regulars include Matthewson's
brother Gordon. When Epic signed her in
January 1984 they wanted her solo, but she in-
sisted that the band was included. She appeared on cover of trendy mag **The Face** April
'84, was featured in **Vogue**, **Cosmopolitan**,
Elle; by the time she made the cover of **Time**

(6 April 1986) she was the queen of cool, and
two albums of laid-back, jazz influenced ca-
baret-style vocals had sold 12 million copies
worldwide.
[Donald Clarke, April 87]

DIAMOND LIFE.
Tracks: / Smooth operator / Your love is king /
Hang on to your love / When am I gonna make
a living / Frankie's first affair / Cherry pie / Sally
/ I will be your friend / Why can't we be together.
Notes: Digital Stereo.
Compact disc: released on Epic, Aug'84 by
CBS Records. Dist: CBS

Album: released on Epic, Jul'84 by CBS Records. Dist: CBS

Cassette: released on Epic, Jul'84 by CBS
Records. Dist: CBS

IS IT A CRIME.
Tracks: / Is it a crime / Punch drunk.
Single (7"): released on Epic, Dec'85 by CBS
Records. Dist: CBS

Single (12"): released on Epic, Dec'85 by CBS
Records. Dist: CBS

NEVER AS GOOD AS THE FIRST TIME.
Tracks: / Never as good as the first time.
Single (7"): released on Epic, Mar'86 by CBS
Records. Dist: CBS

Single (12"): released on Epic, Mar'86 by CBS
Records. Dist: CBS

PROMISE.
Tracks: / Is it a crime / Sweetest taboo / War of
the hearts / Jezebel / Mr. Wong / Never as good
as the first time / Feat / Tar baby / Mauree.
Compact disc: released on Epic, Jan'86 by
CBS Records. Dist: CBS

Album: released on Epic, Nov'85 by CBS Records. Dist: CBS

Cassette: released on Epic, Nov'85 by CBS
Records. Dist: CBS

WHEN AM I GOING TO MAKE A LIVING.
Single (7"): released on Epic, May'84 by CBS
Records. Dist: CBS

Single (12"): released on Epic, May'84 by CBS
Records. Dist: CBS

Sadie Nine
**KISS ME NOT HIM / YOU TAKE A
MORNING.**
Single (7"): released on Precious, Jan'82 by
Precious Records. Dist: CBS, Polygram

Sadista Sisters
RAG DOLL DUCHESS / FOETUS.
Single (7"): released on KD, May'82

Sadler, Sgt. Barry
BALLAD OF THE GREEN BERETS.
Tracks: / Ballad of the green berets / Maria
Elena (Los Indios Tabajaros).
Single (7"): released on Old Gold, Oct'86 by
Old Gold Records. Dist: Lightning, Jazz Music,
Spartan, Counterpoint

BALLADS OF THE GREEN BERETS.
Album: released on RCA International, Jul'84

Cassette: released on RCA International,
Jul'84

Single (7"): released on USA Import. '80

Sad Lovers and Giants
EPIC GARDEN MUSIC.
Album: released on Midnight Music, '82 by Midnight Music Records. Dist: Rough Trade Distribution, Cartel Distribution

FEEDING THE FLAME.
Album: released on Midnight Music, Nov'83 by
Midnight Music Records. Dist: Rough Trade
Distribution, Cartel Distribution

IN THE BREEZE.
Album: released on Midnight Chime, Dec'84

LOST IN A MOMENT.
Single (7"): released on Midnight Music, Nov'82 by Midnight Music Records. Dist: Rough Trade Distribution, Cartel Distribution

MAN OF STRAW / COWBOYS.
Single (7"): released on Midnight Music, Oct'83 by Midnight Music Records. Dist: Rough Trade Distribution, Cartel Distribution

Single (12"): released on Midnight Music, Oct'83 by Midnight Music Records. Dist: Rough Trade Distribution, Cartel Distribution

TOTAL SOUND.
Album: released on Midnight Music, Oct'86 by Midnight Music Records. Dist: Rough Trade Distribution, Cartel Distribution

Sadonians

DISAPPOINTMENTS (see also Clint Eastwood) (Sadonians & Clint Eastwood).
Single (12"): released on Freedom, Aug'80 by Logo Records. Dist: RCA, Discovery, Wellard, Chris

GOODBYE MY LOVE / GOOD LOVE.
Single (12"): released on Freedom, Feb'80 by Logo Records. Dist: RCA, Discovery, Wellard, Chris

Sad Society

CONTAMINATE.
Single (7"): released on X-Cert, 30 May'87

Safari Party

HOPE IN HELL.
Single (7"): released on Pure And Vain, Jun'85 Dist: Probe, Cartel

Saffrice

SUMMER DAYS / WINTER MORNING.
Single (12"): released on S&G, Mar'82 Dist: Pinnacle

Saffron

PHYSICAL CONTACT.
Tracks: / Physical contact / Physical contact (Instrumental).
Special: released on Bolts, Mar'86 by Bolts Records. Dist: PRT, Pinnacle

Safranski, Eddie

Three Kenton's Be Boppers groups 1947-50

Saga

BEHAVIOUR.
Album: released on Portrait, Sep'85 by CBS Records. Dist: CBS

Cassette: released on Portrait, Sep'85 by CBS Records. Dist: CBS

ON THE LOOSE / FRAMED.
Single (7"): released on Portrait, Jan'83 by CBS Records. Dist: CBS

SCRATCHING THE SURFACE / THE SOUND OF STRANGERS.
Single (7"): released on Portrait, Jan'84

Single (12"): released on Portrait, Jan'84

TAKE A CHANCE.
Tracks: / Take a chance / You and the night.
Single (7"): released on Portrait, Jan'86 by CBS Records. Dist: CBS

Single (12"): released on Portrait, Jan'86 by CBS Records. Dist: CBS

WIND HIM UP / AMNESIA.
Single (7"): released on Portrait, Mar'83 by CBS Records. Dist: CBS

Sager, Carole Bayer

EASY TO LOVE AGAIN / WILD AGAIN.
Single (7"): released on Epic, Nov'81 by CBS Records. Dist: CBS

TOO.
Album: released on Elektra, Sep'78 by WEA Records. Dist: WEA

Sahara

LOVE SO FINE.
Single (12"): released on Elite, May'85 Dist: PRT

Sahib, Sahib

ALL STAR SEXTETS.
Double Album:

Sahm, Doug

Biographical Details: Texas singer, songwriter, bandleader Doug Sahm was born 6 November 1942 in San Atonio. His garage band the Sir Douglas Quintet had hits in the 60's including 'She's about a mover'. He has moved on to roots music, bringing Tex-Mex, blues, country to his act; after a few years in San Francisco he relocated to Austin, Texas and was influenced in the 'outlaw' movement in country music there. [Donald Clarke, April 87]

DOUG SAHM & BAND (Sahm, Doug & Band).
Album: released on Edsel, Apr'85 by Demon Records. Dist: Pinnacle, Jazz Music, Projection

LIVE.
Tracks: / Turn on your lovelight / Stagger Lee / Things I used to do / Papa ain't salty / He don't love you like I love you / Next time you see me / Mr Pitiful / James Brown Medley: I'll go crazy / Think / Please please please / Night train.
Notes: Licensed from Charly International APS. (P) 1987 Charly Holdings Inc. (C) 1987 Charly Records Ltd.
Album: released on Topline, Apr'87 by Charly Records. Dist: Charly Distribution

Cassette: released on Topline, Apr'87 by Charly Records. Dist: Charly Distribution

SIR DOUGLAS - HIS FIRST RECORDING.
Album: released on Charly, Jan'81 by Charly Records. Dist: Charly, Cadillac

TEXAS ROAD RUNNER.
Album: released on Moonshine, May'86 Dist: Projection Distribution

Sahuleka, Daniel

VIVA LA LIBERTADE.
Single (7"): released on Polydor, Oct'82 by Polydor Records. Dist: Polygram, Polydor

Single (12"): released on Polydor, Oct'82 by Polydor Records. Dist: Polygram, Polydor

Saigon

DIVING THROUGH SAND.
Single (7"): released on Ryme Time, Nov'81 by Lismor Records. Dist: Lismor Distribution, Pinnacle

GOTHIC BOP (EP).
Single (7"): released on First Floor, May'84 by First Floor Records. Dist: Cartel

GREEN CARNATION / FALLS THE SHADOW.
Single (7"): released on Ryme Time, Nov'81 by Lismor Records. Dist: Lismor Distribution, Pinnacle

WHERE ARE THE ROSES / PARALLEL.
Single (7"): released on Ryme Time, May'81 by Lismor Records. Dist: Lismor Distribution, Pinnacle

Sailor

Biographical Details: Sailor was a keyboard-based pop quartet formed in 1974 by guitarist-vocalist George Kajanus (real name Georg Hultgren), a former member of Australian folk-rockers Eclection (which also included guitarist Trevor Lucas - later with Fairport Convention). Kajanus teamed with Phil Pickett for guitar-keyboard duo, but added Henry Marsh on keyboards, Grant Serpell on drums for unusual group with no bass or electric guitar (Kajanus played acoustic). After a lot of success with eclectic music, sometimes including accordian, etc. until punk took over. Pickett resurfaced as keyboardist and songwriter with **Culture Club**, co-wrote 'Karma Chameleon'. [Donald Clarke, April 87]

DRESSED FOR DROWNING.
Album: released on Caribou, Feb'81 by Epic Records. Dist: CBS

Cassette: released on Caribou, Feb'81 by Epic Records. Dist: CBS

Sailor's Horse

SAILOR'S HORSE, THE May Day: Minehead documentary of Somerset custom.
Cassette: released on Folktracks, Nov'79 by Folktracks Cassettes. Dist: Folktracks

Saint Andrew

PINBALL WIZARD.
Tracks: / Pinball wizard / Skye boat song, (The).
Single (7"): released on Dark Side Of The Haggis, Jul'86 Dist: Fast Forward, Cartel

Saint Andrews...

BRAND NEW SHIRT & TIE (Saint Augustines School Choir).
Single (7"): released on Stage One, Apr'81 by Stage One Records. Dist: Stage One Distribution

THANKS (Saint Andrews School Choir).
Tracks: / Thanks / Black diamonds and green valleys.
Notes: All proceeds to Aid International Foundation Charity
Single (7"): released on E.C.B.P., Apr'86 Dist: Stage One

Saint Austell Band

ST AUSTELL SALUTES GOFF RICHARDS.
Album: released on Polyphonic, Apr'82 by Polyphonic Records. Dist: Taylors

Cassette: released on Polyphonic, Apr'82 by Polyphonic Records. Dist: Taylors

Saint Benedicts...

CHILDREN OF THE WORLD (Saint Benedicts School (Kids Aid)).
Single (7"): released on Twink, Jan'87 Dist: Backs, Cartel, Pinnacle

Saint Brendan's Voyage

SAINT BRENDAN'S VOYAGE Various artists (Various Artists).
Cassette: released on Anvil, Jan'81 Dist: Anvil

Saint Christopher

CRYSTAL CLEAR.
Single (7"): released on Red Rhino, Mar'84 by Indies Records. Dist: Cartel Distribution

GO AHEAD, CRY.....
Single (7"): released on G&M, Nov'86 Dist: PRT

Saint Davids Cathedral

ST. DAVID'S CATHEDRAL CHOIR.
Album: released on Abbey, '79 by Abbey. Dist: PRT, Taylors, Gamut

Saint Elmo's Fire

SAINT ELMO'S FIRE Original film soundtrack.
Album: released on Atlantic, Oct'85 by WEA Records. Dist: WEA

Cassette: released on Atlantic, Oct'85 by WEA Records. Dist: WEA

Saint George's...

CHRISTMAS CAROLS FROM ST. GEORGE'S CHAPEL ABBEY. (Saint George's Chapel Choir).
Compact disc: released on Abbey, Nov'84 by Abbey. Dist: PRT, Taylors, Gamut

Saint James, Jon

FIRST IMPRESSION.
Album: released on Enigma, Nov'86 by Enigma Records. Dist: Rough Trade, Cartel, EMI

Saint James, Michael

FEEL MY LOVE.
Tracks: / Feel my love / Sad song.
Single (7"): released on WEA, Jan'86 by WEA Records. Dist: WEA

Single (12"): released on WEA, Jan'86 by WEA Records. Dist: WEA

Saint John's...

CHRISTMAS AT ST. JOHNS (Saint John's College, Cambridge).
Album: released on Argo, Oct'74 by Decca Records. Dist: Polygram

CHRISTMAS CAROLS (Saint John's College, Cambridge).
Compact disc: released on Chandos, '86 by Chandos Records. Dist: Harmonia Mundi, Taylors

HOSANNA (Saint John the Divine Cathedral Choir).
Album: released on Gramavision (USA), Jul'83 by Gramavison Records (USA). Dist: PRT, IMS, Polygram

ONE STAR / STAR OF BETHLEHEM (Saint John School & Fodens Ots Brass Band).
Single (7"): released on Rebound, Dec'83 by Rebound Records. Dist: Terry Blood Distribution

PSALMS OF CONSOLATION AND HOPE (Saint John's College, Cambridge).
Compact disc: released on Argo, Apr'79 by Decca Records. Dist: Polygram

QUEENS BIRTHDAY, (THE) (Saint John's School Choir / Band of the Grenadier Guards).
Tracks: / Queens birthday, The / Sparkling.
Single (7"): released on Columbia, Apr'86 by EMI Records. Dist: EMI

SAINT JOHNS RC CATHEDRAL PORTSMOUTH BOYS CHOIR (Saint Johns RC Cathedral Portsmouth Boys Choir).
Album: released on Abbey, Apr'77 by Abbey. Dist: PRT, Taylors, Gamut

WORLD OF (Saint John's College Choir).
Album: released on Decca, '74 by Decca Records. Dist: Polygram

WORLD OF XMAS VOL 2 (Saint John's College Choir, Cambridge).
Album: released on Decca, '71 by Decca Records. Dist: Polygram

Cassette: released on Decca, '71 by Decca Records. Dist: Polygram

Saint Joseph's...

BEAUTY OF MAORI SONG (Saint Joseph's Maori Girls Choir).
Album: released on Viking, Aug'79 Dist: Jetstar, Northumbrian Records, H.R. Taylor

Cassette: released on Viking, Aug'79 Dist: Jetstar, Northumbrian Records, H.R Taylor

HYMNS & SONGS FOR CHILDREN, VOL. 1 (Saint Joseph's School Choir, Colwyn Bay.).
Tracks: / Morning has broken / All creatures of our God and King / Dare to be a Daniel / Go tell it on the mountain / Lord of the Dance / Jesus loves me / Put your hand in the hand / Immortal, invisible, God only wise / Holy, holy, holy / Kumbaya / I think when I read / Seek ye first / Oh Jesus, I have promised / God make my life a little light.
Notes: Produced & directed by Gordon Lorenz
Album: released on Word, Jun'86 by Word Records. Dist: Word Distribution, CBS

Cassette: released on Word, Jun'86 by Word Records. Dist: Word Distribution, CBS

HYMNS & SONGS FOR CHILDREN-VOL.2 (Saint Joseph's School Choir).
Album: released on Word, Nov'86 by Word Records. Dist: Word Distribution, CBS

Cassette: released on Word, Nov'86 by Word Records. Dist: Word Distribution, CBS

MY BEST FRIEND (Saint Joseph's School Choir).
Single (7"): released on Weasel, Nov'85 by Weasel Records. Dist: Spartan

Saint Louis...

GERSHWIN IN THE MOVIES VOL.2 1951-1959 (Saint Louis Symphony Orchestra).
Tracks: / I'll build a stairway to paradise / Somebody loves me / An American in Paris / Someone to watch over me / 'S wonderful / Introduction / Porgy sings / Fugue / Ouragan / Bonjour free.
Notes: With Wilhelmina Fernandez. Orchestra directed by : Leonard Slatkin
Album: released on SPI Milan (France), Mar'87 Dist: Silva Screen

Cassette: released on SPI Milan (France), Mar'87 Dist: Silva Screen

GERSHWIN IN THE MOVIES VOL.1 1931-1945 (Saint Louis Symphony Orchestra).
Tracks: / Embraceable you / They all laughed / Love is here to stay / Strike up the band / Fascinating rhythm / But not for me / Rhapsody in blue / Man I love, The / Seconde rhapsodie.
Notes: With Wilhelmina Fernandez Orchestra directed by Leonard Slatkin.
Album: released on SPI Milan (France), Mar'87 Dist: Silva Screen

Cassette: released on SPI Milan (France), Mar'87 Dist: Silva Screen

GERSHWIN IN THE MOVIES 1/2(CD) (Saint Louis Symphony Orchestra).
Notes: With Wilhelmina Fernandez Orchestra led by Leonard Slatkin. Compilation of 'Gershwin in the Movies Vol.1 & 2' albums A 249/250(album) C 249/250(cassette)
Compact disc: released on Milan France, May'87

Saint Louis Blues

SAINT LOUIS BLUES Various artists (Various Artists).
Album: released on Jazz Live, '79

Saint Louis blues march

SAINT LOUIS BLUES MARCH Various artists (Various Artists).
Compact disc: by Polygram Records. Dist: Polygram

Saint Louise's...

SAINT LOUISE'S COLLEGE CHOIR, BELFAST (Saint Louise's College Choir, Belfast).
Album: released on Homespun(Ireland), Jun'85 by Outlet Records. Dist: Outlet

Cassette: released on Homespun(Ireland), Jun'85 by Outlet Records. Dist: Outlet

Saint Magnus...

CHOIR AND ORGAN OF ST. MAGNUS CATHEDRAL (Saint Magnus Cathedral Choir and Organ).
Album: released on Lismor, Nov'76 Dist: Projection, Lismor, Cadillac Music, H.R. Taylor, Outlet

Saint-Marie, Buffy

BEST OF BUFFY, THE.
Album: released on Vanguard (USA), Nov'84

SOLDIER BLUE / I'M GONNA BE A COUNTRY GIRL AGAIN.
Single (7"): released on Flashback, Jan'83 by PRT Records. Dist: PRT

SPOTLIGHT OF BUFFY SAINT-MARIE.
Double Album: released on PRT, Oct'81 by PRT Records. Dist: PRT

Double cassette: released on PRT, Oct'81 by PRT Records. Dist: PRT

Saint Martin...
SERENADE (Saint Martin-In-The-Field/Tommy Reilly).
Notes: Full details see under REILLY, Tommy

Saint Mary....
AVE MARIE (Saint Mary & Saint Anne's Choir, Abbots Bromley).
Album: released on Alpha, Oct'81 by Alpha Records. Dist: H.R. Taylor, Gamut

Cassette: released on Alpha, Oct'81 by Alpha Records. Dist: H.R. Taylor, Gamut

POPULAR CHRISTMAS CAROLS (Saint Mary's Choir, Warwick).
Album: released on Abbey, Nov'83 by Abbey. Dist: PRT, Taylors, Gamut

Cassette: released on Abbey, Nov'83 by Abbey. Dist: PRT, Taylors, Gamut

Saint Mary, Redcliffe
CHANGE RINGING.
Album: released on Saydisc, Jan'81 by Saydisc Records. Dist: Essex, Harmonia Mundi, Roots, H.R. Taylor, Jazz Music, Swift, Projection, Gamut

Cassette: released on Saydisc, Jan'81 by Saydisc Records. Dist: Essex, Harmonia Mundi, Roots, H.R. Taylor, Jazz Music, Swift, Projection, Gamut

Saint Michael-Le-Belfry
MY SPIRIT WILL COME.
Tracks: / This man Jesus / Create in us / My spirit will come / Do what is good / Breathe on me / Holy Lord / Hosanna / Siya hamba / Seeing you daily with wonders and signs / I will build / In your name / Jesus you're with me / Keep movin' on / Shalom.
Notes: Songs from the choir and instrumentalists of St.Michael-Le-Belfry, York.
Album: released on Word, Mar'87 by Word Records. Dist: Word Distribution, CBS

Cassette: released on Word, Mar'87 by Word Records. Dist: Word Distribution, CBS

Saint Paul's...
CAROLLING AT CHRISTMAS (Saint Paul's Cathedral Choir).
Album: released on Ampro, Nov'79

CHRISTMAS MUSIC (Saint Paul's Cathedral Choir).
Album: released on Philips, Nov'74 Dist: IMS-Polygram

LET IT BE / SING A SONG (Saint Paul's Boys Choir).
Album: released on Mean, Nov'81 by Mean Records. Dist: Spartan

NYMPHS AND SHEPHERDS / O FOR THE WINGS OF A DOVE (Saint Paul's Cathedral Choir).
Single (7"): released on Pip, Nov'82 by PRT Records. Dist: PRT

SILENT NIGHT (Saint Paul's Cathedral Choir).
Single (7"): released on Charisma, Nov'80 by Virgin Records. Dist: EMI

Saint Richard's....
SING TO GOD (Saint Richard's with Saint Andrew's Junior School Choir).
Album: released on Sacred, May'82 by Word Records.

Cassette: released on Sacred, May'82 by Word Records.

Saints
ALL FOOLS DAY.
Album: released on Polydor, Oct'86 by Polydor Records. Dist: Polygram, Polydor

Cassette: released on Polydor, Oct'86 by Polydor Records. Dist: Polygram, Polydor

ALWAYS / IN THE MIRROR.
Single (7"): released on New Rose, Jun'82 Dist: Rough Trade, Cartel

BEST OF SAINTS, THE.
Album: released on Razor, Oct'86 by Razor. Dist: Pinnacle

FOLLOW THE LEADER.
Single (7"): released on Flicknife, Feb'83 by

Flicknife Records. Dist: Spartan

GHOST SHIPS.
Single (7"): released on New Rose, Mar'85 Dist: Rough Trade, Cartel

IMAGINATION.
Single (7"): released on New Rose, Dec'84 Dist: Rough Trade, Cartel

JUST LIKE FIREWOULD.
Tracks: / Just like firewould / East is east / Casablanca.
Single (7"): released on Polydor, Mar'87 by Polydor Records. Dist: Polygram, Polydor

Single (12"): released on Polydor, Mar'87 by Polydor Records. Dist: Polygram, Polydor

LIVE IN A MUD HUT.
Album: released on New Rose, May'85 Dist: Rough Trade, Cartel

Compact disc: released on New Rose, May'85 Dist: Rough Trade, Cartel

PARALYTIC TONIGHT DUBLIN TOMORROW.
Single (7"): released on New Rose, Jun'82 Dist: Rough Trade, Cartel

TEMPLE OF THE LORD, THE.
Tracks: / Temple of the Lord, The / Celtic ballad / How to avoid disaster".
Notes: Third track on 12" version only, NOT on 7".
Single (7"): released on Polydor, Oct'86 by Polydor Records. Dist: Polygram, Polydor

Single (12"): released on Polydor, Oct'86 by Polydor Records. Dist: Polygram, Polydor

Saint Vitus
HALLOWS VICTIM.
Album: released on SST, Apr'86 by SST Records. Dist: Pinnacle

SAINT VITUS.
Album: released on SST, Jun'85 by SST Records. Dist: Pinnacle

THIRST & MISERABLE.
Album: released on SST, Aug'87 by SST Records. Dist: Pinnacle

THIRSTY AND MISERABLE.
Extended-play record: released on SST, Jul'87 by SST Records. Dist: Pinnacle

WALKING DEAD, THE.
Single (12"): released on SST, Nov'85 by SST Records. Dist: Pinnacle

Saint Winifred's...
20 ALL TIME CHILDRENS FAVOURITES H (Saint Winifred's School Choir).
Album: released on MFP, Oct'85 by EMI Records. Dist: EMI

Cassette: released on MFP, Oct'85 by EMI Records. Dist: EMI

AND THE CHILDREN SING (Saint Winifred's School Choir).
Album: released on MFP, Jan'80 by EMI Records. Dist: EMI

Cassette: released on MFP, Jan'80 by EMI Records. Dist: EMI

CHILDRENS' PARTY TIME (Saint Winifred's School Choir).
Tracks: / If you're happy and you know it / Farmer's in his den, (The) / Oranges and lemons / Here we go round the muberry bush / Old MacDonald had a farm / London Bridge / Dancing Queen / Brown girl in the ring / Yellow submarine / Rivers of Babylon / Waterloo / Simon says / Matchstick men and matchstick cats and dogs / Bright eyes / When you wish upon a star.
Cassette: released on Hour Of Pleasure, '86 by Music For Pleasure Records. Dist: EMI

CHRISTMAS FOR EVERYONE (Saint Winifred's School Choir).
Album: released on MFP (EMI), Dec'82 by EMI Records. Dist: EMI

Cassette: released on MFP (EMI), Dec'82 by EMI Records. Dist: EMI

IT'S A SMALL WORLD (Saint Winifred's School Choir).
Album: released on Music for Pleasure, Nov'83 by EMI Records. Dist: MFP Distribution

Cassette: released on Music for Pleasure, Nov'83 by EMI Records. Dist: MFP Distribution

MY VERY OWN PARTY REC (Saint Winifred's School Choir).
Album: released on MFP, Dec'80 by EMI Records. Dist: EMI

Cassette: released on MFP, Dec'80 by EMI Records. Dist: EMI

Sainty, Russ
50'S HITS RIGHT HERE ON 45.
Single (7"): released on Russ, Nov'83 Dist: Spartan Distribution

Sakamoto, Kyu
SUKIYAKI.
Single (7"): released on USA Import, '80

Sakamoto, Riuichi
B-2 UNIT.
Album: released on Island, Mar'81 by Island Records. Dist: Polygram

MERRY CHRISTMAS MR. LAWRENCE.
Album: released on Virgin, Oct'83 by Virgin Records. Dist: EMI, Virgin Distribution

Cassette: released on Virgin, Oct'83 by Virgin Records. Dist: EMI, Virgin Distribution

ONCE IN A LIFETIME.
Single (7"): released on Epic, Oct'82 by CBS Records. Dist: CBS

WARHEAD.
Single (7"): released on Island, Aug'81 by Island Records. Dist: Polygram

Single (12"): released on Island, Aug'81 by Island Records. Dist: Polygram

Sakamoto, Ryuichi
FIELD WORK (Sakamoto, Ryuichi/Thomas Dolby).
Tracks: / Field work / Exhibition".
Notes: Third track on 12" version only, NOT on 7".
Single (12"): released on 10, Jan'86 by 10 Records. Dist: Virgin, EMI

Single (7"): released on 10, Jan'86 by 10 Records. Dist: Virgin, EMI

ILLUSTRATED MUSICAL ENCYCLOPEDIA.
Tracks: / Field work / Etude / Paradise lost / M.A.Y. in the backyard / Steppin' into Asia / Tibetan dance / Zen-gun / In a forest of feathers.
Compact disc: released on 10, Jul'87 by 10 Records. Dist: Virgin, EMI

Sakata, Akira
DANCE (Sakata, Akira Trio).
Album: released on Enja (Germany), Apr'82 by Enja Records (W.Germany). Dist: Cadillac Music

Sakhile
NEW LIFE.
Album: released on Jive Africa, Jun'84 by Zomba Records. Dist: RCA

Cassette: released on Jive Africa, Jun'84 by Zomba Records. Dist: RCA

SAKHILE.
Single (7"): released on Jive, Sep'83 by Zomba Records. Dist: RCA, PRT, CBS

Single (12"): released on Jive, Sep'83 by Zomba Records. Dist: RCA, PRT, CBS

Saki
SAKI 1 By H.H. Munro (Burden, Hugh).
Notes: Includes: Sredni Vashtar, The Story Teller and Morivera.
Cassette: released on Talking Tape Company, Sep'84 by Talking Tape Company Records.

SAKI 2 By H.H. Munro (Burden, Hugh).
Notes: Includes: The She Wolf, The Open Window and Music On The Hill.
Cassette: released on Talking Tape Company, '84 by Talking Tape Company Records.

SAKI 3 By H.H. Munro (Burden, Hugh).
Notes: Includes: Mrs Packletide's Daughter and Story of St. Vespaluus.
Cassette: released on Talking Tape Company, '84 by Talking Tape Company Records.

SAKI 4 By H.H. Munro (Burden, Hugh).
Notes: Includes: Tobermoray and The Mettucklume Method.
Cassette: released on Talking Tape Company, '84 by Talking Tape Company Records.

SAKI 5 By H.H. Munro (Burden, Hugh).
Notes: Includes: The Hounds of Fate and The Mouse.
Cassette: released on Talking Tape Company, '84 by Talking Tape Company Records.

SAKI 6 By H.H. Munro (Burden, Hugh).
Notes: Includes: The Brogue, Laura and The Lumber Room.
Cassette: released on Talking Tape Company, '84 by Talking Tape Company Records.

Sakuma, Masahide
LISA.
Album: released on Pan East, Jul'86 by L.O.E. Records. Dist: Nine Mile, PRT, Cartel

Cassette: released on Pan East, Jul'86 by L.O.E. Records. Dist: Nine Mile, PRT, Cartel

Compact disc: released on Pan East, Jul'86 by L.O.E. Records. Dist: Nine Mile, PRT, Cartel

Salad Days
SALAD DAYS Revival London cast (Revival London Cast).
Album: released on That's Entertainment, Jul'82 by That's Entertainment Records. Dist: Pinnacle, PRT

Cassette: released on That's Entertainment, Jul'82 by That's Entertainment Records. Dist: Pinnacle, PRT

Salant, Norman
SAX TALK.
Single (12"): released on C&D, Feb'85 by Phonogram Records. Dist: Polygram

Salazar
1-2-3/LET'S HANG ON.
Single (7"): released on Cricket International, Oct'82 by Cricket International Records. Dist: Stage One

Single (12"): released on Cricket International, Oct'82 by Cricket International Records. Dist: Stage One

Salem 66
ACROSS THE SEA.
Tracks: / Across the sea.
Single (7"): released on Homestead, Feb'86 Dist: Rough Trade, Cartel, Shigaku

FREQUENCY AND URGENCY.
Album: released on Homestead, Apr'87 Dist: Rough Trade, Cartel, Shigaku

Salem Foundation
SAY YOU'RE READY.
Tracks: / Love games / Say you're ready.
Single (12"): released on Solid Music, Sep'86 by Solid Music Records. Dist: Jetstar

Salford Jets
PAIN IN MY HEART.
Single (7"): released on KA, Mar'83

Single (12"): released on KA, Mar'83

Salim, Abdel Gadir
SONGS FROM KORDOFAN.
Album: released on World Circuit, Apr'87 by Taurus Records. Dist: Sterns/Triple Earth Distribution

Salisbury Cathedral
CAROLS FROM SALISBURY.
Album: released on Meridian, Aug'83 Dist: Harmonia Mundi Distributors

CHOIR OF....
Album: released on Saga, Sep'75 Dist: Harmonia Mundi Distributors

MUSIC FROM.
Album: released on BBC, Jul'78 by BBC Records & Tapes. Dist: EMI, PRT

Cassette: released on BBC, '79 by BBC Records & Tapes. Dist: EMI, PRT

Salman, Shukur
OUD RECITAL.
Album: released on Headline, Aug'77 by Creole Records. Dist: PRT

Salmontails
SALMONTAILS.
Album: released on Oblivion, Jan'85 Dist: Projection

Salonisti, I
CAFE VICTORIA.
Tracks: / Los mareados / Poema valseado / Recuerdo / Coral / Romance de barrio / Uno / Payadora / Flores negras / Severina / Flor de lino / Contrabajissimo.
Compact disc: released on Harmonia Mundi (France), Jul'86 Dist: Harmonia Mundi

Salon Music
HUNTING ON PARIS.
Single (7"): released on Mobile Suit Corporation, Apr'82 Dist: Phonogram Distribution, Polygram Distribution

Salonorchester Colln

NOUVEAU SALON, (LE).
Tracks: / Frau Luna (Overture from -) / Murmelindes luftchen / Was eine frau in fruhling traumt / Puppchen, du bist mein augenstern / Avant de mourir / Berliner luft / Linden march / In einer kleinen Konditorei / Cafehaus / Alle englein lachen / Spanish march / Geburtstagsstandchen / Da capo.
Compact disc: released on Harmonia Mundi (France), Jul'86 Dist: Harmonia Mundi

Sal Paradise

MIRACLE.
Single (7"): released on Audiotrax, Nov'84 by Audiotrax. Dist: PRT

SHIMMER.
Album: released on Arista, Mar'84 by Arista Records. Dist: RCA

Cassette: released on Arista, Mar'84 by Arista Records. Dist: RCA

Salsaya Big Band

LIVE IN LUXOR.
Album: released on Timeless, Oct'86

Salsoul Orchestra

CHRISTMAS TIME.
Single (7"): released on Epic, Nov'81 by CBS Records. Dist: CBS

Single (12"): released on Epic, Nov'81 by CBS Records. Dist: CBS

OOH I LOVE IT.
Single (12"): released on Salsoul, Mar'83

Salt

BEYOND A SONG.
Album: released on Pilgrim, '82 by Pilgrim Records. Dist: Rough Trade, Cartel

Salten, Felix

BAMBI.
Notes: Full details see under SALTEN, Felix.
Cassette: released on Tellastory, Dec'86 by Bartlett Bliss Productions. Dist: PRT Distribution, Hayward Promotions Distribution, H.R. Taylor Distribution

Cassette: released on Tellastory, Mar'84 by Bartlett Bliss Productions. Dist: PRT Distribution, Hayward Promotions Distribution, H.R. Taylor Distribution

Salt 'N' Pepa

HOT COOL VICIOUS.
Tracks: / Beauty and the beat / Tramp / I'll take your man / It's all right / Chick on the side / I desire / Showstopper, The / My mike sounds nice.
Album: released on Champion, Jun'87 by Champion Records. Dist: RCA

Cassette: released on Champion, Jun'87 by Champion Records. Dist: RCA

Compact disc: released on Champion, Jun'87 by Champion Records. Dist: RCA

Album: released on Champion, Jul'87 by Champion Records. Dist: RCA

Cassette: released on Champion, Jul'87 by Champion Records. Dist: RCA

MY MIKE SOUNDS NICE.
Single (7"): released on Champion, Feb'87 by Champion Records. Dist: RCA

TRAMP (REMIX).
Tracks: / Tramp (remix) / Push it / Idle chatter.
Single (7"): released on Champion, Jul'87 by Champion Records. Dist: RCA

Single (12"): released on Champion, Jul'87 by Champion Records. Dist: RCA

Salty Dog

OLYMPIC CITY 1992.
Tracks: / Olympic city 1992 / Long distance runner.
Single (7"): released on Sub Zero, May'86 Dist: PRT Distribution

Salu Salu Band

EFRE EOPAS STRING BANDS.
Album: released on Viking, Jan'77 Dist: Harmonia Mundi Distributors

Salute To..

SALUTE TO PERCY GRAINGER various (Various Artists).
Album: released on Decca, '69 by Decca Records. Dist: Polygram

SALUTE TO THE BEE GEES (Various Artists).
Cassette: released on AIM (Budget Cassettes), Feb'83

Saluzzi, Dino

KULTRUM.
Album: released on ECM (Germany), Sep'83 by ECM Records. Dist: IMS, Polygram, Virgin through EMI

ONCE UPON A TIME - FAR AWAY IN THE SOUTH.
Tracks: / Jose, Valeria and Matias / And the Father said... / Revelation, (The) / Silence / ...And he loved his brother, till the end / Far away in the south... / We are the children.
Notes: Dino Saluzzi - bandoneon Palle Mikkelborg - trumpet, flugelhorn Charlie Haden - bass Pierre Favre - percussion
Album: released on ECM (Germany), Apr'86 by ECM Records. Dist: IMS, Polygram, Virgin through EMI

Compact disc: released on ECM (Germany), Apr'86 by ECM Records. Dist: IMS, Polygram, Virgin through EMI

Salvador, Sal

BOO BOO BE DOOP.
Album: released on Affinity, Jul'81 by Charly Records. Dist: Charly, Cadillac

IN OUR OWN SWEET WAY.
Album: released on Stash, Apr'83 Dist: Swift Distribution, Jazz Music Distribution, Jazz Horizons Distribution, Celtic Music Distribution, Cadillac, JSU Distribution, Zodiac Distribution

Salvation

GIRLSCHOOL.
Single (7"): released on Merciful Release, Sep'83 by Sisterhood Records. Dist: WEA

Single (12"): released on Merciful Release, Sep'83 by Sisterhood Records. Dist: WEA

JESSICA'S CRIME.
Tracks: / Jessica's crime.
Single (7"): released on Batfish, Feb'86 Dist: Red Rhino, Cartel

Single (12"): released on Batfish, Feb'86 Dist: Red Rhino, Cartel

SEEK.
Tracks: / Seek.
Single (7"): released on Ediesta, Nov'86 by Ediesta Records. Dist: Red Rhino, Cartel

Single (12"): released on Ediesta, Nov'86 by Ediesta Records. Dist: Red Rhino, Cartel

Salvation Army

CHRISTMAS WITH THE SALVATION ARMY INTERNATIONAL STAFF BAND (Salvation Army International Staff Band, (The)).
Tracks: / O come all ye faithful / We three kings / While shepherds watched their flocks / Away in a manger.
Notes: Also featuring the Internationall Staff Songsters and the Croydon Singing Company.
Album: released on Word, Oct'86 by Word Records. Dist: Word Distribution, CBS

Cassette: released on Word, Oct'86 by Word Records. Dist: Word Distribution, CBS

PEACE IN OUR TIME (Salvation Army Band).
Album: released on Word, May'85 by Word Records. Dist: Word Distribution, CBS

Cassette: released on Word, May'85 by Word Records. Dist: Word Distribution, CBS

Salvation Sunday

COLD GREY EYES.
Tracks: / Cold grey eyes / Torn to pieces* / Cold to the touch* / Measure of the man*.
Notes: Tracks vary between versions.
Single (7"): released on Polydor, Sep'86 by Polydor Records. Dist: Polygram, Polydor

Single (12"): released on Polydor, Sep'86 by Polydor Records. Dist: Polygram, Polydor

Double-pack single: released on Polydor, Sep'86 by Polydor Records. Dist: Polygram, Polydor

COME TO YOUR SENSES.
Single (7"): released on Polydor, Aug'87 by Polydor Records. Dist: Polygram, Polydor

Single (12"): released on Polydor, Aug'87 by Polydor Records. Dist: Polygram, Polydor

HEART IN MOTION.
Tracks: / Heart in motion / Heartbreaking man (demo).
Single (7"): released on Polydor, May'87 by Polydor Records. Dist: Polygram, Polydor

Salvatore Cutungo

INNAMORATI.
Single (7"): released on Sonet, Jun'82 by Sonet Records. Dist: PRT

Salvetti, Tocko

ISLE OF CAPRI.
Single (7"): released on Young Blood, Aug'84 by Young Blood Records. Dist: Pinnacle

Salvo, Joe

LIFE COULD BE BETTER.
Single (7"): released on Towerbell, Aug'84 by Towerbell Records. Dist: EMI

Sam Brothers 5

SAM BROTHERS 5.
Album: released on Arhoolie, May'81 by Arhoolie Records. Dist: Projection, Topic, Jazz Music, Swift, Roots

Sam & Dave

Biographical Details: Soul vocal duo Sam & Dave were Sam Moore, born in 1935 in Miami, Florida, and Dave Prater, born in 1937 in Ocilla, Georgia; they got together onstage in Miami in 1958 and audience response convinced them to team up, but they had no hits during a period on Roulette. They signed with Atlantic in 1965, and Jerry Wexler sent them to Stax to record songs by Isaac Hayes and David Porter with the Memphis Horns, and some of the best loved hits of the soul era resulted. [Donald Clarke, April 87]

18 GREATEST HITS.
Album: released on Masters (Holland), Aug'87. Estim retail price in Sep'87 was £2.99.

Cassette: released on Masters (Holland), Aug'87. Estim retail price in Sep'87 was £2.99.

CAN'T STAND UP FOR FALLING DOWN.
Album: released on Edsel, May'84 by Demon Records. Dist: Pinnacle, Jazz Music, Projection

GREATEST HITS:SAM & DAVE.
Tracks: / Soul man / Summertime / You don't know what you mean to me / When something is wrong with my baby / You send me / Hold on I'm coming / Wonderful world / Said I wouldn't tell anybody / Cupid / I thank you / Soul sister brown sugar / Dock of the bay / You got me hummin' / Don't pull your love out on me baby / Soothe me / Gimme some lovin' / Bring it on home / Another Saturday night / You don't know like I know / Can't you find another way of doing it baby.
Album: released on Showcase, Apr'86 Dist: Counterpoint

Cassette: released on Showcase, Apr'86 Dist: Counterpoint

Compact disc: released on MCS Look Back, Jul'87

HOLD ON, I'M COMING.
Single (7"): released on Atlantic, '80 by WEA Records. Dist: WEA

Single (7"): released on Old Gold, Jan'85 by Old Gold Records. Dist: Lightning, Jazz Music, Spartan, Counterpoint

HOLD ON I'M COMING.
Album: released on Platinum (W.Germany), Nov'85 Dist: Mainline

Cassette: released on Platinum (W.Germany), Nov'85 Dist: Mainline

SAM & DAVE MEDLEY-SOUL REVIEW.
Single (7"): released on Polydor, Nov'85 by Polydor Records. Dist: Polygram, Polydor

Single (12"): released on Polydor, Nov'85 by Polydor Records. Dist: Polygram, Polydor

SAM & DAVE, THE BEST OF.
Album: released on Atlantic, Apr'82 by WEA Records. Dist: WEA

Compact disc: released on Atlantic, Jul'87 by WEA Records. Dist: WEA

SOUL MAN.
Single (12"): released on Perfect, May'87

SOUL SISTER.
Album: released on Platinum (W.Germany), Oct'85 Dist: Mainline

Cassette: released on Platinum (W.Germany), Oct'85 Dist: Mainline

SWEET SOUL MUSIC.
Tracks: / Hold on I'm comin' / 634-5789 / Respect / Funky street / How sweet it is / I thank you / Soul sister brown sugar / I'll be doggone / Satisfaction / Land of 1000 dances / Funky broadway / Sweet soul music.
Album: released on Topline, Feb'87 by Charly Records. Dist: Charly Distribution

Cassette: released on Topline, Feb'87 by Charly Records. Dist: Charly Distribution

WONDERFUL WORLD.
Tracks: / Soul man / Hold on I'm coming / I thank you / Soothe me / Said I wouldn't tell nobody / You don't know like I know / Soul sister (you're brown sugar) / Can't you find another way of doing it / You got me hummin' / Don't pull your love / When something is wrong with my baby / You don't know what you mean to me / Dock of the bay / Another saturday night / What a wonderful world / You send me.
Notes: Licensed from Charly International APS. This CD (P) 1987 Charly Holdings Inc. (C) 1987 Charly Records Ltd.
Compact disc: released on Topline, May'87 by Charly Records. Dist: Charly Distribution

Same

DOWNTOWN.
Single (7"): released on Unlikely, Sep'82

Samhain

NOVEMBER-COMING-FIRE.
Tracks: / Diabolos '88 / In my grip / Mother of mercy / Birthright / To walk the night / Let the day begin / Halloween II / November's fire / Kiss of steel / Unbridled / Human pony girl.
Notes: (P) 1985 O.S.R. made by Caroline Records Inc./Plan 9 Records. A Revolver Records release.
Album: released on Revolver, Aug'86 by Revolver Records. Dist: Revolver, Cartel

Sam, Jeff

DON'T ROCK THE THING SO.
Tracks: / Don't rock the thing so / Body beat (Peter King).
Single (12"): released on Blackbeat, Aug'86 Dist: Jetstar

Sammes, Mike Singers

DOUBLE TAKE, VOLUME 1 - LATE NITE VINYL.
Tracks: / Sam's song / Spread a little happiness / It's been a long, long time / Hope our love lasts / Nevertheless / Strollin' / I've heard that song before / I don't want to walk without you / Always / Sweetest sounds, (The) / Last of the summer wine, (The) / You are my heart's delight / I've told you every little star / All alone / I dream of brownie / Magic world of yesterday, (The) / Feelings / Pieds-en l'air / Begin the beguine / How deep is your love / Tea for two / In the bleak midwinter / Long ago (And far away) / Keep the home fires burning.
Double Album: released on Late Nite Vinyl, Oct'86 by Sammes, Mike Records. Dist: Pinnacle, Taylors

Cassette: released on Late Nite Extra, Oct'86

DOUBLE TAKE - VOLUME 2 - LATE NITE VINYL.
Tracks: / Just for you / I'm always chasing rainbows / Gymnopedie / With you I'm born again / We'll meet again / I'm comin' home / Remember / Mayfair Ladies Quartet, (The) / It had to be you / Summer knows, The / If you were the only girl in the world / I won't last a day without you / So in love with you / So in love with you / Great gnome robbery, (The) / Humming bird / Lest we forget / Why do I love you? / Laughter in the rain / All the things you are / You and I / Very thought of you, (The) / Boy from...,(The) / Sad sweet dreamer / Ballad of the Mary Rose, (The) / As time goes by / Put a little love away / He was beautiful (Cavatina) / Once in a while / Ill wind / Not just for a moment / What'll I do? / Ta-ra.
Double Album: released on Late Nite Vinyl, Oct'86 by Sammes, Mike Records. Dist: Pinnacle, Taylors

Cassette: released on Late Nite Extra, Oct'86

JUST FOR YOU.
Tracks: / Sam's song / Just for you / How deep is your love? / I'm always chasing rainbows / Gymnopedie / Sad sweet dreamer / Boy from..., The / Spread a little happiness / He was beautiful (Cavatina) / I don't want to walk without you / Always / With you I'm born again / In the bleak midwinter / Sweetest sounds, The / Long ago and far away / Why do I love you? / Not for just a moment / Feelings / It's been a long, long time / Pieds-en-L'air.
Compact disc: released on LNV Records, Sep'87

ROYAL WEDDING WALTZ.
Single (7"): released on President, Apr'81 by President Records. Dist: Taylors, Spartan

Sample, Joe

CARMEL.
Compact disc: released on MCA, Apr'87 by MCA Records. Dist: Polygram, MCA

Double cassette: released on MCA, Oct'83 by MCA Records. Dist: Polygram, MCA

FANCY DANCE.
Tracks: / Childrens song / Fancy dance / All the lonely years / Another blues / Svenska flicka / Old town.
Compact disc: released on Sonet, Oct'86 by Sonet Records. Dist: PRT

Album: released on Sonet, Jan'79 by Sonet Records. Dist: PRT

HUNTER, THE.
Album: released on MCA, Mar'83 by MCA Records. Dist: Polygram, MCA

Cassette: released on MCA, Mar'83 by MCA Records. Dist: Polygram, MCA

OASIS.
Compact disc: released on MCA, Mar'86 by

MCA Records. Dist: Polygram, MCA

Album: released on MCA, Sep'85 by MCA Records. Dist: Polygram, MCA

Cassette: released on MCA, Sep'85 by MCA Records. Dist: Polygram, MCA

RAINBOW SEEKER.
Tracks: / Rainbow seeker / In all my wildest dreams / There are many stops along the way / Melodies of love / Fly with wings of love / As long as it lasts / Islands in the rain / Together we'll find a way.
Notes: Produced by Crusaders Productions, Stix Hooper, Joe Sample & Wilton Felder.
Album: released on MCA, Aug'81 by MCA Records. Dist: Polygram, MCA

Cassette: released on MCA, Aug'81 by MCA Records. Dist: Polygram, MCA

Compact disc: released on MCA, Jul'87 by MCA Records. Dist: Polygram, MCA

ROLES.
Tracks: / Woman you're drivin' me mad / Gifted, The / Friends and lovers / Ego mania mambo / Fortune hunter / Ship of fools / Passionist.
Album: released on MCA, Jun'87 by MCA Records. Dist: Polygram, MCA

Cassette: released on MCA, Jun'87 by MCA Records. Dist: Polygram, MCA

Compact disc: released on MCA, Jun'87 by MCA Records. Dist: Polygram, MCA

ROSES.
Album: released on MCA, Jun'87 by MCA Records. Dist: Polygram, MCA

Album: released on MCA, Jun'87 by MCA Records. Dist: Polygram, MCA

SWING STREET CAFE (Sample, Joe & David T.Walker).
Tracks: / Hallelujah, I love her so / Rockhouse / Honest I do / Next time U see me / Woke up this morning / C.C. rider / Honky tonk / After hours.
Album: released on MCA, Aug'86 by MCA Records. Dist: Polygram, MCA

Cassette: released on MCA, Aug'86 by MCA Records. Dist: Polygram, MCA

Compact disc: released on MCA, Jul'87 by MCA Records. Dist: Polygram, MCA

VOICES IN THE RAIN.
Album: released on MCA, '83 by MCA Records. Dist: Polygram, MCA

Cassette: released on MCA, '83 by MCA Records. Dist: Polygram, MCA

Sample Of Blue Notes

SAMPLE OF BLUE NOTES, A Various Artists (Various Artists).
Tracks: / Blowin' the blues away / Blue riff / Sermon, The / Minor's holiday / I guess I'll hang my tears out to dry / Round midnight / Calling all cats / Eye of the hurricane / Love for sale / Dig dis / Midnight blue / Sidewinder, The.
Compact disc: released on Blue Note, Sep'87 by EMI Records. Dist: EMI

Compact disc: released on Blue Note, Sep'87 by EMI Records. Dist: EMI

Album: released on Blue Note, Sep'87 by EMI Records. Dist: EMI

Cassette: released on Blue Note, Sep'87 by EMI Records. Dist: EMI

Sampler..

SAMPLER 82 (Various Artists).
Compact disc: released on Windham Hill (Germany), '86

SAMPLER 84 various artists (Various Artists).
Album: released on Windham Hill (Germany), Dec'84

Cassette: released on Windham Hill (Germany), Dec'84

SAMPLER 86 MCA Master series (Various Artists).
Tracks: / Scrumpy cider / Month of seasons, A / Smiles and smiles to go / Perfect peace / Coco loco / Seventeenth summer / Grant's corner / Time gone by / Cycles / Unfolding.
Album: released on MCA, Jul'87 by MCA Records. Dist: Polygram, MCA

Cassette: released on MCA, Jul'87 by MCA Records. Dist: Polygram, MCA

Compact disc: released on MCA, Jul'87 by MCA Records. Dist: Polygram, MCA

Sampson, Colin

ONLY YOU.
Album: released on Glory Gold, Nov'86 Dist: Jetstar

Sampson, Deryck

BOOGIE EXPRESS.
Album: released on Harlequin, Sep'84 by Harlequin Records. Dist: Swift, Jazz Music, Wellard, Chris, IRS, Taylor, H.R.

Sampson, Edgar

Biographical Details: Edgar Samson (1907-73) played violin and saxophones; he also wrote some of the biggest hits of the Swing Era: he played with Duke Ellington in 1927, Fletcher Henderson 1931-33, Chick Webb 1933-37; he wrote 'Stompin' at the Savoy", Don't be that way', 'Blue Minor', 'If dreams come true', 'Blue Lou', 'Lullaby in rhythm' 1934-38, mostly for Webb, later big hits for Benny Goodman. He led his own band 1949-51, played with Tito Puente and other Latin bands; led his own combos in the 1960's.
[Donald Clarke, April 87]

SWING SOFTLY SWEET SAMPSON.
Album: released on Jasmine, Jun'83 by Jasmine Records. Dist: Counterpoint, Lugtons, Taylor, H.R., Wellard, Chris, Swift, Cadillac

Samson

ARE YOU READY.
Single (7"): released on Polydor, Feb'84 by Polydor Records. Dist: Polygram, Polydor

Single (12"): released on Polydor, Feb'84 by Polydor Records. Dist: Polygram. Polydor

Picture disc single: released on Polydor, Feb'84 by Polydor Records. Dist: Polygram, Polydor

FIGHT GOES ON.
Single (7"): released on Polydor, Apr'84 by Polydor Records. Dist: Polygram, Polydor

Single (12"): released on Polydor, Apr'84 by Polydor Records. Dist: Polygram. Polydor

HEAD TACTICS (Samson (featuring Bruce Dickinson)).
Tracks: / Vice versa / Earth mother / Losing my grip / Take it like a man / Once bitten / Go to hell / Hard times / Nice girl / Too close to rock / Walking out on you.
Notes: Paul Samson originally formed Samson in early '78 with Chris Aylmer on bass, Clive Burr on drums and Paul himself on guitar and vocals. At the end of that year, Clive left the band, later to join Iron Maiden, and was replaced by the mysterious masked character, Thunderstick. A debut album, 'Survivors', was released in October '79. Deciding that more vocal power was needed, Paul enlisted young vocalist Paul Dickinson, at the time a member of the London rock band The Shots. During the next couple of years, with the line-up of Dickinson, Samson, Aylmer and Thunderstick, the band were at the forefront of the so-called New Wave of British Heavy Metal, along with Iron Maiden, Def Leppard and Saxon. They toured extensively in Britain and Europe, and released two albums during this period, 'Head On' and 'Shock Tactics'. Due to the demise of the record company involved, this material became unavailable by mid 82, and following requests by fans of Dickinson and Samson, this album has now been made available. The group disbanded in 1984 and Paul Samson has recently completed his first solo album. The tracks on head tactics were selected from 'Head On' and 'Shock Tactics', and were remixed last year by Jo Julian and Paul Samson at the Music Works in London. An additional track, 'Losing My Grip' was included, this being the only version of the song with Bruce Dickinson on vocals.
Album: released on Capitol, Mar'86 by Capitol Records. Dist: EMI

Cassette: released on Capitol, Mar'86 by Capitol Records. Dist: EMI

LAST RITES.
Album: released on Thunderbolt, Sep'84 by Magnum Music Group Ltd. Dist: Magnum Music Group Ltd, PRT Distribution, Spartan Distribution

LIFE ON THE RUN.
Single (7"): released on Polydor, Oct'82 by Polydor Records. Dist: Polygram, Polydor

Double-pack single: released on Polydor, Oct'82 by Polydor Records. Dist: Polygram, Polydor

LOSING MY GRIP.
Picture disc single: released on Polydor, Jun'82 by Polydor Records. Dist: Polygram, Polydor

Single (12"): released on Polydor, Jun'82 by Polydor Records. Dist: Polygram, Polydor

MR. ROCK 'N' ROLL.
Album: released on Thunderbolt, Apr'84 by Magnum Music Group Ltd. Dist: Magnum Music Group Ltd, PRT Distribution, Spartan Distribution

Single (12"): released on Thunderbolt, Apr'84 by Magnum Music Group Ltd. Dist: Magnum Music Group Ltd, PRT Distribution, Spartan Distribution

RIDIN' WITH THE ANGELS.
Single (7"): released on RCA, May'81 by RCA Records. Dist: RCA, Roots, Swift, Wellard, Chris, I & B, Solomon & Peres Distribution

SHOCK TACTICS.
Album: released on RCA, May'81 by RCA Records. Dist: RCA, Roots, Swift, Wellard, Chris, I & B, Solomon & Peres Distribution

Cassette: released on RCA, May'81 by RCA Records. Dist: RCA, Roots, Swift, Wellard, Chris, I & B, Solomon & Peres Distribution

SURVIVORS.
Album: released on Thunderbolt, Jun'84 by Magnum Music Group Ltd. Dist: Magnum Music Group Ltd, PRT Distribution, Spartan Distribution

Cassette: released on Thunderbolt, Jun'84 by Magnum Music Group Ltd. Dist: Magnum Music Group Ltd, PRT Distribution, Spartan Distribution

THANK YOU AND GOODNIGHT.
Album: released on Razor, Oct'86 by Razor. Dist: Pinnacle

Album: released on Metal Masters, Mar'85 by Razor Records. Dist: Pinnacle

VICE VERSA (Samson (featuring Bruce Dickinson)).
Tracks: / Vice versa / Losing my grip.
Single (7"): released on Capitol, Feb'86 by Capitol Records. Dist: EMI

Single (12"): released on Capitol, Feb'86 by Capitol Records. Dist: EMI

Samson, Paul

JOINT FORCES.
Tracks: / Burning emotion / No turning back / Russians / Tales of the fury / Reach out to love / Chosen few / Tramp / Power of love / Tell me.
Notes: Paul Samson - lead and rhythm guitars. Produced and engineered by Jo Julian. Special guests: Nicky Moore, vocals; John McCoy, bass; Colin Towns, piano on 'Reach Out To Love'; Jo Julian, synths; Edgar Patrik, drums; Chris Sharley, drums on 'No Turning Back'; Jody Turner, co-vocals on 'Tramp'; Rock Goddess, backing vocals on 'Tell Me'. All titles published by Rondor Music (London) Ltd.
Album: released on Raw Power, May'86 Dist: Pinnacle

Cassette: released on Raw Power, May'86 Dist: Pinnacle

Samson, Sam...

SWING IN THE SPRING 1939/42 (Samson, Sam Och Hans Orkester).
Album: released on Dragon, Jun'86 by Dragon Records. Dist: Jazz Music, Projection, Cadillac

Sams Orchestra

DISCO PANTHER.
Single (7"): released on Loose, Sep'83 by Loose Records. Dist: Nine Mile, Cartel

Single (12"): released on Loose, Sep'83 by Loose Records. Dist: Nine Mile, Cartel

Sam The Ram

WOLLY BULLY (Sam The Ram & The Fairisles).
Tracks: / Salt and vinegar.
Single (7"): released on Starblend, Dec'86 by Starblend Records. Dist: PRT Distribution

Single (12"): released on Starblend, Dec'86 by Starblend Records. Dist: PRT Distribution

Sam The Sham

BEST OF SAM THE SHAM & THE PHARAOHS (Sam The Sham & The Pharaohs).
Album: released on Polydor, Aug'86 by Polydor Records. Dist: Polygram, Polydor

Cassette: released on Polydor, Aug'86 by Polydor Records. Dist: Polygram, Polydor

PHARAOHIZATION (Sam The Sham & The Pharaohs).
Album: released on Rhino (USA), May'86 by Rhino Records (USA).

WOOLY BULLY (Sam The Sham & The Pharaohs).
Single (7"): released on Old Gold, Jul'84 by Old Gold Records. Dist: Lightning, Jazz Music, Spartan, Counterpoint

Samuels, Winston

I'LL BE HERE.
Single (12"): released on WE, May'84 by We Records. Dist: Jetstar

Samuri

FIRES OF HELL.
Single (7"): released on Ebony, Dec'84 by Ebony Records. Dist: Pinnacle, Ebony

SACRED BLADE.
Album: released on Ebony, Dec'84 by Ebony Records. Dist: Pinnacle, Ebony

Sanborn, David

AS WE SPEAK.
Album: released on Warner Bros., Jul'82 by Warner Bros Records. Dist: WEA

Album: released on WEA (Import), Jul'83

BACKSTREET.
Album: released on Warner Bros., Sep'83 by Warner Bros Records. Dist: WEA

Cassette: released on Warner Bros., Sep'83 by Warner Bros Records. Dist: WEA

CHANGE OF HEART, A.
Tracks: / Change of heart, A / Chicago song / Imogene / High roller / Tintin / Braeking point / Change of heart, A / Summer / Dream, The.
Compact disc: released on Warner Bros., Feb'87 by Warner Bros Records. Dist: WEA

Album: released on Warner Bros., Jan'87 by Warner Bros Records. Dist: WEA

Cassette: released on Warner Bros., Jan'87 by Warner Bros Records. Dist: WEA

CHICAGO SONG.
Tracks: / Chicago song / Imogene.
Single (7"): released on Warner Bros., May'87 by Warner Bros Records. Dist: WEA

Single (12"): released on Warner Bros., May'87 by Warner Bros Records. Dist: WEA

DREAM, THE (REMIX).
Tracks: / Dream (remix),The / Imogen / Change of heart,A **.
Single (7"): released on Warner Brothers, Feb'87 by Warner Bros Records. Dist: WEA

Single (12"): released on Warner Brothers, Feb'87 by Warner Bros Records. Dist: WEA

HIDEAWAY.
Album: released on Warner Brothers, Mar'81 by Warner Bros Records. Dist: WEA

LET IT SPEAK.
Album: released on Warner Bros., Mar'84 by Warner Bros Records. Dist: WEA

LET'S JUST SAY GOODBYE/SEDUCTION.
Single (7"): released on Warner Brothers, Jul'81 by Warner Bros Records. Dist: WEA

NEITHER ONE OF US/LETS JUST SAY GOODBYE/LOVE IS NOT ENOUGH.
Single (7"): released on Warner Bros., Jan'84 by Warner Bros Records. Dist: WEA

Single (12"): released on Warner Bros., Jan'84 by Warner Bros Records. Dist: WEA

STRAIGHT TO THE HEART.
Tracks: / Hideaway / Straight to the heart / Run for cover / Smile / Lisa / Love and happiness / Lotus blossom / One hundred ways.
Compact disc: released on Warner Bros., Jan'86 by Warner Bros Records. Dist: WEA

Album: released on Logo, '82 by Logo Records. Dist: Roots, BMG

STRAIGHT TO THE HEART.
Album: released on Warner Bros., Nov'84 by Warner Bros Records. Dist: WEA

VOYEUR.
Tracks: / Let's just say goodbye / It's you / Wake me when it's over / One in a million / Run for cover / All I need is you / Just for you.
Album: released on Warner Bros., May'81 by Warner Bros Records. Dist: WEA Deleted '83.

Cassette: released on Warner Bros., May'81 by Warner Bros Records. Dist: WEA

Compact disc: released on Warner Bros., May'81 by Warner Bros Records. Dist: WEA

Sanchez, Pancho

PAPA GATO.
Album: released on Concord Jazz(USA), Feb'87 by Concord Jazz Records (USA). Dist: IMS, Polygram

Sanchez, Poncho

BIEN SABROSO.
Album: released on Concord Jazz(USA), Jun'84 by Concord Jazz Records (USA). Dist: IMS, Polygram

EL CONGUERO.
Tracks: / Siempre me va bien / Mi negra / Shiny stockings / Si no hay amor / Yumbambo / Agua dulce / Night walk / Tin tin deo / Cuidado.
Notes: 'El Conguero' (The Conga Player) follows in the footsteps of Poncho's Grammy nominated album 'Bien Sabroso!' CJP 239. This is his third Concord album as a leader; Poncho's years of association with Cal Tjader were an explosive springboard for his own Latin jazz rhythms. Personnel: Poncho Sanchez - congas & bata/Ramon Banda - timbales/Tony Banda - bass/Sal Cracchiolo - trumpet & flugelhorn/Dick Mitchell - tenor & alto sax, flute/David Romero - bongos/Art Velasco - trombone.
Album: released on Concord Jazz(USA),

Dec'85 by Concord Jazz Records (USA). Dist: IMS, Polygram

GAVIOTA.
Notes: Retail price estimated by Music Master to be 14.39 in December 1966
Compact disc: released on Discovery (USA), Dec'86 in Discovery Records (USA). Dist: Swift, Flexitron-Audio, Jazz Music

PAPA GATO.
Tracks: / Quindembo / Papa Gato / Serenidad / Jumpin' with Symphony Sid / Baila baila / Pan dulce / Tania / Senor blues / Manteca.
Notes: Poncho's fourth Concord Picante release is hot,melodic & danceable...rich with solos & sensible work.Years of performing with vibist Cal Tjader served as a springboard for this giant of Latin jazz. Personnel: Poncho Sanchez: congas & bata/Justo Almario:alto & tenor saxes,flute/ Ramon Banda:timbales/Tony Banda:bass/Sal Cracchiolo: trumpet & flugelhorn/Charlie Otwell: piano/David Romero: bongos/Art Velasco: trombone.
Album: released on Concord Jazz Picante(USA), Mar'87 Dist: IMS, Polygram

SONANDO.
Album: released on Concord Jazz, Mar'83 by Concord Jazz Records (USA). Dist: IMS, Polygram

Cassette: released on Concord Jazz, Mar'83 by Concord Jazz Records (USA). Dist: IMS, Polygram

Sanclous David
BRIDGE THE.
Album: released on Elektra(Musician), Jun'82 by WEA Records. Dist: WEA

Sanctified Country Girls
SANCTIFIED COUNTRY GIRLS 1927-31 (Various Artists).
Notes: Complete recording in chronological order of Jesse May Hill/Rev.Sister Mary Nelson/Sister Cally Fancy. Mono.
Album: released on Wolf, Oct'86 Dist: Jazz Music, Swift

Sanctified Jug Bands
COMPLETE RECORDINGS IN CHRONOLOGICAL ORDER 1928-30.
Notes: Artists: Elder Richard Bryant, Brother Williams, Memphis Sanctified Singers, Holy Ghost Sanctified Singers.

Sanctuary
PRICE TO PAY.
Cassette: released on Vision, Feb'85 Dist: Vision

Sandberg, Paul
HIDING PLACE HE.
Album: on Pilgrim Records. Dist: Rough Trade, Cartel

LATELY HAVE YOU SEEN THE SUN.
Album: on Pilgrim Records. Dist: Rough Trade, Cartel

WELCOME TO THE FAMILY.
Album: on Pilgrim Records. Dist: Rough Trade, Cartel

Sandburg Sound Book
SANDBURG SOUND BOOK FOR CHILDREN Various Artists (Various Artists).
Boxed set: released on Caedmon(USA), '81 by Caedmon (USA) Records. Dist: Gower, Taylors, Discovery

Sandee
YOU'RE THE ONE (MIAMI MIX).
Single (12"): released on Atlantic, 30 May'87 by WEA Records. Dist: WEA

Sandeman, Mary
INTRODUCING MARY SANDEMAN.
Album: released on REL, '79

Cassette: released on REL, Sep'85

MARY SANDEMAN'S REQUESTS.
Album: released on REL, Sep'85

Cassette: released on REL, Sep'85

Sanders, Billy
JA SO NE PARTY.
Album: released on Bear Family, Oct'80 by Bear Family Records. Dist: Rollercoaster Distribution, Swift

Sanders, Joe
JOE SANDERS & HENRY KING 1945.
Album: released on Aircheck, Apr'79

VICTORY PARADE (Sanders, Joe & His Orchestra/Henry King & His Orch.).
Album: released on Aircheck (USA), Oct'86 Dist: Swift, Jazz Music

---

Sanderson, Richard
WHEN FORTUNE REIGNS.
Tracks: / Puissance et Loire.
Single (7"): released on Carrere, Feb'87 by Carrere Records. Dist: PRT, Spartan

Sanderson, Tommy
KEEP ON DANCING (Sanderson, Tommy & His Orchestra).
Album: released on Maestro, Jul'86 by Maestro Records.

Sanders, Pharoah
Biographical Details: Saxophonist Pharoah Sanders real name is Farrell. He was born in 1940 in Little Rock, Arkansas, played with R&B bands; later with Sun Ra, John Coltrane; began making his own albums in 1964 on ESP, in 1969 on Impulse: the 1969 band pursued Coltrane's spiritual quest with an exotic sound at a gentler level of intensity, with Lonnie Liston Smith and the African-inspired yodel of vocalist Leon Thomas (born in 1937 in East St.Louis, Illinois); both had left by the time 'Thembi' was recorded by a sextet, Sanders' fourth Impulse LP and the second to make the pop album chart. 'Love will find a way' on Arista in 1977 was his first USA chart entry, with a 23-piece band plus vocalists. [Donald Clarke, April 87]

BLACK UNITY.
Album: released on Impulse, Oct'85 by Impulse Records. Dist: MCA, Polygram

TAUHID.
Album: released on Impulse, Oct'85 by Impulse Records. Dist: MCA, Polygram

TEMBI.
Album: released on Jasmine, Sep'82 by Jasmine Records. Dist: Counterpoint, Lugtons, Taylor, H.R., Wellard, Chris, Swift, Cadillac

Album: released on Jasmine, Sep'82 by Jasmine Records. Dist: Counterpoint, Lugtons, Taylor, H.R., Wellard, Chris, Swift, Cadillac

Cassette: released on Jasmine, Sep'82 by Jasmine Records. Dist: Counterpoint, Lugtons, Taylor, H.R., Wellard, Chris, Swift, Cadillac

Sanders, Ric
WHENEVER.
Album: released on Waterfront, Jun'84 by Waterfront Records. Dist: Rough Trade, Cartel, Projection, Roots

Sanders, Robert & Tom
DOING BAD.
Tracks: / Doing bad.

Sandford, Chas
TEMPTATION/JULIE.
Single (7"): released on Elektra, Jul'82 by WEA Records. Dist: WEA

Sandglow Marinas
GONE TO CHINA.
Single (7"): released on Spellbound, Jun'84 by Spellbound Records. Dist: CBS

San Diego Blues
SAN DIEGO BLUES Various artists (Various Artists).
Album: released on Advent, Apr'79 Dist: Celtic Music, Projection, Swift

Sandi & The Sunsetz
ALIVE.
Single (7"): released on Alfa, Mar'82 Dist: CBS

DREAMS OF IMMIGRANTS.
Single (7"): released on Sire, Oct'82

Picture disc single: released on Sire, Oct'82

Single (12"): released on Sire, Oct'82

Sandke, Jordan
RHYTHM IS OUR BUSINESS (Sandke, Jordan & Jaki Byard & Co.).
Album: released on Stash, Mar'87 Dist: Swift Distribution, Jazz Music Distribution, Jazz Horizons Distribution, Celtic Music Distribution, Cadillac, JSU Distribution, Zodiac Distribution

Sandler, Albert
GOLDEN AGE OF ALBERT SANDLER.
Tracks: / Londonderry air / In the land of the sky blue water / Bird songs at eventide / Chanson hindoue-sadko / Shy serenade / Serenade les millions d'arlequin / Phantom melody, The / Serenade staendchen / Demande et reponse / Thais-meditation / In an eighteenth century drawing room / An old violin / Dreaming-waltz / On wings of song / Largo.
Album: released on Golden Age, May'86 by Music For Pleasure Records. Dist: EMI

Cassette: released on Golden Age, May'86 by Music For Pleasure Records. Dist: EMI

Sandor Dekl
DIGITAL GIPSY MUSIC SOUND.
Album: released on Hungaraton(Hungary), Nov'83 Dist: Conifer

Sandpipers
GUANTANAMERA.
Cassette: released on Pickwick, Mar'84 by Pickwick Records. Dist: Pickwick Distribution, Prism Leisure Distribution, Lugtons

Single (7"): released on USA Import, '80

LATIN LOVE AFFAIR.
Cassette: released on Pickwick, May'84 by Pickwick Records. Dist: Pickwick Distribution, Prism Leisure Distribution. Lugtons

Sandra
I'LL NEVER BE MARIA MAGDALENA.
Tracks: / I'll never be Maria Magdalena / Party games / Little girl.
Single (7"): released on 10, May'86 by 10 Records. Dist: Virgin, EMI

Single (12"): released on 10, May'86 by 10 Records. Dist: Virgin, EMI

IN THE HEAT OF THE NIGHT.
Tracks: / In the heat of the night / Heatwave.
Single (7"): released on 10, Jan'86 by 10 Records. Dist: Virgin, EMI

Single (12"): released on 10, Jan'86 by 10 Records. Dist: Virgin, EMI

LONG PLAY, THE.
Tracks: / In the heat of the night / On the tray (seven years) / Little girl / You and I / I'll never be Maria Magdalena / Heartbeat (that's emotion) / Sisters and brothers / Change your mind.
Album: released on 10, Jul'86 by 10 Records. Dist: Virgin, EMI

Cassette: released on 10, Jul'86 by 10 Records. Dist: Virgin, EMI

Sands Family
AFTER THE MORNING.
Album: released on EMI, Apr'77 by EMI Records. Dist: EMI

REAL IRISH FOLK.
Album: released on Emerald (Ireland), Oct'81 by Emerald Records. Dist: I & B, Ross, PRT

Cassette: released on Emerald (Ireland), Oct'81 by Emerald Records. Dist: I & B, Ross, PRT

YOU'LL BE WELL LOOKED AFTER.
Album: released on EMI, Jun'76 by EMI Records. Dist: EMI

Sand Storm
ALWAYS AND FOREVER.
Single (12"): released on Unknown, Jun'85

Sandstrom, Nisse
HOME COOKING With Red Mitchell & Tommy Flanagan.
Album: released on Phontastic, Jul'81 Dist: Wellard, Chris

YOUNG FOREVER (Sandstrom, Nisse/Horace Parlan/Red Mitchell).
Album: released on Phontastic, Mar'87 Dist: Wellard, Chris

Sandvik Big Band
SANDVIK BIG BAND.
Notes: Featuring Ann Kristin/Claes Jansson
Album: released on Dragon, Jun'86 by Dragon Records. Dist: Jazz Music, Projection, Cadillac

Sandy Bay
FROZEN ORANGE JUICE (Sandy, Tam & Geordie).
Single (7"): released on Peach River, Apr'83 by Peach River Records. Dist: PRT

Sandy, Freddie
BICYCLE SONG.
Single (7"): released on Mind, Sep'83 by Zella Records. Dist: Taylors

Sandy's Sidemen
PLAYING COMPOSITIONS....
Album: released on Jasmine, Mar'83 by Jasmine Records. Dist: Counterpoint, Lugtons, Taylor, H.R., Wellard, Chris, Swift. Cadillac

Sandy, Tam & Geordie
AMANG THE NEEPS AND BARLEY WITH.
Notes: Retail price estimated by Music Master to be 4.99 in February 1987
Cassette: by Ross Records. Dist: Ross Distribution, Roots Distribution

---

Sane Inmates
GIRL IS MINE.
Single 10": released on Holly Cone, Apr'83 by Ariwa Records. Dist: Jetstar, Rough Trade

Sangria
PEOPLE FROM IBIZA.
Single (7"): released on Sangria, Nov'84 by Sangria Records. Dist: Pinnacle

Single (12"): released on Sangria, Nov'84 by Sangria Records. Dist: Pinnacle

Sangster, John
DOUBLE VIBES HOBBIT.
Album: released on Swaggie (Australia), Jan'83

FOR LEON BISMARCK.
Album: released on Swaggie (Australia), Jan'83

HOBBIT SUITE, THE.
Album: released on Swaggie (Australia), Jan'83

San Jose
HARD TO HANDLE.
Album: released on Sanctum, Dec'83 Dist: Jetstar, Cartel

Sankomota
SANKOMOTA.
Album: released on Earthworks, Jul'85 by Earthworks Records. Dist: Earthworks Distributors, Rough Trade, Cartel, Projection

Sanny X
GOLDEN RULES (Sanny X featuring Mr.P & Little Sally).
Tracks: / Golden rules / She moves.
Single (7"): released on DMC-Arista, Sep'86 by Ariola Records. Dist: RCA, Ariola

Single (12"): released on DMC-Arista, Sep'86 by Ariola Records. Dist: RCA, Ariola

SPLASH DOWN.
Single (12"): released on DRC, Jul'85 by DRC. Dist: Spin-Off

Sano, Motoharu
COMPLICATION SHAKEDOWN.
Single (7"): released on Epic, Jan'85 by CBS Records. Dist: CBS

Single (12"): released on Epic, Jan'85 by CBS Records. Dist: CBS

San, Papa
ANIMAL PARTY.
Album:

San Raphael
SHINE THE LIGHTS (2 PARTS).
Single (12"): released on M&R, Jun'83 by M&R Records (USA). Dist: Jetstar Distribution

San Remo Strings
FESTIVAL TIME/ALL TURNED ON.
Single (7"): released on Motown, Oct'81 by Motown Records. Dist: BMG Distribution

San Sabastian
SOPHIA NATIONAL/EXOTIC LOVE.
Single (7"): released on Sonet, Jun'83 by Sonet Records. Dist: PRT

Sans Harbour
SANS HARBOUR.
Single (7"): released on Camden(RCA), Mar'82 by RCA Records. Dist: Pickwick Distribution, Taylors, Swift

Santa (Claus)
SANTA'S GREATEST HITS Various Artists (Various Artists).
Double Album: released on Atlantic Gap, Nov'85 by Island Records. Dist: Polygram

Cassette: released on Atlantic Gap, Nov'85 by Island Records. Dist: Polygram

Santa Claus-The Movie
SANTA CLAUS-THE MOVIE Original motion picture soundtrack (Various Artists).
Tracks: / Main title:Every Christmas Eve & Santa's theme/ Arrival of the elves / Making toys / Christmas rhapsody / It's Christmas again / March of the elves / Patch,natch! / It's Christmas all over the world / Thought's about Santa / Thank you Santa.
Album: released on EMI America, Nov'85 by EMI Records. Dist: EMI

Cassette: released on EMI America, Nov'85 by EMI Records. Dist: EMI

Santamaria, Mongo

MONGO MAGIC.
Album: released on Roulette (France), Apr'84

MONGO'S GROOVE.
Album: released on BGP, Oct'87 by Ace Records. Dist: PRT. Estim retail price in Oct'87 was £5.67.

Santana

ABRAXAS.
Tracks: / Singing winds / Crying beasts / Black magic woman / Gypsy queen / Oye como va / Incident at Neshabur / Se a cabo / Mother's daughter / Samba pa ti / Hope you're feeling better / El Nicoya.
Notes: Originally CBS 64087.Released in 1970.
Album: released on CBS, Mar'86 by CBS Records. Dist: CBS

Cassette: released on CBS, Mar'86 by CBS Records. Dist: CBS

Compact disc: released on CBS, Mar'86 by CBS Records. Dist: CBS

AMIGOS.
Tracks: / Let me / Tell me are you tired? / Europa / Let it shine / Gitano / Dance sister dance / Take me with you.
Compact disc: released on CBS, Mar'87 by CBS Records. Dist: CBS

Album: released on CBS, '76 by CBS Records. Dist: CBS

Cassette: released on CBS, Jun'84 by CBS Records. Dist: CBS

Cassette: released on CBS, Jun'84 by CBS Records. Dist: CBS

BEYOND APPEARANCES.
Tracks: / Breaking out / Written in sand / How long / Brotherhood / Spirit / Say it again / Who loves you / I'm the one who loves you / Touchdown raiders / Right now.
Album: released on CBS, Mar'86 by CBS Records. Dist: CBS

Cassette: released on CBS, Mar'86 by CBS Records. Dist: CBS

Compact disc: released on CBS, Mar'86 by CBS Records. Dist: CBS

Album: released on CBS, Aug'87 by CBS Records. Dist: CBS

BLACK MAGIC WOMAN.
Single (7"): released on CBS, '80 by CBS Records. Dist: CBS

CARAVANSERAI.
Album: released on CBS, Nov'81 by CBS Records. Dist: CBS

Cassette: released on CBS, Nov'81 by CBS Records. Dist: CBS

FESTIVAL.
Album: released on CBS, Nov'76 by CBS Records. Dist: CBS

Cassette: released on CBS, Nov'76 by CBS Records. Dist: CBS

FREEDOM.
Tracks: / Veracruz / She can't let go / Once it's gotcha / Love is you / Songs of freedom / Deep the deeper / Praise / Mandela / Before we go / Victim of circumstance.
Album: released on CBS, Feb'87 by CBS Records. Dist: CBS

Cassette: released on CBS, Feb'87 by CBS Records. Dist: CBS

GREATEST HITS:SANTANA.
Album: released on CBS, Aug'74 by CBS Records. Dist: CBS

Cassette: released on CBS, Aug'74 by CBS Records. Dist: CBS

Compact disc: by CBS Records. Dist: CBS

INNER SECRET.
Compact disc: by CBS Records. Dist: CBS

LOTUS.
Triple album / cassette: released on CBS, Dec'75 by CBS Records. Dist: CBS

MARATHON.
Tracks: / Marathon / Lightning in the sky / Aqua marine / You know that I love you / All I ever wanted / Stand up / Runnin' / Summer lady / Love / Stay (beside me) / Hard times.
Compact disc: released on CBS, May'87 by CBS Records. Dist: CBS

Album: released on CBS, Oct'79 by CBS Records. Dist: CBS

Cassette: released on CBS, Oct'79 by CBS Records. Dist: CBS

MOONFLOWER.
Double Album: released on CBS, Apr'85 by CBS Records. Dist: CBS

Cassette: released on CBS, Apr'85 by CBS Records. Dist: CBS

SAMBA PA TI.
Tracks: / Samba pa ti / Jin-go-lo-ba / She's not there / Evil ways.
Single (12"): released on Old Gold, Feb'86 by Old Gold Records. Dist: Lightning, Jazz Music, Spartan, Counterpoint

SANTANA.
Compact disc: released on CBS, May'87 by CBS Records. Dist: CBS

SANTANA 3.
Tracks: / Batuka / No one to depend on / Taboo / Toussaint l'overture / Everything's everything / Guajira / Jungle strut / Everything's coming our way / Para los rumberos.
Compact disc: released on CBS, Mar'87 by CBS Records. Dist: CBS

SHANGO.
Tracks: / Nile / Hold on / Night hunting time / Nowhere to run / Neuva York / Oxun / Body surfing / What does it take? / Let me inside / Warrior / Shango.
Compact disc: released on CBS, '83 by CBS Records. Dist: CBS

Album: released on CBS, '83 by CBS Records. Dist: CBS

SWING OF DELIGHT, THE (Santana, Devadip, Carlos).
Double Album: released on CBS, Sep'80 by CBS Records. Dist: CBS

Double cassette: released on CBS, Sep'80 by CBS Records. Dist: CBS

VERA CRUZ.
Tracks: / Vera cruz / Mandela.
Single (7"): released on CBS, May'87 by CBS Records. Dist: CBS

VIVA SANTANA.
Tracks: / She's not there / Well alright / Oye como va / Let the music set you free / I'll be waiting / What does it take (to win your love) / Black magic woman/Gipsy queen / Samba pa ti / Carnaval / Let the children play / Dance sister dance / Se a cabo / Everythings coming our way / Jin go lo ba.
Album: released on K-Tel, Oct'86 by K-Tel Records. Dist: Record Merchandisers Distribution, Taylors, Terry Blood Distribution, Wynd-Up Distribution, Relay Distribution, Pickwick Distribution, Solomon & Peres Distribution, Polygram

Cassette: released on K-Tel, Oct'86 by K-Tel Records. Dist: Record Merchandisers Distribution, Taylors, Terry Blood Distribution, Wynd-Up Distribution, Relay Distribution, Pickwick Distribution, Solomon & Peres Distribution, Polygram

Compact disc: released on K-Tel, Oct'86 by K-Tel Records. Dist: Record Merchandisers Distribution, Taylors, Terry Blood Distribution, Wynd-Up Distribution, Relay Distribution, Pickwick Distribution, Solomon & Peres Distribution, Polygram

ZEBOP.
Tracks: / Changes / E papa re / Primera invasion / Searchin' / Over & over / Winning / Tales of Kilimanjaro / Sensitive kind / American gipsy / I love you too much / Brightest star / Hannibal.
Compact disc: released on CBS, Dec'85 by CBS Records. Dist: CBS

Santana, Carlos

Biographical Details: Guitarist Carlos Santana, born in Mexico in 1947, formed his influential Latin-rock group in 1969, first called Santana Bluesband. The band played at the Woodstock Festival in 1969; His first album 'Santana' was a number 4 LP in the USA, the next two Abraxus and Santana 3 were both number 1. Most of his subsequent albums have charted, but those big hits were the most influential. Abraxus included 'Black magic woman', also a hit for Fleetwood Mac.

HAVANA MOON.
Compact disc: released on CBS, May'87 by CBS Records. Dist: CBS

WATCH YOUR STEP/ LIGHTNIN'.
Single (7"): released on CBS, Apr'83 by CBS Records. Dist: CBS

Santa, Tracy

HELL IN A HANDTRUCK.
Single (7"): released on Exile, May'87 by Exile Records. Dist: Pinnacle

Sante Fe

SANTE FE (Santers).
Album: released on Tank, Nov'79 by Tank Records.

Santers

GUITAR ALLEY.
Album: released on Heavy Metal America, Jun'84 by FM-Revolver Records. Dist: EMI

RACING TIME.
Album: released on Heavy Metal, Dec'82 by FM-Revolver Records. Dist: EMI

Santillan, Facio

EL CONDOR PASA - FLUTES FROM THE ANDES.
Compact disc: released on Barclay (France), Aug'87 by Decca Records. Dist: IMS, Discovery, Conifer, Swift, Polygram

Santing, Mathilde

LOVE OF THE COMMON MAN.
Tracks: / Love of the common man / One day as a lion.
Single (7"): released on WEA International, 23 May'87 by WEA Records. Dist: WEA

OUT OF THIS DREAM.
Tracks: / Love of the common man / Town without pity / Wanting things / One day as a lion / Broken bicycles / tgempted / Is there any way out of this dream? / Twenty tambourines / She needs me / Kings and queens / Too close for comfort / Sheep in fog.
Album: released on WEA, Jun'87 by WEA Records. Dist: WEA

Cassette: released on WEA, Jun'87 by WEA Records. Dist: WEA

WATER UNDER THE BRIDGE.
Album: released on WEA, Jun'85 by WEA Records. Dist: WEA

Cassette: released on WEA, Jun'85 by WEA Records. Dist: WEA

YOU TOOK ADVANTAGE OF ME.
Single (7"): released on WEA, Sep'82 by WEA Records. Dist: WEA

Santo & Johnny

SLEEP WALK.
Tracks: / Sleepwalk / Teardrop.
Single (7"): released on Old Gold, Oct'86 by Old Gold Records. Dist: Lightning, Jazz Music, Spartan, Counterpoint

Santrax

COME AND GET IT/INSTRUMENTAL VERSION.
Single (12"): released on Hitman, Jul'83 by Hitman Records. Dist: Pinnacle

Santrra

OXYD.
Album: released on Zensor, Feb'87 by Zensor Records. Dist: Rough Trade

Sapphire

BURNING (Sapphire feat. Kelly).
Tracks: / Burning / Burning(instrumental).
Single (12"): released on Passion, Apr'86 by Skratch Records. Dist: PRT

Sapphires

GONNA BE A BIG THING/EDDIE REAGAN PLAYING HIDE AND SEEK.
Single (7"): released on ABC, Jun'78 Dist: Pinnacle

MY BABY MUST BE A MAGICIAN/WHATEVER YOU WANT MY LOVE.
Single (7"): released on Stiff, Apr'83 by Stiff Records. Dist: EMI, Record Services Distribution (Ireland)

Single (12"): released on Stiff, Apr'83 by Stiff Records. Dist: EMI, Record Services Distribution (Ireland)

ROCK ME SLOWLY/MAKE LOVE TO THE MUSIC.
Single (12"): released on Becket, Jan'84

Saraband

CLOSE TO IT ALL.
Album: released on Folk Heritage, Jul'82 by Folk Heritage Records. Dist: Roots, Wynd-Up Distribution, Jazz Music, Folk Heritage

Saracan

CHANGE OF HEART.
Album: released on Neat, Jan'85 by Neat Records. Dist: Pinnacle, Neat

NO MORE LONELY NIGHTS.
Single (7"): released on Nucleus, May'82

WE HAVE ARRIVED/A FACE IN THE CROWD.
Single (7"): released on Neat, Aug'83 by Neat Records. Dist: Pinnacle, Neat

Sara Goes Pop

SARA GOES POP.
Double-pack single: released on It's War Boys, Nov'82 Dist: Recommended

Sarah Goes Shopping

MONEY SPEAKS LOUDER THAN WORDS.
Single (7"): released on Crystal, Jul'85 by Crystal Records. Dist: Jetstar, Revolver, Cartel

Sarah & The Planes

TWO CAN HAVE A PARTY.
Single (7"): released on Cloud International, Apr'85 by Creole Records. Dist: Pinnacle

Sarbib Saheb Quartet

IT COULDN'T HAPPEN WITHOUT YOU.
Album: released on Soul Note, May'85 Dist: Harmonia Mundi Distributors

Sarean Quartar

PARIS NEED NOT BE WARM.
Tracks: / Paris need not be warm / Paris need not be warm.
Single (7"): released on Contempo, Nov'86 Dist: Nine Mile, Cartel, Red Rhino

Sargeant & Malone

LOVE MESSAGE/I KNOW WHO YOU ARE.
Single (7"): released on Half Moon, Sep'82 by Rondelet Music And Records. Dist: Spartan

Single (12"): released on Half Moon, Sep'82 by Rondelet Music And Records. Dist: Spartan

MOVING UP/INSTRUMENTAL VERSION.
Single (7"): released on Half Moon, Sep'82 by Rondelet Music And Records. Dist: Spartan

Single (12"): released on Half Moon, Sep'82 by Rondelet Music And Records. Dist: Spartan

Sargeant Pepper

TIME TO GO DREAD/BENGALI DUB.
Single (12"): released on Ariwa, Apr'83 by Ariwa Records. Dist: Revolver, Cartel, Jetstar, Rough Trade

Sargeant, Will

THEMES FOR GRIND.
Album: released on 92 Happy Customers, Jul'83 Dist: Cartel

Sarlo, Teri de

VOICES IN THE WIND.
Album: released on Day Spring, May'86 by Word Records. Dist: Word Distribution, CBS

Sarr Band

STRUT YOUR STUFF.
Single (7"): released on Calendar, Mar'80 Dist: Polygram

Single (12"): released on Calendar, Mar'80 Dist: Polygram

Sarstedt, Clive

LOVE CAN HURT/DON'T KICK ME AGAIN.
Single (7"): released on Spectra, Sep'81 by Spectra Records. Dist: Pinnacle

SUPER LOVE.
Single (7"): released on Spectra, Nov'81 by Spectra Records. Dist: Pinnacle

Sarstedt, Peter

HEMINGWAY.
Tracks: / Hemingway / Don Quixote.
Single (7"): released on Filmtrax, Apr'86 by Filmtrax Records. Dist: Pinnacle

LOVE AMONG THE RUINS/DON QUIXOTE.
Single (7"): released on Peach River, Sep'82 by Peach River Records. Dist: PRT

UP DATE.
Album: released on Steinar (Iceland), Nov'81 Dist: PRT Distribution

VERY BEST OF PETER SARSTEDT.
Tracks: / Where do you go to my lovely / Don Quixote / I am a cathedral / Tall tree / Hollywood sign / Boulevard / Europa / Far pavilions, The / Eternal days / Beirut / Southern belle / Frozen orange juice / Love among the ruins / Take off your clothes / Friends / Don't bury your love / Mulberry dawn / Hemingway.
Compact disc: released on The Collection, Apr'87 by Object Enterprises Ltd. Dist: Counterpoint Distribution

WHERE DO YOU GO TO MY LOVELY/MORNING MOUNTAIN.
Single (7"): released on UA, Jan'69 Dist: EMI

WHERE DO YOU GO TO MY LOVELY/FROZEN ORANGE JUICE.
Single (7"): released on Old Gold, Oct'83 by Old Gold Records. Dist: Lightning, Jazz Music, Spartan, Counterpoint

Sarstedt, Robin

MY RESISTANCE IS LOW.
Single (7"): released on Old Gold, Sep'85 by Old Gold Records. Dist: Lightning, Jazz Music, Spartan, Counterpoint

Sashay, Scion

SUCCESS.
Album: released on Jah Life, Nov'86 by Jah Life Records. Dist: Jetstar

Sash Leon

I REMEMBER NEWPORT.
Album: released on Delmark, Jan'74 Dist: Projection, Swift, Cadillac

S.A.S. Paratroopers

WINGED DAGGER (S.A.S. Paratroopers 3rd Battallion).
Single (7"): released on Bandleader, Mar'83 by Bandleader Records. Dist: PRT

Sass

BABY TALK.
Single (7"): released on 10, Nov'85 by 10 Records. Dist: Virgin, EMI

Single (12"): released on 10, Nov'85 by 10 Records. Dist: Virgin, EMI

I DIDN'T MEAN IT ALL.
Single (7"): released on 10, Jan'85 by 10 Records. Dist: Virgin, EMI

Single (12"): released on 10, Jan'85 by 10 Records. Dist: Virgin, EMI

Satalite

HERE IS TODAY'S NEWS.
Album: released on Brickyard, Nov'84 Dist: Pinnacle

I WONDER WHY/COMBINATION 2.
Single (12"): released on Star Track, Mar'82 Dist: Star Track Distribution

NIGHTMARE (THE) (EP).
Single (7"): released on Kamera, Feb'83

URBAN GORILLA/HIGH RISE HILLBILLIES.
Single (7"): released on Rewind, Aug'80 by Rewind Records. Dist: Spartan

VIETNAM/LUCY IS A PROSTITUTE/I FELL IN LOVE WITH A LESBIAN.
Single (7"): released on Brickyard, Sep'83 Dist: Pinnacle

Satan

COURT IN THE ACT.
Album: released on Neat, Jan'85 by Neat Records. Dist: Pinnacle, Neat

KISS OF DEATH/HEADS WILL ROLL.
Single (7"): released on Guardian, Sep'82 by Guardian Records. Dist: Jazz Music, Pinnacle

Satan Defloration Inc.

SATAN DEFLORATION INCORPORATED.
Album: released on Powerstation Records, Mar'87 by Powerstation Records. Dist: Pinnacle

Satanic Malfunctions

WHO WANTS THE WORLD(EP).
Extended-play record: released on Tea Core, Oct'86 Dist: Red Rhino, Cartel

Satanic Rites

LIVE TO RIDE/HIT AND RUN.
Single (7"): released on Heavy Metal, Sep'81 by FM-Revolver Records. Dist: EMI

Satan, Nick

WE WISH YOU A TEDDY CHRISTMAS (Satan, Nick & The Rockin' Devils).
Single (7"): released on Hot Rock, Nov'80 by Hot Rock Records. Dist: Hot Rock

Satent, Malcolm

LOAD OF BULL, A.
Album: released on Highway, Jan'85 by Highway Records. Dist: Roots, Projection, Ross

Satie, Erik

SEPT TABLEAUX PHONIQUES.
Tracks: / Trois bonbons de York pour Erik Satie / Budapest subway / Welcome / Moving things from A to B / Falz waltz / For memories of an amnesiac / Allair meets / Faction de Satie (I can't get no).
Notes: With Steve Beresford/Tony Coe/Robert Cornford/Lol Coxhill/Alan Hacker/David Holland/Phil Wachsmann.
Album: released on Nato (France), Sep'86 by Disques Nato. Dist: Essex Record Distributors Ltd.

TROIS SARABANDES ET SIX GNOSSIENNES.
Tracks: / Trois sarabandes et six gnossiennes.
Album: released on Nato (France), Sep'86 by Disques Nato. Dist: Essex Record Distributors Ltd.

Satin, C.T.

FINALLY I FOUND A FRIEND.
Tracks: / Finally I found a friend / Finally I found a friend (Garage mix).
Single (7"): released on Nine O Nine, Mar'87 by Creole Records. Dist: Rhino, PRT

Sato, Masahiko

TRINITY.
Album: released on Enja (Germany), Jan'82 by Enja Records (W.Germany). Dist: Cadillac Music

Satriana, Joe

NOT OF THIS EARTH.
Album: released on Food For Thought, Feb'87 by Food For Thought Records. Dist: Pinnacle

Saturday Night Fever

SATURDAY NIGHT FEVER (Various Artists).
Notes: Released on CIC Video

SATURDAY NIGHT FEVER Original film soundtrack (Various Artists).
Tracks: / Stayin' alive / How deep is your love / Night fever / More than a woman / Jive talkin' / You should be dancing / More than a woman / Calypso breakdown / If I can't have you / Fifth of Beethoven (A) / Open sesame / Boogie shoes / M.F.S.B. / K Jee / Disco inferno / Manhattan skyline / Night on disco mountain / Salsation.

Compact disc: released on RSO, '83

Double cassette: released on RSO, Jan'84

Double Album: released on RSO, Jan'84

Saturday Night's Alright

SATURDAY NIGHT'S ALRIGHT Various Artists (Various Artists).
Album: released on Cambra, Mar'85 by Cambra Records. Dist: IDS, Conifer

Cassette: released on Cambra, Mar'85 by Cambra Records. Dist: IDS. Conifer

Saturday Night Scrontch

SATURDAY NIGHT SCRONTCH Various artists (Various Artists).
Notes: Artists include Frankie Jaxon/Tampa Red's Holum Jug Band.
Album: released on Collectors Items, Jul'86 Dist: Jazz Music, Swift, Chris Wellard

Saturday Superstore

SATURDAY SUPERSTORE SELECTION REPLAY VOLUME 2 Various Artists (Various Artists).
Album: released on Chrysalis, Nov'84 by Chrysalis Records. Dist: CBS

Cassette: released on Chrysalis, Nov'84 by Chrysalis Records. Dist: CBS

SATURDAY SUPERSTORE - REPLAY SELECTION Various Artists (Various Artists).
Album: released on BBC, Oct'83 by BBC Records & Tapes. Dist: EMI, PRT, Pye

Cassette: released on BBC, Oct'83 by BBC Records & Tapes. Dist: EMI, PRT, Pye

Saturnalia

GIRL ON THE EIGHTH FLOOR/COLD NIGHT AIR.
Single (7"): released on Burning Words, Jan'83 Dist: Cartel

INSIDE THE DEVILS CIRCUS/THE PROMISE.
Single (7"): released on Burning Words, Jul'82 Dist: Cartel

Saucers

SPRING HAS SPRUNG.
Single (7"): released on BBC, Apr'82 by BBC Records & Tapes. Dist: EMI, PRT, Pye

Saulsberry, Rodney

I WONDER.
Single (7"): released on Allegiance, Nov'84 by PRT Records. Dist: PRT

Single (12"): released on Allegiance, Nov'84 by PRT Records. Dist: PRT

RODNEY SAULSBERRY.
Album: released on Allegiance, Nov'84 by PRT Records. Dist: PRT

Single (12"): released on Allegiance, Nov'84 by PRT Records. Dist: PRT

Saunders, Anthony

DANGER GIRL.
Single (12"): released on The Foundation, May'84 by Foundation Records, The. Dist: Jetstar Distribution

Saunders, Jesse

FUNK YOU UP.
Single (12"): released on Streetfire, Jun'84

Sauter, Eddie

Biographical Details: Eddie Sauter (1914-1981) was one of the great arrangers of the Swing Era, writing for **Charlie Barnet**, then doing virtually all the writing for **Red Norvo** and **Mildred Bailey** in the late 1930's when their popular band was a hit on the radio. Then he worked for **Benny Goodman**, many others; with **Bill Finegan** (born 1917), famous for some of **Glenn Miller's** best arrangements, he formed the Sauter-Finegan band, which had very clever and witty hits in the early 1950's with unusual instrumentation. Finegan revived that band in New York in 1987. [Donald Clarke, April 1987]

RETURN OF THE DOODLETOWN FIFERS, THE (Sauter, Eddie/Bill Finegan).
Tracks: / Doodletown Fifers / April in Paris / Churchmouse / When hearts are young / One is a lonely number / Doodletown races / Midnight sleighride / Moonlight on the ganges / Foggy day, A / Rain / Thursday's child / Darn that dream.
Notes: Eddie Sauter and Bill Finegan and their orchestra were a successful and very adventurous post war band. This album features tracks from the 50's which were re-recorded in stereo in the early 60's. Includes 'Sleighride', their well known Christmas track. Original American sleeve. Nothing currently available from Sauter & Finegan. Similar to the sounds of Ray Anthony, Nelson Riddle and Billy May.
Album: released on UA, Dec'85 Dist: EMI

Cassette: released on UA, Dec'85 Dist: EMI

Savage

HYPERACTIVE.
Album: released on Zebra, Jun'85 by Cherry Red Records. Dist: Pinnacle

Cassette: released on Zebra, Jun'85 by Cherry Red Records. Dist: Pinnacle

LOOSE 'N' LETHAL.
Album: released on Ebony, Nov'83 by Ebony Records. Dist: Pinnacle, Ebony

ONLY YOU.
Single (7"): released on Carrere, Nov'84 by Carrere Records. Dist: PRT, Spartan

Single (12"): released on Carrere, Nov'84 by Carrere Records. Dist: PRT, Spartan

WE GOT THE EDGE.
Single (12"): released on Zebra, Nov'84 by Cherry Red Records. Dist: Pinnacle

Savage, Johnny

JOHNNY SAVAGE ALBUM (THE).
Album:

WINDS OF WARMTH.
Single (7"):

Savage Progress

BURNING BUSH.
Single (7"): released on Ten, Aug'84 Cat. no: **TEN 27**
Single (12"): released on Ten, Aug'84

CELEBRATION.
Album: released on 10, Sep'84 by 10 Records. Dist: Virgin, EMI

HEART BEGIN TO BEAT.
Single (7"): released on 10, Jun'84 by 10 Records. Dist: Virgin, EMI

Single (12"): released on 10, Jun'84 by 10 Records. Dist: Virgin, EMI

MY SOUL UNWRAPS TONIGHT.
Single (7"): released on Virgin, Mar'84 by Virgin Records. Dist: EMI, Virgin Distribution

Single (12"): released on Virgin, Mar'84 by Virgin Records. Dist: EMI, Virgin Distribution

Savage Public

TRUDGE.
Notes: Mini LP
Album: released on Play It Again Sam, Jan'86 Dist: Red Rhino, Cartel

Savage Republic

TRAGIC FIGURES.
Album: released on Sordide Sentimental (France), Mar'84 Dist: Cartel

Savage, Tony

40 GOLDEN OLDIES.
Tracks: / I do like to be beside the seaside / Make it a party / Sing as we go / Songs of the sea / All the nice girls love a sailor / Stein song, The / Sunshine of your smile / Following in father's footsteps / Somewhere my love / This is my song / Roll along covered wagon / Sunset trail, The / Old faithful / Don't fence me in / Horsey horsey / Lilli Marlene / Happy days are here again / Ferry Boat Inn, The / On the crest of a wave / Keep your sunnyside up / White cliffs of Dover / Quartermaster's song, The / Paper doll / I'll be seeing you / Red sails in the sunset / We'll meet again / Bless 'em all / Band played on, The / Goodnight Irene / My bonne / Harbour lights / Always in my heart / On Donna Clara / Washing on the siegfried line, The / Goodbye Sally / Run rabbit run / Hey little hen / Kiss me goodnight Sergeant Major / Roll out the barrel / If I had my way / When they sound the last all clear / Russian rose / Now is the hour.
Notes: 40 Golden Oldies featuring many tunes from the Second World War 1939-1945 with Tony Savage-organ/Dominic-keyboards: Tony Savage, 21 Eaton Road, Margate, Kent CT9 1XB: (Tel 0843-220765)
Album: released on Seaside Records, '86

GOLDEN OLDIES.
Tracks: / Roses of Picardy / One day at a time / Old rugged cross (The) / If I can help somebody / Amazing grace / Please release me / I love you because / Please / Pennies from heaven / It had to be me / Among my souveniers / Deed I do / Tangerine / Quick step (Chicago swing) / Chicago / Five foot two eyes of blue / When the red red robin / I've got sixpence / Foxtrot (break away blues) / All of me / I don't want to set the world on fire / You need hands / Paper roses / Amapola / Arrivederci / And I love you so / Spanish eyes / Birdie song / Edelweiss / Charmaine / Wonderful world of the young / Who's taking you home tonight.
Album: released on Seaside Records. '86

GOOD OLD SONGS IN DANCETIME (THE).
Tracks: / If your face wants to laugh well let it / Gilbert and Filbert / Has anybody here seen Kelly / Coal-black Mammy / I've got rings on my fingers / Broadway melody / Alice blue gown / If those lips could only speak / Sally / If I had my life to live over again / La cumparsita / At the balalaika / She was one of the early birds / Bird in a gilded cage / Cruising down the river / Eton boating song / Harry Lime theme / You were meant for me / Here we are here we are again / Fall and follow me / Man who broke the bank at Monte Carlo / Let's all go down the Strand / Take me back to dear old blighty / Till the boys come home / Pack up your troubles / Goodbye-ee / Anniversary waltz / My old dutch / In apple blossom time / Memories / You belong to my heart / How wonderful to know / I can't begin to tell / Green eyes / Underneath the arches / Hometown / Maybe it's because I'm a Londoner / Show me the way to go home / Lambeth walk / If you were the only girl in the world / Broken doll (A) / Let's have another one.
Notes: With Tony Savage-organ and Dominic-keyboard
Album: released on Seaside Records, '86

MORE SING-ALONG-DANCE TIME.
Tracks: / I wanna say hello / Whispering / Is it true what they say about Dixie? / Give my regards to Broadway / Lonesome and sorry / Ain't she sweet / Are you lonesome tonight / When I grow too old to dream / Ramona / Till we meet again / In a shady nook / Glory of love (The) / Rock-a-bye your baby / Happy days and lonely days / I can't give you anything but love baby / Happy days and lonely nights / Red sails in the sunset / South of the border / Somebody stole my girl / Who's sorry now / Blue skies / When you're smiling / She's a lassie from Lancashire / Meet me tonight in dreamland / Two little girls in blue / By the side of the Zuyder Zee / Joshuah / Marie Elena / Strangers in the night / Somethin' stupid / Marta / Cock o' the north / Wi' a hundred pipers / Annie Laurie / Loch Lomond / Blue bells of Scotland.
Album: released on Seaside Records, '86

SING-ALONG-DANCE TIME.
Tracks: / California here I come / Who were you with last night / Who's sorry now / Four leaf clover / Maggie / Wait till the sun shines Nellie / I wonder who's kissing her now / It's a sin to tell a lie / Let the rest of the world go by / Hello hello who's your lady friend / Pack up your troubles in your old kit bag / Just like the ivy / Daddy wouldn't buy me a bow-wow / I'm Henry the eighth I am / Lily of Laguna / I do like to be beside the seaside / St Bernards waltz / I belong to Glasglow / Two lovely black eyes / Meet me tonight in dreamland / Down at the Old Bull and Bush / Let's twist again / I love a lassie / My old man said follow the van / When the saints go marching in / Tea for two cha cha cha / Wheels cha cha cha / On the sunny side of the street / Me and my shadow / Moonlight and roses / Come back to Erin / My wild Irish rose / After the ball / Daisy bell / She was one of the early birds / Jealousy / Isle of Capri / Heart of my heart / Bye bye blackbird / Carolina in the morning / You made me love you / For me and my girl / We'll meet again.
Notes: A 'Live' recording of Happy Holiday Makers singing and dancing at Cliftonville.
Album: released on Seaside Records, '86

TONY AND HIS SON DOMINIC PLAY THE ORGAN.
Tracks: / Here we are again / I do like to be beside the seaside / Spanish eyes / Edelweiss / Bladen races / Whispering grass / I love you

because / Amazing grace / Keep right on to the end of the road / Aniversary waltz / Men of Harlech / We'll keep a welcome / Tie a yellow ribbon round the old oak tree / Viva Espana / 12th Street rag / When the saints go marching in / We'll meet again / Merry widow waltz / Little Annie Rooney / In the shade of the old apple tree / Give me a little cosy corner / Roaming in the gloaming / I wouldn't leave my little wooden hut / Happy wanderer / Honeysuckle and the bee / Soldiers of the queen / Softly softly / Don't bring Lulu / Ma ma he's making eyes at me / I want a girl just like the girl who married dear old dad / When you're smiling / St Bernard's medley / Oh oh Antonio / In the good old summertime / I'll be your sweetheart / Side by side / On a slow boat to China / Strollin' / Farmer's / Kaiser Bill's batman.
Album: released on Seaside Records, '86

Savanna

I CAN'T TURN AWAY.
Single (7"): released on Red Bus, Sep'81 by Red Bus Records. Dist: PRT

Single (12"): released on Red Bus, Sep'81 by Red Bus Records. Dist: PRT

NEVER LET YOU GO/VERSION.
Single (7"): released on R & B, Mar'82 by Red Bus. Dist: PRT

Single (12"): released on R & B, Mar'82 by Red Bus. Dist: PRT

Savatage

DUNGEONS ARE CALLING THE.
Album: released on Music For Nations, Mar'85 by Music For Nations Records. Dist: Pinnacle

FIGHT FOR THE ROCK.
Tracks: / Fight fo the rock / Out on the streets / Crying for love / Day after day / Edge of midnight, The / Hyde / Lady in disguise / She's only rock 'n' roll / Wishing well / Red light paradise.
Album: released on Atlantic, May'86 by WEA Records. Dist: WEA

Cassette: released on Atlantic, May'86 by WEA Records. Dist: WEA

POWER OF THE NIGHT.
Album: released on Atlantic, Aug'85 by WEA Records. Dist: WEA

SIRENS.
Album: released on Music For Nations, Sep'85 by Music For Nations Records. Dist: Pinnacle

Savers, Charlie

CHARLIE SHAVERS.
Album: released on Phoenix Jazz (USA), Apr'79
Cat. no: **PHOENIX JAZZ LP 21**
Album: released on Hep, Apr'81 by H.R. Taylor Records. Dist: Jazz Music, Cadillac Music, JSU, Taylors, Wellard, Chris, Zodiac, Swift, Fast Forward

Save The Animals

AMERICAN SCHOOL CHOIR WITH VARIOUS SOLOISTS.
Album: released on Ears And Eyes, Apr'83 by Ears And Eyes Records. Dist: Taylors, Ears And Eyes Records

Cassette: released on Ears And Eyes, Apr'83 by Ears And Eyes Records. Dist: Taylors, Ears And Eyes Records

Save The Children...

LITTLE STAR/A MAP OF (Save The Children Fund Choir).
Single (7"): released on Stiff, Nov'81 by Stiff Records. Dist: EMI, Record Services Distribution (Ireland)

Save Us

HISTORY TO THE WOMB.
Tracks: / History to the womb / Man out of context.
Single (7"): released on Quiet, Jan'86 by Quiet Records. Dist: Nine Mile, Cartel

Savile's Time Travels

20 GOLDEN HITS OF 1962.
Album: released on EMI, Oct'83 by EMI Records. Dist: EMI

Cassette: released on EMI, Oct'83 by EMI Records. Dist: EMI

20 GOLDEN HITS OF 1957.
Album: released on Music For Pleasure (Holland), Feb'84 by EMI Records. Dist: EMI

Cassette: released on Music For Pleasure (Holland), Feb'84 by EMI Records. Dist: EMI

20 GOLDEN HITS OF 1958.
Album: released on MFP, Feb'82 by EMI Records. Dist: EMI

Cassette: released on MFP, Feb'82 by EMI Records. Dist: EMI

20 GOLDEN HITS OF 1959.
Album: released on Music For Pleasure, Jul'82 by EMI Records. Dist: EMI

Cassette: released on Music For Pleasure, Jul'82 by EMI Records. Dist: EMI

20 GOLDEN HITS OF 1960.
Album: released on MFP, Oct'81 by EMI Records. Dist: EMI

Cassette: released on MFP, Oct'81 by EMI Records. Dist: EMI

20 GOLDEN HITS OF 1961.
Album: released on MFP, Sep'82 by EMI Records. Dist: EMI

Cassette: released on MFP, Sep'82 by EMI Records. Dist: EMI

20 GOLDEN HITS OF 1968.
Album: released on MFP, Oct'85 by EMI Records. Dist: EMI

Cassette: released on MFP, Oct'85 by EMI Records. Dist: EMI

20 GOLDEN HITS OF 1963.
Album: released on Music For Pleasure, Oct'81 by EMI Records. Dist: EMI

Cassette: released on Music For Pleasure, Oct'81 by EMI Records. Dist: EMI

20 GOLDEN HITS OF 1964.
Album: released on Music For Pleasure, Sep'83 by EMI Records. Dist: EMI

Cassette: released on Music For Pleasure, Sep'83 by EMI Records. Dist: EMI

20 GOLDEN HITS OF 1965.
Album: released on Music For Pleasure, May'84 by EMI Records. Dist: EMI

Cassette: released on Music For Pleasure, May'84 by EMI Records. Dist: EMI

20 GOLDEN HITS OF 1966.
Album: released on Music For Pleasure, Sep'84 by EMI Records. Dist: EMI

Cassette: released on Music For Pleasure, Sep'84 by EMI Records. Dist: EMI

20 GOLDEN HITS OF 1967.
Album: released on MFP, Jul'85 by EMI Records. Dist: EMI

Cassette: released on MFP, Jul'85 by EMI Records. Dist: EMI

SAVILE'S TIME TRAVELS 20 Golden Hits of 1969 (Various Artists).
Tracks: / Tracy / Breakaway / Wonderful world, beautiful people / It's getting better / Delta Lady / Wichita Lineman / My sentimental friend / Melting Pot / Surround yourself with sorrow / Aquarius / Dizzy / I'll never fall in love again / Iraelites / Blackberry Way / Gin gan goolie / Where do you go to (my lovely) / Boom bang-a-bang / Going up the country / Return of Django.
Album: released on MFP, Jun'87 by EMI Records. Dist: EMI

Cassette: released on MFP, Jun'87 by EMI Records. Dist: EMI

Savitt, Jan

Biographical Details: Violinist Jan Savitt was born in Russia, probably in 1908; he died in California in 1948. He was a child prodigy who led one of America's most popular dance bands; several hits 1938-42 included the band's theme, '720 In The Books', so called because that was the number on the arrangement. His popular vocalist Bon-Bon was black, unusual then. [Donald Clarke, April 87]

IN DISCO ORDER VOLUME 1.
Album: released on Ajax, Jul'77

JAN SAVITT - 1938 VOLUME 2.
Album: released on Ajax, Apr'79

JAN SAVITT - 1938 VOLUME 3.
Album: released on Ajax, Apr'79

Savoy Brown

BEST OF SAVOY BROWN, THE.
Album: released on Decca (Rock Echoes), May'82 by Decca Records. Dist: Polygram, IMS

HARDWAY TO GO, A.
Album: released on Platinum (W.Germany), Oct'85 Dist: Mainline

Cassette: released on Platinum (W.Germany), Oct'85 Dist: Mainline

HIGHWAY BLUES.
Album: released on See For Miles, May'85 by See For Miles Records. Dist: Pinnacle

Savoy Brown Blues Band

BLUES ROOTS.
Album: released on Decca, '78 by Decca Records. Dist: Polygram

GETTING TO THE POINT.
Album: released on Decca, '68 by Decca Records. Dist: Polygram

SHAKE DOWN.
Album: released on Decca, '67 by Decca Records. Dist: Polygram

Savoy-Doucet Cajun Band

LES HARIAS.
Album: released on Arhoolie, Jul'84 by Arhoolie Records. Dist: Projection, Topic, Jazz Music, Swift, Roots

WITH SPIRITS.
Album: released on Arhoolie, Dec'86 by Arhoolie Records. Dist: Projection, Topic, Jazz Music, Swift, Roots

Savoy Jazzmen

JUBILEE.
Album: released on Burlington, May'86 by Plant Life Records. Dist: Jazz Music, Celtic Music, Clyde Factors Distributors, I.R.S., Projection, Wellard, Chris, Roots

LATEST RELEASE.
Album: released on Burlington, May'86 by Plant Life Records. Dist: Jazz Music, Celtic Music, Clyde Factors Distributors, I.R.S., Projection, Wellard, Chris, Roots

SAVOY JAZZMEN, THE.
Album: released on Burlington, Oct'86 by Plant Life Records. Dist: Jazz Music, Celtic Music, Clyde Factors Distributors, I.R.S., Projection, Wellard, Chris, Roots

SAVOY RAG.
Album: released on Burlington, Nov'81 by Plant Life Records. Dist: Jazz Music, Celtic Music, Clyde Factors Distributors, I.R.S., Projection, Wellard, Chris, Roots

YOU'VE GOT THE RIGHT KEY....
Album: released on Burlington, May'86 by Plant Life Records. Dist: Jazz Music, Celtic Music, Clyde Factors Distributors, I.R.S., Projection, Wellard, Chris, Roots

YOU'VE GOT THE RIGHT KEY.
Album: released on Burlington, Nov'81 by Plant Life Records. Dist: Jazz Music, Celtic Music, Clyde Factors Distributors, I.R.S., Projection, Wellard, Chris, Roots

Savoy Orphans

STOMP OFF,LET'S GO!.
Album: released on Halcyon (USA), Jan'87 by Halcyon Records (USA). Dist: Jazz Music, Conifer, Taylors

Saw, Tenor

CLASH (Saw, Tenor & Don Angelo).
Album: released on Witty, '85 by Witty Records. Dist: Jetstar

GOLDEN HEN (THE) (Saw, Tenor & Don Angelo).
Album: released on Uptempo, '85 by Uptempo Records. Dist: Jetstar Distribution

Saw Thunder

MANOEUVRES.
Album: released on Bullet, Dec'84 Dist: Bullet Distribution

Sawyer, Nigel

LAST LOVE SONG / TO KIRKHAM & BEYOND.
Single (7"): released on RCA, Sep'82 by RCA Records. Dist: RCA, Roots, Swift, Wellard, Chris, I & B, Solomon & Peres Distribution

Sawyer, Roy

I'M READY TO FALL IN LOVE AGAIN.
Single (7"): released on Premier, Oct'85 by Premier Records. Dist: CBS

Sax Happy

FACTORY SONG.
Single (7"): released on Take A Hammer, Feb'83 by Take A Hammer Records. Dist: Cartel Distribution

Sax Maniacs

NEVER GONNA LOSE ME.
Single (7"): released on Penthouse, Mar'81 by Penthouse Records. Dist: Pinnacle

ONE HUNDRED AND EIGHTY.
Single (7"): released on Penthouse, Nov'81 by Penthouse Records. Dist: Pinnacle

SARA SARA KI KI.
Single (7"): released on Penthouse, Jun'82 by Penthouse Records. Dist: Pinnacle

Saxon

Biographical Details: Heavy metal band Saxon was formed in 1977in Yorkshire, England, by vocalist Peter 'Biff' Byford (born 5 January1951); Paul Quinn, Graham Oliver, guitars; Steve Dawson, bass; Pete Gill, drums. They showed some lyrical ability not restricted to the tired sex and sword-and-sorcery themes of some of the others. [Donald Clarke, April 87]

BACK ON THE STREETS.
Single (7"): released on Parlophone, Jul'85 by EMI Records. Dist: EMI

Single (12"): released on Parlophone, Jul'85 by EMI Records. Dist: EMI

Single (12"): released on Parlophone, Aug'85 by EMI Records. Dist: EMI

BACKS TO THE WALL.
Single (7"): released on Carrere, Jul'80 by Carrere Records. Dist: PRT, Spartan

BIG TEASER.
Single (7"): released on Carrere, Jun'80 by Carrere Records. Dist: PRT, Spartan

Album: released on Carrere, Mar'85 by Carrere Records. Dist: PRT, Spartan

Cassette: released on Carrere, Mar'85 by Carrere Records. Dist: PRT, Spartan

Album: released on Carrere, Mar'85 by Carrere Records. Dist: PRT, Spartan

Album: released on Parlophone, Jan'86 by EMI Records. Dist: EMI

Cassette: released on Parlophone, Jan'86 by EMI Records. Dist: EMI

CRUSADER.
Tracks: / Crusader prelude(The) / Crusader / Little bit of what you fancy (A) / Sailing to America / Set me free / Just let me rock / Bad boys (Like to rock 'n' roll) / Do it all for you / Rock city / Run for your lives.
Notes: Originally released in February 1984. Recorded in America and produced by Kevin Beamish(an American mainstream rock producer who has done a lot of work with Reo Speedwagon). Their whole image while touring in 1984 surrounded the idea of 'Crusader' in their stage set,costumes etc. Original gatefold sleeve.
Album: released on EMI, '86 by EMI Records. Dist: EMI

Cassette: released on EMI, '86 by EMI Records. Dist: EMI

DENIM AND LEATHER.
Album: released on Fame, May'87 by Music For Pleasure Records. Dist: EMI

Cassette: released on Fame, May'87 by Music For Pleasure Records. Dist: EMI

DENIM & LEATHER.
Tracks: / Princess of the night / Never surrender / Out of control / Rough & ready / Play it loud / And the bands played on / Midnight rider / Fire in the sky / Denim & leather.
Album: released on Fame, May'87 by Music For Pleasure Records. Dist: EMI

Cassette: released on Fame, May'87 by Music For Pleasure Records. Dist: EMI

DO IT ALL FOR YOU.
Single (7"): released on Carrere, May'84 by Carrere Records. Dist: PRT, Spartan

Single (12"): released on Carrere, May'84 by Carrere Records. Dist: PRT, Spartan

EAGLE HAS LANDED (THE).
Tracks: / 747 (Strangers in the night) / Princess of the night / Strong arm of the law / Heavy metal thunder / 20,000 ft / Wheels of steel / Never surrender / Fire in the sky / Machine gun / Rock the nations / 747(Strangers in the night) and the band played on.
Notes: Live album recorded on their UK 1982 tour. So called because of the large eagle on their stage backdrop. First album with Nigel Glocker on drums.
Album: released on EMI, '86 by EMI Records. Dist: EMI

Cassette: released on EMI, '86 by EMI Records. Dist: EMI

FLIPHITS (4 TRACK CASSETTE EP).
Cassette: released on Carrere, Jul'83 by Carrere Records. Dist: PRT, Spartan

INNOCENCE IS NO EXCUSE.
Album: released on Parlophone, Sep'85 by EMI Records. Dist: EMI

Cassette: released on Parlophone, Sep'85 by EMI Records. Dist: EMI

Picture disc album: released on Parlophone, Sep'85 by EMI Records. Dist: EMI

LIVE INNOCENCE.
Notes: Number of tracks: 12. Type of recording:Live. Total playing time: 60 minutes.
Video-cassette (VHS): released on PMI, '86 by PMI Records. Dist: EMI

Video-cassette [Betamax]: released on PMI, '86 by PMI Records. Dist: EMI

NEVER SURRENDER.
Single (7"): released on Carrere, Jul'81 by Carrere Records. Dist: PRT, Spartan

NIGHTMARE.
Single (7"): released on Carrere, Jul'83 by Carrere Records. Dist: PRT, Spartan

Single (12"): released on Carrere, Jul'83 by Carrere Records. Dist: PRT, Spartan

Picture disc single: released on Carrere, Jul'83 by Carrere Records. Dist: PRT, Spartan

NORTHERN LADY.
Tracks: / Everybody up(live in madrid) / Dallas 1PM (live in Madrid)*.
Single (7"): released on EMI, Jan'87 by EMI Records. Dist: EMI

Single (12"): released on EMI, Jan'87 by EMI Records. Dist: EMI

POWER AND THE GLORY.
Single (7"): released on Carrere, Apr'83 by Carrere Records. Dist: PRT, Spartan

Single (12"): released on Carrere, Apr'83 by Carrere Records. Dist: PRT, Spartan

Picture disc single: released on Carrere, Apr'83 by Carrere Records. Dist: PRT, Spartan

POWER AND THE GLORY.
Tracks: / Power and the glory / Redline / Warrior / Nightmare / This town rocks / Watching the sky / Midas touch / Eagle has landed (The).
Notes: Originally released in March 1983. First attempt to break in American rock market. Produced by well known American producer Jeff Glixman who has recently worked with Black Sabbath.
Album: released on EMI, '86 by EMI Records. Dist: EMI

Cassette: released on EMI, '86 by EMI Records. Dist: EMI

Album: released on Carrere, Mar'83 by Carrere Records. Dist: PRT, Spartan

Cassette: released on Carrere, Mar'83 by Carrere Records. Dist: PRT, Spartan

PRINCESS OF THE NIGHT.
Single (7"): released on Carrere, Oct'81 by Carrere Records. Dist: PRT, Spartan

ROCKIN AGAIN H.
Single (7"): released on Parlophone, Sep'85 by EMI Records. Dist: EMI

Single (12"): released on Parlophone, Sep'85 by EMI Records. Dist: EMI

ROCK'N'ROLL GIPSY.
Tracks: / Rock 'n' roll gipsy / Krakatoa 1 / Rock 'n' roll gipsy / Krakatoa / Medley (The) : Heavy metal thunder / Stand up and be counted / Taking your chances / Warrior.
Single (7"): released on Parlophone, '86 by EMI Records. Dist: EMI

Single (12"): released on Parlophone, '86 by EMI Records. Dist: EMI

ROCK THE NATIONS.
Tracks: / Rock the nations / Battle cry / Waiting for the night / We came here to rock / You ain't no angel / Running hot / Party 'til you puke / Empty promises / Motorcycle man / Northern lady.
Compact disc: released on EMI, Jan'87 by EMI Records. Dist: EMI

Album: released on EMI, '86 by EMI Records. Dist: EMI

Cassette: released on EMI, '86 by EMI Records. Dist: EMI

Single (7"): released on EMI, '86 by EMI Records. Dist: EMI

Single (12"): released on EMI, '86 by EMI Records. Dist: EMI

Picture disc single: released on EMI, '86 by EMI Records. Dist: EMI

SAILING TO AMERICA.
Single (7"): released on Carrere, Jan'84 by Carrere Records. Dist: PRT, Spartan

Single (12"): released on Carrere, Jan'84 by Carrere Records. Dist: PRT, Spartan

SAXON.
Album: released on Parlophone, Jan'86 by EMI Records. Dist: EMI

Cassette: released on Parlophone, Jan'86 by EMI Records. Dist: EMI

STRONG ARM METAL.
Album: released on Carrere, Dec'84 by Carrere Records. Dist: PRT, Spartan

Cassette: released on Carrere, Dec'84 by Carrere Records. Dist: PRT, Spartan

Album: released on Parlophone, Jan'86 by EMI Records. Dist: EMI. Estim retail price in Jul'87 was £3.99.

Cassette: released on Parlophone, Jan'86 by EMI Records. Dist: EMI

STRONG ARM OF THE LAW.
Tracks: / Heavy metal thunder / To hell & back again / Strong arm of the law / Taking your chances / 20,000 Ft. / Hungry years / Sixth form girls / Dallas 1pm.
Album: released on Fame, May'87 by Music For Pleasure Records. Dist: EMI

Cassette: released on Fame, May'87 by Music For Pleasure Records. Dist: EMI

Single (7"): released on Carrere, Nov'80 by Carrere Records. Dist: PRT, Spartan

Single (12"): released on Carrere, Nov'80 by Carrere Records. Dist: PRT, Spartan

SUZY HOLD ON.
Single (7"): released on Carrere, Sep'80 by Carrere Records. Dist: PRT, Spartan

Single (12"): released on Carrere, Sep'80 by Carrere Records. Dist: PRT, Spartan

WAITING FOR THE NIGHT.
Tracks: / Waiting for the train (Extended Version) / Chase the fade.
Single (7"): released on EMI, '86 by EMI Records. Dist: EMI

Single (12"): released on EMI, '86 by EMI Records. Dist: EMI

WHEELS OF STEEL.
Tracks: / Motorcycle man / Stand up and be counted / 747 (Strangers in the night) / Freeway man / See the light shining / Fighting gang / See the light shining / Fighting gang / Suzi hold on / Machine gun.
Album: released on Carrere, '85 by Carrere Records. Dist: PRT, Spartan

Cassette: released on Carrere, '85 by Carrere Records. Dist: PRT, Spartan

WHEELS OF STEEL.
Single (7"): released on Carrere, Mar'80 by Carrere Records. Dist: PRT, Spartan

Saxon, Sky

TAKES ON GLORY (Saxon, Sky 'Sunlight').
Album: released on Line, Jun'87

Saxon, Sky Blues Band

FULL SPOON OF SEEDY BLUES, (A).
Album: released on Music Box, May'87

Say Amen Somebody

SAY AMEN, SOMEBODY Original Soundtrack.
Album: released on DRG (USA), May'84 by DRG Records. Dist: Conifer, RCA

Cassette: released on DRG (USA), May'84 by DRG Records. Dist: Conifer, RCA

SAY AMEN, SOMEBODY Original soundtrack (Various Artists).
Tracks: / Highway to heaven / Singing in my soul / What manner of man / When I've done my best / Take my hand, precious Lord / I'm his child / He chose me / No ways tired / Jesus dropped the charges / I'll never turn back / Storm is passing over (The) / It's gonna rain / He brought us / Canaan.
Notes: Live recording, including Willie Mae Ford Smith, Thomas A. Dorsey, Delois Barrett Campbell & The Barrett Sisters, The O'Neal Twins, Zella Jackson Price.
Compact disc: released on DRG (USA), Mar'87 by DRG Records. Dist: Conifer, RCA

Sayer, Eddy

WATERGLASS (Sayer, Eddy & Simon Tassano).

Sayer, Leo

Biographical Details: Singer, songwriter Leo Sayer was born in Sussex on 21 May 1948. He went to art college, busked in London streets with Lol Coxhill, formed a writing partnership with David Courtney and had 15 hits in the UK in ten years from 1973, more than half in the top ten. He is still popular on TV variety shows. [Donald Clarke, April '87]

FANTASY.
Double cassette: released on Chrysalis(Take 2), Dec'82 by Chrysalis Records. Dist: CBS

HAVE YOU EVER BEEN IN LOVE.
Album: released on Chrysalis, Nov'83 by Chrysalis Records. Dist: CBS

Cassette: released on Chrysalis, Nov'83 by Chrysalis Records. Dist: CBS

HEART (STOP BEATING IN TIME).
Single (7"): released on Chrysalis, May'82 by Chrysalis Records. Dist: CBS

LEO.
Album: released on Music For Pleasure, Sep'84 by EMI Records. Dist: EMI

Cassette: released on Music For Pleasure, Sep'84 by EMI Records. Dist: EMI

LEO SAYER.
Double Album: released on Pickwick, Sep'80 by Pickwick Records. Dist: Pickwick Distribution, Prism Leisure Distribution, Lugtons

Double cassette: released on Pickwick, Sep'80 by Pickwick Records. Dist: Pickwick Distribution, Prism Leisure Distribution, Lugtons

MOONLIGHTING.
Tracks: / Long tall glasses.
Single (7"): released on Old Gold, Feb'87 by Old Gold Records. Dist: Lightning, Jazz Music, Spartan, Counterpoint

MORE THAN I CAN SAY.
Single (7"): released on Chrysalis, Jun'80 by Chrysalis Records. Dist: CBS

REAL LIFE.
Tracks: / Real life / Girl is with me (The).
Single (7"): released on Chrysalis, '86 by Chrysalis Records. Dist: CBS

SEA OF HEARTBREAK.
Single (7"): released on Chrysalis, Jan'84 by Chrysalis Records. Dist: CBS

Single (12"): released on Chrysalis, Jan'84 by Chrysalis Records. Dist: CBS

SHOW MUST GO ON.
Tracks: / One man band.
Single (7"): released on Old Gold, Feb'87 by Old Gold Records. Dist: Lightning, Jazz Music, Spartan, Counterpoint

SHOW MUST GO ON,THE.
Album: released on Pickwick, May'80 by Pickwick Records. Dist: Pickwick Distribution, Prism Leisure Distribution, Lugtons

Cassette: released on Pickwick, May'80 by Pickwick Records. Dist: Pickwick Distribution, Prism Leisure Distribution, Lugtons

SOLO.
Tracks: / Solo / Passion.
Single (7"): released on Chrysalis, '86 by Chrysalis Records. Dist: CBS

UNCHAINED MELODY.
Tracks: / Unchained melody / Heart for sale / How much love / Orchard road.
Single (7"): released on Chrysalis, '86 by Chrysalis Records. Dist: CBS

Single (12"): released on Chrysalis, '86 by Chrysalis Records. Dist: CBS

VERY BEST OF LEO SAYER.
Tracks: / You make me feel like dancing / Raining in my heart / How much love / Dancing the night away / Thunder in my heart / Can't stop lovin you (Though I try)(I) / One man band / Giving it all away / Train / Let it be / Long tall glasses / Moonlighting / Show must go on.
Album: released on Chrysalis, '79 by Chrysalis Records. Dist: CBS

Cassette: released on Chrysalis, '79 by Chrysalis Records. Dist: CBS

Compact disc: released on Chrysalis, '79 by Chrysalis Records. Dist: CBS

WHEN I NEED YOU.
Tracks: / You make me feel like dancing.
Single (7"): released on Hallmark, Feb'87 by Pickwick Records. Dist: Pickwick Distribution, PRT, Taylors

Album: released on Hallmark, Oct'82 by Pickwick Records. Dist: Pickwick Distribution, PRT, Taylors

Cassette: released on Hallmark, Oct'82 by Pickwick Records. Dist: Pickwick Distribution, PRT, Taylors

WORLD RADIO.
Tracks: / Heart (stop beating in time) / Paris dies in the morning / Have you ever been in love / Rumours / Heroes / Til you let your heart win / End of the game (The) / Wondering where the lions are / We've got ourselves in love / World radio.
Notes: Produced by Arif Mardin
Album: released on Chrysalis, '82 by Chrysalis Records. Dist: CBS

Cassette: released on Chrysalis, '82 by Chrysalis Records. Dist: CBS

Compact disc: released on Chrysalis, '82 by Chrysalis Records. Dist: CBS

Sayer, Pete

CY-CLONE.
Album: released on Country Roads Records, Nov'81 by Country Roads Records. Dist: Stage One

Sayle, Alexei

CAK.
Album: released on Springtime, Oct'82 by Springtime Records. Dist: Island Distribution, Polygram Distribution

Cassette: released on Springtime, Oct'82 by Springtime Records. Dist: Island Distribution, Polygram Distribution

FISH PEOPLE TAPES,THE.
Cassette: released on Springtime, Mar'84 by Springtime Records. Dist: Island Distribution, Polygram Distribution

MEANWHILE.
Tracks: / Meanwhile / Advertising.
Single (7"): released on CBS, '86 by CBS Records. Dist: CBS

Single (12"): released on CBS, '86 by CBS Records. Dist: CBS

PANIC.
Album: released on CBS, Dec'85 by CBS Records. Dist: CBS

Cassette: released on CBS, Dec'85 by CBS Records. Dist: CBS

PLAY THAT FUNKY MUSIC JEWISH BOY.
Single (7"): released on CBS, Nov'85 by CBS Records. Dist: CBS

Single (12"): released on CBS, Nov'85 by CBS Records. Dist: CBS

Sayzer, Michael

WHEN THE LIGHTS GO DOWN.
Single (7"): released on Musik, Oct'85 Dist: PRT Distribution, MIS-EMI Distribution

Scab Aid

LET IT BE.
Single (7"): released on Scum, Jul'87 Dist: Rough Trade, Cartel

Scadding, Sue

SIMPLE LOVER.
Single (7"): released on Speed, Aug'83

Sca-Dows

SKAS ON 45.
Single (7"): released on Penthouse, Sep'81 by Penthouse Records. Dist: Pinnacle

Single (12"): released on Penthouse, Sep'81 by Penthouse Records. Dist: Pinnacle

Scaffold

LILY THE PINK.
Single (7"): released on EMI, Oct'77 by EMI Records. Dist: EMI

SINGLES A'S & B'S.
Tracks: / 2 Day's Monday / Goodbat nightman / Thank you very much / Do you remember / 1 2 3 / Lily the pink / Charity bubbles / Gin gan goolie / Liver birds / Busdreams / Liverpool Lou / Blind jellyfish / Ide B. the first / Carry on krow / Today / Buttons of your mind / Goose / All the way up / Please sorry / Ten years after on strawberry jam / Commercial break / Do the Albert.
Album: released on See For Miles, '86 by See For Miles Records. Dist: Pinnacle

SINGLES A'S & B'S.
Album: released on See For Miles, Oct'82 by Charly Records. Dist: Spartan

Scaggs, Boz

Biographical Details: Rock singer, songwriter Boz Scaggs was born William Ross Scaggs, 8 June 1944, in Ohio. He grew up in Texas,he played in bands with schoolmate Steve Miller in Texas and in Madison, Wisconsin; later in San Francisco; he had gone to Europe with musicians who later bacame Mother Earth, he made his first solo album **Boz** for Polydor in Sweden in 1964, but his proper debut as a confident artist was in 1969 on Atlantic, with Diane Allman and Muscle Shoals Sideman; then on CBS. His albums have been selling strongly ever since, all still in print in the USA. [Donald Clarke, April 87]

BOZ SCAGGS.
Album: released on Atlantic, Jan'74 by WEA Records. Dist: WEA

BOZ SCAGGS AND BAND.
Album: released on CBS, Oct'80 by CBS Records. Dist: CBS

Cassette: released on CBS, Oct'80 by CBS Records. Dist: CBS

DOWN TWO THEN LEFT.
Album: released on CBS, Nov'77 by CBS Records. Dist: CBS

Cassette: released on CBS, Nov'77 by CBS Records. Dist: CBS

HITS.
Album: released on CBS, Dec'80 by CBS Records. Dist: CBS

Cassette: released on CBS, Dec'80 by CBS Records. Dist: CBS

MIDDLE MAN.
Album: released on CBS, May'80 by CBS Records. Dist: CBS

Cassette: released on CBS, May'80 by CBS Records. Dist: CBS

SILK DEGREES.
Tracks: / What can I say / Georgia / Jump street / What do you want the girl to do? / Harbour lights / Lowdown / It's over / Love me tomorrow / Lido shuffle / We're all alone.
Compact disc: released on CBS, '86 by CBS Records. Dist: CBS

SLOW DANCER.
Album: released on CBS, Mar'82 by CBS Records. Dist: CBS

Cassette: released on CBS, Mar'82 by CBS Records. Dist: CBS

Scaggs, Ricky
HIGHWAYS AND HEARTACHES.
Album: released on Epic, Oct'82 by CBS Records. Dist: CBS

HONEY (OPEN THAT DOOR).
Single (7"): released on Epic, Jul'84 by CBS Records. Dist: CBS

Scala
SECRET CEREMONY.
Tracks: / Secret ceremony / Wiping a tear from the all seeing eye.
Single (12"): released on Cocteau, 23 May'87 by Cocteau Records. Dist: Pinnacle, IDS

Scala, Primo
PRIMO SCALA & HIS ACCORDIAN BAND (Scala, Primo & His Accordian Band).
Album: released on Decca (Reflections), Feb'81 by Decca Records. Dist: Polygram, IMS

Scala Timpani
WINDS OF CHANGE.
Single (7"): released on Fire, Apr'85 by Twist and Shout Music. Dist: Nine Mile, Rough Trade, Cartel

Scandal
GOODBYE TO YOU.
Single (7"): released on CBS, Jan'83 by CBS Records. Dist: CBS

HANDS TIED.
Single (7"): released on CBS, Jan'85 by CBS Records. Dist: CBS

I WANNA DO IT (Scandal & Lee Genesis).
Single (7"): released on Creole, Jun'81 by Creole Records. Dist: Rhino, PRT

Single (12"): released on Creole, Jun'81 by Creole Records. Dist: Rhino. PRT

Scandanavian Evergreens
SCANDANAVIAN EVERGREENS (Accordion Orchestra & Choir).
Album: released on ARC (Accordion Records), '84 Dist: Accordion Record Club

Scanjazz
SUNSET CAFE STOMP.
Album: released on Stomp Off (USA), Jan'84

VOLUME 3.
Album: released on Stomp Off, Jun'86 by Stomp Off Records. Dist: Jazz Music Distribution

Scarab
ROCK NIGHT.
Single (7"): released on Inferno, Aug'80 by Inferno Records. Dist: Inferno, Cartel, Pinnacle

Scarbury, Joey
BELIEVE IT OR NOT.
Single (7"): released on Elektra, Oct'81 by WEA Records. Dist: WEA

Scarecrows
DEEP END.
Single (7"): released on Swordfish, Aug'85 Dist: Nine Mile Distribution, Cartel Distribution

NAPALM WITH SILVER.
Single (12"): released on Swordfish, Jan'85 Dist: Nine Mile Distribution Cartel Distribution

Scarilege
BEYOND THE REALMS OF MADNESS.
Album: released on Cor, Oct'85 Dist: Revolver, Cartel

Scarlet Alive
HEAT GOES UP (Scarlet Alive & The Terminal Jive).
Single (7"): released on Jive Alive, Oct'82 Dist: Jungle

ON EARTH AND IN HEAVEN.
Single (7"): released on Small Run, Mar'83 by Small Run Records. Dist: Pinnacle

Scarlet Party
101 DAM-NATIONS.
Single (7"): released on Parlophone, Sep'82 by EMI Records. Dist: EMI

EYES OF ICE.
Single (7"): released on Parlophone, Feb'83 by EMI Records. Dist: EMI

Scarlett
SAD SONGS ON THE RADIO.
Single (7"): released on Lamborghini, Aug'84 by Lamborghini Records. Dist: PRT

SISTERS UNDER THE SKIN.
Single (7"): released on Lamborghini, Mar'84 by Lamborghini Records. Dist: PRT

Single (12"): released on Lamborghini, Mar'84 by Lamborghini Records. Dist: PRT

Single (7"): released on Lamborghini, Oct'84 by Lamborghini Records. Dist: PRT

Scarlett & Black
YOU NEVER UNDERSTOOD ME.
Tracks: / You never understood me / Oliver (Ext.Mix).
Single (7"): released on MDM/Virgin, Sep'86 Dist: Siren, Virgin, EMI

Single (12"): released on MDM/Virgin, Sep'86 Dist: Siren, Virgin, EMI

Scarr, Geoff
CUMALOT Bawdy ballads volume 1.
Album: released on Big Ben, Apr'81 by Big Ben Records. Dist: Spartan, Taylor, H.R.

Scars
AUTHOR AUTHOR.
Album: released on Charisma, Apr'81 by Virgin Records. Dist: EMI

Cassette: released on Charisma, Apr'81 by Virgin Records. Dist: EMI

Scary Thieves
SCARY THIEVES.
Album: released on Parlophone, Mar'85 by EMI Records. Dist: EMI

Cassette: released on Parlophone, Mar'85 by EMI Records. Dist: EMI

Scatterbrain
MOUNTAINS GO RHYTHMIC.
Album: released on Irmgardz, Jul'85 Dist: Nine Mile, Cartel

Scattered Order
CAREER OF THE SILLY THING.
Album: released on Ink, Mar'86 by Red Flame. Dist: Rough Trade, Cartel, Pinnacle

ESCAPE VIA CESSNOCK.
Tracks: / Escape via cessnock.
Single (12"): released on Ink, Mar'86 by Red Flame. Dist: Rough Trade, Cartel, Pinnacle

Scatter, Peter
STRICTLY FOR DANCING (Scatter, Peter & George Charlton).
Album: released on MWM, Jun'82 by Mawson & Wareham. Dist: Spartan Distribution, Jazz Music Distribution, JSU Distribution

STRICTLY PETER SCATTER.
Album: released on MWM, Jun'82 by Mawson & Wareham. Dist: Spartan Distribution, Jazz Music Distribution, JSU Distribution

Scawta Rocks
SUDDENLY.
Single (12"): released on Rite Sound, Apr'83

Scene
GOOD LOVIN'.
Single (7"): released on Diamond, Sep'85 by Revolver Records. Dist: Cartel

Single (12"): released on Diamond, Sep'85 by Revolver Records. Dist: Cartel

I'VE HAD ENOUGH.
Single (7"): released on Inferno, Jul'80 by Inferno Records. Dist: Inferno, Cartel, Pinnacle

SOMETHING THAT YOU SAID.

Single (7"): released on Diamond, Jan'85 by Revolver Records. Dist: Cartel

Scene Of The Crime
SCENE OF THE CRIME. Various artists (Various Artists).
Album: released on Suspect, Oct'81

Schaffer, Janne
CHINESE (THE).
Tracks: / Halkans affair / Air mattress / Mignon / Filet / Daniel Sover / Harvest machine / Chinese, The / Titus / Marbles / No registration.
Album: released on Butt, Dec'86 by Butt Records. Dist: Counterpoint

TRAFFIC.
Tracks: / Emerald city, Theme from the / Flight 05 / Like a new born child / Cats eye. The / Rose tango / September / Traffic / Windshift / Springfire / Belongings.
Notes: Recorded and mixed at Sonet Studio 3. Engineers Lef Allanson and Janne Ugand. Produced by Janne Schaffer and Lef Allanson.
Album: released on Shanghai, Jul'86

Schaubroeck, Armand
ARMAND SCHAUBROECK LIVE AT THE.....
Double Album: released on Mirror, Sep'86 by Priority Records. Dist: Priority Distribution

I CAME TO VISIT, BUT DECIDED TO STAY.
Album: released on Mirror, Sep'86 by Priority Records. Dist: Priority Distribution

I SHOT MY GUARDIAN ANGEL.
Album: released on Mirror, Sep'86 by Priority Records. Dist: Priority Distribution

LOT OF PEOPLE WOULD LIKE TO SEE, A.
Triple album / cassette: released on Mirror, Sep'86 by Priority Records. Dist: Priority Distribution

RATF......
Album: released on Mirror, Sep'86 by Priority Records. Dist: Priority Distribution

SHAKIN'SHAKIN'.
Album: released on Mirror, Sep'86 by Priority Records. Dist: Priority Distribution

Scheer Music
RAPPIN' IT UP.
Album: released on Palo Alto (Italy), Jan'84

Scheid, The Elmer Story
SCHEID, THE ELMER STORY Various artists (Various Artists).
Double Album: released on ARC (Accordion Records), '84 Dist: Accordion Record Club

Schell, Daniel & Karo
IF WINDOWS THEY HAVE.
Album: released on Made To Measure, Feb'87 by Made To Measure Records. Dist: Pinnacle

Schenker, Michael
ARMED AND READY (Schenker, Michael Group).
Single (7"): released on Chrysalis, Aug'80 by Chrysalis Records. Dist: CBS

DANCER (Schenker, Michael Group).
Single (7"): released on Chrysalis, Aug'82 by Chrysalis Records. Dist: CBS

Single (12"): released on Chrysalis, Aug'82 by Chrysalis Records. Dist: CBS

MICHAEL SCHENKER GROUP (Schenker, Michael Group).
Album: released on Fame, Jun'84 by Music For Pleasure Records. Dist: EMI

Cassette: released on Fame, Jun'84 by Music For Pleasure Records. Dist: EMI

ONE NIGHT A BUDOKAN (Schenker, Michael Group).
Double Album: released on Chrysalis, Mar'82 by Chrysalis Records. Dist: CBS

Double cassette: released on Chrysalis, Mar'82 by Chrysalis Records. Dist: CBS

PORTFOLIO.
Tracks: / Doctor doctor / Rock bottom / Rock will never die / Armed and ready / Ready to rock / Assault attack / Ulcer / Attack of the mad axeman.
Compact disc: released on Chrysalis, Apr'87 by Chrysalis Records. Dist: CBS

Album: released on Chrysalis, Jul'87 by Chrysalis Records. Dist: CBS

Cassette: released on Chrysalis, Jul'87 by Chrysalis Records. Dist: CBS

ROCK WILL NEVER DIE (Schenker, Michael Group).

Album: released on Chrysalis, Jun'84 by Chrysalis Records. Dist: CBS

Cassette: released on Chrysalis, Apr'84 by Chrysalis Records. Dist: CBS

Video-cassette (VHS): released on Hendring Video, Oct'84 by Charly Records. Dist: Charly, PVG

MSG.
Tracks: / Ready to rock / Attack of the mad axeman / On and on / Let sleeping dogs lie / I want more / Never trust a stranger / Looking for love / Secondary motion.
Compact disc: released on Chrysalis, May'86 by Chrysalis Records. Dist: CBS

Album: released on Chrysalis, Sep'81 by Chrysalis Records. Dist: CBS

Cassette: released on Chrysalis, Sep'81 by Chrysalis Records. Dist: CBS

Schickele, Peter
SILENT RUNNING.
Album: released on Varese International, Mar'79

Schickert, Gunther
SAMTVOGEL.
Album: released on Brain (Germany), Aug'80

Schiller, Nina
STAY THE NIGHT.
Single (7"): released on Ecstasy, Oct'83 by Creole Records. Dist: CBS

Single (12"): released on Ecstasy, Oct'83 by Creole Records. Dist: CBS

Schilling, Peter
ALL THE LOVE I NEED.
Tracks: / All the love I need / In my youth.
Single (7"): released on WEA Int, Nov'86

Single (12"): released on WEA Int, Nov'86

MAJOR TOM Coming home.
Single (7"): released on WEA International, Sep'83 by WEA Records. Dist: WEA

Single (12"): released on WEA International, Sep'83 by WEA Records. Dist: WEA

MAJOR TOM (2 PARTS).
Single (7"): released on WEA, May'83 by WEA Records. Dist: WEA

Schizophrenia
SCHIZOPHRENIA - A VIEWPOINT (Laing, R.D.).
Cassette: released on Psychology Today, Oct'81

Schlaflose Nachte
DRUM DANCE AND SONG.
Single (12"): released on Red Flame, Jun'82

FLUSTERN.
Single (7"): released on Armageddon, Apr'82 by Armageddon Records. Dist: Revolver, Cartel, Pinnacle

Schlager Parade
SCHLAGER PARADE Various artists (Various Artists).
Notes: Featuring:Marco Bakker,Adam & Eve,Christian Anders,Catherine Valentine,Conny Froboes.
Album: released on Music For Pleasure (Holland), May'86 by EMI Records. Dist: EMI

Cassette: released on Music For Pleasure (Holland), May'86 by EMI Records. Dist: EMI

Schleimer K
FOUR TRACK EP.
Single (7"): released on Glass, Jul'82 by Glass Records. Dist: Nine Mile, Rough Trade, Red Rhino, Play It Again Sam

Schlippenbach, Alexander
PAYAN.
Album: released on Enja (Germany), Jan'82 by Enja Records (W.Germany). Dist: Cadillac Music

Schloss, Cynthia
AS IF I DIDN'T KNOW.
Single (12"): released on Revue, Jan'85 by Revue Records. Dist: Creole

COUNTRY REGGAE.
Album: released on Dub UK, Sep'85

Schmidt, Claudia
OUT OF THE DARK.
Album: released on Flying Fish (USA), Apr'86 by Flying Fish Records (USA). Dist: Roots, Projection

Schmidt, Irmin
FILM MUSIK - VOL.3/4.
Double Album: released on Spoon (Germany), Jun'84

Schmidt, Joey
JOEY, LAWRENCE AND MYRON.
Album: released on ARC (Accordion Records), '84 Dist: Accordion Record Club

Schmitt, Georges
JOY TO THE WORLD (Schmitt, Georges and Bernard Struber).
Compact disc: released on Saydisc, May'86 by Saydisc Records. Dist: Essex, Harmonia Mundi, Roots, H.R. Taylor, Jazz Music, Swift, Projection, Gamut

Schneider, Helen
HOT SUMMER NIGHTS/ SHOUTS.
Single (7"): released on WEA, Jul'82 by WEA Records. Dist: WEA

ROCK AND ROLL GYPSY.
Single (7"): released on WEA, Mar'82 by WEA Records. Dist: WEA

Schneider, John
MEMORY LIKE YOU (A).
Tracks: / What's a memory like you (doing in a love like this) / You're the last thing I needed to-night / Who cares / Somebody's gonna love her / An old rainbow jukebox and you / If we can't have forever (let's take tonight) / One more night / He finally made up her mind / One who got away (The) / Welcome home.
Compact disc: released on MCA, Apr'87 by MCA Records. Dist: Polygram, MCA

Compact disc: released on MCA, May'87 by MCA Records. Dist: Polygram, MCA

Album: released on MCA Import, Mar'86 by MCA Records. Dist: Polygram, IMS

TAKE THE LONG WAY HOME.
Tracks: / At the sound of the tone / Broken promise land, The / She's ready for someone to love her / Sounds like something I would say / Better class of losers / Gettin'even / Auction, The / This time / Just when / Take the long way home.
Album: released on MCA, Nov'86 by MCA Records. Dist: Polygram, MCA

Cassette: released on MCA, Nov'86 by MCA Records. Dist: Polygram, MCA

Compact disc: released on MCA, Apr'87 by MCA Records. Dist: Polygram, MCA

WHAT'S A MEMORY LIKE YOU (DOIN' IN A LOVE LIKE THIS).
Single (7"): released on MCA, Aug'87 by MCA Records. Dist: Polygram, MCA

YOU AIN'T SEEN THE LAST OF ME.
Tracks: / I lost my head last night / So good / When the right one comes along / Angleina / If it was anyone but you / Hillbilly / Credit / Gun-fighter, The / Redneck is the backbone of America, A / Love, you ain't seen the last of me.
Album: released on MCA, Jun'87 by MCA Records. Dist: Polygram, MCA

Cassette: released on MCA, Jun'87 by MCA Records. Dist: Polygram, MCA

Compact disc: released on MCA, Jun'87 by MCA Records. Dist: Polygram, MCA

Schnitter, David
GOLIATH.
Album: released on Muse, Apr'81 by Peerless Records. Dist: Lugtons Distributors

INVITATION.
Album: released on Muse, Apr'81 by Peerless Records. Dist: Lugtons Distributors

THUNDERING.
Album: released on Muse, Apr'81 by Peerless Records. Dist: Lugtons Distributors

Schnitzler, Conrad
CONAL.
Album: released on Uniton Records, Sep'84 by Cartel

Schoener, Eberhard
EVENTS.
Album: released on EMI (Germany), '83 by EMI Records. Dist: Conifer

Scholars
WHEN WINDS BREATHE SOFT.
Album: released on Oiseau Lyre, Apr'79

Scholfield, Stan
CHAMPIONS ENTERTAIN (Scholfield, Stan Accordion Band).

Album: released on ARC (Accordion Records), '84 Dist: Accordion Record Club

Schoof, Manfred
DISTANT THUNDER.
Album: released on Enja (Germany), Jan'82 by Enja Records (W.Germany). Dist: Cadillac Music

School Band
TAKE THEM TO SCHOOL (School Band (Alan Morgan)).
Tracks: / Tonight.
Single (7"): released on Total Eclipse, Feb'87 Dist: Spartan

Schoolboys
MISTER MOUTH/ WHILE THE OTHERS CRY.
Single (7"): released on Avatar, Feb'83 by Ava-tar Communications. Dist: CBS

School Report
THIS SONG IS CRAZY.
Single (7"): released on Mr. Sam, Aug'85

School Sinners
SCHOOLS OUT.
Tracks: / Schools out / Detention.
Single (7"): released on MBS, Jun'87 Dist: PRT

Single (12"): released on MBS, Jun'87 Dist: PRT

School Ties
HOUSE OF THE RISING SUN/ IN-SANITY.
Single (7"): released on Qwest, Dec'82 by WEA Records. Dist: WEA

Schooly-D
DEDICATION TO ALL B-BOYS.
Tracks: / Dedication to all B-Boys / I don't like rock'n'roll radio / Maniac / Gangster boogie.
Single (7"): released on Mute, Jul'87 Dist: Spartan Distribution, Rough Trade Distribution, Cartel Distribution

Single (12"): released on Mute, Jul'87 Dist: Spartan Distribution, Rough Trade Distribution, Cartel Distribution

PUT YOUR FILAS ON.
Tracks: / Put your filas on.
Single (12"): released on Flame, Oct'86 by Nimbus Records. Dist: Nimbus, Swift

SATURDAY NIGHT.
Tracks: / Saturday night / Do it do it.
Notes: Double album.
Single (12"): released on Flame, Feb'87 by Nimbus Records. Dist: Nimbus, Swift

SATURDAY NIGHT (LP).
Album: released on Flame, Jun'87 by Nimbus Records. Dist: Nimbus, Swift

Cassette: released on Flame, Jun'87 by Nim-bus Records. Dist: Nimbus, Swift

SCHOOLY-D.
Album: released on Flame, Nov'86 by Nimbus Records. Dist: Nimbus, Swift

Schroeder, Robert
BODY LOVE.
Compact disc: released on Racket (Germany), May'86

BRAIN VOYAGER.
Compact disc: released on Racket, '86 Dist: Rough Trade

BRAIN VOYAGER.
Album: released on Racket (Deutsche Austro-phon), Sep'86

Cassette: released on Racket (Deutsche Au-strophon), Sep'86

COMPUTER VOICE.
Compact disc: released on Racket (Germany), Oct'86

Album: released on Racket (Germany), Aug'85

PARADISE.
Compact disc: released on Racket, '86 Dist: Rough Trade

SPACE DETECTIVE (DANCE MIX)/ SKY WALKER.
Single (12"): released on IC (Germany), Dec'83 by Innovative Communication Records. Dist: Impex Musik Distribution

Schubert, Adrian
ADRAN SCHUBERT & HIS SALON OR-CHESTRA (Schubert, Adran & His Salon Or-chestra/I.Kaufman/H.Lambert).
Album: released on Collectors Items, Jul'86 Dist: Jazz Music, Swift, Chris Wellard

Schulman, Ira
BLOWIN' WITH THE WIND.
Album: released on Trend (USA), Aug'84 by Discovery Records. Dist: Flexitron Distributors Ltd, Swift

Schultze, Kristian
EXPEDITION EXTRA.
Album: released on Erdenklang (Germany), Jun'84

Schultz & Kurly Band
WEGGIS SONG/ AM BACHALPSEE.
Single (7"): released on Square Peg, Dec'81

Schulze, Klaus
ANGST.
Album: released on Inteam, Apr'84 by Inteam Records. Dist: Impex Distribution

Album: released on Virgin, Mar'84 by Virgin Records. Dist: EMI, Virgin Distribution

APHRICA (Schulze, Klaus / Rainer Bloss).
Album: released on Inteam, Apr'84 by Inteam Records. Dist: Impex Distribution

AUDENTITY.
Compact disc: released on Innovative Com-munication, May'86 by Innovative Communica-tion Records. Dist: Pickwick Distribution

BLACK DANCE.
Tracks: / Ways of change / Some velvet phas-ing / Voices of Syn.
Compact disc: released on Virgin, Jun'87 by Virgin Records. Dist: EMI, Virgin Distribution

BODY LOVE.
Compact disc: released on Brain (Germany), May'86

CYBORG.
Album: released on Isadora(France), Jan'78 Dist: Stage One

DIG IT.
Album: released on Brain, Dec'80

DREAMS.
Album: released on Thunderbolt, Apr'87 by Magnum Music Group Ltd. Dist: Magnum Music Group Ltd, PRT Distribution, Spartan Distribu-tion

DRIVE INN (Schulze, Klaus / Rainer Bloss).
Tracks: / Drive Inn / Sightseeing / Truckin' / Highway / Racing / Road to clear / Drive out.
Notes: Cult act.Former Tangerine Dream members
Album: released on Thunderbolt, Feb'86 by Magnum Music Group Ltd. Dist: Magnum Music Group Ltd, PRT Distribution, Spartan Distribu-tion

Compact disc: released on Thunderbolt, May'86 by Magnum Music Group Ltd. Dist: Magnum Music Group Ltd, PRT Distribution, Spartan Distribution

Album: released on Inteam, Apr'84 by Inteam Records. Dist: Impex Distribution

Album: released on Thunderbolt, Sep'85 by Magnum Music Group Ltd. Dist: Magnum Music Group Ltd, PRT Distribution, Spartan Distribu-tion

DUNE.
Compact disc: released on Brain (Germany), May'86

Album: released on Brain (Germany), May'80

IRRLICHT.
Album: released on Isadora(France), Jan'78 Dist: Stage One

MIRAGE.
Album: released on Thunderbolt, Nov'86 by Magnum Music Group Ltd. Dist: Magnum Music Group Ltd, PRT Distribution, Spartan Distribu-tion

Cassette: released on Thunderbolt, Nov'86 by Magnum Music Group Ltd. Dist: Magnum Music Group Ltd, PRT Distribution, Spartan Distribu-tion

Compact disc: released on Thunderbolt, Nov'86 by Magnum Music Group Ltd. Dist: Mag-num Music Group Ltd, PRT Distribution, Spar-tan Distribution

Album: released on Brain, Jan'78

MOONDAWN.
Album: released on Brain (Germany), '79

Album: released on Isadora(France), Jan'78 Dist: Stage One

PICTURE MUSIC.
Compact disc: released on Thunderbolt, May'87 by Magnum Music Group Ltd. Dist: Magnum Music Group Ltd, PRT Distribution, Spartan Distribution

TIME WIND.
Album: released on Virgin, Mar'84 by Virgin Records. Dist: EMI, Virgin Distribution

Schuman, Mort
SORROW.
Tracks: / Sorrow.
Single (7"): released on Sierra, Sep'86 by Sier-ra Records. Dist: WEA

Schumann, Theo
TANZ IN THEO'S BEAT BAR (Schumann, Theo Formation).
Album: released on Amigo, Sep'79 Dist: Red Rhino, Cartel

Schutz, Dieter
COMET (THE).
Album: released on Sky (Germany), Aug'86

VOYAGE.
Album: released on Sky (Germany), Jan'86

Schuur, Diane
BY DESIGN (Schuur, Dianne & Jose Felicia-no).
Tracks: / By Design.
Single (7"): released on GRP (USA), Apr'86 by GRP Records (USA). Dist: IMS, Polygram

DEEDLES & BASIE.
Album: released on GRP (USA), Aug'87 by GRP Records (USA). Dist: IMS, Polygram. Estim retail price in Sep'87 was £7.15.

Cassette: released on GRP (USA), Aug'87 by GRP Records (USA). Dist: IMS, Polygram. Estim retail price in Sep'87 was £7.15.

Compact disc: released on GRP (USA), Aug'87 by GRP Records (USA). Dist: IMS, Poly-gram. Estim retail price in Sep'87 was £13.59.

SCHUUR THING.
Tracks: / Needle in a haystack / By design / Love dance / Love you back / Someday / Some-day we'll all be free / It don't mean a thing if it ain't got that swing / American wedding song / Take me to the river / Make a plan / Sure thing.
Notes: Special guest Jose Feliciano.Superb second album from Diane Schuur.Stan Getz is featured on the key track 'It Don't Mean a thing....'and on 'Love Dance' a delightful at-mospheric ballad.Her cover of Al Green's 'Take Me To The River' is surprisingly rocky and the duets with Jose Feliciano are positively soulful.
Album: released on GRP (USA), Dec'85 by GRP Records (USA). Dist: IMS, Polygram

Cassette: released on GRP (USA), Dec'85 by GRP Records (USA). Dist: IMS, Polygram

Compact disc: released on GRP (USA), Dec'85 by GRP Records (USA). Dist: IMS, Poly-gram

TIMELESS.
Tracks: / How long has this been going on? / Easy to love / Come rain or come shine / How about me / Do nothin'till you hare from me / Time for love, A / Time for love,A / I can't believe that you're in love with me / Please send me some-one to love / Impossible / Don't like goodbyes.
Notes: 'Timeless' is an enthralling emotion-packed album of unforgettable evergreens, lovingly etched by four brilliant arrangers.They include the legendly Billy May,Pat Wil-liams,Johnny Mandel and Jeremy Lubbock.The compact disc version will inc-lude two additional bonus tracks that do not appear on the album and cassette version.They are 'Travel-lin'Blues'and 'Too Late Now'
Album: released on GRP (USA), Oct'86 by GRP Records (USA). Dist: IMS, Polygram

Cassette: released on GRP (USA), Oct'86 by GRP Records (USA). Dist: IMS, Polygram

Compact disc: released on GRP (USA), Oct'86 by GRP Records (USA). Dist: IMS, Polygram

Schwaller, Schwaller
ROMAN SCHWALLER QUARTET.
Notes: With: Don Freidman, M. Johnson, Heinz Leid.
Album: released on Four Leaf Clover, Jul'87 Dist: Jazz Music, Swift

Schwartz, Arthur
FROM THE PEN OF....
Album: released on RCA, Nov'84 by RCA Rec-ords. Dist: RCA, Roots, Swift, Wellard, Chris, I & B, Solomon & Peres Distribution

Cassette: released on RCA, Nov'84 by RCA Records. Dist: RCA, Roots, Swift, Wellard, Chris, I & B, Solomon & Peres Distribution

Schwartz, Eddie
ALL OUR TOMORROWS/ TONIGHT.
Single (7"): released on Atco, Mar'82 by Atlan-tic Records. Dist: WEA

Schwarz, Brinsley
SILVER PISTOL.
Album: released on Edsel, Apr'86 by Demon

Records. Dist: Pinnacle, Jazz Music, Projection

Schwarzkopf, Elizabeth

BARCAROLLE.
Single (7"): released on H.M.V., Dec'85 by EMI Records. Dist: EMI

Schwarz, Tracey & Eloise

HOME AMONG THE HILLS.
Album: released on Bear Family, Oct'80 by Bear Family Records. Dist: Rollercoaster Distribution, Swift

Schwarzwalder Kirschtprte

UNSER HAUMEISTER.
Cassette: released on Slob, Feb'84 by Slob Records. Dist: Falling A Distribution

Schwingungen

SCHWINGUNGEN(NEW AGE MUSIC) Various artists (Various Artists).
Album: released on Sky (Germany), Jan'86

Science

TOKYO.
Single (7"): released on Rialto, Jan'81 by Rialto Records. Dist: Pinnacle

Science Fiction Soundbook

SCIENCE FICTION SOUNDBOOK (Shatner, William & Leonard Nimoy).
Special: released on Caedmon(USA), Sep'80 by Caedmon (USA) Records. Dist: Gower, Taylors, Discovery

Special: released on Caedmon(USA), Sep'80 by Caedmon (USA) Records. Dist: Gower, Taylors, Discovery

Science Looks At Speech

SCIENCE LOOKS AT SPEECH (Fry, Dr. D.B.).
Cassette: released on Seminar Cassettes, Oct'81

Scientific Americans

LOAD AND GO.
Cassette: released on Reach Out Int, '83

Scientific Approach...

SCIENTIFIC APPROACH TO RELIGION (Hardy, Sir Alister).
Cassette: released on Seminar Cassettes, Oct'81

Scientific View...

SCIENTIFIC VIEW OF MEDITATION (Ornstein, Proffessor Robert).
Cassette: released on Seminar Cassettes, Oct'81

Scientist

BIG SHOWDOWN 1980, THE (Scientist & Prince Jammy).
Album: released on Greensleeves, Feb'80 by Greensleeves Records. Dist: BMG, Jetstar, Spartan

CRUCIAL CUTS.
Album: released on Kingdom, '84 by Kingdom Records. Dist: Kingdom

CRUCIAL CUTS VOL.II.
Album: released on Kingdom Records, Apr'86 by Kingdom Records. Dist: Kingdom Records

Cassette: released on Kingdom Records, Apr'86 by Kingdom Records. Dist: Kingdom Records

DUB DUEL AT KING TUBBY'S (Scientist V The Professor).
Album: released on Kingdom, Sep'83 by Kingdom Records. Dist: Kingdom

HEAVYWEIGHT DUB CHAMPION.
Album: released on Greensleeves, Apr'80 by Greensleeves Records. Dist: BMG, Jetstar, Spartan

HIGH PRIEST OF DUB.
Album: released on Kingdom, Sep'83 by Kingdom Records. Dist: Kingdom

IN THE KINGDOM OF DUB.
Album: released on Kingdom, Sep'83 by Kingdom Records. Dist: Kingdom

KING OF DUB.
Compact disc: released on Motown, Mar'87 by Motown Records. Dist: BMG Distribution

PEOPLE'S CHOICE, THE.
Album: released on Kingdom, Sep'83 by Kingdom Records. Dist: Kingdom

SCIENTIST ENCOUNTERS PAC-MAN.
Album: released on Greensleeves, Nov'82 by Greensleeves Records. Dist: BMG, Jetstar, Spartan

SCIENTIST MEETS THE SPACE INVADERS.
Album: released on Greensleeves, Feb'81 by Greensleeves Records. Dist: BMG, Jetstar, Spartan

SCIENTIST WINS THE WORLD CUP.
Album: released on Greensleeves, May'82 by Greensleeves Records. Dist: BMG, Jetstar, Spartan

Scientists

ATOM BOMB BABY.
Album: released on Au-Go-Go (Australia), Aug'85 by Au-Go-Go Records (Australia). Dist: Rough Trade, Cartel

BLOOD RED RIVER.
Album: released on Au-Go-Go (Australia), '83 by Au-Go-Go Records (Australia). Dist: Rough Trade, Cartel

HAPPY HOUR/SWAMPLAND.
Single (7"): released on Au-Go-Go (Australia), Oct'83 by Au-Go-Go Records (Australia). Dist: Rough Trade, Cartel

HEADING FOR A TRAUMA.
Album: released on Au-Go-Go (Australia), Oct'86 by Au-Go-Go Records (Australia). Dist: Rough Trade, Cartel

HUMAN JUKEBOX, THE.
Album: released on Karbon, Aug'87 by Karbon Records. Dist: Pinnacle, Red Rhino, Cartel

SCIENTISTS & RESPONSIBILITY (Pauling, Proffessor Linus).
Cassette: released on Seminar Cassettes, Oct'81

THIS HEART DOESN'T RUN ON BLOOD.
Album: released on Au-Go-Go (Australia), Nov'84 by Au-Go-Go Records (Australia). Dist: Rough Trade, Cartel

WE HAD LOVE/ CLEAR SPOT.
Single (7"): released on Au-Go-Go (Australia), Oct'83 by Au-Go-Go Records (Australia). Dist: Rough Trade, Cartel

WEIRD LOVE.
Album: released on Karbon, Sep'86 by Karbon Records. Dist: Pinnacle, Red Rhino, Cartel

YOU GET WHAT YOU DESERVE.
Album: released on Karbon, Jul'85 by Karbon Records. Dist: Pinnacle, Red Rhino, Cartel

YOU ONLY LIVE TWICE.
Single (7"): released on Karbon, Oct'85 by Karbon Records. Dist: Pinnacle, Red Rhino, Cartel

Sci-Fi Music Festival

SCI - FI MUSIC FESTIVAL Original Soundtrack.
Album: released on SPI Milan (France), May'85 Dist: Silva Screen

Cassette: released on SPI Milan (France), May'85 Dist: Silva Screen

Sci Fi Sex Stars

ROCKITT MISS USA.
Tracks: / Rockitt Miss USA.
Single (12"): released on Sputnikco, Oct'86

Scion Sashay

DANCEHALL QUEEN.
Single (12"): released on Jah Life, Jun'84 by Jah Life Records. Dist: Jetstar

Scion Sashay Success

PAIN-A-BACK.
Single (12"): released on Greensleeves, Aug'84 by Greensleeves Records. Dist: BMG, Jetstar, Spartan

PUT IT ON.
Single (12"): released on Jah Life, Mar'85 by Jah Life Records. Dist: Jetstar

YOUNG AFRICANS.
Single (12"): released on Jah Life, Oct'85 by Jah Life Records. Dist: Jetstar

Scissor Fits

I DON'T WANT TO WORK FOR BRITISH AIRWAYS.
Single (7"): released on Dubious, Oct'79 by Lobster Factory. Dist: Rough Trade, Stage One

Sclavis, Louis

AD AUGUSTA PER AUGUSTIA.
Tracks: / La signification des choix musicaux / Musique pour une ceromonie / Jour plus tard / Per angustia / Le pardon / Levo levo / Vitesses / Ad augusta.
Album: released on Nato (France), Sep'86 by Disques Nato. Dist: Essex Record Distributors Ltd.

RECONTRES.
Tracks: / Week-end du lundi / L'Echappe / To meet / Les brumes / Simili / Advantage / Russe (The) / Pour memoire.
Album: released on Nato (France), Sep'86 by Disques Nato. Dist: Essex Record Distributors Ltd.

Scobey, Bob

ALEXANDER'S JAZZ BAND (Scobey, Bob, Alexander's Jazz Band).
Album: released on Dawn Club, Dec'86 Dist: Cadillac, Swift, JSU

BOB SCOBEY'S FRISCO BAND.
Compact disc: released on London, Apr'87 by London Records. Dist: Polygram

Scofield, John

9SHINOLA.
Album: released on Enja (Germany), Jan'82 by Enja Records (W.Germany). Dist: Cadillac Music

BLUE MATTER.
Tracks: / Blue matter / Trim / Heaven hill / So you say / Now she's blonde / Make me / Nag, The / Time marches on.
Notes: All compositions written by John Schofield. Executive Producer: Jonathan F.P. Rose. Produced by Steve Swallow. Recorded at Media Sound, New York, N.Y. Septem ber 1986.
Album: released on Sonet, Mar'87 by Sonet Records. Dist: PRT

ELECTRIC OUTLET.
Tracks: / Just my luck / Big break / Best western / Pick hits / Filibuster / Thanks again / King for a day / Phone home.
Compact disc: released on Gramavision (USA), May'86 by Gramavison Records (USA). Dist: PRT, IMS, Polygram

Album: released on Gramavision (USA), Nov'84 by Gramavison Records (USA). Dist: PRT, IMS, Polygram

Cassette: released on Gramavision (USA), Nov'84 by Gramavison Records (USA). Dist: PRT, IMS, Polygram

JOHN SCOFIELD - LIVE.
Album: released on Enja (Germany), Jan'82 by Enja Records (W.Germany). Dist: Cadillac Music

ROUGH HOUSE.
Album: released on Enja (Germany), Jan'82 by Enja Records (W.Germany). Dist: Cadillac Music

STILL WARM.
Album: released on Sonet, Jan'87 by Sonet Records. Dist: PRT

Compact disc: released on Gramavision (USA), May'86 by Gramavison Records (USA). Dist: PRT, IMS, Polygram

Album: released on Gramavision (USA), Apr'86 by Gramavison Records (USA). Dist: PRT, IMS, Polygram

Scooby Doo

GHOSTLY APACHE.
Cassette: released on Look & Listen, Nov'84 by Listen For Pleasure. Dist: EMI

HORROR AT HANGWOOD HALL.
Cassette: released on Look & Listen, Nov'84 by Listen For Pleasure. Dist: EMI

PHANTOM PARROT, THE.
Cassette: released on Look & Listen, Nov'84 by Listen For Pleasure. Dist: EMI

Scoop

PANIC/NEVER DRESS RIGHT.
Single (7"): released on Towerbell, Jan'82 by Towerbell Records. Dist: EMI

Scorched Earth

I DON'T WANT TO FIGHT IN YOUR WARS.
Single (7"): released on Page One, Mar'83 by Page, Larry. Dist: PRT, Spartan

TOMORROW NEVER COMES/QUESTIONS.
Single (12"): released on Carrere, Feb'85 by Carrere Records. Dist: PRT, Spartan

Scorcher

WAKE UP THE PARTY.
Album: released on Scorcher, Dec'86

Scorcher, Erroll

ROACH IN THE CORNER.
Single (7"): released on D. Roy, Apr'80

RUDE BOY STEP/LETTING GO.
Single (12"): released on Jux, Apr'82

Scorpions

Biographical Details: The German heavy metal band the Scorpions was formed in Hanover in 1970 by guitarist brothers Michael and Rudolph Schenker (Rudolf born in 1952) with Klaus Meine, vocals; Lothar Heimberg, bass; Wolfgang Dziony, drums. First album **Lonesome Crow** in 1972 sold well in Germany, led to film score work **The Cold Paradise**, but Michael quit in 1973 to join UFO; Rudy re-formed with Meine and Ulrich Roth, guitar; Francis Buchholz, bass; Jorgen Rosenthal, drums. They went from strength to strength, becoming a top attraction in Japan in the late 70's and having surprising success in America. [Donald Clarke, April 87]

ACTION.
Album: released on Brain (Germany), May'80

ANIMAL MAGNETISM.
Album: released on Harvest, May'80 by EMI Records. Dist: Roots, EMI

Cassette: released on Harvest, May'80 by EMI Records. Dist: Roots, EMI

BEST OF THE SCORPIONS.
Tracks: / Steam rock fever / Pictured life / Robot man / Back stage queen / Speedy's coming / Hellcat / He's a woman she's a man / In trance / Dark lady / Sails of Charon, The / Virgin killer.
Album: released on RCA, Sep'81 by RCA Records. Dist: RCA, Roots, Swift, Wellard, Chris, I & B, Solomon & Peres Distribution

Cassette: released on RCA, Sep'81 by RCA Records. Dist: RCA, Roots, Swift, Wellard, Chris, I & B, Solomon & Peres Distribution

Compact disc: released on RCA, Sep'81 by RCA Records. Dist: RCA, Roots, Swift, Wellard, Chris, I & B, Solomon & Peres Distribution

BLACKOUT.
Tracks: / Blackout / Can't live without you / No one like you / You give me all I need / Now / Dynamite / Arizona / China white / When the smoke is going down.
Album: released on Fame (Harvest), May'85 by Music For Pleasure Records. Dist: EMI

Cassette: released on Fame (Harvest), May'85 by Music For Pleasure Records. Dist: EMI

Compact disc: released on Harvest, Oct'87 by EMI Records. Dist: Roots, EMI

CAN'T LIVE WITHOUT YOU.
Single (7"): released on Harvest, Jul'82 by EMI Records. Dist: Roots, EMI

FIRST STING VIDEO EP.
Notes: A West German heavy rock band showcase four tracks from two albums, among them 'Blackout' and 'Love At First Sting'. Hi-fi soundtrack.
Video-cassette (VHS): released on PMI, Jun'86 by PMI Records. Dist: EMI

Video-cassette [Betamax]: released on PMI, Jun'86 by PMI Records. Dist: EMI

FLY TO THE RAINBOW.
Album: released on RCA, Oct'85 by RCA Records. Dist: RCA, Roots, Swift, Wellard, Chris, I & B, Solomon & Peres Distribution

Cassette: released on RCA, Oct'85 by RCA Records. Dist: RCA, Roots, Swift, Wellard, Chris, I & B, Solomon & Peres Distribution

GOLD ROCK.
Album: released on Brain (Germany), Nov'77

IN TRANCE.
Album: released on RCA International (USA), '84 by RCA Records. Dist: RCA

Cassette: released on RCA International (USA), '84 by RCA Records. Dist: RCA

LONESOME CROW.
Album: released on Heavy Metal, Nov'82 by FM-Revolver Records. Dist: EMI

Picture disc album: released on Heavy Metal, Nov'82 by FM-Revolver Records. Dist: EMI

Cassette: released on Heavy Metal Worldwide, Jul'85 by FM-Revolver Records. Dist: EMI

Album: released on Razor, Oct'86 by Razor. Dist: Pinnacle

LOVE AT FIRST STING.
Tracks: / Bad boys running wild / Rock you like a hurricane / I'm leaving you / Coming home / Same thrill, The / Big city nights / As soon as the good times roll / Crossfire / Still loving you.
Album: released on Harvest, Feb'84 by EMI Records. Dist: Roots, EMI

Cassette: released on Harvest, Feb'84 by EMI Records. Dist: Roots, EMI

Compact disc: released on Harvest, Feb'84 by EMI Records. Dist: Roots, EMI

LOVEDRIVE.
Album: released on Fame (Harvest), Nov'83 by Music For Pleasure Records. Dist: EMI

Cassette: released on Fame (Harvest), Nov'83

by Music For Pleasure Records. Dist: EMI

NO ONE LIKE YOU.
Single (7"): released on Harvest, Jun'85 by EMI Records. Dist: Roots, EMI

ROCK GALAXY.
Album: released on RCA (Germany), '83

TAKEN BY FORCE.
Album: released on RCA, Sep'81 by RCA Records. Dist: RCA, Roots, Swift, Wellard, Chris, I & B, Solomon & Peres Distribution

Cassette: released on RCA, Sep'81 by RCA Records. Dist: RCA, Roots, Swift, Wellard, Chris, I & B, Solomon & Peres Distribution

TAKE OFF.
Album: released on RCA (Germany), '83

TOKYO TAPES.
Tracks: / All night long / Pictured life / Backstage queen / Polar nights / In trance / We'll burn the sky / Suspender love / In search of the peace of the mind / Fly to the rainbow.
Double Album: released on RCA, '84 by RCA Records. Dist: RCA, Roots, Swift, Wellard, Chris, I & B, Solomon & Peres Distribution

Double cassette: released on RCA, '84 by RCA Records. Dist: RCA, Roots, Swift, Wellard, Chris, I & B, Solomon & Peres Distribution

Double compact disc: released on RCA, '84 by RCA Records. Dist: RCA, Roots, Swift, Wellard, Chris, I & B, Solomon & Peres Distribution

VIRGIN KILLER.
Album: released on RCA, Feb'77 by RCA Records. Dist: RCA, Roots, Swift, Wellard, Chris, I & B, Solomon & Peres Distribution

VIRGIN KILLER (IMPORT).
Album: released on RCA (Germany). '83

WORLD WIDE LIVE.
Tracks: / Countdown / Coming home / Blackout / Bad boys running wild / Loving you sunday morning / Make it real / Big city nights / Coast to coast / Holiday / Still loving you / Rock you like a hurricane / Can't live without you / Zoo, The / No-one like you / Dynamite.
Notes: Video information. Type of recording: Live. Total playing time: 60 minutes.
Compact disc: released on Harvest, Feb'86 by EMI Records. Dist: Roots, EMI

Video-cassette (VHS): released on PMI, Jun'86 by PMI Records. Dist: EMI

Video-cassette (Betamax): released on PMI, Jun'86 by PMI Records. Dist: EMI

Album: released on Harvest, Jun'85 by EMI Records. Dist: Roots, EMI

Cassette: released on Harvest, Jun'85 by EMI Records. Dist: Roots, EMI

Scotch
DIACO BAND.
Single (12"): released on Red Bus, Jun'85 by Red Bus Records. Dist: PRT

Scotch Measure
SCOTCH MEASURE.
Album: released on Topic, Nov'86 Dist: Roots Distribution

Scotch Mist
HOOTS MON/RED RIVER VALLEY.
Single (7"): released on Starblend, Nov'82 by Starblend Records. Dist: PRT Distribution

Scotdisc Premiere...
GO COUNTRY WESTERN.
Album: released on Scotdisc, Dec'86 Dist: Clyde Factors Distributors

Cassette: released on Scotdisc, Dec'86 Dist: Clyde Factors Distributors

Scotland
ALL THE BEST FROM SCOTLAND (Various Artists).
Cassette: released on Lismor, Jul'80 by Lismor Records. Dist: Lismor, Roots, Celtic Music

ALL THE BEST FROM SCOTLAND VOL.2 (Various Artists).
Cassette: released on Lochshore, May'81 by Klub Records. Dist: PRT

CALEDONIA (Various Artists).
Album: released on Nonesuch, Jul'84

SCOTLAND - THE DANCES AND THE DANCE BAND Various artists (Various Artists).
Album: released on Lismor, Jul'87 by Lismor Records. Dist: Lismor, Roots, Celtic Music

SCOTLAND - THE MUSIC OF A NATION Various artists (Various Artists).
Album: released on Lismor, Jul'87 by Lismor Records. Dist: Lismor, Roots, Celtic Music

Compact disc: released on Lismor, Aug'87 by Lismor Records. Dist: Lismor, Roots, Celtic Music

SCOTLAND-THE PIPES AND DRUMS
various artists (Scotland-The Pipes and Drums).
Compact disc: released on Lismor, Aug'87 by Lismor Records. Dist: Lismor, Roots, Celtic Music

Album: released on Lismor, Jul'87 by Lismor Records. Dist: Lismor, Roots, Celtic Music

SCOTLAND - THE SINGERS AND THE SONGS Various artists (Various Artists).
Album: released on Lismor, Jul'87 by Lismor Records. Dist: Lismor, Roots, Celtic Music

Compact disc: released on Lismor, Aug'87 by Lismor Records. Dist: Lismor, Roots, Celtic Music

THIS IS SCOTLAND (Various Artists).
Cassette: released on EMI, May'80 by EMI Records. Dist: EMI

VOICE OF SCOTLAND (Various Artists).
Album: released on Encore, Aug'79 by EMI Records. Dist: EMI Deleted '81.

Cassette: released on Encore, Aug'79 by EMI Records. Dist: EMI Deleted '81.

WORLD OF SCOTLAND VOL.2 (Various Artists).
Album: released on Decca, Jun'75 by Decca Records. Dist: Polygram

Cassette: released on Decca, Jun'75 by Decca Records. Dist: Polygram

Scotland Forever
SCOTLAND FOREVER Various artists (Various Artists).
Notes: Alistair Murdoch, Ron Gonella, The Reg. Band of the Scots Guards and The Pipes & Drums of the 2nd. Bn. Scots Guards and various other artists
Album: released on Ross, '86 by Ross Records. Dist: Ross Distribution, Roots Distribution

Cassette: released on Ross, '86 by Ross Records. Dist: Ross Distribution, Roots Distribution

Scotland The What?
HOW ARE THINGS IN AUCHTERTURRA?.
Album: released on STW, Jan'87

Cassette: released on STW, Jan'87

Scotland World Cup Squad
BIG TRIP TO MEXICO.
Tracks: / Big trip to mexico / Carry the hopes of Scotland.
Single (7"): released on Columbia, Apr'86 by EMI Records. Dist: EMI

SCOTLAND WORLD CUP SQUAD Argentina 1978.
Album: released on Klub, Jun'78

Scots Country Comfort
STILL ROLLIN'.
Album: released on Ross, '86 by Ross Records. Dist: Ross Distribution, Roots Distribution

Cassette: released on Ross, '86 by Ross Records. Dist: Ross Distribution, Roots Distribution

Scots Dragoon Guards
ORIGINAL VERSION OF AMAZING GRACE.
Album: released on RCA Camden, '82 by RCA Records. Dist: Pickwick Distribution, Taylor, H.R.

Cassette: released on RCA Camden, '82 by RCA Records. Dist: Pickwick Distribution, Taylor, H.R.

Scots Guards...
CRAGS OF TUMBLEDOWN MOUNTAIN (Scots Guards Pipes & Drums Band).
Single (7"): released on Ross, Jan'83 by Ross Records. Dist: Ross. Distribution, Roots Distribution

Scots Song & Music
SCOTS SONG AND MUSIC Various artists (Volume 1) (Various Artists).
Album: released on Springthyme, '83 by Springthyme Records. Dist: Folksound Distribution

Cassette: released on Springthyme, '83 by Springthyme Records. Dist: Folksound Distribution

SCOTS SONG AND MUSIC Various artists (Volume 2) (Various Artists).
Album: released on Springthyme, '83 by Springthyme Records. Dist: Folksound Distribution

Scott, Amanda
LIES.
Tracks: / Experience.
Single (7"): released on Starbland, Feb'87 by Starbland Records. Dist: PRT Distribution

Single (12"): released on Starbland, Feb'87 by Starbland Records. Dist: PRT Distribution

Scott, Andy
INVISIBLE.
Single (7"): released on Statik, Apr'85 Dist: Rough Trade Distribution, Stage One Distribution

Single (12"): released on Statik, Apr'85 Dist: Rough Trade Distribution, Stage One Distribution

KRUGGERRANDS.
Single (7"): released on Statik, Nov'83 Dist: Rough Trade Distribution, Stage One Distribution

Single (12"): released on Statik, Nov'83 Dist: Rough Trade Distribution, Stage One Distribution

LET HER DANCE.
Single (7"): released on Statik, Sep'84 Dist: Rough Trade Distribution, Stage One Distribution

Single (12"): released on Statik, Sep'84 Dist: Rough Trade Distribution, Stage One Distribution

Scott, Cynthia
JUGGLER OF HEARTS.
Single (7"): released on Red Flame, Jan'84

Single (12"): released on Red Flame, Jan'84

X-BOY, THE.
Single (7"): released on Compact Organisation, Aug'82 Dist: PRT

Single (12"): released on Compact Organisation, Aug'82 Dist: PRT

Scott, Dave
STROLLING ALONG.
Single (7"): released on Telscot, Sep'81 by Telscot Records. Dist: Telscot Distribution

Scott, Elfrida
BY YON CASTLE WA'.
Tracks: / Lovely Argyll / Caledonia / I know a lad / Let him go let him tarry.
Cassette: released on Ross, Dec'86 by Ross Records. Dist: Ross Distribution, Roots Distribution

Scott, Ellie
LOOK FOR ME.
Album: released on Tank, Sep'79 by Tank Records.

Scott-Heron, Gil
Biographical Details: Gil Scott-Heron was born in Chicago in 1949. He published novels The Vulture, The Nigger Factory, also poetry. He began collaborating with Brian Robert Jackson on music so as to get his social message across, half-spoken, half sung; he has a large cult audience.

1980 (Scott-Heron, Gil & Brian Jackson).
Album: released on Arista, May'85 by Arista Records. Dist: RCA

BEST OF GIL SCOTT-HERON, THE.
Album: released on Arista, Sep'84 by Arista Records. Dist: RCA

Cassette: released on Arista, Sep'84 by Arista Records. Dist: RCA

BOTTLE, THE (Scott-Heron, Gil & Brian Jackson).
Single (7"): released on Champagne, Jan'81 by DJM Records.

Single (12"): released on Champagne, Jan'81 by DJM Records.

DOTTLE, THE.
Single (7"): released on Inferno, Jul'80 by Inferno Records. Dist: Inferno, Cartel, Pinnacle

Single (12"): released on Inferno, Jul'80 by Inferno Records. Dist: Inferno, Cartel, Pinnacle

MOVING TARGET.
Album: released on Arista, Sep'82 by Arista Records. Dist: RCA

REFLECTIONS.
Album: released on Arista, Oct'81 by Arista Records. Dist: RCA

WINTER IN AMERICA.
Single (7"): released on Arista, Nov'85 by Arista Records. Dist: RCA

Single 10": released on Arista, Nov'85 by Arista Records. Dist: RCA

Scott, Isaac
ISSAC SCOTT BLUES BAND (Scott, Isaac Blues Band).
Album: released on Red Lightnin', Sep'82 by Red Lightnin' Records. Dist: Roots, Swift, Jazz Music, JSU, Pinnacle, Cartel, Wynd-Up Distribution

Scottish Dance Band...
ACCORDION CLUB NIGHT.
Notes: Robin Brock & His Band, Circassian Circle etc. - Robin Brock & His Band, Dunoon barn dance (Mrs. MacDonald of Dunach etc.) - Charlie Cowie, The Poppy leaf - Robin Brock & His Band, Jig (The rock and the wee pickle tower etc.) - Archie Duncan, De Draufganger - Robin Brock & His Band, Shetland Waltzes (Sunset over Foula etc.) - John Huband, Limehouse Blues - Robin Brock & His Band, Reel (eight men of Moidart etc.) Robin Brock & His Band, Reel (Aitken Drum etc.) - John Huband, Nuages - Robin Brock & His Band, Strathspey (Scottish Rambles etc.) - Charlie Cowie, Kilkenny Races - Archie Duncan, Wakfrieden - Robin Brock & His Band, Dundee Reel etc.) - Robin Brock & His Band, Gay Gordons (Pipe Major Sam Scott etc.)
Album: by Lismor Records. Dist: Lismor, Roots, Celtic Music

Scottish Division...
AMAZING GRACE.
Album: released on RCA Camden, '73 by RCA Records. Dist: Pickwick Distribution, Taylor, H.R.

Scottish Favourites
SCOTTISH FAVOURITES Various artists (Various Artists).
Cassette: released on Klub, Jul'81

Scottish Fiddle Orchestra
FIDDLERS RALLY VOL 1 (KELVIN HALL).
Album: released on REL, '76

Cassette: released on REL, '76

FIDDLERS RALLY VOL 2 (KELVIN HALL).
Album: released on REL, '76

Cassette: released on REL, '76

FIDDLERS TO THE FORE.
Album: released on REL, '83

Cassette: released on REL, '83

GREAT PERFORMANCES.
Album: released on Impression, Aug'84 Dist: CBS

Cassette: released on Impression, Aug'84 Dist: CBS

SCOTTISH FIDDLE ORCHESTRA AT THE ROYAL ALBERT HALL, THE.
Album: released on REL, '78

Cassette: released on REL, '78

SCOTTISH FIDDLERS PROM.
Album: released on REL, '80

Cassette: released on REL, '80

TAM O'SHANTER AND CUTTY-SARK OVERTURE, THE.
Album: released on REL, '84

Cassette: released on REL, '84

Scottish Folk...
FREEDOM COME ALL YE (Scottish Folk Singers For Ethiopia).
Album: released on Whilkie House, May'85

Scottish National...
CHRISTMAS CAROLS Cond. John Currie.
Album: released on ASV, Oct'82 by Academy Sound & Vision Records. Dist: Pinnacle

Cassette: released on ASV, Oct'82 by Academy Sound & Vision Records. Dist: Pinnacle

FIDDLER'S RALLY.
Album: released on BBC, Oct'76 by BBC Records & Tapes. Dist: EMI, PRT, Pye

Cassette: released on BBC, Oct'76 by BBC Records & Tapes. Dist: EMI, PRT, Pye

Scottish Sampler
SCOTTISH SAMPLER Various artists (Various Artists).
Album: released on BBC, Oct'76 by BBC Records & Tapes. Dist: EMI, PRT, Pye

Cassette: released on BBC, Oct'76 by BBC Records & Tapes. Dist: EMI, PRT, Pye

Scottish Tradition

SCOTTISH TRADITION VOL 1 Various artists (Various Artists).
Cassette: released on Tangent, Jan'82 by Tangent Records. Dist: Roots Records Distribution, Impetus Distribution, H.R. Taylor Distribution, Jazz Music Distribution, JSU Distribution, Projection Distribution, Gordon Duncan Distribution, Ross Records Distribution

Scottish World Cup...

WE HAVE A DREAM.
Single (7"): released on WEA, Apr'82 by WEA Records. Dist: WEA

Scott, Issac

BIG TIME BLUES MAN.
Album: released on Red Lightnin', Jul'83 by Red Lightnin' Records. Dist: Roots, Swift, Jazz Music, JSU, Pinnacle, Cartel, Wynd-Up Distribution

Scott, Jack

GREASEBALL.
Album: released on Bison Bop (Germany), Jun'85

GRIZZILY BEAR.
Tracks: / Two timin' woman / Baby she's gone / You can bet your bottom dollar / Baby baby / Found a woman / Oh little one / Patsy / Cruel world / Good deal Lucille / What in the world's come over you / Burning bridges / It only happened yesterday / Now that I / Steps one and two / Little feeling called love, A / Strange desire / My dream come true / One of these days / Grizzily bear / Cry cry cry / You only see what you wanna see / Part where I cry, The / Strangers / Laugh and the world laughs with you / Meo myo / Sad story / I can't hold your letters / If only / Green green valley / Before the bird flies / May you never be alone / Insance / Face to the wall / You're just getting better / As you take a walk through my mind.
Double Album: released on Charly, May'86 by Charly Records. Dist: Charly, Cadillac

JACK SCOTT (16 TRACKS).
Album: released on Krazy Kat, Dec'84 Dist: Jazz Music, Swift, Chris Wellard, H.R. Taylor, Charly, Hotshot, IRS Distribution

LEGENDARY, THE.
Album: released on Rockstar, Sep'82

LEGENDARY, THE (10" LP).
Album: released on Rockstar, Sep'82

SCOTT ON GROOVE.
Album: released on Bear Family (RCA), Sep'84

SPIRIT MOVES ME, THE.
Album: released on Bison Bop(West Germany), Jan'85

Scott, Jeff

KEEP ON PROVING IT (Scott, Jeff & The Hitmakers).
Single (7"): released on Surry, Aug'80

Scott, Jimmy

HUNT, THE.
Tracks: / Hunt (The) / Missing link (The).
Single (7"): released on Move, May'86 by Charly Records. Dist: Charly Distribution, Fast Forward Distribution, Cartel Distribution

Single (12"): released on Move, May'86 by Charly Records. Dist: Charly Distribution, Fast Forward Distribution, Cartel Distribution

Scott, John

SHOOTING PARTY (THE).
Album: released on Vinilo Spain, Aug'86 by Vinilo Spain Records. Dist: Silva Screen

SOUTHWARK CATHEDRAL ORGAN.
Album: released on Alpha, Aug'82 by Alpha Records. Dist: H.R. Taylor, Gamut

Scott, Maggie

DON'T FOOL AROUND WITH HIS FEELINGS.
Single (7"): released on Donut, Oct'83

Scott, Mike

KIND OF LOVING, A.
Tracks: / Kind of loving, A / Hey lady.
Single (7"): released on ESR, Jun'86 by ESR Records. Dist: ESR, Pinnacle

Scott, Millie

AUTOMATIC.
Tracks: / Automatic / Automatic(instrumental).
Single (7"): released on Fourth & Broadway, Aug'86 by Island Records. Dist: Polygram, EMI

Single (12"): released on Fourth & Broadway, Aug'86 by Island Records. Dist: Polygram, EMI

EV'RY LITTLE BIT.
Single (7"): released on Fourth & Broadway, Feb'87 by Island Records. Dist: Polygram, EMI

Single (12"): released on Fourth & Broadway, Feb'87 by Island Records. Dist: Polygram, EMI

LET'S TALK IT OVER.
Single (7"): released on Fourth & Broadway, Jun'87 by Island Records. Dist: Polygram, EMI

Single (12"): released on Fourth & Broadway, Jun'87 by Island Records. Dist: Polygram, EMI

LOVE ME RIGHT.
Tracks: / 2 hot 2 handle / Every little bit / One stop lover / Don't take your love / Love me right / Let's talk it over / Can't stand the heat / Automatic / Prisoner of love.
Album: released on Fourth & Broadway, Mar'87 by Island Records. Dist: Polygram, EMI

Cassette: released on Fourth & Broadway, Mar'87 by Island Records. Dist: Polygram, EMI

Compact disc: released on Fourth & Broadway, Mar'87 by Island Records. Dist: Polygram, EMI

PRISONER OF LOVE.
Tracks: / Prisoner of love / Prisoner of the groove.
Single (7"): released on Fourth & Broadway, Mar'86 by Island Records. Dist: Polygram, EMI

Single (12"): released on Fourth & Broadway, Mar'86 by Island Records. Dist: Polygram, EMI

Scott, Ossie

MY WAY.
Album: released on Third World, Feb'79 Dist: Jetstar Distribution

REGGAE EXPOSURE WITH SAX.
Album: released on Londisc, Jun'84 by Londisc Records.

SUPREME SOUNDS OF OSSIE SCOTT, THE.
Album: released on Vista Sounds, '83 by Vista Sounds Records. Dist: Jetstar

Album: released on Third World, Jun'79 Dist: Jetstar Distribution

WONDERFUL SOUNDS OF OSSIE SCOTT, THE.
Album: released on World Enterprise, Dec'84 Dist: Jetstar

Scott, Peggy

LOVERS' HOLIDAY/PICKING WILD... (Scott, Peggy & Jo Jo Benson).
Single (7"): released on Charly, Jul'80 by Charly Records. Dist: Charly, Cadillac

Scott, Pete

BABY STAY.
Single (7"): released on Rubber, Jul'76 by Rubber Records. Dist: Roots Distribution, Projection Distribution, Jazz Music Distribution, Celtic Music Distribution, JSU Distribution, Spartan Distribution

DON'T PANIC.
Album: released on Rubber, Jun'82 by Rubber Records. Dist: Roots Distribution, Projection Distribution, Jazz Music Distribution, Celtic Music Distribution, JSU Distribution, Spartan Distribution

JIMMY THE MOONLIGHT.
Album: released on Rubber, Jun'82 by Rubber Records. Dist: Roots Distribution, Projection Distribution, Jazz Music Distribution, Celtic Music Distribution, JSU Distribution, Spartan Distribution

Scott, Ray

REAL MEMPHIS SOUND VOLUME 2 (THE).
Album: released on White Label, Feb'87 by White Label Records. Dist: Jetstar

Scott, Raymond

Biographical Details: Bandleader **Raymond Scott** was born in 1909 and was well known for clever novelty arrangements such as **"In An Eighteenth Century Drawing Room"**, **"Dinner Music For A Pack Of Hungry Cannibals"**, **"When Cootie Left The Duke"** (which caused a shock in the music business in 1939, when Cootie Williams left Duke Ellington for more money with Benny Goodman.) His intricate arrangements were played by a first rate sextet. Later he led a big band, became music director on radio and TV of **Your Hit Parade** for many years (all the while he was a CBS staff musician) and was married to Dorothy Collins, a regular on the show he'd discovered as a teenager.

BUSINESS MAN'S BOUNCE.
Album: released on Golden Era, Jul'82 by Import Records. Dist: Wellard, Chris, Swift

POPULAR MUSIC.
Album: released on Swing House, '84 Dist: Jazz Music Distribution, Swift Distribution, Chris Wellard Distribution

Scott, Rhoda

RHODA SCOTT IN NEW YORK.
Album: released on Barclay (Import), Nov'79

Scott, Robin

CRAZY ZULU (LONDON MIX) (Scott, Robin & African Pioneers).

EUREKA.
Single (7"): released on Discovery, Oct'85 Dist: PRT

Single (12"): released on Discovery, Oct'85 Dist: PRT

EUREKA KA KA.
Single (7"): released on Albion, Jun'83 by Albion Records. Dist: Spartan, Pinnacle

Single (12"): released on Albion, Jun'83 by Albion Records. Dist: Spartan, Pinnacle

LEFT HANDED DREAM (Scott, Robin & Riuichi Sakomoto).
Album: released on Epic, Nov'82 by CBS Records. Dist: CBS

Scott, Ronnie

Biographical Details: Tenor saxophonist and bandleader **Ronnie Scott** was born in London in 1927. He is best known as co-operator (with Peter King) of one of the most famous jazz clubs in the world for almost 30 years, also for his elderly and terrible jokes, but he is an underrated (even by himself) musician, having studied jazz in New York at the height of the bop era thanks to Geraldo's Navy (bandleader Geraldo hired musicians to work on the Queen Mary, back and forth across the Atlantic). Among his best-known albums include the **Battle Royal**, made in 1951 with two tenors, **Victor Feldman** on piano; **Serios Gold** was made in 1977 with **John Taylor** on keyboards (lately of Azimuth), **Ron Matthewson** on bass and **Martin Drew** on drums (who still play in the quintet at the club) and **Louis Stewart** on guitar. [Donald Clarke, April 87]

GREAT SCOT VOLUME 1.
Album: released on Esquire, Apr'79 by Titan International Productions. Dist: Jazz Music, Cadillac Music, Swift, Wellard, Chris, Backs, Rough Trade, Revolver, Nine Mile

LIVE AT THE JAZZ CLUB (Scott, Ronnie & His Orchestra).
Tracks: / Popo / Pantagrulian / Mullenium / Bearness of you, The / Nemo / All the things you are / Champ / Day dream / On the alamo / What's new / I may be wrong.
Album: released on Esquire, Jul'87 by Titan International Productions. Dist: Jazz Music, Cadillac Music, Swift, Wellard, Chris, Backs, Rough Trade, Revolver, Nine Mile

MUSIC FROM RONNIE'S.
Special: released on Pye, Sep'78

RONNIE SCOTT'S 20TH ANNIVERSARY ALBUM.
Album: released on PRT, Jul'79 by PRT Records. Dist: PRT

SERIOUS GOLD.
Album: released on PRT, Jan'78 by PRT Records. Dist: PRT

Cassette: released on PRT, Jan'78 by PRT Records. Dist: PRT

Scott, Russell

FRIENDS & NEIGHBOURS.
Album: released on Dansan, Oct'81 by Spartan Records. Dist: Spartan

MUSIC AND DANCING WITH RUSSELL SCOTT.
Album: released on Dansan, Jul'81 by Spartan Records. Dist: Spartan

Cassette: released on Dansan, Jul'81 by Spartan Records. Dist: Spartan

Scott, Sharon

OH WHAT A NIGHT FOR LOVE.
Tracks: / Oh what a night for love / I like it.
Single (7"): released on Debut, Jul'86 by Skratch Music. Dist: PRT

Single (12"): released on Debut, Jul'86 by Skratch Music. Dist: PRT

Scott's Royale...

PIPE MAJOR WILLIE COCHRAN (Scott's Royale Highland Showband).
Album: released on Scotdisc, Jul'87 Dist: Clyde Factors Distributors

Cassette: released on Scotdisc, Jul'87 Dist: Clyde Factors Distributors

Scotts Songs & Music

SCOTTS SONGS AND MUSIC Various artists (Various Artists).
Notes: 'Scotts Songs And Music' at Kinross Festival.
Album: released on Springthyme, Oct'86 by Springthyme Records. Dist: Jazz Music Distribution, Projection Distribution, Roots Distribution

Cassette: released on Springthyme, Oct'86 by Springthyme Records. Dist: Jazz Music Distribution, Projection Distribution, Roots Distribution

Scott's, Tommy

PIPES AND STRINGS OF SCOTLAND.
Album: released on Country House, Sep'84 by BGS Productions Ltd. Dist: Taylor, H.R., Record Merchandisers Distribution, Pinnacle, Sounds of Scotland Records

Cassette: released on Country House, Sep'84 by BGS Productions Ltd. Dist: Taylor, H.R., Record Merchandisers Distribution, Pinnacle, Sounds of Scotland Records

Scott, Tim

HIGH LONESOME SOUND,THE.
Tracks: / Sound of thunder / I could be anything / Great escape,The / Easy time / Release / Low ride / Fire down / In this world / High hopes / Under a new heaven / Hey sister.
Album: released on Geffen, Jun'87 by Geffen Records. Dist: WEA, CBS

Cassette: released on Geffen, Jun'87 by Geffen Records. Dist: WEA, CBS

Scott, Tom

BEST OF TOM SCOTT.
Album: released on CBS, Aug'80 by CBS Records. Dist: CBS

DESIRE.
Tracks: / Desire / Sure enough / Only one, The / Stride / Johnny B. Badd / Meet somebody / Maybe I'm amazed / Chunk of funk.
Album: released on Elektra(Musician), Aug'82 by WEA Records. Dist: WEA

Compact disc: by WEA Records. Dist: WEA

TARGET.
Tracks: / Target / Come back to me / Aerobia / He's too young / Got to get out of New York / Biggest part of me, The / Burindi Bump.
Compact disc: released on Atlantic, '86 by WEA Records. Dist: WEA

Scott, Tommy

GOING HOME.
Single (7"): released on Scot Disc, Aug'84

SCOTLAND-14 ALL TIME SOTTISH FAVOURITES.
Compact disc: released on Scotdisc, Nov'86 Dist: Clyde Factors Distributors

'TIS A GIFT (TO BE SIMPLE) (Scott, Tommy's Strings of Scotland).
Single (7"): released on August (USA), Nov'85 Dist: Taylors

TOMMY SCOTT'S PIPES & STRINGS OF SCOTLAND.
Tracks: / Pride of bonnie Scotland (The) / Ode to joy / Abide with me / Scottish banner (The) / 'tis a gift(to be simple) / Bonnie Mary of Argyle / Send in the clowns / Jesu joy(of mans desiring) / Rose of Kelvingrove (The) / Song of the wind (The) / Scott's choice / Light of the morning / Little drummer boy / Carnival is over, The.
Album: released on Scotdisc, Dec'86 Dist: Clyde Factors Distributors

TOMMY SCOTT'S ROYALE HIGHLAND SHOWBAND Starring Pipe Major Willie Cochrane (Scott, Tommy's Royale Highland Showband).
Tracks: / Red river rose / March march march all the way / Morag of Dunvegan / Mingulay boat song / Maggie may / Day is ended, The / P.K.'s salute / Pigeon at the gate / Pipes o' Drummond / De'il among the tailors / Kilt is my delight, The / Pipers patrol / Mount Fuji / Water is wide / Flute salad / Dark Island / May kway o'may kway / McCleod if Raassey / High road to Linton.

Album: released on Scotdisc, 8 Jun'87 Dist: Clyde Factors Distributors

Cassette: released on Scotdisc, 8 Jun'87 Dist: Clyde Factors Distributors

TOMMY SCOTT'S SCOTLAND.
Tracks: / Annie Laurie / Dark Lochnagar / Great Glen (Colonel Robertson), The / Skye boat song / Amazing Grace / Flower of Scotland / Will ye no come back again / Scotland forever / My love is like a red red rose / Flowers of the forrest / Rowan tree / Green trees of Tyrol / My Ain folk / Auld lang syne.
Album: released on Scotdisc, Dec'86 Dist: Clyde Factors Distributors

Scott, Tony

Biographical Details: **Tony Scott** was born in New Jersey in 1921; with **Buddy DeFranco** he is one of the few musicians to specialise on the clarinet in post-war jazz. He studied ethnic music in the Orient from 1959 to 1965. His verve albums were made in the mid- 60's; **52nd Street Scene** was made in 1958, with **Coleman Hawkins, Jimmy Knepper, Al Cohn, Pee Wee Russell, Oscar Pettiford, Tommy Flanagan**

and others on various tracks. [Donald Clarke, April 87]

52ND STREET SCENE.
Album: released on Jasmine, Feb'83 by Jasmine Records. Dist: PRT

AFRICAN BIRD.
Album: released on Soul Note, May'85 Dist: Projection, Celtic Music, Chris Wellard

MUSIC FOR ZEN MEDITATION.
Tracks: / Is not all one? / Murmuring sound of the mountain / Quivering leaf, ask the wind / After the snow the fragrance / To drift like clouds / Za-Zan (Meditation) / Prajina Paramita Hridya Sutra / Sanzan (moment of truth) / Satori (enlightenment).
Album: released on Verve (Polydor-Germany), Mar'81 by Polydor Records (Germany). Dist: Polygram

Compact disc: released on Verve (Polydor-Germany), Sep'84 by Polydor Records (Germany). Dist: Polygram

SUNG HEROES.
Tracks: / Misery (to lady day) / Portrait of Anne Frank / Remembrance of Art Tatum / Requiem for 'Hot Lips' Page / Blues for an African friend / For Stefan Wolpe / Israel / Memory of my father / Lament to manolete.
Notes: All compositions by Tony Scott. Featuring: Bill Evans, Scott Lafaro, Paul Motian. Published by Ajay music (BMI) except 'Misery (To Lady Day)' published by BigSeven Music (BMI). Produced by Tony Scott. Executive Production: Ray Passman and Francois Zalacain.
Album: released on Sunnyside (USA), Sep'86 Dist: Mole Jazz Distribution, Conifer Distribution

Scott, T T

LOVER GAME.
Tracks: / Lover game / Children of Zion.
Single (12"):

Scott, Willie

SHEPHERD'S SONG, THE.
Album: released on Topic, '81 by Topic Records. Dist: JSU Distribution, Projection Distribution, Jazz Music Distribution

Scraping Foetus...

NAIL (Scraping Foetus Off The Wheel).
Album: released on Self Immolation-Some Bizzare, Nov'85

Cassette: released on Self Immolation-Some Bizzare, Nov'85

Compact disc: released on Some Bizzare, Apr'86 by Charisma Records. Dist: EMI, CBS, Polygram

Scratch

KEEP ON SEARCHING FOR LOVE.
Single (12"): released on Master Funk, Jun'84 by Master Funk Records. Dist: PRT

Scratch Acid

BERSERKER.
Album: released on Fundamental, Feb'87 by Fundamental Records. Dist: Red Rhino, Cartel

JUST KEEP EATING.
Album: released on Fundamental, May'86 by Fundamental Records. Dist: Red Rhino, Cartel

SCRATCH ACID.
Album: released on Fundamental, Apr'86 by Fundamental Records. Dist: Red Rhino, Cartel

Scratch On The Wire

SCRATCH ON THE WIRE Various artists (Various Artists).
Album: released on Island, Sep'79 by Island Records. Dist: Polygram

Scratch & Upsetters

SUPER APE.
Album: released on Island, Aug'76 by Island Records. Dist: Polygram

Scream

WALKING BY MYSELF.
Single (7"): released on Jungle Hop, Mar'87

Scream & Dance

IN RHYTHM/GIACOMETTI.
Single (7"): released on Recreational, Apr'82 by Revolver Records. Dist: Rough Trade

Single (12"): released on Recreational, Apr'82 by Revolver Records. Dist: Rough Trade

Screaming Blue Messiahs

GOOD AND GONE.
Album: released on WEA, May'85 by WEA Records. Dist: WEA

Cassette: released on WEA, May'85 by WEA Records. Dist: WEA

GUNSHY.
Tracks: / Wild blue yonder / Holiday head / Smash the market place / Just for fun / Let's go down to the woods / Talking doll / Twin Cadillac Valentine / President Kennedy's mile / Clear View / Killer born man.
Album: released on WEA, Apr'86 by WEA Records. Dist: WEA

Cassette: released on WEA, Apr'86 by WEA Records. Dist: WEA

PAINT IT BLACK.
Single (7"): released on No Future, Jan'84 by No Future Records. Dist: Pinnacle, Rough Trade, Cartel

PEEL SESSION 24.7.84.
Cassette single: released on Strange Fruit, 13 Jun'87 by Clive Selwood. Dist: Pinnacle

SMASH THE MARKET PLACE.
Tracks: / Smash the market place / Just for fun / Power glide, The.
Single (7"): released on WEA, Apr'86 by WEA Records. Dist: WEA

Single (12"): released on WEA, Apr'86 by WEA Records. Dist: WEA

TWIN CADILLAC VALENTINE.
Single (7"): released on WEA, Oct'85 by WEA Records. Dist: WEA

Single (12"): released on WEA, Oct'85 by WEA Records. Dist: WEA

WILD BLUE YONDER.
Tracks: / Wild blue yonder / Killer born man / I'm mad again.
Single (7"): released on WEA, Sep'86 by WEA Records. Dist: WEA

Single (12"): released on WEA, Sep'86 by WEA Records. Dist: WEA

Screaming Dead

CREATURES OF THE NIGHT.
Single (12"): released on No Future, Jul'83 by No Future Records. Dist: Pinnacle, Rough Trade, Cartel

DANSE MACABRE COLLECTION.
Single (12"): released on Angel, Sep'84

DREAM OF YESTERDAY, A.
Single (12"): released on Angel, Feb'85

NECROMARIA.
Single (7"): released on No Future, Aug'83 by No Future Records. Dist: Pinnacle, Rough Trade, Cartel

VALLEY OF THE DEAD/SCHOOL GIRL....
Single (7"): released on Skull, Sep'82

Screaming Lord Sutch

JACK THE RIPPER.
Album: released on Konnexion, Aug'87 Dist: Roots, Pinnacle

Screaming Nobodies

BURGER KING EP.
Tracks: / Burger king EP / Big fat sucker.
Single (12"): released on Supreme International Editions, Feb'86 Dist: Rough Trade Distribution, Cartel Distribution

Screaming Saxophones

SCREAMING SAXOPHONES VOLUME 1 Various artists (Various Artists).
Album: released on Swingtime, Jan'86 Dist: Jazz Music Distribution, Charly

Screaming Silence

SAME OLD STORY.
Tracks: / Same old story.
Single (7"): released on Acrobat, Sep'86 by Acrobat Records. Dist: Polygram, Red Rhino, Cartel

Screaming Sirens

YOUR GOOD GIRL'S GOING BAD.
Single (7"): released on Beach Culture, Jul'85 Dist: Backs, Cartel

Screaming Trees

BEATEN BY THE UGLY STICK.
Single (12"): released on Native, Feb'87 by Native Records. Dist: Red Rhino, Cartel

IRON GURU (4 TRACK EP).
Single (7"): released on Native, 30 May'87 by Native Records. Dist: Red Rhino, Cartel

Single (12"): released on Native, 30 May'87 by Native Records. Dist: Red Rhino, Cartel

RELEASE.
Tracks: / Release.
Single (12"): released on Native, Mar'86 by Native Records. Dist: Red Rhino, Cartel

Screaming Tribesman

DATE WITH A VAMPYRE.
Single (12"): released on What Goes On, Nov'85 Dist: Rough Trade, Cartel, Shigaku

MOVE A LITTLE CLOSER.
Single (12"): released on What Goes On, Aug'85 Dist: Rough Trade, Cartel, Shigaku

Screecher Nice

HAVE TO GET A FLAT.
Single (12"): released on Jammy's, Oct'84 by Jammy's Records. Dist: Jetstar

Screechie Delton

ANSWER MY QUESTION/DUB ME THE ANSWER.
Single (12"): released on Peoples Choice, Jun'83 by Peoples Choice Records. Dist: Jetstar

MOVING AWAY/VERSION.
Single (12"): released on Peoples Choice, Dec'83 by Peoples Choice Records. Dist: Jetstar

Screechy Jah

WALK AND SHRANK.
Single (12"): released on Blacka Dread, Jul'84

Screen 3

COME INTO MY JUNGLE/THE DIVIDING.
Single (7"): released on Epic, Feb'83 by CBS Records. Dist: CBS

Single (12"): released on Epic, Feb'83 by CBS Records. Dist: CBS

VISITOR (THE).
Single (12"): released on Gross Product, Mar'84 by Gross Product Records. Dist: Backs, Cartel

Screen music...

SCREEN MUSIC FOR LOVERS various artists.
Album: released on Denon, Mar'82 by Denon Records. Dist: Harmonia Mundi

Screen Themes 1985/6

SCREEN THEMES 1985/6 Various artists (Various Artists).
Tracks: / Back to the future / Goonies / Santa Claus. etc..
Compact disc: released on Denon, May'86 by Denon Records. Dist: Harmonia Mundi

Screen Three

NEW BLOOD/EUROPEAN JOURNEY.
Single (7"): released on Romans In Britain, Nov'81 Dist: Rough Trade Distribution

Screwdriver

FAMILY COUNCILOR.
Tracks: / Family councilor / Family councillor (Version).
Single (12"): released on Revelationary Sound, Feb'87 by Revelationary Sound Records. Dist: Jetstar

NO MAMA.
Album: released on Volcano, Jun'87 by Volcano Records. Dist: Jetstar

Scritti Politti

ABSOLUTE.
Picture disc single: released on Virgin, Jul'84 by Virgin Records. Dist: EMI, Virgin Distribution

ASYLUMS IN JERUSALEM/JAQQUES.
Single (7"): released on Rough Trade, Jul'82 by Rough Trade Records. Dist: Rough Trade Distribution, Cartel Distribution

Single (7"): released on Rough Trade, Jul'82 by Rough Trade Records. Dist: Rough Trade Distribution, Cartel Distribution

Single (12"): released on Rough Trade, Jul'82 by Rough Trade Records. Dist: Rough Trade Distribution, Cartel Distribution

CUPID AND PSYCHE '85.
Tracks: / Word girl, the / Small talk / Absolute / Little knowledge, A / Don't work that hard / Perfect way / Lover to fall / Wood beez (pray like Aretha Franklin) / Hypnotize / Flesh and blood / Absolute (Remix) / Hypnotize (Remix) / Wood Beez (Remix).
Compact disc: released on Virgin, Jun'85 by Virgin Records. Dist: EMI, Virgin Distribution

FAITHLESS/INSTRUMENTAL VERSION.
Single (7"): released on Rough Trade, Apr'82 by Rough Trade Records. Dist: Rough Trade Distribution, Cartel Distribution

Single (12"): released on Rough Trade, Apr'82 by Rough Trade Records. Dist: Rough Trade Distribution, Cartel Distribution

HEGAMONY.
Single (7"): released on Rough Trade, Oct'79 by Rough Trade Records. Dist: Rough Trade Distribution, Cartel Distribution

HYPNOTISE.
Single (7"): released on Virgin, Nov'84 by Virgin Records. Dist: EMI, Virgin Distribution

Single (12"): released on Virgin, Nov'84 by Virgin Records. Dist: EMI, Virgin Distribution

PERFECT WAY.
Single (7"): released on Virgin, Aug'85 by Virgin Records. Dist: EMI, Virgin Distribution

Single (12"): released on Virgin, Aug'85 by Virgin Records. Dist: EMI, Virgin Distribution

SCRITLOCKS DOOR/MESSTHETICS.
Single (7"): released on Rough Trade, Nov'79 by Rough Trade Records. Dist: Rough Trade Distribution, Cartel Distribution

SONGS TO REMEMBER.
Compact disc: released on Rough Trade, May'87 by Rough Trade Records. Dist: Rough Trade Distribution, Cartel Distribution

Album: released on Rough Trade, Sep'82 by Rough Trade Records. Dist: Rough Trade Distribution, Cartel Distribution

Cassette: released on Rough Trade, Sep'82 by Rough Trade Records. Dist: Rough Trade Distribution, Cartel Distribution

SWEETEST GIRL/LIONS AFTER SLUMBER.
Single (7"): released on Rough Trade, Oct'81 by Rough Trade Records. Dist: Rough Trade Distribution, Cartel Distribution

Single (12"): released on Rough Trade, Oct'81 by Rough Trade Records. Dist: Rough Trade Distribution, Cartel Distribution

VIDEO EP.
Notes: An EP containing five promos by the successful UK band, including hits like 'The Word Girl' and 'Wood Beez'.1986 production. Number of tracks; 5. Type of recording: EP. Total playing time: 20 minutes.
Video-cassette (VHS): released on Virgin, May'86 by Virgin Records. Dist: EMI, Virgin Distribution

WOOD BEEZ.
Single (7"): released on Virgin, Mar'84 by Virgin Records. Dist: EMI, Virgin Distribution

Single (12"): released on Virgin, Mar'84 by Virgin Records. Dist: EMI, Virgin Distribution

WORD GIRL THE.
Single (7"): released on Virgin, Apr'85 by Virgin Records. Dist: EMI, Virgin Distribution

Single (12"): released on Virgin, Apr'85 by Virgin Records. Dist: EMI, Virgin Distribution

Scrodd, Crystal Belle

BELLE DE JOUR.
Album: released on United Dairies, Dec'86 Dist: Rough Trade, Indies

INEVITABLE CHRYSTAL BELLE SCRODD RECORD.
Album: released on United Dairies, Oct'85 Dist: Rough Trade, Indies

Scrubs

BATTLE.
Tracks: / Battle / Battle narrative.
Single (7"): released on Anubis, Sep'86 Dist: Spartan

TIME FOR YOU.
Tracks: / Time for you / Battle / Lorraine.
Single (7"): released on Flicknife, May'87 by Flicknife Records. Dist: Spartan

Scruffy Gents

SCRUFFY GENTS/IT TAKES TOO LONG.
Single (7"): released on MRS, Jan'82

Scruffy The Cat

HIGH OCTANE REVIVAL.
Album: released on Relativity (USA), Aug'87 Dist: Pinnacle

TINY DAYS.
Album: released on Relativity (USA), Aug'87 Dist: Pinnacle

Scruggs, Earl

STORY TELLER & THE BANJO MAN, THE (Scruggs, Earl & Tom T Hall).
Album: released on CBS, Aug'82 by CBS Records. Dist: CBS

Cassette: released on CBS, Aug'82 by CBS Records. Dist: CBS

TOP OF THE WORLD.

Album: released on CBS, Mar'83 by CBS Records. Dist: CBS

Scrunter

JUDIT.
Tracks: / Judit / Oil in the coil.
Single (12"): released on Hot Vinyl, Jun'86 by Hot Vinyl Records. Dist: Jetstar

Scullion

BALANCE AND CONTROL.
Album: released on WEA Ireland, Mar'87 by WEA Records. Dist: Celtic Distributions, Projection, I & B

Cassette: released on WEA Ireland, Mar'87 by WEA Records. Dist: Celtic Distributions, Projection, I & B

Scum

BORN TOO SOON.
Album: released on Children Of The Revolution, Mar'87 by Revolver Records. Dist: Revolver, Cartel

Sea Breeze

BEND DOWN AND ROLL YOUR BELLY.
Tracks: / Bend down and roll your belly / I don't mind.
Single (12"): released on Hot Vinyl, Aug'86 by Hot Vinyl Records. Dist: Jetstar

Seacombe, Harry

HIGHWAY OF LIFE.
Album: released on Telstar, Nov'86 by Telstar Records. Dist: RCA Distribution

Cassette: released on Telstar, Nov'86 by Telstar Records. Dist: RCA Distribution

Compact disc: released on Telstar, Jan'87 by Telstar Records. Dist: RCA Distribution

Seaford College...

MY COUNTRY (Seaford College Chapel Choir).
Tracks: / Jerusalem / Pie Jesu / My song is love unknown / Be still my soul / Chorale (Commit The Way To Jesus) / Litany of the passion / How great the harvest is / I would be true / Let thy merciful ears'O Lord / God that made earth and heaven / I vow to thee my country / Kyrie / King of love, The / Nunc Dimittis / Sanctus / Dear Lord and Father of mankind / Jesu, joy of man's desiring / Ave verum (Jesu, Word of God Incarnate) / Love Divine.
Notes: Directed by Philip Hill: Produced by Bob Barratt/Organist: Carys Hughes/ Recording Engineer: Stuart Eltham assisted by Andrew Fraser:/Location Engineers Graham Kirby & Richard Hale:/ Recorded at St. Augustine's Church, Kilburn with the Abbey Road Mobile;/ Mastered at EMI's Abbey Road Studios by Harry Moss. Front Cover Photo by Derek Foress FRPS/ shows Salisbury Wiltshire:/Cover Design: Roy Keighley. Rear Photo David Cole, Petworth.
Album: released on Grasmere, Oct'86 by Grasmere Records. Dist: EMI

Cassette: released on Grasmere, Oct'86 by Grasmere Records. Dist: EMI

ROYAL CAROL CONCERT, (A) (Seaford College Chapel Choir).
Album: released on Abbey, Nov'83 by Abbey. Dist: PRT, Taylors, Gamut

Cassette: released on Abbey, Nov'83 by Abbey. Dist: PRT, Taylors, Gamut

Seagulls

GOLDSTONE RAP, THE.
Single (7"): released on Energy, May'83 by Energy Records. Dist: Jazz Music

Single (12"): released on Energy, May'83 by Energy Records. Dist: Jazz Music

Seal, Geof

WHAT I'M GONNA BE.
Tracks: / What I"m gonna be / What I'm gonna be (Instrumental).
Single (7"): released on LBA, Jul'86 by LBA Records.

Seals, Dan

BLUE.
Compact disc: released on EMI America, '87 by EMI Records. Dist: EMI

BOP.
Tracks: / Bop / In San Antone.
Single (7"): released on EMI America, Apr'86 by EMI Records. Dist: EMI

ON THE FRONT LINE.
Tracks: / On the front line / Three time loser / Fewer threads than these / Gonna be easy now / Guitar man out of control / I will be there / You still move me / While I'm here / I'm still strung out on you / Lullaby.
Notes: In 1986, Dan Seals was America's biggest country music star. His last album (not released in the UK) 'Won't Be Blue Anymore' included a US hit single with Marie Osmond called 'Meet Me In Montana'. With the masterful work of producer Kyle Lehning, Dan Seals has selected and written a very impressive work with 'On The Front Line'.
Album: released on EMI America, Mar'87 by EMI Records. Dist: EMI

Cassette: released on EMI America, Mar'87 by EMI Records. Dist: EMI

Compact disc: released on EMI, Mar'87 by EMI Records. Dist: EMI

SAN ANTONE.
Compact disc: released on EMI America, Apr'87 by EMI Records. Dist: EMI

Seals, Son

Biographical Details: Blues singer and guitarist Son Seals' father owned a club in Osceola, Georgia, where Son was born in 1942; he sat in at the club, toured with **Earl Hooker**, **Albert King**, settled in Chicago in 1971. He is part of the marvelous **Alligator** label family of bluesmen whose records are leased to **Sonet** in the UK.

BAD AXE.
Tracks: / Don't pick me for your fool / Going home (where women got meat on their bones) / Just about to lose your clown / Friday again / Cold blood / Out of my way / I think you're fooling me / I can count on my blues / Can't stand to see her cry / Person to person.
Compact disc: released on Sonet, Oct'86 by Sonet Records. Dist: PRT

Album: released on Sonet, Dec'84 by Sonet Records. Dist: PRT

CHICAGO FIRE.
Album: released on Alligator, Sep'80 Dist: Jetstar

LIVE AND BURNING.
Album: released on Sonet, Nov'78 by Sonet Records. Dist: PRT

MIDNIGHT SON.
Album: released on Sonet, Jul'77 by Sonet Records. Dist: PRT

SON SEALS BLUES BAND.
Album: released on Sonet, Jan'75 by Sonet Records. Dist: PRT

Sealy, Joe

LIVE AT ERROLS (Sealy, Joe & Friends).
Album: released on Innovation (Canada), Sep'84 Dist: Mole Jazz

CLEAR VISION.
Notes: With Dave Young / Pete Magadini
Album: released on Sackville, May'86 Dist: JSU, Jazz Music, Jazz Horizons, Cadillac Music, Celtic Music, Swift

Search

LIKE THE WAY YOU FUNK WITH ME.
Single (7"): released on Philly World, Mar'82 by Philly World Records (USA). Dist: Polygram

Single (12"): released on Philly World, Mar'82 by Philly World Records (USA). Dist: Polygram

PEANUT BUTTER AND JAM.
Single (7"):

Single (12"):

SEARCH.
Album:

Searchers

Biographical Details: **The Searchers** are still one of the best-loved pop quartets from the 1960s, as good as the Beatles at the start, though unlike the mop-tops they did not progress from there: lead guitarist **John McNally** was born 30 August 1941; rhythm guitarist **Mike Pender** on 3 March 1942; bassist **Tony Jackson** on 16 July 1940, drummer **Chris Curtis** (the only one not originally from Liverpool) on 16 August 1941 in Oldham. They named themselves after the John Wayne film (Wayne's catchphrase in the film 'That'll be the day!' also providing the title of Buddy Holly's first hit). Their imaginitive harmonies and distinctive guitar sound influenced the **Byrds**; like the Beatles, they played at the Cavern and in Hamburg 1961-62; they had three never-to-be-forgotten no. one hits 1963-64 with 'Sweets For My Sweet','Needles & Pins', 'Don't Throw Your Love Away' (last two were also top 20 USA). [Donald Clarke, April 87]

100 MINUTES.
Cassette: released on PRT, Jun'82 by PRT Records. Dist: PRT

ANOTHER NIGHT.
Single (7"): released on Sire, Mar'81

GOLDEN HOUR: SEARCHERS.
Album: released on Golden Hour, Jan'74 by PRT Records. Dist: PRT

Cassette: released on Golden Hour, Jan'74 by PRT Records. Dist: PRT

GREATEST HITS:SEARCHERS.
Tracks: / Love Potion No. 9 / When you walk in the room / Needles and pins / Sugar and spice / Sweets for my sweet / Magic potion / It's in her kiss / Don't throw your love away / Shimmy shimmy / Hi-heel sneakers / Da doo ron ron / Twist and shout / Stand by me / What have they done to the rain.
Album: released on Showcase, Apr'86 Dist: Counterpoint

Cassette: released on Showcase, Apr'86 Dist: Counterpoint

Album: released on Rhino (USA), Jan'86 by Rhino Records (USA).

I DON'T WANT TO BE THE ONE.
Single (7"): released on PRT, Nov'82 by PRT Records. Dist: PRT

IT'S THE SEARCHERS.
Album: released on PRT, Feb'81 by PRT Records. Dist: PRT

LOVE LIES BLEEDING.
Album: released on PRT, Jul'83 by PRT Records. Dist: PRT

Cassette: released on PRT, Jul'83 by PRT Records. Dist: PRT

MEET THE SEARCHERS.
Album: released on PRT, Feb'81 by PRT Records. Dist: PRT

NEEDLES AND PINS.
Album: released on RCA (Germany), Jan'83 Cat. no: **26 21358**
Single (7"): released on PRT, May'76 by PRT Records. Dist: PRT

Single (7"): released on Flashback, Apr'79 by Flashback Records/PRT Records. Dist: Mainline, PRT

Single (7"): released on Old Gold, Jul'82 by Old Gold Records. Dist: Lightning, Jazz Music, Spartan, Counterpoint Deleted '1.

SILVER SEARCHERS.
Tracks: / Sweets for my sweet / Don't throw your love away / Someday we're gonna love again / What have they done to the rain / Goodbye my love / He's got no love / System, The / Needles and pins / Take me for what I'm worth / Take it or leave it / Have you ever loved somebody / Each time / Till you say you'll be mine / Sugar and spice / When I get home / Everybody come and clap your hands / Till I met you / I don't wabt to go on without you / Everything you do / When you walk in the room / Western Union / Popcorn double feature / Bumble bee / Four strong winds / Too many miles.
Compact disc: released on Nouveau Music, '86 Dist: PRT Distribution

SOUND LIKE THE SEARCHERS.
Album: released on PRT, Feb'81 by PRT Records. Dist: PRT

SPOTLIGHT ON THE SEARCHERS.
Double Album: released on PRT, Jan'80 by PRT Records. Dist: PRT

Cassette: released on PRT, Jan'80 by PRT Records. Dist: PRT

SUGAR AND SPICE.
Album: released on PRT, Feb'81 by PRT Records. Dist: PRT

SWEETS FOR MY SWEET.
Album: released on PRT, Dec'85 by PRT Records. Dist: PRT

Cassette: released on PRT, Dec'85 by PRT Records. Dist: PRT

Single (7"): released on Old Gold, Jul'84 by Old Gold Records. Dist: Lightning, Jazz Music, Spartan, Counterpoint

WHEN YOU WALK IN THE ROOM.
Album: released on PRT, May'80 by PRT Records. Dist: PRT

Cassette: released on PRT, May'80 by PRT Records. Dist: PRT

Single (7"): released on Flashback, Jul'80 by Flashback Records/PRT Records. Dist: Mainline, PRT

Search Party

ALL AROUND THE WORLD.
Single (7"): released on Magnet, Dec'83 by Magnet Records. Dist: BMG

Single (12"): released on Magnet, Dec'83 by Magnet Records. Dist: BMG

URBAN FOXES.
Single (7"): released on Magnet, Mar'82 by Magnet Records. Dist: BMG

Single (12"): released on Magnet, Mar'82 by Magnet Records. Dist: BMG

WALKING ON ICE.
Tracks: / Walking on ice / Walking on ice (rub mix).
Single (7"): released on President, Jul'87 by President Records. Dist: Taylors, Spartan

Searing R & B Sax

SEARING R & B SAX INSTRUMENTALS (1952 - 56) Various artists (Various Artists).
Album: released on Krazy Kat, May'83 Dist: Jazz Music, Swift, Chris Wellard, H.R. Taylor, Charly, Hotshot, IRS Distribution

Seary, Everton

POOR MAN A CRY.
Single (12"): released on Small Acts, Oct'84 by Small Acts Records. Dist: Jetstar

Sease, Marvin

MARVIN SEASE.
Tracks: / Double crosser / Let's get married today / Love me or leave me / Ghetto man / You're number one / Dreaming / Candy licker.
Album: released on London, Apr'87 by London Records. Dist: Polygram

Sea Shanties

SEA SHANTIES various artists.
Album: released on Topic, '81 Dist: Roots Distribution

Sea Songs....

SEA SONGS & SHANTIES (Topic Sampler No.7) (Various Artists).
Album: released on Topic, '74 by Topic Records. Dist: JSU Distribution, Projection Distribution, Jazz Music Distribution

SEA SONGS VOL.1 (Various Artists).
Cassette: released on Folktracks, Nov'79 Dist: Roots

Seasons

SEASONS Various artists (Various Artists).
Album: released on K-Tel, Aug'79 by K-Tel Records. Dist: Record Merchandisers Distribution, Taylors, Terry Blood Distribution, Wynd-Up Distribution, Relay Distribution, Pickwick Distribution, Solomon & Peres Distribution, Polygram

Cassette: released on K-Tel, Oct'79 by K-Tel Records. Dist: Record Merchandisers Distribution, Taylors, Terry Blood Distribution, Wynd-Up Distribution, Relay Distribution, Pickwick Distribution, Solomon & Peres Distribution, Polygram

Sea Stone

AGAINST THE TIDE.
Extended-play record: released on Plankton, Oct'82 by Plankton Records. Dist: Cantio (Sweden)

SUMMER FEVER.
Single (7"): released on Plankton, Oct'80 by Plankton Records. Dist: Cantio (Sweden)

Seaton, B. B.

BORN FREE.
Single (12"): by Jama Records.

EVERYDAY PEOPLE.
Album: released on Creole, Apr'85 by Creole Records. Dist: Rhino, PRT

Single (12"): released on Revue, Mar'85 by Revue Records. Dist: Creole

I'LL NEVER RUN AROUND.
Tracks: / I"ll never run around / Bubbling around.
Single (12"): released on BI, Apr'86 Dist: Jetstar

IT'S DREAD.
Single (12"): released on BI BI, Nov'85

JAN HELPS THOSE THAT HELP THEMSELVES.
Single (12"): released on Disco, Apr'82

JUST A LITTLE MORE TIME.
Single (7"): released on Rhino, May'85 by Creole Records. Dist: PRT, Rhino

MEDLY OF LOVE.
Single (12"): released on King and the I, Jun'85

Seaton, Dennis

I'M INTO SOMETHING GOOD.
Single (7"): released on Creole, Aug'87 by Creole Records. Dist: Rhino, PRT

Single (12"): released on Creole, Aug'87 by Creole Records. Dist: Rhino, PRT

Seaton, Johnny

UPTOWN.
Album: released on Rockhouse, Mar'84 by Rockhouse Records. Dist: Swift Distribution, Charly Distribution

Single (7"): released on Rockhouse, Apr'84 by Rockhouse Records. Dist: Swift Distribution,

Sea Train

BEST OF SEA TRAIN & MARBLED MESSENGER, THE.
Tracks: / Oh my love / Sally goodin' / Creepin' midnight / I'm willin' / Song of job / Home to you / 13 questions / Marbleheaded messenger / London song / Gramercy / State of Georgia's mind / Losing all the years / Mississippi moon / How sweet the song.
Album: released on See For Miles, Jun'87 by See For Miles Records. Dist: Pinnacle

SEA TRAIN.
Album: released on Edsel, Nov'86 by Demon Records. Dist: Pinnacle, Jazz Music, Projection

Sea Wolf

SEA WOLF Jack London (Boland, Arthur).
Cassette: released on Colophone, Feb'81 by Audio-Visual Library Services. Dist: Audio-Visual Library Services

SEA WOLF By Jack London (Quayle, Anthony).
Cassette: released on Caedmon(USA), '82 by Caedmon (USA) Records. Dist: Gower, Taylors, Discovery

Sebastian, David

SINCE YOU WENT AWAY.
Single (12"): released on Noel, Sep'81 by Mainline Record Company. Dist: Mainline

Sebesky, Don

FULL CIRCLE.
Album: released on PRT, Oct'84 by PRT Records. Dist: PRT

MOVING LINES.
Album: released on Dr Jazz, Mar'86 by Doctor Jazz Records. Dist: CBS, PRT

Cassette: released on Dr Jazz, Mar'86 by Doctor Jazz Records. Dist: CBS, PRT

Sebestyen, Marta

MARTA SEBESTYEN WITH MUZIKAS (Sebestyen, Marta with Muzikas).
Album: released on Hannibal, Oct'87 by Hannibal Records. Dist: Charly, Harmonia Mundi, Projection, Celtic Music, Roots. Estim retail price in Sep'87 was £5.99.

Sebo, Ferenc

MUSIC AND DANCES OF HUNGARY (Sebo, Ferenc Ensemble).
Album: released on Arion, Jun'79 Dist: Discovery

Cassette: released on Arion, Jun'79 Dist: Discovery

Secession

BETRAYALS.
Single (7"): released on Garden, Oct'82 Dist: Carmel Distribution

MAGICIAN (THE).
Tracks: / Magician (The) / Killing season (The).
Single (7"): released on Siren, Mar'87 by Virgin Records. Dist: EMI

Single (12"): released on Siren, Mar'87 by Virgin Records. Dist: EMI

PROMISE.
Tracks: / Promise / Havoc.
Single (7"): released on Siren, Jun'87 by Virgin Records. Dist: EMI

Single (12"): released on Siren, Jun'87 by Virgin Records. Dist: EMI

Secombe, Harry

BLESS THIS HOUSE.
Album: released on Warwick, Apr'79 Dist: Multiple Sound Distributors

Cassette: released on Warwick, Apr'79 Dist: Multiple Sound Distributors

HARRY'S CHOICE.
Album: released on Spot, Oct'83 by Pickwick Records. Dist: H.R. Taylor, Lugtons

Cassette: released on Spot, Oct'83 by Pickwick Records. Dist: H.R. Taylor, Lugtons

HARRY SECOMBE COLLECTION.
Double Album: released on Pickwick, Jul'76 by Pickwick Records. Dist: Pickwick Distribution, Prism Leisure Distribution, Lugtons

Double cassette: released on Pickwick, Jul'76 by Pickwick Records. Dist: Pickwick Distribution, Prism Leisure Distribution, Lugtons

HARRY SECOMBE'S HIGHWAY OF SONG.
Album: released on Starblend, May'84 by Starblend Records. Dist: PRT Distribution

---

Cassette: released on Starblend, May'84 by Starblend Records. Dist: PRT Distribution

HIGHWAY COMPANION, THE.
Notes: Features the best of the ITV series "Highway" -an anthology of readings and short music links, presented by Harry Secombe and featuring readings by Wendy Craig and Bernard Cribbins.
Album: released on Word, Aug'87 by Word Records. Dist: Word Distribution, CRS

Cassette: released on Word, Aug'87 by Word Records. Dist: Word Distribution, CBS

HOW GREAT THOU ART.
Album: released on Premier, May'85 by Premier Records. Dist: CBS

Cassette: released on Premier, May'85 by Premier Records. Dist: CBS

IF I RULED THE WORLD.
Single (7"): released on Old Gold, Jul'82 by Old Gold Records. Dist: Lightning, Jazz Music, Spartan, Counterpoint

IF I RULED THE WORLD.
Tracks: / Be my love / Bless this house / Falling in love with love / I believe in love / If I ruled the world / Mama / O Sole Mio / Speak to me of love / This is my song / Younger than springtime.
Album: released on Timeless, Jul'86

Cassette: released on Timeless, Jul'86

MUSICAL WORLD OF HARRY SECOMBE, THE.
Album: released on Cambra, '83 by Cambra Records. Dist: IDS, Conifer

Cassette: released on Cambra, '83 by Cambra Records. Dist: IDS, Conifer

SACRED SONGS.
Album: released on Philips, Nov'84 Dist: IMS-Polygram

Cassette: released on Philips, Nov'84 Dist: IMS-Polygram

SONG AND A PRAYER, A.
Album: released on Celebrity, Aug'81 by Evolution Group records. Dist: Spartan

Cassette: released on Celebrity, Aug'81 by Evolution Group records. Dist: Spartan

SONGS OF PRAISE.
Cassette: released on Autograph, Apr'85 Dist: Record Services Distribution (Ireland)

THESE ARE MY SONGS.
Album: released on Celebrity, Dec'80 by Evolution Group records. Dist: Spartan

Cassette: released on Celebrity, Dec'80 by Evolution Group records. Dist: Spartan

Second Chapter Of Acts

ENCORES.
Album: released on Myrrh, May'82 by Word Records. Dist: Word Distribution

Cassette: released on Myrrh, May'82 by Word Records. Dist: Word Distribution

HOW THE WEST WAS ONE.
Double Album: released on Myrrh, May'82 by Word Records. Dist: Word Distribution

Double cassette: released on Myrrh, May'82 by Word Records. Dist: Word Distribution

IN THE VOLUME OF THE BOOK.
Album: released on Myrrh, May'82 by Word Records. Dist: Word Distribution

Cassette: released on Myrrh, May'82 by Word Records. Dist: Word Distribution

MANSION BUILDER.
Album: released on Sparrow, May'82 by Word Records. Dist: Spartan

Cassette: released on Sparrow, May'82 by Word Records. Dist: Spartan

REJOICE.
Album: released on Sparrow, May'82 by Word Records. Dist: Spartan

Cassette: released on Sparrow, May'82 by Word Records. Dist: Spartan

WITH FOOTNOTES.
Album: released on Myrrh, May'82 by Word Records. Dist: Word Distribution

Cassette: released on Myrrh, May'82 by Word Records. Dist: Word Distribution

Second Coming

INCEST.

Single (7"): released on Torment, Nov'84 Dist: Red Rhino, Cartel

RETURN (EP), THE.
Single (7"): released on Torment, May'85 Dist: Red Rhino, Cartel

Second House Saturday

SONGS OF SCOTTISH MUSIC HALL.
Album: released on Lismor, Apr'78 by Lismor Records. Dist: Lismor, Roots, Celtic Music

Cassette: released on Lismor, Apr'78 by Lismor Records. Dist: Lismor, Roots, Celtic Music

Second Image

STAR.
Single (7"): released on Polydor, Jun'82 by Polydor Records. Dist: Polygram, Polydor

Single (12"): released on Polydor, Jun'82 by Polydor Records. Dist: Polygram, Polydor

STARTING AGAIN.
Single (7"): released on MCA, Jan'85 by MCA Records. Dist: CBS

Single (12"): released on MCA, Jan'85 by MCA Records. Dist: CBS

THERE SHE GOES.
Single (7"): released on MCA, Jan'84 by MCA Records. Dist: CBS

Single (12"): released on MCA, Jan'84 by MCA Records. Dist: CBS

WHAT'S HAPPENING.
Single (7"): released on Polydor, Sep'82 by Polydor Records. Dist: Polygram, Polydor

Single (12"): released on Polydor, Sep'82 by Polydor Records. Dist: Polygram, Polydor

Second Layer

WORLD OF RUBBER.
Album: released on Cherry Red, '82 by Cherry Red Records. Dist: Pinnacle

Seconds Of Pleasure

PULL ME UP.
Single (7"): released on Palladin, Apr'85 by Palladin Records. Dist: Cartel

Single (12"): released on Palladin, Apr'85 by Palladin Records. Dist: Cartel

Second Time Around

SECOND TIME AROUND Various artists (Various Artists).
Album: released on Cambra, Mar'85 by Cambra Records. Dist: IDS, Conifer

Cassette: released on Cambra, Mar'85 by Cambra Records. Dist: IDS, Conifer

Secret 7

EINS ZWEI DREI.
Tracks: / Eins zwei drei / Holiday in Berlin.
Single (7"): released on GTF Records, Jun'87 by GTF Records.

Secret Act

FRED FLINTSTONE WHERE ARE YOU?.
Tracks: / Fred Flintsone where are you? / Heaven.
Single (7"): released on Lifeline, Aug'86 Dist Ideal Music

Secret Affair

BUSINESS AS USUAL.
Album: released on I-Spy, Feb'82 by Arista Records. Dist: Polygram

Cassette: released on I-Spy, Feb'82 by Arista Records. Dist: Polygram

GLORY BOYS.
Album: released on I-Spy, Nov'79 by Arista Records. Dist: Polygram

MY WORLD.
Single (7"): released on I-Spy, Feb'80 by Arista Records. Dist: Polygram

TIME FOR ACTION.
Single (7"): released on I-Spy, Aug'79 by Arista Records. Dist: Polygram

Secretaries From Heaven

ART INTERFACE.
Single (7"): released on Interface, Jun'83 by Interface Records. Dist: Cartel

Secret Garden

SECRET GARDEN By Francis H. Burnett (Gordon, Hannah).
Cassette: released on Pinnacle, '79 by Pinnacle Records. Dist: Pinnacle

---

SECRET GARDEN By Fancis H. Burnett (Watford, Gwen).
Cassette: released on LFP, Feb'80

SECRET GARDEN By Francis H. Burnett (Jackson, Glenda).
Cassette: released on Argo (Spokenword), Nov'82 by Decca Records. Dist: Polygram

Secret Harts

DANCE LIKE BOY DANCE LIKE GIRL.
Single (7"): released on WEA International Jul'83 by WEA Records. Dist: WEA

Single (12"): released on WEA International, Jul'83 by WEA Records. Dist: WEA

Secret Life Of Punks

SECRET LIFE OF PUNKS Various artists (Various Artists).
Album: released on Secret, Nov'82 by Secret Records. Dist: EMI

Cassette: released on Secret, Nov'82 by Secret Records. Dist: EMI

Secret Of My Success

SECRET OF MY SUCCESS (THE) Original soundtrack (Various Artists).
Tracks: / Secret of my success (The) / Sometimes the good guys finish first / I burn for you / Riskin' a romance / Gazabo / Price of love (The) / Water fountain / Don't ask the reason why / Themes / Heaven and the heartaches.
Notes: Music score by David Foster. Music supervision: Tommy Mottola and Jeb Brian.
Album: released on MCA, Apr'87 by MCA Records. Dist: Polygram, MCA

Cassette: released on MCA, Apr'87 by MCA Records. Dist: Polygram, MCA

Secret Of Nimh

SECRET OF NIMH Original Motion Picture Soundtrack.
Album: released on That's Entertainment, Sep'82 by That's Entertainment Records. Dist: Pinnacle, PRT

Secret Places

SECRET PLACES Original soundtrack.
Album: released on Virgin, Sep'84 by Virgin Records. Dist: EMI, Virgin Distribution

Secret Service

FLASH IN THE NIGHT.
Single (7"): released on Sonet, Jan'82 by Sonet Records. Dist: PRT

HOW I WANT YOU.
Single (7"): released on Sonet, Dec'84 by Sonet Records. Dist: PRT

LA GOODBYE.
Single (7"): released on Sonet, Sep'81 by Sonet Records. Dist: PRT

OH SUSIE.
Album: released on Sonet, Jul'80 by Sonet Records. Dist: PRT

OVER TOWN.
Single (7"): released on Sonet, Feb'83 by Sonet Records. Dist: PRT

WHEN THE NIGHT CLOSES IN.
Tracks: / When the night closes in / Let us dance a little bit more.
Single (7"): released on Sonet, Jun'86 by Sonet Records. Dist: PRT

Single (12"): released on Sonet, Jun'86 by Sonet Records. Dist: PRT

Secret Seven

HOLD ON TO LOVE.
Single (7"): released on Bronze, Apr'83 by Polygram Records. Dist: Polydor

Single (12"): released on Bronze, Apr'83 by Polygram Records. Dist: Polydor

Secret Syde

HIDDEN SECRETS.
Album: released on Hosehead, Apr'86 Dist: Red Rhino, Cartel

Secret Troup

JUNCTION 16 - WAITING FOR A CALL.
Single (12"): released on RS, Dec'85 Dist: Revolver Distribution, Cartel Distribution

Sect

FREE ENGLAND.
Tracks: / Free England.
Single (7"): released on Insect, Oct'86 Dist: Nine Mile, Cartel

VOICE OF REASON, THE.
Album: released on Razor, Jun'87 by Razor. Dist: Pinnacle

Section 25

ALWAYS NOW.
Tracks: / Friendly fires / Dirty disco / C.P. / Loose talk costs lives / Inside out / Melt close / Hit / Babies in the Bardo / Be brave / New horizon.
Album: released on Factory, Jan'87 by Factory Records. Dist: Cartel, Pinnacle

Cassette: released on Factory, Jan'87 by Factory Records. Dist: Cartel, Pinnacle

Album: released on Factory, Sep'81 by Factory Records. Dist: Cartel, Pinnacle

BACK TO WONDER.
Single (7"): released on Factory, Jun'83 by Factory Records. Dist: Cartel, Pinnacle

BAD NEWS WEEK.
Tracks: / Bad news week.
Single (12"): released on Factory, Nov'86 by Factory Records. Dist: Cartel, Pinnacle

BEAST,THE.
Single (12"): released on Factory, Jul'82 by Factory Records. Dist: Cartel, Pinnacle

CRAZY WISDOM.
Single (7"): released on Factory Benelux, Sep'85 by Rough Trade Records. Dist: Cartel

FROM THE HIP.
Album: released on Factory, Mar'84 by Factory Records. Dist: Cartel, Pinnacle

GIRLS DON'T COUNT.
Single (12"): released on Factory, Jul'80 by Factory Records. Dist: Cartel, Pinnacle

LOOKING FROM A HILLTOP.
Single (7"): released on Factory, Jun'84 by Factory Records. Dist: Cartel, Pinnacle

Single (12"): released on Factory, Jun'84 by Factory Records. Dist: Cartel, Pinnacle

LOVE AND HATE.
Album: released on Factory, Jul'86 by Factory Records. Dist: Cartel, Pinnacle

Cassette: released on Factory, Jul'86 by Factory Records. Dist: Cartel, Pinnacle

Section 5

WE WON'T CHANGE.
Album: released on Oi!, Nov'85 Dist: Revolver Distribution

Section A

STILETTO.
Single (7"): released on LBA, Apr'85 by LBA Records.

TIME STANDS STILL.
Single (7"): released on Subversive, Jul'82 Dist: Backs, Cartel Distribution

Sector 27

EXCALIBUR.
Single (7"): released on Rocket, May'84 by Phonogram Records. Dist; Polygram Distribution

Single (12"): released on Rocket, May'84 by Phonogram Records. Dist: Polygram Distribution

Security Leak

KEEP THE TEARS.
Single (7"): released on Audiotrax, Jun'84 by Audiotrax. Dist: PRT

Sedaka, Dara & Neil

YOUR PRECIOUS LOVE.
Single (7"): released on MCA, Feb'84 by MCA Records. Dist: CBS

Sedaka, Neil

Biographical Details: Neil Sedaka, born in New York in 1939, is a singer/songwriter who had early success in the Brill Building era of the late 1950s-early 1960s and who turned out to have the talent to stick around. From a piano-playing family, he is a fine pianist himself; writing with **Howard Greenfield**, his success with teen pop was so great from 1959 to 1963 that only **Elvis Presley** outsold him; he switched to MOR during the progressive rock era of the late 1960s, and came back mid-1970s with quality pop: a Tin-Pan-Alley trouper. [Donald Clarke, April 87]

20 GOLDEN PIECES OF NEIL SEDAKA.
Album: released on Bulldog, Jan'83 by Bulldog Records. Dist: President Distribution, Spartan, Swift, Taylor, H.R.

Cassette: released on Bulldog, Jan'83 by Bulldog Records. Dist: President Distribution, Spartan, Swift, Taylor, H.R.

3 GREAT GUYS (see 3 Great Guys) (Sedaka, Neil/Paul Anka/Sam Cooke).

BACKTRACKIN'.
Album: released on Masterpiece, Jan'86

Cassette: released on Masterpiece, Jan'86

BEST OF.
Album: released on Premier, Jan'84 by Premier Records. Dist: CBS

Cassette: released on Premier, Jan'84 by Premier Records. Dist: CBS

BREAKING UP IS HARD TO DO.
Tracks: / Breaking up is hard to do / I go ape.
Single (7"): released on Old Gold, Nov'86 by Old Gold Records. Dist: Lightning, Jazz Music, Spartan, Counterpoint

Single (7"): released on RCA, Jan'80 by RCA Records. Dist: RCA, Roots, Swift, Wellard, Chris, I & B, Solomon & Peres Distribution

COME SEE ABOUT ME.
Album: released on MCA, Apr'84 by MCA Records. Dist: CBS

Cassette: released on MCA, Apr'84 by MCA Records. Dist: CBS

FABULOUS NEIL SEDAKA,THE.
Double Album: released on Cambra, Jan'83 by Cambra Records. Dist: IDS, Conifer

Double cassette: released on Cambra, Jan'83 by Cambra Records. Dist: IDS, Conifer

GOOD TIMES.
Tracks: / Love made me feel this way / Sweet dreams of you / Let me walk with you again / Rosarita / Hungry years / Wonderful world of love / Good times / Paint me again / Tomorrow never came.
Album: released on PRT, Jul'86 by PRT Records. Dist: PRT

Cassette: released on PRT, Jul'86 by PRT Records. Dist: PRT

Compact disc: released on PRT, Jul'86 by PRT Records. Dist: PRT

GOOD TIMES, THE.
Tracks: / Good times, The / Paint me again.
Single (7"): released on PRT, Apr'86 by PRT Records. Dist: PRT

HAPPY BIRTHDAY SWEET 16.
Single (7"): released on RCA, Jan'80 by USA Import. Dist: Lightning

Single (7"): released on RCA Golden Grooves, Jul'81 by RCA Records. Dist: RCA

Tracks: / Happy Birthday Sweet Sixteen / Calendar girl.
Single (7"): released on Old Gold, Oct'86 by Old Gold Records. Dist: Lightning, Jazz Music, Spartan, Counterpoint

I'M A SONG.
Cassette: released on Orchid Music, Feb'82 by Bibi. Dist: Pinnacle

LAUGHTER AND TEARS.
Album: released on Polydor, Jun'87 by Polydor Records. Dist: Polygram, Polydor

Cassette: released on Polydor, Jun'87 by Polydor Records. Dist: Polygram, Polydor

Album: released on Polydor, Jun'76 by Polydor Records. Dist: Polygram, Polydor

Cassette: released on Polydor, Jun'76 by Polydor Records. Dist: Polygram, Polydor

LAUGHTER IN THE RAIN.
Single (7"): released on Old Gold, Jul'84 by Old Gold Records. Dist: Lightning, Jazz Music, Spartan, Counterpoint

LAUGHTER & TEARS.
Compact disc: by Polydor Records. Dist: Polygram, Polydor

MAGIC MOMENTS.
Cassette: released on RCA, Jun'84 by RCA Records. Dist: RCA, Roots, Swift, Wellard, Chris, I & B, Solomon & Peres Distribution

NEIL SEDAKA LIVE AT THE ROYAL FESTIVAL HALL.
Cassette: released on Polydor, Jun'83 by Polydor Records. Dist: Polygram, Polydor

NEIL SEDAKA'S GREATEST HITS.
Album: released on RCA International, Jan'84 Cat. no: **NL 89171**

Cassette: released on RCA International, Jan'84

OH CAROL.
Tracks: / Oh Carol / One way ticket.
Single (7"): released on Old Gold, Oct'86 by Old Gold Records. Dist: Lightning, Jazz Music, Spartan, Counterpoint

Single (7"): released on Golden Grooves, May'82 by RCA. Dist: RCA

Album: released on RCA, Jan'79 by RCA Records. Dist: RCA, Roots, Swift, Wellard, Chris, I & B, Solomon & Peres Distribution

Cassette: released on RCA, Jan'79 by RCA Records. Dist: RCA, Roots, Swift, Wellard, Chris, I & B, Solomon & Peres Distribution

Album: released on RCA (Germany), Jun'83

Cassette: released on RCA (Germany), Jun'83

PRELUDE.
Album: released on Meteor, Nov'83 by Magnum Force Music. Dist: CBS Distribution

Sedgemorons

DROP DEAD DARLING.
Digital audio tape: released on Sheep Worrying, May'85 Dist: Cartel

Sedition

MIGHTY DEVICE, THE.
Tracks: / Mighty device, The.
Single (12"): released on Fun, Sep'86 by Fun Records. Dist: Projection

Seducer

CAUGHT IN THE ACT.
Album: released on Thunderbolt, Oct'85 by Magnum Music Group Ltd. Dist: Magnum Music Group Ltd, PRT Distribution, Spartan Distribution

'EADS DOWN - SEE YOU AT THE END.
Album: released on Stud, Apr'87 by John Sherry.

INDECENT EXPOSURE.
Single (12"): released on Thunderbolt, Nov'84 by Magnum Music Group Ltd. Dist: Magnum Music Group Ltd, PRT Distribution, Spartan Distribution

Seducer Dubwise

SEDUCER DUBWISE Various Artists (Various Artists).
Album: released on Hitbound, Jun'84 by Hitbound Records. Dist: Jetstar

Seduction

ELECTRICITY.
Single (12"): released on Challenge, Feb'85 by Elite Records. Dist: Pinnacle

Seeds

FALLING OFF THE EDGE.
Album: released on Music Box, May'87 Cat. no: **SMB 158**

LEGENDARY MASTER RECORDINGS.
Album: released on Sonet, Aug'78 by Sonet Records. Dist: PRT

SEEDS II : ART (Various Artists).
Tracks: / Puppet life / Life in reverse / F.T.N. / Urban ospreys / Hearts in exile / Trendy / Conspiracy / My mother was a friend of the enemy of the people / So many others.
Notes: Second volume in Cherry Red's 'Seeds' series, featuring deletd indie singles, including The Go-Betweens, The Nightingales, Bone Orchard, The Higsons, Blurt and more. Cassette has Seeds 1 on side 2.
Album: released on Cherry Red, Mar'87 by Cherry Red Records. Dist: Pinnacle

Cassette: released on Cherry Red, Apr'87 by Cherry Red Records. Dist: Pinnacle

SEEDS III: ROCK (Various Artists).
Tracks: / Big time / Roger Wilson said / Dance stance / Standing up / Europeans / Favourite sister / She's fallen in love with a monster man / Cast a long shadow / Terminal Tokyo / King mob / Christine Keeler / So long / I'll remember you / Drunken uncle John.
Notes: (P) Original sound recording made by Cherry Red Records Ltd.
Album: released on Cherry Red, Jun'87 by Cherry Red Records. Dist: Pinnacle

SEEDS I: POP (Various Artists).
Tracks: / World weary / Everybody thinks everybody else is dead bad / Another reason / Shoot to kill / Jack / Every conversation / Heavens above / Stop the rain / Tough Times / Don't ring me up / Sun shines here (The) / Fast boyfriends / Three wishes / Happy feeling / Mark my word / Don't come back / Things have changed (that should have stayed the same) / Patrick / Time goes by so slow.
Album: released on Cherry Red, Mar'87 by Cherry Red Records. Dist: Pinnacle

SEEDS,THE.
Album: released on Line (West Germany), Feb'84

WEB OF SOUND,A.
Album: released on Line (West Germany), Feb'84

Seeger, Peggy

Biographical Details: Peggy Seeger was born in New York in 1935; she is the sister of Mike and half-sister of Pete. Her mother, **Ruth Crawford Seeger**, was a talented composer (her string quartet of the early '30s a particulary fine piece) who gave it up to become a collector and editor of folksongs, especially for children. Peggy studied music at Radcliffe and began performing in public; studied Russian in Holland in 1955, travelled widely, including to Russia and China; came to England in 1956 to act in a Granada TV production of the folk musical **Dark Side Of The Moon**. Joined the **Ramblers**, including **Ewan MacColl**; she settled in Britain, recorded and wrote music for films and TV with MacColl, as well as making more than 30 solo albums, also recording with MacColl, **Tom Paley**, her sisters Penny and Barbara, and publishing anthologies such as **Folk Songs Of Peggy Seeger** '64. Whereas Pete Seeger likes to get crowds singing and Mike prefers to teach traditional music to small groups, Peggy has specialised in ballads, often of a feminist point of view; her solo LPs are on Folkways and Rounder in the USA. [Donald Clarke, April 87]

BLOOD AND ROSES VOL.1 (Seeger, Peggy/Ewen MacColl).

BLOOD AND ROSES VOL.2 (Seeger, Peggy/Ewen MacColl).

BLOOD AND ROSES VOL.3 (Seeger, Peggy/Ewen MacColl).

COLD SNAP (see MacColl, Ewen) (Seeger, Peggy/Ewen MacColl).

Seeger, Pete

Biographical Details: Pete Seeger, was born in 1919 in New York, is the Johnny Appleseed of American music; in his controversial career he taught a whole generation to sing and be brave. He plays a five-string banjo of his own design and wrote a book on how to play it. He formed the **Almanac Singers** with **Woody Guthrie** in 1939, the **Weavers** quartet in 1949; the Weavers' enormous success in 1950 was ruined by an FBI informant who swore that they were all communists, later went to prison for perjury. Seeger was convicted of contempt for refusing to answer the House Un-American Activities Committee's questions in 1955; the case was thrown out in 1962, yet Seeger remained blacklisted. He made many albums for Folkways, and was signed by American Columbia Records despite the fact that the parent CBS TV Network wouldn't have him on screen. He wrote, co-wrote or adapted and popularised **"If I HadA Hammer"**, **"Where Have All The Flowers Gone"**, **"The Bells Of Rhymney"**, **"We Shall Overcome"** (from a Baptist hymn), **"Guantanamera"**, **"Gotta Travel On"**, African songs **"Wimoweh"** (aka 'The Lion Sleeps Tonight), **"Abiyoyo"**; much more. [Donald Clarke, April 87]

GREATEST HITS: PETE SEEGER.
Album: released on CBS(Holland), Jun'84 by CBS Records. Dist: Discovery

PETE SEEGER.
Album: released on Greenwich Village, Jan'87 by Sweet Folk All Records. Dist: Roots, Projection, Lightning, Celtic Music, Wellard, Chris

PETE SEEGER WITH ILLAPU.
Album: released on Greenwich Village, Jan'87 by Sweet Folk All Records. Dist: Roots, Projection, Lightning, Celtic Music, Wellard, Chris

Seekers

Biographical Details: The Seekers were a vocal-instrumental folk/pop group formed in Australia by guitarist **Keith Potger** (born 2 March 1941, Ceylon), lead singer **Judith Durham** (born 7 July 1943) and two others; they came to London and gigged at the Palladium in 1964 with **Dusty Springfield**, who wrote their no.1 hit **"I'll Never Find Another You"** (1965). Other hits include **"A World Of Our Own"**, film theme **"Georgy Girl"**; they split up in 1968, but Potger formed the sextet **New Seekers** the next year, with lead singer **Eve Graham** (born 13 April 1943, Perth, Scotland) this group had hits in 1970-73 including Delaney Bramlett's **"Never Ending Story Of Love"** (no.2 UK), **"Look What They've Done To My Song, Ma'"** written by Melanie Safka (top 50 UK, top 20 USA), **"I'd Like To Teach The World To Sing (In Perfect Harmony)'** no.1 UK/7 USA (a Roger Cook/Roger Greenway song), medley **"Pinball Wizard/See Me Feel Me"** from the Who's **Tommy**, British hits continuing to 1978. [Donald Clarke, April 87]

BEST OF THE SEEKERS.
Album: released on EMI (Holland), '83 by EMI Records. Dist: Conifer

CARNIVAL IS OVER,THE.
Single (7"): released on Old Gold (Reissue), Oct'79

Single (7"): released on EMI (Holland), Jul'84 by EMI Records. Dist: Conifer

I'LL NEVER FIND ANOTHER YOU.
Single (7"): released on Import Music Service (IMS), '80 Dist: Concord Jazz Distributions, Pablo, Polygram

SEEKERS,THE.
Album: released on World Records, Dec'81 Dist: Polygram

Cassette: released on World Records, Dec'81 Dist: Polygram

Album: released on EMI (Holland), '83 by EMI Records. Dist: Conifer

SEEKERS,THE(I'LL NEVER FIND ANOTHER YOU).

Cassette: released on EMI, Jul'80 by EMI Records. Dist: EMI

THIS IS THE SEEKERS.
Album: released on EMI, Sep'80 by EMI Records. Dist: EMI

Cassette: released on EMI, Sep'80 by EMI Records. Dist: EMI

VERY BEST OF THE SEEKERS.
Album: released on EMI, May'74 by EMI Records. Dist: EMI

Cassette: released on EMI, May'74 by EMI Records. Dist: EMI

Seek, Sue

AMERICAN MAN AMERICAN LOVER.
Tracks: / American man American lover / DC Shadow of the white moon / Calling UFO beta.
Single (7"): released on Red Ruby, Jun'87 Dist: Red Ruby

SHADOW OF MY MIND.
Tracks: / Shadow of my mind / Calling.
Single (7"): released on Red Ruby, Jun'87 Dist: Red Ruby

Notes: Self - 134 Oldfield Grove, London SE16

Seeley, Leonard K

TRADITION.
Single (7"): released on Ram, Sep'83 by Ram. Dist: PRT

Single (12"): released on Ram, Sep'83 by Ram. Dist: PRT

Seelos, Ambros

DANCE FESTIVAL (Seelos, Ambros Orchestra).
Compact disc: released on Bridge, Oct'86 Dist: CD Centre Distribution, Pinnacle, Target

DANCE FESTIVAL (Seelos, Ambros show band).
Compact disc: released on Bridge, Jan'87 Dist: CD Centre Distribution, Pinnacle, Target

DANCE FESTIVAL VOL.2 (Seelos, Ambros show band).
Notes: Cha cha, Samba, Tango, Quick Step, Slow Waltz, Rumba, Slow Fox etc.
Compact disc: released on Bridge, Apr'87 Dist: CD Centre Distribution, Pinnacle, Target

Seema, Puseletso

HE O OE OE (Seema, Puseletso & Tau Ea Linare).
Album: released on Globestyle, Aug'85 by Ace Records. Dist: Projection

Seething Wells

RISING SUN OF RANTING VERSE.
Single (7"): released on Radical Wallpaper, Dec'82 Dist: Cartel

See You In Vegas

WORK.
Single (7"): released on Red Rhino, Aug'83 by Indies Records. Dist: Cartel Distribution

Segal, Charles

COME FLY WITH ME (Segal, Charles His Piano & Orchestra).
Cassette: released on VFM Cassettes, Jan'85

SINATRA SONGBOOK,THE (Segal, Charles Orchestra).
Cassette: released on International Artists, Oct'76 by Arrowtabs Records. Dist: Arrowtabs

SLEEPY SHORES(MIDNIGHT STRINGS) (Segal, Charles His Piano & Orchestra).
Cassette: released on VFM Cassettes, Jan'85

Segal, Erich

LOVE STORY.
Cassette: released on Caedmon(USA), Sep'85 by Caedmon (USA) Records. Dist: Gower, Taylors, Discovery

Segami, Y

LATIN PERCUSSION.
Album: released on Denon, Mar'82

Seger, Bob

Biographical Details: Rock singer/songwriter **Bob Seger** was born 6 May 1945 in Ann Arbor, Michigan. He began performing in 1961 and became a local hero who took some years to make an international breakthrough: he formed his first band **Last Heard** in 1964; their single **'Heavy Music'** on the Cameo-Parkway label almost reached the USA national top 100 '67, but the label folded. **'Ramblin' Gamblin' Man'** '68 made the top 20 on Capitol, but he made eight albums before the live two-record set **Silver Bullet** reached the top 40 LPs in the USA, staying in the charts for 140 weeks; since then his LPs have gone platinum. He had 13 top singles in the USA 1977-83, many ballads and almost all his own compositions; none were hits in Britain, although some of his albums have charted. His music is considered to be unpretentious 'working class rock' and his following is similar to that of Bruce Springsteen in terms of audience identification. [Donald Clarke, April 87]

AGAINST THE WIND (Seger, Bob & The Silver Bullet Band).
Tracks: / Horizontal bop, The / You'll accomp'ny me / Her strut / No man's land / Long man's land / Long twin silver line / Against the wind / Good for me / Betty Lou's gettin' out tonight / Fire lake / Shinin' brightly.
Album: released on Capitol, Mar'80 by Capitol Records. Dist: EMI

Cassette: released on Capitol, Mar'80 by Capitol Records. Dist: EMI

Compact disc: released on Capitol, Mar'80 by Capitol Records. Dist: EMI

AMERICAN STORM (Seger, Bob & The Silver Bullet Band).
Tracks: / American Storm / Fortunate son / Hollywood Nights* / (Live version)*.
Single (7"): released on Capitol, Mar'86 by Capitol Records. Dist: EMI

Single (7"): released on Capitol, Mar'86 by Capitol Records. Dist: EMI

DISTANCE,THE (Seger, Bob & The Silver Bullet Band).
Album: released on Capitol, Jan'83 by Capitol Records. Dist: EMI

Cassette: released on Capitol, Jan'83 by Capitol Records. Dist: EMI

Compact disc: released on Capitol, Jan'84 by Capitol Records. Dist: EMI

DISTANCE, THE.
Tracks: / Even now / Makin' thunderbirds / Boomtown blues / Shame on the moon / Love's the last to know / Roll me away / House behind a house / Comin' home / Little victories.
Compact disc: released on Capitol, '86 by Capitol Records. Dist: EMI

EVEN NOW (Seger, Bob & The Silver Bullet Band).
Single (7"): released on Capitol, Mar'83 by Capitol Records. Dist: EMI

HOLLYWOOD NIGHTS.
Single (7"): released on Capitol, Oct'81 by Capitol Records. Dist: EMI

Single (12"): released on Capitol, Oct'81 by Capitol Records. Dist: EMI

LIKE A ROCK (Seger, Bob & The Silver Bullet Band).
Tracks: / American storm / Like a rock / Miami / Ring, The / Tightrope / Aftermath, The / Sometimes / It's you / Somewhere tonight / Tightrope / Aftermath, The / Sometimes / It's you / Somewhere tonight / American storm / Like a rock / Miami / Ring, The / Like a rock (edit) / Livin' inside my heart / Like a rock / Living inside my heart / Katmandu.
Notes: "Like a Rock" is the first album from Bob Seger and the Silver Bullet Band for three years. The subject of a large following here in Britian, the group are best known for the rock 'n' roll anthem "Hollywood Nights". The new album is produced by Bob Seger & Punch and features backing vocals on three tracks by the Weather Girls.
Album: released on Capitol, Mar'86 by Capitol Records. Dist: EMI

Cassette: released on Capitol, Mar'86 by Capitol Records. Dist: EMI

Compact disc: released on Capitol, Jul'86 by Capitol Records. Dist: EMI

Single (7"): released on Capitol, Jun'86 by Capitol Records. Dist: EMI

Single (12"): released on Capitol, Jun'86 by Capitol Records. Dist: EMI

LIVE BULLET.
Album: released on Capitol, Aug'76 by Capitol Records. Dist: EMI

Cassette: released on Capitol, Jan'77 by Capitol Records. Dist: EMI

MONGREL.
Album: released on Fame, Jul'83 by Music For Pleasure Records. Dist: EMI

Cassette: released on Fame, Jul'83 by Music For Pleasure Records. Dist: EMI

NIGHT MOVES.
Album: released on Fame, May'82 by Music For Pleasure Records. Dist: EMI

Cassette: released on Fame, May'82 by Music For Pleasure Records. Dist: EMI

NINE TONIGHT.
Double Album: released on Capitol, Oct'81 by Capitol Records. Dist: EMI

Double cassette: released on Capitol, Oct'81 by Capitol Records. Dist: EMI

ROLL ME AWAY (Seger, Bob & The Silver Bullet Band).
Single (7"): released on Capitol, Jul'83 by Capitol Records. Dist: EMI

SEVEN (Seger, Bob & The Silver Bullet Band).
Album: released on Greenlight-Capitol, Jun'81 by Capitol Records. Dist: EMI

Cassette: released on Greenlight-Capitol, Jun'81 by Capitol Records. Dist: EMI

SHAKEDOWN (Seger, Bob & The Silver Bullet Band).
Tracks: / Shakedown / Aftermath, The.
Notes: Shakedoiwn is taken from the forthcoming Beverly Hills Cop II film soundtrack.
Single (7"): released on MCA, Jun'87 by MCA Records. Dist: Polygram, MCA

Single (12"): released on MCA, Jun'87 by MCA Records. Dist: Polygram, MCA

SHAME ON THE MOON (Seger, Bob & The Silver Bullet Band).
Single (7"): released on Capitol, Jan'83 by Capitol Records. Dist: EMI

SMOKIN O.P.'S.
Album: released on EMI (Germany), Mar'84 by EMI Records. Dist: Conifer

Cassette: released on EMI (Germany), Mar'84 by EMI Records. Dist: Conifer

STRANGER IN TOWN.
Album: released on Capitol, May'78 by Capitol Records. Dist: EMI

Cassette: released on Capitol, May'78 by Capitol Records. Dist: EMI

Seger, Peggy

BLOOD AND ROSES VOL. 4 (Seger, Peggy & Ewan MacColl).
Album: released on Blackthorne, Jul'86 Dist: Projection, Cadillac Music, Celtic Music, Roots

BLOOD AND ROSES VOL. 5 (Seger, Peggy & Ewan MacColl).
Album: released on Blackthorne, Jul'86 Dist: Projection, Cadillac Music, Celtic Music, Roots

Segovia

PORTRAIT OF ANDREAS SEGOVIA,A.
Album: released on Stylus, Aug'87 Dist: Pinnacle, Terry Blood Distribution, Stylus Distribution

Compact disc: released on Stylus, Aug'87 Dist: Pinnacle, Terry Blood Distribution, Stylus Distribution

Segue

THREE ON THE TROT.
Single (7"): released on Tart'n, Aug'83 by Tart'n Records. Dist: Cartel Distribution

VISION OF THE FUTURE.
Single (12"): released on Amazing, May'85 by Amazing Records. Dist: Cartel

Sehorn's Soul Farm

SEHORN'S SOUL FARM (Various Artists).
Album: released on Charly(R&B), Feb'82 by Charly Records. Dist: Charly, Cadillac

Seidel, Jan

ON THE FARM/THE COW POLKA.
Single (7"): released on RCA, Feb'82 by RCA Records. Dist: RCA, Roots, Swift, Wellard, Chris, I & B, Solomon & Peres Distribution

Seize

EVERYBODY DOES (EP).
Single (7"): released on Whynot, Sep'82

Sektion II

TWO OF US.
Single (7"): released on National Health, Aug'84 by National Health Records. Dist: ILA

Selassie I Rockers

30 PIECES OF DUB.
Album: released on Empire World, '83

Selby, Hubert

MR PRESIDENT ENTERTAINS.
Album: released on Amberlee, Jan'77 by Amberlee Records. Dist: Amberlee Records, H.R. Taylor

Selecter

MISSING WORDS.
Single (7"): released on Two-Tone, Mar'80 by Chrysalis Records. Dist: H.R. Taylor

ON MY RADIO.
Tracks: / Three minute hero.
Single (7"): released on Old Gold, Feb'87 by Old Gold Records. Dist: Lightning, Jazz Music, Spartan, Counterpoint

Single (12"): released on Old Gold, Jan'87 by Old Gold Records. Dist: Lightning, Jazz Music, Spartan, Counterpoint

Single (7"): released on Two-Tone, Oct'79 by Chrysalis Records. Dist: H.R. Taylor

THREE MINUTE HERO/JAMES BOND.
Single (7"): released on Two-Tone, Jan'80 by Chrysalis Records. Dist: H.R. Taylor

TOO MUCH PRESSURE.
Album: released on Two-Tone, Feb'80 by Chrysalis Records. Dist: H.R. Taylor

Cassette: released on Two-Tone, Feb'80 by Chrysalis Records. Dist: H.R. Taylor

Selectors

JENNY JENNY.
Single (7"): released on Ethnic, Nov'84 Dist: Kingdom

Self Abuse

SOLDIER, THE (EP).
Single (7"): released on Radical Change, Mar'84 by Backs Records. Dist: Backs, Cartel

Self Control

BROKEN UP.
Album: released on Dancing Sideways, Nov'83 by Dancing Sideways Records. Dist: Pinnacle

Selfish Gene

SELFISH GENE Dawkins, Richard.
Cassette: released on Psychology Today, Oct'81

Self, Jim

CHILDREN AT PLAY (Self, Jim Quintet).
Album: released on Discovery, Aug'83 Dist: PRT

Self Service

HEAVEN'S ABOVE.
Single (7"): released on Racket, May'83 Dist: Rough Trade

Seliga, Frank

ON THE ROCKS - IN STRICT TEMPO RHYTHM (Seliga, Frank & His Dance Orchestra).
Album: released on Austrophon (Germany), Aug'85

Sellers, John

LET PRAISE ARISE.
Album: released on Wing, May'85

Cassette: released on Wing, May'85

Sellers, Peter

BEST OF SELLERS.
Album: released on Starline, Jun'73 by EMI Records. Dist: EMI

HE'S INNOCENT OF WATERGATE (Sellers, Peter & Spike Milligan).
Album: released on Decca, Aug'74 by Decca Records. Dist: Polygram

PARKINSON INTERVIEW, (THE).
Album: released on BBC, Nov'80 by BBC Records & Tapes. Dist: EMI, PRT, Pye

Cassette: released on BBC, Nov'80 by BBC Records & Tapes. Dist: EMI, PRT, Pye

SHE LOVES YOU.
Single (7"): released on Parlophone, Jan'81 by EMI Records. Dist: EMI

SONGS OF SELLERS, (THE).
Album: released on Music For Pleasure (Holland), Oct'83 by EMI Records. Dist: EMI

Cassette: released on Music For Pleasure (Holland), Oct'83 by EMI Records. Dist: EMI

Selvester, Cathryn

IF YOU'RE NOT HERE.
Single (12"): released on Capo, Sep'84 by Capo Records. Dist: Jetstar

Selvin, Ben

1929-32 (Selvin, Ben & His Orchestra).
Album: released on Saville, May'84 by Conifer Records. Dist: Conifer

CHEERFUL LITTLE EARFUL (Selvin, Ben & His Orchestra).
Album: released on Saville, Jan'84 by Conifer Records. Dist: Conifer

Semantics

BWANA JUNCTION.

Album: released on Line, Apr'87

Sembello, Michael
MANIAC.
Single (7"): released on Casablanca, Aug'85 Dist: Polygram, Phonogram

Seminars
TRAFFIC CONTROL (Bonn,Tokyo,London).
Cassette: released on International Report, Oct'81 by Seminar Cassettes. Dist: Audio-Visual Library Services, Davidson Distribution, Eastern Educational Products Distrib., Forlaget Systime Distribution, MacDougall Distribution, Talktapes Distribution, Watkins Books Ltd Distribution, Norton, Jeff Distribution

Semprini
GOLDEN MOMENTS, (THE).
Double Album: released on Music For Pleasure (Holland), Jul'83 by EMI Records. Dist: EMI

Cassette: released on Music For Pleasure (Holland), Jul'83 by EMI Records. Dist: EMI

MOTORWAY SERENADE.
Cassette: released on Mobile Music, '78

SEMPRINI CLASSICAL PIECES.
Cassette: released on Ideal(Tapes), Apr'80 Dist: EMI

Semuta
SEMUTA.
Album: released on Lee Lambert, May'80 by Lee Lambert Records. Dist: Cadillac

Senate
ORIGINAL SIN, (THE).
Single (7"): released on War, Jul'84 by War Records. Dist: PRT

Single (12"): released on War, Jul'84 by War Records. Dist: PRT

Senator, Asher
ABBREVIATION QUALIFICATION.
Single (12"): released on Fashion, Aug'84 by Fashion Records. Dist: PRT, Jetstar

ASHER SENATOR V JOHNNY RINGO (Senator, Asher & Johnny Ringo).
Album: released on Fashion, Dec'84 by Fashion Records. Dist: PRT, Jetstar

BIG MATCH, (THE).
Single (7"): released on Fashion, Nov'85 by Fashion Records. Dist: PRT, Jetstar

Single (12"): released on Fashion, Nov'85 by Fashion Records. Dist: PRT, Jetstar

BORN TO CHAT.
Album: released on Fashion, Nov'86 by Fashion Records. Dist: PRT, Jetstar

BUBBLE WITH I.
Single (7"): released on Fashion, Mar'86 by Fashion Records. Dist: PRT, Jetstar

Sendak Soundbook
SENDAK SOUNDBOOK, (THE) Sendak, Maurice (Grimes, Tammy).
Boxed set: released on Caedmon(USA), '82 by Caedmon (USA) Records. Dist: Gower, Taylors, Discovery

Send No Flowers
PLAYING FOR TIME.
Single (7"): released on Praxis, Aug'82

Sensation 49
SENSATION 49.
Album: released on Nostalgia (Sweden), '82 by Wellard, Chris Distribution. Dist: Wellard, Chris Distribution

Sensational Nightingales
SONGS OF PRAISE.
Album: released on MCA (USA), Jun'84

Sensation Jazz Band
OCEAN QUEEN.
Album: released on Sensation, Dec'82 Dist: Jazz Music

Sensation Of..
SENSATION OF THE EIGHTIES - VOLUME 1 (Various Artists).
Album: released on Band Of Gold, Jan'87 by Stylus Records. Dist: Stylus

Cassette: by Stylus Records. Dist: Stylus

Sensations
BABY LOVE (Sensations & Jah Stone).

Sense
HOLDING ON.
Single (7"): released on Carrere, Nov'83 by Carrere Records. Dist: PRT, Spartan

HOLD ON.
Album: released on Carrere, Feb'84 by Carrere Records. Dist: PRT, Spartan

JAMIE.
Single (7"): released on War, Jul'85 by War Records. Dist: PRT

Single (12"): released on War, Jul'85 by War Records. Dist: PRT

THREE MINUTES LATE.
Single (7"): released on Carrere, Jul'83 by Carrere Records. Dist: PRT, Spartan

Single (12"): released on Carrere, Jul'83 by Carrere Records. Dist: PRT, Spartan

YOU CRY.
Single (7"): released on War, Sep'84 by War Records. Dist: PRT

Sense of Beauty
SENSE OF BEAUTY VOL. 2 (Various Artists).
Album: released on Uniton (Norway), May'86 Dist: Cartel

Cassette: released on Uniton (Norway), May'86 Dist: Cartel

Sense of Vision
DREAM.
Single (7"): released on Clean, Jan'84 by Clean Records. Dist: Cartel

Senses
IF YOU CAN COUNT.
Single (7"): released on West End, Feb'84 by Arista Records. Dist: Polygram

Single (12"): released on West End, Feb'84 by Arista Records. Dist: Polygram

Sensible Jerseys
RIGHT AND WRONG.
Single (7"): released on Jersey, Jun'85

TWO WAY RADIO.
Single (7"): released on Virgin, Sep'85 by Virgin Records. Dist: EMI, Virgin Distribution

Single (12"): released on Virgin, Sep'85 by Virgin Records. Dist: EMI, Virgin Distribution

Sensible Shoes
BUILD ME AN EMPIRE.
Tracks: / Build me an empire / Build me an empire (Version).
Single (7"): released on Lambs To The Slaughter, Jun'86 by Prism Records. Dist: Pinnacle, Red Rhino, Cartel

GAME.
Single (7"): released on Instep, Jan'85 by Instep Records. Dist: Pinnacle

LONE STAR HERO.
Single (7"): released on Lambs To The Slaughter, Mar'87 by Prism Records. Dist: Pinnacle, Red Rhino, Cartel

Senter, Boyd
SOLOS AND SENTERPEDES-VOL.1-1927-28.
Tracks: / Down-hearted blues / Boss of the stomps / Grind out, The / I ain't got nobody / T'aint clean / Eniale blues / Just so-so / Prickly heat / Sister Kate / Mobile blues / No more / Original stack o'lee blues / Original Chinese blues / Somebody's wrong.
Album: released on Harlequin, Dec'86 by Harlequin Records. Dist: Swift, Jazz Music, Wellard, Chris, IRS, Taylor, H.R.

Sent From Coventry
SENT FROM COVENTRY Various artists (Various Artists).
Album: released on Kathedral, '80 by Cherry Red Records. Dist: Pinnacle

Sentimental Guitar
SENTIMENTAL GUITAR Various artists (Various Artists).
Cassette: released on Bravo, Feb'80 by Pickwick Records. Dist: Lugtons

Sentimental Hits...
SENTIMENTAL HITS OF EARLY 60'S (Various Artists).
Tracks: / Sailor / Soldier boy / Michael / Love letters / Why / Breaking up is hard to do / Theme from 'A summer place' / You don't know / Put

your head on my shoulder / Pretty blue eyes / Dr Kildare theme / Go away little girl / Last night was made for love / Next time (The).
Album: released on Old Gold, Nov'86 by Old Gold Records. Dist: Lightning, Jazz Music, Spartan, Counterpoint

Sentimental Journey
SENTIMENTAL JOURNEY Various artists (Various Artists).
Album: released on Cambra, Mar'85 by Cambra Records. Dist: IDS, Conifer

Cassette: released on Cambra, Mar'85 by Cambra Records. Dist: IDS, Conifer

SENTIMENTAL JOURNEY Various bands (Various bands).
Double Album: released on Telefunken, Nov'81

SENTIMENTAL JOURNEY Sterne, Laurence (Sinden, Donald).
Double cassette: released on Argo (Spokenword), Jul'82 by Decca Records. Dist: Polygram

Sentinel Beast
DEPTHS OF DEATH.
Album: released on Roadrunner (Dutch), Aug'86 Dist: Pinnacle

Seona Dancing
BITTER HEART.
Single (7"): released on London, Sep'83 by London Records. Dist: Polygram

Single (12"): released on London, Sep'83 by London Records. Dist: Polygram

MORE TO LOSE.
Single (7"): released on London, May'83 by London Records. Dist: Polygram

Single (12"): released on London, May'83 by London Records. Dist: Polygram

September
LOVER IN ME, (THE).
Single (7"): released on 10, Jun'85 by 10 Records. Dist: Virgin, EMI

SLOWLY.
Tracks: / Slowly / Lover is me, The.
Single (7"): released on 10, Mar'86 by 10 Records. Dist: Virgin, EMI

Single (12"): released on 10, Mar'86 by 10 Records. Dist: Virgin, EMI

Sequence
SEQUENCE.
Album: by PRT Records. Dist: PRT Distribution

Cassette: by PRT Records. Dist: PRT Distribution

Seratt, Kenny
DIESEL DEVIL.
Single (7"): released on Big R, Dec'81 by Big R Records. Dist: Pinnacle, Wynd-Up Distribution, Solomon & Peres Distribution, I & B, JSU, Swift, Record Merchandisers Distribution, Spartan

GIVE ME A TITLE AND I'LL WRITE YOU A SONG.
Album: released on Big R, Nov'80 by Big R Records. Dist: Pinnacle, Wynd-Up Distribution, Solomon & Peres Distribution, I & B, JSU, Swift, Record Merchandisers Distribution, Spartan

Cassette: released on Big R, Nov'80 by Big R Records. Dist: Pinnacle, Wynd-Up Distribution, Solomon & Peres Distribution, I & B, JSU, Swift, Record Merchandisers Distribution, Spartan

RIDIN' THE BIG A.
Album: released on Big R, Nov'80 by Big R Records. Dist: Pinnacle, Wynd-Up Distribution, Solomon & Peres Distribution, I & B, JSU, Swift, Record Merchandisers Distribution, Spartan

Cassette: released on Big R, Nov'80 by Big R Records. Dist: Pinnacle, Wynd-Up Distribution, Solomon & Peres Distribution, I & B, JSU, Swift, Record Merchandisers Distribution, Spartan

SATURDAY NIGHT IN DALLAS.
Album: released on Big R, Nov'80 by Big R Records. Dist: Pinnacle, Wynd-Up Distribution, Solomon & Peres Distribution, I & B, JSU, Swift, Record Merchandisers Distribution, Spartan

Cassette: released on Big R, Nov'80 by Big R Records. Dist: Pinnacle, Wynd-Up Distribution, Solomon & Peres Distribution, I & B, JSU, Swift, Record Merchandisers Distribution, Spartan

Single (12"): released on Big R, Nov'80 by Big R Records. Dist: Pinnacle, Wynd-Up Distribution, Solomon & Peres Distribution, I & B, JSU, Swift, Record Merchandisers Distribution, Spartan

Serenaders
MARIAN.

Single (12"): released on Brown, Jul'83 Dist: Jetstar

SWEET LOVING.
Tracks: / Sweet loving / Sweet loving (Version).
Single (12"): released on Brown, Apr'86 Dist: Jetstar

VELVET MORDE.
Tracks: / Velvet Morde / Velvet morde (Version).
Single (12"): released on Jetstar, Sep'86 Dist: Jetstar, Stage One

Sergeant
LIVING IN THE FAST LANE.
Album: released on Powerstation Records, Sep'86 by Powerstation Records. Dist: Pinnacle

SERGEANT.
Album: released on Mausoleum, Apr'85 by Mausoleum Records. Dist: Pinnacle

Sergeant Frog
BUTTERFLY BALL (LOVE IS ALL).
Single (7"): released on Safari, Oct'82 by Safari Records. Dist: Pinnacle

Sergeant Pepper
DANCING TO REGGAE MUSIC.
Single (12"): released on Ariwa, Sep'83 by Ariwa Records. Dist: Revolver, Cartel, Jetstar, Rough Trade

ONE FAMILY.
Single (12"): released on Jah Shaka, Mar'84 by Jah Shaka Records. Dist: Jetstar

Sergeant, Will
FAVOURITE BRANCHES.
Single (7"): released on WEA, Jul'82 by WEA Records. Dist: WEA

Sergent & Herbtree
RIGHT TO FUNK.
Tracks: / Right to funk / Right to funk (version).
Single (12"): released on Safe House, 23 May'87

Sergion & Herbtree
EASTENDAH.
Tracks: / Eastendah / Eastendah (Dub).
Single (7"): released on Yellow Balloon, May'86 Dist: PRT

Serious Beats
SERIOUS BEATS (Various Artists).
Double Album: released on Serious, Dec'86 by Serious Records. Dist: PRT

Serious Drinking
COUNTRY GIRL (BECOMES DRUGS & SEX PUNK).
Single (7"): released on Upright, May'84 by Upright Records. Dist: Cartel, Rough Trade

HANGOVER.
Single (7"): released on Uptight, Mar'83

LOVE ON THE TERRACES (EP).
Single (7"): released on Upright, Sep'82 by Upright Records. Dist: Cartel, Rough Trade

REVOLUTION STARTS AT CLOSING TIME.
Tracks: / Winters over / Spirit of '66 / Love on the terraces / Bobby Moore was innocent / Hangover / Countdown to Bilko' / Really good kicks / 12XU / Am I coming over to yours / Revolution starts at closing time (The).
Album: released on Upright, Apr'87 by Upright Records. Dist: Cartel, Rough Trade

THEY MAY BE DRINKERS ROBIN, BUT THEY'RE ALSO HUMAN BEINGS.
Album: released on Upright, Apr'87 by Upright Records. Dist: Cartel, Rough Trade

Serious Hip-Hop
SERIOUS HIP-HOP 2 Various artists (Various Artists).
Album: released on Serious, Mar'87 by Serious Records. Dist: PRT

Serious Intention
SERIOUS.
Tracks: / Serious / Serious (Dub).
Single (7"): released on London, Mar'86 by London Records. Dist: Polygram

Single (12"): released on London, Mar'86 by London Records. Dist: Polygram

YOU DON'T KNOW.
Single (7"): released on Important, Oct'85 by EMI

Single (12"): released on Important, Oct Dist: EMI

Serious Posse
I DON'T BELIEVE.
Single (7"): released on Eyes, Jul'84 by Eyes Records.

Single (12"): released on Eyes, Jul'84 by Eyes Records.

Seris, Jaques
FREE TO LOVE-OID.
Single (7"): released on JSO, Jun'80
Cat. no: **EAT 2**

Sern, Lou
SWISS BOY.
Tracks: / Cuckoo clock(int).
Single (12"): released on Greyhound, Nov'86 by Greyhound Records. Dist: PRT, Greyhound

Sertl, Doug
GROOVIN' (Sertl, Doug Big Band).
Album: released on Discovery (USA), Apr'85

UPTOWN EXPRESS.
Album: released on Imported, Jun'84 Dist: Conifer

Servant
LIGHT MANOEUEVRES.
Album: released on Myrrh, May'85 by Word Records. Dist: Word Distribution

Cassette: released on Myrrh, May'85 by Word Records. Dist: Word Distribution

SHE'S ALWAYS HIDING.
Tracks: / She's always hiding / Transpired.
Single (7"): released on Head, Mar'86 by Head Records. Dist: Revolver, Cartel

SUN, A SMALL STAR (THE).
Tracks: / Sun, a small star (The).
Single (12"): released on Head, Oct'86 by Head Records. Dist: Revolver, Cartel

SWIMMING IN A HUMAN OCEAN.
Notes: With their new album, Servant reflect upon the Christian lifestyle lived out in the mainstream of our contemporary culture. In the forefront are two lead vocalists - Sandie Brock; with her husband, Owen, who started the group in Europe 13 years ago; and Eric O, a dynamic new addition to the band. Recorded almost entirely in New York, the album captures post-pop rock nuances married with dance sensibilities. Part of an emerging genre of music influencing the world today. Now located in Cincinnati, Ohio, the group has a full time missionary commitment to share the adventure of being a Christian in today's world.
Album: released on Myrrh, Jun'86 by Word Records. Dist: Word Distribution

Cassette: released on Myrrh, Jun'86 by Word Records. Dist: Word Distribution

Service, Robert
ROBERT SERVICE STORY,THE.
Album: released on R.E.L., Jan'80 by REL Records. Dist: Gordon Duncan Distribution, Celtic Music, Record Merchandisers Distribution, Projection, Graeme Tosh music

Services Silver Jubilee
SERVICES SILVER JUBILEE MUSICAL PAGEANT 1977 various bands (Various bands).
Double Album: released on PRT Special, Aug'77 by PRT Records. Dist: PRT

Sesto, Camilo
CAMILO.
Album: released on Arista, Nov'82 by Arista Records. Dist: RCA

Cassette: released on Arista, Nov'82 by Arista Records. Dist: RCA

SHOULDER TO SHOULDER.
Single (7"): released on Ariola, Feb'83 Dist: RCA, Ariola

Sete, Bola
OCEAN.
Album: released on Sonet, '76 by Sonet Records. Dist: PRT

Setus Productions
ANTHEM.
Single (12"): released on Red Rhino, Jul'85 by Red Rhino Records. Dist: Red Rhino, Cartel

Setzer, Brian
KNIFE FEELS LIKE JUSTICE,THE.
Tracks: / Knife feels like justice,The / Barbwire fence / Haunted river / Boulevard of broken dreams / Bobby's back / Radiation ranch / Chains around your heart / Maria / Three Guys Aztec / Breath of life / Barbwire fence.
Notes: As a guitarist and lead singer with the Stray Cats,Brian Setzer became a well-known figure in the field of popular music at the start of the 80's.A few brief stints with Robert Plant's Honey Drippers were warm-ups for a major musical changeof direction for Setzer,whose appearance at the Farm Aid Benefit drew a five-minute standing ovation.Producer Don Gehman is known mainly for his work with John Cougar Mellencamp.
Single (7"): released on EMI America, Apr'86 by EMI Records. Dist: EMI

Album: released on EMI America, May'86 by EMI Records. Dist: EMI

Cassette: released on EMI America, May'86 by EMI Records. Dist: EMI

Seven...
SEVEN DWARFS & THEIR DIAMOND MINE Various artists (Various Artists).
Extended-play record: released on Disneyland, Apr'81 Dist: EMI

SEVEN HOT AIR MEN AND OTHERS (Seven Hot Air Men & Others).
Album: released on VJM, Apr'79 by VJM (UK) Records. Dist: Swift

STRANGER THAN FICTION.
Single (7"): released on Polydor, Oct'84 by Polydor Records. Dist: Polygram, Polydor

Single (12"): released on Polydor, Oct'84 by Polydor Records. Dist: Polygram, Polydor

Seven Brides...
SEVEN BRIDES FOR SEVEN BROTHERS Original London Cast (Various Artists).
Tracks: / June bride / When you're in love / Overture / Bless your beautiful hide / Wonderful wonderful day / One man / Goin' courtin' / Love never goes away / Sobbin' women / Townsfolk's lament, The / Woman ought to know her place, A / We gotta make it through the winter / Lonesome polecat / Spring spring spring / Glad that you were born / Love never goes away / Wedding dance / Finale.
Notes: Roni Page, Steve Devereaux, Geoff Steer etc. Cond. Martin Yates. Songs by Gene De Paul and Johnny Mercer. New songs by Al Kasha and Joel Hirschhorn.
Album: released on CBS, Feb'87 by CBS Records. Dist: CBS

Cassette: released on CBS, Feb'87 by CBS Records. Dist: CBS

Album: released on First Night, Jun'86 by Safari Records. Dist: Pinnacle

Cassette: released on First Night, Jun'86 by Safari Records. Dist: Pinnacle

Seven Four Seven
SLIPWAY.
Single (7"): released on Floating World, Jun'85 by Neat Records. Dist: Pinnacle

Seven Seance
ANOTHER EMPTY FACE.
Single (12"): by Icon Records. Dist: IKF, Cartel

Seven Seconds
CREW, THE.
Album: released on Better Youth Orginisation, Sep'84 Dist: Cartel, Red Rhino

Seven Stars
SEVEN STARS.
Album: released on Concord Jazz(USA), Jun'83 by Concord Jazz Records (USA). Dist: IMS, Polygram

Compact disc: released on Concord Jazz(USA), Jun'83 by Concord Jazz Records (USA). Dist: IMS, Polygram

Seventeen
CAPTURED IN ICE.
Album: released on Eva-Lolita, Jul'86 Dist: Pinnacle

DON'T LET GO/BANK HOLIDAY WEEKEND.
Single (7"): released on Vendetta, Mar'80

Seventeenth &...
DEATH OR GLORY BOYS, THE (Seventeenth & Twentyfirst Lancers, Regimental Band Of).
Album: released on Parade, May'80 Dist: MSD

Seventh Avenue
ARMED ROBBERY.
Tracks: / Armed robbery / Armed robbery (inst).
Single (7"): released on Nightmare, Jun'87 by Nightmare Records. Dist: PRT

Single (12"): released on Nightmare, Jun'87 by Nightmare Records. Dist: PRT

Single (7"): released on Columbia, Jun'87 by EMI Records. Dist: EMI

ENDING UP ON A HIGH.
Single (7"): released on Record Shack, May'85 by Record Shack Records. Dist: PRT

Single (12"): released on Record Shack, May'85 by Record Shack Records. Dist: PRT

I HEAR THUNDER.
Single (7"): released on Record Shack, Jun'84 by Record Shack Records. Dist: PRT

Single (12"): released on Record Shack, Jun'84 by Record Shack Records. Dist: PRT

LOVE'S GONE MAD.
Tracks: / Love's gone mad / Love's gone mad instrumental / Love's gone mad / Love's gone mad (hot mix).
Single (7"): released on Record Shack, Feb'86 by Record Shack Records. Dist: PRT

Single (12"): released on Record Shack, Feb'86 by Record Shack Records. Dist: PRT

Single (7"): released on Tangerine, Oct'86

Single (12"): released on Tangerine, Oct'86

NO MAN'S LAND.
Tracks: / No man's land / Ending up on a high / Love's gone mad / No man's land instrumental.
Single (7"): released on Record Shack, Aug'86 by Record Shack Records. Dist: PRT

Single (12"): released on Record Shack, Aug'86 by Record Shack Records. Dist: PRT

Single (7"): released on Record Shack, Aug'86 by Record Shack Records. Dist: PRT

Seventh Avenue Stompers
FIDGETY FEET.
Notes: Artists include: Emmett Berry - trumpet, Vic Dickenson - trombone, Buster Bailey - clarinet, Red Richards - piano, Al Lucas - bass, Bobby Donaldson - drums, Joe Wilder - trumpet, Seldon Powell - tenor sax, Ernie Hayes - organ, Bucky Pizzarelli - guitar. Includes two previously unissued tracks: 'Ferry Boat Romp' and 'Blues Like They Used To Be', as well as cuts like 'Basin Street Blues' and St. Louis Blues'.
Album: released on Savoy Jazz, Dec'86 by RCA Records (Germany). Dist: Conifer

Seventh Extension
LIKE AN OPEN DOOR.
Single (12"): released on Dancebeat, Apr'82 by Dancebeat Records. Dist: Jetstar

Seventh Heaven
HANKY PANKY.
Tracks: / Hanky panky / Gemini logic.
Single (7"): released on Mercury, May'87 by Phonogram Records. Dist: Polygram Distribution

Single (12"): released on Mercury, May'87 by Phonogram Records. Dist: Polygram Distribution

HOT SUN.
Single (7"): released on Mercury, Aug'85 by Phonogram Records. Dist: Polygram Distribution

Single (12"): released on Mercury, Aug'85 by Phonogram Records. Dist: Polygram Distribution

LITTLE GIRLS IN BIG CARS.
Tracks: / Hanky panky.
Single (7"): released on Epic, Aug'87 by CBS Records. Dist: CBS

Single (12"): released on Epic, Aug'87 by CBS Records. Dist: CBS

Seventh Seance
ANOTHER EMPTY FACE.
Single (12"): released on Icon, May'84 by Icon Records. Dist: IKF, Cartel

INTO THE OUTSIDE.
Single (7"): released on Icon, Aug'84 by Icon Records. Dist: IKF, Cartel

Seventh Wave
PSI-FI.
Album: released on Gull, Sep'77 by Gull Records. Dist: Pinnacle

THINGS TO COME.
Album: released on Gull, Sep'77 by Gull Records. Dist: Pinnacle

Seventh Wonder
WORDS DON'T SAY ENOUGH.
Album: released on Parachute (USA), May'78 Dist: Polygram

Seventies..
SEVENTIES VOL.2, (THE) Various artists (Various Artists).
Tracks: / Spirit in the sky / Horse with no name, (A) / Hot love / Maggie May / I hear you knocking / Woodstock / When I'm dead and gone / Whiskey in the jar / Black night / Mama told me not to come / Hold your head up / Devil's answer / Witch queen of New Orleans / Meet me on the corner.
Album: released on Old Gold, Nov'85 by Old Gold Records. Dist: Lightning, Jazz Music, Spartan, Counterpoint

Cassette: released on Old Gold, Nov'85 by Old Gold Records. Dist: Lightning, Jazz Music, Spartan, Counterpoint

Seven Traditional Singers
KNIFE IN THE WINDOW, THE.
Cassette: released on Folktracks, Nov'79 by Folktracks Cassettes. Dist: Folktracks

Seventy...
70 GOLDEN NURSERY RHYMES Various Artists (Various Artists).
Album: released on Super Tempo, May'84 by Multiple Sounds Records. Dist: Multiple Sound Distributors

Cassette: released on Super Tempo, May'84 by Multiple Sounds Records. Dist: Multiple Sound Distributors

Seventy-Eighth...
HIGHLANDERS PIPE BAND (Seventy-Eighth Fraser Highlanders Pipe Band).
Album: released on Lismor, Jul'84 by Lismor Records. Dist: Lismor, Roots, Celtic Music

Cassette: released on Lismor, Jul'84 by Lismor Records. Dist: Lismor, Roots, Celtic Music

Seventy-Five...
75 MILLION SELLERS Various Artists (Various Artists).
Album: released on Pickwick, Jul'80 by Pickwick Records. Dist: Pickwick Distribution, Prism Leisure Distribution, Lugtons

Cassette: released on Pickwick, Jul'80 by Pickwick Records. Dist: Pickwick Distribution, Prism Leisure Distribution, Lugtons

Seventy-Nine...
'79 CHARTBUSTERS (Seventy-Nine Chartbusters).
Cassette: released on Aim, Feb'83 Dist: H.R. Taylor

Seventy-Seven's
ALL FALL DOWN.
Album: released on Word, Feb'85 by Word Records. Dist: Word Distribution, CBS

Cassette: released on Word, Feb'85 by Word Records. Dist: Word Distribution, CBS

Seven West
WHEN THE COLOUR STARTS TO FADE.
Tracks: / When the colour starts to fade / Nothing changes.
Single (7"): released on Rebel, Feb'86 Dist: PRT

Severed Heads
CITY SLAB HORROR.
Album: released on Ink, Mar'85 by Red Flame. Dist: Rough Trade, Cartel, Pinnacle

CLIFFORD DARLING Please don't live in the past.
Notes: Double LP set.
Double Album: released on Ink, Dec'85 by Red Flame. Dist: Rough Trade, Cartel, Pinnacle

DEAD EYES OPENED.
Single (12"): released on Rough Trade, Mar'84 by Rough Trade Records. Dist: Rough Trade Distribution, Cartel Distribution

GOODBYE TONSILS.
Single (7"): released on Ink, Feb'85 by Red Flame. Dist: Rough Trade, Cartel, Pinnacle

HEAT SEEKING SUSAN.
Single (12"): released on Ink, Sep'85 by Red Flame. Dist: Rough Trade, Cartel, Pinnacle

HEAVY METAL.
Single (7"): released on Plastic Canvas, Apr'83 Dist: Pinnacle

MEDIA JINGLES.
Cassette: released on Music For Midgets, May'84 Dist: Backs, Cartel Distribution

PROPELLOR.
Tracks: / Propellor / Harold and Cindy hospital.
Single (12"): released on Ink, Jul'86 by Red Flame. Dist: Rough Trade, Cartel, Pinnacle

SIDE 2.
Cassette: released on Music For Midgets, May'84 Dist: Backs, Cartel Distribution

SINCE THE ACCIDENT.
Album: released on Red Ink, Mar'84

Severn Valley Railway
SEVERN VALLEY STEAM.

Album: released on Lugtons, Feb'80

SOUNDS OF SEVERN VALLEY RAILWAY.
Album: released on Response, Feb'81 by Priority Records. Dist: BMG

Sevillia

CAVATINA.
Single (7"): released on Polydor, Mar'79 by Polydor Records. Dist: Polygram, Polydor

Sex Aids

BACK ON THE PISS AGAIN.
Single (7"): released on Riot City, Sep'83 by Riot City Records. Dist: Revolver

Sex Beat

PUMP.
Single (7"): released on ABC, Apr'84 Dist: CBS, Pinnacle

Single (12"): released on ABC, Apr'84 Dist: CBS, Pinnacle

Sex Gang Children

BEASTS.
Tracks: / Beasts / Cannibal queen / Who on earth can that be / Sense of elation / Into the abyss / Dieche / Salvation / Mocnoglia times of our lives.
Album: released on Dojo, Aug'86 by Castle Communications Records. Dist: Cartel

Album: released on Illuminated, Dec'83 by IKF Records. Dist: Pinnacle, Cartel, Jetstar

Single (12"): released on Illuminated, Feb'85 by IKF Records. Dist: Pinnacle, Cartel, Jetstar

DEICHE.
Single (12"): released on Saderal, Sep'85 Dist: Nine Mile, Cartel

Single (12"): released on Illuminated, Feb'85 by IKF Records. Dist: Pinnacle, Cartel, Jetstar

ECSTASY AND VENDETTA OVER NEW YORK.
Cassette: released on Reach Out International, Aug'84 Dist: Red Rhino, Cartel

INTO THE ABYSS.
Single (7"): released on Illuminated, Feb'85 by IKF Records. Dist: Pinnacle, Cartel, Jetstar

MAURITIA MAYER.
Single (7"): released on Clay, Sep'83 by Clay Records. Dist: Pinnacle

Single (12"): released on Clay, Sep'83 by Clay Records. Dist: Pinnacle

RE-ENTER THE ABYSS.
Tracks: / State of mind / Killer k / Shout and scream / Sebastian / Beasts / Into the abyss / Deiche / Times of our lives / Draconian dream.
Album: released on Dojo, Apr'86 by Castle Communications Records. Dist: Cartel

Cassette: released on Dojo, Apr'86 by Castle Communications Records. Dist: Cartel

SEBASTIANE.
Single (12"): released on Illuminated, Mar'85 by IKF Records. Dist: Pinnacle, Cartel, Jetstar

SEX AND LEGEND.
Album: released on Illuminated, Mar'83 by IKF Records. Dist: Pinnacle, Cartel, Jetstar

SONG AND LEGEND.
Tracks: / Crack up (The) / German nun / State of mind / Sebastiane / Draconian dream / Shout and scream / Killer k / Cannibal queen / Kill machine / Song and legend.
Album: released on Dojo, Apr'86 by Castle Communications Records. Dist: Cartel

Single (7"): released on Illuminated, Mar'83 by IKF Records. Dist: Pinnacle, Cartel, Jetstar

Sex, John

BUMP GRIND IT.
Single (12"): released on Southern Studios, Feb'87 by Southern Studio Records. Dist: Pinnacle

Sex Pistols

Biographical Details: The best-known of all the punk bands of the late 1970's, the Sex Pistols were formed in 1975 by vocalist **Johnny Rotten** (born **John Lydon**, 31 January 1956), guitarist **Steve Jones** (born 3 May 1955), bassist **Glen Matlock** (born 27 August 1956), drummer **Paul Cook** (born 27 July 1956). **Matlock** was replaced in 1977 by **Sid Vicious** (born John Simon Ritchie, 10 May 1957; died 2 February 1979 in NYC of a heroin overdose while under indictment for killing his girlfriend **Nancy Spungeon**). They were encouraged by boutique owner/entrepreneur **Malcolm McLaren**, who in turn had been inspired by briefly managing the **New York Dolls**, their American rquivalent. **Cook, Matlock**and **Jones** had formed the **Swankers**, then recruited **Rotten.** They bragged that they had no abilty to play or sing; their object was to make rock and roll exciting and to put superstars out of business. Their EMI single **'Anarchy In The UK'** was a hit in late 1976 but their contract was cancelled due to obnoxious behaviour in public and on TV amid a media circus. A & M sugned them but also cancelled; **'God Save The Queen'** was released on Virgin during Queen Elizabeth II's Silver Jubilee in June 1977 and was banned by the BBC but became a no.2 hit. Six more singles were top 10 and their debut album **Never Mind The Bollocks - Here's The Sex Pistols** was no.1 in 1977. Their film **The Great Rock'n'Roll Swindle** is a record of McLaren at work and a pop artifact. Rotten quit in 1978, changed his name back to Lydon and formed **Public Image Ltd**; the remaining trio completed the film, recorded new material with **Vicious** singing (**'My Way'**, **'C'mon Everybody'**, **Something Else'** - all UK top 10 hits), also recorded a track and additional film footage with train robber **Ronnie Biggs**. They tried new singers including **Jimmy Pursey** and **Tenpole Tudor** (who appeared in the film). The most notorious of the punks, but outlasted by **The Clash** and **The Damned.** (Donald Clarke, April 87)

10TH ANNIVERSARY.
Album: released on McDonald-Lydon, Aug'86 Dist: Pinnacle

6 TRACK MINI LP.
Album: released on Chaos, Jan'85 by Backs Records. Dist: Nine Mile, Cartel

ANARCHYIN THE UK.
Single (7"): released on Unknown, '80

ANARCHY (LIVE VERSION).
Tracks: / Anarchy (Live version) / Anarchy in the UK / I wanna be me / God save the Queen / Did you no wrong / Pretty vacant / Holidays in the sun / No fun / Biggest blow / My way / Something else / Silly thing / C'mon everybody / Steppin stone / Great rock and roll swindle.
Single (12"): released on McDonald-Lydon, Apr'86 Dist: Pinnacle

Album: released on Virgin, Apr'86 by Virgin Records. Dist: EMI, Virgin Distribution

Cassette: released on Virgin, Apr'86 by Virgin Records. Dist: EMI, Virgin Distribution

BEST OF...AND WE DON'T CARE.
Album: released on Flyover, Jan'80 by Flyover Records. Dist: Flyover Records

CARRI ON SEX PISTOLS.
Album: released on Virgin, Jul'79 by Virgin Records. Dist: EMI, Virgin Distribution

C'MON EVERYBODY.
Single (7"): released on Virgin, '79 by Virgin Records. Dist: EMI, Virgin Distribution

FILTH & THE FURY, THE 6 album box set.
Album: released on Macdonald, Jan'87

FLOGGING A DEAD HORSE.
Tracks: / Anarchy in the UK / I wanna be me / God save the Queen / Did you no wrong / Pretty vacant / Holidays in the sun / No fun / Biggest blow / My way / Something else / Silly thing / C'mon everybody / Stepping stone / Great rock'n' roll swindle.
Album: released on Virgin, Apr'86 by Virgin Records. Dist: EMI, Virgin Distribution

Compact disc: released on Virgin, Oct'86 by Virgin Records. Dist: EMI, Virgin Distribution

Album: released on Virgin, Feb'80 by Virgin Records. Dist: EMI, Virgin Distribution

Cassette: released on Virgin, Feb'80 by Virgin Records. Dist: EMI, Virgin Distribution

GOD SAVE THE QUEEN.
Single (7"): released on Virgin, May'77 by Virgin Records. Dist: EMI, Virgin Distribution

GREAT ROCK'N'ROLL SWINDLE.
Tracks: / God save the Queen / Johnny B. Goode / Road runner / Anarchy in the UK / Don't give no lip child / I'm not your stepping stone / L'anarchie pour le UK / Einmal Belsen war wirflich bortreffiich / Silly thing / My way / I wanna be me / Something else / Rock around the clock / Lonely boy / EMI / Great rock'n'roll swindle (The) / Friggin in the riggin / You need hands / Who killed Bambi.
Compact disc: released on Virgin, Jul'86 by Virgin Records. Dist: EMI, Virgin Distribution

Single (7"): released on Virgin, Sep'79 by Virgin Records. Dist: EMI, Virgin Distribution

Double Album: released on Virgin, Jun'79 by Virgin Records. Dist: EMI, Virgin Distribution

Cassette: released on Virgin, '79 by Virgin Records. Dist: EMI, Virgin Distribution

HOLIDAYS IN THE SUN.
Single (7"): released on Virgin, Oct'77 by Virgin Records. Dist: EMI, Virgin Distribution

I'M NOT YOUR STEPPING STONE.
Single (7"): released on Virgin, Jun'80 by Virgin Records. Dist: EMI, Virgin Distribution

LAST CONCERT ON EARTH.
Album: released on Konnexion, Feb'86 Dist: Roots, Pinnacle

LAST SHOW ON EARTH.
Album: released on McDonald-Lydon, May'86 Dist: Pinnacle

LIVE WORLDWIDE.
Album: released on Konnexion, Aug'85 Dist: Roots, Pinnacle

MINI LP (THE).
Album: released on Chaos, Jan'86 by Backs Records. Dist: Nine Mile, Cartel

MY WAY.
Single (7"): released on Virgin, Jun'78 by Virgin Records. Dist: EMI, Virgin Distribution

Single (12"): released on Virgin, Apr'83 by Virgin Records. Dist: EMI, Virgin Distribution

NEVER MIND THE BOLLOCKS.
Tracks: / Holidays in the sun / Bodies / No feelings / Liar / God save the Queen / Problems / Seventeen / Anarchy in the UK / Submission / Pretty vacant / New York / EMI.
Album: released on Virgin, Oct'86 by Virgin Records. Dist: EMI, Virgin Distribution

Cassette: released on Virgin, Oct'86 by Virgin Records. Dist: EMI, Virgin Distribution

Compact disc: released on Virgin, Oct'86 by Virgin Records. Dist: EMI, Virgin Distribution

ORIGINAL PISTOLS.
Album: released on Demon, Jul'86 by Demon Records. Dist: Pinnacle

ORIGINAL PISTOLS LIVE.
Tracks: / No feelings / Anarchy in the U.K. / I'm a lazy sod / Liar / Dolls(New York) / Don't give me no lip child / Dubstitute / Pretty Vacant / I wanna be me / Problems / Submission / No fun.
Album: released on Dojo, Dec'86 by Castle Communications Records. Dist: Cartel

Compact disc: released on Dojo, '86 by Castle Communications Records. Dist: Cartel

PRETTY VACANT.
Single (7"): released on Virgin, Jul'77 by Virgin Records. Dist: EMI, Virgin Distribution

SEX PISTOLS LIVE.
Tracks: / Anarchy in the UK / I'm a lazy sod / Pretty vacant / Substitute.
Single (12"): released on Archive 4, Aug'86 by Castle Communications Records. Dist: Nine Mile, Cartel

SILLY THING.
Single (7"): released on Virgin, Mar'79 by Virgin Records. Dist: EMI, Virgin Distribution

SOMETHING ELSE.
Single (7"): released on Virgin, Feb'79 by Virgin Records. Dist: EMI, Virgin Distribution

SUBMISSION.
Tracks: / Submission / No feelings.
Single (7"): released on Chaos, Mar'87 by Backs Records. Dist: Nine Mile, Cartel

WHO KILLED BAMBI (Sex Pistols & Tenpole Tudor).
Single (7"): released on Virgin, Sep'81 by Virgin Records. Dist: EMI, Virgin Distribution

Sexteto Tango

MAGIA PORTENA: ORIGINAL TANGOS FROM ARGENTINA.
Album: released on RCA (France), Oct'85 by RCA Records. Dist: Discovery

Sexton, Ann

LOVE TRIALS.
Tracks: / I want to be loved / I'm his wife, you're just a friend / Who's gonna love you? / I had a fight with love (and I lost) / Be serious / Colour my world blue / You've been doing me wrong for so long / Have a little mercy / Loving you, loving me / Love, love, love / Come back home / Keep on holding on / You're letting me down / You're gonna miss me.
Album: released on Charly, Jan'87 by Charly Records. Dist: Charly, Cadillac

YOU'VE BEEN GONE TOO LONG.
Single (7"): released on Inferno, Jul'80 by Inferno Records. Dist: Inferno, Cartel, Pinnacle

Sexton, Charlie

BEATS SO LONELY.
Tracks: / Beats so lonely / Attraction / Hold me / Beats so lonely (beat the lonely monster).
Single (7"): released on MCA, Mar'86 by MCA Records. Dist: Polygram, MCA

Picture disc single: released on MCA, Mar'86 by MCA Records. Dist: Polygram, MCA

Single (12"): released on MCA, Mar'86 by MCA Records. Dist: Polygram, MCA

HOLD ME.
Tracks: / Beats so lonely / Control me".
Single (7"): released on MCA, Jan'87 by MCA Records. Dist: Polygram, MCA

Single (12"): released on MCA, Jan'87 by MCA Records. Dist: Polygram, MCA

PICTURES FOR PLEASURE.
Tracks: / Impressed / Beat's so lonely / Restless / Hold me / Pictures for pleasure / Tell me / Attractions / You don't belong / Space.
Notes: (Debut album): Recorded in Los Angeles the beginning of 1985. Produced by Keith Forsey, who has also produced the Psychedelic Furs,Glenn Frey,Billy Idol and Simple Minds. Charlie wrote,sang and played guitar, bass and keyboards. Charlie had his first professional gig at age 11, touring at age 13 as lead guitarist forJoe Ely. He has recorded with Bob Dylan, Don Henley, the Rolling StonesRon Wood and Keith Richards, Joe Ely and Jimmy Barnes (Cold Chisel). Charlie's groups have toured with the Clash and Joe Ely,amongst others. Charlie was born in San Antonio,Texas and raised in Austin, Texas.
Album: released on MCA, Feb'86 by MCA Records. Dist: Polygram, MCA

Cassette: released on MCA, Feb'86 by MCA Records. Dist: Polygram, MCA

Compact disc: released on MCA, Jul'86 by MCA Records. Dist: Polygram, MCA

Sexual Harassment

I NEED A FREAK.
Single (12"): released on Elite, Sep'83 Dist: PRT

Sexy Shorts

SEXY SHORTS Various artists (Various Artists).
Notes: A collection of eleven so called x rated music promo clips which were deemed toohot to show on tv, by naughty chaps like Queen, Duran Duran and the Tubes.
Video-cassette (VHS): released on PMI, Jun'86 by PMI Records. Dist: EMI

Video-cassette [Betamax]: released on PMI, Jun'86 by PMI Records. Dist: EMI

Seymour Orchestra

18 FAVOURITE FILM THEMES (Seymour Studio Orchestra (The)).
Tracks: / Star trek / Star wars / 2001 / Superman / Rocky (gonna fly now) / Chariots of fire / Cavatina (The deer hunter) / Diamonds are forever / Theme for E.T / Close encounters / Good, the bad and the ugly (The) / Bright eyes (watership down) / Do you know where you are going to (mahogany) / Godfather theme (The) / I just called to say I love you / Axel F / Evergreen / Pink panther theme (The).
Album: released on Showcase, Sep'86 Dist: Counterpoint

Cassette: released on Showcase, Sep'86 Dist: Counterpoint

CLASSICAL BREAKS The collectio (Seymour Symphony Orchestra).
Compact disc: by Object Enterprises Ltd. Dis Counterpoint Distribution

ENDLESS LOVE SONGS (Seymour Symphony Orchestra).
Tracks: / Careless whisper / Move closer / Endless Love / Ebony and ivory / For your eyes on / Arthur's theme / Hello again / I love a rai night / Hopelessly devoted to you / I only wa to be with you / I'd rather leave while I'm in lov / Mandy / I write the songs / Nights in white sat / Suddenly / Over the rainbow / With you I' born again / Could it be I'm falling in love.
Notes: All tracks licensed from Coombe Mus International Ltd.
Album: released on Showcase, '86 Dis Counterpoint

Cassette: released on Showcase, '86 Di Counterpoint

Seymour, Robin

CRUISIN' 1956 WKMH Detroit.
Cassette: released on Increase(USA), Jun' by Quicksilver Records (USA).

Seymour, Terry

TERRY SEYMOUR BIG BAND (Seymo Terry Big Band).
Album: released on Wave, Nov'74 by Cha Records. Dist: Charly

SFF

SUNBURST.
Album: released on Brain (Germany), '79

SYMPHONIC PICTURES.
Album: released on Brain (Germany), Jan'

TICKET TO EVERYWHERE.
Album: released on Brain (Germany), May

SFX

ROCKIN' WITH MY RADIO.
Single (7"): released on Lamborghini, Oc by Lamborghini Records. Dist: PRT

SGB

C'EST LA VIE.
Tracks: / C'est la vie / I love the way yo

dancing.
Single (7"): released on Trojan, Mar'86 by Trojan Records. Dist: PRT, Jetstar

INFATUATION.
Single (7"): released on Trojan, Nov'85 by Trojan Records. Dist: PRT, Jetstar

Shade Adejumo

SUMMER DAYS.
Single (12"): released on Solid Groove, Mar'82 Dist: Jetstar, Pinnacle

Shades

ACE OF SHADES.
Album: released on Magnum Force, May'83 by Magnum Music Group Ltd. Dist: Magnum Music Group Ltd, PRT, Spartan

LIVE AT CAISTER.
Single (7"): released on Magnum Force, Apr'81 by Magnum Music Group Ltd. Dist: Magnum Music Group Ltd, PRT, Spartan

RUNNING WILD.
Tracks: / Running wild / Running wild vocal version.
Notes: Running Wild is the theme from the LWT TV Series.
Single (7"): released on Sierra, Mar'87 by Sierra Records. Dist: WEA

Shadow

AH COME OUT TO PARTY.
Single (12"): released on Hot Vinyl, Jun'85 by Hot Vinyl Records. Dist: Jetstar

RAW ENERGY.
Album: released on Hot Vinyl, 30 May'87 by Hot Vinyl Records. Dist: Jetstar

SHADOWS IN THE STREETS.
Album: released on Elektra, Oct'81 by WEA Records. Dist: WEA

STORM(THE).
Single (12"): released on Sunburn, Mar'83 by Orbitone Records. Dist: Jetstar Distribution

WALK AND WINCE.
Single (12"): released on Seara, Jun'82 by Seara Records. Dist: Jetstar

Shadowboys

WAITING FOR TOMORROW.
Single (7"): released on Pete-Nik, Jan'84 by Pete-Nik Records. Dist: Cartel

Shadowdance Theatre

COLOUR OF MIDNIGHT.
Single (7"): released on Ariel, Nov'83

Shadowfax

DREAMS OF CHILDREN,THE.
Album: released on Windham Hill (Germany), Feb'85

SHADOWDANCE.
Tracks: / New electric India / Watercourse way / Ghost bird / Distant voices / Shadowdance / Brown rice/ karmapa chenno / Song for my brother,A.
Album: released on Windham Hill, Feb'85 Dist: AM

Cassette: released on Windham Hill, Feb'85 Dist: AM

Compact disc: released on Windham Hill, Feb'85 Dist: AM

SHADOWFAX.
Album: released on Windham Hill, Nov'85 Dist: AM

Cassette: released on Windham Hill, Nov'85 Dist: AM

Compact disc: released on Windham Hill, Nov'85 Dist: AM

TOO FAR TO WHISPER.
Tracks: / Too far to whisper / What goes around / China blue / Orangutang gang (The) / Road to Anna / Street noise / Slim limbs akimbo / Tsunami / Maceo / Ritual.
Notes: The new album from one of Windham Hill's most commercially successful and critically acclaimed acts. The band's unique sound prompted the noted US jazz critic Leonard Feather to write classifying this album a tougher task than appreciating it and that applies. A blend of so many different national styles into an acoustic/jazz/rock fusion, has resulted in a sound that has continued to evolve and delight. 10 original new songs,with a very varied feeling, including 2 songs with vocals.
Album: released on A&M, Jun'86 by A&M Records. Dist: Polygram

Cassette: released on A&M, Jun'86 by A&M Records. Dist: Polygram

Compact disc: released on A&M, Jun'86 by A&M Records. Dist: Polygram

Shadows, The

Biographical Details: The Shadows were the most influential instrumental rock'n'roll group in Britain, with 24 top 40 hits 1960-66 (more than half in the top ten) beginning with **"Apache"** at no.1. The original line-up was **Hank Marvin**, lead guitar; **Bruce Welch**, rhythm guitar; **Jet Harris**, bass; **Tony Meehan**, drums. They came together to back **Cliff Richard** on his first tour, calling themselves **The Drifters** in 1958, changing their name mod-1959 to avoid confusion with the black American vocal group. Their trademarks were gleaming red Fender Stratocaster guitars and the 'Shadows Step', a three-step onstage movement. They played on all of Richard's hits from '58 to 1961, and many more through 1968, when they split up; they reformed in the early '70s, delighted old fans on tours and sold hit albums and singles well into the 1980s.
[Donald Clarke, April 87]

20 GOLDEN GREATS.
Tracks: / Apache / Frightened city (The) / Guitar tango / Kon-tiki / Foot tapper / Genie with the light brown lamp / Warlord (The) / Place in the sun, A / Place in the sun, A / Atlantis / Wonderful land / FBI / Savage (The) / Geronimo / Shindig / Stingray / Theme for young lovers / Rise and fall of Flingel Bunt (The) / Maroc 7 / Dance on.
Compact disc: released on EMI, Mar'87 by EMI Records. Dist: EMI

Album: released on EMI, Jan'77 by EMI Records. Dist: EMI

Cassette: released on EMI, Jan'77 by EMI Records. Dist: EMI

20 ROCK 'N' ROLL HITS.
Album: released on EMI (Holland), '83 by EMI Records. Dist: Conifer

ANOTHER STRING OF HOT HITS.
Album: released on Music for Pleasure, Nov'83 by EMI Records. Dist: MFP Distribution

Cassette: released on Music for Pleasure, Nov'83 by EMI Records. Dist: MFP Distribution

APACHE.
Album: released on EMI (Holland), '83 by EMI Records. Dist: Conifer

Single (7"): released on EMI (France), '83 by EMI Records. Dist: Conifer

Single (7"): released on EMI, Jan'77 by EMI Records. Dist: EMI

BEST OF THE SHADOWS.
Double Album: released on EMI (Belgium), '83 by EMI Records. Dist: Conifer

Album: released on EMI (Germany), '83 by EMI Records. Dist: Conifer

BOYS,THE.
Single (12"): released on EMI (Holland), '82 by EMI Records. Dist: Conifer

COMPACT SHADOWS.
Tracks: / Equinoxe v / Third man (The) / No dancing / Memory / Chi mai / Africa / Thing-me-jig / Missing / Mozart forte / If you leave me now / Summer love / Hello mr W.A / Queen of hearts / More than I can say / Life in the jungle / Chariots of fire / Sailing / Going home.
Compact disc: released on Polydor, Sep'86 by Polydor Records. Dist: Polygram, Polydor

DANCE WITH THE SHADOWS.
Tracks: / Chattanooga choo-choo / Blue shadows / Tonight(from the film West Side Story) / That's the way it goes / Big b / In the mood / Lonely bull (The) / Dakota / French dressing / High and the mighty (The) / Don't it make you feel good / Zambesi / Temptation / Brazil / Lost city (The) / Little bitty bear, A / Blue sky / Blue sea / Blue me / Bossa roo / Five hundred miles / Cotton pickin / Deep purple / Santa Ana / Windjammer (The) / Dean's theme / Breakthru / Let it be me / National provincial samba.
Notes: Taken from an existing EMI double album (same title). A superb Shadows double which was recorded in 1964-65. Includes really good vintage Shadows material from their classic period. Also an extensive sleeve note by Chris White of Music Week. An excellent double for the Autumn period.
Album: released on Music For Pleasure, Nov'86 by EMI Records. Dist: EMI

Cassette: released on Music For Pleasure, Nov'86 by EMI Records. Dist: EMI

DANCING IN THE DARK.
Tracks: / Dancing in the dark / Turning point.
Single (7"): released on Polydor, Aug'86 by Polydor Records. Dist: Polygram, Polydor

Single (12"): released on Polydor, Aug'86 by Polydor Records. Dist: Polygram, Polydor

DISQUE D'OR.
Album: released on EMI (France), '83 by EMI Records. Dist: Conifer

DON'T CRY FOR ME ARGENTINA.
Single (7"): released on EMI, '80 by EMI Records. Dist: EMI

DOUBLE ALBUM.
Tracks: / Apache / Savage, The / This hammer / Foot tapper / Shadoogie / Perfidia / Kon-tiki / Man of mystery / Theme for young lovers / Alice in Sunderland / Rumble, The / Quartermasters stores / Dakota / Deep purple / Nivram / Mustang / Guitare tango / Dance on / FBI / Lost city / Lonesome fella / Frightened city / Brazil / Lonely bull.
Album: released on Pathe Marconi, Jun'87 Dist: Swift

Cassette: released on Pathe Marconi, Jun'87 Dist: Swift

EST.1958 (Shadows & Cliff Richard).
Album: released on Columbia, '68 by EMI Records. Dist: EMI

GREATEST HITS: SHADOWS.
Album: released on Columbia, '85 by EMI Records. Dist: EMI

Cassette: released on Columbia, '85 by EMI Records. Dist: EMI

GUARDIAN ANGEL.
Tracks: / How do I love thee / Hammerhead / Saturday western (The) / Look back on love (from the film Terminal Choice) / Johnny Staccato / I will return / I'm gonna be your guardian angel / Can't play your game / On a night like this / Turning point / Our Albert.
Compact disc: released on Roll Over Record-Polydor, Nov'86

HITS OF THE SHADOWS VOL 1.
Cassette: released on VFM Cassettes, Jan'85

HITS RIGHT UP YOUR STREET.
Album: released on Polydor, Aug'84 by Polydor Records. Dist: Polygram, Polydor

Cassette: released on Polydor, Aug'84 by Polydor Records. Dist: Polygram, Polydor

LIFE IN THE JUNGLE.
Album: released on Polydor, Feb'85 by Polydor Records. Dist: Polygram, Polydor

Cassette: released on Polydor, Feb'85 by Polydor Records. Dist: Polygram, Polydor

LIFE IN THE JUNGLE/THE SHADOWS 'LIVE' AT ABBEY ROAD.
Double Album: released on Polydor, Sep'82 by Polydor Records. Dist: Polygram, Polydor

Double cassette: released on Polydor, Sep'82 by Polydor Records. Dist: Polygram, Polydor

LIVE.
Notes: Seven track EP recorded live on stage at the national exhibition centre, with ever-green Shads hits like Apache and FBI.
Video-cassette (VHS): released on PMI, Jun'86 by PMI Records. Dist: EMI

Video-cassette [Betamax]: released on PMI, Jun'86 by PMI Records. Dist: EMI

Album: released on Music For Pleasure (Holland), Nov'83 by EMI Records. Dist: EMI

Cassette: released on Music For Pleasure (Holland), Nov'83 by EMI Records. Dist: EMI

MISSING.
Single (7"): released on Polydor, Jul'82 by Polydor Records. Dist: Polygram, Polydor

MOONLIGHT SHADOW.
Tracks: / Moonlight shadow / Johnny Staccato.
Single (7"): released on Polydor, Apr'86 by Polydor Records. Dist: Polygram, Polydor

MOONLIGHT SHADOWS.
Tracks: / Moonlight shadow / Walk of life / I just called to say I love you / Every breath you take / Nights in white satin / Hello / Power of love (The) / Three times a lady / Against all odds / Hey Jude / Dancing in the dark / I know him so well / Memory / Imagine/ woman / Sailing / Whiter shade of pale.
Album: released on Polydor, May'86 by Polydor Records. Dist: Polygram, Polydor

Cassette: released on Polydor, May'86 by Polydor Records. Dist: Polygram, Polydor

Compact disc: released on Polydor, May'86 by Polydor Records. Dist: Polygram, Polydor

MORE HITS.
Album: released on Columbia, Aug'85 by EMI Records. Dist: EMI

Cassette: released on Columbia, Aug'85 by EMI Records. Dist: EMI

MUSTANG.
Single (12"): released on EMI (Holland), '82 by EMI Records. Dist: Conifer

ON A NIGHT LIKE THIS.
Single (7"): released on Polydor, Aug'84 by Polydor Records. Dist: Polygram, Polydor

OUT OF THE SHADOWS.
Tracks: / Rumble (The) / Bandit (The) / Cosy / 1861 / Perfidia / Little b / Bo Diddley / South of the border / Spring is nearly here / Are they all like you / Tales of a raggy tramline / Some are lonely / Kinda cool.
Notes: The Shadows second LP Out Of The Shadows is re-released by Awareness Records. Out Of The Shadows has been deleted for over a decade.
Album: released on Awareness, Aug'86 by Awareness. Dist: EMI

Cassette: released on Awareness, Aug'86 by Awareness. Dist: EMI

RHYTHM & GREENS.
Single (12"): released on EMI (Belgium), '82 by EMI Records. Dist: Conifer

ROCK ON WITH THE SHADOWS.
Album: released on MFP, Feb'80 by EMI Records. Dist: EMI

Cassette: released on MFP, Feb'80 by EMI Records. Dist: EMI

SHADOOGIE.
Double Album: released on EMI (Holland), '83 by EMI Records. Dist: Conifer

Album: released on Pathe MarconiEMI Europe), Jan'85

SHADOW MUSIC.
Album: released on Columbia, May'66 by EMI Records. Dist: EMI Deleted '87.

SHADOWS IN JAPAN.
Single (12"): released on EMI (Holland), '83 by EMI Records. Dist: Conifer

SHADOWS STORY,THE.
Album: released on EMI (Holland), '83 by EMI Records. Dist: Conifer

SHADOWS, THE.
Tracks: / 36-24-36 / FBI / Apache / Savage (The) / This hammer / Foot tapper / Shadoogie / Perfidia / Kon-tiki / Man of mystery / Theme for young lovers / Alice in Sunderland / Rumble (The) / Quarter master's lovers / Dakota / Deep purple / Nivram / Mustang / Guitare tango / Dance on / Lost city (The) / Lonesome fella / Frightened city / Brazil / Lonely bull (The) / Friday on my mind / Winchester Cathedral / Maria Elena / Semi-detached suburban mr James / Jigsaw / Stardust / Trains and boats and planes / Ranka-chank / What a lovely tune / Little b / Shindig / Shazamkin / All my sorrows / I wish I could shimmy like my sister Arthur / Slaughter on tenth avenue.
Album: released on Music For Pleasure (Holland), Oct'86 by EMI Records. Dist: EMI

Cassette: released on Music For Pleasure (Holland), Oct'86 by EMI Records. Dist: EMI

Album: released on Pathe MarconiFrance), Nov'86

Cassette: released on Hour Of Pleasure, Oct'86 by Music For Pleasure Records. Dist: EMI

Single (7"): released on EMI Europe, Sep'82 by EMI Records. Dist: Conifer

Album: released on World Records, Dec'81 Dist: Polygram

Cassette: released on World Records, Dec'81 Dist: Polygram

Album: released on Fame, May'83 by Music For Pleasure Records. Dist: EMI

Cassette: released on Fame, May'83 by Music For Pleasure Records. Dist: EMI

SHADOWS VOCALS,THE.
Album: released on EMI, Jun'84 by EMI Records. Dist: EMI

Cassette: released on EMI, Jun'84 by EMI Records. Dist: EMI

STRING OF HITS.
Tracks: / Riders in the sky / Parisiene walkways / Classical gas / Theme from the deer-hunter (Cavatina) / Bridge over troubled water / You're the one that I want / Heart of glass / Don't cry for me Argentina / Song for duke / Bright eyes / Rodrigo's guitar concerto de aranjuez / Baker street.
Album: released on Music For Pleasure (Holland), Oct'86 by EMI Records. Dist: EMI

Cassette: released on Music For Pleasure (Holland), Oct'86 by EMI Records. Dist: EMI

Album: released on MFP, Sep'85 by EMI Records. Dist: EMI

Compact disc: released on EMI, Oct'87 by EMI Records. Dist: EMI. Estim retail price in Sep'87 was £11.99.

THEME FROM EASTENDERS & HOWARDS WAY.
Tracks: / No dancing.
Single (7"): released on Polydor, Nov'86 by Polydor Records. Dist: Polygram, Polydor

THEME FROM THE DEER HUNTER (CAVATINA).
Single (7"): released on EMI, Apr'79 by EMI Records. Dist: EMI

XXV.
Compact disc: by Polydor Records. Dist: Poly-

gram, Polydor

Shadows Guitar Greats
SHADOWS GUITAR GREATS various artists (Various Session Artists).
Cassette: released on AIM (Budget Cassettes), Feb'83

Shadowshow
ECHOES.
Single (7"): released on Original, Mar'84 Dist: RCA Distribution, Jazz Music Distribution, PRT Distribution

SECURE IN YOU/NOONDAY KISSES.
Single (7"): released on Original, Oct'83 Dist: RCA Distribution, Jazz Music Distribution, PRT Distribution

Shadows of Night
G-L-O-R-I-A.
Album: released on Edsel, Apr'85 by Demon Records. Dist: Pinnacle, Jazz Music, Projection

Shadow & Substance
SHADOW & SUBSTANCE Wonderful world of Glass vol 2 (Various Artists).
Album: released on Glass, Apr'84 by Glass Records. Dist: Nine Mile, Rough Trade, Red Rhino, Play It Again Sam

Shadow Talk
PEOPLE WATCHING PEOPLE.
Single (7"): released on Magnet, May'84 by Magnet Records. Dist: BMG

Single (12"): released on Magnet, May'84 by Magnet Records. Dist: BMG

YOU COULD BE MINE.
Single (7"): released on Magnet, Sep'84 by Magnet Records. Dist: BMG

Shady
GET RIGHT NEXT TO YOU.
Tracks: / Get right next to you.
Single (7"): released on Funkin' Marvellous, May'86 Dist: Priority, RCA, Ariola

Single (12"): released on Funkin' Marvellous, May'86 Dist: Priority, RCA, Ariola

Shafer, Ted
SAN FRANCISCO JAZZ (Shafer, Ted Jelly Roll Jazz Band).
Album: released on GBH, Jun'86 by GBH Records. Dist: Jazz Music, Swift

Shafer, Whitey
MEMPHIS MEMORY.
Album: released on Bear Family, Nov'84 by Bear Family Records. Dist: Rollercoaster Distribution, Swift

MY HOUSE IS YOUR HONKY TONK.
Album: released on Bear Family, Nov'84 by Bear Family Records. Dist: Rollercoaster Distribution, Swift

Shaffer, Doreen
BABY LAY DOWN.
Single (7"): released on Revue, Jun'85 by Revue Records. Dist: Creole

WONDERFUL SOUND.
Album: released on Review, Dec'85 by Jetstar

Shaftesbury
LULL BEFORE THE STORM, (THE).
Album: released on OK, May'80 by Klub Records. Dist: PRT Distribution

WE ARE THE BOYS.
Album: released on OK, Jul'81 by Klub Records. Dist: PRT Distribution

Shaq
LOOP DI LOVE.
Single (7"): released on Old Gold (Reissue), Jul'82

Shah, Idries
FRAMEWORK FOR NEW KNOWLEDGE.
Cassette: released on Seminar Cassettes, Oct'81 by Seminar Cassettes. Dist: Davidson Distribution, Eastern Educational Products Distrib, Fortaget Systems Distribution, Laser Books Ltd Distribution, MacDougall Distribution, Talktapes Distribution, Watkins Books Ltd Distribution, Norton, Jeff Distribution

Shall, Mike
NO HOLES BARD & EEZUM SQUEEZUM.
Cassette: released on Folktracks, Nov'79 by Folktracks Cassettes. Dist: Folktracks

Shaka All Stars
MESSAGE FROM AFRICA.
Album: released on Jah Shaka, Jun'85 by Jah Shaka Records. Dist: Jetstar

Shaka, Jah
COMMANDMENT OF DUB PART |V.
Album: released on Jah Shaka, Dec'85 by Jah Shaka Records. Dist: Jetstar

COMMANDMENTS OF DUB.
Album: released on Chapter 6, Jun'87 by Chapter 6 Records. Dist: Jetstar

COMMANDMENTS OF .. PART 6.
Album: released on Jah Shaka Music. May'87

JAH SHAKA MEETS ASWAD IN ADDIS ABABA STUDIO.
Notes: For full information see under Aswad

Shakatak
CITY RHYTHM.
Single (7"): released on Polydor, Aug'85 by Polydor Records. Dist: Polygram, Polydor

Single (12"): released on Polydor, Aug'85 by Polydor Records. Dist: Polygram, Polydor

DAY BY DAY.
Tracks: / Day by day / Once upon a time / Secret / Physical attraction / City rhythm / I must be dreaming / Africa / Goodbye / Mickey mouse / Viva la fantasy.
Compact disc: released on Polydor, Dec'85 by Polydor Records. Dist: Polygram, Polydor

Album: released on Polydor, Dec'85 by Polydor Records. Dist: Polygram, Polydor

Cassette: released on Polydor, Dec'85 by Polydor Records. Dist: Polygram, Polydor

DOWN ON THE STREET.
Album: released on Polydor, Aug'84 by Polydor Records. Dist: Polygram, Polydor

Cassette: released on Polydor, Aug'84 by Polydor Records. Dist: Polygram, Polydor

DOWN THE STREET.
Album: released on Polydor, Jun'87 by Polydor Records. Dist: Polygram, Polydor

Cassette: released on Polydor, Jun'87 by Polydor Records. Dist: Polygram, Polydor

DRIVING HARD.
Tracks: / Livin in the UK. / Into the night / Toot the shoot / Lumiere / Late night flight / Waves / Steppin (live) / Covina / You never know / Brazilian dawn.
Album: released on Polydor, Jun'86 by Polydor Records. Dist: Polygram, Polydor

Cassette: released on Polydor, Jun'86 by Polydor Records. Dist: Polygram, Polydor

Compact discs: released on Polydor, Jun'86 by Polydor Records. Dist: Polygram, Polydor

Cassette: released on Polydor, Feb'83 by Polydor Records. Dist: Polygram, Polydor

INVITATIONS.
Tracks: / Lose myself / Lonely afternoon / Steppin out / Stranger / Sol fuego / Usual situation / Invitations / In shadows.
Compact disc: released on Polydor, Jan'83 by Polydor Records. Dist: Polygram, Polydor

Album: released on Polydor, Feb'85 by Polydor Records. Dist: Polygram, Polydor

Cassette: released on Polydor, Feb'85 by Polydor Records. Dist: Polygram, Polydor

LIVE.
Tracks: / Dark is the night / Streetwalkin / Watching you / Invitations / Nightbirds / Don't blame it on love / Easier said than done / Down on the street.
Compact disc: released on Polydor, Feb'85 by Polydor Records. Dist: Polygram, Polydor

NIGHTBIRDS.
Tracks: / Takin off / Lisa / Go for it / Rio nights / Nightbirds / Fly the wing / Easier said than done / Bitch to the boys / Light of my life.
Compact disc: released on Polydor, Jan'83 by Polydor Records. Dist: Polygram, Polydor

Album: released on Polydor, Mar'82 by Polydor Records. Dist: Polygram, Polydor

Cassette: released on Polydor, Mar'82 by Polydor Records. Dist: Polygram, Polydor

OUT OF THIS WORLD.
Tracks: / Dark is the night / Don't say that again / Slip away / On nights like tonight / Out of this world / Out of this world / Let's get together / If you can see me now / Sanur.
Compact disc: released on Polydor, Jan'83 by Polydor Records. Dist: Polygram, Polydor

SOMETHING SPECIAL.
Tracks: / Something special / Cavalcante.

Single (7"): released on Polydor, 30 May'87 by Polydor Records. Dist: Polygram, Polydor

Single (12"): released on Polydor, 30 May'87 by Polydor Records. Dist: Polygram, Polydor

STRANGER.
Single (7"): released on Polydor, Nov'82 by Polydor Records. Dist: Polygram, Polydor

Single (12"): released on Polydor, Nov'82 by Polydor Records. Dist: Polygram, Polydor

STREETWALKIN'.
Single (7"): released on Polydor, Jun'82 by Polydor Records. Dist: Polygram, Polydor

Single (12"): released on Polydor, Jun'82 by Polydor Records. Dist: Polygram, Polydor

Shake Around
SHAKE AROUND (Various Artists).
Album: released on Sun, May'85 by Charly Records. Dist: Charly Distribution

Shake'N'Jive
SHAKE'N'JIVE (Various Artists).
Album: released on Spot, Feb'83 by Pickwick Records. Dist: H.R. Taylor,

Cassette: released on Spot, Feb'83 by Pickwick Records. Dist: H.R. Taylor,

Shake, Rattle & Roll
SHAKE, RATTLE & ROLL Various artists (Various Artists).
Tracks: / Shaka, rattle and roll / Clock, The / Have mercy baby / Shake a hand / See you later, alligator / Maybellene / Mailman blues / I can't go on / Every hour / Get a job / That'll be the day / Good golly miss Molly / Reet petite / I met him on a sunday / At my front door / I'm movin on / What about us / New Orleans.
Album: released on New World (USA), Aug'86 by New World Records (USA). Dist: Conifer

Shakers
MISSING LINK (THE).
Tracks: / Missing link (The).
Single (12"): released on Waterfront, Jan'86 by Waterfront Records. Dist: Rough Trade, Cartel, Projection, Roots

TEMPTATION WALK.
Single (7"): released on Waterfront, Feb'84 by Waterfront Records. Dist: Rough Trade, Cartel, Projection, Roots

Shakers/Cobras
THIS STUFF'S GONNA BUST YOUR BRAINS OUT.
Album: released on Arela, Jan'87 Dist: Rough Trade, Cartel

Shake Shake Shake It Baby
SHAKE SHAKE SHAKE IT BABY - SIN ALLEY VOL.3 (Various Artists).
Album: released on Cornball, Jun'87

Shakespeare, Maria
JOEY'S SONGBOOK.
Tracks: / Joey's songbook / Joey's songbook (dub).
Single (12"): released on Dean's, Jun'86 Dist: Jetstar

Shakespeare, Mark
BOHM MUSICA DIGITAL-PERCHANCE TO DREAM.
Album: released on Grosvenor, Nov'96 by Grosvenor Records. Dist: Taylors

SPOTLIGHT ON SHAKESPEARE.
Tracks: / Bohm symphony / Music / Memory / Tocca tocca / Classica (arr.) / Jetzt geht die party los / Kreuzberger nachte / Y viva Espana / Tico tico / Thunder and lightning / Schneewalzer klavierthen muckel / Trompeten echo / Hey, Das ist music / What I did for love / Good the bad and the ugly / Ghost riders in the sky / Yellow rose of texas / Farmer and the cowman / Amor amor / Brazil.
Album: released on Grosvenor, Feb'87 by Grosvenor Records. Dist: Taylors

Cassette: released on Grosvenor, Feb'87 by Grosvenor Records. Dist: Taylors

Shakespeare, William
ALL'S WELL THAT ENDS WELL (COMPLETE TEXT) (Various Artists).
Cassette: released on Argo (Spokenword), Jun'84 by Decca Records. Dist: Polygram

HENRY V (Various Artists).
Cassette: released on Argo (Spokenword), Mar'84 by Decca Records. Dist: Polygram

KING JOHN.
Cassette: released on Argo (Spokenword), Oct'85 by Decca Records. Dist: Polygram

LOVE'S LABOUR'S LOST (COMPLETE

TEXT) (Various Artists).
Cassette: released on Argo (Cassettes), Sep'84 by Decca Records. Dist: Polygram

MACBETH.
Cassette: released on Listen For Pleasure, Oct'85 by MFP Records. Dist: EMI

MERRY WIVES OF WINDSOR, THE.
Cassette: released on Argo, Apr'85 by Decca Records. Dist: Polygram

OTHELLO The complete text (Various Artists).
Cassette: released on Argo (Spokenword), Jul'83 by Decca Records. Dist: Polygram

RICHARD III (Various Artists).
Cassette: released on Argo, Mar'84 by Decca Records. Dist: Polygram

RICHARD III (Marlowe Dramatic Society).
Double cassette: released on Argo, Apr'84 by Decca Records. Dist: Polygram

SONNETS (Pasco, Richard).
Double cassette: released on Argo, Oct'84 by Decca Records. Dist: Polygram

THESE ARE WOMAN.
Cassette: released on Caedmon(USA), Apr'85 by Caedmon (USA) Records. Dist: Gower, Taylors, Discovery

TITUS ADRONICUS.
Cassette: released on Argo, Apr'85 by Decca Records. Dist: Polygram

VENUS AND ADONIS/ RAPE OF LUCRECE, THE.
Cassette: released on Argo, Dec'85 by Decca Records. Dist: Polygram

Shake That Thing
SHAKE THAT THING America's top bands of the 20's (Various bands).
Cassette: released on ASV, Mar'81 by Academy Sound & Vision Records. Dist: Pinnacle

SHAKE THAT THING (Various Artists).
Album: released on ASV, Mar'81 by Academy Sound & Vision Records. Dist: Pinnacle

Shakey Jake
KEY WON'T FIT, THE.
Album: released on Murray Brothers (USA), Mar'84 Dist: Swift Distribution

Shakin' Pyramids
CUMBERLAND GAP (Shakin' Pyramids & Lonnie Donegan).
Single (7"): released on Virgin, Nov'81 by Virgin Records. Dist: EMI, Virgin Distribution

JUST A MEMORY.
Single (7"): released on Virgin, Jun'82 by Virgin Records. Dist: EMI, Virgin Distribution

PHARAOH'S CHANT.
Single (7"): released on Virgin, Mar'82 by Virgin Records. Dist: EMI, Virgin Distribution

SKIN 'EM UP.
Album: released on Virgin, Mar'84 by Virgin Records. Dist: EMI, Virgin Distribution

TAKE A TRIP.
Single (7"): released on Cuba Libre, Mar'81 by Virgin Records. Dist: EMI

TENNESSEE ROCK 'N' ROLL.
Single (7"): released on Virgin, May'81 by Virgin Records. Dist: EMI, Virgin Distribution

Shaky & Bonnie
ROCKIN' GOOD WAY.
Single (7"): released on Epic, Jan'84 by CBS Records. Dist: CBS

Picture disc single: released on Epic, Jan'84 by CBS Records. Dist: CBS

Single (12"): released on Epic, Jan'84 by CBS Records. Dist: CBS

Shalamar
AMNESIA.
Single (7"): released on MCA, Nov'84 by MCA Records. Dist: Polygram, MCA

Single (12"): released on MCA, Nov'84 by MCA Records. Dist: Polygram, MCA

BILL THE GALACTIC HERO.
Album: released on BBC, Sep'84 by BBC Records & Tapes. Dist: EMI, PRT.

Cassette: released on BBC, Sep'84 by BBC Records & Tapes. Dist: EMI, PRT.

CIRCUMSTANTIAL EVIDENCE.
Tracks: / Circumstantial evidence / Games / Loves grown deep / Playthang / Female / Bo

to love / Worth waitin' for / Imaginary love.
Album: released on Solar, Jul'87 by MCA Records. Dist: Polygram Distribution

Cassette: released on Solar, Jul'87 by MCA Records. Dist: Polygram Distribution

Compact disc: released on Solar, Jul'87 by MCA Records. Dist: Polygram Distribution

Single (7"): released on MCA, Aug'87 by MCA Records. Dist: Polygram, MCA

Single (12"): released on MCA, Aug'87 by MCA Records. Dist: Polygram, MCA

DANCING IN THE STREETS.
Single (7"): released on CBS, Jun'84 by CBS Records. Dist: CBS

Single (12"): released on CBS, Jun'84 by CBS Records. Dist: CBS

DEADLINE USA.
Single (7"): released on MCA, Mar'84 by MCA Records. Dist: Polygram, MCA

Single (12"): released on MCA, Mar'84 by MCA Records. Dist: Polygram, MCA

FRIENDS.
Tracks: / Night to remember / Don't try to change me / Help me / On top of the world / I don't wanna be the last to know / Friends / Playing to win / I just stopped by because I had to / There it is / I can make you feel good.
Compact disc: released on Sire, Jan'83

GO FOR IT.
Album: released on Solar, Dec'81

Cassette: released on Solar, Dec'81

GREATEST HITS:SHALAMAR.
Tracks: / Over and over / Night to remember, A / Uptown festival (part 1) / There it is / I can make you feel good / Disappearing act / Dead giveaway / Friends / Amnesia / My girls love me / Make that move / There it is / Second time around, The / Night to remember, A / Take that to the bank / I owe you one.
Album: released on Stylus, Apr'86 Dist: Pinnacle, Terry Blood Distribution, Stylus Distribution

Cassette: released on Stylus, Apr'86 Dist: Pinnacle, Terry Blood Distribution, Stylus Distribution

Compact disc: released on MCA, '86 by MCA Records. Dist: Polygram, MCA

Album: released on Solar, Aug'82

Cassette: released on Solar, Aug'82

HEARTBREAK.
Tracks: / Amnesia / Dancing in the streets / Whenever you need me / Heartbreak / Don't get stopped in Beverly Hills / My girl loves me / Melody (an erotic affair) / Deceiver.
Compact disc: released on Vogue, Jan'87 Dist: Discovery, Jazz Music, PRT, Swift

Album: released on Solar, Jun'87 by MCA Records. Dist: Polygram Distribution

Cassette: released on Solar, Jun'87 by MCA Records. Dist: Polygram Distribution

Album: released on Epic, Jun'84 by CBS Records. Dist: CBS

Cassette: released on Epic, Jun'84 by CBS Records. Dist: CBS

MY GIRL LOVES ME.
Single (7"): released on MCA, Jan'85 by MCA Records. Dist: Polygram, MCA

Single (12"): released on MCA, Jan'85 by MCA Records. Dist: Polygram, MCA

NIGHT TO REMEMBER.
Tracks: / Night to remember / Take that to the bank / Uptown festival.
Single (7"): released on I.R.S.(Independent Record Syndicate), 30 May'87 by I.R.S.. Dist: MCA

Single (12"): released on I.R.S.(Independent Record Syndicate), 30 May'87 by I.R.S.. Dist: MCA

SWEETER AS THE DAYS GO BY.
Single (7"): released on Solar, Nov'81

Single (12"): released on Solar, Oct'81

TAKE THAT TO THE BANK.
Tracks: / Take that to the bank (M & M Mix) / Right in the socket / Right in the socket (Original US 12") / Take that to the band (Original US 12").
Single (7"): released on MCA, Aug'86 by MCA Records. Dist: Polygram, MCA

Single (12"): released on MCA, Aug'86 by MCA Records. Dist: Polygram, MCA

TALK TO ME.
Single (12"): released on Solar, Jan'82

THREE FOR LOVE.
Album: released on Solar, Dec'80

Cassette: released on Solar, Dec'80

UPTOWN FESTIVAL.
Single (7"): released on Solar, Jul'81

Single (12"): released on Solar, Jun'81

WORK IT OUT.
Single (7"): released on Solar, May'82

Single (12"): released on Solar, May'82

Shale, Kerry

HUCKLEBERRY FINN.
Cassette: released on Listen For Pleasure, Aug'85 by MFP Records. Dist: EMI

Shaljean, Bonnie

ROUNDTOWER (Shaljean, Bonnie & Packie Byrne).
Album: released on Dingles, '83 by Dingle's Records. Dist: Projection

Shalobberdop Twins

FAMOUS MAN.
Single (7"): released on Riviera, Nov'84 Dist: Discovery, Pinnacle

Sham 69

ANGELS WITH DIRTY FACES.
Album: released on Receiver, '86 by Receiver Records. Dist: Pinnacle

Cassette: released on Receiver, '86 by Receiver Records. Dist: Pinnacle

Single (7"): released on Polydor, Apr'78 by Polydor Records. Dist: Polygram, Polydor

I DON'T WANNA.
Single (7"): released on Step Forward, Oct'79 by Faulty Products Records. Dist: Faulty Products Distribution, Pinnacle

Single (12"): released on Step Forward, Oct'77 by Faulty Products Records. Dist: Faulty Products Distribution, Pinnacle

LIVE AND LOUD.
Album: released on Link, Feb'87 Dist: DMS, RCA

Album:

RIP AND TEAR.
Single (7"): released on Legacy, Aug'87 Dist: PRT

TELL THE CHILDREN.
Single (7"): released on Polydor, Mar'80 by Polydor Records. Dist: Polygram, Polydor

Shambeko Say Wah

REMEMBER/ CRACK IS A CRACK, A.
Single (7"): released on Eternal, Apr'82 by Eternal Records. Dist: WEA

Single (12"): released on Eternal, Apr'82 by Eternal Records. Dist: WEA

Shambleau

SHAMBLEAU Moore, C.L. (Moore, Catherine).
Cassette: released on Caedmon(USA), Oct'81 by Caedmon (USA) Records. Dist: Gower, Taylors, Discovery

Shame

SHAME, THE.
Tracks: / Shame, The (EP).
Single (12"): released on Shake The Label, Jul'86 Dist: Fast Forward, Cartel

Shamen

DROP.
Album: released on Moshka, Jun'87

Cassette: released on Moshka, Jun'87

SOMETHING ABOUT YOU.
Single (7"): released on Moksha, 23 May'87 Dist: Nine Mile Distribution, Cartel Distribution

Single (12"): released on Moksha, 23 May'87 Dist: Nine Mile Distribution, Cartel Distribution

YOUNG 'TILL YESTERDAY.
Tracks: / Young 'till yesterday / World theatre / Golden hair / Strange days dream / It's all around.
Single (7"): released on Moksha, Nov'86 Dist: Nine Mile Distribution, Cartel Distribution

Single (12"): released on Moksha, Nov'86 Dist: Nine Mile Distribution, Cartel Distribution

Shampoo

EVERLASTING (2 PARTS).
Single (7"): released on Arrival, Aug'81 by Arrival. Dist: Revolver, Cartel

Single (12"): released on Arrival, Aug'81 by Arrival. Dist: Revolver, Cartel

Shamrock Singers

IRISH SINGALONG.
Album: released on Hawk, Oct'76 by Dolphin Records. Dist: I & B, Celtic Music, Solomon & Peres Distribution

Cassette: released on Hawk, Oct'76 by Dolphin Records. Dist: I & B, Celtic Music, Solomon & Peres Distribution

Sha Na Na

Biographical Details: Sha Na Na were a twelve-strong rock'n'roll revival group formed '69 at Columbia University; they played at Woodstock in 1969 and had an American TV series from 1977. With costumes and choreography, they were more popular live than on record, but their several albums made good party music. [Donald Clarke, April 87]

ROCKIN' AND A ROLLIN'.
Tracks: / Rama lama ding dong / Splish splash / Wooley bully / Purple people eater / Monster mash / Rockin' robin / Da doo ron ron / Mr Bass Man / Charlie Brown / Boney Moroney / Alley oop / Little arrows / Get a job / My prayer.
Compact disc: released on The Collection, Apr'87 by Object Enterprises Ltd. Dist: Counterpoint Distribution

SHA NA NA IS HERE TO STAY.
Album: released on Buddah, Jul'85 Dist: Swift, Jazz Music, PRT

Cassette: released on Buddah, Jul'85 Dist: Swift, Jazz Music, PRT

Shand Family

THREE GENERATIONS OF SHAND Family album, The.
Tracks: / Bonnie Kirkwall Bay / Gay Gordons / Way down south / Karlstad valsen / Polka / Dream valley of Glendaurel / Battle of the Somme / Molly Lee / Harveston castle / Ploughboy, The / Bridal path, The / Scottish waltzes / Jigs / Irish hornpipes / Battle is o'er, The / Castle dangerous / Green hills of Tyrol, The / McNamara's band / Hot asphalt / Garden where the pirates grow, The / Irish washerwoman, The / Now is the hour / Aloha land.
Notes: Shand Family include: Jimmy Shand Snr/Jimmy Shand Jnr & Diane Shand.
Album: released on Emerald (Ireland), Nov'84 by Emerald Records. Dist: I & B, Ross, PRT

Shand, Jimmy

50 YEARS ON WITH JIMMY SHAND, HIS BAND AND GUESTS (Shand, Jimmy & His Band).
Album: released on Ross Records, Jan'84

Cassette: released on Ross Records, Jan'84

AUCHTERMUCHTY CEILIDH (Shand, Jimmy & His Band).
Notes: With Robbie Shepherd, Diane Shand and Jimmy Urquart
Album: released on Ross, '86 by Ross Records. Dist: Ross Distribution, Roots Distribution

Cassette: released on Ross, '86 by Ross Records. Dist: Ross Distribution, Roots Distribution

BONNIE SCOTLAND (Shand, Jimmy & His Band).
Notes: Retail price given by ARC excluding P & P (via mail order) is 4.99. Mail order Distribution address: Accordian Music Record Club, 146 Birmingham Road, Kidderminster, Worcs. DY10 2SL. Tel: 0562 746105.
Cassette: released on Accordion Record Club, Jul'86 by Accordion Record Club Records. Dist: Accordion Record Club

ECHOES IN THE GLEN (Shand, Jimmy & His Band).
Album: released on Ross, Dec'86 by Ross Records. Dist: Ross Distribution, Roots Distribution

Cassette: released on Ross, '86 by Ross Records. Dist: Ross Distribution, Roots Distribution

FAMILY ALBUM (Shand, Jimmy, Jimmy Shand Jnr & Diane Shand).
Tracks: / Nina (Rick's wife) / Adam (Rick's second son) / Mum / Chloe (German shepherd) / Oliver (Rick's eldest son) / Kookie (cat) / Black beauty (black rabbit) / Oscar (Rick & Nina's son) / Dad / Tilly (Golden retriever) / Benjamin / Jemma (Rick & Nina's daughter) / Wiggles (Black & white rabbit).
Album: released on Emerald, Oct'81 by Emerald Records. Dist: Ross, PRT, Solomon & Peres Distribution

Cassette: released on Emerald, Oct'81 by Emerald Records. Dist: Ross, PRT, Solomon & Peres Distribution

FIFTY YEARS ON (Shand, Jimmy & His Band).
Notes: With guests
Album: released on Ross, '86 by Ross Records. Dist: Ross Distribution, Roots Distribution

Cassette: released on Ross, '86 by Ross Records. Dist: Ross Distribution, Roots Distribution

Notes: Retail price given by ARC excluding P & P (via Mail Order) is 4.99. Mail order Distribution address: Accordian Record Club, 146 Birmingham Road, Kidderminster, Worcs. DY10 2SL. Tel 0562 746105

FOCUS ON JIMMY SHAND (Shand, Jimmy & His Band).
Double Album: released on Decca, Feb'78 by Decca Records. Dist: Polygram Deleted '80.

Double cassette: released on Decca, Feb'78 by Decca Records. Dist: Polygram

GOLDEN YEARS OF JIMMY SHAND, (THE) (Shand, Jimmy & His Band).
Album: released on Glen, Mar'79 Dist: EMI, Outlet

Cassette: released on Glen, Mar'79 Dist: EMI, Outlet

HAPPY HOURS WITH JIMMY SHAND.
Tracks: / Happy hours / Macdonald of Sleat / De'il amang the tailors / Lucky scap / Masons apron / Lassie / Lord Lovat's Lament / Meeting of the waters / St.Andrews parade / Harveston castle / Breadalbane reel / Bobby Watson / Auld hoose, The / Rothesay Bay / Bonnie Gallowa / Lass from Braco, The / Para handy / White leather club, The / Bonnie Isle of Gletness / Sunset over Foula / Rona's voe / Scotland the brave / We're no awaw tae bide awa / Maggie and Jock / Roll along Kentucky moon / Omaha / Missouri waltz, The / Whispering pines of Nevada, The / New Scotland Strathspey, The / Miss Drummond of Perth / Miss Nancy Frowns / Lady Charlotte Murray's favourite / Stobhall / Howard Lockhart polka.
Notes: Jimmy Shand-accordian/Ian Powrie-fiddle
Album: released on Music For Pleasure, Jun'86 by EMI Records. Dist: EMI

Cassette: released on Music For Pleasure, Jun'86 by EMI Records. Dist: EMI

LEGENDS OF SCOTLAND (Shand, Jimmy & His Band).
Tracks: / Muckin' o' Geordies byre / Lady Nellie Wemyss / Braidley's house / Major Mackie / Cock o' the north / Jeannie King / Lord Lyndoch / Duke of Gordon / Laird o' Thrums, The / Lady Ann Hope / If you're Irish / With my Shillelagh under my arm / Royal Scots polka / Swilcan, The / Gordon B Cosh / Kinkell braes / Ithan bar / Northern lights of old Aberdeen, The / Scotland the brave / Thistle of the north, The / We're no awa tae bide awa / Cailin no min sa / Leaving Barra / Morag of Dunvegan / When you and I were young Maggie / Bluebell polka / I'll take you home again Kathleen / Black dance , The / Wedding / Wandering drummer, The / Breadalbane reel.
Cassette: released on Lochshore, Jun'86 by Klub Records. Dist: PRT

MAGIC SOUNDS OF SHAND, (THE) (Shand, Jimmy & His Band).
Album: released on Music For Pleasure (Holland), May'83 by EMI Records. Dist: EMI

SCOTLAND MY HOME (Shand, Jimmy & His Band).
Album: released on Glen, Oct'81 Dist: EMI, Outlet

Cassette: released on Glen, Oct'81 Dist: EMI, Outlet

SCOTLAND'S OWN (Shand, Jimmy & His Band).
Album: released on Grasmere, Mar'85 by Grasmere Records. Dist: EMI

Cassette: released on Grasmere, Mar'85 by Grasmere Records. Dist: EMI

THREE GENERATIONS OF SHAND (Shand, Jimmy & Family).
Album: released on Emerald, Nov'84 by Emerald Records. Dist: Ross, PRT, Solomon & Peres Distribution

Cassette: released on Emerald, Nov'84 by Emerald Records. Dist: Ross, PRT, Solomon & Peres Distribution

TRIBUTE TO JIMMY SHAND - THE FIRST 46 YEARS (Shand, Jimmy & His Band).
Album: released on Waverley, Jun'80 by EMI Records. Dist: EMI

Cassette: released on Waverley, Jun'80 by EMI Records. Dist: EMI

Shand, Jimmy Jnr.

BONNIE SCOTLAND.
Album: released on Ross, '86 by Ross Records. Dist: Ross Distribution, Roots Distribution

Cassette: released on Ross, '86 by Ross Records. Dist: Ross Distribution, Roots Distribution

COME TO THE DANCE (Shand, Jimmy Jnr. & His Band).
Album: released on Emerald, Oct'81 by Emerald Records. Dist: Ross, PRT, Solomon & Peres Distribution

Cassette: released on Emerald, Oct'81 by Emerald Records. Dist: Ross, PRT, Solomon &

MIST COVERED MOUNTAINS.
Notes: Dance music and vocals from Jimmy Shand Jnr. and his band
Cassette: released on Ross, '86 by Ross Records. Dist: Ross Distribution, Roots Distribution

Shanga

HEY FRED! (YOU NEED A SUNBED).
Single (7"): released on CSA, Jul'86 by CSA Records. Dist: PRT, Jetstar

Single (12"): released on CSA, Jul'86 by CSA Records. Dist: PRT, Jetstar

Shango

SHANGO FUNK THEOLOGY.
Album: released on Carrere, May'84 by Carrere Records. Dist: PRT, Spartan

SHANGO MESSAGE.
Single (12"): released on Celluloid-Carrere, Aug'84 by Celluloid. Dist: PRT, Spartan

Shangri-Las

65.
Album: released on Red Bird, Mar'84 by Charly.

GOLDEN HITS: THE SHANGRI-LAS.
Album: released on Philips (Import), Mar'84

GREATEST HITS:SHANGRI-LAS.
Tracks: / Leader of the pack / Give him a great big kiss / Maybe / Out in the streets / Give us your blessings / Right now and not later / Remember (walkin' in the sand) / I can never go home anymore / Long live our love / Past present and future / Train from Kansas City / Shout / Twist and shout / I'm blue / You cheated, you lied / So much in love.
Notes: A Red Bird recording. Licensed from Charly Records International APS. This CD (P) 1987 Charly Holdings Inc. (C) 1987 Charly Records Ltd.
Compact disc: released on Topline, May'87 by Charly Records. Dist: Charly Distribution

LEADER OF THE PACK.
Album: released on Charly, '83 by Charly Records. Dist: Charly, Cadillac

Album: released on Topline, Nov'84 by Charly Records. Dist: Charly Distribution

Cassette: released on Topline, Nov'84 by Charly Records. Dist: Charly Distribution

Album: released on Astan, Nov'84 by Astan Records. Dist: Counterpoint

Cassette: released on Astan, Nov'84 by Astan Records. Dist: Counterpoint

LEADER OF THE PACK/ GIVE HIM A GREAT BIG KISS.
Single (7"): released on Charly, '80 by Charly Records. Dist: Charly, Cadillac

LEADER OF THE PACK/ WALKING IN THE SAND.
Single (7"): released on Old Gold, Jul'82 by Old Gold Records. Dist: Lightning, Jazz Music, Spartan, Counterpoint

Shankar

SONG FOR EVERYONE.
Compact disc: released on ECM (Germany), Apr'85 by ECM Records. Dist: IMS, Polygram, Virgin through EMI

VISION.
Album: released on ECM (Germany), Mar'84 by ECM Records. Dist: IMS, Polygram, Virgin through EMI

WHO'S TO KNOW.
Tracks: / Ragam-Tanam-Pallavi / Ananda Nadamadum Tillai Sankara.
Notes: Prsonnel: Shankar-double violin, tamboura/Umayalpuram K Sivaraman-Mridangam/Zakir Hurrain-tabla/Lakshminarayana-condutor
Compact disc: released on ECM (Germany), Dec'85 by ECM Records. Dist: IMS, Polygram, Virgin through EMI

Shankar, Ravi

GENISIS(OST).
Compact disc: released on SPI Milan (France), Nov'86 Dist: Silva Screen

GENIUS OF..., THE.
Double Album: released on CBS(Holland), Jun'84 by CBS Records. Dist: Discovery

HIMALAYA (Shankar & Bill Lovelady).
Single (7"): released on WEA, Jul'82 by WEA Records. Dist: WEA

WHO'S TO KNOW.
Album: released on ECM (Germany), Jul'81 by ECM Records. Dist: IMS, Polygram, Virgin through EMI

Shank, Bud

Biographical Details: Bud Shank was born 27 May 1926, Dayton, Ohio; he plays flute and also sax and is also a composer. He went to California in 1947, played in big bands and stidied with trumpeter/bandleader **Shorty Rogers**, becoming a mainstay in the West Coast jazz scene and a regular at Howard Rumsey's famous **Lighthouse Club** in Hermosa Beach; he also did a lot of studio work and was heard in film soundtracks. He made nearly 30 albums as a leader on World Pacific/Pacific Jazz '54-70, mostly small-group sets, always with excellent sidemen, including LPs of pop songs '66-7: **Michelle**, with Baker on flugelhorn, arrangement by Bob Florence, was a hit LP in the USA. He also made **Brazil '65** on Capitol with Sergio Mendez and played as a sideman on LPs by just about everybody. In 1974 he co-formed the **L.A. Four** with Shelly Manne, Ray Brown and Laurindo Almeida (albums on Concord Jazz) and has made several albums on Concord Jazz since '76 with pianist/composer Bill Mays. [Donald Clarke, April 87]

BRAZILVILLE (Shank, Bud & Charlie Byrd).
Album: released on Concord Jazz(USA), Mar'82 by Concord Jazz Records (USA). Dist: IMS, Polygram

Cassette: released on Concord Jazz(USA), Mar'82 by Concord Jazz Records (USA). Dist: IMS, Polygram

BUD SHANK & THE RPO (Shank, Bud & The RPO).
Tracks: / Here's that rainy day / Body and soul / Concerto for jazz alto saxaphone and orchestra.
Notes: Bud Shank and the Royal Philharmonic Orchestra conducted by Vic Lewis, recorded at the Festival Hall in November 1985. The two featured pieces here are "Body and Soul" and "Concerto For Jazz Alto Saxaphone And Orchestra" by Manny Albam were recorded at a royal gala performance celebrating 50 years of the music of Dizzy Gillespie. The concert was in aid of The Royal School For The Blind. The remaining track on this album "Here's That Rainy Day" is performed by the Bud Shank Quartet recorded at the Concord Club, Southampton.
Album: released on Mole Jazz, Apr'87 by Mole Jazz Records. Dist: Mole Jazz Distributors

Compact disc: released on Mole Jazz, Apr'87 by Mole Jazz Records. Dist: Mole Jazz Distributors

LIVE AT THE HAIG.
Album: released on Mole Jazz, Sep'85 by Mole Jazz Records. Dist: Mole Jazz Distributors

THAT OLD FEELING (Shank, Bud Quartet).
Album: released on Contemporary, Jan'87 by Contemporary Records. Dist: Pinnacle

THIS BUD'S FOR YOU.
Tracks: / I'll be seeing you / Nica's dream / Never never land / Space maker / Visa / Cotton Blossom / Bouncing with Bud.
Notes: And the Rhythm section of Ron Carter/Kenny Barron/Al Foster. Produced by Bob Golden. Recorded at Classic Sound Studio-NYC on 14.11.84
Album: released on Muse (USA), May'86 by Muse Records (USA). Dist: Conifer Distribution, Jazz Music Distribution

Shank I Sheck

SHANK I SHECK Various artists (Various Artists).
Album: released on Vista Sounds, '83 by Vista Sounds Records. Dist: Jetstar

Shankly, Bill

SHANKLY ON SOCCER VOLUME 1.
Album: released on Technical, May'81 Dist: Stage One Distribution

Shannon

DANCIN'.
Tracks: / Dancin' / Faces in the crowd.
Single (7"): released on Club, Apr'87 by Phonogram Records. Dist: Polygram

Single (12"): released on Club, Apr'87 by Phonogram Records. Dist: Polygram

LET THE MUSIC PLAY.
Compact disc: released on Bellaphon, '86 by Bellaphon Records. Dist: IMS-Polygram

Album: released on Club, Mar'84 by Phonogram Records. Dist: Polygram

Cassette: released on Club, Mar'84 by Phonogram Records. Dist: Polygram

Single (7"): released on Club, Nov'83 by Phonogram Records. Dist: Polygram

LOVE GOES ALL THE WAY.
Tracks: / Prove me right / Love goes all the way / Dancin' / Sabotage my heart / You put a spark in my life / Right track / Faces in the crowd / You blew.
Notes: The third hit album from Shannon - a return to form with the recent dance hit "Dancin" typifying the "Shannon Sound" that began with "Let The Music Play". Also includes the beautiful ballad "Love Goes All The Way" and the US hit "Prove Me Right" - a soulful dance number proving Shannon has an excellent soul voice. Packaged in a highly provocative sleeve featuring Shannon in both evening dress and (near) undress. Not to be missed!
Album: released on Club, Jun'87 by Phonogram Records. Dist: Polygram

Cassette: released on Club, Jun'87 by Phonogram Records. Dist: Polygram

Shannon, Del

20 ROCK 'N' ROLL HITS.
Album: released on EMI (Germany), '83 by EMI Records. Dist: Conifer

CHEAP LOVE.
Single (7"): released on Demon, May'83 Dist: Jazz Music, Projection

DEL SHANNON.
Album: released on Dakota (Countdown series), Oct'82 by Dakota Records. Dist: PRT

Cassette: released on Dakota (Countdown series), Oct'82 by Dakota Records. Dist: PRT

DROP DOWN AND GET ME.
Album: released on Demon, May'83 Dist: Jazz Music, Projection

HATS OFF TO LARRY.
Single (7"): released on Juke Box, Mar'82

Single (7"): released on Old Gold, Apr'83 by Old Gold Records. Dist: Lightning, Jazz Music, Spartan, Counterpoint

I GO TO PIECES.
Album: released on Edsel, Apr'86 by Demon Records. Dist: Pinnacle, Jazz Music, Projection

KEEP SEARCHIN'.
Single (7"): released on Old Gold, Apr'83 by Old Gold Records. Dist: Lightning, Jazz Music, Spartan, Counterpoint

LITTLE TOWN FLIRT.
Single (7"): released on Old Gold, Apr'83 by Old Gold Records. Dist: Lightning, Jazz Music, Spartan, Counterpoint

LIVE IN ENGLAND.
Album: released on Fame (United Artists), May'82 by Music For Pleasure Records. Dist: EMI

Cassette: released on Fame (United Artists), May'82 by Music For Pleasure Records. Dist: EMI

ROCK'N'ROLL GREATS.
Tracks: / Hats off to Larry / Lightnin' strikes / Little town flirt / Sunny / Summer in the city / Pied Piper, The / She / Handy man / Swiss maid, The / Hey little girl / Crying / Two kinds of teardrops / Keep searchin' (we'll follow the sun) / What's a matter baby (is it hurting you) / Runaway.
Notes: Hats off to Del Shannon- A Rock 'n' Roll Great! A product of the 60's although previosly a member of the Dovells- Remember "The Bristol Stomp"?- Del Shannon had many hits including "Hats Off To Larry", "Little Town Flirt" and of course "Runaway". Side two features highlights of a live concert date and includes many other great Del Shannon Favourites, finishing with a terrific live version of "Runaway". A fabulous sleeve with sleeve notes by Roger St. Pierre.
Album: released on Music For Pleasure, Apr'86 by EMI Records. Dist: EMI

Cassette: released on Music For Pleasure, Apr'86 by EMI Records. Dist: EMI

RUNAWAY.
Tracks: / Runaway / Jody.
Single (7"): released on Old Gold, 30 May'87 by Old Gold Records. Dist: Lightning, Jazz Music, Spartan, Counterpoint

Single (7"): released on JB, Jun'80 by Mr. R&B Records. Dist: Swift

Single (7"): released on London, Mar'81 by London Records. Dist: Polygram

Single (7"): released on Creole, Aug'82 by Creole Records. Dist: Rhino, PRT

Single (7"): released on Old Gold, Apr'83 by Old Gold Records. Dist: Lightning, Jazz Music, Spartan, Counterpoint

RUNAWAY HITS.
Tracks: / Little town flirt / Runaway / Jody / Hats off to Larry / So long baby / Swiss maid / Answer to everything, The / Hey little girl / Cry myself to sleep / Two kinds of tear drops / Kelly / Handy man / Two silouettes / Sue's gotta be mine / Keep searchin' / Stranger in town.
Compact disc: released on Edsel, Nov'86 by Demon Records. Dist: Pinnacle, Jazz Music, Projection

Album: released on Edsel, Mar'84 by Demon Records. Dist: Pinnacle, Jazz Music, Projection

SEA OF LOVE.
Single (7"): released on Demon, Nov'83 Dist: Jazz Music, Projection

SWISS MAID.
Single (7"): released on Old Gold, Apr'83 by Old Gold Records. Dist: Lightning, Jazz Music, Spartan, Counterpoint

Shannon, Jackie De

SKY HIGH.
Cassette: released on Audiotrax, Jul'85 by Audiotrax. Dist: PRT

WINGS OF VICTORY.
Single (7"): released on Audiotrax, Jun'84 by Audiotrax. Dist: PRT

Shannon Jackson, Ronald

MAN DANCE.
Album: released on Antilles, Sep'82 by Island Records. Dist: Polygram

Shannon, Seamus

TRADITIONAL IRISH ACCORDION.
Album: released on Outlet (Ireland), Sep'79

Cassette: released on Outlet (Ireland), Jul'79

Shante, Roxanne

BITE THIS.
Single (7"): released on 10, Nov'85 by 10 Records. Dist: Virgin, EMI

HAVE A NICE DAY.
Tracks: / Have a nice day / Have a nice day (inst).
Single (7"): released on Breakout, Jul'87 by A&M Records. Dist: Polygram

Single (12"): released on Breakout, Jul'87 by A&M Records. Dist: Polygram

Shantung Music Society

MUSIC OF CONFUCIOUS HOMELAND.
Album: released on Lyrichord (USA), Oct'81 by Lyrichord Records (USA). Dist: Flexitron Distributors Ltd

Shanty Crew

SHANTY CREW.
Album: released on Coach House, Mar'85

Cassette: released on Coach House, Mar'85

Shanty Men

SHANTY MEN Various artists (Various Artists).
Album:

Shape Of Finns To Come

SHAPE OF FINNS TO COME Various artists (Various Artists).
Album: released on Cherry Red, '82 by Cherry Red Records. Dist: Pinnacle

Shape Up & Dance

SHAPE UP AND DANCE, VOL 1 (Kendal, Felicity).
Album: released on Lifestyle, '83 by Zomba Records. Dist: CBS, PRT, RCA

Cassette: released on Lifestyle, '83 by Zomba Records. Dist: CBS, PRT, RCA

SHAPE UP AND DANCE, VOL 2 (Rippon, Angela).
Album: released on Lifestyle, '83 by Zomba Records. Dist: CBS, PRT, RCA

Cassette: released on Lifestyle, '83 by Zomba Records. Dist: CBS, PRT, RCA

SHAPE UP AND DANCE, VOL 3 (St.Clair, Isla).
Album: released on Lifestyle, '83 by Zomba Records. Dist: CBS, PRT, RCA

Cassette: released on Lifestyle, '83 by Zomba Records. Dist: CBS, PRT, RCA

SHAPE UP AND DANCE, VOL 4 (Danielle, Suzanne).
Album: released on Lifestyle, '83 by Zomba Records. Dist: CBS, PRT, RCA

Cassette: released on Lifestyle, '83 by Zomba Records. Dist: CBS, PRT, RCA

SHAPE UP AND DANCE, VOL 5 (Brookes, Christina).
Album: released on Lifestyle, '83 by Zomba Records. Dist: CBS, PRT, RCA

Cassette: released on Lifestyle, '83 by Zomba Records. Dist: CBS, PRT, RCA

SHAPE UP AND DANCE, VOL 6 (Lulu).
Album: released on Lifestyle, Mar'84 by Zomba Records. Dist: CBS, PRT, RCA

Cassette: released on Lifestyle, Mar'84 by Zomba Records. Dist: CBS, PRT, RCA

SHAPE UP AND DANCE, VOL 7 (Aston, Jay).
Album: released on Lifestyle, Mar'84 by Zomba Records. Dist: CBS, PRT, RCA

Cassette: released on Lifestyle, Mar'84 by Zomba Records. Dist: CBS, PRT, RCA

SHAPE UP AND DANCE, VOL 8 (Dando, Suzanne).
Album: released on Lifestyle, Mar'84 by Zomba Records. Dist: CBS, PRT, RCA

Cassette: released on Lifestyle, Mar'84 by Zomba Records. Dist: CBS, PRT, RCA

SHAPE UP AND DANCE, VOL 9 (Best, George & Mary Stavin).
Album: released on Lifestyle, '84 by Zomba Records. Dist: CBS, PRT, RCA

Cassette: released on Lifestyle, '84 by Zomba Records. Dist: CBS, PRT, RCA

SHAPE UP AND DANCE, VOL 10 (Boulaye, Patti).
Album: released on Lifestyle, Mar'84 by Zomba Records. Dist: CBS, PRT, RCA

Cassette: released on Lifestyle, Mar'84 by Zomba Records. Dist: CBS, PRT, RCA

Shape Up For..

SHAPE UP FOR MOTHERHOOD Various artists (Various Artists).
Album: released on Lifestyle, '83 by Zomba Records. Dist: CBS, PRT, RCA

Cassette: released on Lifestyle, '83 by Zomba Records. Dist: CBS, PRT, RCA

SHAPE UP FOR SEX Various artists (Various Artists).
Album: released on Lifestyle, '84 by Zomba Records. Dist: CBS, PRT, RCA

Cassette: released on Lifestyle, '84 by Zomba Records. Dist: CBS, PRT, RCA

Shapiro, Helen

Biographical Details: Helen Shapiro was born in Bethnal Green in 1946 and had her fisrt hit at the age of 13, becoming one of the biggest pop stars of the immediately pre-Beatle era. She had eleven hits between 1961 and 1964, including two chart toppers, and starred in films **It's Trad, Dad** (directed by **Richard Lester**) and **Play It Cool** (by **Michael Winner**), both in 1962. She was succesful in clubs, then turned to the stage, including a revival of **Lionel Bart**'s **Oliver!**; more recently she has gigged with **Humphrey Lyttleton** and **George Melley**.

25TH ANNIVERSARY ALBUM, THE.
Tracks: / Walkin' back to happiness / Keep away from other girls / Basin street blues / Don't treat me like a child / It's my party / Little Miss Loenly / She needs company / Stop and you will become aware / Something wonderful / Tell me what he said / Fever / You don't know / Look who it is / St. Louis blues / In my calendar / Let's talk about love / Woe is me / Queen for tonight / Here in your arms / Birth of the blues, The.

Notes: Specially compiled for Music For Pleasure this anniversary album celebrates 25 years of the Music of Helen Shapiro. This album includes eleven chart hits particularly her two No.1's- "You Don't Know" and "Walkin' Back To Happiness". Packaged in a superb sleeve complete with a sleeve note written by Helen's friend, Chris White of Music Week, other featured tracks are "Fever" (her last chart hit) and many blues numbers which Helen still performs to this day at venues up and down the country, including Ronnie Scotts Club.
Album: released on Music For Pleasure, Feb'86 by EMI Records. Dist: EMI

Cassette: released on Music For Pleasure, Feb'86 by EMI Records. Dist: EMI

BEST OF HELEN SHAPIRO.
Album: released on EMI (Holland), '83 by EMI Records. Dist: Conifer

BRICKYARD BLUES.
Single (7"): released on Oval, Jan'84 by Oval Records. Dist: Pinnacle

CRY ME A RIVER.
Single 10": released on Oval, Apr'83 by Oval Records. Dist: Pinnacle

ECHOES OF THE DUKE (Shapiro, Helen & Humphrey Lyttelton & His Band).
Album: released on Calligraph, Feb'85 by Calligraph Records. Dist: PRT

LET YOURSELF GO.
Single (7"): released on Oval, Apr'83 by Oval Records. Dist: Pinnacle

QUALITY OF MERCER, THE.
Album: released on Calligraph, Jun'87 by Calligraph Records. Dist: PRT

STRAIGHTEN UP AND FLY RIGHT.
Album: released on Oval, Jul'83 by Oval Records. Dist: Pinnacle

OPS WITH ME & HELEN HITS OUT.
ouble Album: released on EMI, Aug'83 by MI Records. Dist: EMI

ouble cassette: released on EMI, Aug'83 by MI Records. Dist: EMI

VALKING BACK TO HAPPINESS.
ngle (7"): released on EMI (Holland), Jul'84 EMI Records. Dist: Conifer

YOU DON'T KNOW.
Single (7"): released on Old Gold, Oct'83 by Old Gold Records. Dist: Lightning, Jazz Music, Spartan, Counterpoint

Shapiros

ISOLADE.
Single (7"): released on North Of Watford, Nov'79 by North Of Watford Records. Dist: Wynd-Up Distribution

PERISHED LEATHER.
Single (12"): released on Swim, Mar'85 Dist: Swim Music

Shar

JUNIOR JACKIN'.
Tracks: / Junior jackin' / Junior jackin' dub mix.
Single (12"): released on Debut, Mar'87 by Skratch Music. Dist: PRT

Shara

CAN'T GET OVER YOU.
Tracks: / Can't get over you.
Single (7"): released on Unit 7, Mar'86 by Greensleeves Records. Dist: RCA

Sharazade

REFLECTIONS.
Single (7"): released on Code, Mar'83 by Code Records. Dist: PRT

Single (12"): released on Code, Mar'83 by Code Records. Dist: PRT

Sharif, Omar

TALES OF THE DESERT Spoken Word.
Album: released on Caedmon(USA), '79 by Caedmon (USA) Records. Dist: Gower, Taylors, Discovery

Cassette: released on Caedmon(USA), '79 by Caedmon (USA) Records. Dist: Gower, Taylors, Discovery

Sharing The House..

STAR WARS (Sharing The House With Mother).
Tracks: / Star Wars.
Single (12"): released on Adventures In Clubland, Jul'86 Dist: DMS, RCA

STATIC NATION (Sharing The House With Mother).
Cassette: released on AIC, Nov'86 Dist: Pinnacle, PRT

Sharkey

SHARKEY & HIS KINGS OF DIXIELAND (Sharkey & His Kings of Dixieland).
Album: released on GHB, Jun'86 Dist: Jazz Music, Swift

Sharkey, Feargal

FEARGAL SHARKEY.
Compact disc: released on Virgin, Dec'85 by Virgin Records. Dist: EMI, Virgin Distribution

Tracks: / Good heart, A / You little thief / Someone to somebody.
Video-cassette (VHS): released on Virgin, Apr'86 by Virgin Records. Dist: EMI, Virgin Distribution

GOOD HEART.
Single (7"): released on Virgin, Sep'85 by Virgin Records. Dist: EMI, Virgin Distribution

Single (12"): released on Virgin, Sep'85 by Virgin Records. Dist: EMI, Virgin Distribution

LISTEN TO YOUR FATHER.
Single (7"): released on Charisma, Sep'84 by Virgin Records. Dist: EMI

Single (12"): released on Charisma, Sep'84 by Virgin Records. Dist: EMI

LOVING YOU.
Single (7"): released on Virgin, Jun'85 by Virgin Records. Dist: EMI, Virgin Distribution

Single (12"): released on Virgin, Jun'85 by Virgin Records. Dist: EMI, Virgin Distribution

SOMEONE TO SOMEBODY.
Tracks: / Someone to somebody / Cold water.
Single (7"): released on Virgin, Mar'86 by Virgin Records. Dist: EMI, Virgin Distribution

Single (12"): released on Virgin, Mar'86 by Virgin Records. Dist: EMI, Virgin Distribution

YOU LITTLE THIEF.
Tracks: / You little thief / Living action, The.
Single (7"): released on Virgin, Dec'85 by Virgin Records. Dist: EMI, Virgin Distribution

Single (12"): released on Virgin, Dec'85 by Virgin Records. Dist: EMI, Virgin Distribution

Sharks

PHANTOM ROCKERS.
Album: released on Nervous, Jul'84 by Nervous Records. Dist: Nervous, Rough Trade

Sharks In Italy

PRECIOUS.
Single (7"): released on Clay, Oct'85 by Clay Records. Dist: Pinnacle

TIME.
Single (7"): released on Clay, Nov'84 by Clay Records. Dist: Pinnacle

TIME IS OURS.
Tracks: / Time is ours / Pressure.
Single (7"): released on Bonaire, Sep'86 Dist: RCA, Ariola

Single (12"): released on Bonaire, Oct'86 Dist: RCA, Ariola

Shark Taboo

EVERYONE'S A FREAK.
Album: released on Big Beat, Jan'87 by Ace Records. Dist: Projection, Pinnacle

Album: released on Big Beat, Feb'86 by Ace Records. Dist: Projection, Pinnacle

SECRETS OF A LUNATIC.
Album: released on Crisis, Nov'85 by Prism Records. Dist: Red Rhino, Cartel

Shark Tabu

BIG SELL, THE.
Single (7"): released on Crisis, Oct'85 by Prism Records. Dist: Red Rhino, Cartel

CAGE (EP).
Single (7"): released on Lambs To The Slaughter, May'85 by Prism Records. Dist: Pinnacle, Red Rhino, Cartel

TROINEANN - SIAD.
Single (7"): released on Lambs To The Slaughter, Nov'84 by Prism Records. Dist: Pinnacle, Red Rhino, Cartel

Shark Vegas

YOU HURT ME.
Single (12"): released on Factory, Sep'85 by Factory Records. Dist: Cartel, Pinnacle

Album: released on Virgin, Nov'85 by Virgin Records. Dist: EMI, Virgin Distribution

Cassette: released on Virgin, Nov'85 by Virgin Records. Dist: EMI, Virgin Distribution

Sharma, Shivkumar

MELODIES OF ROMANCE.
Album: released on Gramophone Co. of India, Apr'84 by Gramophone Company Of India, UK Branch. Dist: EMI, Sterns, Triple Earth

Sharmen

THEY MAY BE RIGHT.
Tracks: / They may be right.
Single (12"): released on One Big Guitar, Apr'86 by One Big Guitar Records. Dist: Revolver Distribution, Cartel Distribution, Pinnacle

Sharon

IN YOUR EYES.
Single (7"): released on Starlite, Mar'83 Dist: Swift Distribution, PRT Distribution

Single (12"): released on Starlite, Mar'83 Dist: Swift Distribution, PRT Distribution

SHARON IN SONG.
Album: released on Topspin (Ireland), Mar'77 Dist: I & B, Outlet, Shannon Distribution, S & P Distribution

Sharp

ENTERTAIN ME.
Tracks: / So say harrah(The emporor's new clothes).
Single (7"): released on Unicorn, Nov'86 Dist: Nine Mile, Cartel

Single (12"): released on Unicorn, Nov'86 Dist: Nine Mile, Cartel

Sharp, Al

POKE, THE/ KEEP ON POKIN.
Single (7"): released on Solid, Jul'82 by Solid Records. Dist: Graduate, Spartan

Single (12"): released on Solid, Jul'82 by Solid Records. Dist: Graduate, Spartan

SAVE YOUR LOVE FOR ME (Sharp, Al & Lucy Brill).
Single (7"): released on Solid, Aug'83 by Solid Records. Dist: Graduate, Spartan

Sharp, Brian

BRIAN SHARP IN JAPAN.
Album: released on Grosvenor, Jun'81 by Grosvenor Records. Dist: Taylors

NIGHTHAWK.
Album: released on Grosvenor, Apr'83 by Grosvenor Records. Dist: Taylors

Cassette: released on Grosvenor, Apr'83 by Grosvenor Records. Dist: Taylors

ORCHESTRAL KEYBOARDS.
Album: released on Grosvenor, May'86 by Grosvenor Records. Dist: Taylors

ORCHESTRALLY YOURS.
Album: released on Grosvenor, Mar'82 by Grosvenor Records. Dist: Taylors

ORCHESTRAL SOUNDS OF BRIAN SHARP.
Album: released on Grosvenor, Jul'79 by Grosvenor Records. Dist: Taylors

ORGAN FIESTA VOL.1 (Sharp, Brian & The Riha Orchestra).
Cassette: released on VFM Cassettes, Jan'85

ORGAN FIESTA VOL.2 (Sharp, Brian & The Riha Orchestra).
Cassette: released on VFM Cassettes, Jan'85

ORGAN FIESTA VOL.3 (Sharp, Brian & The Riha Orchestra).
Cassette: released on VFM, Feb'85 by VFM Records. Dist: Taylors, Wynd-Up Distribution

PERSONAL SELECTION FOR YOU, A.
Cassette: released on Grosvenor, Sep'81 by Grosvenor Records. Dist: Taylors

PLAYS MAINLY HAMMOND.
Album: released on Grosvenor, '74 by Grosvenor Records. Dist: Taylors

WURLITZER WONDERLAND.
Album: released on Grosvenor, Jan'77 by Grosvenor Records. Dist: Taylors

Sharp, Debbie

RISING STAT (ALT MIX).
Single (7"): released on Debut, May'87 by Skratch Music. Dist: PRT

Single (12"): released on Debut, May'87 by Skratch Music. Dist: PRT

Sharp, Dee

MAGICIAN.
Single (7"): released on RCA, May'83 by RCA Records. Dist: RCA, Roots, Swift, Wellard, Chris, I & B, Solomon & Peres Distribution

Single (12"): released on RCA, May'83 by RCA Records. Dist: RCA, Roots, Swift, Wellard, Chris, I & B, Solomon & Peres Distribution

RISING TO THE TOP.
Single (12"): released on Fashion, Jul'83 by Fashion Records. Dist: PRT, Jetstar

Sharpe, Bill

CHANGE YOUR MIND (Sharpe, Bill & Gary Numan).
Single (7"): released on Polydor, Jan'85 by Polydor Records. Dist: Polygram, Polydor

Single (12"): released on Polydor, Jan'85 by Polydor Records. Dist: Polygram, Polydor

FAMOUS PEOPLE.
Tracks: / Famous people (U.S. Remix) / Shuffle, (The) / Remix, remake, remodel / Silhouettes / Peach / Change your mind / Catching a train / Fools in a world of fire / Washed away / Fair weather girl.
Album: released on Polydor, Apr'85 by Polydor Records. Dist: Polygram, Polydor

Cassette: released on Polydor, Apr'85 by Polydor Records. Dist: Polygram, Polydor

Compact disc: released on Polydor, Apr'85 by Polydor Records. Dist: Polygram, Polydor

Sharpe, Cecil

AN HOUR WITH... (Sharpe, Cecil / Ashley Hutchings).
Album: released on Projection, Jun'86

Sharpe, Elliot

VIRTUAL STANCE.
Album: released on Dossier, Feb'87 Dist: Red Rhino, Cartel

Sharpees

BACK TO ZERO.
Single (7"): released on Moonlight, May'82 by Lithon Recording & Music Publishing.

Sharp, Elliott

NOTS.
Album: released on Glass, Mar'82 by Glass Records. Dist: Nine Mile, Rough Trade, Red Rhino, Play It Again Sam

TESSALATION ROW.

Album: released on SST, Aug'87 by SST Records. Dist: Pinnacle

Sharp, Emma

IM A MILLIONAIRE (Sharp, Emma & The Features).
Single (7"): released on Mean, Dec'81 by Mean Records. Dist: Spartan

REMEMBER MY JEALOUSY (Sharp, Emma & The Features).
Single (7"): released on EMI, Jul'83 by EMI Records. Dist: EMI

Sharpe & Numan

NEW THING FROM LONDON TOWN.
Tracks: / New thing from London town / Time to die.
Single (7"): released on Numa, Sep'86 by Numa Records. Dist: PRT Distribution

Single (12"): released on Numa, Sep'86 by Numa Records. Dist: PRT Distribution

Picture disc single: released on Numa, May'86 by Numa Records. Dist: PRT Distribution

Sharpe, Ray

LIVE AT THE BLUEBIRD VOLUME I.
Album: released on Flying High, Oct'86 Dist: Mike's Country Music Room Distribution, Projection

Sharpe, Rocky

COME ON LET'S GO (Sharpe, Rocky & The Replays).
Single (7"): released on Chiswick, Sep'81 by Chiswick Records. Dist: Pinnacle

HEART (Sharpe, Rocky & The Replays).
Single (7"): released on Chiswick, Jun'82 by Chiswick Records. Dist: Pinnacle

IF YOU WANNA BE HAPPY (Sharpe, Rocky & The Replays).
Single (7"): released on Polydor, Feb'83 by Polydor Records. Dist: Polygram, Polydor

SHOUT SHOUT (Sharpe, Rocky & The Replays).
Album: released on Chiswick, Jul'82 by Chiswick Records. Dist: Pinnacle

STOP PLEASE STOP (Sharpe, Rocky & The Replays).
Single (7"): released on Polydor, Jun'83 by Polydor Records. Dist: Polygram, Polydor

YOU'RE THE ONE (Sharpe, Rocky & The Replays).
Single (7"): released on Chiswick, Sep'80 by Chiswick Records. Dist: Pinnacle

Sharples, Bob

WORLD OF ALBERT KETELBEY (Sharples, Bob/New Symphony Orchestra).
Album: released on Decca, '72 by Decca Records. Dist: Polygram

Sharp, Rebby

GREEN STREET.
Single (7"): released on Zensor, Aug'82 by Zensor Records. Dist: Rough Trade

Sharrock, Sonny

GUITAR.
Album: released on Enemy, May'86 by Enemy Records. Dist: Rough Trade, Cadillac

MONKEY POCKIE BOO.
Album: released on Affinity, Sep'79 by Charly Records. Dist: Charly, Cadillac

Shaskeen

BACK TO THE GLEN.
Album: released on Harp(Ireland), Oct'81 by Pickwick Records. Dist: Taylors

Cassette: released on Harp(Ireland), Oct'81 by Pickwick Records. Dist: Taylors

DAWN, THE.
Album: released on Release (Ireland), Jan'78

Cassette: released on Release (Ireland), Jan'78

SHASKEEN.
Album: released on Harp(Ireland), Aug'83 by Pickwick Records. Dist: Taylors

Cassette: released on Harp(Ireland), Aug'83 by Pickwick Records. Dist: Taylors

S-Haters

COME.
Album: released on Midnight Music, Jul'84 by Midnight Music Records. Dist: Rough Trade Distribution, Cartel Distribution

SOLITARY HABIT.
Single (12"): released on Midnight Music, May'84 by Midnight Music Records. Dist: Rough Trade Distribution, Cartel Distribution

Single (7"): released on Midnight Music, May'84 by Midnight Music Records. Dist: Rough Trade Distribution, Cartel Distribution

STRANGE GIRL.
Single (7"): released on Midnight Music, Mar'85 by Midnight Music Records. Dist: Rough Trade Distribution, Cartel Distribution

Shatner, William

FOUNDATIONS-PSYCHOHISTORIANS.
Album: released on Caedmon(USA), Nov'76 by Caedmon (USA) Records. Dist: Gower, Taylors, Discovery

Cassette: released on Caedmon(USA), Nov'76 by Caedmon (USA) Records. Dist: Gower, Taylors, Discovery

MIMSY WERE THE BOROGOVES.
Album: released on Caedmon(USA), Jul'77 by Caedmon (USA) Records. Dist: Gower, Taylors, Discovery

Cassette: released on Caedmon(USA), Jul'77 by Caedmon (USA) Records. Dist: Gower, Taylors, Discovery

Shattered Dreams

NOTHING VENTURED NOTHING GAINED.
Single (7"): released on Epigram, Mar'84 by Epigram Records. Dist: Rough Trade

Shaun & The Sounds

YOU ANGEL YOU.
Single (7"): released on Quasar, Jul'83

Shaver, Billy Joe

HELL RAISERS I love country (Shaver, Billy Joe & Johnny Paycheck).
Tracks: / I'm just an old chunk of coal (but ...) / Old five and dimers like me / Fit to kill and going out in style / When the word was thunderbird / AMTRAK (and ain't coming back) / Oklahoma wind / Saturday night / I been to Georgia on a fast train / Take this job and shove it / She's all I got / Drinkin' and drivin' / I'm the only hell (Mama ever raised) / Fifteen beers / Turnin' off a memory / You better move on / Outlaw's prayer.
Notes: Turnin' off a memory features Merle Haggard
Album: released on CBS, Mar'87 by CBS Records. Dist: CBS

Shavers, Charlie

Biographical Details: Charlie Shavers (1917-71) was one of the most original and popular trumpet players of the Swing Era; he played with the bands of **Tiny Bradshaw** and **Lucky Millinder**, then with the **John Kirby Sextet** from 1937 until 1944 ('the biggest little band in the land'). His best known compositions are **Pastel Blue** (became **Why Begin Again** with words) and **Undecided**, a hit (with words by **Sid Robin**) for **Ella Fitzgerald**, the **Ames Brothers**, etc. He later played with **Tommy Dorsey** and many others.

LIVE.
Album: released on Black & Blue (France), Jun'84 Dist: Swift, Target, Discovery

NOVEMBER 1961 & MARCH 1962 (Shavers, Charlie Quartet).
Album: released on From The Jazz Vault, Oct'80 by Damont Records. Dist: Swift, Taylor, H.R.

TRUMPET MAN.
Album: released on Jazz Horizons, Apr'81 Dist: Jazz Horizons

Shaw, Artie

Biographical Details: Artie Shaw was the other clarinet-playing bandleader of the Swing Era; partisans of Shaw and **Benny Goodman** sometimes had heated discussions. Shaw was born in 1910 and was among the busiest freelance musicians in New York when he formed his own band; after half a dozen hits he had an international smash with **Jerry Gray**'s arrangement of **Cole Porter's Begin The Beguine** '38 (copied straight by **Billy Cotton** in this country); his other big hits were **Frenesi** (arranged by the black American composer **William Grant Still**, with oboe, French horn and strings), **Stardust**, **Dancing In The Dark** and **Summit Ridge Drive**, by the small group the **Gramercy Five**, with **Johnny Guarnieri** on harpsichord; all were named among their all time favourite records by disc jockeys in a Billboard poll in 1956. He employed top musicians like **Tony Pastor** (on tenor sax and novelty vocals), drummer **Buddy Rich**, trumpeters **Billy Butterfield** and **Roy Eldridge**, and at one point **Billie Holiday**. An intelligent and unpredictable man, he frequently got fed up with the music business, finally quit around 1954, but came back fronting a band in the early 1980's. He married seven times and wrote a novel called **I Love You, I Hate You, Drop Dead!** in 1965.

1937-1938,VOLUME 2 (Shaw, Artie & The Rhythm Makers).
Album: released on Swingdom, Nov'86 Dist: Jazz Music Distribution

Cassette: released on Swingdom, Nov'86 Dist: Jazz Music Distribution

1938 BAND IN HI-FI, (THE).
Album: released on Fanfare (USA), Apr'79 Dist: Jazz Music

1949-50, VOL 3 (Shaw, Artie & His Orchestra).
Album: released on Solid Sender, Apr'81 Dist: JSU, Jazz Music

1949, VOL 1 (Shaw, Artie & His Orchestra).
Album: released on Solid Sender, Apr'81 Dist: JSU, Jazz Music

1949, VOL 2 (Shaw, Artie & His Orchestra).
Album: released on Solid Sender, Apr'81 Dist: JSU, Jazz Music

ARTIE SHAW.
Album: released on Bright Orange, Apr'79 Dist: Swift

ARTIE SHAW COLLECTION, (THE).
Album: released on Deja Vu, Aug'85 by Deja Vu Records. Dist: Counterpoint Distribution, Record Services Distribution (Ireland)

Cassette: released on Deja Vu, Aug'85 by Deja Vu Records. Dist: Counterpoint Distribution, Record Services Distribution (Ireland)

ARTIE SHAW & HIS MUSICIANS, 1949.
Album: released on First Heard, Jul'77 by Submarine Records. Dist: Conifer, Taylors

ARTIE SHAW & HIS ORCHESTRA PLAY 22 ORIGINAL RECORDINGS (Shaw, Artie & His Orchestra).
Double Album: released on Hindsight(USA), Jun'84 by Hindsight Records (USA). Dist: Swift, Charly

ARTIE SHAW & HIS ORCHESTRA, 1938, VOL 2 (Shaw, Artie & His Orchestra).
Album: released on London, Apr'80 by London Records. Dist: Polygram

ARTIE SHAW & HIS ORCHESTRA, 1938, VOL 1 (Shaw, Artie & His Orchestra).
Album: released on London, Apr'80 by London Records. Dist: Polygram

ARTIE SHAW & HIS ORCHESTRA (Shaw, Artie & His Orchestra).
Album: released on Premier, May'85 by Premier Records. Dist: CBS

Cassette: released on Premier, May'85 by Premier Records. Dist: CBS

ARTIE SHAW ON THE AIR.
Album: released on Aircheck (USA), Apr'79 Dist: Swift, Jazz Music

Album: released on Sandy Hook, Aug'79

AT THE HOLLYWOOD PALLADIUM.
Album: released on Hep, Aug'86 by H.R. Taylor Records. Dist: Jazz Music, Cadillac Music, JSU, Taylors, Wellard, Chris, Zodiac, Swift, Fast Forward

BEST OF ARTIE SHAW, (THE).
Album: released on RCA, '84 by RCA Records. Dist: RCA, Roots, Swift, Wellard, Chris, I & B, Solomon & Peres Distribution

Cassette: released on RCA, '84 by RCA Records. Dist: RCA, Roots, Swift, Wellard, Chris, I & B, Solomon & Peres Distribution

BLUE INTERLUDE.
Album: released on Pathe MarconiFrance), Dec'84

Cassette: released on Pathe MarconiFrance), Dec'84

BORN TO SWING (Shaw, Artie & His Orchestra).
Album: released on Jazz Live, Apr'81

CLARINET MAGIC.
Album: released on Musicraft, Jan'80

DEUX GRANDES ANNEES (1938-39).
Double Album: released on RCA (France), '83 by RCA Records. Dist: Discovery

HOLLYWOOD PALLADIUM.
Album: released on Hep, Apr'81 by H.R. Taylor Records. Dist: Jazz Music, Cadillac Music, JSU, Taylors, Wellard, Chris, Zodiac, Swift, Fast Forward

I CAN'T GET STARTED (Shaw, Artie & His Gramercy Five).
Album: released on Verve (USA), Sep'81 by Polydor. Dist: Polygram

INDISPENSABLE ARTIE SHAW, VOLS. 5/6 (1944-45).
Tracks: / Lady / Jumpin' on the merry-go-round / I'll never be the same / S'wonderful / Bedford drive / Grabtown grapple, The / Sad sack, The / Little jazz / Tea for two / Summertime / Time on my hands / Foggy day, A / Man I love, The / I could write a book / Thrill of a lifetime / Lucky number / Lucky number / Love walked on / Soon / Natch / They can't take that away from me / Someone to watch over me / Things are looking up / Maid with the flaccid air, The / No one but you / Dancing on the ceiling / I can't get started with you / Just floatin' along / I can't escape from you / Scuttlebutt / Gentle grifter, The / Mysterioso / Hop, skip and jump.
Double Album: released on RCA, Jan'87 by RCA Records. Dist: RCA, Roots, Swift, Wellard, Chris, I & B, Solomon & Peres Distribution

Double cassette: released on RCA, Jan'87 by RCA Records. Dist: RCA, Roots, Swift, Wellard, Chris, I & B, Solomon & Peres Distribution

INDISPENSABLE ARTIE SHAW VOLS 1/2 (1938-1939).
Tracks: / Begin the beguine (from 'Jubilee') / Indian love call (from Rose-Marie) / Comin' on / Back bay shuffle / Any old time / I can't believe that you're in love with me / Non-stop light / What is this thing called love (from Wake up and dream) / Copenhagen / Softly, as in a morning sunrise (from New moon) / It had to be you / My heart stood still (from Connecticut Yankee) / Rosalie (from Rosalie) / Rose room / This is it (from Stars in your eyes) / Deep purple / Prosschai (Goodbye, goodbye) / I'm coming, Virginia (from Africana) / Snug as a bug in a rug (from Gracie Allen murder case) / One foot in the groove / Out of nowhere / I can't afford to dream (from Yokel boy) / Serenade to a savage / You're the lucky guy / Nightmare (Theme) / Sobbin' blues / Together / Carioca (from Flying down to Rio) / At sundown / I've got my eyes on you / Sweet Sue, just you / St. Louis blues.
Notes: Monophonic recording.
Double Album: released on Jazz Tribune (USA), Sep'86 Dist: Discovery

Double cassette: released on Jazz Tribune (USA), Sep'86 Dist: Discovery

INDISPENSABLE VOL. 3/4 (Shaw, Artie & His Orchestra).
Tracks: / Frenesi / King for a day / Special delivery stomp / Summit ridge drive / Chantez-les bas / Stardust / Blues / What is there to say? / Who's excited? / Prelude in C major / When the quail come back to San Quentin / Concerto for clarinet / Moonglow / Confessin' / Love me a little little / Beyond the blue horizon / Blues in the night / Rockin' chair / Take your shoes off, baby / Solid Sam / Just kiddin' around / St. James Infirmary / Deuces wild / Someone's rocking my dreamboat / Carnival / Needlenose / Two in one blues / Sometimes I feel like a motherless child.
Notes: Monophonic recording.
Double Album: released on Jazz Tribune, Jun'86 Dist: Discovery

Double cassette: released on Jazz Tribune, Jun'86 Dist: Discovery

Double Album: released on Jazz Tribune (USA), Sep'86 Dist: Discovery

Double Album: released on RCA (France), '83 by RCA Records. Dist: Discovery

MAGIC WITH THE BIG BANDS & STRINGS, VOL 1.
Album: released on Musicraft (USA), Apr'79 by Discovery Records (USA). Dist: Flexitron Distributors Ltd, Swift Distribution

MELODY & MADNESS, VOL 2.
Album: released on Nostalgia (Sweden), '82 by Wellard, Chris Distribution. Dist: Wellard, Chris Distribution

Cassette: released on Nostalgia (Sweden), '82 by Wellard, Chris Distribution. Dist: Wellard, Chris Distribution

MELODY & MADNESS, VOL 1.
Album: released on Nostalgia (Sweden), '82 by Wellard, Chris Distribution. Dist: Wellard, Chris Distribution

MELODY & MADNESS, VOL 4.
Album: released on Nostalgia (Sweden), '82 by Wellard, Chris Distribution. Dist: Wellard, Chris Distribution

MELODY & MADNESS, VOL 5.
Album: released on Nostalgia (Sweden), '82 by Wellard, Chris Distribution. Dist: Wellard, Chris Distribution

MELODY & MADNESS, VOL 3.
Album: released on Nostalgia (Sweden), '82 by Wellard, Chris Distribution. Dist: Wellard, Chris Distribution

Cassette: released on Nostalgia (Sweden), '82 by Wellard, Chris Distribution. Dist: Wellard, Chris Distribution

ORIGINAL SOUNDS OF THE SWING ERA, VOL 7.
Album: released on RCA (Germany), '83

PIED PIPER, (THE) (Shaw, Artie & His Orchestra).
Album: released on First Heard, Jun'81 by Submarine Records. Dist: Conifer, Taylors

RHYTHM MAKERS (Shaw, Artie & His Orchestra).
Album: released on Magic, Jan'87 Dist: Jazz

Music, Submarine, Swift, Chris Wellard, Conifer

Cassette: released on Magic, Jan'87 Dist: Jazz Music, Submarine, Swift, Chris Wellard, Conifer

SONG OF INDIA.
Compact disc: released on Dance Band Days, Jul'87 Dist: Geoff's Records International

SWING GOES ON, VOL 3.
Album: released on EMI (Germany), '83 by EMI Records. Dist: Conifer

SWINGING BIG BANDS, 1938-45, VOL 1.
Album: released on Joker Import, Apr'81

SWINGING BIG BANDS, 1938-40, VOL 2.
Album: released on Joker Import, Apr'81

THIS IS ARTIE SHAW.
Tracks: / Begin the beguine / Indian love call / Any old time / Back bay shuffle / Deep in a dream / It had to be you / Jungle drums / Donkey Serenade, (The) / Deep purple / All the things you are / Frenesi / Cross your heart / Summit ridge drive / Temptation / Star dust / My blue heaven / Smoke gets in your eyes / Moonglow / Dancing in the dark.
Album: released on RCA, Jul'86 by RCA Records. Dist: RCA, Roots, Swift, Wellard, Chris, I & B, Solomon & Peres Distribution

Cassette: released on RCA, Jul'86 by RCA Records. Dist: RCA, Roots, Swift, Wellard Chris, I & B, Solomon & Peres Distribution

Album: released on RCA (Germany), '83

TRAFFIC JAM.
Album: released on Astan (USA), Mar'85

UNCOLLECTED ARTIE SHAW & HIS ORCHESTRA, VOL 5.
Album: released on Hindsight(USA), Apr'85 by Hindsight Records (USA). Dist: Swift, Charly

Shaw, Charles "Bobo"

CHARLES 'BOBO' SHAW.
Album: released on Muse (Import), '81

Shaw, Francis

MARY'S THEME (FROM JAMAICA INN) (Shaw, Francis & The L.S.O.).
Single (7"): released on Peach River, Apr'83 by Peach River Records. Dist: PRT

Shaw, Gene Sextet

DEBUT IN BLUES.
Tracks: / Debut in blues / Karachi / Gentle Princess, (The) / When sunny gets blue / Thieves carnival / Not too cool / Who knows? / Travelog.
Album: released on Arco, '86 by Charly Records. Dist: Charly

Shaw, George Bernard

ARMS & THE MAN A play in three acts (Various Artists).
Cassette: released on Talking Tape Company, '84 by Talking Tape Company Records.

PYGMALION with Alec McCowen & Diana Rigg.
Double cassette: released on Argo (Spokenword), Jul'82 by Decca Records. Dist: Polygram

Shaw, Graham

I AM THE MINSTREL.
Album: released on Tradition, '78 Dist: JSU, Cassion Distribution, Celtic Music, Jazz Music, Projection, Roots Records

Shaw, Martin

CROSS MY HEART.
Single (7"): released on Nouveau Music, Jan'84 Dist: PRT Distribution

Shaw, Milt

PRECIOUS LITTLE THING CALLED LOVE, A (Shaw, Milt & His Orch./Moe Baer & His Wardman Park Orch.).
Album: released on Collectors Items, Feb'87 Dist: Jazz Music, Swift, Chris Wellard

Shawnie, G

MISSION IMPOSSIBLE.
Single (7"): released on Mute, Jul'87 Dist: Spartan Distribution, Rough Trade Distribution, Cartel Distribution

Single (12"): released on Rhythm King, Jul'87 Dist: Rough Trade, Cartel

Shaw, Nina

I BELIEVED IN YOU.
Single (7"): released on Creole, Feb'83 by Creole Records. Dist: Rhino, PRT

Single (12"): released on Creole, Feb'83 by Creole Records. Dist: Rhino, PRT

LOOK AT ME NOW.
Single (7"): released on Red Bus, Apr'84 by Red Bus Records. Dist: PRT

STOP IF YOU LOVE.
Single (7"): released on Ecstasy, Sep'83 by Creole Records. Dist: CBS

Single (12"): released on Ecstasy, Sep'83 by Creole Records. Dist: CBS

Shaw, Phillipe

HOVIS BISCUITS, THE (Shaw, Phillipe & The Fotokopies).
Album: released on DUP, Aug'80

Shaw, Robert

TEXAS BARRELHOUSE BLUES.
Album: released on Arhoolie, May'81 by Arhoolie Records. Dist: Projection, Topic, Jazz Music, Swift, Roots

Shaw, Roland Orchestra

LARCANGE PLAYS TRENET (see Larcange,Maurice/Roland Shaw & His Orchestra).

Shaw, Sandie

Biographical Details: Sandie Shaw's real name is **Sandra Goodrich.** She was born in 1947 in Dagenham. Helped by **Adam Faith** and then the songs of **Chris Andrews**, she became a pop star in the mid-60's, winning the Eurovision Song Contest in 1967 with **Puppet On A String**, in a bouncy style which was widely imitated. She guested on **Heaven 17**'s album **Music of Quality & Distinction** in '81, had a couple of minor hits and played succesful concerts in London in 1986.

20 GOLDEN PIECES OF SANDIE SHAW.
Tracks: / One note samba / Yes my darling daughter / Ne me quitte pas (If you go away) / Everytime we say goodbye / I get a kick out of you / Time after time / You've not changed / Today / Show me / Those were the days / Reviewing the situation / Mama roux / Maybe I'm amazed / Rose garden (I never promised you a -) / Monsieur Dupont / Anytime, anywhere / Think it all over / What now my love / Scarborough fair / Tonight in Tokyo.
Notes: (P) 1986 Bulldog Records. (C) 1986 Bulldog Records
Album: released on Bulldog, Apr'86 by Bulldog Records. Dist: President Distribution, Spartan, Swift, Taylor, H.R.

Cassette: released on Bulldog, Apr'86 by Bulldog Records. Dist: President Distribution, Spartan, Swift, Taylor, H.R.

ALWAYS SOMETHING THERE TO REMIND ME.
Single (7"): released on Old Gold, Jul'82 by Old Gold Records. Dist: Lightning, Jazz Music, Spartan, Counterpoint

ARE YOU READY TO BE HEARTBROKEN?.
Tracks: / Are you ready to be heartbroken? / Steven (You don't eat meat) / Hand in glove*.
Single (7"): released on Polydor, May'86 by Polydor Records. Dist: Polygram, Polydor

Single (12"): released on Polydor, May'86 by Polydor Records. Dist: Polygram, Polydor

CHOSE LIFE.
Album: released on Palace, May'83 Dist: PVG

FREDERICK.
Tracks: / Frederick / Go Johnny go / Girl don't come*.
Single (7"): released on Polydor, Jul'86 by Polydor Records. Dist: Polygram, Polydor

Single (12"): released on Polydor, Jul'86 by Polydor Records. Dist: Polygram, Polydor

GOLDEN HOUR OF GREATEST HITS.
Album: released on Golden Hour, '74 by PRT Records. Dist: PRT

HAND IN GLOVE.
Single (7"): released on Rough Trade, May'84 by Rough Trade Records. Dist: Rough Trade Distribution, Cartel Distribution

Single (12"): released on Rough Trade, May'84 by Rough Trade Records. Dist: Rough Trade Distribution, Cartel Distribution

PUPPET ON A STRING.
Single (7"): released on Old Gold, Jul'82 by Old Gold Records. Dist: Lightning, Jazz Music, Spartan, Counterpoint

Single (7"): released on Flashback, Jul'80 by PRT Records. Dist: PRT

REMINDING YOU.
Album: released on PRT, May'83 by PRT Records. Dist: PRT

Cassette: released on PRT, May'83 by PRT Records. Dist: PRT

WISH I WAS.
Single (7"): released on Palace, May'83 Dist: PVG

Shaw, Thomas

BORN IN TEXAS.
Album: released on Advent (US), May'79 Dist: Swift

Shaw, Tina

SEXUAL ATTRACTION (Shaw, Tina & The Sexual Attractions).
Single (7"): released on Creole, Mar'85 by Creole Records. Dist: Rhino, PRT

Shaw, Tommy

GIRLS WITH GUNS.
Album: released on A&M, Oct'84 by A&M Records. Dist: Polygram

Cassette: released on A&M, Oct'84 by A&M Records. Dist: Polygram

Shaw, Woody

Biographical Details: American jazzman Woody Shaw was born in 1944 in North Carolina. He plays trumpet and flugelhorn and has become a highly regarded composer. He gigged with **Chick Corea, Eric Dolphy, Art Blakey** and many others. He has become a highly regarded composer and bandleader since finding his own voice in the 1970's.

CONCERT ENSEMBLE.
Album: released on Muse, May'81 by Peerless Records. Dist: Lugtons Distributors

ICHI-BAN (Shaw, Woody/Jun. Cook/R. Matthews/S. James/Guilherme).
Album: released on Timeless(import), May'81 Dist: Cadillac

IRON MEN, THE.
Album: released on Muse (Import), '81

LITTLE RED FANTASY.
Album: released on Muse (Import), May'81

LONELY SCHOOL.
Single (7"): released on A&M, Jan'85 by A&M Records. Dist: Polygram

Single (12"): released on A&M, Jan'85 by A&M Records. Dist: Polygram

LOVE DANCE.
Album: released on Muse (Import), May'81

MOONTRANE, THE.
Album: released on Muse (Import), Apr'81

SETTING STANDARDS.
Tracks: / There is no greater love / All the way / Spiderman blues / Touch of your lips / What's new / When lore is new.
Notes: Woody Shaw - flugelhorn Cedar Walton - piano Buster Williams - bass Victor Jones - drums
Album: released on Muse Jazz (USA), Jan'86

Shazam

LOGAN'S RUN.
Single (7"): released on Bulldog, '78 by Bulldog Records. Dist: President Distribution, Spartan, Swift, Taylor, H.R.

She

NEVER SURRENDER.
Single (7"): released on Neat, May'85 by Neat Records. Dist: Pinnacle, Neat

Single (12"): released on Neat, May'85 by Neat Records. Dist: Pinnacle, Neat

Shea, George Beverley

GEORGE BEVERLY SHEA AND FRIENDS.
Notes: Friends include The Gaither Trio, Evie, Cliff Barrows, Amy Grant, Sandi Patti & Billy Graham.
Album: released on Word, Nov'86 by Word Records. Dist: Word Distribution, CBS

Cassette: released on Word, Nov'86 by Word Records. Dist: Word Distribution, CBS

HYMNS YOU KNOW & LOVE.
Album: released on RCA International, Mar'81

Cassette: released on RCA International, Mar'81

OLD RUGGED CROSS, THE.
Album: released on Word, May'82 by Word Records. Dist: Word Distribution. CBS

Cassette: released on Word, May'82 by Word Records. Dist: Word Distribution, CBS

SINGS 20 BEST LOVED HYMNS.
Album: by Pilgrim Records. Dist: Rough Trade, Cartel

Album: released on RCA, Apr'84 by RCA Records. Dist: RCA, Roots, Swift, Wellard, Chris, I & B, Solomon & Peres Distribution

Cassette: released on RCA, Apr'84 by RCA Records. Dist: RCA, Roots, Swift, Wellard, Chris, I & B, Solomon & Peres Distribution

Shearer, John

CHILDREN'S PARTY TIME.
Album: released on Country House, Sep'79 by BGS Productions Ltd. Dist: Taylor, H.R., Record Merchandisers Distribution, Pinnacle, Sounds of Scotland Records

Shearing, George

Biographical Details: Pianist George Shearing was born blind in London in 1919. He was already a highly regarded jazz musician when he went to the USA in 1947, sponsored by British-born critic/composer/producer **Leonard Feather**; in 1949 he invented a much imitated style with his quintet of piano, guitar, vibes, bass and drums, playing in the bop-flavoured 'locked hands' chordal style. He has been one of the mmost popular jazz musicians in the world ever since.

500 MILES HIGH.
Album: released on MPS Jazz, Apr'81

ALONE TOGETHER (Shearing, George & Marian McPartland).
Album: released on Concord Jazz, Dec'81 by Concord Jazz Records (USA). Dist: IMS, Polygram

AN ELEGANT EVENING (Shearing, George & Mel Torme).
Tracks: / I'll be seeing you / Love and the moon / Oh, you crazy moon / No moon at all / After the waltz is over / This time the dream's on me / Last night, when we were young / You changed my life / I had the craziest dream / Darn that dream / Brigg fair / My foolish heart / You're driving me crazy.
Notes: George Shearing - piano Mel Torme - vocals No other accompaniment Recorded March 1985
Personnel: George Shearing - piano / Mel Torme - vocals. Recorded in March 1985
Album: released on Concord Jazz(USA), Feb'86 by Concord Jazz Records (USA). Dist: IMS, Polygram

Cassette: released on Concord Jazz(USA), Feb'86 by Concord Jazz Records (USA). Dist: IMS, Polygram

Compact disc: released on Concord Jazz(USA), Jul'87 by Concord Jazz Records (USA). Dist: IMS, Polygram
Cat. no: **CCD 4294**

AN EVENING WITH (Shearing, George & Mel Torme).
Tracks: / All God's chillun got rhythm / Born to be blue / Give me the simple life / Good morning heartache / Manhattan hoedown / You'd be so nice to come home to / Nightingale sang in Berkeley Square, A / Love / It might as well be spring / Lullaby of birdland.
Notes: Personnel: George Shearing- Piano Mel Torme-vocals Brian Torf-bass
Compact disc: released on Concord Jazz(USA), Mar'87 by Concord Jazz Records (USA). Dist: IMS, Polygram

BEAUTY AND THE BEAT (Shearing, George & Peggy Lee).
Album: released on Capitol T (USA), Jun'83 Dist: Conifer

CHAMPAGNE EVENING (Shearing, George & Mel Torme).
Album: released on Concord Jazz, Aug'82 by Concord Jazz Records (USA). Dist: IMS, Polygram

Cassette: released on Concord Jazz, Aug'82 by Concord Jazz Records (USA). Dist: IMS, Polygram

EVENING AT CHARLIE'S, (AN) (Shearing, George & Mel Torme).
Album: released on Concord Jazz, Sep'84 by Concord Jazz Records (USA). Dist: IMS, Polygram

Cassette: released on Concord Jazz, Sep'84 by Concord Jazz Records (USA). Dist: IMS, Polygram

FIRST EDITION (Shearing, George & Jim Hall).
Album: released on Concord Jazz, Apr'82 by Concord Jazz Records (USA). Dist: IMS, Polygram

Cassette: released on Concord Jazz, Apr'82 by Concord Jazz Records (USA). Dist: IMS, Polygram

GETTING IN THE SWING OF THINGS (Shearing, George Trio).
Album: released on MPS Jazz, May'81

GRAND PIANO.
Tracks: / When a woman loves a man / It never entered my mind / Mack the knife / Nobody else but me / Imitations / Taking a chance on love / If I had you / How insensitive / Easy to love / While we're young.
Album: released on Concord Jazz(USA), Nov'85 by Concord Jazz Records (USA). Dist: IMS, Polygram

Cassette: released on Concord Jazz(USA), Nov'85 by Concord Jazz Records (USA). Dist: IMS, Polygram

Compact disc: released on Concord Jazz(USA), Sep'86 by Concord Jazz Records (USA). Dist: IMS, Polygram

IN CONCERT AT THE PAVILION (Shearing, George & Brian Torff).
Album: released on Concord Jazz, Nov'80 by Concord Jazz Records (USA). Dist: IMS, Polygram

IT'S EASY TO REMEMBER.
Album: released on Jasmine, Feb'83 by Jasmine Records. Dist: Counterpoint, Lugtons, Taylor, H.R., Wellard, Chris, Swift, Cadillac

JAZZ CONCERT.
Tracks: / Walkin' / Love is just around the corner / I cover the waterfront / Love walked in / There with you / Bel Aire.
Album: released on Capitol, Jun'86 by Capitol Records. Dist: EMI

Cassette: released on Capitol, Jun'86 by Capitol Records. Dist: EMI

LET THERE BE LOVE (Shearing, George & Nat King Cole).
Album: released on Music For Pleasure, Apr'83

Cassette: released on Music For Pleasure, Apr'83

LIGHT, AIRY AND SWINGING.
Album: released on MPS Jazz, May'81

LIVE AT THE CAFE CARLYLE (Shearing, George & Don Thompson).
Album: released on Concord Jazz, Sep'84 by Concord Jazz Records (USA). Dist: IMS, Polygram

Cassette: released on Concord Jazz, Sep'84 by Concord Jazz Records (USA). Dist: IMS, Polygram

MANY FACETS OF GEORGE SHEARING, (THE).
Album: released on MPS Jazz, May'81

MORE GRAND PIANO (solo piano).
Tracks: / My silent love / Change partners / My favourite things / You don't know what love is / Ramona / People / East of the sun / I can't get started / Dream / Wind in the willow.
Album: released on Concord Jazz(USA), Jul'87 by Concord Jazz Records (USA). Dist: IMS, Polygram

Cassette: released on Concord Jazz(USA), Jul'87 by Concord Jazz Records (USA). Dist: IMS, Polygram

Compact disc: released on Concord Jazz(USA), Jul'87 by Concord Jazz Records (USA). Dist: IMS, Polygram

MUSIC OF COLE PORTER, THE (Shearing, George / Barry Tuckwell).
Tracks: / I concentrate on you / Everything I love / I've got you under my skin / Easy to love / In the still of the night / Every time we say goodbye / But in the morning, no / So in love / After you / All through the night / Do I love you?.
Album: released on Concord Jazz(USA), Oct'86 by Concord Jazz Records (USA). Dist: IMS, Polygram

Cassette: released on Concord Jazz(USA), Oct'86 by Concord Jazz Records (USA). Dist: IMS, Polygram

Compact disc: released on Concord Jazz(USA), Oct'86 by Concord Jazz Records (USA). Dist: IMS, Polygram

MY SHIP.
Album: released on MPS Jazz, May'81

NAT COLE SINGS, GEORGE SHEARING PLAYS (Shearing, George & Nat King Cole).
Album: released on Capitol, May'78 by Capitol Records. Dist: EMI

Cassette: released on Capitol, May'78 by Capitol Records. Dist: EMI

SOLO PIANO-MY SHIP.
Tracks: / My ship / Happy days are here again / When I fall in love / Londonderry air / April in Paris / Entertainer, The / Tenderly / How deep is the ocean / Autumn in New York / Greensleeves / Send in the clowns.
Notes: A solo performance by the great George Shearing.A programme of popular standards that will appear to all good music lovers. Surprise track 'Send in the Clowns' features Shearing playing and singing.
Compact disc: released on MPS Jazz, May'87

TOP DRAWER (Shearing, George & Mel Torme).
Album: released on Concord Jazz, Jul'83 by Concord Jazz Records (USA). Dist: IMS, Polygram

Cassette: released on Concord Jazz, Jul'83 by Concord Jazz Records (USA). Dist: IMS, Polygram

WINDOW.
Album: released on MPS Jazz, May'81

YOUNG GEORGE SHEARING, (THE).
Album: released on Jasmine, Feb'83 by Jasmine Records. Dist: Counterpoint, Lugtons, Taylor, H.R., Wellard, Chris, Swift, Cadillac

Shear, Jules

DEMO-ITIS.
Album: released on Enigma, Feb'87 by Enigma Records. Dist: Rough Trade, Cartel, EMI

WHISPERING YOUR NAME.
Single (7"): released on EMI America, May'83 by EMI Records. Dist: EMI

Shearston, Gary

I GET A KICK OUT OF YOU.
Single (7"): released on Old Gold, Jul'82 by Old Gold Records. Dist: Lightning, Jazz Music, Spartan, Counterpoint

She Captured

NEW START.
Tracks: / New start.
Single (7"): released on Eve, Mar'86 Dist: Hidden Target Records

Sheeba

HEY EVERYBODY.
Single (7"): released on Multitone, Dec'81

HOROSCOPES.
Single (7"): released on Ritz, Apr'81 by Ritz Records. Dist: Spartan

NEXT NIGHT.
Single (7"): released on Ritz, Aug'81 by Ritz Records. Dist: Spartan

Sheehan, Henry

FADE.
Single (7"): released on Big H, Feb'82

Sheena...

SHEENA: QUEEN OF THE JUNGLE Original soundtrack (Sheena: Queen Of The Jungle).
Album: released on SPI Milan (France), May'85 Dist: Silva Screen

Sheen, Stevie

ALMOST LIVE AT THE VENUE, TOKYO JOE'S CAN PASTILLA.
Album: released on Tollo, Mar'84

Sheer Ecstasy

SHEER ECSTASY Various artists (Various Artists).
Album: released on Ecstasy, Nov'84 by Creole Records. Dist: CBS

Cassette: released on Ecstasy, Nov'84 by Creole Records. Dist: CBS

SHEER ECSTASY (VOL. 2) Various Artists (Various Artists).
Tracks: / Rhythm of your love (Re-mix) / Living for the city / Sizzlin' / With you I could have it all / I don't wanna fall in love again / AM-FM / So shy / Love is like an itching in my heart / Big time operator / Spotlite of love.
Album: released on Ecstasy, May'86 by Creole Records. Dist: CBS

Cassette: released on Ecstasy, May'86 by Creole Records. Dist: CBS

Sheer Elegance

LIFE IS TOO SHORT, GIRL.
Single (7"): released on Old Gold, Jan'85 by Old Gold Records. Dist: Lightning, Jazz Music, Spartan, Counterpoint

Sheer Gold

NO MORE WILL I ROAM.
Single (7"): released on Negro, Dec'84 by Negro Records. Dist: Jetstar

Shequi

AROUND THE WORLD FOR SPORT.
Album: released on Celtic Music, Feb'81 by Celtic Music Distribution. Dist: Celtic Music, Jazz Music, Projection, Roots

IN THE WIND.
Album: released on Highway, Jan'85 by Highway Records. Dist: Roots, Projection, Ross

Sheik, Kid

KID SHEIK & JOHN HANDY (Sheik, Kid & John Handy).
Cassette: released on Nola, Mar'87 Dist: JSU, Jazz Music, Cadillac, Chris Wellard

SHEIK OF ARABY, (THE) (Sheik, Kid Storyville Ramblers).
Album: released on 504, Sep'86 by 504 Records. Dist: Chris Wellard, Jazz Music

Cassette: released on 504, Sep'86 by 504 Records. Dist: Chris Wellard, Jazz Music

Sheila

LITTLE DARLIN'.
Album: released on Carrere America (USA), Dec'81 by Polygram.

Cassette: released on Carrere America (USA), Dec'81 by Polygram.

Sheila B. Devotion

KING OF THE WORLD.
Album: released on Carrere, Jul'80 by Carrere Records. Dist: PRT, Spartan

Cassette: released on Carrere, Jul'80 by Carrere Records. Dist: PRT, Spartan

Single (7"): released on Carrere, Jun'80 by Carrere Records. Dist: PRT, Spartan

Single (12"): released on Carrere, Jun'80 by Carrere Records. Dist: PRT, Spartan

LITTLE DARLIN'.
Single (7"): released on Carrere, Oct'81 by Carrere Records. Dist: PRT, Spartan

SPACER.
Single (12"): released on Carrere, Jun'84 by Carrere Records. Dist: PRT, Spartan

Sheila E

BELLE OF ST. MARK, THE.
Single (7"): released on Warner Bros., Jan'85 by Warner Bros Records. Dist: WEA

GLAMOROUS LIFE, THE.
Album: released on Warner Bros., Aug'84 by Warner Bros Records. Dist: WEA

Cassette: released on Warner Bros., Aug'84 by Warner Bros Records. Dist: WEA

HOLD ME.
Tracks: / Hold me / World is high, The.
Single (7"): released on Paisley Park (usa), Feb'87 by WEA Records. Dist: WEA

Single (12"): released on Paisley Park (usa), Feb'87 by WEA Records. Dist: WEA

LIVE ROMANCE 1600.
Tracks: / Sister fate / Erotic city / Toy box / Love bizarre, A / Merci for the speed of a mad clown in summer / Holly rock / Glamorous life, The / Love bizarre, A.
Notes: Special Guest Prince
Video-cassette (VHS): released on PMI, Nov'86 by PMI Records. Dist: EMI

Video-cassette [Betamax]: released on PMI, Nov'86 by PMI Records. Dist: EMI

LOVE BIZARRE, (A).
Tracks: / Love bizarre, (A) / Love bizarre, (A) (Part 2) / Save the people".
Notes: Third track on 12" version only.
Single (7"): released on Paisley Park (usa), Jan'86 by WEA Records. Dist: WEA

Single (12"): released on Paisley Park (usa), Jan'86 by WEA Records. Dist: WEA

LOVE BIZARRE,A.
Single (7"): released on Warner Bros., Oct'85 by Warner Bros Records. Dist: WEA

ROMANCE 1600.
Tracks: / Sister fate / Dear Michael Angelo / Love bizarre, (A) / Toy box / Yellow / Romance 1600 / Merci for the speed of a mad clown in summer / Bedtime story.
Compact disc: released on Warner Bros., Dec'85 by Warner Bros Records. Dist: WEA

Album: released on Warner Bros., Aug'85 by Warner Bros Records. Dist: WEA

Cassette: released on Warner Bros., Aug'85 by Warner Bros Records. Dist: WEA

SHEILA E.
Tracks: / One day (I'm gonna make you mine) / Wednesday like a river / Touch me / Faded photographs / Koo koo / Pride and passion / Boy's club / Soul salsa / Hon E. man / Love on a blue train.
Album: released on Paisley Park (usa), Feb'87 by WEA Records. Dist: WEA

Cassette: released on Paisley Park (usa), Feb'87 by WEA Records. Dist: WEA

Compact disc: released on Warner Bros., Feb'87 by Warner Bros Records. Dist: WEA

Sheila Shallot

SHEILA SHALLOT & BENNY various artists (Various Artists).
Cassette: released on Tell-A-Tale, '84 by Pickwick Records. Dist: Spartan-Taylors Distribution

Sheldon, Jack

BLUES IN THE NIGHT (Sheldon, Jack & The Swedish All Stars).
Album: released on Phontastic, May'86 Dist: Wellard, Chris

JACK SHELDON QUARTET, THE.
Album: released on Concord Jazz(USA), Nov'83 by Concord Jazz Records (USA). Dist: IMS, Polygram

Sheller, William

QUARTUORS.
Album: released on Another Side, Dec'84 by Les Disques Du Crepuscule Records. Dist: Rough Trade, Cartel

Shelley

POETRY IN MOTION/SAVOIRE FAIRE.
Single (7"): released on Impact, Sep'82 by Ace Records. Dist: Rough Trade, Pinnacle, Swift, Backs, Counterpoint, Jungle, Hotshot, Cartel

Shelley, Anne

INTRODUCING.. (Shelley, Anne & The Marines).
Album: released on Topspin (Ireland), Nov'76 Dist: I & B, Outlet, Shannon Distribution, S & P Distribution

Shelleyan Orphan

ANATOMY OF LOVE.
Tracks: / Anatomy of love.
Single (7"): released on Rough Trade, Apr'87 by Rough Trade Records. Dist: Rough Trade Distribution, Cartel Distribution

Single (12"): released on Rough Trade, Apr'87 by Rough Trade Records. Dist: Rough Trade Distribution, Cartel Distribution

CAVALRY OF CLOUD.
Tracks: / Cavalry cloud.
Single (7"): released on Rough Trade, Sep'86 by Rough Trade Records. Dist: Rough Trade Distribution, Cartel Distribution

Single (12"): released on Rough Trade, Sep'86 by Rough Trade Records. Dist: Rough Trade Distribution, Cartel Distribution

HELLEBORINE.
Album: released on Rough Trade, May'87 by Rough Trade Records. Dist: Rough Trade Distribution, Cartel Distribution

Cassette: released on Rough Trade, May'87 by Rough Trade Records. Dist: Rough Trade Distribution, Cartel Distribution

Compact disc: released on Rough Trade, '87 by Rough Trade Records. Dist: Rough Trade Distribution, Cartel Distribution

Shelley, Howard

SCHUBERT PIANO SONATAS.
Album: released on Amon Ra, Jun'86 by Saydisc Records. Dist: H.R. Taylor, Gamut, PRT, Jazz Music, Essex Record Distributors Ltd., Projection, Swift

Shelley, Percy Bysshe

TREASURY.
Cassette: released on Audio Visual Productions, Aug'78

Shelley, Pete

BLUE EYES.
Tracks: / Blue eyes / Nelson's riddle.
Single (7"): released on Mercury, Jul'86 by Phonogram Records. Dist: Polygram Distribution

Single (12"): released on Mercury, Jul'86 by Phonogram Records. Dist: Polygram Distribution

HEAVEN AND THE SEA.
Tracks: / Waiting for love / On your own / They're coming for you / I surrender / Life without reason / Need a minit / Never again / My dreams / Blue eyes / You can't take that away / No moon....
Notes: Producer Stephen Hague
Album: released on Mercury, Jun'86 by Phonogram Records. Dist: Polygram Distribution

Cassette: released on Mercury, Jun'86 by Phonogram Records. Dist: Polygram Distribution

Compact disc: released on Mercury, Jun'86 by Phonogram Records. Dist: Polygram Distribution

I SURRENDER.
Tracks: / I surrender / I need a minit.
Single (7"): released on Mercury, Nov'86 by Phonogram Records. Dist: Polygram Distribution

Single (12"): released on Mercury, Nov'86 by Phonogram Records. Dist: Polygram Distribution

ON YOUR OWN.
Tracks: / On your own / Please forgive me...but I cannot endure it any longer.
Single (7"): released on Phonogram, May'86 by Phonogram Records. Dist: Polygram

Single (12"): released on Phonogram, May'86 by Phonogram Records. Dist: Polygram

WAITING FOR LOVE.
Tracks: / Waiting for love / Designer lamps.
Single (7"): released on Mercury, Feb'86 by Phonogram Records. Dist: Polygram Distribution

Single (12"): released on Mercury, Feb'86 by Phonogram Records. Dist: Polygram Distribution

Shelley, Peter

BEST OF PETER SHELLEY.
Album: released on Magnet, Oct'77 by Magnet Records. Dist: BMG

GEE BABY.
Single (7"): released on Magnet, Aug'81 by Magnet Records. Dist: BMG

LOVE ME LOVE MY DOG.
Tracks: / Gee baby.
Single (7"): released on Old Gold, Jan'87 by Old Gold Records. Dist: Lightning, Jazz Music, Spartan, Counterpoint

Shell, Ray

EVERYDAY PEOPLE/STREET ANGEL (Shell, Ray & Street Angels).
Single (12"): released on Record Shack, Feb'82 by Record Shack Records. Dist: PRT

Shelly, Pete

NEVER AGAIN.
Single (7"): released on Immaculate, Nov'84 by Immaculate Records. Dist: Cartel

Single (12"): released on Immaculate, Nov'84 by Immaculate Records. Dist: Cartel

Shelton, Allen

SHELTON SPECIAL WITH MCREYNOLD.
Album: released on Rounder (USA Import), Aug'77

Shelton, Anne

Biographical Details: Singer Ann Shelton was born in Dulwich in 1927, and performed on the BBC at age 12. She went to work for bandleader **Ambrose** rather than be evacuated from WWII London. She was under contract to Ambrose for years, but also worked with **Glen Miller and Bing Crosby** during the war at their request. She had many hit records before UK charts began (she was the first to sing **Lili Marlene** in English) and continued into the 1950's. With **Vera Lynn** one of the country's best loved artists from that era, she was also succesful in the USA. She sang **You'll Never Know** for the Queen Mother on her 80th birthday, and sang on UK TV with a Glen Miller ghost band in 1984 during celebrations for the 40th anniversary of D-Day.

ANNE SHELTON SINGS WITH AMBROSE & HIS ORCHESTRA.
Album: released on Decca (Recollections), Apr'84 by Decca Recollections. Dist: Polygram, IMS Deleted '86.

Cassette: released on Decca (Recollections), Apr'84 by Decca Recollections. Dist: Polygram, IMS

ANNE SHELTON'S SENTIMENTAL JOURNEY.
Album: released on President, Oct'82 by President Records. Dist: Taylors, Spartan

CRAZY.
Single (7"): released on President, Sep'82 by President Records. Dist: Taylors, Spartan

I'LL BE SEEING YOU.
Album: released on Decca, Jul'77 by Decca Records. Dist: Polygram

Cassette: released on Decca, Jul'77 by Decca Records. Dist: Polygram

MAGIC OF ANNE SHELTON, (THE).
Album: released on Music For Pleasure, Jun'84 by EMI Records. Dist: EMI

Cassette: released on Music For Pleasure, Jun'84 by EMI Records. Dist: EMI

SING IT AGAIN, ANNE.
Album: released on President, Dec'83 by President Records. Dist: Taylors, Spartan

Cassette: released on President, Jan'84 by President Records. Dist: Taylors, Spartan

Shelto, Steve

DON'T GIVE YOUR LOVE AWAY.
Single (7"): released on Epic, Mar'83 by CBS Records. Dist: CBS

Single (12"): released on Epic, Mar'83 by CBS Records. Dist: CBS

Shenton, Robb

LONELY JOE.
Single (7"): released on Sterling, Sep'82 Dist: Jennifer Distribution

Shepard, Jean

Biographical Details: Jean Shepard was born in Oklahoma in 1933 and became a succesful country singer on Capitol with the help of bandleader **Hank Thompson** in 1953. She was also popular on the Grand Ole Opry and was married to country singer **Hawkshaw Hawkins**, killed in the same plane crash as **Patsy Cline**.

I'M A BELIEVER.
Album: released on MFP, Apr'81 by EMI Records. Dist: EMI

Cassette: released on MFP, Apr'81 by EMI Records. Dist: EMI

VERY BEST OF JEAN SHEPARD, (THE).
Album: released on Liberty, Nov'79 by Liberty-United. Dist: EMI

Cassette: released on Liberty, Nov'79 by Liberty-United. Dist: EMI Deleted '81.

Sheperet, David

PRETTY LOOKS.
Single (12"): released on Rusty International, Jan'83 by Rusty International Records. Dist: Jetstar Distribution

Shepherd

SHEPHERD, (THE) Forsyth, Frederick (Powell, Robert).
Cassette: released on Pickwick Talking Books, '83

Shepherd, Dave

AIRMAIL SPECIAL (Shepherd, Dave Quintet).
Cassette: released on Chevron, Nov'84 Dist: Multiple Sound Distributors

SHEPHERD'S DELIGHT (Shepherd, Dave Quintet).
Album: released on Swift, '74 Dist: Swift Distribution

Shepherd, David

CINEMA ORGAN ENCORES.
Album: released on Deroy, Jun'81 by Deroy Records. Dist: Jazz Music, Swift

DAVID SHEPHERD.
Notes: David Shepherd plays Wyatt Hall & St.Peters College,Adelaide,Australia.
Album: released on Deroy, May'86 by Deroy Records. Dist: Jazz Music, Swift

THAT GOLDEN AGE.
Album: released on Grosvenor, Mar'82 by Grosvenor Records. Dist: Taylors

THEATRELAND.
Album: released on Grosvenor, Feb'82 by Grosvenor Records. Dist: Taylors

Shepherd, Don

ADNAMS ALE.
Album: released on Sweet Folk All, May'81 by Sweet Folk All Records. Dist: Sweet Folk All, Roots, Celtic Music, Dragon, Impetus, Projection, Chris Wellard, Festival Records

SUN AND THE MOON, (THE).
Album: released on Sweet Folk All, May'81 by Sweet Folk All Records. Dist: Sweet Folk All, Roots, Celtic Music, Dragon, Impetus, Projection, Chris Wellard, Festival Records

Shepherd, James

COLNE VALLEY MVC.
Album: released on Look, Nov'79 Dist: R. Smith & Co. Records, H.R. Taylor

JAMES SHEPHERD VERSATILE BRASS, (THE) (Shepherd, James Versatile Brass).
Album: released on Decca, Mar'78 by Decca Records. Dist: Polygram

Cassette: released on Decca, Mar'78 by Decca Records. Dist: Polygram Deleted '81.

POPULAR CONTRASTS (Shepherd, James Versatile Brass).
Album: released on Look, Feb'84 Dist: R. Smith & Co. Records, H.R. Taylor

STRIKE UP THE BAND (Shepherd, James Versatile Brass).
Album: released on Decca, Sep'79 by Decca Records. Dist: Polygram

Cassette: released on Decca, Sep'79 by Decca Records. Dist: Polygram Deleted '81.

Shepherd, Robbie

STORY OF TURRIFF SHOW.
Cassette: released on Ross, '86 by Ross Records. Dist: Ross Distribution, Roots Distribution

UP THE DONS.
Single (7"): released on Ross, May'83 by Ross Records. Dist: Ross Distribution, Roots Distribution

Shepherd, T.G.

STRONG HEART.
Tracks: / What you gonna do about her.
Single (7"): released on CBS, Nov'86 by CBS Records. Dist: CBS

Shepherd, Vic

MOTTY DOWN, A (Shepherd, Vic & John Bowden).
Album: released on Burlington, Oct'86 by Plant Life Records. Dist: Jazz Music, Celtic Music, Clyde Factors Distributors, I.R.S., Projection, Wellard, Chris, Roots

Shepp, Archie

ARCHIE SHEPP/THE NEW YORK CONTEMPORARY FIVE VOL.2 (Shepp, Archie & New York Contemporary Five).
Notes: MONO production.
Album: released on Storyville, May'86 by Storyville Records. Dist: Jazz Music Distribution, Swift Distribution, Chris Wellard Distribution, Counterpoint Distribution

BLASE.
Tracks: / My angel / There is a balm in Gilead / Sophisticated lady / Touareg.
Compact disc: released on Affinity, Mar'87 by Charly Records. Dist: Charly, Cadillac

Album: released on Affinity, Feb'78 by Charly Records. Dist: Charly, Cadillac

DOWN HOME NEW YORK.
Compact disc: released on Soul Note (Italy), '86 Dist: Harmonia Mundi Distributors

Album: released on Soul Note, May'85

DUET (See Brand, Dollar) (Shepp, Archie & Dollar Brand).
Album: released on Denon, Mar'82 by Denon Records. Dist: Harmonia Mundi

FIRE MUSIC.
Album: released on Impulse, Oct'85 by Impulse Records. Dist: MCA, Polygram

FORCE (Shepp, Archie & Max Roach).
Double Album: released on Uni/Base, Apr'81 Dist: Jazz Music, Jazz Horizons
Cat. no: **UNI 28976**

FOUR FOR TRANE.
Album: released on Jasmine, Aug'82 by Jasmine Records. Dist: Counterpoint, Lugtons, Taylor, H.R., Wellard, Chris, Swift, Cadillac

Cassette: released on Jasmine, Aug'82 by Jasmine Records. Dist: Counterpoint, Lugtons, Taylor, H.R., Wellard, Chris, Swift, Cadillac

HOUSE I LIVE IN, (THE) (Shepp, Archie Quintet).
Album: released on Steeplechase Import, May'81

LADYBIRD.
Album: released on Denon, Mar'82

LIVE AT THE PAN AFRICAN FESTIVAL.
Album: released on Affinity, Oct'79 by Charly Records. Dist: Charly, Cadillac

LIVE IN SAN FRANCISCO.
Album: released on Jasmine, Feb'84 by Jasmine Records. Dist: Counterpoint, Lugtons, Taylor, H.R., Wellard, Chris, Swift, Cadillac

LIVE IN TOKYO (Shepp, Archie Quartet).
Album: released on Denon, Mar'82

LOOKING AT BIRD.
Album: released on Steeplechase(USA), Sep'81

MAMA TOO TIGHT.
Album: released on Jasmine, Jun'82 by Jasmine Records. Dist: Counterpoint, Lugtons, Taylor, H.R., Wellard, Chris, Swift, Cadillac

Cassette: released on Jasmine, Jun'82 by Jasmine Records. Dist: Counterpoint, Lugtons, Taylor, H.R., Wellard, Chris, Swift, Cadillac

MONTREUX 1.
Album: released on Black Lion, Sep'85 by Black Lion Records. Dist: Jazz Music, Chris Wellard, Taylor, H.R., Counterpoint, Cadillac

Album: released on Freedom Import, '83 Dist: SP & S Records (Distribution)

MONTREUX 2.
Album: released on Freedom Import, Jan'79 Dist: SP & S Records (Distribution)

NEW THING AT NEWPORT (Shepp, Archie & John Coltrane).
Album: released on Jasmine, Jun'82 by Jasmine Records. Dist: Counterpoint, Lugtons, Taylor, H.R., Wellard, Chris, Swift, Cadillac

Cassette: released on Jasmine, Jun'82 by Jasmine Records. Dist: Counterpoint, Lugtons, Taylor, H.R., Wellard, Chris, Swift, Cadillac

ON GREEN DOLPHIN STREET.
Tracks: / On Green Dolphin Street / Enough / Scene is clean, The / In a mello blues / I thought about you.
Notes: Featuring: Archie Shepp,W.Bishop Jnr.,S.Jones,J.Chambers. recorded at Sound Ideas Studios,New York City,November 28th 1977.
Album: released on Denon, Mar'82 by Denon Records. Dist: Harmonia Mundi

Compact disc: by Denon Records. Dist: Harmonia Mundi

ON THIS NIGHT.
Album: released on Jasmine, Aug'82 by Jasmine Records. Dist: Counterpoint, Lugtons, Taylor, H.R., Wellard, Chris, Swift, Cadillac

Cassette: released on Jasmine, Aug'82 by Jasmine Records. Dist: Counterpoint, Lugtons, Taylor, H.R., Wellard, Chris, Swift, Cadillac

POEM FOR MALCOLM.
Album: released on Affinity, Mar'83 by Charly Records. Dist: Charly, Cadillac

SEA OF FACES, A.
Compact disc: released on Black Saint (Italy), '86 Dist: Target, Jazz Music, Harmonia Mundi

SEA OF FACES, (A).
Album: released on Black Saint, Jul'78 Dist: Projection, IMS, Polygram, Chris Wellard, Harmonia Mundi, Swift

STEAM.
Album: released on Enja (Germany), Jan'82 by Enja Records (W.Germany). Dist: Cadillac Music

THERE'S A TRUMPET IN MY SOUL.
Album: released on Freedom Import, Apr'79 Dist: SP & S Records (Distribution)

THREE FOR A QUARTER ONE FOR A DIME.
Album: released on Jasmine, Mar'83 by Jasmine Records. Dist: Counterpoint, Lugtons, Taylor, H.R., Wellard, Chris, Swift, Cadillac

TRAY OF SILVER.
Album: released on Denon, Mar'82

TROUBLE IN MIND (Shepp, Archie & Horace Parlan).
Album: released on Steeplechase(USA), Sep'81

YASMINIA - BLACK WOMAN.
Album: released on Affinity, May'79 by Charly Records. Dist: Charly, Cadillac

Sheppard, David

IT'S HARD FOR A WOMAN.
Single (12"): released on Red Sea, Jun'85 by Red Sea Records. Dist: Jetstar

Sheppard-Missett, Judi

JAZZERCISE.
Album: released on MCA, Jun'82 by MCA Records. Dist: CBS

Cassette: released on MCA, Jun'82 by MCA Records. Dist: CBS

Sheppard, T.G.

Biographical Details: T.G.Sheppard is a country singer/songwriter with an intimate style that appeals to female fans. He was born **William Bowder** in Tennessee on 20 July 1944. He recorded for Atlantic as **Bryan Stacy** in 1962, but had quit performing to do promotional work in Memphis when he couldn't get anyone to record **The Devil In A Bottle**, a song by **Bobby David** that he believed in, so he recorded it himself and had a no.1 country hit in 1975; he's been a star ever since. Among his many hits was **Make My Day**, a duet with actor **Clint Eastwood.** Hits that crossed over to the pop chart include **I Loved Them Every One.**

FINALLY.
Single (7"): released on Warner Brothers, May'82 by WEA Records. Dist: WEA

I LOVE 'EM ALL.
Album: released on Warner-Curb, Aug'81

I LOVE 'EM EVERY ONE.
Single (7"): released on Curb, Jun'81

MAKE MY DAY (Sheppard, T.G. & Clint Eastwood).
Single (7"): released on Warner Brothers, Feb'84 by WEA Records. Dist: WEA

ONLY ONE YOU.
Single (7"): released on Warner Brothers, Apr'82 by WEA Records. Dist: WEA

PARTY TIME.
Single (7"): released on Curb, Dec'81

Shep's Banjo Band

BIG BAND FAVOURITES.
Cassette: released on Ditto, Aug'84 by Pickwick Records. Dist: H.R. Taylor

Shep's Banjo Boys

BANJO SINGALONG.
Album: released on Spot, Feb'83 by Pickwick Records. Dist: H.R. Taylor, Lugtons

Cassette: released on Spot, Feb'83 by Pickwick Records. Dist: H.R. Taylor, Lugtons

SHEP'S BANJO BOYS.
Album: released on Nevis, May'77 Dist: H.R. Taylor

Shepway Folk

SHEPWAY FOLK Various artists (Various Artists).
Tracks: / Keys of Canterbury / Mandy / Congo River / Flowers of Scotland.
Notes: Artists include: Handbell Hoodeners of Folkestone,Mik & Martyn Danejohn,Pendulum Hackett   Targa.
Traditional & contemporary folk plus sea shanties and humorous george Formby songs. Eron Records,27 Balmoral Road,Kingsdown,Deal,Kent CT 14 8BX.
Album: released on Eron, Sep'85 by Eron Records. Dist: Eron Records

Cassette: released on Eron, Sep'85 by Eron Records. Dist: Eron Records

Sherbourne, Janet

NOBODY BUT YOU.
Tracks: / Nobody but you / Everyday / Ivory.
Single (7"): released on Practical Music, '81

Single (7"): released on Practical, Mar'82 Dist: Rough Trade

SLOWER THAN MOLASSES (Sherbourne, Janet & Mark Lockett).
Tracks: / Heavy set / All you can eat / Tree sequence / Slower than molasses / China / My lovesick hours / Click / 19 to the dozen / Sirian air / Luna.
Album: released on Practical, May'86 Dist: Rough Trade

Sherbs

SKILL, (THE).
Album: released on Atco, May'81 by Atlantic Records. Dist: WEA

Sheredew, Mike

DONNA (Sheredew, Mike & The Nightrider).
Tracks: / Donna / Moonshine.
Single (7"): released on Swoop, '67 Dist: Le Matt Music Distribution

Sheridan, Mike

BIRMINGHAM BEAT (Sheridan, Mike & The Nightriders).
Album: released on Edsel, Jan'84 by Demon Records. Dist: Pinnacle, Jazz Music, Projection

DONNA (Sheridan, Mike & The Nightriders).
Single (7"): released on Swoop, Feb'82 Dist: Le Matt Music Distribution

Sheridan, Tony

HAMBURG 1961 (Sheridan, Tony & The Beatles).
Album: released on Topline, Nov'84 by Charly Records. Dist: Charly Distribution

Cassette: released on Topline, Nov'84 by Charly Records. Dist: Charly Distribution

ICH LIEB'DICH SO.
Tracks: / Ich lieb'dich so / Der kiss me song / Arme kleine lilly* / Eyrst wenn man treu sein kann* / Madison kid / Veedeboom slop slop / Wolgalied / Let's slop / Alles nur arus liebe / Ich will bei dir bleiben / Ich bie dich nie mehr wieder gehn* / Hey ba ba re bop / Vive l'armour / Ya Ya,Parts 1&2 / La bamba (Spanish) / Malaguena (Spanish).
Album: released on Bear Family, Nov'86 by Bear Family Records. Dist: Rollercoaster Distribution, Swift

Sheriff, Dave

FILL MY HAT WITH SILVER.
Album: released on Tank, Sep'79 by Tank Records.

I'LL BE ALONE TONIGHT.
Single (7"): released on Tank, Dec'77 by Tank Records.

WITH FOUR CARD EXPRESS.
Album: released on Tank, Jun'79 by Tank Records.

Sheriff, Jack

LAUGH YOURSELF AWAKE.
Album: released on Midnight Music, Oct'86 by Midnight Music Records. Dist: Rough Trade Distribution, Cartel Distribution

LET'S BE NONCHALANT EP:BUY EVERYBODY A CAKE.
Tracks: / We're gonna be in love / Whatcha gonna do? / Buttered slice of democracy.

Extended-play record: released on Midnight Music, Feb'86 by Midnight Music Records. Dist: Rough Trade Distribution, Cartel Distribution

Sheri & Son

LIES.
Single (7"): released on Precious, Sep'81 by Precious Records. Dist: CBS, Polygram

Sherlock Holmes...

SHERLOCK HOLMES SOUNDBOOK
(Doyle, Arthur Conan).
Cassette: released on Caedmon(USA), Oct'81 by Caedmon (USA) Records. Dist: Gower, Taylors, Discovery

SHERLOCK HOLMES STORIES, VOL 1
Conan Doyle (Rathbone, Basil).
Cassette: released on Caedmon(USA), Oct'81 by Caedmon (USA) Records. Dist: Gower, Taylors, Discovery

SHERLOCK HOLMES STORIES, VOL 2
Conan Doyle (Rathbone, Basil).
Cassette: released on Caedmon(USA), Oct'81 by Caedmon (USA) Records. Dist: Gower, Taylors, Discovery

SHERLOCK HOLMES STORIES, VOL 3
Conan Doyle (Rathbone, Basil).
Cassette: released on Caedmon(USA), Oct'81 by Caedmon (USA) Records. Dist: Gower, Taylors, Discovery

SHERLOCK HOLMES STORIES, VOL 4
Conan Doyle (Rathbone, Basil).
Cassette: released on Caedmon(USA), Oct'81 by Caedmon (USA) Records. Dist: Gower, Taylors, Discovery

SHERLOCK HOLMES STORIES Conan Doyle (Hardy, Robert).
Double cassette: released on Argo (Spokenword), Jul'82 by Decca Records. Dist: Polygram

Sherman, Allan

HELLO MUDDAH HELLO FADDAH.
Single (7"): released on Warner Brothers, Jul'81 by WEA Records. Dist: WEA

GIFT OF LAUGHTER, A Best of Allen Sherman.
Album: released on Rhino (USA), May'86 by Rhino Records (USA).

Sherman, Ben

CHRISTMAS BELLS.
Album: released on Tank, Sep'79 by Tank Records.

Sherman, Bim

CENTURY (Sherman, Bim & The Voluntary).
Album: released on Century, Jun'86 by Century Records. Dist: Rough Trade, Cartel

Album: released on Century, Mar'84 by Century Records. Dist: Rough Trade, Cartel

DANGER.
Album: released on Century, Oct'84 by Century Records. Dist: Rough Trade, Cartel

HAPPINESS.
Single (12"): released on Jah Shaka, Dec'82 by Jah Shaka Records. Dist: Jetstar

HAUNTING GROUND.
Album: released on RDL, Dec'86

KEEP YOU DANCING.
Single 10": released on On-U-Sound, Dec'83 Dist: Rough Trade Distribution, Lightning

LOVERS LEAP.
Album: released on RDL, 30 May'87

REVOLUTION.
Single 10": released on On-U-Sound, Apr'82 Dist: Rough Trade Distribution, Lightning

Sherman, Tony

ELLOVEE-EE.
Single (7"): released on Polydor, Oct'82 by Polydor Records. Dist: Polygram, Polydor

Single (12"): released on Polydor, Oct'82 by Polydor Records. Dist: Polygram, Polydor

Sherrick

JUST CALL.
Tracks: / Just call / I'm scared a'you.
Single (7"): released on Warner Bros., Jul'87 by Warner Bros Records. Dist: WEA

Single (12"): released on Warner Bros., Jul'87 by Warner Bros Records. Dist: WEA

SHERRICK.
Tracks: / Tell me what it is / Just call / Baby I'm for real / This must be love / Do you baby / All because of you / Let's be lovers tonight / Lady you are / Send for me.
Album: released on Warner Brothers, Aug'87 by Warner Bros Records. Dist: WEA

Cassette: released on Warner Brothers, Aug'87 by Warner Bros Records. Dist: WEA

Compact disc: released on Warner Brothers, Aug'87 by Warner Bros Records. Dist: WEA

Sherriff, Dave

DON'T TELL ME LIES.
Single (7"): released on Dapa, Apr'84 by Dapa Records. Dist: PRT

Sherrill, Pappy

33 YEARS OF P&P (Sherrill, Pappy & Snuffy Jenkins).
Album: released on Rounder (USA Import), Jul'77

CRAZY WATER (Sherrill, Pappy & Snuffy Jenkins).
Album: released on Rounder (USA Import), Jun'77

WILEY ZEKE & HOMER (Sherrill, Pappy & The Morris Brothers).
Album: released on Rounder (USA Import), Jun'77

Shertz

YOU'VE GOT YOUR TROUBLES.
Single (7"): released on Wat, Oct'83 by Wat Records. Dist: Owlerton Speedways Distribution

Sherwood, Bobby

ONE NIGHT STAND - 1946.
Album: released on Joyce, Jul'82

POLITELY.
Album: released on Golden Era, Jul'82 by Import Records. Dist: Wellard, Chris, Swift

SHERWOOD SWINGS.
Album: released on Swing House, '84 Dist: Jazz Music Distribution, Swift Distribution, Chris Wellard Distribution

VICTORY PARADE OF SPOTLIGHT BANDS 1945.
Album: released on Aircheck (USA), Apr'79 Dist: Swift, Jazz Music

Sherwood Rise

FROM THE WOOD.
Album: released on Dingles, '83 by Dingle's Records. Dist: Projection

She's Gotta Have It

SHE'S GOTTA HAVE IT Music from the motion picture by Bill Lee (Various Artists).
Notes: Featuring Bill Lee, Ronnie Dyson, Harold Vick, Stanley Conell, Kenny Washington,Virgil Jones, Cedar Walton, Joe Chambers. Produced and arranged by Bill Lee.
Album: released on Antilles, Mar'87 by Island Records. Dist: Polygram

Cassette: released on Antilles, Mar'87 by Island Records. Dist: Polygram

She Sherriff

I FORGOT MORE THAN YOU'LL EVER KNOW.
Single (7"): released on Charisma, Mar'82 by Virgin Records. Dist: EMI

Shetland...

DA MIRRIE BOYS Shetland fiddle tunes (Shetland "Da Mirrie Boys").
Cassette: released on Folktracks, Nov'79 by Folktracks Cassettes. Dist: Folktracks

SHETLAND FIDDLERS VOLUME ONE Various artists (Various Artists).
Cassette: released on Topic, Feb'85 by Topic Records. Dist: JSU Distribution, Projection Distribution, Jazz Music Distribution

SHETLAND FIDDLERS Various artists (Various Artists).
Album: released on Leader, '81 Dist: Jazz Music, Projection

SHETLAND FOLK FIDDLING - VOL.2
(Shetland Folk Fiddling).
Album: released on Topic, '81 by Topic Records. Dist: JSU Distribution, Projection Distribution, Jazz Music Distribution

SILVER BOW, THE Shetland folk fiddling - Vol.1 (Various Artists).
Album: released on Topic, Jul'76 by Topic Records. Dist: JSU Distribution, Projection Distribution, Jazz Music Distribution

Shevlin, Ann

RIGHT ON THE EDGE.
Tracks: / Right on the edge / Lyric of your love.

She Wolf

SHE WOLF & OTHERS Saki (Burden, Hugh).
Cassette: released on Talking Tape Company, Aug'81 by Talking Tape Company Records.

Shields, Duncan

STAY TOGETHER.
Single (7"): released on Markar, May'85 Dist: Fast Forward, Cartel

Shikane

CHANGE YOUR MIND.
Single (7"): released on Red Bus, Feb'84 by Red Bus Records. Dist: PRT

Single (12"): released on Red Bus, Feb'84 by Red Bus Records. Dist: PRT

Shillelagh Sisters

GIVE ME MY FREEDOM.
Single (7"): by CBS Records. Dist: CBS

Single (12"): by CBS Records. Dist: CBS

Picture disc single: released on CBS, Apr'84 by CBS Records. Dist: CBS

PASSION FRUIT.
Single (7"): released on CBS, Aug'84 by CBS Records. Dist: CBS

Single (12"): released on CBS, Aug'84 by CBS Records. Dist: CBS

Shimazu, Hideo

THEN SPRING.
Compact disc: released on Denon, Apr'86 by Denon Records. Dist: Harmonia Mundi

Shine

I DREAM IN BLUE.
Tracks: / Last time round.
Single (7"): released on China, Apr'86 by Chrysalis Records. Dist: Chrysalis

Single (12"): released on China, Apr'86 by Chrysalis Records. Dist: Chrysalis

Shine, Brendan

BEST OF...
Album: released on Play (Ireland), '74

BLUE MISTY EYES.
Album: released on Play (Ireland), Jun'82

Cassette: released on Play (Ireland), Jun'82

BRENDAN SHINE COLLECTION,THE.
Album: released on Play (Ireland), Nov'83

Cassette: released on Play (Ireland), Nov'83

BUNCH OF VIOLETS BLUE.
Single (7"): released on Play (Ireland), Sep'84

CARROTS.
Single (7"): released on Play (Ireland), Sep'80

CATCH ME IF YOU CAN.
Album: released on Play (Ireland), Sep'80

Cassette: released on Play (Ireland), Sep'80

CEILI HOUSE.
Album: released on Play (Ireland), '74

Cassette: released on Play (Ireland), '74

CHRISTMAS TIME IN IRELAND.
Single (7"): released on Play (Ireland), Oct'7

COUNTY DOWN.
Single (7"): released on Play (Ireland), Aug'8

DOOGEENS.
Single (7"): released on Play (Ireland), May't

DO YOU WANT YOUR OLD LOBB WASHED.
Single (7"): released on Play (Ireland), Sep'8

FOUR GREAT TRACKS.
Extended-play record: released on Play (Ireland), Jul'81

HEY LOUISE.
Single (7"): released on Play (Ireland), Apr'8

IRISH SIDE OF BRENDAN SHINE.
Album: released on Harp(Ireland), May'80 Pickwick Records. Dist: Taylors

IRISH STARTIME.
Album: released on Irish Startime, '78 Dist: B

LIVE AT THE THATCH.
Album: released on Thatch, Aug'87 Dist: Spartan Distribution

Cassette: released on Thatch, Aug'87 Dist: Spartan Distribution

LONELINESS.
Tracks: / Accordian (inst) / These are sounds i love / My son.
Single (7"): released on Play, Feb'86 by Play Records. Dist: Spartan

Single (12"): released on Play, May'86 by Play Records. Dist: Spartan

MELODY.
Single (7"): released on Play (Ireland), Jul'85

MEMORIES.
Tracks: / Danny boy / If I were a blackbird / Old bog road / Dublin in the rare ould times / Mountains of Mourne / Banks of my own lovely lee.
Album: released on Play (Ireland), Nov'85

Cassette: released on Play (Ireland), Nov'85

ME OLD BONESHAKER.
Single (7"): released on Play (Ireland), Nov'82

MOONSHINE.
Tracks: / Moonshine / Girl from Clare (The).
Single (7"): released on Play, Mar'87 by Play Records. Dist: Spartan

Album: released on Play, Nov'86 by Play Records. Dist: Spartan

MY OLD COUNTRY HOME.
Single (7"): released on Play (Ireland), Jan'83

MY SON.
Tracks: / My son / Did you kiss me.
Single (7"): released on Play, Jan'86 by Play Records. Dist: Spartan

NEW ROADS.
Album: released on Play (Ireland), Oct'76

Cassette: released on Play (Ireland), Oct'76

NICE AND EASY.
Album: released on Play (Ireland), Jan'78

Cassette: released on Play (Ireland), Jan'78

NOW I'M EASY(COCK FARMER).
Single (7"): released on Play (Ireland), May'84

OLD RUGGED CROSS.
Single (7"): released on Play (Ireland), Jun'82

PUB CRAWL.
Single (7"): released on Play (Ireland), Nov'81

THANK GOD FOR KIDS.
Single (7"): released on Play (Ireland), Dec'83

THIS IS BRENDAN SHINE.
Album: released on Play (Ireland), Nov'76

Cassette: released on Play (Ireland), Nov'76

VILLAGE WHERE I WENT TO SCHOOL.
Single (7"): released on Play (Ireland), May'83

WITH LOVE.
Single (7"): released on Play (Ireland), Sep'84

Cassette: released on Play (Ireland), Sep'84

YOU'LL NEVER GO BACK.
Tracks: / You'll never go back / Biddy from Glenroe.
Single (7"): released on Play, Oct'86 by Play Records. Dist: Spartan

Shinehead
BILLIE JEAN.
Single (12"): released on Hawkeye, Sep'84 by Hawkeye Records. Dist: Hawkeye, Lightning (WEA) Distribution, Jetstar, PRT

TOUGH AND RUGGED.
Album: released on ALM Music, Aug'86 Dist: Jetstar

WHO THE CAP FIT.
Tracks: / Who the cap fit / Billie Jean / Mama said to say.
Single (7"): released on Virgin, Nov'86 by Virgin Records. Dist: EMI, Virgin Distribution

Single (12"): released on Virgin, Nov'86 by Virgin Records. Dist: EMI, Virgin Distribution

Shine, Johnny
COUNTRY BLUES (Shine, Johnny & Blind Will Dukes).
Album: released on JSP, Dec'84 by JSP Records. Dist: Swift, Projection

JOHNNY SHINE'S BAND WITH BIG WALTER HORTON (Shine, Johnny Band & Walter Horton).
Album: released on Testament, May'86 Dist: Swift Distribution, Making Waves Distribution

Shine On Harvey Moon
SHINE ON HARVEY MOON various artists (Various Artists).
Album: released on Images, Oct'82 by MSD Records. Dist: PRT

Cassette: released on Images, Oct'82 by MSD Records. Dist: PRT

Shines, Johnnie
HEY BA-BA-RE-BOP.
Album: released on Rounder (USA), May'79 Dist: Mike's Country Music Room Distribution, Jazz Music Distribution, Swift Distribution, Roots Records Distribution, Projection Distribution, Topic Distribution

Shining
WORKING CLASS HERO.
Single (12"): released on Turbo, Jun'83 Dist: Stage One

Shining, The
SHINING,THE Original film soundtrack.
Album: released on Warner Brothers, '80 by Warner Bros Records. Dist: WEA

Shiny Men
SHINY MEN.
Album: released on Experimental, Oct'81 by United Dairies Records. Dist: Indies

Shiny To Shiny
WAITING FOR US.
Single (7"): released on Red Flame 10, Nov'83
Cat. no: RFB 29
Single (12"): released on Red Flame 10, Nov'83

Ships Company...
SAILING (Ships Company Of HMS Ark Royal).
Single (7"): released on BBC, Jul'82 by BBC Records & Tapes. Dist: EMI, PRT

Shirati Jazz
BENGA BEAT.
Album: released on World Circuit, May'87 by Taurus Records. Dist: Sterns/Triple Earth Distribution

Shirelles
21 GREATEST HITS,THE.
Tracks: / Will you love me tomorrow / Dedicated to the one I love / Foolish little girl / Mama said / Baby it's you / Everybody loves a lover / Big john / Maybe tonight / Mad,mad world / Welcome home baby / Don't say goodnight and mean goodbye / Stop the music / Tonight's the night / I met him on sunday / What does girl do? / Thank you baby / Sha-le-la / To know him is to love him / Boys / My heart belongs to you.
Compact disc: released on Bescol, May'87 Dist: Target

BEST OF...
Cassette: released on Creole (Everest-Europa), Jul'84 by Creole Records. Dist: PRT, Rhino

GREATEST HITS:SHIRELLES.
Compact disc: released on Impact, Aug'87 by Ace Records. Dist: Rough Trade, Pinnacle, Swift, Backs, Counterpoint, Jungle, Hotshot, Cartel

Album: released on Ace, Aug'87 by Ace Records. Dist: Pinnacle, Swift, Hotshot, Cadillac

JUKE BOX GIANTS.
Album: released on Audio Fidelity, May'82 Dist: PRT

LOST AND FOUND.
Album: released on Impact, Feb'87 by Ace Records. Dist: Rough Trade, Pinnacle, Swift, Backs, Counterpoint, Jungle, Hotshot, Cartel

MAMA SAID.
Tracks: / Mama said / Will you love me tomorrow / Tonights the night / Foolish little girl / Everybody loves a lover / Thank you baby / Soldier boy / Dedicated to the one I love / Baby it's you / I met him on a Sunday / Welcome home baby / Boys.
Album: released on Topline, '86 by Charly Records. Dist: Charly Distribution

Cassette: released on Topline, '86 by Charly Records. Dist: Charly Distribution

MAMA SAID.
Album: released on Topline, Jul'85 by Charly Records. Dist: Charly Distribution

Cassette: released on Topline, Jul'85 by Charly Records. Dist: Charly Distribution

SHA LA LA LA.
Album: released on Impact, Apr'85 by Ace Records. Dist: Rough Trade, Pinnacle, Swift, Backs, Counterpoint, Jungle, Hotshot, Cartel

SHIRELLES GREATEST HITS, THE.
Compact disc: released on Impact, Aug'87 by Ace Records. Dist: Rough Trade, Pinnacle, Swift, Backs, Counterpoint, Jungle, Hotshot, Cartel

SOULFULLY YOURS.
Album: released on Kent, Dec'84 by Ace Records. Dist: Pinnacle

WILL YOU LOVE ME TOMORROW/SOLDIER BOY.
Single (7"): released on Old Gold, Apr'83 by Old Gold Records. Dist: Lightning, Jazz Music, Spartan, Counterpoint

WILL YOU LOVE ME TOMORROW.
Single (7"): released on Dakota, Aug'82 by Dakota Records. Dist: PRT

Shirelles, The
SHIRELLES GREATEST HITS,THE.
Album: released on Impact, Aug'87 by Ace Records. Dist: Rough Trade, Pinnacle, Swift, Backs, Counterpoint, Jungle, Hotshot, Cartel

Shirley Anne
GROWING UP IS HARD.
Single (7"): released on Greenhill, Nov'85 by Greenhill Records. Dist: PRT

PAL OF MY CRADLE DAYS.
Tracks: / Pal of my cradle days / Young girl at heart.
Single (7"): released on Greenhill, Feb'86 by Greenhill Records. Dist: PRT

Shirley & Company
SHAME SHAME SHAME.
Single (7"): released on Old Gold, Jul'84 by Old Gold Records. Dist: Lightning, Jazz Music, Spartan, Counterpoint

SHAME SHAME SHAME/RIMSHOTS.
Single (7"): released on Flashback, Jan'83 by Flashback Records/PRT Records. Dist: Mainline, PRT

Shirley Junior Choir
HOMEWARD BOUND/TWENTIETH CENTURY CAROL.
Single (7"): released on Thunderbay, Nov'82 Dist: Spartan Distribution

Shirley & Lee
Biographical Details: Shirley & Lee were Shirley Pixley Goodman, born in 1937, and Leonard Lee, born in 1935; their r&b hits began in 1952 on the Aladin label, and included one of the all-time great party records for teenagers of all ages, Let the Good Times Roll which crossed over to top 20 pop in 1956. Their style was based on the contrast between his big voice & her little one. See also Shirley & Co.. Shirley had one of the first disco hits in 1976, Shame Shame Shame, produced & written by Sylvia Robinson (of Mickey & Sylvia).

BEST OF SHIRLEY & LEE,THE vol 1.
Album: released on Ace, Sep'82 by Ace Records. Dist: Pinnacle, Swift, Hotshot, Cadillac

LET THE GOOD TIMES ROLL.
Single (7"): released on Creole Replay, Aug'84 by Creole Records. Dist: PRT, Rhino

Shirley, Roy
FOR EVERYONE.
Single (7"): released on Shirley, Jan'85 by Shirley, Roy Records. Dist: Pinnacle

Shirra, Tom
MOOD INDIGO (Shirra, Tom & His Friends).
Album: released on Lismor, Nov'76 by Lismor Records. Dist: Lismor, Roots, Celtic Music

Shiva
ANGEL OF MONZ.
Single (7"): released on Heavy Metal, Nov'82 by FM-Revolver Records. Dist: EMI

FIREDANCE.
Album: released on Heavy Metal, Nov'82 by FM-Revolver Records. Dist: EMI

ROCK LIVES.
Single (7"): released on Heavy Metal, Feb'82 by FM-Revolver Records. Dist: EMI

Shiv & Hari
YUGAL BANDI.
Album: released on Sonet, '74 by Sonet Records. Dist: PRT

Album: released on Sonet, '74 by Sonet Records. Dist: PRT

Shoc Corridor
BLIND SIGN.
Single (7"): released on Shout, Oct'82 by Shout Records. Dist: Rough Trade, Cartel

FEVER.
Single (12"): released on Quiet, Nov'84 by Quiet Records. Dist: Nine Mile, Cartel

HOLDING TREASURE.
Single (7"): released on Shout, Jun'84 by Shout Records. Dist: Rough Trade, Cartel

TRAIN OF EVENTS.
Album: released on Quiet, Nov'84 by Quiet Records. Dist: Nine Mile, Cartel

Shock
DYNAMO BEAT.
Single (7"): released on RCA, Oct'81 by RCA Records. Dist: RCA, Roots, Swift, Wellard, Chris, I & B, Solomon & Peres Distribution

Single (12"): released on RCA, Oct'81 by RCA Records. Dist: RCA, Roots, Swift, Wellard, Chris, I & B, Solomon & Peres Distribution

Shockabilly
19TH NERVOUS BREAKDOWN.
Single (7"): released on Rough Trade, Mar'83 by Rough Trade Records. Dist: Rough Trade Distribution, Cartel Distribution

COLOSSEUM.
Album: released on Rough Trade, Apr'84 by Rough Trade Records. Dist: Rough Trade Distribution, Cartel Distribution

DAWN OF SHOCKABILLY.
Single (12"): released on Rough Trade, Nov'82 by Rough Trade Records. Dist: Rough Trade Distribution, Cartel Distribution

EARTH VS SHOCKABILLY.
Album: released on Rough Trade, '84 by Rough Trade Records. Dist: Rough Trade Distribution, Cartel Distribution

SHOCKABILLY HEAVEN.
Album: released on Fundamental, Nov'85 by Fundamental Records. Dist: Red Rhino, Cartel

VIETNAM.
Album: released on Fundamental, Aug'85 by Fundamental Records. Dist: Red Rhino, Cartel

Shocked, Michelle
DISORIENTED.
Tracks: / Disoriented / If love was a train / Chainsmoker* / Stranded in a limousine* / Goodnight Irene*.
Single (7"): released on Cooking Vinyl, Jun'87 Dist: Nine Mile, Cartel, Red Rhino

Single (12"): released on Cooking Vinyl, Jun'87 Dist: Nine Mile, Cartel, Red Rhino

TEXAS CAMPFIRE TAPES.
Album: released on Cooking Vinyl, Nov'86 Dist: Nine Mile, Cartel, Red Rhino

Shock Headed Peters
I BLOODBROTHER BE.
Single (7"): released on EL, Sep'84 by El Records. Dist: Rough Trade, Pinnacle

Single (12"): released on EL, Sep'84 by El Records. Dist: Rough Trade, Pinnacle

Single (7"): released on Island, Nov'84 by Island Records. Dist: Polygram

Single (12"): released on Island, Nov'84 by Island Records. Dist: Polygram

LIFE EXTINGUISHER.
Tracks: / Life extinguisher.
Single (7"): released on Beach Culture, Feb'86 Dist: Backs, Cartel

Shocking Blue
VENUS.
Single (7"): by Old Gold Records. Dist: Lightning, Jazz Music, Spartan, Counterpoint

Shock Taktix
MOROCKO.
Tracks: / Morocko / This is not / Morocko (Mad house mix).
Single (7"): released on RCA, 13 Jun'87 by RCA Records. Dist: RCA, Roots, Swift, Wellard, Chris, I & B, Solomon & Peres Distribution

Single (12"): released on RCA, 13 Jun'87 by RCA Records. Dist: RCA, Roots, Swift, Wellard, Chris, I & B, Solomon & Peres Distribution

Shock Therapy
SHOCK THERAPY.
Album: released on Fundamental, Mar'87 by Fundamental Records. Dist: Red Rhino, Cartel

Shock Treatment
SHOCK TREATMENT Original soundtrack.
Album: released on Warner Brothers, Nov'81 by WEA Records. Dist: WEA

Shock USA
THAT'S A LADY.
Single (7"): released on Fantasy, Aug'82 by RCA Records. Dist: RCA, Jetstar

Single (12"): released on Fantasy, Jul'82 by RCA Records. Dist: RCA, Jetstar

Shoehorn

DO THE BEST I CAN.
Single (7"): released on Monarch, Sep'81 by Chart Records. Dist: Pinnacle

Shoemake, Charlie

AWAY FROM THE CROWD (Shoemake, Charlie Sextet).
Album: released on Discovery, Jun'83 Dist: PRT

BLUE SHOE.
Album: released on Muse, Apr'81 Dist: JSU Distribution, Jazz Horizons Distribution, Jazz Music Distribution, Celtic Music Distribution

CROSS ROADS (Shoemake, Charlie Sextet).
Album: released on Discovery, Aug'83 Dist: PRT

I THINK WE'RE ALMOST THERE.
Compact disc: released on Discovery (USA), Dec'86 by Discovery Records (USA). Dist: Swift, Flexitron-Audio, Jazz Music

PLAYS THE MUSIC OF DAVID RAKSIN (Shoemake, Charlie Sextet).
Album: released on Discovery (USA), Apr'84

SUNSTROKE.
Album: released on Muse, Apr'81 Dist: JSU Distribution, Jazz Horizons Distribution, Jazz Music Distribution, Celtic Music Distribution

Shoes

BOOMERANG.
Album: released on Fan Club, Jul'87 by New Rose. Dist: Rough Trade, Cartel, Pinnacle

SHOES Various artists (Various Artists).
Album: released on Kent, Mar'84 by Ace Records. Dist: Pinnacle

SILHOUETTES.
Album: released on Demon, Sep'84 Dist: Jazz Music, Projection

TONGUE TWISTER.
Album: released on Elektra, Jun'81 by WEA Records. Dist: WEA

WHEN PUSH COMES TO SHOVE.
Single (7"): released on Demon, Jan'85 Dist: Jazz Music, Projection

Shoes For Industry

I CAN'T HELP IT.
Single (7"): released on Fried Egg, Jul'81 by Fried Egg Records. Dist: Rough Trade, Cartel

SPEND.
Single (7"): released on Fried Egg, Jul'81 by Fried Egg Records. Dist: Rough Trade, Cartel

TALK LIKE A WALK.
Album: released on Fried Egg, Jul'81 by Fried Egg Records. Dist: Rough Trade, Cartel

Shoes Were For Sunday

SHOES WERE FOR SUNDAY (Weir, Molly).
Cassette: released on Chivers Audio Books, '81 by Chivers Sound & Vision. Dist: Chivers Sound & Vision

Shogun

HIGH IN THE SKY.
Tracks: / High in the sky.
Single (7"): released on Attack, Aug'86 by Trojan Records. Dist: Trojan, Pinnacle, Red Rhino

SHOGUN.
Album: released on Attack, Oct'86 by Trojan Records. Dist: Trojan, Pinnacle, Red Rhino

Album: released on RSO, Nov'82

Cassette: released on RSO, Nov'82

Shojitabuchi

SHOJITABUCHI FIDDLES AND SINGS.
Album: released on Jin (USA), Feb'79 Dist: Swift

Shokk

LOCK ME OUT.
Single (7"): released on Polydor, Mar'87 by Polydor Records. Dist: Polygram, Polydor

Single (12"): released on Polydor, Mar'87 by Polydor Records. Dist: Polygram, Polydor

Sholle, Jon

CATFISH FOR SUPPER (Sholle, Jon & Grisman Bromberg).
Album: released on Rounder (USA), Mar'79 Dist: Mike's Country Music Room Distribution, Jazz Music Distribution, Swift Distribution, Roots Records Distribution, Projection Distribution, Topic Distribution

Shoot Dispute

GAT GUN.
Single (7"): released on Zanzibar, Jul'85 by Zanzibar Records. Dist: Cartel

Shooting High

SHOOTING HIGH various artists (Various Artists).
Tracks: / Breakaway / Lovely lady / What are you thinkin' about baby? / Star gazing / Whisper sweet / In a blue and pensive mood / Please believe me / Heart to heart / Red sails in the sunset / When did you leave heaven? / Farewell to arms / Just two hearts and a waltz refrain / That's what I like about you / Don't blame me / Deep water / Cheek to cheek / When the poppies bloom again / Don't kiss me goodnight / Little white gardenia, A / I'm shooting high.
Notes: Solo recordings by British dance and vocalists.
Album: released on Saville, May'87 by Conifer Records. Dist: Conifer

Cassette: released on Saville, May'87 by Conifer Records. Dist: Conifer

Shooting Party

I KNOW THAT MOOD.
Tracks: / I know that mood / One shot.
Single (7"): released on Siren, Jan'86 by Virgin Records. Dist: EMI

Single (7"): released on Siren, Jan'86 by Virgin Records. Dist: EMI

TRICK OF THE LIGHT.
Single (7"): released on Siren, Sep'85 by Virgin Records. Dist: EMI

Single (12"): released on Siren, Sep'85 by Virgin Records. Dist: EMI

TRICK OF THE NIGHT.
Tracks: / Trick of the light / Hold that emotion.
Single (7"): released on Towerbell, Jun'86 by Towerbell Records. Dist: EMI

Single (12"): released on Towerbell, Jun'86 by Towerbell Records. Dist: EMI

Shooting Star

FLESH AND BLOOD.
Single (7"): released on Virgin, Jan'82

HANG ON FOR YOUR LIFE.
Album: released on Virgin, Jan'82

SILENT SCREAM.
Album: released on Virgin, Aug'85 by Virgin Records. Dist: EMI, Virgin Distribution

Cassette: released on Virgin, Aug'85 by Virgin Records. Dist: EMI, Virgin Distribution

SUMMER SUN.
Single (7"): released on Virgin, Jul'85 by Virgin Records. Dist: EMI, Virgin Distribution

Single (12"): released on Virgin, Jul'85 by Virgin Records. Dist: EMI, Virgin Distribution

YOU'VE GOT WHAT I NEED.
Single (7"): released on Virgin, Feb'80

Shop Assistants

ALL DAY LONG.
Single (7"): released on Subway Organisation, Jun'85 Dist: Revolver, Cartel

I DON'T WANNA BE FRIENDS WITH YOU.
Tracks: / I don't wanna be friends with you / Look back.
Single (7"): released on Blue Guitar, Sep'86 by Chrysalis Records. Dist: CBS Distribution

Single (12"): released on Blue Guitar, Sep'86 by Chrysalis Records. Dist: CBS Distribution

SHOP ASSISTANTS.
Album: released on Blue Guitar, Nov'86 by Chrysalis Records. Dist: CBS Distribution

Cassette: released on Blue Guitar, Nov'86 by Chrysalis Records. Dist: CBS Distribution

SOMEWHERE IN CHINA.
Tracks: / Somewhere in China / Almost made it.
Single (7"): released on 53rd & 3rd, Feb'86 by Fast Forward Records. Dist: Fast Forward, Cartel

Single (12"): released on 53rd & 3rd, Feb'86 by Fast Forward Records. Dist: Fast Forward, Cartel

Shopping For Girls

SORRY WRONG ONE.
Single (7"): released on Triangle, Jan'82 by Triangle Records. Dist: Pinnacle

Shore, Dinah

DINAH SINGS, PREVIN PLAYS (Shore, Dinah & Andre Previn).
Album: released on Capitol, Apr'84 by Capitol Records. Dist: EMI

Cassette: released on Capitol, Apr'84 by Capitol Records. Dist: EMI

DINAH SINGS SOME BLUES WITH RED (Shore, Dinah & The Red Norvo Quintet).
Album: released on Capitol, Jul'85 by Capitol Records. Dist: EMI

Cassette: released on Capitol, Jul'85 by Capitol Records. Dist: EMI

DINAH, YES INDEED!.
Album: released on Music for Pleasure, Apr'83 by EMI Records. Dist: MFP Distribution

Cassette: released on Music for Pleasure, Apr'83 by EMI Records. Dist: MFP Distribution

HOLDING HANDS AT MIDNIGHT.
Album: released on RCA, Oct'84 by RCA Records. Dist: RCA, Roots, Swift, Wellard, Chris, I & B, Solomon & Peres Distribution

Cassette: released on RCA, Oct'84 by RCA Records. Dist: RCA, Roots, Swift, Wellard, Chris, I & B, Solomon & Peres Distribution

LAVENDER BLUE.
Tracks: / They didn't believe me / They can't take that away from me / I may be wrong (but I think your wonderful) / Gypsy (The) / Anniversary song (The) / It's easy to remember / Come rain or come shine / It all depends on you / Little white lies / Golden earrings / I'll be seeing you / Lavender blue / Laughing on the outside / I get along without you very well.
Album: released on Memoir, Jan'87 by Memoir Records. Dist: PRT Distribution

Cassette: released on Memoir, Jun'86 by Memoir Records. Dist: PRT Distribution

MOMENTS LIKE THESE.
Tracks: / Deep purple / When the world was young / Moments like this / I'll remember April / These foolish things / I fall in love too easily / What's new / I can dream, can't I? / Now I know / How long as this been going on? / Something wonderful.
Album: released on RCA, Jun'87 by RCA Records. Dist: RCA, Roots, Swift, Wellard, Chris, I & B, Solomon & Peres Distribution

Cassette: released on RCA, Jun'87 by RCA Records. Dist: RCA, Roots, Swift, Wellard, Chris, I & B, Solomon & Peres Distribution

Album: released on RCA, Jun'87 by RCA Records. Dist: RCA, Roots, Swift, Wellard, Chris, I & B, Solomon & Peres Distribution

Cassette: released on RCA, Jun'87 by RCA Records. Dist: RCA, Roots, Swift, Wellard, Chris, I & B, Solomon & Peres Distribution

Shorter, Wayne

ADAM'S APPLE.
Tracks: / Adam's apple / 502 Blues (drinkin' and drivin') / El gaucho / Footprints / Teru / Chief Crazy Horse / Collector (The).
Compact disc: released on EMI, Mar'87 by EMI Records. Dist: EMI

Album: released on Blue Note, Oct'85 by EMI Records. Dist: EMI

Cassette: released on Blue Note, Sep'87 by EMI Records. Dist: EMI. Estim retail price in Sep'87 was £5.99.

ATLANTIS.
Album: released on CBS, Oct'85 by CBS Records. Dist: CBS

Cassette: released on CBS, Oct'85 by CBS Records. Dist: CBS

BLUES A LA CARTE.
Album: released on Affinity, Nov'85 by Charly Records. Dist: Charly, Cadillac

JUJU.
Tracks: / Juju / Deluge / House of jade / Mahjong / Yes & no / Twelve more bars to go.
Compact disc: released on Manhattan-Blue Note, May'87 by EMI America Records (USA). Dist: EMI

Cassette: released on Blue Note, Sep'87 by EMI Records. Dist: EMI. Estim retail price in Sep'87 was £5.99.

JU-JU.
Album: released on Blue Note, Apr'85 by EMI Records. Dist: EMI

PHANTOM NAVIGATOR.
Tracks: / Condition red / Mahogany bird / Remote control / Yamanja / Forbidden / Plan-it! / Flagships.
Compact disc: released on CBS, Apr'87 by CBS Records. Dist: CBS

PHANTOM NAVIGATOR.
Tracks: / Condition red / Mahogany bird / Remote control / Ya manja / Forbidden, plan-it! / Flagships.
Album: released on CBS, Mar'87 by CBS Records. Dist: CBS

Cassette: released on CBS, Mar'87 by CBS Records. Dist: CBS

SECOND GENESIS.
Album: released on Affinity, Mar'84 by Charly Records. Dist: Charly, Cadillac

SOOTHSAYER, THE.
Album: released on Liberty-United, Jun'80 by EMI Records. Dist: EMI

Album: released on Affinity, Sep'84 by Charly Records. Dist: Charly, Cadillac

SPEAK NO EVIL.
Tracks: / Witch hunt / Fee-fi-fo-fum / Dance candaverous / Speak no evil / Infant eyes / Wild flower / Out to lunch / Straight up & down / Witch hunt / Fee-fi-fo-fum / Dance cadaverous / Speak no evil / Infant eyes / Wild flower.
Notes: P 1987 Manhattan records,a division of Capitol records Inc.
Compact disc: released on Manhattan-Blue Note, May'87 by EMI America Records (USA). Dist: EMI

Compact disc: released on Blue Note, Jun'87 by EMI Records. Dist: EMI

Album: released on Blue Note (USA Import), Sep'84

WAYNING MOMENTS.
Tracks: / Black orpheus / Devils' Island / Moon of Manakoora / Dead end / Wayning moments / Powder keg / All or nothing at all / Callaway went that-a-way.
Notes: A Vee Jay Recording. Licensed from Charly Records International APS.
Compact disc: released on Charly, Nov'86 by Charly Records. Dist: Charly, Cadillac

Shorthouse, Bert

DANCE AWAY (Shorthouse, Bert & The Glenlomond Scottish Band).
Album: released on Lochshore, May'81 by Klub Records. Dist: PRT

Cassette: released on Lochshore, May'81 by Klub Records. Dist: PRT

...WITH FRIENDS (Shorthouse, Bert & The Glenlomond Scottish Band).
Cassette: released on Lochshore, Jul'82 by Klub Records. Dist: PRT

Album: released on Lochshore, Jul'82 by Klub Records. Dist: PRT

Short, J.D.

EARLY RECORDINGS 1930-33.
Album: released on Wolf (Austria), Aug'85

LEGACY OF THE BLUES.
Album: released on Sonet, '73 by Sonet Records. Dist: PRT

Short, Memphis

I'M JUST ME...COUNTRY STYLE.
Album: released on Tank, Nov'79 by Tank Records.

Short People

WHY'D YOU PUT IT TO ME BABY.
Single (7"): released on Inferno, Sep'79 by Inferno Records. Dist: Inferno, Cartel, Pinnacle

Shorts

COMMENT CA VA.
Single (7"): released on EMI, Jul'83 by EMI Records. Dist: EMI

Shorty The President

PRESENTING SHORTY.
Album: released on Cactus, Aug'76 by Creole Records. Dist: CBS

Shoscombe Old Place

SHOSCOMBE OLD PLACE various artists (Various Artists).
Cassette: released on Anvil, Jan'81 Dist: Anv

Shot

MAIN THING.
Tracks: / Main thing / Main dub.
Notes: Featuring Kim Marsh
Single (12"): released on Affair, Sep'86 Dist: DMS, RCA

Shotgun

BORN TO ROCK.
Album: released on Rockhouse(USA), Nov'

GREY COAT BOY(EP).
Single (7"): released on Billy Goat, Apr'79 Chick-A-Boom Records. Dist: PRT

TENNESSEE ROCKIN'.
Album: released on Magnum Force, Jul'82 Magnum Music Group Ltd. Dist: Magnum Music Group Ltd, PRT, Spartan

Shotgun Brides
RESTLESS.
Single (7"): released on Neat, Apr'87 by Neat Records. Dist: Pinnacle, Neat

Shotgun Express
I COULD FEEL THE WHOLE WORLD TURN AROUND.
Single 10": released on See For Miles, Jun'83 by Charly Records. Dist: Spartan

Shotts & Dykehead...
CHAMPION OF CHAMPIONS (Shotts & Dykehead Caledonia Pipe Band).
Album: released on Lismor, Jul'81 by Lismor Records. Dist: Lismor, Roots, Celtic Music

Cassette: released on Lismor, Jul'81 by Lismor Records. Dist: Lismor, Roots, Celtic Music

SHORES OF LOCH KATRINE (Shotts & Dykehead Caledonia Pipe Band).
Album: released on Lismor, '74 by Lismor Records. Dist: Lismor, Roots, Celtic Music

SHOTTS & DYKEHEAD CALEDONIA PIPE BAND (Shotts & Dykehead Caledonia Pipe Band).
Album: released on Lismor, Nov'76 by Lismor Records. Dist: Lismor, Roots, Celtic Music

Shout
STARTING LINE.
Single (7"): released on Mercury, Apr'82 by Phonogram Records. Dist: Polygram Distribution

SUSPICION.
Single (12"): released on Passion, Jan'85 by Skratch Records. Dist: PRT

TRIBAL.
Single (7"): released on Lost Moments, Feb'85 Dist: Backs, Cartel

Shout-A-Loud
4 MINUTE WARNING.
Single (7"): released on Vroom, Mar'83

Shouters
SHOUTERS various artists (Various Artists).
Album:

Showaddywaddy
GOOD TIMING.
Single (7"): released on Bell, Feb'82 by Arista Records. Dist: Polygram

GOODY GOODY.
Single (7"): released on RCA, Nov'82 by RCA Records. Dist: RCA, Roots, Swift, Wellard, Chris, I & B, Solomon & Peres Distribution

GREATEST HITS:SHOWADDYWADDY.
Album: released on Genie, Nov'86 by Genie Records. Dist: Spartan, CBS

Cassette: released on Genie, Nov'86 by Genie Records. Dist: Spartan, CBS

LIVING LEGENDS.
Album: released on RCA, Feb'83 by RCA Records. Dist: RCA, Roots, Swift, Wellard, Chris, I & B, Solomon & Peres Distribution

Cassette: released on RCA, Feb'83 by RCA Records. Dist: RCA, Roots, Swift, Wellard, Chris, I & B, Solomon & Peres Distribution

ROCK ON WITH SHOWADDYWADDY.
Album: released on MFP, Aug'81 by EMI Records. Dist: EMI

Cassette: released on MFP, Aug'81 by EMI Records. Dist: EMI

SHOWADDYWADDY.
Album: released on Hallmark, Feb'82 by Pickwick Records. Dist: Pickwick Distribution, PRT, Taylors

Cassette: released on Hallmark, Feb'82 by Pickwick Records. Dist: Pickwick Distribution, PRT, Taylors

SOUL & INSPIRATION.
Single (7"): released on RCA, Jan'83 by RCA Records. Dist: RCA, Roots, Swift, Wellard, Chris, I & B, Solomon & Peres Distribution

UNDER THE MOON OF LOVE.
Tracks: / Under the moon of love / Rock 'n' roll lady / When / Heartbeat.
Single (7"): released on Genie, Aug'86 by Genie Records. Dist: Spartan, CBS

Single (12"): released on Genie, Aug'86 by Genie Records. Dist: Spartan, CBS

Album: released on MFP, Apr'85 by EMI Records. Dist: EMI

Cassette: released on MFP, Apr'85 by EMI Records. Dist: EMI

WHO PUT THE BOMP.
Single (7"): released on RCA, Aug'82 by RCA Records. Dist: RCA, Roots, Swift, Wellard, Chris, I & B, Solomon & Peres Distribution

Showbiz Club Of Belfast
MEXICO HERE WE GO.
Tracks: / Mexico here we go / Northern Ireland.
Single (7"):

Showboat
SHOWBOAT Original soundtrack (Various Artists).
Compact disc: released on CBS, May'87 by CBS Records. Dist: CBS

SHOW BOAT Original soundtrack.
Tracks: / Make believe / Bill / Life upon the wicked stage / You are love / Can't help lovin' dat man / Life upon the wicked stage / You are love / I might fall back on you / Why do I love you / Ol' man river.
Album: released on CBS, Jul'86 by CBS Records. Dist: CBS

Cassette: released on CBS, Jul'86 by CBS Records. Dist: CBS

SHOWBOAT Original 1971 London Cast (Various Artists).
Album: released on That's Entertainment, Apr'83 by That's Entertainment Records. Dist: Pinnacle, PRT

Cassette: released on That's Entertainment, Apr'83 by That's Entertainment Records. Dist: Pinnacle, PRT

SHOWBOAT & THE GAY OLD DOG read by Edna Ferber (Ferber, Edna).
Cassette: released on Caedmon(USA), Aug'83 by Caedmon (USA) Records. Dist: Gower, Taylors, Discovery

Showcase Of Stars
SHOWCASE OF STARS various artists (Various Artists).
Album: released on Homespun(Ireland), Jun'83 by Outlet Records. Dist: Outlet

Cassette: released on Homespun(Ireland), Jun'83 by Outlet Records. Dist: Outlet

Show Classics
SHOW CLASSICS various artists (Various Artists).
Triple album / cassette: released on Telstar, Nov'84 by Telstar Records. Dist: RCA Distribution

Triple album / cassette: released on Telstar, Nov'84 by Telstar Records. Dist: RCA Distribution

Show Side Of David Jacobs
SHOW SIDE OF DAVID JACOBS various artists (Jacobs, David with various artists).
Album: released on BBC, Aug'84 by BBC Records & Tapes. Dist: EMI, PRT, Pye

Showstoppers
AIN'T NOTHING BUT A HOUSE PARTY.
Single (7"): released on Inferno, Sep'79 by Inferno Records. Dist: Inferno, Cartel, Pinnacle

Single (7"): released on Neil Rushton, Apr'83

Single (12"): released on Neil Rushton, Apr'83

Single (7"): released on USA Import, '80

Showstoppers 81
DISCO SOUND OF MUSIC.
Single (7"): released on Whisper, Sep'81 by Whisper Records. Dist: Spartan

Single (12"): released on Whisper, Sep'81 by Whisper Records. Dist: Spartan

Shox Lumania
LIVE AT THE PEPPERMINT LOUNGE.
Cassette: released on Reach Out Int, '83

Shreeve, Mark
ASSASSIN.
Album: released on Uniton, Sep'83

Album: released on Jive Electro, Sep'84 by Zomba Records. Dist: RCA

Cassette: released on Jive Electro, Sep'84 by Zomba Records. Dist: RCA

CARE.
Album: released on Y, Mar'83

Cassette: released on Y, Mar'83

LEGION.
Album: released on Jive, Aug'85 by Zomba Records. Dist: RCA, PRT, CBS

Cassette: released on Jive, Aug'85 by Zomba Records. Dist: RCA, PRT, CBS

Single (7"): released on Jive Electro, Aug'85 by Zomba Records. Dist: RCA

Single (12"): released on Jive Electro, Aug'85 by Zomba Records. Dist: RCA

THOUGHTS OF WAR.
Album: released on Uniton, Sep'84

Shrew Kings
GREEN EYED KID.
Tracks: / Green eyed kid / One day in hell / This is the land / Mac the knife (radio version) / Alabama song.
Single (12"): released on Thin Sliced, Feb'87 by Thin Sliced Records. Dist: Rough Trade Distribution, Cartel Distribution

PLAY BRECHT.
Single (7"): released on Thin Sliced, Jun'85 by Thin Sliced Records. Dist: Rough Trade Distribution, Cartel Distribution

SAD BUT TRUE.
Album: released on Thin Sliced, Apr'86 by Thin Sliced Records. Dist: Rough Trade Distribution, Cartel Distribution

Shriekback
ACCRETIONS Monstrous dance mix.
Single (12"): released on Y, Aug'83

BEST OF SHRIEKBACK.
Compact disc:

BIG NIGHT MUSIC.
Tracks: / Underwaterboys / Exquisite / Reptiles and I (The) / Sticky jazz / Cradle song / Black light trap / Gunning for the Buddha / Running on the rocks / Shining path / Pretty little things.
Notes: Produced by Gavin MacKillop and Barry Andrews
Album: released on Island, Jan'87 by Island Records. Dist: Polygram

Cassette: released on Island, Jan'87 by Island Records. Dist: Polygram

Compact disc: released on Island, Jan'87 by Island Records. Dist: Polygram

FISH BELOW THE ICE.
Single (12"): released on Arista, Sep'85 by Arista Records. Dist: RCA

GUNNING FOR BUDDHA.
Tracks: / Bludgeoned / Black light trap*.
Notes: * Extra track on 12" version only
Single (12"): released on Island, Dec'86 by Island Records. Dist: Polygram

Single (12"): released on Island, Dec'86 by Island Records. Dist: Polygram

HAND ON MY HEART.
Single (7"): released on Arista, Jun'84 by Arista Records. Dist: RCA

Single (12"): released on Arista, Jun'84 by Arista Records. Dist: RCA

Single (12"): released on Arista, Jun'84 by Arista Records. Dist: RCA

Picture disc single: released on Arista, Aug'84 by Arista Records. Dist: RCA

INFINITE, THE.
Album: released on Kaz, Oct'85 by Kaz Records. Dist: PRT

Cassette: released on Kaz, Oct'85 by Kaz Records. Dist: PRT

JAM SCIENCE.
Album: released on Arista, Jul'84 by Arista Records. Dist: RCA

Cassette: released on Arista, Jul'84 by Arista Records. Dist: RCA

LINED UP.
Single (7"): released on Y, Feb'83

Single (12"): released on Y, Feb'83

LINED UP (REMIX).
Single (7"): released on Y, Aug'83

MERCY DASH.
Single (7"): released on Arista, Nov'84 by Arista Records. Dist: RCA

Picture disc single: released on Arista, Nov'84 by Arista Records. Dist: RCA

MY SPINE IS THE BASS LINE.
Single (7"): released on Y, Sep'82

Single (12"): released on Y, Sep'82

NEMESIS.
Single (7"): released on Arista, May'85 by Arista Records. Dist: RCA

Single (12"): released on Arista, May'85 by Arista Records. Dist: RCA

Single (12"): released on Arista, Jun'85 by Arista Records. Dist: RCA

OIL AND GOLD.
Album: released on Arista, Jul'85 by Arista Records. Dist: RCA

Cassette: released on Arista, Jul'85 by Arista Records. Dist: RCA

SEXTHINKONE.
Single (7"): released on Y, Jun'82

TENCH.
Extended-play record: released on Y, Jun'82

Extended-play record: released on Y, Jun'82

WORKING ON THE GROUND.
Single (7"): released on Y, Jun'83

Single (12"): released on Y, Jun'83

Shrieve
THROUGH THE FIRE (Shrieve, Hagar, Schon, Aaronson).

Shrinking Men
HAZARDS IN THE HOME.
Extended-play record: released on Pop, Feb'82 by Magnet Records. Dist: RCA

ZAMBESI MISSION.
Single (7"): released on Pop, Mar'81 by Magnet Records. Dist: RCA

Shropshire Lad
SHROPSHIRE LAD, A.
Double Album: released on Meridian, May'80 Dist: Harmonia Mundi Distributors

Double cassette: released on Meridian, May'80 Dist: Harmonia Mundi Distributors

Shtokolov, Boris
RUSSIAN SONGS & ROMANCES (BORIS SHTOKOLOV).
Cassette: released on Melodiya (USSR), Feb'79 Dist: T.B.C Distribution

Shucks
HILLBILLY SWING.
Album: released on Sweet Folk All, May'81 by Sweet Folk All Records. Dist: Sweet Folk All, Roots, Celtic Music, Dragon, Impetus, Projection, Chris Wellard, Festival Records

TWO DAYS TWO TRACKS.
Album: released on Sweet Folk All, May'81 by Sweet Folk All Records. Dist: Sweet Folk All, Roots, Celtic Music, Dragon, Impetus, Projection, Chris Wellard, Festival Records

Shulzhenko, K
FOLK SONGS.
Cassette: released on Melodiya (USSR), Feb'79 Dist: T.B.C Distribution

Shunters
SINCE MORNING.
Album: released on Charly, Feb'82 by Charly Records. Dist: Charly, Cadillac

Shusha
DURABLE FIRE Songs by English poets.
Album: released on Linnet, Sep'82

FROM EAST TO WEST.
Cassette: released on Tangent, Jan'82 by Tangent Records. Dist: Roots Records Distribution, Impetus Distribution, H.R. Taylor Distribution, Jazz Music Distribution, JSU Distribution, Projection Distribution, Gordon Duncan Distribution, Ross Records Distribution

HERE I LOVE YOU.
Album: released on Rhapsody, May'80 by President Records. Dist: Taylors, Swift, Jazz Music, Wellard, Chris

Single (7"): released on President, Oct'80 by President Records. Dist: Taylors, Spartan

Shute, Nevil
ON THE BEACH.
Cassette: released on Listen For Pleasure, Oct'85 by MFP Records. Dist: EMI

Shuttleworth, John
SWIMMING WITH SHARON.
Single (7"): released on Idea, Jun'87 by Idea Records. Dist: Rough Trade, Cartel

Single (12"): released on Idea, Jun'87 by Idea Records. Dist: Rough Trade, Cartel

Shy

BRAVE THE STORM.
Album: released on RCA, May'85 by RCA Records. Dist: RCA, Roots, Swift, Wellard, Chris, I & B, Solomon & Peres Distribution

Cassette: released on RCA, May'85 by RCA Records. Dist: RCA, Roots, Swift, Wellard, Chris, I & B, Solomon & Peres Distribution

EXCESS ALL AREAS.
Tracks: / Emergency / Can't fight the nights / Young heart / Just love me / Break down the walls / Under fire / Devil woman / Talk to me / When the love is over / Telephone.
Album: released on RCA, Jan'87 by RCA Records. Dist: RCA, Roots, Swift, Wellard, Chris, I & B, Solomon & Peres Distribution

Cassette: released on RCA, Jan'87 by RCA Records. Dist: RCA, Roots, Swift, Wellard, Chris, I & B, Solomon & Peres Distribution

Compact disc: released on RCA, Apr'87 by RCA Records. Dist: RCA, Roots, Swift, Wellard, Chris, I & B, Solomon & Peres Distribution

HOLD ON(TO YOUR LOVE).
Single (7"): released on RCA, Mar'85 by RCA Records. Dist: RCA, Roots, Swift, Wellard, Chris, I & B, Solomon & Peres Distribution

Single (12"): released on RCA, Mar'85 by RCA Records. Dist: RCA, Roots, Swift, Wellard, Chris, I & B, Solomon & Peres Distribution

ONCE BITTEN TWICE SHY.
Album: released on Ebony, Nov'83 by Ebony Records. Dist: Pinnacle, Ebony

REFLECTIONS.
Single (7"): released on RCA, May'85 by RCA Records. Dist: RCA, Roots, Swift, Wellard, Chris, I & B, Solomon & Peres Distribution

Single (12"): released on RCA, May'85 by RCA Records. Dist: RCA, Roots, Swift, Wellard, Chris, I & B, Solomon & Peres Distribution

YOUNG HEART.
Tracks: / Young heart / Run for cover / Don't want to lose your love*.
Notes: *Extra track on 12" only
Single (7"): released on RCA, Apr'87 by RCA Records. Dist: RCA, Roots, Swift, Wellard, Chris, I & B, Solomon & Peres Distribution

Single (12"): released on RCA, Apr'87 by RCA Records. Dist: RCA, Roots, Swift, Wellard, Chris, I & B, Solomon & Peres Distribution

Shygula

IT'S MUCH BETTER NOW.
Single (7"): released on Proto, Sep'83 by Proto Records. Dist: WEA

Shy, Jean

TOUGH ENOUGH.
Album: released on Record Shack, Jul'85 by Record Shack Records. Dist: PRT

TOUGH ENOUGH (Shy, Jean & Hannsjorg Scheid).
Tracks: / Are you tough enough / Maze (I just wanna escape) / How can you say that you're the one? / Rock my body tonight / Someday I'll go to Africa / Ricky tick / I wish I could find the way / Then you came.
Album: released on Record Shack, Oct'86 by Record Shack Records. Dist: PRT

Shy Tots

GALLERY.
Album: released on Shy Tots, Mar'83 by Shy Tots Records. Dist: Rough Trade

Siam

FAREWELL.
Album: released on VM, Jan'83 by VM Records. Dist: PRT

Album: released on VM, Jan'83 by VM Records. Dist: PRT

Sian

FIGHT THE DRAGON.
Single (7"): released on Big Ben, Jul'85 by Big Ben Records. Dist: Spartan, Taylor, H.R.

Sibble, Leroy

DANCEHALL STYLE.
Single (12"): released on Ranking Joe, Jun'85 by Ranking Joe Records. Dist: Jetstar

I DON'T KNOW.
Tracks: / I don't know / Your love is real.
Single (12"): released on Ranking Joe, Apr'86 by Ranking Joe Records. Dist: Jetstar

LOVE WON'T COME EASY.
Tracks: / Keep on knocking.
Single (12"): released on Greensleeves, Jan'87 by Greensleeves Records. Dist: BMG, Jetstar, Spartan

NEVER GONNA GIVE YOU UP.
Tracks: / Never gonna give you up.
Single (12"): released on Rhythms, Apr'86 by Rhythms Records. Dist: Jetstar

ONLY WITH YOU.
Single (12"): released on Micron, Dec'83 by Micron Records. Dist: Jetstar Distribution

ON TOP.
Cassette: released on Miccan, Sep'86 by Miccan Records. Dist: Jetstar Distribution

ROCK & COME ON.
Single (12"): released on Micron, Jul'83 by Micron Records. Dist: Jetstar Distribution

Siberian 4

HOMO LIBER.
Album: released on Leo, Sep'84 Dist: Recommended

Siberian Folk Choir

SIBERIAN STATE FOLK CHOIR.
Album: released on Melodiya (USSR), May'78 Dist: T.B.C Distribution

Siberry, Jane

SPECKLESS SKY, THE.
Tracks: / One more colour / Seven steps to the wall / Very large hat, The / Mien bitte / Vladimir - Vladimir / Mimi on the beach / Map of the world / Empty city, The / Taxi ride, The.
Album: released on WEA, Jun'87 by WEA Records. Dist: WEA

Cassette: released on WEA, Jun'87 by WEA Records. Dist: WEA

Sibley, Don E

PUNK BASHING BOOGIE.
Single (7"): released on Hot Rock, Jan'80 by Hot Rock Records. Dist: Hot Rock

Sicily

FOLK MUSIC & SONGS OF SICILY various artists (Various Artists).
Album: released on Lyrichord (USA), Oct'81 by Lyrichord Records (USA). Dist: Flexitron Distributors Ltd

Sickidz

I COULD GO TO HELL FOR YOU (EP).
Single (12"): released on Big Beat, Jun'84 by Ace Records. Dist: Projection, Pinnacle

Sick Rose

FACES.
Album: released on Electric Eye, Mar'87 by Electric Eye Records. Dist: Red Rhino, Cartel

Sick Things

ANTI-SOCIAL DISEASE (EP).
Single (7"): released on Chaos, Nov'83 by Backs Records. Dist: Nine Mile, Cartel

LEGENDARY SICK THINGS (EP).
Single (7"): released on Chaos, Jan'84 by Backs Records. Dist: Nine Mile, Cartel

Sicroff, Elan

JOURNEYS TO INACCESIBLE PLACES AND OTHER MUSIC.
Album: released on E.G., Jul'87 by Virgin Records. Dist: Virgin, EMI

Cassette: released on E.G., Jul'87 by Virgin Records. Dist: Virgin, EMI

JOURNEY TO INACCESIBLE PLACES AND OTHER MUSIC.
Album: released on E.G., Jun'87 by Virgin Records. Dist: Virgin, EMI

Cassette: released on E.G., Jun'87 by Virgin Records. Dist: Virgin, EMI

Siddleys

WHAT WENT WRONG THIS TIME?.
Single (7"): released on Medium Cool, Aug'87 Dist: Red Rhino Distribution, Cartel Distribution

Sideboard, Sid

BUCKET & SPADES (Sideboard, Sid & The Chairs).
Single (7"): released on PRT, Jul'82 by PRT Records. Dist: PRT

Sidebottom, Frank

CHRISTMAS IS REALLY FANTASTIC.
Single (7"): released on In Tape, Dec'86 by In Tape Records. Dist: Red Rhino, Cartel

I'M THE URBAN SPACEMAN.
Tracks: / I'm the urban spaceman / Oh supermum / Sci-fi medley / Space is ace / Robot Frank / Fireball XL5 / Life on Mars / Close encounters of the third kind.
Single (7"): released on Zonophone, Jul'86 by EMI Records. Dist: EMI

Picture disc single: released on Zonophone, Jul'86 by EMI Records. Dist: EMI

Single (12"): released on Zonophone, Jul'86 by EMI Records. Dist: EMI

OH BLIMEY IT'S CHRISTMAS.
Single (7"): released on Regal Zonophone, Nov'85 by EMI Music Ltd.

Single (12"): released on Regal Zonophone, Nov'85 by EMI Music Ltd.

POPULAR MEDLEY.
Single (7"): released on Regal Zonophone, Aug'85 by EMI Music Ltd.

Side By Side

SIDE BY SIDE various artists (Various Artists).
Album: released on CBS, May'80 by CBS Records. Dist: CBS

Cassette: released on CBS, May'80 by CBS Records. Dist: CBS

Side Effect

ALL ABOARD.
Album: released on Elektra, Jul'82 by WEA Records. Dist: WEA

ALWAYS THERE.
Tracks: / Always there.
Single (12"): released on Streetwave, Dec'85 by Streetwave Records. Dist: PRT Distribution

PORTRAITS.
Album: released on Asylum, May'81 by WEA Records. Dist: WEA

Side Effects

SIDE EFFECTS, THE.
Album: released on Armageddon, Jul'82 by Armageddon Records. Dist: Revolver, Cartel, Pinnacle

Side On

MAGIC.
Single (7"): released on Beggars Banquet, Feb'82 by Beggars Banquet Records. Dist: WEA

Single (12"): released on Beggars Banquet, Feb'82 by Beggars Banquet Records. Dist: WEA

Sideway Look

SIDEWAY LOOK.
Album: released on Virgin, Sep'84 by Virgin Records. Dist: EMI, Virgin Distribution

Cassette: released on Virgin, Sep'84 by Virgin Records. Dist: EMI, Virgin Distribution

Sidewinder

ALL WOUND UP.
Album: released on Tank, Jun'79 by Tank Records.

BASIL HEARD / THE GAME.
Single (7"): released on Pope Creation, Dec'83

Sid & Nancy

SID & NANCY - LOVE KILLS Original soundtrack (Various Artists).
Tracks: / Love kills / Haunted / Pleasure and pain / Chinese choppers / She never took no for an answer / Love kills / Off the boat / Dum dum club / Burning room / Junk theme / I wanna be your dog / Taxi to heaven.
Notes: Original soundtrack album to the new Alex Cox movie about the story of Sid Vicious and Nancy Spungen.
Album: released on MCA, Aug'86 by MCA Records. Dist: Polygram, MCA

Cassette: released on MCA, Aug'86 by MCA Records. Dist: Polygram, MCA

Siebel, Paul

LIVE WITH DAVID BROMBERG & GARY WHITE.
Album: released on Rag Baby, Mar'81 Dist: Pinnacle, Red Lightnin' Distribution

Siegel, Janis

AT HOME.
Tracks: / Trouble man / Small day tomorrow / Million dollar secret, the / Night trane / Bob White / (If I had) rhythm in my nursery rhymes / Back coffee / From Vienna with love / Cruel master of my dreams, The.
Album: released on Atlantic, Jul'87 by WEA Records. Dist: WEA

Cassette: released on Atlantic, Jul'87 by WEA Records. Dist: WEA

BACK TO THE ISLAND / DON'T GET SCARED.
Single (7"): released on Atlantic, Oct'82 by WEA Records. Dist: WEA

Siege Of Troy

SIEGE OF TROY Various artists (Various Artists).
Cassette: released on Anvil, Jul'82 Dist: Anvil

Sievey, Chris

BAISER / LAST.
Single (7"): released on Rabid, Sep'82 by Rabid Records. Dist: Pinnacle, Rough Trade

CAMOFLAGE / ZX 81 PROGRAMS / FLYING TRAIN / F T.
Single (7"): released on EMI, Jun'83 by EMI Records. Dist: EMI

Cassette single: released on EMI, Jun'83 by EMI Records. Dist: EMI

RED INDIAN MUSIC.
Single (7"): released on Razz, Sep'82 by Razz. Dist: Pinnacle

WE'RE LIKE YOU (Sievey, Chris & The Freshies).
Single (7"): released on Razz, Sep'81 by Razz. Dist: Pinnacle

Siffre, Labi

IT MUST BE LOVE.
Tracks: / It must be love / Crying, laughing, loving, lying.
Single (7"): released on Old Gold, Oct'86 by Old Gold Records. Dist: Lightning, Jazz Music, Spartan, Counterpoint

LABI SIFFRE COLLECTION (THE).
Tracks: / Make my day / Too late / Watch me / My song / For the children / It must be love / Prayer / Crying, laughing, loving, lying / Nothing in the world like love / If you have faith / Some say / Fool me a good night / Just a little more line / Give love.
Cassette: released on Conifer, Jan'86 by Conifer Records. Dist: Conifer

Cassette: released on Conifer, Jan'86 by Conifer Records. Dist: Conifer

SOMETHING INSIDE.
Single (7"): released on China, Feb'87 by Chrysalis Records. Dist: Chrysalis

Single (12"): released on China, Feb'87 by Chrysalis Records. Dist: Chrysalis

Sigerson, Davitt

DAVITT SIGERSON.
Album: released on Island, Jul'80 by Island Records. Dist: Polygram

FALLING IN LOVE AGAIN.
Album: released on ZE, Jul'84 by Island Records. Dist: Polygram

Cassette: released on ZE, Jul'84 by Island Records. Dist: Polygram

Siglo XX

ART OF WAR.
Single (12"): released on Antler, May'82 by Antler Records (Belgium). Dist: Red Rhino, Cart

DREAMS OF PLEASURE.
Single (12"): released on Antler, Dec'83 by Antler Records (Belgium). Dist: Red Rhino, Car

DUBBEL LP.
Album: released on Antelope, Mar'85 by Red Rhino Records. Dist: Cartel

FLOWERS FOR THE REBELS.
Album: released on Play It Again Sam, Apr Dist: Red Rhino, Cartel

IN THE GARDENS.
Single (7"): released on Paragon, May'84 Paragon Records. Dist: Paragon

TILL THE END OF THE NIGHT.
Single (12"): released on Play It Again Sa Feb'87 Dist: Red Rhino, Cartel

Signal To Noise Set

SIGNAL TO NOISE SET various art (Various Artists).
Album: released on Only A Revolution, Dec by Only A Revolution Records., Rough Tr Distribution, Cartel Distribution, Jungle Distr tion

Signature Tunes

SIGNATURE TUNES (Various Artists).
Tracks: / Christ via wires / Bounds of son,bonds of love / Belle dux on the bea leyasu / Portrait of Jan with moon and st West deep / Feels like winter again / This ill / Highway 2000 / Airfields / Certain bridge Telecommunication.
Album: released on Cocteau, Nov'85 by C teau Records. Dist: Pinnacle, IDS

Cassette: released on Cocteau, Nov'85 Cocteau Records. Dist: Pinnacle, IDS

Sign Language

BELIEF AND OTHER CAUSES.
Tracks: / Belief and other causes.
Single (7"): released on Fire, Mar'86 by Twist and Shout Music. Dist: Nine Mile, Rough Trade, Cartel

MONTREUX.
Album: released on Windham Hill, Aug'87 Dist: AM

Cassette: released on Windham Hill, Aug'87 Dist: AM

Compact disc: released on Windham Hill, Aug'87 Dist: AM

Signorelli, Frank
1946-49

Sigue Sigue Sputnik

21ST CENTURY BOY.
Tracks: / 21st Century boy / Buy.
Single (7"): released on EMI, May'86 by EMI Records. Dist: EMI

Single (12"): released on EMI, May'86 by EMI Records. Dist: EMI

FLAUNT IT.
Tracks: / Love missile F1-11 / Sex bomb boogie / Atari baby / Rocket Miss U.S.A. / 21st Century boy / Massive retaliation / Teenage thunder / She's my man.
Compact disc: released on EMI, Dec'86 by EMI Records. Dist: EMI

Album: released on Parlophone, Jul'86 by EMI Records. Dist: EMI

Cassette: released on Parlophone, Jul'86 by EMI Records. Dist: EMI

Boxed set: released on Parlophone, Jul'86 by EMI Records. Dist: EMI

Boxed set: released on Parlophone, Jul'86 by EMI Records. Dist: EMI

LOVE MISSILE F1-11.
Tracks: / Love missile F1-11 / Hack attack / Love missile(dance mix)".
Notes: Extra track on 12" only
Single (7"): released on Parlophone, Feb'86 by EMI Records. Dist: EMI

Single (12"): released on Parlophone, Feb'86 by EMI Records. Dist: EMI

LOVE MISSILE F1-11(2).
Tracks: / Love missile F1-11 / Love missile F1-11(trailer video mix) / Love missile F1-11 / And actuality sound / Hack attack.
Single (12"): released on EMI, Mar'86 by EMI Records. Dist: EMI

VIDEO SINGLE.
Tracks: / Sex Bomb Boogie / Love Missile F1-11
Notes: The first ever video only single release. This version of "Sex bomb Boogie" is a brand new recording, previously unreleased and produced by Giorgio Moroder. Shot live at the Royal Albert Hall and also featuring spectacular footage from the block buster movie "The Terminator".
Video-cassette (VHS): released on PMI, Dec'86 by PMI Records. Dist: EMI

Sileas

DELIGHTED WITH HARPS.
Album: released on Lapwing, Jul'86 by Lapwing Records Ltd. Dist: Celtic Music, Projection, Roots Records, Ross, Gordon Duncan Distribution, Graham Tosh Distribution, Chans Records

Silencers

CAN'T CRY.
Tracks: / I can't cry / Crucify me / Blue desire".
Single (7"): released on RCA, Jul'87 by RCA Records. Dist: RCA, Roots, Swift, Wellard, Chris, I & B, Solomon & Peres Distribution

Single (12"): released on RCA, Jul'87 by RCA Records. Dist: RCA, Roots, Swift, Wellard, Chris, I & B, Solomon & Peres Distribution

LETTER FROM ST.PAUL, A.
Tracks: / Painted moon / I can't cry / Bullets & spires / God's gift / I need / I ought to know better from St.Paul, A / Blue desire / Possessed.
Cassette: released on RCA, Jun'87 by RCA Records. Dist: RCA, Roots, Swift, Wellard, Chris, I & B, Solomon & Peres Distribution

Album: released on RCA, Jun'87 by RCA Records. Dist: RCA, Roots, Swift, Wellard, Chris, I Solomon & Peres Distribution

Compact disc: released on RCA, May'87 by RCA Records. Dist: RCA, Roots, Swift, Wellard, Chris, I & B, Solomon & Peres Distribution

LETTERS FROM ST. PAUL.

Silence & The Beat

FREEZING POINT.
Tracks: / Freezing point (remix) / Freezing point (Inst).
Single (12"): released on Silver Lining, Nov'86

Single (7"): released on Silver Lining, Oct'86

Silent, B. C.

TAKE IT OR LEAVE IT.
Tracks: / Consequences.
Single (7"): released on Sonet, Jan'87 by Sonet Records. Dist: PRT

Silent Guests

HOUSE OF WAX.
Single (7"): released on Third World, Jun'82 Dist: Jetstar Distribution

IN MY SECRET GARDEN.
Album: released on T.W., May'82 by T.W. Records. Dist: Cartel

Silent Rage

OH BABY.
Single (7"): released on Lost Moment, May'85

Silent Rite

GREATEST SHOW.
Single (7"): released on 46 Records (Germany), Sep'83 by 46 Records (Germany). Dist: Rough Trade

Silent Running

EMOTIONAL WARFARE.
Single (7"): released on EMI, Mar'84 by EMI Records. Dist: EMI

Single (12"): released on EMI, Mar'84 by EMI Records. Dist: EMI

NO FAITH IS BLIND.
Single (12"): released on Parlophone, Oct'85 by EMI Records. Dist: EMI

SILENT RUNNING Original film soundtrack.
Album: released on Varese International, Mar'79

WHEN THE 12TH OF NEVER COMES.
Single (7"): released on EMI, Jun'83 by EMI Records. Dist: EMI

Silent Screen

HANDSTANDS.
Single (7"): released on TMI, May'84 by TMI Records. Dist: Red Rhino Distribution, Cartel Distribution

Silent Underdog

PAPA'S GOT A BRAND NEW PIGBAG.
Single (7"): released on Kaz, Jan'85 by Kaz Records. Dist: PRT

Single (12"): released on Kaz, Jan'85 by Kaz Records. Dist: PRT

Silhouette

CLOWN.
Single (7"): released on Thunderbay, Apr'83 Dist: Spartan Distribution

I CAN TAKE A HINT.
Single (7"): released on Spirit, Jun'84

MAKE THE MOST OF IT.
Single (7"): released on Spirit, Sep'85 by Spirit Records. Dist: WEA

NO GOOD SAYING NO GOOD.
Single (7"): released on Thunderbay, Apr'83 Dist: Spartan Distribution

Silhouettes

AIN'T SHE SWEET.
Album: released on Tema, Jun'86 by Tema Records. Dist: EMI

GET A JOB.
Tracks: / Get a job / Stagger Lee / Ten commandments of love.
Single (7"): released on Stateside, 23 May'87 Dist: EMI

Single (12"): released on Stateside, 23 May'87 Dist: EMI

Single (7"): released on Old Gold, Jul'82 by Old Gold Records. Dist: Lightning, Jazz Music, Spartan, Counterpoint

GO LATIN.
Album: released on Tema, Sep'82 by Tema Records. Dist: EMI

Silicon Chips

THEIR IMPACT.
Cassette: released on International Report, Oct'81 by Seminar Cassettes. Dist: Audio-Visual Library Services, Davidson Distribution, Eastern Educational Products Distrib., Forlaget Systime Distribution, MacDougall Distribution, Talktapes Distribution, Watkins Books Ltd Distribution, Norton, Jeff Distribution

THEIR USES.
Cassette: released on International Report, Oct'81 by Seminar Cassettes. Dist: Audio-Visual Library Services, Davidson Distribution, Eastern Educational Products Distrib., Forlaget Systime Distribution, MacDougall Distribution, Talktapes Distribution, Watkins Books Ltd Distribution, Norton, Jeff Distribution

Silicon Teens

JUDY IN DISGUISE/CHIP'N'ROLL.
Single (7"): released on Mute, Jan'80 Dist: Spartan Distribution, Rough Trade Distribution, Cartel Distribution

JUST LIKE EDDIE.
Single (7"): released on Mute, Jul'80 Dist: Spartan Distribution, Rough Trade Distribution, Cartel Distribution

MEMPHIS TENNESSEE/LET'S DANCE.
Single (7"): released on Mute, Aug'79 Dist: Spartan Distribution, Rough Trade Distribution, Cartel Distribution

MUSIC FOR PARTIES.
Album: released on Mute, '81 Dist: Spartan Distribution, Rough Trade Distribution, Cartel Distribution

Silk

FLY AWAY.
Single (7"): released on Stage One, Apr'84 by Stage One Records. Dist: Stage One Distribution

Silk, J.M.

I CAN'T TURN AROUND.
Tracks: / I can't turn round.
Single (7"): released on RCA, Oct'86 by RCA Records. Dist: RCA, Roots, Swift, Wellard, Chris, I & B, Solomon & Peres Distribution

Single (12"): released on RCA, Oct'86 by RCA Records. Dist: RCA, Roots, Swift, Wellard, Chris, I & B, Solomon & Peres Distribution

LET THE MUSIC TAKE CONTROL.
Tracks: / Insane apella mix.
Single (7"): released on RCA, Feb'87 by RCA Records. Dist: RCA, Roots, Swift, Wellard, Chris, I & B, Solomon & Peres Distribution

Single (12"): released on RCA, Feb'87 by RCA Records. Dist: RCA, Roots, Swift, Wellard, Chris, I & B, Solomon & Peres Distribution

SHE'S SO FAR AWAY.
Tracks: / She's so far away / Jack your body / House in B-minor" / I can't turn around".
Single (7"): released on RCA, 13 Jun'87 by RCA Records. Dist: RCA, Roots, Swift, Wellard, Chris, I & B, Solomon & Peres Distribution

Single (12"): released on RCA, 13 Jun'87 by RCA Records. Dist: RCA, Roots, Swift, Wellard, Chris, I & B, Solomon & Peres Distribution

Silk Stockings

SILK STOCKINGS (Various Artists).
Tracks: / Too many / Paris loves lovers / Stereophonic sound / It's a chemical reaction / That's all/all of you / Satin and silk / Silk stockings / Without love / Fated to be mated / Josephine / Sideria / Red blues.. / Ritz roll and rock / Too bad.
Album: released on CBS, Feb'87 by CBS Records. Dist: CBS

Cassette: released on CBS, Feb'87 by CBS Records. Dist: CBS

Silk & Suede

HITS OF THE 70'S.
Cassette: released on Kingfisher, Nov'81 Dist: PRT

Silk Touch

DREAMING OF BLONDIE.
Cassette: released on Kingfisher, Nov'81 Dist: PRT

Silkwood

SILKWOOD Original film soundtrack.
Album: released on DRG (USA), Apr'84 by DRG Records. Dist: Conifer, RCA

Cassette: released on DRG (USA), Apr'84 by DRG Records. Dist: Conifer, RCA

Silky

LEFT RIGHT CENTRE.
Single (7"): released on Panther, Sep'84 by MCA Records. Dist: CBS

Single (12"): released on Panther, Sep'84 by MCA Records. Dist: CBS

Silky Soul Hits

SILKY SOUL HITS OF THE 70'S various artists (Various Artists).
Album: released on Old Gold, Jun'85 by Old Gold Records. Dist: Lightning, Jazz Music, Spartan, Counterpoint

Cassette: released on Old Gold, Jun'85 by Old Gold Records. Dist: Lightning, Jazz Music, Spartan, Counterpoint

Silly Wizard

BEST OF SILLY WIZARD.
Album: released on Shanachie (Ireland), '85

CALEDONIAS HARDY SONS.
Album: released on Highway, Mar'85 by Highway Records. Dist: Roots, Projection, Ross

FIRST ALBUM.
Album: released on Highway, '85 by Highway Records. Dist: Roots, Projection, Ross

GLINT OF SILVER, A.
Album: released on Green Linnet(USA), Feb'87 by Green Linnet Records (USA). Dist: Projection

Cassette: released on WEA Ireland, Mar'87 by WEA Records. Dist: Celtic Distributions, Projection, I & B

GOLDEN GOLDEN.
Album: released on Rels, May'86 Dist: Projection

Cassette: released on Rels, May'86 Dist: Projection

GOLDEN,GOLDEN.
Album: released on R.E.L., Oct'85 by REL Records. Dist: Gordon Duncan Distribution, Celtic Music, Record Merchandisers Distribution, Projection, Graeme Tosh music

Cassette: released on R.E.L., Oct'85 by REL Records. Dist: Gordon Duncan Distribution, Celtic Music, Record Merchandisers Distribution, Projection, Graeme Tosh music

KISS THE TEARS AWAY.
Album: released on Highway, Nov'83 by Highway Records. Dist: Roots, Projection, Ross

Cassette: released on Highway, Nov'83 by Highway Records. Dist: Roots, Projection, Ross

LIVE IN AMERICA.
Album: released on R.E.L., Jun'85 by REL Records. Dist: Gordon Duncan Distribution, Celtic Music, Record Merchandisers Distribution, Projection, Graeme Tosh music

Cassette: released on R.E.L., Jun'85 by REL Records. Dist: Gordon Duncan Distribution, Celtic Music, Record Merchandisers Distribution, Projection, Graeme Tosh music

SO MANY PARTINGS.
Album: released on Highway, '81 by Highway Records. Dist: Roots, Projection, Ross

TAKE THE HIGH ROAD.
Single (7"): released on Highway, Oct'80 by Highway Records. Dist: Roots, Projection, Ross

WILD AND BEAUTIFUL.
Album: released on Highway, '85 by Highway Records. Dist: Roots, Projection, Ross

Silos

ABOUT HER STEPS.
Album: released on Frontier (USA), Aug'87 Dist: Cherry Red, Zippo, What Goes On

Silsoe

AZTEC GOLD The official ITV theme(World Cup).
Tracks: / Aztec gold / On wings of the wind.
Single (7"): released on CBS, May'86 by CBS Records. Dist: CBS

TWO OF US, THE.
Tracks: / Genesis-A.O.N.
Single (7"): released on Sierra, Dec'86 by Sierra Records. Dist: WEA

Silver

I CRY A RIVER.
Album: released on Orbitone, Aug'78 by Orbitone Records. Dist: Jetstar Distribution

Silvera, Carmen

ALLO'ALLO.
Tracks: / Under the bridges of Paris.
Single (7"): released on First Night, Nov'86 by Safari Records. Dist: Pinnacle

Silvera, Jeanette
WHEN I NEED YOU.
Album: released on Wild Flower, Jun'84 by Wild Flower Records. Dist: Jetstar

Silver Bow
SHETLAND FOLK FIDDLING vol 1.
Album: released on Topic, '81 by Topic Records. Dist: JSU Distribution, Projection Distribution, Jazz Music Distribution

Silver Condor
SILVER CONDOR.
Album: released on CBS, Nov'81 by CBS Records. Dist: CBS

Cassette: released on CBS, Nov'81 by CBS Records. Dist: CBS

Silver Convention
DISCOTHEQUE VOL 2.
Album: released on Magnet, Mar'76 by Magnet Records. Dist: BMG

FLY ROBIN FLY/GET UP & BOOGIE.
Single (7"): released on Magnet, Sep'81 by Magnet Records. Dist: BMG

GET UP AND BOOGIE.
Tracks: Fly Robin fly / Save me° / Everybody's talking 'bout love'.
Single (7"): released on Old Gold, Jan'87 by Old Gold Records. Dist: Lightning, Jazz Music, Spartan, Counterpoint

Single (12"): released on Old Gold, Jan'87 by Old Gold Records. Dist: Lightning, Jazz Music, Spartan, Counterpoint

Single (7"): released on Magnet, Mar'76 by Magnet Records. Dist: BMG

Silver, Damion
PUT YOUR HEAD ON MY SHOULDER.
Single (7"): released on AWA, Jul'84 by AWA Records. Dist: Pinnacle

Silver, Dave
GYM-PANIC.
Single (7"): released on Jungle, Jun'83 by Jungle Records. Dist: Jungle, Cartel

SPARKLING SOUND OF .. (Silver, Dave & His Band).
Album: released on ARC (Accordion Records), '84 Dist: Accordion Record Club

Silverhead
16 AND SAVAGED.
Album: released on Purple, Jun'85 by Purple Records. Dist: EMI

SILVERHEAD.
Album: released on Purple, Jun'85 by Purple Records. Dist: EMI

Silver, Horace
...AND THE JAZZ MESSENGERS.
Tracks: Room 608 / Creepin' in / Stop time / To whom it may concern / Hippy / Preacher, The / Hankerin / Doodlin'.
Compact disc: by EMI Records. Dist: EMI

BLOWIN'THE BLUES AWAY.
Cassette: released on Blue Note, Apr'87 by EMI Records. Dist: EMI

Album: released on Blue Note, Apr'87 by EMI Records. Dist: EMI

BLOWIN' THE BLUES AWAY (Silver, Horace Quintet).
Tracks: Blowin' the blues away / St. Vitus dance, The / Break city / Peace / Sister Sadie / Baghdad, The / Melancholy mood / How did it happen.
Cassette: released on Blue Note, May'87 by EMI Records. Dist: EMI

Compact disc: released on Blue Note, Sep'87 by EMI Records. Dist: EMI. Estim retail price in Sep'87 was £11.99.

FINGER POPPIN'.
Album: released on Blue Note (USA Import), Sep'84

FINGER POPPIN' WITH THE HORACE SILVER QUINTET (Silver, Horace Quintet).
Tracks: Finger poppin' / Juicy Lucy / Swingin' the samba / Sweet stuff / Cookin' at the Continental / Come on home / You happened my way / Mellow D.
Notes: This was the first of many Blue Note albums by Horace Silver's finest and longest-lasting band with trumpeter Blue Mitchell and tenor saxophonist Junior Cook. Like all of Silver's efforts, it is meticuously planned and performed as well as being drenched in earthy, soulful, lyrical feeling. Several Silver classics came out of this album, including 'Juicy Lucy', 'Cookin' at the Continental', 'Come on home' and the title tune.
Album: released on Blue Note, May'86 by EMI Records. Dist: EMI

HORACE SILVER ... AND THE JAZZ MESSENGERS (Silver, Horace & The Jazz Messengers).
Compact disc: released on Blue Note, Sep'87 by EMI Records. Dist: EMI. Estim retail price in Sep'87 was £11.99.

HORACE SILVER AND THE JAZZ MESSENGERS.
Cassette: released on Blue Note, May'87 by EMI Records. Dist: EMI

HORACE SILVER & THE JAZZ MESSENGERS (Silver, Horace & The Jazz Messengers).

Horace Silver & The Jazz Messengers
SERENADE TO A SOUL SISTER.
Tracks: Psychedelic Sally / Serenade to a soul sister / Rain dance / Jungle juice / Kindred spirits / Next time I fall in love.
Album: released on Manhattan, Nov'86 by President Records. Dist: Jazz Music, Swift, Taylors, Chris Wellard

SIX PIECES OF SILVER.
Album: released on Blue Note (USA Import), Sep'84

SONG FOR MY FATHER (Silver, Horace Quintet).
Tracks: Song for my father / Natives are restless tonight, The / Calcutta cutie / Que pasa / Kicker, the / Lonely woman.
Album: released on Blue Note, Mar'86 by EMI Records. Dist: EMI

Cassette: released on Blue Note, Mar'86 by EMI Records. Dist: EMI

Album: released on Blue Note, May'85 by EMI Records. Dist: EMI

Cassette: released on Blue Note, May'85 by EMI Records. Dist: EMI

Silver, Jimmy
RIGHT OLD KNEES UP, (A) (Silver, Jimmy & His Music).
Album: released on Decca, Dec'83 by Decca Records. Dist: Polygram

Silver, Karen
I DON'T WANNA FALL IN LOVE AGAIN.
Single (12"): released on Ecstasy, Apr'85 by Creole Records. Dist: CBS

Silver, Maxwell
17 AND READY.
Single (7"): released on BM, Mar'85 Dist: EMI, M.I.S.

MORE I LOOK, (THE).
Single (7"): released on BM, Jul'85 Dist: EMI, M.I.S.

Silver, Mick
EVERYTHING YOU NEED.
Single (7"): released on Legacy, Apr'85 Dist: PRT

Single (12"): released on Legacy, Apr'85 Dist: PRT

IT'S TRUE.
Tracks: It's true / Life in the shade.
Single (7"): released on Legacy, Apr'86 Dist: PRT

Single (12"): released on Legacy, Apr'86 Dist: PRT

LAST SONG, THE.
Tracks: Last song, The / Home again.
Single (7"): released on Carrere, Oct'86 by Carrere Records. Dist: PRT, Spartan

Single (12"): released on Carrere, Oct'86 by Carrere Records. Dist: PRT, Spartan

Silver, Mike
FREE.
Album: released on Silversound, Nov'85 Dist: Projection

Cassette: released on Silversound, Nov'85 Dist: Projection

Album: released on Silversound, Jan'85 Dist: Projection

NO MACHINE.
Notes: Silversound Distribution - Tel: 0478 832447.
Album: released on Silversound, Feb'87 Dist: Projection

Cassette: released on Silversound, Feb'87 Dist: Projection

Silver Pozzoli
AROUND MY DREAM.
Single (7"): released on Sierra, Jul'85 by Sierra Records. Dist: WEA

Single (12"): released on Sierra, Jul'85 by Sierra Records. Dist: WEA

Silvers, Colonel Jim
COLONEL JIM SILVERS.
Album: released on Rondelet, Nov'81 Dist: Spartan Distribution

CRYING MY HEART OUT OVER YOU.
Single (7"): released on Rondelet, Oct'81 Dist: Spartan Distribution

Silverstein, Shel
FREAKING AT THE FREAKERS' BALL.
Album: released on CBS, Oct'79 by CBS Records. Dist: CBS

Cassette: released on CBS, Oct'79 by CBS Records. Dist: CBS

Silverstone Steel...
SILVERSTONE STEEL ORCHESTRA.
Album: released on Joy, '74 by President Records. Dist: Jazz Music, Swift, President Distribution

Silvertones
SILVER BULLETS.
Album: released on Trojan, '74 by Trojan Records. Dist: PRT, Jetstar

Silvertones Choir
SO DEEP IS THE NIGHT.
Album: released on Praise, '75 Dist: Outlet

Silverwind
BY HIS SPIRIT.
Album: released on Birdwing, Mar'84 by Word Records. Dist: Word Distribution

Cassette: released on Birdwing, Mar'84 by Word Records. Dist: Word Distribution

SILVERWIND.
Album: released on Sparrow, May'82 by Word Records. Dist: Spartan

Cassette: released on Sparrow, May'82 by Word Records. Dist: Spartan

Silverwing
ALIVE AND KICKING.
Album: released on Bullet, Jul'83 by Bullet Distribution

SITTING PRETTY.
Single (7"): released on Neon Music, Apr'82

Single (12"): released on Neon Music, Apr'82

THAT'S ENTERTAINMENT.
Single (7"): released on Mayhem, Nov'82 by International Records & Tapes. Dist: Pinnacle

Silvester, Victor
100 MINUTES.
Cassette: released on PRT, Jun'82 by PRT Records. Dist: PRT

CELEBRATION PARTY DANCES.
Album: released on One Up, Dec'74 by EMI Records.

Cassette: released on One Up, Oct'83 by EMI Records.

GET RHYTHM IN YOUR FEET.
Album: released on EMI Retrospect, Oct'85 by EMI Records. Dist: EMI

Cassette: released on EMI Retrospect, Oct'85 by EMI Records. Dist: EMI

HOLLYWOOD HERITAGE.
Album: released on PRT, Dec'79 by PRT Records. Dist: PRT

Cassette: released on PRT, Dec'79 by PRT Records. Dist: PRT

LET'S HAVE A PARTY.
Album: released on Encore, Oct'79 by EMI Records. Dist: EMI

Cassette: released on Encore, Oct'79 by EMI Records. Dist: EMI Deleted '87.

MORE DANCING FAVOURITES.
Double Album: released on PRT, May'79 by PRT Records. Dist: PRT

Double cassette: released on PRT, May'79 by PRT Records. Dist: PRT

QUICK, QUICK, SLOW.
Album: released on World (Retrospect Series), Feb'84

Cassette: released on World (Retrospect Series), Feb'84

SILVESTER DANCETIME.
Album: released on PRT, Jul'75 by PRT Records. Dist: PRT

SPOTLIGHT ON VICTOR SILVESTER.
Double Album: released on PRT, Oct'81 by PRT Records. Dist: PRT

Double cassette: released on PRT, Oct'81 by PRT Records. Dist: PRT

SPOTLIGHT ON VICTOR SILVESTER, VOL 2.
Double Album: released on PRT, Oct'84 by PRT Records. Dist: PRT

Double cassette: released on PRT, Oct'84 by PRT Records. Dist: PRT

VICTOR SILVESTER'S JIVE BAND.
Album: released on EMI Retrospect, Jun'85 by EMI Records. Dist: EMI

Cassette: released on EMI Retrospect, Jun'85 by EMI Records. Dist: EMI

WALTZES, TANGOS AND MODERN BEAT.
Album: released on PRT, Sep'70 by PRT Records. Dist: PRT

Silvester, Victor Jnr
60 YEARS ON.
Album: released on Dansan, Apr'82 by Spartan Records. Dist: Spartan

I'LL GO WHERE THE MUSIC....
Double Album: released on PRT, Oct'79 by PRT Records. Dist: PRT

Double cassette: released on PRT, Oct'79 by PRT Records. Dist: PRT

JUST THE WAY YOU ARE.
Double Album: released on PRT, Nov'80 by PRT Records. Dist: PRT

VERY THOUGHT OF YOU, (THE).
Double Album: released on PRT, Nov'81 by PRT Records. Dist: PRT

Silvo, Johnny
IN THE SPOTLIGHT.
Album: released on Sweet Folk All, Jan'87 by Sweet Folk All Records. Dist: Sweet Folk All, Roots, Celtic Music, Dragon, Impetus, Projection, Chris Wellard, Festival Records

TIME ENOUGH TO SPARE.
Album: released on Plant Life. Nov'81

Simaryp
SHINHEAD MOONSTOMP.
Album: released on Trojan, Jan'83 by Trojan Records. Dist: PRT, Jetstar

Simeon Andre
SWEET TALKING/HEY FAT MAN.
Single (12"): released on Get Set Sounds Jul'82 by Get Set Sounds Records. Dist: Jetstar

Simeone, Harry
LITTLE DRUMMER BOY THE.
Album: released on Audio Fidelity, Dec'81 Dist: PRT

Simeone, Harry Chorale
LITTLE DRUMMER BOY THE.
Album: released on Audio Fidelity, Oct'84 Dist: PRT

Cassette: released on Audio Fidelity, Oct'84 Dist: PRT

Album: released on 20th Century, Nov'80 Dist: RCA, IMS-Polygram

Simeon, Omer
CHICAGO JAZZ-VOL.2 (Simeon, Omer/Richard M. Jones).

Simlen, Sidney
ZYDECO LUCY GO.
Single (7"): released on Bally Hoo (USA), Dec'82 Dist: Swift

Simlon, Lascell
ALL CREATURES GREAT AND SMALL (Simlon, Lascell & Jah Larry).
Single (12"): released on Clarendon Sounds Apr'82 by Clarendon Sounds Records. Dist: Jetstar

Simmons, Chandra
NEVER GONNA LET YOU GO.
Single (12"): released on Fresh (USA), Aug Dist: Pinnacle

Simmons, Desmond
ALONE ON PENGUIN ISLAND.
Album: released on Dome, Jul'81 Dist: Rough Trade

Simmons, Norman

I'M THE BLUES (Simmons, Norman Quintet/Jimmy Owens/Clifford Jordan).
Album: released on Milljack (USA), Nov'86 Dist: Jazz Horizons Distribution, Jazz Music Distribution

I'M THE BLUES.
Album: released on Milliac, Jul'83

Album: released on Milljac, Jan'81

MIDNIGHT CREEPER.
Album: released on Milljack (USA), Nov'86 Dist: Jazz Horizons Distribution, Jazz Music Distribution

MIDNIGHT CREEPER (Simmons, Norman/Lisle Atkinson/Al Harewood).
Album: released on Milljack, Sep'86 Dist: Jazz Horizons Distribution, Jazz Music Distribution

RAMIRA THE DANCER (Simmons, Norman Quartet).
Album: released on Spotlite, Jan'83 by Spotlite Records. Dist: Cadillac, Jazz Music, Spotlite

Simmons, Patrick

SO WRONG.
Single (7"): released on Elektra, May'83 by WEA Records. Dist: WEA

Single (12"): released on Elektra, May'83 by WEA Records. Dist: WEA

Simmons, Sonny

MANHATTEN EGOS.
Album: released on Arhoolie, May'81 by Arhoolie Records. Dist: Projection, Topic, Jazz Music, Swift, Roots

Simms Brothers

TAKE ME AS I AM.
Single (7"): released on Elektra, Jan'80 by WEA Records. Dist: WEA

Simms, Claudette

LOVERBOY.
Tracks: / Lover boy / Lover boy(version).
Single (12"): released on Speciality, Jul'86 by Relic Records. Dist: Swift

YOU'RE MY NATTY DREAD.
Single (12"): released on Code, Jan'85 by Code Records. Dist: Jetstar, EMI

Simms, Zoot

AFRICAN CHALLENGE.
Single (12"): released on Studio One, Sep'84 Dist: Jetstar

Simon, Carly

ANTICIPATION.
Cassette: released on Elektra, Oct'82 by WEA Records. Dist: WEA

BEST OF CARLY SIMON.
Tracks: / Right thing to do, The / Mockingbird / Legend in your own time / You're so vain / Haven't got time for the pain / (We have) no secrets / Night owl / Anticipation / Attitude dancing / That's the way i've always heard it should be.
Compact disc: released on Elektra (USA), Jul'86 by Elektra/Asylum/Nonesuch Records. Dist: WEA

Album: released on Elektra, Nov'76 by WEA Records. Dist: WEA

Cassette: released on Elektra, Nov'76 by WEA Records. Dist: WEA

Compact disc: released on Elektra, '83 by WEA Records. Dist: WEA

COME UPSTAIRS.
Single (7"): released on Mirage-WEA, Dec'82 by Atlantic Records. Dist: WEA Distribution

Single (12"): released on Mirage-WEA, Dec'82 by Atlantic Records. Dist: WEA Distribution

COMING AROUND AGAIN.
Tracks: / Itsy bitsy spider / If it wasn't love* / Coming around again / Give me all night / As time goes by / Do the walls come down / It should have been me / Stuff that dreams are made of, The / Two hot girls (on a hot summer night) / You have to hurt / All I want is you / Hold what you've got / Itsy bitsy spider.
Single (7"): released on Arista, Jan'87 by Arista Records. Dist: RCA

Single (12"): released on Arista, Jan'87 by Arista Records. Dist: RCA

Album: released on Arista, Jan'87 by Arista Records. Dist: RCA

Cassette: released on Arista, Jan'87 by Arista Records. Dist: RCA

Compact disc: released on Arista, Jan'87 by Arista Records. Dist: RCA

Compact disc single: released on Arista, Feb'87 by Arista Records. Dist: RCA

GIVE ME ALL NIGHT.
Tracks: / Give me all night / Two hot girls (on a hot summer's night) / Hold what you've got.
Single (7"): released on Arista, Apr'87 by Arista Records. Dist: RCA

Single (12"): released on Arista, Apr'87 by Arista Records. Dist: RCA

HELLO BIG MAN.
Tracks: / You know what to do / Menemsha / Damn,you get to me / Is this love / Orpheus / It happens everyday / Such a good day / Hello big man / You don't feel the same / Floundering.
Compact disc: released on Elektra (USA), Jul'86 by Elektra/Asylum/Nonesuch Records. Dist: WEA

HURT.
Single (7"): released on Warner Brothers, Jan'82 by WEA Records. Dist: WEA

JESSE.
Single (7"): released on Warner Brothers, Nov'80 by WEA Records. Dist: WEA

NOBODY DOES IT BETTER.
Single (7"): released on Elektra, Mar'82 by WEA Records. Dist: WEA

NO SECRETS.
Album: released on Elektra, Nov'76 by WEA Records. Dist: WEA

Cassette: released on Elektra, Nov'76 by WEA Records. Dist: WEA

SPOILED GIRL.
Tracks: / My new boyfriend / Come back home / Tonight and forever / Spoiled girl / Tired of being blonde / Wives are in Connecticut / Anyone but me / Make me feel something / Can't give up / Black honeymoon.
Compact disc: released on CBS, Dec'85 by CBS Records. Dist: CBS

Album: released on Epic, Oct'85 by CBS Records. Dist: CBS

Cassette: released on Epic, Oct'85 by CBS Records. Dist: CBS

SPY.
Album: released on Elektra, Jun'79 by WEA Records. Dist: WEA

Cassette: released on Elektra, Jun'79 by WEA Records. Dist: WEA

STUFF THAT DREAMS ARE MADE OF, THE.
Tracks: / As time goes by / Sleight of hand.
Single (12"): released on Arista, Aug'87 by Arista Records. Dist: RCA

TIRED OF BEING BLONDE.
Single (7"): released on Epic, Jul'85 by CBS Records. Dist: CBS

Single (12"): released on Epic, Jul'85 by CBS Records. Dist: CBS

WHY?.
Single (7"): released on Elektra, Jul'82 by WEA Records. Dist: WEA

Single (12"): released on Elektra, Jul'82 by WEA Records. Dist: WEA

YOU'RE SO VAIN.
Single (7"): released on Elektra, Sep'76 by WEA Records. Dist: WEA

Album: released on Hallmark, Apr'81 by Pickwick Records. Dist: Pickwick Distribution, PRT, Taylors

Cassette: released on Hallmark, Apr'81 by Pickwick Records. Dist: Pickwick Distribution, PRT, Taylors

Single (7"): released on Old Gold, Sep'85 by Old Gold Records. Dist: Lightning, Jazz Music, Spartan, Counterpoint

Simone

HIM.
Single (7"): released on Electricity, Aug'84 by Electricity Records. Dist: PRT

Single (12"): released on Electricity, Aug'84 by Electricity Records. Dist: PRT

Picture disc single: released on Electricity, Aug'84 by Electricity Records. Dist: PRT

IT'S TOO LATE.
Single (12"): released on Electricity, 23 May'87 by Electricity Records. Dist: PRT

Single (7"): released on KRP, Nov'83 by High Energy Records. Dist: PRT

Single (12"): released on KRP, Nov'83 by High Energy Records. Dist: PRT

Single (7"): released on Electricity, Mar'84 by Electricity Records. Dist: PRT

Single (12"): released on Electricity, Mar'84 by Electricity Records. Dist: PRT

RED LIGHT SPELLS DANGER.
Tracks: / Red light spells danger / Red light spells danger (Remix) / Heart & soul.
Single (7"): released on Spirit, May'86 by Spirit Records. Dist: WEA

Single (12"): released on Spirit, May'86 by Spirit Records. Dist: WEA

Single (7"): released on Spirit, Nov'85 by Spirit Records. Dist: WEA

Single (12"): released on Spirit, Nov'85 by Spirit Records. Dist: WEA

Simonelli, Dante

MEMORIES OF ITALY.
Album: released on Viking, Dec'79 Dist: Harmonia Mundi Distributors

Simone, Nina

AIN'T GOT NO....I GOT LIFE.
Tracks: / Ain't got no....I got life / To love somebody.
Single (7"): released on Old Gold, Oct'86 by Old Gold Records. Dist: Lightning, Jazz Music, Spartan, Counterpoint

ARTISTRY OF NINA SIMONE, THE.
Album: released on RCA International (USA), '84 by RCA Records. Dist: RCA

Cassette: released on RCA International (USA), '84 by RCA Records. Dist: RCA

BACKLASH.
Album: released on Star Jazz USA, Apr'86 by Charly Records. Dist: Charly Distribution

Cassette: released on Star Jazz USA, Apr'86 by Charly Records. Dist: Charly Distribution

Album: released on Chase Music, Nov'84 by Chase Records. Dist: PRT

Cassette: released on Chase Music, Nov'84 by Chase Records. Dist: PRT

BALTIMORE.
Album: released on CTI, Feb'84 by Polydor Records. Dist: IMS, Polygram

BEST OF NINA SIMONE.
Tracks: / I love you Porgy (from Porgy & Bess) / Break down and let it all out / Four woman / Pirate Jenny I put a spell on you / Sinnerman / Don't let it be misunderstood.
Compact disc: released on Philips, Mar'86 Dist: IMS-Polygram

Album: released on Philips (Timeless), Sep'84

Cassette: released on Philips (Timeless), Sep'84

BLACK SOUL.
Album: released on RCA (Germany), Jul'83

Cassette: released on RCA (Germany), Jul'83

CRY BEFORE I GO.
Album: released on Manhattan, Nov'80 by EMI Records. Dist: EMI

FINE AND MELLOW.
Album: released on Golden Hour, Oct'75 by PRT Records. Dist: PRT

FODDER ON MY WINGS.
Album: released on IMS, Mar'84 by Polydor Records. Dist: IMS, Polygram

HERE COMES THE SUN.
Album: released on RCA International (USA), Jul'80 by RCA Records. Dist: RCA

Cassette: released on RCA International (USA), Jul'80 by RCA Records. Dist: RCA

Album: released on RCA (France), Oct'85 by RCA Records. Dist: Discovery

LIVE AT VINE STREET.
Album: released on Verve (USA), May'87 by Polydor. Dist: Polygram

Cassette: released on Verve (USA), May'87 by Polydor. Dist: Polygram

MAGIC MOMENTS.
Cassette: released on RCA, May'86 by RCA Records. Dist: RCA, Roots, Swift, Wellard, Chris, I & B, Solomon & Peres Distribution

MUSIC FOR THE MILLIONS.
Album: released on Philips Import, Dec'83

Cassette: released on Philips Import, Dec'83

MY BABY JUST CARES FOR ME.
Tracks: / My baby just cares for me / Don't smoke in bed / Mood indigo / He needs me / Love me or leave me / I loves you Porgy / Good bait / Central Park blues / You'll never walk alone / Plain gold ring / Little girl blue / My baby just cares for me (Special extended vesion).
Compact disc: released on Charly, Mar'86 by Charly Records. Dist: Charly, Cadillac

Album: released on Charly, '85 by Charly Records. Dist: Charly, Cadillac

Cassette: released on Charly, '85 by Charly Records. Dist: Charly, Cadillac

Single (7"): released on Charly, Apr'85 by Charly Records. Dist: Charly, Cadillac

Single (12"): released on Charly, Apr'85 by Charly Records. Dist: Charly, Cadillac

NINA'S BACK!.
Tracks: / It's cold out here / Porgy / I sing just to know that I'm alive / For a while / Fodder on her wings / Touching and caring / Saratoga / You must have another lover.
Notes: Nina's first album in four years.
Album: released on VPI, Feb'86 by VPI Records. Dist: IMS, Polygram

Cassette: released on VPI, Feb'86 by VPI Records. Dist: IMS, Polygram

NINA SIMONE.
Album: released on Dakota (Countdown series), Oct'82 by Dakota Records. Dist: PRT

Cassette: released on Dakota (Countdown series), Oct'82 by Dakota Records. Dist: PRT

NINA SIMONE SINGS THE BLUES.
Album: released on RCA, Aug'85 by RCA Records. Dist: RCA, Roots, Swift, Wellard, Chris, I & B, Solomon & Peres Distribution

Cassette: released on RCA, Aug'85 by RCA Records. Dist: RCA, Roots, Swift, Wellard, Chris, I & B, Solomon & Peres Distribution

Album: released on RCA (Germany), '83

OUR LOVE.
Album: released on Barclay (France), May'83 by Decca Records. Dist: IMS, Discovery, Conifer, Swift, Polygram

Cassette: released on Barclay (France), May'83 by Decca Records. Dist: IMS, Discovery, Conifer, Swift, Polygram

PORTRAIT OF NINA SIMONE, (A).
Double Album: released on Musidisc (France), Aug'83 Dist: Discovery Distribution, Swift Distribution

REPLAY ON NINA SIMONE.
Album: released on Sierra, Aug'85 by Sierra Records. Dist: WEA

Cassette: released on Sierra, Aug'85 by Sierra Records. Dist: WEA

VERY RARE EVENING WITH NINA SIMONE, (A).
Album: released on PM, Jan'80

Simon, F.

GUN CONTROL.
Album: released on Chrysalis, May'85 by Chrysalis Records. Dist: CBS

Cassette: released on Chrysalis, May'85 by Chrysalis Records. Dist: CBS

Simon & Garfunkel

BOOKENDS.
Tracks: / Bookends / Save the life of my child / America / Overs / Voice of old people / Old friends / Fakin' it / Punky's dilemma / Hazy shade of winter / At the zoo / Mrs. Robinson.
Compact disc: released on CBS, Dec'85 by CBS Records. Dist: CBS

Album: released on CBS, Nov'82 by CBS Records. Dist: CBS

Cassette: released on CBS, Nov'82 by CBS Records. Dist: CBS

BRIDGE OVER TROUBLED WATER.
Tracks: / Bridge over troubled water / El condor pasa / Cecilia / Keep the customer satisfied / So long, Frank Lloyd Wright / Boxer, The / Baby driver / Only living boy in New York, The / Why don't you write me / Bye bye love / Song for the asking.
Album: released on CBS, '70 by CBS Records. Dist: CBS

Cassette: released on CBS, '70 by CBS Records. Dist: CBS

Compact disc: released on CBS, '82 by CBS Records. Dist: CBS

COLLECTION: SIMON & GARFUNKEL.
Compact disc: by CBS Records. Dist: CBS

CONCERT IN CENTRAL PARK, (THE).
Double Album: released on Geffen, Mar'82 by Geffen Records. Dist: WEA, CBS

Double cassette: released on Geffen, Mar'82 by Geffen Records. Dist: WEA, CBS

GRADUATE, THE Original soundtrack.
Tracks: / Sound of silence / Jungleman party foxtrot / Mrs. Robinson / Sunporch cha-cha / Scarborough Fair / On the strip / April come she will / Folks / Great effect / Big bright green pleasure machine.
Compact disc: released on CBS, Dec'85 by CBS Records. Dist: CBS

GRADUATE, (THE).
Album: released on CBS, Feb'84 by CBS Records. Dist: CBS

Cassette: released on CBS, Feb'84 by CBS Records. Dist: CBS

Album: released on CBS, '74 by CBS Records. Dist: CBS

Cassette: released on CBS, '74 by CBS Records. Dist: CBS

GREATEST HITS: SIMON & GARFUNKEL.
Album: released on CBS, '74 by CBS Records. Dist: CBS

Cassette: released on CBS, '74 by CBS Records. Dist: CBS

IN CENTRAL PARK.
Video-cassette (VHS): released on Warner, Oct'84 by Warner Bros Records. Dist: WEA

MRS ROBINSON.
Single (7"): released on CBS, '80 by CBS Records. Dist: CBS

Single (7"): released on Geffen, Jul'82 by Geffen Records. Dist: WEA, CBS

PARSLEY,SAGE, ROSEMARY & THYME.
Tracks: / Scarborough Fair, Canticle / Patterns / Cloudy / Big bright green pleasure machine, The / 59th Street Bridge song(feelin'groovy) / Dangling conversation, The / Flowers never bend with the rainfall / Simple desultory philippic / For Emily, whenever I may find her / Poem on an underground wall, A / Seven o'clock news / Silent night.
Album: released on CBS, Mar'81 by CBS Records. Dist: CBS

Cassette: released on CBS, Mar'81 by CBS Records. Dist: CBS

Compact disc: by CBS Records. Dist: CBS

SIMON & GARFUNKEL COLLECTION.
Album: released on CBS, Nov'81 by CBS Records. Dist: CBS

Cassette: released on CBS, Nov'81 by CBS Records. Dist: CBS

Compact disc: released on CBS, '83 by CBS Records. Dist: CBS

SIMON & GARFUNKEL COLLECTION, THE.
Tracks: / I am a rock / Homeward bound / America / 59th Street Bridge song / Wednesday morning 3am / El condor pasa / At the zoo / Scarborooough Fair (Canticle) / Boxer, The / Sound of silence / Mrs. Robinson / Keep the customer satisfied / Song for the asking / Hazy shade of winter / Cecilia / Old friends / Bookends theme / Bridge over troubled water.
Compact disc: released on CBS, Apr'85 by CBS Records. Dist: CBS

SOUNDS OF SILENCE.
Tracks: / Sound of silence / Leaves that are green / Blessed / Somewhere they can't find me / Kathy's song / Anji / Homeward bound / Most peculiar man / I am a rock / Richard Cory / April come she will.
Compact disc: released on CBS, Dec'85 by CBS Records. Dist: CBS

SOUNDS OF SILENCE.
Album: released on CBS, Mar'81 by CBS Records. Dist: CBS

Cassette: released on CBS, Mar'81 by CBS Records. Dist: CBS

Single (7"): released on CBS, '80 by CBS Records. Dist: CBS

WEDNESDAY MORNING 3 AM.
Album: released on CBS, Nov'85 by CBS Records. Dist: CBS

Cassette: released on CBS, Nov'85 by CBS Records. Dist: CBS

WEDNESDAY MORNING 3AM.
Tracks: / You can tell the world / Last night I had the strangest dream / Bleecker Street / Sparrow / Benedictus / Peggy-O / He was my brother / Sound of silence / Go tell it on the mountain / Sun is burning / Times are a-changin' / Wednesday morning 3am.
Compact disc: released on CBS, Dec'85 by CBS Records. Dist: CBS

Simonics

IN THIS HEAT.
Single (7"): released on Thin Sliced, Nov'85 by Thin Sliced Records. Dist: Rough Trade Distribution, Cartel Distribution

Single (12"): released on Thin Sliced, Nov'85 by Thin Sliced Records. Dist: Rough Trade Distribution, Cartel Distribution

UNDER A GLASS BELL.
Tracks: / Under a glass bell.
Single (7"): released on Temple, Aug'86 by Temple Records. Dist: Roots Distribution, Folksound Distribution, Celtic Music Distribution, Projection Distribution

Single (12"): released on Temple, Aug'86 by Temple Records. Dist: Roots Distribution, Folksound Distribution, Celtic Music Distribution, Projection Distribution

Simon, Jo

MR. RIGHT.
Album: released on Compleat, Mar'86 by Compleat Records. Dist: PRT

Cassette: released on Compleat, Mar'86 by Compleat Records. Dist: PRT

ONE LAST LOOK.
Tracks: / One last look / One last look(ext) / Always on my mind.
Single (12"): released on Compleat, Feb'86 by Compleat Records. Dist: PRT

Simon, Joe

BRING IT ON HOME TO ME.
Single (7"): by Charly Records. Dist: Charly, Cadillac

SOUL NEIGHBOURS (see Hughes, Jimmy) (Simon, Joe & Jimmy Hughes).
Album: released on Charly(R&B), Nov'84 by Charly Records. Dist: Charly, Cadillac

Simon, Paul

ALLERGIES.
Single (7"): released on Warner Brothers, Nov'83 by WEA Records. Dist: WEA

BOY IN THE BUBBLE.
Tracks: / (remix) / Hearts and bones*.
Single (7"): released on Warner Bros., Nov'86 by Warner Bros Records. Dist: WEA

Single (12"): released on Warner Bros., Nov'86 by Warner Bros Records. Dist: WEA

DIAMONDS ON THE SOLES OF HER SHOES.
Tracks: / All around the world of the myth of fingerprints.
Single (7"): released on Warner Bros., Feb'87 by Warner Bros Records. Dist: WEA

Single (12"): released on Warner Bros., Feb'87 by Warner Bros Records. Dist: WEA

GRACELAND.
Tracks: / Graceland / Crazy Love vol.2 / Late Great Johnny Ace (The)*.
Notes: * = Extra track on 12" only.
Single (7"): released on Warner Bros., Apr'87 by Warner Bros Records. Dist: WEA

Single (12"): released on Warner Bros., Apr'87 by Warner Bros Records. Dist: WEA

GRACELAND.
Tracks: / Boy in the bubble, The / Graceland / I know what I know / Gumboots / Diamonds on the soles of her shoes / You can call me Al / Under African skies / Homeless / Crazy love Vol.II / All around the world or the myth of fingerprints.
Album: released on Warner Brothers, Sep'86 by WEA Records. Dist: WEA

Cassette: released on Warner Brothers, Sep'86 by Warner Bros Records. Dist: WEA

Compact disc: released on Warner Brothers, Sep'86 by Warner Bros Records. Dist: WEA

GREATEST HITS:PAUL SIMON.
Album: released on CBS, Nov'77 by CBS Records. Dist: CBS

Cassette: released on CBS, Nov'77 by CBS Records. Dist: CBS

Compact disc: released on CBS, Nov'77 by CBS Records. Dist: CBS

GREATEST HITS:PAUL SIMON.
Tracks: / Something so right / Fifty ways to leave your lover / Kodachrome / Me and Julio down by the school yard / American tune / Gone at last / Still crazy after all these years / My little town / Mother and child reunion / Loves me like a rock / Stranded in a limousine / Slip slidin' away / Mardi gras.
Compact disc: released on CBS, Mar'87 by CBS Records. Dist: CBS

GREATEST HITS: PAUL SIMON.
Tracks: / Me and Julio down by the schoolyard / Something so right / Kodachrome / I do it for your love / 50 ways to leave your lover / American tune / Mother and the child reunion / Loves me like a rock / Take me to the Mardi Gras / Slip slidin' away / Stranded in a limousine / Still crazy after all these years / Have a good time / Duncan.
Album: released on CBS, Nov'86 by CBS Records. Dist: CBS

Cassette: released on CBS, Nov'86 by CBS Records. Dist: CBS

HEARTS AND BONES.
Tracks: / Think to much / Train in the distance / Cars are cars / Late great Jonny Ace, The / Allergies / Hearts and bones / When numbers get serious / Song about the moon / Rene and Georgette Magritte with their dog after the War.
Compact disc: released on Warner Brothers, '86 by Warner Bros Records. Dist: WEA

Album: released on Warner Brothers, Nov'83 by WEA Records. Dist: WEA

Cassette: released on Warner Brothers, Nov'83 by WEA Records. Dist: WEA

Compact disc: released on Warner Brothers, '83 by WEA Records. Dist: WEA

LATE IN THE EVENING.
Single (7"): released on Warner Brothers, Aug'80 by WEA Records. Dist: WEA

LIVE RHYMIN' - IN CONCERT.
Album: released on CBS, Mar'74 by CBS Records. Dist: CBS

MOTHER AND CHILD REUNION.
Single (7"): released on CBS, '74 by CBS Records. Dist: CBS

OH MARION.
Single (7"): released on Warner Brothers, Jan'81 by WEA Records. Dist: WEA

ONE TRICK PONY.
Compact disc: released on Warner Bros., '87 by Warner Bros Records. Dist: WEA

Album: released on Warner Brothers, Aug'80 by WEA Records. Dist: WEA

Cassette: released on Warner Brothers, Aug'80 by WEA Records. Dist: WEA

PAUL SIMON.
Album: released on CBS, '74 by CBS Records. Dist: CBS

Cassette: released on CBS, '74 by CBS Records. Dist: CBS

STILL CRAZY AFTER ALL THESE YEARS.
Tracks: / Still crazy after all these years / My little town / I do it for your love / 50 ways to leave your lover / Night game / Gone at last / Some folk's lives roll easy / Have a good time / You're kind / Silent eyes.
Album: released on CBS, Oct'75 by CBS Records. Dist: CBS

Cassette: released on CBS, Oct'75 by CBS Records. Dist: CBS

Compact disc: released on CBS, Oct'75 by CBS Records. Dist: CBS

UNDER AFRICAN SKIES.
Tracks: / I know what I know / Homeless.
Single (7"): released on Warner Brothers, Aug'87 by Warner Bros Records. Dist: WEA

Single (12"): released on Warner Brothers, Aug'87 by Warner Bros Records. Dist: WEA

YOU CAN CALL ME AL.
Tracks: / You can call me Al / Gumboots.
Single (7"): released on Warner Brothers, Aug'86 by Warner Bros Records. Dist: WEA

Single (12"): released on Warner Brothers, Aug'86 by Warner Bros Records. Dist: WEA

Simon, Ralph

TIME BEING.
Album: by Gramavison Records (USA). Dist: PRT, IMS, Polygram

Simon Says

SIMON SAYS Various artists (Various Artists).
Album: released on Golden Hour, Mar'77 by PRT Records. Dist: PRT

Simons, Leroy

AT THE DANCE.
Single (12"): released on Neville King, Sep'82 by Neville King Records. Dist: Jetstar

Simon, Tito

CAN'T STOP LOVING YOU (Simon, Tito & Sus Band).
Single (12"): released on Pama, May'83 by Pama Records. Dist: Pama, Enterprise, Jetstar

DARLING (YOU'RE ALL I NEED TO GET BY).
Single (12"): released on Studio 80, Jan'84 by Studio 80 Records. Dist: Jetstar Distribution

HEAT IS ONE, (THE).
Album: released on Tit, Mar'84

MONDAY MORNING FEELING.
Album: released on Trojan, Apr'75 by Trojan Records. Dist: PRT, Jetstar

REGGAE MUSIC COME FROM JAMAICA.
Single (12"): released on Pama, Feb'84 by Pama Records. Dist: Pama, Enterprise, Jetstar

SAD AFFAIR (YOU DON'T LOVE ME AT ALL).
Single (12"): released on TTT, Nov'84

THIS MONDAY MORNING FEELING.
Tracks: / This Monday morning feeling / Feel the rhythm.
Single (12"): released on Body Music, Jul'86 by Body Music Records. Dist: Jetstar

WE MEET AGAIN.
Album: released on NUM. Dec'85

Simon, Vincent

I'VE GOT SOMETHING TO SAY.
Single (12"): released on Crucial Roots, Dec'83 by Crucial Roots Records. Dist: Jetstar

Simper, Nick Fandango

JUST ANOTHER DAY IN THE LIFE OF A FOOL.
Single (7"): released on Paro, Feb'83 by Paro Records. Dist: Spartan

Simple Minds

ALIVE AND KICKING.
Single (7"): released on Virgin, Sep'85 by Virgin Records. Dist: EMI, Virgin Distribution

Single (12"): released on Virgin, Sep'85 by Virgin Records. Dist: EMI Virgin Distribution

ALL THE THINGS SHE SAID.
Tracks: / All the things she said / Don't you forget (about me) / Promised you a miracle.
Single (7"): released on Virgin, Mar'86 by Virgin Records. Dist: EMI, Virgin Distribution

CELEBRATION.
Album: released on Virgin, Sep'82 by Virgin Records. Dist: EMI, Virgin Distribution

Cassette: released on Virgin, Sep'82 by Virgin Records. Dist: EMI, Virgin Distribution

DON'T YOU FORGET ABOUT ME.
Single (7"): released on Virgin, Apr'85 by Virgin Records. Dist: EMI, Virgin Distribution

Single (12"): released on Virgin, Apr'85 by Virgin Records. Dist: EMI. Virgin Distribution

EMPIRE AND DANCE.
Tracks: / I travel / Today I died again / Celebrate / This fear of Gods / Capital city / Constantinople line / Thirty frames a second / Kant-kino / Room / Twist / Run / Repulsion.
Compact disc: released on Virgin, '86 by Virgin Records. Dist: EMI, Virgin Distribution

EMPIRES AND DANCE.
Album: released on Virgin, Sep'82 by Virgin Records. Dist: EMI, Virgin Distribution

Cassette: released on Virgin, Sep'82 by Virgin Records. Dist: EMI, Virgin Distribution

GHOSTDANCING.
Tracks: / Jungleland / Ghostdancing / Jungleland.
Single (7"): released on Virgin, Nov'86 by Virgin Records. Dist: EMI, Virgin Distribution

Single (7"): released on Virgin, Nov'86 by Virgin Records. Dist: EMI, Virgin Distribution

Single (12"): released on Virgin, Nov'86 by Virgin Records. Dist: EMI Virgin Distribution

GLITTERING PRIZE / THEME.
Single (7"): released on Virgin, Aug'82 by Virgin Records. Dist: EMI, Virgin Distribution

Single (12"): released on Virgin, Aug'82 by Virgin Records. Dist: EMI, Virgin Distribution

IN THE CITY OF LIGHT.
Album: released on Virgin, May'87 by Virgin Records. Dist: EMI, Virgin Distribution

Cassette: released on Virgin, May'87 by Virgin Records. Dist: EMI, Virgin Distribution

Double Album: released on Virgin, 30 May'87 by Virgin Records. Dist: EMI, Virgin Distribution

Cassette: released on Virgin, 30 May'87 by Virgin Records. Dist: EMI, Virgin Distribution

Compact disc: released on Virgin, Jun'87 by Virgin Records. Dist: EMI, Virgin Distribution

I TRAVEL / FILM THEME.
Single (12"): released on Virgin, Apr'83 by Virgin Records. Dist: EMI, Virgin Distribution

I TRAVEL / THIRTY FRAMES A SECOND.
Single (7"): released on Arista, Jan'82 by Arista Records. Dist: RCA

Single (12"): released on Arista, Jan'82 by Arista Records. Dist: RCA

LIFE IN A DAY.
Compact disc: released on Virgin, Jul'87 by Virgin Records. Dist: EMI, Virgin Distribution

LOVE SONG.
Single (7"): released on Virgin, Aug'81 by Virgin Records. Dist: EMI, Virgin Distribution

Single (12"): released on Virgin, Aug'81 by Virgin Records. Dist: EMI, Virgin Distribution

NEW GOLD DREAM.
Tracks: / Someone somewhere in summertime / Colours fly and catherine wheel / Promised you a miracle / Big sleep / Somebody up there likes you / New gold dream / Glittering prize / Hunter & the hunted / King is white & in the crowd.
Compact disc: released on Virgin, '86 by Virgin Records. Dist: EMI, Virgin Distribution

Album: released on Virgin, Sep'82 by Virgin Records. Dist: EMI, Virgin Distribution

Cassette: released on Virgin, Sep'82 by Virgin Records. Dist: EMI, Virgin Distribution

ONCE UPON A TIME.
Tracks: / Once upon a time / All the things she said / Ghostdancing / Alive and kicking / Oh jungleland / I wish you were here / Sanctify yourself / Come a long way.
Notes: Their seventh chart album and second number one.
Album: released on Virgin, Oct'85 by Virgin Records. Dist: EMI, Virgin Distribution

Cassette: released on Virgin, Oct'85 by Virgin Records. Dist: EMI, Virgin Distribution

Compact disc: released on Virgin, Oct'85 by Virgin Records. Dist: EMI, Virgin Distribution

PROMISED YOU A MIRACLE (RE-RELEASE).
Tracks: / Promised you a miracle / Book of brilliant things / Glittering prize* / Celebrate*.
Single (7"): released on Virgin, Jun'87 by Virgin Records. Dist: EMI, Virgin Distribution

Single 10": released on Virgin, Jun'87 by Virgin Records. Dist: EMI, Virgin Distribution

Single (12"): released on Virgin, 13 Jun'87 by Virgin Records. Dist: EMI, Virgin Distribution

PROMISED YOU A MIRACLE (LIVE).
Tracks: / Promised you a miracle (live) / Book of brilliant things (live) / Glittering prize (live) / Celebration (live).
Cassette single: released on Virgin, 20 Jun'87 by Virgin Records. Dist: EMI, Virgin Distribution

PROMISED YOU A MIRACLE.
Single (7"): released on Virgin, Mar'82 by Virgin Records. Dist: EMI, Virgin Distribution

Single (12"): released on Virgin, Mar'82 by Virgin Records. Dist: EMI, Virgin Distribution

REEL TO REAL CACOPHONY.
Tracks: / Real to real / Naked eye / Citizen (dance of youth) / Veldt / Carnival (shelter in a suitcase) / Factory / Cacophony / Premonition / Changeling / Film theme / Calling your name / Scar.
Compact disc: released on Virgin, '86 by Virgin Records. Dist: EMI, Virgin Distribution

SANCTIFY YOURSELF.
Tracks: / Sanctify yourself.
Single (7"): released on Virgin, Jan'86 by Virgin Records. Dist: EMI, Virgin Distribution

Single (12"): released on Virgin, Jan'86 by Virgin Records. Dist: EMI, Virgin Distribution

SISTER FEELINGS CALL.
Cassette: released on Virgin, Oct'86 by Virgin Records. Dist: EMI, Virgin Distribution

SOMEONE SOMEWHERE (IN SUMMERTIME) / KING IS WHITE.....
Single (7"): released on Virgin, Nov'82 by Virgin Records. Dist: EMI, Virgin Distribution

Single (12"): released on Virgin, Nov'82 by Virgin Records. Dist: EMI, Virgin Distribution

ONS AND FASCINATION.
ouble Album: released on Virgin, Aug'81 by rgin Records. Dist: EMI, Virgin Distribution

ouble cassette: released on Virgin, Aug'81 Virgin Records. Dist: EMI, Virgin Distribution

ONS & FASCINATION Sister feelings call.
ompact disc: released on Virgin, Apr'86 by rgin Records. Dist: EMI, Virgin Distribution

PARKLE IN THE RAIN.
acks: / Up on the catwalk / Book of brilliant ngs / Speed your love to me / Waterfront / st at easter / Street hassle / White hot day / moon / Cry like a baby / Kick inside of me, e / Shake off the ghosts.

Compact disc: released on Virgin, '86 by Virgin Records. Dist: EMI, Virgin Distribution

Album: released on Virgin, Feb'84 by Virgin Records. Dist: EMI, Virgin Distribution

Cassette: released on Virgin, Feb'84 by Virgin Records. Dist: EMI, Virgin Distribution

SWEAT IN BULLET.
Single (7"): released on Virgin, Oct'81

Single (12"): released on Virgin, Nov'81

WATERFRONT / HUNTER AND THE HUNTED / IF YOU WANT MY LOVE.
Single (7"): released on Virgin, Nov'83 by Virgin Records. Dist: EMI, Virgin Distribution

Single (12"): released on Virgin, Nov'83 by Virgin Records. Dist: EMI, Virgin Distribution

Simple Pip

JAMES REEVES.
Cassette: released on Talking Tape Company, '84 by Talking Tape Company Records.

Simple Simon

BAD MAN.
Album: released on Kingdom, Oct'85 by Kingdom Records. Dist: Kingdom

FOREIGN MINDS.
Single (12"): released on Rosie Uprising, Sep'84 by Rosie Uprising Records. Dist: Jetstar Distribution

LIFE IN THE GHETTO.
Single (12"): released on Greensleeves, Oct'82 by Greensleeves Records. Dist: BMG, Jetstar, Spartan

REGGAE MOVE.
Album: released on Vista Sounds, Mar'85 by Vista Sounds Records. Dist: Jetstar

Simplicious

LET HER FEEL IT.
Single (7"): released on Fourth & Broadway, Sep'84 by Island Records. Dist: Polygram, EMI

Single (12"): released on Fourth & Broadway, Sep'84 by Island Records. Dist: Polygram, EMI

Simplicity

BLACK IS OUR COLOUR.
Single (12"): released on King & City, Oct'81 Dist: Jetstar

LET'S ROCK.
Single (12"): released on S&G, Jul'83 by S&G Records. Dist: Jetstar

LOVIN' KIND.
Tracks: / Lovin' king.
Single (12"): released on King's Records Label, Dec'86

THIS LOVE IS REAL.
Single (12"): released on S&G, Jul'82 by S&G Records. Dist: Jetstar

WAITING.
Single (12"): released on King & City, Oct'81 Dist: Jetstar

Simply Red

COME TO MY AID.
Single (7"): released on Elektra, Aug'85 by WEA Records. Dist: WEA

Single (12"): released on Elektra, Aug'85 by WEA Records. Dist: WEA

HOLDING BACK THE YEARS.
Tracks: / Holding back the years / Drowning in my own tears / Picture book.
Single (7"): released on WEA, May'86 by WEA Records. Dist: WEA

Single (12"): released on WEA, May'86 by WEA Records. Dist: WEA

Single (7"): released on Elektra, Nov'85 by WEA Records. Dist: WEA

Single (12"): released on Elektra, Nov'85 by WEA Records. Dist: WEA

Gatefold sleeve: released on Elektra, Nov'85 by WEA Records. Dist: WEA

Picture disc single: released on Elektra, Nov'85 by WEA Records. Dist: WEA

INFIDELITY.
Tracks: / Infidelity / Lady Godiva's room.
Single (7"): released on WEA, May'87 by WEA Records. Dist: WEA

Single (12"): released on WEA, May'87 by WEA Records. Dist: WEA

JERICO.
Tracks: / Jerico / Jerico (The musical) / Money's too tight to mention (live) / Heaven (live).
Single (7"): released on WEA, Feb'86 by WEA Records. Dist: WEA

Single (12"): released on WEA, Feb'86 by WEA Records. Dist: WEA

MAYBE SOMEDAY.
Tracks: / Maybe someday / Let me have it all.
Single (7"): released on Elektra, Jul'87 by WEA Records. Dist: WEA

Single (12"): released on Elektra, Jul'87 by WEA Records. Dist: WEA

MEN AND WOMEN.
Album: released on WEA, Mar'87 by WEA Records. Dist: WEA

Cassette: released on WEA, Mar'87 by WEA Records. Dist: WEA

Compact disc: released on WEA, Mar'87 by WEA Records. Dist: WEA

MONEYS TOO TIGHT(TO MENTION).
Single (7"): released on Elektra, Jun'85 by WEA Records. Dist: WEA

Single (12"): released on Elektra, Jun'85 by WEA Records. Dist: WEA

Picture disc single: released on Elektra, Jun'85 by WEA Records. Dist: WEA

Special: released on Elektra, Jun'85 by WEA Records. Dist: WEA

OPEN UP THE RED BOX.
Tracks: / Open up the red box / Look at you now / Heaven.
Single (7"): released on WEA, Jul'86 by WEA Records. Dist: WEA

Single (12"): released on WEA, Jul'86 by WEA Records. Dist: WEA

PICTURE BOOK.
Tracks: / Come to my aid / Sad old red / Look at you now / Heaven / Jericho / Money's too tight to mention / Holding back the years / Open up the red box / No direction / Picture book.
Compact disc: released on Elektra (USA), Oct'85 by Elektra/Asylum/Nonesuch Records. Dist: WEA

Picture disc album: released on Elektra (USA), May'86 by Elektra/Asylum/Nonesuch Records. Dist: WEA

Album: released on Elektra, Oct'85 by WEA Records. Dist: WEA

Cassette: released on Elektra, Oct'85 by WEA Records. Dist: WEA

Compact disc: released on Elektra, Oct'85 by WEA Records. Dist: WEA

RIGHT THING, THE.
Tracks: / There's a light / Ev'ry time we say good-bye*.
Single (7"): released on WEA, Jan'87 by WEA Records. Dist: WEA

Single (12"): released on WEA, Jan'87 by WEA Records. Dist: WEA

Simpson and Strong

TWO SOUL CHIEFS.
Album: released on Red Lightnin', May'83 by Red Lightnin' Records. Dist: Roots, Swift, Jazz Music, JSU, Pinnacle, Cartel, Wynd-Up Distribution

Simpson, Chris

LIVING WITH A WOMAN LIKE YOU.
Single (7"): released on Speed, Jul'83

STING OF THE GIN.
Single (7"): released on Juice, Dec'82 by IRS. Dist: A&M, CBS

Simpson, Martin

GOLDEN VANITY.
Album: released on Leader, Jan'81 Dist: Jazz Music, Projection

GRINNING YOUR FACE.
Album: released on Topic, Sep'83 Dist: Roots Distribution

Album: released on Topic, Apr'85 Dist: Roots Distribution

NOBODY'S FAULT BUT MINE.
Album: released on Dambuster, Mar'86 by Dambuster Records. Dist: Projection, Celtic Music, Roots

SAD OR HIGH KICKING.
Album: released on Topic, Nov'86 Dist: Roots Distribution

SPECIAL AGENT.
Album: released on Waterfront, Mar'84 by Waterfront Records. Dist: Rough Trade, Cartel, Projection, Roots

TRUE DARE OR PROMISE (Simpson, Martin & Jessica).
Album: released on Topic, Jul'87 by Topic Records. Dist: JSU Distribution, Projection Distribution, Jazz Music Distribution

Simpson, Mickey

GOOD GOOD LOVING.
Single (12"): released on Sanity, May'84 by Sanity Records. Dist: Pinnacle, Jetstar

STUMBLING BLOCK.
Single (12"): released on Mandingo, Nov'83 Dist: Jetstar. Estim retail price in Jul'87 was £3.99.

Simpson, Raymond

DREAM GIRL.
Single (12"): released on Vibes Corner, Jan'84 by Vibes Corner Records. Dist: Jetstar

TURN YOUR LOVE AROUND.
Single (12"): released on JBM, Feb'82 Dist: T.One Records

Simpson, Ray (Wreckless)

PLEASE DON'T WALK AWAY.
Single (12"): released on Big Youth, Feb'82

Simpson, Red

20 GREAT TRUCK HITS.
Album: released on EMI (Sweden), Jan'83 by EMI Records. Dist: Conifer

Simpson, Sandra

YOU'RE MY EVERYTHING.
Single (12"): released on Innovation, Apr'85 by Innovation Records. Dist: Jetstar

Simpson, Steve

JIVING.
Single (7"): released on Roxon, Oct'81 by Roxon Records. Dist: Pinnacle

Sims, Frankie Lee

WALKING WITH FRANKIE.
Album: released on Krazy Kat, Mar'85 Dist: Jazz Music, Swift, Chris Wellard, H.R. Taylor, Charly, Hotshot, IRS Distribution

Sims, John Haley

JUST FRIENDS (Sims, John Haley/Harry Sweets Edison).
Album: released on Pablo (USA), '82 by Pablo Records (USA). Dist: Wellard, Chris, IMS-Polygram, BMG

Cassette: released on Pablo (USA), '82 by Pablo Records (USA). Dist: Wellard, Chris, IMS-Polygram, BMG

Sims, Joyce

ALL AND ALL.
Tracks: / All and all / All and all (Dub).
Single (7"): released on London, Apr'86 by London Records. Dist: Polygram

Single (12"): released on London, Apr'86 by London Records. Dist: Polygram

LIFETIME LOVE (JAZZY EDIT).
Tracks: / Lifetime love (jazzy edit) / Lifetime love (def edit).
Single (7"): released on London, 30 May'87 by London Records. Dist: Polygram

Single (12"): released on London, 30 May'87 by London Records. Dist: Polygram

Simson, Paul Connection

TREAT HER SWEETER.
Single (7"): released on 10, Jun'85 by 10 Records. Dist: Virgin, EMI

Single (12"): released on 10, Jun'85 by 10 Records. Dist: Virgin, EMI

Sims, Zoot

BASIE AND ZOOT (see under Basie,Count) (Sims, Zoot & Count Basie).
Album: released on Pablo, '82 by Pablo Records. Dist: Wellard, Chris, IMS-Polygram, BMG

Cassette: released on Pablo, '82 by Pablo Records. Dist: Wellard, Chris, IMS-Polygram, BMG

BEST OF ZOOT SIMS, (THE).
Album: released on Pablo, '82 by Pablo Records. Dist: Wellard, Chris, IMS-Polygram, BMG

Cassette: released on Pablo, '82 by Pablo Records. Dist: Wellard, Chris, IMS-Polygram, BMG

BLUES FOR TWO (Sims, Zoot & Joe Pass).
Album: released on Pablo, Mar'83 by Pablo Records. Dist: Wellard, Chris, IMS-Polygram, BMG

Cassette: released on Pablo, Mar'83 by Pablo Records. Dist: Wellard, Chris, IMS-Polygram, BMG

BODY AND SOUL (Sims, Zoot & Al Cohn).
Album: released on Muse, Jun'77 Dist: JSU Distribution, Jazz Horizons Distribution, Jazz Music Distribution, Celtic Music Distribution

DOWN HOME (Sims, Zoot Quartet).
Tracks: / Jive at five / Doggin' around / Ascap / Avalon / I cried for you / Bill Bailey won't you please come home / Good night sweetheart / There'll be some changes made / I've heard that blues before.
Compact disc: released on Affinity, Jan'87 by Charly Records. Dist: Charly, Cadillac

Album: released on Affinity, May'82 by Charly Records. Dist: Charly, Cadillac

HAWTHORNE NIGHTS.
Album: released on Pablo, '82 by Pablo Records. Dist: Wellard, Chris, IMS-Polygram, BMG

Cassette: released on Pablo, '82 by Pablo Records. Dist: Wellard, Chris, IMS-Polygram, BMG

IF I'M LUCKY (Sims, Zoot & Jimmy Rowles).
Album: released on Pablo, '82 by Pablo Records. Dist: Wellard, Chris, IMS-Polygram, BMG

Cassette: released on Pablo, '82 by Pablo Records. Dist: Wellard, Chris, IMS-Polygram, BMG

IN A SENTIMENTAL MOOD.
Album: released on Sonet, Jun'85 by Sonet Records. Dist: PRT

INNOCENT YEARS, (THE) (Sims, Zoot Four).
Album: released on Pablo, Sep'82 by Pablo Records. Dist: Wellard, Chris, IMS-Polygram, BMG

Cassette: released on Pablo, Sep'82 by Pablo Records. Dist: Wellard, Chris, IMS-Polygram, BMG

IN PARIS - 1956.
Album: released on Swing Disque, May'87

I WISH I WERE TWINS.
Album: released on Pablo, '82 by Pablo Records. Dist: Wellard, Chris, IMS-Polygram, BMG

Cassette: released on Pablo, '82 by Pablo Records. Dist: Wellard, Chris, IMS-Polygram, BMG

JOE & ZOOT (Sims, Zoot & Joe Venuti).
Double Album: released on Vanguard, Sep'76 by PRT Records. Dist: PRT

MOTORING ALONG (Sims, Zoot & Al Cohn).
Album: released on Sonet, '76 by Sonet Records. Dist: PRT

NASHVILLE (Sims, Zoot & Dick Nash).
Album: released on Zim, Apr'81 Dist: JSU, Jazz Horizons, Jazz Music, Swift

PASSION FLOWER.
Album: released on Pablo, '82 by Pablo Records. Dist: Wellard, Chris, IMS-Polygram, BMG

Cassette: released on Pablo, '82 by Pablo Records. Dist: Wellard, Chris, IMS-Polygram, BMG

QUIETLY THERE - ZOOT SIMS PLAYS JOHNNY MANDEL.
Album: released on Pablo, Sep'84 by Pablo Records. Dist: Wellard, Chris, IMS-Polygram, BMG

Cassette: released on Pablo, Sep'84 by Pablo Records. Dist: Wellard, Chris, IMS-Polygram, BMG

SOPRANO SAX.
Compact disc: released on Pablo (USA), May'86 by Pablo Records (USA). Dist: Wellard, Chris, IMS-Polygram, BMG

SWEETEST SOUNDS, THE (Sims, Zoot/Rune Gustafsson).
Album: released on Sonet, Jun'86 by Sonet Records. Dist: PRT

SWINGER, (THE).
Album: released on Pablo, '82 by Pablo Records. Dist: Wellard, Chris, IMS-Polygram, BMG

Cassette: released on Pablo, '82 by Pablo Records. Dist: Wellard, Chris, IMS-Polygram, BMG

TENOR CONTRASTS VOLUME 2 (Sims, Zoot/Al Cohn/James Moody).
Album: released on Esquire, Nov'86 by Titan International Productions. Dist: Jazz Music, Cadillac Music, Swift, Wellard, Chris, Backs, Rough Trade, Revolver, Nine Mile

WAITING GAME.
Album: released on Jasmine, Mar'83 by Jasmine Records. Dist: Counterpoint, Lugtons, Taylor, H.R., Wellard, Chris, Swift, Cadillac

WARM TENOR (Sims, Zoot & Jimmy Rowles).
Album: released on Pablo, '82 by Pablo Records. Dist: Wellard, Chris, IMS-Polygram, BMG

Cassette: released on Pablo, '82 by Pablo Records. Dist: Wellard, Chris, IMS-Polygram, BMG

ZOOT! (Sims, Zoot Quartet).
Album: released on Original Jazz Classics (USA), Apr'86 Dist: Fantasy (USA) Distribution, Chris Wellard Distribution, IMS-Polygram Distribution

ZOOT PLAYS SOPRANO.
Album: released on Pablo, '82 by Pablo Records. Dist: Wellard, Chris, IMS-Polygram, BMG

Cassette: released on Pablo, '82 by Pablo Records. Dist: Wellard, Chris, IMS-Polygram, BMG

ZOOT SIMS.
Album:

Album: released on Jazz Reactivation, Jul'82 Dist: PRT

ZOOT SIMS/DICK NASH (Sims, Zoot & Dick Nash).
Album: released on Zim, Apr'79 Dist: JSU, Jazz Horizons, Jazz Music, Swift

ZOOT SIMS/FRANK ROSOLINO (Sims, Zoot/Frank Rosolino).
Compact disc: released on Vogue, Dec'86 Dist: Discovery, Jazz Music, PRT, Swift

ZOOT SIMS & THE GERSHWIN BROTHERS.
Album: released on Pablo, '82 by Pablo Records. Dist: Wellard, Chris, IMS-Polygram, BMG

Cassette: released on Pablo, '82 by Pablo Records. Dist: Wellard, Chris, IMS-Polygram, BMG

ZOOT SIMS WITH THE BOB BROOKMEYER QUINTET (Sims, Zoot & The Bob Brookmeyer Quintet).
Album: released on Pumpkin, Nov'79 Dist: Jazz Music, Wellard, Chris, Cadillac

Simukonda, Ackim

LADY SUNSHINE.
Notes: Daylight Records, The Daylight Co.(Distribution) Ltd, 2 Dorset Place, New Street, Honiton, Devon EX14 8AB.
Album: released on Daylight, '86 by Daylight Records. Dist: Daylight

Sinatra, F.

LEGENDARY CONCERTS VOL. 2.
Compact disc: released on The Compact Collection, Sep'87 by Conifer Records. Dist: Conifer Distribution

Sinatra, Frank

20 CLASSIC TRACKS.
Album: released on MFP, Sep'81 by EMI Records. Dist: EMI

Cassette: released on MFP, Sep'81 by EMI Records. Dist: EMI

20 GOLDEN CLASSICS, VOL 2.
Album: released on Astan, Nov'84 by Astan Records. Dist: Counterpoint

Cassette: released on Astan, Nov'84 by Astan Records. Dist: Counterpoint

20 GOLDEN CLASSICS, VOL 1.
Album: released on Astan, Nov'84 by Astan Records. Dist: Counterpoint

Cassette: released on Astan, Nov'84 by Astan Records. Dist: Counterpoint

20 GOLDEN GREATS.
Album: released on EMI (Capitol), Apr'78 by Capitol Records. Dist: EMI

Cassette: released on EMI (Capitol), Apr'78 by Capitol Records. Dist: EMI

20 GOLDEN PIECES OF FRANK SINATRA.
Album: released on Bulldog, Sep'85 by Bulldog Records. Dist: President Distribution, Spartan, Swift, Taylor, H.R.

Cassette: released on Bulldog, Sep'85 by Bulldog Records. Dist: President Distribution, Spartan, Swift, Taylor, H.R.

ALL THE WAY.
Album: released on Capitol, Sep'84 by Capitol Records. Dist: EMI

Cassette: released on Capitol, Sep'84 by Capitol Records. Dist: EMI

BANG BANG.
Single (7"): released on Reprise, Dec'81 by WEA Records. Dist: WEA

BEST OF FRANK SINATRA.
Album: released on EMI (Holland), '83 by EMI Records. Dist: Conifer

BEST OF FRANK SINATRA & TOMMY DORSEY (Sinatra, Frank & Tommy Dorsey).
Album: released on RCA (Brazil), Jan'84

Cassette: released on RCA (Brazil), Jan'84

BEST OF OL' BLUE EYES.
Album: released on Reprise, May'75 by WEA Records. Dist: WEA

Cassette: released on Reprise, May'75 by WEA Records. Dist: WEA

BROADWAY KICK, (THE).
Album: released on CBS(Blue Diamond), Jun'85 by CBS Records. Dist: CBS

Cassette: released on CBS(Blue Diamond), Jun'85 by CBS Records. Dist: CBS

CAPITOL YEARS (THE).
Tracks: / Where are you? / Swingin' affair, A / This is Sinatra / Wee small hours / Songs for swingin' lovers / Swingin' session / Come swing with me / All the way / Sings of love and things / Point of no return / Nice 'n' easy / No one cares / Look to your heart / Only the lonely / Close to you / Swing easy / Swing easy / Come dance with me / Songs for young lovers / Swingin' affair, A / This is Sinatra - vol.2.
Notes: A 20 cassette box set of the classic albums from Frank Sinatra's Capitol career. All cassettes are on high quality XDR tape and show the original sleeve designs with notes by Alan Dell. Features his best loved songs with orchestrations by Billy May, the late Nelson Riddle, Gordan Jenkins and many more. This deluxe box set comes complete with a full colour booklet, exclusive to the set, tracing Sinatra's "Capitol years" with colour photographs and story by Alan Del. (Track titles are titles of each cassette)
Boxed set: released on Capitol, Sep'85 by Capitol Records. Dist: EMI

Cassette: released on Capitol, Dec'86 by Capitol Records. Dist: EMI

CHRISTMAS ALBUM (THE).
Album: released on Deja Vu, Aug'86 by Deja Vu Records. Dist: Counterpoint Distribution, Record Services Distribution (Ireland)

Cassette: released on Deja Vu, Aug'86 by Deja Vu Records. Dist: Counterpoint Distribution, Record Services Distribution (Ireland)

CLOSE TO YOU.
Tracks: / Close to you / P.S. I love you / Love locked out / Everything happens to me / It's easy to remember / Don't like goodbyes / With every breath I take / Blame it on my youth / It could happen to you / I've had my moments / I couldn't sleep a wink last night / End of a love affair(The) / If it's the last thing I do / There's a flaw in my flue / Wait till you see her.
Compact disc: released on EMI, Mar'87 by EMI Records. Dist: EMI

Album: released on Capitol, Jul'84 by Capitol Records. Dist: EMI

Cassette: released on Capitol, Jul'84 by Capitol Records. Dist: EMI

COME DANCE WITH ME.
Album: released on Capitol, Jun'84 by Capitol Records. Dist: EMI

Cassette: released on Capitol, Jun'84 by Capitol Records. Dist: EMI

COME FLY WITH ME.
Album: released on Capitol, Jun'84 by Capitol Records. Dist: EMI

Cassette: released on Capitol, Jun'84 by Capitol Records. Dist: EMI

COME SWING WITH ME.
Album: released on Capitol, Sep'84 by Capitol Records. Dist: EMI

Cassette: released on Capitol, Sep'84 by Capitol Records. Dist: EMI

CONCERT SINATRA (THE).
Compact disc: released on Reprise, Oct'86 by WEA Records. Dist: WEA

CONCERTS (THE).
Album: released on Deja Vu, Jul'86 by Deja Vu Records. Dist: Counterpoint Distribution, Record Services Distribution (Ireland)

Cassette: released on Deja Vu, Jul'86 by Deja Vu Records. Dist: Counterpoint Distribution, Record Services Distribution (Ireland)

DOOBE DOOBE DOO STRANGERS IN THE NIGHT.
Tracks: / Doobe doobe doo strangers in the night / In the wee small hours of the morning / Last night we were young.
Single (7"): released on Reprise, Apr'86 by WEA Records. Dist: WEA

Single (12"): released on Reprise, Apr'86 by WEA Records. Dist: WEA

DORSEY-SINATRA SESSIONS, 1940-42.
Album: released on RCA, Nov'72 by RCA Records. Dist: RCA, Roots, Swift, Wellard, Chris, I & B, Solomon & Peres Distribution

DUETS (THE).
Notes: Other artists include: Pearl Bailey/Jane Russell/Rosemary Clooney/Elvis Presley/Dinah Shore/Judy Garland etc.
Album: released on Deja Vu, May'86 by Deja Vu Records. Dist: Counterpoint Distribution, Record Services Distribution (Ireland)

Cassette: released on Deja Vu, May'86 by Deja Vu Records. Dist: Counterpoint Distribution, Record Services Distribution (Ireland)

EARLY YEARS, (THE).
Album: released on RCA (Germany), May'83

FRANK SINATRA.
Compact disc: released on Deja Vu, Jul'87 by Deja Vu Records. Dist: Counterpoint Distribution, Record Services Distribution (Ireland)

Boxed set: released on World Records, Dec'81 Dist: Polygram

Double cassette: released on World Records, Dec'81 Dist: Polygram

FRANK SINATRA & BING CROSBY (Sinatra, Frank & Bing Crosby).
Album: released on Joker, Apr'81 Dist: Cadillac, Zodiac Distribution, Jazz Horizons, Jazz Music, JSU, Celtic Music

FRANK SINATRA CHRISTMAS COLLECTION (THE).
Album: released on Deja Vu, Oct'86 by Deja Vu Records. Dist: Counterpoint Distribution, Record Services Distribution (Ireland)

FRANK SINATRA COLLECTION (THE).
Tracks: / I'll dance at your wedding / Lilli Bolero / Little white lies / Tree in the meadow (A) / My happiness / You call everbody darlin' / Now is the hour / One hundred years from today / I'm in the mood for love / After I say I'm sorry / I'll string along with you / This can't be love / Devil and the deep blue sea (The) / When I dance with you / I wonder who's kissing her now / I wish I didn't love her so / How soon / Lady from 29 Palms / You do / Serenade of the bells / Golden earrings / Dance ballerina dance / I'll get by / Pistol packing mama / Speak low / I've found a new baby / Lover is blue (A) / Tenderly / Mimi / Nice 'n' easy / Cheek to cheek / I'm gonna sit right down and right myself a letter / As time goes by / Witchcraft / I've got you under my skin / You make me feel so young / I can't get started / I get a kick out of you / Chicago / Come fly with me / Lady is a tramp (The) / Tender trap (The) / My funny valentine / Night and day / You'd be so nice to come home to / Dancing in the dark / Let's get away from it all / Nice work if you can get it / One for my baby.
Notes: This album contains early recordings which can reveal quality limiations of th tape source. All tracks licensed from San Juan Music Group.
Album: released on Collectors, Apr'86 by Castle Communications Records. Dist: PRT, Pinnacle, Jazz Music

Cassette: released on Collectors, Apr'86 by Castle Communications Records. Dist: PRT, Pinnacle, Jazz Music

Album: released on Capitol, Sep'86 by Capitol Records. Dist: EMI

Cassette: released on Capitol, Sep'86 by Capitol Records. Dist: EMI

FRANK SINATRA COLLECTION, (THE).
Album: released on Deja Vu, Aug'85 by Deja Vu Records. Dist: Counterpoint Distribution, Record Services Distribution (Ireland)

Cassette: released on Deja Vu, Aug'85 by Deja Vu Records. Dist: Counterpoint Distribution, Record Services Distribution (Ireland)

FRANK SINATRA DUETS.
Compact disc: released on Deja Vu, Jul'87 b Deja Vu Records. Dist: Counterpoint Distribu tion, Record Services Distribution (Ireland)

FRANK SINATRA & LENA HORNE (S natra, Frank & Lena Horne).
Album: released on Astan, Nov'84 by Asta Records. Dist: Counterpoint

Cassette: released on Astan, Nov'84 by Asta Records. Dist: Counterpoint

FRANK SINATRA SINGS FOR ONL THE LONELY.
Album: released on Capitol, Jul'84 by Capi Records. Dist: EMI

Cassette: released on Capitol, Jul'84 by Ca tol Records. Dist: EMI

FRANK SINATRA & TOMMY DORSE (Sinatra, Frank & Tommy Dorsey).
Album: released on Jazz Live, Oct'86

GOT THE WORLD ON A STRING.
Album: released on Starburst, Jun'87 by Sta burst Records. Dist: CBS Distribution

Cassette: released on Starburst, Jun'87 Starburst Records. Dist: CBS Distribution

GREATEST HITS: FRANK SINATF VOLS 1 & 2.
Double cassette: released on Reprise, Nov by WEA Records. Dist: WEA

GREATEST HITS: FRANK SINATRA
The early years.
Album: released on Embassy, Jun'78 by CBS Records. Dist: CBS

Cassette: released on Embassy, Jun'78 by CBS Records. Dist: CBS

GREATEST HITS: FRANK SINATRA VOL.2.
Album: released on Reprise, '74 by WEA Records. Dist: WEA

Cassette: released on Reprise, '74 by WEA Records. Dist: WEA

Cassette: released on Reprise, '74 by WEA Records. Dist: WEA

GREATEST HITS: FRANK SINATRA VOL.1.
Album: released on Reprise, '74 by WEA Records. Dist: WEA

Cassette: released on Reprise, '74 by WEA Records. Dist: WEA

GREATEST HITS: FRANK SINATRA.
Double Album: released on Capitol (Holland), '83 by Capitol Records. Dist: Conifer

IN CONCERT.
Double Album: released on Reprise, '74 by WEA Records. Dist: WEA

IN THE BEGINNING.
Double Album: released on CBS, Sep'80 by CBS Records. Dist: CBS

Cassette: released on CBS, Sep'80 by CBS Records. Dist: CBS

IN THE WEE SMALL HOURS.
Tracks: / In the wee small hours of the morning / Mood indigo / Glad to be unhappy / I get along without you very well / Deep in a dream / I see your face before me / Can't we be friends / When your lover has gone / What is this thing called love / I'll be around / Ill wind / It never entered my mind / Dancing on the ceiling / I'll never be the same / This love of mine.
Compact disc: released on EMI, Mar'87 by EMI Records. Dist: EMI

Album: released on Capitol, Sep'84 by Capitol Records. Dist: EMI

Cassette: released on Capitol, Sep'84 by Capitol Records. Dist: EMI

IT MIGHT AS WELL BE SWING (Sinatra, Frank/Count Basie).
Compact disc: released on Reprise, Oct'86 by WEA Records. Dist: WEA

KISSES AND TEARS.
Album: released on Meteor, Apr'87 by Magnum Music Group Ltd. Dist: Magnum Music Group Ltd, PRT Distribution, Spartan Distribution

LA IS MY LADY.
Album: released on Qwest, Aug'84 by WEA Records. Dist: WEA

Cassette: released on Qwest, Aug'84 by WEA Records. Dist: WEA

L.A. IS MY LADY.
Compact disc: released on Qwest, Mar'87 by WEA Records. Dist: WEA

LEGENDARY CONCERTS VOLUME 1.
Compact disc: released on The Compact Collection, Sep'87 by Conifer Records. Dist: Conifer Distribution

LONG AND FAR AWAY.
Tracks: / Little white lies / Suddenly / It's spring / This can't be love / Long ago and far away / One hundred years from today / I'm in the mood for love / Tenderly / Speak low / My happiness / I'll get by / Now is the hour / I found a new baby / You can't be true dear.
Album: released on Topline, '86 by Charly Records. Dist: Charly Distribution

Cassette: released on Topline, '86 by Charly Records. Dist: Charly Distribution

LOOK TO YOUR HEART.
Album: released on Capitol, Jul'84 by Capitol Records. Dist: EMI

Cassette: released on Capitol, Jul'84 by Capitol Records. Dist: EMI

LOVE AND MARRIAGE.
Single (7"): released on EMI Golden 45's, Mar'84 by EMI Records. Dist: EMI

LOVE IS A KICK.
Tracks: / You do something to me / Bim bam baby / My blue heaven / When you're smiling (the whole world smiles with you) / Saturday night (is the loneliest night of the week) / Bye bye baby / Continental (you kiss while you're dancing) (The) / Deep night / Should I? / American beauty rose / Five minutes more / Farewell farewell to love.
Album: released on CBS Cameo, Mar'86 by CBS Records. Dist: CBS

Cassette: released on CBS Cameo, Mar'86 by CBS Records. Dist: CBS

MAN AND HIS MUSIC, A.
Double compact disc: released on Reprise, Jul'87 by WEA Records. Dist: WEA

MUSICAL MONTAGE, A.
Album: released on Artistry, Sep'86 Dist: Jazz Music

MY BEST YEARS, VOL 1.
Album: released on IMS(Import), Oct'82 by Polydor Records. Dist: IMS, Polygram

MY BEST YEARS, VOL 2.
Album: released on IMS(Import), Oct'82 by Polydor Records. Dist: IMS, Polygram

MY WAY.
Tracks: / Watch what happens / Didn't we / Hallelujah, I love her so / Yesterday all my tomorrows / My Way / Day in the life of a fool, A / For once in my life / If you go away / Mrs.Robinson.
Compact disc: released on Reprise, Nov'86 by WEA Records. Dist: WEA

Album: released on Reprise, '74 by WEA Records. Dist: WEA

Cassette: released on Reprise, '74 by WEA Records. Dist: WEA

Single (7"): released on Reprise, '80 by WEA Records. Dist: WEA

Single (7"): released on Reprise, Jul'81 by WEA Records. Dist: WEA

NEW YORK NEW YORK.
Tracks: / Theme from New York, New York / I get a kick out of you / Something stupid / Moon river / What now my love / Summer wind / Mrs Robinson / My way / Strangers in the night / For once in my life / Yesterday / That's life / Girl from Ipanema / Lady is a tramp (The) / Bad, bad Leroy Brown / Ol' man river.
Album: released on Warner Bros., Mar'86 by Warner Bros Records. Dist: WEA

Cassette: released on Warner Bros., Mar'86 by Warner Bros Records. Dist: WEA

Compact disc: released on Warner Bros., '87 by Warner Bros Records. Dist: WEA

NEW YORK, NEW YORK.
Single (7"): released on Reprise, Jul'80 by WEA Records. Dist: WEA

NICE AND EASY.
Tracks: / Nice and easy / Come fly with me / One for my baby.
Single (7"): released on Capitol, Sep'86 by Capitol Records. Dist: EMI

Single (12"): released on Capitol, Sep'86 by Capitol Records. Dist: EMI

NICE 'N' EASY.
Album: released on Capitol, Jul'84 by Capitol Records. Dist: EMI

Cassette: released on Capitol, Jul'84 by Capitol Records. Dist: EMI

NO ONE CARES.
Album: released on Capitol, Jul'84 by Capitol Records. Dist: EMI

Cassette: released on Capitol, Jul'84 by Capitol Records. Dist: EMI

NOW IS THE HOUR.
Tracks: / I wonder who's kissing her now / I wish I didn't love you so / How soon / Lady from 29 Palms / You do / Serenade of the bells / Golden earrings / Dance ballerina dance / I'll dance at your wedding / Lili Bolero / Little white lies / Tree in the meadow (A) / My happiness / You call everybody darling / Now is the hour.
Album: released on Showcase, Apr'86 Dist: Counterpoint

Cassette: released on Showcase, Apr'86 Dist: Counterpoint

Album: released on Meteor, Sep'84 by Magnum Force Music. Dist: CBS Distribution

Album: released on Astan, Nov'84 by Astan Records. Dist: Counterpoint

Cassette: released on Astan, Nov'84 by Astan Records. Dist: Counterpoint

OFF THE RECORD WITH....
Album: released on Sierra, Aug'87 by Sierra Records. Dist: WEA. Estim retail price in Sep'87 was £4.99.

Cassette: released on Sierra, Aug'87 by Sierra Records. Dist: WEA. Estim retail price in Sep'87 was £4.99.

OL' BLUE EYES.
Tracks: / Witchcraft / Come fly with me / Young at heart / Tender trap, The / All the way.
Compact disc: released on Card/Grand Prix, Apr'87 Dist: Target

OL' BLUE EYES IS BACK.
Album: released on Reprise, '73 by WEA Records. Dist: WEA

OL' BLUE EYES IS BACK.
Tracks: / You will be my music / You're so right / Winner's (Theme from 'Maurie') / Nobody wins / Send in the clowns / Dream away / Let me try again / There used to be a ball park / Noah.
Compact disc: released on Reprise, Nov'86 by WEA Records. Dist: WEA

ONE NIGHT STAND WITH FRANK SINATRA.
Album: released on Joyce (USA), May'84 Dist: Swift

ORIGINAL SESSIONS, VOL 1.
Album: released on Meteor, Nov'84 by Magnum Force Music. Dist: CBS Distribution

ORIGINAL SESSIONS, VOL 2.
Album: released on Meteor, Nov'84 by Magnum Force Music. Dist: CBS Distribution

POINT OF NO RETURN.
Album: released on Capitol, Sep'84 by Capitol Records. Dist: EMI

Cassette: released on Capitol, Sep'84 by Capitol Records. Dist: EMI

PORTRAIT OF AN ALBUM.
Video-cassette (VHS): released on MGM, Feb'85 Dist: Polygram Distribution, Swift Distribution

PORTRAIT OF SINATRA.
Double Album: released on Reprise, Mar'77 by WEA Records. Dist: WEA

Double cassette: released on Reprise, Mar'77 by WEA Records. Dist: WEA

RARE SINATRA, (THE).
Album: released on Capitol, '78 by Capitol Records. Dist: EMI

Cassette: released on Capitol, '78 by Capitol Records. Dist: EMI

REPLAY ON (Vol 2).
Album: released on Sierra, May'86 by Sierra Records. Dist: WEA

Cassette: released on Sierra, May'86 by Sierra Records. Dist: WEA

REPLAY ON FRANK SINATRA.
Album: released on Sierra, Feb'85 by Sierra Records. Dist: WEA

Cassette: released on Sierra, Feb'85 by Sierra Records. Dist: WEA

REPRISE YEARS, THE.
Album: released on Reprise, Dec'86 by WEA Records. Dist: WEA

SALOON SONGS.
Tracks: / One for my baby (and one more for the road) / I should care / These foolish things / I guess I'll have to dream the rest / It never entered my mind / When your lover has gone / Body and soul / That old feeling / Ghost of a chance with you, (I don't stand a) / There's no you / Guess I'll hang my tears out to dry / Why try to change me now.
Album: released on CBS, Jul'87 by CBS Records. Dist: CBS

Cassette: released on CBS, Jul'87 by CBS Records. Dist: CBS

SAY HELLO.

Single (7"): released on Reprise, Nov'81 by WEA Records. Dist: WEA

SCREEN SINATRA.
Album: released on Capitol, Sep'80 by Capitol Records. Dist: EMI

Cassette: released on Capitol, Sep'80 by Capitol Records. Dist: EMI

SEPTEMBER OF MY YEARS.
Compact disc: released on Reprise, Oct'86 by WEA Records. Dist: WEA

SEXY, SWINGING SINATRA.
Triple album / cassette: released on Capitol(USA), Jan'85 by Capitol (USA) Records. Dist: EMI

SINATRA.
Double Album: released on Joker, '79 Dist: Cadillac, Zodiac Distribution, Jazz Horizons, Jazz Music, JSU, Celtic Music

SINATRA: A MAN & HIS MUSIC.
Compact disc: released on Reprise, Oct'86 by WEA Records. Dist: WEA

SINATRA AT THE SANDS (Sinatra, Frank/Count Basie).
Compact disc: released on Reprise, Nov'86 by WEA Records. Dist: WEA

SINATRA CHRISTMAS ALBUM.
Tracks: / Jingle bells / Christmas song, The / Mistletoe and holly / I'll be home for Christmas (if only in my dreams) / Have yourself a merry little Christmas / Christmas waltz, The / First Noel, The / Hark! the herald angels sing / O little town of Bethelehem / Adeste Fidelis / It came upon a midnight clear / Silent night.
Notes: Orchestra conducted by Gordon Jenkins.
Album: released on MFP, Sep'87 by EMI Records. Dist: EMI

Cassette: released on MFP, Sep'87 by EMI Records. Dist: EMI

SINATRA CHRISTMAS ALBUM, (THE).
Album: released on Capitol, Nov'83 by Capitol Records. Dist: EMI

Cassette: released on Capitol, Nov'83 by Capitol Records. Dist: EMI

SINATRA LOVE SONGS.
Tracks: / Nearness of you / If I had you / Nevertheless / You go to my head / My melancholy baby / How deep is the ocean / Embraceable you / She's funny that way, (I got a woman crazy for me) / For every man there's a woman / I don't know why (I just do) / Someone to watch over me / Love me.
Album: released on CBS, Jul'87 by CBS Records. Dist: CBS

Cassette: released on CBS, Jul'87 by CBS Records. Dist: CBS

SINATRA SALOON SONGS.
Album: released on CBS, Jul'87 by CBS Records. Dist: CBS

Cassette: released on CBS, Jul'87 by CBS Records. Dist: CBS

SINATRA SCREEN.
Tracks: / Continental, The / It's the same old dream / Laura / Stormy weather / I've got a crush on you / House I live in, The / All through the day / I couldn't sleep a wink last night / Time after time / But beautiful / I fall in love too easily / Brooklyn bridge, The.
Album: released on CBS, Jul'87 by CBS Records. Dist: CBS

Cassette: released on CBS, Jul'87 by CBS Records. Dist: CBS

SINATRA SINGS...OF LOVE AND THINGS.
Album: released on Capitol, Sep'84 by Capitol Records. Dist: EMI

Cassette: released on Capitol, Sep'84 by Capitol Records. Dist: EMI

SINATRA'S SWINGIN' SESSION.
Tracks: / When your smiling / Blue moon / S'posin' / It all depends on you / It's only a paper moon / My blue heaven / Should I / September in the rain / Always / I can't believe you're in love with me / I concentrate on you / You do something to me / Sentimental baby / Ol' MacDonald / Hidden persuasion.
Compact disc: released on EMI, Mar'87 by EMI Records. Dist: EMI

Album: released on Capitol, Sep'84 by Capitol Records. Dist: EMI

Cassette: released on Capitol, Sep'84 by Capitol Records. Dist: EMI

SINATRA STAGE.
Tracks: / There's no business like show business / Song is you, The / September song / Oh what a beautiful morning / They say it's wonderful / Bess oh where is my bess / Where or when / I could write a book / Why was I born / Lost in the stars / All the things you are / Ol'man river.
Album: released on CBS, Jul'87 by CBS Records. Dist: CBS

Cassette: released on CBS, Jul'87 by CBS Records. Dist: CBS

SINATRA STANDARDS.
Tracks: / Saturday night (is the loneliest night in the week) / Poinciana / Try a little tenderness / Autumn in New York / April in Paris / Dream / Nancy (with the laughing face) / Put your dreams away / I'm glad there is you / Day by day / Close to you / I'm a fool to want you.
Album: released on CBS, Jul'87 by CBS Records. Dist: CBS

Cassette: released on CBS, Jul'87 by CBS Records. Dist: CBS

SINATRA SWINGS.
Tracks: / Should I? / Birth of the blues /*Mean to me / It all depends on you / Deep night / Sweet Lorraine / Castle rock / Why can't you behave / My blue heaven / S'posin' / You can take my word for it baby / Blue skies.
Album: released on CBS, Jul'87 by CBS Records. Dist: CBS

Cassette: released on CBS, Jul'87 by CBS Records. Dist: CBS

SONGS FOR SWINGING LOVERS.
Tracks: / Too marvellous for words / Old devil moon / Pennies from heaven / Love is here to stay / I've got you under my skin / I thought about you / We'll be together again / Makin'whoopee / Swingin' down the lane / Anything goes / How about you / You make me feel so young / It happened in Monterey / You're getting to be a habit with me / You brought a new kind of love to me.
Compact disc: released on EMI, Mar'87 by EMI Records. Dist: EMI

SONGS FOR SWINGIN' LOVERS.
Album: released on Capitol, Sep'84 by Capitol Records. Dist: EMI

Cassette: released on Capitol, Sep'84 by Capitol Records. Dist: EMI

SONGS FOR YOUNG LOVERS.
Album: released on Capitol, Jun'84 by Capitol Records. Dist: EMI

Cassette: released on Capitol, Jun'84 by Capitol Records. Dist: EMI

STRANGERS IN THE NIGHT.
Compact disc: released on Reprise, Nov'86 by WEA Records. Dist: WEA

Single (7"): released on Reprise, '80 by WEA Records. Dist: WEA

STRING ALONG.
Album: released on Meteor, Oct'85 by Magnum Force Music. Dist: CBS Distribution

SUDDENLY IT'S SPRING.
Album: released on Meteor, Jun'86 by Magnum Music Group Ltd. Dist: Magnum Music Group Ltd, PRT Distribution, Spartan Distribution

SUPERGOLD.
Double Album: released on EMI (Germany), '83 by EMI Records. Dist: Conifer

SWING EASY.
Album: released on Capitol, Jun'84 by Capitol Records. Dist: EMI

Cassette: released on Capitol, Jun'84 by Capitol Records. Dist: EMI

SWINGIN' AFFAIR, A.
Album: released on Capitol, Mar'84 by Capitol Records. Dist: EMI

Cassette: released on Capitol, Mar'84 by Capitol Records. Dist: EMI

SWINGING SEXY SINATRA.
Double Album: released on EMI (France), '83 by EMI Records. Dist: Conifer

TENDERLY.
Album: released on Meteor, Apr'84 by Magnum Force Music. Dist: CBS Distribution

THAT'S LIFE.
Compact disc: released on Reprise, Oct'86 by WEA Records. Dist: WEA

THEME FROM NEW YORK NEW YORK.
Tracks: / Theme from New York New York / My kind of town / LA is my lady.
Single (7"): released on Warner Bros., Feb'86 by Warner Bros Records. Dist: WEA

Single (12"): released on Warner Bros., Feb'86 by Warner Bros Records. Dist: WEA

THIS IS SINATRA.
Tracks: / I've got the world on a string / Three coins in the fountain / Love and marriage / From here to eternity / South of the border / Rain (falling fron the skies) / Gal that got away, The / Young at heart / Learnin' the blues / My one and only love / Tender trap (The) (Love is) / Don't worry 'bout me.
Notes: (P)1956 Original Sound Recordings made by Capitol Records Inc.
Album: released on Capitol, Mar'87 by Capitol Records. Dist: EMI

Cassette: released on Capitol, Mar'87 by Capitol Records. Dist: EMI

THIS IS SINATRA VOL.2.
Tracks: / Hey! Jealous lover / Everybody loves somebody / Something wonderful happens in summer / Half as lovely / You're cheatin' yourself (if you're cheatin' on me) / You'll always be the one I love / You forgot all the words / How little we know (How little it matters) / Time after time / Crazy love / Johnny Concho theme (wait for me) / If you are but a dream / So long, my love / It's the same old dream / I believe / Put all your dreams away (for another day).
Notes: Orchestra conducted by Nelson Riddle

Album: released on Capitol, Mar'87 by Capitol Records. Dist: EMI

Cassette: released on Capitol, Mar'87 by Capitol Records. Dist: EMI

TO LOVE A CHILD.
Single (7"): released on Reprise, Dec'82 by WEA Records. Dist: WEA

TOMMY DORSEY & HIS ORCHESTRA WITH FRANK SINATRA (see Dorsey, Tommy) (Sinatra, Frank & The Tommy Dorsey Orchestra).

TRILOGY.
Boxed set: released on Reprise, Apr'80 by WEA Records. Dist: WEA

UNOBTAINABLE FRANK SINATRA (THE).
Album: released on Deja Vu, Aug'86 by Deja Vu Records. Dist: Counterpoint Distribution, Record Services Distribution (Ireland)

Cassette: released on Deja Vu, Aug'86 by Deja Vu Records. Dist: Counterpoint Distribution, Record Services Distribution (Ireland)

V-DISC RECORDINGS, VOL 1.
Album: released on Apex, Aug'81 Dist: Jazz Music, Swift

VOICE 1942-1952, THE.
Tracks: / One for my baby / I should care / These foolish things / I guess I'll have to dream the rest / It never entered my mind / When your lover has gone / Body and soul / That old feeling / Ghost of a chance with you (I don't stand a) / There's no you / Guess I'll hang my tears out to dry / Why try to change me now / Nearness of you (The) / If I had you / Never the less / You go to my head / My melancholy baby / How deep is the ocean / Embraceable you / She's funny that way / For every man there's a woman / I don't know why (I just do) / Someone to watch over me / Love me / Saturday night (is the loneliest night in the week) / Poinciana / Try a little tenderness / Autumn in New York / April in Paris / Dream / Nancy (with the laughing face) / Put your dreams away / I'm glad there is you / Day by day / Close to you / I'm a fool to want you / Should I ? / Birth of the blues / Mean to me / It all depends on you / Deep night / Sweet Lorraine / Castle rock / Why can't you behave / My blue heaven / S'posin / You can take my word for it baby / Blue skies / Continental, The / It's the same old dream / Laura / Stormy weather / I've got a crush on you / House I live in, The / All through the day / I couldn't sleep a wink last night / Time after time / But beautiful / I fall in love too easy / Brooklyn bridge, The / There's no business like show business / Song is you (The) / September song / Oh what a beautiful morning / They say it's wonderful / Bess oh where is my Bess / Where or when / I could write a book / Why was I born / Lost in the stars / All the things you are / Ol' man river.
Album: released on CBS, Nov'86 by CBS Records. Dist: CBS

VOICE (THE)(CD).
Compact disc: released on Solid Gold, Oct'86 Dist: MCA

Album: released on CBS Cameo, Oct'84 by CBS Records. Dist: CBS

Cassette: released on CBS Cameo, Oct'84 by CBS Records. Dist: CBS

Compact disc: released on CBS, Jun'87 by CBS Records. Dist: CBS

WELL DID YOU EVAH (Sinatra, Frank & Bing Crosby).
Single (7"): released on Capitol, Nov'83 by Capitol Records. Dist: EMI

WHERE ARE YOU?.
Album: released on Capitol, Mar'84 by Capitol Records. Dist: EMI

Cassette: released on Capitol, Mar'84 by Capitol Records. Dist: EMI

YOU MAKE ME FEEL SO YOUNG.
Tracks: / Night and day / Laura / Somebody loves me / Little white lies / This can't be love / You make me feel so young / Speak low / Yo do something to me / Begin the beguine / Tenderly / On the sunny side of the street / Love me or leave me / They did not believe me / Out of nowhere / I've got my love to keep me warm / For you.
Compact disc: released on Topline, '87 by Charly Records. Dist: Charly Distribution

YOUNG FRANK SINATRA, (THE).
Album: released on Joker, Apr'81 Dist: Cadillac, Zodiac Distribution, Jazz Horizons, Jazz Music, JSU, Celtic Music

Sinatras

BETRAYAL.
Album: released on Hit The Deck, Jan'85 by Hit The Deck Records. Dist: PRT

HAPPY FEELING.
Single (7"): released on Dining Out, Jun'81

I'M LONELY.
Single (7"): released on Shriekback, Sep'85

Single (12"): released on Shriekback, Sep'85

SEEING COMES BEFORE WORDS.
Single (7"): released on Dining Out, Nov'81

SWEAT.
Single (7"): released on Empire, Sep'82 by Empire Records. Dist: Backs, Cartel, Jetstar

Single (12"): released on Empire, Sep'82 by Empire Records. Dist: Backs, Cartel, Jetstar

YOU MAKE ME FEEL....
Single (7"): released on Transmanor, Mar'82

YOU MAKE ME FEEL LIKE I'M WEARING NEW....
Single (7"): released on Empire, Apr'82 by Empire Records. Dist: Backs, Cartel, Jetstar

Sinclair, Belinda

WHITE HORSES.
Single (7"): released on Applause, Jun'81 by Riva Records. Dist: WEA, Discovery

Sinclair, Jimmy

RIVER LOVE SONG (2 PARTS).
Single (12"): released on Thunderbolt, Nov'83 by Magnum Music Group Ltd. Dist: Magnum Music Group Ltd, PRT Distribution, Spartan Distribution

Sinclair, John

NAZ, THE.
Single (7"): released on Charisma, Nov'82 by Virgin Records. Dist: EMI

Sinclair, Loretta

EVERYTIME WE TOUCH.
Tracks: / Everytime we touch / Everytime we touch (instrumental - rhythm mix).
Single (7"): released on Citybeat, Sep'86 Dist: WEA

Single (12"): released on Citybeat, Sep'86 Dist: WEA

Sindy & The Action Men

WHO'S SHE.
Single (7"): released on Wimp, Feb'84 by Wimp Records. Dist: Backs, Cartel

Single (12"): released on Wimp, Feb'84 by Wimp Records. Dist: Backs, Cartel

YOU'RE LUCKY/PINNED AGAINST THE WALL.
Single (7"): released on Wimp, Dec'82 by Wimp Records. Dist: Backs, Cartel

Sinful

GONNA RAISE HELL.
Album: released on Shades, Sep'85 Dist: Pinnacle

Singalong Banjo Party

SINGALONG BANJO PARTY Various artists (Various Artists).
Double Album: released on Platinum, Nov'83 by Geoffs Records.

Double cassette: released on Platinum, Nov'83 by Geoffs Records.

Sing An Irish Song

SING AN IRISH SONG VOL 1 (Cottage by the Lee) (Various Artists).
Tracks: / Turfman from Ardee / Old Arboe / Where is my Nora / Shores of Lough Brann / Four country roads / Cottage on the old Dungannon Road / Boys from the Co Mayo / Cottage by the Lee / Lough sheelin / Marta the flower of sweet Strabane.
Cassette: released on Homespun(Ireland), Jul'86 by Outlet Records. Dist: Outlet

SING AN IRISH SONG VOL 2 (mountains of Mourne) (Various Artists).
Tracks: / If only we had old Ireland over here / Mountains of Mourne / Slievenamon / When you and I were young Maggie / Cottage by the Lee / Hills of Glenswilly / Moonshiner / Mulroy Bay / Dublin in the rare oul times / Bunch of thyme.
Cassette: released on Homespun(Ireland), Jul'86 by Outlet Records. Dist: Outlet

SING AN IRISH SONG VOL 3 (I'll take you home again Kathleen) (Various Artists).
Tracks: / I'll take you home again Kathleen / Come back Paddy Reilly / Mulroy Bay / Castle of Dromore / Noreen Bawn / My wild Irish rose / Old rustic bridge / Carrickfergus / Cottage on the old Dungannon Road / Do you want yer oul lobby washed down.
Cassette: released on Homespun(Ireland), Jul'86 by Outlet Records. Dist: Outlet

SING AN IRISH SONG VOL 4 (Rose of Mooncoin) (Various Artists).
Tracks: / Rose of Aranmore / Spancil Hill / Old mud cabin on the hill / Mother's love is a blessing (A) / Rose of Mooncoin / Old rustic bridge by the hill / Boys from the Co Armagh / Typical Irishman / Any Tipperary town / Sweet Mary.
Cassette: released on Homespun(Ireland), Jul'86 by Outlet Records. Dist: Outlet

SING AN IRISH SONG VOL 5 (spinning wheel) (Various Artists).
Tracks: / Travelling people / Spinning wheel / Hometown on the Foyle / Slaney valley / Stone outside Dan Murphy's door / Faughan side / Lough Sheelin / Mountains of Morne / Dingle Bay / Take me back to Castlebar.
Cassette: released on Homespun(Ireland), Jul'86 by Outlet Records. Dist: Outlet

SING AN IRISH SONG VOL 6 (Galway Bay) (Various Artists).
Tracks: / My Eileen / Boys from Co. Mayo / Gallant John Joe / Emigrants letter / Galway Bay / Old Claddagh ring / Goodbye Johny dear / Westmeath bachelor / Gentle mother / I'll take you home again Kathleen.
Cassette: released on Homespun(Ireland), Jul'86 by Outlet Records. Dist: Outlet

SING AN IRISH SONG VOL 7 (rose of Tralee) (Various Artists).
Tracks: / Donaree / Boys from Co Armagh / Let Mr Maguire sit down / Eileen O'Grady / I'll remember you love in my prayers / Where the three counties meet / Paddy's green shamrock shore / Come back Paddy Reilly / My wild Irish rose / Rose of Tralee.
Cassette: released on Homespun(Ireland), Jul'86 by Outlet Records. Dist: Outlet

SING AN IRISH SONG VOL 8 (village where I went to school) (Various Artists).
Tracks: / Village where I went to school / Kellys (The) / Boys from Co Mayo / If we only had old Ireland over here / Homes of Donegal / Stone outside Dan Murphy's door / My Lagan love / Abbeyshrule / Typical Irishman / Christmastime in Ireland.
Cassette: released on Homespun(Ireland), Jul'86 by Outlet Records. Dist: Outlet

SING AN IRISH SONG VOL 9 (Irish eyes) (Various Artists).
Tracks: / Irish eyes / Gentle mother / Pretty little girl from Omagh / Irish rover / If you're Irish / Doonaree / Little country town in Ireland / Asthoreen bawn / Catch me if you can.
Cassette: released on Homespun(Ireland), Jul'86 by Outlet Records. Dist: Outlet

SING AN IRISH SONG VOL 10 (girl from Donegal) (Various Artists).
Tracks: / Girl form Donegal / These are my mountains / Village in Co Tyrone (A) / Give an Irish girl to me / Moonshiner (The) / Where the three counties meet / Eileen O'Grady / Blacksmith (The) / Sunset years of life / Coastline of Mayo.
Cassette: released on Homespun(Ireland), Jul'86 by Outlet Records. Dist: Outlet

SING AN IRISH SONG VOL 11 (town I love so well) (Various Artists).
Tracks: / Oul Lammas fair / Spancil Hill / Shores of Lough Neagh / Dear old Donegal / Town I love so well / Boys of Killybegs / My Eileen is waiting for me / Give an Irish girl to me / My Kathleen / Real old mountain dew.
Cassette: released on Homespun(Ireland), Jul'86 by Outlet Records. Dist: Outlet

SING AN IRISH SONG VOL 12 (three leaf shamrock) (Various Artists).
Tracks: / Ireland mother Ireland / Boys from Co Armagh / Old Claddagh ring / Three leaf shamrock / Miltown Malbay / Rose of Mooncoin / Cottage by the Lee / Green hills of Kerry / Lovely derry on the banks of the Foyle / McCarthy's party.
Cassette: released on Homespun(Ireland), Jul'86 by Outlet Records. Dist: Outlet

SING AN IRISH SONG VOL 13 (fields of Athenry) (Various Artists).
Tracks: / Fields of Athenry / Spancil hill / Rose of Mooncoin / My beautiful limerick / Slievenamon / Four green fields / Galway shawl / Hills of Kerry / Blacksmith / Catch me if you can.
Cassette: released on Homespun(Ireland), Jul'86 by Outlet Records. Dist: Outlet

SING AN IRISH SONG VOL 14 (St Patrick's Day) (Various Artists).
Tracks: / Three tunes (The) / High caul cap / Soldiers joy / Girl I left behind / Sweets of May / Siege of Ennis / Rocks of Cashel / Farewell to whiskey / Humours of Bandon / Bonie Kate / Sligo maid / Miss Monaghan's / St Patrick's Day / Drops of brandy / Kelly the boy from Killan / Dawning of the day / Roddy McCorley / If you're Irish / Come into the parlour / With me Shillelagh under me arm / Westmeath bachelor / Piper through the meadow strays (The).
Notes: All traditional arrangement.
Cassette: released on Homespun(Ireland), Jul'86 by Outlet Records. Dist: Outlet

SING AN IRISH SONG VOL 15 (a nation once again) (Various Artists).
Tracks: / Ireland's 32 / Take me home to Mayo / Four green fields / Fields of Athenry / Sean South / West awake / Shall my soul pass through old Ireland / Boys of the old brigade / James Connolly / Nation once again (A).
Cassette: released on Homespun(Ireland), Jul'86 by Outlet Records. Dist: Outlet

SING AN IRISH SONG VOL 16 (Old Bog Road) (Various Artists).
Tracks: / Old Bog Road / Noreen Bawn / Life to go / Road by the river / Connemara cradle song / Hills of Connemara / My lovely Irish rose / 40 shades of green / Wreck of No 9.
Cassette: released on Homespun(Ireland), Jul'86 by Outlet Records. Dist: Outlet

SING AN IRISH SONG VOL 17 (Carrickfergus) (Various Artists).
Tracks: / Carrickfergus / Wild rover / McCaffrey / Follow me up to Carlow / Connemara cradle song / Mursheen Durkin / Banks of Ohio / McAlpines Fusiliers / Butcher boy / Santiano.
Cassette: released on Homespun(Ireland), Jul'86 by Outlet Records. Dist: Outlet

SING AN IRISH SONG VOL 18 (Galway shawl) (Various Artists).
Tracks: / Rose of Castlerea / Galway shawl / Stone outside Dan Murphy's door / Abbeyshrule / Take me back to Castlebar / Catch me if you can / Village where I went to school / Any Tipperary town / Do you want your aullobby washed down / Old Bog Road.
Cassette: released on Homespun(Ireland), Jul'86 by Outlet Records. Dist: Outlet

SING AN IRISH SONG VOL 19 (where the River Shannon flows) (Various Artists).
Tracks: / Hometown on the Foyle / 40 shades of green / Mulroy Bay / Any Tipperary town / Where the River Shannon flows / Slaney valley / Mother's love is a blessing (A) / Old cross of Arboe / Shores of Loughbran / Cliffs of Doneen.
Cassette: released on Homespun(Ireland), Jul'86 by Outlet Records. Dist: Outlet

SING AN IRISH SONG VOL 20 (Kevin Barry) (Various Artists).
Tracks: / God save Ireland / Dying rebel / Lonely woods of Upton / Kevin Barry / Blood stained bandage / Bold Fenian men / Fields of Athenry / Father Murphy / Irish soldier boy / Who fears to speak of '98.
Cassette: released on Homespun(Ireland), Jul'86 by Outlet Records. Dist: Outlet

SING AN IRISH SONG VOL 21 (mass rock in the Glen) (Various Artists).
Tracks: / Mass rock in the Glen / Irish soldier boy / Moonshiner / Here's a toast to you Claddagh / Slattery's mounted fut / 50 years of golden jubilee / Goodbye Mick, goodbye Pat / West of the old River Shannon / Castle of Dromore / Hills of Glenswilly.
Cassette: released on Homespun(Ireland), Jul'86 by Outlet Records. Dist: Outlet

SING AN IRISH SONG VOL 22 (old Claddagh ring) (Various Artists).
Tracks: / Sing Irishmen sing / As I roved out / Rocks of Bawn / She moved through the fair / Rattlin' roarin' Willie / Peggy Gordon / Doffin mistress / High Germany / Sam Hall / Old Claddagh ring.
Cassette: released on Homespun(Ireland), Jul'86 by Outlet Records. Dist: Outlet

SING AN IRISH SONG VOL 23 (Ireland mother Ireland) (Various Artists).
Tracks: / Ireland mother Ireland / Three lovely lassies / Town of Galway / If I were a blackbird / Dingle Bay / Molly Bawn boating on Lough Rhee / Do you remeber the good old days / Miltown Malabay / Blarney roses / Typical Irishman.
Cassette: released on Homespun(Ireland), Jul'86 by Outlet Records. Dist: Outlet

SING AN IRISH SONG VOL 24 (Galway races) (Various Artists).
Tracks: / Spanish lady / Lough Erin's lovely shore / Galway races / Rocking the cradle / Singing bird / Big strong man / Ramblin' Irishman / Bunclody / Spancil Hill / Kitty from Baltimore.
Cassette: released on Homespun(Ireland), Jul'86 by Outlet Records. Dist: Outlet

Sing A Song Of Playschool

SING A SONG OF PLAYSCHOOL.

Album: released on BBC, Oct'76 by BBC Records & Tapes. Dist: EMI, PRT, Pye

Cassette: released on BBC, Oct'76 by BBC Records & Tapes. Dist: EMI, PRT, Pye

Sing Children Sing

NEW YORK CITY OPERA CHILDREN'S CHORUS (New York City Opera Childrens Choir).
Album: released on Caedmon(USA), Jan'78 by Caedmon (USA) Records. Dist: Gower, Taylors, Discovery

Cassette: released on Caedmon(USA), Jan'78 by Caedmon (USA) Records. Dist: Gower, Taylors, Discovery

Singelton, Charlie

MODERN MAN.
Album: released on Arista, Dec'85 by Arista Records. Dist: RCA

Singelton, Maxine

DON'T YOU LOVE IT.
Single (7"): released on System, Jan'82 Dist: ERC Records

Single (12"): released on System, Jan'82 Dist: ERC Records

YOU CAN'T RUN AWAY FROM LOVE.
Single (7"): released on Creole, Feb'83 by Creole Records. Dist: Rhino, PRT

Single (12"): released on Creole, Feb'83 by Creole Records. Dist: Rhino, PRT

Singer, Hal

SOUL OF AFICA also see Jef Gilson (Singer, Hal & Jef Gilson).

SWING ON IT.
Album: released on JSP, Aug'81 by JSP Records. Dist: Swift, Projection

Singer, James

ARICA/JAH BLESS THE CHILDREN.
Single (12"): released on Peoples Choice, Oct'82 by Peoples Choice Records. Dist: Jetstar

LEVEL VIBES.
Single (12"): released on BWB, Jun'84 Dist: Jetstar

WORLD SMILING WITH YOU.
Single (12"): released on BWB, Dec'84 Dist: Jetstar

Singers & Players

LEAPS AND BOUNDS.
Album: released on Cherry Red, Feb'84 by Cherry Red Records. Dist: Pinnacle

REVOLUTION/TOO MUCH WORKLOAD.
Single 10": released on On-U-Sound, Apr'82 Dist: Rough Trade Distribution, Lightning

STAGGERING HEIGHTS.
Album: released on On-U-Sound, Aug'83 Dist: Rough Trade Distribution, Lightning

Singers Unlimited

ACAPELLA.
Tracks: / Both sides now / London by night / Here, there and everywhere / Lullaby / Michell / Fool on the hill / Emily / Since you asked / More I can not wish you / Try to remember.
Compact disc: released on Verve, Aug'84 by Phonogram Records. Dist: Polygram

CAPELLA A.
Album: released on MPS (Germany), Sep'84 Dist: IMS-Polygram Distribution, Parnote Distribution (Formerly MDC)

Cassette: released on MPS (Germany), Sep'84 Dist: IMS-Polygram Distribution, Parnote Distribution (Formerly MDC)

CAPELLA A 11.
Album: released on MPS (Germany), Apr'85 Dist: IMS-Polygram Distribution, Parnote Distribution (Formerly MDC)

CAPELLA A 111.
Album: released on MPS (Germany), Aug'85 Dist: IMS-Polygram Distribution, Parnote Distribution (Formerly MDC)

CHRISTMAS.
Tracks: / Dec the halls / Ah bleak and chill the wintry wind / Bright, bright the hollly berries / Nigh Bethlehem / While by my sheep / It came upon a midnight clear / Silent night / Joy to the world / Wassail song carol of the Russian children / Good King Wenceslas / O, come all ye faithful / Coventry carol / Have yourself a merry little Christmas.
Compact disc: released on MPS-Polydor, Nov'84

CHRISTMAS.
Album: released on MPS Jazz, Jan'81

COMPACT JAZZ.
Compact disc: released on MPS, Jul'87

EVENTIDE.
Album: released on MPS (Germany), Aug'85 Dist: IMS-Polygram Distribution, Parnote Distribution (Formerly MDC)

FEELING FREE.
Tracks: / You are the sunshine of my life / Time for love, A / Green Dolphin Street / So many stars / Feeling free with Patrick B / Ja da / Skylark / On a clear day / I'm shadowing you / Where is the love.
Notes: Te group are accompanied by the orchestras of Robert Farnon and Pat Williams.
Album: released on MPS (Germany), Aug'85 Dist: IMS-Polygram Distribution, Parnote Distribution (Formerly MDC)

Compact disc: released on MPS (Germany), Aug'85 Dist: IMS-Polygram Distribution, Parnote Distribution (Formerly MDC)

FOUR OF US.
Album: released on MPS Jazz, May'81

FRIENDS.
Album: released on MPS Jazz, May'81

IN TUNE.
Album:

INVITATION.
Album: released on MPS Jazz, Jan'81

JUST IN TIME.
Album: released on MPS Jazz, May'81

SENIMENTAL JOURNEY.
Album: released on MPS (Germany), Apr'85 Dist: IMS-Polygram Distribution, Parnote Distribution (Formerly MDC)

SINGERS UNLIMITED.
Compact disc: by Polydor Records. Dist: Polygram, Polydor

SPECIAL BLEND A.
Album: released on MPS Jazz, May'81

WALKMAN JAZZ.
Cassette: released on Polydor, Jun'87 by Polydor Records. Dist: Polygram, Polydor

WITH ROB MCCONNELL AND THE BOSS BRASS.
Album: released on MPS (Germany), Apr'85 Dist: IMS-Polygram Distribution, Parnote Distribution (Formerly MDC)

Sing For Joy

SING FOR JOY Various girl guides and boy scouts (Various Artists).
Album: released on BBC, Aug'78 by BBC Records & Tapes. Dist: EMI, PRT, Pye

Cassette: released on BBC, Aug'78 by BBC Records & Tapes. Dist: EMI, PRT, Pye

Singh, Peter

ELVIS I'M ON THE PHONE.
Single (7"): released on Screaming Out For Red, Apr'82 Dist: Spartan

Singh, Romie

DANCING TO FORGET.
Tracks: / Peeping Tom.
Single (7"): released on Portrait, Feb'87 by CBS Records. Dist: CBS

Single (12"): released on Portrait, Feb'87 by CBS Records. Dist: CBS

Single, Singe

LEAVES BADNESS ALONE.
Single (12"): released on Vibes, Jan'85 Dist: Vibes

SHOULDER MOVE/DUB.
Single (12"): released on Tads, Sep'83 by Tads Records. Dist: Jetstar Distribution. Estim retail price in Jul'87 was £3.99.

TWO UPRISING STARS (Singie, Singie/Bobby Melody).
Album: released on Midnight Rock, Nov'85 Dist: Jetstar Distribution, Kingdom Distribution

YES SHE GONE.
Single (12"): released on Blue Mountain, Jul'85 Dist: Jetstar

Singing...

SINGING IN THE BAND Songs from Play School & Play Away (Singing In The Band).
Album: released on BBC, Apr'84 by BBC Records & Tapes. Dist: EMI, PRT, Pye

Cassette: released on BBC, Apr'84 by BBC Records & Tapes. Dist: EMI, PRT, Pye

Singing & Dancing Games

SINGING & DANCING GAMES Various artists (Various Artists).
Album: released on Kiddicraft, Jan'80 by MacDonald Educational Records. Dist: H.R. Taylor

Cassette: released on Kiddicraft, Jan'80 by MacDonald Educational Records. Dist: H.R. Taylor

Singing Detective

SINGING DETECTIVE, THE Various artists (Various Artists).
Notes: Music from the BBC TV series.

Singing Fireman

WELLEPHANT (Singing Fireman (Graham Walker with Claire & Friends)).
Tracks: / Wellephant / What do you do.
Single (7"): released on Island, Oct'86 by Island Records. Dist: Polygram

Singing Nun

DOMINIQUE.
Single (7"): released on Phillips, Jan'80

Singing Preachers

GOSPEL SINGING.
Album: released on Blues Classics (USA), Jul'87 by Arhoolie Records. Dist: Topic, Jazz Music, Projection

Singing Ringing Tree

GOOD DAY GOOD.
Single (7"): released on Sample, Aug'87 by Sample Records. Dist: Red Rhino, Cartel

Singing Sheep

BAA BAA BLACK SHEEP/FLOCK AROUND THE CLOCK.
Single (7"): released on Sheep, Dec'82 by Virgin Records. Dist: CBS

Singin' In The Rain

SINGIN' IN THE RAIN Orininal London Cast (Various Artists).
Tracks: / Singin' in the rain / Temptation / I can't give you anything but love / Be a clown / Too marvellous for words / You are my lucky star / Moses / Good morning / Fit as a fiddle / Fascinating rhythm / Would you / All I do is dream of you / Make 'em laugh / You were meant for me / Broadway ballet / Finale.
Notes: Artists include Tommy Steele, Roy Castle, Danielle Carson etc.
Album: released on CBS, Jul'86 by CBS Records. Dist: CBS

Cassette: released on CBS, Jul'86 by CBS Records. Dist: CBS

Compact disc: released on CBS, Apr'87 by CBS Records. Dist: CBS

Album: released on Safari, Mar'84 by Safari Records. Dist: Pinnacle

Cassette: released on Safari, Mar'84 by Safari Records. Dist: Pinnacle

Cassette: released on MGM, Jan'83 Dist: Polygram Distribution, Swift Distribution

Album: released on EEC Import (Limited Edition), Dec'82 Dist: IMS, Polygram

SINGIN' IN THE RAIN (VIDEO) (Various Artists).
Notes: Released by MGM/UA/Screen Legends

Single English

HEAVEN GONE WRONG.
Single (7"): released on Rebound, Aug'84 by Rebound Records. Dist: Terry Blood Distribution

Single File

OUT IN THE TRAFFIC.
Tracks: / Out in the traffic.
Single (7"): released on Mainline, May'86 Dist: Red Rhino

Singles

ON THE LINE/FOOLS PARTY.
Single (7"): released on Posh, Aug'83 by Posh Records. Dist: Pinnacle

SINGLES various artists (Various Artists).
Cassette: released on Reach Out Int, Jan'83

T.V DETECTIVES/SEND FOR SORROW.
Single (7"):

Singleton, Valerie

STORY OF AJEEB & THE 40 LOVELY GIRLS.
Cassette: released on Chiron Cassettes, Jan'79 by Ivan Berg. Dist: Pinnacle, Record & Tape Sales

STORY OF AJEEB & THE 40 LOVELY GIRLS & STORY OF SHAHRAZ.
Cassette: released on Chiron Cassettes, Jan'79 by Ivan Berg. Dist: Pinnacle, Record & Tape Sales

STORY OF SINBAD THE SAILOR THE STORY OF THE LITTLE HUNCHBACK.
Cassette: released on Chiron Cassettes, Jan'79 by Ivan Berg. Dist: Pinnacle, Record & Tape Sales

STORY OF SINBAD THE SAILOR.
Cassette: released on Chiron Cassettes, Jan'79 by Ivan Berg. Dist: Pinnacle, Record & Tape Sales

STORY OF THE FISHERMAN & THE JINNEE.
Cassette: released on Chiron Cassettes, Jan'79 by Ivan Berg. Dist: Pinnacle, Record & Tape Sales

STORY OF THE FISHERMAN & STORY OF MA'ARUF THE COBBLER.
Double Album: released on Chiron Cassettes, '79 by Ivan Berg. Dist: Pinnacle, Record & Tape Sales

Sing Market

VIA TV.
Tracks: / Via TV.
Single (12"): released on Dark Network, Aug'86 by Dance Network Records. Dist: Backs, Cartel

Sing Out!

SING OUT! Various artists (Various Artists).
Notes: Highlights from the ITV series featuringRoger Whittaker, Gloria Gaynor, George Hamilton IV, Carroll Baker, Dana, The African Childrens Choir.
Album: released on Tembo, Sep'87

Compact disc: released on Tembo, Sep'87

Cassette: released on Tembo, Sep'87

SING OUT various artists.
Compact disc: released on IMS, Aug'87 by Polydor Records. Dist: IMS, Polygram

Sing, Say & Play

SING, SAY & PLAY (Various Artists).
Album: released on Topic, '81 by Topic Records. Dist: JSU Distribution, Projection Distribution, Jazz Music Distribution

Sing Sing & The Crime

LITTLE MAN.
Tracks: / Little man / Leave the cold behind / Happy for a moment*.

Single (12"): released on Wire, Mar'87 Dist: Nine Mile, Cartel

Single (7"): released on Wire, 23 May'87 Dist: Nine Mile, Cartel

Sing Something Disney

CLIFF ADAMS SINGS.
Album: released on BBC, Oct'85 by BBC Records & Tapes. Dist: EMI, PRT, Pye

Cassette: released on BBC, Oct'85 by BBC Records & Tapes. Dist: EMI, PRT, Pye

Singspiration Trio

SONGS FOR CHILDREN NUMBER 1.
Album: by Pilgrim Records. Dist: Rough Trade, Cartel

STORY FOR CHILDREN NUMBER 2.
Album: by Pilgrim Records. Dist: Rough Trade, Cartel

Sinister Cleaners

GOODBYE MS JONES.
Tracks: / Goodbye Ms Jones / I'll never forget this / Bastards / Wild flower.
Single (12"): released on AAZ, Nov'86 by AAZ Records. Dist: Red Rhino, Cartel

LEMON MERINGUE BEDSIT.
Tracks: / Lemon meringue bedsit.
Single (12"): released on AAZ, Jun'86 by AAZ Records. Dist: Red Rhino, Cartel

LONGING FOR NEXT YEAR.
Tracks: / Longing for next year / Bleed / Monkey & the typewriter / Goodbye Ms. Jones / Complication day.
Notes: Contact AAZ Records, 47 Brudenell Mount, Leeds LS6 1HS Tel: 0532 780855.
Single (12"): released on AAZ, Jun'87 by AAZ Records. Dist: Red Rhino, Cartel

Sinitta

CRUISING.
Single (7"): released on Fanfare, Feb'85 by Ferroway/Fanfare Records. Dist: PRT

Single (12"): released on Fanfare, Feb'85 by Ferroway/Fanfare Records. Dist: PRT

FEELS LIKE THE FIRST TIME.
Tracks: / Feels like the first time / Feels like the first time (dub mix).
Single (7"): released on Fanfare, Oct'86 by Ferroway/Fanfare Records. Dist: PRT

Single (12"): released on Fanfare, Oct'86 by Ferroway/Fanfare Records. Dist: PRT

Single (12"): released on Fanfare, Oct'86 by Ferroway/Fanfare Records. Dist: PRT

Single (7"): released on Fanfare, Oct'86 by Ferroway/Fanfare Records. Dist: PRT

FEELS LIKE THE FIRST TIME (EXTENDED).
Tracks: / Feels like the first time / Feels like the first time (instrumental) / So macho* / Cruising*.

I COULD BE.
Single (7"): released on Midas, Nov'83 by Magnet Records. Dist: PRT Distribution

Single (12"): released on Midas, Nov'83 by Magnet Records. Dist: PRT Distribution

NEVER TOO LATE.
Single (7"): released on Midas, Sep'83 by Magnet Records. Dist: PRT Distribution

Single (12"): released on Midas, Sep'83 by Magnet Records. Dist: PRT Distribution

SO MACHO.
Tracks: / So macho / Cruising (remix).
Single (7"): released on Fanfare, Feb'86 by Ferroway/Fanfare Records. Dist: PRT

Single (12"): released on Fanfare, Feb'86 by Ferroway/Fanfare Records. Dist: PRT

Single (7"): released on Fanfare, Jul'85 by Ferroway/Fanfare Records. Dist: PRT

Single (12"): released on Fanfare, Jul'85 by Ferroway/Fanfare Records. Dist: PRT

TOY BOY.
Tracks: / Toy boy / Toy boy (inst).
Single (7"): released on Fanfare, Jul'87 by Ferroway/Fanfare Records. Dist: PRT

Single (12"): released on Fanfare, Jul'87 by Ferroway/Fanfare Records. Dist: PRT

Sinking Of The Lusitania

SINKING OF THE LUSITANIA (1915 Spoken Word) (Various Artists).
Cassette: released on History Makers, May'78 by Ivan Berg. Dist: Pinnacle

Sinking Ships

CINEMA CLOCK.
Single (12"): released on Dead Good, Dec'80 Deleted '81.

Sinnamon

HE'S GONNA TAKE YOU HOME TO HIS HOUSE.
Single (12"): released on Becket, Jan'83

I NEED YOU NOW.
Single (7"): released on Jive, Jul'83 by Zomba Records. Dist: RCA, PRT, CBS

Single (12"): released on Jive, Jul'83 by Zomba Records. Dist: RCA, PRT, CBS

THANKS TO YOU.
Single (7"): released on Becket, Jun'82

Single (12"): released on Becket, Jun'82

Sins

SINS Original soundtrack (Various Artists).
Tracks: / It's hard to be tender / Love and passion / Oath, The / Arrival in Paris / Venezia anziana / Face to face with the mirror / At Susumos / Concerto for Helen / Hubert / Despair / Happy moments / Golden ball / Jeanne death / Remembering / Holland concertino / Roofs of Paris.
Notes: Soundtrack from the forthcoming television series 'Sins' starring Joean Collins.The music is by Francis Lai with additional music by Roland Romanelli and Michael Legrand. The song 'It's Hard To Be Tender' is sung by Carly Simon.
Album:

Cassette:

Sinster Cleaners

GNOMES OF ZURICH.
Single (7"): released on AAZ, Feb'85 by AAZ Records. Dist: Red Rhino, Cartel

Sinster Ducks

MARCH OF THE SINSTER DUCKS.
Single (7"): released on Situation 2, Aug'83 Dist: Cartel, Pinnacle

Sinyx

BLACK DEATH (EP).
Single (7"): released on Reality, Mar'82

Siobhan & Pride

SINGING COUNTRY.
Album: released on Homespun(Ireland), Nov'79 by Outlet Records. Dist: Outlet

Cassette: released on Homespun(Ireland), Nov'79 by Outlet Records. Dist: Outlet

Sio, Teresa De

AFRICANA.
Album: released on Polydor (Italy), Sep'85

Cassette: released on Polydor (Italy), Sep'85

Siouxsie & The Banshees

Biographical Details: Siouxsie & The Banshees began as a UK punk band formed in 1976 by vocalist **Siouxsie Sioux** (real name Susan Janet Dallion; born in London 27 May 1957) and basist **Steve Severin** (born Steve Bailey in 1955) with guitarist **John McKay**, drummer **Kenny Morris**. They were criticised for their tasteless Nazi trappings, moved through psychedelia; **Siouxsie** id still going strong as a sort of voodoo Barbie doll, still concentrating on songs of doom and gloom. [Donald Clarke, April 1987]

CANDYMAN.
Tracks: / Candyman / Lullaby / Umbrella.
Single (7"): released on Wonderland, Feb'86 by Polydor Records. Dist: Polygram

Single (12"): released on Wonderland, Feb'86 by Polydor Records. Dist: Polygram

DAZZLE.
Single (7"): released on Wonderland, Jun'84 by Polydor Records. Dist: Polygram

Single (12"): released on Wonderland, Jun'84 by Polydor Records. Dist: Polygram

HYAENA.
Tracks: / Dazzle / We hunger / Take me back / Belladonna / Swimming horses / Bring me the head of the preacherman / Running town / Pointing bone / Blow the house down.
Compact disc: released on Wonderland, Jun'84 by Polydor Records. Dist: Polygram

Album: released on Wonderland, Jun'84 by Polydor Records. Dist: Polygram

Cassette: released on Wonderland, Jun'84 by Polydor Records. Dist: Polygram

Compact disc: released on Wonderland, Jun'84 by Polydor Records. Dist: Polygram

JU JU.
Album: released on Polydor, Jun'81 by Polydor Records. Dist: Polygram, Polydor

Cassette: released on Polydor, Jun'81 by Polydor Records. Dist: Polygram, Polydor

KALEIDOSCOPE.
Album: released on Polydor, Aug'80 by Polydor Records. Dist: Polygram, Polydor

Cassette: released on Polydor, Aug'80 by Polydor Records. Dist: Polygram, Polydor

KISS IN THE DREAMHOUSE, A.
Album: released on Polydor, Oct'82 by Polydor Records. Dist: Polygram, Polydor

Cassette: released on Polydor, Oct'82 by Polydor Records. Dist: Polygram, Polydor

NOCTURN.
Video-cassette (VHS): released on Polygram/Spectrum, Jan'84 by Polygram Records. Dist: Polygram

NOCTURNE.
Album: released on Wonderland, Nov'83 by Polydor Records. Dist: Polygram

Cassette: released on Wonderland, Nov'83 by Polydor Records. Dist: Polygram

ONCE UPON A TIME.
Video-cassette (VHS): released on Channel 5, Jun'86 Dist: W.H. Smiths

ONCE UPON A TIME 'THE SINGLES'.
Album: released on Polydor, Nov'81 by Polydor Records. Dist: Polygram, Polydor

Cassette: released on Polydor, Nov'81 by Polydor Records. Dist: Polygram, Polydor

PASSENGER(THE).
Tracks: / Passenger (The) / She's cuckoo / Something blue **.
Single (7"): released on Wonderland, Mar'87 by Polydor Records. Dist: Polygram

Single (12"): released on Wonderland, Mar'87 by Polydor Records. Dist: Polygram

PEEL SESSION 5.12.77.
Tracks: / Love in a void / Mirage / Metal postcard / Suburban relapse.
Cassette single: released on Strange Fruit, 13 Jun'87 by Clive Selwood. Dist: Pinnacle

SCREAM, THE.
Album: released on Polydor, '78 by Polydor Records. Dist: Polygram, Polydor

Cassette: released on Polydor, '78 by Polydor Records. Dist: Polygram, Polydor

SIOUXSIE & THE BANSHEES.
Video-cassette (VHS): released on Polygram/Spectrum, Jan'84 by Polygram Records. Dist: Polygram

SONG FROM THE EDGE OF THE WORLD.
Tracks: / Song from the edge of the world / Whole price of blood, The / Mechanical eyes*.
Single (7"): released on Wonderland, Jul'87 by Polydor Records. Dist: Polygram

Single (12"): released on Wonderland, Jul'87 by Polydor Records. Dist: Polygram

SWIMMING HORSES.
Single (7"): released on Polydor, Mar'84 by Polydor Records. Dist: Polygram, Polydor

Single (12"): released on Polydor, Mar'84 by Polydor Records. Dist: Polygram, Polydor

THIS WHEEL'S ON FIRE.
Tracks: / Shooting sun / Sleep walking (on the high wire).
Single (7"): released on Wonderland, Jan'87 by Polydor Records. Dist: Polygram

Single (12"): released on Wonderland, Jan'87 by Polydor Records. Dist: Polygram

THROUGH THE LOOKING GLASS.
Tracks: / Hall of mirrors / Trust in me / This wheels on fire / Strange fruit / This town ain't big enough for the both of us / You're lost little girl / Passenger (The) / Gun / Little Johnny Jewel.
Album: released on Wonderland, Mar'87 by Polydor Records. Dist: Polygram

Cassette: released on Wonderland, Mar'87 by Polydor Records. Dist: Polygram

Compact disc: released on Wonderland, Mar'87 by Polydor Records. Dist: Polygram

TINDERBOX.
Notes: The new album from Siouxsie and the Banshees. Produced by The Banshees, mixed by Steve Churchyard. Includes the hit singles 'Candyman' and 'Cities In Dust'. CD features five extra tracks.
Album: released on Wonderland, Apr'86 by Polydor Records. Dist: Polygram

Cassette: released on Wonderland, Apr'86 by Polydor Records. Dist: Polygram

Compact disc: released on Wonderland, Apr'86 by Polydor Records. Dist: Polygram

VOICES.
Single (12"): released on Wonderland, Oct'84 by Polydor Records. Dist: Polygram

Sioux, Tammi

ACT NATURALLY.
Album: released on Sweet Folk All, May'81 by Sweet Folk All Records. Dist: Sweet Folk All, Roots, Celtic Music, Dragon, Impetus, Projection, Chris Wellard, Festival Records

Siozade, Raymond

PIANO AT BRETELLES, THE.
Album: released on Accordion Record Club, Jul'86 by Accordion Record Club Records. Dist: Accordion Record Club

Sir Alick

IN SEARCH OF THE PERFECT BABY (Sir Alick & The Phrazer).
Single (7"): released on Recommended, Mar'82 by Recommended Records. Dist: Recommended, Impetus, Rough Trade

Siravo & Joseph

RODGERS & HART MEET COLE PORTER (Siravo & Joseph Orchestras).
Album: released on Everest (Premier), '83 by Everest Records. Dist: Pinnacle
Cat. no: **CBR 1001**
Cassette: released on Everest (Premier), '83 by Everest Records. Dist: Pinnacle

Sir Bromwell

SEXY LADY.
Single (12"): released on Three Kings, Jun'84 by Three Kings Records. Dist: Jetstar Distribution

Sirdar Wakefield...

ACCORDEON ORCH. (Sirdar Wakefield Brass Band).
Album: released on ARC (Accordion Records), '84 Dist: Accordion Record Club

Sir Douglas Quintet

COLLECTION: SIR DOUGLAS QUINTET.
Compact disc: released on Collector Series, '86 by Castle Communications Records. Dist: PRT, Pinnacle, RCA, Ariola

EVERY BREATH YOU TAKE.
Single (7"): released on Sonet, Jul'84 by Sonet Records. Dist: PRT

MENDOCINO.
Album: released on Mercury, Aug'81 by Phonogram Records. Dist: Polygram Distribution
Cat. no: **9279 125**
Cassette: released on Mercury, Aug'81 by Phonogram Records. Dist: Polygram Distribution

QUINTESSENCE.
Album: released on Sonet, Feb'82 by Sonet Records. Dist: PRT

Album: released on Rounder (USA), Jan'84 Dist: Mike's Country Music Room Distribution, Jazz Music Distribution, Swift Distribution, Roots Records Distribution, Projection Distribution, Topic Distribution

RIO MEDINA.
Album: released on Sonet, Mar'84 by Sonet Records. Dist: PRT

SHE'S ABOUT A MOVER.
Single (7"): released on USA Import, '80

SIR DOUGLAS QUINTET COLLECTION.
Tracks: / Mendocino / And it didn't even bring me down / At the crossroads / Nuevo laredo / Wasted days & wasted nights / She's about a mover / Old habits die hard / It was fun while it lasted / Down on the border / I keep wishing for you / Revolutionary ways / Dynamite woman / Stoned faces don't lie / Texas me / Magic illusion / Song of everything / You never get too big and..... / You're gonna miss me / Sheila tequila / Tonite tonite / Border wave.
Notes: All tracks licensed from C.ERA Records Ltd.Design:Shoot That Tiger!:(C) 1986 Castle Communications Plc,Unit 7,271 Merton Road,London SW18 5JS.
Double Album: released on Collector, Apr'86 by Castle Communications Records. Dist: PRT, Pinnacle

Double cassette: released on Collector, Apr'86 by Castle Communications Records. Dist: PRT, Pinnacle

WHO WERE YOU THINKING OF.
Single (7"): released on Sonet, Jun'82 by Sonet Records. Dist: PRT

Siren
AMERICAN GIRL.
Single (7"): released on Distant Cousins, Aug'84 Dist: Red Rhino, Cartel

Sirens Of 7th Avenue
SHINE ON.
Single (12"): released on New Rose, 13 Jun'87 Dist: Rough Trade, Cartel

SIRENS OF 7TH AVENUE, THE.
Album: released on New Rose, Oct'86 Dist: Rough Trade, Cartel

Sir Francis Drake
SIR FRANCIS DRAKE-TELL A TALE.
Cassette: released on Pickwick, Mar'84 by Pickwick Records. Dist: Pickwick Distribution, Prism Leisure Distribution, Lugtons

Sir George Presents....
SIR GEORGE PRESENTS PARTY MUSIC (Various Artists).
Album: released on Sir George, Jul'85 by Sir George Records. Dist: Jetstar, Pinnacle

Sir Gibble
SIR GIBBIE (GEOGE MACDONALD)
Read by Tom Flemming.
Cassette: released on Colophone, Nov'81 by Audio-Visual Library Services. Dist: Audio-Visual Library Services

Sir Horatio
ABRACADABRA.
Single (12"): released on Rock Steady, Sep'82 by Rock Steady Records. Dist: Rough Trade Distribution, Indies Distribution, Cartel Distribution

Sir John Mandeville
SIR JOHN MANDEVILLE (Various Artists).
Cassette: released on Anvil, Jan'81 Dist: Anvil

Sirkel & Co.
SIRKEL & COMPANY WITH MICK TAYLOR.
Album: released on Affinity, Jul'77 by Charly Records. Dist: Charly, Cadillac

Sir Mix-a-Lot
SQUARE DANCE RAP.
Tracks: / Square dance rap (version) / Square dance rap.
Single (7"): released on Streetwave, Jun'86 by Streetwave Records. Dist: PRT Distribution

Single (12"): released on Streetwave, Jun'86 by Streetwave Records. Dist: PRT Distribution

Sirrs, Ed
I THINK I THINK TOO MUCH.
Single (7"): released on Oval, May'82 by Oval Records. Dist: Pinnacle

Sir Smasham Uppe
SIR SMASHAM UPPE (Various Artists).
Cassette: released on Anvil, Jan'81 Dist: Anvil

Sir Stephen
TURNTABLE TERROR TRAX VOL.2.
Tracks: / Stephen's overture / Let's begin / In the bass / Rock the bass / Vox.
Single (12"): released on Bluebird, 13 Jun'87 by Bluebird Records. Dist: EMI, Jetstar

Sissle, Noble
SISSLE AND HIS SIZZLING SYNCOPATORS (Sissle, Noble/Tommy Ladnier/Sidney Bechet).
Album: released on Classic Jazz Masters, Dec'86 by Mainline Record Company. Dist: Mainline, Swift, Jazz Music

Sister Annunciata
HEY FATHER CHRISTMAS (Sister Audrey).
Single (7"): released on Mayfield, Dec'81 by Mayfield Records. Dist: PRT

Sister Audrey
HAPPINESS.
Tracks: / Children of the Ghetto.
Single (12"): released on Ariwa, Nov'86 by Ariwa Records. Dist: Revolver, Cartel, Jetstar, Rough Trade

I LOVE YOU.
Single (7"): released on Ariwa, Jul'85 by Ariwa Records. Dist: Revolver, Cartel, Jetstar, Rough Trade

Sister Candy
BLACK CULTURE (Sister Carol).
Album: released on Vista Sounds, '83 by Vista Sounds Records. Dist: Jetstar

KEEP BUBBLING.
Single (12"): released on Raiders, Nov'84 Dist: Jetstar

Single (12"): released on Raiders, Nov'84 Dist: Jetstar

Sister Carol
BLACK CINDERELLA.
Album: released on Jah Life, May'84 by Jah Life Records. Dist: Jetstar

INTERNATIONAL STYLE.
Single (12"): released on Jah Life, May'84 by Jah Life Records. Dist: Jetstar

Sister Chairmain
HOLAREST.
Single (12"): released on Technics, Aug'87 by Technics Records. Dist: Jetstar Distribution

Sisterhood
GIFT.
Album: released on Merciful Release, Jul'86 by Sisterhood Records. Dist: WEA

Cassette: released on Merciful Release, Jul'86 by Sisterhood Records. Dist: WEA

GIVING GROUND.
Tracks: / Giving ground.
Single (7"): released on Merciful Release, Jan'86 by Sisterhood Records. Dist: WEA

Sister Love
DON'T TELL HIM.
Single (12"): released on Future, Feb'82 Dist: Pinnacle

HE IS LEAVING YOU.
Single (12"): released on Loving times, Jul'82

Sister March's Secret
SISTER MARCH'S SECRET (Various Artists).
Double cassette: released on Candlelight, '81 by Audio-Visual Library Services. Dist: Audio-Visual Library Services

Sister Nancy
ONE TWO.
Single (12"): released on Black Music, Jul'82 by Black Music Records. Dist: Jetstar

Sister Orll
D.J.QUEEN.
Single (12"): released on Lost Tribes, May'84 by Lost Tribes Records. Dist: Jetstar

Sisters Are Doin' It
SISTERS ARE DOIN' IT Various artists (Various Artists).
Double Album: released on Towerbell, Apr'86 by Towerbell Records. Dist: EMI

Cassette: released on Towerbell, Apr'86 by Towerbell Records. Dist: EMI

Sister Scene
HOLD BACK YOUR LOVE.
Single (7"): released on Magnet, Nov'84 by Magnet Records. Dist: BMG

Sister Sledge
ALL AMERICAN GIRLS.
Single (7"): released on Atlantic, Mar'81 by WEA Records. Dist: WEA

Single (12"): released on Atlantic, Mar'81 by WEA Records. Dist: WEA

GREATEST HITS:SISTER SLEDGE.
Tracks: / Frankie / Mama never told me / All American girls / Dancing on the jagged edge / When the boys meet the girls / Smile / Lost in music / Thinking of you / He's the greatest dancer / We are family.
Album: released on Atlantic, Apr'86 by WEA Records. Dist: WEA

Cassette: released on Atlantic, Apr'86 by WEA Records. Dist: WEA

HERE TO STAY.
Tracks: / Make a wish / Here to stay".
Single (12"): released on Parlophone, Jan'87 by EMI Records. Dist: EMI

Single (7"): released on Parlophone, Jan'87 by EMI Records. Dist: EMI

HE'S JUST A RUNAWAY.
Single (7"): released on Cotillion (Import), Aug'81 by Atlantic Records. Dist: WEA

Single (12"): released on Cotillion (Import), Aug'81 by Atlantic Records. Dist: WEA

IF YOU REALLY WANT ME.
Single (7"): released on Atlantic, May'81 by WEA Records. Dist: WEA

Single (12"): released on Atlantic, May'81 by WEA Records. Dist: WEA

LOST IN MUSIC.
Single (7"): released on Cotillion (Import), Aug'84 by Atlantic Records. Dist: WEA

Single (12"): released on Cotillion (Import), Aug'84 by Atlantic Records. Dist: WEA

LOVE SOMEBODY TODAY.
Album: released on Atlantic, Feb'80 by WEA Records. Dist: WEA

Cassette: released on Atlantic, Feb'80 by WEA Records. Dist: WEA

MY GUY.
Single (7"): released on Cotillion (Import), Feb'82 by Atlantic Records. Dist: WEA

THINKING OF YOU.
Single (7"): released on Cotillion (Import), May'84 by Atlantic Records. Dist: WEA

Single (12"): released on Cotillion (Import), May'84 by Atlantic Records. Dist: WEA

WE ARE FAMILY.
Album: released on Atlantic, Nov'84 by WEA Records. Dist: WEA

Cassette: released on Atlantic, Nov'84 by WEA Records. Dist: WEA

Single (7"): released on Atlantic, May'79 by WEA Records. Dist: WEA

WHEN THE BOYS MEET THE GIRLS.
Tracks: / When the boys meet girls / Boys most likely (The).
Single (7"): released on Atlantic, Feb'86 by WEA Records. Dist: WEA

Single (12"): released on Atlantic, Feb'86 by WEA Records. Dist: WEA

Album: released on Atlantic, Jun'85 by WEA Records. Dist: WEA

Cassette: released on Atlantic, Jun'85 by WEA Records. Dist: WEA

Sisters Of Mercy
ALICE.
Single (7"): released on Merciful Release, Nov'82 by Sisterhood Records. Dist: WEA

ANACONDA.
Single (7"): released on Merciful Release, Mar'83 by Sisterhood Records. Dist: WEA

BODY AND SOUL.
Single (7"): released on Merciful Release, Jun'84 by Sisterhood Records. Dist: WEA

Single (12"): released on Merciful Release, Jun'84 by Sisterhood Records. Dist: WEA

BODY ELECTRIC.
Single (7"): released on CNT, Apr'82 Dist: Rough Trade, Cartel

DAMAGE DONE.
Single (7"): released on Merciful Release, Feb'83 by Sisterhood Records. Dist: WEA

FIRST AND LAST AND ALWAYS.
Album: released on Merciful Release, Apr'85 by Sisterhood Records. Dist: WEA

Cassette: released on Merciful Release, Apr'85 by Sisterhood Records. Dist: WEA

NO TIME TO CRY.
Single (7"): released on Merciful Release, Feb'85 by Sisterhood Records. Dist: WEA

REPTILE HOUSE.
Single (7"): released on Merciful Release, May'83 by Sisterhood Records. Dist: WEA

TEMPLE OF LOVE.
Single (7"): released on Merciful Release, Oct'83 by Sisterhood Records. Dist: WEA

Single (12"): released on Merciful Release, Oct'83 by Sisterhood Records. Dist: WEA

WAKE, THE.
Notes: A highly-rated band on the UK indie circuit who have now broken up,making this 13-strong live performance something of something memorial.
Video-cassette (VHS): released on Polygram, Aug'86 by Polygram Records. Dist: Polygram

Sister Sonle
FEEL LIKE JUMPING.
Single (12"): released on Chartbound, Nov'84 by Chartbound Records. Dist: Jetstar

Sister Verna
UP FRONT LOVER.
Tracks: / Up front lover / Up front lover (Dub version).
Single (12"): released on Photographer, Apr'86 Dist: Jetstar

Situation
FUN.
Single (7"): released on President, Apr'84 by President Records. Dist: Taylors, Spartan

Single (12"): released on President, Apr'84 by President Records. Dist: Taylors, Spartan

Sivuca
AIN'T NO SUNSHINE.
Single (7"): released on London, Jul'84 by London Records. Dist: Polygram

Single (12"): released on London, Jul'84 by London Records. Dist: Polygram

SIVUCA.
Album: released on Vanguard, Aug'84 by PRT Records. Dist: PRT

Six...
ENTER POLKA HALL OF FAME (Six Fat Dutchman).
Album: released on ARC (Accordion Records), Nov'84 Dist: Accordion Record Club

SEE UNDER 6 IN NUMERICAL SECTION AFTER Z.

SIX COUNTRY HITS Various artists (Various Artists).
Single (7"): released on Scoop 33, Jun'84 by Pickwick Records. Dist: H.R. Taylor

Cassette: released on Scoop 33, Jun'84 by Pickwick Records. Dist: H.R. Taylor

SIX FAT DUTCHMAN Various artists (Various Artists).
Album: released on ARC (Accordion Records), '84 Dist: Accordion Record Club

SIX SEQUENCES POUR ALFRED HITCHCOCK Various artists (Various Artists).
Tracks: / Fear of incarceration / Family plot / Teenage hearthrob / Cafe Mozart / OK / Question de principe / Audition, The / Movie A / Movie B / Pour un demi-poulet.
Notes: With: British Summer Time Ends/Jac Berrocal/Annick Nozati/Denis Levaillant/Alan Tomlinson/Joelle Leandre.
Album: released on Nato (France), Jan'86 by Disques Nato. Dist: Essex Record Distributors Ltd.

SIX NUMBER ONES Various artists (Various Artists).
Extended-play record: released on Scoop 33, Oct'84 by Pickwick Records. Dist: H.R. Taylor

Cassette: released on Scoop 33, Oct'84 by Pickwick Records. Dist: H.R. Taylor

SIX SWINGERS Various original artists (Various Artists).
Album: released on World Records, Sep'77 Dist: Polygram

Six Hands In Tempo
ALL IN GOOD TIME.
Album: released on Burlington, Oct'86 by Plant Life Records. Dist: Jazz Music, Celtic Music, Clyde Factors Distributors, I.R.S., Projection, Wellard, Chris, Roots

DESPERATE DIGITS.
Album: released on Plant Life, Oct'83 Dist: Roots

Six Minute War
MORE SHORT SONGS.
Extended-play record: released on Six Minute War, Jul'82

SIX MINUTE WAR, THE.
Single (7"): released on S&G, Jun'82 Dist: Pinnacle

SLIGHTLY LONGER SONGS.
Single (7"): released on Six Minute War, Oct'82

Six-One-X
WORKING MAN.
Single (7"): released on President, Apr'84 by President Records. Dist: Taylors, Spartan

Sixteen...

16 BIG HITS (Early & late 60's) (Various Artists).
Double Album: released on Motown, Oct'82 by RCA Records. Dist: RCA Distribution

Double cassette: released on Motown, Oct'82 by RCA Records. Dist: RCA Distribution

16 BIG HITS OF THE SIXTIES various artists (Various Artists).
Album: released on MFP, Apr'79 by EMI Records. Dist: EMI

Cassette: released on MFP, Apr'79 by EMI Records. Dist: EMI

16 BLUEGRASS HITS (Various Artists).
Album: released on Starday, Apr'87

Cassette: released on Starday, Apr'87

Album:

16 DANCE PARTY HITS Various artists (Various Artists).
Single (7"): released on Recommended, Aug'86 by Recommended Records. Dist: Recommended, Impetus, Rough Trade

16 FIDDLERS GREATEST HITS (Various Artists).
Album: released on Starday, Apr'87

Cassette: released on Starday, Apr'87

16 GREATEST REGGAE HITS Various artists (Various Artists).
Album: released on Trojan, Jan'83 by Trojan Records. Dist: PRT, Jetstar

16 HOT BULLETS various artists (Various Artists).
Album: released on Hallmark, Jan'82 by Pickwick Records. Dist: Pickwick Distribution, PRT, Taylors

Cassette: released on Hallmark, Jan'82 by Pickwick Records. Dist: Pickwick Distribution, PRT, Taylors

16 NO.1'S OF THE 70'S Various artists (Various Artists).
Album: released on MFP, Apr'85 by EMI Records. Dist: EMI

Cassette: released on MFP, Apr'85 by EMI Records. Dist: EMI

16 NUMBER ONE COUNTRY HITS VOL.2 Various Original artists (Various Artists).
Album: released on CBS, Mar'80 by CBS Records. Dist: CBS

Cassette: released on CBS, Mar'80 by CBS Records. Dist: CBS

16 NUMBER ONE COUNTRY HITS VOL.1 Various Original artists (Various Artists).
Album: released on CBS, Aug'77 by CBS Records. Dist: CBS

Cassette: released on CBS, Aug'77 by CBS Records. Dist: CBS

16 ORCHESTRAL WORLD HITS PART 1 Various artists (Various Artists).
Album: released on Phonogram (Holland), Jul'85 Dist: IMS-Polygram

Cassette: released on Phonogram (Holland), Jul'85 Dist: IMS-Polygram

16 ORCHESTRAL WORLD HITS PART 2 Various artists (Various Artists).
Album: released on Phonogram (Holland), Jul'85 Dist: IMS-Polygram

Cassette: released on Phonogram (Holland), Jul'85 Dist: IMS-Polygram

16 POPULAR CHRISTMAS CAROLS Carious (Various Artists).
Album: released on Abbey, Nov'79 by Abbey. Dist: PRT, Taylors, Gamut

16 RED HOT JUKEBOX HITS Carious artists (Various Artists).
Album: released on String, Oct'79 by Topic Records. Dist: Roots Distribution, Jazz Music Distribution, JSU Distribution, Projection Distribution, Swift Distribution

16 SUPER IRISH HITS various artists (Various Artists).
Album: released on Homespun(Ireland), Dec'82 by Outlet Records. Dist: Outlet

Cassette: released on Homespun(Ireland), Dec'82 by Outlet Records. Dist: Outlet

16 TEARJERKERS VOL 2 various original artists (Various original artists).
Album: released on Hallmark, Jul'84 by Pickwick Records. Dist: Pickwick Distribution, PRT, Taylors

Cassette: released on Hallmark, Jul'84 by Pickwick Records. Dist: Pickwick Distribution, PRT, Taylors

16 TRUCK DRIVER GREATS (Various Artists).
Album: released on Starday, Apr'87

Cassette: released on Starday, Apr'87

KING IS COMING THE (Sixteen Singing Men).
Album: by Pilgrim Records. Dist: Rough Trade, Cartel

SEE UNDER 16 IN NUMERICAL SECTION AFTER Z.

SIXTEEN DYNAMITE REGGAE HITS Various artists (Various Artists).
Album: released on Trojan, Nov'86 by Trojan Records. Dist: PRT, Jetstar

Cassette: released on Trojan, Nov'86 by Trojan Records. Dist: PRT, Jetstar

Sixteen, Earl

BAD COMPANY/HEY GIRL.
Single (12"): released on Clair, Apr'83 by Clair Records. Dist: Jetstar

DANCEHALL QUEEN.
Single (12"): released on Now Generation, Sep'85 Dist: Jetstar Distribution

GIVE JAH PRAISE.
Single (12"): released on Teledec, May'82

GIVE YOUR LOVE.
Single (12"): released on Conqueror, Jan'86 Dist: Jetstar

LEGGO GIRL.
Single (12"): released on Cyprian, Mar'84 by Cyprian Records. Dist: Jetstar

MINE TO LOVE.
Single (12"): released on DATC, Mar'86 by DATC Records. Dist: Rough Trade

NIGHT AND DAY.
Tracks: / Night and day / Changing world.
Single (12"): released on New Generation, Dec'85 Dist: Jetstar

NO MASH UP THE DANCE.
Single (12"): released on Studio One, Sep'84 Dist: Jetstar

PEEK-A-BOO/JULIA.
Single (12"): released on CSA, Jan'84 by CSA Records. Dist: PRT, Jetstar

PROBLEMS.
Single (12"): released on Reggae City, Aug'85 by Reggae City Records. Dist: Jetstar

RUB UPON ME.
Single (12"): released on Fatman Studio, Nov'84 by Fatman Studio Records. Dist: Jetstar

SHINING STAR.
Album: released on Vista Sounds, Jan'83 by Vista Sounds Records. Dist: Jetstar

SONGS OF LOVE AND HARDSHIP.
Album: released on Kingdom, Nov'84 by Kingdom Records. Dist: Kingdom

WARNING.
Single (12"): released on Time, Jul'84 Dist: Jetstar Distribution

WISH IT WAS LOVE.
Tracks: / Wish it was love / You're my love.
Single (12"): released on Original, May'86 Dist: RCA Distribution, Jazz Music Distribution, PRT Distribution

Sixth Festival Of....

SIXTH FESTIVAL OF EVANGELICAL CHOIRS.
Album: by Pilgrim Records. Dist: Rough Trade, Cartel

Sixties..

60'S FILE Various artists (Various Artists).
Double Album: released on PRT, Nov'77 by PRT Records. Dist: PRT

60'S GREATEST HITS Various artists (Various Artists).
Tracks: / You've got your troubles / Everlasting love / Silence is golden / Those were the days / Same old feeling, (The) / Crying game, (The) / Somewhere / Wild thing / Hippy hippy shake / Hitchin' a ride / My old man's a dustbin / You'll never walk alone / Da doo ron ron / He's so fine / Run to him / Young girl / On Broadway / When a man loves a woman / Letter, (The) / Rebel rouser / Zip-a-dee-doo-dah / Let's twist again / Peppermint twist / Yakety yak.
Album: released on Warwick Reflections, Jun'86 by Warwick Records.

Cassette: released on Warwick Reflections, Jun'86 by Warwick Records.

60'S HITS 100 minutes (Various Artists).
Cassette: released on PRT (100 Minute Series), Jun'82

SIXTIES BACKEAT Various artists (Various Artists).
Album: released on See For Miles, Dec'84 by Charly Records. Dist: Spartan

SIXTIES LOST AND FOUND - VOL.3 Various artists (Various Artists).
Album: released on See For Miles, Dec'83 by Charly Records. Dist: Spartan

SIXTIES LOST AND FOUND - VOL 1 1964-1969 (Various Artists).
Notes: Album includes Rod Stewart, The Herd, Love Sculpture
Album: released on See For Miles, Aug'86 by See For Miles Records. Dist: Pinnacle

SIXTIES LOST AND FOUND - VOL 2 Various artists (Various Artists).
Tracks: / I'll cry instead / Good morning little schoolgirl / That's a long time ago / Woman / Money / Don't you just know it / Buckle shoe stomp / Baby please don't go / Just one more chance / London boys / Sister Morphine / Say you don't mind / Will you be my lover tonight / Surprise surprise / Now I know / We love the Beatles / Like dreamers do / That's alright mama / Uncle Willie / Long tall shorty.
Album: released on See For Miles, Nov'86 by See For Miles Records. Dist: Pinnacle

SIXTIES LOST AND FOUND - VOL 3 Various artists (Various Artists).
Tracks: / What's news pussy cat / Please Mr Postman / No response / Elbow baby / Bow Street runner / St James infirmary / You're on my mind / Lonely weekends / Kansas City / Long legged baby / Third time lucky / My baby's crazy bout Elvis / Shang a doo lang / Yes I do / Caroline / Something better / I've got you out of my mind / Country boy / Really gonna shake / There you go.
Album: released on See For Miles, Dec'86 by See For Miles Records. Dist: Pinnacle

SIXTIES LOST AND FOUND - VOL.2 Various artists (Various Artists).
Album: released on See For Miles, Dec'83 by Charly Records. Dist: Spartan

SIXTIES - LOST AND FOUND 1964-1969 Various artists (Various Artists).
Album: released on See For Miles, Oct'82 by Charly Records. Dist: Spartan

SIXTIES MANIA Various artists (Various Artists).
Album: released on Telstar, Nov'86 by Telstar Records. Dist: RCA Distribution

Cassette: released on Telstar, Nov'86 by Telstar Records. Dist: RCA Distribution

SIXTIES MIX (Various Artists).
Album: released on Stylus, Jul'87 Dist: Pinnacle, Terry Blood Distribution, Stylus Distribution

Cassette: released on Stylus, Jul'87 Dist: Pinnacle, Terry Blood Distribution, Stylus Distribution

SIXTIES REVISITED Various artists (Various Artists).
Cassette: released on Decca, Aug'84 by Decca Records. Dist: Polygram

SIXTIES VOLUME 1, THE Various artists (Various Artists).
Tracks: / Wanderer, (The) / Run to him / Will you still love me tomorrow? / Runaway / He's so fine / Sealed with a kiss / Island of dreams / Telstar / Hey baby / Three steps to Heaven / Poetry in motion / Johnny remember me / Running bear / Tell Laura I love her.
Album: released on Old Gold, Nov'85 by Old Gold Records. Dist: Lightning, Jazz Music, Spartan, Counterpoint

Cassette: released on Old Gold, Nov'85 by Old Gold Records. Dist: Lightning, Jazz Music, Spartan, Counterpoint

SIXTIES VOLUME 2, THE Various artists (Various Artists).
Tracks: / Young girl / San Francisco (be sure to wear some flowers in your hair) / Let's go to San Francisco / Everlasting love / California Dreamin' / Pretty flamingo / Massachusetts / Good vibrations / Kites / Excerpt from a teenage opera / Mr Tambourine Man / Something in the air / Waterloo sunset / From the underworld.
Notes: Recalling the Flower Power years of the Sixties.
Album: released on Old Gold, Nov'85 by Old Gold Records. Dist: Lightning, Jazz Music, Spartan, Counterpoint

Cassette: released on Old Gold, Nov'85 by Old Gold Records. Dist: Lightning, Jazz Music, Spartan, Counterpoint

SIXTIES VOLUME 3, THE various artists (Various Artists).
Tracks: / Walk right back / Save the last dance for me / Handy man / Locomotion, The / Swiss maid, The / More than I can say / It might as well rain until September / Halfway to Paradise / Sheila / Rhythms of the rain / Let's dance / Don't ever change / Runaround Sue.
Album: released on Old Gold, Nov'85 by Old Gold Records. Dist: Lightning, Jazz Music, Spartan, Counterpoint

Album: released on Old Gold, Nov'85 by Old Gold Records. Dist: Lightning, Jazz Music, Spartan, Counterpoint

SIXTIES VOLUME 4, THE Various artists (Various Artists).
Tracks: / Sun ain't gonna shine any more, (The) / Itchycoo Park / Whiter shade of pale, (A) / Monday Monday / Mighty Quinn, (The) / Albatross / You've lost that lovin' feeling / Sloop Jon B / Sunny afternoon / For your love / With a girl like you / Hang on Sloopy / We've gotta get out of this place / Friday on my mind.
Album: released on Old Gold, Nov'85 by Old Gold Records. Dist: Lightning, Jazz Music, Spartan, Counterpoint

Cassette: released on Old Gold, Nov'85 by Old Gold Records. Dist: Lightning, Jazz Music, Spartan, Counterpoint

SIXTIES VOLUME 5, THE Various artists (Various Artists).
Tracks: / Wedding, (The) / Just loving you / This is my song / Last waltz, (The) / Carnival is over, (The) / What a wonderful world / Edelweiss / Green green grass of home / Careless hands / There must be a way / It must be him (seul sur son etoile) / Almost there / If only I had time / She wears my ring.
Album: released on Old Gold, Nov'85 by Old Gold Records. Dist: Lightning, Jazz Music, Spartan, Counterpoint

Cassette: released on Old Gold, Nov'85 by Old Gold Records. Dist: Lightning, Jazz Music, Spartan, Counterpoint

Sixties Mania

60'S MANIA Various Artists (Various Artists).
Album: released on Telstar, Aug'87 by Telstar Records. Dist: RCA Distribution

Cassette: released on Telstar, Aug'87 by Telstar Records. Dist: RCA Distribution

Sixty...

60 MINUTES PLUS Heavy metal compilation - Various artists (Various Artists).
Cassette: released on Neat, Jun'83 by Neat Records. Dist: Pinnacle, Neat

SEE UNDER 60 IN NUMERICAL SECTION AFTER Z.

SIXTY YEARS OF MOTORING (Sixty Years Of Motoring).
Album: by Decca Records. Dist: Polygram

Sly Lion

WITHIN.
Tracks: / Within / You are love.
Notes: Irish Eurovision entry
Single (7"): released on Silent, Apr'87 Dist: Stiff

Sizzling Country ....

SIZZLING COUNTRY INSTRUMENTALS (Various Artists).
Album: released on Spot, Mar'85 by Pickwick Records. Dist: H.R. Taylor, Lugtons

Cassette: released on Spot, Mar'85 by Pickwick Records. Dist: H.R. Taylor, Lugtons

Sjazner, Bernard

BIG SCARE, THE.
Album: released on New Rose, May'84 Dist: Rough Trade, Cartel

Sjoesten, Lars Octet

Lee plays the music of Lars Gullin

Sjogren, Irene

SWEET SUPRISE (Sjogren, Irene Quintet).

Sjosten, Lars Trio

BELLS, BLUES AND BROTHERHOOD.
Album: released on Dragon, Jul'83 by Dragon Records. Dist: Jazz Music, Projection, Cadillac

SJOSTEN LARS AND BREWMOORE (Sjosten, Lars Trio/Brew Moore).
Album: released on Sonet, May'74 by Sonet Records. Dist: PRT

Ska City Rockers

TIME IS TIGHT.
Single (7"): released on Inferno, Feb'80 by Inferno Records. Dist: Inferno, Cartel, Pinnacle

Ska, Donny

UNITED AFRICA.
Tracks: / United Africa / Dub it in Africa.
Single (12"): released on Solomonic, Aug'86 by Solomonic Records. Dist: Jetstar, Pinnacle

Ska-Dows

SKA'D FOR LIFE.
Album: released on Cheapskate, '82 by Cheapskate Records. Dist: RCA

SKAS ON 45.
Single (7"): released on Cheapskate, Oct'81 by Cheapskate Records. Dist: RCA

Single (12"): released on Cheapskate, Oct'81 by Cheapskate Records. Dist: RCA

Single (12"): released on Penthouse, Jan'85 by Penthouse Records. Dist: Pinnacle

WE GOTTA GET OUT OF THIS PLACE.
Single (7"): released on Cheapskate, Apr'82 by Cheapskate Records. Dist: RCA

Skafish

OBSESSIONS OF YOU.
Single (7"): released on Illegal, Jul'80 by Faulty Products Records. Dist: Pinnacle, Lightning, Cartel

Skagarack

SKAGARACK.
Tracks: / Move it in the night / I'm alone / Saying Damned woman / Don't turn me upside down Lies / Victim of the system / City child / Double crossed.
Notes: Debut album on Polydor by Scandinavian band Skagarack is a classic combination of traditional rock and ballads.
Album: released on IMS, Nov'86 by Polydor Records. Dist: IMS, Polygram

Cassette: by Polydor Records. Dist: IMS, Polygram

Compact disc: by Polydor Records. Dist: IMS, Polygram

Skaggs, Ricky

Biographical Details: Ricky Scaggs is a country singer and musician, born 18th July 1954 in Cordell, Kentucky, who has dominated the USA charts in the 1980's with his neo-traditional style. He plays mandolin and fiddle as well as guitar. He worked in bluegrass groups and with **Emmylou Harris's Hot Band** 1977-80 (wrote arrangements for her *Roses In The Snow* album) before going solo with an album on the small Sugar Hill label, then switching to Epic. He is married to Sharon White and also produces albums by **The Whites**. [Donald Clarke, April 1987].

ARTIFICIAL HEART.
Tracks: / Artificial Heart / Whell hoss.
Single (7"): released on Epic, Sep'86 by CBS Records. Dist: CBS

AT THE COUNTRY STORE.
Album: released on Country Store, Apr'87 by Starblend Records. Dist: PRT, Prism Leisure Corporation Records

Cassette: released on Country Store, Apr'87 by Starblend Records. Dist: PRT, Prism Leisure Corporation Records

CAJUN MOON.
Tracks: / Cajun Moon / Rockin'the boat.
Single (7"): released on Epic, May'86 by CBS Records. Dist: CBS

COUNTRY BOY.
Tracks: / Country boy / Wheel hoss.
Single (7"): released on Epic, Jan'86 by CBS Records. Dist: CBS

Album: released on Epic, Oct'84 by CBS Records. Dist: CBS

Cassette: released on Epic, Oct'84 by CBS Records. Dist: CBS

DON'T CHEAT IN OUR HOME TOWN.
Album: released on Epic, Nov'83 by CBS Records. Dist: CBS

Cassette: released on Epic, Nov'83 by CBS Records. Dist: CBS

FAMILY AND FRIENDS.
Tracks: / Lost and I'll never find the way / Two different worlds / River of memory / Talk about sufferin' / Think of what you've done / Toy heart Hallelujah I'm ready / Say / Won't you be mine / Won't it be wonderful there / River of Jordan.
Compact disc: released on Rounder (USA), Dec'86 Dist: Mike's Country Music Room Distribution, Jazz Music Distribution, Swift Distribution, Roots Records Distribution, Projection Distribution, Topic Distribution

Album: released on Sundown, Feb'85 by Magnum Music Group Ltd. Dist: Magnum Music Group Ltd, PRT Distribution, Spartan Distribution

Cassette: released on Sundown, Feb'85 by Magnum Music Group Ltd. Dist: Magnum Music Group Ltd, PRT Distribution, Spartan Distribution

FAVOURITE COUNTRY SONGS.
Album: released on Epic, May'85 by CBS Records. Dist: CBS

Cassette: released on Epic, May'85 by CBS Records. Dist: CBS

HEARTBROKE.
Single (7"): released on Epic, Sep'83 by CBS Records. Dist: CBS

HONEY (OPEN THAT DOOR).
Single (7"): released on Epic, Jun'84 by CBS Records. Dist: CBS

LIVE IN LONDON.
Tracks: / Uncle pen / Heartbroke / She didn't say why / Cajun moon / Country boy / I've got a new heartache / You make me feel like a man / Rockin' the boat / Honey (open that door) / Don't get above your raising.
Album: released on Epic, Jan'86 by CBS Records. Dist: CBS

Cassette: released on Epic, Jan'86 by CBS Records. Dist: CBS

LOVES GONNA GET YA!.
Tracks: / Hard row to hoe, A / Love's gonna get you someday / I'm beside myself / I wonder if I care as much / Don't stop Gypsy / Hard row to hoe, A / I won't let you down / Walkin' in Jerusalem / Artificial heart / Love can't ever get better than this / Daddy was a hard working honest man / Raisin' the Dickens / New star shining.
Compact disc: released on Epic, May'87 by CBS Records. Dist: CBS

Album: released on Epic, Nov'86 by CBS Records. Dist: CBS

Cassette: released on Epic, Nov'86 by CBS Records. Dist: CBS

Compact disc: released on Epic, May'87 by CBS Records. Dist: CBS

NEW STAR SHINING (Skaggs, Ricky & James Taylor).
Tracks: / Walking in Jerusalem.
Single (7"): released on Epic, Nov'86 by CBS Records. Dist: CBS

SUNDOWN (Skaggs, Ricky/K. Whitley).
Album: released on Sundown, Apr'87 by Magnum Music Group Ltd. Dist: Magnum Music Group Ltd, PRT Distribution, Spartan Distribution

SWEET TEMPTATION.
Album: released on Ritz, Apr'85 by Ritz Records. Dist: Spartan

Cassette: released on Ritz, Apr'85 by Ritz Records. Dist: Spartan

THAT'S IT.
Compact disc: released on Sundown, Dec'86 by Magnum Music Group Ltd. Dist: Magnum Music Group Ltd, PRT Distribution, Spartan Distribution

Album: released on Rebel (USA), Feb'85 Dist: Mike's Country Music Room Distribution, Projection

Skanga

HEY FRED You need a sunbed.
Tracks: / Hey Fred / Feeling inside.
Single (7"): released on CSA, Jun'87 by CSA Records. Dist: PRT, Jetstar

Single (12"): released on CSA, Jun'87 by CSA Records. Dist: PRT, Jetstar

Skank orchestra

WE ARE THE PEOPLE.
Single (7"): released on Scorpio, Sep'81 by Scorpio Records. Dist: Jetstar

Single (12"): released on Scorpio, Sep'81 by Scorpio Records. Dist: Jetstar

Skara Brae

SKARA BRAE.
Album: released on Shanachie, Jun'85 Dist: Sterns/Triple Earth Distribution, Roots

Skat

FEMME FATALE.
Single (7"): by Graduate Records. Dist: Nine Mile, Cartel

Skatalites

GUNS OF NAVARONE.
Single (7"): released on Island, Jan'80 by Island Records. Dist: Polygram

LIVE AT SUNSPLASH.
Album: released on Synergy, Mar'86 Dist: Jetstar Distribution

RETURN OF THE BIG GUNS.
Album: released on Island, Jul'84 by Island Records. Dist: Polygram

SCATTERED LIGHT.
Album: released on CDB, Sep'84 by CDB Records. Dist: Jetstar

Album: released on Alligator, Feb'85 Dist: Jetstar

SKATALITES WITH SLY & ROBBIE & THE TAXI GANG.
Album: released on Vista Sounds, Feb'84 by Vista Sounds Records. Dist: Jetstar

STRETCHING OUT.
Album: released on Rior (USA), Apr'86

Skaville USA

SKAVILLE USA (Various Artists).
Album: released on Ska, Jan'87 Dist: Revolver, Cartel

Skeelbred, Ray

STOMPIN' 'EM DOWN.
Notes: with Hall Smith.
Album: released on Stomp Off, Mar'87 by Stomp Off Records. Dist: Jazz Music Distribution

Skeete, Beverley

IF THE FEELING IS RIGHT/KEEP ON RUNNING.
Single (12"): released on Elite, Sep'83 Dist: PRT

WARM.
Single (7"): released on Elite, Feb'85 Dist: PRT

YOU CAN'T SAY NO.
Single (7"): released on Elite, Jun'85 Dist: PRT

Single (12"): released on Elite, Jun'85 Dist: PRT

Skeletal Family

ALONE SHE CRIES.
Single (7"): released on Red Rhino, Jan'84 by Red Rhino Records. Dist: Red Rhino, Cartel

Single (12"): released on Red Rhino, Jan'84 by Red Rhino Records. Dist: Red Rhino, Cartel

BURNING OIL.
Album: released on Red Rhino, Aug'84 by Red Rhino Records. Dist: Red Rhino, Cartel

FUTILE COMBAT.
Album: released on Red Rhino, Apr'85 by Red Rhino Records. Dist: Red Rhino, Cartel

GHOSTS.
Album: released on Onsala International, Nov'86

JUST A FRIEND.
Single (7"): released on Luggage, Mar'83 by Luggage. Dist: Multicord

JUST A MINUTE.
Tracks: / Just a minute / Big love.
Single (7"): released on Chrysalis, Aug'86 by Chrysalis Records. Dist: CBS

Single (12"): released on Chrysalis, Aug'86 by Chrysalis Records. Dist: CBS

PROMISED LAND.
Single (7"): released on Red Rhino, Feb'85 by Red Rhino Records. Dist: Red Rhino, Cartel

Single (12"): released on Red Rhino, Feb'85 by Red Rhino Records. Dist: Red Rhino, Cartel

RECOLLECTS.
Single (7"): released on Red, May'84

RESTLESS.
Tracks: / Restless / What goes up.
Single (7"): released on Chrysalis, Mar'86 by Chrysalis Records. Dist: CBS

Single (12"): released on Chrysalis, Mar'86 by Chrysalis Records. Dist: CBS

SO SURE.
Single (7"): released on Red Rhino, Jun'84 by Red Rhino Records. Dist: Red Rhino, Cartel

Single (12"): released on Red Rhino, Jun'84 by Red Rhino Records. Dist: Red Rhino, Cartel

TOGETHER - BURNING OIL/FUTILE COMBAT.
Cassette: released on Red Rhino, Oct'85 by Red Rhino Records. Dist: Red Rhino, Cartel

Skeletons, The

ROCKIN' BONES.
Album: released on N.B.T., 30 May'87

Skellern, Peter

AIN'T LIFE SOMETHING.
Album: released on Decca (Rock Echoes), Mar'84 by Decca Records. Dist: Polygram, IMS

Cassette: released on Decca (Rock Echoes), Mar'84 by Decca Records. Dist: Polygram, IMS

ASTAIRE.
Tracks: / Cheek to cheek / Conitental / Is'nt this a lovely day / No strings / Let's call the whole thing off / Night and day / Puttin' on the Ritz / They can't take that away from me / Top hat / Way you look tonight.
Album: released on Timeless, Jul'86

Cassette: released on Timeless, Jul'86

Album: released on Mercury, Aug'87 by Phonogram Records. Dist: Polygram Distribution

Cassette: released on Mercury, Aug'87 by Phonogram Records. Dist: Polygram Distribution

Compact disc: released on Mercury, Aug'87 by Phonogram Records. Dist: Polygram Distribution

BEST OF PETER SKELLERN, THE.
Double Album: released on Decca, Jun'85 by Decca Records. Dist: Polygram

Double cassette: released on Decca, Jun'85 by Decca Records. Dist: Polygram

BUSY LINE.
Single (7"): released on Mercury, Feb'83 by Phonogram Records. Dist: Polygram Distribution

HAPPY ENDINGS.
Album: released on BBC, Oct'81 by BBC Records & Tapes. Dist: EMI, PRT, Pye

Cassette: released on BBC, Oct'81 by BBC Records & Tapes. Dist: EMI, PRT, Pye

HOW LOVED YOU ARE.
Tracks: / How loved you are / Freewheelin'.
Single (7"): released on Sonet, Jul'87 by Sonet Records. Dist: PRT

INTRODUCING...RIGHT FROM THE START.
Album: released on Elite, Mar'81 Dist: PRT

Cassette: released on Elite, Mar'81 Dist: PRT

ISN'T THIS A LOVELY DAY.
Tracks: / You can't take that away from me.
Single (7"): released on Mercury, Aug'87 by Phonogram Records. Dist: Polygram Distribution

LOVELIGHT.
Tracks: / How loved you are / One in the eye for the moon / These foolish things / What are you doing the rest of your life / All the things you are / What love I've found in you / Folks Who live on the hill. the / Not a day too soon / When you wish upon a star / September song.
Album: released on Sonet, May'87 by Sonet Records. Dist: PRT

Compact disc: released on Sonet, Jul'87 by Sonet Records. Dist: PRT

ME AND MY GIRL.
Single (7"): released on Sierra, Sep'84 by Sierra Records. Dist: WEA

PETER SKELLERN.
Album: released on Decca, '72 by Decca Records. Dist: Polygram

Cassette: released on Decca, '72 by Decca Records. Dist: Polygram

SKELLERN.
Album: released on Mercury, Oct'83 by Phonogram Records. Dist: Polygram Distribution

Cassette: released on Mercury, Oct'83 by Phonogram Records. Dist: Polygram Distribution

STILL MAGIC.
Album: released on Mercury, Jan'85 by Phonogram Records. Dist: Polygram Distribution

Cassette: released on Mercury, Jan'85 by Phonogram Records. Dist: Polygram Distribution

STRING OF PEARLS, A.
Album: released on Mercury, Nov'82 by Phonogram Records. Dist: Polygram Distribution

Cassette: released on Mercury, Nov'82 by Phonogram Records. Dist: Polygram Distribution

YOU'RE A LADY.
Album: released on Contour, Apr'86 by Pickwick Records. Dist: Pickwick Distribution, PRT

Cassette: released on Contour, Apr'86 by Pickwick Records. Dist: Pickwick Distribution, PRT

Single (7"): released on Old Gold (Reissue), Oct'83

Single (7"): released on Decca-Originals, Mar'82 by Decca Records. Dist: Polygram, IMS

Skelmanthorpe

MOVIN' ON (Skelmanthorpe Male Voice Choir).
Album: released on Look, Nov'79 Dist: R. Smith & Co. Records, H.R. Taylor

Cassette: released on Look, Nov'79 Dist: R. Smith & Co. Records, H.R. Taylor

Skeptix

RETURN TO HELL.
Single (7"): released on Zenon, May'84 Dist: Neon, Pinnacle

ROUTINE MACHINE.
Single (7"): released on Zenon, Oct'82 Dist: Neon, Pinnacle

SCARRED FOR LIFE.
Single (7"): released on Neon, Aug'83 by Neon Records. Dist: Neon, Pinnacle

SO THE YOUTH.
Album: released on Rock-O-Rama, Jul'83

VENDETTA.
Single (7"): released on White Rose, Feb'84 by White Rose Records. Dist: Lightning

Skerry Ramblers
RETURN TO THE SHAMROCK SHORE.
Album: released on Homespun(Ireland), Sep'82 by Outlet Records. Dist: Outlet

Cassette: released on Homespun(Ireland), Sep'82 by Outlet Records. Dist: Outlet

Sketch
COLOUR BLIND.
Album: released on Sketch, Jul'87 by Sketch Records. Dist: IMS

CRAZY SUNDAY.
Single (12"): released on Sketch, Jul'87 by Sketch Records. Dist: IMS

SECONDS COUNT.
Tracks: / Feels so good / Fever / Fine & mellow / Heroes / Stormy Monday / Crazy Sunday / Was it something you said? / Cool for love.
Notes: Debut album from London-based jazz quintet featuring the vibrant singer Sue Hawker.Very much a cult band in London with as-trong club following.Their repertoire features an array of jazz styles.As well as Sue Hawker's original compositions the album also show-cases such jazz standards as "Fine & Mellow" &"Stormy Monday".This is definately a band to watch for the future. Personnel:Sue Hawker-vocals / Pete 'Sabbo' Saberton-piano /Jeremy Stacey-drums/ Rob Koral-guitar / Laurence Cottle-'Wal'Bass Guitars.
Album: released on Sketch UK, Mar'87

Skidmore, Alan
EUROPEAN JAZZ QUINTET (Skidmore, Alan & Others).
Album: released on Ego, Oct'79 by Ego Records. Dist: Jazz Services Unlimited Dist. (JSU), Cadillac Music

S.O.H. (Skidmore, Alan, Tony Oxley & Ali Haurand).
Album: released on Ego, Oct'79 by Ego Records. Dist: Jazz Services Unlimited Dist. (JSU), Cadillac Music

S.O.S. (Skidmore, Alan, Mike Osborne & John Surman).
Album: released on Ogun, Jan'77 Dist: Jazz Music, JSU, Cadillac

Skid Row
SKID ROW.
Album: released on CBS, Apr'87 by CBS Records. Dist: CBS

Cassette: released on CBS, Apr'87 by CBS Records. Dist: CBS

Skids
ABSOLUTE GAME, THE.
Album: released on Virgin, Mar'84 by Virgin Records. Dist: EMI, Virgin Distribution

Cassette: released on Virgin, Mar'84 by Virgin Records. Dist: EMI, Virgin Distribution

CHARLES.
Single (7"): released on No Bad, Apr'78 by No Bad Records. Dist: Pinnacle, Wynd-Up Distribution (Scotland)

DAYS IN EUROPA.
Album: released on Virgin, Mar'84 by Virgin Records. Dist: EMI, Virgin Distribution

FANFARE.
Album: released on Virgin, May'82 by Virgin Records. Dist: EMI, Virgin Distribution

Cassette: released on Virgin, May'82 by Virgin Records. Dist: EMI, Virgin Distribution

INTO THE VALLEY.
Single (7"): released on Virgin, Feb'79 by Virgin Records. Dist: EMI, Virgin Distribution

Single (12"): released on Virgin, May'83 by Virgin Records. Dist: EMI, Virgin Distribution

JOY.
Album: released on Virgin, Nov'81 by Virgin Records. Dist: EMI, Virgin Distribution

Cassette: released on Virgin, Nov'81 by Virgin Records. Dist: EMI, Virgin Distribution

SCARED TO DANCE.
Album: released on Virgin, Mar'84 by Virgin Records. Dist: EMI, Virgin Distribution

SWEET SUBURBIA.
Single (7"): released on Virgin, Sep'78 by Virgin Records. Dist: EMI, Virgin Distribution

Skiff Skats
CRIPPLE CREEK.
Single (7"): released on Doggo, Jan'85 Dist: Rough Trade, Cartel

SKIFF SKAT STUFF.
Album: released on Spindrift, Nov'85 Dist: Roots

Skifs, Bjorn
ARBITER.
Single (7"): released on RCA, Apr'85 by RCA Records. Dist: RCA, Roots, Swift, Wellard, Chris, I & B, Solomon & Peres Distribution

Single (12"): released on RCA, Apr'85 by RCA Records. Dist: RCA, Roots, Swift, Wellard, Chris, I & B, Solomon & Peres Distribution

Skin
1000 YEARS.
Tracks: / 1000 years / My own hands.
Single (7"): released on Product Inc., Mar'87 Dist: Cartel

Single (12"): released on Product Inc., Mar'87 Dist: Cartel

BLOOD, WOMEN, ROSES.
Compact disc: released on Product Inc., May'87 Dist: Cartel

GIRL COME OUT.
Tracks: / Girl come out / Girl come out (dub).
Single (7"): released on Product Inc., Jul'87 Dist: Cartel

Single (12"): released on Product Inc., Jul'87 Dist: Cartel

THOUSAND YEARS.
Single (7"): released on Product Inc., Mar'87 Dist: Cartel

Single (12"): released on Product Inc., Mar'87 Dist: Cartel

Skin & Bone
LET IT BE ME.
Tracks: / Summertime blues / Only you / Rhythm of the rain / Have I the right / Singing the blues.
Cassette: released on Ross, Dec'86 by Ross Records. Dist: Ross Distribution, Roots Distribution

SKIN & BONE Various artists (Various Artists).
Cassette: released on Skin & Bone, Jun'85 Dist: Cartel, Rough Trade

Skin & Fingers
BABY'S BACK.
Single (7"): released on Ensign, May'82 by Ensign Records. Dist: CBS Distribution

Skin Flicks
IN THE HEAT.
Single (7"): released on Lost Moments, Jan'85 Dist: Backs, Cartel

Single (12"): released on Lost Moments, Jan'85 Dist: Backs, Cartel

Skin Games
COWBOY JOE.
Tracks: / Cowboy Joe / Blanche.
Single (7"): released on Epic, Jul'87 by CBS Records. Dist: CBS

Single (12"): released on Epic, Jul'87 by CBS Records. Dist: CBS

Skinhead
ROUGH AND RUGGED.
Album: released on ALM Music, Aug'87 Dist: Jetstar

Skinhead Classics
SKINHEAD CLASSICS VOL.1 Various artists (Various Artists).
Extended-play record: released on Trojan, '83 by Trojan Records. Dist: PRT, Jetstar

SKINHEAD CLASSICS VOL.2 Various artists (Various Artists).
Extended-play record: released on Trojan, '83 by Trojan Records. Dist: PRT, Jetstar

SKINHEAD CLASSICS EP Various artists (Various Artists).
Extended-play record: released on Trojan, Feb'80 by Trojan Records. Dist: PRT, Jetstar

Skinner, Barry
ABROAD AS I WAS WORKING.
Album: released on Stoof, May'78 Dist: Roots Distribution

Bushes and briars

Skinner, Bob
ME & MY GUITAR.
Album: released on Lake, Oct'80 by Fellside Recordings. Dist: Jazz Music, Fellside

Skinner, Jimmy
NO.1 IN BLUEGRASS.
Album: released on Starday, Apr'87

Cassette: released on Starday, Apr'87

Skinner, Julian
BLESSED BY YOU.
Single (12"): released on Jungle Rhythm, Oct'85

Skinner, Scott
STRATHSPEY KING, THE.
Album: released on Topic, '81 by Topic Records. Dist: JSU Distribution, Projection Distribution, Jazz Music Distribution

Skinny Puppy
BITE.
Album: released on Scarface, Feb'86 by Scarface Records. Dist: Cartel

DIGIT.
Tracks: / Digit.
Single (12"): released on Play It Again Sam, Nov'86 Dist: Red Rhino, Cartel

MIND:THE PERPETUAL INTERCOURSE.
Tracks: / One time one place / Gods gift / Three blind mice / Love / Stairs and flowers / Antagonism / 200 Years / Dig it / Burnt with water.
Album: released on EMI, Feb'87 by EMI Records. Dist: EMI

SKINNY PUPPY.
Album: released on Scarface, Jun'85 by Scarface Records. Dist: Cartel

Skin Side Out
TO HELL WITH CARNIVAL.
Single (12"): released on Lost Moments, Nov'85 Dist: Backs, Cartel

VIPER PANG.
Single (7"): released on Lost Moments, Nov'85 Dist: Backs, Cartel

Single (12"): released on Lost Moments, Nov'85 Dist: Backs, Cartel

Skin Talk
SKIN TALK Various artists (Various Artists).
Album: released on 101 International, Mar'84

Skin The Peeler
SKIN THE PEELER.
Album: released on STP, Jun'84 by STP Records. Dist: Cartel Distribution

Skin the piper
BEYOND THE PALE.
Cassette: released on Fuller Sounds, Sep'85 Dist: Fuller Sounds

Skint Video
ROGUES.
Tracks: / Cops on 45.
Single (7"): released on Off The Kerb, Dec'86 by Off The Kerb Records. Dist: Rough Trade Distribution, Cartel Distribution

Ski Patrol
BRIGHT SHINY THINGS.
Single (7"): released on Clever Metal, Sep'82 by Clever Metal Records. Dist: Cartel

FAITH IN TRANSITION.
Single (7"): released on Malicious Damage, Jul'81 Dist: Polygram

Skipworth & Turner
HOT PURSUIT.
Single (12"): released on Fourth & Broadway, Sep'85 by Island Records. Dist: Polygram, EMI

SKIPWORTH & TURNER.
Cassette: released on Fourth & Broadway, Nov'85 by Island Records. Dist: Polygram, EMI

THINKING ABOUT YOUR LOVE.
Single (7"): released on Fourth & Broadway, Apr'85 by Island Records. Dist: Polygram, EMI

Single (12"): released on Fourth & Broadway, Jun'85 by Island Records. Dist: Polygram, EMI

Skirted Issue
RUM AND COCA COLA.
Single (7"): released on That's Entertainment, Apr'82 by That's Entertainment Records. Dist: Pinnacle, PRT

Skitts
LIVING WITHOUT YOU/WAS I....
Single (7"): released on Will, Apr'82

Skitzo
SKITZO MANIA.
Album: released on Nervous, 30 May'87 by Nervous Records. Dist: Nervous, Rough Trade

Skjelbred, Ray
SKJELBRED,RAY & HAL SMITH (Skjelbred, Ray & Hal Smith).
Album: released on Stomp Off, Jun'86 by Stomp Off Records. Dist: Jazz Music Distribution

SOLO JAZZ PIANO 1973/1974.
Album: Dist: Jazz Music

Skool Boyz
SLIP AWAY.
Single (7"): released on CBS, Sep'84 by CBS Records. Dist: CBS

Skrewdriver
BACK WITH A BANG.
Single (7"): released on Skrewdriver, Sep'82

Single (12"): released on Skrewdriver, Sep'82

Skroteez
NEW TOWN/WHO'S LAW/LIVI PUNKZ.
Single (7"): released on Overspill, May'82

SKT
YOUR LOVE IS ALRIGHT (Skull).
Single (7"): released on RCA, Jun'84 by RCA Records. Dist: RCA, Roots, Swift, Wellard, Chris, I & B, Solomon & Peres Distribution

Single (12"): released on RCA, Jun'84 by RCA Records. Dist: RCA, Roots, Swift, Wellard, Chris, I & B, Solomon & Peres Distribution

Skull
LIVING.
Single (12"): released on One Little Indian, Feb'87 by One Little Indian Records. Dist: Nine Mile Distribution, Cartel Distribution

Sky
ANIMALS THE (PART 1)/KP 11.
Single (7"): released on Ariola, Jan'83 by RCA, Ariola

CADMIUM.
Tracks: / Troika / Fayre / Girl in winter (The) / Mother Russia / Telex from Peru / Boy from Dundee (The) / Night / Then & Now / Return to me / Son of Hotta.
Notes: The most accessible SKY recording yet,which includes the memorable 'Troika'and 'A Girl In Winter'/'Return To Me',both written by Alan Tarney.'Cadmium'recaptureand expands the appeal of the second album.
Compact disc: released on Arista, '86 by Arista Records. Dist: RCA

Album: released on Ariola, Nov'83 Dist: RCA, Ariola

Cassette: released on Ariola, Nov'83 Dist: RCA, Ariola

Compact disc: released on Ariola, Nov'83 Dist: RCA, Ariola

FOOL ON THE HILL.
Single (7"): released on Ariola, Apr'81 Dist: RCA, Ariola

FORTHCOMING.
Album: released on Ariola, May'82 Dist: RCA, Ariola

GREAT BALLOON RACE,THE.
Tracks: / Desperate for your love / Allegro Land,The / Peter's wedding / Great balloon race,The / Lady & The Imp,The / Caldando Rokey-Stone / Night sky.
Album: released on Epic, Apr'86 by CBS Records. Dist: CBS

Cassette: released on Epic, Apr'86 by CBS Records. Dist: CBS

Compact disc: released on Epic, Apr'86 by CBS Records. Dist: CBS

MASTERPIECES-THE VERY BEST OF SKY.
Tracks: / Toccata / Westway / Fool on the hill / Gymnopedie / Vivaldi / Skylark / Troika / Hotta / Masquerade / Girl in winter / Dance of the little fairies / Chiropodie 1 / Keep me safe and keep me warm,shelter me from darkness.
Compact disc: released on Telstar, May'86 by Telstar Records. Dist: RCA Distribution

MASTERPIECES THE VERY BEST OF SKY.
Album: released on Telstar, Apr'84 by Telstar Records. Dist: RCA Distribution

SKY.
Tracks: / Westway / Cannonball / Trois Gymnopedies / Danza / Carrilon / Where opposites meet(part 1-5).
Album: released on Fame, Oct'86 by Music For Pleasure Records. Dist: EMI

Album: released on Ariola, Sep'82 Dist: RCA, Ariola

SKY 1.
Tracks: / Westway / Carillion / Danza / Gymnopedie No.1 / Cannonball / Where opposites meet-Part 1 / Where opposites meet-Part 2 / Where opposites meet-Part 3 / Where opposites meet-Part 4 / Where opposites meet-Part 5.
Album: released on Fame, Oct'86 by Music For Pleasure Records. Dist: EMI

Cassette: released on Fame, Oct'86 by Music For Pleasure Records. Dist: EMI

SKY 2.
Album: released on Ariola, Jan'82 Dist: RCA, Ariola

Cassette: released on Ariola, Jan'82 Dist: RCA, Ariola

SKY 3.
Album: released on Ariola, Sep'82 Dist: RCA, Ariola

Album: released on Ariola, Sep'82 Dist: RCA, Ariola

SKY 5 LIVE.
Album: released on Arista, Jan'83 by Arista Records. Dist: RCA

Cassette: released on Arista, Jan'83 by Arista Records. Dist: RCA

SKY (BOX SET).
Album: released on Ariola, Nov'81 Dist: RCA, Ariola

Boxed set: released on Ariola, Nov'81 Dist: RCA, Ariola

SONGS THAT MADE AMERICA FAMOUS.
Album: released on Adelphi, May'81 by Adelphi Records. Dist: Jetstar

TOCCATA/VIVALDI.
Single (7"): released on Ariola, Sep'82 Dist: RCA, Ariola

Skyboat

SHIP IN DISTRESS.
Album: released on Plant Life, May'82 Dist: Roots

Sky City Rockers

NICE AND SLOW.
Single (7"): released on Sedition, Aug'87 by Sedition Records. Dist: PRT

Single (12"): released on Sedition, Aug'87 by Sedition Records. Dist: PRT

Skyers,Nathan

OH LOVE.
Tracks: / Oh love / Leave bad company.
Single (12"): released on Mandingo, Apr'86 Dist: Jetstar

Skyes, Roosevelt

1929-1942.
Notes: Mono.
Album: released on Best Of Blues, Oct'86 by Best Of Blues Records. Dist: Swift

Skyliners

SINCE I DON'T HAVE TO.
Album: released on Ace, Aug'83 by Ace Records. Dist: Pinnacle, Swift, Hotshot, Cadillac

Skymasters

BIG BAND FAVOURITES.
Tracks: / Skyliner / Begin the beguine / Trumpet blues and cantabile / I'm getting sentimental over you / Pink panther theme (The) / One o'clock jump / Opus one / Moonlight serenade / Take the A train / Love / Lean Baby / Sing sing sing.
Notes: The Skymasters are one of Holland's most popular radio and concert Big Bands. This superb digital recording features the very best in Big Band repetoire including "Take The A Train" (Billy Strayhorn), "Moonlight Serenade" (Glenn Miller), and "One O'Clock Jump" (Count Basie).
Album:

Cassette:

Compact disc:

Skynyrd, Lynyrd

NUTHIN' FANCY.
Compact disc: released on MCA, Sep'87 by MCA Records. Dist: Polygram, MCA

Skyriders

SNOOPY V THE RED BARON.
Single (7"): released on Airport, Mar'85 Dist: Airport

Skyrockets

Dance band years - the 1940's

Sky Saxon

GROOVY THING,A.
Album: released on New Rose, Aug'86 Dist: Rough Trade, Cartel

Skyscrapers

CHIFFON CHIFFON/JENNY.
Single (7"): released on Zilch, Nov'81 by Zilch Records. Dist: Stage One

HOTLINE FROM WASHINGTON.
Single (7"): released on Zilch, Apr'81 by Zilch Records. Dist: Stage One

WAITING FOR THIS MOMENT ALL NIGHT.
Single (7"): released on Zilch, May'82 by Zilch Records. Dist: Stage One

Sky's the limit, The

SKY'S THE LIMIT, THE Musical (Various Artists).
Notes: Fred Astaire and Joan Leslie team up for 'One for my baby and one for the road' and other hit tunes
Video-cassette (VHS): released on Video Collection, May'87 by Video Collection International Ltd.. Dist: Counterpoint

Sky Sunlight Saxon

MASTERS OF PYSCHEDELIA.
Album: released on New Rose, Nov'84 Dist: Rough Trade, Cartel

Skytrain

FOX ON THE RUN.
Single (7"): released on Half Moon, Jun'83 by Rondelet Music And Records. Dist: Spartan

Single (12"): released on Half Moon, Jun'83 by Rondelet Music And Records. Dist: Spartan

Skyy

FROM THE LEFT SIDE.
Tracks: / Givin'it (to you) / Love attack / Nonstop / Song song / Big fun / Love illogical / Tell her you care / Jealousitis / Rock it.
Album: released on Capitol, Jun'86 by Capitol Records. Dist: EMI

Cassette: released on Capitol, Jun'86 by Capitol Records. Dist: EMI

GIVIN'IT (TO YOU).
Tracks: / Givin'it (to you).
Single (7"): released on Capitol, Jun'86 by Capitol Records. Dist: EMI

INNER CITY.
Album: released on Salsoul, Jan'85

Slab!

MUSIC FROM THE IRON LUNG.
Album: released on Ink, Apr'87 by Red Flame. Dist: Rough Trade, Cartel, Pinnacle

PARALAX AVENUE.
Tracks: / Yukou / Flirt.
Single (12"): released on Ink, Feb'87 by Red Flame. Dist: Rough Trade, Cartel, Pinnacle

SMOKE RINGS.
Tracks: / Smoke rings / Abbasloth.
Single (7"): released on Ink, Jun'87 by Red Flame. Dist: Rough Trade, Cartel, Pinnacle

Single (12"): released on Ink, Jun'87 by Red Flame. Dist: Rough Trade, Cartel, Pinnacle

Slack, Freddie

BOOGIE WOOGIE.
Album: released on Oldie Blues(Sweden), May'85

Slade

ALL JOIN HANDS.
Single (7"): released on RCA, Nov'84 by RCA Records. Dist: RCA, Roots, Swift, Wellard, Chris, I & B, Solomon & Peres Distribution

Single (12"): released on RCA, Nov'84 by RCA Records. Dist: RCA, Roots, Swift, Wellard, Chris, I & B, Solomon & Peres Distribution

AMAZING KAMIKAZE SYNDROME, THE.
Album: released on RCA, Dec'83 by RCA Records. Dist: RCA, Roots, Swift, Wellard, Chris, I & B, Solomon & Peres Distribution

Cassette: released on RCA, Dec'83 by RCA Records. Dist: RCA, Roots, Swift, Wellard, Chris, I & B, Solomon & Peres Distribution

AND NOW THE WALTZ,C'EST LAVIE.
Single (7"): released on RCA, Nov'82 by RCA Records. Dist: RCA, Roots, Swift, Wellard, Chris, I & B, Solomon & Peres Distribution

COZ I LUV YOU.
Album: released on Karussell (Import), Mar'82

Cassette: released on Karussell (Import), Mar'82

CRACKERS' -THE CHRISTMAS PARTY ALBUM.
Album: released on Telstar, Dec'85 by Telstar Records. Dist: RCA Distribution

Cassette: released on Telstar, Dec'85 by Telstar Records. Dist: RCA Distribution

DO YOU BELIEVE IN MIRACLES.
Single (7"): released on RCA, Nov'85 by RCA Records. Dist: RCA, Roots, Swift, Wellard, Chris, I & B, Solomon & Peres Distribution

Single (12"): released on RCA, Nov'85 by RCA Records. Dist: RCA, Roots, Swift, Wellard, Chris, I & B, Solomon & Peres Distribution

KNUCKLE SANDWICH NANCY.
Single (7"): released on Cheapskate, May'81 by Cheapskate Records. Dist: RCA

LOCK UP YOUR DAUGHTERS.
Single (7"): released on RCA, Sep'81 by RCA Records. Dist: RCA, Roots, Swift, Wellard, Chris, I & B, Solomon & Peres Distribution

MERRY XMAS EVERYBODY.
Tracks: / Don't blame me.
Single (12"): released on Polydor, Nov'86 by Polydor Records. Dist: Polygram, Polydor

Single (7"): released on Polydor, Nov'86 by Polydor Records. Dist: Polygram, Polydor

Single (7"): released on Polydor, Nov'85 by Polydor Records. Dist: Polygram, Polydor

Single (12"): released on Polydor, Nov'85 by Polydor Records. Dist: Polygram, Polydor

MYZSTERIOUS MIZSTER JONES.
Single (12"): released on RCA, Mar'85 by RCA Records. Dist: RCA, Roots, Swift, Wellard, Chris, I & B, Solomon & Peres Distribution

Single (12"): released on RCA, Mar'85 by RCA Records. Dist: RCA, Roots, Swift, Wellard, Chris, I & B, Solomon & Peres Distribution

OKEY COKEY.
Single (7"): released on Receiver, Dec'86 by Receiver Records. Dist: Pinnacle
Cat. no: **SPEED 201**
Picture disc single: released on Speed, Dec'82

ON STAGE.
Album: released on RCA, '84 by RCA Records. Dist: RCA, Roots, Swift, Wellard, Chris, I & B, Solomon & Peres Distribution

Cassette: released on RCA, '84 by RCA Records. Dist: RCA, Roots, Swift, Wellard, Chris, I & B, Solomon & Peres Distribution

ROGUES GALLERY.
Album: released on RCA, Feb'85 by RCA Records. Dist: RCA, Roots, Swift, Wellard, Chris, I & B, Solomon & Peres Distribution

Cassette: released on RCA, Feb'85 by RCA Records. Dist: RCA, Roots, Swift, Wellard, Chris, I & B, Solomon & Peres Distribution

RUBY RED.
Single (7"): released on RCA, Mar'82 by RCA Records. Dist: RCA, Roots, Swift, Wellard, Chris, I & B, Solomon & Peres Distribution

SEVEN YEAR (B)ITCH, THE.
Single (7"): released on RCA, Jan'85 by RCA Records. Dist: RCA, Roots, Swift, Wellard, Chris, I & B, Solomon & Peres Distribution

Single (12"): released on RCA, Jan'85 by RCA Records. Dist: RCA, Roots, Swift, Wellard, Chris, I & B, Solomon & Peres Distribution

SLADE ALIVE.
Album: released on Polydor, Nov'84 by Polydor Records. Dist: Polygram, Polydor

Cassette: released on Polydor, Nov'84 by Polydor Records. Dist: Polygram, Polydor

SLADE IN FLAME Film soundtrack.
Album: released on Polydor, Jun'82 by Polydor Records. Dist: Polygram, Polydor

Cassette: released on Polydor, Jun'82 by Polydor Records. Dist: Polygram, Polydor

SLADES GREATS.
Album: released on Polydor, May'84 by Polydor Records. Dist: Polygram, Polydor

Cassette: released on Polydor, May'84 by Polydor Records. Dist: Polygram, Polydor

STILL THE SAME.
Tracks: / Gotta go home.
Single (7"): released on RCA, Jan'87 by RCA Records. Dist: RCA, Roots, Swift, Wellard, Chris, I & B, Solomon & Peres Distribution

STILL THE SAME (EXT).
Tracks: / Gotta go home.
Single (12"): released on RCA, Feb'87 by RCA Records. Dist: RCA, Roots, Swift, Wellard, Chris, I & B, Solomon & Peres Distribution

STORY OF: SLADE.
Double Album: released on Polydor, '81 by Polydor Records. Dist: Polygram, Polydor

Double cassette: released on Polydor, Apr'81 by Polydor Records. Dist: Polygram, Polydor

THAT'S WHAT FRIENDS ARE FOR.
Tracks: / That's what friends are for / Wild party.
Single (7"): released on RCA, Apr'87 by RCA Records. Dist: RCA, Roots, Swift, Wellard, Chris, I & B, Solomon & Peres Distribution

Single (12"): released on RCA, Apr'87 by RCA Records. Dist: RCA, Roots, Swift, Wellard, Chris, I & B, Solomon & Peres Distribution

TILL DEAF DO US PART.
Album: released on RCA, Dec'81 by RCA Records. Dist: RCA, Roots, Swift, Wellard, Chris, I & B, Solomon & Peres Distribution

Cassette: released on RCA, Dec'81 by RCA Records. Dist: RCA, Roots, Swift, Wellard, Chris, I & B, Solomon & Peres Distribution

WE'LL BRING THE HOUSE DOWN.
Tracks: / We'll bring the house down / Night starvation / Wheel's ain't coming down / Hold on to your hats / When I'm dancin' / I ain't fightin' / Dizzy mama / Nuts bolts & screws / My baby's got it / Lemme love into ya / I'm a rocker.
Album: released on RCA, Oct'86 by RCA Records. Dist: RCA, Roots, Swift, Wellard, Chris, I & B, Solomon & Peres Distribution

Cassette: released on RCA, Oct'86 by RCA Records. Dist: RCA, Roots, Swift, Wellard, Chris, I & B, Solomon & Peres Distribution

Album: released on Cheapskate, Mar'81 by Cheapskate Records. Dist: RCA

Cassette: released on Cheapskate, Mar'81 by Cheapskate Records. Dist: RCA

Single (7"): released on Cheapskate, Jan'81 by Cheapskate Records. Dist: RCA

YOU BOYZ MAKE BIG NOIZE.
Tracks: / Love is like a rock / That's what friends are for / Still the same / Fools go grazy / She's heavy / We won't give in / Won't you rock with me / Ooh la la in L.A. / Me and the boys / Sing shout (knock yourself out) / Roaring silence, The / It's hard having fun nowadays.
Album: released on RCA, Jan'87 by RCA Records. Dist: RCA, Roots, Swift, Wellard, Chris, I & B, Solomon & Peres Distribution

Cassette: released on RCA, Jan'87 by RCA Records. Dist: RCA, Roots, Swift, Wellard, Chris, I & B, Solomon & Peres Distribution

Compact disc: released on RCA, Jan'87 by RCA Records. Dist: RCA, Roots, Swift, Wellard, Chris, I & B, Solomon & Peres Distribution

Compact disc: released on RCA, '87 by RCA Records. Dist: RCA, Roots, Swift, Wellard, Chris, I & B, Solomon & Peres Distribution

YOU BOYZ MAKE BIG NOIZE (SINGLE).
Tracks: / You boyz make big noize / Boyz (inst).
Single (7"): released on Cheapskate, Jul'87 by Cheapskate Records. Dist: RCA

Single (12"): released on Cheapskate, Jul'87 by Cheapskate Records. Dist: RCA

Slade, Stanley

MR. STORMALONG Sea Shanties.
Cassette: released on Folktracks, Nov'79 by Folktracks Cassettes. Dist: Folktracks

Slainte

AS TEARS GO BY.
Single (7"): released on Mint, Oct'82 by Emerald Records. Dist: Ross Distribution, PRT Distribution, Solomon & Peres Distribution

WHEN I GROW TOO OLD TO DREAM.
Single (7"): released on Mint, Apr'82 by Em-

erald Records. Dist: Ross Distribution, PRT Distribution, Solomon & Peres Distribution

Slanted View
WHITE PAPER.
Single (12"): released on Tite, Aug'85 Dist: Backs, Cartel Distribution

Slapp Happy
EVERYBODY'S SLIMMIN.
Single (7"): released on Half Cat, Jun'83 by Half Cat Records. Dist: Rough Trade

SORT OF.
Album: released on Recommended, Sep'86 by Recommended Records. Dist: Recommended, Impetus, Rough Trade

Slash Cuts
SLASH CUTS Various artists (Various Artists).
Album: released on Slash, Aug'85 by London Records. Dist: Polygram

Slater, Jim
AMAZING MONSTERS (Slater, Jim & Christopher).
Cassette: released on Delyse, Oct'80 by Delyse Records. Dist: H.R. Taylor

Slater, Les
LES SLATER Pub pianist of the year plays 44 singalong favourites.
Album: released on Grosvenor, Jun'81 by Grosvenor Records. Dist: Taylors

Slater, Roy, L.
WONDER.
Single (7"): released on Jama, Apr'79 by Jama Records.

Slater, Stuart
ALL AROUND THE WORLD.
Single (7"): released on Chrysalis, Apr'83 by Chrysalis Records. Dist: CBS

Slates
FALL.
Single (7"): released on Rough Trade, May'81 by Rough Trade Records. Dist: Rough Trade Distribution, Cartel Distribution

Slatkin, Leonard
MUSIC OF BERNSTEIN.
Tracks: / Candide-overture / Fancy free / Facsimile / On the town-three dance episodes.
Album: released on H.M.V., Feb'87 by EMI Records. Dist: EMI

Cassette: released on H.M.V., Feb'87 by EMI Records. Dist: EMI

Slaughter and the dogs
I'M THE ONE.
Single (7"): released on DJM, Jun'80 by DJM Records. Dist: CBS, Polygram

THE WAY WE WERE.
Album: released on Thrush, Jun'83 Dist: Pinnacle

TWIST AND TURN.
Single (12"): released on Thrush, Feb'83 Dist: Pinnacle

WHERE HAVE ALL THE BOOT BOYS GONE.
Single (7"): released on Decca, Mar'81 by Decca Records. Dist: Polygram

YOU'RE READY NOW.
Single (7"): released on DJM, Nov'79 by DJM Records. Dist: CBS, Polygram

Slaughter, Joe
I'LL FOLLOW YOU DOWN.
Single (7"): released on Creation, Nov'85 Dist: Rough Trade, Cartel

Single (12"): released on Creation, Nov'85 Dist: Rough Trade, Cartel

SHE'S SO OUT OF TOUCH.
Tracks: / She's so out of touch / I know you rider / Lonesome death of Thurston Moore,The.
Single (7"): released on Creation, Nov'86 Dist: Rough Trade, Cartel

Single (12"): released on Creation, Nov'86 Dist: Rough Trade, Cartel

Slave
DONT WASTE MY TIME.
Single (7"): released on Certain, Oct'85 Dist: Priority, EMI, Pinnacle

Single (12"): released on Certain, Oct'85 Dist: Priority, EMI, Pinnacle

---

DO YOU LIKE IT GIRL.
Single (7"): released on Cotillion, Mar'83 by WEA Records. Dist: WEA

Single (12"): released on Cotillion, Mar'83 by WEA Records. Dist: WEA

JUICY-O.
Tracks: / I like your style.
Single (12"): released on Ichiban, Jul'87 by Ichiban Records. Dist: PRT

JUST A TOUCH OF LOVE.
Single (7"): released on Cotillion, May'84 by WEA Records. Dist: WEA

Single (12"): released on Cotillion, May'84 by WEA Records. Dist: WEA

MAKE BELIEVE.
Album: released on Ichiban, Aug'87 by Ichiban Records. Dist: PRT

Cassette: released on Ichiban, Aug'87 by Ichiban Records. Dist: PRT

STEPPIN' OUT.
Single (12"): released on Cotillion, Nov'83 by WEA Records. Dist: WEA

THRILL ME.
Tracks: / Thrill me / Jazzy lady / Unchained at last.
Single (12"): released on Certain, Feb'86 Dist: Priority, EMI, Pinnacle

UCHAINED AT LAST.
Album: released on Certain, Feb'86 Dist: Priority, EMI, Pinnacle

UNCHAINED AT LAST.
Tracks: / Jazzy Lady / I'd like to get you / Don't u be afraid / All we need is time / Thrill me / Don't waste my time / It's my heart thats breakin' / Babe show me.

WAIT FOR ME.
Single (7"): released on Cotillion, Jan'82 by WEA Records. Dist: WEA

Single (12"): released on Cotillion, Jan'82 by WEA Records. Dist: WEA

Slave dance
DEFENDER OF THE LIE.
Album: released on Plague Circuit Of Events, Sep'85 Dist: Backs, Cartel

Slayer
CRIMINALLY INSANE.
Tracks: / Criminally insane (remix) / Aggressive protector / Post mortem*.
Single (7"): released on London, 23 May'87 by London Records. Dist: Polygram

Single (12"): released on London, 23 May'87 by London Records. Dist: Polygram

HAUNTING THE CHAPLE.
Single (12"): released on Road Runner, Oct'84

HELL AWAITS.
Album: released on Road Runner, May'85

INTERVIEW PICTURE DISC.
Album: released on Baktabak, Jun'87 by Baktabak Records. Dist: Arabesque

REIGN IN BLOOD.
Tracks: / Angel of death / Piece by piece / Necrophobic / Altar of sacrifice / Jesus saves / Criminally insane / Reborn / Epidemic / Postmortem / Raining blood.
Notes: This album has already been important and features 'Speed' metal's most important phenomenon, Slayer. Produced by Slayer with Def Jam's Rick Rubin. Slayer is: Kerry King-lead guitars/Jeff Hanneman-lead guitar/Tom Araya-vocals, bass/Dave Lombard-drums.
Album: released on Def Jam (USA), Apr'87 by CBS Records. Dist: CBS

Cassette: released on Def Jam (USA), Apr'87 by CBS Records. Dist: CBS

SHOW NO MERCY.
Album: released on Music For Nations, Jun'84 by Music For Nations Records. Dist: Pinnacle

Sleazee
GIRL ARE OUT.
Single (7"): released on Calibre, Nov'83 by Calibre Records. Dist: PRT

Single (12"): released on Calibre, Nov'83 by Calibre Records. Dist: PRT

Sledgehammer
BLOOD ON THEIR HANDS.
Album: released on Illuminated, Feb'85 by IKF Records. Dist: Pinnacle, Cartel, Jetstar

IN THE QUEUE.
Picture disc single: released on Illuminated, Mar'85 by IKF Records. Dist: Pinnacle, Cartel, Jetstar

---

Sledge, Percy
ANY DAY NOW.
Album: released on Charly(R&B), Mar'84 by Charly Records. Dist: Charly, Cadillac

Cassette: released on Charly(R&B), Mar'84 by Charly Records. Dist: Charly, Cadillac

BEST OF... When A Man Loves A Woman (The Ultimate).
Album: released on Atlantic, Feb'87 by WEA Records. Dist: WEA

Cassette: released on Atlantic, Feb'87 by WEA Records. Dist: WEA

COVER ME.
Tracks: / Cover me / It tears me apart.
Single (7"): released on Atlantic, 23 May'87 by WEA Records. Dist: WEA

Single (12"): released on Atlantic, 23 May'87 by WEA Records. Dist: WEA

GREATEST HITS:PERCY SLEDGE.
Compact disc: released on MCS Look Back, Jul'87

Album: released on Masters (Holland), Jan'87

Cassette: released on Masters (Holland), Jan'87

GREATEST HITS: PERCY SLEDGE.
Cassette: released on K-Tel, Aug'84 by K-Tel Records. Dist: Record Merchandisers Distribution, Taylors, Terry Blood Distribution, Wynd-Up Distribution, Relay Distribution, Pickwick Distribution, Solomon & Peres Distribution, Polygram

HIS TOP HITS.
Compact disc: released on Timeless Treasures, Jul'86 Dist: Counterpoint Distribution

IF LOVING YOU IS WRONG.
Tracks: / If loving you is wrong / When a man loves a woman / Take time to know her / Warm & tender love / It tears me up / Behind closed doors / Try alittle tenderness / Dock of the bay / Tell it like it is / You send me / Bring it on home to me / My special prayer / I've been loving you too long / Cover me.
Notes: Licensed from : Kilo Music Ltd This compilation: P 1986 Charly Records Ltd C 1986 Charly Records Ltd
Album: released on Charly, Aug'87 by Charly Records. Dist: Charly, Cadillac

PERCY.
Tracks: / Bring your lovin' to me / You had to be there / All night train / She's too pretty to cry / I still miss someone / Faithful kind, The / Home type thing / Personality / Ill put angels around you / Hard lovin' woman / When a man loves a woman 87.
Compact disc: released on Charly, Jul'87 by Charly Records. Dist: Charly, Cadillac

Album: released on Charly(R&B), Jul'87 by Charly Records. Dist: Charly, Cadillac

Cassette: released on Charly(R&B), Jul'87 by Charly Records. Dist: Charly, Cadillac

ULTIMATE COLLECTION, THE.
Compact disc: released on Atlantic, Jul'87 by WEA Records. Dist: WEA

WARM AND TENDER LOVE.
Album: released on Blue Moon, Aug'86 Dist: Magnum Music Group Ltd, PRT, Spartan

WHEN A MAN LOVES A WOMAN (LP).
Tracks: / I'll be your everything / If this is the last time / Hard to be friends / Blue water / Love away people / Take time to know her / Out of left field / Warm and tender love / It tears me up / When a man loves a woman / Walkin' in the sun / Behind closed doors / Make it good and make it last / Good love (The) / I believe in you / My special prayer.
Notes: Licensed from Charly International APS. This CD (P) 1987 Charly Holdings Ltd. (C) 1987 Charly Records Ltd.

WHEN A MAN LOVES A WOMAN.
Tracks: / Warm and Tender.
Single (7"): released on Atlantic, Jan'87 by WEA Records. Dist: WEA

Single (12"): released on Atlantic, Jan'87 by WEA Records. Dist: WEA

Album: released on Topline, Apr'87 by Charly Records. Dist: Charly Distribution

Compact disc: released on Topline, Apr'87 by Charly Records. Dist: Charly Distribution

Compact disc: released on Intertape, Jul'87 Dist: Target

Album: released on Hallmark, Jun'81 by Pickwick Distribution. Dist: Pickwick Distribution, PRT, Taylors

Cassette: released on Hallmark, Jun'81 by Pickwick Records. Dist: Pickwick Distribution, PRT, Taylors

Album: released on Topline, Jan'85 by Charly Records. Dist: Charly Distribution

---

Cassette: released on Topline, Jan'85 by Charly Records. Dist: Charly Distribution

Single (7"): released on Atlantic, '74 by WEA Records. Dist: WEA

Single (12"): released on Atlantic, Apr'80 by WEA Records. Dist: WEA

Single (7"): released on Old Gold, Jan'85 by Old Gold Records. Dist: Lightning, Jazz Music, Spartan, Counterpoint

Sleepers
ISLAND OF DREAMS.
Single (7"): released on SMC, Mar'83 by SMC Records. Dist: ILA

Sleep gently in the womb
SLEEP GENTLY IN THE WOMB (Various Artists).
Album: released on Silva, Nov'84 by Silva Records. Dist: Spartan

Cassette: released on Silva, Nov'84 by Silva Records. Dist: Spartan

Sleeping Beauty
SLEEPING BEAUTY Read by Susan Hampshire.
Cassette: released on Storytime Cassettes, Aug'83

SLEEPING BEAUTY (Various Artists).
Cassette: released on Anvil, Jan'81 Dist: Anvil

Album: released on Disneyland, Dec'82 by Disneyland-Vista Records (USA). Dist: BBC Records & Tapes, Rainbow Communications Ltd(Distribution)

Cassette: released on Disneyland, Dec'82 by Disneyland-Vista Records (USA). Dist: BBC Records & Tapes, Rainbow Communications Ltd(Distribution)

SLEEPING BEAUTY..
Cassette: released on Tellastory, Oct'79 by Bartlett Bliss Productions. Dist: PRT Distribution, Hayward Promotions Distribution, H.R. Taylor Distribution

SLEEPING BEAUTY/PUSS IN BOOTS Read by Dora Bryan (Bryan, Dora).
Cassette: released on Listen Productions, Nov'84 Dist: H.R. Taylor, Hayward Promotions Distribution

SLEEPING BEAUTY (THE) Read by Denise Bryer.
Cassette: released on Kiddy Kassettes, Aug'77

Sleeping Dogs
BEWARE.
Single (7"): released on Crass, Jun'83 by Exit-stencil Music. Dist: Rough Trade, Cartel

Sleeping Lions
CELEBRATION.
Single (7"): released on CBS, Feb'83 by CBS Records. Dist: CBS

Sleeping Pictures
POSSESSION.
Single (7"): released on Lost Moments, May'85 Dist: Backs, Cartel

Sleeque
ONE FOR THE MONEY.
Tracks: / One for the money / One for the (Dub).
Single (12"): released on Malaco, Jun'86 by Malaco Records. Dist: Charly

Sleigh, Bob
I WANNA BE THE FAIRY ON THE XMAS TREE.
Single (7"): released on Bulrush, Nov'83 Dist: Pinnacle

Sleighriders
VERY MERRY DISCO, A.
Album: released on Warwick, Nov'84 by MSI Records. Dist: CBS

Cassette: released on Warwick, Nov'84 by MSD Records. Dist: CBS

Sleigh, Robert
FIRST SNOW.
Single (7"): released on Stiff, Nov'83 by Stiff Records. Dist: EMI, Record Services Distribution (Ireland)

Slick
SPACE BASS.
Single (12"): released on Streetwave, Nov' by Streetwave Records. Dist: PRT Distribution

Slickaphonics

CHECK YOUR HEAD AT THE DOOR.
Tracks: / Going,going,gone / Never say never / Dig my way to China / That's it / Jungle in my heart / It's you again / Writing on the wall / Gettin' crazy.
Notes: The Slickaphonics are a five piece jazz-funk band from New York, led by Trombonist Ray Anderson
Album: released on IMS(Import), Jan'87 by Polydor Records. Dist: IMS, Polygram

Slickee Boys

CYBERNETICS DREAMS OF PI.
Album: released on New Rose, May'84 Dist: Rough Trade, Cartel

UH OH...NO BREAKS.
Album: released on New Rose, May'85 Dist: Rough Trade, Cartel

WHEN I GO TO THE BEACH.
Single (7"): released on New Rose, Aug'84 Dist: Rough Trade, Cartel

Slick,Grace

BARON VON TOLBOOTH.
Album: released on RCA (Germany), '83

DREAMS.
Album: released on RCA, Sep'81 by RCA Records. Dist: RCA, Roots, Swift, Wellard, Chris, I & B, Solomon & Peres Distribution

Cassette: released on RCA, Sep'81 by RCA Records. Dist: RCA, Roots, Swift, Wellard, Chris, I & B, Solomon & Peres Distribution

MANHOLE.
Album: released on RCA (Special Imports Service), Jul'84

SOFTWARE.
Album: released on RCA, Mar'84 by RCA Records. Dist: RCA, Roots, Swift, Wellard, Chris, I & B, Solomon & Peres Distribution

Cassette: released on RCA, Mar'84 by RCA Records. Dist: RCA, Roots, Swift, Wellard, Chris, I & B, Solomon & Peres Distribution

Slik

MAKE ME WHEN YOU GO.
Tracks: / Take me when you go.
Single (7"): released on Slik, Oct'86

Slim

IT'S IN THE MIX.
Single (12"): released on Greyhound, Jul'83 by Greyhound Records. Dist: PRT, Greyhound

Slim & Bam

MCVOUTY.
Album: released on Hep, Apr'81 by H.R. Taylor Records. Dist: Jazz Music, Cadillac Music, JSU, Taylors, Wellard, Chris, Zodiac, Swift, Fast Forward

SON OF MCVOUTY.
Album: released on Hep, Sep'86 by H.R. Taylor Records. Dist: Jazz Music, Cadillac Music, JSU, Taylors, Wellard, Chris, Zodiac, Swift, Fast Forward

Album: released on Hep, May'79 by H.R. Taylor Records. Dist: Jazz Music, Cadillac Music, JSU, Taylors, Wellard, Chris, Zodiac, Swift, Fast Forward

SON OF MCVOUTY.
Album: released on Hep, Apr'81 by H.R. Taylor Records. Dist: Jazz Music, Cadillac Music, JSU, Taylors, Wellard, Chris, Zodiac, Swift, Fast Forward

Slim, Bumble Bee

BUMBLE BEE SLIM 1931-37 Amos Eas-
Notes: With: Big Bill Broonzy, Washboard Sam
Album: released on Document, Jul'87

EVERYBODY'S FISHING.
Album: released on Magpie, Jan'77 Dist: Projection

Slim, Lightning

FEATURE SIDES,THE 1954.
Notes: Mono recording.
Album: released on Flyright, Oct'86 by Flyright Records. Dist: Krazy Kat, Swift, Jazz Music

Slimline

YOU CAN DANCE TO IT.
Single (7"): released on Channel, Apr'82 by Channel Records. Dist: Pinnacle

Single (12"): released on Channel, Apr'82 by Channel Records. Dist: Pinnacle

Slim, Memphis

ALL KINDS OF BLUES.
Compact disc: released on Carrere, Apr'87 by Carrere Records. Dist: PRT, Spartan

COLLECTION: MEMPHIS SLIM.
Album: released on Deja Vu, Aug'86 by Deja Vu Records. Dist: Counterpoint Distribution, Record Services Distribution (Ireland)

Cassette: released on Deja Vu, Aug'86 by Deja Vu Records. Dist: Counterpoint Distribution, Record Services Distribution (Ireland)

LIVE! FROM THEATRE MUNICIPAL, BAYONNE,FRANCE.
Album: released on Storyville, Sep'86 by Storyville Records. Dist: Jazz Music Distribution, Swift Distribution, Chris Wellard Distribution, Counterpoint Distribution

LIVE AT RONNIE SCOTTS.
Compact disc: released on Hendring Video, Dec'86 by Charly Records. Dist: Charly, PVG

SEE UNDER MEMPHIS.

TRAVELLING WITH THE BLUES.
Album: released on Storyville, Sep'86 by Storyville Records. Dist: Jazz Music Distribution, Swift Distribution, Chris Wellard Distribution, Counterpoint Distribution

Slim, Tarheel

TOO MUCH COMPETITION.
Album: released on Sundown, Apr'85 by Magnum Music Group Ltd. Dist: Magnum Music Group Ltd, PRT Distribution, Spartan Distribution

WILDCAT TAMER.
Album: released on Krazy Kat, Mar'85 Dist: Jazz Music, Swift, Chris Wellard, H.R. Taylor, Charly, Hotshot, IRS Distribution

Slinger, Cees

CEES/PHILLY/CLIFFORD/ISLA (Slinger, Cees/Philly Joe Jones/Clifford Jordan/Isla Eckinger).
Notes: Full album title: Cees Slinger/Philly Joe Jones/Clifford Jordan/Isla Eckinger.
Album: released on Timeless, Oct'86

Slipstream

SLIPSTREAM Best of British jazz funk (Various Artists).
Album: released on Beggars Banquet, Nov'81 by Beggars Banquet Records. Dist: WEA

Cassette: released on Beggars Banquet, Nov'81 by Beggars Banquet Records. Dist: WEA

Slits

ANIMAL SPACE/ANIMAL SPACIER.
Single (7"): released on Human, Jul'81 Dist: Roots, Stage One Deleted '1.

BOOTLEG/RETROSPECTIVE.
Album: released on Y, May'80

IN THE BEGINNING.
Single (7"): released on Rough Trade, Mar'80 by Rough Trade Records. Dist: Rough Trade Distribution, Cartel Distribution

PEEL SESSION 19.9.77.
Single (12"): released on Strange Fruit, Jan'87 by Clive Selwood. Dist: Pinnacle

Sloane, Carol

AS TIME GOES BY.
Compact disc: released on East Wind, '86 by East Wind Records. Dist: PRT

CAROL SINGS.
Notes: With Jimmy Rowles,Frank Wess, George Mraz
Album: released on Progressive (Import), Apr'81

SOPHISTICATED LADY.
Notes: with Sir Roland Hanna/Richie Pratt
Album: released on Audiophile, Jan'87 by Jazzology Records (USA). Dist: Jazz Music, Swift

Sloley, Andrew

SUPERSTAR.
Tracks: / Superstar / My baby.
Single (12"): released on Moove, Apr'86 Dist: Jetstar Distribution

Sloley, Glen

DON'T PLAY WITH LOVE.
Single (12"): released on Star Disc, Nov'84 by Star Disc Records. Dist: Jetstar Distribution

Slovenly

RISPOSTE.
Album: released on SST, Aug'87 by SST Records. Dist: Pinnacle

Slow Children

PRESIDENT AM I (HARD TIME)/BRAZILIAN MAGAZINES.
Single (7"): released on Ensign, Jun'81 by Ensign Records. Dist: CBS Distribution

SLOW CHILDREN.
Album: released on Ensign, Apr'81 by Ensign Records. Dist: CBS Distribution

Cassette: released on Ensign, Apr'81 by Ensign Records. Dist: CBS Distribution

SPRING IN FIALTA.
Single (7"): released on Ensign, Sep'81 by Ensign Records. Dist: CBS Distribution

Single (12"): released on Ensign, Sep'81 by Ensign Records. Dist: CBS Distribution

Slowfade

SLOWFADE.
Single (7"): released on Third World, Jul'82 Dist: Jetstar Distribution

SOUND OF A BREAKING HEART.
Single (7"): released on T.W., Feb'83 by T.W. Records. Dist: Cartel

Slow Jam

SLOW JAM 1 Various artists (Various Artists).
Album: released on Streetsounds, Sep'86

Cassette: released on Streetsounds, Sep'86

SLOW JAM 2 (Various Artists).
Album: Deleted Nov'86.

Cassette: Deleted Nov'86.

SLOW JAM 3 (Various Artists).
Album: released on Streetsounds, Jul'87

Cassette: released on Streetsounds, Jul'87

Slow, (Le)

TONIGHT I'M IN THE MOOD FOR LOVE.
Single (7"): released on Island, May'83 by Island Records. Dist: Polygram

Slow Motion

CHRISTMAS CHARADE Featuring White Christmas & Good King Wenceslas.
Single (7"): released on RK, Nov'79

Slow 'N' Moody

SLOW 'N' MOODY, BLACK 'N' BLUESY (Various Artists).
Album: released on Kent (Cadet, USA), Jul'83 by Ace Records. Dist: Pinnacle

Slow - Original Pop Hits

SLOW - ORIGINAL POP HITS (Various Artists).
Album: released on Polygram (France), Sep'85

Cassette: released on Polygram (France), Sep'85

Slow Twitch Fibres

THIS IS YOUR LUNCH/ILLICIT SECTS.
Single (7"): released on Rialto, Oct'81 by Rialto Records. Dist: Pinnacle

Single (7"): released on Rialto, Oct'81 by Rialto Records. Dist: Pinnacle

Sluggers

OVER THE FENCE.
Album: released on Arista, Aug'86 by Arista Records. Dist: RCA

Cassette: released on Arista, Aug'86 by Arista Records. Dist: RCA

Sluggers, The

OVER THE FENCE.
Tracks: / Over the fence / Perfect man / Written in the wind / Live wire / As we believe / I can't help myself / Jack in a box / Storm of love / In that magic moment / City lights.
Album: released on Arista, Jan'87 by Arista Records. Dist: RCA

Cassette: released on Arista, Jan'87 by Arista Records. Dist: RCA

Slurpy Gloop

I HEARD IT IN A BATH IN IHIO.
Album: released on Sparkling New Dimensional, Nov'86

Slutz

NOVA THE NERVO.
Single (7"): released on Sky-Hi, Mar'82 Dist: Pinnacle

Sly

ANTHOLOGY (Sly and The Family Stone).
Tracks: / Dance to the music / M'lady / Life / Fun / Sing a simple song / Everyday people / Stand / I want to take you higher / Don't call me nigger, whitey / You can make it if you try / Hot fun in the summertime / Thank you (Falettinme be mice elf agin) / Everybody is a star / Family affair / Runnin' away / You caught me smilin' / Thank you for talking to me Africa / Babies makin' babies / If you want me to stay / Que sera sera (whatever will be, will be).
Album: released on Epic, Sep'87 by CBS Records. Dist: CBS

Cassette: released on Epic, Sep'87 by CBS Records. Dist: CBS

BLACK ASH DUB (Sly And The Revolutionaries).
Album: released on Trojan, '83 by Trojan Records. Dist: PRT, Jetstar

Sly and The Family Stone

AIN'T BUT THE ONE WAY.
Album: released on WEA (Import), Mar'83

DANCE TO THE MUSIC (7").
Single (7"): released on Old Gold, Jul'82 by Old Gold Records. Dist: Lightning, Jazz Music, Spartan, Counterpoint

FREE.
Album: released on Edsel, May'87 by Demon Records. Dist: Pinnacle, Jazz Music, Projection

Cassette: released on Edsel, May'87 by Demon Records. Dist: Pinnacle, Jazz Music, Projection

FRESH.
Notes: Reissue of the 1973 Epic/CBS album, which features the no.12 american hit single'If You Want Me To Stay'.San Francisco Funk/Rock Band,featuring Sly Stone,Freddie Stone,Rosie Stone and Larry Graham.
Album: released on Edsel, Jun'87 by Demon Records. Dist: Pinnacle, Jazz Music, Projection

Cassette: released on Edsel, Jun'87 by Demon Records. Dist: Pinnacle, Jazz Music, Projection

Compact disc: released on Edsel, Aug'87 by Demon Records. Dist: Pinnacle, Jazz Music, Projection

GREATEST HITS.
Album: released on Epic, Mar'81 by CBS Records. Dist: CBS

Cassette: released on Epic, Mar'81 by CBS Records. Dist: CBS

Sly Flack

DELINQUENT FUNK.
Single (7"): released on Ecstasy, Nov'84 by Creole Records. Dist: CBS

Single (12"): released on Ecstasy, Nov'84 by Creole Records. Dist: CBS

Sly Fox

IF PUSH COMES TO SHOVE.
Tracks: / If push comes to shove / Stay true.
Single (7"): released on Capitol, Aug'86 by Capitol Records. Dist: EMI

LET'S GO ALL THE WAY.
Tracks: / Let's go all the way / Don't play with fire / I still remember / Won't let you go / Como tu te llama? / Stay true / If push comes to a shove / Merry go round / Let's go all the way / Come to Te Llama (what is your name).
Notes: Produced by Ted Currier for Platinum Productions, Inc. Co-produced by David Spradley for Platinum Vibe Productions Inc.
Album: released on Capitol, Jun'86 by Capitol Records. Dist: EMI

Cassette: released on Capitol, Jun'86 by Capitol Records. Dist: EMI

Single (7"): released on Capitol, Apr'86 by Capitol Records. Dist: EMI

LET'S GO ALL THE WAY(12").
Tracks: / Let's go all the way / Como to te llama?(what is your name?).
Single (12"): released on Capitol, Jun'86 by Capitol Records. Dist: EMI

Single (12"): released on Capitol, Apr'86 by Capitol Records. Dist: EMI

Sly & Robbie

BOOPS (HERE TO GO).
Tracks: / Boops (here to go) / Don't stop the music.
Single (12"): released on Fourth & Broadway, Apr'87 by Island Records. Dist: Polygram, EMI

Single (12"): released on Fourth & Broadway, Mar'87 by Island Records. Dist: Polygram, EMI

Single (7"): released on Fourth & Broadway, Mar'87 by Island Records. Dist: Polygram, EMI

CLUB PLAYS Various artists (Sly & Robbie with various artists).
Album: released on Taxi, Aug'86 by Taxi Records. Dist: Jetstar Distribution

DON'T STOP THE MUSIC.
Single (7"): released on Island, Dec'81 by Is-

land Records. Dist: Polygram

Single (12"): released on Island, Dec'81 by Island Records. Dist: Polygram

DUB EXTRAVAGANZA.
Album: released on CSA, Feb'84 by CSA Records. Dist: PRT, Jetstar

Cassette: released on CSA, Aug'85 by CSA Records. Dist: PRT, Jetstar

Compact disc: released on CSA, Aug'87 by CSA Records. Dist: PRT, Jetstar

DUB EXTRAVIGANZA, A.
Tracks: / Mystic mix / His imperial majesty / Weeping willow / Bad girls dub / Tonight is the night / Fire house special / African culture / Crisis dub / Dance dub / Soundman style / Loving tonight / Jah is with you / Chipping dub / Pumping dub / Double trouble / See no evil / Pure is the soul / Rise up / Reggae stylee / Eden dub.
Cassette: released on CSA, Dec'86 by CSA Records. Dist: PRT, Jetstar

FIRE.
Tracks: / Fire / Ticket to ride / Miles.
Single (7"): released on Fourth & Broadway, Jul'87 by Island Records. Dist: Polygram, EMI

Single (12"): released on Fourth & Broadway, Jul'87 by Island Records. Dist: Polygram, EMI

GET TO THIS, GET TO THAT.
Single (7"): released on Island, Jul'85 by Island Records. Dist: Polygram

IATOLA.
Single (7"): released on Taxi, Oct'83 by Island Records. Dist: EMI

INSIDE OUTSIDE.
Single (7"): released on Taxi, Oct'83 by Taxi Records. Dist: Jetstar Distribution

LANGUAGE BARRIER.
Tracks: / Make 'em move / Get to this,get to that / No name on the bullet / Miles(black satin) / Bass & trouble / Language barrier.
Compact disc: released on Island, Dec'85 by Island Records. Dist: Polygram

LANGUAGE BARRIER.
Album: released on Island, Apr'87 by Island Records. Dist: Polygram

Cassette: released on Island, Apr'87 by Island Records. Dist: Polygram

MAKE 'EM MOVE.
Single (7"): released on Island, Nov'85 by Island Records. Dist: Polygram

Single (12"): released on Island, Nov'85 by Island Records. Dist: Polygram

PRESENT TAXI.
Album: released on Island, May'81 by Island Records. Dist: Polygram

Cassette: released on Island, May'81 by Island Records. Dist: Polygram

REGGAE GREATS.
Album: released on Island, Jun'85 by Island Records. Dist: Polygram

Cassette: released on Island, Jun'85 by Island Records. Dist: Polygram

RHYTHM KILLERS.
Album: released on Fourth & Broadway, Apr'87 by Island Records. Dist: Polygram, EMI

Cassette: released on Fourth & Broadway, Apr'87 by Island Records. Dist: Polygram, EMI

RHYTHM KILLERS.
Compact disc: released on Fourth & Broadway, '87 by Island Records. Dist: Polygram, EMI

RIVER NIGGER.
Single (7"): released on Taxi, Oct'83 by Taxi Records. Dist: Jetstar Distribution

SEXUAL HEALING/SEARCH AND DESTROY.
Single (12"): released on Taxi, Dec'82 by Island Records. Dist: EMI

SOUND OF TAXI, VOL.1 Various artists (Sly & Robbie with various artists).
Album: released on Taxi, Aug'86 by Taxi Records. Dist: Jetstar Distribution

SOUND OF TAXI VOL.2 Various artists (Sly & Robbie with various artists).
Album: released on Taxi, Aug'86 by Taxi Records. Dist: Jetstar Distribution

STING, THE.
Album: released on Taxi, Jul'86 by Taxi Records. Dist: Jetstar Distribution

TAXI FARE.
Album: released on Heartbeat, Jul'87 Dist: Revolver, Pinnacle

TRIPLET/WATERBED.
Single (12"): released on Taxi, Dec'83 by Island Records. Dist: EMI

UHURU IN DUB.
Album: released on CSA, Jul'87 by CSA Records. Dist: PRT, Jetstar

Cassette: released on CSA, Jul'87 by CSA Records. Dist: PRT, Jetstar

Sly & The Family Stone

DANCE TO THE MUSIC.
Album: released on Thunderbolt, Apr'87 by Magnum Music Group Ltd. Dist: Magnum Music Group Ltd, PRT Distribution, Spartan Distribution

FRESH.
Album: released on Edsel, Jun'87 by Demon Records. Dist: Pinnacle, Jazz Music, Projection

Cassette: released on Edsel, Jun'87 by Demon Records. Dist: Pinnacle, Jazz Music, Projection

THERE'S A RIOT GOING ON.
Album: released on Edsel, Feb'86 by Demon Records. Dist: Pinnacle, Jazz Music, Projection

Cassette: released on Edsel, Feb'86 by Demon Records. Dist: Pinnacle, Jazz Music, Projection

Slyvian, David

FORBIDDEN COLOURS (Slyvian, David and Riuichi Sakamoto).
Single (7"): released on Virgin, Jun'83 by Virgin Records. Dist: EMI, Virgin Distribution

Single (12"): released on Virgin, Jun'83 by Virgin Records. Dist: EMI, Virgin Distribution

Smack

LIVE DESIRE.
Album: released on High Dragon, Jul'87 Dist: Pinnacle

LOVERS CONCERTO/DEEP BREATHING.
Single (7"): released on Jive, Jun'82 by Zomba Records. Dist: RCA, PRT, CBS

Single (12"): released on Jive, Jun'82 by Zomba Records. Dist: RCA, PRT, CBS

Smackee

PARTY LIGHTS.
Album: released on Tank, Jun'79 by Tank Records.

Smack my crack

SMACK MY CRACK (Various Artists).
Compact disc: released on Homestead, Jun'87 Dist: Rough Trade, Cartel, Shigaku

Album: released on Homestead, Jun'87 Dist: Rough Trade, Cartel, Shigaku

Cassette: released on Homestead, Jun'87 Dist: Rough Trade, Cartel, Shigaku

Small Ads

FRIDAY NITE COWBOY.
Single (7"): released on Bronze, Nov'81 by Polygram Records. Dist: Polydor

Small Assassin

SMALL ASSASSIN, THE By Ray Bradbury (Bradbury, Ray).
Cassette: released on Caedmon(USA), '82 by Caedmon (USA) Records. Dist: Gower, Taylors, Discovery

Small Chimes

EYES OF CHRISTMAS/SANTA.
Single (7"): released on Cavendish, Dec'83 Dist: Cavendish Music, ILA

Small Faces

ALL OR NOTHING.
Single (7"): released on Decca, Aug'66 by Decca Records. Dist: Polygram

ALL OR NOTHING/MY MINDS EYE.
Single (7"): released on Old Gold, Oct'83 by Old Gold Records. Dist: Lightning, Jazz Music, Spartan, Counterpoint

AUTUMN STONE.
Tracks: / Here comes the nice / Autumn Stone, The / Collibosher / All or nothing / Red balloon / Lazy sunday / Call it something nice / I can't make it / After glow or your love / Sha la la la lee / Universal (The) / Rollin' over / If I were a carpenter / Every little bit hurts / My mind's eye / Tin soldier / Just passing / Itchycoo park / Hey girl / Wide eyed girl on the wall / Whacha gonna do about it / Wam bam thank you mam.
Compact disc: released on Castle, Nov'86 by Castle Records. Dist: Pinnacle

Album: released on Castle, May'86 by Castle Records. Dist: Pinnacle

Cassette: released on Castle, May'86 by Castle Records. Dist: Pinnacle

AUTUMN STONE.
Album: released on Immediate, Jul'84 by Castle Communications. Dist: Cartel

BIG HITS.
Album: released on Virgin, Jul'80 by Virgin Records. Dist: EMI, Virgin Distribution

Cassette: released on Virgin, Jul'80 by Virgin Records. Dist: EMI, Virgin Distribution

COLLECTION: SMALL FACES.
Tracks: / Lazy Sunday / Rollin' over / If I were a carpenter / Every little bit hurts / All or nothing / Itchycoo Park / My minds eye / Sha la la la lee / Watcha gonna do about it / Afterglow / Here comes the nice / I feel much better / Don't burst my bubble / Autumn stone / Universal,The / Tin soldier / Hey girl / Tell me have you seen me / I can't make it.
Album: released on Castle Communications, Nov'85 by Castle Communications. Dist: Cartel, Pinnacle, Counterpoint

Cassette: released on Castle Communications, Nov'85 by Castle Communications. Dist: Cartel, Pinnacle, Counterpoint

FOR YOUR DELIGHT, THE DARLINGS OF....
Album: released on Virgin, Oct'80 by Virgin Records. Dist: EMI, Virgin Distribution

FROM THE BEGINNING.
Album: released on Decca, Aug'84 by Decca Records. Dist: Polygram

Cassette: released on Decca, Aug'84 by Decca Records. Dist: Polygram

GOLDEN HITS: SMALL FACES.
Album: released on Astan, Nov'84 by Astan Records. Dist: Counterpoint

Cassette: released on Astan, Nov'84 by Astan Records. Dist: Counterpoint

ITCHYCOO PARK.
Tracks: / Itchycoo Park / Lazy Sunday / Sha la la la lee / Here comes the nice.
Notes: Limited edition 12" single. All tracks licensed from Interworld Communications.
Single (12"): released on Archive 4, Aug'86 by Castle Communications Records. Dist: Nine Mile, Cartel

ITCHYCOO PARK.
Single (7"): released on Lightning, '80 by Lightning Records. Dist: Jetstar

ITCHYCOO PARK/HERE COMES THE NICE.
Single (7"): released on Old Gold, Jan'85 by Old Gold Records. Dist: Lightning, Jazz Music, Spartan, Counterpoint

LAZY SUNDAY.
Single (7"): released on Old Gold, Jan'85 by Old Gold Records. Dist: Lightning, Jazz Music, Spartan, Counterpoint

LAZY SUNDAY/AUTUMN STONE.
Single (7"): released on Immediate, Sep'81 by Castle Communications. Dist: Cartel

LAZY SUNDAY/ROLLIN' OVER.
Single (7"): released on Immediate, Oct'82 by Castle Communications. Dist: Cartel

LONDON BOYS (Small Faces/Byrds/David Bowie/Dobie Gray).
Single (7"): released on Decca, Sep'79 by Decca Records. Dist: Polygram

OGDEN'S NUT GONE FLAKE.
Album: released on Immediate, Mar'80 by Castle Communications. Dist: Cartel

OGDEN'S NUT GONE...FLAKE.
Tracks: / Ogden's nut gone flake / After glow / Long agos and worlds apart / Rene / Son of a baker / Lazy Sunday / Happiness Stan / Rollin' over / Hungry intruder, The / Journey, The / Mad John / Happy days toy town.
Compact disc: released on Immediate, Oct'86 by Castle Communications. Dist: Cartel

Album: released on Castle, Sep'86 by Castle Records. Dist: Pinnacle

Cassette: released on Castle, Sep'86 by Castle Records. Dist: Pinnacle

Compact disc: released on Castle Classics, '86 by Castle Communications. Dist: BMG

OGDEN'S NUT GONE FLAKE (IMPORT).
Album: released on Line (West Germany), Feb'84

QUITE NATURALLY.
Tracks: / Rollin' over / Song of a baker / I feel much better / Talk to you / Tin soldier / Autumn stone / Become like you / I can't make it / Donkey rides,a penny,a glass / Rene / I'm only dreaming / Hungry intruder, The / Red balloon / Just passing.
Notes: All tracks licensed from Interworld Communications. Album compiled by:Frank Neilson.Design: Terry Rawlings,Jon Cooke. Matrix number: 5 013428 111451
Album: released on Showcase, Sep'86 Dist: Counterpoint

Cassette: released on Showcase, Sep'86 Dist: Counterpoint

ROCK ROOTS.
Album: released on Decca, Jun'77 by Decca Records. Dist: Polygram

SHA LA LA LA LEE.
Album: released on Decca, Mar'81 by Decca Records. Dist: Polygram

Cassette: released on Decca, Mar'81 by Decca Records. Dist: Polygram

SHA LA LA LA LEE/ALL OR NOTHING.
Single (7"): released on Decca-Originals, Mar'82 by Decca Records. Dist: Polygram, IMS

SHA LA LA LA LEE/WHATCHA GONNA DO ABOUT IT.
Single (7"): released on Old Gold, Oct'83 by Old Gold Records. Dist: Lightning, Jazz Music, Spartan, Counterpoint

SMALL FACES.
Album: released on Decca, '66 by Decca Records. Dist: Polygram

SMALL FACES (GERMAN IMPORT).
Album: released on Line (West Germany) Feb'84

SMALL FACES GREATEST HITS.
Album: released on Immediate, Jan'78 by Castle Communications. Dist: Cartel

Cassette: released on Immediate, Jan'78 by Castle Communications. Dist: Cartel

SMALL FACES, THE.
Album: released on New World, May'80 b President Records. Dist: Swift, Spartan

SORRY SHE'S MINE.
Album: released on Platinum (W.Germany) Oct'85 Dist: Mainline

Cassette: released on Platinum (W.Germany Oct'85 Dist: Mainline

Small, Fred

HEART OF THE APPALOOSA.
Album: released on Rounder (USA), Jan'8 Dist: Mike's Country Music Room Distributio Jazz Music Distribution, Swift Distributio Roots Records Distribution, Projection Distrib. tion, Topic Distribution

NO LIMIT.
Album: released on Rounder (USA), Sep' Dist: Mike's Country Music Room Distributio Jazz Music Distribution, Swift Distributio Roots Records Distribution, Projection Distrib tion, Topic Distribution

Small, Freddie

MEDLEY REGGAE COLLECTIO (PART 2).
Album: released on Pioneer Internation Jun'85 by Pioneer International Records. D Jetstar

Small Hits...

SMALL HITS FROM NEAR MISS (Various Artists).
Album: released on Inevitable, Jul'84 by Ine able Records. Dist: Rough Trade

Cassette: released on Inevitable, Jul'84 by I vitable Records. Dist: Rough Trade

Small In A Big Way

KATIE'S LIPS.
Single (7"): released on Bedlam, Apr'84 D Pinnacle

Smalling, Milton

FIGHTING SPIRIT.
Single (12"): released on CSA, Jul'85 by C Records. Dist: PRT, Jetstar

Small Label Gems

SMALL LABEL GEMS OF THE FORT VOL.1 (Various Artists).
Album: released on Solid Sender, Apr'81 JSU, Jazz Music

SMALL LABEL GEMS OF THE FORT VOL.2 (Various Artists).
Album: released on Solid Sender, Apr'81 JSU, Jazz Music

SMALL LABEL GEMS OF THE FORT VOL.3 (Vakeros, The).
Album: released on Solid Sender, Apr'81 JSU, Jazz Music

Small Labels

SMALL LABELS 1927-1935, THE Various artists (Various Artists).
Notes: Artists include: Chicago redheads/Chick Bullock etc.
Album: released on Collectors Items, Jul'86 Dist: Jazz Music, Swift, Chris Wellard

Smalltown Elephants

WALKING ON ICE.
Tracks: / Walking on ice / Walking on ice (Ext.) / All for you / Inside out.
Single (7"): released on Polydor, Jul'87 by Polydor Records. Dist: Polygram, Polydor

Single (12"): released on Polydor, Jul'87 by Polydor Records. Dist: Polygram, Polydor

Small Woman

SMALL WOMAN (BY ALAN BURGESS)
Filmed as: Inn of the sixth happiness (Bergman, Ingrid).
Cassette: released on Argo (Spokenword), Jul'82 by Decca Records. Dist: Polygram

Small World

LOVE IS DEAD.
Single (7"): released on Whamm, May'82 Dist: Pinnacle

Smart

SMART Various artists (Various Artists).
Album: released on Kent, Mar'86 by Ace Records. Dist: Pinnacle

THIS TIME/MR RIGHT.
Single (7"): released on Complex(R.A.P.), Oct'82 Dist: Complex (R.A.P.), Red Rhino, Cartel

Smart, Charles

ORGAN & CHIMES CHRISTMAS ALBUM (Smart, Charles & James Blades).
Album: released on Eclipse, '70 by Decca Records. Dist: Polygram

Smart, Leroy

BACK TO BACK (see Reid,Junior/Leroy Smart) (Smart, Leroy/Junior Reid).

BANK ACCOUNT.
Album: released on Power House, Nov'85 by Power House Records. Dist: Jetstar

DON, THE.
Single (12"): released on Kaya, Aug'85 by Kaya Records. Dist: Jetstar

DREAD HOT IN AFRICA.
Album: released on Burning Sounds, May'78 by Ross, Bill/Burning Sounds Records. Dist: PRT

GIRL YOU A FRAUD.
Single (7"): released on Bromac, Nov'84 Dist: Jetstar

GIVE ME LOVING.
Single (12"): released on Blue Trac, Oct'84 by Blue Mountain Records. Dist: Jetstar

IMPRESSIONS OF LEROY SMART.
Album: released on Burning Sounds, '78 by Ross, Bill/Burning Sounds Records. Dist: PRT

JAH LOVES EVERYONE.
Album: released on Burning Sounds, '78 by Ross, Bill/Burning Sounds Records. Dist: PRT

LEROY SMART - SUPERSTAR.
Album: released on Third World, Jun'77 Dist: Jetstar Distribution

LIT OFF SUP'M.
Tracks: / Jack Slick.
Single (12"): released on Live & Love, Dec'86 by Third World Records. Dist: Jetstar

LIVE UP ROOTS CHILDREN.
Album: released on Striker Lee, Jul'85 by Striker Lee Records. Dist: Jetstar Distribution

LIVE UP ROOTS CHILDREN (Smart, Leroy & The Rock Studio Posse).
Single (12"): released on Striker Lee, Jun'85 by Striker Lee Records. Dist: Jetstar Distribution

LOVE JAH FOREVER.
Single (12"): released on Get Set Sounds, Jun'83 by Get Set Sounds Records. Dist: Jetstar

LOVE ME TONIGHT.
Single (12"): released on Greensleeves, Aug'87 by Greensleeves Records. Dist: BMG, Jetstar, Spartan

LOVE TONIGHT.
Tracks: / Love tonight / Love tonight (inst).
Single (12"): released on Greensleeves, Jul'87 by Greensleeves Records. Dist: BMG, Jetstar, Spartan

---

Single (12"): released on Greensleeves, Jul'87 by Greensleeves Records. Dist: BMG, Jetstar, Spartan

MAKE THIS LOVE BE TRUE.
Single (7"): released on Ranking Joe, Jun'85 by Ranking Joe Records. Dist: Jetstar

MANKIND IS SO UNJUST.
Single (12"): released on Music Works, Dec'82 Dist: Jetstar Distribution

MONEY IS COMFORT.
Tracks: / Money is comfort / If I give my love.
Single (12"): released on Time One, Jul'86 Dist: Jetstar Distribution

MOTHER LANCHIE.
Single (12"): released on Guidance, Mar'83 Dist: Jetstar

PRETTY LOOKS.
Single (12"): released on Foundation, Dec'83 by Foundation Records, The. Dist: Jetstar

PROPHECY.
Tracks: / Prophecy / Prophecy.
Single (12"): released on Techniques, Oct'86 Dist: Jetstar Distribution

SET IT.
Tracks: / Set it.
Single (12"): released on Java, Mar'86 Dist: Jetstar

SHE JUST A DRAW CARD.
Album: released on World Wide Success, Mar'85 by World Wide Success Records. Dist: Jetstar

Single (12"): released on Tads, Jul'84 by Tads Records. Dist: Jetstar Distribution

SHE LOVE IT IN THE MORNING.
Album: released on GG'S, May'84 by GG'S Records. Dist: Jetstar

SHOWCASE.
Album: released on Fatman Studio, Jan'85 by Fatman Studio Records. Dist: Jetstar

SOUL AND INSPIRATION.
Single (12"): released on Londisc, Jun'84 by Londisc Records.

SWEET LADY.
Single (12"): released on Music Works, Aug'82 Dist: Jetstar Distribution

TALK OF THE TOWN.
Tracks: / Talk of dub.
Single (12"): released on Revue, Dec'86 by Revue Records. Dist: Creole

TEMPTATIONS.
Album: released on Crystal, Nov'85 by Crystal Records. Dist: Jetstar, Revolver, Cartel

THIS IS THE TIME.
Single 10": released on Reggae, Oct'82 by Reggae Records. Dist: Jetstar, Morpheus Distribution

TURN OFF THE LIGHTS.
Single (12"): released on Time, Aug'85 Dist: Jetstar Distribution

WE RULE.
Single (12"): released on Unity Sound, Jun'85 Dist: Jetstar

...WITH ROOTS RADIX & FRIENDS.
Album: released on Vista Sounds, '83 by Vista Sounds Records. Dist: Jetstar

Smashed Gladys

17 GOIN' ON CRAZY.
Single (7"): released on FM, Oct'85 by FM-Revolver Records. Dist: EMI

SMASHED GLADYS.
Album: released on Heavy Metal America, Nov'85 by FM-Revolver Records. Dist: EMI

Cassette: released on Heavy Metal America, Nov'85 by FM-Revolver Records. Dist: EMI

Smash Hits

SMASH HITS - VOL.3 Various artists (Various Artists).
Album: released on Aim (Budget Cassettes), Feb'83

Smashing all stars

SMASHING ALL STARS Various artists (Various Artists).
Notes: Including Don Carlos, Mighty Diamonds etc.
Album: released on CSA, Jul'86 by CSA Records. Dist: PRT, Jetstar

Smashing Time

SMASHING TIME (A countdown compilation) (Various Artists).
Album: released on Re-Elect The President,

Jan'87 Dist: Backs, Cartel

Smash Palace

LIVING ON THE BORDER LINE.
Tracks: / Living on the border line / Night of a thousand faces.
Single (7"): released on Epic, Feb'86 by CBS Records. Dist: CBS

SMASH PALACE.
Tracks: / Living on the borderline / Count the days / Love will find a way / Never say no again / Juliet to me / No love lost / Night to remember, A / Pieces of my heart / Night of a thousand faces.
Album: released on Epic, Apr'86 by CBS Records. Dist: CBS

Cassette: released on Epic, Apr'86 by CBS Records. Dist: CBS

Smeck, Roy

PLAYS HAWAIIAN GUITAR ETC.
Album: released on Yazoo, Mar'77 Dist: Swift, Projection

Smersh

PART OF THE ANIMAL THAT PEOPLE DON'T LIKE, THE.
Album: released on Deadman's Curve, Nov'86 by Dave Henderson.

Smike

SMIKE Original cast recording.
Double Album: released on Smike, Sep'83 by Smike Records. Dist: Pinnacle

Double cassette: released on Smike, Sep'83 by Smike Records. Dist: Pinnacle

SMIKE Various artists (Various Artists).
Album: released on Flashback, Nov'85 by PRT Records. Dist: PRT

Cassette: released on Flashback, Nov'85 by PRT Records. Dist: PRT

Smile Child

SINGLE WILD.
Single (7"): released on Butt, Feb'82 by Butt Records. Dist: Counterpoint

Smiles, Kenny

MAGIC.
Album: released on Black Mountain, Dec'79 by Black Mountain Records.

Smiley, Billy

NEW NIGHT.
Album: released on Meadowlark, Jan'87 by Sparrow Records. Dist: Word Distribution

Cassette: released on Meadowlark, Jan'87 by Sparrow Records. Dist: Word Distribution

Smiley Culture

ORIGINAL SMILEY CULTURE, THE.
Album: released on Top Notch, Dec'86

SCHOOL TIME CHRONICLE.
Tracks: / School time chronicle / So what.
Single (7"): released on Polydor, Aug'86 by Polydor Records. Dist: Polygram, Polydor

Single (12"): released on Polydor, Aug'86 by Polydor Records. Dist: Polygram, Polydor

Smiley, Red

TAKE A RIDE.
Single (7"): released on Jin, Oct'79 by Priority Records. Dist: EMI

Smiley's People

SMILEY'S PEOPLE (Carre, John Le).
Double cassette: released on Listen For Pleasure, Oct'82 by MFP Records. Dist: EMI

SMILEY'S PEOPLE Music from the television soundtrack.
Album: released on BBC, Sep'82 by BBC Records & Tapes. Dist: EMI, PRT, Pye

Cassette: released on BBC, Sep'82 by BBC Records & Tapes. Dist: EMI, PRT, Pye

Smith

HERE COME'S MY BABY.
Single (7"): released on Ram, Nov'81 by Ram. Dist: Greensleeves Records, RCA

Smith, Arthur

GUITAR BOOGIE.
Single (7"): released on USA Import, '80

Smith, Arthur "Guitar" and

ARTHUR "GUITAR" SMITH AND VOICES.
Album: released on Stetson, Oct'86 by Hasmick Promotions Ltd.. Dist: Counterpoint Dis-

---

tribution, H.R. Taylor Distribution, Swift Distribution, Chris Wellard Distribution

Cassette: released on Stetson, Oct'86 by Hasmick Promotions Ltd.. Dist: Counterpoint Distribution, H.R. Taylor Distribution, Swift Distribution, Chris Wellard Distribution

MISTER GUITAR.
Album: released on Starday, Apr'87

Cassette: released on Starday, Apr'87

Smith Band, Richard

PREMIUM BLUES.
Album: released on Blue Swan, Jan'87 Dist: Cartel

Smith, Bessie

ANY WOMAN'S BLUES.
Double cassette: released on CBS, '74 by CBS Records. Dist: CBS

BESSIE SMITH COLLECTION, THE.
Album: released on Deja Vu, Aug'85 by Deja Vu Records. Dist: Counterpoint Distribution, Record Services Distribution (Ireland)

Cassette: released on Deja Vu, Aug'85 by Deja Vu Records. Dist: Counterpoint Distribution, Record Services Distribution (Ireland)

CLASSICS - VOL.3 - 1928/31.
Cassette: released on Neovox, Aug'81 by Neovox Records. Dist: VJM Records, Jazz Music, JSU, Chris Wellard

EMPRESS, THE.
Tracks: / Sing, sing prison blues / Follow the deal on down / Sinful blues / Woman's trouble blues / Love me daddy blues / Dying gambler's blues / St.Louis blues / Reckless blues / Sobbin' hearted blues / Cold in hand blues / You've been a good ole wagon / Cake walkin' babies / Yellow dog blues, The / Soft pedal blues / Dixie flyers blues / Nashville woman's blues / Muddy water / There'll be a hot time in the old town tonight / Trombone cholly / Send me to the 'lectric chair / Them's graveyard words / Hot springs blues / Lock and key / Mean old bedbug blues / Good man is hard to find, A / Homeless blues / Looking for my man blues / Dyin' by the hour / Foolish man blues / Thinking blues / Pickpocket blues.
Double Album: released on Avan-Guard (Australia), Sep'86 by Avan-Guard Records (Australia). Dist: Conifer, Discovery

JAZZ CLASSICS IN DIGITAL STEREO.
Tracks: / Empty bed blues / Alexander's Ragtime Band / Preachin' the blues / Keep it to yourself / Trombone Cholly / At the Christmas Ball / Kitchen man / You've got to give me some / He's got me goin' / Devil's gonna git you / Send me to the 'lectric chair / Baby doll / Take me for a buggy ride / Young woman's blues.
Notes: Features Bessie with such jazz giants as Coleman Hawkins,James P. Johnson, Charlie Green,Joe Smith,Fletcher Henderson And Jack Teagarden
Album: released on BBC, Sep'87 by BBC Records & Tapes. Dist: EMI, PRT, Pye

Cassette: released on BBC, Sep'86 by BBC Records & Tapes. Dist: EMI, PRT, Pye

Compact disc: released on BBC, Sep'86 by BBC Records & Tapes. Dist: EMI, PRT, Pye

NOBODY'S BLUES BUT MINE.
Double cassette: released on CBS, '79 by CBS Records. Dist: CBS

SAINT LOUIS BLUES (Smith, Bessie/Billie Holiday/Trixie Smith).
Album: released on Jazz Live, Oct'86

ST.LOUIS BLUES (Smith, Bessie & Various artists).
Album: released on Jazz Live, Apr'81

WHOLE ST. LOUIS BLUES SOUNDTRACK.
Album: released on Jazz Live, Apr'81

WORLDS GREATEST BLUES SINGER.
Double Album: by CBS Records. Dist: CBS

Smith, Bill

CONVERSATION PIECES (Smith, Bill/Stuart Broomer).
Album: released on Onari (Canada), Jan'87 Dist: Jazz Music Distribution, Jazz Horizons Distribution

Album: released on Onari, Apr'81

PICK A NUMBER.
Album: released on Onari, Apr'81

Smith, Bryan

AN INVITATION TO BRYAN SMITH'S PARTY.
Album: released on Dansan, Nov'79 by Spartan Records. Dist: Spartan

AT THE ROYAL ALBERT HALL.
Album: released on Dansan, Apr'78 by Spartan Records. Dist: Spartan

Cassette: released on Dansan, Apr'78 by Spartan Records. Dist: Spartan

BACK IN YOUR OWN BACKYARD.
Album: released on Dansan, Jul'79 by Spartan Records. Dist: Spartan

Cassette: released on Dansan, Jul'79 by Spartan Records. Dist: Spartan

BANJO TIME (Smith, Bryan & The Boys).
Album: released on Dansan, Apr'82 by Spartan Records. Dist: Spartan

CLASSICALLY YOURS.
Album: released on Dansan, Oct'80 by Spartan Records. Dist: Spartan

COUNTRY AND WESTERN.
Album: released on Dansan, Jul'81 by Spartan Records. Dist: Spartan

Cassette: released on Dansan, Jul'81 by Spartan Records. Dist: Spartan

DANCING FOR PLEASURE (Smith, Bryan & His Festival Orchestra).
Album: released on Music for Pleasure, Jun'85 by EMI Records. Dist: MFP Distribution

Cassette: released on Music for Pleasure, Jun'85 by EMI Records. Dist: MFP Distribution

ENTERTAINER, THE.
Album: released on Savoy, Sep'86

EVERYBODY DANCE.
Album: released on Dansan, Jun'78 by Spartan Records. Dist: Spartan

GOES TO TOWN.
Album: released on Dansan, May'83 by Spartan Records. Dist: Spartan

HAPPY PIANO OF BRYAN SMITH IN SEQUENCE TIME , THE.
Album: released on Dansan, Aug'78 by Spartan Records. Dist: Spartan

HAWAIIAN PARADISE.
Album: released on Dansan, Jul'80 by Spartan Records. Dist: Spartan

Cassette: released on Dansan, Jul'80 by Spartan Records. Dist: Spartan

IN SEQUENCE.
Album: released on Dansan, '74 by Spartan Records. Dist: Spartan

Cassette: released on Dansan, '74 by Spartan Records. Dist: Spartan

LET'S BE HAPPY (Smith, Bryan And Riverboat Band).
Album: released on Dansan, Mar'83 by Spartan Records. Dist: Spartan

MUSIC MUSIC MUSIC (Smith, Bryan & His Happy Band).
Album: released on Dansan, Dec'83 by Spartan Records. Dist: Spartan

PLAY IT AGAIN SAM.
Album: released on Dansan, Sep'81 by Spartan Records. Dist: Spartan

RIVERBOAT SHUFFLE.
Album: released on Dansan, Apr'81 by Spartan Records. Dist: Spartan

Cassette: released on Dansan, Apr'81 by Spartan Records. Dist: Spartan

ROBIN'S RETURN (Smith, Bryan & His Piano).
Album: released on BS Production, Jul'87

SEQUENCE TIME AT THE RADIO 2 BALLROOM VOLUME 2 (Smith, Bryan & His Festival Orchestra).
Album: released on BBC, Sep'78 by BBC Records & Tapes. Dist: EMI, PRT, Pye

Cassette: released on BBC, Sep'78 by BBC Records & Tapes. Dist: EMI, PRT. Pve

SEQUENCE TIME AT THE RADIO 2 BALLROOM VOLUME 3 (Smith, Bryan & His Festival Orchestra).
Album: released on BBC, Jun'79 by BBC Records & Tapes. Dist: EMI, PRT, Pye

Cassette: released on BBC, Jun'79 by BBC Records & Tapes. Dist: EMI, PRT, Pve

SEQUENCE TIME AT THE RADIO 2 BALLROOM (Smith, Bryan & His Festival Orchestra).
Album: released on BBC, '79 by BBC Records & Tapes. Dist: EMI, PRT, Pye

Cassette: released on BBC, '79 by BBC Records & Tapes. Dist: EMI, PRT, Pye

Page 928

TWO'S COMPANY.
Album: released on Dansan, Jul'80 by Spartan Records. Dist: Spartan

YOUR RADIO REQUESTS (Smith, Bryan & His Festival Orchestra).
Album: released on Dansan, Jun'82 by Spartan Records. Dist: Spartan

Smith, Byther
TELL ME HOW YOU LIKE IT.
Album: released on Red Lightnin', Nov'85 by Red Lightnin' Records. Dist: Roots, Swift, Jazz Music, JSU, Pinnacle, Cartel, Wynd-Up Distribution

Smith, Carl
CARL SMITH'S GREATEST HITS VOL 1.
Album: released on Gusto (USA), '80 by Gusto Records (USA). Dist: Crusader

Smith, Carlton
EXCITE ME.
Tracks: / Excite me.
Single (7"): released on Citybeat, Oct'86 Dist: WEA

Single (12"): released on Citybeat, Oct'86 Dist: WEA

Smith, Charles
TESTIFYIN' (Smith,Charles/Chuck Armstrong/Ted Ford).
Tracks: / My great loss (Ashes to ashes) / Glad to be gone / I'm useless / Why can't I cry / Only time you say you love me (The) / Stand up and take it like a man / Pull me out of the water / Two pillows / Why does it hurt so bad / How sweet it is / I'm gonna forget about you / Keep your mind on me / She's gonna come back / Pretty girls everywhere / Please give me another chance / You're gonna need me.
Notes: Original sound recordings made by Sound Stage 7/77 Records.
Album: released on Charly, Mar'87 by Charly Records. Dist: Charly, Cadillac

Smith, Charlie Boy
WASSIT GOTTA DEW WI YEW.
Album: released on Sweet Folk All, May'81 by Sweet Folk All Records. Dist: Sweet Folk All, Roots, Celtic Music, Dragon, Impetus, Projection, Chris Wellard, Festival Records

WEDDING OF THE YEAR (Smith, Chris C).
Single (7"): released on Cool King, Jul'81 Dist: Pinnacle

Smith, Clara
CLARA SMITH VOL.1 (1923).
Album: released on Vintage Jazz Music Society (VJM), '74 by Vintage Jazz Music Society (VJM) Records. Dist: Vintage Jazz Music Society (VJM), Jazz Music, VJM, Swift, Conifer, H.R. Taylor, Chris Wellard

CLARA SMITH VOL.2 (1923-24).
Album: released on Vintage Jazz Music Society (VJM), '74 by Vintage Jazz Music Society (VJM) Records. Dist: Vintage Jazz Music Society (VJM), Jazz Music, VJM, Swift, Conifer, H.R. Taylor, Chris Wellard

CLARA SMITH VOL.3 (1924).
Album: released on Vintage Jazz Music Society (VJM), '74 by Vintage Jazz Music Society (VJM) Records. Dist: Vintage Jazz Music Society (VJM), Jazz Music, VJM, Swift, Conifer, H.R. Taylor, Chris Wellard

Smith, Clarence Pinetop
COMPILATION 1928-29-30.
Album: released on Oldie Blues Holland, Apr'86

Smith, Connie
TWENTY OF THE BEST.
Album: released on RCA International (USA), Apr'85 by RCA Records. Dist: RCA

Cassette: released on RCA International (USA), Apr'85 by RCA Records. Dist: RCA

Smith, Dave
OUT OF THIS WORLD.
Album: released on Grosvenor, Feb'82 by Grosvenor Records. Dist: Taylors

WAITING FOR THE CHASE.
Album: released on Rubber, May'83 by Rubber Records. Dist: Roots Distribution, Projection Distribution, Jazz Music Distribution, Celtic Music Distribution, JSU Distribution, Spartan Distribution

Smith, Derek Trio
DARK EYES.
Album: released on East Wind, Apr'85 by East Wind Records. Dist: PRT

LOVE FOR SALE.

Album: released on Progressive, Apr'81 by Progressive Records. Dist: Jetstar

MAN I LOVE, THE.
Album: released on Progressive, Apr'81 by Progressive Records. Dist: Jetstar

PLAYS THE MUSIC OF JEROME KERN.
Album: released on Progressive, '81 by Progressive Records. Dist: Jetstar

Smith, Dick, Band
WAY OF THE WORLD.
Single (7"): released on Hologram, Jan'81 by Aardvark. Dist: Wynd-Up Distribution

Smith, Dick King
SHHEP-PIG, THE.
Notes: Read by: Stephen Thorne. 2 cassettes-1 hour 50 minutes. Cover to Cover Cassettes, Dene House, Lockeridge, Marlborough, Wiltshire. Telephone 067-286-495.
Special: released on Cover to Cover, Sep'86 by Cover to Cover Cassettes. Dist: Conifer

Smith, Donovan
MR. WALKER.
Single (12"): released on Love Linch, Feb'82 Dist: Jetstar

Smithereens
ESPECIALLY FOR YOU.
Album: released on Enigma (Europe), Nov'86 by Enigma Records. Dist: Rough Trade, Cartel, EMI

ESPECIALLY FOR YOU.
Compact disc: released on Enigma, Mar'87 by Enigma Records. Dist: Rough Trade, Cartel, EMI

IN A LONELY PLACE.
Tracks: / Beauty and sadness / Blood and roses / Mr. Eliminator.
Notes: Extra tracks on 12" only
Single (7"): released on Enigma, Feb'87 by Enigma Records. Dist: Rough Trade, Cartel, EMI

IN A LONELY PLACE.
Single (12"): released on Enigma, Feb'87 by Enigma Records. Dist: Rough Trade, Cartel, EMI

IN A LONELY PLACE (Smithereens With Suzanne Vega).
Single (7"): released on Enigma, Dec'86 by Enigma Records. Dist: Rough Trade, Cartel, EMI

STRANGERS WHEN WE MEET.
Single (7"): released on Enigma, Aug'87 by Enigma Records. Dist: Rough Trade, Cartel, EMI

STRANGERS WHEN WE MEET.
Single (12"): released on Enigma, Aug'87 by Enigma Records. Dist: Rough Trade, Cartel, EMI

(YOU IS)A GUARANTEE OF LOVE.
Single (7"): released on MCA, Aug'87 by MCA Records. Dist: Polygram, MCA

(YOU IS)A GUARANTEE OF LOVE.
Tracks: / (You is)A guarantee for love / Promiscuous / Ask / Cemetary gates.
Single (7"): released on WEA Int, '86

Smith, Ernie
BEND DOWN LOW.
Single (7"): released on KR, Sep'81 by KR Recordings Ltd. Dist: RCA, Revolver, Cartel

BEND DOWN LOW.
Single (12"): released on KR, Sep'81 by KR Recordings Ltd. Dist: RCA, Revolver, Cartel

MR. SMITH'S CLASSICS.
Album: released on KR, Mar'82 by KR Recordings Ltd. Dist: RCA, Revolver, Cartel

Cassette: released on KR, Mar'82 by KR Recordings Ltd. Dist: RCA, Revolver, Cartel

Smith, Eugene
ROCK BY DAY, ROLL BY NIGHT.
Tracks: / Rock by day, roll by night / Streetwise.
Single (7"): released on Tembo, Jul'86 by Tembo (Canada). Dist: IMS Distribution, Polygram Distribution

Smith, Fenton
BOOM IT UP.
Single (12"): released on Fashion, May'84 by Fashion Records. Dist: PRT, Jetstar

GIRLS.
Single (12"): released on Fashion, Nov'84 by Fashion Records. Dist: PRT, Jetstar

I LOST MY GIRL.
Single (12"): released on Ital, Mar'84 Dist: Pinnacle

INTENTION ARE BIG.
Tracks: / Intention are big / Got to get you baby.
Single (12"): released on Style, Jun'86

REGGAE PARTY.
Single (7"): released on Love Birds, Feb'82 Dist: Jetstar

Single (12"): released on Love Birds, Feb'82 Dist: Jetstar

SUGAR SUGAR.
Tracks: / Can't romp with me.
Single (12"): released on Live, Jan'87 Dist: Jetstar, PRT

WOMAN AS NICE, A.
Album: released on S&G, May'83 by S&G Records. Dist: Jetstar

Single (12"): released on S&G, Mar'83 by S&G Records. Dist: Jetstar

Smith, Frankie
DOUBLE DUTCH BUS.
Single (7"): released on Virgin, Feb'82 by Virgin Records. Dist: EMI, Virgin Distribution

Single (12"): released on Virgin, Feb'82 by Virgin Records. Dist: EMI, Virgin Distribution

Smith, Frederick, E
633 SQUADRON READ BY SIMON WARD.
Cassette: released on Listen For Pleasure, May'84 by MFP Records. Dist: EMI

Smith, G.E.
HEART FROZEN UP.
Single (7"): released on Mirage, Jul'81 Dist: Pinnacle

Smith, George 'Harmonica'
ARKANSAS TRAP.
Album: released on Black Cat, Aug'81 Dist: Projection

BOOGIE'N WITH GEORGE.
Album: released on Murray Brothers (USA), May'84 Dist: Swift Distribution

...OF THE BLUES.
Album: released on Crosscut, Aug'87 Dist: Rollercoaster Distribution, Swift

Smith, Gordon
DOWN ON MEAN STREET.
Album: released on Appaloosa, May'81 Dist: Roots, Folksound, JSU, Projection, Celtic Music, Chris Wellard

LONG OVERDUE.
Album: released on Line (West Germany), Jan'85

TAKIN' TIME.
Album: released on Appaloosa, May'81 Dist: Roots, Folksound, JSU, Projection, Celtic Music, Chris Wellard

Smith, Hal
SMITH'S HAL CREOLE SUNSHINE ORCHESTRA (Smith's Hal Creole Sunshine Orchestra).
Album: released on Stomp Off, Jun'86 by Stomp Off Records. Dist: Jazz Music Distribution

Smith, Hobart
OLD TIMEY RAP, THE A collection of American songs and instrumentals.
Album: released on Topic, '81 Dist: Roots Distribution

Smith, Huey "Piano"
IMPERIAL SIDES 1960/61, THE (Smith, Huey & The Clowns).
Album: released on Pathe Marconi, Sep'84 Dist: Swift

SOMEWHERE THERE'S HONEY FRO THE GRIZZLY (Smith, Huey & The Clowns).
Album: released on Ace, May'84 by Ace Records. Dist: Pinnacle, Swift, Hotshot, Cadillac

'TWAS THE NIGHT BEFORE CHRIST-MAS (Smith, Huey & The Clowns).
Single (7"): released on Ace, Apr'79 by Ace Records. Dist: Pinnacle, Swift, Hotshot, Cadillac

DON'T YOU JUST KNOW IT.
Single (7"): released on Kent, Aug'83 by Ace Records. Dist: Pinnacle

ROCKIN' & JIVIN'.
Album: released on Charly, Nov'81 by Charly Records. Dist: Charly, Cadillac

ROCKIN' PNEUMONIA AND BOOGIE WOOGIE FLU.
Album: released on Ace, Mar'79 by Ace Records. Dist: Pinnacle, Swift, Hotshot, Cadillac

Smith, Hurricane

DON''I LET IT DIE.
Single (7"): released on Old Gold, Oct'83 by Old Gold Records. Dist: Lightning, Jazz Music, Spartan, Counterpoint

Smith, Ian

GOLDEN GRATES (Smith, Ian Is The Vagabond King).
Album: released on Cold Harbour, Jan'87 Dist: Pinnacle, Probe Plus Distribution, Cartel, M.I.S., EMI, DMS, RCA, Ariola

Smith, Jabbo

SWEET 'N' LOW DOWN (Smith, Jabbo & His Rhythm Aces).
Tracks: Black and tan fantasy / Ace of rhythm / Sweet and low blues / Jazz battle / Little willie blues / Sleepy time blues / Take your time / Take me to the river / Let's get together / Sau Sha Stomp / Michigander blues / Decatur Stret tutti / Till times get better / What more can a poor fellow do? / Sweet and low down / Sleepytime blues / Jazz battle / Little willie blues / Take your time / Sau sha stomp / Let's get together / Michigander blues / Decatur street tutti / Till times get better / Ace of rhythm.
Album: released on Affinity, Jul'86 by Charly Records. Dist: Charly, Cadillac

Cassette: released on Affinity, Jul'86 by Charly Records. Dist: Charly, Cadillac

Album: released on Affinity, Aug'86 by Charly Records. Dist: Charly, Cadillac

Smith, Jack

WHISPERING BARITONE.
Album: released on Word, Nov'75 by Word Records. Dist: Word Distribution, CBS

Cassette: released on Word, Nov'75 by Word Records. Dist: Word Distribution, CBS

Smith, Jimmy

BACK AT THE CHICKEN SHACK.
Tracks: Back at the Chicken Shack / When I grow too old to dream / Minor chant / Messy Bessie / On the sunny side of the street.
Compact disc: released on EMI, Mar'87 by EMI Records. Dist: EMI

Cassette: released on Blue Note, Sep'8 / by EMI Records. Dist: EMI. Estim retail price in Sep'87 was £5.99.

BASHIN Unpredictable Jimmy Smith, The (Smith, Jimmy & Big Band).
Tracks: Walk on the wild side / Of man river / In a mellow tone / Step right up / Beggar for the blues / Bashin' / I'm an old cowhand.
Album: released on Verve (USA), May'82 by Polydor. Dist: Polygram

Cassette: released on Verve (USA), May'82 by Polydor. Dist: Polygram

Compact disc: released on Verve (USA), May'82 by Polydor. Dist: Polygram

BIG BAND STYLE.
Tracks: Volare / Goody, goody/Always/Happy days are here again / 9 to 5 / Those were the days/Something stupid / Chanson d'amour/Old fashioned way/Mame / Lulu's back in town/Alexander's rag time band / Red sails in the sunset/Shanty in old shanty town / Silly little song / Out of nowhere/If I had my way / Smoke gets in your eyes/On a slow boat to China / Little on the lonely side, A/I'll get by/We'll meet again / If I should fall in love again/Are you lonesome tonight.
Cassette: released on Sounds Ultimate, Aug'87 Dist: PRT, H.R. Taylor

CAT STRIKES AGAIN.
Compact disc: released on Delta, '86 by Delta Records. Dist: Target

CAT STRIKES AGAIN, THE (Smith, Jimmy & Lalo Schifrin).
Compact disc: released on Delta, Feb'86 by Delta Records. Dist: Target

CAT, THE.
Tracks: Joy house theme / Basin Street blues / Cat, The / Carpetbagger's theme / St.Louis blues / Chicago serenade / Delon's blues / Blues in the night.
Compact disc: released on Verve, '83 by Phonogram Records. Dist: Polygram

COMPACT JAZZ.
Compact disc: released on Verve, Jul'87 by Phonogram Records. Dist: Polygram

CRAZY BABY.
Tracks: When Jonny comes marching home / Makin' whoopee / Night in Tunisia / Sonnymoon for two / Mack the knife / What's new / Alfredo.
Notes: Produced by Alfred Lion.
Album: released on Manhattan, Nov'86 by EMI Records. Dist: EMI

DYNAMIC DUO (Smith, Jimmy & Wes Montgomery).
Tracks: Down by the riverside / Night train / James and Wes / 13 (Death march) / Baby, it's cold outside.
Compact disc: released on Verve, Oct'84 by Phonogram Records. Dist: Polygram

---

GO FOR WATCHA KNOW.
Tracks: Fungi mama / Go for watcha know, (Mama said) / Bass face / She's out of my life / We can make it work / No sustitute.
Compact disc: released on Blue Note, Oct'86 by EMI Records. Dist: EMI

GO FOR WHATCHA KNOW.
Compact disc: released on Manhattan-Blue Note, Sep'87 by EMI America Records (USA). Dist: EMI

HOUSE PARTY.
Cassette: released on Blue Note, Apr'87 by EMI Records. Dist: EMI

Album: released on Blue Note, Apr'87 by EMI Records. Dist: EMI

HOUSEPARTY.
Tracks: J.O.S. / What is this thing called love / Just friends / Cherokee / Blues after all.
Notes: (P) 1987 Manhattan Records, a division of Capitol Records.
Compact disc: released on Manhattan-Blue Note, May'87 by EMI America Records (USA). Dist: EMI

Album: released on Blue Note (USA Import), Jul'85

JUST ORGAN...JUST FOR YOU.
Album: released on Sounds Ultimate, Jun'83 Dist: PRT, H.R. Taylor

LIL' DARLIN'.
Album: released on Sounds Ultimate, Jan'85 Dist: PRT, H.R. Taylor

LOVELY WAY TO SPEND AND EVENING, A.
Album: released on Sounds Ultimate, Sep'81 Dist: PRT, H.R. Taylor

Cassette: released on Sounds Ultimate, Sep'81 Dist: PRT, H.R. Taylor

MUSIC TO MOTOR BY.
Cassette: released on Sounds Ultimate, Oct'82 Dist: PRT, H.R. Taylor

OFF THE TOP.
Tracks: I'll drink to that / M-A-S-H, Theme from / Ain't misbehavin' / Jimmy Smith rap / Endless love / Mimosa / Off the top.
Compact disc: released on Elektra (USA), '86 by Elektra/Asylum/Nonesuch Records. Dist: WEA

ON DAYS LIKE THESE.
Tracks: How high the moon / Do that to me one more time / I've got my love to keep me warm / Stsy / Theme from New York New York / Please don't talk about me when I'm gone / Blue moon / Desafinado / I should have known / On a clear day / Easy to love / Strike up the band / For the good times / On days like these.
Cassette: released on Sounds Ultimate, Aug'87 Dist: PRT, H.R. Taylor

Album: released on Sounds Ultimate, Aug'82 Dist: PRT, H.R. Taylor

...ON THE RIVIERA.
Album: released on Grosvenor, Nov'79 by Grosvenor Records. Dist: Taylors

ORGAN GRINDER SWING.
Compact disc: released on Verve, Jan'86 by Phonogram Records. Dist: Polygram

PARTY SIDE OF JIMMY SMITH, THE.
Album: released on Grosvenor, Jun'81 by Grosvenor Records. Dist: Taylors

PLAY PIANO, I.
Album: released on Sounds Ultimate, Apr'83

PRAYER MEETING.
Tracks: Prayer meeting / I almost lost my mind / Stone cold dead / In the market / When the saints go marchin in / Red top / Picnicking.
Album: released on Blue Note, Mar'86 by EMI Records. Dist: EMI

Cassette: released on Blue Note, Mar'86 by EMI Records. Dist: EMI

SERMON.
Cassette: released on Blue Note, Apr'87 by EMI Records. Dist: EMI

Album: released on Blue Note, Apr'87 by EMI Records. Dist: EMI

SO REAL, SO BEAUTIFUL.
Tracks: So real, so beautiful / Trust in me / Charade / You and me against the world / Consuelo's love theme / Time after time / Here's that rainy day / Fly me to the moon / I've got you under my skin / For once in my life / Lover / All of me / Have you met Miss Jones / Begin the beguine.
Cassette: released on Sounds Ultimate, Aug'87 Dist: PRT, H.R. Taylor

Album: released on Sounds Ultimate, Mar'82 Dist: PRT, H.R. Taylor

---

Cassette: released on Sounds Ultimate, Mar'82 Dist: PRT, H.R. Taylor

SWING AND SING ALONG IN THE BIG BAND STYLE.
Album: released on Sounds Ultimate, Aug'83 Dist: PRT, H.R. Taylor

Cassette: released on Sounds Ultimate, Aug'83 Dist: PRT, H.R. Taylor

TALKING HANDS.
Album: released on Grosvenor, Nov'79 by Grosvenor Records. Dist: Taylors

TO WAIT FOR LOVE.
Album: released on Sounds Ultimate, Mar'83 Dist: PRT, H.R. Taylor

TWO SIDES OF JIMMY SMITH.
Album: released on Grosvenor, Apr'79 by Grosvenor Records. Dist: Taylors

WALKMAN JAZZ.
Cassette: released on Polydor, Jun'87 by Polydor Records. Dist: Polygram, Polydor

WHO'S AFRAID OF VIRGINIA WOOLF.
Tracks: Slaughter on Tenth Avenue / Who's afraid of Virginia Woolf? / John Brown's body / Wives and lovers / Women of the world / Bluesette.
Compact disc: released on Polydor, Feb'85 by Polydor Records. Dist: Polygram, Polydor

Smith, Jimmy (USA)

BACK AT THE CHICKEN SHACK.
Album: released on Blue Note, Oct'85 by EMI Records. Dist: EMI

CAT, THE.
Cassette: released on Verve (USA), Jun'84 by Polydor. Dist: Polygram

Compact disc: released on Verve (USA), Jun'84 by Polydor. Dist: Polygram

CHAMP, THE.
Album: released on Blue Note (USA), Sep'84

GOT MY MOJO WORKING.
Album: released on Verve, Mar'83 by Phonogram Records. Dist: Polygram

HOME COOKIN'.
Album: released on Blue Note (USA Import), Sep'84

MIDNIGHT SPECIAL.
Album: released on Blue Note, Sep'84

Cassette: released on Blue Note (USA), Sep'84

OFF THE TOP.
Compact disc: released on Elektra (Musician), Apr'84 by WEA Records. Dist: WEA

SERMON, THE.
Album: released on Blue Note, Apr'85 by EMI Records. Dist: EMI

Smith, Johnny

MOONLIGHT IN VERMONT (Smith, Johnny & Stan Getz).
Double Album: released on Vogue, Jan'78 Dist: Discovery, Jazz Music, PRT, Swift

Smith, Keely

POLITELY.
Tracks: Sweet and lovely / Cocktails for two / Song is you, The / I'll get by / Lullaby of the leaves / On the sunny side of the street / Let's get started / I'll never smile again / S'posin' / East of the sun (and west of the moon) / All the way / I never knew (I could love anybody).
Album: released on Capitol T (USA), Nov'85 Dist: Conifer

SWINGIN' PRETTY.
Album: released on Capitol, May'85 by Capitol Records. Dist: EMI

Cassette: released on Capitol, May'85 by Capitol Records. Dist: EMI

Smith, Keith

BALL OF FIRE.
Album: released on Hefty Jazz, Sep'79 Dist: JSU, Swift, Wellard, Chris, Jazz Music, Cadillac Music

KEITH SMITH & ALTON PURNELL LIVE (Smith, Keith Band & Alton Purnell).
Album: released on 77, 74 by 77 Records. Dist: Chris Wellard, Jazz Music, Jazz Music

KEITH SMITH'S AMERICAN ALL STARS IN EUROPE 1966.
Album: released on Hefty Jazz, Sep'79 Dist: JSU, Swift, Wellard, Chris, Jazz Music, Cadillac Music

---

TORONTO 66 (Smith, Keith with The American All Stars).
Album: released on 77, 74 by 77 Records. Dist: Chris Wellard, Cadillac Music. Jazz Music

UP JUMPED THE BLUES (Smith, Keith, Chosen Five & Benny Waters).
Album: released on Hefty Jazz, Sep'79 Dist: JSU, Swift, Wellard, Chris, Jazz Music, Cadillac Music

WAY DOWN YONDER IN NEW ORLEANS.
Album: released on Hefty Jazz, Sep'79 Dist: JSU, Swift, Wellard, Chris, Jazz Music, Cadillac Music

Smith, Kendra

FELL FROM THE SUN.
Single (12"): released on Rough Trade, Jan'85 by Rough Trade Records. Dist: Rough Trade Distribution, Cartel Distribution

Smith, Leo

DIVINE LOVE.
Album: released on ECM (Germany), May'79 by ECM Records. Dist: IMS, Polygram, Virgin through EMI

SPIRIT CATCHER.
Album: released on Nessa, Sep'79 Dist: Projection, Swift

Smith, Little George

OOPIN' DOOPIN' DOOPIN'.
Album: released on Ace, Nov'82 by Ace Records. Dist: Pinnacle, Swift, Hotshot, Cadillac

Smith, Lonnie

THINK.
Tracks: Son of Ice Bag / Call of the wild, The / Think / Three blind mice / Slouchin'.
Notes: Produced by Francis Wolff.
Album: released on Manhattan, Nov'86 by EMI Records. Dist: EMI

Smith, Lonnie Liston

BEST OF LONNIE LISTON SMITH, THE.
Album: released on CBS, Jan'81 by CBS Records. Dist: CBS

Cassette: released on CBS, Jan'81 by CBS Records. Dist: CBS

DREAMS OF TOMORROW.
Album: released on Doctor Jazz (USA), Jul'83 by Doctor Jazz Records. Dist: CBS

Cassette: released on Doctor Jazz (USA), Jul'83 by Doctor Jazz Records. Dist: CBS

EXPANSIONS.
Single (12"): released on Bluebird, Nov'83 by Bluebird Records. Dist: EMI, Jetstar

IF YOU TAKE CARE OF ME.
Single (7"): released on Doctor Jazz (USA), Feb'85 by Doctor Jazz Records. Dist: CBS

LOVELAND.
Album: released on CBS, '74 by CBS Records. Dist: CBS

REJUVENATION.
Album: released on Dr Jazz, Mar'86 by Doctor Jazz Records. Dist: CBS, PRT

Cassette: released on Dr Jazz, Mar'86 by Doctor Jazz Records. Dist: CBS, PRT

SILHOUETTES.
Album: released on Doctor Jazz (USA), Nov'84 by Doctor Jazz Records. Dist: CBS

Cassette: released on Doctor Jazz (USA), Nov'84 by Doctor Jazz Records. Dist: CBS

Smith, Louis Quintet

LOUIS SMITH QUINTET.
Album: released on Steeplechase, '78

PRANCIN'.
Album: released on Steeplechase Import, Sep'79

Smith, Ludwig

LOVING NONSTOP.
Single (12"): released on Negus Roots, Jul'85 by Negus Roots Records. Dist: Jetstar

Smith, Mack Allen

GOTTA ROCK TONIGHT.
Album: released on Charly, Apr'81 by Charly Records. Dist: Charly, Cadillac

Smith, Mandy

I JUST CAN'T WAIT.
Tracks: You're never alone.
Single (7"): released on PWL, Jan'87

Smith, Margo

BEST OF THE TENNESSEE YODELLER.
Album: released on MCA, Mar'87 by MCA Records. Dist: Polygram, MCA

Cassette: released on MCA, Mar'87 by MCA Records. Dist: Polygram, MCA

MARGO SMITH.
Tracks: / Don't break my heart that loves you / Still a woman / Love's explosion / If I give my heart to you / It only hurts for a little while / Little things mean a lot / Paper lovin' / Shuffle song / There I said it / Save your kisses for me.
Album: released on MCA Import, '86 by MCA Records. Dist: Polygram, IMS

Smith, Mel

SCRATCH 'N' SNIFF (Smith, Mel & Griff Rhys-Jones).
Tracks: / I spy / Antiques roadshow / Hooligans / Drugs / Video nasties / Meryl streep / Autumn / Richard Branson / Christmas / Bob Geldof / V.D. / Mia farrow / Aids / Taboos / Perverts / Animals / Senior citizens / Rigor mortis / Rigor mortis.
Album: released on 10, Nov'86 by 10 Records. Dist: Virgin, EMI

TREMBLING.
Tracks: / Trembling / Easy.
Single (7"): released on 10, '86 by 10 Records. Dist: Virgin, EMI

Smith, Michael

AUSTIN STREAM (Smith, Michael Quartet).
Album: released on SAJ (W.Germany), Mar'78

LA MUSIQUE BLANCHE.
Album: released on Chant du Monde, Jan'78 Dist: Harmonia Mundi

MI CYAAN BELIEVE IT.
Album: released on Island, Nov'82 by Island Records. Dist: Polygram

Cassette: released on Island, Nov'82 by Island Records. Dist: Polygram

Smith, Michael W

BIG PICTURE (THE).
Notes: As a songwriter, Michael has penned such classics as 'How majestic is your name' and 'Great is the Lord'. As a recording artist,he produced two top-selling albums and was awarded a Grammy last year for 'Michael W. Smith 2'. And as a performer,Michael is known for his keyboard magic,contagious energy,and his work for Amy Grant. But there's more to Michael W. Smith - it's called The Big Picture. The Big Picture marks a variation in production for Michael,as well as his musical direction. On this third album,he works for the first time with coproducer John Potoker. Together these producers direct the talents of accomplished session players to create an aggresive and provocative musical package.
Album: released on Reunion, '86

Cassette: released on Reunion, '86

SING UNTO HIM.
Tracks: / How majestic is your name / Friends / Jude doxology / Great is the Lord / Hosanna / Stubborn love.
Notes: Ten Michael W. Smith compositions arranged by Steven V. Taylor and sung by Michael with a youth choir for youth choirs.
Album: released on Word, '86 by Word Records. Dist: Word Distribution, CBS

Cassette: released on Word, '86 by Word Records. Dist: Word Distribution, CBS

Smith, Mike

GLAD ALL OVER.
Single (7"): released on Proto, Aug'85 by Proto Records. Dist: WEA

Single (12"): released on Proto, Aug'85 by Proto Records. Dist: WEA

Smith, Mr.

TWO VERY SIMILAR VIEWS OF...
Album: released on Sweet Folk, Nov'79 Dist: Roots Distribution

Smith, O.C

SON OF HICKORY HOLLER'S TRAMP.
Single (7"): released on Old Gold, Jul'82 by Old Gold Records. Dist: Lightning, Jazz Music, Spartan, Counterpoint

Smith, Orville

GOTTA HOLD ON TO THIS FEELING.
Tracks: / Gotta hold on to this feeling / Gotta hold on to this feeling (Reggae version).
Single (7"): released on Greensleeves, '86 by Greensleeves Records. Dist: BMG, Jetstar, Spartan

Single (12"): released on Greensleeves, '86 by Greensleeves Records. Dist: BMG, Jetstar, Spartan

Smith, Patti

BECAUSE THE NIGHT.
Single (7"): released on Old Gold, Jul'84 by Old Gold Records. Dist: Lightning, Jazz Music, Spartan, Counterpoint

BECAUSE THE NIGHT/GLORIA.
Single (7"): released on Arista, Apr'83 by Arista Records. Dist: RCA

BECAUSE THE NIGHT/REDONO BEAT/DANCING BAREFOOT/FREE-MONEY.
Single (12"): released on Arista, Apr'83 by Arista Records. Dist: RCA

GLORIA/MY GENERATION.
Single (7"): released on Arista, Sep'77 by Arista Records. Dist: RCA

HORSES.
Album: released on Arista, Dec'75 by Arista Records. Dist: RCA

NEVER ENOUGH.
Tracks: / Never enough / Downtown train / Give it time / Call to heaven / River cried, The / Isn't it enough / Sue Lee / Tough love / Heartache heard round the world.
Album: released on CBS, Apr'87 by CBS Records. Dist: CBS

Cassette: released on CBS, Apr'87 by CBS Records. Dist: CBS

WAVES.
Album: released on Arista, Jan'79 by Arista Records. Dist: RCA

Album: released on Arista, Jan'79 by Arista Records. Dist: RCA

Smith, Patti Group

EASTER.
Album: released on Fame (Arista), Jan'83 by Music For Pleasure Records. Dist: EMI

Cassette: released on Fame (Arista), Jan'83 by Music For Pleasure Records. Dist: EMI

RADIO ETHIOPIA.
Album: released on Arista, Oct'76 by Arista Records. Dist: RCA

Cassette: released on Arista, Oct'76 by Arista Records. Dist: RCA

Smith, Paul

LIVE AND LEARN.
Notes: Paul Smith, known as the voice and pen behind manu of the imperials songs,has channelled his songwriting into a new solo album. Together with friends and producer Keith Thomas,Paul's music comes alive. The sounds are dominated by keyboard and frequented by brass. The music changes in texture and feeling with each message - saxaphone solos enhance the atmosphere of tenderness and strength: synthesizer swells parallel the rising emotion in Paul's voice. "Live and Learn" is a musical study of love and faith.
Album: released on Day Spring, '86 by Word Records. Dist: Word Distribution, CBS

Cassette: released on Day Spring, '86 by Word Records. Dist: Word Distribution, CBS

LIVE JAM SESSIONS AT THE HAIG (Smith, Paul & Various Artists).
Album: released on Jam Session (USA), Jan'79 Dist: Jazz Music, Jazz Horizons

Smith, Phoebe

I AM A ROMANY/DOCTOR OF A GIPSY FAMILY.
Cassette: released on Folktracks, Nov'79 Dist: Roots

ONCE I HAD A TRUE LOVE.
Album: released on Topic, Jan'81 Dist: Roots Distribution

Smith, Ray

COUNTRY SIDE THE.
Album: by Charly Records. Dist: Charly, Cadillac

ROOM FULL OF ROSES.
Single (7"): released on Wix (USA), Jan'80 Dist: Billy Goat, Swift

Smith, Rex

CAMOUFLAGE.
Album: released on CBS, Aug'83 by CBS Records. Dist: CBS

Cassette: released on CBS, Aug'83 by CBS Records. Dist: CBS

Smith, Richard Jon

ABC OF KISSING.
Single (7"): released on Jive, Mar'85 by Zomba Records. Dist: RCA, PRT, CBS

Single (12"): released on Jive, Mar'85 by Zomba Records. Dist: RCA, PRT, CBS

Picture disc single: released on Jive, May'85 by Zomba Records. Dist: RCA, PRT, CBS

BABY'S GOT ANOTHER/THIS IS THE MOMENT.
Single (7"): released on Jive, Mar'83 by Zomba Records. Dist: RCA, PRT, CBS

Single (12"): released on Jive, Mar'83 by Zomba Records. Dist: RCA, PRT, CBS

DANCE WITH ME.
Single (7"): released on Jive, Jul'84 by Zomba Records. Dist: RCA, PRT, CBS

Single (12"): released on Jive, Jul'84 by Zomba Records. Dist: RCA, PRT, CBS

DON'T GO WALKING OUT THAT DOOR.
Single (7"): released on Jive, Aug'82 by Zomba Records. Dist: RCA, PRT, CBS

Single (12"): released on Jive, Aug'82 by Zomba Records. Dist: RCA, PRT, CBS

HOLD ON.
Single (7"): released on Jive, Sep'85 by Zomba Records. Dist: RCA, PRT, CBS

Single (12"): released on Jive, Sep'85 by Zomba Records. Dist: RCA, PRT, CBS

IN THE NIGHT/I NEED YOU/DUN VERSION.
Single (7"): released on Jive, Jan'84 by Zomba Records. Dist: RCA, PRT, CBS. Estim retail price in Jul'87 was £3.99.

Single (12"): released on Jive, Jan'84 by Zomba Records. Dist: RCA, PRT, CBS

RICHARD JON SMITH.
Album: released on Jive, Oct'83 by Zomba Records. Dist: RCA, PRT, CBS

Cassette: released on Jive, Oct'83 by Zomba Records. Dist: RCA, PRT, CBS

SHE'S THE MASTER OF THE GAME/LOVE IS WHAT I'M AFTER.
Single (7"): released on Jive, Jul'83 by Zomba Records. Dist: RCA, PRT, CBS

Single (12"): released on Jive, Jul'83 by Zomba Records. Dist: RCA, PRT, CBS

STAY WITH ME TONIGHT.
Single (7"): released on Jive, Feb'82 by Zomba Records. Dist: RCA, PRT, CBS

Compact disc: released on Jive, Feb'82 by Zomba Records. Dist: RCA, PRT, CBS

Smith, Russell

BOY NEXT DOOR THE.
Album: released on Capitol (Holland), Dec'84 by Capitol Records. Dist: Conifer

Smiths

ASK.
Cassette: released on Rough Trade, Nov'86 by Rough Trade Records. Dist: Rough Trade Distribution, Cartel Distribution

Single (7"): released on Rough Trade, '86 by Rough Trade Records. Dist: Rough Trade Distribution, Cartel Distribution

Single (12"): released on Rough Trade, '86 by Rough Trade Records. Dist: Rough Trade Distribution, Cartel Distribution

BIGMOUTH STRIKES AGAIN.

BOY WITH THE THORN IN HIS SIDE THE.
Single (7"): released on Rough Trade, Sep'85 by Rough Trade Records. Dist: Rough Trade Distribution, Cartel Distribution

Single (12"): released on Rough Trade, Sep'85 by Rough Trade Records. Dist: Rough Trade Distribution, Cartel Distribution

CHARMING MAN THE/JEANE.
Single (7"): released on Rough Trade, Nov'83 by Rough Trade Records. Dist: Rough Trade Distribution, Cartel Distribution

Single (12"): released on Rough Trade, Nov'83 by Rough Trade Records. Dist: Rough Trade Distribution, Cartel Distribution

GIRLFRIEND IN A COMA.
Single (7"): released on Rough Trade, Aug'87 by Rough Trade Records. Dist: Rough Trade Distribution, Cartel Distribution

Single (12"): released on Rough Trade, Aug'87 by Rough Trade Records. Dist: Rough Trade Distribution, Cartel Distribution

HAND IN GLOVE.
Single (7"): released on Rough Trade, May'83 by Rough Trade Records. Dist: Rough Trade Distribution, Cartel Distribution

HATFUL OF HOLLOW.
Compact disc: released on Rough Trade, May'87 by Rough Trade Records. Dist: Rough Trade Distribution, Cartel Distribution

Album: released on Rough Trade, Nov'84 by Rough Trade Records. Dist: Rough Trade Distribution, Cartel Distribution

Cassette: released on Rough Trade, Nov'84 by Rough Trade Records. Dist: Rough Trade Distribution, Cartel Distribution

HEADMASTERS RITUAL THE.
Single (12"): released on Import, Jul'85 Dist: Stage One

HEAVEN KNOWS.
Single (7"): released on Rough Trade, Sep'84 by Rough Trade Records. Dist: Rough Trade Distribution, Cartel Distribution

Single (12"): released on Rough Trade, Sep'84 by Rough Trade Records. Dist: Rough Trade Distribution, Cartel Distribution

HOW SOON IS NOW.
Single (7"): released on Rough Trade, Feb'85 by Rough Trade Records. Dist: Rough Trade Distribution, Cartel Distribution

Single (12"): released on Rough Trade, Feb'85 by Rough Trade Records. Dist: Rough Trade Distribution, Cartel Distribution

INTERVIEW PICTURE DISC.
Album: released on Baktabak, May'87 by Baktabak Records. Dist: Arabesque

LOUDER THAN BOMBS.
Compact disc: released on Rough Trade, May'87 by Rough Trade Records. Dist: Rough Trade Distribution, Cartel Distribution

LOUDER THAN BOMBS.
Album: released on Rough Trade, 30 May'87 by Rough Trade Records. Dist: Rough Trade Distribution, Cartel Distribution

Cassette: released on Rough Trade, 30 May'87 by Rough Trade Records. Dist: Rough Trade Distribution, Cartel Distribution

LOVE AND DEVOTION (Smith, S & The Uniques).
Single (12"): released on Rosie Uprising, Sep'84 by Rosie Uprising Records. Dist: Jetstar Distribution

MEAT IS MURDER.
Compact disc: released on Rough Trade, May'87 by Rough Trade Records. Dist: Rough Trade Distribution, Cartel Distribution

Album: released on Rough Trade, '85 by Rough Trade Records. Dist: Rough Trade Distribution, Cartel Distribution

Cassette: released on Rough Trade, '85 by Rough Trade Records. Dist: Rough Trade Distribution, Cartel Distribution

PANIC.
Tracks: / Panic / Vicar in a tutu / Draize train (The).
Single (7"): released on Rough Trade, '86 by Rough Trade Records. Dist: Rough Trade Distribution, Cartel Distribution

Single (12"): released on Rough Trade, '86 by Rough Trade Records. Dist: Rough Trade Distribution, Cartel Distribution

QUEEN IS DEAD, THE.
Tracks: / Frankly, Mr Shankly / I Know it's over / Never had no one ever / Cemetery gates / Big mouth strikes again / Vicar in a tutu / There is a light that never goes out / Some girls are bigger than others / Queen is dead, The.
Compact disc: released on Rough Trade, May'87 by Rough Trade Records. Dist: Rough Trade Distribution, Cartel Distribution

SHAKESPEAR'S SISTER.
Single (7"): released on Rough Trade, Mar'85 by Rough Trade Records. Dist: Rough Trade Distribution, Cartel Distribution

Single (12"): released on Rough Trade, Mar'85 by Rough Trade Records. Dist: Rough Trade Distribution, Cartel Distribution

SHEILA TAKE A BOW.
Tracks: / Sheila take a bow / Is it really so strange? / Sweet and tender hooligan*.
Notes: *Extra track on 12" only
Single (7"): released on Rough Trade, Apr'87 by Rough Trade Records. Dist: Rough Trade Distribution, Cartel Distribution

Single (12"): released on Rough Trade, Apr'87 by Rough Trade Records. Dist: Rough Trade Distribution, Cartel Distribution

SHOPLIFTERS OF THE WORLD.
Tracks: / Unite / Half A Person / London.
Single (7"): released on Rough Trade, Jan'87 by Rough Trade Records. Dist: Rough Trade Distribution, Cartel Distribution

Single (12"): released on Rough Trade, Jan'87 by Rough Trade Records. Dist: Rough Trade Distribution, Cartel Distribution

SMITHS THE.
Album: released on Rough Trade, Feb'84 by Rough Trade Records. Dist: Rough Trade Distribution, Cartel Distribution

Cassette: released on Rough Trade, Feb'84 by Rough Trade Records. Dist: Rough Trade Distribution, Cartel Distribution

SMITHS, THE.
Compact disc: released on Rough Trade, May'87 by Rough Trade Records. Dist: Rough Trade Distribution, Cartel Distribution

THAT JOKE ISN'T FUNNY ANYMORE.
Single (7"): released on Rough Trade, Jun'85 by Rough Trade Records. Dist: Rough Trade Distribution, Cartel Distribution

Single (12"): released on Rough Trade, Jun'85 by Rough Trade Records. Dist: Rough Trade Distribution, Cartel Distribution

WHAT DIFFERENCE DOES IT MAKE/BACK TO THE OLD HOUSE.
Single (7"): released on Rough Trade, Jan'84 by Rough Trade Records. Dist: Rough Trade Distribution, Cartel Distribution

Single (12"): released on Rough Trade, Jan'84 by Rough Trade Records. Dist: Rough Trade Distribution, Cartel Distribution

WILLIAM IT WAS REALLY NOTHING.
Single (7"): released on Rough Trade, Aug'84 by Rough Trade Records. Dist: Rough Trade Distribution, Cartel Distribution

Single (12"): released on Rough Trade, Aug'84 by Rough Trade Records. Dist: Rough Trade Distribution, Cartel Distribution

WORLD WON'T LISTEN.
Compact disc: released on Rough Trade, May'87 by Rough Trade Records. Dist: Rough Trade Distribution, Cartel Distribution

WORLD WON'T LISTEN (THE).
Cassette: released on Rough Trade, Feb'87 by Rough Trade Records. Dist: Rough Trade Distribution, Cartel Distribution

Album: released on Rough Trade, Feb'87 by Rough Trade Records. Dist: Rough Trade Distribution, Cartel Distribution

Smiths, Bob
BETTER THAN AN ORCHESTRA (Smiths, Bob Ideal Band).
Album: released on Topic, Jan'81 by Roots Distribution

IDEAL MUSIC (Smiths, Bob Ideal Band).
Album: released on Topic, Nov'81 by Roots Distribution

Smith, Slim
BLESSED ARE THE POOR.
Tracks: / Blessed are the poor / Promise to be true.
Single (7"): released on Third World, '86 Dist: Jetstar Distribution

DANCE HALL CONNECTION.
Album: released on Third World, '86 Dist: Jetstar Distribution

TIME HAS COME THE.
Album: released on Pama, Mar'84 by Pama Records. Dist: Pama, Enterprise, Jetstar

EVERYBODY NEEDS LOVE.
Single 10": released on Pama Oldies, Jul'82

MEMORIAL.
Album: released on Trojan, Feb'85 by Trojan Records. Dist: PRT, Jetstar

Smith, Stention
SUGAR & SPICE.
Single (12"): released on Clair, Aug'84 by Clair Records. Dist: Jetstar

Smith, Stuff
DESERT SANDS.
Album: released on Verve, May'82 by Phonogram Records. Dist: Polygram

SWINGING STUFF.
Album: released on Storyville, Aug'83 by Storyville Records. Dist: Jazz Music Distribution, Swift Distribution, Chris Wellard Distribution, Counterpoint Distribution

SWINGIN' STUFF (Smith, Stuff Quartet).
Notes: With Kenny Drew/NHOP/Alex Riel
Album: released on Storyville, '86 by Storyville Records. Dist: Jazz Music Distribution, Swift Distribution, Chris Wellard Distribution, Counterpoint Distribution

VARSITY SESSION THE VOLUME 2 Smith, Stuff & His Orchestra).
Album: released on Storyville, Jul'81 by Storyville Records. Dist: Jazz Music Distribution, Swift Distribution, Chris Wellard Distribution, Counterpoint Distribution

Smith, Tab
I DON'T WANNA PLAY IN THE KITCHEN (Smith, Tab & Orchestra).
Album: released on Saxophonograph, May'85 Dist: Swift

Smith, Terry
BRITISH ARTIST JAZZ VOLUME 2 also see Tony Lee Trio (Smith, Terry & Terry Lee Trio).

Smith, Timmy
CRAZY BABY.
Album: released on Blue Note, Nov'86 by EMI Records. Dist: EMI

Smith, Tommy
GIANT STRIDES.
Album: released on GFM, Feb'87 by GFM Records. Dist: Fast Forward, Cartel, PRT, Projection

GIANT STRIDES.
Album: released on GFM, Mar'84 by GFM Records. Dist: Fast Forward, Cartel, PRT, Projection

Smith, Toni
OOH I LIKE THE WAY IT FEELS/OOH DUB.
Single (7"): released on Malaco, Jan'84 by Malaco Records. Dist: Charly

Single (12"): released on Malaco, Jan'84 by Malaco Records. Dist: Charly

Smith, Tono
CAN'T STOP.
Tracks: / Can't stop / Can't stop(Dub mix).
Single (12"): released on Lisson, '86 Dist: PRT

Smith, Tufty
HOW TO MAKE A BAKEWELL TART (Smith, Tufty/Alan Harris/ Sure Harris).
Album: released on Free Reed, Jan'87 by Free Reed Records. Dist: Roots, Projection, Hobgoblin Records, Oblivion

Smith T.V
CHANNEL FIVE.
Album: released on Expulsion, Jul'83 by Expulsion Records. Dist: Stage One

WAR FEVER/LIES.
Single (7"): released on Expulsion, Apr'83 by Expulsion Records. Dist: Stage One

Smith, Warren
LAST DETAIL THE.
Album: released on Charly, Dec'81 by Charly Records. Dist: Charly, Cadillac

LEGENDARY SUN PERFORMANCES.
Album: released on Charly, Nov'77 by Charly Records. Dist: Charly, Cadillac

MEMORIAL ALBUM.
Album: released on Magnum Force, Jul'82 by Magnum Music Group Ltd. Dist: Magnum Music Group Ltd, PRT, Spartan

Smith, Wayne
COME ALONG.
Single (12"): released on Greensleeves, Nov'84 by Greensleeves Records. Dist: BMG, Jetstar, Spartan

DANCING MACHINE.
Single (12"): released on Tonas, Jul'85 Dist: Jetstar Distribution

ICKY ALL OVER.
Single (12"): released on Greensleeves, Jul'85 by Greensleeves Records. Dist: BMG, Jetstar, Spartan

LIFE IS A MOMENT IN SPACE.
Single (12"): released on Black Joy, Dec'82 Dist: Jetstar

NO PUPPY LOVE.
Tracks: / No puppy love / Teach me to dance.
Single (12"): released on Real Authentic Sound, '86

SHUTDOWN VOLUME 7 also see Patrick Andy (Smith,Wayne & Patrick Andy).

SLENG TENG.
Album: released on Greensleeves, '86 by Greensleeves Records. Dist: BMG, Jetstar, Spartan

SLENG TENG MIXDOWN (REMIX).
Single (12"): released on Greensleeves, Apr'85 by Greensleeves Records. Dist: BMG, Jetstar, Spartan. Estim retail price in Jul'87 was £3.99.

SMOKERS HSUPPER.
Album: released on Chartbound, May'85 by Chartbound Records. Dist: Jetstar

SMOKER SUPPER/WHEN YOU'RE YOUNG.
Single (12"): released on Chartbound, Dec'83 by Chartbound Records. Dist: Jetstar

TRY MY LOVE.
Tracks: / Try my love / Murder commit.
Single (12"): released on Unity, '86 by Unity Records. Dist: Jetstar

UNDEHR ME SLENG TENG.
Single (7"): released on Greensleeves, Feb'85 by Greensleeves Records. Dist: BMG, Jetstar, Spartan

Smith Whistling Jack
I WAS KAISER BILL'S BATSMAN.
Single (7"): released on Deram, Jan'80 by Decca Records. Dist: Polygram

I WAS KAISER BILL'S BATSMAN/BRITISH GRIN & BEAR.
Single (7"): released on Decca-Originals, May'82 by Decca Records. Dist: Polygram, IMS

Smith, Wilbur
LEOPARD HUNTS IN THE DARKNESS THE.
Cassette: released on LFP, May'85

Smith, Willie
GRAND PIANO (DUETS) (Smith, Willie 'The Lion'& Don Ewell).
Album: released on Sackville, Apr'81 by JSU, Jazz Music, Jazz Horizons, Cadillac Music, Celtic Music, Swift

Album: released on Swaggie (Australia), Jan'83

HARLEM PIANO (Smith, Willie The Lion & Luckey Roberts).
Album: released on Good Time Jazz (USA), Jul'81 by Good Time Jazz Records (USA). Dist: Polygram

LION THE (Smith, The Memoirs Of Willie).
Album: released on RCA (France), Jan'83 by RCA Records. Dist: Discovery

ORIGINAL 14 PLUS TWO (Smith, Willie 'The Lion'& Don Ewell).
Album: released on Commodore Classics, May'87 by Teldec Records (Germany). Dist: Conifer, IMS, Polygram

Album: released on Teldec (Germany), Sep'83 by Import Records. Dist: IMS Distribution, Polygram Distribution

PORK AND BEANS (Smith, Willie 'The Lion'& Don Ewell).
Album: released on Black Lion, Jan'85 by Black Lion Records. Dist: Jazz Music, Chris Wellard, Taylor, H.R., Counterpoint, Cadillac

TEA FOR TWO.
Album: released on Jazz Live, Apr'81

WILLIE THE LION SMITH VOL 1 (Smith, Willie'The Lion').
Album: released on Jazz Reactivation, Jan'82 Dist: PRT

WILLIE THE LION SMITH VOL 2 (Smith, Willie'The Lion').
Album: released on Jazz Reactivation, May'83 Dist: PRT

Smoke Babe
HOT BLUES.
Album: released on Arhoolie, May'81 by Arhoolie Records. Dist: Projection, Topic, Jazz Music, Swift, Roots

Smokey Valley Boys
SMOKEY VALLEY BOYS.
Album: released on Rounder, Jan'77 Dist: Roots Distribution

Smokey Wilson
88TH STREET BLUES.
Album: released on Murray Brothers (USA), May'84 Dist: Swift Distribution

Smokie
BRIGHT LIGHTS & BACK ALLEYS.
Album: released on RAK, Oct'77 by RAK. Dist: EMI

Cassette: released on RAK, Oct'77 by RAK. Dist: EMI

LOOKING DANCERS/HIDING FROM THE NIGHT.
Single (7"): released on Mean, Nov'82 by Mean Records. Dist: Spartan

SMOKIE'S GREATEST HITS.
Album: released on Fame (RAK), Nov'84 by Music For Pleasure Records. Dist: EMI

Cassette: released on Fame (RAK), Nov'84 by Music For Pleasure Records. Dist: EMI

Smokin
MIDNIGHT.
Single (7"): released on Zone, Jan'83

Smooth & co
HALF STEPPIN'.
Album: released on Move, '85 by Charly Records. Dist: Charly Distribution, Fast Forward Distribution, Cartel Distribution

Smooth Sax:
SMOOTH SAX: LATE NIGHT FAVOURITES Various artists (Various Artists).
Double album: released on Cambra, May'85 by Cambra Records. Dist: IDS, Conifer

Double cassette: released on Cambra, May'85 by Cambra Records. Dist: IDS, Conifer

Smothers Smoky
SMOKY SMOTHERS 1960-1962.
Album: released on Krazy Kat, Jul'82 Dist: Jazz Music, Swift, Chris Wellard, H.R. Taylor, Charly, Hotshot, IRS Distribution

Smurf And Breakdance
SMURF AND BREAKDANCE various artists (Various Artists).
Album: released on RCA (France), Jun'84 by RCA Records. Dist: Discovery

Cassette: released on RCA (France), Jun'84 by RCA Records. Dist: Discovery

Smurfs
CLAPPING AND JUMPING SHOW.
Single (7"): released on Creole, Nov'81 by Creole Records. Dist: Rhino, PRT

JOKING SMURF.
Single (7"): released on Dureco (Holland), Mar'84 Dist: PRT

MERRY CHRISTMAS WITH THE SMURFS.
Album: released on Dureco (Holland), Jan'83 Dist: PRT

Cassette: released on Dureco (Holland), Jan'83 Dist: PRT

SMURF FOR ALL IT'S WORTH IT/INSTRUMENTAL.
Single (12"): released on Celluloid, May'83 by Charly Records. Dist: Charly

SMURFING SING SONG.
Album: released on Decca, Dec'79 by Decca Records. Dist: Polygram

Cassette: released on Decca, Dec'79 by Decca Records. Dist: Polygram

SMURFS PARTY TIME.
Album: released on Dureco (Holland), Jan'83 Dist: PRT

Cassette: released on Dureco (Holland), Jan'83 Dist: PRT

Smyth, Gilli
FAIRY TALES.
Album: released on Charly, Nov'79 by Charly Records. Dist: Charly, Cadillac

MOTHER.
Album: released on Charly, Jun'78 by Charly Records. Dist: Charly, Cadillac

Snake corps
FLESH ON FLESH.
Album: released on Midnight Chime, '85

PARTY'S OVER.
Single (12"): released on Midnight, Aug'85

SCIENCE KILLS.
Single (12"): released on Midnight, Sep'85

VICTORY PARADE.
Tracks: / Victory parade / Always be the same / Painted ocean.
Single (12"): released on Midnight Chime, '86

Snake Finger
AGAINST THE GRAIN.
Album: released on New Ralph, Jan'84 by New Ralph Records. Dist: Rough Trade

GREENER POSTURES.
Album: released on Do-It, Jan'81 by Do-It Records. Dist: Virgin, EMI

NIGHT OF DESIRABLE OBJECTS.
Album: released on Red Rhino, Jun'87 by Red Rhino Records. Dist: Red Rhino, Cartel

Cassette: released on Red Rhino, Jun'87 by Red Rhino Records. Dist: Red Rhino, Cartel

Compact disc: released on Red Rhino, Apr'87 by Red Rhino Records. Dist: Red Rhino, Cartel

Snakes Of Shakes

GRACELANDS AND THE NATURAL WOOD.
Album: released on Making Waves, '86 by Making Waves Records.

Cassette: released on Making Waves, '86 by Making Waves Records.

SOUTHERN CROSS.
Single (7"): released on Making Waves, '86 by Making Waves Records.

Single (12"): released on Making Waves, '86 by Making Waves Records.

Album: released on Tense But Confident, Mar'85 by The Snakes of Shakes. Dist: Cartel Distribution

SOUTHERN CROSS (PT 3).
Single (12"): released on Tense But Confident, Aug'85 by The Snakes of Shakes. Dist: Cartel Distribution

Snap Shot

HALFWAY TO PARADISE/FLY IN MY FACE.
Single (7"): released on Jammy, Jun'83 by Jammy Records. Dist: Jammy

Snatch

SHOPPING FOR CLOTHES/JOEY.
Single (12"): released on Fetish, May'81 by Fetish Records. Dist: Cartel, Pinnacle

SNATCH.
Album: released on Pandemonium, Nov'83

Snatch & The Poontangs

SNATCH AND THE POONTANGS.
Album: released on Snatch, Oct'86 by Charly Records. Dist: Charly

Sneaky Feelings

WAITING FOR TOUCHDOWN.
Album: released on Flying Nun, Apr'87 Dist: Rough Trade, Cartel

Snell, Adrian

ALPHA & OMEGA.
Notes: Alpha & Omega is a major,new contemporay musical with a prophetic message;a cry to God that the church may receive His love and bring His redemption,not only to our own relationships and situations,but also to our nations and world. Co-written by lyracist Phil Thomson,the partnership which also produced Adrian's first internationally sucessful album "Feed the Hungry Heart",Alpha & Omega has already been performed in Jerusalem as a prelude to performances in countries world-wide. The British premier is on 20th September at the Hammersmith Odeon,London.
Album: released on Myrrh, '86 by Word Records. Dist: Word Distribution

Cassette: released on Myrrh, '86 by Word Records. Dist: Word Distribution

LISTEN TO THE PEACE.
Album: released on Dove, May'79 by Dove Records. Dist: Jetstar

SOMETHING NEW UNDER THE SUN.
Album: released on Dove, May'79 by Dove Records. Dist: Jetstar

Snell, David

HARP TRANSPLANT.
Tracks: / Close to you (They long to be) / Do you know the way to San Jose? / This guy's in love with you / Both sides now / Wichita lineman / Call me / Eine kleine nachtmusik / Invention in A minor / Fur Elise / Gavotte in G minor / Praeludium / Trumpet voluntary.
Compact disc: released on PRT, '86 by PRT Records. Dist: PRT

Snell, Nigel (author)

CLARES NEW BABY BROTHER.
Cassette: released on Look & Listen, Nov'84 by Listen For Pleasure. Dist: EMI

DAVIDS FIRST DAY AT SCHOOL.
Cassette: released on Look & Listen, Nov'84 by Listen For Pleasure. Dist: EMI

KATE VISITS THE DOCTOR.
Cassette: released on Look & Listen, Nov'84 by Listen For Pleasure. Dist: EMI

SUE LEARNS TO CROSS THE ROAD.
Cassette: released on Look & Listen, Nov'84 by Listen For Pleasure. Dist: EMI

Cassette: released on Look & Listen, Nov'84 by Listen For Pleasure. Dist: EMI

Sniff N The Tears

DRIVERS SEAT/NIGHTLIFE/PUT YOPUR MONEY WHERE YOUR MOUTH IS.
Single (12"): released on Chiswick, Jun'83 by Chiswick Records. Dist: Pinnacle

FICKLE HEART.
Cassette: released on Chiswick, Aug'82 by Chiswick Records. Dist: Pinnacle

GAMES UP THE.
Album: released on Chiswick, Aug'82 by Chiswick Records. Dist: Pinnacle

HUNGRY EYES/BAGATELLE.
Single (7"): released on Chiswick, Jul'82 by Chiswick Records. Dist: Pinnacle

LOVE/ACTION.
Album: released on Chiswick, Aug'82 by Chiswick Records. Dist: Pinnacle

RETROSPECTIVE.
Album: released on Chiswick, Jun'83 by Chiswick Records. Dist: Pinnacle

RIDE BLUE DIVIDE.
Album: released on Chiswick, Aug'82 by Chiswick Records. Dist: Pinnacle

Snipers

OPEN THE ATTACK.
Album: released on Megaton, '86 by Megaton Records. Dist: Rough Trade Distribution, Cartel Distribution

QUICK AND DEAD.
Album: released on Megaton, '86 by Megaton Records. Dist: Rough Trade Distribution, Cartel Distribution

THREE PIECE SUITE (EP).
Single (7"): released on Crass, Dec'81 by Exitstencil Music. Dist: Rough Trade, Cartel

Snoopy

SNOOPY Original cast (Various Artists).
Album: released on DRG, Jul'79

SNOOPY Original London cast.
Album: released on TER, Oct'83 Dist: Pinnacle

Cassette: released on TER, Oct'83 Dist: Pinnacle

Snowboy

BRING ON THE BEAT.
Tracks: / Bring on the beat.
Single (12"): released on Waterfront-Art, '85

BRING ON THE BEAT (Snowboy & The G.L Band).
Single (7"): released on Waterfront-Art, Nov'85

MAMBO TERESA.
Tracks: / Mambo teresa / Wild spirit.
Single (12"): released on Waterfront, '86 by Waterfront Records. Dist: Rough Trade, Cartel, Projection, Roots

Snowden, Jean & Les

DAY OF THE MIRACLES.
Album: by Pilgrim Records. Dist: Rough Trade, Cartel

Snow, Hank

20 OF THE BEST.
Album: released on RCA, Nov'84 by RCA Records. Dist: RCA, Roots, Swift, Wellard, Chris, I & B, Solomon & Peres Distribution

Cassette: released on RCA, Nov'84 by RCA Records. Dist: RCA, Roots, Swift, Wellard, Chris, I & B, Solomon & Peres Distribution

Cassette: released on RCA, Nov'84 by RCA Records. Dist: RCA, Roots, Swift, Wellard, Chris, I & B, Solomon & Peres Distribution

HITS OF HANK SHOW.
Album: released on RCA (Germany), Oct'84

Cassette: released on RCA (Germany), Oct'84

I'M MOVING ON.
Single (7"): released on RCA, Jan'80 by RCA Records. Dist: RCA, Roots, Swift, Wellard, Chris, I & B, Solomon & Peres Distribution

JUST KEEP A-MOVIN'.
Notes: Issued summer 1983 still available.
Album: released on Detour, May'83 by Detour Records. Dist: Swift, RCA, Jazz Music, Projection

JUST KEEP A-MOVIN'.
Tracks: / Scale to measure love, A / Just keep a-movin / Music makin' mama from Memphis / Bill is falling due, The / Can't have you blues / Scale to measure love, A / Cryin',Prayin',Waitin',hopin' / I can't control my heart / Love's game of let's pretend / My Arabian baby / Blue sea blues / Caribbean / Blossoms in the springtime / Chatin' with a chick in chatanooga / I'm glad I got to see you once again / Cuba Rhumba / Owl and I (The) / Just keep a-movin' / Music makin'mama from memphis / Bill is falling due,The / Can't have you blues / Scale to measure love,A / Cryin',prayin',waitin',hopin' / I can't control my heart / Love's game of let's pretend / My arabian baby / Blue sea blues / Caribbbean / Blossoms in springtime / Chattin'with a chick in chatanooga / I'm glad I got to see you once again / Cuba rhumba / Owl and I,The.
Album: released on Detour, '83 by Detour Records. Dist: Swift, RCA, Jazz Music, Projection

JUST KEEP A MOVING.
Album: released on Detour, Mar'84 by Detour Records. Dist: Swift, RCA, Jazz Music, Projection

RAILROAD MAN.
Tracks: / Waiting for a train / Big wheels / Lat ride, The / Streamlined canon ball, The / Ghost trains / Pan American / Southbound / 'Way out there / Chattanooga choo choo / Wreck of the Number Nine / Lonesome whistle / Crazy engineer, The.
Album: released on RCA, Jan'87 by RCA Records. Dist: RCA, Roots, Swift, Wellard, Chris, I & B, Solomon & Peres Distribution

Cassette: released on RCA, Jan'87 by RCA Records. Dist: RCA, Roots, Swift, Wellard, Chris, I & B, Solomon & Peres Distribution

Snowman

SNOWMAN, THE Film Soundtrack & Story (Film Soundtrack & Story).
Album: released on CBS, Dec'83 by CBS Records. Dist: CBS

Cassette: released on CBS, Dec'83 by CBS Records. Dist: CBS

Snowmen

HOKEY COKEY.
Single (7"): released on Slack, Nov'81 by Stiff Records. Dist: CBS

HOKEY COKEY THE ALBUM.
Album: released on Solid, Dec'84 by Solid Records. Dist: Graduate, Spartan

Cassette: released on Solid, Dec'84 by Solid Records. Dist: Graduate, Spartan

NIK NAK PADDY WAK.
Tracks: / Nik nak paddy wak / Snowmen are rappin' / Nik nak paddy wak / Hokey cokey / Auld lang syne (Medley) / Snowmen rappin'.
Single (7"): released on Priority, '86 by Priority Records. Dist: RCA

Single (12"): released on Priority, '86 by Priority Records. Dist: RCA

XMAS PARTY/DANCE OF THE SNOWMEN.
Single (7"): released on Solid, Dec'83 by Solid Records. Dist: Graduate, Spartan

Snow Phoebe

BEST OF.
Album: released on CBS, Apr'85 by CBS Records. Dist: CBS

Cassette: released on CBS, Apr'85 by CBS Records. Dist: CBS

GAMES/DOWN IN THE BASEMENT.
Single (7"): released on Atlantic, Apr'81 by WEA Records. Dist: WEA

GASOLINE ALLEY.
Single (7"): released on Mirage, Jun'81 Dist: Pinnacle

ROCK AWAY.
Album: released on Mirage, Apr'81 Dist: Pinnacle

Cassette: released on Mirage, Apr'81 Dist: Pinnacle

Snow Queen

SNOW QUEEN Various artists (Various Artists).
Cassette: released on Tellastory, Oct'79 by Bartlett Bliss Productions. Dist: PRT Distribution, Hayward Promotions Distribution, H.R. Taylor Distribution

SNOW QUEEN Adapted by Pamela Matthew (Matthew, Pamela).
Album: released on Tempo, Nov'79 by Warwick Records. Dist: Multiple Sound Distributors

Cassette: released on Tempo, Nov'79 by Warwick Records. Dist: Multiple Sound Distributors

Snow, Tom

SOMEWHERE DOWN THE ROAD.
Single (7"): released on Arista, Jan'83 by Arista Records. Dist: RCA

Snow White

SNOW WHITE Various artists (Various Artists).
Cassette: released on Anvil, Jan'81 Dist: Anvil

SNOW WHITE AND THE ROSE RED
Tell-a-tale series (Various Artists).
Cassette: released on Pickwick (Ladybird), '83

SNOW WHITE & THE SEVEN DWARFS
Various artists (Various Artists).
Cassette: released on Tellastory, Oct'79 by Bartlett Bliss Productions. Dist: PRT Distribution, Hayward Promotions Distribution, H.R. Taylor Distribution

Cassette: released on Pickwick (Ladybird), '83

Album: released on Disneyland, Dec'82 Dist: EMI

Picture disc album: released on Disneyland, Dec'82 Dist: EMI

Extended-play record: released on Disneyland, Dec'82 Dist: EMI

Cassette: released on Disneyland, Dec'82 Dist: EMI

SNOW WHITE & THE SEVEN DWARFS
Film Soundtrack-Various artists (Film Soundtrack-Various artists).
Album: released on Disney, Oct'84 by BBC Records & Tapes. Dist: BBC Records & Tapes, PRT

Cassette: released on Disney, Oct'84 by BBC Records & Tapes. Dist: BBC Records & Tapes, PRT

Snowy Red

I'M RED/MEGADEATH.
Single (7"): released on Dirty Dance, Apr'82 Dist: Pinnacle

SNOWY RED.
Album: released on New Dance, Apr'82 Dist: Rough Trade, Red Rhino, Cartel

VISION.
Album: released on Soundworks, Feb'84 by Rough Trade Records. Dist: Cartel

Snyder, Bill

BEWITCHING HOUR.
Album: released on Memoir, Jan'87 by Memoir Records. Dist: PRT Distribution

BEWITCHING HOUR (THE).
Album: released on Memoir, '86 by Memoir Records. Dist: PRT Distribution

Cassette: released on Memoir, '86 by Memoir Records. Dist: PRT Distribution

Snyder, John

PIECES OF LIGHT (See McPhee, John) (Snyder, John & John McPhee).

Soapy

TOP OF THE BOX.
Single (7"): released on BBC, Nov'86 by BBC Records & Tapes. Dist: EMI, PRT, Pye

Single (12"): released on BBC, Nov'86 by BBC Records & Tapes. Dist: EMI, PRT, Pye

Soca Explosion On 33

SOCA EXPLOSION ON 33 Vol. 1: Ellie matt & g.i. brass (Various Artists).

Soca Syndicate

BOY LIKE YOU/VERSION.
Single (12"): released on Sunburn, Dec'83 by Orbitone Records. Dist: Jetstar Distribution

Soca Train

SOCA TRAIN Various artists (Various Artists).
Album: released on London, Aug'84 by London Records. Dist: Polygram

Album: released on London, Aug'84 by London Records. Dist: Polygram

Soccio, Gino

CLOSER.
Album: released on Atlantic, May'81 by WEA Records. Dist: WEA

HUMAN NATURE.
Single (12"): released on Noir, Oct'85 Dist: Pinnacle, Jetstar, PRT

SOCIAL HARP.
Album: released on Rounder, May'79 Dist: Roots Distribution

TODAY/BULLY BOYS/WORLD AT RANSOM.
Single (7"): released on Karnage, Mar'83 by IFK Records. Dist: IFK

TRY IT OUT/CLOSER.
Single (7"): released on Atlantic, Jun'81 by WEA Records. Dist: WEA

Single (12"): released on Atlantic, Jun'81 by WEA Records. Dist: WEA

Social club,The
RUMOURS.
Tracks: Rumours / Rumours (Shep's version).
Single (7"): released on Cool Tempo, '86 by Chrysalis Records. Dist: CBS

Single (12"): released on Cool Tempo, '86 by Chrysalis Records. Dist: CBS

Social Unrest
BEFORE THE FALL.
Album: released on Konkurrel, Aug'87

Society
SATURN GIRL.
Single (7"): released on Biglife, Aug'87 by Bi-glife Records. Dist: Rough Trade, Cartel

Single (12"): released on Biglife, Aug'87 by Bi-glife Records. Dist: Rough Trade, Cartel

Society Highes
BOOTS/WALKOUT.
Single (7"): released on Out To Lunch, May'83 by Out To Lunch Records. Dist: PRT Distribution

Single (12"): released on Out To Lunch, Jun'83 by Out To Lunch Records. Dist: PRT Distribution

Society's Rejects
SKINS 'N' PUNKS VOLUME 1 (Society's Rejects/Last Rough....).
Album: released on Oil, Nov'86 Dist: Revolver Distribution

Sockit
SWING ON A STAR.
Single (7"): released on FM, Sep'85 by FM-Revolver Records. Dist: EMI

Single (12"): released on FM, Sep'85 by FM-Revolver Records. Dist: EMI

Soda, Frank
OVERSEXED & UNDERFED.
Single (7"): released on Carrere, Jun'81 by Carrere Records. Dist: PRT, Spartan

Sodom
OBSESSED BY CRUELTY.
Album: released on Steamhammer, '86

Sods
MINUTES TO GO.
Album: released on Step Forward, Sep'79 by Faulty Products Records. Dist: Faulty Products Distribution, Pinnacle

So Feww
GET INSIDE/I'M NOT AUTOMATIC.
Single (7"): released on All For One, Nov'82 Dist: Pinnacle

SPIRITS HIGH/RAINMAKER & HIS SON.
Single (7"): released on All For One, Jun'82 Dist: Pinnacle

Soft And Easy
SOFT AND EASY.
Double Album: released on Decca, Oct'75 by Decca Records. Dist: Polygram

Cassette: released on Decca, Oct'75 by Decca Records. Dist: Polygram

VOLUME 2 (VARIOUS ORIGINAL OR-CHESTRAS).
Double Album: released on Decca, Apr'77 by Decca Records. Dist: Polygram

Cassette: released on Decca, Apr'77 by Decca Records. Dist: Polygram

Soft And Tender
SOFT AND TENDER (Various Artists).
Compact disc: Dist: CD Centre Distribution, Pinnacle, Target

SOFT AND TENDER Various artists (Various Artists).
Notes: Star Marketing Services Ltd, 90 Queens Road, Twickenham, Middlesex. TW1 4ET. Tel: 1 891 6487.
Compact disc: released on Bridge, '86 Dist: CD Centre Distribution, Pinnacle, Target

Soft As Ghosts
MYSTIFIED/FACETS OF LOVE.
Single (7"): released on Roundlet, Sep'83

Soft Boys
CAN OF BEES.
Album: released on Aura, Feb'80 by Hollywood Nites Distribution. Dist: Pinnacle

Album: released on Two Crabs, Jun'84 Dist: Rough Trade, Stage One

HE'S A REPTILE/SONG NO 4.
Single (7"): released on Midnight, Apr'83

I WANNA DESTROY YOU.
Single (7"): released on Armageddon, Jul'81 by Armageddon Records. Dist: Revolver, Cartel, Pinnacle

KINGDOM OF LOVE.
Single (7"): released on Armageddon, Jul'82 by Armageddon Records. Dist: Revolver, Cartel, Pinnacle

KINGDOM OF LOVE/VEGETABLE MAN.
Single (7"): released on Armageddon, Jul'82 by Armageddon Records. Dist: Revolver, Cartel, Pinnacle

ONLY THE STONE REMAINS.
Single (7"): released on Armchair, Oct'81

TWO HALVES FOR THE PRICE OF ONE.
Album: released on Armageddon, Mar'82 by Armageddon Records. Dist: Revolver, Cartel, Pinnacle

WAITING FOR A VENTIATOR.
Album: released on De Laurean, Aug'85 by Backs Records. Dist: Cartel

Soft Cell
12 SINGLES THE.
Single (12"): released on Some, Nov'82 Dist: Phonogram, Polygram

ART OF FALLING APART.
Album: released on Some Bizarre, Feb'83 by Virgin Records. Dist: EMI, CBS, Polygram

Cassette: released on Some Bizarre, Feb'83 by Virgin Records. Dist: EMI, CBS, Polygram

LAST NIGHT (THE) (THE FINAL SOFT CELL ALBUM).
Tracks: / Mr self destruct / Slave to this / Little rough rhinestone / Meet murder my angel / Best way to kill (The) / L'esqualita / Down in the subway / Surrender (To a stranger) / Soul inside / Where was your heart (When you needed it most).
Notes: Marc and David's new 'Farewell album',released earlier this year to great critical acclaim.
Compact disc: released on Some Bizarre, '84 by Virgin Records. Dist: EMI, CBS, Polygram

NON STOP ECSTATIC DANCING.
Album: released on Some Bizzare, Jun'82 by Charisma Records. Dist: EMI, CBS, Polygram

Cassette: released on Some Bizzare, Jun'82 by Charisma Records. Dist: EMI, CBS, Polygram

NON STOP EROTIC DANCING.
Album: released on Some Bizzare, Nov'81 by Charisma Records. Dist: EMI, CBS, Polygram
Cat. no: BZLP 2
Cassette: released on Some Bizzare, Nov'81 by Charisma Records. Dist: EMI, CBS, Polygram

NON STOP EROTIC VIDEO SHOW.
Notes: Songs taken from the 'Erotic' and 'Ec-static dancing' albums.
Video-cassette (VHS): released on Video Collection, May'87 by Video Collection International Ltd.. Dist: Counterpoint

NON STOP EXOTIC VIDEOSHOW.
Video-cassette (VHS): released on PMI, '86 by PMI Records. Dist: EMI

Video-cassette (Betamax): released on PMI, '86 by PMI Records. Dist: EMI
Cat. no: MXP 99 1035 4

SINGLES 1981-1985, THE.
Tracks: / Memorabilla / Tainted love / Bedsitter / Say hello, wave goodbye / Torch / What / Where the heart is / Numbers / Soul inside / Down in the subway.
Album:

Cassette:

Compact disc: released on Polydor, Nov'86 by Polydor Records. Dist: Polygram, Polydor

SINGLES, (THE).
Compact disc: by Charisma Records. Dist: EMI, CBS, Polygram

Soft Cell
Video-cassette (VHS): released on Thorn-Emi, '84

Tainted Love.
Single (7"): released on Some Bizarre, Feb'85 by Virgin Records. Dist: EMI, CBS, Polygram

Single (12"): released on Some Bizarre, Feb'85 by Virgin Records. Dist: EMI, CBS, Polygram

TAINTED LOVE (VIDEO).
Tracks: / Tainted love / Say hello, wave good-bye.
Notes: Video single.
Video-cassette (VHS): released on Gold Rushes, Mar'87 by Video Collection International Ltd.. Dist: Counterpoint

Soft Drinks
CINZANO WET DREAM/POP STARS.
Single (7"): released on Outer Himalayen, Apr'82 Dist: Rough Trade Distribution

Soft Heap
SOFT HEAP.
Album: released on Charly, Aug'79 by Charly Records. Dist: Charly, Cadillac

Softly As I Leave You
SOFTLY AS I LEAVE YOU various artists (Various Artists).
Album: released on Music For Pleasure (Holland), Sep'84 by EMI Records. Dist: EMI

Soft Machine
ALIVE & WELL & LIVING IN PARIS.
Album: released on EMI (Germany), Aug'83 by EMI Records. Dist: Conifer

AT THE BEGINNING.
Album: released on Charly, Mar'83 by Charly Records. Dist: Charly, Cadillac

SOFT MACHIME VOLUME 2.
Album: released on Big Beat, May'87 by Ace Records. Dist: Projection, Pinnacle

Cassette: released on Big Beat, May'87 by Ace Records. Dist: Projection, Pinnacle

SOFT MACHINE.
Album: released on Big Beat, Mar'87 by Ace Records. Dist: Projection, Pinnacle

Cassette: released on Big Beat, Mar'87 by Ace Records. Dist: Projection, Pinnacle

Soft Shoe
KOJO.
Single (7"): released on IDM, Aug'84 by IDM Records. Dist: PRT

Soft Touch
I'S MY LIFE/THE SUS SONG.
Single (7"): released on Nems, Nov'80 Dist: Castle Communications Records, Pinnacle Records

Soft verdict
AT HOME.
Single (12"): released on Les Disques Du Cre-puscule, Aug'87 Dist: Rough Trade, Pinnacle, Island, Polygram

AT HOME/NOT HOME.
Single (7"): released on Les Disques Du Cre-puscule, Feb'82 Dist: Rough Trade, Pinnacle, Island, Polygram

CLOSER COVER.
Single (7"): released on Les Disques Du Cre-puscule, Nov'83 Dist: Rough Trade, Pinnacle, Island, Polygram

FOR AMUSEMENT ONLY.
Album: released on Crepescule, '86 by Island Records. Dist: Polygram, Pinnacle

Software
ELECTRONIC UNIVERSE.
Album: released on Innovative Communication, '86 by Innovative Communication Records. Dist: Pickwick Distribution

Soho
WALKING IN THE SAND.
Tracks: / Walking in the sand / Walking in the sand / Rock solid lover / What is it like to be a girl.
Single (7"): released on Big Red Group, '86 by Big Red Group Records. Dist: PRT

Single (12"): released on Big Red Group, '86 by Big Red Group Records. Dist: PRT

So Hot So Sweet
SO HOT SO SWEET Various Artists (Various Artists).

Solal,Martial
BIG A BAND.
Album: released on CY (France), '85 Dist: Discovery

LIVE 1959/85.
Compact disc: released on Accord (France), '86 Dist: Discovery, Target

SOLO SOLAL.
Album: released on MPS Jazz, May'81

SUITE FOR TRIO.
Album: released on MPS Jazz, May'81

Solar Asylum
MADE TO BE BROKEN.
Album: released on Twin Tone, '86

Solar Galaxy Of Stars
SOLAR GALAXY OF STARS Various artists (Various Artists).
Double Album: released on Solar, Oct'80 by MCA Records. Dist: Polygram Distribution

Double cassette: released on Solar, Oct'80 by MCA Records. Dist: Polygram Distribution

Solar System
SOLAR SYSTEM, THE (Various Artists).
Tracks: / Standing on your own / Take a chance on me / Take that to the bank / Romeo where's Juliet / Wet my whistle / It's a love thing / There it is / Get in touch with me / Headlines / Night to remember, A / Sweet sensation / Operator (edited version) / Over and over / Some kinda lover.
Album: released on MCA, May'87 by MCA Records. Dist: Polygram, MCA

Cassette: released on MCA, May'87 by MCA Records. Dist: Polygram, MCA

Compact disc: released on MCA, May'87 by MCA Records. Dist: Polygram, MCA

Soldier
SHERLEE/FORCE.
Single (12"): released on Heavy Metal, Feb'82 by FM-Revolver Records. Dist: EMI

Soldier Dolls
TASTE OF BLOOD A.
Single (7"): released on Sream, Feb'85 by Revolver Records. Dist: Cartel Distribution

WHAT DO THEY KNOW.
Single (7"): released on Revolver, Mar'84 by Revolver Records. Dist: Revolver, Cartel

Soldiers Of Fortune
STARS/AUTONMIA.
Single (7"): released on Total Darkness, May'83 by Rough Trade Records.

Solen, Andrzej
SOLIDARITY DEFIANT/GENERAL FEELINGS.
Single (7"): released on Solidarity, Jul'82

Solid air
IT AIN'T GONNA HAPPEN.
Cassette: released on Plankton, Apr'85 by Plankton Records. Dist: Cantio (Sweden)

WAY PAST BEDTIME.
Tracks: / Anti anti / Now that I've found your love / Living in a real world / Stranger to myself / All of my dreams / Intro / What's missing / Artificial Heart / Borrowed love / Stop me from starting this feeling / Breathless / Don't let love let you down / Never to much / Roses / Passion from a woman / My number / Falling in love / Hold on / What about me / Amityville / Outro.
Cassette: released on Plankton, '86 by Plankton Records. Dist: Cantio (Sweden)

Album: released on Epic, '86 by CBS Records. Dist: CBS

Cassette: released on Epic, '86 by CBS Records. Dist: CBS

Solid Gold...
SOLID GOLD COUNTRY Various artists (Various Artists).
Cassette: released on RCA International, Jun'82

SOLID GOLD MILLION SELLERS Various session artists (Various Session Artists).
Cassette: released on AIM (Budget Cassettes), Feb'83

Solid Gold Swing
SOLID GOLD SWING Various artists.
Cassette: released on RCA International, Nov'84

Solid In Brass

HANDBELL MUSIC.
Cassette: released on Saydisc, Jul'77 by Saydisc Records. Dist: Essex, Harmonia Mundi, Roots, H.R. Taylor, Jazz Music, Swift, Projection, Gamut

Solid Soul

SOLID SOUL (Various Artists).
Tracks: / Stand by me / Soul man / Knock on wood / My guy / Hey there lonely girl / Patches / Rescue me / Mr big stuff / Backfield in motion / Tighten up / Harry hippie / Satisfaction guaranteed / In crowd, The / When a man loves a woman.
Notes: (P) & (C) 1987 K-Tel International (UK) Ltd. K-Tel International (UK) Ltd., 620 Western Avenue, London W3. K-Tel Ireland Ltd, 31 Ballsbridge Terrace, Dublin 4.
Compact disc: released on K-Tel, May'87 by K-Tel Records. Dist: Record Merchandisers Distribution, Taylors, Terry Blood Distribution, Wynd-Up Distribution, Relay Distribution, Pickwick Distribution, Solomon & Peres Distribution, Polygram

Solitaire

BABY BLUE.
Tracks: / Baby blue / Baby blue clarient instrumental.
Single (7"): released on Plaza, '86 by Plaza Records. Dist: Spartan

MY MAN.
Single (7"): released on Plaza, Jan'87 by Plaza Records. Dist: Spartan

WOMAN IN ME, THE.
Tracks: / Woman in me, The / Woman in me, The (inst).
Single (7"): released on Plaza, Jul'87 by Plaza Records. Dist: Spartan

Single (12"): released on Plaza, Jul'87 by Plaza Records. Dist: Spartan

Solitaire Collection

I WRITE THE SONGS various artists (Various original artists).
Album: released on Starblend, '83 by Starblend Records. Dist: PRT Distribution

Cassette: released on Starblend, '83 by Starblend Records. Dist: PRT Distribution

SOLITAIRE COLLECTION.
: by Starblend Records. Dist: PRT Distribution

Solley David

DARK ISLAND THE.
Cassette: released on Lismor, Jan'73 by Lismor Records. Dist: Lismor, Roots, Celtic Music

Album: released on DGG, Nov'84 by Polydor Records. Dist: Polygram

Cassette: released on DGG, Nov'84 by Polydor Records. Dist: Polygram

Compact disc: released on DGG, Nov'84 by Polydor Records. Dist: Polygram

GREAT SONGS OF SCOTLAND.
Album: released on Lismor, May'77 by Lismor Records. Dist: Lismor, Roots, Celtic Music

Cassette: released on Lismor, May'77 by Lismor Records. Dist: Lismor, Roots, Celtic Music

HIGHLANDS AND ISLANDS.
Album: by Lismor Records. Dist: Lismor, Roots, Celtic Music

Cassette: by Lismor Records. Dist: Lismor, Roots, Celtic Music

Sollscher,Goran

CAVATINA.
Tracks: / Granada / Portrait / Sakura / Georgia on my mind / Romance d'amour.
Notes: Digital Stereo
Compact disc: released on DGG, '84 by Polydor Records. Dist: Polygram

Solo

SOLO.
Tracks: / Solo / Right stuff (The).
Single (7"): released on PRT, '85 by PRT Records. Dist: PRT

Single (7"): released on PRT, Nov'85 by PRT Records. Dist: PRT

Solo Album

SOLO ALBUM Various artists (Various Artists).
Album: released on Fried Egg, Jul'81 by Fried Egg Records. Dist: Rough Trade, Cartel

Soloff, Lew

HANALEI BAY.
Notes: Ex-member of Blood,Sweat & Tears trumpeter Lew Soloff presents an album of fusion jazz using both acoustic and electric instruments. The material ranges from the beautiful ballads 'My Buddy' and 'A Felicidade' to the latin percussive 'Handel Bay'. Gil Evans is featured on electric piano. Personnel: Lew Soloff-trumpet,flugehorn/Gil Evans-electric piano/Pete Levin-synthsizer/Hiram Bullock-guitars/Mark Egon-bass/Adam Nussbaum-drums/Kenwood Dennard-drums/Manolo Badrena-percussion.

YESTERDAYS.
Album: released on King (USA), Apr'87 Dist: Gusto Distribution

Soloists of the Bolshoi

RUSSIAN OLD ROMANCES.
Cassette: released on Melodiya (USSR), Feb'79 Dist: T.B.C Distribution

Soloman, Roger

IN THE GROOVE.
Single (12"): released on Raiders, May'85 Dist: Jetstar

Solomon, Diane

LIVE ON TOUR.
Album: released on Bulldog, Aug'81 by Bulldog Records. Dist: President Distribution, Spartan, Swift, Taylor, H.R.

Cassette: released on Bulldog, Aug'81 by Bulldog Records. Dist: President Distribution, Spartan, Swift, Taylor, H.R.

YOU CAN DO IT.
Single (7"): released on Bulldog, Jun'81 by Bulldog Records. Dist: President Distribution, Spartan, Swift, Taylor, H.R.

Solo, Sal

HEART AND SOUL
Tracks: / Heart beat / Poland your spirit won't die / Shout shout / Music and you / Contact / Go now / Forever be.
Album: released on MCA, '85 by MCA Records. Dist: Polygram, MCA

Cassette: released on MCA, '85 by MCA Records. Dist: Polygram, MCA

HOW WAS I TO KNOW.
Tracks: / How was I to know / In innocence.
Single (7"): released on Awesome, Feb'87 by Awesome Records. Dist: Rough Trade, Cartel

Sol Paradise

SLOW PASSION/COME TO MY ROOM.
Single (7"): released on Abstract, Mar'82 by Abstract. Dist: Pinnacle

Solstice

NEW LIFE//PEACE FOR THE NEW AGE.
Cassette: released on Roke, Aug'83 Dist: Roke Distribution

SILENT DANCE.
Album: released on Equinox, Nov'84 by Equinox. Dist: Pinnacle

Solution

HOW TO SOLVE THE RUBIK CUBE.
Cassette: released on Nevis, Nov'81 Dist: H.R Taylor

Some, Belouis

BELOUIS SOME.
Tracks: / Let it be with you / Stranger than fiction / Some girls / Passion play / Animal magic / Dream girl / My body / Wind of change / What I see / Let it be with you (12" mixed by Phil 'Mixmaster' Harding).
Album: released on Parlophone, Jun'87 by EMI Records. Dist: EMI

Cassette: released on Parlophone, Jun'87 by EMI Records. Dist: EMI

Compact disc: released on Parlophone, Jun'87 by EMI Records. Dist: EMI

IMAGINATION.
Tracks: / Imagination / Have you ever been in love? / Imagination / Target pratice.
Single (7"): released on Parlophone, '86 by EMI Records. Dist: EMI

Single (12"): released on Parlophone, '86 by EMI Records. Dist: EMI

Double-pack single: released on Parlophone, '86 by EMI Records. Dist: EMI

Single (7"): released on Parlophone, Mar'85 by EMI Records. Dist: EMI

Single (12"): released on Parlophone, Mar'85 by EMI Records. Dist: EMI

JERUSALEM.
Tracks: / Jerusalem / Target practice / Round round / Stand down.
Single (7"): released on Parlophone, '86 by EMI Records. Dist: EMI

Single (12"): released on Parlophone, '86 by EMI Records. Dist: EMI

Single (7"): released on Parlophone, '86 by EMI Records. Dist: EMI

LET IT BE WITH YOU.
Tracks: / Let it be with you / Wind of change / Let it be with you (ext dance mix) / Imagination (dance mix) / Some people.
Compact disc single: released on Parlophone, May'87 by EMI Records. Dist: EMI

Single (7"): released on Parlophone, Apr'87 by EMI Records. Dist: EMI

Single (7"): released on Parlophone, Apr'87 by EMI Records. Dist: EMI

Single (12"): released on Parlophone, Apr'87 by EMI Records. Dist: EMI

LET IT BE WITH YOU (REMIX).
Tracks: / Let it be with you (remix) / Let it be with you (dub) / Wind of change.
Single (12"): released on EMI, May'87 by EMI Records. Dist: EMI

SOME PEOPLE.
Tracks: / Some way / Walk away / Have you ever been in love / Jerusalem / Some people / Stand down / Imagination / Walk away / Aware of you / Target practice / Have you ever been in love / Tail lights / Jerusalem.
Single (7"): released on Parlophone, '86 by EMI Records. Dist: EMI

Double-pack single: released on Parlophone, '86 by EMI Records. Dist: EMI

Single (12"): released on Parlophone, '86 by EMI Records. Dist: EMI

Single (7"): released on Parlophone, Jun'85 by EMI Records. Dist: EMI

Single (12"): released on Parlophone, Jul'85 by EMI Records. Dist: EMI

Double-pack single: released on Parlophone, Jul'85 by EMI Records. Dist: EMI

SOME PEOPLE (REMIX).
Tracks: / Some people / Walk way.
Single (7"): released on Parlophone, '86 by EMI Records. Dist: EMI

Picture disc single: released on Parlophone, '86 by EMI Records. Dist: EMI

Some Day Blue

DARK ROOM.
Single (7"): released on Raucous, Nov'83 by MK Records. Dist: MK

Some Detergents

MODERN PROBLEMS.
Single (7"): released on Out Of Town, Jun'82

Some fascinating things

SOME FASCINATING THINGS Various Artists (Various Artists).
Album: released on Crepescule, '86 by Island Records. Dist: Polygram, Pinnacle

Some Ghost Stories

SOME GHOST STORIES (Hordern, Sir Michael).

Some Kind Of Wonderful

D'YOU READ MY LETTER.
Single (7"): released on Reekus, Sep'82 by Reekus Records. Dist: Nine Mile, Cartel

SOME KIND OF WONDERFUL Film soundtrack (Various Artists).
Tracks: / Do anything / Brilliant mind / Cry like this / I go crazy / She loves me / Hardest walk (The) / Shyest time (The) / Miss Amanada Jones / Cant help falling in love / Turn to the sky.
Album: released on MCA, Apr'87 by MCA Records. Dist: Polygram, MCA

Cassette: released on MCA, Apr'87 by MCA Records. Dist: Polygram, MCA

Some Now Are

TRUTH TO TELL.
Single (7"): released on Interior, Jan'84 by Interior Records. Dist: Rough Trade

Someone Else

BE MY BABY.
Single (7"): released on Stagmanor, Sep'83 by Stagmanor Records. Dist: Pinnacle

Some People Play Guitar

SOME PEOPLE PLAY GUITAR LIKE A LOTTA PEOPLE DON'T various artists (Various Artists).
Album: released on Kicking Mule, '74 by Sonet Dist: Roots, PRT

Somers, Debroy

DEROY SOMERS & HIS BAND (Somers, Debroy & His Band).
Album: released on Joy, Jul'84 by President Records. Dist: Jazz Music, Swift, President Distribution

Somerset, Arthur

OK YA.
Single (7"): released on Loose End, Mar'84 by MCA Records. Dist: CBS, MCA

Something Fierce

COMPLETELY UNGLUED.
Album: released on Tambourine, Nov'86 by Tambourine. Dist: Backs, Cartel

Something happens

TWO CHANCES.
Tracks: / Two chances (EP).
Single (7"): released on Cooking Vinyl, '86 Dist: Nine Mile, Cartel, Red Rhino

Something Stirs

SOMETHING STIRS various artists (Various Artists).
Album: released on Adventures In Reality, Nov'84 by Backs Records. Dist: Cartel

Something To Shout About

SOMETHING TO SHOUT ABOUT various artists (Various Artists).
Album: released on Seville, Nov'82 by President Records. Dist: Jazz Music, Swift

Something wild

SOMETHING WILD Film soundtrack (Various Artists).
Tracks: / Loco de amor / Ever fallen in love / Zero zero seven charlie / Not my slave / You don't have to cry / With or without you / High life / Man with a gun / Temptation / Wild thing.
Album: released on MCA, Apr'87 by MCA Records. Dist: Polygram, MCA

Cassette: released on MCA, Apr'87 by MCA Records. Dist: Polygram, MCA

Somewhere A Voice

LOVE LOGIC & EGO.
Album: released on Peyote, Sep'84 Dist: Jazz Music

Somewhere In time

SOMEWHERE IN TIME Original soundtrack (Various Artists).
Album: released on MCA, '86 by MCA Records. Dist: Polygram, MCA

Cassette: released on MCA, '86 by MCA Records. Dist: Polygram, MCA

Sommer,Gunter

ASCENSUER POUR LE 28 (Sommer,Gunter et Trois Vieux Amis).
Tracks: / Nelly et Sylvain / Daniel und sein volvo / Makoko apercoit / Toute pour raoul / Jiair und J.E. / Isabel record boxes'.
Album: released on Nato (France), '86 by Disques Nato. Dist: Essex Record Distributors Ltd.

HORMUSIK ZWEI.
Tracks: / Chatenay / Villedieu / Isabelle icebox.
Album: released on Nato (France), '86 by Disques Nato. Dist: Essex Record Distributors Ltd.

Sommers, Joanie

DREAM (Sommers, Joanie /Bob Florence).
Album: released on Discovery (USA), Aug'83 by Discovery Records (USA). Dist: Swift, Flexitron-Audio, Jazz Music

Sommers, Patti

LAST NIGHT, THE.
Album: released on Birds Nest, Jul'78 by Happy Face Records. Dist: Red Rhino, Bulle Distribution, Pinnacle, Birds Nest, PRT

Somo Somo

PARIS.
Album: released on Sterns, Jan'87 by Sterns Records. Dist: Sterns/Triple Earth Distribution

SOMO SOMO.
Album: released on Sterns, Mar'85 by Sterns Records. Dist: Sterns/Triple Earth Distribution

SOMO SOMO'(ZAIRE/UK).
Tracks: / Mosese 2000 / Masikiki ya mola Jamy jamy / Mele / Cheko.
Notes: The whirlwind sounds of Zairean soukous blew new life into the music scene with this tight London recording. "The best African LP to be released anywhere this year (1985).(City Limits)"
Album: released on Sterns, '85 by Sterns Records. Dist: Sterns/Triple Earth Distribution

Album: released on Sterns, '86 by Sterns Records. Dist: Sterns/Triple Earth Distribution
Cat. no: **STERNS 10**

Song and dance

SONG AND DANCE (Various Artists).
Notes: An Andrew Lloyd Webber Spectacular featuring songs from Sarah Brightman in 'Tell me on a Sunday and dance from Wayne Sleep and company to the 'Variations' music.
Video-cassette (VHS): released on RCA, Oct'84 by RCA Records. Dist: RCA, Roots, Swift, Wellard, Chris, I & B, Solomon & Peres Distribution

Songbirds

SONGBIRDS Various original artists (Various original artists).
Double Album: released on Starblend (Solitaire Collection), '83 by Starblend Records. Dist: PRT Distribution

Double cassette: released on Starblend (Solitaire Collection), '83 by Starblend Records. Dist: PRT Distribution

Songbook

SONGBOOK Original Cast (Various Artists).
Album: released on PRT, Sep'79 by PRT Records. Dist: PRT

Song & Dance

SONG & DANCE Original cast recording (Various Artists).
Double Album: released on Polydor, Jun'82 by Polydor Records. Dist: Polygram, Polydor

Cassette: released on Polydor, Jun'82 by Polydor Records. Dist: Polygram, Polydor

Song Is...

SONG IS...GERSHWIN, THE Gershwin 50th anniversary tribute (Various Artists).
Tracks: / I got rhythm / Man I love, The / Half of it, dearie, blues, The / Oh lady be good / Little jazz bird / Do what you do / Funny face / My one and only / I found a four leaf clover / Nashville nightingale / Sweet and low down / That certain feeling / Liza / When do we dance / Someone to watch over me / S'wonderful / Fascinatin' rhythm / I'll build a stairway to paradise / I got plenty o' nuttin'.
Album: released on ASV Living Era, Jul'87 by ASV Records. Dist: PRT

Cassette: released on ASV Living Era, Jul'87 by ASV Records. Dist: PRT

SONG IS JEROME KERN, THE various artists (Various Artists).
Album: released on ASV Living Era, Sep'85 by ASV Records. Dist: PRT

Cassette: released on ASV Living Era, Sep'85 by ASV Records. Dist: PRT

SONG IS, THE Richard Rogers and Lorenz Hart (Various Artists).
Tracks: / We'll be the same / My heart stood still / Blue Room, The / Little things you do, The / Little birdie told me so, A / Why do you suppose? / Maybe it's me / Girl friend, The / Mountain greenery / Step on the Blues / Whats the use of talking / Thou Swell / Its easy to remember / Yours sincerely / Dancing on the ceiling / Blue Moon / Hello / Where's that rainbow / Tree in the park, A / Give her a kiss / With a Song in my heart.
Notes: 'Immortal' say's Capitol radio's Brian Rust of the Rodgers and Hart songwriting partnership,'and one of the cornerstones on which the edifice of American popular music is built'. There is little more to be said: here is a superb blend of all time favourites together with lesser known but remarkable songs by some great artists, and an excellent follow up to the Jerome Kern compillation (AJA 5036)
Album: released on ASV, May'86 by Academy Sound & Vision Records. Dist: Pinnacle

Cassette: released on ASV, May'86 by Academy Sound & Vision Records. Dist: Pinnacle

Song Of A...

SONG OF A DUTCH STREET ORGAN various artists (Various Artists).
Album: released on Sound Stories, Feb'80 Dist: H.R. Taylor

Song Remains The Same

SONG REMAINS THE SAME (Various Artists).

Songs For A Modern Church

SONGS FOR A MODERN CHURCH various artists (Various Artists).

Album: released on Charisma, Apr'83 by Virgin Records. Dist: EMI

Cassette: released on Charisma, Apr'83 by Virgin Records. Dist: EMI

Songs For New Lovers

SONGS FOR NEW LOVERS (Dardanelle (vocal) (Various Artists).
Album: released on Stash, '79 Dist: Swift Distribution, Jazz Music Distribution, Jazz Horizons Distribution, Celtic Music Distribution, Cadillac, JSU Distribution, Zodiac Distribution
Cat. no: **ST 202**

Songs For Tomorrow

SONGS FOR TOMORROW Various artists (Various Artists).
Album: released on BBC, Aug'80 by BBC Records & Tapes. Dist: EMI, PRT, Pye

Cassette: released on BBC, Aug'80 by BBC Records & Tapes. Dist: EMI, PRT, Pye

Songs From

SONGS FROM ORIGINAL SOUND TRACKS Various artists (Various Artists).
Notes: 1985: Original sound recordings owned by Buena Vista Distribution Co. Inc.

SONGS FROM PLAYSCHOOL From children's TV (Various Artists).
Album: released on BBC, Feb'84 by BBC Records & Tapes. Dist: EMI, PRT, Pye

Cassette: released on BBC, Feb'84 by BBC Records & Tapes. Dist: EMI, PRT, Pye

SONGS FROM THE NEW INTERNATIONAL various artists (Various Artists).
Notes: Including, Royal Family and the poor, Muslin Gauze
Album: released on Recloose Organisation, Jun'86 by Recloose Organisation. Dist: Cartel, Rough Trade

SONGS FROM THE NEW REDEMPTION HYMNAL (Songs from the New Redemption Hymnal).
Tracks: / And can it be / Bind us together / great is thy faithfulness / Just as I am / Old Rugged cross, The / Thine be the glory / When I survey the Wonderous cross.
Notes: A live recording of 16 hyns to accompany the new redemption hymnal book.
Album: released on Word, Oct'86 by Word Records. Dist: Word Distribution, CBS

Cassette: released on Word, Oct'86 by Word Records. Dist: Word Distribution, CBS

Songs Of

ALL JOLLY FELLOWS-SONGS OF COUNTRY LIFE various artists (Various Artists).
Cassette: released on Folktracks, Nov'79 by Folktracks Cassettes. Dist: Folktracks

SONGS OF BRER RABBIT (Glass, Dudley).

SONGS OF CHRISTMAS PAST (Various Artists).
Tracks: / Christmas alphabet / Rudolph the red nosed reindeer / Christmas and you / Away in a manger / Christmas island / I'm sending a letter to Santa Claus / Silent night,holy night / St.Nicholas waltz / Santo Natale (Merry christmas) / Little boy that Santa Claus forgot (The) / Jingle bells / White Christmas / Christmas song (merry Christmas to you),The / I saw mommy kissing Santa Claus / Little donkey / Christmas in Killarney / Merry Christmas / Merry christmas / Adeste fideles (o come all ye faithful).
Album: released on Recollections, Dec'86

SONGS OF IRELAND Various artists (Various Artists).
Tracks: / Fields of Athenry / Song for Ireland, A / Men of worth / I'll take you home again Kathleen / Raglan Road / Isle of Innisfree, The / Let it be / When you were sweet sixteen / Cavan girl / Water is wide, The / Red is the rose / Sailing home / Parting glass / Bunch of thyme.
Compact disc: released on K-Tel, Jun'87 by K-Tel Records. Dist: Record Merchandisers Distribution, Taylors, Terry Blood Distribution, Wynd-Up Distribution, Relay Distribution, Pickwick Distribution, Solomon & Peres Distribution, Polygram

SONGS OF LOVE,COUNTRY STYLE various artists (Various Artists).
Album: released on ABC, Mar'82 Dist: CBS, Pinnacle

Cassette: released on ABC, Mar'82 Dist: CBS, Pinnacle

SONGS OF LOVE,LUCK, ANIMALS & MAGIC (Various Artists).
Tracks: / Love Song / Grizzly Bear war song / Rabbit song / Gambling Song / Love Song / Basket Song / Brush dance song(dont make fun of my sweetheart) / Brush dance song(Grandpa Natt's song) / Love Song / Seagull Song / Song to stop the Rain / Hunting Song / Brush dance(Hobo song) / Brush Dance / Gambling Songs / Pelican song / Gambling songs / Gambling songs / Ceremonial dance / Ending Ceremonial dance.
Notes: Music of the Yurok(tracks 1-14) and Tolawa(tracks 15-20)Indians(USA!) Producer Charlotte Heth.
Album: released on New World (USA), Sep'86 by New World Records (USA). Dist: Conifer

SONGS OF THE CIVIL WAR various artists (Various Artists).
Tracks: / I wish I was in Dixies' land / All quiet along the Poromac tonight / We are coming, Father Abra'am / Mother, is the battle over? / Drummer boy of Shiloh, The / Beauregards's retreat from Shiloh / Jeff in petticoats / Weeping, sad and lonely / It's a gold old rebel.
Album: released on New World (USA), Dec'86 by New World Records (USA). Dist: Conifer

SONGS OF THE OPEN ROAD (Gypsies,travellers & country singers) (Various Artists).
Album: released on Topic, '81 by Topic Records. Dist: JSU Distribution, Projection Distribution, Jazz Music Distribution

Songs Of Courtship

AS I ROVED OUT.
Cassette: released on Folktracks, Nov'79 by Folktracks Cassettes. Dist: Folktracks

Songs Of Fellowship

SONGS OF FELLOWSHIP VOL.1 A new song (Various Artists).
Album: released on Dove, May'79 by Dove Records. Dist: Jetstar

SONGS OF FELLOWSHIP VOL.2 City of God (Various Artists).
Album: released on Dove, May'79 by Dove Records. Dist: Jetstar

Songs Of Praise

SONGS OF PRAISE VOL.2 from BBC TV (Various Artists).
Album: released on BBC, Oct'78 by BBC Records & Tapes. Dist: EMI, PRT, Pye

Cassette: released on BBC, Oct'78 by BBC Records & Tapes. Dist: EMI, PRT, Pye

Songs Of Scotland

SONGS OF SCOTLAND VOL.1 various artists (Various Artists).

Album: released on Lochshore, May'83 by Klub Records. Dist: PRT

Cassette: released on Lochshore, May'83 by Klub Records. Dist: PRT

SONGS OF SCOTLAND VOL.2 various artists (Various Artists).
Cassette: released on Lochshore, Jun'84 by Klub Records. Dist: PRT

Album: released on Lochshore, Jun'84 by Klub Records. Dist: PRT

SONGS OF SCOTLAND VOL.3 various artists (Various Artists).
Album: released on Lochshore, Apr'85 by Klub Records. Dist: PRT

Cassette: released on Lochshore, Apr'85 by Klub Records. Dist: PRT

SONGS OF SCOTLAND VOL.4 various artists (Various Artists).
Tracks: / Home to the Kyles(Tighnabruaich) / Auld meal wheel / Bonnie Gallowa / Misty islands of the highlands / Wee sprig o'heather, A / Our ain fireside / Loch Lomond / Island of Arran / Rowan tree / Inverary Inn / Old Rustic Brigg, The / Home that I love.
Album: released on Lochshore, Apr'86 by Klub Records. Dist: PRT

Cassette: released on Lochshore, Apr'86 by Klub Records. Dist: PRT

Songs Of Seduction

SONGS OF SEDUCTION (A) various artists (Various Artists).
Cassette: released on Folktracks, Nov'79 by Folktracks Cassettes. Dist: Folktracks

Songs Of The Depression

SONGS OF THE DEPRESSION various artists (Various Artists).
Album: released on Stash (USA), May'84 Dist: Swift Distribution, Jazz Music Distribution, Jazz Horizons Distribution, Celtic Music Distribution, Cadillac, JSU Distribution, Zodiac Distribution

Songs Of The Emerald Isle

SONGS OF THE EMERALD ISLE VOL.1 (Various Artists).
Tracks: / Galway Bay / Spinning wheel (The) / Star of the County Down(The) / Ballyhoe / Old bog road (The) / Coortin' in the kitchen / Mother Machree / Trottin' to the fair / Banks of my own lovely lee (The) / When Irish eyes are smiling / Pretty Irish girl, A / Mountains of Mourne, The / Castlebar Fair / Eileen Oge.
Notes: Record 2 of a two record set
Album: released on MFP, Apr'87 by EMI Records. Dist: EMI

Cassette: released on MFP, Apr'87 by EMI Records. Dist: EMI

SONGS OF THE EMERALD ISLE VOL.2 (Various Artists).
Tracks: / Rose of Tralee, The / Eileen O'Grady / Danny boy / Connemara / Doonaree / Sweet Marie / Flower of sweet Strabane (The) / Whiskey in the jar / Three drunken maidens / Dan Malone / Liffey barges / Galway races, The / Kitty of Colerane / Bantry Bay.
Album: released on MFP, Apr'87 by EMI Records. Dist: EMI

Cassette: released on MFP, Apr'87 by EMI Records. Dist: EMI

Songs Of Ulster...

SONGS OF THE ULSTER PROTESTANT various artists (Various Artists).
Album: released on Ulster, Aug'82 Dist: Outlet

Cassette: released on Ulster, Aug'82 Dist: Outlet

Songs & Southern...

SONGS & SOUTHERN BREEZES (Country singers from Hampshire & Sussex) (Various Artists).
Album: released on Topic, '81 by Topic Records. Dist: JSU Distribution, Projection Distribution, Jazz Music Distribution

Songs & Stars

SONGS & STARS OF THE FORTIES various artists (Various Artists).
Album: released on EMI Retrospect, Oct'84 by EMI Records. Dist: EMI

Cassette: released on EMI Retrospect, Oct'84 by EMI Records. Dist: EMI

SONGS & STARS OF THE THIRTIES various artists (Various Artists).
Album: released on World (Retrospect Series), Feb'84

Cassette: released on World (Retrospect Series), Feb'84

Songsters & Saints

SONGSTERS & SAINTS VOL.1 various blues & gospel artists (Various Artists).
Double Album: released on Matchbox, Nov'84 by Saydisc Records. Dist: Roots, Projection, Jazz Music, JSU, Celtic Music

SONGSTERS & SAINTS VOL.2 various blues & gospel artists (Various Artists).
Double Album: released on Matchbox, May'85 Dist: Projection

Son house

BLIND LEMON JEFFERSON/SON HOUSE (Son House /Blind Lemon Jefferson).

DEATH LETTER.
Album: released on Edsel, Dec'85 by Demon Records. Dist: Pinnacle, Jazz Music, Projection

Soni

AIN'T HAD ENOUGH LOVE.
Tracks: / Aint had enough Love / Reggae sensation.
Single (12"): released on Chartbound, Aug'86 by Chartbound Records. Dist: Jetstar

Sonia

BOY I LOVE, THE.
Single (12"): released on Starlight, Nov'82 by Starlight Records. Dist: Jetstar Distribution

Single (12"): released on D. Roy, Apr'80

Sonic Youth

BAD MOON RISING.
Compact disc: released on Blast First, Nov'86 by Sonic Youth Records. Dist: Rough Trade, Nine Mile, Red Rhino, Cartel

Album: released on Blast First, Mar'85 by Sonic Youth Records. Dist: Rough Trade, Nine Mile, Red Rhino, Cartel

CONFUSION IN SEX.
Album: released on Neutral, Feb'84 by Zensor Records. Dist: Rough Trade, Cartel

CONFUSION IS SEX.
Compact disc: released on SST, Sep'87 by SST Records. Dist: Pinnacle. Estim retail price in Sep'87 was £13.12.

Album: released on SST, Oct'87 by SST Records. Dist: Pinnacle. Estim retail price in Sep'87 was £6.49.

DEATH VALLEY (see Lunch, Lydia) (Sonic Youth/Lydia Lunch).

DEATH VALLEY 69.
Single (12"): released on Blast First, Jun'85 by Sonic Youth Records. Dist: Rough Trade, Nine Mile, Red Rhino, Cartel

E.V.O.L.
Album: released on Blast First, May'86 by Sonic Youth Records. Dist: Rough Trade, Nine Mile, Red Rhino, Cartel

Cassette: released on Blast First, May'86 by Sonic Youth Records. Dist: Rough Trade, Nine Mile, Red Rhino, Cartel

E.V.O.L..
Compact disc: released on Blast First, Nov'86 by Sonic Youth Records. Dist: Rough Trade, Nine Mile, Red Rhino, Cartel

FLOWER.
Notes: Only Coloured Vinyl

Single (12"): released on Blast First, Jan'86 by Sonic Youth Records. Dist: Rough Trade, Nine Mile, Red Rhino, Cartel

HALLOWEEN 2 ENGRAVED (Sonic Youth/Savage Pencil).
Tracks: / Halloween 2 engraved.
Single (12"): released on Blast First, Jul'86 by Sonic Youth Records. Dist: Rough Trade, Nine Mile, Red Rhino, Cartel

KILL YOUR IDOLS.
Album: released on Zensor, Feb'84 by Zensor Records. Dist: Rough Trade

SISTER.
Album: released on Blast First, Jun'87 by Sonic Youth Records. Dist: Rough Trade, Nine Mile, Red Rhino, Cartel

Cassette: released on Blast First, Jun'87 by Sonic Youth Records. Dist: Rough Trade, Nine Mile, Red Rhino, Cartel

SONIC YOUTH.
Album: released on Zensor, Mar'86 by Zensor Records. Dist: Rough Trade

Album: released on Neutral, Feb'84 by Zensor Records. Dist: Rough Trade, Cartel

Album: released on SST, Oct'87 by SST Records. Dist: Pinnacle. Estim retail price in Sep'87 was £6.49.

STARPOWER.
Tracks: / Starpower / Bubblegum / To your soul".
Single (7"): released on Blast First, Oct'86 by Sonic Youth Records. Dist: Rough Trade, Nine Mile, Red Rhino, Cartel

Single (12"): released on Blast First, Oct'86 by Sonic Youth Records. Dist: Rough Trade, Nine Mile, Red Rhino, Cartel

Son, Joe

DARK SIDE OF TOWN (Son, Joe & The Solar System).
Single (7"): released on Sonet, Oct'84 by Sonet Records. Dist: PRT

Sonnier, Jo El

CAJUN LIFE.
Album: released on Sonet, Oct'80 by Sonet Records. Dist: PRT

Sonnier, Lee

FAIS DO DO BREAKDOWN (Sonnier, Lee & Happy Fats(1940's)).
Tracks: / Setre chandelle / Allons dance colinda / Dans les Grande Meche / Chere Catan / Fais do do breakdown / Dans la Platin / Chere eci et cher laba / Along the river / Cankton two step / War Widow waltz / La valse de hadocol / Crowley two step / La blues de Cajin / Acadian all star special.
Album: released on Flyright, Nov'86 by Flyright Records. Dist: Krazy Kat, Swift, Jazz Music

Sonn, Larry

SOUND OF SONN, THE (Sonn, Larry & His Orchestra).
Album: released on Jasmine, Feb'83 by Jasmine Records. Dist: Counterpoint, Lugtons, Taylor, H.R., Wellard, Chris, Swift, Cadillac

Sonny

DON'T STOP.
Single (12"): released on Chartbound, May'87 by Chartbound Records. Dist: Jetstar

LOVE A LITTLE LATIN (Sonny and the 'Boys from LA').
Tracks: / Cuban love song, The / From Russia with love / Maria elena / Solitaire / If I had a hammer / He's a tramp / Dream a little dream / Sueno que estou junto a ti / That tat cat jive / Girl from Ipanema, The / Desifanado / Meditation(meditacao) / Tell me when(Quando Quando) / Singin' in the rain / O meu Violao / I'm not in love.
Album: released on Sounds Ultimate, Aug'86 Dist: PRT, H.R. Taylor

Sonny & Cher

I GOT YOU BABE.
Single (7"): released on Old Gold, Sep'85 by Old Gold Records. Dist: Lightning, Jazz Music, Spartan, Counterpoint

Single (7"): released on Atlantic, Jul'81 by WEA Records. Dist: WEA

Single (7"): released on Atlantic (Import), '80

VERY BEST OF SONNY & CHER.
Album: released on Hallmark, Jun'81 by Pickwick Records. Dist: Pickwick Distribution, PRT, Taylors

Cassette: released on Hallmark, Apr'81 by Pickwick Records. Dist: Pickwick Distribution, PRT, Taylors

Son of Ind

DELIRIOUS.
Album: released on Reactor, Nov'86 Dist: Fast Forward

Son of Jah

URBAN GUERRILLA.
Album: released on Natty Congo, Mar'86 by Natty Congo Records. Dist: Jetstar

Son of Jazz

SON OF JAZZ FOR ABSOLUTE BEGINNERS (Various Artists).
Tracks: / Doctor Jazz / St. Louis shuffle / Ain't misbehavin' / Handful of keys / Flaming youth / Blue washboard stomp / I got a right to sing the blues / Maple leaf rag / Heyena stomp / Texas stomp / I'm gonna stomp, Mr. Henry Lee / It should be you / Oh didn't he ramble?.
Album: released on RCA, Jan'87 by RCA Records. Dist: RCA, Roots, Swift, Wellard, Chris, I & B, Solomon & Peres Distribution

Cassette: released on RCA, Jan'87 by RCA Records. Dist: RCA, Roots, Swift, Wellard, Chris, I & B, Solomon & Peres Distribution

Son Of John

PEOPLE SHOUTING.
Tracks: / People shouting / Your interpretation.
Single (7"): released on Individual, Jul'86 by Individual Records. Dist: Pinnacle

Son Of Oi!

SON OF OI! various punk artists (Various Artists).
Album: released on Syndicate Oi, Nov'83

Sons & Lovers

SONS & LOVERS D.H.Lawrence (McKellen, Ian).
Double cassette: released on Argo (Spokenword), Mar'83 by Decca Records. Dist: Polygram

Sons Of Arqa

ARQA OLOGY.
Notes: picture disc
Album: released on One G Productions, Feb'86 Dist: Red Rhino Distribution

Sons Of Bix

OSTRICH WALK.
Album: released on Jazzology, Jun'86 Dist: Jazz Music, Swift

Sons Of Cain

END OF SOMETHING.
Single (7"): released on Loppylugs, Jan'82 by Loppylugs Records. Dist: Pinnacle, Loppylugs

Sons Of Jah

JOHNNY TOO LATE.
Single (12"): released on Natty Congo, Nov'82 by Natty Congo Records. Dist: Jetstar

SOMMER LOVE.
Single (12"): released on Natty Congo, Sep'85 by Natty Congo Records. Dist: Jetstar

Sons Of Jobs..

SONS OF JOBS FOR THE BOYS various artists (Various Artists).
Album: released on Natalie, Aug'85 Dist: Stiff, EMI

Sons Of Man

IRON LADY.
Single (7"): released on Croydon Music, Nov'81 Dist: Pinnacle

Sons Of Sam

GOLDEN AGE OF DISCO, THE.
Album: released on Flowmotion, Jun'85 Dist: Red Rhino, Cartel

Sons Of Shane

FLY.
Tracks: / Fly / All I had.
Single (7"): released on Whippet, Jul'87 by Whippet Records. Dist: Nine Mile, Cartel

Sons Of The Arqua

ARQ OF THE ARQUANS.
Album: released on Scarface, Jun'85 by Scarface Records. Dist: Cartel

Sons Of The Pioneers

20 OF THE BEST.
Album: released on RCA International, Apr'85

Cassette: released on RCA International, Apr'85

COWBOY COUNTRY.
Album: released on Bear Family, Sep'84 by Bear Family Records. Dist: Rollercoaster Distribution, Swift

EDITION 1, 1945-46 - COOL WATER.
Tracks: / Cool water / Timber trail / You'll be sorry when I'm gone / Forgive and forget / Gold star mother with silvery hair / You're getting tired of me / Columbus stockade blues / Cool water / Cowboy camp meetin' / I wear your memory in my heart / Tumbling tumbleweeds / No one to cry to / Everlasting hills of Oklahoma, (The) / Grievin' my heart out for you / Out California way / Stars and stripes on Iwo Jima (Isle).
Album: released on Bear Family, May'87 by Bear Family Records. Dist: Rollercoaster Distribution, Swift

EDITION 2, 1946-47 - TEARDROPS IN MY HEART.
Tracks: / Teardrops in my heart / Chant of the wanderer, (The) / Let's pretend / Will there be sagebrush in Heaven? / Penny for your thoughts, (A) / Baby doll / Letter marked unclaimed, (The) / Trees / Cigarettes, whisky and wild, wild women / You don't know what lonesome is / Too high too wide too low / You'll never miss the water (till the well runs dry) / Have I told you lately that I love you / My best to you / Blue prairie / Lead me gently home father.
Album: released on Bear Family, May'87 by Bear Family Records. Dist: Rollercoaster Distribution, Swift

EDITION 3, 1947 - A HUNDRED AND SIXTY ACRES.
Tracks: / Hundred and sixty acres, (A) / Calico apron and gingham gown / Whiffenpoof song, (The) / Wind / Where are you / Out in pioneer town / Two eyes two lips but no heart / Cowboy country / Power in the blood / Let me share your name / Happy birthday polka / Read the Bible every day / Sea walker, (The) / Old Rugged Cross, (The) / Last round-up, (The) / Bar-none ranch (in the sky), (The).
Album: released on Bear Family, May'87 by Bear Family Records. Dist: Rollercoaster Distribution, Swift

EDITION 5, 1949-50 - LAND BEYOND THE SUN.
Tracks: / Land beyond the sun / Wagon's west / Outlaws / Rollin' dust / Song of the wagonmaster / Wind / Love at the country fair / Wedding dolls (from your wedding cake) / Old man atom / I told them about you / Chuckawalla swing / What this country needs / Eagle's heart, (The) / Baby, I ain't gonna cry no more / Little white cross / Roses.
Album: released on Bear Family, May'87 by Bear Family Records. Dist: Rollercoaster Distribution, Swift

LUCKY YOU.
Album: released on JEMF, Mar'85

Sons Of Wonder

FIRE ON ME.
Single (12"): released on Home Boy, Oct'84 by Home Boy Records. Dist: Jetstar

Soolaimon

RAMAYA.
Single (7"): released on Flair, Aug'82 by Flair Records. Dist: Pinnacle

Sophie's Choice

SOPHIE'S CHOICE Original soundtrack.
Album: released on PRT, Jun'83 by PRT Records. Dist: PRT

Soprano Mystics

TELL ME WHY.
Single (12"): released on Horsemouth, Jul'83 Dist: Jetstar, Rough Trade

Soprano Summit

LIVE AT THE BIG HORN JAZZ FEST..
Album: released on Jazzology, Jun'86 Dist: Jazz Music, Swift

Sopwith Camel

FRANTIC DESOLATION.
Album: released on Demon, May'86 by Demon Records. Dist: Pinnacle

Sorcerer

SORCERER Film soundtrack (Tangerine Dream).
Album: released on MCA, Feb'82 by MCA Records. Dist: Polygram, MCA

Cassette: released on MCA, Feb'82 by MCA Records. Dist: Polygram, MCA

Sorcerer, The

SORCERER, THE Gilbert & Sullivan (Various Artists).
Double Album: released on Decca, Jan'59 by Decca Records. Dist: Polygram

Sorkness, Bjorn

BEARBURGER, THE.
Cassette: released on Uniton, Nov'83

Sorrow Come...

SORROW COME PASS ME AROUND Rural black religious music (Various Artists).
Album: released on Advent, Apr'79 Dist: Celtic Music, Projection, Swift

Sorrows

TEENAGE HEARTBREAK.
Album: released on Epic, Sep'80 by CBS Records. Dist: CBS

Sorry

THAT WAY IT IS.
Album: released on Homestead, Dec'86 Dist: Rough Trade, Cartel, Shigaku

S.O.S. Band

12" TAPE, THE.
Tracks: / Just be good to me / Just the way you like it / Weekend Girl / Finest, The / Borrowed Love.
Cassette: released on Tabu, Sep'86 by CBS Records. Dist: CBS Distribution

ARTISTS VOL.3, THE (S.O.S. Band/Kleeer/Womack/O'Jays).
Album: released on Streetsounds, Sep'85

Cassette: released on Streetsounds, Sep'85

BORROWED LOVE.
Tracks: / Borrowed Love / Do you still want to.
Single (7"): released on Tabu, Jun'86 by CBS Records. Dist: CBS Distribution

Single (12"): released on Tabu, Jun'86 by CBS Records. Dist: CBS Distribution

EVEN WHEN YOU SLEEP.
Single (12"): released on Tabu, Nov'86 by CBS Records. Dist: CBS Distribution

FINEST, THE.
Tracks: / Finest, The / I don't want nobody else.
Single (7"): released on Tabu, Mar'86 by CBS Records. Dist: CBS Distribution

Single (12"): released on Tabu, Mar'86 by CBS Records. Dist: CBS Distribution

GROOVIN (THAT'S WHAT WERE DOING) TAKE YOUR TIME.
Single (7"): released on Tabu, Feb'83 by CBS Records. Dist: CBS Distribution

Single (12"): released on Tabu, Feb'83 by CBS Records. Dist: CBS Distribution

JUST THE WAY YOU LIKE IT.
Album: released on Tabu, Aug'84 by CBS Records. Dist: CBS Distribution

Cassette: released on Tabu, Aug'84 by CBS Records. Dist: CBS Distribution

JUST THE WAY YOU LIKE IT (2).
Single (7"): released on Tabu, Aug'84 by CBS Records. Dist: CBS Distribution

Single (12"): released on Tabu, Aug'84 by CBS Records. Dist: CBS Distribution

Double-pack single: released on Tabu, Sep'84 by CBS Records. Dist: CBS Distribution

NO LIES.
Tracks: / No lies / Even when I sleep.
Single (7"): released on Tabu, Mar'87 by CBS Records. Dist: CBS Distribution

ON THE RISE.
Tracks: / Tell me if you still care / Just be good to me / For your love / I'm not runnin' / If you want my love / On the rise / Who's making love / Steppin' the stones.
Album: released on Tabu, Nov'86 by CBS Records. Dist: CBS Distribution

Album: released on Tabu, Sep'83 by CBS Records. Dist: CBS Distribution

Cassette: released on Tabu, Sep'83 by CBS Records. Dist: CBS Distribution

SANDS OF TIME.
Tracks: / Even when you sleep / Sands of time / Borrowed love / Nothing but the best / Finest, The / No lies / Two time lover / Do you still want to? / Sands of time(reprise).
Album: released on Tabu, Apr'86 by CBS Records. Dist: CBS Distribution

Cassette: released on Tabu, Apr'86 by CBS Records. Dist: CBS Distribution

Compact disc: released on CBS, Oct'86 by CBS Records. Dist: CBS

S.O.S.
Album: released on Tabu, Nov'84 by CBS Records. Dist: CBS Distribution

Cassette: released on Tabu, Nov'84 by CBS Records. Dist: CBS Distribution

TELL ME YOU STILL CARE.
Single (7"): released on Tabu, Jun'84 by CBS Records. Dist: CBS Distribution

Single (12"): released on Tabu, Jun'84 by CBS Records. Dist: CBS Distribution

Soso, Winston

I DON'T MIND.
Tracks: / I don't mind / Dancing spell.
Single (12"): released on Strayco, Jul'86 Dist: Jetstar Distribution

Soul

SOUL (BEST OF CHESS, CHECKER, CADET) Various artists (Various Artists).
Album: released on Checker(USA), Apr'81 by PRT. Dist: PRT

TRIBES / LOVE.
Single (7"): released on Cherry Red, Jul'81 by Cherry Red Records. Dist: Pinnacle

Soul Affair

ABC.
Single (7"): released on Rooster, Mar'84 by Rooster Records. Dist: PRT Distribution

Single (12"): released on Rooster, Mar'84 by Rooster Records. Dist: PRT Distribution

Soul Affair Orchestra

SOUL AFFAIR.
Album: released on Creole, Oct'76 by Creole Records. Dist: Rhino, PRT

S.O.U.L. Agents

S.O.U.L. AGENTS Various artists (Various Artists).
Album: released on Kent, Sep'84 by Ace Records. Dist: Pinnacle

Soul All Dayer

SOUL ALL DAYER Various artists (Various Artists).
Album: released on LGR, Aug'87 Dist: Jetstar. Estim retail price in Sep'87 was £5.99.

Soul Asylum

MADE TO BE BROKEN.
Album: released on Rough Trade, Sep'86 by Rough Trade Records. Dist: Rough Trade Distribution, Cartel Distribution

Soul Brothers at Home

SWINGIN' THE BLUES.
Notes: What more can be said about the 16 tracks on this album,16 tracks that are essential to any standard big band & jazz collection. The most famous of the many Basie bands featuring Lester Young,Chu Berry, Henshel Evans,Buck Clay Fin,Harry Edison, Dickie Wells,Jimmy Rushing, & that Rolls Royce of a rhythm section of Basie Freddie Green, Walter page & Jo Jones. The classics by a band that has pleased millions of people & will continue to do as long as there is music.
Album: released on Jazzology, Jun'86 Dist: Jazz Music, Swift

Album: released on Phontastic, '86 Dist: Wellard, Chris

Soul Class of '66

SOUL CLASS OF '66 Various artists (Various Artists).
Album: released on Kent (MCA), Jan'84 by Ace Records. Dist: Pinnacle

Soul Club

I WANT YOUR GUY.
Tracks: / I want your guy / I want your guy (dub).
Single (7"): released on Cool Tempo, Feb'87 by Chrysalis Records. Dist: CBS

Single (12"): released on Cool Tempo, Feb'87 by Chrysalis Records. Dist: CBS

Soul, David

BAND OF FRIENDS.
Album: released on Energy, Mar'80 by E.G. Records. Dist: Taylors

Cassette: released on Energy, Mar'80 by E.G. Records. Dist: Taylors

BEST DAYS OF MY LIFE, THE.
Album: released on Energy, May'82 by E.G. Records. Dist: Taylors

Cassette: released on Energy, May'82 by E.G. Records. Dist: Taylors

FOOL FOR LOVE / YOU'RE A WOMAN NOW.
Single (7"): released on Energy, Feb'81 by E.G. Records. Dist: Taylors

HOW CAN YOU TELL YOU GOT IT.
Single (7"): released on Energy, May'82 by E.G. Records. Dist: Taylors

I CAN'T AFFORD THAT FEELING ANYMORE.
Single (7"): released on Philips, Dec'81 Dist: IMS-Polygram

SURRENDER TO ME / PIPER.
Single (7"): released on Energy, Mar'80 by E.G. Records. Dist: Taylors

Soul daze/Soul nites

SOUL DAZE/SOUL NITES Various artists (Various Artists).
Double Album: released on Ronco, Aug'82

Soul Decade

SOUL DECADE (Various Artists).
Album: released on WEA, Mar'86 by WEA Records. Dist: WEA

Cassette: released on WEA, Mar'86 by WEA Records. Dist: WEA

Soul Deep

SOUL DEEP (Various Artists).
Tracks: / Love of my man, The / Sad shade if blue / Let me down easy / I don't know what you got but it's got me / Faithfull and true / Every little bit hurts / Hymn no.5 / Ashes to ashes / Either way I lose / I love you / I'ts too late / Giving up / It's too late / Giving up / Nothing takes the place of you / What was I supposed to do / Long cold winter / Corn bread row.
Compact disc: released on Charly, Jan'87 by Charly Records. Dist: Charly, Cadillac

Soul Doctor

SOUL DOCTOR.
Tracks: / Soul doctor / Nevermore.
Single (7"): released on Sticky Music, Jul'87 by Sticky Music Records. Dist: Fast Forward Distributors, Cartel Distribution

Soul Factory Collection

SOUL FACTORY COLLECTION, THE (Various Artists).
Tracks: / Love wars / Reet Petite / Tossing and turning / Let's get it on / My Girl / Turn off the lights / Ain't Nobody / I'm still waiting / In the Midnight hour / Sweet soul music / If you don't know me by now / Fingertips / Week-end girl / Endless Love / B.A.B.Y. / Hang on in there Baby / Tell me why / Stand by me / Breaking down / Ghetto Child / Reach out, I'll be there / Thats how heartaches are made / Young hearts run free / Living in the U.K.
Notes: Double album and cassette Compiled by tony Blackburn.
Album: released on Starblend, Dec'85 by Starblend Records. Dist: PRT Distribution

Cassette: released on Starblend, Dec'85 by Starblend Records. Dist: PRT Distribution

Soul Fever

SOUL FEVER Various artists (Various Artists).
Cassette: released on K-Tel Goldmasters, Aug'84 by K-Tel Records. Dist: K-Tel

Soulful Kinda Music

SOULFULL KINDA MUSIC (Various Artists).
Tracks: / Do what you gotta do.
Album: released on Soul Supply, Jan'87 by High Energy Records. Dist: Charly

Soul Galore

SOUL GALORE Various artists (Various Artists).
Album: released on SMP, Nov'85 Dist: Jetstar, PRT

Soul Hunter

MAELSTROM.
Single (12"): released on Contempo, Mar'87 Dist: Nine Mile, Cartel, Red Rhino

Soulin' Vol 1

SOULIN' VOL 1 (Various Artists).
Album: released on Moonshine (Belgium), Dec'85 Dist: Projection Distribution

Soulin' Vol 2

SOULIN' VOL 2 (Various Artists).
Album: released on Moonshine, May'86 Dist: Projection Distribution

Soulin' Vol 3

SOULIN' VOL 3 (Various Artists).
Album: released on Moonshine, Nov'86 Dist: Projection Distribution

Soul, Junior

MESSAGE FROM MARIA.
Tracks: / Message from Maria / Message from Maria (version).
Single (12"): released on Creole, Jun'87 by Creole Records. Dist: Rhino, PRT

Soul Kings

KING OF SOUL.
Single (12"): released on Red Rooster, Apr'84 by Red Rooster Records. Dist: Pinnacle

Soul Man

SOUL MAN Various artists (Various Artists).
Notes: 17 original soul tracks by Sam & Dave, Eddy Floyd, Martha Reeves, Fontella Bass, Rufus Thomas, Percy Sledge.
Compact disc: released on Delta, Apr'87 by Delta Records. Dist: Target

Album: released on A&M, Jan'87 by A&M Records. Dist: Polygram

Cassette: released on A&M, Jan'87 by A&M Records. Dist: Polygram

SOUL MAN (VIDEO) (Various Artists).
Notes: Released on New World Video. 103 minutes.

Soulmates

SOULMATES Various artists (Various Artists).
Album: released on Spot, Feb'83 by Pickwick Records. Dist: H.R. Taylor,

Cassette: released on Spot, Feb'83 by Pickwick Records. Dist: H.R. Taylor,

Soul Mining

SOUL MINING (Various Artists).
Tracks: / Soul Man / Knock on Wood / Patches / Walking the dog / Rescue Me / In Crowd, The / Love wont let me wait / Duck, The / Western movies / I Know / Rainy night in Georgia, A / Get on up.
Album: released on Topline, Sep'86 by Charly Records. Dist: Charly Distribution

Cassette: released on Topline, Sep'86 by Charly Records. Dist: Charly Distribution

Soul of a Man

SOUL OF A MAN Various artists (Various Artists).
Album: released on Kent, May'85 by Ace Records. Dist: Pinnacle

Soul of Black Music

SOUL OF BLACK MUSIC VOL 1 Various artists (Various Artists).
Album: released on Sonet, Sep'79 by Sonet Records. Dist: PRT

SOUL OF BLACK MUSIC VOL 2 Various artists (Various Artists).
Album: released on Sonet, Sep'79 by Sonet Records. Dist: PRT

SOUL OF BLACK MUSIC - GOSPEL SCENE Various artists (Various Artists).
Double Album: released on Vogue (France), Jun'84 Dist: Discovery, Jazz Music, PRT, Swift

Soul of British R'n'B

SOUL OF BRITISH R'N'B 1962-1986 (Various Artists).
Tracks: / Stop stop stop (or honey I'll be gone) / Time it takes (The) / Midnight confession / Mary open the door / Get on the right track baby / Little girl / My love / Precious words / Strut around / Sugar baby-Part 1 / Cross my heart / If your love don't swing / I need your loving / Night time is the right time / Walking the dog / Can you hear me / Love is a beautiful thing / Ooh-la-lah / Sugar baby -part 2.
Album: released on See For Miles, Apr'86 by See For Miles Records. Dist: Pinnacle

Soul on Ice

UNDERWATER / SPLINTERED LENS.
Single (7"): released on Red Rhino, Jan'82 by Red Rhino Records. Dist: Red Rhino, Cartel

Soul on Sound

SOUL ON SOUND NO 33 Various artists (Various Artists).
Cassette: released on Soul On Sound, Jul'84 by Soul On Sound Records. Dist: PRT

Soul Passion

SOUL PASSION Various original artists (Various original artists).
Album: released on Contour, '82 by Pickwick Records. Dist: Pickwick Distribution, PRT

Cassette: released on Contour, '82 by Pickwick Records. Dist: Pickwick Distribution, PRT

Soul & Reggae Favourites

SOUL & REGGAE FAVOURITES Various artists (Various Artists).
Cassette: released on Autograph, Apr'85 Dist: Record Services Distribution (Ireland)

Soul Searching

SOUL SEARCHING (Various Artists).
Compact disc: released on Jive, Apr'87 by Zomba Records. Dist: RCA, PRT, CBS

SOUL SEARCHING VOL.1 (Various Artists).
Album: released on Jive, Jul'87 by Zomba Records. Dist: RCA, PRT, CBS

Cassette: released on Jive, Jul'87 by Zomba Records. Dist: RCA, PRT, CBS

Soul Sensation

SOUL SENSATION Various session artists (Various Session Artists).
Cassette: released on Dynamic, Sep'81 by Creole Records. Dist: CBS, Essex

Cassette: released on AIM (Budget Cassettes), Feb'83

Soul Serenade

SOUL SERENADE Various artists (Various Artists).
Album: released on Kent, Jun'85 by Ace Records. Dist: Pinnacle

Soul Shakin'

SOUL SHAKIN' Various artists (Various Artists).
Album: released on Hallmark, '82 by Pickwick Records. Dist: Pickwick Distribution, PRT, Taylors

Cassette: released on Hallmark, '82 by Pickwick Records. Dist: Pickwick Distribution, PRT, Taylors

Soul Sisters

SOUL SISTERS EP Various artists (Various Artists).
Single (7"): released on Chess, Jul'85 by Charly Records. Dist: Charly, Swift, PRT, Discovery, IMS, Polygram

Soul Sonic Force

PLANET ROCK.
Single (7"): released on 21 Records, Aug'82 by Polydor Records. Dist: Polydor

Single (12"): released on 21 Records, Aug'82 by Polydor Records. Dist: Polydor

Soul Spin

SOUL SPIN Various artists (Various Artists).
Album: released on Kent, Aug'84 by Ace Records. Dist: Pinnacle

Soul Superbowl

SOUL SUPERBOWL-THE SIXTIES V THE SEVENTIES (Various Artists).
Tracks: / Please give me one more chance / Thanks for a little lovin' / Baby boy / She won't come back / Skate a while baby / Keep her guessing / Hey it's love / Where does that leave me / Katrina / Love's the only way to survive / What kind of love / Spread love / Look up with your mind / I fooled you this time.
Album: released on Kent, Nov'86 by Ace Records. Dist: Pinnacle

Soul Survivors

SOUL SURVIVORS (Various Artists).

Tracks: / Troglodyte / Snake, The / Girl watcher / Got to get you off my mind / Only the strong survive / Slipaway / Tonights the night / Show & tell / Supernatural thing / Looking for a love / Can I change my mind / Groovy situation.
Album: released on Milestone USA, Oct'86 Dist: Logo Distribution, RCA Distribution, Discovery Distribution, JSU Distribution, Swift Distribution

Cassette: released on Milestone USA, Oct'86 Dist: Logo Distribution, RCA Distribution, Discovery Distribution, JSU Distribution, Swift Distribution

Album: released on Topline, Jan'87 by Charly Records. Dist: Charly Distribution

Soul Time

SOUL TIME (Various Artists).
Tracks: / Happy hippie / If you need me / Too weak to fight / Turn back the hands of time / Bring it on home / I've never found a girl / B A B Y / Do the funky chicken / Last night / Hey there lonely girl / Love on a mountain top / Trapped by a thing called love.
Album: released on Topline, Jan'87 by Charly Records. Dist: Charly Distribution

Cassette: released on Topline, Jan'87 by Charly Records. Dist: Charly Distribution

SOUL TIME (Various Artists).
Tracks: / Soul Time / Beat, The / Quitter never wins, A / I'm coming to your rescue / Love Trap / More today than yesterday / Little bit of something, A / He who picks a Rose / This heart of mine / There's a pain in my heart / Help me / Walk like a man / Lot of love, A / It's all over me / I need your love so desperately / Stranger in my arms / Seven the loser / Country Road.
Album: released on SMP, Apr'86 Dist: Jetstar, PRT

Soul Train

JAZZ ISVERIGE '86.
Album: released on Caprice, Nov'86 by RCA Records. Dist: RCA

Soul Uprising

SOUL UPRISING Various artists (Various Artists).
Album: released on Kent, Feb'85 by Ace Records. Dist: Pinnacle

Soul Years...

SOUL YEARS OF MINIT RECORDS Struttin' & flirtin' 1966-1969 (Various Artists).
Tracks: / What is this / 60 minutes of your love / Working on your case / Hunk of funk, A / Baby I love you / I know you don't want me no more / Fly me to the moon / How I miss you baby / Get right / I wish it would rain / Worried life blues / My heart is in danger / I've got love for my baby / I'm gonna do all I can to do right by my man.
Notes: Side A - 16.37 mins, Side B - 19.14 mins. Came the 1960's and the age of Soul Music. Rich, gospel-influenced vocals and contemporary instrumentations were thehallmarks of this new form of R & B and Minit was one of the most productive andinnovative home labels. Out front in this Minit/Soul collection is Bobby Womack with three of his first R & B hits, all produced by Chips Moman who crated his recent "Wo-Magic" album. From the songwriting team of Isaac Hayes and David Porter came "60 Minutes Of Your Love" sung by Homer Banks and our line-up also includes "Baby I Love You" written and sung by the late Jimmy Holiday. And when there is soul, there has to be Ike & Tina Turner, who stopped long enough on Minit to cut a live album and some studio single sides including the Temptations/Gladys Knight favourite "I wish It Would Rain" (EMI release sheet - 7/87).
Album: released on EMI America (Stateside), Jul'87 by EMI Records. Dist: EMI

Cassette: released on EMI America (Stateside), Jul'87 by EMI Records. Dist: EMI

Sound

COUNTING THE DAYS.
Compact disc: released on Statik/Caroline '86

Single (7"): released on Statik, May'84 Dist: Rough Trade Distribution, Stage One Distribution

HAND OF LOVE.
Single (7"): released on Play It Again Sam, 30 May'87 Dist: Red Rhino, Cartel

HEADS AND HEARTS.
Album: released on Statik, Oct'85 Dist: Rough Trade Distribution, Stage One Distribution

HEADS & HEARTS & HOTHOUSE & SHOCK OF DAYLIGHT.
Compact disc: released on Static, Dec'86

HEYDAY.
Single (7"): released on Korova, Sep'80 Dist: WEA

HOT HOUSE.
Single (7"): released on Korova, May'82 Dist: WEA

IN THE HOTHOUSE.
Album: released on Statik, Nov'85 Dist: Rough Trade Distribution, Stage One Distribution

JEOPARDY.
Album: released on Korova, Oct'80 Dist: WEA

ONE THOUSAND REASONS.
Single (7"): released on Statik, Nov'84 Dist: Rough Trade Distribution, Stage One Distribution

Single (12"): released on Statik, Nov'84 Dist: Rough Trade Distribution, Stage One Distribution

SHOCK OF DAYLIGHT.
Album: released on Statik, Oct'85 Dist: Rough Trade Distribution, Stage One Distribution

Cassette: released on Statik, Oct'85 Dist: Rough Trade Distribution, Stage One Distribution

SOUND D' AFRIQUE various artists (Various Artists).
Album: released on Island, Oct'81 by Island Records. Dist: Polygram

Cassette: released on Island, Oct'81 by Island Records. Dist: Polygram

SOUND GUIDE TO BRITISH WADERS Various artists (Various Artists).
Album: released on BBC, Nov'84 by BBC Records & Tapes. Dist: EMI, PRT,

Cassette: released on BBC, Nov'84 by BBC Records & Tapes. Dist: EMI, PRT,

SOUND OF APPLAUSE VOL.2 Various artists.
Album: released on K-Tel (Era), Jun'83 by K-Tel Records. Dist: K-Tel

Cassette: released on K-Tel (Era), Jun'83 by K-Tel Records. Dist: K-Tel

SOUND OF APPLAUSE VOL.1 Various artists.
Album: released on K-Tel (Era), Jun'83 by K-Tel Records. Dist: K-Tel

Cassette: released on K-Tel (Era), Jun'83 by K-Tel Records. Dist: K-Tel

SOUND OF EUROPE Various artsists (Various Artists).
Cassette: released on Oak, May'83 by Oak Records. Dist: Spartan Distribution, Pinnacle

SOUND OF GULF COAST Various artists (Various Artists).
Album: released on Ace, May'80 by Ace Records. Dist: Pinnacle, Swift, Hotshot, Cadillac

SOUND OF HARLEM Various artists (Various Artists).
Album: released on Jazz Document, Jul'82 Dist: Jazz Music

SOUND OF THE 70'S Various Original artists (Various original artists).
Double Album: released on K-Tel, Aug'82 by K-Tel Records. Dist: Record Merchandisers Distribution, Taylors, Terry Blood Distribution, Wynd-Up Distribution, Relay Distribution, Pickwick Distribution, Solomon & Peres Distribution, Polygram

Double cassette: released on K-Tel, Aug'82 by K-Tel Records. Dist: Record Merchandisers Distribuuon, Taylors, Terry Blood Distribution, Wynd-Up Distribution, Relay Distribution, Pickwick Distribution, Solomon & Peres Distribution, Polygram

SOUND, THE.
Album: released on Statik, Nov'85 Dist: Rough Trade Distribution, Stage One Distribution

Cassette: released on Statik, Nov'85 Dist: Rough Trade Distribution, Stage One Distribution

TEMPERATURE DROP.
Single (7"): released on Statik, Jun'85 Dist: Rough Trade Distribution, Stage One Distribution

THUNDER UP.
Album: released on Play It Again Sam, Jun'87 Dist: Red Rhino, Cartel

Compact disc: released on Play It Again Sam, Apr'87 Dist: Red Rhino, Cartel

Sound and Motion

SHIPWRECKED.
Tracks: / Shipwrecked / Shipwrecked (Instrumental).
Single (7"): released on K R Recordings, Aug'86 by KR Recordings Ltd. Dist: RCA, Revolver, Cartel

Single (12"): released on K R Recordings, Aug'86 by KR Recordings Ltd. Dist: RCA, Revolver, Cartel

SHIPWRECKED (GC LABEL!).
Single (7"): released on GC, Oct'86 by GC Recordings. Dist: DMS, RCA

Single (12"): released on GC, Oct'86 by GC Recordings. Dist: DMS, RCA

Sound Asleep

I'M COLD OUTSIDE.
Tracks: / I'm cold outside / Kings of the clover Green.
Single (7"): released on Vinyl Solution, Oct'86 Dist: Pinnacle

Sound Barrier

FASTEN YOUR SEAT BELT.
Single (12"): released on Compact Organisation, Jul'85 Dist: PRT

MORNINGTON CRESCENT.
Single (7"): released on Compact Organisation, Jun'84 Dist: PRT

SUBURBIA SUITE, THE.
Album: released on Compact Organisation, Jun'85 Dist: PRT

Sound Effects

SOUND EFFECTS NO.1.
Album: released on BBC, Dec'81 by BBC Records & Tapes. Dist: EMI, PRT.

Cassette: released on BBC, Dec'81 by BBC Records & Tapes. Dist: EMI, PRT,

SOUND EFFECTS NO.10 Music and effects for home movies.
Album: released on BBC, Dec'81 by BBC Records & Tapes. Dist: EMI, PRT,

Cassette: released on BBC, Dec'81 by BBC Records & Tapes. Dist: EMI, PRT.

SOUND EFFECTS NO.11 Off beat sound effects.
Album: released on BBC, Dec'81 by BBC Records & Tapes. Dist: EMI, PRT,

Cassette: released on BBC, Dec'81 by BBC Records & Tapes. Dist: EMI, PRT

SOUND EFFECTS NO.12 Out of this world.
Album: released on BBC, Dec'81 by BBC Records & Tapes. Dist: EMI, PRT.

Cassette: released on BBC, Dec'81 by BBC Records & Tapes. Dist: EMI, PRT.

SOUND EFFECTS NO.13 Death and horror.
Album: released on BBC, Dec'81 by BBC Records & Tapes. Dist: EMI, PRT,

Cassette: released on BBC, Dec'81 by BBC Records & Tapes. Dist: EMI, PRT,

SOUND EFFECTS NO.15 Vanishing sounds in Britain.
Album: released on BBC, Dec'81 by BBC Records & Tapes. Dist: EMI, PRT, .

Cassette: released on BBC, Dec'81 by BBC Records & Tapes. Dist: EMI, PRT,

SOUND EFFECTS NO.16 Disasters.
Album: released on BBC, Dec'81 by BBC Records & Tapes. Dist: EMI, PRT,

Cassette: released on BBC, Dec'81 by BBC Records & Tapes. Dist: EMI, PRT.

SOUND EFFECTS NO.17 Birds and other sounds of the countryside.
Album: released on BBC, Dec'81 by BBC Records & Tapes. Dist: EMI, PRT,

Cassette: released on BBC, Dec'81 by BBC Records & Tapes. Dist: EMI, PRT

SOUND EFFECTS NO.18 Holiday sound effects.
Album: released on BBC, Dec'81 by BBC Records & Tapes. Dist: EMI, PRT,

Cassette: released on BBC, Dec'81 by BBC Records & Tapes. Dist: EMI, PRT.

SOUND EFFECTS NO.19 Doctor who sound effects from TV series.
Album: released on BBC, Dec'81 by BBC Records & Tapes. Dist: EMI, PRT.

Cassette: released on BBC, Dec'81 by BBC Records & Tapes. Dist: EMI, PRT,

SOUND EFFECTS NO.2.
Album: released on BBC, Dec'81 by BBC Records & Tapes. Dist: EMI, PRT,

Cassette: released on BBC, Dec'81 by BBC Records & Tapes. Dist: EMI, PRT,

SOUND EFFECTS NO.20 Sporting sound effects.
Album: released on BBC, Dec'81 by BBC Records & Tapes. Dist: EMI, PRT,

Cassette: released on BBC, Dec'81 by BBC Records & Tapes. Dist: EMI, PRT,

SOUND EFFECTS NO.21 Death and horror Vol.2.
Album: released on BBC, Dec'81 by BBC Records & Tapes. Dist: EMI, PRT.

Cassette: released on BBC, Dec'81 by BBC Records & Tapes. Dist: EMI, PRT

SOUND EFFECTS NO.22 Music for silent movies.
Album: released on BBC, Dec'81 by BBC Records & Tapes. Dist: EMI, PRT.

Cassette: released on BBC, Dec'81 by BBC Records & Tapes. Dist: EMI, PRT.

SOUND EFFECTS NO.23 Relaxing sounds.
Album: released on BBC, Dec'81 by BBC Records & Tapes. Dist: EMI, PRT.

Cassette: released on BBC, Dec'81 by BBC Records & Tapes. Dist: EMI, PRT.

SOUND EFFECTS NO.24 Combat.
Album: released on BBC, Dec'81 by BBC Records & Tapes. Dist: EMI, PRT,

Cassette: released on BBC, Dec'81 by BBC Records & Tapes. Dist: EMI, PRT,

SOUND EFFECTS NO.25 sounds of speed.
Album: released on BBC, Dec'81 by BBC Records & Tapes. Dist: EMI, PRT,

Cassette: released on BBC, Dec'81 by BBC Records & Tapes. Dist: EMI, PRT,

SOUND EFFECTS NO.26 Science fiction.
Album: released on BBC, Dec'81 by BBC Records & Tapes. Dist: EMI, PRT.

Cassette: released on BBC, Dec'81 by BBC Records & Tapes. Dist: EMI, PRT,

SOUND EFFECTS NO.27 Even more death and horror.
Album: released on BBC, Oct'82 by BBC Records & Tapes. Dist: EMI, PRT.

Album: released on BBC, Oct'82 by BBC Records & Tapes. Dist: EMI, PRT

SOUND EFFECTS NO.28 Comedy.
Album: released on BBC, Aug'83 by BBC Records & Tapes. Dist: EMI, PRT.

Cassette: released on BBC, Aug'83 by BBC Records & Tapes. Dist: EMI, PRT.

SOUND EFFECTS NO.29 Hi-Tech FX.
Album: released on BBC, Sep'84 by BBC Records & Tapes. Dist: EMI, PRT.

Cassette: released on BBC, Sep'84 by BBC Records & Tapes. Dist: EMI, PRT.

SOUND EFFECTS NO.3.
Album: released on BBC, Dec'81 by BBC Records & Tapes. Dist: EMI, PRT.

Cassette: released on BBC, Dec'81 by BBC Records & Tapes. Dist: EMI, PRT,

SOUND EFFECTS NO.4.
Album: released on BBC, Dec'81 by BBC Records & Tapes. Dist: EMI, PRT.

Cassette: released on BBC, Dec'81 by BBC Records & Tapes. Dist: EMI, PRT,

SOUND EFFECTS NO.5.
Album: released on BBC, Dec'81 by BBC Records & Tapes. Dist: EMI, PRT.

Cassette: released on BBC, Dec'81 by BBC Records & Tapes. Dist: EMI, PRT.

SOUND EFFECTS NO.6.
Album: released on BBC, Dec'81 by BBC Records & Tapes. Dist: EMI, PRT.

Cassette: released on BBC, Dec'81 by BBC Records & Tapes. Dist: EMI, PRT.

SOUND EFFECTS NO.7.
Album: released on BBC, Dec'81 by BBC Records & Tapes. Dist: EMI, PRT,

Cassette: released on BBC, Dec'81 by BBC Records & Tapes. Dist: EMI, PRT.

SOUND EFFECTS NO.8.
Album: released on BBC, Dec'81 by BBC Records & Tapes. Dist: EMI, PRT,

Cassette: released on BBC, Dec'81 by BBC Records & Tapes. Dist: EMI, PRT.

SOUND EFFECTS NO.9.
Album: released on BBC, Dec'81 by BBC Records & Tapes. Dist: EMI, PRT,

Cassette: released on BBC, Dec'81 by BBC Records & Tapes. Dist: EMI, PRT,

Sound of Mull

GAELIC FOLK SONGS.
Album: released on Lismor, Nov'76 by Lismor Records. Dist: Lismor, Roots, Celtic Music

Cassette: released on Lismor, Nov'76 by Lismor Records. Dist: Lismor, Roots, Celtic Music

Sound Of Music

SOUND OF MUSIC original soundtrack.
Compact disc: released on Epic, May'87 by CBS Records. Dist: CBS

SOUND OF MUSIC Original Motion Picture Sound Track (Various Artists).
Tracks: / Prelude / Sound of Music / Overture and Preludium (Dixit Dominus) / Nuns Chorus / Morning Hymn and Alleluia / Nuns Chorus / Maria / Nuns chorus / I have confidence in me / Sixteen going on seventeen / My Favourite things / Climb every Mountain / Lonely goatherd, The / Do re mi / Something good / Processional and Maria/Nuns Chorus/Edelweiss / Climb every mountain(chorus).
Notes: Digital Stereo Recording. Film score conducted byb Irwin Kostal.
Compact disc: released on RCA, Oct'84 by RCA Records. Dist: RCA, Roots, Swift, Wellard, Chris, I & B, Solomon & Peres Distribution

Album: released on RCA, Sep'81 by RCA Records. Dist: RCA, Roots, Swift, Wellard, Chris, I & B, Solomon & Peres Distribution

Cassette: released on RCA, Sep'81 by RCA Records. Dist: RCA, Roots, Swift, Wellard, Chris, I & B, Solomon & Peres Distribution

SOUND OF MUSIC Original London Cast.
Album: released on CBS Cameo, Aug'85 by CBS Records. Dist: CBS

Cassette: released on CBS Cameo, Aug'85 by CBS Records. Dist: CBS

Sound of New Orleans, The

SOUND OF NEW ORLEANS, THE Various artists (Various Artists).
Tracks: / Working in a coal mine / Barefootin' / Look a py py / Iko iko / Ride your pony / Cissy strutt / Lawdy Miss Clawdy / People say / Down home girl / Holy cow / Tell it like it is / Chapel of love / Release me / Chicken strut / Get out of

Page 938

my life woman / Let the good times roll / Red sails in the sunset / Hercules / Sinner girl / Don't pity me / Gossip gossip / I Think you're jiving me.
Compact disc: released on Charly, Apr'86 by Charly Records. Dist: Charly, Cadillac

Sound of Oi!

SOUND OF OI! The hills are alive with the... (Various Artists).
Tracks: / Coventry / Surfin' in Newquay / My life's fine / Sheila / Fictional kicks / Battle / Old / Norman / Headcase / Coming on strong / Best, The / onfusion / Law, The / Beginning of the end.
Album: released on Link, Jul'87 Dist: DMS, RCA

Sound of Picante

SOUND OF PICANTE Various artists (Various Artists).
Tracks: / Bye bye blues / Summer knows, The / Fiz a cama na varanda / Rainfall / Tango allegra / Don't cry for me Argentina / Maria Cervantes / Happy Lypso / Sin Timbal.
Notes: A collection of classic performances recorded for the Concorde Picante label. Personnel: Monty Alexander-piano/Laurinder Almeida-guitar/Charlie Byre-guitar/Tania Maria-piano, vocal/Tito Puente-vibes & percussion/Poncho Sanchez-congas & percussion/Cal Tjader-vibes.
Album: released on Concord Jazz Picante(USA), Apr'86 Dist: IMS, Polygram

Cassette: released on Concord Jazz Picante(USA), Apr'86 Dist: IMS, Polygram

Sound of St. Louis soul

SOUND OF ST. LOUIS SOUL (Various Artists).
Album: released on Timeless, Jun'87

Sound Of Summer, (The)

SOUND OF SUMMER, THE Various artists (Various Artists).
Tracks: / Surf city * / Surfin' safari / Hey little cobra * / Little Honda * / Tequila / Indian lake * / Ride the wild surf * / Wipe out * / Surfer girl / Baby talk / G.T.O. * / Remember (walking in the sand) / Summer song, A * / Beach baby * / Surfin / Pipeline *.
Compact disc: released on K-Tel, Jun'87 by K-Tel Records. Dist: Record Merchandisers Distribution, Taylors, Terry Blood Distribution, Wynd-Up Distribution, Relay Distribution, Pickwick Distribution, Solomon & Peres Distribution, Polygram

Album: released on K-Tel, Jul'87 by K-Tel Records. Dist: Record Merchandisers Distribution, Taylors, Terry Blood Distribution, Wynd-Up Distribution, Relay Distribution, Pickwick Distribution, Solomon & Peres Distribution, Polygram

Cassette: released on K-Tel, Jul'87 by K-Tel Records. Dist: Record Merchandisers Distribution, Taylors, Terry Blood Distribution, Wynd-Up Distribution, Relay Distribution, Pickwick Distribution, Solomon & Peres Distribution, Polygram

Sounds...

SOUNDS AND SONGS OF LONDON Various artists (Various Artists).
Album: released on EMI, Jun'83 by EMI Records. Dist: EMI

Cassette: released on EMI, Jun'83 by EMI Records. Dist: EMI

SOUNDS FOR CHRISTMAS Various artists (Various Artists).
Cassette: released on Decca, Nov'77 by Decca Records. Dist: Polygram

SOUNDS LATIN Various original artists (Various original artists).
Album: released on Decca, Sep'77 by Decca Records. Dist: Polygram

SOUNDS LIKE ABBA Various artists (Various Artists).
Cassette: released on VFM, May'85 by VFM Records. Dist: Taylors, Wynd-Up Distribution

SOUNDS LIKE BUDDY HOLLY Various session artists (Various Session Artists).
Cassette: released on VFM, Feb'78 by VFM Records. Dist: Taylors, Wynd-Up Distribution

SOUNDS OF BONEY M Various session artists (Various Session Artists).
Cassette: released on AIM (Budget Cassettes), Feb'83

SOUNDS OF CHRISTMAS Various artists (Various Artists).
Cassette: released on Times Cassettes, Jan'79 by Ivan Berg. Dist: Pinnacle

SOUNDS OF LIVING WORLD Various artists (Various Artists).
Album: released on BBC, Jun'78 by BBC Records & Tapes. Dist: EMI, PRT, Pye

Cassette: released on BBC, Jun'78 by BBC Records & Tapes. Dist: EMI, PRT, Pye

SOUNDS OF SCOTLAND Various original artists (Various original artists).
Album: released on Lismor, Jul'78 by Lismor Records. Dist: Lismor, Roots, Celtic Music

Cassette: released on Lismor, Jul'78 by Lismor Records. Dist: Lismor, Roots, Celtic Music

SOUNDS OF THE WEST Various artists (Various Artists).
Album: released on Scotdisc, Jul'85 Dist: Clyde Factors Distributors

Cassette: released on Scotdisc, Jul'85 Dist: Clyde Factors Distributors

SOUNDS OF WARGAMES Various artists (Various Artists).
Cassette: released on Audiocord Cassettes, May'83

Sounds Beautiful

SOUNDS BEAUTIFUL Various artists (Various Artists).
Album: released on Warwick, Nov'85 Dist: Multiple Sound Distributors

Cassette: released on Warwick, Nov'85 Dist: Multiple Sound Distributors

Sound Sensation

I JUST CALLED TO SAY I LOVE YOU.
Cassette: Dist: Multiple Sound Distributors

ROUND AND ROUND.
Cassette: released on Chevron, Feb'85 Dist: Multiple Sound Distributors

TOP HITS OF THE YEAR.
Cassette: released on Chevron, Feb'85 Dist: Multiple Sound Distributors

Sounds Incorporated

SOUNDS INCORPORATED.
Album: released on See For Miles, '83 by Charly Records. Dist: Spartan

Sounds Jamaica

REGGAE FROM SUNSET TO DAWN.
Cassette: released on Chevron, Aug'85 Dist: Multiple Sound Distributors

Sounds Like Music

SOUNDS LIKE MAGIC Various artists (Various Artists).
Album: released on Hallmark, Apr'86 by Pickwick Records. Dist: Pickwick Distribution, PRT, Taylors

Cassette: released on Hallmark, Apr'86 by Pickwick Records. Dist: Pickwick Distribution, PRT, Taylors

Sounds Magic

JUST TIME.
Single (7"): released on Genie, Sep'83 by Genie Records. Dist: Spartan, CBS

Sounds of Carillon

SOUNDS OF CARILLON Bournville & Loughborough Carillons.
Cassette: released on Saydisc, May'79 by Saydisc Records. Dist: Essex, Harmonia Mundi, Roots, H.R. Taylor, Jazz Music, Swift, Projection, Gamut

Sounds of Love

SOUNDS OF LOVE (Various Artists).
Compact disc: released on Delta, '86 by Delta Records. Dist: Target

Sounds Of Motown

SOUNDS OF MOTOWN Ready steady go.
Notes: The bulk of this historically fascinating tape is taken from a special edition of the classic pop TV show of the sixties that was devoted to Motown acts like the Supremes,Stevie Wonder,the Temptations and the Miracles.Dusty Springfield hosts and there is extra footage of Marvin Gaye.Sadly,the picture and sound quality leave a bit to be desired. Recording time 50 minutes.
Video-cassette (VHS): released on PMI, Jun'86 by PMI Records. Dist: EMI

Video-cassette [Betamax]: released on PMI, Jun'86 by PMI Records. Dist: EMI

Sounds of Soweto

SOUNDS OF SOWETO (Various Artists).
Compact disc: released on EMI, Mar'87 by EMI Records. Dist: EMI

Album: released on EMI, Mar'87 by EMI Records. Dist: EMI

Cassette: released on EMI, Mar'87 by EMI Records. Dist: EMI

Sounds of the 60's

SOUNDS OF THE 60'S Various artists (Various Artists).
Cassette: released on Cambra, '83 by Cambra Records. Dist: IDS, Conifer

Sounds of the 70's

SOUNDS OF THE 70'S Various artists (Various Artists).
Double Album: released on Cambra, Nov'83 by Cambra Records. Dist: IDS, Conifer

Cassette: released on Cambra, Nov'83 by Cambra Records. Dist: IDS, Conifer

SOUNDS OF THE 70'S VOL.2 Various artists (Various Artists).
Album: released on Cambra, Apr'84 by Cambra Records. Dist: IDS, Conifer

Cassette: released on Cambra, Apr'84 by Cambra Records. Dist: IDS, Conifer

Sounds Of The Screen

TV GIANTS.
Album: released on Elecstar, Mar'85 by Elecstar Records. Dist: PRT

Album: released on Elecstar, Mar'85 by Elecstar Records. Dist: PRT

Sounds Orchestral

CAST YOUR FATE.
Single (7"): released on Old Gold, Jul'82 by Old Gold Records. Dist: Lightning, Jazz Music, Spartan, Counterpoint

DREAMS.
Album: released on PRT, Jun'83 by PRT Records. Dist: PRT

Cassette: released on PRT, Jun'83 by PRT Records. Dist: PRT

LOVE IS EVERYTHING.
Double cassette: released on Pickwick, Mar'83 by Pickwick Records. Dist: Pickwick Distribution, Prism Leisure Distribution, Lugtons

SLEEPY SHORES.
Tracks: / Family of man / Something / Wigwam / They long to be close to you / He ain't heavy he's my brother / Smoke ritual / Coloured rain / Witchita linesman / Classical gas / By the time I get to Phoenix / Shackled / Sleepy shores.
Compact disc: released on PRT, Nov'85 by PRT Records. Dist: PRT

Sounds Sensations

POP CONCERT-VOLUME 2.
Album: released on Tempo, Jul'80 by Warwick Records. Dist: Multiple Sound Distributors

Cassette: released on Tempo, Jul'80 by Warwick Records. Dist: Multiple Sound Distributors

Sounds Tzigane

SOUNDS TZIGANE Various artists (Various Artists).
Album: released on Decca, '78 by Decca Records. Dist: Polygram

Sounds Visual

SOUNDS VISUAL Various artists (Various Artists).
Cassette: released on Radio Six, May'84 by Radio Six Records. Dist: Radio Six

Soundtrack

CRAZY.
Single (7"): released on Rialto, Jun'82 by Rialto Records. Dist: Pinnacle

GHOST OF LOVE.
Single (7"): released on Rialto, Apr'82 by Rialto Records. Dist: Pinnacle

KISS OF THE SPIDERWOMAN (Soundtrack With Wally Bardarou).
Notes: The soundtrack to William Hurt's critically acclaimed movie.The album includes new music from Wally Badarou,recently in the charts with the club favourite "Chief Inspector".
Album: released on Island, Jan'86 by Island Records. Dist: Polygram

Cassette: released on Island, Jan'86 by Island Records. Dist: Polygram

Soundtracks & Head

RAIN RAIN RAIN.
Single (12"): released on Rough Trade, Jun'82 by Rough Trade Records. Dist: Rough Trade Distribution, Cartel Distribution

Soundwave

SOUNDWAVE NO.7 Various artists (Various Artists).
Cassette: released on Soul On Sound, Jul'84 by Soul On Sound Records. Dist: PRT

Soup Dragons

CAN'T TAKE NO MORE.
Tracks: / Can't take no more / Whitewash / Aha experience*.
Single (7"): released on Raw TV Products, Jun'87 Dist: Fast Forward, Cartel

Single (12"): released on Raw TV Products, Jun'87 Dist: Fast Forward, Cartel

HANG-TEN!.
Tracks: / Just mind your step girl / Slow things down / Man about town with chairs.
Single (7"): released on Raw TV Products, Oct'86 Dist: Fast Forward, Cartel

Single (12"): released on Raw TV Products, Oct'86 Dist: Fast Forward, Cartel

HEAD GONE ASTRAY.
Tracks: / Girl in the world / So sad I feel*.
Single (7"): released on Raw TV Products, Jan'87 Dist: Fast Forward, Cartel

Single (12"): released on Raw TV Products, Jan'87 Dist: Fast Forward, Cartel

SUN IS IN THE SKY EP.
Single (7"): released on Subway, Feb'86 Dist: Revolver Distribution, Spartan Distribution

WHOLE WIDE WORLD.
Tracks: / I know everything / Pleasantly surprised.
Single (7"): released on Subway, May'86 Dist: Revolver Distribution, Spartan Distribution

Single (12"): released on Subway, May'86 Dist: Revolver Distribution, Spartan Distribution

Sources Of Energy

SOURCES OF ENERGY England, N.York, Tel Aviv.
Cassette: released on International Report, Oct'81 by Seminar Cassettes. Dist: Audio-Visual Library Services, Davidson Distribution, Eastern Educational Products Distrib., Forlaget Systime Distribution, MacDougall Distribution, Talktapes Distribution, Watkins Books Ltd Distribution, Norton, Jeff Distribution

Sousa & Pryor Bands,The

SOUSA & PRYOR BANDS, THE Original Recordings- 1901-1926.
Tracks: / Patriot, The / Pasquinade / Glory of the yankee navy / Trombone sneeze / Musical joke on "Bedilia", (A) / Ben-Hur chariot race march / General Pershing march / General mix-up march / March Shannon / Battleship Connecticut shuffle / Alagazam march / Yankee shuffle / Teddy bears picnic / Down the field march / Falcon march / Repasz band march / Federal march / Creole belles / At a Georgia camp meeting.
Notes: Mono recording
Album: released on New World (USA), Apr'87 by New World Records (USA). Dist: Conifer

South America

AFRO - BRAZILIAN RELIGIOUS SONGS.
Album: released on Lyrichord (USA), Oct'81 by Lyrichord Records (USA). Dist: Flexitron Distributors Ltd

AMAZONIA - CULT MUSIC OF NORTHERN BRAZIL.
Album: released on Lyrichord (USA), Oct'81 by Lyrichord Records (USA). Dist: Flexitron Distributors Ltd

INCA HARP - LAMENTS AND DANCES OF THE INCA EMPIRE, THE.
Album: released on Lyrichord (USA), '82 by Lyrichord Records (USA). Dist: Flexitron Distributors Ltd

MUSIC OF THE INCAS.
Album: released on Lyrichord (USA), Oct'81 by Lyrichord Records (USA). Dist: Flexitron Distributors Ltd

Cassette: released on Lyrichord (USA), Oct'81 by Lyrichord Records (USA). Dist: Flexitron Distributors Ltd

PERU - MUSIC FROM THE LAND OF MACCHU PICCHU.
Album: released on Lyrichord (USA), Oct'81 by Lyrichord Records (USA). Dist: Flexitron Distributors Ltd

VIRACOCHA - LEGENDARY MUSIC OF THE ANDES.
Album: released on Lyrichord (USA), Oct'81 by Lyrichord Records (USA). Dist: Flexitron Distributors Ltd

Southampton All Stars

TRIBUTE TO GLENN MILLER.
Cassette: released on All That's Jazz, Jun'86 Dist: Jazz Music

South, April

CHAINS THAT BIND ME/ YOU WANT TO ROCK.
Single (7"): released on President, Jan'83 by President Records. Dist: Taylors, Spartan

HEROES OF THE NIGHT/ BOYS ARE OUT....
Single (7"): released on President, Apr'82 by

President Records. Dist: Taylors, Spartan

South Atlantic Islands

SOUTH ATLANTIC ISLANDS A portrait of the Falkland Islands Wildlife.
Album: released on Saydisc, Oct'79 by Saydisc Records. Dist: Essex, Harmonia Mundi, Roots, H.R. Taylor, Jazz Music, Swift, Projection, Gamut

Southbank Orchestra

DEMPSEY & MAKEPEACE.
Single (7"): released on Sierra, Jan'85 by Sierra Records. Dist: WEA

Southbound

TRACKS.
Album: released on Westwood, May'78 by Westwood Records. Dist: Jazz Music, H.R. Taylor, JSU, Pinnacle, Ross Records

South Coast Ska Stars

SOUTH COAST RUMBLE/ HEAD ON.
Single (7"): released on Safari, Apr'80 by Safari Records. Dist: Pinnacle

South, Eddie

TOGETHER (see Reinhardt, Django) (South, Eddie/Django Reinhardt/Stephane Grappelli).

Southend Rock

SOUTHEND ROCK Various artists (Various Artists).
Album: released on Sonet, Oct'79 by Sonet Records. Dist: PRT

Southern Blues

SOUTHERN BLUES Various artists (Various Artists).
Double Album:

Southern Death Cult

FAT MAN / MOYA.
Single (7"): released on Situation 2, Dec'82 Dist: Cartel, Pinnacle

Single (12"): released on Situation 2, Dec'82 Dist: Cartel, Pinnacle

Southern Eagle...

THAT NASTY SWING (CHRIS COMBER & MIKE PARIS) (Southern Eagle String Band).
Album: released on Bear Family, Sep'84 by Bear Family Records. Dist: Rollercoaster Distribution, Swift

Southern Filmharmonic

SOUND OF MOVIES.
Cassette: released on Kingfisher, Nov'81 Dist: PRT

Southern Jazz Group

JAZZ FROM DOWN UNDER VOL 3.
Album: released on Dawn Club, May'79

JAZZ FROM DOWN UNDER VOL 4.
Album: released on Dawn Club, May'79

JAZZ FROM DOWN UNDER VOL 2.
Album: released on Dawn Club, May'79

JAZZ FROM DOWN UNDER VOL 1.
Album: released on Dawn Club, May'79

VOL.1-1946-1950.
Album: released on Dawn Club, Dec'86 Dist: Cadillac, Swift, JSU

VOL.2-1946-1950.
Album: released on Dawn Club, Dec'86 Dist: Cadillac, Swift, JSU

VOL.3-1946-1950.
Album: released on Dawn Club, Dec'86 Dist: Cadillac, Swift, JSU

VOL.4-1946-1950.
Album: released on Dawn Club, Dec'86 Dist: Cadillac, Swift, JSU

Southern, Jeri

JERI SOUTHERN MEETS COLE PORTER.
Album: released on Capitol, Oct'84 by Capitol Records. Dist: EMI

Cassette: released on Capitol, Oct'84 by Capitol Records. Dist: EMI

LIVE' AT THE CRESCENDO.
Tracks: / I thought of you last night / I get a kick out of you / Dancing on the ceiling / Blame it on my mouth / Remind me / You better go now / I'm just a woman / Something I dreamed last night / Nice work if you can get it / When I fall in love.
Album: released on Capitol T (USA), Nov'85

Dist: Conifer

WHEN I FALL IN LOVE.
Album: released on MCA, Apr'84 by MCA Records. Dist: CBS

Cassette: released on MCA, Apr'84 by MCA Records. Dist: CBS

Southern Lighting

DOWN THE ROAD.
Album: released on Cleopatra, Dec'86 by Musicland Records. Dist: Rough Trade, Cartel

Southern Nights

SOUTHERN NIGHTS - THE VERY BEST OF COUNTRY Various artists (Various Artists).
Album: released on Music For Pleasure, Sep'84 by EMI Records. Dist: EMI

Cassette: released on Music For Pleasure, Sep'84 by EMI Records. Dist: EMI

Southern, Sheila

25 NURSERY RHYMES (Southern, Sheila with Mike Sammes).
Album: released on Damont, '78 by WEA Records. Dist: WEA

Cassette: released on Damont, '78 by WEA Records. Dist: WEA

FOUR CLASSIC STORIES AND 20 POPULAR NURSERY RHYMES.
Album: released on Horatio Nelson, Nov'86 Dist: PRT

Cassette: released on Horatio Nelson, Nov'86 Dist: PRT

SINGS THE BACHARACH & DAVID SONGBOOK.
Album: released on Oak, Sep'82 by Oak Records. Dist: Spartan Distribution, Pinnacle

WHITE WEDDING / GOOD LUCK GOOD HEALTH GOD BLESS Sheila Southern with various artists.
Single (7"): released on EMI, May'81 by EMI Records. Dist: EMI

Southern Soul Belles

SOUTHERN SOUL BELLES Various artists (Various Artists).
Album: released on Charly(R&B), Feb'82 by Charly Records. Dist: Charly, Cadillac

Southern Soul Brothers

SOUTHERN SOUL BROTHERS (Various Artists).
Album: released on Charly, Jul'87 by Charly Records. Dist: Charly, Cadillac

Southern Soul Sisters

SOUTHERN SOUL SISTERS (Various Artists).
Album: released on Charly, Jul'87 by Charly Records. Dist: Charly, Cadillac

Southern Stompers

FASCINATING RHYTHM.
Album: released on VJM, Apr'79 by VJM (UK) Records. Dist: Swift

STEVE LANE'S JUBILEE RECORD.
Album: released on VJM, Apr'79 by VJM (UK) Records. Dist: Swift

Southern Swing

SOUTHERN SWING.
Notes: With C.Walker/G.Brown/J.Haworth/A.Andrews/C.Hillary.
Cassette: released on All That's Jazz, Jun'86 Dist: Jazz Music

Souther, Richard

HEIRBORNE.
Notes: Israeli, Irish and British influences pass through this synthesizer player's first Meadowlark Album. "I prefer the synthesier over other instruments because of its expressiveness", he explains, "For Heirborne I used twenty of them".
Album: released on Meadowlark, Mar'86 by Sparrow Records. Dist: Word Distribution

Cassette: released on Meadowlark, Mar'86 by Sparrow Records. Dist: Word Distribution

Southforks

NOBODY EVER DIES IN DALLAS.
Tracks: / I'm sorry now.
Single (7"): released on Keyhole, Dec'86

South Frisco Jazz Band

VOLUME 3.
Album: released on Stomp Off, Jun'86 by Stomp Off Records. Dist: Jazz Music Distribution

South India

MUSIC OF SOUTH INDIA.
Album: released on Lyrichord (USA), '82 by Lyrichord Records (USA). Dist: Flexitron Distributors Ltd

South, Joe

GAMES PEOPLE PLAY.
Tracks: / Games people play / Rock me gently.
Notes: Also contains:"Rock me gently" by Andy Kim
Single (7"): released on Old Gold, Apr'87 by Old Gold Records. Dist: Lightning, Jazz Music, Spartan, Counterpoint

INTROSPECT.
Tracks: / All my hard times / Rose garden / Mirror of your mind / Redneck / Don't throw your love to the wind / Greatest love, The / Games people play / These are not my people / Don't you be ashamed / Birds of a feather / Gabriel.
Album: released on See For Miles, Jun'86 by See For Miles Records. Dist: Pinnacle

South Louisiana...

MORE SOUTH LOUISIANA JUKE BOX HITS (Various Artists).
Album: released on Jin, Feb'79 Dist: Swift

SOUTH LOUISIANA JUKE BOX HITS Various artists (Various Artists).
Album: released on Jin, Feb'79 Dist: Swift

South Mississippi Blues

SOUTH MISSISSIPPI BLUES Original various artists (Various Artists).
Album: released on Rounder (USA Import), Apr'77

South Pacific

SOUTH PACIFIC Various artists (Various Artists).
Tracks: / Overture / Dites-moi / Cockeyed optimist, A / Twin soliloquies / Some enchanted evening / Bloody Mary / There is nothing like a dame / Bali ha'i / I'm gonna wash that man right out-a-my hair / I'm in love with a wonderful guy / Younger than springtime / This is how it feels / Entr'acte / Happy talk / Honey bun / You've got to be carefully taught / This nearly was mine / March 19, The / Take off, The / Communication established / Finale ultimo / Dites moi / Some enchanted evening.
Album: released on CBS, Sep'86 by CBS Records. Dist: CBS

Cassette: released on CBS, Sep'86 by CBS Records. Dist: CBS

Compact disc: released on CBS, Oct'86 by CBS Records. Dist: CBS

SOUTH PACIFIC Original film soundtrack.
Album: released on RCA, '84 by RCA Records. Dist: RCA, Roots, Swift, Wellard, Chris, I & B, Solomon & Peres Distribution

Cassette: released on RCA, '84 by RCA Records. Dist: RCA, Roots, Swift, Wellard, Chris, I & B, Solomon & Peres Distribution

SOUTH PACIFIC ISLAND MUSIC Various artists (Various Artists).
Album: released on Nonesuch Explorer (USA), Jul'84

South Rebels

ROCKIN' DADDY EP.
Single (7"): released on Red Hot, Feb'80 Dist: Swift

South Side Blues

SOUTH SIDE BLUES - CHICAGO: LIVING LEGENDS Various artists (Various Artists).
Album: released on Riverside, Jan'85 Dist: K-Tel, Jetstar

Southside, Johnny

ALL I WANT IS EVERYTHING (Southside, Johnny & The Ashbury Dukes).
Single (7"): released on Mercury (USA Import), Jul'81

AT LEAST WE GOT SHOES (Southside and the Asbury Jukes).
Tracks: / Hard to find / Tell me (that our love's still strong) / Walk away Renee / Take my love / You can count on me / Till the end of the night / I only want to be with you / Lorraine / I can't wait / Under the sun.
Album: released on RCA, Jul'86 by RCA Records. Dist: RCA, Roots, Swift, Wellard, Chris, I & B, Solomon & Peres Distribution

Cassette: released on RCA, Jul'86 by RCA Records. Dist: RCA, Roots, Swift, Wellard, Chris, I & B, Solomon & Peres Distribution

Compact disc: released on RCA, Jul'86 by RCA Records. Dist: RCA, Roots, Swift, Wellard, Chris, I & B, Solomon & Peres Distribution

HARD TO FIND (Southside, Johnny & The Jukes).
Tracks: / You can count on me / I should have.......
Single (12"): released on RCA, Jan'87 by RCA Records. Dist: RCA, Roots, Swift, Wellard, Chris, I & B, Solomon & Peres Distribution

IN THE HEAT (Southside, Johnny & The Jukes).
Tracks: / Love goes to war / New Romeo / Love is the drug / Captured / I can't live without love / Over my head / Don't look back / Tell me lies / Action speaks louder than words / New coat of paint.
Album: released on Polydor, Nov'84 by Polydor Records. Dist: Polygram, Polydor

Cassette: released on Polydor, Nov'84 by Polydor Records. Dist: Polygram, Polydor

Compact disc: released on Polydor, Nov'84 by Polydor Records. Dist: Polygram, Polydor

TELL ME That our love's still strong (Southside, Johnny & The Jukes).
Tracks: / Tell me / I only want to be with you.
Single (7"): by RCA Records. Dist: RCA, Roots, Swift, Wellard, Chris, I & B, Solomon & Peres Distribution

Single (7"): released on RCA, May'87 by RCA Records. Dist: RCA, Roots, Swift, Wellard, Chris, I & B, Solomon & Peres Distribution

WALK AWAY RENEE.
Tracks: / I can't wait.
Single (7"): released on RCA, Jun'86 by RCA Records. Dist: RCA, Roots, Swift, Wellard, Chris, I & B, Solomon & Peres Distribution

Single (12"): released on RCA, Jun'86 by RCA Records. Dist: RCA, Roots, Swift, Wellard, Chris, I & B, Solomon & Peres Distribution

YOU CAN COUNT ON ME (Southside, Johnny & The Jukes).
Tracks: / Till the end of the night / I should have said I love you.
Single (7"): released on RCA, Oct'86 by RCA Records. Dist: RCA, Roots, Swift, Wellard, Chris, I & B, Solomon & Peres Distribution

Single (12"): released on RCA, Oct'86 by RCA Records. Dist: RCA, Roots, Swift, Wellard, Chris, I & B, Solomon & Peres Distribution

South Side Safari

SOUTH SIDE SAFARI Various artists (Various Artists).
Album: released on Red Lightnin', Apr'82 by Red Lightnin' Records. Dist: Roots, Swift, Jazz Music, JSU, Pinnacle, Cartel, Wynd-Up Distribution

Southside Screamers

SOUTHSIDE SCREAMERS CHICAGO BLUES 1948-58 Various artists (Various Artists).
Album: released on St.George (USA), Feb'85

Southwark Cathedral Choir

SOUTHWARK CATHEDRAL CHOIR.
Album: released on Alpha, '82 by Alpha Records. Dist: H.R. Taylor, Gamut

Cassette: released on Alpha, '82 by Alpha Records. Dist: H.R. Taylor, Gamut

Souvenir de Paris

SOUVENIR DE PARIS Various artists (Various Artists).
Album: released on ASV Living Era, Apr'84 by ASV Records. Dist: PRT

Cassette: released on ASV Living Era, Apr'84 by ASV Records. Dist: PRT

Souvenir d'Italia

SOUVENIR D'ITALIA Various artists (Various Artists).
Cassette: released on Music Masters, Jul'83 by Music Masters Records. Dist: Taylors

Souvenirs

SOUVENIRS (BEST OF BROADWAY AND HOLLYWOOD) Various artists (Various Artists).
Album: released on RCA (Germany), Jun'83

Sovereign's Parade

SOUNDS OF SOUNDHURST Various bands.
Album: released on Major Richards Military Music, Oct'77

Soviet Army...

SOVIET ARMY CHORUS AND BAND (Soviet Army Chorus And Band).
Tracks: / Song of youth / Birch tree in a field did stand / Far away / Volga boat song / You are always beautiful / Along Peter's street / Tipperary / Ah lovely night / Kamarinskaya / Annie Laurie / Song of the plains / Kalinka / Bandura / Oh no John / Snow flakes / Ukrainian poem / Soldiers chorus from 'The Decembrists'.
Notes: Artistic Director and Chief Conductor Boris Alexandrov. Chief Chorus Master. Konstantin Vinogradov. Musical Director and Con-

ductor: Vladimir Alexandrov. Soloists: Track 8 - N. Polozkov. Track 9 - E. Belayaev. Track 10: E. Foektistov.
Compact disc: released on H.M.V., Apr'87 by EMI Records. Dist: EMI

SOVIET ARMY ENSEMBLE Various artists (Various Artists).
Album: released on H.M.V., Nov'66 by EMI Records. Dist: EMI

Cassette: released on H.M.V., Nov'66 by EMI Records. Dist: EMI

WORLD FOLK SONGS (Soviet Army Song & Dance Ensemble).
Cassette: released on Melodiya, Mar'79

Soviet France
ASAULT AND MIRAGE.

ASSAULT AND MIRAGE.
Cassette: released on Red Rhino, Jun'87 by Red Rhino Records. Dist: Red Rhino, Cartel

ELSTRE.
Album: released on Red Rhino, Jul'84 by Red Rhino Records. Dist: Red Rhino, Cartel

FLOCK OF ROTATIONS, A.
Album: released on Red Rhino, Jun'87 by Red Rhino Records. Dist: Red Rhino, Cartel

GESTURE SIGNAL THREAT.
Album: released on Red Rhino, Aug'86 by Red Rhino Records. Dist: Red Rhino, Cartel

MISFITS LOONEY TUNES AND SQUALID CRIMINALS.
Album: released on Red Rhino, Aug'86 by Red Rhino Records. Dist: Red Rhino, Cartel

MOHNOMISCHE.
Album: released on Red Rhino, '84 by Red Rhino Records. Dist: Red Rhino, Cartel

NORSCHE.
Album: released on Red Rhino, '84 by Red Rhino Records. Dist: Red Rhino, Cartel

POPULAR SOVIET SONGS AND YOUTH CULTURE.
Cassette: released on Red Rhino, Nov'85 by Red Rhino Records. Dist: Red Rhino, Cartel

POPULAR SOVIET SONGS AND YOUTH CULTURE.
Cassette: released on Red Rhino, Nov'85 by Red Rhino Records. Dist: Red Rhino, Cartel

RITUAL / MUDBAST BOYS / SEM BOYS / BRING HESSA / MOUNW.
Single (12"): released on Red Rhino, '82 by Red Rhino Records. Dist: Red Rhino, Cartel

Sovine, Red
16 ALL TIME FAVOURITES.
Album: released on Starday, Apr'87

Cassette: released on Starday, Apr'87

16 GREATEST HITS.
Album: released on Starday, Apr'87

Cassette: released on Starday, Apr'87

BEST OF....
Notes: 10 tracks
Album: released on Starday, Apr'87

Cassette: released on Starday, Apr'87

CLASSIC NARRATIONS.
Album: released on Starday, Apr'87

GIDDY-UP-GO.
Album: released on Gusto (USA), '80 by Gusto Records (USA). Dist: Crusader

Single (7"): released on Starday, Sep'81

LITTLE ROSA.
Album: released on Bulldog Records, Jul'82

PHANTOM 309.
Album: released on Gusto (USA), '80 by Gusto Records (USA). Dist: Crusader

SUNDAY WITH SOVINE.
Album: released on Starday, Apr'87

Cassette: released on Starday, Apr'87

TEDDY BEAR.
Album: released on Gusto (USA), '80 by Gusto Records (USA). Dist: Crusader

Album: released on Starday (USA), '80

Cassette: released on Starday (USA), '80

Sowell, Radics
CAUTION / BALI HAI SPECIAL.
Single (12"): released on Attack, Jan'81 by Trojan Records. Dist: Trojan, Pinnacle, Red Rhino

FIGHT.
Single (12"): released on Attack, Apr'81 by Trojan Records. Dist: Trojan, Pinnacle, Red Rhino

GIVE ME YOUR LOVE.
Single (12"): released on DATC, Oct'82 by DATC Records. Dist: Rough Trade

LOVE IS WHAT SHE WANTS.
Single (12"): released on Big Youth, Apr'82

WHEEL O MITILDA.
Single (12"): released on Solid Groove, Dec'81 Dist: Jetstar, Pinnacle

WILD STYLE.
Single (12"): released on Regal, Jul'82

Soweto
COMPILATION, (A).
Album: released on Rough Trade, '84 by Rough Trade Records. Dist: Rough Trade Distribution, Cartel Distribution

Soweto Street Music
SOWETO STREET MUSIC - THE DEFINITIVE COLLECTION Various artists (Various Artists).
Album: released on Audiotrax, Nov'84 by Audiotrax. Dist: PRT

Cassette: released on Audiotrax, Nov'84 by Audiotrax. Dist: PRT

So You Think..
DON'T NEED YOU (So You Think You're A Cowboy).
Single (7"): released on Cheatin'Heart, Jun'84 Dist: Fast, Cartel

Space
JUST BLUE.
Album: released on PRT International, Feb'79

MAGIC FLY.
Single (7"): released on Record Shack, Feb'85

Single (12"): released on Record Shack, Feb'85

VERY BEST OF SPACE, (THE).
Album: released on Record Shack, Apr'85

Space Invaded
SPACE INVADED - BBC SPACE THEMES Various artists (Various Artists).
Album: released on BBC, Sep'82 by BBC Records & Tapes. Dist: EMI, PRT, Pye

Cassette: released on BBC, Sep'82 by BBC Records & Tapes. Dist: EMI, PRT, Pye

Spacelings
LAST NIGHT I HAD THE STRANGEST DREAM.
Single (7"): released on Wise-Z, Nov'85 Dist: Priority, EMI

Spacemen 3
PERFECT PRESCRIPTIONS.
Album: released on Glass, Aug'87 by Glass Records. Dist: Nine Mile, Rough Trade, Red Rhino, Play It Again Sam

SOUND OF CONFUSION.
Album: released on Glass, Jun'86 by Glass Records. Dist: Nine Mile, Rough Trade, Red Rhino, Play It Again Sam

WALKING WITH JESUS.
Single (7"): released on Glass, Dec'86 by Glass Records. Dist: Nine Mile, Rough Trade, Red Rhino, Play It Again Sam

Space Monkey
CAN'T STOP RUNNING.
Single (7"): released on Inner Vision, Sep'83 by CBS Records. Dist: CBS

Single (12"): released on Inner Vision, Sep'83 by CBS Records. Dist: CBS

COME WITH ME.
Single (7"): released on Inner Vision, Sep'84 by CBS Records. Dist: CBS

Single (12"): released on Inner Vision, Sep'84 by CBS Records. Dist: CBS

ONE MORE SHOT.
Single (7"): released on Inner Vision, Aug'85 by CBS Records. Dist: CBS

Single (12"): released on Inner Vision, Aug'85 by CBS Records. Dist: CBS

Space Negros
PINK NOISE.
Album: released on Glass, Sep'85 by Glass Records. Dist: Nine Mile, Rough Trade, Red

Rhino, Play It Again Sam

Spacewalkers
CAPTAIN ZEP.
Single (7"): released on BBC, Jan'83 by BBC Records & Tapes. Dist: EMI, PRT, Pye

Spagna
CALL ME.
Tracks: / Call me / Girl , it's not the end of the world / Easy lady".
Single (7"): released on CBS, May'87 by CBS Records. Dist: CBS

Single (12"): released on CBS, May'87 by CBS Records. Dist: CBS

Single (12"): released on CBS, Jun'87 by CBS Records. Dist: CBS

CALL ME (VIVA MIX).
Single (12"): released on CBS, Aug'87 by CBS Records. Dist: CBS

DEDICATED TO THE MOON.
Tracks: / Call me / Dedicated to the moon / So easy / Power of money, The / Easy lady / Dance dance dance / Why can't I say (I love you Babe) / Baby blue / Girl, It's not the end of the world.
Album: released on CBS, Jun'87 by CBS Records. Dist: CBS

Cassette: released on CBS, Jun'87 by CBS Records. Dist: CBS

EASY LADY.
Tracks: / Jealousy.
Single (7"): released on CBS, Oct'86 by CBS Records. Dist: CBS

Single (12"): released on CBS, Oct'86 by CBS Records. Dist: CBS

Spain..
SPAIN: CANTE FLAMENCO Various artists (Various Artists).
Album: released on Lyrichord (USA), '82 by Lyrichord Records (USA). Dist: Flexitron Distributors Ltd

SPAIN: MAGIC OF SPAIN Various artists (Various Artists).
Album: released on EMI, Aug'80 by EMI Records. Dist: EMI

Cassette: released on EMI, Aug'80 by EMI Records. Dist: EMI

SPAIN: SOUL OF SPANISH FLAMENCO Various artists (Various Artists).
Album: released on Nonesuch Explorer (USA), Jul'84

SPAIN: SPANISH ARMADA Various artists (Various Artists).
Cassette: released on History Makers, Jan'79 by Ivan Berg. Dist: Pinnacle

Spandau Ballet
BEST OF..SPANDAU BALLET.
Compact disc: released on Chrysalis, '86 by Chrysalis Records. Dist: CBS

CHANT NO 1 (I DON'T NEED THIS PRESSURE).
Single (7"): released on Reformation, Jul'81, CBS

Single (12"): released on Reformation, Jul'81, CBS

COLLECTION - 12" MIXES.
Compact disc: released on Reformation, Apr'87, CBS

DIAMOND.
Album: released on Chrysalis, Mar'82 by Chrysalis Records. Dist: CBS

Cassette: released on Chrysalis, Mar'82 by Chrysalis Records. Dist: CBS

Boxed set: released on Chrysalis, Mar'82 by Chrysalis Records. Dist: CBS

FIGHT FOR OURSELVES.
Tracks: / Fight for ourselves / Fight for the Heartache.
Single (7"): released on CBS, Jul'86 by CBS Records. Dist: CBS

Single (12"): released on CBS, Jul'86 by CBS Records. Dist: CBS

GOLD.
Single (7"): released on Chrysalis, Aug'83 by Chrysalis Records. Dist: CBS

Single (12"): released on Chrysalis, Aug'83 by Chrysalis Records. Dist: CBS

HOW MANY LIES.
Single (7"): released on Reformation, Jan'87, CBS

Single (12"): released on Reformation, Jan'87, CBS

I'LL FLY FOR YOU.
Single (7"): released on Reformation, Aug'84, CBS

Single (12"): released on Reformation, Aug'84, CBS

INSTINCTION.
Single (7"): released on Chrysalis, Apr'82 by Chrysalis Records. Dist: CBS

Single (12"): released on Chrysalis, Apr'82 by Chrysalis Records. Dist: CBS

JOURNEYS TO GLORY.
Tracks: / To cut a long story short / Reformation / Mandolin / Muscle bound / Muscle bound / Ages of blows / Freeze, The / Confused / Confused / Toys.
Album: released on Chrysalis, Mar'81 by Chrysalis Records. Dist: CBS

Cassette: released on Chrysalis, Mar'81 by Chrysalis Records. Dist: CBS

Compact disc: released on Chrysalis, '82 by Chrysalis Records. Dist: CBS

Double cassette: released on Chrysalis(Take 2), Dec'82 by Chrysalis Records. Dist: CBS

LIVE OVER BRITTAIN.
Video-cassette (VHS): released on Chrysalis, Oct'84 by Chrysalis Records. Dist: CBS

PAINT ME DOWN.
Single (7"): released on Chrysalis, Nov'81 by Chrysalis Records. Dist: CBS

Single (12"): released on Chrysalis, Nov'81 by Chrysalis Records. Dist: CBS

PARADE.
Tracks: / Only when you leave / Highly strung / I'll fly for you / Nature of the beast / Revenge for love / Always in the back of my mind / With the pride / Round and round.
Compact disc: released on Chrysalis, Jun'87 by Chrysalis Records. Dist: CBS

Album: released on Chrysalis, Jun'84 by Chrysalis Records. Dist: CBS

Cassette: released on Chrysalis, Jun'84 by Chrysalis Records. Dist: CBS

Compact disc: released on Chrysalis, Jun'84 by Chrysalis Records. Dist: CBS

SINGLES COLLECTION, THE.
Tracks: / Gold / Lifeline / Round and around / Only when you leave / Instinction / Highly strung / True / Communication / I'll fly for you / To cut a long story short / Chant no 1 / She loved like a diamond / Paint me down / Freeze / Muscle-bound.
Compact disc: released on Chrysalis, Apr'86 by Chrysalis Records. Dist: CBS

SINGLES COLLECTION, (THE).
Album: released on Chrysalis, Nov'85 by Chrysalis Records. Dist: CBS

Cassette: released on Chrysalis, Nov'85 by Chrysalis Records. Dist: CBS

THROUGH THE BARRICADES.
Tracks: / Barricades-introduction / Cross the line / Man in chains / How many lies / Virgin / Fight for ourselves / Swept / Snakes and lovers / Through the barricades / Through the barricades (s) / With pride.
Album: released on CBS, Nov'86 by CBS Records. Dist: CBS

Cassette: released on CBS, Nov'86 by CBS Records. Dist: CBS

Compact disc: released on CBS, Nov'86 by CBS Records. Dist: CBS

Single (7"): released on Reformation, Oct'86, CBS

Single (12"): released on Reformation, Oct'86, CBS

TO CUT A LONG STORY SHORT.
Tracks: / Chant no.1 (I don't need this pressure on).
Single (7"): released on Chrysalis, Feb'87 by Chrysalis Records. Dist: CBS

Single (7"): released on Chrysalis, Nov'80 by Chrysalis Records. Dist: CBS

Single (12"): released on Chrysalis, Dec'81 by Chrysalis Records. Dist: CBS

TRUE.
Tracks: / Gold / Pleasure / Communication / Code of love / Gold / Life line / Heaven is a secret / Foundation / True.
Single (7"): released on Old Gold, Feb'87 by Old Gold Records. Dist: Lightning, Jazz Music, Spartan, Counterpoint

Album: released on Chrysalis, Mar'83 by Chrysalis Records. Dist: CBS

Cassette: released on Chrysalis, Mar'83 by Chrysalis Records. Dist: CBS

TWELVE INCH MIXES.
Tracks: / Gold / Lifeline / Round & round / Only when you leave / Instinction / Highly restrung / True / Communication / I'll fly for you / To cut a long story short / Chant no.1 / She loved like diamond / Paint me down / Freeze, The / Muscle-bound.
Album: released on Chrysalis, Nov'86 by Chrysalis Records. Dist: CBS

Cassette: released on Chrysalis, Nov'86 by Chrysalis Records. Dist: CBS

Album: released on Bam Caruso, Jan'87 by Bam Caruso Records. Dist: Rough Trade, Revolver, Cartel

Spaniels

GREAT GOOGLEY MOO.
Album: released on Charly, Jul'81 by Charly Records. Dist: Charly, Cadillac

STORMY WEATHER.
Tracks: / Lovey dovey baby / Tree little words / People will say we're in love / I'll be waiting / Stormy weather / Why I love you / Baby come along with me / I owe you / Bounce / Red snails in the sunset / Please don't tease / You painted pictures / Baby sweets / One hundred years from today / Stranger in love (A) / Let's make up.
Album: released on Charly, May'86 by Charly Records. Dist: Charly, Cadillac
Cat. no: **CRB 1114**

Spanier, Muggsy

1924-28.
Notes: Artists include: The Bucktown Five, Stomp Six, Charles Pierce & His Orchestra and The Jungle Kings.

AFTER YOU'VE GONE (see Hines ,Earl).

HESITATIN BLUES.
Tracks: / Hesitatin blues / Little David play your harp / Judy / American patrol / Chicago / Baby brown / When my dream boat comes home / Wreck of the old '97 / No lovers allowed / Careless love / More than you know / Can't we be friends / My wild Irish rose / Oh Dr Ochsner / Since we fell out of love / Washington & Lee swing / Two o'clock jump.
Notes: Mono
Album: released on Affinity, Oct'86 by Charly Records. Dist: Charly, Cadillac

HESITATIN' BLUES.
Tracks: / Hesitating blues / Little David, play your harp / Judy / American patrol / Chicago / Baby Brown / When my dreamboat comes homes / Wreck of the old 97 / No lovers allowed / Careless love (parts 1-3) / More than you know / Can't we be friends / My wild Irish rose / Oh, Doctor Ochsner! / Since we fell out of love / Washington & Lee swing / Two o'clock jump.
Album: released on Affinity, Sep'86 by Charly Records. Dist: Charly, Cadillac

Cassette: released on Affinity, Sep'86 by Charly Records. Dist: Charly, Cadillac

HOT HORN.
Album: released on Storyville (USA), Jun'86 by Moss Music Group Records (USA). Dist: Discovery Distribution, Jazz Music Distribution, Swift Distribution, Chris Wellard Distribution, JSU Distribution, Celtic Music Distribution

HOT HORN 1944 (Spanier, Muggsy & His Ragtimers).
Album: released on Commodore Classics, '87 by Teldec Records (Germany). Dist: Conifer, IMS, Polygram

MUGGSY SPANIER.
Notes: Mono production. Featuring Miff Mole/Lou McGairty/Pee Wee Russell.
Album: released on Storyville, Jun'86 by Storyville Records. Dist: Jazz Music Distribution, Swift Distribution, Chris Wellard Distribution, Counterpoint Distribution

MUGGSY SPANIER AND PEE WEE RUSSELL (Spanier, Muggsy & Pee Wee Russell).
Notes: With Bob Haggart/G Wettling etc.
Cassette: released on Holmia Cassettes, Jun'86 Dist: Jazz Music, Wellard, Chris

MUGGSY SPANIER & FRANK TESCHEMAKER (Spanier, Muggsy & Frank Teschemaker).
Album: released on Joker, Apr'81 Dist: Cadillac, Zodiac Distribution, Jazz Horizons, Jazz Music, JSU, Celtic Music

MUGGSY SPANIER & HIS RAGTIME BAND, VOL 1.
Album: released on Joker, Apr'81 Dist: Cadillac, Zodiac Distribution, Jazz Horizons, Jazz Music, JSU, Celtic Music

MUGGSY SPANIER & HIS ALL STARS.
Album: released on Joker, Apr'81 Dist: Cadillac, Zodiac Distribution, Jazz Horizons, Jazz Music, JSU, Celtic Music

MUGSY SPANIER.
Album: released on Deja Vu, Jan'87 by Deja Vu Records. Dist: Counterpoint Distribution, Record Services Distribution (Ireland)

Cassette: released on Deja Vu, Jan'87 by Deja Vu Records. Dist: Counterpoint Distribution, Record Services Distribution (Ireland)

NICK'S - NEW YORK.
Album: released on Commodore Classics, May'87 by Teldec Records (Germany). Dist: Conifer, IMS, Polygram

ON V-DISC 1944-45.
Album: released on Everybody's, Jul'87 by Everybody's Records. Dist: Jazz Music, Swift

RICHMOND AND CHICAGO DAYS, 1924-28.
Album: released on Swaggie (Australia), Jan'83

SPANIER IN CHICAGO, 1954.
Album: released on VJM, Apr'79 by VJM (UK) Records. Dist: Swift

TIN ROOF BLUES (Spanier, Muggsy & Earl Hines).
Double Album: released on Vogue Jazz (France), May'83

VOL 2 (Spanier, Muggsy & His Dixieland All Stars).
Album: released on Storyville, Nov'86 by Storyville Records. Dist: Jazz Music Distribution, Swift Distribution, Chris Wellard Distribution, Counterpoint Distribution

Spank

OOH BABY.
Single (7"): released on Champion, Apr'85 by Champion Records. Dist: RCA

Single (12"): released on Champion, Apr'85 by Champion Records. Dist: RCA

SPANK YOU.
Album: released on Champion, Mar'85 by Champion Records. Dist: RCA

Spanner, Ranking

SOME SEE THE THRILL.
Tracks: / Some see the thrill (Inst).
Single (12"): released on Stop 'N' Rock, Nov'86

Spann, Otis

BLUES OF OTIS SPANN, (THE).
Album: released on See For Miles, Aug'85 by Charly Records. Dist: Spartan

BLUES OF OTIS SPANN PLUS...,THE.
Notes: This album is from 1964,and featured guests include Eric Clapton,Jimmy Page & Muddy Waters-S.F.M have also added 3 tracks.
Album: released on See For Miles, Jun'87 by See For Miles Records. Dist: Pinnacle

CANDID SPANN, VOL 1.
Album: released on Crosscut, Jan'83

CANDID SPANN, VOL 2.
Album: released on Crosscut, Jan'83

CRYIN' TIME.
Album: released on Vanguard, Apr'78 by PRT Records. Dist: PRT

GOOD MORNING MR BLUES.
Album: released on Storyville (USA), Apr'86 by Moss Music Group Records (USA). Dist: Discovery Distribution, Jazz Music Distribution, Swift Distribution, Chris Wellard Distribution, JSU Distribution, Celtic Music Distribution

NOBODY KNOWS CHICAGO LIKE I DO.
Album: released on Charly, Nov'83 by Charly Records. Dist: Charly, Cadillac

OTIS SPANN IS THE BLUES.
Album: released on Candid, Dec'85 Dist: Counterpoint, Cadillac

RAREST.
Album: released on JSP, Apr'84 by JSP Records. Dist: Swift, Projection

TAKE ME BACK HOME.
Album: released on Black Magic (Holland), Aug'84

WALKING THE BLUES.
Album: released on Candid, Jul'87 Dist: Counterpoint, Cadillac

Spanos, Danny

EXCUSE ME.
Single (7"): released on Epic, Jan'84 by CBS Records. Dist: CBS

Single (12"): released on Epic, Jan'84 by CBS Records. Dist: CBS

Spargo

YOU AND ME.
Single (7"): released on Champagne, Jun'81 by DJM Records.

Single (12"): released on Champagne, Jun'81 by DJM Records.

Spark Gap Wonder Boys

CLUCK OLD HEN.
Album: released on Rounder, May'77

Sparkle

YIP YAP RABBIT.
Single (12"): released on UK Bubblers, Oct'85 by Greensleeves Records. Dist: RCA, Jetstar

Sparkling Bronze

(ENGLISH HANDBELL RINGING).
Album: released on Grosvenor, Nov'77 by Grosvenor Records. Dist: Taylors

Sparks

BEST OF SPARKS.
Album: released on Island, Sep'79 by Island Records. Dist: Polygram

Cassette: released on Island, Oct'79 by Island Records. Dist: Polygram

CHANGE.
Single (7"): released on London, Jul'85 by London Records. Dist: Polygram

Single (12"): released on London, Jul'85 by London Records. Dist: Polygram

COOL PLACES.
Single (7"): released on Atlantic, Jun'83 by WEA Records. Dist: WEA

FUNNY FACES.
Single (7"): released on Why-Fi, Sep'81 by Why-Fi Records. Dist: RCA, Indies

I PREDICT.
Single (7"): released on Atlantic, Jun'82 by WEA Records. Dist: WEA

MUSIC THAT YOU CAN DANCE TO.
Single (7"): released on Consolidated Allied, Nov'86 Dist: Pinnacle

Single (12"): released on Consolidated Allied, Nov'86 Dist: Pinnacle

MUSIC THAT YOU CAN DANCE TO.
Album: released on Car, Nov'86 by Car Records. Dist: Pinnacle

Cassette: released on Car, Nov'86 by Car Records. Dist: Pinnacle

NUMBER ONE SONG IN HEAVEN.
Single (12"): released on Virgin, May'83

ROSEBUD.
Single (7"): released on Consolidated Allied, Feb'87 Dist: Pinnacle

Single (12"): released on Consolidated Allied, Feb'87 Dist: Pinnacle

TERMINAL JIVE.
Album: released on Virgin, Sep'79

WHOMP THAT SUCKER.
Album: released on Why-Fi, May'81 by Why-Fi Records. Dist: RCA, Indies

Cassette: released on Why-Fi, May'81 by Why-Fi Records. Dist: RCA, Indies Deleted '82.

Sparks, J.J.

BRIXTON BLUE BEAT (Sparks, J.J. & The City Gents).
Album: released on Vista Sounds, '83 by Vista Sounds Records. Dist: Jetstar

I AM DREAMING.
Single (12"): released on Ixia, Sep'82 Dist: Jetstar

LET IT BE ME.
Single (12"): released on Echo, Mar'82 by Vista Sounds. Dist: Jazz Music

Sparks, Larry

RAMBLING BLUEGRASS (Sparks, Larry & The Lonsesome Ramblers).
Album: released on Gusto (USA), Oct'79 by Gusto Records (USA). Dist: Crusader

Sparky's Magic Piano

SPARKY'S MAGIC PIANO Various artists (Various Artists).
Tracks: / Sparky's magic piano / Sparky and the talking train.
Notes: Henry Blair featuring Ray Turner at the piano. Narration by Verne Smith/music by Billy May/talking piano Sonovox.
Album: released on Capitol, Nov'86 by Capitol Records. Dist: EMI

Cassette: released on Capitol, Nov'86 by Capitol Records. Dist: EMI

Sparling, Steve

MERCY MERCY ME.
Tracks: / Mercy mercy me / Mercy mercy me (instrumental).
Single (7"): released on Important, Aug'86 Dist: EMI

Single (12"): released on Important, Aug'86 Dist: EMI

Sparrow

KING OF THE WORLD.
Album: released on Dynamic, Aug'84 by Creole Records. Dist: CBS, Essex

SPARROW VS THE REST.
Album: released on Dynamic, Jun'76 by Creole Records. Dist: CBS, Essex

Sparta

ANGEL OF DAEATH/TONIGHT.
Single (7"): released on Suspect, Oct'81

Spartacus

TERMINAL LOVE/(WHAT ARE WE GOING TO DO).
Single (7"): released on Carrere, Oct'81 by Carrere Records. Dist: PRT, Spartan

Spartacus R

AFRICA I SEE.
Album: released on Zara, Dec'83 by Zara Records. Dist: Rough Trade

Cassette: released on Zara, Dec'83 by Zara Records. Dist: Rough Trade

FREEDOM FIRST.
Album: released on Zara, Jan'87 by Zara Records. Dist: Rough Trade

Album: released on Zara, Jun'84 by Zara Records. Dist: Rough Trade

THIRD WORLD WAR.
Album: released on Zara, Oct'83 by Zara Records. Dist: Rough Trade

WOZA MALCOLM.
Single (12"): released on Zara, May'87 by Zara Records. Dist: Rough Trade

Spartan Warriors

STEEL N CHAINS.
Album: released on Guardian, Aug'84 by Guardian Records. Dist: Jazz Music, Pinnacle

SP Band

DON'T SAY IT (SP Band with Shezwae Powell).
Tracks: / Because of heaven.
Single (7"): released on Bond, Mar'86 Dist: Spartan

Spear of Destiny

ALL MY LOVE.
Single (12"): released on Burning Rome, Jun'85 Dist: CBS

FLYING SCOTSMAN/AFRICA THE MAN WHO TUMES THE DRUMS.
Single (7"): released on Epic, Feb'83 by CBS Records. Dist: CBS

Single (12"): released on Epic, Feb'83 by CBS Records. Dist: CBS

Cassette: released on Epic, Apr'83 by CBS Records. Dist: CBS

GRAPES OF WRATH.
Tracks: / Wheel (The) / Flying Scotsman / Roof of the world / Aria / Solution / Murder of love (The) / Preacher (The) / Omen of the times / Man who tunes the drums (The) / Grapes of wrath.
Album: released on Epic, Apr'86 by CBS Records. Dist: CBS

Cassette: released on Epic, Apr'86 by CBS Records. Dist: CBS

NEVER TAKE ME ALIVE.
Tracks: / Never take me alive / Land of shame.
Single (7"): released on 10, Mar'87 by 10 Records. Dist: Virgin, EMI

Single (12"): released on 10, Mar'87 by 10 Records. Dist: Virgin, EMI

ONE EYED JACKS.
Tracks: / Rainmaker / Young men / Everything you ever wanted / Don't turn away / Liberator / Prisoner of love / Playground of the rich / Forbidden planet / Attica / These days are gone.
Album: released on Epic, Apr'84 by CBS Records. Dist: CBS

Cassette: released on Epic, Apr'84 by CBS Records. Dist: CBS

OUTLAND.
Album: released on 10, Apr'87 by 10 Records. Dist: Virgin, EMI

Cassette: released on 10, Apr'87 by 10 Records. Dist: Virgin, EMI

Compact disc: released on 10, May'87 by 10 Records. Dist: Virgin, EMI

PRISONER OF LOVE/ROSIE/GRAPES OF WRATH/RAINMAKER.
Single (7"): released on Epic, Jan'84 by CBS Records. Dist: CBS

Single (12"): released on Epic, Jan'84 by CBS Records. Dist: CBS

Double-pack single: released on Epic, Jan'84 by CBS Records. Dist: CBS

S.O.D. THE EPIC YEARS.
Tracks: / Wheel, The / Rainmaker / Prisoner of love / Playground of the rich / Young men / Up all night / Come back / All my love (ask nothing) / Mickey / Liberator.
Video-cassette (VHS): released on CBS, Apr'87 by CBS Records. Dist: CBS

Album: released on Epic, May'87 by CBS Records. Dist: CBS

Cassette: released on Epic, May'87 by CBS Records. Dist: CBS

Compact disc: released on Epic, Jul'87 by CBS Records. Dist: CBS

STRANGERS IN OUR TOWN.
Tracks: / Somewhere out there / Time of our lives*.
Single (7"): released on 10, Jan'87 by 10 Records. Dist: Virgin, EMI

Single (12"): released on Ten, Jan'87

WAS THAT YOU.
Tracks: / Was that you / Was that you (live version) / Miami Vice (live)* / Outlands (live)*.
Single (7"): released on 10, Jul'87 by 10 Records. Dist: Virgin, EMI

Single (12"): released on 10, Jul'87 by 10 Records. Dist: Virgin, EMI

WHEEL TE/HOP THE/SOLUTION/ROOF OF THE WORLD/LOVE.
Single (12"): released on Epic, May'83 by CBS Records. Dist: CBS

WHEEL, THE.
Tracks: / Wheel (The) / Flying Scotsman / Prisoner of love / Liberator.
Single (12"): released on Old Gold, Feb'86 by Old Gold Records. Dist: Lightning, Jazz Music, Spartan, Counterpoint

WHEEL THE /THE HOP.
Single (7"): released on Epic, Jun'83 by CBS Records. Dist: CBS

Single (12"): released on Epic, Jun'83 by CBS Records. Dist: CBS

WORLD SERVICE.
Album: released on Epic, Aug'85 by CBS Records. Dist: CBS. Estim retail price in Jul'87 was £3.99.

Single (12"): released on Epic, Aug'85 by CBS Records. Dist: CBS

Spears, Billie Jo

17 GOLDEN PIECES OF BILLIE JO SPEARS.
Album: released on Bulldog, Nov'83 by Bulldog Records. Dist: President Distribution, Spartan, Swift, Taylor, H.R.

APOLOGISING ROSE.
Single (7"): released on Ritz, Aug'82 by Outlet Records. Dist: Outlet, Prism Leisure Distribution, Record Services Distribution (Ireland), Roots

BILLIE JO SINGLES ALBUM THE.
Album: released on United Artists, Nov'79

Cassette: released on United Artists, Nov'79

BLANKET ON THE GROUND.
Single (7"): released on United Artists (USA), Jan'84 by EMI Records. Dist: EMI, Swift, Solomon & Peres Distribution

COUNTRY GREATS.
Tracks: / 57 Chevrolet / Loving him was easier(than anything i'll ever do again) / Another somebody done somebody wrong...(Hey won't you play) / Till something better comes along / Sing me an old fashioned song / Every time I sing a love song / See the funny little clown / That's what friends are for / Blanket on the ground / Ode to Billy Joe / Misty blue / I don't wanna play house / Hurt / Stand by your man / He's got more love in his little finger / Take me to your world.
Album: released on MFP, Mar'87 by EMI Records. Dist: EMI

Cassette: released on MFP, Mar'87 by EMI Records. Dist: EMI

FEVER.
Album: released on Premier, May'85 by Premier Records. Dist: CBS

Cassette: released on Premier, May'85 by Premier Records. Dist: CBS

FOR THE GOOD TIMES.
Album: released on MFP, Apr'81 by EMI Records. Dist: EMI

Cassette: released on MFP, Apr'81 by EMI Records. Dist: EMI

I CAN HEAR KENTUCKY CALLING ME
(Spears, Billie Jo & Carrie Duncan).

IF YOU WANT ME/HERE COMES THOSE LIES AGAIN.
Single (7"): released on United Artists, Mar'77

IT COULD HAVE BEEN ME.
Tracks: / He's on the run again / Danny (baby ruby) / Come on home / Which way you gone Billy / You're my man / I'll never be free / Step child / Souveniers and Californian memories / It could've been me.
Album: released on Showcase, Apr'86 Dist: Counterpoint

Cassette: released on Showcase, Apr'86 Dist: Counterpoint

MIDNIGHT BLUE.
Album: released on Premier, Feb'87 by Premier Records. Dist: CBS

Cassette: released on Premier, Feb'87 by Premier Records. Dist: CBS

ODE TO BILLIE JO.
Album: released on Capitol, Apr'85 by Capitol Records. Dist: EMI

Cassette: released on Capitol, Apr'85 by Capitol Records. Dist: EMI

SUNSHINE.
Album: released on Premier, Jan'84 by Premier Records. Dist: CBS

Cassette: released on Premier, Jan'84 by Premier Records. Dist: CBS

TWENTY COUNTRY GREATS.
Tracks: / Queen of the silver dollar / Cryin' time / I'll never love like this again / All I have to do is dream / Tenessee waltz / What I've got in mind / Just the way you are / This ole house / Rocky top / Blue bayou / For the good times / Fire and rain / Crystal chandeliers / It's a heartache / Silver threads and golden needles / Fifty seven Chevrolet / I'm gonna be a country girl / Here you come again / Blue blue day / Blanket on the ground.

Compact disc: released on Warwick, Nov'86 Dist: Multiple Sound Distributors

WE JUST CAME APART AT THE SEAMS.
Album: released on Premier, May'85 by Premier Records. Dist: CBS

Cassette: released on Premier, May'85 by Premier Records. Dist: CBS

WHAT I'VE GOT IN MIND.
Single (7"): released on Liberty, Sep'85 by Liberty-United. Dist: EMI

Special AKA

GANGSTERS.
Single (7"): released on Two-Tone, Jul'79 by Chrysalis Records. Dist: H.R. Taylor

GIRLFRIEND.
Single (7"): released on Two-Tone, Aug'84 by Chrysalis Records. Dist: H.R. Taylor

IN THE STUDIO.
Album: released on Two-Tone, Jun'84 by Chrysalis Records. Dist: H.R. Taylor

Cassette: released on Two-Tone, Jun'84 by Chrysalis Records. Dist: H.R. Taylor

NELSON MENDELLA.
Single (7"): released on Two-Tone, Mar'84 by Chrysalis Records. Dist: Polygram

Single (12"): released on Two-Tone, Mar'84 by Chrysalis Records. Dist: Polygram

Special Binaural Effects

ADVENTURE IN BINAURAL.
Album: released on JVC, Jan'78 Dist: Target

BILLY JO SPEARS.
Album: released on Ritz, Oct'83 by Ritz Records. Dist: Spartan

Cassette: released on Ritz, Oct'83 by Ritz Records. Dist: Spartan

MIDNIGHT BLUE.
Single (7"): released on Premier, Jul'85 by Premier Records. Dist: CBS

SWINGIN/I CAN HEAR KENTUCKY CALLING ME.
Single (7"): released on Ritz, May'83 by Outlet Records. Dist: Outlet, Prism Leisure Distribution, Record Services Distribution (Ireland), Roots

Single (7"): released on Ritz, May'83 by Outlet Records. Dist: Outlet, Prism Leisure Distribution, Record Services Distribution (Ireland), Roots

Special Duties

BULLSHIT CRASS.
Single (7"): released on Rondelet Music And Records, Nov'82 by Rondelet Music And Records. Dist: Pinnacle, Cartel Distribution, Rondelet Music And Records Distribution

POLICE STATE.
Single (7"): released on Rondelet, May'82 Dist: Spartan Distribution

PUNK ROCKER.
Single (7"): released on Expulsion, May'83 by Expulsion Records. Dist: Stage One

VIOLENT SOCIETY.
Single (7"): released on Rondelet, Jan'82 Dist: Spartan Distribution

Special EFX

MODERN MANNERS.
Tracks: / Fountain of you / Fun in the sun / Modern manners / After one empty step / Toy shop (The) / Mystical remedies / Buttermilk falls / Greenway North / High society.
Compact disc: released on GRP (USA), Jul'85 by GRP Records (USA). Dist: IMS, Polygram

Album: released on GRP (USA), Jul'85 by GRP Records (USA). Dist: IMS, Polygram

Cassette: released on GRP (USA), Jul'85 by GRP Records (USA). Dist: IMS, Polygram

Compact disc: released on GRP (USA), Jul'85 by GRP Records (USA). Dist: IMS, Polygram

MYSTIQUE.
Tracks: / Hands of the healer / Rainy Sunday / Udu voodoo / Pleasance / Noel / Islands / Sidestreet paradise, A / When the earth was flat / Sleeping tiger, The / Dreamer of dreams * / Ritual *.
Notes: For their 4th GRP album,guitarist Chieli Minucci and percussionist George Jinda bring a "new age" feel and touch to their colourful diverse blend of music. Extra bonus track on CD only.
Album: released on GRP (USA), May'87 by GRP Records (USA). Dist: IMS, Polygram

Cassette: released on GRP (USA), May'87 by GRP Records (USA). Dist: IMS, Polygram

Compact disc: released on GRP (USA), May'87 by GRP Records (USA). Dist: IMS, Polygram

SLICE OF LIFE.
Notes: Third album of GRP for contemporary jazz group Special EFX. Led by guitarist and chief composer Chieli Minucci and percussionist, composer George Jinda. Moulding acoustic guitar, percussion, Bolivian wood flute alongside synthesizers and electric instruments, Special EFX evoke a vivid collage of endless sounds and musical textures.
Album: released on GRP (USA), Apr'86 by GRP Records (USA). Dist: IMS, Polygram

Compact disc: released on GRP (USA), Apr'86 by GRP Records (USA). Dist: IMS, Polygram

Special Occasion

FLYING TO SANTA BARBARA.
Single (12"): released on Nunk, Nov'84 by Nunk. Dist: Lightning

Special Project

GREEN ONIONS.
Tracks: / Green onions / Elephant man / Nightmare / Nightmare (skratch mix).
Single (12"): released on White Label, Jul'87 by White Label Records. Dist: Jetstar

Special Request

TAKE IT TO THE MAX.
Single (7"): released on Island, Aug'84 by Island Records. Dist: Polygram

Single (12"): released on Island, Aug'84 by Island Records. Dist: Polygram

Specials

DO NOTHING.
Single (7"): released on Two-Tone, Dec'80 by Chrysalis Records. Dist: Polygram

GANGSTERS.
Single (7"): released on Two-Tone, Jul'79 by Chrysalis Records. Dist: Polygram

GHOST TOWN.
Single (7"): released on Two-Tone, Jun'81 by Chrysalis Records. Dist: Polygram

Single (12"): released on Two-Tone, Jun'81 by Chrysalis Records. Dist: Polygram

GHOST TOWN.
Tracks: / Rat race.
Single (7"): released on Old Gold, Feb'87 by Old Gold Records. Dist: Lightning, Jazz Music, Spartan, Counterpoint

MESSAGE TO RUBY.
Single (7"): released on Two-Tone, Oct'79 by Chrysalis Records. Dist: Polygram

MORE SPECIALS.
Album: released on Two-Tone, Sep'80 by Chrysalis Records. Dist: Polygram

Cassette: released on Two-Tone, Sep'80 by Chrysalis Records. Dist: Polygram

PEEL SESSION 29.5.79.
Single (12"): released on Strange Fruit, Jan'87 by Clive Selwood. Dist: Pinnacle

RAT RACE.
Single (7"): released on Two-Tone, May'80 by Chrysalis Records. Dist: Polygram

SPECIALS,THE.
Album: released on Fame (Chrysalis), Nov'84 by Music For Pleasure Records. Dist: EMI

Cassette: released on Fame (Chrysalis), Nov'84 by Music For Pleasure Records. Dist: EMI

Double cassette: released on Chrysalis(Take 2), Dec'82 by Chrysalis Records. Dist: CBS

STEREOTYPE.
Single (7"): released on Two-Tone, Sep'80 by Chrysalis Records. Dist: Polygram

TOO MUCH TOO YOUNG.
Tracks: / Gangsters.
Single (7"): released on Old Gold, Feb'87 by Old Gold Records. Dist: Lightning, Jazz Music, Spartan, Counterpoint

TOO MUCH TOO YOUNG.
Single (7"): released on Two-Tone, Jan'80 by Chrysalis Records. Dist: Polygram

Specialty story

SPECIALTY STORY VOL 1, THE.
Album: released on Ace, Aug'85 by Ace Records. Dist: Pinnacle, Swift, Hotshot, Cadillac

Specific Oceans

DO YOU?.
Single (7"): released on Ugly, Jun'84 by Ugly Records.

Specimen

BEAUTY OF POISON.
Single (7"): released on London, Nov'83 by London Records. Dist: Polygram

Single (12"): released on London, Nov'83 by London Records. Dist: Polygram

RETURNING FROM A JOURNEY.
Single (7"): released on London, May'83 by London Records. Dist: Polygram

Single (12"): released on London, May'83 by London Records. Dist: Polygram

Picture disc single: released on London, Jun'83 by London Records. Dist: Polygram

SHARPE TEETH PRETTY TEETH.
Single (7"): released on Truth (UK), Mar'85 Dist: Stage One

Single (12"): released on Truth (UK), Mar'85 Dist: Stage One

Speckled Red

1929-38.
Album: released on Wolf, Apr'84 Dist: Jazz Music, Swift

SPECKLED RED IN LONDON 1960.
Album: released on VJM, Apr'79 by Wellard, Chris Distribution. Dist: Wellard, Chris Distribution

Spectacular...

SPECTACULAR SOUND EFFECTS-1
(Spectacular sounds effects).
Album: released on EMI, Jun'81 by EMI Records. Dist: EMI

Cassette: released on EMI, Jun'81 by EMI Records. Dist: EMI

SPECTACULAR SOUND EFFECTS-2
(Spectacular sounds effects).
Album: released on EMI, Jun'81 by EMI Records. Dist: EMI

Cassette: released on EMI, Jun'81 by EMI Records. Dist: EMI

Spector, Phil

CHRISTMAS SINGLE, THE (EP).
Single (7"): released on Phil Spector International, Nov'82

ECHOE'S OF THE 60'S.
Album: released on Philips, Oct'77 Dist: IMS-Polygram

GREATEST HITS / CHRISTMAS ALBUM.
Double Album: released on Impression, Nov'84 Dist: CBS

Double cassette: released on Impression, Nov'84 Dist: CBS

PHIL SPECTOR: EARLY PRODUCTIONS '58-61 Various artists (Various Artists).
Album: released on Rhino (USA), Jul'84 by Rhino Records (USA).

PHIL SPECTOR: ECHOES OF THE SIXTIES Various artists (Various Artists).
Album: released on Phil Spector International, Oct'77

Cassette: released on Phil Spector International, Oct'77

PHIL SPECTOR'S CHRISTMAS ALBUM.
Album: released on Phil Spector International, Dec'79

Cassette: released on Phil Spector International, Dec'79

WALL OF SOUND.
Boxed set: released on Phil Spector, Nov'81

Spector, Ronnie
DARLIN' / SETTIN' THE WOODS ON FIRE.
Single (7"): released on Red Shadow, Jan'81 Dist: Pinnacle

HERE TODAY GONE TOMORROW.
Single (7"): released on Red Shadow, Mar'81 Dist: Pinnacle

UNFINISHED BUSINESS.
Tracks: / Who can sleep / Love on a rooftop / Dangerous / Burning love / Unfinished business / Walk away (If I could) / Heart song / True to you / When we danced / Good love is hard to find.
Album: released on CBS, Jul'87 by CBS Records. Dist: CBS

Cassette: released on CBS, Jul'87 by CBS Records. Dist: CBS

WHO CAN SLEEP.
Tracks: / Who can sleep / When we danced.
Single (7"): released on CBS, 13 Jun'87 by CBS Records. Dist: CBS

Single (12"): released on CBS, 13 Jun'87 by CBS Records. Dist: CBS

Spectra
DIGITAL LOVE.
Single (7"): released on Certain, May'86 Dist: Priority, EMI, Pinnacle

Single (12"): released on Certain, May'86 Dist: Priority, EMI, Pinnacle

Spectral Display
IT TAKES A MUSCLE TO FALL IN LOVE / TANGLO.
Single (7"): released on EMI, Feb'83 by EMI Records. Dist: EMI

Spectres
STORIES.
Single (7"): released on Demon, Feb'81 by Demon Records. Dist: Pinnacle

STRANGE EFFECT / GETTING AWAY FROM YOU.
Single (7"): released on Direct Hit, Jul'80

Spectrum
ALL OR NOTHING.
Single (7"): released on Phoenix, Oct'85 by Stiff Records. Dist: EMI

Single (12"): released on Phoenix, Oct'85 by Stiff Records. Dist: EMI

HAVING A GOOD TIME / SHAKE IT UP.
Single (12"): released on Smokey, Jun'82 Dist: Jetstar

LIVE IN JAPAN.
Album: released on Rounder (USA Import), Jan'84

SPECTRUM: (THE COLOURS SAMPLER) Various artists (Various Artists).
Tracks: / Humble thyself in the sight of the lord / Sweet hour of prayer / Joy to the world / I love you lord (Phil Keaggy).
Album: released on Maranatha Music, May'86

Cassette: released on Maranatha Music, May'86

TRIBUTE TO THELONIOUS MONK, THE.
Album: released on Switch, Nov'82 Dist: PRT Distribution, Jazz Music Distribution, PRT Distribution

Spectrum - Volume 1
SPECTRUM - VOLUME 1 Various artists (Various Artists).
Compact disc: released on ECM (Germany), Jul'87 by ECM Records. Dist: IMS, Polygram, Virgin through EMI

Compact disc: released on ECM (Germany), Jul'87 by ECM Records. Dist: IMS, Polygram, Virgin through EMI

Spedding, Chris
CHRIS SPEDDING.
Album: released on RAK, Apr'76 by RAK. Dist: EMI

CRYING GAME, THE / COUNTERFEIT.
Single (7"): released on RAK, Oct'80 by RAK. Dist: EMI

GUITAR GRAFITTI.
Album: released on RAK, Feb'79 by RAK. Dist: EMI

Cassette: released on RAK, Feb'79 by RAK. Dist: EMI Deleted '81.

HURT.
Album: released on RAK, Oct'77 by RAK. Dist: EMI

I'M NOT LIKE EVERYBODY ELSE.
Album: released on RAK, Nov'80 by RAK. Dist: EMI

MEAN 'N' MOODY.
Album: released on See For Miles, Jan'85 by Charly Records. Dist: Spartan

MEAN'N'MOODY.
Album: released on See For Miles, Jul'87 by See For Miles Records. Dist: Pinnacle

Speech and Drama
SPEECH AND DRAMA (Exploring music and sound).
Cassette: released on D'Arblay, Jul'78 by Anemone Records.

Speed Kills
SPEED KILLS Various artists (Various Artists).
Album: released on Music For Nations, Sep'85 by Music For Nations Records. Dist: Pinnacle

SPEED KILLS VOL 2 Various artists (Various Artists).
Notes: Track details not advised
Album: released on Under One Flag, May'86 Dist: Pinnacle

Cassette: released on Under One Flag, May'86 Dist: Pinnacle

Speedstars
Joey Harris & the Speedstars

Speed Trials
SPEED TRIALS, THE Various artists (Various Artists).
Album: released on Homestead, May'85 Dist: Rough Trade, Cartel, Shigaku

Speirs, Sam
TALK TO ME / SHUFFLING.
Single (7"): released on Holyrood, Oct'83 by Holyrood Records. Dist: Pinnacle

Spellbound
ABCDEFGHIJKL.O.V.E I LOVE YOU / DON'T YA DO ME THAT WAY.
Single (7"): released on Chrysalis, Jun'83 by Chrysalis Records. Dist: CBS

Single (12"): released on Chrysalis, Jun'83 by Chrysalis Records. Dist: CBS

MY KINDA GIRL.
Tracks: / My kinda girl / Gone rockin'.
Single (7"): released on Sonet, May'86 by Sonet Records. Dist: PRT

ROCKIN RECKLESS.
Tracks: / Rockin Reckless.
Single (7"): released on Sonet, Sep'86 by Sonet Records. Dist: PRT

Spelleogenisis
SPELLEOGENESIS Original soundtrack.
Album: released on Nomusic, Jun'84 Dist: Red Rhino Distribution, Cartel Distribution

Speller, Jenny
RIDING ON A RAINBOW.

Single (7"): released on Roxon, Apr'81 by Roxon Records. Dist: Pinnacle

Spelling Misteaks
RUBBER DUCK POP STAR.
Single (7"): released on Stortbeat, Nov'79 by Stortbeat Records. Dist: Spartan Distribution

Spellman, Benny
CALLING ALL CARS.
Album: released on Bandy (USA), Jul'84

FORTUNE TELLER / LIPSTICK TRACES.
Single (7"): released on Band (USA), Mar'83 Dist: Swift

Spence, Brian
BROTHERS.
Album: released on Polydor, Sep'86 by Polydor Records. Dist: Polygram, Polydor

Cassette: released on Polydor, Sep'86 by Polydor Records. Dist: Polygram, Polydor

Compact disc: released on Polydor, Sep'86 by Polydor Records. Dist: Polygram, Polydor

HEAR IT FROM THE HEART.
Tracks: / Hear it from the heart / I will call you
Single (7"): released on Polydor, Aug'86 by Polydor Records. Dist: Polygram, Polydor

Single (12"): released on Polydor, Aug'86 by Polydor Records. Dist: Polygram, Polydor

Spence, Derek
SEE A BLACK MAN CRY / TRILOGY.
Single (7"): released on Cha-Cha, Feb'82 by Cha Cha. Dist: Jetstar

Spence, Joseph
BAHAMAN GUITARIST.
Album: released on Arhoolie, May'81 by Arhoolie Records. Dist: Projection, Topic, Jazz Music, Swift, Roots

JOSEPH SPENCE.
Album: released on Rounder (USA Import), Sep'79

Spence, Peter
DON'T LEAVE ME LONELY.
Tracks: / Lonely (Inst) / Don't leave me lonely (P.A.Mix).
Single (12"): released on Greensleeves, Jan'87 by Greensleeves Records. Dist: BMG, Jetstar, Spartan

FRIVOLOUS WOMAN.
Tracks: / Frivolous Woman / Frivolous Woman (Dub Mix).
Single (12"): released on Movin Music, Oct'86

Spencer, Bill
GET ON UP / AFRICAN GIRL.
Single (7"): released on Olympic, Dec'82

Single (12"): released on Olympic, Dec'82

IMAGINE / DO YOU REALLY LOVE ME.
Single (12"): released on Olympic, Sep'82

Spencer, Don
SINGS THE SONGS OF PLAY SCHOOL.
Album: released on Nevis, Jan'79 Dist: H.R. Taylor

Spencer, Earle
EARLE SPENCER & HIS NEW BAND SENSATION OF 1946.
Album: released on First Heard, Jul'77 by Submarine Records. Dist: Conifer, Taylors

Spencer, John
TRYING TO MATTER.
Album: released on Tank, Sep'79 by Tank Records.

Spencer, John B.
OUT WITH A BANG.
Tracks: / Out with a bang / Funny honey / Gingham white and blue / Acceptable losses / Plaisir d'amour and more / Forgotten the blues / Hold on to your heartache / Cry baby cry / Flesh and blood / Chris is in love again / One more whiskey / Sad reunion / Answer only with your eyes.
Album: released on Waterfront, Feb'87 by Waterfront Records. Dist: Rough Trade, Cartel, Projection, Roots

Spencer, John Louts
LAST LP, THE.
Album: released on Beggars Banquet, Sep'78 by Beggars Banquet Records. Dist: WEA

Spencer, Johnny
STRIKE SONG, THE.
Single (7"): released on Pastafont, Oct'84 by Pastafont Records.

Spencer, Juan
I'M ON MY WAY.
Single (7"): by Soul Stop Record 3. Dist: Spartan

Spencer, Mike
OH MY PAPA.
Single (7"): released on Service, Nov'82

Spencer, Tracy
RUN TO ME.
Tracks: / Run to Me / Mama Run.
Single (7"): released on CBS, Aug'86 by CBS Records. Dist: CBS

Single (12"): released on CBS, Aug'86 by CBS Records. Dist: CBS

Spence, Sonya
IN THE DARK.
Cassette: released on Skynote, Sep'84 by Skynote Records. Dist: Jetstar

JAMAICAN JUMP.
Single (12"): released on Cima, Dec'84 by Cima Records. Dist: Jetstar

Spender, Stephen
FOUR TWENTIETH CENTURY POETS.
Double cassette: released on Argo, Apr'85 by Decca Records. Dist: Polygram

Spense, Barrington
FALLING IN LOVE FOR THE FIRST TIME.
Single (12"): released on Exclusive, Feb'82 Dist: Jetstar

Sphere
FOUR FOR ALL.
Album: released on Verve (Germany), Aug'87

Cassette: released on Verve (Germany), Aug'87

Compact disc: released on Verve (Germany), Aug'87

Sphinx
BURNING LIGHTS.
Album: released on Mausoleum, May'85 by Mausoleum Records. Dist: Pinnacle

Spice
YOU'RE ALWAYS THERE.
Tracks: / You're always there / Your always there (Dub Version).
Single (12"): released on Noir, May'86 Dist: Pinnacle, Jetstar, PRT

YOU'RE SO NICE.
Single (7"): released on Jive, Jul'83 by Zomba Records. Dist: RCA, PRT, CBS

Single (12"): released on Jive, Jul'83 by Zomba Records. Dist: RCA, PRT, CBS

Spicer, George
BLACKBERRY FOLD.
Album: released on Topic, '82 Dist: Roots Distribution

Spicer, Terry
GOING TO BRIGHTON.
Single (7"): released on After Hours, Jul'82 Dist: CBS

Spicher, Buddy
BUDDIES (Spicher, Buddy & Buddy Emmons).
Album: released on Sonet, Nov'77 by Sonet Records. Dist: PRT

PLATINUM FIDDLE.
Album: released on President, Aug'80 by President Records. Dist: Taylors, Spartan

Spider
ALL THE TIME.
Single (7"): released on City, '81 by City Records. Dist: Pinnacle

BREAKAWAY.
Single (7"): released on A&M, Jul'84 by A&M Records. Dist: Polygram

Single (12"): released on A&M, Jul'84 by A&M Records. Dist: Polygram

GIMME GIMME IT ALL.
Tracks: / Gimme gimme it all / Rock tonight /

live recording from the Kerrang concert (See notes) / Gimme gimme it all (extended version:see notes) / Did ya Like baby (see notes).
Single (7"): released on PRT, Mar'86 by PRT Records. Dist: PRT

Special: released on PRT, Mar'86 by PRT Records. Dist: PRT

Single (12"): released on PRT, Mar'86 by PRT Records. Dist: PRT

HERE WE GO ROCK 'N' ROLL.
Picture disc single: released on A&M, Mar'84 by A&M Records. Dist: Polygram

ROCK'N'ROLL FOREVER WILL LAST.
Single (7"): released on RCA, Aug'82 by RCA Records. Dist: RCA, Roots, Swift, Wellard, Chris, I & B, Solomon & Peres Distribution

ROCK'N'ROLL GYPSIES.
Album: released on RCA, Oct'82 by RCA Records. Dist: RCA, Roots, Swift, Wellard, Chris, I & B, Solomon & Peres Distribution

Cassette: released on RCA, Oct'82 by RCA Records. Dist: RCA, Roots, Swift, Wellard, Chris, I & B, Solomon & Peres Distribution

TALKIN' 'BOUT ROCK 'N' ROLL / DOWN 'N' OUT.
Single (7"): released on RCA, Nov'82 by RCA Records. Dist: RCA, Roots, Swift, Wellard, Chris, I & B, Solomon & Peres Distribution

THATS RIGHT TALKIN' 'BOUT ROCK 'N' ROLL.
Single (7"): released on Creole, Feb'82 by Creole Records. Dist: Rhino, PRT

WHY D'YA LIE TO ME / FOOTLOOSE / 9 TO 5.
Single (7"): released on RCA, Feb'83 by RCA Records. Dist: RCA, Roots, Swift, Wellard, Chris, I & B, Solomon & Peres Distribution

Single (12"): released on RCA, Feb'83 by RCA Records. Dist: RCA, Roots, Swift, Wellard, Chris, I & B, Solomon & Peres Distribution

Spiderman

SPIDERMAN IN MACHINES & MONSTERS (Various Artists).
Cassette: released on MFP, Oct'85 by EMI Records. Dist: EMI

SPIDERMAN IN THE RETURN OF DR.OCTOPUS.
Cassette: released on MFP, Oct'85 by EMI Records. Dist: EMI

SPIDERMAN IN THE SCORPION TAKES A BRIDE (Various Artists).
Cassette: released on MFP, Oct'85 by EMI Records. Dist: EMI

Spiders

BEST OF THE SPIDERS VOLUME 2.
Album: released on KC, Jun'85 by KC Records. Dist: Cartel

BEST OF THE SPIDERS VOL 1.
Album: released on KC, Jan'85 by KC Records. Dist: Cartel

SPIDERS, THE: THE BEST OF VOL2..
Tracks: / Thats enough / Don't knock / Sukey Sukey Sukey / mmm Mmm baby / I'm searching / Am I the one / Witchcraft / You're the one / I'm slippin' in / True you dont love me / she keeps me wondering / I did'nt want to do it / Walking around in circles.
Album: released on KC, Oct'86 by KC Records. Dist: Cartel

SPIDERS, THE: THE BEST OF VOL.1.
Tracks: / Dont pity me / Bells in my heart / I'll stop crying / Real thing, The / Honey bee / How I feel / Goodbye / For a thrill / Dear Mary / Thats the way to win my heart / tears began to flow / Lost and bewildered / You played the part / All in my heart.
Album: released on KC, Oct'86 by KC Records. Dist: Cartel

Spies Like Us

SPIES LIKE US Original Sound Track (Various Artists).
Notes: Track details not advised. 'Spies like us' is the latest comedy adventure from director John Landis. It stars chevy Chase and Dan Aykroyd. Te Album features all the orchestral music by Elmer bernstein, who also did 'Ghostbusters' and 'The Black Cauldron', and is an action score in the style of 'The Magnificent seven' and 'The Great Escape'. The Film is from the director of 'Into The Night' and the story is by the same writer of 'Ghost Busters'.
Album: released on TER, Feb'86 Dist: Pinnacle

Spikes

SIX SHARP CUTS.
Album: released on Hybrid, Oct'85 by Statik Records. Dist: Pinnacle

Spikes,The

COLOUR IN A BLACK FORREST.
Album: released on Zinger, Jun'87 by Zinger Records. Dist: Pinnacle

Spiking

BREAKTHROUGH.
Single (12"): released on Splendid, May'82 by Splendid Records. Dist: Jetstar

LOCAL DISH.
Single (12"): released on Sunburst, May'82 Dist: Sunburst Records

MY MUSIC.
Single (12"): released on Sunburn, Dec'83 by Orbitone Records. Dist: Jetstar Distribution

PRIED UNE JEUNE FEMME.
Single (12"): released on Splendid, May'82 by Splendid Records. Dist: Jetstar

WIND WITH MISS CARNIVAL.
Single (12"): released on Sunburst, May'82 Dist: Sunburst Records

Spinal Tap

THIS IS SPINAL TAP Tour soundtrack.
Album: released on Philips (Holland), Sep'84
Cat. no: **8178 461**
Cassette: released on Philips (Holland), Sep'84

Spink, Arthur

HAPPY ACCORDION.
Album: released on ARC (Accordion Records), '84 Dist: Accordion Record Club

Spinners

18 GOLDEN FAVOURITES.
Album: released on Note, Apr'79 by EMI Records. Dist: EMI

Cassette: released on Note, Apr'79 by EMI Records. Dist: EMI

AROUND THE WORLD...AND BACK AGAIN.
Album: released on Dingles, '83 by Dingles Records. Dist: Projection

BY ARRANGEMENT.
Cassette: released on EMI, '79 by EMI Records. Dist: EMI

FOLK AT THE PHIL!.
Album: released on Spot, Sep'85 by Pickwick Records. Dist: H.R. Taylor, Lugtons

Cassette: released on Spot, Sep'85 by Pickwick Records. Dist: H.R. Taylor, Lugtons

HERE'S TO THE SPINNERS.
Album: released on Music For Pleasure (Holland), Nov'83 by EMI Records. Dist: EMI

Cassette: released on Music For Pleasure (Holland), Nov'83 by EMI Records. Dist: EMI

HERE'S TO YOU...FROM THE SPINNERS.
Album: released on PRT, Oct'82 by PRT Records. Dist: PRT

Cassette: released on PRT, Oct'82 by PRT Records. Dist: PRT

IN OUR LIVEPOOL HOME.
Double Album: released on PRT, Sep'83 by PRT Records. Dist: PRT

Double cassette: released on PRT, Sep'83 by PRT Records. Dist: PRT

LAST NIGHT WE HAD A DO.
Album: released on PRT, Oct'84 by PRT Records. Dist: PRT

Cassette: released on PRT, Oct'84 by PRT Records. Dist: PRT

LIVERPOOL LOU.
Tracks: / Liverpool lou / Going to the Zoo / Island in the sun.
Single (7"): released on PRT, May'86 by PRT Records. Dist: PRT

MUSIC OF THE SPINNERS 1968/1971.
Cassette: released on Philips, Feb'81 Dist: IMS-Polygram

SINGING CITY, THE.
Album: released on Philips, May'84 Dist: IMS-Polygram

Cassette: released on Philips, May'84 Dist: IMS-Polygram

SONGS OF THE TALL SHIPS.
Album: released on EMI, Aug'84 by EMI Records. Dist: EMI

Cassette: released on EMI, Aug'84 by EMI Records. Dist: EMI

SPINNERS, THE.
Cassette: released on Ideal(Tapes), Apr'80 Dist: EMI

Cassette: released on Ditto Cassettes, Aug'83
Cat. no: **DTO 10068**

SPUN GOLD.
Tracks: / Liverpool lou / Tom Dooley / Morning has broken / Grannie's old armchair / Freight train / Dirty old town / Imagine / Family of man / Going to the zoo / Black and white / Wild Rover / Yellow bird / Little boxes / Matchstalk men and matchstalk cats and dogs / Scarborough fair / Island in the sun / Bring a little water Sylvie / Goodnight Irene.
Cassette: released on PRT, Nov'86 by PRT Records. Dist: PRT

Album: released on PRT, Nov'86 by PRT Records. Dist: PRT

Compact disc: released on PRT, Nov'86 by PRT Records. Dist: PRT

WIND IS BLOWING, THE.
Single (7"): released on PRT, Nov'85 by PRT Records. Dist: PRT

YOUR 20 FAVOURITE CHRISTMAS CAROLS.
Album: released on Columbia, Dec'85 by EMI Records. Dist: EMI

Cassette: released on Columbia, Dec'85 by EMI Records. Dist: EMI

Spinstar

NO I CAN'T STAND IT.
Single (7"): released on KR, Sep'82 by KR Recordings Ltd. Dist: RCA, Revolver, Cartel

Single (12"): released on KR, Sep'82 by KR Recordings Ltd. Dist: RCA, Revolver, Cartel

Spirit

1984.
Single (7"): released on Mercury, Jan'84 by Phonogram Records. Dist: Polygram Distribution

Single (12"): released on Mercury, Jan'84 by Phonogram Records. Dist: Polygram Distribution

FAMILY THAT PLAYS TOGETHER, THE.
Album: released on Edsel, Mar'86 by Demon Records. Dist: Pinnacle, Jazz Music, Projection

Album: released on Edsel, Mar'86 by Demon Records. Dist: Pinnacle, Jazz Music, Projection

JOURNEY TO POTATOLAND.
Album: released on Beggars Banquet, Apr'81 by Beggars Banquet Records. Dist: WEA

Cassette: released on Beggars Banquet, Apr'81 by Beggars Banquet Records. Dist: WEA

LIVE.
Album: released on Illegal, Jan'79 by Faulty Products Records. Dist: Pinnacle, Lightning, Cartel

MR SKIN.
Single (7"): released on Mercury, Apr'84 by Phonogram Records. Dist: Polygram Distribution

Single (7"): released on Mercury, Apr'84 by Phonogram Records. Dist: Polygram Distribution

ROCK GIANTS.
Album: released on CBS(Holland), Jun'84 by CBS Records. Dist: Discovery

THIRTEENTH DREAM, THE.
Tracks: / Black satin nights / Mr skin / Mr skin / Mechanical World / Pick it up / All over the world / 1984 / Uncle Jack / Natures way / Fesh Garbage / I got a line on you.
Notes: Digital stereo recording
Compact disc: released on Mercury, Jul'84 by Phonogram Records. Dist: Polygram Distribution

TURN TO THE RIGHT.
Single (7"): released on Beggars Banquet, Jun'81 by Beggars Banquet Records. Dist: WEA

TWELVE DREAMS OF DR. SARDONICUS.
Album: released on Epic, Mar'81 by CBS Records. Dist: CBS

Cassette: released on Epic, Mar'81 by CBS Records. Dist: CBS

WE'VE GOT TO LEARN.
Single (7"): released on Beggars Banquet, May'81 by Beggars Banquet Records. Dist: WEA

Spiritborn

PITY THE UNBORN CHILD.
Single (7"): released on Spearhead, Sep'84 by Spearhead Records. Dist: Spearhead ILA

Spirit Level

ALONE & HAPPY.
Single (7"): released on Blue Waters, Jan'85 Dist: M.I.S.

GIVE A LITTLE.
Single (7"): released on Ram, Feb'84 by Ram. Dist: PRT

MICE IN THE WALLET.
Album: released on Spotlite, '83 by Spotlite Records. Dist: Cadillac, Jazz Music, Spotlite

SPIRIT LEVEL.
Album: released on Spotlite, Jan'85 by Spotlite Records. Dist: Cadillac, Jazz Music, Spotlite

Spirit of Christmas

SPIRIT OF CHRISTMAS Various artists (Various Artists).
Album: released on Audio Fidelity, Oct'84 Dist: PRT

Cassette: released on Audio Fidelity, Oct'84 Dist: PRT

Spirit Of Praise

SPIRIT OF PRAISE VOL II: VARIOUS ARTISTS.
Tracks: / Don't you know its time / Jesus my lord / Praise ye the Lord / Lord you are more precious / My Lord let me be / Pierce my ear / Ah Lord god / Oh Lord you've done great things / jesus, Jesus, Jesus / Thine be the glory / Jesus is King / What kind of love is this / O breath of life / I delight greatly / My Peace / Spirit of the Living God / Be still and Know / I will sing.
Notes: The second album featuring songs from the Spirit of Praise songbook. 18 songs sensitively produced by John Daniels, arranged by Chris bowater, who directs his own Lincoln singers and shares keyboards with John.
Album: released on Word, Jan'86 by Word Records. Dist: Word Distribution, CBS

Cassette: released on Word, Jan'86 by Word Records. Dist: Word Distribution, CBS

Spirit of Scotland

SPIRIT OF SCOTLAND Various artists (Various Artists).
Album: released on REL, '84

Cassette: released on REL, '84

Spirits of Africa

SPIRITS OF AFRICA VOL.1 (Various Artists).
Album: released on Probe Plus, Jun'87 by Probe Plus Records. Dist: Probe Plus Distribution

Spirits Of Rhythm

RHYTHM PERSONIFIED (1933/4).
Album: released on JSP, Feb'85 by JSP Records. Dist: Swift, Projection

Spirituals

NEGRO SPIRITUAL MUSIC.
Album: released on Joker, Apr'81 Dist: Cadillac, Zodiac Distribution, Jazz Horizons, Jazz Music, JSU, Celtic Music

Spisar party

SPISAR PARTY (Various Artists).
Album: released on Starclub, Jun'87

Spitfire

SO YOU WANT TO BE A ROCK 'N' ROLL STAR.
Single (7"): released on Carrere America (USA), Sep'82 by Polygram.

Spit like paint

FOR THE LIFE OF ME.
Single (12"): released on Dining Out, Jul'82 by Dining Out Records. Dist: IKF, Independent

Spitting Image

CHICKEN SONG, THE.
Tracks: / Chicken song, The / I've never met a nice South African / Hello, you must be going * / We're scared of Bob *.
Single (7"): released on Virgin, Apr'86 by Virgin Records. Dist: EMI, Virgin Distribution

Single (12"): released on Virgin, May'86 by Virgin Records. Dist: EMI, Virgin Distribution

SANTA CLAUS IS ON THE DOLE.
Tracks: / First Athiest / Tabernacle choir.
Single (7"): released on Virgin, Nov'86 by Virgin Records. Dist: EMI, Virgin Distribution

Single (12"): released on Virgin, Nov'86 by Virgin Records. Dist: EMI, Virgin Distribution

SPIT IN YOUR EAR.
Album: released on Virgin, Oct'86 by Virgin Records. Dist: EMI, Virgin Distribution

Cassette: released on Virgin, Oct'86 by Virgin

Records. Dist: EMI, Virgin Distribution

Spittle, Dusty
COUNTRY WORLD OF, THE.
Cassette: released on Viking Publications, Apr'80 by Viking Publications. Dist: Viking Publications, Harmonia Mundi Distributors, Banks Music publications

Spivak, Charlie
1946 (Spivak, Charlie and his orchestra).
Album: released on Circle(USA), Oct'86 by Jazzology Records (USA). Dist: Jazz Music, Swift, Chris Wellard

CHARLIE SPIVAK & JIMMY JOY 1945.
Album: released on Aircheck (USA), Apr'79 Dist: Swift, Jazz Music

HOP SKIP & JUMP.
Cassette: by Astan Records. Dist: Counterpoint

ONE WAY PASSAGE.
Album: released on First Heard, Jun'79 by Submarine Records. Dist: Conifer, Taylors

Spivak, Dubby
SWINGS LIGHTLY.
Album: released on Audiophile, Jan'87 by Jazzology Records (USA). Dist: Jazz Music, Swift

Spizz
PEEL SESSION 7/8/78 (Spizz oil).
Tracks: / Cold city / 6000 crazy / Pure noise / Alien language / Protect from heat / Platform 3 / Switched off.
Single (12"): released on Strange Fruit, Feb'87 by Clive Selwood. Dist: Pinnacle

Spizz Energi
SOLDIER SOLDIER.
Single (7"): released on Rough Trade, Sep'79 by Rough Trade Records. Dist: Rough Trade Distribution, Cartel Distribution

WHERE'S CAPTIAN KIRK.
Single (7"): released on Rough Trade, '79 by Rough Trade Records. Dist: Rough Trade Distribution, Cartel Distribution

Spizzenergi 2
JUNGLE FEVER.
Single (7"): released on Rough Trade, Jul'82 by Rough Trade Records. Dist: Rough Trade Distribution, Cartel Distribution

WORK.
Single (7"): released on Rough Trade, Feb'82 by Rough Trade Records. Dist: Rough Trade Distribution, Cartel Distribution

Spizz oil
6000 CRAZY.
Single (7"): released on Rough Trade, Jan'79 by Rough Trade Records. Dist: Rough Trade Distribution, Cartel Distribution

COLD CITY.
Single (7"): released on Rough Trade, Jan'79 by Rough Trade Records. Dist: Rough Trade Distribution, Cartel Distribution

SPK
AUTO-DA-FE.
Album: released on Walter Ulbright, Jan'84 by Walter Ulbright Records. Dist: Rough Trade

DEKOMPOSITIONES.
Single (12"): released on Side Effects, May'83 by SPK Records. Dist: Rough Trade, Cartel

FROM SCIENCE TO RITUAL.
Album: released on Plasma Tapes, Jan'84 by Plasma Tapes Records. Dist: Rough Trade

IN FLAGRANTE DELICTO.
Tracks: / In flagrante delicto.
Single (12"): released on Side Effects, May'86 by SPK Records. Dist: Rough Trade, Cartel

INFORMATION OVERLOAD.
Album: released on Normal, May'85 Dist: Red Lightnin' Distribution, Rough Trade Distribution, Cartel Distribution

LIVE AT THE CRYPT.
Cassette: released on Sterile, Apr'85 Dist: Red Rhino Distribution, Cartel Distribution

METAL DANCE.
Single (12"): released on Desire, Apr'85 by Desire Records. Dist: Pinnacle

ZAMIA LEHMANNI.
Album: released on Side Effects, Oct'86 by SPK Records. Dist: Rough Trade, Cartel

Splash
EUROPEAN BOY.
Single (7"): released on Rocket, Aug'87 by

Page 946

Phonogram Records. Dist: Polygram Distribution

Single (12"): released on Rocket, Aug'87 by Phonogram Records. Dist: Polygram Distribution

FEAR NO EVIL.
Single (7"): released on Ramkup, Jul'81 Dist: Pinnacle

MODERN WOMEN.
Single (7"): released on Ramkup, Jan'82 Dist: Pinnacle

Q'EST CE QUE C'EST.
Tracks: / Q'est ce que c'est / Dont look back / Ce soir *.
Single (7"): released on Rocket, Aug'86 by Phonogram Records. Dist: Polygram Distribution

Single (12"): released on Rocket, Aug'86 by Phonogram Records. Dist: Polygram Distribution

SPLASH Original soundtrack.
Album: released on Cherry Lane, Jun'84 by Cherry Lane Productions. Dist: PRT

Cassette: released on Cherry Lane, Jun'84 by Cherry Lane Productions. Dist: PRT

Splashdown
BUILD IT UP.
Single (7"): released on Old Convent, Jun'84 by Old Convent Records. Dist: Old Convent

IT'S A BRAND NEW DAY.
Single (7"): released on Red Bus, Jul'82 by Red Bus Records. Dist: PRT

Single (12"): released on Red Bus, Jul'82 by Red Bus Records. Dist: PRT

TO YOUR HEART.
Single (7"): released on Shack, Feb'83 Dist: PRT

Single (12"): released on Shack, Feb'83 Dist: PRT

Splash SF
CHANGE IS GONNA COME.
Single (7"): released on Sucsa, Sep'84 by Sucsa records. Dist: M.I.S. Distribution

SWEET DREAMING.
Single (7"): released on Sucha, Jan'85

Splat
TAXI.
Single (7"): released on Ron Johnson, Jul'84 by Ron Johnson Records. Dist: Nine Mile Distribution, Cartel Distribution

YEAH THE DUM DUM.
Single (7"): released on Ron Johnson, Aug'83 by Ron Johnson Records. Dist: Nine Mile Distribution, Cartel Distribution

Spliff
CARBONARA.
Single (7"): released on CBS, Jan'83 by CBS Records. Dist: CBS

SPLIFF RADIO SHOW.
Album: released on CBS, Feb'81 by CBS Records. Dist: CBS

Spliff Riff
MORE TODAY THAN YESTERDAY.
Tracks: / More today than yesterday / You shook up my world.
Single (7"): released on JK productions, Feb'86

Single (12"): released on JK productions, Feb'86

Spliffy, Herbert
EASY SQUEEZE (Spliffy, Herbert & Eric Donaldson).

Splinter
DANGER ZONE.
Single (7"): released on Barn, Jun'79 by Barn Records. Dist: RCA

Splinteres Sword
SPLINTERED SWORD   Henry Treece (Shedden, John).
Cassette: released on Colophone, Nov'81 by Audio-Visual Library Services. Dist: Audio-Visual Library Services

Split beaver
SAVAGE.
Single (7"): released on Heavy Metal, Sep'81 by FM-Revolver Records. Dist: EMI

WHEN HELL WON'T HAVE YOU.
Album: released on Heavy Metal, Jun'82 by FM-Revolver Records. Dist: EMI

Split Crow
ROCKSTORM.
Album: released on Guardian, Apr'85 by Guardian Records. Dist: Jazz Music, Pinnacle

Split Enz
I SEE RED.
Single (7"): released on Illegal, Nov'79 by Faulty Products Records. Dist: Pinnacle, Lightning, Cartel

SPLIT ENZ Video Cassette.
Video-cassette (VHS): released on Polygram, Oct'84 by Polygram Records. Dist: Polygram

TIME AND TIDE.
Album: released on A&M, Apr'82 by A&M Records. Dist: Polygram

Cassette: released on A&M, Apr'82 by A&M Records. Dist: Polygram

TRUE COLOURS.
Tracks: / Shark attack / I got you / Whats the matter with you / Double happy / I wouldn't dream of it / I hope I never / Nobody takes me seriously / Missing person / Poor boy / How can I resist her / Choral sea, The.
Album: released on A&M, Nov'85 by A&M Records. Dist: Polygram

Cassette: released on A&M, Nov'85 by A&M Records. Dist: Polygram

TRUE COLOURS.
Album: released on A&M, Aug'80 by A&M Records. Dist: Polygram

Cassette: released on A&M, Aug'80 by A&M Records. Dist: Polygram

WAIATA.
Album: released on A&M, May'81 by A&M Records. Dist: Polygram

Cassette: released on A&M, May'81 by A&M Records. Dist: Polygram

Split Knee Loons
SPLIT KNEE LOONS (6 TRACK EP).
Single (7"): released on Avatar, Jul'81 by Avatar Communications. Dist: CBS

Split Level
GIRL.
Single (7"): released on Climate, Apr'84 by Climate Records. Dist: Climate Records

SATISFYIN' FEELING.
Single (7"): released on Carve Up, Mar'81 Dist: Jazz Music, Red Lightnin' Distribution, Rough Trade, Pinnacle

SOUL LIMBO.
Single (7"): released on Red Lightnin', Sep'82 by Red Lightnin' Records. Dist: Roots, Swift, Jazz Music, JSU, Pinnacle, Cartel, Wynd-Up Distribution

Split Second
BODY CHECK (A Split Second).
Tracks: / Body check / Burnout / On command / Flesh.
Single (7"): released on Antler, Nov'86 by Antler Records (Belgium). Dist: Red Rhino, Cartel

RIGORMORTIS.
Tracks: / Rigormortis.
Single (7"): released on Antler, 20 Jun'87 by Antler Records (Belgium). Dist: Red Rhino, Cartel

Single (12"): released on Antler, 20 Jun'87 by Antler Records (Belgium). Dist: Red Rhino, Cartel

Splitt
ALL I EVER WANTED.
Tracks: / All I ever wanted / No great adventure.
Single (7"): released on Legend, Oct'86 by Legend Records. Dist: EMI, Legend Distribution, Island

Single (12"): released on Legend, Oct'86 by Legend Records. Dist: EMI, Legend Distribution, Island

Splodge
IN SEARCH OF THE SEVEN GOLDEN GUSSETS.
Album: released on Razor, Nov'82 by Razor. Dist: Pinnacle

MOUTH AND TROUSERS.
Single (7"): released on Razor, Nov'82 by Razor. Dist: Pinnacle

---

Splodge, Max
PHUT, PHUT, SPLODGENIK.
Tracks: / 86 The year of the bean.
Single (7"): released on Neat, Jan'87 by Neat Records. Dist: Pinnacle, Neat

Splodgenessabounds
SPLODGENESSABOUNDS.
Album: released on Deram, Jan'81 by Decca Records. Dist: Polygram

Cassette: released on Deram, Jan'81 by Decca Records. Dist: Polygram

Spontaneous Music
BIOSYSTEM.
Album: released on Incus, May'78 Dist: Jazz Music, Cadillac

LIVE AT NOTRE DAME HALL.
Notes: Featuring Lou Coxhill
Album: released on Sweet Folk All, Mar'87 by Sweet Folk All Records. Dist: Sweet Folk All, Roots, Celtic Music, Dragon, Impetus, Projection, Chris Wellard, Festival Records

LIVE AT NOTRE DAME THEATRE.
Album: released on Sweet Folk and Country, Oct'86 Dist: Chris Wellard Distribution

SOURCE, THE.
Album: released on Tangent, Apr'81 by Tangent Records. Dist: Lugtons Distributors, Taylors, JSU Distribution, Projection Distribution

SO WHAT DO YOU THINK.
Album: released on Tangent, Apr'81 by Tangent Records. Dist: Lugtons Distributors, Taylors, JSU Distribution, Projection Distribution

SPONTANEOUS MUSIC ENSEMBLE.
Album: released on Affinity, Mar'83 by Charly Records. Dist: Charly, Cadillac

Spoonie Gee
GODFATHER, THE.
Single (12"): released on Tuff City (USA), Aug'87 Dist: Pinnacle

Spoons
ARIAS & SYMPHONIES.
Album: released on A&M, Feb'83 by A&M Records. Dist: Polygram

Sport
MOVE TO THE MUSIC.
Single (7"): released on Baskerville, Jul'84 Dist: Pinnacle

THIS WHEEL'S ON FIRE.
Single (7"): released on Chevy, Oct'83 by Chevy Records.

Single (12"): released on Chevy, Oct'83 by Chevy Records.

Sporting Life
HELP THE CHILDREN.
Single (7"): released on Crash, Oct'82 by Satril Records. Dist: PRT

Single (12"): released on Crash, Oct'82 by Satril Records. Dist: PRT

Sport of Kings
PARADE.
Album: released on Press, Jul'86 by Press Records.

Album: released on Music Galore, Aug'85 by Shanghai records. Dist: Counterpoint Distribution

Sport & Politics
CONTROVERSIES IN WORLD SPORT.
Cassette: released on International Report, Oct'81 by Seminar Cassettes. Dist: Audio-Visual Library Services, Davidson Distribution, Eastern Educational Products Distrib., Forlaget Systime Distribution, MacDougall Distribution, Talktapes Distribution, Watkins Books Ltd Distribution, Norton, Jeff Distribution

Spotlight On.....
SPOTLIGHT ON DANCE   Various Artists (Various Artists).
Album: released on PRT, Oct'83 by PRT Records. Dist: PRT

Cassette: released on PRT, Oct'83 by PRT Records. Dist: PRT

SPOTLIGHT ON HITS OF THE SIXTIES Various Artists (Various Artists).
Album: released on PRT, Oct'81 by PRT Records. Dist: PRT

Cassette: released on PRT, Oct'81 by PRT Records. Dist: PRT

SPOTLIGHT ON HITS OF THE SEVEN-

TIES Various Artists (Various bands).
Album: released on PRT (Spotlight), Oct'82 by PRT Records. Dist: PRT

Cassette: released on PRT (Spotlight), Oct'82 by PRT Records. Dist: PRT

SPOTLIGHT ON LOVE Various Artists (Various Artists).
Double Album: released on PRT, '80 by PRT Records. Dist: PRT

Double cassette: released on PRT, '80 by PRT Records. Dist: PRT

SPOTLIGHT ON ROCK 'N' ROLL Various artists (Various Artists).
Double Album: released on PRT, Oct'81 by PRT Records. Dist: PRT

Double cassette: released on PRT, Oct'81 by PRT Records. Dist: PRT

SPOTLIGHT ON SOUL Various Artists (Various Artists).
Album: released on PRT, Oct'83 by PRT Records. Dist: PRT

Cassette: released on PRT, Oct'83 by PRT Records. Dist: PRT

SPOTLIGHT ON STATESIDE Various Artists (Various Artists).
Album: released on PRT, Oct'83 by PRT Records. Dist: PRT

Cassette: released on PRT, Oct'83 by PRT Records. Dist: PRT

SPOTLIGHT ON THE FABULOUS 50'S Various Artists (Various Artists).
Album: released on PRT, Oct'83 by PRT Records. Dist: PRT

Cassette: released on PRT, Oct'83 by PRT Records. Dist: PRT

SPOTLIGHT ON THE SWINGIN' 60'S Various Artists (Various Artists).
Album: released on PRT, Oct'83 by PRT Records. Dist: PRT

Cassette: released on PRT, Oct'83 by PRT Records. Dist: PRT

Spotnicks

HIGHWAY BOOGIE.
Tracks: / Highway boogie / Lost property / Could it be love? / Mighty bump / Love is a symphony / Truck driver's dream / Just another dream / Just another boy / Dolly H. / delightful / Let it roll roll roll / Besame mucho.
Album: released on Magnum Force, Jun'86 by Magnum Music Group Ltd. Dist: Magnum Music Group Ltd, PRT, Spartan

Compact disc: released on Magnum Force, Jun'86 by Magnum Music Group Ltd. Dist: Magnum Music Group Ltd, PRT, Spartan

IN THE MIDDLE OF THE UNIVERSE.
Album: released on Mill (USA), May'84 Dist: Swift Distribution

Album: released on Astan, Nov'84 by Astan Records. Dist: Counterpoint

Cassette: released on Astan, Nov'84 by Astan Records. Dist: Counterpoint

Album: released on Magnum Force, Apr'85 by Magnum Music Group Ltd. Dist: Magnum Music Group Ltd, PRT, Spartan

MUSIC FOR THE MILLIONS.
Tracks: / Johnny Guitar / Spotnicks theme / Orange blossom special / Rocket man, The / Galloping guitars / Amapola / Ghost riders in the sky / Dark eyes / Joey's song / La rosita / Space party.
Notes: Swedish instrumental group of the sixties. contains two of their UK hits 'Orange blossom special' and 'Rocket man'
Album: released on Polydor (Germany), Dec'85 Dist: IMS-Polygram

Cassette: released on Polydor (Germany), Dec'85 Dist: IMS-Polygram

Spot The Dog

TOY.
Single (7"): released on Diatribe, Sep'82

Sprague,Billy

WHAT A WAY TO GO.
Album: released on Reunion, Aug'85

Cassette: released on Reunion, Aug'85

Sprague,Carl T.

COWBOY SONGS FROM TEXAS.
Album: released on Bear Family, Oct'80 by Bear Family Records. Dist: Rollercoaster Distribution, Swift

FIRST POPULAR SINGING COWBOY,THE.
Album: released on Bear Family, Oct'80 by Bear Family Records. Dist: Rollercoaster Distribution, Swift

Sprague, Peter

MUSICA DEL MAR.
Album: released on Concord Jazz(USA), Apr'84 by Concord Jazz Records (USA). Dist: IMS, Polygram

NA PALI COAST.
Tracks: / Coltrane / Magic miss melissa *.
Album: released on Concord Jazz(USA), Aug'86 by Concord Jazz Records (USA). Dist: IMS, Polygram

NA PALI COAST.
Album: released on Concord Jazz(USA), Sep'85 by Concord Jazz Records (USA). Dist: IMS, Polygram

Album: released on Springtime, May'84 by Springtime Records. Dist: Island Distribution, Polygram Distribution

Sprangeen

SPRANGEEN.
Album: released on Springthyme, Oct'86 by Springthyme Records. Dist: Jazz Music Distribution, Projection Distribution, Roots Distribution

Cassette: released on Springthyme, Oct'86 by Springthyme Records. Dist: Jazz Music Distribution, Projection Distribution, Roots Distribution

Spreadthick Folk Group

MIXED BREW.
Cassette: released on Folktracks, Nov'79 by Folktracks Cassettes. Dist: Folktracks

Spredthick

SPREDTHICK.
Album: released on Actual, May'81 by Import Records. Dist: JSU, Projection

Spreechle,Delton

SWEET AFRICA.
Single 10": released on King Jam, Jul'82 by King Jam Records. Dist: Jetstar

Spring Artist '86

SPRING ARTIST'86 This is your God (Various Artists).
Notes: The Live worship album from this year's Spring harvest. Features songs By graham

Kendrick, Ishmael, Chris Bowater, Morris Chapman and others.
Album: released on Spirit of Praise, Jul'86

Compact disc: released on Spirit of Praise, Jul'86

Springate, John

MY LIFE.
Single (7"): released on Towerbell, Feb'85 by Towerbell Records. Dist: EMI

SONG FOR CHRISTMAS.
Single (7"): released on Terrific, Dec'83 by Creole Records. Dist: CBS Distribution

Single (7"): released on Sedition, Nov'85 by Sedition Records. Dist: PRT

TO BE A MATADOR.
Tracks: / To be a matador / Wake up Madrid.
Single (7"): released on Epic, Jul'87 by CBS Records. Dist: CBS

Gatefold sleeve: released on Epic, Jul'87 by CBS Records. Dist: CBS

Springer,Mark

PIANO.
Album: released on Illuminated, Feb'85 by IKF Records. Dist: Pinnacle, Cartel, Jetstar

Springer, Marvin

MERRY CHRISTMAS.... (Springer, Marvin & The Children of the World Choir).
Single (7"): released on Sold, Dec'86

Springfield

GREAT GUNS.
Album: released on Look, '82 by Look Records. Dist: Jazz Music

Springfield, Dusty

BEAUTIFUL FEELINGS.
Album: released on Mercury (Holland), Apr'85 by Phonogram Records. Dist: Polygram Distribution

Cassette: released on Mercury (Holland), Apr'85 by Phonogram Records. Dist: Polygram Distribution

Compact disc: released on Mercury (Holland), Apr'85 by Phonogram Records. Dist: Polygram Distribution

GREATEST HITS: DUSTY SPRINGFIELD.
Album: released on Mercury (USA), Sep'81 by Import Records. Dist: IMS Distribution, Polygram Distribution

Cassette: released on Mercury (USA), Sep'81 by Import Records. Dist: IMS Distribution, Polygram Distribution

Album: released on Philips, Oct'83 Dist: IMS-Polygram

Cassette: released on Philips, Oct'83 Dist: IMS-Polygram

IN MEMPHIS PLUS.
Album: released on Philips, Mar'85 Dist: IMS-Polygram

Cassette: released on Philips, Mar'85 Dist: IMS-Polygram

I ONLY WANT TO BE WITH YOU.
Single (7"): released on Old Gold, Jul'82 by Old Gold Records. Dist: Lightning, Jazz Music, Spartan, Counterpoint

LOVE SONGS.
Notes: Digital stereo
Compact disc: released on Phillips import, '84

PRIVATE NUMBER.
Single (7"): released on Allegiance, Mar'84 by PRT Records. Dist: PRT

SOMETIMES LIKE BUTTERFLIES.
Single (7"): released on Hippodrome, Aug'85 Dist: EMI

Single (12"): released on Hippodrome, Aug'85 Dist: EMI

SON OF A PREACHER MAN.
Album: released on Spot, Feb'84 by Pickwick Records. Dist: H.R. Taylor, Lugtons

Cassette: released on Spot, Feb'84 by Pickwick Records. Dist: H.R. Taylor, Lugtons

VERY BEST OF DUSTY SPRINGFIELD.
Album: released on K-Tel, Oct'81 by K-Tel Records. Dist: Record Merchandisers Distribution, Taylors, Terry Blood Distribution, Wynd-Up Distribution, Relay Distribution, Pickwick Distribution, Solomon & Peres Distribution, Polygram

Cassette: released on K-Tel, Oct'81 by K-Tel Records. Dist: Record Merchandisers Distribution, Taylors, Terry Blood Distribution, Wynd-Up Distribution, Relay Distribution, Pickwick Distribution, Solomon & Peres Distribution, Polygram

YOU DON'T HAVE TO SAY YOU LOVE ME.
Single (7"): released on Philips, '80 Dist: IMS-Polygram

Springfield, Rick

CELEBRATE YOUTH.
Single (7"): released on RCA, Apr'85 by RCA Records. Dist: RCA, Roots, Swift, Wellard, Chris, I & B, Solomon & Peres Distribution

Single (12"): released on RCA, Apr'85 by RCA Records. Dist: RCA, Roots, Swift, Wellard, Chris, I & B, Solomon & Peres Distribution

DN'T TALK TO STRANGERS.
Single (7"): released on RCA, Apr'82 by RCA Records. Dist: RCA, Roots, Swift, Wellard, Chris, I & B, Solomon & Peres Distribution

HARD TO HOLD.
Album: released on RCA, Aug'84 by RCA Records. Dist: RCA, Roots, Swift, Wellard, Chris, I & B, Solomon & Peres Distribution

Cassette: released on RCA, Aug'84 by RCA Records. Dist: RCA, Roots, Swift, Wellard, Chris, I & B, Solomon & Peres Distribution

Compact disc: released on RCA, Aug'84 by RCA Records. Dist: RCA, Roots, Swift, Wellard, Chris, I & B, Solomon & Peres Distribution

HARD TO HOLD Film Soundtrack.
Tracks: / Love somebody / Dont walk away / Bop 'til you drop / Taxi Dancings / S.F.O. / stand up / when the lights go down / Great lost art of conversation, The / Go swimming.
Notes: Digital Stereo
Compact disc: released on RCA, Sep'84 by RCA Records. Dist: RCA, Roots, Swift, Wellard, Chris, I & B, Solomon & Peres Distribution

HUMAN TOUCH.
Single (7"): released on RCA, Jun'83 by RCA Records. Dist: RCA, Roots, Swift, Wellard, Chris, I & B, Solomon & Peres Distribution

Single (12"): released on RCA, Jun'83 by RCA Records. Dist: RCA, Roots, Swift, Wellard, Chris, I & B, Solomon & Peres Distribution

I'VE DONE ANYTHING FOR YOU.
Single (7"): released on RCA, Nov'81 by RCA Records. Dist: RCA, Roots, Swift, Wellard, Chris, I & B, Solomon & Peres Distribution

JESSIE'S GIRL.
Single (7"): released on RCA, May'81 by RCA Records. Dist: RCA, Roots, Swift, Wellard, Chris, I & B, Solomon & Peres Distribution

Single (7"): released on RCA, Mar'84 by RCA Records. Dist: RCA, Roots, Swift, Wellard, Chris, I & B, Solomon & Peres Distribution

Single 10": released on RCA, Mar'84 by RCA Records. Dist: RCA, Roots, Swift, Wellard, Chris, I & B, Solomon & Peres Distribution

Album: released on RCA, May'83 by RCA Records. Dist: RCA, Roots, Swift, Wellard, Chris, I & B, Solomon & Peres Distribution

Cassette: released on RCA, May'83 by RCA Records. Dist: RCA, Roots, Swift, Wellard, Chris, I & B, Solomon & Peres Distribution

Compact disc: released on RCA, May'83 by RCA Records. Dist: RCA, Roots, Swift, Wellard, Chris, I & B, Solomon & Peres Distribution

LIVING IN OZ.
Tracks: / Human Touch / Alyson / Affair of the heart / Living in Oz / Me and Johnny / Motel eyes / Tiger by the tail / Souls / I can't stap hurting / Like Father like son / I can't stop hurting you.
Notes: Digital Stereo
Compact disc: released on RCA, Apr'84 by RCA Records. Dist: RCA, Roots, Swift, Wellard, Chris, I & B, Solomon & Peres Distribution

LOVE SOMEBODY.
Single (7"): released on RCA, May'84 by RCA Records. Dist: RCA, Roots, Swift, Wellard, Chris, I & B, Solomon & Peres Distribution

Single (12"): released on RCA, May'84 by RCA Records. Dist: RCA, Roots, Swift, Wellard, Chris, I & B, Solomon & Peres Distribution

PLATINUM VIDEOS.
Notes: The promo Video for six major US hits by one of the biggest selling solo performers on the U.S. pop scene, including 'Human Touch' and 'Jessie's Girl'
Video-cassette (VHS): released on RCA, Oct'84 by RCA Records. Dist: RCA, Roots, Swift, Wellard, Chris, I & B, Solomon & Peres Distribution

STATE OF THE HEART.
Single (7"): released on RCA, Aug'85 by RCA Records. Dist: RCA, Roots, Swift, Wellard, Chris, I & B, Solomon & Peres Distribution

Single (12"): released on RCA, Aug'85 by RCA Records. Dist: RCA, Roots, Swift, Wellard, Chris, I & B, Solomon & Peres Distribution

SUCCESS HAS'NT SPOILED ME YET.
Tracks: / Calling all girls / I get excited / What kind of fool am I / Kristina / Tonight / Black is black / Dont talk to strangers / How do you talk to girls / Still crazy for you. / American girl, The / Just one Kiss / April 24,1981.
Album: released on RCA, Jun'82 by RCA Records. Dist: RCA, Roots, Swift, Wellard, Chris, I & B, Solomon & Peres Distribution

Cassette: released on RCA, Jun'82 by RCA Records. Dist: RCA, Roots, Swift, Wellard, Chris, I & B, Solomon & Peres Distribution

Compact disc: released on RCA, Jun'82 by RCA Records. Dist: RCA, Roots, Swift, Wellard, Chris, I & B, Solomon & Peres Distribution

TAO.
Tracks: / Dance this world away / Celebrate Youth / State of the Heart / Written in rock / Power of love(the Tao of Love), The / Walking on the edge / Tao of heaven, The / Walking on the edge / Stranger in the house / My fathers chair / Walk like a man.
Album: released on RCA, May'85 by RCA Records. Dist: RCA, Roots, Swift, Wellard, Chris, I & B, Solomon & Peres Distribution

Cassette: released on RCA, May'85 by RCA Records. Dist: RCA, Roots, Swift, Wellard, Chris, I & B, Solomon & Peres Distribution

Compact disc: released on RCA, May'85 by RCA Records. Dist: RCA, Roots, Swift, Wellard, Chris, I & B, Solomon & Peres Distribution

WHAT KIND OF FOOL AM I.
Single (7"): released on RCA, Sep'82 by RCA Records. Dist: RCA, Roots, Swift, Wellard, Chris, I & B, Solomon & Peres Distribution

WORKING CLASS DOG.
Tracks: / Everybody's girl / Daddy's pearl / Red hot and blue love / Inside Silvia / Love is alright tonight / Jessie's girl / Hole in my heart / Carry me away / I've done everything for you / Light of love, The.
Album: released on RCA, Jan'87 by RCA Records. Dist: RCA, Roots, Swift, Wellard, Chris, I & B, Solomon & Peres Distribution

Cassette: released on RCA, Jan'87 by RCA Records. Dist: RCA, Roots, Swift, Wellard, Chris, I & B, Solomon & Peres Distribution

Springfields

ISLAND OF DREAMS.

Single (7"): released on Old Gold, Jul'82 by Old Gold Records. Dist: Lightning, Jazz Music, Spartan, Counterpoint

Spring Harvest '85
LIGHTS TO THE WORLD.
Album: released on Word, Jul'85 by Word Records. Dist: Word Distribution, CBS

Cassette: released on Word, Jul'85 by Word Records. Dist: Word Distribution, CBS

Spring harvest '87
SPRING HARVEST '87 Where truth & justice meet (Various Artists).
Tracks: / Lord is marching out, The / Rejoice, rejoice, rejoice / He has showed you o man what is good / Be still, for the presence of the Lord / Here is love / Gloria Co. medley / Jesus thou art precious / Hosanna / Whizz kids song / O lord the clouds are gathering / Jesus you are the radiance / He that is in us / Spirit of God show me Jesus / Jesus you are changing me / Holy is the Lord / Lord the light of your love.
Notes: Recorded live at Spring Harvest at both Minehead and Skegness sites, this album features three new Graham Kendrick songs.
Album: released on Spirit of Praise, Jun'87

Cassette: released on Spirit of Praise, Jun'87

Spring,Jane
LOVE BITES BACK.
Single (12"): released on Carrere, Oct'85 by Carrere Records. Dist: PRT, Spartan

Spring Sampler '87
SPRING SAMPLER '87 MCA Master Series (Various Artists).
Tracks: / Mr.Chow / Solving a dream / Dreams of flight / Stone circle / Wunjo / Southern hospitality / Sowelu / Allegro Vivace.
Album: released on MCA, Jul'87 by MCA Records. Dist: Polygram, MCA

Cassette: released on MCA, Jul'87 by MCA Records. Dist: Polygram, MCA

Compact disc: released on MCA, Jul'87 by MCA Records. Dist: Polygram, MCA

Springs, Helena
MIDNIGHT LADY.
Tracks: / Midnight lady / Love satisfaction.
Single (7"): released on Arista, Jul'87 by Arista Records. Dist: RCA

Single (12"): released on Arista, Jul'87 by Arista Records. Dist: RCA

NEW LOVE.
Compact disc: released on Arista, Jul'87 by Arista Records. Dist: RCA

Album: released on Arista, Jul'87 by Arista Records. Dist: RCA

Cassette: released on Arista, Jul'87 by Arista Records. Dist: RCA

PAPER MONEY.
Tracks: / Paper money / Go all the way.
Single (7"): released on Arista, 23 May'87 by Arista Records. Dist: RCA

Single (12"): released on Arista, 23 May'87 by Arista Records. Dist: RCA

Springsteen, Bruce
BORN IN THE U.S.A..
Tracks: / Cover Me / Born in the U.S.A. / Darlington county / Working on the highway / Downbound train / I'm on fire / No surrender / Bobby jean / I'm goin' down / Glory days / Dancing in the dark / My Hometown.
Notes: Digital Stereo
Compact disc: released on CBS, Aug'84 by CBS Records. Dist: CBS

BORN IN THE USA.
Album: released on CBS, Jun'84 by CBS Records. Dist: CBS

Cassette: released on CBS, Jun'84 by CBS Records. Dist: CBS

Compact disc: released on CBS, Aug'84 by CBS Records. Dist: CBS

BORN TO RUN.
Tracks: / Born to run / Johnny 99 / Spirit in the night / Because the night / Seeds.
Single (7"): released on CBS, May'87 by CBS Records. Dist: CBS

Single (12"): released on CBS, May'87 by CBS Records. Dist: CBS

Compact disc single: released on CBS, May'87 by CBS Records. Dist: CBS

Album: released on CBS, Oct'75 by CBS Records. Dist: CBS

Cassette: released on CBS, '79 by CBS Rec-

ords. Dist: CBS

Compact disc: released on CBS, '83 by CBS Records. Dist: CBS

BORN TO RUN: (COMPACT DISC).
Tracks: / Thunder road / Tenth avenue-freeze out / Night Back streets / Born to run / She's the one / Meeting across the river / Jungleland.
Compact disc: released on CBS, '83 by CBS Records. Dist: CBS

BOXED SET OF FOUR 12" SINGLES.
Boxed set: released on CBS, Nov'85 by CBS Records. Dist: CBS

COVER ME.
Double-pack single: released on CBS, Sep'84 by CBS Records. Dist: CBS

DARKNESS ON THE EDGE OF TOWN.
Tracks: / Badlands / Adam raised a cain / Something in the night / Candy's room / Racing in the street / Promised land, The / Factory / Streets of fire / Prove it all / Darkness on the edge of town.
Notes: Digital stereo
Compact disc: released on CBS, Jul'84 by CBS Records. Dist: CBS

DARKNESS ON THE EDGE OF TOWN.
Album: released on CBS, Nov'84 by CBS Records. Dist: CBS

Cassette: released on CBS, Nov'84 by CBS Records. Dist: CBS

Compact disc: released on CBS, Jul'84 by CBS Records. Dist: CBS

FIRE.
Single (7"): released on CBS, Jan'87 by CBS Records. Dist: CBS

Single (12"): released on CBS, Jan'87 by CBS Records. Dist: CBS

GREETINGS FROM ASBURY PARK,N.J..
Tracks: / Blinded by the light / Growin' up / Mary Queen of Arkansas / Does this bus stop at 82nd street / Lost in the flood / Angel for you, The / Spirit in the night / Its hard to be a saint in the city.
Notes: Originally CBS 65480; released 1973.
Album: released on CBS, Nov'82 by CBS Records. Dist: CBS

Cassette: released on CBS, Nov'82 by CBS Records. Dist: CBS

Compact disc: released on CBS, Nov'82 by CBS Records. Dist: CRS

LIVE 1975-1985.
Tracks: / Thunder road / Adam raised a cain / Spirit in the night / 4th of July / Asbury park (Sandy) / Paradiseby the 'c' / Fire / Growin' up / It's hard to be a saint in the city / Backstreets / Rosalita / Raise your hand / hungry heart / Two hearts / Cadillac ranch / You can look (but you better not touch) / Independance day / Badlands / Because the night / Candy's room / Darkness on the edge of town / Racing in the street / This land is your land / Nebraska / Johnny 99 / Reason to beleive / Born in the U'S'A' / Seeds / River, The / War / Darlington county / Working on the highway / Promised land (The) / Cover me / I'm on fire / Bobby Jean / My home town / Born to run / No surrender / Tenth avenue freeze-out / Jersey girl.
Album: released on CBS, Nov'86 by CBS Records. Dist: CBS

Cassette: released on CBS, Nov'86 by CBS Records. Dist: CBS

NEBRASKA.
Tracks: / Nebraska / Atlantic city / Mansion on the hill / Johnny / Highway Patrolman / State trooper / Used cars / Open all night / My fathers house / Reason to believe.
Notes: Nebraska is a solo Accoustic album based on one of the most critically acclaimed musicians of the decade.
Album: released on CBS, Sep'82 by CBS Records. Dist: CBS

Cassette: released on CBS, Sep'82 by CBS Records. Dist: CBS

Compact disc: released on CBS, Sep'82 by CBS Records. Dist: CBS

OPEN ALL NIGHT.
Single (7"): released on CBS, Nov'82 by CBS Records. Dist: CBS

RIVER, THE.
Tracks: / Ties that bind, The / Sherry darling / Jackson Cage / Two hearts / Independance day / Hungry Heart / Out in the street / Crush on you / You can look(But you'd better not touch) / I wanna marry you / River, The / Point Blank / Cadillac Ranch / I'm a rocker / Fade away / Stolen car / Ramrod / Price you pay, The / Wreck on the highway.
Notes: Double album. Double cassette. Double compact disc
Double Album: released on CBS, Oct'80 by CBS Records. Dist: CBS

Double cassette: released on CBS, Oct'80 by CBS Records. Dist: CBS

Double compact disc: released on CBS, Oct'80 by CBS Records. Dist: CBS

WAR What is it good for.
Tracks: / War.
Single (7"): released on CBS, Nov'86 by CBS Records. Dist: CBS

Single (12"): released on CBS, Nov'86 by CBS Records. Dist: CBS

WAR (WHAT IS IT GOOD FOR).
Tracks: / Merry Xmas baby / Incident of 5th street'.
Single (7"): released on CBS, Nov'86 by CBS Records. Dist: CBS

Single (12"): released on CBS, Nov'86 by CBS Records. Dist: CBS

WILD, THE INNOCENT AND THE E.STREET SHUFFLE, THE.
Tracks: / E. Street shuffle, The / 4th of July / Asbury park (Sandy) / Wild Billy's circus / Incident on 57th street / Rosalita (come out tonight) / New york city serenade.
Notes: Originally CBS 65780 released 1974
Album: released on CBS, Nov'83 by CBS Records. Dist: CBS

Compact disc: released on CBS, Nov'83 by CBS Records. Dist: CBS

Compact disc: released on CBS, Nov'83 by CBS Records. Dist: CBS

Springstone, Bruce
TAKE ME OUT TO THE BALLPARK.
Single (7"): released on Food For Thought, Jul'85 by Food For Thought Records. Dist: Pinnacle

Springwater
FIRST TIME.
Single (7"): released on Flying, Nov'82 by Flying Records. Dist: DMS

I WILL RETURN.
Single (7"): released on Old Gold, Jul'84 by Old Gold Records. Dist: Lightning, Jazz Music, Spartan, Counterpoint

Sproule, Daithi
IRONMAN, THE (Sproule, Daithi with Tommy Peoples).

Sprouse, Blaine
BRILLIANCY.
Album: released on Rounder (USA), Aua'85

Sprout Head Uprising
EARLY SPRING.
Album: released on Rock Steady, May'82 by Rock Steady Records. Dist: Rough Trade Distribution, Indies Distribution, Cartel Distribution

I WISH, I WISH.
Single (7"): released on Rock Steady, Sep'82 by Rock Steady Records. Dist: Rough Trade Distribution, Indies Distribution, Cartel Distribution

PUT SOME WATER IN.
Single (7"): released on Stiff, Jul'81

THROW SOME WATER IN.
Single (7"): released on Stiff, Jul'82

Sprulli, Wild Jimmy
HARD GRINDIN' BLUESMAN, (THE).
Album: released on Krazy Kat, Jan'85 Dist: Jazz Music, Swift, Chris Wellard, H.R. Taylor, Charly, Hotshot, IRS Distribution

Sprung aus dem wolkum
PAS ATTENDRE.
Tracks: / Pas Attendre.
Single (12"): released on Les Disques Du Soleil et De L'acier, Feb'86

Spud
SMOKING ON THE BOG.
Album: released on Sonet, Dec'77 by Sonet Records. Dist: PRT

Spur,Silver
COME TO ME (Spur,Silver & Juice Newton).

Spy
WHOLE LOTTA WAYS (TO CATCH A FISH).
Single (7"): released on Mission Discs, Jun'84

Spyder D
I CAN'T WAIT, To rock the mike.
Tracks: / I can't wait / I can't wait.
Single (7"): released on Champion, Jun'86 by

Champion Records. Dist: RCA

Single (12"): released on Champion, Jun'86 by Champion Records. Dist: RCA

Spyri,Johanna
HEIDI.
Cassette: released on Tellastory, Dec'86 by Bartlett Bliss Productions. Dist: PRT Distribution, Hayward Promotions Distribution, H.R. Taylor Distribution

Spyro Gyra
ALTERNATIVE CURRENT.
Album: released on MCA, Oct'85 by MCA Records. Dist: Polygram, MCA

BREAK OUT.
Album: released on MCA, Aug'86 by MCA Records. Dist: Polygram, MCA

Cassette: released on MCA, Aug'86 by MCA Records. Dist: Polygram, MCA

BREAKOUT.
Tracks: / Bob goes to the store / Freefall / Doubletake / Doubletake / Breakout / Body wave / Whirlwind / Swept away / Guiltless.
Compact disc: released on MCA, '87 by MCA Records. Dist: Polygram, MCA

CARNAVAL.
Tracks: / Cafe amore / Dizzy / Awakening / Cashaca / Fox trot / Sweet 'n' savvy / Bittersweet / Carnaval.
Compact disc: released on MCA, '87 by MCA Records. Dist: Polygram, MCA

CARNIVAL.
Album: released on MCA, Sep'82 by MCA Records. Dist: Polygram, MCA

Cassette: released on MCA, Sep'82 by MCA Records. Dist: Polygram, MCA

CATCHING THE SUN.
Tracks: / Catching the sun / Cockatoo / Autumn of our love / Laser material / Percolator / Philly / Lovin' you (interlude) lovin' you / Here again / Safari.
Compact disc: released on MCA, Apr'87 by MCA Records. Dist: Polygram. MCA

CATCHING THE SUN.
Album: released on MCA, '83 by MCA Records. Dist: Polygram, MCA

Cassette: released on MCA, '83 by MCA Records. Dist: Polygram, MCA

CITY KIDS.
Album: released on MCA, Aug'83 by MCA Records. Dist: Polygram, MCA

Cassette: released on MCA, Aug'83 by MCA Records. Dist: Polygram, MCA

FREETIME.
Tracks: / Freetime / Telluride / Summer strut / Elegy for Trane / Pacific sunrise / Amber dream / String soup.
Compact disc: released on MCA, '87 by MCA Records. Dist: Polygram, MCA

MORNING DANCE.
Tracks: / Morning dance / Jubilee / Rasul / Song Lorraine / Starburst / It does'nt matter / Little Linda / End of Romanticism.
Album: released on MCA, Feb'84 by MCA Records. Dist: Polygram. MCA

Cassette: released on MCA, Feb'84 by MCA Records. Dist: Polygram. MCA

Compact disc: released on MCA, Feb'84 by MCA Records. Dist: Polygram, MCA

MORNING DANCE.
Double cassette: released on MCA (Twinpax series), Apr'82

SPYRO GYRA.
Double cassette: released on MCA (Twinpax series), Oct'83

Album: released on Infinity, Aug'81 by MCA Records. Dist: CBS

Cassette: released on Infinity, Aug'81 by MCA Records. Dist: CBS

STORIES WITHOUT WORDS.
Tracks: / Cayo Hueso / Serpentine shelly / Del corazon / Early light / Nu sungo / Chrysalis / Joy ride / Pyramid.
Album: released on MCA, Jul'87 by MCA Records. Dist: Polygram, MCA

Cassette: released on MCA, Jul'87 by MCA Records. Dist: Polygram, MCA

Compact disc: released on MCA, Jul'87 by MCA Records. Dist: Polygram, MCA

Spy who loved me
SPY WHO LOVED ME Film soundtrack (Various Artists).
Album: released on United Artists, Sep'77

Page 948

Cassette: released on United Artists, Sep'77 Deleted '81.

Album: released on EMI (Holland), Mar'84 by EMI Records. Dist: Conifer

Squad

WHY DO YOU MAKE ME WAIT?.
Single (12"): released on Sparkside, May'82

Squadronaires

FLYING HOME.
Album: released on Decca (Recollections), Apr'82 by Decca Recollections. Dist: Polygram, IMS

Square Crows

SQUARE CROWS.
Album: released on Dingles, Jun'84 by Dingles Records. Dist: Projection

Square Department

LOVE ME.
Single (7"): released on Record Shack, Aug'83

Square Peg

ECHOES OF WAR.
Single (7"): released on Stranded, Jun'84 by Stranded Records. Dist: Fast Distribution, Cartel Distribution

Square Roots

SQUARE ROOTS (Various Artists).
Notes: Including June Tabor, Ted Hawkins, Billy Bragg.
Album: released on Folk Roots, Apr'87

Cassette: released on Folk Roots, Apr'87

Squeeze

ARGY BARGY.
Album: released on A&M, Feb'80 by A&M Records. Dist: Polygram

Cassette: released on A&M, Feb'80 by A&M Records. Dist: Polygram

BLACK COFFEE IN BED.
Single (7"): released on A&M, Apr'82 by A&M Records. Dist: Polygram

COOL FOR CATS.
Tracks: / Slap and tickle / Revue / Touching me touching you / Its not cricket / Its so dirty / Hop skip and jump / Up the junction / Hard to find / Slightly drunk / Goodbye girl / Cool for cats / Up the Junction (live)* / Another nail in my heart:* / Pulling mussels (from the shell):* / Is that love: *1 *2 / Tempted:*1,*2 / Labelled with love:*1,*2 Black coffee in bed:*1,*2 / Annie get your gun:*.
Album: released on A&M, Nov'85 by A&M Records. Dist: Polygram

Cassette: released on A&M, Nov'85 by A&M Records. Dist: Polygram

Album: released on A&M, Mar'79 by A&M Records. Dist: Polygram

Cassette: released on A&M, Mar'79 by A&M Records. Dist: Polygram

Single (7"): released on Old Gold, Sep'85 by Old Gold Records. Dist: Lightning, Jazz Music, Spartan, Counterpoint

COSI FAN TUTTI FRUTTI.
Tracks: / Big beng / By your side / I wont ever go drinking again (?) / Hits of the year / Heartbreaking world / No place like home / By your side / Last time forever / I learnt how to pray / King George street.
Album: released on A&M, Aug'85 by A&M Records. Dist: Polygram

Cassette: released on A&M, Aug'85 by A&M Records. Dist: Polygram

Compact disc: released on A&M, Aug'85 by A&M Records. Dist: Polygram

EAST SIDE STORY.
Tracks: / In quintessence / Someone else's heart / Tempted / Piccadily / There's no tomorrow / Woman's world / Is that Love / F-hole / labelled with love / Someone else's bell / Mumbo jumbo / Vanity fair / Messed around.
Album: released on A&M, Sep'86 by A&M Records. Dist: Polygram

Cassette: released on A&M, Sep'86 by A&M Records. Dist: Polygram

Cassette: released on A&M, May'81 by A&M Records. Dist: Polygram

EAST SIDE STORY.
Album: released on A&M, Sep'81 by A&M Records. Dist: Polygram

HOUR GLASS.
Tracks: / Hour glass / Wedding bells / Splitting into three*.
Single (7"): released on A&M, Jul'87 by A&M Records. Dist: Polygram

Single (12"): released on A&M, Jul'87 by A&M Records. Dist: Polygram

KING GEORGE STREET.
Tracks: / King George street / Love's crashing ways (live) / Up the Junction (live)*.
Single (7"): released on A&M, Apr'86 by A&M Records. Dist: Polygram

Single (12"): released on A&M, Apr'86 by A&M Records. Dist: Polygram

LABELLED WITH LOVE.
Single (7"): released on A&M, Sep'81 by A&M Records. Dist: Polygram

SINGLES 45'S AND UNDER.
Tracks: / Take me I'm your's:* / Goodbye girl: * / Cool for cats:* / Up the Junction:* / Slap and tickle.
Notes: The creative backbone of Squeeze songwriters Chris Difford and Glen Tilbrook have; in a few short years; become one of the most respected teams currently writing popular music. Having worked together since 1973 they have been continuously successful since signing with A & M in 1978, delivering 5 fine albums to date. It is this success that is reflected in their first compilation 'Squeeze singles 45's and under'
Tracks in the 'tracks file' not marked with an asterisk written by Difford and tilbrook and published by Rondor music (London) Ltd.
Album: released on A&M, Oct'82 by A&M Records. Dist: Polygram

Cassette: released on A&M, Oct'82 by A&M Records. Dist: Polygram

Compact disc: released on A&M, Oct'82 by A&M Records. Dist: Polygram

SQUEEZE.
Album: released on A&M, Mar'82 by A&M Records. Dist: Polygram

Cassette: released on A&M, Mar'82 by A&M Records. Dist: Polygram

SWEETS FROM A STRANGER.
Album: released on A&M, May'82 by A&M Records. Dist: Polygram

Cassette: released on A&M, May'82 by A&M Records. Dist: Polygram

TAKE ME I'M YOURS.
Single (7"): released on Old Gold, Oct'83 by Old Gold Records. Dist: Lightning, Jazz Music, Spartan, Counterpoint

Squibley, Steve

BAD MAN.
Single (12"): released on White, Nov'84

Squibs

ON THE LINE.
Single (7"): released on Oily, Jul'81 by Oily Records. Dist: Fast Distribution

PARADES.
Single (7"): released on Oily, Jul'81 by Oily Records. Dist: Fast Distribution

Squier, Billy

DON'T SAY NO (Bagatelle).
Tracks: / Don't say no / Golden days.
Single (7"): released on Roxy, May'86 by Ritz Records. Dist: Spartan Distribution

Compact disc: released on Capitol, Apr'87 by Capitol Records. Dist: EMI

EMOTIONS.
Compact disc: released on Capitol, Apr'87 by Capitol Records. Dist: EMI

EMOTIONS IN MOTION.
Tracks: / Everybody wants you / Emotions in motion / Learn how to live / Learn how to live / In your eyes / Keep me satisfied / It keeps you rocking / One good woman / She's a runner / Catch 22 / Listen to the heartbeat.
Compact disc: released on EMI, Jul'87 by EMI Records. Dist: EMI

Single (7"): released on Capitol, Sep'82 by Capitol Records. Dist: EMI

ENOUGH IS ENOUGH.
Tracks: / Shot o' love / Love is the hero / Lady with a tenor Sax / All we have to give / Come home / Break the silence / Powerhouse / Lonely one / Til its over / Wink of an eye.
Compact disc: released on EMI, Jan'87 by EMI Records. Dist: EMI

Album: released on Capitol, Nov'86 by Capitol Records. Dist: EMI

Cassette: released on Capitol, Nov'86 by Capitol Records. Dist: EMI

EVERYBODY WANTS YOU.
Single (7"): released on Capitol, Jan'83 by Capitol Records. Dist: EMI

HOTTEST NIGHT OF THE YEAR, THE.
Album: released on Capitol, Sep'82 by Capitol Records. Dist: EMI

Cassette: released on Capitol, Sep'82 by Capitol Records. Dist: EMI

LIVE IN THE DARK.
Video-cassette (VHS): released on PMI, Jun'86 by PMI Records. Dist: EMI

Video-cassette [Betamax]: released on PMI, Jun'86 by PMI Records. Dist: EMI

LOVE IS THE HERO.
Tracks: / Learn how to live (live).
Single (7"): released on Capitol, Jan'87 by Capitol Records. Dist: EMI

Single (12"): released on Capitol, Jan'87 by Capitol Records. Dist: EMI

ROCK ME TONITE.
Single (7"): released on Capitol, Aug'84 by Capitol Records. Dist: EMI

SIGNS OF LIFE.
Tracks: / All night long / Rock me tonite / Eye on you / Take a look behind ya / Reach for the sky / 1984, (Another) / Fall for love / Can't get next to you / Hand me downs / Sweet release.
Compact disc: released on EMI, Jul'87 by EMI Records. Dist: EMI

SONGS OF LIFE.
Compact disc: released on Capitol, Apr'87 by Capitol Records. Dist: EMI

TOO DAZE GONE.
Single (7"): released on Capitol, Feb'82 by Capitol Records. Dist: EMI

Squire

EVERY TRICK IN THE BOOK OF LOVE.
Single (12"): released on C. More Tone, Oct'83 by Backs Records. Dist: Cartel

GET SMART.
Album: released on Hi-Lo, Mar'86 by Hi-Lo Records & Tapes. Dist: Nine Mile, Cartel

GET SMART.
Album: released on Hi-Lo, Aug'85 by Hi-Lo Records & Tapes. Dist: Nine Mile, Cartel

GIRL ON A TRAIN.
Single (7"): released on Hi-Lo, Jul'82 by Hi-Lo Records & Tapes. Dist: Nine Mile, Cartel

HITS FROM 3,000 YEARS AGO.
Album: released on Hi-Lo, Aug'85 by Hi-Lo Records & Tapes. Dist: Nine Mile, Cartel

JASAMINE.
Single (7"): released on Hi-Lo, Sep'83 by Hi-Lo Records & Tapes. Dist: Nine Mile, Cartel

NO TIME TOMORROW.
Single (7"): released on Hi-Lo, Apr'82 by Hi-Lo Records & Tapes. Dist: Nine Mile, Cartel

SINGLES ALBUM, THE.
Album: released on Hi-Lo, Mar'85 by Hi-Lo Records & Tapes. Dist: Nine Mile, Cartel

SINGLES LP.
Album: released on Hi-Lo, Mar'86 by Hi-Lo Records & Tapes. Dist: Nine Mile, Cartel

YOUNG IDEA, THE.
Single (7"): released on Squire Fan Club, Jun'84 by Hi-Lo Records & Tapes. Dist: Nine Mile Distribution, Cartel Distribution

Squire, Chris

RUN WITH THE FOX (Squire, Chris & Alan White).
Single (7"): released on Atlantic, Dec'82 by WEA Records. Dist: WEA

Squire, John

BROKEN-DOWN GENTLEMEN (Squire, John/John Leonard).
Album: released on Rubber, Jun'82 by Rubber Records. Dist: Roots Distribution, Projection Distribution, Jazz Music Distribution, Celtic Music Distribution, JSU Distribution, Spartan Distribution

Squire, Paul

RAINBOWS END.
Single (7"): released on Roxon, Oct'81 by Roxon Records. Dist: Pinnacle

Squires, Audrey

IN CONCERT.
Album: released on Klub, May'80

Cassette: released on Klub, May'80

SILENT CHRISTMAS.
Tracks: / Silent Christmas / Ding dong on Christmas night.
Notes: All profits to st Raphaels hospice.
Single (7"): released on Lakeside, Nov'86 by Lakeside Records. Dist: Lakeside

Squires, Dorothy

WE CLOWNS.
Album: released on Esban, Dec'84 Dist: Pinnacle

WINE IS THERE,THE.
Tracks: / Try a little tenderness.
Single (7"): released on Esban, Feb'87 Dist: Pinnacle

WITH ALL MY HEART.
Album: released on Decca, Nov'79 by Decca Records. Dist: Polygram

YOU'LL NEVER WALK ALONE.
Single (7"): released on Esban, Jul'85 Dist: Pinnacle

Squirrel Bait

KID DYNAMITE.
Tracks: / Kid dynamite / Slake train coming.
Single (7"): released on Homestead, '86 Dist: Rough Trade, Cartel, Shigaku

SKAG HEAVEN.
Album: released on Homestead, Feb'87 Dist: Rough Trade, Cartel, Shigaku

SQUIRREL BAIT.
Album: released on Homestead, '86 Dist: Rough Trade, Cartel, Shigaku

SRC

REVENGE OF THE QUACKENBUSH BROTHERS.
Album: released on Bam Caruso, Mar'87 by Bam Caruso Records. Dist: Rough Trade, Revolver, Cartel

SSS Soul Survey

SSS SOUL SURVEY Various artists (Various Artists).
Album: released on Charly(R&B), Feb'82 by Charly Records. Dist: Charly, Cadillac

Staa Marx

CRAZY WEEKEND.
Single (7"): released on Cherry Red, Feb'79 by Cherry Red Records. Dist: Pinnacle

Stabbins, Ashley, Duo

FIRE WITHOUT BRICKS.
Album: released on Bead, Dec'77 Dist: Cadillac

Staber, Dick

PICKIN' AROUND THE COOKSTOVE (WITH FRIENDS).
Album: released on Rounder (USA), Aug'77

Stabilizers

TYRANNY.
Tracks: / (If I) found Rome / I don't need the pain / Now I hear you / One simple thing / Underground / Does your love lie open / Place to hide, A / You pull me down / Tyranny / Place to hide, A / Tyranny / (If I) found Rome.
Album: released on CBS, Sep'86 by CBS Records. Dist: CBS

Cassette: released on CBS, Sep'86 by CBS Records. Dist: CBS

Single (7"): released on CBS, Aug'86 by CBS Records. Dist: CBS

Single (12"): released on CBS, Aug'86 by CBS Records. Dist: CBS

Staccato

STACCATO Original Television Soundtrack.
Album: released on That's Entertainment, Apr'83 by That's Entertainment Records. Dist: Pinnacle, PRT

Stacey, Mike

I WANT YOU.
Tracks: / I want you / Everything I am.
Single (7"): released on Sierra, May'87 by Sierra Records. Dist: WEA

Stack-a-records

STACK-A-RECORDS Various artists (Various Artists).
Album: released on Rockhouse, Jun'83 by Rockhouse Records. Dist: Swift Distribution, Charly Distribution

STACK-A-RECORDS Various artists (Various Artists).
Album: released on Nervous, Jul'84 by Nervous Records. Dist: Nervous, Rough Trade

Stacks

YOU'RE ON MY MIND.
Single (7"): released on Brand New, Mar'84 by Brand New Records. Dist: Ace Records, Chiswick Records, Pinnacle

Stacy, Jeff

STACY'N'SUTTON (Stacy, Jeff/Ralph Sutton).
Tracks: / Fascinating rhythm / You took advantage of / Indiana / Oh baby / Stars fell on Alabama / If I could be with you / I want to be happy / I can't get started / Jeepers creepers / I'll dance at your wedding / Fussin' / Eye opener / Tain't nobody's business / Sneakaway / I got rhythm.
Album: released on Affinity, Jun'86 by Charly Records. Dist: Charly, Cadillac

TWO GOOD MEN (Stacy, Jeff & Teddy Wilson).

Stacy, Jess

JESS STACY AND FRIENDS.
Notes: Solos by Lee Wiley, Specs Powell.
Album: released on Commodore Classics, May'87 by Teldec Records (Germany). Dist: Conifer, IMS, Polygram

ON THE AIR.
Album: released on Aircheck (USA), Oct'86 Dist: Swift, Jazz Music

PIANO SOLOS (1935-56).
Album: released on Swaggie (Australia), Jan'83

STACY 'N' SUTTON (Stacy, Jess Quartet).
Tracks: / Fascinating rythym / You took advantage of me / Indiana / Fascinating Rhythm / You took advantage of me / Indiana / Oh baby / Stars fell on Alabama / If I could be with you one hour tonight / I want to be happy / I can't get started / Jeepers creepers / I'll dance at your wedding / Fussin / Eye Opener / Taint nobody's biz-nezz it I do / Snow morning blues / Sneakaway / I got rhythm.
Album: released on Affinity, Apr'86 by Charly Records. Dist: Charly, Cadillac

WITH LEE WILEY, SPECS POWELL & SOLOS - 1938 & 1944.
Album: released on Commodore Class, Aug'82 by Teldec Records (Germany). Dist: Conifer, IMS, Polygram

Stadium Dogs

WHAT'S NEXT.
Album: released on Magnet, '78 by Magnet Records. Dist: BMG

Cassette: released on Magnet, '78 by Magnet Records. Dist: BMG

Staff

TCHA TCHA TCHINA.
Single (7"): released on PRT, Feb'82 by PRT Records. Dist: PRT

Staff, Kathy

BENNY.
Single (7"): released on Monarch, Mar'83 by Chart Records. Dist: Pinnacle

NORA BATTY'S STOCKINGS (Staff, Kathy & Bill Owen).

Stafford, Jim

LITTLE BITS AND PIECES.
Single (7"): released on CBS, Nov'84 by CBS Records. Dist: CBS

SPIDERS AND SNAKES.
Single (7"): released on Old Gold, Jul'84 by Old Gold Records. Dist: Lightning, Jazz Music, Spartan, Counterpoint

Stafford, Jo

AMERICAN FOLK SONGS.
Album: released on Corinthian (USA), Mar'79 Dist: Swift

G.I. JOE Songs of World War 2.
Album: released on Corinthian (USA), Mar'79 Dist: Swift

HITS OF JO STAFFORD, THE.
Album: released on Music For Pleasure, Jul'84 by EMI Records. Dist: EMI

Cassette: released on Music For Pleasure, Jul'84 by EMI Records. Dist: EMI

INTRODUCING JO STAFFORD.
Tracks: / Begin the beguine / Roses of Picardy / If I ever love again / Congratulations / Why can't you behave? / Sometime / Always true to you in my fashion / Scarlet ribbons for her hair / Too marvellous for words / Over the rainbow / Just reminiscing / Walking my baby back home / I remember you / Happy times / Baby, won't you please come home / Smoke dreams.
Album: released on Capitol, Oct'87 by Capitol Records. Dist: EMI. Estim retail price in Jul'87 was £3.99.

Cassette: released on Capitol, Oct'87 by Capitol Records. Dist: EMI

JO PLUS BLUES With the ballad of the blues.
Album: released on Corinthian (USA), Mar'79 Dist: Swift

Dist: Swift

JO PLUS BROADWAY.
Album: released on Corinthian (USA), Mar'79 Dist: Swift

JO PLUS JAZZ.
Album: released on Corinthian (USA), Mar'79 Dist: Swift

JO STAFFORD'S GREATEST HITS.
Album: released on Corinthian (USA), Mar'79 Dist: Swift

OLD RUGGED CROSS (Stafford, Jo and Gordon Macre).
Tracks: / Whispering hope / Abide with me / In the garden / Beyond the sunset / Beautiful Isle of somewhere / It is no secret / I found a friend / Old rugged cross, The / Rock of ages / Star of hope (based on the theme by Emile Waldteufel) / Now the day is over / Perfect day, A.
Album: released on MFP, Jun'87 by EMI Records. Dist: EMI

Cassette: released on MFP, Jun'87 by EMI Records. Dist: EMI

OLD RUGGED CROSS, THE.
Album: released on Music For Pleasure, '78 by EMI Records. Dist: EMI

SKI TRAILS Songs for fireside.
Album: released on Corinthian (USA), Mar'79 Dist: Swift

SONGS OF FAITH HOPE & LOVE.
Album: released on Corinthian (USA), Mar'83 Dist: Swift

STARRING JO STAFFORD.
Album: released on Capitol, Jun'85 by Capitol Records. Dist: EMI

Cassette: released on Capitol, Jun'85 by Capitol Records. Dist: EMI

STARS OF THE 50'S.
Album: released on EMI (Holland), Aug'84 by EMI Records. Dist: Conifer

Stafford, Joe

SINGS SONGS OF SCOTLAND.
Album: released on Ariola (Holland), Apr'84

Cassette: released on Ariola (Holland), Apr'84

THANK YOU FOR CALLING.
Album: released on Ariola (Holland), Apr'84

Cassette: released on Ariola (Holland), Apr'84

Stafford, Johnny

TWENTY HARMONICA GREATS.
Album: released on Music For Pleasure, Jul'84 by EMI Records. Dist: EMI

Cassette: released on Music For Pleasure, Jul'84 by EMI Records. Dist: EMI

Staffordshire Regiment

MUSIC BY THE BAND OF....
Album: released on Music Masters, Jan'83 by Music Masters Records. Dist: Taylors

Cassette: released on Music Masters, Jan'83 by Music Masters Records. Dist: Taylors

Stafford, Terry

SUSPICION.
Album: released on Ace, Apr'87 by Ace Records. Dist: Pinnacle, Swift, Hotshot, Cadillac

Stage

DANCING DAYS.
Tracks: / Dancing days / Too close for comfort.
Single (7"): released on IRS, Sep'86 Dist: Polygram

Single (12"): released on IRS, Sep'86 Dist: Polygram

NOTHING STRANGER THAN TODAY.
Tracks: / Kissing at the station / Stop the time.
Notes: Extra track on 12" only
Single (7"): released on I.R.S.(Independent Record Syndicate), Feb'87 by I.R.S.. Dist: MCA

Stage B

RECALL TO LIFE/ LIGHT ON THE HILLSIDE.
Single (7"): released on Shock Rock, Feb'80 Dist: Clyde Factors Distributors

Stagefright

STRANGER IN THE NIGHT.
Single (7"): released on S.T.N., Jan'85 Dist: M.I.S. Distribution

Stages In Life

STAGES IN LIFE Various artists (Various Artists).

Album: released on All Turn, Sep'85 Dist: Jetstar

Stag Marks Gang

AIN'T NO FUN ON THE DOLE.
Single (7"): released on Double Image, Jul'82 by Double Image Records.

Stained Glass

OPEN ROAD.
Album: released on Sweet Folk All, May'81 by Sweet Folk All Records. Dist: Sweet Folk All, Roots, Celtic Music, Dragon, Impetus, Projection, Chris Wellard, Festival Records

Staines, Bill

WILD WILD HEART.
Album: released on Philo (USA), Dec'85

Staircase to nowhere

STAIRCASE TO NOWHERE (Various Artists).
Album: released on Bam Caruso, Dec'86 by Bam Caruso Records. Dist: Rough Trade, Revolver, Cartel

Stalactite

SHAS.
Single (7"): released on Albatross, Jan'85 Dist: M.I.S.

Stalag 17

STALAG NO. 17 SUPERVISION EXCURSION Various artists (Various Artists).
Album: released on Jammy's, Sep'85 by Jammy's Records. Dist: Jetstar

TRUTH WILL BE HEARD From Belfast with... (Stalag 17 & Toxic Waste).
Single (7"): released on Mortarhate, Sep'85 by Dorane Ltd.

WE WILL BE FREE (Stalag 17/Asylum/Toxic Waste).
Notes: Belfast Community Benefit
Album: released on Warzone, Mar'87

Stallion

STALLION/ DOOM WATCH.
Single (12"): released on Sunsplash, Sep'83 by Sunsplash Records. Dist: Jetstar Distribution

Stamey, Chris

IN THE WINTER OF LOVE/ IT'S A WONDERFUL LIFE.
Album: released on Palo Alto (USA), Jan'84 by Palo Alto Records. Dist: Conifer

Stamm, Marvin

STAMMPEDE.
Cassette: released on Palo Alto (USA), Jul'86 by Palo Alto Records. Dist: Conifer

Stampede

DAYS OF WINE AND ROSES/ PHOTOGRAPHS.
Single (7"): released on Polydor, Sep'82 by Polydor Records. Dist: Polygram, Polydor

Single (12"): released on Polydor, Sep'82 by Polydor Records. Dist: Polygram, Polydor

OTHER SIDE/ RUNNER, THE.
Single (7"): released on Polydor, May'83 by Polydor Records. Dist: Polygram, Polydor

PHOTOGRAPHS/ DAYS OF WINE & ROSES.
Single (7"): released on Polydor, Dec'82 by Polydor Records. Dist: Polygram, Polydor

Single (12"): released on Polydor, Dec'82 by Polydor Records. Dist: Polygram, Polydor

Stampfel, Peter

PETER STAMPFEL & THE BOTTLECAPS (Stampfel, Peter & The Bottlecaps).
Album: released on Rounder Europa, May'87

Stampley, Joe

20 GREATEST HITS.
Album: released on Astan, Nov'84 by Astan Records. Dist: Counterpoint

Cassette: released on Astan, Nov'84 by Astan Records. Dist: Counterpoint

GOOD OL' BOYS - ALIVE AND WELL, THE (Stampley, Joe and Moe Bandy).

JOE STAMPLEY.
Cassette: released on Audio Fidelity, Oct'84 Dist: PRT

Stand By Me

STAND BY ME Original Soundtrack (Various Artists).
Notes: Film soundtrack includes tracks by Buddy Holly, The Coasters etc.
Album: released on Atlantic, Feb'87 by WEA Records. Dist: WEA

Cassette: released on Atlantic, Feb'87 by WEA Records. Dist: WEA

Stand In For Love

STAND IN FOR LOVE (Various Artists).
Tracks: / It's starting to get to me now / Underneath my make up / No, no, I can't help you / I'm through trying to prove my love for you / I found a new love / Let's live / Get out of my life / Quiet place, A / I can't wait until I see my baby's face / Missin' my baby / Anyone who knows what love is (will understand) / That's how much I love you / Every day / Workin' on a groovy thing.
Album: released on Kent, Apr'86 by Ace Records. Dist: Pinnacle

Standing 4

ICE EMOTION.
Tracks: / Ice emotion / Nightmare.
Single (7"): released on Four Records, Sep'87 by Four Records. Dist: Four Records

NIGHTMARE.
Tracks: / Standing still / Nightmare / Ice emotion.
Cassette single: released on Four Records, Sep'87 by Four Records. Dist: Four Records

Standing Ovation

TIMES OF FUN/ WHAT MEANING.
Cassette single: released on Falling A, Dec'83 by Falling A Records. Dist: Falling A Distribution

Standing Stones

STANDING STONES (Various Artists).
Album: released on Coda Landscape, Jan'86 by Coda Records. Dist: WEA

Cassette: released on Coda Landscape, Jan'86 by Coda Records. Dist: WEA

Compact disc: released on Coda Landscape, Feb'86 by Coda Records. Dist: WEA

Stanford - Le - Hope

RED RED WINE.
Single (12"): released on ABL, Oct'83 by ABL Records. Dist: Jetstar

Stangeloves

I WANT CANDY.
Album: released on Line (West Germany) Feb'84

Stanger & Nelson

I'M DOING FINE NOW.
Single (7"): released on Excalibur, Oct'83 by Red Bus Records. Dist: PRT

Single (12"): released on Excalibur, Oct'83 by Red Bus Records. Dist: PRT

Stanisclaus, Olga J

DARLIN' COOL IT/ JAM SOMETHING.
Single (12"): released on Sunburn, Mar'83 by Orbitone Records. Dist: Jetstar Distribution

OLGA (2 PARTS).
Single (12"): released on Sunburn, Mar'83 by Orbitone Records. Dist: Jetstar Distribution

Stanley Brothers

16 GREATEST HITS.
Album: released on Starday, Apr'87

Cassette: released on Starday, Apr'87

20 BLUEGRASS ORIGINALS.
Album: released on Starday, Apr'87

Cassette: released on Starday, Apr'87

BANJO IN THE HILLS.
Album: released on King (USA), Apr'87 Dist: Gusto Distribution

Cassette: released on King (USA), Apr'87 Dist: Gusto Distribution

BEST OF....
Notes: 10 tracks
Album: released on Starday, Apr'87

Cassette: released on Starday, Apr'87

FOLK CONCERT.
Album: released on King (USA), Apr'87 Dist: Gusto Distribution

Cassette: released on King (USA), Apr'87 Dist: Gusto Distribution

FOLK SONG FESTIVAL.
Album: released on Starday, Apr'87

Cassette: released on Starday, Apr'87

ON THE RADIO, VOLUME 1.
Album: released on County (USA), Jul'84 Dist: Mike's Country Music Room Distribution, Projection, Swift

ON THE RADIO, VOLUME 2.
Album: released on County (USA), Jul'84 Dist: Mike's Country Music Room Distribution, Projection, Swift

SONGS THEY LIKE THE BEST.
Album: released on King (USA), Apr'87 Dist: Gusto Distribution

Cassette: released on King (USA), Apr'87 Dist: Gusto Distribution

STANLEY BROTHERS & THE CLINCH MOUNTAIN BOYS (Stanley Brothers & The Clinch Mountain Boys).
Album: released on King (USA), Apr'87 Dist: Gusto Distribution

Cassette: released on King (USA), Apr'87 Dist: Gusto Distribution

Stanley, Chris

INCREDIBLE.
Album: released on Mountain Sounds, Nov'86

Stanley,Chuck

DAY BY DAY.
Tracks: / Day by day / Finer things in life (The).
Single (7"): released on Def Jam (USA), Apr'87 by CBS Records. Dist: CBS

Single (12"): released on Def Jam (USA), Apr'87 by CBS Records. Dist: CBS

FINER THINGS IN LIFE,THE.
Tracks: / Day by day / Love toy / Never gonna let you go / Burning up / Make you mine tonight / Jammin' to the bells / All and all / Real soon / When it all falls down.
Album: released on Def Jam (USA), Mar'87 by CBS Records. Dist: CBS

Cassette: released on Def Jam (USA), Mar'87 by CBS Records. Dist: CBS

Compact disc: released on Def Jam (USA), Mar'87 by CBS Records. Dist: CBS

Compact disc: released on Def Jam (USA), May'87 by CBS Records. Dist: CBS

Stanley, Finton

FINTON STANLEY ON TOUR.
Tracks: / Happy hours polka / Pigalle / St.Patricks day medley / Quando quando / Don't you forget it / Irish reels / Freight train / West's awake / I love Paris / High level reel / Somewhere my love / Black and white rag / Scottish selection.
Album: released on Accordion Record Club, Jul'86 by Accordion Record Club Records. Dist: Accordion Record Club

Cassette: released on Accordion Record Club, Jul'86 by Accordion Record Club Records. Dist: Accordion Record Club

FINTON STANLEY ON TOUR VOL.2.
Tracks: / She taught me to yodel / Greensleeves / French waltz / My lagan love / Scottish island breeze / Medley / Irish reels / Derry air / Hungarian dance no.5 / In the mood / Retour des hirondelles / Viva Espana / Reels / Souveneir musette / Tico tico / Brazil.
Album: released on Accordion Record Club, Jul'86 by Accordion Record Club Records. Dist: Accordion Record Club

Cassette: released on Accordion Record Club, Jul'86 by Accordion Record Club Records. Dist: Accordion Record Club

Stanley, Pamela

COMING OUT OF HIDING.
Single (7"): released on Casablanca, Jun'84 Dist: Polygram, Phonogram

Single (12"): released on Casablanca, Jun'84 Dist: Polygram, Phonogram

Stanley, Ralph

HILLS OF HOME.
Album: released on King (USA), Apr'87 Dist: Gusto Distribution

Cassette: released on King (USA), Apr'87 Dist: Gusto Distribution

Stano

CONTENT TO WRITE I DINE.
Album: released on Scoff, Jun'84 Dist: Rough Trade, Cartel

ROOM, THE.
Single (7"): released on Vox Enterprise, Apr'82
Cat. no: VE 1

Stansfield, Lisa

I GOT A FEELING/ RED LIGHTS.
Single (7"): released on Polydor, Oct'83 by Polydor Records. Dist: Polygram, Polydor

ONLY WAY/ ONLY LOVE.
Single (7"): released on Polydor, Oct'82 by Polydor Records. Dist: Polygram, Polydor

YOUR ALIBIS/ THOUGHT POLICE.
Single (7"): released on Devil, Mar'82 by Devil Records. Dist: Spartan

Stanshall, Vivian

HENRY AT NDIDIS KRAAL.
Album: released on Demon Verbals, Sep'84 by Demon Records. Dist: Demon Records, Pinnacle

SIR HENRY AT RAWLINSON END.
Album: released on Charisma, '78 by Virgin Records. Dist: EMI

TEDDY BOYS DON'T KNIT.
Album: released on Charisma, Jun'81 by Virgin Records. Dist: EMI

Cassette: released on Charisma, Jun'81 by Virgin Records. Dist: EMI

Stan's Soul Shop

STAN'S SOUL SHOP Various artists (Various Artists).
Album: released on Charly, Feb'82 by Charly Records. Dist: Charly, Cadillac

Stan & The Gang

GRANDADS MOTTO.
Single (7"): released on Spy 80, Nov'81

Stanton, Eddie

LUCIFER WANTS ME FOR A SUNBEAM.

Single (7"): released on Black Eyes, May'81 Dist: Rough Trade

MILTON KEYNES WE LOVE YOU.
Single (7"): released on Black Eyes, May'81 Dist: Rough Trade

Stanton Miranda

WHEELS OVER INDIAN TRAILS.
Tracks: / Wheels over Indian trails / Wheels over trails.

Staple Singers

BE ALTITUDE RESPECT YOURSELF.
Album: released on Stax, Aug'87 by Ace Records. Dist: Pinnacle, Chris Wellard, IMS-Polygram

HOLD ON TO YOUR DREAMS.
Album: released on 20th Century, Oct'81 Dist: RCA, IMS-Polygram

Cassette: released on 20th Century, Oct'81 Dist: RCA, IMS-Polygram

I'LL TAKE YOU THERE.
Single (7"): released on Stax, Mar'82 by Ace Records. Dist: Pinnacle, Chris Wellard, IMS-Polygram

LONG WALK TO DC.
Single (7"): released on Stax, Oct'87 by Ace Records. Dist: Pinnacle, Chris Wellard, IMS-Polygram

PLAY ON.
Tracks: / Pray on / Don't drive me away / Downward road / Will the circle be unbroken / Stand by me / Ain't that good news / If I could hear my brother / Going away / Don't knock / Uncloudy day / I know I got religion / Somebody save me / Let's go home / This may be the last time / I had a dream / Calling me.
Album: released on New Cross, Apr'86 by Charly Records. Dist: Charly

RESPECT YOURSELF.
Tracks: / Respect yourself / You're gonna make me cry.
Single (7"): released on Stax, 13 Jun'87 by Ace Records. Dist: Pinnacle, Chris Wellard, IMS-Polygram

Compact disc: released on Stax, Oct'87 by Ace Records. Dist: Pinnacle, Chris Wellard, IMS-Polygram

SLIPPERY PEOPLE.
Single (7"): released on Epic, Sep'84 by CBS Records. Dist: CBS

Single (12"): released on Epic, Sep'84 by CBS Records. Dist: CBS

STAPLE SINGERS.
Album: released on Epic, Nov'85 by CBS Records. Dist: CBS

Cassette: released on Epic, Nov'85 by CBS Records. Dist: CBS

STAPLE SINGERS AT THEIR BEST.
Album: released on Stax, Mar'82 by Ace Records. Dist: Pinnacle, Chris Wellard, IMS-Polygram

Cassette: released on Stax, Mar'82 by Ace Records. Dist: Pinnacle, Chris Wellard, IMS-Polygram

STAPLE SINGERS, THE.
Cassette: released on Audio Fidelity, Oct'84 Dist: PRT

THIS IS OUR NIGHT.
Single (7"): released on Epic, Jan'85 by CBS Records. Dist: CBS

Single (12"): released on Epic, Jan'85 by CBS Records. Dist: CBS

WE'LL GET OVER.
Tracks: / Give a damn / Everyday people / End of the road,The / Tend to your own business / Solon Bushi (Japanese folk song) / Challenge,The / God bless the children / Games people play / Wednesday in your garden,A / Gardner,The / When do I get paid.
Notes: Produced by legendary guitarist,producer and arranger Steve Cropper.Re-issue.
Album: released on Stax, Jan'87 by Ace Records. Dist: Pinnacle, Chris Wellard, IMS-Polygram

Cassette: released on Stax, Jan'87 by Ace Records. Dist: Pinnacle, Chris Wellard, IMS-Polygram

Staple Singers, The

BE ALTITUDE/ RESPECT YOURSELF.
Album: released on Stax, Aug'87 by Ace Records. Dist: Pinnacle, Chris Wellard, IMS-Polygram

Stapleton, Maureen

SUMMER PEOPLE, THE.
Album: released on Caedmon(USA), Sep'77 by Caedmon (USA) Records. Dist: Gower, Taylors, Discovery

Cassette: released on Caedmon(USA), Sep'77 by Caedmon (USA) Records. Dist: Gower, Taylors, Discovery

Star Accordian Band

ALL TIME FAVOURITES.
Album: released on Klub, Nov'86

Compact disc: released on Klub, Nov'86

Star Accordion Band

COUNTRY FAVOURITES - VOL.2.
Album: released on Klub, Oct'85

Cassette: released on Klub, Oct'85

COUNTRY FAVOURITES.
Album: released on Klub, Dec'83

Cassette: released on Klub, Dec'83

PARTY FAVOUTITES.
Album: released on Klub, Nov'85

Album: released on Klub, Nov'85

SCOTTISH FAVOURITES VOL.2.
Tracks: / These are my mountains / Song of the Clyde / Dancing in Kyle / Sottish soldier / Donald where's your trousers / Crookit bawbee / There was a lad.
Notes: The sixth album from the Star Accordion Band. 41 great titles. Another great 'sing along' album.
Album: released on Klub, Apr'86

Cassette: released on Klub, Apr'86

SCOTTISH FAVOURITES.
Compact disc: released on Igus, 20 Jun'87 by Klub. Dist: PRT, Musac Distribution Ltd (Scotland)

SCOTTISH FAVOURITES.
Album: released on Klub, May'85

Cassette: released on Klub, May'85

Star Accordion Dance Band

SCOTTISH DANCE FAVOURITES.
Album: released on Igus, Jul'87 by Klub. Dist: PRT, Musac Distribution Ltd (Scotland)

Cassette: released on Igus, Jul'87 by Klub. Dist: PRT, Musac Distribution Ltd (Scotland)

Starburst

STARBURST (Various Artists).
Album: released on Hallmark, Jul'86 by Pickwick Records. Dist: Pickwick Distribution, PRT, Taylors

Cassette: released on Hallmark, Jul'86 by Pickwick Records. Dist: Pickwick Distribution, PRT, Taylors

Starburst Country

STARBURST COUNTRY Various artists (Various Artists).
Album: released on Meteor, Mar'85 by Magnum Force Music. Dist: CBS Distribution

Starcher, Buddy

COUNTRY LOVE SONGS.
Album: released on Bear Family, Oct'80 by Bear Family Records. Dist: Rollercoaster Distribution, Swift

Star Child

STAR CHILD (Wilde, Oscar).
Cassette: released on Kiddy Kassettes, Feb'81

Star Club Show

STAR CLUB SHOW Various artists (Various Artists).
Album: released on Phonogram Import, Jun'82

Cassette: released on Phonogram Import, Jun'82

Starday Dixie

STARDAY DIXIE ROCKABILLIES Various artists (Various Artists).
Album: released on Gusto (USA), Oct'79 by Gusto Records (USA). Dist: Crusader

STARDAY DIXIE ROCKABILLIES - VOL.2 Various artists (Various Artists).
Album: released on Gusto (USA), Oct'79 by Gusto Records (USA). Dist: Crusader

Stardust, Alvin

ALVIN STARDUST (6 TRACK HITS).
Single (7"): released on Scoop 33, Sep'83 by Pickwick Records. Dist: H.R. Taylor

Cassette: released on Scoop 33, Sep'83 by Pickwick Records. Dist: H.R. Taylor

CLOCK ON THE WALL.
Single (7"): released on Chrysalis, Apr'85 by Chrysalis Records. Dist: CBS

Single (12"): released on Chrysalis, Apr'85 by Chrysalis Records. Dist: CBS

GREATEST HITS: ALVIN STARDUST.
Album: released on Magnet, Oct'77 by Magnet Records. Dist: BMG

Cassette: released on Magnet, Oct'77 by Magnet Records. Dist: BMG

I FEEL LIKE...ALVIN STARDUST.
Album: released on Chrysalis, Nov'84 by Chrysalis Records. Dist: CBS

Cassette: released on Chrysalis, Nov'84 by Chrysalis Records. Dist: CBS

I FEEL LIKE BUDDY HOLLY.
Single (7"): released on Chrysalis, Apr'84 by Chrysalis Records. Dist: CBS

Single (12"): released on Chrysalis, Jun'84 by Chrysalis Records. Dist: CBS

I HOPE AND I PRAY (Stardust, Alvin & Sheila Walsh).
Tracks: / I hope and I pray / Speak of love.
Single (7"): released on Chrysalis, Mar'86 by Chrysalis Records. Dist: CBS

Single (12"): released on Chrysalis, Mar'86 by Chrysalis Records. Dist: CBS

I WANT YOU BACK IN MY LIFE AGAIN.
Single (7"): released on Stiff, Jul'82

Picture disc single: released on Stiff, Jul'82

JAILHOUSE ROCK.
Tracks: / Jailhouse rock / Love is real / My coo-ca-choo.
Single (7"): released on Magnet, Oct'86 by Magnet Records. Dist: BMG

Single (12"): released on Magnet, Oct'86 by Magnet Records. Dist: BMG

Album: released on RCA (Germany), Jan'83

Single (7"): released on RCA, May'77 by RCA Records. Dist: RCA, Roots, Swift, Wellard, Chris, I & B, Solomon & Peres Distribution

Single (7"): released on RCA, May'77 by RCA Records. Dist: RCA, Roots, Swift, Wellard, Chris, I & B, Solomon & Peres Distribution

Single (7"): released on RCA, Jan'83 by RCA Records. Dist: RCA, Roots, Swift, Wellard, Chris, I & B, Solomon & Peres Distribution

Picture disc single: released on RCA, Jan'83 by RCA Records. Dist: RCA, Roots, Swift, Wellard, Chris, I & B, Solomon & Peres Distribution

MY COO CA CHOO.
Single (7"): released on Magnet, Nov'73 by Magnet Records. Dist: BMG

Single (7"): released on Magnet, Sep'81 by Magnet Records. Dist: BMG

PICTURE OF YOU.
Single (7"): released on Stiff, Nov'82 by Stiff Records. Dist: EMI, Record Services Distribution (Ireland)

PRETEND.
Single (7"): released on Stiff, Aug'81 by Stiff Records. Dist: EMI, Record Services Distribution (Ireland)

RED DRESS.
Single (7"): released on Magnet, Apr'74 by Magnet Records. Dist: BMG

SLEEPLESS NIGHTS.
Single (7"): released on Chrysalis, Jun'85 by Chrysalis Records. Dist: CBS

Single (12"): released on Chrysalis, Jun'85 by Chrysalis Records. Dist: CBS

WALK AWAY RENEE.
Single (7"): released on Stiff, Apr'83 by Stiff Records. Dist: EMI, Record Services Distribution (Ireland)

WEEKEND.
Single (7"): released on Stiff, Apr'82 by Stiff Records. Dist: EMI, Record Services Distribution (Ireland)

WONDERFUL TIME UP THERE.
Single (7"): released on Stiff, Nov'81 by Stiff Records. Dist: EMI, Record Services Distribution (Ireland)

Starfighters

ALLEY CAT BLUES.
Single (7"): released on Jive, Aug'81 by Zomba Records. Dist: RCA, PRT, CBS

Single (12"): released on Jive, Aug'81 by Zomba Records. Dist: RCA, PRT, CBS

POWER CRAZY.
Album: released on Jive, Oct'81 by Zomba Records. Dist: RCA, PRT, CBS

Cassette: released on Jive, Oct'81 by Zomba Records. Dist: RCA, PRT, CBS

Single (7"): released on Jive, Oct'81 by Zomba Records. Dist: RCA, PRT, CBS

Single (12"): released on Jive, Oct'81 by Zomba Records. Dist: RCA, PRT, CBS

Starforce on CD

STARFORCE ON CD (Various Artists).
Compact disc: released on WEA, Jun'87 by WEA Records. Dist: WEA

Stargard

BACK 2 BACK.
Album: released on Warner Brothers, Jul'81 by WEA Records. Dist: WEA

WEAR IT OUT.
Single (7"): released on Warner Brothers, Jan'80 by WEA Records. Dist: WEA

Stargazers

AIN'T NOBODY HERE BUT US CHICKENS.
Single (7"): released on Epic, Jan'83 by CBS Records. Dist: CBS

Star Inc.

INNER SPIRITS.
Compact disc: released on The Compact Collection, Sep'87 by Conifer Records. Dist: Conifer Distribution

INTER SYNTHELLITE 28 Synthesizer hits.
Compact disc: released on The Compact Collection, Sep'87 by Conifer Records. Dist: Conifer Distribution

JAMES BOND FILM THEMES.
Compact disc: released on The Compact Collection, Sep'87 by Conifer Records. Dist: Conifer Distribution

Star Is Born

STAR IS BORN, A Original soundtrack (Various Artists).
Album: released on CBS, Feb'77 by CBS Records. Dist: CBS

Cassette: released on CBS, Feb'77 by CBS Records. Dist: CBS

Star is born, (A)

STAR IS BORN, (A) Film soundtrack (Film soundtrack, featuring Barbra Streisand).
Album: released on CBS, Feb'77 by CBS Records. Dist: CBS

Cassette: released on CBS, Feb'77 by CBS Records. Dist: CBS

Starita, Ray

RHAPSODY IN RHYTHM (Starita, Ray & His Ambassadors Band).
Album: released on Saville, Apr'83 by Conifer Records. Dist: Conifer

Stark

COMMUNICATING BALANCE.
Cassette: released on Dead Happy, '82 by Dead Happy Records. Dist: Mason's Music Distributors/Wholesalers, Rough Trade

FOND ADIEU.
Cassette: released on Dead Happy, '86 by Dead Happy Records. Dist: Mason's Music Distributors/Wholesalers, Rough Trade

INSANITY IS ONLY A HAIRBREADTH AWAY.
Cassette: released on Dead Happy, '82 by Dead Happy Records. Dist: Mason's Music Distributors/Wholesalers, Rough Trade

SINGLE,THE.
Cassette: released on Dead Happy, '82 by Dead Happy Records. Dist: Mason's Music Distributors/Wholesalers, Rough Trade

Stark,Bengt

PUPILS AND TEACHERS.
Album: released on Phontastic (Sweden), '82 by Wellard, Chris Distribution. Dist: Wellard, Chris Distribution

Starkman

......AND OTHER VOICES (Leah And The Starkman).
Cassette: released on Dead Happy, '86 by Dead Happy Records. Dist: Mason's Music Distributors/Wholesalers, Rough Trade

BEACH FATIGUE REVUE.
Cassette: released on Dead Happy, '86 by Dead Happy Records. Dist: Mason's Music Distributors/Wholesalers, Rough Trade

BENEFITS OF BALANCE.
Cassette: released on Dead Happy, '86 by Dead Happy Records. Dist: Mason's Music Distributors/Wholesalers, Rough Trade

LAST RESORT.
Cassette: released on Dead Happy, '86 by Dead Happy Records. Dist: Mason's Music Distributors/Wholesalers, Rough Trade

SCANTILY SCULPTURED.
Cassette: released on Dead Happy, '86 by Dead Happy Records. Dist: Mason's Music Distributors/Wholesalers, Rough Trade

STARK CONTRAST.
Cassette: released on Dead Happy, '86 by Dead Happy Records. Dist: Mason's Music Distributors/Wholesalers, Rough Trade

WAKE UP/VIBETHING (It's Krats/Vibething).
Cassette: released on Dead Happy, '86 by Dead Happy Records. Dist: Mason's Music Distributors/Wholesalers, Rough Trade

WEIRD STRATEGY.
Cassette: released on Dead Happy, '86 by Dead Happy Records. Dist: Mason's Music Distributors/Wholesalers, Rough Trade

Starlight

DREAM OF ME.
Single (12"): released on BB, Jul'84 Dist: Jetstar

IF I HAD MONEY.
Tracks: / If I had money / If I had money (inst).
Single (7"): released on Record Shack, Aug'86 by Record Shack Records. Dist: PRT

Single (12"): released on Record Shack, Aug'86 by Record Shack Records. Dist: PRT

Starlight Express

STARLIGHT EXPRESS (Various Artists).
Tracks: / Overture / Rolling stock / Call me rusty / Lotta locomotion, A / Pumping iron / Freight / AC/DC / Hitching and switching / He whistled at me / Race-heat one / There's me / Blues, The / Belle / Race-heat two / Race-heat three / Starlight express / Rap, The / Uncoupled / Rolling stock (reprise) / C.B. / Race-uphill final / Right place, right time / Starlight express / Racedownhill final / No comeback / One rock 'n' roll too many / Only he / Only you / Light at the end of the tunnel.
Notes: Double album & cassette.
Album: released on Starlight Express, Jun'84 by Polydor Records. Dist: Polygram Distribution

Cassette: released on Starlight Express, Jun'84 by Polydor Records. Dist: Polygram Distribution

Compact disc: released on Starlight Express, Jun'84 by Polydor Records. Dist: Polygram Distribution

Starlight Serenades

STARLIGHT SERENADES (Various Artists).
Tracks: / Coming home / After a while / Someone's rocking my dreamboat / Starlight serenade / Maybe / You'll never know / I'm beginning to see the light / I shall be waiting / Wish me luck (as you wave me goodbye) / So-so in love / Tangerine / Don't sweetheart me / I can't begin to tell you / You're in love / Maria Elena / Amapola / By the river of roses / In a shady nook by a babbling brook / Danger ahead / After all / Chibaba chi-baba / It's the bluest kind of blues my baby sings / Stepping out with my baby / Music stopped, The / Judaline / Lovely way to spend an evening / I'd give a million tomorrows / I just dropped in to say hello / Let's keeo it that way / That's the moon my son / Don't ever leave me / How deep is the ocean / Strangers in the dark / I keep forgetting to remember / There's a moon over the ocean / Lili Marlene.
Notes: Four star British vocalists of the forties who all made iontemational breakthroughs. "Forces sweetheart" Vera Lynn and Anned Shelton have topped the chartss on both sides of the atlantic, throughout Europe and Australasia: Denny Dennis along with a sequence of UK band liaisons from Roy Fox to Ambrose to the Squadronaires also cracked the American mrket whenheworked with the Tommy DorseyBand, whilst Donald Peers entertaining career spanned half a century. Here, ourfour celebrities perform a mixture of their own big hits and songs of the day from successful movies and shows.
Album: released on London, Sep'86 by London Records. Dist: Polygram

Cassette: released on London, Sep'86 by London Records. Dist: Polygram

Starlite

GENTLE PEOPLE.
Single (7"): released on Solid Gold, Dec'81

Starman

STARMAN Original Soundtrack.
Album: released on That's Entertainment, Jun'85 by That's Entertainment Records. Dist: Pinnacle, PRT

Starpoint

HE WANTS MY BOYS.
Tracks: / He wants my boys / Satisfy me love.
Single (7"): released on Elektra (USA), Apr'87 by Elektra/Asylum/Nonesuch Records. Dist: WEA

Single (12"): released on Elektra (USA), Apr'87 by Elektra/Asylum/Nonesuch Records. Dist: WEA

IT'S ALL YOURS.
Single (7"): released on Elektra, May'84 by WEA Records. Dist: WEA

OBJECT OF MY DESIRE.
Tracks: / Object of my desire / Am I still the one.
Single (7"): released on Elektra (USA), Jan'86 by Elektra/Asylum/Nonesuch Records. Dist: WEA

Single (12"): released on Elektra (USA), Jan'86 by Elektra/Asylum/Nonesuch Records. Dist: WEA

RESTLESS.
Album: released on Elektra, Aug'85 by WEA Records. Dist: WEA

SENSATIONAL.
Album: released on Elektra (USA), Feb'87 by Elektra/Asylum/Nonesuch Records. Dist: WEA

Cassette: released on Elektra (USA), Feb'87 by Elektra/Asylum/Nonesuch Records. Dist: WEA

Starprest

SCHOOLDAYS.
Single (7"): released on Avatar, Aug'81 by Avatar Communications. Dist: CBS

Starr,Andy

SPUEAKY SHOES.
Single (7"): released on Rollin' Rock, Jun'80

Starr, Bonito

ELECTRIC.
Tracks: / Electric / Shock.
Single (12"): released on New Generation, Jun'86 Dist: Jetstar

Starr, Edwin

20 GREATEST MOTOWN HITS.
Tracks: / Stop her on sight (S.O.S.) / 25 miles / Headline news / Agent double-O soul / Back street / I want my baby back / Funky music sho nuff turns me on / Soul master / You've got my soul on fire / Who's right or wrong / War / Stop the war now / Way over there / take me clear from here / Cloud nine / There you go / Gonna keep on tryin' till I win your love / Time / My weakness is you / Harlem.

25 MILES.
Single (7"): released on Motown, Oct'81 by Motown Records. Dist: BMG Distribution

25 MILES/WAR AND PEACE 2 Classic albums.
Tracks: / Twenty-five miles / Im still a struggling man / Backyard lovin' man / He who picks a rose / Soul city (open your arms to me) / You beat me to the punch / Gonna keep on tryin' till I win your love / Pretty little angel / If my heart could tell the story / Who cares if you're happy or not (I do) / 24 hours to find my baby / Mighty good lovin' / War / Running back and forth / Adios senorita / All around the world / I can't escape your memory / At last (I found a love) / I just wanted to cry / Raindrops keep falling on my head / Time / California soul / I can't replace my old love / She should have been home.

AGENT DOUBLE O SOUL.
Single (7"): released on Motown, Oct'81 by RCA Records. Dist: RCA Distribution

CONTACT.
Single (7"): released on Old Gold, Jan'85 by Old Gold Records. Dist: Lightning, Jazz Music, Spartan, Counterpoint

GRAPEVINE.
Tracks: / Grapevine / I need your love / Grapevine part 1&2 *.
Single (7"): released on Hippodrome, Mar'86 Dist: EMI

Single (12"): released on Hippodrome, Mar'86 Dist: EMI

HITS OF EDWIN STARR/20 GREATEST HITS.
Album: released on Motown, Feb'87 by Motown Records. Dist: BMG Distribution

Cassette: released on Motown, Feb'87 by Motown Records. Dist: BMG Distribution

IT AIN'T FAIR.
Single (7"): released on Hippodrome, May'85 Dist: EMI

Single (12"): released on Hippodrome, May'85 Dist: EMI

I WANNA TAKE YOU HOME.
Single (7"): released on Avatar, Jan'83 by Avatar Communications. Dist: CBS

Single (12"): released on Avatar, Jan'83 by Avatar Communications. Dist: CBS

MISSLES(WE DONT WANT TO DIE).
Single (7"): released on Hippodrome, Oct'85 Dist: EMI

Single (12"): released on Hippodrome, Oct'85 Dist: EMI

SMOOTH.
Single (7"): released on Calibre, Aug'83 by Calibre Records. Dist: PRT

Single (12"): released on Calibre, Aug'83 by Calibre Records. Dist: PRT

SOUL SINGER.
Tracks: / Soul singer / Eye to eye contact (remake).
Single (7"): released on Hippodrome, Jul'86 Dist: EMI

Single (12"): released on Hippodrome, Jul'86 Dist: EMI

STOP HER ON SIGHT.
Single (7"): released on Motown, Oct'81 by Motown Records. Dist: BMG Distribution

TWENTY FIVE MILES / WAR AND PEACE.
Compact disc: released on Motown, Dec'86 by Motown Records. Dist: BMG Distribution

WAR.
Single (7"): released on Motown, Oct'81 by Motown Records. Dist: BMG Distribution

Starr, Freddie

CRYING GAME.
Single (7"): released on Towerbell, Feb'82 by Towerbell Records. Dist: EMI

GREAT PRETENDER.
Single (7"): released on Towerbell, Jul'82 by Towerbell Records. Dist: EMI

HOLLYWOOD.
Single (7"): released on Savoir Faire, Aug'83

SPIRIT OF ELVIS,THE.
Album: released on Kamera, Nov'81

Starr, Jack

OUT OF THE DARKNESS.
Album: released on Music For Nations, Aug'84 by Music For Nations Records. Dist: Pinnacle

ROCK THE AMERICAN WAY.
Album: released on Passport, Nov'85 Dist: Polygram

Page 952

Starr, Kay

1947.
Album: released on Hindsight(UK), Jun'86 Dist: Jazz Music

BLUE STARR.
Tracks: / It's a lonely old town (when you're not around) / You're driving me crazy(what did I do?) / House is haunted (by the echo of your last goodbye), The / We three(my echo,my shadow & me) / I really don't want to know / Blue Starr / Wedding bells / It's funny to everyone but me / Little white lies / Just like a butterfly(that's caught in the trap) / Blue & sentimental.
Album: released on RCA, Jun'87 by RCA Records. Dist: RCA, Roots, Swift, Wellard, Chris, I & B, Solomon & Peres Distribution

IN A BLUE MOOD.
Album: released on Capitol, Jul'85 by Capitol Records. Dist: EMI

Cassette: released on Capitol, Jul'85 by Capitol Records. Dist: EMI

JAZZ SINGER.
Album: released on Capitol, Sep'83 by Capitol Records. Dist: EMI

Cassette: released on Capitol, Sep'83 by Capitol Records. Dist: EMI Deleted '87.

KAY STARR STYLE,THE.
Album: released on Capitol, Oct'84 by Capitol Records. Dist: EMI

Cassette: released on Capitol, Oct'84 by Capitol Records. Dist: EMI

PURE GOLD.
Album: released on RCA International (USA), Jun'81 by RCA Records. Dist: RCA

Cassette: released on RCA International (USA), Jun'81 by RCA Records. Dist: RCA

ROCK AND ROLL WALTZ.
Tracks: / Rock and roll waltz / Wheel of fortune.
Notes: Also contains:"Wheel of fortune" by Kay Starr.
Single (7"): released on Old Gold, Apr'87 by Old Gold Records. Dist: Lightning, Jazz Music, Spartan, Counterpoint

WHEEL OF FORTUNE.
Single (7"): released on Capitol, '80 by Capitol Records. Dist: EMI

Starr, Ringo

BLAST FROM YOUR PAST.
Tracks: / You're sixteen / No no song / It don't come easy / Photograph / Back of boogaloo / Oly you (and you alone) / Beacoups of blues / Oh my my / Early 1970 / I'm the greatest.
Compact disc: released on Parlophone, May'87 by EMI Records. Dist: EMI

GOODNIGHT VIENNA.
Album: released on EMI (Germany), Aug'83 by EMI Records. Dist: Conifor

IT DON'T COME EASY.
Single (7"): released on EMI Golden 45's, May'84 by EMI Records. Dist: EMI

ROTOGRAVURE.
Album: released on Polydor, Jun'82 by Polydor Records. Dist: Polygram, Polydor

Cassette: released on Polydor, Jun'82 by Polydor Records. Dist: Polygram, Polydor

STOP AND SMELL THE ROSES.
Album: released on RCA, Dec'81 by RCA Records. Dist: RCA, Roots, Swift, Wellard, Chris, I & B, Solomon & Peres Distribution

Cassette: released on RCA, Dec'81 by RCA Records. Dist: RCA, Roots, Swift, Wellard, Chris, I & B, Solomon & Peres Distribution

WRACK MY BRAIN.
Single (7"): released on RCA, Nov'81 by RCA Records. Dist: RCA, Roots, Swift, Wellard, Chris, I & B, Solomon & Peres Distribution

YOU'RE SIXTEEN.
Single (7"): released on Parlophone, Feb'74 by EMI Records. Dist: EMI

Starr, Stella

STELLA'S STARR HITS.
Album: released on Pelican, Sep'81 by Stella Starr. Dist: Jazz Music

Starr, Will

THIS IS WILL STARR -The daddy of them all.
Album: released on PRT Special, '73 by PRT Records. Dist: PRT

Cassette: released on Marble Arch, Feb'74 Dist: Taylors

THIS IS WILL STARR IN STARR TIME.
Tracks: / Jacqueline waltz / Frank Jamieson two-step / Plaisance / Dark island / Woodland flowers / Auteuil;-Langchamp / Amazing grace / Household Brigade two-step.
Cassette: released on Highlander, Jun'86 Dist: PRT

THIS IS WILL STARR MUSIC WITH A KICK.
Tracks: / Dancing fingers / Gordon scottishe / Swiss polka / Oslo waltz / Irish hornpipes medley / Circassian circle medley / Looking for a partner / Para handy / Pipe marches medley / Scottish waltz / Scottish waltz medley Scot / March hare / Strathspey and reel medley.
Cassette: released on Highlander, Jun'86 Dist: PRT

Starry Ride

STARRY RIDE various artists (Various Artists).
Album: released on Psycho, Sep'84 Dist: Funhouse, Rough Trade

Starship

IT'S NOT OVER ('TIL IT'S OVER).
Single (7"): released on RCA, Aug'87 by RCA Records. Dist: RCA, Roots, Swift, Wellard, Chris, I & B, Solomon & Peres Distribution

Single (12"): released on RCA, Aug'87 by RCA Records. Dist: RCA, Roots, Swift, Wellard, Chris, I & B, Solomon & Peres Distribution

KNEE DEEP IN HOOPLA.
Tracks: / We built this city / Sara / Tomorrow doesn't matter tonight / Rock myself to sleep / Desperate heart / Private room / Before I go / Hearts of the world will understand / Love rusts.
Album: released on RCA, Nov'85 by RCA Records. Dist: RCA, Roots, Swift, Wellard, Chris, I & B, Solomon & Peres Distribution

Cassette: released on RCA, Nov'85 by RCA Records. Dist: RCA, Roots, Swift, Wellard, Chris, I & B, Solomon & Peres Distribution

Compact disc: released on RCA, Mar'86 by RCA Records. Dist: RCA, Roots, Swift, Wellard, Chris, I & B, Solomon & Peres Distribution

NO PROTECTION.
Tracks: / Beat patrol / Nothing's gonna stop us now / It's not over ('til it's over) / Girls like you / Wings of a lie / Children, The / I don't know why / Transatlantic / Babylon / Set the night to music.
Album: released on RCA, Jul'87 by RCA Records. Dist: RCA, Roots, Swift, Wellard, Chris, I & B, Solomon & Peres Distribution

Cassette: released on RCA, Jul'87 by RCA Records. Dist: RCA, Roots, Swift, Wellard, Chris, I & B, Solomon & Peres Distribution

Compact disc: released on RCA, Jul'87 by RCA Records. Dist: RCA, Roots, Swift, Wellard, Chris, I & B, Solomon & Peres Distribution

NOTHING'S GONNA STOP US NOW.
Tracks: / Nothing's gonna stop us now / Layin' it on the line / We built this city ** / Tomorrow doesn't matter tonight **.
Single (7"): released on RCA, Mar'87 by RCA Records. Dist: RCA, Roots, Swift, Wellard, Chris, I & B, Solomon & Peres Distribution

Single (12"): released on RCA, Mar'87 by RCA Records. Dist: RCA, Roots, Swift, Wellard, Chris, I & B, Solomon & Peres Distribution

SARA.
Tracks: / Sara / Hearts of the world will understand / Jane *.
Single (7"): released on RCA, Jan'86 by RCA Records. Dist: RCA, Roots, Swift, Wellard, Chris, I & B, Solomon & Peres Distribution

Single (12"): released on RCA, Jan'86 by RCA Records. Dist: RCA, Roots, Swift, Wellard, Chris, I & B, Solomon & Peres Distribution

TOMORROW DOESN'T MATTER TONIGHT.
Tracks: / Tomorrow doesn't matter tonight / Love rusts / No way out * / Love rusts * / Laying it on the line *.
Single (7"): released on RCA, May'86 by RCA Records. Dist: RCA, Roots, Swift, Wellard, Chris, I & B, Solomon & Peres Distribution

Single (12"): released on RCA, May'86 by RCA Records. Dist: RCA, Roots, Swift, Wellard, Chris, I & B, Solomon & Peres Distribution

WE BUILT THIS CITY.
Single (7"): released on RCA, Oct'85 by RCA Records. Dist: RCA, Roots, Swift, Wellard, Chris, I & B, Solomon & Peres Distribution

Single (12"): released on RCA, Oct'85 by RCA Records. Dist: RCA, Roots, Swift, Wellard, Chris, I & B, Solomon & Peres Distribution

Starship Orchestra

CELESTIAL SKY.
Album: released on CBS, Sep'80 by CBS Records. Dist: CBS

Star Sisters

DANGER.
Tracks: / Danger / You're my first, you're my last.
Single (7"): released on Carrere, Jan'86 by Carrere Records. Dist: PRT, Spartan

Single (12"): released on Carrere, Jan'86 by Carrere Records. Dist: PRT, Spartan

HE'S THE 1 (I LOVE).
Single (7"): released on Carrere America (USA), Sep'85 by Polygram.

Single (12"): released on Carrere America (USA), Sep'85 by Polygram.

STARS ON 45.
Album: released on CBS, Aug'83 by CBS Records. Dist: CBS

Cassette: released on CBS, Aug'83 by CBS Records. Dist: CBS

Stars of...

STARS OF THE COUNTRY various artists (Various Artists).
Cassette: released on Ditto Cassettes, Sep'83

STARS OF THE GRAND OLE OPREY various artists (Various Artists).
Album: released on Spot, Mar'85 by Pickwick Records. Dist: H.R. Taylor,

Cassette: released on Spot, Mar'85 by Pickwick Records. Dist: H.R. Taylor,

STARS OF THE PEDAL STEEL GUITAR (Various Artists).
Album: released on Starday, Apr'87

Cassette: released on Starday, Apr'87

STARS OF THE STREETS ENCORE various artists (Various Artists).
Album: released on Barclay (Import), Apr'82

STARS OF THE THIRTIES various artists (Various Artists).
Album: released on Decca(American Recollections), Feb'84

STARS OF THE THIRTIES VOL.2 various artists (Various Artists).
Album: released on Decca(American Recollections), Dec'84

STARS OF THE ZIEGFIELD FOLLIES various artists (Various Artists).
Album: released on Sandy Hook, Aug'79

Stars of Faith

OF BLACK NATIVITY.
Double Album: released on Musidisc (France), Sep'83 Dist: Discovery Distribution, Swift Distribution

Stars Of Heaven

CLOTHES OF PRIDE.
Single (7"): released on Hotwire, Jan'86 by Crashed Records. Dist: Rough Trade, Cartel

HOLYHEAD.
Single (7"): released on Rough Trade, Mar'87 by Rough Trade Records. Dist: Rough Trade Distribution, Cartel Distribution

Single (12"): released on Rough Trade, Mar'87 by Rough Trade Records. Dist: Rough Trade Distribution, Cartel Distribution

SACRED HEART HOTEL.
Album: released on Rough Trade, Aug'86 by Rough Trade Records. Dist: Rough Trade Distribution, Cartel Distribution

Stars of the 50's

STARS OF THE 50'S (Various Artists).
Tracks: / Softly softly / Heartbeat / My special angel / Ev'ry day of my life / Stairway of love / Starry eyed / Dreamboat / Never do a tango with an eskimo / Around the world / World outside, The / Wake up little Susie / White sports coat and a pink carnation / My thanks to you / Zambesi / Mandy / Pickin' a chicken / Blue star / Lollipop / Tammy / Be my girl / China tea / Cindy oh Cindy / Only sixteen / Don't laugh at me (cause I'm a fool).
Cassette: released on Hour Of Pleasure, Oct'86 by Music For Pleasure Records. Dist: EMI

Stars On 45 (Video)

Stars on 45 (video)

Starsound

STARS MEDLEY.
Album: released on CBS, Apr'82 by CBS Records. Dist: CBS

Cassette: released on CBS, Apr'82 by CBS Records. Dist: CBS

STARS ON STEVIE.
Single (7"): released on CBS, Feb'82 by CBS Records. Dist: CBS

Single (12"): released on CBS, Feb'82 by CBS Records. Dist: CBS

STARSOUND.
Cassette: released on CBS, Aug'82 by CBS Records. Dist: CBS

Star Spangled Country

STAR SPANGLED COUNTRY The hits of '84 (Various Artists).
Album: released on Epic, Aug'84 by CBS Records. Dist: CBS

Cassette: released on Epic, Aug'84 by CBS Records. Dist: CBS

Stars Sing...

STARS SING LENNON & MCCARTNEY (Various Artists).
Tracks: / Do you want to know a secret / Hello little girl / Yesterday / World without love / It's for you / Long and winding road / With a little help from my friends / Come together / Ob-la di, ob-la da / Eight days a week / I saw her standing there / Day tripper / Hard day's night / Here there and everywhere / Misery / She's leaving home / When I'm sixty four / Back in the USSR / Help / Hey bulldog.
Notes: All titles composed by Lennon & McCartney . All titles published by Northern Songs Ltd.
Album: released on Music For Pleasure, Jun'86 by EMI Records. Dist: EMI

Cassette: released on Music For Pleasure, Jun'86 by EMI Records. Dist: EMI

Starstruck

THRU TO YOU.
Album: released on Mausoleum, May'85 by Mausoleum Records. Dist: Pinnacle

Stars Unlimited Singers, The

20 GOLDEN LOVE SONGS.
Compact disc: released on The Compact Collection, Sep'87 by Conifer Records. Dist: Conifer Distribution

Startled Insects

CURSE OF PHEREMONES.
Cassette: released on Antilles, Apr'87 by Island Records. Dist: Polygram

CURSE OF THE PHERMONES.
Tracks: / Creatures / Igor's horn / Underworld / Shrimps in love / Fastest claw / Lost at sea / Big wheel, The / Loco / Glass mountain / Moho.
Album: released on Antilles, Apr'87 by Island Records. Dist: Polygram

Cassette: released on Antilles, Jun'87 by Island Records. Dist: Polygram

STARLTED INSECTS.
Album: released on Antenna, Apr'84 Dist: Cartel

UNDERWORLD.
Single (12"): released on Antenna, May'85 Dist: Cartel

Startrax

REGGAES GREATEST HITS.
Album: released on Hallmark, Nov'81 by Pickwick Records. Dist: Pickwick Distribution, PRT, Taylors

Cassette: released on Hallmark, Nov'81 by Pickwick Records. Dist: Pickwick Distribution, PRT, Taylors

Star Trek

SEARCH FOR SPOCK (Star Trek III).
Single (12"): released on Disney, Oct'84 by BBC Records & Tapes. Dist: BBC Records & Tapes, PRT

STAR TREK Original soundtrack.
Album: released on PRT, Nov'85 by PRT Records. Dist: PRT

Cassette: released on PRT, Nov'85 by PRT Records. Dist: PRT

Album: released on CBS, Jan'80 by CBS Records. Dist: CBS

Cassette: released on CBS, Jan'80 by CBS Records. Dist: CBS

STAR TREK Storyteller Little L.P. (Various Artists).
Album: released on Disneyland, Feb'84 by WEA Records. Dist: WEA

Cassette: released on Disneyland, Feb'84 by WEA Records. Dist: WEA

STAR TREK III - THE SEARCH FOR SPOCK Original soundtrack (Star Trek III - The Search For Spock).
Album: released on Capitol, Aug'84 by Capitol Records. Dist: EMI

Cassette: released on Capitol, Aug'84 by Capitol Records. Dist: EMI

STAR TREK II - THE WRATH OF KHAN Various artists (Various Artists).
Album: released on Disneyland, Feb'84 by

WEA Records. Dist: WEA

Cassette: released on Disneyland, Feb'84 by WEA Records. Dist: WEA

STAR TREK IV- THE VOYAGE HOME Original Soundtrack (Various Artists).

Album: released on MCA, Feb'87 by MCA Records. Dist: Polygram, MCA

Cassette: released on MCA, Feb'87 by MCA Records. Dist: Polygram, MCA

Starts Here

STARTS HERE various artists (Various Artists).
Album: released on Plezure, Mar'84 by Plezure Records. Dist: Pinnacle

Start To Jump...

START TO JUMP BECAUSE IT'S JUBILEE (Various Artists).
Album: released on Swingtime, Aug'86 Dist: Jazz Music Distribution, Charly

Star Turn

STAR TURN FOR EUROPE.
Tracks: / Star turn for Europe (remix) / Star turn on 45.
Single (7"): released on Star Turn, Apr'86 Dist: PRT Distribution

STARTURN FOR EUROPE.
Single (7"): released on V-Tone, Feb'82 by Relic. Dist: Swift

STARTURN ON 45 (PINTS).
Single (7"): released on V-Tone, Sep'81 by Relic. Dist: Swift

Starvation

STARVATION.
Single (7"): released on Zarjazz, Feb'85 by Virgin. Dist: EMI

Single (12"): released on Zarjazz, Feb'85 by Virgin. Dist: EMI

Star Wars

EMPIRE STRIKES BACK, THE (Star Wars II).
Double Album: released on RSO, May'80

Double cassette: released on RSO, May'80

STAR WARS Original soundtrack (London Symphony Orchestra).
Double Album: released on RSO, Sep'82

STAR WARS Various artists (Various Artists).
Extended-play record: released on Disneyland, Dec'82 Dist: EMI

Cassette: released on Disneyland, Dec'82 Dist: EMI

STAR WARS Original film soundtrack (Various Artists).
Compact disc: released on Polydor, '83 by Polydor Records. Dist: Polygram, Polydor

STAR WARS 3 Return of the Jedi (Star Wars 3).
Album: released on Polydor, May'83 by Polydor Records. Dist: Polygram, Polydor

Cassette: released on Polydor, May'83 by Polydor Records. Dist: Polygram, Polydor

Star Wars Trilogy

STAR WARS TRILOGY Original film scores.
Tracks: / Main title (Star Wars) / Princess Leia's theme / Here they come / Asteroid field, The / Yoda's theme / Imperial march / Parade of the Ewoks / Luke and Leia / Fight with tie fighters / Jabba the Jutt / Darth Vader's death / Forest battle, The / Finale.
Album: released on TER, Dec'83 Dist: Pinnacle

Compact disc: released on TER, Dec'83 Dist: Pinnacle

Starz

BRIGHTEST STARZ.
Album: released on Heavy Metal America, Jan'85 by FM-Revolver Records. Dist: EMI

Cassette: released on Heavy Metal America, Jan'85 by FM-Revolver Records. Dist: EMI

LIVE IN CANADA.
Album: released on Heavy Metal America, Oct'85 by FM-Revolver Records. Dist: EMI

Cassette: released on Heavy Metal America, Oct'85 by FM-Revolver Records. Dist: EMI

PISS PARTY.
Album: released on Heavy Metal America, Nov'85 by FM-Revolver Records. Dist: EMI

SO YOUNG,SO BAD.
Single (7"): released on Heavy Metal America, May'85 by FM-Revolver Records. Dist: EMI

Stash Christmas album

STASH CHRISTMAS ALBUM 16 Blues & Jazz Classics (Various Artists).
Album: released on Stash, Mar'87 Dist: Swift Distribution, Jazz Music Distribution, Jazz Horizons Distribution, Celtic Music Distribution, Cadillac, JSU Distribution, Zodiac Distribution

STASH CHRISTMAS ALBUM various artists (Various Artists).
Album: released on Stash (USA), Feb'85 Dist: Swift Distribution, Jazz Music Distribution, Jazz Horizons Distribution, Celtic Music Distribution, Cadillac, JSU Distribution, Zodiac Distribution

State Academic Choir

FOLK SONGS.
Cassette: released on Melodiya (USSR), Feb'79 Dist: T.B.C Distribution

STATE ACADEMIC RUSSIAN CHOIR.
Album: released on Melodiya (USSR), May'78 Dist: T.B.C Distribution

State Funeral of...

STATE FUNERAL OF SIR WINSTON CHURCHILL,K.G.,OM,C.H. Spoken Word (Spoken Word).
Double Album: released on Decca, Feb'65 by Decca Records. Dist: Polygram

State Northern Chorus

RUSSIAN FOLK SONGS (STATE NORTHERN FOLK CHORUS).
Cassette: released on Melodiya (USSR), Feb'79 Dist: T.B.C Distribution

State of Decay

STATE OF DECAY Doctor Who (Baker, Tom).
Cassette: released on Pickwick Talking Books, '83

State of Emergency

MEN OF ACTION.
Single (7"): released on Northeast Music, Jul'83 by Northeast Music Records. Dist: Northeast Music Distribution, Pinnacle

State of Grace

HELLO WINTERTIME.
Single (7"): released on PRT, Jan'84 by PRT Records. Dist: PRT

Single (12"): released on PRT, Jan'84 by PRT Records. Dist: PRT

WALKING RHYTHM.
Single (7"): released on Flamingo, Nov'81 by Carlin Music Corp. Dist: RCA

State Of Play

BALANCING THE SCALES.
Tracks: / Naked as the day / Natural colour / Rockabye baby / Work-man / Human kind / Winds of change (so many things) / We go under / Take me to the king / Lost souls.
Notes: Cassette also includes "Strange air"/"Trout". Compact disc includes "Strangeair", "Trout" and "Rescue".
Album: released on Virgin, Jul'86 by Virgin Records. Dist: EMI, Virgin Distribution

Cassette: released on Virgin, Jul'86 by Virgin Records. Dist: EMI, Virgin Distribution

Compact disc: released on Virgin, Jul'87 by Virgin Records. Dist: EMI, Virgin Distribution

NATURAL COLOURS.
Tracks: / Natural colours / Lost souls.
Single (7"): released on Virgin, Apr'86 by Virgin Records. Dist: EMI, Virgin Distribution

Single (12"): released on Virgin, Apr'86 by Virgin Records. Dist: EMI, Virgin Distribution

ROCK A BYE BABY.
Tracks: / Rock a bye baby / Metropolis.
Single (7"): released on Virgin, Jun'86 by Virgin Records. Dist: EMI, Virgin Distribution

Single (12"): released on Virgin, Jun'86 by Virgin Records. Dist: EMI, Virgin Distribution

State of The Art

INSTINCT.
Single (7"): released on Big Freeze, 20 Jun'87

State Omsk Folk Chorus

RUSSIAN FOLK SONGS (STATE OMSK FOLK CHORUS).
Cassette: released on Melodiya (USSR), Feb'79 Dist: T.B.C Distribution

State Project

EMPIRE STATE Title track from film.
Tracks: / Empire State / Money.
Single (7"): released on Priority, 20 Jun'87 by Priority Records. Dist: RCA

Single (12"): released on Priority, 20 Jun'87 by Priority Records. Dist: RCA

State Russian Chorus

RUSSIAN FOLK SONGS (STATE RUSSIAN CHORUS).
Cassette: released on Melodiya (USSR), Feb'79 Dist: T.B.C Distribution

State Street Aces

OLD FOLKS SHUFFLE VOL.3.
Album: released on Stomp Off, Oct'86 by Stomp Off Records. Dist: Jazz Music Distribution

PASS OUT LIGHTLY.
Album: released on Stomp Off (USA), Jan'84

Statetrooper

STATETROOPER.
Tracks: / Shape of things to come / Set fire to the night / Dreams of the faithful / Stand me up / Veni vidi vici / Last stop to heaven / She got the look / Too late / Armed and ready.
Notes: Produced by Phil Chilton. (P) 1987 Original Sound Recordings made by London's Pride Management. 1987 An FM release. FM is a division of FM-Revolver Records Ltd.
Album: released on FM, May'87 by FM-Revolver Records. Dist: EMI

Cassette: released on FM, May'87 by FM-Revolver Records. Dist: EMI

Compact disc: released on FM, May'87 by FM-Revolver Records. Dist: EMI

Static Activity

EPICALLY BLAZING ADVENTURES of static activity in the land of Zing.
Single (7"): released on Rapp, Aug'83 by Rapp. Dist: Cartel

Statik Compilation

STATIK COMPILATION 1 various artists (Various Artists).
Album: released on Statik, Jul'85 Dist: Rough Trade Distribution, Stage One Distribution

STATIK COMPILATION 2 various artists (Various Artists).
Album: released on Statik, Jul'85 Dist: Rough Trade Distribution, Stage One Distribution

Station Hall Jazz Band

NEW ORLEANS DIXIE.
Notes: 18 popular jazz standards played by the Staion Hall Jazz Band
Compact disc: released on Delta, May'87 by Delta Records. Dist: Target

Statler Brothers

ATLANTA BLUE.
Tracks: / Atlanta blue / If it makes a difference / Let's just take one night at a time / Angel in her face / Hollywood / One takes the blame / Give it your best / No love lost / One size fits all / My only love.
Notes: Digital stereo.
Compact disc: released on Mercury, Oct'84 by Phonogram Records. Dist: Polygram Distribution

AT THE COUNTRY STORE.
Album: released on Country Store, Dec'85 by Starblend Records. Dist: PRT, Prism Leisure Corporation Records

Cassette: released on Country Store, Dec'85 by Starblend Records. Dist: PRT, Prism Leisure Corporation Records

BROTHERS IN SONG.
Notes: he long-esablished US country group, who once had a hit in Britain with "Flowerson the wall" performing recent material. Total playing time 19 minutes.
Video-cassette (VHS): released on Polygram, Sep'86 by Polygram Records. Dist: Polygram

CHRISTMAS PRESENT.
Album: released on Mercury (Holland), Nov'85 by Phonogram Records. Dist: Polygram Distribution

Cassette: released on Mercury (Holland), Nov'85 by Phonogram Records. Dist: Polygram Distribution

FOUR FOR THE SHOW.
Tracks: / Count on me / You oughta be here with me / We got the memories / I don't dream any more / Forever / Only you / For cryin' out loud / Will you be there / I believe I'll live for him / More like daddy than me.
Notes: Produced by Jerry Kennedy.
Album: released on Mercury, Jun'86 by Phonogram Records. Dist: Polygram Distribution

Cassette: released on Mercury, Jun'86 by Phonogram Records. Dist: Polygram Distribution

Compact disc: released on Mercury, Jun'86 by Phonogram Records. Dist: Polygram Distribution

PARDNERS IN RHYME.
Tracks: / Hello Mary Lou / Sweeter and sweeter / Memory lane / Remembering you / Too much on my heart / I'm sorry you had to be the one / Her heart of mine / You don't wear blue so well / Autumn leaves / Amazing grace.
Compact disc: released on Mercury, Oct'85 by Phonogram Records. Dist: Polygram Distribution

Album: released on Mercury, Oct'85 by Phonogram Records. Dist: Polygram Distribution

Cassette: released on Mercury, Oct'85 by Phonogram Records. Dist: Polygram Distribution

TODAY.
Album: released on Mercury, Jul'83 by Phonogram Records. Dist: Polygram Distribution

Cassette: released on Mercury, Jul'83 by Phonogram Records. Dist: Polygram Distribution

TOO MUCH OF MY HEART.
Tracks: / Too much of my heart / Hello Mary Lou.
Single (7"): released on Mercury, Jan'86 by Phonogram Records. Dist: Polygram Distribution

Statman, Andy

NASHVILLE MORNINGS, NEW YORK NIGHTS.
Album: released on Rounder (USA), Jun'86 Dist: Mike's Country Music Room Distribution, Jazz Music Distribution, Swift Distribution, Roots Records Distribution, Projection Distribution, Topic Distribution

Staton, Candi

CANDI STATON.
Album: released on Warner Brothers, Aug'80 by Warner Bros Records. Dist: WEA

COUNT ON ME.
Single (7"): released on Sugarhill, Jul'82 by PRT Records. Dist: PRT Distribution

Single (12"): released on Sugarhill, Jul'82 by PRT Records. Dist: PRT Distribution

MAKE ME AN INSTRUMENT.
Album: released on Myrrh, May'85 by Word Records. Dist: Word Distribution

Cassette: released on Myrrh, May'85 by Word Records. Dist: Word Distribution

SUSPICIOUS MINDS.
Album: released on Sugarhill, Jul'82 by PRT Records. Dist: PRT Distribution

Cassette: released on Sugarhill, Jul'82 by PRT Records. Dist: PRT Distribution

Single (7"): released on Sugarhill, Mar'82 by PRT Records. Dist: PRT Distribution

Single (12"): released on Sugarhill, Mar'82 by PRT Records. Dist: PRT Distribution

Single (7"): released on Warner Bros. (USA Import), '80 by WEA Records. Dist: WEA

Single (7"): released on Warner Brothers, Jul'81 by WEA Records. Dist: WEA

Single (7"): released on Old Gold, Sep'85 by Old Gold Records. Dist: Lightning, Jazz Music, Spartan, Counterpoint

TELL IT LIKE IT IS (Staton, Candi/Bettye Swann).
Tracks: / Someone you use / I'd rather be an old man's sweetheart / Evidence / Sweet feeling / I'm just a prisoner (of your good lovin') / Do your duty / Get it when I want it / Tell it like it is / These arms of mine / No faith, no love / Cover me / Don't you ever get tired (of hurtin' me) / You're up to your same old tricks again / Today I started loving you again / Willie and Laura Mae Jones.
Notes: One side each for these two phenomenal female R & B singers. Candi Staton best remembered for her hit "Young hearts run free".
Album: released on Stateside, Apr'86 Dist: EMI

Cassette: released on Stateside, Apr'86 Dist: EMI. Estim retail price in Sep'87 was £3.86.

YOUNG HEARTS RUN FREE.
Tracks: / Young hearts run free / Young hearts run free (M & M ' 86 remix).
Single (7"): released on Warner Bros., May'86 by Warner Bros Records. Dist: WEA

Single (12"): released on Warner Bros. May'86 by Warner Bros Records. Dist: WEA

YOU'VE GOT THE LOVE (Staton, Candi featuring The source).
Tracks: / You've got the love (mix).
Single (7"): released on Streetsounds, Nov'86

Single (12"): released on Streetsounds, Nov'86

Staton, Dakota

LATE LATE SHOW, (THE) (Staton, Dakota Orchestra (Cond. Van Alexander)).
Album: released on Capitol, Apr'84 by Capitol Records. Dist: EMI

Cassette: released on Capitol, Apr'84 by Capitol Records. Dist: EMI

Status IV

LOVIN' YOU.
Single (7"): released on Design Communications, Mar'84

Single (12"): released on Design Communications, Mar'84

YOU AIN'T REALLY DOWN.
Single (7"): released on TMT, Jul'83

Single (12"): released on TMT, Jul'83

Single (12"): released on Domino, May'85 by Domino Records. Dist: Charly

Status Quo

100 MINUTES.
Cassette: released on PRT (100 Minute Series), Jun'82

1982.
Tracks: / She don't fool me / Young pretender / Get out and walk / Jealousy / I love rock and roll / Resurrection / Dear John / Doesn't matter / I want the world to know / I should have known / Big man.
Compact disc: released on Vertigo, '83 by Phonogram Records. Dist: Polygram

BACK TO BACK.
Tracks: / Mess of bluees / Ol' rag blues / Can't be done / Too close to the ground / No contract / Win or lose / Margerita time / Your kind of love / Stay the night / Gin down town tonight.
Album: released on Vertigo, Nov'83 by Phonogram Records. Dist: Polygram

Cassette: released on Vertigo, Nov'83 by Phonogram Records. Dist: Polygram

Compact disc: released on Vertigo, Nov'83 by Phonogram Records. Dist: Polygram

BEST OF STATUS QUO (The early years).
Tracks: / Down the dustpipe / Gerdundula / In my chair / Umleitung / Lakky lady / Daughter / Railroad / Tune to the music / April,spring,summer and Wednesdays / Mean girl / Spinning wheel blues.
Compact disc: released on PRT, '86 by PRT Records. Dist: PRT

Album: released on PRT, '73 by PRT Records. Dist: PRT

Cassette: released on PRT, '73 by PRT Records. Dist: PRT

CAROLINE.
Single (7"): released on Old Gold, Sep'85 by Old Gold Records. Dist: Lightning, Jazz Music, Spartan, Counterpoint

COLLECTION: STATUS QUO.
Double Album: released on Castle Communications, Nov'85 by Castle Communications. Dist: Cartel, Pinnacle, Counterpoint

Double cassette: released on Castle Communications, Nov'85 by Castle Communications. Dist: Cartel, Pinnacle, Counterpoint

EAR JOHN.
ingle (7"): released on Vertigo, Mar'82 by Phonogram Records. Dist: Polygram

OG OF TWO HEADS.
racks: / Umleitung / Nanana / Something's oing on in my head / Railroad / Gerdundula / ean girl / Someone's learning.
ompact disc: released on PRT, '86 by PRT Records. Dist: PRT

bum: released on PRT, Nov'71 by PRT Records. Dist: PRT

OWN THE DUSTPIPE.
bum: released on Golden Hour, Oct'75 by PRT Records. Dist: PRT Deleted '80.

ssette: released on Golden Hour, Oct'75 by PRT Records. Dist: PRT

ngle (7"): released on PRT, '74 by PRT Records. Dist: PRT

ngle (12"): released on Big Deal, Jun'77

REAMIN'.
acks: / Long-legged girls / Quo Christmas ke mix (The) *.
gle (7"): released on Vertigo, Nov'86 by Phonogram Records. Dist: Polygram

D OF THE ROAD 84.
leo-cassette (VHS): released on Channel 5, '86 Dist: W.H. Smiths

FRESH QUOTA.
Special: released on PRT, Sep'81 by PRT Records. Dist: PRT

Cassette: released on PRT, Sep'81 by PRT Records. Dist: PRT

FROM THE MAKERS OF.....
Triple album / cassette: released on Vertigo, Nov'82 by Phonogram Records. Dist: Polygram

Double cassette: released on Vertigo, Nov'82 by Phonogram Records. Dist: Polygram

Special: released on Vertigo, Nov'82 by Phonogram Records. Dist: Polygram

GERDUNDULA.
Single (7"): released on PRT, Jun'73 by PRT Records. Dist: PRT

GOING DOWN TOWN TONIGHT.
Single (7"): released on Vertigo, Apr'84 by Phonogram Records. Dist: Polygram

GOLDEN HOUR OF STATUS QUO VOLUME 2.
Album: released on Golden Hour, '75 by PRT Records. Dist: PRT Deleted '80.

Cassette: released on Golden Hour, '75 by PRT Records. Dist: PRT

GOLDEN HOUR OF STATUS QUO.
Album: released on Golden Hour, '73 by PRT Records. Dist: PRT Deleted '80.

Cassette: released on Golden Hour, '73 by PRT Records. Dist: PRT

HELLO.
Album: released on Vertigo, May'83 by Phonogram Records. Dist: Polygram

Cassette: released on Vertigo, May'83 by Phonogram Records. Dist: Polygram

ICE IN THE SUN.
Single (7"): released on Import, '80 Dist: Stage One

IN MY CHAIR.
Single (7"): released on PRT, Jun'79 by PRT Records. Dist: PRT

IN THE ARMY NOW.
Tracks: / In the army now / Heartburn / Late last night *.
Album: released on Vertigo, Aug'86 by Phonogram Records. Dist: Polygram

Cassette: released on Vertigo, Aug'86 by Phonogram Records. Dist: Polygram

Compact disc: released on Vertigo, Aug'86 by Phonogram Records. Dist: Polygram

Single (7"): released on Vertigo, Sep'86 by Phonogram Records. Dist: Polygram

Single (12"): released on Vertigo, Sep'86 by Phonogram Records. Dist: Polygram

JUST FOR THE RECORD.
Album: released on PRT, Jun'79 by PRT Records. Dist: PRT Deleted '80.

Cassette: released on PRT, Jun'79 by PRT Records. Dist: PRT

LIVE.
Double Album: released on Vertigo, Sep'84 by Phonogram Records. Dist: Polygram

Double Album: released on Vertigo, '77 by Phonogram Records. Dist: Polygram

Double cassette: released on Vertigo, Sep'84 by Phonogram Records. Dist: Polygram

LIVE AT THE N.E.C..
Video-cassette (VHS): released on Polygram, Sep'84 by Polygram Records. Dist: Polygram

Album: released on Vertigo (Import), Jul'84 Dist: IMS, Polygram

Cassette: released on Vertigo (Import), Jul'84 Dist: IMS, Polygram

Video-cassette (VHS): released on Channel 5, Mar'86 Dist: W.H. Smiths

MA KELLY'S GREASY SPOON.
Tracks: / Spinning wheel blues / Daughter / Everything / Shy fly / Spring (April) / Summer and Wednesdays / Junior's wailing / Lakky lady / Need your love / Lazy poker blues / Is it really me? / Gotta go home.
Compact disc: released on PRT, '86 by PRT Records. Dist: PRT

Album: released on PRT, '74 by PRT Records. Dist: PRT

MEAN GIRL.
Single (7"): released on PRT, Jul'78 by PRT Records. Dist: PRT

Single (7"): released on Old Gold, Jul'82 by Old Gold Records. Dist: Lightning, Jazz Music, Spartan, Counterpoint

MUSIC OF STATUS QUO, THE (1972-1974).
Album: released on Mercury (USA), Nov'81 by Import Records. Dist: IMS Distribution, Polygram Distribution

Cassette: released on Vertigo, Dec'76 by Phonogram Records. Dist: Polygram

ON THE LEVEL.
Album: released on Vertigo, Aug'83 by Phonogram Records. Dist: Polygram

Cassette: released on Vertigo, Aug'83 by Phonogram Records. Dist: Polygram

PICTURES OF MATCHSTICK MEN.
Single (7"): released on Flashback, Apr'79 by PRT Records. Dist: PRT

Single (7"): released on Old Gold, Apr'83 by Old Gold Records. Dist: Lightning, Jazz Music, Spartan, Counterpoint

PILEDRIVER.
Album: released on Vertigo, May'83 by Phonogram Records. Dist: Polygram

Cassette: released on Vertigo, May'83 by Phonogram Records. Dist: Polygram

PRESERVED.
Notes: Six tracks. Live recording. Total playing time: 27 minutes.
Video-cassette (VHS): released on Channel 5, Nov'86 Dist: W.H. Smiths

QUO.
Album: released on Vertigo, Aug'83 by Phonogram Records. Dist: Polygram

Album: released on Vertigo, '74 by Phonogram Records. Dist: Polygram

Cassette: released on Vertigo, Aug'83 by Phonogram Records. Dist: Polygram

RED SKY.
Tracks: / Red sky / Don't give it up / Milton Keynes medley *.
Single (7"): released on Vertigo, Jul'86 by Phonogram Records. Dist: Polygram

Single (12"): released on Vertigo, Jul'86 by Phonogram Records. Dist: Polygram

REST OF STATUS QUO, THE.
Album: released on PRT, Sep'76 by PRT Records. Dist: PRT

Cassette: released on PRT, Sep'76 by PRT Records. Dist: PRT

ROCKIN' ALL OVER THE WORLD.
Album: released on Vertigo, Aug'85 by Phonogram Records. Dist: Polygram

Cassette: released on Vertigo, Aug'85 by Phonogram Records. Dist: Polygram

ROLLIN' HOME.
Tracks: / Rollin' home / Lonely / Keep me guessing *.
Single (7"): released on Vertigo, Apr'86 by Phonogram Records. Dist: Polygram

Single (12"): released on Vertigo, Apr'86 by Phonogram Records. Dist: Polygram

ROLL OVER LAY DOWN.
Single (7"): released on Vertigo, May'75 by Phonogram Records. Dist: Polygram

SHE DON'T FOOL ME.
Single (7"): released on Vertigo, Jun'82 by Phonogram Records. Dist: Polygram

SPOTLIGHT ON STATUS QUO VOLUME 2.
Album: released on PRT (Spotlight), Oct'82 by PRT Records. Dist: PRT

Cassette: released on PRT (Spotlight), Oct'82 by PRT Records. Dist: PRT

SPOTLIGHT ON STATUS QUO.
Double Album: released on PRT, '80 by PRT Records. Dist: PRT

Double cassette: released on PRT, '80 by PRT Records. Dist: PRT

STATUS QUO.
Album: released on Marble Arch, May'78 Dist: Taylors

Cassette: released on Marble Arch, May'78 Dist: Taylors

Double Album: released on Pickwick, Sep'80

Double cassette: released on Pickwick, Sep'80

STATUS QUO COLLECTION.
Double Album: released on Pickwick, Aug'78

Double cassette: released on Pickwick, Aug'78

TO BE OR NOT TO BE.
Album: released on Contour, Apr'83 by Pickwick Records. Dist: Pickwick Distribution, PRT

Cassette: released on Contour, Apr'83 by Pickwick Records. Dist: Pickwick Distribution, PRT

TWELVE GOLD BARS VOLUME 2.
Compact disc: released on Vertigo, Nov'84 by Phonogram Records. Dist: Polygram

TWELVE GOLD BARS VOLUME 1.
Compact disc: released on Vertigo, Nov'84 by Phonogram Records. Dist: Polygram

TWELVE GOLD BARS VOLS. 1 & 2.
Tracks: / Rockin' all over the world / Down down / Caroline / Paper plane / Break the rules / Again and again / Mystery song / Roll over lay down / Rain / Wild side of life / Whatever you want / Living in an island / What you're proposin' / Lies / Something 'bout you baby I like / Don't drive my car / Dear John / Rock 'n' roll / Ol' rag blues / Mess of blues / Marguerita time / Going down town tonight / Wanderer, The / Caroline.
Notes: Contains all Quo's hits including "The Wanderer".
Compact disc: released on Vertigo, Nov'84 by Phonogram Records. Dist: Polygram

Compact disc: released on Vertigo, Nov'84 by Phonogram Records. Dist: Polygram

YOU AIN'T REALLY DOWN.
Tracks: / You ain't really down / You ain't really down (instr. acapella).
Single (12"): released on Domino, Aug'86 by Domino Records. Dist: Charly

Stavely Makepeace

JUST TELL HER FRED SAID GOODBYE.
Single (7"): released on Sma, Nov'83 by Sma Records. Dist: Spartan

SONGS OF YESTERDAY.

Single (7"): released on Hammer, Apr'80 Dist: PRT

Stavis, George

MORNING MOOD.
Tracks: / Sunlight / Full moon / Morning mood / Finland / Goblins / Kingpins / Carnival / Mistral / Hall of the Mountain King.
Notes: In Stavis's hands, the 5 string banjo sings out in new voices. He unleashes the banjo allowing it to experience the sounds of Indian Raga.East european folk melodies, and Middle Eastern refrains, while never forgetting its American folk roots. Stavis' music will thrill the traditionalist while exploring the world wide heritage of the banjo
Album: released on Polydor (Germany), Sep'96 Dist: IMS-Polygram

Stax blues masters

STAX BLUES MASTERS VOLUME 1 BLUE MONDAY Various Artists (Various Artists).
Album: released on Stax, Mar'82 by Ace Records. Dist: Pinnacle, Chris Wellard, IMS-Polygram

Stax Greatest Hits

STAX GREATEST HITS Various artists (Various Artists).
Tracks: / In the rain / I'll take you there / Who's making love / Do the funky chicken / Hearsay / Dedicated to the one I love / I could never be president / Woman to woman / Good woman turning bad / Respect yourself / I've been lonely for so long / Theme from 'Shaft' / Mr. big stuff / Private number / So I can love you / Starting all over again / That's what love will make you do / Whatcha see is whatcha get.
Compact disc: released on Stax, Mar'87 by Ace Records. Dist: Pinnacle, Chris Wellard, IMS-Polygram

Stax, John

DANCE FOR MY LOVE.
Single (7"): released on Lamborghini, Oct'84 by Lamborghini Records. Dist: PRT

Single (12"): released on Lamborghini, Oct'84 by Lamborghini Records. Dist: PRT

INFATUATION.
Single (7"): released on Lamborghini, Mar'85 by Lamborghini Records. Dist: PRT

WAITING IN THE MIDDLE OF THE NIGHT.
Single (7"): released on Lamborghini, Jan'84 by Lamborghini Records. Dist: PRT

Single (12"): released on Lamborghini, Jan'84 by Lamborghini Records. Dist: PRT

Stax trax

STAX TRAX (18 CLASSIC SOUL HITS)

Various Artists (Various Artists).
Album: released on Premier, '84 by Premier Records. Dist: CBS

Cassette: released on Premier, '84 by Premier Records. Dist: CBS

Stayin' alive
STAYIN' ALIVE Original Soundtrack (Various Artists).
Compact disc: released on RSO, '83

Stay Prest
SCHOOL DAYS.
Single (7"): released on Avatar, '82 by Avatar Communications. Dist: CBS

St.Che
BE MY.....
Tracks: / Be my.... / Exquisite.
Single (7"): released on Siren, Oct'86 by Virgin Records. Dist: EMI

Single (12"): released on Siren, Oct'86 by Virgin Records. Dist: EMI

St.Clair, Isla
CHRISTMAS DREAMS.
Single (7"): released on Deauville, Dec'81 by Stiletto Records. Dist: Pinnacle

ISLAND OF DREAMS / MY GENERATION.
Single (7"): released on Deauville, Mar'82 by Stiletto Records. Dist: Pinnacle

SINGS TRADITIONAL SCOTTISH SONGS.
Album: released on Tangent, Apr'81 Dist: Roots Distribution, Lugtons Distributors, Taylors, JSU Distribution, Spartan Distribution

Cassette: released on Tangent, Apr'81 Dist: Roots Distribution, Lugtons Distributors, Taylors, JSU Distribution, Spartan Distribution

SONG AND THE STORY, THE.
Album: released on Clare, Jul'81 Dist: Jazz Music, Chris Wellard

STILL NO SIGN OF THE LIFEBOATS.
Single (7"): released on Dingles, Aug'83 by Dingles Records. Dist: Projection

Stead, Joe
BAKER'S SCORE.
Album: released on Greenwich Village, Jan'87 by Sweet Folk All Records. Dist: Roots, Projection, Lightning, Celtic Music, Wellard, Chris

HARVEST HAS BEEN TAKEN IN, (THE).
Album: released on Sweet Folk All, Jun'81 by Sweet Folk All Records. Dist: Sweet Folk All, Roots, Celtic Music, Dragon, Impetus, Projection, Chris Wellard, Festival Records

LIVE AT THE WHITTLEBURY FOLK CLUB.
Album: released on Sweet Folk All, May'81 by Sweet Folk All Records. Dist: Sweet Folk All, Roots, Celtic Music, Dragon, Impetus, Projection, Chris Wellard, Festival Records

OBSCENITIES.
Album: released on Sweet Folk All, May'81 by Sweet Folk All Records. Dist: Sweet Folk All, Roots, Celtic Music, Dragon, Impetus, Projection, Chris Wellard, Festival Records

Steady
STEADY Various Artists (Various Artists).
Album: released on Trojan, Jan'82 by Trojan Records. Dist: PRT, Jetstar

Steady b
CHEATIN' GIRL.
Tracks: / Bring the beat back.
Single (7"): released on Jive, Jan'87 by Zomba Records. Dist: RCA, PRT, CBS

Single (12"): released on Jive, Jan'87 by Zomba Records. Dist: RCA, PRT, CBS

STEADY B.
Album: released on Jive, Jan'87 by Zomba Records. Dist: RCA, PRT, CBS

Stealers Wheel
STUCK IN THE MIDDLE.
Single (7"): released on Old Gold, Jul'82 by Old Gold Records. Dist: Lightning, Jazz Music, Spartan, Counterpoint

Steam
NA NA HEY HEY KISS HIM GOODBYE.
Single (7"): released on Old Gold, Jan'85 by Old Gold Records. Dist: Lightning, Jazz Music, Spartan, Counterpoint

Steam Ballads
STEAM BALLADS Various Artists (Various Artists).
Album: released on Broadside, Jun'81 by Broadside Records. Dist: Celtic Distributions, H.R. Taylor, Jazz Music, Projection, Jazz Services Unlimited Dist. (JSU)

Cassette: released on Broadside, Jun'81 by Broadside Records. Dist: Celtic Distributions, H.R. Taylor, Jazz Music, Projection, Jazz Services Unlimited Dist. (JSU)

Steaming towards Oslo
OFF THE HOOK.
Single (7"): released on Deptfordiscs, Jun'83

Steam Jenny
GLEN COE.
Cassette: released on Lochshore, Jul'87 by Klub Records. Dist: PRT

Steampacket
FIRST SUPERGROUP, THE.
Album: released on Decal, Aug'87 by Charly Records. Dist: Charly

Steam Trains
BIG FOUR, (THE).
Cassette: released on Audiocord Cassettes, May'83

BLACK FIVES.
Cassette: released on Audiocord Cassettes, May'83

BRITISH RAILWAYS STANDARD LOCOMOTIVES.
Cassette: released on Audiocord Cassettes, May'83

BUILT SWINDON.
Cassette: released on Audiocord Cassettes, May'83

CASTLES & KINGS.
Album: released on ASV-Transacord, Oct'81 by ASV Records. Dist: PRT

Cassette: released on ASV-Transacord, Apr'85 by ASV Records. Dist: PRT

COPPER CAPPED ENGINES.
Album: released on ASV-Transacord, May'81 by ASV Records. Dist: PRT

Cassette: released on ASV-Transacord, May'81 by ASV Records. Dist: PRT

DOUBLE HEAD OF STEAM.
Album: released on ASV-Transacord, Mar'83 by ASV Records. Dist: PRT

EARLY 60'S STEAM Are you going to get the sound of it coming in.
Notes: Early 60's steam from a personal collection featuring steam train recordings taken from a personal collection and featuring the following railway locations:- Ludlow - Wocferton / Tenbury Wells / Kidderminster (B.R.) / Aberystwyth / Weymouth Harbour / Bewdley (B.R.) / Worcester and Leominster. This cassette is available direct from GLTK Recordings, 20 Church Walk, Kidderminster, Worcestershire.
Cassette: released on GLTK, Jun'87 by GLTK Records. Dist: GLTK Records

ECHOES OF ENGINES.
Album: released on ASV-Transacord, Jun'86 by ASV Records. Dist: PRT

ENGINES FROM DERBY & CREWE.
Album: released on ASV-Transacord, Sep'85 by ASV Records. Dist: PRT

Cassette: released on ASV-Transacord, Sep'85 by ASV Records. Dist: PRT

ENGINES WITH ACCENTS.
Notes: Tracks include Steam locomotives at work on European Railways between 1959 and 1973. A 181 ton Garratt and other locomotives, with freight and passenger trains on the 5' 6" guage Renfe in Spain in 1968. Italian locomotives with freight and passenger trains on the FS in Italy 1973. DB and DR Pacific locomotives and a 38 class 4-6-0 with passenger trains on the DB in West Germany between 1970 and 1973. On the SNCF in France. A Pacific with a Brussels-Paris express in 1959, 141R locomotives with freight trains in 1965 and a 141TA with a freight train in 1966Various locomotives, including an Austrian designed 2-8-4, with passenger and freight trains on the CFR in Romania in 1971. An Austrian built 0-10-0 marshalling a freight train on the JZ in Yugoslavia, on a night in the Istrian mountains in 1970.
Album: released on ASV-Transacord, May'87 by ASV Records. Dist: PRT

Cassette: released on ASV-Transacord, May'87 by ASV Records. Dist: PRT

FAREWELL TO STEAM.
Album: released on Amberlee, Nov'81 by Am-

berlee Records. Dist: Amberlee Records, H.R. Taylor

FLYING SCOTSMAN & OTHER LOCOMOTIVES.
Album: released on President Special Projects, Nov'81

FROM THE FOOTPLATE.
Cassette: released on Audiocord Cassettes, May'83

GONE WITH REGRET (Recordings of once famous Great Western engines).
Album: released on Amberlee, Nov'81 by Amberlee Records. Dist: Amberlee Records, H.R. Taylor

GREAT LITTLE TRAINS OF ENGLAND.
Cassette: released on Audiocord Cassettes, May'83

GREAT NORTHERN FOR THE NORTH.
Cassette: released on Audiocord Cassettes, May'83

GREAT WESTERN IN GLOUCESTERSHIRE Steam recordings of Severn & Wye Railway.
Album: released on Saydisc, Nov'80 by Saydisc Records. Dist: Essex, Harmonia Mundi, Roots, H.R. Taylor, Jazz Music, Swift, Projection, Gamut

Cassette: released on Saydisc, Nov'80 by Saydisc Records. Dist: Essex, Harmonia Mundi, Roots, H.R. Taylor, Jazz Music, Swift, Projection, Gamut

GREAT WESTERN, (THE).
Album: released on ASV-Transacord, Apr'85 by ASV Records. Dist: PRT

Cassette: released on ASV-Transacord, Apr'85 by ASV Records. Dist: PRT

GRESLEY BEAT (Incl. classes A3, A4, V2, D49, K4, J50 & J39.).
Album: released on Amberlee, Nov'81 by Amberlee Records. Dist: Amberlee Records, H.R. Taylor

G.W.R..
Album: released on ASV-Transacord, Aug'81 by ASV Records. Dist: PRT

IRON-ORE STEAMERS.
Album: released on Saydisc, Jul'81 by Saydisc Records. Dist: Essex, Harmonia Mundi, Roots, H.R. Taylor, Jazz Music, Swift, Projection, Gamut

LAST TRAIN TO RYDE.
Album: released on Amberlee, Nov'81 by Amberlee Records. Dist: Amberlee Records, H.R. Taylor

L.M.S..
Album: released on ASV-Transacord, May'81 by ASV Records. Dist: PRT

L.N.E.R..
Album: released on ASV-Transacord, Jul'81 by ASV Records. Dist: PRT

LOCOMOTIVES FROM LEEDS.
Cassette: released on Audiocord Cassettes, May'83

LTTLE TRAINS OF WALES, (THE).
Cassette: released on Audiocord Cassettes, May'83

MAGNIFICENT SEVERN, (THE).
Cassette: released on Audiocord Cassettes, May'83

MAIN LINE STEAM SPECIALS.
Album: released on Sound Stories, Nov'81 Dist: H.R. Taylor

MIDLAND & NORTH WESTERN.
Album: released on ASV-Transacord, Sep'82 by ASV Records. Dist: PRT

Cassette: released on ASV-Transacord, Sep'82 by ASV Records. Dist: PRT

NORTH OF KINGS CROSS.
Album: released on ASV-Transacord, Sep'84 by ASV Records. Dist: PRT

Cassette: released on ASV-Transacord, Sep'84 by ASV Records. Dist: PRT

PACIFIC POWER.
Album: released on ASV-Transacord, Jun'85 by ASV Records. Dist: PRT

Cassette: released on ASV-Transacord, Jun'85 by ASV Records. Dist: PRT

PASSENGERS NO MORE.
Cassette: released on Audiocord Cassettes, May'83

POWER OF STEAM, (THE).
Album: released on ASV-Transacord, May'84 by ASV Records. Dist: PRT

Cassette: released on ASV-Transacord, May'84 by ASV Records. Dist: PRT

RAILWAY RHYTHMS.
Album: released on ASV-Transacord, May'81 by ASV Records. Dist: PRT

Cassette: released on ASV-Transacord, May'81 by ASV Records. Dist: PRT

RAILWAYS RECALLED.
Album: released on ASV-Transacord, Jan'82 by ASV Records. Dist: PRT

Cassette: released on ASV-Transacord, Jan'82 by ASV Records. Dist: PRT

RAILWAYS ROUND THE CLOCK.
Album: released on ASV-Transacord, May'81 by ASV Records. Dist: PRT

Cassette: released on ASV-Transacord, May'81 by ASV Records. Dist: PRT

RAILWAY TO RICCARTON.
Album: released on ASV-Transacord, Sep'81 by ASV Records. Dist: PRT

RAINHILL REMEMBERED.
Cassette: released on Audiocord Cassettes, May'83

REAL DAYS OF STEAM.
Album: released on President Special Projects, Nov'81

REGIONAL ROUND NO. 1 - EASTERN.
Cassette: released on Audiocord Cassettes, May'83

REGIONAL ROUND NO. 2 SOUTHERN.
Cassette: released on Audiocord Cassettes, May'83

REGIONAL ROUND NO. 3 MIDLAND.
Cassette: released on Audiocord Cassettes, May'83

REGIONAL ROUND NO. 4 SCOTTISH.
Cassette: released on Audiocord Cassettes, May'83

RETURN TO STEAM PRESERVED LOCOMOTIVES.
Album: released on Saydisc, Apr'81 by Saydisc Records. Dist: Essex, Harmonia Mundi, Roots, H.R. Taylor, Jazz Music, Swift, Projection, Gamut

Cassette: released on Saydisc, Apr'81 by Saydisc Records. Dist: Essex, Harmonia Mundi, Roots, H.R. Taylor, Jazz Music, Swift, Projection, Gamut

RETURN TO STEAM VOLUME 2.
Album: released on Saydisc, Jul'81 by Saydisc Records. Dist: Essex, Harmonia Mundi, Roots, H.R. Taylor, Jazz Music, Swift, Projection, Gamut

Cassette: released on Saydisc, Jul'81 by Saydisc Records. Dist: Essex, Harmonia Mundi, Roots, H.R. Taylor, Jazz Music, Swift, Projection, Gamut

RHYTHMS OF STEAM.
Notes: The latest in this popular series features lineside recordings of steam locomotives at work on British Railways 1958 and 1961 at: Hitchin, Tyndrum, Templecombe, Tyne Dock, Usan and Barkston Junction; a journey on the 'East Mid- lander' special train, hauled by the then newly-restored Midland Compound 4-4-0 No.1000, between Leicester Central and Oxford in 1960. The disc is superbly packaged with, asusual, an outstandingly informative sleeve note by Peter Handford, the producer recently nominated for this year's Best Film Soundtrack' Oscar in Hollywood, for Sydney Pollack's film "Out of Africa". The disc is mostly re-edited and contains previously un-issued recordings.
Album: released on Transacord, Apr'86 by ASV-Academy Sound and Vision. Dist: PRT, H.R. Taylor

Cassette: released on ASV-Transacord Apr'86 by ASV Records. Dist: PRT

SEVERN VALLEY STEAM.
Album: released on Sound Stories, Nov'81 Dist: H.R. Taylor

SHUNTING THE YARD.

Cassette: released on Audiocord Cassettes, May'83

SOMERSET & DORSET.
Cassette: released on Audiocord Cassettes, May'83

SOMERSET & DORSET, (THE).
Album: released on ASV-Transacord, Feb'85 by ASV Records. Dist: PRT

Cassette: released on ASV-Transacord, Feb'85 by ASV Records. Dist: PRT

SOUND EFFECTS NO.14 STEAM IN STEREO.
Album: released on BBC, Dec'81 by BBC Records & Tapes. Dist: EMI, PRT, Pye

SOUTHERN STEAM.
Album: released on ASV-Transacord, May'81 by ASV Records. Dist: PRT

Cassette: released on ASV-Transacord, May'81 by ASV Records. Dist: PRT

SPECIALS IN STEAM.
Cassette: released on Audiocord Cassettes, May'83

STEAM HAULED BY A STANIER BLACK 5.
Album: released on President Special Projects, Nov'81

STEAM IN ALL DIRECTIONS.
Album: released on ASV-Transacord, Aug'81 by ASV Records. Dist: PRT

Cassette: released on ASV-Transacord, Aug'81 by ASV Records. Dist: PRT

STEAM IN SCOTLAND.
Album: released on ASV-Transacord, May'81 by ASV Records. Dist: PRT

Cassette: released on ASV-Transacord, May'81 by ASV Records. Dist: PRT

STEAM IN THE FIFTIES.
Album: released on ASV-Transacord, May'81 by ASV Records. Dist: PRT

Cassette: released on ASV-Transacord, May'81 by ASV Records. Dist: PRT

STEAM IN THE SEVENTIES.
Cassette: released on Audiocord Cassettes, May'83

STEAM IN TWILIGHT.
Album: released on Sound Stories, Nov'81 Dist: H.R. Taylor

STEAM LOCOMOTIVES ON THE GRADIENT.
Album: released on President Special Projects, Nov'81

STEAM ON THE LICKEY INCLINE.
Album: released on ASV-Transacord, Sep'83 by ASV Records. Dist: PRT

STEAM RAILWAY MISCELLANY, (A).
Album: released on President Special Projects, Nov'81

STEAM'S FINAL HOURS.
Album: released on Saydisc, Nov'80 by Saydisc Records. Dist: Essex, Harmonia Mundi, Roots, H.R. Taylor, Jazz Music, Swift, Projection, Gamut

STEAM SPECIALS OF THE 70S.
Album: released on Sound Stories, Nov'81 Dist: H.R. Taylor

STEAM THROUGH ALL SEASONS.
Album: released on ASV-Transacord, May'81 by ASV Records. Dist: PRT

Cassette: released on ASV-Transacord, May'81 by ASV Records. Dist: PRT

STEAM WEEKEND, (A).
Album: released on President Special Projects, Nov'81

STOREFIELD IN THE RAIN.
Album: released on President Special Projects, Nov'81

STOREFIELD STORY.
Album: released on President Special Projects, Nov'81

TRAINS IN THE HILLS.
Album: released on ASV-Transacord, May'82 by ASV Records. Dist: PRT

Cassette: released on ASV-Transacord, May'82 by ASV Records. Dist: PRT

TRAINS IN THE NIGHT.
Album: released on ASV-Transacord, Jul'82 by ASV Records. Dist: PRT

Cassette: released on ASV-Transacord, Jul'82 by ASV Records. Dist: PRT

TRAINS IN TROUBLE.
Album: released on ASV-Transacord, Nov'81 by ASV Records. Dist: PRT

TRAINS TO REMEMBER.
Notes: Already issued in LP form, this cassette is now issued by public demand. Trains remembered are:- The Cambrian Coast Express at Talerddig station. Some trains in the night at Grantham station. A passenger trains and a goods train at Llangurllo station. The Pines Express on the Lickey Incline. The Whitby Moors special train at Ravenscar and at Goathland. The Northern Irishman passing Killochan.
Cassette: released on ASV-Transacord, May'87 by ASV Records. Dist: PRT

Album: released on ASV-Transacord, May'83 by ASV Records. Dist: PRT

TRIUMPH OF AN A4 PACIFIC.
Album: released on ASV-Transacord, Jul'81 by ASV Records. Dist: PRT

Cassette: released on ASV-Transacord, Jul'81 by ASV Records. Dist: PRT

WESTERN STEAM IN THE MIDLANDS.
Cassette: released on Audiocord Cassettes, May'83

WEST OF EXETER.
Album: released on ASV-Transacord, Jan'84 by ASV Records. Dist: PRT

Cassette: released on ASV-Transacord, Jan'84 by ASV Records. Dist: PRT

WORKING ON THE FOOTPLATE.
Album: released on ASV-Transacord, Jan'83 by ASV Records. Dist: PRT

YORK COLLECTION, (THE).
Cassette: released on Audiocord Cassettes, May'83

Steding, Walter
SECRET SPY.
Single (7"): released on Animal, Aug'82 by Chrysalis Records. Dist: Polygram

Steel
ROCK OUT.
Single (7"): released on Neat, Nov'81 by Neat Records. Dist: Pinnacle, Neat

Steel Angels
AND THE ANGELS WERE MADE OF STEEL.
Album: released on Madrigal (France), Nov'85 Dist: Greyhound

BLONDES HAVE MORE FUN.
Album: released on Riva, Jan'78 Dist: PRT

Cassette: released on Riva, Jan'78 Dist: PRT

Steel Band
ANTIGUA & TRINIDAD.
Tracks: / T et TC / National / Soulful calypso / Panorama / Indes jump / Flamingoes.
Compact disc: released on Sunset (France), Dec'86 Dist: IMS-Polygram Distribution

Cassette: released on Beggars Banquet, Jul'84 by Beggars Banquet Records. Dist: WEA

CARNIVAL ON ANTIGUA VOL.2.
Tracks: / Pusch (steelband) / Keep the pace (chant) / Tune for Pan (steelband) / Lynch scratch band/Monica (steelband) / Brass band/Pan in harmony (steelband) / Sugar cane (chant) / Supa stars (steelband) / Farmers (band) / Explosion (steelband).
Album: released on Sunset (France), Apr'86 Dist: IMS-Polygram Distribution

Steel Breeze
DREAMIN' IS EASY.
Single (7"): released on RCA, Apr'83 by RCA Records. Dist: RCA, Roots, Swift, Wellard, Chris, I & B, Solomon & Peres Distribution

YOU DON'T WANT ME ANYMORE.
Single (7"): released on RCA, Oct'82 by RCA Records. Dist: RCA, Roots, Swift, Wellard, Chris, I & B, Solomon & Peres Distribution

Steele, Davy
LONG TIME GETTING HERE.
Album: released on Bracken, Dec'84 Dist: Celtic Music

Steele, Jan
VOICES & INSTRUMENTS
(Steele,Jan/John Cage).
Album: released on Editions EG, Jan'87 by Virgin Records. Dist: EMI

Steele, Jo Ann
COUNTRY GIRL.
Album: released on Bulldog, May'84 by Bulldog Records. Dist: President Distribution, Spartan, Swift, Taylor, H.R.

LOVE ON BORROWED TIME.
Single (7"): released on Bulldog, May'84 by Bulldog Records. Dist: President Distribution, Spartan, Swift, Taylor, H.R.

Steele, Maureen
BOYS WILL BE BOYS.
Single (7"): released on RCA, Sep'85 by RCA Records. Dist: RCA, Roots, Swift, Wellard, Chris, I & B, Solomon & Peres Distribution

Single (12"): released on RCA, Sep'85 by RCA Records. Dist: RCA, Roots, Swift, Wellard, Chris, I & B, Solomon & Peres Distribution

NATURE OF THE BEAST.
Album: released on Motown, Jun'85 by Motown Records. Dist: BMG Distribution

Cassette: released on Motown, Jun'85 by Motown Records. Dist: BMG Distribution

SAVE THE NIGHT FOR ME.
Single (7"): released on Motown, Jun'85 by Motown Records. Dist: BMG Distribution

Single (12"): released on Motown, Jun'85 by Motown Records. Dist: BMG Distribution

Steeler
RULIN' THE EARTH.
Album: released on Earthshaker (Germany), Jun'85 by Earthshaker Records (Germany). Dist: IMS, Polygram

STEELER.
Notes: Featuring Ron Keel (vocals/guitars) and Yngwie Malmsteen (lead guitar).
Album: released on Earthshaker (Germany), Aug'84 by Earthshaker Records (Germany). Dist: IMS, Polygram
Album: released on Shrapnel (USA), Aug'87

Steele, Sandra
YOU MAKE IT SOUND SO EASY.
Single (7"): released on Precision, Mar'81 by PRT Records. Dist: PRT

Steele, Tommy
20 GREATEST HITS.
Album: released on Spot, Aug'83 by Pickwick Records. Dist: H.R. Taylor, Lugtons

Cassette: released on Spot, Aug'83 by Pickwick Records. Dist: H.R. Taylor, Lugtons

HENRY FIELDING'S HANS ANDERSON
(Steele, Tommy & Sally Ann Howes).
Album: released on Flashback, Oct'85 by Flashback Records/PRT Records. Dist: Mainline, PRT

Cassette: released on Flashback, Oct'85 by Flashback Records/PRT Records. Dist: Mainline, PRT

LITTLE WHITE BULL.
Single (7"): released on Decca, '59 by Decca Records. Dist: Polygram

ROCK WITH THE CAVEMAN.
Single (7"): released on Decca-Originals, Mar'82 by Decca Records. Dist: Polygram, IMS

SINGING IN THE RAIN.
Single (7"): released on Safari Records. Dist: Pinnacle

SINGING THE BLUES.
Single (7"): released on Decca, '80 by Decca Records. Dist: Polygram

Single (7"): released on Old Gold, Sep'85 by Old Gold Records. Dist: Lightning, Jazz Music, Spartan, Counterpoint

Steeleye Span
ALL AROUND MY HAT.
Tracks: / Gaudete / All around my hat.
Single (7"): released on Old Gold, Feb'87 by Old Gold Records. Dist: Lightning, Jazz Music, Spartan, Counterpoint

Album: released on MFP, Jul'85 by EMI Records. Dist: EMI

Cassette: released on MFP, Jul'85 by EMI Records. Dist: EMI

Single (7"): released on Chrysalis, Nov'82 by Chrysalis Records. Dist: CBS

BACK IN LINE.
Compact disc: released on Flutterby, Nov'86 by Flutterby Records. Dist: Pinnacle, Projection

Album: released on Flutterby, May'86 by Flutterby Records. Dist: Pinnacle, Projection

---

BELOW THE SALT.
Album: released on Chrysalis, '74 by Chrysalis Records. Dist: CBS

Cassette: released on Chrysalis, '74 by Chrysalis Records. Dist: CBS

BEST OF STEELEYE SPAN.
Compact disc: by Chrysalis Records. Dist: CBS

Album: released on Chrysalis, Mar'84 by Chrysalis Records. Dist: CBS

Cassette: released on Chrysalis, Mar'84 by Chrysalis Records. Dist: CBS

COMMONERS CROWN.
Double Album: released on Chrysalis, Jan'75 by Chrysalis Records. Dist: CBS

Cassette: released on Chrysalis, Jan'75 by Chrysalis Records. Dist: CBS

FOLK ELECTRIC FOLK Original field recordings.
Cassette: released on Folktracks, Nov'79 by Folktracks Cassettes. Dist: Folktracks

HARK THE VILLAGE WAIT.
Album: released on Mooncrest, '83 by Mooncrest Records. Dist: PRT Distribution

Cassette: released on Mooncrest, '85 by Mooncrest Records. Dist: PRT Distribution

LIVE AT LAST.
Album: released on Chrysalis, '78 by Chrysalis Records. Dist: CBS

Cassette: released on Chrysalis, '78 by Chrysalis Records. Dist: CBS

NOW WE ARE SIX.
Album: released on Chrysalis, '74 by Chrysalis Records. Dist: CBS

Cassette: released on Chrysalis, '74 by Chrysalis Records. Dist: CBS

ORIGINAL MASTERS.
Album: released on Chrysalis, May'77 by Chrysalis Records. Dist: CBS

Cassette: released on Chrysalis, May'77 by Chrysalis Records. Dist: CBS

PARCEL OF ROGUES.
Album: released on Chrysalis, '74 by Chrysalis Records. Dist: CBS

Cassette: released on Chrysalis, '74 by Chrysalis Records. Dist: CBS

PLEASE TO SEE THE KING.
Album: released on Mooncrest, '83 by Mooncrest Records. Dist: PRT Distribution

Cassette: released on Mooncrest, '83 by Mooncrest Records. Dist: PRT Distribution

ROCKET COTTAGE.
Double cassette: released on Chrysalis(Take 2), Dec'82 by Chrysalis Records. Dist: CBS

SAILS OF SILVER.
Album: released on Chrysalis, Nov'80 by Chrysalis Records. Dist: CBS

Cassette: released on Chrysalis, Nov'80 by Chrysalis Records. Dist: CBS

SOMEWHERE IN LONDON.
Single (7"): released on Butterfly, Nov'85 by Priority. Dist: EMI

STEELEYE SPAN.
Album: released on Hallmark, May'80 by Pickwick Records. Dist: Pickwick Distribution, PRT, Taylors

Cassette: released on Hallmark, May'80 by Pickwick Records. Dist: Pickwick Distribution, PRT, Taylors

Double Album: released on Cambra, Feb'85 by Cambra Records. Dist: IDS, Conifer

Cassette: released on Cambra, Feb'85 by Cambra Records. Dist: IDS, Conifer

TEN MAN MOP ..Or Mr Reservoir rides again.
Tracks: / Gower wassail / Jigs: Paddy Clancy's jig/Willie Clancy's fancy / Four nights drunk / When I was on horseback / Marrowbones / Captain Coulston / Reels: Wee weave / Skewball.
Album: released on Mooncrest, Aug'86 by Mooncrest Records. Dist: PRT Distribution

Cassette: released on Mooncrest, Aug'86 by Mooncrest Records. Dist: PRT Distribution

TIME SPAN.
Album: released on Mooncrest, Sep'84 by Mooncrest Records. Dist: PRT Distribution

---

by ASV Records. Dist: PRT

Steel, Ivy

REINCARNATION (Steel, Ivy & friends).
Album: released on Innovation (Canada), Sep'84 Dist: Mole Jazz

Steelover

GLOVE ME.
Album: released on Mausoleum, Mar'85 by Mausoleum Records. Dist: Pinnacle

Steel Pulse

BABYLON THE BANDIT.
Tracks: / Save black music / Not King James version / School boy's crush / Sugar daddy / Kick that habit / Blessed is the man / Love walks out / Don't be afraid / Babylon the bandit.
Album: released on Elektra (USA), Mar'86 by Elektra/Asylum/Nonesuch Records. Dist: WEA

Cassette: released on Elektra (USA), Mar'86 by Elektra/Asylum/Nonesuch Records. Dist: WEA

EARTH CRISIS.
Album: released on Wise Man Doctrine, Feb'84 Dist: Jetstar, Spartan

Cassette: released on Wise Man Doctrine, Feb'84 Dist: Jetstar, Spartan

HANDSWORTH REVOLUTION.
Album: released on Island, Jan'78 by Island Records. Dist: Polygram

Cassette: released on Island, Jan'78 by Island Records. Dist: Polygram

LOVE WALKS OUT.
Tracks: / Love walks out / Kick that habit (cold turkey) / Save black music *.
Single (7"): released on Elektra (USA), Feb'86 by Elektra/Asylum/Nonesuch Records. Dist: WEA

Single (12"): released on Elektra (USA), Feb'86 by Elektra/Asylum/Nonesuch Records. Dist: WEA

RAVERS.
Single (7"): released on Wise Man Doctrine, Apr'82 Dist: Jetstar, Spartan

Single (12"): released on Wise Man Doctrine, Apr'82 Dist: Jetstar, Spartan

REGGAE GREATS.
Album: released on Island, May'85 by Island Records. Dist: Polygram

Cassette: released on Island, May'85 by Island Records. Dist: Polygram

STEPPIN' OUT.
Single (12"): released on Wise Man Doctrine, Mar'84 Dist: Jetstar, Spartan

TRUE DEMOCRACY.
Album: released on Wise Man Doctrine, Apr'82 Dist: Jetstar, Spartan

Cassette: released on Wise Man Doctrine, Apr'82 Dist: Jetstar, Spartan

YOUR HOUSE.
Single (12"): released on Wise Man Doctrine, Jan'83 Dist: Jetstar, Spartan

Steely Dan

AJA.
Tracks: / Black cow / Aja / Deacon blues / Peg / Home at last / I got the news / Josie.
Notes: Originally Abc: ABCL 5225. Released 1977.
Album: released on ABC, '83 Dist: CBS, Pinnacle

Cassette: released on ABC, '83 Dist: CBS, Pinnacle

Compact disc: released on ABC, '83 Dist: CBS, Pinnacle

BERRY TOWN.
Compact disc: released on Bellaphon, '86 by Bellaphon Records. Dist: IMS-Polygram

CAN'T BUT A THRILL.
Cassette: released on ABC, Apr'82 Dist: CBS, Pinnacle

CAN'T BUY A THRILL.
Album: released on ABC, '83 Dist: CBS, Pinnacle

Cassette: released on ABC, '83 Dist: CBS, Pinnacle

COUNTDOWN TO ECSTASY.
Album: released on ABC, Feb'82 Dist: CBS, Pinnacle

Cassette: released on ABC, Feb'82 Dist: CBS, Pinnacle

Album: released on Fame, Jul'83 by Music For Pleasure Records. Dist: EMI

Cassette: released on Fame, Jul'83 by Music For Pleasure Records. Dist: EMI

DECADE OF STEELY DAN, A The best of Steely Dan.
Tracks: / FM / Black friday / Babylon sisters / Deacon blues / Bodhisatva / Hey nineteen / Do it again / Peg / Rikki don't lose that number / Reeling in the years / East t Louis Toodle-oo / Kid Charlemagne / My old school / Bad sneakers.
Compact disc: released on MCA, Aug'85 by MCA Records. Dist: Polygram, MCA

DO IT AGAIN.
Single (7"): released on Old Gold (Reissue), Apr'83

GAUCHO.
Tracks: / Babylon sisters / Hey nineteen / Glamour profession / Gaucho / Time out of mind / My rival / Third world man.
Album: released on MCA, Nov'80 by MCA Records. Dist: Polygram, MCA

Cassette: released on MCA, Nov'80 by MCA Records. Dist: Polygram, MCA

Compact disc: released on MCA, Nov'80 by MCA Records. Dist: Polygram, MCA

GOLD.
Album: released on MCA, Jun'82 by MCA Records. Dist: CBS

Cassette: released on MCA, Jun'82 by MCA Records. Dist: CBS

KATY LIED.
Album: released on MCA, Jun'84 by MCA Records. Dist: CBS

Cassette: released on MCA, Jun'84 by MCA Records. Dist: CBS

KATY LIED/ROYAL SCAM.
Cassette: released on MCA, Oct'83 by MCA Records. Dist: Polygram, MCA

OLD REGIME.
Compact disc: released on Thunderbolt, May'87 by Magnum Music Group Ltd. Dist: Magnum Music Group Ltd, PRT Distribution, Spartan Distribution

Album: released on Thunderbolt, May'87 by Magnum Music Group Ltd. Dist: Magnum Music Group Ltd, PRT Distribution, Spartan Distribution

Cassette: released on Thunderbolt, May'87 by Magnum Music Group Ltd. Dist: Magnum Music Group Ltd, PRT Distribution, Spartan Distribution

PRETZEL LOGIC.
Cassette: released on MCA, Feb'84 by MCA Records. Dist: CBS

Cassette: released on MCA, Feb'84 by MCA Records. Dist: CBS

PRETZEL LOGIC/COUNTDOWN TO ECSTACY.
Cassette: released on MCA (Twinpax Cassettes), Sep'84

REELIN' IN THE YEARS.
Single (7"): released on MCA, Nov'85 by MCA Records. Dist: Polygram, MCA

Album: released on MCA, Oct'85 by MCA Records. Dist: Polygram, MCA

Cassette: released on MCA, Oct'85 by MCA Records. Dist: Polygram, MCA

Single (7"): released on ABC, '80 Dist: CBS, Pinnacle

REELIN' IN THE YEARS/RICKY DON'T LOSE THAT NUMBER.
Single (12"): released on MCA (Re-issue), Dec'83

ROYAL SCAM, THE.
Album: released on MCA (ABC), Sep'82 by MCA Records. Dist: Polygram, MCA

Cassette: released on MCA (ABC), Sep'82 by MCA Records. Dist: Polygram, MCA

SUN MOUNTAIN.
Tracks: / Berry town / Android warehouse / More to come / Sun mountain / Ida Lee / Any world / Stone piano / Caves of Altrimara / Horse in town, A / Roaring of the lamb / Parker's band / Oh, wow it's you / You go where I go / This seat's been taken / Little with sugar, A / Take it out on me.
Cassette: released on Showcase, Apr'86 Dist: Counterpoint

Steenhuis, Wout

HAWAIIAN COUNTRY.
Album: released on Valentine, Apr'83 by Valentine Records. Dist: PRT

Cassette: released on Valentine, Apr'83 by Valentine Records. Dist: PRT

MAGIC OF HAWAII (Steenhuis, Wout & The Kontikis).
Tracks: / Hawaiian wedding song / Trade winds / Bali hai / Lovely hula hands / Pearly shell / Halekulani / Sweet leilani / Song of the islands / Harbour lights / Beyond the reef / Drifting and dreaming / Blue Hawaii / Taboo / Hawaiian war chant / On a little bamboo bridge / Mailkini hula / On the beach at Waikiki / Farewell Hawaii.
Album: released on Warwick Reflections, Jun'86 by Warwick Records.

Cassette: released on Warwick Reflections, Jun'86 by Warwick Records.

Steig, Jeremy

OUTLAWS.
Album: released on Enja (Germany), Jan'82 by Enja Records (W.Germany). Dist: Cadillac Music

Steig, William

DOMINIC chapters 1-7.
Cassette: released on Caedmon(USA), '84 by Caedmon (USA) Records. Dist: Gower, Taylors, Discovery

DOMINIC (CHAPTERS 1-7).
Cassette: released on Caedmon(USA), Oct'84 by Caedmon (USA) Records. Dist: Gower, Taylors, Discovery

DR.DE SOTO AND OTHER STORIES Spoken Word.
Cassette: released on Caedmon(USA), Apr'85 by Caedmon (USA) Records. Dist: Gower, Taylors, Discovery

Steinbeck, John

SNAKE AND JOHNNY BEAR, THE.
Cassette: released on Caedmon(USA), Apr'85 by Caedmon (USA) Records. Dist: Gower, Taylors, Discovery

Stein, Chris

WILD STYLE THEME RAP 1 (see Grandmaster Caz&Chris Stein) (Stein, Chris & Grandmaster Caz).

Steiner, Max

KING KONG 1933 Film music (Steiner, Max & the National Philharmonic Orchestra).
Album: released on Entr'Acte (France), Dec'80 Dist: Unicorn

Stein, Lou

LOU STEIN & FRIENDS (Stein, Lou & Friends).
Album: released on World Jazz, May'81 by World Jazz Records. Dist: World Jazz, JSU, Jazz Music

SOLO. Piano.
Album: released on Audiophile, Jul'87 by Jazzology Records (USA). Dist: Jazz Music, Swift

Stein, Lou Trio

LOU STEIN TRIO.
Album: released on Jump, '82 Dist: Jazz Music, Jazz Horizons

Steinman, Jim

BAD FOR GOOD.
Tracks: / Bad for good / Lost boys and golden girls / Love and death and an American guitar / Stark raving love / Out of the frying pan (and into the fire) / Surf's up / Dance in my pants / Left in the dark.
Notes: Cassette has two extra tracks: "Rock and roll dreams come true" and "The storm"
Album: released on Epic, Aug'86 by CBS Records. Dist: CBS

Cassette: released on Epic, Aug'86 by CBS Records. Dist: CBS

Steinman, Jim Fire Inc.

TONIGHT IS WHAT IT MEANS TO BE YOUNG.
Single (7"): released on MCA, May'84 by MCA Records. Dist: CBS

Single (12"): released on MCA, May'84 by MCA Records. Dist: CBS

Steinman, Lydia

TAKE ME TO THE FOREVER.
Single (12"):

TOUCH ME IN THE MORNING.
Single (12"):

Album: released on Epic, May'81 by CBS Records. Dist: CBS

Cassette: released on Epic, May'81 by CBS Records. Dist: CBS

Steinski & Mass Media

WE'LL BE RIGHT BACK.
Tracks: / (Bonus beats).
Single (7"): released on Fourth & Broadway,

Jan'87 by Island Records. Dist: Polygram, EMI

Single (12"): released on Fourth & Broadway, Jan'87 by Island Records. Dist: Polygram, EMI

Single (12"): released on Fourth & Broadway, Feb'87 by Island Records. Dist: Polygram, EMI

Stella

IF YOU DO LIKE MY MUSIC.
Album: released on President, Apr'82 by President Records. Dist: Taylors, Spartan

SI TU AIMES MA MUSIQUE.
Single (7"): released on President, Apr'82 by President Records. Dist: Taylors, Spartan

Stenberg, Berdien

RONDO RUSSO.
Tracks: / Rondo russo / Fire dance / Ecatacy.
Single (7"): released on Starblend, Jul'86 by Starblend Records. Dist: PRT Distribution

RONDO RUSSO.
Album: released on Lifestyle, Dec'83 by Zomba Records. Dist: CBS, PRT, RCA

Cassette: released on Lifestyle, Dec'83 by Zomba Records. Dist: CBS, PRT, RCA

Single (7"): released on Lifestyle, Nov'83 by Zomba Records. Dist: CBS, PRT, RCA

Stench

RASPBERY CRIPPLE.
Single (7"): released on Sticky, Mar'83

Stender Band

ERFRISCHUNGEN.
Album: released on Burlington, Oct'86 by Platz Life Records. Dist: Jazz Music, Celtic Music, Clyde Factors Distributors, I.R.S., Projection, Wellard, Chris, Roots

Stenson, Bobo

GREEN PRINTS (Stenson, B./Mikkeborg/Landgren/Aberg).

Stent, Malcolm

GO AND PLAY UP YOUR OWN END.
Album: released on Starward, Oct'82 Dist: Roots Distribution, Red Sky Distribution, Celtic Music Distribution, Projection Distribution

LOAD OF BULL, A.
Album: released on Highway, '81 by Highway Records. Dist: Roots, Projection, Ross

Stepaside

SIT DOWN AND RELAPSE.
Single (7"): released on Gale, Apr'80 by Gale Records. Dist: Spartan

Stephanie

IRRESISTABLE.
Tracks: / Irresistable / Ouragan / Irresistable Ouragan *.
Single (7"): released on Carrere, Mar'86 Carrere Records. Dist: PRT, Spartan

Single (12"): released on Carrere, Mar'86 Carrere Records. Dist: PRT, Spartan

LIVE YOUR LIFE.
Tracks: / Les sega Mauricien / Live your life.
Single (7"): released on Carrere, Jan'87 Carrere Records. Dist: PRT, Spartan

Single (12"): released on Carrere, Jan'87 Carrere Records. Dist: PRT, Spartan

Compact disc: released on Carrere, '86 Carrere Records. Dist: PRT, Spartan

SHAME.
Single (7"): released on Banana, Feb'84 Dist: Pinnacle, Fresh

Single (12"): released on Banana, Feb'84 Dist: Pinnacle, Fresh

YOUR LIFE.
Album: released on Carrere, Feb'87 by Carrere Records. Dist: PRT, Spartan

Cassette: released on Carrere, Feb'87 by Carrere Records. Dist: PRT, Spartan

Stephens, Bruce

WHATCH THAT FIRST STEP.
Album: released on Strawberry-Uniton, Nov

Stephens, Greg

BEGGAR BOY OF THE NORTH, (THE) AND OTHER NORTHERN TUNES (Stephens, Greg/Crookfinger Jack).
Album: released on Fellside, Apr'81 by Fellside Records. Dist: Roots, Jazz Music, Celtic Music, Projection

EGGAR BOY OF THE NORTH AND THER,THE (Stephens, Greg/Crookfinger ack).

Stephenson, Craig

OUCH.
ngle (7"): released on Arista, Sep'86 by Aris- Records. Dist: RCA

ngle (12"): released on Arista, Sep'86 by ista Records. Dist: RCA

Stephenson, Kayly

VANNA BE CLOSE TO YOU.
ngle (12"): released on Cassia Music, Jun'86 Solid Gold Records. Dist: Jetstar

Stephenson, Martin

OAT TO BOLIVIA.
acks: / Coleen / Little red bottle / Tribute to late Reverend Gary Davis / Running water / ndle in the middle / Piece of the cake / Look wn, look down / Slow lovin' / Caroline / Rain / ocodile cryer / Boat to Bolivia / Slaughter man holly humble heart.
bum: released on Kitchenware, Mar'87 by chenware Records. Dist: Cartel, CBS, Poly- m, RCA-Ariola Distribution

ssette: released on Kitchenware, Mar'87 by henware Records. Dist: Cartel, CBS, Poly- m, RCA-Ariola Distribution

mpact disc: released on Kitchenware, '87 by Kitchenware Records. Dist: Cartel, S, Polygram, RCA-Ariola Distribution

gle (7"): released on Kitchenware, Oct'86 Kitchenware Records. Dist: Cartel, CBS, gram, RCA-Ariola Distribution

gle (12"): released on Kitchenware, Oct'86 Kitchenware Records. Dist: Cartel, CBS, gram, RCA-Ariola Distribution

OCODILE CRIER.
ks: / Crocodile crier / Louis.
le (7"): released on Kitchenware, Jun'86 Kitchenware Records. Dist: Cartel, CBS, gram, RCA-Ariola Distribution

le (12"): released on Kitchenware, Jun'86 itchenware Records. Dist: Cartel, CBS, gram, RCA-Ariola Distribution

W LOVIN'.
ks: / Slow lovin' / Tribute to the late Rev Davis.
e (7"): released on Kitchenware, Aug'86 itchenware Records. Dist: Cartel, CBS, ram, RCA-Ariola Distribution

ephenson,Pamela

WRONG.
e (7"): released on Mercury, Jan'82 by gram Records. Dist: Polygram Distribu-

ephenson, Van

ERN DAY DELILAH.
(7"): released on MCA, Jun'84 by MCA ds. Dist: Polygram, MCA

TEOUS ANGER.
s: / Modern day Delilah / I know who you nd I saw what you did) / What the big girls on't do that / Others only dream / Righ- anger / Cure will kill you, The / You've ed to before / Heart over mind / All ameri- y.
n: released on MCA, Jun'87 by MCA Rec- Dist: Polygram, MCA

tte: released on MCA, Jun'87 by MCA ds. Dist: Polygram, MCA

ICIOUS HEART.
: released on MCA, Aug'86 by MCA Rec- Dist: Polygram, MCA

tte: released on MCA, Aug'86 by MCA s. Dist: Polygram, MCA

E DOIN' ALRIGHT.
: / We're doin' alright / Suspicious heart the big girls do * / Modern day Delilah *.
(7"): released on MCA, Sep'86 by MCA s. Dist: Polygram, MCA

(12"): released on MCA, Sep'86 by MCA s. Dist: Polygram, MCA

phens, Sam

DILLY DALLY (Stephens, Sam and ennox-Martin).
(7"): released on Dingles, Aug'83 by Records. Dist: Projection

oh means justice

YOU PAY (THE).
7"): released on Exile, May'87 by Exile . Dist: Pinnacle

o'In Out

HER HAPPY CUSTOMER.
Album: released on Monarch, Oct'83 by Chart Records. Dist: Pinnacle

Steppa & the Chosen Few

IT MEK.
Single (12"): released on Easy Street, Dec'83 by Easy Street Records. Dist: Jetstar

Steppenwolf

BORN TO BE WILD.
Single (7"): released on Old Gold, Apr'83 by Old Gold Records. Dist: Lightning, Jazz Music, Spartan, Counterpoint

GOLD.
Album: released on Fame (MCA), Jan'83 by Music For Pleasure Records. Dist: EMI

Cassette: released on Fame (MCA), Jan'83 by Music For Pleasure Records. Dist: EMI

Album: released on MCA, Aug'81 by MCA Records. Dist: Polygram, MCA

Cassette: released on MCA, Aug'81 by MCA Records. Dist: Polygram, MCA

GOLDEN GREATS: STEPPENWOLF.
Album: released on MCA, Jul'85 by MCA Records. Dist: Polygram, MCA

Cassette: released on MCA, Jul'85 by MCA Records. Dist: Polygram, MCA

STEPPENWOLF.
Tracks: / Sookie Sookie / Everybody's next one / Berry rides again / Hoochie coochie man / Born to be wild / Your wall's too high / Desperation / Pusher, The / Girl I knew, A / Take what you need / Ostrich, The.
Album: released on MCA, Jun'87 by MCA Records. Dist: Polygram, MCA

Cassette: released on MCA, Jun'87 by MCA Records. Dist: Polygram, MCA

Compact disc: released on MCA, Jul'87 by MCA Records. Dist: Polygram, MCA

STEPPENWOLF THE SECOND.
Tracks: / Faster than the speed of life / Tighten up your wig / None of your doing / Spiritual fantasy / Don't step on the grass, Sam / 28 / Magic carpet ride / Dissapointment number (unknown) / Lost and found by trial and error / Hodge, podge strained through a leslie / Resurection / Reflections / Faster than the speed of life / Tighten up your wig / None of your doing / Spiritual fantasy / 28 / Don't step on the grass sam / Magic capret ride / Disappointment number (unknown) / Lost and found by trial and error / Hodge, podge strained through a leslie / Resurrection / Reflections.
Compact disc: released on MCA, Aug'87 by MCA Records. Dist: Polygram, MCA

Stepper

OH LOVING SAVIOUR (Stepper & Melody Players).
Single (12"): released on Melody, May'83 by Melody Records. Dist: Jetstar Distribution

Steps Ahead

MAGNETIC.
Tracks: / Trains / Beirut / In a sentimental mood / Magnetic love / Sumo / All the tea in China / Something I said / Reprise.
Album: released on Elektra (USA), Aug'86 by Elektra/Asylum/Nonesuch Records. Dist: WEA

Single (12"): released on Elektra (USA), Aug'86 by Elektra/Asylum/Nonesuch Records. Dist: WEA

MODERN TIMES.
Album: released on Elektra(Musician), Mar'84 by WEA Records. Dist: WEA

STEPS AHEAD.
Tracks: / Pools / Islands / Loxodrome / Both sides of the coin / Skyward bound / Northern cross / Trio.
Compact disc: released on Elektra (USA), Jul'84 by Elektra/Asylum/Nonesuch Records. Dist: WEA

Album: released on Elektra(Musician), Jun'83 by WEA Records. Dist: WEA

Stereo Fun Inc.

GOT YOU WHERE I WANT YOU BABE.
Single (7"): released on Ecstasy, May'83 by Creole Records. Dist: CBS

Single (12"): released on Ecstasy, May'83 by Creole Records. Dist: CBS

Sterling Cooke Force

FULL FORCE.
Album: released on Ebony, Aug'84 by Ebony Records. Dist: Pinnacle, Ebony

Sterling, Dave

PUTTIN' IN OVERTIME AT HOME.
Album: released on Tank, Dec'77 by Tank Records.

Sterling, Pam

IF YOU'RE NOT HERE.
Single (12"): released on Kufe, May'85 by Kufe Records. Dist: Pinnacle

Stern, Michael

M'OCEAN.
Compact disc: released on Sonic Atmospheres, '86 Dist: Target

Stetsasonic

GO STETSA I.
Tracks: / Go stetsa I / On fire.
Single (7"): released on Tommy Boy, Mar'87 by Warner Brothers. Dist: WEA Distribution

Single (12"): released on Tommy Boy, Mar'87 by Warner Brothers. Dist: WEA Distribution

Steve & Bonnie

ONCE IN ROYAL DAVID'S CITY.
Single (7"): released on Jeeves, Dec'83 Dist: Jeeves, ILA

Steve & Eydie

BEST OF STEVE & EYDIE.
Album: released on CBS, Feb'77 by CBS Records. Dist: CBS

Cassette: released on CBS, Feb'77 by CBS Records. Dist: CBS

Stevens, April

ALONE.
Album: released on Mr. Sam, Jul'85

Cassette: released on Mr. Sam, Jul'85

ONCE UPON A VERY SPECIAL TIME.
Single (7"): released on Mr. Sam, May'85

Stevens, Cat

BUDDHA & THE CHOCOLATE BOX.
Album: released on Island, '74 by Island Records. Dist: Polygram

CATCH BULL AT FOUR.
Tracks: / Sitting / Boy with a moon and star on his head / Angelsea / Silent sunlight / Can't keep it in / 18th Avenue (Kansas City nightmare) / Freezing steel / O'Caritas / Sweet scarlet / Ruins.
Compact disc: released on Island, Feb'87 by Island Records. Dist: Polygram

Album: released on Island, Jan'78 by Island Records. Dist: Polygram

Cassette: released on Island, Jun'81 by Island Records. Dist: Polygram

CAT STEVENS.
Cassette: released on Spot, Apr'86 by Pickwick Records. Dist: H.R. Taylor, Lugtons

CAT STEVENS COLLECTION.
Tracks: / First cut is the deepest / School is out / Lovely city / Humming bird / Granny / I love my dog / Kitty / Baby get your head screwed on / Lady / Here comes my wife / Matthew and son / Tramp, The / Come on baby / Blackness of the nights / Portobello Road / Here comes my baby / Come on and dance / Northern wind / I've found a love / I'm gonna be king.
Notes: Licensed from the Decca Record Co Ltd. Design and art direction - Shoot that tiger. (C) Castle Communications Plc, Unit 7, 271 Merton Road, London SW18 5JS. Barcode: 5 013428 131275. Double album. Double cassette.
Album: released on Collectors, Apr'86 by Castle Communications Records. Dist: PRT, Pinnacle, Jazz Music

Cassette: released on Collectors, Apr'86 by Castle Communications Records. Dist: PRT, Pinnacle, Jazz Music

CAT STEVENS' GREATEST HITS.
Album: released on Island, Jul'75 by Island Records. Dist: Polygram

Cassette: released on Island, Jul'75 by Island Records. Dist: Polygram

GREATEST HITS:CAT STEVENS.
Tracks: / Wild world / Oh very young / Can't keep it in / Hard headed woman / Moonshadow / Two fine people / Peace train / Ready / Father and son / Sitting / Morning has broken / Another saturday night.
Compact disc: released on Island, Apr'87 by Island Records. Dist: Polygram

MATTHEW & SON.
Single (7"): released on Old Gold, Oct'83 by Old Gold Records. Dist: Lightning, Jazz Music, Spartan, Counterpoint

Single (7"): released on Deram, Jul'80 by Decca Records. Dist: Polygram

Single (7"): released on Decca-Originals, Mar'82 by Decca Records. Dist: Polygram, IMS

MONA BONE JAKON.
Tracks: / Lady d'Arbanville / Maybe you're / Pop star / I think I see the light / Trouble / Mona Bone Jakon / I wish I wish / Katmandu / Fill my eyes / Timer / Time / Lillywhite.
Compact disc: released on Island, Apr'87 by Island Records. Dist: Polygram

Album: released on Island, Jan'78 by Island Records. Dist: Polygram

Cassette: released on Island, Jun'81 by Island Records. Dist: Polygram

MORNING HAS BROKEN.
Single (7"): released on Island, '80 by Island Records. Dist: Polygram

Single (7"): released on Island, Nov'83 by Island Records. Dist: Polygram

MUSIC FOR THE MILLIONS.
Tracks: / Matthew and son / Here comes my baby / Lovely city / I love my dog / Here comes my wife / Granny / I'm gonna get me a gun / Kitty / First cut is the deepest / Bad night, A / School is out / Where are you.
Album: released on Decca (Germany), Dec'85 by Decca Records. Dist: Polygram, IMS

Cassette: released on Decca (Germany), Dec'85 by Decca Records. Dist: Polygram, IMS

TEA FOR THE TILLERMAN.
Tracks: / Where do the children play / Hard headed woman / Wild world / Sad Lisa / Miles from nowhere / But I might die tonight / Longer boats / Into white / On the road to find out / Father and son / Tea for the tillerman.
Album: released on Island, Oct'86 by Island Records. Dist: Polygram

Cassette: released on Island, Oct'86 by Island Records. Dist: Polygram

Compact disc: released on Island, Sep'86 by Island Records. Dist: Polygram

TEASER AND THE FIRECAT.
Tracks: / Wind, The / Ruby love / If I laugh / Changes IV / How can I tell you / Tuesday's dead / Morning has broken / Bitter blue / Moon shadow / Peace train.
Album: released on Island, Sep'86 by Island Records. Dist: Polygram

Cassette: released on Island, Sep'86 by Island Records. Dist: Polygram

Compact disc: released on Island, Sep'86 by Island Records. Dist: Polygram

VIEW FROM THE TOP.
Double Album: released on Deram, May'75 by Decca Records. Dist: Polygram

Cassette: released on Deram, May'75 by Decca Records. Dist: Polygram Deleted '82.

Stevens, Dane

FOR A RAINY DAY.
Album: released on Tank, Dec'77 by Tank Records.

Stevens, Flo

FLO' GENTLY, SWEET COUNTRY.
Album: released on BGS, Nov'79 by BGS Productions Ltd. Dist: BGS Distribution, Wynd-Up Distribution, Ross Records, Duncan, Gordon Distribution, Taylor, H.R., Record Merchandisers Distribution

Cassette: released on BGS, Nov'79 by BGS Productions Ltd. Dist: BGS Distribution, Wynd-Up Distribution, Ross Records, Duncan, Gordon Distribution, Taylor, H.R., Record Merchandisers Distribution

ROCK'N'ROLL WALTZ.
Cassette single: released on Country House, Jul'82 by BGS Productions Ltd. Dist: Taylor, H.R., Record Merchandisers Distribution, Pinnacle, Sounds of Scotland Records

SWEET DREAMS.
Album: released on Neptune, Jul'78 by Lismor. Dist: Spartan

Cassette: released on Neptune, Jul'78 by Lismor. Dist: Spartan

Stevens, John

APPLICATION, INTERACTION AND... (Stevens, John/Trevor Watts/Barry Guy).
Album: released on Spotlite, '83 by Spotlite Records. Dist: Cadillac, Jazz Music, Spotlite

FREEBOP.
Album: released on Affinity, '83 by Charly Records. Dist: Charly, Cadillac

LONGEST NIGHT, VOL 1 (Stevens, John & Evan Parker).
Album: released on Ogun, Feb'78 Dist: Jazz Music, JSU, Cadillac

LONGEST NIGHT, VOL 2 (Stevens, John & Evan Parker).
Album: released on Ogun, Jun'78 Dist: Jazz

Music, JSU, Cadillac

NO FEAR (Stevens, John/Trevor Watts/Barry Guy).
Album: released on Spotlite, '83 by Spotlite Records. Dist: Cadillac, Jazz Music, Spotlite

Stevens, Keni

ALL DAY ALL NIGHT.
Tracks: / All day all night / All day all night (keep on loving mix) / All day all night (jazz mix) / All day all night (funk mix).
Single (12"): released on Elite, Feb'86 Dist: PRT

BLUE MOODS.
Compact disc: released on Jam Today, Jun'87 Dist: PRT, Jetstar

CANNOT LIVE WITHOUT YOUR LOVE (AT LAST THE DANCE MIX).
Tracks: / Cannot live without your love (dance mix) / Passionate (jam today remix).
Single (7"): released on Elite, Jul'87 Dist: PRT

Single (12"): released on Elite, Jul'87 Dist: PRT

TOO MUCH TOO SOON.
Tracks: / Too much too soon / Night moves (ultra-sensual remix) / Too much too soon (Inst).
Single (12"): released on Elite, Oct'86 Dist: PRT

Stevens, Kenni

NIGHT MOVIES.
Single (7"): released on Elite, Jul'85 Dist: PRT

Single (12"): released on Elite, Jul'85 Dist: PRT

Stevens, Lamona

SONGS OF DONNA SUMMER.
Cassette: released on Kingfisher, Nov'81 Dist: PRT

Stevens, Mackenzie

LET IT PLAY.
Tracks: / Let it play / Rastafari.
Single (12"): released on Trojan, Apr'86 by Trojan Records. Dist: PRT, Jetstar

Stevens, Meic

GITAR YNY TWLLDAN STAR.
Album: released on Sain, '85 by Sain Records. Dist: Projection, Sain

NOS DU NOS DA.
Album: released on Sain, '85 by Sain Records. Dist: Projection, Sain

Stevenson, Doug

STEEL ON MY MIND.
Album: released on Country House, Sep'79 by BGS Productions Ltd. Dist: Taylor, H.R., Record Merchandisers Distribution, Pinnacle, Sounds of Scotland Records

Cassette: released on Country House, Sep'79 by BGS Productions Ltd. Dist: Taylor, H.R., Record Merchandisers Distribution, Pinnacle, Sounds of Scotland Records

Stevenson, N.A.

BOOGIE WOOGIE COUNTRY GIRL.
Single (7"): released on Spade (USA), May'83

Stevenson, Robert Louis

TREASURE ISLAND.
Cassette: released on Listen For Pleasure, Jul'84 by MFP Records. Dist: EMI

Triple album / cassette: released on Cover to Cover, Jun'85 by Cover to Cover Cassettes. Dist: Conifer

Stevenson, Savourna

TICKLED PINK.
Album: released on Springthyme, Oct'86 by Springthyme Records. Dist: Jazz Music Distribution, Projection Distribution, Roots Distribution

Cassette: released on Springthyme, Oct'86 by Springthyme Records. Dist: Jazz Music Distribution, Projection Distribution, Roots Distribution

Stevens, Ray

6 TRACK HITS.
Extended-play record: released on Scoop 33, Sep'83 by Pickwick Records. Dist: H.R. Taylor

Cassette: released on Scoop 33, Sep'83 by Pickwick Records. Dist: H.R. Taylor

BOTH SIDES OF RAY STEVENS.
Tracks: / Gitarzan / Moonlight special / Mr business man / Bridget the midget / Streak / Freddie Feelgood / Misty / Everything is beautiful / Young love / Sunshine / All my trials / Turn your radio on.
Album: released on Crown, Feb'86 by Ace Records. Dist: Pinnacle, Swift

Cassette: released on Crown, Feb'86 by Ace Records. Dist: Pinnacle, Swift

BRIDGET THE MIDGET.
Single (7"): released on Old Gold, Jul'82 by Old Gold Records. Dist: Lightning, Jazz Music, Spartan, Counterpoint

DON'T LAUGH NOW.
Album: released on RCA, Sep'82 by RCA Records. Dist: RCA, Roots, Swift, Wellard, Chris, I & B, Solomon & Peres Distribution

GREATEST HITS:RAY STEVENS.
Album: released on MCA, Apr'87 by MCA Records. Dist: Polygram, MCA

Cassette: released on MCA, Apr'87 by MCA Records. Dist: Polygram, MCA

ME.
Album: released on Mercury (USA), Dec'83 by Import Records. Dist: IMS Distribution, Polygram Distribution

MISSISSIPPI SQUIREL REVIVAL.
Single (7"): released on MCA, Apr'85 by MCA Records. Dist: CBS

Single (12"): released on MCA, Apr'85 by MCA Records. Dist: CBS

RAY STEVENS GREATEST HITS.
Tracks: / Streak, The / Shriner's convention / It's me against Margaret / Turn your radio on / Misty / Mississippi squirrel revival (The) / Gitarzan / Ahab the arab / Along came Jones / Everything is beautiful.
Album: released on MCA, Apr'87 by MCA Records. Dist: Polygram, MCA

Cassette: released on MCA, Apr'87 by MCA Records. Dist: Polygram, MCA

RAY STEVENS GREATEST HITS COLLECTION, THE.
Double Album: released on Pickwick, Jul'79 by Pickwick Records. Dist: Pickwick Distribution, Prism Leisure Distribution, Lugtons

Double cassette: released on Pickwick, Jul'79 by Pickwick Records. Dist: Pickwick Distribution, Prism Leisure Distribution, Lugtons

STREAK, THE.
Single (7"): released on Old Gold, Jul'82 by Old Gold Records. Dist: Lightning, Jazz Music, Spartan, Counterpoint

VERY BEST OF RAY STEVENS.
Album: released on Spot, Sep'84 by Pickwick Records. Dist: H.R. Taylor, Lugtons

Cassette: released on Spot, Sep'84 by Pickwick Records. Dist: H.R. Taylor, Lugtons

Stevens, Ronnie

STORYTIME TOP TEN - VOL.4.
Cassette: released on VFM Cassettes, Jan'85

STORYTIME TOP TEN - VOL.8 (Stevens, Ronnie & Toddy).
Cassette: released on VFM Cassettes, Jan'85

STORYTIME TOP TIME - VOL.5.
Cassette: released on VFM Cassettes, Jan'85

Stevens, Scott

DREAMIN' COUNTRY.
Album: released on Klub, Aug'78

Stevens, Shakin'

Biographical Details: Shakin' Stevens was born **Michael Barratt**, 4 March 1948 in Ely, Wales; he is a rock'n'roll **revivalist** with the style down pat. He began as a frontman with **The Sunsets**, a revival band formed in '69 who were a big live attraction; **A Legend** was originally released in 1970, produced **by Dave Edmunds**, the first of a series by the sunsets. Stevens won a role in the London musical **Elvis**, starring **P.J. Proby**; he starred in the hit TV revival of Jack Good's **Oh Boy** programme; his solo hits and albums began in 1980, produced first by **Stuart Colman**, later by **Edmunds**; his first hit was **"Hot Dog"** (no.24 in 1980); **"Marie Marie"** (top 20 same year) was written by the then-unknown **Dave Alvin** of the Blasters; he had no.1 hits 1981-1982 with **"This Ole House"** (1954 American hit by Rosemary Clooney), **"Green Door"** (American no.1 by deejay Jim Lowe in 1956), **"Oh Julie"** (USA hit by the Crescendos, 1957)
[Donald Clarke, April 87]

20 ROCKABILLY HITS.
Album: released on Meteor, Jun'85 by Magnum Force Music. Dist: CBS Distribution

Cassette: released on Meteor, Jun'85 by Magnum Force Music. Dist: CBS Distribution

AT THE ROCKHOUSE.
Album: released on Magnum Force, Jul'82 by Magnum Music Group Ltd. Dist: Magnum Music Group Ltd, PRT, Spartan
Cat. no: **MFLP 004**

Cassette: released on Magnum Force, Jul'82 by Magnum Music Group Ltd. Dist: Magnum Music Group Ltd, PRT, Spartan

BECAUSE I LOVE YOU.
Tracks: / Tell me one more time.
Single (7"): released on Epic, Oct'86 by CBS Records. Dist: CBS

Single (12"): released on Epic, Oct'86 by CBS Records. Dist: CBS

BOP WON'T STOP.
Tracks: / Bop won't stop, The / Why do you treat me this way / Diddle I / Don't be two faced / Livin' lovin' wreck / Rockin' good way, A / Brand new man / I cry just a little bit / As long as / Love worth waiting for, A / Love me tonight / It's late.
Notes: Digital stereo
Compact disc: released on Epic, Jul'84 by CBS Records. Dist: CBS

BOP WON'T STOP, THE.
Compact disc: released on Epic, Jul'84 by CBS Records. Dist: CBS

CLASSICS.
Album: released on Magnum Force, Nov'83 by Magnum Music Group Ltd. Dist: Magnum Music Group Ltd, PRT, Spartan

COLLECTION PARTS 1 & 2 (Stevens, Shakin' & The Sunsets).
Tracks: / Sweet little sixteen / Monkey's uncle / Tear it up / Silver wings / Ready Teddy / Reet petite / Outlaw man / Queen of the hop / Lady lizard / Story of the rockers / Jungle rock / Justine / You mostest girl / Girl in red / Rock around with Ollie Vee / Blue swingin' mama / Sugaree / I don't care / Tiger / Frantic.
Notes: All; tracks licensed from Philip H.A. Bailey (PHAB). (C) 1986. Matrix No. 5 013428 131534.Double album and cassette.
Album: released on Castle Collectors, Sep'86 by Castle Communications Records. Dist: Pinnacle

Cassette: released on Castle Collectors, Sep'86 by Castle Communications Records. Dist: Pinnacle

COLLECTION: SHAKIN' STEVENS.
Album: released on EMI (Germany), '83 by EMI Records. Dist: Conifer

HEY MAE.
Single (7"): released on Epic, Apr'82 by CBS Records. Dist: CBS

SHAKIN' STEVENS & THE SUNSETS (Shakin' Stevens & The Sunsets).
Double Album: released on Premier, Dec'84 by Premier Records. Dist: CBS

Tracks: / Jungle rock / You mostest girl / Girl in red / Rock around with Ollie Vee / Blue's swingin' mama / Sugaree / Baby I don't care / Tiger / Frantic / Sweet little sixteen / Monkey's uncle / Tear it up / Silver wings / Ready Teddy / Reet petite / Outlaw man / Queen of the hop / Lady lizard / Story of the rockers.
Compact disc: released on Collector Series, '86 by Castle Communications Records. Dist: PRT, Pinnacle, RCA, Ariola

EXTRA.
Album: released on Teldec (Germany), Oct'83 by Import Records. Dist: IMS Distribution, Polygram Distribution

Cassette: released on Teldec (Germany), Oct'83 by Import Records. Dist: IMS Distribution, Polygram Distribution

FRANTIC (Stevens, Shakin' & The Sunsets).
Single (7"): released on Magnum Force, Feb'82 by Magnum Music Group Ltd. Dist: Magnum Music Group Ltd, PRT, Spartan

GREATEST HITS: SHAKIN STEVENS.
Album: released on Epic, Nov'84 by CBS Records. Dist: CBS

Cassette: released on Epic, Nov'84 by CBS Records. Dist: CBS

GREATEST ORIGINAL HITS.
Extended-play record: released on Epic, Mar'83 by CBS Records. Dist: CBS

GREEN DOOR.
Single (7"): released on Epic, Jul'81 by CBS Records. Dist: CBS

HOT DOG.
Album: released on Epic, Apr'82 by CBS Records. Dist: CBS Deleted '87.

Cassette: released on Epic, Apr'82 by CBS Records. Dist: CBS

Single (7"): released on Epic (Reissue), Apr'82 by CBS Records. Dist: CBS

JUNGLE ROCK.
Single (7"): released on Battle Of The Bands, Apr'81 Dist: Stage One

JUSTINE (Stevens, Shakin' & The Sunsets).
Single (7"): released on Magnum Force, Feb'83 by Magnum Music Group Ltd. Dist: Magnum Music Group Ltd, PRT, Spartan

LIGHT UP THE DYNAMITE (Stevens, Shakin' & Nick Lowe).
Album: released on Magnum Force (Limited Edition), '83

LIPSTICK, POWDER AND PAINT.
Album: released on Epic, Nov'85 by CBS Records. Dist: CBS

Cassette: released on Epic, Nov'85 by CBS Records. Dist: CBS

LITTLE BOOGIE WOOGIE, A.
Tracks: / Little boogie woogie, A / If you'r[e] gonna cry.
Single (7"): released on Epic, 13 Jun'87 by CBS Records. Dist: CBS

Single (12"): released on Epic, 13 Jun'87 by CBS Records. Dist: CBS

Cassette single: released on Epic, 27 Jun'8[7] by CBS Records. Dist: CBS

Cassette single: released on Epic, Jul'87 by CBS Records. Dist: CBS

MANHATTAN MELODRAMA.
Tracks: / Manhattan melodrama / Blue moon [of] Kentucky / Alan Freed / California cowboy / Lady lizard / Punk / Outlaw man / Riot in c[ell] block number 9 / I told you so / Tallahassee la[s]sie / Longer stronger love / Like a teenage[r] / Don't jive no more / Holy roller / No other ba[by] / Get back John.
Notes: Production licensed from Philip H. Bailey (PHAB). Original sound recordin[g] owned by Dureco Benelux. (P) & (C) Warw[ick] Records. A Warwick Leisure product. Made [&] printed in the UK. Bar code: 5 012106 2200[...]
Album: released on Warwick Reflection[s], Jun'86 by Warwick Records.

Cassette: released on Warwick Reflectio[ns], Jun'86 by Warwick Records.

Album: released on Mint (Ireland), Jul'81

Cassette: released on Mint (Ireland), Jul'81

MEMPHIS EARTHQUAKE (Steve[ns], Shakin' & The Sunsets).
Single (7"): released on Magnum Force, Apr[...] by Magnum Music Group Ltd. Dist: Magn[um] Music Group Ltd, PRT, Spartan

MERRY CHRISTMAS.
Tracks: / Merry Christmas / Blue Christmas.
Single (7"): released on Epic, Nov'86 by C[BS] Records. Dist: CBS

MERRY CHRISTMAS EVERYONE.
Single (7"): released on Epic, Nov'85 by C[BS] Records. Dist: CBS

Single (12"): released on Epic, Nov'85 by C[BS] Records. Dist: CBS

NO OTHER BABY.
Single (7"): released on Mint, Aug'81 by [Em]erald Records. Dist: Ross Distribution, PRT [Dis]tribution, Solomon & Peres Distribution

ORIGINAL SHAKIN' STEVENS, T[HE] (Stevens, Shakin' & The Sunsets).
Cassette: released on Chevron, Feb'85 Multiple Sound Distributors

ORIGINAL SHAKIN' STEVENS A[ND] THE SUNSET - VOL.2.
Cassette: released on Chevron, Aug'85 Multiple Sound Distributors

PLATINUM HIGH SCHOOL (Ste[vens], Shakin', Jets & Jonny Storm).
Album: released on Magnum Force, Nov'[...] Magnum Music Group Ltd. Dist: Magnum M[usic] Group Ltd, PRT, Spartan

PROFILE.
Album: released on Teldec (Germany), J[...] by Import Records. Dist: IMS Distribution, [Poly]gram Distribution

Cassette: released on Teldec (Germ[any]), Jun'82 by Import Records. Dist: IMS Dis[tribu]tion, Polygram Distribution

ROCKIN' & SHAKIN' (Stevens, Sha[kin' &] The Sunsets).
Album: released on Hallmark, Sep'84 by [Pick]wick Records. Dist: Pickwick Distribution, [H.R.] Taylors

Cassette: released on Hallmark, Sep'[84 by] Pickwick Records. Dist: Pickwick Distri[bution], PRT, Taylors

ROCKIN' SHAKY.
Picture disc album: released on Astan, [...] by Astan Records. Dist: Counterpoint

Picture disc album: released on Astan, [...] by Astan Records. Dist: Counterpoint

ROCK ON WITH A LEGEND (Ste[vens], Shakin' & The Sunsets).
Album: released on Music for Pleasure, [...] by EMI Records. Dist: MFP Distribution

Cassette: released on Music for Ple[asure], Oct'81 by EMI Records. Dist: MFP Distr[ibution]

HAKIN' STEVENS.
icture disc album: released on Astan, Dec'85
y Astan Records. Dist: Counterpoint

ouble Album: released on Everest (Premier),
2 by Everest Records. Dist: Pinnacle

lbum: released on Hallmark, Jun'81 by Pick-
ick Records. Dist: Pickwick Distribution, PRT,
aylors

assette: released on Hallmark, Jun'81 by
ickwick Records. Dist: Pickwick Distribution,
RT, Taylors

HAKIN' STEVENS 4 track cassette EP.
assette: released on Epic, Aug'82 by CBS
ecords. Dist: CBS

HAKY SINGS ELVIS.
ngle (7"): released on Solid Gold, Sep'81
st: MCA

HATTERED GLASS (Stevens, Shelley &
arry Santana).
acks: / Shattered glass / Rock 'n' roll winter.
ngle (7"): released on Recoil Prism, Dec'85

HATTERIN - VOL.2 (Stevens, Shakin' &
e Sunsets).
bum: released on Contour, Sep'81 by Pick-
k Records. Dist: Pickwick Distribution, PRT

ssette: released on Contour, Sep'81 by
kwick Records. Dist: Pickwick Distribution,
T

LVER WINGS.
um: released on Astan, Nov'84 by Astan
cords. Dist: Counterpoint

ssette: released on Astan, Nov'84 by Astan
cords. Dist: Counterpoint

OOKEY.
gle (7"): released on Epic (Reissue), Apr'82
BS Records. Dist: CBS

KE ONE.
um: released on Epic, Oct'79 by CBS Rec-
. Dist: CBS

ssette: released on Epic, Oct'79 by CBS
ords. Dist: CBS

ARDROPS.
gle (7"): released on Epic, Dec'84 by CBS
ords. Dist: CBS

S OLE HOUSE.
le (7"): released on Epic, Feb'82 by CBS
ords. Dist: CBS Deleted '86.

ER.
m: released on Premier, '84 by Premier
ords. Dist: CBS

sette: released on Premier, '84 by Premier
rds. Dist: CBS

le (7"): released on Everest (Premier),
2 by Everest Records. Dist: Pinnacle

le (7"): released on Everest (Premier),
3 by Everest Records. Dist: Pinnacle

CK YEARS.
ks: / Somebody touched me / Just walking
rain / Mountain of love / Rebound / You
s hurt the one you love / No other baby /
down yonder in New Orleans / Keep a
king / Gotta lotta livin' to do / Ruby baby /
/ Tossin' 'n' turning / Hound dog.
n: released on MFP, Oct'86 by EMI Rec-
Dist: EMI

tte: released on MFP, Oct'86 by EMI
ds. Dist: EMI

CK YEARS, THE.
s: / Somebody touched me / Just walkin'
rain / Mountain of love / Rebound / You
s hurt the one you love / No other baby /
down yonder in New Orleans / Keep a
in' / Gotta lotta livin' to do / Ruby baby /
/ Tossin' and turnin' / Hound dog.
s: This compilation 1983 Mediamotion
eas.
: released on MFP, Aug'86 by EMI Rec-
Dist: EMI

tte: released on MFP, Aug'86 by EMI
ds. Dist: EMI

ING AWAY.
: / Turning away / Diddle I.
(7"): released on Epic, Jan'86 by CBS
s. Dist: CBS

(12"): released on Epic, Jan'86 by CBS
s. Dist: CBS

IATE ROCK 'N' ROLLER, THE
ns, Shakin' & The Sunsets).
: released on Big Beat (France), Jul'84

vens, Shelly

ET LOVE.
(7"): released on Rialto, Oct'80 by Rialto Records. Dist: Pinnacle

Stevens, Stu

ALBERT AND MARY.
Single (7"): released on Young Blood, Jan'84 by Young Blood Records. Dist: Pinnacle

COMMAND PERFORMANCE.
Cassette: released on VFM Cassettes, Jan'85

COWBOY IN PARIS.
Single (7"): released on Crazy Viking, Sep'82 by Crazy Vikings Records. Dist: Pinnacle

Single (12"): released on Crazy Viking, Sep'82 by Crazy Vikings Records. Dist: Pinnacle

Album: released on Ash, Jul'82 by Ash Records. Dist: Ash

DREAM IT BACK.
Tracks: / Dream it back / Cherokee mountain.
Notes: Distributed by Ash Records Ltd, Cropwell House, Salmon Lane, Kirkby-in-Ashfield,Nottingham, NGH17 9HB. Tel: 0623 752448
Single (7"): released on Ash, May'86 by Ash Records. Dist: Ash

EMMA AND I.
Tracks: / Mind painter / When I dream / That old brown dog / Loving arms / Emma and I / My woman my wife / Sunday morning coming down / Got my guitar / Room for a boy / Lady lay down / Bridge over troubled water / Hard to be humble / Three kinds of flowers.
Album: released on Ash, Apr'86 by Ash Records. Dist: Ash

EYES OF MY CHILD.
Single (7"): released on Ash, Nov'82 by Ash Records. Dist: Ash

FOREVER.
Single (7"): released on Crazy Viking, Jul'83 by Crazy Vikings Records. Dist: Pinnacle

FUNNY FACE.
Tracks: / Funny face / Choking kind / Four strong winds / I don't want to cry / Tree in the meadow / Revelation / Mexico City / Good hearted woman / Derby's castle / Love me tender / Colorado / Yours love / Streets I have walked.
Cassette: released on Ash, Apr'86 by Ash Records. Dist: Ash

LONER, THE.
Tracks: / Lady luck / Riverboat / America you are my woman / Love of the common people / West side of Texas / Miami sunset / Wrap my arms around the world / Rain / Had to run / Every night when I cry myself to sleep.
Album: released on Ash, Apr'86 by Ash Records. Dist: Ash

Album: released on Ash, Jul'82 by Ash Records. Dist: Ash

MAN AND HIS MUSIC, THE.
Tracks: / Rose, The / Dry your eyes / Little boy genius / Three times a lady / Nancy Lee / My heroes have always been cowboys / Always on my mind / Dream it back / Imagine / Suspicious minds / While the feelings good / Girl you love, The.
Cassette: released on Ash, Apr'86 by Ash Records. Dist: Ash

MAN FROM OUTER SPACE.
Single (7"): released on Eagle (London), '81 by Eagle Records (London). Dist: Stage One

OLD RUGGED CROSS.
Tracks: / Eltigre / I can't keep my hands off you / Winter world away / Red cloud's day / Cowboys and daddies / Biff / Beautiful noise / Lady oh / American trilogy / Old rugged cross / Eyes of my child.
Cassette: released on Ash, Apr'86 by Ash Records. Dist: Ash

OUTER RUGGED CROSS.
Cassette: released on Ash, Jul'82 by Ash Records. Dist: Ash

REMEMBER ME AT SUNSHINE.
Single (7"): released on Young Blood, Sep'81 by Young Blood Records. Dist: Pinnacle

SAD OLD SPANISH GUITAR.
Single (7"): released on Young Blood, Aug'84 by Young Blood Records. Dist: Pinnacle

SONGS THAT MADE STU STEVENS (THE VOICE), THE.
Album: released on Young Blood, Jan'81 by Young Blood Records. Dist: Pinnacle

STU STEVENS.
Cassette: released on VFM Cassettes, Jan'85

TOGETHER AGAIN.
Album: released on Ash, Jul'82 by Ash Records. Dist: Ash

WAY LOVE'S SUPPOSED TO BE, THE.
Single (7"): released on Ritz, Aug'85 by Ritz Records. Dist: Spartan

WHEN I DREAM.
Single (7"): released on Eagle (London), Apr'81 by Eagle Records (London). Dist: Stage One

Stevens, Tony

TILL WE MEET AGAIN.
Tracks: / Till we meet again / If I can forget her.
Single (7"): by Outlet Records. Dist: Outlet, Prism Leisure Distribution, Record Services Distribution (Ireland), Roots

WAY LOVE'S SUPPOSED TO BE.
Album: released on Ritz, Aug'86 by Outlet Records. Dist: Outlet, Prism Leisure Distribution, Record Services Distribution (Ireland), Roots

Cassette: released on Ritz, Aug'86 by Outlet Records. Dist: Outlet, Prism Leisure Distribution, Record Services Distribution (Ireland), Roots

Stevie Wonder Songbook

STEVIE WONDER SONGBOOK (Various Artists).
Album: released on Starblend, Dec'86 by Starblend Records. Dist: PRT Distribution

Stewart, Al

BEST OF AL STEWART.
Album: released on RCA, May'85 by RCA Records. Dist: RCA, Roots, Swift, Wellard, Chris, I & B, Solomon & Peres Distribution

Album: released on RCA, May'85 by RCA Records. Dist: RCA, Roots, Swift, Wellard, Chris, I & B, Solomon & Peres Distribution

EARLY YEARS.
Tracks: / Bedsitter images / In Brooklyn / Electric Los Angeles sunset / Clifton in the rain / You should have listened to Al / Manuscript / Small fruit song / Life and life only / Love chronicles.
Notes: Tracks 1, 3, 4, 6, 7 produced by Roy Guest. Tracks 2, 5, 8, 9 produced by Roy Guest with John Woods & Al Stewart. All titles composed by Al Stewart and published by Gwyneth Music Ltd.
Album: released on Fame, Sep'86 by Music For Pleasure Records. Dist: EMI

Cassette: released on Fame, Sep'86 by Music For Pleasure Records. Dist: EMI

INDIAN SUMMER/LIVE.
Album: released on RCA, '84 by RCA Records. Dist: RCA, Roots, Swift, Wellard, Chris, I & B, Solomon & Peres Distribution

Cassette: released on RCA, '84 by RCA Records. Dist: RCA, Roots, Swift, Wellard, Chris, I & B, Solomon & Peres Distribution

LORI DON'T GO RIGHT NOW.
Single (7"): released on RCA, Jun'84 by RCA Records. Dist: RCA, Roots, Swift, Wellard, Chris, I & B, Solomon & Peres Distribution

LOVE CHRONICLES.
Album: released on RCA International (USA), May'82 by RCA Records. Dist: RCA

Cassette: released on RCA International (USA), May'82 by RCA Records. Dist: RCA

ORANGE.
Album: released on CBS, Nov'81 by CBS Records. Dist: CBS

RUSSIANS & AMERICANS.
Album: released on RCA, May'84 by RCA Records. Dist: RCA, Roots, Swift, Wellard, Chris, I & B, Solomon & Peres Distribution

Cassette: released on RCA, May'84 by RCA Records. Dist: RCA, Roots, Swift, Wellard, Chris, I & B, Solomon & Peres Distribution

TIME PASSAGES.
Tracks: / Valentina way / Life in dark water / Man for all seasons / Almost lucky / Time passages / Palace of Versailles / Timeless skies / End of the day / Song on the radio.
Album: released on RCA, Nov'86 by RCA Records. Dist: RCA, Roots, Swift, Wellard, Chris, I & B, Solomon & Peres Distribution

Cassette: released on RCA, Nov'86 by RCA Records. Dist: RCA, Roots, Swift, Wellard, Chris, I & B, Solomon & Peres Distribution

Compact disc: released on RCA, Nov'86 by RCA Records. Dist: RCA, Roots, Swift, Wellard, Chris, I & B, Solomon & Peres Distribution

YEAR OF THE CAT.
Tracks: / Lord Grenville / On the border / Midas shadow / Sand in your shoes / If it doesn't come naturally, leave it / Flying sorcery / Broadway hotel / One stage before / Year of the cat.
Compact disc: released on Mobile Fidelity, '86 by Mobile Fidelity Records.

Album: released on RCA, Nov'84 by RCA Records. Dist: RCA, Roots, Swift, Wellard, Chris, I & B, Solomon & Peres Distribution

Cassette: released on RCA, Nov'84 by RCA Records. Dist: RCA, Roots, Swift, Wellard, Chris, I & B, Solomon & Peres Distribution

YEAR OF THE CAT (7").
Tracks: / Year of the cat / Couldn't get it right.
Single (7"): released on Old Gold, Nov'86 by Old Gold Records. Dist: Lightning, Jazz Music, Spartan, Counterpoint

ZERO SHE FLIES.
Album: released on RCA, Oct'85 by RCA Records. Dist: RCA, Roots, Swift, Wellard, Chris, I & B, Solomon & Peres Distribution

Cassette: released on RCA, Oct'85 by RCA Records. Dist: RCA, Roots, Swift, Wellard, Chris, I & B, Solomon & Peres Distribution

Stewart, Amii

AMII.
Tracks: / Time is tight / Power play / Easy on your love / Easy on your love / Love's in disguise / Lover to lover / Break these chains / Love ain't no toy / Mystery of love, The / Conspiracy / This generation.
Album: released on RCA, Jan'87 by RCA Records. Dist: RCA, Roots, Swift, Wellard, Chris, I & B, Solomon & Peres Distribution

Cassette: released on RCA, Jan'87 by RCA Records. Dist: RCA, Roots, Swift, Wellard, Chris, I & B, Solomon & Peres Distribution

AMII STEWART.
Album: released on Atlantic, May'79 by WEA Records. Dist: WEA

Cassette: released on Atlantic, May'79 by WEA Records. Dist: WEA

ASH 48.
Single (12"): released on Sedition, Oct'85 Dist: PRT

FRIENDS.
Single (7"): released on RCA, Jan'85 by RCA Records. Dist: RCA, Roots, Swift, Wellard, Chris, I & B, Solomon & Peres Distribution

HITS, THE.
Album: released on Sedition, Nov'85 Dist: PRT

Cassette: released on Sedition, Nov'85 Dist: PRT

KNOCK ON WOOD.
Single (7"): released on Atlantic, '78 by WEA Records. Dist: WEA

Single (7"): released on Sedition, Jul'85 Dist: PRT

Single (12"): released on Sedition, Jul'85 Dist: PRT

LIGHT MY FIRE.
Single (7"): released on Atlantic, Jun'79 by WEA Records. Dist: WEA

Single (12"): released on Sedition, Aug'85 Dist: PRT

LOVE AIN'T NO TOY.
Tracks: / Lover to lover / Friends.
Notes: Friends-on 12" version only
Single (7"): released on RCA, Feb'87 by RCA Records. Dist: RCA, Roots, Swift, Wellard, Chris, I & B, Solomon & Peres Distribution

Single (12"): released on RCA, Feb'87 by RCA Records. Dist: RCA, Roots, Swift, Wellard, Chris, I & B, Solomon & Peres Distribution

MY GUY, MY GIRL (Stewart, Amii & Deon Estus).
Tracks: / My guy, my girl / Bring it on back / Knock on wood * / Light my fire *.
Single (12"): released on Sedition, Jan'86 Dist: PRT

Single (7"): released on Sedition, Nov'85 Dist: PRT

Single (12"): released on Sedition, Nov'85 Dist: PRT

PARADISE BIRD.
Album: released on Atlantic, Oct'79 by WEA Records. Dist: WEA

Cassette: released on Atlantic, Nov'79 by WEA Records. Dist: WEA

THAT LOVING FEELING.
Single (7"): released on RCA, Mar'85 by RCA Records. Dist: RCA, Roots, Swift, Wellard, Chris, I & B, Solomon & Peres Distribution

Single (12"): released on RCA, Mar'85 by RCA Records. Dist: RCA, Roots, Swift, Wellard, Chris, I & B, Solomon & Peres Distribution

WHERE DID OUR LOVE GO.
Single (7"): released on Atlantic, Apr'81 by WEA Records. Dist: WEA

Single (12"): released on Atlantic, Apr'81 by WEA Records. Dist: WEA

YOU REALLY TOUCH MY HEART.
Single (7"): released on Sedition, Oct'85 Dist: PRT

Single (12"): released on Sedition, Oct'85 Dist: PRT

Double-pack single: released on Sedition, Nov'85 Dist: PRT

Stewart, Andy

20 SCOTTISH FAVOURITES-COLLECTION.
Album: released on Music For Pleasure, Jun'85 by EMI Records. Dist: EMI

Cassette: released on Music For Pleasure, Jun'85 by EMI Records. Dist: EMI

ANDY STEWARTS GREATSET HITS.
Album: released on PRT Special, May'77 by PRT Records. Dist: PRT

BEST OF ANDY STEWART, THE.
Album: released on Emerald, Aug'87 by Emerald Records. Dist: Ross, PRT, Solomon & Peres Distribution

Cassette: released on Emerald, Aug'87 by Emerald Records. Dist: Ross, PRT, Solomon & Peres Distribution

BRAND NEW FROM ANDY.
Cassette: released on PRT Special, May'75 by PRT Records. Dist: PRT

Cassette: released on PRT Special, May'75 by PRT Records. Dist: PRT

COME IN COME IN.
Album: released on Lismor, Sep'83 by Lismor Records. Dist: Lismor, Roots, Celtic Music

COUNTRY BOY (Stewart Andy with Ann Williams).
Album: released on PRT, Nov'75 by PRT Records. Dist: PRT

Cassette: released on PRT, Nov'75 by PRT Records. Dist: PRT

FIRE IN THE GLEN (Stewart, Andy M/Phil Cunningham/Manus Lunny).
Album: released on Topic, Nov'86 Dist: Roots Distribution

LEGENDS OF SCOTLAND.
Tracks: / Campbelltown loch / Battle is o'er, The / Take me back / Donald where's yer troosers / Muckin' o' Geordie's byre / Scottish soldier, A / Barren rocks of Aden / Road to Dundee / Dancing in Kyle / Cailin mo ruin-sa / Morag of Dunvegan / By the lochside / Tunes of glory / D'ye mind lang syne.
Cassette: released on Lochshore, Jun'86 by Klub Records. Dist: PRT

SCOTLAND IS ANDY STEWART.
Album: released on Emerald (Ireland), Oct'81 by Emerald Records. Dist: I & B, Ross, PRT

Cassette: released on Emerald (Ireland), Oct'81 by Emerald Records. Dist: I & B, Ross, PRT

Stewart, Andy M.

BY THE HUSH.
Album: released on Highway, Apr'86 by Highway Records. Dist: Roots, Projection, Ross

Stewart, Angela

COULD I HAVE THIS DANCE/INSTRUMENTAL.
Single (12"): released on Thunderbolt, Nov'83 by Thunderbolt Records. Dist: Jetstar Distribution

FEEL LIKE DANCING.
Single (7"): released on Nura, Oct'83 by Nura Records. Dist: Jetstar Distribution

MOONLIGHT LOVER.
Single (12"): released on Kingdom, Jun'84 by Kingdom Records. Dist: Kingdom

WHEN LOVES COME KNOCKING.
Single (12"): released on Dynamic, Jun'82 by Creole Records. Dist: CBS, Essex

Stewart, Belle

QUEEN AMONG THE HEATHER.
Album: released on Topic, Jan'81 by Topic Records. Dist: Distribution, Projection Distribution, Jazz Music Distribution

STEWARTS O'BLAIR (Stewart, Belle & family).
Album: released on Lismor, Jul'85 by Lismor Records. Dist: Lismor, Roots, Celtic Music

Stewart, Babs

EASY WAY OUT (Stewart, Babs & Rocky Cambell).
Single (12"): released on Private I, Oct'84 Dist: CBS

IT HURTS SO GOOD.
Single (12"): released on Sunburn, Jul'83 by Orbitone Records. Dist: Jetstar Distribution

Stewart, Billy

SUMMERTIME.
Single (7"): released on Chess, Jul'85 by Charly Records. Dist: Charly, Swift, PRT, Discovery, IMS, Polygram

Stewart, Bob

TOMORROW WE PART.
Album: released on Broadside, Jun'81 by Broadside Records. Dist: Celtic Distributions, H.R. Taylor, Jazz Music, Projection, Jazz Services Unlimited Dist. (JSU)

Cassette: released on Broadside, Jun'81 by Broadside Records. Dist: Celtic Distributions, H.R. Taylor, Jazz Music, Projection, Jazz Services Unlimited Dist. (JSU)

Stewart, Dave

BUSY DOIN NOTHING/THE WORLD (Stewart, Dave & Barbara Gaskin).
Single (7"): released on Broken, Aug'83 by Broken Records. Dist: Stiff Records, EMI

Picture disc single: released on Broken, Aug'83 by Broken Records. Dist: Stiff Records, EMI

I'M IN A DIFFERENT WORLD (Stewart, Dave & Barbara Gaskin).
Single (7"): released on Broken, Jun'84 by Broken Records. Dist: Stiff Records, EMI

IT'S MY PARTY (Stewart, Dave & Barbara Gaskin).
Single (7"): released on Broken, Aug'81 by Broken Records. Dist: Stiff Records, EMI

JOHNNY ROCCO/HAMBURGER SONG (Stewart, Dave & Barbara Gaskin).
Single (7"): released on Broken, Nov'82 by Broken Records. Dist: Stiff Records, EMI

LEIPZIG/RICH FOR A DAY (Stewart, Dave & Barbara Gaskin).
Single (7"): released on Broken, Jan'84 by Broken Records. Dist: Stiff Records, EMI

LOCOMOTION, THE (Stewart, Dave & Barbara Gaskin).
Tracks: / Locomotion, The / Make me promises.
Single (7"): released on Broken, May'86 by Broken Records. Dist: Stiff Records, EMI

Single (12"): released on Broken, May'86 by Broken Records. Dist: Stiff Records, EMI

SIAMESE CAT SONG/EMPERORS GUITAR (Stewart, Dave & Barbara Gaskin).
Single (7"): released on Broken, Feb'83 by Broken Records. Dist: Stiff Records, EMI

WHAT BECOMES OF THE BROKEN HEARTED.
Single (7"): released on Broken, Feb'81 by Broken Records. Dist: Stiff Records, EMI

Stewart, Davie

DAVIE STEWART.
Album: released on Topic, Jan'81 Dist: Roots Distribution

LIFE TRAVELLING ROADS.
Cassette: released on Folktracks, Nov'79 by Folktracks Cassettes. Dist: Folktracks

SCOTS BALLADS (ACC).
Cassette: released on Folktracks, Nov'79 by Folktracks Cassettes. Dist: Folktracks

SHORES OF THE FORTH (Stewart, Davie & John Watt with the Beggar's Mantle Band).
Album: released on Springthyme, '83 by Springthyme Records. Dist: Jazz Music Distribution, Projection Distribution, Roots Distribution

Cassette: released on Springthyme, '83 by Springthyme Records. Dist: Jazz Music Distribution, Projection Distribution, Roots Distribution

TWO SCOTS TINKER TALES.
Cassette: released on Folktracks, Nov'79 by Folktracks Cassettes. Dist: Folktracks

Stewart, Eric

FROOTY ROOTIES.
Album: released on Mercury, Aug'82 by Phonogram Records. Dist: Polygram Distribution

Cassette: released on Mercury, Aug'82 by Phonogram Records. Dist: Polygram Distribution

Stewart Family

STEWARTS OF BLAIR THE.

Album: released on Topic, Jan'81 by Topic Records. Dist: , Projection Distribution, Jazz Music Distribution

TRAVELLING STEWARTS THE.
Album: released on Topic, Jan'81 by Topic Records. Dist: Projection Distribution, Jazz Music Distribution

Stewart, Gary

20 OF THE BEST.
Album: released on RCA, Mar'84 by RCA Records. Dist: RCA, Roots, Swift, Wellard, Chris, I & B, Solomon & Peres Distribution

Cassette: released on RCA, Mar'84 by RCA Records. Dist: RCA, Roots, Swift, Wellard, Chris, I & B, Solomon & Peres Distribution

Stewart, Jermaine

DON'T EVER LEAVE ME.
Tracks: / Give your love to me.
Single (7"): released on 10, Jan'87 by 10 Records. Dist: Virgin, EMI

Single (12"): released on Ten, Jan'87

FRANTIC ROMANTIC.
Tracks: / We don't have to take our clothes off / Versatile / Moonlight carnival / Don't ever leave me / Dance floor / Jody / Give your love to me / Out to punish / Frantic romantic.
Compact disc: released on 10, Jul'87 by 10 Records. Dist: Virgin, EMI

GET IT OVER WITH.
Single (7"): released on 10, Jun'84 by 10 Records. Dist: Virgin, EMI

Single (12"): released on 10, Jun'84 by 10 Records. Dist: Virgin, EMI

GET OVER IT.
Single (7"): released on 10, Jun'84 by 10 Records. Dist: Virgin, EMI

Single (12"): released on 10, Jun'84 by 10 Records. Dist: Virgin, EMI

I LIKE IT.
Single (7"): released on 10, May'85 by 10 Records. Dist: Virgin, EMI

Single (12"): released on 10, May'85 by 10 Records. Dist: Virgin, EMI

JODY.
Tracks: / Jody / Dance floor.
Single (7"): released on 10, Oct'86 by 10 Records. Dist: Virgin, EMI

Single (12"): released on 10, Oct'86 by 10 Records. Dist: Virgin, EMI

WE DON'T HAVE TO TAKE OUR CLOTHES OFF.
Tracks: / We don't have to take our clothes off / Brilliance.
Single (7"): released on 10, Feb'86 by 10 Records. Dist: Virgin, EMI

Single (12"): released on 10, Feb'86 by 10 Records. Dist: Virgin, EMI

WORD IS OUT.
Single (7"): released on Virgin, Mar'84 by Virgin Records. Dist: EMI, Virgin Distribution

Single (12"): released on Virgin, Mar'84 by Virgin Records. Dist: EMI, Virgin Distribution

WORD IS OUT THE.
Album: released on Ten, Nov'84

Cassette: released on Ten, Nov'84

Stewart, Jimmy

TOUCH, THE.
Notes: American guitarist Jimmy Stewart With a programme of his own compositions. Each piece is dedicated to the foremost jazz guitarists, simulating the styles and sounds of their respective eras. As well as his collaboration with one of the most important guitarists of the 60's and 70's Gabor Szabo, Stewart has performed with countless other stars, including Ray Charles, Quincey Jones, Andy Williams and Michael Jackson Personnel: Ryo Okomoto-synthesiser
Album: released on Blackhawk, Jan'87 by Blackhawk Records (USA). Dist: IMS-Polygram

TOUCH, THE.
Album: released on Blackhawk, Aug'86 by Blackhawk Records (USA). Dist: IMS-Polygram

Cassette: released on Blackhawk, Aug'86 by Blackhawk Records (USA). Dist: IMS-Polygram

Stewart, John

CALIFORNIA BLOODLINES PLUS.
Tracks: / California bloodlines / Razor back woman / She believes in me / Omaha rainbow / Pirates of Stone County Road, The / Shakles and chains / Heart full of woman and a bellyfull of Tennessee / Willard / Big Joe / Mother country / Lonesome picker / You can't look back / Missouri birds / July, you're a woman / Never goin' back / Friend of Jesus / Marshall wind.
Album: released on See For Miles, Mar'87 by See For Miles Records. Dist: Pinnacle
Cat. no: **SEE 87**

PHOENIX CONCERTS THE.
Album: released on RCA (Germany), Jul'83

TRANCAS.

Album: released on Sunstorm, Nov'84 by Sunstorm Records. Dist: Stage One Records

Album: released on Sierra, Jul'85 by Sierra Records. Dist: WEA

Cassette: released on Sierra, Jul'85 by Sierra Records. Dist: WEA

Stewart & Kyle

ISN'T IT STRANGE.
Album: by Pilgrim Records. Dist: Rough Trade, Cartel

YOURS FOREVER.
Album: by Pilgrim Records. Dist: Rough Trade, Cartel

Stewart, Louis

BAUBLES,BANGLES & BEADS (Stewa Louis & Peter Ind).
Album: released on Wave, Apr'79 by Wav Records. Dist: JSU, Swift, Jazz Music, Cadilla Chris Wellard

Stewart, Mark & Mafia

AS THE VENEER OF DECEMOCRAC STARTS TO FADE.
Album: released on Mute, Nov'85 Dist: Spa tan Distribution, Rough Trade Distribution, Ca tel Distribution

COPING WITH COWARDICE.
Album: released on On-U-Sound, Jun'83 Di Rough Trade Distribution, Lightning

HIGH IDEALS AND CRAZ DREAMS/JERUSALEM.
Single (12"): released on On-U-Sound, Oct' Dist: Rough Trade Distribution, Lightning

HYPNOTISED.
Single (7"): released on Mute, May'85 Di Spartan Distribution, Rough Trade Distributio Cartel Distribution

Single (12"): released on Mute, May'85 D Spartan Distribution, Rough Trade Distributi Cartel Distribution

Stewart, Norman

MUSIC AND SONG FROM SCOTLAN
Album: released on Celtic Music, May'80 Celtic Music Distribution. Dist: Celtic Mu Jazz Music, Projection, Roots

Stewart, Rex

BIGG JAZZ 1940 also see Teagerden J (Stewart, Rex & Jack Teagarden).

BIG JAZZ 1940 (Stewart, Rex & Jack garden).
Album: released on Everybody's, Jul'87 Everybody's Records. Dist: Jazz Music, Sw

HOLLYWOOD JAM Featuring Duke Ell ton (Stewart, Rex All Stars Band).
Album: released on Duke, Jul'87 by Melo Records. Dist: Jazz Horizons, Jazz Music, tic Music, Swift

Album: released on Duke, Oct'82 by Melo Records. Dist: Jazz Horizons, Jazz Music, tic Music, Swift

RENDEZVOUS WITH REX.
Tracks: / Tillie's twist / Pretty ditty / Tell me / Trade winds / My kind of gal / Blue echo.
Notes: Licensed from Decca Records Ltd pyright Control
Album: released on Affinity, Dec'86 by C Records. Dist: Charly, Cadillac

Stewart, Rod

ABSOLUTELY LIVE.
Compact disc: released on Riva, Mar'87 PRT

Album: released on Riva, Nov'82 Dist: P

Cassette: released on Riva, Nov'82 Dist:

AN OLD RAINCOAT WON'T LET DOWN.
Album: released on Mercury, Aug'83 by nogram Records. Dist: Polygram Distribu

Cassette: released on Mercury, Aug' Phonogram Records. Dist: Polygram Di tion

ANOTHER HEARTACHE.
Tracks: / Another heartache / You're heart.
Single (7"): released on Warner Bros., by Warner Bros Records. Dist: WEA

Single (12"): released on Warner Bros., by Warner Bros Records. Dist: WEA

ATLANTIC CROSSING.
Tracks: / Three times a loser / Alright for a / All in the name of r'n'roll / Drift away / cold sober / I don't want to talk about it / the spotlight / This old heart of mine(is w you) / Still love you / Sailing.

ompact disc: released on Riva, Feb'87 Dist: RT

bum: released on Riva, Jul'77 Dist: PRT

assette: released on Riva, Jul'77 Dist: PRT

TLANTIC CROSSING/A NIGHT ON HE TOWN.
assette: released on Riva Warner Bros, ov'83

ABY JANE/READY NOW/IF LOVING OU WAS WRONG.
ngle (7"): released on Warner Bros., Jun'83 Warner Bros Records. Dist: WEA

ngle (12"): released on Warner Bros., Jun'83 Warner Bros Records. Dist: WEA

EST OF ROD STEWART THE.
bum: released on Mercury, Sep'85 by Phogram Records. Dist: Polygram Distribution

assette: released on Mercury, Sep'85 by onogram Records. Dist: Polygram Distribun

EST OF THE.
ouble Album: released on Mercury, Jun'77 Phonogram Records. Dist: Polygram Disution

ouble cassette: released on Mercury, Jun'77 Phonogram Records. Dist: Polygram Disution

EST OF THE BEST THE.
bum: released on Mercury, May'81 by Phogram Records. Dist: Polygram Distribution

ODY WISHES.
acks: / Dancin' alone / Baby Jane / Move me ody wishes / Sweet surrender / What am I nna do / Ghetto blaster / Ready now / Strans / Again / Satisfied.
bum: released on Warner Brothers, Jun'83 Warner Bros Records. Dist: WEA

ssette: released on Warner Brothers, Jun'83 Warner Bros Records. Dist: WEA

mpact disc: released on Warner Bros., 84 by Warner Bros Records. Dist: WEA

AMOUFLAGE.
um: released on Warner Brothers, Jun'84 WEA Records. Dist: WEA

ssette: released on Warner Brothers, Jun'84 WEA Records. Dist: WEA

mpact disc: released on Warner Brothers, 84 by WEA Records. Dist: WEA

N I GET A WITNESS.
um: released on Astan, Nov'84 by Astan cords. Dist: Counterpoint

ssette: released on Astan, Nov'84 by Astan cords. Dist: Counterpoint

ERY BEAT OF MY HEART.
cks: / Who's gonna take me home / Another rtache / Night like this, A / Red hot in black / e to eternity / Love touch / In my own crazy / Every beat of my heart / Ten days of rain my life / Every beat of my heart * / Trouble.
um: released on Warner Bros., Jul'86 by ner Bros Records. Dist: WEA

sette: released on Warner Bros., Jul'86 by ner Bros Records. Dist: WEA

mpact disc: released on Warner Bros., 6 by Warner Bros Records. Dist: WEA

gle (7"): released on Warner Bros., Jun'86 Varner Bros Records. Dist: WEA

gle (12"): released on Warner Bros., Jun'86 Varner Bros Records. Dist: WEA

ERY PICTURE TELLS A STORY.
cks: / True blue / You wear it well / I don't t to discuss it / You're my girl / Sweet little 'n' roller / Sailor / Dixie toot / Street fighting / Every picture tells a story / Seems like a time / That's all right / Amazing grace / Toow is such a long time / Henry / Maggie May ndolin wind / I'm losing you (I know) / Reao believe.
npact disc: released on Mercury, Oct'84 by nogram Records. Dist: Polygram Distribu-

m: released on Mercury, May'83 by Phoam Records. Dist: Polygram Distribution

sette: released on Mercury, May'83 by nogram Records. Dist: Polygram Distribu-

OTLOOSE AND FANCY FREE.
m: released on Riva, Oct'77 Dist: PRT

sette: released on Riva, Oct'77 Dist: PRT

SOLINE ALLEY.
npact disc: by Phonogram Records. Dist: gram

EATEST HITS: ROD STEWART.
Compact disc: released on Riva, Jan'81 Dist: PRT

GREATEST HITS:ROD STEWART.
Tracks: / Hot legs / Maggie May / Do ya think I'm sexy / You're in my heart / Sailing / I don't want to talk about it / Tonight's the night / Killing of Georgie / First cut is the deepest / I was only joking.
Compact disc: released on Riva, '83 Dist: PRT

GREATEST HITS: ROD STEWART VOL.2.
Compact disc: by CBS Records. Dist: CBS

GREATEST HITS: ROD STEWART VOL.1.
Album: released on Riva, Oct'79 Dist: PRT

Cassette: released on Riva, Oct'79 Dist: PRT

HITS OF ROD STEWART THE.
Album: released on Contour, Sep'85 by Pickwick Records. Dist: Pickwick Distribution, PRT

Cassette: released on Contour, Sep'85 by Pickwick Records. Dist: Pickwick Distribution, PRT

I WAS ONLY JOKING/HOT LEGS.
Single (7"): released on Riva, Jan'80 Dist: PRT

JUKE BOX HEAVEN 14 rock'n'roll greats.
Album: released on Contour, Jan'87 by Pickwick Records. Dist: Pickwick Distribution, PRT

Cassette: released on Contour, Jan'87 by Pickwick Records. Dist: Pickwick Distribution, PRT

LITTLE MISS UNDERSTOOD/SO MUCH TO SAY.
Single (7"): released on Immediate, Feb'83 by Castle Communications. Dist: Cartel

LOVE TOUCH.
Tracks: / Love touch / Heart is on the line / Hard lesson to learn *.
Single (7"): released on Warner Bros., May'86 by Warner Bros Records. Dist: WEA

Single (12"): released on Warner Bros., May'86 by Warner Bros Records. Dist: WEA

Album: released on A&M, Sep'76 by A&M Records. Dist: Polygram

MAGGIE MAY.
Album: released on Contour, Sep'81 by Pickwick Records. Dist: Pickwick Distribution, PRT

Cassette: released on Contour, Sep'81 by Pickwick Records. Dist: Pickwick Distribution, PRT

Single (7"): released on Mercury, Oct'84 by Phonogram Records. Dist: Polygram Distribution

MUSIC OF 1970-71 THE.
Cassette: released on Mercury, Jan'77 by Phonogram Records. Dist: Polygram Distribution

MY GIRL/SHE WON'T DANCE WITHOUT ME.
Single (7"): released on Riva, Dec'80 Dist: PRT

NIGHT ON THE TOWN A.
Album: released on Riva, Jan'76 Dist: PRT

Cassette: released on Riva, Jan'76 Dist: PRT

OH GOD I WISH I WAS HOME.
Single (7"): released on Riva, Mar'81 Dist: PRT

OH NO NOT MY BABY (COMPILATION).
Album: released on Japanese Import, May'79

PASSION.
Single (7"): released on Riva, Oct'80 Dist: PRT

Single (12"): released on Riva, Oct'80 Dist: PRT

PEOPLE GET READY (Stewart, Rod & Jeff Beck).
Single (7"): released on Epic, Jun'85 by CBS Records. Dist: CBS

ROD STEWART.
Album: released on Contour, Oct'82 by Pickwick Records. Dist: Pickwick Distribution, PRT

Cassette: released on Contour, Oct'82 by Pickwick Records. Dist: Pickwick Distribution, PRT

Cassette: released on Cambra, Jan'83 by Cambra Records. Dist: IDS, Conifer

Album: released on Mercury (Holland), Jul'85 by Phonogram Records. Dist: Polygram Distribution

Cassette: released on Mercury (Holland), Jul'85 by Phonogram Records. Dist: Polygram Distribution

SAILING.
Tracks: / Sailing / Stone cold sober.
Notes: All proceeds to The Channel Ferry Disaster Fund

Single (7"): released on Warner Bros., Mar'87 by Warner Bros Records. Dist: WEA

SAILING/STONE COLD SOBER.
Single (7"): released on Riva, Jun'77 Dist: PRT

Single (7"): released on Warner Bros., Jan'84 by Warner Bros Records. Dist: WEA

SING IT AGAIN ROD.
Compact disc: by Phonogram Records. Dist: Polygram Distribution

SOME DAY.
Album: released on Platinum (W.Germany), Oct'85 Dist: Mainline

Cassette: released on Platinum (W.Germany), Oct'85 Dist: Mainline

SWEET SURRENDER/GHETTO BLASTER/GOD I WISH I WAS HOME TONIGHT.
Single (7"): released on Warner Brothers, Nov'83 by WEA Records. Dist: WEA

Single (12"): released on Warner Brothers, Nov'83 by WEA Records. Dist: WEA

TONIGHT I'M YOURS.
Album: released on Riva, Nov'81 Dist: PRT

Cassette: released on Riva, Nov'81 Dist: PRT

TONIGHT IS YOURS.
Video-cassette (VHS): released on Embassy Home Entertainment, Jan'84 by CBS. Dist: Gold & Sons

TONIGHTS THE NIGHT.
Single (7"): released on Riva (import), Jan'80

WEREDSUCCESSEN SERIES.
Album: released on Mercury (europe), Jun'82

Cassette: released on Mercury (europe), Jun'82

WIDE EYED GIRL.
Album: released on Platinum (W.Germany), Oct'85 Dist: Mainline

Cassette: released on Platinum (W.Germany), Oct'85 Dist: Mainline

YOU WEAR IT WELL.
Single (7"): released on Phillips import, Jan'80

Stewart, Roma

TODAY/LISTEN TO MUMMY AND DADDY.
Single (12"): released on S&G, Dec'82 by S&G Records. Dist: Jetstar

Stewart, Roman

WHAT YOU WANNA DO.
Single (12"): released on D. Roy, Apr'80

Stewart, Sandy

IF YOU'RE NOT HERE.
Single (7"): released on Vista Sounds, Mar'85 by Vista Sounds Records. Dist: Jetstar

SINGS THE SONGS OF JEROME KERN.
Notes: with Dick Hyman piano.
Album: released on Audiophile, Jan'87 by Jazzology Records (USA). Dist: Jazz Music, Swift

Stewart, Slam

Biographical Details: Stewart, Slam is a bassist and vocalist, born Leroy Stewart on 21 September 1914in Englewood, New Jersey. He teamed with **Slim Gaillard** in 1937 as **Slim & Slam**; their hits included **'Flat Foot Floogie'**. He practices one of the most distinctive and delightful gimmicks in jazz, bowing a bass solo and humming in unison and octave above. One of his best know recording sessions was late '43 with the **Lester Young Quartet**. He appeared in the early 1980's with **Illinois Jacquet** at the late lamented Canteen. Guitarist **Bucky Pizzerelli** was born in 1926, also in New Jersey, which also gave us Count Basie, Frank Sinatra, Bruce Springsteen...

DIALOGUE.
Album: released on Sonet, Jan'80 by Sonet Records. Dist: PRT

Album: released on Stash, Apr'81 Dist: Swift Distribution, Jazz Music Distribution, Jazz Horizons Distribution, Celtic Music Distribution, Cadilac, JSU Distribution, Zodiac Distribution

NEW YORK NEW YORK.
Album: released on Stash, Apr'81 Dist: Swift Distribution, Jazz Music Distribution, Jazz Horizons Distribution, Celtic Music Distribution, Cadillac, JSU Distribution, Zodiac Distribution

Cassette: released on Stash, Apr'81 Dist: Swift Distribution, Jazz Music Distribution, Jazz Horizons Distribution, Celtic Music Distribution, Cadillac, JSU Distribution, Zodiac Distribution

Stewart & Stax

I GOT FAITH IN YOU.
Tracks: / Rita's baby (Inst) / I got faith in you.
Single (7"): released on Rainbow, Jan'87 Dist: I & B, CBS

Stewart, Tinga

GONE AGAIN.
Single (12"): released on Jedi, Nov'84 Dist: Jetstar Deleted '1.

GYPSY RASTS/RUNNING UP AND DOWN.
Single (12"): released on Gog, Apr'83 by Gog Records. Dist: Jetstar

KEY TO YOUR HEART.
Album: released on Londisc, Aug'84 by Londisc Records.

KEY TO YOUR HEAT/INSTRUMENTAL VERSION.
Single (12"): released on Calabash, Aug'83 by Calabash Records. Dist: Jetstar

NUMBER ONE SONG (RUB A DUB).
Single (7"): released on Vista Sounds, Mar'85 by Vista Sounds Records. Dist: Jetstar

RED RED WINE/YOU SHOULD NEVER DO THAT.
Single (12"): released on Jama, Sep'83 by Jama Records.

TAKE YOU TO THE DANCE.
Tracks: / Take you to the dance / She pan wee mine.
Single (12"): released on Twin Explosion, Aug'86 Dist: Jetstar

Stewart, Tinker

DRY UP YOUR TEARS.
Single (12"): released on White, Feb'85

Stewart, Wayne

ASPEN SKYLINE (Stewart Wayne & Friends).
Album: released on Sierra, May'79 by Sierra Records. Dist: WEA

Sticky Wicket

TALKING CRICKET.
Single (12"): released on CSA, Jul'84 by CSA Records. Dist: PRT, Jetstar
Cat. no: **12CSA 503**
Single (7"): released on CSA, Jun'84 by CSA Records. Dist: PRT, Jetstar

Stiff Kittens

CONTEMPT.
Tracks: / Contempt / Light.
Single (7"): released on Chris, May'86 Dist: Prism, Red Rhino, Cartel

HAPPY NOW.
Single (7"): released on Crisis, Aug'86 by Prism Records. Dist: Red Rhino, Cartel

Stiff Little Fingers

ALL THE BEST.
Album: released on Chrysalis, Jan'83 by Chrysalis Records. Dist: CBS

Cassette: released on Chrysalis, Jan'83 by Chrysalis Records. Dist: CBS

ALTERNATIVE ULSTER.
Single (7"): released on Rough Trade, Jan'79 by Rough Trade Records. Dist: Rough Trade Distribution, Cartel Distribution

AT THE EDGE.
Single (7"): released on Chrysalis, Feb'80 by Chrysalis Records. Dist: CBS

BITS OF KIDS.
Single (7"): released on Chrysalis, Aug'82 by Chrysalis Records. Dist: CBS

Single (12"): released on Chrysalis, Aug'82 by Chrysalis Records. Dist: CBS

GO FOR IT.
Album: released on Chrysalis, Apr'81 by Chrysalis Records. Dist: CBS

Cassette: released on Chrysalis, Apr'81 by Chrysalis Records. Dist: CBS

GOTTA GETTAWAY.
Single (7"): released on Rough Trade, May'79 by Rough Trade Records. Dist: Rough Trade Distribution, Cartel Distribution

HANX.
Cassette: released on Chrysalis, Sep'80 by Chrysalis Records. Dist: CBS

Album: released on Chrysalis, Sep'80 by Chrysalis Records. Dist: CBS

INFLAMMABLE MATERIAL.
Album: released on Rough Trade, Aug'79 by Rough Trade Records. Dist: Rough Trade Distribution, Cartel Distribution

Cat. no: XPRES

JUST FADE AWAY.
Single (7"): released on Chrysalis, Mar'81 by Chrysalis Records. Dist: CBS

LISTEN.
Single (7"): released on Chrysalis, Jan'82 by Chrysalis Records. Dist: CBS

NOBODY'S HERO.
Single (7"): released on Chrysalis, May'80 by Chrysalis Records. Dist: CBS

Album: released on Chrysalis, Mar'80 by Chrysalis Records. Dist: CBS

Cassette: released on Chrysalis, Mar'80 by Chrysalis Records. Dist: CBS

NOW THEN.
Album: released on Chrysalis, Sep'82 by Chrysalis Records. Dist: CBS

Cassette: released on Chrysalis, Sep'82 by Chrysalis Records. Dist: CBS

PEEL SESSION 12.9.78.
Tracks: / Johnny was / Law and order / Barbed wire love / Suspect device.

PEEL SESSIONS.
Cassette single: released on Strange Fruit, 30 May'87 by Clive Selwood. Dist: Pinnacle

SILVERLINING.
Single (7"): released on Chrysalis, May'81 by Chrysalis Records. Dist: CBS

SUSPECT DEVICE.
Single (7"): released on Rigid Digits, Jun'78 Dist: PRT

Single (7"): released on Rough Trade, Jan'79 by Rough Trade Records. Dist: Rough Trade Distribution, Cartel Distribution

TALK BACK.
Single (7"): released on Chrysalis, Apr'82 by Chrysalis Records. Dist: CBS

Stiffs

GOODBYE MY LOVE.
Single (7"): released on Stiff, Feb'81 by Stiff Records. Dist: EMI, Record Services Distribution (Ireland)

Stiffs '85

YOUNG GUITARS, THE.
Single (12"): released on Dork, Jun'85 by Dork Records. Dist: Probe, Cartel

Stiffy Dread

JAH DREADFUL (2 parts).
Single (12"): released on Twinkle, Sep'83 by Twinkle Records. Dist: Jetstar

Stigma

REMEMBER.
Single (12"): released on Stigmatic Sound, Sep'81

Stikki Stuff

YO YO.
Tracks: / Yo yo / For all those who sail with us.
Single (7"): released on Total Eclipse, Oct'86 Dist: Spartan

Stiletto

VIDEO.
Single (7"): released on Wonderful, Aug'81 Dist: Spartan

Stiletto Rox

TAKE ME WHEN YOU GO.
Tracks: / Take me when you go / Shouting out a reason.
Single (7"): released on Slik, Oct'86

Still

CHORUS OF BLOWS.
Extended-play record: released on Open Door, Aug'82 by Open Door Records. Dist: Open Door Distribution

Still groove-jumping

STILL GROOVE - JUMPING Various artists (Various Artists).
Tracks: / High low Jack / Mr Bear comes to town / I'm gonna keep my good eye on you / Peek-a-boo / Bear hug, The / When I get married / Rockin with red / Jump man jump / She's got no hair / Country boy / You better heed my warning / Down in the bottom / Midnight hours / Right now baby / All my life / Drink up.
Album: released on Detour, Jul'87 by Detour Records. Dist: Swift, RCA, Jazz Music, Projection

Still Life

AWAY FROM THIS TOWN.
Single (7"): released on Regard, Sep'82

PASSION PLAY.
Single (7"): released on Funzone, Aug'83 by Funzone Records.

Stills, Stephen

Biographical Details: Stephen Stills was born on 3 January 1945 in Dallas, Texas; a singer, guitarist and songwriter who worked in **Buffalo Springfield**, auditioned to be a **Monkee**, then became a superstar with **Crosby, Stills, Nash & Young**. He wrote many of Buffalo's songs and has been doing it ever since; also played on **Supersession** in 1968 with **Al Kooper** and **Mike Bloomfield**; his first solo album **Stephen Stills** in 1970 was a smash hit and is still selling, with hit song **'Love the one you're with'**.

LOVE THE ONE YOU'RE WITH.
Single (7"): released on Atlantic, '75 by WEA Records. Dist: WEA

STEPHEN STILLS.
Album: released on Atlantic, '73 by WEA Records. Dist: WEA

TWO ORIGINALS OF STEPHEN STILLS
Stephen Stills and Stephen Stills 2.
Double Album: released on Atlantic, Oct'75 by WEA Records. Dist: WEA

Still thinking

FIRST ROMANCE.
Single (7"): released on Last Minute, Apr'83 by Initial Records. Dist: Pinnacle

Still Waters Trio

LIFE'S RAILROAD.
Album: by Pilgrim Records. Dist: Rough Trade, Cartel

Stilts

WAITNG FOR A MIRACLE ('Til Tuesday).
Single (7"): released on Rondelet, Dec'81 Dist: Spartan Distribution

Stimulators

LOUD, FAST RULES.
Cassette: released on Reach Out International, '83 Dist: Red Rhino, Cartel

Sting

BRING ON THE NIGHT.
Tracks: / Bring on the night / Consider me gone / Low life / We work the black seam / Driven to tears / Dream of the blue turtles, The / Demolition man / One world / Love is seventh wave / Moon over bourbon street / I burn for you / Another day / Children's crusade / Down so long / Tea in the Sahara.
Notes: Sting:'Bring on the night'-the ultimate performance album! In 1985,Sting took a brand new band on the road.Later that year the band recorded and released the world-wide smash album 'The Dream of The Blue Turtles'The band consisted of:Bra-nford Marsalis on saxophone (worked with Art Blakey,Dizzie Gillespie,Miles DavisWynton Marsalis & Clark Terry):Kenny Kirkland on keyboards (worked with Wyntonl Marsalis,Dizzie Gillespie & Elvin Jones): Omar Hakim on Drums(previously with Weather Report):Darryl Jones on bass (previously with Miles Davis): Dolette McDonald on backing vocals (worked with The Police,Talking Heads and Laurie Anderson):Janice Pendarvis on backing vocals (worked with Philip Glass,Laurie Anderson,Roberta Flack and Peter Tosh). Whilst on tour,selected gigs in Rome and Paris were singled out and recorded "Bring On The Night" is the result of those recordings,and is without doubt one of the most exiting albums ever released. A 15 track'live'double album,cassette & compact disc,including 6 tracks from 'The Dream Of The Blue Turtles'8 Police songs and a superb re-working of 'Down So Long'
Double Album: released on A&M, Jun'86 by A&M Records. Dist: Polygram

Double cassette: released on A&M, Jun'86 by A&M Records. Dist: Polygram

Compact disc: released on A&M, Jun'86 by A&M Records. Dist: Polygram

DREAM OF THE BLUE TURTLES,THE.
Tracks: / If you love somebody set them free / Love is the seventh wave / We work the black seam / Russians / Children's crusade / Shadows in the rain / Consider me gone / Dream of the blue turtles, The / Moon over bourbon street / Fortress around your heart.
Notes: The much anticipated debut solo album from Police frontman.'The Dream Of The Blue Turtles'is superbly packaged,including an inner-sleeve and large folded in-sert.It features 9 new songs,plus a complete re-working of 'Shadows In The Rain'(from the'Zenyatta Mondatta'album).Sting's songwriting has never been stronger from the superb new soul-flavoured single 'If You Love Somebody Set Them Free' (already on route to be a smash),through the haunting 'Russians',to Carribean flavoured 'Love Is The Seventh Wave'.Sting has picked a stunning array of music-ians to play on this album. Omar Harkin (Weather Report)-Drums;Darryl Jones (Miles Davis Band)-Bass;Kenny Kirkland-Keyboards;Branfield Marsalis-Sax and Percussion and,ofcourse,Sting on Vocals and Guitar.
Album: released on A&M, Jun'85 by A&M Records. Dist: Polygram

Cassette: released on A&M, Jun'85 by A&M Records. Dist: Polygram

Compact disc: released on A&M, Jun'85 by A&M Records. Dist: Polygram

Picture disc album: released on A&M, Jan'86 by A&M Records. Dist: Polygram

FORTRESS.
Single (7"): released on A&M, Sep'85 by A&M Records. Dist: Polygram

Single (12"): released on A&M, Sep'85 by A&M Records. Dist: Polygram

IF YOU LOVE SOMEBODY SET THEM FREE.
Single (7"): released on A&M, May'85 by A&M Records. Dist: Polygram

MOON OVER BOURBON STREET.
Tracks: / Moon over bourbon street / Mack the knife / Fortress around your heart.
Single (7"): released on A&M, Feb'86 by A&M Records. Dist: Polygram

Single (12"): released on A&M, Feb'86 by A&M Records. Dist: Polygram

RUSSIANS.
Single (7"): released on A&M, Nov'85 by A&M Records. Dist: Polygram

Single (12"): released on A&M, Nov'85 by A&M Records. Dist: Polygram

SEVENTH WAVE.
Single (7"): released on A&M, Aug'85 by A&M Records. Dist: Polygram

Single (12"): released on A&M, Aug'85 by A&M Records. Dist: Polygram

STING Soundtrack (Soundtrack).
Album: released on MCA, '83 by MCA Records. Dist: Polygram, MCA

Cassette: released on MCA, '83 by MCA Records. Dist: Polygram, MCA

Stinga, Paul

CHARMS OF THE RUMANIAN MUSIC (Stinga, Paul & His Orchestra).
Tracks: / Sirba de la seaca / Batrineasca / Taraneasca de la burau Jeni / Suite de Moldavie I / Suite de Moldavie II / Purtata de la bistrica / Suite de muntenie / Hora din rasomiresti / Joc din bihor / Suite de banat / Suite de Transilvanie.
Compact disc: released on Pierre Verany (France), May'87 Dist: Conifer

Stingrays

BEHIND THE BEYOND.
Tracks: / Behind the beyond.
Single (7"): released on Kaleidoscope, Nov'86

Single (12"): released on Kaleidoscope, Nov'86

COUNTDOWN.
Single (7"): released on Fried Egg, Jul'81 by Fried Egg Records. Dist: Rough Trade, Cartel

DINOSAURS.
Single (7"): released on Big Beat, Feb'83 by Ace Records. Dist: Projection, Pinnacle

Album: released on Big Beat, Jul'83 by Ace Records. Dist: Projection, Pinnacle

DON'T BREAK DOWN.
Single (7"): released on Big Beat, Aug'85 by Ace Records. Dist: Projection, Pinnacle

Single (12"): released on Big Beat, Aug'85 by Ace Records. Dist: Projection, Pinnacle

ESCALATOR.
Single (7"): released on Ace, Mar'84 by Ace Records. Dist: Pinnacle, Swift, Hotshot, Cadillac

ESSENTIAL STING-RAYS, THE.
Album: released on Big Beat, Jun'87 by Ace Records. Dist: Projection, Pinnacle

JUNE RHYME.
Tracks: / June rhyme / Wedding ring / Militant tendency.
Single (12"): released on ABC, Apr'86 Dist: CBS, Pinnacle

LIVE RETALIATION.
Album: released on Media burn, Jul'85 by Rocks Off Record Emporium. Dist: Rough Trade, Cartel

NEVER DO.
Single (7"): released on Circus, Apr'81 Dist: Circus, Recommended

RADIATOR ROCK.
Single (7"): released on Rocket, Apr'82 by Phonogram Records. Dist: Polygram Distribution

STINGRAYS STORY.
Single (7"): released on Media Burn, Mar'86 Rocks Off Record Emporium. Dist: Rou Trade Distribution, Cartel Distribution

Stingrites

BABY'S GOT A BRAND NEW BRAIN.
Tracks: / Baby's got a brand new brain.
Single (7"): released on Snaffle, Feb'86 Di Fast Forward, Cartel

Sting,The

STING,THE Original Film Soundtrack (Va ous Artists).
Tracks: / Solace / Entertainer,The / Easy wi ners / Pineapple rag / Gladiolus rag / Merry round music / Listen to the mocking bird / D ling Nellie Gray / Turkey in the straw / Ragtin dance / Hooker's hooker / Luther / Glove,Th Little girl.
Compact disc: released on MCA, Feb'87 MCA Records. Dist: Polygram, MCA

Stirling, Leigh

DELIGHTFUL DOLORES.
Single (7"): released on Wikk, Apr'79

Stitched Back Foot Airman

SEVEN EGG TIMING GREATS.
Album: released on Very Mouth, May'86 Very Mouth Records. Dist: Cartel

WOULDN'T YOU LIKE TO KNO
(Stiched Back Foot Airman).
Single (7"): released on Very Mouth, Feb'87 Very Mouth Records. Dist: Cartel

Stitt, Sonny

Biographical Details: see under - Miles Da "Live in Stockholm, 1960".

CHAMP, THE.
Album: released on Muse, Apr'81 by Peerl Records. Dist: Lugtons Distributors

CONSTELLATION.
Tracks: / Constellation / (I don't stand a) gh of a chance / Webb city / By accident / Rays k / Casbah / It's magic / Topsy.
Notes: Personnel: Sonny Stitt - alto & te saxophones/Barry Harris - piano/Sam Jon bass/Roy Brooks - drun Produced by Don Schlitten. A&R co-ordina Joe Fields. Recorded at RCA studio, NYC J 27 1972. Enginerr: Paul Goodman. Maste engineer: Joe Brescio, the cutting room NY
Album: released on Muse (USA), May'86 Muse Records (USA). Dist: Conifer Distributi Jazz Music Distribution

EVERY DAY I HAVE THE BLUES (S Sonny, Joe Turner and Pee Wee Crayton).
Album: released on Pablo (USA), '82 by P Records (USA). Dist: Wellard, Chris, IMS-P gram, BMG

Cassette: released on Pablo (USA), '82 Pablo Records (USA). Dist: Wellard, C IMS-Polygram, BMG

IN WALKED SONNY.
Album: released on Sonet, '76 by Sonet F ords. Dist: PRT

JUST FRIENDS With Red Holloway.
Album: released on Affinity, Jan'81 by Ch Records. Dist: Charly, Cadillac

LAST STITT SESSION, THE.
Album: released on Muse, May'83 by Peer Records. Dist: Lugtons Distributors

LOOSE WALK (Stitt, Sonny & Milt Jacks

MADE FOR EACH OTHER.
Album: released on Delmark, '74 Dist: Pr tion, Swift, Cadillac

MOONLIGHT IN VERMONT.
Album: released on Denon, Mar'82 by De Records. Dist: Harmonia Mundi

MY BUDDY Sonny Stitt plays G.Ammor
Album: released on Muse, Jun'77 by Pee Records. Dist: Lugtons Distributors

NIGHT WORK.
Album: released on Black Lion, Sep'8 Black Lion Records. Dist: Jazz Music, Wellard, Taylor, H.R., Counterpoint. Cadill

NOW!.
Album: released on Jasmine, Jun'82 by mine Records. Dist: Counterpoint, Lug Taylor, H.R., Wellard, Chris, Swift, Cadilla

Cassette: released on Jasmine, Jun'82 by mine Records. Dist: Counterpoint, Lug Taylor, H.R., Wellard, Chris, Swift, Cadilla

SALT AND PEPPER (Stitt, Sonny & Gonsalves).
Album: released on Jasmine, Jun'82 by mine Records. Dist: Counterpoint, Lug Taylor, H.R., Wellard, Chris, Swift, Cadilla

Cassette: released on Jasmine, Jun'82 by Jasmine Records. Dist: Counterpoint, Lugtons, Taylor, H.R., Wellard, Chris, Swift, Cadillac

SALT & PEPPER (see Gonsalves, Paul & Sonny Stitt) (Stitt, Sonny & Paul Gonsalves).

SONNY'S BACK.
Album: released on Muse (Import), '81

SONNY'S BUBBA'S SESSIONS.
Album: released on Gateway, Nov'83 by Kingdom. Dist: Pinnacle

SONNY STITT MEETS SADIK HAKIM.
Album: released on Progressive (Import), '81

SUPER STITT.
Album: released on Phoenix, Apr'81 Dist: Jazz Horizons

SUPER STITT VOL.2.
Album: released on Phoenix, Apr'81 Dist: Jazz Horizons

SWEETS.
Album: released on Gateway, '84 by Kingdom. Dist: Pinnacle

TENOR BATTLES (With Eddie 'Lockjaw' Davis).
Album: released on Phoenix, Apr'81 by Audio Fidelity Enterprises. Dist: Stage One, Lugtons

Stiv Bators

HAVE LOVE WILL TRAVEL.
Single (12"): released on Bomp (USA), Aug'87 Dist: Pinnacle

Stivell, Alan

ALAN STIVELL.
Album: released on Impact, Mar'79 by Ace Records. Dist: Rough Trade, Pinnacle, Swift, Backs, Counterpoint, Jungle, Hotshot, Cartel

CHIMINS DE TERRE.
Album: released on Fontana (Europe), Nov'82 by Phonogram Records. Dist: Polygram

Cassette: released on Fontana (Europe), Nov'82 by Phonogram Records. Dist: Polygram

HARPES DU NOUVEL AGE.
Album: released on Rounder (USA), Jun'86 Dist: Mike's Country Music Room Distribution, Jazz Music Distribution, Swift Distribution, Roots Records Distribution, Projection Distribution, Topic Distribution

Compact disc: released on Rounder, May'86 Dist: Roots Distribution

RENAISSANCE OF THE CELTIC HARP.
Compact disc: released on Rounder (USA), Dec'86 Dist: Mike's Country Music Room Distribution, Jazz Music Distribution, Swift Distribution, Roots Records Distribution, Projection Distribution, Topic Distribution

Album: released on Philips Applause, Dec'83

[illegible] released on Philips Applause, '83

St. James, John

FIRST IMPRESSIONS.
Album: released on Enigma, Apr'87 by Enigma Records. Dist: Rough Trade, Cartel, EMI

St James, Michael

THERE IS ONLY ONE LOVE IYZ 44.

Stobart, Kathy

ARBEIA (Featuring Marion Williams Vocal).
Album: released on Spotlite, '83 by Spotlite Records. Dist: Cadillac, Jazz Music, Spotlite

Stock/Aitken/Waterman

ROADBLOCK.
Tracks: / Roadblock / Roadblock (horn jammin').
Single (7"): released on Breakout, Jul'87 by A&M Records. Dist: Polygram

Single (12"): released on Breakout, Jul'87 by A&M Records. Dist: Polygram

Stock, Catherine

TO HAVE AND TO HOLD.
Tracks: / To have and to hold (Theme song from thr LWT TV series) / Don't be afraid.
Single (7"): released on Sierra, Oct'86 by Sierra Records. Dist: WEA

Stockhausen, Karlheinz

SYLON.
Album: released on Chrysalis, Mar'76 by Chrysalis Records. Dist: CBS

Cassette: released on Chrysalis, Mar'76 by Chrysalis Records. Dist: CBS

Stockholm Monsters

ALL AT ONCE.
Single (7"): released on Factory, Jun'84 by Factory Records. Dist: Cartel, Pinnacle

ALMER MATER.
Album: released on Factory, Mar'84 by Factory Records. Dist: Cartel, Pinnacle

FAIRY TALES.
Single (7"): released on Factory, Jan'82 by Factory Records. Dist: Cartel, Pinnacle

HAPPY EVER AFTER.
Single (7"): released on Factory, Aug'82 by Factory Records. Dist: Cartel, Pinnacle

Stockholm Police Choir

POLISKOREN.
Album: released on Phontastic (Sweden), '82 by Wellard, Chris Distribution. Dist: Wellard, Chris Distribution

Stockingcap

WAVE CRAZE.
Single (12"): released on GRP, Mar'84 by Ariola/Arista. Dist: Greyhound

Stockton's Wing

AMERICAN SPECIAL.
Album: released on Tara (Ireland), Nov'84 by Tara Records. Dist: I & B Records Distribution, Record Services Distribution (Ireland), Roots Distribution

BEAUTIFUL AFFAIR.
Single (7"): released on DJM, Jan'82 by DJM Records. Dist: CBS, Polygram

BEAUTIFUL WING.
Single (7"): released on Ritz, Apr'83 by Outlet Records. Dist: Outlet, Prism Leisure Distribution, Record Services Distribution (Ireland), Roots

FULL FLIGHT.
Tracks: / Over the moors / So many miles / Dancing in the dark / Full flight / Why wait until tomorrow / Hey Marsha / New Clare revival / Avondale / Fox's hasp / Over the moors / So many miles / Dancing in the dark / Full flight / Why wait until tomorrow / Hey Marsha / New Clare revival / Avondale / Fox's hasp.
Notes: Stockton's wing are currently Ireland's no.1 band.Fusing traditional Irish Folk with Contemporary Rock and Pop idioms they have created a huge following throughout the Republic & Northern Ireland.This new album has just been released in Ireland and is currently riding high in the charts."Full Flight"features the bands'last four hit singles,"So Many Miles","Why Wait Until Tomorrow"and "Avondale"Their next single will be "Hey Marsha"
Album: released on Polydor (Ireland), Oct'86 by Polydor Records. Dist: Polygram, I & B

Cassette: released on Polydor (Ireland), Oct'86 by Polydor Records. Dist: Polygram, I & B

IN OUR WORLD.
Single (7"): released on Revolving, Oct'83 by Revolving Records. Dist: Spartan

LIGHT IN THE WESTERN SKY.
Cassette: released on Tara (Ireland), '83 by Tara Records. Dist: I & B Records Distribution, Record Services Distribution (Ireland), Roots Distribution

Cassette: released on Tara (Ireland), '83 by Tara Records. Dist: I & B Records Distribution, Record Services Distribution (Ireland), Roots Distribution

STOCKTON'S WING.
Album: released on Tara (Ireland), '82 by Tara Records. Dist: I & B Records Distribution, Record Services Distribution (Ireland), Roots Distribution

Cassette: released on Tara (Ireland), '82 by Tara Records. Dist: I & B Records Distribution, Record Services Distribution (Ireland), Roots Distribution

TAKE A CHANCE.
Album: released on Tara (Ireland), '82 by Tara Records. Dist: I & B Records Distribution, Record Services Distribution (Ireland), Roots Distribution

Cassette: released on Tara (Ireland), '82 by Tara Records. Dist: I & B Records Distribution, Record Services Distribution (Ireland), Roots Distribution

TAKE ONE LIVE.
Album: released on Revolving, Nov'84 by Revolving Records. Dist: Spartan

Stoddart, P

WORLD'S GREATEST PIPERS VOL 3 (Stoddart, P/M G N M).
Album: released on Limsor, Dec'86

Stoker, Bram

DRACULA (Various Artists).
Cassette: released on Argo, Mar'84 by Decca Records. Dist: Polygram

DRACULA (Valentine, Anthony).
Cassette: released on Pickwick Talking Books, '83

Stokes, Doris

WELCOME TO MY WORLD.
Album: released on Lipp, Oct'84 by Lipp Records. Dist: PRT, Lipp

Cassette: released on Lipp, Oct'84 by Lipp Records. Dist: PRT, Lipp

Stokes, Frank

1927-29 THE REMAINING TITLES.
Album: released on Matchbox, Nov'84 by Saydisc Records. Dist: Roots, Projection, Jazz Music, JSU, Celtic Music

Stokes, Loretta

MY CONSCIENCE WON'T LET ME.
Single (12"): released on Nightmare Gold, Feb'87 Dist: PRT

Stokes, Val

LEAVING.
Single (7"): released on BBC, Jun'84 by BBC Records & Tapes. Dist: EMI, PRT, Pye

Stolen Pets

CHANGES.
Single (7"): released on Carrere, Jun'82 by Carrere Records. Dist: PRT, Spartan

Single (12"): released on Carrere, Jun'82 by Carrere Records. Dist: PRT, Spartan

Stolen Power

WHEELS STILL TURNING (EP).
Single (7"): released on Hornsea Rising, Mar'82 Dist: Rough Trade

Stompin' At The...

STOMPIN' AT THE HONKY TONK (Western swing in Houston 1936-1941) (Various Artists).
Album: released on String, '81 by Topic Records. Dist: Roots Distribution, Jazz Music Distribution, JSU Distribution, Projection Distribution, Swift Distribution

STOMPIN' AT THE KLUB FOOT various artists (Various Artists).
Album: released on ABC, Oct'84 Dist: CBS, Pinnacle

STOMPIN' AT THE KLUB FOOT VOL.II Various artists (Various Artists).
Album: released on ABC, Nov'85 Dist: CBS, Pinnacle

STOMPIN' AT THE KLUB FOOT-VOL.3 various artists (Various Artists).
Album: released on ABC, Nov'86 Dist: CBS, Pinnacle

STOMPIN' AT THE SAVOY various artists (Various Artists).
Album: released on Savoy, Jun'83

Cassette: released on Savoy, Jun'83

Stone

CRAZY.
Single (7"): released on Sound Of New York, Jul'83 by Sound Of New York Records. Dist: PRT

GIRL I LIKE THE WAY YOU MOVE.
Single (7"): released on Carrere, Jan'83 by Carrere Records. Dist: PRT, Spartan

Single (12"): released on Carrere, Jan'83 by Carrere Records. Dist: PRT, Spartan

TIME.
Single (7"): released on Carrere, Apr'82 by Carrere Records. Dist: PRT, Spartan

Single (12"): released on Carrere, Apr'82 by Carrere Records. Dist: PRT, Spartan

Stone Alliance

HEAD UP.
Album: released on Import, Jul'82 Dist: Stage One

Stonebolt

STONEBOLT.
Album: released on Sierra, '79 by Sierra Records. Dist: WEA

Stone City Band

ALL DAY AND ALL OF THE NIGHT.
Single (7"): released on Motown, Oct'81 by RCA Records. Dist: RCA Distribution

Single (12"): released on Motown, Oct'81 by RCA Records. Dist: RCA Distribution

BOYS ARE BACK, THE.
Album: released on Motown, Oct'81 by RCA Records. Dist: RCA Distribution

LADIES CHOICE.
Single (7"): released on Motown, Sep'83 by RCA Records. Dist: RCA Distribution

Single (12"): released on Motown, Sep'83 by RCA Records. Dist: RCA Distribution

Single (7"): released on Motown, Oct'81 by RCA Records. Dist: RCA Distribution

OUT FROM THE SHADOW.
Album: released on Motown, Nov'83 by RCA Records. Dist: RCA Distribution

Cassette: released on Motown, Nov'83 by RCA Records. Dist: RCA Distribution

STRUT YOUR STUFF.
Single (7"): released on Motown, Oct'81 by RCA Records. Dist: RCA Distribution

Stoned Aid

ARE YOU GOING TO STONEHENGE?.
Tracks: / Are you going to Stonehenge?.
Single (7"): released on Hit, Jun'86 by Hit Records. Dist: Pinnacle, Backs, Cartel

Stone, Davina

FOR THE LOVE OF YOU.
Single (12"): released on Ariwa, Oct'82 by Ariwa Records. Dist: Revolver, Cartel, Jetstar, Rough Trade

LOVE POWER.
Single (7"): released on Ariwa, Feb'82 by Ariwa Records. Dist: Revolver, Cartel, Jetstar, Rough Trade

Stonefree

CAN'T SAY BYE.
Tracks: / Can't say bye / Night train.
Single (7"): released on Ensign, Apr'87 by Ensign Records. Dist: CBS Distribution

Single (12"): released on Ensign, Apr'87 by Ensign Records. Dist: CBS Distribution

Stone Fury

BURNS LIKE A STAR.
Album: released on MCA, Mar'85 by MCA Records. Dist: CBS

Cassette: released on MCA, Mar'85 by MCA Records. Dist: CBS

Stoneham, Ernest V.

ERNEST V.STONEHAM & BLUE RIDGE CORN SHUCKERS (Stoneham, Ernest V./Blue Ridge Corn Shuckers).
Album: released on Rounder (USA), '82 Dist: Mike's Country Music Room Distribution, Jazz Music Distribution, Swift Distribution, Roots Records Distribution, Projection Distribution, Topic Distribution

Stoneham, Harry

BY MYSELF.
Cassette: released on DJM, '79 by DJM Records. Dist: CBS, Polygram

IN THE STILL OF THE NIGHT.
Album: released on DJM, Nov'77 by DJM Records. Dist: CBS, Polygram

SOLID GOLD HAMMOND.
Double Album: released on MFP, Sep'81 by EMI Records. Dist: EMI

Double cassette: released on MFP, Sep'81 by EMI Records. Dist: EMI

Stonehenge

LEAVE IT UP TO ME.
Single (7"): released on Jet, Nov'81 by Jet Records. Dist: CBS

Stonehill, Randy

BETWEEN THE GLORY & THE FLAME.
Album: released on Myrrh, May'82 by Word Records. Dist: Word Distribution

Cassette: released on Myrrh, May'82 by Word Records. Dist: Word Distribution

CELEBRATE THIS HEARTBEAT.
Album: released on Myrrh, Dec'84 by Word Records. Dist: Word Distribution

Cassette: released on Myrrh, Dec'84 by Word Records. Dist: Word Distribution

STONEHILL.
Album: released on Street Tunes, Oct'84 by Street Tunes Records. Dist: Pinnacle

WILD FRONTIER,THE.
Album: released on Myrrh, Apr'87 by Word

Cassette: released on Myrrh, Apr'87 by Word Records. Dist: Word Distribution

Stone, Jah

BABY LOVE (see Sensations) (Stone, Jah & Sensations).

Stone, Lew

10.30 TUESDAY NIGHT (Stone, Lew & His Band).
Album: released on Ace Of Clubs, '63 by Decca Records. Dist: Polygram

COFFEE IN THE MORNING (Stone, Lew & His Band).
Album: released on President, Sep'83 by President Records. Dist: Taylors, Spartan

Cassette: released on President, Jan'84 by President Records. Dist: Taylors, Spartan

ECHO OF A SONG (Stone, Lew & His Band).

ECHO OF A SONG, THE (Stone, Lew & His Band).
Album: released on Halcyon, Mar'83 by Halcyon Records. Dist: Jazz Music

Album: released on Halcyon, Dec'82 by Halcyon Records. Dist: Jazz Music

GOLDEN AGE OF LEW STONE (Stone, Lew & His Band).
Album: released on Golden Age, Jul'85 by Music For Pleasure Records. Dist: EMI

Cassette: released on Golden Age, Jul'85 by Music For Pleasure Records. Dist: EMI

PRESENTING LEW STONE 1934-35 (Stone, Lew & His Band).
Double Album: released on World, '73 Dist: Jetstar

RIGHT FROM THE HEART (Stone, Lew & His Band (feat.Al Bowlly)).
Album: released on Old Bean, Aug'85 Dist: Jazz Music

Cassette: released on Old Bean, Aug'85 Dist: Jazz Music

WITH AL BOWLLY.
Album: released on Halcyon, Aug'87 by Halcyon Records. Dist: Jazz Music. Estim retail price in Sep'87 was £5.25.

Stoneman, Scotty

LIVE IN L.A. (WITH THE KENTUCKY COLONELS).
Album: released on Sierra, May'79 on Briar Records. Dist: Projection

Stone, Ricky

JENNY PLEASE.
Single (7"): released on Magnet, Feb'85 by Magnet Records. Dist: BMG

SOMETHING'S COOKING (Theme from Crazy Kitchen).
Single (7"): released on Magnet, Nov'85 by Magnet Records. Dist: BMG

Stone, R & J

WE DO IT.
Tracks: / We do it.
Single (7"): released on Old Gold, Mar'87 by Old Gold Records. Dist: Lightning, Jazz Music, Spartan, Counterpoint

Stone Roses

SALLY CINNAMON.
Tracks: / Sally Cinammon / Here it comes / All across the sands.
Single (12"): released on Black, May'87 by FM-Revolver Records. Dist: Revolver, Probe Plus Distribution, Cartel

SALLY CINNAMON.
Tracks: / Here it comes / All across the sands.

SO YOUNG.
Single (12"): released on Thin Line, Sep'85 Dist: Rough Trade Distribution, Cartel Distribution

Stonier, Nigel Band

STILL NOT OVER YOU.
Single (7"): released on Cargo, Jul'81 Dist: Rough Trade

Stooges

NO FUN (Stooges(feat. Iggy Pop)).
Album: released on Elektra Asylum, Aug'80 by Elektra/Asylum/Nonesuch Records. Dist: WEA

Stookey, Noel Paul

BAND & BODYWORKS.
Album: released on Myrrh, May'82 by Word Records. Dist: Word Distribution

---

Cassette: released on Myrrh, May'82 by Word Records. Dist: Word Distribution

Stop Look & Listen

STOP LOOK & LISTEN various artists (Various Artists).
Album: released on Impact, Mar'85 by Ace Records. Dist: Rough Trade, Pinnacle, Swift, Backs, Counterpoint, Jungle, Hotshot, Cartel

Stoppard, Tom

DOG IT WAS THAT DIED/DISSOLUTION OF DOMINIC BOOT various artists (Various Artists).

Stop The World

STOP THE WORLD I WANT TO GET OFF Original London cast.
Album: released on That's Entertainment, Sep'84 by That's Entertainment Records. Dist: Pinnacle, PRT

Cassette: released on That's Entertainment, Sep'84 by That's Entertainment Records. Dist: Pinnacle, PRT

WORK.
Single (7"): released on Juice, Jan'85 by Juice. Dist: PRT

Single (12"): released on Juice, Jan'85 by Juice. Dist: PRT

Storball

DOG IT WAS THAT DIED.
Cassette: released on BBC, May'84 by BBC Records & Tapes. Dist: EMI, PRT, Pye

Storeyville Jazz Band

STOREYVILLE JAZZ BAND.
Notes: Daylight Records, The Daylight Co. (Distribution), Ltd, 2 Dorset Place New Street, Honiton, Devon EX 14 8AB.
Album: released on Daylight, May'86 by Daylight Records. Dist: Daylight

Stories..

STORIES FOR A RAINY DAY (Craig, Wendy).
Album: released on Super Tempo, May'84 by Multiple Sounds Records. Dist: Multiple Sound Distributors

Cassette: released on Super Tempo, May'84 by Multiple Sounds Records. Dist: Multiple Sound Distributors

STORIES FROM THE BIBLE 1 various artists (Various Artists).
Cassette: released on Anvil, Jan'81 Dist: Anvil

STORIES FROM THE BIBLE 2 various artists (Various Artists).
Cassette: released on Anvil, Jan'81 Dist: Anvil

STORIES FROM THE DUKES OF HAZZARD various artists (Various Artists).
Album: released on Spot, May'84 by Pickwick Records. Dist: H.R. Taylor, Lugtons

Cassette: released on Spot, May'84 by Pickwick Records. Dist: H.R. Taylor, Lugtons

STORIES & SONGS OF PORTLAND BILL, THE (Grace, John).
Notes: For Full information see under "Grace,John".

Storm

LOVE LOVE LOVE.
Single (12"): released on 4 Way, Nov'84

MALICE IN WONDERLAND.
Tracks: / Malice in wonderland / Malice in wonderland (Dub Mix) / Doctor storm.
Single (12"): released on Silent Record Company, Mar'86 Dist: Pinnacle

Stormbringer

STORMBRINGER.
Album: released on Mausoleum, Jun'85 by Mausoleum Records. Dist: Pinnacle

Storm, Gale

GALE STORM HITS.
Album: released on Ace, May'84 by Ace Records. Dist: Pinnacle, Swift, Hotshot, Cadillac

Storm, Johnny

FAST EDDIE.
Single (7"): released on Magnum Force, May'81 by Magnum Music Group Ltd. Dist: Magnum Music Group Ltd, PRT, Spartan

FLAME ON!.
Album: released on Magnum Force, May'83 by Magnum Music Group Ltd. Dist: Magnum Music Group Ltd, PRT, Spartan

PLATINUM HIGH SCHOOL (Storm, Johnny/Shakin' Stevens & The Jets).

Album: released on Magnum Force, Nov'82 by Magnum Music Group Ltd. Dist: Magnum Music Group Ltd, PRT, Spartan

Storm, Rebecca

MAMA MAMA MAMA.
Album: released on Flyright, Oct'86 by Flyright Records. Dist: Krazy Kat, Swift, Jazz Music

MR.LOVE.
Tracks: / Mr.Love / Mr.King.
Single (7"): released on Columbia, Feb'86 by EMI Records. Dist: EMI

SHOW, THE (Theme from Connie).
Single (12"): released on Telebell, Jul'85 by Towerbell Records. Dist: EMI

Single (12"): released on Telebell, Jul'85 by Towerbell Records. Dist: EMI

WRONG GIRL,THE.
Tracks: / Wrong girl,The / Swansong.
Single (7"): released on Spirit, Jul'86 by Spirit Records. Dist: WEA

Stormtroopers Of Death

SPEAK ENGLISH OR DIE.
Album: released on Roadrunner (Dutch), Dec'85 Dist: Pinnacle

Storm, Warren

BOPPIN' TONIGHT (Storm, Warren/ Al Ferrier).
Album: released on Flyright, Apr'77 by Flyright Records. Dist: Krazy Kat, Swift, Jazz Music

MAMA MAMA MAMA.
Album: released on Flyright, Nov'84 by Flyright Records. Dist: Krazy Kat, Swift, Jazz Music

Stormwitch

STRONGER THAN HEAVEN.
Album: released on Powerstation Records, Sep'86 by Powerstation Records. Dist: Pinnacle

Storybook

STORYBOOK Read by Glenda Jackson.
Double cassette: released on Argo (Spokenword), Jul'83 by Decca Records. Dist: Polygram

Story, Carl

16 GREATEST HITS.
Album: released on Starday, Apr'87

Cassette: released on Starday, Apr'87

GOSPEL REVIVAL.
Album: released on Starday, Apr'87

Cassette: released on Starday, Apr'87

Story, Little Bob

LIGHT OF MY TOWN.
Album: released on RCA, Feb'81 by RCA Records. Dist: RCA, Roots, Swift, Wellard, Chris, I & B, Solomon & Peres Distribution

Story, Liz

SOLID COLOURS.
Tracks: / Wedding rain / Pacheco pass / Without you / Hymn / Things with wings / Solid colours / Bradley's dream / Water caves / Peace piece.
Notes: The stunning debut album from the then 25 year old composer and pianist who wrote 8 of the featured pieces.
Album: released on Windham Hill (Germany), Sep'84

Compact disc: released on Windham Hill (Germany), Sep'84

UNACCOUNTABLE EFFECT.
Album: released on Windham Hill (Germany), Aug'85

Story of....

STORY OF BABAR By Jean de Brunhoff (Story of Babar).
Notes: For full information see under "De Brunhoff, Jean"

STORY OF BACH (Hart, Derek & London Theatre Players).
Cassette: released on Kiddy Kassettes, Aug'77

STORY OF BEETHOVEN (Devlin, William & London Theatre Players).
Cassette: released on Kiddy Kassettes, Aug'77

STORY OF CHOPIN (Hardy, Robert & London Theatre Players).
Cassette: released on Kiddy Kassettes, Aug'77

STORY OF LITTLE BLACK SAMBO (Bannerman, Helen).

STORY OF: MERSEYBEAT various artists (Beatles & Various).

A Documentary of the world beating success the Beatles and those who followed them fr in the 1960's. Narrated by Roger McGou 1986 Productio
Total playing time = 50 minute
Type of recording = Documentary.
Video-cassette (VHS): released on MC May'86 Dist: Polygram Distribution, Swift tribution

STORY OF MOZART (McCowan, Ale London Theatre Players).
Cassette: released on Kiddy Kassettes, Au;

STORY OF POP Various artists (Various tists).
Notes: 20 tracks by The Merseybeats, Swing Blue Jeans, Troggs, Chris Andrews, Fred & Dreamers etc.
Compact disc: released on Delta, May'87 Delta Records. Dist: Target

STORY OF SIR GALAHAD (Richards Ian).
Album: released on Caedmon(USA), May by Caedmon (USA) Records. Dist: Gower, T lors, Discovery

Cassette: released on Caedmon(US May'80 by Caedmon (USA) Records. Dist: Gower, Taylors, Discovery

STORY OF STAR WARS various art (Various Artists).
Album: released on Disneyland, Jul'83 by W Records. Dist: WEA

STORY OF STAR WARS Original sou track adaptation (Story of Star Wars).
Album: released on Twentieth Century, Nov by Twentieth Century Records. Dist: BMG, IN Polygram

Cassette: released on Twentieth Centu Nov'79 by Twentieth Century Records. D BMG, IMS-Polygram

STORY OF SWAN LAKE adapted by W Botsford (Various Artists).
Cassette: released on Caedmon(USA), '82 Caedmon (USA) Records. Dist: Gower, T lors, Discovery

STORY OF THE BLUES various art (Various Artists).
Double Album: released on CBS, May'82 CBS Records. Dist: CBS

Double cassette: released on CBS, May'82 CBS Records. Dist: CBS Deleted '86.

STORY OF THE BLUES VOL.1 various tists (Various Artists).
Triple album / cassette: released on C Oct'84 by CBS Records. Dist: CBS

STORY OF THE EMPIRE STRIK BACK various artists (Various Artists).
Album: released on Disneyland, Jul'83 by W Records. Dist: WEA

STORY OF THE GIANTS OF JAZZ v ous artists (Various Artists).
Compact disc: released on Vogue, Dec Dist: Discovery, Jazz Music, PRT, Swift

STORY OF THE NUTCRACKER Hoffi (Bloom, Claire).
Album: by Caedmon (USA) Records. Gower, Taylors, Discovery

Cassette: released on Caedmon(USA), Ja by Caedmon (USA) Records. Dist: Gower, lors, Discovery

STORY OF THE RETURN OF THE J various artists (Various Artists).
Album: released on Disneyland, Jul'83 by W Records. Dist: WEA

STORY OF THE THREE KINGS Jol Hildesheim (Rose, George).
Cassette: released on Caedmon(USA), '8 Caedmon (USA) Records. Dist: Gower, lors, Discovery

Story So Far

STORY SO FAR, THE various artists (V ous Artists).
Album: released on Sub Zero, Jul'85 Dist: Distribution

Story Teller

SAKI By H H Munro (Burden, Hugh).
Cassette: released on Talking Tape Compa Aug'81 by Talking Tape Company Records

Story, Tim

IN ANOTHER COUNTRY.
Album: released on Uniton Records, Ma Dist: Cartel

THREE FEET FROM THE MOON.
Album: released on Uniton (Norway), Ma Dist: Cartel

Cassette: released on Uniton (Norwa May'86 Dist: Cartel

UNTITLED.
Album: released on Uniton Records, Sep'84
Dist: Cartel

Single (7"): released on SCC, Dec'83 Dist: Pinnacle

Strange Relations

PARTY.
Single (7"): released on Rocket, Feb'84 by Phonogram Records. Dist: Polygram Distribution

Strange, Richard

INTERNATIONAL LANGUAGE.
Single (7"): released on Cherry Red, Jan'80 by Cherry Red Records. Dist: Pinnacle

NEXT.
Single (12"): released on Albion, May'83 by Albion Records. Dist: Spartan, Pinnacle

PHENOMENAL RISE OF RICHARD STRANGE, THE.
Album: released on Virgin, May'81 by Virgin Records. Dist: EMI, Virgin Distribution

Strangers and Brothers

CANDI TRAIN.
Tracks: / Candi train / In the heat of the night / What did we do?.
Single (7"): released on Magnet, Sep'86 by Magnet Records. Dist: BMG

Single (12"): released on Magnet, Sep'86 by Magnet Records. Dist: BMG

SENSATIONAL.
Tracks: / Sensational.
Single (7"): released on Magnet, Mar'86 by Magnet Records. Dist: BMG

Single (12"): released on Magnet, Mar'86 by Magnet Records. Dist: BMG

Strangers at Black...

STRANGER RIDERS AT BLACK PONY INN.
Cassette: released on Pickwick, Mar'84 by Pickwick Records. Dist: Pickwick Distribution, Prism Leisure Distribution, Lugtons

Strangers In Rome

FURTHER ROOM/PSYCHEDELIA.
Single (7"): released on AFR, Feb'83 by AFR Records. Dist: AFR Records

Stranger Still

SOLITUDE/SURVIVOR.
Single (7"): released on Exit, Apr'82 by Exit Records. Dist: Backs

Stranger than fiction

PRELUDE.
Single (12"): released on Constitution, Jul'87 by Constitution Records. Dist: Rough Trade, Cartel

Strange, Steve

IN THE YEAR 2525.
Single (7"): released on Stiff, Jun'82 by Stiff Records. Dist: EMI, Record Services Distribution (Ireland)

Strangeways

CLOSE TO THE EDGE.
Tracks: / Close to the edge / Hold back your love / Heartbeat zone.
Single (7"): released on Bonaire, Mar'86 Dist: RCA, Ariola

Single (12"): released on Bonaire, Mar'86 Dist: RCA, Ariola

ONLY A FOOL.
Tracks: / Only a fool / Empty street / Stand up & shout (live) ** / Breaking down the barriers(live) **.
Single (7"): released on Bonaire, Mar'87 Dist: RCA, Ariola

Single (12"): released on Bonaire, Mar'87 Dist: RCA, Ariola

STRANGE WAYS.
Album: released on Arista, Mar'86 by Arista Records. Dist: RCA

Cassette: released on Arista, Mar'86 by Arista Records. Dist: RCA

Stranglers

5 MINUTES.
Single (7"): released on United, Jan'78 Dist: Swift

ALWAYS THE SUN.
Tracks: / Always the sun / Normal normal.
Single (7"): released on Epic, Oct'86 by CBS Records. Dist: CBS

Single (12"): released on Epic, Oct'86 by CBS Records. Dist: CBS

AURAL SCULPTURE.
Tracks: / Ice queen / Skin deep / Let me down easy / No mercy / North winds / Uptown / Punch & Judy / Spain / Laughing / Souls / Mad hatter.
Album: released on Epic, May'87 by CBS Records. Dist: CBS

Cassette: released on Epic, May'87 by CBS Records. Dist: CBS

BIG IN AMERICA.
Tracks: / Dry day.
Single (7"): released on Epic, Nov'86 by CBS Records. Dist: CBS

BIG IN AMERICA (SINGLE).
Tracks: / Dry day.
Single (7"): released on Epic, Nov'86 by CBS Records. Dist: CBS

Single (12"): released on Epic, Nov'86 by CBS Records. Dist: CBS

BLACK AND WHITE.
Album: released on Epic, Jan'86 by CBS Records. Dist: CBS

Cassette: released on Epic, Jan'86 by CBS Records. Dist: CBS

Album: released on United Artists, '85

Cassette: released on United Artists, '85

CHOOSEY SUSIE/MEAN TO ME.
Single (7"): released on King (USA), Apr'79 by Gusto Records. Dist: Gusto Distribution, IMS, Swift

COLLECTION 1977-1982,THE.
Tracks: / Get a grip on yourself / Peaches / Hanging around / No more heroes / Duchess / Walk on by / Waltzinblack / Something better change / Nice 'n' Sleazy / Who wants the world / Golden Brown / Strange little girl / La Folie / Bearcage.
Notes: Superb fourteen track compilation.All their best known tracks including 'Peaches'Duchess','Nice and Sleazy','Golden Brown','Who Wants The world','Strange Little Girl'.
Album: released on EMI, Sep'82 by EMI Records. Dist: EMI

Cassette: released on EMI, Sep'82 by EMI Records. Dist: EMI

Compact disc: released on EMI, Sep'82 by EMI Records. Dist: EMI

DON'T BRING HARRY (FRENCH VERSION).
Single (12"): released on New Rose, 30 May'87 Dist: Rough Trade, Cartel

DREAMTIME.
Tracks: / Always the sun / Dreamtime / Was it you / You'll always reap what you sow / Ghost train / Nice in Nice / Big in America / Shakin' like a leaf / Mayan skies / Too precious.
Album: released on Epic, Oct'86 by CBS Records. Dist: CBS

Cassette: released on Epic, Oct'86 by CBS Records. Dist: CBS

Compact disc: released on Epic, Oct'86 by CBS Records. Dist: CBS

DUCHESS/FOOLS RUSH OUT.
Single (7"): released on United Artists, Aug'79

FELINE.
Tracks: / Midnight summer dream / It's a small world / Ships that pass in the night / European female,The / Let's tango in paris / Paradise / All roads lead to Rome / Blue sister / Never say goodbye.
Album: released on Epic, Apr'86 by CBS Records. Dist: CBS

Cassette: released on Epic, Apr'86 by CBS Records. Dist: CBS

GOLDEN BROWN.
Single (7"): released on EMI Golden 45's, Mar'84 by EMI Records. Dist: EMI

GOLDEN BROWN (12").
Single (12"): released on EMI (Germany), May'84 by EMI Records. Dist: Conifer

GOLDEN BROWN (VIDEO).
Tracks: / Golden Brown / Strange little girl.
Notes: Video single.
Video-cassette (VHS): released on Gold Rushes, Mar'87 by Video Collection International Ltd.. Dist: Counterpoint

HANGING AROUND.
Single (7"): released on United Artists, '80

INTERVIEW PICTURE DISC.
Album: released on Baktabak, May'87 by Baktabak Records. Dist: Arabesque

LA FOLIE.
Album: released on Fame (Liberty), Nov'83 by Music For Pleasure Records. Dist: EMI

Cassette: released on Fame (Liberty), Nov'83 by Music For Pleasure Records. Dist: EMI

LIVE (X-CERT).
Album: released on United Artists, '85

Cassette: released on United Artists, '85

MENINBLACK.
Album: released on Liberty, '85 by Liberty-United. Dist: EMI

Cassette: released on Liberty, '85 by Liberty-United. Dist: EMI

MIDNIGHT SUMMER DREAM.
Single (7"): released on Epic, Feb'83 by CBS Records. Dist: CBS

Single (12"): released on Epic, Feb'83 by CBS Records. Dist: CBS

NICE IN NICE.
Tracks: / Nice in Nice / Since you went away.
Single (7"): released on Epic, Aug'86 by CBS Records. Dist: CBS

Single (12"): released on Epic, Aug'86 by CBS Records. Dist: CBS

NO MORE HEROES.
Tracks: / I feel like a wog / Bitching / Dead ringer / Dagenham Dave / Bring on the nubiles / Something better change / No more heroes / Peasant in the big shitty / Burning up time / English towns / School mam.
Album: released on United Artists, '85

Cassette: released on United Artists, '85

Album: released on Fame, Sep'87 by Music For Pleasure Records. Dist: EMI. Estim retail price in Sep'87 was £3.49.

Cassette: released on Fame, Sep'87 by Music For Pleasure Records. Dist: EMI. Estim retail price in Sep'87 was £3.49.

NO MORE HEROES/IN THE SHADOWS.
Single (7"): released on United Artists, Sep'77

OFF THE BEATEN TRACK.
Tracks: / Go buddy go / Top secret / Old codger / Man in white / Rock it to the moon / Love 30 / Shut up / Walk on by(full length version) / Vietnamerica / Meak to me / Cruel garden / Yellowcake UF6 / 5 Minutes.
Album: released on Liberty, Sep'86 by Liberty-United. Dist: EMI

Cassette: released on Liberty, Sep'86 by Liberty-United. Dist: EMI

PEACHES/GO BUDDY GO.
Single (7"): released on United Artists, Apr'79

RATTUS NORVEGICUS.
Tracks: / Sometimes / Goodbye Toulouse / London lady / Princess of the streets / Hanging around / Peaches / Get a grip on yourself / Ugly / Down in the sewer:falling / Down in the sewer:Trying to get out again / Rats rally.
Compact disc: released on EMI, Jun'87 by EMI Records. Dist: EMI

RAVEN.
Album: released on United Artists, '85

Cassette: released on United Artists, '85

RAVEN, THE.
Album: released on Fame, Sep'85 by Music For Pleasure Records. Dist: EMI

Cassette: released on Fame, Sep'85 by Music For Pleasure Records. Dist: EMI

SHAKIN' LIKE A LEAF.
Notes: Was it you?-on 12" only
Single (7"): released on Epic, Feb'87 by CBS Records. Dist: CBS

Single (12"): released on Epic, Feb'87 by CBS Records. Dist: CBS

Single (12"): released on Epic, Feb'87 by CBS Records. Dist: CBS

STRANGE LITTLE GIRL/CRUEL GARDEN.
Single (7"): released on Liberty, Jul'82 by Liberty-United. Dist: EMI

STRANGLERS VOL.4 (RATTUS NORVEGICUS).
Album: released on Fame (United Artists), May'82 by Music For Pleasure Records. Dist: EMI

Cassette: released on Fame (United Artists), May'82 by Music For Pleasure Records. Dist: EMI

VIDEO COLLECTION 1972-1982,THE.
Tracks: / Get a grip on yourself / Something better change / Peaches / Hanging around / Straighten out / No more heroes / Five minutes / Sweden / Nice 'n' Sleazy / Duchess / Nuclear Device / Bearcage / Who wants the world / Golden brown / Strange Little Girl.
Notes: Following the band through their early hit singles and videos to their recent renewed success,is a fascinating biography of the band,as well as a comment on their grasp of what makes a good video,which they consistantly apply through themany different periods of fashion which the tracks cover.They know what they want in a video,be it gimmicks on 'Nuclear Device',erotica on 'Nice and Sleazy' or the pleasing mellow images of 'Golden Brown'.Almost all of the tracks have an'edge'on them which makes them often very funny(as in"Duchess" for example)or very telling (as in "Strange Little Girl") Biographical,16 track recording which is 60 minutes long.
Video-cassette (VHS): released on EMI, Nov'82 by EMI Records. Dist: EMI

Video-cassette [Betamax]: released on EMI, Nov'82 by EMI Records. Dist: EMI

VIDEO COLLECTION,THE.
Video-cassette (VHS): released on PMI, Jun'86 by PMI Records. Dist: EMI

Video-cassette [Betamax]: released on PMI Jun'86 by PMI Records. Dist: EMI

WALK ON BY.
Single (7"): released on United Artists, Jul'78

Straps

BRIXTON.
Single (7"): released on Donut, Jul'82

STRAPS ALBUM, THE.
Album: released on Cyclops, Jan'83

Strasse

STAIRWAY TO YOU.
Single (7"): released on RCA, May'83 by RCA Records. Dist: RCA, Roots, Swift, Wellard Chris, I & B, Solomon & Peres Distribution

Single (12"): released on RCA, May'83 by RCA Records. Dist: RCA, Roots, Swift, Wellard Chris, I & B, Solomon & Peres Distribution

Strasser, Hugo

BEST OF....
Album: released on EMI (Holland), '83 by EMI Records. Dist: Conifer

DANCE HITS 1983.
Album: released on EMI (Germany), '83 by EMI Records. Dist: Conifer

DANCE INTO 1982.
Album: released on Dansan, Oct'81 by Spartan Records. Dist: Spartan

DANCE INTO '81 WITH HUGO STRASSER.
Album: released on Dansan, Jan'81 by Spartan Records. Dist: Spartan

Cassette: released on Dansan, Jan'81 by Spartan Records. Dist: Spartan

DANCE INTO THE EIGHTIES WITH....
Album: released on Dansan, Feb'80 by Spartan Records. Dist: Spartan

Cassette: released on Dansan, Feb'80 by Spartan Records. Dist: Spartan

DANCE RECORD '81.
Album: released on EMI (Germany), '83 by EMI Records. Dist: Conifer

DANCE RECORD OF THE YEAR.
Album: released on Sydney Thompson, Jun'

DANCING CLARINET.
Album: released on Dansan, Jul'79 by Spartan Records. Dist: Spartan

DANCING CLARINET, THE.
Album: released on EMI (Germany), '83 by EMI Records. Dist: Conifer

DER GOLDENE TANZSCHUH.
Album: released on Sydney Thompson, '75

DIE TANNZPLATTE.
Album: released on EMI (Germany), '83 by EMI Records. Dist: Conifer

DIE TANZPLATTE DES JAHRES '86.
Album: released on EMI (Germany), Sep'85 EMI Records. Dist: Conifer

DIE TANZPLATTE DES JAHRES '78.
Album: released on Sydney Thompson, Jan

DIE TANZPLATTE DES JAHRES 75/7
Album: released on Sydney Thompson, '75

HIT PARTY.
Album: released on EMI (Germany), '83 by EMI Records. Dist: Conifer

HIT PARTY OF THE YEAR VOL.2.
Album: released on Sydney Thomps May'76

ROMANTIC CLARINET.
Album: released on EMI (Germany), '83 by EMI Records. Dist: Conifer

SUPERGOLD.

Album: released on EMI (Germany), '83 by EMI Records. Dist: Conifer

TANGO-ERFOLGE MIT HUGO STRASSER.
Album: released on Sydney Thompson, '75

TANGOS.
Album: released on EMI (Germany), Sep'84 by EMI Records. Dist: Conifer

TANZ GALA INTERNATIONAL VOL. 2.
Album: released on EMI (Germany), Apr'86 by EMI Records. Dist: Conifer

TANZ MIT..VOL.1.
Album: released on EMI (Germany), '83 by EMI Records. Dist: Conifer

TANZ MIT...VOL.2.
Album: released on EMI (Germany), '83 by EMI Records. Dist: Conifer

TANZPLATTE 1985.
Album: released on EMI (Germany), Sep'84 by EMI Records. Dist: Conifer

TANZPLATTE '87.
Album: released on EMI (Germany), Dec'86 by EMI Records. Dist: Conifer

UND SEIN TANZORCHESTER.
Album: released on EMI (Germany), '83 by EMI Records. Dist: Conifer

Stratas, Teresa
STRATAS SINGS WEILL.
Album: released on Nonesuch, Jan'87

Cassette: released on Nonesuch, Jan'87

Compact disc: released on Nonesuch, Jan'87

TERESA STRATAS.
Compact disc:

Strategy
DON'T EVER TRUST YOUR HEART.
Single (7"): released on Ocean, Mar'81 by Ocean Records. Dist: PRT

Strathclyde Police Pipers
CHAMPION OF CHAMPIONS.
Album: released on Lismor, '83 by Lismor Records. Dist: Lismor, Roots, Celtic Music

Cassette: released on Lismor, '83 by Lismor Records. Dist: Lismor, Roots, Celtic Music

Strathspey, Elgin
ELGIN STRATHSPEY & REEL FIDDLE SOCIETY (Strathspey, Elgin Reel Fiddle Society).
Album: released on Country House, Jan'81 by BGS Productions Ltd. Dist: Taylor, H.R., Record Merchandisers Distribution, Pinnacle, Sounds of Scotland Records

Cassette: released on Country House, Jan'81 by BGS Productions Ltd. Dist: Taylor, H.R., Record Merchandisers Distribution, Pinnacle, Sounds of Scotland Records

Stratus
THROWING SHAPES.
Album: released on Steeltrax, Sep'85 by Steeltrax Records. Dist: PRT Distribution

Cassette: released on Steeltrax, Sep'85 by Steeltrax Records. Dist: PRT Distribution

Strauss
STRAUSS WALTZES (Various Artists).
Cassette: released on Pickwick (Ditto series), '82

Strauss's greatest hits
STRAUSS'S GREATEST HITS (Various artists).
Cassette: released on CBS, Jul'83 by CBS Records. Dist: CBS

Strawberry Alarm Clock
STRAWBERRIES MEAN LOVE.
Cassette: released on Big Beat, Mar'87 by Ace Records. Dist: Projection, Pinnacle

Album: released on Big Beat, Mar'87 by Ace Records. Dist: Projection, Pinnacle

Strawberry Park
SUMMER IS COMING/BEACH PARTY.
Single (7"): released on Sonet, Jun'82 by Sonet Records. Dist: PRT

Strawberry Switchblade
LENE.
Single (7"): released on Korova, Aug'85 Dist: WEA

Cassette: released on Korova, Aug'85 Dist: WEA

STRAWBERRY SWITCHBLADE.
Album: released on Korova, Apr'85 Dist: WEA

Cassette: released on Korova, Apr'85 Dist: WEA

TREES AND FLOWERS/GO AWAY.
Single (7"): released on 92 Happy Customers, Jul'83 Dist: Cartel

Single (12"): released on 92 Happy Customers, Jul'83 Dist: Cartel

Strawbs
BEST OF THE STRAWBS.
Album: released on A&M, Sep'78 by A&M Records. Dist: Polygram

PART OF THE UNION/LAY DOWN.
Single (7"): released on Old Gold, Jul'82 by Old Gold Records. Dist: Lightning, Jazz Music, Spartan, Counterpoint

STRAWBS.
Album: released on Toots, May'87

Cassette: released on Toots, May'87

Straw Dogs
YELLOW AND BLUE ATTACK.
Album: released on Enigma, Feb'87 by Enigma Records. Dist: Rough Trade, Cartel, EMI

Strawhead
GENTLEMEN OF FORTUNE (FOLK).
Album: released on Traditional Sound, May'84 by Cadillac Music Records.

SEDGEMOOR.
Album: released on Dragon, Jun'86 by Dragon Records. Dist: Jazz Music, Projection, Cadillac

THROUGH SMOKE & FIRE.
Album: released on Tradition, '82 Dist: JSU, Cassion Distribution, Celtic Music, Jazz Music, Projection, Roots Records

Stray
LIVE AT THE MARQUEE.
Album: released on Gull, Jan'84 by Gull Records. Dist: Pinnacle

Cassette: released on Gull, Jan'84 by Gull Records. Dist: Pinnacle

Stray Cats
GONNA BALL.
Album: released on Arista, Nov'81 by Arista Records. Dist: RCA

Cassette: released on Arista, Nov'81 by Arista Records. Dist: RCA

RANT 'N' RAVE WITH THE STRAY CATS.
Album: released on Arista, Aug'83 by Arista Records. Dist: RCA

Cassette: released on Arista, Aug'83 by Arista Records. Dist: RCA

ROCK THIS TOWN/CAN'T HURRY LOVE.
Single (7"): released on Arista, Jan'81 by Arista Records. Dist: RCA

STRAY CATS.
Album: released on Arista, Feb'81 by Arista Records. Dist: RCA

Cassette: released on Arista, Feb'81 by Arista Records. Dist: RCA

STRAY CATS/GONNA BALL.
Cassette: released on Arista, Aug'83 by Arista Records. Dist: RCA

Strayhorn, Billy
CUE FOR SAXAPHONE (Strayhorn, Billy Septet).
Tracks: / Cue's blue now / Gone with the wind / Cherry / Watch your cue / You brought a new kind of love to me / When I dream of you / Rose room.
Album: released on Affinity, Dec'86 by Charly Records. Dist: Charly, Cadillac

Strazzerl, Frank
RELAXIN'.

Streep, Meryl
AMAZING GRACE.
Single (7"): released on PRT, May'84 by PRT Records. Dist: PRT

Street Angel
DRESSING UP.
Single (7"): released on Street Beat, Nov'83 by

Pinnacle Records. Dist: Pinnacle

Single (12"): released on Street Beat, Nov'83 by Pinnacle Records. Dist: Pinnacle

ONE BITE.
Single (7"): released on Calibre, Oct'85 by Calibre Records. Dist: PRT

Single (12"): released on Calibre, Oct'85 by Calibre Records. Dist: PRT

Single (12"): released on Calibre, Nov'85 by Calibre Records. Dist: PRT

Single (7"): released on Calibre, Oct'85 by Calibre Records. Dist: PRT

Single (12"): released on Calibre, Oct'85 by Calibre Records. Dist: PRT

ONE BITE (REMIX).
Single (12"): released on Calibre, Nov'85 by Calibre Records. Dist: PRT

Street Angels
DRESSING UP.
Single (7"): released on Street Beat, Nov'83 by Decca Records. Dist: Polygram Distribution

Single (12"): released on Street Beat, Nov'83 by Decca Records. Dist: Polygram Distribution

Streetband
STREETBAND (Streetband with Paul Young).
Double Album: released on Cambra, Feb'85 by Cambra Records. Dist: IDS, Conifer

Double cassette: released on Cambra, Feb'85 by Cambra Records. Dist: IDS, Conifer

Streetbeat
IN LOVE.
Single (7"): released on Steinar, Sep'85

Single (7"): released on Steinar, Sep'85

RAP 'N' SCRATCH.
Single (7"): released on Steinar, Dec'84

Single (12"): released on Steinar, Dec'84

Street Beats
STREET BEATS VOL.1 (Various Artists).
Album: released on Sugarhill (USA), Aug'84 by PRT Records. Dist: PRT Distribution

Cassette: released on Sugarhill (USA), Aug'84 by PRT Records. Dist: PRT Distribution

Street Boys
SOME FOLK.
Single (7"): released on Sonet, Jul'81 by Sonet Records. Dist: PRT

Single (7"): released on Sonet, Jul'81 by Sonet Records. Dist: PRT

Street Car Named Desire
STREET CAR NAMED DESIRE, A (Various artists (Various Artists).
Notes: Compilation of Norwich bands.
Cassette: released on Norwich Venue Campaign, Nov'85 Dist: Backs, Cartel Distribution

Street Corner Memories
STREET CORNER MEMORIES VOL.1 (Various Artists).
Album: released on Ace, Mar'87 by Ace Records. Dist: Pinnacle, Swift, Hotshot, Cadillac

STREET CORNER MEMORIES Various artists (Various Artists).
Notes: 16 examples of (mainly) white Italian/American Doo-wop from the late 50's & early 60's.

STREET CORNER MEMORIES VOL.2 Various artists (Various Artists).
Double Album: released on Ace, May'87 by Ace Records. Dist: Pinnacle, Swift, Hotshot, Cadillac

Street Fleet
STREET FLEET Original soundtrack (Various Artists).
Album: released on MCA, Apr'84 by MCA Records. Dist: Polygram, MCA

Streetheart
SNOW WHITE.
Single (7"): released on President, Nov'84 by President Records. Dist: Taylors, Spartan

Street History
STREET HISTORY Hip-Hop (Hip Hop).
Notes: Narrated by rapper Gary Byrd,this is a musical and visual documentary of the new body dancing and electro-music which has come off the New York streets.
Video-cassette (VHS): released on Polygram

Music, Sep'84 by Polygram Records. Dist: Polygram

Street, Judy
WHAT.
Single (7"): released on Soul Stop, Aug'82 by Soul Stop Record 3. Dist: Spartan

Street Level
NEVER KNEW.
Single (7"): released on Embryo Arts, Dec'84 by Embryo Arts Records. Dist: Plankton Distribution

STREET LEVEL (Various Artists).
Album: released on Ronco, Oct'80

Cassette: released on Ronco, Oct'80

Streetlife
ACT ON INSTINCT.
Single (12"): released on Factory, Feb'84 by Factory Records. Dist: Cartel, Pinnacle

SILENCE.
Single (12"): released on Factory, Apr'85 by Factory Records. Dist: Cartel, Pinnacle

Streetlife Fantasy
GOTTA STOP IT Nuclear war.
Tracks: / Gotta stop it / We're in this together (club mix).
Single (7"): released on Tidalwave, 20 Jun'87

Streetmark
DREAMS.
Album: released on Sky (Germany), Jan'86

Streetnoise
STREETNOISE Various artists.
Album: released on Epic, Oct'82 by CBS Records. Dist: CBS

Cassette: released on Epic, Oct'82 by CBS Records. Dist: CBS

Street Organ (De Arabier)
AMSTERDAM IN MUSIC.
Tracks: / Geef mij maar Amsterdam / By the side of the Zuyderzee / Als op het leidseplein de lichtjes / Weer eens branden gaan / O mooie westertoren / Ik hou van jou, mooi Amsterdam / Bloesem van seringen / In de jordaan / Pieromentwals / Amsterdam, dat eew Amsterdam / M'n wiegie was een stijfselkissie / Nou tabe dan / Op de sluizen der ijmuiden / Bij ons in de jordaan / Het lied van het pieroment.
Notes: Melodies from Amsterdam played by Holland's best known street organ 'De Arabier' Sleeve contains interesting notes on famous tourist spots in Amsterdam.

Cassette:

Street Organ Music
HOLLAND SOUVENIR.
Album:

Cassette:

Street, Pamela
MILL RACE, THE.
Cassette: released on Soundings, Feb'85 Dist: Soundings

MILL RACE, (THE).
Cassette: released on Soundings, Feb'85 Dist: Soundings

Streetrods
ROCK ROCK ROCK.
Single (7"): released on Rock Shop, Sep'83

ROCK ROCK ROCK.
Single (7"): released on Rock Shop, Sep'83

Streets...
STREETS OF FIRE Original soundtrack (Various Artists).
Album: released on MCA, May'84 by MCA Records. Dist: CBS

Cassette: released on MCA, May'84 by MCA Records. Dist: CBS

STREETS OF GLASGOW Various artists (Various Artists).
Album: by Topic Records. Dist: JSU Distribution, Projection Distribution, Jazz Music Distribution

Streets Ahead
BACK TO MONO (EP).
Single (7"): released on Dead Duck, Feb'82

Single (7"): released on Dead Duck, Feb'82

Street Scene

STREET SCENE (Various Artists).
Album: released on K-Tel, Nov'82 by K-Tel Records. Dist: Record Merchandisers Distribution, Taylors, Terry Blood Distribution, Wynd-Up Distribution, Relay Distribution, Pickwick Distribution, Solomon & Peres Distribution, Polygram

Cassette: released on K-Tel, Nov'82 by K-Tel Records. Dist: Record Merchandisers Distribution, Taylors, Terry Blood Distribution, Wynd-Up Distribution, Relay Distribution, Pickwick Distribution, Solomon & Peres Distribution, Polygram

Street Soca

STREET SOCA (Various Artists).
Album: released on Streetwave, Sep'84 by Streetwave Records. Dist: PRT Distribution

Cassette: released on Streetwave, Sep'84 by Streetwave Records. Dist: PRT Distribution

Streets Of Blairgowrie

STREETS OF BLAIRGOWRIE.
Cassette: released on Folktracks, Nov'79 by Folktracks Cassettes. Dist: Folktracks

Streets of Fire

STREETS OF FIRE Soundtrack.
Album: released on MCA, May'84 by MCA Records. Dist: CBS

Cassette: released on MCA, May'84 by MCA Records. Dist: CBS

Streets of Glasgow

STREETS OF GLASGOW Various artists.
Album: released on Topic, '81 by Topic Records. Dist: JSU Distribution, Projection Distribution, Jazz Music Distribution

Street Sound hip hop 16

STREET SOUND HIP HOP 16 (Various Artists).
Album: released on Streetsounds, 30 May'87

Cassette: released on Streetsounds, 30 May'87

Street Sounds

STREET SOUNDS 19/20 Various Artists (Various Artists).
Cassette: released on Streetsounds, Nov'86

Album: released on Streetsounds, Nov'86

STREET SOUNDS 20 Various Artists (Various Artists).
Album: released on Streetsounds, Jan'87

Cassette: released on Streetsounds, Jan'87

STREET SOUNDS 87 Various Artists (Various Artists).
Album: released on Streetsounds, Jun'87

Cassette: released on Streetsounds, Jun'87

STREET SOUNDS ANTHEMS 3 Various artists (Various Artists).
Album: released on Streetsounds, Jul'87

Cassette: released on Streetsounds, Jul'87

STREET SOUNDS ANTHEMS Various Artists (Various Artists).
Cassette: released on Streetsounds, Jan'87

Album: released on Streetsounds, Jan'87

STREET SOUNDS ANTHEMS 2 Various Artists (Various Artists).
Album: released on Streetsounds, Jun'87

Cassette: released on Streetsounds, Jun'87

STREET SOUNDS ARTISTS VOL.3 Various artists (Various Artists).
Album: released on Streetsounds, Oct'85

Cassette: released on Streetsounds, Oct'85

STREET SOUNDS ARTISTS Various Artists (Various Artists).
Album: released on Streetsounds, Sep'84

Cassette: released on Streetsounds, Sep'84

STREET SOUNDS BREAKBEATS Various Artists (Various Artists).
Album: released on Streetsounds, 30 May'87

STREET SOUNDS EDITION 5 Various artists (Various Artists).
Album: released on Streetsounds, Aug'83

Cassette: released on Streetsounds, Aug'83

STREET SOUNDS EDITION 4 Various artists (Various Artists).
Album: released on Streetsounds, Jul'83

STREET SOUNDS EDITION 8 Various artists (Various Artists).
Album: released on Streetsounds, Jan'84

Cassette: released on Streetsounds, Jan'84

STREET SOUNDS EDITION 6 Various artists (Various Artists).
Album: released on Streetsounds, Sep'83

Cassette: released on Streetsounds, Sep'83

STREET SOUNDS EDITION 10 Various artists (Various Artists).
Album: released on Streetsounds, Jul'84

Cassette: released on Streetsounds, Jul'84

STREET SOUNDS EDITION 3 (Various Artists).
Album: released on Streetsounds, May'83

Cassette: released on Streetsounds, May'83

STREET SOUNDS EDITION 15 Various Artists (Various Artists).
Album: released on Streetsounds, Jan'86

Cassette: released on Streetsounds, Jan'86

STREET SOUNDS EDITION 7 Various artists (Various Artists).
Album: released on Streetsounds, Dec'83

Cassette: released on Streetsounds, Dec'83

STREET SOUNDS EDITION 14 Various artists (Various Artists).
Notes: Artists include: Five Star/Three Degrees/Read For The World/Jeff Tyzik/Starpoint-Collage/Frankie Kelly/Tramaine/Gardenia/Bernard Wright.

STREET SOUNDS EDITION 17 Various artists (Various Artists).
Notes: 10 tracks by: Janet Jackson/Beau Williams/Jaki Graham/Princess/Michael Jonzun/Colors/Cashflow/Zapp/Sleeque/Gwen Guthrie.
Album: released on Streetsounds, Jun'86

Cassette: released on Streetsounds, Jun'86

STREET SOUNDS EDITION 9 Various artists (Various Artists).
Album: released on Streetsounds, May'84

Cassette: released on Streetsounds, May'84

STREET SOUNDS EDITION 12 Various artists (Various Artists).

STREET SOUNDS EDITION 11 Various artists (Various Artists).
Album: released on Streetsounds, Apr'85

Cassette: released on Streetsounds, Apr'85

STREET SOUNDS EDITION 16 Various Artists (Various Artists).
Album: released on Streetsounds, Apr'86

Cassette: released on Streetsounds, Apr'86

STREET SOUNDS EDITION 18 Various artists (Various Artists).
Tracks: / Rumours (Long Version) / Dreamer (Long Version - Vocal) / Falling / Breaking away (Extended Version) / Holiday rap / Midas touch (Vocal/Ext. Version) / What does it take (to win your love) (Rerapped mix) / Give me your love (extended version) / Excite me / Fool's paradise (Paradise mix).
Album: released on Streetsounds, Sep'86

Cassette: released on Streetsounds, Sep'86

STREET SOUNDS ELECTRO 2 Various artists (Various Artists).
Album: released on Streetsounds, Dec'83

Cassette: released on Streetsounds, Dec'83

STREET SOUNDS ELECTRO 3 Various artists (Various Artists).
Album: released on Streetsounds, Jan'84

Cassette: released on Streetsounds, Jan'84

STREET SOUNDS ELECTRO 1 Various artists (Various Artists).
Album: released on Streetsounds, Sep'83

Cassette: released on Streetsounds, Sep'83

STREET SOUNDS ELECTRO 9 Various artists (Various Artists).
Album: released on Streetsounds, Oct'85

Cassette: released on Streetsounds, Oct'85

STREET SOUNDS ELECTRO 10 Various artists (Various Artists).
Album: released on Streetsounds, Jan'86

Cassette: released on Streetsounds, Jan'86

STREET SOUNDS ELECTRO 11 Various artists (Various Artists).
Album: released on Streetsounds, Mar'86

Cassette: released on Streetsounds, Mar'86

STREET SOUNDS ELECTRO 15 Various artists (Various Artists).
Album: released on Streetsounds, Nov'86

Cassette: released on Streetsounds, Nov'86

STREET SOUNDS ELECTRO 7 Various artists (Various Artists).
Album: released on Streetsounds, May'85

Cassette: released on Streetsounds, May'85

STREET SOUNDS HI-ENERGY NO.1 Various artists (Various Artists).
Album: released on Streetsounds, Feb'84

Cassette: released on Streetsounds, Feb'84

STREET SOUNDS HI-ENERGY NO.2 Various artists (Various Artists).
Album: released on Streetsounds, May'84

Cassette: released on Streetsounds, May'84

STREET SOUNDS HIP-HOP ELECTRO 12 Various artists (Various Artists).
Tracks: / Fastest man alive / Square dance rap / Trow the D and ghetto bass / Ultimate III live! / MC story / Girls (Rulin' the world) / Funky beat.
Album: released on Streetsounds, May'86

Cassette: released on Streetsounds, May'86

STREET SOUNDS HIP-HOP ELECTRO 13 Various artists (Various Artists).
Album: released on Streetsounds, Jun'86

Cassette: released on Streetsounds, Jun'86

STREET SOUNDS HIP-HOP ELECTRO 14 Various artists (Various Artists).
Tracks: / Monster beat / Leave it to the drums (here come the drums) / Breaking bells / Manipulator, The / Me and my possee / She's a skeezer / Downbeats / Rip the cut.
Album: released on Streetsounds, Aug'86

Cassette: released on Streetsounds, Aug'86

STREET SOUNDS INSPIRATION DANCE Various artists (Various Artists).
Album: released on Streetsounds, Nov'85

STREET SOUNDS NO. 1S OF 1983 Various Artists (Various Artists).
Special: released on Streetsounds, Jun'84

Double cassette: released on Streetsounds, Jun'84

STREET SOUNDS PICTURE BOX NO. 1 Various artists (Various Artists).
Video-cassette (VHS): released on Streetsounds, Jul'86

STREET SOUNDS PREVIEW Various Artists (Various Artists).
Album: released on Streetsounds, 30 May'87

Cassette: released on Streetsounds, 30 May'87

STREET SOUNDS (UK ELECTRO 1) Various artists.
Album: released on Streetsounds, Jun'84

Cassette: released on Streetsounds, Jun'84

Street Suite

STREET SUITE Various artists.
Album: released on CBS, May'83 by CBS Records. Dist: CBS

Cassette: released on CBS, May'83 by CBS Records. Dist: CBS

STREET SUITE Various artists (Various Artists).
Album: released on CBS, May'83 by CBS Records. Dist: CBS

Cassette: released on CBS, May'83 by CBS Records. Dist: CBS

Street System

DELIRIOUS (IN A TRANCE).
Single (7"): released on Vogue, May'84 Dist: Discovery, Jazz Music, PRT, Swift

Single (12"): released on Vogue, May'84 Dist: Discovery, Jazz Music, PRT, Swift

Street to Street

STREET TO STREET (VOL.1) Various artists.
Album: released on Open Eye, Sep'79 by Open Eye Records. Dist: Rough Trade Distribution

STREET TO STREET (VOL.2) Various artists.
Album: released on Open Eye, '81 by Open Eye Records. Dist: Rough Trade Distribution

Street to street vol 2

STREET TO STREET VOL 2 Various artists (Various Artists).
Album: released on Open Eye, '81 by Open Eye Records. Dist: Rough Trade Distribution

STREET TO STREET VOL 1 Various artists (Various Artists).
Album: released on Open Eye, Sep'79 by Open Eye Records. Dist: Rough Trade Distribution

Streetwalking Blues

STREETWALKING BLUES Various artists (Various Artists).
Album: released on Stash, Apr'81 Dist: Swift Distribution, Jazz Music Distribution, Jazz Horizons Distribution, Celtic Music Distribution, Cadillac, JSU Distribution, Zodiac Distribution

Streetwave

STREETWAVE The first 3 years vol. 1 (Various Artists).
Cassette: released on Streetwave, Oct'86 by Streetwave Records. Dist: PRT Distribution

Album: released on Streetwave, Oct'86 by Streetwave Records. Dist: PRT Distribution

STREETWAVE - THE FIRST 3 YEARS VOL. 1 Various artists (Various Artists).
Compact disc: released on Streetsounds Oct'86

STREETWAVE - THE FIRST 3 YEARS VOL. 2 Various artists (Various Artists).
Compact disc: released on Streetsounds Oct'86

Streisand, Barbra

BARBRA JOAN STREISAND.
Album: released on CBS, Nov'82 by CBS Records. Dist: CBS

Cassette: released on CBS, Nov'82 by CBS Records. Dist: CBS Deleted '86.

BARBRA STREISAND ALBUM, (THE).
Album: released on CBS, Mar'81 by CBS Records. Dist: CBS

Cassette: released on CBS, Mar'81 by CBS Records. Dist: CBS

BROADWAY ALBUM, THE.
Tracks: / Putting it together / If I love you / Something's coming / Not while I'm around / Being alive / I have dreamed / We kiss in a shadow / Something wonderful / Send in the clowns / Pretty women / Ladies who lunch, The / Can't help lovin' that man / I loves you Porgy / Porgy I's your woman now (Bess, you is my woman) / Somewhere.
Album: released on CBS, Jan'86 by CBS Records. Dist: CBS

Cassette: released on CBS, Jan'86 by CBS Records. Dist: CBS

Compact disc: released on CBS, Feb'86 by CBS Records. Dist: CBS

BUTTERFLY.
Tracks: / Love in the afternoon / Guava jelly / Grandma's hands / I won't last a day without you / Jubilation / Simple man / Life on mars / Since I don't have you / Crying time / Let the good times roll.
Compact disc: released on CBS, Jul'87 by CBS Records. Dist: CBS

CHRISTMAS ALBUM.
Album: released on CBS, Dec'80 by CBS Records. Dist: CBS

Cassette: released on CBS, Dec'80 by CBS Records. Dist: CBS

CHRISTMAS ALBUM, A.
Tracks: / Jingle bells / Have yourself a merry little Christmas / Christmas song, The / Chestnuts roasting on an open fire / White Christmas / My favourite things / Best of gifts / Sleep in heavenly peace (Silent night) / Gounod's Ave Maria / O little town of Bethlehem / I wonder as I wander / Lord's prayer, The.
Compact disc: released on CBS, Nov'85 by CBS Records. Dist: CBS

CLASSICAL BARBRA.
Album: released on CBS, '76 by CBS Records. Dist: CBS

Cassette: released on CBS, '76 by CBS Records. Dist: CBS

CLASSICAL BARBRA.
Compact disc: released on CBS, Jun'86 by CBS Records. Dist: CBS

COLOUR ME BARBRA.
Tracks: / Yesterdays / One kiss / Minute waltz, The / Gotta move / Non C'est Bien / Where or when / Medley; Animal crackers in my soup / Medley: Funny Face / Medley: That face / Medley: They didn't believe me / Medley: Were thine that special face / Medley: I've grown accustomed

tomed to her face / Medley: I've grown accustomed to her face / Medley; let's face the music and dance / Medley: Sam, you made the pants too long / Medley: What's new pussycat / Medley: Small world / Medley: I love you / Medley: I stayed too long at the fair / Medley: Look at that face / C'est Si Bon (it's so good) / Where am I going / Starting here, starting now.
Compact disc: released on CBS, Jul'87 by CBS Records. Dist: CBS

EMOTION.
Tracks: / Emotion / Make no mistake / He's mine / Time machine / Best I could / Left in the dark / Heart don't change my mind / When I dream your a step in the right direction / Clear sailing / Here we are at last.
Album: released on CBS, Oct'84 by CBS Records. Dist: CBS

Cassette: released on CBS, Oct'84 by CBS Records. Dist: CBS

Compact disc: released on CBS, Oct'84 by CBS Records. Dist: CBS

FUNNY GIRL.
Tracks: / Overture / If a girl isn't pretty / I'm the greatest star / Cornet man / Who taught her everything / His love makes me beautiful / I want to be seen with you tonight / Henry Street / People / You are woman / Don't rain on my parade / Sadie, Sadie / Find yourself a man / Rat-tat-tat-tat / Who are you now / Dance that makes me dance.
Notes: Music by Jule Styne, Lyrics by Robert Merrill, book by Isobel Lennart.
Compact disc: released on Capitol, May'87 by Capitol Records. Dist: EMI

Album: released on Capitol, May'85 by Capitol Records. Dist: EMI

Cassette: released on Capitol, May'85 by Capitol Records. Dist: EMI

GOLDEN HIGHLIGHTS OF ... (XMAS).
Album: released on CBS(Import), Jun'86 by CBS Records. Dist: Conifer, Discovery, Swift

Cassette: released on CBS(Import), Jun'86 by CBS Records. Dist: Conifer, Discovery, Swift

GREATEST HITS: BARBRA STREISAND VOL.2.
Album: released on CBS, Aug'79 by CBS Records. Dist: CBS

Cassette: released on CBS, Aug'79 by CBS Records. Dist: CBS

Compact disc: released on CBS, Jul'84 by CBS Records. Dist: CBS

GREATEST HITS:BARBRA STREISAND.
Tracks: / People / Second hand Rose / Why did I choose you / He touched me / Free again / Don't rain on my parade / My colouring book / Sam / You made the pants too long / My man (Mon homme) / Gotta move / Happy days are here again.
Compact disc: released on CBS, Apr'86 by CBS Records. Dist: CBS

GREATEST HITS: BARBARA STREISAND VOL.2.
Tracks: / Evergreen / Prisoner / My heart belongs to me / Songbird / You don't bring me flowers anymore / Way we were (The) / Sweet inspiration / Where you lead / All in love is fair / Superman / Stoney end
Compact disc: released on CBS, '86 by CBS Records. Dist: CBS

GREATEST HITS: BARBRA STREISAND.
Album: released on CBS, '74 by CBS Records. Dist: CBS

Cassette: released on CBS, '74 by CBS Records. Dist: CBS

GUILTY.
Album: released on CBS, Oct'80 by CBS Records. Dist: CBS

Cassette: released on CBS, Oct'80 by CBS Records. Dist: CBS

Album: released on CBS, '82 by CBS Records. Dist: CBS
Cat. no: MASTERSOUND H 86122
Compact disc: released on CBS, '83 by CBS Records. Dist: CBS

GUILTY.
Compact disc: released on CBS, '83 by CBS Records. Dist: CBS

LIVE CONCERT AT THE FORUM.
Tracks: / Sing / Make your own kind of music / Starting here,starting now / Don't rain on my parade / Monologue / On a clear day (you can see forever) / Sweet inspiration / Where you lead / Didn't we / My man / Stoney end / Sing / Happy days are here again / People.
Compact disc: released on CBS, Mar'87 by CBS Records. Dist: CBS

LOVE SONGS.
Album: released on CBS, Jan'82 by CBS Records. Dist: CBS

Cassette: released on CBS, Jan'82 by CBS

Records. Dist: CBS

Compact disc: released on CBS, '83 by CBS Records. Dist: CBS

LOVE SONGS.
Tracks: / Memory / You don't bring me flowers / My heart belongs to me / Wet / New York state of mind / Man I loved / No more tears / Comin' in and out of your life / Evergreen / I don't break easily / Kiss me in the rain / Lost inside of you / Way we were / Love inside.
Compact disc: released on CBS, Sep'84 by CBS Records. Dist: CBS

MAKE NO MISTAKE, HE'S MINE (Streisand, Barbra & Kim Carnes).
Single (7"): released on CBS, Jan'85 by CBS Records. Dist: CBS

MEMORY.
Single (7"): released on CBS, Feb'83 by CBS Records. Dist: CBS

NO MATTER WHAT HAPPENS.
Single (7"): released on CBS, Jan'84 by CBS Records. Dist: CBS

ONE VOICE.
Tracks: / Somewhere / Evergreen / Something's coming / People / Over the rainbow / Guilty / What kind of fool / Papa, can you hear me / Way we were, The / It's a new world / Happy days are here again / America, the beautiful.
Album: released on CBS, May'87 by CBS Records. Dist: CBS

Cassette: released on CBS, May'87 by CBS Records. Dist: CBS

Compact disc: released on CBS, May'87 by CBS Records. Dist: CBS

OVER THE RAINBOW.
Tracks: / Over the rainbow / Guilty.
Single (7"): released on CBS, 30 May'87 by CBS Records. Dist: CBS

PEOPLE.
Single (7"): released on CBS, '80 by CBS Records. Dist: CBS

SECOND BARBRA STREISAND ALBUM, (THE).
Album: released on CBS, Mar'81 by CBS Records. Dist: CBS Deleted '86.

Cassette: released on CBS, Mar'81 by CBS Records. Dist: CBS

SEND IN THE CLOWNS.
Tracks: / Send in the clowns / Being alive / Somewhere.
Single (7"): released on CBS, Mar'86 by CBS Records. Dist: CBS

Double-pack single: released on CBS, Mar'86 by CBS Records. Dist: CBS

SOMEWHERE.
Tracks: / Somewhere / Not while I'm around.
Single (7"): released on CBS, Dec'85 by CBS Records. Dist: CBS

SOMEWHERE.
Single (7"): released on CBS, Nov'85 by CBS Records. Dist: CBS

SONG BIRD.
Compact disc: released on CBS, May'87 by CBS Records. Dist: CBS

STAR IS BORN, A.
Album: released on CBS, Feb'77 by CBS Records. Dist: CBS

Cassette: released on CBS, Feb'77 by CBS Records. Dist: CBS

STONEY END.
Album: released on CBS, Feb'85 by CBS Records. Dist: CBS

Cassette: released on CBS, Feb'85 by CBS Records. Dist: CBS

SUPERMAN.
Tracks: / Superman / Don't believe what you read / Baby me / My heart belongs to me / Answer me / Cabin fever / Love comes from unexpected places / New York State of mind / Lullaby for myself.
Compact disc: released on CBS, Jul'87 by CBS Records. Dist: CBS

THIRD ALBUM.
Album: released on CBS, Jun'81 by CBS Records. Dist: CBS

Cassette: released on CBS, Jun'81 by CBS Records. Dist: CBS

WAY WE WERE, (THE).
Album: released on CBS, Apr'74 by CBS Records. Dist: CBS

Cassette: released on CBS, Apr'74 by CBS Records. Dist: CBS

WAY YOU MAKE ME FEEL.
Single (7"): released on CBS, Nov'83 by CBS Records. Dist: CBS

WET.
Tracks: / Wet / Come rain or come shine / Splish splash / On rainy afternoons / After the rain / No more tears (enough is enough) / Niagara / I ain't gonna cry tonight / Kiss me in the rain.
Album: released on CBS, '79 by CBS Records. Dist: CBS

Cassette: released on CBS, '79 by CBS Records. Dist: CBS

Compact disc: released on CBS, '86 by CBS Records. Dist: CBS

WOMAN IN LOVE.
Single (7"): released on CBS, Apr'82 by CBS Records. Dist: CBS

YENTL.
Album: released on CBS, Nov'83 by CBS Records. Dist: CBS

Cassette: released on CBS, Nov'83 by CBS Records. Dist: CBS

Strength
UNDERSTANDING YOU.
Single (7"): released on Big A, Mar'85 Dist: Red Rhino, Cartel

Strength through Oi
STRENGTH THROUGH OI Various artists (Various Artists).
Album: released on Wonderful World, Aug'85 Dist: M.I.S., EMI, Stage One

Stren, Patti
HUG ME.
Cassette: released on Caedmon(USA), '84 by Caedmon (USA) Records. Dist: Gower, Taylors, Discovery

Strensall Haxby
MACK THE KNIFE.
Tracks: / Mack the knife / Here I am.
Single (7"): released on Mr. Sam, Oct'86

Stress
BIG WHEEL, THE.
Album: released on Adventures In Reality, Jul'85 by Backs Records. Dist: Cartel

PLAYING GAMES.
Single (7"): released on Out Of Town, Jun'82

REALITY SYNDROME, THE.
Cassette: released on Out Of Town, Jun'82

RESTRAINT.
Cassette: released on Adventures In Reality, Jul'84 by Backs Records. Dist: Cartel

Stretch
WYH DID YOU DO IT.
Single (7"): released on Old Gold, Jun'84 by Old Gold Records. Dist: Lightning, Jazz Music, Spartan, Counterpoint

Strevens, Eddie
TAKING A CHANCE ON LOVE.
Album: released on Halcyon, Dec'82 by Halcyon Records. Dist: Jazz Music

Strickler, Benny
YERBA BUENA DAYS (Strickler, Benny/Wally Rose /Lu Watters).

Strictly for...
SRICTLY FOR LOVERS Various artists (Various Artists).
Album: released on Island, Jul'85 by Island Records. Dist: Polygram

Cassette: released on Island, Jul'85 by Island Records. Dist: Polygram

STRICTLY FOR KONNOISEURS Various artists (Various Artists).
Album: released on Music For Nations, Feb'85 by Music For Nations Records. Dist: Pinnacle

Cassette: released on Music For Nations, Feb'85 by Music For Nations Records. Dist: Pinnacle

STRICTLY FOR ROCKERS Various 'Reggae greats' artists (Various Artists).
Album: released on Island, Aug'85 by Island Records. Dist: Polygram

Cassette: released on Island, Aug'85 by Island Records. Dist: Polygram

Strike
STRIKE.
Album: released on Music For Nations, Jan'85

---

by Music For Nations Records. Dist: Pinnacle

Strike 1
CAN'T TOUCH ME ANYMORE.
Single (12"): released on Elite, Jun'83 Dist: PRT

Stringbean
SALUTE TO UNCLE DAVE MACON (Stringbean & His Banjo).
Album: released on Starday, Apr'87

Cassette: released on Starday, Apr'87

Stringdusters
STRINGDUSTERS, THE.
Album: released on Folk Heritage, Jul'82 by Folk Heritage Records. Dist: Roots, Wynd-Up Distribution, Jazz Music, Folk Heritage

Stringer
THAT'S WHEN THE CRYING STARTS.
Single (7"): released on Arrival, Oct'82 by Arrival. Dist: Revolver, Cartel

Strings
YUM YUM.
Extended-play record: released on Parsley (Belgium), Dec'82 Dist: Pinnacle, Rough Trade

String trio of New York
FIRST STRING.
Album: released on Black Saint, Sep'79 Dist: Projection, IMS, Polygram, Chris Wellard, Harmonia Mundi, Swift

Striplin, Sylvia
GIVE ME YOUR LOVE.
Tracks: / Give me your love / Give me your love (alternative mix).
Single (12"): released on Music Of Love, Oct'86

Strizzi Rizzi
DRESSED UP LIKE ANIMALS.
Tracks: / Dressed up like animals.
Single (12"): released on Organik, Dec'85 Dist: Rough Trade Distribution, Cartel Distribution

Stroe, Corneliu
TRANSYLVANIAN SUITE (Stroe, Corneliu/Harry Tavitian).

Strollers
FIVE CATS DOWN....BOPPIN AND STROLLIN.
Album: released on Magnum Force, Jul'83 by Magnum Music Group Ltd. Dist: Magnum Music Group Ltd, PRT, Spartan

LONDON PRIDE.
Album: released on Magnum Force, Jul'83 by Magnum Music Group Ltd. Dist: Magnum Music Group Ltd, PRT, Spartan

WE SAY YEAH.
Single (7"): released on Magnum Force, Aug'82 by Magnum Music Group Ltd. Dist: Magnum Music Group Ltd, PRT, Spartan

Strong, Bob
ONE NIGHT STAND.
Album: released on Joyce, Jul'82

ON THE AIR.
Album: released on Aircheck, May'79

TONE COLOR SERENADE.
Album: released on Golden Era, Jul'82 by Import Records. Dist: Wellard, Chris, Swift

Strong, John
LOVER IN DISGRACE.
Single (7"): released on Flying, May'85 by Flying Records. Dist: DMS

Strong, Patience
QUIET CORNER WITH GAVIN DEARD.
Cassette: released on Meridian, Feb'81 Dist: Harmonia Mundi Distributors

Strong, Rob
FAREWELL TO HARLEM (Strong, Rob & The Rockets).
Single (7"): released on Strong, Sep'81

Strozier, Frank
REMEMBER ME (Strozier, Frank Sextet).
Album: released on Steeplechase, Jul'77

Struggle
WALTZ OF THE DEMONS.
Tracks: / W K Blues / Waltz of the demons / Starlings theme / I don't know / Runnin' / Off shore.
Album: released on Charly, Dec'86 by Charly

Records. Dist: Charly, Cadillac

Cassette: released on Charly, Dec'86 by Charly Records. Dist: Charly, Cadillac

Album: released on Affinity, Jan'81 by Charly Records. Dist: Charly, Cadillac

WHAT'S GOING ON? (Direct Cut album) (Strozier, Frank Quintet).
Album: released on Steeplechase, Feb'79

Struggle

NO STRONGER MUSIC.
Single (12"): released on Regal, Jul'82

ROCKY MUSIC (Sly & Robbie).
Single (12"): released on Taxi, Oct'83 by Island Records. Dist: EMI

SILENT BASHERS.
Single (7"): released on Volcana, Oct'83

Strummer, Joe

LOVE KILLS.
Tracks: / Love kills / Dum dum club.
Single (7"): released on CBS, Jul'86 by CBS Records. Dist: CBS

Single (12"): released on CBS, Jul'86 by CBS Records. Dist: CBS

Strunz & Farah

FRONTERA.
Tracks: / Quetzal / Zona liberada / Reng / Cassiopeia / Rio nuevo / Abrazo (Embrace) / Amritsar / Dervish,The.
Notes: Spanish and Latin guitar music fused with jazz Personell:Jorge Strunze/Ardeshir Farah/Alex Acuna/Omaya Alghanim/Stanley Clarke/Luis Conte/Miguel Cruz/Eduardo del Barrio/Majid Ghorbani/Steve Kajula/Aris Quiroga/Walfredo Reyes/Manoochehr Sadeghi/Steve Tavaglione/Randy Tico
Compact disc: released on Fantasy (USA), Jan'87 by Fantasy Inc USA Records. Dist: IMS, Polygram

Strutter, Harry

BORNEO (Strutter, Harry Hot Rhythm Orchestra).
Album: released on Black Lion, Jul'87 by Black Lion Records. Dist: Jazz Music, Chris Wellard, Taylor, H.R., Counterpoint, Cadillac

Strutting...

STRUTTING AT THE BRONZE PEACOCK (Various Artists).
Double Album: released on Ace, Aug'87 by Ace Records. Dist: Pinnacle, Swift, Hotshot, Cadillac

Album: released on Ace, Aug'87 by Ace Records. Dist: Pinnacle, Swift, Hotshot, Cadillac

Strutz

START.
Single (7"): released on Fast Products, Feb'82 by Fast Product Records. Dist: Spartan

Stryker, Scott

LESS THAN LOVERS, MORE THAN FRIENDS.
Tracks: / Less than lovers... / Less than lovers... (inst).
Single (7"): released on Nightmare, 23 May'87 by Nightmare Records. Dist: PRT

Single (12"): released on Nightmare, 23 May'87 by Nightmare Records. Dist: PRT

Stryper

CALLING ON YOU.
Single (7"): released on Music For Nations, Apr'87 by Music For Nations Records. Dist: Pinnacle

Single (12"): released on Music For Nations, Apr'87 by Music For Nations Records. Dist: Pinnacle

INTERVIEW PICTURE DISC.
Album: released on Baktabak, Jul'87 by Baktabak Records. Dist: Arabesque

SOLDIERS UNDER COMMAND.
Album: released on Music For Nations, Nov'86 by Music For Nations Records. Dist: Pinnacle

SOLDIERS UNDER COMMAND.
Notes: The album that really broke the band in the States,having sold over 300,000 units,it was the label's best selling album of the year (released on a secular label).Forget the controversy of their make-up and the way they dress.Listen to the music and read the lyrics and then make up your own mind.The music is their own individual style,with Michael Sweet's vocals cutting through the heavy rock guitar sound.Just listen to the closing note on "Makes me wanna sing"-but make sure there is no glass around!This is one album you should warn the neighbours about.It demands to be played as loud as the plaster on the walls can take but you'll have a street party outside by the end of the album!
Album: released on Myrrh, Feb'87 by Word Records. Dist: Word Distribution
Cat. no: **MYR R 1228**

Cassette: released on Myrrh, Feb'87 by Word Records. Dist: Word Distribution
Cat. no: **MYR C 1228**

TO HELL WITH THE DEVIL.
Tracks: / Abyss (to hell with the devil) / To hell with the devil / Calling on you / Free / Honestly / Way / Sing along song / Rockin' the world / All of me / More from a man.
Album: released on Music For Nations, Oct'86 by Music For Nations Records. Dist: Pinnacle
Cat. no: **MFN 70**

Album: released on Myrrh, Feb'87 by Word Records. Dist: Word Distribution
Cat. no: **MYR R 1129**

Album: released on Myrrh, Feb'87 by Word Records. Dist: Word Distribution
Cat. no: **MYR C 1229**

Compact disc: released on MFN, Aug'87 by Music For Nations Records. Dist: Pinnacle
Cat. no: **CDMFN 70**

Cassette: released on Music For Nations, Sep'87 by Music For Nations Records. Dist: Pinnacle. Estim retail price in Sep'87 was £5.99.
Cat. no: **TMFN 70**

Compact disc: released on Music For Nations, Aug'87 by Music For Nations Records. Dist: Pinnacle
Cat. no: **CD MFN 70**

WINTER WONDERLAND.
Single (7"): released on Enigma, Nov'85 by Enigma Records. Dist: Rough Trade, Cartel, EMI
Cat. no: **STRY 1**

YELLOW AND BLACK ATTACK, THE.
Notes: Debut album
Album: released on Music For Nations, Apr'87 by Music For Nations Records. Dist: Pinnacle
Cat. no: **MFN 74**

Stuart

FEELIN' LONELY.
Tracks: / Feelin' lonely / Lady.
Single (7"): released on First Time Music, Aug'87 by First Time Records. Dist: First Time Records
Cat. no: **STR 5453**

Stuart, Alice

ALL THE GOOD TIMES.
Album: released on Arhoolie, May'81 by Arhoolie Records. Dist: Projection, Topic, Jazz Music, Swift, Roots
Cat. no: **ARHOOLIE 4002**

Stuart, Bridgette

KEEP AN EYE ON YOU.
Single (12"): released on SS Music, Apr'82
Cat. no: **SSMD 021**

Stuart, Colin

TOURING SCOTLAND.
Album: released on Lismor, Jul'81 by Lismor Records. Dist: Lismor, Roots, Celtic Music
Cat. no: **LILP 5110**

Cassette: released on Lismor, Jul'81 by Lismor Records. Dist: Lismor, Roots, Celtic Music
Cat. no: **LICS 5110**

Stuart, Gene

DARLIN' THINK OF ME.
Album: released on Release, Nov'76 by Release Records. Dist: I & B, Wynd-Up Distribution, Taylors, Solomon & Peres Distribution
Cat. no: **BRL 4067**

FIRST CLASS COUNTRY.
Album: released on Homespun(Ireland), '82 by Outlet Records. Dist: Outlet
Cat. no: **PHL 413**

Cassette: released on Homespun(Ireland), '82 by Outlet Records. Dist: Outlet
Cat. no: **CPHL 413**

GREATEST HITS: GENE STUART.
Album: released on Hawk, '76 by Dolphin Records. Dist: I & B, Celtic Music, Solomon & Peres Distribution
Cat. no: **HALP 120**

GREATEST HITS: GENE STUART VOL.2.
Album: released on Sharp, Jan'77 by Sharp Records. Dist: Red Rhino, Cartel
Cat. no: **SHARP 2**

Cassette: released on Sharp, Mar'77 by Sharp Records. Dist: Red Rhino, Cartel
Cat. no: **SHARP 2 (TC)**

JUST FOR WHAT I AM.
Album: released on Release, Jun'78 by Release Records. Dist: I & B, Wynd-Up Distribution, Taylors, Solomon & Peres Distribution
Cat. no: **BRL 4099**

ME & MY BOYS (With the Homesteaders).
Album: released on Release, Sep'76 by Release Records. Dist: I & B, Wynd-Up Distribution, Taylors, Solomon & Peres Distribution
Cat. no: **DRL 2014**

PRECIOUS MEMORIES.
Album: released on Release, Jan'78 by Release Records. Dist: I & B, Wynd-Up Distribution, Taylors, Solomon & Peres Distribution
Cat. no: **BRL 4089**

Album: released on Release, Jan'78 by Release Records. Dist: I & B, Wynd-Up Distribution, Taylors, Solomon & Peres Distribution
Cat. no: **CBRL 4089**

Stuart, James

ONLY WHEN I LAUGH.
Single (7"): released on Radioactive, Aug'82
Cat. no: **RAD 506**

Stuart, John

SUMMER BREEZE (Stuart, John & The Heavenly Music Corporation).
Tracks: / Summer breeze / Black and blue.
Single (7"): released on Fon, Jul'87 by Fon Records. Dist: Rough Trade, Red Rhino, Cartel

Single (12"): released on Fon, Aug'87 by Fon Records. Dist: Rough Trade, Red Rhino, Cartel

Students' Choir Utrecht

OFFICIUM TENEBRARUM.
Album: released on Celestial Harmonies, Jul'87 by TM Records. Dist: PRT

Studio London Orchestra, The

ALL NIGHT LONG.
Compact disc: released on The Compact Collection, Sep'87 by Conifer Records. Dist: Conifer Distribution

FEELINGS.
Compact disc: released on The Compact Collection, Sep'87 by Conifer Records. Dist: Conifer Distribution

MEMORY. 20 LOVE THEMES.
Compact disc: released on The Compact Collection, Sep'87 by Conifer Records. Dist: Conifer Distribution

MUSIC OF ENNIO MORRICONE,THE.
Compact disc: released on The Compact Collection, Sep'87 by Conifer Records. Dist: Conifer Distribution

WHITE CHRISTMAS.
Compact disc: released on The Compact Collection, Sep'87 by Conifer Records. Dist: Conifer Distribution

Studio Two

DEVEL AND DEVIL BLUE SEA.
Single (7"): released on Albion, Jul'82 by Albion Records. Dist: Spartan, Pinnacle

Studioz

I SAW HER STANDING THERE.
Single (7"): released on Warm, '82 Dist: EMI

Stuff

STUFF.
Album: released on Warner Brothers, Jan'77 by WEA Records. Dist: WEA

Stuff The Neighbours

STUFF THE NEIGHBOURS, PLAY IT LOUD various artists (Various Artists).
Single (7"): released on Cause For Concern, Sep'84 Dist: Cartel

Stump

GRAB HANDS EP.
Single (12"): released on Ron Johnson, Mar'86 by Ron Johnson Records. Dist: Nine Mile Distribution, Cartel Distribution

PEEL SESSION 5.2.86.
Single (12"): released on Strange Fruit, Jan'87 by Clive Selwood. Dist: Pinnacle

QUIRK OUT.
Cassette: released on Stuff, May'87 Dist: Rough Trade Distribution, Cartel Distribution

Stunt Kites

HAIL TO THE ROOTS.
Single (7"): released on Criminal Damage, Oct'83 by Criminal Damage Records. Dist: Backs, Cartel

LEBENSTRAUM.
Single (7"): released on Pax, Nov'81 by Pax Records. Dist: Red Rhino, Cartel

LEONARA.
Single (7"): released on Criminal Damage, Feb'83 by Criminal Damage Records. Dist: Backs, Cartel

Stunt Man

STUNT MAN original motion picture soundtrack.
Album: released on 20th Century, Feb'81 Dist: RCA, IMS-Polygram

Stupids

FRANKFURTER.
Single (12"): released on Vinyl Solution, Aug'87 Dist: Pinnacle

PERUVIAN VACATION.
Album: released on Children Of The Revolution, May'86 by Revolver Records. Dist: Revolver, Cartel

RETARD PICNIC.
Album: released on Children Of The Revolution, Oct'86 by Revolver Records. Dist: Revolver, Cartel

VAN STUPID.
Special: released on Vinyl Solution, May'87 Dist: Pinnacle

VIOLENT NUN.
Single (7"): released on Children Of The Revolution, Mar'85 by Revolver Records. Dist: Revolver, Cartel

Sturm Group

CENTURY HO.
Album: released on Green Shoes (Canada), Apr'86 by Green Shoes Records (Canada). Dist: Red Rhino, Cartel

Sturm Und Drang

RIVER.
Tracks: / River.
Single (12"): released on Torso, Mar'86 by Torso Records. Dist: Rough Trade, Cartel, EMI

Stutter, Marvin

GOING SOFA (Stutter,Marvin & The Open Air Team).
Single (7"): released on Ritz, Feb'87 by Outlet Records. Dist: Outlet, Prism Leisure Distribution, Record Services Distribution (Ireland), Roots

Stutz Bear Cats

2 4 6 8 99.
Single (7"): released on PRT, Jun'84 by PRT Records. Dist: PRT

RUNNING IN THE NIGHT.
Single (7"): released on PRT, May'85 by PRT Records. Dist: PRT

Single (12"): released on PRT, May'85 by PRT Records. Dist: PRT

SONGS WE SING.
Album: released on Multi-Media, Jun'82 by Multi Media Tapes Records. Dist: Pinnacle, Conifer Distribution, H.R. Taylor Distribution, Stage One Distribution

Cassette: released on Multi-Media, Jun'82 by Multi Media Tapes Records. Dist: Pinnacle, Conifer Distribution, H.R. Taylor Distribution, Stage One Distribution

SONG THAT I SING.
Single (7"): released on Multi-Media, Apr'82 by Multi Media Tapes Records. Dist: Pinnacle, Conifer Distribution, H.R. Taylor Distribution, Stage One Distribution

St Vitus Dance

LOVE ME LOVE MY DOGMA.
Album: released on Probe Plus, Jun'87 by Probe Plus Records. Dist: Probe Plus Distribution

Style

BUBBLE.
Single (7"): released on West Ham FC, Dec'81

WE'LL MEET AGAIN.
Single (7"): released on Fatal, Oct'82 by WBL (White Bell Records Ltd.). Dist: CBS

Style Council

CAFE BLEU.
Tracks: / Mick's blessing / Me ship came in / Blue cafe / Paris match (The) / My ever changing moods / Dropping bombs on the whitehouse / Gospel, A / Strength of your nature / You're the best thing / Here's one that got away / Headstart for happiness / Council meeting.
Album: released on Polydor, Feb'84 by Polydor Records. Dist: Polygram, Polydor

Cassette: released on Polydor, Feb'84 by Polydor Records. Dist: Polygram, Polydor

Compact disc: released on Polydor, Feb'84 by Polydor Records. Dist: Polygram, Polydor

COME TO MILTON KEYNES.
Single (7"): released on Polydor, Jun'85 by Polydor Records. Dist: Polygram, Polydor

Single (12"): released on Polydor, Jun'85 by Polydor Records. Dist: Polygram, Polydor

Gatefold sleeve: released on Polydor, Jun'85 by Polydor Records. Dist: Polygram, Polydor

COST OF LOVING,THE.
Compact disc: released on Polydor, Jan'87 by Polydor Records. Dist: Polygram, Polydor

EVER CHANGING MOODS.
Single (7"): released on Polydor, Feb'84 by Polydor Records. Dist: Polygram, Polydor

Single (12"): released on Polydor, Feb'84 by Polydor Records. Dist: Polygram, Polydor

FAR EAST & FAR OUT- COUNCIL MEETING IN JAPAN.
Tracks: / Big boss groove, The / Here's one that got away / You're the best thing / It just came to pieces in my hands / Mick's up / Dropping bombs on the White House / Long hot summer / My ever changing moods / Le depart / Whole point of no return (The) / Money go round / Headstart for happiness / Speak like a child.
Video-cassette (VHS): released on Polygram Music, Aug'84 by Polygram Records. Dist: Polygram

Video-cassette [Betamax]: released on Polygram Music, Aug'84 by Polygram Records. Dist: Polygram

HAVE YOU EVER HAD IT BLUE.
Single (7"): released on Polydor, Mar'86 by Polydor Records. Dist: Polygram, Polydor

Single (12"): released on Polydor, Mar'86 by Polydor Records. Dist: Polygram, Polydor

HOME AND ABROAD (LIVE).
Album: released on Polydor, Aug'86 by Polydor Records. Dist: Polygram, Polydor

Cassette: released on Polydor, Aug'86 by Polydor Records. Dist: Polygram, Polydor

Compact disc: released on Polydor, Aug'86 by Polydor Records. Dist: Polygram, Polydor

INTRODUCING THE STYLE COUNCIL.
Compact disc: by Polydor Records. Dist: Polygram, Polydor

IT DIDN'T MATTER.
Tracks: / All year round.
Single (7"): released on Polydor, Jan'87 by Polydor Records. Dist: Polygram, Polydor

Single (12"): released on Polydor, Jan'87 by Polydor Records. Dist: Polygram, Polydor

LODGERS, THE.
Single (7"): released on Polydor, Sep'85 by Polydor Records. Dist: Polygram, Polydor

Single (12"): released on Polydor, Sep'85 by Polydor Records. Dist: Polygram, Polydor

Double-pack single: released on Polydor, Sep'85 by Polydor Records. Dist: Polygram, Polydor

LONG HOT SUMMER.
Single (7"): released on Polydor, Aug'83 by Polydor Records. Dist: Polygram, Polydor

Single (12"): released on Polydor, Aug'83 by Polydor Records. Dist: Polygram, Polydor

MONEY GO ROUND.
Single (7"): released on Polydor, May'83 by Polydor Records. Dist: Polygram, Polydor

Single (12"): released on Polydor, May'83 by Polydor Records. Dist: Polygram, Polydor

OUR FAVOURITE SHOP.
Tracks: / Homebreakers / All gone away / Come to Milton Keynes / Internationalist / Stones throw away, A / Stand up comics instructions (The) / Boy who cried wolf / Man of great promise, A / Down in the Seine / Lodgers (The) / Luck / With everything to lose / Our favourite shop / Walls come tumbling down / Shout to the top.
Album: released on Polydor, Apr'85 by Polydor Records. Dist: Polygram, Polydor

Cassette: released on Polydor, Apr'85 by Polydor Records. Dist: Polygram, Polydor

Compact disc: released on Polydor, Apr'85 by Polydor Records. Dist: Polygram, Polydor

SHOUT TO THE TOP.
Single (7"): released on Polydor, Sep'84 by Polydor Records. Dist: Polygram, Polydor

Cassette: released on Polydor, Sep'84 by Polydor Records. Dist: Polygram, Polydor

SHOWBIZ.
Video-cassette (VHS): released on Polygram, May'86 by Polygram Records. Dist: Polygram

SPEAK LIKE A CHILD.
Single (7"): released on Polydor, Mar'83 by Polydor Records. Dist: Polygram, Polydor

STYLE COUNCIL: INTERVIEW PICTURE DISC.
Album: released on Baktabak, Apr'87 by Baktabak Records. Dist: Arabesque

VIDEO EP.
Video-cassette (VHS): released on PMI, Jul'86 by PMI Records. Dist: EMI

Video-cassette (VHS): released on Polygram/Spectrum, Jan'84 by Polygram Records. Dist: Polygram

VIDEO SINGLE (THE).
Video-cassette (VHS): released on Channel 5, '86 Dist: W.H. Smiths

WAITING.
Tracks: / Waiting / Francoise / Theme from Jerusalem **.
Single (7"): released on Polydor, Feb'87 by Polydor Records. Dist: Polygram, Polydor

Single (12"): released on Polydor, Feb'87 by Polydor Records. Dist: Polygram, Polydor

WALLS COME TUMBLING DOWN.
Single (7"): released on Polydor, Apr'85 by Polydor Records. Dist: Polygram, Polydor

Single (12"): released on Polydor, Apr'85 by Polydor Records. Dist: Polygram, Polydor

WHAT WE.
Video-cassette (VHS): released on Polygram, Jan'86 by Polygram Records. Dist: Polygram

YOU'RE THE BEST THING.
Single (12"): released on Polydor, May'84 by Polydor Records. Dist: Polygram, Polydor

Single (7"): released on Polydor, May'84 by Polydor Records. Dist: Polygram, Polydor

Styler

BEND DOWN AND ROLL YOUR BELLY.
Tracks: / Bend down and roll your belly / We gonna jam.
Single (12"): released on Seara, Jul'86 by Seara Records. Dist: Jetstar

OB LA DI OB LA DA.
Tracks: / Ob la di ob la da / Ob la di ob la da (away version).
Single (7"): released on Seara, Nov'86 by Seara Records. Dist: Jetstar

Style X

NO SECRET AFFAIR.
Single (12"): released on Rygel, Oct'81 by Alan Osborne. Dist: Pinnacle

Stylistics

ALL ABOUT LOVE.
Album: released on Contour, Sep'81 by Pickwick Records. Dist: Pickwick Distribution, PRT

Cassette: released on Contour, Sep'81 by Pickwick Records. Dist: Pickwick Distribution, PRT

GREAT LOVE HITS, THE.
Album: released on Contour, Apr'83 by Pickwick Records. Dist: Pickwick Distribution, PRT

Cassette: released on Contour, Apr'83 by Pickwick Records. Dist: Pickwick Distribution, PRT

HURRY UP THIS WAY AGAIN.
Album: released on Philadelphia International, Oct'80 by CBS Records. Dist: CBS

Cassette: released on Philadelphia International, Oct'80 by CBS Records. Dist: CBS

I'M STONE IN LOVE WITH YOU.
Single (7"): released on Old Gold, Sep'85 by Old Gold Records. Dist: Lightning, Jazz Music, Spartan, Counterpoint

LOVE IS NOT THE ANSWER.
Single (7"): released on Virgin, Jul'85 by Virgin Records. Dist: EMI, Virgin Distribution

Single (12"): released on Virgin, Jul'85 by Virgin Records. Dist: EMI, Virgin Distribution

SOME THINGS NEVER CHANGE.
Compact disc: released on Bellaphon, '86 by Bellaphon Records. Dist: IMS-Polygram

Album: released on Virgin, May'85 by Virgin Records. Dist: EMI, Virgin Distribution

Cassette: released on Virgin, May'85 by Virgin Records. Dist: EMI, Virgin Distribution

VERY BEST OF THE STYLISTICS.
Album: released on H & L, Jun'83 by H&L Records (USA).

Cassette: released on H & L, Jun'83 by H&L Records (USA).

YOU MAKE ME FEEL BRAND NEW.
Single (7"): released on Old Gold, Jul'82 by Old Gold Records. Dist: Lightning, Jazz Music, Spartan, Counterpoint

Styrene, Poly

GODS AND GODESSES.
Tracks: / Gods and Godesses.
Single (7"): released on Awesome, Jul'86 by Awesome Records. Dist: Rough Trade, Cartel

Single (12"): released on Awesome, Jul'86 by Awesome Records. Dist: Rough Trade, Cartel

Styx

BABE.
Tracks: / Best of the times / Prime time / White punks on dope.
Single (12"): released on Old Gold, Jan'87 by Old Gold Records. Dist: Lightning, Jazz Music, Spartan, Counterpoint

Single (7"): released on Old Gold, Sep'85 by Old Gold Records. Dist: Lightning, Jazz Music, Spartan, Counterpoint

BEST OF, THE.
Tracks: / You need love / Lady / I'm gonna make you feel it / What has come between us / Southern woman / Rock and roll feeling / Winner take all / Best thing / Witch wolf / Grove of Eglantine (The) / Man of miracles.
Album: released on RCA, Oct'79 by RCA Records. Dist: RCA, Roots, Swift, Wellard, Chris, I & B, Solomon & Peres Distribution

Cassette: released on RCA, Oct'79 by RCA Records. Dist: RCA, Roots, Swift, Wellard, Chris, I & B, Solomon & Peres Distribution

Compact disc: released on RCA, Oct'79 by RCA Records. Dist: RCA, Roots, Swift, Wellard, Chris, I & B, Solomon & Peres Distribution

CAUGHT IN THE ACT.
Video-cassette (VHS): released on A&M Sound Pictures, Sep'84 by A&M Records. Dist: PVG

Album: released on CBS, Apr'84 by CBS Records. Dist: CBS

CORNERSTONE.
Album: released on A&M, Feb'80 by A&M Records. Dist: Polygram

Cassette: released on A&M, Feb'80 by A&M Records. Dist: Polygram

EQUINOX.
Album: released on A&M, Jan'76 by A&M Records. Dist: Polygram

GRAND ILLUSION, THE.
Album: released on A&M, Aug'77 by A&M Records. Dist: Polygram

Cassette: released on A&M, Aug'77 by A&M Records. Dist: Polygram

GRAN ILLUSION.
Tracks: / Gran illusion (The) / Fooling yourself / Superstar / Come sail away / Miss America / Man in the wilderness / Castle walls / Grand finale (The).
Album: released on A&M, Nov'85 by A&M Records. Dist: Polygram

Cassette: released on A&M, Nov'85 by A&M Records. Dist: Polygram

KILROY WAS HERE.
Tracks: / Mr Roboto / Cold war / Don't let it end / High time / Heavy metal poisoning / Just get through this night / Double life / Haven't we been here before / Don't let it end.
Compact disc: released on A&M, Apr'84 by A&M Records. Dist: Polygram

Compact disc: released on A&M, Apr'84 by A&M Records. Dist: Polygram

KILROY WAS HERE.
Album: released on A&M, Mar'83 by A&M Records. Dist: Polygram

MAN OF MIRACLES.
Album: released on RCA (Germany), '83

PARADISE THEATER.
Tracks: / AD 1928 / Rockin in paradise / Too much time on my hands / Nothing ever goes as planned / Best of times (The) / Lonely people / She cares / Snowblind / Half-penny, two penny / AD 1958 / State street Sadie.
Compact disc: released on A&M, Jun'84 by A&M Records. Dist: Polygram

PARADISE THEATRE.
Album: released on A&M, Jan'81 by A&M Records. Dist: Polygram

Cassette: released on A&M, Jan'81 by A&M Records. Dist: Polygram

Compact disc: released on A&M, Jan'81 by A&M Records. Dist: Polygram

PIECES OF EIGHT.
Album: released on A&M, Sep'78 by A&M Records. Dist: Polygram

Cassette: released on A&M, Sep'78 by A&M Records. Dist: Polygram

ROCK GALAXY.
Double Album: released on RCA (Germany), Jul'83

Cassette: released on RCA (Germany), Jul'83

SERPENT IS RISING, THE.
Album: released on RCA (Germany), '83

STYX.
Album: released on RCA (Germany), '83

Sub Culture

LOUD AND CLEAR.
Single (7"): released on Essential, Dec'83 Dist: Rough Trade

Subhumans

DAY THE COUNTRY DIED.
Album: released on Spiderleg, Jan'83 Dist: Rough Trade

DEMOLITION WAR.
Single (7"): released on Spiderleg, Nov'81 Dist: Rough Trade

EPLP.
Album: released on Bluurg, Oct'86 by Bluurg Records. Dist: Rough Trade, Nine Mile

EVOLUTION.
Single (7"): released on BLWRG, Jun'83 by Rough Trade Records. Dist: Cartel

RATS.
Single (7"): released on Bluurg, Dec'84 by Bluurg Records. Dist: Rough Trade, Nine Mile

REASONS FOR EXISTANCE.
Single (7"): released on Spiderleg, Apr'82 Dist: Rough Trade

RELIGIOUS WARS.
Single (7"): released on Spiderleg, Aug'82 Dist: Rough Trade

TIME FLIES BUT AEROPLANES CRASH.
Single (7"): released on Bluurg, Nov'83 by Bluurg Records. Dist: Rough Trade, Nine Mile

Sublime Harmony

SUBLIME HARMONY (Victorian Musical Boxes and Polyphons) (Various Artists).
Album: released on Saydisc, Oct'79 by Saydisc Records. Dist: Essex, Harmonia Mundi, Roots, H.R. Taylor, Jazz Music, Swift, Projection, Gamut

Cassette: released on Saydisc, Oct'79 by Saydisc Records. Dist: Essex, Harmonia Mundi, Roots, H.R. Taylor, Jazz Music, Swift, Projection, Gamut

Submarines

GREY SKIES BLUES.
Single (7"): released on Head, Jan'87 by Head Records. Dist: Revolver, Cartel

Sub Muris

HONESTY.
Single (7"): released on Dog Rock, Dec'83 by Dog Rock Records. Dist: Backs, Cartel

Subramaniam

BLOSSOM.
Album: released on Crusaders (Audiophile series), Apr'82

Subramaniam, L

FANTASY WITHOUT LIMITS.
Tracks: / Fantasy without limits / Feeling lonely / Mani talks / 5-3/4 / Frenzy.
Notes: L. Subramaniam- violin/ Emil Richards- vibes, marimba/ Milcho leviev- keyboards/David Edelstein- electric bass/ Frank Morgan- saxophone/ Zakir Hussain-tabla, naal,duggis/ Bob Forte- Ralph Humphrey- drums/ S. Vijayashree- tampura,surmandal
Compact disc: released on Trend (USA), Sep'86 by Discovery Records. Dist: Flexitron Distributors Ltd, Swift

INDIAN CLASSICAL MUSIC.
Compact disc: released on Discovery (USA), Jun'87 by Discovery Records (USA). Dist: Swift, Flexitron-Audio, Jazz Music

Subrimaniam, Dr L

GARLAND.
Album: released on Storyville, Aug'86 by Storyville Records. Dist: Jazz Music Distribution, Swift Distribution, Chris Wellard Distribution, Counterpoint Distribution

SOUTH INDIAN STRINGS-THE ART OF DR.L.SUBRANIAM.

Subterraneans

MY FLAMINGO.
Single (7"): released on Demon, Feb'81 by Demon Records. Dist: Pinnacle

SLUM.
Tracks: / Slum / Maxi joy / Heading for the light*.
Notes: * = Extra track on 12" only
Single (7"): released on Mother, Apr'87 Dist: Island Distribution

Single (12"): released on Mother, Apr'87 Dist: Island Distribution

Subtonics

TAKE IT EASY FLORENCE.
Tracks: / Take it easy Florence / Nothing to lose.
Single (7"): released on Life of Man, Jul'87 by Life Of Man Records. Dist: Backs, Cartel

Subway
SUBWAY Original soundtrack.
Album: released on Virgin, Nov'85 by Virgin Records. Dist: EMI, Virgin Distribution

Sub Zero
OUT OF THE BLUE.
Single (7"): released on Sub Zero, Apr'84 Dist: PRT Distribution

Success Allstars
CHRISTMAS RUSH.
Single (12"): released on Success, Dec'83 Dist: Counterpoint Distribution

Such, Ernst
APHRICA (see Schulze, Klaus) (Such, Ernst/Klaus Schulze/Rainier Bloss).

Suck
SUCK Various artists (Various Artists).
Album: released on Instant, Sep'86 by Instant Records. Dist: Cartel

Suckers
GET SUCKED.
Cassette: released on Hearing Protection, Nov'84 by Falling A Records. Dist: Falling A Distribution

Sudatan Creche
KINDERGARTEN.
Single (12"): released on Illuminated, Jul'83 by IKF Records. Dist: Pinnacle, Cartel, Jetstar

Sudden Afternoon
ACID RAIN.
Tracks: / Acid Rain / Red sun / City of night dreams / Die neue ahnung.
Single (12"): released on Midnight Music, Oct'86 by Midnight Music Records. Dist: Rough Trade Distribution, Cartel Distribution

DANCING SHADOWS.
Single (12"): released on Midnight, Nov'85

DANCING SHOES.
Album: released on Midnight Chime, Nov'85

INDUSTY & NATURE.
Single (12"): released on Midnight Music, Sep'85 by Midnight Music Records. Dist: Rough Trade Distribution, Cartel Distribution
Cat. no: DONG 16

Sudden Impact...
SUDDEN IMPACT AND THE BEST OF DIRTY HARRY Various Artists (Various Artists).

Sudden, Nikki
BACK TO THE START.
Single (7"): released on Rather, Jun'81 Dist: Rough Trade

BIBLE BELT,THE.
Album: released on Flicknife, May'83 by Flicknife Records. Dist: Spartan

CHANNEL STEAMER.
Single (7"): released on Abstract, Apr'82 by Abstract. Dist: Pinnacle

DEAD MEN TELL NO TALES.
Album: released on Creation, May'87 Dist: Rough Trade, Cartel

JACOBITES (Sudden, Nikki & Dave Kusworth).
:
Album: released on Glass, Apr'84 by Glass Records. Dist: Nine Mile, Rough Trade, Red Rhino, Play It Again Sam
Cat. no: GLALP 008
LAST BANDITS IN THE WORLD, THE (Sudden, Nikki/Fean, Johnny/Carmody,Simon).

LAST BANDITS IN THE (THE) (Sudden, Nikki, Johnny Fean & Simon Carmody).

LAST BANDIT (THE).
Tracks: / Last bandit (The).
Single (7"): released on Creation, Sep'86 Dist: Rough Trade, Cartel

Single (12"): released on Creation, Sep'86 Dist: Rough Trade, Cartel

LUNACY IS LEGEND EP (Sudden, Nikki/Times/Necessitarians).
Single (12"):

SHAME OF THE ANGELS,THE (Sudden, Nikki & Dave Kusworth).
Single (7"): released on Pawnhearts, Sep'84 by Pawnhearts Records. Dist: Cartel

TEXAS (Sudden, Nikki & The Jacobites).
Album: released on Creation, Oct'86 Dist: Rough Trade, Cartel

---

WAITING ON EGYPT.
Album: released on Abstract, Mar'86 by Abstract. Dist: Pinnacle

Album: released on Abstract, May'82 by Abstract. Dist: Pinnacle

Sudden Sway
AUTUMN CUT BACK JOB LOT OFFER.

JOB LOT OFFER.
Single (7"): released on Rough Trade, Jan'87 by Rough Trade Records. Dist: Rough Trade Distribution, Cartel Distribution

PEEL SESSION 16.11.83.
Cassette single: released on Strange Fruit, 13 Jun'87 by Clive Selwood. Dist: Pinnacle

PEEL SESSION, THE.
Tracks: / Let's evolve / Relationships.
Single (7"): released on Strange Fruit, Sep'86 by Clive Selwood. Dist: Pinnacle

SINGASONG.
Tracks: / Singasong.
Single (7"): released on Blanco Y Negro, Apr'86 by WEA Records. Dist: WEA

Single (12"): released on Blanco Y Negro, Apr'86 by WEA Records. Dist: WEA

SUDDEN SWAY.
Album: released on Blanco Y Negro, Aug'86 by WEA Records. Dist: WEA

TO YOU WITH REGARD.
Single (7"): released on Chant, Aug'81 by Rough Trade

Sudquist,Ragnar Hylen Sven
SUDQUIST, RAGNAR HYLEN SVEN Various Artists (Various Artists).
Album: released on ARC (Accordion Records), '84 Dist: Accordion Record Club

Suede Crocodiles
STOP THAT TRAIN.
Single (7"): released on No Strings, Aug'83 Dist: Rough Trade, Cartel

Sue Instrumentals
SUE INSTRUMENTALS 1959-1967 The beat is on (Various Artists).
Tracks: / I've got a woman pt.1 / Going home / Fat back / June's blues / So far away / Stick shift / Good time tonight / New breed, The pt.1 / Chicken scratch / Monkey hips and rice / Soul at sunrise / All about my girl / New breed, The pt.2 / M.G. blues.
Album: released on EMI America (Stateside), Jul'87 by EMI Records. Dist: EMI

Cassette: released on EMI America (Stateside), Jul'87 by EMI Records. Dist: EMI

SUE INSTRUMENTALS Various Artists (Various Artists).
Single (7"): released on Sue-Ensign, Oct'83 by Island Records. Dist: EMI

Sue,Peggy
GENTLY HOLD ME (Sue,Peggy with Sonny Wright).
Single (7"): released on Big R, Nov'80 by Big R Records. Dist: Pinnacle, Wynd-Up Distribution, Solomon & Peres Distribution, I & B, JSU, Swift, Record Merchandisers Distribution, Spartan

Cassette: released on Big R, Nov'80 by Big R Records. Dist: Pinnacle, Wynd-Up Distribution, Solomon & Peres Distribution, I & B, JSU, Swift, Record Merchandisers Distribution, Spartan

Sue Records...
SUE RECORDS-MAXIMUM R&B Various Artists (Various Artists).
Cassette: released on Sue-Ensign, Oct'83 by Island Records. Dist: EMI

Sue Story,The
SUE STORY,THE Various Artists (Various Artists).
Album: released on Line (West Germany), Feb'84

Sugar Blue
CROSSROADS.
Album: released on T.O.L, Oct'80

PONTIAC.
Single (7"): released on Blue Sound, Oct'80

Sugar Creek
SUGAR CREEK.
Album: released on Music For Nations, Nov'85 by Music For Nations Records. Dist: Pinnacle

Sugar Cubes
BIRTHDAY.
Single (12"): released on One Little Indian,

Jul'87 by One Little Indian Records. Dist: Nine Mile Distribution, Cartel Distribution

Sugar D
BUBBLE TO ROOTS ROCK REGGAE (Sugar D & The Offbeat Posse).
Single (12"): released on Y & D, Jul'87

Sugarhill Gang
8TH WONDER.
Album: released on Sugarhill (USA), Apr'82 by PRT Records. Dist: PRT Distribution

Cassette: released on Sugarhill (USA), Apr'82 by PRT Records. Dist: PRT Distribution

Single (12"): released on Sugarhill, Apr'81 by PRT Records. Dist: PRT Distribution

APACHE.
Single (7"): released on Sugarhill, Feb'82 by PRT Records. Dist: PRT Distribution

Single (12"): released on Sugarhill, Feb'82 by PRT Records. Dist: PRT Distribution

BAD NEWS DON'T BOTHER ME.
Single (7"): released on Sugarhill, Feb'80 by PRT Records. Dist: PRT Distribution

Single (12"): released on Sugarhill, Feb'80 by PRT Records. Dist: PRT Distribution

BE A WINNER.
Single (7"): released on Sugarhill, Apr'83 by PRT Records. Dist: PRT Distribution

Single (12"): released on Sugarhill, Apr'83 by PRT Records. Dist: PRT Distribution

HOT HOT SUMMER DAY.
Single (7"): released on Sugarhill, Aug'80 by PRT Records. Dist: PRT Distribution

Single (12"): released on Sugarhill, Aug'80 by PRT Records. Dist: PRT Distribution

KICK IT LIVE FROM 9 TILL 5.
Single (12"): released on Sugarhill, Oct'83 by PRT Records. Dist: PRT Distribution

LIVIN' IN THE FAST LANE.
Single (12"): released on Sugarhill, Jun'84 by PRT Records. Dist: PRT Distribution

LOVER ON YOU.
Single (7"): released on Sugarhill, Jul'82 by PRT Records. Dist: PRT Distribution

Single (12"): released on Sugarhill, Jul'82 by PRT Records. Dist: PRT Distribution

WORK WORK THE BODY.
Single (12"): released on Sugarhill, Mar'85 by PRT Records. Dist: PRT Distribution

Sugar Ray Dinkle
CABRINI GREEN RAP.
Single (7"): released on Flame, May'87 by Nimbus Records. Dist: Nimbus, Swift

Single (12"): released on Flame, May'87 by Nimbus Records. Dist: Nimbus, Swift

Sugar & Spice
SWEET LOVING.
Single (7"): released on Salamo, Oct'82 by Aitken, Laurel Records. Dist: Pinnacle

Sugar Star
NINE O NINE (THE BEAT IS MINE).
Tracks: / Nine o nine (The beat is mine) / Nine o nine (The beat is mine) (Version).
Single (12"): released on Nine O Nine, Mar'87 by Creole Records. Dist: Rhino, PRT

Suggestive Motion
LOVING YOU.
Single (7"): released on Bodie, Oct'83

Suicidal Tendencies
JOIN THE ARMY.
Album: released on Virgin, Apr'87 by Virgin Records. Dist: EMI, Virgin Distribution

Cassette: released on Virgin, Apr'87 by Virgin Records. Dist: EMI, Virgin Distribution

Compact disc: released on Virgin, Jun'87 by Virgin Records. Dist: EMI, Virgin Distribution

POSSESED TO SKATE.
Tracks: / Possesed to skate / Human guinea pig / Two wrongs dont make a right.
Single (7"): released on Virgin, May'87 by Virgin Records. Dist: EMI, Virgin Distribution

Single (12"): released on Virgin, May'87 by Virgin Records. Dist: EMI, Virgin Distribution

SUICIDAL TENDENCIES.
Album: released on Frontier (USA), Aug'87 Dist: Cherry Red, Zippo, What Goes On

---

Suicide
CHEREE.
Tracks: / Cheree / I remember.
Single (12"): released on Demon, Nov'86 by Demon Records. Dist: Pinnacle

Album: released on Demon, Sep'86 by Demon Records. Dist: Pinnacle

GHOST RIDERS.
Cassette: released on Raw, Nov'86 by Raw Records. Dist: Spartan

HALF-ALIVE.
Cassette: released on Reach Out International, '83 Dist: Red Rhino, Cartel

SUICIDE.
Compact disc: released on Demon, Nov'86 by Demon Records. Dist: Pinnacle

Suicide Twins
SILVER MISSILES AND HAND GRENADES.
Album: released on Lick, May'86 by Cherry Bombz. Dist: Pinnacle

Cassette: released on Lick, May'86 by Cherry Bombz. Dist: Pinnacle

Sullivan, Frank
FIRST IMPRESSIONS.
Album: released on Revelation, '81

Sullivan, Flo
HIGHER.
Single (7"): released on Red Flame, Jun'85 by Red Flame Records. Dist: Nine Mile, Cartel

Sullivan, Gene
QUEEN - VOL.4.
Album: released on Kenneth, Jan'87 Dist: Chris Wellard

Sullivan, Ira
BIRD LIVES (Sullivan, Ira & Chicago Jazz Quintet).
Album: released on Affinity, Dec'81 by Charly Records. Dist: Charly, Cadillac

HORIZONS.
Album: released on Discovery, Sep'83 by PRT

INCREDIBLE IRA SULLIVAN PLAYS VARIOUS INSTRUMENTS.
Album: released on Stash, Apr'81 Dist: Swift Distribution, Jazz Music Distribution, Jazz Horizons Distribution, Celtic Music Distribution, Cadillac, JSU Distribution, Zodiac Distribution

IRA SULLIVAN.
Album: released on Flying Fish (USA), May'79 by Flying Fish Records (USA). Dist: Roots, Projection

IRA SULLIVAN QUARTET.
Album: released on Delmark, '74 Dist: Projection, Swift, Cadillac

NICKY'S TUNE.
Album: released on Delmark, '74 Dist: Projection, Swift, Cadillac

Sullivan, Jim Band
ROCK AND ROLL WRECKS.
Album: released on Street Tunes, Oct'83 by Street Tunes Records. Dist: Pinnacle

Sullivan,Joe
AND THE ALLSTARS.
Album: released on Shoestring, '81 by Shoestring Records. Dist: Shoestring

AT THE PIANO.
Album: released on Shoestring, Apr'81 by Shoestring Records. Dist: Shoestring

Sullivan, Maxine
Biographical Details: see under - Bobby Hackett.

CLOSE AS PAGES IN A BOOK.
Album: released on Monmouth, Mar'79

GOOD MORNING LIFE.
Album: released on Audiophile, Jun'86 by Jazzology Records (USA). Dist: Jazz Music, Swi

GREAT SONGS FROM THE COTTO CLUB.
Album: released on SPI Milan, Jul'85 Dist: Silva Screen

Cassette: released on SPI Milan, Jul'85 Dist: Silva Screen

GREAT SONGS OF THE COTTON CLUB, THE.

Tracks: / Happy as the day is long / You gave me ev'rything but love / As long as I live / Raisin' the rent / 'Neath the pale Cuban moon / Ill wind / Between the devil and the deep blue sea / I love a parade / Harlem holiday / Get yourself a new broom / Stormy weather / In the silence of the night / That's what I hate about love / Primitive Prima Donna / I've got the world on a string.
Notes: Maxine Sullivan was one of the original Cotton Club stars. On this new recording she sings the songs of Harold Arlen and Ted Koehler, house writers for the Cotton Club between 1930 and 1934. This album features three songs previously not recorded and three others which have never appeared on LP.
Compact disc: released on GRP (USA), Jul'87 by GRP Records (USA). Dist: IMS, Polygram

MAXINE SULLIVAN WITH THE BOB HAGGART QUINTET... (Sullivan, Maxine with The Bob Haggart Quintet).
Double Album: released on Audiophile, Jul'87 by Jazzology Records (USA). Dist: Jazz Music, Swift

QUEEN, THE.
Album: released on Kenneth, Jul'82 Dist: Chris Wellard

SINGS THE MUSIC OF BURTON LANE.
Album: released on Stash, Sep'86 Dist: Swift Distribution, Jazz Music Distribution, Jazz Horizons Distribution, Celtic Music Distribution, Cadillac, JSU Distribution, Zodiac Distribution

SULLIVAN SHAKESPEARE HYMAN.
Album: released on Monmouth, Mar'79

UPTOWN (Sullivan, Maxine with the Scott Hamilton Quintet).
Tracks: / You were meant for me / I thought about you / Goody goody / Something to remember you by / Wrap your troubles in dreams / You're a lucky guy / Georgia on my mind / By myself / I got the right to sing the blues / Just one of those things.
Notes: And yet another legend comes to Concord Records. Cotton Club veteran Maxine Sullivan will take you uptown for a great set of swingin standards backed by the impeccable Scott Hamilton and his band. Maxine is a classic with new release her great delivery and rhythmic control confirm her stture as a seasoned pro.
Album: released on Concord Jazz(USA), Dec'85 by Concord Jazz Records (USA). Dist: IMS, Polygram

Cassette: released on Concord Jazz(USA), Dec'85 by Concord Jazz Records (USA). Dist: IMS, Polygram

Sullivan, Norman

JOY BELLS RINGING.
Single (12"): released on Black Joy, '82 Dist: Jetstar

Sullivan, Rocky

BRING BACK THE NIGHT.
Single (7"): released on Rag Baby, Mar'81 Dist: Pinnacle, Red Lightnin' Distribution

ILLEGAL ENTRY.
Album: released on Rag Baby, Mar'81 Dist: Pinnacle, Red Lightnin' Distribution

Sullivan's, Dan

DAN SULLIVAN'S SHAMROCK BAND.
Album: released on Topic, '81 Dist: Roots Distribution

Sultry Soul Sisters

SULTRY SOUL SISTERS -WONNDER WOMAN VOL.3 Various artists (Various Artists).
Album: released on Rhino (USA), Feb'85 by Rhino Records (USA).

Sulzmann, Stan

EVERYBODY'S SONG BUT MY OWN (Sulzmann, Stan & John Taylor).
Tracks: / Introduction to no particular song / Little fella, The / Old ballad / Miold man / Everybody's song but my own? / Gigolo / Sea lady / Gnu suite-part one / Sweet Yakity Waltz / In the mood.
Album: released on Loose Tubes, Jul'87 Dist: IMS-Polygram

ON LOAN WITH GRATITUDE.
Album: released on Mosaic, Aug'77 by Mosaic Records. Dist: Jazz Music Distribution, Impetus Distribution, JSU Distribution, Cadillac

Sumac, Yma

FUEGO DEL ANDE.
Tracks: / La molina (the mill song) / Flor de canela (cinnamon flower) / Gallito Caliente (the hot rooster) / La pampa y la puna (the plains and the mountain) / Dale que dale / Llora corazon (crying heart) / Huanchina (enchanted lake) / La perla de chira (the pear) / Mi palomita / Virgenes del sol (virgins of the sun) / Gallito ciego (one eyed rooster) / Clamour (I won't forget you).
Album: released on Capitol T (USA), Dec'85 Dist: Conifer

LEGEND OF THE JIVARO.
Album: released on Capitol, Oct'84 by Capitol Records. Dist: EMI

Cassette: released on Capitol, Oct'84 by Capitol Records. Dist: EMI

Sumlin, Hubert

HUBERT SUMLIN'S BLUES PARTY.
Album: released on Demon, Jun'87 by Demon Records. Dist: Pinnacle

Summer Breeze

SUMMER BREEZE VOL.1 & 2 Various Original artists (Various original artists).
Album: released on Telstar, May'83 by Telstar Records. Dist: RCA Distribution

Cassette: released on Telstar, May'83 by Telstar Records. Dist: RCA Distribution

Summer, Donna

ARE YOU READY/DEAR MISS LONELY.
Single (7"): released on Vertigo, Apr'81 by Phonogram Records. Dist: Polygram

BAD GIRLS.
Compact disc: released on Casablanca, Feb'87 Dist: Polygram, Phonogram

BAD GIRLS.
Double Album: released on Casablanca, Nov'81 Dist: Polygram, Phonogram

Double cassette: released on Casablanca, Nov'81 Dist: Polygram, Phonogram

BAD REPUTATION.
Album: released on Vertigo, May'83 by Phonogram Records. Dist: Polygram

Cassette: released on Vertigo, May'83 by Phonogram Records. Dist: Polygram

BLACK ROSE-A ROCK LEGEND.
Album: released on Vertigo, Apr'79 by Phonogram Records. Dist: Polygram

Cassette: released on Vertigo, Apr'79 by Phonogram Records. Dist: Polygram

CATS WITHOUT CLAWS.
Tracks: / Supernatural love / It's not the way / There goes my baby / Suzanna / Cats without claws / Oh Billy please / Eyes / Maybe it's over / I'm free / Forgive me.
Compact disc: released on Warner Bros., Sep'84 by Warner Bros Records. Dist: WEA

Album: released on Warner Bros., Sep'84 by Warner Bros Records. Dist: WEA

Cassette: released on Warner Bros., Sep'84 by Warner Bros Records. Dist: WEA

Compact disc: released on Warner Bros., Sep'84 by Warner Bros Records. Dist: WEA

COLD LOVE/GRAND ILLUSION.
Single (7"): released on Warner, Dec'80 by Warner Bros Records. Dist: WEA

Album: released on Warner Bros., Jul'82 by Warner Bros Records. Dist: WEA

Cassette: released on Warner Bros., Jul'82 by Warner Bros Records. Dist: WEA

Compact disc: released on Warner Bros., Jul'82 by Warner Bros Records. Dist: WEA

DONNA SUMMER.
Tracks: / Love is in control (finger on the trigger) / Mystery of love / Woman in me (The) / State of independence / Livin in America / Protection / If it hurts just a little / Love is just a breath away / Lush life.
Compact disc: released on Warner Bros., Jan'84 by Warner Bros Records. Dist: WEA

GREATEST HITS: DONNA SUMMER VOL.1.
Album: released on Casablanca, Apr'82 Dist: Polygram, Phonogram

Cassette: released on Casablanca, Apr'82 Dist: Polygram, Phonogram

GREATEST HITS: DONNA SUMMER VOL.2.
Album: released on Casablanca, Apr'82 Dist: Polygram, Phonogram

Cassette: released on Casablanca, Apr'82 Dist: Polygram, Phonogram

I FEEL LOVE.
Single (7"): released on Casablanca, Oct'84 Dist: Polygram, Phonogram

Single (12"): released on Casablanca, Oct'84 Dist: Polygram, Phonogram

I LOVE TO DANCE.
Album: released on Perfect, Aug'87

Cassette: released on Perfect, Aug'87

I REMEMBER YESTERDAY.
Album: released on Casablanca, May'83 Dist: Polygram, Phonogram

Cassette: released on Casablanca, May'83 Dist: Polygram, Phonogram

LIVE AND MORE.
Double Album: released on Casablanca, Nov'81 Dist: Polygram, Phonogram

Double cassette: released on Casablanca, Nov'81 Dist: Polygram, Phonogram

LOVE IS IN CONTROL/SOMETIMES.
Single (7"): released on Warner Brothers, Jun'82 by Warner Bros Records. Dist: WEA

Single (12"): released on Warner Brothers, Jun'82 by Warner Bros Records. Dist: WEA

LOVE'S UNKIND.
Single (7"): released on Old Gold, Sep'85 by Old Gold Records. Dist: Lightning, Jazz Music, Spartan, Counterpoint

ONCE UPON A TIME.
Compact disc: released on Casablanca, Feb'87 Dist: Polygram, Phonogram

ON THE RADIO.
Compact disc: released on Casablanca, Feb'87 Dist: Polygram, Phonogram

SHE WORKS HARD FOR THE MONEY.
Tracks: / She works hard for the money / Stop, look and listen / He's a rebel / Woman / Unconditional love / Love has a mind of it's own / Tokyo / People people / I do believe (I feel in love).
Compact disc: released on Mercury, Jul'84 by Phonogram Records. Dist: Polygram Distribution

STATE OF INDEPENDENCE/LOVE IS JUST A BREATH AWAY.
Single (7"): released on Warner Brothers, Nov'82 by Warner Bros Records. Dist: WEA

Single (12"): released on Warner Brothers, Nov'82 by Warner Bros Records. Dist: WEA

SUMMER COLLECTION (THE).
Tracks: / She works hard for the money / Bad girls / On the radio / Stop, look and listen / Last dance / MacArthur park / Heaven knows / Unconditional love / I love you / Enough is enough (no more tears).

SUMMER COLLECTION THE.
Album: released on Mercury, Nov'85 by Phonogram Records. Dist: Polygram Distribution

Cassette: released on Mercury, Nov'85 by Phonogram Records. Dist: Polygram Distribution

Compact disc: released on Mercury, Nov'85 by Phonogram Records. Dist: Polygram Distribution

WALK AWAY.
Tracks: / Bad girls / Hot stuff / On the radio / I feel love / Walk away / Last dance / Sunset people / Mac Arthur park.
Compact disc: released on Casablanca, Jan'83 Dist: Polygram, Phonogram

Album: released on Casablanca, Nov'81 Dist: Polygram, Phonogram

Cassette: released on Casablanca, Nov'81 Dist: Polygram, Phonogram

Compact disc: released on Casablanca, Jan'83 Dist: Polygram, Phonogram

WHO DO YOU THINK YOUR FOOLING.
Single (7"): released on Warner-Geffen, Mar'81 by Warner Bros Records. Dist: WEA

WOMAN IN ME/ LIVING IN AMERICA.
Single (7"): released on Warner Brothers, Nov'83 by Warner Bros Records. Dist: WEA

Single (12"): released on Warner Brothers, Nov'83 by Warner Bros Records. Dist: WEA

Summerfield, Saffron

FANCY MEETING YOU HERE.
Album: released on Mother Earth, Sep'76 Dist: Folksound Distribution, JSU Distribution, Jazz Music Distribution, Projection Distribution, Celtic Music Distribution

Summerlands Tapes

BIBLE TRUTH SERIES.
Cassette: released on Summerlands Tapes, Nov'82

CURRENT EVENTS & PROPHECY SERIES.
Cassette: released on Summerlands Tapes, Nov'82

HEALING,PRAYER,SPIRITUAL GIFTS ETC..
Cassette: released on Summerlands Tapes, Nov'82

SCIECE OF THE SPIRIT SERIES (Summer Means Fun).
Cassette: released on Summerlands Tapes, Nov'82

SUCCESSFUL LIVING SERIES.
Cassette: released on Summerlands Tapes, Nov'82

Summer Means Fun

SUMMER MEANS FUN Various artists (Various Artists).
Album: released on CBS, '84 by CBS Records. Dist: CBS

Cassette: released on CBS, '84 by CBS Records. Dist: CBS

Summer, Ray

STARLIGHT SOUNDS OF SUMMER.
Album: released on Ultimate, Nov'84 by Ultimate Records. Dist: Spartan

YOURS.
Album: released on Sounds Ultimate, Apr'85 Dist: PRT, H.R. Taylor

Summers And Sanders

PHD GIRL.
Single (7"): released on Dawn Break, Aug'84 by Dawn Break Records. Dist: Pinnacle

Summers, Andy

BEWITCHED (Summers, Andy & Robert Fripp).
Album: released on A&M, Sep'84 by A&M Records. Dist: Polygram

Cassette: released on A&M, Sep'84 by A&M Records. Dist: Polygram

I ADVANCE MASKED (Summers, Andy & Robert Fripp).

LOVE IS THE STRANGEST WAY.
Tracks: / Love is the strangest way / XYZ.
Single (7"): released on MCA, Jul'87 by MCA Records. Dist: Polygram, MCA

Single (12"): released on MCA, Jul'87 by MCA Records. Dist: Polygram, MCA

XYZ.
Tracks: / Love is the strangest way / How many days / Almost there / Eyes of a stranger / Change, The / Scary voices / Nowhere / XYZ / Only road, The / Hold me / Love is the strangest way / How many days.
Album: released on MCA, Jul'87 by MCA Records. Dist: Polygram, MCA

Cassette: released on MCA, Jul'87 by MCA Records. Dist: Polygram, MCA

Compact disc: released on MCA, Jul'87 by MCA Records. Dist: Polygram, MCA

Summers, Bill

ON SUNSHINE.
Album: released on Prestige, Oct'79 by Prestige Records (USA). Dist: RCA, JSU, Swift

Summers, Bob

INSIDE OUT (Summers, Bob Quintet).
Album: released on Discovery (USA), Jun'84 by Discovery Records (USA). Dist: Swift, Flexitron-Audio, Jazz Music

Summers, Dave

SUMMERS IN CLEVELAND.
Album: released on Outlet (Ireland), '75

Summers, Dee J

MY BEST FRIEND TOLD ME.
Single (7"): released on Creole, Aug'87 by Creole Records. Dist: Rhino, PRT

Single (12"): released on Creole, Aug'87 by Creole Records. Dist: Rhino, PRT

Summers, Gene

DANCE DANCE DANCE.
Album: released on Charly, Dec'81 by Charly Records. Dist: Charly, Cadillac

EARLY ROCKING RECORDINGS.
Album: released on White, Dec'86

GENE SUMMERS IN NASHVILLE.
Album: released on Magnum Force, Jul'82 by Magnum Music Group Ltd. Dist: Magnum Music Group Ltd, PRT, Spartan

TEXAN REBEL ROCK A BOOGIE SHAKE, THE.
Album: released on Bear Family, Jul'81 by Bear Family Records. Dist: Rollercoaster Distribution, Swift

Summers, Loraine

COME TO ME.
Album: released on Klub, Nov'80

Cassette: released on Klub, Nov'80

Summers, Lorraine

LAY DOWN BESIDE ME.
Single (7"): released on Klub, May'81

Summertime on Icarus

SUMMERTIME ON ICARUS/ INTO THE COMET Clarke, Arthur C. (Mower, Patrick).
Cassette: released on Pickwick, '83 by Pickwick Records. Dist: Pickwick Distribution, Prism Leisure Distribution, Lugtons

Summertime Serenade

SUMMERTIME SERENADE The famous Dubbledick Carl Frei street organ.
Album: released on Amberlee, Apr'79 by Amberlee Records. Dist: Amberlee Records, H.R. Taylor

Cassette: released on Amberlee, Nov'81 by Amberlee Records. Dist: Amberlee Records, H.R. Taylor

Sun

DANCE.
Single (7"): released on Air, Mar'85 by Chrysalis Records. Dist: Polygram

Single (12"): released on Air, Mar'85 by Chrysalis Records. Dist: Polygram

LEGS.
Single (7"): released on Air City (USA), Dec'85 Dist: PRT

Single (12"): released on Air City (USA), Dec'85 Dist: PRT

START THE COUNTDOWN / THE X FACTOR.
Single (7"): released on Chevy, Sep'83 by Chevy Records.

SUN THE BLUES YEARS 1950-1956 Various artists (Various Artists).
Boxed set: released on Sun, Oct'85 by Charly Records. Dist: Charly Distribution

Sunbury Junior Singers

CHRISTMAS SONGS & CAROLS.
Album: released on Sacred, May'82 by Word Records.

Cassette: released on Sacred, May'82 by Word Records.

GOSPEL SONGS & SPIRITUALS.
Album: released on Sacred, May'82 by Word Records.

Cassette: released on Sacred, May'82 by Word Records.

MORNING HAS BROKEN.
Album: released on Banners & Bonnets, May'82 by Word Records. Dist: Word Distribution

Cassette: released on Banners & Bonnets, May'82 by Word Records. Dist: Word Distribution

Suncats

JAILHOUSE ROCKABILLY.
Album: released on Rockhouse, Aug'87 by Rockhouse Records. Dist: Swift Distribution, Charly Distribution

Sun country box

SUN COUNTRY BOX (Various Artists).
Album: released on Bear Family, Nov'86 by Bear Family Records. Dist: Rollercoaster Distribution, Swift

Sundance

MONTEGO BAY.
Single (7"): released on Passion, Jun'84 by Skratch Records. Dist: PRT
Cat. no: **PASH 31**
Single (12"): released on Passion, Jun'84 by Skratch Records. Dist: PRT

WHAT'S LOVE?.
Single (7"): released on Bronze, Oct'81 by Polygram Records. Dist: Polydor

Sunday Evening's...

SUNDAY EVENING'S FAVOURITE HYMNS Various artists (Various Artists).
Album: released on Emerald (Ireland), Oct'81 by Emerald Records. Dist: I & B, Ross, PRT

Cassette: released on Emerald (Ireland), Oct'81 by Emerald Records. Dist: I & B, Ross, PRT

Sundholm, Roy

EAST TO WEST.
Album: released on Ensign, May'81 by Ensign Records. Dist: CBS Distribution

Cassette: released on Ensign, May'81 by Ensign Records. Dist: CBS Distribution

GOOD GIRLS DON'T WEAR WHITE.
Single (7"): released on Ensign, Jul'81 by Ensign Records. Dist: CBS Distribution

Sundown

HAPPY STATE OF MIND.
Album: released on Tank, Dec'77 by Tank Records.

Sundown Band

ALL ALONE TOGETHER.
Album: released on Folk Heritage, Jul'82 by Folk Heritage Records. Dist: Roots, Wynd-Up Distribution, Jazz Music, Folk Heritage

Sundown, Lonesome

BEEN GONE TOO LONG.
Album: released on Sonet, Jun'80 by Sonet Records. Dist: PRT

Sunfire

STEP IN THE NIGHT.
Single (7"): released on Warner Brothers, May'83 by WEA Records. Dist: WEA

Single (12"): released on Warner Brothers, May'83 by WEA Records. Dist: WEA

SUNFIRE.
Album: released on Warner Brothers, Jun'83 by WEA Records. Dist: WEA

Sunglasses After Dark

MORBID SILENCE.
Single (7"): released on Anagram, Mar'84 by Cherry Red Records. Dist: Pinnacle

Single (12"): released on Anagram, Mar'84 by Cherry Red Records. Dist: Pinnacle

UNTAMED CULTURE.
Album: released on Anagram, Jan'85 by Cherry Red Records. Dist: Pinnacle

Sun, Joe

OLD FLAMES.
Album: released on Ovation, Mar'80 by Gull Records. Dist: PRT Distribution

OUT OF YOUR MIND.
Album: released on Ovation, Mar'80 by Gull Records. Dist: PRT Distribution

SUN NEVER SETS, (THE) (Sun, Joe & The Solar System).
Album: released on Sonet, Dec'84 by Sonet Records. Dist: PRT

Sun Life Stanshawe Band

CARNIVAL.
Album: released on Chandos, Aug'81 by Chandos Records. Dist: Harmonia Mundi, Taylors

Cassette: released on Chandos, Aug'81 by Chandos Records. Dist: Harmonia Mundi, Taylors

Sun, Nicci

WHO SAVED WHO?.
Single (7"): released on RAK, Sep'82 by RAK. Dist: EMI

Sunny afternoon

SUNNY AFTERNOON Various artists (Various Artists).
Album: released on Impression, Aug'83 Dist: CBS

Cassette: released on Impression, Aug'83 Dist: CBS

Sunny afternoon, Vol 2

SUNNY AFTERNOON, VOL 2 Various artists (Various Artists).
Album: released on Impression, Jul'84 Dist: CBS

Cassette: released on Impression, Jul'84 Dist: CBS

Sunnyland, Slim

LEGACY OF THE BLUES, VOL 2.
Album: released on Sonet, '75 by Sonet Records. Dist: PRT

LITTLE BROTHER MONTGOMERY.
Album: released on 77, Sep'79 by 77 Records. Dist: Chris Wellard, Cadillac Music, Jazz Music

Sunny & Mel

HERE'S A LITTLE SUNSHINE.
Album: released on Dulcima, Jun'83 by Living Productions Records. Dist: H.R. Taylor

Cassette: released on Dulcima, Jun'83 by Living Productions Records. Dist: H.R. Taylor

Sunny & Showboat

SUNNY & SHOWBOAT Original London casts.
Album: released on World Records, Feb'77 Dist: Polygram

Sun Palace

WINNING.
Single (12"): released on Passion, Nov'83 by Skratch Records. Dist: PRT

Sun Ra

COSMOS.
Album: released on Cobra, May'79 by Cobra Records. Dist: Projection, EMI

COSMOS SUN CONNECTION.
Album: released on Saturn, Feb'86 Dist: Recommended, Rough Trade, Cartel

DANCING SHADOWS.
Album: released on Happy Bird (Germany), Sep'84 Dist: Polygram, IMS

HELIOCENTRIC WORLDS OF SUN RA.
Album: released on ESP, Apr'81 by ESP Records. Dist: Jazz Horizons, Jazz Music

OTHER WORLDS.
Album: released on Happy Bird (Germany), Sep'84 Dist: Polygram, IMS

SOLAR-MYTH APPROACH, VOL 2.
Album: released on Affinity, '83 by Charly Records. Dist: Charly, Cadillac

SOLAR-MYTH APPROACH, VOL 1.
Album: released on Affinity, Feb'78 by Charly Records. Dist: Charly, Cadillac

SOLO PIANO, VOL 1.
Album: released on Improvising Artists, Jul'78 Dist: Swift

SOLO PIANO, VOL 2.
Album: released on Improvising Artists, '78 Dist: Swift

SOUND OF JOY.
Album: released on Delmark, '74 Dist: Projection, Swift, Cadillac

STRANGE CELESTIAL ROAD.
Album: released on Y, Sep'82

SUN MYTH, (THE).
Album: released on Happy Bird (Germany), Sep'84 Dist: Polygram, IMS

SUN RA.
Album: released on Inner City, Apr'79 Dist: Jetstar

SUN RA ARKESTRA NEETS SALAH RAGAB IN EGYPT.
Album: released on Praxis (Greece), May'84 Dist: Mole Jazz

SUN SONG.
Album: released on Delmark, '74 Dist: Projection, Swift, Cadillac

Sun Records

SUN RECORDS - THE ROCKING YEARS Various artists (Various Artists).
Tracks: / I don't mind / Sentimental fool / I need a man / Voice of a fool / I'm getting better all the time / Bop bop baby / Don't need your lovin' / Wild woman / Don't need your lovin' / Cindy Lou / Honey love / Fine little baby / Move baby move / Ooby dooby / Go go go / Rockhouse / Domino / Have you ever been lonely / Fool proof / Sorry I lied / Rockabilly gal / Flat foot Sam / Rakin' and scrapin' / Lordy Hoody / Long time gone / I dig you baby-1 / You better believe it-1 / Sweetie pie / I dig you baby-2 / Shake around / You better beleive it-2 / Rock boppin' baby / That's the way I love / Eight wheel driver / Sweet woman / Baby that's good / King of fools / Memories never grow old / Good lovin' / Fool fool fool / Dreamy nights / Hey heart / Right behind you baby / So young / Why why why / You made a hit / Sail away / Rockin' bandit / Willing and ready / Forever yours / Shake around / Breakup / Mona Lisa / Rockin' love / Pretend / Too young / Thousand guitars / Is it too late? / Is it me? / Southbound line / Beat it / Today is blue day / Breeze / Hey little girl / Mystery train-1 / This kinda love / Sweet and easy to love / Mystery train-2 / Thinkin' of me / Have a little party / Whole lotta shakin' / I'll change my ways / This old heart of mine / Love is my business / I lost my baby / Walkin' (the stroll) / With your love, with your kiss / No more crying the blues / No name girl / Got your water boiling / Blues at midnight / Pop and mama / Chains of love / Juicy fruit / Drinkin' wine / I done told you / Crazy woman / I don't love you baby / Money money money / If I'm not wanted / Love my baby / One broken heart / Fairlane rock / Blues blues blues / Love my baby / Mad man / Carl Perkins in Memphis / Heartbreakin' love / You can't make love to somebody / Everybody's tryin'to be my baby / Miss Pearl / Dixie fried / Put your cat clothes on - 1 / Take me from this garden of evil / That don't move me / Mad man / Only you / Pink pedal pushers / That's right / Crawdad hole / If you don't mind / Slow down / Fool for loving you / Whole lotta shakin' goin' on / Somehow we'll find a way / Sign it on the dotted line / All night rock / You win again / College man / I'll be around / After the hop / I'll wait forever / High school confidential / Be wise, don't cry / Crazy heart / Breakup / Sally's got a sister / Come on little mama - 1 / Little bitty pretty girl / Where'd you stay last night / Hey good lookin' / Sugarfoot / Love dumb baby / Greenback dollar, watch and chain - 1 / Foolish heart / Charlie's boogie / Lonely wolf / Hey Bo Diddley / Greenback dollar, watch and chain - 2 / Tuff (Cattywampus) / That's just too bad / 706 Union / Cotton pickin' boogie / Rockin' at the wood choppers ball / It makes no difference now / Bernero's boogie / Put your cat clothes on - 2 / Sign on the dotted line / Come on little mama - 2 / Rock baby, rock it / Tennessee zip / I feel like rockin' / Love crazy baby / Treat me right / Get it off your mind / What's the reason / You call everybody darlin' / Go ahead baby / Huh babe / High high high / My baby don't rock / That's what I tell my heart / Born to sing the blues / I need your lovin' kiss / Goin' crazy / Mad at you / Good lookin' woman / Rock-a-bye baby / Sweet rocking mama / Sonny boy / Fire engine red / All I want is you / My one desire / Tomorrow / Please don't cry over me / That depends on you / Down on the border / Don't let me down / Shake rattle and roll / It's me baby / Rocking with my baby / Trumpet / Ten cats down / Fools hall of fame / Cheese and crackers / Sally Jo / We wanna boogie / Red headed woman / Ain't got a thing / Feelin' good / Truckin' down the avenue / Restless / Find my baby for me / Sadie Brown / Itchy / Rock'n' roll Ruby / Stop the world / Uranium rock / Dear John / Flyin' saucer rock and roll / I want you baby / Red hot / No name girl / Got your water boiling / Blues at midnight / Pop and mama / Chains of love / Juicy fruit / Drinkin' wine / I done told you / Crazy woman / I don't love you baby / Money money money / If I'm not wanted / Love my baby - 1 / Love my baby - 2 / One broken heart / Fairlane rock / Blues blues blues / Mad man / Heartbreakin' love / Miss pearl / Take me (from this garden of evil) / Mad man / Whole lotta shakin' goin' on / You win again / High school confidential / Crazy heart / Charlie's boogie / Blue suede shoes / My baby done left me / Rebound / Lonely weekends / Stairway to nowhere / She's gone away / Did you tell me you don't care / I wanta rock / Memories of you / Judy / Drive in / Fool proof / Have you ever been lonely / Sorry I lied / Flat foot Sam / Lordy hoody / I dig you baby / You better believe it / Sweetie pie / I dig you baby - 2 / Shake around / You better believe it / Rock boppin' baby / Eight wheel driver / Sweet woman / Baby that's good / King of fools / Memories never grow old / Good lovin' / Fool fool fool / Dreamy nights / Hey heart / Right behind you baby / So young / Sail away / Breakup / Rockin' bandit / Willing and ready / Shake around / You made a hit / Forever yours / Mona Lisa / Rockin' love / Pretend / Too young / Thousand guitars, A / Is it too late? / Southbound line / Beat it / Is it me? / Your lovin' man / Today is blue day / Breeze / Hey little girl / Mystery train / This kinda love / Sweet and easy to love / Mystery train - 2 / Thinkin' of me / Have a iittle party / Whole lotta shaking going on / I'll change my ways / This old heart of mine / Love is my business / I lost my baby / With your love, with your kiss / No more crying the blues / Raunchy / Midnight man / Somehow we'll find a way / Wild rice / College man / Scroungle / After the hop / Sally's got a sister / Bop train / Flip flop and bop / Rolando / Little bitty pretty girl / Hey good lookin' / Sugarfoot rag / Hey bo diddley / That's the way I feel / Tuff (cattywampus) / That's just too bad / 706 union.
Boxed set: released on Sun, Feb'87 by Charly Records. Dist: Charly Distribution

Sunset All Stars

JAMMIN' AT SUNSET.
Album: released on Black Lion, Jan'85 by Black Lion Records. Dist: Jazz Music, Chris Wellard, Taylor, H.R., Counterpoint, Cadillac

SUNSET ALLSTARS.
Album: released on Black Lion, '83 by Black Lion Records. Dist: Jazz Music, Chris Wellard, Taylor, H.R., Counterpoint, Cadillac

Sunset Dance Orchestra

DANCING YEARS OF BING CROSBY, THE.
Album: released on Sunset, '78 Dist: EMI Deleted '80.

Cassette: released on Sunset, '78 Dist: EMI

Sunset Gun

IN AN IDEAL WORLD.
Album: released on CBS, Sep'85 by CBS Records. Dist: CBS

Cassette: released on CBS, Sep'85 by CBS Records. Dist: CBS

Sunset special

SUNSET SPECIAL Various artists (Various Artists).
Tracks: / Your honey love / Willing and ready / Judy / Shake around / You made a hit / Behind you baby / Why why why / Show me / Broke my guitar / Break up / This old heart of mine / Christine / Sweet love on my mind / I lost my baby.
Album: released on Sun, Jan'86 by Charly Records. Dist: Charly Distribution

Sun's gold hits

SUN'S GOLD HITS Various artists (Various Artists).
Album: released on Sun, Feb'81 by Charly Records. Dist: Charly Distribution

Sun's greatest hits

SUN'S GREATEST HITS Various artists (Various Artists).
Album: released on Rhino (USA), Feb'85 by Rhino Records (USA).

Sunshine, Monty

MONTY SUNSHINE'S JAZZ BAND (Sunshine's, Monty Jazz Band).
Album: released on Stomp Off, Jun'86 by Stomp Off Records. Dist: Jazz Music Distribution

ON SUNDAY.
Album: released on Wam, May'87

PORTRAIT VOL 2.
Album: released on Wam, May'87

SUNSHINE IN LONDON.
Album: released on Black Lion, Dec'79 by Black Lion Records. Dist: Jazz Music, Chris Wellard, Taylor, H.R., Counterpoint, Cadillac

Sunshine Special

SUNSHINE SPECIAL Various artists (Various Artists).
Album: released on VJM, Apr'79 by VJM (UK) Records. Dist: Swift

Sunshine & the Radics

MOUNT ZION.
Single (12"): released on DATC, Mar'83 by DATC Records. Dist: Rough Trade

Suns of Arqa

ECLECTICISM.
Cassette: released on One G, Oct'84

GD MAGICK (EP).
Single (12"): released on Antler, Jan'84 by Antler Records (Belgium). Dist: Red Rhino, Cartel

GET DOWN MAGIC.
Single (12"): released on Rock Steady, Sep'83 by Rock Steady Records. Dist: Rough Trade Distribution, Indies Distribution, Cartel Distribution

INDIA.
Album: released on One G, Sep'84

REVENGE OF THE MOZABITES.
Album: released on Rock Steady, Sep'82 by Rock Steady Records. Dist: Rough Trade Distribution, Indies Distribution, Cartel Distribution

Single (12"): released on Rock Steady, Oct'83 by Rock Steady Records. Dist: Rough Trade Distribution, Indies Distribution, Cartel Distribution

SOUL TO SAVE / ANATA SNAKE DANCE.
Single (7"): released on Rock Steady, '81 by Rock Steady Records. Dist: Rough Trade Distribution, Indies Distribution, Cartel Distribution

WADADA MAGIC.
Album: released on Antler, Jan'84 by Antler Records (Belgium). Dist: Red Rhino, Cartel

Sun Sounds Special

MEMPHIS BEAT.
Album: released on Sun, '82 by Charly Records. Dist: Charly Distribution

Sunsplash

SUNSPLASH Various original artists (Various original artists).

Album: released on K-Tel, Jul'83 by K-Tel Records. Dist: Record Merchandisers Distribution, Taylors, Terry Blood Distribution, Wynd-Up Distribution, Relay Distribution, Pickwick Distribution, Solomon & Peres Distribution, Polygram

Cassette: released on K-Tel, Jul'83 by K-Tel Records. Dist: Record Merchandisers Distribution, Taylors, Terry Blood Distribution, Wynd-Up Distribution, Relay Distribution, Pickwick Distribution, Solomon & Peres Distribution, Polygram

Sunsplash Showcase

SUNSPLASH SHOWCASE Various Jamaican artists (Various Artists).
Album: released on Kingdom, Sep'83 by Kingdom Records. Dist: Kingdom

Sunwind

SUN BELOW (THE).
Tracks: / Mr Yang / Under the trees / Two ladies / Happy tune shephardis / Sun below (The) / Rising / Sun below (The).
Compact disc: released on MMC, Oct'86 by MMC Records. Dist: PRT Distribution, Pinnacle

SUN BELOW, THE.
Album: released on MMC, Nov'83 by MMC Records. Dist: PRT Distribution, Pinnacle

Sun Yama

SUBTERRANEAN HOMESICK BLUES.
Single (7"): released on Trans, Jul'82 by Trans Records. Dist: Statik, Stage One

Super All Star

SUPER ALL STAR Various artists (Various Artists).
Album: released on Globestyle, Mar'87 by Ace Records. Dist: Projection

Super black

BAD BOY GONE A SAIL.
Tracks: / One time girl friend.
Single (12"): released on Jammy's, Jan'87 by Jammy's Records. Dist: Jetstar

BUBBLING TIME.
Tracks: / Take life easy.
Single (7"): released on United Sound, Mar'86 Dist: Jetstar

LOVESICK.
Tracks: / Boom shakatak (General Tree).
Single (12"): released on Unity, Apr'86 by Unity Records. Dist: Jetstar

OLD TIME PEOPLE.
Tracks: / Old time people / Dancehall night.
Single (12"): released on Live & Love, Nov'86 by Third World Records. Dist: Jetstar

RAMBO.
Tracks: / Rambo / Can't conquer me.
Single (12"): released on Live & Love, Oct'86 by Third World Records. Dist: Jetstar

Super Blues

SUPER BLUES Various artists (Various Artists).
Album: released on Chess, Oct'86 by Charly Records. Dist: Charly, Swift, PRT, Discovery, IMS, Polygram

Supercats

BOOPS.
Single (7"): released on Techniques, Jun'86 Dist: Jetstar Distribution

Single (12"): released on Techniques, Jun'86 Dist: Jetstar Distribution

BOOPS DEH.
Album: released on Technique, May'86 by Technique. Dist: CBS

CRY FOR THE YOUTH.
Tracks: / Boops.
Single (12"): released on Techniques, Apr'86 Dist: Jetstar Distribution

Supercharge

PEACHES 'N' CREAM.
Single (7"): released on Criminal, Oct'80 by Criminal Records. Dist: Jetstar

Superchart

SUPERCHART : 83 various artists (Various Artists).
Album: released on Telstar, Nov'83 by Telstar Records. Dist: RCA Distribution

Cassette: released on Telstar, Nov'83 by Telstar Records. Dist: RCA Distribution

Super Country

SUPER COUNTRY VOL.1 various artists (Various Artists).
Cassette: released on Homespun(Ireland), Feb'83 by Outlet Records. Dist: Outlet

SUPER COUNTRY VOL.2 various artists (Various Artists).
Cassette: released on Homespun(Ireland), Feb'83 by Outlet Records. Dist: Outlet

Cassette: released on Homespun(Ireland), Feb'83 by Outlet Records. Dist: Outlet

SUPER COUNTRY VOL.3 various artists (Various Artists).

Super Diamono de Dakar

PEOPLE.
Album: released on Encore, Feb'87 by EMI Records. Dist: EMI

Super Enigmatix

TOUCH THE BEAT.
Single (7"): released on MDM, Mar'87 Dist: Siren, Virgin, EMI

Single (12"): released on MDM, Mar'87 Dist: Siren, Virgin, EMI

Supergirl

FILM SOUNDTRACK.
Compact disc: released on TER, Jul'85 Dist: Pinnacle

SUPERGIRL Original soundtrack (Various Artists).
Album: released on Colosseum(West Germany), Feb'86 Dist: Silva Screen

Supergrass

SUPERGRASS, THE various artists (Various Artists).
Album: released on Island Visual Arts, Nov'85 by Island Records. Dist: Polygram

Cassette: released on Island Visual Arts, Nov'85 by Island Records. Dist: Polygram

Supergroove

YAWNS ON 45.
Single (7"): released on Swamp, Aug'81 by Swamp Records. Dist: PRT Distribution

Super Hits

SUPERHITS 1 & 2 various artists (Various original artists).
Double Album: released on Ronco, Sep'81

Double cassette: released on Ronco, Sep'81

SUPER HITS: 1953 various artists (Various Artists).

SUPER HITS: 1956 various artists (Various Artists).
Album: released on Gusto (USA), Oct'79 by Gusto Records (USA). Dist: Crusader

Album: released on Gusto (USA), Oct'79 by Gusto Records (USA). Dist: Crusader

SUPER HITS: 1959 various artists (Various Artists).
Album: released on Gusto (USA), Oct'79 by Gusto Records (USA). Dist: Crusader

SUPER HITS: 1960 various artists (Various Artists).
Album: released on Gusto (USA), Oct'79 by Gusto Records (USA). Dist: Crusader

SUPER HITS: 1961 various artists (Various Artists).
Album: released on Gusto (USA), Oct'79 by Gusto Records (USA). Dist: Crusader

SUPER HITS: 1965 various artists (Various Artists).
Album: released on Gusto (USA), Oct'79 by Gusto Records (USA). Dist: Crusader

SUPER HITS OF THE 80'S various artists (Various Artists).
Cassette: released on Bi Bi(Budget Cassettes), Jan'83

Superiors

BE MY GIRL.
Single (7"): released on Polo, May'84 by Polo Records. Dist: PRT

Superman

SUPERMAN III Original Soundtrack (Superman III).
Album: released on Warner Brothers, Jul'83 by WEA Records. Dist: WEA

SUPERMAN IN DEATH FROM A DISTANT GALAXY (Super Heroes series) (Various Artists).
Cassette: released on MFP, Oct'85 by EMI Records. Dist: EMI

SUPERMAN & THE CONQUERER FROM THE PAST (Super Heroes series) (Various Artists).
Cassette: released on MFP, Oct'85 by EMI Records. Dist: EMI

SUPERMAN & THE NEUTRON NIGHTMARE (Super Heroes series) (Various Artists).
Cassette: released on MFP, Oct'85 by EMI Records. Dist: EMI

Superman and Spiderman

SUPERMAN AND SPIDERMAN.
Album: released on Kingdom Records, Apr'86 by Kingdom Records. Dist: Kingdom Records

Cassette: released on Kingdom Records, Apr'86 by Kingdom Records. Dist: Kingdom Records

Super Maxi's

SUPER MAXI'S VOL 2 Various artists (Various Artists).
Tracks: / After the love has gone / Sayonara (don't stop) / Ocean of crime (we're movin on) / Cenerentola / Heaven I need (The) / Call my name (the final disco remix) / Frontline / Boat (The) / Eye to eye / Mary is a clerk / Rock & rock / Step by step.
Album: released on Teldec (Germany), Apr'86 by Import Records. Dist: IMS Distribution, Polygram Distribution

Cassette: released on Teldec (Germany), Apr'86 by Import Records. Dist: IMS Distribution, Polygram Distribution

Super Mazembe

SHAURI YAKO.
Single (12"): released on Earthworks, Jan'84 by Earthworks Records. Dist: Earthworks Distributors, Rough Trade, Cartel, Projection

Supernatural Stories

EXORCISM OF BROTHER SIMEON (Various Artists).
Cassette: released on Chiron Cassettes, '79 by Ivan Berg. Dist: Pinnacle, Record & Tape Sales

MONSTERS OF THE EARTH (Various Artists).
Cassette: released on Chiron Cassettes, '79 by Ivan Berg. Dist: Pinnacle, Record & Tape Sales

NOSTRADAMUS (Various Artists).
Cassette: released on Chiron Cassettes, '79 by Ivan Berg. Dist: Pinnacle, Record & Tape Sales

UFO'S/ THE PYRAMID MYSTERY (Various Artists).
Cassette: released on Chiron Cassettes, '79 by Ivan Berg. Dist: Pinnacle, Record & Tape Sales

Super Oldies

SUPER OLDIES (Various Artists).
Tracks: / Love letters in the sand / Duke of Earl / To know you is to love you / Keep a knockin' / Fernandos hideaway / Singing the blues / Rave on / This ole house / Who's sorry now / Tennessee waltz / Purple people eater, The / Because they're young / Tom Dooley / Concrete and clay.
Compact disc: released on The Collection, Apr'87 by Object Enterprises Ltd. Dist: Counterpoint Distribution

SUPER OLDIES OF THE FIFTIES (Various Artists).
Compact disc: released on Bridge, '86 Dist: CD Centre Distribution, Pinnacle, Target

SUPER OLDIES OF THE SIXTIES (Various Artists).
Compact disc: released on Bridge, '86 Dist: CD Centre Distribution, Pinnacle, Target

SUPER OLDIES OF THE SIXTIES, VOL.2 Various artists (Various Artists).
Notes: Tracks by Sam & Dave, Lou Christie, Billy J.Kramer, Mary Hopkins, The Equals etc.
Compact disc: released on Bridge, Apr'87 Dist: CD Centre Distribution, Pinnacle, Target

SUPER OLDIES OF THE FIFTIES, VOL.2 Various artists (Various Artists).
Notes: Tracks by Ronnie Ray, Patti Page, Little Richard, The Drifters, Coasters etc.

SUPER OLDIES OF THE SEVENTIES, VOL.1 Various artists (Various Artists).
Notes: Tracks by Marmalade, Melanie, Daniele Boone, New Seekers, Paper Lace, Lobo etc.
Compact disc: released on Bridge, Apr'87 Dist: CD Centre Distribution, Pinnacle, Target

SUPER OLDIES OF THE SIXTIES Various artists (Various Artists).
Compact disc: released on Bridge, Oct'86 Dist: CD Centre Distribution, Pinnacle, Target

SUPER OLDIES- THE FIFTIES Various artists (Various Artists).
Compact disc: released on Bridge, Dec'85 Dist: CD Centre Distribution, Pinnacle, Target

Super Rail Band

NEW DIMENSIONS IN RAIL CULTURE (Super Rail Band of the Buffet de la Gare de Bamako, Mali).
Album: released on Globestyle, Mar'85 by Ace Records. Dist: Projection

Super Rhythm 'N' Blues

SUPER RHYTHM 'N' BLUES Various artists (Various Artists).
Tracks: / Keep on knowin' / I found my baby there / Letter, The / Could this be love / I thank god / Big fine woman / Lovin' woman / Blues are bluer / Cry baby cry / Need him / Wild child / Walkin' and talkin' / Please love me / I'm tramping / Porgy / Deep river / My man / See what you have done / Blues for christmas / That's heaven to me / Feel like I wanna cry / I just can't take it / I'm wonderin' / Milky white way / Maybelline / Memphis / Lover come back to me / Did you cry the blues / Peace breaker / Why don't you love me / Long tall Sally / Baby call on me / Let the good times roll / My prayer / Good night Irene / Sweet little sixteen.
Notes: Artists Include: Sam Cooke/Little Richard/Wilson Pickett: And more star names, as well as classic cuts from Billie Holiday and Ray Charles.
Album: released on Pathe Marconi, Dec'85 Dist: Swift

Supersax

CHASIN' THE BIRD.
Tracks: / Shaw nuff / Night in Tunisia, A / Drifting on a reed / Song is you, The / Oop bop sh'bam / Round midnight / Now's the time / Dizzy atmosphere / Chasin' the bird / Parker's mood.
Compact disc: released on Polydor, Nov'84 by Polydor Records. Dist: Polygram. Polydor

EMBRACEABLE YOU (Supersax & L.A. Voices).
Album: released on CBS(France), Aug'84 by CBS Records. Dist: Conifer, Discovery, Swift

Cassette: released on CBS(France), Aug'84 by CBS Records. Dist: Conifer, Discovery, Swift

SUPERSAX & L.A. VOICES VOL.2 (Supersax & L.A. Voices).
Album: released on CBS(France), May'85 by CBS Records. Dist: Conifer, Discovery, Swift

Cassette: released on CBS(France), May'85 by CBS Records. Dist: Conifer, Discovery, Swift

Supershow

SUPERSHOW.
Notes: A lost rock-jam supression from the end of the 60's, held in a disused London factory, and featuring the likes of Eric Clapton, Buddy Guy and Led Zepplin. 1969 production. Total playing time: 82 minutes
Video-cassette (VHS): released on Virgin Music Video, Sep'86 by Virgin Records. Dist: EMI

Supersonic Syd

SUPERSONIC SYD SINGS - OR DOES HE (Supersonic Syd(Sid Little)).

Super Sounds

SUPER SOUNDS Various artists (Various Artists).
Tracks: / I know him so well / Every breath you take / Oh lady be good / Manana / Diamonds are a girls best friend / Mambo jambo / Certain smile, A / Aquarius / Love letters in the sand / Jersey bounce / Dance to the music / Crazy rhythm / Something's gotta give / When I fall in love / Why do I love you / Take me home country roads / Have you ever been lonely / That old funky rolls / S'posin'.
Cassette: released on Sounds Ultimate, Jun'86 Dist: PRT, H.R. Taylor

Superstar Mix Up

SUPERSTAR MIX UP Various artists (Various Artists).
Single (12"): released on Greensleeves, Dec'84 by Greensleeves Records. Dist: BMG, Jetstar, Spartan

Superstar Session

SUPERSTAR SESSION Various artists (Various Artists).
Album: released on Astan, Nov'84 by Astan Records. Dist: Counterpoint

Cassette: released on Astan, Nov'84 by Astan Records. Dist: Counterpoint

Superstars Hit Parade

SUPERSTARS HIT PARADE Various artists (Various Artists).
Notes: Inc. Dennis Brown, King Kong.
Album: released on Greensleeves, May'86 by Greensleeves Records. Dist: BMG, Jetstar, Spartan

SUPERSTARS HIT PARADE VOL.1 Various artists (Various Artists).
Album: released on Live & Love, May'86 by Third World Records. Dist: Jetstar

SUPERSTARS HIT PARADE VOL.2 Various artists (Various Artists).
Album: released on World Enterprise, Sep'86 Dist: Jetstar

Superstar Symphonies

SUPERSTAR SYMPHONIES Various artists (Various Artists).
Double cassette: released on Cambra, Jan'82 by Cambra Records. Dist: IDS, Conifer

Superted

SUPERTED THEME AND OVERTURE/ SPOTTY MAN SONG.
Single (7"): released on Rainbow Communication, Jan'84

Supertramp

AUTOBIOGRAPHY OF SUPERTRAMP.
Album: released on A&M, Oct'86 by A&M Records. Dist: Polygram

Cassette: released on A&M, Oct'86 by A&M Records. Dist: Polygram

Compact disc: released on A&M, Oct'86 by A&M Records. Dist: Polygram

BREAKFAST IN AMERICA.
Tracks: / Gone Hollywood / Logical song, The / Goodbye stranger / Breakfast in America / Oh darling / Take the long way home / Lord is it mine / Just another nervous wreck / Casual conversation / Child of vision.
Album: released on A&M, '82 by A&M Records. Dist: Polygram

Cassette: released on A&M, '82 by A&M Records. Dist: Polygram

Compact disc: released on A&M, '82 by A&M Records. Dist: Polygram

BROTHER WHERE YOU BOUND.
Tracks: / Cannonball / Still in love / No inbetween / Better days / Brother where you bound / Ever open door.
Album: released on A&M, May'85 by A&M Records. Dist: Polygram

Cassette: released on A&M, May'85 by A&M Records. Dist: Polygram

Cassette: released on A&M, May'85 by A&M Records. Dist: Polygram

CANNONBALL.
Tracks: / Every open door.
Single (7"): released on A&M, Feb'86 by A&M Records. Dist: Polygram

Single (12"): released on A&M, Feb'86 by A&M Records. Dist: Polygram

CRIME OF THE CENTURY.
Tracks: / School / Bloody well right / Hide in your shell / Asylum / Dreamer / Rudy / If everyone was listening / Crime of the century.
Album: released on A&M, '82 by A&M Records. Dist: Polygram

Cassette: released on A&M, '82 by A&M Records. Dist: Polygram

Compact disc: released on A&M, '82 by A&M Records. Dist: Polygram

CRISIS WHAT CRISIS/ EVEN IN THE QUIETEST MOMENTS.
Double Album: released on A&M, May'81 by A&M Records. Dist: Polygram

CRISIS ? WHAT CRISIS ?.
Album: released on A&M, Nov'75 by A&M Records. Dist: Polygram

Cassette: released on A&M, Nov'75 by A&M Records. Dist: Polygram

DREAMER.
Single (7"): released on Old Gold, Sep'85 by Old Gold Records. Dist: Lightning, Jazz Music, Spartan, Counterpoint

EVEN IN THE QUIETEST MOMENTS.
Tracks: / Give a little bit / Lover boy / Even in the quietest moments / Downstream / Babaj / From now on / Fool's overture.
Album: released on A&M, Apr'86 by A&M Records. Dist: Polygram

Cassette: released on A&M, Apr'86 by A&M Records. Dist: Polygram

FAMOUS LAST WORDS.
Tracks: / Crazy / Put on your old brown shoes / It's raining again / Bonnie / Know who you are / My kind of lady / C'est le bon / Waiting so long / Don't leave me now.
Notes: Words and music by Rick Davies and Roger Hodgson-Published by Delicate Music administered by Almo Music Corp.
Album: released on A&M, Oct'82 by A&M Records. Dist: Polygram

Cassette: released on A&M, Oct'82 by A&M Records. Dist: Polygram

Compact disc: released on A&M, Oct'82 by A&M Records. Dist: Polygram

INDELIBLY STAMPED.
Album: by A&M Records. Dist: Polygram

Cassette: by A&M Records. Dist: Polygram

LOGICAL SONG.
Tracks: / Goodbye stranger.
Single (7"): released on A&M, Sep'86 by A&M Records. Dist: Polygram

MY KIND OF LADY/ KNOW WHO YOU ARE.
Single (7"): released on A&M, Jan'83 by A&M Records. Dist: Polygram

PARIS (LIVE DOUBLE).
Double Album: released on A&M, Sep'80 by A&M Records. Dist: Polygram

Double cassette: released on A&M, Sep'80 by A&M Records. Dist: Polygram

SUPERTRAMP.
Album: released on Pickwick (A&M), May'84

Cassette: released on Pickwick (A&M), May'84

Album: released on A&M, Mar'82 by A&M Records. Dist: Polygram

Cassette: released on A&M, Mar'82 by A&M Records. Dist: Polygram

Supply Demand & Curve

SUPPLY DEMAND & CURVE.
Album: released on Mulligan (Ireland), Jan'77 by Topic Records. Dist: Roots Distribution, Jazz Music Distribution, JSU Distribution, I & B Distribution, Projection Distribution, Wynd-Up Distribution, Celtic Distributions

Support Band

HIGH HEEL SNEAKERS.
Tracks: / Long legged lady.
Single (7"): released on School, Feb'87 Dist: RCA

Supporters

PLAY THE GAME(THE ANTHEM).
Single (7"): released on Sonic Communications, Oct'85 by Priority Records. Dist: EMI

Supremes

BACK IN MY ARMS AGAIN.
Single (7"): released on Motown, '80 by Motown Records. Dist: BMG Distribution

DIANA ROSS & THE SUPREMES JOIN THE TEMPTATIONS (Supremes, Diana Ross & The Temptations).
Album: released on Motown, Oct'81 by RCA Records. Dist: RCA Distribution

Cassette: released on Motown, Oct'81 by RCA Records. Dist: RCA Distribution

FLOY JOY/ BAD WEATHER.
Single (7"): released on Motown, Oct'81 by Motown Records. Dist: BMG Distribution

GREATEST HITS: SUPREMES.
Album: released on Motown, Jun'83 by Motown Records. Dist: BMG Distribution

Cassette: released on Motown, Jun'83 by Motown Records. Dist: BMG Distribution

MAGNIFICENT 7, THE (Supremes/Four Tops).
Album: released on Motown, Oct'81 by Motown Records. Dist: BMG Distribution

Cassette: released on Motown, Oct'81 by Motown Records. Dist: BMG Distribution

REACH OUT AND TOUCH.
Single (7"): released on Motown, Oct'81 by Motown Records. Dist: BMG Distribution

REFLECTIONS/ HAPPENING, THE.
Single (7"): released on Motown, '80 by Motown Records. Dist: BMG Distribution

RIVER DEEP MOUNTAIN HIGH.
Single (7"): released on Motown, Oct'81 by Motown Records. Dist: BMG Distribution

SOMEDAY WE'LL BE TOGETHER.
Single (7"): released on Motown, '80 by Motown Records. Dist: BMG Distribution

STONED LOVE.
Single (7"): released on Motown, '80 by Motown Records. Dist: BMG Distribution

STONED LOVE/ NATHAN JONES.
Single (7"): released on Motown, Oct'81 by Motown Records. Dist: BMG Distribution

STOP IN THE NAME OF LOVE.
Single (7"): released on Motown, '80 by Motown Records. Dist: BMG Distribution

UP THE LADDER TO THE ROOF.
Single (7"): released on Motown, Oct'81 by Motown Records. Dist: BMG Distribution

YOU CAN'T HURRY LOVE.
Single (7"): released on Motown, '80 by Motown Records. Dist: BMG Distribution

YOU KEEP ME HANGIN' ON.
Single (7"): released on Motown, Apr'85 by Motown Records. Dist: BMG Distribution

Single (12"): released on Motown, Apr'85 by Motown Records. Dist: BMG Distribution

Single (7"): released on Motown, '80 by Motown Records. Dist: BMG Distribution

Surface

FALLING IN LOVE.
Single (7"): released on Salsoul, Jun'83

Single (12"): released on Salsoul, Jun'83

HAPPY.
Tracks: / Let's try again.
Single (7"): released on CBS, Feb'87 by CBS Records. Dist: CBS

Compact disc: released on Scotti Brothers (USA), Mar'87 by Scotti Brothers Records. Dist: Polydor

Single (12"): released on CBS, Aug'87 by CBS Records. Dist: CBS

RACE THE NIGHT.
Album: released on Killerwatt, May'86 Dist: Kingdom Records, Pinnacle

SURFACE.
Tracks: / Let's try again / Happy / We're all searching / Lately / Gotta make love tonight / Who loves you / You're fine / Lady wants a man / Girls were made to love / Feels so good.
Album: released on CBS, Dec'86 by CBS Records. Dist: CBS

Cassette: released on CBS, Dec'86 by CBS Records. Dist: CBS

Surface Band

JAH BIBLE/ NEW STYLE.
Single (12"): released on Surface, Aug'83 by Surface Records. Dist: Jetstar Distribution

SHE HAS GONE AWAY/ WARM AND TENDER LOVE.
Single (12"): released on Lucky Dice, Dec'83 by Lucky Dice Records. Dist: Jetstar

Surface Mutants

ANAESTHETIC (EP).
Single (7"): released on Clone, Sep'82 Dist: Spartan

TRAIN/ SOMEWHERE STRANGE/ HELP.
Single (12"): released on Rock Steady, Sep'82 by Rock Steady Records. Dist: Rough Trade Distribution, Indies Distribution, Cartel Distribution

Surfadelics

BAD LITTLE GIRL.
Album: released on Media Burn, Dec'86 by Rocks Off Record Emporium. Dist: Rough Trade Distribution, Cartel Distribution

BAD LITTLE GIRL, THE.
Album: released on Media burn, Aug'87 by Rocks Off Record Emporium. Dist: Rough Trade, Cartel

TOO GOOD TO BE TRUE.
Single (7"): released on Armchair, Nov'85

Surfaris

SINGLES 1963-1967.
Album: released on MCA, Mar'87 by MCA Records. Dist: Polygram, MCA

Cassette: released on MCA, Mar'87 by MCA Records. Dist: Polygram, MCA

WIPE OUT.
Single (7"): released on Old Gold, Jul'82 by Old Gold Records. Dist: Lightning, Jazz Music, Spartan, Counterpoint

Surf City Drag City

SURF CITY DRAG CITY Various artists (Various Artists).
Tracks: / Surfin' USA / Surf city / Surf route 101 / Shoot the curl / I live for the sun / Be true to your school / Summer means fun / Warmth of the sun, The / Hot rod USA / Drag city / Repossession blues / Little Honda / I get around / Don't worry baby / Beach blanket bingo / Ride the wild surf.
Album: released on Capitol, Jul'86 by Capitol Records. Dist: EMI

Cassette: released on Capitol, Jul'86 by Capitol Records. Dist: EMI

Surf Drums

THESE 7 YEARS.
Single (12"): released on Swordfish, Sep'85 Dist: Nine Mile Distribution, Cartel Distribution

WALK AWAY.
Single (7"): released on Kaleidoscope Sound, Mar'87

Single (12"): released on Kaleidoscope Sound, Mar'87

Surfin' Dave

STATESIDE CENTRE.
Single (7"): released on Nine Mile, Sep'85 by Nine Mile Records. Dist: Nine Mile, Cartel

Surfin' Lungs

COWABUNGA.
Album: released on Off-Beat, Aug'85 by Off-Beat Records. Dist: Jetstar Distribution

MICKEY'S CAR.
Single (7"): released on Lovers Leap, Mar'84 by Backs. Dist: Cartel

PRAY FOR SUN.
Single (7"): released on Lovers Leap, Mar'85 by Backs. Dist: Cartel

SURF JET GIRL.
Tracks: / Surf-jet girl / Girls are feelin' alright / Big man on campus.

Single (7"): released on Big Beat, Jun'86 by Ace Records. Dist: Projection, Pinnacle

Surfin' USA

SURFIN' USA Various original artists (Various original artists).

Album: released on Hallmark, Mar'79 by Pickwick Records. Dist: Pickwick Distribution, PRT, Taylors

Cassette: released on Hallmark, Mar'79 by Pickwick Records. Dist: Pickwick Distribution, PRT, Taylors

Surf Punks

MY BEACH.
Album: released on Epic, Sep'80 by CBS Records. Dist: CBS

Surgin

WHEN MIDNIGHT COMES.
Album: released on Music For Nations, Dec'85 by Music For Nations Records. Dist: Pinnacle

Surkamp, David

LONIE.
Tracks: / Lonie.
Single (7"): released on Shanghai, Aug'86

Surman

Miroslav Vitous group

Surman, John

AMAZING ADVENTURES OF SIMON SIMON.
Tracks: / Nestor's saga (the tale of the ancient) / Buccaneers / Kentish hunting (Lady Margaret's air) / Pilgrim's way (to the seventeenth walls) / Within the halls of Neptune / Phoenix and the fire / Fide et amore (by faith and love) / Merry pranks (the jester's song) / Fitting epitaph, A.
Notes: Personnel: John Surman-soprano and baritone saxophones, bass clarinet, synthesizer/Jack DeJohnette-drums, congas, electric piano.
Compact disc: released on ECM (Germany), Aug'86 by ECM Records. Dist: IMS, Polygram, Virgin through EMI

Album: released on ECM, Dec'81 by ECM Records. Dist: IMS, Polygram, Virgin through EMI

SONATINAS.
Album: released on Steam, Apr'81 Dist: JSU, Chris Wellard, Jazz Music, Projection, Cadillac

SUCH WINTERS OF MEMORY (see Krog,Karin/John Surman).

SURMAN FOR ALL SAINTS.
Album: released on Ogun, Jun'79 Dist: Jazz Music, JSU, Cadillac

Album: released on ECM (Germany), May'85 by ECM Records. Dist: IMS, Polygram, Virgin through EMI

UPON REFLECTION.
Tracks: / Edges of illusion / Filigree / Caithness to Kerry / Beyond a shadow / Prelude and rustic dance / Lampfighter / Following behind / Constellation.
Notes: Personnel: John Surman-soprano and baritone saxophone, bass, clarinet, synthesizers.
Album: released on ECM (Germany), '82 by ECM Records. Dist: IMS, Polygram, Virgin through EMI

Compact disc: released on ECM (Germany), '82 by ECM Records. Dist: IMS, Polygram, Virgin through EMI

WITHHOLDING PATTERN.
Tracks: / Doxology / Changes of season / All cat's whiskers and bees' knees / Holding pattern I / Skating on thin ice / Snooper, The / Wildcat blues / Holding pattern 2.
Notes: Another long awaited solo album from John Surman-who has just finished a very successful Jazz Services tour in the UK. Surman has built up a strong following in the UK over the years and plays here as often as he can.
Compact disc: released on ECM (Germany), May'86 by ECM Records. Dist: IMS, Polygram, Virgin through EMI

Surprize

IN MOVIMENTO.
Album: released on Factory Benelux, Mar'84 by Rough Trade Records. Dist: Cartel

Surreal Estate

CURTAIN CALL.
Single (12"): released on Letharge, Nov'86 Dist: Red Rhino

Single (12"): released on Letharge, Sep'86 Dist: Red Rhino

Survival

WRITE TO ME.
Single (12"): released on Riff-Raff, Feb'82 Dist: Jetstar

Survival Dance Report

SURVIVAL DANCE REPORT Various artists (Various Artists).
Triple album / cassette: released on Survival, Nov'83 by Survival Records. Dist: Backs, Cartel Distribution

Special: released on Survival, Nov'83 by Survival Records. Dist: Backs, Cartel Distribution

Survival Singles

SURVIVAL SINGLES COLLECTION Various artists (Various Artists).
Single (7"): released on Survival, Jan'84 by Survival Records. Dist: Backs, Cartel Distribution

Survivor

BURNING HEART.
Tracks: / Feels like love / Eye of the tiger.
Single (7"): released on Scotti Brothers (USA), Feb'86 by Scotti Brothers Records. Dist: Polydor

Picture disc single: released on Scotti Brothers (USA), Feb'86 by Scotti Brothers Records. Dist: Polydor

Double-pack single: released on Scotti Brothers (USA), Feb'86 by Scotti Brothers Records. Dist: Polydor

Single (12"): released on Scotti Brothers (USA), Feb'86 by Scotti Brothers Records. Dist: Polydor

CAUGHT IN THE GAME.
Album: released on Epic, Oct'83 by CBS Records. Dist: CBS

Cassette: released on Epic, Oct'83 by CBS Records. Dist: CBS

EYE OF THE TIGER.
Tracks: / Hesitation dance / One that really matters / I'm not that man anymore / Children of the night / Ever since the world began / American heart beat / Silver girl / Eye of the tiger / Feels like love.
Album: released on Scotti Brothers (USA), Feb'86 by Scotti Brothers Records. Dist: Polydor

Cassette: released on Scotti Brothers (USA), Feb'86 by Scotti Brothers Records. Dist: Polydor

Compact disc: released on Scotti Brothers (USA), Feb'86 by Scotti Brothers Records. Dist: Polydor

EYE OF THE TIGER (ALBUM).
Tracks: / Eye of the tiger / Feels like love / Hesitation dance / One that really matters, The / I'm not that man any more / Children of the night / Ever since the world began / American heartbeat / Silver girl.
Compact disc: released on Scotti Brothers (USA), '86 by Scotti Brothers Records. Dist: Polydor

EYE OF THE TIGER/ TAKE YOU ON A SUNDAY.
Single (7"): released on Scotti Brothers (USA), Jan'84 by Scotti Brothers Records. Dist: Polydor

Single (12"): released on Scotti Brothers (USA), Jan'84 by Scotti Brothers Records. Dist: Polydor

HIGH ON YOU.
Single (7"): released on Scotti Brothers (USA), Jan'85 by Scotti Brothers Records. Dist: Polydor

I CAN'T HOLD BACK.
Tracks: / Burning heart / Rosanna / Make believe / I won't hold you back / Good for you / It's a feeling / Afraid of love / Lovers in the night / We made it / Waiting for your love / Africa.
Single (7"): released on Scotti Brothers (USA), Mar'86 by Scotti Brothers Records. Dist: Polydor

Single (12"): released on Scotti Brothers (USA), Mar'86 by Scotti Brothers Records. Dist: Polydor

Compact disc: released on CBS, '83 by CBS Records. Dist: CBS

IS THIS LOVE.
Tracks: / Can't let you go / Is this love / Can't let you go.
Single (7"): released on Scotti Brothers (USA), Nov'86 by Scotti Brothers Records. Dist: Polydor

Single (12"): released on Scotti Brothers (USA), Nov'86 by Scotti Brothers Records. Dist: Polydor

MOMENT OF TRUTH.
Single (7"): released on Casablanca, Aug'84 Dist: Polygram, Phonogram

ONE THAT REALLY MATTERS/ HESITATION DANCE.
Single (7"): released on Scotti Brothers (USA), Jan'83 by Scotti Brothers Records. Dist: Polydor

SEARCH IS OVER (THE).
Tracks: / Search is over (The) / It's the singer not the song.
Single (7"): released on Scotti Brothers (USA), May'86 by Scotti Brothers Records. Dist: Polydor

Single (12"): released on Scotti Brothers (USA), May'86 by Scotti Brothers Records. Dist: Polydor

SURVIVOR.
Album: released on Scotti Brothers (USA), Nov'80 by Scotti Brothers Records. Dist: Polydor

VERY BEST OF SURVIVOR.
Compact disc: released on Bellaphon, '86 by Bellaphon Records. Dist: IMS-Polygram

VITAL SIGNS.
Tracks: / I can't hold back / High on you / First night / Search is over (The) / Broken promises / Popular girl / Everlasting / It's the singer not the song / I see you in everyone / Moment of truth.
Compact disc: released on Bellaphon, '86 by Bellaphon Records. Dist: IMS-Polygram

Album: released on Scotti Brothers (USA), Apr'86 by Scotti Brothers Records. Dist: Polydor

Cassette: released on Scotti Brothers (USA), Apr'86 by Scotti Brothers Records. Dist: Polydor

WHEN SECONDS COUNT.
Tracks: / How much love / Keep it right here / This love / Man against the world / Rebel son / Oceans / When seconds count / Backstreet love affair / In good faith / Can't let you go.
Album: released on Scotti Brothers (USA), Jan'86 by Scotti Brothers Records. Dist: Polydor

Cassette: released on Scotti Brothers (USA), Jan'86 by Scotti Brothers Records. Dist: Polydor

Sus

YEARNING FOR YOUR LOVE.
Single (12"): released on Tit, Jun'84 by Tit Records.

Suso

SUSO.
Album: released on Carrere, Jul'84 by Carrere Records. Dist: PRT, Spartan

Suspicions

OUR LOVE IS IN THE POCKET.
Single (7"): released on Inferno, Apr'84 by Inferno Records. Dist: Inferno, Cartel, Pinnacle

Sussed

I'VE GOT ME PARKA.
Tracks: / I've got me parka.
Single (7"): released on Graduate, Jul'86 by Graduate Records. Dist: Nine Mile, Cartel

Sussex Harvest

COLLECTION OF TRADITIONAL SONGS FROM SUSSEX, A.
Album: released on Topic, '81 Dist: Roots Distribution

Sutch, Screaming Lord

ALIVE AND WELL.
Album: released on IMS(Import), Oct'82 by Polydor Records. Dist: IMS, Polygram

Cassette: released on IMS(Import), Oct'82 by Polydor Records. Dist: IMS, Polygram

ALL BLACK AND HAIRY/ JACK THE RIPPER.
Single (7"): released on Ace, Jun'81 by Ace Records. Dist: Pinnacle, Swift, Hotshot, Cadillac

JACK THE RIPPER.
Cassette: released on Autograph, Apr'85 Dist: Record Services Distribution (Ireland)

JACK THE RIPPER/ I'M A HOG.
Single (7"): released on Decca-Originals, May'82 by Decca Records. Dist: Polygram, IMS

ROCK AND HORROR.
Album: released on Ace, Nov'82 by Ace Records. Dist: Pinnacle, Swift, Hotshot, Cadillac

ROCK'N'ROLL MADMAN (EP).
Single (7"): released on Magnum Force, May'82 by Magnum Music Group Ltd. Dist: Magnum Music Group Ltd, PRT, Spartan

SCREAMING LORD SUTCH & THE SAVAGES.
Album: released on Ace, Jul'81 by Ace Records. Dist: Pinnacle, Swift, Hotshot, Cadillac

Sutcliff, Bobby

ANOTHER JANGLY MESS EP.
Single (7"): released on Tambourine, Mar'87 by Tambourine. Dist: Backs, Cartel

Sutcliff/Something Fierce

ANOTHER COMPLETE MESS.
Notes: Double pack containing album & 12" single and highlighting Tambourines American branch. Featuring Bobby Sutcliff (ex The Windbreakers) and Minneapolis' Some- thing Fierce.
Special: released on Tambourine, Sep'87 by The Dentists. Dist: Pinnacle

Suter Blind Date

FIRST RENDEZ-VOUS.
Album: released on Jungle, May'83 by Jungle Records. Dist: Jungle, Cartel

Sutherland Brothers

ARMS OF MARY.
Tracks: / Secrets.
Single (7"): released on Old Gold, Jan'87 by Old Gold Records. Dist: Lightning, Jazz Music, Spartan, Counterpoint

REACH FOR THE SKY.
Album: released on CBS, Jun'85 by CBS Records. Dist: CBS

Cassette: released on CBS, Jun'85 by CBS Records. Dist: CBS

Sutherland, Iain

IT COULDA BEEN BUDDY HOLLY.
Single (7"): released on Avatar, Sep'83 by Avatar Communications. Dist: CBS

MIXED EMOTIONS.
Album: released on Avatar, Sep'83 by Avatar Communications. Dist: CBS

WHEEL, THE (FAITES VOS JEUX).
Single (7"): released on Avatar, Feb'84 by Avatar Communications. Dist: CBS

Sutherland, Isabel

LICHT BOB'S LASSIE, THE.
Cassette: released on Folktracks, Nov'79 by Folktracks Cassettes. Dist: Folktracks

VAGRANT SONGS OF SCOTLAND.
Album: released on Topic, '81 Dist: Roots Distribution

Sutherland, Joan

WORLD OF JOAN SUTHERLAND, THE.
Album: released on Decca, '70 by Decca Records. Dist: Polygram

Cassette: released on Decca, '70 by Decca Records. Dist: Polygram

Sutherland, Mackie

LITTLE MISS BLUE EYES.
Album: released on Ross, '86 by Ross Records. Dist: Ross Distribution, Roots Distribution

Cassette: released on Ross, '86 by Ross Records. Dist: Ross Distribution, Roots Distribution

Sutherland, Nadine

UNTIL.
Album: released on Tuff Gong, Dec'85 by Tuff Gong Records. Dist: Jetstar

Sutherland, Willie

LIVE AT THE TOWER HOTEL,ELGIN.
Cassette: released on Torfness, Jan'87

Sutter, Art

ART OF LOVE (THE).
Tracks: / When I fall in love / I love you because / When your old wedding ring was new / As time goes by / Anniversary waltz / Wedding song / Our house / I only have eyes for you / Those endearing young charms / And I love you so / If / Song for you / Looking through the eyes of love / Best days of my life.
Album: released on Lismor, Nov'85 by Lismor Records. Dist: Lismor, Roots, Celtic Music

Cassette: released on Lismor, Nov'85 by Lismor Records. Dist: Lismor, Roots, Celtic Music

ART OF THE COUNTRY (THE).
Tracks: / Fool such as I / That'll be the day / Only love / You were always on my mind / Evening star / I fall to pieces / Dreams of the everyday housewife / Still / Me and Bobby McGee / Send me the pillow that you dream on / You never can tell / Your cheating heart / Wolverton mountain / Please help me I'm falling.
Album: released on Lismor, Nov'85 by Lismor Records. Dist: Lismor, Roots, Celtic Music

Cassette: released on Lismor, Nov'85 by Lismor Records. Dist: Lismor, Roots, Celtic Music

Sutton, Chris

CHRIS SUTTON.
Tracks: / Trouble / Tell it like this / Prince of jus-

tice / Voices / (You just can't)tear it from a heart / Don't get me wrong / You worry me / Know it all / That one love / Don't push your love / Money ain't worth it.
Album: released on Polydor, Nov'86 by Polydor Records. Dist: Polygram, Polydor

Cassette: released on Polydor, Nov'86 by Polydor Records. Dist: Polygram, Polydor

Compact disc: released on Polydor, Nov'86 by Polydor Records. Dist: Polygram, Polydor

DON'T GET ME WRONG.
Tracks: / Don't get me wrong / Love is the reason.
Single (7"): released on Polydor, Jul'86 by Polydor Records. Dist: Polygram, Polydor

Single (12"): released on Polydor, Jul'86 by Polydor Records. Dist: Polygram, Polydor

PRINCE OF JUSTICE.
Tracks: / Prince of justice / Money ain't worth it.
Single (7"): released on Polydor, Apr'86 by Polydor Records. Dist: Polygram, Polydor

Single (12"): released on Polydor, Apr'86 by Polydor Records. Dist: Polygram, Polydor

YOU WORRY ME.
Tracks: / You worry me / All of my life / Know it all.
Single (7"): released on Boiling Point, Oct'86 by Polydor Records. Dist: Polygram

Single (12"): released on Boiling Point, Oct'86 by Polydor Records. Dist: Polygram

Sutton, Mike & Brenda

DON'T LET GO OF ME.
Single (7"): released on Silvertown, Nov'82 by Silvertown Records.

Single (12"): released on Silvertown, Nov'82 by Silvertown Records.

WE'LL MAKE IT.
Single (7"): released on Virgin, Feb'82 by Virgin Records. Dist: EMI, Virgin Distribution

Single (12"): released on Virgin, Feb'82 by Virgin Records. Dist: EMI, Virgin Distribution

Sutton, Ralph

BIX BEIDERBECKE SUITE.
Album: released on Commodore Classics, May'87 by Teldec Records (Germany). Dist: Conifer, IMS, Polygram

BIX BEIDERBECKE SUITE & PIANO PORTRAITS.
Album: released on Commodore Classics, Feb'84 by Teldec Records (Germany). Dist: Conifer, IMS, Polygram

LIVE.
Album: released on Flyright, Aug'79 by Flyright Records. Dist: Krazy Kat. Swift, Jazz Music

OFF THE CUFF Live.
Album: released on Audiophile, Jul'87 by Jazzology Records (USA). Dist: Jazz Music, Swift

PARTNERS IN CRIME (Sutton, Ralph & Bob & Len Barnard).
Tracks: / Swing that music / One morning in May / Old folks / Rain / I never knew / Slow boat to China / It's wonderful / How can you face me? / West End Avenue blues / Diga diga doo.
Notes: Produced by Mark Hewitt. Recording co-ordinator Horst Liepold NYC. Recorded by Jimmie Madison at Jimmie Madison Studio NYC 25/8/83. Remix at Unison Sound, Sydney by Julian Lee with Mike Dodd assisting 12/12/83. Master tape assembled by Ivan Fisher. This project was assisted by the Music Board of The Australia Council, the Federal Government's Arts Funding and Advisory Body.
Album: released on Vanguard (CBS), Aug'86 by Vanguard (CBS) Records. Dist: Conifer

Cassette: released on Vanguard (CBS), Aug'86 by Vanguard (CBS) Records. Dist: Conifer

SUTTON, RALPH QUARTET (Sutton, Ralph Quartet).
Album: released on Storyville, Nov'86 by Storyville Records. Dist: Jazz Music Distribution, Swift Distribution, Chris Wellard Distribution, Counterpoint Distribution

SUTTON, RALPH & THE ALL STARS (Sutton, Ralph & The All Stars).
Notes: Mono.
Album: released on Jazz Archives, Jul'86 by Jazz Archives Records. Dist: Jazz Music

Suuka

C'EST LA VIE/ DON'T CRY FOR ME.
Single (7"): released on Paro, Nov'83 by Paro Records. Dist: Spartan

Single (12"): released on Paro, Nov'83 by Paro Records. Dist: Spartan

Suxy May

CRAZY HOUND DOG.
Single (7"): released on Sheet, Jul'82 Dist: Rough Trade

Suzie

DANCE/ MIDAS MAJESTIC.
Single (7"): released on Speed, Nov'82

Suziki, Yoshio

MORNING PICTURE.
Notes: L.O.E. Entertainment Ltd., 159 Broadhurst Gardens, London NW6 3AU. Tel: 01-328-6100/6215/6228
Album: released on Pan East, Jul'86 by L.O.E. Records. Dist: Nine Mile, PRT, Cartel

Cassette: released on Pan East, Jul'86 by L.O.E. Records. Dist: Nine Mile, PRT, Cartel

Suzy And The Red Stripes

SEASIDE WOMAN.
Tracks: / Seaside woman / B-side to seaside.
Single (7"): released on EMI, Jul'86 by EMI Records. Dist: EMI

Single (12"): released on EMI, Jul'86 by EMI Records. Dist: EMI

SWA

YOUR FUTURE (IF YOU HAVE ONE).
Album: released on SST, Sep'85 by SST Records. Dist: Pinnacle

Swaffield Junior School

YULE CHANT/ GET DOWN YULE.
Single (7"): released on Spectra, Dec'81 by Spectra Records. Dist: Pinnacle

Single (12"): released on Spectra, Nov'81 by Spectra Records. Dist: Pinnacle

Swallow Records

SWALLOW RECORDS LOUISIANA CAJAN SPECIAL NO.1 Various artists (Various Artists).
Album: released on Ace, Jun'85 by Ace Records. Dist: Pinnacle, Swift, Hotshot. Cadillac

SWALLOW RECORDS LOUISIANA CAJUN SPECIAL NO. 2 Various artists (Various Artists).
Notes: Artists include: Nathan Abshire/Lionel Cormier & Sundown Playboys/Austin Pitre/Barro & Teardrops/August Broussard & Calcasieu Ramblers/Doris Matte/Bobby Leger & Lake Charles Playboys/Aldus Mouton/Mamou Playboys/Adam Herbert & Country Playboys/Balfa Brothers/Leeman Pejean & Happy Playboys of Scott D.L. Menard/Phil Menard/Don Guillory & L.A. Travellers/Rambling Aces/Louis Cormier.
Album: released on Ace, Feb'86 by Ace Records. Dist: Pinnacle, Swift, Hotshot. Cadillac

Swallows & Amazons

SWALLOWS & AMAZONS Ransome, Arthur (Cribbins, Bernard).
Double cassette: released on Listen For Pleasure, Nov'81 by MFP Records. Dist: EMI

Swallow Tongue

GOT TO BE THERE/ HITCH UP HONEY.
Single (7"): released on Cherry Red, Sep'83 by Cherry Red Records. Dist: Pinnacle

Single (12"): released on Cherry Red, Sep'83 by Cherry Red Records. Dist: Pinnacle

STAIN UPON THE SILENCE. A.
Album: released on Cherry Red, Oct'83 by Cherry Red Records. Dist: Pinnacle

Swamp Blues

LOOKING THE WORLD OVER.
Album: released on Sonet, Sep'78 by Sonet Records. Dist: PRT

SWAMP BLUES (VOLUME 2).
Album: released on Sonet, Sep'78 by Sonet Records. Dist: PRT

Swamp Children

LITTLE VOICES/ CALL ME HONEY.
Single (12"): released on Factory, Oct'81 by Factory Records. Dist: Cartel, Pinnacle

Swamp Dog

UNCUT & CLASSIFIED 1A.
Album: released on Charly(R&B), Sep'81 by Charly Records. Dist: Charly, Cadillac

Swamp Dogg

UNMUZZLED.
Album: released on Charly(R&B), Aug'83 by Charly Records. Dist: Charly, Cadillac

Swamplands Beat

SWAMPLANDS BEAT Various artists (Various Artists).
Album: released on Goldband, Sep'84 by Charly Records. Dist: Charly

Swampland Soul

SWAMPLAND SOUL Various artists (Various Artists).
Album: released on Goldband, Feb'79 by Charly Records. Dist: Charly

Swamp Rats

UNRELATED SEGMENTS.
Album: released on Eva-Lolita, Jan'87 Dist: Pinnacle

Swan Arcade

DIVING FOR PEARLS.
Notes: Artists also include: Rick Kemp/Maddy Price.
Album: released on Fellside, Jul'86 by Fellside Records. Dist: Roots, Jazz Music, Celtic Music, Projection

MATCHLESS.
Album: released on Stoof, '82 Dist: Roots Distribution

SWAN ARCADE.
Album: released on Leader, '81 Dist: Jazz Music, Projection

TOGETHER FOREVER.
Album: released on Fellside, May'85 by Fellside Records. Dist: Roots, Jazz Music, Celtic Music, Projection

Swan, Billy

I CAN HELP.
Single (7"): released on Monument, '80 by CBS Records. Dist: CBS Distribution

Swan Down Gloves

SWAN DOWN GLOVES Original London cast.
Album: released on That's Entertainment, Apr'83 by That's Entertainment Records. Dist: Pinnacle, PRT

Cassette: released on That's Entertainment, Apr'83 by That's Entertainment Records. Dist: Pinnacle, PRT

Swanerud, Thore

MORE THAN YOU KNOW.
Notes: With J. Moody, Red Mitchell, P. Wickeman.
Album: released on Dragon, Jun'86 by Dragon Records. Dist: Jazz Music, Projection, Cadillac

STAR DUST.
Album: released on Dragon, '86 by Dragon Records. Dist: Jazz Music, Projection, Cadillac

Swanhunters

BLOODSPORT.
Single (12"): released on Fon, Nov'86 by Fon Records. Dist: Rough Trade, Red Rhino, Cartel

Swan In Love

SWAN IN LOVE.
Album: released on Milan, Jun'84, IMS Distribution, Conifer Distribution, Discovery Distribution

Swan, John

TEMPORARY HEARTACHE.
Single (7"): released on WEA, Dec'82 by WEA Records. Dist: WEA

Swann, Donald

AT THE DROP OF A HAT With Michael Flanders.
Album: released on Encore, Nov'78 by EMI Records. Dist: EMI

Cassette: released on Encore, Nov'78 by EMI Records. Dist: EMI

AT THE DROP OF ANOTHER HAT.
Album: released on Encore, Nov'78 by EMI Records. Dist: EMI

Cassette: released on Encore, Nov'78 by EMI Records. Dist: EMI

EVENING IN CRETE.
Album: released on World Records, '78 Dist: Polygram

Cassette: released on World Records, '78 Dist: Polygram

Swans

COP.
Album: released on Kelvin 4.22, Nov'84 by Some Bizzare Records. Dist: Rough Trade, Cartel

FILTH.
Album: released on Zensor, Apr'85 by Zensor Records. Dist: Rough Trade

GREED.
Album: released on K 422, Mar'86 by K 422 Records. Dist: Rough Trade Cartel

HOLY MONEY.
Album: released on K 422, Sep'86 by K 422 Records. Dist: Rough Trade. Cartel

RAPING A SLAVE EP.
Single (12"): released on K 422, Mar'85 by K 422 Records. Dist: Rough Trade, Cartel

SCREW, A.
Tracks: / Screw, A.
ingle (12"): released on Kelvin 4.22, Sep'86 by Some Bizzare Records. Dist: Rough Trade, Cartel

TIME IS MONEY (BASTARD).
Tracks: / Time is money (bastard) / Sealed in skin / Time is money (mix).
Single (12"): released on K 422, Jan'86 by K 422 Records. Dist: Rough Trade, Cartel

Swan Silvertones

GET YOUR SOUL RIGHT.
Tracks: / Is God satisfied with me / At the cross / I'll search heaven / What about you? / Great day in September / Seek, seek / Singin' in my soul / Sinner man / Sign of the judgement / Oh Mary don't you weep / Lady called mother, A / Get your soul right / Move somewhere / Stand up and testify / He saved my soul / Brighter day ahead.
Album: released on New Cross, Apr'86 by Charly Records. Dist: Charly

Swansway

BALCONY THEME.
Single (7"): released on Exit International, Aug'82 by Phonogram Records. Dist: Polygram

Single (12"): released on Exit International, Aug'82 by Phonogram Records. Dist: Polygram

FUGITIVE KIND (THE).
Tracks: / Soul train / Keeping it strong / Club secrets / In trance / Je joue / Blade (The) / Anchor (The) / When the wild calls / Stay / Illuminations.
Notes: Digital stereo.
Compact disc: released on Exit International, Oct'84 by Phonogram Records. Dist: Polygram

HISTORY AND IMAGE.
Notes: A live recording of this newly successful rock band, recorded live at the Astoria, Charing Cross Road, in London. Eleven tracks in all, including their hit 'Soul Train'. Number of tracks: 11. Type of recording: Live. Total playing time: 50 minutes.
Video-cassette (VHS): released on Polygram, Oct'84 by Polygram Records. Dist: Polygram

Swarbrick, Dave

CEILIDH ALBUM.
Album: released on Sonet, Jun'79 by Sonet Records. Dist: PRT

FLITTIN'.
Album: released on Spindrift, Sep'84 Dist: Roots

LIFT THE LID AND LISTEN.
Album: released on Sonet, Aug'78 by Sonet Records. Dist: PRT

LIVE AT THE WHITE BEAR.
Album: released on White Bear, Sep'84 Dist: Celtic Music, Jazz Music

SMIDDYBURN.
Album: released on Logo, Jul'81 by Logo Records. Dist: Roots, BMG

Cassette: released on Logo, Jul'81 by Logo Records. Dist: Roots, BMG

Album: released on Transatlantic (Italy), Mar'85

SWARBRICK.
Album: released on Transatlantic, Mar'82 by Logo Records. Dist: Roots Distribution, RCA Distribution

Cassette: released on Transatlantic, Mar'82 by Logo Records. Dist: Roots Distribution, RCA Distribution

WHEN THE BATTLE IS OVER.
Tracks: / It suits me well / My singing bird / Once I loved a maiden / Bonaparte's retreat / Nightingale (The) / Wishing / Kallarney boys of pleasure (The) / Shepherd's hey / When the battle is over / Ace & the deuce of Pipering (the) / Rocky Road to Dublin (The) / Coulin (The).
Notes: Licensed from Logo Records. Compiled by John Howard.
Album: released on Conifer, May'86 by Conifer Records. Dist: Conifer

Cassette: released on Conifer, May'86 by Conifer Records. Dist: Conifer

Swarbriggs
SWARBRIGGS GREATEST HITS.
Album: released on EMI (Ireland), Mar'77 by EMI Records (Ireland). Dist: Conifer, I & B Records Distribution

Swartz, Harvey
URBAN EARTH.
Album: released on Gramavision (USA), Dec'85 by Gramavison Records (USA). Dist: PRT, IMS, Polygram

Swartz, Harvie
UNDERNEATH IT ALL.
Album: released on Gramavision (USA), Jul'83 by Gramavison Records (USA). Dist: PRT, IMS, Polygram

Swat
DEVIL WOMAN.
Single (12"): released on Rockas, May'85 by Rockas Records, Inc. Dist: Jetstar Distribution, Revolver, Cartel

Swaye
COLD OPEN DOOR.
Single (12"): released on Kalabash, Jan'85 by Kalabash Records. Dist: Jetstar

Swayne, Giles
CRY.
Double Album: released on BBC, May'85 by BBC Records & Tapes. Dist: EMI, PRT, Pve

Double cassette: released on BBC, May'85 by BBC Records & Tapes. Dist: EMI PRT Pve

Swaysland
NO MONEY NO LOVE.
Single (7"): released on Hemiola, Aug'85 by Hemiola Records. Dist: Hemiola

Sweden Through The Ages
IT HELPS TO CRY.
Tracks: / It helps to cry.
Single (12"): released on Snappy, Feb'86 Dist: Fast Forward, Cartel

Swede, Simon
SIMON SWEDE & AVRIL APRICOT Various artists (Various Artists).
Cassette: released on Tell-a-tale (Cassettes) '84

Swedish Christmas Songs
SWEDISH CHRISTMAS SONGS Various artists (Various Artists).
Album: released on Phontastic (Sweden), '82 by Wellard, Chris Distribution. Dist: Wellard, Chris Distribution

Swedish Evergreens
SVENSKA EVERGREENS.
Double Album: released on Phontastic (Sweden), '82 by Wellard, Chris Distribution. Dist: Wellard, Chris Distribution

Double cassette: released on Phontastic (Sweden), '82 by Wellard, Chris Distribution. Dist: Wellard, Chris Distribution

Swedish Fiddle Music
SWEDISH FIDDLE MUSIC Various original artists (Various original artists).
Album: released on Sonet, '77 by Sonet Records. Dist: PRT

Swedish Heavy Metal
SWEDISH HEAVY METAL Various artists (Various Artists).
Album: released on Sonet, Feb'85 by Sonet Records. Dist: PRT

Swedish Jazz Kings
TRIBUTE TO CLARENCE WILLIAMS, A.
Album: released on Stomp Off, Oct'86 by Stomp Off Records. Dist: Jazz Music Distribution

Swedish Radio Jazz Group
RAINBOW SKETCHES.
Album: released on Four Leaf Clover, '78 Dist: Jazz Music, Swift

Sweeney
I'VE BEEN MEANING TO SAY / TAKE A LITTLE TIME.
Single (7"): released on Small Run, Feb'83 by Small Run Records. Dist: Pinnacle

Sweep, Jimmy
LONDON TOWN / BRIDGETOWN GIRLS.
Single (7"): released on PRT, Feb'82 by PRT Records. Dist: PRT

Sweet
BALLROOM BLITZ / WIGWAM BAM.
Single (7"): released on Golden Grooves, May'82 by RCA. Dist: RCA

BIGGEST HITS.
Album: released on RCA (Germany), '83

BLOCKBUSTER.
Tracks: / Blockbuster / Little Willy.
Single (7"): released on Old Gold, Apr'87 by Old Gold Records. Dist: Lightning, Jazz Music, Spartan, Counterpoint

BLOCKBUSTER / HELLRAISER.
Single (7"): released on RCA Golden Grooves, Aug'81 by RCA Records. Dist: RCA

DESOLATION BOULEVARD.
Album: released on RCA (Germany), '83

FOX ON THE RUN.
Tracks: / Fox on the run / Ballroom blitz.
Single (7"): released on Old Gold, Apr'87 by Old Gold Records. Dist: Lightning, Jazz Music, Spartan, Counterpoint

HARD CENTRES The rock years.
Album: released on Zebra, Jul'87 by Cherry Red Records. Dist: Pinnacle

Cassette: released on Zebra, Jul'87 by Cherry Red Records. Dist: Pinnacle

IDENTITY CRISIS.
Album: released on Polydor, Nov'82 by Polydor Records. Dist: Polygram, Polydor

IT'S IT'S THE SWEET MIX.
Single (7"): released on Anagram, Dec'84 by Cherry Red Records. Dist: Pinnacle

Single (12"): released on Anagram, Dec'84 by Cherry Red Records. Dist: Pinnacle

SIX TEENS, THE.
Single (7"): released on Anagram, Sep'84 by Cherry Red Records. Dist: Pinnacle

Single (12"): released on Anagram, Sep'84 by Cherry Red Records. Dist: Pinnacle

STRUNG UP.
Album: released on RCA (Germany), '83

SWEET FANNY ADAMS.
Album: released on RCA (Germany), '83

SWEETS GOLDEN GREATS.
Album: released on RCA (Germany), '83

SWEET SIXTEEN.
Album: released on Anagram, Aug'84 by Cherry Red Records. Dist: Pinnacle

Cassette: released on Anagram, Aug'84 by Cherry Red Records. Dist: Pinnacle

Compact disc: released on Anagram, Aug'84 by Cherry Red Records. Dist: Pinnacle

WIG WAM WILLY MIX.
Single (7"): released on Anagram, May'85 by Cherry Red Records. Dist: Pinnacle

Single (12"): released on Anagram, May'85 by Cherry Red Records. Dist: Pinnacle

Sweet charity
SWEET CHARITY Original soundtrack (Various Artists).
Compact disc: released on EMI America, Apr'87 by EMI Records. Dist: EMI

SWEET CHARITY Original Broadway cast (Various Artists).
Album: released on CBS Cameo, Sep'85 by CBS Records. Dist: CBS

Cassette: released on CBS Cameo, Sep'85 by CBS Records. Dist: CBS

Sweet Comfort Band
BREAKIN' THE ICE.
Album: released on Light USA, May'82 by Lexicon Music. Dist: Word Distribution

Cassette: released on Light USA, May'82 by Lexicon Music. Dist: Word Distribution

HEARTS OF FIRE.
Album: released on Light USA, May'82 by Lexicon Music. Dist: Word Distribution

Cassette: released on Light USA, May'82 by Lexicon Music. Dist: Word Distribution

HOLD ON TIGHT.
Album: released on Light USA, May'82 by Lexicon Music. Dist: Word Distribution

Cassette: released on Light USA, May'82 by Lexicon Music. Dist: Word Distribution

Sweet Dreams
LIFE AND TIMES OF PATSY CLINE
(THE).
Tracks: / San Antonio rose / Seven lonely days / Your cheatin' heart / Lovesick blues / Walking after midnight / Foolin' around / Half as much / I fall to pieces / Crazy / Blue moon of Kentucky / She's got you / Sweet dreams.
Notes: Directed by Harold Reidz (The French Lieutenants' Woman) and produced by Bernard Schwartz (Coal Miner's Daughter), 'Sweet Dreams' starring Jessica Lange as Patsy Cline has opened to excellent reviews in the UK which will certainly lead to demand for this attractive album. In essence a 'Greatest Hits', 'Sweet Dreams' contains twelve of Patsy Cline's most successful recordings including 'She's Got You', 'Heartaches', 'Crazy', 'Leavin' On Your Mind', and the classic 'I Fall To Pieces'. Produced by Owen Bradley the album features Patsy Cline's original vocal tracks complemented by new backing tracks performed by the cream of Nashville session musicians including Hargus Robbins, Floyd Cramer and The Jordanaires. The end result brings a sparkling new dimension to the sound of Patsy Cline which has resulted in millions of record sales in the past and will continue to do so in the future.
Album: released on MCA, Feb'86 by MCA Records. Dist: Polygram, MCA

Cassette: released on MCA, Feb'86 by MCA Records. Dist: Polygram, MCA

Sweet Ecstacy
PULL OUR LOVE TOGETHER / JAM PARTY.
Single (12"): released on Excalibur, Apr'83 by Red Bus Records. Dist: PRT

Sweet Heat
THIS IS THE NIGHT.
Tracks: / Tis is the night / Tis is the night (inst) / Tis is the night (dub).
Single (12"): released on Champion, 30 May'87 by Champion Records. Dist: RCA

Sweet Home Chicago
SWEET HOME CHICAGO Various artists (Various Artists).
Album: released on Delmark, '82 Dist: Projection, Swift, Cadillac

Sweet Honey In The Rock
FEEL SOMETHING DRAWING ME ON.
Album: released on Spindrift, Mar'86 Dist: Roots

OTHER SIDE (THE).
Album: released on Spindrift, Mar'86 Dist: Roots

WE ALL...EVERYONE OF US.
Album: released on Spindrift, Jun'84

Cassette: released on Spindrift, Jun'84

Sweet Light
ADIOS.
Single (7"): released on OK, Jul'80 by Klub Records. Dist: PRT Distribution

HOLD TIGHT.
Single (7"): released on Klub, Oct'79

Sweet Memories
SWEET MEMORIES Various Artists (Various Artists).
Compact disc: released on K-Tel, Aug'87 by K-Tel Records. Dist: Record Merchandisers Distribution, Taylors, Terry Blood Distribution, Wynd-Up Distribution, Relay Distribution, Pickwick Distribution, Solomon & Peres Distribution, Polygram

Sweet 'N' Bitter Band
WOMAN IN LOVE.
Tracks: / Woman in love / Loving dub.
Single (12"): released on ITS, Apr'86 by I.T.S. Records. Dist: Jetstar

Sweet People
AND THE BIRDS WERE SINGING.
Tracks: / And the birds were singing / Perse.
Single (7"): released on Polydor, Jul'87 by Polydor Records. Dist: Polygram, Polydor

MUSIC FOR THE MILLIONS.
Album: released on Polydor (Holland), Feb'85

Cassette: released on Polydor (Holland), Feb'85

Sweet, Phil
MEMPHIS BLUE STREAK.
Album: released on Charly, Jul'81 by Charly Records. Dist: Charly, Cadillac

Sweet, Rachel
...AND THEN HE KISSED ME.
Album: released on CBS, Oct'81 by CBS Records. Dist: CBS

Cassette: released on CBS, Oct'81 by CBS Records. Dist: CBS

BABY LETS PLAY HOUSE.
Single (7"): released on Stiff, Nov'79

FOOLS GOLD.
Single (7"): released on Stiff, Jan'80

SPELLBOUND.
Single (7"): released on Stiff, May'80

Sweet Revenge
NOTHING EVER GOES THE WAY IT'S PLANNED.
Single (7"): released on Revenge, Apr'85 by Revolver Records. Dist: Cartel

Sweet Savage
TAKE NO PRISONERS / KILLING TIME.
Single (7"): released on Park, Dec'81 Dist: Jazz Music

Sweet Sensation
SAD SWEET DREAMER.
Tracks: / Sad sweet dreamer (sensational mix) / Purely by coincidence / Sad sweet dreamer (original mix) / Purely by coincidence (saccarine mix).
Single (7"): released on PRT, Aug'86 by PRT Records. Dist: PRT

Single (12"): released on PRT, Aug'86 by PRT Records. Dist: PRT

SAD SWEET DREAMER / PAPER DOLLS / SOMETHING HERE IN MY HEART.
Single (7"): released on Flashback, Jan'83 by PRT Records. Dist: PRT

Sweet soulful Chicago
SWEET SOULFUL CHICAGO various (Various Artists).
Album: released on Kent, Jun'87 by Ace Records. Dist: Pinnacle

Sweet Soul Music
SWEET SOUL MUSIC Various original artists (Various original artists).
Double Album: released on Cambra, '83 by Cambra Records. Dist: IDS, Conifer

Double cassette: released on Cambra, '83 by Cambra Records. Dist: IDS, Conifer

Sweet Substitute
I GIVE IN.
Single (7"): released on Decca, '78 by Decca Records. Dist: Polygram

LULLABY OF BROADWAY / SLEEPY SUZIE.
Single (7"): released on Black Lion, Nov'82 by Black Lion Records. Dist: Jazz Music, Chris Wellard, Taylor, H.R., Counterpoint, Cadillac

SOPHISTICATED LADIES.
Album: released on Black Lion, Oct'82 by Black Lion Records. Dist: Jazz Music, Chris Wellard, Taylor, H.R., Counterpoint, Cadillac

TEN CENTS A DANCE.
Album: released on Decca, Aug'77 by Decca Records. Dist: Polygram

Cassette: released on Decca, Aug'77 by Decca Records. Dist: Polygram Deleted '81.

Sweet, Suzanna
CORNER LOVE.
Single (12"): released on CDJ, Apr'83 by CDJ Records. Dist: Jetstar

Sweet Tee
IT'S MY BEAT (Sweet Tee & Jazzy Joyce).
Single (7"): released on Champion, Feb'87 by Champion Records. Dist: RCA

Single (12"): released on Champion, Feb'87 by Champion Records. Dist: RCA

Sweet Thunder
EVERYBODY'S SINGING LOVE SONGS.
Tracks: / Everybody's singing love songs / Space bass (slick).
Single (12"): released on Streetwave, Dec'85 by Streetwave Records. Dist: PRT Distribution

Swell Maps
COLLISION TIME.
Album: released on Rough Trade, '84 by Rough Trade Records. Dist: Rough Trade Distribution, Cartel Distribution

DRESDEN STYLE.
Single (7"): released on Rather, Jun'81 Dist: Rough Trade

JANE FROM OCCUPIED EUROPE.
Album: released on Rather, Jun'81 Dist: Rough Trade

LET'S BUILD A CAR.
Single (7"): released on Rather, Jun'81 Dist: Rough Trade

READ ABOUT SEYMOUR.
Single (7"): released on Rather, Jun'81 Dist: Rough Trade

REAL SHOCKS.
Single (7"): released on Rather, Jun'81 Dist: Rough Trade

SWELL MAPS (EP).
Single (7"): released on Rather, Jun'81 Dist: Rough Trade

TRIP TO MARINEVILLE, A.
Album: released on Rather, Jun'81 Dist: Rough Trade

WHATEVER HAPPENS NEXT.
Album: released on Rather, Jun'81 Dist: Rough Trade

Swenson, May
POETRY & VOICE OF MAY SWENSON.
Album: released on Caedmon(USA), Nov'76 by Caedmon (USA) Records. Dist: Gower, Taylors, Discovery

Swift Jewel Cowboys
CHUCK WAGON SWING.
Album: released on String, '81 by Topic Records. Dist: Roots Distribution, Jazz Music Distribution, JSU Distribution, Projection Distribution, Swift Distribution

Swift, Jonathan
GULLIVER'S TRAVELS.
Tracks: / Gulliver's travels (cont).
Cassette: released on Tellastory, Dec'86 by Bartlett Bliss Productions. Dist: PRT Distribution, Hayward Promotions Distribution, H.R. Taylor Distribution

Swift, Tully
HOW TO MAKE A BAKEWELL TART.
Album: released on Freereed, Nov'77 by Topic Records. Dist: JSU

Swim
TALKING TO A SHADOW.
Single (7"): released on Zim Zam, Aug'82

Swimming In Sand
POWER.
Tracks: / Power.
Single (7"): released on Powerstation Records, Jul'86 by Powerstation Records. Dist: Pinnacle

Swimming In The Sea
HERO FOR THE HEROINE.
Single (7"): released on Squanderlust, Aug'82 Dist: Backs, Cartel Distribution

Swimming Pool Queues
DEEP END, THE.
Album: released on Armageddon, Sep'83 by Armageddon Records. Dist: Revolver, Cartel, Pinnacle

PRETTY ON THE INSIDE.
Tracks: / Pretty on the inside / Blue tomorrow / Purple rivers / Bells ring.
Notes: In Doublepack.
Single (7"): released on A&M, Jan'86 by A&M Records. Dist: Polygram

SWIMMING POOL Q'S, THE.
Album: released on A&M, Jul'85 by A&M Records. Dist: Polygram

Cassette: released on A&M, Jul'85 by A&M Records. Dist: Polygram

Swimming To France
YOU NEVER EVEN ASKED MY NAME (EP).
Single (12"): released on Oval, Feb'84 by Oval Records. Dist: Pinnacle

Swinburne, Algernon..
SELECTED POETRY OF SWINBURNE.
Album: released on Caedmon(USA), '79 by Caedmon (USA) Records. Dist: Gower, Taylors, Discovery

Cassette: released on Caedmon(USA), '79 by Caedmon (USA) Records. Dist: Gower, Taylors, Discovery

Swinburne, Lara Band
MADNESS & LIES.
Single (7"): released on Bridge, Mar'84 Dist: Starr Marketing Distribution

Swindells, Steve
FRESH BLOOD.

Page 982

Album: released on Cotillion, Oct'80 by WEA Records. Dist: WEA

Swing
SWING.
Album: released on Planet, Nov'81 Dist: WEA

Single (7"): released on EMI Golden 45's, Feb'85 by EMI Records. Dist: EMI

SHAKE:THE BEST OF THE SWINGING BLUE JEANS.
Tracks: / Hipps hippy shake / Don't make me over / Good golly Miss Molly / Do you know / Long tall Sally / You're so good / Tutti frutti / It isn't there / Shakin' all over / Make me know you're mine / Shake, rattle and roll / Save the last dance for me / Lawdy Miss Clawdy / It's too late now / Good lovin' / Tremblin' / Around and around / Rumours, gossip, words, untrue / That's the way it goes / Some sweat day.
Notes: Including all their hit singles between 1963 and 1966. The 'Bluegeans' began their career in the Cavern Club of Liverpool. They came up with the idea and ran a Guest Night which included such names as Gerry, The Searcher's Billy Kramer, The Coasters and of course, The Beatles. They were originally regarded as a skiffle band and their stage outfits were rather 'square' compared to what other groups were wearing. Onced they'd changed Bluegenes to Blue Jeans, actually wore jeans on stage and turned to rock 'n' roll, things began to hapen very swiftly for them. 1964 was their peak year and yet they continued to perform for a further 20 years and in 1964 appeared in at least 12 different countries around the world.
Album: released on EMI, Jan'86 by EMI Records. Dist: EMI

Cassette: released on EMI, Jan'86 by EMI Records. Dist: EMI

SWINGING BLUE JEANS.
Album: released on EMI (Holland), '83 by EMI Records. Dist: Conifer

Swinging' joy
SWINGIN' FOR JOY Piano portraits, volume three (Various Artists).
Tracks: / Swingin' for joy / Mississippi moan / Rosetta / Boogie woogie maxixe / Yancey special / Jingles / When a woman loves a man / Three little words / Shaik of Araby / Twinklin' / Just you, just me / Oh! Red / Boogie Woogie cocktail / (I don' stand a) ghost of a chance (with you) / If I were a bell / Blues for Django.
Album: released on Affinity, Apr'87 by Charly Records. Dist: Charly, Cadillac

Swinging Laurels
LONELY BOY.
Single (7"): released on WEA, Mar'83 by WEA Records. Dist: WEA

Single (12"): released on WEA, Mar'83 by WEA Records. Dist: WEA

OFF THE RECORD.
Single (12"): released on Dining Out, Mar'82 by Dining Out Records. Dist: IKF, Independent

RODEO.
Single (7"): released on WEA, Oct'82 by WEA Records. Dist: WEA

Single (12"): released on WEA, Oct'82 by WEA Records. Dist: WEA

Swinging Rock
SWINGING ROCK (Various Artists).
Album: released on Collector (White Label Holland), Jan'85 Dist: Swift

Swinging Sixties
SWINGING SIXTIES Various artists (Various Artists).
Album: released on Hallmark, Feb'86 by Pickwick Records. Dist: Pickwick Distribution, PRT, Taylors

Swinging Soul Machine
Cassette: released on Planet, Nov'81 Dist: WEA

Swingadilla
IN THE MOOD.
Single (7"): released on Safari, Jun'82 by Safari Records. Dist: Pinnacle

Swing Classics
SWING CLASSICS VOLUME 1 1944-1945.
Notes: Mono production: With Hot Lips Page/Shavers etc.
Album: released on Storyville, Jun'86 by Storyville Records. Dist: Jazz Music Distribution, Swift Distribution, Chris Wellard Distribution, Counterpoint Distribution

Swing Collection
42ND STREET.
Single (7"): released on Hobo, Nov'84 by Hobo Records. Dist: Hobo

---

MUSIC GOES ROUND AND ROUND THE 30'S, THE.
Album: released on Hobo, Jul'85 by Hobo Records. Dist: Hobo

Album: released on Hobo, Jul'85 by Hobo Records. Dist: Hobo

SWING COLLECTION Various artists (Various Artists).
Album: released on Deja Vu, Nov'85 by Deja Vu Records. Dist: Counterpoint Distribution, Record Services Distribution (Ireland)

Cassette: released on Deja Vu, Nov'85 by Deja Vu Records. Dist: Counterpoint Distribution, Record Services Distribution (Ireland)

SWING COLLECTION, THE Various artists (Various Artists).
Cassette: released on Deja Vu, Aug'85 by Deja Vu Records. Dist: Counterpoint Distribution, Record Services Distribution (Ireland)

Swing Era
SWING ERA Various artists (Various Artists).
Album: released on Joker (Import), Apr'81

Swingers
COUNTING THE BEAT.
Single (7"): released on Carrere, Feb'82 by Carrere Records. Dist: PRT, Spartan

Swinging 60's
SWINGING 60'S (Various Artists).
Boxed set: released on Readers Digest Ass., Mar'85 by Readers Digest Ass.. Dist: Readers Digest Ass.

Swinging Blue Jeans
BRAND NEW AND FADED.
Album: released on Dart, Jul'74 by President Records. Dist: Jazz Music, Swift

DANCIN'.
Cassette: released on Autograph, Apr'85 Dist: Record Services Distribution (Ireland)

HIPPY HIPPY SHAKE.
Single (7"): released on H.M.V., Nov'80 by EMI Records. Dist: EMI

Single (7"): released on Old Gold, Oct'83 by Old Gold Records. Dist: Lightning, Jazz Music, Spartan, Counterpoint

BOOKER T'S GREATEST HITS (EP).
Single (7"): released on Inferno, Aug'80 by Inferno Records. Dist: Inferno, Cartel, Pinnacle

Single (12"): released on Inferno, Aug'80 by Inferno Records. Dist: Inferno, Cartel, Pinnacle

Swinging UK
SWINGING UK.
Notes: A survey of the early '60's UK beat group scene, made at the time as a cinema documentary, and featuring The Hollies, Animals, Lulu and many others. Reissue of a Precision film. 1964 production. Type of recording: Documentary. Total playing time: 53 minutes.
Video-cassette (VHS): released on Polygram, Oct'86 by Polygram Records. Dist: Polygram

Swing Jackpot
SWING JACKPOT (Various Artists).
Album: released on Jazz Archives, Jul'87 by Jazz Archives Records. Dist: Jazz Music

Swinglehurst, Richie
HOCUSPOCUS.
Single (7"): released on Tembo, Jun'85 by Tembo (Canada). Dist: IMS Distribution, Polygram Distribution

Single (12"): released on Tembo, Jun'85 by Tembo (Canada). Dist: IMS Distribution, Polygram Distribution

Swingles
CACHAPAYA.
Tracks: / Cahapaya / Peter Gunn.
Single (7"): released on Rainbow, May'87 Dist: ! & B, CBS

CHRISTMAS.
Tracks: / Rudolph the red nosed reindeer / O tannenbaum / Little drummer boy / Santa Claus is coming to town / Jingle bells / Silent night / Ave Maria.
Album: released on Polydor, Nov'86 by Polydor Records. Dist: Polygram, Polvdor

Cassette: released on Polydor, Nov'86 by Polydor Records. Dist: Polygram, Polydor

I BELEIVE IN FATHER CHRISTMAS.
Tracks: / Albatross.
Single (7"): released on Polydor, Nov'86 by Polydor Records. Dist: Polygram, Polydor

INSTRUMENTALS.
Album: released on Polydor, Nov'86 by Poly-

---

dor Records. Dist: Polygram, Polydor

Cassette: released on Polydor, Nov'86 by Polydor Records. Dist: Polygram, Polydor

Swingle Singers
ANYONE FOR MOZART, BACH, HANDEL, VIVALDI ?.
Compact discs: released on Philips (Germany), Nov'86

BEST OF THE SWINGLE SINGERS, (THE).
Cassette: released on Verve, May'87 by Phonogram Records. Dist: Polygram

COMPACT JAZZ.
Tracks: / Air for G String / Etude Op 25 No 2 / Aranjuez.
Compact disc: by Phonogram Records. Dist: Polygram

Cassette: released on Phonogram, Jul'87 by Phonogram Records. Dist: Polygram

Compact disc: released on Mercury, Jul'87 by Phonogram Records. Dist: Polygram Distribution

PLACE VENDOME (Swingle Singers & MJQ).
Album: released on Phillips Europe, Sep'85

Cassette: released on Phillips Europe, Sep'85

Swingle Singles
JAZZ SEBASTION BACH.
Album: released on Philips (Europe), Sep'85

Cassette: released on Philips (Europe), Sep'85

Swing Out Sister
BLUE MOOD.
Tracks: / Blue mood / Wake me when its over.
Single (7"): released on Mercury, May'86 by Phonogram Records. Dist: Polygram Distribution

Single (12"): released on Mercury, Nov'85 by Phonogram Records. Dist: Polygram Distribution

BREAKOUT.
Tracks: / Breakout / Dirty money.
Single (12"): released on Mercury, Sep'86 by Phonogram Records. Dist: Polygram Distribution

FOOLED BY A SMILE.
Tracks: / Fooled by a smile / Fever.
Single (7"): released on Mercury, Jun'87 by Phonogram Records. Dist: Polygram Distribution

Single (12"): released on Mercury, Jun'87 by Phonogram Records. Dist: Polygram Distribution

IT'S BETTER TO TRAVEL.
Compact disc: released on Mercury, May'87 by Phonogram Records. Dist: Polygram Distribution

Album: released on Mercury, May'87 by Phonogram Records. Dist: Polygram Distribution

Cassette: released on Mercury, May'87 by Phonogram Records. Dist: Polygram Distribution

SURRENDER.
Tracks: / Who's to blame.
Single (7"): released on Mercury, Dec'86 by Phonogram Records. Dist: Polygram Distribution

Single (12"): released on Mercury, Dec'86 by Phonogram Records. Dist: Polygram Distribution

Swing Piano
SWING PIANO Various artists.
Notes: Mono production. Featuring Earl Hines; Art Tatum; Teddy Wilson.
Album: released on Storyville, May'86 by Storyville Records. Dist: Jazz Music Distribution, Swift Distribution, Chris Wellard Distribution, Counterpoint Distribution

Swingshow
SWINGSHOW Various artists (Various Artists).
Album: released on RCA (Brazil). '84

Cassette: released on RCA (Brazil). '84

Swing Sounds
SWING SOUNDS (Various Artists).
Album: released on Jazz Live, Apr'81

Swing's the thing
SWING'S THE THING Various artists (Various Artists).
Album: released on JSP, Sep'84 by JSP Rec-

ords. Dist: Swift, Projection

Swing That Music
SWING THAT MUSIC Original Artists (Original artists).
Compact disc: released on The Compact Collection. Sep'87 by Conifer Records. Dist: Conifer Distribution

Swingtime Jive
SWINGTIME JIVE Various artists (Various Artists).
Album: released on Stash, Apr'81 Dist: Swift Distribution, Jazz Music Distribution, Jazz Horizons Distribution, Celtic Music Distribution, Cadillac, JSU Distribution, Zodiac Distribution

Swing Under The Nazis
CLANDESTINE RECORDINGS OF THE... ...Frankfurt Hot Club 1941-1944.
Tracks: / Bugle call rag / Stomp / Blues / Margie / Sheik of Araby (Thu) / Blues / Honeysuckle rose / I can't give you... / Undecided / I've found a new baby / On the sunny side of the street / My blue heaven / Sweet Sue / Lady be good.
Notes: Artists include: Hans Otto Jung/Karlo Bohlander/Rudi Thomsen/Mark Bunner/Karl Petry/Hans Berry/Freddy De Bondt/Robert Pauwels/Tinus Bruyn/Andre Smit/Horst Lippman. Mono recording.
Album: released on Harlequin, Nov'86 by Harlequin Records. Dist: Swift, Jazz Music, Wellard, Chris, IRS, Taylor, H.R.

SWING UNDER THE NAZIS 1941-44 (Various Artists).
Album: released on Harlequin, Jan'87 by Harlequin Records. Dist: Swift, Jazz Music, Wellard, Chris, IRS, Taylor, H.R.

Swing Your Partners
SWING YOUR PARTNERS Various original square dance artists (Various Artists).

Swiss Navy
BACK TO THE WALL.
Single (7"): released on Phonogram, May'83 by Phonogram Records. Dist: Polygram

Single (12"): released on Phonogram, May'83 by Phonogram Records. Dist: Polygram

Switch
AM I STILL YOUR BOYFRIEND?.
Album: released on Total Experience, Jan'85 by Phonogram. Dist: Polygram

Switchblade
SOUNDS IN OUR MINDS.
Single (7"): released on Crezent, Sep'83 by Crezent Records. Dist: Pinnacle

WE ARE ROCKIN'.
Single (7"): released on Crezent, Feb'84 by Crezent Records. Dist: Pinnacle

Switchback
VINTAGE TREND.
Single (7"): released on Bombay Ltd, Nov'83

Switched on in Italy
SWITCHED ON IN ITALY Various artists (Various Artists).
Album: released on Klub, Oct'83

Cassette: released on Klub, Oct'83

Switzerland, Michael
MARILYN MONROE'S SISTER.
Single (7"): released on Red Rhino, Oct'83 by Indies Records. Dist: Cartel Distribution

Swope, Earl
LOST SESSION, THE.
Album: released on Nostalgia (Sweden), Nov'82 by Wellard, Chris Distribution. Dist: Wellard, Chris Distribution

Sword and the Sorcerer
SWORD AND THE SORCERER Original Soundtrack.
Album: released on That's Entertainment, Apr'83 by That's Entertainment. Dist: Pinnacle, PRT

Sword of Jah Mouth
INVASION.
Album: released on Metrosound, Dec'84 by Metrosound Records. Dist: Jetstar Distribution

Syar
DEATH BEFORE DISHONOUR.
Album: released on Mausoleum, Apr'84 by Mausoleum Records. Dist: Pinnacle

Cassette: released on Mausoleum, Jul'84 by Mausoleum Records. Dist: Pinnacle

Sybil
FALLING IN LOVE.
Tracks: / Falling in love / Falling in love (dub mix).
Single (7"): released on Champion, Oct'86 by Champion Records. Dist: RCA

Single (12"): released on Champion, Oct'86 by Champion Records. Dist: RCA

LET YOURSELF GO.
Tracks: / Falling in love (remix) / Let yourself go / Let yourself go (inst).
Notes: Pic bag *Extra track on 12" only
Single (7"): released on Champion, Apr'87 by Champion Records. Dist: RCA

Single (12"): released on Champion, Apr'87 by Champion Records. Dist: RCA

Album: released on Champion, Aug'87 by Champion Records. Dist: RCA

Cassette: released on Champion, Aug'87 by Champion Records. Dist: RCA

MY LOVE IS GUARANTEED.
Single (7"): released on Champion, Aug'87 by Champion Records. Dist: RCA

Single (12"): released on Champion, Aug'87 by Champion Records. Dist: RCA

Sydney Salvation Army
DANIEL.
Album: released on Key, May'79 by Key Records. Dist: Spartan

Sve
TURN ON THE FIRE.
Album: released on Road Runner, Jun'85

Sykes, Roosevelt
BLUES FROM BOTTOMS.
Album: released on 77, '73 by 77 Records. Dist: Chris Wellard, Cadillac Music, Jazz Music

FEEL LIKE BLOWING MY HORN.
Album: released on Delmark, '74 Dist: Projection, Swift, Cadillac

HONEYDRIPPER'S DUKE'S MIXTURE (VOLUME 4), THE.
Album: released on Barclay (Import), Nov'79

Sylum
I'M IMPRESSED.
Single (7"): released on Heavy Metal, Sep'85 by FM-Revolver Records. Dist: EMI

SYLUM.
Album: released on FM, Oct'85 by FM-Revolver Records. Dist: EMI

Sylva, Mynus
REGGAE DOWN CARNIVAL SHOWCASE '84.
Album: released on Circle, May'84 Dist: Jazz Music

Sylvantone Showcase
SYLVANTONE SHOWCASE Various artists (Various Artists).
Album: released on Sylvantone, Jul'85 Dist: Outlet Distribution, Sylvantone Distribution

Cassette: released on Sylvantone, Jul'85 Dist: Outlet Distribution, Sylvantone Distribution

Sylvester
BAND OF GOLD.
Single (7"): released on London, Aug'83 by London Records. Dist: Polygram

Single (12"): released on London, Aug'83 by London Records. Dist: Polygram

CALL ME.
Album: released on Ecstasy, Apr'84 by Creole Records. Dist: CBS

Cassette: released on Ecstasy, Apr'84 by Creole Records. Dist: CBS

DON'T STOP.
Single (7"): released on London, May'83 by London Records. Dist: Polygram

Single (12"): released on London, May'83 by London Records. Dist: Polygram

DO YA WANNA FUNK (Sylvester/Patrick Cowley).
Single (7"): released on London, Sep'82 by London Records. Dist: Polygram

Single (12"): released on London, Sep'82 by London Records. Dist: Polygram

Tracks: / Do you wanna funk (Brighton summer mix) / Menergy / Do you wanna funk (original mix).
Single (12"): released on Domino, Aug'86 by Domino Records. Dist: Charly

GREATEST HITS: SYLVESTER.
Album: released on Fantasy, Nov'83 by RCA Records. Dist: RCA, Jetstar

Cassette: released on Fantasy, Nov'83 by RCA Records. Dist: RCA, Jetstar

LIVING FOR THE CITY.
Tracks: / Living for the city / Living for the city (dub mix).
Single (7"): released on Creole, Mar'86 by Creole Records. Dist: Rhino, PRT

Single (12"): released on Creole, Mar'86 by Creole Records. Dist: Rhino, PRT

MENERGY.
Single (7"): released on ERC, Aug'84 by ERC Records. Dist: PRT

Single (12"): released on ERC, Aug'84 by ERC Records. Dist: PRT

MUTUAL ATTRACTION.
Tracks: / Someone like you / Living for the city / Summertime / Mutual attraction / Talk to me / Cool of the evening / Sooner or later / Anything can happen.
Album: released on Warner Brothers, Jan'87 by Warner Bros Records. Dist: WEA

Cassette: released on Warner Brothers, Jan'87 by Warner Bros Records. Dist: WEA

SYLVESTER - GREATEST HITS.
Tracks: / Do ya wanna funk / Dance (disco heat) / You make me feel (mighty real) / I need somebody to love / Stars' intro / Can't stop dancing / Stars.
Notes: During the 70's Sylvester was one of the most outrageous and flamboyant artists on the scene. This album contains three of his four UK hits.
Album: released on Fantasy (USA), Jun'86 by Fantasy Inc USA Records. Dist: IMS, Polygram

Sylvia
HASTA LA VISTA.
Single (7"): released on Sonet, Sep'76 by Sonet Records. Dist: PRT

NOBODY.
Single (7"): released on RCA, Jan'83 by RCA Records. Dist: RCA, Roots, Swift, Wellard, Chris, I & B, Solomon & Peres Distribution

ONE STEP CLOSER.
Album: released on RCA, May'85 by RCA Records. Dist: RCA, Roots, Swift, Wellard, Chris, I & B, Solomon & Peres Distribution

Cassette: released on RCA, May'85 by RCA Records. Dist: RCA, Roots, Swift, Wellard, Chris, I & B, Solomon & Peres Distribution

PILLOW TALK.
Single (7"): released on London, '80 by London Records. Dist: Polygram

Single (7"): released on Old Gold, Jul'84 by Old Gold Records. Dist: Lightning, Jazz Music, Spartan, Counterpoint

READ ALL ABOUT IT.
Single (7"): released on RCA, Jun'85 by RCA Records. Dist: RCA, Roots, Swift, Wellard, Chris, I & B, Solomon & Peres Distribution

SOMEBODY LOVES YOU.
Album: released on Sonet, Oct'76 by Sonet Records. Dist: PRT

SWEET YESTERDAY.
Album: released on RCA, Feb'83 by RCA Records. Dist: RCA, Roots, Swift, Wellard, Chris, I & B, Solomon & Peres Distribution

Cassette: released on RCA, Feb'83 by RCA Records. Dist: RCA, Roots, Swift, Wellard, Chris, I & B, Solomon & Peres Distribution

Sylvian, David
ALCHEMY AND INDEX OF POSSIBILITIES.
Cassette: released on Virgin, Dec'85 by Virgin Records. Dist: EMI, Virgin Distribution

BAMBOO HOUSES (Sylvian, David & Riuichi Sakamoto).
Single (7"): released on Virgin, Jul'82 by Virgin Records. Dist: EMI, Virgin Distribution

Single (12"): released on Virgin, Jul'82 by Virgin Records. Dist: EMI, Virgin Distribution

BRILLIANT TREES.
Tracks: / Pulling punches / Ink in the well (The) / Nostalgia / Red guitar / Weathered wall / Backwaters / Brilliant trees.
Album: released on Virgin, Jun'84 by Virgin Records. Dist: EMI, Virgin Distribution

Cassette: released on Virgin, Jun'84 by Virgin Records. Dist: EMI, Virgin Distribution

Compact disc: released on Virgin, Jun'84 by Virgin Records. Dist: EMI, Virgin Distribution

GONE TO EARTH.
Album: released on Virgin, Aug'86 by Virgin

Records. Dist: EMI, Virgin Distribution.

Cassette: released on Virgin, Aug'86 by Virgin Records. Dist: EMI, Virgin Distribution

Compact disc: released on Virgin, Aug'86 by Virgin Records. Dist: EMI, Virgin Distribution

SILVER MOON.
Tracks: / Silver moon / Gone to Earth.
Single (7"): released on Virgin, Sep'86 by Virgin Records. Dist: EMI, Virgin Distribution

Single (12"): released on Virgin, Sep'86 by Virgin Records. Dist: EMI, Virgin Distribution

STEEL CATHEDRALS.
Video-cassette (VHS): released on Virgin, Jan'86 by Virgin Records. Dist: EMI, Virgin Distribution

TAKING THE VEIL (Symbol of freedom).
Tracks: / Taking the veil / Answered prayers.
Single (7"): released on Virgin, Jul'86 by Virgin Records. Dist: EMI, Virgin Distribution

Single (12"): released on Virgin, Jul'86 by Virgin Records. Dist: EMI, Virgin Distribution

WORDS WITH THE SHAMAN (EP).
Single (12"): released on Virgin, Nov'85 by Virgin Records. Dist: EMI, Virgin Distribution

Sylvia & The Sapphires
BABY I'M A FOOL FOR YOU.
Single (7"): released on Stiff, Oct'82 by Stiff Records. Dist: EMI, Record Services Distribution (Ireland)

Single (12"): released on Stiff, Nov'82 by Stiff Records. Dist: EMI, Record Services Distribution (Ireland)

SHOPPING AROUND.
Single (7"): released on Stiff, Jul'82

Single (12"): released on Stiff, Jul'82

Symarip
SKINHEAD MOONSTOMP.
Album: released on Trojan, '83 by Trojan Records. Dist: PRT, Jetstar

Single (7"): released on Trojan, Jun'79

Symbolic Three
NO SHOW.
Tracks: / No show / We're treacherous / Tell off.
Single (7"): released on PRT, Jan'86 by PRT Records. Dist: PRT

Single (12"): released on PRT, Jan'86 by PRT Records. Dist: PRT

Symphonion
SYMPHONION MUSIC BOX (Eroica three disc, (The)).
Album: released on Bornard Music Box Co.(USA), Nov'80

Cassette: released on Bornard Music Box Co.(USA), Nov'80

Syncbeat
MUSIC (DANCE).
Tracks: / Music (Dance mix) / Music (Original mix).
Single (12"): released on Streetwise, Aug'84 Dist: Greyhound

Syncopation
MARKING TIME.
Single (7"): released on Factory, Feb'82 by Factory Records. Dist: Cartel, Pinnacle

Syndicate
DANCE YOU TO THE GROUND.
Single (7"): released on EMI, Jul'81 by EMI Records. Dist: EMI

Single (12"): released on EMI, Jun'81 by EMI Records. Dist: EMI

GOLDEN KEY.
Single (12"): released on Supreme, Jun'85 by Supreme Records. Dist: PRT Distribution

Syndrome
SHINE ON US.
Single (7"): released on Sometimes, Jul'83 Dist: Sometimes Distribution

Album: released on Logo, Mar'82 by Logo Records. Dist: Roots, BMG

Synergy
AUDION.
Compact disc: by Pacific Records (USA). Dist: Atlantic

COMPUTER EXPERIMENTS VOL.1.

Compact disc: by Pacific Records (USA). Dist: Atlantic

CORDS.
Compact disc: by Pacific Records (USA). Dist: Atlantic

ELECTRONIC REALISATIONS FOR ROCK ORCHESTRA.
Compact disc: by Pacific Records (USA). Dist: Atlantic

GAMES.
Compact disc: by Pacific Records (USA). Dist: Atlantic

JUPITER MENACE.
Album: released on Shanghai, Sep'84

METROPOLITIAN SUITE.
Compact disc: by Pacific Records (USA). Dist: Atlantic

SEMI-CONDUCTOR.
Album: released on Passport (USA), May'84 by Logo. Dist: BMG

Album: released on Passport (USA), May'84 by Logo. Dist: BMG

SEQUENCER.
Compact disc: by Pacific Records (USA). Dist: Atlantic

Synphonic variations
SNOWMEN.
Tracks: / Seasons.
Single (7"): released on CBS, Nov'86 by CBS Records. Dist: CBS

Syntax
FOOL, THE.
Single (7"): released on Pith, Oct'81

Synthetic
SULPHATE SUICIDE.
Single (7"): released on Logic Step, May'82

Synthetic Dreams
OBSESSION.
Single (7"): released on Logical step, Oct'81

Synthetic Orchestra
THEME FROM E.T..
Single (7"): released on PRT, Feb'83 by PRT Records. Dist: PRT

Synthetics
JAPANESE TOYS.
Single (7"): released on Cheapskate, Jul'82 by Cheapskate Records. Dist: RCA

Synthphonic Variations
SEASONS.
Tracks: / Moonlight sonata / Move closer / One more night / Greatest love of all, The / Snowman, The / One day I'll fly away / Pictures of winter / Careless whisper / Cover me / Fur Elise / Holding back the years / On my own / Seasons / Don't give up / Pachebel-canon (Theme from "Ordinary People") / Your love is King / Power of love, The / Raining in my heart.
Album: released on CBS, Oct'86 by CBS Records. Dist: CBS

Cassette: released on CBS, Oct'86 by CBS Records. Dist: CBS

Syreeta
BEST OF SYREETA, THE.
Album: released on Motown, Oct'81 by RCA Records. Dist: RCA Distribution

Cassette: released on Motown, Oct'81 by RCA Records. Dist: RCA Distribution

---

CAN'T SHAKE YOUR LOVE.
Single (7"): released on Motown, Aug'82 by RCA Records. Dist: RCA Distribution

Single (12"): released on Motown, Aug'82 by RCA Records. Dist: RCA Distribution

---

FOREVER IS NOT ENOUGH.
Single (7"): released on Motown, May'83 by RCA Records. Dist: RCA Distribution

Single (12"): released on Motown, May'83 by RCA Records. Dist: RCA Distribution

---

GO FOR IT.
Single (7"): released on Motown, Oct'81 by RCA Records. Dist: RCA Distribution

---

HE'S GONE.
Single (7"): released on Motown, Oct'81 by RCA Records. Dist: RCA Distribution

---

I MUST BE IN LOVE.
Single (7"): released on Motown, Apr'82 by RCA Records. Dist: RCA Distribution

Single (12"): released on Motown, Apr'82 by RCA Records. Dist: RCA Distribution

---

IT WILL COME IN TIME.
Single (7"): released on Motown, Oct'81 by RCA Records. Dist: RCA Distribution

---

ONE MORE TIME FOR LOVE.
Single (7"): released on Motown, Oct'81 by RCA Records. Dist: RCA Distribution

---

PLEASE STAY.
Single (7"): released on Motown, Oct'81 by RCA Records. Dist: RCA Distribution

---

QUICK SLICK..
Single (7"): released on Motown, Nov'81 by

RCA Records. Dist: RCA Distribution

Single (12"): released on Motown, Dec'81 by RCA Records. Dist: RCA Distribution

---

SET MY LOVE IN MOTION.
Album: released on Motown, Dec'81 by RCA Records. Dist: RCA Distribution

Cassette: released on Motown, Dec'81 by RCA Records. Dist: RCA Distribution

---

STEVIE WONDER PRESENTS.
Album: released on Motown, Oct'82 by RCA Records. Dist: RCA Distribution

Cassette: released on Motown, Oct'82 by RCA Records. Dist: RCA Distribution

---

SYREETA.
Album: released on Motown, Oct'81 by RCA Records. Dist: RCA Distribution

Cassette: released on Motown, Oct'81 by RCA Records. Dist: RCA Distribution

---

WITH YOU I'M BORN AGAIN.
Single (7"): released on Motown, Oct'81 by RCA Records. Dist: RCA Distribution

---

YOUR KISS IS SWEET.
Single (7"): released on Motown, Oct'81 by RCA Records. Dist: RCA Distribution

---

Syro Gyra
INCOGNITO.
Compact disc: released on MCA, Feb'87 by MCA Records. Dist: Polygram, MCA

Syron Danes
BRINGER OF EVIL.
Album: released on Ebony, Nov'84 by Ebony Records. Dist: Pinnacle, Ebony

---

System
COME AS YOU ARE (SUPERSTAR).
Tracks: / Modern girl.
Single (7"): released on Atlantic, Feb'87 by WEA Records. Dist: WEA

Single (12"): released on Atlantic, Feb'87 by WEA Records. Dist: WEA

DON'T DISTURB THIS GROOVE.
Tracks: / Don't disturb the groove / Save me.
Album: released on Atlantic, Mar'87 by WEA Records. Dist: WEA

Cassette: released on Atlantic, Mar'87 by WEA Records. Dist: WEA

PLEASURE SEEKERS, THE.
Album: released on Polydor, Aug'85 by Polydor Records. Dist: Polygram, Polydor

---

Cassette: released on Polydor, Aug'85 by Polydor Records. Dist: Polygram, Polydor

---

WARFARE (EP).
Single (7"): released on Spiderleg, Jun'82 Dist: Rough Trade

Systems
TOTAL RECALL.
Single (7"): released on Open Eye, Oct'81 by Open Eye Records. Dist: Rough Trade Distribution

---

Szajner, Bernard
BIG SCARE, THE (EP).
Single (12"): released on New Rose, Aug'84 Dist: Rough Trade, Cartel

---

BRUTE REASON.
Album: released on Island, May'83 by Island Records. Dist: Polygram

Cassette: released on Island, May'83 by Island Records. Dist: Polygram

---

SOME DEATHS TAKE FOREVER.
Album: released on Initial, Sep'81 by Initial Records. Dist: Pinnacle

---

SUPERFICIAL MUSIC.
Album: released on Initial, Sep'81 by Initial Records. Dist: Pinnacle

---

Szajner's, Bernard 'ZED'
VISIONS OF DUNE.
Album: released on Initial, Sep'81 by Initial Records. Dist: Pinnacle

---

Szalai, Antal
HUNGARIAN SONGS POPULAR ALL OVER THE.. (Szalai, Antal & His Gypsy Band).
Tracks: / Pretty Kati / Blue forgetmenot / They fiddle, they make fine music / Down at the end of the village / Come tonight, late at night / Ten pairs of kisses all in one / Leaves of the shimmering aspen fell, The / Wheat it's ripening, The / My sweet heart sent word / All, all, all I feel bitter for / My tiny wee dove / My fiddle's broken / My saucy rose / Listen my rose, my little Kati / It's no good standing at the gate every night / Three pretzels / Cane starts out, The / Little girl, do you hear the music / Pretty girls, pretty girls have blue eyes / Harken, gypsies / May bug, yellow may bug / There's only one girl in the world / Girls, girls, Simongat girls / Blonde is pretty, dark hairs pretty / There are no rosenbushes in the Puszta / I had thirteen lovers / Badacsony csardas / My lover comes from Transdanubla / It's over, over, over.
Compact disc: released on Hungaraton(Hungary), Sep'86 Dist: Conifer

---

T.34
ROCK ON.
Single (7"): released on Galaxy, Feb'83 by Galaxy Records. Dist: RCA, Red Lightnin' Distribution, Discovery, Swift

Taaga
FRIEND OF MINE.
Single (7"): released on Taaga Trax, Nov'83 by Taaga Trax Records. Dist: Cartel Distribution

Tabackin, Lew
Insights

Tabloids
PIXIE HAMMERS.
Single (7"): released on Hackney, Jun'84 by Hackney Records. Dist: Hackney

Tabor, June
ABYSSINIANS.
Album: released on Topic, Nov'86 Dist: Roots Distribution

Cassette: released on Topic, Nov'86 Dist: Roots Distribution

Album: released on Topic, Jan'84 by Topic Records. Dist: JSU Distribution, Projection Distribution, Jazz Music Distribution

AIR AND GRACES.
Cassette: released on Shanachie, Nov'86 Dist: Sterns/Triple Earth Distribution, Roots

AIRS AND GRACES.
Album: released on Topic, '77 by Topic Records. Dist: JSU Distribution, Projection Distribution, Jazz Music Distribution

ASHES & DIAMONDS.
Album: released on Topic, '77 by Topic Records. Dist: JSU Distribution, Projection Distribution, Jazz Music Distribution

BEES ON HORSEBACK (Tabor, June & Bob Davenport).
Album: released on Freereed, Nov'77 by Topic Records. Dist: JSU

CUT ABOVE,A (Tabor, June & Martin Simpson).
Album: released on Topic, '81 by Topic Records. Dist: JSU Distribution, Projection Distribution, Jazz Music Distribution

SPY SHIP THEME.
Single (7"): released on BBC, Nov'83 by BBC Records & Tapes. Dist: EMI, PRT, Pye

Tabor, Laszlo
Echoes of Italy

WORLD OF GYPSY ROMANCE.
Album: released on Decca, '71 by Decca Records. Dist: Polygram

Cassette: released on Decca, '71 by Decca Records. Dist: Polygram

Tabu Ley
AFRICA SELECTION.
Album: released on Sterns African, Sep'85 by Sterns African Records. Dist: Stern's Distribution, Rough Trade

IN AMERICA AND CANADA.
Album: released on Genidia (Zaire), Jul'84 Dist: Earthworks Distributors, Rough Trade

Tackhead
GAME (THE)[YOU'LL NEVER WALK ALONE].
Picture disc single: released on Fourth & Broadway, Apr'87 by Island Records. Dist: Polygram, EMI

WHAT'S MY MISSION NOW?.
Single (7"): released on On-U-Sound, Oct'85 Dist: Rough Trade Distribution, Lightning

Taco
AFTER EIGHT.
Tracks: / Singin' in the rain / Tribute to Tino / Puttin' on the Ritz / I should care / Carmella / La vie en rose / Cheek to cheek / After eight / Livin' in my dreamworld / Encore / Thanks a million.
Compact disc: released on RCA, '84 by RCA Records. Dist: RCA, Roots, Swift, Wellard, Chris, I & B, Solomon & Peres Distribution

Album: released on RCA (Germany), Nov'83

Cassette: released on RCA (Germany), Nov'83

Compact disc: released on RCA (Germany), Jan'84

LET'S FACE THE MUSIC AND DANCE.
Single (7"): released on RCA, May'84 by RCA Records. Dist: RCA, Roots, Swift, Wellard, Chris, I & B, Solomon & Peres Distribution

Single (12"): released on RCA, May'84 by RCA Records. Dist: RCA, Roots, Swift, Wellard, Chris, I & B, Solomon & Peres Distribution

PUTTIN' ON THE RITZ.
Single (7"): released on RCA, Sep'83 by RCA Records. Dist: RCA, Roots, Swift, Wellard, Chris, I & B, Solomon & Peres Distribution

SINGIN' IN THE RAIN.
Single (7"): released on RCA, Apr'83 by RCA Records. Dist: RCA, Roots, Swift, Wellard, Chris, I & B, Solomon & Peres Distribution

Tactic
VIDEO VIDEO.
Single (7"): released on Sonet, Jun'83 by Sonet Records. Dist: PRT

Tacticos, Manos
MUSIC FROM THE GREEK ISLANDS
(Tacticos, Manos & his Bouzoukis).
Double Album: released on Music For Pleasure, Feb'83

Double cassette: released on Music For Pleasure, Feb'83

Tacuma, Jamaaladeen
MUSIC WORLD.
Tracks: / Kimono queen / Tokyo cosmopolitaan / Matsuru / Rouge / Kismet / Creator has a master plan / Jamila's theme / One more night.
Album: released on Sonet, Jan'87 by Sonet Records. Dist: PRT

RENAISSANCE MAN.
Tracks: / Renaissance man / Flash back / Let's have a good time / Next stop, The / Dancing in your head / There he stood / Battle of images, The / Sparkle.
Compact disc: released on Gramavision (USA), '86 by Gramavision Records (USA). Dist: PRT, IMS, Polygram

Album: released on Gramavision (USA), Nov'84 by Gramavision Records (USA). Dist: PRT, IMS, Polygram

Cassette: released on Gramavision (USA), Nov'84 by Gramavision Records (USA). Dist: PRT, IMS, Polygram

Compact disc: released on Gramavision (USA), Nov'84 by Gramavision Records (USA). Dist: PRT, IMS, Polygram

SHOW STOPPER.
Album: released on Gramavision (USA), Dec'83 by Gramavision Records (USA). Dist: PRT, IMS, Polygram

Tadley Band
AT THE LAKESIDE.
Album: released on Music Masters, Jan'83 by Music Masters Records. Dist: Taylors

Tad & Marry Anne
FOLLOW ME.
Tracks: / Follow me / Ezungizeng (Tad & Micky).

Single (12"): released on Jay Dee, Apr'86 by Jaydee Records. Dist: Jetstar

Tad's Logic Band
CHAPTER 1 DUB MIX.
Album: released on Tads, Jun'84 by Tads Records. Dist: Jetstar Distribution

Taff, Russ
MEDALS.
Album: released on Myrrh, Sep'85 by Word Records. Dist: Word Distribution

Cassette: released on Myrrh, Sep'85 by Word Records. Dist: Word Distribution

Taffy
I LOVE MY RADIO.
Single (7"): released on Transglobal Rhythm King, Nov'86 by Mute Records. Dist: Rough Trade, Cartel

Single (12"): released on Transglobal Rhythm King, Nov'86 by Mute Records. Dist: Rough Trade, Cartel

STEP BY STEP.
Single (7"): released on Trans Global, Jul'87

Single (12"): released on Trans Global, Jul'87

Single (12"): released on Transglobal Rhythm King, Aug'87 by Mute Records. Dist: Rough Trade, Cartel

T.A.G.G.
BIG SEX.
Tracks: / Ocean,The.
Single (7"): released on Sweatbox, Feb'87 by Sweatbox Records. Dist: Rough Trade, Cartel

Single (12"): released on Sweatbox, Feb'87 by Sweatbox Records. Dist: Rough Trade, Cartel

Taggart, Blind Joe
1926-1934.
Notes: Mono
Album: released on Wolf, Jan'87 Dist: Jazz Music, Swift

Tahiti
DREAM ISLAND.
Notes: Track details:A TAMAUA,Chant de gloire/HOE,ANA,Chant des Piroguiers/MARCHE DES JEUX DU PACIFIQUE SUD/MA-RAAMU,Ratal/KAVA,Aparima vava/HUE,Aparima/TEVA,Himene Popaa/TERO,Himene tarava/IAORA RA,Aparima/TE RAI,Paoa/TIARE TAHITI HERE E,Himene Popaa/MAHANA RUI RUI,Hivinau/ORIORIO,Pata'uta'u/MANU E,Aparima/PAHUA NIHO KEKA,Danse du cochon sauvage/UMAHA TO HAA IKE TE-META,Ruu/OTEA VAIETE,Otea/PAOA NO FAAA,Paoa/UTE NO ARUE,Ute/OTEA TE-MAEVA,Otea/HIVINAU NO MOOREA,Hivinau/OTEA FETIA OE,Otea/APARIMA NO PIRAE,maururu a vau,Chant d'adieu Authentic Polynesian music.
Compact disc: released on Sunset (France), Jan'87 Dist: IMS-Polygram Distribution

Tailgators
MUMBO JUMBO.
Album: released on Zippo, Sep'86

SWAMP ROCK.
Album: released on Food For Thought, Aug'85 by Food For Thought Records. Dist: Pinnacle

Tajah, Paulette
COS YOU LOVE ME BABY.
Single (7"): released on Raiders, Sep'84 Dist: Jetstar

GLAD YOU'RE AROUND.
Tracks: / Glad you're around.
Single (12"): released on Exclusive, Jan'86 Dist: Jetstar

Single (12"): released on Exclusive Productions, Dec'85 Dist: Jetstar

MOVE UP CLOSE TO ME BABY.
Single (12"): released on LGR, Dec'83 by Jetstar

STOP LOOK LISTEN.
Single (12"): released on Ariwa, Aug'87 by Ariwa Records. Dist: Revolver, Cartel, Jetstar, Rough Trade

YOU'RE THE ONE.
Single (7"): released on Exclusive Productions, Jun'85 Dist: Jetstar

Single (12"): released on Exclusive Productions, Jun'85 Dist: Jetstar

Taj Mahal
EVERYBODY IS SOMEBODY.
Tracks: / French letter / Deed I do".
Single (7"): released on Gramavision (USA), Mar'87 by Gramavision Records (USA). Dist: PRT, IMS, Polygram

Single (12"): released on Sonet, Mar'87 by Sonet Records. Dist: PRT

FIRST LP.
Cassette: released on Demon, Nov'85 by Demon Records. Dist: Pinnacle

GOING HOME.
Album: released on CBS, Jul'80 by CBS Records. Dist: CBS

Cassette: released on CBS, Jul'80 by CBS Records. Dist: CBS

NATCH'L BLUES, THE.
Album: released on Edsel, May'87 by Demon Records. Dist: Pinnacle, Jazz Music, Projection

TAJ MAHAL.
Album: released on Edsel, Dec'85 by Demon Records. Dist: Pinnacle, Jazz Music, Projection

Cassette: released on Edsel, Dec'85 by Demon Records. Dist: Pinnacle, Jazz Music, Projection

TAJ MAHAL LIVE WITH THE INTERNATIONAL RHYTHM BAND.
Album: released on Magnet, '83 by Magnet Records. Dist: BMG

Cassette: released on Magnet, '83 by Magnet Records. Dist: BMG

Taka Boom
IN THE MIDDLE OF THE NIGHT.
Tracks: / In the middle of the night / In the middle of the night (LP version).
Single (7"): released on Boiling Point, Jan'86 by Polydor Records. Dist: Polygram

Single (12"): released on Boiling Point, Jan'86 by Polydor Records. Dist: Polygram

Takahashi, Yukihiro
BEATNIKS, (THE).
Album: released on Statik, '82 Dist: Rough Trade Distribution, Stage One Distribution

DISPOSABLE LOVE.
Single (7"): released on Alfa, Jul'82 Dist: CBS

MURDERED BY THE MUSIC.
Single (7"): released on Statik, May'82 Dist: Rough Trade Distribution, Stage One Distribution

NEUROMANTIC.
Album: released on Alfa, Jan'82 Dist: CBS

Cassette: released on Alfa, Jan'82 Dist: CBS

STAY CLOSE.
Tracks: / Stay Close / Betsu-Ni.
Single (7"): released on Rime, Oct'86 Dist: DMS-RCA

STRANGER THINGS HAVE HAPPENED.
Single (12"): released on Cocteau, Apr'85 by Cocteau Records. Dist: Pinnacle, IDS

WILD AND MOODY.
Tracks: / Wild and moody / Stranger things have happened / Kill that thermostat / Helpless / Price to pay / Bounds of reason, bonds of love / Walking to the beat.
Album: released on Cocteau, Feb'85 by Cocteau Records. Dist: Pinnacle, IDS

Takanaka, Masayoshi
SAUDADE.
Album: released on Polydor (Germany), Jul'83 Dist: IMS-Polygram

Cassette: released on Polydor (Germany), Jul'83 Dist: IMS-Polygram

Takase, Aki
SONG FOR HOPE (Takase, Aki Trio).
Album: released on Enja (Germany), Jan'82 by Enja Records (W.Germany). Dist: Cadillac Music

Take 3
CAN'T GET ENOUGH.
Single (7"): released on Elite, May'85 Dist: PRT
Single (12"): released on Elite, May'85 Dist: PRT

MUSICAL AND TIME.
Single (12"): released on Elite, Jun'84 Dist: PRT

THIS GOOD GOOD FEELING.
Single (12"): released on Elite, Nov'84 Dist: PRT

Take my youth
TAKE MY YOUTH (AN ANTHOLOGY OF POETRY FROM THE GREAT WAR) Various Authors (Hardy, Robert/Martin Jarvis).
Cassette: released on Talking Tape Company, '84 by Talking Tape Company Records.

Takes three
TONITE'S THE NITE.
Single (12"): released on Fast Forward, Sep'83 by Fast Forward Records. Dist: Independant, Cartel

Take The Subway...
TAKE THE SUBWAY TO YOUR SUBURB Various Artists).
Album: released on Subway, Dec'86 Dist: Revolver Distribution, Spartan Distribution

Take Us Two
I WANNA BE A ROCK STAR.
Single (7"): released on Raw Dance Music, Apr'84 by Raw Dance Music. Dist: ILA

Taking The Strain
TAKING THE STRAIN Various artists (Various Artists).
Album: released on BBC, Jul'81 by BBC Records & Tapes. Dist: EMI, PRT, Pye

Cassette: released on BBC, Jul'81 by BBC Records & Tapes. Dist: EMI, PRT, Pye

Taking The Trains Out
TAKING THE TRAINS OUT Various Artists (Various Artists).
Extended-play record: released on Wildcat, Jun'83

Talas
SINK YOUR TEETH INTO THAT.
Album: released on Food For Thought, Aug'86 by Food For Thought Records. Dist: Pinnacle

Talbot, Alan
JC THE NAZ.
Single (7"): released on Hobo, Dec'81 by Mr. Sam Records. Dist: Jazz Music

Talbot, Jamie
ALTITUDE.
Album: released on Move, Sep'86 by Charly Records. Dist: Charly Distribution, Fast Forward Distribution, Cartel Distribution

MORNIN'.
Tracks: / Mornin' / In your day dreaming.
Single (12"): released on Move, Sep'86 by Charly Records. Dist: Charly Distribution, Fast Forward Distribution, Cartel Distribution

Talbot, John Michael
BE EXALTED.
Notes: Today, John Michael is the foremost voice in Catholic music. He is known around the world for his rich musical sites, powerful orchestrations, and a dynamic message that touches

countless hearts through his popular albums and sell-out concert performances. "Be Exalted" is an album of worship which attempts to capture spiritual reality and, although most of the songs are familiar, being used in many churches throughout the world, some are new and fresh. Both trained and untrained singers join together as one chorus of charismatic freedom and melodic creativity to make a pleasing harmony for God.
Album: released on Birdwing, Aug'86 by Word Records. Dist: Word Distribution

Cassette: released on Birdwing, Aug'86 by Word Records. Dist: Word Distribution

COME TO THE QUIET.
Album: released on Birdwing, May'82 by Word Records. Dist: Word Distribution

Cassette: released on Birdwing, May'82 by Word Records. Dist: Word Distribution

FOR THE BRIDE.
Album: released on Birdwing, May'82 by Word Records. Dist: Word Distribution

Cassette: released on Birdwing, May'82 by Word Records. Dist: Word Distribution

GOD OF LIFE.
Cassette: released on Birdwing, Nov'84 by Word Records. Dist: Word Distribution

LORD'S SUPPER, THE.
Cassette: released on Birdwing, May'85 by Word Records. Dist: Word Distribution

NEW EARTH, THE.
Album: released on Sparrow, May'82 by Word Records. Dist: Spartan

Cassette: released on Sparrow, May'82 by Word Records. Dist: Spartan

PAINTER, THE.
Album: released on Sparrow, May'82 by Word Records. Dist: Spartan

Cassette: released on Sparrow, May'82 by Word Records. Dist: Spartan

QUIET, THE.
Notes: The musician who first put down the drums and picked up the guitar at age nine once again showcases the blessed dimensions of that decision- perhaps more clearly than ever.
Album: released on Meadowlark, Mar'86 by Sparrow Records. Dist: Word Distribution

Cassette: released on Meadowlark, Mar'86 by Sparrow Records. Dist: Word Distribution

SONGS FOR WORSHIP VOLUME 11.
Album: released on Birdwing, Sep'85 by Word Records. Dist: Word Distribution

Cassette: released on Birdwing, Sep'85 by Word Records. Dist: Word Distribution

TROUBADOUR OF THE GREAT KING.
Album: released on Birdwing, May'82 by Word Records. Dist: Word Distribution

Cassette: released on Birdwing, May'82 by Word Records. Dist: Word Distribution

Talbot, Terry
TIME TO LAUGH, A TIME TO SING, A.
Album: released on Sparrow, May'82 by Word Records. Dist: Spartan

Cassette: released on Sparrow, May'82 by Word Records. Dist: Spartan

Talents
OUT OF LOVE.
Single (12"): released on Kaya, Nov'85 by Kaya Records. Dist: Jetstar

TEN PERCENT INSPIRATION.
Single (12"): released on Kaya, Sep'85 by Kaya Records. Dist: Jetstar

Tale Of A Donkey's....
TALE OF A DONKEY'S TAIL (And other Playschool stories) (Various Artists).
Album: released on BBC, Jun'76 by BBC Records & Tapes. Dist: EMI, PRT, Pye

Cassette: released on BBC, Jun'76 by BBC Records & Tapes. Dist: EMI, PRT, Pye

Tale of Ale
STORY OF THE ENGLISHMAN AND HIS BEER.
Album: released on Free Reed, Jan'87 by Free Reed Records. Dist: Roots, Projection, Hobgoblin Records, Oblivion

Tale Of Tuppeny
TALE OF TUPPENY (Plus other Stories by Beatrix Potter) (Spoken Word).
Cassette: released on Tellastory, May'82 by Bartlett Bliss Productions. Dist: PRT Distribu-

tion, Hayward Promotions Distribution, H.R. Taylor Distribution

Tale of two cities, A
TALE OF TWO CITIES, A Dickens, Charles (Gielgud, Sir John).
Cassette: released on Argo, Nov'84 by Decca Records. Dist: Polygram

TALE OF TWO CITIES, A (See under Gielgud, Sir John) (Dickens, Charles).

Tales From...
TALES FROM THE WEST INDIES Various Artists (Various Artists).
Cassette: released on Anvil, Jan'81 Dist: Anvil

Tales From Arabia
TALES FROM ARABIA Various Artists (Various Artists).
Cassette: released on Anvil, Jan'81 Dist: Anvil

Tales From India
TALES FROM INDIA VOL. 1 Various Artists (Various Artists).
Cassette: released on Anvil, Jan'81 Dist: Anvil

TALES FROM INDIA VOL.2 Various Artists (Various Artists).
Cassette: released on Anvil, Jan'81 Dist: Anvil

Tales From Japan
TALES FROM JAPAN Various Artists (Various Artists).
Cassette: released on Anvil, Jan'81 Dist: Anvil

Tales From Lapland
TALES FROM LAPLAND Various Artists (Various Artists).
Cassette: released on Anvil, Jul'82 Dist: Anvil

Tales From Moomin Valley
TOVE JANSSON.

Tales From Norway
TALES FROM NORWAY Various Artists (Various Artists).
Cassette: released on Anvil, Jan'81 Dist: Anvil

Tales From Persia
TALES FROM PERSIA Various Artist (Various Artists).
Cassette: released on Anvil, Jan'81 Dist: Anvil

Tales From Turkey
TALES FROM TURKEY Various Artists (Various Artists).
Cassette: released on Anvil, Jan'81 Dist: Anvil

Tales from two in a bed
TALES FROM TWO IN A BED Ahlbert, Allan (Boyd, Carole).
Cassette: released on Tellastory, Mar'84 by Bartlett Bliss Productions. Dist: PRT Distribution, Hayward Promotions Distribution, H.R. Taylor Distribution

Tales Of Beatrix Potter
TALES OF BEATRIX POTTER Film Soundtrack (Film soundtrack).
Album: released on H.M.V., Mar'71 by EMI Records. Dist: EMI

Tales Of Chivalry
TALES OF CHIVALRY Various Artists (Various Artists).
Cassette: released on Anvil, Jul'82 Dist: Anvil

Tales of Terror
TALES OF TERROR.
Album: released on CD Presents, Aug'86 Dist: IMS, Polygram

Talisman
RUN COME GIRL.
Single (12"): released on Recreational, '81 by Revolver Records. Dist: Rough Trade

Single (12"): released on Recreational, '81 by Revolver Records. Dist: Rough Trade

TAKIN THE STRAIN.
Album: released on Embryo, Jul'84 by Embryo Records. Dist: Revolver, Cartel, WEA

TALISMAN.
Album: released on SRT, Jan'77 by SRT Records. Dist: Pinnacle, Solomon & Peres Distribution, SRT Distribution, H.R. Taylor Distribution, PRT Distribution

Talk Back
I CAN'T LET YOU GO.
Single (7"): released on CBS, Jan'83 by CBS Records. Dist: CBS

Single (12"): released on CBS, Jan'83 by CBS Records. Dist: CBS

PLEASURE.
Single (7"): released on Cottage Records, Mar'84

Talking Drums
COURAGE.
Single (12"): released on Sticky Music, May'84 by Sticky Music Records. Dist: Fast Forward Distributors, Cartel Distribution

PRETEND A STRANGER.
Tracks: / Pretend a stranger.
Single (7"): released on Sticky, Jul'86

REASSEMBLY.
Album: released on Sticky, May'86

Talking Heads
77.
Cassette: released on Sire, Oct'82

AND SHE WAS.
Single (7"): released on EMI, Feb'86 by EMI Records. Dist: EMI

Single (12"): released on EMI, Feb'86 by EMI Records. Dist: EMI

Picture disc single: released on EMI, Feb'86 by EMI Records. Dist: EMI

BURNING DOWN THE HOUSE.
Single (7"): released on Sire, Jul'83

Single (12"): released on Sire, Jul'83

Album: released on Sire, Aug'79

Cassette: released on Sire, Aug'79

FEAR OF MUSIC.
Tracks: / Zimbra / Mind / Cities / Paper / Life during wartime / Memories can't wait / Air / Heaven / Animals / Electric guitar / Drugs.
Compact disc: released on Sire, Jul'84

Compact disc: released on Sire, Jul'84

GIRLFRIEND IS BETTER.
Single (7"): released on EMI, Nov'84 by EMI Records. Dist: EMI

Single (12"): released on EMI, Jan'85 by EMI Records. Dist: EMI

HOUSES IN MOTION.
Single (7"): released on Sire, May'81

Single (12"): released on Sire, May'81

INTERVIEW PICTURE DISC.
Album: released on Baktabak, May'87 by Baktabak Records. Dist: Arabesque

LADY DON'T MIND.
Single (7"): released on EMI, May'85 by EMI Records. Dist: EMI

Single (12"): released on EMI, May'85 by EMI Records. Dist: EMI

LADY DON'T MIND, THE.
Double-pack single: released on EMI, Jun'85 by EMI Records. Dist: EMI

Single (12"): released on EMI, Jun'85 by EMI Records. Dist: EMI

LIFE DURING WARTIME (LIVE VERSION).
Single (7"): released on Sire, Mar'82

Single (12"): released on Sire, Mar'82

LIFE DURING WARTIMES.
Single (7"): released on Sire, Oct'79

LITTLE CREATURES.
Tracks: / And she was / Give me back my name / Creatures of love / Lady don't mind, The / Perfect world / Stay up late / Walk it down / Television man / Road to nowhere.
Album: released on EMI, Jun'85 by EMI Records. Dist: EMI

Cassette: released on EMI, Jun'85 by EMI Records. Dist: EMI

Compact disc: released on EMI, Jun'85 by EMI Records. Dist: EMI

MORE SONGS ABOUT BUILDINGS & FOOD.
Album: released on Sire, Jul'78

Cassette: released on Sire, Jul'78

MORE SONGS ABOUT BUILDINGS AND FOOD.
Compact disc: released on Sire, Jan'87

NAME OF THIS BAND IS TALKING HEADS, THE.
Double Album: released on Sire, Mar'82

Double cassette: released on Sire, Mar'82

ONCE IN A LIFETIME.
Single (7"): released on Sire, Feb'81

Single (7"): released on Sire, Feb'81

Single (12"): released on Sire, Mar'81

RADIO HEAD.
Tracks: / Radio head (LP version) / Hey Now (Movie version) / Radio Head (Ext. Remix) / Radio Head (Movie version) / Hey now (Milwaukee mix).
Notes: Original sound recordings made by Talking Heads Tours Inc. under exclusive licence to EMI Records.
Double-pack single: released on EMI, May'87 by EMI Records. Dist: EMI

Compact disc single: released on EMI, Apr'87 by EMI Records. Dist: EMI

RADIO HEAD (LP VERSION).
Tracks: / Radio head (LP version) / Hey now.
Single (7"): released on EMI, Apr'87 by EMI Records. Dist: EMI

Single (12"): released on EMI, Apr'87 by EMI Records. Dist: EMI

REMAIN IN LIGHT.
Tracks: / Great curve / Crosseyed and painless / Born under punches (Heat goes on) / Houses in motion / Once in a lifetime / Listening wind / Seen and not seen / Overload.
Compact disc: released on Sire, '83

Album: released on Sire, Nov'80

Cassette: released on Sire, Nov'80

ROAD TO NOWHERE.
Single (7"): released on EMI, Sep'85 by EMI Records. Dist: EMI

Single (12"): released on EMI, Sep'85 by EMI Records. Dist: EMI

Picture disc single: released on EMI, Oct'85 by EMI Records. Dist: EMI

SLIPPERY PEOPLE.
Single (7"): released on EMI, Oct'84 by EMI Records. Dist: EMI

Single (12"): released on EMI, Oct'84 by EMI Records. Dist: EMI

SPEAKING IN TONGUES.
Tracks: / Burning down the house / Making flippy floppy / Swamp / Girlfriend is letter / Slippery people / I get wild- Wild gravity / Pull up the roots / Moon rocks / This must be the place.
Compact disc: released on Sire, '83

Cassette: released on Sire, Jun'83

STOP MAKING SENSE.
Tracks: / Psycho Killer / Swamp / Slippery people / Burning down the house / Girl friend is letter / Once in a lifetime / What a day that was / Life during wartime / Take me to the river.
Notes: New live album from Talking Heads, their first release on EMI. Their last studio album was released in June 1983 and a previous live album was released in 1982. The band have a large following in this country, all of their recent albums have gone Top 30. This album also has live versions of classic tracks such as "Psycho Killer", "Once in A Lifetime" and "Burning Down the House". "Once in A Lifetime" was a No.14 in 1981. The cassette contains several extended versions of the album tracks.
Album: released on EMI, Oct'84 by EMI Records. Dist: EMI

Cassette: released on EMI, Oct'84 by EMI Records. Dist: EMI

Compact disc: released on EMI, Oct'84 by EMI Records. Dist: EMI

Video-cassette (VHS): released on Palace, '86 Dist: PVG

TAKE ME TO THE RIVER.
Single (7"): released on Sire, Jun'79

TALKING HEADS'77.
Tracks: / Uh-oh, love comes to town / New feeling / Tentative decisions / Happy day / Who is it / No compassion / Book I read / Don't worry about the government / First week / Last week...carefree / Psycho killer / Pulled up.
Compact disc: released on Sire, Oct'87

THIS MUST BE THE PLACE.
Tracks: / This must be the place / Moon rocks.
Single (7"): released on EMI, Jan'86

TRUE STORIES.
Tracks: / Love for sale / Pussiln' evidence / Hey / Papa Legba / Wild wild life / Radio head / City of dreams / People like us / City of dreams.
Notes: All tracks by: David Byrne. (P)1986 original Sound Recordings. Made by Talking Heads Tour Inc. Under exclusive licence to EMI Records.
Album: released on EMI, Sep'86 by EMI Records. Dist: EMI

Cassette: released on EMI, Sep'86 by EMI Records. Dist: EMI

Compact disc: released on EMI, Oct'86 by EMI Records. Dist: EMI

WILD WILD LIFE.
Tracks: / Wild wild life / People like us (movie version).
Single (7"): released on EMI, Aug'86 by EMI Records. Dist: EMI

Single (12"): released on EMI, Aug'86 by EMI Records. Dist: EMI

COLOUR OF SPRING (THE).
Compact disc: by EMI Records. Dist: EMI

COLOUR OF SPRING, THE.
Tracks: / Happiness is easy / I don't believe in you / Life's what you make it / April 15th / Living in another world / Give it up / Chameleon day / Time it's time.
Album: released on EMI, Feb'86 by EMI Records. Dist: EMI

Cassette: released on EMI, Feb'86 by EMI Records. Dist: EMI

Compact disc: released on EMI, Apr'86 by EMI Records. Dist: EMI

GIVE IT UP.
Tracks: / Give it up / Pictures of Bernadette.
Single (7"): released on Parlophone, May'86 by EMI Records. Dist: EMI

Single (12"): released on Parlophone, May'86 by EMI Records. Dist: EMI

I DON'T BELIEVE IN YOU.
Tracks: / I don't believe in you / Does Caroline know / Happiness is easy.

IT'S MY LIFE.
Tracks: / Dum dum girl / Such a shame / Renee / It's my life / Tomorrow / Started / Last time, The / Call in the night boy / Does Caroloine know / It's you.
Album: released on EMI, Feb'84 by EMI Records. Dist: EMI

Cassette: released on EMI, Feb'84 by EMI Records. Dist: EMI

Compact disc: released on EMI, Feb'84 by EMI Records. Dist: EMI

Single (7"): released on EMI, Jan'84 by EMI Records. Dist: EMI

Single (12"): released on EMI, Jan'84 by EMI Records. Dist: EMI

LIFE'S WHAT YOU MAKE IT.
Tracks: / Life's what you make it / It's getting late in the evening / Life's what you make it (EXT) / It's my life / Does Caroline know.
Single (7"): released on EMI, Feb'86 by EMI Records. Dist: EMI

Single (12"): released on EMI, Feb'86 by EMI Records. Dist: EMI

Single (12"): released on EMI, Feb'86 by EMI Records. Dist: EMI

Double-pack single: released on EMI, Feb'86 by EMI Records. Dist: EMI

LIVING IN ANOTHER WORLD.
Tracks: / Living in another world / For what it's worth / Living in another world / For what it's worth / Living in another world (US mix) / Original.
Single (7"): released on EMI, Mar'86 by EMI Records. Dist: EMI

Single (12"): released on EMI, Mar'86 by EMI Records. Dist: EMI

Picture disc single: released on EMI, Mar'86 by EMI Records. Dist: EMI

Single (12"): released on EMI, Mar'86 by EMI Records. Dist: EMI

MY FOOLISH FRIEND.
Single (7"): released on EMI, Feb'83 by EMI Records. Dist: EMI

Single (12"): released on EMI, Feb'83 by EMI Records. Dist: EMI

PARTY'S OVER.
Tracks: / Talk Talk / It's so serious / Today / Party's over / Hate / Have you heard the news / Mirror man / Another word / Candy.
Compact disc: released on EMI, Mar'87 by EMI Records. Dist: EMI

PARTY'S OVER, THE.
Tracks: / Talk Talk / It's so serious / Today / Party's over, The / Hate / Have you heard the news / Mirror man / Another word / Candy.
Album: released on EMI, Jul'82 by EMI Records. Dist: EMI

Cassette: released on EMI, Jul'82 by EMI Records. Dist: EMI

Album: released on Fame, Sep'87 by Music For Pleasure Records. Dist: EMI. Estim retail

---

price in Sep'87 was £3.49.

Cassette: released on Fame, Sep'87 by Music For Pleasure Records. Dist: EMI. Estim retail price in Sep'87 was £3.49.

SUCH A SHAME.
Single (7"): released on EMI, Mar'84 by EMI Records. Dist: EMI

Single (12"): released on EMI, Mar'84 by EMI Records. Dist: EMI

TODAY.
Single (7"): released on EMI, Jun'82 by EMI Records. Dist: EMI

BRAND NEW GUN.
Tracks: / Brand new gun / Last house on the left / Took a long time.
Single (12"): released on Big Beat, Mar'86 by Ace Records. Dist: Projection, Pinnacle

FINAL KICK.
Single (7"): released on Big Beat, Jun'85 by Ace Records. Dist: Projection, Pinnacle

Single (12"): released on Big Beat, Jun'85 by Ace Records. Dist: Projection, Pinnacle

ISLAND OF LOST SOULS.
Single (7"): released on Big Beat, Sep'82 by Ace Records. Dist: Projection, Pinnacle

WEDNESDAY ADDAMS' BOYFRIEND.
Single (7"): released on Big Beat, Aug'84 by Ace Records. Dist: Projection, Pinnacle

AMERICAN ORIGINALS.
Tracks: / Find somebody and love them / Bury me in New Orleans / Baby she loves a rocker / Whiskey on the side / Are they gonna make us outlaws again / Way to say I love you, (A) / New York town / Open all night / Montana song / Ready to please / We're all one family (all over the world).
Compact disc: released on Bear Family, Aug'86 by Bear Family Records. Dist: Rollercoaster Distribution, Swift

BYRD. GREAT SERVICE.
Album: released on Abbey, Feb'87 by Abbey. Dist: PRT, Taylors, Gamut

Compact disc: released on Abbey, Feb'87 by Abbey. Dist: PRT, Taylors, Gamut

HOT ROD IS HER NAME.
Tracks: / Goldie Jo Mahome / Underway / Give me a chance / If you knew what I know / Please be careful / Are you mine / Out of line / Boom boom boomerang / Will this dream of mine come true / Hot Rod is her name / Whose pidgeon are you / Don't you know, don't you know I want to walk with you / Come with me / Remembering you / You loved another one better than me / Why must I wonder / I gave my heart to two people.
Album: released on Bear Family, Feb'86 by Bear Family Records. Dist: Rollercoaster Distribution, Swift

STACK-A-RECORDS (Tall, Tom & His Tom Cats).
Single (7"): released on Rock Star, Dec'80 Dist: Lightning, Swift Distribution, Superdisc Distribution

Album: released on Bear Family, Jun'85 by Bear Family Records. Dist: Rollercoaster Distribution, Swift

NEVER LOOK BACK.
Album: released on Steamhammer, Nov'85

BEATNIK BOY.
Tracks: / My best friend.
Single (7"): released on 53rd & 3rd, Dec'86 by Fast Forward Records. Dist: Fast Forward, Cartel

STEAMING TRAIN.
Tracks: / Just a dream / Steaming train / Beatnik.
Single (7"): released on 53rd & 3rd, Dec'86 by Fast Forward Records. Dist: Fast Forward, Cartel

Single (12"): released on 53rd & 3rd, Dec'86 by Fast Forward Records. Dist: Fast Forward, Cartel

---

Single (7"): released on 53rd & 3rd, 30 May'87 by Fast Forward Records. Dist: Fast Forward, Cartel

Single (12"): released on 53rd & 3rd, 30 May'87 by Fast Forward Records. Dist: Fast Forward, Cartel

PANGE LINGUA (JOSHQUIN).
Album: released on Abbey, Nov'86 by Abbey. Dist: PRT, Taylors, Gamut

Cassette: released on Abbey, Nov'86 by Abbey. Dist: PRT, Taylors, Gamut

Compact disc: released on Abbey, Nov'86 by Abbey. Dist: PRT, Taylors, Gamut

EDWARD THOMAS.
Album: released on Response, Feb'81 by Priority Records. Dist: BMG

AFFECTION.
Tracks: / Affection / Everybody dance / Summertime love'.
Single (7"): released on A&M, Feb'86 by A&M Records. Dist: Polygram

Single (12"): released on A&M, Feb'86 by A&M Records. Dist: Polygram

LOST PROPERTIES.
Cassette single: released on LTC, Sep'83 Dist: LTC

HOSANNA IN EXCELSIS!.
Album: released on Apollo, '74

TAMING OF THE SHREW, THE. By William Shakespeare.
Double cassette: released on Argo (Spoken-word), May'83 by Decca Records. Dist: Polygram

GOING TO A PARTY.
Tracks: / Party verion (Bubblers crew).
Single (12"): released on UK Bubblers, Nov'86 by Greensleeves Records. Dist: RCA, Jetstar

BABY LOVE.
Single (7"): released on Reggae, Mar'82 by Reggae Records. Dist: Jetstar, Morpheus Distribution

Single (12"): released on Reggae, Mar'82 by Reggae Records. Dist: Jetstar, Morpheus Distribution

BOOMERANG.
Single (12"): released on Reggae, Mar'83 by Reggae Records. Dist: Jetstar, Morpheus Distribution

EBONY EYES.
Single (12"): released on Earthquake, Mar'83 by Earthquake Records. Dist: Jetstar

GO AWAY DREAM.
Single (12"): released on Taxi, Oct'83 by Island Records. Dist: EMI

HERE I GO AGAIN.
Tracks: / Home training.
Single (12"): released on Skynote, Dec'86 Dist: Sidewalk Records

HEY GRANDMA.
Single (12"): released on Smash Apartheid Music Works, Sep'85

HOLD ON.
Single (12"): released on Plantation, May'82 Dist: Jetstar

JOY IN THE MORNING.
Single (12"): released on Arrival, Oct'83 by Arrival. Dist: Revolver, Cartel

JUKI JAMMY.
Single (12"): released on Londisc, Sep'85 by Londisc Records.

LAYING BESIDE YOU.
Single (7"): released on D. Roy, Apr'80

SMILING FACES SOMETIMES.
Single (12"): released on Island, Mar'81 by Island Records. Dist: Polygram

SWEAT FOR YOU BABY.
Single (12"): released on Taxi, Aug'82 by Taxi Records. Dist: Jetstar Distribution

---

TRUE TRUE.
Single (7"): released on Dancebeat, Dec'81 by Dancebeat Records. Dist: Jetstar

WHO DAT SAY DAT.
Single (12"): released on Revue, Jan'85 by Revue Records. Dist: Creole

Tammy

OLD ENOUGH TO KNOW BETTER.
Tracks: / Old enough to know better / Do it to me.
Single (7"): released on Mix Factory, May'86 Dist: Creole Distribution, PRT Distribution

Tampa Red

GUITAR WIZARD,THE 1935-53.
Album: released on Blues Classics (USA), Jul'87 by Arhoolie Records. Dist: Topic, Jazz Music, Projection

IT'S TIGHT LIKE THAT 1928-1942.
Album: released on Blues Document, Jul'84 Dist: Swift

TAMPA RED WITH JOHNNY JONES
(Tampa Red & Johnny Jones).
Album: released on Krazy Kat (USA), May'83

Tams

ATLANTA SOUL CONNECTION.
Album: released on Charly, Nov'83 by Charly Records. Dist: Charly, Cadillac

BEACH MUSIC FROM...THE TAMS.
Album: released on Compleat, Jul'84 by Compleat Records. Dist: PRT

HEY GIRL DON'T BOTHER ME.
Tracks: / Hey girl don't bother me / Our love is getting stronger.
Single (7"): released on Casino Classics, Apr'86 by RK Records. Dist: PRT

Single (7"): released on Old Gold, Jul'82 by Old Gold Records. Dist: Lightning, Jazz Music, Spartan, Counterpoint

Tamson, Jock Bairns

JOCK TAMSON'S BAIRNS.
Album: released on Temple, Jan'83 by Temple Records. Dist: Rough Trade Distribution, Cartel Distribution

LASSES FASHION, THE.
Album: released on Topic, '82 by Topic Records. Dist: JSU Distribution, Projection Distribution, Jazz Music Distribution

Tan

I'VE GOT TO GET TO INDIANA.
Album: released on White Dove, Dec'81 by White Dove Records. Dist: Pinnacle

Single (7"): released on White Dove, Jan'80 by White Dove Records. Dist: Pinnacle

SUMMER PLACE.
Single (7"): released on Rough Trade, Jun'81 by Rough Trade Records. Dist: Rough Trade Distribution, Cartel Distribution

THERE'S A FIRE.
Single (7"): released on White Dove, Aug'79 by White Dove Records. Dist: Pinnacle

Tandoori Cassette

ANGEL TALK.
Single (7"): released on IKA, Nov'82 Dist: IDS

Tandy-Morgan Band

EARTH RISE.
Tracks: / Earth rise / Under the blue / Asteroid / Suddenly / Escape from the citadel / Caesar of the galaxy / One thousand worlds / Spaceship Earth / Zero zero / Third planet, (The) / Ria / Princeton / Pictures in my pillow / Secret, (The).
Album: released on FM, Jul'86 by FM-Revolver Records. Dist: EMI

Cassette: released on FM, Jul'86 by FM-Revolver Records. Dist: EMI

Tandy, Sharon

HOLD ON.
Single (12"): released on Atlantic, Apr'80 by WEA Records. Dist: WEA

Tanega, Norma

WALKING MY CAT NAMED DOG.
Single (7"): released on Old Gold, Jul'84 by Old Gold Records. Dist: Lightning, Jazz Music, Spartan, Counterpoint

Tanganyika

I'M LIL ROXANNE.
Tracks: / I'm lil Roxanne / I'm lil Roxanne (Instrumental version).
Single (7"): released on Revue, Aug'86 by Revue Records. Dist: Creole

Single (12"): released on Revue, Aug'86 by Revue Records. Dist: Creole

Tangerine Dream

ALPHA CENTAURI/ATEM.
Album: released on Virgin, Jul'76

ATEM.
Compact disc: released on Jive, Jan'87 by Zomba Records. Dist: RCA, PRT, CBS

COLLECTION-PART ONE, THE.
Tracks: / Genesis / Circulation of events / Fauni-gena / Alpha centauri.
Album: released on Collector Series, Mar'87 by Castle Communications Records. Dist: PRT, Pinnacle, RCA, Ariola

Cassette: released on Collector Series, Mar'87 by Castle Communications Records. Dist: PRT, Pinnacle, RCA, Ariola

COLLECTION-PART TWO, THE.
Notes: Bar code number: 5 013428 131619.
Album: released on Collector Series, Mar'87 by Castle Communications Records. Dist: PRT, Pinnacle, RCA, Ariola

Cassette: released on Collector Series, Mar'87 by Castle Communications Records. Dist: PRT, Pinnacle, RCA, Ariola

CYCLONE.
Tracks: / Bent cold sidewalk / Rising runner missed by endless sender / Madrigal meridian.
Album: released on Virgin, '82 by Virgin Records. Dist: EMI, Virgin Distribution Deleted '84.

Cassette: released on Virgin, '82 by Virgin Records. Dist: EMI, Virgin Distribution

Compact disc: released on Virgin, Jul'87 by Virgin Records. Dist: EMI, Virgin Distribution

DREAM SEQUENCE.
Tracks: / Dream is always the same, (The) / Phaedra / Rubicon (Part 1) / Stratosfear (Exc) / Choronzon / Cherokee land (live) / Cinnamon Road / Kiew mission / Ricochet (part 2) / Cloudburst fight / Force majeure / Tangram (part 1) / Beach scene / Logos (parts 1 & 2) / White eagle / Dominion / Love on a real train.
Double Album: released on Virgin, Nov'85 by Virgin Records. Dist: EMI, Virgin Distribution

Double cassette: released on Virgin, Nov'85 by Virgin Records. Dist: EMI, Virgin Distribution

Double compact disc: released on Virgin, Nov'85 by Virgin Records. Dist: EMI, Virgin Distribution

ENCORE.
Compact disc: by Virgin Records. Dist: EMI, Virgin Distribution

EXIT.
Tracks: / Kiew mission / Pilots of purple twilight / Choronzon / Exit / Network 23 / Remote viewing.
Album: released on Virgin, Sep'81 by Virgin Records. Dist: EMI, Virgin Distribution

Cassette: released on Virgin, Sep'81 by Virgin Records. Dist: EMI, Virgin Distribution

Compact disc: released on Virgin, Sep'81 by Virgin Records. Dist: EMI, Virgin Distribution

FIRESTARTER Film soundtrack.
Album: released on MCA, Jul'84 by MCA Records. Dist: CBS

Cassette: released on MCA, Jul'84 by MCA Records. Dist: CBS

FLASHPOINT.
Tracks: / Going west / Afternoon in the desert / Plane ride / Mystery tracks / Lost in the dunes / Highway patrol / Love phantasy / Madcap story / Dirty cross roads / Flashpoint.
Notes: Hit film soundtrack from the German synthesizer stars. Moody, atmospheric themes with an underlying feeling of power and menace.
Album: released on Heavy Metal Worldwide, Apr'87 by FM-Revolver Records. Dist: EMI

Cassette: released on Heavy Metal Worldwide, Apr'87 by FM-Revolver Records. Dist: EMI

Compact disc: released on Heavy Metal Worldwide, Apr'87 by FM-Revolver Records. Dist: EMI

Album: released on Heavy Metal, Feb'85 by FM-Revolver Records. Dist: EMI

Cassette: released on Heavy Metal, Feb'85 by FM-Revolver Records. Dist: EMI

FORCE MAJEURE.
Tracks: / Force Majeure / Cloudburstflight / Thru Metamorphic rocks.
Album: released on Virgin, Jun'79 by Virgin Records. Dist: EMI, Virgin Distribution Deleted '85.

Cassette: released on Virgin, Jun'79 by Virgin Records. Dist: EMI, Virgin Distribution Deleted '85.

Compact disc: released on Virgin, Jul'87 by Virgin Records. Dist: EMI, Virgin Distribution

GREEN DESERT.
Compact disc: by Zomba Records. Dist: RCA, PRT, CBS

Album: released on Relativity (USA), Aug'87 Dist: Pinnacle

HYPERBOREA.
Album: released on Virgin, Nov'83 by Virgin Records. Dist: EMI, Virgin Distribution

Cassette: released on Virgin, Nov'83 by Virgin Records. Dist: EMI, Virgin Distribution

Compact disc: released on Virgin, Nov'83 by Virgin Records. Dist: EMI, Virgin Distribution

IN THE BEGINNING.
Boxed set: released on Jive Electro, Mar'86 by Zomba Records. Dist: RCA

LIVE-ENCORE.
Tracks: / Cherokee lane / Moonlight / Coldwater canyon / Desert dream.
Double Album: released on Virgin, Oct'77 by Virgin Records. Dist: EMI, Virgin Distribution

Double cassette: released on Virgin, Oct'77 by Virgin Records. Dist: EMI, Virgin Distribution

Compact disc: by Virgin Records. Dist: EMI, Virgin Distribution

LOGOS-LIVE.
Tracks: / Logos, parts 1 & 2 / Dominion.
Notes: Live at the Dominion, london 82.
Album: released on Virgin, Apr'86 by Virgin Records. Dist: EMI, Virgin Distribution

Cassette: released on Virgin, Apr'86 by Virgin Records. Dist: EMI, Virgin Distribution

Compact disc: released on Virgin, Apr'86 by Virgin Records. Dist: EMI, Virgin Distribution

LOGOS LIVE AT THE DOMINION, LONDON 1982.
Album: released on Virgin, Jan'83

Cassette: released on Virgin, Jan'83

PARC, LE.
Album: released on Jive, Aug'85 by Zomba Records. Dist: RCA, PRT, CBS

Cassette: released on Jive, Aug'85 by Zomba Records. Dist: RCA, PRT, CBS

PHAEDRA.
Tracks: / Phaedra / Msterious semblance at the strand of nightmares / Movements of a visionary / Sequent C.
Notes: Originallt virgin: V 2010 released 1974
Album: released on Virgin, Mar'84 by Virgin Records. Dist: EMI, Virgin Distribution

Cassette: released on Virgin, Mar'84 by Virgin Records. Dist: EMI, Virgin Distribution

Compact disc: released on Virgin, Jul'87 by Virgin Records. Dist: EMI, Virgin Distribution

POLAND.
Album: released on Jive Electro, Nov'84 by Zomba Records. Dist: RCA

Cassette: released on Jive Electro, Nov'84 by Zomba Records. Dist: RCA

Picture disc album: released on Jive Electro, Nov'84 by Zomba Records. Dist: RCA

RICOCHET.
Tracks: / Ricochet part 1 / Ricochet part 2.
Notes: Originally Virgin: V 2044, released 1975
Album: released on Virgin, Mar'84 by Virgin Records. Dist: EMI, Virgin Distribution

Compact disc: released on Virgin, Jul'87 by Virgin Records. Dist: EMI, Virgin Distribution

RUBYCON.
Tracks: / Rubycon part 1 / Rubycon part 2.
Notes: Originally Virgin: V 2025, released 1975
Album: released on Virgin, Mar'84 by Virgin Records. Dist: EMI, Virgin Distribution

Cassette: released on Virgin, Mar'84 by Virgin Records. Dist: EMI, Virgin Distribution

Compact disc: released on Virgin, Jul'87 by Virgin Records. Dist: EMI, Virgin Distribution

SORCERER Film soundtrack.
Album: released on MCA, Feb'82 by MCA Records. Dist: CBS

Cassette: released on MCA, Feb'82 by MCA Records. Dist: CBS

STRATOSFEAR.
Tracks: / Stratosfear / Big sleep in search of Hades, The / 3am At the border of the marsh from Okenfeokee / Invisible Limits.
Notes: Originally released October 1976
Album: released on Virgin, '82 by Virgin Records. Dist: EMI, Virgin Distribution Deleted '84.

Cassette: released on Virgin, '82 by Virgin Records. Dist: EMI, Virgin Distribution Deleted '84.

Cassette: released on Virgin, Jul'87 by Virgin Records. Dist: EMI, Virgin Distribution

STREET HAWK.
Single (7"): released on Jive Electro, Aug'85 by Zomba Records. Dist: RCA

Single (12"): released on Jive Electro, Aug'85 by Zomba Records. Dist: RCA

TANGERINE DREAM COLLECTION, THE.
Tracks: / Genesis / Circulation of events / Fauni-Gena / Alpha centauri / Fly and collision of comas sola / Journey through a burning brain / Zeit first movement - birth of liquid plejades / White clouds.
Double Album: released on Castle Collectors, Jul'87 by Castle Communications Records. Dist: Pinnacle

Double cassette: released on Castle Collectors, Jul'87 by Castle Communications Records. Dist: Pinnacle

Compact disc: released on Castle Collectors, Jul'87 by Castle Communications Records. Dist: Pinnacle

TANGRAM.
Tracks: / Tangram sets nos 1 & 2.
Compact disc: released on Virgin, Oct'85 by Virgin Records. Dist: EMI, Virgin Distribution

THIEF.
Compact disc: released on Virgin, '86 by Virgin Records. Dist: EMI, Virgin Distribution

TYGER.
Tracks: / Tyger / 21st century common mar (part 2).
Single (7"): released on Jive, 13 Jun'87 by Zomba Records. Dist: RCA, PRT, CBS

Single (12"): released on Jive, 13 Jun'87 b Zomba Records. Dist: RCA, PRT, CBS

TYGER (LP).
Compact disc: released on Jive, Jun'87 b Zomba Records. Dist: RCA, PRT, CBS

Album: released on Jive, Jun'87 by Zomb Records. Dist: RCA, PRT, CBS

Cassette: released on Jive, Jun'87 by Zomb Records. Dist: RCA, PRT, CBS

UNDERWATER SUNLIGHT.
Tracks: / Song of the whale / From dawn.../... dusk / Dolphin dance / Ride on the Ray / Scub Scuba / Underwater twilight.
Album: released on Jive Electro, Aug'86 b Zomba Records. Dist: RCA

Cassette: released on Jive Electro, Aug'86 b Zomba Records. Dist: RCA

Compact disc: released on Jive Electr Aug'86 by Zomba Records. Dist: RCA

UNDERWATER SUNLIGHT.
Tracks: / Song of the whale / From dawn.../.. dusk / Dolphin dance / Rideon the ray / Scu scuba / Underwater twilight.
Compact disc: released on Jive, Jan'87 b Zomba Records. Dist: RCA, PRT, CBS

WARSAW IN THE SUN.
Single (7"): released on Jive, Sep'84 by Zomb Records. Dist: RCA, PRT, CBS

Single (12"): released on Jive, Sep'84 b Zomba Records. Dist: RCA, PRT, CBS

Picture disc single: released on Jive, Sep'8 by Zomba Records. Dist: RCA, PRT, CBS

WHITE EAGLE.
Tracks: / Mojave-plan / Midnight in Tula / Co vention of the Twenty Four / White Eagle.
Album: released on Virgin, Mar'82 by Virg Records. Dist: EMI, Virgin Distribution

Cassette: released on Virgin, Mar'82 by Virg Records. Dist: EMI, Virgin Distribution

Compact disc: released on Virgin, Mar'82 Virgin Records. Dist: EMI, Virgin Distribution

ZEIT.
Compact disc: released on Jive, Jan'87 Zomba Records. Dist: RCA, PRT, CBS

Double Album: released on Virgin, Jun'76

Tanglewood

RISE AND SHINE.
Album: released on Creole, Apr'85 by Cre Records. Dist: Rhino, PRT

Tango Echo Delta Delta

CHINA.
Single (7"): released on China Disques, Sep by China Disques. Dist: Pinnacle

LATELY.
Single (7"): released on China Disques, Jar by China Disques. Dist: Pinnacle

Tango Fran Argentina
TANGO FRAN ARGENTINA A dazzling musical adventure (Various Artists).
Album: released on Phontastic, Mar'87 Dist: Wellard, Chris

Tanh Chi
HOW LONG IS A DAY?.
Tracks: / How long is a day / Live for me / Make time".
Single (12"): released on Arista, Jul'87 by Arista Records. Dist: RCA

Single (7"): released on Arista, Jul'87 by Arista Records. Dist: RCA

Single (7"): released on Arista, Aug'87 by Arista Records. Dist: RCA

Single (12"): released on Arista, Aug'87 by Arista Records. Dist: RCA

RIBBON.
Tracks: / Silent night.
Single (7"): released on Arista, Jan'87 by Arista Records. Dist: RCA

Single (12"): released on Arista, Jan'87 by Arista Records. Dist: RCA

Tanhol
RUDEBOYS.
Tracks: / Rudeboys / Gunshot salute.
Single (12"): released on UK Bubblers, May'86 by Greensleeves Records. Dist: RCA, Jetstar

Tank
ARMOURED PLATED.
Tracks: / Dont walk away / Power of the Hunter / Run Like Hell / Filth hounds of Hades / (He fell in love with a) Storm Trooper / Red Skull Rock / Snake, the / Who needs Love songs / Stepping on a Land mine / Turn your head around / Crazy horses / Some came running / Hammer on / Shellshock / T.W.D.A.M.O. / Biting & Scratching / Used Leather (Hanging Loose) / Blood Guts and Beer / Filth Bitch Boogie / T.A.N.K.
Notes: Double LP. Bar Code: 5 013428 140093   Side 1-Tracks 1,2,4,5,6,7,8,9,10 Licensed from This Records Co.Ltd. Track 3 Licensed from EDT
                                    t   d
Side 2-tracks 1,2,3,4,5,6,7,9,10 Licensed from EDT   Ltd
This Records Co.Ltd. Track 8 Licensed from
EDT   Ltd
Front cover illustration:Melvyn. design and Art Direction: Shoot that Tiger! This compilation (C) 1985 Castle Communications Ltd. Unit 7, 771 Merton Rd, London SW18 5JS
Album: released on Raw Power, Apr'86 Dist: Pinnacle

Cassette: released on Raw Power, Apr'86 Dist: Pinnacle

ECHOES OF A DISTANT BATTLE.
Single (7"): released on Music For Nations, Jul'83 by Music For Nations Records. Dist: Pinnacle

Single (12"): released on Music For Nations, Jul'83 by Music For Nations Records. Dist: Pinnacle

HONOUR AND BLOOD.
Album: released on Music For Nations, Dec'84 by Music For Nations Records. Dist: Pinnacle

THIS MEANS WAR.
Album: released on Music For Nations, May'83 by Music For Nations Records. Dist: Pinnacle

Picture disc album: released on Music For Nations, Jun'83 by Music For Nations Records. Dist: Pinnacle

Cassette: released on Music For Nations, May'83 by Music For Nations Records. Dist: Pinnacle

Tannahill Weavers
ARE YE SLEEPING, MAGGIE.
Album: released on Plant Life, Nov'81 Dist: Roots

LAND OF LIGHT.
Album: released on Green Linnet(USA), Jul'87 by Green Linnet (USA). Dist: Projection

Cassette: released on WEA Ireland, Mar'87 by WEA Records. Dist: Celtic Distributions, Projection, I & B

OLD WOMAN'S DANCE, THE.
Album: released on Plant Life, Nov'81 Dist: Roots

TANNAHILL WEAVERS IV.
Album: released on Plant Life, Nov'81 Dist: Roots

TANNAHILL WEAVERS, THE.
Album: released on Plant Life, Nov'81 Dist: Roots

Tanned Leather
NOODLE SOAP.

Album: released on Response, Apr'81 by Priority Records. Dist: BMG

Tannen, Holly
FROSTY MORNING (Tannen, Holly & Pete Cooper).
Album: released on Plant Life, Nov'81 Dist: Roots

Tanner, Gid
GID TANNER & SKILLET LICKERS.
Album: released on Rounder (USA), Jun'77

Tanner, Phil
GREAT MAN OF GOWER, THE.
Cassette: released on Folktracks, Nov'79 by Folktracks Cassettes. Dist: Folktracks

Tannol
WORRIES AND TROUBLES.
Single (12"): released on UK Bubblers, Sep'85 by Greensleeves Records. Dist: RCA, Jetstar

Tansey, Seamus
SEAMUS TANSEY.
Album: released on Leader, '81 Dist: Jazz Music, Projection

Tansey's Fancy
TANSEY'S FANCY.
Album: released on Plant Life, Jul'84 Dist: Roots

Tansin, Jo
STEAL MY HEART.
Tracks: / Steal my heart / I wonder if I'm making it.
Single (7"): released on Zuma, Jul'86 by Zuma Records. Dist: CBS, PRT

Tantallon
TARTAN HUSTLE.
Single (7"): released on DJM, May'76 by DJM Records. Dist: CBS, Polygram Deleted '77.

Tan Tan
MUSICAL NOSTALGIA TODAY.
Album: released on Rainbow, Jun'82 Dist: I & B, CBS

Tantara
I.D.O..
Tracks: / I.D.O. / Rumours.
Single (7"): released on President, Mar'86 by President Records. Dist: Taylors, Spartan

Single (12"): released on President, Mar'86 by President Records. Dist: Taylors, Spartan

Tantra
HILLS OF KATMANDU.
Single (7"): released on Automatic, Jul'81 Dist: WEA, Independant

Single (12"): released on Automatic, Jun'81 Dist: WEA, Independant

Tanzania Yetu
OUR TANZANIA.
Album: released on Triple Earth, Mar'85 by Sterns Records. Dist: Sterns/Triple Earth Distribution

Tanzschau
SOMEONE ON MY STAIRS.
Single (7"): released on Tao Dance, Oct'83 by Tao Dance Records. Dist: Cartel Distribution

Tap Dance Kid
TAP DANCE KID Broadway dance recording.
Album: released on TER, Mar'85 Dist: Pinnacle

Cassette: released on TER, Mar'85 Dist: Pinnacle

Tara
FOLK BALLADS FROM IRELAND.
Tracks: / Home by the Lee / This land we love / Right says she / Any Tipperary Town / German Clockwinder / Slievegallion Braes / John O'Dreams / Shane O'Neil / Juice of the Barley / Lovely Leitrim / Mary Mac / Rose of Allendale / Take me back to castlebar / Carrickfergus.
Album: released on Homespun(Ireland), Feb'86 by Outlet Records. Dist: Outlet

Cassette: released on Homespun(Ireland), Feb'86 by Outlet Records. Dist: Outlet

Tara, Folk Group
BELFAST CITY BY THE LAGAN SIDE.
Album: released on Homespun(Ireland), Mar'84 by Outlet Records. Dist: Outlet

---

Cassette: released on Homespun(Ireland), Mar'84 by Outlet Records. Dist: Outlet

Tar Bables
FRIED MILK.
Album: released on SST, Oct'87 by SST Records. Dist: Pinnacle. Estim retail price in Sep'87 was £6.49.

Tarbuck, Jimmy
AGAIN.
Single (7"): released on Safari, Oct'85 by Safari Records. Dist: Pinnacle

ANY DREAM WILL DO.
Tracks: / Any dream will do.
Single (7"): released on Safari, Sep'86 by Safari Records. Dist: Pinnacle

LET'S HAVE A PARTY.
Single (7"): released on Towerbell, Dec'82 by Towerbell Records. Dist: EMI

Targe
TARGE.
Album: released on Agra, May'81

Tarheel Slim
NUMBER 9 TRAIN.
Single (7"): released on Charly, Jul'82 by Charly Records. Dist: Charly, Cadillac

TOO MUCH COMPETITION.
Album: released on Sundown (Holland), May'85

WILDCAT TAMER.
Single (7"): released on Charly, '82 by Charly Records. Dist: Charly, Cadillac

Tarka The Otter
TARKA THE OTTER / THE RELUCTANT DRAGON.
Double cassette: released on Argo (Spoken-word), May'83 by Decca Records. Dist: Polygram

Tarleton's Jig
FOR KING AND PARLIAMENT I.
Tracks: / Prince Rupert's march (4.21) / French report (2.14) / Vive le Roy (2.31) / Battle of Worcester (3.47) / Gather your rosebuds (1.45) / Halfe Hannikin (2.48) / We be soldiers three (1.37) / Cuckold's all in a row / Sir Thomas Fairfax:his march (2.10) / Padua CXVII / Scots march (1.48) / Drive the cold winter away (4.47) / Lord of Carnavans jegg (2.19) / When cannons are roaring (2.32) / Clean contrary way (2.42) / King (3.00) / Millfield (2.36) / Rump song (2.04).
Album: released on Nuns Meadows Productions, Nov'86 by James Bisgood & Sharon Lindo. Dist: Nuns Meadows Productions Distribution

Tarmigan
TIME IS GETTING ON.
Single (7"): released on New World, Nov'81 by President Records. Dist: Swift, Spartan

Tarragon, Steve
TERRACOTTA WARRIOR.
Single (7"): released on Scratch, Apr'82

Tartan Album
TARTAN ALBUM Various artists (Various Artists).
Album: released on REL, '79 Dist: Roots

Tartan Brass
OUR SCOTLAND.
Album: released on Limsor, Dec'86

Tartan Lads
AN EVENING WITH THE TARTAN LADS.
Album: released on REL, '77 Dist: Roots

Cassette: released on REL, '77 Dist: Roots

BY THE LOCHSIDE.
Album: released on Lismor, '75 by Lismor Records. Dist: Lismor, Roots, Celtic Music

Cassette: released on Lismor, '75 by Lismor Records. Dist: Lismor, Roots, Celtic Music

CHRISTMAS DREAM, THE.
Single (7"): released on R.E.L. '77 by REL Records. Dist: Gordon Duncan Distribution, Celtic Music, Record Merchandisers Distribution, Projection, Graeme Tosh music

LEGENDS OF SCOTLAND.
Cassette: released on Lochshore, Mar'87 by Klub Records. Dist: PRT

MEMORIES OF SCOTLAND.
Album: released on Klub, Nov'84

Cassette: released on Klub, Nov'84

OLD FLAMES.
Single (7"): released on Lochshore, Oct'84 by Klub Records. Dist: PRT

SCOTLAND EVER MORE.
Single (7"): released on Lochshore, May'82 by Klub Records. Dist: PRT

Album: released on Lochshore, Oct'82 by Klub Records. Dist: PRT

Cassette: released on Lochshore, Oct'82 by Klub Records. Dist: PRT

SCOTLAND'S OWN....
Album: released on Lochshore, May'81 by Klub Records. Dist: PRT

Cassette: released on Lochshore, May'81 by Klub Records. Dist: PRT

SCOTLAND YET.
Album: released on Lismor, Nov'76 by Lismor Records. Dist: Lismor, Roots, Celtic Music

Cassette: released on Lismor, Nov'76 by Lismor Records. Dist: Lismor, Roots, Celtic Music

SCOTTISH COUNTRY ROADS.
Album: released on R.E.L., '78 by REL Records. Dist: Gordon Duncan Distribution, Celtic Music, Record Merchandisers Distribution, Projection, Graeme Tosh music

Cassette: released on R.E.L, '78 by REL Records. Dist: Gordon Duncan Distribution, Celtic Music, Record Merchandisers Distribution, Projection, Graeme Tosh music

SEASONS.
Album: released on Lochshore, Apr'82 by Klub Records. Dist: PRT

Cassette: released on Lochshore, Apr'82 by Klub Records. Dist: PRT

WELCOME TO OUR MUSIC.
Album: released on R.E.L., '79 by REL Records. Dist: Gordon Duncan Distribution, Celtic Music, Record Merchandisers Distribution, Projection, Graeme Tosh music

Cassette: released on R.E.L., '79 by REL Records. Dist: Gordon Duncan Distribution, Celtic Music, Record Merchandisers Distribution, Projection, Graeme Tosh music

Tarzen
TARZEN.
Album: released on Valentino, Oct'85

Tasavallan Presidentti
LAMBERTLAND.
Album: released on Sonet, 74 by Sonet Records. Dist: PRT

MILKY WAY MOSES.
Album: released on Sonet, 74 by Sonet Records. Dist: PRT

Tasby, Finis
BLUES MECHANIC.
Album: released on Ace, Jan'85 by Ace Records. Dist: Pinnacle, Swift, Hotshot, Cadillac

Tashan
CHASING A DREAM.
Tracks: / Read the dream / Strung out on you / If words can express / Thank you father / Love is...... / I don't ever / So much in love / Read my mind / Ooh we baby / Chasin' a dream / Got the right attitude.
Album: released on Def Jam (USA), Oct'86 by CBS Records. Dist: CBS

Album: released on Def Jam (USA), Dec'86 by CBS Records. Dist: CBS

Cassette: released on Def Jam (USA), Dec'86 by CBS Records. Dist: CBS

JUST CHASIN' A DREAM.
Single (7"): released on Def Jam (USA), Jul'87 by CBS Records. Dist: CBS

Single (12"): released on Def Jam (USA), Jul'87 by CBS Records. Dist: CBS

Single (12"): released on Def Jam (USA), Jul'87 by CBS Records. Dist: CBS

THANK YOU FATHER.
Tracks: / Thank you father / Got the right attitude / Love is".
Notes: / = Extra track on 12" only
Single (7"): released on Def Jam (USA), Apr'87 by CBS Records. Dist: CBS

Single (12"): released on Def Jam (USA), Apr'87 by CBS Records. Dist: CBS

Task Force
FORBIDDEN FRUIT.
Album: released on Thunderbolt, May'83 by Magnum Music Group Ltd. Dist: Magnum Music

Group Ltd, PRT Distribution, Spartan Distribution

Tassano,Simon

WATERGLASS (Tassano,Simon & Eddy Sayer).
Cassette: released on Touch, Sep'84 by Touch Records. Dist: Rough Trade, Cartel

Taste

ON THE BOARDS.
Album: released on Polydor (Germany), Aug'85 Dist: IMS-Polygram

TASTE.
Album: released on Polydor, '79 by Polydor Records. Dist: Polygram, Polydor

Album: released on Polydor (Germany), Aug'85 Dist: IMS-Polygram

Taste Of Honey

BOOGIE OOGIE OOGIE.
Tracks: / Boogie oogie oogie / Heaven must be missing an angel.
Notes: Also contains:"Heaven must be missing an angel" by Tavares
Single (7"): released on Old Gold, Apr'87 by Old Gold Records. Dist: Lightning, Jazz Music, Spartan, Counterpoint

Single (7"): released on Capitol, Apr'85 by Capitol Records. Dist: EMI

Single (12"): released on Capitol, Apr'85 by Capitol Records. Dist: EMI

Taste Of Summer

TASTE OF SUMMER (Various Artists).
Album: released on Afro-Euro, Aug'86 by Polydor Records. Dist: Polygram

Cassette: released on Afro-Euro, Aug'86 by Polydor Records. Dist: Polygram

Taster, A

TASTER, A Various artists (Various Artists).
Album: released on Relentless, Nov'82 by Relentless Records. Dist: Cartel

Tasty Tim

SUGAR SUGAR.
Single (7"): released on Carrere, Mar'84 by Carrere Records. Dist: PRT, Spartan

Single (12"): released on Carrere, Mar'84 by Carrere Records. Dist: PRT, Spartan

TOO HOT TO HANDLE.
Single (7"): released on Carrere, Jan'85 by Carrere Records. Dist: PRT Spartan

Single (12"): released on Carrere, Jan'85 by Carrere Records. Dist: PRT Spartan

Tatar People (Music Of)

MUSIC OF TATAR PEOPLE.
Album: released on Tangent, Apr'81 by Tangent Records. Dist: Lugtons Distributors, Taylors, JSU Distribution, Projection Distribution

Tate, Buddy

BUDDY TATE AND THE MUSE ALL STARS.
Album: released on Muse (Import), Apr'81

BUDDY TATE WITH... Humphrey Lyttleton & his band (Tate, Buddy with Humphrey Lyttleton & his Band).
Notes: Full title: Buddy Tate with Humphrey Lyttleton & his band
Album: released on Calligraph, Aug'86 by Calligraph Records. Dist: PRT

GREAT BUDDY TATE, (THE).
Album: released on Concord Jazz, Nov'81 by Concord Jazz Records (USA). Dist: IMS, Polygram

INSTRUMENTAL FOR DANCING.......
Album: released on Krazy Kat (USA), Dec'84

JUST JAZZ (Tate, Buddy/Al Grey).
Album: released on Uptown (USA), Nov'86 by Uptown Records. Dist: Jazz Music

KANSAS CITY JOYS, (THE).
Album: released on Sonet, May'77 by Sonet Records. Dist: PRT

KANSAS CITY WOMAN.
Album: released on Black Lion, May'79 by Black Lion Records. Dist: Jazz Music, Chris Wellard, Taylor, H.R., Counterpoint, Cadillac

KANSAS CITY WOMEN (Tate, Buddy & Humphrey Lyttleton).
Album: released on Black Lion, Jul'87 by Black Lion Records. Dist: Jazz Music, Chris Wellard, Taylor, H.R., Counterpoint, Cadillac

LONG TALL TENOR (Tate, Buddy & Humphrey Lyttleton).
Album: released on Calligraph, Sep'86 by Calligraph Records. Dist: PRT

QUARTET.
Album: released on Sackville (Import), Apr'83 Dist: Cadillac

SWINGING LIKE....TATE (Tate,Buddy & His Orchestra).
Tracks: / Bottle it / Walk that walk / Miss Sadie Brown / Moon eyes / Rockin' Steve / Rompin' with Buck.
Notes: Licensed from Decca Records Ltd. A Felsted recording
Album: released on Affinity, Nov'86 by Charly Records. Dist: Charly, Cadillac

TOUR DE FORCE (see Cohn,Al/Scott Hamilton/Buddy Tate).

Tate, Grady

AIN'T BUT A FEW OF US (see Jackson, Milt) (Tate, Grady/ Milt Jackson/ Ray Brown/ Oscar Peterson).

Tate, Howard

GET IT WHILE YOU CAN.
Album: released on Verve, Mar'83

LOOK AT GRANNY RUN RUN.
Single (7"): released on Verve, Apr'83

Tate, Roy

LIFELINE.
Single 10": released on Why-Fi, Jan'82 by Why-Fi Records. Dist: RCA, Indies

Tate, Tommy

TOMMY TATE.
Album: released on Move, Nov'85 by Charly Records. Dist: Charly Distribution, Fast Forward Distribution, Cartel Distribution

Album: released on Timeless, Jul'86

Tate, Troy

LOVE IS.
Single (7"): released on Rough Trade, Jul'83 by Rough Trade Records. Dist: Rough Trade Distribution, Cartel Distribution

Single (12"): released on Rough Trade, Jul'83 by Rough Trade Records. Dist: Rough Trade Distribution, Cartel Distribution

THOMAS.
Single (7"): released on Why-Fi, Jun'81 by Why-Fi Records. Dist: RCA, Indies

Tati, Jacques

ORIGINAL SOUNDTRACKS.
Album: released on Phonogram (France), Aug'83

Cassette: released on Phonogram (France), Aug'83

Tatum, Art

1945.
Album: released on Joker Import, Apr'81

ART TATUM COLLECTION,(THE).
Album: released on Deja Vu, Jul'86 by Deja Vu Records. Dist: Counterpoint Distribution, Record Services Distribution (Ireland)

Cassette: released on Deja Vu, Jul'86 by Deja Vu Records. Dist: Counterpoint Distribution, Record Services Distribution (Ireland)

ART TATUM, VOLS 1 & 2.
Double Album: released on Vogue, Jun'75 Dist: Discovery, Jazz Music, PRT, Swift

BEST OF ART TATUM, (THE).
Album: released on Pablo Jazz (USA), Oct'84 by United Artists. Dist: Swift

ERROLL GARNER & ART TATUM, VOL 1 (see Garner, Erroll) (Tatum, Art & Erroll Garner).

FIRST RECORDINGS/IN CONCERT.
Tracks: / Tiger Rag / Tea for two / St.Louis blues / Tiger rag / Sophistacated lady / How High the moon / Humouresque / Tatum ole boogie / Someone to watch over me / Yesterdays / I know that you Know / Willow weep for me / Man I love, The / Kerry dance, the.
Album: released on CBS, Jul'86 by CBS Records. Dist: CBS

Cassette: released on CBS, Jul'86 by CBS Records. Dist: CBS

GENIUS, (THE).
Album: released on Black Lion, Jan'85 by Black Lion Records. Dist: Jazz Music, Chris Wellard, Taylor, H.R., Counterpoint, Cadillac

GET HAPPY.
Album: released on Black Lion, Jul'77 by Black Lion Records. Dist: Jazz Music, Chris Wellard, Taylor, H.R., Counterpoint, Cadillac

GROUP MASTERPIECES (Tatum, Art Trio).
Tracks: / Just one of those things / More than you know / Some other Spring / Blue Lou / Love For Sale / Is'nt it romantic / I,ll never be the same / I'll gyuess I'll have to change my plans / Trio Blues.
Notes: Personnel: Art Tatum.,Red Callender.,Jo Jones.
Compact disc: released on Pablo (USA), Jul'86 by Pablo Records (USA). Dist: Wellard, Chris, IMS-Polygram, BMG

KEYSTONE SESSIONS.
Album: released on Varese International, Mar'79

LIVE AT THE CRESCENDO.
Compact disc: released on Vogue, Dec'86 Dist: Discovery, Jazz Music, PRT, Swift

MASTERS OF JAZZ VOL.8.
Album: released on Storyville, May'86 by Storyville Records. Dist: Jazz Music Distribution, Swift Distribution, Chris Wellard Distribution, Counterpoint Distribution

ON THE AIR.
Album: released on Aircheck, Feb'78

PIANO GENIUS.
Album: released on Charly, Dec'86 by Charly Records. Dist: Charly, Cadillac

Cassette: released on Charly, Dec'86 by Charly Records. Dist: Charly, Cadillac

PIANO GENIUS.
Tracks: / Young and Healthy / Morning noon and night / When day is done / Stardust / China Town my China Town / Man I love, The / Tabu / Somebody loves Me / Why was I born / If I could be with you one hour tonight / Tea for two / Mean to me / It's only a paper Moon / Just a gigolo / Three little Words / I Gotta right to sing the blues.
Album: released on Affinity, Sep'86 by Charly Records. Dist: Charly, Cadillac

Cassette: released on Affinity, Sep'86 by Charly Records. Dist: Charly, Cadillac

PIANO MASTERY.
Album: released on Shoestring, Apr'81

PIANO SOLO.
Album: released on EMI (France), Mar'84 by EMI Records. Dist: Conifer

Cassette: released on EMI (France), Mar'84 by EMI Records. Dist: Conifer

PURE GENIUS.
Album: released on Affinity, May'84 by Charly Records. Dist: Charly, Cadillac

SONG OF THE VAGABONDS.
Album: released on Black Lion, Jul'87 by Black Lion Records. Dist: Jazz Music, Chris Wellard, Taylor, H.R., Counterpoint, Cadillac

Album: released on Black Lion, Jul'76 by Black Lion Records. Dist: Jazz Music, Chris Wellard, Taylor, H.R., Counterpoint, Cadillac

STRANGE AS IT SEEMS.
Album: released on Collectors Items, Jul'86 Dist: Jazz Music, Swift, Chris Wellard

Album: released on Collectors Items, Feb'85 Dist: Jazz Music, Swift, Chris Wellard

TATUM GROUP MASTERPIECES, VOL 4.
Album: released on Pablo, Mar'78 by Pablo Records. Dist: Wellard, Chris, IMS-Polygram, BMG

TATUM GROUP MASTERPIECES, VOL 2.
Album: released on Pablo, Aug'77 by Pablo Records. Dist: Wellard, Chris, IMS-Polygram, BMG

Cassette: released on Pablo, Aug'77 by Pablo Records. Dist: Wellard, Chris, IMS-Polygram, BMG

TATUM GROUP MASTERPIECES, VOL 7.
Album: released on Pablo, Mar'78 by Pablo Records. Dist: Wellard, Chris, IMS-Polygram, BMG

Cassette: released on Pablo, Mar'78 by Pablo Records. Dist: Wellard, Chris, IMS-Polygram, BMG

TATUM GROUP MASTERPIECES, VOL 8.
Album: released on Pablo, Aug'77 by Pablo Records. Dist: Wellard, Chris, IMS-Polygram, BMG

Cassette: released on Pablo, Aug'77 by Pablo Records. Dist: Wellard, Chris, IMS-Polygram, BMG

TATUM GROUP MASTERPIECES, VOL 3.
Album: released on Pablo, Mar'78 by Pablo Records. Dist: Wellard, Chris, IMS-Polygram, BMG

Cassette: released on Pablo, Mar'78 by Pablo Records. Dist: Wellard, Chris, IMS-Polygram, BMG

TATUM GROUP MASTERPIECES, VOL 9.
Album: released on Pablo, Mar'79 by Pablo Records. Dist: Wellard, Chris, IMS-Polygram, BMG

Cassette: released on Pablo, Mar'79 by Pablo Records. Dist: Wellard, Chris, IMS-Polygram, BMG

TATUM GROUP MASTERPIECES, VOL 5.
Cassette: released on Pablo, Aug'77 by Pablo Records. Dist: Wellard, Chris, IMS-Polygram, BMG

TATUM GROUP MASTERPIECES, VOL 6.
Album: released on Pablo, Aug'77 by Pablo Records. Dist: Wellard, Chris, IMS-Polygram, BMG

Cassette: released on Pablo, Aug'77 by Pablo Records. Dist: Wellard, Chris, IMS-Polygram, BMG

TATUM GROUP MASTERPIECES, THE (Sept. 1956) (Tatum, Art/ Ben Webster).
Compact disc: released on Pablo (USA), May'86 by Pablo Records (USA). Dist: Wellard Chris, IMS-Polygram, BMG

TATUM GROUP MASTERPIECES (SEPTEMBER 1946) (THE) (Tatum, Art/ Ben Webster).

TATUM GROUP MASTERPIECES, VOL 1.
Album: released on Pablo, Jul'75 by Pabl Records. Dist: Wellard, Chris, IMS-Polygram BMG

Cassette: released on Pablo, Jul'75 by Pabl Records. Dist: Wellard, Chris, IMS-Polygran BMG

TATUM SOLO MASTERPIECES, VOL 1
Album: released on Pablo, Apr'78 by Pab Records. Dist: Wellard, Chris, IMS-Polygrar BMG

Cassette: released on Pablo, Apr'78 by Pab Records. Dist: Wellard, Chris, IMS-Polygrar BMG

TATUM SOLO MASTERPIECES, VOL
Album: released on Pablo, '78 by Pablo Re ords. Dist: Wellard, Chris, IMS-Polygram, BM

Cassette: released on Pablo, '78 by Pablo Re ords. Dist: Wellard, Chris, IMS-Polygram, BM

TATUM SOLO MASTERPIECES, VOL
Album: released on Pablo, '78 by Pablo Re ords. Dist: Wellard, Chris, IMS-Polygram, BM

Cassette: released on Pablo, '78 by Pablo Re ords. Dist: Wellard, Chris, IMS-Polygram, BM

TATUM SOLO MASTERPIECES, V 10.
Album: released on Pablo, May'81 by Pa Records. Dist: Wellard, Chris, IMS-Polygra BMG

Cassette: released on Pablo, May'81 by Pa Records. Dist: Wellard, Chris, IMS-Polygra BMG

TATUM SOLO MASTERPIECES, V 11.
Album: released on Pablo, Sep'81 by Pa Records. Dist: Wellard, Chris, IMS-Polygra BMG

Cassette: released on Pablo, Sep'81 by P Records. Dist: Wellard, Chris, IMS-Polygr BMG

TATUM SOLO MASTERPIECES, V 12.
Cassette: released on Pablo, '82 by Pablo R ords. Dist: Wellard, Chris, IMS-Polygram, B

TATUM SOLO MASTERPIECES, VO
Album: released on Pablo, Aug'78 by P Records. Dist: Wellard, Chris, IMS-Polyg BMG

Cassette: released on Pablo, Aug'78 by P Records. Dist: Wellard, Chris, IMS-Polyg BMG

TATUM SOLO MASTERPIECES, VO
Album: released on Pablo, May'78 by P Records. Dist: Wellard, Chris, IMS-Polyg BMG

Cassette: released on Pablo, May'78 by P Records. Dist: Wellard, Chris, IMS-Polyg BMG

TATUM SOLO MASTERPIECES, VO
Album: released on Pablo, Apr'78 by P Records. Dist: Wellard, Chris, IMS-Polyg BMG

Cassette: released on Pablo, Apr'78 by P Records. Dist: Wellard, Chris, IMS-Polyg BMG

TATUM SOLO MASTERPIECES, VOL 3.
Album: released on Pablo, May'78 by Pablo Records. Dist: Wellard, Chris, IMS-Polygram, BMG

Cassette: released on Pablo, May'78 by Pablo Records. Dist: Wellard, Chris, IMS-Polygram, BMG

TATUM SOLO MASTERPIECES, VOL 5.
Album: released on Pablo, May'78 by Pablo Records. Dist: Wellard, Chris, IMS-Polygram, BMG

Cassette: released on Pablo, May'78 by Pablo Records. Dist: Wellard, Chris, IMS-Polygram, BMG

TATUM SOLO MASTERPIECES, VOL 6.
Album: released on Pablo, Aug'78 by Pablo Records. Dist: Wellard, Chris, IMS-Polygram, BMG

Cassette: released on Pablo, Aug'78 by Pablo Records. Dist: Wellard, Chris, IMS-Polygram, BMG

V-DISCS, (THE).
Album: released on Black Lion, '79 by Black Lion Records. Dist: Jazz Music, Chris Wellard, Taylor, H.R., Counterpoint, Cadillac

Tauber, Richard

GOLDEN AGE OF RICHARD TAUBER.
Album: released on Golden Age, Jul'83 by Music For Pleasure Records. Dist: EMI

GOLDEN MELODIES.
Album: released on Pearl, Mar'83 by Pavillion (USA). Dist: Taylors, Swift

GREAT VOICES OF THE CENTURY.
Album: released on Bulldog, Mar'85 by Bulldog Records. Dist: President Distribution, Spartan, Swift, Taylor, H.R.

SONGS AND DUETS.
Album: released on EMI Retrospect, Aug'84 by EMI Records. Dist: EMI

Cassette: released on EMI Retrospect, Aug'84 by EMI Records. Dist: EMI

THIS WAS RICHARD TAUBER.
Album: released on Starline, May'71 by EMI Records. Dist: EMI

Cassette: released on Starline, May'71 by EMI Records. Dist: EMI

VOICE OF ROMANCE, (THE).
Boxed set: released on World Records, Dec'81 Dist: Polygram

Taupin, Bernie

BE.
Tracks: / Friend of the flag / Corrugated iron / Lebon Jane / Hold back the night / She sends flowers / Billy Fury / I still can't believe that you're one / Conquistador / New Lone Ranger, The / Desperation train.
Album: released on RCA, Jun'87 by RCA Records. Dist: RCA, Roots, Swift, Wellard, Chris, I & B, Solomon & Peres Distribution

Cassette: released on RCA, Jun'87 by RCA Records. Dist: RCA, Roots, Swift, Wellard, Chris, I & B, Solomon & Peres Distribution

Taurus

HE IS TIGHT.
Single (7"): released on RCA, Jul'82 by RCA Records. Dist: RCA, Roots, Swift, Wellard, Chris, I & B, Solomon & Peres Distribution

Single (12"): released on RCA, Jul'82 by RCA Records. Dist: RCA, Roots, Swift, Wellard, Chris, I & B, Solomon & Peres Distribution

Taurus Boyz

ROKIN' FOR A LOVER.
Single (7"): Lookin' for a lover / Lookin' for a lover
Single (7"): released on Cool Tempo, Feb'87 by Chrysalis Records. Dist: CBS

Single (12"): released on Chrysalis, Feb'87 by Chrysalis Records. Dist: CBS

Tavagna

Centru

Tavares

BEST OF TAVARES, (THE).
Album: released on Fame (Capitol), May'82 by Music For Pleasure Records. Dist: EMI

Cassette: released on Fame (Capitol), May'82 by Music For Pleasure Records. Dist: EMI

DEEPER IN LOVE.
Single (7"): released on RCA, Sep'83 by RCA Records. Dist: RCA, Roots, Swift, Wellard, Chris, I & B, Solomon & Peres Distribution

Single (12"): released on RCA, Sep'83 by RCA Records. Dist: RCA, Roots, Swift, Wellard, Chris, I & B, Solomon & Peres Distribution

HEAVEN MUST BE MISSING AN ANGEL See Taste of Honey - Boogie oogie oogie.
Notes: Also contains:"Boogie oogie oogie" by Taste of Honey

HEAVEN MUST BE MISSING AN ANGEL.
Tracks: / Heaven must be missing an angel / Don't take away the music / Whodunnit".
Single (7"): released on Capitol, Feb'86 by Capitol Records. Dist: EMI

Single (12"): released on Capitol, Feb'86 by Capitol Records. Dist: EMI

Single (7"): released on Capitol, Jun'76 by Capitol Records. Dist: EMI

IT ONLY TAKES A MINUTE.
Tracks: / It only takes a minute / More than a woman / One minute(Inst)".
Single (7"): released on Capitol, Apr'86 by Capitol Records. Dist: EMI

Single (12"): released on Capitol, Apr'86 by Capitol Records. Dist: EMI

LOVE UPRISING.
Album: released on Capitol, Mar'81 by Capitol Records. Dist: EMI

NEVER HAD A LOVE LIKE THIS BEFORE.
Single (7"): released on Capitol, Mar'79 by Capitol Records. Dist: EMI

NEW DIRECTIONS.
Album: released on RCA, Nov'82 by RCA Records. Dist: RCA, Roots, Swift, Wellard, Chris, I & B, Solomon & Peres Distribution

Cassette: released on RCA, Nov'82 by RCA Records. Dist: RCA, Roots, Swift, Wellard, Chris, I & B, Solomon & Peres Distribution

TURN OUT THE NIGHTLIGHT.
Single (7"): released on Capitol, Oct'81 by Capitol Records. Dist: EMI

VERY BEST OF TAVARES, THE.
Tracks: / Heaven must be missing an angel,(Remixed 12" version) / She's gone / Mighty Power of love,the / Check it out / One step away / I wanna see you soon / More than a woman(Remixed Version) / Whodunnit(Remixed 12" Version) / Bein' with you / It only takes a minute / Love I never had, the / My ship / Don't take away the Music (Remixed 12" version).
Album: released on Capitol, Mar'86 by Capitol Records. Dist: EMI

Cassette: released on Capitol, Mar'86 by Capitol Records. Dist: EMI

Tavares, Victor

SHOW ME.
Single (7"): released on Malaco, May'83

Single (12"): released on Malaco, May'83

Taverners

BLOWING SANDS.
Album: released on Leader, Sep'81 by Jazz Music, Projection

LAZY AFTERNOON.
Album: released on Folk Heritage, Jul'82 by Folk Heritage Records. Dist: Roots, Wynd-Up Distribution, Jazz Music, Folk Heritage

SAME OLD FRIENDS.
Album: released on Folk Heritage, Jul'82 by Folk Heritage Records. Dist: Roots, Wynd-Up Distribution, Jazz Music, Folk Heritage

Tav Falco
See under Falco, Tav

SHAKE RAG.
Single (12"): released on New Rose, Aug'86 Dist: Rough Trade, Cartel

Tavitian, Harry

TRANSYLVANIAN SUITE (Tavitian, Harry/Corneliu Stroe).
Album: released on Leo, Jan'87 Dist: Recommended

Tawatha

THIGH RIDE.
Tracks: / Thigh ride / Welcome to my dreams.
Single (7"): released on Epic, Jun'87 by CBS Records. Dist: CBS

THIGH RIDE (THIGH HIGH MIX).
Tracks: / Thigh ride (dub mix) / Thigh ride (thigh high mix) / Welcome to my dream.

Single (12"): released on Epic, Jun'87 by CBS Records. Dist: CBS

WELCOME TO MY DREAM.
Tracks: / Thigh ride / Did I dream you / Love shine / Love goes higher / Welcome to my dream (tears of joy) / Are you serious / More than before / Waiting's over, The / No more tears.
Album: released on Epic, Jul'87 by CBS Records. Dist: CBS

Cassette: released on Epic, Jul'87 by CBS Records. Dist: CBS

Tawney, Cyril

DOWN AMONGST THE BARLEY STRAW.
Album: released on Leader, Sep'81 Dist: Jazz Music, Projection

Taxi

VOICES.
Single (7"): released on Trial, Jul'82 by Trial Records. Dist: Pinnacle

Taxi connection...

TAXI CONNECTION LIVE IN LONDON (Various Artists).
Tracks: / Red hot / When you're hot you're hot / Trouble you a trouble me / Call the police / One in a million / Mr. Land-Lord / Greetings / Reggae calypso.
Notes: Featuring ROBBIE SHAKES-PEARS/LY DUNBAR/DEAN FRAZER/FRANK-LYN WAUL/HANDEL TUCKER/JUNIOR CHIN/RON ROBINSON AND WINSTON BOWEN
Album: released on Island, Jan'86 by Island Records. Dist: Polygram

Cassette: released on Island, Jan'86 by Island Records. Dist: Polygram

Taxi Gang

DOWN ON THE CORNER.
Single (7"): released on Island, Sep'85 by Island Records. Dist: Polygram Deleted May'87.

Single (12"): released on Island, Sep'85 by Island Records. Dist: Polygram Deleted May'87.

ELECTRO REGGAE-VOL.1.
Tracks: / Triplet Interpolating don't go / Peter Gunn / Pastor Dub / Pumping Iron / Twilight Zone / Taxi Connection / Sting,The / Waterbed.
Album: released on Island, Jul'86 by Island Records. Dist: Polygram

Cassette: released on Island, Jul'86 by Island Records. Dist: Polygram

Taxi Girl

AUSSI BELLE QU'UNE BALLE.
Tracks: / Aussi belle qu'une balle.
Single (7"): released on Play It Again Sam, Jan'86 Dist: Red Rhino, Cartel

Single (12"): released on Play It Again Sam, Jan'86 Dist: Red Rhino, Cartel

Taxman

WELL ARMED AND DANGEROUS.
Tracks: / Well armed and dangerous / Well armed and dangerous (version).
Single (7"): released on Sir George, Jul'87 by Sir George Records. Dist: Jetstar, Pinnacle

Taxman & Nagata

IT'S GONE.
Single (7"): released on Senator, Dec'84 by Senator records. Dist: Jetstar

Taylor, Al

YOU DIDN'T CALL ME.
Tracks: / You didn't call me / Living it up.
Single (7"): released on Buzzin, Sep'86 by DMS, RCA, Pinnacle

Taylor, Alan

WIN OR LOOSE.
Album: released on T Records, Jan'85 Dist: Celtic Music

Taylor, Allan

CIRCLE ROUND AGAIN.
Album: released on Black Crow, May'83 by Mawson & Wareham Records. Dist: Projection

ROLL ON THE DAY.
Album: released on Rubber. Jun'82

TRAVELLER, (THE).
Album: released on Rubber. Jun'82

Taylor, Alpheus

RAID.
Tracks: / Raid.
Single (12"): released on Black Anet, Aug'86 by Factory Records. Dist: Factory, Rough Trade, Cartel, Pinnacle

---

STRUGGLIN'.
Album: released on Black Anet, May'86 by Factory Records. Dist: Factory, Rough Trade, Cartel, Pinnacle

Taylor, Andy

DON'T LET ME DIE YOUNG.
Single (7"): released on MCA, Aug'87 by MCA Records. Dist: Polygram, MCA

Single (12"): released on MCA, Aug'87 by MCA Records. Dist: Polygram, MCA

LIFE GOES ON.
Tracks: / Life goes on / Broken window.
Single (7"): released on MCA, Apr'87 by MCA Records. Dist: Polygram, MCA

Single (12"): released on MCA, Apr'87 by MCA Records. Dist: Polygram, MCA

TAKE IT EASY.
Tracks: / Take it easy / Angel eyes.
Single (7"): released on Atlantic, Jul'86 by WEA Records. Dist: WEA

Single (12"): released on Atlantic, Jul'86 by WEA Records. Dist: WEA

THUNDER.
Tracks: / I might lie / Don't let me die young / Life goes on / Thunder / Night train / Tremblin' / Bringin' me down / Broken window / French guitar.
Compact disc: released on MCA, May'87 by MCA Records. Dist: Polygram, MCA

Album: released on MCA, May'87 by MCA Records. Dist: Polygram, MCA

Cassette: released on MCA, May'87 by MCA Records. Dist: Polygram, MCA

Taylor, Art

A.T'S DELIGHT.
Album: released on Blue Note, Oct'81 by EMI Records. Dist: EMI

TAYLORS WAILERS.
Album: released on Original Jazz Classics (USA), Jun'86 Dist: Fantasy (USA) Distribution, Chris Wellard Distribution, IMS-Polygram Distribution

Album: released on Prestige (USA). Aug'84

Taylor, Billy

I WISH I KNEW (how it would feel to be free).
Tracks: / I wish I knew(how it would feel to be free)(themefromfilm86) / Right here, right now / Freedom".
Notes: The Billy Taylor Trio with orchestra conducted by Oliver Nelson.
Single (7"): released on Capitol, Sep'86 by Capitol Records. Dist: EMI

Single (12"): released on Capitol, Sep'86 by Capitol Records. Dist: EMI

WHERE'VE YOU BEEN (Taylor, Billy Quartet).
Album: released on Concord Jazz, Aug'81 by Concord Jazz Records (USA). Dist: IMS, Polygram

Taylor, Bob

DON'T BE UNFAIR.
Single (7"): released on Rollin, Jun'80

Taylor, Bram

BIDE A WHILE.
Album: released on Fellside, May'85 by Fellside Records. Dist: Roots, Jazz Music, Celtic Music, Projection

DREAMS & SONGS TO SING.
Album: released on Fellside, Feb'87 by Fellside Records. Dist: Roots, Jazz Music, Celtic Music, Projection

Taylor, Cecil

3PHASIS.
Notes: Jimmy Lyons - alto saxophone
Raphe   Malik   -   trumpet
Ramsay   Ameen   -   violin
Sirone   -   bass
Ronald Shannon Jackson - drums
(P) & (C) 1979 Recording Anthology of American Music Inc.   Publisher - Mayflower   Music   Corp.
Producer - Sam Parkins.
Album: released on New World (USA), Sep'86 by New World Records (USA). Dist: Conifer

AIR ABOVE MOUNTAINS.
Album: released on Enja (Germany), Jan'82 by Enja Records (W.Germany). Dist: Cadillac Music

CECIL TAYLOR QUARTET IN EUROPE (Taylor, Cecil Quartet).
Album: released on Jazz Connoisseur, Apr'79 Dist: Jazz Horizons, Jazz Music, Swift, Wellard, Chris

CECIL TAYLOR UNIT.
Tracks: / Idut / Serdab / Holiday en masque.
Notes: Jimmy Lyons - alto saxophone
Raphe Malik - trumpet
Ramsay Ameen - violin
Sirone - bass
Ronald Shannon Jackson - drums
Album: released on New World (USA), Jul'86 by New World Records (USA). Dist: Conifer

CONQUISTADOR.
Tracks: / Conquistador / With (exit).
Compact disc: released on Manhattan-Blue Note, Jun'87 by EMI America Records (USA). Dist: EMI

Album: released on Blue Note (USA Import), Sep'84

DARK TO THEMSELVES (Taylor, Cecil Unit).
Album: released on Enja (Germany), Jan'82 by Enja Records (W.Germany). Dist: Cadillac Music

EMBRACED.
Double Album: released on Pablo, May'78 by Pablo Records. Dist: Wellard, Chris, IMS-Polygram, BMG

Cassette: released on Pablo, May'78 by Pablo Records. Dist: Wellard, Chris, IMS-Polygram, BMG

INDENT.
Album: released on Freedom, Nov'77 by Logo Records. Dist: RCA, Discovery, Wellard, Chris

INNOVATIONS.
Album: released on Freedom, Jul'74 by Logo Records. Dist: RCA, Discovery, Wellard, Chris

JUMPIN' PUMPKINS.
Album: released on Candid, Jul'87 Dist: Counterpoint, Cadillac

LIVE IN THE BLACK FOREST.
Album: released on MPS Jazz, Jun'81

LOOKING AHEAD.
Tracks: / Luyah, the glorious step / African violets / Of what / Wallering / Toll / Excursion on a wobbly rail.
Album: released on Boplicity, Sep'86 by Boplicity Records. Dist: Ace Records, Pinnacle

NEFERTITI-BEAUTIFUL ONE.
Double Album: released on Freedom, Oct'76 by Logo Records. Dist: RCA, Discovery, Wellard, Chris

NEW YORK CITY RYTHM & BLUES (Taylor, Cecil/Buell Neidlinger).
Album: released on Candid/Black Lion, Jun'86 Dist: Jazz Music, Swift

PRAXIS.
Double Album: released on Praxis (Greece), May'84 Dist: Mole Jazz

SILENT TONGUES.
Album: released on Freedom, Jun'79 by Logo Records. Dist: RCA, Discovery, Wellard, Chris

STUDENT STUDIES.
Double Album: released on Affinity, Mar'83 by Charly Records. Dist: Charly, Cadillac

WHAT'S NEW.
Album: released on Black Lion, Sep'85 by Black Lion Records. Dist: Jazz Music, Chris Wellard, Taylor, H.R., Counterpoint, Cadillac

WINGED SERPENT (Taylor,Cecil Segments 11).
Compact disc: released on Soul Note (Italy), '86 Dist: Harmonia Mundi Distributors

WORLD OF CECIL TAYLOR, (THE).
Album: released on Candid, Dec'85 Dist: Counterpoint, Cadillac

WORLD OF, THE.
Album: released on Candid, Jul'87 Dist: Counterpoint, Cadillac

Taylor, Charlie

FILLIN IN THE BLUES (1928/30).
Album: released on Herwin, May'76 Dist: Jazz Music

Taylor, Christopher

QUIET NIGHTS.
Cassette: released on Grosvenor, May'86 by Grosvenor Records. Dist: Taylors

STEPPING OUT.
Album: released on Grosvenor, Dec'86 by Grosvenor Records. Dist: Taylors

THEME FOR 1983.
Single (7"): released on Grosvenor, Mar'83 by Grosvenor Records. Dist: Taylors

Taylor, C.P

AND A NIGHTINGALE SANG.

Page 992

Cassette: released on Soundings, Mar'85 Dist: Soundings

Taylor, Dave

CADILLAC CAR.
Single (7"): released on Charly, Mar'80 by Charly Records. Dist: Charly, Cadillac

MIDNIGHT ROCK.
Album: released on Nervous, Jul'84 by Nervous Records. Dist: Nervous, Rough Trade

STEPPIN' OUTTA LINE.
Album: released on Rockhouse, Oct'86 by Rockhouse Records. Dist: Swift Distribution, Charly Distribution

Taylor, Derek

SALUTE TO JOLSON (MEDLEY).
Single (7"): released on OK, May'83 by Klub Records. Dist: PRT Distribution
Cat. no: **OK 004**

Single (12"): released on OK, May'83 by Klub Records. Dist: PRT Distribution

Taylor, Doris

HAVE I TOLD YOU LATELY.
Single (12"): released on Time, May'85 Dist: Jetstar Distribution

Taylor, Eddie

BIG TOWN PLAYBOY.
Album: released on Charly, Mar'81 by Charly Records. Dist: Charly, Cadillac

I FEEL SO BAD.
Album: released on Advent (US), Apr'79 Dist: Swift

READY FOR EDDIE (Taylor, Eddie Playboy).
Album: released on Big Bear, May'82 by Big Bear Records. Dist: Big Bear, Swift

READY FOR EDDIE TAYLOR.
Album: released on Big Bear, Oct'86 by Big Bear Records. Dist: Big Bear, Swift

Taylor, Felice

I FEEL LOVE COMIN' ON.
Single (7"): released on President, May'80 by President Records. Dist: Taylors, Spartan

Taylor, Greg Fingers

HARPOON MAN.
Album: released on Red Lightnin', Jun'85 by Red Lightnin' Records. Dist: Roots, Swift, Jazz Music, JSU, Pinnacle, Cartel, Wynd-Up Distribution

Taylor, Hound Dog

BEWARE OF THE DOG.
Album: released on Sonet, May'76 by Sonet Records. Dist: PRT

HOUND DOG TAYLOR & THE HOUSE ROCKERS.
Album: released on Sonet, May'75 by Sonet Records. Dist: PRT

HOUSE ROCKIN' BOOGIE.
Album: released on JSP, Dec'82 by JSP Records. Dist: Swift, Projection

KINGS OF SLIDE GUITAR.
Album: released on JSP, Jun'84 by JSP Records. Dist: Swift, Projection

Taylor, James

BEST OF JAMES TAYLOR, THE.
Compact disc: released on CBS, Mar'87 by CBS Records. Dist: CBS

Album: released on CBS, Mar'87 by CBS Records. Dist: CBS

Cassette: released on CBS, Mar'87 by CBS Records. Dist: CBS

BLOW UP (Taylor, James Quartet).
Single (7"): released on Re-Elect The President, Apr'87 Dist: Backs, Cartel

B.S.U.R.
Single (7"): released on CBS, Aug'79 by CBS Records. Dist: CBS Deleted May'80.

CLASSIC SONGS.
Tracks: / Fire and rain / Mexico / You've got a friend / How sweet it is (to be loved by you) / Carolina on my mind / Something in the way she moves / Shower the people / Sweet baby James / That's why I'm there / Everyday / Up on the roof / Your smiling face / Her town too / Handyman / Don't let me be lonely tonight / Only a dream in Rio.
Album: released on WEA-CBS, Apr'87

Album: released on WEA-CBS, Apr'87

Compact disc: released on WEA-CBS, Apr'87

DAD LOVES HIS WORK.
Compact disc: released on CBS, May'87 by CBS Records. Dist: CBS

Album: released on CBS, Apr'81 by CBS Records. Dist: CBS

Cassette: released on CBS, Apr'81 by CBS Records. Dist: CBS

EVERYDAY.
Tracks: / Everyday / Limousine driver.
Single (7"): released on CBS, Mar'86 by CBS Records. Dist: CBS

FLAG.
Tracks: / Company man / Johnnie come back / Day tripper / I will not lie for you / Brother trucker / Is that the way you look? / B.S.U.R. / Rainy day man / Millworker / Up on the roof / Chanson Francaise / Sleep come free me.
Album: released on CBS, Feb'86 by CBS Records. Dist: CBS

Cassette: released on CBS, Feb'86 by CBS Records. Dist: CBS

Album: released on CBS, Aug'79 by CBS Records. Dist: CBS

Cassette: released on CBS, Aug'79 by CBS Records. Dist: CBS Deleted May'81.

GREATEST HITS:JAMES TAYLOR.
Compact disc: released on Warner Bros., Jan'87 by Warner Bros Records. Dist: WEA

Album: released on Warner Brothers, May'82 by WEA Records. Dist: WEA

Cassette: released on Warner Brothers, May'82 by WEA Records. Dist: WEA

J.T..
Tracks: / Your smiling face / There we are / Honey don't leave L.A. / Another grey morning / Bartender's blues / Secret o'life / Handy man / I was only telling a lie / Looking for love on broadway / Terra nova / If I keep my heart out of sight / Traffic jam.
Compact disc: released on CBS, Jun'87 by CBS Records. Dist: CBS

Album: released on CBS, Feb'85 by CBS Records. Dist: CBS

Cassette: released on CBS, Feb'85 by CBS Records. Dist: CBS

MISSION IMPOSSIBLE (Taylor, James Quartet).
Album: released on Re-Elect The President, Jun'87 Dist: Backs, Cartel

SWEET BABY JAMES.
Tracks: / Sweet baby James / Lo and behold / Sunny skies / Steam Roller / Country Road / Oh Susanna / Fire and rain biossom / Anywhere like heaven / Oh baby don't you lose your lip on me / Suite for 20G / Love has brought me around / You've got a friend / Places in my past / Riding on a railroad / Soldiers / Mud slide slim / Hey Mister, that's me upon the jukebox / You can close your eyes / Machine gun / Kelly / Long ago and far away / Let me ride / Highway song / Isn't it nice to be home again.
Compact disc: released on Warner Brothers, Apr'84 by Warner Bros Records. Dist: WEA

THAT'S WHY I'M HERE.
Tracks: / That's why I'm here / Song for you far away / Only a dream in Rio / Turn away / Going around one more time / Everyday / Limousine driver / Only one / Mona / Man who shot Liberty Valence, The / That's why I'm here (reprise).
Album: released on CBS, Jan'86 by CBS Records. Dist: CBS

Cassette: released on CBS, Jan'86 by CBS Records. Dist: CBS

Compact disc: released on CBS, '86 by CBS Records. Dist: CBS

TWO ORIGINALS OF (SWEET BABY JAMES & MUD SLIDE SLIM).
Double Album: released on Warner Brothers, Oct'75 by WEA Records. Dist: WEA

UP ON THE ROOF.
Tracks: / Fire and rain.
Single (7"): released on CBS, Jan'87 by CBS Records. Dist: CBS

YOU'VE GOT A FRIEND.
Tracks: / You've got a friend / Fire & rain.
Single (7"): released on Old Gold, Mar'86 by Old Gold Records. Dist: Lightning, Jazz Music, Spartan, Counterpoint

YOU'VE GOT A FRIENDLY.
Single (7"): released on Warner Brothers, Jul'81 by WEA Records. Dist: WEA

Taylor, Jeremy

DONE IN A FLASH.
Album: released on Sweet Folk & Country, May'78 Dist: Chris Wellard Distribution

JOBSWORTH.
Single (7"): released on BBC, Sep'82 by BBC Records & Tapes. Dist: EMI, PRT, Pye

LIVE AT THE YOUNG VIC.
Album: released on Jeremy Taylor Records, May'82

Taylor, John

AZIMUTH (Taylor, John/N. Winstone/K. Wheeler).
Album: released on ECM, Aug'77 by ECM Records. Dist: IMS, Polygram, Virgin through EMI

I DO WHAT I DO.
Tracks: / I do what I do / Jazz / I do what I do (Film mix).
Single (7"): released on Parlophone, Mar'86 by EMI Records. Dist: EMI

Single (12"): released on Parlophone, Mar'86 by EMI Records. Dist: EMI

IT TAKES TWO TO TEMPO (Taylor, John & Howard Beaumont).

Taylor, Johnnie

EVER READY.
Album: released on CBS, Jun'78 by CBS Records. Dist: CBS

IT'S SEPTEMBER.
Single (7"): released on Stax, Jan'85 by Ace Records. Dist: Pinnacle, Chris Wellard, IMS-Polygram

TESTIFY (I WONNA).
Single (7"): released on Stax, Oct'87 by Ace Records. Dist: Pinnacle, Chris Wellard, IMS-Polygram

THIS IS YOUR NIGHT.
Album: released on Malaco, Dec'84

WALL TO WALL.
Album: released on Malaco, Feb'86 by Malaco Records. Dist: Charly

WHO'S MAKING LOVE.
Tracks: / Who's making love / I'm trying.
Single (7"): released on Stax, 13 Jun'87 by Ace Records. Dist: Pinnacle, Chris Wellard, IM Polygram

Single (7"): released on Stax, Mar'82 by Ace Records. Dist: Pinnacle, Chris Wellard, IM Polygram

Single (7"): released on Old Gold, Sep'85 by Old Gold Records. Dist: Lightning, Jazz Music, Spartan, Counterpoint

Album: released on Stax, 7 Sep'87 by Ace Records. Dist: Pinnacle, Chris Wellard, IMS-Polygram

Taylor, Johnny

20 GREATEST HITS.
Compact disc: released on London, Apr'87 London Records. Dist: Polygram

LOVERBOY.
Album: released on Malaco, Feb'87 by Malaco Records. Dist: Charly

Taylor, Joseph

UNTO BRIGG FAIR.
Album: released on Leader, Sep'81 Dist: Jazz Music, Projection

Taylor, Joyce

SING ALONG HAMMOND STYLE.
Album: released on Joy, May'74 by President Records. Dist: Jazz Music, Swift, President Distribution

Taylor,Kevin

PIANO & PIANO ACCORDIAN.
Album: released on Shanachie (Ireland)

Taylor, Koko

EARTHSHAKER,THE.
Album: released on Sonet, Aug'78 by Sonet Records. Dist: PRT

FROM THE HEART OF A WOMAN.
Album: released on Sonet, Sep'81 by Sonet Records. Dist: PRT

I GOT WHAT IT TAKES.
Album: released on Sonet, Aug'76 by Sonet Records. Dist: PRT

LIVE FROM CHICAGO An audience with the queen.
Tracks: / Let the good times roll / I'm a woman / Going back to IUKA / Devil's gonna have a day, the / Come to Mama / I'd rather go blind / Let me love you / Wang dang doodle.
Album: released on Sonet, May'87 by Sonet Records. Dist: PRT

QUEEN OF THE BLUES.
Album: released on Sonet, Aug'85 by Sonet Records. Dist: PRT

Taylor, Linda

EVERY WAKING HOUR.
Tracks: / Every waking hour (inst)..
Single (7"): released on Nightmare, Jan'87 by Nightmare Records. Dist: PRT

Single (12"): released on Nightmare, Jan'87 by Nightmare Records. Dist: PRT

TAYLOR MADE.
Album: released on Groove PR, May'82 by Beggars Banquet Records. Dist: WEA, PRT

YOU AND ME JUST STARTED.
Single (7"): released on Groove PR, Apr'82 by Beggars Banquet Records. Dist: WEA, PRT

Single (12"): released on Groove PR, Apr'82 by Beggars Banquet Records. Dist: WEA, PRT

YOU'RE IN THE POCKET.
Single (7"): released on Groove PR, Sep'81 by Beggars Banquet Records. Dist: WEA, PRT

Single (12"): released on Groove PR, Sep'81 by Beggars Banquet Records. Dist: WEA, PRT

Taylor, Little Johnny

AS LONG AS I DON'T SEE YOU.
Single (7"): released on Charly, Jul'80 by Charly Records. Dist: Charly, Cadillac

I SHOULDA BEEN A PREACHER.
Album: released on Red Lightnin', Sep'82 by Red Lightnin' Records. Dist: Roots, Swift, Jazz Music, JSU, Pinnacle, Cartel, Wynd-Up Distribution

PART-TIME LOVE.
Album: released on Charly, Mar'81 by Charly Records. Dist: Charly, Cadillac

Taylor, Madeline

GYPSIES, TRAMPS AND THIEVES.
Single (7"): released on Rubicon, 30 May'87

Taylor, Marla

BABY YOU GOT ME.
Single (12"): released on KNK, Mar'83 by KNK Records. Dist: Jetstar

JUST LOVERS.
Single 10": released on Sight, Oct'82

Taylor, Martin

SKYE BOAT.
Album: released on Concord, Jun'82 by Import Records. Dist: IMS, Polygram

TRIBUTE TO ART TATUM.
Album: released on Hep, Nov'86 by H.R. Taylor Records. Dist: Jazz Music, Cadillac Music, JSU, Taylors, Wellard, Chris, Zodiac, Swift, Fast Forward

Taylor, Mike, Lee

BIG 10-4.
Single (7"): released on Buffalo (UK), Nov'81

PIG OF THE YEAR.
Single (7"): released on Orbit, Jul'83 by Orbit Records. Dist: PRT Distribution

Taylor, Neil

CHRISTMAS CRACKER, A.
Single (7"): released on Cherub, Dec'81 by Cherub Records. Dist: Pinnacle

Taylor, Paddy

BOY IN THE GAP, THE.
Album: released on Claddagh, '74 by Claddagh Records. Dist: I & B, Record Services Distribution (Ireland), Roots, Topic, Impetus, Projection, CM

SLOW AIRS & DANCES.
Cassette: released on Folktracks, Nov'79 by Folktracks Cassettes. Dist: Folktracks

Taylor, R. Dean

GOTTA SEE JANE.
Single (7"): released on Motown, Oct'81 by Motown Records. Dist: BMG Distribution

INDIANA WANTS ME.
Single (7"): released on Motown, Oct'81 by Motown Records. Dist: BMG Distribution

THERE'S A GHOST IN MY HOUSE.
Single (7"): released on Motown, Feb'83 by Motown Records. Dist: BMG Distribution

Taylor, Rod

GIRL OF MY COMPLEXION.
Single (12"): released on DATC, Mar'83 by DATC Records. Dist: Rough Trade

MIDNIGHT COWBOY.
Single (12"): released on Sweetcorn, Nov'84

---

by Sweetcorn Records. Dist: Jetstar

MISS CARTER WORE PINK.
Single (7"): released on Rampage, Nov'80

MOVING OUT OVER.
Single (12"): released on Unity, Apr'80 by Unity Records. Dist: Jetstar

SUN MOON AND STARS (Taylor, Rod & Blackstar).
Single (7"): released on DATC, Oct'82 by DATC Records. Dist: Rough Trade

WHERE IS YOUR LOVE MANKIND.
Single (7"): released on Greensleeves, Nov'80 by Greensleeves Records. Dist: BMG, Jetstar, Spartan

Taylor, Roger

STRANGE FRONTIER.
Album: released on EMI, Jun'84 by EMI Records. Dist: EMI

Cassette: released on EMI, Jun'84 by EMI Records. Dist: EMI

Taylor, Rusty

GOOD OLD BAD OLD DAYS.
Album: released on Stomp Off, Dec'82 by Stomp Off Records. Dist: Jazz Music Distribution

TAYLOR, RUSTY & STEVE LANE'S STOMPERS (Taylor, Rusty & Steve Lane's Stompers).
Album: released on Stomp Off, Jun'86 by Stomp Off Records. Dist: Jazz Music Distribution

Taylor, Steve

LIMELIGHT.
Tracks: / Disco, this / I want to be a clone / You don't owe me nothing / On the fritz / We don't need no colour code / Whatever happened to sin / Meltdown / Not gonna fall away.
Notes: Recorded live at Greenbelt, and therefore contains all the excitement and atmosphere generally missing from a studio album.
Album: released on Sparrow, Jun'86 by Word Records. Dist: Spartan

Cassette: released on Sparrow, Jun'86 by Word Records. Dist: Spartan

MELTDOWN.
Compact disc: released on Word, Aug'85 by Word Records. Dist: Word Distribution, CBS

ON THE FRITZ.
Album: released on Sparrow, Jun'85 by Word Records. Dist: Spartan

Cassette: released on Sparrow, Jun'85 by Word Records. Dist: Spartan

Taylor, Ted

IT'S TOO LATE.
Single (7"): released on Charly, Jul'80 by Charly Records. Dist: Charly, Cadillac

KEEP WALKING ON.
Album: released on Charly, Mar'81 by Charly Records. Dist: Charly, Cadillac

Taylor, Thomas

LOVE SOMEBODY.
Tracks: / Love somebody / Love somebody (inst).
Single (7"): released on Raise The Roof, Jun'87 by Orbit Records. Dist: PRT

Single (12"): released on Raise The Roof, Jun'87 by Orbit Records. Dist: PRT

Taylor, Tot

ARISE SIR TOT.
Tracks: / Arise Sir Tot / Mr Strings / People will talk / Ballad of Jackie & Ivy.
Single (12"): released on London Popular Arts, Oct'86

AUSTRALIA.
Tracks: / Australia / Inside story, The.
Single (7"): released on LPA, Apr'87

BOX OFFICE POISON.
Album: released on London Popular Arts, Jun'86

DON'T SPY ON ME.
Single (7"): released on Compact Organisation, Nov'81 Dist: PRT

INSIDE STORY, THE.
Album: released on Easy Listeners, Aug'84 by Easy Listeners Records.

IT'S GOOD FOR YOU.
Single (7"): released on LPA, Jul'87 by LPA Records. Dist: Revolver, Cartel

I WANT TO PLAY THE DRUMS.
Single (7"): released on Compact Organisation, Aug'82 Dist: PRT

MY BLUE PERIOD.
Album: released on London Popular Arts, Jul'87

POPTOWN.
Single (7"): released on Easy Listeners, Sep'84 by Easy Listeners Records.

Taylor, T.T.

ACCORDIAN GOLDS.
Album: released on ARC (Accordion Records), '84 Dist: Accordion Record Club

REMEMBER.
Single (7"): released on Solid Groove, Oct'81 Dist: Jetstar, Pinnacle

Taylor, Tut

FRIAR TUT.
Album: released on Rounder, '77

Taylor, Tyrone

COME TO ME.
Single (12"): released on Londisc, Mar'84 by Londisc Records.

COTTAGE IN NEGRIL.
Single (7"): by MCA Records. Dist: CBS

Single (12"): by MCA Records. Dist: CBS

Album: released on Diamond C, Dec'84 by Diamond C Records. Dist: Jetstar

ENERGY.
Single (7"): released on MCA, Jun'84 by MCA Records. Dist: CBS

Single (12"): released on MCA, Jun'84 by MCA Records. Dist: CBS

GOT TO COME BACK.
Tracks: / Got to come back / Roslyn.
Single (12"): released on Hawkeye, Dec'85 by Hawkeye Records. Dist: Hawkeye, Lightning (WEA) Distribution, Jetstar, PRT

HEAVY WAISTLINE.
Single (12"): released on Real Wax, Jun'84

HOLD YOUR HAND IN PUBLIC.
Tracks: / Hold your hand in public / Bird of a feather.
Single (12"): released on Diamond C, Jul'86 by Diamond C Records. Dist: Jetstar

JAMMING IN THE HILLS.
Album: released on World Enterprise, Dec'86 Dist: Jetstar

LOVE YOU BACK TO LOVING ME.
Single (12"): released on Londisc, Apr'85 by Londisc Records.

MEMBERS ONLY.
Tracks: / Members only / Let me rock you tonight.
Single (12"): released on Technique, Aug'86 by Technique. Dist: CBS

SEND A LETTER.
Tracks: / Send a letter / Send a letter (version) / Take your time / Too fast (Ringcraft Posse).
Single (12"): released on Starlight, Mar'86 by Starlight Records. Dist: Jetstar Distribution

Single (12"): released on World Enterprise, Nov'86 Dist: Jetstar

TAKE YOUR TIME.
Tracks: / Girl your mine.
Single (12"): released on Blue Trac, Jan'87 by Blue Mountain Records. Dist: Jetstar

Taylor, Vince

BRAND NEW CADILLAC (Taylor, Vince & Playboy).
Single (7"): released on EMI, May'79 by EMI Records. Dist: EMI

CHANGING FOR YOU.
Single (12"): released on Clouds, Dec'83 by Clouds Records. Dist: Jetstar

HOUR OF MAGIC, THE.
Single (12"): released on Time, Oct'85 Dist: Jetstar Distribution

I'LL BE YOUR HERO.
Single (7"): released on T & P, May'83 by T & P Records. Dist: Swift

Tay Pan

BREAK OUT.
Single (12"): released on Bullet, Jan'84 Dist: Bullet Distribution

T-Birds

MY LIFE.
Single (7"): released on Epic, Jul'81 by CBS Records. Dist: CBS

T.Bones/Gary Farr

DEM BONES.
Album: released on EVA, Jun'84

T. Booker & The MG's

SOUL LIMBO.
Single (7"): released on Stax, Aug'87 by Ace Records. Dist: Pinnacle, Chris Wellard, IMS-Polygram

Single (12"): released on Stax, Aug'87 by Ace Records. Dist: Pinnacle, Chris Wellard, IMS-Polygram

TIME IS TIGHT.
Tracks: / Time is tight / Johnny, I love you.
Single (12"): released on Stax, 13 Jun'87 by Ace Records. Dist: Pinnacle, Chris Wellard, IMS-Polygram

Single (7"): released on Old Gold, Sep'85 by Old Gold Records. Dist: Lightning, Jazz Music, Spartan, Counterpoint

T-Boys

ONE WAY STREET.
Single (7"): released on Almost Animal, Oct'81 by Almost Animal Records. Dist: Almost Animal Records

Tchaikousky

TCHAIKOVSKY'S GREATEST HITS various artists (Various Artists).
Cassette: released on CBS, Jul'83 by CBS Records. Dist: CBS

Tchaikovsky, Bram

BREAKING DOWN THE WALLS OF HEARTACHE.
Single (7"): released on Arista, May'81 by Arista Records. Dist: RCA

FUNLAND.
Album: released on Arista, May'81 by Arista Records. Dist: RCA

SHALL WE DANCE.
Single (7"): released on Arista, Mar'81 by Arista Records. Dist: RCA

T-Charm

RHYTHM IN RHAPSODY.
Single (7"): released on Liberty, Feb'80 by Liberty-United. Dist: EMI

Tchical, John

CONTINENT (Tchical, John/Hartmut Gerkin).
Album: released on Praxis (Greece), May'84 Dist: Mole Jazz

LIVE IN ATHENS.
Album: released on Praxis (Greece), May'84 Dist: Mole Jazz

Tchico

FULL STREAM AHEAD (Tchico & Les officers of African Music).
Tracks: / Nostagie d'Afrique / Veronica-Linda / Au revoir adely / Detty Ioveinda / Sane-mamdou.
Album: released on Globestyle, Jan'86 by Ace Records. Dist: Projection

TC Matic

O LA LA LA.
Single (7"): released on Statik, Apr'82 Dist: Rough Trade Distribution, Stage One Distribution

T-Connection

LOVE ODYSSEY.
Single (7"): released on Capitol, Mar'83 by Capitol Records. Dist: EMI

Single (12"): released on Capitol, Mar'83 by Capitol Records. Dist: EMI

T-Coy

CARINO.
Single (12"): released on De Construction, 23 May'87 Dist: PRT

T.D.A. (Test Department)

FACES OF FREEDOM, 1, 2. AND 3.
Tracks: / Faces of freedom. 1,2.and3.
Single (12"): released on Some Bizzarre, Mar'86 by Virgin Records. Dist: EMI, CBS, Polygram

Teachers

TEACHERS Original motion picture soundtrack (Various Artists).
Tracks: / Teacher teacher / One foot back in the door / Edge of a dream (Theme from "Teacher") / Interstate love affair / Fooling around / Cheap sunglasses / Understanding / I can't stop the fire / In the jungle (concrete jungle) / I'm the teacher.

Notes: Teachers' stars Nick Nolte in a contemporary comic drama about daily life in an urban American high school. The film is produced by Aaron Russo, producer of Eddie Murphy's "Trading Places". Russo is also responsible for compiling the soundtrack which features ten artists, nine of whom perform original material written specially for the film. Featured artists include Freddie Mercury of Queen, Ian Hunter and ZZ Top. Bob Seger and the Silver Bullet Band.
Album: released on Capitol, Feb'85 by Capitol Records. Dist: EMI

Cassette: released on Capitol, Feb'85 by Capitol Records. Dist: EMI

Compact disc: released on Capitol, Feb'85 by Capitol Records. Dist: EMI

Teach Us..

TEACH US YOUR WAY various artists (Various Artists).
Album: released on Word, May'82 by Word Records. Dist: Word Distribution, CBS

Cassette: released on Word, May'82 by Word Records. Dist: Word Distribution, CBS

Teach Yourself To..

TEACH YOURSELF TO:CHA-CHA various artists (Various Artists).
Cassette: released on Kiddy Kassettes, Aug'77

TEACH YOURSELF TO: QUICKSTEP various artists (Various Artists).
Cassette: released on Kiddy Kassettes, Aug'77

TEACH YOURSELF TO: WALTZ various artists (Various Artists).
Cassette: released on Kiddy Kassettes, Aug'77

Teagarden, Jack

1943.
Album: released on Queen-Disc, Apr'81 Dist: Celtic Music, JSU, Jazz Horizons, Jazz Music

BIG JAZZ 1940 also see Stewart Rex (Teagarden, Jack & Stewart, Rex).

BIG JAZZ 1940 (& Rex stewart).
Album: released on Everbody's (Import), Jul'82

BIG T AND MIGHTY MAX (Teagarden, Jack/Max Kaminsky).
Album: released on Commodore Classics, May'87 by Teldec Records (Germany). Dist: Conifer, IMS, Polygram

BIRTH OF A BAND.
Album: released on Giants of Jazz, May'86 by Hasmick Promotions Ltd.. Dist: Counterpoint, Jazz Music, Taylors, Swift, Mainline, Wellard, Chris

Cassette: released on Giants of Jazz, May'86 by Hasmick Promotions Ltd.. Dist: Counterpoint, Jazz Music, Taylors, Swift, Mainline, Wellard, Chris

HOLLYWOOD BOWL 1963 (Teagarden, Jack & Bobby Hackett).
Album: released on Shoestring, Apr'81

JACK TEAGARDEN.
Album: released on Queen-Disc, Apr'81 Dist: Celtic Music, JSU, Jazz Horizons, Jazz Music

Album: released on Queen-Disc, Apr'81 Dist: Celtic Music, JSU, Jazz Horizons, Jazz Music

JACK TEAGARDEN.. In San Francisco.
Album: released on Rarities, Apr'81

JACK TEAGARDEN & Frankie Trumbauber TNT (& Frankie Trumbauber TNT).
Album: released on Aircheck, '79

JACK TEAGARDEN AND Max Kaminsky (& Max Kaminsky).
Album: released on Commodore Class, Jul'82 by Teldec Records (Germany). Dist: Conifer, IMS, Polygram

JACK TEAGARDEN & EARL HINES (Teagarden, Jack & Earl Hines).
Album: released on Magic, Jun'86 Dist: Jazz Music, Submarine, Swift, Chris Wellard, Conifer

JACK TEAGARDEN & THE CONDON GANG 1944 (Teagarden, Jack/Condon Gang).
Album: released on Pumpkin, '79 Dist: Jazz Music, Wellard, Chris, Cadillac

JAZZ ORIGINAL.
Tracks: / King Porter stomp / Eccentric / Davenport blues / Original dixieland one-step / Bad actin' woman / Mis'ry and the blues / High society / Music to love by / Meet me where they play the blues / Riverboat shuffle / Milenberg joys / Blue funk.
Notes: An original Bethlehem recording.
Compact disc: released on Charly, '87 by Charly Records. Dist: Charly, Cadillac

Album: released on Affinity, Jun'85 by Charly Records. Dist: Charly, Cadillac

LESTER MEETS MILES (Teagarden, Jack all stars & M.J.Q).
Notes: For full information see: MJQ & Jack Teagarden all Stars.

MASTERS OF JAZZ VOL.10.
Album: released on Storyville, May'86 by Storyville Records. Dist: Jazz Music Distribution, Swift Distribution, Chris Wellard Distribution, Counterpoint Distribution

MEMORIAL.
Album: released on Musidisc (France), '74 Dist: Discovery Distribution, Swift Distribution

ON THE AIR 1936,1938.
Album: released on Aircheck (USA), May'79 Dist: Swift, Jazz Music

SHINE (& Pee Wee Russell).
Album: released on Joker (Import), Apr'81

STANDARD LIBRARY OF JAZZ VOL 2.
Album: released on Storyville, Jul'81 by Storyville Records. Dist: Jazz Music Distribution, Swift Distribution, Chris Wellard Distribution, Counterpoint Distribution

SWINGING GATE,THE.
Album: released on Giants of Jazz, Oct'84 by Hasmick Promotions Ltd.. Dist: Counterpoint, Jazz Music, Taylors, Swift, Mainline, Wellard, Chris

TROMBONE T FROM TEXAS.
Tracks: / I gotta right to sing the blues / Love me or leave me / Jeepers creepers / Basin street blues / Blues to the lonely / Beal Street blues / Someday sweetheart / After you've gone / Nobody knows the trouble I've seen / Body & soul / River boat shuffle / Love me / Prelude to the blues / Farewell blues / Aunt Hagar's blues / Somebody loves me.
Album: released on Affinity, Jan'86 by Charly Records. Dist: Charly, Cadillac

Cassette: released on Affinity, Jan'86 by Charly Records. Dist: Charly, Cadillac

UNFORGETTABLE JACK TEAGARDEN, THE.
Album: released on Halcyon (USA), Jul'86 by Halcyon Records (USA). Dist: Jazz Music, Conifer, Taylors

VARSITY SIDES.
Tracks: / If I could be with you one hour tonight / My melancholy baby / Can't we talk it over / Can't we talk it over / Blues, The / Love for sale / Moon and the willow tree, The / Wham / Devil may care / Night on the Shalimar / I hear bluebirds / Fatima's drummer boy / Now I lay me down to dream / Wait 'til I catch you in my dreams / And so do I / River home.
Album: released on RCA, Jan'87 by RCA Records. Dist: RCA, Roots, Swift, Wellard, Chris, I & B, Solomon & Peres Distribution

Cassette: released on RCA, Jan'87 by RCA Records. Dist: RCA, Roots, Swift, Wellard, Chris, I & B, Solomon & Peres Distribution

V DISC ALL STARS,THE (& Louis Armstrong).
Album: released on Pumpkin, Apr'79 Dist: Jazz Music, Wellard, Chris, Cadillac

Teahouse Camp

TO KILL,STAB IN BACK.
Single (7"): released on Realman-Demon, Jun'85

Teale, Steve

MISS COSTELLO.
Single (7"): released on Ramkup, Nov'81 Dist: Pinnacle

Team 10

MISSION IMPOSSIBLE (Team 10 and The Jazz Pretenders).
Tracks: / Mission imposible.
Single (12"): released on Portrait, Sep'86 by CBS Records. Dist: CBS

Team 23

MOVE INTO THE RHYTHM.
Single (7"): released on Race, Feb'81

team 38

CLOSER TO YOU.
Single (12"): released on Elite, Aug'84 Dist: PRT

Team feat,Gee Bello

WE ARE THE TEAM.
Single (7"): released on EMI, Oct'85 by EMI Records. Dist: EMI

Single (12"): released on EMI, Oct'85 by EMI Records. Dist: EMI

Team (The)

WICKI WACKY HOUSE PARTY.
Single (7"): released on EMI, Jun'85 by EMI Records. Dist: EMI

Single (12"): released on EMI, Jun'85 by EMI Records. Dist: EMI

Single (12"): released on EMI, Jun'85 by EMI Records. Dist: EMI

Teamwork

BEST OF YOUR FAMILY REQUESTS.
Album: released on Homespun(Ireland), Jun'85 by Outlet Records. Dist: Outlet

Cassette: released on Homespun(Ireland), Jun'85 by Outlet Records. Dist: Outlet

SAD MOVIES(MAKE ME CRY).
Single (7"): released on Homespun(Ireland), Jan'85 by Outlet Records. Dist: Outlet

SING ME AN OLD FASIONED SONG.
Album: released on Homespun(Ireland), Jun'83 by Outlet Records. Dist: Outlet

Cassette: released on Homespun(Ireland), Jun'83 by Outlet Records. Dist: Outlet

TERRACE TALK.
Single (7"): released on Kingdom, Apr'82 by Kingdom Records. Dist: Kingdom

Tea Pad Songss

TEA PAD SONGS VOL.1 various artists (Various Artists).
Album: released on Stash, Apr'81 Dist: Swift Distribution, Jazz Music Distribution, Jazz Horizons Distribution, Celtic Music Distribution, Cadillac, JSU Distribution, Zodiac Distribution

TEA PAD SONGS VOL.2 various artists (Various Artists).
Album: released on Stash, Apr'81 Dist: Swift Distribution, Jazz Music Distribution, Jazz Horizons Distribution, Celtic Music Distribution, Cadillac, JSU Distribution, Zodiac Distribution

Teardrop explodes

KILIMANJARO.
Album: released on Mercury, Jul'84 by Phonogram Records. Dist: Polygram Distribution

Cassette: released on Mercury, Jul'84 by Phonogram Records. Dist: Polygram Distribution

REWARD.
Single (7"): released on Mercury, Jun'85 by Phonogram Records. Dist: Polygram Distribution

Single (12"): released on Mercury, Jun'85 by Phonogram Records. Dist: Polygram Distribution Deleted '87.

TINY CHILDREN.
Single (12"): released on Mercury, Jun'82 by Phonogram Records. Dist: Polygram Distribution

WILDER.
Album: released on Mercury, Nov'81 by Phonogram Records. Dist: Polygram Distribution

Cassette: released on Mercury, Nov'81 by Phonogram Records. Dist: Polygram Distribution

Teardrop Time

TEARDROP TIME various artists (Various Artists).
Cassette: released on K-Tel, Aug'84 by K-Tel Records. Dist: Record Merchandisers Distribution, Taylors, Terry Blood Distribution, Wynd-Up Distribution, Relay Distribution, Pickwick Distribution, Solomon & Peres Distribution, Polygram

Tear Garden

TEAR GARDEN (EP), THE.
Tracks: / Tear garden, The.
Single (12"): released on Play It Again Sam, Nov'86 Dist: Red Rhino, Cartel

Tearjerkers..

TEARJERKERS & HEARTBREAKERS various artists (Various Artists).

Tear, Robert

FOLK SONGS (Tear, Robert & Phillip Ledger).
Album: released on H.M.V., '82 by EMI Records. Dist: EMI

Tears For Fears

HURTING, THE.
Tracks: / Mad world / Pale shelter / Ideas as opiates / Memories fade / Suffer the children / Hurting / Watch me bleed / Change / Prisoner / Start of the breakdown.
Compact disc: released on Mercury, '83 by Phonogram Records. Dist: Polygram Distribution

Album: released on Mercury, Mar'83 by Phonogram Records. Dist: Polygram Distribution
Cat. no: **MERS 17**

Cassette: released on Mercury, Mar'83 by Phonogram Records. Dist: Polygram Distribution

IN MY MIND'S EYE.
Tracks: / Mother's talk / Pale shelter / Mad world / Hurting (The).
Notes: A live concert by the band at Hammersmith Odeon, with 13 tracks in all, including several hit singles. Number of tracks:13. Live. Total playing time: 60 minutes.
Video-cassette (VHS): released on Polygram Music, Oct'84 by Polygram Records. Dist: Polygram

Video-cassette [Betamax]: released on Polygram Music, Oct'84 by Polygram Records. Dist: Polygram

SCENES FROM ....
Video-cassette (VHS): released on Polygram, Jan'86 by Polygram Records. Dist: Polygram

SHOUT.
Single (7"): released on Mercury, Nov'84 by Phonogram Records. Dist: Polygram Distribution

SONGS FROM THE BIG CHAIR.
Tracks: / Shout / Working hour (The) / Everybody wants to rule the world / Mother's talk / I believe / Broken / Head over heels / Broken (live) / Listen.
Notes: Digital stereo. Produced once more by Chris Hughes who was responsible for all their previous hits plus the Platinum 'The Hurting' album. The album features some of the most superb sounds on record with a breadth of material covering a range of styles.
Compact disc: released on Mercury, Mar'85 by Phonogram Records. Dist: Polygram Distribution

SONGS FROM THE BIG CHAIR.
Album: released on Mercury, Mar'85 by Phonogram Records. Dist: Polygram Distribution

Cassette: released on Mercury, Mar'85 by Phonogram Records. Dist: Polygram Distribution

Compact disc: released on Mercury, Mar'85 by Phonogram Records. Dist: Polygram Distribution

VIDEOSINGLES (THE).
Video-cassette (VHS): released on Channel 5 Mar'86 Dist: W.H. Smiths

Tears In my eyes

TEARS IN MY EYES Various Artists (Various Artists).
Tracks: / Should I let him go / I don't want to g / I ain't myself anymore / He made woman fo man / It's private tonight / First love / I wann make you happy / Beginning of my end (The) Shopping for love / I need your love to comfo me / Let me hear it from you / Inside story / Long walk on a short pier (A) / Thrill is gone (The) / Tears in my eyes / This must end.
Album: released on Kent, Oct'85 by Ace Rec ords. Dist: Pinnacle

Tease

FIRESTARTER.
Tracks: / Firestarter / Baby, be mine.
Single (7"): released on Epic, Apr'86 by CBS Records. Dist: CBS

Single (12"): released on Epic, Apr'86 by CBS Records. Dist: CBS

TEASE.
Tracks: / Note, The / Better wild (than mild) Firestarter / Body heat / Total control / So music / Baby be mine / I wish you were here.
Album: released on Epic, Jun'86 by CBS Re ords. Dist: CBS

Cassette: released on Epic, Jun'86 by CB Records. Dist: CBS

Tea set

SOUTH PACIFIC.
Single (7"): released on Demon, Jul'81 Demon Records. Dist: Pinnacle

Teaze

ONE NIGHT STANDS.
Album: released on Heavy Metal Americ Feb'85 by FM-Revolver Records. Dist: EMI

TASTE OF TEAZE.
Album: released on Heavy Metal Ameri Aug'84 by FM-Revolver Records. Dist: EMI

Technics

YOU DON'T CARE FOR ME (Te nics/Ranking Devon).
Single (12"): released on Treasure Isla Mar'84 by Treasure Island Records. Dist: star

Technique

HEAVEN TO ME.
Single (7"): released on ERC, Jun'84 by E Records. Dist: PRT

Single (12"): released on ERC, Jun'84 by ERC Records. Dist: PRT

Techniques

NEVER FALL IN LOVE AGAIN.
Single (12"): released on Black Joy, Jun'82 Dist: Jetstar

Technofunk

Mirada Rock

Technology...

TECHNOLOGY TWO EDGED SWORD King, Dr. Alexander (King, Dr. Alexander).
Cassette: released on Seminar Cassettes, Oct'81

Techno Orchestra

CASUAL TEASE.
Album: released on Street Tunes, Sep'83 by Street Tunes Records. Dist: Pinnacle

Technos

FALLING IN LOVE AGAIN.
Single (7"): released on PRT, Jul'85 by PRT Records. Dist: PRT

Single (12"): released on PRT, Jul'85 by PRT Records. Dist: PRT

FOREIGN LAND.
Album: released on PRT, Aug'85 by PRT Records. Dist: PRT

FOREIGN LAND.
Single (7"): released on PRT, Jul'83 by PRT Records. Dist: PRT

Single (12"): released on PRT, Jul'83 by PRT Records. Dist: PRT

FOREIGN LAND.
Single (7"): released on PRT, Oct'85 by PRT Records. Dist: PRT

Single (12"): released on PRT, Oct'85 by PRT Records. Dist: PRT

NIGHT TIME HEAVEN.
Single (7"): released on PRT, Jan'84 by PRT Records. Dist: PRT

Single (12"): released on PRT, Jan'84 by PRT Records. Dist: PRT

SPIRIT OF THE THING.
Single (7"): released on PRT, Aug'84 by PRT Records. Dist: PRT

Single (12"): released on PRT, Aug'84 by PRT Records. Dist: PRT

Techno Twins

TECHNOSTALGIA.
Album: released on PRT, Sep'82 by PRT Records. Dist: PRT

Cassette: released on PRT, Sep'82 by PRT Records. Dist: PRT

Ted And The Tall Tops

CRAZY DATE.
Album: released on New Rose, 30 May'87 Dist: Rough Trade, Cartel

Tedd, Simon

YESTERDAY'S MEMORIES.
Single (7"): released on China Disques, Jun'83 by China Disques. Dist: Pinnacle

Teddy Bear

TEDDY BEAR Various Artists (Various Artists).
Cassette: released on Bibi, Sep'81

Teddy Bears

TO KNOW HIM IS TO LOVE HIM.
Single (7"): released on Old Gold, Jul'82 by Old Gold Records. Dist: Lightning, Jazz Music, Spartan, Counterpoint

Teddy Bear's Picnic

TEDDY BEAR'S PICNIC Various artists (Various Artists).
Cassette: released on Storyteller, Jun'86

Teddy & the Frat Girls

I WANNA BE A MAN.
Single (12"): released on Alternative Tentacles, Feb'85 by Alternative Tentacles Records. Dist: Rough Trade, Pinnacle

Tedesco, Tommy

CARNIVAL TIME (Tedesco, Tommy Trio).
Album: released on Trend (USA), Jun'84 by Discovery Records. Dist: Flexitron Distributors Ltd, Swift

Cassette: released on Trend (USA), Nov'84 by Discovery Records. Dist: Flexitron Distributors Ltd, Swift

HOLLYWOOD GYPSY,A (Tedesco,Tommy Trio).
Compact disc: released on Discovery (USA), Dec'86 by Discovery Records (USA). Dist: Swift, Flexitron-Audio, Jazz Music

MY DESIREE (Tedesco, Tommy Quintet).
Album: released on Discovery (USA), Jan'84

Cassette: released on Discovery (USA), Jan'84

Tedesco,Tommy Trio

CARNIVAL TIME.
Tracks: / Carnival time / Lo yisa goy / Brenda's song / Petals / Chops shop / Bull's eye / Mister Mairants I persume / Four brothers / Waltz for Carma-lee / D's doze and dem.
Notes: Tommy Tedesco-acoustic and electric guitar/John Kurnick-acoustic and electric guitar/Jim Bruno-acoustic and electric guitar.
Compact disc: released on Trend (USA), Sep'86 by Discovery Records. Dist: Flexitron Distributors Ltd, Swift

Ted & The Tall Tops

CRAZY DATE.
Notes: Honky-Tonk album from Austin,Texas (USA) combo,featuring Mike Buck from the Leroi Brothers on bass.
Album: released on New Rose, Jun'87 Dist: Rough Trade, Cartel

Tee, Lynneth

HELLO STRANGER.
Single (7"): released on True World, Jan'85 by True World Records. Dist: PRT, Jetstar

Tee-Mac

SOUND OF THE UNIVERSE.
Single (7"): released on Ensign, Jun'81 by Ensign Records. Dist: CBS Distribution

Single (12"): released on Ensign, Jun'81 by Ensign Records. Dist: CBS Distribution

Teenage....

TEENAGE LOVE Various Artists (Various Artists).
Double Album: released on Cambra, '83 by Cambra Records. Dist: IDS, Conifer

Double cassette: released on Cambra, '83 by Cambra Records. Dist: IDS, Conifer

TEENAGE LOVE SONGS OF THE LATE 50S Various Artists (Various Artists).
Album: released on Old Gold, Jun'85 by Old Gold Records. Dist: Lightning, Jazz Music, Spartan, Counterpoint

Cassette: released on Old Gold, Jun'85 by Old Gold Records. Dist: Lightning, Jazz Music, Spartan, Counterpoint

TEENAGE MEETING Various Artists (Various Artists).
Album: released on Seville, Nov'82 by President Records. Dist: Jazz Music, Swift

TEENAGE ROCK 'N' PARTY VOLUME 3 Various Artists (Various Artists).
Album: released on Ace, Jul'84 by Ace Records. Dist: Pinnacle, Swift, Hotshot, Cadillac

TEENAGE ROCK 'N' ROLL PARTY VOLUME 1 Various Artists (Various Artists).
Album: released on Ace, Nov'80 by Ace Records. Dist: Pinnacle, Swift, Hotshot, Cadillac

TEENAGE ROCK 'N' ROLL PARTY VOLUME 2 Various Artists (Various Artists).
Album: released on Ace, May'83 by Ace Records. Dist: Pinnacle, Swift, Hotshot, Cadillac

TEENAGE ROCK 'N' ROLL PARTY VOLUME 4 Various Artists (Various Artists).
Album: released on Ace, Apr'85 by Ace Records. Dist: Pinnacle, Swift, Hotshot, Cadillac

Teenage Head

FRANTIC CITY.
Album: released on Attic, Jun'82 Dist: Pinnacle

Teena Marie

BEHIND THE GROOVE.
Single (7"): released on Motown, Apr'85 by RCA Records. Dist: RCA Distribution

Single (12"): released on Motown, Apr'85 by RCA Records. Dist: RCA Distribution

BEHIND THE GROOVE.
Single (7"): released on Motown, Oct'81 by RCA Records. Dist: RCA Distribution

Single (12"): released on Motown, Oct'81 by RCA Records. Dist: RCA Distribution

CAN IT BE LOVE.
Single (7"): released on Motown, Oct'81 by RCA Records. Dist: RCA Distribution

EMERALD CITY.
Tracks: / Emerald city / Once is not enough / Lips to find you / You so heavy / Shangri-la / Batucaca suite / Love me down easy / Sunny skies.
Album: released on Epic, Jul'86 by CBS Records. Dist: CBS

Cassette: released on Epic, Jul'86 by CBS Records. Dist: CBS

GREATEST HITS: TEENA MARIE.
Album: released on Gordy (USA), Sep'86 by Motown Records. Dist: RCA

Cassette: released on Gordy (USA), Sep'86 by Motown Records. Dist: RCA

GREATEST HITS: TEENA MARIE ...and more.
Tracks: / Behind the groove / It must be magic / I'm a sucker for your love / Square biz / Why can't I get next to you / Lonely desire / Revolution / Co-pilot to pilot / I need your lovin' / 365 / Portuguese love / Love just wouldn't be right / Where's California / Don't look back / Every little bit hurts.
Album: released on Gordy (USA), Oct'86 by Motown Records. Dist: RCA

Cassette: released on Gordy (USA), Oct'86 by Motown Records. Dist: RCA

I'M A SUCKER FOR YOUR LOVE.
Single (7"): released on Motown, Oct'81 by RCA Records. Dist: RCA Distribution

Single (12"): released on Motown, Oct'81 by RCA Records. Dist: RCA Distribution

I NEED YOUR LOVIN'.
Single (7"): released on Motown, Oct'81 by RCA Records. Dist: RCA Distribution

Single (12"): released on Motown, Oct'81 by RCA Records. Dist: RCA Distribution

IRONS IN THE FIRE.
Album: released on Motown, Oct'81 by RCA Records. Dist: RCA Distribution

Cassette: released on Motown, Oct'81 by RCA Records. Dist: RCA Distribution

IT MUST BE MAGIC.
Album: released on Motown, Oct'81 by RCA Records. Dist: RCA Distribution

Cassette: released on Motown, Oct'81 by RCA Records. Dist: RCA Distribution

Single (7"): released on Motown, Nov'81 by RCA Records. Dist: RCA Distribution

Single (12"): released on Motown, Nov'81 by RCA Records. Dist: RCA Distribution

LADY T.
Album: released on Motown, Oct'81 by RCA Records. Dist: RCA Distribution

LIPS TO FIND YOU.
Tracks: / Lips to find you / Lips to find you.
Single (7"): released on Epic, Jun'86 by CBS Records. Dist: CBS

Single (12"): released on Epic, Jun'86 by CBS Records. Dist: CBS

LONELY DESIRE.
Single (7"): released on Motown, Oct'81 by RCA Records. Dist: RCA Distribution

LOVE ME DOWN EASY.
Tracks: / Love me down easy / Love me down easy (instrumental).
Single (7"): released on Epic, Oct'86 by CBS Records. Dist: CBS

Single (12"): released on Epic, Oct'86 by CBS Records. Dist: CBS

LOVERGIRL.
Single (7"): released on Epic, Mar'85 by CBS Records. Dist: CBS

PORTUGUESE LOVE.
Single (7"): released on Motown, Jan'82 by RCA Records. Dist: RCA Distribution

Single (12"): released on Motown, Jan'82 by RCA Records. Dist: RCA Distribution

ROBBERY.
Album: released on Epic, Nov'83 by CBS Records. Dist: CBS

Cassette: released on Epic, Nov'83 by CBS Records. Dist: CBS

SQUARE B12.
Single (7"): released on Motown, Oct'81 by RCA Records. Dist: RCA Distribution

Single (12"): released on Motown, Oct'81 by RCA Records. Dist: RCA Distribution

STAR CHILD.
Album: released on Epic, Feb'85 by CBS Records. Dist: CBS

Cassette: released on Epic, Feb'85 by CBS Records. Dist: CBS Deleted May'87.

WILD AND PEACEFUL.
Album: released on Motown, Oct'81 by RCA Records. Dist: RCA Distribution

Cassette: released on Motown, Oct'81 by RCA Records. Dist: RCA Distribution

Teen Beat

TEEN BEAT Various Artists (Various Artists).
Album: released on Capitol, Nov'81 by Capitol Records. Dist: EMI

Cassette: released on Capitol, Nov'81 by Capitol Records. Dist: EMI

Teenbeats

I CAN'T CONTROL MYSELF.
Single (7"): released on Safari, '79 by Safari Records. Dist: Pinnacle

STRENGTH OF THE NATION.
Single (7"): released on Safari, '80 by Safari Records. Dist: Pinnacle

Teen Dreams

LETS GET BUSY (Teen Dreams with Valentino).
Tracks: / Let's get busy / Let's get busy (inst) / Let's get busy (Boy crazy mix) / Let's get busy (dub).
Single (7"): released on Warner Bros., Jun'87 by Warner Bros Records. Dist: WEA

Single (12"): released on Warner Bros., Jun'87 by Warner Bros Records. Dist: WEA

TEEN DREAMS Various Artists (Various Artists).
Album: released on Laurie, Mar'82 by RCA Records. Dist: RCA

Cassette: released on Laurie, Mar'82 by RCA Records. Dist: RCA

Teen, Judy

LOVE BITE (Teen,Judy & the Rat Pack).
Single (7"): released on GFM, Jan'87 by GFM Records. Dist: Fast Forward, Cartel, PRT, Projection

LOVE BITES (Teen,Judy & the Brat Pack).
Tracks: / Second bite / Again and again.
Notes: Extra track on 12" only.
Single (12"): released on GFM, Feb'87 by GFM Records. Dist: Fast Forward, Cartel, PRT, Projection

Teen Queens

GOOD ROCKIN' DADDY.
Single (7"): released on Ace, Mar'81 by Ace Records. Dist: Pinnacle, Swift, Hotshot, Cadillac

ROCK EVERYBODY.
Tracks: / Rock everybody / Red top / Eddie my love / Zig zag / All my love / Baby mine / Riding the boogie / Just goofed / Love sweet love / So all alone / My heart's desire / Teenage gold / Let's make up / Billy Boy.
Notes: Mono
Album: released on Ace, Oct'86 by Ace Records. Dist: Pinnacle, Swift, Hotshot, Cadillac

Tee, Richard

BOTTOM LINE (THE).
Tracks: / If you want it / What can I say / Bottom line (The) / Nippon lights / Rhapsody in blue / Miss-Understanding / Spring is you / No real way / Moving on.
Notes: Ace session keyboard man and veteran of a thousand Atlantic studio sessions. Member of New York session band Stuff, whose personnel included Cornell, Dupree, Eric Gale and Steve Gadd. This band have played with just about everyone of any consequence from Aretha Franklin, Paul Simon, Quincy Jones to Joe Cocker and many many more too numerous to mention here. 'The Bottom Line' features an all-star band including Steve Gadd, Dave Weckl and Marcus Miller. Richard Tee does some great vocals as well as his superb keyboard work. Superb contemporary soul/R & B Richard Tee is featured on the latest Peter Gabriel album. All compositions by Richard Tee except for Gershwin;s 'Rhapsody in Blue'. Personnel: Richard Tee-acoustic piano, electric piano, vocal, Linnclaps/Steve Gadd-drums/Dave Weckl-drums/Marcus Miller-bass/Will Lee-bass/Ralph McDonald-percussion//John Tropes-guitar. Guest vocal on 'Miss-Understanding'-William Eaton and Zack Sanders.
Album: released on King (Japan), Jul'86 Dist: IMS, Polygram

Tees-side fettlers

RING OF IRON.
Album: released on Tradition, Aug'76 Dist: JSU, Cassion Distribution, Celtic Music, Jazz Music, Projection, Roots Records

TRAVELLING THE TEES.
Album: released on Tradition, Aug'76 Dist: JSU, Cassion Distribution, Celtic Music, Jazz Music, Projection, Roots Records

Teeze
TEEZE.
Album: released on Road Runner, Nov'85

Teezers
BEST PART OF BREAKING UP, (THE).
Single (7"): released on Arrival, May'81 by Arrival. Dist: Revolver, Cartel

Teitelbaum, Richard
TIME ZONES.
Album: released on Freedom, Apr'79 by Logo Records. Dist: RCA, Discovery, Wellard, Chris

Te Kanawa, Kiri
CHRISTMAS WITH KIRI.
Compact disc: released on Decca, Nov'86 by Decca Records. Dist: Polygram

MY FAVOURITE THINGS.
Album: released on Hallmark, Oct'87 by Pickwick Records. Dist: Pickwick Distribution, PRT, Taylors

Cassette: released on Hallmark, Oct'87 by Pickwick Records. Dist: Pickwick Distribution, PRT, Taylors

WHITE CHRISTMAS.
Tracks: / Mary's boy child.
Single (7"): released on Decca, Jan'87 by Decca Records. Dist: Polygram

Tekla Irie
REGGAE RHYTHM.
Single (12"): released on Fulani, Sep'84 by Fulani. Dist: Fualni-ILA

Telegents
GET OUT.
Single (7"): released on Genie, Apr'81 by Genie Records. Dist: Spartan, CBS

Telephone
AU COEUR DE LA NUIT.
Album: released on Virgin, Jul'81

CHATTERBOX,CLASSICS VOL.1 Telephone answering machine messages (Telephone answering machine messages).
Cassette: released on Chatterbox, Jun'82 by RCA. Dist: RCA

CHATTERBOX, HUMOUR,VOL.1 Telephone answering machine messages (Telephone answering machine messages).
Cassette: released on Chatterbox, Jun'82 by RCA. Dist: RCA

CHATTERBOX, MIXED BAG VOL.1 Telephone answering machine messages (Telephone answering machine messages).
Cassette: released on Chatterbox, Jun'82 by RCA. Dist: RCA

CHATTERBOX,POPS-VOL.1 Telephone answering machine messages (Telephone answering machine messages).
Cassette: released on Chatterbox, Jun'82 by RCA. Dist: RCA

TELEPHONE.
Album: released on Virgin, Oct'82

UN AUTRE MONDE.
Album: released on Virgin, Jul'84

Telephone Bill
MANHATTAN DOLL (Telephone Bill/Smooth Operators).
Album: released on Dingles, Aug'82 by Dingles Records. Dist: Projection

Television
BLOW UP, (THE).
Cassette: released on Reach Out International, '83 Dist: Red Rhino, Cartel

PAINTED WORD, (THE) (Television Personalities).
Album: released on Illuminated, Jan'85 by IKF Records. Dist: Pinnacle, Cartel, Jetstar

SENSE OF BELONGING (Television Personalities).
Single (7"): released on Rough Trade, Dec'83 by Rough Trade Records. Dist: Rough Trade Distribution, Cartel Distribution

TELEVISION'S GREATEST HITS VOL.1. 65 themes from the 50's and 60's (Various Artists).
Album: released on T.V. Toons, Jun'87

Cassette: released on T.V. Toons, Jun'87

TELEVISION'S GREATEST HITS VOL.2 65 themes from the 50's and 60's (Various Artists).
Album: released on T.V. Toons, Jun'87

Cassette: released on T.V. Toons, Jun'87

Television Personalities
I KNOW WHERE SYD BARRETT LIVES.
Single (7"): released on Rough Trade, Feb'81 by Rough Trade Records. Dist: Rough Trade Distribution, Cartel Distribution

Telex
AMOUR TOUJOURS, (L').
Single (7"): released on Interdisc, Sep'82 by Interdisc Records. Dist: Island, EMI

Single (12"): released on Interdisc, Sep'82 by Interdisc Records. Dist: Island, EMI

BIRDS & BEES.
Album: released on Interdisc, Sep'82 by Interdisc Records. Dist: Island, EMI

Cassette: released on Interdisc, Sep'82 by Interdisc Records. Dist: Island, EMI

HAVEN'T WE MET SOMEWHERE BEFORE.
Single (7"): released on Interdisc, Jul'82 by Interdisc Records. Dist: Island, EMI

Single (12"): released on Interdisc, Jul'82 by Interdisc Records. Dist: Island, EMI

LOOKING FOR ST. TROPEZ.
Album: released on Sire, Jun'79

NEUROVISION.
Album: released on Sire, May'80

Telfer, John
Rubadub-pop goes the nursery rhymes

Telham Tinkers
HOT IN ALICE SPRINGS.
Album: released on Eron, Sep'85 by Eron Records. Dist: Eron Records

Tella & Collins
WHEN YOU'RE YOUNG.
Tracks: / When you're young / When you're young (instrumental).
Single (7"): released on AI, Oct'86

Single (12"): released on AI, Oct'86

Tella, Sylvia
HE'S MY BABY.
Single (12"): released on Boss, Oct'85

I STILL FEEL.
Album: released on Boss, Nov'84

SPELL.
Album: released on Sarge, Apr'86 by Sarge Records. Dist: Jetstar

SWEETER HE IS.
Single (12"): released on SRL, Apr'82

Tell-A-Tale
CHRISTOPHER COLUMBUS.
Cassette: released on Pickwick (Tell-a-tale), Apr'84 by Pickwick Records. Dist: Pickwick Distribution

OLIVER CROMWELL.
Cassette: released on Pickwick (Tell-a-tale), Mar'84 by Pickwick Records. Dist: Pickwick Distribution

Tellers
JENNIFER CLARKE.
Single (12"): released on Calypso Joe, Aug'85 by Calypso Joe Records. Dist: Jetstar

Tell me on sunday
MARTI WEBB & ORIG. TV CAST.
Album: released on Polydor, '80 by Polydor Records. Dist: Polygram, Polydor

Cassette: released on Polydor, '80 by Polydor Records. Dist: Polygram, Polydor

Tell Tale Hearts
FALLING DOWN.
Tracks: / Falling down.
Single (12"): released on Teden's Doorbell, Ma:'87

TELLTALE HEARTS.
Album: released on Lolita, Apr'86 by Lolita Records. Dist: Rough Trade, Cartel

Telly hits
TELLY HITS Various Artists (Various Artists).
Album: released on Stylus, Nov'85 Dist: Pinnacle, Terry Blood Distribution, Stylus Distribution

Cassette: released on Stylus, Nov'85 Dist: Pinnacle, Terry Blood Distribution, Stylus Distribution

Telsa
MODERN DAY COWBOY.
Tracks: / Love me (live) / Cover queen (live).
Single (7"): released on Geffen, Aug'87 by Geffen Records. Dist: WEA, CBS

Single (12"): released on Geffen, Aug'87 by Geffen Records. Dist: WEA, CBS

Temiz, Okay
ORIENTAL WIND.
Album: released on Sonet, Aug'78 by Sonet Records. Dist: PRT

TURKISH FOLK JAZZ.
Album: released on Sonet, '75 by Sonet Records. Dist: PRT

Tempchin, Jack
JACK TEMPCHIN.
Album: released on Arista, '78 by Arista Records. Dist: RCA

Temper
NO FAVOURS.
Single (7"): released on MCA, Sep'84 by MCA Records. Dist: Polygram, MCA

Single (12"): released on MCA, Sep'84 by MCA Records. Dist: Polygram, MCA

Temperance Seven
HOT TEMPERANCE SEVEN.
Album: released on Wam, May'87

YOU'RE DRIVING ME CRAZY.
Single (7"): released on Old Gold, Oct'83 by Old Gold Records. Dist: Lightning, Jazz Music, Spartan, Counterpoint

Temperley, Joe
JUST FRIENDS (Temperley Joe & Jimmy Knepper).
Album: released on Hep, Apr'81 by Taylor Records. Dist: Jazz Music, Cadillac Music, JSU, Taylors, Wellard, Chris, Zodiac, Swift, Fast Forward

SAXPLOITATION (Temperley, Joe & Kathy Stobart).
Album: released on Spotlite, May'77 by Spotlite Records. Dist: Cadillac, Jazz Music, Spotlite

Tempest
ALWAYS THE SAME.
Single (7"): released on Magnet, May'85 by Magnet Records. Dist: BMG

78 rpm record: released on Magnet, Aug'85 by Magnet Records. Dist: BMG

BLUEBELLE.
Single (7"): released on Magnet, Sep'85 by Magnet Records. Dist: BMG

Single (12"): released on Magnet, Sep'85 by Magnet Records. Dist: BMG

DIDN'T WE HAVE A NICE TIME (and all my friends...).
Tracks: / Didn't we have a nice time (and all my friends are here) / Physical act (The) / Didn't we have a nice time (and all my friends are here).
Notes: Writer: Michael Sheerin. Producer Glenn Tilbrook except "The Tempest.
Single (7"): released on Magnet, May'86 by Magnet Records. Dist: BMG

Single (12"): released on Magnet, May'86 by Magnet Records. Dist: BMG

FIVE AGAINST THE HOUSE.
Album: released on Anagram, Jun'84 by Cherry Red Records. Dist: Pinnacle

LADY LEFT THIS.
Single (7"): released on Glass, Jul'83 by Glass Records. Dist: Nine Mile, Rough Trade, Red Rhino, Play It Again Sam

LAZY SUNDAY.
Tracks: / Lazy Sunday / You've always got something to say.
Single (7"): released on Magnet, Aug'86 by Magnet Records. Dist: BMG

Single (12"): released on Magnet, Aug'86 by Magnet Records. Dist: BMG

MONTEZUMA.
Single (12"): released on Anagram, Dec'83 by Cherry Red Records. Dist: Pinnacle

Single (12"): released on Anagram, Dec'83 by Cherry Red Records. Dist: Pinnacle

TEMPEST, THE.
Tracks: / Lazy Sunday / Tonight / Diane / Tempest, The / "Bluebell / Didn't we have a nice Michael Sheerin time / Don't you realise / Leave the boy alone / "Always the same / This is the world.
Album: released on Magnet, Nov'86 by Magnet Records. Dist: BMG

Temple Church Choir
TEMPLE TRADITION.
Album: released on Abbey, Feb'80 by Abbey. Dist: PRT, Taylors, Gamut

Temple, Johnny
JOHNNY TEMPLE 1935-9.
Album: released on Document, Jul'87

Templemore Band
CONCERT BRASS.
Album: released on Homespun(Ireland), Aug'82 by Outlet Records. Dist: Outlet

Temple, Paul and...
PAUL TEMPLE AND THE HARKDALE ROBBERY Durbridge, Francis (Durbridge, Francis).
Cassette: released on Pickwick Talking Books, '83

Temporary Title
CHEONG SAM (SUMMER SONG).
Single (7"): released on Secret, Oct'81 by Secret Records. Dist: EMI

CHEONG SONG (SUMMER SONG).
Single (7"): released on Secret, Oct'81 by Secret Records. Dist: EMI

Temptations
17 GREATEST HITS.
Tracks: / Girl (why you wanna make me blue) / My girl / Since I lost my baby / Ain't to proud to beg / (I know) I'm losing you / You're my everything / I wish it would rain / I can never love another (after loving you) / Cloud / Runaway child running wild / I can't get next to you / Psychedelic shack / Ball of confusion (that's what the world is today) / Just my imagination (running away with me) / Superstar (remember how you got where you are)/ Papa was a rollin' stone / Hey girl (I like your style).
Compact disc: released on Motown, Jul'85 by Motown Records. Dist: BMG Distribution

20 GOLDEN GREATS.
Album: released on Motown, Oct'81 by RCA Records. Dist: RCA Distribution

Cassette: released on Motown, Oct'81 by RCA Records. Dist: RCA Distribution

25TH ANNIVERSARY.
Tracks: / I want a love I can see / So much joy / It don't have to be this way / Further you look the less you see / My girl / Since I lost my baby / I can't get next to you / Cloud nine / Just my imagination / Come to me / Soulmate / Tear from a woman's eyes / Wherever I lay my hat / Don't look back / Get ready / Ain't too proud to beg / Truly yours / Papa was a rollin' stone / Thanks to you / Glasshouse / Power / Treat her like a lady.
Album: released on Tamla Motown, Jun'86 by Motown Records. Dist: RCA Distribution

Cassette: released on Tamla Motown, Jun'86 by Motown Records. Dist: RCA Distribution

AIMING AT YOUR HEART.
Single (7"): released on Motown, Oct'81 by Motown Records. Dist: BMG Distribution

Single (12"): released on Motown, Oct'81 by Motown Records. Dist: BMG Distribution

ALL DIRECTIONS.
Album: released on Motown, Mar'82 by Motown Records. Dist: BMG Distribution

Cassette: released on Motown, Mar'82 by Motown Records. Dist: BMG Distribution

ALL THE MILLION SELLERS.
Album: released on Motown, Apr'84 by Motown Records. Dist: BMG Distribution

Cassette: released on Motown, Apr'84 by Motown Records. Dist: BMG Distribution

Double Album: released on Motown, Oct'81 by Motown Records. Dist: BMG Distribution

Double cassette: released on Motown, Oct'81 by Motown Records. Dist: BMG Distribution

ANTHOLOGY Volumes 1 & 2.
Tracks: / Way you do the things you do, The / I'll be in trouble / Girl's alright with me, The / Girl (why you wanna make me blue) / My girl / I'm growing / Since I lost my baby / My baby / Don't look back / get ready / Ain't too proud to beg / Beauty is only skin deep / I'm losing you,

know) / All I need / You're my everything / It's you that I need (Loneliness made me realize) / I wish it would rain / I truly, truly believe / I could never love another (after loving you) / Runaway child, running wild / Ol' man river / Try to remember / Impossible dream, The / I'm gonna make you love me / Please return your love to me / Cloud nine / Don't let the Joneses get you down / I can't get next to you / Psychedelic shack / Ball of confusion (that's what the world is today / Funky music sho nuff turns me on / I ain't got nothin' / Just my imagination (running away with me) / Superstar (remember how you got where you are) / Mother nature / Love woke me up this morning / Papa was a rollin' stone / Masterpiece / Shakey ground / Power / Sail away / Treat her like a lady.
Compact disc: released on Motown, Jan'87 by Motown Records. Dist: BMG Distribution

Double Album: released on Motown, Oct'81 by RCA Records. Dist: RCA Distribution

Double cassette: released on Motown, Oct'81 by RCA Records. Dist: RCA Distribution

BACK TO BASICS.
Album: released on Motown, Dec'83 by Motown Records. Dist: BMG Distribution

Cassette: released on Motown, Dec'83 by Motown Records. Dist: BMG Distribution

BALL OF CONFUSION.
Single (7"): released on Motown, Apr'85 by Motown Records. Dist: BMG Distribution

Single (12"): released on Motown, Apr'85 by Motown Records. Dist: BMG Distribution

BEST OF THE TEMPTATIONS.
Album: released on Telstar, Nov'86 by Telstar Records. Dist: RCA Distribution

Cassette: released on Telstar, Nov'86 by Telstar Records. Dist: RCA Distribution

CLOUD NINE.
Album: released on Motown, Oct'81 by Motown Records. Dist: BMG Distribution

Cassette: released on Motown, Oct'81 by Motown Records. Dist: BMG Distribution

Single (7"): released on Motown, Mar'83 by Motown Records. Dist: BMG Distribution

CLOUD NINE/PUZZLE PEOPLE (2 classic albums).
Tracks: / Cloud nine / I heard it through the grapevine / Runaway child, running wild / Love is a hurtin' thing / Hey girl / Why did she have to leave me (why did she have to go?) / I need your lovin' / Don't let him take your love from me / I gotta find a way (to get you back) / I can't get next to you / Hey Jude / Don't let the Joneses get you down / Message from a black man / It's your thing / Little green apples / You don't love me no more / Since I've lost you / Running away (ain't gonna help you) / That's the way love is / Slave.
Compact disc: released on Motown, Oct'86 by Motown Records. Dist: BMG Distribution

CLOUD NINE/PUZZLE PEOPLE 2 Classic albums.
Tracks: / Cloud nine / I heard it through the grapevine / Runaway child, running wild / Love is a hurtin' thing / Hey girl / Why did she have to leave me (why did she have to go) / I need your lovin' / Don't let him take your love from me / I gotta find a way (to get you back) / Gonna keep on tryin' till I win your love / I can't get next to you / Hey Jude / Don't let the Joneses get you down / Message from a black man / It's your thing / Little green apples / You don't love me no more / Since I've lost you / Running away (ain't gonna help you) / That's the way love is / Slave.
Compact disc: released on Motown, Jan'87 by Motown Records. Dist: BMG Distribution

Diana Ross joins The Temptations/together

DO YOU REALLY LOVE YOUR BABY.
Single (7"): released on Motown, Nov'85 by Motown Records. Dist: BMG Distribution

Single (12"): released on Motown, Nov'85 by Motown Records. Dist: BMG Distribution

GET READY.
Single (7"): released on Motown, Oct'81 by RCA Records. Dist: RCA Distribution

Album: released on Motown, '82 by RCA Records. Dist: RCA Distribution

Cassette: released on Motown, '82 by RCA Records. Dist: RCA Distribution

GIVE LOVE AT CHRISTMAS.
Album: released on Motown, Nov'85 by RCA Records. Dist: RCA Distribution

Cassette: released on Motown, Nov'85 by RCA Records. Dist: RCA Distribution

I'M SO FASCINATED.
Tracks: / I'm fascinated / How can you say that it's over / Treat her like a lady / M & M remix.
Single (7"): released on Motown, Mar'86 by Motown Records. Dist: BMG Distribution

Single (12"): released on Motown, Mar'86 by Motown Records. Dist: BMG Distribution

JUST MY IMAGINATION.
Single (7"): released on Motown, Mar'83 by RCA Records. Dist: RCA Distribution

Single (7"): released on Motown, Oct'81 by RCA Records. Dist: RCA Distribution

LADY SOUL.
Tracks: / Lady soul / Fine mess (A) / Papa was a rolling stone.
Single (7"): released on Motown, Aug'86 by Motown Records. Dist: BMG Distribution

Single (12"): released on Motown, Aug'86 by Motown Records. Dist: BMG Distribution

LAW OF THE LAND.
Single (7"): released on Motown, Apr'85 by RCA Records. Dist: RCA Distribution

Single (12"): released on Motown, Apr'85 by RCA Records. Dist: RCA Distribution

LIVE AT THE COPA/WITH A LOT O' SOUL 2 Classic albums.
Tracks: / Introduction / Get ready / You're my everything / I truly, truly believe / I wish it would rain / For once in my life / I could never love another (after loving you) / Introduction to Band and Group / Hello young lovers / With these hands / Swanee / Impossible dream, The / Please return your love to me / I'm losing you, (I know) / Ain't no sun since you've been gone / All I need / It's you that I need, (Loneliness made me realize) / No more water in the well / Save my love for a rainy day / Just one last look / Sorry is a sorry word / You're my everything / Now that you've won me / Two sides to love / Don't send me away.
Compact disc: released on Motown, Feb'87 by Motown Records. Dist: BMG Distribution

LIVE AT THE COPA/WITH A LOT O'SOUL.

LOVE ON MY MIND TONIGHT.
Single (7"): released on Motown, Mar'83 by RCA Records. Dist: RCA Distribution

Single (12"): released on Motown, Mar'83 by RCA Records. Dist: RCA Distribution

MASTERPIECE.
Album: released on Motown, Oct'81 by RCA Records. Dist: RCA Distribution

Cassette: released on Motown, Oct'81 by RCA Records. Dist: RCA Distribution

MEDLEY OF HITS (Temptations & Four Tops).
Single (7"): released on Motown, Oct'83 by RCA Records. Dist: RCA Distribution

Single (7"): released on Motown, Oct'83 by RCA Records. Dist: RCA Distribution

MY GIRL.
Tracks: / My girl / Wherever I lay my hat / Way you the the things you do (The) / My baby.
Single (7"): released on Motown, Jun'86 by Motown Records. Dist: BMG Distribution

Single (12"): released on Motown, Jun'86 by Motown Records. Dist: BMG Distribution

MY LOVE IS TRUE(TRULY FOR YOU).
Single (7"): released on Motown, Mar'85 by Motown Records. Dist: BMG Distribution

Single (12"): released on Motown, Mar'85 by Motown Records. Dist: BMG Distribution

NITE AT THE APOLLO LIVE, A (see also Daryl Hall, John Oates) (Daryl Hall & John Oates with The temptations).

PAPA WAS A ROLLING STONE.
Single (7"): released on Motown, Aug'87 by Motown Records. Dist: BMG Distribution

Single (12"): released on Motown, Aug'87 by Motown Records. Dist: BMG Distribution

PAPA WAS A ROLLIN' STONE.
Single (7"): released on Motown, Oct'81 by Motown Records. Dist: BMG Distribution

POWER.
Single (7"): released on Motown, Oct'81 by Motown Records. Dist: BMG Distribution

Cassette: released on Motown, Oct'81 by Motown Records. Dist: BMG Distribution

PSYCHEDELIC SHACK.
Album: released on Motown, Mar'82 by Motown Records. Dist: BMG Distribution

Cassette: released on Motown, Mar'82 by Motown Records. Dist: BMG Distribution

PSYCHEDELIC SHACK/ALL DIRECTIONS 2 Classic albums.
Tracks: / Psychedelic shack / You make your own heaven and hell right here on Earth / Hum along and dance / Take a stroll thru your mind / It's summer / War / You need love like I do / Friendship train / Funky music / Psychedelic shack / You make your own heaven and hell right here on earth / Hum along and dance / Take a stroll thru your mind / It's summer / War / You need love like I do (don't you?) / Friendship train / Funky music sho nuff turns me on / Run Charlie run / Papa was a rollin' stone / Love woke me up this morning / I ain't got nothin' / First time ever (I saw your face), The / Mother nature / Do your thing.
Compact disc: released on Motown, Nov'86 by Motown Records. Dist: BMG Distribution

PUZZLE PEOPLE.
Album: released on Motown, Mar'82 by Motown Records. Dist: BMG Distribution

Cassette: released on Motown, Mar'82 by Motown Records. Dist: BMG Distribution

...SING SMOKEY.
Album: released on Motown, Oct'81 by Motown Records. Dist: BMG Distribution

Cassette: released on Motown, Oct'81 by Motown Records. Dist: BMG Distribution

SONG FOR YOU/MASTERPIECE 2 Classic albums.
Tracks: / Happy people (2) / Glasshouse / Shakey ground / Prophet, The / Happy people (1) / Song for you, A / Memories / I'm a bachelor / Firefly / Hey girl (I like your style) / Masterpiece / Ma / Law of the land / Plastic man / Hurry tomorrow.
Compact disc: released on Motown, Dec'86 by Motown Records. Dist: BMG Distribution

STANDING ON THE TOP (2 parts) (Temptations Featuring Rick James).
Single (7"): released on Motown, May'82 by Motown Records. Dist: BMG Distribution

Single (12"): released on Motown, May'82 by Motown Records. Dist: BMG Distribution

STRUCK BY LIGHTNING TWICE.
Single (7"): released on Motown, Oct'81 by RCA Records. Dist: RCA Distribution

SURFACE THRILLS.
Album: released on Motown, Mar'83 by RCA Records. Dist: RCA Distribution

Cassette: released on Motown, Mar'83 by RCA Records. Dist: RCA Distribution

TAKE ME AWAY.
Single (7"): released on Motown, Oct'81 by RCA Records. Dist: RCA Distribution

T.C.B.-THE ORIGINAL SOUNTRACK (Temptations with Diana Ross & The Supremes).
Album: released on Motown, Mar'82 by RCA Records. Dist: RCA Distribution

Cassette: released on Motown, Mar'82 by RCA Records. Dist: RCA Distribution

TEMPTATIONS 4 track cassette EP.
Cassette: released on Motown, May'83 by RCA Records. Dist: RCA Distribution

TEMPTATIONS, THE.
Album: released on Motown, Jun'82 by RCA Records. Dist: RCA Distribution

Cassette: released on Motown, Jun'82 by RCA Records. Dist: RCA Distribution

TO BE CONTINUED....
Tracks: / Lady soul / Message to the world / To be continued / Put us together again / Someone / Girls (they like it) / More love, your love / Fine mess, A / You're the one / Love me right.
Album: released on Motown, Sep'86 by Motown Records. Dist: BMG Distribution

Cassette: released on Motown, Sep'86 by Motown Records. Dist: BMG Distribution

TOUCH ME.
Tracks: / Magic / Give her some attention / Deeper than love / I'm fascinated / Touch me / Don't break your promise to me / She got tired of loving me / Do you really love your baby / Oh lover.
Album: released on Motown, Nov'85 by Motown Records. Dist: BMG Distribution

Cassette: released on Motown, Nov'85 by Motown Records. Dist: BMG Distribution

TREAT HER LIKE A LADY.
Single (7"):

Single (12"):

TRULY FOR YOU.
Album: released on Motown, Dec'84 by RCA Records. Dist: RCA Distribution

Cassette: released on Motown, Dec'84 by RCA Records. Dist: RCA Distribution

Tems, Mick

GOWERTON FAIR.
Album: released on Sweet Folk All, May'81 by Sweet Folk All Records. Dist: Sweet Folk All, Roots, Celtic Music, Dragon, Impetus, Projection, Chris Wellard, Festival Records

Ten...

"10" Original soundtrack.
Album: released on Warner Brothers, Apr'80 by Warner Bros Records. Dist: WEA

10 DANCE RECORDS VOL.1 Various artists (Various Artists).
Album: released on 10, Apr'86 by 10 Records. Dist: Virgin, EMI

Cassette: released on 10, Apr'86 by 10 Records. Dist: Virgin, EMI

TEN BEST HITS Various artists (Various Artists).
Cassette: released on Homespun(Ireland), Dec'85 by Outlet Records. Dist: Outlet

TEN GREAT HITS Various artists (Various Artists).
Cassette: released on Homespun(Ireland), Dec'83 by Outlet Records. Dist: Outlet

TEN SOUVENIR SONGS OF IRELAND Various artists (Various Artists).
Cassette: released on Homespun(Ireland), Jun'84 by Outlet Records. Dist: Outlet

TEN YEARS OF OFFSHORE RADIO Various artists (Various Artists).
Double Album: released on East Anglian Productions, Jan'78 by East Anglian Productions. Dist: Lightning

Double cassette: released on East Anglian Productions, Jan'78 by East Anglian Productions. Dist: Lightning

Tena Four

GOLDEN HEN.
Single (12"): released on Uptempo, Aug'85 by Uptempo Records. Dist: Jetstar Distribution

Tenants

TENANTS, THE.
Album: released on Epic, Aug'83 by CBS Records. Dist: CBS

Tenbury, St. Michaels...

CHOIR OF ST. MICHAELS, THE.
Album: released on Abbey, Nov'79 by Abbey. Dist: PRT, Taylors, Gamut

Ten-By-Twelve

10 BY 12 Various artists (Various Artists).
Tracks: / Living in America / Alice, I want you just for me / I wonder if I take you home / House rocker / Hot / Saturday love / Sugar free / New York eyes / If I were here tonight / Finest, The.
Album: released on Portrait, Apr'86 by CBS Records. Dist: CBS

Cassette: released on Portrait, Apr'86 by CBS Records. Dist: CBS

Ten CC

24 HOURS.
Single (7"): released on Mercury, Apr'83 by Phonogram Records. Dist: Polygram Distribution

Single (12"): released on Mercury, Apr'83 by Phonogram Records. Dist: Polygram Distribution

BEST OF 1975-77.
Album: released on Mercury, Nov'81 by Phonogram Records. Dist: Polygram Distribution

BLOODY TOURISTS.
Compact disc: by Phonogram Records. Dist: Polygram Distribution

DONNA.
Single (7"): released on Import, '80 Dist: Stage One

DREADLOCK HOLIDAY.
Album: released on Mercury (Holland), Apr'84 by Phonogram Records. Dist: Polygram Distribution

FEEL THE LOVE.
Single (7"): released on Mercury, Jul'83 by Phonogram Records. Dist: Polygram Distribution

GREATEST HITS: TEN CC.
Album: released on Mercury, Sep'79 by Phonogram Records. Dist: Polygram Distribution

Cassette: released on Mercury, Sep'79 by Phonogram Records. Dist: Polygram Distribution

Compact disc: released on Mercury, Sep'79 by Phonogram Records. Dist: Polygram Distribution

GREATEST HITS: TEN CC.
Tracks: / Rubber bullets / Donna / Silly love / Dean and I / Life is a minestrone / Wall street

shuffle / Art for art's sake / I'm Mandy, fly me / Good morning judge / Things we do for love / Dreadlock holiday / I'm not in love.
Compact disc: released on Mercury, '83 by Phonogram Records. Dist: Polygram Distribution

HOW DARE YOU?.
Album: released on Mercury, Dec'83 by Phonogram Records. Dist: Polygram Distribution
Cat. no: PRICE 60
Cassette: released on Mercury, Dec'83 by Phonogram Records. Dist: Polygram Distribution

I'M NOT IN LOVE.
Single (7"): released on Mercury, Oct'84 by Phonogram Records. Dist: Polygram Distribution

Single (7"): released on Old Gold, Jan'85 by Old Gold Records. Dist: Lightning, Jazz Music, Spartan, Counterpoint

IN CONCERT.
Album: released on Contour, Oct'82 by Pickwick Distribution, PRT

Cassette: released on Contour, Oct'82 by Pickwick Distribution, PRT

IT DOESN'T MATTER AT ALL.
Single (7"): released on Mercury, May'80 by Phonogram Records. Dist: Polygram Distribution

LIVE AND LET LIVE.
Double Album: released on Mercury (Germany), Apr'85 by Phonogram Records. Dist: Polygram Distribution

LIVE AT THE INTERNATIONAL MUSIC SHOW (VIDEO).
Notes: Inc. 'I'm not in love'
Video-cassette (VHS): released on Video Collection, May'87 by Video Collection International Ltd.. Dist: Counterpoint

LIVE IN CONCERT.
Tracks: / Good morning Judge / Things we do for love / People in love / Wall street shuffle / Feel the benefit.
Notes: A live concert of 10CC filmed at the Hammersmith Odean by Bruce Gowers.
Video-cassette (VHS): released on VCL, Sep'86 by Elecstar Records. Dist: PRT

LOOK HEAR.
Album: released on Mercury, Apr'80 by Phonogram Records. Dist: Polygram Distribution

Cassette: released on Mercury, Apr'80 by Phonogram Records. Dist: Polygram Distribution Deleted '81.

NOUVEAU RICHE.
Single (7"): released on Mercury, May'81 by Phonogram Records. Dist: Polygram Distribution

ONE TWO FIVE.
Single (7"): released on Mercury, Feb'80 by Phonogram Records. Dist: Polygram Distribution

ORIGINAL SOUNDTRACK, (THE).
Album: released on Mercury, Oct'83 by Phonogram Records. Dist: Polygram Distribution

Cassette: released on Mercury, Oct'83 by Phonogram Records. Dist: Polygram Distribution

POWER OF LOVE.
Single (7"): released on Mercury, Feb'82 by Phonogram Records. Dist: Polygram Distribution

PROFILE.
Album: released on Teldec, Jul'81

Cassette: released on Teldec, Jul'81

RUBBER BULLETS.
Single (7"): released on Import, '80 Dist: Stage One

RUN AWAY.
Single (7"): released on Mercury, Jul'82 by Phonogram Records. Dist: Polygram Distribution

SHEET MUSIC.
Album: released on Mercury, May'83 by Phonogram Records. Dist: Polygram Distribution

Cassette: released on Mercury, May'83 by Phonogram Records. Dist: Polygram Distribution

SONGS WE DO FOR LOVE, (THE).
Album: released on Flyover, Apr'79 by Flyover Records. Dist: Flyover Records

TEN OUT OF 10.
Album: released on Mercury, Nov'81 by Phonogram Records. Dist: Polygram Distribution
Cat. no: 6359 048
Cassette: released on Mercury, Nov'81 by Phonogram Records. Dist: Polygram Distribution

Compact disc: released on Mercury, '83 by Phonogram Records. Dist: Polygram Distribution

TEN OUT OF TEN.
Tracks: / Don't ask / Overdraft on overdrive / Don't turn me away / Nouveaux riches, Les / Memories / Notall hotel / Action man in Motown suit / Listen with your eyes / Lying here with you / Survivor.
Compact disc: released on Mercury, '83 by Phonogram Records. Dist: Polygram Distribution

WINDOWS IN THE JUNGLE.
Album: released on Mercury, Oct'83 by Phonogram Records. Dist: Polygram Distribution

Cassette: released on Mercury, Oct'83 by Phonogram Records. Dist: Polygram Distribution

CHAIN GANG.
Single (7"): released on Ritz, Jun'82 by Ritz Records. Dist: Spartan

STILL IN LOVE WITH YOU.
Tracks: / Still in love with you.
Single (7"): released on Stiff, Mar'86 by Stiff Records. Dist: EMI, Record Services Distribution (Ireland)

Single (12"): released on Stiff, Mar'86 by Stiff Records. Dist: EMI, Record Services Distribution (Ireland)

ENJOY YOURSELF.
Tracks: / If I were you / Teenage cream / Closer to god.
Single (12"): released on Kick, Jan'87 by Mike Collier. Dist: Pinnacle

JOHNNY ORGY.
Album: released on Kick, Aug'86 by Mike Collier. Dist: Pinnacle

THERE'S GOLD IN THEM THERE HILLS.
Single (7"): released on Risk, Apr'84 by Rough Trade Records. Dist: Rough Trade

TENEBRAE Original soundtrack.
Album: released on That's Entertainment, Jul'83 by That's Entertainment Records. Dist: Pinnacle, PRT

BLIND FAITH.
Single (7"): released on Nosrednas, Dec'83 Dist: Cartel Distribution

MILK AND HONEY.
Single (7"): released on Milk & Honey, Mar'84 Dist: Pinnacle

TEN HITS (Various Artists).
Cassette: released on Homespun(Ireland), Dec'82 by Outlet Records. Dist: Outlet

LET THE GOOD TIMES ROLL.
Album: released on Criminal Damage, Nov'86 by Criminal Damage Records. Dist: Backs, Cartel

TENNESSEE CHRISTMAS Various artists.
Tracks: / Away in a manger / Tennessee Christmas / Please come home for Christmas / One bright star / First Noel, The / Greatest little Christmas ever was / Christmas song, The / Christmas in the Caribbean / Christmas is paintin' the town / Winter wonderland.
Notes: Artists: Loretta Lynn, Oak Ridge Boys, Barbara Mandrell, Reba McEntire, John Schneider, Steve Wariner, Nicolette Larson, Jimmy Buffett, Ray Stevens, Brenda Lee.
Album: released on MCA Import, Mar'86 by MCA Records. Dist: Polygram, IMS

TENNESSEE COUNTRY Various artists (Various Artists).
Album: released on Charly, '78 by Charly Records. Dist: Charly, Cadillac

TENNESSEE LEGENDS Various artists (Various Artists).
Notes: Artists include: Sleepy John Estes/Furry Lewis/Gus Cannon etc.
Album: released on Southland (USA), Jun'86 by Jazzology Records (USA). Dist: Jazz Music, Swift

1924-1926.
Double Album: released on Fountain-Retrieval, Dec'82 by Retrieval Records. Dist: Retrieval, VJM, Swift, Jazz Music, Wellard, Chris

CORPORAL BROWN.
Tracks: / Corporal Brown / Corporal Brown (version).
Single (12"): released on Blue Trac, Jun'87 by Blue Mountain Records. Dist: Jetstar

FEVER.
Album: released on Blue Mountain, Nov'85 Dist: Jetstar

NO WORK ON SUNDAY.
Single (12"): released on White, Nov'85

RING THE ALARM.
Single (12"): released on Techniques, Sep'85 Dist: Jetstar Distribution

TENOR SAX ALBUM Various artists (Various Artists).
Tracks: / Girl of my dreams / I.Q. Blues / Scuffin' / Jim Dawgs / Honeysuckle rose / I surrender, dear / Blue skies / Kat's fur / Body & soul / Lunatic / Can't help lovin' dat man / Bad man's bounce / Baby watch that stuff / Misty morning blues / Take the 'A' train / Don't blame me / Savoy blip / Jacquet in the box / Doggin' with doggett / Minor romp / Berry's blues / Last stop (USA) / Flight eleven / Modern fantasy / Confessin' / September song / They can't take that away from me.
Double Album: released on Savoy (USA), Mar'85 by Arista Records. Dist: Polygram, Swift

CRACKING UP.
Single (7"): released on Good Vibration, May'83 by Good Vibrations Records. Dist: Pinnacle, Rough Trade

EDDIE, OLD BOB, DICK & GARY.
Album: released on Stiff, Mar'81

LET THE FOUR WINDS BLOW.
Album: released on Stiff, Nov'81

Cassette: released on Stiff, Nov'81

Single (7"): released on Stiff, Feb'82

SWORDS OF A THOUSAND MEN.
Single (7"): released on Stiff, Mar'81

THREE BELLS IN AROW.
Single (7"): released on Stiff, Oct'80

THROWING MY BABY OUT WITH THE BATHWATER.
Single (7"): released on Stiff, Oct'81

WHO KILLED BAMBI.
Single (7"): released on Virgin, Sep'81

WUNDERBAR.
Single (7"): released on Stiff, Jul'81

PERFECTION.
Single (7"): released on Sirocco, Feb'85 by Sirocco Records. Dist: Pinnacle

LAST WORDS.
Tracks: / Last words / White gold.
Single (7"): released on Epic, May'86 by CBS Records. Dist: CBS

Single (12"): released on Epic, May'86 by CBS Records. Dist: CBS

BREAKING POINT.
Album: released on Roadrunner, Aug'87 by Roadrunner Records (Germany). Dist: Pinnacle

SIX EMPTY PLACES.
Album: released on Cherry Red, Oct'81 by Cherry Red Records. Dist: Pinnacle

MILLION MILES AWAY.
Tracks: / Million miles away / Secret life of Madeline / Peace and love.
Single (7"): released on Chrysalis, Apr'86 by Chrysalis Records. Dist: CBS

Single (12"): released on Chrysalis, Apr'86 by Chrysalis Records. Dist: CBS

Tracks: / When it rains / There goes everything / Rags / This one in you / Where the flowers grow / One life / Beyond me / Walk on / Million miles away / Silver heaven.
Notes: Produced by Stephen Street.
Album: released on Chrysalis, May'86 by Chrysalis Records. Dist: CBS

Cassette: released on Chrysalis, May'86 by Chrysalis Records. Dist: CBS

WHEN IT RAINS.
Tracks: / When it rains / Walk on.
Single (12"): released on Chrysalis, Sep'86 by Chrysalis Records. Dist: CBS

CAN'T IGNORE THE TRAIN.
Single (7"): released on Elektra, Jun'85 by WEA Records. Dist: WEA

Single (12"): released on Elektra, Jun'85 by WEA Records. Dist: WEA

HUMAN CONFLICT NUMBER FIVE.
Album: released on Press (USA). Jun'84

IN MY TRIBE.
Tracks: / What's the matter here? / Hey Jack Kerouac / Like the weather / Cherry tree / Painted desert / Don't talk / Peace train / Gun shy / My sister Rose / Campfire song, A / City of angels / Verdi cries.
Album: released on Elektra, Aug'87 by WEA Records. Dist: WEA

Cassette: released on Elektra, Aug'87 by WEA Records. Dist: WEA

Compact disc: released on Elektra, Aug'87 by WEA Records. Dist: WEA

JUST AS THE TIDE IS A FLOWING.
Single (7"): released on Elektra, Nov'85 by WEA Records. Dist: WEA

MY MOTHER THE WAR.
Single (12"): released on Reflex Records Mar'84 by Reflex Records. Dist: Rough Trade Cartel

PEACE TRAIN.
Single (7"): released on Elektra, Aug'87 by WEA Records. Dist: WEA

SCORPIO RISING.
Tracks: / Scorpio rising / Arbor day.
Single (7"): released on Elektra (USA), Jan'87 by Elektra/Asylum/Nonsuch Records. Dist: WEA

SECRETS OF THE I-CHING.
Album: released on Press (USA), Aug'87

WISHING CHAIR, THE.
Album: released on Elektra, Nov'85 by WE Records. Dist: WEA

Cassette: released on Elektra, Nov'85 by WE Records. Dist: WEA

TEN TO ONE SUPPER HITS VOLUME.
Various artists (Various Artists).
Notes: Catalogue number unknown.
Album: released on Jammy's, Dec'85 by Jammy's Records. Dist: Jetstar

10 YEARS AFTER THE GOLDRUSH
(Various Artists).
Notes: Inc. Philip Boa, Gaye Bikers, Creepers
Album: released on Constrictor, Jun'87 Dist: Rough Trade, Red Rhino, Cartel

ALVIN LEE & COMPANY.
Album: released on Deram, '72 by Decca Records. Dist: Polygram

Cassette: released on Deram, '74 by Decca Records. Dist: Polygram

CLASSIC PERFORMANCES OF TEN YEARS AFTER.
Album: released on Chrysalis, Jan'77 by Chrysalis Records. Dist: CBS

Cassette: released on Chrysalis, Jan'77 by Chrysalis Records. Dist: CBS

COLLECTION: TEN YEARS AFTER.
Double Album: released on Castle Communications, Nov'85 by Castle Communications Dist: Cartel, Pinnacle, Counterpoint

Cassette: released on Castle Communications, Nov'85 by Castle Communications. Dist: Cartel, Pinnacle, Counterpoint

CRICKLEWOOD GREEN.
Album: released on Chrysalis, Jul'75 by Chrysalis Records. Dist: CBS

Cassette: released on Chrysalis, '74 by Chrysalis Records. Dist: CBS

CRICKLEWOOD GREEN.
Album: released on Chrysalis, Jul'75 by Chrysalis Records. Dist: CBS

Cassette: released on Chrysalis, '74 by Chrysalis Records. Dist: CBS

GOIN' HOME.
Album: released on Chrysalis, Apr'75 by Chrysalis Records. Dist: CBS

Cassette: released on Chrysalis, '74 by Chrysalis Records. Dist: CBS

GREATEST HITS: TEN YEARS AFTER VOL.1.
Cassette: released on Teldec, Feb'79 Dist: Pinnacle, Celtic Music

HEAR ME CALLING.
Single 7": released on Deram, '80 by London Records. Dist: Polygram

LOVE LIKE A MAN.
Single 7": released on Old Gold, Oct'83 by Old Gold Records. Dist: PRT, Counterpoint, Lightning, Jazz Music, Taylors

ORIGINAL RECORDINGS VOL.2.
Tracks: / One of these days / Over the hill / Two time mama / Stoned woman / Good morning little schoolgirl / Fifty thousand miles beneath my brain / If you should love me / My baby left me / Think about the times / Working on the road / Love like a man.
Notes: The comprehensive sequel to vol.1,this time covering The Chrysalis period.Includes the 8-minute live version of the 1970 U.K top-tenner 'Love Like A Man',together with tracks from 'SSSSH','WATT','Cricklewood Green',ETC.
Album: released on See For Miles, Jun'87 by See For Miles Records. Dist: Pinnacle

POSITIVE VIBRATIONS.
Album: released on Chrysalis, '74 by Chrysalis Records. Dist: CBS

Cassette: released on Chrysalis, '74 by Chrysalis Records. Dist: CBS

ROCK & ROLL MUSIC TO THE WORLD.
Album: released on Chrysalis, '74 by Chrysalis Records. Dist: CBS

Cassette: released on Chrysalis, '74 by Chrysalis Records. Dist: CBS

SPACE IN TIME, A.
Album: released on Chrysalis, '74 by Chrysalis Records. Dist: CBS

Cassette: released on Chrysalis, '74 by Chrysalis Records. Dist: CBS

SSSH.
Album: released on Chrysalis, Jul'75 by Chrysalis Records. Dist: CBS

Cassette: released on Chrysalis, '79 by Chrysalis Records. Dist: CBS

STONEDHENGE.
Album: released on Deram, '69 by London Records. Dist: Polygram

Cassette: released on Deram, '74 by London Records. Dist: Polygram

TEN YEARS AFTER Original recordings vol.1.
Tracks: / I'm going home / Feel it for me / Portable people / Love until I die / Speed kills / Help me / Going to try / Hear me calling / Don't want you / Woman / Spider in your web / Sounds, The Losing the dogs.
Album: released on See For Miles, Feb'87 by See For Miles Records. Dist: Pinnacle

TEN YEARS AFTER Recorded live.
Double Album: released on Chrysalis, '73 by Chrysalis Records. Dist: CBS

Double cassette:

TEN YEARS AFTER.
Album: released on Hallmark, May'80 by Pickwick Records.

Cassette: released on Hallmark, May'80 by Pickwick Records.

UNDEAD.
Album: released on Deram, '68 by London Records. Dist: Polygram

Cassette: released on Deram, '68 by London Records. Dist: Polygram Deleted '81.

Tenyue, Wayne

MURDEROUS TIME.
Single 12": released on Red Nail, Feb'82 by B & C Music Ltd.. Dist: Jetstar

Tepper, Robert

NO EASY WAY OUT.
Tracks: / No easy way out / Domination.
Single 7": released on Scotti Bros (USA), Feb'86 by Scotti Brothers Records. Dist: Polydor

Terminal

AM I DOING IT RIGHT.
Single 7": released on Termite, Nov'82 Dist: Termite Distribution

Terminal Beach

LOVE ON AUTO.
Single 7": released on TB, Jul'82

Terminal Fun

TWIST AND SURVIVE.
Single 7": released on Projected Image, Nov'82

Terms Of Endearment

TERMS OF ENDEARMENT.
Single 7": released on Capitol, Apr'84 by Capitol Records. Dist: EMI

Ternent, Billy

SHE'S MY LOVELY (Ternent, Billy & His Orchestra).
Album: released on President, Sep'83 by President Records. Dist: President, Jazz Music, Taylors, Spartan

Cassette: released on President, Jan'84 by President Records. Dist: President, Jazz Music, Taylors, Spartan

TERNENT SOUND, THE (Ternent, Billy and His Orchestra).
Tracks: / She's my lovely / How about you / Mr Wonderful / Unforgetable / Hold my hand / Gipsy in my soul, The / Zing went the strings of my heart / Certain smile (A) / Pretty girl is like a melody (A) / Happy days and lonely nights / Tammy / I'll be with you in apple blossom time.
Album: released on President, Apr'86 by President Records. Dist: President, Jazz Music, Taylors, Spartan

THAT UNMISTAKABLE SOUND (Ternent, Billy & His Orchestra).
Album: released on Jasmine, Mar'83 by Jasmine Records. Dist: Counterpoint, Cadillac, Taylors, Wellard, Swift, Jazz Music

Terrahawks

TERRAHAWKS THEME.
Single 7": released on Anderburr, Nov'83 by Anderburr.

Single 12": released on Anderburr, Nov'83 by Anderburr.

Terraplane

GOOD THING GOING.
Tracks: / Good thing going / Night of madness, A / Good life, The*.
Single 7": released on Epic, Jun'87 by CBS Records. Dist: CBS

Single 12": released on Epic, Jun'87 by CBS Records. Dist: CBS

Cassette single: released on Epic, Jun'87 by CBS Records. Dist: CBS

I SURVIVE.
Single 7": released on City, Mar'83 by City Records. Dist: Pinnacle

MOVING TARGET.
Tracks: / Moving target / When I sleep alone / I survive (live) / I can't live without your love (live) / If that's what it takes / Good things going / Promised land / Moving target / Hostage to fortune / Heartburn / Hearts on fire / I will come out fighting / Nothing on but the radio.

CD Index

Issue No.7 Price £1.25

Order from: John Humphries Publishing Ltd.,
Music House,
1 De Cham Avenue,
Hastings, East Sussex.
TN37 6HE
Or phone: 0424 71518

Single 7": released on Epic, Aug'87 by CBS Records. Dist: CBS

Single 12": released on Epic, Aug'87 by CBS Records. Dist: CBS

Gatefold sleeve: released on Epic, Aug'87 by CBS Records. Dist: CBS

Album: released on Epic, Sep'87 by CBS Records. Dist: CBS

Cassette: released on Epic, Sep'87 by CBS Records. Dist: CBS

Compact disc: released on Epic, Sep'87 by CBS Records. Dist: CBS

THAT'S WHAT IT TAKES.
Tracks: / Living after dark / Drugs*.
Single 7": released on Epic, Jan'87 by CBS Records. Dist: CBS

Single 12": released on Epic, Jan'87 by CBS Records. Dist: CBS

WHEN YOU'RE HOT.
Single 7": released on Epic, Jul'85 by CBS Records. Dist: CBS

Single 12": released on Epic, Jul'85 by CBS Records. Dist: CBS

Terrell, Dino

YOU CAN DO IT.
Tracks: / You can do it / You can do it (instrumental) / Acal-poco / You can do it (Dub).
Single 7": released on Lovebeat Int., Mar'86 Dist: PRT, Spartan, Gypsy

Single 12": released on Lovebeat Int., Mar'86 Dist: PRT, Spartan, Gypsy

Terrell, Tammi

GREATEST HITS: TAMMI TERRELL (Terrell, Tammi & Marvin Gaye).
Album: released on Motown, Jul'82 by Motown Records. Dist: BMG

Cassette: released on Motown, Jul'82 by Motown Records. Dist: BMG

Single 7": released on Motown, Oct'81 by Motown Records. Dist: BMG

ONION SONG (Terrell, Tammi & Marvin Gaye).
Single 7": released on Motown, Oct'81 by Motown Records. Dist: BMG

UNITED (Terrell, Tammi & Marvin Gaye).
Album: released on Motown, Mar'82 by Motown Records. Dist: BMG

Cassette: released on Motown, Mar'82 by Motown Records. Dist: BMG

YOU'RE ALL I NEED (see Gaye, Marvin) (Terrell, Tammi & Marvin Gaye).
Album: released on Motown, Oct'81 by Motown Records. Dist: BMG

Cassette: released on Motown, Oct'81 by Motown Records. Dist: BMG

YOU'RE ALL I NEED TO GET BY (Terrell, Tammi & Marvin Gaye).
Single 7": released on Motown, Oct'81 by Motown Records. Dist: BMG

Terri, Billy

SOME GIRLS ARE LADIES.
Tracks: / Some girls are ladies / Love and tears.
Single 7": released on Sonet, May'87 by Sonet Records. Dist: Jazz Music, Swift, Celtic Music, Roots, PRT, Sonet

Territories

TERRITORIES - VOL.1 Various artists (Various artists).
Album: released on Arcadia(USA), Apr'79 by Halcyon Records (USA). Dist: Wellard, Swift, VJM

TERRITORIES- VOL.2 Various artists (Various artists).
Album: released on Arcadia(USA), Apr'79 by Halcyon Records (USA). Dist: Wellard, Swift, VJM

TERRITORIES - VOL.3 THE SOUTH Various artists (Various artists).
Album: released on Arcadia(USA), Apr'79 by Halcyon Records (USA). Dist: Wellard, Swift, VJM

Territory bands (The)

TERRITORY BANDS THE Various artists (Various artists).
Notes: Artists include: Don Albert and his Orchestra/Ernie Fields and his Orchestra/Carolina Cotton Pickers Orchestra/Boots and his Bdds.
Album: released on Jazz Information, Oct'86 by Mr.R&B Records. Dist: Swift

Album: released on Classic Jazz Masters, Aug'87 by Mainline Record Company. Dist: Mainline, Swift

Album: released on Tax, Aug'87 Dist: Jazz Music, Swift, Zodiac

Territory Blues

TERRITORY BLUES 1934-1941 Various artists (Various artists).
Album: released on Magpie, Apr'79 by Flyright Records. Dist: Swift, Jazz Music, Wellard, Cadillac

Terry, Al

AL TERRY & JIM NEWMAN (Terry, Al/Jim Newman).
Album: released on Flyright, Jul'86 by Flyright Records. Dist: Swift, Jazz Music, Wellard, Cadillac

GOOD DEAL LUCILLE.
Album: released on Bear Family, Nov'84 by Bear Family Records(Germany). Dist: Celtic Music, Swift, Rollercoaster

Terry, Alistair

YOUNG AT HEART.
Album: released on FM, Jan'86 by FM-Revolver Records. Dist: BMG

Terry, Clark

AIN'T MISBEHAVIN'.
Album: released on Pablo, Sep'79 by Pablo Records. Dist: Wellard, IMS, BMG, Polygram

Cassette: released on Pablo, Sep'79 by Pablo Records. Dist: Wellard, IMS, BMG, Polygram

ALTERNATIVE BLUES (Terry, Clark, F. Hubbard, D. Gillespie & O. Peterson).
Album: released on Pablo, Sep'82 by Pablo Records. Dist: Wellard, IMS, BMG, Polygram

Cassette: released on Pablo, Sep'82 by Pablo Records. Dist: Wellard, IMS, BMG, Polygram

BIG B-A-D BAND LIVE AT BUDDY'S PLACE.
Album: released on Vanguard, Jan'77 by PRT Records.

CLARK TERRY & HIS JOLLY GIANTS (Terry, Clark & His Jolly Giants).
Album: released on Vanguard, Nov'77 by PRT Records.

COLOR CHANGES.
Compact disc: released on Candid, Jul'87 Dist: Counterpoint, Cadillac, Jazz Music, Wellard. Estim retail price in Nov'87 was £11.99.

Album: released on Candid, Dec'86 Dist: Counterpoint, Cadillac, Jazz Music, Wellard

DUKE WITH A DIFFERENCE.
Album:

FUNK DUMPLIN'S (Terry, Clark Quintet).
Album: released on Matrix(Denmark), Apr'81 Dist: Jazz Horizons, Jazz Music

HAPPY HORNS OF, THE.
Album: released on Jasmine, Jun'82 by Jasmine Records. Dist: Counterpoint, Cadillac, Taylors, Wellard, Swift, Jazz Music

Cassette: released on Jasmine, Jun'82 by Jasmine Records. Dist: Counterpoint, Cadillac, Taylors, Wellard, Swift, Jazz Music

IT'S WHAT'S HAPPENIN'.
Album: released on Jasmine, Aug'82 by Jasmine Records. Dist: Counterpoint, Cadillac, Taylors, Wellard, Swift, Jazz Music

Cassette: released on Jasmine, Aug'82 by Jasmine Records. Dist: Counterpoint, Cadillac, Taylors, Wellard, Swift, Jazz Music

LIVE ON 57TH STREET (Terry, Clark Big Bad Band).
Album: released on Big Bear, Jul'78 by Big Bear Records. Dist: Big Bear, Swift, Jazz Music

MEMORIES OF DUKE.
Album: released on Pablo, '78 by Pablo Records. Dist: Wellard, IMS, BMG, Polygram

Cassette: released on Pablo, '78 by Pablo Records. Dist: Wellard, IMS, BMG, Polygram

MOTHER - MOTHER (Terry, Clark & Zoot Sims).
Album: released on Pablo, Aug'80 by Pablo Records. Dist: Wellard, IMS, BMG, Polygram

Cassette: released on Pablo, Aug'80 by Pablo Records. Dist: Wellard, IMS, BMG, Polygram

OSCAR PETERSON & CLARK TERRY (Terry, Clark & Oscar Peterson).
Album: released on Pablo(USA), '82 by Ace Records. Dist: PRT

Cassette: released on Pablo(USA), '82 by Ace Records. Dist: PRT

SERENADE TO A BUS SEAT (Terry, Clark Quintet).
Album: released on Original Jazz Classics (USA), Jun'86 by Fantasy(USA). Dist: IMS, Polygram

YES THE BLUES.
Album: released on Pablo, Jul'81 by Pablo Records. Dist: Wellard, IMS, BMG, Polygram

Cassette: released on Pablo, Jul'81 by Pablo Records. Dist: Wellard, IMS, BMG, Polygram

Terry & Gerry

BANKING ON SIMON.
Single 7": released on In Tape, Jul'85 by In Tape Records. Dist: Red Rhino, Cartel

Single 12": released on In Tape, Jul'85 by In Tape Records. Dist: Red Rhino, Cartel

BUTLERS ON THE BREAD.
Single 7": released on Vindaloo, Sep'84 by Vindaloo Records. Dist: WEA, Cartel

CLOSED SHOP.
Single 7": released on In Tape, Feb'85 by In Tape Records. Dist: Red Rhino, Cartel

CLOTHES SHOP.
Single 12": released on In Tape, Aug'85 by In Tape Records. Dist: Red Rhino, Cartel

FROM LUBBOCK AND CLINTWOOD EAST.
Album: released on In Tape, Oct'85 by In Tape Records. Dist: Red Rhino, Cartel

Cassette: released on In Tape, Oct'85 by In Tape Records. Dist: Red Rhino, Cartel

LAST BULLET IN THE GUN (THE).
Tracks: / Last bullet in the gun (The).
Single 7": released on In Tape, Aug'86 by In Tape Records. Dist: Red Rhino, Cartel

Single 12": released on In Tape, Aug'86 by In Tape Records. Dist: Red Rhino, Cartel

RESERVATION.
Tracks: / Reservation.
Single 7": released on In Tape, Mar'86 by In Tape Records. Dist: Red Rhino, Cartel

Single 12": released on In Tape, Mar'86 by In Tape Records. Dist: Red Rhino, Cartel

Terry, Helen

ACT OF MERCY.
Tracks: / Act of mercy / Over the border.
Single 7": released on Virgin, Jul'86 by Virgin Records. Dist: Virgin, EMI

Single 12": released on Virgin, Jul'86 by Virgin Records. Dist: Virgin, EMI

BLUE NOTES.
Album: released on Virgin, Sep'86 by Virgin Records. Dist: Virgin, EMI

Cassette: released on Virgin, Sep'86 by Virgin Records. Dist: Virgin, EMI

Compact disc: released on Virgin, Oct'86 by Virgin Records. Dist: Virgin, EMI

COME ON AND FIND ME.
Tracks: / Come on and find me / Come on and find me / Reach out / River (The).
Single 7": released on Virgin, Oct'86 by Virgin Records. Dist: Virgin, EMI

Single 12": released on Virgin, Oct'86 by Virgin Records. Dist: Virgin, EMI

Terry, Lillian

OO-SHOO-BE-DOO-BE....OO,OO.
Notes: With Dizzy Gillespie
Compact disc: released on Soul Note (Italy), '86 Dist: Harmonia Mundi Distributors

Terry, M

I LOVE MUSIC.
Tracks: / I love music / Moustachio.
Single 7": released on MCA, May'86 by MCA Records. Dist: Polygram

Single 12": released on MCA, May'86 by MCA Records. Dist: Polygram

Album: released on Storyville, Sep'86 by Storyville Records. Dist: Swift, Wellard

Terry, Mike

30 PIANO FAVOURITES.
Album: released on President, Apr'82 by President Records. Dist: President, Jazz Music, Taylors, Spartan

CLACKERS.
Album: released on Joy, May'74 by President Records. Dist: President, Jazz Music, Taylors, Spartan

LIVE AT THE PAVILLION THEATRE GLASGOW VOL.2.
Album: released on President, Sep'77 by President Records. Dist: President, Jazz Music, Taylors, Spartan

LIVE AT THE PAVILLION THEATRE GLASGOW, VOL.1.
Album: released on President, Sep'77 by President Records. Dist: President, Jazz Music, Taylors, Spartan

QUEEN OF CLUBS.
Album: released on President, Jul'84 by President Records. Dist: President, Jazz Music, Taylors, Spartan

TRIBUTE TO WINIFRED ATTWELL.
Album: released on President, Jul'85 by President Records. Dist: President, Jazz Music, Taylors, Spartan

Cassette: released on President, Jul'85 by President Records. Dist: President, Jazz Music, Taylors, Spartan

Terry, Sonny

SONNY TERRY 1952.
Album: released on Krazy Kat(USA), Jan'87 Dist: Swift, Celtic Music, Wellard, Projection, Taylors, Charly, Hotshot, IRS

SONNY'S STORY.
Album: released on Prestige, Jun'84 by Prestige Records (USA). Dist: BMG, Swift

WALK ON (Terry, Sonny/Brownie McGhee).
Album: released on Astan, Nov'84 by Astan Records.

Cassette: released on Astan, Nov'84 by Astan Records.

WHOOPIN'.
Notes: with Johnny Winter/Willie Dixon/Styve Homnick.
Album: released on Sonet, Mar'87 by Sonet Records. Dist: Jazz Music, Swift, Celtic Music, Roots, PRT, Sonet

WHOOPIN' THE BLUES.
Tracks: / Whoopin' the blues / All alone blues / Worried man blues / Leaving' blues / Scream' and cryin' blues / Riff and harmonica jump / Crow Jane blues / Beer garden blues / Hot headed woman / Custard pie blues / Early morning blues / Harmonica rag / Dirty mistreater don't you know / Telephone blues.
Album: released on Charly (R&B), May'86 by Charly Records. Dist: Charly, Cadillac

WIZARD OF THE HARMONICA.
Album: released on Storyville(Denmark), Jul'81

Terry, Tony

SHE'S FLY.
Tracks: / She's fly.
Single 7": released on Epic, Oct'87 by CBS Records. Dist: CBS

Single 12": released on Epic, Oct'87 by CBS Records. Dist: CBS

Teschemaker, Frank

MUGGSY SPANIER & FRANK TESCHEMAKER (see Spanier, Muggsy).

Tesco Bombers

HERNANDO'S HIDEAWAY.
Single 7": released on Y, Jan'82 by Y Records.

Tesla

LITTLE SUZIE (little Suzie's on the up).
Tracks: / Little Suzie / Before my eyes / Comin' atcha live (remix).
Single 7": released on Geffen, Mar'87 by Geffen Records. Dist: WEA

Single 12": released on Geffen, Mar'87 by Geffen Records. Dist: WEA

MECHANICAL RESONANCE.
Tracks: / Ez come ez go / Cumin' atcha live / Gettin' better / 2 Late 4 love / Rock me to the top / We're no good together / Modern day cowboy / Changes / Little Suzi / Love me / Cover queen / Before my eyes.
Album: released on WEA, Jan'87 by WEA Records. Dist: WEA

Cassette: released on WEA, Jan'87 by WEA Records. Dist: WEA

Tess

TESS Original soundtrack.
Album: released on Import, Apr'81 Dist: Stage One

TESS OF THE D'URBERVILLES Hardy, Thomas (Shearer, Moira).
Double cassette: released on Argo(Spokenword), Nov'82 by Decca Classics. Dist: Polygram

Test compact disc

TEST COMPACT DISC Various artists (Various artists).
Notes: Digital stereo
Compact disc: released on RCA, Feb'85 Dist: BMG

Test Department

BEATING THE RETREAT.
Album: released on Some Bizzare, Jul'84 by Charisma Records. Dist: EMI, CBS, Polygram

Cassette: released on Some Bizzare, Jul'84 by Charisma Records. Dist: EMI, CBS, Polygram

Album: released on Some Bizzare, Nov'84 by Charisma Records. Dist: EMI, CBS, Polygram

Cassette: released on Some Bizzare, Nov'84 by Charisma Records. Dist: EMI, CBS, Polygram

Album: released on Mercury, Sep'87 by Phonogram Records. Dist: Polygram

COMPULSION.
Single 12": released on Some Bizzare, Dec'83 by Charisma Records. Dist: EMI, CBS, Polygram

GOODNIGHT OUT, A.
Album: released on Some Bizzare, 21 Nov'87 by Charisma Records. Dist: EMI, CBS, Polygram

SECOND EDITION BOXED SET.
Album: released on Some Bizzare, Dec'84 Dist: Rough Trade, Cartel

SHOULDER TO SHOULDER.
Album: released on Ministry Of Powert, Feb'85 Dist: Red Rhino, Cartel

UNACCEPTABLE FACE OF FREEDOM.
Album: released on Ministry Of Powert, Mar'86 Dist: Red Rhino, Cartel

Test disc (BBC)

BBC STEREO TEST DISC.
Album: released on BBC, May'75 by BBC Records & Tapes. Dist: EMI

Test Tubes

PRESSED FOR CASH.
Single 12": released on Trapper, Mar'84 Dist: Pinnacle, Rough Trade

Testament

LEGACY,THE.
Tracks: / Over the wall / Haunting,The / Burnt offerings / Raging waters / Curse of the legions of death / First strike is deadly / Do or die / Alone in the dark / Apocalypitc city.
Album: released on Atlantic, Jun'87 by WEA Records. Dist: WEA, Swift, Celtic Music

Cassette: released on Atlantic, Jun'87 by WEA Records. Dist: WEA, Swift, Celtic Music

Testament Of Rock

TESTAMENT OF ROCK, VOL 1 Various artists (Various artists).
Tracks: / Buena sera / Let's have a party / Be-bop-a-lula / Loop de loop / Medley / Stupid Cupid / Ma he's making eyes at me / Tweedle Dee / Woman lore / Pennies from heaven / Telephone baby / Over the rainbow / Race the devil / Rip it up / Hum ding a ling / Nothing's too good for my baby / She she little Sheila / Rock your baby / Willie and the hand jive / Jump, jive and wail / Dona'a wan'a / Five feet of lovin' / Three girls named Molly / Banana split for my baby / Oh Marie! / Mumble Rosie / Candy man / Little mama / I ain't got nobody / Dance to the bop / Kansas city / Maybelline / When it's sleepy time down south / Such a night / Long tall Sally / Blue jean bop.
Notes: In short...some great names...great music.
Album: released on Pathe Marconi (France), Dec'85 Dist: Swift

Testcard F

BANDWAGON TANGO.
Single 7": released on Backs, Apr'83 by Backs Records. Dist: Backs, Cartel

THIRD STROKE.
Single 7": released on Backs, Mar'84 by Backs Records. Dist: Backs, Cartel

Teugels, Walem

MORTIER ORGAN VOL.1.
Album: released on Joy, May'74 by President Records. Dist: President, Jazz Music, Taylors, Spartan

MORTIER ORGAN VOL.2.
Album: released on Joy, May'74 by President Records. Dist: President, Jazz Music, Taylors, Spartan

Teupen, Johnny

GOLDEN MELODIES.
Compact disc: released on Delta, Oct'86 by Delta Records. Dist: Target, Zodiac

Teutonic Invasion

TEUTONIC INVASION PT.1 (Various artists).
Notes: Inc. Paradox, Crows.
Album: released on Rock Hard, May'87

Tew, Alan

YOU ARE THE SUNSHINE OF MY LIFE (Tew, Alan Orchestra).
Album: released on Golden Hour, Sep'77 by PRT Records.

Cassette: released on Golden Hour, Sep'77 by PRT Records.

Tewkesbury Abbey

CHAPEL HOUR - BLUE COAT SCHOOL, BIRMINGHAM.
Album: released on Abbey, Jan'77 by SCS Music Ltd.. Dist: PRT, Taylors, Gamut

Tex and the Horseheads

LIFE IS COOL.
Album: released on Enigma, Nov'85 by Enigma Records. Dist: Rough Trade, Cartel, EMI, Pinnacle, Silva Screen Records

LIVE: TEX & THE HORSEHEADS.
Album: released on Enigma, Dec'86 by Enigma Records. Dist: Rough Trade, Cartel, EMI, Pinnacle, Silva Screen Records

Tex, Joe

AIN'T GONNA BUMP NO MORE.
Single 7": released on Old Gold, Jul'82 by Old Gold Records. Dist: PRT, Counterpoint, Lightning, Jazz Music, Taylors

BEST OF JOE TEX.
Album: released on Atlantic, Jul'84 by WEA Records. Dist: WEA, Swift, Celtic Music

Cassette: released on Atlantic, Jul'84 by WEA Records. Dist: WEA, Swift, Celtic Music

Tex, John

GUESS WHO'S A SUCKER FOR YOU.
Single 12": released on Disco Tex, Nov'84 by Disco Tex Records. Dist: Jetstar

Tex Mex

TEX MEX BORDER MUSIC VOL.24 Various artists (Various artists).
Album: released on Folklyric(USA), Aug'85 by Arhoolie Records. Dist: Jazz Music, Projection, Roots, Celtic Music, Cadillac, Ross, Duncans, Impetus

TEX MEX (VOL 17) Various female artists (Various artists).
Album: released on Folklyric(USA), Mar'85 by Arhoolie Records. Dist: Jazz Music, Projection, Roots, Celtic Music, Cadillac, Ross, Duncans, Impetus

Texas Blues

TEXAS BLUES Dallas 1928.
Album: released on Fountain-Retrieval, Jul'87 by Retrieval Records. Dist: Retrieval, Wellard, Swift

TEXAS BLUES Various artists (Various artists).
Album: released on Arhoolie(USA), May'81 by Arhoolie Records. Dist: Jazz Music, Projection, Roots, Celtic Music, Cadillac, Ross, Duncans, Impetus

TEXAS BLUES 1928-29 (Various artists).
Album: released on HK, Sep'87 Dist: Swift

Texas chainsaw massacre 2

TEXAS CHAINSAW MASSACRE 2 (Various artists).
Album: released on MCA, Nov'86 by MCA Records. Dist: Polygram

Cassette: released on MCA, Nov'86 by MCA Records. Dist: Polygram

Texas Country Blues

TEXAS COUNTRY BLUES 1948-1952 (Various artists).
Album: released on Krazy Kat(USA), Nov'86 Dist: Swift, Celtic Music, Wellard, Projection, Taylors, Charly, Hotshot, IRS

Album: released on Krazy Kat(USA), Dec'86 Dist: Swift, Celtic Music, Wellard, Projection, Taylors, Charly, Hotshot, IRS

Texas Dance Hall

TEXAS DANCE HALL FAVOURITES Various artists (Various artists).
Album: released on Big Beat, May'82 by Ace Records. Dist: Celtic Music, Pinnacle, Jazz Music, Projection

Texas Flashbacks

TEXAS FLASHBACKS (Various artists).
Album: released on Antar, Oct'87 by Bam Caruso Records. Dist: Fast Forward, Revolver Cartel, Probe, Red Rhino

TEXAS FLASHBACKS VOL 2 (Various artists).
Album: released on Antar, Oct'87 by Bam Caruso Records. Dist: Fast Forward, Revolver Cartel, Probe, Red Rhino

TEXAS FLASHBACKS VOL.3 (Various artists).
Album: released on Antar, Aug'86 by Bam Caruso Records. Dist: Fast Forward, Revolver Cartel, Probe, Red Rhino

TEXAS FLASHBACKS VOL.4 (Various artists).
Album: released on Antar, Aug'86 by Bam Caruso Records. Dist: Fast Forward, Revolver Cartel, Probe, Red Rhino

TEXAS FLASHBACKS VOL.5 (Various artists).
Album: released on Antar, Nov'86 by Bam Caruso Records. Dist: Fast Forward, Revolver Cartel, Probe, Red Rhino

Texas hillbilly boogie

TEXAS HILLBILLY BOOGIE Various artists (Various artists).
Notes: Artists include Hess, Sergent, York.
Album: released on Esoldun, Sep'87 by Esoldun Records. Dist: Swift

Texas Mavericks

WHO ARE THESE MASKED MEN?.
Album: released on New Rose, Jun'87 Dist: Pinnacle

Texas Psychedelia

TEXAS PSYCHEDELIA FROM THE 60'S Various artists (Various artists).
Album: released on Eva-Lolita, Jul'86 Dist: Pinnacle

Texas Rhythm & Blues

TEXAS RHYTHM & BLUES Various artists (Various artists).
Album: released on Ace, Mar'81 by Ace Records. Dist: PRT, Pinnacle, Celtic Music, Cadillac, Jazz Music, Wellard

Texas Rockabilly

TEXAS ROCKABILLY (Various artists).
Tracks: / Love come back to me / Let me slide / I'm not skukin / Oakies in the pokie / High class feelin / Pour me a glass of wine / Sleep rock a roll rock a baby / Swing bop boogie / I gottum / Lay your head on my shoulder / Don't mean maybe,baby / Oklahoma blues / Don't come cryin'.
Album: released on Esoldun, Dec'87 by Esoldun Records. Dist: Swift

TEXAS ROCKABILLY VOL. 2 various artists (Various artists).
Notes: Jerry Irby, Hank Stanford etc.
Album: released on Esoldun, Oct'87 by Esoldun Records. Dist: Swift

Texas sand

TEXAS SAND Various artists (Various artists).
Album: released on Rambler, Jul'81 Dist: Swift, Wellard

Texas Seaport

TEXAS SEAPORT 1934-37 Various artists (Various artists).
Album: released on Magpie, Jan'79 by Flyright Records. Dist: Swift, Jazz Music, Wellard, Cadillac

Texas-Mexican

TEXAS-MEXICAN BORDER MUSIC VOL. 1 First Women duets, The (Various artists).
Notes: with Hermanas Padilla, Hermanas Mendoza, Carmen y Laura etc. 1930-1950. Mono.
Album: released on Folklyric(USA), Feb'87 by Arhoolie Records. Dist: Jazz Music, Projection, Roots, Celtic Music, Cadillac, Ross, Duncans, Impetus

Textones

CEDAR CREEK.
Album: released on Enigma, Oct'87 by Enigma Records. Dist: Rough Trade, Cartel, EMI, Pinnacle, Silva Screen Records

CEDAR RIDGE.
Compact disc: released on Enigma, Oct'87 by Enigma Records. Dist: Rough Trade, Cartel, EMI, Pinnacle, Silva Screen Records

VACATION/ TIME IS RIGHT, THE.
Single 7": released on Big Beat, Aug'82 by Ace Records. Dist: Celtic Music, Pinnacle, Jazz Music, Projection

Teyte, Dame Maggie

HER LIFE & ART.
Album: released on BBC, Oct'79 by BBC Records & Tapes. Dist: EMI

Cassette: released on BBC, Oct'79 by BBC Records & Tapes. Dist: EMI

Thackray, Jake

JAKE THACKRAY AND SONGS.
Album: released on Dingles, '83 by Dingles Records. Dist: Projection, Celtic Music, Roots, Spartan

LIVE PERFORMANCE.
Album: released on EMI, Nov'76 by EMI Records(UK). Dist: EMI

VERY BEST OF JAKE THACKRAY.
Album: released on EMI, Dec'75 by EMI Records(UK). Dist: EMI

Cassette: released on EMI, Dec'75 by EMI Records(UK). Dist: EMI

Thailand

LAO MUSIC OF THE NORTH EAST.
Album: released on Lyrichord(USA), '82 by Lyrichord Records(USA). Dist: Flexitron Ltd., Roots

THAILAND Various traditional Asian music (Various artists).
Album: released on IMS, Sep'85 by Polydor Records. Dist: IMS, Polygram

Thamby

ACQUAINTANCES/ AQUAINTANCES IN B.
Single 7": released on Freshly Cut, Oct'82 Dist: Backs, Cartel

Thamesdown Singers

SING.
Album: released on Abbey, Jul'76 by SCS Music Ltd.. Dist: PRT, Taylors, Gamut

Thanes

MY GIRL EP.
Single 7": released on DDT, Sep'87 by D.D.T Records. Dist: Fast Forward, Cartel

Thanet Gospel Choir

BEST LOVED CAROLS.
Album: by Pilgrim Records. Dist: Rough Trade, Cartel

Thank For The Memory

THANK FOR THE MEMORY Various artists (Various artists).
Album: released on Swinghouse, '84 Dist: Jazz Music, Swift, Wellard, Celtic Music

Tharpe, Sister Rosetta

SWINGS & ROCKS.
Album: released on Rosetta(USA), Sep'87 Dist: Swift

That Beatin' Rhythm

THAT BEATIN' RHYTHM Various artists (Various artists).
Album: released on Inferno, May'84 by Inferno Records. Dist: Inferno, Cartel, Pinnacle

That Dobro Sound...

THAT DOBRO SOUND'S GOIN' ROUND (Various artists).
Album: released on Starday, Apr'87

Cassette: released on Starday, Apr'87

That Driving Beat

THAT DRIVIN' BEAT (Various artists).
Album: released on Soul Supply, Jun'86 Dist: Backs, Cartel

Album: released on Soul Supply, Jan'87 Dist: Backs, Cartel

Cassette: released on Soul Supply, Dec'84 Dist: Backs, Cartel

That Good Ole...

THAT GOOD OLE ROCK'N'ROLL SOUND (Various artists).
Album: released on White, Jul'87 by White Records. Dist: CSA

That Newport Jazz

THAT NEWPORT JAZZ All star performances recorded live at Newport Jazz Festival (Various artists).
Tracks: / Undecided / These foolish things (remind me of you) / Sweet Georgia Brown / Stardust / Chasin' at Newport / Rosetta / Just you, just me / When your lover has gone / Lester leaps in.
Album: released on CBS, Jul'87 by CBS Records. Dist: CBS

Cassette: released on CBS, Jul'87 by CBS Records. Dist: CBS

That Ole Devil...

THAT OLE DEVIL CALLED LOVE (Various artists).
Tracks: / Can't smile without you / Crying / First time ever I say your face / Hard to say I'm sorry / I love a rainy night / Endless love / Lyin' eyes / Mandy / Move closer / Knights in white satin / One day I'll fly away / One more night / Pie Jesu / She's out of my life / Tara's theme / That ole devil called love / Keep on loving you / With you I'm born again / You might need somebody / I made it through the rain.
Compact disc: released on The Collection, Aug'87 by Object Enterprises Ltd. Dist: Jazz Music

That Petrol Emotion

BABBLE.
Album: released on Polydor, May'87 by Polydor Records. Dist: Polygram, Polydor

Cassette: released on Polydor, May'87 by Polydor Records. Dist: Polygram, Polydor

Compact disc: released on Polydor, May'87 by Polydor Records. Dist: Polygram, Polydor

BIG DECISION.
Tracks: / Big decision / Souldeep.
Single 7": released on Polydor, Mar'87 by Polydor Records. Dist: Polygram, Polydor

Single 12": released on Polydor, Mar'87 by Polydor Records. Dist: Polygram, Polydor

GENIUS MOVE.
Tracks: / Genius move / Party games.
Single 7": released on Virgin, Oct'87 by Virgin Records. Dist: Virgin, EMI

IT'S A GOOD THING.
Tracks: / It's a good thing / Mine.
Single 7": released on Demon, Apr'86 by Demon Records. Dist: Celtic Music, Pinnacle, Jazz Music

Single 12": released on Demon, Apr'86 by Demon Records. Dist: Celtic Music, Pinnacle, Jazz Music

KEEN.
Tracks: / Keen.
Single 12": released on Pink, Oct'86 by Pink Records. Dist: Rough Trade

Single 7": released on Pink, Jul'85 by Pink Records. Dist: Rough Trade

MANIC POP THRILL.
Album: released on Demon, Jul'86 by Demon Records. Dist: Celtic Music, Pinnacle, Jazz Music

Cassette: released on Demon, Jul'86 by Demon Records. Dist: Celtic Music, Pinnacle, Jazz Music

Compact disc: released on Demon, Jul'86 by Demon Records. Dist: Celtic Music, Pinnacle, Jazz Music

NATURAL KIND OF JOY.
Tracks: / Natural kind of joy.
Single 7": released on Demon, Aug'86 by Demon Records. Dist: Celtic Music, Pinnacle, Jazz Music

Single 12": released on Demon, Jun'86 by Demon Records. Dist: Celtic Music, Pinnacle, Jazz Music

PEEL SESSION, THE.
Tracks: / V2 / Lettuce / Blind spot / Can't stop.
Single 12": released on Strange Fruit, Sep'87 by Clive Selwood. Dist: Pinnacle

SWAMP.
Tracks: / Swamp (Remix) / Swamp (Ext. Mix) / Swamp / Me and baby brother, Creeping to the cross / Dance your ass off / Creeping to the cross (Shorter & better).
Single 7": released on Polydor, Jul'87 by Polydor Records. Dist: Polygram, Polydor

Single 12": released on Polydor, Jul'87 by Polydor Records. Dist: Polygram, Polydor

Extended-play record: released on Polydor, Jul'87 by Polydor Records. Dist: Polygram, Polydor

VS.
Single 7": released on Noise A Noise, Oct'85 Dist: Rough Trade, Cartel

Single 12": released on Noise A Noise, Oct'85 Dist: Rough Trade, Cartel

That Toddlin' Town

THAT TODDLIN' TOWN - CHICAGO 1926-28 Various artists (Various artists).
Album: released on Swaggie(Australia), Jan'83 Dist: Jazz Music

That Was Rock

THAT WAS ROCK Various artists (Various artists).
Video-cassette (VHS): released on Channel 5, '87 Dist: W.H. Smiths

Thatcher on Acid

ANOTHER ONE GIRL.
Tracks: / Another one girl.
Single 12": released on All The Madmen, Jul'86 by All The Madmen Records. Dist: Rough Trade, Cartel

That's Entertainment

THAT'S ENTERTAINMENT (Various artists).
Album: released on BBC, Apr'87 by BBC Records & Tapes. Dist: EMI

Cassette: released on BBC, Apr'87 by BBC Records & Tapes. Dist: EMI

THAT'S ENTERTAINMENT-PART II Original soundtrack (Various artists).
Tracks: / Rebound / Lonely weekenends / Stairway to nowhere / She's gone away / You don't care / I wanna rock / Memories of you / Judy / Overture / Drive in / That's entertainment / For me and my gal / I've got a feelin' you're foolin' / Hi-Lili, Hi-Lo / All of you / Lady is a tramp / Smoke gets in your eyes / Rock baby rock it / Temptation / Tennessee zip / Takin' a chance on love / Love crazy baby / Treat me right / Inka dinka doo / Get it off your mind / What's the reason / Easter parade / You call everybody darlin' / Couple of swells, A / Go ahead baby / Huh babe / High high high / Good morning / My baby don't rock / That's what I tell my heard / Triplets / Last time I saw Paris, The / Born to sing the blues / I need your lovin' kiss / I'll build a stairway to paradise / Goin' crazy / There's no business like show buiness / Mad at you / Have yourself a merry little Christmas / Good lookin' woman / Rock-a-bye baby / I got rhythm / Sweet rocking mama / Sonny boy / Fire engine red / Tomorrow / Please don't cry over me / That depends on you / All I want is you / I remember it well / My one desire / Down on the border / Don't let me down / Shake rattle and roll / It's me baby / Rocking with my baby / Trumpet / Ten cats down / Fools hall of fame / Cheese and crackers / Sally Jo / We wanna boogie / Red headed woman / Ain't got a thing / Feelin' good / Truckin' down the avenue / Restless / Find my baby for me / Sadie Brown / Itch / Rock'n'roll Ruby / Stop the world / Uranium rock / Dear John / Flyin' saucer rock and roll / I want you baby / Red hot / Blue suede shoes / My baby done left me.
Compact disc: released on CBS, Mar'87 by CBS Records. Dist: CBS

That's Funk

THAT'S FUNK VOL.2 Various artists (Various artists).
Album: released on Teldec, Sep'84 Dist: Pinnacle, Celtic Music

Cassette: released on Teldec, Sep'84 Dist: Pinnacle, Celtic Music

That's My Rabbit...

THAT'S MY RABBIT, MY DOG CAUGHT IT (Various artists).
Tracks: / Groundhog / Old grey horse / My pretty little pink / Granny went to the meeting with her old shoes on / Spanish fandango / Run banjo / Pearly dew / Blues / Lights in the valley / Lost boy blues / Fe fe phochaux / Kimball house / Last of Sizemore / Hunky dory / Big-footed nigger / That's my rabbit, my dog caught it / Rymer's favourite / Le Rille Cajun / Lost Indian / Jig / Bibb county hoe down / Peakock rag.

That's Soul

THAT'S SOUL 20 Original hits (Various artists).
Notes: 20 original hits by: Martha Reeves,Soloman Burke,sam Cooke,Sam&Dave,Eddie Floyd,Percy Sledge, etc.
Compact disc: released on Delta, May'87 by Delta Records. Dist: Target, Zodiac

That's the way I feel now

THAT'S THE WAY I FEEL NOW A tribute to Thelonious Monk (Various artists).
Album: released on A&M, Aug'84 by A&M Records. Dist: Polygram

Cassette: released on A&M, Aug'84 by A&M Records. Dist: Polygram

The Name Escapes Me

HEARTBEAT.
Single 7": released on Piranha, Oct'87 Dist: BMG

The The

HEARTLAND.
Tracks: / Heartland / Born in New S.A. / Flesh and bones / Sweet bird of truth.
Single 7": released on Epic, Jul'86 by CBS Records. Dist: CBS

Single 12": released on Epic, Jul'86 by CBS Records. Dist: CBS

Single 12": released on Some Bizarre, Aug'86 by Virgin Records. Dist: EMI, CBS, Polygram

INFECTED.
Tracks: / Infected / Out of the blue (into the fire) / Heartland / Angels of deception / Sweet bird of truth / Slow train to dawn / Twilight of a champion / Mercy beat, The / Infected / Out of the blue (into the fire) / Heartland / Angels of deception / Sweet bird of truth / Slow train to dawn / Twilight of a champion / Mercy beat / Infected / Disturbed.
Compact disc: released on Epic, May'87 by CBS Records. Dist: CBS

Album: released on Epic, Nov'86 by CBS Records. Dist: CBS

Cassette: released on Epic, Nov'86 by CBS Records. Dist: CBS

Video-cassette (VHS): released on CBS, Apr'87 by CBS Records. Dist: CBS

Single 7": released on Epic, Oct'86 by CBS Records. Dist: CBS

Single 12": released on Epic, Oct'86 by CBS Records. Dist: CBS

NATURE OF VIRTURE, THE.
Single 7": released on Epic, Feb'83 by CBS Records. Dist: CBS

Single 12": released on Epic, Feb'83 by CBS Records. Dist: CBS

SLOW TRAIN TO DAWN.
Tracks: / Harbour lights.
Single 7": released on Epic, Jan'87 by CBS Records. Dist: CBS

Single 12": released on Epic, Jan'87 by CBS Records. Dist: CBS

SOUL MINING.
Album: released on Epic, Oct'83 by CBS Records. Dist: CBS

Cassette: released on Epic, Oct'83 by CBS Records. Dist: CBS

SWEET BIRD OF TRUTH.
Notes: Limited edition of 7,5000
Single 7": released on Epic, May'86 by CBS Records. Dist: CBS

SWEET BIRD OF TRUTH.
Tracks: / Soul mining / Sweet bird of truth / Sleeping juice / Harbour lights.
Single 7": released on Epic, May'87 by CBS Records. Dist: CBS

Single 12": released on Epic, May'87 by CBS Records. Dist: CBS

Compact disc single: released on Epic, May'87 by CBS Records. Dist: CBS

Cassette single: released on Epic, May'87 by CBS Records. Dist: CBS

THIS IS THE DAY.
Single 7": released on Some Bizzare, Jul'84 by Charisma Records. Dist: EMI, CBS, Polygram

Theatre of Hate

DO YOU BELIEVE IN THE WEST WORLD.
Single 7": released on Burning Rome, Jan'82 Dist: CBS

Single 12": released on Burning Rome, Jan'82 Dist: CBS

Single 7": released on Burning Rome, Jul'84 Dist: CBS

EASTWORLD.
Single 7": released on Burning Rome, Nov'82 Dist: CBS

Single 12": released on Burning Rome, Nov'82 Dist: CBS

HOP, THE.
Single 7": released on Burning Rome, May'82 Dist: CBS

Single 12": released on Stiff, Nov'85 by Stiff Records. Dist: EMI, Record Services(Ireland), Jazz Music

ORIGINAL SIN (LIVE).
Tracks: / Original sin / Westworld / Klan (The) / Conquistador / Poppies / Incinerator / Judgement hymn / 63 / Rebel without a brain / Legion.
Album: released on Dojo, Apr'86 by Castle Communications Records. Dist: Nine Mile, Cartel

REVOLUTION (SINGLES ALBUM).
Album: released on Burning Rome, Aug'84 Dist: CBS

Cassette: released on Burning Rome, Aug'84 Dist: CBS

Thee People

IT HAPPENED ON A SUNDAY MORNING.
Single 7": released on Deb, Feb'83 by Deb Records. Dist: Spartan

Theilmans, Toots

AQUARELA DO BRASIL.
Compact disc: released on Philips (Germany), '86 Dist: IMS, Polygram

AUTUMN LEAVES.
Album: released on Soul Note, May'85

Cassette: released on Soul Note, May'85

HARMONICA JAZZ.
Album: released on CBS, Feb'84 by CBS Records. Dist: CBS

Cassette: released on CBS, Feb'84 by CBS Records. Dist: CBS

LIVE: TOOTS THEILMANS.
Album: released on Polydor, Aug'81 by Polydor Records. Dist: Polygram, Polydor

MUSIC FOR THE MILLIONS.
Album: released on Polydor (Germany), Jun'83 Dist: IMS-Polygram

Cassette: released on Polydor (Germany), Jun'83 Dist: IMS-Polygram

NE ME QUITTE PAS.
Tracks: / Ne me quitte pas / Blue 'n' green / All Blues / Stardust / Autumn leaves / Velas.
Album: released on SPI Milan (France), Jul'87, IMS

Cassette: released on SPI Milan (France), Jul'87, IMS

Compact disc: released on SPI Milan (France), Jul'87, IMS

SUN GAMES.
Album: released on Timeless, Dec'83 Dist: Pinnacle, Cadillac, Jazz Music

YOUR TIMELESS LOVE.
Album: released on Sonet, Aug'85 by Sonet Records. Dist: Jazz Music, Swift, Celtic Music, Roots, PRT, Sonet

Them

BABY PLEASE DON'T CRY.
Single 7": released on Old Gold, Oct'83 by Old Gold Records. Dist: PRT, Counterpoint, Lightning, Jazz Music, Taylors

GLORIA.
Single 7": released on Decca, May'82 by Decca Records. Dist: Polygram

HERE COMES THE NIGHT.
Single 7": released on Deram, Sep'73 by London Records. Dist: Polygram

Single 7": released on Old Gold, Oct'83 by Old Gold Records. Dist: PRT, Counterpoint, Lightning, Jazz Music, Taylors

ONE MORE TIME.
Album: released on Decca (Holland), Apr'84 by Decca Records. Dist: Polygram, IMS

SINGLES, THE.
Cassette: released on See For Miles, Sep'87 by See For Miles Records. Dist: Pinnacle

THEM.
Tracks: / Don't start crying now / Baby please don't go / Here comes the night / One more time / It won't hurt half as much / Mystic eyes / Call my name / Richard Cory / Gloria / Story of them, The / One two brown eyes / Philosophy / All for myself / How long baby / I'm gonna dress in black / If you and I could be as two / Bring 'em on in / Don't you know / Friday's child.

Album: released on See For Miles, Aug'86 by See For Miles Records. Dist: Pinnacle

Album: released on Decca, '65 by Decca Records. Dist: Polygram

THEM AGAIN.
Album: released on Decca, '66 by Decca Records. Dist: Polygram

THEM THE COLLECTION.
Tracks: / Baby please don't go / Bright lights, big city / I put a spell on you / Hello Josephine / Turn on your love light / Don't start crying know / Gloria / Story of Them (The) / It's all over now, baby blue / I got a woman / My little baby / How long baby.
Notes: Featuring Van Morrison
Double Album: released on Collectors, Apr'86 by Castle Communications Records. Dist: Jazz Music, Pinnacle

Double cassette: released on Collectors, Apr'86 by Castle Communications Records. Dist: Jazz Music, Pinnacle

Them Belfast Gypsies

THEM BELFAST GYPSIES.
Album: released on Sonet, Jan'78 by Sonet Records. Dist: Jazz Music, Swift, Celtic Music, Roots, PRT, Sonet

Them Howling Horrors

CHANGING TIDE.
Album: released on Criminal Damage, Feb'86 by Criminal Damage Records. Dist: Backs, Cartel

DIG DOWN DEEPER.
Tracks: / Wise up little girl / Ain't got a clue / We copped the first shot at the gunfight.
Single 12": released on Criminal Damage, Nov'86 by Criminal Damage Records. Dist: Backs, Cartel

Them Indoors

THEM INDOORS Various session artists (Various Session Artists).
Album: released on Innovation, Nov'84 by Innovation Records. Dist: Jetstar

Cassette: released on Innovation, Nov'84 by Innovation Records. Dist: Jetstar

Them Two

BREAKFAST IN BED.
Single 12": released on White Label, Feb'85 by White Label Records. Dist: Jetstar

Theme Songs...

THEME SONGS OF THE BIG BANDS Various artists (Various artists).
Album: released on Bright Orange, Apr'79 Dist: Swift

Themes

THEMES Various artists (Various artists).
Album: released on K-Tel, Apr'81 by K-Tel Records. Dist: K-Tel, Celtic Music, Terry Blood, Wynd-Up, Taylors, Pickwick, Solomon & Peres, Polygram

Cassette: released on K-Tel, May'81 by K-Tel Records. Dist: K-Tel, Celtic Music, Terry Blood, Wynd-Up, Taylors, Pickwick, Solomon & Peres, Polygram

Themes Album

THEMES ALBUM (THE) Various artists (Various artists).
Compact disc: released on K-Tel, Nov'86 by K-Tel Records. Dist: K-Tel, Celtic Music, Terry Blood, Wynd-Up, Taylors, Pickwick, Solomon & Peres, Polygram

Double Album: released on K-Tel, May'84 by K-Tel Records. Dist: K-Tel, Celtic Music, Terry Blood, Wynd-Up, Taylors, Pickwick, Solomon & Peres, Polygram

Cassette: released on K-Tel, May'84 by K-Tel Records. Dist: K-Tel, Celtic Music, Terry Blood, Wynd-Up, Taylors, Pickwick, Solomon & Peres, Polygram

Themes And Dreams

THEMES AND DREAMS Various artists (Various artists).
Album: released on Sierra, Apr'85 by Sierra Records. Dist: WEA

Cassette: released on Sierra, Apr'85 by Sierra Records. Dist: WEA

Boxed set: released on Innovative Music Production, Feb'85 by Pickwick Records.

Boxed set: released on Innovative Music Production, Feb'85 by Pickwick Records.

Themes And Screens

THEMES AND SCREENS Various artists (Various artists).
Tracks: / Somewhere my love / Love theme from 'the Godfather' / What I did for love / Aquarius/let the sun shine in / Tomorrow / How deep is your love / Evergreen / Maria / Climb every mountain / Wouldn't it be lovely / Memory / Windmills of your mind (The) / I don't know how to love him / Born free / Up where we belong / Last of the summer wine.
Notes: 16 great hits from cinema, stage and TV.
Album: released on Warwick Reflections, Jun'86 by Warwick Records. Dist: CBS, MSD, Taylors, Solomon & Peres

Cassette: released on Warwick Reflections, Jun'86 by Warwick Records. Dist: CBS, MSD, Taylors, Solomon & Peres

Themes & Dreams

THEMES & DREAMS VOLUME 2 Various artists (Various artists).
Album: released on Hallmark, Sep'84 by Pickwick Records.

Cassette: released on Hallmark, Sep'84 by Pickwick Records.

Themes In Brass

THEMES IN BRASS Various artists (Various artists).
Double cassette: released on Pickwick(Ditto series), Jul'82 by Pickwick Records. Dist: PRT

Themis, John

ATMOSPHERIC CONDITIONS.
Tracks: / Emily / Trick (The) / Post hypnotic suggestions / Cinderella's last waltz / Electric storm / Transition / Black mamba samba / Trouble.
Album: released on Coda Landscape, Jan'86 by Coda Records. Dist: WEA

Cassette: released on Coda Landscape, Jan'86 by Coda Records. Dist: WEA

Compact disc: released on Coda Landscape, Jan'86 by Coda Records. Dist: WEA

ENGLISH RENAISSANCE.
Album: released on Coda, Apr'86 by Coda Records. Dist: Celtic Music, Cartel, WEA, Roots, Pinnacle

Cassette: released on Coda, Apr'86 by Coda Records. Dist: Celtic Music, Cartel, WEA, Roots, Pinnacle

Compact disc: released on Coda, Jul'86 by Coda Records. Dist: Celtic Music, Cartel, WEA, Roots, Pinnacle

FINAL CRUISE.
Tracks: / Final cruise / English renaissance.
Single 7": released on Coda, Mar'86 by Coda Records. Dist: Celtic Music, Cartel, WEA, Roots, Pinnacle

SIRENS.
Tracks: / Goblins of Sherwood / Emily / Sirens / Trick (The) / Post hypnotic suggestions / Trouble / Raid at the brothel / Electric storm / Transitions / Black mamba samba / Cinderella's last waltz.
Album: released on Coda, Jun'83 by Coda Records. Dist: Celtic Music, Cartel, WEA, Roots, Pinnacle

Cassette: released on Coda, Jun'83 by Coda Records. Dist: Celtic Music, Cartel, WEA, Roots, Pinnacle

Compact disc: released on Coda, Jun'83 by Coda Records. Dist: Celtic Music, Cartel, WEA, Roots, Pinnacle

ULYSSES AND THE CYCLOPS.
Tracks: / Atmospheric conditions / Final cruise / Free fall / Whales / Live at Camelot / Ulysses and the Cyclops / Run for miles / Lethal blow.
Album: released on Coda, Aug'84 by Coda Records. Dist: Celtic Music, Cartel, WEA, Roots, Pinnacle

Cassette: released on Coda, Aug'84 by Coda Records. Dist: Celtic Music, Cartel, WEA, Roots, Pinnacle

Compact disc: released on Coda, Aug'84 by Coda Records. Dist: Celtic Music, Cartel, WEA, Roots, Pinnacle

Then Came Rock 'N' Roll

THEN CAME ROCK 'N' ROLL Various artists (Various artists).
Album: released on EMI, May'84 by EMI Records(UK). Dist: EMI

Cassette: released on EMI, May'84 by EMI Records(UK). Dist: EMI

Then Jerico

BIG SWEEP, THE.
Single 12": released on Immaculate, Aug'85 by Immaculate Records. Dist: Cartel

FAULT.
Single 7": released on London, Sep'85 by London Records. Dist: Polygram

Single 12": released on London, Sep'85 by London Records. Dist: Polygram

FIRST (The Sound of Music).
Album: released on London, Mar'87 by London Records. Dist: Polygram

Cassette: released on London, Mar'87 by London Records. Dist: Polygram

FIRST (THE SOUND OF MUSIC).
Tracks: / Let her fall / Blessed days / Laughter party / Stable boy / Motive, The / Muscle deep / Quiet place, A (apathy and sympathy) / Play dead / Hitcher, The / Prairie rose / Blessed days (Tokyo mix) / Fault (dub).
Notes: This impressive debut album from Then Jerico was produced, engineered and mixed by Owen Davies. Included are the acclaimed singles 'Muscle Deep' and 'Let Her Fall' as well as the new single "Prairie Rose' released 30.3.87. The cassette and the compact disc have two extra tracks:-'Blessed Days (Tokyo Mix) and Fault (Dub).
Compact disc: released on London, Mar'87 by London Records. Dist: Polygram

MOTIVE, THE.
Tracks: / Word, The / Motive, The / Motive, The (Extended) / Motive, The (Midnight mix).
Single 7": released on London, Jul'87 by London Records. Dist: Polygram

Single 12": released on London, Jul'87 by London Records. Dist: Polygram

MUSCLE DEEP.
Tracks: / Muscle deep / Clank (countdown to oblivian) / Fault / Muscle deep (extended).
Single 7": released on London, Mar'86 by London Records. Dist: Polygram

Single 12": released on London, Mar'86 by London Records. Dist: Polygram

Single 7": released on London, Oct'87 by London Records. Dist: Polygram

Single 12": released on London, Oct'87 by London Records. Dist: Polygram

PRAIRIE ROSE.
Tracks: / Prairie rose / Electric / One life / Fault.
Single 7": released on London, Mar'87 by London Records. Dist: Polygram

Single 12": released on London, Mar'87 by London Records. Dist: Polygram

Theobald, Mike & Jack

BLUEGRASS COUNTRY.
Album: released on Shiloh, Mar'79 Dist: Projection

Theodorakis, Mikis

BALLAD OF MAUTHAUSEN.
Compact disc: released on Sound, '86 Dist: Target

BOUZOUKIS OF..., THE.
Album: released on Disc AZ(France), Aug'84

Cassette: released on Disc AZ(France), Aug'84

CANTO GENERAL.
Compact disc: released on Sound, '86 Dist Target

ZORBA THE GREEK.
Album: released on Phonogram, Sep'83 by Phonogram Records. Dist: Polygram

Cassette: released on Phonogram, Sep'83 by Phonogram Records. Dist: Polygram

Therapy

ONLY A FOOL/ THUNDER AND LIGHTNING.
Single 7": released on Revo, Sep'82 by Albion Dist: Spartan, Pinnacle

STAY BY ME/ SOFT TOUCH.
Single 7": released on Smile, Apr'82 by Smil Records. Dist: Spartan

There Is No Future

THERE IS NO FUTURE Various artist (Various artists).
Album: released on No Future, Nov'84 Dis Pinnacle, Rough Trade, Cartel Deleted '87.

There Was This Bloke

THERE WAS THIS BLOKE Various artis (Various artists).
Album: released on Rubber, Jun'82 by Rubb Records. Dist: Projection, Roots, Jazz Musi Celtic Music, Spartan

These Cats Ain't Nothin'...

THESE CATS AIN'T NOTHIN' BU TRASH Various artists (Various artists).
Album: released on Big Beat, Feb'83 by A Records. Dist: Celtic Music, Pinnacle, Ja Music, Projection

These Future Kings

AFTER THIS.
Extended-play record: released on Rampa (Australia), Sep'87 Dist: Pinnacle

These Modern Times

THESE MODERN TIMES (Various artist
Album: released on Soul Supply, Jan'87 Di Backs, Cartel

These Mortal Souls

GET LOST (DON'T LIE).
Compact disc: released on Mute, Oct'87 D Spartan, Rough Trade, Cartel

Album: released on Mute, Oct'87 Dist: Spart Rough Trade, Cartel. Estim retail price in Oct was £6.29.

MARRY ME (LIE LIE).
Tracks: / Open up and bleed / Blood and sa / She said.
Single 12": released on Mute, Aug'87 D Spartan, Rough Trade, Cartel

These Tender Virtues

WALTZ.
Single 7": released on Carousel, Jun'85 by Carousel Records. Dist: Spartan, Rough Trade

They All Played..

THEY ALL PLAYED MAPLE LEAF RAG various artists (Various artists).
Album: released on Herwin, '74 Dist: Jazz Music, Projection, Swift, Celtic Music, Cadillac, Ross, Duncans, Impetus

They Call That...

THEY CALL THAT AN ACCIDENT various artists (Soundtrack).
Album: released on Island, Mar'83 by Island Records. Dist: Polygram, Celtic Music

Cassette: released on Island, Mar'83 by Island Records. Dist: Polygram, Celtic Music

They Called It..

THEY CALLED IT CROONING Various artists (Various artists).
Album: released on ASV-Living Era, Feb'84 by Academy Sound & Vision Records. Dist: Pinnacle

Cassette: released on ASV-Living Era, Feb'84 by Academy Sound & Vision Records. Dist: Pinnacle

They Might Be Giants

THEY MIGHT BE GIANTS.
Album: released on Rough Trade, Oct'87 by Rough Trade Records. Dist: Rough Trade, Cartel. Estim retail price in Sep'87 was £4.99.

Cassette: released on Rough Trade, Oct'87 by Rough Trade Records. Dist: Rough Trade, Cartel. Estim retail price in Oct'87 was £5.99.

They Must Be Russians

AND OTHER GROUNDLESS ACCUSATIONS.
Album: released on Native, Sep'85 by Native Records. Dist: Red Rhino, Cartel

CHAINS.
Single 12": released on First Floor, Jul'83 by First Floor Records. Dist: Cartel

DEVOTION.
Single 7": released on Office Box, Oct'84 by Office Box Records. Dist: Red Rhino, Cartel

Single 12": released on Office Box, Oct'84 by Office Box Records. Dist: Red Rhino, Cartel

DON'T TRY TO CURE YOURSELF.
Single 7": released on Fresh, Apr'81 Dist: Jetstar

RED SQUARE.
Tracks: / Red square.
Single 12": released on Native, Feb'86 by Native Records. Dist: Red Rhino, Cartel

THEY MUST BE RUSSIANS.
Album: released on First Floor, Aug'83 by First Floor Records. Dist: Cartel

They Only Come Out at..

THEY ONLY COME OUT AT NIGHT Various artists (Various artists).
Album: released on Clay, Sep'85 by Clay Records. Dist: Pinnacle

They Played The..

THEY PLAYED THE HIPPODROME (Various artists).
Tracks: / Japanese sandman / Somebody stole my gal / It all belongs to me / Mister Brown of London town / Nice kind Sergeant-Major / Blasted oak, The / Crest of a wave, The / Leaning on a lamp post / Underneath the arches / Sandy furnishes the home (on hire purchase) / When you play with fire / Singing a vagabond song / I've got sixpence (as I go rolling home) / In all the world / Theophilus and his operation / Fan, The / I like riding on a choo choo choo / Won't we 'ave a party when it's over / Reflections on the water (looking down at me) / I wouldn't take a million for the old grey mare / We three (my echo, my shadow and me) / Give me you (Ou es-tu mon amour) / Put your shoes on Lucy / Gipsy, The / Only a glass of champagne / Dream / My heart isn't in it / I'm in love with two sweethearts / As time goes by / No one but you / Breathless / Beware / You're not alone / I still believe / Story of Tina, The (dio prasina matia) / Yes, I'll be here / Same old crowd, The / Garden in the rain, A / Danger ahead / I'll make up for everything / Papa's in bed with his breeches on / Don't ever walk in the shadows / Murder.
Notes: This is a double album and a double cassette.
Double Album:

Cassette: released on Decca (London), Mar'87 by Decca Records. Dist: Polygram, IMS

THEY PLAYED THE PALLADIUM Various artists (Various artists).
Cassette: released on Ditto, Mar'86 by Pickwick Records. Dist: Taylors

They Shall Not Pass

THEY SHALL NOT PASS Various artists
Album: released on Abstract, Mar'85 by Abstract. Dist: Pinnacle

They'll Never Keep Us...

THEY'LL NEVER KEEP US DOWN... Various artists (Various artists).
Album: released on Rounder(USA), Jan'85 Dist: Jazz Music, Projection, Swift, Celtic Music, Cadillac, Ross, Duncans, Impetus

They're Off!

THEY'RE OFF! (Racing game with 2 LP's).
Double Album: released on Ronco, Jun'76 by Ronco Records.

They're Playing Our Song

THEY'RE PLAYING OUR SONG Original London cast.
Album: released on That's Entertainment, Apr'83 by That's Entertainment Records. Dist: Pinnacle

Cassette: released on That's Entertainment, Apr'83 by That's Entertainment Records. Dist: Pinnacle

Thielemans, Toots

JUST FRIENDS (Thielemans, Toots/Johnny Teupen/Paul kuhn).
Compact disc: released on Delta, '86 by Delta Records. Dist: Target, Zodiac

LIVE IN THE NETHERLANDS (Thielemans, Toots,Joe Pass,Niels Henning,Orsted Pedersen).
Album: released on Pablo, Sep'82 by Pablo Records. Dist: Wellard, IMS, BMG, Polygram

Cassette: released on Pablo, Sep'82 by Pablo Records. Dist: Wellard, IMS, BMG, Polygram

Compact disc: released on Pablo(USA), May'86 by Ace Records. Dist: PRT

SILVER COLLECTION, THE.
Tracks: / Do it for your love / My little suede shoes / You're my blues machine / Dirty old man / Summer of '42 / Bluesette / Muskrat ramble / Mooche (The) / What are you doing with the rest of your life / Gentle rain (The) / First time I ever saw your face / Big bossa / Ben / You've got it bad girl / Love remembered / Old friend.
Compact disc: released on Polydor, Jun'85 by Polydor Records. Dist: Polygram, Polydor

TOOT AND SYEND (Thielemans, Toots & Svens Asmussen).
Album: released on Sonet, Nov'87 by Sonet Records. Dist: Jazz Music, Swift, Celtic Music, Roots, PRT, Sonet

WORLD HITS PLAYED ON THE MOUTH ORGAN (Thielemans, Toots/Benny clark).
Compact disc: released on Delta, Oct'86 by Delta Records. Dist: Target, Zodiac

Album: released on Storyville, May'86 by Storyville Records. Dist: Swift, Wellard

Thieves

TALK YOUR HEAD OFF.
Single 7": released on Planetarium Discs, 30 May'87

Thieves like us

MIND MADE.
Single 7": released on Earlobe, May'80 by Earlobe Records. Dist: Pinnacle Deleted '87.

Thigpen, Ed

ACTION-RE-ACTION.
Album: released on Sonet, '76 by Sonet Records. Dist: Jazz Music, Swift, Celtic Music, Roots, PRT, Sonet

Thin Lizzy

BEST OF PHIL LYNOT & THIN LIZZY, THE.
Compact disc: released on Telstar, 7 Nov'87 by Telstar Records. Dist: BMGg*

Album: released on Telstar, 7 Nov'87 by Telstar Records. Dist: BMGg*

Cassette: released on Telstar, 7 Nov'87 by Telstar Records. Dist: BMGg*

BLACK ROSE.
Tracks: / Do anything you want / Toughest street in town / S & M / Waiting for an alibi / Sarah / Got to give it up / Get out of here / With love / Roisin dubh.
Notes: From 1979, Lizzy's hit album featuring the singles 'Waiting for an Alibi', 'Sarah' and 'Do anything you want to'.
Album: released on Vertigo, Oct'86 by Phonogram Records. Dist: Polygram

Cassette: released on Vertigo, Oct'86 by Phonogram Records. Dist: Polygram

BOYS ARE BACK IN TOWN.
Album: released on Contour, Nov'83 by Pickwick Records. Dist: Pickwick

Cassette: released on Contour, Nov'83 by Pickwick Records. Dist: Pickwick

CHINATOWN.
Tracks: / We will be strong / Chinatown / Sweetheart / Sugar blues / Killer on the loose / Having a good time / Genocide / Didn't I / Hey you.
Notes: Lizzy's 1980 LP featuring the hit single 'Killer On The Loose'. Great sleeve.
Album: released on Vertigo, Oct'86 by Phonogram Records. Dist: Polygram

Cassette: released on Vertigo, Oct'86 by Phonogram Records. Dist: Polygram

COLLECTION: THIN LIZZY.
Album: released on Castle Communications, Nov'85 by Castle Communications. Dist: PRT, Pinnacle, Cartel

Cassette: released on Castle Communications, Nov'85 by Castle Communications. Dist: PRT, Pinnacle, Cartel

Compact disc: released on Castle Collectors, Jul'87 by Castle Communications Records. Dist: Pinnacle

DANCIN IN THE MOONLIGHT.
Single 7": released on Old Gold, Jan'85 by Old Gold Records. Dist: PRT, Counterpoint, Lightning, Jazz Music, Taylors

FIGHTING.
Album: released on Vertigo, Aug'83 by Phonogram Records. Dist: Polygram

Album: released on Vertigo, Aug'83 by Phonogram Records. Dist: Polygram

HOLLYWOOD/THE PRESSURE WILL BLOW.
Single 7": released on Vertigo, Feb'82 by Phonogram Records. Dist: Polygram

Picture disc single: released on Vertigo, Feb'82 by Phonogram Records. Dist: Polygram

JAILBREAK.
Album: released on Vertigo, Oct'83 by Phonogram Records. Dist: Polygram

Cassette: released on Vertigo, Oct'83 by Phonogram Records. Dist: Polygram

JOHNNY THE FOX.
Album: released on Vertigo, May'83 by Phonogram Records. Dist: Polygram

Cassette: released on Vertigo, May'83 by Phonogram Records. Dist: Polygram

LIFE.
Double Album: released on Vertigo, Nov'83 by Phonogram Records. Dist: Polygram

Double cassette: released on Vertigo, Nov'83 by Phonogram Records. Dist: Polygram

LITTLE DARLING.
Single 7": released on Decca, Apr'74 by Decca Records. Dist: Polygram

LIVE AND DANGEROUS - IN CONCERT.
Tracks: / Boys are back in town (The) / Dancing in the moonlight / Massacre / I'm still in love with you / Me and the boys were wondering... / Don't believe a word / Warriors / Are you ready? / Sha la la la / Baby drives me crazy.
Notes: The great Irish rock band live at the Rainbow Theatre playing to an ecstatic audience - one of the classic rock concerts of the 70's. Number of tracks: 9. Type of recording: live. Total playing time: 50 minutes.
Video-cassette (VHS): released on VCL, Sep'86 by Elecstar Records.

Album: released on Vertigo, Nov'84 by Phonogram Records. Dist: Polygram

Cassette: released on Vertigo, Nov'84 by Phonogram Records. Dist: Polygram

LIZZY KILLERS.
Tracks: / Do anything you want to / Sarah / Whiskey in the jar / Jailbreak Chinatown / Boys are back in town (The) / Killer on the loose / Don't believe a word / Dancing in the moonlight / Waiting for an alibi.
Compact disc: released on Vertigo, '83 by Phonogram Records. Dist: Polygram

NIGHT LIFE.
Album: released on Vertigo, Aug'83 by Phonogram Records. Dist: Polygram

Cassette: released on Vertigo, Aug'83 by Phonogram Records. Dist: Polygram

REMEMBERING.
Album: released on Teldec, Jun'81 Dist: Pinnacle, Celtic Music

REMEMBERING (PART 1).
Album: released on Decca, Aug'76 by Decca Records. Dist: Polygram

Cassette: released on Decca, Aug'76 by Decca Records. Dist: Polygram

RENEGADE.
Album: released on Vertigo, Nov'81 by Phonogram Records. Dist: Polygram

Cassette: released on Vertigo, Nov'81 by Phonogram Records. Dist: Polygram

ROCKERS.
Album: released on Decca, Dec'81 by Decca Records. Dist: Polygram

Cassette: released on Decca, Dec'81 by Decca Records. Dist: Polygram

SHADES OF BLUE ORPHANAGE.
Album: released on Decca, '72 by Decca Records. Dist: Polygram

THUNDER AND LIGHTNING.
Album: released on Vertigo, Mar'83 by Phonogram Records. Dist: Polygram

Cassette: released on Vertigo, Mar'83 by Phonogram Records. Dist: Polygram

Single 7": released on Vertigo, Apr'83 by Phonogram Records. Dist: Polygram

Single 12": released on Vertigo, Apr'83 by Phonogram Records. Dist: Polygram

WAITING FOR AN ALIBI.
Single 7": released on Vertigo, Feb'79 by Phonogram Records. Dist: Polygram

WHISKEY IN THE JAR.
Tracks: / Whiskey in the jar / Rocker (The) Sarah / Black boys on the corner.
Album: released on Contour, Apr'86 by Pickwick Records. Dist: Pickwick

Cassette: released on Contour, Apr'86 by Pickwick Records. Dist: Pickwick

Album: released on Karussell(Germany), Nov'85 Dist: IMS, Polygram

Cassette: released on Karussell(Germany), Nov'85 Dist: IMS, Polygram

Single 12": released on Archive 4, Aug'86 by Castle Communications Records.. Cartel

WHISKY IN THE JAR.
Single 7": released on Decca, Oct'79 by Decca Records. Dist: Polygram

Single 7": released on Old Gold, Oct'83 by Old Gold Records. Dist: PRT, Counterpoint, Lightning, Jazz Music, Taylors

Double-pack single: released on Polydor, Nov'85 by Polydor Records. Dist: Polygram, Polydor

Thin Red Line

ONLY DREAMING OF YOU.
Single 7": released on MTM-Privacy, Jul'84 Dist: Rough Trade, Cartel

Single 12": released on MTM-Privacy, Jul'84 Dist: Rough Trade, Cartel

Thin White Rope

BOTTOM FEEDERS.
Album: released on Demon, Oct'87 by Demon Records. Dist: Celtic Music, Pinnacle, Jazz Music

EXPLORING THE AXIS.
Album: released on Zippo, Nov'85 by Demon Records. Dist: Projection, Pinnacle

MOONHEAD.
Album: released on Zippo, Feb'87 by Demon Records. Dist: Projection, Pinnacle

Thing

ALIEN ATTACK.
Single 12": released on Electricity, Jun'84 by Electricity Records.

THING, THE Original soundtrack.
Album: released on MCA, Sep'82 by MCA Records. Dist: Polygram

Thing Called Love

THING CALLED LOVE, A Various artists (Various artists).
Album: released on Hallmark, Aug'85 by Pickwick Records.

Cassette: released on Hallmark, Aug'85 by Pickwick Records.

Things

OUTSIDE MY WINDOW.
Album: released on Eva-Lolita, Jul'86 Dist: Pinnacle

Things That Go

THINGS THAT GO Various artists (Various artists).
Cassette: released on Invicta, Jul'84 by Audio-Visual Productions(AVP). Dist: Spartan

Think Pink

IN AND OUT OF LOVE.
Single 7": released on Red Bus, Jun'84 by Red Bus Records. Dist: PRT

Think Smart Soul Stirrers.......

THINK SMART SOUL STIRRERS JERK IT AT THE PARTY IN CHINATOWN (Various artists).
Album: released on Kent, Jan'87 by Kent Records. Dist: Pinnacle, Cadillac, Jazz Music

Thinking Plague

MOON SONGS.
Album: released on Deadman's Curve, Mar'87 by Dave Henderson. Dist: Red Rhino, Cartel

Third Army

MARCH OF 10 000 SOLDIERS.
Single 7": released on No, Nov'81 Dist: Rough Trade

Single 12": released on No, Nov'81 Dist: Rough Trade

Third Circle

GOODBYE TO YESTERDAY.
Single (12"): released on Rouska, Mar'87 Dist:
Red Rhino Distribution, Cartel Distribution

LAST NIGHT WAS THE BEST NIGHT OF
MY LIFE.
Tracks: / Last night was the best night of my life
/ Man who fell apart (The) / Real eyes.
Single (7"): released on Rouska, Apr'86 Dist:
Red Rhino Distribution, Cartel Distribution

Single (12"): released on Rouska, Oct'86 Dist:
Red Rhino Distribution, Cartel Distribution

Third Eye

PASS MYSELF.
Single (7"): released on Scarlet, Feb'82 by
Scarlet Records. Dist: Cartel

Third Festival

1000 STRONG (Third Festival Of Massed
English Male Choirs, The).
Album: released on Bandleader, Jul'83 by Band-
leader Records. Dist: PRT

Third Fusiliers

REGIMENTAL BAND & CORPS OF
DRUMS Recorded on location in Germany
(Third Fusiliers In Concert).
Album: released on Music Masters, Jun'81 by
Music Masters Records. Dist: Taylors

Third Light

SHINE.
Single (7"): released on Blue Train, Oct'84 by
Checkmount Distribution. Dist: Spartan

Third Man

ORAL PLEASURE.
Single (7"): released on Uniton, Sep'84

Single (7"): released on Uniton, Sep'84

THIRD MAN, The Read by James Mason
(Greene, Graham).
Cassette: released on Listen For Pleasure,
Sep'82 by MFP Records. Dist: EMI

Third World

96 DEGREES IN THE SHADE.
Album: released on Island, Jul'77 by Island
Records. Dist: Polygram

Cassette: released on Island, Jul'77 by Island
Records. Dist: Polygram

DANCING ON THE FLOOR (HOOKED
ON LOVE).
Single (7"): released on CBS, May'81 by CBS
Records. Dist: CBS

Single (12"): released on CBS, May'81 by CBS
Records. Dist: CBS

HOLD ON TO LOVE.
Tracks: / Spirit lives, The / Get outta town / Hold
on to love / We could be Jammin' Reggae / Corruption / Reggae radio station / Pyramid / Simplicity / Manners / Peace Flags.
Album: released on CBS, Aug'87 by CBS Records. Dist: CBS

Cassette: released on CBS, Aug'87 by CBS
Records. Dist: CBS

Album: released on CBS, Aug'87 by CBS Records. Dist: CBS

Cassette: released on CBS, Aug'87 by CBS
Records. Dist: CBS

JOURNEY TO ADDIS.
Album: released on Island, Sep'78 by Island
Records. Dist: Polygram

Cassette: released on Island, Jul'81 by Island
Records. Dist: Polygram

LAGOS JUMP.
Single (7"): released on CBS, Jan'84 by CBS
Records. Dist: CBS

Single (12"): released on CBS, Jan'84 by CBS
Records. Dist: CBS

NOW THAT WE'VE FOUND LOVE.
Single (7"): released on Island, Mar'85 by Island Records. Dist: Polygram Deleted '87.

Picture disc single: released on Island, Mar'85
by Island Records. Dist: Polygram

Single (12"): released on Island, Mar'85 by Island Records. Dist: Polygram

Single (12"): released on Island, Mar'85 by Island Records. Dist: Polygram

ONE MORE TIME.
Tracks: / One more time.
Single (7"): released on CBS, Jan'86 by CBS
Records. Dist: CBS

Single (12"): released on CBS, Jan'86 by CBS

Records. Dist: CBS

PRISONER IN THE STREET.
Album: released on Island, Jun'80 by Island
Records. Dist: Polygram

Cassette: released on Island, Jun'80 by Island
Records. Dist: Polygram

REGGAE GREATS.
Album: released on Island, Mar'85 by Island
Records. Dist: Polygram

Cassette: released on Island, Mar'85 by Island
Records. Dist: Polygram

ROCK THE WORLD.
Album: released on CBS, Nov'85 by CBS Records. Dist: CBS

Cassette: released on CBS, Nov'85 by CBS
Records. Dist: CBS

SENSE OF PURPOSE.
Album: released on CBS, Apr'85 by CBS Records. Dist: CBS

Cassette: released on CBS, Apr'85 by CBS
Records. Dist: CBS

STANDING IN THE RAIN.
Single (7"): released on CBS, Aug'81 by CBS
Records. Dist: CBS

THIRD WORLD.
Album: released on Island, May'76 by Island
Records. Dist: Polygram

YOU'VE GOT THE POWER.
Tracks: / Try jah love / Ride on / You're playing
too close / before you make the move (melt with
everyone) / Jah Jah children moving up / You've
got the power (to make a change) / Inna time
like this / I wake up cryin' / Low key jammin'.
Album: released on CBS, Jan'87 by CBS Records. Dist: CBS

Cassette: released on CBS, Jan'87 by CBS
Records. Dist: CBS

Third World Disco

THIRD WORLD DISCO - VOL.1 Various
reggae artists (Various Artists).
Album: released on Third World, Jun'77 Dist:
Jetstar Distribution

THIRD WORLD DISCO - VOL.3 Various
reggae artists (Various Artists).
Album: released on Third World, Aug'78 Dist:
Jetstar Distribution

Thirteen

CLIMB DOWN (Thirteen At Midnight).
Single (7"): released on Survival, '83 by Survival Records. Dist: Backs, Cartel Distribution

Single (12"): released on Survival, '83 by Survival Records. Dist: Backs, Cartel Distribution

LAST TRUE FRIENDS (Thirteen At Midnight).
Album: released on Survival, Feb'85 by Survival Records. Dist: Backs, Cartel Distribution

Thirteen At Midnight

OTHER PASSENGERS.
Single (7"): released on Pure, May'82 by Group
13 At Midnight.

SKIN DEEP.
Single (7"): released on Survival, Nov'83 by
Survival Records. Dist: Backs, Cartel Distribu-
tion

Single (12"): released on Survival, Nov'83 by
Survival Records. Dist: Backs, Cartel Distribution

TIME IS TIGHT.
Single (7"): released on Survival, Jun'84 by
Survival Records. Dist: Backs, Cartel Distribu-
tion

Single (12"): released on Survival, Jun'84 by
Survival Records. Dist: Backs, Cartel Distribution

Thirteen Moons

LITTLE DREAMING BOY.
Album: released on Wire, May'86 Dist: Nine
Mile, Cartel

ORIGINS.
Album: released on Wire, Aug'87 Dist: Nine
Mile, Cartel. Estim retail price in Sep'87 was
£5.99.

SUDDENLY ONE SUMMER.
Tracks: / Where did you all go.
Single (7"): released on Wire, Nov'86 Dist:
Nine Mile, Cartel

Single (12"): released on Wire, Nov'86 Dist:
Nine Mile, Cartel

TRUE STORY, (A).

Tracks: / True story, (A) / Night parade / Daddy
come home / Last train to San Antone.
Single (7"): released on Wire, Sep'86 Dist:
Nine Mile, Cartel

Single (12"): released on Wire, Sep'86 Dist:
Nine Mile, Cartel

Thirteenth...

EASTER EVERYWHERE (Thirteenth Floor
Elevators).
Album: released on Radar, May'79 by WEA
Music Ltd. Dist: WEA, PRT

PSYCHEDELIC SOUNDS OF... (Thir-
teenth Floor Elevators).
Album: released on Radar, '78 by WEA Music
Ltd. Dist: WEA, PRT

Thirteenth Chime

CURSED.
Single (7"): released on Chime, Jan'82 Dist:
Rough Trade

FIRE.
Single (7"): released on 13th Crime, Nov'82
Dist: Backs

Thirty...

30 BRITISH HITS OF THE 60'S Various
artists (Various Artists).
Album: released on Philips (Holland), Jul'84

Cassette: released on Philips (Holland), Jul'84

30 MINUTES Various artists (Various Artists).
Cassette: released on Falling A, Nov'84 by Falling A Records. Dist: Falling A Distribution

Thirty Bob Sults

SIX FOOT UNDER.
Single (7"): released on Tanner Made, May'82

Thirty Eight Special

IF I HAD BEEN THE ONE.
Single (7"): released on A&M, Jan'84 by A&M
Records. Dist: Polygram

LIKE NO OTHER NIGHT.
Single (7"): released on A&M, May'86 by A&M
Records. Dist: Polygram

Single (12"): released on A&M, May'86 by A&M
Records. Dist: Polygram

SPECIAL FORCES.
Album: released on A&M, Jun'82 by A&M Records. Dist: Polygram

STRENGTH IN NUMBERS.
Tracks: / Somebody like you / Like no other
night / Last time / Once in a lifetime / Just a little
love / Has there ever been a good goodbye? /
Once in a million / Heart's on fire / Against the
night / Never give an inch.
Album: released on A&M, May'86 by A&M Records. Dist: Polygram

Cassette: released on A&M, May'86 by A&M
Records. Dist: Polygram

TOUR DE FORCE.
Album: released on A&M, Feb'84 by A&M Records. Dist: Polygram

Cassette: released on A&M, Feb'84 by A&M
Records. Dist: Polygram

WILD EYED SOUTHERN BOYS.
Album: released on A&M, Apr'81 by A&M Records. Dist: Polygram

Thirty Nine Clocks

BLADES IN YOUR MASQUERADE.
Album: released on Flicknife, Jul'83 by Flicknife Records. Dist: Spartan

Thirty Seconds

AUTOMATIC.
Single (7"): released on Initial, Jun'81 by Initial
Records. Dist: Pinnacle

Thirty Three Seconds

SKYLIGHT ROCK.
Single (7"): released on Fractured, Mar'85 Dist:
Backs-Cartel

Thirty Two Golden...

32 GOLDEN COUNTRY HITS - VOL.1
Various artists (Various Artists).
Album: released on RCA (Germany), Jan'85

Cassette: released on RCA (Germany), Jan'85

32 GOLDEN COUNTRY HITS - VOL.2
Various artists (Various Artists).
Album: released on RCA (Germany), Jan'85

Cassette: released on RCA (Germany), Jan'85

This Are Two Tone

THIS ARE TWO TONE Various artists
(Various Artists).
Album: released on Two-Tone, Nov'83 by
Chrysalis Records. Dist: Polygram

Cassette: released on Two-Tone, Nov'83 by
Chrysalis Records. Dist: Polygram

This England

THIS ENGLAND Special Double Compila-
tion -various artists (Various Artists).
Album: released on Decca, Jun'76 by Decca
Records. Dist: Polygram

Cassette: released on Decca, Jun'76 by Decca
Records. Dist: Polygram

This Final Frame

DIARY, THE.
Single (7"): released on Scratch, Mar'82

MASK, THE.
Single (7"): released on Pnegwan, Apr'85

TAKE NO PRISONERS.
Single (7"): released on Direct, Mar'85 by Phonogram Records. Dist: Polygram

Single (12"): released on Direct, Mar'85 by
Phonogram Records. Dist: Polygram

This Future

DAY BREAKS AGAIN.
Tracks: / Young dogs / Another one / Break
(The).
Extended-play record: released on Press,
Apr'86 by Press Records.

This Heat

DECEIT.
Album: released on Rough Trade, '84 by
Rough Trade Records. Dist: Rough Trade Dis-
tribution, Cartel Distribution

HEAT LP.
Album: released on Piano, Aug'79 Dist: Recommended

This Is...

THIS IS DIGITAL RECORDING Various
artists sampler (Various Artists).
Album: released on EMI, Apr'80 by EMI Records. Dist: EMI

Cassette: released on EMI, Jul'80 by EMI Records. Dist: EMI

THIS IS DIXIELAND Various artists (Vari-
ous Artists).
Album: released on Import, Dec'83 Dist: Stage
One

THIS IS HOT Various artists (Various Artists).
Album: released on Hot, Aug'85 by Hot Records. Dist: Rough Trade, Cartel

THIS IS JAZZ BROADCASTS VOL.
(Various Artists).
Tracks: / High society / Tiger rag / Basin street
blues / Dippermouth blues / Sister Kate / Ain't
misbehavin' / That's a plenty / Baby won't you
please come home / I know that you know
Blues / Caprice rag / Charleston.
Album: released on Rhapsody, May'87 by
President Records. Dist: Taylors, Swift, Jazz
Music, Wellard, Chris

THIS IS JAZZ BROADCASTS VOL.
(Various Artists).
Tracks: / Theme (way down yonder in New Or-
leans) / Sensation rag / You're some pretty doll
/ Twelfth street rag / Buddy Bolden's blues /
Black and blue / Summertime / Farewell blues /
Maple leaf rag / Basin street blues / Polka dot
stomp / Kansas City man blues / Jazz me blues
/ Carolina shout / Panama march (rag).
Album: released on Rhapsody, May'87 by
President Records. Dist: Taylors, Swift, Jazz
Music, Wellard, Chris

THIS IS JAZZ VOL.1 Broadcasts (Broadcasts).
Album: released on Rarities, Apr'81

THIS IS JAZZ VOL.2 Various artists (Various Artists).
Album: released on Rarities, Apr'81

THIS IS LONDON Various artists (Various
Artists).
Album: released on Decca, May'81 by Decca
Records. Dist: Polygram

Cassette: released on Decca, May'81 by
Decca Records. Dist: Polygram

THIS IS MAMOU CAJUN RADIO Various
artists (Various Artists).
Album: released on Sonet, Jan'80 by Sonet
Records. Dist: PRT

THIS IS MOTOWN Various artists (Various
Artists).

Album: released on Motown, May'84 by RCA Records. Dist: RCA Distribution

Cassette: released on Motown, May'84 by RCA Records. Dist: RCA Distribution

THIS IS MUSIC VOL.3 Various artists (Various Artists).

Cassette: released on Chevron, Sep'84 Dist: Multiple Sound Distributors

THIS IS MUSIC VOL.4 Various artists (Various Artists).
Cassette: released on Chevron, Nov'84 Dist: Multiple Sound Distributors

THIS IS MUSIC VOL.5 Various artists (Various Artists).
Cassette: released on Chevron, Feb'85 Dist: Multiple Sound Distributors

THIS IS NORTHERN SOUL Various artists (Various Artists).
Album: released on Grape-Vine, Jul'80 Dist: RCA, Swift

THIS IS ROCK 'N' ROLL Various artists (Various Artists).
Album: released on Pickwick IMP, Aug'84

Cassette: released on Pickwick IMP, Aug'84

THIS IS SOCA (1984) Various artists (Various Artists).
Album: released on Oval, Aug'84 Dist: Projection

THIS IS SOUL Various artists (Various Artists).
Album: released on Starblend, Jan'85 by Starblend Records. Dist: PRT Distribution

Cassette: released on Starblend, Jan'85 by Starblend Records. Dist: PRT Distribution

Album: released on Atlantic, Jul'84 by WEA Records. Dist: WEA

Cassette: released on Atlantic, Jul'84 by WEA Records. Dist: WEA

THIS IS THE BIG BAND ERA Dorsey,Berigan,Goodman,Etc... (Dorsey,Berigan,Goodman,Etc...).
Album: released on RCA (Germany), '83

THIS IS WALES Various artists (Various Artists).
Album: released on EMI, May'80 by EMI Records. Dist: EMI

Cassette: released on EMI, May'80 by EMI Records. Dist: EMI

This is country music

THIS IS COUNTRY MUSIC various artists (Various Artists).
Tracks: / End of the world, The / Fantasy / Abilene / Too many rivers / 500 miles away from home / Theme from Dukes of Hazzard / She called me baby / Nobody's child / Sea of heartbreak / Legend in my time,A (I'd be) / Guitar man / Once a day / He'll have to go / Send me the pillow (you dream on) / Here you come again / Kiss an angel good morning.
Notes: Tracks 6, Mono; 10,11-Electronic Stereo.
Album: released on Music For Pleasure, Apr'87 by EMI Records. Dist: EMI

Cassette: released on Music For Pleasure, Apr'87 by EMI Records. Dist: EMI

THIS IS COUNTRY MUSIC Various artists (Various Artists).
Album: released on Bear Family, Oct'80 by Bear Family Records. Dist: Rollercoaster Distribution, Swift

This Is Easy Listening

THIS IS EASY LISTENING Various artists (Various Artists).

Double cassette: released on Memoir, '85 by Memoir Records. Dist: PRT Distribution

This Is Hot Too

THIS IS HOT TOO Various artists (Various Artists).
Notes: Artists include The Triffids/Celibate Rifles
Album: released on Hot, Apr'86 by Hot Records. Dist: Rough Trade, Cartel

This Island Earth

SEE THAT GLOW.
Tracks: / Euroglow.
Single (7"): released on Magnet, Jan'87 by Magnet Records. Dist: BMG

Single (12"): released on Magnet, Jan'87 by Magnet Records. Dist: BMG

Single (7"): released on Magnet, Sep'84 by Magnet Records. Dist: BMG

Single (12"): released on Magnet, Sep'84 by Magnet Records. Dist: BMG

TAKE ME TO THE FIRE.
Single (7"): released on Magnet, Apr'85 by Magnet Records. Dist: BMG

Single (12"): released on Magnet, Apr'85 by Magnet Records. Dist: BMG

This Is Oi!

THIS IS OI! (a street punk comilation) (Various Artists).
Album: released on Oi!, Jan'86 Dist: Revolver Distribution

This Is Roots Music

THIS IS ROOTS MUSIC-VOL.1 (Various Artists).
Album: released on Virgo, Jan'87

This Is Scotland

THIS IS SCOTLAND (Various Artists).
Tracks: / Hundred thousand welcomes, A / Hundred thousand welcomes, A / Amazing grace / Come to the Ceilidh-John Worth's jig / Dancing in the Kyle / Abide with me / Massacre of Glencoe / Jaqueline waltz / Always argyle / Punch bowl reel / Archaracle midgie / Bonnie Mary of Argyle / Skyline of Skye / Reels / 4/4 marches.
Cassette: released on Scotdisc, Dec'86 Dist: Clyde Factors Distributors

THIS IS SCOTLAND VOLUME II Various artists (Various Artists).
Tracks: / Bluebell polka / Come by the hills / Barren rocks of Aden, The / Highland laddie / Mhairi's wedding / Black bear, The / Take me home / Jans dance / Mathematician, The / High level, The / Dark Island / Scotland again (Caledonia) / Annie Laurie / Addie Harper Jig, The / Garstairs dream / Unshackled Lord of the hills / Mull of Kintyre / Yer mither / Ice on the road / John Gillespie's dog / Bird bone, The / Oor wullie / Wild mountain thyme / Cowal gathering / Ellenor.
Cassette: released on Scotdisc, May'87 Dist: Clyde Factors Distributors

This Is Soca 2

THIS IS SOCA 2 Various artists (Various Artists).
Tracks: / Neighbour, neighbour / Bend down and rock / Bahia girl / I don'tmind / Party people rock / Hammer (The) / To young to soca / We want more grynner / Miss Barbados / Pan rising.

Album: released on London, Jul'86 by London Records. Dist: Polygram

Cassette: released on London, Jul'86 by London Records. Dist: Polygram

This Is Soca 3

THIS IS SOCA 3 Various artists (Various Artists).
Tracks: / Calypso music / Jourvert music / Madness / Yes darling / Bahia girl / Kojak / Dedication / Permission to mash up the place / Tabanca / One day / Sing ram bam / Say say / Thunder / Doctor, doctor / Spring garden on fire / Burn dem.
Notes: Consists of: Record one - David Rudder with Charlie's Roots. Record two - Various artists (The Soca Hits of '87).
Double Album: released on London, Aug'87 by London Records. Dist: Polygram. Estim retail price in Sep'87 was £6.29.

Double cassette: released on London, Aug'87 by London Records. Dist: Polygram. Estim retail price in Sep'87 was £6.29.

This Is Soul

THIS IS SOUL (Various Artists).
Tracks: / Dancing in the street / Warm and tender love / Under the boardwalk / What becomes of the broken hearted / Stand by me / Drift away / Spanish Harlem / Jimmy Mack / Knock on wood / Take time to know her / Hey girl don't bother me / Rescue me / If you don't know me by now.
Compact disc: released on The Collection, Apr'87 by Object Enterprises Ltd. Dist: Counterpoint Distribution

This Is This

HATE AND THE SHAME, THE.
Single (12"): released on Touch, Jun'85 by Touch Records. Dist: Rough Trade, Cartel

This Is WOMAD

THIS IS WOMAD (Various Artists).
Album: released on Womad, Jul'87 by Womad Records. Dist: Revolver, Cartel

This Mortal Coil

16 DAYS.
Single (12"): released on 4AD, Sep'83 by 4AD Records. Dist: Rough Trade

DRUGS.
Tracks: / Drugs / Come here my love.
Single 10": released on 4AD, Aug'86 by 4AD Records. Dist: Rough Trade

FILIGREE AND SHADOW.
Album: released on 4AD, Sep'86 by 4AD Records. Dist: Rough Trade

Cassette: released on 4AD, Sep'86 by 4AD Records. Dist: Rough Trade

FILIGREE AND SHADOW.
Compact disc: released on 4AD, Oct'86 by 4AD Records. Dist: Rough Trade

IT'LL END IN TEARS.
Tracks: / Kangaroo / Song to the siren / Holocaust / Fyt / Fond affections / Last ray, The / Waves become wings / Another day / Barramundi / Dreams made flesh / Not me / Single wish, A.
Compact disc: released on 4AD, '86 by 4AD Records. Dist: Rough Trade

Album: released on 4AD, Oct'84 by 4AD Records. Dist: Rough Trade

Cassette: released on 4AD, Oct'84 by 4AD Records. Dist: Rough Trade

KANGAROO.
Single (7"): released on 4AD, Aug'84 by 4AD Records. Dist: Rough Trade

SONG TO THE SIREN.
Single (7"): released on 4AD, Sep'83 by 4AD Records. Dist: Rough Trade

This Parade

EROTICA.
Single (12"): released on Rumpo, Apr'85 Dist: Nine Mile Distribution, Cartel Distribution

This Poison

ENGINE FAILURE.
Tracks: / You;-Think.
Single (7"): released on Reception, Feb'87 Dist: Red Rhino, Cartel

This Way Up

TELL ME WHY.
Tracks: / Tell me why / Move on up to heaven.
Single (7"): released on Virgin, Jul'87 by Virgin Records. Dist: EMI, Virgin Distribution

Single (12"): released on Virgin, Jul'87 by Virgin Records. Dist: EMI, Virgin Distribution

Cassette single: released on Virgin, Jul'87 by Virgin Records. Dist: EMI, Virgin Distribution

This Years Blonde

PLATINUM POP (Blondie Medley).
Single (7"): released on Creole, Sep'81 by Creole Records. Dist: Rhino, PRT

Single (12"): released on Creole, Sep'81 by Creole Records. Dist: Rhino, PRT

Thomas, Andrew

SINGAPORE MASQUERADE.
Single (7"): released on Arena, May'83 by Arena Records. Dist: Spartan

Thomas, B.J.

AMAZING GRACE.
Album: released on Word, May'82 by Word Records. Dist: Word Distribution, CBS

Cassette: released on Word, May'82 by Word Records. Dist: Word Distribution, CBS

BEST OF.
Cassette: released on Creole (Everest-Europa), Jul'84 by Creole Records. Dist: PRT, Rhino

B.J.THOMAS.
Cassette: released on Audio Fidelity, Oct'84 Dist: PRT

CLOSE TO YOU.
Cassette: released on Orchid Music, Feb'82 by Bibi. Dist: Pinnacle

MIRACLE.
Album: released on Myrrh, May'82 by Word Records. Dist: Word Distribution

Cassette: released on Myrrh, May'82 by Word Records. Dist: Word Distribution

NEW LOOKS.
Album: released on Epic, Aug'83 by CBS Records. Dist: CBS

Cassette: released on Epic, Aug'83 by CBS Records. Dist: CBS

YOU GAVE ME LOVE.
Album: released on World, Jun'84 Dist: Jetstar Cat. no: **WRD 3006**
Cassette: released on World, Jun'84 Dist: Jetstar

Thomas, Buddy

KITTY PUSS FIDDLER.
Album: released on Rounder (USA Import), May'77

Thomas,Carla

I LIKE WHAT YOU'RE DOING TO ME.
Single (7"): released on Stax, Oct'87 by Ace Records. Dist: Pinnacle, Chris Wellard, IMS-Polygram

Thomas, Carter

SONOMA.
Album: released on Press Avant, Oct'85 by Compendium International Records.

Thomas, Charlie

Greatest hits live: Charlie Thomas

Thomas,David

BLAME THE MESSENGER.
Album: released on Rough Trade, Feb'87 by Rough Trade Records. Dist: Rough Trade Distribution, Cartel Distribution

MONSTER WALKS ON WINTER LAKE, THE (Thomas, David & the Wooden Buds).
Album: released on Rough Trade, Feb'86 by Rough Trade Records. Dist: Rough Trade Distribution, Cartel Distribution

MORE PLACES FOREVER (Thomas,David & The Pedestrians).
Album: released on Rough Trade, May'85 by Rough Trade Records. Dist: Rough Trade Distribution, Cartel Distribution

SOUND OF THE SAND, THE (Thomas,David & The Pedestrians).
Album: released on Rough Trade, '84 by Rough Trade Records. Dist: Rough Trade Distribution, Cartel Distribution

VARIATIONS ON A THEME (Thomas,David & The Pedestrians).
Album: released on Rough Trade, '84 by Rough Trade Records. Dist: Rough Trade Distribution, Cartel Distribution

WINTER COMES HOME.
Album: released on Recommended, Sep'86 by Recommended Records. Dist: Recommended, Impetus, Rough Trade

Thomas, Dylan

DYLAN THOMAS SOUNDBOOK.
Boxed set: released on Caedmon(USA), May'80 by Caedmon (USA) Records. Dist: Gower, Taylors, Discovery

Boxed set: released on Caedmon(USA), May'80 by Caedmon (USA) Records. Dist: Gower, Taylors, Discovery

MAN BE MY METAPHOR.
Cassette: released on Talking Tape Company, '84 by Talking Tape Company Records.

Cassette: released on Talking Tape Company, '84 by Talking Tape Company Records.

UNDER MILK WOOD (Featuring Richard Burton) (Various Artists).
Cassette: released on Argo (Spokenword), Jun'82 by Decca Records. Dist: Polygram

UNDER MILK WOOD (NARRATED) Narrated by Donald Houston (Tracey, Stan/Donald Houston).
Album: released on Steam, Apr'81 Dist: JSU, Chris Wellard, Jazz Music, Projection, Cadillac

Thomas, Evelyn

COLD SHOULDER.
Tracks: / Cold shoulder / Hot mix.
Single (7"): released on Record Shack, Mar'86 by Record Shack Records. Dist: PRT

Single (12"): released on Record Shack, Mar'86 by Record Shack Records. Dist: PRT

Single (12"): released on Record Shack, Mar'86 by Record Shack Records. Dist: PRT

HEARTLESS.
Single (7"): released on Record Shack, Nov'84 by Record Shack Records. Dist: PRT

Single (12"): released on Record Shack, Nov'84 by Record Shack Records. Dist: PRT

HIGH ENERGY.
Album: released on Record Shack, Oct'86 by Record Shack Records. Dist: PRT

Single (7"): released on Record Shack, May'84 by Record Shack Records. Dist: PRT

Single (12"): released on Record Shack, May'84 by Record Shack Records. Dist: PRT

Picture disc single: released on Record Shack, May'84 by Record Shack Records. Dist: PRT

MASQUERADE.
Single (7"): released on Record Shack, Aug'84

by Record Shack Records. Dist: PRT

Single (12"): released on Record Shack, Aug'84 by Record Shack Records. Dist: PRT

REFLECTIONS.
Tracks: / Reflections / Tightrope / Number one lover / How many hearts / Cold shoulder / Standing at the crossroads / Sorry, wrong number / Heartless.
Album: released on Record Shack, Aug'86 by Record Shack Records. Dist: PRT

Cassette: released on Record Shack, Aug'86 by Record Shack Records. Dist: PRT

Single (12"): released on Record Shack, Nov'85 by Record Shack Records. Dist: PRT

Single (7"): released on Record Shack, Sep'83 by Record Shack Records. Dist: PRT

Single (12"): released on Record Shack, Sep'83 by Record Shack Records. Dist: PRT

SORRY WRONG NUMBER.
Single (7"): released on Record Shack, Apr'85 by Record Shack Records. Dist: PRT

Single (12"): released on Record Shack, Apr'85 by Record Shack Records. Dist: PRT

STANDING AT THE CROSS ROADS.
Tracks: / Standing at the cross roads / Standing at the cross roads (inst).
Single (7"): released on Nightmare, Apr'87 by Nightmare Records. Dist: PRT

Single (12"): released on Nightmare, Apr'87 by Nightmare Records. Dist: PRT

STANDING AT THE CROSSROADS.
Tracks: / Standing at the crossroads / How many hearts? / Cold shoulder / Sorry wrong number / Reflections suite, The / Reflections (love tempo) / Tightrope / Number one lover / Reflections / Tightrope.
Album: released on Record Shack, Sep'86

Cassette: released on Record Shack, Sep'86

TIGHTROPE.
Tracks: / Tightrope / Tightrope (INST).
Single (7"): released on Nightmare, Oct'86 by Nightmare Records. Dist: PRT

Single (12"): released on Nightmare, Oct'86 by Nightmare Records. Dist: PRT

Thomas, Henry

RAGTIME TEXAS.
Double Album: released on Herwin, Sep'75 Dist: Jazz Music

Thomas, Irma

BREAKAWAY.
Tracks: / Without love (there is nothing) / Take a look / Time is on my side / Wish someone would care / It's starting to get me now / He's my guy / What are you trying to do / I'm gonna cry till my tears run dry / You don't miss a good thing (until it's gone) / Anyone who knows what love is (will understand) / It's raining / Please send me someone to love / Another woman's man / While the city sleeps / Straight from the heart / It's a man's woman's world / I've been there before / I need you so / Breakaway / Without love (there is nothing).
Album: released on Stateside, Sep'87 Dist: EMI

Cassette: released on Stateside, Sep'87 Dist: EMI

Album: released on Parlophone, Sep'87 by EMI Records. Dist: EMI. Estim retail price in Sep'87 was £5.99.

Cassette: released on Parlophone, Sep'87 by EMI Records. Dist: EMI. Estim retail price in Sep'87 was £5.99.

HIP SHAKING MAMA.
Album: released on Charly, Dec'81 by Charly Records. Dist: Charly, Cadillac

IN BETWEEN TEARS.
Album: released on Charly, Mar'81 by Charly Records. Dist: Charly, Cadillac

IRMA THOMAS SINGS (Minit and Bandy Originals).
Album: released on Bandy (USA), Apr'79

NEW RULES, THE.
Compact disc: released on Rounder (USA), '86 Dist: Mike's Country Music Room Distribution, Jazz Music Distribution, Swift Distribution, Roots Records Distribution, Projection Distribution, Topic Distribution

Album: released on Rounder Europa, Feb'87

Album: released on Rounder Europa, Apr'86

SAFE WITH ME.
Single (7"): released on Polo, Apr'81 by Polo Records. Dist: PRT

Single (12"): released on Polo, Apr'81 by Polo

Records. Dist: PRT

SOUL QUEEN OF NEW ORLEANS.
Album: released on Maison de Soul, Mar'79 Dist: Swift

TIME IS ON MY SIDE.
Cassette: released on Kent, Jan'85 by Ace Records. Dist: Pinnacle

Cassette: released on Kent, Jan'85 by Ace Records. Dist: Pinnacle

WISH SOMEONE WOULD CARE.
Album: released on Flyover, Apr'79 by Flyover Records. Dist: Flyover Records

Thomas, Jah

Best dressed chicken in town

CLEAN YOUR TEETH.
Single (12"): released on Midnight Rock, Mar'84 Dist: Jetstar Distribution, Kingdom Distribution

DANCE HALL CONNECTION.
Album: released on Silver Camel, '83 Dist: Jetstar, Rough Trade

LONDON SKANK.
Single (7"): released on Midnight Rock, Nov'81 Dist: Jetstar Distribution, Kingdom Distribution

NAH FIGHT OVER WOMAN.
Album: released on Vista Sounds, '83 by Vista Sounds Records. Dist: Jetstar

POSSIE (Thomas, Jah & Jim Brown).
Single (7"): released on Midnight Rock, Oct'83 Dist: Jetstar Distribution, Kingdom Distribution

STOP YU LOAFIN'.
Album: released on Greensleeves, Sep'78 by Greensleeves Records. Dist: BMG, Jetstar, Spartan

SWEET MEMORIES.
Single (12"): released on Midnight, Feb'82

TRIBUTE TO RAGGAE KING, BOB N.MARLEY.
Album: released on Vista Sounds, '83 by Vista Sounds Records. Dist: Jetstar

Thomas, Jameson

PLAYS AND SINGS DELTA BLUES CLASSICS.
Album: released on Swingmaster, Oct'82 Dist: Jazz Music Distribution

Thomas, Jimmy

HANG RIGHT ON IN THERE (2 Parts).
Single (7"): released on Osceola, Feb'82 by Osceola Records. Dist: Charly, Pinnacle

STANDING ALONE IN A CROWD.
Single (7"): released on Cricket International, Oct'82 by Cricket International Records. Dist: Stage One

Thomas, Joe

BLOWNIN' IN FROM K.C..
Album: released on Uptown, Jul'83 by Uptown Records. Dist: PRT, Cartel

RAW MEAT.
Album: released on Uptown (USA), Nov'86 by Uptown Records. Dist: Jazz Music

Album: released on Uptown, Feb'83 by Uptown Records. Dist: PRT, Cartel

Thomas, Joy

JUMP AROUND.
Single (12"): released on Half Moon, Apr'83 by Rondelet Music And Records. Dist: Spartan

Thomas, Kid

Biographical Details: see under - Punch Miller.

AT MOULIN ROUGE.
Album: released on Center(USA), Mar'77 Dist: Swift, VJM

AT THE OLD GRIST MILL (Thomas, Kid & His New Orleans Joymakers).
Album: released on GHB, Jun'86 Dist: Jazz Music, Swift

ECHOES OF NEW ORLEANS VOL.2.
Album: released on Storyville, '78 by Storyville Records. Dist: Jazz Music Distribution, Swift Distribution, Chris Wellard Distribution, Counterpoint Distribution

HIS NEW ORLEANS JAZZ BAND.
Album: released on Arhoolie, Jun'75 by Arhoolie Records. Dist: Projection, Topic, Jazz Music, Swift, Roots

IN DENMARK VOL.1 (Thomas, Kid & Louis Nelson).
Album: released on Storyville, Jun'77 by Storyville Records. Dist: Jazz Music Distribution, Swift Distribution, Chris Wellard Distribution, Counterpoint Distribution

IN SCANDINAVIA (Thomas, Kid Jazz Band).
Album: released on Rarities, Sep'74

JAZZOLOGY POLL WINNERS 1964 (Thomas,Kid/George Lewis/Don Ewell).
Album: released on GHB, Sep'86 Dist: Jazz Music, Swift

KID THOMAS' DIXIELAND BAND (Recorded New Orleans 1968) (Thomas, Kid & His Dixieland band).
Album: released on Nola, Apr'79 Dist: JSU, Jazz Music, Cadillac, Chris Wellard

Cassette: released on Nola, Apr'79 Dist: JSU, Jazz Music, Cadillac, Chris Wellard

KID THOMAS, EMANUEL PAUL & BARRY MARTYN.
Album: released on 77, '74 by 77 Records. Dist: Chris Wellard, Cadillac Music, Jazz Music

KID THOMAS/RAYMOND BURKE & THE ORIGINAL ALGIERS STOMPERS (Thomas, Kid/Raymond Burke).
Album: released on Jazzology, Feb'87 Dist: Jazz Music, Swift

KID THOMAS & THE NEW BLACK EAGLE JAZZ BAND (Thomas, Kid & The New Black Eagle Jazz Band).
Album: released on GHB, Jun'86 Dist: Jazz Music, Swift

LOVE SONGS OF THE NILE.
Album: released on GHB, Mar'87 Dist: Jazz Music, Swift

NEW ORLEANS JAZZ.
Album: released on Arhoolie, May'81 by Arhoolie Records. Dist: Projection, Topic, Jazz Music, Swift, Roots

ROCKIN' THIS JOINT TONITE (With Dixon and Ace Holder).
Album: released on JSP, Feb'79 by JSP Records. Dist: Swift, Projection

Thomas, Leon

PIECE OF CAKE, A (Thomas, Leon & Freddy Hubbard).
Album: released on Palcoscenico (Italy), '81 Dist: Jazz Music

Thomas, Lillo

DOWNTOWN.
Tracks: / Downtown / I'm in love.
Single (7"): released on Capitol, Jul'87 by Capitol Records. Dist: EMI

Single (12"): released on Capitol, Jul'87 by Capitol Records. Dist: EMI

I'M IN LOVE.
Tracks: / I'min love (longer luv mix) / Sexy girl / Sexy girl (sexy mix) / I've been loving you too long (to stop now).
Double-pack single: released on Capitol, 23 May'87 by Capitol Records. Dist: EMI

I'M IN LOVE (RADIO MIX).
Tracks: / I'm in love / I'm in love (short love dub) / I've been loving you too long to stop now.
Single (7"): released on Capitol, May'87 by Capitol Records. Dist: EMI

Single (12"): released on Capitol, May'87 by Capitol Records. Dist: EMI

I'M IN LOVE (REMIX).
Tracks: / I'm in love (remix) / Sexy girl (sexy mix) / Sexy girl (inst).
Single (12"): released on Capitol, Jun'87 by Capitol Records. Dist: EMI

LET ME BE YOURS.
Album: released on Capitol, Sep'83 by Capitol Records. Dist: EMI

Cassette: released on Capitol, Sep'83 by Capitol Records. Dist: EMI

LILLO.
Tracks: / I'm in love / Her love / Sweet surrender / That guy (could have been me) / Sexy girl / Wanna make love (all night long) / I've been loving you too long (to stop now) / Downtown / Put your foot down.
Notes: Lillo Thomas' third album for Capitol sees him in strongest form yet. Already quite a name on the soul scene both here and in the States, Lillo has yet to have a really big hit single. However that day may be very near because the first single from his album, *Sexy girl* is shaping up to be a massive club record here

in britain. *Sexy girl* is written by Lillo's label mate Paul Laurence, along with Tommy Allen, renowned bass player with the group Change. Lillo also shows off his talents as composer and producer on this album, which features some fine ballads, including a cover of Otis Redding's hit *I've been loving you too long* [EMI release sheet, April 87].
Album: released on Capitol, Apr'87 by Capitol Records. Dist: EMI

Cassette: released on Capitol, Apr'87 by Capitol Records. Dist: EMI

Compact disc: released on EMI, Jul'87 by EMI Records. Dist: EMI

SEXY GIRL.
Single (7"): released on Capitol, Mar'87 by Capitol Records. Dist: EMI

Single (12"): released on Capitol, Mar'87 by Capitol Records. Dist: EMI

Thomas, Louise

CAST ASIDE MY STUBBORN HEART.
Tracks: / I've got to tell you goodbye.
Single (12"): released on Red Bus, Nov'86 by Red Bus Records. Dist: PRT

DOUBLE VISION.
Tracks: / Double vision / Double vision (inst).
Single (7"): released on Nightmare, May'87 by Nightmare Records. Dist: PRT

Single (12"): released on Nightmare, May'87 by Nightmare Records. Dist: PRT

HEAD OVER HEELS.
Tracks: / Head over heels / Head over heels (INST).
Single (12"): released on Debut, Feb'86 by Skratch Music. Dist: PRT

REFLEX ACTION.
Tracks: / Reflex action (INST).
Single (7"): released on R & B, Apr'86 by Red Bus. Dist: PRT

Single (12"): released on R & B, Apr'86 by Red Bus. Dist: PRT

Thomas, Luther

....CREATIVE ENSEMBLE & LESTER BOWIE.
Album: released on Circle, Jan'80 Dist: Jazz Music

Thomas, Michael Tilson

GERSHWIN LIVE.
Album: released on CBS, Sep'82 by CBS Records. Dist: CBS

Thomas, Nicky

LOVE OF THE COMMON PEOPLE.
Single (7"): released on Old Gold, Jul'84 by Old Gold Records. Dist: Lightning, Jazz Music, Spartan, Counterpoint

Single (7"): released on Trojan, Feb'83 by Trojan Records. Dist: PRT, Jetstar

Single (12"): released on Trojan, Feb'83 by Trojan Records. Dist: PRT, Jetstar

Single (7"): released on Trojan, Aug'81 by Trojan Records. Dist: PRT, Jetstar

Album: released on Trojan, '77 by Trojan Records. Dist: PRT, Jetstar

TELL IT LIKE IT IS.
Album: released on Trojan, '74 by Trojan Records. Dist: PRT, Jetstar

Thomas, Pat

IN ACTION VOL.2.
Album: released on Earthworks, Feb'84 by Earthworks Records. Dist: Earthworks Distributors, Rough Trade, Cartel, Projection

NINE MILES HIGH.
Single (7"): released on Tout Ensemble, Aug'86 Dist: Pinnacle

Single (12"): released on Tout Ensemble, Aug'86 Dist: Pinnacle

PAT THOMAS & EBO TAYLOR (Thomas, Pat & Ebo Taylor).
Album: released on Dannytone, Apr'85 b Dannytone Records.

Thomas, Pauline

IF I FOLLOW MY HEART.
Tracks: / If I folow my heart (Remix version).
Single (12"): released on Neville King, Aug'8 by Neville King Records. Dist: Jetstar

SAVING ALL MY LOVE FOR YOU.
Tracks: / Saving all my love for you / This is
Single (12"): released on Neville King, Jan' by Neville King Records. Dist: Jetstar

Thomas, Philip Michael

JUST THE WAY I PLANNED IT.
Tracks: / Just the way I planned it / All my lo
Single (7"): released on WEA, Jan'86 by WE Records. Dist: WEA

Single (12"): released on WEA, Jan'86 by WE Records. Dist: WEA

LIVIN' THE BOOK OF LIFE.
Tracks: / Livin' the book of life / Just the way I planned it / You might be the lucky one / Fish & chips / Everything happens in it's own time / She's a liar / I'm in love with the love that you give me / Stay(in my loving arms tonight) / All my love / La Mirada.
Album: released on Atlantic, Mar'86 by WEA Records. Dist: WEA

Cassette: released on Atlantic, Mar'86 by WEA Records. Dist: WEA

Thomas, Ramblin'
RAMBLIN' THOMAS (1928-1932).
Album: released on Matchbox, Nov'83 by Saydisc Records. Dist: Roots, Projection, Jazz Music, JSU, Celtic Music

Thomas, Rockin' Tabby
BLUES TRAIN.
Album: Dist: Swift

ROCKIN' TABBY THOMAS Rockin' with the blues.
Album: Dist: Swift

Thomas, R.S.
R.S. THOMAS READS HIS POEMS.
Album: released on Oriel, Feb'77 Dist: Welsh Arts Council Distribution

Thomas, Ruddy
AM I CRAZY.
Tracks: / Am I crazy / Sitting in the park.
Single (12"): released on Hawkeye, Dec'85 by Hawkeye Records. Dist: Hawkeye, Lightning (WEA) Distribution, Jetstar, PRT

COME TO ME.
Tracks: / Cindy.
Single (12"): released on C & E, Nov'86 Dist: Jetstar

LET'S DANCE.
Single (12"): released on Greensleeves, Jun'85 by Greensleeves Records. Dist: BMG, Jetstar, Spartan

LONG LOST LOVER.
Tracks: / Long lost lover / Twilight zone / Peter Gunne.
Single (12"): released on Island, Mar'86 by Island Records. Dist: Polygram

PERHAPS.
Tracks: / Waking my baby.
Single (12"): released on World Enterprise, Dec'86 Dist: Jetstar

SHE'S MY PRE-RELEASE.
Tracks: / She's my pre-release (version).
Single (12"): released on Orbitone, Nov'86 by Orbitone Records. Dist: Jetstar Distribution

TELL IT LIKE IT IS.
Tracks: / Tell it like it is / Make up your mind.
Single (12"): released on Hawkeye, Mar'86 by Hawkeye Records. Dist: Hawkeye, Lightning (WEA) Distribution, Jetstar, PRT

TIME FOR LOVE (Thomas, Ruddy & June Lodge).
Tracks: / Time for love / In the summertime.
Single (12"): rel: released on Greensleeves, Feb'86 by Greensleeves Records. Dist: BMG, Jetstar, Spartan

Single (12"): released on Greensleeves, Feb'86 by Greensleeves Records. Dist: BMG, Jetstar, Spartan

Single (12"): released on Greensleeves, Nov'85 by Greensleeves Records. Dist: BMG, Jetstar, Spartan

Thomas, Rudi
HESE SONGS.
ngle (12"): released on Charm, 30 May'87 st: Jetstar

Thomas, Rudy
LL THIS LOVE.
ngle (12"): released on Tads, Jan'84 by Tads cords. Dist: Jetstar Distribution

LESS YOU (Thomas, Rudy with Neville own & John Wayne).
gle (12"): released on Shuttle, Apr'83 Dist:

EJA VU.
um: released on Mobiliser, Apr'83 by st: Jetstar Distribution

ON'T WANT TO LOSE YOU.
um: released on World Enterprise, Jan'87 st: Jetstar

ST ONE MOMENT AWAY.
ngle (12"): released on Creole, Dec'81 by Cre- Records. Dist: Rhino, PRT

ngle (12"): released on Creole, Dec'81 by ole Records. Dist: Rhino, PRT

KEY TO THE WORLD (Thomas, Rudy & Sound Inc.).
Single (12"): released on Hawkeye, Apr'82 by Hawkeye Records. Dist: Hawkeye, Lightning (WEA) Distribution, Jetstar, PRT

LOVE YOU NEED, THE.
Single (12"): released on Londisc, Jun'84 by Londisc Records.

LOVING PAUPER.
Single (12"): released on Real Wax, Jul'84

NICE AND EASY (Thomas, Rudy & Sound Inc.).
Single (12"): released on Hawkeye, Feb'83 by Hawkeye Records. Dist: Hawkeye, Lightning (WEA) Distribution, Jetstar, PRT

RAIN FROM THE SKY (2 Parts).
Single (12"): released on Revue, May'83 by Revue Records. Dist: Creole

REFLECTIONS (Thomas, Rudy & Barry Biggs).
Single (12"): released on Mobiliser, Mar'83 by Jetstar Records. Dist: Jetstar Distribution

Single (7"): released on Stars Recording, Aug'83

Single (7"): released on Stars Recording, Aug'83

SITTING OUT NIGHT TIME.
Single (12"): released on Revue, Oct'84 by Revue Records. Dist: Creole

SWEET REGGAE MUSIC (Leroy Smart).
Single (12"): released on Mobiliser, Feb'84 by Jetstar Records. Dist: Jetstar Distribution

SWING OUT NIGHT TIME.

TONIGHT'S THE NIGHT.
Single (12"): released on Diamond C, Jun'84 by Diamond C Records. Dist: Jetstar

WHEN I THINK OF YOU.
Single (12"): released on Hawkeye, Aug'80 by Hawkeye Records. Dist: Hawkeye, Lightning (WEA) Distribution, Jetstar, PRT

Thomas, Rufus
BEAR CAT.
Single (7"): released on Charly, Dec'76 by Charly Records. Dist: Charly, Cadillac

DO THE FUNKY CHICKEN.
Single (7"): released on Old Gold, Sep'85 by Old Gold Records. Dist: Lightning, Jazz Music, Spartan, Counterpoint

JUMP BACK.
Album: released on Edsel, May'84 by Demon Records. Dist: Pinnacle, Jazz Music, Projection

Thomas, Tabby
BLUES TRAIN.
Album: released on Ace, May'87 by Ace Records. Dist: Pinnacle, Swift, Hotshot, Cadillac

Thomas & Taylor
I LOVE YOU.
Tracks: / Love and affection.
Single (12"): released on In Recordings, Feb'87 Dist: RCA, DMS

Single (12"): released on In Recordings, Feb'87 Dist: RCA, DMS

TRUE LOVE (BOOK 1).
Tracks: / Lonely too long / True love / Freedom / You can't blame love (remix) / you can't blame love / Freedom / My room / Love and affection (remix) / Call me / I love you.
Album: released on Recordings, Jan'87

Cassette: released on Recordings, Jan'87

YOU CAN'T BLAME LOVE.
Tracks: / You can't blame love / We need company.
Single (7"): released on Cool Tempo, May'86 by Chrysalis Records. Dist: CBS

Single (12"): released on Cool Tempo, May'86 by Chrysalis Records. Dist: CBS

Thomas the Voice
STONE CUTTER BOY.
Single (7"): released on North West, Jun'87 by North West Records. Dist: Red Rhino Distribution, Cartel Distribution

Single (12"): released on North West, Jun'87 by North West Records. Dist: Red Rhino Distribution, Cartel Distribution

Thomas, Timmy
WHY CAN'T WE LIVE TOGETHER.
Single (7"): released on Import, '80 Dist: Stage One

Thomas, T.J.
NICE THINGS WE SAID WORTH MORE THAN MONEY.
Tracks: / Nice things we said worth more than money / Nice things we said worth more than money(version).
Single (12"): released on VIP, Aug'86 Dist: Jetstar Distribution

Thomas, Vaneese
LET'S TALK IT OVER.
Single (7"): released on Geffen, Aug'87 by Geffen Records. Dist: WEA, CBS

Single (12"): released on Geffen, Aug'87 by Geffen Records. Dist: WEA, CBS

VANEESE THOMAS.
Album: released on Geffen, Jul'87 by Geffen Records. Dist: WEA, CBS

Cassette: released on Geffen, Jul'87 by Geffen Records. Dist: WEA, CBS

Album: released on Geffen, Aug'87 by Geffen Records. Dist: WEA, CBS

Thomas, Willard
RAMBLIN.
Album: released on Collectors, 78 by Castle Communications Records. Dist: PRT, Pinnacle, Jazz Music

Thom, Lou
IT SEEMS TO ME.
Single (7"): released on Half Moon, Sep'82 by Rondelet Music And Records. Dist: Spartan

Single (12"): released on Half Moon, Sep'82 by Rondelet Music And Records. Dist: Spartan

Thompson, Ally
FALLING FOR YOU.
Cassette: released on Ross, '86 by Ross Records. Dist: Ross Distribution, Roots Distribution

TRUCK DRIVIN' MAN.
Cassette: released on Ross, '86 by Ross Records. Dist: Ross Distribution, Roots Distribution

Cassette: released on Ross, Aug'84 by Ross Records. Dist: Ross Distribution, Roots Distribution

Thompson, B
B.THOMPSON AND THE BLACK EAGLE JAZZ BAND (Thompson, B & The Black Eagle Jazz Band).

Thompson, Barbara
FANTASY.
Album: released on Original, Mar'84 by RCA Distribution, Jazz Music Distribution, PRT Distribution

Cassette: released on Original, Mar'84 Dist: RCA Distribution, Jazz Music Distribution, PRT Distribution

HEAVENLY BODIES.
Compact disc: released on TM Records, '86

MOTHER EARTH (Thompson, Barbara Paraphernalia).
Album: released on TM, Sep'84 by TM Records. Dist: PRT Distribution

Cassette: released on TM, Sep'84 by TM Records. Dist: PRT Distribution

PURE FANTASY (Thompson, Barbara Paraphernalia).
Tracks: / Pure fantasy / Mother earth suite.
Album: released on TM, Sep'86 by TM Records. Dist: PRT Distribution

Cassette: released on TM, Sep'86 by TM Records. Dist: PRT Distribution

Compact disc: released on TM, Sep'86 by TM Records. Dist: PRT Distribution

WITH YOU (Thompson, Barbara & Rod Argent).
Single (7"): released on MCA, Feb'82 by MCA Records. Dist: Polygram, MCA

Single (12"): released on MCA, Feb'82 by MCA Records. Dist: Polygram, MCA

Thompson, Bobby
7 IN 7 OUT.
Album: released on Rainbow (USA), Feb'85 by Rainbow (USA). Dist: IMS, Polygram

Cassette: released on Rainbow (USA), Feb'85 by Rainbow (USA). Dist: IMS, Polygram

BOBBY THOMPSON LAUGH-IN, THE.
Album: released on Rubber, Jun'82 by Rubber

Single (7"): released on Old Gold, Jul'84 by Old Gold Records. Dist: Lightning, Jazz Music, Spartan, Counterpoint

Records. Dist: Roots Distribution, Projection Distribution, Jazz Music Distribution, Celtic Music Distribution, JSU Distribution, Spartan Distribution

Cassette: released on Rubber, Jun'82 by Rubber Records. Dist: Roots Distribution, Projection Distribution, Jazz Music Distribution, Celtic Music Distribution, JSU Distribution, Spartan Distribution

LITTLE WASTER, THE.
Album: released on Rubber, Jun'82 by Rubber Records. Dist: Roots Distribution, Projection Distribution, Jazz Music Distribution, Celtic Music Distribution, JSU Distribution, Spartan Distribution

Cassette: released on Rubber, Jun'82 by Rubber Records. Dist: Roots Distribution, Projection Distribution, Jazz Music Distribution, Celtic Music Distribution, JSU Distribution, Spartan Distribution

WHAT FETTLE.
Album: released on M & W, Nov'85

Cassette: released on M & W, Nov'85

Thompson, Butch
A' SOLAS.
Album: released on Stomp Off (USA), Jan'84

BUTCH THOMPSON & HAL SMITH (Thompson, Butch & Hal Smith).
Album: released on Stomp Off, Jun'86 by Stomp Off Records. Dist: Jazz Music Distribution

BUTCH THOMPSON & HIS BERKELEY GANG (Thompson, Butch & his Berkeley Gang).
Album: released on Stomp Off, Mar'87 by Stomp Off Records. Dist: Jazz Music Distribution

IN CHICAGO (Thompson, Butch & His Boys & Frank Chase).
Album: released on Jazzology, Jul'87 Dist: Jazz Music, Swift

MILENBERG JOYS (Thompson, Butch/Hal Smith/Charlie Devore).
Album: released on Stomp Off, Oct'86 by Stomp Off Records. Dist: Jazz Music Distribution

PLAYS JELLY ROLL MORTON VOL.2.
Album: released on Center(USA), Mar'77 Dist: Swift, VJM

PLAYS JELLY ROLL MORTON.
Album: released on Center(USA), Mar'77 Dist: Swift, VJM

Thompson, Carl
BABY.
Single (12"): released on Skynote, Sep'85 Dist: Sidewalk Records

Thompson, Carol
HAPPY SONG.
Single (7"): released on S&G, Nov'81 Dist: Pinnacle

STRANGEST LOVE AFFAIR.
Tracks: / Strangest love affair / Tonight / S.l.a.- s.l.a.'.
Single (7"): released on Virgin, Aug'86 by Virgin Records. Dist: EMI, Virgin Distribution

Single (12"): released on Virgin, Aug'86 by Virgin Records. Dist: EMI, Virgin Distribution

Thompson, Carroll
APPLE OF MY EYE.
Single (12"): released on Virgin, Dec'84 by Virgin Records. Dist: EMI, Virgin Distribution

CARROLL THOMPSON.
Album: released on Carousel, '83 by Carousel Records. Dist: Spartan, Rough Trade

HONIS I DO.
Single (7"): released on Carousel, Jan'84 by Carousel Records. Dist: Spartan, Rough Trade

Single (12"): released on Carousel, Dec'83 by Carousel Records. Dist: Spartan, Rough Trade

HOPELESSLY IN LOVE.
Album: released on Carib Jems, Jan'84 by Carib Jems. Dist: Spartan, Jetstar

Cassette: released on Carib Jems, Jan'84 by Carib Jems. Dist: Spartan, Jetstar

JUST A LITTLE BIT.
Single (7"): released on Red Bus, Jan'82 by Red Bus Records. Dist: PRT

Single (12"): released on Red Bus, Jan'82 by Red Bus Records. Dist: PRT

LOVE WITHOUT PASSION.
Tracks: / Ready or not / Tonite*.

Single (7"): released on Virgin, Jan'87 by Virgin Records. Dist: EMI, Virgin Distribution

Single (12"): released on Virgin, Jan'87 by Virgin Records. Dist: EMI, Virgin Distribution

LOVE WON'T LET ME WAIT (Thompson, Carroll & Trevor Walters).
Single (12"): released on Sanity, Jul'84 by Sanity Records. Dist: Pinnacle, Jetstar

MAKE IT WITH YOU.
Single (12"): released on Carousel, May'83 by Carousel Records. Dist: Spartan, Rough Trade

Single (12"): released on Carousel, May'83 by Carousel Records. Dist: Spartan, Rough Trade

YOU MAKE IT HEAVEN.
Single (12"): released on Carousel, Aug'83 by Carousel Records. Dist: Spartan, Rough Trade

YOUR LOVE.
Single (12"): released on S&G, Aug'82 Dist: Pinnacle

Thompson, Charles

DAY I JOIN THE GOLF CLUB, THE.
Cassette: released on Dead Happy, '82 by Dead Happy Records. Dist: Mason's Music Distributors/Wholesalers, Rough Trade

Thompson, Charles Sir

FOR THE EARS (Honda/Corea/Vitous/Haynes).
Double Album: released on Vogue Jazz (France), May'83

Thompson, Chris

BYE BYE LOVE.
Single (7"): released on Simple, Jul'84 by Simple Records. Dist: EMI

HIGH COST OF LIVING, THE.
Tracks: / Love & loneliness / What a woman wants / It don't bother me / High cost of living, The / Empty house / It's not over / Living for the thrill / Missing / She's dangerous / This is not a world of our making.
Album: released on Atlantic, Aug'86 by WEA Records. Dist: WEA

Cassette: released on Atlantic, Aug'86 by WEA Records. Dist: WEA

IT'S NOT OVER.
Tracks: / It's not over / Make it a holiday.
Single (7"): released on Parlophone, Mar'87 by EMI Records. Dist: EMI

LOVE & LONELINESS.
Tracks: / Love & loneliness / Easy street.
Single (7"): released on Atlantic, Aug'86 by WEA Records. Dist: WEA

Single (12"): released on Atlantic, Aug'86 by WEA Records. Dist: WEA

PUSH AND SHOVE (see O'Connor, Hazel) (Thompson, Chris & Hazel O'Connor).

Thompson, Colin

THREE KNIGHTS.
Album: released on Fellside (Cumbria), '83 by Fellside Records. Dist: Roots, Projection, CM, Jazz Music

Thompson, Danny

WHATEVER.
Album: released on Hannibal, Jul'87 by Hannibal Records. Dist: Charly, Harmonia Mundi, Projection, Celtic Music, Roots

Compact disc: released on Hannibal, Aug'87 by Hannibal Records. Dist: Charly, Harmonia Mundi, Projection, Celtic Music, Roots. Estim retail price in Sep'87 was £11.99.

Thompson, Don

BEAUTIFUL FRIENDSHIP, A (Thompson, Don Quartet).
Album: released on Concord Jazz, Jul'84 by Concord Jazz Records (USA). Dist: IMS, Polygram

COAST TO COAST.
Album: released on Amberlee, '74 by Amberlee Records. Dist: Amberlee Records, H.R. Taylor

COUNTRY PLACE.
Album: released on PM, Jan'80 Deleted '80.

LIVE AT THE CAFE CARLYLE (see Shearing, George) (Thompson, Don & George Shearing).

LIVE AT THE CAFE CARLYLE.
Album: released on Concord Jazz(USA), Sep'84 by Concord Jazz Records (USA). Dist: IMS, Polygram

Cassette: released on Concord Jazz(USA), Sep'84 by Concord Jazz Records (USA). Dist: IMS, Polygram

Thompson, Eddie

AIN'T SHE SWEET (Thompson, Eddie Trio/Spike robinson).
Album: released on Hep, Apr'81 by H.R. Taylor Records. Dist: Jazz Music, Cadillac Music, JSU, Taylors, Wellard, Chris, Zodiac, Swift, Fast Forward

AT CHESTERS (Thompson, Eddie Trio/Spike robinson).
Album: released on Hep, Aug'85 by H.R. Taylor Records. Dist: Jazz Music, Cadillac Music, JSU, Taylors, Wellard, Chris, Zodiac, Swift, Fast Forward

AT CHESTERS VOL.2 (Thompson, Eddie Trio/Spike robinson).
Notes: Full details see under ROBINSON, Spike

BY MYSELF.
Album: released on 77, '74 by 77 Records. Dist: Chris Wellard, Cadillac Music, Jazz Music

EDDIE THOMPSON WITH ROY WILLIAMS (Thompson, Eddie & Roy Williams).
Album: released on Hep, Apr'81 by H.R. Taylor Records. Dist: Jazz Music, Cadillac Music, JSU, Taylors, Wellard, Chris, Zodiac, Swift, Fast Forward

MEMORIES OF YOU (Thompson, Eddie Trio/Spike robinson).
Album: released on Hep, Jul'84 by H.R. Taylor Records. Dist: Jazz Music, Cadillac Music, JSU, Taylors, Wellard, Chris, Zodiac, Swift, Fast Forward

PUT ON A HAPPY FACE.
Single (7"): released on Hobo, Aug'79 by Hobo Records. Dist: Hobo Deleted '80.

Thompson, Eric

BLUEGRASS GUITAR.
Album: released on Kicking Mule, Jul'79 by Sonet. Dist: Roots, PRT-Pye Distribution

MAGIC ROUNDABOUT STORIES.
Album: released on BBC, Oct'76 by BBC Records & Tapes. Dist: EMI, PRT.

Cassette: released on BBC, Oct'76 by BBC Records & Tapes. Dist: EMI, PRT,

Thompson, Everand

OBSERVATION BABYLON (Thompson, Everand & Eusi Simba).
Single (12"): released on Ultimate, Jun'81 by Ultimate Records. Dist: Spartan

Thompson, Francis

ITALIAN MAN.
Single (7"): released on Ark, Nov'82 Dist: ILA

Thompson, Hank

20 GOLDEN PIECES OF HANK THOMPSON.
Album: released on Bulldog, May'85 by Bulldog Records. Dist: President Distribution, Spartan, Swift, Taylor, H.R.

Cassette: released on Bulldog Records, Jul'85

BEST OF BEST, THE.
Album: released on Gusto (USA), '80 by Gusto Records (USA). Dist: Crusader

DANCE RANCH.
Album: released on Stetson, Oct'86 by Hasmick Promotions Ltd.. Dist: Counterpoint Distribution, H.R. Taylor Distribution, Swift Distribution, Chris Wellard Distribution

Cassette: released on Stetson, Oct'86 by Hasmick Promotions Ltd.. Dist: Counterpoint Distribution, H.R. Taylor Distribution, Swift Distribution, Chris Wellard Distribution

HANK THOMPSON.
Album: released on MCA, Mar'87 by MCA Records. Dist: Polygram, MCA

Cassette: released on MCA, Mar'87 by MCA Records. Dist: Polygram, MCA

Thompson, Hayden

BOONEVILLE MISSISSIPPI FLASH.
Album: released on Charly, Aug'85 by Charly Records. Dist: Charly, Cadillac

FUNNY HOW TIME SLIPS AWAY.
Album: released on Meteor, Apr'87 by Magnum Music Group Ltd.. Dist: Magnum Music Group Ltd, PRT Distribution, Spartan Distribution

ROCKABILLY GUY 1954-1962.
Tracks: / I feel the blues coming on / Act like you love me / Rockabilly gal / Love my baby / One broken heart / Blues,blues,blues / You are my sunshine / Mama,mama,mama / Call me shorty / Brown-eyed handsome man / I hold you in my heart / Kansas City / It won't be long until the summer / Old Kris Kringle / Pardon me / Queen bee / Goin' steady.

Compact disc: released on Charly, '86 by Charly Records. Dist: Charly, Cadillac

Album: released on Charly, Nov'86 by Charly Records. Dist: Charly, Cadillac

Thompson, Johnny

SHE GIVES ME LOVING.
Tracks: / Shje gives me loving / Substitute.
Single (12"): released on Megastar, Jul'86

SILENT NIGHT (Thompson, Johnny Singers).
Compact disc: released on Hi Grade, '86 Dist: Target

SPIRIT OF GOSPEL, THE (Thompson, Johnny Singers).
Compact disc: released on Bridge, Apr'87 Dist: CD Centre Distribution, Pinnacle, Target

Thompson, Leroy

HARD TIMES CRIMINAL TIMES.
Single (12"): released on Noel, Sep'81 by Mainline Record Company. Dist: Mainline

Thompson, Lincoln

COME SPRING.
Single (12"): released on God Sent, May'82 by Third World Records. Dist: Jetstar

NATURAL WILD.
Album: released on Ballistic, Aug'80 by Ballistic Records. Dist: EMI, Mojo Distribution

ONE COMMON NEED.
Single (12"): released on God Sent, Apr'82 by Third World Records. Dist: Jetstar

Thompson, Linda

ONE CLEAR MOMENT.
Album: released on Warner Bros., Apr'85 by Warner Bros Records. Dist: WEA

Cassette: released on Warner Bros., Apr'85 by Warner Bros Records. Dist: WEA

Thompson, Linval

ALL NIGHT LONG.
Single (12"): released on Greensleeves, Dec'82 by Greensleeves Records. Dist: BMG, Jetstar, Spartan

BABY FATHER.
Album: released on Greensleeves, Feb'83 by Greensleeves Records. Dist: BMG, Jetstar, Spartan

BUBBLES UP.
Single (12"): released on Gamble, Aug'84 by Gamble Records. Dist: Jetstar

HOLDING ON TO MY GIRLFRIEND.
Single (12"): released on Greensleeves, Dec'81 by Greensleeves Records. Dist: BMG, Jetstar, Spartan

I LOVE MARIJUANA.
Album: released on Trojan, Sep'81 by Trojan Records. Dist: Jetstar

I NEVER RUN I NEVER HIDE.
Single (12"): released on Greensleeves, Feb'79 by Greensleeves Records. Dist: BMG, Jetstar, Spartan

I REALLY LOVE YOU.
Single (12"): released on Gamble, May'84 by Gamble Records. Dist: Jetstar

LOOK HOW ME SEXY.
Album: released on Greensleeves, '82 by Greensleeves Records. Dist: BMG, Jetstar, Spartan

LOVE IS THE QUESTION.
Album: released on Burning Sounds, Dec'78 by Ross, Bill/Burning Sounds Records. Dist: PRT

NEGREA LOVE DUB.
Album: released on Trojan, Sep'78 by Trojan Records. Dist: PRT, Jetstar

POOR PEOPLE.
Single (12"): released on A.1, Apr'82 by A.1 Records. Dist: PRT

POP NO STYLE.
Single (12"): released on Attack, Jan'81 by Trojan Records. Dist: Trojan, Pinnacle, Red Rhino

YOU BABY.
Single (7"): released on Thompson Sound, Dec'82 by Thompson Sound Records. Dist: PRT Distribution

Thompson, Lucky

LUCKY THOMPSON FEATURING OSCAR PETTIFORD.
Album: released on Jasmine, Mar'84 by Jasmine Records. Dist: Counterpoint, Lugtons, Taylor, H.R., Wellard, Chris, Swift, Cadillac

TEST PILOT.
Album: released on Swingtime, Jan'86 Dist: Jazz Music Distribution, Charly

Thompson, Mayo

CORKY'S DEBT TO HIS FATHER.
Album: released on Glass, Sep'85 by Glass Records. Dist: Nine Mile, Rough Trade, Red Rhino, Play It Again Sam

Thompson, Otis

PLEASE DON'T GO.
Single (12"): released on Sunburn, Oct'84 by Orbitone Records. Dist: Jetstar Distribution

Thompson, Paul

CAN I TAKE YOU HOME.
Single (12"): released on Chams, Sep'83 by Chams Records. Dist: Jetstar

Thompson, Prince Lincoln

HUMANITY.
Album: released on Vista Sounds, '83 by Vista Sounds Records. Dist: Jetstar

NATURAL WILD.
Album: released on Vista Sounds, Dec'84 by Vista Sounds Records. Dist: Jetstar

PRINCE LINCOLN AND THE ROYAL RASSES.
Album: released on Vista Sounds, '83 by Vista Sounds Records. Dist: Jetstar

Thompson, Rev. Johnny

GLORIOUS FEELING.
Album: released on Calligraph, Sep'86 by Calligraph Records. Dist: PRT

Thompson, Richard

ACROSS A CROWDED ROOM.
Tracks: / When the spell is broken / You don't say / I ain't going to drag my feet no more / Love is a faithless country / Fire in the engine room / Walking through a wasted land / Little blue number / She twists the knife again / Ghosts in the wind.
Album: released on Polydor, Apr'86 by Polydor Records. Dist: Polygram, Polydor

Cassette: released on Polydor, Apr'86 by Polydor Records. Dist: Polygram, Polydor

Compact disc: released on Polydor, Apr'86 by Polydor Records. Dist: Polygram, Polydor

DARING ADVENTURES.
Compact disc: released on Polydor, Nov'86 by Polydor Records. Dist: Polygram, Polydor

GUITAR/VOCAL.
Tracks: / Hpart needs a home, A / Free as bird / Night comes in / Pitfall/Excursion / Calvari cross / Time will show the wiser / Throw-away street puzzle / Mr Lacey / Ballad of easy rider Poor Will' and the jolly hangman / Sweet little Rock'n'roller / Heart needs a home, A / Dark end of the street / It'll be me.
Notes: Album originally released in 1976 Double LP including live recording of an Oxford concert and early solos such as 'Throwaway street puzzle', a single B-side.
Album: released on Hannibal, Jun'86 by Hannibal Records. Dist: Charly, Harmonia Music Projection, Celtic Music, Roots

HAND OF KINDNESS.
Tracks: / Poisoned heart and a twisted memory, A / Tear stained letter / How I wanted to Both ends burning / Poisoned heart and twisted memory, A / Wrong heartbeat / Hand kindness / Devonside / Two left feet.
Album: released on Hannibal, Jun'86 by Hannibal Records. Dist: Charly, Harmonia Mundi, Projection, Celtic Music, Roots

Cassette: released on Hannibal, Jun'86 by Hannibal Records. Dist: Charly, Harmonia Mundi, Projection, Celtic Music, Roots

Compact disc: released on Hannibal, Jun'86 by Hannibal Records. Dist: Charly, Harmonia Mundi, Projection, Celtic Music, Roots

SMALL TOWN ROMANCE.
Tracks: / Heart needs a home, A / Time to some changes / Beat the retreat / Woman man? / For shame of doing wrong / Honky tonk blues / Small town romance / I want to see bright lights tonight / Down where the drunkard roll / Love is bad for business / Great Valerie Don't let a thief steal into your heart / Ne again.
Album: released on Hannibal, Jun'86 by Hannibal Records. Dist: Charly, Harmonia Mund Projection, Celtic Music, Roots

Cassette: released on Hannibal, Jun'86 by Hannibal Records. Dist: Charly, Harmonia Mundi, Projection, Celtic Music, Roots

Compact disc: released on Hannibal, Jun'86 by Hannibal Records. Dist: Charly, Harmonia Mundi, Projection, Celtic Music, Roots

STRICT TEMPO.
Album: released on Carthage, Jul'87

Album: released on Elixir, Sep'81 by Richard & Linda Thompson. Dist: Folksound

WRONG HEARBEAT.
Single (7"): released on Hannibal, Aug'83 by Hannibal Records. Dist: Charly, Harmonia Mundi, Projection, Celtic Music, Roots

YOU DON'T SAY.
Single (7"): released on Polydor, Jun'85 by Polydor Records. Dist: Polygram, Polydor

Thompson, Richard & Linda
DON'T RENEGE ON OUR LOVE.
Single (7"): released on Hannibal, Apr'82 by Hannibal Records. Dist: Charly, Harmonia Mundi, Projection, Celtic Music, Roots

FIRST LIGHT.
Tracks: / Restless highway / Sweet surrender / Don't let a thief steal your heart / Choice wife / Died for love / Strange affair / Layla / Pavanne / House of cards / First light.
Album: released on Hannibal, Jun'86 by Hannibal Records. Dist: Charly, Harmonia Mundi, Projection, Celtic Music, Roots

Compact disc: released on Chrysalis, '86 by Chrysalis Records. Dist: CBS

Album: released on Chrysalis, '78 by Chrysalis Records. Dist: CBS

Cassette: released on Chrysalis, '78 by Chrysalis Records. Dist: CBS

HOKEY POKEY.
Tracks: / Heart needs a home, A / Hokey pokey / I'll regret it all in the morning / Smiffy's glass eye / Egypt / Never again / Georgie on a spree / Old man inside a young man / Sun never shines on the poor / Heart needs a home, A / Mole in a hole.
Album: released on Hannibal, Jun'86 by Hannibal Records. Dist: Charly, Harmonia Mundi, Projection, Celtic Music, Roots

Album: released on Hannibal, Aug'85 by Hannibal Records. Dist: Charly, Harmonia Mundi, Projection, Celtic Music, Roots

I WANT TO SEE THE BRIGHT LIGHTS TONIGHT.
Album: released on Island, '74 by Island Records. Dist: Polygram

Cassette: released on Island, '74 by Island Records. Dist: Polygram

POUR DOWN LIKE SILVER.
Tracks: / Streets of paradise / For shame of doing wrong / Poor boy is taken away / Night comes in / Jet plane is a rocking chair / Beat the retreat / Hard luck stories / Dimming of the day / Dargai.
Album: released on Hannibal, Jun'86 by Hannibal Records. Dist: Charly, Harmonia Mundi, Projection, Celtic Music, Roots

SHOOT OUT THE LIGHTS.
Tracks: / Man in need / Walking on a wire / Don't renege on our love / Just the motion / Shoot out the lights / Back street slide / Did she jump or was she pushed? / Wall of death.
Album: released on Hannibal, Jun'86 by Hannibal Records. Dist: Charly, Harmonia Mundi, Projection, Celtic Music, Roots

Cassette: released on Hannibal, Jun'86 by Hannibal Records. Dist: Charly, Harmonia Mundi, Projection, Celtic Music, Roots

Compact disc: released on Hannibal, Jun'86 by Hannibal Records. Dist: Charly, Harmonia Mundi, Projection, Celtic Music, Roots

SHOUT OUT THE LIGHTS.
Album: released on Hannibal, '84 by Hannibal Records. Dist: Charly, Harmonia Mundi, Projection, Celtic Music, Roots

Thompson, Sonny
WINGS IN PARIS.
Album: released on Black & Blue (France), Mar'74 Dist: Swift, Target, Discovery

Thompson, Sue
SWEET MEMORIES.
Album: released on Sundown, Sep'85 by Magnum Music Group Ltd. Dist: Magnum Music Group Ltd, PRT Distribution, Spartan Distribution

Thompson, Sydney
IN DANCE CHAMPIONSHIP DANCING
(Thompson, Sydney & His Orchestra).
Album: released on BBC, Apr'84 by BBC Records & Tapes. Dist: EMI, PRT, Pye

Cassette: released on BBC, Apr'84 by BBC Records & Tapes. Dist: EMI, PRT, Pye

AN EVENING WITH SYDNEY THOMPSON.
Album: released on Sydney Thompson, '81

Cassette: released on Sydney Thompson, '81

Album: released on Sydney Thompson, '81

Cassette: released on Sydney Thompson, '81

...AT THE RADIO 2 BALLROOM.
Album: released on BBC, '78 by BBC Records & Tapes. Dist: EMI, PRT, Pye

Cassette: released on BBC, '78 by BBC Records & Tapes. Dist: EMI, PRT, Pye

BALLROOM DANCING GREATS.
Album: released on Sydney Thompson, '81

BALLROOM IN TEMPO.
Album: released on Sydney Thompson, Dec'79

Cassette: released on Sydney Thompson, Dec'79

BALLROOM & LATIN REPRISE.
Album: released on Sydney Thompson, '81

BARN DANCES & TWO STEPS.
Extended-play record: released on Sydney Thompson, Dec'79

CHA CHA CHAS.
Extended-play record: released on Sydney Thompson, Dec'79

CHA CHA CHAS AND SAMBAS.
Album: released on Sydney Thompson, '80

Cassette: released on Sydney Thompson, May'81

DANCING GUITARS.
Album: released on Sydney Thompson, Aug'79

Cassette: released on Sydney Thompson, Aug'79

DANCING GUITARS IN THE BALLROOM.
Album: released on Sydney Thompson, Dec'79

Cassette: released on Sydney Thompson, Dec'79

DOWN AT THE OLD BULL AND BUSH
(Thompson, Sydney & His Orchestra).
Album: released on Sydney Thompson, Sep'83

FAVOURITES IN DANCE & SONG.
Album: released on Sydney Thompson, Dec'77

Cassette: released on Sydney Thompson, Jan'78

FAVOURITES IN DANCE AND SONG - VOL.3 BALLROOM AND LATIN.
Album: released on Sydney Thompson, Jun'83

FAVOURITES IN DANCE AND SONG - VOL.2.
Album: released on Sydney Thompson, Aug'79

Cassette: released on Sydney Thompson, Aug'79

FIFTH COLLECTION-QUICKSTEPS & FOXTROTS.
Album: released on Sydney Thompson, '81

FIFTH COLLECTION-WALTZES & TANGOS.
Album: released on Sydney Thompson, '81

FOXTROTS.
Extended-play record: released on Sydney Thompson, Dec'79

HAWAIIAN SERENADE.
Album: released on Sydney Thompson, '78

Cassette: released on Sydney Thompson, '78

JOIN SYDNEY THOMPSON FOR LATIN AMERICAN DANCING.
Album: released on Sydney Thompson, Jun'77

JOIN SYDNEY THOMPSON IN THE BALLROOM.
Album: released on Sydney Thompson, Jun'77

LATIN DANCING GREATS.
Album: released on Sydney Thompson, '81

LATIN IN TEMPO.
Album: released on Sydney Thompson, Dec'79

Cassette: released on Sydney Thompson, Dec'79

LILTING WALTZES & TANGOS.

MEMORIES.
Album: released on Sydney Thompson, '81

MORE BALLROOM FAVOURITES
(Thompson, Sydney & His Orchestra).
Album: released on Sydney Thompson, Jul'80

MORE LATIN FAVOURITES (Thompson, Sydney & His Orchestra).
Album: released on Sydney Thompson, Jul'80

MUSIC FOR CELEBRATING SPECIAL OCCASIONS.
Extended-play record: released on Sydney Thompson, Dec'79

MUSIC FOR LEISURE (Thompson, Sydney & His Orchestra).
Compact disc: released on Sydney Thompson, Dec'86

OLDE TIME DANCING PARTY (Thompson, Sydney & His Orchestra).
Album: released on Note, Sep'79 by EMI Records. Dist: EMI

Cassette: released on Note, Sep'79 by EMI Records. Dist: EMI

OLDE TIME & SEQUENCE DANCING
(Thompson, Sydney & His Orchestra).
Album: released on Sydney Thompson, '77

OLD TIME AND SEQUENCE CHAMPIONSHIP DANCING.
Album: released on Sydney Thompson, '77

OLD TIME AND SEQUENCE DANCING.
Album: released on Sydney Thompson, Oct'82

PASO DOBLES AND JIVES.
Extended-play record: released on Sydney Thompson, Dec'79

PAUL JONES WITH SYDNEY THOMPSON.
Album: released on Sydney Thompson, '79

PLAYS FOR STRICT TEMPO BALLROOM DANCING.
Album: released on Sydney Thompson, Aug'79

Cassette: released on Sydney Thompson, Aug'79

QUICKSTEPS.
Extended-play record: released on Sydney Thompson, Dec'79

QUICKSTEPS AND FOXTROTS.
Album: released on Sydney Thompson, '80

Cassette: released on Sydney Thompson, '80

Album: released on Sydney Thompson, May'81

QUICKSTEPS AND FOXTROTS (Thompson, Sydney & His Orchestra).
Album: released on Sydney Bron Music, Jun'83

RUMBAS.
Extended-play record: released on Sydney Bron Music, Dec'79

RUMBAS AND JIVES.
Album: released on Sydney Bron Music, May'81

RUMBAS AND PASO DOBLES.
Extended-play record: released on Sydney Thompson, Dec'79

Album: released on Sydney Thompson, '80

Cassette: released on Sydney Thompson, '80

SAMBAS.
Extended-play record: released on Sydney Thompson, Dec'79

SAUNTERS & BARN DANCES.
Extended-play record: released on Sydney Thompson, Dec'79

SYDNEY THOMPSON FOXTROTS
(Thompson, Sydney & His Orchestra).
Album: released on Sydney Thompson, Sep'83

SYDNET THOMPSON PLAYS A LATIN ENCORE.
Album: released on Sydney Thompson, '78
Cat. no: C-VOC 307
Cassette: released on Sydney Thompson, Aug'79

SYDNEY THOMPSON CHA CHA CHAS
(Thompson, Sydney & His Orchestra).
Extended-play record: released on Sydney Thompson, Sep'83

SYDNEY THOMPSON COLLECTION (WALTZES & TANGOS).
Album: released on Sydney Thompson, May'76

Cassette: released on Sydney Thompson, Dec'78 Deleted '80.

Album: released on Sydney Thompson, Jun'77

Cassette: released on Sydney Thompson, Dec'78

SYDNEY THOMPSON COLLECTION (RUMBAS & PASO DOBLES).
Album: released on Sydney Thompson, Jun'77

Cassette: released on Sydney Thompson, Dec'78

SYDNEY THOMPSON COLLECTION (QUICKSTEPS & FOXTROTS).
Album: released on Sydney Thompson, May'76

Cassette: released on Sydney Thompson, May'76

Album: released on Sydney Thompson, Jun'77

Cassette: released on Sydney Thompson, Jun'77

SYDNEY THOMPSON COLLECTION (VIENNSE WALTZES & JIVES).
Album: released on Sydney Thompson, May'76

Cassette: released on Sydney Thompson, Dec'78

SYDNEY THOMPSON INVITES YOU TO TAKE YOU PARTNERS.
Album: released on Sydney Thompson, '77

SYDNEY THOMPSON PLAYS A BALLROOM ENCORE.
Album: released on Sydney Thompson, '78

Cassette: released on Sydney Thompson, Aug'79

SYDNEY THOMPSON PLAYS FOR SEQUENCE DANCING.
Album: released on Sydney Thompson, '77

SYDNEY THOMPSON PLAYS FOR BALLROOM & LATIN DANCING.
Album: released on Sydney Thompson, '81

Cassette: released on Sydney Thompson, '81

Album: released on Sydney Thompson, Jun'83

SYDNEY THOMPSON PLAYS LATIN DANCING FAVOURITES.
Album: released on Sydney Thompson, Dec'77

Album: released on Sydney Thompson, Jan'78

SYDNEY THOMPSON PLAYS FOR OLD TIME AND SEQUENCE DANCING.
Album: released on Sydney Thompson, Nov'77

SYDNEY THOMPSON PLAYS FOR LATIN DANCING.
Album: released on Sydney Thompson, Aug'79

Cassette: released on Sydney Thompson, Aug'79

SYDNEY THOMPSON QUICKSTEPS.
Extended-play record: released on Sydney Thompson, Sep'83

SYDNEY THOMPSON RUMBAS.
Extended-play record: released on Sydney Thompson, Sep'83

SYDNEY THOMPSON WALTZES
(Thompson, Sydney & His Orchestra).
Extended-play record: released on Sydney Thompson, Sep'83

SYDNEY THOMPSON COLLECTION (CHA CHA CHAS & SAMBAS).
Album: released on Sydney Thompson, Jun'77

Cassette: released on Sydney Thompson, Jun'77

TANGOS.
Extended-play record: released on Sydney Thompson, Dec'79

TWENTY ALL TIME PARTY DANCE FAVOURITES.
Album: released on Sydney Thompson, Aug'79

Album: released on Sydney Thompson, Aug'79

VIENNESE WALTZES & JIVES.
Extended-play record: released on Sydney Thompson, Dec'79

Album: released on Sydney Thompson, Nov'77

Cassette: released on Sydney Thompson, Dec'78

WALTZES.
Extended-play record: released on Sydney Thompson, Dec'79

WALTZES AND TANGOS.
Album: released on Sydney Thompson, '80

Cassette: released on Sydney Thompson, '80

Album: released on Sydney Thompson, May'81

Album: released on Sydney Thompson, Jun'83

Thompson Twins

CLOSE TO THE BONE.
Tracks: / Follow your heart / Bush baby / Get that love / 20th Century / Long goodbye / Stillwaters / Savage moon / Gold fever / Dancing in your shoes / Perfect day.
Album: released on Arista, Apr'87 by Arista Records. Dist: RCA

Cassette: released on Arista, Apr'87 by Arista Records. Dist: RCA

Compact disc: released on Arista, Jan'87 by Arista Records. Dist: RCA

DON'T MESS WITH DR. DREAM.
Single (7"): released on Arista, Aug'85 by Arista Records. Dist: RCA

Single (12"): released on Arista, Aug'85 by Arista Records. Dist: RCA

Picture disc single: released on Arista, Aug'85 by Arista Records. Dist: RCA

GET THAT LOVE.
Tracks: / Get that love.
Single (12"): released on Arista, Mar'87 by Arista Records. Dist: RCA

Compact disc single: released on Arista, Apr'87 by Arista Records. Dist: RCA

HERE'S TO THE FUTURE.
Tracks: / Don't mess with doctor dream / Bay your hands on me / Future days / You killed the clown / Revolution / King for a day / Love is the law / Emperor's clothes(part1) / Tokyo / Breakaway.
Notes: Album contained limited edition free 5-track 12". the cassette contains extra tracks for life.
Album: released on Arista, Sep'86 by Arista Records. Dist: RCA

Cassette: released on Arista, Sep'86 by Arista Records. Dist: RCA

Compact disc: released on Arista, Sep'86 by Arista Records. Dist: RCA

IN THE NAME OF LOVE.
Single (7"): released on T Label, Jan'82 by Arista Records. Dist: Polygram Distribution

Single (12"): released on T Label, Jan'82 by Arista Records. Dist: Polygram Distribution

INTO THE GAP.
Album: released on T Label, Feb'84 by Arista Records. Dist: Polygram Distribution

Cassette: released on T Label, Feb'84 by Arista Records. Dist: Polygram Distribution

Compact disc: released on T Label, Jun'84 by Arista Records. Dist: Polygram Distribution

INTO THE GAP.
Tracks: / Doctor doctor / You take me up / Day after day / No peace for the wicked / Sister mercy / Into the gap / Hold me now / Storm on the sea / Who can stop the rain.
Compact disc: released on Arista, Jun'84 by Arista Records. Dist: RCA

KING FOR A DAY.
Single (7"): released on Arista, Oct'85 by Arista Records. Dist: RCA

Single (12"): released on Arista, Oct'85 by Arista Records. Dist: RCA

Single (12"): released on Arista, Oct'85 by Arista Records. Dist: RCA

Single (12"): released on Arista, Oct'85 by Arista Records. Dist: RCA

LAY YOUR HANDS ON ME.
Single (7"): released on Arista, Nov'84 by Arista Records. Dist: RCA

Single (12"): released on Arista, Nov'84 by Arista Records. Dist: RCA

Single (7"): released on Arista, Nov'84 by Arista Records. Dist: RCA

Single (12"): released on Arista, Dec'84 by Arista Records. Dist: RCA

Special: released on Arista, Dec'84 by Arista Records. Dist: RCA

LIVE.
Video-cassette (VHS): released on PMI, Jun'86 by PMI Records. Dist: EMI

Video-cassette [Betamax]: released on PMI, Jun'86 by PMI Records. Dist: EMI

LIVE/BEACH CULTURE.
Single (7"): released on Tee, Oct'82 by Arista Records. Dist: Polydor

Single (12"): released on Tee, Oct'82 by Arista Records. Dist: Polydor

LIVE IN LIVERPOOL (VIDEO).
Notes: Inc.'Detectives', 'In the name of love', 'Love on your side' etc. 60 minutes
Video-cassette (VHS): released on Video Collection, May'87 by Video Collection International Ltd.. Dist: Counterpoint

LONG GOODBYE, THE.
Tracks: / Long goodbye (The) / Dancing in your shoes / Hold me now (dance mix).
Single (7"): released on Arista, May'87 by Arista Records. Dist: RCA

Single (12"): released on Arista, May'87 by Arista Records. Dist: RCA

Compact disc single: released on Arista, May'87 by Arista Records. Dist: RCA

LOVE ON YOUR SIDE.
Single (7"): released on Arista, Jan'83 by Arista Records. Dist: RCA

Cassette: released on Arista, Jan'83 by Arista Records. Dist: RCA

NOTHING IN COMMON.
Tracks: / Nothing in common / Nothing to lose.
Single (7"): released on Arista, Sep'86 by Arista Records. Dist: RCA

Single (12"): released on Arista, Sep'86 by Arista Records. Dist: RCA

OUT OF THE GAP.
Cassette: released on Arista, Jun'84 by Arista Records. Dist: RCA

PERFECT DAY.
Single (7"): released on Arista, Mar'87 by Arista Records. Dist: RCA

PERFECT GAME, THE.
Single (7"): released on T Label, Feb'81 by Arista Records. Dist: Polygram Distribution

PRODUCT OF.....
Album: released on Fame (Arista), Jul'83 by Music For Pleasure Records. Dist: EMI

Cassette: released on Fame (Arista), Jul'83 by Music For Pleasure Records. Dist: EMI

Cassette: released on T Label, Aug'83 by Arista Records. Dist: Polygram Distribution

QUICK STEP AND SIDE KICK.
Tracks: / Kamikazee / Love on your side / If you were here / Judy do / Tears / Watching / We are detective / Love lies bleeding / All fall out.
Notes: Digital stereo
Compact disc:

QUICKSTEP AND SIDE KICK.
Album: released on Fame, Jul'85 by Music For Pleasure Records. Dist: EMI

Cassette: released on Fame, Jul'85 by Music For Pleasure Records. Dist: EMI

REVOLUTION.
Single (7"): released on Arista, Nov'85 by Arista Records. Dist: RCA

Single (12"): released on Arista, Nov'85 by Arista Records. Dist: RCA

Single (12"): released on Arista, Nov'85 by Arista Records. Dist: RCA

ROLL OVER.
Single (7"): released on Arista, Apr'85 by Arista Records. Dist: RCA

Single (12"): released on Arista, Apr'85 by Arista Records. Dist: RCA

SET.
Album: released on Fame, Sep'84 by Music For Pleasure Records. Dist: EMI

Cassette: released on Fame, Sep'84 by Music For Pleasure Records. Dist: EMI

Thor

KEEP THE DOGS AWAY.
Album: released on Gull, Jun'85 by Gull Records. Dist: Pinnacle

KNOCK 'M' DOWN.
Single (7"): released on Road Runner, Jul'85

Single (12"): released on Road Runner, Jul'85

LET THE BLOOD RUN RED.
Single (7"): released on Albion, Apr'84 by Albion Records. Dist: Spartan, Pinnacle

Single (12"): released on Albion, Apr'84 by Albion Records. Dist: Spartan, Pinnacle

Picture disc single: released on Albion, Apr'84 by Albion Records. Dist: Spartan, Pinnacle

LIVE IN DETROIT.
Tracks: / Thunder on the tundra / Let the blood run red / Knock 'em down / Rock the city / Lightning strikes / Anger / Keep the dogs away / Hot flames / Now comes the storm / When gods collide.
Notes: Bar code: 5 013428 140086 All tracks licensed from EDT Ltd. This compilation: C 1985 Castle Communications Ltd.,Unit 7,271 Merton Road,London, SW18 5JS.
Album: released on Raw Power, Apr'86 Dist: Pinnacle

Cassette: released on Raw Power, Apr'86 Dist: Pinnacle

ONLY THE STRONG.
Album: released on MFN, Apr'85 by Music For Nations Records. Dist: Pinnacle

OVER TO YOU.
Single (7"): released on KA, Nov'82

THUNDER ON THE TUNDRA.
Single (7"): released on Albion, Jun'84 by Albion Records. Dist: Spartan, Pinnacle

Single (12"): released on Albion, Jun'84 by Albion Records. Dist: Spartan, Pinnacle

Picture disc single: released on Albion, Jun'84 by Albion Records. Dist: Spartan, Pinnacle

UNCHAINED.
Album: released on Ultranoise, Feb'84 by Ultranoise Records. Dist: Cartel

Thorburn, Billy

LET'S BREAK THE GOOD NEWS.
Tracks: / Let's break the good news / With the wind & the rain in your hair / Wish me luck / I'd never fall in love again / All over the place / All alone with my shadow / Memory of a rose, The / Love makes the world go round / It's foolish but it's fun / Faithful forever / If I could paint a memory / There'll come another day / I-spy / You're so sweet to remember / Too many irons in the fire / I'm happy for your sake.
Notes: A new 16-track compilation from Billy Thorburn's highly successful group The Organ,Dance Band & Me featuring renowned organist Robinson Cleaver who celebrates his 80th birthday in May.Jazz enthusiast,Hugh Palmer provides us with full personnels for each track plus an informative sleeve note tracing the history of Billy Thorburn and his musicians through his varied and successful employment from beginning as a 9 years old choirmaster to the height of his recording career.This album will have 3-fold appeal,satisfying the followers of Billy Thorburn as well as dance band enthusiast and fans of the largely extinct theatre organ.All tracks have been transferred using the direct metal mastering technique for the best sound quality.
Album: released on EMI Retrospect, May'86 by EMI Records. Dist: EMI

Cassette: released on EMI Retrospect, May'86 by EMI Records. Dist: EMI

ORGAN, THE DANCE BAND AND ME, THE.
Cassette: released on President, Jun'85 by President Records. Dist: Taylors, Spartan

Thore Jederby

MORNING JUMP (Thore Jederby Jazz Groups(1940-1948)).
Album: released on Dragon, Jun'86 by Dragon Records. Dist: Jazz Music, Projection, Cadillac

Thornally, Phil

ANOTHER WORLD.
Single (7"): released on Riva, Sep'84 Dist: PRT

SO THIS IS LOVE/ LAST TOO LONG.
Single (7"): released on Riva, Jul'83 Dist: PRT

Cassette: released on Riva, Jul'83 Dist: PRT

Thornberry, Russell

TEN DOLLAR SONGS.
Album: released on Emerald, '78 by Emerald Records. Dist: Ross, PRT, Solomon & Peres Distribution

Thorn Birds & Other BBC ...

THORN BIRDS & OTHER BBC TV THEMES Various artists (Various Artists).
Album: released on BBC, Sep'84 by BBC Records & Tapes. Dist: EMI, PRT, Pye

Cassette: released on BBC, Sep'84 by BBC Records & Tapes. Dist: EMI, PRT, Pye

Thornborough, Julie

I'M YOUR COUNTRY GIRL.
Album: released on Folk Heritage, Jul'82 by Folk Heritage Records. Dist: Roots, Wynd-Up Distribution, Jazz Music, Folk Heritage

Thorne, Kirk

MR MAGIC/ PARTY FOR TWO.
Single (12"): released on JKO, Feb'85 by JKO Records. Dist: Pinnacle

Thornhill, Claude

1941 & 1947 (Thornhill, Claude and his Orchestra).
Album: released on Circle(USA), Jun'86 by Jazzology Records (USA). Dist: Jazz Music, Swift, Chris Wellard

SONG IS YOU, THE.
Album: released on Hep, Apr'81 by H.R. Taylor Records. Dist: Jazz Music, Cadillac Music, JSU, Taylors, Wellard, Chris, Zodiac, Swift, Fast Forward

Thorns Of Affliction

PANIC STRICKEN/ EYES OF THE DEAD.
Single (7"): released on Cargo, Aug'81 Dist: Rough Trade

Thornton, Big Mama

BIG MAMA THORNTON & CHICAGO BLUES BAND.
Album: released on Arhoolie, '81 by Arhoolie Records. Dist: Projection, Topic, Jazz Music, Swift, Roots

IN EUROPE.
Album: released on Arhoolie, May'81 by Arhoolie Records. Dist: Projection, Topic, Jazz Music, Swift, Roots

Thornton, Clifford

PANTHER & THE LASH.
Album: released on Musi-disc, '74

Thornton, Willie Mae

BALL & CHAIN.
Album: released on Arhoolie, Jul'87 by Arhoolie Records. Dist: Projection, Topic, Jazz Music, Swift, Roots

Album: released on Arhoolie, May'81 by Arhoolie Records. Dist: Projection, Topic, Jazz Music, Swift, Roots

IN EUROPE Blues singer.
Album: released on Arhoolie, Jul'87 by Arhoolie Records. Dist: Projection, Topic, Jazz Music, Swift, Roots

QUIT SNOOPIN' ROUND MY DOOR.
Tracks: / Rock a bye baby / Hard times / I ain't no fool either / You don't move me no more / No Jody for me / Let your tears fall baby / Every time I think of you / Mischievious boogie / How come / Just like a dog / I've searched the world over / Nightmare / Story of my blues / Stop a-hoppin on me / Laugh,laugh,laugh / Fish.
Album: released on Ace, Sep'86 by Ace Records. Dist: Pinnacle, Swift, Hotshot, Cadillac

Thorn, Tracey

DISTANT SHORE, A.
Tracks: / Small town girl / Simply couldn't care / Seascape / Femme fatale / Dreamy / Plain sailing / New opened eyes / Too happy.
Notes: (P) 1987 Original sound recording made by Cherry Red Records Ltd. Produced by Tracey Thorn.
Compact disc: released on Cherry Red, Jun'87 by Cherry Red Records. Dist: Pinnacle

Album: released on Cherry Red, Feb'85 by Cherry Red Records. Dist: Pinnacle

Cassette: released on Cherry Red, Feb'85 b Cherry Red Records. Dist: Pinnacle

PLAIN SAILING.
Single (7"): released on Cherry Red, Dec'84 b Cherry Red Records. Dist: Pinnacle

Thorogood,George

BETTER THAN THE REST (Thorogoo George & The Destroyers).
Album: released on MCA, Aug'81 by MCA Re ords. Dist: Polygram, MCA

Cassette: released on MCA, Aug'81 by MC Records. Dist: Polygram, MCA

GEORGE THOROGOOD (Thorogoo George & The Destroyers).
Album: released on Demon, Mar'86 by Dem Records. Dist: Pinnacle

Cassette: released on Demon, Mar'86 Demon Records. Dist: Pinnacle

GEORGE THOROGOOD & THE D STROYERS (Thorogood, George & The D stroyers).
Album: released on Sonet, Jun'78 by So

Records. Dist: PRT

GEORGE THOROGOOD & THE DESTROYERS (Thorogood, George & The Destroyers).
Tracks: / You got to lose / Madison blues / One bourbon, one scotch, one beer / Kind hearted woman / Can't stop lovin' / Ride on Josephine / Homesick boy / John Hardy / I'll change my style / Delaware slide.
Album: released on Demon, Mar'86 by Demon Records. Dist: Pinnacle

Cassette: released on Demon, Mar'86 by Demon Records. Dist: Pinnacle

Compact disc: released on Demon, Mar'86 by Demon Records. Dist: Pinnacle

HOUSE OF BLUE LIGHTS (Thorogood, George & The Destroyers).
Single (7"): released on Sonet, May'81 by Sonet Records. Dist: PRT

LIVE.
Tracks: / Who do you love? / Bottom of the sea / Night time / I drink alone / One bourbon,one scotch,one beer / Alley oop / Madison blues / Bad to the bone / Sky is crying, The / Reelin' & rockin'.
Notes: Produced by Terry Manning & The Delaware Destroyers.
Album: released on EMI America, Sep'86 by EMI Records. Dist: EMI

Cassette: released on EMI America, Sep'86 by EMI Records. Dist: EMI

MAVERICK (Thorogood, George & The Destroyers).
Album: released on EMI America, May'85 by EMI Records. Dist: EMI

Cassette: released on EMI America, May'85 by EMI Records. Dist: EMI

MORE GEORGE THOROGOOD & THE DESTROYERS (Thorogood, George & The Destroyers).
Album: released on Sonet, Oct'80 by Sonet Records. Dist: PRT

MORE GEORGE THOROGOOD & THE DESTROYERS (Thorogood, George & The Destroyers).
Album: released on Demon, Mar'86 by Demon Records. Dist: Pinnacle

MOVE IT ON OVER (Thorogood,George and The Destroyers).
Cassette: released on Demon, Feb'87 by Demon Records. Dist: Pinnacle
Cat. no: **FIENDCASS 58**
Album: released on Sonet, '78 by Sonet Records. Dist: PRT

MOVE IT ON OVER (Thorogood, George & The Destroyers).
Album: released on Demon, Mar'86 by Demon Records. Dist: Pinnacle

NIGHT TIME/ KIDS FROM PHILLY (Thorogood, George & The Destroyers).
Single (7"): released on Sonet, Sep'80 by Sonet Records. Dist: PRT

NOBODY BUT ME/ THAT PHILLY THING (Thorogood, George & The Destroyers).
Single (7"): released on EMI America, Jul'82 by EMI Records. Dist: EMI

Thoroughly Modern Millie

THOROUGHLY MODERN MILLIE Original soundtrack.
Album: released on MCA, Oct'82 by MCA Records. Dist: Polygram, MCA

Cassette: released on MCA, Oct'82 by MCA Records. Dist: Polygram, MCA

Those French Girls

CLOSE UP.
Single (7"): released on Safari, Nov'81 by Safari Records. Dist: Pinnacle

SORRY SORRY.
Single (7"): released on Safari, Jan'82 by Safari Records. Dist: Pinnacle

Those Golden Birdies

ENNUI.
Single (12"): released on Headless Horse, Dec'86 Dist: Revolver

Those Golden No.1's

THOSE GOLDEN NO.1'S Various session artists (Various Session Artists).
Cassette: released on AIM (Budget Cassettes), Feb'83

Those Helicopters

DR.JANOV.
Single (7"): released on Lavender, Jun'81

Those Obnoxious Types

LOVE IS DEAD.
Notes: Distributed by Esoteric 33 Barberry House,Shannon Road,Kings Norton, Birmingham,B38 9BX. Tele: 021 458 7503
Single (7"): released on Exoteric, '85 by Exoteric Records. Dist: Rough Trade

Those Oldies But Goodies

THOSE OLDIES BUT GOODIES FROM DEL FI Various artists (Various Artists).
Album: released on Ace(Del Fi-Rhino USA), Apr'83 by Ace Records. Dist: Pinnacle, Swift, Hotshot

Those Ragtime Years

THOSE RAGTIME YEARS 1899-1916 Original artists (Various Artists).
Double Album: released on World Records, Feb'77 Dist: Polygram

Those Were The Days

THOSE WERE THE DAYS Various artists (Various Artists).
Notes: 18 original tracks by Mary Hopkins, Del Shannon, Crystals, Drifters, Bobby Vee, Nashville Teens etc.
Compact disc: released on Delta, Apr'87 by Delta Records. Dist: Target

Those Were The Hits

THOSE WERE THE HITS OF 1960 Various artists (Various Artists).
Album: released on EMI (Holland), Jan'85 by EMI Records. Dist: Conifer

Cassette: released on EMI (Holland), Jan'85 by EMI Records. Dist: Conifer

THOSE WERE THE HITS OF 1961 Various artists (Various Artists).
Album: released on EMI (Holland), Jan'85 by EMI Records. Dist: Conifer

Cassette: released on EMI (Holland), Jan'85 by EMI Records. Dist: Conifer

THOSE WERE THE HITS OF 1962 Various artists (Various Artists).
Album: released on EMI (Holland), Jan'85 by EMI Records. Dist: Conifer

Cassette: released on EMI (Holland), Jan'85 by EMI Records. Dist: Conifer

THOSE WERE THE HITS OF 1963 Various artists (Various Artists).
Album: released on EMI (Holland), Jan'85 by EMI Records. Dist: Conifer

Cassette: released on EMI (Holland), Jan'85 by EMI Records. Dist: Conifer

THOSE WERE THE HITS OF 1964 Various artists (Various Artists).
Album: released on EMI (Holland), Jan'85 by EMI Records. Dist: Conifer

Cassette: released on EMI (Holland), Jan'85 by EMI Records. Dist: Conifer

Thoughts

WAIT ALONG TIME FOR YOU.
Single (7"): released on Straight 8, Jul'83

Single (12"): released on Straight 8, Jul'83

Thousand All Britain

1000 TONGUES TO SING Various Artists (Various Artists).
Album: released on Word, May'82 by Word Records. Dist: Word Distribution, CBS

Cassette: released on Word, May'82 by Word Records. Dist: Word Distribution, CBS

Thousand Miles...

JIMMY HIGHLIFE (Thousand Miles Of Sunshine).
Single (7"): released on Go Discs, Jun'84 by Go Discs Records. Dist: CBS Distribution

Single (12"): released on Go Discs, Jun'84 by Go Discs Records. Dist: CBS Distribution

Thou Shall Not Pass

THOU SHALL NOT PASS Various artists (Various Artists).
Album: released on Abstract, Mar'85 by Abstract. Dist: Pinnacle

Thrasher

BURNING AT THE SPEED OF LIGHT.
Album: released on Music For Nations, Jun'85 by Music For Nations Records. Dist: Pinnacle

Thrashing Doves

BEAUTIFUL IMBALANCE.
Tracks: / Self-infliction crew.
Single (7"): released on A&M, Jan'87 by A&M Records. Dist: Polygram

Single (12"): released on A&M, Jan'87 by A&M Records. Dist: Polygram

BEDROCK VICE.
Tracks: / Beautiful imbalance / Matchstick flotilla / Ginding stone / Killer for you / Rochdale house / Biba's basement / Castroville street / Magdalene / Tinderbox man / Northern civil war party / Jesus on the payroll / Grinding Stone, The.
Notes: The debut album from this much tipped band includes their recent chart single "Beautiful Imbalance" plus 10 other original songs which reveal a quite exceptional song-writing talent.
Album: released on A&M, Apr'87 by A&M Records. Dist: Polygram

Cassette: released on A&M, Apr'87 by A&M Records. Dist: Polygram

Compact disc: released on A&M, Apr'87 by A&M Records. Dist: Polygram

BIBA'S BASEMENT.
Tracks: / Biba's basement / Tinder box, The / All night chemist*.
Single (7"): released on A&M, Sep'86 by A&M Records. Dist: Polygram

Single (12"): released on A&M, Sep'86 by A&M Records. Dist: Polygram

GRINDING STONE, THE.
Tracks: / Grinding stone (Let me climb your ladder), The / Receiver, The / Last train to Bedrock*.
Notes: * extra track on 12" version only

MATCHSTICK.
Tracks: / Matchstick / Lotilla / Hollywood maids* / Sympathy for the devil*.
Notes: *=Extra track on 12" only
Single (7"): released on A&M, May'86 by A&M Records. Dist: Polygram

Single (12"): released on A&M, May'86 by A&M Records. Dist: Polygram

Threats

GO TO HELL.
Single (7"): released on Rondelet, Jun'82 Dist: Spartan Distribution

POLITICIANS AND MINISTERS.
Single (7"): released on Rondelet, Nov'82 Dist: Spartan Distribution

Single (12"): released on Rondelet, Nov'82 Dist: Spartan Distribution

Three...

3 BILLY GOATS GRUFF & OTHER FAVOURITE STORIES (for children aged 3-7) (Various Artists).
Cassette: released on VFM Cassettes, Jul'85

3 GREAT GIRLS (Ann-Margaret/Kitty Kallen/Della Reese).
Cassette: released on RCA, Nov'84 by RCA Records. Dist: RCA, Roots, Swift, Wellard, Chris, I & B, Solomon & Peres Distribution

Album: released on RCA, Nov'84 by RCA Records. Dist: RCA, Roots, Swift, Wellard, Chris, I & B, Solomon & Peres Distribution

3 GREAT GUYS Paul Anka/Sam Cooke/Neil Sedaka (Paul Anka/Sam Cooke/Neil Sedaka).
Album: released on RCA, Nov'84 by RCA Records. Dist: RCA, Roots, Swift, Wellard, Chris, I & B, Solomon & Peres Distribution

Cassette: released on RCA, Nov'84 by RCA Records. Dist: RCA, Roots, Swift, Wellard, Chris, I & B, Solomon & Peres Distribution

EVER AFTER (Three O'clock).
Tracks: / Suzie's on the ball now / Look into your eyes / When we can / Penny girls (The) / Follow him around / Warm aspirations / Step out of line / We are one / If you could see my way / Songs and gentle words.
Album: released on I.R.S.(Independent Record Syndicate), Feb'87 by I.R.S.. Dist: MCA

Cassette: released on I.R.S.(Independent Record Syndicate), Feb'87 by I.R.S.. Dist: MCA

THREE T'S AT THE HICKORY HOUSE 1936-37 various artists (Various Artists).
Album: released on Broadway, Apr'79 Dist: Jetstar

Three Action

ON THE JOURNEY OF A LIFETIME.
Tracks: / On the journey of a lifetime.
Single (7"): released on Ediesta, Sep'86 by Ediesta Records. Dist: Red Rhino, Cartel

Single (12"): released on Ediesta, Sep'86 by Ediesta Records. Dist: Red Rhino, Cartel

Three Amigos

THREE AMIGOS Original soundtrack (Various Artists).
Tracks: / Ballad of the 3 Amigos / Main title / Big sneak, The / My little buttercup / Santa Poco / Fiesta and Flamenco / El Guapo / Return of the Amigos / Blue shadows on the trail / Singing bush, The / Amigos at the mission / Capture / El Guapo's birthday / Chase, The / Amigo's, amigo's, amigo's / Farewell / End credits.
Album: released on Warner Bros., Jul'87 by Warner Bros Records. Dist: WEA

Cassette: released on Warner Bros., Jul'87 by Warner Bros Records. Dist: WEA

Three Angry Poles

MOTOR CYCLE MANIAC.
Tracks: / Motorcycle maniac.
Single (12"): released on Play It Again Sam, Sep'86 Dist: Red Rhino, Cartel

Three Bears

THREE BEARS, THE Children's story (Various Artists).
Cassette: released on Tellastory, Oct'79 by Bartlett Bliss Productions. Dist: PRT Distribution, Hayward Promotions Distribution, H.R. Taylor Distribution

Three Choirs Festival

THREE CHOIRS FESTIVAL (250th. Anniversary) (Various Artists).
Album: released on Abbey, '78 by Abbey. Dist: PRT, Taylors, Gamut

Three Colours

ONE BIG TREE.
Tracks: / One big tree.
Single (7"): released on Pinnacle, Nov'86 by Pinnacle Records. Dist: Pinnacle

SITTING PRETTY.
Tracks: / Sitting pretty / I called him by his mane / Eventually* / Here comes your saviour*.
Single (7"): released on Souls Select, Jul'87 by Souls Select Records. Dist: Nine Mile, Cartel

Single (12"): released on Souls Select, Jul'87 by Souls Select Records. Dist: Nine Mile, Cartel

Single (12"): released on Souls Select, Jul'87 by Souls Select Records. Dist: Nine Mile, Cartel

THIS IS NORWOOD.
Album: released on Souls Select, Apr'87 by Souls Select Records. Dist: Nine Mile, Cartel

Three Courgettes

SUBSTITUTE.
Single (7"): released on Island, Jul'82 by Island Records. Dist: Polygram

THREE COURGETTES, THE.
Single (7"): released on Island, May'82 by Island Records. Dist: Polygram

Picture disc single: released on Island, May'82 by Island Records. Dist: Polygram

Three D

BREAK THE FIX(ATION).
Single (12"): released on RAK, Aug'84 by RAK. Dist: EMI Deleted '87.

Single (7"): released on RAK, Aug'84 by RAK. Dist: EMI

DANCE TO BELIEVE.
Single (7"): released on RAK, Apr'85 by RAK. Dist: EMI

Single (12"): released on RAK, Apr'85 by RAK. Dist: EMI

NEARER.
Single (7"): released on RAK, Jan'85 by RAK. Dist: EMI

Three Degrees

20 GOLDEN GREATS.
Album: released on Hallmark, Sep'84 by Pickwick Records. Dist: Pickwick Distribution, PRT, Taylors

Cassette: released on Hallmark, Sep'84 by Pickwick Records. Dist: Pickwick Distribution, PRT, Taylors

6 TRACK HITS.
Extended-play record: released on Scoop 33, Sep'83 by Pickwick Records. Dist: H.R. Taylor

Cassette: released on Scoop 33, Sep'83 by Pickwick Records. Dist: H.R. Taylor

GOLD.
Album: released on K-Tel, Aug'80 by K-Tel Records. Dist: Record Merchandisers Distribution, Taylors, Terry Blood Distribution, Wynd-Up Distribution, Relay Distribution, Pickwick Distribution, Solomon & Peres Distribution, Polygram

Cassette: released on K-Tel, Aug'80 by K-Tel Records. Dist: Record Merchandisers Distribution, Taylors, Terry Blood Distribution, Wynd-Up Distribution, Relay Distribution, Pickwick Distribution, Solomon & Peres Distribution, Polygram

HEAVEN I NEED, THE.
Single (7"): released on Supreme, Sep'85 by Supreme Records. Dist: PRT Distribution

Single (12"): released on Supreme, Sep'85 by Supreme Records. Dist: PRT Distribution

HEAVEN I NEED, THE (REMIX).
Single (12"): released on Supreme, Nov'85 by Supreme Records. Dist: PRT Distribution

HITS HITS HITS.
Album: released on Hallmark, Sep'81 by Pickwick Records. Dist: Pickwick Distribution, PRT, Taylors

Cassette: released on Hallmark, Sep'81 by Pickwick Records. Dist: Pickwick Distribution, PRT, Taylors

LIAR (YOU'VE BEEN CHEATING ON ME).
Single (7"): released on 3D, Nov'83 Dist: Spartan

NEW DIMENSIONS.
Album: released on Ariola, Feb'79 Dist: RCA, Ariola

Cassette: released on Ariola, Feb'79 Dist: RCA, Ariola

THIS IS THE HOUSE.
Tracks: / This is the house / This is the house(mega dance version) / Senza voce / Heaven I need,The / Gimme gimme gimme.
Single (12"): released on Supreme, Mar'86 by Supreme Records. Dist: PRT Distribution

Single (12"): released on Supreme, Mar'86 by Supreme Records. Dist: PRT Distribution

Single (12"): released on Supreme, Mar'86 by Supreme Records. Dist: PRT Distribution

Single (7"): released on RCA, Apr'82 by RCA Records. Dist: RCA, Roots, Swift, Wellard, Chris, I & B, Solomon & Peres Distribution

THREE DEGREES, THE.
Album: released on Philadelphia International, Jun'81 by CBS Records. Dist: CBS

Cassette: released on Philadelphia International, Jun'81 by CBS Records. Dist: CBS

Album: released on MFP, Oct'81 by EMI Records. Dist: EMI

Cassette: released on MFP, Oct'81 by EMI Records. Dist: EMI

TWENTY OF THEIR GREATEST HITS.
Album: released on Epic, Jun'84 by CBS Records. Dist: CBS

Cassette: released on Epic, Jun'84 by CBS Records. Dist: CBS

WHEN WILL I SEE YOU AGAIN.
Single (7"): released on Old Gold, Apr'83 by Old Gold Records. Dist: Lightning, Jazz Music, Spartan, Counterpoint

WITHOUT YOU.
Single (7"): released on Ariola, May'82 Dist: RCA, Ariola

WOMAN IN LOVE.
Tracks: / Woman in love / Runner (The).
Single (7"): released on Old Gold, Apr'87 by Old Gold Records. Dist: Lightning, Jazz Music, Spartan, Counterpoint

Single (7"): released on Ariola, Dec'78 Dist: RCA, Ariola

Three Disc Symphonion

THREE DISC SYMPHONION, THE (Victorian musical boxes) (Victorian Musical Boxes).
Album: released on Saydisc, Nov'84 by Saydisc Records. Dist: Essex, Harmonia Mundi, Roots, H.R. Taylor, Jazz Music, Swift, Projection, Gamut

Cassette: released on Saydisc, Nov'84 by Saydisc Records. Dist: Essex, Harmonia Mundi, Roots, H.R. Taylor, Jazz Music, Swift, Projection, Gamut

Three Dixons

HIGHWAYMAN.
Single (7"): released on Music Power, Jun'85 Dist: Greyhound, Jetstar Distribution

Single (12"): released on Music Power, Jun'85 Dist: Greyhound, Jetstar Distribution

Three Dog Night

BEST OF THREE DOG NIGHT.
Compact disc: released on MCA, Feb'87 by MCA Records. Dist: Polygram, MCA

EVERY ONE A MASTERPIECE.
Tracks: / It's for you / Change is gonna come, A / Mama told me not to come / Woman / I can hear you calling / I'll be creeping / It ain't easy / I've got enough heartache / Joy to the world / Murder in my heart for the judge / My impersonal life / Freedom for the stallion / My old Kentucky home / Shambala / I'd be so happy / Til the world ends / Everybody's a masterpiece.
Notes: All tracks produced by Richard Podolor except 1&2 Gabriel Mekler Original sound recordings made by ABC/MCA Records Inc. This compilation published 1987 by See For Miles Records Ltd Copyright 1987 See For Miles Records Ltd A Colin Miles Compilation Side 2 all tracks produced by Richard Podolor except 6&7 Jimmy Lenner & Bob Monaco.
Album: released on See For Miles, May'87 by See For Miles Records. Dist: Pinnacle

GOLDEN GREATS: THREE DOG NIGHT.
Album: released on MCA, Oct'85 by MCA Records. Dist: Polygram, MCA

Cassette: released on MCA, Oct'85 by MCA Records. Dist: Polygram, MCA

IT'S A JUNGLE(MINI LP).
Single (12"): released on Lamborghini, Jun'84 by Lamborghini Records. Dist: PRT

IT'S A JUNGLE OUT THERE.
Single (7"): released on Lamborghini, Mar'84 by Lamborghini Records. Dist: PRT

MAMA TOLD ME NOT TO COME.
Single (7"): released on Old Gold, Jul'82 by Old Gold Records. Dist: Lightning, Jazz Music, Spartan, Counterpoint

Three Fat Women...

THREE FAT WOMEN OF ANTIBES Maugham, Somerset (Burden, Hugh).
Cassette: released on Talking Tape, '84

Three Flying Bigoudis

CHRISTMAS TIME.
Single (7"): released on Nuclear, Nov'83 by Nuclear Records.

Three Guys Naked..

THREE GUYS NAKED FROM THE WAIST DOWN Off Broadway cast (Off Broadway Cast).
Album: released on TER, Apr'85 Dist: Pinnacle

Cassette: released on TER, Apr'85 Dist: Pinnacle

Three Jacksons

36 ACCORDION SUCCESSEN VAN THE THREE JACKSONS.
Album: released on Music For Pleasure (Holland), May'86 by EMI Records. Dist: EMI

Cassette: released on Music For Pleasure (Holland), May'86 by EMI Records. Dist: EMI

Three Johns

ATOM DRUM BOP.
Notes: Misicassette plus 2 bonus tracks.
Cassette: released on Abstract, Nov'85 by Abstract. Dist: Pinnacle

ATOM DRUM BOY.
Album: released on Abstract, Aug'84 by Abstract. Dist: Pinnacle

A.W.O.L..
Single (7"): released on Abstract, Oct'83 by Abstract. Dist: Pinnacle

Single (7"): released on Abstract, Oct'83 by Abstract. Dist: Pinnacle

BRAINBOX.
Single (7"): released on Abstract, Nov'85 by Abstract. Dist: Pinnacle

Single (12"): released on Abstract, Nov'85 by Abstract. Dist: Pinnacle

DEATH OF THE EUROPEAN.
Single (12"): released on Abstract, May'85 by Abstract. Dist: Pinnacle

Single (7"): released on Abstract, May'85 by Abstract. Dist: Pinnacle

DO THE SQUARE.
Single (7"): released on Abstract, Mar'84 by Abstract. Dist: Pinnacle

Single (12"): released on Abstract, Mar'84 by Abstract. Dist: Pinnacle

ENGLISH WHITE BOY ENGINEER.
Single (7"): released on CNT, May'82 Dist: Rough Trade, Cartel

NEVER & ALWAYS.
Single (7"): released on Abstract, Jul'87 by Abstract. Dist: Pinnacle

Single (12"): released on Abstract, Jul'87 by Abstract. Dist: Pinnacle

ROCK'N'ROLL DEMOCRACY.
Album: released on Abstract, Nov'86 by Abstract. Dist: Pinnacle

SOLD DOWN THE RIVER.
Tracks: / Sold down the river.
Single (7"): released on Abstract, Apr'86 by Abstract. Dist: Pinnacle

Single (12"): released on Abstract, Apr'86 by Abstract. Dist: Pinnacle

SOME HISTORY.
Single (12"): released on Abstract, Jan'84 by Abstract. Dist: Pinnacle

WORLD BY STORM.
Album: released on Abstract, Apr'86 by Abstract. Dist: Pinnacle

Cassette: released on Abstract, Apr'86 by Abstract. Dist: Pinnacle

Three Little Pigs

THREE LITTLE PIGS various artists (Various Artists).
Album: released on Disneyland, Dec'78 by Disneyland-Vista Records (USA). Dist: BBC Records & Tapes, Rainbow Communications Ltd(Distribution)

Extended-play record: released on Disneyland, Apr'81 by Disneyland-Vista Records (USA). Dist: BBC Records & Tapes, Rainbow Communications Ltd(Distribution)
Cat. no: **DISNEYLAND 303**
Cassette: released on Pickwick (Ladybird), Feb'83

Three Million

I'VE BEEN ROBBED.
Single (7"): released on Cotillion, Jan'84 by WEA Records. Dist: WEA

Single (12"): released on Cotillion, Jan'84 by WEA Records. Dist: WEA

Three Minute Symphony

THREE MINUTE SYMPHONY various artists (Various Artists).
Album: released on Xtract, May'84 by Xtract Records. Dist: Cartel

Three Mustaphas Three

BAM. MUSTAPHA PLAY STEREC.
Album: released on Globestyle, Mar'85 by Ace Records. Dist: Projection

L'ORCHESTRE "BAM" DE GRAND MUSTAPHA INT.& PARTY HITS.
Notes: Mini LP
Album: released on Globestyle, Aug'86 by Ace Records. Dist: Projection

SHOPPING.
Album: released on Globestyle, Aug'87 by Ace Records. Dist: Projection

Compact disc: released on Globestyle, Aug'87 by Ace Records. Dist: Projection

SHOUFFI RHIROU.
Single (12"): released on Globestyle, Aug'87 by Ace Records. Dist: Projection

SI VOUS PASSEZ PAR LA.
Tracks: / Si vous passez par la / Starehe mustapha.
Single (7"): released on Globestyle, Feb'86 by Ace Records. Dist: Projection

Three O'clock

16 TAMBOURINES-BARBEQUE HOEDOWN.
Compact disc: released on Lolita, May'86 by Lolita Records. Dist: Rough Trade, Cartel

ARRIVE WITHOUT TRAVELLING.
Album: released on IRS, Oct'85 Dist: Polygram

Cassette: released on IRS, Oct'85 Dist: Polygram

HAND IN HAND.
Single (7"): released on IRS, Sep'85 Dist: Polygram

Single (12"): released on IRS, Sep'85 Dist: Polygram

SIXTEEN TAMBOURINES.
Album: released on Lolita, Feb'84 by Lolita Records. Dist: Rough Trade, Cartel

WARM ASPIRATIONS.
Tracks: / Warm aspirations / Regina Caeli / Suzie's on the ball".
Notes: "Extra track on 12" only
Single (7"): released on I.R.S.(Independent Record Syndicate), Apr'87 by I.R.S.. Dist: MCA

Single (12"): released on I.R.S.(Independent Record Syndicate), Apr'87 by I.R.S.. Dist: MCA

Three Of A Kind

THREE OF A KIND various artist (Various Artists).
Album: released on BBC, Sep'83 by BBC Records & Tapes. Dist: EMI, PRT

Cassette: released on BBC, Sep'83 by BBC Records & Tapes. Dist: EMI, PRT,

Threepenny Opera

THREEPENNY OPERA Original cast.
Album: released on TER, Apr'85 Dist: Pinnacle

Cassette: released on TER, Apr'85 Dist: Pinnacle

Three Phase

ALL I WANT TO DO.
Single (7"): released on Speed, Jan'83

Three P Sweet

TOO CLOSE TO THE MOON.
Single (7"): released on Record, Feb'82

Three Rockies

STOP WASTING YOUR TIME.
Single (7"): released on 10, Oct'84 by 10 Records. Dist: Virgin, EMI

Three Shades Of The Blues

THREE SHADES OF THE BLUES various artists (Various Artists).
Album: released on Relic (US), Mar'85

Three Sounds

BABE'S BLUES.
Tracks: / Babe's blues / Wait a minute / Work song / Blue Daniel / Sweet and lovely / Shiny stockings / Walking the floor over you / Between the devil and the deep blue sea / Stairway to the stars / Lazy cat.
Notes: Imported by Pathe Marconi copyright paid in France.
Album: released on Manhattan, Nov'86 by EMI Records. Dist: EMI

INTRODUCING THE THREE SOUNDS.
Tracks: / Tenderly / Willow weep for me / Both sides / Blue bells / It's nice / Goin' home / Would'n you / O sole mio / Bobby / Mo-ge / It might as well be spring / Soft touch / Don't get around much anymore / Goin' home (alternative take).
Compact disc: released on Blue Note, Jun'87 by EMI Records. Dist: EMI

Three Strangers

THREE STRANGERS, THE Hardy, Thomas (Morant, Richard).
Cassette: released on Talking Tape, '84

Three Teens Kill Four

NO MOTIVE.
Album: released on LD, May'84 by LD Records. Dist: Rough Trade, Cartel

Three Times A Day

I CRAVE TO BE A HERMAPHRODITE.
Single (7"): released on Abstract, Nov'81 by Abstract. Dist: Pinnacle

Three + Two

WINDOW SHOPPING.
Single (12"): released on Bluesville International, Jun'84 Dist: Jetstar

Threeway Street

DRUNKARDS AND LOVERS.
Tracks: / Marvo the mighty magician / Carnival song / Drunkards and Lovers / I wish you'd squeeze me (like you squeeze your squeezebox) / Midnight / Al comes around again / Money come the hard way easy go / Derek's hotel / When the circus comes to town / Moving on out Pierre / Unknown soldier,The / Fragments of a world.
Album: released on Fellside, May'85 by Fellside Records. Dist: Roots, Jazz Music, Celtic Music, Projection

Three Way Switch

LEAVING ON A JET PLANE.
Single (7"): released on Ariola, Nov'80 Dist: RCA, Ariola

Three-Wheel

AT THE ELEVENTH HOUR.
Album: released on Sweet Folk Country, Aug'77 Dist: Chris Wellard Distribution

Three Wise Men

REFRESH YOURSELF.
Single (12"): released on Rhythm King, May'87 Dist: Rough Trade, Cartel

URBAN HELL.
Single (12"): released on Rhythm King, Nov'86 Dist: Rough Trade, Cartel

Single (7"): released on Rhythm King, Nov'86 Dist: Rough Trade, Cartel

Page 1012

Three Worlds Of Gulliver

THREE WORLDS OF GULLIVER Original soundtrack.
Album: released on Cloud Nine, Sep'85 by Cloud Nine Records. Dist: Silva Screen, Harmonia Mundi

Threshing & Cultivating

THRESHING AND CULTIVATING BY STEAM POWER.
Album: released on Abbey, '74 by Abbey. Dist: PRT, Taylors, Gamut

Thrillers

SHOOTING TO THE TOP.
Single (7"): released on Big Bear, Jul'80 by Big Bear Records. Dist: Big Bear, Swift

Thrilling Wonder Stories

TWO WAY VIDEO.
Single (7"): released on Made In Space, Jul'83 Dist: Pinnacle

Throbbing Gristle

20 JAZZ FUNK GREATS.
Album: released on Mute, Nov'83 Dist: Spartan Distribution, Rough Trade Distribution, Cartel Distribution

2ND ANNUAL REPORT.
Album: released on Fetish, '81 by Fetish Records. Dist: Cartel, Pinnacle

D.O.A..
Album: released on Mute, Nov'83 Dist: Spartan Distribution, Rough Trade Distribution, Cartel Distribution

D.O.A. THE THIRD AND FINAL REPORT OF THROBBING GRISTLE.
Album: released on Industrial, '78 by Industrial Records. Dist: Rough Trade

GREATEST HITS: THROBBING GRISTLE.
Album: released on Rough Trade, Dec'84 by Rough Trade Records. Dist: Rough Trade Distribution, Cartel Distribution

HEATHEN EARTH.
Album: released on Mute, Nov'83 Dist: Spartan Distribution, Rough Trade Distribution, Cartel Distribution

IN THE SHADOW OF THE SUN.
Album: released on Illuminated, Feb'84 by IKF Records. Dist: Pinnacle, Cartel, Jetstar

IT'S THE PSYCHICK SACRIFICE.
Album: released on Illuminated, Nov'82 by IKF Records. Dist: Pinnacle, Cartel, Jetstar

MISSION IN DEAD SOULS.
Album: released on Mute, Nov'83 Dist: Spartan Distribution, Rough Trade Distribution, Cartel Distribution

NOTHING SHORT OF TOTAL WAR.
Cassette: released on Cause For Concern, May'84 Dist: Cartel

ONCE UPON A TIME.
Album: released on Casual Abandon, Apr'84 Dist: Jetstar, Cartel

SACRIFICE.
Tracks: / Weapon training / Convincing people / Hamburger lady / Chat up / Day song / Persuasion.
Album: released on Dojo, Aug'86 by Castle Communications Records. Dist: Cartel

SECOND ANNUAL REPORT.
Album: released on Mute, Nov'83 Dist: Spartan Distribution, Rough Trade Distribution, Cartel Distribution

THROBBING GRISTLE.
Boxed set: released on Fetish, Feb'82 by Fetish Records. Dist: Cartel, Pinnacle

Through The Looking Glass

THROUGH THE LOOKING GLASS Carroll, Lewis (Rushton, William).
Double cassette: released on Listen For Pleasure, '83 by MFP Records. Dist: EMI

Throwdown

CAMP.
Tracks: / (Rap mix).
Single (7"): released on Hardback, Dec'86 by Streetwave Records. Dist: PRT, Priority, DMS, RCA

Single (12"): released on Hardback, Dec'86 by Streetwave Records. Dist: PRT, Priority, DMS, RCA

Thrower, Percy

GOOD GUIDE TO GARDENING, A.
Double Album: released on Response, Dec'76 by Priority Records. Dist: BMG

GREENFINGER GUIDE (Thrower, Percy & June Whitfield).
Album: released on Lifestyle, '83 by Zomba Records. Dist: CBS, PRT, RCA

Cassette: released on Lifestyle, '83 by Zomba Records. Dist: CBS, PRT, RCA

Throwing Muses

CHAINS CHANGES (EP).
Tracks: / Finished / Reel / Snail Head / Cry baby cry.
Cassette single: released on 4AD, Mar'87 by 4AD Records. Dist: Rough Trade

Single (12"): released on 4AD, Feb'87 by 4AD Records. Dist: Rough Trade

FAT SKIER, THE.
Album: released on 4AD, Aug'87 by 4AD Records. Dist: Rough Trade. Estim retail price in Sep'87 was £3.99.

Cassette: released on 4AD, Aug'87 by 4AD Records. Dist: Rough Trade. Estim retail price in Sep'87 was £3.99.

THROWING MUSES.
Compact disc: released on 4AD, Nov'86 by 4AD Records. Dist: Rough Trade

THROWING MUSES.
Album: released on 4AD, Jul'86 by 4AD Records. Dist: Rough Trade

Compact disc: released on 4AD, Oct'86 by 4AD Records. Dist: Rough Trade

THROWING MUSES.
Tracks: / Call me / Green / Green / Hate my way / Vicky's box / Rabbits dying / America (she can't say no) / Fear / Stand up / Soul soldier / Delicate cutters.
Album: released on 4AD, Nov'86 by 4AD Records. Dist: Rough Trade

Cassette: released on 4AD, Nov'86 by 4AD Records. Dist: Rough Trade

Thrust

PUT YOUR BODY TO IT.
Single (7"): released on Arista, Aug'84 by Arista Records. Dist: RCA

Single (12"): released on Arista, Aug'84 by Arista Records. Dist: RCA

T.H.S. (The horn section)

LADY SHINE.
Single (7"): released on Fourth & Broadway, Aug'84 by Island Records. Dist: Polygram, EMI

Single (12"): released on Fourth & Broadway, Aug'84 by Island Records. Dist: Polygram, EMI

Thumann, Harry

UNDERWATER.
Single (7"): released on Decca, Jan'81 by Decca Records. Dist: Polygram

Single (12"): released on Decca, Jan'81 by Decca Records. Dist: Polygram

Thumbelina

THUMBELINA Tell-a-tale series (Various Artists).
Cassette: released on Pickwick (Ladybird), '83

THUMBELINA / THE LITTLE MATCH GIRL.
Cassette: released on Listen Productions, Nov'84 Dist: H.R. Taylor, Hayward Promotions Distribution

Thumper's Race

THUMPER'S RACE Various artists (Various Artists).
Extended-play record: released on Disneyland, Apr'81 Dist: EMI

Thunderball

THUNDERBALL James Bond Original Soundtrack.
Tracks: / Thunderball (main title) / Chateau fight / Electrocution - searching Lippe's room / Switching the body / Vulcan crash landing - loading bombs into Disco Volante / Cape Martinique - Mr. Kiss Kiss Bang Bang / Thunderball / Death of Fiona / Bond below Disco Volante / Search for vulcan / 007 / Mr. Kiss Kiss Bang Bang.
Notes: Produced by Kevin McClory. Conducted by John Barry. Published by SBK United Partnerships.
Album: released on Liberty, Jul'87 by Liberty-United. Dist: EMI

Cassette: released on Liberty, Jul'87 by Liberty-United. Dist: EMI

Album: released on EMI (Germany), Aug'83 by EMI Records. Dist: Conifer

Thunderbolt...

THUNDERBOLT HARD ROCK SAMPLER Various artists (Various Artists).
Notes: Special budget price album. Top rock musicians. Import release-limited edition.
Album: released on Thunderbolt, Jan'86 by Magnum Music Group Ltd. Dist: Magnum Music Group Ltd, PRT Distribution, Spartan Distribution

Thunderbolts

DUST ON ME NEEDLE.
Single (7"): released on Stiff, Oct'80

Thunderclap Newman

SOMETHING IN THE AIR.
Single (7"): released on Old Gold, Jul'84 by Old Gold Records. Dist: Lightning, Jazz Music, Spartan, Counterpoint

Thunder, Sam

DON'T TAKE FOREVER.
Single (12"): released on Bullet, Jan'84 Dist: Bullet Distribution

MANOEUVERS.
Picture disc album: released on Bulleon, Dec'84 Dist: Pinnacle

Thunder, Shelley

SMALL HORSE WOMAN.
Album: released on Hawkeye, May'86 by Hawkeye Records. Dist: Hawkeye, Lightning (WEA) Distribution, Jetstar, PRT

Cassette: released on Hawkeye, May'86 by Hawkeye Records. Dist: Hawkeye, Lightning (WEA) Distribution, Jetstar, PRT

Thunders, Johnny

BORN TO LOSE (Thunders, Johnny & The Heartbreakers).
Single (7"): released on Twins, Feb'85

CHINESE ROCKS (Thunders, Johnny & The Heartbreakers).
Single (7"): released on Jungle, May'85 by Jungle Records. Dist: Jungle, Cartel

Single (12"): released on Jungle, May'85 by Jungle Records. Dist: Jungle, Cartel

CRAWFISH (Thunders, Johnny & Patti Palladin).
Tracks: / Crawfish / Tie me up.
Notes: Pic bag
Single (7"): released on Jungle, Apr'87 by Jungle Records. Dist: Jungle, Cartel

Single (12"): released on Jungle, Apr'87 by Jungle Records. Dist: Jungle, Cartel

Picture disc single: released on Jungle, Apr'87 by Jungle Records. Dist: Jungle, Cartel

CRAWFISH (Thunders, Johnny & The Heartbreakers).
Single (7"): released on Jungle, Oct'85 by Jungle Records. Dist: Jungle, Cartel

Single (12"): released on Jungle, Oct'85 by Jungle Records. Dist: Jungle, Cartel

Picture disc single: released on Jungle, Nov'85 by Jungle Records. Dist: Jungle, Cartel

D.T.K./L.A.M.F. (Thunders, Johnny & The Heartbreakers).
Compact disc: released on Jungle, Nov'86 by Jungle Records. Dist: Jungle, Cartel

DTK-LAMP (Thunders, Johnny & The Heartbreakers).
Compact disc: released on Jungle, Oct'86 by Jungle Records. Dist: Jungle, Cartel

GET OFF THE PHONE (Thunders, Johnny & The Heartbreakers).
Single (7"): released on Jungle, Mar'84 by Jungle Records. Dist: Jungle, Cartel

Single (12"): released on Jungle, Sep'84 by Jungle Records. Dist: Jungle, Cartel

HURT ME.
Album: released on New Rose, Jan'84 Dist: Rough Trade, Cartel

Single (7"): released on New Rose, Feb'84 Dist: Rough Trade, Cartel

IN COLD BLOOD.
Album: released on New Rose, Mar'84 Dist: Rough Trade, Cartel

L.A.M.F. - REVISITED (Thunders, Johnny & The Heartbreakers).
Album: released on Jungle, May'84 by Jungle Records. Dist: Jungle, Cartel

Cassette: released on Jungle, May'84 by Jungle Records. Dist: Jungle, Cartel

LIVE AT LYCEUM BALLROOM, LONDON 1984.
Album: released on ABC, Jun'84 Dist: CBS, Pinnacle

QUE SERA SERA.
Album: released on Jungle, Nov'85 by Jungle Records. Dist: Jungle, Cartel

Cassette: released on Jungle, Nov'85 by Jungle Records. Dist: Jungle, Cartel

QUE SERA SERA Whatever will be will be (Thunders, Johnny & Patti Palladin).
Single (7"): released on Jungle, Jun'87 by Jungle Records. Dist: Jungle, Cartel

Single (12"): released on Jungle, Jun'87 by Jungle Records. Dist: Jungle, Cartel

QUE SERA SERA.
Compact disc: released on Jungle, Dec'86 by Jungle Records. Dist: Jungle, Cartel

STATIONS OF THE CROSS.
Cassette: released on Roir, Feb'87 by Reach Out International Records. Dist: Red Rhino Distribution, Cartel Distribution

TOO MUCH JUNKIE BUSINESS.
Cassette: released on Reach Out International, '83 Dist: Red Rhino, Cartel

VINTAGE '77 (Thunders, Johnny & The Heartbreakers).
Single (7"): released on Jungle, May'83 by Jungle Records. Dist: Jungle, Cartel

Thunderstick

ALECIA.
Single (7"): released on Thunderbolt, Nov'83 by Magnum Music Group Ltd. Dist: Magnum Music Group Ltd, PRT Distribution, Spartan Distribution

BEAUTY & THE BEASTS.
Album: released on Thunderbolt, Apr'84 by Magnum Music Group Ltd. Dist: Magnum Music Group Ltd, PRT Distribution, Spartan Distribution

Cassette: released on Thunderbolt, Apr'84 by Magnum Music Group Ltd. Dist: Magnum Music Group Ltd, PRT Distribution, Spartan Distribution

FEEL LIKE ROCK 'N' ROLL.
Album: released on Thunderbolt, Nov'83 by Magnum Music Group Ltd. Dist: Magnum Music Group Ltd, PRT Distribution, Spartan Distribution

Thunderthumbs

FREEDOM (Thunderthumbs/Toetsenman).
Single (7"): released on Polydor, Jul'82 by Polydor Records. Dist: Polygram, Polydor

Single (12"): released on Polydor, Jul'82 by Polydor Records. Dist: Polygram, Polydor

Thurrock Marching Brass

THURROCK MARCHING BRAS.
Album: released on Grosvenor, Jun'81 by Grosvenor Records. Dist: Taylors

Thurso & Donreal...

NORTH OF THE HIGHLANDS (Thurso & Donreal Strathspey & Reel Society).
Album: released on Lapwing, Jul'86 by Lapwing Records Ltd. Dist: Celtic Music, Projection, Roots Records, Ross, Gordon Duncan Distribution, Graham Tosh Distribution, Chans Records

Tibbetts, Steve

EXPLODED VIEW.
Tracks: / Name everything / Another year / Clear day,A / And no memories / Your cat / Forget / Drawing down the moon / X festival,The / Metal summer / Assembly field.
Notes: Steve Tibbetts - guitars, kalimba, tapes Marc Anderson - congas, steel drum, percussion, berimba Bob Hughes - bass
Marcus Wise - tabla
Claudia Schmidt - vocal
Bruce Henry - vocal
Jan Reimer - vocal
Album: released on ECM (Germany), Jan'87 by ECM Records. Dist: IMS, Polygram, Virgin through EMI

Compact disc: released on ECM (Germany), Jan'87 by ECM Records. Dist: IMS, Polygram, Virgin through EMI

NORTHERN SONG.
Album: released on ECM, May'82 by ECM Records. Dist: IMS, Polygram, Virgin through EMI

SAFE JOURNEY.
Album: released on ECM (Germany), Apr'84 by ECM Records. Dist: IMS, Polygram, Virgin through EMI

Tibbs, Fredi

ALL I HAVE TO DO IS DREAM.
Tracks: / All I have to do is dream / Mede mahoma besona-menyanie.
Single (7"): released on Tulip, Feb'86 Dist: M.I.S., Jetstar

Tibet
ASIAN TRADITIONAL MUSIC.
Album: Dist: Conifer, Discovery

SONGS OF MILAREPA, (THE).
Album: released on Lyrichord (USA), Oct'81 by Lyrichord Records (USA). Dist: Flexitron Distributors Ltd

TIBETAN FOLK & MINSTREL MUSIC.
Album: released on Lyrichord (USA), Oct'81 by Lyrichord Records (USA). Dist: Flexitron Distributors Ltd

TIBETAN FOLK SONGS FROM LHASA & AMDO.
Album: released on Lyrichord (USA), Oct'81 by Lyrichord Records (USA). Dist: Flexitron Distributors Ltd

TIBETAN MYSTIC SONGS.
Album: released on Lyrichord (USA), Oct'81 by Lyrichord Records (USA). Dist: Flexitron Distributors Ltd

TIBETAN SONGS OF GODS AND DEMONS.
Album: released on Lyrichord (USA), Oct'81 by Lyrichord Records (USA). Dist: Flexitron Distributors Ltd

Tibetan Ritual
TIBETAN RITUAL MUSIC.
Single (12"): released on Sub Rosa, Jul'87 by Sub Rosa Records. Dist: Red Rhino Distribution, Cartel Distribution

Tibet/Bhutan
TIBETAN & BHUTANESE INSTRUMENTAL & FOLK MUSIC.
Album: released on Lyrichord (USA), Oct'81 by Lyrichord Records (USA). Dist: Flexitron Distributors Ltd

Tickell, Kathryn
BORDERLANDS.
Album: released on Black Crow, Feb'87 by Mawson & Wareham Records. Dist: Projection

Cassette: released on Black Crow, Feb'87 by Mawson & Wareham Records. Dist: Projection

ON KEILDER SIDE.
Notes: Northumbrian pipes and fiddle.
Compact disc: released on Saydisc, Jun'87 by Saydisc Records. Dist: Essex, Harmonia Mundi, Roots, H.R. Taylor, Jazz Music, Swift, Projection, Gamut

ON KEILDER SIDE (Tickell,Kathryn Northumbrian Pipes).
Album: released on Saydisc, Sep'84 by Saydisc Records. Dist: Essex, Harmonia Mundi, Roots, H.R. Taylor, Jazz Music, Swift, Projection, Gamut

Cassette: released on Saydisc, Sep'84 by Saydisc Records. Dist: Essex, Harmonia Mundi, Roots, H.R. Taylor, Jazz Music, Swift, Projection, Gamut

Tidee-T
SMURF DANCE.
Single (12"): released on Carrere, Jun'84 by Carrere Records. Dist: PRT, Spartan

Tidworth Tattoo
MUSIC FROM TIDWORTH TATTOO 1975.
Album: released on Lismor, '82 by Lismor Records. Dist: Lismor, Roots, Celtic Music

Tied Logs
BLUEBELL POLKA / CAT ON THE MIXER.
Single (7"): released on Button, Oct'83 by Musical Characters Records. Dist: Spartan

CAPTAIN PUGWASH.
Single (7"): released on Button, Aug'84 by Musical Characters Records. Dist: Spartan

STAMP AND SWING.
Single (7"): released on Button, Oct'82 by Musical Characters Records. Dist: Spartan

Tier Garden
AFRIKAAN.
Single (7"): released on Cogent, Aug'84 by Cogent Records. Dist: Rough Trade

INDIA.
Tracks: / India.
Single (7"): released on Cogent, Mar'86 by Cogent Records. Dist: Rough Trade

Tierney, Harry
IRENE.
Album: released on Monmouth Evergreen, Mar'79 Dist: Jazz Music Distribution, Swift Distribution

Tiers Opera
GIRLS VOICES.
Single (7"): released on Tiers Opera, Mar'85 by Priority Records. Dist: EMI

Single (12"): released on Tiers Opera, Mar'85 by Priority Records. Dist: EMI

Tietchens, Asmus
WATCHING THE BURNING BRIDE (Tietchens, Asmus & Terry Burrows).
Album: released on Hamster, Aug'86 by Hamster Records And Tapes. Dist: Backs, Cartel

Tiger
CAN'T STAY YASO.
Tracks: / Can't stay yaso / Sitting in LA LA.
Single (12"): released on Hawkeye, Mar'87 by Hawkeye Records. Dist: Hawkeye, Lightning (WEA) Distribution, Jetstar, PRT

GUILTY / HAVE YOU EVER BEEN HURT / THREE DOG NIGHT.
Single 10": released on Pama, Sep'82 by Pama Records. Dist: Pama, Enterprise, Jetstar

LIVE: TIGER MEETS GENERAL TREES (Tiger & General Trees).
Tracks: Me name is Tiger / Don is Don / Puppy love / Mi lover / Bad boy style / Lyrics fi yu / Money / Hill and gully style / No wanga gut / Na lef ya so / Mind reader / No way home / Peanut man / No way home / So so so so / Toothache / Minibus / Negril / Check fi police (medley).
Album: released on CSA, Jun'87 by CSA Records. Dist: PRT, Jetstar

ME NAME TIGER.
Album: released on Mango, Apr'87 by Inferno Records. Dist: Inferno

Cassette: released on Mango, Apr'87 by Inferno Records. Dist: Inferno

NO PUPPY LOVE.
Tracks: / No puppy love / Country girl.
Single (12"): released on Thunderbolt, Sep'86

Tiger Lily
ANTHEM FROM A RUPERT OPERA.
Single (7"): released on Rose, Aug'85

Tiger Moth
SPEED THE PLOUGH.
Single (7"): released on Rogue, Oct'84 by Fast Forward Records. Dist: Nine Mile Distribution, Cartel Distribution

TIGER MOTH.
Album: released on Rogue, Oct'84 by Fast Forward Records. Dist: Nine Mile Distribution, Cartel Distribution

Tiger Rag
TIGER RAG 1931 Various artists (Various Artists).
Album: released on Nostalgia (Sweden), '82 by Wellard, Chris Distribution. Dist: Wellard, Chris Distribution

Tiger Tails
WORDS WITHOUT CONVICTION.
Single (7"): released on Snotty Snail, Dec'80 Dist: Rough Trade

Tiger Tailz
SHOOT TO KILL.
Tracks: / Shoot to kill.
Single (12"): released on T.T., Mar'87

Tighten up
TIGHTEN UP, VOL 2 Various artists (Various Artists).
Album: released on Trojan, '83 by Trojan Records. Dist: PRT, Jetstar

Tight Fit
BACK TO THE 60'S.
Album: released on Fame (Jive), Nov'83 by Music For Pleasure Records. Dist: EMI

Cassette: released on Fame (Jive), Nov'83 by Music For Pleasure Records. Dist: EMI

Single (7"): released on Jive, Nov'85 by Zomba Records. Dist: RCA, PRT, CBS

Single (12"): released on Jive, Nov'85 by Zomba Records. Dist: RCA, PRT, CBS

BACK TO THE 60'S, PART 2.
Single (7"): released on Jive, Sep'81 by Zomba Records. Dist: RCA, PRT, CBS

Single (12"): released on Jive, Sep'81 by Zomba Records. Dist: RCA, PRT, CBS

BACK TO THE SIXTIES.
Tracks: / Back to the sixties / Cocoa night.
Single (12"): released on Jive, Dec'85 by Zomba Records. Dist: RCA, PRT, CBS

Single (12"): released on Jive, Dec'85 by Zomba Records. Dist: RCA, PRT, CBS

FANTASY ISLAND.
Single (7"): released on Jive, Apr'82 by Zomba Records. Dist: RCA, PRT, CBS

Single (12"): released on Jive, Apr'82 by Zomba Records. Dist: RCA, PRT, CBS

Picture disc single: released on Jive, Apr'82 by Zomba Records. Dist: RCA, PRT, CBS

I'M UNDECIDED.
Single (7"): released on Jive, Oct'82 by Zomba Records. Dist: RCA, PRT, CBS

Picture disc single: released on Jive, Oct'82 by Zomba Records. Dist: RCA, PRT, CBS

LION SLEEPS TONIGHT (WIMOWEH).
Single (7"): released on Jive, Jan'82 by Zomba Records. Dist: RCA, PRT, CBS

Single (12"): released on Jive, Jan'82 by Zomba Records. Dist: RCA, PRT, CBS

Album: released on Music for Pleasure, Nov'83 by EMI Records. Dist: MFP Distribution

Cassette: released on Music for Pleasure, Nov'83 by EMI Records. Dist: MFP Distribution

LOVE THE ONE YOU'RE WITH.
Single (7"): released on Jive, Oct'83 by Zomba Records. Dist: RCA, PRT, CBS

Single (12"): released on Jive, Oct'83 by Zomba Records. Dist: RCA, PRT, CBS

SECRET HEART.
Single (7"): released on Jive, Jul'82 by Zomba Records. Dist: RCA, PRT, CBS

Single (12"): released on Jive, Jul'82 by Zomba Records. Dist: RCA, PRT, CBS

Tightrope
EVEREST THE HARD WAY.
Single (7"): released on Do it, Mar'82

Single (12"): released on Do it, Mar'82

Tights
BAD HEARTS.
Single (7"): released on Cherry Red, Jun'78 by Cherry Red Records. Dist: Pinnacle

HOWARD HUGHES.
Single (7"): released on Cherry Red, Sep'78 by Cherry Red Records. Dist: Pinnacle

Tijuana
TIJUANA Various artists (Various Artists).
Album: released on Aim (Budget Cassettes), Sep'83

Tik & Tok
COOL RUNNING.
Single (7"): released on Survival, Sep'83 by Survival Records. Dist: Backs, Cartel Distribution

Single (12"): released on Survival, Sep'83 by Survival Records. Dist: Backs, Cartel Distribution

Picture disc single: released on Survival, Sep'83 by Survival Records. Dist: Backs, Cartel Distribution

EVERYTHING WILL CHANGE.
Single (7"): released on Survival, Jul'84 by Survival Records. Dist: Backs, Cartel Distribution

Single (12"): released on Survival, Jul'84 by Survival Records. Dist: Backs, Cartel Distribution

Picture disc single: released on Survival, Jul'84 by Survival Records. Dist: Backs, Cartel Distribution

HIGHER GROUND.
Single (7"): released on Survival, Aug'84 by Survival Records. Dist: Backs, Cartel Distribution

Single (12"): released on Survival, Aug'84 by Survival Records. Dist: Backs, Cartel Distribution

INTOLERANCE.
Album: released on Survival, Aug'84 by Survival Records. Dist: Backs, Cartel Distribution

Cassette: released on Survival, Aug'84 by Survival Records. Dist: Backs, Cartel Distribution

Picture disc album: released on Survival, Aug'84 by Survival Records. Dist: Backs, Cartel Distribution

SCREEN ME I'M YOURS.
Single (7"): released on Survival, Dec'83 by Survival Records. Dist: Backs, Cartel Distribution

Single (12"): released on Jive, Dec'85 by Zomba Records. Dist: RCA, PRT, CBS

Picture disc single: released on Survival, Dec'83 by Survival Records. Dist: Backs, Cartel Distribution

Boxed set: released on Survival, Dec'83 by Survival Records. Dist: Backs, Cartel Distribution

Boxed set: released on Survival, Dec'83 by Survival Records. Dist: Backs, Cartel Distribution

SUMMER IN THE CITY.
Single (7"): released on Survival, Sep'82 by Survival Records. Dist: Backs, Cartel Distribution

Picture disc single: released on Survival, Sep'82 by Survival Records. Dist: Backs, Cartel Distribution

Single (12"): released on Survival, Sep'82 by Survival Records. Dist: Backs, Cartel Distribution

Till, Emmitt
AMERICAN POLICE.
Single (7"): released on PVK, Aug'85

FIGHT-GAME.
Tracks: Fight-game / Nothing like a motorbike.
Notes: Le Matt Music distribution: 0789 750474/0494 36301
Single (7"): released on Swoop, Sep'86 Dist: Le Matt Music Distribution

HIT MAN.
Tracks: / Hit man / American police / Hit man (album) / American police (album) / New York Jets / Crime wave / Turn it up / Messin' / Alligator man / Groovin' / Oh momma blues / Is there anyone out there / Latin / Hot revs.
Single (7"): released on PVK, Jun'87

Album: released on PVK, Apr'87

Album: released on PVK, Jun'85

NEW YORK JETS.
Tracks: / New York Jets / Alligator man.
Single (7"): released on PVK, '87

Single (7"): released on PVK, May'84

NIGHT WALKIN'.
Tracks: / Night walkin' / Latin.
Single (7"): released on Swoop, '86 Dist: Le Matt Music Distribution

Tiller Boys
BIG NOISE FROM THE JUNGLE (EP).
Single (7"): released on New Hormones, Jul'81 by New Hormones Records.

Tillis, Mel
AT THE COUNTRY STORE.
Album: released on Country Store, Dec'85 by Starblend Records. Dist: PRT, Prism Leisure Corporation Records

Cassette: released on Country Store, Dec'85 by Starblend Records. Dist: PRT, Prism Leisure Corporation Records

LONG WAY TO DAYTONA, (A).
Album: released on Elektra, Apr'82 by WEA Records. Dist: WEA

MEL TILLIS THE GREATEST.
Album: released on Gusto (USA), Oct'79 by Gusto Records (USA). Dist: Crusader

NEW PATCHES.
Album: released on MCA, Jun'84 by MCA Records. Dist: CBS

Cassette: released on MCA, Jun'84 by MCA Records. Dist: CBS

VERY BEST OF MEL TILLIS, THE.
Tracks: / Coca-Cola Cowboy / What did I promise her last night / Good woman blues / Ain't no California / I got the hoss / Send me down to Tuscon / I believe in you / Heart healer / Charlie's angel / Burning memories.
Album: released on MCA Import, Mar'86 by MCA Records. Dist: Polygram, IMS

Tillotson, Johnny
POETRY IN MOTION.
Album: released on Ace(Barnaby USA), Aug'84 by Ace Records. Dist: Pinnacle, Swift, Hotshot

Single (7"): released on Old Gold, Jul'82 by Old Gold Records. Dist: Lightning, Jazz Music, Spartan, Counterpoint

SCRAPBOOK.
Album: released on Bear Family, Jul'84 by Bear Family Records. Dist: Rollercoaster Distribution, Swift

Till Tuesday
WHAT ABOUT LOVE.
Tracks: / What about love / Will she just fall down.
Single (7"): released on Epic, Oct'86 by CBS

Records. Dist: CBS

Single (12"): released on Epic, Oct'86 by CBS Records. Dist: CBS

Tilson Thomas, Michael
GERSHWIN LIVE (see Vaughan, Sarah).

Tilston, Steve
DON'T LOOK DOWN.
Single (7"): released on T.W., Sep'84 by T.W. Records. Dist: Cartel

IN FOR A PENNY, IN FOR A POUND.
Album: released on T.W., Dec'84 by T.W. Records. Dist: Cartel

LIFE BY MISADVENTURE.
Album: released on Run River, Feb'87 by Run River Records. Dist: In-Market Ltd., PRT

SONGS FROM THE DRESS REHEARSAL.
Album: released on Cornucopia, Apr'77 Dist: JSU

THESE DAYS.
Tracks: / These days / Lazy tango.
Single (7"): released on Run River, Aug'87 by Run River Records. Dist: In-Market Ltd., PRT

Tilt
RIDE THE TIGER.
Album: released on Meteor, Apr'87 by Magnum Music Group Ltd. Magnum Music Group Ltd, PRT Distribution, Spartan Distribution

Tilt O' The Kilt
TILT O' THE KILT Various artists (Various Artists).
Double Album: released on PRT, Jul'81 by PRT Records. Dist: PRT

Double cassette: released on PRT, Jul'81 by PRT Records. Dist: PRT

TILT O' THE KILT VOL 2 Various artists (Various Artists).
Album: released on PRT, Jun'83 by PRT Records. Dist: PRT

Cassette: released on PRT, Jun'83 by PRT Records. Dist: PRT

'Til Tuesday
VOICES CARRY.
Album: released on Epic, Jun'85 by CBS Records. Dist: CBS Deleted '87.
Cat. no: EPC 26434
Cassette: released on Epic, Jun'85 by CBS Records. Dist: CBS

WELCOME HOME.
Tracks: / What about love / Coming up close / No one / Life's but a call down / David denies / Lover's day / Have mercy / Sleeping and walking / Angels never call / No one is watching you now.
Album: released on Epic, Feb'87 by CBS Records. Dist: CBS

Cassette: released on Epic, Feb'87 by CBS Records. Dist: CBS

WELCOME HOME.
Compact disc: released on Epic, Mar'87 by CBS Records. Dist: CBS

WHAT ABOUT LOVE.
Tracks: / Voices carry.
Single (7"): released on Epic, Jan'87 by CBS Records. Dist: CBS

Single (12"): released on Epic, Jan'87 by CBS Records. Dist: CBS

Single (12"): released on Epic, Feb'87 by CBS Records. Dist: CBS

Timbuk 3
AIRWAVE JUNGLE (EP).
Tracks: / Airwave jungle.
Extended-play record: released on Illegal, Aug'86 by Faulty Products Records. Dist: Pinnacle, Lightning, Cartel

FUTURE'S SO BRIGHT I GOTTA WEAR SHADES.
Tracks: / I'll do alright / Shame on you*.
Single (7"): released on I.R.S.(Independent Record Syndicate), Jan'87 by I.R.S. Dist: MCA

Single (12"): released on I.R.S.(Independent Record Syndicate), Jan'87 by I.R.S. Dist: MCA

GREETINGS FROM.
Tracks: / Future so bright I gotta wear shades (The) / Life is hard / Hairstyles and attitudes / Facts about cats / I need your / Just another movie / Friction / Cheap black & white / Shame on you / I love you in the strangest ways.
Compact disc: released on I.R.S./MCA, Apr'87 by MCA Records. Dist: Polygram, MCA

HAIRSTYLES AND ATTITUDES.
Tracks: / Hairstyles and attitudes / I love you in

---

the strongest way / Airwave jungle/I just want to make love to you (medley).
Single (7"): released on I.R.S.(Independent Record Syndicate), Mar'87 by I.R.S. Dist: MCA

Single (12"): released on I.R.S.(Independent Record Syndicate), Mar'87 by I.R.S. Dist: MCA

Time...
AFRICAN WOMAN (Time Unlimited).
Single (12"): released on Time Unlimited, Oct'85 Dist: Spartan Distribution

COOL (PART ONE) / COOL (PART TWO).
Single (7"): released on Warner Brothers, Feb'82 by Warner Bros Records. Dist: WEA

Single (12"): released on Warner Brothers, Feb'82 by Warner Bros Records. Dist: WEA

GOT YOUR NUMBER / GRACE.
Single (7"): released on Warner Brothers, Jan'83 by Warner Bros Records. Dist: WEA

Single (12"): released on Warner Brothers, Jan'83 by Warner Bros Records. Dist: WEA

ICE CREAM CASTLE.
Tracks: / Ice cream castles / My drawers / Chilli sauce / Jungle love / If the kid can't make you come / Bird, The.
Compact disc: released on Warner Bros., Jul'86 by Warner Bros Records. Dist: WEA
Album: released on Warner Brothers, Aug'84 by Warner Bros Records. Dist: WEA

IT'S TIMELESS Curtis Fuller, Harold Land etc (Timeless All Stars).
Album: released on Timeless (Holland), Apr'84 Dist: JSU Distribution, Jazz Music Distribution, Jazz Horizons Distribution, Cadillac, Celtic Music Distribution

TIME Various artists (Various Artists).
Tracks: / Born to rock 'n' roll / Time talkin' / Time / Ascention (The music of the spheres) / Law of the Universe / Time lord theme / John Christie / One human family / What on Earth / I know, I know / Your brother in soul / Case for the prosecution / Starmaker / Time will teach us all / Object / In my defence / Within my world / Because / Move the judge / She's so beautiful / Beauty, truth love freedom, peace / If only you knew / We're the UFO / Theme from time / Harmony / Return, The / Time (reprise) / It's in everyone of us.
Notes: Dave Clark's 'Time' premieres at the Dominion Theatre, Tottenham Court Rd, London on April 9th 1986. The album features Cliff Richard, Julian Lennon, Leo Sayer, Stevie Wonder, Freddie Mercury, Ashford & Simpson, Dionne Warwick and Murray Head. Double album in gatefold sleeve with 20 page full colour booklet.
Album: released on EMI, Apr'86 by EMI Records. Dist: EMI

Cassette: released on EMI, Apr'86 by EMI Records. Dist: EMI

TIME.
Album: released on Warner Brothers, Mar'82 by Warner Bros Records. Dist: WEA

Cassette: released on Warner Brothers, Mar'82 by Warner Bros Records. Dist: WEA

TIME FOR MEMEORIES.
Cassette: released on Decca, Apr'81 by Decca Records. Dist: Polygram

TIME MACHINE (H.G.WELLS) Read by Robert Hardy.
Cassette: released on Listen For Pleasure, Apr'79 by MFP Records. Dist: EMI

WHAT TIME IS IT?.
Album: released on Warner Brothers, Jan'83 by Warner Bros Records. Dist: WEA

WORLD DESTRUCTION (Time zone).
Single (7"): released on Virgin, Jan'85 by Virgin Records. Dist: EMI, Virgin Distribution

Single (12"): released on Virgin, Jan'85 by Virgin Records. Dist: EMI, Virgin Distribution

Time After Time
TIME AFTER TIME Original Soundtrack (Various Artists).
Compact disc: released on Silva Screen, May'87 by Silva Screen Records. Dist: Silva Screen, PRT

Time Bandits
ENDLESS ROAD.
Tracks: / Fiction.
Single (7"): released on CBS, Jan'87 by CBS Records. Dist: CBS

FICTION.
Tracks: / Dancing on a string / I want to live / I won't steal away / You are every world / Runaway / Only a fool / Back against the wall / Endless road / America / I'm only shooting love.
Album: released on CBS, May'86 by CBS Records. Dist: CBS

Cassette: released on CBS, May'86 by CBS

Records. Dist: CBS

HOW DOES IT FEEL.
Single (7"): released on CBS, Apr'84 by CBS Records. Dist: CBS

I'M ONLY SHOOTING LOVE.
Single (7"): released on CBS, Jul'84 by CBS Records. Dist: CBS

Single (12"): released on CBS, Jul'84 by CBS Records. Dist: CBS

I'M SPECIALISED IN YOU.
Single (7"): released on CBS, Feb'83 by CBS Records. Dist: CBS

Single (12"): released on CBS, Feb'83 by CBS Records. Dist: CBS

LISTEN TO THE MAN WITH THE GOLDEN VOICE.
Single (12"): released on CBS, May'83 by CBS Records. Dist: CBS

Single (7"): released on CBS, May'83 by CBS Records. Dist: CBS

ONLY A FOOL.
Tracks: / 123.
Single (7"): released on CBS, Mar'86 by CBS Records. Dist: CBS

Single (12"): released on CBS, Mar'86 by CBS Records. Dist: CBS

WHEN YOU'RE DANCING.
Single (7"): released on CBS, Aug'87 by CBS Records. Dist: CBS

Timebox
TIMEBOX (Various Artists).
Notes: Mid-priced 16 track selection of bands featured at London's Timebox club. Studio tracks by: Blyth Power, Black Cillas, Menticide, Thatcher On Acid, Stump, Stitched Backfoot Airmen, Saviours Of Pop music, Children Held Hostage etc.
Album: released on Timebox, Apr'87 by Timebox records. Dist: Pinnacle

Time code
LOUIE LOUIE.
Tracks: / Village house stomp.
Single (7"): released on Jive, Nov'86 by Zomba Records. Dist: RCA, PRT, CBS

Single (12"): released on Jive, Nov'86 by Zomba Records. Dist: RCA, PRT, CBS

Time Dance
PICTURE.
Single (7"): released on Midnight, Sep'83

Time for Hits
TIME FOR HITS Various artists (Various Artists).
Album: released on Spartan, Nov'85 by Spartan Records. Dist: Spartan

Cassette: released on Spartan, Nov'85 by Spartan Records. Dist: Spartan

Time in Motion
I WANNA BE YOUR TELEPHONE.
Single (7"): released on Red Rhino, Sep'82 by Red Rhino Records. Dist: Red Rhino, Cartel

QUIET TYPE.
Single (7"): released on Red Rhino, May'82 by Red Rhino Records. Dist: Red Rhino, Cartel

Time Machine
SUMMER OF LOVE.
Tracks: / Summer of love (EP) / San Francisco / Papar sun / Flowers in the rain / Whiter shade of pale / California dreaming / All you need is love / Summer of love.
Single (7"): released on Bam Caruso, Jun'86 by Bam Caruso Records. Dist: Rough Trade, Revolver, Cartel

Time & patience
TRIBULATION.
Single (12"): released on Creole, Apr'85 by Creole Records. Dist: Rhino, PRT

Times
BLUE FIRE.
Single (7"): released on Art Pop, Oct'84 by Art Pop Records. Dist: Rough Trade, Cartel, Pinnacle

BLUE PERIOD.
Album: released on Art Pop, Apr'85 by Art Pop Records. Dist: Rough Trade, Cartel, Pinnacle

BOYS ABOUT TOWN.
Single (12"): released on Art Pop, Oct'85 by Art Pop Records. Dist: Rough Trade, Cartel, Pinnacle

---

BOYS BRIGADE.
Single (7"): released on Art Pop, Aug'84 by Art Pop Records. Dist: Rough Trade, Cartel, Pinnacle

DANGER MAN THEME.
Single (7"): released on Art Pop, Sep'83 by Art Pop Records. Dist: Rough Trade, Cartel, Pinnacle

ENJOY.
Album: released on Art Pop, Nov'86 by Art Pop Records. Dist: Rough Trade, Cartel, Pinnacle

HELLO EUROPE.
Album: released on Art Pop, Nov'84 by Art Pop Records. Dist: Rough Trade, Cartel, Pinnacle

I HELPED PATRICK MCGOOHAN ESCAPE.
Album: released on Art Pop, Dec'83 by Art Pop Records. Dist: Rough Trade, Cartel, Pinnacle
Single (7"): released on Art Pop, Jan'84 by Art Pop Records. Dist: Rough Trade, Cartel, Pinnacle

POP GOES ART.
Album: released on Whaam, Jul'82 Dist: Pinnacle

RED WITH PURPLE FLASHES.
Single (7"): released on Whaam, Jul'81 Dist: Pinnacle

THIS IS LONDON.
Album: released on Art Pop, Jul'83 by Art Pop Records. Dist: Rough Trade, Cartel, Pinnacle

TIMES'TV.
Tracks: / Time TV / Trailor from 'Enjoy' / Policeforce, The / El Aragua / Pick it up.
Single (7"): released on Fire, Oct'86 by Twist and Shout Music. Dist: Nine Mile, Rough Trade, Cartel

Single (12"): released on Fire, Oct'86 by Twist and Shout Music. Dist: Nine Mile, Rough Trade, Cartel

UP AGAINST IT.
Album: released on Art Pop, Apr'86 by Art Pop Records. Dist: Rough Trade, Cartel, Pinnacle

Times Square
JOANNE.
Single (7"): released on Northeast Music, Jun'83 by Northeast Music Records. Dist: Northeast Music Distribution, Pinnacle

Time To Rock
TIME TO ROCK Various artists (Various Artists).
Tracks: / Jailhouse rock / Bathroom wall / Never forgive / Here it comes / Cumin' atcha live / Start the fire / Fighting for the world / Breakout / Shadow of your love / License to kill / Burnt offerings.
Album: released on WEA, Jul'87 by WEA Records. Dist: WEA

Cassette: released on WEA, Jul'87 by WEA Records. Dist: WEA

Compact disc: released on WEA, Jul'87 by WEA Records. Dist: WEA

Time UK
CABERET(THE).
Single (7"): released on Red Bus, Sep'83 by Red Bus Records. Dist: PRT

Single (12"): released on Red Bus, Sep'83 by Red Bus Records. Dist: PRT

PLAY GROUND OF PRIVELGE.
Single (7"): released on Arista, Jan'85 by Arista Records. Dist: RCA

Single (12"): released on Arista, Jan'85 by Arista Records. Dist: RCA

YOU WON'T STOP.
Single (7"): released on Arista, Sep'85 by Arista Records. Dist: RCA

Single (12"): released on Arista, Sep'85 by Arista Records. Dist: RCA

Timex Social club
MIXED UP WORLD.
Tracks: / Mixed up world.
Single (7"): released on Cool Tempo, Nov'86 by Chrysalis Records. Dist: CBS

Single (12"): released on Cool Tempo, Nov'86 by Chrysalis Records. Dist: CBS

VICIOUS RUMORS.
Album: released on Cool Tempo, Jan'87 by Chrysalis Records. Dist: CBS

Cassette: released on Cool Tempo, Jan'87 by Chrysalis Records. Dist: CBS

Timmons, Bobby

JENKINS, JORDAN & TIMMONS (Timmons, Bobby/Clifford Jordan/John Jenkins).
Notes: For full information see: Jenkins, John/Clifford Jordan & Bobby Timmons.

THIS HERE.
Album: released on Riverside (USA), Aug'84 Dist: Fantasy (USA) Distribution

THIS HERE IS ....
Compact disc: released on Carrere, Apr'87 by Carrere Records. Dist: Spartan

THIS HERE IS BOBBY TIMMONS.
Compact disc: released on Vanguard (USA), Apr'86

Timms, Sally

LONG BLACK VEIL (Timms, Sally & The Wandering Cowgirls).
Tracks: / Butchers boy / Margherita / Down to Dover.
Single (7"): released on T.I.M., Nov'86 by T.I.M. Records. Dist: Backs, Cartel Distribution

Single (12"): released on T.I.M., Nov'86 by T.I.M. Records. Dist: Backs, Cartel Distribution

THIS HOUSE IS A HOUSE OF TROUBLE (Timms, Sally & The Wandering Cowgirls).
Single (7"): released on T.I.M., 13 Jun'87 by T.I.M. Records. Dist: Backs, Cartel Distribution

Single (12"): released on T.I.M., 13 Jun'87 by T.I.M. Records. Dist: Backs, Cartel Distribution

Tim & Nell

THERE WILL COME LOVE / TOGETHER AGAIN.
Single (12"): released on Orbitone, May'82 by Orbitone Records. Dist: Jetstar Distribution

Timothy, Christopher

ALL CREATURES GREAT AND SMALL.
Cassette: released on Listen For Pleasure, Aug'85 by MFP Records. Dist: EMI

Tims, Alfonia

FUTURE FUNK - UNCUT (Tims, Alfonia and his Flying Tigers).
Cassette: released on Reach Out Int. '83

Ti-Na-Na

KISSING FOR FUN.
Tracks: / Kissing for fun / You're so attractive.
Single (7"): released on Genie, Jul'86 by Genie Records. Dist: Spartan, CBS

Tinder box

TINDER BOX (Asher, Jane).
Cassette: released on Listen Productions, Nov'84 Dist: H.R. Taylor, Hayward Promotions Distribution

Tin Drum

AMOURER, (L').
Tracks: / L'Amourer.
Single (7"): released on Fun After All, Apr'86 Dist: Pinnacle

Single (12"): released on Fun After All, Apr'86 Dist: Pinnacle

Tin Kan

THOUSAND MILES OF WHITE.
Single (7"): released on White Dove, Oct'79 by White Dove Records. Dist: Pinnacle

Tinniswood, Peter

MORE TALES FROM A LONG ROOM
Read by Robin Bailey.
Cassette: released on Listen For Pleasure, '83 by MFP Records. Dist: EMI

TALES FROM A LONG ROHOM VOL.1 & 2.
Cassette: released on Listen Productions, Nov'84 Dist: H.R. Taylor, Hayward Promotions Distribution

TALES FROM A LONG ROOM VOL 1 AND 11.
Cassette: released on Listen Productions, Nov'84 Dist: H.R. Taylor, Hayward Promotions Distribution

Tinsley, John

SUNRISE BLUES.
Album: released on Swingmaster, May'86 Dist: Jazz Music Distribution

Tin Star

SOMEBODY'S DREAMS.
Album: released on Special Delivery, Aug'87 Dist: Nine Mile, Cartel. Estim retail price in Sep'87 was £5.99.

Tin Tin

HOLD IT.
Single (7"): released on WEA, Jul'83 by WEA Records. Dist: WEA

Single (12"): released on WEA, Jul'83 by WEA Records. Dist: WEA

KISS ME.
Single (7"): released on WEA, Oct'82 by WEA Records. Dist: WEA

Single (12"): released on WEA, Mar'84 by WEA Records. Dist: WEA

Tiny Lights

FLOWERS IN THE AIR.
Single (12"): released on Temple, Dec'86 by Temple Records. Dist: Roots Distribution, Folksound Distribution, Celtic Music Distribution, Projection Distribution

Tiny Town

DROP BY DROP.
Single (7"): released on Elastic Music, May'84 by Elastic Records. Dist: Revolver, Cartel

LITTLE TIN GOD.
Album: released on Elastic Music, Jun'85 by Elastic Records. Dist: Revolver, Cartel

LIVING OUT OF LIVING.
Single (7"): released on Elastic Music, Nov'84 by Elastic Records. Dist: Revolver, Cartel

NO PLACE LIKE HOME.
Tracks: / No place like home.
Single (12"): released on Very Mouth, Feb'86 by Very Mouth Records. Dist: Cartel

Tipinifini

FEVER.
Single (7"): released on Spartan, Aug'85 by Spartan Records. Dist: Spartan

Single (12"): released on Spartan, Aug'85 by Spartan Records. Dist: Spartan

Tip of the iceberg

TIP OF THE ICEBERG Various artists (Various Artists).
Cassette: released on York Music, Mar'85 Dist: Bomb Alley Music, Spartan

TIP OF THE ICEBERG VOL II Various artists (Various Artists).
Cassette: released on Bomb Alley, Jul'85 Dist: Red Rhino, Cartel

Tippa Ranking

GOOD LOOKING.
Single (7"): released on Red Man, Aug'82 by Red Man Records. Dist: Jetstar

KNIFE CUT.
Single (7"): released on Red Man, Aug'83 by Red Man Records. Dist: Jetstar

ROSE MARIE.
Single (7"): released on Red Man, Aug'82 by Red Man Records. Dist: Jetstar

SOLOMON YOU CAN'T KEEP A GOOD MAN DOWN.
Single (7"): released on Reggae Delight, Nov'84

Single (12"): released on Reggae Delight, Nov'84

Tipper Ranking

ECHO GET SHOT.
Single (12"): released on Form, Oct'81 by Form Records. Dist: Pinnacle

Tippett, Keith

IN FOCUS (Tippett, Keith/Howard Riley).

LIVE (Tippett's, Keith Septet).
Album: released on Ogun, Jun'86 Dist: Jazz Music, JSU, Cadillac

MERCY DASH (Tippett, Keith/Gallivan, Joe/Dean, Elton/Hopper, Hugh).
Album: released on Culture Press, Dec'86 by Vista Sounds Records. Dist: Jetstar, Rough Trade

OVARY LODGE (WITH VARIOUS ARTISTS).
Album: released on Ogun, Jan'77 Dist: Jazz Music, JSU, Cadillac

T 'N' T (Tippett, Keith/Stan Tracey).
Album: released on Steam, Apr'81 Dist: JSU, Chris Wellard, Jazz Music, Projection, Cadillac

Tippetts, J

VOICE (Tippetts, J/M Nichols/P Minton/B Eley).

Album: released on Ogun, Apr'74 Dist: Jazz Music, JSU, Cadillac

Tippetts, Julie

ENCORE (see Auger, Brian) (Tippetts, Julie & Brian Auger).

Tircolea, Catalin

PANPIPE AND ORGAN.
Compact disc: released on Delta, '86 by Delta Records. Dist: Target

Tired of living

KISS A LOTTA FROGS.
Single (7"): released on Initial, Aug'81 by Initial Records. Dist: Pinnacle

Tirez Tirez

ETUDES.
Album: released on Aura, '81 by Hollywood Nites Distribution. Dist: Pinnacle

RAZOR BLADE.
Single (7"): released on Aura, Sep'81 by Hollywood Nites Distribution. Dist: Pinnacle

SOCIAL RESPONSIBILITY.
Album: released on Rough Trade, Jul'87 by Rough Trade Records. Dist: Rough Trade Distribution, Cartel Distribution

STORY OF THE YEAR.
Single (7"): released on Les Disques Du Crepuscule, Nov'83 Dist: Rough Trade, Pinnacle, Island, Polygram

UNDER THE DOOR.
Single (12"): released on Himalaya, Jun'84 by Himalaya Records. Dist: Rough Trade, Cartel

Tiselius, Lars

HAMMOND DANCE PARTY.
Album: released on Joy, '74 by President Records. Dist: Jazz Music, Swift, President Distribution

Titan

IMAGINARY LADY.
Single (7"): released on After Hours, Feb'83 Dist: CBS

Titanic

SULTANA.
Single (7"): released on CBS, '80 by CBS Records. Dist: CBS

Tito Puente

EL REY.
Compact disc: released on Concord Jazz(USA), Dec'86 by Concord Jazz Records (USA). Dist: IMS, Polygram

Tjader, Cal

A FUEGO VIVO.
Album: released on Concord, Apr'82 by Import Records. Dist: IMS, Polygram

Cassette: released on Concord, Apr'82 by Import Records. Dist: IMS, Polygram

GAZAME.
Album: released on Concord Jazz, Nov'80 by Concord Jazz Records (USA). Dist: IMS, Polygram

GOOD VIBES.
Album: released on Concord Jazz(USA), Oct'84 by Concord Jazz Records (USA). Dist: IMS, Polygram

SHINING SEA, THE.
Album: released on Concord Jazz, Nov'81 by Concord Jazz Records (USA). Dist: IMS, Polygram

SOLAR HEAT.
Album: released on Rhapsody, Oct'82 by President Records. Dist: Taylors, Swift, Jazz Music, Wellard, Chris

SONA LIBRE.
Tracks: / Hip walk / Sally's tomato / O barquinho / El muchacho / Insight / My reverie / Morning of the animal / Azul / Invitation / Alonzo.
Notes: Digital stereo recording.
Compact disc: released on Verve, Apr'84 by Phonogram Records. Dist: Polygram

TJ Express

WORKING WITH THE PEOPLE.
Single (7"): released on Blue Chip, Jan'81 by Blue Chip Records.

T.K.O.

IN YOUR FACE.
Album: released on Music For Nations, Dec'84 by Music For Nations Records. Dist: Pinnacle

---

T LA Rock

BACK TO BURN.
Single (7"): released on 10, Jan'87 by 10 Records. Dist: Virgin, EMI

Single (12"): released on Ten, Jan'87

BREAKIN' BELLS.
Tracks: / Breakin' bells / Bass machine.
Single (7"): released on 10, Sep'06 " y 10 Records. Dist: Virgin, EMI

Single (12"): released on 10, Sep'86 by 10 Records. Dist: Virgin, EMI

THIS BEAT KICKS (THE CHAD BEAT REMIX).
Tracks: / This beat kicks / Having fun / Back to burn (club version).
Single (12"): released on 10, Jun'87 by 10 Records. Dist: Virgin, EMI

T-Life

SOMETHING THAT YOU DO TO ME.
Single (7"): released on Arista, Oct'81 by Arista Records. Dist: RCA

Single (12"): released on Arista, Sep'81 by Arista Records. Dist: RCA

Tillo de Piscop

STOP BAJON....PRIMAVERA.
Tracks: / Stop bajon ... (inst) / Stadera.
Single (12"): released on Greyhound, Jan'87 by Greyhound Records. Dist: PRT, Greyhound

TNT

BACK ON THE ROAD.
Single (7"): released on Noat, Apr'84 by Neat Records. Dist: Pinnacle, Neat

KNIGHTS OF THE NEW THUNDER.
Album: released on Vertigo (Holland), Mar'85 Cat. no: 8188651
Cassette: released on Vertigo (Holland), Mar'85

TELL NO TALES.
Tracks: / Everyone's a star / 10,000 lovers (in one) / Sapphire / Northern lights.
Album: released on Vertigo, May'87 by Phonogram Records. Dist: Polygram

Cassette: released on Vertigo, Dec'1 by Phonogram Records. Dist: Polygram

Compact disc: released on Vertigo, May'87 by Phonogram Records. Dist: Polygram

Toba

MOVING UP.
Single (12"): released on Connection, Mar'82 by Connection Records. Dist: Pinnacle

To Be

TO BE.
Album: released on Brain (Germany), '79

To Be Continued

FIRST CUT (EP), THE.
Single (7"): released on Visual, Dec'82

To Be Or Not To Be

TO BE OR NOT TO BE Original Soundtrack (Various Artists).
Cassette: released on Island, Feb'84 by Island Records. Dist: Polygram

Cassette: released on Island, Feb'84 by Island Records. Dist: Polygram

Tobermory...

TOBERMORY & OTHER STORIES (Newth, Jonathan).
Cassette: released on Colophone, Jun'81 by Audio-Visual Library Services. Dist: Audio-Visual Library Services

Tobisawa,H & M Ohishi

TRANSIT ON THE WIND.
Notes: New Age Music for piano,bass and strings.
Compact disc: released on Denon, May'86 by Denon Records. Dist: Harmonia Mundi

Tobruk

WILD ON THE RUN.
Album: released on Parlophone, Mar'85 by EMI Records. Dist: EMI

Cassette: released on Parlophone, Mar'85 by EMI Records. Dist: EMI

Single (7"): released on Neat, Sep'83 by Neat Records. Dist: Pinnacle, Neat

Toczek, Nick

BRITANARCHIST.
Tracks: / Britanarchist / More to hate than

meets the eye.
Single (12"): released on Acrimonya, Feb'86 by Acrimony Records. Dist: Red Rhino, Cartel

BRITANARCHIST DEMO, THE.
Cassette: released on Bluurg, Jan'84 by Bluurg Records. Dist: Rough Trade, Nine Mile

Today's country classics
TODAY'S COUNTRY CLASSICS Various artists (Various Artists).
Tracks: / Cowboy rides again,The / How blue / Make my life with you / Knock on wood / Mississippi squirrel revival / Country girls / Sweet country music / What I didn't do / Happy birthday dear heartache / God bless the U.S.A.
Album: released on MCA Import, Mar'86 by MCA Records. Dist: Polygram, IMS

Todays Pops....
TODAYS POPS FOR TODAYS TOTS Various Artists (Various Artists).
Cassette: released on Bravo, Feb'80 by Pickwick Records. Dist: Lugtons

Todays Smash Hits
TODAYS SMASH HITS VOL.111 Various Session Artists (Various Session Artists).
Cassette: released on Aim, Feb'83 Dist: H.R. Taylor

Todd
THANK YOU.
Single (7"): released on Disques Du Grand Michel, Sep'84 by Disques Du Grand Michel. Dist: December Songs, Independents Distribution

Todd, Dick
BLUE ORCHIDS.
Album: released on RCA, Aug'87 by RCA Records. Dist: RCA, Roots, Swift, Wellard, Chris, I & B, Solomon & Peres Distribution

Cassette: released on RCA, Aug'87 by RCA Records. Dist: RCA, Roots, Swift, Wellard, Chris, I & B, Solomon & Peres Distribution

Todd,H.F.
ILLY SHOES.
assette: released on VFM, Sep'78 by VFM ecords. Dist: Taylors, Wynd-Up Distribution

Todd,Jimmy
IAPPY HOURS.
lbum: released on Grampian, '71 by Grampin Records. Dist: Grampian, Clyde Factors Disibutors, Ross

ALMON TAILS UP THE WATER.
lbum: released on Grampian, '73 by Grampin Records. Dist: Grampian, Clyde Factors Disibutors, Ross

Todd,Leslie
'EART TO HEART.
racks: / Heart to heart / Heart to heart / Tener in the dark.
'ingle (7"): released on Sonet, Jan'86 by onet Records. Dist: PRT

Todd,Tony
OU'RE BREAKING MY HEART.
ngle (7"): released on Crash, Jan'83 by Sa- Records. Dist: PRT

Toddy
TORYTIME TOP TEN VOL.6.
ssette: released on VFM Cassettes, Jan'85

Todorow,Camy
URSTING AT THE SEAMS.
ngle (7"): released on Virgin, Sep'85 by Vir- Records. Dist: EMI, Virgin Distribution

ngle (12"): released on Virgin, Sep'85 by Vir- Records. Dist: EMI, Virgin Distribution

HAIN OF FOOLS.
acks: / Chain of fools / Day of the storm.
ngle (7"): released on Virgin, Mar'87 by Vir- Records. Dist: EMI, Virgin Distribution

ngle (7"): released on Virgin, Mar'87 by Vir- Records. Dist: EMI, Virgin Distribution

Together
AYING GAMES.
gle (12"): released on Mausoleum, May'85 Mausoleum Records. Dist: Pinnacle

um: released on K-Tel, Oct'79 by K-Tel cords. Dist: Record Merchandisers Distribu-, Taylors, Terry Blood Distribution, Wynd-Up tribution, Relay Distribution, Pickwick Disution, Solomon & Peres Distribution, Polym

ssette: released on K-Tel, Oct'79 by K-Tel cords. Dist: Record Merchandisers Distribu-, Taylors, Terry Blood Distribution, Wynd-Up

Distribution, Relay Distribution, Pickwick Distribution, Solomon & Peres Distribution, Polygram

TOGETHER Various artists (Various Artists).
Tracks: / There'll be sad songs(to make you cry) / Should have known better / Tender love / Zoom / Power of love,The / Amoureuse / I'm in love baby / You're everything to me / Move closer / My favourite waste of time / Starting together / Only love / Anyone who had a heart / If you don't know me by now / Me and Mrs Jones / Secret Lovers.
Album: released on K-Tel, Oct'86 by K-Tel Records. Dist: Record Merchandisers Distribution, Taylors, Terry Blood Distribution, Wynd-Up Distribution, Relay Distribution, Pickwick Distribution, Solomon & Peres Distribution, Polygram

Cassette: released on K-Tel, Oct'86 by K-Tel Records. Dist: Record Merchandisers Distribution, Taylors, Terry Blood Distribution, Wynd-Up Distribution, Relay Distribution, Pickwick Distribution, Solomon & Peres Distribution, Polygram

Album: released on CBS, Nov'84 by CBS Records. Dist: CBS

Cassette: released on CBS, Nov'84 by CBS Records. Dist: CBS

Together again
TOGETHER AGAIN (Various Artists).
Tracks: / Something to brag about / Together again / What's in your heart / Heart to heart talk / Let your love flow / Somethin''bout you baby I like / We've got tonight / Love story (you and me) / Don't fall in love with a dreamer / Willingly / Forgive me John / Why don't we just sleep on it tonight / Yaya con dio.
Album: released on MFP, Mar'87 by EMI Records. Dist: EMI

Cassette: released on MFP, Mar'87 by EM Records. Dist: EMI

Togo
KABI YE MUSIC FROM.
Album: released on Ocora (France), Jul'74 Dist: Discovery Distribution

Tokalon
COMING TO GET YOU.
Single (7"): released on Champagne, Feb'82 by DJM Records.

Single (12"): released on Champagne, Feb'82 by DJM Records.

Tokens
LION SLEEPS TONIGHT,THE.
Tracks: / Lion sleeps tonight,The / Three bells,The.
Single (7"): released on Old Gold, Nov'86 by Old Gold Records. Dist: Lightning, Jazz Music, Spartan, Counterpoint

Single (7"): released on RCA, '80 by USA Import. Dist: Lightning

Tokio Jo
VENUE, MAJORCA.
Album: released on Mafia Records, May'83

Tokyo Blade
BLACK HEARTS AND JADED SPADES.
Album: released on Tokyo Blade, Feb'86

CAVE SESSION,THE.
Single (12"): released on Powerstation Records, Jun'85 by Powerstation Records. Dist: Pinnacle

LIGHTNING STRIKES.
Single (12"): released on Powerstation Records, Sep'84 by Powerstation Records. Dist: Pinnacle

MADAM GUILLOTINE.
Single (12"): released on Powerstation Records, Jan'85 by Powerstation Records. Dist: Pinnacle

MIDNIGHT RENDEZVOUS.
Single (12"): released on Powerstation Records, Feb'84 by Powerstation Records. Dist: Pinnacle

NIGHT OF THE BLADE.
Album: released on Powerstation Records, Sep'84 by Powerstation Records. Dist: Pinnacle

POWER GAME.
Single (7"): released on Powerstation Records, Oct'83 by Powerstation Records. Dist: Pinnacle

TOKYO BLADES.
Album: released on Powerstation Records, Oct'83 by Powerstation Records. Dist: Pinnacle

UNDERCOVER HONEYMOON.
Tracks: / Underground honeymoon.
Single (12"): released on Tokyo Blade, Apr'86

WARRIOR OF THE RISING SUN.
Tracks: / Madam Guillotine / Fever / Night of the blade / Breakout / Unleash the beat / Attack Attack / Lightning strikes (Extended version) / Warrior of the rising sun / Someone to love / Mean Streak / If heaven is hell (Extended Version) / Break the chains / Dead of the night / Powergame / Highway Passion / Midnight rendezvous / Sunrise in Tokyo / Killer City / Liar / Death on mainstreet.
Notes: Double LP and Cassette.The recordings are licensed from Powerstation Records LtdThis compilation (C) 1985 Castle Communications Ltd,Unit 7,Merton Road,Ind.Est, 271 Merton Road,London,SW18.
Double Album: released on Raw Power, Apr'86 Dist: Pinnacle

Double cassette: released on Raw Power, Apr'86 Dist: Pinnacle

Tokyo Brass Ensemble
DIGITAL MARCH.
Notes: Digital Stereo Marches by J.F Wagner,Sousa,Sugiyama,Pierne.
Compact disc: released on Denon, Jan'85 by Denon Records. Dist: Harmonia Mundi

Tokyo Charm
RUNAWAY.
Single (7"): released on RCA, Aug'82 by RCA Records. Dist: RCA, Roots, Swift, Wellard, Chris, I & B, Solomon & Peres Distribution

Tokyo Mobile Music
TOKYO MOBILE MUSIC 1 Various artists (Various Artists).
Album: released on Mobile Suit Corporation, Apr'82 Dist: Phonogram Distribution, Polygram Distribution

Cassette: released on Mobile Suit Corporation Apr'82 Dist: Phonogram Distribution, Polygran Distribution

Tokyo Olypics
RADIO (TURN HER ON).
Single (7"): released on Ritz, Jun'83 by Ritz Records. Dist: Spartan

Single (12"): released on Ritz, Jun'83 by Ritz Records. Dist: Spartan

SHOT BY LOVE (2 PARTS).
Single (7"): released on Ritz, Jan'83 by Ritz Records. Dist: Spartan

Single (12"): released on Ritz, Jan'83 by Ritz Records. Dist: Spartan

Tokyo Reggae
TOKYO REGGAE CLASH Various Artists (Various Artists).
Album: released on Wackies, Nov'84 by Wackies Records. Dist: Jetstar

To Let
TO LET Galsworthy, John (Hordern, Sir Michael).
Notes: To Let is the third of nine novels by John Galsworthy which make up The Forsyte Saga. The books cover fifty years of the decline of the Forsyte family, from the1880's to the 1930's. In seeking to insulate themselves by property from realityand the disintegration of their class, the Forsytes are gradually blinded to thethreats of social change. Sir Michael Hordern reads this abridgement of Galsworthy's to Let which has become a classic of English literature. Running time 2 hrs30 mins approx.
Cassette: released on LFP, Jun'87

Tolkien,J.R.R.
HOBBITT,THE.
Album: released on Caedmon(USA), Jul'77 by Caedmon (USA) Records. Dist: Gower, Taylors, Discovery

Cassette: released on Caedmon(USA), Jul'77 by Caedmon (USA) Records. Dist: Gower, Taylors, Discovery

J.R.R. TOLKIEN SOUNDBOOK.
Album: released on Caedmon(USA), May'80 by Caedmon (USA) Records. Dist: Gower, Taylors, Discovery

Cassette: released on Caedmon(USA), May'80 by Caedmon (USA) Records. Dist: Gower, Taylors, Discovery

POEMS & SONGS OF MIDDLE EARTH.
Album: released on Caedmon(USA), Jul'77 by Caedmon (USA) Records. Dist: Gower, Taylors, Discovery

Cassette: released on Caedmon(USA), Jul'77 by Caedmon (USA) Records. Dist: Gower, Taylors, Discovery

SILMARLLION-EXCERPTS,THE.
Album: released on Caedmon(USA), Jul'79 by Caedmon (USA) Records. Dist: Gower, Taylors, Discovery

Cassette: released on Caedmon(USA), Jul'79 by Caedmon (USA) Records. Dist: Gower, Taylors, Discovery

SILMARLLION,THE.
Album: released on Caedmon(USA), Nov'77 by Caedmon (USA) Records. Dist: Gower, Taylors, Discovery

Cassette: released on Caedmon(USA), Nov'77 by Caedmon (USA) Records. Dist: Gower, Taylors, Discovery

Tollefsen, Toralf
ACCORDION EVERGREENS.
Album: released on ARC (Accordion Records), '86 Dist: Accordion Record Club

Tolliver,Charles
IMPACT.
Album: released on Enja (Germany), Jan'82 by Enja Records (W.Germany). Dist: Cadillac Music

Tolly,Maria
VOICES.
Album: released on Stroppy Cow, Sep'86 by stroppy cow records. Dist: WRPM Distribution

Tolman,Russ
TOTEM POLES AND GLORY HOLES.
Album: released on Zippo, Sep'86

Tolonen,Jukka
CROSSECTION.
Album: released on Sonet, '76 by Sonet Records. Dist: PRT

MONTREUX BOOGIE.
Album: released on Sonet, Jan'79 by Sonet Records. Dist: PRT

MOUNTAIN STREAM.
Album: released on Sonet, Feb'80 by Sonet Records. Dist: PRT

PASSENGER TO PARAMARIBO, A.
Album: released on Sonet, Aug'78 by Sonet Records. Dist: PRT

RADIO ROMANCE.
Compact disc: released on Sonet, '86 by Sonet Records. Dist: PRT

TOLONEN.
Album: released on Sonet, '74 by Sonet Records. Dist: PRT

TOUCH WOOD.
Album: released on Sonet, Jul'81 by Sonet Records. Dist: PRT

Tolstoy, Leo
ANNA KARENINA Read by Irene Worth.
Album: released on Caedmon(USA), '79 by Caedmon (USA) Records. Dist: Gower, Taylors, Discovery

Cassette: released on Caedmon(USA), '78 by Caedmon (USA) Records. Dist: Gower, Taylors, Discovery

Tolvan Big Band
SPLIT VISION.
Album: released on Dragon, Jun'86 by Dragon Records. Dist: Jazz Music, Projection, Cadillac

Tom Brown's Schooldays
TOM BROWN'S SCHOOLDAYS By Thomas Hughes (Hughes, Tom).
Cassette: released on Colophone, Sep'81 by Audio-Visual Library Services. Dist: Audio-Visual Library Services

Tomcat
OLD FATHER CHRISTMAS / DONROY & TOMCAT / GOOD KING WENCESLAS.
Single (7"): released on Denmar, Nov'82 Dist: Denmar, ILA

TOMBS OF ATUAN Le Guin, Ursula (Hood, Morag).
Cassette: released on Colophone, Nov'81 by Audio-Visual Library Services. Dist: Audio-Visual Library Services

Tomfoolery
TOMFOOLERY Various artists (Various Artists).
Album: released on Multi-Media, Apr'82 by Multi Media Tapes Records. Dist: Pinnacle, Conifer Distribution, H.R. Taylor Distribution, Stage One Distribution

Cassette: released on Multi-Media, Apr'82 by Multi Media Tapes Records. Dist: Pinnacle, Conifer Distribution, H.R. Taylor Distribution, Stage One Distribution

Tomita

BERMUDA TRIANGLE.
Album: released on RCA, '84 by RCA Records. Dist: RCA, Roots, Swift, Wellard, Chris, I & B, Solomon & Peres Distribution

Cassette: released on RCA, '84 by RCA Records. Dist: RCA, Roots, Swift, Wellard, Chris, I & B, Solomon & Peres Distribution

BOLERO.
Album: released on RCA, Mar'80 by RCA Records. Dist: RCA, Roots, Swift, Wellard, Chris, I & B, Solomon & Peres Distribution

Cassette: released on RCA, Mar'80 by RCA Records. Dist: RCA, Roots, Swift, Wellard, Chris, I & B, Solomon & Peres Distribution

DAWN CHORUS.
Tracks: / Cannon of the three stars / Whistle train / Vocalise / Dawn chorus / Adagio of the sky / Pegasus / Cosmic chorale / Vela-x pulsar.
Album: released on RCA, Nov'84 by RCA Records. Dist: RCA, Roots, Swift, Wellard, Chris, I & B, Solomon & Peres Distribution

Cassette: released on RCA, Nov'84 by RCA Records. Dist: RCA, Roots, Swift, Wellard, Chris, I & B, Solomon & Peres Distribution

Compact disc: released on RCA, Nov'84 by RCA Records. Dist: RCA, Roots, Swift, Wellard, Chris, I & B, Solomon & Peres Distribution

FIREBIRD Original television soundtrack.
Tracks: / Firebird suite,The / Prelude a l'apres midi d'un faune / Night on the bare mountain.
Notes: Originally released February 1976.
Album: released on RCA, May'82 by RCA Records. Dist: RCA, Roots, Swift, Wellard, Chris, I & B, Solomon & Peres Distribution

Cassette: released on RCA, May'82 by RCA Records. Dist: RCA, Roots, Swift, Wellard, Chris, I & B, Solomon & Peres Distribution

Compact disc: released on RCA, May'82 by RCA Records. Dist: RCA, Roots, Swift, Wellard, Chris, I & B, Solomon & Peres Distribution

Album: released on Leader, '81 Dist: Jazz Music, Projection

GRAND CANYON SUITE.
Album: released on RCA (Special Imports Service), Jul'84

GROFE / GRAND CANYON SUITE.
Album: released on Red Seal, Jul'82 by RCA Records. Dist: RCA

Cassette: released on Red Seal, Jul'82 by RCA Records. Dist: RCA

PICTURES AT AN EXHIBITION.
Tracks: / Gnome,The / Old castle ,The / Tuileries / Bydlo / Ballet of the chicks in their shells / Samuel Goldenberg and Schmuyle / Limoges / Calacombs / Cum mortuis in lingua mortua / Hut of baba yaba,The / Great gate of kiev,The.
Album: released on RCA, Sep'86 by RCA Records. Dist: RCA, Roots, Swift, Wellard, Chris, I & B, Solomon & Peres Distribution

Cassette: released on RCA, Sep'81 by RCA Records. Dist: RCA, Roots, Swift, Wellard, Chris, I & B, Solomon & Peres Distribution

Compact disc: released on RCA, Sep'81 by RCA Records. Dist: RCA, Roots, Swift, Wellard, Chris, I & B, Solomon & Peres Distribution

PLANETS, THE.
Album: released on RCA, Aug'85 by RCA Records. Dist: RCA, Roots, Swift, Wellard, Chris, I & B, Solomon & Peres Distribution

Cassette: released on RCA, Aug'85 by RCA Records. Dist: RCA, Roots, Swift, Wellard, Chris, I & B, Solomon & Peres Distribution

RAVEL ALBUM.
Tracks: / Daphinest chloesuite no.2 / Pavane pour une infante defunte / Bolero / Ma merie l'oye suite.
Notes: Digital stereo recording.
Compact disc: released on RCA, Dec'84 by RCA Records. Dist: RCA, Roots, Swift, Wellard, Chris, I & B, Solomon & Peres Distribution

SNOWFLAKES ARE DANCING
..
Tracks: / Snowflakes are dancing(children's corner suite no.4) / Reverie / Gardens in the rain (estampes no 3) / Clair de lune(suite Bergamasque no.3) / Arabesque no.1 / Engulfed cathedral, The (preludes book no.8) / Goliwog's cake walk(childrens corner suite no.6) / Footprints in the snow(preludes book no.6).
Notes: Music from Debussy's piano score,electronically arranged by Isao Tomita for moogsynthesizer,tape recorders,mixers and accessories.
Compact disc: released on RCA, May'83 by RCA Records. Dist: RCA, Roots, Swift, Wellard, Chris, I & B, Solomon & Peres Distribution

Album: released on RCA, '84 by RCA Records. Dist: RCA, Roots, Swift, Wellard, Chris, I & B, Solomon & Peres Distribution

Cassette: released on RCA, '84 by RCA Records. Dist: RCA, Roots, Swift, Wellard, Chris, I & B, Solomon & Peres Distribution

SOUND CREATURE.
Album: released on Japanese Import, May'79

SPACE FANTASY.
Album: released on RCA (Germany), '83

SPACE WALK....IMPRESSIONS OF AN ASTRONAUT.
Album: released on RCA, Aug'84 by RCA Records. Dist: RCA, Roots, Swift, Wellard, Chris, I & B, Solomon & Peres Distribution

Cassette: released on RCA, Aug'84 by RCA Records. Dist: RCA, Roots, Swift, Wellard, Chris, I & B, Solomon & Peres Distribution

TOMITA'S GREATEST HITS.
Album: released on RCA, Sep'81 by RCA Records. Dist: RCA, Roots, Swift, Wellard, Chris, I & B, Solomon & Peres Distribution

Cassette: released on RCA, Sep'81 by RCA Records. Dist: RCA, Roots, Swift, Wellard, Chris, I & B, Solomon & Peres Distribution

Tomita,Isao

KOSMOS.
Tracks: / Space fantasy / Unanswered question / Solvejg's song / Hora stacto / Sea named solaris.
Notes: Originally released in 1976.
Album: released on RCA, May'82 by RCA Records. Dist: RCA, Roots, Swift, Wellard, Chris, I & B, Solomon & Peres Distribution

Cassette: released on RCA, May'82 by RCA Records. Dist: RCA, Roots, Swift, Wellard, Chris, I & B, Solomon & Peres Distribution

Compact disc: released on RCA, May'82 by RCA Records. Dist: RCA, Roots, Swift, Wellard, Chris, I & B, Solomon & Peres Distribution

Tomlin, Calton

WEENY TEENY BIT.
Single (12"): released on Original Sounds, Sep'85 Dist: Jetstar Distribution

Tomlinson,Jill

OWL WHO WAS AFRAID OF THE DARK, THE.
Cassette: released on Cover to Cover, Jun'85 by Cover to Cover Cassettes. Dist: Conifer

Tommies

LET'S TAKE YOU BACK.
Single (7"): released on Elecstar, Nov'85 by Elecstar Records. Dist: PRT

Tommy

TOMMY VOL 1 Various artists (Various Artists).
Album: released on Polydor (Italy), May'84

Cassette: released on Polydor (Italy), Mav'84

TOMMY VOL 2 Various artists (Various Artists).
Album: released on Polydor (Italy), May'84

Cassette: released on Polydor (Italy), May'84

Tommy Armstrong...

TOMMY ARMSTRONG OF TYNESIDE Various artists (Various Artists).
Album: released on Topic, '74 Dist: Roots Distribution

Tommy Boy

TOMMY BOY - GREATEST HITS Various artists (Various Artists).
Double Album: released on Tommy Boy, Mar'85 by Warner Brothers. Dist: WEA Distribution

Cassette: released on Tommy Boy, Mar'85 by Warner Brothers. Dist: WEA Distribution

Tommy 'J'

RIDIN' IN MY CAR / HEY YOU.
Single (7"): released on RAK, Jun'81 by RAK. Dist: EMI

SAME TIME SAME CHANNEL / UP ON YOUR WALL.
Single (7"): released on EMI, Mar'83 by EMI Records. Dist: EMI

WHY DON'THEY UNDERSTAND / SAIL AWAY.
Single (7"): released on Regard, Jul'82

Tommy Makem

BEST OF TOMMY MAKEM & THE CLANCY BROTHERS (Tommy Makem & The Clancy Brothers).
Album: released on Emerald, '69 by Emerald Records. Dist: Ross, PRT, Solomon & Peres Distribution

Tomorrow

MY WHITE BICYCLE / SABRE DANCE.
Single (7"): released on Old Gold (Reissue), Oct'83

PARANOID.
Tracks: / Paranoid / Remember me this way.
Notes: Distributed by Esoteric 33 Barberry House,Shannon Road,Kings Norton,Birmingham B38 9BX
Single (7"): released on Tomorrows, May'85

TOMORROW.
Tracks: / My white bicycle / Colonel Brown / Real life permanant dream / Shy boy / Claremount lake / Revolution / Incredible journey of Timothy Chase,The / Auntie Mary's dress shop / Strawberry fields forever / Three jolly little dwarfs / Now your time has come / Hallucinations.

Notes: Licensed from EMI Records Ltd.This compilation (P) 1986 Charly Records Ltd.(C)1986 Charly Records Ltd.
Album: released on Charly, Jun'86 by Charly Records. Dist: Charly, Cadillac

Tomorrow's Edition

YOU TURN ME ON.
Single (7"): released on CBS, Feb'82 by CBS Records. Dist: CBS

Single (12"): released on CBS, Feb'82 by CBS Records. Dist: CBS

Tomorrow We Part

TOMORROW WE PART Various artists (Various Artists).
Album: released on Broadside, Jun'81 by Broadside Records. Dist: Celtic Distributions, H.R. Taylor, Jazz Music, Projection, Jazz Services Unlimited Dist. (JSU)

Cassette: released on Broadside, Jun'81 by Broadside Records. Dist: Celtic Distributions, H.R. Taylor, Jazz Music, Projection, Jazz Services Unlimited Dist. (JSU)

Tompall

AT THE COUNTRY STORE (Tompall & The Glaser Brothers).
Album: released on Starblend Country Store, Aug'86 by Starblend Records. Dist: PRT Distribution

Cassette: released on Starblend Country Store, Aug'86 by Starblend Records. Dist: PRT Distribution

LOVIN' HER WAS EASIER (Tompall & The Glaser Brothers).
Album: released on Elektra, Nov'81 by WEA Records. Dist: WEA

Tom Sawyer

TOM SAWYER Mark Twain (Sherman, Bob).
Cassette: released on Pinnacle, '79 by Pinnacle Records. Dist: Pinnacle

Tom the Voice

I WAS A YOUNG MAN.
Single (7"): released on Northwest, Nov'85 by Rough Trade Records. Dist: Cartel Distribution

Tom Thumb

TOM THUMB (Hampshire, Susan).
Cassette: released on Storytime Cassettes, Aug'83

TOM THUMB Various artists (Various Artists).
Cassette: released on Pickwick (Ladybird), Feb'83

Tom Tom Club

CLOSE TO THE BONE.
Album: released on Island, Aug'83 by Island Records. Dist: Polygram

Cassette: released on Island, Aug'83 by Island Records. Dist: Polygram

LORELEI / ON AND ON.
Single (7"): released on Island, Jun'82 by Island Records. Dist: Polygram

Single (12"): released on Island, Jun'82 by Island Records. Dist: Polygram

TOM TOM CLUB (WORDY RAPPINGHOOD).
Tracks: / Wordy rappinghood / Genius of love / Tom Tom theme / L'Elephant / As above so below / Loreli / On On On On / Booming and zooming.
Album: released on Island, Oct'86 by Island Records. Dist: Polygram

Cassette: released on Island, Oct'86 by Island Records. Dist: Polygram

Compact disc: released on Island, May'87 by Island Records. Dist: Polygram

Toned F

TONE DEAF / JEALOUS.
Single (7"): released on Extra Bit, Sep'81 Dist: Rough Trade

Tones On Tail

BURNING SKIES / OK THIS IS THE POPS.
Single (7"): released on Situation 2, May'83 Dist: Cartel, Pinnacle

BURNING SKIES / OK THIS IS THE POPS / WHEN YOU'RE SMILING.
Single (12"): released on Situation 2, May'83 Dist: Cartel, Pinnacle

CHRISTIAN SAYS.
Single (7"): released on Beggars Banquet, Nov'84 by Beggars Banquet Records. Dist: WEA

Single (12"): released on Beggars Banquet, Nov'84 by Beggars Banquet Records. Dist: WEA

LIONS.
Single (7"): released on Beggars Banquet, May'84 by Beggars Banquet Records. Dist: WEA

Single (12"): released on Beggars Banquet, May'84 by Beggars Banquet Records. Dist: WEA

PERFORMANCE.
Single (7"): released on Beggars Banquet, Mar'84 by Beggars Banquet Records. Dist: WEA

Single (12"): released on Beggars Banquet, Mar'84 by Beggars Banquet Records. Dist: WEA

POP.
Album: released on Beggars Banquet, Mar'84 by Beggars Banquet Records. Dist: WEA

Cassette: released on Beggars Banquet, Mar'84 by Beggars Banquet Records. Dist: WEA

TONES ON TAIL.
Album: released on Situation 2, Jan'85 Dist: Cartel, Pinnacle

Cassette: released on Situation 2, Jan'85 Dist: Cartel, Pinnacle

Tonga

FRIENDLY ISLANDS, THE (Tonga: Music From).
Album: released on Tangent, Apr'81 by Tangent Records. Dist: Lugtons Distributors, Taylors, JSU Distribution, Projection Distribution

Cassette: released on Tangent, Jan'82 by Tangent Records. Dist: Lugtons Distributors, Taylors, JSU Distribution, Projection Distribution

Tongue In Cheek

DON'T STOP THE LOVE.
Tracks: / Don't stop the love / Don't stop the love (version).
Single (12"): released on Criminal, Jul'87 by Criminal Records. Dist: Jetstar

Tongue'n'Cheek

I SHOULD CO-CO (NUTS TO YOU).
Single (7"): released on Towerbell, Sep'81

Tong,Winston

THEORETICAL CHINA.
Single (12"): released on Le Disques Du Crepuscule, Dec'84

THEORETICALLY CHINESE.
Album: released on Operation Afterglow Nov'85 Dist: Pinnacle

Compact disc: released on Himalaya, May'8 by Himalaya Records. Dist: Rough Trade, Cartel

Tonics

ALL SUMMER LONG / STANDBACK.
Single (7"): released on Magnet, Aug'81 b Magnet Records. Dist: BMG

Tonik, Terry

JUST A LITTLE MOD / SMASHE AND.....
Single (7"): released on Posh, Feb'80 by Pos Records. Dist: Pinnacle

Tonix

STRANGERS / TALK TO ME.
Single (7"): released on 109 Product, Aug'8

Tonnaugwenn

TONNAUGWENN Various artists (Vario Artists).

Album:

Tony J. & Alton Ellis
TELEPHONE LINE.
Single (12"): released on Cypron, Aug'83

Tony Lee Trio
BRITISH ARTIST JAZZ VOLUME 2 also see Terry Smith (Tony Lee Trio & Terry Smith).
Album: released on Lee Lambert, May'77 by Lee Lambert Records. Dist: Cadillac

Tony & Marla
ROSES ARE RED / SONG OF LOVE.
Single (7"): released on Hollywood, Feb'84 by Hollywood Records. Dist: Pinnacle

Tony The Turtle
TONY THE TURTLE Various artists (Various Artists).
Cassette: released on Anvil, Jan'81 Dist: Anvil

Too good...
TOO GOOD TO BE FORGOTTEN MORE SOUL CLASSICS Various artists (Various Artists).
Tracks: / Whispers (getting louder) / Oh no not my baby / Have you seen her / There was a time / I just don't know what to do with myself / Love of my man, The / Washed ashore / Hook & sling in the naked city (no pity) / To good to be forgotten / Love makes a woman / I'm gonna miss you / Tell him I'm not home / Long after tonight is all over / With this ring / Midsummer night in Harlem.
Album: released on Charly(R&B), Jul'87 by Charly Records. Dist: Charly, Cadillac

Cassette: released on Charly(R&B), Jul'87 by Charly Records. Dist: Charly, Cadillac

Too Hot To Handle
TOO HOT TO HANDLE Capitol country vol.1 (Various Artists).
Tracks: / I believe in lovin' em / Merle's boogie woogie / Butane blues / Automatic mama / Too hot to handle / Okee fi nokee / If you ain't livin'(you ain't livin) / Playin' dominoes & boootin' dice / Smokey mountain boogie / Lost john boogie / I get the blues / Double up & catch / My Tennessee talkin' doll / Done gone crazy / I'm a poor boy / Humpty dumpty boogie.
Album: released on Charly, Jan'87 by Charly Records. Dist: Charly, Cadillac

TOO HOT TOO HANDLE(CAPITAL COUNTRY VOL.1) Various artists (Various artists).
Notes: Artists:Merle Travis,Gene Quinn,Leon Chappel,Lee Bond,Faron Young,Ramblin'Jimmie Dolan,Tennessee Ernie Ford,Hank Thompson.
Album: released on Charly, Jul'86 by Charly Records. Dist: Charly, Cadillac

Tools
GOTTA MAKE SOME MONEY SOMEHOW.
Single (7"): released on Olly, Jul'81 by Olly Records. Dist: Fast Distribution

Tools you can trust
AGAIN AGAIN AGAIN.
Album: released on Red Energy Dynamo, Apr'86 by Red Energy Dynamo Records. Dist: Rhino, Cartel

AT A NEW SEAM.
Single (7"): released on Red Energy Dynamo, Apr'84 by Red Energy Dynamo Records. Dist: Red Rhino, Cartel

JESSY BODY THRUST.
Single (7"): released on Red Energy Dynamo, Apr'84 by Red Energy Dynamo Records. Dist: Red Rhino, Cartel

SAY IT LOW.
Tracks: / Say it Low.
Single (7"): released on Red Energy Dynamo, Apr'86 by Red Energy Dynamo Records. Dist: Red Rhino, Cartel

SHARPEN THE TOOLS.
Boxed set: released on Red Energy Dynamo, Apr'85 by Red Energy Dynamo Records. Dist: Red Rhino, Cartel

WORKING AND SHOPPING.
Single (7"): released on Red Energy Dynamo, Apr'83 by Red Energy Dynamo Records. Dist: Red Rhino, Cartel

MORE PROOF.
Album: released on Red Energy Dynamo, Apr'85 by Red Energy Dynamo Records. Dist: Red Rhino, Cartel

Tootsie Roll
PERFECT LOVERS.
Single (7"): released on Creole, May'82 by Creole Records. Dist: Rhino, PRT

Toots & The Maytals
BAM BAM.
Single (7"): released on Island, Aug'82 by Island Records. Dist: Polygram

BEAUTIFUL WOMAN.
Single (12"): released on Island, Sep'81 by Island Records. Dist: Polygram

Single (7"): released on Island, Sep'81 by Island Records. Dist: Polygram

BEST OF TOOTS & THE MAYTALS.
Album: released on Trojan, Jul'84 by Trojan Records. Dist: PRT, Jetstar

Cassette: released on Trojan, Jul'84 by Trojan Records. Dist: PRT, Jetstar

FROM THE ROOTS.
Album: released on Trojan, '83 by Trojan Records. Dist: PRT, Jetstar

FUNKY KINGSTON.
Album: released on Trojan, '83 by Trojan Records. Dist: PRT, Jetstar

JUST LIKE THAT.
Album: released on Island, Oct'79 by Island Records. Dist: Polygram

Cassette: released on Island, Oct'79 by Island Records. Dist: Polygram

LIVE AT REGGAE SUNSPLASH.
Album: released on Vista Sounds, Feb'84 by Vista Sounds Records. Dist: Jetstar

PASS THE PIPE.
Album: released on Island, Apr'79 by Island Records. Dist: Polygram

Cassette: released on Island, Apr'79 by Island Records. Dist: Polygram

REGGAE GOT SOUL.
Album: released on Island, Mar'76 by Island Records. Dist: Polygram

Cassette: released on Island, Mar'76 by Island Records. Dist: Polygram

REGGAE GREATS.
Album: released on Island, May'85 by Island Records. Dist: Polygram

Cassette: released on Island, May'85 by Island Records. Dist: Polygram

STICK IT UP MISTER.
Extended-play record: released on Island, Jul'80 by Island Records. Dist: Polygram

Top 25 From....
TOP 25 FROM YOUR HUNDRED BEST TUNES Various Artists (Various Artists).
Double Album: released on Decca, Nov'75 by Decca Records. Dist: Polygram

Cassette: released on Decca, Nov'75 by Decca Records. Dist: Polygram

Top Country Sound
IN CONCERT.
Album: released on Folk Heritage, Jul'82 by Folk Heritage Records. Dist: Roots, Wynd-Up Distribution, Jazz Music, Folk Heritage

IN THE MIDDLE OF NOWHERE.
Album: released on Folk Heritage, Jul'82 by Folk Heritage Records. Dist: Roots, Wynd-Up Distribution, Jazz Music, Folk Heritage

RIDIN EASY.
Album: released on Folk Heritage, Jul'82 by Folk Heritage Records. Dist: Roots, Wynd-Up Distribution, Jazz Music, Folk Heritage

Cassette: released on Folk Heritage, Jul'82 by Folk Heritage Records. Dist: Roots, Wynd-Up Distribution, Jazz Music, Folk Heritage

Top Gear
DREAM MACHINE.
Single (7"): released on EMI, Jul'81 by EMI Records. Dist: EMI

Top Gun
TOP GUN Original soundtrack (Various Artists).
Tracks: / Danger zone / Mighty Wings / Playing with the boys / Lead Me On / Take my breath away(Love theme from Top Gun / Hot summer nights / Heaven in your eyes / Heaven in your eyes / through the fire / Destination Unknown / Top Gun anthem.
Album: released on CBS, Sep'86 by CBS Records. Dist: CBS

Cassette: released on CBS, Sep'86 by CBS Records. Dist: CBS

TOP GUN Original Soundtrack (Various Artists).
Compact disc: released on CBS, '86 by CBS

Records. Dist: CBS

Top Of The Bill
TOP OF THE BILL Various Artists (Various Artists).
Album: released on Rhapsody, '74 by President Records. Dist: Taylors, Swift, Jazz Music, Wellard, Chris

Top Of The Morning
TOP OF THE MORNING Various Artists (Various Artists).
Album: released on Harp(Ireland), May'80 by Pickwick Records. Dist: Taylors

Cassette: released on Harp(Ireland), May'80 by Pickwick Records. Dist: Taylors

Top Of The Poppers
BEST OF TOP THE POPS,THE.
Album: released on Hallmark, Dec'84 by Pickwick Records. Dist: Pickwick Distribution, PRT, Taylors

Cassette: released on Hallmark, Dec'84 by Pickwick Records. Dist: Pickwick Distribution, PRT, Taylors

Topol
FIDDLER ON THE ROOF.
Album: released on Embassy, '70 by CBS Records. Dist: CBS

IF I WERE A RICH MAN.
Single (7"): released on CBS, Jun'83 by CBS Records. Dist: CBS

TOPOL'S ISRAEL.
Album: released on BBC, Oct'84 by BBC Records & Tapes. Dist: EMI, PRT

Cassette: released on BBC, Oct'84 by BBC Records & Tapes. Dist: EMI, PRT.

Topping,Frank
CALVARY.
Single (7"): released on Multi Media Tapes, Dec'82 by Multi Media Tapes Records. Dist: Stage One Distribution, Conifer Distribution, H.R. Taylor Distribution, Pinnacle

SLEEP WELL MY SON.
Single (7"): released on President, Nov'76 by President Records. Dist: Taylors, Spartan

Topping,Simon
PROSPECT PARK.
Single (7"): released on Factory Benelux, Aug'85 by Rough Trade Records. Dist: Cartel

Top Secret
ANOTHER CRAZY DAY.
Album: released on Cheapskate, Oct'81 by Cheapskate Records. Dist: RCA

Cassette: released on Cheapskate, Oct'81 by Cheapskate Records. Dist: RCA

TOP SECRET Original Soundtrack (Various Artists).
Album: released on That's Entertainment, Dec'84 by That's Entertainment Records. Dist: Pinnacle, PRT

Top Ten Groups...
TOP TEN GROUPS OF THE SEVENTIES (Various Artists).
Album: released on Pickwick, Feb'86 by Pickwick Records. Dist: Pickwick Distribution, Prism Leisure Distribution, Lugtons

Cassette: released on Pickwick, Feb'86 by Pickwick Records. Dist: Pickwick Distribution, Prism Leisure Distribution

Top Ten Hymns
TOP TEN HYMNS FROM SONGS OF PRAISE Various Artists (Various Artists).
Album: released on BBC, Feb'85 by BBC Records & Tapes. Dist: EMI, PRT.

Cassette: released on BBC, Feb'85 by BBC Records & Tapes. Dist: EMI, PRT.

Top Twelve...
TOP TWELVE BIRD SONGS Various Artists (Various Artists).
Album: released on BBC, Mar'84 by BBC Records & Tapes. Dist: EMI, PRT.

Cassette: released on BBC, Mar'84 by BBC Records & Tapes. Dist: EMI, PRT.

TOP TWELVE DISCO SINGLES (Various Artists).
Album: released on KMK, Dec'85 Dist: Revolver, Jetstar

Toquinho
TOQUINHO.
Album: released on Sign (France), Apr'86 Dist: Greyhound

Torcello,John
STATE OF THE ART ACCORDION.
Album: released on ARC (Accordion Records), '84 Dist: Accordion Record Club

Torch
ELECTIKISS.
Album: released on Music For Nations, Nov'84 by Sword Records. Dist: Pinnacle

TORCH.
Album: released on Road Runner, Jan'85

Torch Song
CAN'T FIND MY WAY HOME.
Tracks: / Can't find my way home / Spear* / Living out of time.
Single (7"):

Single (12"):

ODE TO BILLY JOE.
Single (7"): released on IRS, Jan'85 Dist: Polygram

Single (12"): released on IRS, Jan'85 Dist: Polygram

WHITE NIGHT.
Tracks: / White Night / Mothdub / Microdot daylight.
Single (12"):

WISH THING.
Album: released on IRS, Jul'84 Dist: Polygram

Cassette: released on IRS, Jul'84 Dist: Polygram

Torch,Sydney
AT THE CINEMA ORGAN (The Regal cinema, Marble Arch).
Album: released on World Records, Jan'79 Dist: Polygram

Cassette: released on World Records, Jan'79 Dist: Polygram

SIDNEY TORCH AT THE THEATRE ORGAN(1932-39).
Album: released on Doris, Apr'79 by Amberlee. Dist: Lugtons

Torero Band
TIJUANA CHRISTMAS.
Album: released on Music For Pleasure, Sep'84

Cassette: released on Music For Pleasure, Sep'84

TIJUANA CHRISTMAS.
Album: released on Music For Pleasure (Holland), Sep'84 by EMI Records. Dist: EMI

Cassette: released on music For Pleasure (Holland), Sep'84 by EMI Records. Dist: EMI

Torme
DIE PRETTY,DIE YOUNG.
Notes: Led by former Gillan guitarist Bernie Torme.
Album: released on Heavy Metal, Jun'87 by FM-Revolver Records. Dist: EMI

OFFICIAL LIVE BOOTLEG.
Album: released on Onsala, Jul'87 Dist: Making Waves, Pinnacle

START.
Tracks: / Start / T.V.O.D. / Kerrap / Love, Guns & Money.
Single (7"): released on Zebra, Apr'86 by Cherry Red Records. Dist: Pinnacle

Single (12"): released on Zebra, Apr'86 by Cherry Red Records. Dist: Pinnacle

Torme, Bernie
ALL AROUND THE WORLD.
Album: released on Zebra, Sep'85 by Cherry Red Records. Dist: Pinnacle

ALL AROUND THE WORLD.
Single (7"): released on Zebra, Aug'85 by Cherry Red Records. Dist: Pinnacle

ALL DAY AND ALL OF THE NIGHT.
Single (7"): released on Fresh, Apr'81 Dist: Jetstar

BACK TO BABYLON.
Album: released on Zebra, Sep'85 by Cherry Red Records. Dist: Pinnacle

BACK WITH THE BOYS.

Tracks: / Come Tomorrow / My baby loves a vampire / No Easy Way / Try and stop me* / Don't give up your day Job * / Turn out the lights / Wild West / Whats next* / Lies* / Night Lights / All day and all of the night / Back with the boys*.
Notes: Bar code: 5 013428 140109 Side 1: Ttracks 1,4,5 licensed by Chippa wood Ltd. Tracks 2,3,6 Licensed by Zebra Records, a division of Cherry Red Records. Side 2: Track 1 Licensed by Zebra records, a division of Cherry Red records. Tracks 2,3,4,5,6 Licensed by chippawood Ltd. Design: Shoot that Tiger. (C) Castle communications Ltd, Unit 7, 271 Merton Rd, London, SW18 5JS.

Album: released on Raw Power, Apr'86 Dist: Pinnacle

Cassette: released on Raw Power, Apr'86 Dist: Pinnacle

ELECTRIC GYPSIES.
Album: released on Zebra, Oct'83 by Cherry Red Records. Dist: Pinnacle

Cassette: released on Zebra, Oct'83 by Cherry Red Records. Dist: Pinnacle

I CAN'T CONTROL MYSELF.
Single (7"): released on Zebra, Oct'83 by Cherry Red Records. Dist: Pinnacle

LIVE.
Album: released on Zebra, '84 by Cherry Red Records. Dist: Pinnacle

MY BABY LOVES A VAMPIRE.
Single (7"): released on Zebra, Jan'84 by Cherry Red Records. Dist: Pinnacle

Single (12"): released on Zebra, Jan'84 by Cherry Red Records. Dist: Pinnacle

OFFICIAL BOOTLEG.
Tracks: / Frontline / Turn out the lights / Hardcore / Star / Burning bridges / T.V.O.D. / My baby loves a vampire / New Orleans / Love, guns and money / All around the world / Mystery train / Frontline 2.
Notes: Live album recorded in London now on compact disc and including three bonus tracks.
Compact disc: released on The CD Label, Jul'87

TURN OUT THE LIGHTS.
Album: released on Kamaflage, Jun'82 by DJM Records. Dist: CBS, Polygram

Cassette: released on Kamaflage, Jun'82 by DJM Records. Dist: CBS, Polygram

Torme, Mel

AN EVENING AT CHARLE'S (Torme, Mel & George Shearing).
Album: released on Concord Jazz(USA), Sep'84 by Concord Jazz Records (USA). Dist: IMS, Polygram

Cassette: released on Concord Jazz(USA), Sep'84 by Concord Jazz Records (USA). Dist: IMS, Polygram

BACK IN TOWN (Torme, Mel & The Mel-Tones).
Album: released on Verve (France), Feb'84

DUKE ELLINGTON & COUNT BASIE SONGBOOK, THE.
Tracks: / I'm gonna go fishin / Don't get around much anymore / I like the Sunrise / Take the "A" train / Reminiscin' in tempo / Outskirts of town, the / Just a sittin' and a rockin' / Down for double / I'm gonna move to the outskirts of town / Blue and sentimental / Oh what a night for love / Sent for you yesterday (and here you come today) / In the evening(When the sun goes down).
Album: released on Verve, Aug'85 by Phonogram Records. Dist: Polygram

Cassette: released on Verve, Aug'85 by Phonogram Records. Dist: Polygram

Compact disc: released on Verve, Aug'85 by Phonogram Records. Dist: Polygram

GREAT SINGERS OF THE FIFTIES.
Album: released on Jazz Greats (US), Jan'79

GREAT SONG STYLISTS VOLUME 2,THE.
Album: released on Apex, Jun'83 Dist: Jazz Music, Swift

I CAN'T GIVE YOU ANYTHING BUT LOVE.
Album: released on Musicraft(Import), Aug'83

I DIG DUKE & COUNT.
Album: released on Verve (USA), Dec'79 by Polydor. Dist: Polygram

IT'S A BLUE WORLD.
Album: released on Affinity, May'85 by Charly Records. Dist: Charly, Cadillac

LIVE AT THE CRESCENDO.
Double Album: released on Affinity, Oct'82 by Charly Records. Dist: Charly, Cadillac

LIVE AT THE CRESCENDO.
Tracks: / Love is just a bug / Nobody's heart / It's only a paper moon / What is this thing called love / I got plenty o'nuttin / Taking a chance / One for my baby / Nightingale sang in Berkeley Square / Just one of those things / Autumn leaves / Girl next door / Lover come back to me / I'm beginning to see the light / Looking at you / Tender trap / Tenderly / I wish I was in love again / It's d'lovely / It's allright with me / Home by the sea / Manhattan.
Compact disc: released on Affinity, Jan'87 by Charly Records. Dist: Charly, Cadillac

Compact disc: released on Charly, Jan'87 by Charly Records. Dist: Charly, Cadillac

LULU'S BACK IN TOWN (Torme Mel & the Marty Paich Dek-Tette).
Tracks: / Lulu's back in town / When the sun Comes out / I love to watch the moonlight / Fascinatin' Rhythm / Blues, the / Carioca, the / Lady is a tramp, the / I like to recognise a tune / Keeping myself for you / Lullaby of birdland / When april comes again / sing for your supper.
Compact disc: released on Charly, Mar'86 by Charly Records. Dist: Charly, Cadillac

LULU'S BACK IN TOWN (Torme Mel & the Marty Paich Dek-Tette).
Album: released on Affinity, May'82 by Charly Records. Dist: Charly, Cadillac

MEL TORME.
Cassette: released on Audio Fidelity, Oct'84 Dist: PRT

MEL TORME (Torme,Mel & Rob McConnell and The Boss Brass).
Compact disc: released on Concord Jazz(USA), Dec'86 by Concord Jazz Records (USA). Dist: IMS, Polygram

MEL TORME.
Album: released on Deja Vu, Nov'85 by Deja Vu Records. Dist: Counterpoint Distribution, Record Services Distribution (Ireland)

Album: released on Deja Vu, Nov'85 by Deja Vu Records. Dist: Counterpoint Distribution, Record Services Distribution (Ireland)

MEL TORME AND.. (Torme,Mel & Rob McConnell and The Boss Brass).
Tracks: / Just friends / September song / Don'cha go 'way mad / House is not a home,A / Song is you,The / Cow cow boogie / Handful of stars,A / Stars fell on Alabama / Duke Ellington medley:It don't mean a thing / Do nothing till you hear from me / Mood indigo / Take the A train / Sophisticated lady / Satin doll.
Notes: Mel Torme-vocals/Rob McConnell-trombone/The Boss Brass
Compact disc: released on Concord Jazz(USA), Jan'87 by Concord Jazz Records (USA). Dist: IMS, Polygram

MEL TORME & FRIENDS REC. LIVE AT MARTY'S NEW YORK CITY (Torme',Mel & Friends).
Album: released on Finesse, Apr'84 by PRT Records. Dist: PRT

Cassette: released on Finesse, Apr'84 by PRT Records. Dist: PRT

MEL TORME/ROB MCCONNELL & BOSS BRASS (Torme,Mel & Rob McConnell and The Boss Brass).
Album: released on Concord Jazz(USA), Oct'86 by Concord Jazz Records (USA). Dist: IMS, Polygram

Cassette: released on Concord Jazz(USA), Oct'86 by Concord Jazz Records (USA). Dist: IMS, Polygram

MEL TORME SINGS.
Album: released on Bulldog Records, Jul'82

Album: released on Astan, Nov'84 by Astan Records. Dist: Counterpoint

Cassette: released on Astan, Nov'84 by Astan Records. Dist: Counterpoint

MUSICAL SOUNDS ARE THE BEST SONGS.
Album: released on Jasmine, Feb'83 by Jasmine Records. Dist: Counterpoint, Lugtons, Taylor, H.R., Wellard, Chris, Swift, Cadillac

PRIME TIME.
Album: released on Jazz Greats (US), Jan'79

ROUND MIDNIGHT.
Album: released on Stash, Jun'86 Dist: Swift Distribution, Jazz Music Distribution, Jazz Horizons Distribution, Celtic Music Distribution, Cadillac, JSU Distribution, Zodiac Distribution

SINGS FRED ASTAIRE.
Compact disc: released on Charly, Aug'87 by Charly Records. Dist: Charly, Cadillac

SINGS HIS CALIFORNIA SUITE (Torme',Mel Orchestra).
Album: released on Discovery (USA), Nov'84 by Discovery Records (USA). Dist: Swift, Flexitron-Audio, Jazz Music

SWING SCHUBERT ALLEY (Torme',Mel & Marty Paich).
Album: released on Verve (USA), Sep'81 by Polydor. Dist: Polygram

SWINGS SCHUBERT ALLEY.
Tracks: / Too close for comfort / Once in love with Amy / Sleepin' Bee / On the street where you live / just in time / Whatever Lola wants / Surrey with the fringe on top / Old devil moon / too darn hot / Lonely town.
Compact disc: released on Verve, Oct'84 by Phonogram Records. Dist: Polygram

THERE'S NO BUSINESS LIKE SHOW BUSINESS (Torme,Mel & His Mel-Tones).
Album: released on Musicraft(Trend USA), Oct'82

TORME.
Album: released on Bulldog, Aug'77 by Bulldog Records. Dist: President Distribution, Spartan, Swift, Taylor, H.R.

Album: released on Rhapsody, Aug'80 by President Records. Dist: Taylors, Swift, Jazz Music, Wellard, Chris

Album: released on Verve (USA), Oct'84 by Polydor. Dist: Polygram

Album: released on Verve (USA), Oct'84 by Polydor. Dist: Polygram

TORME'.
Tracks: / All in love is fair / First time I ever saw your face / New York state of mind / Stars / Send in the clowns / Ordinairy fool / When the world was young / Yesterday when I was young / Bye bye blackbird.
Compact disc: released on Rhapsody, Jan'87 by President Records. Dist: Taylors, Swift, Jazz Music, Wellard, Chris

TORME SINGS ASTAIRE (Torme,Mel & The Marty Paich).
Album: released on Affinity, Nov'83 by Charly Records. Dist: Charly, Cadillac

TORME SINGS ASTAIRE (Torme Mel & the Marty Paich Dek-Tette).
Tracks: / Nice work if you can get it / Somethings gotta give / Foggy day, A / Fine romance, A / Let's call the whole thing off / Top hat, white tie and tails / Way you look tonight, The / Piccolino, The / They can't take that away from me / Cheek to cheek / Let's face the music and dance / They all laughed.
Compact disc: released on Charly, Aug'87 by Charly Records. Dist: Charly, Cadillac

Torment

MYSTERY MEN EP, THE.
Tracks: / Mystery man / Rock strong / Conscription plan / Red red death.
Notes: Self-4/36 Dabbs Hill Lane, Northolt, Middx. - 01 422 3462
Single (12"): released on Nervous, Mar'87 by Nervous Records. Dist: Nervous, Rough Trade

PSYCLOPS CARNIVAL.
Album: released on Nervous, Sep'86 by Nervous Records. Dist: Nervous, Rough Trade

Tormentors

GODDESS OF LOVE.
Album: released on Mausoleum, Sep'84 by Mausoleum Records. Dist: Pinnacle

HANGING AROUND.
Album: released on Eva-Lolita, Apr'86 Dist: Pinnacle

Tornados

REMEMBERING.
Album: released on Decca, Sep'76 by Decca Records. Dist: Polygram

Cassette: released on Decca, Sep'76 by Decca Records. Dist: Polygram

TELSTAR.
Single (7"): released on Decca, Mar'82 by Decca Records. Dist: Polygram

Single (7"): released on Old Gold, Oct'83 by Old Gold Records. Dist: Lightning, Jazz Music, Spartan, Counterpoint

Torn,David

BEST LAID PLANS.
Tracks: / Before the bitter wind / Best Laid plans / Hum of its parts, the / removable toungue / In the fifth direction / Two face flash / Angle of incidents.
Notes: Best Laid Plans is the first solo effort of David torn, member of the Jan Garbarek group and the everyman band. Guitarist Torn creates modern sound scapes with his innovative technique. He explores the tonal possibilities of his instrument and develops his very own phrasing. Together with Drummer Geoffrey Gordon he offers music that is inspired by various contemporary styles and displays the mere joy of p l a y i n g . personnel: David Tor - guitars/ Geoffrey Gordon - Percussion.
Compact disc: released on ECM, Mar'85 by ECM Records. Dist: IMS, Polygram, Virgin through EMI

BEST LAID PLANS.
Album: released on ECM (Germany), Mar'85 by ECM Records. Dist: IMS, Polygram, Virgin through EMI

Compact disc: released on ECM (Germany Mar'85 by ECM Records. Dist: IMS, Polygram Virgin through EMI

CLOUD ABOUT MERCURY.
Tracks: / Suyafhu skin..snapping the hollo reed / Mercury grid, the / 3 minutes of pure en tertainment / Previous man / Network of spark
Notes: David Torn has established himself a one of the most inventive & respected electr guitarists."Cloud About Mercury"will furthe conform this. Teamed with Tor Levin,Bill Bruford (both ex-King Crimson) Mark Isham.Together they present a capturir statement on the borders of avante garde ro & contempory jazz Personnel: David Torn-elec.& accoustic gu tars/Mark Isham-trumpet,piccolo trumpet,fl gelhorn,synthesizer/ Tony levin-Chapma Stick,synthesizer bass/bill Bruford-Simmor drums,synthesizer-drums,percussion.
Compact disc: released on ECM (Germany Mar'87 by ECM Records. Dist: IMS, Polygrar Virgin through EMI

Album: released on ECM (Germany), Feb'8 by ECM Records. Dist: IMS, Polygram, Virg through EMI

Torner,Gosta

LIVING LEGEND.
Album: released on Nostalgia, '82 Dist: Ja Music, Counterpoint

Toronto

GIRLS NIGHT OUT.
Album: released on MCA, Mar'84 by MCA Re ords. Dist: CBS

Cassette: released on MCA, Mar'84 by M(Records. Dist: CBS

LOOKIN' FOR TROUBLE.
Album: released on A&M, Oct'80 by A&M Re ords. Dist: Polygram

Torrance,Bill

BILL TORRANCE SINGS.
Album: released on Klub, Dec'82

CALEDONIA.
Single (7"): released on Klub, Jun'80

MAGGIE.
Single (7"): released on Klub, Mar'83

REFLECTION.
Album: released on Klub, Apr'84

Cassette: released on Klub, Apr'84

Torres,Jaime

CHARANGO.
Tracks: / Chimba chica / La diablada / Nau tiempos jinan tatay / Mambo de machahua Ch'isi / Caminos en la puna / La perigrinack El dia que me quieras / Chacarera del tiem Zamba de la candeleria / Sirvinaco / Milonga mis amores.
Notes: The charango is a guitar-like instrum favoured by the folk musicians of B via,Peru,Chile and North Argentir It is played here in a contemporary m ner,much like the group Incantation. Ot featured instruments include the pan-pipes
Compact disc: released on Messidor (C many), Jan'87 Dist: IMS Distribution, Polyg

MUSIC FROM THE INCAS.
Album: released on Philips Import, Apr'83

Tortilla Flats

GIANT SKY.
Tracks: / Giant Sky / Waiting for the rain to / Shall ever be.
Single (12"): released on Bam Caruso, Aug by Bam Caruso Records. Dist: Rough Tra Revolver, Cartel

Torvill & Dean

BOLERO.
Single (7"): released on Safari, Dec'83 by fari Records. Dist: Pinnacle

Single (12"): released on Safari, Dec'83 by fari Records. Dist: Pinnacle

Toshiko/Mariano, the

TOSHIKO MARIANO QUARTET, TH
Album: released on Candid, May'86 Counterpoint, Cadillac

Tosh, Peter

BUSH DOCTOR.
Tracks: / (You Gotta' walk)Don't look ba Pick myself up / I'm the toughest / Soon co Moses the prophet / Bush doctor / Stand f dem Ha Fe Get A Beatin' / Creation.
Notes: A striking sleeve on this brilliant alb for the Reggae man himself-Peter\Tosh duced by the 'Glimmer twins' (Jagger and chard). Mick Jagger is Co Vocalist on the r track ('you've gotta' walk')Don't look b which reached No.43 in the charts in 1

backing players include the great Sly and Robbie and of course Keith Richard.
Album: released on Fame, Nov'85 by Music
for Pleasure Records. Dist: EMI

Cassette: released on Fame, Nov'85 by Music
for Pleasure Records. Dist: EMI
___
N MY SONG.
racks: / In my song / Come together.
ngle (7"): released on Parlophone, Jul'87 by
MI Records. Dist: EMI

ngle (12"): released on Parlophone, Jul'87 by
MI Records. Dist: EMI
___
OHNNY B. GOODE.
ngle 10": released on Radic, Mar'83 by
dic. Dist: EMI
___
IVE.
deo-cassette (VHS): released on PMI,
un'86 by PMI Records. Dist: EMI

deo-cassette [Betamax]: released on PMI,
un'86 by PMI Records. Dist: EMI
___
MAMA AFRICA.
bum: released on Radic, Apr'83 by Radic.
st: EMI

assette: released on Radic, Apr'83 by Radic.
st: EMI
___
MAMA AFRICA (SINGLE).
ngle (7"): released on Radic, Sep'83 by
dic. Dist: EMI

ngle 10": released on Radic, Sep'83 by
dic. Dist: EMI
___
O NUCLEAR WAR.
racks: / No nuclear war / Nah Goa Jail / Fight
arlod / Vampire / In my song / Lesson in my
y / Testify / Come together.
bum: released on Parlophone, Mar'87 by
MI Records. Dist: EMI

assette: released on Parlophone, Sep'87 by
MI Records. Dist: EMI. Estim retail price in
ep'87 was £5.99.

mpact disc: released on Parlophone, Mar
'87 by EMI Records. Dist: EMI
___
OTHING BUT LOVE.
ngle (7"): released on Rolling Stones, Jun'81
st: EMI, WEA Distribution

ngle (12"): released on Rolling Stones,
n'81 Dist: EMI, WEA Distribution
___
ANTED DREAD & ALIVE.
bum: released on Rolling Stones, Jun'81
st: EMI, WEA Distribution Deleted '87.

assette: released on Rolling Stones, Jun'81
st: EMI, WEA Distribution
___
oss & The Detachables
DICATED TO JOHN HUMPHRIES
R.
racks: / Stephen Rodgers Rock / Simon Mil-
s Bum / Wotcha Sinius / Oh f*** off Dodge /
nes is me mate / Julian don't give a sh** /
dge & the Deutchmarks.
bum: released on Lodge Records, Mar'84
___
otal Chaos
CTORY MAN.
ngle (7"): released on Volume, Sep'82 by
ume Records. Dist: Pinnacle

LDS AND FOREVER.
ngle (12"): released on Volume, Sep'83 by
ume Records. Dist: Pinnacle

ERE ARE NO RUSSIANS IN AF-
ANISTAN.
ngle (7"): released on Volume, Jul'83 by Vol-
e Records. Dist: Pinnacle
___
otal Contrast
WITH YOU TONIGHT.
ngle (7"): released on Total Contrast, Jan'84
otal Contrast Records. Dist: PRT

ngle (12"): released on Total Contrast,
84 by Total Contrast Records. Dist: PRT

ngle (12"): released on Total Contrast, Oct'85
otal Contrast Records. Dist: PRT

ngle (12"): released on Total Contrast,
35 by Total Contrast Records. Dist: PRT

Y.
racks: / Jody / Jody (inst).
le (7"): released on London, Jul'87 by Lon-
Records. Dist: Polygram

le (12"): released on London, Jul'87 by
on Records. Dist: Polygram

Y.
le (7"): released on London, Aug'87 by

le (12"): released on London, Aug'87 by

London Records. Dist: Polygram
___
NEXT TIME I'LL KNOW BETTER.
Single (12"): released on Total Contrast,
Nov'84 by Total Contrast Records. Dist: PRT
___
RIVER, THE.
Tracks: / River, the / River, the(Instrumental) /
Takes a Little time(US Remix)*.
Single (7"): released on London, Feb'86 by
London Records. Dist: Polygram

Single (12"): released on London, Feb'86 by
London Records. Dist: Polygram
___
TAKES A LITTLE TIME.
Single (7"): released on London, Jul'85 by Lon-
don Records. Dist: Polygram

Single (12"): released on London, Jul'85 by
London Records. Dist: Polygram
___
TOTAL CONTRAST.
Tracks: / Hit and Run / River, the / Where is
love / How many reasons / Takes a Little time /
What you gonna do about it / Sunshine / Entan-
gled.
Album: released on London, Nov'85 by London
Records. Dist: Polygram

Cassette: released on London, Nov'85 by London Records. Dist: Polygram

Compact disc: released on London, Mar'86 by
London Records. Dist: Polygram
___
WHAT YOU GONNA DO ABOUT IT.
Tracks: / What you gonna do about it / I'm still
waiting.
Single (7"): released on London, Apr'86 by
London Records. Dist: Polygram

Single (12"): released on London, Apr'86 by
London Records. Dist: Polygram
___
Total Noise
TOTAL NOISE (EP) Various artists (Vari-
ous Artists).
Single (7"): released on Total Noise, Jun'82
___
Total Strangers
SHE'S SO FINE.
Single (7"): released on Bandit Records,
Sep'82 by Bandit Records. Dist: Pinnacle, King-
dom

WORKING WORLD.
Single (7"): released on Small Run, Apr'83 by
Small Run Records. Dist: Pinnacle
___
Totem
ON THE AIR VOL.2.
Album: released on Totem, May'79 Dist: Jazz
Music, Projection, Swift
___
To the bride
TO THE BIRDE Various artists (Various Ar-
tists).
Album: released on Myrrh, May'82 by Word
Records. Dist: Word Distribution

Cassette: released on Myrrh, May'82 by Word
Records. Dist: Word Distribution
___
To The Finland Station
DOMINO THEORY.
Single (7"): released on Melodia, Jan'82 Dist:
Rough Trade Distribution
___
Toto
FAHRENHEIT.
Tracks: / Till the end / We can Make it Tonight
/ Without your love / Can't stand it any longer /
I'll be over you / Fahrenheit / Somewhere to-
night / Could this be Love / Lea / Don't stop me
now.
Album: released on CBS, Sep'86 by CBS Rec-
ords. Dist: CBS

Cassette: released on CBS, Sep'86 by CBS
Records. Dist: CBS

Compact disc: released on CBS, Sep'86 by
CBS Records. Dist: CBS
___
HOLD THE LINE.
Album: released on Hallmark, Sep'84 by Pick-
wick Records. Dist: Pickwick Distribution, PRT,
Taylors

Cassette: released on Hallmark, Sep'84 by
Pickwick Records. Dist: Pickwick Distribution,
PRT, Taylors

Single (7"): released on Old Gold, Sep'85 by
Old Gold Records. Dist: Lightning, Jazz Music,
Spartan, Counterpoint
___
HOW DOES IT FEEL?.
Single (7"): released on CBS, Feb'85 by CBS
Records. Dist: CBS
___
HYDRA.
Album: released on CBS, Feb'85 by CBS Rec-
ords. Dist: CBS

Cassette: released on CBS, Feb'85 by CBS

Records. Dist: CBS
___
I'LL BE OVER YOU.
Tracks: / In a word / Africa / 99.
Single (7"): released on CBS, Sep'86 by CBS
Records. Dist: CBS

Single (12"): released on CBS, Sep'86 by CBS
Records. Dist: CBS
___
I WON'T HOLD YOU BACK.
Single (7"): released on CBS, Jun'83 by CBS
Records. Dist: CBS

Single (12"): released on CBS, Jun'83 by CBS
Records. Dist: CBS

Picture disc single: released on CBS, Jun'83
by CBS Records. Dist: CBS
___
ROSANNA.
Single (7"): released on CBS, Mar'83 by CBS
Records. Dist: CBS

Picture disc single: released on CBS, Apr'83
by CBS Records. Dist: CBS
___
TOTO.
Tracks: / Child's Anthem / I'll supply the love /
Georgy porgy / Manuella run / You are the
flower / Girl Goodbye / Takin' it back / Rock-
maker / Hold the line / Angela.
Compact disc: released on CBS, Oct'86 by
CBS Records. Dist: CBS

Album: released on CBS, Jun'84 by CBS Records. Dist: CBS

Cassette: released on CBS, Jun'84 by CBS
Records. Dist: CBS
___
TOTO IV.
Tracks: / Rossana / Make beleive / I won't hold
you back / Good for you / It's a feeling / Afraid
of love / Lovers in the night / We made it / Waiting for your love / Africa.
Album: released on CBS, Nov'86 by CBS Records. Dist: CBS

Cassette: released on CBS, Nov'86 by CBS
Records. Dist: CBS

Album: released on CBS, Apr'82 by CBS Records. Dist: CBS

Cassette: released on CBS, Apr'82 by CBS
Records. Dist: CBS

Compact disc: released on CBS, '83 by CBS
Records. Dist: CBS
___
TURN BACK.
Compact disc: released on CBS, May'87 by
CBS Records. Dist: CBS
___
Toto Coelo
DRACULA'S TANGO (SUCKER FOR
YOUR LOVE).
Single (7"): released on Radial Choice, Oct'82

Single (12"): released on Radial Choice,
Oct'82
___
GIMME SOME LOVIN'.
Single (7"): released on Debut-Passion, Oct'85

Single (12"): released on Debut-Passion,
Oct'85
___
GIRLS' NIGHT OUT.
Single (7"): released on Debut, Apr'85 by
Skratch Music. Dist: PRT

Single (12"): released on Debut, Apr'85 by
Skratch Music. Dist: PRT
___
I EAT CANNIBALS.
Single (7"): released on Radial Choice, Jul'82

Single (12"): released on Radial Choice, Jul'82
___
MILK FROM THE COCONUT.
Single (7"): released on Radial Choice, May'83

Single (12"): released on Radial Choice,
May'83
___
Tottenham Hotspur
HOT SHOT TOTTENHAM.
Tracks: / Hot shot Tottenham / Ossie's dream.
Single (7"): released on Rainbow, Apr'87 Dist:
I & B, CBS
___
HOT SHOT TOTTENHAM.
Tracks: / Hot shot Tottenham (special remix) /
Ossie's dream.
Single (12"): released on Rainbow, May'87
Dist: I & B, CBS
___
OSSIE'S DREAM.
Single (7"): released on Shelf, May'81 by Shelf
Records.
___
TOTTENHAM TOTTENHAM.
Single (7"): released on Shelf, Jun'82 by Shelf
Records.

Picture disc single: released on Shelf, Jun'82
by Shelf Records.

Totterdell, Dave
ROOM FOR THOUGHT.
Album: released on Burlington, Nov'81 by Plant
Life Records. Dist: Jazz Music, Celtic Music,
Clyde Factors Distributors, I.R.S., Projection,
Wellard, Chris, Roots
___
Tottle, Jack
BACK ROAD.
Album: released on Rounder (USA Import),
Aug'77
___
Toucan Jive
I WANT YOU TO BE MY BABY.
Single (7"): released on Kay-Drum, Jun'83 by
Kay-Drum Records. Dist: Pinnacle

Single (12"): released on Kay-Drum, Jun'83 by
Kay-Drum Records. Dist: Pinnacle
___
Touch
BACK ALLEY VICES.
Album: released on Ebony, Jan'85 by Ebony
Records. Dist: Pinnacle, Ebony

FEATURE MIST.
Cassette: released on Touch, Feb'83 by Touch
Records. Dist: Rough Trade, Cartel

ISLANDS IN BETWEEN.
Cassette: released on Touch, May'84 by Touch
Records. Dist: Rough Trade, Cartel

KEEP ON.
Single (12"): released on Elite, Jan'82 Dist:
PRT

LOVE SOMETHING SPECIAL.
Single (7"): released on Elite, Apr'82 Dist: PRT

Single (12"): released on Elite, Apr'82 Dist:
PRT

MERIDIANS 1.
Cassette: released on Touch, May'83 by Touch
Records. Dist: Rough Trade, Cartel

MERIDIANS 2.
Cassette: released on Touch, Jun'83 by Touch
Records. Dist: Rough Trade, Cartel

THAT'S WHAT THEY SAY ABOUT
LOVE.
Single (7"): released on Arista, Feb'85 by Aris-
ta Records. Dist: RCA

Single (12"): released on Arista, Feb'85 by
Arista Records. Dist: RCA

TOUCH 33.
Cassette: released on Touch, Mar'83 by Touch
Records. Dist: Rough Trade, Cartel
___
Touchdown
BREAKOUT.
Single (7"): released on Excalibur, Oct'82 by
Red Bus Records. Dist: PRT

Single (12"): released on Excalibur, Oct'82 by
Red Bus Records. Dist: PRT

DO YOU NEED?.
Single (12"): released on Krack, Dec'84 by
Krack Records. Dist: Pinnacle

EASE YOUR MIND.
Single (7"): released on Excalibur, May'82 by
Red Bus Records. Dist: PRT

ENDZONE, THE.
Tracks: / Endzone, The.
Single (12"): released on Debut, Apr'86 by
Skratch Music. Dist: PRT
___
Touched
DEATH ROW.
Album: released on Ebony, Mar'86 by Ebony
Records. Dist: Pinnacle, Ebony

DREAM GIRL.
Single (7"): released on Ebony, Jan'85 by
Ebony Records. Dist: Pinnacle, Ebony
___
Touchet Brothers
TOUCHET BROTHERS CAJUN MUSIC
BAND, THE.
Album:
___
Touch more brass
TOUCH MORE BRASS Various artists
(Various Artists).
Double Album: released on Cambra, May'85
by Cambra Records. Dist: IDS, Conifer

Double cassette: released on Cambra, May'85
by Cambra Records. Dist: IDS, Conifer
___
Touch of brass, (A)
TOUCH OF BRASS, A Various artists
(Various Artists).
Double Album: released on Cambra, Apr'85 by

Cambra Records. Dist: IDS, Conifer

Double cassette: released on Cambra, Apr'85 by Cambra Records. Dist: IDS, Conifer

Touchstone
JEALOUSY.
Album: released on WEA Ireland, Mar'87 by WEA Records. Dist: Celtic Distributions, Projection, I & B

Cassette: released on WEA Ireland, Mar'87 by WEA Records. Dist: Celtic Distributions, Projection, I & B

Touchton, Timothy
GREAT BIG MAMA.
Tracks: / Great big mama / Great big mama (variation).
Single (7"): released on Response, Jul'87 by Priority Records. Dist: BMG

SAVE YOUR LOVE FOR ME.
Single (7"): released on Response, May'85

Tough stuff
TOUGH STUFF Various Artists (Various Artists).
Album: released on Charly, May'80 by Charly Records. Dist: Charly, Cadillac

Touplanx
SAXOPHONE SONG.
Single (7"): released on DC, Feb'82

Toups, Wayne
CAJUN PARADISE.
Album: released on Sonet, Jun'80 by Sonet Records. Dist: PRT

Tour de force
BEAT THE CLOCK.
Single (7"): released on Wongo, Jun'82

SCHOOL RULES.
Single (7"): released on Phantom, Nov'81 by Mean Records. Dist: Pinnacle

Touring Co.
EVERY STEP OF THE WAY.
Single (7"): released on Radioactive, Jul'82

Tourist
HOOKED ON YOU.
Tracks: / Hooked on you (inst).
Single (12"): released on Groove & Move, Nov'86 by G&M Records. Dist: G&M Records, PRT

Tourists, (THE)
TOURISTS, (THE).
Album: released on RCA International (USA), Jun'81 by RCA Records. Dist: RCA

Cassette: released on RCA International (USA), Jun'81 by RCA Records. Dist: RCA

Toussaint, Allen
FROM A WHISPER TO A SCREAM.
Album: released on Kent, Mar'85 by Ace Records. Dist: Pinnacle

SOUTHERN NIGHTS.
Album: released on Edsel, Mar'85 by Demon Records. Dist: Pinnacle, Jazz Music, Projection

WITH THE STOKES.
Album: released on Bandy (USA), Jul'84

Tout Sweet
ANOTHER MAN IS TWICE AS NICE.
Single (7"):

Compact disc:

Tovey, Frank
EASY LISTENING FOR THE HARD OF HEARING (Tovey, Frank & Boyd Rice).
Album: released on Mute, Nov'86 Dist: Spartan Distribution, Rough Trade Distribution, Cartel Distribution

FAD GADGET SINGLES.
Album: released on Mute, Nov'86 Dist: Spartan Distribution, Rough Trade Distribution, Cartel Distribution

Cassette: released on Mute, Nov'86 Dist: Spartan Distribution, Rough Trade Distribution, Cartel Distribution

LUDDITE JOE.
Tracks: / Clean this act up / Small world.
Single (7"): released on Mute, Apr'86 Dist: Spartan Distribution, Rough Trade Distribution, Cartel Distribution

Single (12"): released on Mute, Apr'86 Dist: Spartan Distribution, Rough Trade Distribution,

Cartel Distribution
LUXURY.
Single (7"): released on Mute, Jul'85 Dist: Spartan Distribution, Rough Trade Distribution, Cartel Distribution

Single (12"): released on Mute, Jul'85 Dist: Spartan Distribution, Rough Trade Distribution, Cartel Distribution

SNAKES AND LADDERS.
Album: released on Mute, May'86 Dist: Spartan Distribution, Rough Trade Distribution, Cartel Distribution

Cassette: released on Mute, May'86 Dist: Spartan Distribution, Rough Trade Distribution, Cartel Distribution

Compact disc: released on Mute, '86 Dist: Spartan Distribution, Rough Trade Distribution, Cartel Distribution

Tower of power
TOWER OF POWER.
Album: released on Sheffield Lab, Oct'82

WHAT IS HIP.
Album: released on Edsel, Nov'86 by Demon Records. Dist: Pinnacle, Jazz Music, Projection

Towner, Ralph
BATIK.
Album: released on ECM (Germany), '78 by ECM Records. Dist: IMS, Polygram, Virgin through EMI

BLUE SUN.
Compact disc: released on ECM (Germany), Oct'86 by ECM Records. Dist: IMS, Polygram, Virgin through EMI

Album: released on ECM (Germany), Apr'83 by ECM Records. Dist: IMS, Polygram, Virgin through EMI

DEPART (see Azymuth with Ralph Towner) (Towner, Ralph with Azymuth).

DIARY.
Tracks: / Dark spirit / Entry in a diary / Images unseen / Icarus / Mon enfant / Ogden road / Erg / Silence of a candle /The.
Notes: Ralph Towner-12 string and classical guitar, piano, gongs.
Compact disc: released on ECM (Germany), Aug'86 by ECM Records. Dist: IMS, Polygram, Virgin through EMI

Album: released on ECM (Germany), Feb'75 by ECM Records. Dist: IMS, Polygram, Virgin through EMI

FIVE YEAR LATER (Towner, Ralph/John Abercrombie).
Album: released on ECM (Germany), Mar'82 by ECM Records. Dist: IMS, Polygram, Virgin through EMI

MATCHBOOK (Towner, Ralph/Gary Burton).
Album: released on ECM (Germany), Jun'75 by ECM Records. Dist: IMS, Polygram, Virgin through EMI

OLD FRIENDS, NEW FRIENDS.
Compact disc: released on ECM (Germany), Oct'86 by ECM Records. Dist: IMS, Polygram, Virgin through EMI

SLIDE SHOW (Towner, Ralph & Gary Burton).
Tracks: / Maelstrom / Vessel / Around the bend / Blue in green / Beneath an evening sky / Donkey jamboree / Continental breakfast / Charlotte's tangle / Innocenti.
Notes: More than 10 years after their duet album "Matchbook", these two musicians got together again to record a fresh and inspired statement of the art of improvisors. "Slide show" presents both new and familiar compositions by Ralph Towner plus a vital version of the Miles Davis/Bill Evans standard "Blue & Green". The tunes range from fine lyrical songs to humorous calypso-like music. The interaction between these two fine musicians is breathtaking. Ralph Towner-classical and 12-string guitars. Gary Burton-vibraphone, marimba.
Album: released on ECM (Germany), Feb'86 by ECM Records. Dist: IMS, Polygram, Virgin through EMI

Compact disc: released on ECM (Germany), Feb'86 by ECM Records. Dist: IMS, Polygram, Virgin through EMI

SOLO CONCERT.
Tracks: / Oceanus / Visitation / Drifting petals / Nimbus / Winter solstice / Piscean dance / Red and black / Sand.
Notes: Personnel: Ralph Towner-12 string and classical guitar, piano/Jan Garbarek-tenor and soprano saxophones, flute/Eberhard Weber-bass cello/John Christensen-drums, percussion.

Album: released on ECM (Germany), '82 by ECM Records. Dist: IMS, Polygram, Virgin through EMI

Compact disc: released on ECM (Germany), '82 by ECM Records. Dist: IMS, Polygram, Virgin through EMI

SOUNDS & SHADOWS (Towner, Ralph's Solstice).
Album: released on ECM (Germany), Nov'77 by ECM Records. Dist: IMS, Polygram, Virgin through EMI

TRIOS.
Album: released on ECM (Germany), '75 by ECM Records. Dist: IMS, Polygram, Virgin through EMI

WORKS.
Album: released on ECM (Germany), Nov'84 by ECM Records. Dist: IMS, Polygram, Virgin through EMI

Compact disc: released on ECM (Germany), Nov'84 by ECM Records. Dist: IMS, Polygram, Virgin through EMI

Cassette: released on ECM (Germany), Nov'83 by ECM Records. Dist: IMS, Polygram, Virgin through EMI

Townes, Carol Lynn
BELIEVE IN THE BEAT.
Single (7"): released on Polydor, Jan'85 by Polydor Records. Dist: Polygram, Polvdor

Single (12"): released on Polydor, Jan'85 by Polydor Records. Dist: Polygram, Polvdor

Town Hall Jazz Festival
LIVE - ON THE SUNNY SIDE OF THE STREET.
Album: released on JRC & JATH, Apr'81

Townley, John
SLIPPING AWAY.
Single (7"): released on EMI, Jun'81 by EMI Records. Dist: EMI

Single (12"): released on EMI, Jun'81 by EMI Records. Dist: EMI

Town mouse...
TOWN MOUSE AND THE COUNTRY MOUSE, THE Various artists (Various Artists).
Cassette: released on Pickwick (Ladybird), '83

Townsend, Graham
CANADIAN FIDDLER.
Album: released on Rounder, Aug'77

CLASSIS OF IRISH' SCOTTISH & FRENCH-CANADIAN FIDDLING.
Album: released on Rounder, Mar'79

Townsend, Henry & Vernell
ST. LOUIS BLUES.
Album: released on Wolf, Mar'87 Dist: Jazz Music, Swift

ST LOUIS BLUES.
Album: released on Wolf, Oct'82 Dist: Jazz Music, Swift

Townsend, John
ALL KINDS OF EVERYTHING VOLUME 2.
Album: released on Sweet Folk All, May'81 by Sweet Folk All Records. Dist: Sweet Folk All, Roots, Celtic Music, Dragon, Impetus, Projection, Chris Wellard, Festival Records

Townsend, Kim
READ ALL ABOUT IT.
Tracks: / Dance away / Silver tears / Dreamin'on.
Single (7"): released on Individual, Jul'86 by Individual Records. Dist: Pinnacle

Single (12"): released on Individual, Oct'84 by Individual Records. Dist: Pinnacle

Cassette: released on AIRC, May'85

SILVER TEARS.
Single (7"): released on AIRC, May'85

Single (12"): released on AIRC, May'85

Townsend, Mike
DAWN LIGHT (Townsend, Mike band).
Single (7"): released on BBC, Jan'82 by BBC Records & Tapes. Dist: EMI, PRT, Pye

Townsend, Sally
JUST ONE LOOK.
Single (7"): released on OBM-RK, Mar'80

LOVE AT FIRST SIGHT.
Single (7"): released on OBM-RK, Jan'80

Townsend,Sue
GROWING PAINS OF ADRIAN MOLE THE.
Cassette: released on Listen For Pleasure Mar'85 by MFP Records. Dist: EMI

SECRET DIARY OF ADRIAN MOLE (PART 1).
Cassette: released on Talking Tape Company '84 by Talking Tape Company Records.

SECRET DIARY OF ADRIAN MOLE (PART 1).
Cassette: released on Talking Tape Company '84 by Talking Tape Company Records.

SECRET RECORD OF ADRIAN MOLE AGED 13 3/4.
Album: released on Columbia, Nov'84 by EMI Records. Dist: EMI

Cassette: released on Columbia, Nov'84 by EMI Records. Dist: EMI

Townshend, Pete
EMPTY GLASS.
Tracks: / Rough boys / I am an animal / And moved / Let my love open the door / Jools and Jim / Keep on working / Cats in the cupboard / Little is enough. A / Empty glass / Gonna get ya.
Compact disc: released on Atco, '84 by Atlantic Records. Dist: WEA

FACE THE FACE.
Single (7"): released on Atco, Oct'85 by Atlantic Records. Dist: WEA

Single (12"): released on Atco, Oct'85 by Atlantic Records. Dist: WEA

GIVE BLOOD.
Tracks: / Magic bus (live) / Won't get fooled again (live).
Single (7"): released on Atco, Apr'86 by Atlantic Records. Dist: WEA

Single (12"): released on Atco, Apr'86 by Atlantic Records. Dist: WEA

ROUGH BOYS.
Single (7"): released on Atco, Mar'80 by Atlantic Records. Dist: WEA

STOP HURTING PEOPLE.
Single (7"): released on Atco, Jul'82 by Atlantic Records. Dist: WEA

Picture disc single: released on Atco, Jul by Atlantic Records. Dist: WEA

UNIFORMS.
Single (7"): released on Atco, Jul'82 by Atlantic Records. Dist: WEA

Single (12"): released on Atco, Jul'82 by Atlantic Records. Dist: WEA

WHITE CITY.
Tracks: / Secondhand love / Give blood / Brilliant blues / Crashing by design / Lonely words / White city fighting / Face the face / All shall be well / Hiding out / Closing sequence.
Album: released on Atco, Oct'85 by Atlantic Records. Dist: WEA

Cassette: released on Atco, Oct'85 by Atlantic Records. Dist: WEA

Townshend, Simon
I'M THE ANSWER.
Single (7"): released on 21 Records, Jan'83 Polydor Records. Dist: Polvdor

Single (12"): released on 21 Records, Jan'83 by Polydor Records. Dist: Polydor

SO REAL.
Single (7"): released on 21 Records, May by Polydor Records. Dist: Polydor

Single (12"): released on 21 Records, May by Polydor Records. Dist: Polvdor

Town south of bakersfield
TOWN SOUTH OF BAKERSFIELD (ous Artists).
Album: released on Enigma, Dec'86 by Enigma Records. Dist: Rough Trade, Cartel, E

Tox
PRINCE OF DARKNESS.
Album: released on Mausoleum, May'85 Mausoleum Records. Dist: Pinnacle

Toxic Ephex
PUNK AS F...
Single (7"): released on Green Vomit, O Dist: Fast Forward

Toxic Reasons
BULLETS FOR YOU.
Album: released on Alternative Tenta

...ot'86 by Alternative Tentacles Records. Dist: Rough Trade, Pinnacle

GOD BLESS AMERICA.
Single (7"): released on Skysaw, Sep'84 by Skysaw Records. Dist: Red Rhino, Cartel

KILL BY REMOTE CONTROL.
Album: released on Alternative Tentacles, Nov'84 by Alternative Tentacles Records. Dist: Rough Trade, Cartel

Toxic Shock
DUBIOUS DEAL.
Single (7"): released on Vindaloo, Sep'84 by Vindaloo Records. Dist: WEA, Cartel

JUST ANOTHER DAY.
Single (12"): released on Vindaloo, Nov'85 by Vindaloo Records. Dist: WEA, Cartel

Toyah
ANTHEM.
Compact disc: released on Safari, '86 by Safari Records. Dist: Pinnacle

Album: released on Safari, May'81 by Safari Records. Dist: Pinnacle

Cassette: released on Safari, May'81 by Safari Records. Dist: Pinnacle

BE LOUD BE PROUD BE HEARD.
Single (7"): released on Safari, Oct'82 by Safari Records. Dist: Pinnacle

BRAVE NEW WORLD.
Single (7"): released on Safari, May'82 by Safari Records. Dist: Pinnacle

CHANGELING, (THE).
Album: released on Safari, Jun'82 by Safari Records. Dist: Pinnacle

Cassette: released on Safari, Jun'82 by Safari Records. Dist: Pinnacle

DANCED (LIVE).
Single (7"): released on Safari, '81 by Safari Records. Dist: Pinnacle

DESIRE.
Album: released on E.G., 30 May'87 by Virgin Records. Dist: Virgin, EMI

Cassette: released on E.G., 30 May'87 by Virgin Records. Dist: Virgin, EMI

Compact disc: released on E.G., '87 by Virgin Records. Dist: Virgin, EMI

ECHO BEACH.
Tracks: / Echo beach / Plenty.
Single (7"): released on E.G., Apr'87 by Virgin Records. Dist: Virgin, EMI

Single (12"): released on E.G., Apr'87 by Virgin Records. Dist: Virgin, EMI

FOUR FROM TOYAH.
Extended-play record: released on Safari, Nov'81 by Safari Records. Dist: Pinnacle

FOUR MORE FROM TOYAH.
Single (7"): released on Safari, Nov'81 by Safari Records. Dist: Pinnacle

IEYA.
Single (7"): released on Safari, '81 by Safari Records. Dist: Pinnacle

Single (12"): released on Safari, '81 by Safari Records. Dist: Pinnacle

Picture disc single: released on Safari, Jun'82 by Safari Records. Dist: Pinnacle

I WANT TO BE FREE.
Single (7"): released on Safari, May'81 by Safari Records. Dist: Pinnacle

LOVE IS THE LAW.
Album: released on Safari, Oct'83 by Safari Records. Dist: Pinnacle

Cassette: released on Safari, Oct'83 by Safari Records. Dist: Pinnacle

MAYHEM.
Album: released on Safari, Nov'85 by Safari Records. Dist: Pinnacle

Cassette: released on Safari, Nov'85 by Safari Records. Dist: Pinnacle

MINX.
Tracks: / Soldier of fortune / Terrorist of love / Vigilante / I fall in love (I said) / Soul passing through / Sympathy / I'll serve you well / All in a rage / Space between the sounds / School's out / Good in action / America for beginners / Over the city one / Vigilante.
Album: released on Epic, Jul'85 by CBS Records. Dist: CBS

Cassette: released on Epic, Jul'85 by CBS Records. Dist: CBS

Compact disc: released on Epic, Jul'85 by CBS Records. Dist: CBS

MOONLIGHT DANCING.
Tracks: / Moonlight dancing / Sun up / R-e-n-t-r-y into dance.
Single (7"): released on E.G., 20 Jun'87 by Virgin Records. Dist: Virgin, EMI

Single (12"): released on E.G., 20 Jun'87 by Virgin Records. Dist: Virgin, EMI

REBEL RUN.
Single (7"): released on Safari, Aug'83 by Safari Records. Dist: Pinnacle

SHEEP FARMING IN BARNET.
Album: released on Safari, Feb'80 by Safari Records. Dist: Pinnacle

Cassette: released on Safari, '80 by Safari Records. Dist: Pinnacle

SHEEP FARMING IN BARNET (SINGLE).
Single (7"): released on Safari, '80 by Safari Records. Dist: Pinnacle

THUNDER IN THE MOUNTAINS.
Single (7"): released on Safari, Sep'81 by Safari Records. Dist: Pinnacle

Single (12"): released on Safari, Oct'81 by Safari Records. Dist: Pinnacle

TOYAH TOYAH TOYAH.
Album: released on Safari, Dec'80 by Safari Records. Dist: Pinnacle

Cassette: released on Safari, Dec'80 by Safari Records. Dist: Pinnacle

TRIBAL LOOK.
Single (7"): released on Safari, '80 by Safari Records. Dist: Pinnacle

VICTIMS OF THE RIDDLE.
Single (7"): released on Safari, Jul'79 by Safari Records. Dist: Pinnacle

VOW, (THE).
Single (7"): released on Safari, Nov'83 by Safari Records. Dist: Pinnacle

Single (12"): released on Safari, Nov'83 by Safari Records. Dist: Pinnacle

WARRIOR ROCK.
Double Album: released on Safari, Nov'82 by Safari Records. Dist: Pinnacle

Double cassette: released on Safari, Nov'82 by Safari Records. Dist: Pinnacle

Toyah/Fripp
LADY OR THE TIGER.
Album: released on Editions EG, Jan'87 by Virgin Records. Dist: EMI

Cassette: released on Editions EG, Jan'87 by Virgin Records. Dist: EMI

Toyan
DJ CLASH - NICODEMUS V TOYAN
(Toyan/Nicodemus).
HOT BUBBLEGUM.
Album: released on Power House, Nov'84 by Power House Records. Dist: Jetstar

HOW THE WEST WAS WON.
Album: released on Greensleeves, Jul'81 by Greensleeves Records. Dist: BMG, Jetstar, Spartan

MARJORIE.
Single (12"): released on Rusty International, Jan'83 by Rusty International Records. Dist: Jetstar Distribution

MURDER (Toyan/Tipper Lee/Johnny Slaughter).
Album: released on Vista Sounds, Apr'84 by Vista Sounds Records. Dist: Jetstar

SLENG TING KING.
Single (12"): released on Witty, May'85 by Witty Records. Dist: Jetstar

Toy Dolls
ALFIE FROM THE BRONX.
Single (7"): released on Volume, Nov'83 by Volume Records. Dist: Pinnacle

CHEERIO AND TOODLE PIP.
Single (7"): released on Volume, Aug'83 by Volume Records. Dist: Pinnacle

DIG THAT GROOVE BABY.
Album: released on Volume, Jan'85 by Volume Records. Dist: Pinnacle

---

Cassette: released on Volume, Jan'85 by Volume Records. Dist: Pinnacle

FAR OUT DISC, (THE).
Album: released on Volume, Apr'85 by Volume Records. Dist: Pinnacle

Cassette: released on Volume, Apr'85 by Volume Records. Dist: Pinnacle

GEORDIES GONE TO JAIL.
Single (7"): released on Volume, Jul'86 by Volume Records. Dist: Pinnacle

Single (12"): released on Volume, Jul'86 by Volume Records. Dist: Pinnacle

IDOL GOSSIP.
Single (7"): released on Volume, Sep'86 by Volume Records. Dist: Pinnacle

Single (12"): released on Volume, Sep'86 by Volume Records. Dist: Pinnacle

INTRO.
Single (7"): released on Volume, Sep'85 by Volume Records. Dist: Pinnacle

Single (12"): released on Volume, Sep'85 by Volume Records. Dist: Pinnacle

NELLIE THE ELEPHANT (NOT THE ORIGINAL VERSION).
Single (7"): released on Volume, Nov'84 by Volume Records. Dist: Pinnacle

Single (12"): released on Volume, Nov'84 by Volume Records. Dist: Pinnacle

NELLIE THE ELEPHANT.
Single (7"): released on Volume, Jul'83 by Volume Records. Dist: Pinnacle

SHE GOES TO FINO'S.
Single (7"): released on Volume, Mar'85 by Volume Records. Dist: Pinnacle

Single (12"): released on Volume, Mar'85 by Volume Records. Dist: Pinnacle

SINGLES 1983-84.
Album: released on Volume, Feb'86 by Volume Records. Dist: Pinnacle

TOMMY KOWIE'S CAR.
Single (7"): released on GRC, Oct'81 Dist: Indies

TOY DOLLS, (THE).
Special: released on Wonderful World, Jul'85 Dist: M.I.S., EMI, Stage One

WE ARE MAD.
Single (7"): released on Volume, Jul'84 by Volume Records. Dist: Pinnacle

Single (12"): released on Volume, Jul'84 by Volume Records. Dist: Pinnacle

Toyin
HIP HIP HOORAY.
Single (7"): released on Parlophone, Aug'86 by EMI Records. Dist: EMI

Single (12"): released on Parlophone, Aug'86 by EMI Records. Dist: EMI

IT ONLY TAKES A MINUTE.
Tracks: / It only takes a minute / Six-o-secs flat / Some part of me / Trucks / Suddenly / Pat Nevin's eyes / Final one.
Notes: Tel: 01 806 9295
Single (7"): released on Criminal, Mar'87 by Criminal Records. Dist: Jetstar

Single (12"): released on Criminal, Mar'87 by Criminal Records. Dist: Jetstar

Single (12"): released on Probe Plus, Mar'87 by Probe Plus Records. Dist: Probe Plus Distribution

Toyla
HERE I GO AGAIN.
Single (7"): released on Criminal, Apr'86 by Criminal Records. Dist: Jetstar

Single (12"): released on Criminal, Apr'86 by Criminal Records. Dist: Jetstar

Toyota pipes & drums
AMAZING GRACE.
Album: released on Lismor, Jul'84 by Lismor Records. Dist: Lismor, Roots, Celtic Music

Cassette: released on Lismor, Jul'84 by Lismor Records. Dist: Lismor, Roots, Celtic Music

MOUNT FUJI.
Single (7"): released on Toyota, Apr'82

Toys
DOCTOR DOCTOR.
Single (7"): released on RAK, Jun'80 by RAK. Dist: EMI

Cassette: released on Volume, Jan'85 by Volume Records. Dist: Pinnacle

Lover's Concerto
LOVER'S CONCERTO.
Single (7"): released on Liberty (USA), '80 by United Artists

LOVER'S CONCERTO.
Single (7"): released on Old Gold, Jul'84 by Old Gold Records. Dist: Lightning, Jazz Music, Spartan, Counterpoint

Toy Shop
ATTACK DECADE.
Single (7"): released on Towerbell .Jan'84

Toy Traders
MC210.
Single (7"): released on Action, Nov'81 Dist: Rough Trade, Cartel

Tozzi, Umberto
AMORE.
Album: released on Carrere, Sep'83 by Carrere Records. Dist: PRT, Spartan

Cassette: released on Carrere, Sep'83 by Carrere Records. Dist: PRT, Spartan

GREATEST HITS: UMBERTO TOZZI In concert.
Album: released on CBS(Import), '80 by CBS Records. Dist: Conifer, Discovery, Swift

HURRAH.
Album: released on Ariola (Germany), Sep'84

T-Party
YOU'RE THE ONLY ONE.
Single (7"): released on Wax, Oct'85 by Wax Records. Dist: Pinnacle

T'pau
HEART AND SOUL.
Tracks: / On the wing / Takin' time out".
Single (7"): released on Siren, Jan'87 by Virgin Records. Dist: EMI

Single (12"): released on Siren, Jan'87 by Virgin Records. Dist: EMI

INTIMATE STRANGERS.
Tracks: / Intimate strangers / No sense of pride.
Single (7"): released on Siren, Jun'87 by Virgin Records. Dist: EMI

Single (12"): released on Siren, Jun'87 by Virgin Records. Dist: EMI

Trace, Natchez
BEST OF THE IMMORTAL NATCHEZ TRACE.
Album: released on Sweet Folk All, May'81 by Sweet Folk All Records. Dist: Sweet Folk All, Roots, Celtic Music, Dragon, Impetus, Projection, Chris Wellard, Festival Records

Tracey, Clark
SUDDENLY LAST TUESDAY (Tracey's, Clark Quintet).
Album: released on Cadillac, Jun'86 by Cadillac Records. Dist: Cadillac

Tracey, James
YOU ARE MY WORLD.
Single (7"): released on BMW, Jun'85 Dist: M.I.S., PRT

Tracey, Stan
ALONE (AT WIGMORE HALL 1974).
Album: released on Cadillac, Jul'78 by Cadillac Records. Dist: Cadillac

BRACKNELL CONNECTION, THE.
Album: released on Steam, Apr'81 Dist: Chris Wellard, Jazz Music, Projection, Cadillac

CAPTAIN ADVENTURE.
Album: released on Steam, Apr'81 Dist: Chris Wellard, Jazz Music, Projection, Cadillac

GENESIS (Tracey, Stan, Orchestra).
Tracks: / Beginning, The / Light, The / Firmament, The / Gathering, The / Sun, moon & the stars, The / Feather,fin & limb / Sixth day, The.
Notes: A prolific composer,Stan Tracey is probably best known for his interpretation of Dylan Thomas's "Under Milk Wood".His new work "Genesis" based on the creation has already been performed at Ronnie Scott's Club (residency 28th February–7th March). Reviews have been extremely good for both the performance and the album. An exciting Big Band recording that really swings,featuring some of the best British jazz musicians.
Album: released on SJ, Mar'87

HELLO, OLD ADVERSARY.
Album: released on Steam, Apr'81 Dist: Chris Wellard, Jazz Music, Projection, Cadillac

LIVE AT RONNIE SCOTTS (Tracey's, Stan Hexad).
Album: released on Steam, Jun'86 Dist:

Chris Wellard, Jazz Music, Projection, Cadillac

ORIGINAL (Tracey, Stan & Mike Osborne).
Album: released on Cadillac, '74 by Cadillac Records. Dist: Cadillac

PLAYS DUKE ELLINGTON.
Album: released on Mole, Jan'87 by Mole Records. Dist: Mole Music Co., Spartan Distribution

POET'S SUITE.
Album: released on Steam, Oct'84 Dist: Chris Wellard, Jazz Music, Projection, Cadillac

SALISBURY SUITE.
Album: released on Steam, Apr'81 Dist: Chris Wellard, Jazz Music, Projection, Cadillac

SONATINAS (Tracey, Stan & John Surman).
Album: released on Steam, '78 Dist: Chris Wellard, Jazz Music, Projection, Cadillac

TANDEM (Tracey, Stan & Mike Osborne).
Album: released on Ogun, Mar'77 Dist: Jazz Music, Cadillac

T'n' T
Album: released on Steam, '79 Dist: JSU, Chris Wellard, Jazz Music, Projection, Cadillac

Tracks West

TRACKS WEST-PLATFORM 1 (Various Artists).
Album: released on T.W., Dec'83 by T.W. Records. Dist: Cartel

Tractor

AVERAGE MAN'S HERO.
Single (7"): released on Roach, Oct'81 by Roach Records.

TRACTOR.
Album: released on Thunderbolt, Jul'83 by Thunderbolt Records. Dist: Jetstar Distribution

Tracy, Arthur

ALWAYS IN SONG.
Album: released on Eclipse, '71 by Decca Records. Dist: Polygram

GIVE ME A HEART TO SING.
Notes: Arthur Tracey, often referred to as "The Street Singer" has been enjoying healthy record sales with Decca since the early 1930's and is the subject of endless enquiry letters to Decca offices. "When are you releasing another disc" is the most common plea, and so far Arthur's loyal follower's all over the world we happily offer this double package. Despite advancing years-he's in his mid-eighties-the Tracy tonsils are in immaculate condition and he still tours his native America, Britain and Europe. Featured here are several items still regularly in his repertoire, including his 'show stopper'"Danny Boy".

I BRING A SONG (Tracy, Arthur (The Street Singer)).
Tracks: / Lovely to look at / With every breath I take / I bring a song / Last round-up, The / Love in bloom / Rollin' home / As you desire me / Kiss me goodnight / Dreaming / In old Vienna / Trouble in paradise / June in January / Just a year ago to-night / Love me forever / All of my life / Take me in your arms / Gypsy fiddles / Wandering.
Album: released on Halcyon (USA), May'87 by Halcyon Records (USA). Dist: Jazz Music, Conifer, Taylors

Cassette: released on Halcyon (USA), May'87 by Halcyon Records (USA). Dist: Jazz Music, Conifer, Taylors

STREET SINGER/STREET SERENADE.
Album: released on Decca (Recollections), Mar'83 by Decca Recollections. Dist: Polygram, IMS

STREET SINGER, THE Give me a heart to sing to.
Double Album: released on London, May'87 by London Records. Dist: Polygram

Cassette: released on London, May'87 by London Records. Dist: Polygram

Tracy, Jeanie

DON'T LEAVE ME THIS WAY.
Tracks: / Don't leave me this way (Sylvester mix).
Single (7"): released on Domino, Aug'86 by Domino Records. Dist: Charly

Single (12"): released on Domino, Aug'86 by Domino Records. Dist: Charly

ME AND YOU.
Album: released on Fantasy, Mar'82 by RCA Records. Dist: RCA, Jetstar

Tracy, Kim

LOVE ME/THROUGH THE LOOKING GLASS.
Single (7"): released on Free Range, Apr'80 Dist: Pinnacle

Tradition

EVERY LITTLE BEAT OF MY HEART.
Single (12"): released on Music Scene, Aug'85 by Music Scene Records. Dist: Jetstar Distribution

GIVE A HELPING HAND IF YOU CAN.
Single (12"): released on Music Scene, Aug'85 by Music Scene Records. Dist: Jetstar Distribution

LOVE MECHANICS.
Tracks: / Love mechanics / Give a helping hand.
Single (7"): released on Rhino, Jun'87 by Creole Records. Dist: PRT, Rhino

Single (12"): released on Rhino, Jun'87 by Creole Records. Dist: PRT, Rhino

SPIRIT OF ECSTACY.
Album: released on Solid Groove, May'82 Dist: Jetstar, Pinnacle

TRIBUTE TO THE KING.
Single (12"): released on Solid Groove, Feb'82 Dist: Jetstar, Pinnacle

WE'RE HAVING A PARTY.
Single (12"): released on Music Scene, Aug'84 by Music Scene Records. Dist: Jetstar Distribution

Traditional asian music

KOREA:VARIOUS TRADITIONAL ASIAN MUSIC.
Album: released on Unknown, Sep'85

Traditional Fairy Stories

TRADITIONAL FAIRY STORIES (Reid, Beryl).
Cassette: released on Pinnacle, '79 by Pinnacle Records. Dist: Pinnacle

Traditional Irish Favourites

TRADITIONAL IRISH FAVOURITES Various artists (Various Artists).
Album: released on Harp(Ireland), Jul'81 by Pickwick Records. Dist: Taylors

Traditional Marches

TRADITIONAL MARCHES VOL 1 Various artists (Various Artists).
Double Album: released on Telefunken (Germany), '81 Dist: Decca Distribution, IMS, Polygram

Traditional Music Of Kenya

MWANA WAMBELE.
Album: released on Orchid, Jan'85 Dist: Impetus Distribution, Orchid

Trad Jazz Festival

TRAD JAZZ FESTIVAL (Various Artists).
Cassette: released on Pickwick (Ditto series), Jul'82

Traffic

BEST OF TRAFFIC.
Album: released on Island, '74 by Island Records. Dist: Polygram

Cassette: released on Island, '74 by Island Records. Dist: Polygram

HOLE IN MY SHOE / NO FACE, NO NAME, NO NUMBER / I'M A MAN.
Single (7"): released on Island, Mar'78 by Island Records. Dist: Polygram

JOHN BARLEYCORN MUST DIE.
Tracks: / Glad / Freedom rider / Empty pages / Stranger to himself / John Barleycorn / Every mother's son.
Notes: All tracks published by Island Music Ltd.
Album: released on Island, Sep'86 by Island Records. Dist: Polygram

Cassette: released on Island, Sep'86 by Island Records. Dist: Polygram

Compact disc: released on Island, Sep'86 by Island Records. Dist: Polygram

LAST EXIT.
Album: released on Island, '74 by Island Records. Dist: Polygram

LOW SPARK OF HIGH-HEELED BOYS (THE).
Tracks: / Hidden treasure / Low spark of high-heeled boys (The) / Light up or leave me alone / Rock & roll stew / Many a mile to freedom / Rainmaker.
Album: released on Island, Sep'86 by Island Records. Dist: Polygram

Cassette: released on Island, Sep'86 by Island Records. Dist: Polygram

MR.FANTASY.
Tracks: / Heaven is in your mind / Berkshire poppies / House for everyone / No face, no name and no number / Dear Mr.Fantasy / Dealer / Utterly simple / Coloured rain / Hope I never find me here / Giving to you.
Album: released on Island, Feb'87 by Island Records. Dist: Polygram

Cassette: released on Island, Feb'87 by Island Records. Dist: Polygram

MR FANTASY.
Album: released on Island, '74 by Island Records. Dist: Polygram

SHOOT OUT AT THE FANTASY FACTORY.
Album: released on Island, '74 by Island Records. Dist: Polygram

Cassette: released on Island, '74 by Island Records. Dist: Polygram Deleted '78.

TRAFFIC.
Tracks: / You can all join in / Pearly queen / Don't be sad / Who knows what tomorrow may bring / Feelin' alright / Vagabond vigin / Forty thousand headmen / Cryin' to be heard / o time to live / Means to an end.
Album: released on Island, Feb'87 by Island Records. Dist: Polygram

Cassette: released on Island, Feb'87 by Island Records. Dist: Polygram

Album: released on Island, Mar'87 by Island Records. Dist: Polygram

TRAFFIC ON THE ROAD.
Double Album: released on Island, '74 by Island Records. Dist: Polygram

Double cassette: released on Island, '74 by Island Records. Dist: Polygram

TRAFFIC / YOU CAN ALL JOIN IN.
Album: released on Island, '74 by Island Records. Dist: Polygram

WELCOME TO THE CANTEEN.
Album: released on Island, '74 by Island Records. Dist: Polygram

Cassette: released on Island, '74 by Island Records. Dist: Polygram Deleted '78.

WHEN THE EAGLE FLIES.
Album: released on Island, Sep'74 by Island Records. Dist: Polygram

Cassette: released on Island, '74 by Island Records. Dist: Polygram Deleted '78.

Tragic Mulatto

JUDO FOR THE BLIND.
Album: released on Alternative Tentacles, Jan'85 by Alternative Tentacles Records. Dist: Rough Trade, Pinnacle

Trail Blazers

TRAIL BLAZERS (Various Artists).
Album: released on Spot, Feb'83 by Pickwick Records. Dist: H.R. Taylor, Lugtons

Cassette: released on Spot, Feb'83 by Pickwick Records. Dist: H.R. Taylor, Lugtons

Trail Of..

TRAIL OF THE PINK PANTHER Original film music (Mancini, Henry).
Album: released on Liberty, Dec'82 by Liberty-United. Dist: EMI

Cassette: released on Liberty, Dec'82 by Liberty-United. Dist: EMI

Trainer, Bunny

JAH HOUSE ID HELL.
Single (12"): released on Big Ship, Sep'84 by Big Ship Records. Dist: Jetstar

Trainspotters

HIGH RISE.
Single (7"): released on Arista, Feb'84 by Arista Records. Dist: RCA

UNFAITHFUL.
Single (7"): released on Arista, Nov'79 by Arista Records. Dist: RCA

Trains (Various)

CHANGING TRAINS.
Album: released on ASV-Transacord, Feb'82 by ASV Records. Dist: PRT

GREAT TRAIN RECORD, (THE).
Cassette: released on Flightstream, Jan'82 by Flightstream Records. Dist: Taylor

THIS IS YORK.
Album: released on ASV-Transacord, Sep'81 by ASV Records. Dist: PRT

Cassette: released on ASV-Transacord, Sep'81 by ASV Records. Dist: PRT

WEST SOMERSET RAILWAY (sounds of).
Album: released on Response, Feb'81

Traitors Gate

DEVIL TAKES THE HIGH ROAD.
Single (12"): released on Bullet, Apr'85 Dist: Bullet Distribution

Tralala

ALWAYS CLOSE AT HAND.
Single (7"): released on Floating World, Jan'85 by Indiet Records. Dist: Pinnacle

ROOM TO BE CRUEL.
Single (7"): released on Floating World, May'84 by Indiet Records. Dist: Pinnacle

Trammell, Bobby Lee

TOOLIE FROLLIE.
Album: released on Bison Bop (Germany), Jan'85

Trammps

HOLD BACK THE NIGHT.
Single (7"): released on Old Gold, Apr'83 by Old Gold Records. Dist: Lightning, Jazz Music, Spartan, Counterpoint

SLIPPING OUT.
Album: released on Atlantic, Jan'81 by WEA Records. Dist: WEA

Tramshed Forever

TRAMSHED FOREVER (Various Artists).
Double Album: released on Sweet Folk All, May'81 by Sweet Folk All Records. Dist: Sweet Folk All, Roots, Celtic Music, Dragon, Impetus, Projection, Chris Wellard, Festival Records

Trance Dance

DO THE DANCE.
Tracks: / Do the dance / Sail away / Do the dance / Do the dance (alt) / Sail away.
Single (7"): released on CBS, Jul'86 by CBS Records. Dist: CBS

Single (12"): released on CBS, Jul'87 by CBS Records. Dist: CBS

Single (7"): released on CBS, Aug'87 by CBS Records. Dist: CBS

Tran Quang Hai

MUSIC OF VIETNAM (Tran Quang Hai/Hoang Mong Thuy).
Album: released on Lyrichord (USA), Oct'81 by Lyrichord Records (USA). Dist: Flexitron Distributors Ltd

Tranquility

TRANQUILITY.
Album: Dist: RCA, Swift

Cassette: Dist: RCA, Swift

TRANQUILITY Various artists (Various Artists).
Double Album: released on Cambra, '83 Cambra Records. Dist: IDS, Conifer

Double cassette: released on Cambra, '83 Cambra Records. Dist: IDS, Conifer

Transatlantic...

TRANSATLANTIC NUMBER ONES Various artists (Various Artists).
Double Album: released on Cambra, Apr'84 Cambra Records. Dist: IDS, Conifer

Double cassette: released on Cambra, Apr by Cambra Records. Dist: IDS, Conifer

Transformers

TRANSFORMERS-THE MOVIE Original soundtrack.
Tracks: / Touch / Instruments of destruction / Death of Optimus prime / Dare / Nothin's gonna stand in our way / Tranformers (theme) / Escape / Hunger / Autobot/Deception / battle / Dare to be stupid.
Album: released on Epic, Dec'86 by CBS Records. Dist: CBS

Cassette: released on Epic, Dec'86 by CBS Records. Dist: CBS

Transfusion

TRANSFUSION - ANTHOLGY Various artists (Various Artists).
Album: released on Union Pacific, Sep'82 Dist: Swift, Jazz Music, Red Lightnin' Distribution

Transistors

RIOT SQUAD.
Single (7"): released on Open Circuit, Sep

Translator

ALONE.
Single (7"): released on CBS, Nov'83 by C

NO TIME LIKE NOW.
Album: released on CBS, Oct'83 by CBS Records. Dist: CBS

Cassette: released on CBS, Oct'83 by CBS Records. Dist: CBS

TRANSLATOR.
Album: released on CBS, Jun'85 by CBS Records. Dist: CBS

Cassette: released on CBS, Jun'85 by CBS Records. Dist: CBS

Trans Lux
BIG APPLE NOISE.
Single (7"): released on Malaco, Feb'84 by Malaco Records. Dist: Charly

Single (12"): released on Malaco, Feb'84 by Malaco Records. Dist: Charly

Transmitters
AND WE CALL THAT LEISURE TIME.
Album: released on Heartbeat, '82 Dist: Revolver, Pinnacle

UGLY MAN, THE.
Single (7"): released on Step Forward, Oct'79 by Faulty Products Records. Dist: Faulty Products Distribution. Pinnacle

Transporter
KIDS ON HER RUN.
Single (7"): released on High Force, Nov'82 Dist: Pinnacle

Transports
TRANSPORTS, THE Various artists (Various Artists).
Double Album: released on Freereed, Nov'77 by Topic Records. Dist: JSU

Tranzista
HEAVEN WITH HER.
Single (7"): released on Atlantic, Jul'83 by WEA Records. Dist: WEA

Single (12"): released on Atlantic, Jul'83 by WEA Records. Dist: WEA

Trapeze
DON'T ASK ME HOW I KNOW.
Single (7"): released on Aura, Jan'80 by Hollywood Nites Distribution. Dist: Pinnacle

HOLD ON.
Album: released on Aura, Oct'79 by Hollywood Nites Distribution. Dist: Pinnacle

LIVE IN TEXAS - DEAD ARMADILLOS.
Album: released on Aura, Nov'81 by Hollywood Nites Distribution. Dist: Pinnacle

RUNNING AWAY.
Single (7"): released on Aura, Mar'81 by Hollywood Nites Distribution. Dist: Pinnacle

WAY BACK TO THE BONE.
Album: released on Killerwatt, Oct'86 Dist: Kingdom Records, Pinnacle

Trapezold
THREE FOLKS OF CHEAT.
Album: released on Rounder (USA Import), May'79

Trash
ROCK ME ROCK YOU.
Single (7"): released on Atlantic, Jun'85 by WEA Records. Dist: WEA

WATCH OUT.
Album: released on RCA, Jun'83 by RCA Records. Dist: RCA, Roots, Swift, Wellard, Chris, I B, Solomon & Peres Distribution

Trash Museum
I'D RATHER DIE YOUNG.
Album: released on Das Buro, Mar'86 Dist: Rough Trade, Cartel

Trash On Delivery
TRASH ON DELIVERY Various artists (Various Artists).
Album: released on Flicknife, Sep'83 by Flicknife Records. Dist: Spartan

Trash Town
UNLUCKY NUMBERS.
Single (7"): released on Course, Oct'85 Dist: Red Rhino, Cartel, Course

Trash Twang & Thunder
TRASH TWANG & THUNDER Various artists (Various Artists).
Album: released on Demon, Apr'85 by Demon

Trauma
TRAUMA Various artists (Various Artists).
Album: released on Hallmark, Oct'82 by Pickwick Records. Dist: Pickwick Distribution, PRT, Taylors

Cassette: released on Hallmark, Oct'82 by Pickwick Records. Dist: Pickwick Distribution, PRT, Taylors

Traum, Artie
LIFE ON EARTH.
Album: released on Rounder (USA Import), Jun'77

Traum, Happy
AMERICAN STRANGER.
Album: released on Kicking Mule, Jan'78 by Sonet. Dist: Roots, PRT-Pye Distribution

HARD TIMES IN THE COUNTRY (Traum, Happy & Art).
Album: released on Rounder (USA Import), May'77

Travaganza
STAY WITH ME.
Single (7"): released on Aura, Jan'85 by Hollywood Nites Distribution. Dist: Pinnacle

TRAVAGANZA.
Album: released on Aura, Nov'84 by Hollywood Nites Distribution. Dist: Pinnacle

Travellers
SONGS,STORIES AND TUNES FROM ENGLISH GYPSIES.
Album: released on Topic, May'86 Dist: Roots Distribution

TRAVELLERS Songs, tunes & tales of English Gypsies.
Album: released on Topic, '81 by Topic Records. Dist: JSU Distribution, Projection Distribution, Jazz Music Distribution

Travelling folk
TRAVELLING FOLK Various artists (Various Artists).
Notes: Artists include Clarke Sisters, Keith Pearson & Treacle Line, Mariners, Merruwyn, Skinners Flats and Tundra. Commemorative album of concerts for the European Parliament Folk Club given in the Foyer European, Luxembourg. Traditional songs, Irish reels, bluegrass banjo and some fine original songs.
Album: released on Eron, Sep'85 by Eron Records. Dist: Eron Records

Cassette: released on Eron, Sep'85 by Eron Records. Dist: Eron Records

Travelling Man
TRAVELLING MAN.
Album: released on Towerbell, Sep'85 by Towerbell Records. Dist: EMI

Cassette: released on Towerbell, Sep'85 by Towerbell Records. Dist: EMI

Travelling Songster
TRAVELLING SONGSTER An anthology from Gypsy singers.
Album: released on Topic, '81 by Topic Records. Dist: JSU Distribution, Projection Distribution, Jazz Music Distribution

Travers, Pat
GO FOR WHAT YOU KNOW (Travers, Pat Band).
Album: released on Polydor, Aug'79 by Polydor Records. Dist: Polygram, Polydor

MAKING MAGIC.
Album: released on Polydor (Germany), Aug'85 Dist: IMS-Polygram

Travis
GET THE LIFE.
Single (7"): released on Charity, Jan'85 by Charity Records. Dist: M.I.S.

GIMME SOME LOVIN.
Tracks: / Anybody but you / Gimme some lovin / Anybody but you.
Single (7"): released on Wag, Jan'87 by Wag Records. Dist: Priority/EMI Distribution

Single (7"): released on Wag, Nov'86 by Wag Records. Dist: Priority/EMI Distribution

Travis, Dave Lee
GUIDE TO CB RADIO (Travis, Dave Lee & Richard Hudson Evans).
Cassette: released on Radiomobile, Nov'82 Dist: Pinnacle

ROCKABILLY FEVER.
Album: released on Spark, Mar'78 by Spark

Cassette: released on Spark, May'78 by Spark Records. Dist: Spark

Travis, Lane
I'M MOVIN' ON.
Album: released on Tank, Jun'79 by Tank records.

Travis, Merle
WALKIN' THE STRINGS.
Album: released on Pathe Marconi/EMI Europe), Jun'84

Travis, Randy
ALWAYS AND FOREVER.
Tracks: / Too gone too long / My house / Good intentions / What'll you do about me? / I won't need you anymore / Forever and ever, Amen / I told you so / Anything / Truth is lyin' next to you, The / Tonight we're gonna tear down the walls.
Album: released on WEA, Jun'87 by WEA Records. Dist: WEA

Cassette: released on WEA, Jun'87 by WEA Records. Dist: WEA

ON THE OTHER HAND.
Tracks: / Can't stop now.
Single (7"): released on Warner Brothers, Jan'87 by Warner Bros Records. Dist: WEA

STORMS OF LIFE.
Tracks: / On the other hand / Storms of life (The) / My heart cracked / Diggin up bones / No place like home / 1982 / Send my body / Messin with my mind / Reasons I cheat / There'll always be a honky tonk somewhere.
Album: released on Warner Bros., Oct'86 by Warner Bros Records. Dist: WEA

Cassette: released on Warner Bros., Oct'86 by Warner Bros Records. Dist: WEA

Compact disc: released on Warner Bros., Mar'87 by Warner Bros Records. Dist: WEA

Travis, Steve
GHOST RIDES IN THE SKY.
Single (7"): released on Frontier, Dec'82 by Funhouse. Dist: Rough Trade

Travolta, John
20 GOLDEN PIECES OF JOHN TRAVOLTA.
Album: released on Bulldog, May'81 by Bulldog Records. Dist: President Distribution, Spartan, Swift, Taylor, H.R.

Cassette: released on Bulldog, Jul'81 by Bulldog Records. Dist: President Distribution, Spartan, Swift, Taylor, H.R.

TWO OF A KIND Film soundtrack.
Album: released on EMI, Nov'83 by EMI Records. Dist: EMI

Cassette: released on EMI, Nov'83 by EMI Records. Dist: EMI

Trax
TELL ME THIS IS LOVE.
Tracks: / Tell me this is love / Tell me this is love (dub mix).
Single (7"): released on Buzzin, Jul'86 Dist: DMS, RCA, Pinnacle

Treacherous Three
GOTTA ROCK.
Single (12"): released on Sugarhill, Nov'85 by PRT Records. Dist: PRT Distribution

SANTA'S RAP.
Single (12"): released on Sugarhill, Nov'84 by PRT Records. Dist: PRT Distribution

YES WE CAN CAN.
Single (7"): released on Sugarhill, Jan'83 by PRT Records. Dist: PRT Distribution

Single (12"): released on Sugarhill, Jan'83 by PRT Records. Dist: PRT Distribution

Treasure girl
TREASURE GIRL / CHEE CHEE Richard Lewine - Betty Comden.
Album: released on That's Entertainment, Apr'83 by That's Entertainment Records. Dist: Pinnacle, PRT

Treasure Island
TREASURE ISLAND Read by Anthony Bate (Stevenson, Robert Louis).
Double cassette: released on Listen For Pleasure, '77 by MFP Records. Dist: EMI

TREASURE ISLAND Narrator Jon Pertwee.
Cassette: released on Storyteller, '79

TREASURE ISLAND Narrated by Paul Daneman.
Cassette: released on Kiddy Kassettes, Feb'81

TREASURE ISLAND Various artists (Various Artists).
Extended-play record: released on Disneyland, Apr'81 Dist: EMI
Cat. no: DISNEYLAND 361
Album: released on That's Entertainment, Sep'84 by That's Entertainment Records. Dist: Pinnacle, PRT

TREASURE ISLAND (Stevenson, Robert Louis).
Cassette: released on Listen For Pleasure, Jul'84 by MFP Records. Dist: EMI

Treasures Of Scotland
TREASURES OF SCOTLAND Various artists (Various Artists).
Album: released on Lismor, '81 by Lismor Records. Dist: Lismor, Roots, Celtic Music

Cassette: released on Lismor, '81 by Lismor Records. Dist: Lismor, Roots, Celtic Music

Treasures Of The Explorer
TREASURES OF THE EXPLORER SERIES Various artists (Various Artists).
Album: released on Nonesuch Explorer (USA), Jul'84

Treasury Of...
TREASURY OF FIELD RECORDINGS - VOL.1 (Treasury Of Field Recordings).
Album: released on 77, 74 by 77 Records. Dist: Chris Wellard, Cadillac Music, Jazz Music

TREASURY OF FIELD RECORDINGS - VOL.2 (Treasury Of Field Recordings).
Album: released on 77, 74 by 77 Records. Dist: Chris Wellard, Cadillac Music, Jazz Music

Treat
SCRATCH AND BITE.
Album: released on Mercury (Sweden), Sep'85
Cat. no: 824 3531
Cassette: released on Mercury (Sweden), Sep'85

Treatment, Steve
HOOKED ON A TREND.
Single (7"): released on Rather, Jun'81 Dist: Rough Trade

Tredegar...
BOUND IN BRASS (Tredegar Town Band).
Album: released on Black Mountain, '82 by Black Mountain Records.

DUMA.
Single (7"): released on Aires, Jun'86 by Aires Records. Dist: EMI

SEND IN THE CLOWNS (Tredegar Band Band).
Single (7"): released on RAK, Nov'79 by RAK. Dist: EMI

SONGS FOR EVERYONE (Tredegar Orpheus Male Voice Choir).
Album: released on PRT, Oct'81 by PRT Records. Dist: PRT

Cassette: released on PRT, Oct'81 by PRT Records. Dist: PRT

TREDEGAR.
Album: released on Aires, Jun'86 by Aires Records. Dist: PRT

Treebound Story
I REMEMBER.
Tracks: / I remember.
Single (12"): released on Fon, Jun'86 by Fon Records. Dist: Rough Trade, Red Rhino, Cartel

MY LIFE'S EXAMPLE.
Tracks: / My life's example.
Single (7"): released on Fon, Apr'87 by Fon Records. Dist: Rough Trade, Red Rhino, Cartel

Single (12"): released on Fon, Apr'87 by Fon Records. Dist: Rough Trade, Red Rhino, Cartel

Trees
GARDEN OF JANE DELAWNEY.
Tracks: / Nothing special / Great silkie, The / Garden of Jane Delawney, The / Lady Margaret / Glasperlon / She moves thro' the fair / Road / Epitaph / Snail's lament.
Notes: Original sound recording made by CBS Records who are exclusive licensees for the UK. (P)1970 CBS Records. (C)1987 Charly Records Ltd.
Album: released on Decal, Aug'87 by Charly Records. Dist: Charly

ON THE SHORE.
Tracks: / Soldiers three / Murdoch / Streets of Derry / Sally free & easy / Fool / Adams toon / Geordie / While the iron is hot / Little Sadie / Polly on the shore.
Notes: Original sound recording made by CBS Records who are exclusive licensees for the UK. (P)1970 CBS Records. (C)1987 Charly

---

Records Ltd.
Album: released on Decal, Aug'87 by Charly Records. Dist: Charly

Trelawny
TRELAWNY Original London cast.
Album: released on TER, May'85

Trelford, Donald
SNOOKERED.
Notes: With the currant craze for the game of snooker, this release is extremely topical. Written by Donald Trelford, editor of the Observer, it describes everything from the great moments to backstage dramas, the money, the rows and the scandals of this seemingly civilised game.
Cassette: released on Listen For Pleasure, Nov'86 by MFP Records. Dist: EMI

Tremblers
TWICE NIGHTLY.
Album: released on Epic, Oct'80 by CBS Records. Dist: CBS

Tremeloes
6 TRACK HITS.
Extended-play record: released on Scoop 33, Mar'84 by H.R. Taylor

Cassette: released on Scoop 33, Mar'84 by Pickwick Records. Dist: H.R. Taylor

AS IT HAPPENED.
Album: released on CBS, Apr'83 by CBS Records. Dist: CBS

Cassette: released on CBS, Apr'83 by CBS Records. Dist: CBS

GREATEST HITS: TREMELOES.
Album: released on Hallmark, Dec'81 by Pickwick Records. Dist: Pickwick Distribution, PRT, Taylors

Cassette: released on Hallmark, Dec'81 by Pickwick Records. Dist: Pickwick Distribution, PRT, Taylors

Album: released on Meteor, Apr'85 by Magnum Force Music. Dist: CBS Distribution

SILENCE IS GOLDEN.
Single (7"): released on Old Gold, Aug'82 by Old Gold Records. Dist: Lightning, Jazz Music, Spartan, Counterpoint

Single (7"): released on CBS, Jul'84 by CBS Records. Dist: CBS

SILENCE IS GOLDEN (1984).
Single (7"): released on Meteor, Oct'84 by Magnum Force Music. Dist: CBS Distribution

WORDS.
Single (7"): released on CBS, Mar'83 by CBS Records. Dist: CBS

Tremeloes, The
TREMELOES GREATEST HITS, THE.
Album:

Tremor toes
LET'S GET THIS (LOVING THING GOING).
Tracks: / Let's get this (loving thing going).
Single (12"): released on World International, Jul'86 Dist: Jetstar

Trendy Dendy
DA DA DA DA.
Single (7"): released on Double L, Feb'82

DO IT AGAIN.
Single (7"): released on Double L, Nov'83

Trenet, Charles
CHARLES TRENET.
Tracks: / Je chante / Boum / Il pleut dans ma chambre / L'a d' la joie / Menilmontant / La romance de Paris / Bonsoir jolie madame / Que feste-tal de nos amours / Debit de l'eau, debit de lait / Chacun son reve / N'y pensez pas trop / Douce France / Mes jeunes annees / L'ame des poetes / Une noix / La jolie sardane / Coin de rue / Source bleue / Route nationale no.7 / La java du dibble / Moi j'aime le music hall / Lorelei / La jardine extraordinaire / Le piano de la plage / Narbonne mon amie / La famille musicienne / Dudrtier Latin / La mer.
Album: released on Pathe Marconi(France), Nov'86

Double Album: released on EMI (France), Apr'83 by EMI Records. Dist: Conifer

Double cassette: released on EMI (France), Apr'83 by EMI Records. Dist: Conifer

DISQUE D'OR.
Album: released on EMI (France), '83 by EMI Records. Dist: Conifer

DOUBLE ALBUM.
Tracks: / Je chante / Bouml / Il pleut dans ma chambre / Y'a d'la joie / Menilmontant / La romance de Paris / Bonsoir jolie madame / Que reste-t-il de nos amours / Debit de l'eau, debit de lait / Chacun son reve / Une noix / La jolie sardane / Coin de rue / Source bleue / Route nationale No.7 / La java du diable / Moi j'aime e music hall / Lorelei / La jardin / Le piano de la plage / Narbonne, mon amie / Quartier Latin / La mer.
Album: released on Pathe Marconi, Jun'87 Dist: Swift

Cassette: released on Pathe Marconi, Jun'87 Dist: Swift

FLORILEGE 86.
Album: released on CBS(Import), Sep'86 by CBS Records. Dist: Conifer, Discovery, Swift

J'AI TA MAIN.
Double Album: released on EMI (France), '83 by EMI Records. Dist: Conifer

Treniers
ROCKIN' IS OUR BUSINESS.
Album: released on Edsel, Feb'83 by Demon Records. Dist: Pinnacle, Jazz Music, Projection

YOUR KILLING ME.
Album: released on Dr. Horse (Sweden), Nov'85 by Mr. R&B Records. Dist: Swift

Trent, Jackie
NIGHT, THE MUSIC AND..., THE.
Cassette: released on Pye, '79

WHERE ARE YOU NOW.
Single (7"): released on Old Gold (Reissue), Jul'82

Treorchy...
CWM RHONDDA (Treorchy Male Choir & Cory Band).
Album: released on Note, Jul'80 by EMI Records. Dist: EMI

Cassette: released on Note, Jul'80 by EMI Records. Dist: EMI

DAVID OF THE WHITE ROCK (Treorchy Male Choir).
Album: released on Columbia, Mar'81 by EMI Records. Dist: EMI

Cassette: released on Columbia, Mar'81 by EMI Records. Dist: EMI

GREATEST HITS: TREORCHY MALE CHOIR (Treorchy Male Choir).
Album: released on Columbia, Feb'75 by EMI Records. Dist: EMI

Cassette: released on Columbia, Feb'75 by EMI Records. Dist: EMI

INSPIRATIONAL BEST OF THE..., THE (Treorchy Male Choir).
Album: released on Word Twenty, May'85

Cassette: released on Word Twenty. May'85

LAND OF MY FATHERS (Treorchy Male Choir).
Cassette: released on Ideal(Tapes), Apr'80 Dist: EMI

MAGIC SOUNDS OF..., THE (Treorchy Male Choir).
Album: released on Music For Pleasure, May'83 by EMI Records. Dist: EMI

MARCH OF THE MEN OF HARLECH (Treorchy Male Choir).
Album: released on BBC, Jun'78 by BBC Records & Tapes. Dist: EMI, PRT, Pye

Cassette: released on BBC, Jun'78 by BBC Records & Tapes. Dist: EMI, PRT, Pye

ON GREAT LONE HILLS... (Treorchy Male Choir).
Album: released on Grasmere, Sep'84 by Grasmere Records. Dist: EMI

Cassette: released on Grasmere, Sep'84 by Grasmere Records. Dist: EMI

SOSPAN FACH (Treorchy Coal Miners).
Cassette: released on Folktracks, Nov'79 by Folktracks Cassettes. Dist: Folktracks

VALLEY CALLED RHONDDA, A (Treorchy Male Choir).
Album: released on EMI, Jun'83 by EMI Records. Dist: EMI

Cassette: released on EMI, Jun'83 by EMI Records. Dist: EMI

WE'LL KEEP A WELCOME - VOL.2 (Treorchy Male Choir & Cory Band).
Album: released on Lugtons Special Products, Jun'83

Treorchy Male Choir
MY WAY.
Tracks: / Rachie / How Lovely Are Thy Dwellings / March of the Men of Harlech / Cymru Fach / With a voice of singing / All through the night / Wachet Auf (Sleepers Wake From Bach's Cantata) / Llef (Deus Salutis) / Wonderous Love / Click Go The Shears / Bugeilio'r Gwenth Gwyn / Arwella / My Way / March of the men of Harlech / Cymru fach / With a voice of singing / All through the night / Rachie (I Bob un syd ffyddlon) / How lovely are thy dwellings / Wachet auf' / Llef (deus salutis) / Wondrous love / Click go the shears / Bugeilio'r gwenith gwyn / Arwela / A/ My way.
Album: released on MFP, Jun'87 by EMI Records. Dist: EMI

Cassette: released on MFP, Jun'87 by EMI Records. Dist: EMI

Tresize, Artie
BALCANQUHAL (see Fisher, Cilla) (Tresize, Artie & Cilla Fisher).

CILLA & ARTIE (see Fisher, Cilla) (Tresize, Artie & Cilla Fisher).

FOR FOUL DAY AND FAIR (see Fisher, Clare_ (Tresize, Artie & Cilla Fisher).

Trespass
BRIGHT LIGHTS.
Single (7"): released on Trial, Jan'82 by Trial Records. Dist: Pinnacle

Single (7"): released on Trial, Oct'83 by Trial Records. Dist: Pinnacle

JEALOUSY.
Single (7"): released on Trial, Sep'82 by Trial Records. Dist: Pinnacle

ONE OF THESE DAYS.
Single (7"): released on Trial, Jan'80 by Trial Records. Dist: Pinnacle

Trespassers W
PRETTY LIPS.
Album: released on Deadman's Curve, Feb'87 by Dave Henderson.

Trespasses W
PARIS INBETWEEN THE WARDS.
Tracks: / Paris inbetween two wards.
Single (12"): released on TW Import, May'86

Trevillion & Nine
ANYONE FOR TENNIS.
Single (7"): released on Service, Sep'82

Trevor Willetts
DOUBLE TOUCH also see Smitton Charles (Trevor Willetts & Smitton Charles).
Album: released on Acorn, Sep'79 Dist: Folksound, Jazz Music

Trew, Gerry
DEEPER.
Single (7"): released on Bluebird, Nov'83 by Bluebird Records. Dist: EMI, Jetstar

Single (12"): released on Bluebird, Nov'83 by Bluebird Records. Dist: EMI, Jetstar

HEARTACHE.
Tracks: / Heartache / Heartache(Instrmental).
Single (7"): released on Billy Boy, May'86 by Bluebird Records. Dist: PRT

Single (12"): released on Billy Boy, May'86 by Bluebird Records. Dist: PRT

I'M DOING FINE NOW.
Tracks: / (Backing track).
Single (12"): released on Bluebird, Dec'86 by Bluebird Records. Dist: EMI, Jetstar

T.Rex
20TH CENTURY BOY.
Single (7"): released on EMI, Aug'82 by EMI Records. Dist: EMI

BEARD OF STARS, (A).
Double Album: released on Cube, Oct'81 by Dakota Records. Dist: PRT

Double cassette: released on Cube, Oct'81 by Dakota Records. Dist: PRT

BOLAN BOOGIE.
Album: released on Cube, Oct'81 by Dakota Records. Dist: PRT

Cassette: released on Cube, Oct'81 by Dakota Records. Dist: PRT

BOLAN'S ZIP GUN.
Compact disc: released on Marc On Wax, Nov'86 Dist: RCA. Spartan

CHILDREN OF THE REVOLUTION.
Notes: Extra track on 12" only

Single (7"): released on Marc On Wax, Feb'87 Dist: RCA, Spartan

Single (12"): released on Marc On Wax, Feb'87 Dist: RCA, Spartan

Single (7"): released on EMI, Jul'82 by EMI Records. Dist: EMI

COLLECTION: T. REX.
Tracks: / Hod rod mama / Strange orchestra's / Chateau in Virginia Waters / Mustang Ford / Graceful Fat Shake / Deborah / Stacey Grove / Travelling Tragition / Salamanda Palaganda / Chariots of Silk / Seal of Seasons / Cat Black (The Wizard's Hat) / She Was Born To Be My Unicorn / Warlord Of The Royal Crocodiles / Woodland Bop / Dove / Beard of Stars, A / Elemental Child / One Inch Rock / Seagull Woman / Mambo Sun / Life's a Gas / Ride a White Swan / Jeepster.
Album: released on Castle, Dec'86 by Castle Records. Dist: Pinnacle

Cassette: released on Castle, Dec'86 by Castle Records. Dist: Pinnacle

Compact disc: released on Castle, Dec'86 by Castle Records. Dist: Pinnacle

DEBORA.
Single (7"): released on Old Gold, Aug'82 by Old Gold Records. Dist: Lightning, Jazz Music, Spartan, Counterpoint

ELECTRIC WARRIOR (T.Rex and Marc Bolan).
Compact disc: released on Sierra, May'87 by Sierra Records. Dist: WEA

ELECTRIC WARRIOR.
Album: released on Cube, Oct'81 by Dakota Records. Dist: PRT

Cassette: released on Cube, Oct'81 by Dakota Records. Dist: PRT

FUTURISTIC DRAGON.
Compact disc: released on Marc On Wax, Nov'86 Dist: RCA, Spartan

GET IT ON.
Tracks: / Get it on / Jeepster / Stand by me Cadillac (demo) / Truck on (yke demo) / Get on.
Notes: (B)= Extra track on blue vinyl (Y)= Extra track on yellow vinyl
Single (7"): released on Marc On Wax, Apr'8 Dist: RCA, Spartan

Single (12"): released on Marc On Wax, Apr'8 Dist: RCA, Spartan

Single (12"): released on Marc On Wax, Apr'8 Dist: RCA, Spartan

GET IT ON.
Compact disc single: released on Marc On Wax, 23 May'87 Dist: RCA, Spartan

Single (7"): released on Cube, Aug'82 by Dakota Records. Dist: PRT

Single (7"): released on EMI, '80 by EMI Records. Dist: EMI

Single (7"): released on Old Gold, Aug'82 by Old Gold Records. Dist: Lightning, Jazz Music, Spartan, Counterpoint

Single (12"): released on T. Rex, May'85

GREATEST HITS: T. REX.
Album: released on Platinum (W.Germany), Oct'85 Dist: Mainline

Cassette: released on Platinum (W.Germany), Oct'85 Dist: Mainline

GREATEST HITS:T.REX (T.Rex and Marc Bolan).
Compact disc: released on Sierra, May'87 by Sierra Records. Dist: WEA

HOT LOVE.
Single (7"): released on Old Gold, Jul'82 by Old Gold Records. Dist: Lightning, Jazz Music, Spartan, Counterpoint

Single (7"): released on Cube, Aug'82 by Dakota Records. Dist: PRT

MAIN MAN.
Album: released on Cambra, Mar'85 by Cambra Records. Dist: IDS, Conifer

Cassette: released on Cambra, Mar'85 by Cambra Records. Dist: IDS, Conifer

OFF THE RECORD WITH T. REX.
Album: released on Sierra, Nov'84 by Sierra Records. Dist: WEA

Cassette: released on Sierra, Nov'84 by Sierra Records. Dist: WEA

ONE INCH ROCK.
Single (7"): released on Cube, Aug'82 by Dakota Records. Dist: PRT

PEEL SESSION, THE.
Single (12"): released on Strange Fruit, Aug'

by Clive Selwood. Dist: Pinnacle

PLATINUM COLLECTION.
Double Album: released on Cube (Platinum Coll), Oct'81

Double cassette: released on Cube (Platinum Coll), Oct'81

PROPHETS.
Double album: released on Cube, Oct'81 by Dakota Records. Dist: PRT

Double cassette: released on Cube, Oct'81 by Dakota Records. Dist: PRT

REPLAY ON (A BEARD OF STARS).
Album: released on Sierra, May'86 by Sierra Records. Dist: WEA

Cassette: released on Sierra, May'86 by Sierra Records. Dist: WEA

REPLAY ON T. REX: BOLAN BOOGIE.
Album: released on Sierra, Feb'85 by Sierra Records. Dist: WEA

Cassette: released on Sierra, Feb'85 by Sierra Records. Dist: WEA

REPLAY ON T. REX: ELECTRIC WARRIOR.
Album: released on Sierra, Feb'85 by Sierra Records. Dist: WEA

Cassette: released on Sierra, Feb'85 by Sierra Records. Dist: WEA

RIDE A WHITE SWAN.
Tracks: Ride a white swan / Jeepster / Hot love.
Notes: All tracks released by Tony Visconti for Straight Ahead Productions Ltd. All tracks written by M. Bolan. All tracks licensed from C-Rex Records Ltd
Single (12"): released on Archive 4, Aug'86 by Castle Communications Records. Dist: Nine Mile, Cartel

SINGLES COLLECTION VOL.3.
Compact disc: released on Marc On Wax, Nov'86 Dist: RCA, Spartan

SINGLES COLLECTION VOLUME 1.
Album: released on Marc On Wax, Mar'87 Dist: RCA, Spartan

Cassette: released on Marc On Wax, Mar'87 Dist: RCA, Spartan

SINGLES COLLECTION VOL.2.
Compact disc: released on Marc On Wax, Nov'86 Dist: RCA, Spartan

SOLID GOLD T. REX.
Album: released on Fame (EMI), May'82 by Music For Pleasure Records. Dist: EMI

Compact disc: released on Fame (EMI), May'82 by Music For Pleasure Records. Dist: EMI

TANK.
Compact disc: released on Marc On Wax, Nov'86 Dist: RCA, Spartan

Compact disc: released on Marc On Wax, Nov'86 Dist: RCA, Spartan

TEENAGE DREAM.
Album: released on Hallmark, Oct'87 by Pickwick Records. Dist: Pickwick Distribution, PRT, Taylors

Cassette: released on Hallmark, Oct'87 by Pickwick Records. Dist: Pickwick Distribution, PRT, Taylors

TELEGRAM SAM.
Single (7"): released on EMI, '80 by EMI Records. Dist: EMI

Single (7"): released on T. Rex, Mar'82

Single (7"): released on T. Rex, Sep'82

T-REX.
Album: released on Dakota (Countdown Series), Oct'82 by Dakota Records. Dist: PRT

Cassette: released on Dakota (Countdown Series), Oct'82 by Dakota Records. Dist: PRT

Cassette: released on Sierra, May'85 by Sierra Records. Dist: WEA

T-REX COLLECTION.
Double Album: released on Pickwick, Aug'78 by Pickwick Records. Dist: Pickwick Distribution, Prism Leisure Distribution, Lugtons

Double cassette: released on Pickwick, Aug'78 by Pickwick Records. Dist: Pickwick Distribution, Prism Leisure Distribution, Lugtons

T-REX IN CONCERT.
Album: released on Marc, Aug'81 Dist: Pinnacle

T. REX - THE COLLECTION.
Tracks: Hot rod mama / Strange orchestra's / Chateau in Virginia Waters / Mustang Ford / Graceful fat Sheba / Deborah / Stacey Grove / Salamanda Palaganda / Travelling tragtion, The / Chariots of silk / Seal of seasons / Cat black (the wizards hat) / She was born to be my unicorn / Warlord of the royal crocodiles / Woodland bop / Dove / Beard of stars, A / Elemental child / One inch rock / Seagull woman / Mambo Sun / Life's a gas / Ride a white swan / Jeepster.
Notes: All Compositions by Marc Bolan: All tracks produced by: Tony Visconti: For straight Ahead Productions: All Tracks licensed from C-REX Records Ltd: Other titles in the collector series on Double LP and Twin Cassette include: CCSLP/SMC 102=The Immediate Singles Collection/106=The Nice Collection/108=The Small Faces Collection/113=The Kinks Collection/117=Thin Lizzy-The Collection/120=Procol Harum - The Collection/124=David Bowie - The Collection: Design: Shoot That Tiger. This compilation (c) 1986 Castle Communications Olc, Unit 7,271 Merton Road, London SW18 5JS. Bar Code: 5 013428 131367: Double Album - Double Cassette:
Album: released on Collector, Apr'86 by Castle Communications Records. Dist: PRT, Pinnacle

Cassette: released on Collector, Apr'86 by Castle Communications Records. Dist: PRT, Pinnacle

TRUCK ON (TYKE).
Single (7"): released on T. Rex, Sep'82

UNOBTAINABLE T. REX, (THE).
Album: released on Nut, Sep'80 by EMI Records. EMI Deleted '83.

Cassette: released on Nut, Sep'80 by EMI Records. Dist: EMI

Trial of Mrs Maybrick....
TRIAL OF MRS MAYBRICK (1889) & MRS MERRIFIELD (1953).
Cassette: released on Vanbera. May'78

Triarchy
SAVE THE KHAN.
Single (7"): released on SRT, Mar'80 by SRT Records. Dist: Pinnacle, Solomon & Peres Distribution, SRT Distribution, H.R. Taylor Distribution, PRT Distribution

Triban
TRIBAN.
Album: released on Black Mountain, May'82 by Black Mountain Records.

Tribble, T.N.T.
T.N.T. TRIBBLE.
Album: released on Krazy Kat (USA), Apr'87

Tribe
STICKING TO MY GUN.
Tracks: Sticking to my gun / Music.
Single (7"): released on TSU, Jun'87

Single (12"): released on TSU, Jun'87

Tribe of Benn
FILTHY CLEAN.
Single (7"): released on Drastic Plastic, 30 May'87 Dist: Fast Forward

Tribesman
SUNBURST.
Single (7"): released on Direct, Sep'80 Dist: Pinnacle

Tribe, Tony
RED RED WINE (EP).
Single (7"): released on Trojan, Nov'83 by Trojan Records. Dist: PRT, Jetstar

Single (12"): released on Trojan, Nov'83 by Trojan Records. Dist: PRT, Jetstar

Tribute to...
TRIBUTE IN SONG TO ROBERT BURNS
Various artists (Various Artists).
Tracks: / There was a man / Bonnie Lassie O'Ballochmyle / John Anderson my Jo / There was a lad / Ae fond kiss / My love is like a red red rose / Man s a man, A / Ye banks and braes / Ca' the Yowes / Corn rigs / Aye waukin' O / Sweet afton / Lea Rig, The / Star O'Rabbie Burns.
Notes: At last a tribute to Robert Burns from today's most Popular Scottish Artists.
Album: released on Lochshore, Apr'86 by Klub Records. Dist: PRT

Cassette: released on Lochshore, Apr'86 by Klub Records. Dist: PRT

TRIBUTE TO ANDY WILLIAMS Various artists (Various Artists).
Cassette: released on Dynamic, Sep'81 by Dynamic Records. Dist: Taylors

---

TRIBUTE TO CARL ALAN AWARD WINNERS Various artists (Various Artists).
Album: released on Dansan, Jan'82 by Spartan Records. Dist: Spartan

TRIBUTE TO DIANA ROSS Various artists (Various Artists).
Cassette: released on AIM (Budget Cassettes), Feb'83

TRIBUTE TO ELVIS Various artists (Various Artists).
Cassette: released on AIM (Budget Cassettes), Feb'83

TRIBUTE TO GALWAY Various artists (Various Artists).
Album: released on Harp(Ireland), Aug'83 by Pickwick Records. Dist: Taylors

Cassette: released on Harp(Ireland), Aug'83 by Pickwick Records. Dist: Taylors

TRIBUTE TO GLEN CAMPBELL Various artists (Various Artists).
Cassette: released on Oak, Sep'82 by Oak Records. Dist: Spartan Distribution, Pinnacle

TRIBUTE TO JOHN FAHEY Various artists (Various Artists).
Album: released on Kicking Mule, Feb'80 by Sonet. Dist: Roots, PRT-Pye Distribution

TRIBUTE TO KENNY ROGERS Various artists (Various Artists).
Cassette: released on AIM (Budget Cassettes), Feb'83

TRIBUTE TO PRESIDENT KENNEDY
Various artists (Various Artists).
Album: released on Shamrock (Ireland), Oct'75 Dist: I & B, EMI (Ireland), Swift, Chris Wellard, Solomon & Peres Distribution, Jazz Music

TRIBUTE TO R.A.F Various artists (Various Artists).
Cassette: released on Dynamic, Sep'81 by Dynamic Records. Dist: Jetstar

TRIBUTE TO SCOTLAND, A Various artists (Various Artists).
Album: released on Emerald, Jan'84 by Emerald Records. Dist: Ross, PRT, Solomon & Peres Distribution

Cassette: released on Emerald, Jan'84 by Emerald Records. Dist: Ross, PRT, Solomon & Peres Distribution

TRIBUTE TO THELONIOUS MONK, (A)
Various artists (Various Artists).
Double Album: released on A&M, Aug'84 by A&M Records. Dist: Polygram

Double cassette: released on A&M, Aug'84 by A&M Records. Dist: Polygram

TRIBUTE TO TRICKY RICKY, A Various artists (Tribute to tricky Ricky, A).
Notes: Artists Include: June Brides/Shop Assistants)
Album: released on Rouska, Apr'86 Dist: Red Rhino Distribution, Cartel Distribution

Trichot, Andre
26 SUCCESSES.
Double Album: released on ARC (Accordion Records), May'84 Dist: Accordion Record Club

COMME AU BAL.
Album: released on ARC (Accordion Records), May'84 Dist: Accordion Record Club

VIENS DANSER.
Album: released on ARC (Accordion Records), May'84 Dist: Accordion Record Club

Trick
HEART OF HEARTS.
Single (7"): released on Unit, May'85 by Unit Records. Dist: PRT

MY WORLD.
Single (7"): released on Unit, Oct'84 by Unit Records. Dist: PRT

Single (12"): released on Unit, Oct'84 by Unit Records. Dist: PRT

TURN TO STONE.
Single (7"): released on Unit, Mar'85 by Unit Records. Dist: PRT

Single (12"): released on Unit, Mar'85 by Unit Records. Dist: PRT

Trick Dog
WHAT A SHAME.
Single (7"): released on Radioactive, Feb'81

Trick or treat
TRICK OR TREAT (Brand, Oscar).
Album: released on Caedmon(USA), May'80 by Caedmon (USA) Records. Dist: Gower, Taylors, Discovery

---

Trick Switch
AN EXCHANGE OF CLIENTS.
Cassette: released on Cockpit, Apr'84 Dist: Vibes

T.S.T.S.
Cassette: released on Cockpit, Apr'84 Dist: Vibes

WHERE'S THE RAFT.
Cassette: released on Cockpit, Apr'84 Dist: Vibes

WHERE'S THE RAFT/AN EXCHANGE OF CLIENTS.
Cassette: released on Cockpit, Apr'84 Dist: Vibes

Triffids
BORN SANDY DEVOTIONAL.
Album: released on Hot, Jun'88 by Hot Records. Dist: Rough Trade, Cartel

FIELD OF GLASS.
Single (12"): released on Hot, Apr'85 by Hot Records. Dist: Rough Trade, Cartel

IN THE PINES.
Album: released on Hot, Nov'86 by Hot Records. Dist: Rough Trade, Cartel

PEEL SESSION, THE.
Tracks: / Life of crime / Chicken killer / Lonely stretch.
Single (12"): released on Strange Fruit, Sep'87 by Clive Selwood. Dist: Pinnacle

RAINING PLEASURE.
Album: released on Hot, Dec'84 by Hot Records. Dist: Rough Trade, Cartel

TREELESS PLAIN.
Album: released on Hot, Oct'84 by Hot Records. Dist: Rough Trade, Cartel

WIDE OPEN ROAD.
Tracks: / Wide open road / Time of weakness / Dear Miss Lonely Hearts / Native bride.
Single (7"): released on Hot, Jun'86 by Hot Records. Dist: Rough Trade, Cartel

Single (12"): released on Hot, Jun'86 by Hot Records. Dist: Rough Trade, Cartel

YOU DON'T MISS YOUR WATER.
Single (7"): released on Hot, May'85 by Hot Records. Dist: Rough Trade, Cartel

Single (12"): released on Hot, May'85 by Hot Records. Dist: Rough Trade, Cartel

Trilogy
NEXT IN LINE.
Album: released on Axe Killer, Jan'87 Dist: Pinnacle

Trimmer & Jenkins
LIVE FROM LONDON'S FABULOUS COMIC STRIP.
Album: released on Charisma, Jun'81 by Virgin Records. Dist: EMI

Trinidad Steel Band
TRINIDAD STEEL BAND, (THE).
Album: released on Nonesuch Explorer (USA), Jul'84

Trinidad Tropicana
ORIGINAL TRINIDAD TROPICANA STEEL BAND.
Album: released on Polydor, May'74 by Polydor Records. Dist: Polygram, Polydor

Trinity
BAD CARD.
Album: released on Blue Moon, Jun'87 Dist: Magnum Music Group Ltd, PRT, Spartan

BEST OF......
Album: released on Culture Press, May'85 by Vista Sounds Records. Dist: Jetstar, Rough Trade

ROCK IN THE GHETTO.
Album: released on Trojan, Sep'81

SIDE KICKS.
Album: released on Vista Sounds, May'83 by Vista Sounds Records. Dist: Jetstar

TEEN JAM.
Album: released on Kingdom, Sep'83

WE LOVE THE PIRATE STATIONS.
Tracks: / We love the pirate stations / Pretty.
Single (7"): released on R2 Records, Jun'87 by R2 Records. Dist: R2

Trio
ANNA LETMEIN LETMEOUT.
Single (7"): released on Mercury, Feb'83 by

Phonogram Records. Dist: Polygram Distribution

Single (12"): released on Mercury, Feb'83 by Phonogram Records. Dist: Polygram Distribution

TRIO.
Album: released on Mobile Suit Corporation, Jun'82 Dist: Phonogram Distribution, Polygram Distribution

Cassette: released on Mobile Suit Corporation, Jun'82 Dist: Phonogram Distribution, Polygram Distribution

TUTTI FRUTTI.
Single (7"): released on Mercury, Nov'83 by Phonogram Records. Dist: Polygram Distribution

Triplet Trouble

BEST OF TRIPLET TROUBLE.
Tracks: / I'll never regret loving you / Sweet soul music / Gentle rain, The / Indoor games / True love.
Notes: Triplet Trouble's first album, recorded in Canada in 1984; has been released in the UK following the groups modestly successul UK tour in the summer of '85. Line-up of the group: Phil Atkins, John Edwardes, Vincent Narechal, Peter Stubtoe, Luc Wan, Adrian Scott-Smith. Bar codes: (A) 5011946-206116 (C) 5011946-206117
Album: released on Antimony, Nov'85 Dist: Precious Metal

Cassette: released on Antimony, Nov'85 Dist: Precious Metal

Trip round the north

TRIP ROUND THE NORTH Various artists (Various Artists).
Album: released on Harp(Ireland), Aug'83 by Pickwick Records. Dist: Taylors

Cassette: released on Harp(Ireland), Aug'83 by Pickwick Records. Dist: Taylors

Trip to the dentist

TRIP TO THE DENTIST Various artists (Various Artists).
Album: released on Skeleton, May'80 by Skeleton Records. Dist: Cartel, Probe

Trischka, Tony

BLUEGRASS LIGHT (BANJO).
Album: released on Rounder (USA), Aug'77

HEARTLANDS.
Album: released on Rounder (USA), Jun'77

HILL COUNTRY.
Album: released on Rounder (USA), Apr'86 Dist: Mike's Country Music Room Distribution, Jazz Music Distribution, Swift Distribution, Roots Records Distribution, Projection Distribution, Topic Distribution

Trish

WARRIOR.
Single (7"): released on Arista, Jan'85 by Arista Records. Dist: RCA

Single (12"): released on Arista, Jan'85 by Arista Records. Dist: RCA

Trisomie 21

CHAPTER 4.
Album: released on Scarface, Jan'86 by Scarface Records. Dist: Cartel

JOH'BURG.
Tracks: / Joh'Burg.
Single (12"): released on Play It Again Sam, Aug'86 Dist: Red Rhino, Cartel

JOH'BURGH.
Single (12"): released on Play It Again Sam, Nov'86 Dist: Red Rhino, Cartel

PASSIONS DIVISEES.
Album: released on Stechak, Feb'85 by Stechak Records. Dist: Rough Trade Distribution, Cartel Distribution

SHIFT AWAY.
Tracks: / Shift away.
Single (12"): released on Play It Again Sam, Mar'87 Dist: Red Rhino, Cartel

WAIT AND DANCE.
Single (12"): released on Scareface, Sep'85

Tristan De Cunha

TRISTAN DE CUNHA Songs Dances & Customs.
Cassette: released on Folktracks, Nov'79 by Folktracks Cassettes. Dist: Folktracks

Tristano, Lennie

COOL IN JAM.
Album: released on Jazz Live (Import), Apr'81

CROSS CURRENTS (Tristano, Lennie/Tadd Dameron).
Tracks: / Wow / Crosscurrent / Yesterdays / Marionette / Sax of a King / Intuition / Digression / Sid'd delight / Casbah / John's Delight / What's new / Heaven's door are open wide / Focus.
Album: released on Affinity, '86 by Charly Records. Dist: Charly, Cadillac

LOST SESSION, (THE) With Earl Swope.
Album: released on Nostalgia (Sweden), Nov'82 by Wellard, Chris Distribution. Dist: Wellard, Chris Distribution

NEW SOUNDS IN THE FORTIES (Tristano, Lennie/Boyd Raeburn).
Album: released on Jazz Live (Import), Apr'81

SOLO IN EUROPE (Tristano, Lennie/Lee Konitz).
Album: released on Unique Jazz (Import), Apr'81

Triton

WILDERNESS OF GLASS.
Album: released on Mosaic, May'79 by Mosaic Records. Dist: Jazz Music Distribution, Impetus Distribution, JSU Distribution, Cadillac

Tritten, Charles

HEIDI GROWS UP.
Notes: The Sequel to Heidi. Read by Jan Francis. Double Cassette. For the children we have one of the favourite characters of our time. Heidi hasalways captured our imaginations and the story of her life in the Swiss Alps with her grandfather and his goats is very special"Heidi Grows Up" tells of her schooling at Rosiaz, home-sickness, her return to the mountains and her subsequent plans which will ensure that she never leaves again.
Cassette: released on Listen For Pleasure, Nov'86 by MFP Records. Dist: EMI

Triumph

ALLIED FORCES.
Tracks: / Fool for your love / Magic power / Air raid / Allied forces / Hot time (In this city tonight) / Fight the good fight / Ordinary man / Petite etude / Say Good Bye.
Compact disc: released on MCA, '87 by MCA Records. Dist: Polygram, MCA

Album: released on RCA, Sep'81 by RCA Records. Dist: RCA, Roots, Swift, Wellard, Chris, I & B, Solomon & Peres Distribution

Cassette: released on RCA, Sep'81 by RCA Records. Dist: RCA, Roots, Swift, Wellard, Chris, I & B, Solomon & Peres Distribution

JUST A GAME.
Album: released on RCA International, Sep'81

Cassette: released on RCA International, Sep'81

MAGIC POWER.
Single (7"): released on RCA, Mar'82 by RCA Records. Dist: RCA, Roots, Swift, Wellard, Chris, I & B, Solomon & Peres Distribution

NEVER SURRENDER.
Album: released on RCA, Feb'83 by RCA Records. Dist: RCA, Roots, Swift, Wellard, Chris, I & B, Solomon & Peres Distribution

Cassette: released on RCA, Feb'83 by RCA Records. Dist: RCA, Roots, Swift, Wellard, Chris, I & B, Solomon & Peres Distribution

PROGRESSIONS OF POWER.
Tracks: / I live for the weekend / I can survive / In the night / Nature's child / Woman in love / Take my heart / Tear the roof off / Fingertalkin' / Hard road.
Album: released on MCA, Jun'87 by MCA Records. Dist: Polygram, MCA

Cassette: released on MCA, Jun'87 by MCA Records. Dist: Polygram, MCA

Album: released on RCA, Sep'81 by RCA Records. Dist: RCA, Roots, Swift, Wellard, Chris, I & B, Solomon & Peres Distribution

Cassette: released on RCA, Sep'81 by RCA Records. Dist: RCA, Roots, Swift, Wellard, Chris, I & B, Solomon & Peres Distribution

ROCK'N'ROLL MACHINE.
Tracks: / Takes time / Bringing it on home / Rocky mountain way / Street fighter / Street fighter (reprise) / 24 hours a day / Blinding light show/Moonchild / Rock 'n' roll machine.
Album: released on MCA, Jun'87 by MCA Records. Dist: Polygram, MCA

Cassette: released on MCA, Jun'87 by MCA Records. Dist: Polygram, MCA

ROCK & ROLL MACHINE.
Album: released on Attic, Jun'82 Dist: Pinnacle

SOMEBODY'S OUT THERE.
Notes: Extra tracks on 12" only
Single (7"): released on MCA, Feb'87 by MCA Records. Dist: Polygram, MCA

Single (12"): released on MCA, Feb'87 by MCA Records. Dist: Polygram, MCA

SPORT OF KINGS (THE).
Tracks: / Tears in the rain / Somebody's out there / What rules my heart / If only / Hooked on you / Take a stand / Just one night / Embrujo / Play with the fire / Don't love anybody else but me / In the middle of the night.
Compact disc: released on MCA, Apr'86 by MCA Records. Dist: Polygram, MCA

SPORT OF KINGS, THE.
Album: released on MCA, Sep'86 by MCA Records. Dist: Polygram, MCA

Cassette: released on MCA, Sep'86 by MCA Records. Dist: Polygram, MCA

STAGES.
Tracks: / When the lights go down / Never surrender / Hold on / Magic power / Rock and roll machine / Lay it on the line / A world of fantasy / Midsummer's daydream / Spellbound / Follow your heart / Follow your heart / Fight the good fight / Mind games / Empty inside.
Album: released on MCA, Nov'85 by MCA Records. Dist: Polygram, MCA

Cassette: released on MCA, Nov'85 by MCA Records. Dist: Polygram, MCA

Compact disc: released on MCA, '87 by MCA Records. Dist: Polygram, MCA

Compact disc: released on MCA, Jul'87 by MCA Records. Dist: Polygram, MCA

THUNDER 7.
Tracks: / Spellbound / Midsummer's daydream / Killing time / Little boy blues / Follow your heart / Rock out, roll on / Time goes by / Time canon / Stranger in a strange land / Cool down.
Compact disc: released on MCA, '86 by MCA Records. Dist: Polygram, MCA

Album: released on MCA, Mar'85 by MCA Records. Dist: CBS

Cassette: released on MCA, Mar'85 by MCA Records. Dist: CBS

TRIUMPH.
Album: released on RCA International, Sep'81

Cassette: released on RCA International, Sep'81

Album: released on Attic, Mar'82 Dist: Pinnacle

WORLD OF FANTASY.
Single (7"): released on RCA, Mar'83 by RCA Records. Dist: RCA, Roots, Swift, Wellard, Chris, I & B, Solomon & Peres Distribution

Triumphant

GIVE PRAISES.
Album: released on Triumphant, Sep'83 by Triumphant Records. Dist: Jetstar

Triumph Street Pipe Band

DRAM BEFORE YOU GO, A.
Album: released on Limsor, Dec'86

Triumvirat

RUSSIAN ROULETTE.
Album: released on EMI (Germany), May'83 by EMI Records. Dist: Conifer

Trix

IN THIS UNIVERSE.
Single (7"): released on Splash, Nov'82 by Splash Records. Dist: CBS

Single (7"): released on Splash, Nov'82 by Splash Records. Dist: CBS

Trixie's Red Motorbike

NORMAN AND NARCISSUS.
Single (7"): released on Lobby Ludd, Jan'84 by Red Rhino Records. Dist: Red Rhino, Cartel

Troccoli, Kathy

HEART & SOUL.
Album: released on Reunion, Jan'85

Cassette: released on Reunion, Jan'85

Trockener Kecks

BETAALDE LIEFDE.
Tracks: / Betaalde liefde / Dood van een held / Souvenir / De split go to the mosk / Naar de top / Betaalde liefde kom terug rosa / Los Zand / Mijn Laatse beer.
Notes: Trockener Kecks, Post Box. 4204, 1009 AE Amsterdam, (0) 20-92.18.90.73.71.55.
Album: released on Trockener Kecks, '85

HOOP DOET LEVEN.
Tracks: / Hoop doet leven / Faam.
Single (7"): released on Trockener Kecks, '86

IEMAND ANDERS.
Tracks: / Iemand anders / De passagier.
Notes: In september '84, "Ieman Anders" is released as single. Paul Berding (Gruppo Spotivo) plays saxophone and the single reaches the top- 5 for dutch-sung singles and bubbling-under. OOR "...the only true successors of Doe Maar are Trockener Kecks of course. Fine Text a subtle sax nice arranged chorus and a powerful composition...". Artists: Leo Kenter- drums/Rick De Leeuw- vocals, guitar/Theo Vogelaars- bass, vocals/Rob De Weer- guitar, vocals. Information: Trockener Kecks, Post Box 4204, 1009 AE Amsterdam, (O) 20-92.18.90.73.71.55.
Single (7"): released on Trockener Kecks, '84

IN DE KROCKTEN VAN DE GEETS.
Tracks: / Afrodisiac / Inde Krockten Van De Geets / Asfalt / Iemand anders / Huurmoordenaar de man in de lucht / Koud en donker / Pumps nooit meer honger / Levend vlees / Speelkwartier.
Notes: After a few changes in the line-up and playing the final of "de grote prijs van Nederland" (a contest for non-commercial music) the second album was released. "...10 songs in the best trditions of Kinks and Undertones" ..."an adventurous search into the crypts of human thinking. The listener gets dragged along to the most distant canyons of the mind.."(OOR 14.02.'84). "...The songs fit tight, singer Rick De leeuw has a beautiful raw voice and the most striking are the lovely backing vocals..."(PAROOL 28.03.'84). "...In De Krockten Van De Geets is a really powerful record and I like it..."(VINYL, May '84). Artists: Leo Kenter-drums/Rick De Leeuw- vocals, guitar/Theo Vogelaars- bass, vocals/Rob De Weerd- guitar,vocals. Infomation: Trockener Kecks, Post Box 4204, 1009 AE Amsterdam, (O)20-92.18.90.73.71.55.
Album: released on Trockener Kecks, '84

KOM TERUG, ROSA.
Tracks: / Kom terug rosa / Slagboom.
Notes: In January '85 the third single in a row. "...a catchy text on the stirring rhythm of an exciting build- up tear- jerker...(OOR. 25.01.'85). The song was broadcasted by Vara's "Je Ziet Maar" on television January 15th. It will appear on the forthcoming album "Betaalde Liefde". Artists: Leo Kenter- drums/Rick De Leeuw- vocals, guitar/Theo Vogelaars- bass, vocals/Rob De Weers- guitar. vocals. Information: Trockener Kecks, Post Box: 4204, 1009 AE Amsterdam, (O)20-92.18.90.73.71.55.
Single (7"): released on Trockener Kecks, '85

LIEVER BLIND.
Tracks: / Liever blind / De buldog.
Notes: Two months later "Liever Blind" came out. The reception of it was very positive. It was played alot on both dutch an belgian radio. "...an adulterous woman turns the holiday of Trockener Kecks into a nightmare..." The video-clip of "Liever Blind" was broadcast by BBC's "Old Grey Whistle Test". Artists: Leo Kenter-drums/Rick De Leeuw- vocals, guitar/Theo Vogelaars- bass, vocals/Rob De Weerd- guitar vocals. Information: Trockener Kecks, Post Box.4204, 1009 AE Amsterdam.(O)20-92.18.90.73.71.55.
Single (7"): released on Trockener Kecks, '84

LOS ZAND.
Tracks: / Los zand / Turning point, the.
Notes: Because of the "Holland Tour '85" together with Ivy Green, Trockener Kecks and Ivy Green released in March '85 the double-A sided single. "Turning Point/Los Zand" NRC Handelsbald" ...Trockener Kecks is a rare exception to the dutch pop tradition, a tradition of soft music and doggerel. Their songs belong in the dutch hitparade. Artists: Leo Kenter drums/Rick De Leeuw- vocals, guitar/Theo Vogelaars- bass. vocals/Rob De Weerd- guitar vocals. Information: Trockener Kecks, Post Box 4204, 1009 AE Amsterdam, (O)20 92.18.90.73.71.55.
Single (7"): released on Trockener Kecks, '85

NAAR DE TOP.
Tracks: / Naar de top / De split.
Single (7"): released on Trockener Kecks, '85

NIET ALLE MEISJES ZIJN VERLIEFD OP KORS.
Tracks: / Niet alle meisjes zijn verliefd op kors / Lang zo aardig niet.
Notes: The second single was a break-through on the radio. The song was played on the dutch and belgian radio a lot and appears on the, Holland, well-known, independent sampler "Stirred, Not Shaken". March '85 the single was played on television. Artists: Leo Kenter drums/Rick De Leeuw- vocals, guitar/Theo Vogelaars- bass. vocals/Rob De Weerd- guitar vocals. Information" Trockener Kecks, Post Box 4204, 1009 AE Amsterdam, (O).20 92.18.90.73.71.55.
Single (7"): released on Trockener Kecks, '8

RICK RINGERS.
Tracks: / Rick ringers / Heineken bier.
Notes: After playing their first gig in November '80, Trockener Kecks decided in February '8 to make a single. Raw, Loud and Fast, "Rik Ringers" became a cult-hit and single of the year the dutch music magazine "OOR". Artists: Leo Kenter- drums/Rick De Leeuw- vocals, guitar/Theo Vogelaars- bass, vocals/Rob De Weerd- guitar. vocals. Information: Trockener Kecks, Post Box 4204, 1009 AE Amsterdam (O)20-92.18.90.73.71.55.
Single (7"): released on Trockener Kecks, '8

SCHLIESSBAUM.
Tracks: / Schliessbaum / Het meisje van de donutshop / De gifbekker mokerslagen / Trotto terreur / Samen met Jose 1 film / Slagboom, (Z was een) / Bouquet / Gienlijn zeuws meisje

2.22 / Samen met Jose / Lidmaatschap / Ik slik
e zever niet / Femme fatale.
Notes: In September the first album came out,
n which you can hear both tempo and more
ppy songs. Songs like "(Zij Was Een) Stag-
oom". "Het Meisje Van De Donut-Shop" and
..Mokerslagen" (appearing in the movie "An
oem") show "Trockener Kecks are capable of
riting powerful and compact popsongs.."
OR 10.09.'81). Artists: Leo Kenter-
ums/Rick De Leeuw- vocals, guitar/Theo
ogelaars-bass, vocals/Rob De Weerd- guitar,
cals. Information: Trockener Kecks, Post Box
204, 1009 AE Amsterdam, (O)20-
.18.90.73.71.55.
lbum: released on Trockener Kecks, '81

OUVENIR.
ecks: / Souvenir / Tegen alles in.
ngle (7"): released on Trockener Kecks, '86

Troggs

EST OF.....
bum: released on Rhino (USA), Feb'85 by
hino Records (USA).

assette: released on Rhino (USA), Feb'85 by
hino Records (USA).

LACK BOTTOM.
ngle (7"): released on RCA (Germany), May'83

ngle (7"): released on Stagecoach, May'83

VERY LITTLE THING.
ngle (7"): by 10 Records. Dist: Virgin, EMI
ngle (12"): by 10 Records. Dist: Virgin, EMI

OLDEN HITS: TROGGS.
bum: released on Astan, Nov'84 by Astan
cords. Dist: Counterpoint

assette: released on Astan, Nov'84 by Astan
cords. Dist: Counterpoint

REATEST HITS: TROGGS.
oum: released on Masters (Holland), Aug'87.
tim retail price in Sep'87 was £2.99.

ssette: released on Masters (Holland),
g'87. Estim retail price in Sep'87 was £2.99.

ST DAYS.
ssette: released on Autograph, Apr'85 Dist:
cord Services Distribution (Ireland)

AN'T CONTROL MYSELF.
ngle (7"): released on Old Gold (Reissue),
82

VE AT MAX'S-KANSAS CITY.
um: released on Max's Kansas City, Mar'81
President Records. Dist: President Distribu-
, Jazz Music, Taylors, Spartan

VE IS ALL AROUND.
ngle (7"): released on Old Gold (Reissue),
82

CK IT BABY.
um: released on Action Replay, Aug'84 by
ion Replay Records. Dist: PRT

CK IT UP.
um: released on Action Replay, Nov'85 by
ion Replay Records. Dist: PRT

LUME 1/VOLUME 2.
ssette: released on DJM, Nov'81 by DJM
ords. Dist: CBS, Polygram

D THING.
gle (7"): released on Old Gold (Reissue),
82

roggs, The

LD THINGS.
um: released on Konnexion, Aug'87 Dist:
ts, Pinnacle

rolka

RAINIAN FOLK MUSIC.
sette: released on Dartington, May'84

RANIAN FOLK MUSIC.
sette: released on Dartington, May'84

rolka voices

NERAL FOR A DAY.
gle (7"): released on Plum, Nov'85 Dist:
th Trade, Cartel

rojan

ASING THE STORM.
um: released on Roadrunner, Sep'85 by
drunner Records (Germany). Dist: Pinnacle

rojan Explosion

OJAN EXPLOSION various artists.
tes: / You can get it if you really want it /
gae in your reggae / Johnny too bad / Liqui-
/ Wonderful world, beautiful people / Them
Ghan and Kiki. 54-46 was my number / Cherry

---

oh baby / Let your yeh be yeh / Dollar of soul /
Young gifted and black / Sweet sensation / Elizabethan reggae.
Notes: It's almost 10 years since the famous
Trojan Explosion Maxi Single series first hit the
streets. During that time legions of Trojan Reggae followers the world over have made each
and every treasured release in this series part
of their Trojan collection. So, as we near that
10th anniversary, the streets are being hit once
again, this time by the release of 'Trojan Explosion' in glorious 12" black vinyl and cassette - in
a stunning sleeve. This compilation combines
some of the very best tracks from the 'Explosion' series together with choice cuts from deep
in the Trojan vaults and is set to join Trojans
other best sellingcompilations.

TROJAN EXPLOSION   Various artists
(Various Artists).
Boxed set: released on Trojan, Mar'83

TROJAN EXPLOSION, VOL 1 Various artists (Various Artists).
Extended-play record: released on Trojan, '83

TROJAN EXPLOSION, VOL 2 Various artists (Various Artists).
Extended-play record: released on Trojan, '83

TROJAN EXPLOSION, VOL 3 Various artists (Various Artists).
Extended-play record: released on Trojan, '83

TROJAN EXPLOSION, VOL 4 Various artists (Various Artists).
Extended-play record: released on Trojan, '83

TROJAN EXPLOSION, VOL 5 Various artists (Various Artists).
Extended-play record: released on Trojan, '83

TROJAN EXPLOSION, VOL 6 Various artists (Various Artists).
Extended-play record: released on Trojan, '83

TROJAN EXPLOSION, VOL 7 Various artists (Various Artists).
Extended-play record: released on Trojan, '83

TROJAN EXPLOSION, VOL 8 Various artists (Various Artists).
Extended-play record: released on Trojan, '83

Trojan hits

TROJAN HITS Various artists (Various Artists).
Album: released on Cambra, Mar'85 by Cambra Records. Dist: IDS, Conifer

Cassette: released on Cambra, Mar'85 by
Cambra Records. Dist: IDS, Conifer

Trojans

GAELIC SKA.
Single (7"): released on Gaz's, Jul'87 by Gaz's
Records. Dist: Backs, Cartel

Single (12"): released on Gaz's, Aug'87 by
Gaz's Records. Dist: Backs, Cartel

RINGO.
Tracks: / Ringo / Good friends.
Single (7"): released on Gaz's Rockin' Rec-
ords, May'87 by Stiff Records, EMI

Trojan's greatest hits

TROJAN'S GREATEST HITS Various artists (Various Artists).
Album: released on Trojan, '83 by Trojan Records. Dist: PRT, Jetstar

Trojan story

TROJAN STORY, VOL 1 Various artists
(Various Artists).

TROJAN STORY, VOL 2 Various artists
(Various Artists).

TROJAN STORY, VOL 1 Various artists
(Various Artists).
Triple album / cassette: released on Trojan,
'83 by Trojan Records. Dist: PRT, Jetstar

Triple album / cassette: released on Trojan,
'83 by Trojan Records. Dist: PRT, Jetstar

TROJAN STORY, VOL 2 Various artists
(Various Artists).
Triple album / cassette: released on Trojan,
'83 by Trojan Records. Dist: PRT, Jetstar

Triple album / cassette: released on Trojan,
'83 by Trojan Records. Dist: PRT, Jetstar

Trollope,Anthony

BARCHESTER TOWERS.
Notes: Read by Timothy West. Produced by
Betty Davis. 3 volumes;14 cassettes. Listen-
ing Time: 19 hours 5 mins.
Cassette: released on Cover to Cover, Apr'87
by Cover to Cover Cassettes. Dist: Conifer

Trombone album, (The)

TROMBONE ALBUM, (THE) Various Artists (Various Artists).
Double Album: released on Savoy (France),

Oct'85

Tron

TRON Various artists (Various Artists).
Extended-play record: released on Disneyland, Dec'82 by WEA Records. Dist: WEA

Cassette: released on Disneyland, Dec'82 by
WEA Records. Dist: WEA

Tronics

LOVE BACKED BY FORCE.
Single (7"): released on Alien, Jul'81

TRANZISTER SISTER.
Single (12"): released on Press, Jul'82

WILDCAT ROCK.
Single (7"): released on Red Rhino, May'83 by
Red Rhino Records. Dist: Red Rhino, Cartel

Trooping the Colour

TROOPING THE COLOUR, 1977 Various
bands (Various bands).
Album: released on Major Richards Military
Music, Oct'77

TROOPING THE COLOUR, 1979 Various
bands (Various bands).
Album: released on Major Richards Military
Music, Nov'79

Cassette: released on Major Richards Military
Music, Nov'79

TROOPING THE COLOUR, 1978 Grena-
dier Guards (Grenadier Guards).
Album: released on Major Richards Military
Music, Jun'78

Cassette: released on Major Richards Military
Music, Jun'78

Troops

SAVE THE BOY.
Single (7"): released on Aura, Aug'79 by Hollywood Nites Distribution. Dist: Pinnacle

TROOPS OF TOMORROW.
Single (12"): released on Just When You
Thought It Was Quiet, Sep'82

Troops For Tomorrow

SONGS OF JOY AND FAITH.
Single (7"): released on Rhythmic, May'82 by
Rhythmic Records. Dist: Havoc Distribution

Tropea,John

N.Y. CATS DIRECT.
Notes: With Jack Cavari,David Spinozza,War-
ren Bernhardt,Don Grolnick,Tom McFaul,Ri-
chard Tee,Steve Gadd etc.
Compact disc: released on DMP, '86 by DMP
Records. Dist: Venture

Compact disc: released on DMP, '86 by DMP
Records. Dist: Venture

Tropical Heatwave

LIMBO ROCK.
Single (7"): released on Bronze, Aug'82 by
Polygram Records. Dist: Polygram

Tropic Amber

AND I LOVE YOU SO.
Single (7"): released on Tropical, Mar'85 by
Tropical Records. Dist: Jetstar

Tropicana Steel Band

TRINIDAD TROPICANA.
Album: released on Polydor, '74 by Polydor
Records. Dist: Polygram, Polydor

Tropics

I'VE BEEN HAD.
Single (12"): released on Cave Music, Apr'85
by Cave Music. Dist: Jetstar

OOH-LA-LA (HOW I LOVE YOU).
Single (7"): released on Hive, Aug'83 Dist: PRT

Single (12"): released on Hive, Aug'83 Dist:
PRT

Trostel, Rolf

DER PROPHET.
Album: released on Uniton, Sep'34

Trotter, John Scott

MUSIC HALL HIGHLIGHTS.
Notes: For full information see under Crosby,
Bing/ John Scott Trotter Orchestra

Trotto

TROTTO Music and song from middle ages
to present day.
Album: released on Free Reed, Sep'79 by Free
Reed Records. Dist: Roots, Projection, Hobgoblin Records, Oblivion

---

Troubadors

NED O' THE HILL.
Album: released on Silver Hill, Nov'76 Dist:
Jazz Music

Trouble

RUN TO THE LIGHT.
Album: released on Roadrunner (Dutch),
Jul'87 Dist: Pinnacle

SKULL.
Album: released on Road Runner, Jul'85

TROUBLE IN MY LIFE.
Tracks: / Trouble in my life / Last time.
Single (7"): released on MDM, Jul'87 Dist:
Siren, Virgin, EMI

Single (12"): released on MDM, Jul'87 Dist:
Siren, Virgin, EMI

Trouble Funk

DROP THE BOMB.
Album: released on Sugarhill, Feb'85 by PRT
Records. Dist: PRT Distribution

Single (12"): released on Sugarhill, Feb'85 by
PRT Records. Dist: PRT Distribution

GOOD TO GO.
Tracks: / Good to go / Say what / Good to go
(instrumental).
Single (7"): released on Island, Jul'86 by Island
Records. Dist: Polygram

Single (12"): released on Island, Jul'86 by Island Records. Dist: Polygram

SAY WHAT.
Album: released on Fourth & Broadway, Oct'86
by Island Records. Dist: Polygram, EMI

Cassette: released on Fourth & Broadway,
Oct'86 by Island Records. Dist: Polygram, EMI

STILL SMOKIN.
Tracks: / Still smokin / Beat is bad (The) / Don't
touch that stereo.
Single (7"): released on Fourth & Broadway,
Oct'86 by Island Records. Dist: Polygram, EMI

Single (12"): released on Fourth & Broadway,
Oct'86 by Island Records. Dist: Polygram, EMI

STILL SMOKING.
Single (7"): released on D.E.T.T., Sep'85 by Island Records. Dist: Polygram

Single (12"): released on D.E.T.T., Sep'85 by
Island Records. Dist: Polygram

STILL SMOKIN RADIO.
Tracks: / Still smokin radio / Beat is bad (The) /
Live in Montreaux / It's all in the mix (don't touch
that stereo).
Cassette single: released on Gogo Island,
Oct'86 by Island Records. Dist: Polygram

TROUBLE FUNK EXPRESS.
Single (12"): released on Greyhound, Jun'83
by Greyhound Records. Dist: PRT, Greyhound

TROUBLE OVER HERE.
Tracks: / Trouble / Woman of principle / Hey
tee bone / All over the world / Stroke / New
money / Sexy / Break it up.
Album: released on Fourth & Broadway,
Aug'87 by Island Records. Dist: Polygram, EMI

Cassette: released on Fourth & Broadway,
Aug'87 by Island Records. Dist: Polygram, EMI

Compact disc: released on Fourth & Broadway, Aug'87 by Island Records. Dist: Polygram,
EMI

TROUBLE OVER HERE TROUBLE
OVER THERE.
Compact disc: released on Fourth & Broad-
way, Jul'87 by Island Records. Dist: Polygram,
EMI

TROUBLE OVER HERE TROUBLE
OVER THERE.
Album: released on Fourth & Broadway, Jul'87
by Island Records. Dist: Polygram, EMI

Cassette: released on Fourth & Broadway,
Jul'87 by Island Records. Dist: Polygram, EMI

WOMAN OF PRINCIPLE.
Tracks: / Woman of principle / Don't touch that
stereo / Woman of principle (Special remix).
Single (7"): released on Fourth & Broadway,
13 Jun'87 by Island Records. Dist: Polygram,
EMI

Single (12"): released on Fourth & Broadway,
13 Jun'87 by Island Records. Dist: Polygram,
EMI

Troubles

LET'S MAKE A DEN.
Tracks: / Terrorism!.
Single (7"): released on Virgin, Jan'87 by Vir-
gin Records. Dist: EMI, Virgin Distribution

Single (12"): released on Virgin, Jan'87 by Virgin Records. Dist: EMI, Virgin Distribution

Troup, Bobby

BOBBY TROUP PLAYS JOHNNY MERCER.
Tracks: / Jamboree ones / Midnight sun / Come rain or come shine / Laura / That old black magic / One for my baby / Cuckoo in the clock / Day in, day out / Jeepers, creepers / Lazy Mood (Love's got me in a) / Skylark / I'm with you.
Notes: A Bethlaham Recording. This compilation P 1987 Charly Records Ltd. This compilation C 1987 Charly Records Ltd.
Album: released on Affinity, Jun'87 by Charly Records. Dist: Charly, Cadillac

DISTINCTIVE STYLE OF BOBBY TROUP, THE.
Album: released on Fresh Sounds, Aug'87 by Charly Records. Dist: Charly

PLAYS JOHNNY MERCER.
Album: released on Affinity, Jul'87 by Charly Records. Dist: Charly, Cadillac

Trowbridge, Douglas

SONGS UNSPOKEN.
Notes: Douglas Trowbridge began his fascination with the piano at the age of 2. He was considered a musical prodigy when at 3 he began studying classical piano with University of Utah's dean of music. Before he was 4 Douglas gave his first of many recitals at church, playing pieces by Bach, Brahms and Scarlotti.
Album: released on Meadowlark, Mar'86 by Sparrow Records. Dist: Word Distribution

Cassette: released on Meadowlark, Mar'86 by Sparrow Records. Dist: Word Distribution

Trower, Robin

BEYOND THE MIST.
Album: released on Music For Nations, Jun'85 by Music For Nations Records. Dist: Pinnacle

Cassette: released on Music For Nations, Jun'85 by Music For Nations Records. Dist: Pinnacle

B.L.T..
Album: released on Chrysalis, Feb'81 by Chrysalis Records. Dist: CBS

BRIDGE OF SIGHS.
Tracks: / Day of the eagle / Bridge of sighs / In this place / Fool and me (The) / Too rolling stoned / About to begin / Lady love / Little bit of sympathy.
Album: released on Chrysalis, Jan'82 by Chrysalis Records. Dist: CBS

Cassette: released on Chrysalis, Jan'82 by Chrysalis Records. Dist: CBS

Compact disc: released on Chrysalis, Jan'82 by Chrysalis Records. Dist: CBS

CARAVAN TO MIDNIGHT.
Cassette: released on Chrysalis, Dec'78 by Chrysalis Records. Dist: CBS

Cassette: released on Chrysalis, Dec'78 by Chrysalis Records. Dist: CBS

FOR EARTH BELOW.
Cassette: released on Chrysalis, Jan'75 by Chrysalis Records. Dist: CBS

Cassette: released on Chrysalis, '75 by Chrysalis Records. Dist: CBS

LONG MISTY DAYS.
Album: released on Chrysalis, Oct'76 by Chrysalis Records. Dist: CBS

Cassette: released on Chrysalis, Oct'76 by Chrysalis Records. Dist: CBS

PASSION.
Album: released on PRT, Feb'87 by PRT Records. Dist: PRT

Cassette: released on PRT, Feb'87 by PRT Records. Dist: PRT

PORTFOLIO The classic collection.
Tracks: / Bridge of sighs / Too rolling stoned / For earth below / Caravan to midnight.
Album: released on Chrysalis, Jul'87 by Chrysalis Records. Dist: CBS

Cassette: released on Chrysalis, Jul'87 by Chrysalis Records. Dist: CBS

Compact disc: released on Chrysalis, Jul'87 by Chrysalis Records. Dist: CBS

TWICE REMOVED FROM YESTERDAY.
Album: released on Chrysalis, '74 by Chrysalis Records. Dist: CBS

Cassette: released on Chrysalis, '74 by Chrysalis Records. Dist: CBS

Troy

LOVE AND HARMONY.
Single (12"): released on Love Linch, Mar'82 Dist: Jetstar

Troy, Doris

WHATCHA GONNA DO ABOUT IT.
Single (12"): released on Atlantic, Apr'80 by WEA Records. Dist: WEA

Troy, Tony

I CAN'T THINK OF ANTHING MORE BEAUTIFUL.
Single (7"): released on Beautiful, Nov'85 Dist: M.I.S.

Truck Driver Songs

TRUCK DRIVER SONGS (Various Artists).
Album: released on King (USA), Apr'87 Dist: Gusto Distribution

Cassette: released on King (USA), Apr'87 Dist: Gusto Distribution

Trucker songs 2

TRUCKER SONGS 2 (Various Artists).
Compact disc: released on Bridge, '86 Dist: CD Centre Distribution, Pinnacle, Target

Truckin' U.S.A.

TRUCKIN' U.S.A. (Various Session Artists).
Cassette: released on AIM (Budget Cassettes), Feb'83

Trudy

CAPTAIN SCARLETT.
Tracks: / Captain Scarlett.
Single (7"): released on Primitive, Feb'87 Dist: O.I.D

INVISIBLE MAN.
Single (7"): by Torso Records. Dist: Rough Trade, Cartel, EMI

True

LONG AFTER TONIGHT.
Single (7"): released on Rock City Records, Oct'84 by Rock City Records. Dist: PRT Distribution

Single (12"): released on Rock City Records, Oct'84 by Rock City Records. Dist: PRT Distribution

True Believers

SPIDERMAN MEETS THE GREEN GOBLIN.
Single (7"): released on LBS, Dec'83 by LBS Records. Dist: Pinnacle

TRUE BELIEVERS.
Tracks: / Tell her / Ring the bell / So blue about you / Rebel kind / Train round the bend / Lucky moon / We're wrong / I get excited / Sleep enough to dream / Rain won't help you when it's over.
Album: released on EMI America, Aug'86 by EMI Records. Dist: EMI

Cassette: released on EMI America, Aug'86 by EMI Records. Dist: EMI

True Colours

FALLING APART AT THE SEAMS.
Single (7"): released on Body & Soul, May'85

True Confessions

TRUE CONFESSIONS Original motion picture soundtrack.
Album: released on That's Entertainment, Dec'81 by That's Entertainment Records. Dist: Pinnacle, PRT

True Life Confessions

DON'T CALL ME CHICKENHEAD.
Single (7"): released on Speed, Apr'83

Picture disc single: released on Speed, Apr'83

Single (12"): released on Speed, Apr'83

HAVING A BATH.
Single (7"): released on Speed, Oct'82

WITCHDOCTOR (OO EE OO AH).
Single (7"): released on Speed, Nov'82

True Love Orchestra

WEDDING SONG (THE).
Tracks: / Wedding song (The) / Sad movies.
Single (7"): released on BBC, Aug'86 by BBC Records & Tapes. Dist: EMI, PRT.

True mathematics

AFTER DARK.
Tracks: / After dark / Greeks in the house.
Notes: Pic bag
Single (7"): released on Champion, Apr'87 by Champion Records. Dist: RCA

Single (12"): released on Champion, Apr'87 by Champion Records. Dist: RCA

True romances

TRUE ROMANCES (Various Artists).
Tracks: / Donna / Tell Laura I love her / Susie Darlin' / Mr.Lee / Teen girl / Maybe / Poetry in motion / Mountain of love / Sea of love / At the hop / To know him is to love him / Come softly to me.
Album: released on Topline, Feb'87 by Charly Records. Dist: Charly Distribution

Cassette: released on Topline, Feb'87 by Charly Records. Dist: Charly Distribution

True Stories

TRUE STORIES Original soundtrack (Various Artists).
Tracks: / Cocktail desperado / Freeway son / Brownie's theme / Mall musak / Dinner music / Disco hits! / City of steel / Love theme from true stories / Festa para um rei negro / Buster's theme / Soy de bejas / I love metal buildings / Glass operator.
Notes: Apart from being the latest album from Talking Heads . True Stories is also the title of the film that marks David Byrne's debut as a film director. True Stories (The Soundtrack) features an electric collection of tracks that represent the complete musical spectrum that David Byrne's career has spanned. This album features country classics like "Cocktail Desperado" and "City of Steel" Avant-garde classical pieces comparable with Philip Glass at his best. "Glass Operator". Traditional classics that equal Vaughan Villiams & Pucell. Cluver Diner's a fine example. The finest Tijuana/Mexicana like 'Fiesta Para un Rey Negro' and 'Latino Hawaiian',Salsa. The film opened in London on Nov 14. Sounds from True Stories (David Byrne)
Album: released on EMI, Nov'86 by EMI Records. Dist: EMI

Cassette: released on EMI, Nov'86 by EMI Records. Dist: EMI

TRUE STORIES OF THE SUPERNATURAL (Dyall, Valentine).
Double cassette: released on Chiron Cassettes, Apr'82 by Ivan Berg. Dist: Pinnacle, Record & Tape Sales

True West

DRIFTERS.
Album: released on Zippo, Dec'84 Cat. no: ZONG 004

HOLLYWOOD HOLIDAY.
Album: released on New Rose (France), '83 Dist: Cartel

Truffauts

FANNY.
Album: released on Sputnik, Jul'87

Truman, Freddie

UMPIRE STRIKES BACK, THE.
Album: released on Vlad, Jun'81 Dist: Revolver

Truman, Harry S.

TRUMAN TAPES, THE.
Album: released on Caedmon(USA), '79 by Caedmon (USA) Records. Dist: Gower, Taylors, Discovery

Cassette: released on Caedmon(USA), Dec'79 by Caedmon (USA) Records. Dist: Gower, Taylors, Discovery

Trumbauer, Frankie

BIX AND TRAM (see Beiderbecke, Bix).

JACK TEAGARDEN & FRANKIE TRUMBAUER TNT.
Album: released on Aircheck, Apr'79

Trummer Jazz

JAZZ & HOT DANCE AFTER THE NAZIS 1946-49.
Album: released on Harlequin, Sep'86 by Harlequin Records. Dist: Swift, Jazz Music, Wellard, Chris, IRS. Taylor, H.R.

Trumpet.

TRUMPET CALLS FOR THE ARMY (Close, A.E.).
Cassette: released on Major Richards, Jul'83 by Major Richards Records. Dist: Taylors

Trumpet Kings

TRUMPET KINGS (Various Artists).
Album: released on Pablo (USA), Oct'75 by Pablo Records (USA). Dist: Wellard, Chris, IMS-Polygram, BMG

Cassette: released on Pablo (USA), Oct'75 by Pablo Records (USA). Dist: Wellard, Chris, IMS-Polygram, BMG

Trumpet Album

TRUMPET ALBUM (Various Artists).
Album:

Trumpet Blues

TRUMPET BLUES 1925/29 (Various Artists).
Album: released on Historical(USA), '78 Dist: Swift, VJM

Trumpet time

TRUMPET TIME (Various Artists).
Notes: Including Louis Armstrong, Buck Clayton, Eldridge, B. Hackett, Y. Lawson.
Album: released on Jazz Society, Mar'87 Dist: Jazz Music, Swift

Trunkles

TRADITIONAL.
Album: released on Sweet Folk All, May'87 by Sweet Folk All Records. Dist: Sweet Folk Roots, Celtic Music, Dragon, Impetus, Projection, Chris Wellard, Festival Records

Truss & Bucket Band

TRUSS & BUCKET BAND.
Album: released on Carlos, Sep'84 by Car Records. Dist: Folksound

Trust

MARCHE OUR CREVE.
Album: released on CBS(France), Sep'84 by CBS Records. Dist: Conifer, Discovery, Sw

REPRESSION.
Cassette: released on CBS, Feb'81 by C Records. Dist: CBS

Album: released on CBS, Feb'81 by CBS Records. Dist: CBS

Truth

CONFUSION (HITS US EVERY TIME
Single (7"): released on Formation, Jun'83 WEA Records. Dist: WEA

Single (12"): released on Formation, Jun'8 WEA Records. Dist: WEA

Double-pack single: released on WEA, Ju by WEA Records. Dist: WEA

EXCEPTION OF LOVE.
Single (7"): released on IRS, Jun'85 Dist: F gram

Single (12"): released on IRS, Jun'85 Polygram

PLAYGROUND.
Album: released on I.R.S.(Independent ord Syndicate), May'85 by I.R.S. Dist: MC

Cassette: released on I.R.S.(Independe Record Syndicate), May'85 by I.R.S. Dist: M

Single (7"): released on Illegal, Mar'85 Faulty Products Records. Dist: Pinnacle, L ning, Cartel

Single (12"): released on Illegal, Mar'8 Faulty Products Records. Dist: Pinnacle, L ning, Cartel

STEP IN THE RIGHT DIRECTION.
Single (7"): released on Formation, Aug'8 WEA Records. Dist: WEA

Single (12"): released on Formation, Aug'8 WEA Records. Dist: WEA

WEAPONS OF LOVE.
Tracks: / Weapons of love / This way fore Soul deep fascination / Another new day / C or back to me / Respect / Cover up my t Edge of town, the / Until it burns / Whitha s Single (7"): released on MCA, May'87 by Records. Dist: Polygram, MCA

Single (12"): released on MCA, May'8 MCA Records. Dist: Polygram, MCA

Truths Of Dune

TRUTHS OF DUNE (Herbert, Frank).
Album: released on Caedmon(USA), M by Caedmon (USA) Records. Dist: Gower lors, Discovery

Cassette: released on Caedmon(U May'80 by Caedmon (USA) Records. Gower, Taylors. Discovery

Trux

BAD LUCK.
Single (7"): released on Trux, Mar'83 Dist

Trying To Make A Living
RYING TO MAKE A LIVING (Various Ar- ists).
lbum: released on Red Lightnin', Sep'82 by ed Lightnin' Records. Dist: Roots, Swift, Jazz lusic, JSU, Pinnacle, Cartel, Wynd-Up Dis- ibution

TSA
EAVY HEAVY METAL.
lbum: released on American Phonogram, ar'85 by PRT Records. Dist: PRT

PUNK.
lbum: released on Mega (Supermusic), eb'84 by Pinnacle Records. Dist: Pinnacle

Tsai-Ping, Liang Professor
HINESE CHENG-ANCIENT & MOD- RN.
lbum: released on Lyrichord (USA), Oct'81 by richord Records (USA). Dist: Flexitron Dis- butors Ltd

T.S.Eliot
LD POSSUM'S BOOK OF PRACTICAL ATS (John Gielgud & Irene Worth).
ssette: released on Caedmon(USA), Aug'83 Caedmon (USA) Records. Dist: Gower, Tay- s, Discovery

Tse-Tung Mao
UOTATIONS FROM THE CHAIRMAN.
bum: released on Peerless, Jan'75

Tshala Muana
POKOLA.
bum: released on Safari sound (African), g'85

Tsiboe, Reggie
THER AND CHILD REUNION.
gle (7"): released on Arista, Nov'85 by Aris- Records. Dist: RCA

gle (12"): released on Arista, Nov'85 by sta Records. Dist: RCA

Tsol
IANGE TODAY.
bum: released on Enigma, Nov'86 by Enig- Records. Dist: Rough Trade, Cartel, EMI

AND RUN.
um: released on Enigma, Jun'76 by Enigma cords. Dist: Rough Trade, Cartel, EMI

um: released on Enigma, Jun'87 by Enigma cords. Dist: Rough Trade, Cartel, EMI

VENGE.
um: released on Enigma, Nov'86 by Enig- Records. Dist: Rough Trade, Cartel, EMI

Tsumani
IT IS.
gle (12"): released on Neon, Jan'82 by n Records. Dist: Neon, Pinnacle

Tsunami
JNAMI.
m: released on Music For Nations, Dec'83 usic For Nations Records. Dist: Pinnacle

Tsunami Ride
FAR BY FAR.
ks: / Too far by far / I had.
le (7"): released on Ocean, Sep'86 by an Records. Dist: PRT

le (12"): released on Ocean, Sep'86 by an Records. Dist: PRT

T Highlights
IGHLIGHTS 1957/64 VOL 1 (TT High- 1957/64 vol 1).
m: released on Sound Stories, Feb'80 H.R. Taylor

IGHLIGHTS 1965/8 VOL 2 (TT High- 1965/8 vol 2).
m: released on Sound Stories, Feb'80 H.R. Taylor

T Quick
AL OF HONOUR.
ks: / Metal of honour / Front burner / Hard ck / Child of sin / Asleep at the wheel / beat the band / Hell to pay queen of the / Glad all over / Glad all over / Siren song.
s: T T Quick are David Dipetro guitar, Mark lo vocals, Walt Fortune-bass Eric -drums
m: released on Island, Oct'86 by Island rds. Dist: Polygram

ette: released on Island, Oct'86 by Island Records. Dist: Polygram

Tuatara
TUATARA Various artists (Various Artists).
Album: released on Flying Nun, Oct'86 Dist: Rough Trade, Cartel

Tubal Cain
LOOK OUT.
Album: released on Myrrh, Jun'85 by Word Records. Dist: Word Distribution

Cassette: released on Myrrh, Jun'95 by Word Records. Dist: Word Distribution

Tubb, Ernest
BLUE CHRISTMAS (Tubb, Ernest And His Texas Troubadours).
Album: released on Stetson, Oct'86 by Hasmick Promotions Ltd.. Dist: Counterpoint Distribution, H.R. Taylor Distribution, Swift Distribution, Chris Wellard Distribution

Cassette: released on Stetson, Oct'86 by Hasmick Promotions Ltd.. Dist: Counterpoint Distribution, H.R. Taylor Distribution, Swift Distribution, Chris Wellard Distribution

COUNTRY MUSIC HALL OF FAME.
Album: released on MCA Coral, May'79 by MCA Records. Dist: Polygram

DADDY OF EM ALL (THE).
Album: released on Stetson, Apr'86 by Hasmick Promotions Ltd.. Dist: Counterpoint Distribution, H.R. Taylor Distribution, Swift Distribution, Chris Wellard Distribution

Cassette: released on Stetson, Apr'86 by Hasmick Promotions Ltd.. Dist: Counterpoint Distribution, H.R. Taylor Distribution, Swift Distribution, Chris Wellard Distribution

ERNEST TUBB STORY (THE).
Tracks: / I'll get along somehow / Slippin around / Filipino baby / When the world has turned you down / Have you ever been lonely / There's a little bit of everything in Texas / Walkin the floor over you / Driftwood on the river / There's nothing more to say / Rainbow at midnight / I'll be glad to take you back / Let's say goodbye like we said hello / Careless darlin don't rob another man's castle / I wonder why you said goodbye / Last night I dreamed / Letters have no arms / Though the days were only seven / I love you because / You nearly lose your mind / I'll miss you when you go / It's been so long darlin / Tomorrow never comes / Blue christmas.
Double Album: released on MCA Import, Mar'86 by MCA Records. Dist: Polygram, IMS

FAVOURITES.
Album: released on Stetson, Jun'86 by Hasmick Promotions Ltd.. Dist: Counterpoint Distribution, H.R. Taylor Distribution, Swift Distribution, Chris Wellard Distribution

Cassette: released on Stetson, Jun'86 by Hasmick Promotions Ltd.. Dist: Counterpoint Distribution, H.R. Taylor Distribution, Swift Distribution, Chris Wellard Distribution

Album: released on Stetson, Feb'86 by Hasmick Promotions Ltd.. Dist: Counterpoint Distribution, H.R. Taylor Distribution, Swift Distribution, Chris Wellard Distribution

Cassette: released on Stetson, Feb'86 by Hasmick Promotions Ltd.. Dist: Counterpoint Distribution, H.R. Taylor Distribution, Swift Distribution, Chris Wellard Distribution

GOLDEN FAVOURITES.
Tracks: / I'll get along somehow / Slipping around / Filipino baby / Have you ever been lonely (have you ever been blue) / There's a little bit of everything in Texas / Walking the floor over you / Driftwood on the river / There's nothing more to say / Rainbow at midnight / I'll always be glad to take you back / Let's say goodbye like we said hello / When the world has turned you down.
Album: released on MCA Import, Mar'86 by MCA Records. Dist: Polygram, IMS

GREATEST HITS:ERNEST TUBB.
Tracks: / Walking the floor over you / Rainbow at midnight / Let's say goodbye like we said hello / Another story / Thanks a lot / Half a mind / I'll get along somehow / Waltz across Texas / It's been so long darling / Mr Juke Box / I wonder you said goodbye.
Album: released on MCA Import, Mar'86 by MCA Records. Dist: Polygram, IMS

IMPORTANCE OF BEING ERNEST (THE).
Tracks: / I'm a long gone daddy / All those yesterdays / San Antonio rose / That, my darlin, is me / Educated mama / I wonder why I worry over you / Your cheatin heart / It makes no difference now / Ships that never come in / Don't change your old fashioned sweetheart / It's the age that makes the difference.
Album: released on Stetson, Nov'85 by Hasmick Promotions Ltd.. Dist: Counterpoint Distribution, H.R. Taylor Distribution, Swift Distribution, Chris Wellard Distribution

Cassette: released on Stetson, Nov'85 by Hasmick Promotions Ltd.. Dist: Counterpoint Distribution, H.R. Taylor Distribution, Swift Distribution, Chris Wellard Distribution

MIDNIGHT JAMBOREE.
Album: released on Stetson, Apr'87 by Hasmick Promotions Ltd.. Dist: Counterpoint Distribution, H.R. Taylor Distribution, Swift Distribution, Chris Wellard Distribution

Cassette: released on Stetson, Apr'87 by Hasmick Promotions Ltd.. Dist: Counterpoint Distribution, H.R. Taylor Distribution, Swift Distribution, Chris Wellard Distribution

Tubb, Justin
JUSTIN TUBB.
Album: released on MCA, Mar'87 by MCA Records. Dist: Polygram, MCA

Cassette: released on MCA, Mar'87 by MCA Records. Dist: Polygram, MCA

Tubby, King
SHALUM DUB (Tubby, King & the Aggrovators).
Album: released on Klik, Mar'76 by Relic. Dist: Swift Deleted '79.

Tube Album
TUBE ALBUM Various Artists (Various Artists).
Album: released on Starblend, Nov'85 by Starblend Records. Dist: PRT Distribution

Cassette: released on Starblend, Nov'85 by Starblend Records. Dist: PRT Distribution

Tubes
COMPLETION BACKWARD PRINCIPLE,THE.
Album: released on Capitol, May'81 by Capitol Records. Dist: EMI

DON'T WANT TO WAIT ANYMORE.
Single (7"): released on Capitol, Jul'81 by Capitol Records. Dist: EMI

OUTSIDE/INSIDE.
Album: released on Capitol, May'83 by Capitol Records. Dist: EMI

Cassette: released on Capitol, May'83 by Capitol Records. Dist: EMI

PRIME TIME.
Album: released on Plastic Head, Nov'86 Dist: Pinnacle, Rough Trade, Cartel

REMOTE CONTROL.
Album: released on A&M, Mar'79 by A&M Records. Dist: Polygram

Cassette: released on A&M, Mar'79 by A&M Records. Dist: Polygram

SHE'S A BEAUTY/WHEN YOU'RE READY TO COME/FANTASTIC DELUSION.
Single (7"): released on Capitol, Apr'83 by Capitol Records. Dist: EMI

Single (12"): released on Capitol, Apr'83 by Capitol Records. Dist: EMI

SUSHI GIRL/MR HATE.
Single (7"): released on Capitol, Oct'81 by Capitol Records. Dist: EMI

TRASH.
Tracks: / Drivin all night / What do you want from life / Turn me on / Slipped my disco / Mondo bondage / Love will keep us together / I'm just a mess / Only the strong survive / Don't touch me there / White punks on dope / Prime time.
Notes: This title means Tubes Rarities and Smash Hits and the album lives up to that title with a collection of gems including Don't touch me there and White punks on dope and Prime time.
Album: released on A&M, Apr'86 by A&M Records. Dist: Polygram

Cassette: released on A&M, Apr'86 by A&M Records. Dist: Polygram

TUBES (THE).
Double compact disc: released on Mobile Fidelity Sound, Dec'85 by Mobile Fidelity Records.

TUBES, THE.
Compact disc: released on Mobile Fidelity, '86 by Mobile Fidelity Records.

TUBES THE.
Album: released on Fame, May'83 by Music For Pleasure Records. Dist: EMI

Cassette: released on Fame, May'83 by Music For Pleasure Records. Dist: EMI

TUBES, THE (VIDEO).
Notes: Inc. 'Mondo bondage', 'White punks on dope' etc.
Video-cassette (VHS): released on Video Collection, May'87 by Video Collection International Ltd.. Dist: Counterpoint

TUBES VIDEO (THE).
Video-cassette (VHS): released on PMI, Nov'84 by PMI Records. Dist: EMI

Video-cassette [Betamax]: released on PMI, Nov'84 by PMI Records. Dist: EMI

WHAT DO YOU WANT FROM LIFE.
Double Album: released on A&M, Feb'78 by A&M Records. Dist: Polygram

Cassette: released on A&M, Feb'78 by A&M Records. Dist: Polygram

Tube, The
TUBE, THE Various artists (Various Artists).
Album: released on K-Tel, Mar'84 by K-Tel Records. Dist: Record Merchandisers Distribution, Taylors, Terry Blood Distribution, Wynd-Up Distribution, Relay Distribution, Pickwick Distribution, Solomon & Peres Distribution, Polygram

Tubeway Army
ARE FRIENDS ELECTRIC/WE ARE FRAGILE.
Single (7"): released on Beggars Banquet, May'79 by Beggars Banquet Records. Dist: WEA

PEEL SESSION, THE.
Single (12"): released on Strange Fruit, Aug'87 by Clive Selwood. Dist: Pinnacle

THAT'S TOO BAD/BOMBERS/OH DIDN'T I SAY.
Single (7"): released on Beggars Banquet, Aug'79 by Beggars Banquet Records. Dist: WEA

THATS TOO BAD/DO YOU NEED THE SERVICE/BOMBERS.
Single (12"): released on Beggars Banquet, Aug'83 by Beggars Banquet Records. Dist: WEA

TUBEWAY ARMY.
Album: released on Fame, May'83 by Music For Pleasure Records. Dist: EMI

Cassette: released on Fame, May'83 by Music For Pleasure Records. Dist: EMI

Tubridy, Michael
EAGLE'S WHISTLE THE.
Album: released on Claddagh, Jan'78 by Claddagh Records. Dist: I & B, Record Services Distribution (Ireland), Roots, Topic, Impetus, Projection, CM

Tuccedo
TO TOUCH YOU.
Tracks: / To touch you / To touch you (version).
Single (7"): released on Chartsounds, Jul'87 by Chartsounds Records. Dist: Jetstar

Single (12"): released on Chartsounds, Jul'87 by Chartsounds Records. Dist: Jetstar

Tucker Adrian
SKYPORT'S LONDON BLUES.
Cassette: released on Folktracks, Nov'79 by Folktracks Cassettes. Dist: Folktracks

Tucker, Bessie
1928 RECORDINGS also see Ida Mae Mack (Tucker, Bessie & Ida Mae Mack).
Album: released on Magpie, Jul'79 Dist: Projection

RARE BLUES (927 - 1935).
Album: released on Historical(USA), Jan'74 Dist: Swift, VJM

Tucker, Colin Lloyd
HEAD.
Tracks: / Head / Sex slave.
Picture disc single: released on DJ, Apr'86 Dist: Rough Trade

MIND BOX.
Album: released on Plastic Head, Jan'87 Dist: Pinnacle, Rough Trade, Cartel

USE IT!.
Tracks: / Mindbox.
Single (12"): released on Plastic Head, Feb'87 Dist: Pinnacle, Rough Trade, Cartel

Tucker, Collin Lloyd
TOY BOX.
Album: released on Glass, Apr'84 by Glass Records. Dist: Nine Mile, Rough Trade, Red Rhino, Play It Again Sam

Tucker, George
DEATH OF FLOYD COLLINS.
Album: released on Rounder (USA), Jun'77

Tucker, Junior
ONE OF THE POOREST PEOPLE.
Single (7"): released on Island, Mar'81 by Island Records. Dist: Polygram

SOME GUYS HAVE ALL THE LUCK.
Single (7"): released on Island, Sep'80 by Island Records. Dist: Polygram

Tucker, Louise
NO TEARS TO CRY/RUNNING MAN/MIDNIGHT BLUE/ONLY FOR YOU.
Single (7"): released on Ariola, Jan'84 Dist: RCA, Ariola

Single (12"): released on Ariola, Jan'84 Dist: RCA, Ariola

Tucker, Marshall Band
RUNNING LIKE THE WIND.
Album: released on Warner Brothers, Jun'79 by WEA Records. Dist: WEA

Tucker, Mickey, Trio
SWEET LOTUS LIPS.
Album: released on Denon, Mar'82

Tucker, Mikey
CRAWL THE.
Album: released on Muse, Apr'81 by Import Records. Dist: Jazz Horizons Distribution, Jazz Music Distribution, JSU Distribution, Swift Distribution

MYSTER MYSTERIOUS.
Album: released on Muse, Apr'81 by Import Records. Dist: Jazz Horizons Distribution, Jazz Music Distribution, JSU Distribution, Swift Distribution

THEME FROM A WOOGIE BOOGIE.
Album: released on Denon, Mar'82 by Denon Records. Dist: Harmonia Mundi

Tucker, Sophie
FOLLOW A STAR.
Notes: 16 tracks from 1922-1931.
Album: released on ASV, Mar'87 by Academy Sound & Vision Records. Dist: Pinnacle

Cassette: released on ASV, Mar'87 by Academy Sound & Vision Records. Dist: Pinnacle

GOLDEN AGE OF SOPHIE TUCKER THE.
Album: released on Golden Age, Jul'85 by Music For Pleasure Records. Dist: EMI

Cassette: released on Golden Age, Jul'85 by Music For Pleasure Records. Dist: EMI

SOME OF THESE DAYS.
Album: released on World Records, Aug'76 Dist: Polygram

Cassette: released on World Records, Aug'76 Dist: Polygram

SOPHIE TUCKER.
Album: released on Deja Vu, Jan'87 by Deja Vu Records. Dist: Counterpoint Distribution, Record Services Distribution (Ireland)

Cassette: released on Deja Vu, Jan'87 by Deja Vu Records. Dist: Counterpoint Distribution, Record Services Distribution (Ireland)

VINTAGE SHOE BIZS GREATS also see Lewis, Ted (Tucker, Sophie & Lewis Ted).

Tucker, Tanya
AT THE COUNTRY STORE.
Album: released on Country Store, Apr'87 by Starblend Records. Dist: PRT, Prism Leisure Corporation Records

Cassette: released on Country Store, Apr'87 by Starblend Records. Dist: PRT, Prism Leisure Corporation Records

GIRLS LIKE ME.
Tracks: / One love at a time / I'll come back as another woman / Fool fool heart / Just another love / Girls like me / Somebody to care / It's only over for you / Daddy long legs / You could change my mind / Still hold on.
Album: released on Capitol, Apr'86 by Capitol Records. Dist: EMI

Cassette: released on Capitol, Apr'86 by Capitol Records. Dist: EMI

LOVE ME LIKE YOU USED TO.
Tracks: / If it don't come easy / Love me like you used to / I won't take less than your love / I wonder what he's doing tonight / I'll Tennessee you in / Alien / Temporarily blue / If I didn't love you / Heartbreaker / Hope you find what you're loving for.
Album: released on Capitol, Aug'87 by Capitol Records. Dist: EMI

Cassette: released on Capitol, Aug'87 by Capitol Records. Dist: EMI

Compact disc: released on Capitol, Aug'87 by Capitol Records. Dist: EMI

Cassette: released on Capitol, Aug'87 by Capitol Records. Dist: EMI

Compact disc: released on Capitol, Aug'87 by Capitol Records. Dist: EMI

Album: released on Capitol, Aug'87 by Capitol Records. Dist: EMI

ONE LOVE AT A TIME.
Tracks: / One love at a time / Fool fool heart.
Single (7"): released on Capitol, Mar'86 by Capitol Records. Dist: EMI

Tucker, Tommy
HI HEEL SNEAKERS/IS THAT THE WAY GOD PLANNED IT.
Single (7"): released on Red Lightnin', Sep'82 by Red Lightnin' Records. Dist: Roots, Swift, Jazz Music, JSU, Pinnacle, Cartel, Wynd-Up Distribution

MOTHER TUCKER.
Album: released on Red Lightnin', Aug'84 by Red Lightnin' Records. Dist: Roots, Swift, Jazz Music, JSU, Pinnacle, Cartel, Wynd-Up Distribution

ROCKS IS MY PILLOW THE- THE COLD GROUND IS MY BED.
Album: released on Red Lightnin', Sep'82 by Red Lightnin' Records. Dist: Roots, Swift, Jazz Music, JSU, Pinnacle, Cartel, Wynd-Up Distribution

Tucker, Tyke & Tina
CUDDLY BEAR/WHOA MULE WHOA.
Single (7"): released on Thrust, Jul'82 by Chiswick Records. Dist: Pinnacle

Tuckwell, Barry
MUSIC OF COLE PORTER, THE (Tuckwell, Barry / George Shearing).
Notes: For full details see under Shearing, George & Barry Tuckwell

PLAY THE MUSIC OF COLE PORTER (Tuckwell, Barry / George Shearing).
Notes: For full information see under Shearing, George & Barry Tuckwell

Tudor.Eddie Tempole
HAYRICK SONG/TAKE YOU TO THE DANCE.
Single (7"): released on Stiff, Apr'83 by Stiff Records. Dist: EMI, Record Services Distribution (Ireland)

Single (12"): released on Stiff, Jun'83 by Stiff Records. Dist: EMI, Record Services Distribution (Ireland)

Tudor, Johnny
RATTLE MY BONES.
Album: released on President, Nov'82 by President Records. Dist: Taylors, Spartan

RHYMNEY.
Single (7"): released on President, Aug'85 by President Records. Dist: Taylors, Spartan

Tudors
TIED UP WITH LOU COOL/CRY BABY CRY.
Single (7"): released on Stiff, Feb'83 by Stiff Records. Dist: EMI, Record Services Distribution (Ireland)

Tudor, Stanley
CINEMA ORGAN ENCORES.
Album: released on Deroy, Jun'81 by Deroy Records. Dist: Jazz Music, Swift

Album: released on Deroy, Jun'81 by Deroy Records. Dist: Jazz Music, Swift

LET YOURSELF GO also see Heyler Jack (Tudor, Stanley & Jack Heyler).

WURLITZER ORGAN ENCORES.
Album: released on Deroy, May'86 by Deroy Records. Dist: Jazz Music. Swift

Album: released on Deroy, May'86 by Deroy Records. Dist: Jazz Music, Swift

Tuesday Blue
TUNNEL VISION.
Tracks: / Tunnel vision / Tell the boys / Don't go away.
Single (7"): released on Mother-Island, Mar'86

Single (12"): released on Mother-Island, Mar'86

Tuff Monks
AFTER THE FIREWORKS (2 PARTS).
Single (7"): released on Au-Go-Go (Australia), Oct'83 by Au-Go-Go Records (Australia). Dist: Rough Trade, Cartel

Tuff, Tony
BEST OF ONY TUFF THE.
Album: released on Vista Sounds, Jan'83 by Vista Sounds Records. Dist: Jetstar

---

BIG BOUT YA/TRADITION (BOURI).
Single (12"): released on Reggae Sound, Sep'83 by Reggae Sound Records. Dist: Jetstar

BORDER.
Single (12"): released on Volcano, Sep'84 by Volcano Records. Dist: Jetstar

CATCH A FIRE.
Album: released on Music Master, Mar'86 Dist: Jetstar Distribution

COME SEE ME.
Single (12"): released on GG'S, Oct'83 by GG'S Records. Dist: Jetstar

DANCE HALL STYLE.
Tracks: / Dance hall style / Mini bus black tree.
Single (12"): released on Black Star, Aug'86 by Black Star Records. Dist: Jetstar

GALLOP FOR ME.
Single (12"): released on Foundation, Dec'83 by Foundation Records, The. Dist: Jetstar

GIRL WATCHER.
Single (12"): released on Londisc, Mar'84 by Londisc Records.

GOOD TO CONTROL ME.
Tracks: / Good to control me / Every time.
Single (12"): released on Greensleeves, Jun'86 by Greensleeves Records. Dist: BMG, Jetstar, Spartan

HOLD THEM.
Tracks: / Hold them / Tell me.
Single (12"): released on Top Rank, Mar'86

HOLY BIBLE.
Single (12"): released on SJS, Sep'85 Dist: Jetstar

IT GOES THERE AGAIN.
Single (12"): released on SJS, Sep'85 Dist: Jetstar

JAM IT AGAIN.
Single (12"): released on Top Rank, Oct'84 by Top Rank Records. Dist: Jetstar Distribution

MARY ANN/HEAD ON STRAIGHT.
Single (12"): released on Up Tempo, Dec'83 by Up Tempo Records. Dist: Jetstar

MIX ME DOWN.
Single (12"): released on Kaya, Aug'84 by Kaya Records. Dist: Jetstar

RENDER YOUR HEART.
Album: released on CSA, Feb'84 by CSA Records. Dist: PRT, Jetstar

SETTLE.
Single (12"): released on Top Rank, Sep'84 by Top Rank Records. Dist: Jetstar Distribution

SHOW ON THE ROAD.
Single (7"): released on Island, Aug'82 by Island Records. Dist: Polygram

Single 10": released on Island, Aug'82 by Island Records. Dist: Polygram

SPIN YOUR ROLL.
Single (12"): released on Unknown, Jul'85

TONY TUFF.
Album: released on Island, Oct'80 by Island Records. Dist: Polygram

TUFF SELECTION.
Album: released on Island, Aug'82 by Island Records. Dist: Polygram

WELL TRASH.
Tracks: / Campion Jockey.
Single (12"): released on GG'S, Nov'86 by GG'S Records. Dist: Jetstar

WHA WE A GO DO.
Album: released on Top Rank, Nov'84 by Top Rank Records. Dist: Jetstar Distribution

Tuff turf
TUFF TURF Original soundtrack (Various Artists).
Album: released on Rhino (USA), Jan'86 by Rhino Records (USA).

Tullo De Piscopo
PRIMAVERA.
Tracks: / Primavera (Stop Bajon) / Primavera (Stop Bajon) (Inst).
Single (12"): released on ZYX (Germany), Mar'86 by ZYX Records. Dist: Greyhound

Tulla, Celli Band
BATTERING RAM + JIGS MEDLEY.
Single (7"): released on Shamrock (Ireland), Nov'76 Dist: I & B, EMI (Ireland), Swift, Chris Wellard, Solomon & Peres Distribution, Jazz Music

---

SWEETHEARTS IN THE SPRING.
Album: released on EMI (Ireland), Jan'73 by EMI Records (Ireland). Dist: Conifer, I & B Records Distribution

Tullio De Piscopo
PRIMAVERA.
Tracks: / Primavera (stop bajon) / Stadera.
Single (7"): released on Greyhound, Feb'87 by Greyhound Records. Dist: PRT, Greyhound

Tull, Jethro
"A".
Album: released on Chrysalis, Sep'80 by Chrysalis Records. Dist: CBS

Cassette: released on Chrysalis, Sep'80 by Chrysalis Records. Dist: CBS

BENEFIT.
Album: released on Chrysalis, Jan'74 by Chrysalis Records. Dist: CBS

Cassette: released on Chrysalis, Jan'74 by Chrysalis Records. Dist: CBS

BEST OF JETHRO TULL THE.
Album: released on Chrysalis, Jan'76 by Chrysalis Records. Dist: CBS

Cassette: released on Chrysalis, Jan'76 by Chrysalis Records. Dist: CBS

HEAVY HORSES.
Album: released on Chrysalis, Apr'78 by Chrysalis Records. Dist: CBS

Cassette: released on Chrysalis, Apr'78 by Chrysalis Records. Dist: CBS

LIVE - BURSTING OUT.
Double Album: released on Chrysalis, Jan'7 by Chrysalis Records. Dist: CBS

Double cassette: released on Chrysalis, Jan'78 by Chrysalis Records. Dist: CBS

LIVING IN THE PAST.
Double Album: released on Chrysalis, Jan'7 by Chrysalis Records. Dist: CBS

Double cassette: released on Chrysalis, Jan'74 by Chrysalis Records. Dist: CBS

MINSTRAL IN THE GALLERY.
Album: released on Chrysalis, Sep'75 by Chrysalis Records. Dist: CBS

Cassette: released on Chrysalis, Sep'75 by Chrysalis Records. Dist: CBS

MU/REPEAT.
Double cassette: released on Chrysalis(Tall 2), Dec'82 by Chrysalis Records. Dist: CBS

ORIGINAL MASTERS.
Album: released on Chrysalis, Oct'85 by Chrysalis Records. Dist: CBS

Cassette: released on Chrysalis, Oct'85 Chrysalis Records. Dist: CBS

PASSIONATE PLAY A.
Album: released on Chrysalis, Jan'73 by Chrysalis Records. Dist: CBS

Cassette: released on Chrysalis, Jan'73 Chrysalis Records. Dist: CBS

REPEAT THE BEST OF VOL LL.
Album: released on Chrysalis, Oct'77 by Chrysalis Records. Dist: CBS

SONGS FROM THE WOOD.
Album: released on Chrysalis, Feb'77 by Chrysalis Records. Dist: CBS

Cassette: released on Chrysalis, Feb'77 Chrysalis Records. Dist: CBS

STAND UP.
Album: released on Fame (Chrysalis), Nov by Music For Pleasure Records. Dist: EMI

Cassette: released on Fame (Chrysalis Nov'83 by Music For Pleasure Records. Dist: EMI

STORM WATCH.
Album: released on Chrysalis, Sep'79 by Chrysalis Records. Dist: CBS

Cassette: released on Chrysalis, Sep'79 Chrysalis Records. Dist: CBS

THICK AS A BRICK.
Album: released on Chrysalis, Jan'74 by Chrysalis Records. Dist: CBS

Cassette: released on Chrysalis, Jan'74 Chrysalis Records. Dist: CBS

THIS WAS.
Album: released on Chrysalis, Jan'74 by Chrysalis Records. Dist: CBS

Cassette: released on Chrysalis, Jan'74 by Chrysalis Records. Dist: CBS

OO OLD TO ROCK N ROLL: TOO OUNG TO DIE.
lbum: released on Chrysalis, Apr'76 by Chrysalis Records. Dist: CBS

assette: released on Chrysalis, Apr'76 by hrysalis Records. Dist: CBS

VAR CHILD.
lbum: released on Chrysalis, Sep'74 by Chrysalis Records. Dist: CBS

lbum: released on Chrysalis, Sep'74 by Chrysalis Records. Dist: CBS

assette: released on Chrysalis, Sep'74 by hrysalis Records. Dist: CBS

ORKING JOHN WORKING JOE.
ngle (7"): released on Chrysalis, Oct'80 by hrysalis Records. Dist: CBS

Tulloch Lynette

VILL/I BELIEVE YOU.
ngle (12"): released on World International, g'83 Dist: Jetstar

Tullo, Pappa

END ME A CHOPPER (see Osbourne, hnny) (Tullo, Pappa & Johnny Osbourne).

OCK AND COME ON YA (see Osbourne, hnny) (Tullo, Pappa & Johnny Osbourne).

Tulpa

OSAIC FISH.
bum: released on Midnight, Jul'85

Tumbling hearts

OU MAY NEVER KNOW.
ngle (7"): released on Exile, May'87 by Exile cords. Dist: Pinnacle

Tummings, Chris

EEDOM (see Connolly, Billy) (Tummings, ris & Billy Connolly).

Tundra

ENTISH GARLAND THE.
um: released on Sweet Folk All, May'81 by eet Folk All Records. Dist: Sweet Folk All, ots, Celtic Music, Dragon, Impetus, Projec-, Chris Wellard, Festival Records

NTISH SONGSTER THE.
um: released on Greenwich Village, May'81 Sweet Folk All Records. Dist: Roots, Projec-, Lightning, Celtic Music, Wellard, Chris

NGS FROM GREEWICH.
um: released on Greenwich Village, Jun'81 Sweet Folk All Records. Dist: Roots, Projec-, Lightning, Celtic Music, Wellard, Chris

unes

E'S MY GIRL.
um: released on RSO, Jan'80 Deleted '81.

unes of Glory

NES OF GLORY (Pipes/Drums/Military d of Scottish Div.School of Music).
um: released on Parade, Jan'81 Dist: MSD

ssette: released on Parade, Jan'81 Dist: D

une, Wranglerb Plus

STERN SWING VOL 2.
um: released on Old Timey, Jan'76

unisian Music

NISIAN MUSIC (Various Artists).
um: released on Caprice, May'76 by RCA ords. Dist: RCA

unji A to Z

NAMAN.
cks: / Bonaman / Loro.
le (7"): released on A-Z, Aug'87 by A-Z ords. Dist: Atlas, PRT

unnel Users

NCE.
le (7"): released on Xjukey, Jul'82

unnelvision

GONNA CRY.
le (7"): released on Octave, Jun'85 by Oc- Records. Dist: M.I.S. Distribution

TCHING THE HYDROPLANES.
le (7"): released on Factory, Jun'81 by ory Records. Dist: Cartel, Pinnacle

unney, Paddy

WERY VALE, THE.
um: released on Topic, '81 by Topic Rec- Dist: JSU Distribution, Projection Distribu-tion, Jazz Music Distribution

IRISH EDGE, THE.
Album: released on Topic, '81 by Topic Records. Dist: JSU Distribution, Projection Distribution, Jazz Music Distribution

LOUGH ERNE SHORE.
Album: released on Mulligan (Ireland), Sep'78 by Topic Records. Dist: Roots Distribution, Jazz Music Distribution, JSU Distribution, I & B Distribution, Projection Distribution, Wynd-Up Distribution, Celtic Distributions

MOUNTAIN STREAMS WHERE THE MOORCOCKS GROW, THE.
Album: released on Topic, '81 by Topic Records. Dist: JSU Distribution, Projection Distribution, Jazz Music Distribution

WILD BEES' NEST, A.
Album: released on Topic, '81 by Topic Records. Dist: JSU Distribution, Projection Distribution, Jazz Music Distribution

Tunnoch Brae Ceildn Band

SCOTTISH NATIONAL DANCES VOL.1.
Album: released on Grampian, '68 by Grampian Records. Dist: Grampian, Clyde Factors Distributors, Ross

Tupac-Amura

FLUTES OF THE ANDES.
Album: released on Sonet, '74 by Sonet Records. Dist: PRT

Tupou, Manu

RAVEN.
Album: released on Caedmon(USA), Aug'77 by Caedmon (USA) Records. Dist: Gower, Taylors, Discovery

Cassette: released on Caedmon(USA), Aug'77 by Caedmon (USA) Records. Dist: Gower, Taylors, Discovery

Turbines

LAST DANCE BEFORE THE HIGHWAY.
Album: released on Big Time, May'86 by Mainline Record Company. Dist: Mainline

MAGIC FINGERS AND HOURLY RATES.
Album: released on New Rose, Jun'87 Dist: Rough Trade, Cartel

Turbo

CHARGED FOR GLORY.
Single (7"): released on Turbo, Sep'82 Dist: Stage One

Turbos

REGGAE SERENADE.
Single (12"): released on Sun Set, Sep'84 by Sun Set Records. Dist: Jetstar Distribution

Turbo Trax

TURBO TRAX (Various Artists).
Album: released on K-Tel, Jun'82 by K-Tel Records. Dist: Record Merchandisers Distribution, Taylors, Terry Blood Distribution, Wynd-Up Distribution, Relay Distribution, Pickwick Distribution, Solomon & Peres Distribution, Polygram

Cassette: released on K-Tel, Jun'82 by K-Tel Records. Dist: Record Merchandisers Distribution, Taylors, Terry Blood Distribution, Wynd-Up Distribution, Relay Distribution, Pickwick Distribution, Solomon & Peres Distribution, Polygram

Turkey

FOLK MUSIC OF TURKEY.
Album: released on Topic, Jan'78 by Topic Records. Dist: JSU Distribution, Projection Distribution, Jazz Music Distribution

Album: released on Topic, '81 by Topic Records. Dist: JSU Distribution, Projection Distribution, Jazz Music Distribution

MUSICAL JOURNEY, A.
Album:

TALES FROM TURKEY.
Cassette: released on Anvil, Apr'80 Dist: Anvil

TRADITIONAL SONGS AND MUSIC.
Album: released on Lyrichord, '82 Dist: Roots

TURKISH FOLK MUSIC.
Album: released on Lyrichord (USA), Oct'81 by Lyrichord Records (USA). Dist: Flexitron Distributors Ltd

TURKISH VILLAGE MUSIC.
Album: released on Explorer, '74 by Nonesuch Records. Dist: Transatlantic Records

Turkey Bones

GOLDFISH (Turkey Bones & The Wild Dogs).
Single (7"): released on Anagram, Jul'83 by Cherry Red Records. Dist: Pinnacle

NO WAY BEFORE THE WEEKEND (Turkey Bones & The Wild Dogs).
Album: released on Big Beat, Mar'85 by Ace Records. Dist: Projection, Pinnacle

RAYMOND (Turkey Bones & The Wild Dogs).
Single (12"): released on McKechnie, Mar'84 by McKechnie Records. Dist: Cartel, Jetstar

Turn Blue

EMOTIONAL ORGASM.
Cassette: released on Dead Happy, '86 by Dead Happy Records. Dist: Mason's Music Distributors/Wholesalers, Rough Trade

TOURNIQUET BLUE.
Notes: Turn Blue are Dave Arnold and Paul Mitten.
Cassette: released on Dead Happy, '86 by Dead Happy Records. Dist: Mason's Music Distributors/Wholesalers, Rough Trade

Turncoats

MOTORBALL MELTBEAT.
Tracks: / Motorball meltbeat.
Single (12"): released on Noise A Noise, Oct'86 Dist: Rough Trade, Cartel

Turner, Ann

YOUR LIFE.
Single (7"): released on Centridge, Aug'82 by Centridge Records. Dist: PRT

Turner, Anne

TOO HOT TO HANDLE.
Tracks: / Don't stop* / Too hot to handle / Love was never easy.
Notes: * = Extra track on 12" only
Single (7"): released on RCA, Mar'87 by RCA Records. Dist: RCA, Roots, Swift, Wellard, Chris, I & B, Solomon & Peres Distribution

Single (12"): released on RCA, Mar'87 by RCA Records. Dist: RCA, Roots, Swift, Wellard, Chris, I & B, Solomon & Peres Distribution

Turner, Big Joe

BIG JOE TURNER MEMORIAL ALBUM RHYTHM AND BLUES YEARS.
Tracks: / Miss Bump Suzie / Chill is on, The / I'll never stop loving you / Don't you cry / Poor lover's blues / Still in love / Baby I still want you / TV Mama / Married woman / You know I love you / Midnight Cannonball / In the evening / Morning noon and night / Ti-Ri-Lee / Lipstick, powder and paint / Rock a while / After a while / Trouble in mind / World of trouble / Love roller coaster / I need a girl / Teenage letter / Wee baby blues (oh wee baby) / (We're gonna) Jump for joy / Sweet Sue just you / My reasons for living / Love oh careless love / Got you on my mind / Chains of love / My little honeydripper / Tomorrow night / Honey, hush.
Double Album: released on Atlantic, Jun'87 by WEA Records. Dist: WEA

Double cassette: released on Atlantic, Jun'87 by WEA Records. Dist: WEA

BLUES TRAIN (Turner,Big Joe & Roomful of Blues).
Tracks: / Crawdad hole / Red sails in the sunset / Cocka-doodle-doo / Jumpin' for Joe / I want a little girl / I know you love me / Last night / I love the way (my baby sings the blues).
Cassette: released on Muse (USA), Feb'87 by Muse Records (USA). Dist: Conifer Distribution, Jazz Music Distribution

BLUES TRAIN (Turner,Big Joe & Roomful of Blues).
Tracks: / Crawdad hole / Red sails in the sunset / Cocka-doodle doo / Jumpin' for Joe (Instrumental) / I want a little / Blues train / I know you love me / Last night(Instrumental) / I love the way (my baby sings the blues).
Notes: Big Joe Turner - vocals (except 4 & 7). Greg Piccolo - tenor saxophone & leaderRich Lataille - alto saxophone. Doug James - baritone saxophone, Bob Enos - trupet. Porkey Cohen - trombone. Al Copley - piano(except 5). Ronnie Earl Horvath - guitar. Preston Hubbard - bass, Fender bass (7only). John Rossie - drums. Special Guest: Dr. John - piano track 5). Produced by Doc Pomus & Bob Porter. Arrangements: Al Copley with Doug James, Greg Piccolo assisted by D. Stuart Hemmingway Jr. Engineer Malcolm Addey. * 4 & 7:- Jumpin' For Joe (Instrumental)/I know you love me * 5 :- I want a little
Album: released on Muse (USA), Aug'86 by Muse Records (USA). Dist: Conifer Distribution, Jazz Music Distribution

Cassette: released on Muse (USA), Aug'86 by Muse Records (USA). Dist: Conifer Distribution, Jazz Music Distribution

HAVE NO FEAR, BIG JOE IS HERE.
Tracks: / S.K. Blues / Watch that jive / Howlin' winds / Low down dog / Mad blues / Playboy blues / My gal's a Jockey / Sally Zu-Zazz / Oowee baby blues / Lucille Lucille / Careless love / Hollywood bed / Johnson & Turner blues / I got love for sale.
Album: released on RCA, Jul'86 by RCA Records. Dist: RCA, Roots, Swift, Wellard, Chris, I & B, Solomon & Peres Distribution

Cassette: released on RCA, Jul'86 by RCA Records. Dist: RCA, Roots, Swift, Wellard, Chris, I & B, Solomon & Peres Distribution

I DON'T DIG IT.
Album: released on Juke Box Lil (Sweden), May'86 by Mr. R&B Records. Dist: Swift

Turner, Bruce

DIRTY BOPPER, THE (Turner, Bruce Quartet).
Album: released on Calligraph, Sep'85 by Calligraph Records. Dist: PRT

Turner, Chris

SHINING DIAMOND.
Single (7"): released on WEA, Feb'81 by WEA Records. Dist: WEA

Turner, Chuck

TEARS.
Single (12"): released on Jammy's, Aug'87 by Jammy's Records. Dist: Jetstar

Turner, Earl

LOVE CAUGHT YOU BY SURPRISE.
Tracks: / Love caught you by surprise / Love caught you by suprise(Instrumental).
Single (7"): released on Fourth & Broadway, Jan'86 by Island Records. Dist: Polygram, EMI

Single (12"): released on Fourth & Broadway, Jan'86 by Island Records. Dist: Polygram, EMI

Turner, Ike

HEY HEY (Turner, Ike & The Kings of Rhythm).
Album: released on Red Lightnin', Apr'84 by Red Lightnin' Records. Dist: Roots, Swift, Jazz Music, JSU, Pinnacle, Cartel, Wynd-Up Distribution

IKE TURNER & HIS KINGS OF RHYTHM - VOL.1 (Turner, Ike & The Kings of Rhythm).
Album: released on Ace, Nov'80 by Ace Records. Dist: Pinnacle, Swift, Hotshot, Cadillac

IKE TURNER & THE KINGS OF RHYTHM From Cobra & Artistic 1958-1959 (Turner, Ike & The Kings of Rhythm).
Album: released on Flyright, Jun'81 by Flyright Records. Dist: Krazy Kat, Swift, Jazz Music

I'M TORE UP (Turner, Ike & The Kings of Rhythm).
Album: released on Red Lightnin', Sep'82 by Red Lightnin' Records. Dist: Roots, Swift, Jazz Music, JSU, Pinnacle, Cartel, Wynd-Up Distribution

KINGS OF RHYTHM.
Album: released on Flyright, Oct'86 by Flyright Records. Dist: Krazy Kat, Swift, Jazz Music

ROCKIN' BLUES.
Tracks: / Prancing / Things I used to do, The / Gully, The / Think / You're still my baby / Katanga / Tacks in my shoes / Right on / Rockin' blues / That's alright / Broken heart / If you love me like you say / Bootie lip / (You can have) the city / Neckin' / These dreams / Soppin' molasses.
Album: released on Stateside, Oct'86 Dist: EMI

Cassette: released on Stateside, Oct'86 Dist: EMI

VOLUME 2.
Album: released on Ace, Aug'85 by Ace Records. Dist: Pinnacle, Swift, Hotshot, Cadillac

Turner, Ike & Tina

BEST OF IKE & TINA TURNER.
Tracks: / I idolize you / Fool in love, A / Sexy Ida (part 2) / It's gonna work out fine / Stagger Lee and Billy / Man's crazy (The) / Letter from Tina, A / River deep mountain high / Workin'together / Nutbush City Limits / Proud Mary / Acid Queen / Baby get it on / Honky tonk woman / Funky Street (live).
Compact disc: released on United Artists, Apr'87

BLACK ANGEL.
Album: released on Musi-disc, Oct'76

BLACK BEAUTY.
Album: released on Musi-disc, Jan'77

Cassette: released on Musi-disc, Jan'77

CRAZY 'BOUT YOU.
Album: released on Platinum (W.Germany), Oct'85 Dist: Mainline

Cassette: released on Platinum (W.Germany), Oct'85 Dist: Mainline

DYNAMIC DUO, THE.
Tracks: / If I can't be first / Goodbye so long / I don't need / Flee flee flee / It's crazy baby / Hard times / Don't you blame it on Mr / Gonna have fun / I wish my dream would come true / Am I a fool in love / Something came over me / Hurt is all you gave me.
Album: released on Crown, Feb'86 by Ace Records. Dist: Pinnacle, Swift

Cassette: released on Crown, Feb'86 by Ace Records. Dist: Pinnacle, Swift

FANTASTIC IKE & TINA.
Album: released on Sunset, '74 Dist: EMI

Cassette: released on Sunset, '74 Dist: EMI

FOOL IN LOVE, A.
Compact disc: released on MCS Look Back, Jul'87

GOLDEN EMPIRE.
Tracks: / Mississippi rolling stone / Living for the city / Golden empire / I'm looking for my mind / Shake a hand / Bootsie whitelaw / Too much man for one woman / I know (you don't want me no more) / Rockin' and rollin' / Never been to Spain.
Notes: Musicians: Warren Datson- bass guitar. Rick Ellis- rhythm guitar. Richard Gibbs- keyboard. Richard Griffin- rhythm guitar, drums. Kerry Hatch- bass guitar. Soko Richardson- drums. Ike Turner- lead guitar, drums, keyboard. Ike Turner Jr.- bass guitar, drums, keyboard. Michael Turner- rhythm guitar, lead guitar. Ronnie Turner- bass guitar. Claude Williams- horns, keyboard. Eric Williams- rhythm guitar. Charles Wilson- keyboards. Robert Wilson- bass guitar. Ronny Wilson- horns, keyboard. Produced, engineered and arranged by Ike Turner. Exec. Producers: Carlo Nasi & Don Murray. Recorded at Bolic Studio, Los Angeles, CA. Remixed at Sunset Sound Factory by Carlo Nasi and Don Murray assisted by Doug Schwartz and Tchad Blake.
Album: released on Teldec (Germany), Apr'86 by Import Records. Dist: IMS Distribution, Polygram Distribution

Cassette: released on Teldec (Germany), Apr'86 by Import Records. Dist: IMS Distribution, Polygram Distribution

GOLDEN EMPIRE 1 & 2.
Tracks: / Mssissippi rolling stone / Living in the city / Golden empire / I'm looking for my mind / Shake a hand / Bootsie whitelaw / Too much man for one woman / I know (you don't want me no more) / Rockin' and rollin' / Never been to Spain.
Album: released on Spartan, Aug'86 by Spartan Records. Dist: Spartan

GREAT ALBUM, THE.
Double Album: released on Musidisc (France), Jun'84 Dist: Discovery Distribution, Swift Distribution

HER MAN...HIS WOMAN.
Album: released on Stateside, Oct'85 Dist: EMI
Cat. no: EG 2607331
Cassette: released on Stateside, Oct'85 Dist: EMI

Cassette: released on Audio Fidelity, Oct'84 Dist: PRT

IKE AND TINA SESSIONS.
Compact disc: released on Kent, Mar'87 by Ace Records. Dist: Pinnacle

IKE & TINA SESSIONS.
Album: released on Kent, Feb'87 by Ace Records. Dist: Pinnacle

Cassette: released on Kent, Feb'87 by Ace Records. Dist: Pinnacle

IKE & TINA TURNER.
Compact disc: released on Intertape, Jul'87 Dist: Target

IKE & TINA TURNER SHOW LIVE, THE.
Album: released on Edsel, Apr'85 by Demon Records. Dist: Pinnacle, Jazz Music, Projection

JUKE BOX GIANTS.
Album: released on Audio Fidelity, May'82 Dist: PRT

LIVING FOR THE CITY.
Tracks: / Living for the city / Push.
Single (7"): released on Spartan, Apr'86 by Spartan Records. Dist: Spartan

Single (12"): released on Spartan, Apr'86 by Spartan Records. Dist: Spartan

NICE AND ROUGH.
Album: released on Liberty, Mar'84 by Liberty-United. Dist: EMI

Cassette: released on Liberty, Mar'84 by Liberty-United. Dist: EMI

NUTBUSH CITY LIMITS.
Single (7"): released on United Artists, Aug'73

RIVER DEEP, MOUNTAIN HIGH.
Album: released on Music For Pleasure, Dec'79 by EMI Records. Dist: EMI

Album: released on Spot, May'84 by Pickwick Records. Dist: H.R. Taylor, Lugtons

Cassette: released on Spot, May'84 by Pickwick Records. Dist: H.R. Taylor, Lugtons

Single (7"): released on Old Gold (Reissue), Jul'82

ROCK ME BABY.
Tracks: / Crazy 'bout you baby / Too hot to hold / Please love me / I smell trouble / It sho' ain't me / We need an understanding / Beauty is just skin deep / Shake a tail feather / Rock me baby / So fine / My babe / Ain't nobody's business / I better getta steppin' / Betcha can't kiss me (just one time) / Fool in love, A / You're so fine.
Compact disc: released on Topline, Apr'87 by Charly Records. Dist: Charly Distribution

Album: released on Bulldog, Sep'82 by Bulldog Records. Dist: President Distribution, Spartan, Swift, Taylor, H.R.

Album: released on Astan, Nov'84 by Astan Records. Dist: Counterpoint

Cassette: released on Astan, Nov'84 by Astan Records. Dist: Counterpoint

Album: released on Topline, Nov'84 by Charly Records. Dist: Charly Distribution

Cassette: released on Topline, Nov'84 by Charly Records. Dist: Charly Distribution

SO FINE.
Album: released on Happy Bird (Germany), Jun'83 Dist: Polygram, IMS

Cassette: released on Happy Bird (Germany), Jun'83 Dist: Polygram, IMS

SOUL OF IKE & TINA, THE.
Album: released on Kent, Apr'84 by Ace Records. Dist: Pinnacle

SOUL OF IKE & TINA TURNER.
Album: released on Musi-disc, May'78

SOUL SELLERS.
Album: released on Liberty, Oct'79 by Liberty-United. Dist: EMI

Cassette: released on Liberty, Nov'79 by Liberty-United. Dist: EMI Deleted '81.

TOO HOT TO HANDLE.
Cassette: released on Orchid Music, Feb'82 by Bibi. Dist: Pinnacle

TOUGH ENOUGH.
Album: released on Liberty, Sep'84 by Liberty-United. Dist: EMI

Cassette: released on Liberty, Sep'84 by Liberty-United. Dist: EMI

Turner, Joe

ANOTHER EPOCH STRIDE PIANO.
Album: released on Pablo (USA), '82 by Pablo Records (USA). Dist: Wellard, Chris, IMS-Polygram, BMG

Cassette: released on Pablo (USA), '82 by Pablo Records (USA). Dist: Wellard, Chris, IMS-Polygram, BMG

BEST OF JOE TURNER, THE.
Album: released on Pablo (USA), '82 by Pablo Records (USA). Dist: Wellard, Chris, IMS-Polygram, BMG

Cassette: released on Pablo (USA), '82 by Pablo Records (USA). Dist: Wellard, Chris, IMS-Polygram, BMG

BOSSES, THE (See Basie, Count) (Turner, Joe & Count Basie).
Album: released on Pablo (USA), '82 by Pablo Records (USA). Dist: Wellard, Chris, IMS-Polygram, BMG

Cassette: released on Pablo (USA), '82 by Pablo Records (USA). Dist: Wellard, Chris, IMS-Polygram, BMG

BOSSES, THE (Turner, Joe & Count Basie).
Album: released on Pablo (USA), '82 by Pablo Records (USA). Dist: Wellard, Chris, IMS-Polygram, BMG

Cassette: released on Pablo (USA), '82 by Pablo Records (USA). Dist: Wellard, Chris, IMS-Polygram, BMG

BOSS OF THE BLUES That's jazz - Vol.14.
Album: released on Atlantic, Jul'76 by WEA Records. Dist: WEA

EVERYDAY I HAVE THE BLUES (Turner, Joe, Pee Wee Crayton & Sonny Stitt).
Album: released on Pablo (USA), '82 by Pablo Records (USA). Dist: Wellard, Chris, IMS-Polygram, BMG

Cassette: released on Pablo (USA), '82 by Pablo Records (USA). Dist: Wellard, Chris, IMS-Polygram, BMG

GREAT RHYTHM & BLUES - VOL.4.
Album: released on Bulldog, Jul'82 by Bulldog Records. Dist: President Distribution, Spartan, Swift, Taylor, H.R.

GREAT RHYTHM & BLUES OLDIES.
Album: released on Carosello, Feb'83 Dist: Jazz Music, Jazz Horizons

HAVE NO FEAR, JOE TURNER IS HERE.
Album: released on Pablo (USA), '82 by Pablo Records (USA). Dist: Wellard, Chris, IMS-Polygram, BMG

Cassette: released on Pablo (USA), '82 by Pablo Records (USA). Dist: Wellard, Chris, IMS-Polygram, BMG

Double Album: released on Savoy (USA), Mar'85 by Arista Records. Dist: Polygram, Swift

IN THE EVENING.
Album: released on Pablo (USA), '82 by Pablo Records (USA). Dist: Wellard, Chris, IMS-Polygram, BMG

Cassette: released on Pablo (USA), '82 by Pablo Records (USA). Dist: Wellard, Chris, IMS-Polygram, BMG

JUMPIN' THE BLUES (Turner,Joe/Pete Johnson).
Album: released on Arhoolie, May'81 by Arhoolie Records. Dist: Projection, Topic, Jazz Music, Swift, Roots

JUMPIN' TONIGHT.
Album: released on Pathe MarconiFrance), Apr'85

JUMPIN' WITH JOE.
Album: released on Charly(R&B), Apr'84 by Charly Records. Dist: Charly, Cadillac

Cassette: released on Charly(R&B), Apr'84 by Charly Records. Dist: Charly, Cadillac

KANSAS CITY, HERE I COME.
Album: released on Pablo (USA), Sep'84 by Pablo Records (USA). Dist: Wellard, Chris, IMS-Polygram, BMG

KANSAS CITY SHOUT (Turner, Joe, Count Basie & Eddie Vinson).
Album: released on Pablo (USA), '82 by Pablo Records (USA). Dist: Wellard, Chris, IMS-Polygram, BMG

Cassette: released on Pablo (USA), '82 by Pablo Records (USA). Dist: Wellard, Chris, IMS-Polygram, BMG

LIFE AIN'T EASY.
Album: released on Pablo (USA), May'83 by Pablo Records (USA). Dist: Wellard, Chris, IMS-Polygram, BMG

Cassette: released on Pablo (USA), May'83 by Pablo Records (USA). Dist: Wellard, Chris, IMS-Polygram, BMG

MIDNIGHT SPECIAL, THE.
Album: released on Pablo (USA), '82 by Pablo Records (USA). Dist: Wellard, Chris, IMS-Polygram, BMG

Cassette: released on Pablo (USA), '82 by Pablo Records (USA). Dist: Wellard, Chris, IMS-Polygram, BMG

NOBODY IN MIND.
Album: released on Pablo (USA), '82 by Pablo Records (USA). Dist: Wellard, Chris, IMS-Polygram, BMG

PATCHA PATCHA (Turner, Joe & Jimmy Witherspoon).
Album: released on Pablo (USA), Sep'86 by Pablo Records (USA). Dist: Wellard, Chris, IMS-Polygram, BMG

Cassette: released on Pablo (USA), Sep'86 by Pablo Records (USA). Dist: Wellard, Chris, IMS-Polygram, BMG

ROCK THIS JOINT (Turner, Big Joe).
Album: released on Magnum Force, Dec'84 by Magnum Music Group Ltd. Dist: Magnum Music Group Ltd, PRT, Spartan

ROOMFUL OF BLUES (Turner, Big Joe).
Album: released on Muse, May'83 Dist: JSU Distribution, Jazz Horizons Distribution, Jazz Music Distribution, Celtic Music Distribution

THINGS THAT I USED TO DO.
Album: released on Pablo (USA), '82 by Pablo Records (USA). Dist: Wellard, Chris, IMS-Polygram, BMG

Cassette: released on Pablo (USA), '82 by Pablo Records (USA). Dist: Wellard, Chris, IMS-Polygram, BMG

TRUMPET KINGS MEET JOE TURNER, THE.
Album: released on Pablo (USA), '82 by Pablo Records (USA). Dist: Wellard, Chris, IMS-Polygram, BMG

Cassette: released on Pablo (USA), '82 by Pablo Records (USA). Dist: Wellard, Chris, IMS-Polygram, BMG

Turner, Joe Lynn

ENDLESSLY.
Single (7"): released on Elektra, Oct'85 by WEA Records. Dist: WEA

RESCUE YOU.
Album: released on Elektra, Nov'85 by WEA Records. Dist: WEA

Cassette: released on Elektra, Nov'85 by WEA Records. Dist: WEA

Turner, John

JEWEL.
Album: released on Jewel, Feb'87

Turner, Ken

KEN TURNER COLLECTION THE.
Album: released on Dansan, Oct'79 by Spartan Records. Dist: Spartan

Cassette: released on Dansan, Oct'79 by Spartan Records. Dist: Spartan

Turner, Ken & His Orchestra

FOUR FESTIVAL REQUESTS IN STRICT TEMPO.
Album: released on Dansan, '82 by Spartan Records. Dist: Spartan

Cassette: released on Dansan, '82 by Spartan Records. Dist: Spartan

Turner, Ken Orchestra

BLACPOOL SALUTES THE CHAMPION.
Album: released on Dansan, Jul'80 by Spartan Records. Dist: Spartan

Cassette: released on Dansan, Jul'80 by Spartan Records. Dist: Spartan

Turner, Nik

BONES OF ELVIS/SIDS SONG.
Single (7"): released on Avatar, Feb'82 by Avatar Communications. Dist: CBS

SPHYNX-XITINTODAY.
Tracks: / Awakening, The / Pyramid spell / H... of double truth, The / Anubis Thoth / Horos, Is... & Nepthys.
Notes: Originally released April 1986
Album: by Virgin Records. Dist: EMI Delet... Oct'86.

Turner, Pierce

HE'S ONLY A LONG WAY ACROSS.
Album: released on Beggars Banquet, Oct'... by Beggars Banquet Records. Dist: WEA

Cassette: released on Beggars Banque... Oct'86 by Beggars Banquet Records. Di... WEA

HOW IT SHONE.
Tracks: / How it shone / How it shone(... strumental).
Single (7"): released on Beggars Banqu... Aug'86 by Beggars Banquet Records. D... WEA

Single (12"): released on Beggars Banqu... Aug'86 by Beggars Banquet Records. D... WEA

ORANGE COLOURED SUN.
Tracks: / Orange coloured sun / Musha G... help her.
Single (7"): released on Beggars Banqu... Mar'87 by Beggars Banquet Records. D... WEA

UNCERTAIN SMILE.
Single (7"): released on Beggars Banqu... Jun'87 by Beggars Banquet Records. D... WEA

WICKLOW HILLS.
Tracks: / Everyone loves a virgin (in their pa...
Single (7"): released on Beggars Banqu... Dec'86 by Beggars Banquet Records. D... WEA

Single (12"): released on Beggars Banqu... Dec'86 by Beggars Banquet Records. D... WEA

Turner, Roger

SUNDAY BEST (Turner, Roger & G... Todd).
Album: released on Incus, Jan'80 Dist: J... Music, Cadillac

Turner, Ruby

BYE BABY.
Tracks: / Bye Baby / Story of a man a... woman, The / If you're ready come go with... / If you're ready come go with me / Still o... mind / Won't cry no more.
Single (7"): released on Jive, Aug'86 by Zo... Records. Dist: RCA, PRT, CBS

Single (12"): released on Jive, Aug'8... Zomba Records. Dist: RCA, PRT, CBS

Single (7"): released on Jive, Aug'86 by Zo... Records. Dist: RCA, PRT, CBS

CHECKING IT OUT (EP).
Single (12"): released on Sunflower, A... Dist: Pinnacle

EVERY SOUL/FIRST STEP.
Single (7"): released on Sunflower, M...

Dist: Pinnacle

Single (12"):

Single (12"): released on Sunflower, Mar'83 Dist: Pinnacle

I'D RATHER GO BLIND.
Tracks: / I'd rather go blind / I'm livin' a life of love / OOh baby baby* / If you're ready (come go with me)+ / Bye baby+ / I'm living a life of love.
Notes: * extra track on 12" version only + tracks included on compact disc
Single (7"): released on Jive, Feb'87 by Zomba Records. Dist: RCA, PRT, CBS

Single (12"): released on Jive, Feb'87 by Zomba Records. Dist: RCA, PRT, CBS

Single (7"): released on Jive, Jul'87 by Zomba Records. Dist: RCA, PRT, CBS

Single (12"): released on Jive, Feb'87 by Zomba Records. Dist: RCA, PRT, CBS

Compact disc: released on Jive, Feb'87 by Zomba Records. Dist: RCA, PRT, CBS

I'D RATHER GO BLIND/IF YOU'RE READY COME GO....
Tracks: / I'd rather go blind / Still on my mind / I'm living a life of love.
Notes: Doublepack single **Still on my mind** in doublepack with **If you're ready, come go with me**
Double-pack single: released on Jive, Mar'87 by Zomba Records. Dist: RCA, PRT, CBS

IF YOU'RE READY (COME GO WITH ME).
Tracks: / If you're ready (come go with me) / Still on my mind / I won't cry no more.
Single (7"): released on Jive, Jan'86 by Zomba Records. Dist: RCA, PRT, CBS

Single (12"): released on Jive, Jan'86 by Zomba Records. Dist: RCA, PRT, CBS

I'M IN LOVE.
Tracks: / I'm in love / Story of a man and a woman (The) / I'm in love / Living the life of love / I'm in love / I'm living a life of love / Feel my love / Someday soon / Still on my mind.
Single (7"): released on Jive, May'87 by Zomba Records. Dist: RCA, PRT, CBS

Single (12"): released on Jive, May'87 by Zomba Records. Dist: RCA, PRT, CBS

Compact disc single: released on Jive, May'87 by Zomba Records. Dist: RCA, PRT, CBS

Single (7"): released on Jive, Mar'86 by Zomba Records. Dist: RCA, PRT, CBS

Single (12"): released on Jive, Mar'86 by Zomba Records. Dist: RCA, PRT, CBS

Single (12"): released on Jive, Apr'86 by Zomba Records. Dist: RCA, PRT, CBS

Album: released on Blue Goose, May'79 Dist: Projection, Swift

IN MY LIFE.
Tracks: / In my life / He's mine.
Single (7"): released on Jive, Jun'87 by Zomba Records. Dist: RCA, PRT, CBS

Single (12"): released on Jive, Jun'87 by Zomba Records. Dist: RCA, PRT, CBS

WOMEN HOLD UP HALF THE SKY.
Compact disc: by Zomba Records. Dist: RCA, PRT, CBS

Album: released on Jive, Oct'86 by Zomba Records. Dist: RCA, PRT, CBS

Cassette: released on Jive, Oct'86 by Zomba Records. Dist: RCA, PRT, CBS

Turner, Ruby, Band

SEPERATE WAYS/I SHALL BE RELEASED.
Single (7"): released on Sunflower, Sep'80 Dist: Pinnacle

Turner, Simon Fisher

BONE OF DESIRE.
Album: released on Papier Mache, Nov'85 by Papier Mache Records. Dist: Rough Trade, Cartel

CARAVAGGIO 1610.
Tracks: / Hills of Abruzzi, The / Dog star, The / Ali paths lead to Rome / Fantasia, childhood memories / How blue sky was / Light and dark (From Missa Lux Et Orrigo) / Umber wastes / Cafe of the moors / Timeout and mind / In the still of the night / Michele of the shadows / Waters of forgetfullness, The / Running, running / Frescobaldi, the greatest organist of our time / Hourglass, The / I love you more than my eyes.
Album: released on EL, Jun'85 by El Records. Dist: Rough Trade, Cartel, Pinnacle

Turner's Merry-Go-Round

TURNERS MERRY-GO-ROUND VOL.1
Various Organs (Various Artists).
Album: released on Grosvenor, May'83 by Grosvenor Records. Dist: Taylors

Cassette: released on Grosvenor, May'83 by Grosvenor Records. Dist: Taylors

Turner, Spyder

SPYDERMAN.
Single (7"): released on Shatter, Nov'83

Single (12"): released on Shatter, Nov'83

Turner, Steve

BRAIDING.
Notes: With George Faux, Dave Walters, B. Martin.
Album: released on Fellside, Mar'87 by Fellside Records. Dist: Roots, Jazz Music, Celtic Music, Projection

Cassette: released on Fellside, Jul'87 by Fellside Records. Dist: Roots, Jazz Music, Celtic Music, Projection

ECLOGUE.
Album: released on Fellside, May'85 by Fellside Records. Dist: Roots, Jazz Music, Celtic Music, Projection

JIGGING ONE NOW.
Album: released on Fellside (Cumbria), Jan'83 by Fellside Records. Dist: Roots, Projection, CM, Jazz Music

OUT STACK.
Album: released on Fellside (Cumbria), Jan'83 by Fellside Records. Dist: Roots, Projection, CM, Jazz Music

Turner, Tich

DON'T REALLY WANT YOU BACK (Turner, Tich Escalators).
Single (7"): released on Cheapskate, Jun'81 by Cheapskate Records. Dist: RCA

Turner, Tina

ACID QUEEN.
Tracks: / Under my thumb / Let's spend the night together / Acid queen / I can see for miles / Whole lotta love / Baby git it on / Bootsey whitelaw / Pick me tonight / Rockin' and rollin'.
Notes: The Acid Queen herself- Tina Turner comes to the Fame label with this classic album from United Artists. Side two features compositions by Ike Turner, while side one includes the Stones' "Under My Thumb" and "Let's spend the night together" and Pet Townsend's "Acid Queen" and "I Can See For Miles". Another high spot is her version of Led Zeppelin's "Whole Lotta Love"- Just terrific! The band includes Ray Parker Jnr. and hornsman Tom Scott. An electric sleeve from a very 'current' artist indeed!
Album: released on Fame, Nov'85 by Music For Pleasure Records. Dist: EMI

Cassette: released on Fame, Nov'85 by Music For Pleasure Records. Dist: EMI

BETTER BE GOOD TO ME.
Tracks: / Better be good to me / When I was young.
Single (7"): released on Capitol, Jan'86 by Capitol Records. Dist: EMI

Single (12"): released on Capitol, Jan'86 by Capitol Records. Dist: EMI

BREAK EVERY RULE.
Tracks: / Afterglow / Back where you started / What you get is what you see / What you get is what you see / Overnight sensation / Change is gonna come,A / Two people.. / Addicted to love / In the midnight hour / 634-5789 / Land of 1,000 dances / Paradise is here / Girls / Typical male / What you get is what you see / Two people / Till the right man comes along / Afterglow / Girls / Back where you started / Break every rule / Overnight sensation / Paradise is here / I'll be thunder.
Notes: Tina filmed 'Live' at the Club Zero....Somewhere in Paris.Tina looking her raunchy best,performs songs from her new album together with steawy versions of such classics as "In the midnight hour" and "Land of 1,000 dances" No. of tracks:12 Type of recording:live Total playing time:60 mins. approx.
Video-cassette (VHS): released on PMI, Feb'87 by PMI Records. Dist: EMI

Album: released on Capitol, Sep'86 by Capitol Records. Dist: EMI

Cassette: released on Capitol, Sep'86 by Capitol Records. Dist: EMI

BREAK EVERY RULE.
Tracks: / Typical male / what you see is what you see / Two people / Till the right man comes along / Afterglow / girls / Back where you started / Break every rule / Overnight sensation / Paradise is here / I'll be thunder.
Compact disc: released on Capitol, Oct'86 by Capitol Records. Dist: EMI

BREAK EVERY RULE (SINGLE).
Tracks: / Break every rule / Girls.
Single (7"): released on Capitol, 23 May'87 by Capitol Records. Dist: EMI

Single (12"): released on Capitol, 23 May'87 by Capitol Records. Dist: EMI

Picture disc single: released on Capitol, 23 May'87 by Capitol Records. Dist: EMI

I CAN'T STAND THE RAIN.
Single (7"): released on Capitol, Feb'85 by Capitol Records. Dist: EMI

Single (12"): released on Capitol, Feb'85 by Capitol Records. Dist: EMI

LET'S STAY TOGETHER.
Single (7"): released on Capitol, Nov'83 by Capitol Records. Dist: EMI

Single (12"): released on Capitol, Nov'83 by Capitol Records. Dist: EMI

Picture disc single: released on Capitol, Nov'83 by Capitol Records. Dist: EMI

NICE 'N' ROUGH.
Tracks: / River deep mountain high / Nutbush city limits / Proud Mary / Honky Tonk Woman / Jumping Jack flash / Hollywood nights / Crazy in the night / Giving it up for your love / Acid queen / Tonight's the night / It's only rock'n'roll / Kill his wife(foolish behaviour).
Notes: No fancy tricks are needed to hold the eyes and attention when Tina is in motion. 'nutbush City Limuts' itself can only be performed the way it should be by the wrtiter herself and tina takes it to the limit on this Video. She performs every song with such raunchy fervour and strength that each becomes a Tina turner classic-not just 'River deep mountain high' and 'Proud Mary'but also'jumping Jack Flash','Acid Queen' and the rest besides. Total playing time 55 minutes.12 tracks.
Video-cassette (VHS): released on EMI, Nov'82 by EMI Records. Dist: EMI

Video-cassette [Betamax]: released on EMI, Nov'82 by EMI Records. Dist: EMI

NICE'N'ROUGH (VIDEO).
Notes: Inc. 'River deep, mountain high', 'Proud Mary', a couple of Stones songs and more!
Video-cassette (VHS): released on Video Collection, May'87 by Video Collection International Ltd.. Dist: Counterpoint

ONE OF THE LIVING.
Single (7"): released on Capitol, Sep'85 by Capitol Records. Dist: EMI

Single (12"): released on Capitol, Sep'85 by Capitol Records. Dist: EMI

PARADISE IS HERE.
Tracks: / In the midnight hour.
Single (7"): released on Capitol, Aug'87 by Capitol Records. Dist: EMI

Single (12"): released on Capitol, Aug'87 by Capitol Records. Dist: EMI

Special: released on Capitol, Aug'87 by Capitol Records. Dist: EMI

PRIVATE DANCER.
Tracks: / I might have been queen / Whats love got to do with it / Show some respect / I can't stand the rain / Private dancer / Lets stay together / Better be good to me / Steel claw / Help.
Notes: Digital Stereo.
Compact disc: released on Capitol, Sep'84 by Capitol Records. Dist: EMI

Album: released on Capitol, Jun'84 by Capitol Records. Dist: EMI

Cassette: released on Capitol, Jun'84 by Capitol Records. Dist: EMI

Compact disc: released on Capitol, Jun'84 by Capitol Records. Dist: EMI

Single (7"): released on Capitol, Nov'84 by Capitol Records. Dist: EMI

Single (12"): released on Capitol, Nov'84 by Capitol Records. Dist: EMI

Picture disc album: released on Capitol, Apr'85 by Capitol Records. Dist: EMI

PRIVATE DANCER CONCERT TOUR.
Notes: Number of Tracks 13. type of Recording:Live. Total playing time:55 minutes.
Video-cassette (VHS): released on PMI, Jun'86 by PMI Records. Dist: EMI

Video-cassette [Betamax]: released on PMI, Jun'86 by PMI Records. Dist: EMI

PRIVATE DANCER VIDEO EP.
Notes: Type of Recording:EP. Total playing time:17 minutes.
Video-cassette (VHS): released on PMI, Jun'86 by PMI Records. Dist: EMI

Video-cassette [Betamax]: released on PMI, Jun'86 by PMI Records. Dist: EMI

Tearing us apart

TOO HOT TO HANDLE.
Tracks: / Please love me / I better get to stepping / Crazy 'bout you baby / My babe / Shake a tail feather / We need an understanding / You're so fine / Here's your heart.
Album: released on Thunderbolt, Jun'87 by Magnum Music Group Ltd. Dist: Magnum Music Group Ltd, PRT Distribution, Spartan Distribution

TWO PEOPLE.
Tracks: / Two people / Havin' a party.
Single (7"): released on Capitol, Oct'86 by Capitol Records. Dist: EMI

Single (12"): released on Capitol, Oct'86 by Capitol Records. Dist: EMI

TWO PEOPLE (DOUBLE PACK).
Tracks: / Two people,(Dance mix) / Having a party / Let's stay together,(Live) / Private dancer,(Live).
Special: released on Capitol, Nov'86 by Capitol Records. Dist: EMI

TYPICAL MALE.
Tracks: / Typical male / Don't turn around / Typical male,(version)*.
Single (7"): released on Capitol, Aug'86 by Capitol Records. Dist: EMI

Single (12"): released on Capitol, Aug'86 by Capitol Records. Dist: EMI

TYPICAL MALE,(PICTURE DISC).
Tracks: / Typical male,Dance mix / Typical male,Dub mix / Typical male,Single mix / Don't turn around.
Single (12"): released on Capitol, Sep'86 by Capitol Records. Dist: EMI

WE DON'T NEED ANOTHER HERO.
Single (7"): released on Capitol, Jul'85 by Capitol Records. Dist: EMI

Picture disc single: released on Capitol, Jul'85 by Capitol Records. Dist: EMI

Single (12"): released on Capitol, Jul'85 by Capitol Records. Dist: EMI

WHAT'S LOVE GOT TO DO WITH IT.
Single (7"): released on Capitol, Jun'84 by Capitol Records. Dist: EMI Deleted May'87.

Single (12"): released on Capitol, Jun'84 by Capitol Records. Dist: EMI

WHAT YOU GET IS WHAT YOU SEE.
Tracks: / What you get is what you see (dance mix) / Tina Turner montage mix.
Notes: Track details:What you get is what you see/(live)/Take me to the river* Double-pack in gatefold sleeve inc.:(dance mix)/Tina Turner montage mix:I can't stand the rain/Two people/We don't need another hero(Thunderdome)/What's love got to do with it/Typical male/Let's stay together.
Single (7"): released on Capitol, Feb'87 by Capitol Records. Dist: EMI

Single (12"): released on Capitol, Feb'87 by Capitol Records. Dist: EMI

Double-pack single: released on Capitol, Feb'87 by Capitol Records. Dist: EMI

Single (12"): released on Capitol, Mar'87 by Capitol Records. Dist: EMI

WHAT YOU SEE IS WHAT YOU GET.
Tracks: / Typical male / Two people / What you get is what you see / Break every rule / Two people (Tina's Hollywood version).
Video-cassette (VHS): released on PMI, Jul'87 by PMI Records. Dist: EMI

Turner, Zeb

JERSEY ROCK.
Album: released on Bear Family, Nov'84 by Bear Family Records. Dist: Rollercoaster Distribution, Swift

Turning Curious

SOUL LIGHT SEASON.
Notes: Mini LP:
Album: released on Closer (France), Mar'86 Dist: Nine Mile, Cartel

Turning Point

CREATURES OF THE NIGHT.
Album: released on Gull, Sep'77 by Gull Records. Dist: Pinnacle

SILENT PROMISE.
Album: released on Gull, Jun'78 by Gull Records. Dist: Pinnacle

Turning Shrines

FACE OF ANOTHER.
Single (12"): released on Temple, Dec'86 by Temple Records. Dist: Roots Distribution, Folksound Distribution, Celtic Music Distribution, Projection Distribution

Turn It Up

TURN IT UP A 10 dance record (Various Artists).
Album: released on 10, Aug'85 by 10 Records. Dist: Virgin, EMI

Cassette: released on 10, Aug'85 by 10 Records. Dist: Virgin, EMI

Turnpike Cruisers

AMSTERDAMAGED.
Notes: Recorded live in November 1986

CRUISIN'UNHOLY.
Tracks: / Cruisin'Unholy.
Notes: 5 Track
Single (7"): released on Jettisoundz, Dec'85
Dist: Red Rhino, Cartel

CRUISIN' UNTIDY.
Single (12"): released on Jettisoundz, Apr'85
Dist: Red Rhino, Cartel

EXTRA FLESH.
Tracks: / Etra flesh.
Single (12"): released on Jettisoundz, Jun'86
Dist: Red Rhino, Cartel

Turnstyle
ONCE MORE FROM THE TOP.
Single (7"): released on Pye, Mar'78 Deleted
May'78.

Turquoise blue
IN THE END.
Single (7"): released on A.R.I.A., Dec'86 by
A.R.I.A. Records. Dist: A.R.I.A., BMG

WE ARE LOST.
Single (7"): released on A.R.I.A., May'87 by
A.R.I.A. Records. Dist: A.R.I.A., BMG

Single (12"): released on A.R.I.A., May'87 by
A.R.I.A. Records. Dist: A.R.I.A., BMG

Turquoise Days
GREY SKIES.
Single (7"): released on Disques Strategie,
Aug'84 Dist: ILA

Turrentine, Stanley
BLUE HOUR.
Tracks: / I want a little girl / Gee baby ain't I
good to you / Blue riff / Since I fell for you / Wil-
low weep for ma.
Album: released on Blue Note, Dec'85 by EMI
Records. Dist: EMI

JOYRIDE.
Tracks: / River's invitation / I wonder where our
love has gone / Little Sheri / Mattie / Bayou /
Taste of honey, A.
Compact disc: released on EMI, Mar'87 by
EMI Records. Dist: EMI
Album: released on Blue Note, Apr'85 by EMI
Records. Dist: EMI

JUBILEE SHOUT.
Tracks: / Jubilee shout / My ship / You said it /
Brother Tom / Cotton walk / You better go now.
Album: released on Manhattan-Blue Note,
Jul'86 by EMI America Records (USA). Dist:
EMI

LOOK OUT.
Tracks: / Look out / Journey into melody / Return engagement / Little Sheri / Tin tin deo / Yesterdays.
Compact disc: released on Blue Note, Aug'87
by EMI Records. Dist: EMI

NEW TIME SHUFFLE.
Album: released on Liberty-United, Jun'80 by
EMI Records. Dist: EMI

PIECES OF A DREAM.
Compact disc: released on Fantasy (USA),
Nov'86 by Fantasy Inc USA Records. Dist: IMS,
Polygram

STANLEY TURRENTINE.
Album: released on Blue Note, May'79 by EMI
Records. Dist: EMI

STRAIGHT AHEAD.
Tracks: / Plum / child is born,(A) / Other side of
time / Straight ahead / Longer you wait,(The) /
Ah rio.
Notes: Another member of the original Blue
Note roster, Stanley Turrentine returns to the
label to produce an album with enormous appeal within and beyond the mainstream
jazz audience. An all star line up for the album
features Jimmy Smith, Les McCann, Ron Carter and George Benson.
Album: released on Blue Note, Dec'85 by EMI
Records. Dist: EMI

THAT'S WHERE IT'S AT.
Tracks: / Smile Stacey / Soft pedal blues / Pia
/ We'll se yaw'll after while, ya heah / I Dorene
Don't cry / Light blue.
Notes: Produced by Alfred Lion.
Album: released on Manhattan, Nov'86 by EMI
Records. Dist: EMI

WONDERLAND Stanley Turrentine plays
the music of Stevie Wonder.
Tracks: / Bird of beauty / Creepin' / You and I /
Living for the city / Boogie on reggae women /
Rocket love / Don't you worry 'bout a thing / Sir
Duke / Bird of beauty / Creepin' you and I / Living for the city / Boogie on reggae women /
Rocket love / Don't you worry about a thing / Sir
Duke.
Notes: The master of the soulful tenor sax has
come up with an extraordinary album in "Wonderland". Conceived as a vehicle to explore the
compositions of Stevie Wonder, Turrentine has
not selected a stack of singles and done cover
versions of them. Here he has selected the pro-
ducer-pianist Ronnie Foster a wide range of
sophisticated (and swinging) Wonder tunes that
make sense in the jazz/R & B realm. With
apowerhouse rhythm section that bassist Abe
Laboriel, drummer Harvey Mason and percus-
sionistPaulinho Da Costa, Turrentine brings
new life and flavour to Stevie's music. The ballad "You And I" is among Stanley's most tender
and soulful achievments. The cookers like
"Boogie On, Reggae Woman", which features
a hot harmonica solo by Wonder himself, get
plenty of jazz fire from Stanley. And Stevies
jazzy pieces like "Sir Duke" and "Living For The
City" are given new dimension. This should
prove to be Stanley Turrentine's strongest selling album to date with its wide appeal to all
areas of jazz and black progressive audiences.
[EMI release sheet, May 1987]
Album: released on Blue Note, May'87 by EMI
Records. Dist: EMI

Compact disc: released on Manhattan-Blue
Note, Jul'87 by EMI America Records (USA).
Dist: EMI

Z.T.'S BLUES.
Album: released on Blue Note, Sep'85 by EMI
Records. Dist: EMI

Cassette: released on Blue Note, Sep'87 by
EMI Records. Dist: EMI. Estim retail price in
Sep'87 was £5.99.

Turriff & District...
PIPING FROM THE NORTH (Turriff & District Pipe Band).
Album: released on Ross, '86 by Ross Records. Dist: Ross Distribution, Roots Distribution

Cassette: released on Ross, '86 by Ross Records. Dist: Ross Distribution, Roots Distribution

Turriff Schoolchildren
SCHOOLDAYS.
Cassette: released on Ross, '86 by Ross Rec-
ords. Dist: Ross Distribution, Roots Distribution

Turtle, Gideon
**GIDEON TURTLE & THE MIDNIGHT
CHOIR** (Turtle, Gideon/Midnight Choir).
Single (12"): released on Golden Dawn,
Aug'84 by Artery Records. Dist: Cartel

Turtle, Henry
98.6.
Single (7"): released on Riviera, Apr'84 Dist:
Discovery, Pinnacle

BUST LOOSE.
Single (7"): released on Variety, May'83 by
Variety Records. Dist: PRT

DREAMING.
Single (7"): released on Variety, Nov'82 by Variety Records. Dist: PRT

**HE'S TAKEN SHEILA OFF HIS WIND-
SCREEN.**
Single (7"): released on Variety, Jul'83 by Var-
iety Records. Dist: PRT

HOUND DOG MAN.
Single (7"): released on Variety, Mar'83 by Variety Records. Dist: PRT

Turtles
20 GREATEST HITS.
Compact disc: released on Rhino (USA), '86
by Rhino Records (USA).

ELANORE.
Single (7"): released on Old Gold (Reissue),
Jul'82

HAPPY TOGETHER.
Single (7"): released on Old Gold (Reissue),
Jul'82

IT AIN'T ME. BABE.
Album: released on Teldec (Germany), May'84
by Import Records. Dist: IMS Distribution, Polygram Distribution

**PRESENT THE BATTLE OF THE
BANDS.**
Album: released on Rhino (USA), May'86 by
Rhino Records (USA).

TURTLE SOUP.
Album: released on Rhino (USA), May'86 by
Rhino Records (USA).

WOODEN HEAD.
Album: released on Rhino (USA), Jul'84 by
Rhino Records (USA).

Tusa, Frank
FATHER TIME.
Album: released on Enja (Germany), Jan'82 by
Enja Records (W.Germany). Dist: Cadillac
Music

Tusk
SHE'S SO COOL.
Single (7"): released on Automatic, May'81
Dist: WEA, Independant

Tutankhamun
ART ENSEMBLE OF CHICAGO.
Album: released on Freedom, '83 by Logo Rec-
ords. Dist: RCA, Discovery, Wellard, Chris

Tutone, Tommy
GET AROUND GIRL.
Single (7"): released on CBS, Jan'84 by CBS
Records. Dist: CBS

TUTONE 2.
Album: released on CBS, Oct'82 by CBS Records. Dist: CBS

Tutti's...
TUTTI'S TROMBONES (inc. Joe Howard)
(Various Artists).
Album: released on B.Vista, '74

TUTTI'S TRUMPETS (inc.Peter Candoli)
(Various Artists).
Album: released on B.Vista, '74

Tuxedo
TO TOUCH YOU.
Tracks: / To touch you / To touch you (version).
Single (7"): released on Chartsounds, Jul'87 by
Chartsounds Records. Dist: Jetstar

Single (12"): released on Chartsounds, Jul'87
by Chartsounds Records. Dist: Jetstar

Tuxedo Moon
DESIRE.
Album: released on Charisma, Mar'81 by Vir-
gin Records. Dist: EMI

Cassette: released on Charisma, Mar'81 by
Virgin Records. Dist: EMI

Album: released on Cramboy, Oct'85 by
Crammed Discs/Joeboy Productions. Dist: Nine
Mile, Cartel

HALF-MUTE.
Album: released on Joe Boy (Belgium), Oct'84
Dist: Impex Distribution

HOLY WARS.
Album: released on Cramboy, Apr'85 by
Crammed Discs/Joeboy Productions. Dist: Nine
Mile, Cartel

NINOTCHKA.
Single (7"): released on Les Disques Du Cre-
puscule, Apr'82 Dist: Rough Trade, Pinnacle,
Island, Polygram

NO TEARS EP.
Tracks: / No tears (EP).
Single (12"): released on Cramboy, Mar'86 by
Crammed Discs/Joeboy Productions. Dist: Nine
Mile, Cartel

SCREAM WITH A VIEW.
Album: released on Cramboy, Oct'85 by
Crammed Discs/Joeboy Productions. Dist: Nine
Mile, Cartel

**SCREAM WITH A VIEW - NERVOUS
GUY..**
Tracks: / Scream with a view - nervous guy /
Where interests lie (special treatment for
the)family man / Midnite stroll.
Single (7"): released on Cramboy, Dec'85 by
Crammed Discs, Cartel

SHIP OF FOOLS.
Notes: Mini LP
Album: released on Cramboy, Jun'86 by
Crammed Discs/Joeboy Productions. Dist: Nine
Mile, Cartel

SOMA.
Single (7"): released on Joe Boy (Belgium),
Jul'84 Dist: Impex Distribution

THOUSAND LIVES BY PICTURES, A.
Album: released on New Ralph, Jan'84 by New
Ralph Records. Dist: Rough Trade

TIME TO LOSE (EP).
Single (12"): released on Les Disques Du Cre-
puscule, Aug'82 Dist: Rough Trade, Pinnacle,
Island, Polygram

TV 21
ALL JOIN HANDS.
Single (7"): released on Deram, Feb'82 by
Decca Records. Dist: Polygram

ON THE RUN.
Single (7"): released on Demon, Feb'81 by
Demon Records. Dist: Pinnacle

SNAKES AND LADDERS.
Single (7"): released on Deram, May'81 by

Decca Records. Dist: Polygram

SOMETHING'S WRONG.
Single (7"): released on Deram, Oct'81 by
Decca Records. Dist: Polygram

THIN RED LINE, A.
Album: released on Deram, Nov'81 by Decca
Records. Dist: Polygram

Cassette: released on Deram, Nov'81 by
Decca Records. Dist: Polygram

T.V. Hits
T.V HITS ALBUM Various artists (Various
Artists).
Album: released on Telebell, Sep'85 by Tower-
bell Records. Dist: EMI

Cassette: released on Telebell, Sep'85 by
Towerbell Records. Dist: EMI

T.V. HITS VOL.2 Various artists (Various Ar-
tists).
Album: released on Towerbell, Apr'86 by
Towerbell Records. Dist: EMI

Cassette: released on Towerbell, Apr'86 by
Towerbell Records. Dist: EMI

TV Personalities
AND DON'T THE KIDS JUST LOVE IT.
Album: released on Rough Trade, Jan'84 by
Rough Trade Records. Dist: Rough Trade Dis-
tribution, Cartel Distribution

BILL GRUNDY EP.
Single (7"): released on Rough Trade, Nov'79
by Rough Trade Records. Dist: Rough Trade
Distribution, Cartel Distribution

HOW I LEARNED TO LOVE THE BOMB.
Tracks: / How I learned to love the bomb / Girl
called charity,(A) / She's only the grocers
daughter.
Single (7"): released on Dreamworld, Oct'86 by
TV Personalities, The. Dist: Rough Trade

MUMMY, YOU'RE NOT WATCHING.
Album: released on Dreamworld, Feb'87 by TV
Personalities, The. Dist: Rough Trade

PAINTED WORD THE.
Album: released on Whaam, Nov'83 Dist: Pinnacle

PRETTIEST GIRL IN THE WORL (THE).
Tracks: / Prettiest girl in the world (The).
Single (7"): released on Constrictor, Mar'87
Dist: Rough Trade, Red Rhino, Cartel

**THEY COULD HAVE BEEN BIGGER
THAN THE BEATLES.**
Album: released on Hot, Jun'86 by Hot Rec-
ords. Dist: Rough Trade, Cartel

**THEY COULD HAVE BEEN BIGGER
THAN THE BEETLES.**
Album: released on Whamm, Nov'82 Dist: Pin-
nacle

**THREE WISHES/GEOFFREY ING-
RAM/DON'T THE KIDS JUST LOVE IT.**
Single (7"): released on Whaam, Sep'82 Dist:
Pinnacle

T.V.Themes
T.V. THEMES (Various Artists).
Compact disc: released on Bridge, '86 Dist:
CD Centre Distribution, Pinnacle, Target

Twain, Mark
PRINCE AND THE PAUPER THE.
Album: released on Caedmon(USA), Jan'79 by
Caedmon (USA) Records. Dist: Gower, Tay-
lors, Discovery

Cassette: released on Caedmon(USA), Jan'79
by Caedmon (USA) Records. Dist: Gower, Taylors, Discovery

Twain Soundbook
TWAIN SOUNDBOOK Marl Twain read by
various artists (Various Artists).
Cassette: released on Caedmon(USA), '81 by
Caedmon (USA) Records. Dist: Gower, Tay-
lors, Discovery

Twang
KICK AND COMPLAIN.
Tracks: / Kick and complain.
Single (12"): released on Ron Johnson, Mar'87
by Ron Johnson Records. Dist: Nine Mile Dis-
tribution, Cartel Distribution

ORIGINAL LONDON CAST.
Album: released on That's Entertainment,
Apr'83 by That's Entertainment Records. Dist:
Pinnacle, PRT

Cassette: released on That's Entertainment,
Apr'83 by That's Entertainment Records. Dist:
Pinnacle, PRT

TWANG! Original London Cast (Various Artists).
Album: released on TER, May'87 Dist: Pinnacle

Cassette: released on TER, May'87 Dist: Pinnacle

Twa Toots

PEEL SESSION 31.12.83.
Tracks: / Peel session,(the)(31st october 1983).
Cassette single: released on Strange Fruit, 13 Jun'87 by Clive Selwood. Dist: Pinnacle

PLEASE DON'T PLAY A RAINY DAY IN GEORGIA.
Album: released on Crystal Clear, Oct'86 by Crystal Records. Dist: Revolver, Cartel

Tweets

BIRDIE SONG.
Single (7"): released on PRT, Nov'84 by PRT Records. Dist: PRT

EVERYBODY GO/WILLY NILLY.
Single (7"): by RCA Records. Dist: RCA, Roots, Swift, Wellard, Chris, I & B, Solomon & Peres Distribution Deleted Mar'82.

LETS ALL SING LIKE THE BIRDIES SONG.
Single (7"): released on PRT, Nov'81 by PRT Records. Dist: PRT

Single (12"): released on PRT, Nov'81 by PRT Records. Dist: PRT

PATRICIA.
Single (7"): released on PRT, Nov'85 by PRT Records. Dist: PRT

Single (12"): released on PRT, Nov'85 by PRT Records. Dist: PRT

PLUMP SONG.
Single (7"): released on Crash, Dec'83 by Satril Records. Dist: PRT

TWEETS ON 45/HERITAGE.
Single (7"): released on RCA, Aug'82 by RCA Records. Dist: RCA, Roots, Swift, Wellard, Chris, I & B, Solomon & Peres Distribution

Twelfth..

IT'S JUST NOT CRITIC (Twelfth Night).
Single (12"): released on EMI, Aug'85 by EMI Records. Dist: EMI

Single (12"): released on EMI, Aug'85 by EMI Records. Dist: EMI

Twelfth Night

ART AND ILLUSION.
Album: released on Music For Nations, Oct'84 by Music For Nations Records. Dist: Pinnacle

FACT AND FICTION.
Album: released on Twelfth Night, Jan'83 Dist: Pinnacle

LIVE AND LET LIVE (LIVE AT THE MARQUEE).
Album: released on Music For Nations, Feb'84 by Music For Nations Records. Dist: Pinnacle

LIVE AT THE TARGET.
Album: released on Twelfth Night, Feb'81 Dist: Pinnacle

SHAME.
Tracks: / Shame / Blue powder monkey.
Single (7"): released on Charisma, May'86 by Virgin Records. Dist: EMI

Single (12"): released on Charisma, May'86 by Virgin Records. Dist: EMI

SMILING AT GRIEF.
Cassette: released on Twelfth Night, Jan'82 Dist: Pinnacle

TAKE A LOOK.
Tracks: / Take a look / Blondon fair.
Single (7"): released on Charisma, Aug'86 by Virgin Records. Dist: EMI

Single (12"): released on Charisma, Aug'86 by Virgin Records. Dist: EMI

TWELFTH NIGHT.
Tracks: / Last song / Pressure / Jungle / Craft,(the) / Blue powder monkey / Theatre / Shame / This is war / Take a look.
Album: released on Charisma, Jul'86 by Virgin Records. Dist: EMI

Cassette: released on Charisma, Jul'86 by Virgin Records. Dist: EMI

Twelve...

BEATLES IN CLASSICS, THE (Twelve Cellists Of The BPO).
Album: released on Teldec (Germany), Dec'84 by Import Records. Dist: IMS Distribution, Polygram Distribution

Cassette: released on Teldec (Germany), Dec'84 by Import Records. Dist: IMS Distribution, Polygram Distribution

LONELY (Twelve Drummers Drumming).
Single (12"): released on Vertigo, Dec'83 by Phonogram Records. Dist: Polygram

TWELVE CARAT GOLD Reggae Hits (Various Artists).
Album: released on Melodisc, Jul'76

TWELVE CHAIRS Original soundtrack (Various Artists).
Album: released on That's Entertainment, Apr'83 by That's Entertainment Records. Dist: Pinnacle, PRT

TWELVE COMMANDMENTS IN METAL (Various Artists).
Album: released on Roadrunner, Sep'85 by Roadrunner Records (Germany). Dist: Pinnacle

Cassette: released on Road Runner, Oct'85

TWELVE ENGLE STREET (Various Artists).
Single (12"): released on Pye, May'80

TWELVE INCHES OF PLEASURE VOL.2 (Various Artists).
Album: released on Proto, Apr'84 by Proto Records. Dist: WEA

TWELVE INCH TAPES - EXTENDED MIXES VOL.2 (Various Artists).
Cassette: released on CBS, Mar'85 by CBS Records. Dist: CBS

TWELVE INCH TAPES - EXTENDED MIXES (Various Artists).
Cassette: released on CBS, Mar'85 by CBS Records. Dist: CBS

TWELVE INCH TAPES - EXTENDED MIXES VOL.4 (Various Artists).

TWELVE INCH TAPES - EXTENDED MIXES VOL.5 (Various Artists).
Cassette: released on CBS, Mar'85 by CBS Records. Dist: CBS

TWELVE INCH TAPES - EXTENDED MIXES VOL.3 (Various Artists).
Cassette: released on CBS, Mar'85 by CBS Records. Dist: CBS

TWELVE MEGAMIXES (Various Artists).
Album: released on Starblend, Jun'85 by Starblend Records. Dist: PRT Distribution

Cassette: released on Starblend, Jun'85 by Starblend Records. Dist: PRT Distribution

TWELVE X TWELVE (Various Artists).
Album: released on Starblend, Feb'85 by Starblend Records. Dist: PRT Distribution

Cassette: released on Starblend, Feb'85 by Starblend Records. Dist: PRT Distribution

WE'LL BE THE FIRST ONES (Twelve Drummers Drumming).
Single (7"): released on Mercury, Mar'84 by Phonogram Records. Dist: Polygram Distribution

Single (12"): released on Mercury, Mar'84 by Phonogram Records. Dist: Polygram Distribution

Twelve 88 Cartel

SWEATING FURORE EP.
Extended-play record: released on Bite Back, Mar'87 Dist: Revolver, Cartel

Twelve Cellists

BEATLES IN CLASSIC, THE (Twelve Cellists Of The BPO).
Tracks: / Yellow submarine / Let it be / Something / Fool on the hill, The / Help / Yesterday / Michelle / Hard days night, a / Norwegian wood / Here there and everywhere / Can't buy me love / Hey Jude.
Compact disc: released on Teldec, May'87

Cassette: released on Teldec, May'87

Album: released on Teldec, May'87

Twentieth...

20TH ALL TIME CHRISTMAS HITS Various artists (Various Artists).
Cassette: released on Ampro Cassettes, Sep'81

Twentieth Century Blues

20TH CENTURY BLUES.
Tracks: / In former times / Marathon / Study to be quiet / Four pieces / Solo piano / Brass choir / Trio for moog synthesizer / violin and bass / Solo violins:.
Compact disc: released on MMC, '86 by MMC Records. Dist: PRT Distribution, Pinnacle

Album: released on MMC, Nov'83 by MMC Records. Dist: PRT Distribution, Pinnacle

Twenty...

20 ALL TIME PARTY HITS Party singalong (Various Artists).
Album: released on Hallmark, Sep'75 by Pickwick Records. Dist: Pickwick Distribution, PRT, Taylors

Cassette: released on Hallmark, Sep'75 by Pickwick Records. Dist: Pickwick Distribution, PRT, Taylors

20 ALL TIME VOCAL CHARTBUSTERS (Various original artists) (Various original artists).
Album: released on MFP (EMI), Sep'82 by EMI Records. Dist: EMI

Cassette: released on MFP (EMI), Sep'82 by EMI Records. Dist: EMI

20 BBC DRAMA THEMES Carious artists (Various Artists).
Album: released on BBC, Apr'83 by BBC Records & Tapes. Dist: EMI, PRT,

Cassette: released on BBC, Apr'83 by BBC Records & Tapes. Dist: EMI, PRT,

20 BEACH BOY HITS various session artists (Various Session Artists).
Cassette: released on AIM (Budget Cassettes), Feb'83

20 CHRISTMAS CLASSICS (Motown christmas album) (Various Artists).
Album: released on Motown, Oct'81 by RCA Records. Dist: RCA Distribution

Cassette: released on Motown, Oct'81 by RCA Records. Dist: RCA Distribution

20 CLASSIC REGGAE TRACKS Various artists (Various Artists).
Album: released on Starburst, Jan'85 by Starburst Records. Dist: CBS Distribution

Cassette: released on Starburst, Jan'85 by Starburst Records. Dist: CBS Distribution

20 CLASSIC ROCK 'N' ROLL TRACKS Various artists (Various Artists).
Album: released on Meteor, Apr'85 by Magnum Music Group Ltd. Dist: Magnum Music Group Ltd, PRT Distribution, Spartan Distribution

Album: released on Starburst, Jan'85 by Starburst Records. Dist: CBS Distribution

20 DISCO DANCIN HITS Various artists (Various Artists).
Album: released on Pickwick, Jan'78 by Pickwick Records. Dist: Pickwick Distribution, Prism Leisure Distribution, Lugtons

Cassette: released on Pickwick, Jan'78 by Pickwick Records. Dist: Pickwick Distribution, Prism Leisure Distribution, Lugtons

20 EXPLOSIVE HITS various artists (Various Artists).
Album: released on Trojan, Jan'83 by Trojan Records. Dist: PRT, Jetstar

20 FAVOURITE HYMNS (From the royal naval college chapel, Grenwich) (Twenty Favourite Hymns).
Album: released on Abbey, Sep'83 by Abbey. Dist: PRT, Taylors, Gamut

Cassette: released on Abbey, Sep'83 by Abbey. Dist: PRT, Taylors, Gamut

20 GEANTS DU PIANO JAZZ (Various Artists).
Compact disc: released on Vogue, Jul'87 Dist: Discovery, Jazz Music, PRT, Swift

20 GOLDEN GREATS (Various Artists).
Notes: Big band hits by Basie, Dorsey, Ellington, Shaw etc. played by a session orchestra featuring Ben Webster, Al Cohn, Mel Lewis, Bud Shank, Conte, Condoli etc.
Compact disc: released on Hermes, Jul'87 by Nimbus Records. Dist: Target

20 GOSPEL SONGS Various artists (Various Artists).
Tracks: / Where the soul never dies / Where the soul never dies / Where the soul never dies / It is no secret / Holy Bible / Royal telephone / I love you Jesus / Three rusty nails / One day at a time / In the garden / I'm using my Bible for a roadmap / Soft and tenderly / Last look at Momma / How great thou art / Dear God / Old rugged cross / Family Bible / If Jesus came to your house / What a friend we have in Mother / Precious memories / Dust on the Bible.
Cassette: released on Homespun(Ireland), Apr'86 by Outlet Records. Dist: Outlet

20 GOSPEL SONGS FROM N. IRELAND Various artists (Various Artists).
Tracks: / What a friend we have in Jesus / Old account, (The) / One day at a time / Dust on mother's Bible / Kneel at the cross / Whispering hope / On a tree at Calvary / In my heart there is a melody / Mother of a wandering boy / On a tree at Calvary / Whispering hope / In my heart there is a melody / Mother of a wandering boy / His banner over me is love / Just a closer walk with you / Turn your radio on / He the pearly gates will open / Mama sang a song / Pull for the shore / Trouble in Amen Corner / Spring of living waters / Life's railway to Heaven / Over the deadline / Stone was rolled away, (The).
Album: released on Homespun(Ireland), May'86 by Outlet Records. Dist: Outlet

20 GREAT BIG BAND HITS Various artists (Various Artists).
Cassette: released on Astan, Jun'86 by Astan Records. Dist: Counterpoint

20 GREATEST SONGS IN MOTOWN HISTORY Various artists (Various Artists).
Tracks: / Three times a lady / Touch me in the morning / I heard it through the grapevine / For once in my life / Never can say goodbye / My girl / Love hangover / Where did our love go? / Dancing in the street / Still / Stop! In the name of love / Tracks of my tears, (The) / You keep me hangin' on / Easy / Reach out I'll be there / Ain't no mountain high enough / You can't hurry love / Standing in the shadows of love / Just my imagination (running away with me) / How sweet it is (to be loved by you).
Compact disc: released on Motown, Mar'86 by Motown Records. Dist: BMG Distribution

20 GREAT ITALIAN LOVE SONGS various artists (Various Artists).
Album: released on Telstar, Apr'83 by Telstar Records. Dist: RCA Distribution
Cat. no: **STAR 2230**
Cassette: released on Telstar, Apr'83 by Telstar Records. Dist: RCA Distribution

20 GREAT "UNKNOWN" SOUL CLASSICS VOL 1 Various artists (Various Artists).
Tracks: / And the rains came / Ain't that soul? / Hey stoney face / Dance, children, dance / Think it over baby / Slow and easy / If I could turn back the hands of time / Get lost / Sweet temptation / You just cheat and lie / If I could do it all over / You are my sunshine / Let freedom ring / I've got a right to lose my mind / I'm not ashamed / With all my heart / You know it ain't right / Blue on blue / Woman needs a man, (A) / It's raining.
Album: released on Cascade, Aug'86 by Ace Records. Dist: Pinnacle

Cassette: released on Cascade, Aug'86 by Ace Records. Dist: Pinnacle

20 HOLIDAY HITS various artists (Various Artists).
Album: released on Creole, Jul'85 by Creole Records. Dist: Rhino, PRT

Cassette: released on Creole, Jul'85 by Creole Records. Dist: Rhino, PRT

20 INSTRUMENTAL FAVOURITES Various artists (Various Artists).
Album: released on MFP, Feb'82 by EMI Records. Dist: EMI

Cassette: released on MFP, Feb'82 by EMI Records. Dist: EMI

20 IRISH HITS Various artists (Various Artists).
Album: released on Harp(Ireland), Jul'81 by Pickwick Records. Dist: Taylors

20 JACKPOT HITS Various artists (Various Artists).
Album: released on Pye, Jan'78

Cassette: released on Pye, Jan'78

20 MOD CLASSICS Various artists (Various Artists).
Album: released on Motown, Oct'81 by RCA Records. Dist: RCA Distribution

Cassette: released on Motown, Oct'81 by RCA Records. Dist: RCA Distribution

20 MOD CLASSICS - VOL.2 Various artists (Various Artists).
Album: released on Motown, Oct'81 by RCA Records. Dist: RCA Distribution

Cassette: released on Motown, Oct'81 by RCA Records. Dist: RCA Distribution

20 MORE ORIGINAL HITS OF THE 70'S Various artists (Various Artists).
Album: released on MFP, Apr'85 by EMI Records. Dist: EMI

Cassette: released on MFP, Apr'85 by EMI Records. Dist: EMI

20 OF THE BEST COUNTRY DUETS Various artists (Various Artists).
Album: released on RCA International, Apr'85

Cassette: released on RCA International, Apr'85

20 OF YOUR HUNDRED BEST TUNES Various artists (Various Artists).
Tracks: / Fingal's cave / Abridged / Sheep may safely graze / Elizabethan serenade / 1812 Overture - end / Blue Danube, (The) / Meditation / Largo (Xerxes) / Nessun Dorma - none shall sleep / Op 42 Toccata (Organ symphony no 5) / K525 1ST Met (Eine Kleine Nachtmusik) / Easter hymn / Fantasia on Greensleeves / Barcarolle (Tales of Hoffman) / Toccata and fugue in D Minor / Arrival of the Queen of Sheba, (The) / Elijah (o rest in the Lord) / Symphony No 7, second movement

/ Dance of the sugar plum fairy.
Album: released on Collector, Apr'86 by Castle Communications Records. Dist: PRT, Pinnacle

Cassette: released on Collector, Apr'86 by Castle Communications Records. Dist: PRT, Pinnacle

20 ONE HIT WONDERS Various artists (Various Artists).
Album: released on See For Miles, Oct'82 by Charly Records. Dist: Spartan

20 ONE HIT WONDERS - VOL.2 Various artists (Various Artists).
Album: released on See For Miles, Dec'83 by Charly Records. Dist: Spartan

20 ORIGINAL HITS OF THE 70'S (1970-1974) Various artists (Various Artists).
Album: released on MFP, Apr'85 by EMI Records. Dist: EMI

Cassette: released on MFP, Apr'85 by EMI Records. Dist: EMI

20 ORIGINAL ROCK AND ROLL CLASSICS Various artists (Various Artists).
Album: released on Pickwick (Limited Edition), '78

Cassette: released on Pickwick (Limited Edition), '78

20 ORIGINAL ROCK HITS Various artists (Various Artists).
Album: released on Pickwick (Limited Edition), '78

Cassette: released on Pickwick (Limited Edition), '78

20 ORIGINALS FROM THE COUNTRY & WESTERN HALL OF FAME Various artists (Various Artists).
Album: released on Pickwick (Limited Edition), '78

Cassette: released on Pickwick (Limited Edition), '78

20 PIECES OF GOLD Various artists (Various Artists).
Cassette: released on AIM (Budget Cassettes), Feb'83

20 REGGAE BLOCKBUSTERS Various artists (Various Artists).
Notes: Including: Young gifted & black, Double Barrel, Everything I own, You can get it, Liquidator, Black & white, It mek, Love of the common people etc.
Compact disc: released on Sound, '86 Dist: Target

20 REGGAE CLASSICS - VOL.2 Various artists (Various Artists).
Album: released on Trojan, Nov'84 by Trojan Records. Dist: PRT, Jetstar

Cassette: released on Trojan, Nov'84 by Trojan Records. Dist: PRT, Jetstar

20 REGGAE CLASSICS Various artists (Various Artists).
Album: released on Trojan, Apr'84 by Trojan Records. Dist: PRT, Jetstar

Cassette: released on Trojan, Apr'84 by Trojan Records. Dist: PRT, Jetstar

20 REQUESTED BALLADS OF IRELAND - VOL.4 Various artists (Various Artists).
Album: released on Homespun(Ireland), Jul'83 by Outlet Records. Dist: Outlet

Cassette: released on Homespun(Ireland), Jul'83 by Outlet Records. Dist: Outlet

20 STAR STUDDED COUNTRY HITS Various artists (Various Artists).
Album: released on Pickwick (Limited Edition), '78

Cassette: released on Pickwick (Limited Edition), '78

20 SUPER HITS Various artists (Various Artists).
Album: released on Pickwick (Limited Edition), '78

Cassette: released on Pickwick (Limited Edition), '78

20 TRADITIONAL CHRISTMAS CAROLS Various artists (Various Artists).
Album: released on BBC, Oct'77 by BBC Records & Tapes. Dist: EMI, PRT,

Cassette: released on BBC, Oct'77 by BBC Records & Tapes. Dist: EMI, PRT

20 WELSH MALE CHOIR FAVOURITES Various artists (Various Artists).
Album: released on Note, Jan'80 by EMI Records. Dist: EMI

Cassette: released on Note, Jan'80 by EMI Records. Dist: EMI

TWENTY CHRISTMAS CLASSICS Various artists (Various Artists).
Tracks: / White Christmas / Rudolph the rednosed reindeer / Frosty the snowman / What Christmas means to me / Twinkle twinkle little me / Jingle bells / Little Christmas tree / Someday at Christmas / Let it snow, let it snow, let it snow / I saw mommy kissing Santa Claus / Christmas lullaby / My Christmas tree / Up on the house top / Christmas song, The (Merry Christmas to you) / Little bright star / Silent night / God rest ye merry gentlemen / Christmas won't be the same this year / Silver bells.
Album: released on Motown, Nov'86 by Motown Records. Dist: BMG Distribution

Cassette: released on Motown, Nov'86 by Motown Records. Dist: BMG Distribution

TWENTY CRUISING FAVOURITES-VOLUME 2 (Various Artists).
Cassette: released on Cascade, Mar'87 by Ace Records. Dist: Pinnacle

TWENTY CRUISING FAVOURITES-VOLUME 1 (Various Artists).
Album: released on Cascade, Mar'87 by Ace Records. Dist: Pinnacle

Cassette: released on Cascade, Mar'87 by Ace Records. Dist: Pinnacle

TWENTY REGGAE BLOCKBUSTERS Various artists (Various Artists).
Notes: Includes: Young gifted & black, double barrel, everything I own, you can get it, liquidator, black & white, it mek, love of the common people, etc.
Album: released on Sound, '86 Dist: Target

TWENTY TRACKS OF COUNTRY HITS-VOL.3 (Various Artists).
Notes: Artists as fof Vols.1&2
Cassette: released on Ross, '86 by Ross Records. Dist: Ross Distribution, Roots Distribution

TWENTY TRACKS OF COUNTRY HITS-VOL.2 (Various Artists).
Notes: Artists as for Vol.1
Cassette: released on Ross, Feb'87 by Ross Records. Dist: Ross Distribution, Roots Distribution

TWENTY TRACKS OF COUNTRY HITS-VOL1 (Various Artists).
Notes: Manson Grant, Mackie Sutherland, Jim Holiday, Mike Devine, Scots Country Comfort-Tracy Wells, Moira Kerr, Tug Wilson
Cassette: released on Ross, '86 by Ross Records. Dist: Ross Distribution, Roots Distribution

Twenty Bluegrass ....

20 BLUEGRASS INSTRUMENTALS (Various Artists).
Album: released on Starday, Apr'87

Cassette: released on Starday, Apr'87

20 BLUEGRASS ORIGINALS (Various Artists).
Album: released on Starday, Apr'87

Cassette: released on Starday, Apr'87

20 BLUEGRASS ORIGINALS VOL.2 (Various Artists).
Album: released on Starday, Apr'87

Cassette: released on Starday, Apr'87

20 BLUEGRASS ORIGINAL HYMNS (Various Artists).
Album: released on Starday, Apr'87

Cassette: released on Starday, Apr'87

Twenty Country...

20 CLASSIC COUNTRY TRACKS various artists (Various Artists).
Album: released on Starburst, Jan'85 by Starburst Records. Dist: CBS Distribution

Cassette: released on Starburst, Jan'85 by Starburst Records. Dist: CBS Distribution

Album: released on Meteor, Apr'85 by Magnum Music Group Ltd. Dist: Magnum Music Group Ltd, PRT Distribution, Spartan Distribution

20 COUNTRY CLASSICS Various artists (Various Artists).
Album: released on Premier, Jan'84 by Premier Records. Dist: CBS

Cassette: released on Premier, Jan'84 by Premier Records. Dist: CBS

20 COUNTRY GREATS various original artists (Various original artists).
Album: released on Pickwick (Limited Edition), Jan'78

Cassette: released on Pickwick (Limited Edition), Jan'78

20 COUNTRY LOVE SONGS various artists (Various Artists).
Album: released on MFP, Sep'85 by EMI Records. Dist: EMI

Cassette: released on MFP, Sep'85 by EMI Records. Dist: EMI

Twenty Days

FREEFALL.
Single (7"): released on Sonar, May'85 by Sonar Records. Dist: Sonar

Twenty Fab...

20 FAB NO.1'S OF THE 50'S Various artists (Various Artists).
Album: released on Music For Pleasure, Feb'84 by EMI Records. Dist: EMI

Cassette: released on Music For Pleasure, Feb'84 by EMI Records. Dist: EMI

20 FAB NO. 1'S OF THE 60'S Various artists (Various Artists).
Album: released on Music For Pleasure, May'84 by EMI Records. Dist: EMI

Cassette: released on Music For Pleasure, May'84 by EMI Records. Dist: EMI

20 FAB NO. 2'S OF THE 60'S Various artists (Various Artists).
Album: released on Music For Pleasure, May'84 by EMI Records. Dist: EMI

Cassette: released on Music For Pleasure, May'84 by EMI Records. Dist: EMI

Twenty First...

21ST CENTURY DUB (Various Artists).
Cassette: released on Roir, Feb'87 by Reach Out International Records. Dist: Red Rhino Distribution, Cartel Distribution

Twenty Five...

25 COUNTRY BALLADS Various artists (Various Artists).
Cassette: released on Westwood, Apr'76 by Westwood Records. Dist: Jazz Music, H.R. Taylor, JSU, Pinnacle, Ross Records

25 COUNTRY BALLADS - VOL.2 Various artists (Various Artists).
Cassette: released on Westwood, '78 by Westwood Records. Dist: Jazz Music, H.R. Taylor, JSU, Pinnacle, Ross Records

25 COUNTRY STORIES Various artists (Various Artists).
Cassette: released on Westwood, Apr'76 by Westwood Records. Dist: Jazz Music, H.R. Taylor, JSU, Pinnacle, Ross Records

25 GREATEST ROCK'N'ROLL HITS,PART1 Various artists (Various Artists).
Compact disc: released on Maybellene, May'87

25 GREATEST ROCK'N'ROLL HITS,PART2 Various artists (Various Artists).
Compact disc: released on Maybellene, May'87

25 IRISH REPUBLICAN SONGS Various artists (Various Artists).
Cassette: released on Derry, Jul'85 by Outlet Records. Dist: Outlet Records

25 MOTOWN NO 1 HITS Various artists (Various Artists).
Double compact disc: released on Motown, Nov'85 by Motown Records. Dist: BMG Distribution

25 ROCK 'N' ROLL GREATS Various artists (Various Artists).
Cassette: released on AIM (Budget Cassettes), Feb'83

25 USA NO.1 HITS FROM 25 YEARS Various artists (Various Artists).
Double Album: released on Motown, Oct'83 by RCA Records. Dist: RCA Distribution

Double cassette: released on Motown, Oct'83 by RCA Records. Dist: RCA Distribution

25 YEARS OF MOTOWN CLASSICS Various artists (Various Artists).
Album: released on Motown, Oct'83 by RCA Records. Dist: RCA Distribution

Cassette: released on Motown, Oct'83 by RCA Records. Dist: RCA Distribution

Twenty Flight Rockers

JOHNNY SEVEN.
Tracks: / Johnny Seven / Tower block rock.
Single (7"): released on WEA, Jul'86 by WEA Records. Dist: WEA

TOWERBLOCK ROCK.
Single (7"): released on ABC, Oct'85 Dist: CBS, Pinnacle

Single (12"): released on ABC, Oct'85 Dist: CBS, Pinnacle

Twenty Four...

24 CAROT ROCK Various artists (Various Artists).
Album: released on Starblend, Jun'85 by Starblend Records. Dist: PRT Distribution

Cassette: released on Starblend, Jun'85 by Starblend Records. Dist: PRT Distribution

24 ORIGINAL NUMBER ONE COUNTRY HITS Various artists (Various Artists).
Album: released on RCA (S.I.S.), Aug'84

Cassette: released on RCA (S.I.S.), Aug'84

24 ROCK'N'ROLL HOUSE SHAKERS Various artists (Various Artists).
Tracks: / Whole lotta shakin' goin' on / What'd I say? / Good golly miss molly / Long tall Sally / Bebopalula / Say mama / Ain't that a shame? / I'm gonna be a wheel someday / Maybelline / Rockhouse / Lotta lovin' / Jungle rock / Tear it up / Ready Teddy / Dancin' party / Remember then / Midnight dynamos / Rockabilly rebel / Shout shout (knock yourself out) / Rama lama ding dong / Rockabilly baby / Crazy little teddy girl / Hey you guys / Maybe that's why I care.
Album: released on Warwick Reflections, Jun'86 by Warwick Records.

Cassette: released on Warwick Reflections, Jun'86 by Warwick Records.

Twenty Four Hours

SHIPWRECKED (I'M NOT COMING BACK).
Single (7"): released on Charisma, Sep'82 by Virgin Records. Dist: EMI

Single (12"): released on Charisma, Sep'82 by Virgin Records. Dist: EMI

SIBERIAN SID.
Single (7"): released on Charisma, Jun'82 by Virgin Records. Dist: EMI

Single (12"): released on Charisma, Jun'82 by Virgin Records. Dist: EMI

Twenty Four Jukebox Hits

24 JUKEBOX HITS OF THE 50'S Original Artists (Original artists).

20 GREAT ROCKABILLY HITS OF THE 50'S Various artists (Various Artists).
Album: released on Cascade, Nov'82 by Ace Records. Dist: Pinnacle

Cassette: released on Cascade, Nov'82 by Ace Records. Dist: Pinnacle

20 GREAT ROCKABILLY HITS OF THE 50'S VOL.2 Various artists (Various Artists).
Album: released on Cascade, Sep'84 by Ace Records. Dist: Pinnacle

Cassette: released on Cascade, Sep'84 by Ace Records. Dist: Pinnacle

20 GREAT ROCK 'N' ROLL HITS OF THE 50'S Various artists (Various Artists).
Album: released on Cascade, Nov'82 by Ace Records. Dist: Pinnacle

Cassette: released on Cascade, Nov'82 by Ace Records. Dist: Pinnacle

20 GREAT TEEN BALLADS OF THE 50'S AND 60'S various artists (Various Artists).
Album: released on Cascade, Aug'85 by Ace Records. Dist: Pinnacle

Cassette: released on Cascade, Aug'85 by Ace Records. Dist: Pinnacle

Twenty Inches At Knee

SPY IN THE HOUSE OF LOVE.
Single (7"): released on Pre, Apr'82 by Charisma. Dist: Polygram

Twenty one...

21 SUPER GOLDEN OLDIES various artists (Various Artists).
Compact disc: released on Bescol, Aug'87 Dist: Target

Compact disc: released on Manhattan-Blue Note, Jul'87 by EMI America Records (USA). Dist: EMI

Twenty One Strangers

MORE CAIN THAN ABEL.
Single (7"): released on Charisma, Feb'85 by Virgin Records. Dist: EMI

Single (12"): released on Charisma, Feb'85 by Virgin Records. Dist: EMI

Twenty Thousand

20,000 LEAGUES UNDER THE SEA Various artists (Various Artists).
Extended-play record: released on Disneyland, Apr'81 Dist: EMI

Compact disc: released on The Compact Collection, Sep'87 by Conifer Records. Dist: Conifer Distribution

Twenty Fourth Street...

24TH STREET BAND.
Album: released on Denon, Mar'82 by Denon Records. Dist: Harmonia Mundi

Twenty Golden...

20 GOLDEN GREATS FROM THE BIG BAND ERA Various Artists (Various Artists).
Tracks: / Trumpet blues / One o'clock jump / Yes indeed / Intermission riff / You made me love you / Four brothers / Artistry in rhythm / Kalamazoo / I'll never smile again / Jeeps blues / Solitude / Don't be that way / Midnight sun / Red bank boogie / La paloma / Stardust / Skyliner / Goosey gander / Well, get it.
Notes: Featuring: Ben Webster, Conte Candoli, Juan Tizol, Vido Musso, Nick Fatool, Al Cohn and other members of the original big band.
Compact disc: released on Hermes, Jun'87 by Nimbus Records. Dist: Target

20 GOLDEN HITS OF THE ROLLING STONES Various session artists (Various Session Artists).
Cassette: released on AIM (Budget Cassettes), Feb'83

20 GOLDEN NUMBER ONES Various original artists (Various original artists).
Album: released on MFP, Oct'80 by EMI Records. Dist: EMI

Cassette: released on MFP, Oct'80 by EMI Records. Dist: EMI

20 GOLDEN PIECES OF VINTAGE ROCK 'N' ROLL Various artists (Various Artists).
Album: released on Bulldog, Mar'81 by Bulldog Records. Dist: President Distribution, Spartan, Swift, Taylor, H.R.

Cassette: released on Bulldog, Mar'81 by Bulldog Records. Dist: President Distribution, Spartan, Swift, Taylor, H.R.

20 GOLDEN PIECES OF COUNTRY MUSIC Various artists (Various Artists).
Album: released on Bulldog, Jan'80 by Bulldog Records. Dist: President Distribution, Spartan, Swift, Taylor, H.R.

20 GOLDEN PIECES OF COUNTRY HITS Various artists (Various Artists).
Album: released on Bulldog, Jan'80 by Bulldog Records. Dist: President Distribution, Spartan, Swift, Taylor, H.R.

20 GOLDEN PIECES OF COUNTRY CHARTS Various artists (Various Artists).
Album: released on Bulldog, '80 by Bulldog Records. Dist: President Distribution, Spartan, Swift, Taylor, H.R.

20 GOLDEN PIECES OF COUNTRY NOSTALGIA Various artists (Various Artists).
Album: released on Bulldog, Jan'80 by Bulldog Records. Dist: President Distribution, Spartan, Swift, Taylor, H.R.

20 GOLDEN PIECES OF THE 50'S AND 60'S Various artists (Various Artists).
Album: released on Bulldog, Jun'79 by Bulldog Records. Dist: President Distribution, Spartan, Swift, Taylor, H.R.

20 GOLDEN SONGS OF FIJI VOL.2 Various artists (Various Artists).
Album: released on Viking, '78 by Viking Records. Dist: Lugtons

Cassette: released on Viking, '78 by Viking Records. Dist: Lugtons

Twenty Great...

20 GREAT BLUES RECORDINGS OF THE 50'S AND 60'S Various artists (Various Artists).
Album: released on Cascade, Jun'83 by Ace Records. Dist: Pinnacle

Cassette: released on Cascade, Jun'83 by Ace Records. Dist: Pinnacle

20 GREAT BLUES RECORDINGS OF THE 50'S AND 60'S VOL.2 Various artists (Various Artists).
Album: released on Cascade, Sep'84 by Ace Records. Dist: Pinnacle

Cassette: released on Cascade, Sep'84 by Ace Records. Dist: Pinnacle

20 GREAT COUNTRY RECORDINGS VOL.2 Various artists (Various Artists).
Cassette: released on Cascade, May'85 by Ace Records. Dist: Pinnacle

Album: released on Cascade, Apr'85 by Ace Records. Dist: Pinnacle

20 GREAT COUNTRY RECORDINGS OF THE 50'S AND 60'S Various artists (Various Artists).
Album: released on Cascade, Jun'83 by Ace Records. Dist: Pinnacle

Cassette: released on Cascade, Jun'83 by Ace Records. Dist: Pinnacle

20 GREAT DOOWOP RECORDINGS Various artists (Various Artists).
Album: released on Cascade, May'84 by Ace Records. Dist: Pinnacle

Cassette: released on Cascade, May'84 by Ace Records. Dist: Pinnacle

20 GREAT GUITAR INSTRUMENTALS Various artists (Various Artists).
Album: released on Cascade, Jun'83 by Ace Records. Dist: Pinnacle

Cassette: released on Cascade, Jun'83 by Ace Records. Dist: Pinnacle

20 GREAT HITS OF HE 60'S Various artists (Various Artists).
Album: released on Cascade, May'84 by Ace Records. Dist: Pinnacle

Cassette: released on Cascade, May'84 by Ace Records. Dist: Pinnacle

20 GREAT RHYTHM & BLUES OF THE 50'S Various artists (Various Artists).
Album: released on Cascade, Nov'82 by Ace Records. Dist: Pinnacle

Cassette: released on Cascade, Nov'82 by Ace Records. Dist: Pinnacle

Twenty Three Most...

23 MOST FAMOUS INTERNATIONAL MILITARY MARCHES Various artists (Various Artists).
Album: released on Vogue (France), Dec'84 Dist: Discovery, Jazz Music, PRT, Swift

Cassette: released on Vogue (France), Dec'84 Dist: Discovery, Jazz Music, PRT, Swift

Twenty Three Skidoo

7 SONGS.
Album: released on Fetish, Feb'82 by Fetish Records. Dist: Cartel, Pinnacle

ASSASSINS WITH SOUL, (THE).
Single (12"): released on Illuminated, Sep'86 by IKF Records. Dist: Pinnacle, Cartel, Jetstar

COUP.
Single (12"): released on Illuminated, Feb'85 by IKF Records. Dist: Pinnacle, Cartel, Jetstar

ETHICS.
Single (7"): released on Pineapple, Jul'82

GOSPEL COMES TO NEW GUINEA.
Single (12"): released on Fetish, Oct'81 by Fetish Records. Dist: Cartel, Pinnacle

JUST LIKE EVERYBODY.
Album: released on Bleeding Chin, Apr'87 by Bleeding Chin Records. Dist: Rough Trade, Cartel

LANGUAGE.
Single (12"): released on Illuminated, Feb'85 by IKF Records. Dist: Pinnacle, Cartel, Jetstar

OOZE.
Single (12"): released on Illuminated, Mar'85 by IKF Records. Dist: Pinnacle, Cartel, Jetstar

SEVEN SONGS.
Album: released on Illuminated, Feb'85 by IKF Records. Dist: Pinnacle, Cartel, Jetstar

TEARING UP THE PLANS.
Single (12"): released on Fetish, May'82 by Fetish Records. Dist: Cartel, Pinnacle

THOUGHT OF YOU.
Single (12"): released on Illuminated, Aug'86 by IKF Records. Dist: Pinnacle, Cartel, Jetstar

URBAN GAMELAN.
Album: released on Illuminated, Feb'85 by IKF Records. Dist: Pinnacle, Cartel, Jetstar

Twice

LOVERBOY.
Tracks: / Loverboy / Good friend.
Single (12"): released on TVT, Apr'86 Dist: Fast Forward, Cartel

Twice A Man

WALK ON YELLOW.
Album: released on Deadman's Curve, Aug'86 by Dave Henderson.

Twice Shy

WANNA DANCE/WHITE BOY.
Single (7"): released on Monarch, Jan'80 by Chart Records. Dist: Pinnacle

Twiggy

DIAMOND.
Single (7"): released on Arista, Mar'86 by Arista Records. Dist: RCA

Single (12"): released on Arista, Mar'86 by Arista Records. Dist: RCA

FEEL EMOTION.
Single (7"): released on Arista, Sep'85 by Arista Records. Dist: RCA

Single (12"): released on Arista, Sep'85 by Arista Records. Dist: RCA

Twilight

JUST ME ALONE.
Single (7"): released on Polydor, Oct'85 by Polydor Records. Dist: Polygram, Polydor

Single (12"): released on Polydor, Oct'85 by Polydor Records. Dist: Polygram, Polydor

MODERN FOLK ARRANGEMENTS.
Tracks: / Skewball / Greenan Castle / Mermaid's song / Golden keyboards / Hunter's purse / Silkie / Alchemist / Astrologer / Fine flowers in the valley / Peter's tune / Leaving Lismore / Major Kord's jig / Captain Ward / Trip to Sligo.
Notes: A German-based folk trio,totally acoustic.Winners of the1985 Edinburgh Folk Festival Competition.
Album: released on Lismor, May'86 by Lismor Records. Dist: Lismor, Roots, Celtic Music

Cassette: released on Lismor, May'86 by Lismor Records. Dist: Lismor, Roots, Celtic Music

Twilight 22

MYSTERIOUS.
Single (12"): released on WEA, Mar'85 by WEA Records. Dist: WEA

Twilly, Dwight

GIRLS.
Single (7"): released on EMI America, May'84 by EMI Records. Dist: EMI

Twin Image

KISS AND MAKE IT BETTER.
Single (7"): released on Capitol, Oct'84 by Capitol Records. Dist: EMI

Single (12"): released on Capitol, Oct'84 by Capitol Records. Dist: EMI

Twink

APOCALIPSTIC.
Tracks: / Apocalipstic / He's crying.
Single (7"): released on Twink, Apr'86 Dist: Backs, Cartel, Pinnacle

DRIVING MY CAR.
Tracks: / Driving my car / Wargirl.
Single (7"): released on Twink, Jun'87 Dist: Backs, Cartel, Pinnacle

Twinkle

TERRY/GOLDEN LIGHTS.
Single (7"): released on Old Gold, Jul'82 by Old Gold Records. Dist: Lightning, Jazz Music, Spartan, Counterpoint

Twinkle and the Fairies

SPACE LOVER.
Tracks: / Space lover.
Single (12"): released on Twinkle, May'86 by Twinkle Records. Dist: Jetstar

Twinkle Brothers

ANTI-APARTHEID.
Album: released on Twinkle, Jan'86 by Twinkle Records. Dist: Jetstar

CRUCIAL CUTS.
Album: released on Virgin, Apr'83 by Virgin Records. Dist: EMI, Virgin Distribution

DON'T JUMP THE FENCE/LET JAH IN.
Single (12"): released on Tsinkle, Jul'83

DUB MASSACRE PART 3.
Album: released on Twinkle, Dec'85 by Twinkle Records. Dist: Jetstar

ENTER ZION.
Album: released on Twinkle, Dec'84 by Twinkle Records. Dist: Jetstar

EVERYBODY NEEDS SOMEBODY/MORE DUB.
Single (12"): released on Twinkle, Jan'83 by Twinkle Records. Dist: Jetstar

FAITH CAN MOVE A MOUNTAIN.
Tracks: / Faith can move a mountain / Mob fury.
Single (12"): released on Jah Shaka, Oct'86 by Jah Shaka Records. Dist: Jetstar

GIVE RASTA PRAISE/CAN'T CHANGE AGAIN.
Single (12"): released on Twinkle, Feb'82 by Twinkle Records. Dist: Jetstar

KILIMANJARO.
Album: released on Twinkle, Oct'85 by Twinkle Records. Dist: Jetstar

LIVE FROM REGGAE SUNSPLASH.
Album: released on Vista Sounds, May'84 by Vista Sounds Records. Dist: Jetstar

MAGNET/CHANT RASTAFARI.
Single (12"): released on Twinkle, Jul'82 by Twinkle Records. Dist: Jetstar

ME NO YOU.
Album: released on Twinkle, Jul'81 by Twinkle Records. Dist: Jetstar

RASTA PON TOP.
Album: released on Vista Sounds, Sep'84 by Vista Sounds Records. Dist: Jetstar

RESPECT AND HONOUR.
Album: released on Twinkle, Mar'87 by Twinkle Records. Dist: Jetstar

TWINKLE LOVE SONGS.
Album: released on Twinkle, Feb'87 by Twinkle Records. Dist: Jetstar

Twins

BALLET DANCERS.
Single (7"): released on Carrere, Mar'84 by Carrere Records. Dist: PRT, Spartan

Single (12"): released on Carrere, Mar'84 by Carrere Records. Dist: PRT, Spartan

FACE TO FACE HEART TO HEART/NEW DAYS NEW WAYS.
Single (7"): released on Carrere, May'83 by Carrere Records. Dist: PRT, Spartan

Single (12"): released on Carrere, May'83 by Carrere Records. Dist: PRT, Spartan

Twisted Ace

FIREBIRD / I WON'T SURRENDER.
Single (7"): released on Heavy Metal, Nov'81 by FM-Revolver Records. Dist: EMI

Twisted Hand

SHORT STRINGS (EP).
Single (7"): released on M.A.P., Apr'82 by M.A.P. Records. Dist: M.A.P., Indies

Twisted Nerve

CAUGHT IN SESSION (EP).
Single (7"): released on Playlist, Sep'82

FIVE MINUTES OF FAME / STRANGE SENSATION.
Single (7"): released on Criminal Damage, Mar'83 by Criminal Damage Records.. Dist: Backs, Cartel

MEDUSA.
Single (12"): released on Criminal Damage, Sep'83 by Criminal Damage Records. Dist: Backs, Cartel

SEANCE.
Album: released on Plus One, Feb'84 by Plus One Records. Dist: Cartel

SEASON OF THE WITCHES (EP).
Single (12"): released on Criminal Damage, Aug'83 by Criminal Damage Records. Dist: Backs, Cartel

YOUTH / OPPORTUNITY KNOCKS / ALWAYS ALONE.
Single (7"): released on Troubador, Nov'82

Twisted Sister

COME OUT & PLAY.
Tracks: / Come out & play / Leader of the pack / You want what we got / I believe in rock'n'roll / Fire still burns. The / Be chrool to your scuel / I believe in you / Out in the streets / Lookin' out for number 1 / Kill or be killed.
Album: released on Atlantic, Dec'85 by WEA Records. Dist: WEA

Picture disc album: released on Atlantic, Dec'85 by WEA Records. Dist: WEA

Compact disc: released on Atlantic, Dec'85 by WEA Records. Dist: WEA

I WANNA ROCK.
Single (7"): released on Atlantic, Oct'84 by WEA Records. Dist: WEA

Single (12"): released on Atlantic, Oct'84 by WEA Records. Dist: WEA

LEADER OF THE PACK.
Tracks: / Leader of the pack / I wanna rock.
Single (7"): released on Atlantic, Jan'86 by WEA Records. Dist: WEA

Single (12"): released on Atlantic, Jan'86 by WEA Records. Dist: WEA

LOVE IS FOR SUCKERS.
Album: released on Atlantic, Jul'87 by WEA Records. Dist: WEA

Cassette: released on Atlantic, Jul'87 by WEA Records. Dist: WEA

Album: released on Atlantic, Aug'87 by WEA Records. Dist: WEA

Cassette: released on Atlantic, Aug'87 by WEA Records. Dist: WEA

Compact disc: released on Atlantic, Aug'87 by WEA Records. Dist: WEA

Compact disc: released on Atlantic, Aug'87 by WEA Records. Dist: WEA

PRICE.
Single (7"): released on Atlantic, Mar'85 by WEA Records. Dist: WEA

RUFF CUTTS (EP).
Single (12"): released on Secret, Jul'82 by Secret Records. Dist: EMI

STAY HUNGRY.
Notes: The American heavy metal outrage band,playing 11 hard-rocking numbers including their familiar anthems!"We're not gonna take it" & "You can't stop rock'n'roll".Total playing time:60minutes.
Video-cassette (VHS): released on Virgin, Oct'84 by Virgin Records. Dist: EMI, Virgin Distribution

Album: released on Atlantic, Jun'84 by WEA Records. Dist: WEA

Cassette: released on Atlantic, Jun'84 by WEA Records. Dist: WEA

UNDER THE BLADE.
Tracks: / What don't you know / Bad boys of rock'n'roll / Run for your life / Sin after sin / Shoot 'em down / Destroyer / Under the blade / Tear it loose / Day of the rocker / Leader of the pack.
Compact disc: released on Secret, Apr'86 by Secret Records. Dist: EMI

Album: released on Secret, Sep'82 by Secret Records. Dist: EMI

Cassette: released on Secret, Sep'82 by Secret Records. Dist: EMI

YOU CAN'T STOP ROCK 'N' ROLL.
Album: released on Atlantic, Jun'83 by WEA Records. Dist: WEA

Cassette: released on Atlantic, Jun'83 by WEA Records. Dist: WEA

YOU WANT WHAT WE GOT.
Tracks: / You want what we got / Stay hungry / We're not gonna take it* / King of fools*.
Single (7"): released on Warner Bros., Apr'86 by Warner Bros Records. Dist: WEA

Single (12"): released on Warner Bros., Apr'86 by Warner Bros Records. Dist: WEA

Twist & Shout...

TWIST AND SHOUT AT THE CAMDEN PALACE (Various Artists).
Notes: Including Jackie Wilson, Len Barry.
Picture disc single: released on Impact, May'87 by Ace Records. Dist: Rough Trade, Pinnacle, Swift, Backs, Counterpoint, Jungle, Hotshot, Cartel

Cassette: released on Impact, May'87 by Ace Records. Dist: Rough Trade, Pinnacle, Swift, Backs, Counterpoint, Jungle, Hotshot, Cartel

Twits

TWITS, THE Roald Dahl (Kinnear, Roy).
Cassette: released on Pickwick Talking Books, '83

Twitty, Conway

20 CONWAY CLASSICS.
Album: released on MCA, Nov'85 by MCA Records. Dist: Polygram, MCA

Cassette: released on MCA, Nov'85 by MCA Records. Dist: Polygram, MCA

BEAT GOES ON, THE.
Album: released on Charly, Jul'85 by Charly Records. Dist: Charly, Cadillac

BEST OF CONWAY AND LORETTA, (THE) (Twitty, Conway and Loretta Lynn).
Tracks: / Louisianna woman, Mississippi man / Lead me on / As soon as I hang up the phone / Let me be there / It's only make believe / From seven till ten / Let your love flow / Letter, (The) / Back home again / Lovin' what your lovin' does to me / Release me / It's true love / Feelins' / I can't love you enough / Hey good lookin'.
Album: released on MCA, May'86 by MCA Records. Dist: Polygram, MCA

BIG TOWN.
Tracks: / Ever since you went away / Big town / Blue is the way I feel / Treat me mean, treat me cruel / Road that I walk, The / Don't go too far / Broken heart / Angel's wings / Turn the other cheek / Wonder if you told her / Midnight / You made me what I am / Big train / Sitting in a dim cafe / Let me be the judge / Diggin' / Have I been away too long / Where I stand / Riskin' one.
Album: released on Showcase, Sep'86 Dist: Counterpoint

Cassette: released on Showcase, Sep'86 Dist: Counterpoint

BIG TRAIN.
Album: released on Astan, Nov'84 by Astan Records. Dist: Counterpoint

Cassette: released on Astan, Nov'84 by Astan Records. Dist: Counterpoint

BORDERLINE.
Tracks: / Julia / Lonely town / I want to know before we make love / Borderline / Not enough love to go 'round / Snake boots / I'm for awhile / Fifteen to forty-three / Everybody needs a hero / That's my job.
Album: released on MCA, Jun'87 by MCA Records. Dist: Polygram, MCA

Cassette: released on MCA, Jun'87 by MCA Records. Dist: Polygram, MCA

Compact disc: released on MCA, Jun'87 by MCA Records. Dist: Polygram, MCA

CLASSIC CONWAY.
Tracks: / Tight fittin' jeans / I can't believe she gives it all to me / Play guitar play / Grandest lady of them all, The / We had it all / Georgia keeps pulling on my ring / Your love has taken me that high / Over thirty(not over the hill) / I am the dreamer(you are the dream) / Red neckin' love makin' night.
Album: released on MCA Import, Mar'86 by MCA Records. Dist: Polygram, IMS

CONWAY TWITTY.
Album: released on Sierra, May'85 by Sierra Records. Dist: WEA

Cassette: released on Sierra, May'85 by Sierra Records. Dist: WEA

DYNAMIC DUO (Twitty, Conway and Loretta Lynn).
Album: released on Music For Pleasure, Jan'83

Cassette: released on Music For Pleasure, Jan'83

GREAT COUNTRY HITS.
Cassette: released on MCA, Mar'85 by MCA Records. Dist: CBS

Cassette: released on MCA, Mar'85 by MCA Records. Dist: CBS

Album: released on Warwick, Mar'81 by MSD Records. Dist: CBS

Cassette: released on Warwick, Mar'81 by MSD Records. Dist: CBS

GREATEST HITS: CONWAY TWITTY VOL.1.
Tracks: / Hello darlin' / I wonder what she'll think about me leaving / Fifteen years ago / Darling,you know I wouldn't lie to you / Darling,you know I wouldn't lie / That's when she started to stop loving you / To see my angel cry / I can't me without you / Next in line / How much more can she stand / Image of me, The / I love you more today.
Album: released on MCA Import, Mar'86 by MCA Records. Dist: Polygram, IMS

IT'S ONLY MAKE BELIEVE.
Single (7"): released on MGM, '80 Dist: Polygram Distribution, Swift Distribution

ROCK'N'ROLL YEARS (1956-1963), THE.
Album: released on Bear Family, Nov'85 by Bear Family Records. Dist: Rollercoaster Distribution, Swift

SHAKE IT UP BABY.
Album: released on Bulldog, Sep'82 by Bulldog Records. Dist: President Distribution, Spartan, Swift, Taylor, H.R.

Compact disc single: released on Bulldog, Sep'82 by Bulldog Records. Dist: President Distribution, Spartan, Swift, Taylor, H.R.

Album: released on Astan, Nov'84 by Astan Records. Dist: Counterpoint

Cassette: released on Astan, Nov'84 by Astan Records. Dist: Counterpoint

SONGWRITER.
Tracks: / Hello darlin' / (Lost her love) on the first date / Baby's gone / You've never been this far before / I'm not through loving you yet / Linda on my mind / After all the good is gone / Games that daddies play, the / I can't believe she gives it all to me / I've already loved you in my mind.
Album: released on MCA Import, Mar'86 by MCA Records. Dist: Polygram, IMS

TAKE GOOD CARE OF MY BABY.
Single (7"): released on Old Gold, Jul'84 by Old Gold Records. Dist: Lightning, Jazz Music, Spartan, Counterpoint

YOU MADE ME WHAT I AM.
Album: released on Allegiance, Apr'84 by PRT Records. Dist: PRT

Cassette: released on Allegiance, Apr'84 by PRT Records. Dist: PRT

Two

2X2.
Single (12"): released on Reflex, Sep'84

CHAINS OF DESIRE.
Tracks: / Chains of desire / Time is on your side / I had love / Will you catch me.
Single (7"): released on North Of South, May'87

Single (12"): released on North Of South, May'87

DREAMING SPIRES.
Album: released on No Future, Jan'84 by No Future Records. Dist: Pinnacle, Rough Trade, Cartel

TRACE OF RED.
Single (7"): released on No Future, Sep'83 by No Future Records. Dist: Pinnacle, Rough Trade, Cartel

WAITING FOR WINTER.
Single (12"): released on No Future, Nov'83 by No Future Records. Dist: Pinnacle, Rough Trade, Cartel

Two A.M.

SOMEBODY SOMEDAY.
Tracks: / Somebody someday / Deams and promises.
Single (7"): released on RCA, Jul'87 by RCA Records. Dist: RCA, Roots, Swift, Wellard, Chris, I & B, Solomon & Peres Distribution

Single (12"): released on RCA, Jul'87 by RCA Records. Dist: RCA, Roots, Swift, Wellard, Chris, I & B, Solomon & Peres Distribution

SOMEBODY SOMEDAY.
Single (7"): released on RCA, Aug'87 by RCA Records. Dist: RCA, Roots, Swift, Wellard, Chris, I & B, Solomon & Peres Distribution

Single (12"): released on RCA, Aug'87 by RCA Records. Dist: RCA, Roots, Swift, Wellard, Chris, I & B, Solomon & Peres Distribution

Two Beggarmen

FLOWERS OF MANCHESTER.
Album: released on Sweet Folk All, May'81 by Sweet Folk All Records. Dist: Sweet Folk All, Roots, Celtic Music, Dragon, Impetus, Projection, Chris Wellard, Festival Records

Two Brothers

TWO BROTHERS Various artists (Various Artists).
Cassette: released on Anvil, Jan'81 Dist: Anvil

Two Daughters

KISS THE CLOTH.
Album: released on United Dairies, Mar'86 Dist: Rough Trade, Indies

Two Fingered Approach

MY WORD WAR ALBUM (Two Helens).
Single (7"): released on Virus, May'83

Two Helens

REFLECTIONS IN RED.
Album: released on Sharko, Oct'86

Two Hundred And Fifty

250 DISCO JINGLES various studio recordings.
Album: released on East Anglian Productions, Jan'78 by East Anglian Productions. Dist: Lightning

Cassette: released on East Anglian Productions, Jan'78 by East Anglian Productions. Dist: Lightning

Two Hundred Days..

200 DAYS & 200 WAYS Various artists (Various Artists).
Album: released on Zoo, Dec'81

Two Man Sound

DISCO SAMBA.
Album: released on Ovation, Jul'80 by Gull Records. Dist: PRT Distribution

Single (7"): released on Ovation, '79 by Gull Records. Dist: PRT Distribution

Two Minds Crack

CRY CRY CRY.
Tracks: / Now the love has gone.
Single (7"): released on Warner Bros., Jan'87 by Warner Bros Records. Dist: WEA

Single (12"): released on Warner Bros., Jan'87 by Warner Bros Records. Dist: WEA

ENEMIES OF PROMISE.
Single (7"): released on Sedition, Oct'84 by Sedition Records. Dist: PRT

Single (12"): released on Sedition, Oct'84 by Sedition Records. Dist: PRT

HUNGER AND GREED.
Single (7"): released on Sedition, Feb'85 by Sedition Records. Dist: PRT

Single (12"): released on Sedition, Feb'85 by Sedition Records. Dist: PRT

Single (12"): released on Sedition, Feb'85 by Sedition Records. Dist: PRT

VICTORY PARADE.
Tracks: / One sky above us / Walk on back / Hunger and greed / Fire / Find the key / Cry cry cry / Upside down / Love is in control / Live to die / Sense that never sleeps.
Album: released on Sire, Nov'86

Cassette: released on Sire, Nov'86

Two Minutes Mr. Smith...

SAVIN' UP.
Single (7"): released on Falcon, Oct'85 Dist: Jetstar, M.I.S.

Two Nations

ANY LUCK.
Tracks: / Any luck / Brand X / Everything I Own*.
Notes: *=Extra track on 12" only.
Single (7"): released on 10, Sep'86 by 10 Records. Dist: Virgin, EMI

Single (12"): released on 10, Sep'86 by 10 Records. Dist: Virgin, EMI

BOTH SIDES.
Album: released on Virgin, Oct'87 by Virgin Records. Dist: EMI, Virgin Distribution

Cassette: released on Virgin, Oct'87 by Virgin Records. Dist: EMI, Virgin Distribution

INDEPENDANCE.
Single (7"): released on 10, Aug'87 by 10 Records. Dist: Virgin, EMI

Single (12"): released on 10, Aug'87 by 10 Records. Dist: Virgin, EMI

Two Ninety Nine

TWO NINETY NINE Various artists (Various Artists).
Album: released on Rot, Jul'84 by Rot Records. Dist: Red Rhino Through Cartel Distributions

Two of a Kind

TWO OF A KIND Original film soundtrack.
Album: released on EMI, Dec'83 by EMI Records. Dist: EMI

Cassette: released on EMI, Dec'83 by EMI Records. Dist: EMI

Two Of Us

BLUE NIGHT SHADOW.
Single (7"): released on Genie, Sep'85 by Genie Records. Dist: Spartan, CBS

Single (12"): released on Genie, Sep'85 by Genie Records. Dist: Spartan, CBS

TWO OF US Various artists (Various Artists).
Album: released on K-Tel, Sep'83 by K-Tel Records. Dist: Record Merchandisers Distribution, Taylors, Terry Blood Distribution, Wynd-Up Distribution, Relay Distribution, Pickwick Distribution, Solomon & Peres Distribution, Polygram

Cassette: released on K-Tel, Sep'83 by K-Tel Records. Dist: Record Merchandisers Distribution, Taylors, Terry Blood Distribution, Wynd-Up Distribution, Relay Distribution, Pickwick Distribution, Solomon & Peres Distribution, Polygram

Two People

HEAVEN.
Tracks: / Run to him.
Single (7"): released on Polydor, Jan'87 by Polydor Records. Dist: Polygram, Polydor

Single (12"): released on Polydor, Jan'87 by Polydor Records. Dist: Polygram, Polydor

MOUTH OF AN ANGEL.
Tracks: / Mouth of an angel / Let's raise murder / Dig it*.
Notes: *=Extra track on 12" only.
Single (7"): released on Polydor, Sep'86 by Polydor Records. Dist: Polygram, Polydor

Single (12"): released on Polydor, Sep'86 by Polydor Records. Dist: Polygram, Polydor

THIS IS THE SHIRT.
Tracks: / This is the shirt./ People in love (never have much fun) / It's obvious.
Single (7"): released on Polydor, Mar'87 by Polydor Records. Dist: Polygram, Polydor

Single (12"): released on Polydor, Mar'87 by Polydor Records. Dist: Polygram, Polydor

Single (7"): released on Polydor, Apr'85 by Polydor Records. Dist: Polygram, Polydor

Single (12"): released on Polydor, Apr'85 by Polydor Records. Dist: Polygram, Polydor

Two Points To Tonka
TWO POINTS TO TONKA Various artists (Various Artists).
Cassette: released on Son Of Inevitable, Feb'85 Dist: Probe Plus Distribution, Cartel

Two Point Two
RUSSIAN DOLL.
Single (7"): released on Rock City Records, Sep'84 by Rock City Records. Dist: PRT Distribution

Two Puerto Ricans
DO IT PROPERLY.
Single (7"): released on Chrysalis, Jun'87 by Chrysalis Records. Dist: CBS

Single (12"): released on Chrysalis, Jun'87 by Chrysalis Records. Dist: CBS

Two Ronnies
BEST OF THE TWO RONNIES, THE.
Album: released on Spot, Feb'82 by Pickwick Records. Dist: H.R. Taylor, Lugtons

Cassette: released on Spot, Feb'82 by Pickwick Records. Dist: H.R. Taylor, Lugtons

VERY BEST OF ME AND THE VERY BEST OF HIM, THE.
Album: released on BBC, Oct'84 by BBC Records & Tapes. Dist: EMI, PRT, Pye

Cassette: released on BBC, Oct'84 by BBC Records & Tapes. Dist: EMI, PRT, Pye

Two's Company
LET'S START ALL OVER AGAIN.
Album: released on Harp(Ireland), Oct'81 by Pickwick Records. Dist: Taylors

MADE FOR EACH OTHER.
Album: released on Release, Jan'78 by Release Records. Dist: I & B, Wynd-Up Distribution, Taylors, Solomon & Peres Distribution

TWO'S COMPANY Various artists.
Album: released on Towerbell, Apr'86 by Towerbell Records. Dist: EMI

Cassette: released on Towerbell, Apr'86 by Towerbell Records. Dist: EMI

YOU'RE MY BEST FRIEND.
Album: released on Release, May'76 by Release Records. Dist: I & B, Wynd-Up Distribution, Taylors, Solomon & Peres Distribution

Two Sisters
DESTINY.
Album: released on Streetwave, Mar'84 by Streetwave Records. Dist: PRT Distribution

Two Thousand And One
2001: A SPACE ODYSSEY Spoken word (Spoken Word).

2001: A SPACE ODYSSEY Original soundtrack.
Tracks: / Also sprach Zarathustra / Requiem for soprano, mezzo soprano, 2 mixed choirs and ... / Blue Danube, (The) / Gayne ballet suite / Atmospheres / Blue Danube, (The) (reprise) / Also sprach Zarathustra (reprise).
Album: released on CBS, Jul'86 by CBS Records. Dist: CBS

Compact disc: released on CBS, Nov'86 by CBS Records. Dist: CBS

Two Thousand And Ten
2010 Original music from the motion picture (Original Music From The Motion Picture).
Album: released on A&M, Mar'85 by A&M Records. Dist: Polygram

Cassette: released on A&M, Mar'85 by A&M Records. Dist: Polygram

2010: ODESSEY TWO Arthur C Clarke (Clarke, Arthur C.).
Cassette: released on Caedmon(USA), Apr'83 by Caedmon (USA) Records. Dist: Gower, Taylors, Discovery

Two Three
ALL THE TIME LOW (Two Timer).
Single (7"): released on Rough Trade, '79 by Rough Trade Records. Dist: Rough Trade Distribution, Cartel Distribution

---

Two Timer
ROCK TO ROCK.
Album: released on Heavy Metal America, Feb'86 by FM-Revolver Records. Dist: EMI

Two Ton Machine
CHINATOWN.
Album: released on Dublar, Aug'85 by Dublar Records. Dist: Jetstar

Two Two
INSUFFICIENT DATA.
Single (7"): released on Chiswick, Feb'82 by Chiswick Records. Dist: Pinnacle

KING SOLOMON'S MINES.
Single (7"): released on Chiswick, Oct'82 by Chiswick Records. Dist: Pinnacle

Single (12"): released on Chiswick, Oct'82 by Chiswick Records. Dist: Pinnacle

KWAGAYO.
Single (7"): released on Chiswick, Jun'82 by Chiswick Records. Dist: Pinnacle

KWAGYO.
Single (7"): released on Chiswick, Jul'82 by Chiswick Records. Dist: Pinnacle

Two Way
ALL DRESSED UP.
Single (7"): released on PRT, Mar'84 by PRT Records. Dist: PRT

Single (12"): released on PRT, Mar'84 by PRT Records. Dist: PRT

FACE IN THE WINDOW.
Single (7"): released on PRT, Jan'83 by PRT Records. Dist: PRT

Two White Horses...
TWO WHITE HORSES STANDIN' IN LINE Various original artists (Various original artists).
Album: released on Matchbox, Oct'76 by Saydisc Records. Dist: Roots, Projection, Jazz Music, JSU, Celtic Music

TXT
GIRLS GOT A BRAND NEW TOY.
Single (7"): released on Portrait, Jul'85 by CBS Records. Dist: CBS

Single (12"): released on Portrait, Jul'85 by CBS Records. Dist: CBS

Tygers of Pan Tang
BURNING IN THE SHADE.
Album: released on Zebra, May'87 by Cherry Red Records. Dist: Pinnacle

CAGE, THE.
Album: released on MCA, Jun'84 by MCA Records. Dist: CBS

Cassette: released on MCA, Jun'84 by MCA Records. Dist: CBS

FIRST KILL.
Album: released on Neat, Aug'86 by Neat Records. Dist: Pinnacle, Neat

SPELLBOUND.
Tracks: / Gangland / Take it / Minotaur / Hellbound / Mirror / Silver and gold / Tyger bay / Story so far, The / Blackjack / Don't stop by.
Album: released on MCA, Jun'87 by MCA Records. Dist: Polygram, MCA

Cassette: released on MCA, Jun'87 by MCA Records. Dist: Polygram, MCA

WILD CAT.
Album: released on Fame, May'83 by Music For Pleasure Records. Dist: EMI

Cassette: released on Fame, May'83 by Music For Pleasure Records. Dist: EMI

WRECK-AGE, THE.
Album: released on Music For Nations, Jun'85 by Music For Nations Records. Dist: Pinnacle

Cassette: released on Music For Nations, Jun'85 by Music For Nations Records. Dist: Pinnacle

Tyla Gang
SUICIDE JOCKEY.
Single (7"): released on Skydog, Apr'77 by Skydog Records.

Tyla, Sean
SEAN TYLA'S JUST POPPED OUT.
Album: released on Zilch, May'81 by Zilch Records. Dist: Stage One

Cassette: released on Zilch, May'81 by Zilch Records. Dist: Stage One

---

Tyla, Sean & English Electric
LANDING LIGHTS.
Single (7"): released on Zilch, Aug'81 by Zilch Records. Dist: Stage One

Tyler, Alvin
ROCKIN' AND ROLLIN' (Tyler, Alvin and The Gyros).
Album: released on Ace, Aug'86 by Ace Records. Dist: Pinnacle, Swift, Hotshot, Cadillac

Tyler, Alvin Red
HERITAGE.
Compact disc: released on Rounder (USA), Dec'86 Dist: Mike's Country Music Room Distribution, Jazz Music Distribution, Swift Distribution, Roots Records Distribution, Projection Distribution, Topic Distribution

Album: released on Rounder Europa, Feb'87

Tyler, Bonnie
BAND OF GOLD.
Tracks: / Band of gold / It's not enough.
Single (7"): released on CBS, May'86 by CBS Records. Dist: CBS

Single (12"): released on CBS, May'86 by CBS Records. Dist: CBS

BONNIE TYLER.
Cassette single: released on RCA, May'83 by RCA Records. Dist: RCA, Roots, Swift, Wellard, Chris, I & B, Solomon & Peres Distribution

FASTER THAN THE SPEED OF NIGHT/CAN GET BETTER.
Single (7"): released on CBS, Apr'83 by CBS Records. Dist: CBS

Single (12"): released on CBS, Apr'83 by CBS Records. Dist: CBS

FASTER THAN THE SPEED OF NIGHT.
Tracks: / Have you ever seen the rain? / Faster than the speed of night / Getting so excited / Total eclipse of the heart / It's a jungle out there / Going through the motions / Tears / Take me back / Straight from the heart.
Notes: Produced and directed by Jim Steinman, it features two Steinman songs, the titletrack and the full-length version of the number one single "Total eclipse of theheart".
Album: released on CBS, Apr'83 by CBS Records. Dist: CBS

Cassette: released on CBS, Apr'83 by CBS Records. Dist: CBS

Compact disc: released on CBS, Apr'83 by CBS Records. Dist: CBS

Picture disc single: released on CBS, May'83 by CBS Records. Dist: CBS

GETTING SO EXCITED.
Single (7"): released on CBS, Mar'84 by CBS Records. Dist: CBS

Single (12"): released on CBS, Mar'84 by CBS Records. Dist: CBS

GREATEST HITS:BONNIE TYLER.
Cassette: released on Telstar, Nov'86 by Telstar Records. Dist: RCA Distribution

Compact disc: released on Telstar, Nov'86 by Telstar Records. Dist: RCA Distribution

Album: released on Telstar, Nov'86 by Telstar Records. Dist: RCA Distribution

HAVE YOU EVER SEEN THE RAIN/TIME.
Single (7"): released on CBS, Jun'83 by CBS Records. Dist: CBS

Single (12"): released on CBS, Jun'83 by CBS Records. Dist: CBS

IF YOU WERE A WOMAN (LIMITED EDITION).
Tracks: / If you were a woman / Under suspicion / If you were a woman (limited edition) / Under suspicion.
Notes: Poster bag limited edition (10,000)
Single (7"): released on CBS, Mar'86 by CBS Records. Dist: CBS

Single (7"): released on CBS, Apr'86 by CBS Records. Dist: CBS

IT'S A HEARTACHE.
Tracks: / It's a heartache / Lost in France.
Single (7"): released on Old Gold, Nov'86 by Old Gold Records. Dist: Lightning, Jazz Music, Spartan, Counterpoint

Single (7"): released on Golden Grooves, Aug'81 by RCA. Dist: RCA

LOVERS AGAIN.
Tracks: / I do it for you.
Single (7"): released on CBS, Jan'87 by CBS Records. Dist: CBS

MORE THAN A LOVER.
Single (7"): released on RCA, Jan'77 by RCA Records. Dist: RCA, Roots, Swift, Wellard, Chris, I & B, Solomon & Peres Distribution Deleted '78.

MY GUNS ARE LOADED.
Single (7"): released on RCA, Mar'79 by RCA Records. Dist: RCA, Roots, Swift, Wellard, Chris, I & B, Solomon & Peres Distribution Deleted May'80.

REBEL WITHOUT A CLUE.
Tracks: / Rebel without a clue / I do it for you.
Single (7"): released on CBS, Oct'86 by CBS Records. Dist: CBS

BATTLE OF WILLS.
Album: released on Y, Oct'82

Tyndall, Nik
EINKLANG.
Album: released on Sky (Germany), Apr'86

ENTSPANNUNG.
Album: released on Sky (Germany), Aug'85

Tyner, McCoy
EXPANSIONS.
Album: released on Blue Note, Apr'85 by EMI Records. Dist: EMI

FLY WITH THE WIND.
Compact disc: released on Fantasy (USA), Nov'86 by Fantasy Inc USA Records. Dist: IMS, Polygram

Compact disc: released on Carrere, Apr'87 by Carrere Records. Dist: PRT, Spartan

IT'S ABOUT TIME (Tyner, McCoy and Jackie McLean).
Tracks: / Spur of the moment / You taught my heart to sing / It's about time / Hip toe / No flowers please / Travelin' / Spur of the moment / You taught my heart to sing / It's about time / Hip toe / No flowers please / Travelin'.
Notes: Featuring Ron Carter on bass, Al Foster on drums and an exceptional trumpeter, Jon Faddis, the material was all composed by McCoy Turner with the exception of one title by Carter.
Album: released on Blue Note, Dec'85 by EMI Records. Dist: EMI

Cassette: released on Blue Note, Dec'85 by EMI Records. Dist: EMI

Compact disc: released on Blue Note, Sep'87 by EMI Records. Dist: EMI. Estim retail price in Sep'87 was £11.99.

NIGHTS OF BALLADS & BLUES.
Album: released on Jasmine, Aug'82 by Jasmine Records. Dist: Counterpoint, Lugtons, Taylor, H.R., Wellard, Chris, Swift, Cadillac

Cassette: released on Jasmine, Aug'82 by Jasmine Records. Dist: Counterpoint, Lugtons, Taylor, H.R., Wellard, Chris, Swift, Cadillac

PLAYS ELLINGTON.
Album: released on Jasmine, '82 by Jasmine Records. Dist: Counterpoint, Lugtons, Taylor, H.R., Wellard, Chris, Swift, Cadillac

Cassette: released on Jasmine, '82 by Jasmine Records. Dist: Counterpoint, Lugtons, Taylor, H.R., Wellard, Chris, Swift, Cadillac

REAL MCCOY, THE.
Tracks: / Passion dance / Contemplation / Four by five / Search for peace / Blues on the corner / Passion dance / Contemplation / Four by five / Search for peace / Blues on the corner.
Compact disc: released on Manhattan-Blue Note, May'87 by EMI America Records (USA). Dist: EMI

Album: released on Blue Note, Jul'87 by EMI Records. Dist: EMI

Album: released on Blue Note, Aug'87 by EMI Records. Dist: EMI

REFLECTIONS.
Double Album: released on Milestone, Mar'82 by Ace Records. Dist: PRT
Single (12"): released on CBS, Oct'86 by CBS Records. Dist: CBS

SECRET DREAMS AND FORBIDDEN FIRE.
Tracks: / Ravishing / If you were a woman / Loving you's a dirty job / No way to treat a lady / Band of gold / Rebel without a clue / Lovers again / Holding out for a hero.
Album: released on CBS, Jul'86 by CBS Records. Dist: CBS

Cassette: released on CBS, Jul'86 by CBS Records. Dist: CBS

Compact disc: released on CBS, Jul'86 by CBS Records. Dist: CBS

STRAIGHT FROM THE HEART.
Single (7"): released on CBS, Aug'83 by CBS Records. Dist: CBS

TOTAL ECLIPSE OF THE HEART.
Tracks: / Total eclipse of the heart / Dead ringer for love / Keep on loving you / Who's crying now?
Single (12"): released on Old Gold, Feb'86 by Old Gold Records. Dist: Lightning, Jazz Music, Spartan, Counterpoint

VIDEO, (THE).
Tracks: / Holding out for a hero / Total eclipse of the heart.
Notes: Eight promo clips from one of Britain's top female rock singers, including hit singles like "Holding out for a hero" and Total eclipse of the heart.
Video-cassette (VHS): released on CBS, Nov'86 by CBS Records. Dist: CBS

Tyler, Charles
60 MINUTE MAN.
Album: released on Adelphi(USA), May'81 by Adelphi Records (USA). Dist: Projection, Swift

DEFINITES VOL 1.
Album: released on Storyville, May'86 by Storyville Records. Dist: Jazz Music Distribution, Swift Distribution, Chris Wellard Distribution, Counterpoint Distribution

SAGA OF THE OUTLAWS.
Album: released on Nessa, Mar'79 Dist: Projection, Swift

Tyler, Charles Ensemble
FOLK AND MYSTERY STORIES.
Album: released on Sonet, Mar'81 by Sonet Records. Dist: PRT

Tyler, Red
HERITAGE.
Album: released on Rounder Europa, Apr'86

Album: released on Rounder Europa, Apr'86

Tymes
MS. GRACE.
Tracks: / Ms. Grace / You little trustmaker.
Single (7"): released on Old Gold, Apr'87 by Old Gold Records. Dist: Lightning, Jazz Music, Spartan, Counterpoint

Single (7"): released on Golden Grooves, Jul'78 by RCA. Dist: RCA

Tymon Dogg
BATTLE WILLS.
Album: released on Y, Sep'84

Tymon Dogs
TENDER MOMENTS.
Album: released on Blue Note, Jul'85 by EMI Records. Dist: EMI

TIME FOR TYNER.
Tracks: / African village / Little Madimba / May street / I didn't know what time it was / Surrey with the fringe on top / I've grown accustomed to your face.
Notes: For this 1968 recording Tyner's regular trio was joined by another outstanding Blue Note artist, vibist Bobby Hutcherson.
Album: released on Blue Note, May'86 by EMI Records. Dist: EMI

Typhoons
TELSTAR.
Single (7"): released on Bohemian, Aug'81 Dist: Spartan

Typhoon Saturday
I HAVE LOVE.
Single (7"): released on Polydor, Sep'82 by Polydor Records. Dist: Polygram, Polydor

Typically Tropical
BARBADOS.
Single (7"): released on PRT, Jun'82 by PRT Records. Dist: PRT

Single (7"): released on Old Gold, Jul'82 by Old Gold Records. Dist: Lightning, Jazz Music, Spartan, Counterpoint

LADY D.
Single (7"): released on Whisper, Jun'81 by Whisper Records. Dist: Spartan

MY RUBBER BALL.
Single (7"): released on Hobo, May'79 by Hobo Records. Dist: Hobo

Tyranosaurus Rex
MY PEOPLE WERE FAIR AND HAD SKY IN....
Album: released on Sierra, Jun'85 by Sierra Records. Dist: WEA

Cassette: released on Sierra, Jun'85 by Sierra Records. Dist: WEA

PROPHETS, SEERS & SAGES.
Album: released on Sierra, Aug'85 by Sierra Records. Dist: WEA

Cassette: released on Sierra, Aug'85 by Sierra Records. Dist: WEA

UNICORN.
Album: released on Sierra, Aug'85 by Sierra Records. Dist: WEA

Cassette: released on Sierra, Aug'85 by Sierra Records. Dist: WEA

Tyrant
FIGHT FOR YOUR LIFE.
Album: released on Powerstation Records, Jul'86 by Powerstation Records. Dist: Pinnacle

LEGIONS OF THE DEAD.
Album: released on Road Runner, Aug'85

MEAN MACHINE.
Album: released on Mausoleum, Mar'85 by Mausoleum Records. Dist: Pinnacle

Tyree
I FEAR THE NIGHT.
Tracks: / I fear the night / I fear the night (remix) / I fear the night (subterranean mix) / I fear the night (fear the dub mix).
Single (12"): released on Ruby, Jun'87 Dist: Red Rhino Distribution, Cartel Distribution

Tyrone
AIN'T GOT NO LOVE.
Single (12"): released on Solid Groove, Feb'82 Dist: Jetstar, Pinnacle

COME ON OVER TO MY PLACE.
Single (12"): released on La Femme Noire, Mar'83 by La Femme Noire Records. Dist: Jetstar

I'M FALLING IN LOVE.
Single (12"): released on Music Scene, Sep'85 by Music Scene Records. Dist: Jetstar Distribution

I'M GONNA MAKE YOU LOVE ME (Tyrone & Samantha Rose).
Single (12"): released on Music Scene, Jun'84 by Music Scene Records. Dist: Jetstar Distribution

I'M GONNA MAKE YOU LOVE ME.
Single (7"): released on Total Control, Nov'85

Single (12"): released on Total Control, Nov'85

I NEED A WOMAN TONIGHT.
Single (12"): released on Eargasm, Jul'80 Dist: Jetstar

MARGATE.
Single (12"): released on Chans, Jul'83 by Chans Records. Dist: Jetstar

REJOICE IT'S CHRISTMAS TIME AGAIN.

Single (12"): released on Thunderbay, Dec'83 Dist: Spartan Distribution

Tyrrall, Gordon
HOW CAN I LIVE AT THE TOP OF A MOUNTAIN.
Album: released on Celtic Music, Mar'84 by Celtic Music Distribution. Dist: Celtic Music, Jazz Music, Projection, Roots

Tyson Dog
BEWARE OF THE DOG.
Album: released on Neat, '85 by Neat Records. Dist: Pinnacle, Neat

Cassette: released on Neat, '85 by Neat Records. Dist: Pinnacle, Neat

CRIMES OF INSANITY.
Album: released on Neat, Oct'86 by Neat Records. Dist: Pinnacle, Neat

EAT THE RICH.
Single (7"): released on Neat, Dec'83 by Neat Records. Dist: Pinnacle, Neat

HAMMERHEAD.
Single (12"): released on Neat, Mar'85 by Neat Records. Dist: Pinnacle, Neat

SCHOOL'S OUT.
Single (7"): released on Neat, Sep'86 by Neat Records. Dist: Pinnacle, Neat

SHOOT TO KILL.
Single (12"): released on Neat, Jul'85 by Neat Records. Dist: Pinnacle, Neat

Tytan
ROUGH JUSTICE.
Album: released on Razor, Aug'85 by Razor. Dist: Pinnacle

Tywyll, Tynal
73 HEB FLARES.
Single (7"): released on Anhrefn, Dec'86 Dist: Revolver, Cartel

Tyzik, Jeff
JAMMIN' IN MANHATTAN.
Tracks: / New York woman / When I look in your eyes / You're my woman, you're my lady / Killer Joe / Jammin' in Manhattan / Better and better / Melange / Echoes.
Notes: Polydor have released the title track of trumpeter Tyzik's album as a single.
Album: released on Polydor, Jul'84 by Polydor Records. Dist: Polygram, Polydor

Compact disc: released on Polydor, Jul'84 by Polydor Records. Dist: Polygram, Polydor

SMILE.
Tracks: / Smile / Sweet surrender / Face / Prized possession / Love won't wait / Hip hop / My heart's desire / I'm in love again / Rare moments.
Album: released on Polydor, Nov'85 by Polydor Records. Dist: Polygram, Polydor

Cassette: released on Polydor, Nov'85 by Polydor Records. Dist: Polygram, Polydor

Tziganka Ensemble
SONGS OF RUSSIA'S GYPSIES.
Album: released on Sweet Folk All, May'81 by Sweet Folk All Records. Dist: Sweet Folk All, Roots, Celtic Music, Dragon, Impetus, Projection, Chris Wellard, Festival Records

Tzuke, Judie
BEST OF JUKIE TZUKE, THE.
Album: released on Rocket, Jun'83 by Phonogram Records. Dist: Polygram Distribution

Cassette: released on Rocket, Jun'83 by Phonogram Records. Dist: Polygram Distribution

---

BLACK FURS.
Single (7"): released on Rocket, May'83 by Phonogram Records. Dist: Polygram Distribution

CAT IS OUT, THE.
Compact disc: released on Legacy, '86 Dist: PRT

CAT IS OUT, THE.
Album: released on Legacy, Jun'85 Dist: PRT

Cassette: released on Legacy, Jun'85 Dist: PRT

HOW DO I FEEL.
Single (7"): released on Rocket, Nov'83 by Chrysalis Records. Dist: CBS

Single (12"): released on Chrysalis, Nov'83 by Chrysalis Records. Dist: CBS

I AM THE PHOENIX.
Album: released on Rocket, Aug'83 by Phonogram Records. Dist: Polygram Distribution

Cassette: released on Rocket, Aug'83 by Phonogram Records. Dist: Polygram Distribution

I'LL BE THE ONE.
Single (7"): released on Legacy, Mar'85 Dist: PRT

JEANNIE NO.
Single (7"): released on Chrysalis, Aug'83 by Chrysalis Records. Dist: CBS

Single (12"): released on Chrysalis, Aug'83 by Chrysalis Records. Dist: CBS

JUDIE TZUKE.
Album: released on Legacy, Jun'85 Dist: PRT

Cassette: released on Legacy, Jun'85 Dist: PRT

Compact disc: released on Legacy, Jun'85 Dist: PRT

LOVE LIKE FIRE.
Single (7"): released on Legacy, Jun'85 Dist: PRT

Single (12"): released on Legacy, Jun'85 Dist: PRT

RITMO.
Album: released on Chrysalis, Sep'83 by Chrysalis Records. Dist: CBS

Cassette: released on Chrysalis, Sep'83 by Chrysalis Records. Dist: CBS

ROAD NOISE-THE OFFICIAL BOOTLEG.
Cassette: released on Chrysalis, Oct'82 by Chrysalis Records. Dist: CBS

Album: released on Chrysalis, Oct'82 by Chrysalis Records. Dist: CBS

SHOOT THE MOON.
Cassette: released on Chrysalis, Apr'82 by Chrysalis Records. Dist: CBS

Album: released on Chrysalis, Apr'82 by Chrysalis Records. Dist: CBS

SPORTS CAR.
Album: released on Rocket, Aug'83 by Phonogram Records. Dist: Polygram Distribution

Cassette: released on Rocket, Aug'83 by Phonogram Records. Dist: Polygram Distribution

THIS SIDE OF HEAVEN.
Single (7"): released on Legacy, Sep'85 Dist: PRT

WELCOME TO THE CRUISE.
Album: released on Rocket, Nov'84 by Phonogram Records. Dist: Polygram Distribution

Cassette: released on Rocket, Nov'84 by Phonogram Records. Dist: Polygram Distribution

YOU.
Single (7"): released on Legacy, Sep'84 Dist: PRT

U2

11 O'Clock tick tick.
Single (7"): released on Island in May'80 by Island Records. Distributed by: Polygram

Boy.
Tracks: / Twilight / An cat dubh / Out of control / Stories for the boys / Ocean, The / Day without me, A / Another time another place / Electric co., The / Shadows and tall trees.
Album: released on Island in Nov'80 by Island Records..Distributed by: Polygram

Musicassette: released on Island in Nov'80 by Island Records. Distributed by: Polygram

Compact disc: released on Island in '86 by Island Records. Distributed by: Polygram

Celebration.
Single (7"): released on Island in Mar'82 by Island Records. Distributed by: Polygram

Day without me, A.
Single (7"): released on Island in Aug'80 by Island Records. Distributed by: Polygram

Fire.
Single (7"): released on Island in Jul'81 by Island Records. Distributed by: Polygram

Gloria.
Single (7"): released on Island in Sep'81 by Island Records. Distributed by: Polygram

I still haven't found what I'm looking for.
Tracks: / I still haven't... / Spanish eyes / Deep in the heart / (Jukebox version)".
Single (7"): released on Island in 23 May'87 by Island Records. Distributed by: Polygram

Single (12"): released on Island in 23 May'87 by Island Records. Distributed by: Polygram

Single (cassette): released on Island in 23 May'87 by Island Records. Distributed by: Polygram

will follow.
Single (7"): released on Island in Oct'80 by Island Records. Distributed by: Polygram

oshua tree.
Compact disc: released on Island in Mar'87 by Island Records. Distributed by: Polygram

lbum: released on Island in Mar'87 by Island Records. Distributed by: Polygram

usicassette: released on Island in Mar'87 by Island Records. Distributed by: Polygram

ew Years Day.
ouble-pack single: released on Island in an'83 by Island Records. Distributed by: Polyam

ctober.
ompact disc: released on Island in '86 by Island Records. Distributed by: Polygram

lbum: released on Island in Oct'81 by Island Records. Distributed by: Polygram

usicassette: released on Island in Oct'81 by and Records. Distributed by: Polygram

de.
cks: / Pride / 4th July / (Sunday bloody Sunay) / Two hearts / Two hearts beat as one / omerang 1 & 2) / (Love comes tumbling) / Seconds in kingdom / 3 Sunrises (out takes).
gle (7"): released on Arabesque in Apr'86. tributed by: D Sharp Records, Pinnacle

gle (12"): released on Island in Oct'84 by Is-Records. Distributed by: Polygram

Sunday Bloody Sunday.
Single (7"): released on Island in Nov'85 by Island Records. Distributed by: Polygram

Single (12"): released on Island in Nov'85 by Island Records. Distributed by: Polygram

Two hearts beat as one.
Double-pack single: released on Island in Mar'83 by Island Records. Distributed by: Polygram

Single (12"): released on Island in Mar'83 by Island Records. Distributed by: Polygram

Under a blood red sky 'Live'.
Tracks: / 11 O'Clock tick tock / Will follow, I / Party girl / Gloria / Sunday bloody Sunday / Electric Co, The / New year's day / '40' / America / Send in the clowns.
Notes: This compilation (P) 1983 Original sound recording made by Island Records Ltd.
Video-cassette (VHS): released on Virgin in Jan'86 by Virgin Records. Distributed by: EMI, Virgin Distribution

Compact disc: released on Island in May'86 by Island Records. Distributed by: Polygram

Album: released on Island in Nov'83 by Island Records. Distributed by: Polygram

Musicassette: released on Island in Nov'83 by Island Records. Distributed by: Polygram

Unforgettable fire, The.
Tracks: / Sort of homecomming / Pride in the name of love / 4th of July / Wire / Unforgettable fire / Promenade / Indian summer sky / MLK / Elvis Presley & America.
Album: released on Island in Sep'84 by Island Records. Distributed by: Polygram

Musicassette: released on Island in Sep'84 by Island Records. Distributed by: Polygram

Compact disc: released on Island in Sep'84 by Island Records. Distributed by: Polygram. Estim retail price in Aug'87 was £11.99.

Video-cassette (VHS): released on Island in '85 by Island Records. Distributed by: Polygram

Single (7"): released on Island in Apr'85 by Island Records. Distributed by: Polygram

Single (12"): released on Island in Apr'85 by Island Records. Distributed by: Polygram

Double-pack single: released on Island in Apr'85 by Island Records. Distributed by: Polygram

War.
Tracks: / Sunday bloody Sunday / Seconds / Like a song / New Years day / Two hearts beat as one / Surrender / Drowning man / Red light / 409 / Surrender.
Compact disc: released on Island in Dec'85 by Island Records. Distributed by: Polygram

Album: released on Island in Feb'83 by Island Records. Distributed by: Polygram

Musicassette: released on Island in Feb'83 by Island Records. Distributed by: Polygram

Wide awake in America.
Album: released on Island in Jun'85 by Island Records. Distributed by: Polygram

With or without you.
Tracks: / With or without you / Luminous times (hold onto love) / Walk to the water.
Compact disc-single: released on Island in Apr'87 by Island Records. Distributed by: Polygram

With or without you (single)8*.
Single (7"): released on Island in Mar'87 by Island Records. Distributed by: Polygram

Single (12"): released on Island in Mar'87 by Island Records. Distributed by: Polygram

Single (cassette): released on Island in Mar'87 by Island Records. Distributed by: Polygram

UB 40

All I want to do.
Tracks: / All I want to do / All I want to do.
Single (7"): released on DEP International in Sep'86 by DEP International Records. Distributed by: Virgin Records, EMI

Single (12"): released on DEP International in Sep'86 by DEP International Records. Distributed by: Virgin Records, EMI

Baggariddim.
Tracks: / King step Mk.1, The / Buzz feeling, The / Lyric officer / Demonstrate / Two in a one Mk.1 / Hold your position Mk.1 / Hip hop lyrical robot / Style Mk.4 / Vi's version / Don't break my heart / I got you babe / Mi spliff.
Compact disc: released on DEP International in Oct'85 by DEP International Records. Distributed by: Virgin Records, EMI

Album: released on DEP International in Oct'85 by DEP International Records. Distributed by: Virgin Records, EMI

Musicassette: released on DEP International in Oct'85 by DEP International Records. Distributed by: Virgin Records, EMI

Cherry oh baby.
Single (7"): released on Virgin in Mar'84 by Virgin Records. Distributed by: EMI, Virgin Distribution

Single (12"): released on Virgin in Mar'84 by Virgin Records. Distributed by: EMI, Virgin Distribution

Don't break my heart.
Single (7"): released on DEP International in Oct'85 by DEP International Records. Distributed by: Virgin Records, EMI

Single (12"): released on DEP International in Oct'85 by DEP International Records. Distributed by: Virgin Records, EMI

Don't slow down.
Single (7"): released on DEP International in May'81 by DEP International Records. Distributed by: Virgin Records, EMI

Single (12"): released on DEP International in May'81 by DEP International Records. Distributed by: Virgin Records, EMI

Earth dies screaming.
Single (7"): by Graduate Records. Distributed by: Nine Mile, Cartel

Single (12"): by Graduate Records. Distributed by: Nine Mile, Cartel

Food for thought.
Single (7"): by Graduate Records. Distributed by: Nine Mile, Cartel

Geffery Morgan.
Tracks: / Riddle me / As always you were wrong again / If it happens again / D.U.B. / Pillow, The / Nkomo a-go-go / Seasons / You're not an army / I'm not fooled so easily / You're eyes were open.
Album: released on DEP International in Oct'84 by DEP International Records. Distributed by: Virgin Records, EMI

Musicassette: released on DEP International in Oct'84 by DEP International Records. Distributed by: Virgin Records, EMI

Compact disc: released on DEP International in Oct'84 by DEP International Records. Distributed by: Virgin Records, EMI

If it happens again.
Single (7"): released on DEP International in Sep'84 by DEP International Records. Distributed by: Virgin Records, EMI

Single (12"): released on DEP International in Sep'84 by DEP International Records. Distributed by: Virgin Records, EMI

I got you babe (Ubieta).
Single (7"): released on DEP International in Jul'85 by DEP International Records. Distributed by: Virgin Records, EMI

Single (12"): released on DEP International in Jul'85 by DEP International Records. Distributed by: Virgin Records, EMI

I'm not fooled.
Single (7"): released on DEP International in Mar'85 by DEP International Records. Distributed by: Virgin Records, EMI

Single (12"): released on DEP International in Mar'85 by DEP International Records. Distributed by: Virgin Records, EMI

I've got mine.
Single (7"): released on DEP International in Jan'83 by DEP International Records. Distributed by: Virgin Records, EMI

Single (12"): released on DEP International in Jan'83 by DEP International Records. Distributed by: Virgin Records, EMI

I won't close my eyes.
Single (7"): released on DEP International in Jan'82 by DEP International Records. Distributed by: Virgin Records, EMI

Labour of love.
Tracks: / Johnny too bad / Guilty / Sweet sensation / Many rivers to cross / Red red wine / Please don't make me cry / She caught the train / Keep on moving / Cherry oh baby / Version girl.
Compact disc: released on DEP International in Jul'86 by DEP International Records. Distributed by: Virgin Records, EMI

Musicassette: released on DEP International in Sep'83 by DEP International Records. Distributed by: Virgin Records, EMI

Album: released on DEP International in Sep'83 by DEP International Records. Distributed by: Virgin Records, EMI

Labour of love (video).
Notes: The hit-making reggae band from Birmingham featuring tracks from the album of the same name,including several big hit singles like"Red red Wine" & "Cherry Oh Baby".Total playing time: 31 minutes.
Video-cassette (VHS): released on Virgin in Oct'84 by Virgin Records. Distributed by: EMI, Virgin Distribution

Live.
Video-cassette (VHS): released on Virgin in Feb'84 by Virgin Records. Distributed by: EMI, Virgin Distribution

Album: released on DEP International in Feb'83 by DEP International Records. Distributed by: Virgin Records, EMI

Musicassette: released on DEP International in Feb'83 by DEP International Records. Distributed by: Virgin Records, EMI

Love is alright.
Single (7"): released on DEP International in May'82 by DEP International Records. Distributed by: Virgin Records, EMI

Single (12"): released on DEP International in May'82 by DEP International Records. Distributed by: Virgin Records, EMI

Many rivers to cross.
Single (7"): released on DEP International in Nov'83 by DEP International Records. Distributed by: Virgin Records, EMI

Single (12"): released on DEP International in Nov'85 by DEP International Records. Distributed by: Virgin Records, EMI

More music.
Compact disc: released on Sound in '86. Distributed by: Target

My way of thinking.
Single (7"): by Graduate Records. Distributed by: Nine Mile, Cartel

Single (12"): by Graduate Records. Distributed by: Nine Mile, Cartel

Night run.
Tracks: / Night run(remix) / Heaven's gate(US mix).
Single (7"): released on Chrysalis in Feb'86 by Chrysalis Records. Distributed by: CBS

Single (12"): released on Chrysalis in Feb'86 by Chrysalis Records. Distributed by: CBS

One in ten.
Single (7"): released on DEP International in Jul'81 by DEP International Records. Distributed by: Virgin Records, EMI

Please don't make me cry.
Single (7"): released on DEP International in Oct'83 by DEP International Records. Distributed by: Virgin Records, EMI

Single (12"): released on DEP International in Oct'83 by DEP International Records. Distributed by: Virgin Records, EMI

Present arms.
Album: released on DEP International in Feb'83 by DEP International Records. Distributed by: Virgin Records, EMI

Musicassette: released on DEP International in Feb'83 by DEP International Records. Distributed by: Virgin Records, EMI

Present arms in dub.
Album: released on DEP International in Feb'83 by DEP International Records. Distributed by: Virgin Records, EMI

Musicassette: released on DEP International in Feb'83 by DEP International Records. Distributed by: Virgin Records, EMI

Album: released on DEP International in Feb'83 by DEP International Records. Distributed by: Virgin Records, EMI

Rat in mi kitchen.
Tracks: / Rat in mi kitchen.
Single (7"): released on DEP International in Jan'87 by DEP International Records. Distributed by: Virgin Records, EMI

Single (12"): released on DEP International in Jan'87 by DEP International Records. Distributed by: Virgin Records, EMI

Rat in the kitchen.
Album: released on DEP International in '86 by DEP International Records. Distributed by: Virgin Records, EMI

Musicassette: released on DEP International in '86 by DEP International Records. Distributed by: Virgin Records, EMI

Compact disc: released on DEP International in '86 by DEP International Records. Distributed by: Virgin Records, EMI

Red red wine.
Single (7"): released on DEP International in Aug'83 by DEP International Records. Distributed by: Virgin Records, EMI

Single (12"): released on DEP International in Aug'83 by DEP International Records. Distributed by: Virgin Records, EMI

Riddle me.
Single (7"): released on DEP International in Nov'84 by DEP International Records. Distributed by: Virgin Records, EMI

Single (12"): released on DEP International in Nov'84 by DEP International Records. Distributed by: Virgin Records, EMI

Signing off.
Compact disc: released on Sound in '86. Distributed by: Target

Album: released on Graduate in '80 by Graduate Records. Distributed by: Nine Mile, Cartel

Musicassette: released on Graduate in '80 by Graduate Records. Distributed by: Nine Mile, Cartel

Singles album.
Album: released on Graduate in Aug'82 by Graduate Records. Distributed by: Nine Mile, Cartel

Musicassette: released on Graduate in Aug'82 by Graduate Records. Distributed by: Nine Mile,. Cartel

Sing our own song.
Tracks: / Sing our own song / Sing our own song(remix).
Single (7"): released on DEP International in Jul'86 by DEP International Records. Distributed by: Virgin Records, EMI

Single (12"): released on DEP International in Jul'86 by DEP International Records. Distributed by: Virgin Records, EMI

So here I am.
Single (7"): released on DEP International in Aug'82 by DEP International Records. Distributed by: Virgin Records, EMI

Single (12"): released on DEP International in Aug'82 by DEP International Records. Distributed by: Virgin Records, EMI

Tyler.
Single (7"): released on Graduate in Feb'83 by Graduate Records. Distributed by: Nine Mile, Cartel

Single (12"): released on Graduate in Feb'83 by Graduate Records. Distributed by: Nine Mile, Cartel

UB40 file, The.
Tracks: / Tyler / King / 12 bar / Burden of shame / Adella / I think it's going to rain today / 25 per cent / Food for thought / Little by little / Signing off / Madame Medusa / Strange fruit / Reefer madness / My way of thinking / Earth dies screaming, The / Dream a lie.
Double compact disc: released on DEP International in Jul'86 by DEP International Records. Distributed by: Virgin Records, EMI

Album: released on DEP International in Mar'85 by DEP International Records. Distributed by: Virgin Records, EMI

Musicassette: released on DEP International in Mar'85 by DEP International Records. Distributed by: Virgin Records, EMI

UB44.
Album: released on DEP International in Apr'86 by DEP International Records. Distributed by: Virgin Records, EMI

Musicassette: released on DEP International in Apr'86 by DEP International Records. Distributed by: Virgin Records, EMI

Album: released on DEP International in Feb'83 by DEP International Records. Distributed by: Virgin Records, EMI

Watchdogs.
Tracks: / Watchdogs / Don't blame me.
Single (7"): released on DEP International in Apr'87 by DEP International Records. Distributed by: Virgin Records, EMI

Single (12"): released on DEP International in Apr'87 by DEP International Records. Distributed by: Virgin Records, EMI

U-Bahnx

Young hearts of Europe.
Single (7"): released on EMI in Mar'85 by EMI Records. Distributed by: EMI

Single (12"): released on EMI in Mar'85 by EMI Records. Distributed by: EMI

U-Brown

Bad habits.
Single (12"): released on Time in Oct'85. Distributed by: Jetstar Distribution

Mister Brown Something.
Album: released on Front line in '78 by Virgin. Distributed by: EMI Deleted '80.

Superstar.
Album: released on Culture Press in Mar'85 by Vista Sounds Records. Distributed by: Jetstar, Rough Trade

You can't keep a good man down.
Album: released on Front line in '79 by Virgin. Distributed by: EMI Deleted '81.

Ubu, Pere

390 degrees of simulated stereo Live volume 1.
Album: released on Rough Trade in '84 by Rough Trade Records. Distributed by: Rough Trade Distribution, Cartel Distribution

Art of walking, The.
Album: released on Rough Trade in '84 by Rough Trade Records. Distributed by: Rough Trade Distribution, Cartel Distribution

Modern dance, The.
Album: released on Rough Trade in '84 by Rough Trade Records. Distributed by: Rough Trade Distribution, Cartel Distribution

Not happy.
Single (7"): released on Rough Trade in Feb'81 by Rough Trade Records. Distributed by: Rough Trade Distribution, Cartel Distribution

Song of the Bailing Man.
Album: released on Rough Trade in '84 by Rough Trade Records. Distributed by: Rough Trade Distribution, Cartel Distribution

UCS All Stars

Live at Frognall.
Album: released on Spotlite in '83 by Spotlite Records. Distributed by: Cadillac, Jazz Music, Spotlite

UFO

Anthology.
Tracks: / Rock bottom / Built for comfort / Highway lady / Can you roll her / Fool for love, A / Shoot shoot / too hot to handle / Gettin' ready / Only you can rock me / Looking for No.1 / Hot'n'ready / Mystery train / No place to run / Proffesion and violence / Chains chains / Something else / Doing it for all of you / When it's time to rock / Diesel in the dust.
Compact disc: released on Raw Power in Apr'87. Distributed by: Pinnacle

Album: released on Raw Power in Mar'87. Distributed by: Pinnacle

Album: released on Raw Power in Mar'87. Distributed by: Pinnacle

C'mon everybody.
Album: released on Teldec (Germany) in Dec'81 by Import Records. Distributed by: IMS Distribution, Polygram Distribution

Collection: UFO.
Double Album: released on Castle Communications in Nov'85 by Castle Communications. Distributed by: Cartel, Pinnacle, Counterpoint

Double musicassette: released on Castle Communications in Nov'85 by Castle Communications. Distributed by: Cartel, Pinnacle, Counterpoint

Couldn't get it right.
Single (7"): released on Chrysalis in Oct'80 by Chrysalis Records. Distributed by: CBS

Force it.
Album: released on Fame in Jun'84 by Music For Pleasure Records. Distributed by: EMI

Musicassette: released on Fame in Jun'84 by Music For Pleasure Records. Distributed by: EMI

Headstone - The best of UFO.
Double Album: released on Chrysalis in Aug'83 by Chrysalis Records. Distributed by: CBS

Musicassette: released on Chrysalis in Aug'83 by Chrysalis Records. Distributed by: CBS

Lights out.
Album: released on Chrysalis in Aug'77 by Chrysalis Records. Distributed by: CBS

Musicassette: released on Chrysalis in Aug'77 by Chrysalis Records. Distributed by: CBS Deleted '87.

Lonely hearts.
Single (7"): released on Chrysalis in Jan'81 by Chrysalis Records. Distributed by: CBS

Making contact.
Album: released on Chrysalis in Jan'83 by Chrysalis Records. Distributed by: CBS

Musicassette: released on Chrysalis in Jan'83 by Chrysalis Records. Distributed by: CBS

Mechanix.
Album: released on Chrysalis in Feb'82 by Chrysalis Records. Distributed by: CBS

Musicassette: released on Chrysalis in Feb'82 by Chrysalis Records. Distributed by: CBS

Mechanix / Lights out.
Musicassette: released on Chrysalis in Dec'82 by Chrysalis Records. Distributed by: CBS

Misdemeanor.
Album: released on Chrysalis in Nov'85 by Chrysalis Records. Distributed by: CBS

Musicassette: released on Chrysalis in Nov'85 by Chrysalis Records. Distributed by: CBS

No heavy petting.
Album: released on Chrysalis in May'76 by Chrysalis Records. Distributed by: CBS

Musicassette: released on Chrysalis in May'76 by Chrysalis Records. Distributed by: CBS Deleted '83.

No place to run.
Album: released on Chrysalis in Jan'80 by Chrysalis Records. Distributed by: CBS

Musicassette: released on Chrysalis in Jan'80 by Chrysalis Records. Distributed by: CBS

Obsessions.
Album: released on Chrysalis in Jun'78 by Chrysalis Records. Distributed by: CBS

Musicassette: released on Chrysalis in Jun'78 by Chrysalis Records. Distributed by: CBS

Phenomenon.
Album: released on Chrysalis in '74 by Chrysalis Records. Distributed by: CBS

Musicassette: released on Chrysalis in '74 by Chrysalis Records. Distributed by: CBS

Space metal.
Album: released on Teldec (Germany) in Jan'85 by Import Records. Distributed by: IMS Distribution, Polygram Distribution

Strangers in the night.
Double Album: released on Chrysalis in '79 by Chrysalis Records. Distributed by: CBS

Double musicassette: released on Chrysalis in '79 by Chrysalis Records. Distributed by: CBS

This time.
Single (7"): released on Chrysalis in Oct'85 by Chrysalis Records. Distributed by: CBS

Single (12"): released on Chrysalis in Oct'85 by Chrysalis Records. Distributed by: CBS

When it's time to rock.
Single (7"): released on Chrysalis in Mar'83 by Chrysalis Records. Distributed by: CBS

Single (12"): released on Chrysalis in Mar'83 by Chrysalis Records. Distributed by: CBS

You can rock me.
Single (7"): released on Chrysalis in Jul'76 by Chrysalis Records. Distributed by: CBS

Young blood.
Single (7"): released on Chrysalis in Jan'80 by Chrysalis Records. Distributed by: CBS

Ugly Americans

Who's sleeping in my bed.
Album: released on Armageddon in Jul'86 by Armageddon Records. Distributed by: Revolver, Cartel, Pinnacle

Ugly Duckling

Hans Christian Anderson.
Notes: For full information see under:'Anderson, Hans Christian'

Ugly duckling Various artists (Various Artists).
Musicassette: released on Storyteller Cassettes in Jun'86. Distributed by: Pinnacle

Ugly duckling Story told by Susan Hampshire (Hampshire, Susan).
Musicassette: released on Storytime Cassettes in Aug'83

Ugly duckling, The Various artists (Various Artists).
Musicassette: released on Tellastory in Oct by Bartlett Bliss Productions. Distributed by: PRT Distribution, Hayward Promotions Distribution, H.R. Taylor Distribution

Musicassette: released on Pickwick (Ladybird) in Feb'83

U-Griffiths

Memories by the score.
Tracks: / Memories by the score / Trouble times.
Single (12"): released on Blue Trac in Mar'86 by Blue Mountain Records. Distributed by: Jet-star

UK Band

Funky Dallas.
Single (7"): released on Hot Rod in Aug'85 by Hot Rod Records. Distributed by: Jetstar

UK Decay

Black cat.
Single (7"): released on Plastic in Oct'81 by Plastic Records. Distributed by: Pinnacle

For madmen only.
Album: released on Fresh in Jul'83. Distributed by: Jetstar

For my country.
Single (7"): released on Fresh in Apr'81. Distributed by: Jetstar

Rising from the dread.
Extended-play record: released on Corpus Christi in Aug'82 by Exitstencil Music. Distributed by: Cartel

Sexual.
Single (7"): released on Fresh in Oct'81. Distributed by: Jetstar

Unexpected guest.
Single (7"): released on Fresh in Feb'81. Distributed by: Jetstar

UK/DK The Original Soundtrack

UK/DK the original soundtrack Various groups (Various Artists).
Album: released on Anagram in Aug'83 by Cherry Red Records. Distributed by: Pinnacle

UK New Country

UK New country Vol.1 Various artists (Various Artists).
Notes: Stage One/Jay Cee Distribution 051 430 9001
Album: released on Barge in Sep'86 by Barge Records. Distributed by: Stage One, Jay-Cee Records
Musicassette: released on Barge in Sep'86 by Barge Records. Distributed by: Stage One, Jay-Cee Records

UK Players

...irl.
...ingle (7"): released on A&M in Sep'81 by A&M records. Distributed by: Polygram

...ingle (12"): released on A&M in Sep'81 by ...&M Records. Distributed by: Polygram

...ove's gonna get you.
...ngle (7"): released on RCA in Apr'83 by RCA ...ords. Distributed by: RCA, Roots, Swift, ...ellard, Chris, I & B, Solomon & Peres Distribu-...n

...ngle (12"): released on RCA in Apr'83 by ...A Records. Distributed by: RCA, Roots, ...ift, Wellard, Chris, I & B, Solomon & Peres ...stribution

...ssbehavin.
...ngle (7"): released on A&M in Jul'82 by A&M ...cords. Distributed by: Polygram

...gle (12"): released on A&M in Jul'82 by ...M Records. Distributed by: Polygram

...way out.
...gle (7"): released on A&M in May'82 by ...M Records. Distributed by: Polygram

...gle (12"): released on A&M in May'82 by ...M Records. Distributed by: Polygram

...make me feel.
...gle (7"): released on RCA in Aug'83 by RCA ...ords. Distributed by: RCA, Roots, Swift, ...ard, Chris, I & B, Solomon & Peres Distribu-...n

...gle (12"): released on RCA in Aug'83 by ... Records. Distributed by: RCA, Roots, ...ift, Wellard, Chris, I & B, Solomon & Perer ...stribution

Ukraine

I can see clearly now.
Single (7"): released on Safari in Oct'82 by Safari Records. Distributed by: Pinnacle

Ukraine, National Choir

Memories of the Ukraine.
Album: released on Viking in Dec'79. Distributed by: Jetstar, Northumbrian Records, H.R. Taylor

Ukridge's Accident

Ukridge's accident sydicate (P.G.Wodehouse).
Musicassette: released on Talking Tape Company in '84 by Talking Tape Company Records

UK Subs

Another typical city.
Single (7"): released on Fall Out in Aug'83. Distributed by: Fresh, Cartel, Jetstar

Single (12"): released on Fall Out in Aug'83. Distributed by: Fresh, Cartel, Jetstar

C.I.D.
Single (7"): released on Pinnacle in Oct'79 by Pinnacle Records. Distributed by: Pinnacle

Countdown.
Single (7"): released on Nems in Nov'81. Distributed by: Castle Communications Records, Pinnacle Records

Crash course, live.
Album: released on Gem in Sep'80 by Gem Records. Distributed by: RCA

Musicassette: released on Gem in Sep'80 by Gem Records. Distributed by: RCA

Demonstration tapes.
Musicassette: released on Mausoleum in Jun'84 by Mausoleum Records. Distributed by: Pinnacle

Album: released on Mausoleum in Apr'84 by Mausoleum Records. Distributed by: Pinnacle

Flood of lies.
Album: released on Fall Out in Jun'87. Distributed by: Swift, Red Rhino, Cartel

Album: released on Fall Out in Jun'87. Distributed by: Swift, Red Rhino, Cartel

Gross out USA.
Album: released on Fall Out in Jan'85. Distributed by: Fresh, Cartel, Jetstar

Huntington Beach.
Album: released on UK Subs in Dec'85. Distributed by: Pinnacle

Musicassette: released on Demon in Jul'86 by Demon Records. Distributed by: Pinnacle

In action.
Single (7"): released on Red Flame in Apr'86 by Red Flame Records. Distributed by: Nine Mile, Cartel

Musicassette: released on Red Flame in Apr'86 by Red Flame Records. Distributed by: Nine Mile, Cartel

Left for dead.
Musicassette: released on Roir in Jun'86 by Reach Out International Records. Distributed by: Red Rhino Distribution, Cartel Distribution

Live at gossips.
Single (cassette): released on Chaos Cassettes in Jun'87 by Backs Records. Distributed by: Nine Mile, Cartel

Live in Holland.
Tracks: / Live in Holland.
Single (7"): released on UK Subs in Mar'86. Distributed by: Pinnacle

Magic.
Single (12"): released on Fall Out in Sep'84. Distributed by: Fresh, Cartel, Jetstar

Party in Paris.
Single (7"): released on Gem in Oct'80 by Gem Records. Distributed by: RCA

Raw material.
Album: released on Killerwatt in Jul'86. Distributed by: Kingdom Records, Pinnacle

Recorded 1979-81.
Album: released on Abstract in Oct'82 by Abstract. Distributed by: Pinnacle

Shake up the city.
Single (7"): released on Abstract in Oct'82 by Abstract. Distributed by: Pinnacle

She's not there.
Single (7"): released on Gem in Nov'79 by Gem Records. Distributed by: RCA

Subs standards.
Tracks: / C.I.D. / Tomorrows girls / Telephone numbers / You don't belong / Rockers / T.V. blues / Crash course / New York Stae police / New order / Violent city / Emotional blackmail / Warhead / Brand new age.
Album: released on Gem in Apr'86 by Castle Communications Records. Distributed by: Cartel

Teenage.
Single (7"): released on Gem in May'80 by Gem Records. Distributed by: RCA

This gun says.
Single (7"): released on Fall Out in Jun'85. Distributed by: Fresh, Cartel, Jetstar

Tomorrow's girls.
Single (7"): released on Gem in Aug'79 by Gem Records. Distributed by: RCA

Warhead.
Single (7"): released on Gem in Feb'80 by Gem Records. Distributed by: RCA

UK Supporters

Viva Espana.
Single (7"): released on Polo in May'82 by Polo Records. Distributed by: PRT

Single (12"): released on Polo in May'82 by Polo Records. Distributed by: PRT

U.K. Symphony Orchestra

Green and pleasant land (United Kingdom Symphony Orchestra).
Album: released on Telstar in May'86 by Telstar Records. Distributed by: RCA Distribution

Musicassette: released on Telstar in May'86 by Telstar Records. Distributed by: RCA Distribution

Compact disc: released on Telstar in Jul'86 by Telstar Records. Distributed by: RCA Distribution

Ullman, Tracey

Breakaway.
Single (7"): released on Stiff in Feb'83 by Stiff Records. Distributed by: EMI, Record Services Distribution (Ireland)

Forever.
Album: released on Stiff in Nov'85 by Stiff Records. Distributed by: EMI, Record Services Distribution (Ireland)

Musicassette: released on Stiff in Nov'85 by Stiff Records. Distributed by: EMI, Record Services Distribution (Ireland)

Helpless.
Single (7"): released on Stiff in Oct'84 by Stiff Records. Distributed by: EMI, Record Services Distribution (Ireland)

Single (7"): released on Stiff in Oct'84 by Stiff Records. Distributed by: EMI, Record Services Distribution (Ireland)

Move over darling.
Single (7"): released on Stiff in Nov'83 by Stiff Records. Distributed by: EMI, Record Services Distribution (Ireland)

Single (12"): released on Stiff in Nov'83 by Stiff Records. Distributed by: EMI, Record Services Distribution (Ireland)

Picture disc single: released on Stiff in Nov'83 by Stiff Records. Distributed by: EMI, Record Services Distribution (Ireland)

My Guy.
Single (7"): released on Stiff in Mar'84 by Stiff Records. Distributed by: EMI, Record Services Distribution (Ireland)

Single (12"): released on Stiff in Mar'84 by Stiff Records. Distributed by: EMI, Record Services Distribution (Ireland)

Picture disc single: released on Stiff in Mar'84 by Stiff Records. Distributed by: EMI, Record Services Distribution (Ireland)

Sunglasses.
Single (7"): released on Stiff in Jun'84 by Stiff Records. Distributed by: EMI, Record Services Distribution (Ireland)

Picture disc single: released on Stiff in Jun'84 by Stiff Records. Distributed by: EMI, Record Services Distribution (Ireland)

Terry.
Single (7"): released on Stiff in Dec'84 by Stiff Records. Distributed by: EMI, Record Services Distribution (Ireland)

They don't know.
Single (7"): released on Stiff in Sep'83 by Stiff Records. Distributed by: EMI, Record Services Distribution (Ireland)

Single 10": released on Stiff in Sep'83 by Stiff Records. Distributed by: EMI, Record Services Distribution (Ireland)

You broke my heart in 17 places.
Compact disc: released on Stiff Records. Distributed by: EMI, Record Services Distribution (Ireland)

Album: released on Stiff in Oct'83 by Stiff Records. Distributed by: EMI, Record Services Distribution (Ireland)

Musicassette: released on Stiff in Oct'83 by Stiff Records. Distributed by: EMI, Record Services Distribution (Ireland)

You caught me out.
Album: released on Stiff in Nov'84 by Stiff Records. Distributed by: EMI, Record Services Distribution (Ireland)

Musicassette: released on Stiff in Nov'84 by Stiff Records. Distributed by: EMI, Record Services Distribution (Ireland)

Ulloa, Francisco

Merengue!.
Album: released on Globestyle in May'87 by Ace Records. Distributed by: Projection

Ulmer, James 'Blood'

America: Do you remember the love?.
Tracks: / I belong in the USA / Lady blue / After dark / Show me your love / Black sheep / Wings / I belong in th' USA / Lady blue / After dark / Show me your love / Black sheep / Wings.
Notes: From his sixties roots in R & B bars bands to the first ranks of funk-jazz with organist John Patton (with whom he recorded on Blue note some 16 years ago) to harmelodic experiments with jazz pioneer Ornette Coleman, guitarist James 'Blood' Ulmer has always been a true American original, absorbing and assimilating all that passes through him. After a self produced album with Ornette and three successful albums on CBS, Ulmer established himself on the international jazz and avant garde scenes as a distinctive and creative voice, for his Blue Note debut, he has surrounded himself with his visionary peers: bassist and producer Bill Laswell and drummer and band leader Ronald Shannon Jackson. On six high individual pieces, two of which include Blood's haunting vocals, Ulmer draws upon American echoes that conjure up every sound from Charlie Christian to Grant Green to Ry Cooder to Duane Eddy. Here is an American original. Someone to deal with ...someone to enjoy: James'Blood'Ulmer.
Album: released on Blue Note in Mar'87 by EMI Records. Distributed by: EMI

Compact disc: released on Manhattan-Blue Note in Jun'87 by EMI America Records (USA). Distributed by: EMI

Are you glad to be in America.
Album: released on Rough Trade in '84 by Rough Trade Records. Distributed by: Rough Trade Distribution, Cartel Distribution

Eye level.
Single (12"): released on Rough Trade in Aug'84 by Rough Trade Records. Distributed by: Rough Trade Distribution, Cartel Distribution

Live at the caravan.
Album: released on Caravan Of Dreams (USA) in Apr'87 by Caravan Of Dreams Records (USA). Distributed by: IMS, Polygram

Part time.
Album: released on Rough Trade in '84 by Rough Trade Records. Distributed by: Rough Trade Distribution, Cartel Distribution

Ulster Heritage

Ulster heritage Various artists (Various Artists).
Tracks: / Intro: Lambeg drum / Derry's walls / Ould Orange flute / Protestant boys / Shepherd's boy / Green grassey slopes / Enniskillen Dragoons / South Down militia / Orange & blue / Orange tree, The / Blackman's dream / Sprigs of Kilrea / Ducks of Magheralin / Sash, The / Aughalee heroes.
Musicassette: released on Ulster in May'86. Distributed by: Outlet

Ulster On The March..

Ulster on the march for God & Ulster Various artists (Various Artists).
Tracks: / What a friend we have in Jesus / Onward christian soldiers / Battle of the Somme / Archie McKinley / Amazing grace / Old rugged cross / Church in the wildwood, The / Nearer my God to thee / When the roll is called / Mine eyes have seen the glory / Along the river / Battle of Garvagh / Tartan soldier / Aghalee Heroes / Blackman's dream / Ramblin' Ulsterman / Aurelia / Abide with me / Onward christian soldiers / Stand up for Jesus / Keep right on to the end of the road / Land of hope & glory / No surrender.
Musicassette: released on Ulster music in May'87

Ulster Says No

Ulster says no Various artists (Various Artists).
Tracks: / No surrender / Lily O / Boyne water / Sash / Sprigs of Kilrea / Orange & Blue / Battle of Garvagh / Union cruiser / Aghalee heroes / Green grassy slopes of the Boyne / Derry's walls / Protestant boys / Auld Orange flute / Blackman's dream.
Musicassette: released on Ulster in Apr'86. Distributed by: Outlet

Ulster Will Always Say No

Ulster will always say no Various artists (Various Artists).
Tracks: / In the defence of the orange & blue / Bold Orange heroes of Comber / Aughalee heroes / Waringford rising star / Biddy McDowal / Battle of Garvagh / Sash / Rifles,the / Protestant boys / Derry's walls / Paisley / Dolly's Brae / Crimson banner / God be with you till we meet again.
Musicassette: released on Ulster music in May'87

Ultimate Selection

Ultimate selection Various artists (Various Artists).
Musicassette: released on Sounds Ultimate in Nov'85. Distributed by: PRT, H.R. Taylor

Ultimate Sway

Here we stand.
Single (7"): released on International Records & Tapes in Aug'82 by International Records & Tapes. Distributed by: Pinnacle

Ultimate Trax

Ultimate trax Vol.1 (Battle of the D.J.'s vol.1) (Various Artists).
Notes: Special full-length 12" versions plus bonus exclusive Battle of the DJ's vol.1. Featuring:Dj.Jazzy Fresh Prince/Raze/Darryl Patterson/Wanda of Raze/Sybil/Kinkina/Marshall Jefferson/Harlequin 4's/Word of Mouth feat.dj.Cheese/Ice Cream T.D.Album.
Album: released on Champion in Nov'86 by Champion Records. Distributed by: RCA

Musicassette: released on Champion in Nov'86 by Champion Records. Distributed by: RCA

Ultimate trax Vol.2 Various artists (Various Artists).
Album: released on Champion in Feb'87 by Champion Records. Distributed by: RCA

Musicassette: released on Champion in Feb'87 by Champion Records. Distributed by: RCA

Ultimate Trax Vol.3 Battle of the D.J.'s (Various Artists).
Album: released on Champion in Jul'87 by Champion Records. Distributed by: RCA

Musicassette: released on Champion in Jul'87 by Champion Records. Distributed by: RCA

Ultimatum

Cross section.
Notes: Daylight records,The Daylight Co.(Distribution)Ltd.,2 Dorset Place,New Street,Honiton,Devon EX14 8AB
Musicassette: released on Daylight in '86 by Daylight Records. Distributed by: Daylight

Ultra Magnetic MC's

Travelling at the speed of thought.
Tracks: / Travelling at the speed of thought / MC's ultra part 11 / B-Boy bonus break*.
Single (7"): released on Citybeat in 20 Jun'87. Distributed by: WEA

Single (12"): released on Citybeat in 20 Jun'87. Distributed by: WEA

Ultra-Violent

Crime for revenge.
Extended-play record: released on Riot City in May'83 by Riot City Records. Distributed by: Revolver

Ultravox

3 into 1.
Tracks: / Young savage / Rockwork / Dangerous rythm / Man who dies everyday / Wild, the beautiful and the damned;The / Slow motion / Just for a moment / My sex / Quiet man / Hiroshima mon amour.
Album: released on Island in Nov'86 by Island Records. Distributed by: Polygram

Musicassette: released on Island in Nov'86 by Island Records. Distributed by: Polygram

All fall down.
Tracks: / All fall down / Dreams.
Single (7"): released on Chrysalis in Nov'86 by Chrysalis Records. Distributed by: CBS

Single (12"): released on Chrysalis in Nov'86 by Chrysalis Records. Distributed by: CBS

All in one day.
Tracks: / All in one day / Prize, The (live) / Stateless.
Single (7"): released on Chrysalis in May'87 by Chrysalis Records. Distributed by: CBS

Single (12"): released on Chrysalis in May'87 by Chrysalis Records. Distributed by: CBS

Collection: Ultravox.
Tracks: / Dancing with tears in my eyes / Hymn / Thin wall, The / Voice, the / Vienna / Passing strangers / Sleepwalk / Reap the wild wind / All stood still / Visions in blue / We came to dance / One small day / Love's great adventure / Lament.
Notes: Digital stereo.
Compact disc: released on Chrysalis in Mar'85 by Chrysalis Records. Distributed by: CBS

Collection: Ultravox (video).
Video-cassette (VHS): released on Palace in Jan'86. Distributed by: PVG

Dancing with tears in my eyes.
Tracks: / Dancing with tears in my eyes / Reap the wild wind.
Single (7"): released on Old Gold in Apr'87 by Old Gold Records. Distributed by: Lightning, Jazz Music, Spartan, Counterpoint

Single (7"): released on Island in May'84 by Island Records. Distributed by: Polygram

Single (12"): released on Island in May'84 by Island Records. Distributed by: Polygram

Ha ha ha.
Album: released on Island in Oct'77 by Island Records. Distributed by: Polygram

Hymn.
Single (7"): released on Chrysalis in Nov'82 by Chrysalis Records. Distributed by: CBS

Single (12"): released on Chrysalis in Nov'82 by Chrysalis Records. Distributed by: CBS

Lament.
Tracks: / White China / One small day / Dancing with tears in my eyes / Lament / Man of two worlds / Heart of the country / When the time comes i'll cry / Friend I call desire.
Compact disc: released on Chrysalis in Sep'84 by Chrysalis Records. Distributed by: CBS

Single (12"): released on Chrysalis in Jun'84 by Chrysalis Records. Distributed by: CBS

Monument.
Video-cassette (VHS): released on Chrysalis in Jan'86 by Chrysalis Records. Distributed by: CBS

Musicassette: released on Chrysalis in Oct'83 by Chrysalis Records. Distributed by: CBS

Album: released on Chrysalis in Oct'83 by Chrysalis Records. Distributed by: CBS

One small day.
Single (12"): released on Chrysalis in Jan'84 by Chrysalis Records. Distributed by: CBS

Passing strangers.
Single (7"): released on Chrysalis in Sep'80 by Chrysalis Records. Distributed by: CBS

Single (12"): released on Chrysalis in Sep'80 by Chrysalis Records. Distributed by: CBS

Quartet.
Tracks: / Reap the wild wind / Serenade / Mine for life / Hymn / Visions in blue / When the scream subsides / We came to dance / Cut & run / Song(we go), The.
Notes: Produced by George Martin.
Album: released on Chrysalis in Oct'82 by Chrysalis Records. Distributed by: CBS

Musicassette: released on Chrysalis in Oct'82 by Chrysalis Records. Distributed by: CBS

Compact disc: by Chrysalis Records. Distributed by: CBS

Rage in Eden.
Tracks: / Voice / We stand alone / I remember death in the afternoon / Thin wall / Stranger within / Accent on youth / Ascent / Rage in Eden / Your name has slipped my mind again.
Compact disc: released on Chrysalis in Jun'87 by Chrysalis Records. Distributed by: CBS

Reap the wild wind.
Single (7"): released on Chrysalis in Sep'82 by Chrysalis Records. Distributed by: CBS

Single (12"): released on Chrysalis in Sep'82 by Chrysalis Records. Distributed by: CBS

Rockwrock.
Single (7"): released on Island in Jul'81 by Island Records. Distributed by: Polygram

Same old story.
Tracks: / Same old story / 3".
Single (7"): released on Chrysalis in Sep'86 by Chrysalis Records. Distributed by: CBS

Single (12"): released on Chrysalis in Sep'86 by Chrysalis Records. Distributed by: CBS

Sleepwalk.
Single (7"): released on Chrysalis in Jul'80 by Chrysalis Records. Distributed by: CBS

Slow motion.
Single (7"): released on Island in Feb'81 by Island Records. Distributed by: Polygram

Systems of romance.
Album: released on Island in Sep'78 by Island Records. Distributed by: Polygram

Musicassette: released on Island in Sep'78 by Island Records. Distributed by: Polygram

Thin wall.
Single (7"): released on Chrysalis in Aug'81 by Chrysalis Records. Distributed by: CBS

Single (12"): released on Chrysalis in Aug'81 by Chrysalis Records. Distributed by: CBS

Ultravox.
Album: released on Island in Feb'77 by Island Records. Distributed by: Polygram

U-vox.
Compact disc: released on Chrysalis in Nov'86 by Chrysalis Records. Distributed by: CBS

U-Vox.
Tracks: / Same old story / Sweet surrender / Dream on / Prize, The / All fall down / Time to kill / Moon madness / Follow your heart / All in one day.
Notes: Produced by Conny Plank & Ultravox.
Album: released on Chrysalis in Oct'86 by Chrysalis Records. Distributed by: CBS

Musicassette: released on Chrysalis in Oct'86 by Chrysalis Records. Distributed by: CBS

Vienna.
Tracks: / Astradyne / New Europeans / Private lives / Passing stranger / Mr. X / Sleepwalk / Western promise / Vienna / All stood still.
Album: released on Chrysalis in '80 by Chrysalis Records. Distributed by: CBS

Compact disc: by Chrysalis Records. Distributed by: CBS

Musicassette: released on Chrysalis in '80 by Chrysalis Records. Distributed by: CBS

Vienna.
Tracks: / Voice,The.
Single (7"): released on Old Gold in Feb'87 by Old Gold Records. Distributed by: Lightning, Jazz Music, Spartan, Counterpoint

Double musicassette: released on Chrysalis(Take 2) in Dec'82 by Chrysalis Records. Distributed by: CBS

Visions in blue.
Single (7"): released on Chrysalis in Mar'83 by Chrysalis Records. Distributed by: CBS

Single (12"): released on Chrysalis in Mar'83 by Chrysalis Records. Distributed by: CBS

Voice.
Single (7"): released on Chrysalis in Nov'81 by Chrysalis Records. Distributed by: CBS

Single (12"): released on Chrysalis in Nov'81 by Chrysalis Records. Distributed by: CBS

We came to dance.
Single (7"): released on Chrysalis in May'83 by Chrysalis Records. Distributed by: CBS

Single (12"): released on Chrysalis in May'83 by Chrysalis Records. Distributed by: CBS

Ultrepe

In between/Hot on spot

U-Mandell

Africa must be free by 1983.
Album: released on Greensleeves in Jun'86 by Greensleeves Records. Distributed by: BMG, Jetstar, Spartan

Umbrella

Make hell for the beautiful people.
Single (12"): released on Immaculate in Jul'85 by Immaculate Records. Distributed by: Cartel

Umbrellas Of Cherbourg

Umbrellas of Cherbourg Various artists (Various Artists).
Double Album: released on Philips (France) in Dec'84

U-Men

Stop spinning.
Album: released on Homestead in Sep'85. Distributed by: Rough Trade, Cartel, Shigaku

Umo Vogue

Just my love.
Single (7"): released on EMI in Jun'84 by EMI Records. Distributed by: EMI

Umps & Dumps

Moon's in a fit, The.
Album: released on Topic in Jun'81 by Topic Records. Distributed by: JSU Distribution, Projection Distribution, Jazz Music Distribution

Uncle Mac

Uncle Mac's nursery rhymes.
Album: released on Starline in Oct'72 by EM Records. Distributed by: EMI

Uncle Ulick

Star of County Down (Uncle Ulick & McMara's Nu Vo Trad Band).
Tracks: / Star of County Down / Are you righ there Michael / Dingle regatta / McNamara Band.
Single (7"): released on Homespun(Ireland) i Jul'86 by Outlet Records. Distributed by: Outle

Unconquerables

Ping pong poppin'.
Tracks: / Ping pong poppin' / Cowboy flix / Doctor Beat / Breakhoven / Hong Kong maiden Storm warning / Nineteen 68 / Jungle voodoo Head spin / Morning chorus / Scorpion sting Rain dance / Reaction man / Mexico / Jeter,The / Helicopter / Dark,The / Off the hook Webb, The / Six point star rap / Take off.
Album: released on Creole in Jan'86 by Creo Records. Distributed by: Rhino, PRT

Undead

It's corruption.
Single (7"): released on Riot City in Apr'82 Riot City Records. Distributed by: Revolver

Killing of reality, The.
Album: released on Riot City in Feb'84 by R City Records. Distributed by: Revolver

Never say die.
Single (7"): released on Rebel in May'86. Distributed by: PRT

Violent visions.
Single (7"): released on Riot City in Oct'82 by Riot City Records. Distributed by: Revolver

Under a glass bell

Over the moon.
Single (7"): released on Trumpet in Nov'86. Distributed by: Backs, Cartel

Undercover

Boys & girls.
Album: released on A&S in Sep'85

Musicassette: released on A&S in Sep'85

Underdog

Rabies in town.
Album: released on Mausoleum in Oct'84 by Mausoleum Records. Distributed by: Pinnacle

Underdog.
Album: released on Thunderbolt in Nov'83 by Magnum Music Group Ltd. Distributed by: Magnum Music Group Ltd, PRT Distribution, Spartan Distribution

Underdogs

East of Dachau.
Single (7"): released on Riot City in Jun'83 by Riot City Records. Distributed by: Revolver

Under Fire

Under fire   Original Motion Picture Soundtrack.
Album: released on Warner Bros. in Mar'84 by Warner Bros Records. Distributed by: WEA

Underground arrows

Change to escape, The.
Single (7"): released on Unicorn in 23 May'87. Distributed by: Nine Mile, Cartel

Underground Zero

Never reach the stars.
Album: released on Flicknife in Jan'85 by Flicknife Records. Distributed by: Spartan

Through the looking glass.
Album: released on Flicknife in Jan'87 by Flicknife Records. Distributed by: Spartan

Underlings

That little girl.
Tracks: / That little girl / Lemon drops / King leech / Resolutions crack.
Single (12"): released on Midnight Music in Oct'86 by Midnight Music Records. Distributed by: Rough Trade Distribution, Cartel Distribution

Under me sleng teng extravagan-

Under me sleng teng extravaganza   Various arists (Various Artists).
Album: released on Tad   in May'85 by Tads Records. Distributed by: Je star Distribution

Under Milk Wood

Under Milk Wood

Underneath

Imp of the perverse.
Tracks: / Imp of the perverse (EP) / Fire / Short   erm agreement.
Single (7"): released on EL in Oct'86 by El Records. Distributed by: Rough Trade, Cartel, Pinnacle

Single (12"): released on EL in Oct'86 by El Records. Distributed by: Rough Trade, Cartel, Pinnacle

** unatic dawn of the dismantler.**
Tracks: / Positive force for good and evil / Thick lack angular / Black England/White bomb / No Tragedy boys and girls / Zophia / Bayonet / mear / Another death in the family / Paren cide / Partyclones plus / This lady devoid / Hang g / Letter from an institution.
Album: released on EL in May'87 by El Records. Distributed by: Rough Trade, Cartel, Pinnacle

Underneath the arches

** nderneath the arches   Original Cast   /arious Artists).**
Album: released on That's Entertainment in   r'82 by That's Entertainment Records. Distributed by: Pinnacle, PRT

Musicassette: released on That's Entertainment in Apr'82 by That's Entertainment Records. Distributed by: Pinnacle, PRT

Underscore

Underscore   Original Soundtrack (Underscore (featuring Wednesday Week)).
Album: released on Enigma in Jun'87 by Enigma Records. Distributed by: Rough Trade, Cartel, EMI

Understanding....

Understanding & coping with anxiety May, Rollo.
Musicassette: released on Psychology in '81

Understanding & managing jealousy Clanton, Gordon.
Musicassette: released on Psychology in '81

Understanding & overcoming loneliness Peplau, L. A..
Musicassette: released on Psychology in '81

Under The Greenwood Tree

Under the Greenwood tree (Mellstock Band).
Notes: For full information see: Mellstock Band

Under the Streetlamp

Under the streetlamp (Various Artists).
Tracks: / Stop hiding in the closet / Under the streetlamp / Dearest one / Lost in a city / You're the beat of my heart / I'll be hangin' on / Baby I need you / Beware! beware! / Someone / Just remember me / Looking for a love of my own / Running wild / There'll still be a sweet tomorrow / Cryin' bitter tears / All the way / Weeping baby all the time.
Album: released on Soul Supply in Jan'87 by High Energy Records. Distributed by: Charly

Under The Sun

My love is a river.
Tracks: / My love is a river / Get ready / Sister salvation / Protect your love.
Single (12"): released on Sierra in Feb'86 by Sierra Records. Distributed by: WEA

Undertones

All wrapped up.
Double Album: released on Ardeck in Nov'83. Distributed by: EMI

Double musicassette: released on Ardeck in Nov'83. Distributed by: EMI

Chain of love.
Single (7"): released on Ardeck in Apr'83. Distributed by: EMI

Cher O'Bowlies   Pick of the Undertones.
Tracks: / Teenage kicks / True confessions / Get over you / Family entertainment / Jimmy Jimmy / Here comes the summer / You got my number (why don't you use it) / My perfect cousin / See that girl / Tearproof / Wednesday week / It's goin' to happen / Julie Ocean / You're welcome / Forever paradise / Beautiful friend / Save me / Love parade / Valentine's treatment / Love before romance.
Notes: The definitive Undertones compilation, including all their hit singles and most popular album and EP tracks.
Album: released on Ardeck in May'86. Distributed by: EMI

Musicassette: released on Ardeck in May'86. Distributed by: EMI

Compact disc: released on EMI in Mar'87 by EMI Records. Distributed by: EMI

Got to have you back.
Single (7"): released on Ardeck in Mar'83. Distributed by: EMI

Single (12"): released on Ardeck in Mar'83. Distributed by: EMI

Here comes the summer.
Single (7"): released on Sire in Apr'82

Hypnotised.
Album: released on Fame in Mar'86 by Music For Pleasure Records. Distributed by: EMI

Musicassette: released on Fame in Mar'86 by Music For Pleasure Records. Distributed by: EMI

Love parade.
Single (7"): released on Ardeck in Jan'83. Distributed by: EMI

Single (12"): released on Ardeck in Jan'83. Distributed by: EMI

My perfect cousin.
Single (7"): released on Ardeck in Oct'83. Distributed by: EMI

Single (12"): released on Ardeck in Oct'83. Distributed by: EMI Deleted '87.

Peel session 21st January 1979.
Single (12"): released on Strange Fruit in Nov'86 by Clive Selwood. Distributed by: Pinnacle

Positive touch.
Album: released on Ardeck in '85. Distributed by: EMI

Musicassette: released on Ardeck in '85. Distributed by: EMI

Save me.
Single (7"): / Save me / Tearproof / I know a girl.
Single (7"): released on Ardeck in May'86. Distributed by: EMI

Single (12"): released on Ardeck in May'86. Distributed by: EMI

Sin of pride, (The).
Album: released on Ardeck in Mar'83. Distributed by: EMI

Album: released on Ardeck in Mar'83. Distributed by: EMI

Musicassette: released on Ardeck in Mar'83. Distributed by: EMI

Musicassette: released on Ardeck in Mar'83. Distributed by: EMI

Teenage kicks.
Single (7"): released on Ardeck in Jun'83. Distributed by: EMI

Single (12"): released on Ardeck in Jun'83. Distributed by: EMI

Undertones.
Video-cassette (VHS): released on PMI in Jun'86 by PMI Records. Distributed by: EMI

Video-cassette [Betamax]: released on PMI in Jun'86 by PMI Records. Distributed by: EMI

Undertones, (The).
Album: . Distributed by: EMI

Album: released on Ardeck in Jul'83. Distributed by: EMI

Musicassette: released on Ardeck in Jul'83. Distributed by: EMI

Musicassette: . Distributed by: EMI

Wednesday week.
Single (7"): released on Sire in Apr'82

You've got my number.
Single (7"): released on Sire in Apr'82

Under two flags

Lest we forget.
Single (7"): released on Situation 2 in Sep'83. Distributed by: Cartel, Pinnacle

Single (12"): released on Situation 2 in Sep'83. Distributed by: Cartel, Pinnacle

Masks.
Single 10": released on Situation 2 in Jun'84. Distributed by: Cartel, Pinnacle

Single (7"): released on Situation 2 in Apr'84. Distributed by: Cartel, Pinnacle

Single (12"): released on Situation 2 in Jun'84. Distributed by: Cartel, Pinnacle

Undivided

Original undivided.
Album: released on Must Dance in Jul'86 by Must Dance Records. Distributed by: Jetstar Distribution

Undivided Roots

Bubbles.
Single (12"): released on Classic Roots in Jun'82

Live Up.
Single (12"): released on Classic Roots in Sep'82

Party nite.
Single (12"): released on Entente in Nov'85 by Entente Records. Distributed by: Jetstar

Rock reggae music.
Single (12"): released on Rough Cut in Jan'85

Rock this yah music.
Tracks: / Rock this yah music.
Single (12"): released on Entente in Jun'86 by Entente Records. Distributed by: Jetstar

Sweet woman.
Single (12"): released on Ruff Cut in Jun'83 by Ruff Cut Records. Distributed by: Jetstar Distribution

Telling me lies.
Single (12"): released on Undivided Roots in Jun'84

True love.
Single (12"): released on CSA in Jun'83 by CSA Records. Distributed by: PRT, Jetstar

Ultimate experience.
Album: released on Entente in Mar'87 by Entente Records. Distributed by: Jetstar

Unexpected guest

Unexpected guest Christie, Agatha.
Musicassette: released on BBC in Sep'84 by BBC Records & Tapes. Distributed by: EMI, PRT, Pye

Unfinished boogie

Unfinished boogie   Various Artists (Various Artists).
Album: released on Muskadine in Apr'79. Distributed by: Swift Distribution

Unforgettable

Unforgettable Various Artists (Various Artists).
Double Album: released on Starblend in '82 by Starblend Records. Distributed by: PRT Distribution

Double musicassette: released on Starblend in '82 by Starblend Records. Distributed by: PRT Distribution

Unforgettable Performances Of The World War Years (Various Artists).
Notes: Artists include Count Basie, Art Tatum etc.
Album: released on Kaydee in Nov'86. Distributed by: Jazz Music, Swift

Unforgettable performances ofthe world war years (Various Artists).
Album: released on Kaydee in Nov'86. Distributed by: Jazz Music, Swift

Unforgettable sound of the 50s, (The) Various Artists (Various Artists).
Album: released on K-Tel (Era) in Jun'83 by K-Tel Records. Distributed by: K-Tel

Musicassette: released on K-Tel (Era) in Jun'83 by K-Tel Records. Distributed by: K-Tel

Unforgettable sound of the 60s, (The) Various Artists (Various Artists).
Album: released on K-Tel (Era) in Jun'83 by K-Tel Records. Distributed by: K-Tel

Musicassette: released on K-Tel (Era) in Jun'83 by K-Tel Records. Distributed by: K-Tel

Unforgiven

I hear the call.
Tracks: / I hear the call / Ghost dance.
Single (7"): released on Elektra (USA) in Aug'86 by Elektra/Asylum/Nonesuch Records. Distributed by: WEA

Unforgiven.
Tracks: / All in quiet on the western front / Hang 'em high / I hear the call / Roverpack / Cheyenne / Gauntlet, The / With my boots on / Ghost dance, The / Loner, The / Preacher, The / Grace.
Album: released on Elektra (USA) in Jul'86 by Elektra/Asylum/Nonesuch Records. Distributed by: WEA

Musicassette: released on Elektra (USA) in Jul'86 by Elektra/Asylum/Nonesuch Records. Distributed by: WEA

Ungar, Jay

Catskill mountain goose chase.

Album: released on Philo (USA) in May'79

Songs, ballads & fiddle tunes.
Album: released on Philo in May'79 by Philo Records (USA). Distributed by: Mike's Country Music Room Distribution, Swift, Roots, Projection, Topic

Union

Harrod's don't sell them.
Single (7"): released on Academy Sound & Vision in Mar'87 by Academy Sound & Vision Records. Distributed by: Pinnacle

Mainstreet, USA.
Single (7"): released on Portrait in Jul'81 by CBS Records. Distributed by: CBS

Union Gap

Young girl.
Single (7"): released on CBS in Feb'78 by CBS Records. Distributed by: CBS

Uniques

Showcase volume 1.
Album: released on Third World in Jun'78. Distributed by: Jetstar Distribution

You don't miss your water.
Single (7"): released on Charly in Jul'80 by Charly Records. Distributed by: Charly, Cadillac

Unissued ..

Unissued 1963 blues festival Various artists (Various Artists).
Notes: Unreleased American Folk Blues Festival set from 1963, featuring Memphis Slim, Sonny Boy Williamson, amazing guitar from Blues Brother Matt 'Guitar' Murphy anda bottom provided by Billy Stepney and Willie Dixon.
Album: released on Red Lightnin' in Apr'86 by Red Lightnin' Records. Distributed by: Roots, Swift, Jazz Music, JSU, Pinnacle, Cartel, Wynd-Up Distribution

Unit 4 + 2

Concrete & clay.
Single (7"): released on Old Gold in Apr'83 by Old Gold Records. Distributed by: Lightning, Jazz Music, Spartan, Counterpoint

Unit 5

Scared of the dark.
Album: released on Clone in May'82. Distributed by: Spartan

United Jazz & Rock Ensemble

Live opus 6.
Album: released on Original in Sep'84. Distributed by: RCA Distribution, Jazz Music Distribution, PRT Distribution

United Nations

First move, The.
Album: released on Magnet in Feb'86 by Magnet Records. Distributed by: BMG

United Kingdom Symphony Or-

Shades.
Single (7"): released on Food For Thought in Jun'85 by Food For Thought Records. Distributed by: Pinnacle

You cheated.
Tracks: / You cheated / Paying the price.
Single (7"): released on Magnet in Feb'86 by Magnet Records. Distributed by: BMG

United Skins

United Skins Various Artists (Various Artists).
Album: released on Boots & braces in '82

United States...

Introducing the United States Of Existance (United States Of Existance).
Album: released on Bam Caruso in Aug'86 by Bam Caruso Records. Distributed by: Rough Trade, Revolver, Cartel

United States of America (United States Of America).
Album: released on Edsel in May'87 by Demon Records. Distributed by: Pinnacle, Jazz Music, Projection

Unitone

M. R. guy.
Single (7"): released on Shoc in May'80

Units, Vincent

Carnival song.
Single (7"): released on Y in Jan'81

Unity

Changes.
Album: released on Pilgrim in '79 by Pilgrim Records. Distributed by: Rough Trade, Cartel

Unity Creates...

Unity creates strength Various artists (Various Artists).
Album: released on Nevis in May'77. Distributed by: H.R. Taylor

Unity Rockers

Everything to me (see Black Harmony & Unity Rockers) (Unity Rockers/Black Harmony).

Unity Station

Day after day.
Single (12"): released on Restless in 23 May'87. Distributed by: Revolver, Cartel

See 1177 the triangle.
Single (7"): released on Restless in Sep'86. Distributed by: Revolver, Cartel

Universal Congress

Universal Congress of....
Album: released on SST in Oct'87 by SST Records. Distributed by: Pinnacle. Estim retail price in Sep'87 was £6.49.

Universe

Every single night.
Single (7"): released on MBT in Jun'84 by MBT Records. Distributed by: Pinnacle

Musicassette: released on MBT in Jun'84 by MBT Records. Distributed by: Pinnacle

Universe Zero

Triomphe de mouches.
Single (7"): released on Recommended in Nov'82 by Recommended Records. Distributed by: Recommended, Impetus, Rough Trade

University Of Missouri...

University of Missouri Kansas City accordian orchestra Various artists (Various Artists).
Album: released on ARC (Accordion Records) in '84. Distributed by: Accordion Record Club

University Six

University Six Volume 1 : 1926 - 26.
Album: released on Harlequin in Jan'86 by Harlequin Records. Distributed by: Swift, Jazz Music, Wellard, Chris, IRS, Taylor, H.R.

Volume 2 1926-27.
Album: released on Harlequin in Apr'87 by Harlequin Records. Distributed by: Swift, Jazz Music, Wellard, Chris, IRS, Taylor, H.R.

Unknown

Unknown.
Tracks: / All over the place / All the things you are / Badge from your coat, The / Ferry boat serenade, The (La Piccinina) / I've got sixpence / One o'clock jump / That's for me / When the moon comes over Madison Square / Bless 'em all / Blueberry hill / I didn't know what time it was / Just one of those things / My romance / On the isle of May / Only forever / Riding high / Trade winds / We three (my echo, my shadow and me) / Ain't it a shame about a name / All this and heaven too / Beat me daddy eight to a bar / Crn silk / Five o'clock whistle, The / Mama yo quiero (I want my mama) / Rhythm on the river / Room five hundred and four / Scrub me mama with a boogie beat / Whispering grass / You say the sweetest things, baby / I remember nothing.
Notes: Under this recording name are placed all songs for which we have some information, such as writer/publisher/date published etc, but for which we do not know the recording name. The computer will not allow a song to be entered without a recording name, so we use "Unknown" as the recording name. John Humphries 25.4.87.

Unknown Cases

If you want me to stay.
Single (12"): released on Rough Trade in Oct'85 by Rough Trade Records. Distributed by: Rough Trade Distribution, Cartel Distribution

Masimbabele.
Single (12"): released on Rough Trade in May'84 by Rough Trade Records. Distributed by: Rough Trade Distribution, Cartel Distribution

Unknowns

Dream sequence.
Album: released on Sire in Jan'82

Unlimited Touch

Searching to find the one.
Single (7"): released on Epic in Jul'81 by CBS Records. Distributed by: CBS

Unmarried Woman

Unmarried Woman, An Original soundtrack (Various Artists).
Album: released on 20th Century in Aug'78. Distributed by: RCA, IMS-Polygram

Unpleasant Goblins

In the nude.
Single (7"): released on Observation in Jul'82

Un Project

Ki-ah.
Single (7"): released on Rygel in Apr'82 by Alan Osborne. Distributed by: Pinnacle

Untouchables

Free yourself.
Single (7"): released on Stiff in Mar'85 by Stiff Records. Distributed by: EMI, Record Services Distribution (Ireland)

Single (12"): released on Stiff in Mar'85 by Stiff Records. Distributed by: EMI, Record Services Distribution (Ireland)

I spy for FBI.
Single (7"): released on Stiff in Jul'85 by Stiff Records. Distributed by: EMI, Record Services Distribution (Ireland)

Single (12"): released on Stiff in Jul'85 by Stiff Records. Distributed by: EMI, Record Services Distribution (Ireland)

Keep your distance.
Single (7"): released on Fried Egg in Jul'81 by Fried Egg Records. Distributed by: Rough Trade, Cartel

Untouchables, (The) Various Artists (Various Artists).
Album: released on Soul Supply in Apr'85 by High Energy Records. Distributed by: Charly

What's gone wrong.
Single (7"): released on Stiff in Nov'85 by Stiff Records. Distributed by: EMI, Record Services Distribution (Ireland)

Single (12"): released on Stiff in Nov'85 by Stiff Records. Distributed by: EMI, Record Services Distribution (Ireland)

Wild child.
Album: released on Stiff in Jun'85 by Stiff Records. Distributed by: EMI, Record Services Distribution (Ireland)

Musicassette: released on Stiff in Jun'85 by Stiff Records. Distributed by: EMI, Record Services Distribution (Ireland)

Untouchables, The

Untouchables, The (Various Artists).
Tracks: / What goes up (must come down) / I need a helping hand / Darling, darling / I'm gonna hurt you / I'm getting tired / You can forget it / Standing at a standstill / I want to be free / Talking eyes / You got me in the palm of your hand / You left me / This time you're wrong / This heart, these hands / Where were you.
Album: released on Soul Supply in Jan'87 by High Energy Records. Distributed by: Charly

Unwanted

Secret past, (The).
Album: released on De Laurean in Jan'85 by Backs Records. Distributed by: Cartel

Unwin, Stanley

Rotatey diskeys with Unwin.
Tracks: / Pidey pipeload of Hamling / Goldyloppers and the three bearloaders / Olympicold B.C. / Hi-de-fido / Arty-craft / Professor Unwin meetit the press and chettery on / Populode of the musicolly / Classicold musee / Professor Unwin answery most questions on manifold subjy.
Album: released on Flashback in Jul'86 by Flashback Records/PRT Records. Distributed by: Mainline, PRT

Musicassette: released on Flashback in Jul'86 by Flashback Records/PRT Records. Distributed by: Mainline, PRT

Up...

Up country Various artists (Various Artists).
Musicassette: released on Dynamic in Sep'81 by Creole Records. Distributed by: CBS, Essex

Up like the swallow Various artists (Various Artists).
Album: released on Broadside in Jun'81 by Broadside Records. Distributed by: Celtic Distributions, H.R. Taylor, Jazz Music, Projection, Jazz Services Unlimited Dist. (JSU)

Musicassette: released on Broadside in Jun'81 by Broadside Records. Distributed by: Celtic Distributions, H.R. Taylor, Jazz Music, Projection, Jazz Services Unlimited Dist. (JSU)

Up the academy Original soundtrack (Up The Academy).
Album: released on Capitol in Aug'80 by Capitol Records. Distributed by: EMI

Musicassette: released on Capitol in Aug'80 by Capitol Records. Distributed by: EMI

Up the town Various artists (Various Artists).
Album: released on Rubber in Jun'82 by Rubber Records. Distributed by: Roots Distribution, Projection Distribution, Jazz Music Distribution, Celtic Music Distribution, JSU Distribution, Spartan Distribution

UPB

Love you forever.
Single (12"): released on Island in Apr'82 by Island Records. Distributed by: Polygram

Upchurch, Phil

Companions.
Album: released on Palladin in Apr'85 by Palladin Records. Distributed by: Cartel

Musicassette: released on Palladin in Apr'85 by Palladin Records. Distributed by: Cartel

When and if I fall in love.
Single (7"): released on Physical in Jul'83 by Physical Records

Single (12"): released on Physical in Jul'83 by Physical Records

Upfront

I want your love.
Tracks: / I want your love.
Single (7"): released on Atlas in Feb'87 by Atlas Records. Distributed by: PRT

Single (12"): released on Atlas in Feb'87 by Atlas Records. Distributed by: PRT

Up front 1 Various artists (Various Artists).
Notes: Artists: Princess, Joyce Sims, Tota Contrast, Crown Heights Affair, Steve Harley George Clinton, T.C. Curtis, Cool Notes, Rochelle Fleming, Ice T, William Bell, Spyder D Cut Master D.C., M.C. Boob.
Album: released on Serious in Jul'86 by Serious Records. Distributed by: PRT

Up front 2 Various artists (Various Ar tists).
Notes: Artists include: Princess/Main Ingredient/Pieces of a Dream/Fatback Band/Nova Casper/Mondo Kane/Willie Colon/Debby Blackwell/Willie Collins/Cultural Vibes/ Real Roxanne/Eric B./Salt 'n' Pepper/Steady B.
Double Album: released on Serious in Aug'86 by Serious Records. Distributed by: PRT

Double musicassette: released on Serious in Aug'86 by Serious Records. Distributed by PRT

Up front 4 (Various Artists).
Album: released on Serious in Jan'87 by Serious Records. Distributed by: PRT

Musicassette: released on Serious in Jan'8 by Serious Records. Distributed by: PRT

Up front 6 (Various Artists).
Album: released on Serious in May'87 by Serious Records. Distributed by: PRT

Musicassette: released on Serious in May'87 by Serious Records. Distributed by: PRT

Upfront 7

Upfront 7 Various artists (Various Artists).
Album: released on Needle in Aug'87. Distributed by: Pinnacle

Musicassette: released on Needle in Aug'87. Distributed by: Pinnacle

Up Jam Crew

Jack me up.
Tracks: / Jack me up / Jack me up Scotty.
Single (7"): released on Nine O Nine in Jul'87 by Creole Records. Distributed by: Rhino, PRT

Upper Norwood Band...

All things bright & beautiful.
Album: released on Banners & Bonnets in May'82 by Word Records. Distributed by: Word Distribution
Cat.no . . . . BAB 3513
Musicassette: released on Banners & Bonnets in May'82 by Word Records. Distributed by: Word Distribution

Uppers on the south down

Uppers on the south down Various artists (Various Artists).
Album: released on Safari in Jun'84 by Safari Records. Distributed by: Pinnacle

Uprights

World turned upside down.
Single (7"): released on Loppylugs in Jan'82 by Loppylugs Records. Distributed by: Pinnacle, Loppylugs

Uproar

Die for me (EP).
Single (7"): released on Lightbeat in Mar'83 by Lightbeat Records. Distributed by: Pinnacle

Nothing can stop you (EP).
Single (7"): released on Volume in Jan'84 by Volume Records. Distributed by: Pinnacle

Rebel youth.
Single (7"): released on Beat-The-System in Feb'83 by Lightbeat Records. Distributed by: Pinnacle

Ups And Downs

In the shadows.
Tracks: / In the shadows.
Single (7"): released on What Goes On in Sep'86. Distributed by: Rough Trade, Cartel, Shigaku

Living kind, The.
Single (12"): released on What Goes On in Oct'86. Distributed by: Rough Trade, Cartel, Shigaku

Sleepless.
Album: released on What Goes On in Nov'86. Distributed by: Rough Trade, Cartel, Shigaku

Upsetters

Best of Lee Perry & The Upsetters Vol.2

New Orleans connection, (The).
Album: released on Charly in Jun'84 by Charly Records. Distributed by: Charly, Cadillac

Return of Django.
Single (7"): released on Old Gold in Apr'83 by Old Gold Records. Distributed by: Lightning, Jazz Music, Spartan, Counterpoint

Upsetter box set Various Artists (Various Artists).
Boxed set: released on Trojan in Jul'85 by Trojan Records. Distributed by: PRT, Jetstar

Upsetters collection.
Album: released on Trojan in '83 by Trojan Records. Distributed by: PRT, Jetstar

Upsetters & Friends

Upsetter collection.
Tracks: / Cold sweat / Return of Django / Check it out / Django shoots first / Kill them all / Vampire, The / Drugs & poison / Sipreano / Black IPA / Bucky skank / Words of my mouth / Tipster special / Cow thief skank / French connection / Better days / Freak out skank.
Album: released on Trojan in Feb'86 by Trojan Records. Distributed by: PRT, Jetstar

---

Musicassette: released on Trojan in Feb'86 by Trojan Records. Distributed by: PRT, Jetstar

Upton, Barry

Ask the D.J..
Tracks: / Ask the DJ / Ask the DJ (version) / Music to my ears.
Single (7"): released on DMC-Arista in Nov'86 by Ariola Records. Distributed by: RCA, Ariola
Cat.no . . . . DECK 3
Single (12"): released on DMC-Arista in Nov'86 by Ariola Records. Distributed by: RCA, Ariola

Upton, Glen

Christmastime is children.
Single (7"): released on Ash in Nov'82 by Ash Records. Distributed by: Ash

Upton, Harry

Why can't it always be Saturday?.
Album: released on Topic in '81 by Topic Records. Distributed by: JSU Distribution, Projection Distribution, Jazz Music Distribution

Uptown is Kicking it

Uptown is Kicking it (Various Artists).
Notes: Seven-track compilation of rising young Hip-Hop acts. Album compiled and produced by Andre harrel, better known to veterans of 'Fresh '86' as Dr.Jeckell.

Uptown is kicking it (Various Artists).
Album: released on MCA in Dec'86 by MCA Records. Distributed by: Polygram, MCA

Musicassette: released on MCA in Dec'86 by MCA Records. Distributed by: Polygram, MCA

Urban Blight

From the Eastside to the Westside.
Single (12"): released on Stickman USA in Aug'87

Urban blues

Urban blues Various original artists 1940's/50's (Various original artists).
Album: released on Speciality in Aug'77 by Relic Records. Distributed by: Swift

Urban Cowboys

Broken promises.
Single (7"): released on Denbeat in Feb'87 by Denbeat Records. Distributed by: Revolver, Cartel

Keys to your heart.
Single (7"): released on Dembeat in Sep'84

Urban De Luxe

De luxe blues band.
Album: released on Appaloosa in Jan'84. Distributed by: Roots, Folksound, JSU, Projection, Celtic Music, Chris Wellard

Urban Dogs

Limo life.
Single (7"): released on Fall Out in Mar'83. Distributed by: Fresh, Cartel, Jetstar

No pedigree.
Album: released on Flicknife in Nov'85 by Flicknife Records. Distributed by: Spartan

Urbane Gorillas

Only the eyes.
Single (7"): released on Inane in Aug'81. Distributed by: Rough Trade

Urbane Gorillas.
Single (7"): released on Inane in Jun'82. Distributed by: Rough Trade

Urbane Planners

Fashion is not enough.
Single (7"): released on Mays in Dec'83 by Mays Records. Distributed by: Roots, Spartan, Projection

Spirit of the thing.
Single (7"): released on Mays in Jan'87 by Mays Records. Distributed by: Roots, Spartan, Projection

Spirit of the thing (Urbane Planners Featuring Milt & Mandy Moreton).
Single (7"): released on Mays in Aug'83 by Mays Records. Distributed by: Roots, Spartan, Projection

---

Urban Gypsy

Japanese girls.
Single (7"): released on Public in Nov'79 by Patrick Cambell-Lyons. Distributed by: Spartan

Urbaniax

Burning circuits.
Single (7"): released on Sonet in Oct'84 by Sonet Records. Distributed by: PRT

Single (12"): released on Sonet in Oct'84 by Sonet Records. Distributed by: PRT

Urbaniax.
Album: released on Sonet in Nov'84 by Sonet Records. Distributed by: PRT

Urbanik, Michel

Nanava.
Single (7"): released on Motown in Oct'81 by RCA Records. Distributed by: RCA Distribution

Single (12"): released on Motown in Oct'81 by RCA Records. Distributed by: RCA Distribution

Urban Sax

Part 3 & 4.
Album: released on Cobra in Sep'79 by Cobra Records. Distributed by: Projection, EMI

Urban sax.
Album: released on Cobra in May'79 by Cobra Records. Distributed by: Projection, EMI

Urbianak, Michael

Recital (Urbaniak, Michel/Vladislav Sendecki).
Album: released on Four Leaf Clover in Jul'86. Distributed by: Jazz Music, Swift

Ure, Midge

Call of the wild.
Tracks: / Call of the wild / When the wind blows / After a fashion.
Single (7"): released on Chrysalis in May'86 by Chrysalis Records. Distributed by: CBS

Single (12"): released on Chrysalis in May'86 by Chrysalis Records. Distributed by: CBS

Gift, The.
Tracks: / If I was / When the winds blow / Living in the past / That certain smile / Gift, The / Antilles / Wastelands / Edo / Chieftan, The / She cried.
Compact disc: released on Chrysalis in '86 by Chrysalis Records. Distributed by: CBS

Album: released on Chrysalis in Oct'85 by Chrysalis Records. Distributed by: CBS

Musicassette: released on Chrysalis in Oct'85 by Chrysalis Records. Distributed by: CBS

If I was.
Single (7"): released on Chrysalis in Aug'85 by Chrysalis Records. Distributed by: CBS

No regrets.
Single (7"): released on Chrysalis in Jun'82 by Chrysalis Records. Distributed by: CBS

That certain smile.
Single (7"): released on Chrysalis in Nov'85 by Chrysalis Records. Distributed by: CBS

Single (12"): released on Chrysalis in Nov'85 by Chrysalis Records. Distributed by: CBS

Wastelands.
Tracks: / Wastelands.
Single (7"): released on Chrysalis in Jan'86 by Chrysalis Records. Distributed by: CBS

Single (12"): released on Chrysalis in Jan'86 by Chrysalis Records. Distributed by: CBS

Uriah Heep

Abominog.
Tracks: / Too scared to run / Chasing shadows / On the rebound / Hot night in a cold town / Running all night / That's the way it is / Prisoner sell your soul / Hot persuasion / Think it over / Too scared to run / Chasing shadows / On the rebound / Hot night in a cold town / Running all night (with the lion) / That's the way it is / Prisoner / Hot persuasion / Sell your soul / Think it over.
Album: released on Castle Communications in Nov'86 by Castle Communications. Distributed by: Cartel, Pinnacle, Counterpoint

---

Musicassette: released on Castle Communications in Nov'86 by Castle Communications. Distributed by: Cartel, Pinnacle, Counterpoint

Compact disc: released on Castle Classics in Nov'86 by Castle Communications. Distributed by: BMG

Album: released on Castle Classics in Apr'86 by Castle Communications. Distributed by: BMG

Musicassette: released on Castle Classics in Apr'86 by Castle Communications. Distributed by: BMG

Album: released on Castle Classics in Mar'82 by Polygram Records. Distributed by: Polydor

Abominog junior.
Extended-play record: released on Bronze in Mar'82 by Polygram Records. Distributed by: Polydor

Anthology.
Tracks: / Gypsy / Bird of prey / Lady in black / Look at yourself / Salisbury / Love machine / Easy livin' / Wizard, The / Sweet Lorraine / Magician's birthday / Come back to me / Free me / Fools / Too scared to run / Think it over.
Compact disc: released on Legacy in '86. Distributed by: PRT

Double Album: released on Raw Power in Apr'86. Distributed by: Pinnacle

Musicassette: released on Raw Power in Apr'86. Distributed by: Pinnacle

Compact disc: released on Raw Power in Apr'86. Distributed by: Pinnacle

Best of...., The.
Album: released on Bronze in Apr'77 by Polygram Records. Distributed by: Polydor

Conquest.
Album: released on Bronze in Feb'80 by Polygram Records. Distributed by: Polydor

Demons and wizards.
Tracks: / Wizard, The / Traveller in time / Easy lovin' / Poet's justice / Circle of hands / Rainbow demon / All my life / Paradise / Spell, The.
Album: released on Castle Classics in Apr'86 by Castle Communications. Distributed by: BMG

Musicassette: released on Castle Classics in Apr'86 by Castle Communications. Distributed by: BMG

Compact disc: released on Castle Communications in '86 by Castle Communications. Distributed by: BMG

Demons & wizards.
Album: released on Bronze in Apr'77 by Polygram Records. Distributed by: Polydor

Album: released on Bronze in Apr'77 by Polygram Records. Distributed by: Polydor

Equator.
Album: released on Portrait in Mar'85 by CBS Records. Distributed by: CBS

Fallen angel.
Album: released on Bronze in Sep'78 by Polygram Records. Distributed by: Polydor

Firefly.
Album: released on Bronze in Apr'77 by Polygram Records. Distributed by: Polydor

Head first.
Album: released on Bronze in May'83 by Polygram Records. Distributed by: Polydor

Musicassette: released on Bronze in May'83 by Polygram Records. Distributed by: Polydor

High & Mighty.
Album: released on Bronze in Apr'77 by Polygram Records. Distributed by: Polydor

Innocent victim.
Album: released on Bronze in '77 by Polygram Records. Distributed by: Polydor

Live.
Double Album: released on Bronze in Apr'77 by Polygram Records. Distributed by: Polydor

Live in Europe, 1979.
Tracks: / Easy livin' / Look at yourself / Lady in black / Free me / Stealin' / Wizard / July morning / Falling in love / Woman of the night / I'm alive / Who needs me / Sweet Lorraine / Free'n'easy / Gypsy.

Album: released on Raw Power in Mar'87. Distributed by: Pinnacle

Musicassette: released on Raw Power in Mar'87. Distributed by: Pinnacle

Look at yourself.
Tracks: / Look at yourself / I wanna be free / July morning / Tears in my eyes / Shadows of grief / What should be done / Love machine.
Album: released on Castle Classics in Apr'86 by Castle Communications. Distributed by: BMG

Musicassette: released on Castle Classics in Apr'86 by Castle Communications. Distributed by: BMG

Magician's birthday, The.
Tracks: / Sunrise / Spider woman / Blind woman / Echoes in the dark / Rain / Sweet Lorraine / Tales / Magician's birthday.
Album: released on Castle Classics in Apr'86 by Castle Communications. Distributed by: BMG

Magicians birthday.
Album: released on Bronze in Jul'77 by Polygram Records. Distributed by: Polydor

On the rebound.
Single (7"): released on Bronze in Feb'82 by Polygram Records. Distributed by: Polydor

Return to fantasy.
Album: released on Bronze in Jul'77 by Polygram Records. Distributed by: Polydor

Salisbury.
Tracks: / Bird of prey / Park, The / Time to live / Lady in black / High priestess / Salisbury.
Album: released on Castle Classics in Apr'86 by Castle Communications. Distributed by: BMG

Album: released on Bronze in Jul'77 by Polygram Records. Distributed by: Polydor

Stay on top.
Gatefold sleeve: released on Bronze in Aug'83 by Polygram Records. Distributed by: Polydor

Single (7"): released on Bronze in Aug'83 by Polygram Records. Distributed by: Polydor

Sweet freedom.
Album: released on Bronze in '79 by Polygram Records. Distributed by: Polydor

That's the way that it is.
Single (7"): released on Bronze in Jun'82 by Polygram Records. Distributed by: Polydor

Very 'eavy ...very 'umble.
Tracks: / Gypsy / Walking in your shadow / Came away Melinda / Lucy blues / Dreammare / Real turned on / I'll keep on trying / Wake up (set your sights).
Album: released on Castle Classics in Apr'86 by Castle Communications. Distributed by: BMG

Urock

No war no more.
Single (7"): released on FM productions in Jun'85. Distributed by: Spartan

Uropa Lula

Our love has just begun.
Single (7"): released on Arista in Jul'82 by Arista Records. Distributed by: RCA

Single (12"): released on Arista in Jul'82 by Arista Records. Distributed by: RCA

U-Roy

African soldier.
Tracks: / African soldier / African soldier (version).
Single (12"): released on Tappa in Aug'86. Distributed by: Jetstar

Baby come back.
Tracks: / Baby come back / Baby come back (INST).
Single (12"): released on Tappa in Sep'86. Distributed by: Jetstar

Best of U-Roy.
Album: released on Live & Love in Jun'77 by Third World Records. Distributed by: Jetstar

Crucial cuts.
Album: released on Virgin in Apr'83 by Virgin Records. Distributed by: EMI, Virgin Distribution

DJ Masterpieces (U-Roy & Friends).

Album: released on Vista in May'84 by Vista Records. Distributed by: Gamut, H.R. Taylor Distribution

Dread in babylon.
Album: released on Virgin in Apr'83 by Virgin Records. Distributed by: EMI, Virgin Distribution

Hustlers taking over.
Single (12"): released on Music Works in Dec'82. Distributed by: Jetstar Distribution

Jah call you.
Tracks: / Jah call you / Great stories.
Single (12"): released on Third World in Jul'86. Distributed by: Jetstar Distribution

Music addict.
Album: released on Ras in Aug'87 by Real Authentic Sound. Distributed by: Greensleeves Records, RCA, Jetstar

Natty rebel.
Album: released on Virgin in Apr'83 by Virgin Records. Distributed by: EMI, Virgin Distribution

Seven goals.
Tracks: / Bullet the sky / Running to stand still / Red hill mining town / In god's country / Trip through the wires / One tree hill / Exit / Mothers of the disappeared / Where the streets have no name / I still haven't found what I'm looking for / With or without you.
Album: released on Ujama in Feb'87 by Ujama Records. Distributed by: Spartan, Jetstar

Version galore.
Album: released on Treasure Isle in Jul'84 by Treasure Isle Records. Distributed by: Jetstar

Urry, Mick

Cockney capers (Urry, Mick With His Showband & Singers).
Album: released on Tank in Jun'79 by Tank Records

I'm in the mood for dancing (Urry, Mick & his Orchestra).
Album:

In a dancing mood (Urry, Mick & his Orchestra).
Album: released on Maestro in Jul'86 by Maestro Records

In a party mood (Urry, Mick His Orchestra & Singers).
Album: released on Maestro in Oct'85 by Maestro Records

Musicassette: released on Maestro in Oct'85 by Maestro Records

US

Keep on looking.
Single (7"): released on Excaliber in Aug'84 by Red Bus Records. Distributed by: PRT

Single (12"): released on Excaliber in Aug'84 by Red Bus Records. Distributed by: PRT

U.S.A.

I love you.
Single (7"): released on Philly World in Nov'82 by Philly World Records (USA). Distributed by: Polygram

Single (12"): released on Philly World in Nov'82 by Philly World Records (USA). Distributed by: Polygram

U.S.A..
Album: released on Philly World in Nov'82 by Philly World Records (USA). Distributed by: Polygram

USA for Africa

We are the world.
Video-cassette (VHS): released on PMI in Jun'86 by PMI Records. Distributed by: EMI

Video-cassette (Betamax): released on PMI in Jun'86 by PMI Records. Distributed by: EMI

Single (7"): released on CBS in Mar'85 by CBS Records. Distributed by: CBS

Single (12"): released on CBS in Mar'85 by CBS Records. Distributed by: CBS

We are the world.....
Album: released on CBS in May'85 by CBS Records. Distributed by: CBS

Musicassette: released on CBS in May'85 by CBS Records. Distributed by: CBS

US country charts

US country charts 1950-1959 various artists (Various Artists).
Album: released on Mercury (Germany) in Apr'85 by Phonogram Records. Distributed by: Polygram Distribution

US country charts 1960-1969 various artists (Various Artists).
Album: released on Mercury (Germany) in Apr'85 by Phonogram Records. Distributed by: Polygram Distribution

Usher, Claire

Superclaire.
Tracks: / Superman / I'm into something good / Shadows / My guy / Rainbow / My boy lollipop / It's 'orrible being in love when you're eight and a half / Raining in my heart / Big sister / Rubber ball / Born too late / Zip-a-dee-doo-dah/Give a little whistle.
Album: released on BBC in Sep'86 by BBC Records & Tapes. Distributed by: EMI, PRT, Pye

Musicassette: released on BBC in Sep'86 by BBC Records & Tapes. Distributed by: EMI, PRT, Pye

U.S.Scooters

Young girls.
Album: released on EMI America in Jul'80 by EMI Records. Distributed by: EMI

USSR Academic Choir

Russian Folk Songs.
Musicassette: released on Melodiya (USSR) in Mar'79. Distributed by: T.B.C Distribution

Album: released on Cosmopolitan in Apr'76 by Oryx Records

USSR Defence Ministry

Famous Russian marches.
Album: released on H.M.V. in '77 by EMI Records. Distributed by: EMI

Ustinov, Peter

Many voices of..., The.
Album: released on BBC in Nov'76 by BBC Records & Tapes. Distributed by: EMI, PRT, Pye

Musicassette: released on BBC in Nov'76 by BBC Records & Tapes. Distributed by: EMI, PRT, Pye

Usual Suspects

Above suspicion.
Album: released on Projection in Dec'83

Usual Suspects, The various artists (Various Artists).
Album: released on Waterfront in Mar'86 by Waterfront Records. Distributed by: Rough Trade, Cartel, Projection, Roots

Usual suspects Vol.1 Various artists (Various Artists).
Album: released on Waterfront in Mar'84 by Waterfront Records. Distributed by: Rough Trade, Cartel, Projection, Roots

Usual suspects Vol.2 (It's all music) (Various Artists).
Album: released on Waterfront in Mar'84 by Waterfront Records. Distributed by: Rough Trade, Cartel, Projection, Roots

UT

Confidential.
Single (12"): released on Outer in Jun'85. Distributed by: Rough Trade Distribution

Conviction.
Album: released on Out in Apr'86 by Out Records. Distributed by: Chris Wellard Distribution, Pinnacle, Rough Trade Distribution, Cartel Distribution

Early life live.
Album: released on Blast First in Jun'87 by Sonic Youth Records. Distributed by: Rough Trade, Nine Mile, Red Rhino, Cartel

U.T.F.O

Roxanne,Roxanne.
Single (7"): released on Streetwave in Mar'85 by Streetwave Records. Distributed by: PRT Distribution

Single (12"): released on Streetwave in Mar'85 by Streetwave Records. Distributed by: PRT Distribution

Single (cassette): released on Streetwave in Mar'85 by Streetwave Records. Distributed by: PRT Distribution

Skeezer pleezer.
Tracks: / Just watch / Where did you go / We work hard / Kangol & Doc / House will rock, The / Split personality / Pick up the pace / Bad luck Barry.
Album: released on Chrysalis in Aug'86 by Chrysalis Records. Distributed by: CBS

Musicassette: released on Chrysalis in Aug'86 by Chrysalis Records. Distributed by: CBS

We work hard.
Tracks: / We work hard / Kangol & Doc.
Single (7"): released on Cool Tempo in Jul'86 by Chrysalis Records. Distributed by: CBS

Single (12"): released on Cool Tempo in Jul'86 by Chrysalis Records. Distributed by: CBS

Ya cold, wanna be with me.
Single (7"): released on Select (USA) in Aug'87

Utopia

Crybaby.
Single (7"): released on WEA International in May'84 by WEA Records. Distributed by: WEA

Oblivion.
Album: released on WEA International in Apr'84 by WEA Records. Distributed by: WEA

Musicassette: released on WEA International in Apr'84 by WEA Records. Distributed by: WEA

One world.
Single (7"): released on Bearsville (USA) in Apr'82 by Warner Bros Records. Distributed by: WEA

Swing to the right.
Album: released on Bearsville (USA) in May'82 by Warner Bros Records. Distributed by: WEA

Trivia 12 track compilation.
Compact disc: by Pacific Records (USA). Distributed by: Atlantic

Uttley, Alison

Brown mouse & the little red fox, The.
Musicassette: released on Listen For Pleasure in Dec'80 by MFP Records. Distributed by: EMI

U Turn

Biological EP.
Single (7"): by Epigram Records. Distributed by: Rough Trade

UV Pop

Anyone for me.
Single (7"): released on Flowmotion in Mar'85. Distributed by: Red Rhino, Cartel

Single (12"): released on Flowmotion in Mar'85. Distributed by: Red Rhino, Cartel

Just a game.
Single (7"): released on Pax in Nov'82 by Pax Records. Distributed by: Red Rhino, Cartel

No songs tomorrow.
Album: released on Flowmotion in '84. Distributed by: Red Rhino, Cartel

Serious.
Single (12"): released on Native in Sep'85 by Native Records. Distributed by: Red Rhino, Cartel

Uwandile

Apartheid.
Album: released on Probe Plus in Jun'87 by Probe Plus Records. Distributed by: Probe Plus Distribution

Crazy today.
Single (7"): released on Crazy Plane in Jul'87. Distributed by: Pinnacle

Uzi

Sleep asylum.
Album: released on Homestead in Aug'86. Distributed by: Rough Trade, Cartel, Shigaku

V

own away by love.
ngle (7"): released on Ram in May'85 by
am. Distributed by: PRT

ngle (12"): released on Ram in May'85 by
am. Distributed by: PRT

**Various artists-Robert Wyatt, Mike Old-
ld, etc. (Various Artists).**
bum: released on Virgin in Jan'75 by Virgin
ocords. Distributed by: EMI, Virgin Distribution

usicassette: released on Virgin in '74 by Vir-
n Records. Distributed by: EMI, Virgin Dis-
bution

Vache, Allan

arinet climax (see Hedges, Chuck)
ache, Allan & Chuck Hedges).

gh speed swing.
bum: released on Audiophile in Jan'87 by
zzology Records (USA). Distributed by: Jazz
sic, Swift

azz moods.
bum: released on Audiophile in Jul'87 by Jaz-
y Records (USA). Distributed by: Jazz
sic, Swift

ache, Warren

**es walk (Vache, Warren With Scott
milton & John Bunch.).**
bum: released on Dreamstreet in Jan'79.
stributed by: Swift

sy going (Vache, Warren Sextet).
cks: / Little girl / Easy going bounce / Warm
y / You'd be so nice to come home to / Mi-
ge / It's been so long / Was I to blame for
ng in love with you? / London by night /
dy make up your mind / Moon song (That
n't meant for me).
es: Personnel: Warren Vache - cornet & flu-
rn / Howard Alden - guitar / Dan Barrett -
bone / John Harkins - piano / Jack Lesberg
ss / Chuck Riggs - drums.
bum: released on Concord Jazz (USA) in
87 by Concord Jazz Records (U). Dis-
ted by: IMS, Polygram

usicassette: released on Concord Jazz
A) in Jul'87 by Concord Jazz Records
A). Distributed by: IMS, Polygram

pact disc: released on Concord Jazz in
7 by Concord Jazz Records (USA). Dis-
ted by: IMS, Polygram

t time out.
es: with Bucky Pizzarelli/Kenny Davern etc.
bum: released on Audiophile in Jan'87 by Jazz
ology Records (USA). Distributed by: Jazz
c, Swift

um: released on Monmouth in Mar'79

escence.
um: released on Concord in Aug'81 by Im-
Records. Distributed by: IMS, Polygram

own jazz.
um: released on Concord Jazz (USA) in
83 by Concord Jazz Records (USA). Dis-
ted by: IMS, Polygram

**t Hamilton and Warren Vache
he, Warren & Scott Hamilton).**
um: released on Concord in Apr'79 by Im-
ecords. Distributed by: IMS, Polygram

Vagina Dentata

Music for Hashasins.
Album: released on Temple in Aug'87 by
Temple Records. Distributed by: Rough Trade
Distribution, Cartel Distribution. Estim retail
price in Sep'87 was £5.99.

Vagrants

What's in my soul.
Single (7"): released on Riktashadz in Jul'82

Valaltis, Lena

Johnny blue.
Single (7"): released on Ariola in Apr'81. Distributed by: RCA, Ariola

Valdor, Frank

**Shall we dance....In strict tempo
rhythm.**
Album: released on Condor(Germany) in
Jul'85

Vale, Jerry

Greatest hits: Jerry Vale.
Album: released on CBS Cameo in Jul'84 by
CBS Records. Distributed by: CBS

Valence, Ricky

Rainbow.
Album: released on Tank in Sep'79 by Tank
Records

Tell Laura I love her.
Single (7"): released on Old Gold in Oct'83 by
Old Gold Records. Distributed by: Lightning,
Jazz Music, Spartan, Counterpoint

Single (7"): released on Old Gold in Oct'83 by
Old Gold Records. Distributed by: Lightning,
Jazz Music, Spartan, Counterpoint

Single (7"): released on EMI in Jul'75 by EMI
Records. Distributed by: EMI

Musicassette: released on Autograph in
Apr'85. Distributed by: Record Services Distribution (Ireland)

Tell laura I love her.

Time after time.
Single (7"): released on Revolver in Mar'81 by
Revolver Records. Distributed by: Revolver,
Cartel

Valens, Ritchie

Donna.
Single (7"): released on Creole Replay in
Aug'84 by Creole Records. Distributed by: PRT,
Rhino

Single (7"): released on Old Gold in Jul'82 by
Old Gold Records. Distributed by: Lightning,
Jazz Music, Spartan, Counterpoint

Greatest hits: Ritchie Valens.
Album: released on RCA in Aug'87 by RCA
Records. Distributed by: RCA, Roots, Swift,
Wellard, Chris, I & B, Solomon & Peres Distribu-
tion

Musicassette: released on RCA in Aug'87 by
RCA Records. Distributed by: RCA, Roots,
Swift, Wellard, Chris, I & B, Solomon & Peres
Distribution

His greatest hits.
Album: released on President in '74 by President Records. Distributed by: Taylors, Spartan

---

History of..., A.
Album: released on Rhino (USA) in Feb'85 by
Rhino Records (USA)

La bamba.
Single (7"): released on RCA in Aug'87 by RCA
Records. Distributed by: RCA, Roots, Swift,
Wellard, Chris, I & B, Solomon & Peres Distribu-
tion

Single (12"): released on RCA in Aug'87 by
RCA Records. Distributed by: RCA, Roots,
Swift, Wellard, Chris, I & B, Solomon & Peres
Distribution

Rock I'll darlin'.
Album: released on Joy in '74 by President
Records. Distributed by: Jazz Music, Swift,
President Distribution

Valente, Caterina

Caterina's greatest hits.
Album: released on Decca in '66 by Decca
Records. Distributed by: Polygram

Caterina Valente's greatest hits.
Album: released on Jasmine in Mar'85 by Jasmine Records. Distributed by: Counterpoint,
Lugtons, Taylor, H.R., Wellard, Chris, Swift, Cadillac

Edition 1 1954/55 Schwarze engel.
Tracks: / Ganz Paris traunt von der liebe /
Schwarze engel / Bambino / Wenn es necht
wird in Paris / Ja in Madrid und Barcelona / O
mama, O mamejo / Die damen welt in Chile /
Malaguena / Baiao Bongo / Babko / Breeze and
I, The (English) / Jalousie (English) / Just for
you, just me (Englisch) / Istanbul (Englisch) / El
Mosculto (Spanisch) / Malaguena (Spanish).
Album: released on Bear Family in Nov'86 by
Bear Family Records. Distributed by: Roller-
coaster Distribution, Swift

Edition 2 1955 Part 1 Chanson d'amour.
Tracks: / Coco Polka (Franzoisch) / Casanova
(Franz) / Fiesta Cubana (Franzoisch) / Chanson
d'amour / Oho aha / Es ist so schon bei dir nach
den sternen / Chanson d'amour (Italienisch) /
Fiesta Cubana (Italienisch) / Begin the beguine
(Englisch) / Siboney (Englisch) / Fiesta Cubana
/ This must be serveol (Englisch) / Donne ta main
et viens (Franzoisch).
Notes: Tracks 7-15 All in Kursiv Bisher Uneröf-
fentlicht. Original Polydor Aufnahmen.
Album: released on Bear Family in Nov'86 by
Bear Family Records. Distributed by: Roller-
coaster Distribution, Swift

Edition 3 (1955-56) - Sing baby sing.
Tracks: / Sing, baby, sing / Bim-bam-bim-bam-
bina / Eventuell / Andalucia / Pietro, zeeg mir
dein herz / Mackie messer / Wir kamen in die
strasse / My lonely lover / It hearts could talk /
Temptation / This ecstasy / Way you love me,
(The) / Chanson d'amour / Bouquet des reves /
Dot ar nog fel / Chanson d'amour.
Album: released on Bear Family in May'87 by
Bear Family Records. Distributed by: Roller-
coaster Distribution, Swift

**Edition 4 (1955-56) - Komm ein biss-
chen mit nach Italien.**
Tracks: / Bonjour Kathrin / Es geht besser,
besser, besser / Eine frau aus Paris / Komm ein
bisschen mit nach Italien / Wie war's / Steig in
das traumboot der liebe / Gaucho / Gespenster
blues / Bitte nach ihnen / Granada / Similau /
There but for the grace of God / Look into my
eyes / Bim-bam-bina, (The) / Sunny day, (A) /
Oho aha / Una donna di Parigi / Bonjour Kathrin.
Album: released on Bear Family in May'87 by
Bear Family Records. Distributed by: Rollercoaster Distribution, Swift

Edition 5 (1956) - O Billy Boy.
Tracks: / Du bist musik / Das hab ich gleich ge-
wusst / Daisy, crazy Daisy / Tschi-bam, tschi-
bam-bo-bam-billa / Goldenan spangen, (Die) /
O Billy boy / Ukulele, du musst weinen / Ja das
sind die kleinen geschichten (hat sie gesagt) /
Bonjour Catherine / Femme dans Paris, (Une) /
Si tout etait fini / Les filles de Paris / L'amour

---

defendu / Dans ma vie / Vie me pousse, (La) /
Granada.
Album: released on Bear Family in May'87 by
Bear Family Records. Distributed by: Roller-
coaster Distribution, Swift

**Hier bin Ich- hier bleib Ich... und abends
in die Scala Original filmmusik (Valente,
Caterina/Bill Haley).**
Tracks: / Immer wieder neu / Mal sehn, Kapitan / Gondoliera sang nie mehr so schon, (Der)
/ Pardon Madame / Bisschen pompadour
(mademoiselle), (Ein) / Immer wieder neu / Spiel
noch einmal fur mich, habanero / Bei dir ist alles
Anders / Ich lass dich niemals mehr allein / Ich
lass dich niemals mehr allein (instrumental) /
Eine nacht am Rio Grand / Djiko / Musik liegt in
der luft / Kleine revue.
Album: released on Bear Family in May'87 by
Bear Family Records. Distributed by: Rollercoaster Distribution, Swift

Album: released on Bolts in Aug'87 by Bolts
Records. Distributed by: PRT, Pinnacle

In a swinging mood.
Tracks: / I've got you under my skin / Come fly
with me / Old devil moon / Cherokee / Let's fall
in love / My funny valentine / There will never
be another you / Take the "A" train / New York,
N.Y. / Chinatown, my Chinatown / What a difference a day made.
Compact disc: released on Teldec in May'87

Valentin, Dave

Flute juice.
Album: released on GRP (USA) in Jun'84 by
GRP Records (USA). Distributed by: IMS, Poly-
gram

Musicassette: released on GRP (USA) in
Jun'84 by GRP Records (USA). Distributed by:
IMS, Polygram

Light struck.
Tracks: / Miss V. / One thing I can't change is
my heart, The / Grandslam / Village, The / AM-
FM / Chris-Cross / Prince of wands / Prelude to
a kiss.
Notes: Jazz flautist Dave Valentin's most commercial artist album to date. Superbly recorded, this album contains both new and
familiar material. Special guest appearance by
singer Angela Bofill who joins Dave Valentin on
'The one thing I can't change is my heart' written by one of Brazil's most popular stars and
composers, Ivan Lins.
Album: released on GRP (USA) in Jul'86 by
GRP Records (USA). Distributed by: IMS, Polygram

Musicassette: released on GRP (USA) in
Jul'86 by GRP Records (USA). Distributed by:
IMS, Polygram

Compact disc: released on GRP (USA) in
Jul'86 by GRP Records (USA). Distributed by:
IMS, Polygram

Valentine

Rocky Valley festival song.
Single (7"): released on Valentine in May'86 by
Valentine Records. Distributed by: PRT

Tina are you ready.
Single (7"): . Distributed by: Pinnacle, Fresh

Single (12"): . Distributed by: Pinnacle, Fresh

Valentine Brothers

Money's too tight.
Single (7"): released on Energy in Mar'83 by
Energy Records. Distributed by: Jazz Music

Single (12"): released on Energy in Mar'83 by
Energy Records. Distributed by: Jazz Music

No better love.
Single (7"): released on EMI America in Aug'87
by EMI Records. Distributed by: EMI

Single (12"): released on EMI America in Aug'87 by EMI Records. Distributed by: EMI

Picture this.
Tracks: / Somebody took my love / No better love / She loves me / In my time / Cut backs / Used to be lovers / What you gonna do with love? / Ladies' delight / Funk attack / Starship / Somebody took my love / No better love / She loves me / In my time / Ladies delight / Cutbacks / Used to be lovers / What you gonna do with love / Starship / Funk attack.
Album: released on EMI America in Aug'87 by EMI Records. Distributed by: EMI

Musicassette: released on EMI America in Aug'87 by EMI Records. Distributed bv: EMI

Compact disc: released on EMI America in Aug'87 by EMI Records. Distributed by: EMI

Valentine, Cindy

In your midnight hour.
Tracks: / Work it out / In your midnight hour.
Single (7"): released on Urban in Apr'87 by Polydor Records. Distributed by: Polygram

Single (12"): released on Urban in Apr'87 by Polydor Records. Distributed by: Polygram

Valentine, Dave

Jungle garden.
Tracks:/ Awakening / Oasis / Bones / Love light in flight / Jungle garden / Very nice indeed / I loves you Porgy / Eighty-one / Tabasco.
Compact disc: released on GRP (USA) in Jul'85 by GRP Records (USA). Distributed by: IMS, Polygram

Album: released on GRP (USA) in Jul'85 by GRP Records (USA). Distributed by: IMS, Polygram

Musicassette: released on GRP (USA) in Jul'85 by GRP Records (USA). Distributed by: IMS, Polygram

We can only dream.
Single (7"): released on Aura in Jul'86 by Holywood Nites Distribution. Distributed by: Pinnacle

Valentine, Dickie

Unchained melodies Four stars of the 50's (Valentine, Dickie/Joan Regan/Jimmy Young/Lita Roza).
Notes: For full details see under Jimmy Young.

Very best of Dickie Valentine, The.
Album: released on Decca in May'84 by Decca Records. Distributed by: Polygram

World of....
Album: released on Decca in '81 by Decca Records. Distributed by: Polygram

Valentine, Kid Thomas

Kid Thoman Valentine's Creole Jazz Band.
Album: released on 77 in Sep'79 by 77 Records. Distributed by: Chris Wellard, Cadillac Music, Jazz Music

Kid Thomas Valentine.
Album: released on Arhoolie in Jan'87 by Arhoolie Records. Distributed by: Projection, Topic, Jazz Music, Swift, Roots

Kid Thomas Valentine With Louis Nelson/New Iberia Stompers.
Musicassette: released on 504 in Sep'86 by 504 Records. Distributed by: Chris Wellard, Jazz Music

Valentine Music Group

Once upon a fairy tale.
Musicassette: released on EMI in Nov'79 by EMI Records. Distributed by: EMI

Valentine, Thomas

At Kohlman's Tavern.
Album: released on New Orleans in Sep'86. Distributed by: Swift, Zodiac Distribution, Jazz Music, JSU

Kohlman's Tavern.
Album: released on New Orleans in Apr'79. Distributed by: Swift, Zodiac Distribution, Jazz Music, JSU

Valentino

Anniversary.
Tracks: / More / And I love you so / Side by side medley / Love / Anniversary Waltz / Always / Let me call you seetheart / Only girl in the world,The(You belong to me) / Can't help falling / Man & woman / Made me love you / Evergreen / True love.
Notes: Mail order distribution address:Accordion Record Club,146 Birmingham Road,Kidderminster,Worcs.DY10 2SL.Tel:0562 746105.
Album: released on Accordion Record Club in Jul'86 by Accordion Record Club Records. Distributed by: Accordion Record Club

Around the world.
Album: released on ARC (Accordion Records) in '84. Distributed by: Accordion Record Club

Best of Valentino, The.
Album: released on ARC (Accordion Records) in '84. Distributed by: Accordion Record Club

Incredible sounds, The.
Tracks: / El Bimbo / Good, Bad & The Ugly / Morning has broken / Toccato / Hawaiian wedding song / Zorba's dance / Star wars / Load of old Cobras / Zither medley / Barrel organ med / Czardas / If I never sang another song / It's now or never.
Notes: Retail price given by ARC excluding P & P (via Mail Order) is 6.00. Mail order distribution address: Accordion Record Club, 146 Birmingham Road, Kidderminster, Worcs. DY10 2SL. Tel: 0562 - 746105.
Musicassette: released on Accordion Record Club in Jul'86 by Accordion Record Club Records. Distributed by: Accordion Record Club

Singalong-a-cupid (Valentino & the Valentines).
Single (7"): released on Polydor in Feb'83 by Polydor Records. Distributed by: Polygram, Polydor

To the one I love.
Tracks: / There's a kind of hush/till there was you / Change your mind / Killing me softly / Don't you forget it / You don't have to say / All my love/with all of your heart / love me tender / My honeysuckle / Love is / When I'm sixty four / Feelings.
Notes: Retail price given by ARC excluding P & P (via Mail Order) is 6.00. Mail Order distribution address: Accordion Record Club, 146 Birmingham Road, Kidderminster, Worcs. DY10 2SL. Tel: 0562 - 746105.
Album: released on Accordion Record Club in Jul'86 by Accordion Record Club Records. Distributed by: Accordion Record Club

Musicassette: released on Accordion Record Club in Jul'86 by Accordion Record Club Records. Distributed by: Accordion Record Club

Valentino Show, The.
Album: released on ARC (Accordion Records) in '84. Distributed by: Accordion Record Club

Valentino, Betty

Keep it up.
Single (7"): released on Design Communications in Jun'84

Single (12"): released on Design Communications in Jun'84

Vale of Atholl Pipe Band

Both sides of the tracks.
Album: released on Lapwing in Jul'87 by Lapwing Records Ltd. Distributed by: Celtic Music, Projection, Roots Records, Ross, Gordon Duncan Distribution, Graham Tosh Distribution, Chans Records

Musicassette: released on Lapwing in Jul'87 by Lapwing Records Ltd. Distributed by: Celtic Music, Projection, Roots Records, Ross, Gordon Duncan Distribution, Graham Tosh Distribution, Chans Records

Valerie

Crest of a wave.
Single (7"): released on Elecstar in Nov'85 by Elecstar Records. Distributed by: PRT

Real surprise (Valerie & The Week Of Wonders).
Single (7"): released on Piggy Bank in Oct'84

Single (12"): released on Piggy Bank in Oct'84

Valeri, Michele

Dinosaur rock (Valeri, Michele & Michael Stein).
Musicassette: released on Caedmon(USA) in '84 by Caedmon (USA) Records. Distributed by: Gower, Taylors, Discovery

Valey, T. Ski

Sexual rapping.
Single (12"): released on Pama in Mar'83 by Pama Records. Distributed by: Pama, Enterprise, Jetstar

Valez, Marth

Escape from Babylon.
Album: released on Sire in Sep'78

Valhalla

Coming home.
Single (7"): released on Neat in Nov'82 by Neat Records. Distributed by: Pinnacle, Neat

Still in love with you.
Single (7"): released on Neat in Jan'84 by Neat Records. Distributed by: Pinnacle, Neat

Valiant Sailor

Songs & ballads of Nelson's Navy.
Album: released on Topic in '81 by Topic Records. Distributed by: JSU Distribution, Projection Distribution, Jazz Music Distribution

Valida

High hat trumpet & rhythm With Billy Mason & His Orchestra.
Album: released on World Records in Mar'79 Distributed by: Polygram

Swing is the thing.
Album: released on World Records in '80. Distributed by: Polygram

Val, Joe

Not a word from home (Val, Joe & New England Bluegrass Boys).
Album: released on Rounder (USA) in Nov'77. Distributed by: Mike's Country Music Room Distribution, Jazz Music Distribution, Swift Distribution, Roots Records Distribution, Projection Distribution, Topic Distribution

One morning in may (Val, Joe & New England Bluegrass Boys).
Album: released on Rounder (USA) in Oct'77. Distributed by: Mike's Country Music Room Distribution, Jazz Music Distribution, Swift Distribution, Roots Records Distribution, Projection Distribution, Topic Distribution

Vallee, Rudy

Heigh-ho everybody, this is.
Album: released on ASV Living Era in Nov'81 by ASV Records. Distributed by: PRT

Musicassette: released on ASV Living Era in Nov'81 by ASV Records. Distributed by: PRT

On the air.
Album: released on Totem Import in Jan'78

Rudy Vallee and his Connecticut Yankees (Vallee, Rudy And His Connecticut Yankees).
Tracks: / Deep night / Little kiss each morning (a little kiss each night), A / I love the moon / M-a-r-y I love you / Stein song / St. Louis blues / Kitty from Kansas city / How come you do me like you do ? / Betsy co-ed / Would you like to take a walk ? / Ninety-nine out of a hundred wanna be loved / When yuba plays the rumba on the tuba / This is the missus / Life is just a bowl of cherries.
Notes: Produced by submarine records.
Album: released on Halcyon (USA) in Sep'86 by Halcyon Records (USA). Distributed by: Jazz Music, Conifer, Taylors

Musicassette: released on Halcyon (USA) in Sep'86 by Halcyon Records (USA). Distributed bv: Jazz Music, Conifer, Taylors

Vallelly, Brian

Song of Chanter

Valley Folk

All bells in paradise.
Album: released on Wynd-up in '81. Distributed by: Wynd-Up Distribution

Valley Girls

Navy lark

Valli, Frankie

Book of love, The (Valli, Frankie & The Four Seasons).
Tracks: / Book of love, The / Deep inside your love.
Single (7"): released on MCA in Apr'86 by MCA Records. Distributed by: Polygram, MCA

Frankie Valli & The Four Seasons (Valli, Frankie & The Four Seasons).
Album: released on K-Tel in Aug'82 by K-Tel Records. Distributed by: Record Merchandisers Distribution, Taylors, Terry Blood Distribution, Wynd-Up Distribution, Relay Distribution, Pickwick Distribution, Solomon & Peres Distribution, Polygram

Musicassette: released on K-Tel in Aug'82 by K-Tel Records. Distributed by: Record Merchandisers Distribution, Taylors, Terry Blood Distribution, Wynd-Up Distribution, Relay Distribution, Pickwick Distribution, Solomon & Peres Distribution, Polygram

Grease.
Single (7"): released on RSO in Aug'78

Heaven must have sent you (Valli, Frankie & The Four Seasons).
Single (7"): released on Warner Bros. (USA Import) in Mar'81 by WEA Records. Distributed by: WEA

My eyes adored you.
Single (7"): released on Old Gold in Apr'83 by Old Gold Records. Distributed by: Lightning, Jazz Music, Spartan, Counterpoint

Night, The (Valli, Frankie & The Four Seasons).
Single (7"): released on Mowest in Oct'81

Reunited love (Valli, Frankie & The Four Seasons).
Album: released on Warner Brothers in Feb'8[illegible] by WEA Records. Distributed by: WEA

Musicassette: released on Warner Brothers i[illegible] Feb'81 by Warner Bros Records. Distributed by: WEA

Streetfighter.
Album: released on MCA in May'86 by MC[illegible] Records. Distributed by: Polygram, MCA

Musicassette: released on MCA in May'86 b[illegible] MCA Records. Distributed by: Polygram, MC[illegible]

Valmouth

Valmouth Original cast from the Chiche[illegible]ter Festival Theatre (Various Artists).
Album: released on That's Entertainment [illegible] Jul'82 by That's Entertainment Records. Di[illegible]tributed by: Pinnacle, PRT

Musicassette: released on That's Entertai[illegible]ment in Jul'82 by That's Entertainment Re[illegible]ords. Distributed by: Pinnacle, PRT

Valotti, Willi

Akkordeon Zauber.
Tracks: / Tanzende finger / Jurafahrt / D'Ga[illegible] Ab / Czardas / Avec plaisir / Flurina / Frieda[illegible] Traum / Retour des hirondelles / Dizzy finger[illegible] Ole guappa / Brijou / Schlitzaugli / Zeughau[illegible] keller - Marsch.
Notes: Mail order distribution address: Acco[illegible]ion Record Club, 146, Birmingham Road, K[illegible]derminster, Worcs. DY10 2SL. Tel: 056[illegible] 746105.
Album: released on Accordion Record Club[illegible] Jul'86 by Accordion Record Club Records. D[illegible]tributed by: Accordion Record Club

Val, Steve

Flex-able.
Tracks: / Little green men / Viv women / Lov[illegible] are crazy / Salamanders in the sun / Boy, Th[illegible] Girl song / Attitude song / Call it sleep / Junk[illegible] Bill's private parts / Next stop earth / Ther[illegible] something dead in here.
Album: released on Food For Thought [illegible] Aug'86 by Food For Thought Records. D[illegible]tributed by: Pinnacle

Album: released on Music For Nations [illegible] Sep'84 by Music For Nations Records. D[illegible]tributed by: Pinnacle

Musicassette: released on Food For Thou[illegible] in Sep'87 by Food For Thought Records. D[illegible]tributed by: Pinnacle. Estim retail price[illegible] Sep'87 was £5.99.

Vampire Bats...

Mr Clean (Vampire Bats From Lewis[illegible]am).
Single (7"): released on Sheet in Jan'82. [illegible]tributed by: Rough Trade

Vampires

Harry's house.
Single (7"): released on Next Record Comp[illegible] in Jul'82. Distributed by: Next Record Comp[illegible]

Van Cleef, Lee

Foreign a no paradise.
Single (12"): released on D&H in Dec'82. [illegible]tributed by: Jetstar

Look how she fat.
Single (7"): released on Joe Gibbs in Apr'8[illegible] Joe Gibbs Records. Distributed by: Jetstar

exy chickens.
Single (12"): released on Carib Gems in
Jun'82. Distributed by: Spartan

Van Cooten, Kay

Day of life

Vandals

when in Rome do as the vandals.
Album: released on Hybrid in Oct'85 by Statik
Records. Distributed by: Pinnacle

Album: released on National Trust in Dec'84 by
National Trust Records. Distributed by: Rough
Trade, Cartel

Van Dam

how do you know.
Single (7"): released on Sticky in May'83

Van Damme, Art & Friends

Van Damme, Art and Friends Various Artists (Various Artists).
Album: released on ARC (Accordion Records)
in '84. Distributed by: Accordion Record Club

Van Day, David

singing the bell.
Single (7"): released on Record Shack in
'85 by Record Shack Records. Distributed
by: PRT

Single (12"): released on Record Shack in
'85 by Record Shack Records. Distributed
by: PRT

young Americans talking.
Single (7"): released on WEA in Apr'83 by WEA
Records. Distributed by: WEA

Single (12"): released on WEA in Apr'83 by
WEA Records. Distributed by: WEA

picture disc single: released on WEA in
'83 by WEA Records. Distributed by: WEA

Van De Broeck, Rob Trio

heavy duty.
Album: released on Timeless in Oct'86

Vandenbos, Conny

beste van Conny Vandenbos.
Album: released on Music For Pleasure (Holland) in '86 by EMI Records. Distributed by:

Musicassette: released on Music For Pleasure
(Holland) in '86 by EMI Records. Distributed by:

Van Denbroeck, R

affair (Van Denbroeck, R/D. Ven-DE. Ineke/H. Emmery/R. Burnet).
Album: released on Timeless in Sep'86

Vandenburg

Album: released on Atco in Oct'85 by Atlantic
Records. Distributed by: WEA

Musicassette: released on Atco in Oct'85 by
Atco Records. Distributed by: WEA

once in a lifetime.
Single (7"): released on Atco in Oct'85 by Atco
Records. Distributed by: WEA

Vander, Christian

tristan et iseult.
Album: released on Barclay in Sep'78 by
Barclay Records. Distributed by: Polygram, DiscConifer, IMS, Swift

Van Der Graaf Generator

generation.
Album: released on Virgin in Feb'87 by Virgin
Records. Distributed by: EMI, Virgin Distribution

h to c.
Album: released on Charisma in Mar'83 by Virgin Records. Distributed by: EMI

Musicassette: released on Charisma in Mar'83
by Virgin Records. Distributed by: EMI

I, who am the only one.
Album: released on Charisma in Jun'81 by Virgin Records. Distributed by: EMI

Least we can do is wave to each other, The.
Album: released on Charisma in Sep'83 by Virgin Records. Distributed by: EMI

Musicassette: released on Charisma in Sep'83
by Virgin Records. Distributed by: EMI

Pawn hearts.
Musicassette: released on Charisma in Mar'83
by Virgin Records. Distributed by: EMI

Pawn Hearts.
Tracks: / Lemmings / Man erg / Plague of lighthouse Keepers, A / Eyewitness pictures / Lighthouse / Eyewitness / SHM presence of the night / Kosmos tours (Custards last stand) / Clot thickens, The / Land's end / We go now.
Notes: Originally released 1971.
Album: released on Charisma in Oct'86 by Virgin Records. Distributed by: EMI

Second generation.
Compact disc: released on Virgin in Feb'87 by
Virgin Records. Distributed by: EMI, Virgin Distribution

Still life.
Tracks: / Pilgrims / Still life / La Rossa / My room
(waiting for wonderland) / Childlike faith in childhood's end.
Notes: Originally released April 1976.
Album: released on Charisma in Oct'86 by Virgin Records. Distributed by: EMI

Time Vaults.
Album: released on Demi Monde in May'85.
Distributed by: Charly

World record.
Album: released on Charisma in Sep'83 by Virgin Records. Distributed by: EMI

Vandike, Greg

Dr Rain.
Single (7"): released on Korova in Feb'82. Distributed by: WEA

Marie Celeste.
Single (7"): released on Korova in Jun'80. Distributed by: WEA

Vandross, Luther

Busy body.
Album: released on Epic in Jan'84 by CBS Records. Distributed by: CBS

Musicassette: released on Epic in Jan'84 by
CBS Records. Distributed by: CBS

Forever, for always, for love.
Tracks: / Bad boy/Having a party / You're the
sweetest one / Since I lost my baby / Forever,
for always, for love / Better love / Promise me /
She loves me back / Once you know how.
Album: released on Epic in Jun'87 by CBS Records. Distributed by: CBS

Musicassette: released on Epic in Jun'87 by
CBS Records. Distributed by: CBS

Give me the reason.
Tracks: / Stop to love / See me / I gave it up
(when I fell in love) / So amazing / Give me the
reason / There's nothing better than love / I really didn't mean it / Because it's really love /
Anyone who had a heart.
Album: released on Epic in Jan'87 by CBS Records. Distributed by: CBS

Musicassette: released on Epic in Jan'87 by
CBS Records. Distributed by: CBS

Single (7"): released on Epic in Jan'87 by
CBS Records. Distributed by: CBS

Single (12"): released on Epic in Jan'87 by
CBS Records. Distributed by: CBS

Compact disc: released on Epic in Jan'87 by
CBS Records. Distributed by: CBS

Single (7"): by CBS Records. Distributed by:
CBS

Single (12"): released on Epic in Jun'86 by
CBS Records. Distributed by: CBS

Single (7"): released on Epic in Nov'86 by CBS
Records. Distributed by: CBS

Single (12"): released on Epic in Nov'86 by
CBS Records. Distributed by: CBS

I didn't really mean it.
Single (7"): released on Epic in 13 Jun'87 by
CBS Records. Distributed by: CBS

Single (12"): released on Epic in 13 Jun'87 by
CBS Records. Distributed by: CBS

I really didn't mean it.
Single (7"): released on Epic in 20 Jun'87 by
CBS Records. Distributed by: CBS

It's over now.
Single (7"): released on Epic in Jun'85 by CBS
Records. Distributed by: CBS

Single (12"): released on Epic in Jun'85 by
CBS Records. Distributed by: CBS

I wanted your love.
Single (7"): by CBS Records. Distributed by:
CBS

Single (12"): by CBS Records. Distributed by:
CBS

Luther Vandross.
Album: released on Epic in Dec'82 by CBS
Records. Distributed by: CBS

Musicassette: released on Epic in Dec'82 by
CBS Records. Distributed by: CBS

Never too much.
Tracks: / Never too much / Sugar and spice (I
found me a girl) / Don't you know that? / I've
been working / She's a super lady / You stopped
loving me / House is not a home, A.
Album: released on Epic in Aug'86 by CBS
Records. Distributed by: CBS

Musicassette: released on Epic in Aug'86 by
CBS Records. Distributed by: CBS

Album: released on Epic in Nov'81 by CBS
Records. Distributed by: CBS

Single (7"): released on Epic in Nov'81 by CBS
Records. Distributed by: CBS

Single (12"): released on Epic in Nov'81 by
CBS Records. Distributed by: CBS

Single (7"): released on Epic in Feb'83 by CBS
Records. Distributed by: CBS

Single (12"): released on Epic in Feb'83 by
CBS Records. Distributed by: CBS

Night I fell in love, The.
Tracks: / Til my baby comes home / Night I fell
in love, The / If only for one night / Creepin' / It's
over now / Wait for love / My sensitivity (Gets in
the way) / Other side of the world.
Album: released on Epic in Mar'85 by CBS
Records. Distributed by: CBS

Musicassette: released on Epic in Mar'85 by
CBS Records. Distributed by: CBS

Compact disc: released on Epic in Mar'85 by
CBS Records. Distributed by: CBS

See me.
Tracks: / See me / House is not a home.
Single (7"): released on Epic in Mar'87 by CBS
Records. Distributed by: CBS

Single (12"): released on Epic in Mar'87 by
CBS Records. Distributed by: CBS

Single (12"): by CBS Records. Distributed by:
CBS

Sugar and spice (I found me a girl).
Single (7"): released on Epic in Oct'81 by CBS
Records. Distributed by: CBS

You're the sweetest one.
Single (7"): released on Epic in Apr'83 by CBS
Records. Distributed by: CBS

Single (12"): released on Epic in Apr'83 by
CBS Records. Distributed by: CBS

Vandross, Wayne

Woman, A.
Single (7"): released on Solid Groove in
May'82. Distributed by: Jetstar, Pinnacle

Van Duser, Guy

Finger-style guitar solos.
Album: released on Rounder in Jan'87. Distributed by: Roots Distribution

Got the world on a string.
Album: released on Rounder (USA) in Dec'85.
Distributed by: Mike's Country Music Room Distribution, Jazz Music Distribution, Swift Distribution, Roots Distribution, Projection
Distribution, Topic Distribution

Van Dyke, Earl

6 by 6.
Single (7"): released on Motown in Oct'81 by
Motown Records. Distributed by: BMG Distribution

Van-Dyke, Jaki

Matter of time.
Single (7"): released on Pectcode in Feb'87.
Distributed by: Spartan

Van Dyke, Leroy

Walk on by.
Single (7"): released on Mercury in '80 by Phonogram Records. Distributed by: Polygram Distribution

Vangelis

8237562.

Albedo 0.39.
Album: released on RCA in '84 by RCA Records. Distributed by: RCA, Roots, Swift, Wellard, Chris, I & B, Solomon & Peres Distribution

Musicassette: released on RCA in '84 by RCA
Records. Distributed by: RCA, Roots, Swift,
Wellard, Chris, I & B, Solomon & Peres Distribution

Apocalypse des animaux, (L').
Compact disc: by Polydor Records. Distributed by: Polygram, Polydor

Beaubourg.
Tracks: / Beaubourg (Part 1) / Beaubourg (Part 2).
Notes: Produced, arranged and performed by
Vangelis.
Album: released on Fame in Sep'86 by Music
For Pleasure Records. Distributed by: EMI

Album: released on Fame in Sep'86 by Music
For Pleasure Records. Distributed by: EMI

Best of Vangelis.
Album: released on RCA in '84 by RCA Records. Distributed by: RCA, Roots, Swift, Wellard, Chris, I & B, Solomon & Peres Distribution

Musicassette: released on RCA in '84 by RCA
Records. Distributed by: RCA, Roots, Swift,
Wellard, Chris, I & B, Solomon & Peres Distribution

Chariots of Fire Original film soundtrack.
Album: released on Polydor in Mar'81 by Polydor Records. Distributed by: Polygram, Polydor

Musicassette: released on Polydor in Mar'81
by Polydor Records. Distributed by: Polygram,
Polydor

Compact disc: released on Polydor in Mar'83
by Polydor Records. Distributed by: Polygram,
Polydor

Chariots of Fire.
Single (7"): released on Polydor in Aug'84 by
Polydor Records. Distributed by: Polygram,
Polydor

China.
Tracks: / Chunk Ko / Dragon / Himalaya / Little
fete / Long march / Plum blossom / Summit /
Tao of love / Yin and Yang.
Compact disc: released on Polydor in '83 by
Polydor Records. Distributed by: Polygram,
Polydor

Album: released on Polydor in Aug'83 by Polydor Records. Distributed by: Polygram, Polydor

Musicassette: released on Polydor in Aug'83
by Polydor Records. Distributed by: Polygram,
Polydor

Compact disc: released on Polydor in '83 by
Polydor Records. Distributed by: Polygram,
Polydor

Dragon, The.
Album: released on Charly in '80 by Charly
Records. Distributed by: Charly, Cadillac

Earth.
Album: released on Polydor (Germany) in
Dec'81. Distributed by: IMS-Polygram

Fete sauvage, La.
Tracks: / Fete sauvage, La (Parts 1 & 2).
Compact disc: released on Phonogram Import
in Jul'85

Greatest hits: Vangelis.
Album: released on RCA (Special Imports Service) in Jul'84

Heaven and hell.
Album: released on RCA in Oct'86 by RCA
Records. Distributed by: RCA, Roots, Swift,
Wellard, Chris, I & B, Solomon & Peres Distribution

Musicassette: released on RCA in Oct'86 by RCA Records. Distributed by: RCA, Roots, Swift, Wellard, Chris, I & B, Solomon & Peres Distribution

Album: released on RCA in '84 by RCA Records. Distributed by: RCA, Roots, Swift, Wellard, Chris, I & B, Solomon & Peres Distribution

Musicassette: released on RCA in '84 by RCA Records. Distributed by: RCA, Roots, Swift, Wellard, Chris, I & B, Solomon & Peres Distribution

Single (7"): released on BBC in Jun'81 by BBC Records & Tapes. Distributed by: EMI, PRT, Pye

Hypothesis.
Album: released on Affinity in May'78 by Charly Records. Distributed by: Charly, Cadillac

Ignacio.
Notes: Music from the film "Entends-Tu - Les Chiens Aboyer ?".
Compact disc: released on Phonogram Import in Jul'85

Invisible connections.
Tracks: / Invisible connections / Atom blaster / Thermo vision.
Compact disc: released on DGG in Mar'85 by Polydor Records. Distributed by: Polygram

Album: released on DGG in Mar'85 by Polydor Records. Distributed by: Polygram

Musicassette: released on DGG in Mar'85 by Polydor Records. Distributed by: Polygram

Compact disc: released on DGG in Mar'85 by Polydor Records. Distributed by: Polygram

L'Apocalypse des animaux.
Double musicassette: released on Polydor in Aug'82 by Polydor Records. Distributed by: Polygram, Polydor

Album: released on Polydor in Apr'84 by Polydor Records. Distributed by: Polygram, Polydor

Musicassette: released on Polydor in Apr'84 by Polydor Records. Distributed by: Polygram, Polydor

Magic moments.
Album: released on RCA in Jun'84 by RCA Records. Distributed by: RCA, Roots, Swift, Wellard, Chris, I & B, Solomon & Peres Distribution

Mask.
Tracks: / Movement 1 / Movement 2 / Movement 3 / Movement 4 / Movement 5 / Movement 6.
Compact disc: released on Polydor in Apr'85 by Polydor Records. Distributed by: Polygram, Polydor

Album: released on Polydor in Apr'85 by Polydor Records. Distributed by: Polygram, Polydor

Musicassette: released on Polydor in Apr'85 by Polydor Records. Distributed by: Polygram, Polydor

Compact disc: released on Polydor in Apr'85 by Polydor Records. Distributed by: Polygram, Polydor

Opera Sauvage.
Album: released on Polydor in Nov'84 by Polydor Records. Distributed by: Polygram, Polydor

Musicassette: released on Polydor in Nov'84 by Polydor Records. Distributed by: Polygram, Polydor

Opera sauvage.
Tracks: / Hymne / Reve / L'enfant / Mouettes / Chromatique / Irlande / Flamants roses.
Compact disc: released on Polydor in '87 by Polydor Records. Distributed by: Polygram, Polydor

Savage beast, The.
Album: released on RCA (Germany) Import in '83

Soil festivities.
Tracks: / Movement 1 / Movement 2 / Movement 3 / Movement 4 / Movement 5.
Album: released on Polydor in Sep'84 by Polydor Records. Distributed by: Polygram, Polydor

Musicassette: released on Polydor in Sep'84 by Polydor Records. Distributed by: Polygram, Polydor

Compact disc: released on Polydor in Sep'84 by Polydor Records. Distributed by: Polygram, Polydor

Album: released on Polydor in Jun'87 by Polydor Records. Distributed by: Polygram, Polydor

---

Musicassette: released on Polydor in Jun'87 by Polydor Records. Distributed by: Polygram, Polydor

Spiral.
Album: released on RCA in Nov'84 by RCA Records. Distributed by: RCA, Roots, Swift, Wellard, Chris, I & B, Solomon & Peres Distribution

Musicassette: released on RCA in Nov'84 by RCA Records. Distributed by: RCA, Roots, Swift, Wellard, Chris, I & B, Solomon & Peres Distribution

To the unknown man Vols 1 & 2.
Double Album: released on RCA in Nov'82 by RCA Records. Distributed by: RCA, Roots, Swift, Wellard, Chris, I & B, Solomon & Peres Distribution

Double musicassette: released on RCA in Nov'82 by RCA Records. Distributed by: RCA, Roots, Swift, Wellard, Chris, I & B, Solomon & Peres Distribution

Van Halen

1984.
Tracks: / 1984 / Jump / Panama / Top Jimmy / Drop dead / Legs / Hot for teacher / I'll wait / Girl gone bad / House of pain.
Album: released on Warner Bros. in Jan'84 by Warner Bros Records. Distributed by: WEA

Musicassette: released on Warner Bros. in Jan'84 by Warner Bros Records. Distributed by: WEA

Compact disc: released on Warner Bros. in Jan'84 by Warner Bros Records. Distributed by: WEA

5150.
Tracks: / Good enough / Why can't this be love / Get up / Dreams / Summer nights / Best of both worlds / Love walks in / "5150" / Inside.
Album: released on Warner Bros. in Apr'86 by Warner Bros Records. Distributed by: WEA

Musicassette: released on Warner Bros. in Apr'86 by Warner Bros Records. Distributed by: WEA

Compact disc: released on Warner Bros. in Apr'86 by Warner Bros Records. Distributed by: WEA

Dance the night away.
Single (7"): released on Warner Bros. in May'79 by Warner Bros Records. Distributed by: WEA

Dancing in the street.
Single (7"): released on Warner Bros. in May'82 by Warner Bros Records. Distributed by: WEA

Diver down.
Tracks: / Where have all the good times gone / Hang 'em high / Cathedral / Secrets / Intruder / Oh pretty woman / Dancing in the street / Little guitar (intro) / Little guitars / Big bad Bill is sweet William now / Bull bug, The / Happy trails.
Compact disc: released on Warner Brothers in Jan'84 by WEA Records. Distributed by: WEA

Album: released on Warner Brothers in Apr'82 by WEA Records. Distributed by: WEA

Musicassette: released on Warner Brothers in Apr'82 by WEA Records. Distributed by: WEA

Dreams.
Tracks: / Dreams / Inside.
Single (7"): released on Warner Bros. in Jun'86 by Warner Bros Records. Distributed by: WEA

Single (12"): released on Warner Bros. in Jun'86 by Warner Bros Records. Distributed by: WEA

Fair warning.
Album: released on Warner Brothers in May'81 by WEA Records. Distributed by: WEA

Musicassette: released on Warner Brothers in May'81 by WEA Records. Distributed by: WEA

Hot for teacher.
Single (7"): released on Warner Brothers in Jun'85 by WEA Records. Distributed by: WEA

Single (12"): released on Warner Brothers in Jun'85 by WEA Records. Distributed by: WEA

I'll wait.
Single (7"): released on Warner Brothers in Jul'84 by WEA Records. Distributed by: WEA

Jump.
Single (7"): released on Warner Brothers in Jan'84 by WEA Records. Distributed by: WEA

Single (12"): released on Warner Brothers in Jan'84 by WEA Records. Distributed by: WEA

Live without a net (video).
Video-cassette (VHS): released on WEA in May'87 by WEA Records. Distributed by: WEA

Pretty woman.
Single (7"): released on Warner Brothers in Feb'85 by WEA Records. Distributed by: WEA

Runnin' with the devil.
Single (7"): released on Warner Bros. in Jul'80 by Warner Bros Records. Distributed by: WEA

Van Halen.
Tracks: / You really got me / Jamie's cryin' / On fire / Runnin' with the Devil / I'm the one / Ain't talkin' bout love / Little dreamer / Feel your love tonight / Atomic Punk / Eruption / Ice cream man.
Compact disc: released on Warner Bros. in Jul'86 by Warner Bros Records. Distributed by: WEA

Album: released on Warner Brothers in May'78 by WEA Records. Distributed by: WEA

Musicassette: released on Warner Brothers in May'78 by WEA Records. Distributed by: WEA

Album: released on Warner Brothers in Apr'79 by WEA Records. Distributed by: WEA

Van Halen I.
Musicassette: released on Warner Brothers in Oct'82 by WEA Records. Distributed by: WEA

Van Halen II.
Compact disc: released on Warner Brothers in Mar'87 by Warner Bros Records. Distributed by: WEA

W 5150.

W 5150C.

Why can't this be love.
Tracks: / Why can't this be love / Get up.
Single (7"): released on Warner Bros. in Mar'86 by Warner Bros Records. Distributed by: WEA

Single (12"): released on Warner Bros. in Mar'86 by Warner Bros Records. Distributed by: WEA

Women & children first.
Album: released on Warner Brothers in Feb'80 by WEA Records. Distributed by: WEA

Musicassette: released on Warner Brothers in Apr'80 by WEA Records. Distributed by: WEA

Van Hove, Fred
Kkwit.
Tracks: / Kkwit: 1re partie / 2e partie / 3e partie (Marche finale).
Album: released on Nato (France) in Sep'86 by Disques Nato. Distributed by: Essex Record Distributors Ltd.

Vanilla Fudge
Mystery.
Album: released on Atco in Jul'84 by Atlantic Records. Distributed by: WEA Deleted '87.

Musicassette: released on Atco in Jul'84 by Atlantic Records. Distributed by: WEA

Vanishing Indians
Vanishing Indians - The Mayans of Guatemala and Belize.
Album: released on Lyrichord (Import) in May'83

Vanishing Point
Vanishing point Soundtrack (Soundtrack).
Album: released on London in Jun'71 by London Records. Distributed by: Polygram

Vanishing Sounds
Vanishing sounds of Britain Sound compilation (Vanishing Sounds of Britain).
Album: released on BBC in Oct'76 by BBC Records & Tapes. Distributed by: EMI, PRT, Pye

Musicassette: released on BBC in Oct'76 by BBC Records & Tapes. Distributed by: EMI, PRT, Pye

---

Vanity
Mechanical emotion.
Single (7"): released on Motown in Jan'85 RCA Records. Distributed by: RCA Distributi

Single (12"): released on Motown in Jan'85 RCA Records. Distributed by: RCA Distributi

Pretty mess.
Single (7"): released on Motown in Sep'84 RCA Records. Distributed by: RCA Distribut

Single (12"): released on Motown in Sep'84 RCA Records. Distributed by: RCA Distribut

Skin on skin.
Tracks: / Under the influence / Manhunt / H mantic voyage / Confidential / Animals / Skin / Gun shy / Ouch / In the jungle.
Album: released on Motown in Jun'86 by town Records. Distributed by: BMG Distribution

Musicassette: released on Motown in Jun by Motown Records. Distributed by: BMG tribution

Under the influence.
Tracks: / Under the influence / Wild animal.
Single (7"): released on Motown in Apr'86 Motown Records. Distributed by: BMG Distribution

Single (12"): released on Motown in Apr'86 Motown Records. Distributed by: BMG Distribution

Wild animal.
Album: released on Motown in Oct'84 by I Records. Distributed by: RCA Distribution

Musicassette: released on Motown in O by RCA Records. Distributed by: RCA Dist

Vanity 6
He's so dull / Make up / Wet dream.
Single (7"): released on Warner Brothe Apr'83 by WEA Records. Distributed by: W

Single (12"): released on Warner Brothe Apr'83 by WEA Records. Distributed by: W

Vanity 6.
Album: released on Warner Brothers in A by WEA Records. Distributed by: WEA

Vanity Fair
Vanity Fair A portrait of Becky Sh Thackeray (Thackeray).
Musicassette: released on Caedmon(US Oct'81 by Caedmon (USA) Records. Distrib by: Gower, Taylors, Discovery

Vanity Fare
Dreamer.
Tracks: / Dreamer / Win or loose.
Single (7"): released on Polydor in Apr' Polydor Records. Distributed by: Polygram Polydor

Hitchin' a ride / Early in the morni
Single (7"): released on Old Gold (Reiss Jul'82

Vannelli, Gino
Black cars.
Album: released on Polydor (Disques De in Apr'85 by Polydor Records. Distribut Polygram

Musicassette: released on Polydor (D Dreyfus) in Apr'85 by Polydor Record tributed by: Polygram

Brother to brother.
Album: released on A&M in '78 by A& ords. Distributed by: Polygram

Living inside myself / Stay with m
Single (7"): released on Arista in Apr'8 ta Records. Distributed by: RCA

Nightwalker.
Album: released on Arista in Apr'81 by Records. Distributed by: RCA

Pauper in paradise.
Album: released on A&M in Jan'78 b Records. Distributed by: Polygram

Powerful people.
Album: released on A&M in '79 by A& rds. Distributed by: Polygram

---

an Ronk, Dave

nday Street.
um: released on Philo in May'79. Dis-
...ted by: Roots

ur basic Dave Van Ronk.
... released on Sonet in Mar'87 by Sonet
...ords. Distributed by: PRT

n't Hof, Jasper

...pill.
...le (12"): released on WEA in Jan'85 by
...A Records. Distributed by: WEA

nwarmer, Randy

...ging on to heaven.
...le (7"): released on Avatar in Dec'81 by
...ar Communications. Distributed by: CBS

...when I needed you most.
...le (7"): released on Island in Jul'81 by Is-
...Records. Distributed by: Polygram

...found a weapon / I guess it never
...s to hurt.....
...(7"): released on Avatar in Feb'82 by
...r Communications. Distributed by: CBS

...lrov, Anatoly

...cations (Vapirov, Anatoly Quintet).
...: released on Leo in Sep'84. Distributed
...ecommended

...enced to silence (see also Sergey
...khin) (Vapirov, Anatoly & Sergey Ku-
...in).
...: released on Leo Records in Sep'84 by
...cords. Distributed by: Impetus, Leo Rec-

...ors

...ets.
...: released on Liberty in Mar'81 by Lib-
...nited. Distributed by: EMI

...assette: released on Liberty in Mar'81 by
...-United. Distributed by: EMI

...hare, The.
...'): released on Liberty in Feb'81 by
...United. Distributed by: EMI Deleted

...g Japenese.
...'): released on Liberty in Jan'80 by
...United. Distributed by: EMI

...s

...P.H..
...: released on Razor in Dec'86 by Razor.
...ed by: Pinnacle

...'ll ever need.
...7"): released on Logo in May'81 by
...Records. Distributed by: Roots, BMG

... King.
...'): released on Castle Communica-
...pr'80 by Castle Communications. Dis-
...y: Cartel, Pinnacle, Counterpoint

...here, The.
...: released on Razor in Jul'83 by Razor
...Distributed by: IDS

...dls.
**...released on Logo in Mar'82 by RCA
...cords. Distributed by: RCA

...sette: released on Logo in Mar'82 by
...Records. Distributed by: RCA

...g in the need.
...): released on Big Beat in Jan'85 by
...rds. Distributed by: Projection, Pin-

..."): released on Big Beat in Jan'85 by
...rds. Distributed by: Projection, Pin-

...th you / Gary Glitter part one.
..."): released on Logo in Feb'82 by
...rds. Distributed by: RCA

**...Don't mess with the best / Radio rock-
...how to shoot straight / All the world's
...nna be a guitar hero (just for you) /
...any (the contract) / I must be mad /
...d / Radio-active / Running.**

Album: released on Raw Power in Sep'86. Distributed by: Pinnacle

Musicassette: released on Raw Power in
Sep'86. Distributed by: Pinnacle

World's Insane, The.
Album: released on Logo in Apr'81 by RCA
Records. Distributed by: RCA

Musicassette: released on Logo in Apr'81 by
RCA Records. Distributed by: RCA

Vards, Miljo Verket

Now's the "frippe" time.
Album: released on Dragon in Jun'86 by Dragon Records. Distributed by: Jazz Music, Projection, Cadillac

Various Artists

Acclaim! Great classical performers.
Album: released on Hallmark in Oct'87 by Pickwick Records. Distributed by: Pickwick Distribution, PRT, Taylors

Musicassette: released on Hallmark in Oct'87
by Pickwick Records. Distributed by: Pickwick
Distribution, PRT, Taylors

Blues Volume 2, The.
Album: released on Chess in Oct'87 by Charly
Records. Distributed by: Charly, Swift, PRT,
Discovery, IMS, Polygram

Musicassette: released on Chess in Oct'87 by
Charly Records. Distributed by: Charly, Swift,
PRT, Discovery, IMS, Polygram

Do It like you feel It Jazz Dance 2.
Notes: Including Bunky Green and Buck Clark.
Album: released on Chess in Oct'87 by Charly
Records. Distributed by: Charly, Swift, PRT,
Discovery, IMS, Polygram

Musicassette: released on Chess in Oct'87 by
Charly Records. Distributed by: Charly, Swift,
PRT, Discovery, IMS, Polygram

Rock 'n' roll cannibals.
Tracks: / Rock 'n' roll cannibals / Jungle hop /
Come on / Uncle Tom got caught / School bus
love affair / Nancy / Cutie / My little girl / Boo be
ah be / Down on the farm / Oh babel / Wail man
wail / Nothing but tough / Ooh yeah baby / She
got eyes / Shadow street / Hello Mr Dee-Jay /
Make her love me.
Album: released on Bear Family in Sep'87 by
Bear Family Records. Distributed by: Roller-
coaster Distribution, Swift. Estim retail price in
Aug'87 was £8.99.

**Sealed with a kiss-million sellers of the
swinging sixties.**
Album: released on Hallmark in Oct'87 by Pickwick Records. Distributed by: Pickwick Distribution, PRT, Taylors

Musicassette: released on Hallmark in Oct'87
by Pickwick Records. Distributed by: Pickwick
Distribution, PRT, Taylors

Speed kills III.
Notes: Including Agent Steel, Bathory and Pos-
sessed.
Album: released on Under One Flag in Oct'87.
Distributed by: Pinnacle. Estim retail price in
Sep'87 was £4.09.

Musicassette: released on Under One Flag in
Oct'87. Distributed by: Pinnacle. Estim retail
price in Sep'87 was £4.09.

Speed metal hell, Vol.3.
Notes: New Renaissance sampler featuring
tracks from: Papsmear, Wehrmacht, Necropolis, Dream Death, Regurgitation, Necrophagia, Blood Feast, Metal Onslaught, Prong, The
Kill and Outrage.
Album: released on New Renaissance (USA)
in Aug'87

Thrash metal attack.
Notes: New Renaissance bands' compilation
featuring: Anvil Bitch, Ripping Corpse, Post Mortem, Necrophagia, Blood Feast, Necropolis,
Aggression, Hellwitch, Des Exult, Wehrmach
and Wargod.
Album: released on New Renaissance (USA)
in Aug'87

Truelove.
Album: released on K-Tel in Oct'87 by K-Tel
Records. Distributed by: Record Merchandisers
Distribution, Taylors, Terry Blood Distribution,
Wynd-Up Distribution, Relay Distribution, Pick-
wick Distribution, Solomon & Peres Distribution,
Polygram

Musicassette: released on K-Tel in Oct'87 by
K-Tel Records. Distributed by: Record Merc-
handisers Distribution, Taylors, Terry Blood
Distribution, Wynd-Up Distribution, Relay Dis-
tribution, Pickwick Distribution, Solomon &
Peres Distribution, Polygram

Compact disc: released on K-Tel in Aug'87 by
K-Tel Records. Distributed by: Record Merchandisers Distribution, Taylors, Terry Blood
Distribution, Wynd-Up Distribution, Relay Distribution, Pickwick Distribution, Solomon &
Peres Distribution, Polygram. Estim retail price
in Sep'87 was £6.99.

Ultimate history of the punk universe.
Notes: Including The Damned, X Ray Spex and
the Adverts.
Boxed set: released on MBC in Oct'87. Distributed by: Pinnacle

Various Traditions

Various traditions Various folk artists
(Various Artists).
Musicassette: released on Tradition in Aug'76.
Distributed by: JSU, Cassion Distribution, Cel-
tic Music, Jazz Music, Projection, Roots Rec-
ords

Varner, Don

Sensitive mind / Lovin' time (Varner,
Don & General Assembly).
Single (7"): released on Neil Rushden (Import)
in Mar'83

Varney, Reg

Variety of Varney.
Tracks: / Vienna time medley / Abi my boy /
Night and day / Mistakes / Rag medley / Smoke
gets in your eyes / Waltz medley / Jingling rag /
Jeane / Rose in a garden of weeds / Cornish
rhapsody / Anniversary.
Album: released on PRT Flashback in Jul'86

Musicassette: released on PRT Flashback in
Jul'86

Vartan, Sylvie

20 years of hits Vol 2.
Album: released on RCA (France) in Oct'85 by
RCA Records. Distributed by: Discovery

Musicassette: released on RCA (France) in
Oct'85 by RCA Records. Distributed by: Discovery

20 years of hits Vol 1.
Album: released on RCA (France) in Oct'85 by
RCA Records. Distributed by: Discovery

Musicassette: released on RCA (France) in
Oct'85 by RCA Records. Distributed by: Discovery

At the Palais du Congres.
Double Album: released on RCA (France) in
Feb'84 by RCA Records. Distributed by: Dis-
covery

Double musicassette: released on RCA
(France) in Feb'84 by RCA Records. Distributed
by: Discovery

Golden album.
Album: released on RCA (France) in Feb'85 by
RCA Records. Distributed by: Discovery

Musicassette: released on RCA (France) in
Feb'85 by RCA Records. Distributed by: Discovery

Varukers

Another religion another war.
Album: released on Riot City in Jun'84 by Riot
City Records. Distributed by: Revolver

Blood suckers.
Album: released on Riot City in Oct'83 by Riot
City Records. Distributed by: Revolver

Led to the slaughter (3 track EP).
Single (7"): released on Riot City in Jan'84 by
Riot City Records. Distributed by: Revolver

Massacred millions.
Single (12"): released on Red Rhino in Nov'84
by Red Rhino Records. Distributed by: Red
Rhino, Cartel

One struggle, one fight.
Album: released on Lib in Mar'86

Prepare for the attack.
Album: released on Attack in Nov'86 by Trojan
Records. Distributed by: Trojan, Pinnacle, Red
Rhino

Vasconcelos, Nana

Bush dance.
Tracks: / Mamae cade baleia / Bush dance /
Xingo xango / Paleto / Eyes and smiles / Cal-
maria / Aguela do milton / Estrella brilhante /
Futebol.
Notes: Featuring Nana Vasconcelos, Arto Lind-
say, Peter Scherer, Clive Stevens, Mario Tole-
do.
Musicassette: released on Antilles in Mar'87
by Island Records. Distributed by: Polygram

Compact disc: released on Antilles in Mar'87
by Island Records. Distributed by: Polygram

Album: released on Antilles in Jun'87 by Island
Records. Distributed by: Polygram

Album: released on Antilles in Mar'87 by Island
Records. Distributed by: Polygram

Duas vozes

Vasey, Al

**George Kelly & Al Vasey / Fessors Ses-
sion Boys**

Vatten

Dreamer, The / Rely back.
Single (7"): released on Gutta in Jun'81

Plain water.
Album: released on Gutta (Sweden) in May'81.
Distributed by: Plankton Distribution

Smelt vatten.
Album: released on Gutta (Sweden) in May'81.
Distributed by: Plankton Distribution

Vattendrag.
Album: released on Gutta in Mar'84

Vaudeville Blues

Vaudeville blues Various artists (Various
Artists).
Album: released on VJM in Apr'78 by VJM (UK)
Records. Distributed by: Swift

Vaughan, Billy

Christmas songs.
Album: released on Audio Fidelity in Oct'84.
Distributed by: PRT

Musicassette: released on Audio Fidelity in
Oct'84. Distributed by: PRT

Day and night (Vaughan, Billy Orchestra).
Double musicassette: released on Cambra in
'83 by Cambra Records. Distributed by: IDS,
Conifer

Moonlight serenade (Vaughan, Billy Orchestra).
Album: released on Lotus in Mar'79

Musicassette: released on Lotus in Mar'79

Vaughan, Dale

How can you be mean to me.
Single (7"): released on Record Mart in Apr'78
by Record Mart Records. Distributed by: Tonal
Distribution, Record Mart

Vaughan, Frankie

Dreamers.
Single (7"): released on PRT in May'84 by PRT
Records. Distributed by: PRT

Garden of Eden / Green door.
Single (7"): released on Old Gold (Reissue) in
Aug'82

Greatest hits: Frankie Vaughan.
Album: released on Spot in Oct'83 by Pickwick
Records. Distributed by: H.R. Taylor, Lugtons

Musicassette: released on Spot in Oct'83 by
Pickwick Records. Distributed by: H.R. Taylor,
Lugtons

Love hits & high kicks.
Double Album: released on Creole in Oct'85
by Creole Records. Distributed by: Rhino, PRT

Musicassette: released on Creole in Oct'85 by
Creole Records. Distributed by: Rhino, PRT

Many moods of....
Album: released on Spindrift in Apr'86. Distributed by: Roots

Moonlight & love songs.
Album: released on SRT in Nov'79 by SRT Records. Distributed by: Pinnacle, Solomon & Peres Distribution, SRT Distribution, H.R. Taylor Distribution, PRT Distribution

Mr Moonlight.
Double Album: released on Music for Pleasure in Jul'83 by EMI Records. Distributed by: MFP Distribution

Double musicassette: released on Music for Pleasure in Jul'83 by EMI Records. Distributed by: MFP Distribution

Music maestro please.
Tracks: / One / Mr. Sandman / You're nobody / I'll never smile again / Music Maestro please / Sonny boy / Hava Nagila / Feelings / Red sails in the sunset / Ragtime piano Joe / With these hands / Who's sorry now.
Album: released on PRT Flashback in Jul'86

Musicassette: released on PRT Flashback in Jul'86

Showmanship.
Single (7"): released on TER in Nov'83

Think beautiful things / Simple kiss.
Single (7"): released on SRT in Dec'79 by SRT Records. Distributed by: Pinnacle, Solomon & Peres Distribution, SRT Distribution, H.R. Taylor Distribution, PRT Distribution

Time after time.
Tracks: / There must be a way / I can't begin to tell you / Call me irresponsible / I don't know why (i just do) / That old feeling / There I've said me again / Games that lovers play / My sweetie went away / My son, my son / You're nobody 'till somebody loves you / So tired / Maybe you'll be there / Serenata / If I had a dozen hearts / Time after time / One i love belongs to somebody else, The / I'll never smile again / Mame / Red roses for a blue lady / Nevertheless (i'm in love with you) / If i had my way / More i see you, The.
Musicassette: released on Hour Of Pleasure in '86 by Music For Pleasure Records. Distributed by: EMI

Tower of strength / Wanderin' eyes.
Single (7"): released on Old Gold (Reissue) in Aug'82

When your old wedding ring was new.
Tracks: / When your old wedding ring was new / Lucky.
Single (7"): released on Spartan in 30 May'87 by Spartan Records. Distributed by: Spartan

Vaughan, Malcolm

Very best of Malcolm Vaughan - 16 favourites of the 50's,The.
Album: released on Music for Pleasure in Feb'84 by EMI Records. Distributed by: MFP Distribution

Musicassette: released on Music for Pleasure in Feb'84 by EMI Records. Distributed by: MFP Distribution

Vaughan, Sarah

Best of, The Walkman jazz series.
Musicassette: released on Verve in May'87 by Phonogram Records. Distributed by: Polygram

Broken hearted melody.
Single (7"): released on Old Gold in Jan'85 by Old Gold Records. Distributed by: Lightning, Jazz Music, Spartan, Counterpoint

Compact jazz.
Tracks: / Lullaby of birdland / Summertime / Embraceable you.
Compact disc: released on Phonogram in Jul'87 by Phonogram Records. Distributed by: Polygram

Musicassette: released on Phonogram in Jul'87 by Phonogram Records. Distributed by: Polygram

Copacabana.
Album: released on Pablo in '82 by Pablo Records. Distributed by: Wellard, Chris, IMS-Polygram, BMG

Musicassette: released on Pablo in '82 by Pablo Records. Distributed by: Wellard, Chris, IMS-Polygram, BMG

Crazy and mixed up.
Tracks: / I didn't know what time it was / That's all / Autumn leaves / Love dance / Island, The / In love in vain / Seasons / You are too beautiful.
Compact disc: released on Pablo (USA) in Jul'86 by Pablo Records (USA). Distributed by: Wellard, Chris, IMS-Polygram, BMG

Divine one (The).
Tracks: / Have you met Miss Jones / Ain't no use / Evert time I see you / You stepped out of a dream / Gloomy Sunday / What do you see in her / Jump for joy / When your lover has gone / I'm gonna laugh you out of my life / Wrap your troubles in dreams / Somebody else's dream / Trouble is a man.
Compact disc: released on Vogue in Dec'86. Distributed by: Discovery, Jazz Music, PRT, Swift

Dizzy Gillespie/Sarah Vaughan/Charlie Parker

Duke Ellington song book, 2.
Album: released on Pablo in '82 by Pablo Records. Distributed by: Wellard, Chris, IMS-Polygram, BMG

Musicassette: released on Pablo in '82 by Pablo Records. Distributed by: Wellard, Chris, IMS-Polygram, BMG

Duke Ellington song book, 1.
Album: released on Pablo in '82 by Pablo Records. Distributed by: Wellard, Chris, IMS-Polygram, BMG

Musicassette: released on Pablo in '82 by Pablo Records. Distributed by: Wellard, Chris, IMS-Polygram, BMG

Foggy Day, (A).
Album: released on Astan in Nov'84 by Astan Records. Distributed by: Counterpoint

Musicassette: released on Astan in Nov'84 by Astan Records. Distributed by: Counterpoint

Gershwin live (Vaughan, Sarah & Michael Tilson Thomas).
Album: released on CBS in Sep'82 by CBS Records. Distributed by: CBS

Musicassette: released on CBS in Sep'82 by CBS Records. Distributed by: CBS

Golden hits: Sarah Vaughan.
Album: released on Mercury (Import) in Apr'83

Musicassette: released on Mercury (Import) in Apr'83

How long has this been going on.
Tracks: / I got the world on a string / Midnight sun / How long has this been going on? / You're blase / Easy living / More than you know / My old flame / Teach me tonight / Body and soul / When your lover has gone.
Compact disc: released on Pablo (USA) in Jul'86 by Pablo Records (USA). Distributed by: Wellard, Chris, IMS-Polygram, BMG

How long has this been going on?.
Album: released on Pablo in '82 by Pablo Records. Distributed by: Wellard, Chris, IMS-Polygram, BMG

Musicassette: released on Pablo in '82 by Pablo Records. Distributed by: Wellard, Chris, IMS-Polygram, BMG

In the land of hi-fi.
Compact disc: released on Philips in Jul'87. Distributed by: IMS-Polygram

Irving Berlin songbook (Vaughan, Sarah & Billy Eckstein).
Tracks: / Alexander's ragtime band / Isn't this a lovely day / I've got my love to keep me warm / All of my life / Cheek to cheek / You're just in love / Remember / Always / Always / Easter parade / Girl that i marry / Now it can be told / Thanks for the memory / Start believing me now / My funny valentine / Foggy day, A / Send in the clowns / Like someone in love / Detour ahead / Three little words / You may not be an angel / If you could see me now.
Compact disc: released on Emarcy(USA) in Apr'85 by Emarcy Records(USA). Distributed by: Polygram

Album: released on Topline in '86 by Charly Records. Distributed by: Charly Distribution

Musicassette: released on Topline in '86 by Charly Records. Distributed by: Charly Distribution

Irving Berlin songbook, (The) (Vaughan, Sarah & Billy Eckstein).
Album: released on Emarcy(Holland) in Feb'85. Distributed by: IMS, Polygram

Musicassette: released on Emarcy(Holland) in Feb'85. Distributed by: IMS, Polygram

Compact disc: released on Emarcy(Holland) in Feb'85. Distributed by: IMS, Polygram

Like someone in love.
Tracks: / Detour ahead / Three little words / I'll string along with you (You may not be an angel) / If you could see me now / Thanks for the memory / Start believing me now / My funny valentine / Foggy day, A / Send in the clowns / Like someone in love.
Notes: Licensed from Charly Records APS. This CD (P) 1987 Charly Holdings inc. (C) Charly Records Ltd.
Compact disc: released on Topline in May'87 by Charly Records. Distributed by: Charly Distribution

Lullaby of Birdland.
Album: released on Mercury (USA) in Dec'83 by Import Records. Distributed by: IMS Distribution, Polygram Distribution

Man I love, (The).
Album: released on Musicraft (USA) in Jan'84 by Discovery Records (USA). Distributed by: Flexitron Distributors Ltd, Swift Distribution

No count Sarah.
Tracks: / Smoke gets in your eyes / Doodlin' / Darn that dream / Just one of those things / Moonlight in Vermont / No 'count blues / Cheek to cheek / Stardust / Missing you.
Notes: Personnel: Sarah Vaughan- vocals/Wendell Culley, Thad Jones, Snooky Young, Joe Newman- trumpets/Henry Coker, Al grey, Benny Powell- trombones/Frank Wess, Frank Foster, Billy Mitchell, Charlie Fowlkes, Marchall Royal- reeds/Freddie Green- guitar/Ronnell Bright- piano/Richard Davis- bass/Sonny Payne- drums. Recorded in New York.
Compact disc: released on Emarcy(USA) in May'86 by Emarcy Records(USA). Distributed by: Polygram

O, some Brasileiro de.
Album: released on RCA (Brazil) in Jan'84

Musicassette: released on RCA (Brazil) in Jan'84

Passing strangers (Vaughan, Sarah & Billy Eckstein).
Album: released on Mercury in Jul'84 by Phonogram Records. Distributed by: Polygram Distribution

Musicassette: released on Mercury in Jul'84 by Phonogram Records. Distributed by: Polygram Distribution

Single (7"): released on Old Gold in Jan'85 by Old Gold Records. Distributed by: Lightning, Jazz Music, Spartan, Counterpoint

Single (7"): released on Mercury (Classic Cuts) in Oct'80

Double Album: released on Mercury in '78 by Phonogram Records. Distributed by: Polygram Distribution

Double musicassette: released on Mercury in '78 by Phonogram Records. Distributed by: Polygram Distribution

Rodgers & Hart songbook, The.
Tracks: / My funny valentine / Little girl blue / Tree in the park, A / It's got to be love / Ship without a sail, A / Bewitched / Thou swell / It never entered my mind / It's easy to remember / Why can't I / My romance / My heart stood still.
Notes: The programme on this record has been compiled from recordings made between 1954 and 1958 and has never been issued in this format before. These recordings have been digitally remastered.
Album: released on Pablo (USA) in Dec'85 by Pablo Records (USA). Distributed by: Wellard, Chris, IMS-Polygram, BMG

Musicassette: released on Pablo (USA) in Dec'85 by Pablo Records (USA). Distributed by: Wellard, Chris, IMS-Polygram, BMG

Compact disc: released on Pablo (USA) in Dec'85 by Pablo Records (USA). Distributed by: Wellard, Chris, IMS-Polygram, BMG

Sarah Vaughan.
Tracks: / Lullaby of birdland / April in Paris / He's my guy / Jim / You're not the kind / Embraceable you / I'm glad there is you / September song / It's crazy.
Notes: Personnel: Orchestra conducted by Ernie Wilkins/H. Mann- flute/C. Brown- trumpet/P. Quiochette- tener sax/J. Benjamin- bass/J. Jones- piano/R. Haynes- drums. Recorded New York 1954.
Compact disc: released on Emarcy(USA) in May'85 by Emarcy Records(USA). Distributed by: Polygram

Musicassette: released on Audio Fidelity in Oct'84. Distributed by: PRT

Sarah Vaughan collection.
Album: released on Deja Vu in Nov'85 by Deja Vu Records. Distributed by: Counterpoint Distribution, Record Services Distribution (Ireland)

Musicassette: released on Deja Vu in Nov'85 by Deja Vu Records. Distributed by: Counterpoint Distribution, Record Services Distribution (Ireland)

Sarah Vaughan/Count Basie (Vaugha[n], Sarah & Count Basie).
Notes: With the Benny Carter Orchestra
Compact disc: released on Vogue in Dec'[...] Distributed by: Discovery, Jazz Music, P[...] Swift

Sarah Vaughan, Vol 1.
Album: released on Jazz Reactivation [...] Jan'82. Distributed by: PRT

Sarah Vaughan, Vol 2.
Album: released on Pye in May'79

Musicassette: released on Pye in May'79

Album: released on Jazz Reactivatior[...] May'83. Distributed by: PRT

Sassy swings again.
Tracks: / Sweet Georgia Brown / Take the [...] train / I left my heart in San Francisco / S'p[...] / Everyday / I have the blues / I want to be ha[...] / All alone / Sweetest sounds / On the other [...] of the tracks / I had a ball.
Compact disc: released on Verve (USA[...] Sep'84 by Polydor. Distributed by: Polygra[...]

Send in the clowns (Vaughan, Sara[h &] Count Basie).
Album: released on Pablo in '82 by Pablo [Rec]ords. Distributed by: Wellard, Chris, IMS-[Poly]gram, BMG

Musicassette: released on Pablo in '8[...] Pablo Records. Distributed by: Wellard, C[...] IMS-Polygram, BMG

Songbook 2 (Vaughan, Sarah & D[uke] Ellington).
Album: released on Pablo in '81 by Pablo [Rec]ords. Distributed by: Wellard, Chris, IMS-[Poly]gram, BMG

Musicassette: released on Pablo in '8[...] Pablo Records. Distributed by: Wellard, C[...] IMS-Polygram, BMG

Sounds of Sarah Vaughan.
Musicassette: released on Vogue Ja[...] May'83

Spotlight on Sarah Vaughan.
Album: released on PRT in Oct'84 by PRT [Rec]ords. Distributed by: PRT

Musicassette: released on PRT in Oct'[...] PRT Records. Distributed by: PRT

Summertime.
Album: released on CBS(I love Jazz) in A[...] by CBS Records. Distributed by: CBS

Musicassette: released on CBS(I love Ja[...] Aug'84 by CBS Records. Distributed by: [...]

Tenderly.
Album: released on Bulldog Records in [...]

Album: released on Astan in Nov'84 by [...] Records. Distributed by: Counterpoint

Musicassette: released on Astan in No[...] Astan Records. Distributed by: Counterp[...]

Time after time (Vaughan, Sa[rah &] Teddy Wilson).
Album: released on Musicraft(Imp[...] Aug'83

Time in my life, A.
Compact disc: released on Mobile F[...] Oct'86 by Mobile Fidelity Records

Vaughan and violins.
Tracks: / Gone with the wind / Day b[...] Please be kind / Live for love / I'll close m[...] / Misty / Midnight sun will never set, The[...] all / I'm lost / Love me / Thrill is gone, T[...]
Notes: Also featuring Quincy Jones Orc[...]
Album: released on Memoir in Dec'85 b[...] oir Records. Distributed by: PRT Distrib[...]

Musicassette: released on Memoir in [...] by Memoir Records. Distributed by: P[...] tribution

Couldn't stand the weather.
Album: released on Epic in Jun'84 by C[...] ords. Distributed by: CBS

Musicassette: released on Epic in J[...] CBS Records. Distributed by: CBS

alive.
: / Say what! / Ain't gone 'n' give up on / Pride and joy / Mary had a little lamb / erstition / I'm leaving you (commit a crime) d shot / Willie the wimp / Look at little sis- Texas flood / Voodoo chile (slight return) / struck baby / Change it / Life without love.
m: released on Epic in Jan'87 by CBS Rec-
Distributed by: CBS

cassette: released on Epic in Jan'87 by Records. Distributed by: CBS

pect disc: released on Epic in May'87 by Records. Distributed by: CBS

to soul.
s: / Say what / Lookin' out the window / little sister / Ain't gone and give up on Gone home / Change it / You'll be mine / y arms / Come on / Life without love.
pect disc: released on Epic in Apr'86 by Records. Distributed by: CBS

to soul.
a: released on Epic in Sep'85 by CBS Distributed by: CBS

assette: released on Epic in Sep'85 by Records. Distributed by: CBS

flood.
a: released on Epic in Aug'83 by CBS cords. Distributed by: CBS

cassette: released on Epic in Aug'83 by cords. Distributed by: CBS

nes, The
fix it.
: / Midnight sun.
(7"): released on Vanity in Feb'87. Dis-
by: Red Rhino, Cartel

oltch.
t silence.
(7"): released on Cathexis in Jul'85. Dis-
by: Fast Forward, Cartel

er.
ssette: released on CRV in 30 May'87
Forward Records. Distributed by: Car-

ngs your tongues.
eleased on CRV in Nov'86 by Fast For-
cords. Distributed by: Cartel

or the assassins, in memory of
Sabbath.
released on VDO in Jan'84 by VDO
Distributed by: WSNS Distribution

y.
): released on Thin Sliced in Apr'80

Charles
best.
e: released on Capitol in Nov'80 by Capi-
ds. Distributed by: EMI

m
mystery.
eleased on Powerstation Records in
Powerstation Records. Distributed

volution.
eleased on Powerstation Records in
Powerstation Records. Distributed

iceva, A
gs.
tte: released on Melodiya (USSR)
Distributed by: T.B.C Distribution

obby
n' roll hits.
on EMI (Germany) in '83 by
ds. Distributed by: Conifer

obby Vee, (The).
eased on Music for Pleasure (Hol-
'83

Musicassette: released on Music for Pleasure (Holland) in Apr'83

Album: released on Liberty in Oct'85 by Liberty-United. Distributed by: EMI

Musicassette: released on Liberty in Oct'85 by Liberty-United. Distributed by: EMI

Bobby Vee meets The Ventures.
Album: released on EMI (France) in '83 by EMI Records. Distributed by: Conifer

Bobby Vee meets The Crickets.
Album: released on EMI (France) in '83 by EMI Records. Distributed by: Conifer

Bobby Vee singles album, (The).
Album: released on Fame (Liberty) in May'82 by Music For Pleasure Records. Distributed by: EMI

Musicassette: released on Fame (Liberty) in May'82 by Music For Pleasure Records. Distributed by: EMI

Bobby Vee sings rare rock & roll tracks.
Album: released on Freedom in Jul'87 by Logo Records. Distributed by: RCA, Discovery, Wellard, Chris

Devil or angel.
Single (7"): released on Hammer in Sep'79. Distributed by: PRT

I remember Buddy Holly.
Album: released on Pathe Marconi in Jun'84. Distributed by: Swift

Night has a thousand eyes, (The).
Single (7"): released on United Artists (USA) in Sep'79 by EMI Records. Distributed by: EMI, Swift, Solomon & Peres Distribution

Rubber ball.
Single (7"): released on Creole in Aug'82 by Creole Records. Distributed by: Rhino, PRT

Run to him.
Tracks: / Run to him / More than I can say.
Single (7"): released on Old Gold in Mar'87 by Old Gold Records. Distributed by: Lightning, Jazz Music, Spartan, Counterpoint

Single (7"): released on USA Import in '80

Take good care of my baby.
Single (7"): released on United Artists (USA) in Sep'79 by EMI Records. Distributed by: EMI, Swift, Solomon & Peres Distribution

Single (7"): released on EMI Golden 45's in Jul'84 by EMI Records. Distributed by: EMI

Vee Jay Blues

Vee Jay Blues Various artists (Various Artists).
Album: released on Charly(R&B) in Jun'85 by Charly Records. Distributed by: Charly, Cadillac

Vee, Vivienne

Destiny.
Single (7"): released on Banana in Apr'84. Distributed by: Pinnacle, Fresh

Single (12"): released on Banana in Apr'84. Distributed by: Pinnacle, Fresh

Vee VV

Boom slump EP.
Single (7"): released on Vinyl Drip in Mar'86. Distributed by: Backs, Cartel

Kindest cut.
Single (7"): released on Cathexis in Jul'85. Distributed by: Fast Forward, Cartel

Vega

Mother Egypt.
Single (7"): released on Red Bus in Feb'83 by Red Bus Records. Distributed by: PRT

Nostradamus.
Single (7"): released on Red Bus in Aug'82 by Red Bus Records. Distributed by: PRT

Single (12"): released on Red Bus in Aug'82 by Red Bus Records. Distributed by: PRT

Vega, Alan

Jukebox babe.
Single (7"): released on Celluloid in Nov'81 by Island Records. Distributed by: Polygram

Single (12"): released on Celluloid in Nov'81 by Island Records. Distributed by: Polygram

Just a million dreams.
Album: released on Elektra in Nov'85 by WEA

Musicassette: released on Elektra in Nov'85 by WEA Records. Distributed by: WEA

On the run.
Single (7"): released on Elektra in Oct'85 by WEA Records. Distributed by: WEA

Single (12"): released on Elektra in Oct'85 by WEA Records. Distributed by: WEA

Vega Brothers

Into something good.
Album: released on MCA Import in Mar'86 by MCA Records. Distributed by: Polygram, IMS

Vega, Suzanne

At The Albert Hall.
Video-cassette (VHS): released on A&M in May'87 by A&M Records. Distributed by: Polygram

Gypsy.
Tracks: / Gypsy / Cracking (live) / Knight movies (live).
Single (7"): released on A&M in Oct'86 by A&M Records. Distributed by: Polygram

Single (12"): released on A&M in Oct'86 by A&M Records. Distributed by: Polygram

Left of centre.
Tracks: / Left of centre / Undertow / Left of centre (live) / Freeze tag (live) / Cracking.
Notes: Suzanne Vega, A&M's brightest new star, follows her hit 'Marlene On The Wall' with a previously unavailable new single 'Left Of Centre'. Taken from the forthcoming U.S. smash album soundtrack 'Pretty In Pink', 'Left Of Center' shows a new side to Suzanne's talents, brilliantly showcasing her new band at their strongest to date: Available on 7", special 4-track 10" and 3 track CD. The CD includes the superb 'Craking' taken from her debut album whilst the 4-track 10" includes two exclusive live tracks, 'Left Of Centre' and 'Freeze Tag'. A major campaign supports this release with full colour in store posters, press adds, and more.
Single (7"): released on A&M in May'86 by A&M Records. Distributed by: Polygram

Single 10": released on A&M in May'86 by A&M Records. Distributed by: Polygram

Compact disc single: released on A&M in May'86 by A&M Records. Distributed by: Polygram

Luka.
Tracks: / Luka / Straight lines (live version) / Neighborhood girls.
Single (7"): released on A&M in May'87 by A&M Records. Distributed by: Polygram

Single (12"): released on A&M in May'87 by A&M Records. Distributed by: Polygram

Single 10": released on A&M in May'87 by A&M Records. Distributed by: Polygram

Single (cassette): released on A&M in 23 May'87 by A&M Records. Distributed by: Polygram

Marlene on the wall.
Tracks: / Marlene on the wall / Small blue thing (live) / Neighbourhood girls / Straight lines (live).
Single (7"): released on A&M in Mar'86 by A&M Records. Distributed by: Polygram

Single 10": released on A&M in Mar'86 by A&M Records. Distributed by: Polygram

Single (12"): released on A&M in Aug'85 by A&M Records. Distributed by: Polygram

Small blue thing.
Tracks: / Small blue thing / Queen and the soldier, The / Black wido station / Some journey.
Single (7"): released on A&M in Jan'86 by A&M Records. Distributed by: Polygram

Solitude standing.
Tracks: / Tom's diner / Luka / Ironbound / Fancy poultry / In the eye / Night vision / Solitude standing / Calypso / Language / Gypsy / Wooden horse / Tom's diner.
Album: released on A&M in May'87 by A&M Records. Distributed by: Polygram

---

Musicassette: released on A&M in May'87 by A&M Records. Distributed by: Polygram

Compact disc: released on A&M in May'87 by A&M Records. Distributed by: Polygram

Suzanne Vega.
Tracks: / Cracking / Freeze tag / Marlene on the wall / Small blue thing / Straight lines / Undertow / Some journey / Queen and the soldier, The / Night movies / Neighbourhood girls.
Compact disc: released on A&M in Feb'86 by A&M Records. Distributed by: Polygram

Album: released on A&M in Jul'85 by A&M Records. Distributed by: Polygram

Musicassette: released on A&M in Jul'85 by A&M Records. Distributed by: Polygram

Tom's diner.
Tracks: / Tom's diner / Left of center / Luka (live).
Notes: The 12" and limited collectors' edition of 10", cassette and C.D. carry exclusive live versions of "Luka" and "Tom's Diner".
Single (7"): released on A&M in Jul'87 by A&M Records. Distributed by: Polygram

Single 10": released on A&M in Jul'87 by A&M Records. Distributed by: Polygram

Single (12"): released on A&M in Jul'87 by A&M Records. Distributed by: Polygram

Single (cassette): released on A&M in Jul'87 by A&M Records. Distributed by: Polygram

Compact disc single: released on A&M in Jul'87 by A&M Records. Distributed by: Polygram

Vega, Tata

Get it up for love.
Single (7"): released on Motown in Oct'81 by RCA Records. Distributed by: RCA Distribution

Single (12"): released on Motown in Oct'81 by RCA Records. Distributed by: RCA Distribution

Love your neighbour.
Single (7"): released on Motown in Oct'81 by RCA Records. Distributed by: RCA Distribution

Single (12"): released on Motown in Oct'81 by RCA Records. Distributed by: RCA Distribution

Miss Celie's blues (sister).
Tracks: / Celie shaves Mr. / Sarification ceremony.
Single (7"): released on Qwest in Jul'86 by WEA Records. Distributed by: WEA

You keep me hangin' on.
Single (7"): released on Motown in Oct'81 by RCA Records. Distributed by: RCA Distribution

Single (12"): released on Motown in Oct'81 by RCA Records. Distributed by: RCA Distribution

Veil

Heavy heart.
Tracks: / Is this sin (watching the nite world work).
Single (12"): released on Andusias International in Apr'86

Manikin.
Single (12"): released on Clay in Oct'84 by Clay Records. Distributed by: Pinnacle

Surrender.
Album: released on Clay in Mar'85 by Clay Records. Distributed by: Pinnacle

Twist.
Single (7"): released on Clay in Aug'85 by Clay Records. Distributed by: Pinnacle

Veiled lady

Veiled lady and the third floor flat, The.
Christie, Agatha (Rees, Roger).
Musicassette: released on Caedmon(USA) in Sep'85 by Caedmon (USA) Records. Distributed by: Gower, Taylors, Discovery

Veitch, Champion Doug

Jumping into love.
Single (7"): released on Making Waves in Sep'85 by Making Waves Records

Single (12"): released on Making Waves in Sep'85 by Making Waves Records

Lumiere urban.
Single (7"): released on Greensleeves in Oct'82 by Greensleeves Records. Distributed by: BMG, Jetstar, Spartan

Single (7"): released on Greensleeves in Oct'82 by Greensleeves Records. Distributed by: BMG, Jetstar, Spartan

Magarita.
Tracks: / Margarita (Mescales mix) / One black night.
Single (12"): released on Conga in Aug'86 by Conga Records. Distributed by: Revolver, Cartel

One black night.
Single (12"): released on Drum in May'85 by Drum Records. Distributed by: Cartel

Vela, Rosie

Interlude.
Tracks: / Interlude / Taxi.
Single (7"): released on A&M in Feb'87 by A&M Records. Distributed by: Polygram

Single (12"): by A&M Records. Distributed by: Polygram

Magic smile.
Tracks: / Magic smile / Second emotion.
Single (7"): released on A&M in Nov'86 by A&M Records. Distributed by: Polygram

Zazu.
Album: released on A&M in Nov'86 by A&M Records. Distributed by: Polygram

Musicassette: released on A&M in Nov'86 by A&M Records. Distributed by: Polygram

Compact disc: released on A&M in Nov'86 by A&M Records. Distributed by: Polygram

Album: released on A&M in Nov'86 by A&M Records. Distributed by: Polygram

Musicassette: released on A&M in Nov'86 by A&M Records. Distributed by: Polygram

Velez, Martha

Escape from Babylon.
Album: released on Sire in Mar'78

Velons

Moonlight & music.
Album: released on Solid Smoke (USA) in Feb'85

Velvelettes

Needle in a haystack.
Single (7"): released on Motown in Mar'83 by RCA Records. Distributed by: RCA Distribution

These things will keep me loving you.
Single (7"): released on Motown in Oct'81 by RCA Records. Distributed by: RCA Distribution

Velvet

Velvet.
Album: released on Black Lion in Oct'79 by Black Lion Records. Distributed by: Jazz Music, Chris Wellard, Taylor, H.R., Counterpoint, Cadillac

Velvette

Got to have your love.
Single (7"): released on Electricity in Jul'84 by Electricity Records. Distributed by: PRT

Nothing's worse than being alone.
Single (12"): released on Electricity in Apr'84 by Electricity Records. Distributed by: PRT

Velvet Underground

1969 with Lou Reed, live.
Album: released on Mercury (Import) in Feb'83

Andy Warhols.
Double Album: released on Polydor in '74 by Polydor Records. Distributed by: Polygram, Polydor

Another view.
Compact disc: released on Polydor (Germany) in Nov'86. Distributed by: IMS-Polygram

Album: released on Polydor in Aug'86 by Polydor Records. Distributed by: Polygram, Polydor

Musicassette: released on Polydor in Aug'86 by Polydor Records. Distributed by: Polygram, Polydor

Greatest hits: Velvet Underground.
Double Album: released on Polydor in Nov'80 by Polydor Records. Distributed by: Polygram, Polydor

Double musicassette: released on Polydor in Nov'80 by Polydor Records. Distributed by: Polygram, Polydor

Live, 1969.
Double Album: released on Mercury in Nov'84 by Phonogram Records. Distributed by: Polygram Distribution

Lou Reed & The Velvet Underground.
Album: released on Polydor in '74 by Polydor Records. Distributed by: Polygram, Polydor

Velvet Underground and Nico.
Tracks: / Sunday morning / I'm waiting for the man / Femme fatale / Venus in furs / Run run run / All tomorrows parties / Heroin / There she goes again / I'll be your mirror / Black Angels death song / European son (to Delmore Schwartz).
Compact disc: released on Polydor in '86 by Polydor Records. Distributed by: Polygram, Polydor

Album: released on Polydor in Aug'83 by Polydor Records. Distributed by: Polygram, Polydor

Musicassette: released on Polydor in Aug'83 by Polydor Records. Distributed by: Polygram, Polydor

Velvet Underground.
Tracks: / White light/white heat / What goes on / Venus in furs / That's the story of my life / Here she comes now / Beginning to see the light / Jesus / Run run run / Some kinda love / Gift, The / I'm so free / I heard her call my name.
Notes: On Sunday night millions of people watched the documentary on this legendary band on the ITV programme "The South Bank Show". Contains 5 albums: "Velvet Underground & Nico/White Light White Heat/The Velvet Underground/VU-in their original sleeves-plus "Another View", an album of ten previously unissued tracks.
Album: released on Polydor in May'86 by Polydor Records. Distributed by: Polygram, Polydor

Compact disc: released on Polydor in May'86 by Polydor Records. Distributed by: Polygram, Polydor

Velvet Underground, (The).
Album: released on MGM in Sep'83. Distributed by: Polygram Distribution, Swift Distribution

Musicassette: released on MGM in Sep'83. Distributed by: Polygram Distribution, Swift Distribution

VU.
Album: released on Polydor in Feb'85 by Polydor Records. Distributed by: Polygram, Polydor

Musicassette: released on Polydor in Feb'85 by Polydor Records. Distributed by: Polygram, Polydor

V.U..
Compact disc: by Polydor Records. Distributed by: Polygram, Polydor

Compact disc: released on Polydor in 20 Jun'87 by Polydor Records. Distributed by: Polygram, Polydor

White light, white heat.
Compact disc: by Polydor Records. Distributed by: Polygram, Polydor

Album: released on Polydor in Apr'84 by Polydor Records. Distributed by: Polygram, Polydor

Musicassette: released on Polydor in Apr'84 by Polydor Records. Distributed by: Polygram, Polydor

Velvet Waters

Velvet waters **Various artists (Various Artists).**
Album: released on Stylus in Nov'86. Distributed by: Pinnacle, Terry Blood Distribution, Stylus Distribution

Musicassette: released on Stylus in Nov'86. Distributed by: Pinnacle, Terry Blood Distribution, Stylus Distribution

Vendetta

Could have done without it.
Tracks: / Row, The / Living one day at a time.
Single (7"): released on Plaza in Aug'86 by Plaza Records. Distributed by: Spartan

Single (12"): released on Plaza in Aug'86 by Plaza Records. Distributed by: Spartan

If you want my love.
Single (7"): released on Plaza in Jun'84 by Plaza Records. Distributed by: Spartan

Single (12"): released on Plaza in Jun'84 by Plaza Records. Distributed by: Spartan

Single (7"): released on Plaza in Jun'85 by Plaza Records. Distributed by: Spartan

I've gotta see Jane.
Single (7"): released on Plaza in Apr'83 by Plaza Records. Distributed by: Spartan

I've got you in my sights.
Single (7"): released on Plaza in Jan'84 by Plaza Records. Distributed by: Spartan

Single (12"): released on Plaza in Jan'84 by Plaza Records. Distributed by: Spartan

Larsen effect, (The).
Single (7"): released on Plaza in Oct'85 by Plaza Records. Distributed by: Spartan

So do I.
Tracks: / So do I (remix 86) / One step at a time.
Single (7"): released on Plaza in Feb'86 by Plaza Records. Distributed by: Spartan

Single (7"): released on Plaza in Oct'83 by Plaza Records. Distributed by: Spartan

Somewhere in the night.
Single (7"): released on Plaza in Mar'85 by Plaza Records. Distributed by: Spartan

Single (12"): released on Plaza in Mar'85 by Plaza Records. Distributed by: Spartan

Vendino Pact

Identical twins.
Single (7"): released on Manifesto in May'82

Veneice

This good good feeling.
Tracks: / This good good feeling / Radio mix.
Single (12"): released on LGR in Nov'86. Distributed by: Jetstar

Vengeance

We have ways.
Album: released on CBS(France) in Sep'86 by CBS Records. Distributed by: Conifer, Discovery, Swift

Musicassette: released on CBS(France) in Sep'86 by CBS Records. Distributed by: Conifer, Discovery, Swift

Venice

Nobody.
Single (7"): released on Foxy in Mar'83 by Foxy. Distributed by: PRT

Venigmas

Red revenge.
Single (7"): by Graduate Records. Distributed by: Nine Mile, Cartel

Strangelove.
Single (7"): released on Biba in Feb'82 by Venigmas Records. Distributed by: Spartan

Venika

In the fun.
Single (12"): released on E.G. in Nov'85 by Virgin Records. Distributed by: Virgin, EMI

Venna

Watching you watching you.
Single (7"): released on Buddah in Apr'83. Distributed by: Swift, Jazz Music, PRT

Single (12"): released on Buddah in Apr'83. Distributed by: Swift, Jazz Music, PRT

Vennick, Dick

Free fair.
Notes: For full information see under: Van Denbroeck, R/D.Vennick/E.Ineke/H.Emmery/R.Burnet.

Free fair **With Bob Van Den Foech,Harry Emmery,Raul Burnet & Erik Ineke.**
Album: released on Timeless(import) in Apr'81. Distributed by: Cadillac

Modal soul (Venom).
Notes: For full information see under: De Graaff, Rein/Dick Vennick Quartet.

Venom

At war with satan.
Tracks: / At war with satan / Rip pride / G cide / Cry wolf / Stand up (and be count Women, leather and hell / Aaaaarrghh.
Album: released on Neat in '85 by Neat ords. Distributed by: Pinnacle, Neat

Musicassette: released on Neat in '85 by Records. Distributed by: Pinnacle, Neat

Compact disc: released on Neat in '85 by Records. Distributed by: Pinnacle, Neat

Black metal.
Tracks: / Side black / Black metal / To he back / Buried alive / Raise the dead / Tea pet / Leave me in hell / Sacrifice / Heave fire / Countess Bathory / Don't burn the w At war with satan (intro).
Album: released on Neat in '85 by Neat ords. Distributed by: Pinnacle, Neat

Compact disc: released on Neat in '85 by Records. Distributed by: Pinnacle, Neat

Blood lust.
Single (7"): released on Neat in Aug'82 by Records. Distributed by: Pinnacle, Neat

Die hard.
Single (7"): released on Neat in May'83 b Records. Distributed by: Pinnacle, Neat

Single (12"): released on Neat in May Neat Records. Distributed by: Pinnacle.

Eine kleine nachtmusik.
Double Album: released on Neat in Dec Neat Records. Distributed by: Pinnacle,

Not one of the other formats: releas Neat in Dec'86 by Neat Records. Distribu Pinnacle, Neat

From hell to the unknown.....
Tracks: / Sons of satan / Welcome to he zo / Mayhem with mercy / Poison / Live angel (die like a devil) / Witching hour days in sodom / Angel dust / In leag satan / Red light fever / Bursting out / At w satan (intro) / Die hard (live version) / M Senile decay / Black metal / Possessed gates of hell (live version) / Buried aliv loud for the crowd / Radio interview (met with Alan Robson).
Album: released on Raw Power in Apr' tributed by: Pinnacle

Musicassette: released on Raw Po Apr'86. Distributed by: Pinnacle

From hell to the unknown.
Album: released on Castle Collectors by Castle Communications Record tributed by: Pinnacle

In league with Santan.
Single (7"): released on Neat in Jan'82 Records. Distributed by: Pinnacle, Ne

Live'84'85.
Album: released on American Phono ternational in Feb'86. Distributed by: P

Live in '85.
Tracks: / Teachers pet / Witching hour
Single (12"): released on Neat in D Neat Records. Distributed by: Pinnacl

Live official bootleg.
Compact disc: released on Magnum by Bulldog Records. Distributed by: S

Manitou.
Single (7"): released on Neat in Oct'8 Records. Distributed by: Pinnacle, Ne

Single (12"): released on Neat in Neat Records. Distributed by: Pinnac

Picture disc single: released on Feb'85 by Neat Records. Distribute nacle, Neat

Single (cassette): released on Neat by Neat Records. Distributed by: Pinn

Nightmare.
Single (7"): released on Neat in Aug' Records. Distributed by: Pinnacle, N

Single (12"): released on Neat in Neat Records. Distributed by: Pinna

Musicassette: released on Neat in Neat Records. Distributed by: Pinna

Single (12"): released on Neat in Neat Records. Distributed by: Pinna

Picture disc single: released on Neat in Sep'85 by Neat Records. Distributed by: Pinnacle, Neat

Obscene miracle.
Picture disc album: released on Demon in Jul'86 by Demon Records. Distributed by: Pinnacle, Neat

Possessed.
Album: released on Neat in '85 by Neat Records. Distributed by: Pinnacle, Neat

Musicassette: released on Neat in '85 by Neat Records. Distributed by: Pinnacle, Neat
Cat.no .... NEATC 1024
Picture disc single: released on Neat in '85 by Neat Records. Distributed by: Pinnacle, Neat

Seventh date of hell.
Tracks: / Bloodlust / Don't burn the witch / Warhead / In league with satan / Live like an angel / Blood lust / In nomine satanus / Die hard / Acid Queen / Busting out / War head / Lady lust / Seven gates of hell / Manitou / Dead of the nite. Notes: One of the most over-the-top of Heavy Metal bands, live on stage at Hammersmith Odeon, and performing eleven outrageously hard-rocking tricks.
Video-cassette (VHS): released on Polygram Music in Oct'84 by Polygram Records. Distributed by: Polygram

Video-cassette [Betamax]: released on Polygram Music in Oct'84 by Polygram Records. Distributed by: Polygram

Singles 80-86.
Musicassette: released on Raw Power in Sep'86. Distributed by: Pinnacle

Compact disc: released on Raw Power in Sep'86. Distributed by: Pinnacle

Compact disc: released on Raw Power in Jun'87. Distributed by: Pinnacle

Speed revolation.
Album: released on Powerstation Records in Jul'86 by Powerstation Records. Distributed by: Pinnacle

Warhead.
Single (7"): released on Neat in Jan'84 by Neat Records. Distributed by: Pinnacle, Neat

Single (12"): released on Neat in Jan'84 by Neat Records. Distributed by: Pinnacle, Neat

Wellcome to hell.
Album: released on Neat in '85 by Neat Records. Distributed by: Pinnacle, Neat

Picture disc album: released on Neat in '85 by Neat Records. Distributed by: Pinnacle, Neat

Ventura, Charlie

Aces at the deuces

Jb for the people (Ventura, Charlie featuring Jackie Cain/Roy kral).
Album: released on Affinity in '83 by Charly Records. Distributed by: Charly, Cadillac

Charlie boy (1946).
Album: released on Phoenix in Apr'81 by Im Jazz Music, JSU, Swift

Charlie Ventura & his band.
Album: released on Jazz Reactivation in '82. Distributed by: PRT

Charlie Ventura Quintet in HI-FI(1956) (Ventura Quintet,Charlie).
Album: released on Harlequin in Aug'84 by Harlequin Records. Distributed by: Swift, Jazz Music, Wellard, Chris, IRS, Taylor, H.R.

Euphoria.
Album:

Chicago-1947 (Ventura Quintet,Charlie).
Album: released on Zim in Apr'81. Distributed by: JSU, Jazz Horizons, Jazz Music, Swift

Live at the 3 deuces

Town hall concert 1945

Town hall concert vol.2.
Album: released on London in '74 by London Records. Distributed by: Polygram

Venture

Love comes around.
Tracks: / Shine.
Single (12"): released on Disco Tex in Oct'86 by Disco Tex Records. Distributed by: Jetstar

Ventures

20 rock'n'roll hits.
Album: released on EMI (Germany) in '83 by EMI Records. Distributed by: Conifer

Best of....
Tracks: / Apache 65 / Ram-bunk-shush / Telstar / Wipe out / Cruel sea / Perfidia / Rebel rouser / Walk, don't run / Penetration / Pipeline / Diamond head / Hawaii Five-O / Out of limits / Slaughter on Tenth Avenue / Journey to the stars / Apache 65 / Ram-bunk-shush / Telstar / Wipe out / Cruel sea / Perfidia / Rebel rouser / Walk don't run / Penetration / Pipeline / Diamond head / Hawaii five-o / Out of limits / Slaughter on Tenth Avenue(live) / Journey to the stars(live).
Compact disc: released on EMI America in Apr'87 by EMI Records. Distributed by: EMI

Collection: Ventures.
Compact disc: released on Collectors Series in '86 by Castle Communications Records. Distributed by: PRT, Pinnacle, RCA, Ariola

Hawaii Five O'.
Single (7"): released on Liberty in '80 by Liberty-United. Distributed by: EMI

Legendary masters.
Album: released on Liberty in '74

Now playing.
Album: released on EMI (Germany) in '83 by EMI Records. Distributed by: Conifer

Ventures Collection, The.
Tracks: / Telstar / Hawaii Five O / Tequila / Wheels / Bumble Bee Rock / Slaughter on tenth avenue / Ghost riders in the sky / Perfidia / Walk don't run / Memphis / Rebel rouser / Apache / Pipeline.
Notes: Produced by: The Ventures/Bob Bogle Bass/Don Wilson Rhythm Guitar/Nokie Edwards Lead Guitar/Mel Taylor Drums. Special thanks to Bob Commack on Keyboards. Recorded at Front Page Productions, Costa Mesa, C.A.
Double Album: released on Castle Communications in Dec'86 by Castle Communications. Distributed by: Cartel, Pinnacle, Counterpoint

Double musicassette: released on Castle Communications in Dec'86 by Castle Communications. Distributed by: Cartel, Pinnacle, Counterpoint

Ventures today,The.
Album: released on Valentine in Jul'83 by Valentine Records. Distributed by: PRT

Musicassette: released on Valentine in Jul'83 by Valentine Records. Distributed by: PRT

Walk don't run.
Tracks: / Walk don't run / Perfidia.
Single (7"): released on Old Gold in Mar'87 by Old Gold Records. Distributed by: Lightning, Jazz Music, Spartan, Counterpoint

Single (7"): released on Liberty in '80

Single (7"): released on EMI (Holland) in Aug'84 by EMI Records. Distributed by: Conifer

Venus

Twilight zone.
Tracks: / Twilight zone / (I'm gonna) set you alight.
Single (12"): released on Passion in Jun'86 by Skratch Records. Distributed by: PRT

Venus in Furs

Love lies.
Single (12"): released on Backs in May'86 by Backs Records. Distributed by: Backs, Cartel

Memento Mori.
Single (7"): released on Movement in Jul'84. Distributed by: Cartel Distribution

Momento Mori.
Picture disc single: released on Backs in Dec'85 by Backs Records. Distributed by: Backs, Cartel

Platonic love.
Album: released on Movement in Dec'84. Distributed by: Cartel Distribution

Real moral fibre.
Album: released on Backs in Sep'86 by Backs Records. Distributed by: Backs, Cartel

Strip.
Album: released on Backs in May'85 by Backs Records. Distributed by: Backs, Cartel

Venus & Razorblades

Songs from sunshine jungle.
Album: released on Spark in May'78 by Spark Records. Distributed by: PRT

Venuti, Joe

Big bands of Joe Venuti 1928-30 Vol.1 (Venuti, Joe Big Band).
Notes: Mono.
Album: released on JSP in Feb'87 by JSP Records. Distributed by: Swift, Projection

Electric Joe.
Album: released on Jump (Import) in '81

Incredible Joe Venuti, The.
Album: released on Audiophile in Jul'87 by Jazzology Records (USA). Distributed by: Jazz Music, Swift

January 28th & 30th,1957 (Venuti, Joe & His Blue Four).
Album: released on From The Jazz Vault in Oct'80 by Damont Records. Distributed by: Swift, Taylor, H.R.

Jazz me blues.
Album: released on Jump (Import) in Apr'81

Joe in Chicago.
Album: released on Flying Fish (USA) in May'79 by Flying Fish Records (USA). Distributed by: Roots, Projection

Joe Venuti and Eddie Lang (With Eddie Lang 1927-28).
Album: released on Swaggie (Australia) in Jan'83

Joe Venuti and his band-1945 (Venuti, Joe & His Band).
Album: released on Golden Era in Jul'82 by Import Records. Distributed by: Wellard, Chris, Swift

Joe Venuti & his orchestra.
Album: released on London in Mar'76 by London Records. Distributed by: Polygram

Joe Venuti Quartet (Venuti,Joe Quartet).
Album: released on Jump in Apr'81. Distributed by: Jazz Music, Jazz Horizons

Joe Venuti's jazz group.
Album: released on Jump in Apr'81. Distributed by: Jazz Music, Jazz Horizons

Joe & Zoot (Venuti, Joe & Zoot Sims).

Mad fiddler from Philly,The.
Album: released on Shoestring in Apr'81 by Shoestring Records. Distributed by: Shoestring

Plays George Gershwin & Jerome Kern.
Album: released on Jump in Apr'81. Distributed by: Jazz Music, Jazz Horizons

Sliding by.
Album: released on Sonet in Jan'78 by Sonet Records. Distributed by: PRT

'S wonderful giants of swing.
Album: released on Flying Fish (USA) in Feb'79 by Flying Fish Records (USA). Distributed by: Roots, Projection

Venupelli blues

Venutiana.
Album: released on Jump in Apr'81 by Jazz Music, Jazz Horizons

Violin jazz.
Album: released on Yazoo in Jan'79. Distributed by: Swift, Projection

Vera

Take me to the bridge.
Single (7"): released on Carrere America (USA) in Sep'81 by Polygram

Single (12"): released on Carrere America (USA) in Sep'81 by Polygram

Vera, Billy

At this moment (live) (Vera, Billy & the Beaters).
Single (7"): released on Fanfare in Feb'87 by Ferroway/Fanfare Records. Distributed by: PRT

Single (12"): released on Fanfare in Feb'87 by Ferroway/Fanfare Records. Distributed by: PRT

Verano, Mario

Get up.
Single (7"): released on EMI in Mar'81 by EMI Records. Distributed by: EMI

Single (12"): released on EMI in Mar'81 by EMI Records. Distributed by: EMI

Verbal Abuse

Rocks your liver.
Album: released on Boner in Mar'87. Distributed by: Revolver

Verbeke, Harry

Shirt stop (Verbeke, Harry Quartet).
Album: released on Timeless in '79

Verden, Jake

Doin' what I like doin.
Album: released on Tank in Jun'79 by Tank Records

Verelli,Andre

Master performance volume 5.
Musicassette: released on Aim in Sep'83. Distributed by: H.R. Taylor

Vergat, Vic

Down to the bone.
Single (7"): released on Harvest in Oct'81 by EMI Records. Distributed by: Roots, EMI

Walk away Renee.
Single (7"): released on Harvest in Jan'83 by EMI Records. Distributed by: Roots, EMI

Vergo, Danny

Kick a hack.
Tracks: / Nanny goat.
Single (12"): released on Uptempo in Mar'86 by Uptempo Records. Distributed by: Jetstar Distribution

Verity

Interrupted journey.
Album: released on PRT in Oct'83 by PRT Records. Distributed by: PRT

Musicassette: released on PRT in Oct'83 by PRT Records. Distributed by: PRT

Stay with me baby.
Single (7"): released on PRT in Oct'83 by PRT Records. Distributed by: PRT

Single (12"): released on PRT in Oct'83 by PRT Records. Distributed by: PRT

Verity, John

Honesty & emotion.
Single (7"): released on PRT in Mar'85 by PRT Records. Distributed by: PRT

Single (12"): released on PRT in Mar'85 by PRT Records. Distributed by: PRT

Truth of the matter.
Album: released on PRT in May'85 by PRT Records. Distributed by: PRT

Musicassette: released on PRT in May'85 by PRT Records. Distributed by: PRT

Two hearts burning.
Tracks: / Two hearts burning / Broken wing / Two hearts burning (Ext. Mix).
Single (7"): released on Sierra in Jul'87 by Sierra Records. Distributed by: WEA

Single (12"): released on Sierra in Jul'87 by Sierra Records. Distributed by: WEA

What about me.
Single (7"): released on PRT in Aug'84 by PRT Records. Distributed by: PRT

Verlaines, The

Hallelujah all the way home.
Album: released on Flying Nun in Oct'86. Distributed by: Rough Trade, Cartel

Jvenilla.
Album: released on Flying Nun in Oct'87. Distributed by: Rough Trade, Cartel

---

Verlaine, Tom

Always.
Single (7"): released on Warner Bros. in Sep'81 by Warner Bros Records. Distributed by: WEA

Single (12"): released on Warner Bros. in Sep'81 by Warner Bros Records. Distributed by: WEA

Album: released on Virgin in Sep'84 by Virgin Records. Distributed by: EMI, Virgin Distribution

Musiccassette: released on Virgin in Sep'84 by Virgin Records. Distributed by: EMI, Virgin Distribution

Cover.
Tracks: / Five miles of you / Let go the mansion / Travelling / O foolish heart / Dissolve-reveal / Miss Emily / Rotation / Swim.
Album: released on Virgin in Apr'86 by Virgin Records. Distributed by: EMI, Virgin Distribution

Musiccassette: released on Virgin in Apr'86 by Virgin Records. Distributed by: EMI, Virgin Distribution

Cry mercy judge.
Tracks: / Cry mercy judge / Call me the / Circling / At this moment (live) / Lover of the night (live) / Strange things happening.
Single (7"): released on Fontana in Mar'87 by Phonogram Records. Distributed by: Polygram

Single (12"): released on Fontana in Mar'87 by Phonogram Records. Distributed by: Polygram

Flash light.

Funniest thing, The.
Tracks: / Funniest thing, The / One time at sundown / Marquee moon ('87).
Single (7"): released on Fontana in May'87 by Phonogram Records. Distributed by: Polygram

Single (12"): released on Fontana in May'87 by Phonogram Records. Distributed by: Polygram

Tom Verlaine.
Album: released on Elektra in Sep'79 by WEA Records. Distributed by: WEA

Town called Walkers, A.
Tracks: / Town called Walkers, A / Smoother than Jones / Caveman flashlight / Town called Walkers, A.
Single (7"):

Single (12"):

Verne, Jules

Around the world in 80 days.
Album: released on Caedmon(USA) in Jul'78 by Caedmon (USA) Records. Distributed by: Gower, Taylors, Discovery

Musiccassette: released on Caedmon(USA) in Jul'78 by Caedmon (USA) Records. Distributed by: Gower, Taylors, Discovery

---

Vernon, Dave

Back to back (EP) (Vernon, Dave & Jed McCoy).
Tracks: / Back to back (EP) / Roamin' country singer / One touch away / Best bar room in town / Rolled the rock away.
Notes: (Self - 0923 47129)
Single (7"): released on Cabin in Feb'87 by Cabin Records. Distributed by: Cabin

Child of 1945.
Album: released on Lakeside in Jul'85 by Lakeside Records. Distributed by: Lakeside

Single (7"): released on Viking in Sep'84. Distributed by: Jetstar, Northumbrian Records, H.R. Taylor

---

Vernon & GI's

Ghost train boogie.
Single (7"): released on Billy Goat in Aug'78 by Chick-A-Boom Records. Distributed by: PRT

GI bop.
Album: released on Billy Goat in Jan'79 by Chick-A-Boom Records. Distributed by: PRT

I wanna be a ted.
Single (7"): released on Billy Goat in Nov'80 by Chick-A-Boom Records. Distributed by: PRT

Vernon & Gwynfor

Welcome H.
Single (7"): released on VIP in May'82. Distributed by: Jetstar Distribution

---

Vernon, Lucy

Jackdaw & other stories,The.
Album: released on Response in Feb'81

Vernons Banjo Trio

When I think of you.
Single (7"): released on Whoopee in May'79 by Whoopee Records. Distributed by: Whoopee Records, Waterfront Records, Jazz Music, JSU, Chris

---

Vernons Girls

Lover please.
Single (7"): released on Decca-Originals in May'82 by Decca Records. Distributed by: Polygram, IMS

Single (7"): released on Old Gold in Sep'85 by Old Gold Records. Distributed by: Lightning, Jazz Music, Spartan, Counterpoint

---

VerPlanck, Marlene

Sings Alec Wilder.
Notes: Mel Lewis - drums. Double album.
Double Album: released on Audiophile in Feb'87 by Jazzology Records (USA). Distributed by: Jazz Music, Swift

---

Verplank, Marlene

I like to sing.
Album: released on Audiophile in Sep'86 by Jazzology Records (USA). Distributed by: Jazz Music, Swift

---

Versatility

Tequila madness.
Single (7"): released on President in Mar'75 by President Records. Distributed by: Taylors, Spartan

---

Vertical Hold

Angel dust.
Single (7"): released on VH in May'84 by VH Records. Distributed by: Backs, Cartel

Bio hazzard.
Single (7"): released on Vertigo in Jun'85 by Phonogram Records. Distributed by: Polygram

Rubber cross.
Single (7"): released on Vertical Hold Ind. in Oct'81. Distributed by: Rough Trade

---

Vertinsky, Alexander

Folk music.
Musiccassette: released on Melodiya (USSR) in Feb'79. Distributed by: T.B.C Distribution

---

Verukas

Blood suckers.
Album: released on Riot City in Jul'83 by Riot City Records. Distributed by: Revolver

Die for your government.
Single (7"): released on Riot City in Jul'83 by Riot City Records. Distributed by: Revolver

Don't wanna be a victim.
Single (7"): released on Inferno in Jun'82 by Inferno Records. Distributed by: Inferno, Cartel, Pinnacle

Protest and survive.
Single (7"): released on Inferno in Dec'81 by Inferno Records. Distributed by: Inferno, Cartel, Pinnacle

---

Verve Jazz Best

Verve Jazz best vol.3 Various artists (Various Artists).
Tracks: / Organ grinder's swing / Cheek to cheek / Samba triste / Aqua de beber / You'd be so nice to come home to / Too close for comfort / Caravan / I can't give you anything but love / Moonglow / Just a sittin' and a rockin' / East of

---

the sun (and west of the moon) / Moonlight in Vermont / You look good to me.
Album: released on Verve (USA) in Apr'86 by Polydor. Distributed by: Polygram

Musiccassette: released on Verve (USA) in Apr'86 by Polydor. Distributed by: Polygram

---

Very Best Of....

Very Best of Jazz, The. Best of British Jazz (Various Artists).
Album: released on Polyphonic in Apr'84 by Polyphonic Records. Distributed by: Taylors

Musiccassette: released on Polyphonic in Apr'84 by Polyphonic Records. Distributed by: Taylors

Very best of: Military Bands Various military bands (Various military bands).
Album: released on EMI Records. Distributed by: EMI

Very best of Motown love songs Various Artists (Various Artists).
Double Album: released on Telstar(Motown) in Feb'84

Musiccassette: released on Telstar(Motown) in Feb'84

Very best of trash horror (Various Artists).
Notes: Includes: Bobby 'Boris' Pickett, Screaming Lord Sutch.
Album: released on McDonald Brothers in May'87

Very best of trash horror vol.2 (Various Artists).
Album: released on MBC in Aug'87. Distributed by: Pinnacle

Very best of Welsh choirs Various Artists (Various Artists).
Album: released on EMI in Nov'75 by EMI Records. Distributed by: EMI

Musiccassette: released on EMI in Nov'75 by EMI Records. Distributed by: EMI

Very Big In America

Very big in America right now Various Artists (Various Artists).
Album: released on Cherry Red in Jun'84 by Cherry Red Records. Distributed by: Pinnacle

---

Very Merry Disco, A

Very merry disco,A Various Artists (Various Artists).
Album: released on Warwick in Nov'83 by MSD Records. Distributed by: CBS

Musiccassette: released on Warwick in Nov'83 by MSD Records. Distributed by: CBS

Veryovka Ukranian Choir

Veryovka Ukranian Folk Choir.
Album: released on Melodiya (USSR) in May'78. Distributed by: T.B.C Distribution

---

Very Things

Bushes scream while my daddy prunes,The.
Album: released on Reflex in Sep'84

Single (7"): released on Reflex in Jun'84

Ghost in my house.
Single (7"): released on One Little Indian in 23 May'87 by One Little Indian Records. Distributed by: Nine Mile Distribution, Cartel Distribution

Single (12"): released on One Little Indian in 23 May'87 by One Little Indian Records. Distributed by: Nine Mile Distribution, Cartel Distribution

Mummy you're a wreck.
Single (12"): released on Reflex in Aug'85

This is Motortown.
Tracks: / Motortown epilogue.
Single (7"): released on DCL Electronic in Nov'86. Distributed by: Nine Mile, Cartel

Single (12"): released on DCL Electronic in Nov'86. Distributed by: Nine Mile, Cartel

---

Vesala, Edward & Sound and Fury

Lumi.
Tracks: / Wind, The / Frozen melody / Calypso Bulbosa / Third moon / Lumi / Camel walk / Fingo / Early messenger / Together.
Notes: Personnel: Edward Vesala -drums, per-

---

cussion/Eskko Heikkinen - trumpet, piccolo trumpet/ Penti Lahti - alto & baritone saxophones, flutes/Jorma Tapio -alto saxophone, clarinet, bass clarinet, flute/Tapani Rinne - tenor & soprano saxophones,clarinet, bass clarinet/Kari Heinila - tenor & soprano saxophones, flute/Tom Bildo - trombone, tuba/Iro Haarla - piano, harp/Raoul Bjorkenheim - guitar/Haka - bass.

Album: released on ECM (Germany) in Jul'87 by ECM Records. Distributed by: IMS, Polygram, Virgin through EMI

Compact disc: released on ECM (Germany) in Jul'87 by ECM Records. Distributed by: IMS, Polygram, Virgin through EMI

Veshara

Shadow of love.
Single (7"): released on Sub Zero in Oct'84. Distributed by: PRT Distribution

---

Vesty, John

First month of spring,The.
Album: released on Shanachie in Sep'79. Distributed by: Sterns/Triple Earth Distribution Roots

---

Veterans

There ain't no age for rock'n'roll.
Single (7"): released on Rantin in Mar'83

Veterans Of Variety

Veterans of variety Various Artists (Various Artists).
Album: released on World in Jun'80 by EMI Records. Distributed by: Conifer

---

Veto

Veto.
Album: released on Powerstation Records in Jul'86 by Powerstation Records. Distributed by: Pinnacle

---

Vetoes

It's only now.
Single (7"): released on RCA in Aug'82 by RCA Records. Distributed by: RCA, Roots, Swift Wellard, Chris, I & B, Solomon & Peres Distribution

Not tonight.
Single (7"): released on RCA in Jan'83 by RCA Records. Distributed by: RCA, Roots, Swift Wellard, Chris, I & B, Solomon & Peres Distribution

---

Vets

World in action.
Single (7"): released on Deck Chair in Jul'8? Distributed by: Pinnacle

---

VHF

Love in the night.
Tracks: / Love in the night / Love in the night (inst).
Single (12"): released on Record Shack Jul'87 by Record Shack Records. Distributed by: PRT

Very high frequency (anti static mix)
Tracks: / Very high frequency.
Single (12"): released on Record Shack Aug'86 by Record Shack Records. Distributed by: PRT

Vhutemus/Archtypi

Vhutemus/Archtypi Various artists (Various Artists).
Album: released on Side Effects in Apr'86 SPK Records. Distributed by: Rough Trade Cartel

---

Via Vagabond

Hip today.
Single 10": released on Albion in Jul'83 by Albion Records. Distributed by: Spartan, Pinnacle

Who likes jazz.
Single (7"): released on Stiff in Aug'82 by Stiff Records. Distributed by: EMI, Record Service Distribution (Ireland)

Via Verdi

Diamond.
Tracks: / Diamonds (dance version).
Single (7"): released on WEA in Jan'8? WEA Records. Distributed by: WEA

Single (12"): released on WEA in Jan'8? WEA Records. Distributed by: WEA

Vibes

an you feel ... the underestimated
man.
ngle (7"): released on Big Beat in Oct'84 by
e Records. Distributed by: Projection, Pin-
acle

nderestimated man.
bum: released on Big Beat in Sep'84 by
e Records. Distributed by: Projection, Pin-
acle

hat's inside.
bum: released on Chainsaw in Jul'85 by
ainsaw Records. Distributed by: Red Rhino,
artel

ithin the wardrobe of your mind.
ngle (7"): released on Chainsaw in Jan'85 by
ainsaw Records. Distributed by: Red Rhino,
rtel

gle (12"): released on Chainsaw in Jan'85
Chainsaw Records. Distributed by: Red
ino, Cartel

ibe Tribe

nscious as a daisy.
ngle (7"): released on Tribal in Jul'87 by Tri-
Records. Distributed by: Revolver, Cartel

ibrations of ....

erations of the sixties Volume 1 (Vari-
Artists).
um: released on Band Of Gold in Jan'87 by
us Records. Distributed by: Stylus

alcassette: released on Band Of Gold in
'87 by Stylus Records. Distributed by: Sty-

ibrators

ska 127.
um: released on Ram in Mar'84 by Ram.
ibuted by: PRT

um: released on Carrere in May'84 by Car-
Records. Distributed by: PRT, Spartan

y baby.
(7"): released on Anagram in Nov'82 by
rry Red Records. Distributed by: Pinnacle

y blue eyes.
(7"): released on Carrere in Jul'84 by
re Records. Distributed by: PRT, Spartan

le (12"): released on Carrere in Jul'84 by
e Records. Distributed by: PRT, Spartan

amendment.
um: released on Ram in Jun'85 by Ram.
buted by: PRT

assette: released on Ram in Jun'85 by
Distributed by: PRT

g home.
(7"): released on Ram in Mar'84 by Ram.

(12"): released on Ram in Mar'84 by
Distributed by: PRT

(7"): released on Carrere in May'84 by
e Records. Distributed by: PRT, Spartan

(12"): released on Carrere in May'84 by
e Records. Distributed by: PRT, Spartan

e some lovin.
(7"): released on Rat Race in Feb'80

: released on Anagram in Jan'83 by
Red Records. Distributed by: Pinnacle

(7"): released on Anagram in May'83 by
Red Records. Distributed by: Pinnacle

: released on FM-Revolver in Oct'86 by
volver Records. Distributed by: BMG
riola], Pathe Marconi, Polygram

erica.
(7"): released on Anagram in Nov'83 by
distributed by: PRT

: released on Epic in Apr'78 by CBS Rec-
distributed by: CBS

Vibrators live.
Album: released on Revolver in Mar'87 by Revolver Records. Distributed by: Revolver, Cartel

Vic & Carol's Crazy..

These boots are made (Vic & Carol's
Crazy Circus).
Single (7"): released on Harbour in May'81 by
Harbour Records. Distributed by: Wellard, Chris

Viceroys

Brethren and sistren.
Album: released on CSA in Mar'83 by CSA
Records. Distributed by: PRT, Jetstar

Can't stop us now.
Single (12"): released on Music Hawk in Apr'82
by Music Hawk Records. Distributed by: Jetstar
Distribution

Chancery Lane.
Album: released on Greensleeves in Jul'84 by
Greensleeves Records. Distributed by: BMG,
Jetstar, Spartan

New clothes.
Single (12"): released on Greensleeves in
Jun'84 by Greensleeves Records. Distributed
by: BMG, Jetstar, Spartan

We must unite.
Album: released on Trojan in '83 by Trojan
Records. Distributed by: PRT, Jetstar

Ya ho.
Album: released on Burning Sounds in Feb'85
by Ross, Bill/Burning Sounds Records. Distributed by: PRT

Vice Squad

Black sheep.
Single (7"): released on Anagram in Nov'83 by
Cherry Red Records. Distributed by: Pinnacle

Single (12"): released on Anagram in Nov'83
by Cherry Red Records. Distributed by: Pinnacle

Citizen.
Single (7"): released on Zonophone in Sep'82
by EMI Records. Distributed by: EMI

Last rockers.
Single (7"): released on Riot City in '81 by Riot
City Records. Distributed by: Revolver

No cause for concern.
Album: released on Zonophone in Oct'81 by
EMI Records. Distributed by: EMI

Out of reach.
Single (7"): released on Riot City in Jan'82 by
Riot City Records. Distributed by: Revolver

Resurrection.
Single (7"): released on Riot in May'81. Distributed by: Rough Trade

Stand strong stand proud.
Single (7"): released on Riot City in Apr'82 by
Riot City Records. Distributed by: Revolver

Teenage rampage.
Single (7"): released on Anagram in Jan'85 by
Cherry Red Records. Distributed by: Pinnacle

You'll never know.
Single (7"): released on Anagram in Apr'84 by
Cherry Red Records. Distributed by: Pinnacle

Single (12"): released on Anagram in Apr'84 by
Cherry Red Records. Distributed by: Pinnacle

Vicious Barreka

Outrage, insanity, profanity.
Album: released on Killer in Mar'86

Vicious Circle

Price of progress.
Album: released on Cor in Nov'85. Distributed
by: Revolver, Cartel

Vicious Pink

C C Can't You See.
Single (7"): released on EMI in May'85 by EMI
Records. Distributed by: EMI

Single (12"): released on EMI in May'85 by EMI
Records. Distributed by: EMI

Single (7"): released on EMI in May'85 by EMI
Records. Distributed by: EMI

Single (12"): released on EMI in May'85 by EMI
Records. Distributed by: EMI

Fetish.
Single (12"): released on EMI in Mar'85 by EMI
Records. Distributed by: EMI

Picture disc single: released on EMI in Mar'85
by EMI Records. Distributed by: EMI

Spooky.
Single (7"): released on EMI in Feb'85 by EMI
Records. Distributed by: EMI

Single (12"): released on EMI in Feb'85 by EMI
Records. Distributed by: EMI

Take me now.
Tracks: / Always hoping / I confess.
Single (7"): released on EMI in Jan'86 by EMI
Records. Distributed by: EMI

Single (12"): released on EMI in Jan'86 by EMI
Records. Distributed by: EMI

Vicious Pink Phenomena

Je t'aime moi non plus.
Single (7"): released on Warehouse in Feb'83
by Warehouse Records. Distributed by: PRT

Single (12"): released on Warehouse in Feb'83
by Warehouse Records. Distributed by: PRT

My private Tokyo.
Single (7"): released on Mobile Suit Corporation in Mar'82. Distributed by: Phonogram Distribution. Polygram Distribution

Single (12"): released on Mobile Suit Corporation in Mar'82. Distributed by: Phonogram Distribution, Polygram Distribution

Vicious rumour club

Whole lotta love.
Single (7"): released on Music Of Life in
Mar'87. Distributed by: Streetwave

Single (12"): released on Music Of Life in
Mar'87. Distributed by: Streetwave

Vicious Rumours

Anytime day or night.
Album: released on Olli in May'86. Distributed
by: Revolver Distribution

Rita.
Single (7"): released on Dork in Nov'84 by Dork
Records. Distributed by: Probe, Cartel

Soldier of the night.
Album: released on Road Runner in Nov'85

Vicious, Sid

Live at CBGB's New York (Vicious, Sid
& Johnny Thunders).
Album: released on Konnexion in Feb'87. Dis-
tributed by: Roots, Pinnacle

Live at the electric ballroom.
Musicassette: released on McDonald-Lydon in
Aug'86. Distributed by: Pinnacle

Love kills N.Y.C.
Album: released on Konexion in Oct'85 by Konexion Records. Distributed by: Pinnacle

Naked.
Single (7"): released on Wonderful in Jul'80.
Distributed by: Spartan

Real Sid and Nancy (The).
Album: released on McDonald-Lydon in
Aug'86. Distributed by: Pinnacle

Sid versus Eddie (Vicious, Sid & Eddie
Cochran).
Album: released on McDonald in Feb'87. Dis-
tributed by: Pinnacle

Vicky

December serenade.
Single (7"): released on JVF in Dec'83

Victim

Teenage, (The).
Single (7"): released on Illuminated in Jun'82
by IKF Records. Distributed by: Pinnacle, Cartel, Jetstar

Victims

Strange things by night.
Single (7"): released on Good in '79. Distributed by: M.I.S., EMI

Teenager, (The).
Single (7"): released on Illuminated in Sep'80
by IKF Records. Distributed by: Pinnacle, Cartel, Jetstar

Victims Family

Voltage & Violets.
Album: released on Konkurrel in Jul'87

Musicassette: released on Konkurrel in Jul'87

Victims of pleasure

Jack & Jill.
Single (7"): released on Rialto in Apr'82 by
Rialto Records. Distributed by: Pinnacle

Slave to fashion.
Single (7"): released on Rialto in Oct'81 by
Rialto Records. Distributed by: Pinnacle

Single (12"): released on Rialto in Oct'81 by
Rialto Records. Distributed by: Pinnacle

When you're young.
Single (7"): released on Rialto in Oct'82 by
Rialto Records. Distributed by: Pinnacle

Victor

Victor, (The) Various Artists (Various Ar-
tists).
Album: released on Liveoak in May'85

Musicassette: released on Liveoak in May'85

Victor Herbert

Victor Herbert- souvenir Various Artists
(Various Artists).
Album: released on Arabesque in Nov'85. Dis-
tributed by: D Sharp Records, Pinnacle

Musicassette: released on Arabesque in
Nov'85. Distributed by: D Sharp Records, Pinnacle

Victoria & her ministers

Victoria & her ministers (History alive
series).
Musicassette: released on D'Arblay in Aug'78
by Anemone Records

Victorian Parents

All American hero.
Single (7"): released on Polydor in Sep'81 by
Polydor Records. Distributed by: Polygram,
Polydor

Silence follows.
Album: released on Polydor in Oct'81 by Polydor Records. Distributed by: Polygram, Polydor

Musicassette: released on Polydor in Oct'81
by Polydor Records. Distributed by: Polygram,
Polydor

Victorian Sunday

Victorian Sunday (The road to Heaven)
Various Artists (Various Artists).
Album: released on Saydisc in Nov'82 by Sayd-
isc Records. Distributed by: Essex, Harmonia
Mundi, Roots, H.R. Taylor, Jazz Music, Swift,
Projection, Gamut

Musicassette: released on Saydisc in Nov'82
by Saydisc Records. Distributed by: Essex, Harmonia Mundi, Roots, H.R. Taylor, Jazz Music,
Swift, Projection, Gamut

Victoria Plum

Victoria Plum (Four favourite stories)
Rippon, Angela (Rippon, Angela).
Not one of the other formats: released on
Tempo Storytime in May'84

Victoria Plum gives Ben a surprise Rip-
pon, Angela (Hyks, Veronika).
Not one of the other formats: released on
Tempo in Aug'84 by Warwick Records. Distributed by: Multiple Sound Distributors

Victoria Plum has a treasure hunt Rippon, Angela (Hyks, Veronika).
Not one of the other formats: released on Tempo in Aug'84 by Warwick Records. Distributed by: Multiple Sound Distributors

Victoria Plum helps the badgers Rippon, Angela (Hyks, Veronika).
Not one of the other formats: released on Tempo in Aug'84 by Warwick Records. Distributed by: Multiple Sound Distributors

Victoria Plum & the.... Rippon, Angela (Hyks, Veronika).
Not one of the other formats: released on Tempo in Aug'84 by Warwick Records. Distributed by: Multiple Sound Distributors

Victor Victoria

Victor Victoria Original Soundtrack.
Album: released on MGM in Apr'82. Distributed by: Polygram Distribution, Swift Distribution

Musiccassette: released on MGM in Apr'82. Distributed by: Polygram Distribution, Swift Distribution

Album: released on MGM (USA) in Aug'83 by Polydor. Distributed by: Polygram, Swift

musiccassette: released on MGM (USA) in Aug'83 by Polydor. Distributed by: Polygram, Swift

Victory in Europe

Victory In Europe Various archive sound recordings (Various Artists).
Album: released on BBC in May'85 by BBC Records & Tapes. Distributed by: EMI, PRT

Musiccassette: released on BBC in May'85 by BBC Records & Tapes. Distributed by: EMI, PRT.

Vidal, Maria

Body rock.
Single (7"): released on EMI America in Aug'85 by EMI Records. Distributed by: EMI

Single (12"): released on EMI America in Aug'85 by EMI Records. Distributed by: EMI

Video Aid

Feed the world compilation.
Video-cassette (VHS): released on Virgin in Jan'86 by Virgin Records. Distributed by: EMI, Virgin Distribution

Video Hits

Video hits.
Video-cassette (VHS): released by Thorn-Emi in Jan'84

Video Hits 1 14 Videostars (Various Artists).
Notes: 56 minutes. Dolby stereo. Inc. Jim Diamond, Bryan Ferry etc.
Video-cassette (VHS): released on Video Collection in May'87 by Video Collection Records. Distributed by: Counterpoint

Video Hits 2 14 Videostars (Various Artists).
Notes: Phil Collins, Billy Ocean, Elton John, Depeche Mode etc.
Video-cassette (VHS): released on Video Collection in May'87 by Video Collection Records. Distributed by: Counterpoint

Video hits collection 2.
Video-cassette (VHS):

Video kids

Never too young to dance.
Album: released on Video Kids in Oct'81

Musiccassette: released on Video Kids in Oct'81

Woodpeckers from space.
Single (7"): released on Record Shack in Nov'84 by Record Shack Records. Distributed by: PRT

Single (12"): released on Record Shack in Nov'84 by Record Shack Records. Distributed by: PRT

Single (7"): released on Epic in Aug'85 by CBS Records. Distributed by: CBS

Video People

On our own.
Single (7"): released on Round in Apr'84. Distributed by: PRT, Red Rhino, Cartel

---

Video Snap

Best of jam (The).
Video-cassette (VHS): released on Polygram Music in Oct'84 by Polygram Records. Distributed by: Polygram

Video stars

Video stars Various Artists (Various Artists).
Album: released on K-Tel in Jan'80 by K-Tel Records. Distributed by: Record Merchandisers Distribution, Taylors, Terry Blood Distribution, Wynd-Up Distribution, Relay Distribution, Pickwick Distribution, Solomon & Peres Distribution, Polygram

Musiccassette: released on K-Tel in Jan'80 by K-Tel Records. Distributed by: Record Merchandisers Distribution, Taylors, Terry Blood Distribution, Wynd-Up Distribution, Relay Distribution, Pickwick Distribution, Solomon & Peres Distribution, Polygram

Video Waves

Video waves.
Video-cassette (VHS): released on Polygram/Spectrum in Jan'84 by Polygram Records. Distributed by: Polygram

Vie en rose, (La)

Vie en rose, (La) Various Artists (Various Artists).
Album: released on New Rose in Feb'85. Distributed by: Rough Trade, Cartel

Vienna Boys Choir

Waltzes & Polkas by Johann Strauss.
Album: released on Red Seal in '78 by RCA Records. Distributed by: RCA

Musiccassette: released on Red Seal in '78 by RCA Records. Distributed by: RCA

Vienna Conservatory

Sing children sing.
Album: released on Caedmon(USA) in Jul'79 by Caedmon (USA) Records. Distributed by: Gower, Taylors, Discovery

Musiccassette: released on Caedmon(USA) in Jul'79 by Caedmon (USA) Records. Distributed by: Gower, Taylors, Discovery

Vienna gold

Vienna gold Various Artists (Various Artists).
Boxed set: released on Effects Gold in Nov'80 by Ronco Records. Distributed by: Ronco Records

Boxed set: released on Effects Gold in Nov'80 by Ronco Records. Distributed by: Ronco Records

Vienna Philharmonic

Onedin Line theme.
Single (7"): released on Decca in '71 by Decca Records. Distributed by: Polygram

Vienna Symphony Orchestra

Symphonic rock.
Album: released on Stylus in Feb'87. Distributed by: Pinnacle, Terry Blood Distribution, Stylus Distribution

Musiccassette: released on Stylus in Feb'87. Distributed by: Pinnacle, Terry Blood Distribution, Stylus Distribution

Compact disc: released on Stylus in Feb'87. Distributed by: Pinnacle, Terry Blood Distribution, Stylus Distribution

Viennese folk music

Viennese folk music Various Artists (Various Artists).
Double Album: released on Telefunken (Germany) in Jul'81. Distributed by: Decca Distribution, IMS, Polygram

Vietnamese Rose

Curtains you.
Single (7"): released on Aaron B in Jul'83 by Aaron B. Distributed by: Spartan

Vietnam Veterans

Green pees.
Double Album: released on Music Maniac in Feb'86. Distributed by: Rough Trade Distribution, Cartel Distribution

---

In ancient times.
Album: released on Music Maniac in Oct'86. Distributed by: Rough Trade Distribution, Cartel Distribution

Album: released on Music Maniac in Jun'86. Distributed by: Rough Trade Distribution, Cartel Distribution

Viewers

Accident.
Single (7"): released on Fire Exit in Aug'80. Distributed by: PRT

View from the hill

Heart to heart.
Single (12"): released on Zara in Jul'84 by Zara Records. Distributed by: Rough Trade

I'm no rebel.
Tracks: / Stay and let me love you / For the sake of love / Turn out the light.
Double-pack single: released on EMI in Feb'87 by EMI Records. Distributed by: EMI

Single (cassette): released on EMI in Feb'87 by EMI Records. Distributed by: EMI

Single (7"): released on Survival in Aug'85 by Survival Records. Distributed by: Backs, Cartel Distribution

Single (12"): released on Survival in Aug'85 by Survival Records. Distributed by: Backs, Cartel Distribution

On the corner.
Tracks: / Living it up.
Single (7"): released on EMI in Aug'87 by EMI Records. Distributed by: EMI

Single (12"): released on EMI in Aug'87 by EMI Records. Distributed by: EMI

View from a hill.
Album: released on Zara in Jun'84 by Zara Records. Distributed by: Rough Trade

View From The Hill, A

No conversation.
Tracks: / No conversation / Everytime I hear your name.
Single (7"): released on EMI in Jun'86 by EMI Records. Distributed by: EMI

Single (12"): released on EMI in Jun'86 by EMI Records. Distributed by: EMI

Vigil

Vigil.
Album: released on Chrysalis in Apr'87 by Chrysalis Records. Distributed by: CBS

Vigilants

Run for cover.
Album: released on Heavy Metal in Nov'85 by FM-Revolver Records. Distributed by: EMI

Vignoles, Roger

Cabaret songs (see Walker, Sarah).

Cabaret songs (Vignoles, Roger & Sarah Walker).
Album: released on Meridian in Jan'83 by Meridean Records. Distributed by: Taylors, Harmonia Mundi Distributors,

Vig, Tommy Orchestra

Space race.
Compact disc: released on Discovery (USA) in Dec'86 by Discovery Records (USA). Distributed by: Swift, Flexitron-Audio, Jazz Music

Viking, Del

They sing...they swing.
Album: released on DJ in Jun'87. Distributed by: Rough Trade

Vikings

Albatross.
Single (7"): released on Ritz in Aug'85 by Outlet Records. Distributed by: Outlet, Prism Leisure Distribution, Record Services Distribution (Ireland), Roots

Vikki

Love is....
Single (7"): released on PRT in Apr'85 by PRT Records. Distributed by: PRT

Single (12"): released on PRT in Apr'85 by PRT Records. Distributed by: PRT

Villa De Ville

Everything counts.
Single (7"): released on Admiral in Oct'82 by Admiral. Distributed by: PRT

For the time being.
Album: released on RCA in Sep'81 by RCA Records. Distributed by: RCA, Roots, Swift, Wellard, Chris, I & B, Solomon & Peres Distribution

Musiccassette: released on RCA in Sep'81 by RCA Records. Distributed by: RCA, Roots, Swift, Wellard, Chris, I & B, Solomon & Peres Distribution

Subcul*ure 22.
Single (7"): released on RCA in Aug'81 by RCA Records. Distributed by: RCA, Roots, Swift, Wellard, Chris, I & B, Solomon & Peres Distribution

Single (7"): released on Admiral in May'83 by Admiral. Distributed by: PRT

Village People

Medley - in the navy.
Single (7"): released on Record Shack in Nov'85 by Record Shack Records. Distributed by: PRT

Single (12"): released on Record Shack in Nov'85 by Record Shack Records. Distributed by: PRT

New York city.
Album: released on Record Shack in Mar'85 Record Shack Records. Distributed by: PRT

Musiccassette: released on Record Shack in Mar'85 by Record Shack Records. Distributed by: PRT

Single (7"): released on Record Shack in Mar'85

Single (12"): released on Record Shack in Mar'85

Renaissance.
Album: released on Mercury in Jul'81 by Phonogram Records. Distributed by: Polygram Distribution

Musiccassette: released on Mercury in Jul'81 by Phonogram Records. Distributed by: Polygram Distribution

Sex over the phone.
Single (7"): released on Record Shack in Jan'85

Single (12"): released on Record Shack in Jan'85

Village School

Village school By Miss Read (Watfield, Gwen).
Musiccassette: released on Chivers Audio Books in '81 by Chivers Sound & Vision. Distributed by: Chivers Sound & Vision

Villard, Michel

Music from the films of Charlie Chaplin.
Tracks: / Titina / Le violeter / Green land snag / Smile / Mandolin serenade / Marchetaire / Evening star / Hungarian dance number / Limelight / Pilgrim (The) (medley) / This is my song / Shoulder arms (medley) / Spring song / Goldrush (medley).
Compact disc: released on Vogue (France) in Sep'86. Distributed by: Discovery, Jazz Music, PRT, Swift

Ville, Roland De

Little Jimmy Brown The 3 bells (Ville, Roland De Orchestra).
Single (7"): released on Precision in Oct'83 PRT Records. Distributed by: PRT

Vince & Claudia

You me and he.
Single (12"): released on Time in Jun'86. Distributed by: Jetstar Distribution

Vincent, Carrie

Holding out for a hero.
Musiccassette: released on Chevron in Nov'86. Distributed by: Multiple Sound Distributors

Vincent, Gene

20 rock 'n' roll hits.
Album: released on EMI (Germany) in EMI Records. Distributed by: Conifer

2 originals of Gene Vincent.
Double Album:

Ain't that too much.
Album: released on Premier in '84 by Premier Records. Distributed by: CBS

Musicassette: released on Premier in '84 by Premier Records. Distributed by: CBS

Baby blue.
Tracks: / Story of the rockers / Pickin poppies / Be-bop-a-lula / Pistol packin mama / Say mama / Rocky road blues / Baby blue / Whole lotta shakin goin on / Day the world turned blue, The / Story of the rockers (instrumental).
Album: released on Showcase in Apr'86. Distributed by: Counterpoint

Musicassette: released on Showcase in Apr'86. Distributed by: Counterpoint

Be-bop-a-lula.
Single (7"): released on EMI (France) in Apr'83 by EMI Records. Distributed by: Conifer

Best of Gene Vincent and his Blue Caps, The.
Album: released on Capitol in Oct'85 by Capitol Records. Distributed by: EMI

Musicassette: released on Capitol in Oct'85 by Capitol Records. Distributed by: EMI

Bird doggin'.
Album: released on Bulldog in Aug'82 by Bulldog Records. Distributed by: President Distribution, Spartan, Swift, Taylor, H.R.

Musicassette: released on Bulldog in Nov'82 by Bulldog Records. Distributed by: President Distribution, Spartan, Swift, Taylor, H.R.

Blue jean bop.
Album: released on EMI (France) in '83 by Conifer Records. Distributed by: Conifer

Cop they couldn't stop, The.
Album: released on Magnum Force in Jul'82 by Magnum Music Group Ltd. Distributed by: Magnum Music Group Ltd, PRT, Spartan

Musicassette: released on Magnum Force in Jul'82 by Magnum Music Group Ltd. Distributed by: Magnum Music Group Ltd, PRT, Spartan

Born to be a rolling stone.
Tracks: / Born to be a rolling stone / Hi-lilli, hi-lo / Bird doggin' / Love is a bird / Ain't that too much / Am I that easy to forget / Hurtin' for you baby / I'm a lonesome fugitive / Poor mans prison / Words and music / I've got my eyes on you / Lonely street.
Compact disc: released on Topline in Jan'87 by Charly Records. Distributed by: Charly Distribution

Album: released on Topline in Apr'87 by Charly Records. Distributed by: Charly Distribution

Born to be a Rolling Stone.
Album: released on Topline in Jan'85 by Charly Records. Distributed by: Charly Distribution

Musicassette: released on Topline in Jan'85 by Charly Records. Distributed by: Charly Distribution

Crazy beat.
Album: released on Capitol (France) in '83 by Capitol Records. Distributed by: Conifer

Cruisin' with Gene Vincent (Vincent, Gene & The Bluecats).
Album: released on Rockstar in Mar'85

Dressing in black.
Album: released on Magnum Force in Nov'82 by Magnum Music Group Ltd. Distributed by: Magnum Music Group Ltd, PRT, Spartan

Eddie Cochran & Gene Vincent

For the collectors only.
Album: released on Magnum Force in Jun'84 by Magnum Music Group Ltd. Distributed by: Magnum Music Group Ltd, PRT, Spartan

From LA to 'Frisco.
Album: released on Magnum Force in Nov'83 by Magnum Music Group Ltd. Distributed by: Magnum Music Group Ltd, PRT, Spartan

Gene sings Vincent, '56.
Album: released on Capitol (France) in '83 by Capitol Records. Distributed by: Conifer

Gene sings Vincent, '57-'59.
Album: released on Capitol (France) in '83 by Capitol Records. Distributed by: Conifer

Gene Vincent and the Blue Caps.
Album: released on EMI (France) in '83 by EMI Records. Distributed by: Conifer

Gene Vincent & Eddie Cochran (Vincent, Gene & Eddie Cochran).
Picture disc album: released on Pathe MarconiEMI Europe) in Jun'84

Gene Vincent record date, A.
Album: released on EMI (France) in '83 by EMI Records. Distributed by: Conifer

Gene Vincent rocks and the Blues Caps Roll.
Album: released on EMI (France) in '83 by EMI Records. Distributed by: Conifer

Gene Vincent's greatest.
Album: released on Fame (Capitol) in May'82 by Music For Pleasure Records. Distributed by: EMI

Musicassette: released on Fame (Capitol) in May'82 by Music For Pleasure Records. Distributed by: EMI

Gene Vincent singles album, The.
Album: released on Capitol in May'81 by Capitol Records. Distributed by: EMI

Musicassette: released on Capitol in May'81 by Capitol Records. Distributed by: EMI

I'm back and I'm proud.
Tracks: / Rockin robin / In the pines / Be-bop-a-lula / Rainbow at midnight / Black letter / White lightning / Saxy ways / Ruby baby / Lotta lovin / Circle never broken / I heard that lonesome whistle / Scarlet ribbons.
Notes: The first CD from Nightfite label is the classic I'm back and I'm proud album from Gene Vincent. The album recorded full stereo on 24 tracks at Elektra Studiosin Los Angeles, was produced by Kim Fowley and Skip Battyn. Vincent's recently published biography quotes Gene makes Johnny Rotten look a schoolboy once he hit that microphone he'd be the greatest rock n roll singer ever. Sex drugs and rock n roll - Gene invented it. This compact disc features the original very collectable full colour Dandelion packing and sleeve notes with an additional not to provide an update. This is the only Gene Vincent CD in the world to date.
Compact disc: released on Nightfite in Sep'86 by Adrian Owlett. Distributed by: Charly, Spartan

Compact disc: released on Nightflite in Aug'87 by Adrian Owlett. Distributed by: Charly, Spartan

Memorial album.
Double Album: released on EMI (France) in '83 by EMI Records. Distributed by: Conifer

Rainy day sunshine.
Single (7"): released on Magnum in Jan'81 by Bulldog Records. Distributed by: Spartan

Rock n Roll greats.
Tracks: / Say mama / Blue jean bop / Wild cat / Right here on earth / Who slapped John / Walkin home from school / Five feet of lovin / She-she little Sheila / Be-bop-a-lula / Jump back honey / Dance in the street / Pistol packin mama / Crazy beat / High blood pressure / Five days, five days / B-i-bickey bi bo be boo.
Notes: Gene Vincent- a rock and roll great.16 fabulous tracks from the man in black leather Say mama, Pistol packin mama, Wild cat, Be-bop-a-lula everyone is a must.Also included are some b sides and rare tracks to complete this superb package. A terrific sleeve with a sleeve note by Roger St Pierre detailing the life and hard times of Capitol Records one time answer to Elvis.
Album: released on Music For Pleasure in Apr'86 by EMI Records. Distributed by: EMI

Musicassette: released on Music For Pleasure in Apr'86 by EMI Records. Distributed by: EMI

Rock'n'roll heroes

Rock 'n' roll legends.
Boxed set: released on EMI (France) in '83 by EMI Records. Distributed by: Conifer

Rock on with Gene Vincent.
Album: released on MFP in Feb'80 by EMI Records. Distributed by: EMI

Musicassette: released on MFP in Feb'80 by EMI Records. Distributed by: EMI

Roll over Beethoven.
Single (7"): released on Beeb in '74 by BBC Records. Distributed by: PRT

Shakin' up a storm (Vincent, Gene & The Shouts).
Album: released on EMI in Jun'83 by EMI Records. Distributed by: EMI

Musicassette: released on EMI in Jun'83 by EMI Records. Distributed by: EMI

Album: released on Pathe MarconiEMI Europe) in Jun'84

Songs of the James Dean era.
Tracks: / Bop street / Race with the devil / Be-bop-a-lula / Blue jean bop / Important words / Yes I love you baby / Little lover / Crazy legs / Who slapped John / Lotta lovin / Unchained melodies.
Compact disc: released on Capitol in Sep'86 by Capitol Records. Distributed by: EMI

Sounds like Gene Vincent.
Album: released on EMI (France) in '83 by EMI Records. Distributed by: Conifer

Star - '56-'58.
Boxed set: released on Pathe MarconiFrance) in Jun'85

Their finest years (Vincent, Gene & Eddie Cochran).
Album: released on EMI (Germany) in '83 by EMI Records. Distributed by: EMI

Thier finest years 1958 & 1956 (Vincent, Gene & Eddie Cochran).
Album: released on Capitol in Nov'81 by Capitol Records. Distributed by: EMI

Musicassette: released on Capitol in Nov'81 by Capitol Records. Distributed by: EMI

Twist crazy times.
Album: released on EMI (France) in '83 by EMI Records. Distributed by: Conifer

For what it's worth.
Single (7"): released on Virgin in Oct'82

Single (12"): released on Virgin in Oct'82

Holly & the Italians.
Album: released on Virgin in Sep'82

Musicassette: released on Virgin in Sep'82

Honolu.
Single (7"): released on Virgin in Aug'82

Enter in.
Album: released on Sparrow in May'82 by Word Records. Distributed by: Spartan

Musicassette: released on Sparrow in May'82 by Word Records. Distributed by: Spartan

Deadwood stage (Vincent, Jean & The Nitecaps).
Single (7"): released on Abacus in Dec'85 by Abacus. Distributed by: Spartan

17 electric.
Single (7"): released on Buzzzbee Records in Jun'84. Distributed by: Pinnacle

Fantasy of love.
Single (7"):

Feel the need (Vincent, Kathy/Nigel Dean).
Tracks: / Feel the need / Close to the edge.
Single (7"): released on Buzzin in Sep'86. Distributed by: DMS, RCA, Pinnacle

Hotter than fire.
Album: released on Buzzin in Jan'87. Distributed by: DMS, RCA, Pinnacle

One too many heartaches.
Tracks: / Hold tight-don't fight / Sweet dynamite".
Single (7"): released on Buzzin in Jan'87. Distributed by: DMS, RCA, Pinnacle

Single (12"): released on Buzzin in Jan'87. Distributed by: DMS, RCA, Pinnacle

Shakin' all over.
Tracks: / Shakin all over / Sweet dynamite (86 mix).
Single (7"): released on Buzzin in Jul'86. Distributed by: DMS, RCA, Pinnacle

Sweet dynamite.
Single (7"): released on Buzzzbee Records in Sep'85. Distributed by: Pinnacle

Single (12"): released on Buzzzbee Records in Sep'85. Distributed by: Pinnacle

Love blonde.
Musicassette: released on Chevron in Feb'85. Distributed by: Multiple Sound Distributors

Vinnie Vincent Invasion.
Tracks: / Boys are gonna rock / Shoot u full of love / No substitute / Animal / Twisted / Do you wanna make love / Back on the streets / I wanna be your victim / Baby o / Invasion.
Album: released on Chrysalis in Aug'86 by Chrysalis Records. Distributed by: CBS

Musicassette: released on Chrysalis in Aug'86 by Chrysalis Records. Distributed by: CBS

I've got to get you into my life.
Single (7"): released on Gun in Aug'80 by B&C Records. Distributed by: Trojan, Pinnacle, Spartan

Fire in the back streets.
Single (7"): released on Pan Polychord in Dec'84 by Pan Polychord Records. Distributed by: PRT

1928-36 (Vincson, Walter & Charlie McCoy).
Notes: For full information see under: McCoy, Charlie.

Rockin with Rita.
Tracks: / Rockin with Rita / Let's surf.
Single (7"): released on Vindaloo in Jul'86 by Vindaloo Records. Distributed by: WEA, Cartel

Single (12"): released on Vindaloo in Jul'86 by Vindaloo Records. Distributed by: WEA, Cartel

Leroy walks.
Album: released on Contemporary Jazz (USA Import) in Jul'81

Leroy walks again (Vinnegar, Leroy Quintet).
Album: released on Contemporary (USA) in Sep'82. Distributed by: Fantasy (USA) Distribution

My fair lady

Night flight to Dakar

Leroy walks.
Tracks: / Walk in / Would you like to take a walk / On the sunny side of the street / Wakin / Walkin my baby back home / I'll walk alone / Walk on the river.
Album: released on Contemporary in Jan'86 by Contemporary Records. Distributed by: Pinnacle

And the Muse All Stars live at Sandy's (Vinson, Eddie 'Cleanhead'.
Album: released on Muse (Import) in '81

Album: released on Charly in Mar'83 by Charly Records. Distributed by: Charly, Cadillac

Clean machine, The (Vinson, Eddie 'Cleanhead'.
Album: released on Muse in Apr'81 by Import Records. Distributed by: Jazz Horizons Distribution, Jazz Music Distribution, JSU Distribution, Swift Distribution

Eddie 'Cleanhead' Vinson and a roomful of blues (Vinson, Eddie 'Cleanhead'.
Album: released on Muse in Aug'82 by Import Records. Distributed by: Jazz Horizons Distribution, Jazz Music Distribution, JSU Distribution, Swift Distribution

Fun In London (Vinson, Eddie 'Cleanhead').
Album: released on JSP in Mar'82 by JSP Records. Distributed by: Swift, Projection

I want a little girl (Vinson, Eddie 'Cleanhead').
Album: released on Pablo (USA) in '82 by Pablo Records (USA). Distributed by: Wellard, Chris, IMS-Polygram, BMG

Musicassette: released on Pablo (USA) in '82 by Pablo Records (USA). Distributed by: Wellard, Chris, IMS-Polygram, BMG

Jamming the blues.
Album: released on Black Lion in Jul'87 by Black Lion Records. Distributed by: Jazz Music, Chris Wellard, Taylor, H.R., Counterpoint, Cadillac

Kansas City shout (Vinson, Eddie, Count Basie & Joe Turner).
Album: released on Pablo (USA) in '82 by Pablo Records (USA). Distributed by: Wellard, Chris, IMS-Polygram, BMG

Musicassette: released on Pablo (USA) in '82 by Pablo Records (USA). Distributed by: Wellard, Chris, IMS-Polygram, BMG

Mr Cleanhead's back in town (Vinson, Eddie 'Cleanhead').
Album: released on JSP in Jul'82 by JSP Records. Distributed by: Swift, Projection

Mr Cleanhead steps out.
Album: released on Saxonograph (Sweden) in Aug'85

Vinson, Eddie 'Cleanhead'

Back in town.
Tracks: / Cleanhead's back in town / That's the way to treat your woman / Trouble in mind / Kidney stew / Sweet lovin' baby / Caldonia / It ain't necessarily so / Cherry red / I you or is you ain't my baby / I just can't keep the tears from tumblin down / Your baby ain't sweet like mine / Hold it right there.
Notes: Original Bethlehem Recordings P 1957.
Compact disc: released on Charly in Jan'87 by Charly Records. Distributed by: Charly, Cadillac

Cleanhead & roomful of blues.
Tracks: / House of joy / Friend of mine / Movin with Lester / No bones / That's the groovy thing / Past sixty blues / Street light / Farmer's daughter blues.
Notes: All tunes except 1 and 4 arranged by Roomful of Blues and Eddi Cleanhead vinson.Personnel: Eddie cleanhead Vinson-alto saxophone (plus vocals on 2,6,8) Greg Piccolo-tenor saxophone & leader. Rich Ltaille-alto saxophone. Doug James- baritonesaxophone. Bob Enos-trumpet. Porky Cohen- trombone. Al Copley- piano. Ronnie Earl Horvath- guitar. Jimmy Wimpfheimer- bass. John Rossi- drums.
Album: released on Muse (USA) in Aug'86 by Muse Records (USA). Distributed by: Conifer Distribution, Jazz Music Distribution

Vintage...

Vintage blues Various artists (Various Artists).
Album: released on RCA International in '84

Musicassette: released on RCA International in '84

Vintage melodies Songs of the Victorian era - Various artists (Various Artists).
Album: released on Neptune in '78 by Lismor. Distributed by: Spartan

Vintage performances Various artists (Various Artists).
Album: released on Cambra in Apr'84 by Cambra Records. Distributed by: IDS, Conifer

Musicassette: released on Cambra in Apr'84 by Cambra Records. Distributed by: IDS, Conifer

Vintage quiz (Palm Court Theatre Orchestra).
Album: released on Chandos in Apr'84 by Chandos Records. Distributed by: Harmonia Mundi, Taylors

Musicassette: released on Chandos in Apr'84 by Chandos Records. Distributed by: Harmonia Mundi, Taylors

Vintage Bands

Vintage bands Various artists (Various Artists).
Tracks: / Music, maestro, please / Have you met miss Jones / Alexander's ragtime band / She had to go and lose it at the Astoria / Nagaski / I can't dance, I got ants in my pants / Nobody loves a fairy when she's forty / Shine / My brother makes the noises for the talkies / Say it with music / Stay as sweet as you are / It's easy to remember / In the mood / Change partners / Let's face the music and dance / Night is young and you're so beautiful, The / Nightingale sang in Berkely square, The / I'm going to get lit up when the lights go up in London / Here's to the next time / Have you ever seen a dream walkin.
Musicassette: released on Hour Of Pleasure in Oct'86 by Music For Pleasure Records. Distributed by: EMI

Album: released on I Love Country in Sep'86. Distributed by: Counterpoint

Musicassette: released on I Love Country in Sep'86. Distributed by: Counterpoint

Vintage Country
I love country

Vintage country I love country (Various Artists).
Tracks: / Back in the saddle again / I love you a thousand years / Strawberry roan (The) / Foggy mountain breakdown / When it's springtime in Alaska (it's forty below) / Deep water / Rawhide / Folsom Prison blues / Big iron / All for the love of a girl / Wabash Cannonball / Big river / High noon (Do not foresake me) / Mom and dad's waltz / Goodnight Irene / Pride.
Album: released on CBS in Mar'87 by CBS Records. Distributed by: CBS

Musicassette: released on CBS in Mar'87 by CBS Records. Distributed by: CBS

Vintage Irving Berlin

Vintage Irving Berlin Various artists (Various Artists).
Tracks: / Oh how I hate to get up in the morning / Mandy / Pretty girl is like a melody ,A / Rock-a-bye baby / Shaking the blues way / It all belongs to me / Where is the song of songs for me / Let me sing and I'm happy / Puttin on the ritz / Not for all the tea in China / How's chances / Heat wave / How deep is the ocean / Cheek to cheek / Louisiana purchas.
Album: released on New World (USA) in Sep'86 by New World Records (USA). Distributed by: Conifer

Vintage Reggae vol 2

Vintage reggae vol 2 Various artists (Various Artists).
Album: released on Germaine in Apr'86 by Germaine Records. Distributed by: Jetstar

Vinton, Bobby

Roses are red.
Single (7"): released on Old Gold (Reissue) in Jul'82

Vinyl Solution

Vinyl solution Various artists (Various Artists).
Tracks: / Orgasm addict / Valley of the dolls / Peaches / I'm stranded / Straw dogs / Little red riding hood / Kill the poor / Ever fallen in love / One hundred punks / Go Buddy go / Stranglehold / Greatest cockney rip off / White riot / Jet boy, jet girl / Wildkat ways / You crack me up.
Album: released on Dojo in Apr'86 by Castle Communications Records. Distributed by: Cartel

Violators

Die with dignity.
Album: released on No Future in Jan'84 by No Future Records. Distributed by: Pinnacle, Rough Trade, Cartel

Gangland.
Single (7"): released on No Future in Jul'82 by No Future Records. Distributed by: Pinnacle, Rough Trade, Cartel

Life on the red line.
Single (7"): released on Future in Mar'83. Distributed by: Pinnacle

Summer of '81 6 track EP.
Single (12"): released on No Future in Nov'83 by No Future Records. Distributed by: Pinnacle, Rough Trade, Cartel

Single (7"): released on No Future in Jan'84 by No Future Records. Distributed by: Pinnacle, Rough Trade, Cartel

There's a guitar burning.
Single (12"): released on No Future in Nov'83 by No Future Records. Distributed by: Pinnacle, Rough Trade, Cartel

Violent Blue

I won't give in loving you.
Single (7"): released on Magnet in Nov'85 by Magnet Records. Distributed by: BMG

Single (12"): released on Magnet in Nov'85 by Magnet Records. Distributed by: BMG

You've got to stay young.
Album: released on Magnet in Dec'85 by Magnet Records. Distributed by: BMG

Violent Breed

Violent breed.
Album: released on Music For Nations in Nov'83 by Music For Nations Records. Distributed by: Pinnacle

Violent Femmes

Blind leading the naked, The.
Tracks: / Old mother Reagan / No killing / Love and make me three / Faith / Breakin hearts / Special / I held her in my arms / Children of the revolution / Good friends / Heartaches / Cold canyon / Two people / Candlelight song / Country death song / Black girls / World without mercy.
Album: released on Slash in Feb'86 by London Records. Distributed by: Polygram

Musicassette: released on Slash in Feb'86 by London Records. Distributed by: Polygram

Compact disc: released on London in Apr'86 by London Records. Distributed by: Polygram

Children of the revolution.
Tracks: / Children of the revolution / Heartache / Good feeling.
Single (7"): released on Slash in Jan'86 by London Records. Distributed by: Polygram

Single (12"): released on Slash in Jan'86 by London Records. Distributed by: Polygram

Gone daddy gone.
Single (7"): released on Slash in Jun'84 by London Records. Distributed by: Polygram

Single (12"): released on Slash in Jun'84 by London Records. Distributed by: Polygram

Hallowed ground.
Album: released on Slash-London in Jun'85

Musicassette: released on Slash-London in Jun'85

Ugly.
Single (7"): released on Rough Trade in Dec'83 by Rough Trade Records. Distributed by: Rough Trade Distribution, Cartel Distribution

Single (12"): released on Rough Trade in Dec'83 by Rough Trade Records. Distributed by: Rough Trade Distribution, Cartel Distribution

Violent Femmes.
Musicassette: released on Slash in Jan'87 by London Records. Distributed by: Polygram

Album: released on Slash in Jan'87 by London Records. Distributed by: Polygram

Album: released on Rough Trade in Sep'83 by Rough Trade Records. Distributed by: Rough Trade Distribution, Cartel Distribution

Violet White

Sweet disease.
Album: released on Jerkin Crocus in Sep'85. Distributed by: MIS-EMI Distribution

Violin Sect

High days and holidays.
Single (7"): released on Cheek One in Dec'81 by Battersea. Distributed by: PRT

Violinsky

Clog dance.
Single (7"): released on Jet in Jan'79 by Jet Records. Distributed by: CBS

Violin Summit

Violin summit Various artists (Various Artists).
Tracks: / Summit soul / Pentup house / Timme's blues / It don't mean a thing / Pennies from heaven / Only time will tell / Hot toddy.
Notes: Perosonnel: Stuff Smith, Stephane Grappelli,Svend Asmussen,Jean Luc Ponty-violins/Kenny Drew- piano/Niels Henning Orsted Pedersen-bass/Alex Riel-drums. Four of the greatest and most active exponents of jazz violin gathered together under the title Violin Summit for a concert performance recorded in Basel, Switzerland on 30 September 1966. It represents a universal zenith of jazz violin performancein that all four musicians incoporate in their playing virtually every approach to the instrument there has been in jazz history right up to the arrival of freejazz. Essential listening for lovers of jazz violin.
Compact disc: released on Verve (USA) in Jun'86 by Polydor. Distributed by: Polygram

Viorst, Judith

Alexander and the terrible, horrible, ...day.
Musicassette: released on Caedmon(USA) in '84 by Caedmon (USA) Records. Distributed by: Gower, Taylors, Discovery

Vipers

I've got you.
Single (7"): released on Mulligan (Ireland) in Jan'79 by Topic Records. Distributed by: Roots Distribution, Jazz Music Distribution, JSU Distribution, I & B Distribution, Projection Distribution, Wynd-Up Distribution, Celtic Distributions

Vipers Skiffle Group

Coffee bar session.
Tracks: / Gloryland / John B. sails / Wanderin / I saw the light / Precious memories darlin / know the lord laid his hands on me / This lan is your land / If I had a hammer / Easy rider / Cumberland gap, The / Hey Liley Liley o / Don you rock me daddy o / It takes a wo ried man / Maggie Mae / 10,000 years ago / Streamline train / Pick a bale of cotton / Ain't yo glad.
Album: released on Rollercoaster in May'86 b Rollercoaster Records. Distributed by: Sw Distribution, Rollercoaster Distribution

Saludando a los rumberos.
Album: released on Globestyle in Feb'87 b Ace Records. Distributed by: Projection

Virgin Dance

Are you ready (for that feeling).
Single (7"): released on Probe Plus in Jun'8 by Probe Plus Records. Distributed by: Pro Plus Distribution

Single (7"): released on Spartan in Jul'83 Spartan Records. Distributed by: Spartan

Single (7"): released on Spartan in Nov'84 Spartan Records. Distributed by: Spartan

Single (12"): released on Spartan in Nov'84 Spartan Records. Distributed by: Spartan

Desire.
Single (7"): released on Spartan in Jan'84 Spartan Records. Distributed by: Spartan

Single (12"): released on Spartan in Jan'84 Spartan Records. Distributed by: Spartan

Dream is over, The.
Single (7"): released on Spartan in Jul'84 Spartan Records. Distributed by: Spartan

Single (12"): released on Spartan in Jul'84 Spartan Records. Distributed by: Spartan

No disguise.
Single (7"): released on Spartan in Oct'83 Spartan Records. Distributed by: Spartan

Single (12"): released on Spartan in Oct'83 Spartan Records. Distributed by: Spartan

Virgin & Gypsy

Virgin and the Gypsy, The D.H. Lawre **(Bell, Elizabeth).**
Musicassette: released on Pickwick in '8 Pickwick Records. Distributed by: Pickwick tribution, Prism Leisure Distribution, Lugto

Virginians

Ballads & bluegrass

Virgin Prunes

Baby turns blue.
Single (7"): released on Rough Trade in O by Rough Trade Records. Distributed Rough Trade Distribution, Cartel Distributi

Single (12"): released on Rough Trac Oct'82 by Rough Trade Records. Distrib by: Rough Trade Distribution, Cartel Dis tion

Beasts (Seven bastard suck).
Single (12"): released on Rough Trac Mar'82 by Rough Trade Records. Distril by: Rough Trade Distribution, Cartel Dis tion

Come to daddy.
Single 10": released on Rough Trade in M by Rough Trade Records. Distribute Rough Trade Distribution, Cartel Distribu

Single (7"): released on Rough Trade in Jul'81 by Rough Trade Records. Distributed by: Rough Trade, Cartel Distribution

Hidden ile, The, Live in Paris.
Notes: Live recording, made at the Theatre Elysees, Paris, France - June 1986. Contains nine tracks, including 'Pagan Lovesong'.
Album: released on Zebra in May'87 by Cherry Red Records. Distributed by: Pinnacle

Musicassette: released on Zebra in May'87 by Cherry Red Records. Distributed by: Pinnacle

Hidden life-live in paris.
Compact disc: released on Baby in May'87 by New Rose Records. Distributed by: Cartel

die I die.
Album: released on Rough Trade in Nov'82 by Rough Trade Records. Distributed by: Rough Trade, Cartel Distribution

love lasts forever.
Tracks: / Love lasts forever / True life story / Lovelornalimbo / Like the way you're frightened.
Single (7"): released on Baby in Jun'86 by New Rose Records. Distributed by: Cartel

Single (12"): released on Baby in Jun'86 by New Rose Records. Distributed by: Cartel

moon looked down and laughed, The.
Album: released on New Rose in Jul'86. Distributed by: Rough Trade, Cartel

Musicassette: released on New Rose in Jul'86. Distributed by: Rough Trade, Cartel

new form of beauty part 2.
Single (7"): released on Rough Trade in Nov'81 by Rough Trade Records. Distributed by: Rough Trade Distribution, Cartel Distribution

over the rainbow.
Album: released on Baby in Mar'85 by New Rose Records. Distributed by: Cartel

Musicassette: released on Baby in Mar'85 by New Rose Records. Distributed by: Cartel

pagan love songs.
Single (7"): released on Rough Trade in Apr'82 by Rough Trade Records. Distributed by: Rough Trade Distribution, Cartel Distribution

Single (12"): released on Rough Trade in '82 by Rough Trade Records. Distributed by: Rough Trade Distribution, Cartel Distribu...

sandpaper lullaby.
Single (7"): released on Rough Trade in Mar'82 by Rough Trade Records. Distributed by: Rough Trade Distribution, Cartel Distribution

show children.
Single (7"): released on Rough Trade in Dec'81 by Rough Trade Records. Distributed by: Rough Trade Distribution, Cartel Distribution

twenty tens (I've been smoking...).
Single (7"): released on Baby in Jan'81 by New Rose Records. Distributed by: Cartel

gin Star
in the reds.
Single (7"): released on Official in Dec'84 by ... Records. Distributed by: Revolver Distribution, Cartel Distribution

in Steele
in the night.
Single (12"): released on Music For Nations in ... by Music For Nations Records. Distributed by: Pinnacle

in Steele II
villans of the flame.
...: released on Music For Nations in Jul'83 by Music For Nations Records. Distributed by: ...

o, Danny
hall Nice.
Single (12"): released on Worries in Jan'85 by ... Records. Distributed by: Jetstar

...als
come back.
...: released on Wimp in May'83 by Wimp ... Distributed by: Backs, Cartel

Virtue, Frank
Guitar boogie shuffle (Virtue, Frank & The Virtues).
Album: released on President in Oct'80 by President Records. Distributed by: Taylors, Spartan

Virtue In Danger
Virtue in danger Original London cast.
Album: released on TER in May'85

Musicassette: released on TER in May'85

Virus
Pray for war.
Album: released on Metalworks in May'87

Stepping stone.
Single (7"): released on 5th Column in Dec'82 by Graduate Records. Distributed by: Pinnacle

Virus II
Wipe out.
Single (7"): released on Big Sleep in Jun'85 by Big Sleep Records. Distributed by: M.I.S.

Visage
Anvil, The.
Tracks: / Damned don't cry / Move up / Night train / Horseman / Look what they've done / Again we love / Wild life / Whispers / Anvil.
Compact disc: released on Polydor in Jan'83 by Polydor Records. Distributed by: Polygram, Polydor

Fade to grey.
Tracks: / Fade to grey / Mind of a toy.
Single (7"): released on Old Gold in May'86 by Old Gold Records. Distributed by: Lightning, Jazz Music, Spartan, Counterpoint

Fade to grey - The singles collection.
Album: released on Polydor in Oct'83 by Polydor Records. Distributed by: Polygram, Polydor

Musicassette: released on Polydor in Oct'83 by Polydor Records. Distributed by: Polygram, Polydor

Visage.
Tracks: / Blocks on blocks / Dancer / Tar / Fade to grey / Malpaso man / Mind of a toy / Moon over Moscow / Visa-age / Steps.
Compact disc: released on Polydor in Jan'83 by Polydor Records. Distributed by: Polygram, Polydor

Visage (Remix).
Single (7"): released on Polydor in Jul'81 by Polydor Records. Distributed by: Polygram, Polydor

Single (12"): released on Polydor in Jul'81 by Polydor Records. Distributed by: Polygram, Polydor

Visage / The Anvil.
Double musicassette: released on Polydor in Feb'83 by Polydor Records. Distributed by: Polygram, Polydor

Visby Big Band
All of me.
Notes: Featuring: Sonya Hedenbratt, Arne Domnerus.
Album: released on Phontastic in Mar'87. Distributed by: Wellard, Chris

Viseur, Gus
Souvenirs musette.
Tracks: / Soir de dispute / Josseline / Bouurasque / Belle touche / Gracieuzette / Adios Pepita / Bolajo.
Album: released on Accordion Record Club in Jul'86 by Accordion Record Club. Distributed by: Accordion Record Club

Visible Frame
Visible frame Various artists (Various Artists).
Album: released on Future in Jan'84. Distributed by: Pinnacle

Visible Target
Every now and then.
Single (7"): released on Simple in Apr'84 by Simple Records. Distributed by: EMI

Single (12"): released on Simple in Apr'84 by Simple Records. Distributed by: EMI

Vision
Calling of the wild.
Single (7"): released on PRT in Oct'85 by PRT Records. Distributed by: PRT

Single (12"): released on PRT in Oct'85 by PRT Records. Distributed by: PRT

Exposed.
Tracks: / Exposed / Victim,The / Can't let her go / Do it tonight / Kisses don't lie / Seduction,The / Private passion / Where did our love go / Lust 4 U.
Album: released on Domino in May'87 by Domino Records. Distributed by: Charly

Introducing Vision.
Album: released on Tank in Nov'79 by Tank Records

Love dance.
Single (7"): released on MVM in Jun'83

Single (12"): released on MVM in Jun'83

Lucifer's friend.
Single (7"): released on MVM in Oct'82

Single (7"): released on Rerun in Oct'85. Distributed by: Backs, Cartel

Single (12"): released on Rerun in Oct'85. Distributed by: Backs, Cartel

Tears idle tears.
Single (7"): released on PRT in Feb'85 by PRT Records. Distributed by: PRT

Single (12"): released on PRT in Feb'85 by PRT Records. Distributed by: PRT

Walk on the outside.
Single (7"): released on Roxon in Aug'81 by Roxon Records. Distributed by: Pinnacle

Who's that stranger?.
Tracks: / Who's that stranger / Breakdown.
Single (7"): released on PRT in Oct'86 by PRT Records. Distributed by: PRT

Single(12"): released on PRT in Oct'86 by PRT Records. Distributed by: PRT

Vision Of Reggae
Vision of reggae (Various Artists).
Album: released on Wambesi in Mar'86 by Wambesi records. Distributed by: Jetstar

Visions
Paper kids.
Single (7"): released on Top Hold in Jun'82

Visions Various artists (Various Artists).
Tracks: / Flying (theme from ET) / Theme from Harry's Game / Mash theme / Hill Street Blues / Chariots of Fire / Theme from Brideshead Revisited / Arthur's theme / I don't know how to love him / Don't cry for me Argentina / Eve of the war, (The) / Star wars / Fame / For your eyes only / Dallas / Shoestring / Chain, The / Angela / Take that look off your face.
Compact disc: released on K-Tel in Nov'86 by K-Tel Records. Distributed by: Record Merchandisers Distribution, Taylors, Terry Blood Distribution, Wynd-Up Distribution, Relay Distribution, Pickwick Distribution, Solomon & Peres Distribution, Polygram

Album: released on K-Tel in Dec'82 by K-Tel Records. Distributed by: Record Merchandisers Distribution, Taylors, Terry Blood Distribution, Wynd-Up Distribution, Relay Distribution, Pickwick Distribution, Solomon & Peres Distribution, Polygram

Musicassette: released on K-Tel in Dec'82 by K-Tel Records. Distributed by: Record Merchandisers Distribution, Taylors, Terry Blood Distribution, Wynd-Up Distribution, Relay Distribution, Pickwick Distribution, Solomon & Peres Distribution, Polygram

Visions - 15 hit love songs Various artists (Various Artists).
Album: released on Hallmark in Feb'85 by Pickwick Records. Distributed by: Pickwick Distribution, PRT, Taylors

Musicassette: released on Hallmark in Feb'85 by Pickwick Records. Distributed by: Pickwick Distribution, PRT, Taylors

Visions - 28 screen smashes Various artists (Various Artists).
Double Album: released on Cambra in May'85 by Cambra Records. Distributed by: IDS, Conifer

Double musicassette: released on Cambra in May'85 by Cambra Records. Distributed by: IDS, Conifer

Visit
All the walls.
Single (7"): released on Future in Jun'83. Distributed by: Pinnacle

Visitors
Visitors.
Album: released on RCA in Mar'82 by RCA Records. Distributed by: RCA, Roots, Swift, Wollard, Chris, I & B, Solomon & Peres Distribution

Musicassette: released on RCA in Mar'82 by RCA Records. Distributed by: RCA, Roots, Swift, Wollard, Chris, I & B, Solomon & Peres Distribution

Visit to Morin, (A)
Visit to Morin, (A) Greene, Graham (Burden, Hugh).
Musicassette: released on Talking Tape Company in '84 by Talking Tape Company Records

Vist To Morin
Vist to Morin, A (Greene, Graham).
Musicassette: released on Talking Tape Company in '84 by Talking Tape Company Records

Visual
Music got me (2 parts).
Single (7"): released on Prelude in Apr'83. Distributed by: CBS

Single (12"): released on Prelude in Apr'83. Distributed by: CBS

Vital Disorders
Prams.
Single (7"): released on Lowther International in Sep'81 by Lowther International Records. Distributed by: Backs, Cartel

Some people.
Single (7"): released on Lowther International in Feb'85 by Lowther International Records. Distributed by: Backs, Cartel

Zombie.
Single (7"): released on Vital disorders in Jun'82

Vital Dub
Well charged.
Album: released on Virgin in Jan'77

Vitale, Joe
Plantation harbour.
Album: released on Elektra Asylum in Jun'81 by Elektra/Asylum/Nonesuch Records. Distributed by: WEA

Vital Sines
Ice statue.
Single (7"): released on Midnight Music in Mar'85 by Midnight Music Records. Distributed by: Rough Trade Distribution, Cartel Distribution

Vital vinyl (vol.1)
Vital vinyl (vol.1) Various artists (Various Artists).
Album: released on Hallmark in May'80 by Pickwick Records. Distributed by: Pickwick Distribution, PRT, Taylors

Musicassette: released on Hallmark in May'80 by Pickwick Records. Distributed by: Pickwick Distribution, PRT, Taylors

Vital vinyl (vol.2)
Vital vinyl (vol.2) Various artists (Various Artists).
Album: released on Hallmark in May'80 by Pickwick Records. Distributed by: Pickwick Distribution, PRT, Taylors

Musicassette: released on Hallmark in May'80 by Pickwick Records. Distributed by: Pickwick Distribution, PRT, Taylors

Vitamin Z
Burning flame.
Single (7"): released on Mercury in Feb'84 by Phonogram Records. Distributed by: Polygram Distribution

Single (12"): released on Mercury in Feb'84 by Phonogram Records. Distributed by: Polygram Distribution

Circus ring (we scream about).
Single (7"): released on Mercury in May'85 by Phonogram Records. Distributed by: Polygram Distribution

Single (12"): released on Mercury in May'85 by Phonogram Records. Distributed by: Polygram Distribution

Everytime that I see you.
Single (7"): released on Mercury in Jul'85 by Phonogram Records. Distributed by: Polygram Distribution

Single (12"): released on Mercury in Jul'85 by Phonogram Records. Distributed by: Polygram Distribution

Double-pack single: released on Mercury in Aug'85 by Phonogram Records. Distributed by: Polygram Distribution

Hi hi friend.
Single (7"): released on Mercury in Nov'85 by Phonogram Records. Distributed by: Polygram Distribution

Single (12"): released on Mercury in Nov'85 by Phonogram Records. Distributed by: Polygram Distribution

Rites of passage.
Tracks: Hi hi friend / Casablanca / Circus ring / Something we can do / Burning flame / Angela / Every time that I see you / Anybody out there.
Notes: Vitamin Z's debut album.
Compact disc: released on Mercury in Nov'85 by Phonogram Records. Distributed by: Polygram Distribution

Album: released on Mercury in Nov'85 by Phonogram Records. Distributed by: Polygram Distribution

Musicassette: released on Mercury in Nov'85 by Phonogram Records. Distributed by: Polygram Distribution

Compact disc: released on Mercury in Nov'85 by Phonogram Records. Distributed by: Polygram Distribution

Vitous

Miroslav Vitous group (Vitous/Surman/Kirkland/Christensen).
Album: released on ECM (Import) in Apr'81 by ECM Records. Distributed by: IMS, Polygram, Virgin through EMI

Vitous, Miroslav

**Dream
Emergence.**
Tracks: / Epilogue / Transformation / Atlantis suite: / Atlantis suite-Matter and spirit / Atlantis suite-Emergence of the spirit / Atlantis suite-Choice (The) / Atlantis suite-Destruction into energy / Wheel of fortune (when the face gets pale) / Regards to Gershwin's honeyman / Alice in Wonderland / Morning Lake for ever / Variations on Spanish themes.
Compact disc: released on ECM (Germany) in Dec'86 by ECM Records. Distributed by: IMS, Polygram, Virgin through EMI

Album: released on ECM (Germany) in Jan'87 by ECM Records. Distributed by: IMS, Polygram, Virgin through EMI

Compact disc: released on ECM (Germany) in Jan'87 by ECM Records. Distributed by: IMS, Polygram, Virgin through EMI

Journey's end.
Album: released on ECM (Germany) in Mar'83 by ECM Records. Distributed by: IMS, Polygram, Virgin through EMI

Mountain in the clouds (That's Jazz Series).
Album: released on Atlantic in Oct'77 by WEA Records. Distributed by: WEA

Rypdal/Vitous/Dejohnette

Viva

Chris must stay.
Single (7"): released on Cambra in Nov'81 by Cambra Records. Distributed by: IDS, Conifer

Dealers of the night.
Album: released on Metronome (Germany) in Sep'83. Distributed by: Jazz Music Distribution

Radio saviour.
Single (7"): released on Square in Jan'80

Viva El Ritmo...

Viva El Ritmo:Cuban-Baila Various artists (Various Artists).
Album: released on Earthworks Int. in Sep'85 by Earthworks Records. Distributed by: Earthworks Distributors, Rough Trade, Cartel, Projection

Viva la revolution

Viva la revolution Various artists (Various Artists).
Album: released on Cambra in Mar'85 by Cambra Records. Distributed by: IDS, Conifer

Musicassette: released on Cambra in Mar'85 by Cambra Records. Distributed by: IDS, Conifer

Viva Marconi

Serious dreaming.
Single (7"): released on Zim Zam in Feb'83

Vivat Regina

Vivat Regina (A Royal portrait in sound).
Album: released on BBC in Apr'77 by BBC Records & Tapes. Distributed by: EMI, PRT, Pye

Musicassette: released on BBC in Apr'77 by BBC Records & Tapes. Distributed by: EMI, PRT, Pye

Viva um khomto

Viva um khomto (Various Artists).
Album: released on Konkurrel in 30 May'87

Viva Zimbabwe

Viva Zimbabwe Various artists (Various Artists).
Album: released on Rough Trade in Sep'83 by Rough Trade Records. Distributed by: Rough Trade Distribution, Cartel Distribution

Vocal group album

Vocal group album Various Artists (Various Artists).
Double Album:

Vocal group R'N'B

Vocal group R'n'B from Joe Davis vol 2 1954-56 Various artists (Various Artists).
Album: released on Krazy Kat in Sep'85. Distributed by: Jazz Music, Swift, Chris Wellard, H.R. Taylor, Charly, Hotshot, IRS Distribution

Vocal group R'N'B volume 1 Various artists (Various Artists).
Album: released on Krazy Kat in Jul'85. Distributed by: Jazz Music, Swift, Chris Wellard, H.R. Taylor, Charly, Hotshot, IRS Distribution

Vocal groups (Doo-Wop)

Vocal groups vol.21 (Doo-Wop) Various artists (Various Artists).
Album: released on Relic (US) in Mar'85

Vocal groups vol.22 (Doo-Wop) Various artists (Various Artists).
Album: released on Relic (US) in Mar'85

Vocal groups vol.23 (Doo-Wop) Various artists (Various Artists).
Album: released on Relic (US) in Mar'85

Vocal groups vol.24 (Doo-Wop) Various artists (Various Artists).
Album: released on Relic (US) in Mar'85

Vocal groups vol.25 (Doo-Wop) Various artists (Various Artists).
Album: released on Relic (US) in Mar'85

Vocal groups vol.26 (Doo-Wop) Various artists (Various Artists).
Album: released on Relic (US) in Mar'85

Vocal groups vol.27 (Doo-Wop) Various artists (Various Artists).
Musicassette: released on Relic (US) in Mar'85

Vogue

Dancing the night away.
Single (7"): released on Mercury in Jul'81 by Phonogram Records. Distributed by: Polygram Distribution

Single (12"): released on Mercury in Jul'81 by Phonogram Records. Distributed by: Polygram Distribution

Love buzz.
Single (7"): released on Mercury in May'82 by Phonogram Records. Distributed by: Polygram Distribution

Single (12"): released on Mercury in May'82 by Phonogram Records. Distributed by: Polygram Distribution

Voice

Sign your name.
Single (7"): released on Secret in Dec'80

Voice Farm

Double garage.
Single (7"): released on Alternative Tentacles in Oct'82 by Alternative Tentacles Records. Distributed by: Rough Trade, Pinnacle

Voice of America

I will tell.
Album: released on Decca (Elite) in Jul'81 by Decca Records. Distributed by: Polygram, IMS

Story of love.
Tracks: Story of love / V.O.A.
Single (7"): released on Virgin in Jul'87 by Virgin Records. Distributed by: EMI, Virgin Distribution

Single (12"): released on Virgin in Jul'87 by Virgin Records. Distributed by: EMI, Virgin Distribution

Voice Of Authority

Very big in America right now.
Album: released on Cherry Red in Oct'84 by Cherry Red Records. Distributed by: Pinnacle

Single (12"): released on Cherry Red in Aug'84 by Cherry Red Records. Distributed by: Pinnacle

Voice Of God Collective

Sounds like Bromley.
Album: released on Plymouth Sounds in Dec'84 by Plymouth Sounds Records. Distributed by: Backs, Cartel

Voice of The Beehive

I walk the earth.

Just a city.
Tracks: Just a city / I walk the earth / Shocks.
Single (12"): released on Food in Mar'87 by Food Records. Distributed by: Rough Trade, Cartel, WEA

Just a city.
Tracks: Just a city.
Single (7"): released on Food in Mar'87 by Food Records. Distributed by: Rough Trade, Cartel, WEA

Voices

Beauty is the beast.
Single (7"): released on Mercury in Oct'83 by Phonogram Records. Distributed by: Polygram Distribution

Single (12"): released on Mercury in Oct'83 by Phonogram Records. Distributed by: Polygram Distribution

Sacrificial rites.
Single (7"): released on Voice in Apr'83

Single (12"): released on Voice in Apr'83

Voices in the dark

Keep it warm.
Tracks: Keep it warm / Keep it warm (remix) / Keep it warm (inst).
Single (7"): released on Champion in May'87 by Champion Records. Distributed by: RCA

Single (12"): released on Champion in May'87 by Champion Records. Distributed by: RCA

Voices Of Progress

Mini-bus driver.
Album: released on Negus Roots in Oct'82 by Negus Roots Records. Distributed by: Jetstar

Single (12"): released on Negus Roots in Sep'82 by Negus Roots Records. Distributed by: Jetstar

Voice, Steve

Back on my feet.
Single (7"): released on Red Bus in Jun'84 by Red Bus Records. Distributed by: PRT

I can't get over you.
Single (7"): released on Red Bus in Jul'82 by Red Bus Records. Distributed by: PRT

Why don't you call me.
Single (7"): released on Red Bus in Mar'81 by Red Bus Records. Distributed by: PRT

Vold, E

Shadows.
Single (7"): released on WEA International in Jan'84 by WEA Records. Distributed by: WEA

Voi Vod

Killing technology.
Album:

Rrrooooaaarrr.
Album: released on Noise in May'86 by Dorane. Distributed by: Revolver, Cartel

War and pain.
Album: released on Music For Nations in Sep'84 by Music For Nations Records. Distributed by: Pinnacle

Volz

Boanerges.
Album: by Pilgrim Records. Distributed by: Rough Trade, Cartel

Volcano

It's not the time.
Single (7"): released on Volcano in Feb'83 by Volcano Records. Distributed by: Jetstar

I wanna make it (yeah I do).
Single (7"): released on Krr-unch in Feb'82

Volcanoes

Into the psyche.
Album: released on Hybrid in Oct'86 by Staff Records. Distributed by: Pinnacle

Strangers in the night.
Single (7"): released on Volcanic in Jan'84

Volcano Suns

All night lotus party.
Album: released on Homestead in Oct'86. Distributed by: Rough Trade, Cartel, Shigaku

Bright Orange, (The).
Album: released on Homestead in Aug'85. Distributed by: Rough Trade, Cartel, Shigaku

Sea cruise.
Tracks: / Sea cruise / Greasy spine.
Single (7"): released on Homestead in Nov'. Distributed by: Rough Trade, Cartel, Shigaku

Vollenweider, Andreas

Down to the moon.
Tracks: / Down to the moon / Moon dance / Steam forest / Water moon / Might fire dance / Quiet observer / Silver wheel / Drown in p... light / Secret, the candle and love (The) / H... patience at bamboo forest / Three silver lad... dance / La luna at l'enfant.
Album: released on CBS in Nov'86 by C... Records. Distributed by: CBS

Musicassette: released on CBS in Nov'86 CBS Records. Distributed by: CBS

Compact disc: released on CBS in Nov'86 CBS Records. Distributed by: CBS

Night fire dance.
Tracks: / Play of five balls.
Single (7"): released on CBS in Nov'86 by ... Records. Distributed by: CBS

Single (12"): released on CBS in Nov'86 by CBS Records. Distributed by: CBS

Pace verde.
Single (7"): released on Geffen in Apr'8... Geffen Records. Distributed by: WEA, CB...

White winds.
Tracks: / White winds the white boat, (T... Hall of the stairs hall of the mosaic (meeting...

Glass hall (choose the crystal), (The) / Play of
e five planets canopy choir /
'oman and the stone, (The) / Stone (close up),
ne. / Phases of the three moons / Flight feet
d root hands / Brotherhood / Sisterseed / Tri-
gy (at the white magic gardens) / White winds.
ompact disc: released on CBS in Jun'85 by
3S Records. Distributed by: CBS

bum: released on CBS in May'85 by CBS
cords. Distributed by: CBS

usicassette: released on CBS in May'85 by
3S Records. Distributed by: CBS

ompact disc: released on CBS in May'85 by
3S Records. Distributed by: CBS

ollerman, Scarlett Von

ld obsessions.
gle (7"): released on Jet in Nov'82 by Jet
cords. Distributed by: CBS

olti

orazon money.
cks: / Corazon money / Bucks.
gle (12"): released on Cram in Mar'86. Dis-
uted by: Nine Mile, Cartel

olz, Greg

er is rising,The.
es: Greg says: "I want to push out the walls
nat Christian music can infiltratethe world
more."
um: released on Myrrh in Nov'86 by Word
ords. Distributed by: Word Distribution

icassette: released on Myrrh in Nov'86 by
d Records. Distributed by: Word Distribu-

n Deyen, Adelbert

essions.
m: released on Sky (Germany) in Aug'85

n Freeman

nade and Blues.
n: released on Nessa in Sep'79. Dis-
d by: Projection, Swift

nk, Henny

otin' Henny Vonk.
n: released on Timeless(import) in
2. Distributed by: Cadillac

negut Soundbook

egut Soundbook Vonnegut, Kurt
us Artists).
assette: released on Caedmon(USA) in
I by Caedmon (USA) Records. Dis-
d by: Taylors, Discovery

o

leben.
: released on Sky (Germany) in May'84

Wernherr

ic climb (Von Wernherr, Otto and
nne).
/ Cosmic climb / We are the gods.
(7"): released on Receiver in May'86 by
r Records. Distributed by: Pinnacle

Voodoo

Crying my heart out.
Single (12"): released on Leo in Nov'82

Voodoo Child

Acid tails and mermaids.
Album: released on Aftermath in Sep'86 by
Aftermath Records. Distributed by: Cartel

Rain (summer mix).
Tracks: / Rain (summer mix) / Glory to the lo-
vers.
Single (7"): released on Aftermath in Jul'87 by
Aftermath Records. Distributed by: Cartel

Voodoo Dolls

Problems with girls.
Album: released on Sunjay in Jun'87

Voodoo Dolls.
Album: released on Red Dynamite (Germany)
in Aug'85

Voodoo Gang

Return of the turtle.
Album: released on Enja (Germany) in Nov'84
by Enja Records (W.Germany). Distributed by:
Cadillac Music

V.O.P

Heroes.
Single (12"): released on Rialto in Jul'83 by
Rialto Records. Distributed by: Pinnacle

Vorhaus, David

White noise.
Album: released on Virgin in May'75

Musicassette: released on Virgin in May'75

Voronezh Vocal Group

**Voronezh girls vocal group (Traditional
songs).**
Album: released on Melodiya (USSR) in
May'78. Distributed by: T.B.C Distribution

Vow Wow

Cyclone.
Album: released on East Rock in Jul'86 by
L.O.E. Entertainment Records. Distributed by:
PRT

Musicassette: released on East Rock in Jul'86
by L.O.E. Entertainment Records. Distributed
by: PRT

Live.
Album: released on Passport in Feb'87. Distributed by: Polygram

Voxpop

Sleeping in a strangers bed.
Single (7"): released on Hollywood in Mar'82
by Hollywood Records. Distributed by: Pinnacle

Voyager

King of Siam.
Single (7"): released on RCA in Jul'81 by RCA
Records. Distributed by: RCA, Roots, Swift,
Wellard, Chris, I & B, Solomon & Peres Distribu-
tion

Like a stone.
Single (7"): released on Flying in Nov'82 by Flying Records. Distributed by: DMS

Rosie.
Single (7"): released on RCA in Oct'81 by RCA
Records. Distributed by: RCA, Roots, Swift,
Wellard, Chris, I & B, Solomon & Peres Distribu-
tion

Voyager.
Album: released on RCA in Oct'81 by RCA
Records. Distributed by: RCA, Roots, Swift,
Wellard, Chris, I & B, Solomon & Peres Distribu-
tion

Musicassette: released on RCA in Oct'81 by
RCA Records. Distributed by: RCA, Roots,
Swift, Wellard, Chris, I & B, Solomon & Peres
Distribution

Voyager Various artists (Various Artists).
Album: released on Start in Jul'85. Distributed
by: CBS, PRT

Musicassette: released on Start in Jul'85. Distributed by: CBS, PRT

Voyages Of Sinbad (I to III)

Voyages Of Sinbad (I to III) (Jones,
Terry).
Musicassette: released on Listen Productions
in Nov'84. Distributed by: H.R. Taylor, Hayward
Promotions Distribution

Voyages of Sinbad (IV to VI) (Jones,
Terry).
Musicassette: released on Listen Productions
in Nov'84. Distributed by: H.R. Taylor, Hayward
Promotions Distribution

Vrethammar, Sylvia

In Goodman's land

Rio de Janeiro.
Album: released on Sonet in Jan'86 by Sonet
Records. Distributed by: PRT

Y Viva Espana.
Album: released on Sonet in Aug'74 by Sonet
Records. Distributed by: PRT

Vriar

Too young.
Musicassette: released on Heavy Metal in
Oct'85 by FM-Revolver Records. Distributed by:
EMI

Vrtacek, Charles

Monkey on a hard roll.

Album: released on Leisure Time in Sep'86.
Distributed by: Recommended

V.S.O.P. The Quintet

Five stars.
Album: released on Japanese Import in Jan'80

Live under the sky.
Album: released on Japanese Import in Jan'80

V-SOR X

Authors 2.
Single (7"): released on DOX in Feb'83 by DOX
Records. Distributed by: Neon Distribution

Cue.
Single (7"): released on Dox Music in Aug'87

V. Spy V. Spy

A.O. Mod. T.V. Vers..
Tracks: / Don't tear it down / Credit cards /
Mission man / Pockets of pride / Go to work /
Sallie-Anne / Snowblind / Use your heard /
Peace and quiet / Take me away.
Album: released on WEA in Jul'87 by WEA
Records. Distributed by: WEA

Musicassette: released on WEA in Jul'87 by
WEA Records. Distributed by: WEA

V-Squad

Eat the meat.
Single (7"): released on Carrere America
(USA) in Jul'81 by Polygram

Vuchovich, Larry

City sounds, village voices.
Album: released on Palo Alto (Italy) in Jan'84

Vuckovich, Larry Trio

Quintet blues for red.
Album: released on Hot House in Dec'85. Distributed by: Jazz Music

Vyllies, The

Ahla.
Single (7"): released on Music For Nations in
May'86 by Music For Nations Records. Dis-
tributed by: Pinnacle

Musicassette: released on Music For Nations
in May'86 by Music For Nations Records. Distributed by: Pinnacle

Lillith.
Tracks: / Whispers in the shadows / Seventh
heaven / Bad trip / Food prayer, (The) / Nuit des
Vyllies, (La) / Give me a name / Beautiful diseases / Black raven, (The) / Desire (repetition
desperation).
Album: released on Fun After All in Jul'86. Distributed by: Pinnacle

Sacred games.
Notes: Second album from Swiss all-girl trio.
Indie-type 'Gothic' act.
Album: released on Fun After All in Jun'87. Dis-
tributed by: Pinnacle

Compact disc: released on Fun After All in
Jun'87. Distributed by: Pinnacle

Scared games.
Album: released on Fun After All in 30 May'87.
Distributed by: Pinnacle

W

Wackie's Rhythm Force
AFRICAN ROOTS ACT IV.
Album: released on Jetstar, Jul'84 Dist: Jetstar, Stage One

AFRICAN ROOTS ACT V.
Album: released on Wackies, Nov'84 by Wackies Records. Dist: Jetstar

Wadada
REGGAE SUNSPLASH.
Single (12"): released on Solomonic, Aug'83 by Solomonic Records. Dist: Jetstar, Pinnacle

Waddington, Bill
DON'T FORGET THE OLD FOLKS AT CHRISTMAS.
Tracks: / Don't forget the old folks at Christmas / Tra la la.
Single (7"): released on Ritz, Nov'86 by Outlet Records. Dist: Outlet, Prism Leisure Distribution, Record Services Distribution (Ireland), Roots

Wade, Decca
IF IT WASN'T FOR RITA.
Single (7"): released on EMI, Apr'83 by EMI Records. Dist: EMI

Wade in the Water
WADE IN THE WATER.
Album: released on Jazz Reactivation, Jul'82 Dist: PRT

Wade, Norman
REAL COUNTRY.
Album: Dist: Swift

Wade, Paul
SHAKESPEARE SONGS OF THE TWENTIETH CENTURY.
Album: by Look Music. Dist: Jazz Music

Waders
QWACKER SONG.
Single (7"): released on KAR, Sep'81

Wade, Terri
LIGHT.
Tracks: / Light (7" mix) / Light (inst) / Light.
Single (12"): released on Big Top, Jun'87 Dist: Cartel

LIVE FOR TONIGHT.
Single (12"): released on Big Top, Sep'85 Dist: Cartel

SINGLE GIRL.
Single (7"): released on Big Top, Apr'85 Dist: Cartel

Single (12"): released on Big Top, Cartel

Wade, Wayne
I'M THE PROMOTER.
Tracks: / I'm the promoter / I'm the promoter (version).
Single (12"): released on Greensleeves, Jun'87 by Greensleeves Records. Dist: BMG, Jetstar, Spartan

IT AIN'T EASY.
Single (12"): released on Revue, Oct'84 by Revue Records. Dist: Creole

LADY.
Single (7"): released on Epic, Jun'83 by CBS Records. Dist: CBS

Single (12"): released on Epic, Jun'83 by CBS Records. Dist: CBS

LOOKING FOR LOVE.
Album: released on Dub, Oct'85

Wagner, Jack
DON'T GIVE UP YOUR DAY JOB.
Tracks: / Weatherman says / Island fever / Love...find it / It's what we don't say / Easy way out / Common man / Lovers in the night / Sneakin' suspicions / It's been a long time / Back home again.
Album: released on Qwest, Jul'87 by WEA Records. Dist: WEA

Cassette: released on Qwest, Jul'87 by WEA Records. Dist: WEA

Wagner, Roger Chorale
BEST OF THE ROGER WAGNER CHORALE CHRISTMAS CAROLS.
Album: released on MFP (Capitol), Dec'82 by EMI Records. Dist: EMI

Cassette: released on MFP (Capitol), Dec'82 by EMI Records. Dist: EMI

Wagners Greatest Hits
WAGNERS GREATEST HITS Various artists (Various Artists).
Cassette: released on CBS, Jul'83 by CBS Records. Dist: CBS

Wagoner, Porter
20 OF THE BEST.
Album: released on RCA International, '84

Cassette: released on RCA International, '84

BEST OF PORTER WAGONER.
Album: released on Victor, '74

COUNTRY MEMORIES.
Cassette: released on K-Tel Goldmasters, Aug'84 by K-Tel Records. Dist: K-Tel

HITS OF DOLLY PARTON & PORTER WAGONER.
Album: released on RCA, Oct'77 by RCA Records. Dist: RCA, Roots, Swift, Wellard, Chris, I & B, Solomon & Peres Distribution

Cassette: released on RCA, Oct'77 by RCA Records. Dist: RCA, Roots, Swift, Wellard, Chris, I & B, Solomon & Peres Distribution

HITS OF PORTER WAGONER.
Album: released on RCA, Jun'78 by RCA Records. Dist: RCA, Roots, Swift, Wellard, Chris, I & B, Solomon & Peres Distribution

Cassette: released on RCA, Jun'78 by RCA Records. Dist: RCA, Roots, Swift, Wellard, Chris, I & B, Solomon & Peres Distribution

LOVE SHINE.
Album: released on Astan, Nov'84 by Astan Records. Dist: Counterpoint

Cassette: released on Astan, Nov'84 by Astan Records. Dist: Counterpoint

PORTER WAGONER.
Tracks: / One more time / Love paid it all / Sugar foot rag / For a good time call Naomi / Louisiana Saturday night / Same way you cam in, (The) / Sorrow on the rocks / What a memory we'd make / Satan wore satin / Uncle Pen.
Album: released on MCA Import, Mar'86 by MCA Records. Dist: Polygram, IMS

Cassette: released on Audio Fidelity, Oct'84 Dist: PRT

Wah
COME BACK.
Single (7"): released on Beggars Banquet, Jun'84 by Beggars Banquet Records. Dist: WEA

Single (12"): released on Beggars Banquet, Jun'84 by Beggars Banquet Records. Dist: WEA

FORGET THE DOWN.
Single (7"): released on Eternal, Jun'81 by Eternal Records. Dist: WEA

HOPE(I WISH YOU'D BELIEVE ME).
Single (7"): released on WEA, Mar'83 by WEA Records. Dist: WEA

SOME DAY.
Single (7"): released on Eternal, Oct'81 by Eternal Records. Dist: WEA

Single (12"): released on Eternal, Oct'81 by Eternal Records. Dist: WEA

STORY OF THE BLUES.
Single (7"): released on Eternal, Nov'82 by Eternal Records. Dist: WEA

Single (12"): released on Eternal, Nov'82 by Eternal Records. Dist: WEA

WAY WE WAH, THE.
Album: released on WEA, Nov'84 by WEA Records. Dist: WEA

Cassette: released on WEA, Nov'84 by WEA Records. Dist: WEA

YOU CAN'T PUT YOUR ARMS AROUND A MEMORY.
Single (12"): released on WEA, Mar'83 by WEA Records. Dist: WEA

Wah Heat
7 MINUTES TO MIDNIGHT.
Single (7"): released on Inevitable, Feb'83 by Inevitable Records. Dist: Rough Trade

Wahib
MY EYES.
Single (7"): released on Hits From Heaven, Apr'82 Dist: Rough Trade

Wahl, Jan
RUNAWAY JONAH & OTHER BIBLICAL ADVENTURES.
Cassette: released on Caedmon(USA), Sep'85 by Caedmon (USA) Records. Dist: Taylors, Discovery

Wahnfried, Richard
MAGATONE.
Album: released on Thunderbolt, Apr'86 by Magnum Music Group Ltd. Dist: Magnum Music Group Ltd, PRT Distribution, Spartan Distribution

Compact disc: released on Thunderbolt, Apr'86 by Magnum Music Group Ltd. Dist: Magnum Music Group Ltd, PRT Distribution, Spartan Distribution

MEGATONE.
Tracks: / Angry young boys / Aganemory / Rich meets Max.
Compact disc: released on Thunderbolt, Oct'86 by Magnum Music Group Ltd. Dist: Magnum Music Group Ltd, PRT Distribution, Spartan Distribution

PLAYS MEGATONE.
Album: released on In Team(W.Germany), Feb'85 Dist: Impex Distribution

Waihirere Maori Club
MUSIC OF AOTEAROA.
Album: released on Viking, Jul'79 Dist: Harmonia Mundi Distributors

Cassette: released on Viking, Jul'79 Dist: Harmonia Mundi Distributors

Waikiki Beach Boys
HAWAIIAN FAVOURITES.
Tracks: / Hawaiian wedding song / Hawaiian march / Analani E / Ports of Paradise / Shimmering sands / My little green shack in Kealakua / Kono knoi / Mamoola moon / Kahola march / Hawaiia calls / Hawaii tattoo / Sweet Leilani / Flower of the islands / Honi kaua / Garlands for your hair / Song of the islands / Tiny bubbles / Beautiful Moorea / Hawaiian honeymoon / March to Diamond Head.
Cassette: released on Hour Of Pleasure, Oct'86 by Music For Pleasure Records. Dist: EMI

PLAY YOUR 40 ALL-TIME HAWAII FAVOURITES.
Double Album: released on MFP, Sep'8 EMI Records. Dist: EMI

Double cassette: released on MFP, Sep'8 EMI Records. Dist: EMI

Waikikis
HAWAII TATTOO (The best of the Wak
Album: released on Emerald, May'78 by erald Records. Dist: Ross, PRT, Solom Peres Distribution

Cassette: released on Emerald, May'78 by erald Records. Dist: Ross, PRT, Solom Peres Distribution

WAIKIKI WELCOME.
Album: released on Emerald, '78 by Em Records. Dist: Ross, PRT, Solomon & F Distribution

Cassette: released on Emerald, '78 by Em Records. Dist: Ross, PRT, Solomon & F Distribution

Waller, Bunny
ARAB OIL.
Single (12"): released on Nighthawk, Jun Faulty Products Records. Dist: Pinnacle.

BACK TO SCHOOL (Waller, Bunny Iomic Players).
Single (12"): released on Solomonic, N by Solomonic Records. Dist: Jetstar, Pinna

BACK TO SCHOOL.
Tracks: / School days dub.
Single (7"): released on Solomonic, Nov Solomonic Records. Dist: Jetstar, Pinna

Single (12"): released on Solomonic, by Solomonic Records. Dist: Jetstar, Pir

Single (12"): released on Solomonic, Oc Solomonic Records. Dist: Jetstar, Pinna

BLACKHEART MAN.
Album: released on Island, Sep'76 by Records. Dist: Polygram

BUNNY WAILER LIVE.
Album: released on Solomonic, Jan'84 Iomonic Records. Dist: Jetstar, Pinnacle

BUNNY WAILER SINGS THE WAI
Album: released on Island, Feb'81 by Records. Dist: Polygram

Cassette: released on Island, Feb'81 by Records. Dist: Polygram

COLLIE MAN.
Single (12"): released on Solomonic, Solomonic Records. Dist: Jetstar, Pinn

CONQUEROR.
Single (12"): released on Solomonic, J Solomonic Records. Dist: Jetstar, Pinn

ELECTRO RAP.
Single (7"): released on Solomonic, J Solomonic Records. Dist: Jetstar, Pinna

Single (12"): released on Solomonic, Solomonic Records. Dist: Jetstar, Pinna

LIVE!.
Album: released on Solomonic, Mar'1 Iomonic Records. Dist: Jetstar, Pinna

MARKET PLACE.
Album: released on Solomonic, Sep' Iomonic Records. Dist: Jetstar, Pinna

MARKETPLACE.
Album: released on CSA, Feb'86 by ords. Dist: PRT, Jetstar

MODERATION.
Single (7"): released on Solomonic, Solomonic Records. Dist: Jetstar, Pinna

ngle (12"): released on Solomonic, Aug'83
r Solomonic Records. Dist: Jetstar, Pinnale

ROTEST.
bum: released on Island, Oct'77 by Island
cords. Dist: Polygram

DING.
gle (7"): released on Solomonic, Sep'81 by
lomonic Records. Dist: Jetstar, Pinnacle

OCK'N'ROLL GROOVE.
bum: released on Solomonic, Mar'84 by Solomonic Records. Dist: Jetstar, Pinnacle

OTS MAN SKANKING.
bum: released on Shanachie, Jul'87 Dist:
rns/Triple Earth Distribution, Roots

OTS RADICS ROCKERS REGGAE.
bum: released on Shanachie, Jan'84

LE DANCE HALL.
bum: released on Solomonic, Aug'87 by So-
onic Records. Dist: Jetstar, Pinnacle

RIOUS THING.
cks: / Food / Serious thing.
gle (12"): released on Solomonic, Jul'86 by
lomonic Records. Dist: Jetstar, Pinnacle

G THE WAILERS.
bum: released on Island, Mar'81 by Island
cords. Dist: Polygram

RS IN YOUR EYES.
gle (7"): released on Solomonic, Jun'86 by
omonic Records. Dist: Jetstar, Pinnacle
gle (12"): released on Solomonic, Jun'86 by
omonic Records. Dist: Jetstar, Pinnacle

BUTE.
m: released on Solomonic, Mar'86 by Sonic Records. Dist: Jetstar, Pinnacle

bum: released on Solomonic, Mar'84 by Sonic Records. Dist: Jetstar, Pinnacle

ailers

NIN'.
m: released on Island, May'74 by Island
rds. Dist: Polygram

ette: released on Island, May'74 by Island
rds. Dist: Polygram

CH THE FIRE.
m: released on Island, May'74 by Island
rds. Dist: Polygram

ette: released on Island, May'74 by Island
rds. Dist: Polygram

GAE GREATS.
m: released on Island, Apr'85 by Island
rds. Dist: Polygram

ette: released on Island, Apr'85 by Island
rds. Dist: Polygram

iling Souls

OF THE WAILING SOULS, THE.
: released on Empire (reggae), Jun'84
star

CE BACK.
(7"): released on Greensleeves, Apr'83
sleeves Records. Dist: BMG, Jetstar,
n

ONDS AND PEARLS (Wailing Souls
Tullo).
(12"): released on Greensleeves, Apr'83
By Greensleeves Records. Dist: BMG,
star

OUSE ROCK.
: released on Greensleeves, Jul'81 by
sleeves Records. Dist: BMG, Jetstar,

BING AND RUNNING.
12"): released on Cha-Cha, Dec'82 by
a. Dist: Jetstar

GAN RACE.
7"): released on Taxi, Oct'83 by Taxi
. Dist: Jetstar Distribution

NCHERS.
on Greensleeves, Feb'83 by
eeves Records. Dist: BMG, Jetstar,

OM RISE KINGDOM FALL.
on Greensleeves,
y Greensleeves Records. Dist: BMG,
star

ON THE LINE.
eleased on Live & Learn, Nov'86 Dist:

OOM.
2"): released on Island, Mar'81 by Is-

---

land Records. Dist: Polygram

ON THE ROCKS.
Album: released on Greensleeves, Sep'83 by
Greensleeves Records. Dist: BMG, Jetstar,
Spartan

SEE BABA JOE.
Single (12"): released on Greensleeves,
Nov'80 by Greensleeves Records. Dist: BMG,
Jetstar, Spartan

SOUL & POWER.
Album: released on Studio 1, Mar'84 by Studio
1 Records. Dist: Jetstar Distribution

STICKY STAY.
Single (12"): released on Greensleeves,
Oct'83 by Greensleeves Records. Dist: BMG,
Jetstar, Spartan

STRANDED.
Album: released on Greensleeves, Oct'84 by
Greensleeves Records. Dist: BMG, Jetstar,
Spartan

TAKE A TASTE.
Single (12"): released on Upfront, Nov'82 by
Serious Records. Dist: PRT

TAKE ME BACK.
Single (7"): released on Upfront, Aug'82 by
Serious Records. Dist: PRT

THEY DON'T KNOW JAH.
Single (12"): released on Greensleeves,
Dec'82 by Greensleeves Records. Dist: BMG,
Jetstar, Spartan

UP FRONT.
Single (12"): released on Greensleeves,
Sep'81 by Greensleeves Records. Dist: BMG,
Jetstar, Spartan

VERY BEST OF THE WAILING SOULS.
Album: released on Greensleeves, Jun'87 by
Greensleeves Records. Dist: BMG, Jetstar,
Spartan

Cassette: released on Greensleeves, Jun'87
by Greensleeves Records. Dist: BMG, Jetstar,
Spartan

WAR DEH ROUND A JOHN SHOP.
Single (12"): released on Greensleeves, Jul'84
by Greensleeves Records. Dist: BMG, Jetstar,
Spartan

WATER PUMPEE.
Single(12"): released on Greensleeves, Jul'83
by Greensleeves Records. Dist: BMG, Jetstar,
Spartan

Wailing Ultimate

WAILING ULTIMATE (Various Artists).
Album: released on Homestead, Jun'87 Dist:
Rough Trade, Cartel, Shigaku

Cassette: released on Homestead, Jun'87
Dist: Rough Trade, Cartel, Shigaku

Compact disc: released on Homestead, Jul'87
Dist: Rough Trade, Cartel, Shigaku

Waine, Raney

**FOURMOST GUITARS WITH RANEY
WAINE** (Waine, Raney/Fourmost Guitars).

**FOURMOST GUITARS WITH RANEY
WAINE.**
Album: released on Jasmine, Jun'84 by Jas-
mine Records. Dist: PRT

Wain, John

...READING THEIR POETRY (Wain, John
& Ted Hughes).
Cassette: released on Audio Visual Produc-
tions, Aug'78

Wainwright, Loudon

ALBUM 3.
Album: released on CBS, '73 by CBS Records.
Dist: CBS

ALBUM III.
Album: released on Edsel, Dec'85 by Demon
Records. Dist: Pinnacle, Jazz Music, Projection

Cassette: released on Edsel, Dec'85 by
Demon Records. Dist: Pinnacle, Jazz Music,
Projection

CARDBOARD BOXES.
Single (7"): released on Demon, Jul'85 by
Demon Records. Dist: Pinnacle

FAME AND WEALTH.
Album: released on Demon, Apr'83 by Demon
Records. Dist: Pinnacle

FIVE YEARS OLD.
Single (7"): released on Demon, Apr'83 by
Demon Records. Dist: Pinnacle

HAPPY ANNIVERSARY.
Single (7"): released on Demon, Aug'86 by

Demon Records. Dist: Pinnacle

I'M ALRIGHT.
Album: released on Demon, Sep'85 by Demon
Records. Dist: Pinnacle

Cassette: released on Demon, Sep'85 by
Demon Records. Dist: Pinnacle

LIVE ONE, A.
Album: released on Edsel, Jun'87 by Demon
Records. Dist: Pinnacle, Jazz Music, Projection

Cassette: released on Edsel, Jun'87 by Demon
Records. Dist: Pinnacle, Jazz Music, Projection

MORE LOVE SONGS.
Album: released on Demon, Sep'86 by Demon
Records. Dist: Pinnacle

Cassette: released on Demon, Sep'86 by
Demon Records. Dist: Pinnacle

Compact disc: released on Demon, Sep'86 by
Demon Records. Dist: Pinnacle

UNREQUITED.
Album: released on CBS, Mar'75 by CBS Records. Dist: CBS

Wait

CRY WITHOUT TEARS.
Single (7"): released on B.O.D., Mar'86 by
Pinnacle

Waite, John

CHOICE, THE.
Tracks: / Choice. The / No breaks.
Single (7"): released on EMI America, Jan'86
by EMI Records. Dist: EMI

EVERY STEP OF THE WAY.
Single (7"): released on EMI America, Sep'85
by EMI Records. Dist: EMI

IF ANYBODY HAD A HEART.
Tracks: / If anybody had a heart / Just like lovers.
Single (7"): released on EMI America, Aug'86
by EMI Records. Dist: EMI

IGNITION.
Album: released on Chrysalis, Jun'82 by Chrysalis Records. Dist: CBS

Cassette: released on Chrysalis, Jun'82 by
Chrysalis Records. Dist: CBS

MASK OF SMILES.
Album: released on EMI, Oct'85 by EMI Records. Dist: EMI

Cassette: released on EMI, Oct'85 by EMI Records. Dist: EMI

MISSING YOU.
Single (7"): released on EMI America, Aug'84
by EMI Records. Dist: EMI

Single (12"): released on EMI America, Aug'84
by EMI Records. Dist: EMI

NO BRAKES.
Album: released on EMI America, Nov'84 by
EMI Records. Dist: EMI

Cassette: released on EMI America, Nov'84 by
EMI Records. Dist: EMI

RESTLESS HEART.
Single (7"): released on EMI America, Mar'85
by EMI Records. Dist: EMI

Single (12"): released on EMI America, Mar'85
by EMI Records. Dist: EMI

ROVER'S RETURN.
Tracks: / These times are hard for lovers / Act
of love / Encircled / Woman's touch / Wild one /
Don't lose any sleep / Sometimes / She's the
one / Big time for love / Encircled.
Album: released on EMI America, Aug'87 by
EMI Records. Dist: EMI

Cassette: released on EMI America, Aug'8/ by
EMI Records. Dist: EMI

Compact disc: released on EMI America,
Sep'87 by EMI Records. Dist: EMI. Estim retail
price in Sep'87 was £11.99.

Compact disc: released on Blue Note, Sep'87
by EMI Records. Dist: EMI. Estim retail price in
Sep'87 was £11.99.

TEARS.
Single (7"): released on EMI America, Nov'84
by EMI Records. Dist: EMI

THESE TIMES ARE HARD.
Tracks: / These times are hard / For lovers /
Missing you"
Single (7"): released on EMI America, Jul'87
by EMI Records. Dist: EMI

Single (12"): released on EMI America, Jul'87
by EMI Records. Dist: EMI

Waiting for Willa

WAITING FOR WILLA By D. Eden (Bloom,
Claire).
Cassette: released on Chivers Audio Books,
Apr'81 by Chivers Sound & Vision. Dist: Chivers
Sound & Vision

Waitresses

BRUISEOLOGY.
Album: released on Polydor, May'83 by Polydor Records. Dist: Polygram, Polydor

Cassette: released on Polydor, May'83 by
Polydor Records. Dist: Polygram, Polydor

MAKE THE WEATHER.
Single (7"): released on Polydor, May'83 by
Polydor Records. Dist: Polygram, Polydor

Single (12"): released on Polydor, May'83 by
Polydor Records. Dist: Polygram, Polydor

Waits, Tom

ASYLUM YEARS.
Tracks: / Diamonds on my windshield / (look-
ing for) the heart of Saturday night / Martha /
Ghosts of Saturday night, (The) / Grapefruit
moon / Small change / Burma shave / I never
talk to strangers / Tom Traubert's blues / Blue
valentines / Potter's field / Kentucky Avenue /
Somewhere / Ruby's arms.
Compact disc: released on Asylum, Oct'86 by
WEA Records. Dist: WEA

Album: released on Asylum, Apr'84 by WEA
Records. Dist: WEA

Cassette: released on Asylum, Apr'84 by WEA
Records. Dist: WEA

BLUE VALENTINE.
Album: released on WEA, Aug'79 by WEA
Records. Dist: WEA

CLOSING TIME.
Album: released on Asylum, Jun'76 by WEA
Records. Dist: WEA

DOWNTOWN TRAIN.
Single (7"): released on Island, Nov'85 by Island Records. Dist: Polygram

Single (12"): released on Island, Nov'85 by Island Records. Dist: Polygram Deleted '87.

FOREIGN AFFAIRS.
Album: released on Asylum, Oct'77 by WEA
Records. Dist: WEA

FRANKS WILD YEARS.
Tracks: / Hang on St. Christopher / Staight to
the top (Rhumba) / Blow wind blow / Tempta-
tion / Innocent when you dream / I'll be gone /
Yesterday is here / Please wake me up / Franks
theme / More than rain / Way down in the hole
/ Straight to the top / I'll take New York / Tele-
phone call from Istanbul / Cold cold ground /
Train song / Innocent when you dream.
Album: released on Island, Aug'87 by Island
Records. Dist: Polygram

Cassette: released on Island, Aug'87 by
Island Records. Dist: Polygram

Compact disc: released on Island, Aug'87 by
Island Records. Dist: Polygram

HEART ATTACK & VINE.
Album: released on Elektra Asylum, '80 by
Elektra/Asylum/Nonesuch Records. Dist: WEA

Cassette: released on Elektra Asylum, Mar'81
by Elektra/Asylum/Nonesuch Records. Dist:
WEA

Single (12"): released on Island, Feb'86 by Island Records. Dist: Polygram

Single (7"): released on Island, Oct'83 by Island Records. Dist: Polygram Deleted '87.

NIGHTHAWKS AT THE DINER.
Double Album: released on Asylum, Jun'76 by
WEA Records. Dist: WEA

RAIN DOGS.
Tracks: / Singapore / Clap hands / Cemetery
polka / Jockey full of Bourbon / Tango till they're
sore / Big black Marah / Diamonds and gold /
Hang down your head / Time / Rain dogs / Midtown / 9th and headpin / Gun Street girl / Union
Square / Blind love / Walking Spanish / Downtown train / Bride of raindog / Anywhere I lay my
head.
Album: released on Island, Oct'85 by Island
Records. Dist: Polygram

Cassette: released on Island, Oct'85 by Island
Records. Dist: Polygram

Compact disc: released on Island, Oct'85 at
Island Records. Dist: Polygram

SMALL CHANGE.
Album: released on Asylum, May'77 by WEA
Records. Dist: WEA

Album: released on Asylum, Jun'76 by WEA
Records. Dist: WEA

SWORDFISH TROMBONES.
Tracks: / Underground / Shore leave / Dave the butcher / Johnsburg, Illinois / 16 shells from a thirty-ought-six / Town with no cheer / In the neighbourhood / Just another sucker on the vine / Frank's wild years / Swordfish trombones / Down, down, down / Soldier's things / Gin soaked boy / Trouble's braids / Rainbirds.
Album: released on Island, Sep'86 by Island Records. Dist: Polygram

Cassette: released on Island, Sep'86 by Island Records. Dist: Polygram

Wake
GRUESOME CASTLE.
Single (12"): released on Factory, May'87 by Factory Records. Dist: Cartel, Pinnacle

HARMONY.
Album: released on Factory, Jan'83 by Factory Records. Dist: Cartel, Pinnacle

HERE COMES EVERYBODY.
Album: released on Factory, Dec'85 by Factory Records. Dist: Cartel, Pinnacle

ON OUR HONEYMOON.
Single (7"): released on Scan, Jan'82 Dist: Rough Trade

ON THE MATTER.
Single (7"): released on Factory, Mar'85 by Factory Records. Dist: Cartel, Pinnacle

SOMETHING OUTSIDE.
Cassette single: released on Factory Benelux, Nov'83 by Rough Trade Records. Dist: Cartel

SOMETHING THAT NO-ONE ELSE CAN BRING (EP).
Tracks: / Gruesome castle / Pale spectre / Furious sex / Plastic flowers.
Extended-play record: released on Factory, 13 Jun'87 by Factory Records. Dist: Cartel, Pinnacle

TALK ABOUT THE PAST.
Single (7"): released on Factory, Mar'84 by Factory Records. Dist: Cartel, Pinnacle

Single (12"): released on Factory, Mar'84 by Factory Records. Dist: Cartel, Pinnacle

Wakeford, Alan
ALAN WAKEFORD PLAYS FOR YOU.
Album: by Pilgrim Records. Dist: Rough Trade, Cartel

Wakeley, Jimmy
SANTA FE TRAIL.
Album: released on Stetson, Apr'86 by Hasmick Promotions Ltd.. Dist: Counterpoint Distribution, H.R. Taylor Distribution, Swift Distribution, Chris Wellard Distribution

Cassette: released on Stetson, Apr'86 by Hasmick Promotions Ltd.. Dist: Counterpoint Distribution, H.R. Taylor Distribution, Swift Distribution, Chris Wellard Distribution

Wakelin, Johnny
BRUNO.
Single (7"): released on Chrysalis, Jun'86 by Chrysalis Records. Dist: CBS

Single (12"): released on Chrysalis, Jun'86 by Chrysalis Records. Dist: CBS

IN ZAIRE.
Single (7"): released on PRT, Aug'86 by PRT Records. Dist: PRT

Single (12"): released on PRT, Aug'86 by PRT Records. Dist: PRT

Single (7"): released on Old Gold (Reissue), Jul'82

REGGAE, SOUL & ROCK 'N' ROLL.
Album: released on Pye, Mar'76

Cassette: released on Pye, Mar'76

WHERE SEAGULLS FLY.
Single (7"): released on Wide Awake, May'83 Dist: PRT

Wakeman, Rick
1984.
Album: released on Charisma, Jun'81 by Virgin Records. Dist: EMI

Cassette: released on Charisma, Jun'81 by Virgin Records. Dist: EMI

Cassette: released on Charisma, Mar'83 by Virgin Records. Dist: EMI

COUNTRY AIRS.
Album: released on Coda, Apr'86 by Coda Records. Dist: Pinnacle, Cartel, WEA, Roots

Cassette: released on Coda, Apr'86 by Coda Records. Dist: Pinnacle, Cartel, WEA. Roots

---

Compact disc: released on Coda, Apr'86 by Coda Records. Dist: Pinnacle, Cartel, WEA, Roots

CRIMES OF PASSION Original motion picture soundtrack.
Album: released on President, Mar'87 by President Records. Dist: Taylors, Spartan

CRIMINAL RECORD.
Album: released on A&M, Mar'82 by A&M Records. Dist: Polygram

Cassette: released on A&M, Mar'82 by A&M Records. Dist: Polygram

DATABASE.
Single (7"): released on TBG, Jun'85 by President Records. Dist: H.R. Taylor Distribution

Single (12"): released on TBG, Jun'85 by President Records. Dist: H.R. Taylor Distribution

FAMILY ALBUM, THE.
Album: released on President, Aug'87 by President Records. Dist: Taylors, Spartan

Cassette: released on President, Aug'87 by President Records. Dist: Taylors, Spartan

GLORY BOYS.
Single (7"): released on TBG, Dec'84 by President Records. Dist: H.R. Taylor Distribution

Single (12"): released on TBG, Dec'84 by President Records. Dist: H.R. Taylor Distribution

G'OLE.
Album: released on Charisma, Apr'83 by Virgin Records. Dist: EMI

Cassette: released on Charisma, Apr'83 by Virgin Records. Dist: EMI

Single (7"): released on Charisma, Apr'83 by Virgin Records. Dist: EMI

GOSPELS.
Album: released on Stylus, Nov'86 Dist: Pinnacle, Terry Blood Distribution, Stylus Distribution

Cassette: released on Stylus, Nov'86 Dist: Pinnacle, Terry Blood Distribution, Stylus Distribution

GOSPELS (THE).
Compact disc: released on Stylus, '87 Dist: Pinnacle, Terry Blood Distribution, Stylus Distribution

GOSPELS, THE.
Album: released on Stylus, Apr'87 Dist: Pinnacle, Terry Blood Distribution, Stylus Distribution

Cassette: released on Stylus, Apr'87 Dist: Pinnacle, Terry Blood Distribution, Stylus Distribution

I'M SO STRAIGHT I'M A WIERDO.
Single (7"): released on Moon, Jun'83 by Moon Records. Dist: PRT Distribution

JOURNEY TO THE CENTRE OF THE EARTH.
Album: released on Hallmark, Feb'85 by Pickwick Records. Dist: Pickwick Distribution, PRT, Taylors

Album: released on Hallmark, Feb'85 by Pickwick Records. Dist: Pickwick Distribution, PRT, Taylors

KING ARTHUR.
Album: released on A&M, Nov'85 by A&M Records. Dist: Polygram

Cassette: released on A&M, Nov'85 by A&M Records. Dist: Polygram

Album: released on TBG-President, Nov'85

Cassette: released on TBG-President, Nov'85

LIVE AT HAMMERSMITH.
Tracks: / Arthur / Three wives / Journey / Merlin.
Compact disc: released on President, Jan'87 by President Records. Dist: Taylors, Spartan

ROCK'N'ROLL PROPHET.
Album: released on Moon, Dec'82 by Moon Records. Dist: PRT Distribution

Cassette: released on Moon, Dec'82 by Moon Records. Dist: PRT Distribution

SILENT NIGHTS.
Album: released on TBG-President, Mar'85

Cassette: released on TBG-President, Mar'85

SIX WIVES OF HENRY VIII.
Cassette: released on A&M, May'81 by A&M Records. Dist: Polygram

WATERFALLS.
Tracks: / Waterfalls / Heather carpets.

Single (7"): released on Code, Apr'86 by Code Records. Dist: Jetstar, EMI

Wakenin, Ulf
AQUARELA DO BRAZIL.
Album: released on Sonet, Aug'85 by Sonet Records. Dist: PRT

Wake Up
WAKE UP EP (THE) (Various Artists).
Tracks: / Change is gonna come, A / Garage land / Levi Stubbs tears / This fragile life / Forty years / Change is gonna come, A.
Single (12"): released on Wake-Up, Apr'87 by Wake-Up Records.

Waking Dream
WAKING DREAM, THE Various artists (Various Artists).
Album: released on Funhouse, Jul'85 by Funhouse. Dist: Psycho, Rough Trade

Walcott, Collin
CLOUD DANCE.
Album: released on ECM, Jan'76 by ECM Records. Dist: IMS, Polygram, Virgin through EMI

CODONA 2 (Walcott/Cherry/Vasconcelos).
Album: released on ECM, Apr'81 by ECM Records. Dist: IMS, Polygram, Virgin through EMI

GRAZING DREAMS.
Tracks: / Song of the morrow, (A) / Gold sun / Swarm, (The) / Mountain morning / Jewel ornament / Grazing dreams / Samba tala / Moon lake.
Compact disc: released on ECM (Germany), Jun'86 by ECM Records. Dist: IMS, Polygram, Virgin through EMI

Album: released on ECM, Aug'77 by ECM Records. Dist: IMS, Polygram, Virgin through EMI

Walcott, Dennis
SISTER MILLIE.
Single (7"): released on Sonic Sounds, May'82 by Sonic Sound Records. Dist: Jetstar

Walden, Narada Michael
AWAKENING.
Album: released on Atlantic, Apr'79 by WEA Records. Dist: WEA

GIMME,GIMME,GIMME.
Single (7"): released on Warner Bros, Mar'85 by Warner Bros Records. Dist: WEA

Single (12"): released on Warner Bros, Mar'85 by Warner Bros Records. Dist: WEA

I'M READY.
Single (7"): released on Atlantic, Jan'83 by WEA Records. Dist: WEA

Single (12"): released on Atlantic, Jan'83 by WEA Records. Dist: WEA

I WANT YOU.
Single (7"): released on Atlantic, Nov'80 by WEA Records. Dist: WEA

Single (12"): released on Atlantic, Nov'80 by WEA Records. Dist: WEA

NATURE OF THINGS.
Album: released on Warner Bros., Feb'85 by Warner Bros Records. Dist: WEA

Cassette: released on Warner Bros., Feb'85 by Warner Bros Records. Dist: WEA

NATURE OF THINGS, THE.
Single (7"): released on Warner Bros., Jun'85 by Warner Bros Records. Dist: WEA

Single (12"): released on Warner Bros., Jun'85 by Warner Bros Records. Dist: WEA

REACH OUT.
Single (7"): released on Atlantic, Mar'83 by WEA Records. Dist: WEA

REAL THANG.
Single (7"): released on Atlantic, Mar'81 by WEA Records. Dist: WEA

Single (12"): released on Atlantic, Mar'81 by WEA Records. Dist: WEA

SUMMER LADY.
Single (7"): released on Atlantic, Aug'82 by WEA Records. Dist: WEA

Single (12"): released on Atlantic, Aug'82 by WEA Records. Dist: WEA

VICTORY.
Album: released on Atlantic, Oct'80 by WEA Records. Dist: WEA

Cassette: released on Atlantic, Oct'80 by WEA Records. Dist: WEA

YOU OUGHTA TO LOVE ME.
Single (7"): released on Atlantic, Jun'82 by WEA Records. Dist: WEA

Single (12"): released on Atlantic, Jun'82 by WEA Records. Dist: WEA

Walden, Wanda
DON'T YOU WANT MY LOVIN'.
Single (7"): released on Elektra Asylum, May'81 by Elektra/Asylum/Nonesuch Records. Dist: WEA

Single (12"): released on Elektra Asylum, May'81 by Elektra/Asylum/Nonesuch Records. Dist: WEA

SEARCHING FOR LOVE.
Album: released on Asylum, May'81 by WEA Records. Dist: WEA

Walder, Russel
ELEMENTS (Walder, Russel/Ira Stein).
Album: released on Windham Hill (Germany), Sep'84

Wald, Jerry
CALL OF THE WILD, THE.
Album: released on Golden Era, Jul'82 by port Records. Dist: Wellard, Chris, Swift

Waldo's Ragtime Orchestra
VOLUME 2.
Album: released on Stomp Off, Jun'86 Stomp Off Records. Dist: Jazz Music Distribution

Waldo, Terry
TERRY WALDO & THE GOTHAM CITY BAND (Waldo. Terry & The Gotham band).
Album: released on Stomp Off, Mar'85 Stomp Off Records. Dist: Jazz Music Distribution

Waldron
FREE AT LAST (Eckinger,Beckton).
Album: released on ECM, '76 by ECM Records. Dist: IMS, Polygram, Virgin through EMI

Waldron, Conrad
YOUR LOVE'S A VOODOO.
Single (7"): released on Sonet, Sep'81 Sonet Records. Dist: PRT

Waldron, Mal
BLACK GLORY.
Album: released on Enja (Germany), Jan'81 Enja Records (W.Germany). Dist: Celtic Music

BLUES FOR LADY DAY.
Album: released on Black Lion, Jul'87 by Lion Records. Dist: Jazz Music, Chris Wellard, Taylor, H.R., Counterpoint, Cadillac

CALL, THE.
Album: released on Japo (ECM), '79 Dist: Polygram

HARD TALK (Waldron, Mal Quintet).
Album: released on Enja (Germany), Jan'81 Enja Records (W.Germany). Dist: Celtic Music

MAL 4 TRIO.
Compact disc: released on Carrere, Apr'82 Carrere Records. Dist: PRT, Spartan

MOODS.
Album: released on Enja (Germany), Jan'81 Enja Records (W.Germany). Dist: Celtic Music

Album: released on Enja (Germany), Jan'81 Enja Records (W.Germany). Dist: Celtic Music

ONE ENTRANCE MANY EXITS.
Album: released on Palo Alto (Italy), Jan'81

Cassette: released on Palo Alto (Italy).

ONE UPMANSHIP (Waldron, Mal Quintet/Steve Lacy).
Album: released on Enja (Germany), Jan'81 Enja Records (W.Germany). Dist: Celtic Music

SET ME FREE.
Album: released on Affinity, Apr'85 by Charly Records. Dist: Charly, Cadillac

SIGNALS.
Album: released on Freedom, Feb'79 Records. Dist: RCA, Discovery, Wellard

TOUCH OF BLUES, A.
Album: released on Enja (Germany), Jan'81 Enja Records (W.Germany). Dist: Celtic Music

---

UP POPPED THE DEVIL.
Album: released on Enja (Germany), Jan'82 by Enja Records (W.Germany). Dist: Cadillac Music

WHAT IT IS (Waldron, Mal Quartet).
Album: released on Enja (Germany), Apr'82 by Enja Records (W.Germany). Dist: Cadillac Music

YOU AND THE NIGHT AND THE MUSIC.
Tracks: / Way you look tonight, The / Bag's groove / Round midnight / You and the night and the music / Georgia on my mind / Billie's bounce / Waltz for my mother
Album: released on King (Japan), Jul'86 Dist: Polygram

Waldron, Mal Quintet

MAL - 1.
Notes: With Gigi Gryce etc.
Compact disc: released on JVC Fantasy (Japan), May'87

Waldron, Mal trio

MAL 4.
Compact disc: released on JVC Fantasy (Japan), Nov'86

Walem Teugels

PORTIER ORGAN VOL.1.
Album: released on Joy, '74 by President Records. Dist: Jazz Music, Swift, President Distribution

PORTIER ORGAN VOL.2.
Album: released on Joy, '74 by President Records. Dist: Jazz Music, Swift, President Distribution

Wales:

WALES-THE DRAGON ARMY (Wales Football Squad & Supporters).
Single (7"): released on Spartan, Sep'85 by Spartan Records. Dist: Spartan

Single (12"): released on Spartan, Sep'85 by Spartan Records. Dist: Spartan

Wales, Josey

BOUNCING.
Single (12"): released on Volcano, Sep'84 by Volcano Records. Dist: Jetstar

LOVE TO SAY SO.
Album: released on Jammy's, Jul'87 by Jammy's Records. Dist: Jetstar

ME T FOUR.
Single (12"): released on Mobiliser, Jan'84 by Mobiliser Records. Dist: Jetstar Distribution

JOSEY WALES MEETS EARLY B (Wales, Josey & Early B).

NAH NO BETTER THAN YARD.
Album: released on Greensleeves, Nov'84 by Greensleeves Records. Dist: BMG, Jetstar, Pan

OUTLAW JOSEY WALES, THE.
Album: released on Greensleeves, May'83 by Greensleeves Records. Dist: BMG, Jetstar, Pan

THEY COME CALL ME.
Single (12"): released on Cornerstone, Sep'84 Dist: Jetstar

TWO GIANTS CLASH (Wales, Josey & Yellowman).
Album: released on Greensleeves, Jan'84 by Greensleeves Records. Dist: BMG, Jetstar, Pan

UNDERCOVER LOVER.
Single (12"): released on S.C.O.M.B.N. 023, April'87

Wales, Josie

Album: released on Black Solidarity, Nov'86 by Black Solidarity Records. Dist: Jetstar

Walk

CAN'T CATCH YOUR NAME.
Single (7"): released on Geneva, Feb'84 by Geneva Records. Dist: Pinnacle, PRT

Walk, Dennis

EAT FISH & CORN BREAD.
Single (12"): released on Greensleeves, by Greensleeves Records. Dist: BMG, Spartan

Walker, Billy

SEVER GAME/BYE BYE LOVE (Walker, Billy & Barbara Fairchild).

BILLY WALKER

Album: released on MCA, Mar'87 by MCA Records. Dist: Polygram, MCA

Cassette: released on MCA, Mar'87 by MCA Records. Dist: Polygram, MCA

FOR MY FRIENDS.
Tracks: / Singing those lovesick blues again / Jesse / He sang the songs about El Paso / Charlie's shoes / Touch of my woman / Don't ever leave me in Texas / Instead of giving up (I'm giving in) / Love boat / Cross the Brazos at Waco / Anything your heart desires / Cool in the daylight (fire in the dark) / Funny how time slips away.
Album: released on Bulldog, Aug'87 by Bulldog Records. Dist: President Distribution, Spartan, Swift, Taylor, H.R.

PRECIOUS MEMORIES.
Album: released on Word, Sep'85 by Word Records. Dist: Word Distribution, CBS

Cassette: released on Word, Sep'85 by Word Records. Dist: Word Distribution, CBS

Walker, Bobbi

SOMETHING ABOUT YOU.
Single (7"): released on Casablanca, Oct'80 Dist: Polygram, Phonogram

Single (12"): released on Casablanca, Oct'80 Dist: Polygram, Phonogram

Walker Bros.

SUN AIN'T GONNA SHINE ANYMORE, THE.
Tracks: / Sun ain't gonna... / In my room.
Single (12"): released on Bam Caruso, 23 May'87 by Bam Caruso Records. Dist: Rough Trade, Revolver, Cartel

Walker Brothers

GREATEST HITS: WALKER BROTHERS.
Album: released on Philips, Aug'81 Dist: IMS-Polygram

Cassette: released on Philips, Aug'81 Dist: IMS-Polygram

HITS.
Album: released on Philips, Aug'83 Dist: IMS-Polygram

Cassette: released on Philips, Aug'83 Dist: IMS-Polygram

LIVE IN JAPAN.
Double Album: released on Bam Caruso, Jun'87 by Bam Caruso Records. Dist: Rough Trade, Revolver, Cartel

Cassette: released on Bam Caruso, Jun'87 by Bam Caruso Records. Dist: Rough Trade, Revolver, Cartel

MOTIVE SERIES.
Album: released on Mercury (USA), Dec'81 by Import Records. Dist: IMS Distribution, Polygram Distribution

Cassette: released on Mercury (USA), Dec'81 by Import Records. Dist: IMS Distribution, Polygram Distribution

MUSIC FOR THE MILLIONS.
Album: released on Polydor (Holland), Dec'83

Cassette: released on Polydor (Holland), Dec'83

NO REGRETS.
Single (7"): released on Old Gold, Sep'85 by Old Gold Records. Dist: Lightning, Jazz Music, Spartan, Counterpoint

SHUT OUT.
Single (7"): released on GTO, Jun'81 by GTO Records. Dist: CBS

SUN AIN'T GONNA SHINE ANYMORE, THE.
Tracks: / Sun ain't gonna shine anymore / (Baby)you don't have to tell me / Stay with me / Annabella / Joanna / Love her / Make it easy on yourself / Walking in the rain / Another tear falls / Deadlier than the male / Jackie / My ship is coming in.
Notes: 12 hits including 2 number 1's.
Album: released on Karussell Gold, Dec'85

Cassette: released on Karussell Gold, Dec'85

SUN AIN'T GONNA SHINE ANYMORE.
Single (7"): released on Philips, Oct'82 Dist: IMS-Polygram

SUN AIN'T GONNA SHINE ANYMORE (2).
Single (7"): released on Old Gold, Jan'85 by Old Gold Records. Dist: Lightning, Jazz Music, Spartan, Counterpoint

WALKER BROTHERS GALA, THE.
Compact disc: released on Philips, Jul'87 Dist: IMS-Polygram

Walker, Bryon

DON'T LOOK ANY FURTHER (Walker, Bryon/Sandra Edwards).
Single (7"): released on Sir George, Aug'85 by Sir George Records. Dist: Jetstar, Pinnacle

Walker, Charlie

CHARLIE WALKER.
Album: released on MCA, Mar'87 by MCA Records. Dist: Polygram, MCA

Cassette: released on MCA, Mar'87 by MCA Records. Dist: Polygram, MCA

Walker, Dean

BABY PLEASE DON'T GO.
Single (7"): released on Sumatra, Mar'84 by Sumatra Records. Dist: Pinnacle

OVER NOW.
Album: released on Sumatra, Nov'83 by Sumatra Records. Dist: Pinnacle

Cassette: released on Sumatra, Nov'83 by Sumatra Records. Dist: Pinnacle

OVER NOW (7").
Single (7"): released on Sumatra, Nov'83 by Sumatra Records. Dist: Pinnacle

Walker, Dee

DIAL L FOR LOVE.
Album: released on Arts Network, Aug'85 Dist: Rough Trade, Cartel

JUMP BACK.
Single (7"): released on Dance Network, Aug'84 by Dance Network Records. Dist: Backs, Cartel

Walker, Eddie

RED SHOES ON MY FEET.
Album: released on Ragged, Jan'85 Dist: Roots, Projection

Walker Jazz Band

BIG BAND STORY VOLUME 2.
Compact disc:

Walker, Joe Louis

COLD IS THE NIGHT.
Tracks: / Why do you run / Madness of it all (was once was and still is (inst version)).
Notes: Debut album from American blues guitarist/vocalist, licenced from Hightone Records (Robert Cray), and produced by Bromberg/Walker (producers of Robert Cray and Ted Hawkins).
Album: released on Ace, Apr'87 by Ace Records. Dist: Pinnacle, Swift, Hotshot, Cadillac

Walker, Junior

ANTHOLOGY (Walker, Junior & The All Stars).
Double Album: released on Motown, Oct'81 by RCA Records. Dist: RCA Distribution

BLOW THE HOUSE DOWN(2).
Single (7"): released on Motown, Oct'83 by RCA Records. Dist: RCA Distribution

Single (12"): released on Motown, Oct'83 by RCA Records. Dist: RCA Distribution

BLOW THE HOUSE DOWN.
Album: released on Motown, Oct'83 by RCA Records. Dist: RCA Distribution

Cassette: released on Motown, Oct'83 by RCA Records. Dist: RCA Distribution

COMPACT COMMAND PERFORMANCES 19 greatest hits (Walker, Junior & The All Stars).
Tracks: / Shotgun / Do the boomerang / Shake and fingerpop / Cleo's mood / Road runner. (I'm ready) / How sweet it is / Money (that's what I want) / Pucker up buttercup / Shoot your shot / Come see about me / Hip city, part 2 / Home cookin' / What does it take (to win your love)? / These eyes / Gotta hold on to this feeling / Do you see my love (for you growing) / Take me girl, I'm ready / Way back home / Walk in the night.
Compact disc: released on Motown, Mar'87 by Motown Records. Dist: BMG Distribution

JUNIOR WALKER'S GREATEST HITS.
Album: released on Motown, Mar'82 by RCA Records. Dist: RCA Distribution

Cassette: released on Motown, Mar'82 by RCA Records. Dist: RCA Distribution

JUNIOR WALKER & THE ALL STARS (EP) 4-track cassette (Walker, Junior & The All Stars).
Cassette: released on Motown, May'83 by RCA Records. Dist: RCA Distribution

ROAD RUNNER (Walker, Junior & The All Stars).
Single (7"): released on Motown, Jun'83 by RCA Records. Dist: RCA Distribution

SHOTGUN/ROADRUNNER 2 Classic albums (Walker, Junior & The All Stars).
Tracks: / Cleo's mood / Do the boomerang /

Shake and fingerpop / Shoot your shot / Tune up / Hot cha / Monkey jump / Tally ho / Monkey jump / Tally ho / Cleo's back / Ain't that the truth / Road runner (I'm a) / How sweet it is / Pucker up Buttercup / Money (that's what I want / Last call / Anyway you wanta, (Dance) / Baby you know you ain't right / Ame' cherie (Soul darling) / Twist lackawanna / Sam-ho-zay / Mutiny.
Compact disc: released on Motown, Dec'86 by Motown Records. Dist: BMG Distribution

Walker, Larry

24 HOURS.
Single (7"): released on International Records & Tapes, Jun'82 by International Records & Tapes. Dist: International Records & Tapes

Walker, Lawrence

LEGEND AT LAST, A.
Album:

Walker, Paulette

IS THERE A PLACE IN YOUR HEART ME?.
Album: released on Bushranger, Mar'85 Dist: Jetstar

Walker, Philip

SOMEDAY YOU'LL HAVE THE BLUES.
Album: released on Sonet, May'80 by Sonet Records. Dist: PRT

TOUGH AS I WANT TO BE.
Album: released on Black & Blue (France), Jan'85 Dist: Swift, Target, Discovery

Walkers

HEY! THAT'S WASTE MY TIME.
Single (7"): released on Club, Feb'86 by Phonogram Records. Dist: Polygram

Single (12"): released on Club, Feb'86 by Phonogram Records. Dist: Polygram

WHATEVER HAPPENED TO THE PARTY GROOVE.
Single (7"): released on London, Nov'83 by London Records. Dist: Polygram

Single (12"): released on London, Nov'83 by London Records. Dist: Polygram

WHO IS YOUR LOVE?.
Single (7"): released on Club, Aug'86 by Phonogram Records. Dist: Polygram

Single (12"): released on Club, Aug'86 by Phonogram Records. Dist: Polygram

Walker, Sarah

CABARET SONGS (Walker, Sarah/Roger Vignoles).
Album: released on Meridian, Jan'83 Dist: Harmonia Mundi Distributors

Walker, Scott

BEST OF SCOTT WALKER.
Album: released on Philips, Oct'83 Dist: IMS-Polygram

Cassette: released on Philips, Oct'83 Dist: IMS-Polygram

CLIMATE OF HUNTER.
Album: released on Virgin, Mar'84 by Virgin Records. Dist: EMI, Virgin Distribution

Cassette: released on Virgin, Mar'84 by Virgin Records. Dist: EMI, Virgin Distribution

FIRE ESCAPE IN THE SKY The Godlike genius of Scott Walker.
Album: released on Zoo, Sep'81

JOANNA.
Single (7"): released on Old Gold, Aug'82 by Old Gold Records. Dist: Lightning, Jazz Music, Spartan, Counterpoint

SCOTT WALKER SINGS JACQUES BREL.
Album: released on Philips, Nov'81 Dist: IMS-Polygram

Walker, T-Bone

I DON'T BE JIVIN'.
Tracks: / T-Bone's back on the scene / I used to be a good boy / Session chatter & I ain't your fool no more / Baby she's a hit / Reconsider baby (hate to see you go) / Session chatter & don't let your heartache catch you / Sometimes I wonder / I don't be jivin' / T-Bone's jam / I ain't your fool no more / I wonder why / Further up the road / All night long / How long blues (that evening train) / Louisiana bayou blues.
Album: released on Bear Family, Sep'87 by Bear Family Records. Dist: Rollercoaster Distribution, Swift. Estim retail price in Aug'87 was £8.99.

I GET SO WEARY.
Album: released on Pathe Marconi/France), Apr'85

LOW DOWN BLUES.
Tracks: / Don't leave me baby / I'm gonna find my baby / It's a low down dirty deal / I know your wig has gone / T-Bone jumps again / Call it stormy monday / She's my old time used to be / Midnight blues / Long skirt baby blues / Too much trouble blues / Hypin' woman blues / Natural blues, The / That's better for me / Lonesome woman blues / Inspiration blues / T-Bone shuffle / That feeling is gone / I wish you were mine / She's the no sleepin'est woman / Plain old downhome blues / Go back to the one you love / You're my best poker hand.
Compact disc: released on Charly, Feb'86 by Charly Records. Dist: Charly, Cadillac

MORE LOW DOWN BLUES.
Tracks: / I got a break baby / Mean old world / Bobby sox blues / First love blues / On your way blues / Wise man blues / Born to be no good / No worry blues / I'm in an awful mood / Goodbye blues / West side baby / Prison blues / Dream girl blues / Long lost lover blues / Triflin' woman blues / Vacation blues / She had to let me down / Don't give me the runaround / Hard pain blues / So blue blues / I'm waiting for your call / I want a little girl.
Notes: Licensed from Capitol Records Inc. This CD (P) 1987 Charly Records Ltd. (C) 1987 Charly Records Ltd
Compact disc: released on Charly, '87 by Charly Records. Dist: Charly, Cadillac

NATURAL BLUES, THE (18 tracks recorded 1946-48).
Album: released on Charly(R&B), Aug'83 by Charly Records. Dist: Charly, Cadillac

PLAIN OLE BLUES.
Album: released on Charly(R&B), Mar'82 by Charly Records. Dist: Charly, Cadillac

STORMY MONDAY BLUES.
Album: released on Charly, Sep'78 by Charly Records. Dist: Charly, Cadillac

T-BONE JUMPS.
Album: released on Charly(R&B), '85 by Charly Records. Dist: Charly, Cadillac

Cassette: released on Charly(R&B), '85 by Charly Records. Dist: Charly, Cadillac

T-BONE WALKER.
Album: released on Deja Vu, Nov'85 by Deja Vu Records. Dist: Counterpoint Distribution, Record Services Distribution (Ireland)

Walkie Talkies

COVER UP.
Single (7"): released on Rialto, Oct'80 by Rialto Records. Dist: Pinnacle

MAN ON COBO BAY.
Single (7"): released on Rialto, Mar'81 by Rialto Records. Dist: Pinnacle

SURVEILLANCE.
Album: released on Rialto, Oct'80 by Rialto Records. Dist: Pinnacle

Cassette: released on Rialto, Oct'80 by Rialto Records. Dist: Pinnacle

WHOSE WORLD IS THIS.
Single (7"): released on Rialto, Aug'80 by Rialto Records. Dist: Pinnacle

Walking Blues

WALKING BLUES Various artists (Various Artists).
Notes: MONO recording.Superlative 1941-42 country blues.
Album: released on Flyright, Jul'86 by Flyright Records. Dist: Krazy Kat, Swift, Jazz Music

Album: released on Flyright, Feb'79 by Flyright Records. Dist: Krazy Kat, Swift, Jazz Music

Walks, Dennis

FISHERMAN.
Single (7"): released on Midnight Rock, Oct'83 Dist: Jetstar Distribution, Kingdom Distribution

Walk the West

WALK THE WEST.
Album: released on EMI, Feb'87 by EMI Records. Dist: EMI

Cassette: released on EMI, Feb'87 by EMI Records. Dist: EMI

WALK THE WEST.
Tracks: / Living at night / Backside / Too much of a good thing / Precious times / Lonely boy / Sheriff of love / Think it over / Solitary man / Calvary hill / Do you wanna dance.
Notes: Composer Paul Kirby. Except track 4 Paul Kirby-R. Watson. Produced by Josef and Winny Nuyens for Castle Productions Inc.

Wall

DAY TRIPPER (EP) (10 track EP).
Single (7"): released on No Future, Nov'82 by No Future Records. Dist: Pinnacle, Rough Trade, Cartel

Single (12"): released on No Future, Nov'82 by No Future Records. Dist: Pinnacle, Rough Trade, Cartel

DIRGES & ANTHEMS.
Album: released on Polydor, Mar'82 by Polydor Records. Dist: Polygram, Polydor

EPITAPH.
Single (7"): released on Polydor, Nov'81 by Polydor Records. Dist: Polygram, Polydor

GHETTO (EP).
Single (7"): released on Fresh, Apr'81 Dist: Jetstar

HOBBY FOR A DAY.
Single (7"): released on Fresh, Jul'81 Dist: Jetstar

PERSONAL TROUBLES & PUBLIC ISSUES.
Album: released on Fresh, Jan'81 Dist: Jetstar

REMEMBERANCE.
Single (7"): released on Polydor, Apr'81 by Polydor Records. Dist: Polygram, Polydor

Wallace, Bennie

BENNIE WALLACE PLAYS MONK.
Album: released on Enja (Germany), Jan'82 by Enja Records (W.Germany). Dist: Cadillac Music

FOURTEEN BAR BLUES.
Album: released on Enja (Germany), Jan'82 by Enja Records (W.Germany). Dist: Cadillac Music

FREE WILL.
Album: released on Enja (Germany), Jan'82 by Enja Records (W.Germany). Dist: Cadillac Music

LIVE AT THE PUBLIC THEATER.
Album: released on Enja (Germany), Jan'82 by Enja Records (W.Germany). Dist: Cadillac Music

SWEEPING THROUGH THE CITY.
Album: released on Enja (Germany), Nov'84 by Enja Records (W.Germany). Dist: Cadillac Music

Wallace Collection

DAYDREAM.
Single (7"): released on EMI (France), Apr'83 by EMI Records. Dist: Conifer

Wallace, Edgar

MIND OF MR. J.G.REEDER, THE (West, Timothy).
Double cassette: released on Argo (Cassettes), Sep'84 by Decca Records. Dist: Polygram

Mind of Mr. J.G.Reeder Vol.2

SHEER MELODRAMA AND OTHER STORIES (West, Timothy).
Cassette: released on Argo, Nov'81 by Decca Records. Dist: Polygram

Wallace, Hugh & Tillie

WARINGSFORD RISING STAR.
Cassette: released on Outlet, May'80 by Outlet Records. Dist: Outlet Distribution

Wallace, Ian

CELEBRATION.
Album: released on Cambra, Jun'85 by Cambra Records. Dist: IDS, Conifer

Cassette: released on Cambra, Jun'85 by Cambra Records. Dist: IDS, Conifer

CHRISTMAS COLLECTION (Wallace, Ian & St.Joseph's School Choir).
Tracks: / Storke carol, The / I wonder as I wander / Virgin Mary had a baby boy, The / Little road to Bethlehem, The / Monkey's carol, The / First mercy, The / Now we go to Bethlehem.
Notes: Ian Wallace and the Choir of St.Joseph's School put together a selection of eternal favourites like'Silent night' & 'In the bleak midwinter'.with less familiar choices.
Album: released on Word, Oct'86 by Word Records. Dist: Word Distribution, CBS

Cassette: released on Word, Oct'86 by Word Records. Dist: Word Distribution, CBS

MY KIND OF MUSIC.
Album: released on Music For Pleasure, Jul'82 by EMI Records. Dist: EMI

Cassette: released on Music For Pleasure, Jul'82 by EMI Records. Dist: EMI

Wallace, Michelle

JAZZ RHYTHM.
Single (7"): released on System, Dec'82 Dist: ERC Records

Single (12"): released on System, Dec'82 Dist: ERC Records

YOU OUGHT TO KNOW.
Single (7"): released on Lovebeat Int., Mar'86 Dist: Gipsy, Spartan

Single (12"): released on Lovebeat Int., Mar'86 Dist: Gipsy, Spartan

Wallchmore Cellidh Band

HIGHLANDERS COMPANION, THE.
Album: released on Lapwing, Apr'86 by Lapwing Records Ltd. Dist: Celtic Music, Projection, Roots Records, Ross, Gordon Duncan Distribution, Graham Tosh Distribution, Chans Records

Wall, Dan

SONG FOR THE NIGHT.
Album: released on Landslide (USA), Mar'85 Dist: Compendium, Rough Trade, Cartel

Wallenstein

FRAULEINS.
Album: released on EMI (Germany), '83 by EMI Records. Dist: Conifer

Waller, Fats

1939.
Album: released on Joker, Apr'81 Dist: Counterpoint, Mainline, Record Services Distribution (Ireland)

1943.
Album: released on Jazz Live, Apr'81

20 GOLDEN PIECES OF....
Album: released on Bulldog Records, Jul'82

AFRICAN RIPPLES.
Album: released on RCA International, '84

Cassette: released on RCA International, '84

AIN'T MISBEHAVIN' (Waller, Fats and His Rhythm).
Album: released on RCA International, '84

Cassette: released on RCA International, '84

ARMFUL O' SWEETNESS (Waller, Fats and His Rhythm).
Tracks: / Porter's love song to a chambermaid, A / I wish I were twins / Armful o' sweetness / Do me a favour / Georgia May / Then I'll be tired of you / Don't let it bother you / Have a little dream on me / Serenade for a wealthy widow / How can you face me / Sweetie pie / Mandy / Lets pretend there's a moon / You're not the only oyster in the stew / I'm growing fonder of you / If it isn't love / Breakin' the ice / Porter's love song to a chambermaid, A.
Notes: Mono recording
Album: released on Saville, Feb'87 by Conifer Records. Dist: Conifer

Cassette: released on Saville, Feb'87 by Conifer Records. Dist: Conifer

BEST OF FATS WALLER, THE.
Album: released on Joker, Apr'81 Dist: Counterpoint, Mainline, Record Services Distribution (Ireland)

BOUNCIN' ON A V DISC.
Album: released on Swaggie (Australia), Jan'83

CHRONOLOGICAL VOL.1 (Waller, Fats & his Rhythm).
Album: released on JSP, Sep'86 by JSP Records. Dist: Swift, Projection

COLLECTION: FATS WALLER.
Album: released on Deja Vu, May'86 by Deja Vu Records. Dist: Counterpoint Distribution, Record Services Distribution (Ireland)

Cassette: released on Deja Vu, May'86 by Deja Vu Records. Dist: Counterpoint Distribution, Record Services Distribution (Ireland)

DINAH (Waller, Fats & his Rhythm).
Album: released on Joker, Apr'81 Dist: Counterpoint, Mainline, Record Services Distribution (Ireland)

FATS AT THE ORGAN.
Album: released on Academy Sound & Vision, Apr'81 by Academy Sound & Vision Records. Dist: Pinnacle

Cassette: released on Academy Sound & Vision, Apr'81 by Academy Sound & Vision Records. Dist: Pinnacle

"FATS" WALLER.
Notes: Plays, sings and talks.
Album: released on Jazz Treasury, Mar'87 Dist: Jazz Music

FATS WALLER IN LONDON.
Album: released on EMI Retrospect, Jun'85 by EMI Records. Dist: EMI

Cassette: released on EMI Retrospect, Jun'85 by EMI Records. Dist: EMI

FATS WALLER LIVE Volume 1.
Cassette: released on Giants of Jazz, Oct'86 by Hasmick Promotions Ltd.. Dist: Counterpoint, Jazz Music, Taylors, Swift, Mainline, Wellard, Chris

FATS WALLER & MORRIS HOT BABIES.
Album: released on Joker, Jul'81 Dist: Counterpoint, Mainline, Record Services Distributio (Ireland)

FINE ARABIAN STUFF.
Album: released on Deluxe, Apr'81 by Delux Records. Dist: Pinnacle

FRIENDS OF FATS VOL. 2.
Album: released on Collectors Items, Feb'8 Dist: Jazz Music, Swift, Chris Wellard

GREAT ORIGINAL PERFORMANCE 1927-1934.
Notes: Original 78's digitally remastered ar stereo enhanced This entirely new techniqu has received universal critical acclaim.
Album: released on BBC, Aug'86 by BBC Re ords & Tapes. Dist: EMI, PRT, Pye

Cassette: released on BBC, Aug'86 by BE Records & Tapes. Dist: EMI, PRT, Pye

HANDFUL OF KEYS.
Tracks: / Handful of keys / You're not the o oyster in the stew / Valentino stomp / Hone suckle rose / St.Louis blues / I'm crazy 'bout baby / Alligator crawl / Blue turning grey ov you / Viper's drag / Your feet's too big / Car na shout / Ain't misbehavin'.
Notes: MONO recording.
Album: released on RCA, Jul'86 by RCA Re ords. Dist: RCA, Roots, Swift, Wellard, Chri & B, Solomon & Peres Distribution

Album: released on RCA, Jul'86 by RCA R ords. Dist: RCA, Roots, Swift, Wellard, Chri & B, Solomon & Peres Distribution

HIS PIANO & HIS RHYTHM VOL 3.
Album: released on Vogue (France), Jan Dist: Discovery, Jazz Music, PRT, Swift

HONEY ON THE MOON.
Album: released on Meteor, Apr'86 by M num Music Group Ltd. Dist: Magnum Mu Group Ltd, PRT Distribution, Spartan Distri tion

HONEYSUCKLE ROSE.
Album: released on Decca (Recollectio Apr'85 by Decca Recollections. Dist: Polygr IMS

INDISPENSABLE FATS WALL (1926-1935) VOL. 1/2, THE.
Double Album: released on RCA (France) by RCA Records. Dist: Discoverv

INDISPENSABLE FATS WALL VOL.3/4 (1935-1936), THE.
Double Album: released on RCA (France) by RCA Records. Dist: Discovery

INDISPENSABLE VOLS.3/4 (1935-3
Tracks: / Night wind / Because of once up time / I believe in miracles / You ain't got no / Whose honey are you? / Rosetta / What' reason / Oh Susannah,dust off that piar Lulu's back in town / I'm gonna sit right and write myself a letter / Dinah / My very friend the milkman / Blue because of you / Street rag / Sweet Sue / Truckin' / Ge rockin' chair / Got a bran' new suit / I've g fingers crossed / Fat & greasy / Funtioniz got rhythm / Sugar rose / West wind / C topher Columbus / Cabin in the sky / I's a tell a lie / Why do I lie to myself about you Chief De Sota / Black raspberry jam / Pasw / I'm crazy 'bout my baby.
Notes: MONO recording.
Double cassette: released on Jazz Tr (USA), Sep'86 Dist: Discoverv

INDISPENSABLE VOLS.1/2, THE.
Tracks: / St.Louis blues / Soothin' syrup / Beale street blues / Fats Waller stomp / V tree / Thou swell / Handful of keys / Minor The / Harlem fuss / Gladyse / Valentine st Lookin' good but feelin' bad / I wish I were / Armful of sweetness / Do me a favor / Do it bother you / Serenade for a wealthy w How can you face me? / Sweetie pie / M Let's pretend there's a moon / You're n only oyster in the stew / Honeysuckle ros lieve it,beloved / Dream man / I'm growir der of you / Breakin' the ice / Alligator Viper's drag / I'm a hundred percent fo Baby brown / Baby brown(instrumental).
Notes: MONO recording.
Double Album: released on RCA, Mar RCA Records. Dist: RCA, Roots, Swift, W Chris, I & B, Solomon & Peres Distributi

Double cassette: released on RCA, Ma RCA Records. Dist: RCA, Roots, Swift, W Chris, I & B, Solomon & Peres Distributi

INDISPENSABLE VOLS.5/6.
Tracks: / S'posin' / Hallelujah / Cryin' Boo hoo / Honeysuckle rose / Smarty / B / How ya baby / Neglected / Florida Skrontch / Sheik of Araby / T ain't good
Double Album: released on RCA, Au RCA Records. Dist: RCA, Roots, Swift, V Chris, I & B, Solomon & Peres Distribut

Double cassette: released on RCA, Au RCA Records. Dist: RCA, Roots, Swift, V Chris, I & B, Solomon & Peres Distribut

JOINT IS JUMPIN', THE.
Tracks: / Ain't misbehavin' / Crazy'b

baby / Handful of keys / Nagasaki / Joint is jumpin', The / Sweet Sue / Just you / Honeysuckle rose / I'm gonna sit right down & write myself a letter / It's a sin to tell alie / Until the real thing comes along / Christopher Columbus / Your feet's too big.
Album: released on Topline, May'86 by Charly Records. Dist: Charly Distribution

Cassette: released on Topline, May'86 by Charly Records. Dist: Charly Distribution

JUGGLING JIVE OF FATS WALLER
Live.
Album: released on Giants of Jazz, Oct'86 by Hasmick Promotions Ltd.. Dist: Counterpoint, Jazz Music, Taylors, Swift, Mainline, Wellard, Chris

Cassette: released on Giants of Jazz, Oct'86 by Hasmick Promotions Ltd.. Dist: Counterpoint, Jazz Music, Taylors, Swift, Mainline, Wellard, Chris

LIVE AT THE YACHT CLUB.
Album: released on Giants of Jazz, Jul'84 by Hasmick Promotions Ltd.. Dist: Counterpoint, Jazz Music, Taylors, Swift, Mainline, Wellard, Chris

LIVE VOL.2.
Album: released on Giants of Jazz, Jan'85 by Hasmick Promotions Ltd.. Dist: Counterpoint, Jazz Music, Taylors, Swift, Mainline, Wellard, Chris

MAGIC MOMENTS.
Cassette: released on RCA, May'86 by RCA Records. Dist: RCA, Roots, Swift, Wellard, Chris, I & B, Solomon & Peres Distribution

MASTERS OF JAZZ.
Album: released on RCA (Germany), '83

MY VERY GOOD FRIEND THE MILKMAN (Waller, Fats & his Rhythm).
Tracks: / I'm gonna sit down & write myself a etter / Dinah / My very good friend the milkman Baby brown / Whose honey are you / Blue beause of you / 12th Street rag / You've been takng lessons in love / Somebody stole my girl / reakin' the ice / I ain't got nobody / Just as long s the world goes round & round / I'm on a seeaw / I got rhythm / Sweet Sue,just you / Rhythm romance / Sweet thing / Serenade for a ealthy widow
Notes: MONO recording.All vocals by Fats /aller.
lbum: released on President, Sep'86 by resident Records. Dist: Taylors, Spartan

IANO SOLOS (1929-1941).
racks: / Blue black bottom / Handful of keys / umb fumblin' / Ain't misbehavin' / Sweet saannah Sue / I've got a feeling i'm falling / Love e or leave me / Gladyse / Valentine stomp / aiting at the end of the road / Baby,oh where an you be / Goin' about / My feelin's are hurt / mashing thirds / My fate is in your hands / Turn the heat / St.Louis blues / After you've gone African ripples / Clothes line ballet / Alligator awl / Viper's drag / Down home blues / E flat ues / Zonky / Keepin' out of mischief now / ardust / Basin street blues / Tea for two / I ain't t nobody / Georgia on my mind / Rockin' chair arolina shout / Honeysuckle rose / Ring dem lls.
otes: MONO recording.
uble Album: released on Jazz Tribune SA), Sep'86 Dist: Discovery

uble cassette: released on Jazz Tribune SA), Sep'86 Dist: Discovery

ANO SOLOS (1929-41).
uble Album: released on RCA (France), '83 RCA Records. Dist: Discovery

RE FATS WALLER (1927-42).
um: released on Swaggie (Australia), '83

RE PIANO BOOGIE.
um: released on RCA (Import), Jun'84

ssette: released on RCA (Import), Jun'84

AT OLD FEELING.
um: released on Swaggie (Australia), 83

AT'S FATS.
npact disc: released on Vogue, Dec'86 : Discovery. Jazz Music, PRT, Swift

CAL FATS, THE.
cks: / My very good friend the milkman / 't let it bother you / You're not the only oysn the stew / Dinah / It's a sin to tell a lie / tight / Honey suckle rose / I'm gonna sit down and write myself a letter / When ebody thinks you're wonderful / You're not kind / Joint is jumpin',The / Two sleepy le / Your feet's too big / Shiek of Araby,The l the real things comes along / Ain't misbe-'.
m: released on RCA, Mar'86 by RCA Rec- Dist: RCA, Roots, Swift, Wellard, Chris, I Solomon & Peres Distribution

ette: released on RCA, Mar'86 by RCA rds. Dist: RCA, Roots, Swift, Wellard, , I & B, Solomon & Peres Distribution

YOUNG FATS WALLER.
Album: released on Joker, Apr'81 Dist: Counterpoint, Mainline, Record Services Distribution (Ireland)

YOU RASCAL YOU.
Tracks: / Georgia may / I'm crazy 'bout my baby / Breakin' the ice / Baby, oh where can you be / If it isn't love / Won't you get off it, please / I wish I were twins / Numb fumblin' / You rascal you / Ain't misbehavin' / Porters love song to a chambermaid,A / Draggin' my heart around / Minor drag, The / My fate is in your hands / That's what I like about you / Harlem fuss / Believe it, beloved / Honeysuckle rose.
Album: released on ASV Living Era, Mar'86 by ASV Records. Dist: PRT

Cassette: released on ASV Living Era, Mar'86 by ASV Records. Dist: PRT

Wallflowers

83.7.
Single (7"): released on Ideal Music, Aug'87 by Ideal Music Records. Dist: Ideal Music

Single (12"): released on Ideal Music, Aug'87 by Ideal Music Records. Dist: Ideal Music

BLUSHING GIRL NERVOUS SMILE.
Tracks: / Blushing girl nervous smile.
Single (12"): released on Mantra, Oct'86 Dist: Revolver, Cartel

Wallgren, Jan

LAVORO INCORSO (Wallgren, Jan Edvard/Swedish Radio Jazz Group).
Album: released on Dragon, '86 by Dragon Records. Dist: Jazz Music, Projection, Cadillac

Wallington,George

AT THE CAFE BOHEMIA.
Album: released on Progressive, Jun'86 by Progressive Records. Dist: Jetstar

BE-BOP KEYBOARD MASTERS.
Double Album: released on Vogue Jazz (France), May'83

JAZZ FOR THE CARRIAGE TRADE.
Notes: With Phil Woods,Donald Byrd etc.
Compact disc: released on JVC Fantasy (Japan), May'87

SYMPHONY OF A JAZZ PIANO.
Compact disc: released on Denon, May'86 by Denon Records. Dist: Harmonia Mundi

Wallin,Per Henrik

BLUES WORK (Wallin,Per Henrik Trio).
Album: released on Dragon, Jun'86 by Dragon Records. Dist: Jazz Music, Projection, Cadillac

Album: released on Krazy Kat, Apr'85 Dist: Jazz Music, Swift, Chris Wellard, H.R. Taylor, Charly, Hotshot, IRS Distribution

BLUES WORK.
Album: released on Dragon, Jul'83 by Dragon Records. Dist: Jazz Music, Projection, Cadillac

Wallis,Bob

LIVE (Wallis,Bob,Storyville Jazzmen).
Album: released on Storyville (USA), Jun'86 by Moss Music Group Records (USA). Dist: Discovery Distribution, Jazz Music Distribution, Swift Distribution, Chris Wellard Distribution, JSU Distribution, Celtic Music Distribution

Wallis, Julie

SUN ARISE/ SOME KINDA FOOL.
Single (7"): released on Speed, Nov'82

WILD THING/ I USED TO BE YOUR NUMBER ONE.
Single (7"): released on Speed, Nov'82

Wallis, Shani

BEST OF SHANI WALLIS, THE.
Album: released on MCA, Oct'85 by MCA Records. Dist: Polygram, MCA

Wall of Voodoo

7 DAYS IN SAMMYSTOWN.
Album: released on IRS, May'86 Dist: Polygram

BIG CITY.
Single (7"): released on IRS, Nov'84 Dist: Polygram

CALL OF THE WEST.
Album: released on Illegal, Oct'82 by Faulty Products Records. Dist: Pinnacle, Lightning, Cartel

DARK CONTINENT.
Album: released on A&M, Oct'81 by A&M Records. Dist: Polygram

DO IT AGAIN.
Tracks: / Do it again / Back in the laundromat / Far side of crazy.
Single (7"): released on I.R.S.(Independent Record Syndicate), May'87 by I.R.S.. Dist: MCA

Single (12"): released on I.R.S.(Independent Record Syndicate), May'87 by I.R.S.. Dist: MCA

FAR SIDE OF CRAZY.
Tracks: / Far side of crazy / Wrong way to Hollywood, The.
Single (7"): released on IRS, Mar'86 Dist: Polygram

Single (12"): released on IRS, Mar'86 Dist: Polygram

GRANMA'S HOUSE.
Album: released on IRS, Jul'84 Dist: Polygram

HAPPY PLANET.
Tracks: / Do it again / Hollywood the second time / Empty room / Chains of luck / When the lights go out / Love is a happy thing/Country of man / Joanne / Elvis bought Dora a cadillac / Grass is greener, The / Ain't my day.
Album: released on I.R.S.(Independent Record Syndicate), Jun'87 by I.R.S.. Dist: MCA

Cassette: released on I.R.S.(Independent Record Syndicate), Jun'87 by I.R.S.. Dist: MCA

INTERSTATE 15.
Single (7"): released on Illegal, Oct'82 by Faulty Products Records. Dist: Pinnacle, Lightning, Cartel

MEXICAN RADIO.
Single (7"): released on Illegal, Jan'83 by Faulty Products Records. Dist: Pinnacle, Lightning, Cartel

Single (12"): released on Illegal, Jan'83 by Faulty Products Records. Dist: Pinnacle, Lightning, Cartel

Wall Street Crash

EUROPEAN AFFAIR.
Cassette: released on Magnet, Dec'83 by Magnet Records. Dist: BMG

Album: released on Magnet, Dec'83 by Magnet Records. Dist: BMG

WALL STREET CRASH.
Album: released on Magnet, '83 by Magnet Records. Dist: BMG

Cassette: released on Magnet, '83 by Magnet Records. Dist: BMG

YOU'RE MY WORLD.
Single (7"): released on Magnet, Dec'83 by Magnet Records. Dist: BMG

Wall, The

WALL, THE Various artists (Various Artists).
Video-cassette (VHS): released on Thorn-Emi, Jan'84

Wally

WASTE OF TIME/ GOOD MORNING MRS....
Single (7"): released on Radioactive, Oct'81

Wally Goes To Holloway

ALL OUR VERY BEST.
Tracks: / All our very best / Wally's yarn.
Single (7"): released on Well Cut, Jun'86 by Well Cut Records. Dist: Well Cut

Walrath, Jack

MASTER OF SUSPENCE.
Compact disc: released on Blue Note, Aug'87 by EMI Records. Dist: EMI

Album: released on Blue Note, Aug'87 by EMI Records. Dist: EMI

MASTER OF SUSPENSE.
Tracks: / Meat / Children / No mystery / Study in porcine / Bouquet of roses / Lord's calypso, The / I'm so lonesome I could cry / Monk on the moon / Hymn for the discontented, A.

PLEA FOR SANITY, A.
Album: released on Stash, Jan'83 Dist: Swift Distribution, Jazz Music Distribution, Jazz Horizons Distribution, Celtic Music Distribution, Cadillac, JSU Distribution, Zodiac Distribution

Walrus

FORGET THE TEARS/ CENTRIFUGE.
Single (7"): released on Dovetail, Jul'82 by Key Records.

Walsh, Adian

LIFE STORY OF MY LIFE.
Album: released on Kaleidoscope Sound, May'87

Walsh, Joe

BEST OF JOE WALSH, THE.
Compact disc: released on MCA, Jul'87 by MCA Records. Dist: Polygram, MCA

Album: released on MCA (ABC), '83 by MCA Records. Dist: Polygram, MCA

Cassette: released on MCA (ABC), '83 by MCA Records. Dist: Polygram, MCA

BUT SERIOUSLY FOLKS.
Album: released on Asylum, May'78 by WEA Records. Dist: WEA

Cassette: released on Asylum, May'78 by WEA Records. Dist: WEA

CONFESSOR.
Album: released on Warner Bros., Jun'85 by Warner Bros Records. Dist: WEA

Cassette: released on Warner Bros., Jun'85 by Warner Bros Records. Dist: WEA

GOT ANY GUM.
Tracks: / Radio song, The / Fun / In my car / Malibu / Half of the time / Got any gum ? / Up to me / No peace in the jungle / Memory lane / Time.
Album: released on Warner Bros., Jul'87 by Warner Bros Records. Dist: WEA

Cassette: released on Warner Bros., Jul'87 by Warner Bros Records. Dist: WEA

JOE WALSH The best of.
Tracks: / Turn to stone / Mother says / Help me through the night / Rocky mountain way / Meadows / Country fair / Funk#49 / Time out / Walk away / Help me thru' the night / Turn to stone.
Compact disc: released on MCA, '87 by MCA Records. Dist: Polygram, MCA

JOE WALSH LIVE You can't argue with a sick mind.
Tracks: / Walk away / Meadows / Rocky mountain way / Time out.
Album: released on MCA, Jun'86 by MCA Records. Dist: Polygram, MCA

Cassette: released on MCA, Jun'86 by MCA Records. Dist: Polygram, MCA

LIFE OF ILLUSION.
Single (7"): released on Elektra Asylum, May'81 by Elektra/Asylum/Nonesuch Records. Dist: WEA

ROCKY MOUNTAIN WAY.
Tracks: / Rocky mountain way / Rose of Cimarron.
Single (7"): released on Old Gold, Apr'86 by Old Gold Records. Dist: Lightning, Jazz Music, Spartan, Counterpoint

YOU BOUGHT IT YOU NAME IT.
Compact disc: released on Warner Bros., Jul'84 by Warner Bros Records. Dist: WEA

YOU CAN'T ARGUE WITH A SICK MIND.
Album: released on Fame, Jan'83 by Music For Pleasure Records. Dist: EMI

Cassette: released on Fame, Jan'83 by Music For Pleasure Records. Dist: EMI

Walsh, Paddy

MAINSAIL HAUL.
Cassette: released on Folktracks, Nov'79 by Folktracks Cassettes. Dist: Folktracks

Walsh,Sheila

DON'T HIDE YOUR HEART.
Album: released on Sparrow, May'85 by Word Records. Dist: Spartan

Cassette: released on Sparrow, May'85 by Word Records. Dist: Spartan

DRIFTING.
Tracks: / Drifting / Turn turn turn / Mystery / Sunset skies / Private Life / Private life / Yes he lives / Fooled by a feeling / Sleepwalking / It's lonely when the lights on / Fighter.
Album: released on Myrrh, Jul'86 by Word Records. Dist: Word Distribution

Cassette:

Album: released on DJM, Jun'83 by DJM Records. Dist: CBS, Polygram

Cassette: released on DJM, Jun'83 by DJM Records. Dist: CBS, Polygram

DRIFTING (Walsh,Sheila & Cliff Richard).
Single (7"): released on DJM, Jun'83 by DJM Records. Dist: CBS, Polygram

Single (12"): released on DJM, Jun'83 by DJM Records. Dist: CBS, Polygram

DRIFTING (EP) (see Richard, Cliff) (Walsh,Sheila & Cliff Richard).

FUTURE EYES.
Album: released on Word, Feb'85 by Word Records. Dist: Word Distribution, CBS

Cassette: released on Word, Feb'85 by Word Records. Dist: Word Distribution, CBS

GROWING UP TO BE A CHILD.
Single (7"): released on DJM, May'84 by DJM

Records. Dist: CBS, Polygram

HIS EYES.
Single (7"): released on DJM, Nov'84 by DJM Records. Dist: CBS, Polygram

PORTRAIT.
Album: released on Sparrow, May'87 by Word Records. Dist: Spartan

Cassette: released on Sparrow, May'87 by Word Records. Dist: Spartan

SHADOWLANDS.
Notes: Produced and arranged by Richard Osborne and Jon Sweet of Cliff Richard songwriting renown and featuring the single recorded with Alvin and released by Chrysalis records,"I hope and I pray".
Album: released on Myrrh, Apr'86 by Word Records. Dist: Word Distribution

Cassette: released on Myrrh, Apr'86 by Word Records. Dist: Word Distribution

TRIUMPH IN THE AIR.
Album: released on Sparrow, Jun'84 by Word Records. Dist: Spartan

Album: released on Sparrow, Jun'84 by Word Records. Dist: Spartan

TURN TURN.
Single (7"): released on DJM, Oct'83 by DJM Records. Dist: CBS, Polygram

Walsh, Steve

EDGE OF NIGHT.
Single (7"): released on Pre, Sep'82 by Charisma. Dist: Polygram

Single (12"): released on Pre, Sep'82 by Charisma. Dist: Polygram

I FOUND LOVING.
Tracks: / I found loving / Nana hey hey (kiss him goodbye).
Single (7"): released on A.1, Jun'87 by A.1 Records. Dist: PRT

Single (12"): released on A.1, Jun'87 by A.1 Records. Dist: PRT

Waltermelon Men

SEVEN YEARS.
Tracks: / Seven years / I've been told.
Single (7"): released on What Goes On, Mar'86 Dist: Rough Trade, Cartel, Shigaku

Walters, Dave

COMES SAILING IN (Folk Guitarist).
Album: released on Fellside, Jan'79 by Fellside Records. Dist: Roots, Jazz Music, Celtic Music, Projection

KITES.
Album: released on Highway, '85 by Highway Records. Dist: Roots, Projection, Ross

Album: released on Greenwich Village, May'81 by Sweet Folk All Records. Dist: Roots, Projection, Lightning, Celtic Music, Wellard, Chris

Walters, Hank

PROGRESS.
Album: released on Rox, Dec'79 by Rox Records. Dist: Spartan Distribution

Walters, Rosemary

JUST ROSE.
Album: released on Negus Roots, Mar'84 by Negus Roots Records. Dist: Jetstar

Walters, Trevor

BABY, I'VE BEEN MISSING YOU.
Tracks: / Baby, I've been missing you / Baby, I've been missing you (version).
Single (12"): released on Starlight, Jul'87 by Starlight Records. Dist: Jetstar Distribution

BETCHA BY GOLLY WOW.
Tracks: / Save it for the night.
Single (7"): released on Priority, Jan'87 by Priority Records. Dist: RCA

Single (12"): released on Priority, Jan'87 by Priority Records. Dist: RCA

HANDYMAN.
Single (12"): released on Ital, Mar'83 Dist: Pinnacle

LOVE ME TONIGHT.
Single (7"): released on Magnet, Sep'81 by Magnet Records. Dist: BMG

Single (12"): released on Magnet, Sep'81 by Magnet Records. Dist: BMG

LOVERS MEDLEY.
Single (12"): released on Must Dance, Nov'82 by Must Dance Records. Dist: Jetstar Distribution

LOVE WILL FIND A WAY.
Tracks: / Love will find a way / Alway's on my mind.
Single (12"): released on Adelphi, Feb'86 by Adelphi Records. Dist: Jetstar

Single (7"): released on Bare, Jan'80 Dist: Pinnacle

LOVING AS ONE.
Single (12"): released on Magnet, Jul'82 by Magnet Records. Dist: BMG

Single (7"): released on Magnet, Jun'82 by Magnet Records. Dist: BMG

PENNY LOVER.
Single (12"): released on I & S, Dec'83 by I & S Records. Dist: Jetstar, I & S

SHAKE YOU DOWN.
Tracks: / Down and out.
Single (12"): released on Starlight, Dec'86 by Starlight Records. Dist: Jetstar Distribution

STUCK ON YOU.
Single (7"): released on I & S, May'84 by I & S Records. Dist: Jetstar, I & S

Single (12"): released on I & S, May'84 by I & S Records. Dist: Jetstar, I & S

THAT'S HOW HEARTACHES ARE MADE.
Tracks: / That's how heartaches are made / That's how heartaches are made (Instr.).
Single (7"): released on Time, Sep'86 Dist: Jetstar Distribution

Single (12"): released on Time, Sep'86 Dist: Jetstar Distribution

WALTERS GOLD WITH LOVE.
Album: released on Adelphi, Dec'86 by Adelphi Records. Dist: Jetstar

WE WILL BE LOVERS (Walters, Trevor & Carol Brown).
Single (12"): released on Beta, Sep'85 Dist: Jetstar

Walther, Gisela

ACCORDIAN CONCERTO (Solo Acc).
Album: released on ARC (Accordion Records), '84 Dist: Accordion Record Club

Walton, C.

NIGHT AT BOOMERS, (A) (see Jordan, Clifford) (Walton, C./Clifford Jordan).

Walton, Cedar

BREAKTHROUGH (Walton, Cedar & Hank Mobley).
Album: released on Muse (Import), Apr'81

CEDAR WALTON (Walton,Cedar/David Williams/Billy Higgins).
Album: released on Timeless, Oct'86

EASTERN REBELLION (Walton,Cedar/George Coleman/Sam Jones/Billy Higgins).
Album: released on Timeless(import), Sep'86 Dist: Cadillac

Cassette: released on Timeless(import), Sep'86 Dist: Cadillac

Album: released on Timeless(import), Apr'81 Dist: Cadillac

EASTERN REBELLION VOL.2 (With Bob Berg,Sam jones & Billy Higgins).
Album: released on Timeless(import), Apr'81 Dist: Cadillac

EASTERN REBELLION VOL.3 (With Curtis Fuller,Bob Berg,Sam jones & Billy Higgins).
Album: released on Timeless(import), Apr'81 Dist: Cadillac

FIRM ROOTS.
Album: released on Muse, Apr'81 by Peerless Records. Dist: Lugtons Distributors

HEART & SOUL (Walton, Cedar & Ron Carter).
Album: released on Timeless(import), Jul'82 Dist: Cadillac

LOVE....
Notes: with BillyHiggins, David Williams, Steve Grossman.
Album: released on Red, Jan'87 Dist: Projection, Jazz Horizons

NIGHT AT BOOMERS, A (VOL.1).
Album: released on Muse (Import), Apr'81

NIGHT AT BOOMERS, A (VOL.2).
Album: released on Muse (Import), Apr'81

SECOND SET (Walton, Cedar Quartet).
Album: released on Steeplechase, Sep'79

TRIO, THE (Walton,Cedar/David Williams/Billy Higgins).
Album: released on Red Pepper, Sep'86 Dist: Jazz Music, Wellard, Chris

Walton, Jake

GLOAMING GREY, THE.
Album: released on Plant Life, Nov'81 Dist: Roots

Walton, Mercy Dee

MERCY DEE WALTON AND HIS PIANO.
Album: released on Arhoolie, May'81 by Arhoolie Records. Dist: Projection, Topic, Jazz Music, Swift, Roots

Waltons

BROWN RICE.
Single (7"): released on Excaliber, Sep'85 by Red Bus Records. Dist: PRT

Single (12"): released on Excaliber, Sep'85 by Red Bus Records. Dist: PRT

DOWNHILL.
Single (7"): released on Medium Cool, May'87 Dist: Red Rhino Distribution, Cartel Distribution

Waltzer

MORGEN BLASTER.
Single (12"): released on Mercury, Jul'85 by Phonogram Records. Dist: Polygram Distribution

Single (7"): released on Mercury, Jul'85 by Phonogram Records. Dist: Polygram Distribution

Wanderers

ONLY LOVERS LEFT ALIVE, THE.
Album: released on Polydor, May'81 by Polydor Records. Dist: Polygram, Polydor

READY TO SNAP.
Single (7"): released on Polydor, Apr'81 by Polydor Records. Dist: Polygram, Polydor

WANDERERS-COLLECTION OF JUKE BOX HITS Various artists (Various Artists).
Album: released on Hallmark, Jun'81 by Pickwick Records. Dist: Pickwick Distribution, PRT, Taylors

Cassette: released on Hallmark, Jun'81 by Pickwick Records. Dist: Pickwick Distribution, PRT, Taylors

WANDERERS, THE.
Notes: The time is 1963. The place, New York...but not the City seen by commuters and tourists. This is a world of back alleys and tenements...where the sounds of the Shireeles and the Crystals are never far away...where the gangs challenge each other for supremacy. This is the world of the Wanderers, gangland warfare and teenage conflict. Type of recording: Film. Total playing time: 112 minutes.
Video-cassette (VHS): released on Picture Time Video, Sep'86 Dist: VCL

Wandering Souls

DOGS IN THE NIGHT.
Single (7"): released on Lost Moments, Feb'85 Dist: Backs, Cartel

Wanderley, Walter

BAZIL'S GREATEST HITS.
Album: released on PRT International, May'81

Wang Brothers

WHILE MY GUITAR GENTLY WEEPS.
Single (12"): released on Communique, Oct'85 Dist: Backs, Cartel

Wang Chung

DANCE HALL DAYS.
Single (7"): released on Geffen, Jan'84 by Geffen Records. Dist: WEA, CBS

Single (12"): released on Geffen, Jan'84 by Geffen Records. Dist: WEA, CBS

Picture disc single: released on Geffen, Jan'84 by Geffen Records. Dist: WEA, CBS

DON'T BE MY ENEMY.
Single (7"): released on Epic, Jun'83 by CBS Records. Dist: CBS

Single (12"): released on Epic, Jun'83 by CBS Records. Dist: CBS

Picture disc single: released on Epic, Jun'83 by CBS Records. Dist: CBS

DON'T LET GO.
Single (7"): released on Geffen, Apr'84 by Geffen Records. Dist: WEA, CBS

Single (12"): released on Geffen, Apr'84 by Geffen Records. Dist: WEA, CBS

Picture disc single: released on Geffen, Apr'84 by Geffen Records. Dist: WEA, CBS

EVERYBODY HAVE FUN TONIGHT.
Tracks: / Fun tonight (the early years).
Single (7"): released on Geffen, Oct'86 by Geffen Records. Dist: WEA, CBS

Single (12"): released on Geffen, Oct'86 by Geffen Records. Dist: WEA, CBS

FIRE IN THE TWILIGHT.
Single (7"): released on A&M, May'85 by A&M Records. Dist: Polygram

Single (12"): released on A&M, May'85 by A&M Records. Dist: Polygram

LET'S GO.
Tracks: / Let's go / To live and die in L.A..
Single (7"): released on Geffen, Mar'87 by Geffen Records. Dist: WEA, CBS

MOSAIC.
Tracks: / Fun tonite / Hypnotize me / Flat horizon / Betrayal / Let's go / Eyes of the girl / Fool and his money / World in which we live.
Album: released on Geffen, Oct'86 by Geffen Records. Dist: WEA, CBS

Cassette: released on Geffen, Oct'86 by Geffen Records. Dist: WEA, CBS

Compact disc: released on WEA, Oct'86 by WEA Records. Dist: WEA

POINTS OF A CURVE.
Tracks: / Don't let go / Dance hall days / Devoted friends / Talk it out / Even if you dream / Don't be my enemy / Waves, The / Look at me now / Wait.
Album: released on WEA, Sep'86 by WEA Records. Dist: WEA

Cassette: released on WEA, Sep'86 by WEA Records. Dist: WEA

TO LIVE AND DIE IN L.A.
Tracks: / To live and die in L.A / Lullaby / Wake up, stop dreaming / Wait / City of the angels / Red stare, The / Black-blue-white / Every big city / Dance hall days / Black, blue, white".
Album: released on Geffen, Jan'86 by Geffen Records. Dist: WEA, CBS

Cassette: released on Geffen, Jan'86 by Geffen Records. Dist: WEA, CBS

Single (7"): released on Geffen, Jun'86 by Geffen Records. Dist: WEA, CBS

Single (12"): released on Geffen, Jun'86 by Geffen Records. Dist: WEA, CBS

Wangford, Hank

ARE YOU THE VICTIM OF AGEIS (Wangford, Hank Band).
Single (7"): released on Charisma, Jan'84 Virgin Records. Dist: EMI

Single (12"): released on Charisma, Jan'84 Virgin Records. Dist: EMI

COWBOYS STAY ON LONGER (Wangford, Hank Band).
Tracks: / Cowboys stay on longer.
Single (12"): released on Honky, Mar'87
Cat. no: HONKY TX
Single (7"): released on WEA, Mar'81 by W Records. Dist: WEA

HANK WANGFORD.
Album: released on Cow Pie, May'85 by C Pie Records. Dist: Rough Trade, Spartan

HANK WANGFORD BUMPER PAC THE.
Cassette: released on Cow Pie, Dec'84 by C Pie Records. Dist: Rough Trade, Spartan

HANK WANGFORD CHRISTMAS THE.
Cassette: released on Cow Pie, Dec'84 by C Pie Records. Dist: Rough Trade, Spartan

LIVE.
Album: released on Cow Pie, Mar'86 by Pie Records. Dist: Rough Trade, Spartan

Album: released on Cow Pie, May'82 by Pie Records. Dist: Rough Trade, Spartan

RODEO RADIO.
Album: released on Situation 2, Sep'85 Cartel, Pinnacle

Cassette: released on Situation 2, Sep'85 Cartel, Pinnacle

ROOTIN' TOOTIN' SANTA CLA (Wangford, Hank Band).
Single (7"): released on Cow Pie, Nov'8 Cow Pie Records. Dist: Rough Trade, Sp

WILD THING.
Single (7"): released on Cow Pie, Jun'8 Cow Pie Records. Dist: Rough Trade, Sp

Wansell, Dexter

CAPTURED.
Tracks: / Captured / Do what you wanna theme from The year of living dangerou Heart on the line / Each moment / Cnversa / Turn me on / Nam (I can't sleep at nigh the wind / East meets west.
Album: released on Ten, Jul'86

Cassette: released on Ten, Jul'86

Page 1074

APTURED (Wansell, Dexter Featuring the nes Girls).
acks: / Captured / Conversation.
ngle (7"): released on 10, May'86 by 10 Recs. Dist: Virgin, EMI

ngle (12"): released on 10, May'86 by 10 cords. Dist: Virgin, EMI

FE ON MARS.
acks: / Life on mars / Always There.
ngle (12"): released on Streetwave, Apr'86 Streetwave Records. Dist: PRT Distribution

YAGER.
um: released on Philadelphia International, '78 by CBS Records. Dist: CBS

ssette: released on Philadelphia International, Jun'78 by CBS Records. Dist: CBS

Wappat, Frank

TH SIDES OF FRANK WAPPAT.
um: released on Rubber, Jun'82

TH OF OUR FATHERS SONGS FOR GING.
um: released on MWM, Jun'82 by Mawson Vareham. Dist: Spartan Distribution, Jazz ic Distribution, JSU Distribution

AISE YE THE LORD-SONGS FOR GING VOL.2.
um: released on MWM, Jun'82 by Mawson Vareham. Dist: Spartan Distribution, Jazz ic Distribution, JSU Distribution

War

OOVIN'.
ks: / Groovin'(Vocal) / Groovin'(Instumen-

le (7"): released on Bluebird, Aug'86 by bird Records. Dist: EMI, Jetstar

le (12"): released on Bluebird, Aug'86 by bird Records. Dist: EMI, Jetstar

T BECAUSE.
le (7"): released on RCA, Jul'82 by RCA rds. Dist: RCA, Roots, Swift, Wellard, , I & B, Solomon & Peres Distribution

V RIDER.
ks: / Low rider (remix) / Low rider (orig) / n' into darkness.
e (7"): released on Lax, May'87 Dist: CBS

e (12"): released on Lax, May'87 Dist:

IRE.
n: released on Thunderbolt, Jun'87 by um Music Group Ltd. Dist: Magnum Music Ltd, PRT Distribution, Spartan Distribu-

LAW.
n: released on RCA, Mar'82 by RCA Rec- Dist: RCA, Roots, Swift, Wellard, Chris, I olomon & Peres Distribution

GIVE YOU...THE FREEDOM TO K.
: released on War, Nov'85 by War Rec- Dist: PRT

tte: released on War, Nov'85 by War ds. Dist: PRT

LIVE.
: released on MCA, Oct'79 by MCA Rec- ist: Polygram, MCA

GOT THE POWER.
(7"): released on RCA, Mar'82 by RCA s. Dist: RCA, Roots, Swift, Wellard, & B, Solomon & Peres Distribution

(12"): released on RCA, Mar'82 by RCA s. Dist: RCA, Roots, Swift, Wellard, & B, Solomon & Peres Distribution

r And Peace

AND PEACE Original soundtrack.
: released on That's Entertainment, by That's Entertainment Records. Dist: e, PRT

d, Anita

WARD.
released on Timeless, Aug'87

d Brothers

S THAT BRIDGE.
/ Cross that bridge (Instrumental).
7"): released on Siren, Nov'86 by Vir- rds. Dist: EMI

12"): released on Siren, Nov'86 by Vir- rds. Dist: EMI

PREY.
/ Easy prey / Bridge too far, A.
7"): released on Siren, Sep'86 by Vir- rds. Dist: EMI

Single (12"): released on Siren, Sep'86 by Virgin Records. Dist: EMI

I TRUSTED YOU.
Tracks: / I trusted you / I trusted you (inst).
Single (7"): released on Siren, 30 May'87 by Virgin Records. Dist: EMI

Single (12"): released on Siren, 30 May'87 by Virgin Records. Dist: EMI

MADNESS OF IT ALL.
Album: released on Siren, Apr'87 by Virgin Records. Dist: EMI

Cassette: released on Siren, Apr'87 by Virgin Records. Dist: EMI

Compact disc: released on Siren, May'87 by Virgin Records. Dist: EMI

MADNESS OF IT ALL, THE.
Album: released on Siren, Apr'87 by Virgin Records. Dist: EMI

Cassette: released on Siren, Apr'87 by Virgin Records. Dist: EMI

WHY DO YOU RUN.
Single (7"): released on Siren, Mar'87 by Virgin Records. Dist: EMI

Single (12"): released on Siren, Mar'87 by Virgin Records. Dist: EMI

Compact disc single: released on Siren, Apr'87 by Virgin Records. Dist: EMI

Ward, Clifford T.

BEST IS YET TO COME.
Single (7"): released on WEA, Jan'81 by WEA Records. Dist: WEA

BOTH OF US.
Album: released on Philips, Mar'84 Dist: IMS-Polygram

Cassette: released on Philips, Mar'84 Dist: IMS-Polygram

CONTRARY.
Single (7"): released on WEA, Apr'81 by WEA Records. Dist: WEA

CRICKET.
Tracks: / Cricket / Computer.
Single (7"): released on Tembo, Mar'86 by Tembo (Canada). Dist: IMS Distribution, Polygram Distribution

ESCALATOR.
Album: released on Charisma, Oct'86 by Virgin Records. Dist: EMI

GAYE.
Single (7"): released on Old Gold, Jul'82 by Old Gold Records. Dist: Lightning, Jazz Music, Spartan, Counterpoint

GAYE - AND OTHER STORIES.
Compact disc: released on Virgin, Mar'87 by Virgin Records. Dist: EMI, Virgin Distribution

HOME THOUGHTS.
Cassette: released on Charisma, Mar'83 by Virgin Records. Dist: EMI

HOME THOUGHTS FROM ABROAD.
Tracks: / Gaye / Wherewithal / Dubious circus company,(the) / Where would that leave me / Traveller,(the) / Home thoughts from abroad / Where's it going to end / Time / Magician, (the) / Give me one more chance / Cold wind blowing / Open university, (the) / Crisis.
Album: released on Charisma, Oct'86 by Virgin Records. Dist: EMI

SOMETIME NEXT YEAR:(7" SINGLE).
Tracks: / Sometime next year / Turbo.
Single (7"): released on Tembo, Nov'86 by Tembo (Canada). Dist: IMS Distribution, Polygram Distribution

SOMETIME NEXT YEAR.
Tracks: / Prams / Who cares / Another radio station / Quiz show / They must think me a fool / Sometime next year / Losin' after all (nothin' new) / Stains / Turbo / Like an old song / Today in parliament / Lost in the flow of your love.
Notes: Clifford T Ward is well known to you all. his previous album 'Both Of Us' released three years ago has never been out of our top twenty best sellers. his songs have been covered by countless other artists including Cliff Richard and his albums have received critical acclaim. In 1973 he had a top ten hit with his song 'Gaye' which still receives regular airplay. 'Sometime Next Year' features twelve of his new compositions ranging from beautiful love songs to 'toungue-in-cheek' obsrvations on life. As well as writing he also produced the album.
Album: released on Tembo, Oct'86 by Tembo (Canada). Dist: IMS Distribution, Polygram Distribution

Cassette: released on Tembo, Oct'86 by Tembo (Canada). Dist: IMS Distribution, Polygram Distribution

Warden, (The)

WARDEN, (THE) Trollope, Anthony (Sutcliffe, Irene).

Boxed set: released on Cover to Cover, Jun'85 by Cover to Cover Cassettes. Dist: Conifer

Ward, Herb

STRANGE CHANGE.
Single (7"): released on Neil Rushden (Import), Mar'83

Ward, Jack

AN ORGAN SELECTION VOL.1.
Cassette: released on Word, '74 by Word Records. Dist: Word Distribution, CBS

AN ORGAN SELECTION VOL.2.
Cassette: released on Word, '74 by Word Records. Dist: Word Distribution, CBS

MORE SANKEYS FAVOURITES.
Album: by Pilgrim Records. Dist: Rough Trade, Cartel

SANKEY MEDLEY.
Album: by Pilgrim Records. Dist: Rough Trade, Cartel

SANKEYS FAVOURITES.
Album: by Pilgrim Records. Dist: Rough Trade, Cartel

Ward, Matthew

ARMED AND DANGEROUS.
Notes: It's been seven years since the 2'nd Chapter of Acts' Mathew Ward released his first solo Album 'Toward Eternity'. Happily ARMED AND DANGEROUS makes a musical leap into the 80's and it was worth the wait. It features synth and guitar driven rock and Ward's Awesome vocal prowess which adequately demonstrate why he may be the best rock vocalist in Christian music. Ward wrote all the Lyrics on the Album, most of which are directed to God like as if they were rock and roll psalms. He also produced and co-wrote all of the music with Jim Tenneboe, and they've come up with a solid package of rock-praise which, by the way, bears no resemblance to the 2nd Chapter of Acts
Album: released on Oak, Aug'86 by Oak Records. Dist: Spartan Distribution, Pinnacle

Cassette: released on Oak, Aug'86 by Oak Records. Dist: Spartan Distribution, Pinnacle

TOWARD ETERNITY.
Album: released on Sparrow, May'82 by Word Records. Dist: Spartan

Cassette: released on Sparrow, May'82 by Word Records. Dist: Spartan

War Dog

WAR DOG Read by David Steuart (Treece, H).
Album: released on Colophone, Sep'81 by Audio-Visual Library Services. Dist: Audio-Visual Library Services

Ward, Pete

BETWEEN THE EYES.
Cassette: released on Plankton, Apr'85 by Plankton Records. Dist: Cantio (Sweden)

DISTANCE GROWS.
Notes: Plankton (Distribution): 01-534 8500
Album: released on Plankton, Jan'87 by Plankton Records. Dist: Cantio (Sweden)

RON GOES TO TOWN.
Cassette: released on Plankton, Mar'83 by Plankton Records. Dist: Cantio (Sweden)

UNUSUAL SHADE.
Cassette: released on Plankton, Feb'85 by Plankton Records. Dist: Cantio (Sweden)

WHEN I MEETS I (Ward, Pete & Intransit).
Single (7"): released on Embryo Arts, Aug'85 by Embryo Arts Records. Dist: Plankton Distribution

Ware, Leon

LEON WARE.
Album: released on Elektra, Jul'82 by WEA Records. Dist: WEA

ROCKING YOU ETERNALLY.
Album: released on Elektra Asylum, Apr'81 by Elektra/Asylum/Nonesuch Records. Dist: WEA

Ware, Tom

FOURTH CIRCLE, THE.
Album: released on Sky (Germany), Aug'85

Warfare

ADDICTED TO LOVE (MAYHEM MIX).
Tracks: / Addicted to love / Hungry dogs (live).
Single (7"): released on Neat, Jul'87 by Neat Records. Dist: Pinnacle, Neat

MAYHEM F*ING MAYHEM.**
Single 10": released on Neat, Dec'86 by Neat Records. Dist: Pinnacle, Neat

METAL ANARCHY.
Album: released on Neat, Jan'86 by Neat Records. Dist: Pinnacle, Neat

NOISE, FILTH & FURY EP, THE.
Single (7"): released on Neat, Jul'84 by Neat Records. Dist: Pinnacle, Neat

PURE FILTH.
Album: released on Neat, '85 by Neat Records. Dist: Pinnacle, Neat

TOTAL DEATH EP.
Extended-play record: released on Neat, Jun'85 by Neat Records. Dist: Pinnacle, Neat

TWO TRIBES.
Single (12"): released on Neat, Nov'84 by Neat Records. Dist: Pinnacle, Neat

Wargasm

WARGASM Various artists (Various Artists).
Album: released on Pax, Jun'82 by Pax Records. Dist: Red Rhino, Cartel

Warhead

SPEEDWAY.
Album: released on Mausoleum, Apr'85 by Mausoleum Records. Dist: Pinnacle

Warholas

POP ART'S DEAD.
Tracks: / Pop art's dead / Moving around / We will.
Single (12"): released on Piranha, May'87

Warhorse

RED SEA.
Album: released on Thunderbolt, May'84 by Magnum Music Group Ltd. Dist: Magnum Music Group Ltd, PRT Distribution, Spartan Distribution

Cassette: released on Thunderbolt, May'84 by Magnum Music Group Ltd. Dist: Magnum Music Group Ltd, PRT Distribution, Spartan Distribution

VULTURE BLOOD.
Album: released on Thunderbolt, Sep'83 by Magnum Music Group Ltd. Dist: Magnum Music Group Ltd, PRT Distribution, Spartan Distribution

Wariner, Steve

IT'S A CRAZY WORLD.
Tracks: / Small town girl / Lynda / If I could make a livin' (out of lovin' you) / There's always a first time / Why do heroes die so young / When it rains / It's a crazy world / Hey alarm clock / Weekend, The / Fastbreak.
Album: released on MCA, Apr'87 by MCA Records. Dist: Polygram, MCA

Cassette: released on MCA, Apr'87 by MCA Records. Dist: Polygram, MCA

Compact disc: released on MCA, Jul'87 by MCA Records. Dist: Polygram, MCA

Waring, Fred

MEMORIAL ALBUM.
Album: released on Stash (USA), Feb'85 Dist: Swift Distribution, Jazz Music Distribution, Jazz Horizons Distribution, Celtic Music Distribution, Cadillac, JSU Distribution, Zodiac Distribution

Warley, Steve

TONIGHTS THE NIGHT.
Single (7"): released on Jive, Oct'82 by Zomba Records. Dist: RCA, PRT, CBS

Warlock

BURNING THE WITCHES.
Tracks: / Signs of satan / After the bomb / dark fade / Homicide rocker / Without you / Metal racer / Burning the witches / Hateful guy / Holding me.
Notes: Warlock's first album 'Burning The Witches' brought them to the attention of the British metal fraternity. A classic of its kind, this 1984 album is one of the best examples of German speed-metal. The band have gone on to produce more commercially orientated albums, most recently 'True As Steel' and as their success has increased, so has the demand for this album. Unavailable, even on import for at least a year 'Burning The Witches' is bound to do well in all heavy metal outlets. [Phonogram release sheet, May 1987]
Album: released on Vertigo, Mar'87 by Phonogram Records. Dist: Polygram

Cassette: released on Vertigo, Mar'87 by Phonogram Records. Dist: Polygram

Cassette: released on Mausoleum, May'84 by Mausoleum Records. Dist: Pinnacle

Album: released on Mausoleum, Mar'84 by Mausoleum Records. Dist: Pinnacle

HELLBOUND.
Tracks: / Hellbound / All night / Earth shaker rock / Wrath child / Ddown and out / Out of control / Time to die / Shout it out / Catch my heart.
Compact disc: released on Phonogram (Germany), Jul'85

Album: released on Phonogram (Germany), Jul'85

Cassette: released on Phonogram (Germany), Jul'85

TRUE AS STEEL.
Tracks: / Mr gold / Fight for rock / Love in the danger zone / Speed of sound / Midnight in china / Vorwarts..all right! / True as steel / Lady in a rock'n'roll hell / Love song. / Igloo on the moon (reckless) / T.O.L.
Notes: Produced by Harry Staroste: Mixed by Michaek Wagener: Each album and cassette includes free tattoo of the 'True As Steel' logo
Album: released on Vertigo, Aug'86 by Phonogram Records. Dist: Polygram

Cassette: released on Vertigo, Aug'86 by Phonogram Records. Dist: Polygram

Compact disc: released on Vertigo, Aug'86 by Phonogram Records. Dist: Polygram

WITHOUT YOU.
Single (7"): released on Mausoleum, Nov'84 by Mausoleum Records. Dist: Pinnacle

Warlord
ALPHA AND OMEGA.
Single (7"): released on Creole, Apr'81 by Creole Records. Dist: Rhino, PRT

Warm
NOVA VAGA.
Album: released on Warm, May'79 Dist: EMI

TIRED OF WAITING FOR YOU.
Single (7"): released on MHG. Jan'80

War Machine
UNKNOWN SOLDIER.
Album: released on Pinnacle, Sep'86 by Pinnacle Records. Dist: Pinnacle

Warm and tender
WARM AND TENDER Various artists (Various Artists).
Album: released on Hallmark, Apr'83 by Pickwick Records. Dist: Pickwick Distribution, PRT, Taylors

Cassette: released on Hallmark, Apr'83 by Pickwick Records. Dist: Pickwick Distribution, PRT, Taylors

Warman, Johnny
HERE COMES THE BEAT PATROL.
Single (7"): released on RAK, Sep'84 by RAK. Dist: EMI

WALKING INTO MIRRORS.
Album: released on Rocket, Jun'81 by Phonogram Records. Dist: Polygram Distribution

Warm Feelings
WARM FEELINGS Various original artists (Solitaire Collection) (Various original artists).
Double Album: released on Starblend, '83 by Starblend Records. Dist: PRT Distribution

Double cassette: released on Starblend, '83 by Starblend Records. Dist: PRT Distribution

Warmington, Keith
EVENING SONG.
Single (7"): released on Right Track, Jul'83 by Right Track Records. Dist: Cartel, Jetstar

Warner
LIVE AND LEARN.
Single (7"): released on Oscar, Jul'83 Dist: Pinnacle

Warner, Florence
OUT OF THE BLUE.
Single (7"): released on Mercury, Jul'82 by Phonogram Records. Dist: Polygram Distribution

Warner, Frank
STORY OF A FOLKSONG U.S.A..
Cassette: released on Folktracks, Nov'79 by Folktracks Cassettes. Dist: Folktracks

Warner, Jack
ORDINARY COPPER, AN.
Single (7"): released on H.M.V., Jun'81 by EMI Records. Dist: EMI Deleted '82.

Warner, Kai
MOTIVE SERIES.
Album: released on Philips, Sep'81 Dist: IMS-Polygram

Cassette: released on Philips, Sep'81 Dist: IMS-Polygram

VERY BEST OF KAI WARNER.
Album: released on Polydor, '74 by Polydor Records. Dist: Polygram, Polydor

Warner, Simon
PERFECT DAY BABY.
Single (7"): released on E.G., Sep'85 by Virgin Records. Dist: Virgin, EMI

Single (12"): released on E.G., Sep'85 by Virgin Records. Dist: Virgin, EMI

Warner's seven aces
1923-1927 White jazz and hot dance from atlanta.
Notes: Mono recording
Album: released on Harlequin, Jan'86 by Harlequin Records. Dist: Jazz Music, Wellard, Chris, IRS, Taylor, H.R.

Warnes, Jennifer
BEST OF JENNIFER WARNES.
Album: released on Arista, Aug'82 by Arista Records. Dist: RCA

BIRD ON A WIRE.
Tracks: / Coming back to you.
Single (7"): released on RCA, Aug'87 by RCA Records. Dist: RCA, Roots, Swift, Wellard, Chris, I & B, Solomon & Peres Distribution

Single (12"): released on RCA, Aug'87 by RCA Records. Dist: RCA, Roots, Swift, Wellard, Chris, I & B, Solomon & Peres Distribution

COULD IT BE LOVE.
Single (7"): released on Arista, Mar'82 by Arista Records. Dist: RCA

FAMOUS BLUE RAINCOAT.
Tracks: / First we take Manhattan / Bird on a wire / Famous blue raincoat / Joan of Arc / Ain't no cure for love / Coming back to you / Song of Bernadette / Singer must die, A / Came so far for beauty.
Album: released on RCA, Jun'87 by RCA Records. Dist: RCA, Roots, Swift, Wellard, Chris, I & B, Solomon & Peres Distribution

Cassette: released on RCA, Jun'87 by RCA Records. Dist: RCA, Roots, Swift, Wellard, Chris, I & B, Solomon & Peres Distribution

Compact disc: released on RCA, Jun'87 by RCA Records. Dist: RCA, Roots, Swift, Wellard, Chris, I & B, Solomon & Peres Distribution

Single (12"): released on Mab, Dec'84 by MAD Records. Dist: Jetstar

FIRST WE TAKE MANHATTAN.
Tracks: / First we take Manhattan / Famous blue raincoat / Joan of Arc.
Single (7"): released on RCA, Jul'87 by RCA Records. Dist: RCA, Roots, Swift, Wellard, Chris, I & B, Solomon & Peres Distribution

Single (12"): released on RCA, Jul'87 by RCA Records. Dist: RCA, Roots, Swift, Wellard, Chris, I & B, Solomon & Peres Distribution

I KNOW A HEARTACHE WHEN I SEE ONE.
Single (7"): released on Arista, Jul'82 by Arista Records. Dist: RCA

RIGHT TIME OF THE NIGHT.
Single (7"): released on Arista, Feb'83 by Arista Records. Dist: RCA

Single (7"): released on Old Gold, Jul'84 by Old Gold Records. Dist: Lightning, Jazz Music, Spartan, Counterpoint

SHOT THROUGH THE HEART.
Album: released on Arista, Jun'79 by Arista Records. Dist: RCA

Cassette: released on Arista, Jun'79 by Arista Records. Dist: RCA

UP WHERE WE BELONG (Warnes, Jennifer & Joe Cocker).
Single (7"): released on Celluloid, Jan'83 by Island Records. Dist: Polygram

Warne, Toni
ANY DREAM WILL DO.
Tracks: / Any dream will do / Ben.
Single (7"): released on Emerald (Ireland), Apr'87 by Emerald Records. Dist: I & B, Ross, PRT

War of the World
WAR OF THE WORLD Original soundtrack.
Compact disc: by CBS Records. Dist: CBS

War Of The Worlds
WAR OF THE WORLDS (Wells) (Hardy, Robert).
Cassette: released on Listen For Pleasure, Nov'77 by MFP Records. Dist: EMI

Warp 9
FADE IN FADE OUT.
Tracks: / Skips a beat / Dirty looks / Big fun / Reach for your star / Cutting edge, The / You'll got over it / To the last drop.
Album: released on Motown, Mar'86 by Motown Distribution

Cassette: released on Motown, Mar'86 by Motown Records. Dist: BMG Distribution

LIGHT YEARS AWAY.
Single (12"): released on Arista, May'83 by Arista Records. Dist: RCA

MASTER OF THE MIX.
Single (7"): released on Fourth & Broadway, Aug'84 by Island Records. Dist: Polygram, EMI

NO MAN IS AN ISLAND.
Single (7"): released on Fourth & Broadway, Jun'84 by Island Records. Dist: Polygram, EMI

NUNK.
Single (7"): released on Arista, Nov'82 by Arista Records. Dist: RCA

Single (12"): released on Arista, Nov'82 by Arista Records. Dist: RCA

SKIPS A BEAT.
Tracks: / Skips a beat / Skips a beat, (dub).
Single (7"): released on Motown, Feb'86 by Motown Records. Dist: BMG Distribution

Single (12"): released on Motown, Feb'86 by Motown Records. Dist: BMG Distribution

War Party
MY NAME IS FATE.
Single (7"): released on EE Records, Sep'85 by E E Records. Dist: Backs

Warren, Alan
GIVE US A KISS FOR CHRISTMAS.
Single (7"): released on Battersea, Dec'82 by Battersea Records. Dist: Pinnacle

Warren, Elile
CAMOUFLAGE.
Single (7"): released on Jet, Sep'82 by Jet Records. Dist: CBS

FALLING IN LOVE WITH YOURSELF.
Single (7"): released on Precision, Jan'81 by PRT Records. Dist: PRT

Single (12"): released on Precision, Jan'81 by PRT Records. Dist: PRT

I WAS MADE FOR LOVING YOU.
Single (7"): released on Precision, Jul'81 by PRT Records. Dist: PRT

ON A NIGHT LIKE THIS.
Tracks: / On a night like this / Feel my love / Loving game/Feel my love, The / Shattered glass / Can't give you up.
Single (7"): released on Columbia, Mar'87 by EMI Records. Dist: EMI

Single (12"): released on Columbia, Mar'87 by EMI Records. Dist: EMI

PRETENDER.
Single (7"): released on Carrere, Oct'83 by Carrere Records. Dist: PRT, Spartan

PRIMITIVE LOVE.
Single (7"): released on Jet, Jul'82 by Jet Records. Dist: CBS

Single (12"): released on Jet, Jul'82 by Jet Records. Dist: CBS

SATELLITES.
Tracks: / Satellites / Satellites,(instrumental).
Single (7"): released on Columbia, May'86 by EMI Records. Dist: EMI

Single (12"): released on Columbia, May'86 by EMI Records. Dist: EMI

Warren,Harry
SONGS OF HARRY WARREN.
Album: released on Citadel, Mar'79 Dist: Swift

Warren, James
BURNING QUESTIONS (Warren, James (Korgis)).
Album: released on Sonet, Jan'87 by Sonet Records. Dist: PRT

IT WONT BE THE SAME OLD PLACE.
Tracks: / It won't be the same old place.
Single (7"): released on Sonet, Oct'86 by Sonet Records. Dist: PRT

THAT WAS MY BIG MISTAKE (Warren, James (Korgis)).
Single (7"): released on Rialto, Apr'81 by Rialto Records. Dist: Pinnacle

THEY DON'T BELIEVE IN MAGIC.
Single (7"): released on Sonet, Jul'86 by Sonet Records. Dist: PRT

Warren, Peter
SOLIDARITY.
Album: released on Japo (ECM Germany), Jun'82

Warren, Robert Penn
SELECTED POEMS Read by Robert Penn Warren.
Cassette: released on Caedmon(USA), '81 by Caedmon (USA) Records. Dist: Gower, Taylors, Discovery

Warrenty
HITS YOU.
Tracks: / Hits you / One of a kind.
Single (7"): released on Warner Bros., Oct'86 by Warner Bros Records. Dist: WEA

Warren, Zed
MUSCLE FOR ME.
Single (7"): released on Wav. Jul'83

MUSIC TO WATCH GIRLS BY.
Single (7"): released on Airebeat, Jun'84 Dist: Red Rhino

Warrington, Mick
AIN'T GONNA VOTE NO MORE.
Single (7"): released on Speed, Dec'82

Warrior
BREAKOUT.
Single (7"): released on Warrior, Mar'84 by Warrior Records. Dist: Pinnacle

DEAD WHEN IT COME TO LOVE.
Single (7"): released on Neat, Aug'82 by Neat Records. Dist: Pinnacle, Neat

FIGHTING FOR THE EARTH.
Single (7"): released on 10, Feb'85 by 10 Records. Dist: Virgin, EMI

Single (12"): released on 10, Feb'85 by 10 Records. Dist: Virgin, EMI

FOR EUROPE ONLY.
Album: released on Warrior, Dec'83 by Warrior Records. Dist: Pinnacle

Single (12"): released on Warrior, Jul'83 Warrior Records. Dist: Pinnacle

Warriors
BEHIND THE MASK.
Album: released on Ensign, Sep'82 by Ensign Records. Dist: CBS Distribution

Cassette: released on Ensign, Sep'82 by Ensign Records. Dist: CBS Distribution

WARRIORS Original soundtrack. (Various Artists).
Album: released on A&M, Jun'79 by A&M Records. Dist: Polygram

Warsaw Accordion Quintet
WARSAW ACCORDION QUINTET Various artists (Various Artists).
Album: released on ARC (Accordion Record) '84 Dist: Accordion Record Club

Warum, Joe
DANS LE BLIZZARD.
Single (7"): released on New Rose, Jul Dist: Rough Trade, Cartel

TANZEN UND DRINKEN.
Single (7"): released on New Rose, Jul Dist: Rough Trade, Cartel

TOCARE LA VERITA.
Album: released on New Rose, Aug'84 Rough Trade, Cartel

Warwick, Dionne
20 GOLDEN PIECES OF DIONNE WARWICK.
Album: released on Bulldog, Oct'82 by Bulldog Records. Dist: President Distribution, Spartan, Swift, Taylor, H.R.

Cassette: released on Bulldog, Oct'82 by Bulldog Records. Dist: President Distribution, Spartan, Swift, Taylor, H.R.

ALL THE LOVE IN THE WORLD.
Single (7"): released on Arista, Dec'82 by Arista Records. Dist: RCA

Single (12"): released on Arista, Dec'82 by Arista Records. Dist: RCA

ANTHOLOGY 1962-1971.
Album: released on Rhino (USA), Feb'87 by Rhino Records (USA).

BEST OF....
Cassette: released on Creole (Everest), Jul'84 by Creole Records. Dist: PRT

DIONNE WARWICK COLLECTION.
Double Album: released on Pickwick, by Pickwick Records. Dist: Pickwick Distribution, Prism Leisure Distribution, Lugtons

ONNE.
oum: released on Arista, Jun'79 by Arista cords. Dist: RCA

ssette: released on Arista, Jun'79 by Arista cords. Dist: RCA

ONNE WARWICK.
um: released on Dakota (Countdown es), Oct'82 by Dakota Records. Dist: PRT

ssette: released on Dakota (Countdown es), Oct'82 by Dakota Records. Dist: PRT

ONNE WARWICK 6 TRACK HITS.
gle (7"): released on Scoop 33, Sep'83 by kwick Records. Dist: H.R. Taylor

ssette single: released on Scoop 33, '83 by Pickwick Records. Dist: H.R. Taylor

ONNE WARWICK COLLECTION, E.
um: released on Pickwick, Dec'79 by Pick- Records. Dist: Pickwick Distribution, Prism ure Distribution, Lugtons

sette: released on Pickwick, Dec'79 by wick Records. Dist: Pickwick Distribution, n Leisure Distribution, Lugtons

NNE WARWICK VOL 4.
sette: released on Audio Fidelity, Oct'84 PRT

NNE WARWICK VOL 3.
sette: released on Audio Fidelity, Oct'84 PRT

NNE WARWICK VOL 1.
sette: released on Audio Fidelity, Oct'84 PRT

YOU KNOW THE WAY TO SAN E.
e (7"): released on Old Gold, Apr'83 by Gold Records. Dist: Lightning, Jazz Music, an, Counterpoint

NDS.
n: released on Arista, Dec'85 by Arista ds. Dist: RCA

ette: released on Arista, Dec'85 by Arista ds. Dist: RCA

act disc: released on Arista, Dec'85 by Records. Dist: RCA

NDS IN LOVE.
n: released on Arista, May'82 by Arista ds. Dist: RCA

tte: released on Arista, May'82 by Arista ds. Dist: RCA

NDS IN LOVE (Warwicke, Dionne & Mathis).
(7"): released on CBS, May'82 by CBS ds. Dist: CBS

DEN HITS: DIONNE WARWICK 2.
: released on Phoenix, Oct'82 by Audio Enterprises. Dist: Stage One, Lugtons

DEN HITS: DIONNE WARWICK .
: released on Phoenix, Oct'82 by Audio Enterprises. Dist: Stage One, Lugtons

A DATE.
(7"): released on Arista, Jan'84 by Aris- rds. Dist: RCA

(12"): released on Arista, Jan'84 by Aris- rds. Dist: RCA

YOU WHERE I WANT YOU (War- Dionne & Johnny Mathis).
(7"): released on CBS, Jan'83 by CBS . Dist: CBS

TEST HITS: DIONNE WARWICK.
released on MFP (Holland), Mar'84 by cords. Dist: EMI

e: released on MFP (Holland), Mar'84 Records. Dist: EMI

cassette: released on Pickwick, Jul'82 wick Records. Dist: Pickwick Distribu- sm Leisure Distribution, Lugtons

BREAKER.
"): released on Arista, Oct'82 by Aris- ds. Dist: RCA

t disc: released on Arista, '83 by Aris- ds. Dist: RCA

released on Arista, Oct'82 by Arista Dist: RCA

released on Arista, Oct'82 by Arista Dist: RCA

OVE & OTHERWISE.
Album: released on Arista, Jun'81 by cords. Dist: RCA

Double cassette: released on Arista, Jun'81 by Arista Records. Dist: RCA

I DON'T CARE WHAT PEOPLE SAY.
Single (7"): released on Arista, Jul'82 by Arista Records. Dist: RCA

I'LL NEVER LOVE THIS WAY AGAIN.
Single (7"): released on Arista, May'83 by Arista Records. Dist: RCA

Single (12"): released on Arista, May'83 by Arista Records. Dist: RCA

NO NIGHT SO LONG.
Album: released on Arista, Aug'80 by Arista Records. Dist: RCA

Cassette: released on Arista, Aug'80 by Arista Records. Dist: RCA

NOW WE'RE STARTING OVER AGAIN.
Single (7"): released on Arista, Jul'81 by Arista Records. Dist: RCA

RESERVATIONS FOR TWO.
Compact disc: released on Arista, Aug'87 by Arista Records. Dist: RCA

Album: released on Arista, Aug'87 by Arista Records. Dist: RCA

Cassette: released on Arista, Aug'87 by Arista Records. Dist: RCA

RUN TO ME (Warwick, Dionne & Barry Manilow).
Single (7"): released on Arista, Mar'85 by Arista Records. Dist: RCA

Single (12"): released on Arista, Mar'85 by Arista Records. Dist: RCA

SO AMAZING.
Compact disc: released on Arista, Apr'84 by Arista Records. Dist: RCA

Album: released on Arista, Oct'83 by Arista Records. Dist: RCA

Cassette: released on Arista, Oct'83 by Arista Records. Dist: RCA

THAT'S WHAT FRIENDS ARE FOR (Warwick & Friends).
Single (7"): released on Arista, Oct'85 by Arista Records. Dist: RCA

Single (12"): released on Arista, Oct'85 by Arista Records. Dist: RCA

THIS GIRL'S IN LOVE.
Album: released on Cambra, Feb'85 by Cambra Records. Dist: IDS, Conifer

Cassette: released on Cambra, Feb'85 by Cambra Records. Dist: IDS, Conifer

VERY BEST OF DIONNE WARWICK, THE.
Cassette: released on Ditto Cassettes, Aug'83

WALK ON BY.
Single (7"): released on Old Gold, Apr'83 by Old Gold Records. Dist: Lightning, Jazz Music, Spartan, Counterpoint

Single (7"): released on Dakota, Aug'82 by Dakota Records. Dist: PRT

Cassette single: released on Orchid Cassettes, Feb'82 Dist: H.R. Taylor Distribution

WE'LL BURN OUR BRIDGES BEHIND US.
Single (7"): released on Warner Bros., Mar'83 by Warner Bros Records. Dist: WEA

WITHOUT YOUR LOVE.
Single (7"): released on Arista, Dec'84 by Arista Records. Dist: RCA

Single (12"): released on Arista, Dec'84 by Arista Records. Dist: RCA

YOURS.
Single (7"): released on Arista, Feb'83 by Arista Records. Dist: RCA

Single (12"): released on Arista, Feb'83 by Arista Records. Dist: RCA

Warwicke, Dionne

16 GOLDEN CLASSICS.
Tracks: / Games people play / Hey Jude / Look of love / If I ruled the world / Going out of my head / Only love can break a heart / Summertime / Unchained melody / Yesterday / You'll never walk alone / Alfie / Trains and boats and planes / You've lost that loving feeling / Anyone who had a heart / Walk on by / Always something there to remind me.
Notes: All tracks licensed by CBS Sepcial Products. Design. Shoot That Tiger! (C) 1986. Castle Communications Place, Unit 7, 271 Merton Road, London SW18 5JS. Bar code: 5/013428/920053
Album: released on Unforgettable, Dec'86 by Castle Communications Records. Dist: Counterpoint

Compact disc: released on Unforgettable, '86 by Castle Communications Records. Dist: Counterpoint

20 GREATEST HITS, THE.
Tracks: / Walk on by / I say a little prayer / (Theme from) Valley of the dolls / I'll never fall in love again / Anyone who had a heart / Message to michael / Do you the way to san jose / Are you there with another / Who can I turn to / House is not a home,A / Don't make me over / You'll never get to heaven / Make it easy on yourself / Reach out for me / Alfie / You've lost that lovin' feeling / Trains and boats and planes / I just don't know what to do with myself / Window of the world,The / Promises,promises.
Compact disc: released on Bescol, May'87 Dist: Target

COLLECTION: DIONNE WARWICKE.
Tracks: / Then came you / Heartbreaker / I'll never love this way / Friends in love / Deja vu / No night so long / Take the short way home / All the love in the world / Love so right, A / Letter, The / Betcha by golly wow / Easy love / Our day will come / Yours / Who,what,when,where,why? / It's the falling in love / With a touch / All the time / What is this? / Walk on by / Anyone who had a heart / You'll never get to heaven / House is not a home, A / Message to Michael / Trains and boats and planes / Look of love (The) / Close to you / Close to you / Do you know the way to San Jose? / Valley of the dolls / There's always something there to remind me / Make it easy on yourself / Promises,promises / What the world needs now.
Compact disc: released on Starblend, '86 by Starblend Records. Dist: PRT Distribution

Double Album: released on Starblend, May'83 by Starblend Records. Dist: PRT Distribution

Double cassette: released on Starblend, May'83 by Starblend Records. Dist: PRT Distribution

DIONNE WARWICK CLASSICS.
Compact disc: released on K-Tel, '86 by K-Tel Records. Dist: Record Merchandisers Distribution, Taylors, Terry Blood Distribution, Wynd-Up Distribution, Relay Distribution, Pickwick Distribution, Solomon & Peres Distribution, Polygram

DO YOU KNOW THE WAY TO SAN JOSE.
Tracks: / You'll never get to heaven.
Single (7"): released on Old Gold, Jan'87 by Old Gold Records. Dist: Lightning, Jazz Music, Spartan, Counterpoint

FRIENDS.
Tracks: / That's what friends are for / Whisper in the dark / Remember your heart / Love at second sight / Moments are moments / Stronger than before / Stay devoted / No one there to sing me a love song / How long / Extravagent gestures.
Compact disc: released on Arista, Jan'86 by Arista Records. Dist: RCA

HEARTBREAKER.
Tracks: / All the love in the world / I can't see anything but you / You are my love / Just one more night / Our day will come / Heartbreaker / yours / Take the short way home / It makes no difference / Misunderstood.
Compact disc: released on Arista, '83 by Arista Records. Dist: RCA

IN CONCERT (VIDEO).
Video-cassette (VHS): released on Video Collection, May'87 by Video Collection International Ltd.. Dist: Counterpoint

LOVE POWER (Warwicke, Dionne & Jeffrey Osbourne).
Tracks: / Love power / In a world such as this / No one in the world*.
Single (7"): released on Arista, Jul'87 by Arista Records. Dist: RCA

Single (12"): released on Arista, Jul'87 by Arista Records. Dist: RCA

SAY A LITTLE PRAYER.
Notes: OCI - Oliver Crombie Imports
Compact disc: released on Dunhill Compact Classics (USA), '86

SO AMAZING.
Tracks: / How many times can we say goodbye / I do it 'cause I like it / Will you still love me tomorrow / Got a date / I can let go now.
Notes: Digital Stereo
Compact disc: released on Arista, Apr'84 by Arista Records. Dist: RCA

WALK ON BY.
Tracks: / Anyone who had a heart.
Single (7"): released on Old Gold, Jan'87 by Old Gold Records. Dist: Lightning, Jazz Music, Spartan, Counterpoint

WHISPER IN THE DARK.
Tracks: / Whisper in the dark / Extravagent gestures / No one there (to sing me a love song)*.
Single (7"): released on Arista, Apr'86 by Arista Records. Dist: RCA

Single (12"): released on Arista, Apr'86 by Arista Records. Dist: RCA

WITHOUT YOUR LOVE.
Tracks: / No one in the world / Without your love / Run to me / Finder of lost loves / Love does'nt live here anymore / Its you / It's love / Bedroom eyes / Weakness / You made me want to love again.
Notes: Brand new album from Dionne, includes single 'Without your love'. Produced by Barry Manilow, and features duet with Barry,'Run to me'. Also features 'Its you', a duet with Stevie wonder, taken from the movie 'A Woman in red'
Album: released on Arista, Feb'85 by Arista Records. Dist: RCA

Cassette: released on Arista, Feb'85 by Arista Records. Dist: RCA

Compact disc: released on Arista, Feb'85 by Arista Records. Dist: RCA

Wasa Express

WASA EXPRESS.
Album: released on Sonet, Jan'80 by Sonet Records. Dist: PRT

Washboard Willie

MOTOR TOWN BOOGIE.
Album: released on JSP, Jul'82 by JSP Records. Dist: Lugtons, Pinnacle

Washburn, Lalomie

MY MUSIC IS HOT.
Album: released on Parachute (USA), Feb'78 Dist: Polygram

Washington Behind Closed...

WASHINGTON BEHIND CLOSED DOORS Original TV soundtrack.
Album: released on BBC, Aug'78 by BBC Records & Tapes. Dist: EMI, PRT,

Cassette: released on BBC, Aug'78 by BBC Records & Tapes. Dist: EMI, PRT,

Washington, Bobby

TAKE AWAY/TAKE AWAY DUB.
Single (12"): released on Selection Exclusive, Sep'82

Washington Dead Cats

MONSTER TALES.
Cassette: released on Chainsaw International, Apr'86 by Chainsaw Records. Dist: Red Rhino, Cartel

Washington, Delroy

FOR YOUR LOVE.
Single (7"): released on Ankh, Apr'81

Single (12"): released on Ankh, Apr'81

I AIN'T NO SLEEPER.
Single (12"): released on International Records & Tapes, Oct'85 by International Records & Tapes. Dist: Pinnacle

Washington, Dinah

BESSIE SMITH SONGBOOK.
Tracks: / After you've gone / Send me to the 'lectric chair / Jailhouse blues / Trombone butter / You've been a good old wagon / Careless love / Back water blues / If I could be with you one hour tonight / Me and my gin / Fine fat daddy.
Notes: Dinah Washington, who died in 1963, combined the power of Bessie Smith with the emotion of Billie Holiday. Whether performing R & B, jazz or popular songs, the blues were never far away, indeed she was called the Queen of the Blues. This moving tribute to Bessie Smith was recorded between December 57-January 58 and originally released as *Bessie Smith Blues*. Digitally remastered from the original mono tapes.
Album: released on Polydor, Nov'86 by Polydor Records. Dist: Polygram, Polydor

Cassette: released on Polydor, Nov'86 by Polydor Records. Dist: Polygram, Polydor

Compact disc: released on Mercury, '86 by Phonogram Records. Dist: Polygram Distribution

BEST OF DINAH WASHINGTON THE.
Album: released on Carosello, Feb'83 Dist: Jazz Music, Jazz Horizons

BEST OF, THE Walkman jazz series.
Cassette: released on Verve, May'87 by Phonogram Records. Dist: Polygram

COMPACT JAZZ.
Tracks: / What a difference a day makes / All of me / I wanna be loved.
Compact disc: released on Phonogram, Jul'87 by Phonogram Records. Dist: Polygram

Cassette: released on Phonogram, Jul'87 by Phonogram Records. Dist: Polygram

DINAH JAMS.
Tracks: / Lover come back to me / Alone together / Summertime / Come rain or shine / No more / I've got you under my skin / There is

no greater love / You go to my head.
Notes: Artists include: Dinah washington, Clifford Brown, Max Roach.
Compact disc: released on Phonogram Import, '84

DINAH WASHINGTON/BROOK BENTON. (Washington, Dinah & Brook Benton).
Album: released on Mercury, Jun'83 by Phonogram Records. Dist: Polygram Distribution

Cassette: released on Mercury, Jun'83 by Phonogram Records. Dist: Polygram Distribution

DINAH WASHINGTON SINGS VOL 1.
Tracks: / After you've gone / Send me to the 'lectric chair / Jailhouse blues / Trombone butter / You've been a good ole wagon / Careless love / Back water blues / If I could be with you one hour tonight / Me and my girl / Fine fat daddy.
Album: released on Jazz Reactivation, Jan'82 Dist: PRT

DINAH WASHINGTON VOL 2.
Album: released on Jazz, May'83

FATS WALLER SONGBOOK THE.
Album: released on Emarcy(Holland), Feb'85 Dist: IMS, Polygram

Cassette: released on Emarcy(Holland), Feb'85 Dist: IMS, Polygram

Compact disc: released on Emarcy(Holland), Feb'85 Dist: IMS, Polygram

FATS WALLER SONGBOOK.
Tracks: / Christopher columbus / T'aint nobody's bizness if I do / Jitterbug waltz / Someone's rocking my dreamboat / Ain't cha glad / Squeeze me / Ain't misbehavin' / Black and blue / Everybody loves my baby / I've got a feeling I'm falling / Honeysuckle rose / Keeping out of mischief now.
Compact disc: released on Emarcy(USA), Apr'85 by Emarcy Records(USA). Dist: Polygram

IF YOU DON'T BELIEVE I'M LEAVING.
Album: released on Juke Box Lil (Sweden), Apr'86 by Mr. R&B Records. Dist: Swift

IMMORTAL.
Album: released on Carosello, Feb'83 Dist: Jazz Music, Jazz Horizons

IN THE LAND OF HI-FI.
Compact disc: released on Philips, Jul'87 Dist: IMS-Polygram

JAZZ SIDES THE.
Album: released on Mercury (USA), Oct'83 by Import Records. Dist: IMS Distribution, Polygram Distribution

VERY BEST THE.
Album: released on Mercury, Jul'84 by Phonogram Records. Dist: Polygram Distribution

Cassette: released on Mercury, Jul'84 by Phonogram Records. Dist: Polygram Distribution

WHAT A DIFFERENCE A DAY MADE.
Tracks: / Remember you / I thought about you / That's all there is to that / I'm thru with love / Cry me a river / what a difference a day made / Nothing in the world(could make me love you more than I do) / Manhattan / Time after time / Its magic / A sunday kind of love / I won't cry anymore.
Compact disc: released on Mercury, Oct'84 by Phonogram Records. Dist: Polygram Distribution

Washington, Ella

NOBODY BUT ME.
Tracks: / All the time / Stop giving your man away / I'm losing the feeling / Doin' the best I can / Starving for love / He'll be back / Too weak to fight / Nobody but me / Sweet talking candy man / Cry cry cry (You're gonna) / Sit down and cry / He called me baby / Grass is always greener, The (on the other side ..) / I want to walk through this life with you.
Album: released on Charly, Feb'87 by Charly Records. Dist: Charly, Cadillac

Washington, Geno

HAND CLAPPIN' FOOT STOMPIN' FUNKY BUTT (Washington, Geno & The Ram Jam Stars).
Album: released on Pye, Aug'80

LIVE SIDEWAYS (Washington, Geno & The Ram Jam Stars).
Album: released on Ammunition, Dec'86 Dist: Pinnacle

MICHAEL THE LOVER.
Single (7"): released on Soul Supply, Jun'84 by High Energy Records. Dist: Charly

Single (12"): released on Soul Supply, Jun'84 by High Energy Records. Dist: Charly

PUT OUT THE CAT.
Album: released on Teldec (Germany), Sep'81 by Import Records. Dist: IMS Distribution, Polygram Distribution

TAKE THAT JOB AND STUFF IT.
Album: released on Konnexion, Aug'87 Dist: Roots, Pinnacle

Washington, Grover Jr

ALL THE KINGS HORSES.
Album: released on Motown, Mar'82 by Motown Records. Dist: BMG Distribution

Cassette: released on Motown, Mar'82 by Motown Records. Dist: BMG Distribution

ANTHOLOGY.
Album: released on Motown, Sep'82 by RCA Records. Dist: RCA Distribution

Cassette: released on Motown, Sep'82 by RCA Records. Dist: RCA Distribution

Album: released on Elektra, Nov'85 by WEA Records. Dist: WEA

Cassette: released on Elektra, Nov'85 by WEA Records. Dist: WEA

AT HIS BEST.
Tracks: / It feels so good / Mister magic / Do dat / Summer song / Secret place / Ain't no sunshine / Master piece.
Compact disc: released on Motown, Apr'85 by Motown Records. Dist: BMG Distribution

BADDEST.
Album: released on Motown, Oct'81 by RCA Records. Dist: RCA Distribution

Cassette: released on Motown, Oct'81 by RCA Records. Dist: RCA Distribution

BE MINE/LITTLE BLACK SAMBA.
Single (7"): released on Elektra, Feb'82 by WEA Records. Dist: WEA

BEST IS YET TO COME THE.
Album: released on Elektra, Jan'83 by WEA Records. Dist: WEA

Cassette: released on Elektra, Jan'83 by WEA Records. Dist: WEA

BEST IS YET TO COME, THE.
Compact disc: released on Elektra, Feb'87 by WEA Records. Dist: WEA

COME MORNING.
Tracks: / East river driver / Come morning / Be mine (tonight) / Reaching out / Jamming / Little black samba / Making love to you / I'm all yours.
Notes: Digital Stereo recording
Compact disc: released on Elektra (USA), Apr'84 by Elektra/Asylum/Nonesuch Records. Dist: WEA

COME MORNING.
Album: released on Elektra, Nov'81 by WEA Records. Dist: WEA

Cassette: released on Elektra, Nov'81 by WEA Records. Dist: WEA

FEELS SO GOOD.
Album: released on Motown, Oct'81 by RCA Records. Dist: RCA Distribution

Cassette: released on Motown, Oct'81 by RCA Records. Dist: RCA Distribution

GREATEST PERFORMANCES.
Cassette: released on Motown, Jun'83 by RCA Records. Dist: RCA Distribution

INNER CITY BLUES.
Album: released on Motown, Mar'82 by Motown Records. Dist: BMG Distribution

Cassette: released on Motown, Mar'82 by Motown Records. Dist: BMG Distribution

INSIDE MOVES.
Compact disc: released on Elektra, Feb'87 by WEA Records. Dist: WEA

Album: released on Elektra, Oct'84 by WEA Records. Dist: WEA

Cassette: released on Elektra, Oct'84 by WEA Records. Dist: WEA

JAMMING/EAST RIVER DRIVE.
Single (7"): released on Elektra, Apr'82 by WEA Records. Dist: WEA

JUST THE WAY YOU ARE/LORANS DANCE.
Single (7"): released on Motown, Oct'81 by RCA Records. Dist: RCA Distribution

LET IT FLOW (FOR DR J)/WINELIGHT.
Single (7"): released on Elektra Asylum, Dec'80 by Elektra/Asylum/Nonesuch Records. Dist: WEA

Single (12"): released on Elektra Asylum, Dec'80 by Elektra/Asylum/Nonesuch Records. Dist: WEA

LIVE AT THE BIJOU.
Tracks: / On the cusp / You make me dance / Look it in the pocket / Sausalito / Funkfoot / Summer song / Juffure / Days in our lives / Mr magic.

Double Album: released on Motown, Jun'86 by Motown Records. Dist: BMG Distribution

Double cassette: released on Motown, Jun'86 by Motown Records. Dist: BMG Distribution

MISTER MAGIC.
Album: released on Motown, Oct'81 by RCA Records. Dist: RCA Distribution

Cassette: released on Motown, Oct'81 by RCA Records. Dist: RCA Distribution

MISTER MAGIC/FEELS SO GOOD 2 Classic albums.
Tracks: / Earth tones / Passion flower / Mister Magic / Black frost / Sea lion, The / Moonstreams / Knucklehead / It feels so good / Hydra.
Compact disc: released on Motown, Nov'86 by Motown Records. Dist: BMG Distribution

PARADISE.
Album: released on Elektra, Jun'79 by WEA Records. Dist: WEA

PARADISE.
Compact disc: released on Elektra, Jul'87 by WEA Records. Dist: WEA

REED SEED.
Album: released on Motown, Jun'82 by RCA Records. Dist: RCA Distribution

Cassette: released on Motown, Jun'82 by RCA Records. Dist: RCA Distribution

SECRET PLACE A.
Album: released on Motown, Oct'81 by Motown Records. Dist: BMG Distribution

Cassette: released on Motown, Oct'81 by Motown Records. Dist: BMG Distribution

SECRET PLACE, A All the king's horses.
Compact disc: released on Motown, Dec'86 by Motown Records. Dist: BMG Distribution

SECRET PLACE, A/ALL THE KING'S HORSES 2 Classic albums.
Tracks: / Secret place, A / Dolphin dance / Not yet / Love makes it better / No tears, in the end / All the king's horses / Where is the love / Body and soul / Lean on me / Lover man / Love song 1700.
Compact disc: released on Motown, Jan'87 by Motown Records. Dist: BMG Distribution

SKY LARKIN.
Album: released on Motown, Apr'84 by RCA Records. Dist: RCA Distribution

Cassette: released on Motown, Apr'84 by RCA Records. Dist: RCA Distribution

STRAWBERRY MOON.
Album: released on CBS, Aug'87 by CBS Records. Dist: CBS

Cassette: released on CBS, Aug'87 by CBS Records. Dist: CBS

Album: released on Memoir, Aug'87 by Memoir Records. Dist: PRT Distribution

Cassette: released on Memoir, Aug'87 by Memoir Records. Dist: PRT Distribution

WINELIGHT.
Tracks: / Winelight / Let it flow (for Dr.J) / In the name of love / Take me there / Just the two of us / Make me a memory (sad samba).
Album: released on Elektra Asylum, Nov'80 by Elektra/Asylum/Nonesuch Records. Dist: WEA

Compact disc: released on Elektra Asylum, Nov'80 by Elektra/Asylum/Nonesuch Records. Dist: WEA

WINELIGHT/PARADISE.
Cassette: released on Elektra, Oct'82 by WEA Records. Dist: WEA

Washington, J.R. Grover

PLAYBOY JAZZ FESTIVAL.
Album: released on Elektra, May'84 by WEA Records. Dist: WEA

STRAWBERRY MOON.
Tracks: / Strawberry moon / Look of love, The / Shivaree Ride / Caught a touch of your love / Maddie's Blues / I will be here for you / Monte Carlo nights / Keep in touch / Summer nights.
Album: released on CBS, Aug'87 by CBS Records. Dist: CBS

Cassette: released on CBS, Aug'87 by CBS Records. Dist: CBS

Washington, Leroy

LEROY WASHINGTON (volume 25 in the Legendary Jay Miller session 1957-61).
Album: released on Flyright, Jun'81 by Flyright Records. Dist: Krazy Kat, Swift, Jazz Music

WILD CHERRY.
Album: released on Flyright, Oct'86 by Flyright Records. Dist: Krazy Kat, Swift, Jazz Music

Washington, Tony

TRIBUTE TO MOHAMMED ALI/ I GOING TO LOVE YOU (Washington, T & Matumbi).
Single (7"): released on Code, Jul'8 by C Records. Dist: Jetstar, EMI

Single (12"): released on Code, Jul'82 by C Records. Dist: Jetstar, EMI

Washington, Tuts

NEW ORLEANS PIANO PROFESSO
Compact disc: released on Pablo (US Dec'86 by Pablo Records (USA). Dist: Well Chris, IMS-Polygram, BMG

Album: released on Rounder (USA), Ja Dist: Mike's Country Music Room Distribu Jazz Music Distribution, Swift Distribut Roots Records Distribution, Projection Dist tion, Topic Distribution

Washington, Walter

WOLF MAN.
Album: released on Rounder Europa, Ma

Wasington, Geno

QUE SERA SERA (EP) (Wasington, And Ram Jam Band).
Single (7"): released on Flashback, Jul' Flashback Records/PRT Records. Dist: line, PRT

Was (Not Was)

OUT COME THE FREAKS.
Single (7"): released on ZE, Jul'81 by Records. Dist: Polygram

Single (12"): released on ZE, Jul'81 by I Records. Dist: Polygram

Single (7"): released on Geffen, Jan'84 by fen Records. Dist: WEA, CBS

Single (12"): released on Geffen, Jan' Geffen Records. Dist: WEA, CBS

OUT COME THE FREAKS.
Album: released on ZE, Apr'84 by Island ords. Dist: Polygram

Cassette: released on ZE, Apr'84 by Records. Dist: Polygram

PROFESSOR NIGHT.
Single (7"): released on Geffen, Apr'84 b fen Records. Dist: WEA, CBS

Single (12"): released on Geffen, Apr' Geffen Records. Dist: WEA, CBS

ROBOT GIRL.
Tracks: / Robot girl / Earth to doris.
Single (7"): released on Mercury, Dec Phonogram Records. Dist: Polygram D tion

Single (12"): released on Mercury, Dec Phonogram Records. Dist: Polygram D tion

SPY IN THE HOUSE OF LOVE.
Tracks: / Spy in the house of love / Da jail.
Single (7"): released on Fontana, 13 Ju Phonogram Records. Dist: Polygram

Single (12"): released on Fontana, 13 by Phonogram Records. Dist: Polygram

TELL ME THAT I'M DANCING.
Single (7"): released on ZE, Mar'82 by Records. Dist: Polygram

Single (12"): released on ZE, Mar'82 b Records. Dist: Polygram

WAS (NOT WAS).
Album: released on ZE, Jul'81 by Isla ords. Dist: Polygram

Cassette: released on ZE, Jul'81 by Isla ords. Dist: Polygram

WHERE DID YOU HEART GO.
Single (7"): released on ZE, Sep'81 b Records. Dist: Polygram

Single (12"): released on ZE, Sep'81 b Records. Dist: Polygram

Waso

LIVE IN A LAREN.
Cassette: released on Polydor (Import

W.A.S.P.

95-NASTY.
Tracks: / 95-Nasty / Easy living / Flesh
Single (7"): released on Capitol, S Capitol Records. Dist: EMI

Single (12"): released on Capitol, S Capitol Records. Dist: EMI

ANIMAL (FUCK LIKE A BEAST).
Single (7"): released on Music For Nations, Apr'84 by Music For Nations Records. Dist: Pinnacle

Single (12"): released on Music For Nations, Apr'84 by Music For Nations Records. Dist: Pinnacle

Picture disc single: released on Music For Nations, Apr'84 by Music For Nations Records. Dist: Pinnacle

Single (7"): released on Music For Nations, May'85 by Music For Nations Records. Dist: Pinnacle

LIND IN TEXAS.
icture disc single: released on Capitol, ct'85 by Capitol Records. Dist: EMI

ingle (7"): released on Capitol, Sep'85 by apitol Records. Dist: EMI

ingle (12"): released on Capitol, Sep'85 by apitol Records. Dist: EMI

ISIDE THE ELECTRIC CIRCUS.
racks: / Big welcome,(the) / I need no doctor / asty restless gypsy / Shoot from the hip / I'm ive / Easy livin' / Sweet cheetah / Mantronic / ng of sodom and gomorrah / Rock rolls on, ne).
ompact disc: released on Capitol, Feb'87 by apitol Records. Dist: EMI

bum: released on Capitol, Oct'86 by Capitol ecords. Dist: EMI

ssette: released on Capitol, Oct'86 by Capi- Records. Dist: EMI

VANNA BE SOMEBODY.
ngle (7"): released on EMI, Aug'84 by EMI cords. Dist: EMI

ture disc single: released on EMI, Aug'84 EMI Records. Dist: EMI

ST COMMAND THE.
um: released on Capitol, Oct'85 by Capitol cords. Dist: EMI

ssette: released on Capitol, Oct'85 by Capi- Records. Dist: EMI

E IN THE RAW.
cks: / Inside the Electric Circus / I don't need doctor / L.O.V.E. machine / Wild child / 9.5 ty / Sleeping (in the fire) / Manimal, The / I ana be somebody / Harder faster / Blind in as / Scream until you like it.
npact disc: released on Capitol, Sep'87 by itol Records. Dist: EMI. Estim retail price in '87 was £11.99.

um: released on Capitol, Sep'87 by Capitol ords. Dist: EMI. Estim retail price in Sep'87 £5.99.

sette: released on Capitol, Sep'87 by Capi- Records. Dist: EMI. Estim retail price in '87 was £5.99.

HOOL DAZE.
le (12"): released on Capitol, Nov'84 by tol Records. Dist: EMI

REAM UNTIL YOU LIKE IT.
le (7"): released on Capitol, Aug'87 by tol Records. Dist: EMI

le (12"): released on Capitol, Aug'87 by tol Records. Dist: EMI

EO EP.
o-cassette (VHS): released on PMI, 36 by PMI Records. Dist: EMI

o-cassette [Betamax]: released on PMI, 6 by PMI Records. Dist: EMI

.S.P.
m: released on Capitol, Aug'84 by Capitol rds. Dist: EMI

ette: released on Capitol, Aug'84 by Capi- ecords. Dist: EMI

S.P. INTERVIEW PICTURE DISC.
n: released on Baktabak, Apr'87 by Bak- Records. Dist: Arabesque

CHILD *.
s: / Wild child / Mississippi queen / Wild / Mississippi queen* / On your knees* / n *.
s: Double pack. Limited edition in Gate- ag.
(7"): released on Capitol, May'86 by l Records. Dist: EMI

e-pack single: released on Capitol, 6 by Capitol Records. Dist: EMI

(12"): released on Capitol, May'86 by l Records. Dist: EMI

ssailers

SAILERS.
: released on Fellside (Cumbria), '83 by e Records. Dist: Roots, Projection, CM, usic

Waste

NOT JUST SOMETHING.
Single (7"): released on Mortarhate, Nov'86 by Dorane Ltd.

Wasted Youth

FROM THE: INNER DEPTHS.
Album: released on V.C., Dec'85 Dist: Jetstar

I'LL REMEMBER YOU/MY FRIENDS ARE.
Single (7"): released on Bridgehouse, Sep'80 Dist: Pinnacle

JEALOUSY/BABY.
Single (12"): released on Bridgehouse, Mar'82 Dist: Pinnacle

REACH OUT/GONE MIDNIGHT.
Single (7"): released on Bridgehouse, Aug'82 Dist: Pinnacle

REBECCA'S ROOM.
Single (7"): released on Fresh, Jun'81 Dist: Jetstar

WASTED YOUTH.
Album: released on Bridgehouse, Jul'82 Dist: Pinnacle

WILD AND WONDERFUL CRIES.
Album: released on Bridgehouse, Oct'81 Dist: Pinnacle

WILD LIFE/GAMES.
Single (7"): released on Bridgehouse, Apr'82 Dist: Pinnacle

Waste Land

WASTE LAND Eliot, T.S. (Guinness, Alec).
Double cassette: released on Argo (Spoken-word), Jul'82 by Decca Records. Dist: Polygram

Watanabe, Kazumi

LONESOME CAT.
Tracks: / Somebody somebody / Mirrors / Aqua beauty / Blackstone / Moving nozzle / Lonesome cat.
Notes: Recorded at Sound Ideas Studio, New York City, 14th December 1977.
Album: released on Denon, Feb'82 by Denon Records. Dist: Harmonia Mundi

Compact disc: released on Denon, Feb'82 by Denon Records. Dist: Harmonia Mundi

MOBO 1.
Album: released on Gramavision (USA), Oct'84 by Gramavison Records (USA). Dist: PRT, IMS, Polygram

Cassette: released on Gramavision (USA), Oct'84 by Gramavison Records (USA). Dist: PRT, IMS, Polygram

MOBO II.
Tracks: / Voyage / Yatokesa / Alicia / Shang hi / All beets are coming.
Compact disc: released on Gramavision (USA), May'85 by Gramavison Records (USA). Dist: PRT, IMS, Polygram

MOBO LL.
Album: released on Gramavision (USA), Feb'85 by Gramavison Records (USA). Dist: PRT, IMS, Polygram

Cassette: released on Gramavision (USA), Feb'85 by Gramavison Records (USA). Dist: PRT, IMS, Polygram

Compact disc: released on Gramavision (USA), Feb'85 by Gramavison Records (USA). Dist: PRT, IMS, Polygram

Watanabe, Sadao

CLIFORNIA SHOWER.
Album: released on Miracle, Jun'79 by Gull Records. Dist: PRT Distribution

DUO CREATURES/TURNING PAGES OF WIND.
Single (7"): released on Miracle, Oct'79 by Gull Records. Dist: PRT Distribution

FILL UP THE NIGHT.
Album: released on WEA, Mar'84 by WEA Records. Dist: WEA

GOOD TIME FOR LOVE.
Tracks: / Good time for love / Love birds whisper in my ear / When we make a home / Step out on the street / I love to say your name / Pogo / All the way / Loving you is easy.
Album: released on WEA, Aug'86 by WEA Records. Dist: WEA

Cassette: released on WEA, Aug'86 by WEA Records. Dist: WEA

GOOD TIME FOR LOVING, A.
Compact disc: released on WEA Int, '86

JAZZ & BOSSA.
Compact disc: released on Denon, May'86 by Denon Records. Dist: Harmonia Mundi

MAISHA.
Album: released on WEA, Jul'85 by WEA Records. Dist: WEA

RENDEZVOUS.
Album: released on WEA, Sep'84 by WEA Records. Dist: WEA

SADAO MEETS BRAZILLIAN FRIENDS.
Compact disc: released on Denon, May'86 by Denon Records. Dist: Harmonia Mundi

Watanabe, Toshyuki

PAUSED WIND.
Notes: New Age Music for piano, flute, oboe and strings.
Compact disc: released on Denon, May'86 by Denon Records. Dist: Harmonia Mundi

Watanbe, Sadao

IF I'M STILL AROUND TOMORROW.
Single (7"): released on WEA Int, Oct'84

Single (12"): released on WEA Int, Oct'84

Wat, Angor

GENERAL STRIKE.
Album: released on Cor, Mar'86 Dist: Revolver, Cartel

Watch

WATCH Music & songs from the schools TV series (Various Artists).
Album: released on BBC, Sep'78 by BBC Records & Tapes. Dist: EMI, PRT, Pye

Cassette: released on BBC, Sep'78 by BBC Records & Tapes. Dist: EMI, PRT, Pye

WATCH - THE THIRD WATCH Various artists (Various Artists).
Album: released on BBC, Oct'83 by BBC Records & Tapes. Dist: EMI, PRT, Pye

Cassette: released on BBC, Oct'83 by BBC Records & Tapes. Dist: EMI, PRT, Pye

Watch Again

WATCH AGAIN Music from the BBC TV schools series (Various Artists).
Album: released on BBC, Jan'80 by BBC Records & Tapes. Dist: EMI, PRT, Pye

Cassette: released on BBC, Jan'80 by BBC Records & Tapes. Dist: EMI, PRT, Pye

Watch With Mother

SUZANNE.
Tracks: / Suzanne / Something so wonderful.
Single (7"): released on Surfin Pict, Oct'86

Water

WATER Original soundtrack.
Album: released on London, Jun'85 by London Records. Dist: Polygram

Water Babies

CHARLES KINGSLEY.
Cassette: released on Caedmon(USA), Jan'84 by Caedmon (USA) Records. Dist: Gower, Taylors, Discovery

WATER BABIES Original film soundtrack (Various Artists).
Album: released on Ariola, Aug'79 Dist: RCA, Ariola

Cassette: released on Ariola, Aug'79 Dist: RCA, Ariola

Waterboys

GIRL CALLED JOHNNY/READY FOR THE MONKEY HOUSE/OUT OF CONTROL.
Single (12"): released on Chicken Jazz, May'83 by Chicken Jazz Records. Dist: Rough Trade

PAGAN PLACE (A).
Tracks: / Church not made with hands / All of the things she gave me / Thrill is gone (The) / Rags / Somebody might come back / Big music (The) / Red army blues / Pagan place.
Compact disc: released on Chrysalis, '86 by Chrysalis Records. Dist: CBS

Album: released on Ensign, May'84 by Ensign Records. Dist: CBS Distribution

Cassette: released on Ensign, May'84 by Ensign Records. Dist: CBS Distribution

THIS IS THE SEA.
Compact disc: released on Ensign, Nov'86 by Ensign Records. Dist: CBS Distribution

Compact disc: by Ensign Records. Dist: CBS Distribution

WATERBOYS (THE).
Tracks: / Church not made with hands / All the things she gave me / Thrill is gone (The) / Rags / Somebody might wave back / Big music (The) / Red army blues / Pagan place (A) / Don't bang the drum / Whole of the moon (The) / Spirit / Pan within (The) / Medicine bow / Old England / Be my enemy / Trumpets / This is the sea.
Album: released on Ensign, Aug'86 by Ensign Records. Dist: CBS Distribution

Cassette: released on Ensign, Aug'86 by Ensign Records. Dist: CBS Distribution

Album: released on Ensign, Aug'86 by Ensign Records. Dist: CBS Distribution

Cassette: released on Ensign, Aug'86 by Ensign Records. Dist: CBS Distribution

WATERBOYS THE.
Album: released on Ensign, Jul'83 by Ensign Records. Dist: CBS Distribution

Cassette: released on Ensign, Jul'83 by Ensign Records. Dist: CBS Distribution

WHOLE OF THE MOON THE.
Single (7"): released on Ensign, Oct'85 by Ensign Records. Dist: CBS Distribution

Cassette: released on Ensign, Oct'85 by Ensign Records. Dist: CBS Distribution

Waterfall

BENEATH THE STARS.
Album: released on Gundog, Jan'82 Dist: Spartan

THREE BIRDS.
Album: released on Avada, Jan'82 Dist: Roots

Waterfoot Damby

14 DAYS.
Single (7"): released on Tape, May'85

Waterman, Dennis

COME AWAY WITH ME.
Single (7"): released on EMI, May'81 by EMI Records. Dist: EMI

I COULD BE SO GOOD FOR YOU.
Album: released on Music For Pleasure, Nov'83 by EMI Records. Dist: EMI

Cassette: released on Music For Pleasure, Nov'83 by EMI Records. Dist: EMI

Single (7"): released on EMI, Sep'80 by EMI Records. Dist: EMI

WE DON'T MAKE LOVE ON SUNDAYS/INDIAN SILK.
Single (7"): released on C&D, Mar'82 by Phonogram Records. Dist: Polygram

Watermelon men

PAST PRESENT AND FUTURE.
Album: released on What Goes On, Sep'85 Dist: Rough Trade, Cartel, Shigaku

Water Pumping Top Ten

WATER PUMPING TOP TEN Various artists (Various Artists).
Album: released on Tads, Nov'83 by Tads Records. Dist: Jetstar Distribution

Waters, Benny

ON THE SUNNY SIDE OF THE STREET.
Album: released on JSP Records, Sep'81 by JSP Records. Dist: Jazz Music, Pinnacle

Waters, Bob

GREAT RIVERS (Waters, Bob & Country Union).
Single (7"): released on Starcrest, '82 by Starcrest Records. Dist: Starcrest Distribution

Waters, Ethel

1938-39 (the complete Bluebird sessions).
Notes: MONO
Album: released on Rosetta, Oct'86 Dist: WRPM Distribution, Jazz Music Distribution, JSU Distribution, Swift Distribution

ETHEL WATERS.
Album: released on Monmouth, Mar'79

FOREMOTHERS Volume 6 (Waters, Ethel).
Cassette: released on Rosetta, Dec'86 Dist: WRPM Distribution, Jazz Music Distribution, JSU Distribution, Swift Distribution

NO-ONE CAN LOVE ME.
Notes: MONO
Cassette: released on Emporium Cassettes, Jul'86 by Emporium Cassettes Records. Dist: Jazz Music

ON THE AIR.
Album: released on Totem (USA), Jun'84 by Totem Records. Dist: Swift, JSU

Watership Down

WATERSHIP DOWN (Dotrice, Roy).
Boxed set: released on Argo, Nov'76 by Decca Records. Dist: Polygram

Boxed set: released on Argo, Nov'76 by Decca Records. Dist: Polygram

Waters, Mira

YOU HAVE INSPIRED ME.
Single (7"): released on Motown, Oct'81 by RCA Records. Dist: RCA Distribution

Waters, Muddy

20 BLUES GREATS.
Album: released on Deja Vu, Nov'85 by Deja Vu Records. Dist: Counterpoint Distribution, Record Services Distribution (Ireland)

Cassette: released on Deja Vu, Aug'85 by Deja Vu Records. Dist: Counterpoint Distribution, Record Services Distribution (Ireland)

BACK IN THE EARLY DAYS VOL.1/2.
Album: released on Syndicate Chapter, Sep'82 Dist: JSU Distribution, Projection Distribution, Red Lightnin' Distribution, Swift Distribution

BEST OF MUDDY WATERS.
Album: released on Chess, Oct'87 by Charly Records. Dist: Charly, Swift, PRT, Discovery, IMS, Polygram

Cassette: released on Chess, Oct'87 by Charly Records. Dist: Charly, Swift, PRT, Discovery, IMS, Polygram

Album: released on Vogue (France), Jul'84 Dist: Discovery, Jazz Music, PRT, Swift

CHESS MASTERS.
Double Album: released on Checker(USA), Apr'81 by PRT. Dist: PRT

CHESS MASTERS...MUDDY WATERS.
Double Album: released on Chess(USA), Apr'82 by Sugar Hill (USA). Dist: PRT, Swift

CHESS MASTERS VOL.3.
Album: released on Chess(USA), May'83 by Sugar Hill (USA). Dist: PRT, Swift

DOWN ON STOVALL'S PLANTATION.
Album: released on Testament, May'86 Dist: Swift Distribution, Making Waves Distribution

FATHERS AND SONS (Waters, Muddy/Michael Bloomfield).
Notes: A star-studded live spectacular from the late sixties, featuring Buddy Mills, Phil Upchurch and Paul Butterfield, to name but three.
Double Album: released on Chess, Dec'85 by Charly Records. Dist: Charly, Swift, PRT, Discovery, IMS, Polygram

FOLK SINGERS.
Album: released on Chess, Oct'87 by Charly Records. Dist: Charly, Swift, PRT, Discovery, IMS, Polygram

Cassette: released on Chess, Oct'87 by Charly Records. Dist: Charly, Swift, PRT, Discovery, IMS, Polygram

GOOD NEWS VOL.3.
Album: released on Syndicate Chapter, Sep'82 Dist: JSU Distribution, Projection Distribution, Red Lightnin' Distribution, Swift Distribution

HARD AGAIN.
Album: released on Blue Sky, Sep'83 by CBS Records. Dist: CBS

Cassette: released on Blue Sky, Sep'83 by CBS Records. Dist: CBS

HOOCHIE COOCHIE MAN.
Album: released on Blue Sky, Jul'83 by CBS Records. Dist: CBS

Cassette: released on Blue Sky, Jul'83 by CBS Records. Dist: CBS

I CAN'T BE SATISFIED.
Tracks: / I can't call her sugar / You can't lose what you ain't never had / Sad letter / I can't be satisfied / Baby please don't go / Walkin' thru the park / Trainfare blues / Sittin' here drinkin' / I got a rich man's woman / Mean mistreater.
Cassette: released on Showcase, Apr'86 Dist: Counterpoint

IN MEMORIAM.
Notes: German pressings of some of the gems such as 'I'm Your Hoochie Coohie Man' and 'Got My Mojo Workin'.
Double Album: released on Chess, Dec'85 by Charly Records. Dist: Charly, Swift, PRT, Discovery, IMS, Polygram

KING BEE.
Album: released on Blue Sky, May'81 by CBS Records. Dist: CBS

LIVE 65-68.
Album: released on Onsala, Aug'87 Dist: Making Waves, Pinnacle

LIVE AT MR KELL'S.
Album: released on Vogue-Chess (France), Mar'84

LIVE AT NEWPORT 1960.
Album: released on Vogue (France), Jul'84 Dist: Discovery, Jazz Music, PRT, Swift

LONDON MUDDY WATERS SESSIONS THE.
Album: released on Chess(USA), Apr'82 by Sugar Hill (USA). Dist: PRT, Swift

MISSISSIPPPI ROLLIN STONE.
Album: released on Blue Moon, Sep'84 Dist: Magnum Music Group Ltd, PRT, Spartan

MUDDY MISSISSIPPI WATERS LIVE.
Album: released on Blue Sky, Jan'79 by CBS Records. Dist: CBS

MUDDY WATERS AT NEWPORT.
Album: released on Chess, Apr'87 by Charly Records. Dist: Charly, Swift, PRT, Discovery, IMS, Polygram

Cassette: released on Chess, Apr'87 by Charly Records. Dist: Charly, Swift, PRT, Discovery, IMS, Polygram

MUD IN YOUR EAR.
Album: released on Muse, Apr'81 by Import Records. Dist: Jazz Horizons Distribution, Jazz Music Distribution, JSU Distribution, Swift Distribution

Album: released on Happy Bird (Germany), Jul'83 Dist: Polygram, IMS

ON CHESS VOL 1 1948-51.
Compact disc: released on Vogue (France), Dec'85 Dist: Discovery, Jazz Music, PRT, Swift

ON CHESS VOL 2 1951-59.
Compact disc: released on Vogue (France), Dec'85 Dist: Discovery, Jazz Music, PRT, Swift

ORIGINAL HOOCHIE COOCHIE MAN.
Album: released on Blue Moon, May'85 Dist: Magnum Music Group Ltd, PRT, Spartan

ORIGINAL HOOCHIE COOCHIE.
Album: released on Astan, Nov'84 by Astan Records. Dist: Counterpoint

Cassette: released on Astan, Nov'84 by Astan Records. Dist: Counterpoint

PROFILE.
Album: released on Teldec (Germany), Apr'84 by Import Records. Dist: IMS Distribution, Polygram Distribution

RARE AND UNISSUED.
Tracks: / Little Anna Mae / Mean disposition / Feel like going home / You're gonna miss me / Stand here trembling / Last time I fool around with you / Where's my woman been / Gal you gotta watch / Lonesome day / Iodine in my coffee / Smoke stack lightning / Let me hang around / Born lover / Down in my heart.
Album: released on Chess, Aug'86 by Charly Records. Dist: Charly, Swift, PRT, Discovery, IMS, Polygram

Cassette: released on Chess, Aug'86 by Charly Records. Dist: Charly, Swift, PRT, Discovery, IMS, Polygram

ROCK ME.
Album: released on Masters (Holland), Apr'87

Cassette: released on Masters (Holland), Apr'87

ROLLIN STONE.
Album: released on Blue Moon, Jul'83 Dist: Magnum Music Group Ltd, PRT, Spartan

SEET HOME CHICAGO.
Album: released on Astan, Nov'84 by Astan Records. Dist: Counterpoint

Cassette: released on Astan, Nov'84 by Astan Records. Dist: Counterpoint

SINGS BIG BILL BROONZY.
Album: released on Chess, Apr'87 by Charly Records. Dist: Charly, Swift, PRT, Discovery, IMS, Polygram

Cassette: released on Chess, Apr'87 by Charly Records. Dist: Charly, Swift, PRT, Discovery, IMS, Polygram

THEY CALL ME MUDDY WATERS.
Album: released on Vogue-Chess (France), Mar'84

VOLUME 2.
Notes: From the 'Blues Roots' catalogue, here we have 13 great tracks, including 'Tiger In Your Tank' and 'Country Boy' (live recording 1971.
Album: released on Chess, Dec'85 by Charly Records. Dist: Charly, Swift, PRT, Discovery, IMS, Polygram

WARSAW SESSIONS VOL.1 1976, THE (Waters, Muddy Blues Band).
Album: released on Poljazz, Jul'87

WARSAW SESSIONS VOL.2 1976, THE (Waters, Muddy Blues Band).
Album: released on Poljazz, Jul'87

WE THREE KINGS (Waters, Muddy/ Little Walter/ Howlin' Wolf).
Album: released on Syndicate Chapter, Sep'82 Dist: JSU Distribution, Projection Distribution, Red Lightnin' Distribution, Swift Distribution

Waters Of The World

WATERS OF THE WORLD (Heyerdahl, Dr.T./ Dr. D. George).
Cassette: released on Seminar Cassettes, '81 by Seminar Cassettes. Dist: Davidson Distribution, Eastern Educational Products Distrib., Forlaget Systime Distribution, Laser Books Ltd Distribution, MacDougall Distribution, Talktapes Distribution, Watkins Books Ltd Distribution, Norton, Jeff Distribution

Waterson, Lal & Mike

BRIGHT PHOEBUS.
Album: released on Highway, Aug'85 by Highway Records. Dist: Roots, Projection, Ross

Waterson, Lal & Norma

TRUE HEARTED GIRL A.
Album: released on Topic, Jan'81 by Topic Records. Dist: JSU Distribution, Projection Distribution, Jazz Music Distribution

Waterson, Mike

MIKE WATERSON.
Album: released on Topic, Jan'81 by Topic Records. Dist: JSU Distribution, Projection Distribution, Jazz Music Distribution

Watersons

BRIGHT PHOEBUS.
Album: released on Leader, Jun'86 Dist: Jazz Music, Projection

Album: released on Leader, Jan'81 Dist: Jazz Music, Projection

FOUR PENCE AND SPICY ALE.
Album: released on Topic, Jan'81 by Topic Records. Dist: JSU Distribution, Projection Distribution, Jazz Music Distribution

FROST & FIRE.
Album: released on Wynd-up, Jan'81 Dist: Wynd-Up Distribution

GREENFIELDS.
Album: released on Topic, Jun'81 by Topic Records. Dist: JSU Distribution, Projection Distribution, Jazz Music Distribution

SOUND, SOUND YOUR INSTRUMENTS OF JOY.
Album: released on Topic, '81 Dist: Roots Distribution

WATERSONS THE.
Album: released on Wynd-up, Jan'81 Dist: Wynd-Up Distribution

YORKSHIRE GARLAND A.
Album: released on Topic, Jan'81 by Topic Records. Dist: JSU Distribution, Projection Distribution, Jazz Music Distribution

Waters, Roger

5.06 AM Every strangers eyes.
Single (7"): released on Harvest, Jun'84 by EMI Records. Dist: Roots, EMI

MUSIC FROM THE BODY (Waters, Roger/Ron Geesin).
Notes: Album originally released 1970.
Album: released on Harvest, Jun'85 by EMI Records. Dist: Roots, EMI

Cassette: released on Harvest, Jun'85 by EMI Records. Dist: Roots, EMI

Album: released on Harvest, Jun'85 by EMI Records. Dist: Roots, EMI

PROS AND CONS OF HITCH HIKING.
Single (7"): released on Harvest, Apr'84 by EMI Records. Dist: Roots, EMI

PROS AND CONS OF HITCH HIKING (THE).
Tracks: / Apparently they were travelling abroad / Running shoes / Arabs with knives and West German skies / For the first time today - part 2 / Sexual revolution / Remains of our love (The) / Go fishing / For the first time today - part 1 / Dunroamin duncarin dunlivin' / Pros and cons of hitch hiking (The) / Every strangers eyes / Moment of clarity (The).
Notes: First solo album from Roger Walters, the major creative force behind Pink Floyd. Features excellent guest musicians including Eric Clapton on guitar and Madeline Bell on vocals, Ray Cooper on percussion, Andy Newmark on drums and appearances by Jack Palance, Cherry Vanilla and others.
Album: released on Harvest, May'84 by EMI Records. Dist: Roots, EMI

Cassette: released on Harvest, May'84 by EMI Records. Dist: Roots, EMI

Compact disc: released on Harvest, May'84 by EMI Records. Dist: Roots, EMI

RADIO K.A.O.S..
Tracks: / Radio waves / Who needs information / Me or him / Powers that be, The / Sunset strip / Home / Four minutes / Tide is turning, The.
Album: released on Harvest, Jun'87 by EMI Records. Dist: Roots, EMI

Cassette: released on Harvest, Jun'87 by EMI Records. Dist: Roots, EMI

Compact disc: released on EMI, Jun'87 by EMI Records. Dist: EMI

RADIO WAVES.
Tracks: / Radio waves / Going to live in LA.
Single (7"): released on EMI, May'87 by EM Records. Dist: EMI

Single (12"): released on EMI, May'87 by EM Records. Dist: EMI

Compact disc single: by EMI Records. Dis EMI

Waters, Ron

MYSTERIOUS PEOPLE.
Album: released on SRT, Jan'77 by SRT Rec ords. Dist: Pinnacle, Solomon & Peres Distribu tion, SRT Distribution, H.R. Taylor Distributio PRT Distribution

Watkins, Geraint

I'M A FOOL TO CARE.
Single (7"): released on Beeb, Sep'81 by BB Records. Dist: PRT

Watkins, Kit

LABYRINTH.
Album: released on Strawberry-Uniton, Nov'

Watkins, Mary

WINDS OF CHANGE.
Album: released on Palo Alto (Italy). Jan'84

Watkins, Otis

YOU TALK TOO MUCH/YOU'R READY.
Single (7"): released on Stiff, Jul'80 by S Records. Dist: EMI, Record Services Distrib tion (Ireland)

Watkiss, Clive

GIMME WHAT YOU GOT/VERSION.
Single (12"): released on S&G, Feb'82 by S Records. Dist: Jetstar

Watkiss, Gerald

PURGATORY & PARADISE.
Album:

Watley, Jody

JODY WATLEY.
Tracks: / Looking for a new love / Still a th Some kind of lover / For the girls / Love in tion / Don't you want me / Do it to the beat / M of all / Learn to say no / Looking for a new l (extended club version).
Album: released on MCA, Feb'87 by MCA R ords. Dist: Polygram, MCA

Cassette: released on MCA, Feb'87 by M Records. Dist: Polygram, MCA

Compact disc: released on MCA, Feb'87 MCA Records. Dist: Polygram, MCA

LOOKING FOR A NEW LOVE.
Tracks: / Looking for a new love / Looking f new love (acappella).
Single (7"): released on MCA, Apr'87 by M Records. Dist: Polygram, MCA

Single (12"): released on MCA, Apr'87 by M Records. Dist: Polygram, MCA

STILL A THRILL.
Tracks: / Sillath / Looking for a new love (a pella).
Single (7"): released on MCA, Jul'87 by Records. Dist: Polygram, MCA

Single (12"): by MCA Records. Dist: gram, MCA

Watrous, Bill

LIVE AT THE PIZZA EXPRESS 198
Album: released on Mole, Jul'83 by Mole ords. Dist: Mole Music Co., Spartan Distrib

Watson, Beasley

BREAKAWAY/DON'T LET YOUR.
Single (7"): released on Creole, Mar'81 by ole Records. Dist: Rhino, PRT

Single (12"): released on Creole, Mar' Creole Records. Dist: Rhino, PRT

Watson, Diz

HUMBALERO.
Album: released on Ace, Jan'85 by Ace Rec-ds. Dist: Pinnacle, Swift, Hotshot, Cadillac

Watson, Doc

SSENTIAL DOC WATSON THE.
ouble **Album:** released on Vanguard, Jan'74 PRT Records. Dist: PRT

THE PINES.
bum: released on Sundown, Nov'84 by Mag-m Music Group Ltd. Dist: Magnum Music oup Ltd, PRT Distribution, Spartan Distribu-n

ssette: released on Sundown, Aug'85 by agnum Music Group Ltd. Dist: Magnum Music oup Ltd, PRT Distribution, Spartan Distribu-n

CKIN' THE BLUES (Watson, Doc/Merle atson).
oum: released on Flying Fish (USA), Jan'86 Flying Fish Records (USA). Dist: Roots, Pro-tion

Watson, Doc & Merle

WN SOUTH.
um: released on Sugarhill, Mar'85 by PRT cords. Dist: PRT Distribution

Watson, Doc/Merle Watson

LK AND COUNTRY LEGEND,A.
um: released on L & R, '82 Dist: Swift

Watson, Ed

OW THEM.
cks: / Show them.
gle (12"): released on Hot Vinyl, Jun'86 by Vinyl Records. Dist: Jetstar

Watson, Ed Brass Circle

IO.
gle (12"): released on Charlie's, Jun'85 by rlie's Records. Dist: Jetstar

Watson Family

ADITION.
um: released on Rounder, Jan'87 Dist: ts Distribution

TSON FAMILY TRADITION THE.
im: released on Topic, Jan'81 Dist: Roots ibution

atson, Gene

EATEST HITS:GENE WATSON.
ks: / Between this time and next time / e I should have been listening / Fourteen mind / Speak softly (you're talking to my) / This dream's on me / What she don't won't hurt her / You're out doing what I'm doing without / Sometimes I get lucky and t / Drinkin' my way back home / Forever
m: released on MCA Import, Mar'86 by Records. Dist: Polygram, IMS

RTACHES LOVE & STUFF.
m: released on MCA, Feb'85 by MCA Rec-Dist: Polygram, MCA

LE BY LITTLE.
n: released on MCA, Apr'84 by MCA Rec-Dist: Polygram, MCA

ette: released on MCA, Apr'84 by MCA rds. Dist: Polygram, MCA

LOVE NEVER DIES.
s: / Old love never dies / Girl I used to run d on (The) / Roads and other reasons / 'Til da comes round / Speak softly (you're talk-my heart) / Nothing about her reminds me / Fourteen carat mind / Lonely me / Sun comes up again (The) / Missing you just d hittin' home.
n: released on MCA Import, Mar'86 by Records. Dist: Polygram, IMS

ETIMES I GET LUCKY.
s: / Speak well of me / Sometimes I get She sure makes leaving look easy / You d yourself right into my life / You put out flame last night / You're just another beer song / Thinkin' 'bout leaving / If I were fall in love with me.
: released on MCA Import, Mar'86 by Records. Dist: Polygram, IMS

S SATURDAY NIGHT.
s: / Texas Saturday night / Got no reason goin' home / You waltzed yourself right life / My memories of you / If I were you in love with me / You're just another beer song / One hell of a heartache / You sure cheatin' seem easy / I'm tellin' me a lie / my way back home.
: released on MCA Import, Mar'86 by Records. Dist: Polygram, IMS

DREAM'S ON ME.
s: / This dream's on me / Fightin' fire with aby me baby / Full time fool / This torch that I carry for you / What she don't know won't hurt her / From cotton to satin / You sure make cheatin' seem easy / Last thing I planned to do today was cheat,The / Somethin' 'bout bein' gone.
Album: released on MCA Import, Mar'86 by MCA Records. Dist: Polygram, IMS

Watson, George

ITRODUCING BIG GEORGE.
Album: released on Emerald, Mar'77 by Emerald Records. Dist: Ross, PRT, Solomon & Peres Distribution

Watson, Helen

BLUE SLIPPER.
Tracks: / You're not the rule (you're the exception) / Boys own world / When you love me I get lazy / New island rock line / Blue slipper / Don't stop now / I'm jealous dear / Sway / Chrome solder / Don't forget to say your prayers / Rock myself to sleep.
Album: released on Columbia, Oct'87 by EMI Records. Dist: EMI

Cassette: released on Columbia, Oct'87 by EMI Records. Dist: EMI

Watsonian Institute

MASTER FUNK.
Album: released on DJM, Mar'78 by DJM Records. Dist: CBS, Polygram

Cassette: released on DJM, Mar'78 by DJM Records. Dist: CBS, Polygram

Watson, John L

DON'T BLAME IT ON LOVE.
Single (7"): released on Satril, Oct'85 by Satril Records. Dist: PRT

Watson, Johnny 'Guitar'

AIN'T THAT A BITCH.
Album: released on DJM, Nov'81 by DJM Records. Dist: CBS, Polygram

Cassette: released on DJM, Nov'81 by DJM Records. Dist: CBS, Polygram

...AND THE FAMILY CLONE.
Album: released on DJM, Jun'81 by DJM Records. Dist: CBS, Polygram

Cassette: released on DJM, Jun'81 by DJM Records. Dist: CBS, Polygram

FUNK BEYOND THE CALL OF DUTY.
Album: released on DJM, Nov'81 by DJM Records. Dist: CBS, Polygram

Cassette: released on DJM, Nov'81 by DJM Records. Dist: CBS, Polygram

GANGSTER IS BLACK, THE.
Album: released on Red Lightnin', Sep'82 by Red Lightnin' Records. Dist: Roots, Swift, Jazz Music, JSU, Pinnacle, Cartel, Wynd-Up Distribution

GANGSTER OF LOVE.
Single (7"): released on DJM, Oct'83 by DJM Records. Dist: CBS, Polygram

Single (12"): released on DJM, Oct'83 by DJM Records. Dist: CBS, Polygram

GETTIN' DOWN WITH....
Album: released on Chess, Jan'87 by Charly Records. Dist: Charly, Swift, PRT, Discovery, IMS, Polygram

Cassette: released on Chess, Jan'87 by Charly Records. Dist: Charly, Swift, PRT, Discovery, IMS, Polygram

GIANT.
Album: released on DJM, Nov'81 by DJM Records. Dist: CBS, Polygram

Cassette: released on DJM, Nov'81 by DJM Records. Dist: CBS, Polygram

HIT THE HIGHWAY.
Album: released on Ace(Cadet), Jul'83 by Ace Records. Dist: Pinnacle, Swift, Hotshot

I HEARD THAT!.
Album: released on Charly(R&B), Jul'85 by Charly Records. Dist: Charly, Cadillac

Cassette: released on Charly(R&B), Jul'85 by Charly Records. Dist: Charly, Cadillac

I HEARD THAT.
Tracks: / Highway 60P / Motor head baby P1953 / No I can't P 1953 / What's going on / Walking to my baby / Thinking / I got eyes / Space guitar / Half-pint-a-whisky / Gettin' drunk / You can't take it with you / Cuttin' in / Sweet lovin mama / In the evening / Those lonely, lonely feelings / Gangster of love.
Notes: Composer John Watson except 1-3 with Mario Delagarde, 9-Rudolph Toombs. 14-traditional. 15 Earl King and Johnny Vincent. Original King recordings.
Compact disc: released on Charly, Jan'87 by Charly Records. Dist: Charly, Cadillac

LOVE JONES.
Album: released on DJM, Nov'81 by DJM Records. Dist: CBS, Polygram

Cassette: released on DJM, Nov'81 by DJM Records. Dist: CBS, Polygram

REAL MOTHER A.
Album: released on DJM, Nov'81 by DJM Records. Dist: CBS, Polygram

Cassette: released on DJM, Nov'81 by DJM Records. Dist: CBS, Polygram

STRIKE ON COMPUTERS.
Tracks: / You do me bad so good / Boogie down party down / Scratching "85" / Let's get together / Strike on computers / Byrd ball train / Statue of Liberty / Please send me somebody to love.
Album: released on Polygram, Jul'87 by Polygram Records. Dist: Polygram

Cassette: released on Polygram, Jul'87 by Polygram Records. Dist: Polygram

Compact disc: released on Polygram, Jul'87 by Polygram Records. Dist: Polygram

THREE HOURS PAST MIDNIGHT.
Compact disc: released on Ace, Mar'87 by Ace Records. Dist: Pinnacle, Swift, Hotshot, Cadillac

VERY BEST OF JOHNNY 'GUITAR' WATSON.
Album: released on DJM, Oct'81 by DJM Records. Dist: CBS, Polygram

Cassette: released on DJM, Oct'81 by DJM Records. Dist: CBS, Polygram

VERY BEST OF..., THE / MR GUITAR.
Double cassette: released on DJM, Nov'81 by DJM Records. Dist: CBS, Polygram

WHAT THE HELL IS THIS.
Album: released on DJM, Nov'81 by DJM Records. Dist: CBS, Polygram

Cassette: released on DJM, Nov'81 by DJM Records. Dist: CBS, Polygram

Watson, Robert

ALL BECAUSE OF YOU.
Album: released on Pye International, Apr'79

BEATITTUDES (Watson, Robert & Curtis Lundy).
Album: released on Hep, Mar'84 by H.R. Taylor Records. Dist: Jazz Music, Cadillac Music, JSU, Taylors, Wellard, Chris, Zodiac, Swift, Fast Forward

ESTIMATED TIME OF ARRIVAL.
Album: released on Pye International, Apr'78

MIXED TRAFFIC.
Album: released on Greenwich Village, May'81 by Sweet Folk All Records. Dist: Roots, Projection, Lightning, Celtic Music, Wellard, Chris

Watson, Robert Sextet

JEWEL.
Album: released on Amigo, Jun'86 Dist: Red Rhino, Cartel

Watson, Wayne

GIANTS IN THE LAND.
Notes: Wayne Watson isn't just a fine vocalist, songwriter and producer-he is a communicator with a strong ability to interpret a lyric. With his new LP-a debut album for Dayspring Records-Wayne intensifies his sound vocally and instrumentally. The striking keyboards and powerful Chicagoish ballards carry his themes of holiness and aggressive faith. He describes the album as 'the most personal statement I have ever made message-wise'.
Album: released on Day Spring, Jun'86 by Word Records. Dist: Word Distribution, CBS

Cassette: released on Day Spring, Jun'86 by Word Records. Dist: Word Distribution, CBS

Watt, Ben

CAN'T.
Single (7"): released on Cherry Red, Jun'81 by Cherry Red Records. Dist: Pinnacle

NORTH MARINE DRIVE.
Tracks: / On Box Hill / Some things don't matter / Lucky one / Empty bottles / North Marine Drive / Waiting like mad / Thirst for knowledge / Long time no sea / You're gonna make me lonesome when you go / Walter and John / Aquamarine / Slipping slowly / Another conversation with myself / Girl in winter, A.
Notes: Tracks 10, 11, 12, 13 and 14 also feature Robert Wyatt. Produced by Ben Watt and mike Gregovich. (P) 1987 Original sound recording made by Cherry red Records Ltd
Compact disc: released on Cherry Red, Jun'87 by Cherry Red Records. Dist: Pinnacle

Album: released on Cherry Red, Feb'83 by Cherry Red Records. Dist: Pinnacle

SOME THINGS DON'T MATTER.
Single (7"): released on Cherry Red, Feb'83 by Cherry Red Records. Dist: Pinnacle

SUMMER INTO WINTER (Watt, Ben & Robert Wyatt).
Single (12"): released on Cherry Red, Apr'82 by Cherry Red Records. Dist: Pinnacle

Watters, Lu

50'S RECORDINGS VOL 2 (Watters, Lu & the Yerba Buena Jazz Band).
Album: released on Dawn, Jun'79

50'S RECORDINGS VOL 1 (Watters, Lu & the Yerba Buena Jazz Band).
Album: released on Dawn, Jun'79

LU WATTERS & BUNK JOHNSON (Watters, Lu & Bunk Johnson).
Album: released on Contemporary(Import), May'83 Dist: IMS, Polygram

YERBA BUENA DAYS.
Album: released on Dawn Club, Jun'79 Dist: Cadillac, Swift, JSU

Watt Government

WORKING MY FINGERS TO THE BONE.
Tracks: / Working my fingers to the bone.
Single (7"): released on Volume, Mar'86 by Volume Records. Dist: Pinnacle

Watt, John

HERE WE GO, HERE WE GO YOUNG BARRY MCGUIGAN.
Single (7"): released on Homespun(Ireland), Jul'85 by Outlet Records. Dist: Outlet

IRELAND'S SINGING FARMER.
Album: released on Homespun(Ireland), '82 by Outlet Records. Dist: Outlet

Cassette: released on Homespun(Ireland), '82 by Outlet Records. Dist: Outlet

JOEY DUNLOP.
Single (7"): released on Homespun(Ireland), Jul'83 by Outlet Records. Dist: Outlet

KELTY CLIPPIE (Watt, John/Davey Stewart).
Single (7"): released on Springthyme, Aug'83 by Springthyme Records. Dist: Jazz Music Distribution, Projection Distribution, Roots Distribution

SHORES OF THE NORTH (Watt, John/Davey Stewart).
Album: released on Springthyme Records, Oct'86 by Springthyme Records. Dist: Jazz Music Distribution, Projection Distribution, Roots Distribution

SINGING FARMER.
Album: released on Homespun(Ireland), Jul'82 by Outlet Records. Dist: Outlet

Cassette: released on Homespun(Ireland), Jul'82 by Outlet Records. Dist: Outlet

SONG OF HOME.
Album: released on Homespun(Ireland), Jul'84 by Outlet Records. Dist: Outlet

Cassette: released on Homespun(Ireland), Jul'84 by Outlet Records. Dist: Outlet

THREE CHEERS FOR BILLY BINGHAM & HIS BOYS.
Single (7"): released on Homespun(Ireland), Apr'82 by Outlet Records. Dist: Outlet

Watt, John/Davey Stewart

SHORES OF THE FORTH.
Album: released on Springthyme, '83 by Springthyme Records. Dist: Jazz Music Distribution, Projection Distribution, Roots Distribution

Cassette: released on Springthyme, '83 by Springthyme Records. Dist: Jazz Music Distribution, Projection Distribution, Roots Distribution

Watts, Alan

ZEN-THE ETERNAL NOW.
Cassette: released on Seminar Cassettes, Oct'81 by Seminar Cassettes. Dist: Davidson Distribution, Eastern Educational Products Distrib., Forlaget Systime Distribution, Laser Books Ltd Distribution, MacDougall Distribution, Talktapes Distribution, Watkins Books Ltd Distribution, Norton, Jeff Distribution

Watts, Andre

GERSHWIN SOLO PIANO MUSIC.
Album: released on CBS, Sep'82 by CBS Records. Dist: CBS

Cassette: released on CBS, Sep'82 by CBS Records. Dist: CBS

Watt, Sandy

I'M JUST ME.
Cassette: released on Ross, '86 by Ross Records. Dist: Ross Distribution, Roots Distribution

LIFE'S RAILWAY TO HEAVEN.
Cassette: released on Ross, Jul'84 by Ross Records. Dist: Ross Distribution, Roots Distribution

SINGING FISHERMAN, THE.
Cassette: released on Ross, Jun'87 by Ross Records. Dist: Ross Distribution, Roots Distribution

Watts, Brenda

WHO NEEDS LOVE LIKE THAT.
Single (7"): released on System, Dec'82 Dist: ERC Records

Single (12"): released on System, Dec'82 Dist: ERC Records

Watts, Charlie

LIVE AT FULHAM TOWN HALL (Watts, Charlie and his Orchestra).
Tracks: / Stomping at the Savoy / Lester leaps in / Moonglow / Robbins nest / Scrapple from the apple / Flying home.
Album: released on CBS, Dec'86 by CBS Records. Dist: CBS

Cassette: released on CBS, Dec'86 by CBS Records. Dist: CBS

Watts, Ernie

CHARIOTS OF FIRE.
Album: released on Qwest, Feb'82 by WEA Records. Dist: WEA

JUST HOLDIN' ON.
Single (7"): released on Elektra, Dec'80 by WEA Records. Dist: WEA

LOOK IN YOUR HEART.
Album: released on Elektra, Oct'80 by WEA Records. Dist: WEA

MUSICIAN.
Album: released on Qwest, Aug'85 by WEA Records. Dist: WEA

Watts, John

I SMELT ROSES IN THE UNDERGROUND.
Single (7"): released on EMI, Jan'83 by EMI Records. Dist: EMI

MAYDAY, MAYDAY.
Single (7"): released on EMI, May'83 by EMI Records. Dist: EMI

ONE VOICE.
Single (7"): released on EMI, Mar'82 by EMI Records. Dist: EMI

SPEAKING IN A DIFFERENT LANGUAGE.
Single (7"): released on EMI, Oct'81 by EMI Records. Dist: EMI

YOUR FAULT.
Single (7"): released on EMI, Jun'82 by EMI Records. Dist: EMI

Watts, Noble Thin Man

RETURN OF THE THIN MAN.
Album: released on Bedrock, Jun'87 by Upright Records. Dist: Pinnacle

Watts Noys

HEART IN FLAMES.
Single (7"): released on Noys, Apr'82 by Noys Records., Pinnacle

Watts, Phil

DO IT WITH LOVE.
Tracks: / Do it with love / Do it with love / Till the end of time.
Single (7"): released on Wattsco, Sep'86 Dist: PRT

Single (12"): released on Wattsco, Sep'86 Dist: PRT

Album: released on Wattsco, Sep'86 Dist: PRT

Cassette: released on Wattsco, Sep'86 Dist: PRT

SPARE ME CONFUSION.
Single (7"): released on Wattco, Nov'85 Dist: M.I.S., EMI

THIS WORLDS AT WAR.
Tracks: / This worlds at war / Sleeping alone.
Single (7"): released on Wattsco, May'86 Dist: PRT

TONIGHT.
Tracks: / No direction.
Single (7"): released on Wattsco, Aug'87 Dist: PRT

Page 1082

Watts, Sammy

SOCO LOVER.
Tracks: / Soco lover / Use me up.
Single (7"): released on Sunburn, Mar'86 by Orbitone Records. Dist: Jetstar Distribution

Single (12"): released on Sunburn, Mar'86 by Orbitone Records. Dist: Jetstar Distribution

TURN ME LOOSE.
Tracks: / Turn me loose / Turn me loose (alternative version).
Single (7"): released on Sunburn, Aug'86 by Orbitone Records. Dist: Jetstar Distribution

Watts, Trevor

APPLICATION, INTERACTION AND... (see Stevens, John / Watts, Trevor/John Stevens/Barry Guy).

CLOSER TO YOU.
Album: released on Ogun, May'79 Dist: Jazz Music, JSU, Cadillac

MOIRE MUSIC (Watts, Trevor Moire Music).
Notes: Featuring Lol Coxhill
Album: released on Arc, Oct'86 Dist: Arc

STELLA MALU (Watts, Trevor & Katrina Krimsky).
Album: released on ECM, Dec'81 by ECM Records. Dist: IMS, Polygram, Virgin through EMI

Watt, Tom

SUBTERRANEAN HOMESICK BLUES.
Tracks: / Subterranean homesick blues / Subterranean homesick blues / I had too much to drink last night.
Single (7"): released on Watt The Duck, Aug'86 by Watt The Duck Records. Dist: M.I.S., EMI

Single (7"): released on Watt The Duck, May'86 by Watt The Duck Records. Dist: M.I.S., EMI

Waulking Songs...

SCOTTISH TRADITION (Waulking Songs from Barra).
Album: released on Tangent, Apr'81 by Tangent Records. Dist: Lugtons Distributors, Taylors, JSU Distribution, Projection Distribution

Waut, Elisa

ELISA WAUT.
Album: released on Statik, Jul'85 Dist: Rough Trade Distribution. Stage One Distribution

Wavelength

DON'T MAKE ME DO IT.
Single (7"): released on Ariola, Mar'82 Dist: RCA, Ariola

HURRY HOME.
Album: released on Ariola, Apr'82 Dist: RCA, Ariola

Cassette: released on Ariola, Sep'82 Dist: RCA, Ariola

Single (7"): released on Ariola, Sep'82 Dist: RCA, Ariola

RIO.
Single (7"): released on Ariola, Nov'82 Dist: RCA, Ariola

SITTING IN THE PARK.
Single (7"): released on Outlook, Sep'83 by Brian Poole. Dist: Spartan Distribution

WIN SOME LOSE SOME.
Single (7"): released on Ariola, Sep'82 Dist: RCA, Ariola

Wavelinx

WE FOUND LOVE.
Tracks: / We found love / Happiness.
Single (12"): released on MGX, 20 Jun'87

Waves

BROWN EYES SON.
Single (7"): released on Albion, Aug'82 by Albion Records. Dist: Spartan, Pinnacle

NIGHTMARE.
Single (7"): released on Armageddon, Apr'82 by Armageddon Records. Dist: Revolver, Cartel, Pinnacle

Waving All Excuses

PATRICK CAMBELL.
Cassette: released on Listen Productions, Nov'84 Dist: H.R. Taylor, Hayward Promotions Distribution

Wa wa nee

STIMULATION.
Tracks: / Headlines / Simulation.
Single (7"): released on CBS, Feb'87 by CBS Records. Dist: CBS

Single (12"): released on CBS, 13 Jun'87 by CBS Records. Dist: CBS

Wax

AMERICAN ENGLISH.
Album: released on RCA, Aug'87 by RCA Records. Dist: RCA, Roots, Swift, Wellard, Chris, I & B, Solomon & Peres Distribution

Cassette: released on RCA, Aug'87 by RCA Records. Dist: RCA, Roots, Swift, Wellard, Chris, I & B, Solomon & Peres Distribution

AMERICAN ENGLISH.
Album: released on RCA, Oct'87 by RCA Records. Dist: RCA, Roots, Swift, Wellard, Chris, I & B, Solomon & Peres Distribution

Cassette: released on RCA, Oct'87 by RCA Records. Dist: RCA, Roots, Swift, Wellard, Chris, I & B, Solomon & Peres Distribution

BALL AND CHAIN.
Single (7"): released on RCA, Oct'85 by RCA Records. Dist: RCA, Roots, Swift, Wellard, Chris, I & B, Solomon & Peres Distribution

Single (12"): released on RCA, Oct'85 by RCA Records. Dist: RCA, Roots, Swift, Wellard, Chris, I & B, Solomon & Peres Distribution

BRIDGE TO YOUR HEART.
Tracks: / Bridge to your heart / Heaven in her bed.
Single (7"): released on RCA, Jun'87 by RCA Records. Dist: RCA, Roots, Swift, Wellard, Chris, I & B, Solomon & Peres Distribution

Single (12"): released on RCA, Jun'87 by RCA Records. Dist: RCA, Roots, Swift, Wellard, Chris, I & B, Solomon & Peres Distribution

MAGNETIC HEAVEN.
Tracks: / Right between the eyes / Hear no evil / Shadows of love / Marie Claire / Ball and chain / Systematic / Breakout / Only a visitor / Rise up / Magnetic heaven.
Album: released on RCA, Jun'86 by RCA Records. Dist: RCA, Roots, Swift, Wellard, Chris, I & B, Solomon & Peres Distribution

Cassette: released on RCA, Jun'86 by RCA Records. Dist: RCA, Roots, Swift, Wellard, Chris, I & B, Solomon & Peres Distribution

Compact disc: released on RCA, Jun'86 by RCA Records. Dist: RCA, Roots, Swift, Wellard, Chris, I & B, Solomon & Peres Distribution

RIGHT BETWEEN THE EYES.
Tracks: / Right between the eyes / Only a visitor.
Single (7"): released on RCA, Mar'86 by RCA Records. Dist: RCA, Roots, Swift, Wellard, Chris, I & B, Solomon & Peres Distribution

Single (12"): released on RCA, Mar'86 by RCA Records. Dist: RCA, Roots, Swift, Wellard, Chris, I & B, Solomon & Peres Distribution

SHADOWS OF LOVE.
Tracks: / Shadows of love / Magnetic house / People all over the world.
Single (7"): released on RCA, Jun'86 by RCA Records. Dist: RCA, Roots, Swift, Wellard, Chris, I & B, Solomon & Peres Distribution

Single (12"): released on RCA, Jun'86 by RCA Records. Dist: RCA, Roots, Swift, Wellard, Chris, I & B, Solomon & Peres Distribution

SYSTEMATIC.
Tracks: / Systematic / Breakout.
Single (7"): released on RCA, Sep'86 by RCA Records. Dist: RCA, Roots, Swift, Wellard, Chris, I & B, Solomon & Peres Distribution

Single (12"): released on RCA, Sep'86 by RCA Records. Dist: RCA, Roots, Swift, Wellard, Chris, I & B, Solomon & Peres Distribution

Waxface

GRAVES OF GOD.
Album: released on Mausoleum, Jul'85 by Mausoleum Records. Dist: Pinnacle

Waxing the winners

WAXING THE WINNERS VOL.1 Melody Maker all star poll winners (Various Artists).
Notes: Melody Maker all star poll winners feature John Dankworth and Jack Parnell. 1951-53.
Album: released on Esquire, Nov'86 by Titan International Productions. Dist: Jazz Music, Cadillac Music, Swift, Wellard, Chris, Backs, Rough Trade, Revolver, Nine Mile

WAXING THE WINNERS VOL.2 Melody Maker all star poll winners (Various Artists).
Notes: Melody Maker all star poll winners feature John Dankworth and Eric Delaney. 1954-55.
Album: released on Esquire, Nov'86 by Titan International Productions. Dist: Jazz Music, Cadillac Music, Swift, Wellard, Chris, Backs, Rough Trade, Revolver, Nine Mile

Way, Darryl

AS LONG AS THERE'S A SPARK.
Single (7"): released on Venturi, Aug'83 by Venturi Records.

LITTLE PLUM.

Single (7"): released on Charisma, Nov'84 by Virgin Records. Dist: EMI

Single (12"): released on Charisma, Nov'84 by Virgin Records. Dist: EMI

Single (7"): released on Snat, Oct'82

Waye, Steve

QUEEN OF MY SOUL.
Single (7"): released on Sway, Feb'85

Wayfarers

WAYFARERS.
Album: released on Eva-Lolita, Dec'85 Dist: Pinnacle

WAYFARERS, THE.
Album: released on Folk Heritage, Jul'82 by Folk Heritage Records. Dist: Roots, Wynd-Up Distribution, Jazz Music, Folk Heritage

WORLD FARE.
Album: released on Eva-Lolita, Jun'86 Dist: Pinnacle

Wayman, Mike

I'LL MAKE YOUR BODY ROCK.
Tracks: / I'll make your body rock / Don't think twice.
Single (7"): released on In Touch, Jul'87 by Touch Records. Dist: Spartan

Single (12"): released on In Touch, Jul'87 by Touch Records. Dist: Spartan

Waymon, Sam

CHICO.
Tracks: / Chico / Circus.
Notes: US composer, jazz pianist, singer & actor. Has worked and toured with legendary greats: Ray Charles, Sarah Vaughan and Nina Simone.
Single (12"): released on IMS, May'87 by Pondor Records. Dist: IMS, Polygram

Wayne, Alvis

I GOTTUM +3.
Single (7"): released on Rollin, Jun'80

I WANNA EAT YOUR PUDDING.
Single (7"): released on Rollin, Jun'80

Wayne, Carl

MISS YOU NIGHTS (Wayne, Carl & Choc Union).
Single (7"): released on Jet, Dec'82 by Jet Records. Dist: CBS

Wayne, Charlie

AERIAL PICTURES.
Single (7"): released on Jet, Apr'82 by Jet Records. Dist: CBS

DEEPER THAN LOVE.
Single (7"): released on Jet, Jan'82 by Jet Records. Dist: CBS

Wayne, Chuck

CHARLIE PRIDE SONGBOOK VOL THE.
Cassette: released on AIM (Budget Cassettes), Sep'83

TASTY PUDDING (Wayne, Chuck, Bill Moore, Zoot Sims).
Album: released on Savoy (France), Oct'86

TRAVELLING.
Album: released on Progressive, Apr'81 Progressive Records. Dist: Jetstar

Wayne, Dig

MASTER MIND.
Tracks: / Master mind / No such love.
Single (7"): released on Polydor, May'87 Polydor Records. Dist: Polygram, Polydor

Single (12"): released on Polydor, May'87 Polydor Records. Dist: Polygram, Polydor

Wayne, Jeff

HIGHLIGHTS/WAR OF THE WORLDS.
Album: released on CBS, Apr'85 by CBS Records. Dist: CBS

Cassette: released on CBS, Apr'85 by Records. Dist: CBS

WAR OF THE WORLDS.
Compact disc: released on CBS, Dec'85 CBS Records. Dist: CBS

Double Album: released on CBS, Jun'77 CBS Records. Dist: CBS

Double cassette: released on CBS, Jun'77 CBS Records. Dist: CBS

Wayne, John
CANTA.
Tracks: / Canta / Mix up blender.
Single (12"): released on Firehouse, Apr'86 Dist: Jetstar

JOHN WAYNE WITH SLY & ROBBIE AND THE AGGROVATORS.
Album: released on Vista Sounds, '83 by Vista Sounds Records. Dist: Jetstar

Wayne, Jon
TEXAS FUNERAL.
Album: released on Hybrid, Aug'85 by Statik Records. Dist: Pinnacle

Wayne, Kld &...
BRIGHT LIGHTS AND COUNTRY MUSIC (Wayne, Kid & The Islanders).
Album: released on Homespun(Ireland), '82 by Outlet Records. Dist: Outlet

Cassette: released on Homespun(Ireland), '82 by Outlet Records. Dist: Outlet

Wayne, Wee Willie
TRAVELLIN' MOOD.
Album: released on Sundown, Oct'82 by Magnum Music Group Ltd. Dist: Magnum Music Group Ltd, PRT Distribution, Spartan Distribution

Album: released on Imperial(France), '83 by K-Tel records. Dist: K-Tel, Taylors, Polygram
Cat. no: 2C 068 83294

Way Of The West
CITY FOR LOVERS (HEY YOU).
Single (7"): by MCA Records. Dist: Polygram, MCA

Single (12"): by MCA Records. Dist: Polygram, MCA

FEEL THE STEEL.
Single (7"): released on MCA, Sep'84 by MCA Records. Dist: Polygram, MCA

Single (12"): released on MCA, Sep'84 by MCA Records. Dist: Polygram, MCA

Way Out
THIS WALKING WAY.
Single (7"): released on Diamond, Nov'85 by Revolver Records. Dist: Cartel

TIME MOVES US ON.
Single (7"): released on Flux, Oct'84 by Flux Records. Dist: Cartel

Waysted
BLACK AND BLUE.
Tracks: / Black and blue / Out of control / Wild night.
Single (7"): released on Parlophone, Nov'86 by EMI Records. Dist: EMI

Single (7"): released on Parlophone, Nov'86 by EMI Records. Dist: EMI

CAN'T TAKE THAT LOVE AWAY.
Single (7"): released on Chrysalis, Oct'83 by Chrysalis Records. Dist: CBS

COMPLETELY WAYSTED.
Tracks: / Women in chains / Hang 'em high / Won't get out alive / Sleazy / Hot love / Dead on your legs / Hurt so good / Somebody to love / Around and around / Rock steady / Love loaded / Hi ho my baby / Toy with passion.
Album: released on Raw Power, Sep'86 Dist: Pinnacle

Cassette: released on Raw Power, Sep'86 Dist: Pinnacle

HEAVEN TONIGHT.
Single (7"): released on Music For Nations, May'85 by Music For Nations Records. Dist: Pinnacle

Single (7"): released on Music For Nations, May'85 by Music For Nations Records. Dist: Pinnacle

HEAVEN TONIGHT.
Tracks: / Fire under the wheels / Hell comes home.
Notes: Extra track on 12" only
Single (7"): released on Parlophone, Feb'87 by EMI Records. Dist: EMI

Single (12"): released on Parlophone, Feb'87 by EMI Records. Dist: EMI

SAVE YOUR PRAYERS.
Tracks: / Walls fall down / Black & blue / Singing to the night / Hell comes home / Heroes die young / Heaven tonight / How the west was won / Wild night / Out of control / Sway.
Notes: Waysted are a four-piece heavy rock band centered around bass player - Peter Way - Ex of UFO, produced by Simon Hanhart (renowned for his work on Marillion's Misplaced childhood album. A single, Black & blue was released 10th November. Waysted are currently on tour in Europe with Status Quo.
Album: released on Parlophone, Nov'86 by EMI Records. Dist: EMI

Cassette: released on EMI, Nov'86 by EMI Records. Dist: EMI

VICES.
Album: released on Chrysalis, Sep'83 by Chrysalis Records. Dist: CBS

Wayward Souls
PAINTED DREAMS.
Album: released on Hybrid, Aug'85 by Statik Records. Dist: Pinnacle

Wazis & Mambetis
THANK YOU VERY MUCH.
Single (7"): released on London, Sep'82 by London Records. Dist: Polygram

Single (12"): released on London, Sep'82 by London Records. Dist: Polygram

We.....
WE ARE MOST AMUSED (The very best of British comedy) (Various original artists).
Double Album: released on Ronco, Nov'82

Double cassette: released on Ronco, Nov'82

WE DON'T WANT YOUR F...... WAR Various artists (Various Artists).
Album: released on Fight Back, Dec'84 by Fight Back Records. Dist: Jungle, Cartel

WE HAVE A DREAM Various artists (Various Artists).
Album: released on One World Peacesongs, Mar'85 by One World Peacesongs Records. Dist: One World Peacesongs Distribution

Cassette: released on One World Peacesongs, Mar'85 by One World Peacesongs Records. Dist: One World Peacesongs Distribution

WE LOVE ELLINGTON various artists (Various Artists).
Album: released on Phontastic (Sweden), '82 by Wellard, Chris Distribution. Dist: Wellard, Chris Distribution

WE WON'T BE YOUR F...... WHORE various artists (Various Artists).
Double Album: released on Mortarhate, Sep'85 by Dorane Ltd.

Weapon Of Peace
FOUL PLAY.
Single (7"): released on Safari, Apr'82 by Safari Records. Dist: Pinnacle

Single (12"): released on Safari, Apr'82 by Safari Records. Dist: Pinnacle

HIT AND RUN.
Single (7"): released on Safari, Oct'82 by Safari Records. Dist: Pinnacle

Single (12"): released on Safari, Oct'82 by Safari Records. Dist: Pinnacle

JAH LOVE.
Single (7"): released on Safari, Oct'81 by Safari Records. Dist: Pinnacle

STANDING ON THE EDGE.
Single (12"): released on Safari, May'83 by Safari Records. Dist: Pinnacle

WEAPON OF PEACE.
Album: released on Safari, Nov'81 by Safari Records. Dist: Pinnacle

Cassette: released on Safari, Nov'81 by Safari Records. Dist: Pinnacle

Weapons
CAPTIVE AUDIENCE.
Album: released on Samurai, May'86 Dist: Pinnacle

Cassette: released on Samurai, May'86 Dist: Pinnacle

Weards, Roy, Last Post
MONOPOLY.
Single (7"): released on Parasol, Jun'82 by Parasol Records. Dist: Pinnacle

We Are Going To Eat You
I WISH I KNEW.
Extended-play record: released on All The Madmen, Jul'87 by All The Madmen Records. Dist: Rough Trade, Cartel

Weatherburn, Ronn
AFTER THE BALL.
Album: released on Stomp Off, Oct'86 by Stomp Off Records. Dist: Jazz Music Distribution

Weather Girls
BIG GIRLS DON'T CRY.
Album: released on CBS, Sep'85 by CBS Rec-

---

ords. Dist: CBS

Cassette: released on CBS, Sep'85 by CBS Records. Dist: CBS

NO ONE CAN LOVE YOU MORE.
Single (7"): released on CBS, Aug'85 by CBS Records. Dist: CBS

Single (12"): released on CBS, Aug'85 by CBS Records. Dist: CBS

SUCCESS.
Single (7"): released on CBS, May'84 by CBS Records. Dist: CBS

Single (12"): released on CBS, May'84 by CBS Records. Dist: CBS

Album: released on CBS, Nov'83 by CBS Records. Dist: CBS

Weatherley, Roy
PIANO PARTY.
Notes: Accompaniment directed by Denis Hayward.
Album: released on Savoy, Nov'86

Weather Men
DEEP DOWN SOUTH.
Tracks: / Deep down south / Redneck blues (The).
Single (7"): released on Play It Again Sam, Jan'86 Dist: Red Rhino, Cartel

DEEP DOWN SOUTH.
Single (12"): released on Play It Again Sam, Nov'85 Dist: Red Rhino, Cartel

LIFE.
Single (7"): released on Pre, Mar'82 by Charisma. Dist: Polygram

Single (12"): released on Pre, Mar'82 by Charisma. Dist: Polygram

OLD FRIEND SAM.
Single (12"): released on Play It Again Sam, Jun'85 Dist: Red Rhino, Cartel

TEN DEADLY KISSES.
Album: released on Play It Again Sam, Feb'87 Dist: Red Rhino, Cartel

Weather Prophets
ALMOST PRAYED.
Tracks: / Almost prayed / Your heartbeat breathes the life into me / Like Frankie Lymon / Wide open arms / Almost prayed / Your heartbeat / Stone in my passway / Downbound train.
Single (7"): released on Creation, May'86 Dist: Rough Trade, Cartel

Single (12"): released on Creation, May'86 Dist: Rough Trade, Cartel

Double-pack single: released on Creation, Jun'86 Dist: Rough Trade, Cartel

MAYFLOWER.
Tracks: / Why does the rain / Key to my love is green, The / Can't keep my mind off you / Mayflower / Head over heels / She comes from the rain / Almost prayed / Faithfull / Swimming pool blues / Walking under a spell / Naked as the day you were born / Sleep.
Album: released on Elevation, Jun'87 by WEA Records. Dist: WEA

Cassette: released on Elevation, Jun'87 by WEA Records. Dist: WEA

NAKED AS THE DAY YOU WERE BORN.
Tracks: / Naked as the day you were born / In my room / Worst friend I ever had (The).
Single (7"): released on Creation, Oct'86 Dist: Rough Trade, Cartel

Single (12"): released on Creation, Oct'86 Dist: Rough Trade, Cartel

PROCESSION.
Tracks: / Procession / Plaza real / Two lines / Where the moon goes / Well (The) / Molasses run.
Notes: A Weather Report album is always a special event but this one more so than most as it features Wayne Shorter and Josef Zawinul fronting a completely new Weather Report.
Album: released on CBS, Feb'83 by CBS Records. Dist: CBS

Cassette: released on CBS, Feb'83 by CBS Records. Dist: CBS

Compact disc: released on CBS, Feb'83 by CBS Records. Dist: CBS

SHE COMES FROM THE RAIN.
Single (7"): released on Elevation, Mar'87 by WEA Records. Dist: WEA

Single (12"): released on Elevation, Mar'87 by WEA Records. Dist: WEA

WHY DOES THE RAIN.
Tracks: / Why does the rain / Midnight mile / Mayflower / Annelea*.
Single (7"): released on Elevation, Jun'87 by

WEA Records. Dist: WEA

Single (12"): released on Elevation, Jun'87 by WEA Records. Dist: WEA

Weather Report
BLACK MARKET.
Compact disc: released on CBS, May'87 by CBS Records. Dist: CBS

DOMINO THEORY.
Tracks: / Can it be done / D flat waltz / Peasant (The) / Predator / Blue sound-note / Swamp cabbage / Domino theory.
Compact disc: by CBS Records. Dist: CBS

Album: released on CBS, Feb'84 by CBS Records. Dist: CBS

Cassette: released on CBS, Feb'84 by CBS Records. Dist: CBS

Compact disc: released on CBS, Feb'84 by CBS Records. Dist: CBS

HEAVY WEATHER.
Album: released on CBS, Sep'83 by CBS Records. Dist: CBS

Cassette: released on CBS, Sep'83 by CBS Records. Dist: CBS

MR GONE.
Tracks: / Pursuit of the woman in the feathered hat (The) / River people / Young and fine / Elders (The) / Mr Gone / Punk jazz / Pinocchio / And then.
Album: released on Prix D'Ami (France), Sep'86

Cassette: released on Prix D'Ami (France), Sep'86

NIGHT PASSAGE.
Tracks: / Dream clock / Port of entry / Forlorn / Rockin' in rhythm / Fast city / Night passage / Three views of a secret / Madagascar.
Compact disc: released on CBS, '83 by CBS Records. Dist: CBS

SPORTIN' LIFE.
Album: released on CBS, Jun'85 by CBS Records. Dist: CBS

Cassette: released on CBS, Jun'85 by CBS Records. Dist: CBS

THIS IS THIS.
Tracks: / This is this / Face the fire / I'll never forget you / Jungle stuff part 1 / Man with the copper fingers / Consequently / Update / China blues.
Album: released on CBS, Jul'86 by CBS Records. Dist: CBS

Cassette: released on CBS, Jul'86 by CBS Records. Dist: CBS

WEATHER REPORT.
Album: released on CBS, Mar'81 by CBS Records. Dist: CBS

Weaver, Patty
DON'T WANT A HEARTACHE.
Single (7"): released on Warner Brothers, Apr'82 by WEA Records. Dist: WEA

SHOT IN THE DARK.
Single (7"): released on Warner Brothers, Aug'82 by WEA Records. Dist: WEA

Single (7"): released on Warner Brothers, May'82 by WEA Records. Dist: WEA

Weavers
BEST OF..... THE.
Album: released on MCA, Dec'84 by MCA Records. Dist: CBS

Cassette: released on MCA, Dec'84 by MCA Records. Dist: CBS

Weaver, Sylvester
REMAINING TITLES OF....
Notes: Mono. Full title: the remaining titles of Sylvester Weaver, 1924-1927
Album: released on Earl Archives, Jan'87 Dist: Swift, Jazz Music

Webb, Cassell
CASSELL WEBB.
Album: released on Statik, Feb'84 Dist: Rough Trade Distribution, Stage One Distribution

Webb, Chick
1936 (Webb, Chick & His Orchestra).
Notes: Mono.
Album: released on Circle(USA), Jan'87 by Jazzology Records (USA). Dist: Jazz Music, Swift, Chris Wellard

CHICK WEBB VOL.1.
Album: released on Kings Of Jazz, Aug'81 Dist: Jazz Horizons, Jazz Music, Celtic Music

Page 1083

IN THE GROOVE.
Album: released on Affinity (MCA), Sep'83

STOMPIN' AT THE SAVOY 1936 (Webb, Chick & His Orchestra).
Notes: With Ella F.
Album: released on Circle(USA), Jun'86 by Jazzology Records (USA). Dist: Jazz Music, Swift, Chris Wellard

Webber, A.J.

CLEVEDON PIER 1.
Single (7"): released on Gundog, Feb'80 Dist: Spartan

OF THIS LAND.
Album: released on Gundog, Sep'84 Dist: Spartan

Webber, Andrew Lloyd

REQUIEM.
Album: released on EMI, Mar'85 by EMI Records. Dist: EMI

Cassette: released on EMI, Mar'85 by EMI Records. Dist: EMI

Compact disc: released on EMI, Mar'85 by EMI Records. Dist: EMI

Webber, Julian Lloyd

PIECES.
Album: released on Polydor, Aug'85 by Polydor Records. Dist: Polygram, Polydor

Cassette: released on Polydor, Aug'85 by Polydor Records. Dist: Polygram, Polydor

Compact disc: released on Polydor, Aug'85 by Polydor Records. Dist: Polygram, Polydor. Estim retail price in Jul'87 was £3.99.

RITUAL FIRE DANCE.
Single (7"): released on Red Seal, Jan'82 by RCA Records. Dist: RCA

RODRIGO CELLO CONCERTO.
Album: released on Red Seal, Jul'82 by RCA Records. Dist: RCA

Cassette: released on Red Seal, Aug'82 by RCA Records. Dist: RCA

TRAVELS WITH MY CELLO.
Album: released on Philips, Nov'84 Dist: IMS-Polygram

Cassette: released on Philips, Nov'84 Dist: IMS-Polygram

Album: released on ECM (Germany), Mar'85 by ECM Records. Dist: IMS, Polygram, Virgin through EMI

Compact disc: released on ECM (Germany), Mar'85 by ECM Records. Dist: IMS, Polygram, Virgin through EMI

Webber, Marlene

JUST FOR YOU.
Tracks: / For you.
Single (12"): released on Joe Frazer, Nov'86 by Joe Frazer Records. Dist: Jetstar

Webb Ivory Newhall Band

FROM BANDSTAND TO CONCERT HALL.
Album: released on Grosvenor, Nov'79 by Grosvenor Records. Dist: Taylors

Webb, Jimmy

SONGWRITERS FOR THE STARS 1 (Webb, Jimmy & Rupert Holmes).
Album: released on Polydor (Norway), Oct'83

Webb, John

EXPERIMENT OF LOVE (THE).
Tracks: / Experiment of love (The) / Cry of the sea.
Single (7"): released on Numa, Jan'86 by Numa Records. Dist: PRT Distribution

Single (12"): released on Numa, Jan'86 by Numa Records. Dist: PRT Distribution

RED HOT GUITARS (Webb, John & R.Warner).
Album: released on VJM, '74 by Wellard, Chris Distribution. Dist: Wellard, Chris Distribution

Webb, Marney

NERVOUS BREAKDOWN.
Single (7"): released on Crash, Mar'81 by Satril Records. Dist: PRT

STILL SEARCHING.
Single (7"): released on Creole, Oct'81 by Creole Records. Dist: Rhino, PRT

Webb, Marti

ALWAYS THERE.
Tracks: / Always there (theme from Howards Way) / Onedin line / Reilly ace of spies / Moonlighting / To have and to hold / I could be so good for you (theme from Minder) / To serve them all my days / EastEnders.
Notes: Marti's top twenty hits.
Album: released on BBC, Nov'86 by BBC Records & Tapes. Dist: EMI, PRT, Pye

Cassette: released on BBC, Nov'86 by BBC Records & Tapes. Dist: EMI, PRT, Pye

ALWAYS THERE (Webb, Marti with the Simon May Orchestra).
Single (7"): released on BBC, Sep'86 by BBC Records & Tapes. Dist: EMI, PRT, Pye

BEN.
Single (7"): released on Starblend, Jun'85 by Starblend Records. Dist: PRT Distribution

DIDN'T MEAN TO FALL IN LOVE.
Single (7"): released on Polydor, Jun'83 by Polydor Records. Dist: Polygram, Polydor

ENCORE.
Album: released on Starblend, Oct'85 by Starblend Records. Dist: PRT Distribution

Cassette: released on Starblend, Oct'85 by Starblend Records. Dist: PRT Distribution

GERSHWIN.
Album: released on BBC, Jul'87 by BBC Records & Tapes. Dist: EMI, PRT, Pye

I CAN'T LET GO.
Tracks: / I can't let go / Why forget.
Single (7"): released on Rainbow, Apr'87 Dist: I & B, CBS

I COULD BE SO GOOD FOR YOU Theme from Minder (Webb, Marti with Paul Jones).
Tracks: / It's still the same dream.
Single (7"): released on BBC, Nov'86 by BBC Records & Tapes. Dist: EMI, PRT, Pye

LAST MAN IN MY LIFE.
Single (7"): released on Polydor, Mar'82 by Polydor Records. Dist: Polygram, Polydor

READY FOR ROSES NOW.
Single (7"): released on Starblend, Dec'85 by Starblend Records. Dist: PRT Distribution

SOMEDAY SOON Theme from Onedin Line.
Tracks: / Someday soon / Moonlighting.
Single (7"): released on BBC, Mar'87 by BBC Records & Tapes. Dist: EMI, PRT, Pye

TELL ME ON A SUNDAY.
Single (7"): released on Polydor, Mar'80 by Polydor Records. Dist: Polygram, Polydor

Album: released on Polydor, Jan'80 by Polydor Records. Dist: Polygram, Polydor

Cassette: released on Polydor, Jan'80 by Polydor Records. Dist: Polygram, Polydor

Webb, Peta

I HAVE WANDERED INTO EXILE.
Album: released on Topic, '81 Dist: Roots Distribution

Webb, Roger

GENTLE TOUCH (Webb, Roger, His Piano & Orchestra).
Single (7"): released on Chandos, Mar'82 by Chandos Records. Dist: Harmonia Mundi, Taylors

Album: released on Chandos, Aug'84 by Chandos Records. Dist: Harmonia Mundi, Taylors

Cassette: released on Chandos, Aug'84 by Chandos Records. Dist: Harmonia Mundi, Taylors

MAGIC OF COLE PORTER, THE.
Album: released on Warwick, Nov'83 by Warwick Records. Dist: Pinnacle

Cassette: released on Warwick, Nov'83 by Warwick Records. Dist: Pinnacle

PARADISE POSTPONED (Webb, Roger Orchestra (The)).
Tracks: / Paradise postponed / Main theme / In the chilterns / Meadows and streams / Romance / Pastorale / Encounters / Letter (The) / Lady Grace's waltz / Love theme / Journey to London / Picton Hall.
Single (7"): released on Columbia, Sep'86 by EMI Records. Dist: EMI

Album: released on Columbia, Oct'86 by EMI Records. Dist: EMI

Cassette: released on Columbia, Oct'86 by EMI Records. Dist: EMI

ROMANTIC PIANO (THE) (Webb, Roger Orchestra (The)).
Tracks: / One day in your life / Blue eyes / Evergreen / One day I'll fly away / Lately / Cavatina / Fool if you think it's over / Misty / Ebony and ivory / Chariots of fire / MASH / Way we were (Tjhe) / Just the way you are / Lady / As time goes by / Memory / Arthur's theme / Send in the clowns / Hill Street blues / Imagine.
Album: released on Warwick Reflections, Jun'86 by Warwick Records.

Cassette: released on Warwick Reflections, Jun'86 by Warwick Records.

SPACE INVADERS.
Single (7"): released on Muti Media Tapes, '81

Webb, Stan 'Chicken Shack'

ROADIES CONCERTO.
Album: released on RCA, Apr'81 by RCA Records. Dist: RCA, Roots, Swift, Wellard, Chris, I & B, Solomon & Peres Distribution

Cassette: released on RCA, Apr'81 by RCA Records. Dist: RCA, Roots, Swift, Wellard, Chris, I & B, Solomon & Peres Distribution

Webb, Steve

DEAR LOVE.
Single (7"): released on Sedition, Aug'85 Dist: PRT

Single (12"): Dist: PRT

IT'S OVER.
Single (7"): released on Big Pop, Jul'87 by Big Pop Records. Dist: Pinnacle

Webcore

RUNNING FOR THE PRECEDENT EP.
Single (12"): released on Jungle, Jun'87 by Jungle Records. Dist: Jungle, Cartel

Weber, Eberhard

CHORUS.
Tracks: / Part 1 / Part 2 / Part 3 / Part 4 / Part 5 / Part 6 / Part 7.
Notes: Digital stereo. Bassist Eberhard Weber's new album is entirely taken up by his long composition 'Chorus' (parts 1-7). It describes the slow development from quiet, static passages to rhythmically dense moments. Sheets of sound and minimalist synthesizer patters (played by Weber himself) are broken up by Jan Garbarek's vital, intense improvisations. 'Chorus' demonstrates Weber's brilliant technique as well as his compositional faculty. He perfectly balances contemplation and vitality. Personnel: Eberhard Weber-bass, synthesizer/Jan Garbarek-soprano and tenor saxophones/Ralph R Rubner-drums/Manfred Hoffbauer-clarinet and flute parts/Martin Kunstner-oboe and English horn.
Compact disc: released on ECM (Germany), Mar'85 by ECM Records. Dist: IMS, Polygram, Virgin through EMI

COLOURS OF CHLOE,THE.
Album: released on ECM, '75 by ECM Records. Dist: IMS, Polygram, Virgin through EMI

FOLLOWING MORNING (THE).
Tracks: / T on a white horse / Moana I / Following morning (The) / Moana II.
Notes: Personnel: Rainer Bruninghaus-piano/Eberhard Weber-bass/Oslo Philharmonic Orchestra.
Compact disc: released on ECM (Germany), Jun'86 by ECM Records. Dist: IMS, Polygram, Virgin through EMI

FOLLOWING MORNING,THE.
Album: released on ECM, Feb'77 by ECM Records. Dist: IMS, Polygram, Virgin through EMI

LATER THAT EVENING.
Album: released on ECM (Germany), Oct'82 by ECM Records. Dist: IMS, Polygram, Virgin through EMI

PASSENGERS (Weber, Eberhard & G.Burton).

WORKS.
Tracks: / Sand / Dark spell (A) / More colours / Touch / Eyes that can see in the dark / Moana II.
Compact disc: released on ECM (Germany), May'85 by ECM Records. Dist: IMS, Polygram, Virgin through EMI

Album: released on ECM/Works (Germany), May'85 by ECM Records. Dist: IMS, Polygram, Virgin through EMI

Weber, Eberhard Colours

LITTLE MOVEMENTS.
Album: released on ECM, Nov'80 by ECM Records. Dist: IMS, Polygram, Virgin through EMI

SILENT FEET.
Album: released on ECM, '78 by ECM Records. Dist: IMS, Polygram, Virgin through EMI

Weber, Hajo

WINTEREISE (A winter journey) (Weber, Hajo & Ulrich Ingenbold).
Album: released on ECM (Germany), Sep'82 by ECM Records. Dist: IMS, Polygram, Virgin through EMI

Webley, George

I'M GONNA LOVE YOU JUST A LITTLE BIT MORE BABE.
Single (7"): released on Simple, Sep'84 by Simple Records. Dist: EMI

Single (12"): released on Simple, Sep'84 by Simple Records. Dist: EMI

TASTY.
Single (7"): released on Simple, Feb'84 by Simple Records. Dist: EMI

Single (12"): released on Simple, Feb'84 by Simple Records. Dist: EMI

Webster, Ben

ALUMNI MASTERS, (THE) (see Gray, Wardell) (Webster, Ben & Wardell Gray).

...AND ASSOCIATES.
Album: released on Verve, Dec'81 by Phonogram Records. Dist: Polygram

ATMOSPHERE FOR LOVERS AND THIEVES.
Album: released on Black Lion, Jan'85 by Black Lion Records. Dist: Jazz Music, Chris Wellard, Taylor, H.R., Counterpoint, Cadillac

AT THE NUWAY CLUB.
Album: released on Nostalgia (Sweden), Oct'82 by Wellard, Chris Distribution. Dist: Wellard, Chris Distribution

AT THE RENAISSANCE.
Album: released on Contemporary, Jun'86 by Contemporary Records. Dist: Pinnacle

BALLADS.
Double Album: released on Verve, Jan'75 by Phonogram Records. Dist: Polygram

BALLADS AND BLUES.
Compact disc: released on The Compact Collection, Sep'87 by Conifer Records. Dist: Conifer Distribution

BEAN & BEN (Webster, Ben & Coleman Hawkins).
Album: released on Harlequin, Oct'83 by Harlequin Records. Dist: Swift, Jazz Music, Wellard, Chris, IRS, Taylor, H.R.

BEN WEBSTER.
Album: released on Commodore Classics, Dec'84 by Teldec Records (Germany). Dist: Conifer, IMS, Polygram

BEN WEBSTER & FRIENDS.
Album: released on Verve, Jun'77 by Phonogram Records. Dist: Polygram

BEN WEBSTER IN EUROPE VOL.2.
Album: released on Rarities, Apr'81

BEN WEBSTER & JIMMY WITHERSPOON (That's Jazz Series) (Webster, Ben & Jimmy Witherspoon).

BEN WEBSTER MEETS DON BYAS (Webster, Ben/Don Byas).
Notes: Personnel: Don Byas-tenor sax/Ben Webster-tenor sax/Tete Monoliu-piano/Peter Trunk-bass/Al 'Tootie' Heath-drums. Tenor giants Ben Webster and Don Byas are two of the handful of great tenor saxophonists in the melodic/harmonic tradition established before and during the swing era. Recorded 1968.
Compact disc: released on ECM (Germany), Jun'86 by ECM Records. Dist: IMS, Polygram, Virgin through EMI

BEN WEBSTER MEETS OSCAR PETERSON.
Compact disc: released on Polydor, Aug'86 by Polydor Records. Dist: Polygram, Polydor
Cat. no: **829 167-2**
Album: released on Verve, Apr'81 by Phonogram Records. Dist: Polygram

BEN WEBSTER (SMALL GROUPS).
Notes: Mono
Album: released on Jazz Archives, Jul'86 by Jazz Archives Records. Dist: Jazz Music

BIG BEN TIME.
Tracks: / Just a sittin' and a-rockin' / Exactly like you / How deep is the ocean / My one and only love / Honeysuckle rose / Jeep is jumpin' / Where or when / Wrap your troubles in dreams / Solitude / Remember.
Notes: Digital stereo.
Compact disc: released on Verve (USA), Sep'84 by Polydor. Dist: Polygram

BLUE LIGHT.
Album: released on Polydor (Holland), Apr'84

DID YOU CALL.
Album: released on Nessa, Mar'79 Dist: Projection, Swift

DUKE'S IN BED.
Album: released on Black Lion, Apr'85 by Black Lion Records. Dist: Jazz Music, Chris Wellard, Taylor, H.R., Counterpoint, Cadillac

FOR THE GUV'NOR.
Tracks: / I got it bad and that ain't good / Drop me off in Harlem / One for the guv'nor / Prelude to a kiss / In a sentimental mood / John Brown's body / Worksong / Preacher, The / Straight no chaser / Rockin' in rhythm / John Brown's body / Worksong / Preacher / Straight no chaser / Rockin' in rhythm.

Notes: An EMI-Holland recording. Produced by Joop Visser. Engineered by Klass Leyen.
Compact disc: released on Charly, May'87 by Charly Records. Dist: Charly, Cadillac

FOR THE GUVNOR.
Double Album: released on Affinity, Oct'79 by Charly Records. Dist: Charly, Cadillac

HORN 1944 (THE) (Webster, Ben and His Orchestra).
Album: released on Circle(USA), Jun'86 by Jazzology Records (USA). Dist: Jazz Music, Swift, Chris Wellard

KID & THE BRUTE,THE (Webster, Ben & Illinois Jacquet).

LIVE AT PIO'S.
Album:

MASTERS OF JAZZ VOL 5.
Album: released on Storyville, May'86 by Storyville Records. Dist: Jazz Music Distribution, Swift Distribution, Chris Wellard Distribution, Counterpoint Distribution

MEETS GERRY MULLIGAN.
Album: released on Verve (USA), May'84 by Polydor. Dist: Polygram

MPS JAZZ TIME VOL.9.
Album: released on MPS, Jun'79

NO FOOL, NO FUN.
Album: released on Spotlite, '83 by Spotlite Records. Dist: Cadillac, Jazz Music, Spotlite

SCANDINAVIAN DAYS.
Album: released on Rarities, Apr'81

SEE YOU AT THE FAIR.
Album: released on Jasmine, Aug'82 by Jasmine Records. Dist: Counterpoint, Lugtons, Taylor, H.R., Wellard, Chris, Swift, Cadillac

Cassette: released on Jasmine, Aug'82 by Jasmine Records. Dist: Counterpoint, Lugtons, Taylor, H.R., Wellard, Chris, Swift, Cadillac

SOULMATES.
Album: released on Riverside (USA), Aug'84 Dist: Fantasy (USA) Distribution

SOULVILLE.
Album: released on Verve, Mar'81 by Phonogram Records. Dist: Polygram

SUNDAY MORNING AT THE MONTMARTRE.
Album: released on Black Lion, '83 by Black Lion Records. Dist: Jazz Music, Chris Wellard, Taylor, H.R., Counterpoint, Cadillac

TATUM GROUP MASTERPIECES (SEPTEMBER 1956) (THE) (Webster, Ben/ Art Tatum).

TWO KINGS OF THE TENOR SAX 44-45 (Webster, Ben/Don Byas).

Webster, Ben Quartet

BEN AT THE NUWAY CLUB.
Album: released on Pumpkin, Sep'79 Dist: Jazz Music, Wellard, Chris, Cadillac

MAKIN WHOOPEE.
Album: released on Spotlite, '83 by Spotlite Records. Dist: Cadillac, Jazz Music, Spotlite

Webster, Katie

POUNDS OF BLUES.
Album: released on Charly(R&B), Jan'85 by Charly Records. Dist: Charly, Cadillac

YOU KNOW THAT'S RIGHT (Webster, Katie (with Hot Licks)).
Album: released on Arhoolie (Germany), Aug'85

Webster, Max

MAGNETIC AIR.
Album: released on Capitol, '80 by Capitol Records. Dist: EMI

Cassette: released on Capitol, '80 by Capitol Records. Dist: EMI

MUTINY UP MY SLEEVE.
Album: released on Capitol, Aug'78 by Capitol Records. Dist: EMI

Wechter, Julius

NATURALLY (Wechter, Julius & The Baja Marimba Band).
Album: released on President, May'85 by President Records. Dist: Taylors, Spartan

Weckl, Dave

LAYIN BACK WITH BEN.
Album: released on Honeydew, Oct'79 Dist: Swift, JSU

Wedding

TOMORROW I SET SAIL.
Tracks: / Tomorrow I set sail / Cry.
Single (7"): released on War, Feb'86 by War Records. Dist: PRT

Single (12"): released on War, Feb'86 by 'Var Records. Dist: PRT

Wedding Present

GO OUT AND GET 'EM BOY.
Single (7"): released on City Slang, Sep'85 Dist: Red Rhino, Cartel

MY FAVOURITE DRESS.
Tracks: / Every mother's son / Never said.
Single (7"): released on Reception, Feb'87 Dist: Red Rhino, Cartel

Single (12"): released on Reception, Feb'87 Dist: Red Rhino, Cartel

ONCE MORE.
Tracks: / Once more.
Single (12"): released on Reception, Jan'86 Dist: Red Rhino, Cartel

PEEL SESSION 26.2.86.
Tracks: / Peel session (26th February 1986) (The).
Cassette single: released on Strange Fruit, 13 Jun'87 by Clive Selwood. Dist: Pinnacle

THIS BOY CAN WAIT.
Tracks: / This boy can wait / You should always keep in touch with your friends.
Single (7"): released on Reception, Jul'86 Dist: Red Rhino, Cartel

Single (12"): released on Reception, Jul'86 Dist: Red Rhino, Cartel

Wedlock, Fred

FOLKER,THE.
Album: released on Village Thing, Mar'81 by Saydisc Records. Dist: Saydisc

FROLLICKS.
Album: released on Village Thing, Mar'81 by Saydisc Records. Dist: Saydisc

Wednesday Afternoon

OUT OF MY MIND.
Single (7"): released on Swagbag, Nov'82 Dist: Alternative Music

Wednesday, Jamie

VOTE FOR LOVE.
Single (12"): released on Pink, Nov'85 by Pink Records. Dist: Rough Trade

WE THREE KINGS OF ORIENT AREN'T.
Tracks: / We three kings of orient aren't.
Notes: 3 track
Single (12"): released on Pink, Aug'86 by Pink Records. Dist: Rough Trade

Wednesday Page

WEDNESDAY PAGE.
Tracks: / Wednesday Page.
Extended-play record: released on Golden Pathway, Aug'86 Dist: Revolver, Cartel

Wednesday Week

WHAT WE HAD.
Album: released on Enigma, Mar'87 by Enigma Records. Dist: Rough Trade, Cartel, EMI

Wee Cherubs

DREAMING.
Single (7"): released on Bogaten, Sep'84 Dist: Fast Forward

Weed A Rare Batch

WEED A RARE BATCH Various artists (Various Artists).
Album: released on Stash (Import), Apr'81 Dist: Swift Distribution, Jazz Music Distribution, Jazz Horizons Distribution, Celtic Music Distribution, Cadillac, JSU Distribution, Zodiac Distribution

Weed, Buddy Septet

FEBRUARY 4TH & 6TH, 1958.
Album: released on From The Jazz Vault, Oct'80 by Damont Records. Dist: Swift, Taylor, H.R.

Weedon, Bert

16 COUNTRY GUITAR GREATS.
Album: released on Polydor, Apr'78 by Polydor Records. Dist: Polygram, Polydor

20 GUITAR GREATS.
Album: released on Pickwick, Oct'79 by Pickwick Records. Dist: Pickwick Distribution, Prism Leisure Distribution, Lugtons

Cassette: released on Pickwick, Oct'79 by Pickwick Records. Dist: Pickwick Distribution, Prism Leisure Distribution, Lugtons

40 GUITAR GREATS.
Album: released on Pickwick, Sep'79 by Pickwick Records. Dist: Pickwick Distribution, Prism Leisure Distribution, Lugtons

Cassette: released on Pickwick, Sep'79 by Pickwick Records. Dist: Pickwick Distribution, Prism Leisure Distribution, Lugtons

AN HOUR OF BERT WEEDON.
Tracks: / China boogie / Flannel foot / Guitar boogie shuffle / Bert's boogie / Blue guitar / Stardust / Nashville boogie / King size guitar / Big beat boogie / Summer place, A (Theme) / Twelfth St. rag / Apache / Lonely guitar / Sorry Robbie / Easy beat / Ginchy / Mr. Guitar / Ghost train / China doll / Night cry / Lonely night / Gin mill guitar / Tokyo melody / Limelight (Theme) / Twelve-string shuffle / High steppin' / Malaguena.
Cassette: released on Hour Of Pleasure, Sep'87 by Music For Pleasure Records. Dist: EMI. Estim retail price in Sep'87 was £1.99.

BERT WEEDON & HIS DANCING GUITARS.
Album: released on Dansan, Mar'82 by Spartan Records. Dist: Spartan

BLUE ECHOES.
Album: released on Polydor, May'77 by Polydor Records. Dist: Polygram, Polydor

GUITAR GOLD - 20 GREATEST HITS.
Album: released on Pickwick, '78

Cassette: released on Pickwick, '78

HEART STRINGS.
Album: released on Celebrity, Dec'80 by Evolution Group records. Dist: Spartan

HONKY TONK GUITAR PARTY.
Album: released on Starline, Nov'77 by EMI Records. Dist: EMI

Cassette: released on Starline, Nov'77 by EMI Records. Dist: EMI Deleted '79.

LOVE LETTERS.
Album: released on Everest (Premier), '83 by Everest Records. Dist: Pinnacle

Cassette: released on Everest (Premier), '83 by Everest Records. Dist: Pinnacle

MR GUITAR.
Double Album: released on Music For Pleasure, Oct'84 by EMI Records. Dist: EMI

Cassette: released on Music For Pleasure, Oct'84 by EMI Records. Dist: EMI

Weeds

CHINA DOLL.
Tracks: / China doll.
Single (7"): released on In Tape, Aug'86 by In Tape Records. Dist: Red Rhino, Cartel

Weekend

CHRISTMAS PARTY EP - CHRISTMAS MEDLEY.
Single (7"): released on Jive, Nov'85 by Zomba Records. Dist: RCA, PRT, CBS

Single (12"): released on Jive, Nov'85 by Zomba Records. Dist: RCA, PRT, CBS

DRUMBEAT FOR BABY / SLEEPY FAIRIES / WEEKEND OFF.
Single (7"): released on Rough Trade, Oct'82 by Rough Trade Records. Dist: Rough Trade Distribution, Cartel Distribution

Single (12"): released on Rough Trade, Oct'82 by Rough Trade Records. Dist: Rough Trade Distribution, Cartel Distribution

LA VARIETE.
Album: released on Rough Trade, Nov'82 by Rough Trade Records. Dist: Rough Trade Distribution, Cartel Distribution

LIVE AT RONNIE SCOTTS.
Album: released on Rough Trade, Aug'83 by Rough Trade Records. Dist: Rough Trade Distribution, Cartel Distribution

MIDNIGHT SLOWS / PAST MEETS PRESENT.
Single (7"): released on Rough Trade, Jun'82 by Rough Trade Records. Dist: Rough Trade Distribution, Cartel Distribution

VIEW FROM HER ROOM / LEAVES OF SPRING.
Single (7"): released on Rough Trade, May'82 by Rough Trade Records. Dist: Rough Trade Distribution, Cartel Distribution

Single (12"): released on Rough Trade, May'82 by Rough Trade Records. Dist: Rough Trade Distribution, Cartel Distribution

Weeks, Alan & The Players

WHAT MORE CAN I SAY.
Single (12"): released on Sanity, Dec'82 by Sanity Records. Dist: Pinnacle, Jetstar

Weeks, Anson

& ORCHESTRA 1932.
Album: released on London, Apr'80 by London Records. Dist: Polygram

Weeks & Co

ROCK CANDY / KNOCK KNOCK.
Single (7"): released on Salsoul, Jun'83

Single (12"): released on Salsoul, Jun'83

Wee MacGreegor

WEE MACGREEGOR (Copeland, James).
Cassette: released on Colophone, Jun'81 by Audio-Visual Library Services. Dist: Audio-Visual Library Services

Weems, Ted

MARVELLOUS (Weems, Ted & His Orchestra).
Album: released on ASV Living Era, May'84 by ASV Records. Dist: PRT

Cassette: released on ASV Living Era, May'84 by ASV Records. Dist: PRT

TED WEEMS BAND 1940/1 BEAT THE BAND SHOWS.
Album: released on Fanfare, Jun'79 by Ferroway/Fanfare Records. Dist: PRT

Wee Papa Girl Rappers

ROCK THE CLOCK.
Single (7"): released on Jive, Jul'87 by Zomba Records. Dist: RCA, PRT, CBS

Single (12"): released on Jive, Jan'87 by Zomba Records. Dist: RCA, PRT, CBS

Weeping Messerschmitts

NOTHING YET.
Tracks: / Nothing yet.
Notes: 3 tracks
Extended-play record: released on Upright, Oct'86 by Upright Records. Dist: Cartel, Rough Trade

Weevil, Bo

WOOLY BULLY / COS IT FEELS GOOD.
Single (7"): released on Fore, May'82 Dist: Pinnacle

Wee Willie Water Melon

WEE WILLIE WATER MELON & BETTY BEETROOT Various artists (Various Artists).
Cassette: released on Tell-a-tale (Cassettes), Aug'84

We Free Kings

DEATH OF THE WILD COLONIAL BOY.
Tracks: / Death of the wild colonial boy / Love is in the air.
Single (7"): released on Howl, Jul'86 Dist: Fast Forward, Cartel

OCEANS.
Single (7"): released on DDT, Mar'87 by D.D.T Records. Dist: Fast Forward, Cartel

We Got Latin Soul

WE GOT LATIN SOUL (Various Artists).
Compact disc: released on Charly, Jun'87 by Charly Records. Dist: Charly, Cadillac

Album: released on Charly, Mar'87 by Charly Records. Dist: Charly, Cadillac

Cassette: released on Charly, Mar'87 by Charly Records. Dist: Charly, Cadillac

WE GOT LATIN SOUL VOL. 1 Various artists (Various Artists).
Tracks: / El Watusi / Taking over / Sock it to me / T P Treat / It's a good feeling (riot) / Bang, bang / Soul drummers / Pata pata / Son cuero y boogaloo / Oh yeah / Boolgaloo con soul.
Notes: Licensed from Musica Latina
Compact disc: released on Charly, May'87 by Charly Records. Dist: Charly, Cadillac

We Heel

BY DANNY & DAD.
Album: released on Cobblers, Mar'84

Wehrmacht

SHARK ATTACK.
Album: released on New Renaissance (USA), Aug'87

Weidlin, Jane

JANE WEIDLIN.
Tracks: / Blue kiss / Goodbye cruel world / Sometimes you really get on my nerves / East meets west / Somebody's going to get into this house / Forever / Modern romance / I will wait for you / One hudred years of solitude / Where we can go / My travelling heart.
Notes: By the time the Go-Go's split hit the press Jane Weidlin was already underway in production of her first solo LP. Recording the

first Jane Weidlin album took place May through to July of 1985. During the demo sessions, Jane worked with a triumvirate of producers - George Massenburg, Bill Payne and Russ Kunkel for half the album, and former Psycadellic Fur Vince Fly, for the other half. It was her feeling that having two production teams would result in a wide spectrum of viewpoints and hopefully more singles. The finished product title simply Jane Weidlin reflects the craftmanship and elegance to which her contributions to the Go-Go's has alluded.
Album: released on I.R.S.(Independent Record Syndicate), Mar'86 by I.R.S.. Dist: MCA

Cassette: released on I.R.S.(Independent Record Syndicate), Mar'86 by I.R.S.. Dist: MCA

Weill, Kurt
GOOD VIBES FOR KURT WEILL.
Album: released on Monmouth, Mar'79

Weird Science
WEIRD SCIENCE Original soundtrack.
Album: released on MCA, Nov'85 by MCA Records. Dist: Polygram, MCA

:

Weirdstone of Brisingamen
WEIRDSTONE OF BRISINGAMEN (Layton, George).
Cassette: released on Pinnacle, '79 by Pinnacle Records. Dist: Pinnacle

Weird Strings
OSCAR AUTOMOBILE / ANCIENT & SQUARE.
Single (7"): released on Velvet Moon, Feb'80 Dist: Rough Trade

Weird Strings 11
MILLIONAIRE / CRIMINAL CAGE.
Single (7"): released on Ace, May'80 by Ace Records. Dist: Pinnacle, Swift, Hotshot, Cadillac

Weisberg, Steve
I CAN'T STAND ANOTHER NIGHT ALONE (IN BED WITH YOU).
Tracks: / Table for one / Walking home alone / Waking up alone / Trapped in true love / You can't have anything.
Notes: EMC's last release for 86 and the first album on Carla Bley and Michael Mantler's newlabel "Xtra Watt", a side label to Watt. This new label is dedicated to theWatt family musicians.
Music composed and arranged by Steve Weisberg. Featured Soloists- Lew Soloff-trumpet(on Trapped)/ Baikida Carroll-trumpet(on Table)/Gary Valente-trombone/John Clark-french horn/Wolfgang Puschnig-alto sax, flute/Howard Johnson-baritone sax, contrabassclarinet,tuba/Hiram Bullock-guitar Steve Weisberg-piano,synthesiser,organ (on Table and You can't)/Steve Swallow- bass/Victor Lewis-drums(on I can't stand)/Anton Fierdrums(on Table and Trapped)
Album: released on Xtra Watt, Jan'87

I CAN'T STAND ANOTHER NIGHT ALONE.
Album: released on ECM (Germany), Dec'86 by ECM Records. Dist: IMS, Polygram, Virgin through EMI

Weissberg, Eric
DUELLING BANJOS.
Tracks: / Delling banjos / Theme from 'Deliverence' / Reuben's train.
Single (7"): released on Old Gold, Mar'86 by Old Gold Records. Dist: Lightning, Jazz Music, Spartan, Counterpoint

Single (7"): released on Automatic, Nov'79 Dist: WEA, Independant

Weiss, Harold
DRUM WHISPERS.
Album: released on ECM (Germany), Apr'83 by ECM Records. Dist: IMS, Polygram, Virgin through EMI

Weiss, Klaus
KLAUS WEISS.
Album: released on Calig, Jul'82 Dist: JSU

Weiss, Michael
MICHAEL WEISS QUINTET FEATURING... Tom Kirkpatrick/R. Lalama/R. Drummond.
Album: released on Criss Cross Jazz, Jan'87 Dist: Jazz Music, Jazz Horizons

Welch, Bob
BOB WELCH.
Album: released on RCA, Mar'82 by RCA Records. Dist: RCA, Roots, Swift, Wellard, Chris, I & B, Solomon & Peres Distribution

Cassette: released on RCA, Mar'82 by RCA Records. Dist: RCA, Roots, Swift, Wellard, Chris, I & B, Solomon & Peres Distribution

COLLECTION: BOB WELCH.
Album: released on EMI (Germany), '83 by EMI Records. Dist: Conifer

FRENCH KISS.
Album: released on Capitol, Nov'77 by Capitol Records. Dist: EMI

THREE HEARTS.
Album: released on Capitol, Apr'79 by Capitol Records. Dist: EMI

TWO TO DO / IMAGINARY FOOL.
Single (7"): released on RCA, Feb'82 by RCA Records. Dist: RCA, Roots, Swift, Wellard, Chris, I & B, Solomon & Peres Distribution

Welch, Ed
GUS HONEYBUN SONG, THE.
Single (7"): released on TSW, 30 May'87

Picture disc single: released on TSW, 30 May'87

IF YOU WOULD TAKE THE TIME / MAKE A FRIEND OF YOU (see also Diane Carter) (Welch, Ed & Diane Carter).
Single (7"): released on Tycos, Sep'83 by Tycos Records. Dist: Tycos

MOONSHOT.
Album: released on United Artists (USA), Aug'79 by EMI Records. Dist: EMI, Swift, Solomon & Peres Distribution

SPIKE MILLIGAN & ED WELCH SING SONGS FROM Q8.
Album:

Welch, Elisabeth
MISS ELISABETH WELCH (1933-1940).
Album: released on World Records, Jul'79 Dist: Polygram

Welch, Elizabeth
IN CONCERT.
Album: released on First Night, Sep'86 by Safari Records. Dist: Pinnacle

Cassette: released on First Night, Sep'86 by Safari Records. Dist: Pinnacle

WHERE HAVE YOU BEEN.
Tracks: / It was worth it / I got it bad and that ain't good / My love is a wanderer / I always say hello (to a flower) / ow little we know / Where have you been / Manhattan madness / He was too good for me / Little girl blue / You were there / Dancing in the dark / Mean to me / As long as I live / Come rain or come shine / Remember.
Album: released on DRG (USA), Mar'87 by DRG Records. Dist: Conifer, RCA

Cassette: released on DRG (USA), Mar'87 by DRG Records. Dist: Conifer, RCA

Welcome to Comboland
WELCOME TO COMBOLAND Various artists (Various Artists).
Album: released on Spindrift, May'86 Dist: Roots

Welcome to Ireland
WELCOME TO IRELAND Various artists (Various Artists).
Tracks: / Forty shades of green / Boys from the county Armagh / I'll take you home again Kathleen / My lagan softly flowing / Mountains of Mourne / Jarvey was a leprechaun (The) / When Irish eyes are smiling / Spinning wheel (The) / Isle of Innisfree (The) / Peter Byrnes' fancy creeping docken / Ballybunion by the sea / Castle of Dromore.
Album: released on Emerald (Ireland), Oct'82 by Emerald Records. Dist: I & B, Ross, PRT

Cassette: released on Emerald, Oct'82 by Emerald Records. Dist: Ross, PRT, Solomon & Peres Distribution

Welcome to Mission England
WELCOME TO MISSION ENGLAND Various artists (Various Artists).
Album: released on Word, Dec'84 by Word Records. Dist: Word Distribution, CBS

Cassette: released on Word, Dec'84 by Word Records. Dist: Word Distribution, CBS

Welcome to Scotland
WELCOME TO SCOTLAND Various artists (Various Artists).
Tracks: / Scotland the brave / Highland laddie / Earl of Mansfield (The) / Barren rock of Aden (The) / Northern lights of Aberdeen (The) / Rothesay bay / I belong to Glasgow / Tommy darling / Horo my nut brown maiden / Jeannie's bawbee / Piper o'Dundee (The) / Mull of Kintyre / De'ils awa' wi' the exciseman (The) / Conundrum (The) / De'il amang the tailors (The) / Maggie / Up in the morning early / O'er the water to Charlie / Cam ye by atholl / Haggis song / Dark island (The) / Mist covered mountains (The) / Roxburgh castle / Hamilton rant / Miss Jane of Violetbank / Moving cloud / Song of the Clyde / Isle of Mull / Kilworth hills / Highland laddie / Scotch on the rocks / Scots wha ha'e / Duncan Gray / We kirkcudbright centipede / Scottish soldier (The) / Road and the miles to Dundee (The) / Take me back / Cambeltown Loch / Muckin' o' Geordie's byre / Donald, where's yer troosers / Wild rover (The) / Farewell my love / I belong to Glasgow / Stop yer ticklin' Jock / Loch Lommond / Scotland the brave / Flowers of Scotland / Will ye come back again / We're no awa' tae bide awa' / Auld lang syne.
Album: released on Emerald (Ireland), Dec'83 by Emerald Records. Dist: I & B, Ross, PRT

Welcome to the Canteen
WELCOME TO THE CANTEEN Various artists (Various Artists).
Album: by Island Records. Dist: Polygram

Welcome to the Highlands
WELCOME TO THE HIGHLANDS (Various Artists).
Notes: Bobby Coghill, Ina Miller, Alex MacArthur and His Scottish Dance Band, Alistair Murdoch, Argo Cameron, Tommy Darkie.
Album: released on Ross, '86 by Ross Records. Dist: Ross Distribution, Roots Distribution

Cassette: released on Ross, '86 by Ross Records. Dist: Ross Distribution, Roots Distribution

Welcome to the Metal Zone
WELCOME TO THE METAL ZONE Various artists (Various Artists).
Album: released on Music For Nations, Apr'85 by Music For Nations Records. Dist: Pinnacle

Cassette: released on Music For Nations, Apr'85 by Music For Nations Records. Dist: Pinnacle

Weldon, Liam
DARK HORSE ON THE WIND.
Album: released on Mulligan, Jan'77 by Topic Records. Dist: Roots Distribution, Jazz Music Distribution, JSU Distribution, I & B Distribution, Projection Distribution, Wynd-Up Distribution, Celtic Distributions

Well Done the Secret Seven
WELL DONE THE SECRET SEVEN (Blyton, Enid).
Album: released on Super Tempo, May'84 by Multiple Sounds Records. Dist: Multiple Sound Distributors

Cassette: released on Super Tempo, May'84 by Multiple Sounds Records. Dist: Multiple Sound Distributors

Weller, Don
DON WELLER.
Album: released on Affinity, Oct'79 by Charly Records. Dist: Charly, Cadillac

Weller, Don Spring Quartet
COMMIT NO NUISANCE.
Album: released on Affinity, Jan'81 by Charly Records. Dist: Charly, Cadillac

Weller, Freddy
BACK ON THE STREET.
Tracks: / Midnight driver / Right in the prime of her love / Shootin' from the heart / Trying to get around to 'em all / If you knew how much I wanted you / Back on the street / Time machine / Intensive care / You believed in a dreamer / Midlife crisis / One dream at a time / Atlanta.
Album: released on Bulldog, Aug'87 by Bulldog Records. Dist: President Distribution, Spartan, Swift, Taylor, H.R.

Welles, Orson
I KNOW WHAT IT IS TO BE YOUNG.
Single (7"): released on Splash, Jan'85 by Splash Records. Dist: CBS

Wellington Citadel Band
MARCHES.
Album: released on Viking, Aug'79 Dist: Harmonia Mundi Distributors

Cassette: released on Viking, Aug'79 Dist: Harmonia Mundi Distributors

Wellington, Duke of
DUKES IN KONZERT, THE.
Album: released on Music Masters, Dec'79 by Music Masters Records. Dist: Taylors

Wellington, Roland
WHEN JAH COMES / COME A ME.
Single (12"): released on Carib Jems, Jun'82 by Carib Jems. Dist: Spartan, Jetstar

Wellington, Sheena
KERELAW.
Cassette: released on Dunkeld, Feb'87 by Dunkeld Records. Dist: Projection

Wellins, Bobby
PRIMROSE PATH (Wellins, Bobby & Jimmy Knepper).

We'll Meet Again
WE'LL MEET AGAIN Various original artists (Various original artists).
Album: released on K-Tel, Sep'82 by K-Tel Records. Dist: Record Merchandisers Distribution, Taylors, Terry Blood Distribution, Wynd-Up Distribution, Relay Distribution, Pickwick Distribution, Solomon & Peres Distribution, Polygram

Cassette: released on K-Tel, Sep'82 by K-Tel Records. Dist: Record Merchandisers Distribution, Taylors, Terry Blood Distribution, Wynd-Up Distribution, Relay Distribution, Pickwick Distribution, Solomon & Peres Distribution, Polygram

Well Red
GET LUCK.
Single (7"): released on Virgin, Jul'87 by Virgin Records. Dist: EMI, Virgin Distribution

Single (12"): released on Virgin, Jul'87 by Virgin Records. Dist: EMI, Virgin Distribution

HONEY.
Tracks: / Honey / Saturday.
Special: released on Virgin, Apr'87 by Virgin Records. Dist: EMI, Virgin Distribution

LIMIT OF YOUR LOVING.
Single (7"): released on Palladin, May'85 by Palladin Records. Dist: Cartel

Single (12"): released on Palladin, May'85 by Palladin Records. Dist: Cartel

LOVE GONE CRAZY.
Single (7"): released on Virgin, Nov'85 by Virgin Records. Dist: EMI, Virgin Distribution

Single (12"): released on Virgin, Nov'85 by Virgin Records. Dist: EMI, Virgin Distribution

MOTION.
Tracks: / Yes we can / Love gone crazy / Come back / System / Get lucky / Mixed up / Turn me on / Honey / Saturday* / Limit of your lovin'* / Let me out*.
Compact disc: released on Virgin, Jun'87 by Virgin Records. Dist: EMI, Virgin Distribution

Album: released on Virgin, Jun'87 by Virgin Records. Dist: EMI, Virgin Distribution

Cassette: released on Virgin, Jun'87 by Virgin Records. Dist: EMI, Virgin Distribution

YES WE CAN.
Tracks: / Don't rush me.
Single (7"): released on Virgin, Jan'87 by Virgin Records. Dist: EMI, Virgin Distribution

Single (12"): released on Virgin, Jan'87 by Virgin Records. Dist: EMI, Virgin Distribution

Wells, Brandi
FANTASY / GOLDEN MOMENT / I LOVE YOU.
Boxed set: released on Wmot, Jul'82

Single (12"): released on Wmot, Jul'82

WATCH OUT.
Album: released on Virgin, Jan'82

Cassette: released on Virgin, Jan'82

WATCH OUT.
Single (7"): released on Virgin, Jan'82

Single (12"): released on Virgin, Jan'82

WHITE BOY DANCE.
Single (7"): released on Virgin, Apr'82 by Virgin Records. Dist: EMI, Virgin Distribution

Single (12"): released on Virgin, Apr'82

Wells Cathedral Choir
CHRISTMAS CAROLS.
Compact disc: released on ASV, Oct'83 by Academy Sound & Vision Records. Dist: Pinnacle

Cassette: released on ASV, Oct'83 by Academy Sound & Vision Records. Dist: Pinnacle

WELLS CATHEDRAL CHOIR & SCHOOL CHAMBER ORCHESTRA.
Album: released on Alpha, '82 by Alpha Records. Dist: H.R. Taylor, Gamut

Cassette: released on Alpha, '82 by Alpha Records. Dist: H.R. Taylor, Gamut

Wells,Dick
TROMBONE FOUR-IN-HAND.
Tracks: / Blue moon / Airlift / It's all over now / Wine-o Junction / Heavy duty / Short,tall,fat and small. / Girl hunt.
Notes: Licensed from Dacca Records ltd. A Felsted recording.
Album: released on Affinity, Nov'86 by Charly Records. Dist: Charly, Cadillac

Wells, Dicky

BONES FOR THE KING.
Tracks: / Bones for the king / Sweet daddy spo-de-o / You took my heart / Hello, smack! / Come and get it / Stan's dance.
Album: released on Affinity, Dec'86 by Charly Records. Dist: Charly, Cadillac

LONESOME ROAD.
Album: released on Uptown, Dec'82 by Uptown Records. Dist: PRT, Cartel

TROMBONE FOUR IN HAND.
Tracks: / Blue moon / Airlift / It's all over now / Wine O junction / Heavy duty / Short, tall fat & small / Girl hunt.
Album: released on Affinity, Oct'86 by Charly Records. Dist: Charly, Cadillac

Wells Fargo

WHO'S BUYING.
Album: released on Tank, Nov'79 by Tank Records.

Wells, James & Susan

LOVE THE CURE FOR ME.
Single (7"): released on Nitemare, Dec'86

Single (12"): released on Nightmare, Dec'86 by Nightmare Records. Dist: PRT

MIRROR IMAGE.
Single (7"): released on Fanfare, Jun'85 by Ferroway/Fanfare Records. Dist: PRT

Single (12"): released on Fanfare, Jun'85 by Ferroway/Fanfare Records. Dist: PRT

RSVP.
Single (7"): released on Fanfare, Feb'85 by Ferroway/Fanfare Records. Dist: PRT

Single (12"): released on Fanfare, Feb'85 by Ferroway/Fanfare Records. Dist: PRT

Wells, Junior

CHIEFLY WELLS.
Album: released on Flyright, Apr'85 by Flyright Records. Dist: Krazy Kat, Swift, Jazz Music

CHIEFLY WELLS (Wells, Junior/Magic Sam).
Album: released on Flyright, Oct'86 by Flyright Records. Dist: Krazy Kat, Swift, Jazz Music

Drinking TNT and smoking dynamite

HOODOO MAN BLUES.
Album: released on Delmark, '74 Dist: Projection, Swift, Cadillac

IN MY YOUNGER DAYS.
Album: released on Red Lightnin', Sep'82 by Red Lightnin' Records. Dist: Roots, Swift, Jazz Music, JSU, Pinnacle, Cartel, Wynd-Up Distribution

MESSING WITH THE KID.
Tracks: / Messin with the kid / I'm a stranger / Little by little / Come on in this house / Cha cha cha in blues / Prison bars all around me / Love me / It hurts me to / Things I'd do for you, The / I could cry / Lovey dovey lovely one / So tired / I need me a car / You sure look good to me / You don't care / Two headed woman.
Album: released on Charly, May'86 by Charly Records. Dist: Charly, Cadillac

MESSIN' WITH THE KID.
Tracks: / Messin' with the kid / I'm a stranger / Come on in this house / Little by little / Cha cha cha in blues / Prison bars all round me / Love me / It hurts me too / Things I'd do for you / I could cry / So tired / Lovey dovey lovely one / I need me a car / You sure look good to me / You don't care / Two headed woman.
Album: released on Charly(R&B), Oct'86 by Charly Records. Dist: Charly, Cadillac

ON TAP.
Album: released on Delmark, '75 Dist: Projection, Swift, Cadillac

ORIGINAL BLUES BROTHERS - LIVE (Wells, Junior & Buddy Guy).
Album: released on Blue Moon, Sep'83 Dist: Magnum Music Group Ltd, PRT, Spartan

SOUTHSIDE BLUES JAM.
Album: released on Delmark, '74 Dist: Projection, Swift, Cadillac

UNIVERSAL ROCK.
Album: released on Flyright, Oct'86 by Flyright Records. Dist: Krazy Kat, Swift, Jazz Music

Album: released on Flyright, '82 by Flyright Records. Dist: Krazy Kat, Swift, Jazz Music

Wells, Kitty

COUNTRY HIT PARADE.
Album: released on Stetson, Apr'87 by Hasmick Promotions Ltd.. Dist: Counterpoint Distribution, H.R. Taylor Distribution, Swift Distribution, Chris Wellard Distribution

Cassette: released on Stetson, Apr'87 by Hasmick Promotions Ltd.. Dist: Counterpoint Distribution, H.R. Taylor Distribution, Swift Distribution, Chris Wellard Distribution

GREATEST HITS:KITTY WELLS.
Tracks: / It wasn't God that made Honky Tonk angels / This white circle / Mommy for a day / Release me / I gave my wedding dress away / Amigo's guitar / Heartbreak USA / I'll repossess my heart / Password / Searching (for someone like you) / Making believe.
Album: released on MCA Import, Mar'86 by MCA Records. Dist: Polygram, IMS

GREATEST HITS: KITTY WELLS.
Cassette: released on K-Tel Goldmasters, Aug'84 by K-Tel Records. Dist: K-Tel

KITTY'S CHOICE.
Album: released on Stetson, Sep'86 by Hasmick Promotions Ltd.. Dist: Counterpoint Distribution, H.R. Taylor Distribution, Swift Distribution, Chris Wellard Distribution

Cassette: released on Stetson, Sep'86 by Hasmick Promotions Ltd.. Dist: Counterpoint Distribution, H.R. Taylor Distribution, Swift Distribution, Chris Wellard Distribution

KITTY WELLS STORY (THE).
Tracks: / It wasn't God who made Honky Tonk angels / I heard the juke box playing / Wedding ring ago (A) / Paying for that back street affair / I don't claim to be an angel / Whose shoulder will you cry on / I gave my wedding dress away / Release me / After dark / Lonely side of town / Making believe / Searching (for someone like you) / Repenting / Your wild life's gonna get you down / Three ways to love you / She's no angel / Touch and go heart / Jealousy / I can't help wondering / Mommy for a day / Amigo's guitar / All the time / Other cheek (The) / Left to right.
Double Album: released on MCA Import, Mar'86 by MCA Records. Dist: Polygram, IMS

MAKIN' BELIEVE.
Album: released on Colorado, Dec'85 Dist: Counterpoint

Cassette: released on Colorado, Dec'85 Dist: Counterpoint

ORIGINAL QUEEN OF COUNTRY MUSIC, (THE).
Album: released on Bulldog Records, Jul'82

Cassette: released on Bulldog Records, Jul'82

SONGS MADE FAMOUS BY JIM REEVES.
Album: released on Stetson, Jun'86 by Hasmick Promotions Ltd.. Dist: Counterpoint Distribution, H.R. Taylor Distribution, Swift Distribution, Chris Wellard Distribution

Cassette: released on Stetson, Jun'86 by Hasmick Promotions Ltd.. Dist: Counterpoint Distribution, H.R. Taylor Distribution, Swift Distribution, Chris Wellard Distribution

Wells, Mary

CHRISTMAS BELLS.
Single (7"): released on Solid Gold, Nov'81

COMPACT COMMAND PERFORMANCES 22 greatest hits.
Tracks: / Bye bye baby / I don't want to take a chance / One who really loves you (The) / You beat me to the punch / Two lovers / Laughing boy / Your old standby / Old love (let's try it again) / Oh little boy / What love has joined together / You lost the sweetest boy / What's easy for two is so hard for one / My guy / Two wrongs don't make a right / Everybody needs love / I'll be available / One block from heaven / When I'm gone / He's the one I love / Whisper you love me boy / Does he love me? / Was it worth it?.
Compact disc: released on Motown, Mar'87 by Motown Records. Dist: BMG Distribution

DON'T BURN YOUR BRIDGES.
Tracks: / Don't burn your bridges / Don't burn your bridges (inst).
Single (7"): released on Nightmare, May'87 by Nightmare Records. Dist: PRT

Single (12"): released on Nightmare, May'87 by Nightmare Records. Dist: PRT

GREATEST HITS: MARY WELLS.
Album: released on Motown, Feb'83 by RCA Records. Dist: RCA Distribution

Cassette: released on Motown, Feb'83 by RCA Records. Dist: RCA Distribution

MARY WELLS SINGS MY GUY.
Album: released on Motown, Mar'82 by RCA Records. Dist: RCA Distribution

Cassette: released on Motown, Mar'82 by RCA Records. Dist: RCA Distribution

MY GUY.
Single (7"): released on Motown, Mar'83 by RCA Records. Dist: RCA Distribution

Single (7"): released on Allegiance, Feb'84 by PRT Records. Dist: PRT

Single (12"): released on Allegiance, Feb'84 by PRT Records. Dist: PRT

MY HANDS ARE TIED.
Tracks: / My hands are tied / My hands are tied (dub mix).
Single (7"): released on Nightmare, May'87 by Nightmare Records. Dist: PRT

Single (12"): released on Nightmare, May'87 by Nightmare Records. Dist: PRT

OLD, NEW AND BEST OF MARY WELLS.
Album: released on Allegiance, Feb'84 by PRT Records. Dist: PRT

Cassette: released on Allegiance, Feb'84 by PRT Records. Dist: PRT

YOU BEAT ME TO THE PUNCH.
Single (7"): released on Allegiance, Jun'84 by PRT Records. Dist: PRT

Wells, Phil

SHANA THE STAR DANCER.
Single (7"): released on Solid Gold, Jan'82

Wells, Phillip J.

LAST SURVIVORS, (THE).
Album: released on Solid Gold, Jun'79

Wells, Susan

NIGHTMARE.
Single (12"): released on Nightmare Gold, Feb'87 Dist: PRT

Wells, Terri

JUST LIKE DREAMIN'.
Album: released on Philly World, Sep'84

Cassette: released on Philly World, Sep'84

YOU MAKE IT HEAVEN.
Single (7"): released on Philly World, Jun'83

Single (12"): released on Philly World, Jun'83

Wells, Tony

DANNY BOY.
Single (7"): released on Artesian, Dec'81 Dist: Pinnacle, PRT

HOLY CITY, (THE).
Single (7"): released on Play, Dec'85 by Play Records. Dist: Spartan

ONLY YOU.
Single (7"): released on Artesian, Aug'83 Dist: Pinnacle, PRT

Wellstood, Dick

IN A MELLO ROLL (Wellstood, Dick/Kenny Davern Quartet).
Album: released on Black Eagle, Apr'79 Dist: Swift, Chris Wellard

SOME HEFTY CATS.
Album: released on Hefty Jazz, Sep'79 Dist: JSU, Swift, Wellard, Chris, Jazz Music, Cadillac Music

Wells, Tracy

BEST OF TRACY WELLS.
Album: released on Homespun(Ireland), Feb'79 by Outlet Records. Dist: Outlet

Cassette: released on Homespun(Ireland), Feb'79 by Outlet Records. Dist: Outlet

COUNTRY ROADS.
Album: released on Outlet, '75 by Outlet Records. Dist: Outlet Distribution

COUNTRY SUNSHINE.
Album: released on Homespun(Ireland), Jan'77 by Outlet Records. Dist: Outlet

Cassette: released on Homespun(Ireland), Jan'77 by Outlet Records. Dist: Outlet

GIVE DADDY BACK TO ME.
Album: released on Homespun(Ireland), Jan'76 by Outlet Records. Dist: Outlet

JUST BECAUSE I'M A WOMAN.
Album: released on Homespun(Ireland), '82 by Outlet Records. Dist: Outlet

Cassette: released on Homespun(Ireland), '82 by Outlet Records. Dist: Outlet

OTHER SIDE OD THE MORNING.
Cassette: released on Ross, '86 by Ross Records. Dist: Ross Distribution, Roots Distribution

Wells, William

CONSTANT BILLY.
Cassette: released on Folktracks, Nov'79 Dist: Roots

Well Up...And Bubble

WELL UP...AND BUBBLE Various artists (Various Artists).
Notes: Artists include: Three Johns, Nightingales, Mekons.
Album: released on Bigger Bank Balance, Nov'85 Dist: Cartel

We Love Norway

WE LOVE NORWAY (Vi Alskar Norge).
Album: released on Phontastic (Sweden), '82 by Wellard, Chris Distribution. Dist: Wellard, Chris Distribution

Welsh, Alex

ALEX WELSH SHOWCASE VOLUME 2.
Album: by Black Lion Records. Dist: Jazz Music, Chris Wellard, Taylor, H.R., Counterpoint, Cadillac

AN EVENING WITH ALEX WELSH PART 1.
Album: released on Polydor, '74 by Polydor Records. Dist: Polygram, Polydor

DIXIELAND TO DUKE.
Album: released on Dormouse, Nov'86 by Dormouse Records. Dist: Swift

IN A PARTY MOOD (Welsh, Alex Band).
Album: released on One Up, Nov'77 by EMI Records.

SALUTE TO SATCHMO (Welsh, Alex/Humphrey Lyttleton/Bruce Turner/George Chisholm).
Double Album: released on Black Lion, '79 by Black Lion Records. Dist: Jazz Music, Chris Wellard, Taylor, H.R., Counterpoint, Cadillac

Welsh Choirs

IDEAL WELSH CHOIRS Various Artists (Various Artists).
Cassette: released on Ideal(Tapes), Jul'84 Dist: EMI

Welsh Guards

FAMOUS MARCHES.
Cassette: released on VFM Cassettes, Jan'85

GILBERT AND SULLIVAN (Welsh Guards Band).
Album: released on Bandleader, Feb'86 by Bandleader Records. Dist: PRT

Cassette: released on Bandleader, Feb'86 by Bandleader Records. Dist: PRT

NIMROD (Welsh Guards Band).
Tracks: / Nimrod / Always Vienna (Wien Bleibt Wien) / Trumpet trio (nine busy fingers) / Hoch heidecksburg! / Children's patrol / Bilitis (theme from the film) / Norwegian carnival / Cardiff arms / Sailing by / Sutherland's law theme / Entry of the boyards / I hope I get better / At the ballet / I can do that / Nothing / One / What I did for love / Abide wih me.
Album: released on Grasmere, Oct'86 by Grasmere Records. Dist: EMI

Cassette: released on Grasmere, Oct'86 by Grasmere Records. Dist: EMI

SING THE SONGS OF OUR HOMELAND (Welsh Guards/London Welsh Male Voice Choir).
Notes: The very first time that both these London based 'bodies' have recorded together. It is very rare these days to find a new album of Military Band and Welsh Male Choir together. The London Welsh Male Choir have previously had success with their album 'Songs From The Valleys' (out on K-Tel).
Album: released on Columbia, Apr'86 by EMI Records. Dist: EMI

Cassette: released on Columbia, Apr'86 by EMI Records. Dist: EMI

TROOPING THE COLOUR.
Cassette: released on Bi Bi(Budget Cassettes), Jan'83

Welsh Guards Band

AT HICKSTEAD.
Album: released on Major Richards, Oct'77
Cat. no: **DR 1**

CHRISTMAS WITH THE WELSH GUARDS.
Album: released on Major Richards Military Music, Dec'82

CYMRU AM BYTH.
Album: released on Daffodil, '74 Dist: Swift

GOD BLESS THE PRINCE OF WALES.
Album: released on Academy Sound & Vision, Jul'81 by Academy Sound & Vision Records. Dist: Pinnacle

Cassette: released on Academy Sound & Vision, Jul'81 by Academy Sound & Vision Records. Dist: Pinnacle

PRINCESS OF WALES.
Single (7"): released on ASV, Jun'81 by Academy Sound & Vision Records. Dist: Pinnacle

THEIR MOST POPULAR RECORDINGS.

Album: released on BBC, '78 by BBC Records & Tapes. Dist: EMI, PRT.

Cassette: released on BBC, '78 by BBC Records & Tapes. Dist: EMI, PRT,

TROOPING OF THE COLOUR 1981, (THE).
Album: released on Major Richards, Jul'81

WELSH GUARDS SHOWCASE NO. 1.
Album: released on Major Richards Military Music, Aug'83

Cassette: released on Major Richards Military Music, Aug'83

Welsh Ladies Choirs

FIRST FESTIVAL OF WELSH LADIES CHOIRS Various Artists (Various Artists).
Album: released on Black Mountain, '82 by Black Mountain Records.

Welsh, Lillie

Let me have the chance

Welsh male choirs

AN HOUR OF WELSH MALE CHOIRS.
Tracks: / Hymn from Finlandia / Unwaith eto'n nghymru annwyl / Lest we forget / Shepherd,shepherd / Lord's prayer (The) / Finnish forest (The) / Cadwyn O Emyn-Donau Cymreig / Joanna,Crugybar,Ebenezer / Cymru fach / Dies Irae / Bryn Myrddin / Memory / Diolch I'r Ior / Soldiers chorus from "Faust" / Lily of the valley, The / Bandits'Chorus / Deus Salutis(Llef) / Silver birch,The / Nant y Mynydd / Hava Nagila.
Cassette: released on Hour Of Pleasure, '87 by Music For Pleasure Records. Dist: EMI. Estim retail price in Sep'87 was £1.99.

WELSH MALE CHOIRS (Various Artists).
Album: released on Hour Of Pleasure, Jun'87 by Music For Pleasure Records. Dist: EMI. Estim retail price in Sep'87 was £1.99.

Welsh Male Voice Choir

WE'LL KEEP A WELCOME.
Tracks: / We'll keep a welcome / Bryan Myrddin / How great thou art / Memory (from 'Cats') / Aberystwyth (Jesu lover of my soul) / Sound of silence (The) / Hymn (from 'Finlandia') / Christus redemptor (hyfrydol) / Softly as I leave you / Comrades arms / Let it be me / Creation's hymn / You'll never walk alone (from 'Carousel') / Martyrs of the arena.
Notes: Includes Canoldir Male Choir/Trerorchy Male Choir/Pontarddulais Male Choir/Morriston Orpheus Choir. Four superb Welsh Choirs - singing a fine selection of traditional and popular classics, from Bryn Mayrddin to 'Memory' from Lloyd Webber's 'Cats'. The album was produced by Bob Barrett of Grasmere Music, who specialises in Welsh Choir productions.
Album: released on Conifer, Dec'85 by Conifer Records. Dist: Conifer

Cassette: released on Conifer, Dec'85 by Conifer Records. Dist: Conifer

WELSH MALE VOICE CHOIRS, A FESTIVAL Various artists (Various Artists).
Tracks: / Myfanwy / Cwn rhondda / Speed your journey / Steal away / March of the men of Harlech / Kumbaya / Sospan fach / Bless this house / Jacobs ladder / O Mary, don't you weep / Comrades in arms / Counting the goats / All through the night / Soldiers chorus from 'Faust' (The) / Lord's prayer (The) / Jerusalem / Immortal, invisible God only wise / Ave Maria / We'll keep a welcome / Michael, row the boat ashore / God bless the Prince of Wales / A-Rockin' all night / Lily of the valley / Mae hen wlad fy nhadau (Welsh National Anthem).
Notes: Featuring some of the top male choirs of Wales: The Treorchy Male Choir/The Morriston Orpheus Choir/Mommouthshire Massed Choir/The Third Festival of One Thousand Welsh Male Voices. 24 tracks beautifully sung titles include: 'Cwm Rhondda', 'Myfanwy', 'Steal Away', 'Ave Maria', 'Kumbaya', 'Sospan Fach'.
Album: released on Music For Pleasure, Apr'86 by EMI Records. Dist: EMI

Cassette: released on Music For Pleasure, Apr'86 by EMI Records. Dist: EMI

Welsh male voices

SOUND AN ALARM (One Thousand Welsh Male).
Album: released on BBC, '78 by BBC Records & Tapes. Dist: EMI, PRT, Pye

Cassette: released on BBC, '78 by BBC Records & Tapes. Dist: EMI, PRT, Pye

Welsh Mixed Voices

THIRD FESTIVAL WELSH MIXED VOICES Various Artists (Various Artists).
Album: released on Black Mountain, '82 by Black Mountain Records.

Welsh Rugby

OTHER SIDE OF THE DRAGON, (THE) (Welsh Rugby All Stars).
Album: released on Evolution, Sep'80 Dist: RCA, Folksound

Weltons

HOW LONG.
Single (7"): released on Carrere America (USA), Apr'82 by Polygram.

Wembley Festival 1977

SERVICES SILVER JUBILEE MUSICAL PAGEANT, (THE) Various Artists (Various Artists).
Album:

Wendy House

STOREYS EP BELLE OF THE BALL.
Tracks: / Storeys ep - belle of the ball / Charmaine / See no reason / Today.
Single (7"): released on Wendy House, Jan'86 by Wendy House Records. Dist: Wendy House

Wendy & Lemmy

STAND BY YOUR MAN.
Single (7"): released on Bronze, Sep'82 by Polygram Records. Dist: Polydor

Wendy & Lisa

WATERFALL.
Single (7"): released on Virgin, Aug'87 by Virgin Records. Dist: EMI, Virgin Distribution

Single (12"): released on Virgin, Aug'87 by Virgin Records. Dist: EMI, Virgin Distribution

Wendy & the Rockets

HAVE YOU BEEN TELLING ME LIES.
Single (7"): released on Oz, Nov'83 by A&M Records. Dist: CBS Distribution

Single (12"): released on Oz, Nov'83 by A&M Records. Dist: CBS Distribution

Wenzani

WENZANI Original Cast (Various Artists).
Cassette: released on Plankton, Dec'84 by Plankton Records. Dist: Cantio (Sweden)

We're Dancing...

WE'RE DANCING (STRICT DANCE TEMPO) VOLUME 4 Various artists (Various Artists).
Album: released on Polydor (Holland), Nov'85

Cassette: released on Polydor (Holland), Nov'85

WE'RE DANCING (STRICK DANCING TEMPO) VOLUME 5 Various artists (Various Artists).
Album: released on Polydor (Holland), Nov'85

Cassette: released on Polydor (Holland), Nov'85

WE'RE DANCING (STRICT DANCE TEMPO) VOLUME 6 Various artists (Various Artists).
Album: released on Polydor (Holland), Nov'85

Cassette: released on Polydor (Holland), Nov'85

We're only human

HOLD YOUR HEAD UP HIGH.
Tracks: / Hold your head up high / I wouldn't treat a dog like you treat me.
Single (7"): released on V.C., Dec'85 Dist: Jetstar

Werewolves of London

NOCTURNE.
Single (7"): released on Wabbit, May'82 by Wabbit Records. Dist: Pinnacle

Werner, Ken

BEYOND THE FOREST OF MIRKWOOD.
Album: released on Enja (Germany), Jan'82 by Enja Records (W.Germany). Dist: Cadillac Music

Werner, Lasse

TRIPLE PLAY JAZZ PIANO (Werner, Lasse/Jan Wallgren/Bobo Stenson).
Album: released on Dragon, Jun'86 by Dragon Records. Dist: Jazz Music, Projection, Cadillac

Werner, Max

RAIN IN MAY.
Single (7"): released on CBS, Feb'82 by CBS Records. Dist: CBS

Werth, Howard

RESPECTABLE.
Single (7"): released on Demon, May'82 Dist: Jazz Music, Projection

Wertz, Kimberley

I'LL BAKE ME A MAN.
Single (12"): released on Pandisc, Jun'84 Dist: Greyhound

Wesker, Arnold

DRAMATIST SPEAKS, (THE) (Wesker, Arnold/John Arden).
Double cassette: released on Argo (Spokenword), Jul'83 by Decca Records. Dist: Polygram

Wessex 82

WESSEX 82 (Various Artists).
Single (7"): released on BLWRG, Feb'83 by Rough Trade Records. Dist: Cartel

Wess, Frank

FLUTE JUICE.
Album: released on Progressive, Aug'82 by Progressive Records. Dist: Jetstar

I HEAR YA TALKIN'.
Notes: For some unknown reason, this album was never released by Savoy when first recorded in 1959, and, in fact, this is its first release- and a real gem too! When Wess recorded this he was 37 years old and a member of the Count Basie Orchestra, which he joined in 1953. The Basie influence is there, of course, added to the fact that trumpeter Thad Jones also appears here- he, too, was part of the Basie Orchestra at the time. Artists include: Frank Wess (flute, tener, alto sax)/Thad Jones (trumpet)/Curtis Fuller (trombone)/Charlie Fowlkes (baritone saxophone)/Hank Jone (piano)/Eddie Jones (bass)/Gus Johnson (drums). Recorded in New Jersey 1959.
Album: released on Savoy Jazz, Dec'85 by RCA Records (Germany). Dist: Conifer

I HEAR YA TALKIN.
Album: released on Savoy (France), Nov'84

WESS OF THE MOON.
Album: released on Commodore Classics, '87 by Teldec Records (Germany). Dist: Conifer, IMS, Polygram

Westbrook, Forrest

THIS IS THEIR TIME, OH YES.
Album: released on Revelation, Mar'87

Westbrook, Kate & Mike

HUMAN ABSTRACT.
Single (7"): released on Original, Dec'82 Dist: RCA Distribution, Jazz Music Distribution, PRT Distribution

LITTLE WESTBROOK MUSIC, (A).
Album: released on Original, Oct'83 Dist: RCA Distribution, Jazz Music Distribution, PRT Distribution

Cassette: released on Original, Oct'83 Dist: RCA Distribution, Jazz Music Distribution, PRT Distribution

PIER RIDES.
Album: released on Westbrook, May'86 Dist: Rough Trade, Cartel

Westbrook, Mike

CORTEGE.
Double Album: released on Original, Jul'82 Dist: RCA Distribution, Jazz Music Distribution, PRT Distribution

GOOSE SAUCE.
Album: released on Original, '80 Dist: RCA Distribution, Jazz Music Distribution, PRT Distribution

I SEE THY FORM.
Single (7"): released on Original, Jan'83 Dist: RCA Distribution, Jazz Music Distribution, PRT Distribution

MAMA CHICAGO.
Double Album: released on RCA, Oct'79 by RCA Records. Dist: RCA, Roots, Swift, Wellard, Chris, I & B, Solomon & Peres Distribution

PARIS ALBUM, (THE).
Double Album: released on Polydor, Dec'81 by Polydor Records. Dist: Polygram, Polydor

PIANO.
Album: released on Original, '80 Dist: RCA Distribution, Jazz Music Distribution, PRT Distribution

WESTBROOK BLAKE BRIGHT AS A FIRE, (THE) (setting of William Blake).
Album: released on Original, Sep'81 Dist: RCA Distribution, Jazz Music Distribution, PRT Distribution
Cat. no: **ORA 203**

Westbrook, Roger

I'N'T 'EE A GRAND LAD.
Album: released on Sweet Folk All, May'81 by Sweet Folk All Records. Dist: Sweet Folk All, Roots, Celtic Music, Dragon, Impetus, Projection, Chris Wellard, Festival Records
Cat. no: **SFA 069**

STILL HE SINGS.
Album: released on Sweet Folk All, Jan'87 by Sweet Folk All Records. Dist: Sweet Folk All, Roots, Celtic Music, Dragon, Impetus, Projection, Chris Wellard, Festival Records

WESTBROOK WRIGLEY (Westbrook, Roger/Bernard Wrigley).
Album: released on Sweet Folk All, Jan'87 by Sweet Folk All Records. Dist: Sweet Folk All, Roots, Celtic Music, Dragon, Impetus, Projection, Chris Wellard, Festival Records

West, Bruce & Laing

WHY DON'TCHA.
Album: released on RSO (Germany), Aug'85

Westbury, Kent

MY BABY DON'T ROCK ME.
Single (7"): released on Record Mart, Mar'78 by Record Mart Records. Dist: Tonal Distribution, Record Mart

Westcliff High School

CAROLS.
Album: released on AJP, Nov'77 by AJP Records.

West, Clint

CLINT WEST.
Album: released on Jin, Feb'79 Dist: Swift

CLINT WEST AT THE PURPLE PEACOCK.
Album: released on Jin, Feb'79 Dist: Swift

CLINT WEST & THE BOOGIE KINGS (West, Clint/Boogie Kings).
Album: released on Jin, Feb'79 Dist: Swift

FABULOUS KINGS.
Album: Dist: Swift

West Coast....

WEST COAST DOOWOP Various Artists (Various Artists).
Album: released on Ace(Cadet USA), Feb'84 by Ace Records. Dist: Pinnacle, Swift, Hotshot

WEST COAST JAM SESSIONS, 1952 Various Artists (Various Artists).
Triple album / cassette: released on Scarecrow, Apr'81 Dist: Jazz Music

WEST COAST JAZZ VOLUME 1 1922-31 Various Artists (Various Artists).
Album: released on Arcadia, Apr'79 Dist: Cartel

WEST COAST JAZZ VOLUME 2 1925-31 Various Artists (Various Artists).
Album: released on Arcadia, Apr'79 Dist: Cartel

WEST COAST SCENE Various Artists (Various Artists).
Double cassette: released on Vogue Jazz, May'83

WEST COAST SCENE VOLUME 2 Various Artists (Various Artists).
Double Album: released on Vogue Jazz, May'83

Double cassette: released on Vogue Jazz, May'83

WEST COAST SCENE VOLUME 3 Various Artists (Various Artists).
Double Album: released on Vogue Jazz, May'83

WEST COAST WINNERS (R & B 1953-57) Various Artists (Various Artists).
Album: released on Moonshine (Holland), Feb'85 Dist: Projection Distribution

West coast guitar greats

WEST COAST GUITAR GREATS Various artists (Various Artists).
Album: released on Moonshine (Belgium), Dec'85 Dist: Projection Distribution

West Coast Pop...

TRANSPARENT DAYS (West coast pop art experimental band).
Album: released on Demon, May'86 by Demon Records. Dist: Pinnacle

Cassette: released on Demon, May'86 by Demon Records. Dist: Pinnacle

West, Dottie

20 OF THE BEST.
Tracks: / Let me off at the corner / Love is no excuse / Gettin' married has made us strangers / Would you hold it against me / Mommy, can I still call him daddy ? / There's story (goin' round) / Paper mansions / Forever yours / Rings of gold / Last time I saw him / Here comes my baby / Before the ring on your finger turns green / What's come over my baby ? / Like a fool / Sweet memories / Country girl / Reno / Reno / Slowly / House of love / Country sushine.
Album: released on RCA, Mar'86 by RCA Records. Dist: RCA, Roots, Swift, Wellard, Chris, I & B, Solomon & Peres Distribution

Cassette: released on RCA, Mar'86 by RCA Records. Dist: RCA, Roots, Swift, Wellard, Chris, I & B, Solomon & Peres Distribution

CLASSICS (see Rogers, Kenny) (West, Dottie/Kenny Rogers).

West, Dotty
EVERY TIME TWO FOOLS COLLIDE (West, Dotty & Kenny Rogers).
Album: released on United Artists, Apr'78

West End
HOT FOR ROCKING.
Single (7"): released on Sound Recordings, Feb'84

Single (12"): released on Sound Recordings, Feb'84

OTHER SIDE OF MIDNIGHT, (THE).
Single (7"): released on EMI, Feb'85 by EMI Records. Dist: EMI

Single (12"): released on EMI, Feb'85 by EMI Records. Dist: EMI

WEST END NIGHT OUT Various Artists (Various Artists).
Cassette: released on Aim (Budget Cassettes), Feb'83

West End Boys
SUMMERTIME.
Single (7"): released on Hippodrome, Sep'85 Dist: EMI

West End Jazz Band
VOLUME 2.
Album: released on Stomp Off, Jun'86 by Stomp Off Records. Dist: Jazz Music Distribution

West End Stompers
AIN'T YOU GLAD.
Album: released on Sweet Folk All, May'81 by Sweet Folk All Records. Dist: Sweet Folk All, Roots, Celtic Music, Dragon, Impetus, Projection, Chris Wellard, Festival Records

TOO BUSY.
Album: released on Sweet Folk All, May'81 by Sweet Folk All Records. Dist: Sweet Folk All, Roots, Celtic Music, Dragon, Impetus, Projection, Chris Wellard, Festival Records

West End story
WEST END STORY Various artists (Various Artists).
Album: released on Streetsounds, Jan'87

Cassette: released on Streetsounds, Jan'87

Compact disc: released on Streetsounds, Jan'87

Western, Billy's Brass
WESTERN RAILROAD.
Album: released on Intersound, Dec'86 by Intersound Records. Dist: Jazz Music

Western, Johnny
GUNFIGHTER, (THE).
Album: released on Bear Family, Sep'84 by Bear Family Records. Dist: Rollercoaster Distribution, Swift

Western Promise
JUSTICE.
Single (12"): released on Midnight Music, Apr'85 by Midnight Music Records. Dist: Rough Trade Distribution, Cartel Distribution

MY WAR.
Tracks: / My war / Stay hungry / England hot / I'll tell you something I think you should know (Part 1)
Single (12"): released on Midnight Music, Jan'86 by Midnight Music Records. Dist: Rough Trade Distribution, Cartel Distribution

West, Gordie
ALBERTA BOUND.
Album: released on Westwood, '82 by Westwood Records. Dist: Jazz Music, H.R. Taylor, JSU, Pinnacle, Ross Records

Westhall, Robert
MACHINE GUNNERS.
Notes: Read by James Bolam. 1 volume: 4 cassettes. Listening time 5 hours 10 minutes.
Cassette: released on Cover to Cover, Feb'87 by Cover to Cover Records. Dist: Conifer

West Hampstead Ladies
IT'S A BIG BIG BEAUTIFUL WORLD.
Single (7"): released on Magic, Mar'83 Dist: Jazz Music, Submarine, Swift, Chris Wellard, Conifer

West Ham United
I'M FOREVER BLOWING BUBBLES.
Single (7"): released on Pve, '80

West, Hedy
BALLADS.
Album: released on Topic, '81 by Topic Records. Dist: JSU Distribution, Projection Distribution, Jazz Music Distribution

GETTING FOLK OUT OF THE COUNTRY (West, Hedy/Bill Clifton).
Album: released on Bear Family, Sep'84 by Bear Family Records. Dist: Rollercoaster Distribution, Swift

LOVE, HELL & BISCUITS.
Album: released on Bear Family, Sep'84 by Bear Family Records. Dist: Rollercoaster Distribution, Swift

OLD TIMES & HARD TIMES.
Album: released on Topic, '81 by Topic Records. Dist: JSU Distribution, Projection Distribution, Jazz Music Distribution

PRETTY SARO.
Album: released on Topic, '81 by Topic Records. Dist: JSU Distribution, Projection Distribution, Jazz Music Distribution

West Indian Company
AVA MARIE.
Single (7"): released on London, Nov'84 by London Records. Dist: Polygram

Single (12"): released on London, Nov'84 by London Records. Dist: Polygram

West Indies
TALES FROM.
Cassette: released on Anvil, Apr'80 Dist: Anvil

West Java
FLUTE & GAMELAN.
Album: released on Tangent, Apr'81 by Tangent Records. Dist: Roots Records Distribution, Impetus Distribution, H.R. Taylor Distribution, Jazz Music Distribution, JSU Distribution, Projection Distribution, Gordon Duncan Distribution, Ross Records Distribution

West, Jim
Biographical Details: see under - Forrest Westbrook.

West, John
BEYOND THE SUNSET (West, John & Family).
Cassette: released on Ross, '86 by Ross Records. Dist: Ross Distribution, Roots Distribution

West, Keith
EXCERPT FROM A TEENAGE OPERA.
Single (7"): released on Import, '80 Dist: Stage One

Single (7"): released on Video Music, May'82

EXCERPTS FROM A TEENAGE OPERA.
Tracks: / Excerpts from a teenage opera.
Single (7"): released on Old Gold, Mar'87 by Old Gold Records. Dist: Lightning, Jazz Music, Spartan, Counterpoint

EXERPTS FROM A TEENAGE OPERA.
Tracks: / Exerpts from a teenage opera / Kites.
Single (7"): released on Old Gold, Mar'87 by Old Gold Records. Dist: Lightning, Jazz Music, Spartan, Counterpoint

West, Keith/Tony
FOR THOSE WHO CARE.
Album: released on Tank, Jun'79 by Tank Records.

Westminster...
20 FAVOURITE (Westminster Central Hall).
Compact disc: by Abbey. Dist: PRT, Taylors, Gamut

FESTIVAL OF CAROLS, A (Westminster Cathedral Choir).
Compact disc: released on Pickwick, Nov'86 by Pickwick Records. Dist: Pickwick Distribution, Prism Leisure Distribution, Lugtons

PORTUGUESE POLYPHONY (Westminster Cathedral Choir).
Album: released on Hyperion, Nov'86 by Hyperion Records. Dist: Taylors, PRT, Gamut

Westminster Abbey Choir
STORY OF (WESTMINSTER) ABBEY.
Cassette: released on Sound Fact, Jul'81 by H.R. Taylor. Dist: Essex

WESTMINSTER ABBEY CHOIR.
Album: released on Abbey, Jun'78 by Abbey. Dist: PRT, Taylors, Gamut

Westminster Cathedral Choir
IN HONOUR OF OUR LADY.
Cassette: released on Abbey, Aug'81 by Abbey. Dist: PRT, Taylors, Gamut

WESTMINSTER CATHEDRAL CHOIR.
Cassette: released on Aim, Feb'83 Dist: H.R. Taylor

Westminster Symphony
TCHAIKOVSKY BALLET.
Double cassette: released on Pickwick (Ditto series), Jul'82

Weston, Kim
It takes two

Weston, Paul & His Orchestra
CINEMA CAMEOS.
Album: released on Corinthian (USA), Mar'79 Dist: Swift

EASY JAZZ.
Album: released on Corinthian (USA), Mar'79 Dist: Swift

Weston, Randy
BERKSHIRE BLUES.
Album: released on Freedom, Mar'79 by Logo Records. Dist: RCA, Discovery, Wellard, Chris

BLUES TO AFRICA.
Album:

NUIT AFRICAINE.
Album: released on Enja (Germany), Jan'82 by Enja Records (W.Germany). Dist: Cadillac Music

Weston, Tom, Four
BRANDED.
Album: released on Tank, Dec'77 by Tank Records.

West Side Story
WEST SIDE STORY Original score (Various Artists).
Notes: Featuring Kiri te Kanawa, Jose Carreras, Tatiana Troyanos, Kurt-Ollmann, Marilyn Horne. Conducted by Leonard Bernstein.
Double Album: released on DGG, May'85 by Polydor Records. Dist: Polygram

Double cassette: released on DGG, May'85 by Polydor Records. Dist: Polygram

Double compact disc: released on DGG, May'85 by Polydor Records. Dist: Polygram

WEST SIDE STORY Original soundtrack (Various Artists).
Tracks: / Jet song / Something's coming / Dance at the gym (blues promenade jump) / America / Maria / Tonight / Gee officer Krupke / I feel pretty / One hand one heart / Quintet / Rumble, The / Cool / Boy like that, A / I have a love / Somewhere.
Compact disc: released on CBS, '86 by CBS Records. Dist: CBS

WEST SIDE STORY Various artists (Various Artists).
Picture disc album: released on Astan, Dec'85 by Astan Records. Dist: Counterpoint

WEST SIDE STORY Original Soundtrack (Various Artists).
Album: released on CBS, '61 by CBS Records. Dist: CBS

Cassette: by CBS Records. Dist: CBS

WEST SIDE STORY Original Cast (Various Artists).
Album: released on CBS, Sep'82 by CBS Records. Dist: CBS

Cassette: released on CBS, Sep'82 by CBS Records. Dist: CBS

West Street Mob
BREAK DANCIN'-ELECTRIC BOOGIE.
Single (12"): released on Sugarhill, Sep'83 by PRT Records. Dist: PRT Distribution

I CAN'T STOP.
Single (12"): released on Sugarhill, Jul'84 by PRT Records. Dist: PRT Distribution

MOSQUITO (aka Hobo scratch).
Single (12"): released on Sugarhill, Nov'84 by PRT Records. Dist: PRT Distribution

WEST STREET MOB.
Album: by PRT Records. Dist: PRT Distribution

Cassette: by PRT Records. Dist: PRT Distribution

Westworld
BA-NA-NA-BAM BOO.
Tracks: / Ba-na-na-bam boo / Cheap'n'nasty.
Single (7"): released on RCA, Apr'87 by RCA Records. Dist: RCA, Roots, Swift, Wellard, Chris, I & B, Solomon & Peres Distribution

Single (12"): released on RCA, Apr'87 by RCA Records. Dist: RCA, Roots, Swift, Wellard, Chris, I & B, Solomon & Peres Distribution

SONIC BOOM BOY.
Tracks: / Mission impossible / Bubble Bo Diddley.
Notes: EXTRA track on 12" only
Single (7"): released on RCA, Feb'87 by RCA Records. Dist: RCA, Roots, Swift, Wellard, Chris, I & B, Solomon & Peres Distribution

Single (12"): released on RCA, Feb'87 by RCA Records. Dist: RCA, Roots, Swift, Wellard, Chris, I & B, Solomon & Peres Distribution

WHERE THE ACTION IS.
Tracks: / Where the action is / Fly Westworld / King Creole / Johnny Blue.
Single (7"): released on RCA, Jul'87 by RCA Records. Dist: RCA, Roots, Swift, Wellard, Chris, I & B, Solomon & Peres Distribution

Single (12"): released on RCA, Jul'87 by RCA Records. Dist: RCA, Roots, Swift, Wellard, Chris, I & B, Solomon & Peres Distribution

Compact disc: released on RCA, Aug'87 by RCA Records. Dist: RCA, Roots, Swift, Wellard, Chris, I & B, Solomon & Peres Distribution

Album: released on RCA, Aug'87 by RCA Records. Dist: RCA, Roots, Swift, Wellard, Chris, I & B, Solomon & Peres Distribution. Estim retail price in Sep'87 was £6.29.

Wet dreams
WET DREAMS Various artists (Various Artists).
Album: released on Rot, May'84 by Rot Records. Dist: Red Rhino Through Cartel Distributions

Wetherby
WETHERBY Original Soundtrack.
Album: released on TER, Mar'85 Dist: Pinnacle

Wet 'n' Wild
DON'T STOP THE BOP.
Album: released on Magnum Force, Jun'83

Wettbewerb, Hugo Herrmann
HUGO HERRMANN WETTBEWERB 1977 Various Artists (Various Artists).
Album: released on ARC (Accordion Records), '84 Dist: Accordion Record Club

Album: released on ARC (Accordion Records), '84 Dist: Accordion Record Club

Wettling, George
GEORGE WETTLING JAZZ BAND (Wettling, George Jazz Band).
Notes: Jonah Jones, Bud Freeman, M. Hinton, G. Barnes.
Album:

WETTLING, GEORGE.
Notes: With Pee Wee Russell/Lou McGarity/Wild Billvetc.
Cassette: released on Holmia Cassettes, Jun'86 Dist: Jazz Music, Wellard, Chris

Wetton, John
CAUGHT IN THE CROSSFIRE.
Album: released on Polydor, Oct'80 by Polydor Records. Dist: Polygram, Polydor

Cassette: released on Polydor, Oct'80 by Polydor Records. Dist: Polygram, Polydor

Wetton/Manzanera
WETTON/MANZANERA.
Tracks: / It's just love / Keep on loving yourself / You don't have to leave my life / Suzanne / Round in circles / Do it again / Every trick in the book / One world / I can't let you go / Have you seen her tonight.
Album: released on Geffen, Jun'87 by Geffen Records. Dist: WEA, CBS

Cassette: released on Geffen, Jun'87 by Geffen Records. Dist: WEA, CBS

Wet Wet Wet
SWEET LITTLE MYSTERY.
Tracks: / Sweet little mystery / Don't let me be lonely tonight.
Single (7"): released on Precious, Jul'87 by Phonogram Records. Dist: Polygram

Single (12"): released on Precious, Jul'87 by Phonogram Records. Dist: Polygram

WISHING I WAS LUCKY.
Tracks: / Wishing I was lucky / Words of wisdom / Still can't remember your name.
Single (7"): released on Precious, Mar'87 by Phonogram Records. Dist: Polygram

Single (12"): released on Precious, Mar'87 by Phonogram Records. Dist: Polygram

WORDS OF WISDOM.

We've Got A Fuzzbox...

BOSTIN STEVE AUSTIN (We've Got A Fuzzbox And We're Gonna Use It).
Album: released on Vindaloo, Jan'87 by Vindaloo Records. Dist: WEA, Cartel

Cassette: released on Vindaloo, Jan'87 by Vindaloo Records. Dist: WEA, Cartel

LOVE IS A SLUG (We've Got A Fuzzbox And We're Gonna Use It).
Tracks: / Love is a slug / Console me / Justine / Spirit in the sky.
Single (7"): released on Vindaloo, Oct'86 by Vindaloo Records. Dist: WEA, Cartel

Single (12"): released on Vindaloo, Oct'86 by Vindaloo Records. Dist: WEA, Cartel

Cassette single: released on Vindaloo, Oct'86 by Vindaloo Records. Dist: WEA, Cartel

WHAT'S THE POINT (We've Got A Fuzzbox And We're Gonna Use It).
Tracks: / Fuzzy ramblings fever* / Bohemian Rhapsody*.
Single (7"): released on Vindaloo, Jan'87 by Vindaloo Records. Dist: WEA, Cartel

Single (12"): released on Vindaloo, Jan'87 by Vindaloo Records. Dist: WEA, Cartel

XXSEX (We've Got A Fuzzbox And We're Gonna Use It).
Tracks: / Xxsex / Rules and regulations / Do I want to ? / She / Aaarrrggghhh.
Single (7"): released on Vindaloo, Feb'86 by Vindaloo Records. Dist: WEA, Cartel

Single (12"): released on Vindaloo, Apr'86 by Vindaloo Records. Dist: WEA, Cartel

We've suffered, now it's your

WE'VE SUFFERED, NOW IT'S YOUR TURN Various artists (Various Artists).
Album: released on Lounging, Dec'84 by Lounging Records. Dist: Revolver, Cartel

We Won't Be...

WE WON'T BE YOUR F**** POOR** Various artists (Various Artists).
Album: released on Mortarhate, Feb'86 by Dorane Ltd.

Weyman, Mike

I'LL MAKE YOUR BODY ROCK.
Tracks: / I'll make your body rock / Don't think twice.
Single (7"): released on In Touch, 30 May'87 by In Touch Records. Dist: Spartan

Single (12"): released on In Touch, 30 May'87 by In Touch Records. Dist: Spartan

WGBC

LOVE ME ANYWAY.
Tracks: / Love me anyway.
Single (7"): released on Expansion, Aug'86 Dist: PRT

Wham

12" TAPE, THE.
Tracks: / Wham rap! / Careless whisper / Freedom / Everything she wants / I'm your man.
Cassette: released on Epic, Sep'86 by CBS Records. Dist: CBS

BAD BOYS/INSTRUMENTAL VERSION.
Single (7"): released on Inner Vision, May'83 by CBS Records. Dist: CBS

Single (12"): released on Inner Vision, May'83 by CBS Records. Dist: CBS

Picture disc single: released on Inner Vision, May'83 by CBS Records. Dist: CBS

EDGE OF HEAVEN, THE.
Tracks: / Edge of heaven, The / Battlestations / Where did your heart go.
Single (7"): released on Epic, Jun'86 by CBS Records. Dist: CBS

Single (12"): released on Epic, Jun'86 by CBS Records. Dist: CBS

FANTASTIC.
Tracks: / Bad boys / Ray of sunshine, A / Love machine / Wham rap (Enjoy what you do) / Club Tropicana / Nothing looks the same in the light / Come on / Young guns (go for it).
Compact disc: released on Inner Vision, '83 by CBS Records. Dist: CBS

Album: released on Inner Vision, Jul'83 by CBS Records. Dist: CBS

Cassette: released on Inner Vision, Jul'83 by CBS Records. Dist: CBS

FINAL.
Notes: No of tracks: 3. Type of recording: EP. Total playing time: 15 minutes.
Video-cassette (VHS): released on CBS-Fox, '86 by CBS Records. Dist: CBS, Fox

FINAL, THE.
Tracks: / Wham rap / Young guns / Bad boys / Club tropicana / Wake me up before you go go / Careless whisper / Freedom / Last Christmas / Everything she wants / I'm your man / Blue / Different corner / Battlestations / Where did your heart go / Edge of heaven.
Album: released on Epic, '86 by CBS Records. Dist: CBS

Cassette: released on Epic, '86 by CBS Records. Dist: CBS

Compact disc: released on Epic, '86 by CBS Records. Dist: CBS

I'M YOUR MAN.
Single (7"): released on Epic, Nov'85 by CBS Records. Dist: CBS

Picture disc single: released on Epic, Nov'85 by CBS Records. Dist: CBS

IN CHINA Foreign skies.
Notes: A documentary of the superstar duo's vist to and concert in China in 1985, with much familiar music mingling with spectacular scenery. 1986 production.
Video-cassette (VHS): released on CBS, Sep'86 by CBS Records. Dist: CBS

LAST CHRISTMAS.
Tracks: / Last Christmas / Where did your heart go.
Single (7"): released on Epic, Nov'85 by CBS Records. Dist: CBS

Single (12"): released on Epic, Nov'85 by CBS Records. Dist: CBS

LAST CHRISTMAS.
Single (7"): released on Epic, Dec'85 by CBS Records. Dist: CBS

MAKE IT BIG.
Tracks: / Wake me up before you go go / Everything she wants / Heartbeat / Like a baby / Freedom / If you were there / Credit card baby / Careless whisper.
Album: released on Epic, Nov'84 by CBS Records. Dist: CBS

Cassette: released on Epic, Nov'84 by CBS Records. Dist: CBS

Compact disc: released on Epic, Nov'84 by CBS Records. Dist: CBS

VIDEO, THE.
Video-cassette (VHS): released on CBS-Fox, '85 by CBS Records. Dist: CBS, Fox

WHAM '85.
Video-cassette (VHS): released on CBS-Fox, '85 by CBS Records. Dist: CBS, Fox

WHAM BOXED SET.
Tracks: / Where did your heart go / Edge of heaven / Different corner, A / Wham rap (enjoy what you do) / Young guns (go for it) / Bad boys / Club Tropicana / Wake me up before you go go / Careless whisper / Freedom / Last Christmas (pudding mix) / Everything she wants-remix / I'm your man / Blue (armed with love) / Different corner, A / Battlestations.
Album: released on Epic, Dec'86 by CBS Records. Dist: CBS

WHAM - IN CHINA.
Notes: Number of tracks: 12. Type of recording: Live. Total playing time: 1 hr 2 mins.
Video-cassette (VHS): released on CBS-Fox, '86 by CBS Records. Dist: CBS, Fox

WHAM RAP (SOCIAL MIX)/WHAM RAP (UNSOCIAL MIX).
Single (12"): released on Inner Vision, Jun'82 by CBS Records. Dist: CBS

YOUNG GUNS GO FOR IT/GOING FOR IT.
Single (7"): released on Inner Vision, Sep'82 by CBS Records. Dist: CBS

What A Crazy World

WHAT A CRAZY WORLD Original film soundtrack.
Album: released on President, Jan'84 by President Records. Dist: Taylors, Spartan

What A Mess

WHAT A MESS Muir, Frank (Muir, Frank).
Cassette: released on Tellastory Tapes, Apr'81

What a nice way to turn 17

WHAT A NICE WAY TO TURN 17 LP Various artists (Various Artists).
Album: released on Seventeen, Nov'84 by Seventeen Records. Dist: Cartel, Nine Mile

Single (7"): released on Rather, Jul'84 Dist: Rough Trade

What If

IT BE WHAT IT BE.
Album: released on Line, Apr'87

What Katy Did

WHAT KATY DID Coolidge, S (Watford, Gwen).
Cassette: released on Listen For Pleasure, Nov'77 by MFP Records. Dist: EMI

What one dance can do

WHAT ONE DANCE CAN DO Various artists (Various Artists).
Album: released on Germaine, Mar'86 by Germaine Records. Dist: Jetstar

What one rhythm can do

WHAT ONE RHYTHM CAN DO Various artists (Various Artists).
Album: released on Germaine, Mar'86 by Germaine Records. Dist: Jetstar

What's happening...

WHAT'S HAPPENING...STATESIDE (Various Artists).
Tracks: / Ready, willing and able / Dead end street / Working on your case / Lookin' for a love / Girls from Texas / As long as I have you.
Notes: Inc. Bobby Womack, Lou Rawls.
Album: released on Stateside, Mar'87 Dist: EMI

Cassette: released on Stateside, Mar'87 Dist: EMI

What To Listen For

WHAT TO LISTEN FOR Exploring music and sound (Various Artists).
Cassette: released on D'Arblay Sound, Jul'78

What To Say

WHAT TO SAY Various artists (Various Artists).
Double cassette: released on BBC English, Aug'78

Wheeler, Ian

REED ALL ABOUT IT (Wheeler, Ian/ Sammy Rimington).
Album: released on Hefty Jazz, Apr'79 Dist: JSU, Swift, Wellard, Chris, Jazz Music, Cadillac Music

Wheeler, Kenny

DEER WAN.
Album: released on ECM, Jan'78 by ECM Records. Dist: IMS, Polygram, Virgin through EMI

DOUBLE DOUBLE YOU.
Album: released on ECM (Germany), Feb'84 by ECM Records. Dist: IMS, Polygram, Virgin through EMI

GNU HIGH.
Tracks: / Heyoke / Smatter / Gnu suite.
Compact disc: released on ECM (Germany), Aug'85 by ECM Records. Dist: IMS, Polygram, Virgin through EMI

Album: released on ECM, Mar'76 by ECM Records. Dist: IMS, Polygram, Virgin through EMI

SONG FOR SOMEONE.
Album: released on Incus, Jan'74 Dist: Jazz Music, Cadillac

Wheel To Reel

WHEEL TO REEL Various artists (Various Artists).
Cassette: released on Island, Nov'81 by Island Records. Dist: Polygram

Whelen, Cliff

CLIFF WHELEN.
Album: released on Sweet Folk All, Aug'77 by Sweet Folk All Records. Dist: Sweet Folk All, Roots, Celtic Music, Dragon, Impetus, Projection, Chris Wellard, Festival Records

COUNTRY BOY.
Album: released on Sweet Folk All, May'81 by Sweet Folk All Records. Dist: Sweet Folk All, Roots, Celtic Music, Dragon, Impetus, Projection, Chris Wellard, Festival Records

HEAVEN TOGETHER.
Album: released on Sweet Folk All, May'81 by Sweet Folk All Records. Dist: Sweet Folk All, Roots, Celtic Music, Dragon, Impetus, Projection, Chris Wellard, Festival Records

WLCOME TO MY WORLD.
Album: released on Sweet Folk All, May'81 by Sweet Folk All Records. Dist: Sweet Folk All, Roots, Celtic Music, Dragon, Impetus, Projection, Chris Wellard, Festival Records

Whelen, John

PRIDE OF WEXFORD.
Album: released on Outlet, Jan'75 by Outlet Records. Dist: Outlet Distribution

Whellans, Mike

DIRT WATER FOX.
Album: released on Dara, Oct'76 by CML Distributors. Dist: MK, Projection

MIKE WHELLANS & ALY BAIN (Whellans, Mike & Aly Bain).
Album: released on Leader, '81 Dist: Jazz Music, Projection

When...

WHEN THE WIND BLOWS By Raymond Briggs (When The Wind Blows).
Cassette: released on BBC, May'84 by BBC Records & Tapes. Dist: EMI, PRT, Pye

WHEN YOU WISH UPON A STAR 16 Disney Favourites (Disney Favourites).
Album: released on Premier, Dec'84 by Premier Records. Dist: CBS

Cassette: released on Premier, Dec'84 by Premier Records. Dist: CBS

When A Man Loves A Woman

WHEN A MAN LOVES A WOMAN Various artists (Various Artists).
Notes: Featuring Percy Sledge, The Marcels, Paul & Paula, Lobo, Tremeloes, Brook Benton, etc.
Compact disc: released on Delta, '86 by Delta Records. Dist: Target

WHEN A MAN LOVES A WOMAN various artists.
Compact disc: released on Delta, Oct'86 by Delta Records. Dist: Target

When Father's Away...

WHEN FATHER'S AWAY ON A BUSINESS TRIP various artists (Various Artists).
Album: released on Milan France, Dec'85

When Girls Do It

WHEN GIRLS DO IT Various artists (Various Artists).
Double Album: released on Red Lightnin', Sep'82 by Red Lightnin' Records. Dist: Roots, Swift, Jazz Music, JSU, Pinnacle, Cartel, Wynd-Up Distribution

When Greek meets Greek

WHEN GREEK MEETS GREEK Greene, Graham (Burden, Hugh).
Cassette: released on Talking Tape Company, '84 by Talking Tape Company Records.

When I Was A Cowboy

WHEN I WAS A COWBOY: SONGS OF COWBOY LIFE Various artists (Various Artists).
Album: released on Morning Star, Sep'84 Dist: Projection Distribution

When Jenny Lost Her Scarf

WHEN JENNY LOST HER SCARF (Grimes, Tammy).
Cassette: released on Caedmon(USA), Oct'79 by Caedmon (USA) Records. Dist: Gower, Taylors, Discovery

When Malindy Sings

WHEN MALINDY SINGS (JAZZ VOCALISTS 1938-1961) Various artists (Various Artists).
Tracks: / Can't get started / I left my baby / Piney Brown blues / Careless love / Ja-da / It's the tune that counts / Robbins nest / Blowtop blues / Key largo / Moonlight in Vermont / Thou swell / Can't we be friends / Misty / Love / When Malindy sings / End of the love affair, The.
Album: released on New World (USA), Aug'86 by New World Records (USA). Dist: Conifer

When Sheepshearing's Done

WHEN SHEEPSHEARING'S DONE: SONGS FROM SOUTHERN ENGLAND Various artists (Various Artists).
Album: released on Topic, '81

When The Wind Blows

WHEN THE WIND BLOWS Oriinal soundtrack (Various Artists).
Compact disc: released on Virgin, Jan'87 by Virgin Records. Dist: EMI, Virgin Distribution

Where Eagles Dare

WHERE EAGLES DARE (read by Martin Jarvis).
Cassette: released on Listen For Pleasure, Nov'81 by MFP Records. Dist: EMI

Where Have We Met Before

WHERE HAVE WE MET BEFORE Various artists (Various Artists).
Tracks: / We'll be the same / You forgot your gloves / And so to bed / How do you it+Riddle me this / Where have we met before / Let's call it a day / Are you making any money / Coffee in the morning, kisses in the night / What can you

say in a love song / That lucky fellow / Boys and girls like you and me / Only another boy and girl / Nobody else but me / Can you just see yourself.
Notes: Also featuring: Frank Luther & Leo Reisman's Orchestra/Lew Sherwood & Eddie Duchin's Orchestra/Joey Nash & Richard Himber's Orchestra/Jane Harvey & Benny Goodman's Quintet/Frank Munn & Arden & Ohman/Ethel Shutta & Paul Smith & George Olsen's Orchestra/Lois Lee & Mark Dawson & Orchestra directed by Milt Rosenstock/Jack Leonard & Tommy Dorsey's Orchestra/Frank Luther & Arden's & Ohman Orchestra/Smith Leonard & Tommy Dorsey's Orchestra/Frank Luther & Arden's & Ohman Orchestra/Smith Ballew & Victor Young's Orchestra/Clare Hanton & Fred Waring & His Pennsylvanians/Jan Clayton/Judy Garland & George Stoll's Orchestra & Paul Whiteman's Orchestra. Mono.
Album: released on New World (USA), Dec'86 by New World Records (USA). Dist: Conifer

Where's Charlie?

WHERE'S CHARLEY? Original London Cast (Loesser, Frank).
Album: released on Monmouth, Mar'79

Where's Lisse

RED LIGHT AND TUTORIAL (EP).
Single (12"): released on Glass, Jun'82 by Glass Records. Dist: Nine Mile, Rough Trade, Red Rhino, Play It Again Sam

TALK TAKES TOO LONG.
Single (7"): released on Glass, Jul'81 by Glass Records. Dist: Nine Mile, Rough Trade, Red Rhino, Play It Again Sam

Where The Blarney Roses

WHERE THE BLARNEY ROSES GROW Various artists (Various Artists).
Album: released on Harp(Ireland), Oct'81 by Pickwick Records. Dist: Taylors

Where The Girls Are

WHERE THE GIRLS ARE Various artists (Various Artists).
Album: released on Ace, Mar'84 by Ace Records. Dist: Pinnacle, Swift, Hotshot, Cadillac

Where The Wild Things Are

WHERE THE WILD THINGS ARE & OTHER STORIES Sendak, Maurice (Grimes, Tammy).
Album: released on Caedmon(USA), '79 by Caedmon (USA) Records. Dist: Gower, Taylors, Discovery

Cassette: released on Caedmon(USA), '79 by Caedmon (USA) Records. Dist: Gower, Taylors, Discovery

Where Would You...

WHERE WOULD YOU RATHER BE TONIGHT Various artists (Various Artists).
Notes: Artists Mike Oldfield: Fairport Convention, Jake Thackery, Steeleye Span, Mike Silver. Jon Benns, Martin Simpson, Paul Metsers, Arizona Snake Review, Johnny Coppin, The Albion Band, Allen Taylor, Les Barker, Phil Beer and Mike Oldfield, Shep Woolley Grant Baynham, Wurzel from Motorhead. None of the tracks on this LP appear on any other album currently available. All Proceeds will go to Broadreach house rehabilitation centre for drug addicts and Alcoholics.
Album: released on Sunrise, Feb'87

While I Work....

WHILE I WORK I WHISTLE (Songs and humour of the Cotswolds) (Various Artists).
Album: released on Saydisc, Oct'79 by Saydisc Records. Dist: Essex, Harmonia Mundi, Roots, H.R. Taylor, Jazz Music, Swift, Projection, Gamut

Whip Crackaway

HORSES TAIL,THE.
Tracks: / Horses tail,The.
Single (7"): released on In Tape, Aug'86 by In Tape Records. Dist: Red Rhino, Cartel

Whippersnapper

PROMISES (Whippersnapper Featuring Dave Swarbrick).
Album: released on Oblivion, Mar'85 Dist: Projection

WHIPPERSNAPPER.
Album: released on WPS, May'87 Dist: Roots, Projection

Whirlpool Guest House

CHANGING FACE (THE).
Single (7"): released on Summerhouse, Feb'87 Dist: Red Rhino Distribution, Cartel

Whirlwind

BLOWING UP A STORM.
Album: released on Chiswick, Sep'78 by Chiswick Records. Dist: Pinnacle

FULL TIME THING.
Single (7"): released on Pye International, Jan'77 Deleted '79.

MIDNIGHT BLUE.
Album: released on Chiswick, May'82 by Chiswick Records. Dist: Pinnacle

Cassette: released on Chiswick, May'82 by Chiswick Records. Dist: Pinnacle

Whiskers

DOOLALLY SONG, THE.
Tracks: / Doolally song, The / What life means to me.
Single (7"): released on Foul Play, Jul'87 by Foul Play Records. Dist: Spartan

Whiskey and Soda

DIRTY DEN RAP.
Tracks: / Dirty Den rap.
Single (7"): released on Spartan, Mar'86 by Spartan Records. Dist: Spartan

Single (12"): released on Spartan, Mar'86 by Spartan Records. Dist: Spartan

Whiskey, Nancy

FREIGHT TRAIN (Whiskey, Nancy & Chas McDevitt).

Whispering Wind Band

WHISPERING WIND BAND.
Album: released on Music From York, Jun'81 Dist: H.R. Taylor Distribution

Cassette: released on Music From York, Jun'81 Dist: H.R. Taylor Distribution

Whispers

AND THE BEAT GOES ON.
Tracks: / And the beat goes on / Some kinda lover / It's a love thing / Contagious.
Single (7"): released on MCA, Mar'87 by MCA Records. Dist: Polygram, MCA

Single (12"): released on MCA, Mar'87 by MCA Records. Dist: Polygram, MCA

Single (7"): released on Soul Train-Solar, Jul'81

Single (12"): released on Soul Train-Solar, Jul'81

BEST OF,THE.
Album: released on Solar, '82

Cassette: released on Solar, '82

CONTAGIOUS.
Single (7"): released on MCA, Jan'85 by MCA Records. Dist: CBS

Single (12"): released on MCA, Jan'85 by MCA Records. Dist: CBS

EMERGENCY.
Single (7"): released on Solar, Apr'82

Single (12"): released on Solar, Apr'82

I CAN MAKE IT BETTER.
Single (7"): released on Solar, May'81

Single (12"): released on Solar, May'81

IN THE RAW.
Single (7"): released on Solar, Jan'82

Single (12"): released on Solar, Jan'82

IT'S A LOVE THING.
Single (7"): released on Solar, Feb'81

Single (12"): released on Solar, Feb'81

JUST GETS BETTER WITH TIME.
Tracks: / I want you / Special FIX / Rock steady / No pain, no gain / In the mood / Just gets better with time / Love's calling / Give it to me.
Album: released on MCA, May'87 by MCA Records. Dist: Polygram, MCA

Cassette: released on MCA, May'87 by MCA Records. Dist: Polygram, MCA

Album: released on I.R.S.(Independent Record Syndicate), May'87 by I.R.S.. Dist: MCA

Cassette: released on I.R.S.(Independent Record Syndicate), May'87 by I.R.S.. Dist: MCA

ROCK STEADY.
Tracks: / Rock steady / Are you going my way.
Single (7"): released on MCA, May'87 by MCA Records. Dist: Polygram, MCA

Single (12"): released on Solar, May'87 by MCA Records. Dist: Polygram Distribution

SO GOOD.
Album: released on MCA, Mar'87 by MCA Records. Dist: Polygram, MCA

Cassette: released on MCA, Mar'87 by MCA Records. Dist: Polygram, MCA

Album: released on MCA, Jan'85 by MCA Records. Dist: CBS

Cassette: released on MCA, Jan'85 by MCA Records. Dist: CBS

SOME KINDS LOVER.
Single (7"): released on MCA, Apr'85 by MCA Records. Dist: CBS

Single (12"): released on MCA, Apr'85 by MCA Records. Dist: CBS

SPECIAL F.
Single (7"): released on MCA, Aug'87 by MCA Records. Dist: Polygram, MCA

Single (12"): released on MCA, Aug'87 by MCA Records. Dist: Polygram, MCA

THIS KIND OF LOVIN.
Album: released on Solar, Oct'81

Cassette: released on Solar, Oct'81

Single (7"): released on Solar, Sep'81

Single (12"): released on Solar, Sep'81

Whistle

(NOTHING SERIOUS)JUST BUGGIN'.
Tracks: / (Nothing serious)Just Buggin' / Buggin'much hard / (Nothing serious)Just buggin'-Remix.
Single (7"): released on Champion, Mar'86 by Champion Records. Dist: RCA

Picture disc single: released on Champion, Mar'86 by Champion Records. Dist: RCA

Single (12"): released on Champion, Mar'86 by Champion Records. Dist: RCA

Single (12"): released on Champion, Mar'86 by Champion Records. Dist: RCA

PLEASE LOVE ME.
Tracks: / Please love me / Just for fun / (Nothing serious)Just Buggin'-Dutch remix.
Single (7"): released on Champion, Jun'86 by Champion Records. Dist: RCA

Single (12"): released on Champion, Jun'86 by Champion Records. Dist: RCA

WHISTLE.
Notes: First 5000 with free 12" singles (nothing serious just buggin')
Album: released on Champion, Jul'86 by Champion Records. Dist: RCA

Cassette: released on Champion, Jul'86 by Champion Records. Dist: RCA

Whistlebinkies

WHISTLEBINKIES VOL.1.
Album: released on Claddagh, '83 by Claddagh Records. Dist: I & B, Record Services Distribution (Ireland), Roots, Topic, Impetus, Projection, CM

Cassette: released on Claddagh, '83 by Claddagh Records. Dist: I & B, Record Services Distribution (Ireland), Roots, Topic, Impetus, Projection, CM

WHISTLEBINKIES VOL.2.
Album: released on Claddagh, '83 by Claddagh Records. Dist: I & B, Record Services Distribution (Ireland), Roots, Topic, Impetus, Projection, CM

Cassette: released on Claddagh, '83 by Claddagh Records. Dist: I & B, Record Services Distribution (Ireland), Roots, Topic, Impetus, Projection, CM

WHISTLEBINKIES VOL.3.
Album: released on Claddagh, '83 by Claddagh Records. Dist: I & B, Record Services Distribution (Ireland), Roots, Topic, Impetus, Projection, CM

Cassette: released on Claddagh, '83 by Claddagh Records. Dist: I & B, Record Services Distribution (Ireland), Roots, Topic, Impetus, Projection, CM

Whistle power, The

WHISTLE POWER, THE Original soundtrack (Original Soundtrack).
Album: released on That's Entertainment, Aug'87 by That's Entertainment Records. Dist: Pinnacle, PRT

Whistling Jack Smith

I WAS KAISER BILL'S BATMAN.
Single (7"): released on Decca-Originals, May'82 by Decca Records. Dist: Polygram, IMS

Whitaker, Mick

LOOKING FOR LOVE IN A STRANGER.
Single (7"): released on State, Jul'81 by State Records.

Whitbread, Sharon

WHY DON'T YOU DO IT.
Single (7"): released on Pye, Jan'77

Whitburn Burgh Band

CHRISTMAS WITH BRASS.
Album: by EMI Records. Dist: EMI

WITHBURN BRASS.
Album: released on Neptune, Jun'79 by Lismor. Dist: Spartan

Whitchurch Male Choir

ABIDE WITH ME (Whitchurch Male Voice Choir).
Album: released on Big Ben, Apr'81 by Big Ben Records. Dist: Spartan, Taylor, H.R.

Whitcomb, Ian

MY WIFE IS DANCING MAD (Whitcomb, Ian & Dick Zimmerman).

OCEANS OF LOVE.
Album: released on I.T.W., Jun'87 by Ian Whitcomb Records. Dist: Pinnacle

ON THE STREET OF DREAMS.
Album: released on I.T.W., Jun'87 by Ian Whitcomb Records. Dist: Pinnacle

PIANOMELT.
Album: released on I.T.W., Jun'87 by Ian Whitcomb Records. Dist: Pinnacle

RAG ODYSSEY.
Album: released on Meteor, Jun'84 by Magnum Force Music. Dist: CBS Distribution

THIS SPORTING LIFE (Whitcomb, Ian & Bluesville).
Single (7"): released on Big Beat, Nov'82 by Ace Records. Dist: Projection, Pinnacle

White, Andy

RAVE ON ANDY WHITE.
Album: released on Decca, Oct'86 by Decca Records. Dist: Polygram

Cassette: released on Decca, Oct'86 by Decca Records. Dist: Polygram

REALITY NOW.
Tracks: / Reality row / Rembrandt hat / Raindance,The.
Single (7"): released on Decca, Sep'86 by Decca Records. Dist: Polygram

Single (12"): released on Decca, Sep'86 by Decca Records. Dist: Polygram

RELIGIUOS PERSUASION.
Single (12"): released on Stiff, Nov'85 by Stiff Records. Dist: EMI, Record Services Distribution (Ireland)

RELIGOUS PERSUASION.
Tracks: / Religious persuasion / Rembradnt persuasion.
Single (7"): released on Stiff, Jan'86 by Stiff Records. Dist: EMI, Record Services Distribution (Ireland)

White, Artie

NOTHING TAKES THE PLACE OF YOU.
Album: released on Ichiban, Aug'87 by Ichiban Records. Dist: PRT

Cassette: released on Ichiban, Aug'87 by Ichiban Records. Dist: PRT

White,Barry

BARRY WHITE-HEART AND SOUL.
Tracks: / You're the first,the last,my everything / I'm gonna love you just that little bit more babe / Standing in the shadows of love / What am I gonna do about you? / Never never gonna give ya up / I love to sing the songs I sing / Don't make me wait too long / Don't make me wait too long / You see the trouble with me / Love serenade / It's ecstacy when you lay down next to me / I can't get enough of you're love babe / I'm qualified to satisfy you / Sha la la means I love you / Honey please can't you see / I've found someone / Let me live my life loving you babe / Let the music play / Baby we better try to get it together / Playing your game baby / I've got so much to give / September(when I first met you) / Love's theme.
Album: released on K-Tel, Nov'85 by K-Tel Records. Dist: Record Merchandisers Distribution, Taylors, Terry Blood Distribution, Wynd-Up Distribution, Relay Distribution, Pickwick Distribution, Solomon & Peres Distribution, Polygram

Cassette: released on K-Tel, Nov'85 by K-Tel Records. Dist: Record Merchandisers Distribution, Taylors, Terry Blood Distribution, Wynd-Up Distribution, Relay Distribution, Pickwick Distribution, Solomon & Peres Distribution, Polygram

BARRY WHITE'S SHEET MUSIC.
Album: released on Unlimited Gold (USA), Jul'80 Dist: CBS (USA) Distribution, CBS

Cassette: released on Unlimited Gold (USA), Jul'80 Dist: CBS (USA) Distribution, CBS

BEST OF BARRY WHITE,THE.
Album: released on Polydor (Holland), Jul'83

Cassette: released on Polydor (Holland), Jul'83

DEDICATED.
Album: released on Unlimited Gold (USA), Sep'83 Dist: CBS (USA) Distribution, CBS

Cassette: released on Unlimited Gold (USA), Sep'83 Dist: CBS (USA) Distribution, CBS

GREATEST HITS: BARRY WHITE VOL.1.
Album: released on 20th Century, May'83 Dist: RCA, IMS-Polygram

Cassette: released on 20th Century, May'83 Dist: RCA, IMS-Polygram

LET THE MUSIC PLAY.
Single (7"): released on 20th Century, Oct'81 Dist: RCA, IMS-Polygram

MESSAGE IS LOVE,THE.
Album: released on Unlimited Gold (USA), Apr'79 Dist: CBS (USA) Distribution, CBS

Cassette: released on Unlimited Gold (USA), Apr'79 Dist: CBS (USA) Distribution, CBS

YOU'RE THE FIRST, THE LAST, MY EVERYTHING.
Single (7"): released on 20th Century, Jul'81 Dist: RCA, IMS-Polygram

White, Barry & Glodean

BARRY AND GLODEAN.
Album: released on Unlimited Gold (USA), May'81 Dist: CBS (USA) Distribution, CBS

Cassette: released on Unlimited Gold (USA), May'81 Dist: CBS (USA) Distribution, CBS

White, Booker

BIG DADDY.
Album: released on Blue Moon, Apr'87 Dist: Magnum Music Group Ltd, PRT, Spartan

White boy blues

COLLECTION VOL.1.
Tracks: / Snake drive / West coast idea / Chocker / I'm your witch doctor / Tribute to elmore / Freight loader / Miles road / Telephone blues / Draggin' my tail / Down in the boots / Steelin' / Chuckles / L.A. Breakdown / Piano shuffle / Someday baby / Porcupine juice / Rubber monkey / Albert / who's knocking / Look down at my woman.
Compact disc: released on Castle Communications, May'86 by Castle Communications. Dist: Cartel, Pinnacle, Counterpoint

Album: released on Castle Communications, Nov'85 by Castle Communications. Dist: Cartel, Pinnacle, Counterpoint

Cassette: released on Castle Communications, Nov'85 by Castle Communications. Dist: Cartel, Pinnacle, Counterpoint

VOLUME 2 PARTS 1 & 2.
Tracks: / Tried / Cold blooded woman / Can't quit you baby / True blue / I feel so good / Ain't gonna cry no more / You don't love me / When you got a good friend / Someone to love me / Dealing with the devil / Roll 'em Pete / Next milestone,The / Water on my fire / Crosstown link / Flapjacks / Not fade away / So much to say / On top of the world / Hideaway / Suprenatural,The / Standing at the crossroads / I want to know.
Double Album: released on Castle Collectors, Sep'86 by Castle Communications Records. Dist: Pinnacle

Double cassette: released on Castle Collectors, Sep'86 by Castle Communications Records. Dist: Pinnacle

Compact disc: released on Collector Series, '86 by Castle Communications Records. Dist: PRT, Pinnacle, RCA, Ariola

White Boys

HARDCORE, IS IT NOT?.
Single (12"): released on Polygram (USA), Aug'87 Dist: Pinnacle

White, Bukka

ABERDEEN MISSISSIPPI BLUES 1937-40.
Tracks: / Pine bluff arkansas / Shake 'em on down / Black train blues / Strange places blues / Where I change my clothes / Sleepy man blues / Parchman farm blues / Good gin blues / High fever blues / District attorney blues / Fixin' to die / Aberdeen Mississippi Blues / Bukka's jitterbug swing / Special streamline.
Album: released on Travellin' Man, Sep'85 Dist: Jazz Music

MISSISSIPPI BLUES.
Album: released on Sonet, '74 by Sonet Records. Dist: PRT

SKY SONGS VOL.1.
Album: released on Arhoolie, May'81 by Arhoolie Records. Dist: Projection, Topic, Jazz Music, Swift, Roots

SKY SONGS VOL.2.
Album: released on Arhoolie, May'81 by Arhoolie Records. Dist: Projection, Topic, Jazz Music, Swift, Roots

White, Chalky

ONE SHOT (White, Chalky & The Shamrastas).
Single (7"): released on Solar Sound, Sep'83 Dist: Chris Wellard

White, Christine

CAUGHT BY LOVE.
Single (7"): released on Black Jack, Jan'81 Dist: Jetstar, Spartan

Single (12"): released on Black Jack, Jan'81 Dist: Jetstar, Spartan

PURE LOVE.
Album: released on Black Jack, Mar'85 Dist: Jetstar, Spartan

White, Christine Joy

FOR YOUR PRECIOUS LOVE.
Single (12"): released on ABL, Aug'84 by ABL Records. Dist: Jetstar

GET READY.
Single (12"): released on Real Wax, Nov'82

White, Clarence

MULESKINNER.
Album: released on Ridgerunner, May'79

White Door

FLAME IN MY HEART.
Single (7"): released on Clay, Aug'84 by Clay Records. Dist: Pinnacle

Single (12"): released on Clay, Aug'84 by Clay Records. Dist: Pinnacle

JERUSALEM.
Single (7"): released on Clay, Jan'86 by Clay Records. Dist: Pinnacle

LOVE BREAKDOWN.
Single (7"): released on Clay, Jun'83 by Clay Records. Dist: Pinnacle

Single (12"): released on Clay, Jun'83 by Clay Records. Dist: Pinnacle

WAY OF THE WORLD.
Single (7"): released on Clay, Apr'82 by Clay Records. Dist: Pinnacle

WINDOWS.
Album: released on Clay, Oct'83 by Clay Records. Dist: Pinnacle

Single (7"): released on Clay, Sep'83 by Clay Records. Dist: Pinnacle

White, Edward

GREAT GATES WEST COAST R 'N' B, THE (White, Edward 'Great Gates').
Album: released on Krazy Kat (USA), Feb'86

White Europeans

SUN ARISE.
Single (7"): released on Aura, Feb'81 by Hollywood Nites Distribution. Dist: Pinnacle

White Fire

PARADES OF GLORY.
Single (7"): released on Vibes, Aug'79 Dist: Vibes

TELL MICHELLE.
Single (7"): released on Record Trading Co., Jul'80

White flag/ Necros

GEIGER COUNTER.
Album: released on Homestead, Feb'87 Dist: Rough Trade, Cartel, Shigaku

White, Frank

WHAT YOU GONNA DO.
Single (7"): released on Wat, May'83 by Wat Records. Dist: Owlerton Speedways Distribution

White,Freddie

LIVE TOUR 1978.
Album: released on Mulligan, Oct'79 by Topic Records. Dist: Roots Distribution, Jazz Music Distribution, JSU Distribution, I & B Distribution, Projection Distribution, Wynd-Up Distribution, Celtic Distributions

LONG DISTANCE RUNNER.
Tracks: / Werewolf / Wedding in Cherokee county / Frozen heart / Long distnace runner / It's you / Voices / Love like blood / Down without a fight / Christmas in Capetown / Goodbye this time.
Album: released on Tara (Ireland), Feb'86 by Tara Records. Dist: I & B Records Distribution, Record Services Distribution (Ireland), Roots Distribution

Cassette: released on Tara (Ireland), Feb'86 by Tara Records. Dist: I & B Records Distribution, Record Services Distribution (Ireland), Roots Distribution

White, Georgia

SINGS AND PLAYS THE BLUES.
Album: released on Rosetta (USA), Mar'84

Whitehall Flute Band

MARCHING WITH....
Cassette: released on Zip, May'80 by Zip Records. Dist: Zip Distribution, Graduate

White Hart

IN SEARCH OF REWARD.
Album: released on Tradition, Sep'79 Dist: JSU, Cassion Distribution, Celtic Music, Jazz Music, Projection, Roots Records

Whitehead, Annie

ALIEN STYLE.
Single (7"): released on Paladin, Mar'85 by Paladin Records. Dist: Rough Trade, Pinnacle
Cat. no: **PALS 100**
Single (12"): released on Paladin, Mar'85 by Paladin Records. Dist: Rough Trade, Pinnacle

MIX UP.
Album: released on Paladin, Jun'85 by Paladin Records. Dist: Rough Trade, Pinnacle

Cassette: released on Paladin, Jun'85 by Paladin Records. Dist: Rough Trade, Pinnacle

Whitehead's, Tim

ENGLISH PEOPLE (Whitehead's, Tim Borderline).
Album: released on Spotlite, Mar'83 by Spotlite Records. Dist: Cadillac, Jazz Music, Spotlite

White Heart

DON'T WAIT FOR THE MOVIE.
Notes: High-energy: aggressive; bold; honest; fun; serious; sensitive. Those are the varied descriptions the six members of White Heart use when asked to describe their latest album. It is their first album on the Sparrow label and marks the debut with White Heart of new lead singer Rick Florian and drummer Chris McHugh, who states, 'Don't wait for the movie', really captures a lot of the energy we portray live and outs it on record. We've taken alot of chances on this album. It's more of a rock oriented album than the previous ones. The songs which make up this new release are all co-written by Billy Smiley, Mark Gersmehl and Gordon Kennedy.
Album: released on Birdwing, Nov'86 by Word Records. Dist: Word Distribution

Cassette: released on Birdwing, Nov'86 by Word Records. Dist: Word Distribution

White Heat

CITY BEAT.
Single (7"): released on Valium, Aug'81 by Mawson & Wareham Records. Dist: Spartan

FINISHED WITH THE FASHIONS.
Single (7"): released on Valium, Oct'80 by Mawson & Wareham Records. Dist: Spartan

IN THE ZERO HOUR.
Album: released on Valium, Jun'82 by Mawson & Wareham Records. Dist: Spartan

NERVOUS BREAKDOWN.
Single (7"): released on Valium, Mar'80 by Mawson & Wareham Records. Dist: Spartan

White Heather Show

WHITE HEATHER SHOW Various Artists (Various Artists).
Cassette: released on Ditto, Jan'85 by Pickwick Records. Dist: H.R. Taylor

White Hot Jazz

WHITE HOT JAZZ VOL.1 Various Artists (Various Artists).
Album: released on Broadway (USA), Mar'84

White House Connection

QUEEN OF THE DISCO.
Tracks: / Queen of the disco (remix).
Single (12"): released on Total Eclipse, Sep'86 Dist: Spartan

Single (12"): released on Total Eclipse, Oct'86 Dist: Spartan

White, James

JAMES WHITE & THE BLACKS (White, James & The Blacks).
Album: released on Island, May'80 by Island Records. Dist: Polygram

SAX MANIAC (White, James & The Blacks).
Album: released on Animal, Sep'82 by Chrysalis Records. Dist: Polygram

White, John

NIGHT PEOPLE.
Tracks: / I need your love / Can't get you out of my system / Night people / Forbidden love / Victim / Don't let it be too late / Fooled around / Mood for love / I wanna get close to you / Let's talk it over / Keep it up / Heading in the right direction / Rockin' & lovin' / New love / Ultimate love / I'm gonna love you.
Album: released on Geffen, Aug'87 by Geffen Records. Dist: WEA, CBS

Cassette: released on Geffen, Aug'87 by Geffen Records. Dist: WEA, CBS

Album: released on Geffen, Aug'87 by Geffen Records. Dist: WEA, CBS

Cassette: released on Geffen, Aug'87 by Geffen Records. Dist: WEA, CBS

White, Josh

BLUES & SPIRITUALS (White, Josh & The Ronnie Sisters).
Album: released on Joker, Apr'81 Dist: Counterpoint, Mainline, Record Services Distribution (Ireland)

WORLD OF JOSH WHITE, THE.
Album: released on Decca, '69 by Decca Records. Dist: Polygram

White, Josh Jnr.

JOSH WHITE JUNIOR.
Album: released on Vogue, May'78 Dist: Discovery, Jazz Music, PRT, Swift

White, Joy

TAKES A MIRACLE.
Single (12"): released on Exclusive, Jul'82 Dist: Jetstar

White, K.C.

ANYWHERE BUT NOWHERE.
Single (12"): released on Solid Groove, Sep'82 Dist: Jetstar, Pinnacle

White, Kevin

COMMUTERS DANCE (White, Kevin & The Yellow Parade).
Single (7"): released on Primitive, Feb'87 Dist: O.I.D

Whitelaw Brothers

WHITELAW BROTHERS - VOL.1.
Album: released on ARC (Accordion Records) '84 Dist: Accordion Record Club

White, Lenny

KIDS STUFF.
Single (7"): released on Elektra Asylum Feb'81 by Elektra/Asylum/Nonesuch Records Dist: WEA

Single (12"): released on Elektra Asylum Feb'81 by Elektra/Asylum/Nonesuch Records Dist: WEA

STREAMLINE.
Album: released on Elektra, '78 by WEA Records. Dist: WEA

TWENNYNINE WITH LENNY WHITE.
Album: released on Elektra Asylum, Oct'80 by Elektra/Asylum/Nonesuch Records. Dist: WE

White Lie

EMOTIONAL BLACKMAIL.
Single (7"): released on Epic, Apr'83 by CB Records. Dist: CBS

Single (12"): released on Epic, Apr'83 by CB Records. Dist: CBS

White lies

WALK ON THE WILD SIDE.
Tracks: / Walk on the wild side / Pepperco blue.
Single (12"): released on WEA, Feb'87 WEA Records. Dist: WEA

White Lightnin

THIS POISON FOUNTAIN.
Single (7"): released on Wild Party, Apr'85 Wild Party Records. Dist: Wild Party

White Line Fever

WHITE LINE FEVER Various Artists (Various Artists).
Album: released on Liberty-United, Apr'82 EMI Records. Dist: EMI

Cassette: released on Liberty-United, Apr by EMI Records. Dist: EMI

White Lion

FIGHT TO SURVIVE.
Album: released on Grand Slam (USA), Aug'87 Dist: Pinnacle

PRIDE.
Tracks: / Hungry / Lonely nights / Don't give up / Sweet little loving / Lady of the valley / Wait / All you need is rock 'n' roll / Tell me / All join our hands / When the children cry.
Album: released on Atlantic, Jul'87 by WEA Records. Dist: WEA

Cassette: released on Atlantic, Jul'87 by WEA Records. Dist: WEA

White, Lynn

SUCCESS.
Album: released on Timeless, Jun'87

Whiteman, Paul

1938 (Whiteman, Paul & His Orchestra).
Album: released on Solid Sender, Apr'81 Dist: JSU, Jazz Music

IN CONCERT AT QUEEN ELIZABETH HALL (Whiteman, Paul & His Orchestra).
Album: released on Wave, Apr'79 by Wave Records. Dist: JSU, Swift, Jazz Music, Cadillac, Chris Wellard

JAZZ A LA KING 1920-1936.
Double Album: released on RCA (France), '83 by RCA Records. Dist: Discovery

MUSIC OF THE ROARING 20'S (Whiteman, Paul & His Orchestra).
Album: released on Wave, Dec'77 by Wave Records. Dist: JSU, Swift, Jazz Music, Cadillac, Chris Wellard

NEW PAUL WHITEMAN ORCHESTRA, THE (Whiteman, Paul & His Orchestra).
Album: released on Monmouth, Mar'79

SHAKING THE BLUES AWAY 1920-1927 (Whiteman, Paul & His Orchestra).
Album: released on Halcyon, Mar'83 by Halcyon Records. Dist: Jazz Music

WANG WANG BLUES.
Cassette: released on Astan, Jun'86 by Astan Records. Dist: Counterpoint

White Mansions

WHITE MANSIONS (A tale from the America Civil War 1861-65) (Various Artists).
Album: released on A&M, May'78 by A&M Records. Dist: Polygram

Cassette: released on A&M, May'78 by A&M Records. Dist: Polygram

White, Maurice

MAURICE WHITE.
Tracks: / Switch on your radio / Jamboree / Stand by me / Sea of glass / I need you / Believe in magic / Lady is love / Invitation / Sleeping flame / Alpha dance / Children of Afrika.
Compact disc: released on CBS, '86 by CBS Records. Dist: CBS

Album: released on CBS, Oct'85 by CBS Records. Dist: CBS

Cassette: released on CBS, Oct'85 by CBS Records. Dist: CBS

STAND BY ME.
Single (12"): released on CBS, Aug'85 by CBS Records. Dist: CBS

Single (7"): released on CBS, Aug'85 by CBS Records. Dist: CBS

White, Michael

MICHAEL WHITE.
Tracks: / Fantasy / I know you need someone / Bring on the night / Matriach / One good turn / Psychometry / Deja vu / Jumpin' the fence / Radio.
Album: released on Atlantic, Aug'87 by WEA Records. Dist: WEA

Cassette: released on Atlantic, Aug'87 by WEA Records. Dist: WEA

MICHAEL WHITE'S NEW ORLEANS MUSIC.
Album: released on Nola, Jul'82 Dist: JSU, Jazz Music, Cadillac, Chris Wellard

SHAKE IT... (White, Michael & his New Orleans Music).
Album: released on 504, Sep'86 by 504 Records. Dist: Chris Wellard, Jazz Music

Cassette: released on 504, Sep'86 by 504 Records. Dist: Chris Wellard, Jazz Music

SHAKE IT BREAK IT.
Album: released on Nola, Aug'81 Dist: JSU, Jazz Music, Cadillac, Chris Wellard

FACTOR, THE.
Album: released on Elektra, Aug'78 by WEA Records. Dist: WEA

White Nights

WHITE NIGHTS Various Artists (Various Artists).
Album: released on Atlantic, Oct'85 by WEA Records. Dist: WEA

Cassette: released on Atlantic, Oct'85 by WEA Records. Dist: WEA

White Noise

AN ELECTRIC STORM.
Album: released on Island, '74 by Island Records. Dist: Polygram

TWO.
Album: released on Virgin, Jun'75 by Virgin Records. Dist: EMI, Virgin Distribution

White, Norma

RIGHT PLACE WRONG TIME.
Single (12"): released on Londis, Oct'85

YOU KEEP ME HANGIN' ON.
Single (12"): released on Sunburn, Jul'83 by Orbitone Records. Dist: Jetstar Distribution

White Plains

MY BABY LOVES LOVIN'.
Single (7"): released on Old Gold, Oct'83 by Old Gold Records. Dist: Lightning, Jazz Music, Spartan, Counterpoint

WHEN YOU ARE A KING.
Single (7"): released on Decca-Originals, Apr'82 by Decca Records. Dist: Polygram, IMS

Single (7"): released on Old Gold, Sep'85 by Old Gold Records. Dist: Lightning, Jazz Music, Spartan, Counterpoint

White, Robert

AGE OF SELF, THE (White, Robert/ Grimethorpe Brass Band).
Single (7"): released on 7.84, Sep'85

BEAUTIFUL DREAMER Robert White sings Stephen Foster.
Album: released on RCA, '84 by RCA Records. Dist: RCA, Roots, Swift, Wellard, Chris, I & B, Solomon & Peres Distribution

Cassette: released on RCA, '84 by RCA Records. Dist: RCA, Roots, Swift, Wellard, Chris, I & B, Solomon & Peres Distribution

BY THE LIGHT OF THE SILVERY MOON.
Album: released on RCA Digital, '84

Cassette: released on RCA Digital, '84

DANNY BOY.
Album: released on RCA, Apr'80 by RCA Records. Dist: RCA, Roots, Swift, Wellard, Chris, I & B, Solomon & Peres Distribution

Cassette: released on RCA, Apr'80 by RCA Records. Dist: RCA, Roots, Swift, Wellard, Chris, I & B, Solomon & Peres Distribution

GALLANT TROUBADOUR, THE.
Album: released on H.M.V., Nov'85 by EMI Records. Dist: EMI

Cassette: released on H.M.V., Nov'85 by EMI Records. Dist: EMI

HOLD ME TIGHT.
Single (7"): released on Calibre, Jan'86 by Calibre Records. Dist: PRT

Single (12"): released on Calibre, Jan'86 by Calibre Records. Dist: PRT

MEMORIES OF JOHN MCCORMACK.
Album: released on RCA Gold Seal, May'85

Cassette: released on RCA Gold Seal, May'85

SINGS THE AMERICAN SONG BOOK.
Album: released on RCA, '84 by RCA Records. Dist: RCA, Roots, Swift, Wellard, Chris, I & B, Solomon & Peres Distribution

Cassette: released on RCA, '84 by RCA Records. Dist: RCA, Roots, Swift, Wellard, Chris, I & B, Solomon & Peres Distribution

WHEN YOU & I WERE YOUNG, MAGGIE.
Album: released on RCA, '84 by RCA Records. Dist: RCA, Roots, Swift, Wellard, Chris, I & B, Solomon & Peres Distribution

Cassette: released on RCA, '84 by RCA Records. Dist: RCA, Roots, Swift, Wellard, Chris, I & B, Solomon & Peres Distribution

White Rock

WHITE ROCK Original Soundtrack (Various Artists).
Album: released on A&M, Jan'77 by A&M Records. Dist: Polygram

Cassette: released on A&M, Jan'77 by A&M Records. Dist: Polygram

White, Roy

LEST WE FORGET.
Single (7"): released on CBS, Sep'85 by CBS Records. Dist: CBS

Single (12"): released on CBS, Sep'85 by CBS Records. Dist: CBS

SHANTY.
Album: released on CBS, Dec'85 by CBS Records. Dist: CBS

Album: released on CBS, Dec'85 by CBS Records. Dist: CBS

STRANGE TO BE WITH YOU.
Tracks: / You are America.
Single (7"): released on CBS, Jan'86 by CBS Records. Dist: CBS

Single (12"): released on CBS, Jan'86 by CBS Records. Dist: CBS

Whites

FOREVER YOU.
Tracks: / Forever you / Pins and needles / Mama don't you know your little girl / (Our own) Jole' Blon / Ring of clover / Move it on over / Blue baby now / I didn't come here to cry / I just started living today / Living in the name of love.
Album: released on MCA Import, Mar'86 by MCA Records. Dist: Polygram, IMS

WHITES GREATEST HITS (THE).
Tracks: / You put the blue in me / Hangin' around / Give me back the old familiar feeling / If it ain't love (let's leave it alone) / I wonder who's holding my baby tonight / Love won't wait / Pins and needles / Forever you / When the new wears off our love / Hometown gossip.
Album: released on MCA, Apr'87 by MCA Records. Dist: Polygram, MCA

Cassette: released on MCA, Apr'87 by MCA Records. Dist: Polygram, MCA

White Sister

FASHION BY PASSION.
Tracks: / Place in the heart, A / Fashion by passion / Dancin' on midnight / Save me tonight / Ticket to ride / April / Until it hurts / Troubleshooters / Lonely teardrops / Place in my heart, A.
Album: released on FM, Mar'87 by FM-Revolver Records. Dist: EMI

Cassette: released on FM-Revolver, Oct'86 by FM-Revolver Records. Dist: BMG (RCA/Ariola), Pathe Marconi, Polygram

Compact disc: released on FM, Mar'87 by FM-Revolver Records. Dist: EMI

TICKET TO RIDE.
Tracks: / Fashion B passion.
Single (7"): released on FM-Revolver, Oct'86 by FM-Revolver Records. Dist: BMG (RCA/Ariola), Pathe Marconi, Polygram

Single (12"): released on FM-Revolver, Oct'86 by FM-Revolver Records. Dist: BMG (RCA/Ariola), Pathe Marconi, Polygram

WHITE SISTER.
Tracks: / Don't say that you're mine / Straight from the heart / Love don't make it right / Breakin' all the rules / Whips / Can't say no / Promises / Walk away / One more night / Just for you.
Album: released on Heavy Metal America, Mar'87 by FM-Revolver Records. Dist: EMI

Whitesnake

AIN'T NO LOVE IN THE HEART OF THE CITY.
Single (7"): released on United Artists, Nov'80

Single (12"): released on United Artists, Nov'80 Deleted '87.

COME AN' GET IT.
Album: released on Liberty, Apr'81

Cassette: released on Liberty, Apr'81

FOOL FOR YOUR LOVING.
Single (7"): released on Liberty, Apr'80

FOURPLAY video ep.
Notes: Four videos spanning the last four years of Whitesnake singles on video, the classic 'Fool for your loving' from 1980, and their worldwide hit of 1981 'Don't break my heart again', both of which feature, David Coverdale, John Lord (keyboards), Ian Paice (drums), Mickey Moody (guitar), and Bernie Marsden (guitar). 'Gere i go again' recorded in 1982, marks the change in line-up and features Colin Hodgkinson (bass), Mel Galley (guitar) and Cozy Powell (drums). The fourth track 'Guilty of love' recorded in August 1983 is taken from the forthcoming album 'Slide it in'.
Video-cassette (VHS): released on PMI, Jan'84 by PMI Records. Dist: EMI

Video-cassette [Betamax]: released on PMI, Jan'84 by PMI Records. Dist: EMI

FOURPLAY (VIDEO).
Notes: OK! Time for you mean muthas to stuff your socks down your spandex trousers and get down to some 'Fourplay'. Shake your hair to 'Fool for your loving, 'Guilty of love' and two more clas(sic) tracks. Yeah!
Video-cassette (VHS): released on Video Collection, May'87 by Video Collection International Ltd.. Dist: Counterpoint

GIVE ME MORE TIME.
Single (7"): released on Liberty, Jan'84

Single (12"): released on Liberty, Jan'84 Deleted '87.

GUILTY OF LOVE.
Single (7"): released on Liberty, Aug'83

Picture disc single: released on Liberty, Aug'83

HERE I GO AGAIN.
Single (7"): released on Liberty, Oct'82

IS THIS LOVE.
Tracks: / Is this love / Standing in the shadows / Need your love so bad / Still of the night.
Notes: Tracks 1 and Produced by Mike Stone for Mike Stone Enterprises & Keith Olsen for Pogo Logo Productions on behalf of Whitesnake Overseas Productions (P) 1987 Original Sound recordings made by Whitesnake Overseas Ltd, under licence to EMI Records Ltd. Tracks 2 and 3:- Produced by Martin Birch. Remixed by Keith Olsen. (P) 1984 Original Sound recordings made by Whitesnake Overseas Ltd, under licence to EMI Records Ltd.
Compact disc single: released on EMI, May'87 by EMI Records. Dist: EMI

Single (7"): released on EMI, May'87 by EMI Records. Dist: EMI

Extended-play record: released on EMI, May'87 by EMI Records. Dist: EMI

Single (12"): released on EMI, May'87 by EMI Records. Dist: EMI

Picture disc single: released on EMI, 30 May'87 by EMI Records. Dist: EMI

LIVE.
Video-cassette (VHS): released on PMI, Jun'86 by PMI Records. Dist: EMI

Video-cassette [Betamax]: released on PMI, Jun'86 by PMI Records. Dist: EMI

LIVE AT DONNINGTON PARK.
Video-cassette (VHS): released on PMI, Sep'84 by PMI Records. Dist: EMI

LIVE IN THE HEART OF THE CITY.
Double Album: released on United Artists, Oct'80

Double cassette: released on United Artists, Oct'80

LOVE AIN'T NO STRANGER.
Single (7"): released on Liberty, Jan'85

Single (12"): released on Liberty, Feb'85

LOVEHUNTER.
Album: released on Fame, Apr'84 by Music For Pleasure Records. Dist: EMI

Cassette: released on Fame, Apr'84 by Music For Pleasure Records. Dist: EMI

READY AN' WILLING.
Album: released on Fame, Sep'85 by Music For Pleasure Records. Dist: EMI

Cassette: released on Fame, Sep'85 by Music For Pleasure Records. Dist: EMI

SAINT AN' SINNERS.
Tracks: / Young blood / Rough and ready / Bloody luxury / Victim of love / Crying in the rain / Here I go again / Love and affection / Rock and roll angels / Dancing girls / Saints and sinners.
Album: released on Fame, May'87 by Music For Pleasure Records. Dist: EMI

Cassette: released on Fame, May'87 by Music For Pleasure Records. Dist: EMI

Album: released on Liberty, '85

Cassette: released on Liberty, '85

SLIDE IT IN.
Album: released on Liberty, Mar'85 Deleted '87.

Cassette: released on Liberty, Mar'85

SNAKEBITE.
Album: released on EMI (Holland), '83 by EMI Records. Dist: Conifer

STANDING IN THE SHADOW.

Single (7"): released on Liberty, Apr'84

Picture disc single: released on Liberty, Apr'84

STILL OF THE NIGHT.
Tracks: / Still of the night / Here I go again (1987) / You're gonna break my heart.
Single (7"): released on EMI, Mar'87 by EMI Records. Dist: EMI

Single (12"): released on EMI, Mar'87 by EMI Records. Dist: EMI

STILL OF THE NIGHT (EXT).
Tracks: / Still of the night / Here I go again (1987) / You're gonna break my heart again.
Picture disc single: released on EMI, Mar'87 by EMI Records. Dist: EMI

TROUBLE.
Tracks: / Take me with you / Love to keep you warm / Lie down (a modern love song) / Day tripper / Nighthawk (vampire blues) / Time is right for love, The / Trouble / Belgian Tom's hat trick / Free flight / Don't mess with me / Take me with you / Love to keep you warm / Lie down (a modern love song) / Day tripper / Nighthawk (vampire blues) / Time is right for love, The / Trouble / Belgian Tom's hat trick / Free light / Don't mess with me.
Notes: Produced by Martin (The Wasp) Birch for Sunburst Records and You. (P) 1978 Original Sound recordings made by Sunburst Records Ltd.
Album: released on Liberty, Jun'87 by Liberty-United. Dist: EMI

Cassette: released on Liberty, Jun'87 by Liberty-United. Dist: EMI

Album: released on Fame, May'82 by Music For Pleasure Records. Dist: EMI

Cassette: released on Fame, May'82 by Music For Pleasure Records. Dist: EMI

WHITESNAKE 1987.
Tracks: / Still of the night / Bad boys / Give me all your love / Looking for love / Crying in the rain / Is this love / Straight for the heart / Don't turn away / Children of the night.
Notes: Whitesnake's first album release since february 1984, sees an unparalled return to form. Produced by Mike Stone and Keith Olsen, the album has been recorded in LA and Compass Point. Features David Coverdale on vocals, John Sykes on guitar, Neil Murray on bass and Aynsley Dunbar on drums. Special guests include Don Airey, Bill Cuomo and Adrian Vandenberg. The album has been preceded by a single *Still of the night c/w Here I go again (1987)*, a re-recording of one of their most popular tracks. The LP also features one other rerecording *Crying in the rain*. Shatter your darkness with *Still of the night*. The music speaks for itself. [EMI release sheet, April 87].
Picture disc album: released on EMI, Apr'87 by EMI Records. Dist: EMI

Album: released on EMI, Apr'87 by EMI Records. Dist: EMI

Cassette: released on EMI, Apr'87 by EMI Records. Dist: EMI

Compact disc: released on EMI, Apr'87 by EMI Records. Dist: EMI

Compact disc: released on EMI, Mar'87 by EMI Records. Dist: EMI

Compact disc: released on EMI, May'87 by EMI Records. Dist: EMI

White, Snowy

BIRD OF PARADISE.
Single (7"): released on Towerbell, Dec'83 by Towerbell Records. Dist: EMI

Single (12"): released on Towerbell, Dec'83 by Towerbell Records. Dist: EMI

Single (7"): released on R4, Oct'85 by R & R. Dist: EMI

Single (12"): released on R4, Oct'85 by R & R. Dist: EMI

FORTUNE.
Single (7"): released on Towerbell, Feb'85 by Towerbell Records. Dist: EMI

Single (12"): released on Towerbell, Feb'85 by Towerbell Records. Dist: EMI

FOR YOU.
Notes: Extra track on 12" only
Single (7"): released on Legend, Feb'87 by Legend Records. Dist: EMI, Legend Distribution, Island

Single (12"): released on Legend, Feb'87 by Legend Records. Dist: EMI, Legend Distribution, Island

I CAN'T LET GO.
Tracks: / Rush hour / I can't let go (inst)* / Changing ways*.
Single (7"): released on Legend, Jul'86 by Legend Records. Dist: EMI, Legend Distribution, Island

Single (12"): released on Legend, Jul'86 by Legend Records. Dist: EMI, Legend Distribution, Island

LAND OF FREEDOM.
Single (7"): released on Towerbell, Oct'84 by Towerbell Records. Dist: EMI

LIVE IN LONDON.
Notes: British guitarist/singer successful in his own right as well as previously being with Thin Lizzy, shown live in concert at the Dominion London. 1985 production
Video-cassette (VHS): released on Polygram, Aug'86 by Polygram Records. Dist: Polygram

PEACE ON EARTH.
Single (7"): released on Towerbell, May'84 by Towerbell Records. Dist: EMI

SNOWY WHITE.
Album: released on Towerbell, Oct'84 by Towerbell Records. Dist: EMI

Cassette: released on Towerbell, Oct'84 by Towerbell Records. Dist: EMI

THAT CERTAIN THING.
Tracks: / Muddy fingers.
Single (7"): released on Legend, Oct'86 by Legend Records. Dist: EMI, Legend Distribution, Island

Single (12"): released on Legend, Oct'86 by Legend Records. Dist: EMI, Legend Distribution, Island

WHITE FLAMES.
Album: released on Towerbell, May'83 by Towerbell Records. Dist: EMI

Cassette: released on Towerbell, May'83 by Towerbell Records. Dist: EMI

White Spirit

BACK TO THE GRIND.
Single (7"): released on Neat, May'80 by Neat Records. Dist: Pinnacle, Neat

White Summer

POWER POISON.
Single (7"): released on White Summer, Mar'85 by Probe Records. Dist: Cartel

White, Tam

LET THE GOOD TIMES ROLL (White, Tam & The Dexters).
Album:

White, T.H.

BOOK OF MERLYN, THE Excerpts read by Christopher Plummer.
Album: released on Caedmon(USA), Jul'79 by Caedmon (USA) Records. Dist: Gower, Taylors, Discovery

Cassette: released on Caedmon(USA), Jul'79 by Caedmon (USA) Records. Dist: Gower, Taylors, Discovery

MERLYN'S ANIMAL COUNCIL.
Cassette: released on Caedmon(USA), '81 by Caedmon (USA) Records. Dist: Gower, Taylors, Discovery

White, Thomas

IVORY GIRL.
Single (7"): released on Hit Run, Sep'79 Dist: Independent

White Tiger

YEAR OF THE TIGER.
Notes: Band features Mark St. John (Kiss) and David Denato (Black Sabbath).
Album: released on E.M.C (USA), Aug'87 Dist: Pinnacle

White, Tony Joe

ROOSEVELT & IRA LEE.
Album: released on Astan, Nov'84 by Astan Records. Dist: Counterpoint

Cassette: released on Astan, Nov'84 by Astan Records. Dist: Counterpoint

White & Torch

BURY MY HEART.
Single (7"): released on RCA, Jan'84 by RCA Records. Dist: RCA, Roots, Swift, Wellard, Chris, I & B, Solomon & Peres Distribution

Single (12"): released on RCA, Jan'84 by RCA Records. Dist: RCA, Roots, Swift, Wellard, Chris, I & B, Solomon & Peres Distribution

MIRACLE.
Single (7"): released on RCA, Oct'83 by RCA Records. Dist: RCA, Roots, Swift, Wellard, Chris, I & B, Solomon & Peres Distribution

Single (12"): released on RCA, Oct'83 by RCA Records. Dist: RCA, Roots, Swift, Wellard, Chris, I & B, Solomon & Peres Distribution

White Wedding

WHITE WEDDING Various Artists (Various Artists).
Extended-play record: released on EMI, May'81 by EMI Records. Dist: EMI

White Wolf

STANDING ALONE.
Album: released on RCA, Nov'84 by RCA Records. Dist: RCA, Roots, Swift, Wellard, Chris, I & B, Solomon & Peres Distribution

Cassette: released on RCA, Nov'84 by RCA Records. Dist: RCA, Roots, Swift, Wellard, Chris, I & B, Solomon & Peres Distribution

White, Znow

ALL HAIL TO THEM.
Album: released on Thunderbolt, Aug'85 by Magnum Music Group Ltd. Dist: Magnum Music Group Ltd, PRT Distribution, Spartan Distribution

Whitfield, Barrence

CALL OF THE WILD.
Album: released on Rounder Europa, Jul'87

DIG YOURSELF.
Album: released on Rounder Europa, Feb'87

Album: released on Rounder (USA), Dec'85 Dist: Mike's Country Music Room Distribution, Jazz Music Distribution, Swift Distribution, Roots Records Distribution, Projection Distribution, Topic Distribution

Cassette: released on Rounder (USA), Dec'85 Dist: Mike's Country Music Room Distribution, Jazz Music Distribution, Swift Distribution, Roots Records Distribution, Projection Distribution, Topic Distribution

Whitfield, David

GREATEST HITS: DAVID WHITFIELD.
Album: released on Decca (Elite), Feb'83 by Decca Records. Dist: Polygram, IMS

Cassette: released on Decca (Elite), Feb'83 by Decca Records. Dist: Polygram, IMS

SINGS THE GREAT SONGS.
Cassette: released on Ditto, Sep'86 by Pickwick Records. Dist: H.R. Taylor

WORLD OF DAVID WHITFIELD, THE.
Album: released on Decca, '69 by Decca Records. Dist: Polygram

Cassette: released on Decca, '69 by Decca Records. Dist: Polygram

WORLD OF DAVID WHITFIELD - VOL.2.
Album: released on Decca, Jul'75 by Decca Records. Dist: Polygram

Whiting, Margaret

GOIN' PLACES.
Album: released on Jasmine, Mar'85 by Jasmine Records. Dist: Counterpoint, Lugtons, Taylor, H.R., Wellard, Chris, Swift, Cadillac

LADY'S IN LOVE WITH YOU, THE.
Album: released on Audiophile, Jun'86 by Jazzology Records (USA). Dist: Jazz Music, Swift

LOVE SONGS BY MARGARET WHITING.
Album: released on Capitol, Jun'85 by Capitol Records. Dist: EMI

Cassette: released on Capitol, Jun'85 by Capitol Records. Dist: EMI

Whitman, Jim

GREEN FIELDS OF IRELAND.
Tracks: / Green fields of Ireland / My lovely Lagan River / Up in the Paltry Mountains / Just a blind Irish boy / My heart is in Connemara / Today you say you are leaving / Kiss the Blarney Stone / In Annalee / River Bann flows on forever / Girl from Carlow Town / Pride of County Down / Take me back to Ireland.
Notes: All royalty proceeds to Mencap.
Album: released on Pastafont, Jun'87 by Pastafont Records.

Cassette: released on Pastafont, Jun'87 by Pastafont Records.

STOLEN KISS, A.
Single (7"): released on Priority, Jan'87 by Priority Records. Dist: RCA

Whitman, Jim & Texas

CUTTIN' LOOSE.
Album: released on Lady London, Sep'84 by Joanne Barrett.

Whitman, Paul

SHAKING THE BLUES AWAY (Whitman, Paul & His Orchestra).
Album: released on Halcyon, Sep'84 by Halcyon Records. Dist: Jazz Music

Whitman, Slim

BEST OF SLIM WHITMAN.
Album: released on EMI (Holland), '83 by EMI Records. Dist: Conifer
Cat. no: **IA 022 58098**

BIRMINGHAM JAIL.
Album: released on RCA/Camden, '69
Cat. no: **CDM 1018**
Cassette: released on RCA/Camden, '69
Cat. no: **CAM 433**

BIRMINGHAM JAIL & OTHER COUNTRY ARTISTS.
Tracks: / Birmingham jail / Wabash waltz / Let's go to church / I'm casting my lasso towards the sky / Tears can never drown the flame (that's in my heart) / I'll never pass this way again.
Album: released on RCA/Camden, Apr'86
Cat. no: **CDM 1018**

CAN'T HELP FALLING IN LOVE WITH YOU.
Single (7"): released on Liberty, Jan'82 by Liberty-United. Dist: EMI
Cat. no: **BP 408**

COUNTRY CLASSICS.
Album: released on Liberty, Aug'85 by Liberty-United. Dist: EMI
Cat. no: **ED 2606821**
Cassette: released on Liberty, Aug'85 by Liberty-United. Dist: EMI
Cat. no: **ED 2606824**

COUNTRY STYLE.
Album: released on Music For Pleasure, Jan'85
Cat. no: **MFP 41 5688 1**
Cassette: released on Music For Pleasure, Jan'85
Cat. no: **MFP 41 5688 4**

GREATEST HITS: SLIM WHITMAN.
Album: released on Liberty, Apr'84
Cat. no: **LBR 2600531**
Cassette: released on Liberty, Apr'84
Cat. no: **TC LBR 2600534**

HAPPY ANNIVERSARY.
Tracks: / Happy anniversary / Indian love call.
Notes: Also contains:"Indian love call" by Slim Whitman
Single (7"): released on Old Gold, Apr'87 by Old Gold Records. Dist: Lightning, Jazz Music, Spartan, Counterpoint
Cat. no: **OG 9716**
Single (7"): released on United Artists (USA), '74 by EMI Records. Dist: EMI, Swift, Solomon & Peres Distribution
Cat. no: **UP 35728**
Single (7"): released on EMI Golden 45's, Mar'84 by EMI Records. Dist: EMI
Cat. no: **G 45 14**

I'LL TAKE YOU HOME AGAIN, KATHLEEN.
Album: released on Hallmark, Apr'78 by Pickwick Records. Dist: Pickwick Distribution, PRT, Taylors
Cat. no: **SHM 959**
Cassette: released on Hallmark, Apr'78 by Pickwick Records. Dist: Pickwick Distribution, PRT, Taylors
Cat. no: **HSC 334**

INDIAN LOVE CALL.
Single (7"): released on Liberty, '80
Cat. no: **LR 0986**

LOVE SONGS OF THE WATERFALL.
Album: released on Sunset, '70 Dist: EMI
Cat. no: **SLS 50153**
Special: released on Sunset, '70 Dist: EMI
Cat. no: **8XS 50153**
Cassette: released on Sunset, '81 Dist: EMI
Cat. no: **TCS 50153**

MR SONGMAN.
Album: released on Liberty, Feb'82 by Liberty-United. Dist: EMI
Cat. no: **LBG 30343**
Cassette: released on Liberty, Feb'82 by Liberty-United. Dist: EMI
Cat. no: **TCLBG 30343**

ROSE MARIE.
Tracks: / Rose Marie / I'll take you home again Kathleen.
Single (7"): released on Old Gold, May'87 by Old Gold Records. Dist: Lightning, Jazz Music, Spartan, Counterpoint
Cat. no: **OG 9712**
Single (7"): released on Liberty, '80 by Liberty-United. Dist: EMI
Cat. no: **LR 8186**

SLIM WHITMAN.
Cassette: released on Ideal(Tapes), Jun'81 Dist: EMI
Cat. no: **TC IDL 20**
Album: released on Hallmark, Feb'82 by Pickwick Records. Dist: Pickwick Distribution, PRT Taylors
Cat. no: **SHM 3089**
Cassette: released on Hallmark, Feb'82 by Pickwick Records. Dist: Pickwick Distribution PRT, Taylors
Cat. no: **HSC 3089**
Cassette: released on Cambra, '83 by Cambra Records. Dist: IDS, Conifer
Cat. no: **CRT 01**

SLIM WHITMAN CHRISTMAS ALBUM (THE).
Album: released on Liberty, Dec'85
Cat. no: **ED 260734**
Cassette: released on Liberty, Dec'85
Cat. no: **ED 260734**

SLIM WHITMAN STORY, (THE).
Boxed set: released on World Records, Dec'8 Dist: Polygram
Cat. no: **ALBUM 2**
Boxed set: released on World Records, Dec'8 Dist: Polygram
Cat. no: **CASSETTE 2**

SONG I LOVE TO SING.
Tracks: / When / Secret love / Since you went away / I could only dream / Last farewell, The / I remember you / Rose Marie / Where do i go from here / Silver haired daddy of mine, The / Beautiful dreamer.
Album: released on Epic, Apr'86 by CBS Records. Dist: CBS

Cassette: released on Epic, Apr'86 by CBS Records. Dist: CBS

'TILL WE MEET AGAIN.
Album: released on United Artists (USA), Apr'80 by EMI Records. Dist: EMI, Swift, Solomon & Peres Distribution

Cassette: released on United Artists (USA), Apr'80 by EMI Records. Dist: EMI, Swift, Solomon & Peres Distribution

VERY BEST OF SLIM WHITMAN, (THE).
Album: released on United Artists (USA), Jan'76 by EMI Records. Dist: EMI, Swift, Solomon & Peres Distribution

Cassette: released on United Artists (USA), Jan'76 by EMI Records. Dist: EMI, Swift, Solomon & Peres Distribution

Whitmore, Iain

WOULD YOU LIKE TO LEAVE.
Single (7"): released on RCA, May'81 by RCA Records. Dist: RCA, Roots, Swift, Wellard, Chris, I & B, Solomon & Peres Distribution

Whitren, Jackie

INTERNATIONAL TIMES (Whitren, Jackie & John Cartwright).
Album: released on Living, Jul'83 Dist: Pinnacle

Cassette: released on Living, Jul'83 Dist: Pinnacle

Single (7"): released on Living, Jul'83 Dist: Pinnacle

Single (12"): released on Living, Jul'83 Dist: Pinnacle

Whitstein Brothers

ROSE OF MY HEART.
Album: released on Rounder (USA), Apr'85 Dist: Mike's Country Music Room Distribution, Jazz Music Distribution, Swift Distribution, Roots Records Distribution, Projection Distribution, Topic Distribution

TROUBLE AIN'T NOTHIN' BUT THE BLUES.
Album: released on Rounder Europa, May'87

Whittaker, Heather

TAKE HER WITH HEART.
Album: released on Dingles, Mar'84 by Dingles Records. Dist: Projection

Whittaker, Roger

16 GOLDEN CLASSICS.
Tracks: / Stranger on the shore / I's now or never / Home loving man / Show me the way / Yarmouth Quay / Mother of mine sleep on / Angels of love / Kids ain't bad / Imagine / What a wonderful world / Bright eyes / Child within me, The / Smiler / Idle dreamer / Thorn trees of Africa / Everybodys looking for an answer.
Notes: All tracks licensed from Tembo Records Ltd/Design: Shoot That Tiger! (C) 1986/Castle Communications Place, Unit 7, 271 Merton Road, London SW18 5JS. Bar code: 5/013428 920121.
Album: released on Unforgettable, Dec'86 by Castle Communications Records. Dist: Counterpoint

Cassette: released on Unforgettable, Dec'86 by Castle Communications Records. Dist: Counterpoint

Compact disc: released on Unforgettable, '86 by Castle Communications Records. Dist: Counterpoint

20 ALL-TIME GREATS.
Album: released on Polydor, Jul'79 by Polydor Records. Dist: Polygram, Polydor

Cassette: released on Polydor, Jul'79 by Polydor Records. Dist: Polygram, Polydor

ALBANY.
Single (7"): released on EMI, May'82 by EMI Records. Dist: EMI

BEST OF ROGER WHITTAKER, THE.
Compact disc: released on Polydor, 30 May'87 by Polydor Records. Dist: Polygram, Polydor

BEST OF ROGER WHITTAKER, 1967-75.
Tracks: / New world in the morning / I kon't believe in if anymore / River lady / Mexican whistler / Streets of London / Why / Mamy blue / Morning please don't come / Durham town / If i were a rich man / Sunrise sunset / Morning hass broken / Dirty old town / Minstral / Moonshadow / Last farewell, The.
Compact disc: released on Polydor (MGM), Apr'84

BITTER AND SWEET.
Single (7"): released on Tembo, Jun'84

BUTTERFLY.
Album: released on Contour, Sep'85 by Pickwick Records. Dist: Pickwick Distribution, PRT

Cassette: released on Contour, Sep'85 by Pickwick Records. Dist: Pickwick Distribution, PRT

CANDLE.
Tracks: / Jerusalem goodbye.
Single (7"): released on Tembo, Jun'86 by Tembo (Canada). Dist: IMS Distribution, Polygram Distribution

CHANGES.
Single (7"): released on EMI, Feb'82 by EMI Records. Dist: EMI

COUNTRY FEEL OF ROGER WHITTAKER.
Double Album: released on Tembo, May'85

Double cassette: released on Tembo, May'85

DURHAM TOWN.
Album: released on Contour, Oct'82 by Pickwick Records. Dist: Pickwick Distribution, PRT

Cassette: released on Contour, Oct'82 by Pickwick Records. Dist: Pickwick Distribution, PRT

DURHAM TOWN.
Tracks: / Durham town (the leavin') / I don't believe in if anymore.
Single (7"): released on Old Gold, Apr'86 by Old Gold Records. Dist: Lightning, Jazz Music, Spartan, Counterpoint

GENIUS OF LOVE.
Single (7"): released on Tembo UK, Apr'86

GENIUS OF LOVE, THE.
Tracks: / Genius of love / Miss Lapotaire / Your voice / Railway hotel / Destiny / Jerusalem goodbye / Candle, The / Yur fool / One more chance / Too emotional / Everybody's got a lonely heart / Only the lonely.
Notes: Roger's latest album features 12 songs ranging from up tempo disco to gentle ballads. Using rock band and full string section the album is well produced and offers several strong tracks for airplay. Recommended tracks 'The genius of love and Roy Orbison's 'Only the lonely'. The band's personnel includes: Brian Bennett of the Shadows on drums and Paul Jones ex-Manfred Mann on harmonica for 'Railway Hotel'/
Album: released on Tembo, Feb'86 by Tembo (Canada). Dist: IMS Distribution, Polygram Distribution

Cassette: released on Tembo, Feb'86 by Tembo (Canada). Dist: IMS Distribution, Polygram Distribution

HAPPY EVERYTHING.
Single (7"): released on Tembo, Nov'84

HEART-TOUCHING FAVOURITES.
Album: released on Tembo, Mar'85

Cassette: released on Tembo, Mar'85

HIS FINEST COLLECTION.
Compact disc: released on Polydor, 30 May'87 by Polydor Records. Dist: Polygram, Polydor

I'M BACK.
Single (7"): released on Tembo, Nov'83

LAST FAREWELL, THE.
Tracks: / New world in the morning.
Single (7"): released on Old Gold, Apr'86 by Old Gold Records. Dist: Lightning, Jazz Music, Spartan, Counterpoint

LOVE ALBUM, THE.
Album: released on Arcade Music Gala, Apr'86 Dist: Stage One

Cassette: released on Arcade Music Gala, Apr'86 Dist: Stage One

MAKE WAY FOR MAN.
Single (7"): released on Tembo, Mar'84

MUSIC FOR THE MILLIONS.
Album: released on Polydor (Holland), Jul'83

Cassette: released on Polydor (Holland), Jul'83

MY FAVOURITE LOVE SONGS.
Album: released on EMI, Apr'83 by EMI Records. Dist: EMI

Cassette: released on EMI, Apr'83 by EMI Records. Dist: EMI

NEW WORLD IN THE MORNING.
Album: released on Philips (Import), Mar'84

Cassette: released on Philips (Import), Mar'84

ROGER WHITTAKER His finest collection.
Compact disc: released on Tembo, '87 by Tembo (Canada). Dist: IMS Distribution, Polygram Distribution

Album: released on Contour, Feb'82 by Pickwick Records. Dist: Pickwick Distribution, PRT

Cassette: released on Contour, Feb'82 by Pickwick Records. Dist: Pickwick Distribution, PRT

Double cassette: released on Cambra, '83 by Cambra Records. Dist: IDS, Conifer

ROGER WHITTAKER ALBUM, (THE).
Album:

Cassette:

ROGER WHITTAKER COLLECTION, THE.
Tracks: / Durham Town / All of my love / Before she breaks my heart / My world / Why / I was born / My son / Time / Summer days / Man without love, A / Man without love, A.
Notes: Double album and double cassette. Bar code: 5/013428/131558.
Album: released on Collectors, Dec'86 by Castle Communications Records. Dist: PRT, Pinnacle, Jazz Music

Cassette: released on Collectors, Dec'86 by Castle Communications Records. Dist: PRT, Pinnacle, Jazz Music

Compact disc: released on Collector Series, '86 by Castle Communications Records. Dist: PRT, Pinnacle, RCA, Ariola

ROGER WHITTAKER IN KENYA.
Album: released on Tembo, Sep'83

ROGER WHITTAKER,THE BEST OF,II
The best of.
Compact disc: released on Polydor, '87 by Polydor Records. Dist: Polygram, Polydor

ROMANTIC SIDE OF ROGER WHITTAKER.
Double Album: released on Tembo, May'85

Double cassette: released on Tembo, May'85

SHENANDOAH.
Tracks: / Shanandoah / Amazing Grace / Skye boat song.
Compact disc single: released on Tembo, Mar'87 by Tembo (Canada). Dist: IMS Distribution, Polygram Distribution

Single (7"): released on Tembo, Feb'87 by Tembo (Canada). Dist: IMS Distribution, Polygram Distribution

SINGING THE HITS.
Double Album: released on Tembo, May'85

Double cassette: released on Tembo, May'85

SKYE BOAT SONG (Whittaker, Roger & Des O'Connor).
Tracks: / Remember romance / Time.
Single (7"): released on Tembo, Sep'86 by Tembo (Canada). Dist: IMS Distribution, Polygram Distribution

SKYE BOAT SONG AND OTHER GREAT SONGS.
Album: released on Tembo, Dec'86 by Tembo (Canada). Dist: IMS Distribution, Polygram Distribution

Cassette: released on Tembo, Dec'86 by Tembo (Canada). Dist: IMS Distribution, Polygram Distribution

Compact disc: released on Tembo, Dec'86 by Tembo (Canada). Dist: IMS Distribution, Polygram Distribution

SO GOOD, SO BAD, SO SOON.
Single (7"): released on EMI, Oct'81 by EMI Records. Dist: EMI

SONGS OF LOVE AND LIFE.
Album: released on Contour, Sep'84 by Pickwick Records. Dist: Pickwick Distribution, PRT

Cassette: released on Contour, Sep'84 by Pickwick Records. Dist: Pickwick Distribution, PRT

STRANGER ON THE SHORE.
Single (7"): released on EMI, Mar'83 by EMI Records. Dist: EMI

TAKE A LITTLE, GIVE A LITTLE.
Single (7"): released on Tembo, Sep'84

Album: released on Tembo, Oct'84

Cassette: released on Tembo, Oct'84

TIDINGS OF COMFORT AND JOY.
Double Album: released on Tembo, Nov'84

Double cassette: released on Tembo, Nov'84

WELCOME HOME.
Tracks: / Welcome home / Now the pain begins.
Single (7"): released on Tembo, Jul'87 by Tembo (Canada). Dist: IMS Distribution, Polygram Distribution

WISHES.
Album: released on Columbia, Jan'80 by EMI Records. Dist: EMI

Cassette: released on Columbia, Jan'80 by EMI Records. Dist: EMI

Whittle, Tommy

JIG SAW (Whittle, Tommy Quartet).
Album: released on Alamo, Jun'79 Dist: Jazz Music

STRAIGHT EIGHT (Whittle, Tommy & Alan Barnes).
Album: released on Music Maniac, May'86 Dist: Rough Trade Distribution, Cartel Distribution

WAXING WITH WHITTLE.
Album: released on Esquire, Apr'79 by Titan International Productions. Dist: Jazz Music, Cadillac Music, Swift, Wellard, Chris, Backs, Rough Trade, Revolver, Nine Mile

WHY NOT (Whittle, Tommy Quartet).
Album: released on Jam, Apr'79 Dist: Jazz Music

Whitworth, Karl

MYTHS OF CONSTANCE (Who).
Single (7"): released on Binji, May'82 by Bulk Cement Marketing International. Dist: Pinnacle

NAMES NUMBERS AND PLACES.
Single (7"): released on Binji, Aug'81 by Bulk Cement Marketing International. Dist: Pinnacle

Whiz Kid

HE'S GOT THE BEAT.
Single (7"): released on Tommy Boy, May'85 by Warner Brothers. Dist: WEA Distribution

Single (12"): released on Tommy Boy, May'85 by Warner Brothers. Dist: WEA Distribution

Whizz

MAXIMUM VOLUME.
Single (7"): released on Rock City Records, Aug'85 by Rock City Records. Dist: PRT Distribution

Single (12"): released on Rock City Records, Aug'85 by Rock City Records. Dist: PRT Distribution

Whizz For Atoms

THAT SINKING FEELING.
Single (7"): released on Graduate, Sep'84 by Graduate Records. Dist: Nine Mile, Cartel

Whizz Kids

PAYE AS YOU EARN.
Single (7"): released on Dead Good, Oct'79

Whizz & Voice

WHIZZ RAP.
Single (7"): released on BBC, Apr'85 by BBC Records & Tapes. Dist: EMI, PRT, Pye

Cassette: released on BBC, Apr'85 by BBC Records & Tapes. Dist: EMI, PRT, Pye

Who

ATHENA.
Single (7"): released on Polydor, Sep'82 by Polydor Records. Dist: Polygram, Polydor

Picture disc single: released on Polydor, Sep'82 by Polydor Records. Dist: Polygram, Polydor

Single (12"): released on Polydor, Sep'82 by Polydor Records. Dist: Polygram, Polydor

Special: released on Polydor, Sep'82 by Polydor Records. Dist: Polygram, Polydor

BEST OF THE SIXTIES.
Album: released on Karussell Gold (Germany), Aug'85

Cassette: released on Karussell Gold (Germany), Aug'85

BEST, THE (MUSIC FOR THE MILLIONS).
Album: released on Polydor (Holland), Feb'85

Cassette: released on Polydor (Holland), Feb'85

BY NUMBERS.
Album: released on Polydor, '75 by Polydor Records. Dist: Polygram, Polydor

Cassette: released on Polydor, '75 by Polydor Records. Dist: Polygram, Polydor

FACE DANCES.
Album: released on Polydor, Mar'81 by Polydor Records. Dist: Polygram, Polydor

Cassette: released on Polydor, Mar'81 by Poly-

dor Records. Dist: Polygram, Polydor

GREATEST HITS: WHO.
Album: released on Arcade Music Gala, Apr'86 Dist: Stage One

Cassette: released on Arcade Music Gala, Apr'86 Dist: Stage One

I CAN'T EXPLAIN.
Single (7"): released on Import, '80 Dist: Stage One

IT'S HARD.
Tracks: / Athena / It's your turn / Cooks county / Dangerous / Eminence front / I've known no war / One life's enough / It's hard / One at a time / Why did i fall for that? / Man is a man / Cry if you want.
Compact disc: released on Polydor, '83 by Polydor Records. Dist: Polygram, Polydor

KIDS ARE ALRIGHT, THE.
Notes: Reissue of the Who's own history of their life and times as a group, with musical and film footage from the mid-60's to the late 70's.
Video-cassette (VHS): released on Polygram, Sep'84 by Polygram Records. Dist: Polygram

LIVE AT LEEDS.
Tracks: / Magic box / My generation / Shaking all over / Substitute / Summer time blues / Young man blues.
Album: released on Track, Nov'83 by Polydor Records. Dist: Polygram

Cassette: released on Track, Nov'83 by Polydor Records. Dist: Polygram

Compact disc: released on Track, Nov'83 by Polydor Records. Dist: Polygram

MEATY, BEATY BIG AND BOUNCY.
Album: released on Track, '74 by Polydor Records. Dist: Polygram

Cassette: released on Track, '74 by Polydor Records. Dist: Polygram

MY GENERATION.
Album: released on Virgin, Oct'80 by Virgin Records. Dist: EMI, Virgin Distribution

Album: released on Polydor, May'81 by Polydor Records. Dist: Polygram, Polydor

Cassette: released on Polydor, May'81 by Polydor Records. Dist: Polygram, Polydor

Album: released on Karussell (Import), Mar'82

Cassette: released on Karussell (Import), Mar'82

ODDS AND SODS.
Album: released on Track, Nov'74 by Polydor Records. Dist: Polygram

Cassette: released on Track, Nov'74 by Polydor Records. Dist: Polygram

ONCE UPON A TIME.
Album: released on Polydor (Germany), Dec'83 Dist: IMS-Polygram

Cassette: released on Polydor (Germany), Dec'83 Dist: IMS-Polygram

PINBALL WIZARD.
Single (7"): released on Import, '80 Dist: Stage One

QUADROPHENIA.
Tracks: / I am the sea / Real me (The) / Cut my hair / Punk and the godfather (The) / I'm one / Dirty jobs (The) / Helpless dancer / Is it in my head / I've had enough / 5:15 / Sea and sand / Drowned / Bell boy / Doctor Jimmy / Rock (The) / Love,reign o'er me.
Notes: Double album
Compact disc: released on Polydor, Jan'87 by Polydor Records. Dist: Polygram, Polydor

Album: released on Polydor, Sep'79 by Polydor Records. Dist: Polygram, Polydor

Cassette: released on Polydor, Sep'79 by Polydor Records. Dist: Polygram, Polydor

QUADROPHENIA (ORIGINAL SOUNDTRACK).
Album: released on Polydor, Sep'79 by Polydor Records. Dist: Polygram, Polydor

Cassette: released on Polydor, Sep'79 by Polydor Records. Dist: Polygram, Polydor

QUICK ONE AND THE WHO SELL OUT, A.
Album: released on Track, '74 by Polydor Records. Dist: Polygram

Cassette: released on Track, '74 by Polydor Records. Dist: Polygram

RARITIES.
Album: released on Track (Import), Oct'82

Cassette: released on Track (Import), Oct'82

RARITIES VOLUME 1 (1966-68).
Album: released on Track, Aug'83 by Polydor Records. Dist: Polygram

Cassette: released on Track, Aug'83 by Polydor Records. Dist: Polygram

RARITIES VOLUME 2 (1970-1973).
Album: released on Polydor, Aug'83 by Polydor Records. Dist: Polygram, Polydor

Cassette: released on Polydor, Aug'83 by Polydor Records. Dist: Polygram, Polydor

SEE ME FEEL ME.
Single (7"): released on Import, '80 Dist: Stage One

SINGLES, THE.
Tracks: / Substitute / I'm a boy / Happy Jack / Pictures of lily / I can see for miles / Magic bus / Pinball wizard / My generation / Summertime blues / Won't get fooled again / Let's see action / Join together / Squeeze box / Who are you / You better you bet.
Compact disc: released on Polydor, Nov'84 by Polydor Records. Dist: Polygram, Polydor

Album: released on Polydor, Nov'84 by Polydor Records. Dist: Polygram, Polydor

Cassette: released on Polydor, Nov'84 by Polydor Records. Dist: Polygram, Polydor

STORY OF THE WHO, THE.
Album: released on Polydor, Oct'76 by Polydor Records. Dist: Polygram, Polydor

Cassette: released on Polydor, Oct'76 by Polydor Records. Dist: Polygram, Polydor

SUMMERTIME BLUES.
Single (7"): released on Import, '80 Dist: Stage One

TOMMY.
Tracks: / Overture / It's a boy / 1921 / Amazing journey / Sparks / Eyesight for the blind / Miracle cure / Sally Simpson / I'm free / Welcome / Tommy's holiday camp / We're not gonna take it / Christmas / Cousin Kevin / Acid Queen,The / Underture / Do you think it's alright / Fiddle about / Pinball wizard / There's a doctor / Go to the mirror / Tommy can you hear me / Smash the mirror / Sensation.
Album: released on Track, '74 by Polydor Records. Dist: Polygram

Cassette: released on Track, '74 by Polydor Records. Dist: Polygram

Compact disc: released on Polydor, '83 by Polydor Records. Dist: Polygram, Polydor

TOMMY - PART 2.
Album: released on Track, '74 by Polydor Records. Dist: Polygram

Cassette: released on Track, '74 by Polydor Records. Dist: Polygram

TWIST AND SHOUT.
Single (7"): released on MCA, Nov'84 by MCA Records. Dist: CBS

WHO ARE YOU.
Album: released on Polydor, Aug'84 by Polydor Records. Dist: Polygram, Polydor

Cassette: released on Polydor, Aug'84 by Polydor Records. Dist: Polygram, Polydor

Single (7"): released on Polydor, Jul'78 by Polydor Records. Dist: Polygram, Polydor

WHO BY NUMBERS, THE.
Album: released on Polydor, Mar'84 by Polydor Records. Dist: Polygram, Polydor

Cassette: released on Polydor, Mar'84 by Polydor Records. Dist: Polygram, Polydor

WHO COLLECTION, THE.
Album: released on Impression, Oct'85 Dist: CBS

Cassette: released on Impression, Oct'85 Dist: CBS

WHO SELL OUT, THE.
Cassette: released on Polydor, Oct'84 by Polydor Records. Dist: Polygram, Polydor

WHO'S LAST.
Album: released on MCA, Dec'84 by MCA Records. Dist: CBS

Cassette: released on MCA, Dec'84 by MCA Records. Dist: CBS

WHO'S NEXT.
Tracks: / Baba O'Riley / Getting in tune / Love ain't for keeping / My wife / Song is over / Bargain / Going mobile / Behind blue eyes / Won't get fooled again.
Album: released on Track, Nov'83 by Polydor Records. Dist: Polygram

Cassette: released on Track, Nov'83 by Polydor Records. Dist: Polygram

Compact disc: released on Polydor, '83 by Polydor Records. Dist: Polygram, Polydor

Cassette: released on Polydor, Feb'83 by Polydor Records. Dist: Polygram, Polydor

WON'T GET FOOLED AGAIN.
Single (7"): released on Polydor, Aug'79 by Polydor Records. Dist: Polygram, Polydor

YOU BETTER YOU BET.
Single (7"): released on Polydor, Feb'81 by Polydor Records. Dist: Polygram, Polydor

Who cares

DOCTOR IN DISTRESS.
Single (7"): released on Record Shack, Apr'85

Single (12"): released on Record Shack, Apr'85

Whodini

BIG MOUTH.
Single (7"): released on Jive, Jun'85 by Zomba Records. Dist: RCA, PRT, CBS

Single (12"): released on Jive, Jun'85 by Zomba Records. Dist: RCA, PRT, CBS

ESCAPE.
Single (7"): released on Jive, Aug'84 by Zomba Records. Dist: RCA, PRT, CBS

Single (12"): released on Jive, Aug'84 by Zomba Records. Dist: RCA, PRT, CBS

FREAKS COME OUT AT NIGHT.
Single (12"): released on Jive, Jan'85 by Zomba Records. Dist: RCA, PRT, CBS

Single (7"): released on Jive, Oct'85 by Zomba Records. Dist: RCA, PRT, CBS

Single (12"):

FUNKY BEAT.
Tracks: / Funky beat.
Single (7"): released on Jive, May'86 by Zomba Records. Dist: RCA, PRT, CBS

Single (12"): released on Jive, May'86 by Zomba Records. Dist: RCA, PRT, CBS

HAUNTED HOUSE OF ROCKS (2 PARTS).
Single (7"): released on Jive, Apr'83 by Zomba Records. Dist: RCA, PRT, CBS

Single (12"): released on Jive, Apr'83 by Zomba Records. Dist: RCA, PRT, CBS

MAGIC'S WAND.
Single (7"): released on Jive, Nov'82 by Zomba Records. Dist: RCA, PRT, CBS

Single (12"): released on Jive, Nov'82 by Zomba Records. Dist: RCA, PRT, CBS

Picture disc single: released on Jive, Feb'83 by Zomba Records. Dist: RCA, PRT, CBS

Cassette: released on Jive, May'84 by Zomba Records. Dist: RCA, PRT, CBS

MAGIC WAND.
Single (7"): released on Zomba, Mar'84 Dist: BMG

Single (12"): released on Zomba, Mar'84 Dist: BMG

NASTY LADY.
Single (7"): released on Jive, Jan'84 by Zomba Records. Dist: RCA, PRT, CBS

Single (12"): released on Jive, Jan'84 by Zomba Records. Dist: RCA, PRT, CBS

ONE LOVE (exit).
Tracks: / One Love(Exit) / One love(exit)[album mix] / One love(exit)[instrumental mix].
Single (12"): released on Jive, Sep'86 by Zomba Records. Dist: RCA, PRT, CBS

RAP MACHINE.
Single (7"): released on Jive, Nov'83 by Zomba Records. Dist: RCA, PRT, CBS

Single (12"): released on Jive, Nov'83 by Zomba Records. Dist: RCA, PRT, CBS

WHODINI.
Album: released on Jive, Nov'83 by Zomba Records. Dist: RCA, PRT, CBS

Cassette: released on Jive, Nov'83 by Zomba Records. Dist: RCA, PRT, CBS

Album: released on Jive, Mar'85 by Zomba Records. Dist: RCA, PRT, CBS

Cassette: released on Jive, Mar'85 by Zomba Records. Dist: RCA, PRT, CBS

Whole Lot Of Soul Here

WHOLE LOT OF SOUL HERE Various artists (Various Artists).
Notes: Artists include: Trends, Marvelows, Bunny Sigler, Little charles & Sidewinders, Bobby Williams, Impressions, Mirettes, Anna Craig, Donna Burkes, Darrow Fletcher, Marvin Sims, Bobby Bland, Bobby Connerly, B.B.King, Garland Green, Little Mr Lee, & Cherokees.
Album: released on Kent, Jan'86 by Ace Records. Dist: Pinnacle

Whole lotta shakin' goin' on

WHOLE LOTTA SHAKIN' GOIN' ON Various artists (Various Artists).
Album: released on Gusto (USA), Nov'79 by Gusto Records (USA). Dist: Crusader

WHOLE LOTTA SHAKIN' GOIN' ON Various artists (Various Artists).

Whole new generation of DJ

WHOLE NEW GENERATION OF DJ Various artists (Various Artists).
Album: released on Greensleeves, Dec'81 by Greensleeves Records. Dist: BMG, Jetstar, Spartan

Who Me

EVERY BA T ROCK.
Single (12"): by Creole Records. Dist: PRT

Whoopee Cushions

SO GOODBYE ROLF HARRIS.
Single (7"): released on Dubious, Oct'79

Whoopee, John

40 GREATEST HITS.
Album: released on ARC (Accordion Records), '84 Dist: Accordion Record Club

40 POLKA'S AND WALTZES.
Album: released on ARC (Accordion Records), '84 Dist: Accordion Record Club

Who Plays Wins

WHO PLAYS WINS Various artists (Various Artists).
Album: released on Safari, Dec'85 by Safari Records. Dist: Pinnacle

Cassette: released on Safari, Dec'85 by Safari Records. Dist: Pinnacle

Who put the bomp

WHO PUT THE BOMP Various original artists (Various original artists).
Double Album: released on London, Apr'81 by London Records. Dist: Polygram

Who Said Charge

SUNARISE.
Single (7"): released on Art-Life, Feb'83

Who Said That

LOVERBOY.
Tracks: / Loverboy / Work don't play.
Single (7"): released on Media Clone, Jun'86 by Media Clone Records. Dist: Media Clone Distribution

Who's George

DIDN'T CATCH YOUR NAME.
Single (7"): released on Impact, Aug'80 by Ace Records. Dist: Rough Trade, Pinnacle, Swift, Backs, Counterpoint, Jungle, Hotshot, Cartel

FOREVER.
Single (7"): released on Compact Organisation, Jul'81 Dist: PRT

I CAN'T RESIST YOU.
Single (7"): released on Cheapskate, Jul'82 by Cheapskate Records. Dist: RCA

Who's Harry Warren

WHO'S HARRY WARREN-EVERGREEN (VOL 2-42ND STREET).
Album: released on Phontastic (Sweden), '82 by Wellard, Chris Distribution. Dist: Wellard, Chris Distribution

Cassette: released on Phontastic (Sweden), '82 by Wellard, Chris Distribution. Dist: Wellard, Chris Distribution

WHO'S HARRY WARREN-EVERGREEN(VOL 1 JEEPERS CREEPERS).
Album: released on Phontastic (Sweden), '82 by Wellard, Chris Distribution. Dist: Wellard, Chris Distribution

Cassette: released on Phontastic (Sweden), '82 by Wellard, Chris Distribution. Dist: Wellard, Chris Distribution

Who's That Girl

WHO'S THAT GIRL Original soundtrack (Various Artists).
Tracks: / Who's that girl / Causing a commotion / Look of love, The / 24 hours / Turn it up / Best thing ever / Can't stop / El coco loco.
Album: released on Sire, Jul'87

Cassette: released on Sire, Jul'87

Page 1096

WHO'S THAT GIRL Original soundtrack (Original Soundtrack).
Compact disc: released on Sire, Aug'87

Who The Hell...
USE IMAGINATION (Who The Hell Does Jane Smith Think She Is?).
Tracks: / In your eyes / How many hours.
Notes: Extra track on 12" only
Single (7"): released on Influx, Jan'87 Dist: DMS, RCA

Single (12"): released on Influx, Feb'87 Dist: DMS, RCA

Who? What? Why? Where?
WHO? WHAT? WHY? WHERE? WHEN? Various artists (Various Artists).
Album: released on Mortarhate, Mar'84 by Dorane Ltd.

Whyos
FULL ARMS AND AN EMPTY HEART.
Single (7"): released on Rock House, Jun'84 Dist: Pinnacle

TALK TO ME LIKE THE RAIN.
Single (7"): released on Rock House, Apr'85 Dist: Pinnacle

WHYOS, THE.
Album: released on Rock House, Sep'84 Dist: Pinnacle

Why Overtime
WHY OVERTIME Moscow,New York,London.
Cassette: released on International Report, Oct'81 by Seminar Cassettes. Dist: Audio-Visual Library Services, Davidson Distribution, Eastern Educational Products Distrib., Forlaget Systime Distribution, MacDougall Distribution, Talktapes Distribution, Watkins Books Ltd Distribution, Norton. Jeff Distribution

Whyte, Norma
RIGHT PLACE RIGHT TIME.
Single (7"): released on Londisc, Nov'85 by Londisc Records.

Whyton, Wally
50 ALL TIME CHILDREN'S FAVOURITES.
Album: released on Hallmark, Aug'79 by Pickwick Records. Dist: Pickwick Distribution, PRT, Taylors

CHILDREN'S FAVOURITE NURSERY RHYMES.
Album: released on Dakota, Apr'82 by Dakota Records. Dist: PRT

Cassette: released on Dakota, Apr'82 by Dakota Records. Dist: PRT

CHILDREN'S PARTY TIME.
Album: released on Dakota, Apr'82 by Dakota Records. Dist: PRT

Cassette: released on Dakota, Apr'82 by Dakota Records. Dist: PRT

CHILDREN'S SING-A-LONG.
Album: released on Dakota, Apr'82 by Dakota Records. Dist: PRT

Cassette: released on Dakota, Apr'82 by Dakota Records. Dist: PRT

Wiata, Inia Te
WAIATA MAORI.
Album: released on Kiwi-Pacific (New Zealand), Aug'83 Dist: Flexitron Distributors Ltd

WIATA MAORI.
Cassette: released on Viking, Jul'79 Dist: Harmonia Mundi Distributors

Wibbley Brothers
FIRST AID.
Single (7"): released on Rondelet Music And Records, Aug'81 by Rondelet Music And Records. Dist: Pinnacle, Cartel Distribution, Rondelet Music And Records Distribution

GO WEIRD.
Album: released on Rondelet Music And Records, Nov'82 by Rondelet Music And Records. Dist: Pinnacle, Cartel Distribution, Rondelet Music And Records Distribution

Wibbly Wobbly Walk
WIBBLY WOBBLY WALK Various artists (Various Artists).
Notes: Novelty numbers from phonographic cylinders and old 78 rpm records.
Album: released on Saydisc, Nov'85 by Saydisc Records. Dist: Essex, Harmonia Mundi, Roots, H.R. Taylor, Jazz Music, Swift, Projection, Gamut

Cassette: released on Saydisc, Nov'85 by Saydisc Records. Dist: Essex, Harmonia Mundi, Roots, H.R. Taylor, Jazz Music, Swift,

---

Projection, Gamut

Wibler, Bob
BOB WIBLER & HIS FAMOUS JAZZ BAND (Wibler, Bob & his famous jazz band).
Notes: Guest Star:S.Bechet.
Album: released on Jazzology, Jun'86 Dist: Jazz Music, Swift

Wichen Kopf
PLAYS WITH MARIONETTES.
Single (7"): released on Missing Link, Oct'82

Wicked Prince..
WICKED PRINCE AND THE WONDERFUL MUSICIAN (read by Michele Dotrice).
Cassette: released on Listen Productions, Jun'83 Dist: H.R. Taylor, Hayward Promotions Distribution

Wicker, Mike
MOVING FORCE, THE.
Album: by Pilgrim Records. Dist: Rough Trade, Cartel

Wickets
24 HOURS FROM TULSA.
Single (7"): released on Completely Different, Oct'84 Dist: Pinnacle

Wickman, Putte
PUTTE WICKMAN & TRIO (Wickman, Putte & Trio).
Album: released on Bluebell, Feb'87 Dist: Conifer, Jazz Music

Wick Scottish Dance Band
BY PEAT FIRE.
Album: released on Grampian, '67 by Grampian Records. Dist: Grampian, Clyde Factors Distributors, Ross

HEATHER AND SHAMROCK.
Album: released on Grampian, '85 by Grampian Records. Dist: Grampian, Clyde Factors Distributors, Ross

Wide Boy Awake
BILLY HYENA.
Single (7"): released on RCA, Feb'84 by RCA Records. Dist: RCA, Roots, Swift, Wellard, Chris, I & B, Solomon & Peres Distribution

Single (12"): released on RCA, Feb'84 by RCA Records. Dist: RCA, Roots, Swift, Wellard, Chris, I & B, Solomon & Peres Distribution

BONA VENTURA.
Single (7"): released on RCA, Feb'83 by RCA Records. Dist: RCA, Roots, Swift, Wellard, Chris, I & B, Solomon & Peres Distribution

Single (12"): released on RCA, Mar'83 by RCA Records. Dist: RCA, Roots, Swift, Wellard, Chris, I & B, Solomon & Peres Distribution

CHICKEN OUTLAW.
Single (7"): released on RCA, Oct'82 by RCA Records. Dist: RCA, Roots, Swift, Wellard, Chris, I & B, Solomon & Peres Distribution

Picture disc single: released on RCA, Oct'82 by RCA Records. Dist: RCA, Roots, Swift, Wellard, Chris, I & B, Solomon & Peres Distribution

Single (12"): released on RCA, Oct'82 by RCA Records. Dist: RCA, Roots, Swift, Wellard, Chris, I & B, Solomon & Peres Distribution

Wide Boys
STOP THAT BOY.
Single (7"): released on Big Bear, Aug'80 by Big Bear Records. Dist: Big Bear, Swift

Wide connections
WIDE CONNECTIONS (Various Artists).
Album: released on Bold Reprieve, 30 May'87 by Bold Reprieve Records. Dist: Pinnacle

Cassette: released on Bold Reprieve, 30 May'87 by Bold Reprieve Records. Dist: Pinnacle

Wide Midlands
SONGS,STORIES & TUNES FROM THE CENTRAL COUNTIES.
Album: released on Topic, '81 Dist: Roots Distribution

Wide Open
WIDE OPEN (Various Artists).
Album: released on Cracked, 30 May'87 by Cracked Records. Dist: Fast Forward, Cartel

Widespread Depression Or-
BOOGIE IN THE BARNYARD.
Album: released on Stash (Import), Apr'81 Dist: Swift Distribution, Jazz Music Distribution, Jazz Horizons Distribution, Celtic Music Distribution,

---

Cadillac, JSU Distribution, Zodiac Distribution

DOWNTOWN UPROAR.
Album: released on Stash (Import), Apr'81 Dist: Swift Distribution, Jazz Music Distribution, Jazz Horizons Distribution, Celtic Music Distribution, Cadillac, JSU Distribution, Zodiac Distribution

ROCKIN' IN RHYTHM.
Album: released on Phontastic (Sweden), '82 by Wellard, Chris Distribution. Dist: Wellard, Chris Distribution

TIME TO JUMP AND SHOUT.
Album: released on Stash (Import), '81 Dist: Swift Distribution, Jazz Music Distribution, Jazz Horizons Distribution, Celtic Music Distribution, Cadillac, JSU Distribution, Zodiac Distribution

Widespread Jazz Orchestra
PARIS BLUES.
Album: released on CBS(France), Oct'85 by CBS Records. Dist: Conifer, Discovery, Swift

Cassette: released on CBS(France), Oct'85 by CBS Records. Dist: Conifer, Discovery, Swift

PRIS BLUES.
Album: released on CBS(Import), Jun'86 by CBS Records. Dist: Conifer, Discovery, Swift

Wiedlin, Janet
BLUE KISS.
Tracks: / Blue kiss / One hundred years.
Single (7"): released on I.R.S.(Independent Record Syndicate), Jan'86 by I.R.S. Dist: MCA

Single (12"): released on I.R.S.(Independent Record Syndicate), Jan'86 by I.R.S.. Dist: MCA

Wiedorje
WIEDORJE.
Album: released on Cobra, Sep'79 by Cobra Records. Dist: Projection, EMI

Wieldin, Jane
BLUE KISS.
Single (7"): released on IRS, Oct'85 Dist: Polygram

Single (12"): released on IRS, Oct'85 Dist: Polygram

Wiesel, Elie
NIGHT(EXCERPTS).

Cassette: released on Caedmon(USA), Sep'82 by Caedmon (USA) Records. Dist: Gower, Taylors, Discovery

Wigan Metro Schools..
WIGAN METRO SCHOOLS BRASS BAND.
Album: released on Castle Studio, '81 by Castle Studio Records.

Wigans Chosen Few
FOOTSEE.
Single (7"): released on Disco Demand, '80 Dist: MCA

Wigans Ovation
AFTER LOVING YOU (2 PTS.).
Single (7"): released on RK, Apr'78

Wigan, Trevor
STRANGE FEELING (Wigan, Trevor/Jimmy Mack & The Tropics).
Tracks: / Strange feeling / Strange feeling (version).
Single (12"): released on LJC, 23 May'87

Wigg, David
BEATLES TAPES (Wigg, David Interviews 69-73).
Double Album: released on Polydor, Jul'76 by Polydor Records. Dist: Polygram, Polydor

Wiggin, Kate Douglas
REBBECCA OF SUNNYBROOK FARM.
Album: released on Caedmon(USA), Sep'80 by Caedmon (USA) Records. Dist: Gower, Taylors, Discovery

Cassette: released on Caedmon(USA), Sep'80 by Caedmon (USA) Records. Dist: Gower, Taylors, Discovery

Wigs
END OF THE OBVIOUS.
Tracks: / End of the obvious.
Notes: 5 track EP
Single (12"): released on Media Burn, Dec'85 by Rocks Off Record Emporium. Dist: Rough Trade Distribution, Cartel Distribution

SIX O'CLOCK SHUFFLE.
Tracks: / Seven and seven is / Loose.
Single (12"): released on Media Burn, Dec'86 by Rocks Off Record Emporium. Dist: Rough

---

Trade Distribution. Cartel Distribution

Wijnkamp, Leo Jr
RAGS TO RICHES.
Album: by Sonet. Dist: Roots, PRT-Pye Distribution

RETURN OF DR HACKENBUSH.
Album: released on Kicking Mule, Sep'79 by Sonet. Dist: Roots, PRT-Pye Distribution

Wikkyd Vikker
BLACK OF THE NIGHT.
Single (7"): released on Boogie, Jun'83 Dist: Pinnacle

Wilber, Bob
GROOVIN AT THE GRUNEWALD.
Album: released on Phontastic (Sweden), '82 by Wellard, Chris Distribution. Dist: Wellard, Chris Distribution

IN THE MOOD FOR SWING.
Album: released on Phontastic (Sweden), '82 by Wellard, Chris Distribution. Dist: Wellard, Chris Distribution

MOZART K581. K498.
Album: released on Artemis, Feb'81 Dist: Chris Wellard

MUSIC OF HOAGY CARMICHAEL (Wilber, Bob/Kenny Davern).
Album: released on Monmouth, May'79

ODE TO BECHET (Wilber, Bob/The Bechet Legacy).
Album: released on Bodeswell, Jul'83

Cassette: released on Bodeswell, Jul'83

ON THE ROAD (Wilber, Bob/The Bechet Legacy).
Album: released on Bodeswell, Jul'83

Cassette: released on Bodeswell, Jul'83

ORIGINAL WILBER.
Album: released on Phontastic (Sweden), '82 by Wellard, Chris Distribution. Dist: Wellard, Chris Distribution

RAPTUROUS REEDS.
Album: released on Phontastic (Sweden), '82 by Wellard, Chris Distribution. Dist: Wellard, Chris Distribution

REFLECTIONS.
Album: released on Bodeswell, Oct'84

SOPRANO SUMMIT (Wilber, Bob/Kenny Davern).
Album: released on World Jazz (Import), Apr'81

SOPRANO SUMMIT 2 (Wilber, Bob/Kenny Davern).
Album: released on World Jazz (Import), Apr'81

SOPRANO SUMMIT CONCERTO (Wilber, Bob/Kenny Davern).
Album: released on Concord Jazz, Jun'77 by Concord Jazz Records (USA). Dist: IMS, Polygram

VITAL WILBER.
Album: released on Phontastic (Sweden), '82 by Wellard, Chris Distribution. Dist: Wellard, Chris Distribution

Wilber Bob,Sextet
DIZZY FINGERS.
Album: released on Bodeswell, May'81

BOB WILBER & THE BECHET LEGACY.
Album: released on Bodeswell, May'81

Wilber's, Bob Jazz Repertory
MUSIC OF KING OLIVER-VOL 1, THE.
Album: released on Bodeswell, Oct'84

Wilbrandt, Thomas
ELECTRIC V, (THE).

Tracks: / Crescendo of Spring,(the) / Electric bird,(the) / Sketches of spring / Idyll / Twilight / Heat,(the) / Hot stuff / Meditation,(the) / Thunder and lightning / Leaves and chutes / Hi celebration / Wide white horizon / Electric harpsichord,(the) / Radio music / Dancing / Breaking the ice / Beating the cold / Farewell,(the) / Winter song,(the).
Notes: Double LP, Double Compact Disc. Music composed by Antonio Vivaldi. Special adaption composed and arranged by Thomas Wilbrandt, Simon Jeffes 9 the creative mastermind of the Penguin Cafe Orchestra and German composer specialist Klaus Buhlet. The Electric V is a journey into the past, present and future. The Musical source is Vivaldi's The Four Seasons.
Album: released on Mercury (Germany),

Sep'84 by Phonogram Records. Dist: Polygram Distribution

Cassette: released on Mercury (Germany), Sep'84 by Phonogram Records. Dist: Polygram Distribution

Compact disc: released on Mercury (Germany), Sep'84 by Phonogram Records. Dist: Polygram Distribution

Wilbur, Bob

SWINGIN' FOR THE KING.
Album: released on Phontastic (Sweden), '82 by Wellard, Chris Distribution. Dist: Wellard, Chris Distribution

Wilburn Brothers

COUNTRY GOLD.
Album: released on Stetson, Nov'85 by Hasmick Promotions Ltd.. Dist: Counterpoint Distribution, H.R. Taylor Distribution, Swift Distribution, Chris Wellard Distribution

Cassette: released on Stetson, Nov'85 by Hasmick Promotions Ltd.. Dist: Counterpoint Distribution, H.R. Taylor Distribution, Swift Distribution, Chris Wellard Distribution

TEDDY & DOYLE.
Album: released on Stetson, Apr'87 by Hasmick Promotions Ltd.. Dist: Counterpoint Distribution, H.R. Taylor Distribution, Swift Distribution, Chris Wellard Distribution

Cassette: released on Stetson, Apr'87 by Hasmick Promotions Ltd.. Dist: Counterpoint Distribution, H.R. Taylor Distribution, Swift Distribution, Chris Wellard Distribution

WILBURN BROTHERS SHOW,(THE).
Album: released on Stetson, Sep'86 by Hasmick Promotions Ltd.. Dist: Counterpoint Distribution, H.R. Taylor Distribution, Swift Distribution, Chris Wellard Distribution

Cassette: released on Stetson, Sep'86 by Hasmick Promotions Ltd.. Dist: Counterpoint Distribution, H.R. Taylor Distribution, Swift Distribution, Chris Wellard Distribution

Wilce, Malcolm

FAMILY FAVOURITES - DANCE (Wilce, Malcolm Duo).
Album: released on Maestro, Jul'87 by Maestro Records.

GOING PLACES (Wilce, Malcolm Duo).
Album: released on Maestro, Jul'86 by Maestro Records.

LET IT SWING (Wilce, Malcolm Duo).
Album: released on Maestro, Jul'86 by Maestro Records.

THERE GOES THAT SONG AGAIN (Wilce, Malcolm Duo,The/Tommy Sanderson).
Album: released on Maestro, Jul'86 by Maestro Records.

Wilcox, David

WHEN YOU MISTREAT HER.
Single (7"): released on Capitol, Nov'85 by Capitol Records. Dist: EMI

Wild!!!

WILD!!! Various artists (Various Artists).
Tracks: / Shtiggy boom / Snatch & grab / That's a plenty / Fever / Baby please don't go / Cleo's boogie / This joint's too hip for me / Take a chance on me / Slow smooth and easy / Fujiyama Mama / For you my love / Why don't you do right / Lake Charles boogie / I love my baby / Somebody put a jukebox in the study hall / It's raining / Buddy stay off that wine / Last call.
Album: released on Stateside, Sep'87 Dist: EMI. Estim retail price in Sep'87 was £3.86.

Wild and Wandering

2,000 LIGHT ALES FROM HOME........
Tracks: / 2,000 light ales from home....dust me down / Stand by me / Real cool time / Interlong / Apply tree part 1 & 2.
Notes: Most of whom went on to become Pop Will Eat Itself...
Single (12"): released on Iguana, Feb'86 by Iguana Records. Dist: ILA, Grapevine

Wild Angels

SHE'S BLACK AND WHITE.
Single (12"): released on Supreme International, Jun'87 by Supreme International Records. Dist: Fast Forward Distributors, Cartel Distribution

Wild Beasts

MINIMUM MAXIMUM.
Single (7"): released on Fried Egg, Jul'81 by Fried Egg Records. Dist: Rough Trade, Cartel

Wild Blue

NO MORE JINX.
Tracks: / Only You / Fire with fire / Nowhere left to run / When I think about you / Blue daze / Give me a reason / Leather blues / Taboo / International language of dance.
Notes: Produced by: Gary Stevenson, Chas Sandfrod, Michael frondelli & Wild Blue.
Album: released on Chrysalis, May'86 by Chrysalis Records. Dist: CBS

Cassette: released on Chrysalis, May'86 by Chrysalis Records. Dist: CBS

Wild Bunch

COUNTRY LIVING.
Single (12"): released on Ariwa, Apr'85 by Ariwa Records. Dist: Revolver, Cartel, Jetstar, Rough Trade

CREATION.
Single (7"): released on Ariwa, May'84 by Ariwa Records. Dist: Revolver, Cartel, Jetstar, Rough Trade

GINA.
Single (7"): released on Red, Apr'80

MR PRESIDENT MAN.
Single (12"): released on Ariwa, Jan'84 by Ariwa Records. Dist: Revolver, Cartel, Jetstar, Rough Trade

PLEASE BE WITH ME.
Album: released on Sweet Folk All, May'81 by Sweet Folk All Records. Dist: Sweet Folk All, Roots, Celtic Music, Dragon, Impetus, Projection, Chris Wellard, Festival Records

RUNAROUND.
Single (12"): released on Ariwa, Aug'84 by Ariwa Records. Dist: Revolver, Cartel, Jetstar, Rough Trade

WILD BUNCH, THE.
Album: released on Ariwa, Aug'84 by Ariwa Records. Dist: Revolver, Cartel, Jetstar, Rough Trade

Wild Bunch,(the)

WILD BUNCH,(THE) Various artists (Various Artists).
Cassette: released on R.O.I.R.. Nov'85

Wild Canyon

NEW WRAPPING.
Tracks: / Teen scene / Entertainer / Canyon hop / Dobro / My memories / New wrapping medley (My grandfathers clock/San Antonia) etc / Enchanted canyon 86 / Skip along / Flamingo shuffle / What is happiness / Country gentleman / Sail place.
Album: released on Bear Family, Nov'86 by Bear Family Records. Dist: Rollercoaster Distribution, Swift

WORLD OF OURS, THIS.
Album: released on Bear Family, Nov'85 by Bear Family Records. Dist: Rollercoaster Distribution, Swift

Single (7"): released on Old Gold, Jul'82 by Old Gold Records. Dist: Lightning, Jazz Music, Spartan, Counterpoint

WildCat

LOVE ATTACK.
Album: released on Road Runner, Nov'85

Wild Cherry

PLAY THAT FUNKY MUSIC.
Single (7"): released on Old Gold, Jul'82 by Old Gold Records. Dist: Lightning, Jazz Music, Spartan, Counterpoint

Wild Connections

WILD CONNECTIONS Various artists (Various Artists).
Notes: Album based on the life amid the last Iron & Whaling communities in the north-east of england.Features Phil Collins,Gary Moore,Clive Bunker,Rod Argent and many top session musicians.First release.
Album: released on Bold Reprieve, Jun'87 by Bold Reprieve Records. Dist: Pinnacle

Cassette: released on Bold Reprieve, Jun'87 by Bold Reprieve Records. Dist: Pinnacle

Compact disc: released on Bold Reprieve, Jun'87 by Bold Reprieve Records. Dist: Pinnacle

Wilde, Errol

FIRST TIME LOVE.
Single (12"): released on Lucky, Jul'82 by Lucky Records.

Wilde, Eugene

CHEY CHEY KULE.
Single (7"): released on Fourth & Broadway, Jul'85 by Island Records. Dist: Polygram, EMI

Single (12"): released on Fourth & Broadway, Jul'85 by Island Records. Dist: Polygram, EMI Deleted '87.

DIANA.
Tracks: / Diana / I want you / Diana(instrumental version)*.
Single (7"): released on MCA, Jun'86 by MCA Records. Dist: Polygram, MCA

Single (12"): released on MCA, Jun'86 by MCA Records. Dist: Polygram, MCA

EUGENE WILDE.
Album: released on Fourth & Broadway, Nov'84 by Island Records. Dist: Polygram, EMI

Cassette: released on Fourth & Broadway, Nov'84 by Island Records. Dist: Polygram, EMI

GOTTA GET YOU HOME TONIGHT.
Single (7"): released on Fourth & Broadway, Sep'84 by Island Records. Dist: Polygram, EMI Deleted '87.

Single (12"): released on Fourth & Broadway, Sep'84 by Island Records. Dist: Polygram, EMI

Picture disc single: released on Fourth & Broadway, Nov'84 by Island Records. Dist: Polygram, EMI

PERSONALITY.
Single (7"): released on Fourth & Broadway, Jan'85 by Island Records. Dist: Polygram, EMI

Single (12"): released on Fourth & Broadway, Jan'85 by Island Records. Dist: Polygram, EMI Deleted '87.

REIGN OF TERROR.
Album: released on Enigma, Apr'87 by Enigma Records. Dist: Rough Trade, Cartel, EMI

SERENADE.
Album: released on MCA, May'86 by MCA Records. Dist: Polygram, MCA

Cassette: released on MCA, May'86 by MCA Records. Dist: Polygram, MCA

Wilde, Jamie

HEAVEN IS IN YOU.
Album: released on Bare, Nov'79 Dist: Pinnacle

Cassette: released on Talking Tape Company, '84 by Talking Tape Company Records.

Wilde, Kim

ANOTHER STEP.
Tracks: / Say you really want me / You keep me hangin' on / You keep me hangin' on* / Hit him / Another step (closer to you)* / Thrill of it, The / I've got so much love / She hasn't got time for you / Brothers / Don't say nothing's changed / Schoolgirl / Say you really want me* / Missing / How do you want my love / Victim**.
Notes: * Tracks also on free 12" single given with album KIML 1. ** Extra track on cassette. Also included on cassette and compact disc - Megamix: You keep me hangin'on/Another step (closer to you)/Say you really want me. Extra tracks on compact disc: Another step (closer to you)/Say you really want me.
Album: released on MCA, Sep'87 by MCA Records. Dist: Polygram, MCA

Cassette: released on MCA, Sep'87 by MCA Records. Dist: Polygram, MCA

Compact disc: released on MCA, Dec'86 by MCA Records. Dist: Polygram, MCA

Cassette: released on MCA, Nov'86 by MCA Records. Dist: Polygram. MCA

Album: released on MCA, Nov'86 by MCA Records. Dist: Polygram, MCA

Video-cassette (VHS): released on CIC Video, Sep'87 by CBS Records. Dist: CBS, Pickwick Distribution

Compact disc: released on MCA, Aug'87 by MCA Records. Dist: Polygram, MCA

ANOTHER STEP (CLOSER TO YOU) (Wilde, Kim & Junior).
Tracks: / Another step (closer to you) / Hold back / Another step (closer to you) / Say you really want me.
Single (7"): released on MCA, Mar'87 by MCA Records. Dist: Polygram, MCA

Single (12"): released on MCA, Mar'87 by MCA Records. Dist: Polygram, MCA

CAMBODIA.
Single (7"): released on RAK, Nov'81 by RAK. Dist: EMI

CHILD COME AWAY.
Single (7"): released on RAK, Oct'82 by RAK. Dist: EMI

KIDS IN AMERICA.
Single (7"): released on RAK, Jan'81 by RAK. Dist: EMI

KIM WILDE.
Album: released on RAK, Jul'81 by RAK. Dist: EMI

Cassette: released on RAK, Jul'81 by RAK. Dist: EMI

Boxed set: released on Pathe MarconiFrance), Jun'85

KIM WILDE (VIDEO).
Tracks: / Love Blonde / View from a bridge / Kids in America.
Notes: 22 minutes
Video-cassette (VHS): released on Video Collection, May'87 by Video Collection International Ltd.. Dist: Counterpoint

RAGE TO LOVE.
Single (7"): released on MCA, Apr'85 by MCA Records. Dist: CBS

Single (12"): released on MCA, Apr'85 by MCA Records. Dist: CBS

Picture disc single: released on MCA, Apr'85 by MCA Records. Dist: CBS

SAY YOU REALLY WANT ME.
Tracks: / Don't say nothing's changed.
Single (7"): released on MCA, Jul'87 by MCA Records. Dist: Polygram, MCA

Single (12"): released on MCA, Jul'87 by MCA Records. Dist: Polygram, MCA

Single (12"): released on MCA, Aug'87 by MCA Records. Dist: Polygram, MCA

Single (7"): released on MCA, Aug'87 by MCA Records. Dist: Polygram, MCA

SELECT.
Album: released on Fame, Jul'85 by Music For Pleasure Records. Dist: EMI

Cassette: released on Fame, Jul'85 by Music For Pleasure Records. Dist: EMI

TEASES AND DARES.
Tracks: / Touch, The / Is it over / Suberbs of moscow / Fit in / Rage to love / Second time, The / Blade runner / Janine / Shangri-la / Thought it was goodbye.
Album: released on MCA, Dec'84 by MCA Records. Dist: Polygram, MCA

Cassette: released on MCA, Dec'84 by MCA Records. Dist: Polygram, MCA

Compact disc: released on MCA, Dec'84 by MCA Records. Dist: Polygram, MCA

VERY BEST OF KIM WILDE, (THE).
Album: released on RAK, Nov'84 by RAK. Dist: EMI

Cassette: released on RAK, Nov'84 by RAK. Dist: EMI

VIDEO EP.
Tracks: / Kids in america / Cambodia / Child come away / Chequered love / View from a bridge / Love blond.
Notes: kim Wilde is one of Britain's most exciting young female singers and this video release co-incides with a period of intense activity for her. Not only is she riding high in the charts with a new album and single, but her 'Greatest Hits' album featuring tracks from this video and more, is also now available. This video is a visual collection of her best work, and its sales potential will be enhanced by Kim's current high profile throughout the media. Number of tracks:6. Type of recording:EP. Total playing time:22 minutes.
Video-cassette (VHS): released on PMI, Nov'84 by PMI Records. Dist: EMI

Video-cassette [Betamax]: released on PMI, Nov'84 by PMI Records. Dist: EMI

VIEW FROM A BRIDGE.
Single (7"): released on RAK, Apr'82 by RAK. Dist: EMI

WATER ON GLASS.
Single (7"): released on RAK, Jul'81 by RAK. Dist: EMI

YOU KEEP ME HANGIN' ON.
Tracks: / You keep me hangin' on / Loving you / You keep me hangin' on*.
Single (7"): released on MCA, Sep'86 by MCA Records. Dist: Polygram, MCA

Single (12"): released on MCA, Oct'86 by MCA Records. Dist: Polygram, MCA

Wilde, Marty

BAD BOY.
Album: released on Philips (Import), Nov'81
Cat. no: **6831 048**
Cassette: released on Philips (Import). Nov'81

Single (7"): released on Old Gold, Aug'82 by Old Gold Records. Dist: Lightning, Jazz Music, Spartan, Counterpoint

ENDLESS SLEEP.
Single (7"): released on Old Gold, Aug'82 by Old Gold Records. Dist: Lightning, Jazz Music, Spartan, Counterpoint

GOOD ROCKIN' - THEN AND NOW.
Album: released on Philips, Jul'74 Dist: IMS-Polygram

HITS OF MARTY WILDE, (THE).

...bum: released on Philips (Timeless), Nov'84

...ssette: released on Philips (Timeless), ...v'84

DREAMS.
...gle (7"): released on KRL, Feb'82

...ENAGER IN LOVE.
...gle (7"): released on Old Gold, Aug'82 by ...Gold Records. Dist: Lightning, Jazz Music, ...artan, Counterpoint

...LDCAT ROCKER.
...gle (7"): released on Bear Family, Jul'81 by ...ar Family Records. Dist: Rollercoaster Dis-...ution, Swift

Wilde, Oscar
...AIRY STORIES VOL.1 READ BY ...BERT RIETTY.
...ssette: released on Kiddy Kassettes, Aug'77

...AIRY STORIES VOL.2 READ BY ...BERT RIETTY.
...ssette: released on Kiddy Kassettes, Aug'77

...APPY PRINCE & OTHER STORIES.
...acks:/ Model millionaire / Nightingale and the ...e / Selfish giant.
...ssette: released on Tellastory, Dec'86 by ...rlett Bliss Productions. Dist: PRT Distribu-...n, Hayward Promotions Distribution, H.R. ...ylor Distribution

...APPY PRINCE & OTHER STORIES, ...E.
...tes: For full information see under: WILDE, ...car - "The Happy prince & other stories"

...APPY PRINCE, THE.
...ssette: released on Talking Tape Company, ...by Talking Tape Company Records.

...RD ARTHUR SAVILE'S CRIME.
...ssette: released on Talking Tape Company, ...by Talking Tape Company Records.

Wilde, Rich
...OY WANTS TO BE ALONE, THE.
...gle (7"): released on Ovation, Jun'80 by ...l Records. Dist: PRT Distribution

Wilder, Matthew
...REAK MY STRIDE.
...gle (7"): released on Epic, Nov'83 by CBS ...cords. Dist: CBS

...gle (12"): released on Epic, Nov'83 by CBS ...cords. Dist: CBS

...ON'T SPEAK THE LANGUANGE.
...gle (7"): released on Epic, Jun'84 by CBS ...cords. Dist: CBS

...OS AMERICAN.
...m: released on CBS, Mar'84 by CBS ...cords. Dist: CBS

Wilderness
...UE LIFE.
...gle (7"): released on EMI, Aug'85 by EMI ...cords. Dist: EMI

...gle (12"): released on EMI, Aug'85 by EMI ...cords. Dist: EMI

Wilder, Tim
...RATHER BE LUCKY THAN GOOD.
...gle (7"): released on Cheapskate, Aug'81 ...Cheapskate Records. Dist: RCA

Wild Fantasy
...T READY.
...gle (7"): released on Dazzle, May'80

...NGLE DRUMS.
...um: released on Magnet, Feb'79 by Mag-...Records. Dist: BMG

...ssette: released on Magnet, Feb'79 by Mag-...Records. Dist: BMG

Wildfire
...UTE FORCE AND IGNORANCE.
...ssette: released on Mausoleum, Jul'84 by ...soleum Records. Dist: Pinnacle

...RUSALEM.
...gle (7"): released on Mausoleum, Mar'85 by ...soleum Records. Dist: Pinnacle

...THING LASTS FOREVER.
...gle (7"): released on Mausoleum, Nov'84 by ...soleum Records. Dist: Pinnacle

...MMER LIGHTNING.
...um: released on Mausoleum, Sep'84 by ...soleum Records. Dist: Pinnacle

Wildflower
...DFLOWER (Original London Cast).
Album: released on World Records, '79 Dist: Polygram

Wild flowers
IT AIN'T SO EASY.
Tracks: / It ain't so easy.
Notes: EP record
Single (7"): released on Chapter 22, Apr'86 by Chapter 22 Records. Dist: Nine Mile, Cartel

JOY OF IT ALL, THE.
Album: released on Reflex Records, Jun'84 by Reflex Records. Dist: Rough Trade, Cartel

KIND OF KINGDOM,(A).
Tracks: / Kind of kingdom.(A).
Single (7"): released on Chapter 22, Oct'86 by Chapter 22 Records. Dist: Nine Mile, Cartel

Single (12"): released on Chapter 22, Oct'86 by Chapter 22 Records. Dist: Nine Mile, Cartel

MELT LIKE ICE.
Single (7"): released on No Future, Jan'84 by No Future Records. Dist: Pinnacle, Rough Trade, Cartel

THINGS HAVE CHANGED.
Single (7"): released on Reflex Records, Apr'84 by Reflex Records. Dist: Rough Trade, Cartel

WILDFLOWER ROOTS Various Reggae Artists (Various Artists).
Album: released on Opal, Mar'76 Dist: Pavilion Distribution

WILDFLOWERS (NEW YORK LOFT JAZZ SESSIONS 1976)VOL.1 Various artists (Various Artists).
Album: released on Douglas (USA Imports), Jun'77

WILDFLOWERS (NEW YORK LOFT JAZZ SESSIONS 1976) VOL.2 Various artists (Various Artists).
Album: released on Douglas (USA Imports), Jun'77

WILDFLOWERS (NEW YORK LOFT JAZZ SESSIONS 1976) VOL.3 Various artists (Various Artists).
Album: released on Douglas (USA Imports), Jun'77

WILDFLOWERS (NEW YORK LOFT JAZZ SESSIONS 1976)VOL.4 Various artists (Various Artists).
Album: released on Douglas (USA Imports), Jun'77

WILDFLOWERS (NEW YORK LOFT JAZZ SESSIONS 1976)VOL.5 Various artists (Various Artists).
Album: released on Douglas (USA Imports), Jun'77

Wild Flowers, The
DUST.
Album: released on Chapter 22, Aug'87 by Chapter 22 Records. Dist: Nine Mile, Cartel

Wild,Gay
ACTION ACTION.
Single (7"): released on Rocket, Sep'80 by Phonogram Records. Dist: Polygram Distribution

Wild Geese
FLIGHT 2.
Album: released on Joke, Jul'82 Dist: Jazz Music, Celtic Music

Album: released on Joker (Italy), Jul'82 Dist: Cadillac, Zodiac Distribution, Jazz Horizons, Jazz Music, JSU, Celtic Music

FULL FLIGHT, THE.
Album: released on Joke, Jun'84 Dist: Jazz Music, Celtic Music

WILD GEESE IN FULL FLIGHT,THE.
Cassette: released on Joke, Feb'85 Dist: Jazz Music, Celtic Music

Wild Geese, The
WILD GEESE(THE) original film soundtrack.
Album: released on A&M, Jul'78 by A&M Records. Dist: Polygram

Wild Hills O'Wannie
WILD HILLS O'WANNIE The small pipes of Northumbria.
Album: released on Topic, '81 Dist: Roots Distribution

Wild Honey
SWEET COUNTRY.
Album: released on Country House, '82 by BGS Productions Ltd. Dist: Taylor, H.R., Record Merchandisers Distribution, Pinnacle, Sounds of Scotland Records

Cassette: released on Country House, '82 by BGS Productions Ltd. Dist: Taylor, H.R., Record Merchandisers Distribution, Pinnacle, Sounds of Scotland Records

Wild Horses
WILD HORSES.
Album: released on EMI, May'80 by EMI Records. Dist: EMI

Cassette: released on EMI, May'80 by EMI Records. Dist: EMI

Wild Indians
LOVE OF MY LIFE.
Single (12"): released on Hulla Balloo, Sep'84 by Hulla Balloo Records. Dist: Nine Mile, Cartel

PENNILESS.
Tracks: / Penniless / Take a tumble / Give up the ghost.
Single (7"): released on Rosebud, Nov'86 Dist: Fast Forward Distributors

Wilding, griselda
PARISIAN ROMANCE.
Notes: Read by Janet Maw
Compact disc: released on Cover to Cover, Nov'86 by Cover to Cover Cassettes. Dist: Conifer

Wildlife
AFRICAN BABY.
Single (7"): released on Polo, Mar'82 by Polo Records. Dist: PRT

Single (12"): released on Polo, Mar'82 by Polo Records. Dist: PRT

Wild Men Of Wonga
WHY DON'T PRETTY GIRLS LOOK AT ME.
Single (7"): released on MCA, May'85 by MCA Records. Dist: Polygram, MCA

Single (12"): released on MCA, May'85 by MCA Records. Dist: Polygram, MCA

Wild Oats
AGINCOURT.
Album: released on Sweet Folk, May'81 Dist: Roots Distribution

Wild Party Sounds
WILD PARTY SOUNDS Various Artists (Various Artists).
Album: released on Cherry Red, Nov'81 by Cherry Red Records. Dist: Pinnacle

Wild Passion
LETTERS TO SEND.
Tracks: / Letters to send / Charlie's a div.
Single (7"): released on Warm, Jun'86 Dist: EMI

Wildroot Orchestra
TOWN WITHOUT PITY/ HURRICANE FREDA.
Single (7"): released on Attic, Apr'82 Dist: Pinnacle

WILDROOT ORCHESTRA, (THE).
Album: released on Attic, Apr'82 Dist: Pinnacle

Wild Seeds
BRAVE, CLEAN AND REVERENT.
Album: released on Zippo, Jun'87

Wild Side
COLD AS ICE.
Single (7"): released on Sounds From The Crypt, Feb'82 Dist: Indies

Wild Strawberries
WILD STRAWBERRIES.
Notes: Produced by Kit Woolven (Thin Lizzy), keyboards by Don Airy.
Album: released on Metal Masters, Apr'87 by Razor Records. Dist: Pinnacle

Wild Style
WILD STYLE Original film soundtrack.
Album: released on Animal, Oct'83 by Chrysalis Records. Dist: Polygram

Cassette: released on Animal, Oct'83 by Chrysalis Records. Dist: Polygram

Wild summer,wow
WILD SUMMER,WOW Various Artists (Various Artists).
Album: released on Creation, Sep'84 Dist: Rough Trade, Cartel

Wild Swans
PEEL SESSION 1.5.82.
Tracks: / Peel Session,(the),No bleeding / Enchanted / Thirst.
Single (12"): released on Strange Fruit, Sep'86 by Clive Selwood. Dist: Pinnacle

Cassette single: released on Strange Fruit, 13 Jun'87 by Clive Selwood. Dist: Pinnacle

REVOLUTIONARY SPIRIT,A.
Single (12"): released on Zoo, Dec'81

Wild Thyme
WILD THYME PLAYS FALLISBROOME.
Album: released on Saydisc, Nov'83 by Saydisc Records. Dist: Essex, Harmonia Mundi Roots, H.R. Taylor, Jazz Music, Swift, Projection, Gamut

Cassette:

Wild Weekend
WILD WEEKEND 60's U.S.pop Vol.2 (Various Artists).
Tracks: / Everyday I have to cry / Palisades Park / Wild weekend / Surfin' bird / You baby / Land of 1000 dances / Eleanore / Judy in disguise / Last kiss / Hey baby / Hey Paula / Cry like a baby.
Album: released on Topline, Aug'86 by Charly Records. Dist: Charly Distribution

Cassette: released on Topline, Aug'86 by Charly Records. Dist: Charly Distribution

Wildwood
GOOD HEARTED FRIENDS.
Album: released on Westwood, Oct'77 by Westwood Records. Dist: Jazz Music, H.R. Taylor, JSU, Pinnacle, Ross Records

WILDWOOD.
Album: released on Westwood, Nov'76 by Westwood Records. Dist: Jazz Music, H.R. Taylor, JSU, Pinnacle, Ross Records

Wildwood, John
GOOD OLD COUNTRY MUSIC.
Album: released on Tank, Dec'77 by Tank Records.

Wiley, Ken
VISAGE.
Compact disc: by Pacific Records (USA). Dist: Atlantic

Wiley, Lee
BACK HOME AGAIN.
Album: released on Monmouth, Mar'79

LEE WILEY SINGS GERSHWIN AND COLE PORTER.
Album: released on Monmouth, Mar'79

LEE WILEY SINGS RODGERS AND HART AND HAROLD ARLEN.
Album: released on Monmouth, Mar'79

SINGS THE SONGS OF GEORGE & IRA GERSHWIN & COLE PORTER.
Album: released on Audiophile, Jun'86 by Jazzology Records (USA). Dist: Jazz Music, Swift

SWEET AND LOWDOWN.
Album: released on Halcyon, Dec'82 by Halcyon Records. Dist: Jazz Music

TOUCH OF THE BLUES, A.
Tracks: / Memphis blues, The / From the land of the sky blue water / Ace in the hole, The / Someday you'll be sorry / My melancholy baby / Hundred years from today, A / Blues in my heart / Maybe you'll be there / Between the devil & the deep blue sea / I don't want to walk without you / Make believe / Touch of the blues, A.
Album: released on RCA, Jun'87 by RCA Records. Dist: RCA, Roots, Swift, Wellard, Chris, I & B, Solomon & Peres Distribution

Cassette: released on RCA, Jun'87 by RCA Records. Dist: RCA, Roots, Swift, Wellard, Chris, I & B, Solomon & Peres Distribution

Wilf & Squint
WHEN THE DAWN BREAKS.
Single (7"): released on Lorall Productions, Apr'85

Wilhelm, Michael
MEAN OLE FRISCO.
Album: released on New Rose, Nov'85 Dist: Rough Trade, Cartel

Wilkerson, Don
PREACH BROTHER.
Album: released on Blue Note (USA Import), Sep'84

Wilkin, Marijohn
ONE DAY AT A TIME.
Album: released on Word 20, May'82

Cassette: released on Word 20, May'82

Wilkins, Ernie
ERNIE WILKINS ALMOST BIG BAND LEVEL.
Album: released on Matrix, Dec'82

WILKINS, ERNIE & THE ALMOST BIG BAND/KENNY DREW/ED THIGPEN
(Wilkins, Ernie and the Almost Big Band/Kenny Drew/Ed Thigpen).
Album: released on Storyville, Sep'86 by Storyville Records. Dist: Jazz Music Distribution, Swift Distribution, Chris Wellard Distribution, Counterpoint Distribution

Wilkinson, Colm
BRING HIM HOME.
Tracks: / Bring him home / Who am I?.
Single (7"): released on First Night, Mar'87 by Safari Records. Dist: Pinnacle

Wilkinson, Sue
LOOKING FOR COVER.
Album: released on Hustler, Dec'86 Dist: PRT

POSERS/ HOLLYWOOD SHEIK.
Single (7"): released on Cheapskate, Nov'80 by Cheapskate Records. Dist: RCA

WOMEN ONLY/ RICH MAN'S SON.
Single (7"): released on Cheapskate, Jun'81 by Cheapskate Records. Dist: RCA

Wilkins, Robert
BEFORE THE REVERENCE.
Album: released on Magpie, Sep'76 Dist: Projection

Wilkins, Yvonne
ON AND ON....
Single (7"): released on RCA, Aug'81 by RCA Records. Dist: RCA, Roots, Swift, Wellard, Chris, I & B, Solomon & Peres Distribution

Willard, Kelly
BLAME IT ON THE ONE I LOVE.
Album: released on Marantha Music, May'82

Cassette: released on Marantha Music, May'82

WILLING HEART.
Album: released on Marantha Music, May'82

Cassette: released on Marantha Music, May'82

Willesden Dodgers
1ST BASE.
Album: released on Jive, Sep'86 by Zomba Records. Dist: RCA, PRT, CBS

Cassette: released on Jive, Sep'86 by Zomba Records. Dist: RCA, PRT, CBS

BREAKIN' OUT.
Single (7"): released on Jive, Jun'84 by Zomba Records. Dist: RCA, PRT, CBS

Single (12"): released on Jive, Jun'84 by Zomba Records. Dist: RCA, PRT, CBS

GUNSMOKE BREAKOUT.
Single (7"): released on Jive, Jul'84 by Zomba Records. Dist: RCA, PRT, CBS

Single (12"): released on Jive, Jul'84 by Zomba Records. Dist: RCA, PRT, CBS

NOT THIS PRESIDENT.
Tracks: / Not this president / Zero og.
Single (7"): released on Jive, Jun'86 by Zomba Records. Dist: RCA, PRT, CBS

Cassette: released on Jive, Jun'86 by Zomba Records. Dist: RCA, PRT, CBS

Willett Family
ROVING JOURNEYMEN, THE.
Album: released on Topic, '81 Dist: Roots Distribution

William, Don
DON WILLIAMS VOL.1.
Album: released on ABC, Aug'81 Dist: CBS, Pinnacle

Cassette: released on ABC, Aug'81 Dist: CBS, Pinnacle

Williams, Al
I AM NOTHING.
Single (7"): released on Grapevine(Religious), Apr'80 Dist: Polygram Deleted Sep'81.

Williams, Alan
COUNTRY SIDE OF ME, (THE).
Album: released on Tank, Dec'77 by Tank Records.

DOING THINGS WITH YOU.
Single (7"): released on Carrere America (USA), Feb'81 by Polygram

LONESOME LEAVIN' BLUES.
Album: released on Tank, Sep'79 by Tank Records.

MIXED FEELIN'.
Album: released on Tank, Dec'77 by Tank Records.

Williams, Andy
ALMOST THERE.
Single (7"): released on Old Gold, Jul'82 by Old Gold Records. Dist: Lightning, Jazz Music, Spartan, Counterpoint

ANDY WILLIAMS CHRISTMAS ALBUM, (THE).
Compact disc: released on Hallmark, Nov'84 by Pickwick Records. Dist: Pickwick Distribution, PRT, Taylors

Cassette: released on Hallmark, Nov'84 by Pickwick Records. Dist: Pickwick Distribution, PRT, Taylors

Album: released on Hallmark, Sep'75 by Pickwick Records. Dist: Pickwick Distribution, PRT, Taylors

Cassette: released on Hallmark, Sep'79 by Pickwick Records. Dist: Pickwick Distribution, PRT, Taylors

ANDY WILLIAMS COLLECTION.
Album: released on Pickwick, Aug'78

Cassette: released on Pickwick, Aug'78

ANDY WILLIAMS' GREATEST HITS.
Album: released on CBS, '74 by CBS Records. Dist: CBS Deleted '87.

Cassette: released on CBS, '74 by CBS Records. Dist: CBS

BUTTERFLY.
Single (7"): released on Old Gold, Apr'83 by Old Gold Records. Dist: Lightning, Jazz Music, Spartan, Counterpoint

BY THE TIME I GET TO PHOENIX.
Extended-play record: released on Scoop, Oct'84

Cassette: released on Scoop, Oct'84

CAN'T GET USED TO LOSING YOU.
Single (7"): released on Old Gold, Jul'82 by Old Gold Records. Dist: Lightning, Jazz Music, Spartan, Counterpoint

CAN'T TAKE MY EYES OFF YOU.
Album: released on Hallmark, '77 by Pickwick Records. Dist: Pickwick Distribution, PRT, Taylors

Cassette: released on Hallmark, '77 by Pickwick Records. Dist: Pickwick Distribution, PRT, Taylors

CLOSE ENOUGH FOR LOVE.
Tracks: / How do you keep the music playing / Moon river / Change partners / Lucky to be me / My funny Valentine / Days of wine and roses / Through the eyes of love / Close enough for love / Music of goodbye / Round midnight.
Album: released on WEA, Nov'86 by WEA Records. Dist: WEA

Cassette: released on WEA, Nov'86 by WEA Records. Dist: WEA

Compact disc: released on WEA, Nov'86 by WEA Records. Dist: WEA

FROM ANDY WITH LOVE.
Album: released on Hallmark, Feb'85 by Pickwick Records. Dist: Pickwick Distribution, PRT, Taylors

Cassette: released on Hallmark, Feb'85 by Pickwick Records. Dist: Pickwick Distribution, PRT, Taylors

GREATEST LOVE CLASSICS (Williams, Andy & the Royal Philharmonic Orchestra.).
Tracks: / Romeo & Juliet / Love made me a fool / Vino de amor / Different light, (A) / Another winters day / Vision, (the) / Journey's end / Twist of fate, (A) / Home / Brave new world / She'll never know / In my world of illusion / Words.
Notes: Digital Stereo
Compact disc: released on EMI, Oct'84 by EMI Records. Dist: EMI

Cassette: released on EMI, Oct'84 by EMI Records. Dist: EMI

Compact disc: released on EMI, Oct'84 by EMI Records. Dist: EMI Deleted '87.

Album: released on Music For Pleasure, Oct'86 by EMI Records. Dist: EMI

Cassette: released on Music For Pleasure, Oct'86 by EMI Records. Dist: EMI

GREAT SONGS OF THE SEVENTIES.
Album: released on CBS, Nov'79 by CBS Records. Dist: CBS

Cassette: released on CBS, Nov'79 by CBS Records. Dist: CBS

HOME LOVING MAN.
Single (7"): released on Old Gold, Jul'82 by Old Gold Records. Dist: Lightning, Jazz Music, Spartan, Counterpoint

I'M OLD FASHIONED.
Album: released on Hallmark, Sep'86 by Pickwick Records. Dist: Pickwick Distribution, PRT, Taylors

Cassette: released on Hallmark, Sep'86 by Pickwick Records. Dist: Pickwick Distribution, PRT, Taylors

LET'S LOVE WHILE WE CAN.
Album: released on CBS, Feb'80 by CBS Records. Dist: CBS

Cassette: released on CBS, Feb'80 by CBS Records. Dist: CBS

REFLECTIONS.
Album: released on CBS, '79 by CBS Records. Dist: CBS

Cassette: released on CBS, '79 by CBS Records. Dist: CBS

REGRETS.
Single (7"): released on CBS, Oct'81 by CBS Records. Dist: CBS

STAR COLLECTION.
Double Album: released on Pickwick, Feb'80 by Pickwick Records. Dist: Pickwick Distribution, Prism Leisure Distribution, Lugtons

Cassette: released on Pickwick, Feb'80 by Pickwick Records. Dist: Pickwick Distribution, Prism Leisure Distribution, Lugtons

UNCHAINED MELODY.
Album: released on Hallmark, Dec'77 by Pickwick Records. Dist: Pickwick Distribution, PRT, Taylors

Cassette: released on Hallmark, Dec'77 by Pickwick Records. Dist: Pickwick Distribution, PRT, Taylors

VERY BEST OF ANDY WILLIAMS, (THE).
Album: released on Hallmark, Apr'84 by Pickwick Records. Dist: Pickwick Distribution, PRT, Taylors

Cassette: released on Hallmark, Apr'84 by Pickwick Records. Dist: Pickwick Distribution, PRT, Taylors

VINO DES ARMOUR.
Single (7"): released on Columbia, Jun'85 by EMI Records. Dist: EMI

WAY WERE, (THE).
Album: released on CBS Cameo, Jul'84 by CBS Records. Dist: CBS

Cassette: released on CBS Cameo, Jul'84 by CBS Records. Dist: CBS

WEDDING AND ANNIVERSARY ALBUM.
Album: released on CBS, Jul'81 by CBS Records. Dist: CBS

Williams, Anthony
LIFETIME.
Album: released on Blue Note (USA Import), Sep'84

SPRING.
Tracks: / Extras / Echo / From before / Love song / Tee / Extras / Echo / From before / Love song / Tee.
Compact disc: released on Manhattan-Blue Note, Jul'87 by EMI America Records (USA). Dist: EMI

Album: released on Blue Note, Jul'85 by EMI Records. Dist: EMI

Williams, Art
INTERPLAY.
Single (7"): released on Soul Stop, Jan'84 by Soul Stop Record 3. Dist: Spartan

Williams, Big Joe
LEGACY OF THE BLUES VOL.6.
Album: released on Sonet, May'74 by Sonet Records. Dist: PRT

NINE STRING GUITAR BLUES.
Album: released on Delmark, May'74

PINEY WOOD BLUES.
Album: released on Delmark, May'74

THINKING OF WHAT THEY DID.
Album: released on Arhoolie, May'81 by Ar-

---

hoolie Records. Dist: Projection, Topic, Jazz Music, Swift, Roots

THINKING OF WHAT THEY DID TO ME
Album: released on Arhoolie, Oct'86 by Arhoolie Records. Dist: Projection, Topic, Jazz Music, Swift, Roots

TOUGH TIMES.
Album: released on Arhoolie, Oct'86 by Arhoolie Records. Dist: Projection, Topic, Jazz Music, Swift, Roots

Album: released on Arhoolie, May'81 by Arhoolie Records. Dist: Projection, Topic, Jazz Music, Swift, Roots

Williams, Billy
CAUGHT IN A WORLD OF MY OWN.
Tracks: / Evernbody rock & roll.
Single (7"): released on S.B., Sep'86

Williams Brothers
SOME BECOME STRANGERS.
Tracks: / Some become strangers / Spark of life / Straight A's in love' / All pumped up"
Single (7"): released on Warner Bros., 20 Jun'87 by Warner Bros Records. Dist: WEA

Single (12"): released on Warner Bros., 20 Jun'87 by Warner Bros Records. Dist: WEA

TWO STORIES.
Tracks: / Some become strangers / Inch by inch / How long / Keeping me alive / Spark of life / You like me / Straight A's in love / State of mind / All pumped up / Rain came down.
Album: released on Warner Bros., Apr'87 by Warner Bros Records. Dist: WEA

Cassette: released on Warner Bros., Apr'87 by Warner Bros Records. Dist: WEA

Williams, Buster
CRYSTAL REFLECTIONS.
Album: released on Muse (Import), Apr'81

HEARTBEAT.
Album: released on Muse (Import), Apr'81

PINNACLE.
Album: released on Muse (Import), Apr'81

TOKUDO.
Album: released on Denon, Mar'82

Williams, Carol
YOU'VE REACHED THE BOTTOM LINE
Single (7"): released on Vanguard, Apr'83 by PRT Records. Dist: PRT

Single (12"): released on Vanguard, Apr'83 by PRT Records. Dist: PRT

Williams, Clarence
1929-1931.
Tracks: / Breeze / Mountain city blues / In our cottage of love / Them things got me / Whoop up / I'm not worrying / Pane in the glass / Freez out / Nervous breakdown / Railroad rhythm / Zonky / You've got to be modernistic / High society blues / Lazy levee loungers / Shout sister shout / Papa de da-da / Baby won't you please come home.
Notes: Mono
Album: released on VJM, '86 by Wellard, Chris Distribution. Dist: Wellard, Chris Distribution

1933-1935 VOL. 1 (WITH HIS WASH BOARD BAND).
Album: released on Swaggie (Australia), Jan'83

CLARENCE WILLIAMS JAZZ KINGS VOL.2 1929/31.
Album: released on VJM, Apr'79 by VJM (UK) Records. Dist: Swift

CLARENCE WILLIAMS JAZZ KINGS 1927/9.
Album: released on VJM, Apr'79 by VJM (UK) Records. Dist: Swift

WILD CAT BLUES.
Notes: Mono
Album: released on Rhapsody, Jan'87 by President Records. Dist: Taylors, Swift, Jazz Music, Wellard, Chris

WNYC JAZZ FESTIVAL.
Album: released on Jazz Unlimited, Dec'86 Dist: Wellard, Chris

Williams, Claude
KANSAS CITY GIANTS.
Album: released on Big Bear, May'82 by B Bear Records. Dist: Big Bear, Swift

Williams, Cootie
BOYS FROM HARLEM 1937-40, (THE)
Album: released on Swaggie (Australia), Jan'83

OYS FROM HARLEM VOL.2 1937-39, THE).
lbum: released on Swaggie (Australia), an'83

OOTIE WILLIAMS & HIS ORCHESRA.
lbum: released on Storyville (Denmark) ul'81

CHOES OF HARLEM (Williams, Cootie nd His Orchestra).
racks: / Echoes of Harlem / Things ain't the hat they used to be / Tess 'torch song / You lk a little trash / Sweet Lorraine / Cherry red ues / 'Round midnight / Is you is or is you ain't Blue garden blues / Floogie boo / I don't know Gotta do some work / My old flame / Now i ow / Somebody's gotta go / Honeysuckle se.
bum: released on Affinity, Jul'86 by Charly ecords. Dist: Charly, Cadillac

EMORIAL.
bum: released on RCA, Feb'86 by RCA Recds. Dist: RCA, Roots, Swift, Wellard, Chris, I B, Solomon & Peres Distribution

assette: released on RCA, Feb'86 by RCA ecords. Dist: RCA, Roots, Swift, Wellard, hris, I & B, Solomon & Peres Distribution

EXTET AND ORCHESTRA.
bum: released on Phoenix (Import), Apr'81

YPHOON.
bum: released on Swingtime, Jan'86 Dist: zz Music Distribution, Charly

Williams, D.A

AKE ME HAPPY.
ngle (7"): released on Pan Polychord, Aug'84 Pan Polychord Records. Dist: PRT

ngle (12"): released on Pan Polychord, g'84 by Pan Polychord Records. Dist: PRT

Williams, Danny

ADDY WRITE A LETTER SOON.
ngle (7"): released on Piccadilly, Sep'80

REEN EYES.
ngle (7"): released on Columbia, Apr'85 by l Records. Dist: EMI

ON RIVER.
ngle (7"): released on Old Gold (Reissue), '82

Williams, Dave

TE THE APPLE TREE.
bum: released on New Orleans, Apr'79 Dist: ift, Zodiac Distribution, Jazz Music, JSU

Williams, David

TE UP THE APPLE TREE.
bum: released on New Orleans, Sep'86 Dist: ift, Zodiac Distribution, Jazz Music, JSU

Williams, Delroy

STAND BLACK.
bum: released on Message, Jun'85 by Messe Records. Dist: Making Waves

TOP THE FIGHTING.
acks: / You'll never know.
ngle (12"): released on Island, Nov'86 by Isd Records. Dist: Polygram

Williams, Deniece

WHAT YOU FEEL.
ngle (7"): released on CBS, May'83 by CBS ecords. Dist: CBS

EE.
ngle (7"): released on Old Gold (Reissue), '83

T ON THE TRAIL.
acks: / Wiser and weaker / Hot on the trail / loves me, he loves me not / Video / I feel the ht / We're together / Straight from the heart / aling.
bum: released on CBS, Sep'86 by CBS Recs. Dist: CBS

ssette: released on CBS, Sep'86 by CBS cords. Dist: CBS

SO PROUD.
um: released on CBS, Jul'83 by CBS Recs. Dist: CBS

ssette: released on CBS, Jul'83 by CBS cords. Dist: CBS

S GONNA TAKE A MIRACLE.
gle (7"): released on CBS, Feb'83 by CBS cords. Dist: CBS

S YOUR CONSCIENCE.
gle (7"): released on CBS, Jun'81 by CBS cords. Dist: CBS

NEVER SAY NEVER.
Tracks: / Never say never / Love finds you.
Single (7"): released on CBS, Apr'87 by CBS Records. Dist: CBS

Single (12"): released on CBS, Apr'87 by CBS Records. Dist: CBS

NEXT LOVE.
Single (7"): released on CBS, Jul'84 by CBS Records. Dist: CBS

Single (12"): released on CBS, Jul'84 by CBS Records. Dist: CBS

SILLY.
Single (7"): released on CBS, Nov'81 by CBS Records. Dist: CBS

SO GLAD I KNOW.
Notes: The release of her first total inspirational album has already been greeted by an overwhelming reception from fans and industry observers alike. It has been attempted many times before- a well known mainstream recording artist taking definitive measures to express their spiritual convictions in music- but rarely has the anticipation been so great and so justified.
Album: released on Bird, Jul'86

Cassette: released on Bird, Jul'86

THIS IS NIECY.
Album: released on CBS, Nov'84 by CBS Records. Dist: CBS

Cassette: released on CBS, Nov'84 by CBS Records. Dist: CBS

TOO MUCH, TOO LITTLE (Williams, Deniece & Johnny Mathis).
Single (7"): released on CBS, Mar'78 by CBS Records. Dist: CBS Deleted May'80.

WATER UNDER THE BRIDGE.
Tracks: / I confess / Never say never / Water under the bridge / Love finds you / Not by chance / One less lonely heart / I believe in you / Someone for someone / Baby this is love / Don't blame it on my heart.
Album: released on CBS, May'87 by CBS Records. Dist: CBS

Cassette: released on CBS, May'87 by CBS Records. Dist: CBS

Williams, Diana

TEDDY BEAR'S LAST RIDE.
Single (7"): released on Capitol, Jun'81 by Capitol Records. Dist: EMI

Williams, Don

ESPECIALLY YOU.
Single (7"): released on MCA, Jul'81 by MCA Records. Dist: CBS

EXPRESSIONS.
Album: released on ABC, Sep'78 Dist: CBS, Pinnacle

Cassette: released on ABC, Sep'78 Dist: CBS, Pinnacle

Cassette: released on MCA (Twinpax series), Apr'82

GOLDEN GREATS: DON WILLIAMS.
Album: released on MCA, Oct'85 by MCA Records. Dist: Polygram, MCA

Cassette: released on MCA, Oct'85 by MCA Records. Dist: Polygram, MCA

GREATEST HITS: DON WILLIAMS VOL.1.
Album: released on MCA (ABC), May'83

Cassette: released on MCA (ABC), May'83

Album: released on Hallmark, Sep'86 by Pickwick Records. Dist: Pickwick Distribution, PRT, Taylors

Cassette: released on Hallmark, Sep'86 by Pickwick Records. Dist: Pickwick Distribution, PRT, Taylors

HARMONY.
Tracks: / Till the rivers run dry / You keep coming 'round / Don't you think it's time / I don't want the money / Where the Arkansas river / Leaves Oklahoma / Say it again / Maybe I just don't know / Magic carpet / Time / Ramblin' (instrumental) / She never knew me.
Album: released on MCA, Feb'86 by MCA Records. Dist: Polygram, MCA

Cassette: released on MCA, Feb'86 by MCA Records. Dist: Polygram, MCA

Cassette: released on MCA (Twinpax series), Oct'83

HEARTBEAT IN THE DARKNESS.
Tracks: / Light in your eyes, The.
Single (7"): released on Capitol, Jun'86 by Capitol Records. Dist: EMI

I BELIEVE IN YOU.
Album: released on MCA, Aug'80 by MCA Records. Dist: CBS

Cassette: released on MCA, Aug'80 by MCA Records. Dist: CBS

IN MY LIFE.
Tracks: / Where do we go from here / Strawberry fields / Something / Apartment 9 / Ruby Tiesday / Always something there / Follow me back / To Louisville / On her way to be a woman / Take my hand for a while / Long walk from childhood / In my life.
Album: released on Showcase, Apr'86 Dist: Counterpoint

Cassette: released on Showcase, Apr'86 Dist: Counterpoint

Album: released on Astan, Nov'84 by Astan Records. Dist: Counterpoint

Cassette: released on Astan, Nov'84 by Astan Records. Dist: Counterpoint

I RECALL GYPSY WOMAN.
Single (7"): released on Old Gold (Reissue), Apr'83

LISTEN TO THE RADIO.
Single (7"): released on MCA, Mar'82 by MCA Records. Dist: CBS

LOVERS AND BEST FRIENDS.
Tracks: / You're my best friend / Story of my life / Pressure makes diamonds / Love me tonight / You get to me / Love me over again / I wouldn't want to live if you didn't love me / Ain't it amaziong / Love is on a roll / I'll need someone to hold me when I cry / We're all the way / I'll be faithful to you.
Album: released on MCA, Mar'87 by MCA Records. Dist: Polygram, MCA

Cassette: released on MCA, Mar'87 by MCA Records. Dist: Polygram, MCA

LOVE STORIES.
Album:

Cassette:

NEW MOVES.
Tracks: / Heartbeat in darkness / I'll never love this way again / Shot full of love / We got love / Send her roses / Senorita / Light in your eyes, The / It's about time / Then it's love / We've got a good fire goin'.
Album: released on Capitol, Mar'86 by Capitol Records. Dist: EMI

Cassette: released on Capitol, Mar'86 by Capitol Records. Dist: EMI

ONLY LOVE.
Single (7"): released on MCA, Jun'82 by MCA Records. Dist: CBS

RUBY TUESDAY.
Extended-play record: released on Scoop, Oct'84

Cassette: released on Scoop, Oct'84

SENORITA.
Single (7"): released on Capitol, Feb'87 by Capitol Records. Dist: EMI

THAT'S THE THING ABOUT LOVE.
Single (7"): released on MCA, Apr'84 by MCA Records. Dist: CBS

VERY BEST OF DON WILLIAMS.
Tracks: / You're my best friend / Lay down beside me / Till the river runs dry / Ghost story / Good ole boys like me / Love me over again / It must be love / Amanda / Tulsa time / Shelter of your eyes, The / She's in love with a Rodeo man / I believe in you / Time on my hands / Turn down the lights / Some broken hearts never mend / I recall a gypsy woman.
Album: released on MCA, Nov'80 by MCA Records. Dist: Polygram, MCA

Cassette: released on MCA, Nov'80 by MCA Records. Dist: Polygram, MCA

Compact disc: released on MCA, Nov'80 by MCA Records. Dist: Polygram, MCA

VERY BEST OF DON WILLIAMS VOL.2.
Album: released on MCA, Feb'84 by MCA Records. Dist: CBS

Cassette: released on MCA, Feb'84 by MCA Records. Dist: CBS

WALKING A BROKEN HEART.
Single (7"): released on MCA, Mar'85 by MCA Records. Dist: CBS

WE'VE GOT A GOOD FIRE GOING.
Tracks: / Shot full of love.
Single (7"): released on Capitol, Feb'86 by Capitol Records. Dist: EMI

WHERE DO WE GO FROM HERE.
Album: released on Sundown, Nov'83 by Magnum Music Group Ltd. Dist: Magnum Music Group Ltd, PRT Distribution, Spartan Distribution

YEARS FROM NOW.
Single (7"): released on MCA, Oct'81 by MCA Records. Dist: CBS

YOU'RE MY BEST FRIEND.
Album: released on MCA (ABC), May'83

Cassette: released on MCA (ABC), May'83

YOU'RE MY BEST FRIEND/VOL.II.
Double cassette: released on MCA (Twinpax Cassettes), Sep'84

Williams, Donnett

CAN'T STAND THE PRESSURE.
Single (12"): released on Real Wax, Nov'82

Williams, E.A.

JESUS FOR THE PEOPLE.
Album: released on Faith, Jun'87 by Faith Records. Dist: Jazz Music, Swift

Williams, Esther

I'LL BE YOUR PLEASURE.
Single (7"): released on RCA, May'81 by RCA Records. Dist: RCA, Roots, Swift, Wellard, Chris, I & B, Solomon & Peres Distribution

INSIDE OF ME.
Album: released on RCA, Jun'81 by RCA Records. Dist: RCA, Roots, Swift, Wellard, Chris, I & B, Solomon & Peres Distribution

Cassette: released on RCA, Jun'81 by RCA Records. Dist: RCA, Roots, Swift, Wellard, Chris, I & B, Solomon & Peres Distribution

Single (7"): released on RCA, Sep'81 by RCA Records. Dist: RCA, Roots, Swift, Wellard, Chris, I & B, Solomon & Peres Distribution

Single (12"): released on RCA, Sep'81 by RCA Records. Dist: RCA, Roots, Swift, Wellard, Chris, I & B, Solomon & Peres Distribution

Williams-Fairey

GOLDEN JUBILEE (Williams-Fairey Engineering Band).
Tracks: / Tritsch-tratsch polka / Carnival for Bass / Serenade (Derek Bourgeois) / Piper in the meadow / Pie Jesu (from Requiem) / Blue rondo a la Turk / Marching with Sousa / Kim / Scarecrow & Mrs. King,theme from the / Swing low sweet chariot / Bohemian Rhapsody / Folk festival.
Notes: National Brass Band Champions,Autumn 1986,and well deserved! It seems a very long time since Fairey's were last on record. This new LP celebrates their Golden Jubilee and demonstrates admirably why they won the title,under the baton of RoyNewsome.The Fairey Band add a new dimension to brass-band music,placing it on a higher plane.
Cassette: released on Grasmere, May'87 by Grasmere Records. Dist: EMI

WILLIAMS-FAIREY ENGINEERING BAND (Williams-Fairey Engineering Band).
Tracks: / Tritsch-tratsch polka / Swing low sweet chariot / Kim / Piper in the meadow / Pie Jesu / Marching with Souza / Carnival for bass / Scarecrow and Mrs. King (The), Theme from / Serenade / Bohemian Rhapsody / Folk festival.
Notes: Musical director: Roy Newsome. Resident conductor: Garry Cutt. Produced by Bob Barrett. Recording engineer: Richard Scott at Strawberry Studios,Stockport. (C) & (P) 1987 Original Sound Recordings made by Grasmere Music Ltd. Mastered at EMI's Abbey Road (London) Studios by Harry Moss
Album: released on Grasmere, Mar'87 by Grasmere Records. Dist: EMI

Williams, Fess

FESS WILLIAMS & HIS ROYLE FLUSH ORCHESTRA (Williams, Fess & His Royle Flush Orchestra).
Album: released on Fountain, Jul'78 by Retrieval Records. Dist: Jazz Music, Swift, VJM, Wellard, Chris, Retrieval

FESS WILLIAMS VOLUME ONE 1929.
Album: released on Harlequin, Nov'85 by Harlequin Records. Dist: Swift, Jazz Music, Wellard, Chris, IRS, Taylor, H.R

VOLUME 2 - COMPLETE SESSIONS 1929-30, THE.
Tracks: / Do shuffle (2 takes) / Betsy Brown / She's still dizzy / Hot mama / 11.30 Saturday night / I'm feelin devilish / Al for grits and gravy / Playing my saxophone (2 takes) / You can't go wrong / Ida, sweet as apple cider / Everything's ok with me / Dinah / Just to be with you tonight.
Notes: Mono
Album: released on Harlequin, Dec'86 by Harlequin Records. Dist: Swift, Jazz Music, Wellard, Chris, IRS, Taylor, H.R.

Williams, Gari

GALW GARI.
Album: released on Cwmni'r Castell, Mar'83

Cassette: released on Cwmni'r Castell, Mar'83

Williams, Geoff

I WANT YOU TO STOP(CALLING ME UP).
Single (7"): released on Code, Oct'84 by Code

Records. Dist: Jetstar, EMI

Single (12"): released on Code, Oct'84 by Code Records. Dist: Jetstar, EMI

Williams, George

YOU HEARD A LIE.
Single (12"): released on Clair, Jun'85 by Clair Records. Dist: Jetstar

Williams, G.O.

BACK TO BOOGIE WOOGIE (Williams, G.O. & Dave Collett).
Album: released on Black Lion, Oct'82 by Black Lion Records. Dist: **Jazz Music, Chris Wellard,** Taylor, H.R., **Counterpoint, Cadillac**

William Shakespeare

TRAGEDY OF KING RICHARD II (complete text) (The Marlowe Dramatic Society).
Double cassette: released on Argo (Spoken-word), May'83 by Decca Records. Dist: Polygram

Williams, Hank

GREAT HITS OF... THE.
Album: released on Contour, Aug'85 by Pickwick Records. Dist: Pickwick Distribution, PRT

Cassette: released on Contour, Aug'85 by Pickwick Records. Dist: Pickwick Distribution, PRT

HANK WILLIAMS.
Album: released on Deja Vu, Jan'87 by Deja Vu Records. Dist: Counterpoint Distribution, Record Services Distribution (Ireland)

Cassette:

HANK WILLIAMS 40 GREATEST HITS.
Album: released on MGM, Jan'78 Dist: Polygram Distribution, Swift Distribution

Cassette: released on MGM, Jan'78 Dist: Polygram Distribution, Swift Distribution

HANK WILLIAMS AND THE DRIFTING COWBOYS (Williams, Hank and The Drifting Cowboys).
Album: released on Jambalaya, Feb'87 by Charly Records. Dist: Charly

Cassette: released on Jambalaya, Feb'87 by Charly Records. Dist: Charly

HANK WILLIAMS GREATEST HITS VOL 1.
Album: released on MGM, Jun'81 Dist: Polygram Distribution, Swift Distribution

Cassette: released on MGM, Jun'81 Dist: Polygram Distribution, Swift Distribution

HEALTH AND HAPPINESS SHOWS 1949.
Album: released on Jambalaya, Sep'85 by Charly Records. Dist: Charly

HOME IN HEAVEN.
Single (7"): released on Arhoolie, Mar'83 by Arhoolie Records. Dist: Projection, Topic, Jazz Music, Swift, Roots

I AIN'T GOT NOTHIN' BUT TIME.
Tracks: / You're gonna change (or I'm gonna leave) / My son calls another man daddy / First year blues / Are you building a temple in heaven / No one will ever know / I'm so lonesome I could cry / House without love, A / When the book of life is read / You better keep it in your mind / Fool about you / Wedding bells / I've just told mama goodbye / If you'll be a baby to me / House of gold. A / We're getting close to the grave each day / Thy burdens are greater than mine / I just don't like this kind of living / My bucket's got a hole in it / Waltz of the wind / How can you refuse now / Fool about you.
Double Album: released on MGM, Oct'86 Dist: Polygram Distribution, Swift Distribution

Double Album: released on Polydor (USA), Sep'86

Cassette: released on Polydor (USA), Sep'86

I'M SO LONESOME.
Single (7"): released on MGM, '80 Dist: Polygram Distribution, Swift Distribution

I'M SO LONESOME I COULD CRY.
Album: released on IMS, Jan'87 by Polydor Records. Dist: IMS, Polygram

LIVE AT THE GRAND OLE OPREY.
Album: released on MGM, Oct'86 Dist: Polygram Distribution, Swift Distribution

LOST HIGHWAY (DECEMBER '48-MARCH '49).
Tracks: / There'll be no teardrops tonight / Lost on the river / I heard my mother praying for me / California Zephyr / Teardrop on a rose, A / Honky tonk blues / Mind your own business / I'm free at last / Wait for the light to shine / No, not now / Lost highway / May you never be alone / Dixie cannonball / Blue love in my heart / Angel of death, The / Jesus remembered me / Dear brother / Singing waterfall / I'm going home / Sundown and sorrow / Alabama waltz.
Notes: Third in a series of Hank's studio and best known non-session recordings in chronilogical order. All recordings are in their original undubbed mono form. Contains versions of two songs that have not been previously released, plus two tunes that have never been available commercially. Remastered for the cleanest possible sound quality. Striking gatefold package contains reproductions of the original trade ads, rare photographs, and extensive liner notes.
Double Album: released on MGM, Jul'86 Dist: Polygram Distribution, Swift Distribution

Cassette: released on MGM, Jul'86 Dist: Polygram Distribution, Swift Distribution

LOVESICK BLUES.
Album: released on MGM, Oct'86 Dist: Polygram Distribution, Swift Distribution

Single (7"): released on MGM, '80 Dist: Polygram Distribution, Swift Distribution

MORE RARE RADIO PROGRAMMES VOL.2.
Album: released on Jambalaya, May'86 by Charly Records. Dist: Charly

MORE RARE RADIO PROGRAMMES 1949.
Album: released on Jambalaya, May'86 by Charly Records. Dist: Charly

MORE RARE RADIO PROGRAMMES VOL.1.
Album: released on Jambalaya, May'86 by Charly Records. Dist: Charly

Album: released on Jambalaya, May'86 by Charly Records. Dist: Charly

ON THE AIR.
Album: released on MGM, Oct'86 Dist: Polygram Distribution, Swift Distribution

RARE RADIO BROADCASTS 1949.
Album: released on Jambalaya, Jul'85 by Charly Records. Dist: Charly

RARE TAKES AND RADIO CUTS.
Album: released on MGM, Oct'86 Dist: Polygram Distribution, Swift Distribution

VERY BEST OF HANK WILLIAMS.
Album: released on Arcade Music Gala, Apr'86 Dist: Stage One

Cassette: released on Arcade Music Gala, Apr'86 Dist: Stage One

VERY BEST OF HANK WILLIAMS VOL.1, THE.
Album: released on Pickwick, Mar'87 by Pickwick Records. Dist: Pickwick Distribution, Prism Leisure Distribution, Lugtons

Cassette: released on Pickwick, Mar'87 by Pickwick Records. Dist: Pickwick Distribution, Prism Leisure Distribution, Lugtons

Williams, Hank Jnr

ARE YOU SURE HANK DONE IT THIS WAY.
Tracks: / Family tradition / Kaw-liga / Whiskey bant and hell bound / Are you sure Hank done it this way / Women I've never had / Old habits / Dixie on my mind / If you don't like Hank Williams / Move it on over / Texas women / All my rowdy friends are coming over tonight / Heaven ain't a lot like Dixie / Country boy can survive, A / Honky tonkin' / Leave them boys alone / Man of steel.
Album: released on Warner Bros., Mar'86 by Warner Bros Records. Dist: WEA

Cassette: released on Warner Bros., Mar'86 by Warner Bros Records. Dist: WEA

HIGH NOTES.
Album: released on Elektra Asylum, Jun'82 by Elektra/Asylum/Nonesuch Records. Dist: WEA

Williams, Heather

NIGHTLIFE (Williams, Heather & The Clima. Orchestra).
Single (12"): released on Challenge, Feb'85 by Elite Records. Dist: Pinnacle

Williams, Iris

BEAUTIFUL.
Tracks: / He was beautiful / Love me good / Send in the clowns / He's out of my life / Now while I still remember how / My prayer / I have loved me a man / Dearest friend / We don't make each other laugh anymore / Run like the wind / Let the music begin / No regrets / Above the tears / Hi there / Men in my life, The / I'll never love this way again.
Notes: For the first time on Music For Pleasure a new collection of great songs performed by one of the U.K.'s best female ballad singer - Iris Williams. Sixteen great tracks including a recent best seller 'Hi There', superb versions of 'We Don'tMake Each Other Laugh Anymore' and 'I'll Never Love this Way Again', a vocal version of Chi Mai 'Dearest Friend' and, of course, her biggest hit 'He Was Beautiful' the vocal version of 'Cavatina' the theme from 'The Deer Hunter'.
Album: released on Music For Pleasure, Feb'86 by EMI Records. Dist: EMI

Cassette: released on Music For Pleasure, Feb'86 by EMI Records. Dist: EMI

DON'T MAKE MY WHITE CHRISTMAS BLUE.
Single (7"): released on Polydor, Dec'82 by Polydor Records. Dist: Polygram, Polydor

HE WAS BEAUTIFUL.
Album: released on Columbia, Jan'80 by EMI Records. Dist: EMI

Cassette: released on Columbia, Jan'80 by EMI Records. Dist: EMI

HE WAS BEAUTIFUL / WE DON'T MAKE EACH.....
Single (7"): released on Columbia, Sep'79 by EMI Records. Dist: EMI

HI THERE!.
Single (7"): released on Columbia, Jan'85 by EMI Records. Dist: EMI

I'LL NEVER LOVE THIS WAY AGAIN.
Single (7"): released on Columbia, May'85 by EMI Records. Dist: EMI

I'M LOOKING FORWARD TO TOMORROW.
Tracks: / I'm looking forward to tomorrow / Let's pretend.
Single (7"): released on President, Mar'87 by President Records. Dist: Taylors, Spartan

JUST FOR YOU / NO REGRETS.
Single (7"): released on EMI, Jul'81 by EMI Records. Dist: EMI

MANY MOODS OF IRIS WILLIAMS.
Album: released on Music World, Jan'77

MEMORY / IF YOU GO AWAY.
Single (7"): released on Polydor, Jan'83 by Polydor Records. Dist: Polygram, Polydor

PEACE MUST COME AGAIN.
Tracks: / Peace must come again / Next time I see you, The.
Album: released on President, Sep'86 by President Records. Dist: Taylors, Spartan

Single (7"): released on President, Jun'86 by President Records. Dist: Taylors, Spartan

WATER IS WIDE (THE).
Tracks: / Water is wide (The) / Let's pretend.
Single (7"): released on President, Apr'87 by President Records. Dist: Taylors, Spartan

YOU ARE MY STORY / SONG ON THE SEASHORE.
Single (7"): released on Polydor, Jan'84 by Polydor Records. Dist: Polygram, Polydor

YOU BELONG TO ME.
Album: released on EMI, Oct'82 by EMI Records. Dist: EMI

Cassette: released on EMI, Oct'82 by EMI Records. Dist: EMI

Williams, James

ALTER EGO.
Tracks: / Black scholars / Alter ego / Havana days / Fourplay / Touching affair, A / Waltz and monk / Beauty witin.
Notes: All compositions by James Williams except 'Waltz and Monk'and 'Havana Days'. Composed by Donald Brown. All Music Published by Second Floor Music (EMI).
Album: released on Sunnyside Jazz (USA), Jan'86

ARIOSO TOUCH, THE (Williams, James Trio).
Album: released on Concord Jazz(USA), Sep'82 by Concord Jazz Records (USA). Dist: IMS, Polygram

FLYING COLOURS (Williams, James/Slide Hampton).
Album: released on Zim, Apr'81 Dist: JSU, Jazz Horizons, Jazz Music, Swift

IMAGES OF THINGS TO COME.
Album: released on Concord, Mar'81 by Import Records. Dist: IMS, Polygram

MIRACLES OF THE HEART (Williams, James 'D Train').
Tracks: / You are everything / Oh how I love you (girl) / Miracle of the heart / Misunderstandings / Let me love you / Ice melts into rain / I got your number / Stand up and fight.
Album: released on CBS, Sep'86 by CBS Records. Dist: CBS

Cassette: released on CBS, Sep'86 by CBS Records. Dist: CBS

MISUNDERSTANDING (Williams, James 'D Train').
Single (7"): released on CBS, Feb'87 by CBS Records. Dist: CBS

Single (12"): released on CBS, Feb'87 by C[...]
Records. Dist: CBS

PROGRESS REPORT (Williams, Jam[...]
Sextet).
Tracks: / Progress report / Episode from a [...]lage dance / Affaire d'amour / Mr. Day's drea[...] / Unconscious behaviour / Renaissance love[...]
Notes: Personnel: James Williams - accous[...] piano/Bill Easley - Alto saxophon[...] flute,clarinet/Kevin Eubanks - Electric g[...]tar/Billy Pierce - Tenor saxophone and sopra[...] saxophone/Tony Reedus - Drums/Rufus Re[...] Accoustic bass/Jerry Gonzales-Congas, add[...] on 'Episode from a Village Dance' only. [...] compositions except 'Unconscious Behavio[...] are published by Second Floor Music, BMI. 'E[...]sode from a Village Dance' is dedicated [...] Bobby Hutcherson and 'Affaire d'Amour' is de[...]cated to the memory of Edward Kennedy 'Du[...] Ellington.
Album: released on Sunnyside (USA), Feb [...] Dist: Mole Jazz Distribution, Conifer Distribut[...]
Cat. no: **SSC 10[...]**
Compact disc: released on Sunnyside (US[...] Feb'86 Dist: Mole Jazz Distribution, Conifer D[...]tribution

Williams, Janet

KEEP IT COMING(FUNK MIX).
Single (12"): released on Justice, May'84 D[...]
Pinnacle

Williams, Jaye

LET ME BE THE ONE.
Single (12"): released on Local, Jan'85 [...]
Local Records. Dist: Pinnacle

Williams, Jerry

CRUISIN' ON A SATURDAY NIGHT.
Single (7"): released on Sonet, Sep'82 [...]
Sonet Records. Dist: PRT

GOD BLESS ROCK'N'ROLL.
Single (7"): released on Sonet, Oct'82 by So[...]
Records. Dist: PRT

TOO FAST TO LIVE,TOO FAST TO D[...]
Album: released on Sonet, Feb'79 by So[...]
Records. Dist: PRT

Williams, Jessica

CASANOVA.
Tracks: / Casanova / Casanova (inst).
Single (12"): released on Passion, Jul'87 [...]
Skratch Records. Dist: PRT

NOTHIN' BUT THE BLUES.
Album: released on Blackhawk, Aug'86 [...]
Blackhawk Records (USA). Dist: IMS-Polygr[...]

QUEENS OF FOOLS.
Single (12"): by Skratch Records. Dist: PR[...]

Single (12"): released on Passion, Sep'83 [...]
Skratch Records. Dist: PRT

Williams, Jimmy

DO YOU REALLY WANT TO WAIT.
Tracks: / Do you really want to wait / Do you [...]ally want to wait (remix).
Single (12"): released on Hardcore, 30 May[...] by Hardcore Records. Dist: PRT

Williams, Joe

EVERYDAY I HAVE THE BLUES.
Album:

JOE WILLIAMS & COUNT BASIE ([...]liams,Joe/Count Basie).
Album: released on Vogue Jazz (Fran[...]
May'83

NOTHIN' BUT THE BLUES.
Tracks: / Who she do / Just a dream / Ple[...] send me someone to love / Alright, OK, you [...] / Hold it right there / In the evening / Rock [...] my bed / Sent for you yesterday / Going to [...]cago blues / Ray Brown's in town.
Notes: Veteran blues giant and ex-Basie [...]calist, singing his way through nine classic bl[...] supported by an all star band. This album [...] a Grammy last year in the States. Digital re[...]ding. Personnel: Joe Williams - vocals/[...] Holloway - leader & tenor sax/ Eddie Cleanh[...] Vinson - vocal & alto sax/Jack McDuff - or[...] &piano/Phil Upchurch - guitar/Ray Brow[...] bass/Gerryck King - drums.
Album: released on DMS USA, Jul'86 by D[...]
Records. Dist: IMS, Polygram

Compact disc: released on DMS USA, Ju[...]
by DMS Records. Dist: IMS, Polygram

Williams, John

16 GOLDEN CLASSICS.
Tracks: / Cavatina (he was beautiful).
Notes: All tracks licensed from C-ERA R[...]ords/Cube Records Ltd. Design: Shoot [...] Tiger! (C) 1986: Castle Communications Pl[...] Unit 7, 271 Merton Road, London SW18 [...] Bar code: 5/013428/920039.
Album: released on Unforgettable, Dec'8[...]
Castle Communications Records. D[...]
Counterpoint

assette: released on Unforgettable, Dec'86
/ Castle Communications Records. Dist:
ounterpoint

ompact disc: released on Unforgettable, '86
/ Castle Communications Records. Dist:
ounterpoint

ISLE SEAT (Williams, John & Boston
ops).
acks: / E.T. / Chariots of fire / Raiders of the
st ark / Yes, Giorgio / New York, New York /
one with the wind / Wizard of Oz, The / Sin-
' in the rain / Friendly persuasion / Meet me
St. Louis.
bum: released on Philips, Jan'83 Dist: IMS-
olygram

assette: released on Philips, Jan'83 Dist:
IS-Polygram

ompact disc: released on Philips, Jan'83
st: IMS-Polygram

RIDGES.
ompact disc: released on K-Tel, Nov'86 by
Tel Records. Dist: Record Merchandisers
stribution, Taylors, Terry Blood Distribution,
ynd-Up Distribution, Relay Distribution, Pick-
ck Distribution, Solomon & Peres Distribution,
olygram

bum: released on Lotus, Aug'79 Dist:
ounterpoint

AVATINA.
ngle (7"): released on Cube, May'77 by Data Records. Dist: PRT

ngle (7"): released on Old Gold, Aug'82 by
d Gold Records. Dist: Lightning, Jazz Music,
partan, Counterpoint

HANGES.
bum: released on Sierra, May'85 by Sierra
ecords. Dist: WEA

assette: released on Sierra, May'85 by Sier-
Records. Dist: WEA

ONCERTO FOR GUITAR AND JAZZ RCHESTRA-PAUL HART.
acks: / Rondo la ronde / Song without words
D minot / Duet for two.
bum: released on CBS, May'87 by CBS Rec-
ds. Dist: CBS

assette: released on CBS, May'87 by CBS
ecords. Dist: CBS

EER HUNTER (ORIGINAL THEME).
bum: released on Cube, Oct'81 by Dakota
ecords. Dist: PRT

assette: released on Cube, Oct'81 by Dako-
Records. Dist: PRT

MPIRE STRIKES BACK, THE.
bum: released on Chalfont (USA), Oct'80 by
rese Sarabande.

T. THEME / OVER THE MOON.
ngle (7"): released on MCA, Nov'82 by MCA
ecords. Dist: CBS

EELINGS (Williams, John & Cleo Laine).
ngle (7"): released on RCA, Mar'77 by RCA
ecords. Dist: RCA, Roots, Swift, Wellard,
aris, I & B, Solomon & Peres Distribution

ESSOR'S NIGHTHAWKS (Williams,
hn/Doc Cheatham/Herb Hall).
bum: released on Storyville, '86 by Storyville
ecords. Dist: Jazz Music Distribution, Swift
stribution, Chris Wellard Distribution,
ounterpoint Distribution

UITAR IS THE SONG, THE.
oum: released on CBS, Jun'83 by CBS Rec-
ls. Dist: CBS

ssette: released on CBS, Jun'83 by CBS
ecords. Dist: CBS

ERE'S WHAT I'M HERE FOR (Williams,
n & Company).
mpact disc: released on Discovery (USA),
c'86 by Discovery Records (USA). Dist:
ift, Flexitron-Audio, Jazz Music

WAS BEAUTIFUL (Williams, John &
o Laine).
gle (7"): released on RCA, Dec'77 by RCA
cords. Dist: RCA, Roots, Swift, Wellard,
ris, I & B, Solomon & Peres Distribution

T THE MUSIC TAKE YOU (Williams,
n & Cleo Laine).
um: released on CBS, Dec'83 by CBS Rec-
s. Dist: CBS

ssette: released on CBS, Dec'83 by CBS
cords. Dist: CBS

AGIC GUITAR OF, THE.
um: released on Hallmark, Feb'86 by Pick-
k Records. Dist: Pickwick Distribution, PRT,
lors

ssette: released on Hallmark, Feb'86 by
wick Records. Dist: Pickwick Distribution,
, Taylors

OFF THE RECORD WITH JOHN WILLIAMS.
Album: released on Sierra, Nov'84 by Sierra Records. Dist: WEA

Cassette: released on Sierra, Nov'84 by Sierra Records. Dist: WEA

OUT OF THIS WORLD (Williams, John & Boston Pops).
Album: released on Philips, Dec'83 Dist: IMS-Polygram

Cassette: released on Philips, Dec'83 Dist: IMS-Polygram

PAUL MCCARTNEY'S THEME FROM HONORARY CONSUL / CLARA'S THEME.
Single (7"): released on Island, Dec'83 by Island Records. Dist: Polygram

PLATINUM COLLECTION.
Double Album: released on Cube (Platinum coll), Oct'81

Double cassette: released on Cube (Platinum coll), Oct'81

PORTRAIT OF JOHN WILLIAMS.
Album: released on CBS(Masterworks), Oct'82 by CBS Records. Dist: CBS
Cat. no: **D 37791**

Cassette: released on CBS(Masterworks), Oct'82 by CBS Records. Dist: CBS

RECOLLECTIONS.
Album: released on CBS, Jun'79 by CBS Records. Dist: CBS

Cassette: released on CBS, Jun'79 by CBS Records. Dist: CBS

REPLAY ON (THE HEIGHT BELOW).
Album: released on Sierra, May'86 by Sierra Records. Dist: WEA

Cassette: released on Sierra, May'86 by Sierra Records. Dist: WEA

ROMANZA / CAVATINA.
Single (7"): released on Cube, Jan'82 by Dakota Records. Dist: PRT

SPOTLIGHT ON JOHN WILLIAMS.
Double Album: released on PRT, '80 by PRT Records. Dist: PRT

Double cassette: released on PRT, '80 by PRT Records. Dist: PRT

STOMPIN' AT THE SAVOY (Williams, John & Boston Pops).
Tracks: / Opus one / Begin the beguine / Sunrise serenade / Stompin' at the Savoy / Tuxedo Junction / Satin doll / In the mood / Sing sing sing / Moonlight serenade / String of pearls / Sleepy lagoon / Song of India / Snowfall / Swing swing swing.
Album: released on Philips, Apr'86 Dist: IMS-Polygram

Cassette: released on Philips, Apr'86 Dist: IMS-Polygram

Compact disc: released on Philips, Apr'86 Dist: IMS-Polygram

SUPERMAN THEME.
Single (7"): released on Warner Brothers, Jan'79 by WEA Records. Dist: WEA

SYMPHONIC SUITES.
Album: released on Music For Pleasure (Holland), Mar'83 by EMI Records. Dist: EMI

Cassette: released on Music For Pleasure (Holland), Mar'83 by EMI Records. Dist: EMI

THAT'S ENTERTAINMENT (Williams, John & Boston Pops).
Tracks: / That's entertainment / Let me entertain you / Fiddler on the roof / Little night music / Pops on Broadway / Gigi / Richard Rodgers waltz.
Compact disc: released on Philips, '86 Dist: IMS-Polygram

TRAVELLING.
Album: released on Sierra, Aug'85 by Sierra Records. Dist: WEA

Cassette: released on Sierra, Aug'85 by Sierra Records. Dist: WEA

WERELD SUCCESSEN (Williams, John & Cleo Laine).
Double Album: released on IMS(Import), Oct'82 by Polydor Records. Dist: IMS, Polygram

WORLD OF JOHN WILLIAMS, (THE).
Tracks: / Travelling / Lorelei / Spanish trip / Nuages / All at sea minor / Duet for guitar and koto / Sarabande / River god, The / Horizon / Theme from "Z" / Raga vilasakhani todi / Good morning freedom.
Compact disc: released on K-Tel, Jun'87 by K-Tel Records. Dist: Record Merchandisers Distribution, Taylors, Terry Blood Distribution, Wynd-Up Distribution, Relay Distribution, Pickwick Distribution, Solomon & Peres Distribution, Polygram

Album: released on K-Tel, Jul'87 by K-Tel Records. Dist: Record Merchandisers Distribution, Taylors, Terry Blood Distribution, Wynd-Up Distribution, Relay Distribution, Pickwick Distribution, Solomon & Peres Distribution, Polygram

Cassette: released on K-Tel, Jul'87 by K-Tel Records. Dist: Record Merchandisers Distribution, Taylors, Terry Blood Distribution, Wynd-Up Distribution, Relay Distribution, Pickwick Distribution, Solomon & Peres Distribution, Polygram

Williams JR, Hank

AIN'T MISBEHAVIN'.
Tracks: / I've been around.
Single (7"): released on Warner Bros., Apr'86 by Warner Bros Records. Dist: WEA

ALL MY ROWDY FRIENDS ARE COMING OVER TONIGHT.
Tracks: / Video blues.
Single (7"): released on Curb (USA), Feb'86 by Warner Bros Records. Dist: CBS, WEA

AT THE COUNTRY STORE.
Album: released on Country Store, Dec'85 by Starblend Records. Dist: PRT, Prism Leisure Corporation Records

Cassette: released on Country Store, Dec'85 by Starblend Records. Dist: PRT, Prism Leisure Corporation Records

FIVE-O.
Tracks: / I'm for love / I really like girls / Nashville scene, The / Ain't misbehavin' / Something to believe in / Lawyers, guns and money / This ain't Dallas / I've been around / New Orleans / Outlaws reward.
Album: released on Warner Bros., Jul'86 by Warner Bros Records. Dist: WEA

Cassette: released on Warner Bros., Jul'86 by Warner Bros Records. Dist: WEA

GREATEST HITS:HANK WILLIAMS JNR.
Compact disc: released on Elektra (USA), '84 by Elektra/Asylum/Nonesuch Records. Dist: WEA

MAGIC GUITAR OF HANK WILLIAMS JR, THE.
Album: released on Hallmark, Feb'86 by Pickwick Records. Dist: Pickwick Distribution, PRT, Taylors

Cassette: released on Hallmark, Feb'86 by Pickwick Records. Dist: Pickwick Distribution, PRT, Taylors

Williams, Kenneth

MORE WILLO THE WISP STORIES.
Album: released on BBC, Jul'83 by BBC Records & Tapes. Dist: EMI, PRT,

Cassette: released on BBC, Jul'83 by BBC Records & Tapes. Dist: EMI, PRT,

PARLOUR POETRY.
Album: released on Saydisc, May'79 by Saydisc Records. Dist: Essex, Harmonia Mundi, Roots, H.R. Taylor, Jazz Music, Swift, Projection, Gamut

Cassette: released on Saydisc, May'79 by Saydisc Records. Dist: Essex, Harmonia Mundi, Roots, H.R. Taylor, Jazz Music, Swift, Projection, Gamut

STORYTIME TOP TEN VOL 9.
Cassette: released on VFM Cassettes, Jan'85

WILLO THE WISP DOWN IN THE WOODS / EDNA'S SONG.
Single (7"): released on BBC, Nov'83 by BBC Records & Tapes. Dist: EMI, PRT, Pye

Williams, Kymm

KYMM.

Album: released on Nevis, Jan'79 Dist: H.R. Taylor

Williams, Larry

ALACAZAM.
Album: released on Ace, Apr'87 by Ace Records. Dist: Pinnacle, Swift, Hotshot, Cadillac

BONY MARONIE.
Single (7"): released on Old Gold, Jan'85 by Old Gold Records. Dist: Lightning, Jazz Music, Spartan, Counterpoint

DIZZY MISS LIZZY.
Single (7"): released on Specialty, Jul'77

Album: released on Ace, Jan'85 by Ace Records. Dist: Pinnacle, Swift, Hotshot, Cadillac

ON STAGE.
Notes: Re-issue of old UK Sue album.
Album: released on Starclub, Jul'87

Williams, Lawton

LIGHTNING JONES.
Album: released on Bear Family, Nov'85 by Bear Family Records. Dist: Rollercoaster Distribution, Swift

Williams, Lenny

TEN WAYS OF LOVING YOU.
Tracks: / Ten ways of loving you / Waiting for your love.
Single (7"): released on Malaco Dance, Sep'86 Dist: PRT

Williams, Leona

LEONA WILLIAMS AND HER DIXIE BAND (Williams, Leona & Her Dixie Band).
Album: released on Fountain, Apr'79 by Retrieval Records. Dist: Jazz Music, Swift, VJM, Wellard, Chris, Retrieval

Williams, Lester

DOWLING STREET HOP.
Album: released on Krazy Kat (USA Import), Mar'83

TEXAS TROUBADOUR.
Album: released on Ace, Feb'87 by Ace Records. Dist: Pinnacle, Swift, Hotshot, Cadillac

Williams, Mallory

REGGAE GONE GRAMMY.
Single (12"): released on Diamond C, May'85 by Diamond C Records. Dist: Jetstar

Williams, Marion

I'VE COME SO FAR.
Album: released on Spirit Feel, Jul'87

Williams, Mary Lou

BEST OF MARY LOU WILLIAMS.
Cassette: released on Pablo (USA), '82 by Pablo Records (USA). Dist: Wellard, Chris, IMS-Polygram, BMG

Cassette: released on Pablo (USA), '82 by Pablo Records (USA). Dist: Wellard, Chris, IMS-Polygram, BMG

EMBRACED (Williams, Mary Lou/Cecil Taylor).
Album: released on Pablo, Apr'78 by Pablo Records. Dist: Wellard, Chris, IMS-Polygram, BMG

Album: released on Pablo, Apr'78 by Pablo Records. Dist: Wellard, Chris, IMS-Polygram, BMG

MY MAMA PINNED A ROSE ON ME.
Album: released on Pablo (USA), '82 by Pablo Records (USA). Dist: Wellard, Chris, IMS-Polygram, BMG

Cassette: released on Pablo (USA), '82 by Pablo Records (USA). Dist: Wellard, Chris, IMS-Polygram, BMG

SOLO RECITAL MONTREUX JAZZ FESTIVAL 1978.
Album: released on Pablo (USA), '82 by Pablo Records (USA). Dist: Wellard, Chris, IMS-Polygram, BMG

Cassette: released on Pablo (USA), '82 by Pablo Records (USA). Dist: Wellard, Chris, IMS-Polygram, BMG

WALKIN' & SWINGIN'.
Album: released on Saar Giants Of Jazz (Italy), Sep'85 Dist: Mainline

Album: released on Saar Giants Of Jazz (Italy), Sep'85 Dist: Mainline

Williams, Mason

CLASSICAL GAS.
Tracks: / Classical gas / Baroque-a-nova.
Single (7"): released on Old Gold, Mar'86 by Old Gold Records. Dist: Lightning, Jazz Music, Spartan, Counterpoint

Single (7"): released on Warner Brothers, Jul'81 by WEA Records. Dist: WEA

Williams, Maurice

BEST OF:MAURICE WILLIAMS & THE ZODIACS (Williams, Maurice & The Zodiacs).
Album: released on Herald, Sep'79 by Relic Records. Dist: Swift

STAY (Williams, Maurice & The Zodiacs).
Single (7"): released on Old Gold, Jul'82 by Old Gold Records. Dist: Lightning, Jazz Music, Spartan, Counterpoint

STAY (JUST A LITTLE BIT LONGER).
Single (7"): released on Creole Replay, Aug'84 by Creole Records. Dist: PRT, Rhino

Williams, Michelle

DANCIN' WITH SOUL (see Williams,Jerry 'Swamp Dogg').
Album: released on Rare Bullet, Jan'84 by Neon Records. Dist: Pinnacle

Williamson, Ann

BLUE BABY BLUE.
Album: released on Mint, Oct'81 by Emerald Records. Dist: Ross Distribution, PRT Distribution, Solomon & Peres Distribution

Cassette: released on Mint, Oct'81 by Emerald Records. Dist: Ross Distribution, PRT Distribution, Solomon & Peres Distribution

BLUE EYES CRYING IN THE RAIN.
Tracks: / Blue eyes crying in the rain / She's got you.
Single (7"):

COUNTRY EVERGREENS.
Album: released on Emerald (Ireland), Oct'81 by Emerald Records. Dist: I & B, Ross, PRT

Cassette: released on Emerald (Ireland), Oct'81 by Emerald Records. Dist: I & B, Ross, PRT

MORE EVERGREEN.
Album: released on Emerald, Jul'87 by Emerald Records. Dist: Ross, PRT, Solomon & Peres Distribution

Cassette: released on Emerald, Jul'87 by Emerald Records. Dist: Ross, PRT, Solomon & Peres Distribution

PAL OF MY CRADLE DAYS.
Single (7"): released on Mint, Dec'82 by Emerald Records. Dist: Ross Distribution, PRT Distribution, Solomon & Peres Distribution

PRECIOUS MEMORIES.
Tracks: / Precious memories / In the garden / Abide with me / Rock of ages / Just a closer walk with thee / What a friend we have in Jesus / When the roll is called up yonder / It is no secret / Tell me the old old story / Nearer my God to thee / One day at a time / Lord's my shepherd, The / Old time religion / Shall we gather at the river.
Album: released on Emerald (Ireland), Apr'86 by Emerald Records. Dist: I & B, Ross, PRT

Cassette: released on Emerald (Ireland), Apr'86 by Emerald Records. Dist: I & B, Ross, PRT

TINY BUBBLES.
Tracks: / Just out of reach / Heart of my heart / You don't have to tell me / Tiny bubbles / Nightingale sang in Berkley Square / Rose coloured glasses / Among my souvenirs / Cryin' time / Softly softly / Baby blue / Let bygones be bygones / Behind the footlights.
Notes: All MCPS/Chappell/Group/Control (P) 1983
Album: released on Emerald (Ireland), Nov'83 by Emerald Records. Dist: I & B, Ross, PRT

Cassette: released on Emerald (Ireland), Nov'83 by Emerald Records. Dist: I & B, Ross, PRT

TINY BUBBLES.
Single (7"): released on Mint, Oct'83 by Emerald Records. Dist: Ross Distribution, PRT Distribution, Solomon & Peres Distribution

WHEN YOU AND I WERE YOUNG MAGGIE.
Tracks: / When you and I were young Maggie / Forsaking all the rest.
Single (7"): released on Emerald (Ireland), May'86 by Emerald Records. Dist: I & B, Ross, PRT

Single (7"): released on Mint, Oct'82 by Emerald Records. Dist: Ross Distribution, PRT Distribution, Solomon & Peres Distribution

Williamson, Bob

SUPER TURN.
Album: released on Sweet Folk All, May'81 by Sweet Folk All Records. Dist: Sweet Folk All, Roots, Celtic Music, Dragon, Impetus, Projection, Chris Wellard, Festival Records

Williamson, Claude

HOLOGRAPHY.
Album: released on Interplay, Sep'79 by Interplay Records. Dist: Jazz Music, Swift

KEYS WEST.
Album: released on Affinity, Apr'81 by Charly Records. Dist: Charly, Cadillac

LA FIESTA.
Album: released on Discovery, Sep'83 Dist: PRT

NEW DEPARTURE.
Album: released on Interplay, Aug'79 by Interplay Records. Dist: Jazz Music, Swift

SALUTE TO BUD.
Album: released on Affinity, Sep'82 by Charly Records. Dist: Charly, Cadillac

Williamson, Malcolm

PROCESSION OF PALMS.
Album: released on Abbey, Mar'80 by Abbey. Dist: PRT, Taylors, Gamut

Williamson, Mark

MARK WILLIAMSON.
Album: by Pilgrim Records. Dist: Rough Trade, Cartel

Williamson, Mark Band

MISSING IN ACTION.
Album: released on Myrrh, Jun'84 by Word Records. Dist: Word Distribution

Cassette: released on Myrrh, Jun'84 by Word Records. Dist: Word Distribution

Williamson, Robin

DRAGON HAS TWO TONGUES, THE.
Album: released on TER, Aug'87 Dist: Pinnacle

Cassette: released on TER, Aug'87 Dist: Pinnacle

DRAGON HAS TWO TONGUES,THE.
Album: released on Towerbell, Feb'85 by Towerbell Records. Dist: EMI

Cassette: released on Towerbell, Feb'85 by Towerbell Records. Dist: EMI

GLINT AT THE KINDLING, A.
Notes: 'A masterpiece' - Sunday Telegraph
Album: released on Awareness, Apr'87 by Awareness. Dist: EMI

Cassette: released on Awareness, Apr'87 by Awareness. Dist: EMI

GLINT AT THE KINDLING, A (Williamson, Robin & His Merry Band).
Tracks: / Five denials on Merlin's grave / Me and the mad girl / Woodcutter's song, The.
Album: released on Awareness, Jun'86 by Awareness. Dist: EMI

Cassette: released on Awareness, Jun'86 by Awareness. Dist: EMI

LEGACY OF SCOTTISH HARPERS.
Album: released on Claddagh, Nov'84 by Claddagh Records. Dist: I & B, Record Services Distribution (Ireland), Roots, Topic, Impetus, Projection, CM

MUSIC FOR THE MABINOG-I.

Album: released on Claddagh, Sep'84 by Claddagh Records. Dist: I & B, Record Services Distribution (Ireland), Roots, Topic, Impetus, Projection, CM

SONGS AND MUSIC 1977 (Williamson, Robin & His Merry Band).
Tracks: / Tune I hear so well, The / Mythic times / When evening shadows fall / Bells, the.
Notes: A selection of Songs & music from Robin's 'American Stonhenge' & 'Journey's Edge' albums. Founder member of 'The Incredible String Band'. Deluxe Gatefold Sleeve.
Album: released on Awareness, Jun'86 by Awareness. Dist: EMI

Cassette: released on Awareness, Jun'86 by Awareness. Dist: EMI

SONGS OF LOVE AND PARTING.
Album: released on Claddagh, Sep'84 by Claddagh Records. Dist: I & B, Record Services Distribution (Ireland), Roots, Topic, Impetus, Projection, CM

Williamson, Sonny Boy

20 BLUES GREATS.
Album: released on Deja Vu, Oct'86 by Deja Vu Records. Dist: Counterpoint Distribution, Record Services Distribution (Ireland)

BEST OF SONNY BOY WILLIAMSON.
Compact disc: released on Greenline, Dec'86 by Charly Records. Dist: Charly

BLUES OF SONNY BOY WILLIAMSON, THE.
Notes: Recorded in Copenhagen, Nov 1st 1963, Ivar Rosenberg.
Compact disc: released on Storyville, Jun'87 by Storyville Records. Dist: Jazz Music Distribution, Swift Distribution, Chris Wellard Distribution, Counterpoint Distribution

CHESS MASTERS.
Album: released on Checker(USA), Apr'81 by PRT. Dist: PRT

CHESS MASTERS VOL.2.
Double Album: released on Chess, Apr'83 by Charly Records. Dist: Charly, Swift, PRT, Discovery, IMS, Polygram

COLLECTION: SONNY BOY WILLIAMSON.
Album: released on Deja Vu, Aug'86 by Deja Vu Records. Dist: Counterpoint Distribution, Record Services Distribution (Ireland)

Cassette: released on Deja Vu, Aug'86 by Deja Vu Records. Dist: Counterpoint Distribution, Record Services Distribution (Ireland)

JAM SESSION.
Album: released on Charly, '82 by Charly Records. Dist: Charly, Cadillac

JAM SESSIONS (see Auger, Brian).

KING BISCUIT TIME.
Album: released on Arhoolie, May'81 by Arhoolie Records. Dist: Projection, Topic, Jazz Music, Swift, Roots

NEWCASTLE DECEMBER 1963.
Album: released on Charly, '82 by Charly Records. Dist: Charly, Cadillac

ONE WAY OUT.
Album: released on Chess, Aug'86 by Charly Records. Dist: Charly, Swift, PRT, Discovery, IMS, Polygram

Cassette: released on Chess, Aug'86 by Charly Records. Dist: Charly, Swift, PRT, Discovery, IMS, Polygram

PORTRAIT IN BLUES, A.
Album: released on Storyville, May'86 by Storyville Records. Dist: Jazz Music Distribution, Swift Distribution, Chris Wellard Distribution, Counterpoint Distribution

SONNY BOY WILLIAMSON.
Notes: 6 LP Box Set.
Album: released on Chess, '86 by Charly Records. Dist: Charly, Swift, PRT, Discovery, IMS, Polygram

TAKE IT EASY BABY.
Tracks: / Bye Bye Bird / I don't care no more / Baby don't worry / Twenty three hours too long / Take it easy baby.
Notes: Live set recorded in London with the Yardbirds and Eric Clapton in support.
Extended-play record: released on Blue Moon, Jul'87 Dist: Magnum Music Group Ltd, PRT, Spartan

UNISSUED 1963 BLUES FESTIVAL, THE.
Notes: For full information see: Memphis Slim.

Williams, Paul

CLASSICS.
Cassette: released on Spot, Apr'86 by Pickwick Records. Dist: H.R. Taylor, Lugtons

IN MEMORY OF ROBERT JOHNSON.
Album: released on Speciality, '73 Dist: PRT

Album: released on Teldec (Germany), Mar'84 by Import Records. Dist: IMS Distribution, Polygram Distribution

JUST AN OLD FASHIONED LOVE SONG.
Album: released on A&M, '74 by A&M Records. Dist: Polygram

Cassette: released on A&M, '74 by A&M Records. Dist: Polygram

Williams, Richard

NEW HORN IN TOWN.
Album: released on Candid, Dec'85 Dist: Counterpoint, Cadillac

Compact disc: released on Candid, Jul'87 Dist: Counterpoint, Cadillac

REJOICE (Williams, Richard, Junior Singers).
Album: released on Black Mountain, '82 by Black Mountain Records.

RICHARD WILLIAMS COLLECTION,THE.
Album: released on Black Mountain, '82 by Black Mountain Records.

Williams, Robert Pete

LEGACY OF THE BLUES.
Album: released on Sonet, '73 by Sonet Records. Dist: PRT

THOSE PRISON BLUES.
Album: released on Arhoolie, May'81 by Arhoolie Records. Dist: Projection, Topic, Jazz Music, Swift, Roots

Williams, Robin

REALITY....WHAT A CONCEPT.
Album: released on Casablanca(Import), Apr'82 Dist: IMS, Polygram

Williams, Roger

GOLDEN CHRISTMAS.
Album: released on Audio Fidelity, Oct'84 Dist: PRT

Cassette: released on Audio Fidelity, Oct'84 Dist: PRT

Williams, Roy

ROYAL TROMBO.
Album: released on Phontastic (Sweden), Jan'85 by Wellard, Chris Distribution. Dist: Wellard, Chris Distribution

SOMETHING WONDERFUL.
Album: released on Hep, Jul'82 by H.R. Taylor Records. Dist: Jazz Music, Cadillac Music, JSU, Taylors, Wellard, Chris, Zodiac, Swift, Fast Forward

WHEN YOU'RE SMILING (Williams, Roy & Benny Waters).
Album: released on Hep, Aug'81 by H.R. Taylor Records. Dist: Jazz Music, Cadillac Music, JSU, Taylors, Wellard, Chris, Zodiac, Swift, Fast Forward

Williams, Shine

AGBOJU LOGUN (Williams, Shine & His African Percussionists).
Single (12"): released on Earthworks, Jul'84 by Earthworks Records. Dist: Earthworks Distributors, Rough Trade, Cartel, Projection

Williams, Simon

WHASHINGTONS OF ENGLAND,THE.
Album: released on Loose, '83 by Loose Records. Dist: Nine Mile, Cartel

ROMPIN', STOMPIN', SINGIN', SWINGIN'. (Williams, Tex/ Spade Cooley).
Album: released on Bear Family, Sep'84 by Bear Family Records. Dist: Rollercoaster Distribution, Swift

Williams, Texas T,

14 ALL TIME COUNTRY HITS.
Album: released on Homespun(Ireland), Feb'78 by Outlet Records. Dist: Outlet

Williams, Tommy

SPRINGTIME IN BATTERSEA.
Album: released on Free Reed, Jan'87 by Free Reed Records. Dist: Roots, Projection, Hobgoblin Records, Oblivion

Album: released on Freereed, Nov'76 by Topic Records. Dist: JSU

Williams, Tony

CIVILIZATION.
Tracks: / Geo rose / Warrior / Ancient eyes / Soweto nights / Slump, The / Civilization / Mutants on the beach / Citadel / Geo rose / Warrior / Ancient eyes / Soweto nights / Slump, The / Civilization / Mutants on the beach / Citadel.
Notes: Master drummer Tony Williams returned to his own recording career,after five years playing only on other people's projects, in 1985 with "Foreign Intrigue". Although Tony was one of the innovators of both avant garde and fusion, that album brought him solidly into the contemporary jazz mainstream. The enthusiastic reputation of "Foreign Intrigue" prompted Williams to form a working group using many of the same musicians from the album. Throughout 1986, the Tony Williams Quintet with Bill Pierce on sax, Wallace Roney on trumpet, Mulgrew Miller on piano and another Blue Note recording artist Charnette Moffett on bass toured various cities in the US as well as South America and Europe. The results of that close-knit ensemble are now heard on "Civilization", recorded at the end of the band's most recent tour. The eight new Williams originals include the haunting beauty of "Soweto Nights", "The Slump" with is humorous, catchy bass line turnarounds, the soaring, contemporary sound of "Mutants On The Beach" and the lovely title tune ballad [EMI release sheet, May 1987]
Album: released on Blue Note, May'87 by EMI Records. Dist: EMI

Single (7"): released on Capitol, Jun'84 by Capitol Records. Dist: EMI

Compact disc: released on Manhattan-Blue Note, Jun'87 by EMI America Records (USA). Dist: EMI

THIRD PLANE (Williams, Tony/Herbie Hancock/Ron Carter).
Notes: For full details see under Herbie Hancock.

Williams, Vesta

DON'T BLOW A GOOD THING.
Tracks: / Don't blow a good thing / You make me want to love again.
Single (7"): released on A&M, Mar'87 by A&M Records. Dist: Polygram

Single (12"): released on A&M, Mar'87 by A&M Records. Dist: Polygram

ONCE BITTEN, TWICE SHY.
Tracks: / Once bitten, twice shy / My heart yours.
Single (7"): released on A&M, Nov'86 by A&M Records. Dist: Polygram

Single (12"): released on A&M, Nov'86 by A&M Records. Dist: Polygram

SUDDENLY IT'S MAGIC.
Tracks: / Suddenly it's magic / Don't let me down / Don't blow a good thing.
Single (7"): released on Breakout, May'87 by A&M Records. Dist: Polygram

VESTA.
Tracks: / Something about you / Sweet thang / Don't blow out a good thing / Get out of my life / I can make your dreams come true / My heart is yours / You make me want to (love again

ou / Don't let me down / Once bitten twice

es: For the past few years, Vesta Williams oeen working non-stop singing back-up vo- with the likes of Bobby Womack, Chaka n, Miles Davies, Jeffrey Osborne, The Cru- ers and many more, but now with the re- e on A&M Records of her debut album sta", it's her turn to enjoy the limelight. sta" is mostly produced by Bryan Loren 's also a new A&M signing, and Billy Valen- of the Valentine Brothers. The album fea- s eleven tracks, two of which are co-written esta. Leon Ware, Bryan Loren and Bill ntine have also contributed songs to the m: Vesta Williams is without doubt one of most talented youngsingers to emerge in re- years and the quality of her performance 'esta 'is testament to that'
um: released on A&M, Nov'86 by A&M Rec- Dist: Polygram

sette: released on A&M, Nov'86 by A&M ords. Dist: Polygram

npact disc: released on A&M, Mar'87 by I Records. Dist: Polygram

Villiams, Victoria

PPY, COME HOME.
ks: / Shoes / Fryin' Pan / Merry-go-round / oy / TC / I'll do his will / Big fish / Animal d / Main road / Lights / Opalousas / Statue bum / Poetry.
um: released on WEA, Jul'87 by WEA Rec- Dist: WEA

sette: released on WEA, Jul'87 by WEA ords. Dist: WEA

PPY LOVE HOME.
um: released on Blanco Y Negro, Jun'87 by Records. Dist: WEA

sette: released on Blanco Y Negro, Jun'87 'EA Records. Dist: WEA

Illiams, Vince

(Williams, Vince & BDO).
le (7"): released on Smile, Feb'81 by Smile rds. Dist: Spartan

Illiams, Wallace W.

TER BED.
le (7"): released on Trindisc, Jan'82 by disc Records. Dist: Jetstar, Pinnacle, gh Trade, Cartel

le (12"): released on Trindisc, Jan'82 by disc Records. Dist: Jetstar, Pinnacle, gh Trade, Cartel

Illiams,Willie

ME ALONG.
le 10": released on Stin Jac, Jul'83 by Stin Records. Dist: Jetstar Distribution

LOVE.
le (12"): released on Uptempo, Jun'84 by mpo Records. Dist: Jetstar Distribution

ATRIATION.
le (12"): released on WLM Music, Jul'83

Illiam Tell

LIAM TELL (Daneman, Paul).
sette: released on Kiddy Kassettes, Aug'77

Illianson, Ann

Y BLUE.
le (7"): released on Mint, Apr'83 by Em- Records. Dist: Ross Distribution, PRT Dis- ion, Solomon & Peres Distribution

Illie And The Poor Boys

SE ARMS OF MINE.
ks: / These arms of mine / Poor boy e.
e (7"): released on Decca, Jan'86 by a Records. Dist: Polygram

LIE AND THE POOR BOYS Various s (Various Artists).
es: Featuring: Charlie Watts - Drums/Bill an - Bass & Vocals/Geraint Watkins - Key- s & vocals/Mickey Gee - Guitar & Vo- Andy Fairweather Low -Guitar & Vocals Ray Cooper/Jimmy Page/Willie Gar- Chris Rea/Steve Gregory/Paul Rod- Kenney Jones/Henry Spinetti/Terry ams. All net proceeds from this albumpro- ill be donated directly to ARMS (Action for arch into Multiple Sclerosis)
pact disc: released on Decca, May'85 by a Records. Dist: Polygram

n: released on Decca, May'85 by Decca ds. Dist: Polygram

ette: released on Decca, May'85 by a Records. Dist: Polygram

Ills,Billy Jack

ZY MAN CRAZY (Willis,Billy Jack & His rn Swing Band).
n: released on Western (USA), Feb'85 by lie Records. Dist: Projection, Topic

Willis, Bob

KING OF WESTERN SWING,THE (Willis, Bob & The Texas Playboys).
Album: released on Charly, Nov'83 by Charly Records. Dist: Charly, Cadillac

TIFFANY TRANSCRIPTIONS VOL.1 (Willis, Bob & The Texas Playboys).
Album: released on Kaleidoscope, Jul'87

TIFFANY TRANSCRIPTIONS VOL.2 (Willis, Bob & The Texas Playboys).
Album: released on Kaleidoscope, Jul'87

TIFFANY TRANSCRIPTIONS VOL.3 (Willis, Bob & The Texas Playboys).
Album: released on Kaleidoscope, Jul'87

TIFFANY TRANSCRIPTIONS VOL.4 (Willis, Bob & The Texas Playboys).
Album: released on Kaleidoscope, Jul'87

TIFFANY TRANSCRIPTIONS VOL.5 (Willis, Bob & The Texas Playboys).
Album: released on Kaleidoscope, Jul'87

Willis Brothers

BEST OF....
Notes: 10tracks
Album: released on Starday, Apr'87

Cassette: released on Starday, Apr'87

Willis, Bruce

RESPECT YOURSELF.
Tracks: / Furniture.
Single (7"): released on Motown, Feb'87 by Motown Records. Dist: BMG Distribution

Single (12"): released on Motown, Feb'87 by Motown Records. Dist: BMG Distribution

RETURN OF BRUNO, THE.
Tracks: / Comin' right up / Respect yourself / Down in Holywood / Young blood / Under the boardwalk / Secret agent man/James Bond is back / Jackpot (Bruno's bop) / Fun time / Lose myself / Firting with disaster.
Album: released on Motown, Jan'87 by Motown Records. Dist: BMG Distribution

Cassette: released on Motown, Jan'87 by Motown Records. Dist: BMG Distribution

Compact disc: released on Motown, Jan'87 by Motown Records. Dist: BMG Distribution

UNDER THE BOARDWALK.
Tracks: / Under the boardwalk / Jack Pot.
Single (7"): released on Motown, May'87 by Motown Records. Dist: BMG Distribution

Tracks: / Under the boardwalk (vocal version) / Under the boardwalk (inst version) / Respect yourself (inst) / Jackpot / Bruno's bop.
Cassette single: released on Motown, 13 Jun'87 by Motown Records. Dist: BMG Distribution

YOUNG BLOOD.
Tracks: / Young blood / Flirting with danger.
Single (7"): released on RCA, Apr'87 by RCA Records. Dist: RCA, Roots, Swift, Wellard, Chris, I & B, Solomon & Peres Distribution

Single (12"): released on RCA, Apr'87 by RCA Records. Dist: RCA, Roots, Swift, Wellard, Chris, I & B, Solomon & Peres Distribution

Willis, Chick

CHICK SINGS CHUCK.
Album: released on Ichiban, Aug'87 by Ichiban Records. Dist: PRT

Cassette: released on Ichiban, Aug'87 by Ichiban Records. Dist: PRT

Willis, Chuck

BE GOOD OR BE GONE.
Album: released on Edsel, Feb'86 by Demon Records. Dist: Pinnacle, Jazz Music, Projection

Cassette: released on Edsel, Feb'86 by Demon Records. Dist: Pinnacle, Jazz Music, Projection

KEEP A DRIVIN.
Album: released on Charly(R&B), Mar'84 by Charly Records. Dist: Charly, Cadillac

Cassette: released on Charly(R&B), Mar'84 by Charly Records. Dist: Charly, Cadillac

Willis, Jack

ORLEANS STREET SHUFFLE (Willis, Jack & His New Orleans Band).
Album: released on 504, Sep'86 by 504 Records. Dist: Chris Wellard, Jazz Music

Cassette: released on 504, Sep'86 by 504 Records. Dist: Chris Wellard, Jazz Music

Willis, Rod

CAT,(THE).
Single (7"): released on Northwood, Mar'84 by Northwood Records. Dist: Backs-Cartel

Willliams, Larry

LARRY WILLIAMS SHOW, THE.
Album: released on Edsel, May'83 by Demon Records. Dist: Pinnacle, Jazz Music, Projection

Willo The Wisp

BEANSTALK, THE Various artists (Various Artists).
Cassette: released on Listen For Pleasure, Jun'84 by MFP Records. Dist: EMI

CHRYSALIS, THE Various artists (Various Artists).
Cassette: released on Listen For Pleasure, Jun'84 by MFP Records. Dist: EMI

GAMES WITH EDNA Various artists (Various Artists).
Cassette: released on Listen For Pleasure, Jun'84 by MFP Records. Dist: EMI

JOYS OF SPRING, THE Various artists (Various Artists).
Cassette: released on Listen For Pleasure, Jun'84 by MFP Records. Dist: EMI

MAGIC GOLF Various artists (Various Artists).
Cassette: released on Listen For Pleasure, Jun'84 by MFP Records. Dist: EMI

WILLO THE WISP (Williams, Kenneth).
Album: released on BBC, Oct'81 by BBC Records & Tapes. Dist: EMI, PRT, Pye

Cassette: released on BBC, Oct'81 by BBC Records & Tapes. Dist: EMI, PRT, Pye

WISHBONE, THE Various artists (Various Artists).
Cassette: released on Listen For Pleasure, Jun'84 by MFP Records. Dist: EMI

Willow

UNDERGROUND MAN.
Notes: First Time Music, 12 Trewartha Road, Praa Sands, Penzance, Cornwall, TR 20 9ST, Tel: Penzance 762826
Cassette: released on First Time/Fugore, Jan'87 by First Time Records. Dist: First Time Records

YOUNG GIRL FROM THE MOUNTAINS.
Tracks: / Here I stand.
Notes: First Time Music- see Willow "Underground man"
Cassette: released on First Time/Fugore, Jan'87 by First Time Records. Dist: First Time Records

Wills, Bob

BASIN ST. BLUES.
Album: released on Kaleidoscope (USA), Feb'85 by Flying Fish Records (USA). Dist: Flying Fish (USA)

BEST OF BOB WILLS, THE.
Tracks: / San Antonio Rose / Eight'r from decatur / Deep in the heart of Texas / Silver bells / Across the alley from the Alamo / Cimarron / South of the border / Milk cow blues / Milk cow blues / My adobe Hacienda / Southwestern Waltz / Big Ball in Cowtown, A.
Album: released on MCA Import, Mar'86 by MCA Records. Dist: Polygram, IMS

BEST OF BOB WILLS VOL.2, THE.
Tracks: / San Antonio rose / Eight'r from decatur / Deep in the heart of Texas / Silver bells (that ring in the night) / Across the valley from the Alamo / South of the border (down Mexico way) / Milk cow blues / My adobe hacienda / Southwestern waltz / Four or five times / Time changes everything / Texas double eagle / You're the only star in my blue heaven / Song of the wanderer (where shall I go?) / Pan handle rag / My mary / Beaumont rag / Whose heart are you breaking now / Brown skin gal / Cimarron.
Double Album: released on MCA Import, Mar'86 by MCA Records. Dist: Polygram, IMS

BEST OF THE TIFFANYS.
Album: released on Kaleidoscope (USA), Feb'85 by Flying Fish Records (USA). Dist: Flying Fish (USA)

BOB WILLS ANTHOLOGY,THE Bob Wills & His Texas Playboys.
Album: released on Embassy, Dec'77 by CBS Records. Dist: CBS

GREATEST HITS OF TEXAS,THE (Wills, Bob & His Texas Playboys).
Album: released on Rhino (USA), Feb'85 by Rhino Records (USA).

PAPA'S JUMPIN'.
Album: released on Bear Family, May'85 by Bear Family Records. Dist: Rollercoaster Distribution, Swift

TIME CHANGES EVERYTHING.
Album: released on Stetson, Oct'86 by Hasmick Promotions Ltd.. Dist: Counterpoint Distribution, H.R. Taylor Distribution, Swift Distribution, Chris Wellard Distribution

Cassette: released on Stetson, Oct'86 by Hasmick Promotions Ltd.. Dist: Counterpoint Distribution, H.R. Taylor Distribution, Swift Distribution, Chris Wellard Distribution

VERY BEST OF BOB WILLS & THE TEXAS PLAYBOYS,THE.
Album: released on Liberty, Apr'84

Cassette: released on Liberty, Apr'84

Wills, Charlie

CHARLIE WILLS.
Album: released on Leader, '81 Dist: Jazz Music, Projection

UP TO THE RIGS (20 Songs from the Dorset Shepherd).
Cassette: released on Folktracks, Nov'79 Dist: Roots

Wills, Johnny Lee

OPERAORS SPECIALS.
Album: released on String, '81 by Topic Records. Dist: Roots Distribution, Jazz Music Distribution, JSU Distribution, Projection Distribution, Swift Distribution

REUNION.
Album: released on Flying Fish (USA), May'79 by Flying Fish Records (USA). Dist: Roots, Projection

ROMPIN', STOMPIN', SWINGIN' (Wills, Johnny Lee & His Boys).
Album: released on Bear Family, Sep'84 by Bear Family Records. Dist: Rollercoaster Distribution, Swift

Wills, Nikki

SOME GUYS HAVE ALL THE LUCK.
Single (7"): released on Avatar, Feb'82 by Avatar Communications. Dist: CBS

Wills, Viola

DARE TO DREAM.
Tracks: / Dare to dream.
Single (7"): released on Streetwise, Feb'86 Dist: Greyhound

Single (12"): released on Streetwise, Feb'86 Dist: Greyhound

GONNA GET ALONG WITHOUT YOU NOW.
Single (7"): released on Ariola-Hansa, Sep'82 by Hansa Records. Dist: Polygram

Single (12"): released on Touch, Jul'84 by Touch Records. Dist: Rough Trade, Cartel

LOVE LETTERS.
Single (7"): released on Charly, Mar'80 by Charly Records. Dist: Charly, Cadillac

REGGAE HIGH.
Single (7"): released on Island, Aug'87 by Island Records. Dist: Polygram

Single (12"): released on Island, Aug'87 by Island Records. Dist: Polygram

SOMEBODY'S EYES.
Tracks: / Somebody's eyes / You love.
Single (7"): released on Sedition, Sep'86 Dist: PRT

Single (12"): released on Sedition, Sep'86 Dist: PRT

TAKE ONE STEP FORWARD (Wills, Viola & Noel McCalla).
Tracks: / Take one step forward (inst).
Single (7"): released on Nitemares, Dec'86

Single (12"): released on Nitemares, Dec'86

YOU ARE THE REASON WHY.
Tracks: / You are the reason why / You are the reason why (alternative version).

Single (7"): released on Streetsounds, May'86

Single (12"): released on Streetsounds, May'86

Will The Circle...

WILL THE CIRCLE BE UNBROKEN Various artists (Various Artists).
Notes: Artists include: Mother/Maybelle Carter/Earl Scruggy/Roy Acuff/Merle Jarvis/Jimmy Martin/Vassar Clements/Junior Huskey/Norman Blake/Pete Oswald Kirley/Kitty/Dritty Dirt Band/Jimmie Faddon/Jeff Haddon/Jim Abbotson/John McEuen and Jes Thompson.
Album: released on European Import, Dec'86 Dist: Conifer

Willy Jive

MONA.
Single (7"): released on Cheapskate, Aug'81 by Cheapskate Records. Dist: RCA

Wilmot, Gary
DON'T FIGHT DESTINY.
Tracks: / Don't fight destiny / Don't fight destiny (inst).

Wilson
DANCE WITH ME.
Tracks: / Dance with me / If that's the way.
Single (7"): released on EMI, Feb'87 by EMI Records. Dist: EMI

Single (12"): released on EMI, Feb'87 by EMI Records. Dist: EMI

Wilson, Ada
IN THE QUIET OF MY ROOM.
Single (12"): released on Thin Sliced, Oct'84 by Thin Sliced Records. Dist: Rough Trade Distribution, Cartel Distribution

TATTOO HOSTS VISION ON.
Album: released on Ambergris, Nov'80

WHAT THE WORLD WANTS.
Album: released on Native, Jan'87 by Native Records. Dist: Red Rhino, Cartel

Wilson, Al
SNAKE.
Single (7"): released on Casino Classics, Aug'84 by RK Records. Dist: PRT

Wilson, Art
DANCING HAMMOND.
Tracks: / Mr Sandman / Mack the knife / Unsentimental / I'll be seeing you / Come fly with me / Yeh, yeh / When the red red robin comes bobbing along / Bye bye blackbird / Nikita / This is all I ask / Once in a while / If love is good to me / You always hurt the one you love / I know I'll never love this way again / I get a kick out of you.
Album: released on Sounds Ultimate, Nov'85 Dist: PRT, H.R. Taylor

Cassette: released on Sounds Ultimate, Nov'85 Dist: PRT, H.R. Taylor

TEA DANCE.
Tracks: / Would you / For you / Sweetest sounds, The / Golden days / Spread a little happiness / Dancing with my shadow / Everything stops for tea / I'll do anything / Neighbours / Nice cup of tea, A / Nice people / I'm ready willing & able / I enjoy being a girl / Sons & daughters / One day in your life / You are the sunshine of my life / Embraceable you / Just good friends / Storm in a teacup / Love is here to stay / That old feeling / Livin' doll / Aunti V's / Some of these days / Play to me gypsy / Golden tango.
Album: released on Sounds Ultimate, May'87 Dist: PRT, H.R. Taylor

Wilson, Bob & Pauline
SOMEBODY LOVES YOU.
Album: released on Myrrh, May'82 by Word Records. Dist: Word Distribution

Cassette: released on Myrrh, May'82 by Word Records. Dist: Word Distribution

Wilson, Calum
...AND HIS SCOTTISH COUNTRY DANCE BAND.
Album: released on Lismor, Jul'80 by Lismor Records. Dist: Lismor, Roots, Celtic Music

Cassette: released on Lismor, Jul'80 by Lismor Records. Dist: Lismor, Roots, Celtic Music

Wilson, Carl
WHAT YOU DO TO ME.
Single (7"): released on Caribou, May'83 by Epic Records. Dist: CBS

YOUNGBLOOD.
Album: released on Caribou, Feb'83 by Epic Records. Dist: CBS

Cassette: released on Caribou, Feb'83 by Epic Records. Dist: CBS

Wilson, Chris
MUSIC FOR TWO LUTES (Wilson,Chris & Tom Finucane).
Album: released on Plant Life, Oct'83 Dist: Roots

Wilson, Clive
PLAYS NEW ORLEANS JAZZ.
Album: released on New Orleans, Sep'86 Dist: Swift, Zodiac Distribution, Jazz Music, JSU

Wilson, Danny
MARY'S PRAYER.
Tracks: / Monkeys shiny day / Mary's prayer.
Single (7"): released on Virgin, Feb'87 by Virgin Records. Dist: EMI, Virgin Distribution

Single (12"): released on Virgin, Feb'87 by Virgin Records. Dist: EMI, Virgin Distribution

Wilson, Delroy
20 GOLDEN HITS.
Double Album: released on Third World, Jun'77 Dist: Jetstar Distribution

22 SUPER HITS.
Album: released on Multiview, Nov'85 Dist: PRT Distribution

BEST OF DELROY WILSON, THE.
Album: released on Empire (reggae), Jun'84 Dist: Jetstar

BREAK UP TO MAKE UP.
Single (12"): released on Plantation, Apr'82 Dist: Jetstar

CHERISH.
Tracks: / Cherish / Cherish (alternative version).
Single (12"): released on Top Rank, Jan'86

COOL OPERATOR.
Album: released on Vista Sounds, '83 by Vista Sounds Records. Dist: Jetstar

DANCING MOOD.
Single (12"): released on Greensleeves, Sep'84 by Greensleeves Records. Dist: BMG, Jetstar, Spartan

DEAN OF REGGAE, THE.
Album: released on Mr.Tipsey (Jamaica), Feb'85 Dist: Jetstar Distribution

DOING ME WRONG.
Tracks: / Doing me wrong / Doing me wrong (alternative version).
Single (12"): released on Blue Mountain, Dec'85 Dist: Jetstar

GIRL OF TODAY.
Tracks: / Girl of today / Stuggling dub.
Single (12"): released on Tulip, Aug'86 Dist: M.I.S., Jetstar

HAPPY BIRTHDAY.
Tracks: / Happy birthday / Have a little faith.
Single (12"): released on Top Rank, Sep'86

I'M STILL WAITING.
Single (12"): released on Sarge, Jun'84 by Sarge Records. Dist: Jetstar

ISLANDS IN THE STREAM (see also Jennifer Lara) (Wilson, Delroy & Jennifer Lara).
Single (12"): by Londisc Records.

KISS AN ANGEL GOOD MORNING.
Single (12"): released on Londisc, Aug'84 by Londisc Records.

LIVING IN THE FOOTSTEPS / SO LONG JENNY.
Single (12"): released on Live & Love, Dec'82 by Live & Love Records. Dist: Jetstar

LOOKIN' FOR LOVE.
Album:

NICE TIMES.
Album: released on Vista Sounds, '83 by Vista Sounds Records. Dist: Jetstar

NO MORE HEARTACHE / ONE WHO LOVES YOU.
Single (12"): released on Black Music, Jul'82 by Black Music Records. Dist: Jetstar

NOTHING GONNA CHANGE MY LOVE FOR YOU.
Single (12"): released on Hawkeye, Nov'85 by Hawkeye Records. Dist: Hawkeye, Lightning (WEA) Distribution, Jetstar, PRT

OLDIES BUT GOLDIES (see also Owen Gray) (Wilson, Delroy & Owen Gray).
Album: released on Vista Sounds, '83 by Vista Sounds Records. Dist: Jetstar

Cassette: released on Vista Sounds, '83 by Vista Sounds Records. Dist: Jetstar

PEOPLE ARE DOING IT EVERY DAY.
Single (12"): released on Revue, Jul'85 by Revue Records. Dist: Jetstar

PLACE IN THE SUN.
Album: released on Culture Press, Sep'84 by Vista Sounds Records. Dist: Jetstar, Rough Trade

PLAY SOMETHING PRETTY.
Single (12"): released on J & J, Aug'83 by J & J Records. Dist: Jetstar

PLEASE DON'T LEAVE ME.
Single (12"): released on High Power, Nov'85 by High Power Records. Dist: Jetstar

REGGAE CLASSICS.
Album: released on Londisc, Aug'84 by Londisc Records.

RUN RUN.
Single (12"): released on Studio One. See'84

Dist: Jetstar

SUPER MIX HITS.
Album: released on Vista Sounds, '83 by Vista Sounds Records. Dist: Jetstar

SUSPICION.
Single (12"): released on Revue, May'83 by Revue Records. Dist: Jetstar

WHICH WAY IS UP.
Album: released on Blue Mountain, Apr'87 Dist: Jetstar

WHO DONE IT.
Album: released on Third World, Feb'79 Dist: Jetstar Distribution

WON'T YOU COME HOME.
Single (12"): released on Starlight, Jul'82 by Starlight Records. Dist: Jetstar Distribution

WORTH YOUR WEIGHT IN GOLD.
Album: released on Burning Sounds, Aug'84 by Ross, Bill/Burning Sounds Records. Dist: PRT

YOU HAVE MY HEART / ONE LITTLE THING.
Single (12"): released on Jah Congo, Oct'82 by Jah Congo Records. Dist: Jetstar

Wilson, Eddie
DANKESCHON, BITTESCHON, WIEDERSEHEN.
Album: released on Starday-Gusto, Oct'80

Wilson, Edith
EDITH WILSON WITH JOHNNY DUNN'S JAZZ HOUNDS.
Album: released on Fountain, Apr'79 by Retrieval Records. Dist: Jazz Music, Swift, VJM, Wellard, Chris, Retrieval

Wilson, Ernest
BIG ENOUGH.
Tracks: / Big enough / Big enough (version).
Single (12"): released on Natty Congo, 23 May'87 by Natty Congo Records. Dist: Jetstar

COME TO ME.
Tracks: / Come to me / Come to me (alternative version).
Single (12"): released on Natty Congo, Sep'86 by Natty Congo Records. Dist: Jetstar

FIRST LOVE.
Single (12"): released on Techniques, Aug'87 Dist: Jetstar Distribution

TALKING IN MY SLEEP.
Tracks: / Talking in my sleep / Who control them.
Single (12"): released on Ozzy Music, May'86 Dist: Jetstar Distribution

Wilson, Flick
MY LADY.
Single (12"): released on Greensleeves, Nov'80 by Greensleeves Records. Dist: BMG, Jetstar, Spartan

SLAVEMASTER (Wilson, Flick & Roots Radic Band).
Single (12"): released on Greensleeves, Aug'80 by Greensleeves Records. Dist: BMG, Jetstar, Spartan

Wilson, Frank
DO I LOVE YOU (INDEED I DO).
Single (7"): released on Motown, Oct'81 by RCA Records. Dist: RCA Distribution

Wilson, Garland
WAY I FEEL, THE.
Notes: Artists also include: Nat Gonella/Nina Mae McKinney.
Album: released on Collectors Items, Jul'86 Dist: Jazz Music, Swift, Chris Wellard

WAY I FEEL, (THE).
Album: released on Collectors Items, Feb'85 Dist: Jazz Music, Swift, Chris Wellard

Wilson, Gary
CRY.
Single (7"): released on Sundance, Jun'84

DREAMIN'.
Single (7"): released on Avatar, May'82 by Avatar Communications. Dist: CBS

HELP ME RHONDA.
Single (7"): released on Avatar, Jul'81 by Avatar Communications. Dist: CBS

MOVIE QUEEN.
Single (7"): released on Sour Grapes, Aug'83

Wilson, Gerald
CALAFIA (Wilson's, Gerald Orchestra Of The 80's).

Tracks: / Prince Albert / Calafia / Eloy / Red The / 3/4 for Mayor Tom / Viva tirado '85 / P gon / Jessica . Blues bones and bobby.
Notes: Featuring - Ernie Watts, Harold Le Milcho Leviev, Al Aarons, Anthony Wils Oscar Brashear, Rick Baptists, Garnett Bro George (Buster) Cooper, Stanley Gilbert, thony Ortega.
Compact disc: released on Trend (US Sep'86 by Discovery Records. Dist: Flexili Distributors Ltd, Swift

GROOVIN' HIGH (Wilson, Gerald/Willi Baranco/Jimmy Mundy).
Album: released on Hep, Apr'81 by H.R. T lor Records. Dist: Jazz Music, Cadillac M JSU, Taylors, Wellard, Chris, Zodiac, S Fast Forward

JESSICA (Wilson, Gerald and His Orches
Album: released on Trend (USA), Jan'84 Discovery Records. Dist: Flexitron Distribu Ltd, Swift

Cassette: released on Trend (USA), Jan'8 Discovery Records. Dist: Flexitron Distribu Ltd, Swift

TORERO IMPRESSIONS IN JAZZ son, Gerald and His Orchestra).
Album: released on Discovery (USA), Feb

Wilson, Harold
PRIME MINISTER ON PMS, (A).
Double cassette: released on Listen For F sure, Sep'78 by MFP Records. Dist: EMI

Wilson, Herman
AT THE WOODWINDS BALL (Wi Herman Chamber Group).
Album: released on Spotlite, '83

Wilson, Jack
CORCOVADO (Wilson, Jack Quartet).
Album: released on Discovery, Sep'83 PRT

Wilson, Jackie
CLASSIC JACKIE WILSON, (THE).
Album: released on Skratch, Jan'84 by Skr Records. Dist: PRT

Cassette: released on Skratch, Jun'84 Skratch Records. Dist: PRT

HIGHER AND HIGHER Your love keeps ing me.
Tracks: / Higher and higher / Who who sa
Single (7"): released on SMP, 20 Jun'87 Jetstar, PRT

Single (12"): released on SMP, 20 Jun'87 Jetstar, PRT

HIGHER & HIGHER.
Compact disc: released on Kent, May'8 Ace Records. Dist: Pinnacle

I DON'T WANT TO LOSE YOU.
Single (7"): released on Kent, Apr'85 by Records. Dist: Pinnacle

I GET THE SWEETEST FEELING.
Tracks: / Lonley teardrops / Whispers ge louder.
Notes: Extra track on 12" only.
Single (7"): released on Skratch, Mar'8 Skratch Records. Dist: PRT

Single (12"): released on Skratch, Mar'8 Skratch Records. Dist: PRT

REET PETITE.
Compact disc: released on Ace, May'8 Ace Records. Dist: Pinnacle, Swift, Hotshot dillac

Album: released on Ace, Mar'85 by Ace ords. Dist: Pinnacle, Swift, Hotshot, Cadill

Cassette: released on Ace, Mar'85 by Ace ords. Dist: Pinnacle, Swift, Hotshot, Cadill

Single (7"): released on Skratch, Mar'8 Skratch Records. Dist: PRT

Single (12"): released on Skratch, Mar'8 Skratch Records. Dist: PRT

REET PETITE (VIDEO).
Tracks: / Reet petite / I get the sweetes ing.
Notes: Video single.
Video-cassette (VHS): released on Rushes, Mar'87 by Video Collection Inte tional Ltd.. Dist: Counterpoint

SOUL YEARS, (THE).
Album: released on Kent, Jan'85 by Ace ords. Dist: Pinnacle

Cassette: released on Kent, Jan'85 by Records. Dist: Pinnacle

SOUL YEARS VOL 2, THE.
Tracks: / Whispers (gettin' louder) / Since showed me how to be happy / Uptight (e things's alright) / You can count on n

omebody up there likes you / My heart is call-
ng / Hard to get a thing called love / Those
eartaches / Don't you know I love you / I've
arned about life / It's all over / Do it the right
ay / You keep me hanging on / To change my
ve / Love is funny that way / Nobody but you.
lbum: released on Kent, May'86 by Ace Recrds. Dist. Pinnacle

ERY BEST OF JACKIE WILSON, THE.
ompact discs: released on Ace, Jun'87 by Ace
ecords. Dist. Pinnacle, Swift, Hotshot, Cadil-
c

Wilson, Jimmy
ROUBLE IN MY HOUSE.
lbum: released on Diving Duck (Holland),
ay'85

Wilson, Jock
X STREET.
acks: / Six street / Live stock.
ngle (12"): released on Uptempo, Jul'86 by
ptempo Records. Dist. Jetstar Distribution

Wilson, Joe Lee
ECRETS FROM THE SUN.
bum: released on Inner City, Apr'79 Dist: Jet-
ar

ITHOUT A SONG.
bum: released on Inner City, Apr'79 Dist: Jet-
ar

Wilson, John
TTER, (THE).
gle (7"): released on Legacy, Feb'85 Dist:

'N AIN'T GONNA SHINE ANYMORE.
cks: / Sun ain't gonna shine anymore /
erything I need.
gle (7"): released on Legacy, Nov'86 Dist:

gle (12"): released on Legacy, Nov'86 Dist:

IDERSTANDING.
cks: / Everything I need.
gle (7"): released on Legacy, Jan'87 Dist:

ALL WANNA BE IN LOVE.
gle (7"): released on Legacy, Jun'85 Dist:

gle (12"): released on Legacy, Jun'85 Dist:

Vilson, John Singers
VE SINGALONG.
um: by Pilgrim Records. Dist: Rough
e, Cartel

Vilson, Junior
MBO.
cks: / Cassandra.
le (12"): released on Rockers Plantation,
37 Dist: Jetstar

Vlson, Justin
UN CHRISTMAS, A.
m:

ISTMAS STORIES.
m:

TRUE.
m:

ITING.
m:

RBIT.
m:

OXICATED TALES.
m:

P IT CLEAR.
m:

MASTER STORY TELLER, THE.
m:

S A GOOD TIME.
m:

RT, THE.
m:

ison, Kerry
CTION SELECTION, THE.
(7"): released on Lambs To The
hter, Jun'87 by Prism Records. Dist: Pin-
Red Rhino, Cartel

(12"): released on Lambs To The
hter, Jun'87 by Prism Records. Dist: Pin-
Red Rhino, Cartel

Wilson, Kevin
KEV'S BACK (RETURN OF THE YOBBO).
Tracks: / Last wager waltz / That's what he really said / Kev's courtin song / Breathe through
my ears / Mick the master farter / Pubic hair
song / It was over (Kev's lament) / Dick ta'phone
/ Hey Santa Claus.
Album: released on Epic, Jan'87 by CBS Records. Dist. CBS

Cassette: released on Epic, Jan'87 by CBS
Records. Dist. CBS

Wilson, Mari
AIN'T THAT PECULIAR?.
Single (7"): released on Compact Organisa-
tion, Apr'84 Dist: PRT

Single (12"): released on Compact Organisation, Apr'84 Dist: PRT

BABY IT'S TRUE (I CAN'T STOP MY-SELF).
Single (7"): released on Compact Organisation, Apr'82 Dist: PRT

Single (12"): released on Compact Organisation, Apr'82 Dist: PRT

BEAT THE BEAT.
Single (7"): released on Compact Organisation, Feb'82 Dist: PRT

BEWARE BOYFRIEND.
Single (7"): released on Compact Organisation, Nov'82 Dist: PRT

Single (12"): released on Compact Organisation, Nov'82 Dist: PRT

CRY ME A RIVER.
Single (7"): released on Compact Organisation, Mar'83 Dist: PRT

Single (12"): released on Compact Organisation, Mar'83 Dist: PRT

DANCE CARD.
Single (7"): released on Compact Organisation, Aug'81 Dist: PRT

DANCE WITH A STRANGER.
Album: released on Compact Organisation,
Jul'85 Dist: PRT

Cassette: released on Compact Organisation,
Jul'85 Dist: PRT

JUST WHAT I ALWAYS WANTED.
Single (7"): released on Compact Organisation, Aug'82 Dist: PRT

Single (12"): released on Compact Organisation, Aug'82 Dist: PRT

LET'S MAKE THIS LAST.
Single (7"): released on Compact Organisation, Sep'84 Dist: PRT

Single (12"): released on Compact Organisation, Sep'84 Dist: PRT

MY LONG-PLAYING GIFT TO THE NA-TION.
Album: released on Compact Organisation,
Feb'83 Dist: PRT

Cassette: released on Compact Organisation,
Feb'83 Dist: PRT

WONDERFUL.
Single (7"): released on Compact Organisation, May'83 Dist: PRT

Single (12"): released on Compact Organisation, May'83 Dist: PRT

WOULD YOU DANCE WITH A STRANGER?.
Single (7"): released on Compact Organisation, Jun'85 Dist: PRT

Wilson, Mary
DON'T GET MAD GET EVEN.
Tracks: / Don't get mad get even / Don't get
mad get even (inst).
Single (7"): released on Nightmare, 23 May'87
by Nightmare Records. Dist: PRT

Single (12"): released on Nightmare, 23
May'87 by Nightmare Records. Dist: PRT

MARY WILSON.
Album: released on Motown, Oct'81 by Motown Records. Dist: BMG Distribution

PICK UP THE PIECES.
Single (7"): released on Motown, Oct'81 by
RCA Records. Dist: RCA Distribution

Wilson, Meri
FIRST TAKE.
Album: released on Pye International, '78

Cassette: released on Pye International, '78

Wilson, Nancy
GODSEND.
Tracks: / Feel like makin' love / Dindi / It's all
been said / Loneliness / Godsend / Ribbon in
the sky / Heart to heart / How could I have know
/ I believe in you / Another place in time.
Compact disc: released on Demon, Dec'84 by
Demon Records. Dist. Pinnacle

LUSH LIFE.
Album: released on Capitol, Apr'84 by Capitol
Records. Dist: EMI

Cassette: released on Capitol, Apr'84 by Capitol Records. Dist. EMI

TWO OF US, (THE).
Album: released on CBS, Sep'84 by CBS Records. Dist. CBS

Cassette: released on CBS, Sep'84 by CBS
Records. Dist. CBS Deleted '87.

Wilson, Paketo
ON TOP OF THE WORLD.
Single (12"): released on Child Of God, Nov'83
by Child Of God Records. Dist: Jetstar

SNEAKING OUT.
Single (12"): released on Child Of God, Nov'83
by Child Of God Records. Dist: Jetstar

Wilson, Paul
ONE-EYED FIDDLER, (THE) (Wilson,
Paul & Ben Van Weede).
Album: released on Saydisc, Nov'80 by Sayd-
isc Records. Dist: Essex, Harmonia Mundi,
Roots, H.R. Taylor, Jazz Music, Swift, Projec-
tion, Gamut

Wilson, Phil
TEN MILES.
Single (7"): released on Creation, Jun'87 Dist:
Rough Trade, Cartel

Single (12"): released on Creation, Jun'87 Dist:
Rough Trade, Cartel

WAITING FOR A CHANGE.
Single (7"): released on Creation, Feb'87 Dist:
Rough Trade, Cartel

Single (12"): released on Creation, Feb'87
Dist: Rough Trade, Cartel

Double-pack single: released on Creation,
Mar'87 Dist: Rough Trade, Cartel

Wilson, Precious
I'LL BE YOUR FRIEND.
Single (7"): released on Jive, Sep'85 by Zomba
Records. Dist: RCA, PRT, CBS

Single (12"): released on Jive, Sep'85 by
Zomba Records. Dist: RCA, PRT, CBS

JEWEL OF THE NILE.
Tracks: / Jewel of the Nile / Didn't take it away.
Single (7"): released on Jive, Apr'86 by
Zomba Records. Dist: RCA, PRT, CBS

Single (12"): released on Jive, Apr'86 by
Zomba Records. Dist: RCA, PRT, CBS

NICE GIRLS DON'T LAST.
Tracks: / Nice girls don't last / Nice girls don't
last (LA mix).
Single (7"): released on Jive, Jul'86 by Zomba
Records. Dist: RCA, PRT, CBS

Single (12"): released on Jive, Jul'86 by Zomba
Records. Dist: RCA, PRT, CBS

ONLY THE STRONG SURVIVE.
Single (7"): released on Jive, Jul'87 by Zomba
Records. Dist: RCA, PRT, CBS

Single (12"): released on Jive, Jul'87 by Zomba
Records. Dist: RCA, PRT, CBS

PRECIOUS WILSON.
Album: released on Jive, Sep'86 by Zomba
Records. Dist: RCA, PRT, CBS

Cassette: released on Jive, Sep'86 by Zomba
Records. Dist: RCA, PRT, CBS

YOU HAVEN'T HEARD THE LAST OF ME.
Single (7"): released on Epic, Feb'83 by CBS
Records. Dist. CBS

Wilson, Robert Anton
SECRETS OF POWER, THE.
Album: released on Illuminated, May'86 by IKF
Records. Dist: Pinnacle, Cartel, Jetstar

Cassette: released on Illuminated, May'86 by
IKF Records. Dist: Pinnacle, Cartel, Jetstar

Wilson, Sandy
DIVORCE ME, DARLING.
Album: released on DRG, Jul'79

Wilson Sisters
PRICE OF LOVE.
Single (7"): released on President, Jul'83 by
President Records. Dist: Taylors, Spartan

Wilson, Smokey
88TH STREET BLUES.
Album: released on Murray Brothers (USA),
May'84 Dist: Swift Distribution

Wilson, Teddy
BODY AND SOUL.
Double Album: released on Vogue, Jul'77

COLE PORTER CLASSICS.
Double Album: released on Black Lion, '79 by
Black Lion Records. Dist: Jazz Music, Chris
Wellard, Taylor, H.R., Counterpoint, Cadillac

Album: released on Black Lion, Jul'84 by Black
Lion Records. Dist: Jazz Music, Chris Wellard,
Taylor, H.R., Counterpoint, Cadillac

D.S.C.B. MEETS TEDDY WILSON (Wilson, Teddy/Dutch Swing College Band).
Album: released on Timeless, Oct'86

ELEGANT PIANO (Wilson, Teddy & Marion
McPartland).
Album: released on Swaggie (Australia),
Jan'83

HOW HIGH THE MOON.
Album: released on Kings Of Jazz, Apr'81 Dist:
Jazz Horizons, Jazz Music, Celtic Music

I GOT RHYTHM.
Double Album: released on Vogue Jazz
(France), May'83

I LOVE A PIANO (Wilson, Teddy Trio/Mary
Lou Williams Quartet).
Album: released on Esquire, Apr'79 by Titan In-
ternational Productions. Dist: Jazz Music, Ca-
dillac Music, Swift, Wellard, Chris, Backs,
Rough Trade, Revolver, Nine Mile

IMPECCABLE MR WILSON, (THE).
Album: released on Verve, Dec'81 by Phonogram Records. Dist: Polygram

IN TOKYO.
Album: released on Sackville, Apr'81 Dist:
JSU, Jazz Music, Jazz Horizons, Cadillac
Music, Celtic Music, Swift

LIVE AT SANTA TECLA.
Album: released on Carosello, Feb'83 Dist:
Jazz Music, Jazz Horizons

MASTERS OF JAZZ VOL.11.
Album: released on Storyville, May'86 by Story-
ville Records. Dist: Jazz Music Distribution,
Swift Distribution, Chris Wellard Distribution,
Counterpoint Distribution

MOONGLOW.
Album: released on Black Lion, Apr'85 by Black
Lion Records. Dist: Jazz Music, Chris Wellard,
Taylor, H.R., Counterpoint, Cadillac

MR WILSON & MR GERSHWIN.
Album: released on CBS(France), May'85 by
CBS Records. Dist: Conifer, Discovery, Swift

Cassette: released on CBS(France), May'85
by CBS Records. Dist: Conifer, Discovery, Swift

NOBLE ART OF..., THE.
Notes: With Niels-Henning Pederson.
Album: released on Storyville, May'86 by Sto-
ryville Records. Dist: Jazz Music Distribution,
Swift Distribution, Chris Wellard Distribution,
Counterpoint Distribution

REVISITS THE GOODMAN YEARS (Wil-
son, Teddy Trio).
Notes: With Ed Thigpen / J. Lundgard.
Album: released on Storyville, May'86 by Sto-
ryville Records. Dist: Jazz Music Distribution,
Swift Distribution, Chris Wellard Distribution,
Counterpoint Distribution

RUNNIN' WILD.
Album: released on Black Lion, Sep'85 by
Black Lion Records. Dist: Jazz Music, Chris
Wellard, Taylor, H.R., Counterpoint, Cadillac

STOMPING AT THE SAVOY.
Album: released on Black Lion, Jan'85 by Black
Lion Records. Dist: Jazz Music, Chris Wellard,
Taylor, H.R., Counterpoint, Cadillac

STRIDING AFTER FATS.
Album: released on Carrere(France), Apr'84 by
Carrere Records (France). Dist: PRT

Album: released on Black Lion, Sep'85 by
Black Lion Records. Dist: Jazz Music, Chris
Wellard, Taylor, H.R., Counterpoint, Cadillac

Cassette: released on Black Lion, Sep'85 by
Black Lion Records. Dist: Jazz Music, Chris
Wellard, Taylor, H.R., Counterpoint, Cadillac

TEDDY WILSON & HIS ALL STARS, VOL 1.

Album: released on Musicraft, Apr'79

TEDDY WILSON, VOL 1.
Album: released on Jazz Reactivation, Jan'82 Dist: PRT

TEDDY WILSON, VOL 2.
Album: released on Jazz Reactivation, May'83 Dist: PRT

TIME AFTER TIME (see Vaughan, Sarah) (Wilson, Teddy & Sarah Vaughan).

TWO HOT FOR WORDS (Wilson, Teddy & His Orchestra with Billie Holiday).
Album: released on Hep, May'86 by H.R. Taylor Records. Dist: Jazz Music, Cadillac Music, JSU, Taylors, Wellard, Chris, Zodiac, Swift, Fast Forward

VOLUME 2 (Wilson, Teddy Sextet).
Album: released on Jazz Archives, Jul'86 by Jazz Archives Records. Dist: Jazz Music

Wilson, Tug
COUNTRY MUSIC LOVIN' KINDA GUY.
Album: released on Ross, '86 by Ross Records. Dist: Ross Distribution, Roots Distribution

Cassette: released on Ross, '86 by Ross Records. Dist: Ross Distribution, Roots Distribution

NASHVILLE HALL OF FAME.
Cassette: released on Country House, '79 by BGS Productions Ltd. Dist: Taylor, H.R., Record Merchandisers Distribution, Pinnacle, Sounds of Scotland Records

Wiltshire Moonrakers
DIALECT STORIES, SONGS, DANCES & CUSTOMS.
Cassette: released on Folktracks, Nov'79 by Folktracks Cassettes. Dist: Folktracks

Wimps
AT THE DISCOTHEQUE.
Single (7"): released on Sniff, May'82 by Sniff Records. Dist: Stiff

HAMBURGER RADIO.
Single (7"): released on Sniff, '82 by Sniff Records. Dist: Stiff

Win
SHAMPOO TEARS.
Tracks: / Shampoo tears / Empty holster / Slider, The.
Single (7"): released on London, Apr'86 by London Records. Dist: Polygram

Single (12"): released on London, Apr'86 by London Records. Dist: Polygram

SUPER POPOID GROOVE.
Tracks: / Super popoid groove / Baby cutting / You've got the power.
Single (7"): released on London, Mar'87 by London Records. Dist: Polygram

Single (12"): released on London, Mar'87 by London Records. Dist: Polygram

UH, TEARS BABY.
Tracks: / Super popoid groove / Shampoo tears / Binding love spell / Un-American broadcasting / Hollywood baby too / Empty holsters / You've got the power / Charms of a powerful trouble / It may be a beautiful sky tonight........ / Charms / Baby cutting / Shampoo tears (remix) / You've got the power (remix).
Notes: Extra tracks on cassette and compact disc only:- Shampoo Tears (Remix), You've got the power (Remix).
This is the debut album from Scottish ban 'Win' (ex Fire Engines) and includes their previous and current single as well as 'You've Got The Power' (the track featured heavily on the award winning commercial for McEwans lager). Produced by David Motion. LP sleeve available in two different colours.
Album: released on London, Apr'87 by London Records. Dist: Polygram

Cassette: released on London, Apr'87 by London Records. Dist: Polygram

Compact disc: released on London, Apr'87 by London Records. Dist: Polygram

UNAMERICAN BROADCASTING.
Single (7"): released on Swamplands, Mar'85

Single (12"): released on Swamplands, Mar'85

YOU'VE GOT THE POWER.
Tracks: / You've got the power / Unamerican broadcasting / In heaven (ladies in the radiator song).
Single (7"): released on Swamplands, Mar'86

Double-pack single: released on Swamplands, Mar'86

Single (12"): released on Swamplands, Mar'85

Single (12"): released on Swamplands, Jun'85

Winans
DECISIONS.
Album: released on Qwest, Oct'87 by WEA Records. Dist: WEA

Cassette: released on Qwest, Oct'87 by WEA Records. Dist: WEA

Compact disc: released on Qwest, Aug'87 by WEA Records. Dist: WEA

LET MY PEOPLE GO.
Tracks: / Choose ye / Redeemed / Perfect love / Straighten my life out / Let my people go / I'll follow where you lead / Special lady / Very real way / Let me people go / Part 2 / Let me people go / Let me people go (raw inst).
Album: released on Qwest, Dec'85 by WEA Records. Dist: WEA

Single (7"): released on Warner Brothers, Jan'86 by Warner Bros Records. Dist: WEA

Single (12"): released on Warner Brothers, Jan'86 by Warner Bros Records. Dist: WEA

TOMORROW.
Album: released on Light, Mar'84 by Light Records. Dist: Cord

Cassette: released on Light, Mar'84 by Light Records. Dist: Cord

VERY REAL WAY.
Tracks: / Let my people go.
Single (7"): released on Qwest, Mar'86 by WEA Records. Dist: WEA

Single (12"): released on Qwest, Mar'86 by WEA Records. Dist: WEA

WINANS.
Album: released on Light, May'82 by Light Records. Dist: Cord

Cassette: released on Light, May'82 by Light Records. Dist: Cord

Winchester Cathedral Choir
CAROLS FROM....
Album: released on ASV, Nov'81 by Academy Sound & Vision Records. Dist: Pinnacle

Cassette: released on ASV, Nov'81 by Academy Sound & Vision Records. Dist: Pinnacle

EVENSONG FOR ASH WEDNESDAY.
Album: released on ASV, Apr'82 by Academy Sound & Vision Records. Dist: Pinnacle

Cassette: released on ASV, Apr'82 by Academy Sound & Vision Records. Dist: Pinnacle

HEAR MY PRAYER.
Double Album: released on PRT, Dec'81 by PRT Records. Dist: PRT

Double cassette: released on PRT, Dec'81 by PRT Records. Dist: PRT

MESSIAH HIGHLIGHTS.
Compact disc: released on ASV, Dec'85 by Academy Sound & Vision Records. Dist: Pinnacle

Wind
FUR ALIVE.
Single (7"): released on Proto, May'85 by Proto Records. Dist: WEA

Windbreakers
RUN.
Album: released on Zippo, Jan'87

TERMINAL.
Album: released on Homestead, Jan'85 Dist: Rough Trade, Cartel, Shigaku

Windham Hill Artists...
WINDHAM HILL ARTISTS LIVE AT MONTREAUX Various artists (Various Artists).
Compact disc: released on Windham Hill (Germany), '86

Windham Hill Sampler '82
WINDHAM HILL SAMPLER '82 Various Artists (Various Artists).
Album: released on Windham Hill (Germany), Sep'84

Windies
HERE COME THE WINDIES.
Single (7"): released on Wicket, Jul'83 by Wicket Records. Dist: Pinnacle

Winding, Kai
GIANTS BONES 80.
Album: released on Sonet, Jun'80 by Sonet Records. Dist: PRT

KAI AND JAY (Winding, Kai & Jay Jay Johnson).
Tracks: / Out of this world / Thous sweet / Lover

/ Lope City / Stolen bass / It's alright with me / Mad about the boy / Yes sir, that's my baby / That's how I feel about you / Gong rock.
Album: released on Affinity, Oct'86 by Charly Records. Dist: Charly, Cadillac

Cassette: released on Affinity, Sep'86 by Charly Records. Dist: Charly, Cadillac

TROMBONE BY THREE (Winding, J.J./Kai Winding/Bennie Green).
Notes: For full details see under: Johnson, J.J./Kai Winding/Bennie Green.

GREAT KAI & JJ,THE.
Album: released on Jasmine, Jun'82 by Jasmine Records. Dist: Counterpoint, Lugtons, Taylor, H.R., Wellard, Chris, Swift, Cadillac

Cassette: released on Jasmine, Jun'82 by Jasmine Records. Dist: Counterpoint, Lugtons, Taylor, H.R., Wellard, Chris, Swift, Cadillac

Winding, Kal,Trombones
JANUARY 31ST & FEBRUARY 15TH,1963.
Album: released on From The Jazz Vault, Oct'80 by Damont Records. Dist: Swift, Taylor, H.R.

Wind In The Willows
WIND IN THE WILLOWS Various Artists (Various Artists).
Album: released on President, Jul'85 by President Records. Dist: Taylors, Spartan

Album: released on Red Bus, Nov'84 by Red Bus Records. Dist: PRT

Cassette: released on Red Bus, Nov'84 by Red Bus Records. Dist: PRT

Windjammer
LIVE WITHOUT YOUR LOVE.
Single (7"): released on MCA, Sep'84 by MCA Records. Dist: CBS

Single (12"): released on MCA, Sep'84 by MCA Records. Dist: CBS

TOSSING AND TURNING.
Single (7"): released on MCA, Jun'84 by MCA Records. Dist: CBS

Single (12"): released on MCA, Jun'84 by MCA Records. Dist: CBS

WINDJAMMER II.
Album: released on MCA, Jul'84 by MCA Records. Dist: CBS

Cassette: released on MCA, Jul'84 by MCA Records. Dist: CBS

WINDJAMMER III.
Album: released on MCA, Oct'85 by MCA Records. Dist: CBS

Cassette: released on MCA, Oct'85 by MCA Records. Dist: CBS

Windows
REARRANGE.
Single (7"): released on Skeleton, '81 by Skeleton Records. Dist: Cartel, Probe

UPPERS ON DOWNERS.
Album: released on Skeleton, '81 by Skeleton Records. Dist: Cartel, Probe

Wind Rush Primary School
WIND RUSH WEDDING SONG.
Tracks: / I need your love (Patrick Grant).
Single (7"): released on Hive, Jul'86 Dist: PRT

Winds of War
WINDS OF WAR Original film soundtrack.
Album: released on TER, Sep'83 Dist: Pinnacle

Cassette: released on TER, Sep'83 Dist: Pinnacle

Windsor, James
CITY LIGHTS.
Single (7"): released on Free Dee, May'82 by ASV. Dist: PRT

Windsor Parish Church
CAROLS FROM WINDSOR PARISH CHURCH.
Album: released on Joy, '74 by President Records. Dist: Jazz Music, Swift, President Distribution

Windy City blues
WINDY CITY BLUES 1935-1953 (Various Artists).
Notes: Featuring: Robert Lockwood, Johnny Shines, Pinetop Perkins etc.
Album: released on Nighthawk, Dec'86 by Faulty Products Records. Dist: Pinnacle, Swift

Wine And Candlelight
WINE AND CANDLELIGHT Various Session Artists (Various Session Artists).
Cassette: released on AIM (Budget Cassettes), Feb'83

Winesburg...Ohio: the con-
WINESBURG, OHIO: THE CONSCIENCE OF WINESBURG Anderson Sherwood (Marshall, E.G. and cast).
Cassette: released on Caedmon(USA), '84 by Caedmon (USA) Records. Dist: Gower, Taylors, Discovery

Wingates Temperance Band
FIREWORKS AND SPARKLERS.
Album: released on Grosvenor, Nov'76 by Grosvenor Records. Dist: Taylors

SOUNDS OF BRASS SERIES VOL. 38.
Album: released on Decca, Sep'79 by Decca Records. Dist: Polygram

Wingfield, Pete
18 WITH A BULLET.
Single (7"): released on Island, Jul'81 by Island Records. Dist: Polygram

THEY ALL CAME BACK.
Single (7"): released on Chipping Norton, Jun'81 Dist: Pinnacle

Wings
BACK TO THE EGG (SUNNY SIDE UF
Album: released on Parlophone, Jun'79 by EMI Records. Dist: EMI

Cassette: released on Parlophone, Jun'79 by EMI Records. Dist: EMI

GETTING CLOSER.
Single (7"): released on Parlophone, Aug'79 by EMI Records. Dist: EMI

GIVE IRELAND BACK TO THE IRISH (PARTS).
Single (7"): released on Parlophone, Feb'72 by EMI Records. Dist: EMI

GOODNIGHT TONIGHT.
Single (7"): released on Parlophone, Mar'79 by EMI Records. Dist: EMI

Single (12"): released on Parlophone, Apr by EMI Records. Dist: EMI

HI HI HI.
Single (7"): released on Parlophone, Dec'72 by EMI Records. Dist: EMI

I'VE HAD ENOUGH.
Single (7"): released on Parlophone, Jun'78 by EMI Records. Dist: EMI

LET 'EM IN.
Single (7"): released on Parlophone, Jul'76 by EMI Records. Dist: EMI

LETTING GO.
Single (7"): released on Parlophone, Sep'75 by EMI Records. Dist: EMI

LISTEN TO WHAT THE MAN SAID.
Single (7"): released on Parlophone, May by EMI Records. Dist: EMI

LIVE AND LET DIE.
Single (7"): released on Parlophone, Jun'73 by EMI Records. Dist: EMI

LONDON TOWN.
Album: released on Parlophone, '85 by EMI Records. Dist: EMI

Cassette: released on Parlophone, '85 by EMI Records. Dist: EMI

Single (7"): released on Parlophone, Aug'78 by EMI Records. Dist: EMI

MARY HAD A LITTLE LAMB.
Single (7"): released on Parlophone, May by EMI Records. Dist: EMI

MAYBE I'M AMAZED.
Single (7"): released on Parlophone, Feb'77 by EMI Records. Dist: EMI

MULL OF KINTYRE.
Single (7"): released on Parlophone, Nov'77 by EMI Records. Dist: EMI

OLD SIAM SIR.
Single (7"): released on Parlophone, Jun'79 by EMI Records. Dist: EMI

SILLY LOVE SONGS.
Single (7"): released on Parlophone, Apr'76 by EMI Records. Dist: EMI

VENUS AND MARS.
Tracks: / Venus and Mars / Rock show / in song / You gave me the answer / Mag

nd Titanium man / Letting go / Venus and Mars prise / Spirits of ancient egypt / Medicine jar / all me back again / Listen to what the man said Treat her gently - lonely old people / Crossads.
lbum: released on Parlophone, '85 by EMI ecords. Dist: EMI

assette: released on Parlophone, '85 by EMI ecords. Dist: EMI

ngle (7"): released on Parlophone, Nov'75 by l Records. Dist: EMI

mpact disc: released on Parlophone, p'87 by EMI Records. Dist: EMI

LD LIFE.
bum: released on Fame (Parlophone), '84 by Music For Pleasure Records. Dist: l

ssette: released on Fame (Parlophone), '84 by Music For Pleasure Records. Dist: l

NGS AT THE SPEED OF SOUND.
um: released on Parlophone, '85 by EMI cords. Dist: EMI

ssette: released on Parlophone, '85 by EMI ords. Dist: EMI

NGS GREATEST.
cks: / Another day / Silly love songs / Live let die / Junior's farm / With a little luck / d on the run / Uncle Albert / Admiral Halsey hi hi / Let'em in / My love / Mull of Kintyre.
um: released on Parlophone, '85 by EMI ords. Dist: EMI

sette: released on Parlophone, '85 by EMI ords. Dist: EMI

pact disc: released on Parlophone, '85 by Records. Dist: EMI

H A LITTLE LUCK.
le (7"): released on Parlophone, Mar'78 by Records. Dist: EMI

ings of Doom, The
GS OF DOOM, THE Various artists ous Artists).
sette: released on Tell-a-tale (Cassettes), 34

ings of History (Vol 4)
VER IN THE SKY.
sette: released on Flightstream, Jun'83 by tstream Records. Dist: Taylor, H.R.

DEZVOUS - SHUTTLEWORTH.
m: released on Flightstream, Jun'83 by tstream Records. Dist: Taylor, H.R.

sette: released on Flightstream, Jun'83 by tstream Records. Dist: Taylor, H.R.

URN TO SHUTTLEWORTH.
m: released on Flightstream, Jun'83 by tstream Records. Dist: Taylor, H.R.

ette: released on Flightstream, Jun'83 by tstream Records. Dist: Taylor, H.R.

NDS AT SHUTTLEWORTH 1909 -
m: released on Flightstream, Jun'83 by tstream Records. Dist: Taylor, H.R.

ette: released on Flightstream, Jun'83 by stream Records. Dist: Taylor, H.R.

nkler, Harold
AR BACH.
s: Sarabande, improvisations, polonaise, ott, etc.
act disc: released on Delta, '86 by Delta ds. Dist: Target

nners
YONE'S A WINNER.
(7"): released on Alibi, Nov'85

ERS.
s: / Soulful melody.
es: With Basie/Duke/Billie/Louise/Art -Live Performances.
: released on Giants of Jazz, Jun'86 by ck Promotions Ltd.. Dist: Counterpoint, lusic, Taylors, Swift, Mainline, Wellard,

(12"): released on Fine Style, Apr'86 by Style Records. Dist: Revolver, Jetstar, Cartel

nners' Pieces
ERS' PIECES Various artists (9th Annthesizer tape contest) (Various Artists).
: / Ribesurito / Sign of four / Demon's Die Alpen / War an dawn / Alla Hornpipe Wassermusik) / Fugitive, The / Toys / Lion's dance / Theme / Motivation / g cat / I know I've known you before / tears.
te: released on Roland, Jun'86 by .. Dist: E.S.S.P. Distributors, Synsound tions

Cassette: released on Roland, '84 by E.S.S.P.. Dist: E.S.S.P. Distributors, Synsound Distributions

Cassette: released on Roland, Jun'84 by E.S.S.P.. Dist: E.S.S.P. Distributors, Synsound Distributions

Cassette: released on Roland, Jun'85 by E.S.S.P.. Dist: E.S.S.P. Distributors, Synsound Distributions

Winner takes all
WINNER TAKES ALL Various artists (Various Artists).
Album: released on Kent, Apr'85 by Ace Records. Dist: Pinnacle

Winnick, Maurice and his Or-
SWEETEST MUSIC THIS SIDE OF HEAVEN, THE.
Album: released on World, May'75 by EMI Records. Dist: Conifer

Winnie the Pooh
WINNIE THE POOH Milne, A.A. (Jeffries, Lionel).
Cassette: released on Listen For Pleasure, Sep'79 by MFP Records. Dist: EMI

WINNIE THE POOH Milne, A.A. (Shelley, Norman).
Double cassette: released on Argo (Spokenword), Oct'83 by Decca Records. Dist: Polygram

WINNIE THE POOH Milne, A.A. (Bennett, Alan).
Album: released on BBC, Sep'84 by BBC Records & Tapes. Dist: EMI, PRT, Pye

Cassette: released on BBC, Sep'84 by BBC Records & Tapes. Dist: EMI, PRT, Pye

WINNIE THE POOH AND KANGA AND ROO Milne, A.A. (Channing, Carol).
Cassette: released on Caedmon(USA), Apr'83 by Caedmon (USA) Records. Dist: Gower, Taylors, Discovery

WINNIE THE POOH & THE HONEY TREE Various artists (Various Artists).
Album: released on Disneyland, Dec'82 by WEA Records. Dist: WEA

Cassette: released on Disneyland, Dec'82 Dist: EMI

WINNIE THE POOH & TIGGER TOO Various artists (Various Artists).
Album: released on Disneyland, Dec'82 by WEA Records. Dist: WEA

Cassette: released on Disneyland, Dec'82 Dist: EMI

Wins, Diana
PEACE ON EARTH.
Single (7"): released on Button, Nov'84 by Musical Characters Records. Dist: Spartan

Winslow, Michael
I AM MY OWN WALKMAN.
Single (7"): released on Island, Jun'85 by Island Records. Dist: Polygram

Single (12"): released on Island, Jun'85 by Island Records. Dist: Polygram

Winsome
AM I THE SAME GIRL.
Tracks: / Am I the same girl / Can't take the lies.
Single (7"): released on Fine Style, Jun'87 by Fine Style Records. Dist: Revolver, Jetstar, PRT, Cartel

Single (12"): released on Fine Style, Jun'87 by Fine Style Records. Dist: Revolver, Jetstar, PRT, Cartel

BORN FREE.
Tracks: / Can't take the lies.
Single (7"): released on Fine Style, Sep'86 by Fine Style Records. Dist: Revolver, Jetstar, PRT, Cartel

Single (12"): released on Fine Style, Sep'86 by Fine Style Records. Dist: Revolver, Jetstar, PRT, Cartel

HOMEBREAKER.
Single (12"): released on Fine Style, Feb'87 by Fine Style Records. Dist: Revolver, Jetstar, PRT, Cartel

ROCK WITH ME BABY (Winsome & Nerious Joseph).
Single (7"): released on Fine Style, Nov'86 by Fine Style Records. Dist: Revolver, Jetstar, PRT, Cartel

Single (12"): released on Fine Style, Nov'86 by Fine Style Records. Dist: Revolver, Jetstar, PRT, Cartel

Compact disc: released on Bridge, Dec'86 Dist: CD Centre Distribution, Pinnacle, Target

Winston
WAITING ROOM.
Single (7"): released on Rural Tension, Jan'82 Dist: Backs, Cartel Distribution

Album: released on Windham Hill (Germany), Sep'84

Album: released on Windham Hill (Germany), Sep'84

Winston Brothers
TRUCKER SONGS.
Compact disc: released on Bridge, '86 Dist: CD Centre Distribution, Pinnacle, Target

Album: released on Bridge, Apr'87 Dist: CD Centre Distribution, Pinnacle, Target

TRUCKER SONGS VOL.2.
Compact disc: released on Bridge, Oct'86 Dist: CD Centre Distribution, Pinnacle, Target

Winstone, Eric and His Or-
AFTER MIDNIGHT.
Cassette: released on AIM (Budget Cassettes), Feb'83

Winstone, Norma
SOMEWHERE CALLED HOME.
Tracks: / Cafe / Somewhere called home / Sea lady / Some time ago / Prologue / Celeste / Hi lilli hi lo / Out of this world / Tea for two.
Notes: After four albums with the trio Azimuth,British singer Norma winstone comes up with a highly individual statement in "Somewhere Called Home".Supported by John Taylor,pianist with Azimuth and Tony Coe on tenor sax & clarinet,the programme features compositions by Egberto Gismonti, Ralph Towner,Pat Smythe,Kenny Wheeler & Bill Evans.Norma has written lyrics for several of the songs and interprets them as ballads. Personnel:Norma Winstone-voice/John Taylor-piano/Tony Coe-clarinet,tenor sax.
Album: released on ECM (Germany), Feb'87 by ECM Records. Dist: IMS, Polygram, Virgin through EMI

Winston, George
AUTUMN.
Notes: George grew up influenced mainly by pop instrumental music (Floyd Cramer, The Ventures and many others), listening to the radio faithfully for the 30 seconds before the hourly news, when they would play instrumentals! George has subsequently studied a whole variety of 20th century piano forms, evolving a unique and personalised style. That style has now reached literally millions of people throughout the USA, Canada, Japan and Europe.
Album: released on Windham Hill, Nov'85 Dist: AM

Cassette: released on Windham Hill, Nov'85 Dist: AM

Compact disc: released on Windham Hill, Nov'85 Dist: AM

Cassette: released on Windham Hill (Germany), Feb'85

DECEMBER.
Album: released on Windham Hill, Nov'85 Dist: AM

Cassette: released on Windham Hill, Nov'85 Dist: AM

Compact disc: released on Windham Hill, Nov'85 Dist: AM

Cassette: released on Windham Hill (Germany), Feb'85

WINTER INTO SPRING.
Album: released on Windham Hill, Nov'85 Dist: AM

Cassette: released on Windham Hill, Nov'85 Dist: AM

Compact disc: released on Windham Hill, Nov'85 Dist: AM

Album: released on Windham Hill (Germany), Sep'84

Cassette: released on Windham Hill (Germany), Feb'85

Winston & The Churchills
WINSTON & THE CHURCHILLS.
Album: released on Cold Harbour, Jan'87 Dist: Pinnacle, Probe Plus Distribution, Cartel, M.I.S., EMI, DMS, RCA, Ariola

Winter, Angela
HEART TO HEART.
Single (12"): released on Survival, Jul'85 by Survival Records. Dist: Backs, Cartel Distribution

Winter Babies
BOSSANOVA SUICIDE.
Single (7"): released on Stiff, Oct'85 by Stiff Records. Dist: EMI, Record Services Distribution (Ireland)

Winter, Chris
SATURDAY NIGHT.
Single (7"): released on PVK, Jul'81

Winter/Dixon/Homnick
WHOOPIN'.
Tracks: / I got my eyes on you / Sonny's whoopin' the doop / Burnt child afraid of fire / Dhoee Whoee / Crow Jane / So tough with me / Whoo wee baby / I think I got the blues / Ya ya / Roll me baby.
Compact disc: released on Sonet, Jan'87 by Sonet Records. Dist: PRT

Winter, Edgar group
FRANKENSTEIN.
Single (7"): released on Blue Sky (USA), '80 Dist: CBS

Winterfolk '80
WINTERFOLK '80 Various artists (Various Artists).
Album: released on Stoof, '82 Dist: Roots Distribution

Winter, Johnny
1ST LP.
Album: released on Demon, Nov'85 by Demon Records. Dist: Pinnacle

Cassette: released on Demon, Nov'85 by Demon Records. Dist: Pinnacle

EARLY WINTER.
Tracks: / Ease my pain / That's what love does / Crying in my heart / Guy you left behind (The) / Shed so many tears / Creepy / Gangster of love / Roadrunner / Leave my woman (wife) alone / I can't believe you want to leave / Broke and lonely / Oh my darling / By the light of the silvery moon / Five after four A.M..
Compact disc: released on President, Jan'87 by President Records. Dist: Taylors, Spartan

Album: released on President, Jul'84 by President Records. Dist: Taylors, Spartan

GUITAR SLINGER.
Tracks: / It's my life baby / Iodine in my coffee / Trick bag / Mad dog / Boot hill / Ismell trouble / Lights out / Kiss tomorrow goodbye / My soul / Don't take advantage of me.
Compact disc: released on Sonet, Oct'86 by Sonet Records. Dist: PRT

Album: released on Sonet, Mar'84 by Sonet Records. Dist: PRT

LIVIN' IN THE BLUES.
Tracks: / Out of sight / Low down gal of mine / Going down slow / Avocado green / Parchman farm / Livin' in the blues / Leavin' blues / 48-32-20 / Bad news / Kind hearted woman / Mojo boogie / Love, life and money / Evil on my mind / See see baby / Tin pan alley / I'm good / Third degree / Shake your money maker / Bad girl blues / Broke and lonely.
Album: released on Showcase, Apr'86 Dist: Counterpoint

Cassette: released on Showcase, Apr'86 Dist: Counterpoint

Album: released on Sonet, Sep'86 by Sonet Records. Dist: PRT

OUT OF SIGHT.
Tracks: / Road runner / Gangster of love / Leave my wife alone / I can't believe you want to leave / That's what love does / Five after four AM / Out of sight / Parchman farm / Low down gal of mine / Going down slow / Leaving blues / Kind hearted woman / Livin' in the blues / Bad news / Oh my darling / Guy you left behind / Road runner / Gangster of love / Leave my woman alone / I can't believe you want to leave / That's what love does / Five after four AM / Out of sight / Parchman farm / Low down gal of mine / Going down slow / Leaving blues / Kind hearted woman.
Notes: Licensed from Charly International APS. this CD (P) 1987 Charly Holdings inc. (C) 1987 Charly Records Ltd
Album: released on Topline, Mar'87 by Charly Records. Dist: Charly Distribution

Cassette: released on Topline, Mar'87 by Charly Records. Dist: Charly Distribution

Compact disc: released on Topline, May'87 by Charly Records. Dist: Charly Distribution

PROGRESSIVE BLUES EXPERIMENT.
Album: released on Razor, Nov'86 by Razor. Dist: Pinnacle

RAISED ON ROCK.
Album: released on Blue Sky, Feb'81 by CBS Records. Dist: CBS

Cassette: released on Blue Sky, Feb'81 by CBS Records. Dist: CBS

SERIOUS BUSINESS.
Tracks: / Master mechanic / Sound the bell / Murdering the blues / It ain't your business / Good time woman / Unseen eye / My time after a while / Serious as a heart attack / Give it back / Route 90.
Compact disc: released on Sonet, Jan'87 by Sonet Records. Dist: PRT

Album: released on Sonet, Sep'85 by Sonet Records. Dist: PRT

Cassette: released on Sonet, Jan'87 by Sonet Records. Dist: PRT

THIRD DEGREE.
Tracks: / Mojo boggie / Love life and money / Evil on my mind / See see baby / Tin pan alley / I'm good / Third degree / Shake your money-maker / Bad girl blues / Broke and lonely.
Compact disc: released on Sonet, '86 by Sonet Records. Dist: PRT

Album: released on Sonet, Oct'86 by Sonet Records. Dist: PRT

Winters, Bernie

FINANCILLY I'M EMBARRASSED.
Single (7"): released on P & L, Mar'83 by P & L Records. Dist: Spartan

SCHNORBITZ SONG, THE.
Single (7"): released on Spartan, Oct'85 by Spartan Records. Dist: Spartan

Winter's, Chris shout

OOSTA BE A PARROT.
Single (7"): released on PVK, Oct'80

Winters, Mike

FOR MUMS & DADS OF ALL AGES (Winters, Mike & Bernie).
Album: released on Spiral, Oct'76 by President Records. Dist: Jazz Music

Winters, Robert

MAGIC MAN (Winters, Robert & Fall).
Album: released on Buddah, Jul'81 Dist: Swift, Jazz Music, PRT

Single (7"): released on Buddah, Aug'81 Dist: Swift, Jazz Music, PRT

Single (12"): released on Buddah, Aug'81 Dist: Swift, Jazz Music, PRT

Winters, Rocky

WISHING.
Single (7"): released on PRT, Feb'86 by PRT Records. Dist: PRT

Single (12"): released on PRT, Feb'86 by PRT Records. Dist: PRT

Winters, Rudy

BABY LAY DOWN.
Single (7"): released on Creole, May'79 by Creole Records. Dist: Rhino, PRT

BACK TO THE LOVE.
Compact disc: released on Creole, Aug'79 by Creole Records. Dist: Rhino, PRT

Single (12"): released on Creole, Aug'79 by Creole Records. Dist: Rhino, PRT Deleted '80.

COME TO ME.
Compact disc: released on Creole, Mar'78 by Creole Records. Dist: Rhino, PRT

FOR THE GOOD TIME.
Single (7"): released on Creole, '78 by Creole Records. Dist: Rhino, PRT

Single (7"): released on Creole Replay, Aug'84 by Creole Records. Dist: PRT, Rhino

I WILL.
Tracks: / I love the nightlife (disco round) / I will.
Single (7"): released on Old Gold, Mar'86 by Old Gold Records. Dist: Lightning, Jazz Music, Spartan, Counterpoint

RUBY WINTERS.
Album: released on Creole, Nov'80 by Creole Records. Dist: Rhino, PRT

SONGBIRD.
Album: released on K-Tel, May'79 by K-Tel Records. Dist: Record Merchandisers Distribution, Taylors, Terry Blood Distribution, Wynd-Up Distribution, Relay Distribution, Pickwick Distribution, Solomon & Peres Distribution, Polygram

Cassette: released on K-Tel, May'79 by K-Tel Records. Dist: Record Merchandisers Distribution, Taylors, Terry Blood Distribution, Wynd-Up Distribution, Relay Distribution, Pickwick Distribution, Solomon & Peres Distribution, Polygram

Winters, Shelley

NINE TIMES OUT OF TEN (Winters Solstice, A).
Single (7"): released on Inferno, Oct'79 by Inferno Records. Dist: Inferno, Cartel, Pinnacle

Winters, Smiley

SMILEY WINTERS.
Album: released on Arhoolie, May'81 by Arhoolie Records. Dist: Projection, Topic, Jazz Music, Swift, Roots

Winters Solstice, A

WINTER SOLSTICE, A Various artists (Various Artists).
Album: released on Windham Hill, Jul'86 Dist: AM

Winters, Tiny

CAFE SOCIETY ORCHESTRA (Winters, Tiny, Cafe Society Orchestra).
Album: released on Zodiac, May'82 Dist: Jazz Music

Winwood, Steve

ARC OF A DIVER.
Tracks: / While you see a change / Arc of a diver / Second hand woman / Slowdown sundown / Spanish dancer / Night train / Dust / While you see a chance / Arc of a diver / Second hand woman / Slowdown sundown / Spanish dancer / Night train / Dust.
Compact disc: released on Island, Jan'87 by Island Records. Dist: Polygram

Compact disc: released on Island, Sep'86 by Island Records. Dist: Polygram

Album: released on Island, Dec'80 by Island Records. Dist: Polygram

Cassette: released on Island, Dec'80 by Island Records. Dist: Polygram

BACK IN THE HIGHLIFE AGAIN.
Tracks: / Help me angel / Night train (inst)*.
Single (7"): released on Island, Jan'87 by Island Records. Dist: Polygram

Single (12"): released on Island, Jan'87 by Island Records. Dist: Polygram

BACK IN THE HIGH LIFE.
Tracks: / Higher love / Take it as it comes / Freedom overspill / Back in the highlife again / Finer things / Wake me up on judgement day / Split decision / My love's leavin'.
Album: released on Island, Jul'86 by Island Records. Dist: Polygram

Cassette: released on Island, Jul'86 by Island Records. Dist: Polygram

Compact disc: released on Island, Jul'86 by Island Records. Dist: Polygram

FREEDOM OVERSPILL.
Tracks: / Spanish dancer.
Single (7"): released on Island, Aug'86 by Island Records. Dist: Polygram

Single (12"): released on Island, Aug'86 by Island Records. Dist: Polygram

Single (12"): released on Island, Aug'86 by Island Records. Dist: Polygram

HIGHER LOVE.
Tracks: / And I go / Higher love / And I go.
Single (7"): released on Island, Jun'86 by Island Records. Dist: Polygram

Single (12"): released on Island, Jun'86 by Island Records. Dist: Polygram

SHOOT OUT AT THE FANTASY FACTORY.
Tracks: / Shoot out at the fantasy factory / Roll right stones / Evening blue / Tragic magic / Sometimes I feel so uninspired.

Notes: Produced by Steve Winwood.
Album: released on Island, Feb'87 by Island Records. Dist: Polygram

Cassette: released on Island, Feb'87 by Island Records. Dist: Polygram

STEVE WINWOOD.
Compact disc: released on Island, May'87 by Island Records. Dist: Polygram

TALKING BACK TO THE NIGHT.
Compact disc: released on Island, Feb'87 by Island Records. Dist: Polygram

Album: released on Island, Sep'82 by Island Records. Dist: Polygram

Cassette: released on Island, Sep'82 by Island Records. Dist: Polygram

THERE'S A RIVER.
Single (7"): released on Island, Nov'81 by Island Records. Dist: Polygram

VALERIE.
Tracks: / Valerie / Talking back to the night / Finer things, The *.
Notes: * Extra track on 12" version only.
Single (7"): released on Island, Sep'87 by Island Records. Dist: Polygram

Single (12"): released on Island, Sep'87 by Island Records. Dist: Polygram

Cassette single: released on Island, Sep'87 by Island Records. Dist: Polygram

Compact disc single: released on Island, Sep'87 by Island Records. Dist: Polygram

Wipeout

BABY PLEASE DON'T GO.
Single (7"): released on M & L, May'82

COME JOIN THE DANCE.
Single (7"): released on Out, May'84 by Out Records. Dist: Chris Wellard Distribution, Pinnacle, Rough Trade Distribution, Cartel Distribution

WIPEOUT - 20 INSTRUMENTAL GREATS Various artists (Various Artists).
Album: released on Impression, Jul'84 Dist: CBS

Cassette: released on Impression, Jul'84 Dist: CBS

Wipers

IS THE REAL?.
Album: released on Psycho (USA), Apr'84

LAND OF THE LOST.
Album: released on Enigma (Europe), Nov'86 by Enigma Records. Dist: Rough Trade, Cartel, EMI

LIVE.
Album: released on Enigma, Mar'86 by Enigma Records. Dist: Rough Trade, Cartel, EMI

OVER THE EDGE.
Album: released on Enigma, Mar'87 by Enigma Records. Dist: Rough Trade, Cartel, EMI

Album: released on Braineater, Nov'84 Dist: Rough Trade, Cartel

YOUTH OF AMERICA.
Album: released on Psycho (USA), Apr'84

Wire

AHEAD.
Tracks: / Ahead / Feed me / Ambulance chases (live) / Vivid riot of red (live).
Single (7"): released on Mute, Mar'87 Dist: Spartan Distribution, Rough Trade Distribution, Cartel Distribution

Single (12"): released on Mute, Mar'87 Dist: Spartan Distribution, Rough Trade Distribution, Cartel Distribution

CHAIRS MISSING.
Album: released on Harvest, Sep'78 by EMI Records. Dist: Roots, EMI

Cassette: released on Harvest, Sep'78 by EMI Records. Dist: Roots, EMI

CRAZY ABOUT LOVE.
Single (12"): released on Rough Trade, Mar'83 by Rough Trade Records. Dist: Rough Trade Distribution, Cartel Distribution

DOCUMENT AND EYEWITNESS.
Album: released on Rough Trade, '84 by Rough Trade Records. Dist: Rough Trade Distribution, Cartel Distribution

Cassette: released on Rough Trade, '84 by Rough Trade Records. Dist: Rough Trade Distribution, Cartel Distribution

IDEAL COPY, THE.
Album: released on Mute, Apr'87 Dist: Spartan Distribution, Rough Trade Distribution, Cartel Distribution

Cassette: released on Mute, Apr'87 Dist: Spartan Distribution, Rough Trade Distribution, Cartel Distribution

IN THE PINK.
Tracks: / Pink flag / 12XU / Map ref 41 degrees N.95 degrees S.W / Reuters / Brazil / Different to me / Practice makes perfect / Outdoor miner / I am the fly / I should have known better / Other window / Single K.O. / Mutual friend.
Album: released on Dojo, Aug'86 by Castle Communications Records. Dist: Cartel

OUR SWIMMER.
Single (7"): released on Rough Trade, May'81 by Rough Trade Records. Dist: Rough Trade Distribution, Cartel Distribution

PINK FLAG.
Album: released on Harvest, Nov'77 by EMI Records. Dist: Roots, EMI

Cassette: released on Harvest, Nov'77 by EMI Records. Dist: Roots, EMI Deleted '79.

SNAKEDRILL (EP).
Tracks: / Serious of snakes / Drill / An advantage in height / Vivid riot of red, A.
Single (12"): released on Mute, Nov'86 Dist: Spartan Distribution, Rough Trade Distribution, Cartel Distribution

WIRE PLAY POP.
Album: released on Pink, Mar'86 by Pink R ords. Dist: Rough Trade

TO THE BEAT OF A DRUM.
Tracks: / To the beat of the drum / George
Single (12"): released on Nine O Nine, Ma by Creole Records. Dist: Rhino, PRT

Wire Train

BETWEEN TWO WORDS.
Tracks: / Last perfect thing / Skills of summ When she was a girl / With god on our si Love, love / I will / No pretties / Ocean, T Two persons / Home.
Album: released on CBS, Mar'86 by CBS ords. Dist: CBS

Cassette: released on CBS, Mar'86 by Records. Dist: CBS

CHAMBER OF HELLOS.
Single (7"): released on CBS, Jan'84 by Records. Dist: CBS

Single (12"): released on CBS, Jan'84 by Records. Dist: CBS

DIVING.
Tracks: / Diving / Mercy mercy.
Single (7"): released on CBS, Apr'87 by Records. Dist: CBS

Single (12"): released on CBS, Apr'87 by Records. Dist: CBS

IN A CHAMBER.
Album: released on CBS, Jan'84 by CBS ords. Dist: CBS

Cassette: released on CBS, Jan'84 by Records. Dist: CBS

LOVE'S PERFECT THING.
Tracks: / Half a lifetime.
Single (7"): released on CBS, Feb'86 by Records. Dist: CBS.

Single (12"): released on CBS, Feb'86 by Records. Dist: CBS

SHE COMES ON She comes on.
Tracks: / She comes on / Compassion.
Single (7"): released on CBS, Mar'87 by Records. Dist: CBS

Single (12"): released on CBS, Mar'87 by Records. Dist: CBS

SKILLS OF SUMMER.
Tracks: / When she was a girl.
Single (7"): released on CBS, May'86 by Records. Dist: CBS

Single (12"): released on CBS, May'86 b Records. Dist: CBS

TEN WOMEN.
Album: released on CBS, Apr'87 by CBS ords. Dist: CBS

Cassette: released on CBS, Apr'87 by Records. Dist: CBS

Wisdom

KLUNG KLUSION.
Single (12"): released on Simbal, Jul'8 Works Records Distribution, Jetstar

Wisdom, Norman

JINGLE JANGLE Original London ca
Album: released on That's Entertai May'83 by That's Entertainment Record Pinnacle, PRT

Wise Blood

DIRTDISH.
Album: released on Some Bizzare, Ja Charisma Records. Dist: EMI, CBS, Po

Cassette: released on Some Bizzare, by Charisma Records. Dist: EMI, CBS gram

MOTOR SLUG.
Single (12"): released on Some Bizarre by Virgin Records. Dist: EMI, CBS, Pol

STUMBO.
Tracks: / Someone drowned in my poo
Single (12"): released on K 422, Dec' 422 Records. Dist: Rough Trade, Carte

Wise Guise

I GUESS SOMEONE UP THERE LIKE ME.
Single (12"): released on Strike, De Strike Records. Dist: Fresh Distribution Trade Distribution, Strike Distribution

Wiseman, Mac

BLUEGRASS FAVOURITES.
Album: released on Stetson, Jul'87 by

...notions Ltd. Dist: Counterpoint Distribu-
...H.R. Taylor Distribution, Swift Distribution,
...s Wellard Distribution

...sette: released on Stetson, Jul'87 by Has-
...Promotions Ltd. Dist: Counterpoint Dis-
...tribution. H.R. Taylor Distribution. Swift
...bution, Chris Wellard Distribution

...NTRY MUSIC MEMORIES.
...m: released on Checkmate, Oct'77 Dist: I

...DEN CLASSICS.
...m: released on Gusto (USA), Oct'79 by
...o Records (USA). Dist: Crusader

...NANDOAH VALLEY MEMORIES.
...m: released on Canaan(USA), Aug'77 by
...Records. Dist: Word Distribution

...se Men

...WLEDGE.
...e (7"): released on Glass, May'83 by
...Records. Dist: Nine Mile, Rough Trade,
...Rhino, Play It Again Sam

...shbone Ash

...US.
...m: released on MCA, Feb'84 by MCA Rec-
...

...ette: released on MCA, Feb'84 by MCA
...ds. Dist: CBS

...SIC ASH.
...m: released on MCA, Aug'81 by MCA Rec-
...

...tte: released on MCA, Aug'81 by MCA
...ds. Dist: CBS

...m: released on Fame (MCA), Jan'83 by
...For Pleasure Records. Dist: EMI

...ette: released on Fame (MCA), Jan'83 by
...For Pleasure Records. Dist: EMI

...NE OVERHEAT.
...(7"): released on AVM, Oct'82 Dist: PRT
...Cat. no: WISH 1

...T PAGE NEWS.
...: released on MCA, Jan'82 by MCA Rec-
...st: CBS

...te: released on MCA, Jan'82 by MCA
...s. Dist: CBS

...DATES.
... Album: released on MCA, '74 by MCA
...s. Dist: CBS

...cassette: released on MCA, '74 by
...ecords. Dist: CBS

...ENGLAND.
...: released on MCA, Jul'82 by MCA Rec-
...st: CBS

...te: released on MCA, Jul'82 by MCA
...s. Dist: CBS

...ORE LONELY NIGHTS.
...(7"): released on AVM, Dec'82 Dist:

...IMAGE.
...: released on MCA, '83 by MCA Rec-
...st: CBS

...te: released on MCA, '83 by MCA Rec-
...st: CBS

...e: released on MCA (Twinpax series),
...

...O THE BONE.
...released on Neat, '85 by Neat Records.
...nacle, Neat

...e: released on Neat, '85 by Neat Rec-
...st: Pinnacle, Neat

...disc album: released on Neat, '85 by
...cords. Dist: Pinnacle, Neat

...ARRELS BURNING.
...released on AVM, Oct'82 Dist: PRT

...ful Thinking

...JL THINKING.
..."): released on Organic, Sep'83 by Or-
...cords. Dist: Pinnacle

...ing stones

...IRL.
...): released on Head, Sep'86 by Head
...Dist: Revolver, Cartel

...AYS.
..."): released on Head, Apr'87 by Head
...Dist: Revolver, Cartel

...2"): released on Head, Apr'87 by Head
...rds. Dist: Revolver, Cartel

Wish You Were Here
WISH YOU WERE HERE Various artists
(Various Artists).
Album: released on Flying Fish (USA), May'79
by Flying Fish Records (USA). Dist: Roots, Pro-
jection

Wiss
MR SUNSHINE.
Album: released on Jah Life, Mar'85 by Jah Life
Records. Dist: Jetstar

Witch
HEX IS ON, THE.
Album: released on Heavy Metal America,
Jun'85 by FM-Revolver Records. Dist: EMI

Witcher, Wolfie
INDOOR BUSKIN' - A LIVE ALBUM.
Album: released on Elefanztrunk, Sep'85 Dist:
Revolver, Hotshot, Cartel

NO MONEY DOWN (Witcher, Wolfie & The
Nightriders).
Single (7"): released on Speed, Nov'82

Witchfinder General
BURNING A SINNER.
Single (7"): released on Heavy Metal, Sep'81
by FM-Revolver Records. Dist: EMI

DEATH PENALTY.
Album: released on Heavy Metal, Nov'82 by
FM-Revolver Records. Dist: EMI

FRIENDS OF HELL.
Album: released on Heavy Metal, Nov'83 by
FM-Revolver Records. Dist: EMI

MUSIC.
Single (7"): released on Heavy Metal, Dec'83
by FM-Revolver Records. Dist: EMI

Picture disc single: released on Heavy Metal,
Dec'83 by FM-Revolver Records. Dist: EMI

SOVIET INVASION.
Single (7"): released on Heavy Metal, Jan'83
by FM-Revolver Records. Dist: EMI

Witchfynde
CLOAK AND DAGGER.
Album: released on Expulsion, Nov'83 by Ex-
pulsion Records. Dist: Stage One

CONSPIRACY.
Single (7"): released on Mausoleum, Mar'85 by
Mausoleum Records. Dist: Pinnacle

GIVE 'EM HELL.
Album: released on Rondelet, May'80 Dist:
Spartan Distribution

Cassette: released on Rondelet, May'80 Dist:
Spartan Distribution

Single (7"): released on Rondelet, Feb'80 Dist:
Spartan Distribution

I'D RATHER GO WILD.
Single (7"): released on Expulsion, Jul'83 by
Expulsion Records. Dist: Stage One

IN THE STARS.
Single (7"): released on Rondelet, Sep'80 Dist:
Spartan Distribution

LORDS OF SIN.
Album: released on Mausoleum, Dec'84 by
Mausoleum Records. Dist: Pinnacle

Cassette: released on Mausoleum, Dec'84 by
Mausoleum Records. Dist: Pinnacle

STAGE FRIGHT.
Album: released on Rondelet, Oct'80 Dist:
Spartan Distribution

Cassette: released on Rondelet, Oct'80 Dist:
Spartan Distribution

Withered Arm
WITHERED ARM Read by Corin Redgrave
(Hardy, Thomas).
Cassette: released on Colophone, Nov'81 by
Audio-Visual Library Services. Dist: Audio-Vis-
ual Library Services

WITHERED ARM (Hardy, Thomas).
Cassette: released on Talking Tape Company,
'84 by Talking Tape Company Records.

Withers, Benny
UP JUMPED THE BLUES (Withers, Benny
& Keith Smith's Chosen 5).
Album: released on Hefty Jazz, Oct'79 Dist:
JSU, Swift, Wellard, Chris, Jazz Music, Cadillac
Music

Withers, Bill
GREATEST HITS: BILL WITHERS.
Album: released on CBS, Jul'83 by CBS Rec-

...ords. Dist: CBS
Cassette: released on CBS, Jul'83 by CBS
Records. Dist: CBS

I WANT TO SPEND THE NIGHT.
Single (7"): released on CBS, Jul'81 by CBS
Records. Dist: CBS

LEAN ON ME.
Single (7"): released on Old Gold (Reissue),
Jul'82

LOVELY DAY.
Tracks: / Lovely day / Lovely night for dancing.
Single (7"): released on CBS, Jul'87 by CBS
Records. Dist: CBS

Tracks: / Lovely day (ext) / Lean on me / Love-
ly night for dancing.
Single (12"): released on CBS, Jul'87 by CBS
Records. Dist: CBS

MENAGERIE.
Album: released on CBS, Nov'85 by CBS Records. Dist: CBS

Cassette: released on CBS, Nov'85 by CBS
Records. Dist: CBS

USA.
Single (7"): released on CBS, Jan'82 by CBS
Records. Dist: CBS

WATCHING YOU, WATCHING ME.
Album: released on CBS, Jun'85 by CBS Records. Dist: CBS

Cassette: released on CBS, Jun'85 by CBS
Records. Dist: CBS

Witherspoon, Jimmy
AIN'T NOBODY'S BUSINESS.
Album: released on Black Lion, Sep'85 by
Black Lion Records. Dist: Jazz Music, Chris
Wellard, Taylor, H.R., Counterpoint, Cadillac

**BEN WEBSTER & JIMMY WITHER-
SPOON** (That's Jazz Series).
Album: released on Warner Brothers, Mar'77
by WEA Records. Dist: WEA

BIG BLUES.
Album: released on JSP, Aug'81 by JSP Records. Dist: Swift, Projection

CRY THE BLUES.
Album: released on Bulldog Records, Jul'82

HEY, MR.LANDLORD.
Album: released on Route 66, Oct'86

LIVE IN PARIS.
Album: released on Vogue, Jan'77

MIDNIGHT LADY CALLED THE BLUES.
Tracks: / New York City blues / Barber / Blinded
by love / Happy hard times / Something rotten
in East St Louis / Midnight lady called the blues
/ Blues hall of fame.
Album: released on Muse (USA), Feb'87 by
Muse Records (USA). Dist: Conifer Distribution,
Jazz Music Distribution

**SINGS THE BLUES WITH PANAMA
FRANCIS AND THE SAVOY SULTANS.**
Album: released on Muse, Feb'83 by Import
Records. Dist: Jazz Horizons Distribution, Jazz
Music Distribution, JSU Distribution, Swift Dis-
tribution

WHO'S BEEN JIVIN' YOU.
Album: released on Ace(Cadet), Jan'84 by Ace
Records. Dist: Pinnacle, Swift, Hotshot

Withers, Tex
BLUE RIBBON COUNTRY.
Cassette: released on Homespun(Ireland),
May'84 by Outlet Records. Dist: Outlet

TRUCK DRIVING MAN.
Cassette: released on VFM Cassettes, Jan'85

Withers, Vivian
WHAT IS MAN.
Tracks: / What is man / Joe Blake / Hangin' on.
Single (12"): released on Trojan, Jun'87 by
Trojan Records. Dist: PRT, Jetstar

With My Hands Liftes Up
WITH MY HANDS LIFTED UP Scripture
songs.
Album: released on Dove, May'79 by Dove
Records. Dist: Jetstar

Witness
LOUDHAILER SONGS....
Album: released on Ron Johnson, Dec'85
by Ron Johnson Records. Dist: Nine Mile Distribution, Cartel Distribution

WITNESS Original soundtrack.
Album: released on That's Entertainment,
Jun'85 by That's Entertainment Records. Dist:

Pinnacle, PRT

Witness, A
I AM JOHN PANCREAS.
Album: released on Ron Johnson, Oct'86 by
Ron Johnson Records. Dist: Nine Mile Distribu-
tion, Cartel Distribution

Witness, The
WITNESS, THE A musical by Jimmy & Carol
Owens.
Album: released on Light, May'82

Cassette: released on Light, May'82

Wittlcombe Fair
WITTICOMBE FAIR HAPPY DAYS.
Album: released on SRT, Dec'76 by SRT Rec-
ords. Dist: Pinnacle, Solomon & Peres Distribu-
tion, SRT Distribution, H.R. Taylor Distribution,
PRT Distribution

Witt, Joachim
TRI TRA TRULLALA.
Single (7"): released on WEA, Sep'82 by WEA
Records. Dist: WEA

Single (12"): released on WEA, Sep'82 by
WEA Records. Dist: WEA

Wittstatt, Hans "Pepe"
LOVE IS THE KEY.
Tracks: / Caligari / Las Canteras / Terminal
symbol / Love is the key / Dream of Westerland
/ Nautical march / Sir Edward-Georg / A.B.A.D..
Album:

Wizard Merlyn MMC
LOLLIPOPS AND DRAGONS (Wizard
Merlyn MMC & The Wizpops).
Single (7"): released on Wizard Merlyn, Nov'82
Dist: Wizard Merlyn Distribution

Wizard of Earthsea
WIZARD OF EARTHSEA (Hood, Moraig).
Cassette: released on Colophone, Nov'81 by
Audio-Visual Library Services. Dist: Audio-Vis-
ual Library Services

Wizard of Oz
WIZARD OF OZ Various Artists (Various Ar-
tists).
Album: released on Disneyland, Dec'82 by
WEA Records. Dist: WEA

Cassette: released on Disneyland, Dec'82
Dist: EMI

WIZARD OF OZ, THE Original soundtrack
(Various Artists).
Tracks: / Over the rainbow / Munchkinland / If
only I had a brain / If only I had a heart / If only
I had the nerve / If I were king of the forest /
Courage / Ding dong! The witch is dead / If
There's no place like home.
Album: released on CBS, Jul'86 by CBS Rec-
ords. Dist: CBS

Cassette: released on CBS, Jul'86 by CBS
Records. Dist: CBS

Compact disc: released on CBS, Jun'87 by
CBS Records. Dist: CBS

Wizard of Oz, (The)
WIZARD OF OZ, (THE) Baum, Frank
(Moore, Stephen).
Double cassette: released on Listen For Plea-
sure, Mar'84 by EMI Records. Dist: MFP

Wizards...
WIZARDS FROM THE SOUTHSIDE Vari-
ous artists (Various Artists).
Album: released on Chess, Aug'86 by Charly
Records. Dist: Charly, Swift, PRT, Discovery,
IMS, Polygram

Cassette: released on Chess, Aug'86 by Charly Records. Dist: Charly, Swift, PRT, Discovery,
IMS, Polygram

Wizzard
ANGEL FINGERS.
Single (7"): released on Harvest, Aug'73 by
EMI Records. Dist: Roots, EMI

I WISH IT COULD BE CHRISTMAS
EVERY DAY.
Single (7"): released on Harvest, Nov'73 by
EMI Records. Dist: Roots, EMI

SEE MY BABY JIVE.
Single (7"): released on Harvest, Feb'76 by
EMI Records. Dist: Roots, EMI

Single (7"): released on Old Gold, Oct'83 by
Old Gold Records. Dist: Lightning, Jazz Music,
Spartan, Counterpoint

WKGB

NON STOP.
Single (7"): released on Fetish, Jul'81 by Fetish Records. Dist: Cartel, Pinnacle

WNW6 Moonlight Radio

WNW6 MOONLIGHT RADIO Various artists (Various Artists).

Album: released on Armageddon, Mar'82 by Armageddon Records. Dist: Revolver, Cartel, Pinnacle

Wobble, Jah

BETWEEN TWO FREQUENCIES (Wobble, Jah & Brett Wickens).
Single (12"): released on General Music (France), Apr'86 by General Music Records (France). Dist: Studio Import & Export Distribution, Silva Screen

TRADEWINGS (Wobble, Jah & Ollie Marland).
Album: released on Lago, Oct'86 by Lago Records. Dist: Pinnacle, Rough Trade

Wobblesox

GET YOU SOCKS OFF.
Single (7"): released on Freewave, Oct'80 Dist: Rough Trade

Wobbly Jellies

MAGIC.
Single (7"): released on Wimp, May'84 by Wimp Records. Dist: Backs, Cartel

Wodehouse, P.G.

ANSELM GETS HIS CHANCE.
Cassette: released on Talking Tape Company, Sep'84 by Talking Tape Company Records.

CLICKING OF CUTHBERT.
Cassette: released on Talking Tape Company, '84 by Talking Tape Company Records.

JEEVES AND THE YULETIDE SPIRIT.
Cassette: released on Talking Tape Company, '84 by Talking Tape Company Records

LORD EMSWORTH & THE GIRLFRIEND.
Cassette: released on Talking Tape Company, '84 by Talking Tape Company Records.

MULLINER'S BUCK U UPPO.
Cassette: released on Talking Tape Company, Sep'84 by Talking Tape Company Records.

UKRIDGE'S ACCIDENT SYNDICATE.
Cassette: released on Talking Tape Company, '84 by Talking Tape Company Records.

Wofford, Mike

PLAYS JEROME KERN.
Tracks: / All the things you are / Long ago and far away / Folks who live on the hill, The / Song is you, The / In love in vain / Smoke gets in your eyes / I won't dance.
Notes: Mike Wofford on Piano,and Anthony Ortega on Alto Tenor sax & flute/Andy Simpkins bass/Jim Plank drums.
Compact disc: released on Discovery (USA), Sep'86 by Discovery Records (USA). Dist: Swift, Flexitron-Audio, Jazz Music

Wogan, Terry

FLORAL DANCE.
Single (7"): released on Philips, Jan'78 Dist: IMS-Polygram

TWO HEADS ARE BTTER THAN ONE/ BEER IS BEST (Wogan, Terry & Jimmy Young).

Wogan, Terry & Jimmy Young

TWO HEADS ARE BETTER THAN ONE.
Single (7"): released on Paramount, Nov'83 by Paramount Records. Dist: PRT

Wolf

CANIS LUPUS.

Album: released on Deram, '73 by Decca Records. Dist: Polygram

EDGE OF THE WORLD.
Album: released on Mausoleum, Jun'84 by Mausoleum Records. Dist: Pinnacle

Cassette: released on Mausoleum, Jun'84 by Mausoleum Records. Dist: Pinnacle

NIGHT MUSIC.
Album: released on Deram, Nov'74 by Decca Records. Dist: Polygram

Wolf And The......

WOLF AND THE SEVEN LITTLE KIDS,THE (Tell-A-Tale Series) (Various Artists).
Cassette: released on Pickwick, '83 by Pickwick Records. Dist: Pickwick Distribution, Prism Leisure Distribution, Lugtons

Wolfe, Jerri

STILL LIFE.
Single (7"): released on Polydor, Aug'82 by Polydor Records. Dist: Polygram, Polydor .

Wolfer, Bill

CALL ME.
Single (7"): released on Solar, May'83

Single (12"): released on Solar, May'83

PAPA WAS A ROLLIN' STONE.
Single (7"): released on Solar, Feb'83

Single (12"): released on Solar, Feb'83

WOLF.
Album: released on Elektra, Jan'83 by WEA Records. Dist: WEA

Wolfe Tones

ACROSS THE BROAD.
Album: released on Triskel, Nov'76 Dist: EMI (Ireland), I & B, Celtic Music

ALIVE ALIVE OH.
Album: released on Triskel, May'81 Dist: EMI (Ireland), I & B, Celtic Music

FAREWELL TO DUBLIN.
Single (7"): released on Triskel, Aug'76 Dist: EMI (Ireland), I & B, Celtic Music

GREATEST HITS:WOLFE TONES.
Tracks: / My heart is in Ireland / Streets of New York / Dreams of home / Only our rivers / Quare things in Dublin / Padraic pearse / On the one road / God save Ireland / Irish eyes / Songs of liberty / Uncle Nobby's steamboat / Sapncill hill / Paddle your own canoe / Some say the devil is dead / Let the people sing / Nation once again, A.
Album: released on K-Tel, Oct'86 by K-Tel Records. Dist: Record Merchandisers Distribution, Taylors, Terry Blood Distribution, Wynd-Up Distribution, Relay Distribution, Pickwick Distribution, Solomon & Peres Distribution, Polygram

Cassette: released on K-Tel, Oct'86 by K-Tel Records. Dist: Record Merchandisers Distribution, Taylors, Terry Blood Distribution, Wynd-Up Distribution, Relay Distribution, Pickwick Distribution, Solomon & Peres Distribution, Polygram

IRISH TO THE CORE.
Album: released on Triskel, Jun'76 Dist: EMI (Ireland), I & B, Celtic Music

LET THE PEOPLE SING.
Album: released on Dolphin, Nov'76 Dist: I & B Records Distribution, Prism Leisure Corporation Records, Record Services Distribution (Ireland)

MY HEART IS IN IRELAND.
Single (7"): released on MCA, Sep'85 by MCA Records. Dist: Polygram, MCA

RIFLES OF THE I.R.A..
Album: released on Dolphin, Nov'76 Dist: I & B Records Distribution, Prism Leisure Corporation Records, Record Services Distribution (Ireland)

TEDDY BEAR'S HEAD (Wolff, Francis).
Album: released on Dolphin, Nov'76 Dist: I & B Records Distribution, Prism Leisure Corporation Records, Record Services Distribution (Ireland)

TILL IRELAND'S A NATION.
Album: released on Dolphin, Nov'76 Dist: I & B Records Distribution, Prism Leisure Corporation Records, Record Services Distribution (Ireland)

UP THE REBELS.
Album: released on Dolphin, Nov'76 Dist: I & B Records Distribution, Prism Leisure Corporation Records, Record Services Distribution (Ireland)

VALE OF AVOCA.
Single (7"): released on Triskel, Jun'76 Dist: EMI (Ireland), I & B, Celtic Music

WOLFE TONES, THE.
Tracks: / My heart is in Ireland / Wearing of the green / Mullinger fleadh / Plastic bullets / Masushla Mavoureen / Song of liberty / Women of Ireland / Butcher's apron / Little Jimmy Murphy / Sailor of St Brendan / Too ra loo / Far away in Australia.
Album: released on MCA, Oct'85 by MCA Records. Dist: Polygram, MCA

Cassette: released on MCA, Oct'85 by MCA Records. Dist: Polygram, MCA

Wolff, Henry

TIBETAN SPELLS 11 (Wolff, Henry & Nancy Hennings).
Album: released on Celestial Harmonies, Jul'87 by TM Records. Dist: PRT

Cassette: released on Celestial Harmonies, Jul'87 by TM Records. Dist: PRT

Wolfgamme, Bill

HAWAIIAN SUNSET.
Album: released on Viking, Nov'79 by Viking Records. Dist: Lugtons

Wolfgamme, Nani

HAWAIIAN COCKTAIL (Wolfgamme, Nani & South Pacific Strings).
Album: released on Viking, Nov'79 by Viking Records. Dist: Lugtons

HAWAII CALLS (Wolfgamme, Nani & His Islanders).
Album: released on Viking, Feb'79 by Viking Records. Dist: Lugtons

Cassette: released on Viking, Feb'79 by Viking Records. Dist: Lugtons

POLYNESIAN LOVE SONG (Wolfgamme, Nani & His Islanders).
Album: released on Viking, '78 by Viking Records. Dist: Lugtons

Cassette: released on Viking, '78 by Viking Records. Dist: Lugtons

Wolfgang Press

BIG SEX (EP).
Tracks: / Big sex (ep) / Wedding (The) / Geat leveller (The) / That heat / God's number.
Extended-play record: by 4AD Records. Dist: Rough Trade

Cassette single: released on 4AD, Apr'87 by 4AD Records. Dist: Rough Trade

BURDEN OF MULES,THE.
Album: released on 4AD, Jul'83 by 4AD Records. Dist: Rough Trade

LEGENDARY WOLFGANG PRESS AND OTHER....
Compact disc: released on 4AD, Feb'87 by 4AD Records. Dist: Rough Trade

Album: released on 4AD, Nov'85 by 4AD Records. Dist: Rough Trade

SCARECROW.
Single (12"): released on 4AD, Jul'84 by 4AD Records. Dist: Rough Trade

STANDING UP STRAIGHT.
Tracks: / Dig a hole / My life / Hammer the halo / Bless my brother / Fire-fly / Rotten fodder / Forty days, thirty nights / I am the crime.
Compact disc: released on 4AD, Feb'87 by 4AD Records. Dist: Rough Trade

Cassette: released on 4AD, May'86 by 4AD Records. Dist: Rough Trade

SWEAT BOX.
Single (12"): released on 4AD, Sep'85 by 4AD Records. Dist: Rough Trade

WATER.
Single (12"): released on 4AD, Mar'85 by 4AD Records. Dist: Rough Trade

Wolfhounds

ANTI MIDAS TOUCH, THE.
Tracks: / Anti Midas touch, The.
Single (7"): released on Pink, Oct'86 by Pink Records. Dist: Rough Trade

Single (12"): released on Pink, Oct'86 by Pink Records. Dist: Rough Trade

CUT THE CAKE.
Tracks: / Cut the cake.
Single (12"): released on Pink, Mar'86 by Pink Records. Dist: Rough Trade

IRELAND BOY'S HURRAGH.
Album: released on Derby, Aug'76

Wolf, Howlin'

HOWLIN' FOR MY BABY.
Tracks: / My baby walked off / Smile at me / Bluebird blues / Everybody's in the mood / Chocolate drop / Come back home / Dorothy Mae / Highway man / Oh Red / My last affair / Howlin for my baby / Sweet woman / C.V. wine blues / Look-a-here baby / Decoration Day blues / Well that's alright / California blues / My troubles and me / California boogie.
Compact disc: released on Charly, Apr'87 by Charly Records. Dist: Charly, Cadillac

Wolf, Peter

COME AS YOU ARE.
Tracks: / Cme as you are / Thick as thieves.
Single (7"): released on EMI America, Apr'87 by EMI Records. Dist: EMI

Single (12"): released on EMI America, Apr'87 by EMI Records. Dist: EMI

Tracks: / Can't get started / Run silent run de / 2 Lane / Magic moon / Mamma said / Fla of love / Come as you are / Wind me up / B avenue / Thick as thieves / Love on ice.
Album: released on EMI America, Jun'87 EMI Records. Dist: EMI

LIGHTS OUT.
Tracks: / Lights out / I need you tonight / (EE-Diddley-bob! / Gloomy Sunday / B please don't let me go / Crazy / Poor girl's h / Here comes that hurt / Pretty lady (tell me w / Mars need women / Billy bigtime.
Notes: Peter Wolf's first solo project, after long association with the J.Geils Band. Alb features 'Pretty lady', with backing vocals Mick Jagger.
Album: released on EMI America, Aug'86 EMI Records. Dist: EMI

Cassette: released on EMI America, Aug'8 EMI Records. Dist: EMI

Compact disc: released on EMI Amer Aug'86 by EMI Records. Dist: EMI

Single (7"): released on EMI America, Au by EMI Records. Dist: EMI

Wolf, Virginia

ACTION.
Single (7"): released on Creole, Mar'82 by ole Records. Dist: Rhino, PRT

DON'T BREAK AWAY.
Tracks: / Open door.
Single (7"): released on Atlantic, Aug'8 WEA Records. Dist: WEA

Single (12"): released on Atlantic, Aug'8 WEA Records. Dist: WEA

PUSH.
Tracks: / Don't break away / One night / St ing on the edge of time / Open door / Man i moon / Let it go / You don't know what y got / Can you feel the fire / Tables have tu / Strangest thing, The.
Album: released on Atlantic, Jul'87 by Records. Dist: WEA

Cassette: released on Atlantic, Jul'87 by Records. Dist: WEA

VIRGINIA WOLF.
Tracks: / Are we playing with fire? / Make night / Only love / It's in your eyes / Waiti your love / Livin' on a knife edge / For a know / Don't run away / Take a chance.
Album: released on Atlantic, Apr'86 by Records. Dist: WEA

Cassette: released on Atlantic, Apr'86 by Records. Dist: WEA

WAITING FOR YOUR LOVE.
Tracks: / Waiting for your love / Take a ch
Single (7"): released on Atlantic, Feb' WEA Records. Dist: WEA

WALKIE TALKIE BOY.
Single (7"): released on Creole, Jun'82 b ole Records. Dist: Rhino, PRT

Wolf & Wolf

DON'T TAKE THE CANDY.
Single (7"): released on Morocco, Jul'84

WOLF & WOLF.
Album: released on Morocco, Apr'84

Cassette: released on Morocco, Apr'84

Wolverines Orchestra

1924.
Album: released on Swaggie (Aust Jan'83

WOLVERINES ORCHESTRA 1924
Album: released on Fountain, Apr'79 by val Records. Dist: Jazz Music, Swift, VJM lard, Chris, Retrieval

Womack And Womack

STAR BRIGHT.
Tracks: / Soul love, soul man / Family / party / Starbright / New York city / Find y another girl / Reason(The)(must be love me / Rejoice.
Album: released on Manhattan, Jan President Records. Dist: Jazz Music, Sw lors, Chris Wellard

Cassette: released on Manhattan, Ja President Records. Dist: Jazz Music, Sw lors, Chris Wellard

Womack, Bobby

CHECK IT OUT.
Tracks: / Interlude / I don't know / Hold my baby's love / That's heaven to me get you back / Tarnished rings / Preache than I can stand / Check it out / Womar have it / Point of no return / It's all ove Daylight / Yes, Jesus loves me.
Album: released on Stateside, Oct'86 D

Cassette: released on Stateside, Oct EMI

Page 1112

ssette: released on Stateside, Oct'86 Dist:
Al

HESS MASTERS (Womack, Bobby & The
lentinos).
bum: released on Chess, Oct'84 by Charly
ecords. Dist: Charly, Swift, PRT, Discovery,
S, Polygram

PSY WOMAN.
acks: / Gipsy woman / Whatever happened
the times.
ngle (7"): released on MCA, May'86 by MCA
ecords. Dist: Polygram, MCA

ngle (12"): released on MCA, May'86 by
A Records. Dist: Polygram, MCA

OME IS WHERE THE HEART IS.
oum: released on Edsel, Feb'86 by Demon
ecords. Dist: Pinnacle, Jazz Music, Projection

ssette: released on Edsel, Feb'86 by Demon
cords. Dist: Pinnacle, Jazz Music, Projection

W COULD YOU BREAK MY HEART.
cks: / How could you break my heart / Give
o / Mr DJ don't stop the music.
gle (7"): released on Arista, 20 Jun'87 by
sta Records. Dist: RCA

gle (12"): released on Arista, 20 Jun'87 by
ta Records. Dist: RCA

ANNA MAKE LOVE TO YOU.
cks: / Whatever happened to the times?.
gle (7"): released on MCA, Jan'87 by MCA
ords. Dist: Polygram, MCA

gle (12"): released on MCA, Jan'87 by MCA
ords. Dist: Polygram, MCA

ISH YOU DIDN'T TRUST ME SO
CH.
gle (7"): released on MCA, Sep'85 by MCA
ords. Dist: Polygram, MCA

le (12"): released on MCA, Sep'85 by MCA
ords. Dist: Polygram, MCA

T.
pact disc: by Pacific Records (USA). Dist:
tic

T II.
pact disc: by Pacific Records (USA). Dist:
tic

T II,THE.
m: released on Motown, Apr'84 by RCA
rds. Dist: RCA Distribution

ette: released on Motown, Apr'84 by RCA
rds. Dist: RCA Distribution

T, THE.
n: released on Motown, Jun'82 by RCA
ds. Dist: RCA Distribution

ette: released on Motown, Jun'82 by RCA
ds. Dist: RCA Distribution

RETS.
(7"): released on Motown, Sep'82 by
Records. Dist: RCA Distribution

n: released on MCA, Sep'85 by MCA Rec-
Dist: CBS

tte: released on MCA, Sep'85 by MCA
ds. Dist: CBS

ANY RIVERS.
s: / I wish he didn't trust me so much / So
lon't leave home without it / So many ri-
Got to be with you tonight / What ever hap-
to those times / Let me kiss it where it
Only survivor / That's where it's at / Check

act disc: released on MCA, Mar'86 by
Records. Dist: Polygram, MCA

ANY SIDES OF YOU.
(7"): released on Motown, Jul'82 by
ecords. Dist: RCA Distribution

(12"): released on Motown, Jul'82 by
ecords. Dist: RCA Distribution

BODY SPECIAL.
: released on Liberty, Sep'84

te: released on Liberty, Sep'84

RIZE SURPRIZE.
(7"): released on Motown, Sep'84 by
ecords. Dist: RCA Distribution

(12"): released on Motown, Sep'84 by
ecords. Dist: RCA Distribution

ME WHY.
(7"): released on Motown, Jun'84 by
ecords. Dist: RCA Distribution

(12"): released on Motown, Jun'84 by
ecords. Dist: RCA Distribution

RSTANDING.
released on Liberty (USA), Apr'81 Dist:
Artists

WOMAGIC.
Compact disc: released on MCA, Mar'87 by MCA Records. Dist: Polygram, MCA

WOMAGIC.
Tracks: / I wanna make love to you / When the weekend comes / All the things you do / I can't stay mad too long / Hear the music / Outside myself / I ain't got to love nobody else / More than love / More than love / It ain't me.
Album: released on MCA, Nov'86 by MCA Records. Dist: Polygram, MCA

Cassette: released on MCA, Nov'86 by MCA Records. Dist: Polygram, MCA

Womack, Steve

NORTHERN COMFORT.
Album: released on Plant Life, Sep'84 Dist: Roots

Womack & Womack

EYES.
Single (7"): released on Elektra, Aug'85 by WEA Records. Dist: WEA

Single (12"): released on Elektra, Aug'85 by WEA Records. Dist: WEA

LOVE WARS.
Single (7"): released on Elektra, Apr'84 by WEA Records. Dist: WEA

Single (12"): released on Elektra, Apr'84 by WEA Records. Dist: WEA

RADIO M.U.S.C. MAN.
Album: released on Elektra, Jun'85 by WEA Records. Dist: WEA

Cassette: released on Elektra, Jun'85 by WEA Records. Dist: WEA

SOUL LOVE SOUL MAN.
Tracks: / Soul love soul man / Soul love soul man (insrumental) / Your man's on fire.
Single (7"): released on Manhattan, Nov'86 by EMI Records. Dist: EMI

Single (12"): released on Manhattan, Nov'86 by EMI Records. Dist: EMI

STARBRIGHT.
Tracks: / Soul love, soul man / It's my party / Starbright / New York city / Find yourself another girl / Reason (must be love), The / Take me / Rejoice.
Album: released on Manhattan, Oct'86 by EMI Records. Dist: EMI

Cassette: released on Manhattan, Oct'86 by EMI Records. Dist: EMI

STRANGE AND FUNNY (Womad talking book volume 2, The).
Single (7"): released on Elektra, Jun'85 by WEA Records. Dist: WEA

Single (12"): released on Elektra, Jun'85 by WEA Records. Dist: WEA

WOMACK & WOMACK.
Album: released on Elektra, Dec'83 by WEA Records. Dist: WEA

Cassette: released on Elektra, Dec'83 by WEA Records. Dist: WEA

Womad talking book

WOMAD TALKING BOOK VOL.1,THE Various Artists (Various Artists).
Album: released on Womad, Apr'85 by Womad Records. Dist: Revolver, Cartel

WOMAD TALKING BOOK VOLUME 2 Various artists (Various Artists).
Album: released on Womad, Nov'85 by Womad Records. Dist: Revolver, Cartel

WOMAD TALKING BOOK VOLUME 3 Europe (Various Artists).
Album: released on Womad, Sep'86 by Womad Records. Dist: Revolver, Cartel

WOMAD TALKING BOOK VOLUME 4 Asia (Various Artists).
Album: released on Womad, Jun'87 by Womad Records. Dist: Revolver, Cartel

Woman In Love

WOMAN IN LOVE Various artists (Various Artists).
Album: released on Starblend, Jan'86 by Starblend Records. Dist: PRT Distribution

Cassette: released on Starblend, Jan'86 by Starblend Records. Dist: PRT Distribution

Wombats

MUD PUDDLES.
Album: released on Homestead, Nov'86 Dist: Rough Trade, Cartel, Shigaku

Wombles

MINUETTO ALLEGRETTO.
Album: released on CBS, '79 by CBS Records. Dist: CBS

WOMBLING MERRY CHRISTMAS.
Single (7"): released on CBS, Dec'83 by CBS Records. Dist: CBS

Women In Jazz

WOMEN IN JAZZ: ALL WOMEN GROUPS Various Artists (Various Artists).
Album: released on Stash, Apr'81 Dist: Swift Distribution, Jazz Music Distribution, Jazz Horizons Distribution, Celtic Music Distribution, Cadillac, JSU Distribution, Zodiac Distribution

WOMEN IN JAZZ: PIANISTS Various Artists (Various Artists).
Album: released on Stash, Apr'81 Dist: Swift Distribution, Jazz Music Distribution, Jazz Horizons Distribution, Celtic Music Distribution, Cadillac, JSU Distribution, Zodiac Distribution

WOMEN IN JAZZ: SWINGTIME TO MODERN Various Artists (Various Artists).
Album: released on Stash, Apr'81 Dist: Swift Distribution, Jazz Music Distribution, Jazz Horizons Distribution, Celtic Music Distribution, Cadillac, JSU Distribution, Zodiac Distribution

Women In Love

WOMEN IN LOVE VOL.3 Various Artists (Various Artists).
Double Album: released on EEC Import (Limited Edition), Dec'82 Dist: IMS, Polygram

Women's Guitar Workshop

WOMEN'S GUITAR WORKSHOP Various Artists (Various Artists).
Album: released on Kicking Mule, '78 by Sonet. Dist: Roots, PRT-Pye Distribution

Women, whisky and wailin'

WOMEN, WHISKY AND WAILIN' Various artists (Various Artists).
Tracks: / Bloodshot eyes / Good morning judge / Sittin' on it all the time / Boogie at midnight / My girl from Kokomo / Fannie Brown got married / My gal / Pedal pushin' papa / My baby's 3-D / South Shore drive / Just a gigolo / I ain't got nobody / Jump, jive and wail / Buona sera / Hucklebuck with Jimmy / Too much boogie / Ain't that just like a woman.
Notes: (A) Original **king** recordings licensed from **Gusto** Records Inc. (B) Original **Vee-Jay** recordings licensed from **Charly** Records International APS. (C) Original **Capitol** recordings licensed from **EMI** Records Ltd. (D) Original **Aladdin** recordinglicensed from Capitol Records Inc. (E) Original **Decca** recordings licensed from **MCA** Records Ltd. This compilation (P) Charly Records Ltd. (C) Charly Records Ltd.
Album: released on Charly, Oct'86 by Charly Records. Dist: Charly, Cadillac

Womersley, Barry

YOU'RE MY WIFE.
Single (7"): released on Da Doo Ron Ron, May'83 by Da Doo Ron Ron Records. Dist: PRT

Wonder boys

WONDER BOYS Various artists (Various Artists).
Album: released on Soul Supply, Dec'86 by High Energy Records. Dist: Charly

Wonder Dog

CHRISTMAS TAILS.
Single (7"): released on ERC, Dec'83 by ERC Records. Dist: PRT

Single (12"): released on ERC, Dec'83 by ERC Records. Dist: PRT

RUFF MIX.
Single (7"): released on Flip, Aug'82 Dist: CBS

Wonderful Town

WONDERFUL TOWN Original London Cast.
Album: released on First Night, Nov'86 by Safari Records. Dist: Pinnacle

Cassette: released on First Night, Nov'86 by Safari Records. Dist: Pinnacle

Wonderful Wizard of Oz

WONDERFUL WIZARD OF OZ (Percival, Lance).
Cassette: released on Storyteller, '79

Wonderful world

WONDERFUL WORLD Various artists (Various Artists).
Album: released on Keyman, Nov'86 by Keyman Records. Dist: Keyman, Revolver

WONDERFUL WORLD OF CHILDREN'S CHRISTMAS Various artists (Various Artists).
Album: released on Audio Fidelity, Oct'84 Dist: PRT

Cassette: released on Audio Fidelity, Oct'84 Dist: PRT

WONDERFUL WORLD OF CHILDREN'S CHRISTMAS - VOL.2 Various artists (Various Artists).
Album: released on Audio Fidelity, Oct'84 Dist: PRT

Cassette: released on Audio Fidelity, Oct'84 Dist: PRT

WONDERFUL WORLD OF CHRISTMAS Various artists (Various Artists).
Album: released on Audio Fidelity, Oct'84 Dist: PRT

Cassette: released on Audio Fidelity, Oct'84 Dist: PRT

WONDERFUL WORLD OF COUNTRY Various artists (Various Artists).
Album: released on Spot, Mar'85 by Pickwick Records. Dist: H.R. Taylor, Lugtons

Cassette: released on Spot, Mar'85 by Pickwick Records. Dist: H.R. Taylor, Lugtons

WONDERFUL WORLD OF COUNTRY MUSIC Various artists (Various Artists).
Album: released on RCA Camden, Feb'80 by RCA Records. Dist: Pickwick Distribution, Taylor, H.R.

Cassette: released on RCA Camden, Feb'80 by RCA Records. Dist: Pickwick Distribution, Taylor, H.R.

WONDERFUL WORLD OF NURSERY RHYMES Vocals - Vera Lynn & Kenneth McKell.
Album: released on Decca, Nov'76 by Decca Records. Dist: Polygram

WONDERFUL WORLD OF GLASS Various artists (Various Artists).
Album: released on Glass, Nov'81 by Glass Records. Dist: Nine Mile, Rough Trade, Red Rhino, Play It Again Sam

Wonder, Jackie

TOO MUCH PRESSURE ON THE KID.
Single (7"): released on Red Stripe, Sep'80 Dist: Sonet, PRT

Wonders

THIS HEART OF MINE.
Single (7"): released on Creole, May'83 by Creole Records. Dist: Rhino, PRT

Wonder, Stevie

12-YEAR-OLD GENIUS - RECORDED LIVE.
Album: released on Motown, Oct'81 by RCA Records. Dist: RCA Distribution

Cassette: released on Motown, Oct'81 by RCA Records. Dist: RCA Distribution

2 CLASSIC ALBUMS: FOR ONCE IN MY LIFE/UPTIGHT.
Tracks: / For once in my life / Shoo-be-doo-be-doo-da-day / You met your match / I wanna make her love me / I'm more than happy (I'm satisfied) / Don't know why I love you / Sunny / I'd be a fool right now / Ain't no lovin / God bless the child / Do I love her / House on the hill, (The) / Love a go go / Hold me / Blowin' in the wind / Nothing's too good for my baby / Teach me tonight / Uptight (Everything's alright) / Ain't that asking for trouble / I want my baby back / Pretty little angel / Music talk / Contract on love / With a child's heart.
Compact disc: released on Motown, Oct'86 by Motown Records. Dist: BMG Distribution

2 CLASSIC ALBUMS: MY CHERIE AMOUR/ SIGNED, SEALED......
Tracks: / My cherie amour / Hello young lovers / At last / Light my fire / Shadow of your smile, (The) / You and me / Pearl / Somebody knows, somebody cares / Yester-me, yester-you, yesterday / Angie girl / Give your love / I've got you / Never had a dream come true / We can work it out / Signed, sealed & delivered, I'm yours / Heaven help us all / You can't judge a book by its cover / Sugar / Don't wonder why / Anything you want me to do / I can't let my heaven walk away / Joe (takes over me) / I gotta have a song / Something to say.
Compact disc: released on Motown, Oct'86 by Motown Records. Dist: BMG Distribution

ANTHOLOGY A.
Triple album / cassette: released on Motown, Oct'81 by RCA Records. Dist: RCA Distribution

AS.
Single (7"): released on Motown, Oct'81 by RCA Records. Dist: RCA Distribution

BLACK ORCHID.
Single (7"): released on Motown, Oct'81 by RCA Records. Dist: RCA Distribution

BOOGIE ON REGGAE WOMAN.
Single (7"): released on Motown, Oct'81 by RCA Records. Dist: RCA Distribution

DO I DO.
Single (7"): released on Motown, May'82 by RCA Records. Dist: RCA Distribution

Single (7"): released on Motown, Apr'85 by RCA Records. Dist: RCA Distribution

Single (12"): released on Motown, Apr'85 by RCA Records. Dist: RCA Distribution

DON'T DRIVE DRUNK.
Single (7"): released on Motown, Dec'84 by RCA Records. Dist: RCA Distribution

Single (12"): released on Motown, Dec'84 by RCA Records. Dist: RCA Distribution

DOWN TO EARTH.
Album: released on Motown, Oct'81 by RCA Records. Dist: RCA Distribution

Cassette: released on Motown, Oct'81 by RCA Records. Dist: RCA Distribution

DOWN TO EARTH/I WAS MADE TO LOVE HER.
Tracks: / Place in the sun, A / Bang bang (My baby shot me down) / Down to earth / Thank you love / Be cool, be calm (and keep yourself together) / Sylvia / My world is empty without you / Lonesome road, The / Angel baby (don't you ever leave me) / Mr. Tambourine man / Sixteen tons / Hey love / I was made to love her / Send me some lovin' / I'd cry / Everybody needs somebody (I need you) / Respect / My girl / Baby don't you do it / Fool for you, A / Can I get a witness / I pity the fool / Please, please, please / Every time I see you I go wild.
Compact disc: released on Motown, Jul'87 by Motown Records. Dist: BMG Distribution

EBONY & IVORY/ RAINCLOUDS (Wonder, Stevie & Paul McCartney).

ESSENTIAL STEVIE WONDER.
Tracks: / Yester-me,yester-you,yesterday / My cherie amour / If you really love me / We can work it out / Signed sealed delivered I'm yours / Never had a dream come true / Something out of the blue / Heaven help us all / Do yourself a favour / I was made to love her / Thank you love / Until you come back to me / I'm wondering / Shoo-be-doo-be-doo-da-day / Angie girl / More than a dream / For once in my life / You met your match / Don't know why I love you / Uptight / Music talk / Ain't that asking for trouble / Love a-go-go / Nothing's too good for my baby / Be cool,be calm (and keep yourself together) / I'd cry / Travelin' man / Place in the sun, A / Blowin' in the wind / Fingertips / Workout Stevie,workout / Hey harmonica man / Kiss me baby / High heel sneakers / Happy street / Don't you feel it / Castles in the sand / Contract on love / I call it pretty music,but the old folks call it the blues(1.
Double Album: released on Motown, Jun'87 by Motown Records. Dist: BMG Distribution

Double cassette: released on Motown, Jun'87 by Motown Records. Dist: BMG Distribution

Double compact disc: released on Motown, Jun'87 by Motown Records. Dist: BMG Distribution

FOR ONCE IN MY LIFE.
Album: released on Motown, Jun'82 by RCA Records. Dist: RCA Distribution

Cassette: released on Motown, Jun'82 by RCA Records. Dist: RCA Distribution

Single (7"): released on Motown, Oct'81 by RCA Records. Dist: RCA Distribution

Single (7"): released on Motown, Apr'85 by RCA Records. Dist: RCA Distribution

Single (12"): released on Motown, Apr'85 by RCA Records. Dist: RCA Distribution

FOR ONCE IN MY LIFE/UPTIGHT 2 Classic albums.
Tracks: / For once in my life / Shoo-be-doo-be-doo-da-day / You met your match / I wanna make her love me / I'm more than happy (I'm satisfied) / Don't know why I love you / Sunny / I'd be a fool right now / Ain't no lovin' / God bless the child / Do I love her / House on the hill, The / Love a go go / Hold me / Blowin' in the wind / Nothing's too good for my baby / Teach me tonight / Teach me tonight / Uptight (everything's alright) / Ain't that asking for trouble / I want my baby back / Pretty little angel / Music talk / Contract on love / With a child's heart.
Compact disc: released on Motown, Jan'87 by Motown Records. Dist: BMG Distribution

FRONTLINE.
Single (7"): released on Motown, Jan'83 by RCA Records. Dist: RCA Distribution

Single (12"): released on Motown, Jan'83 by RCA Records. Dist: RCA Distribution

FULFILLINGNESS FIRST FINALE.
Album: released on Motown, Oct'81 by RCA Records. Dist: RCA Distribution

Cassette: released on Motown, Oct'81 by RCA Records. Dist: RCA Distribution

GO HOME.
Single (7"): released on Motown, Nov'85 by RCA Records. Dist: RCA Distribution

Single (12"): released on Motown, Nov'85 by RCA Records. Dist: RCA Distribution

GREATEST HITS: STEVIE WONDER.
Album: released on Motown, Oct'81 by RCA Records. Dist: RCA Distribution

Cassette: released on Motown, Oct'81 by RCA Records. Dist: RCA Distribution

GREATEST HITS: STEVIE WONDER VOL.2.
Album: released on Motown, Oct'81 by RCA Records. Dist: RCA Distribution

Cassette: released on Motown, Oct'81 by RCA Records. Dist: RCA Distribution

HAPPY BIRTHDAY.
Single (7"): released on Motown, Oct'81 by RCA Records. Dist: RCA Distribution

Single (12"): released on Motown, Oct'81 by RCA Records. Dist: RCA Distribution

Single (12"): released on Motown, Jan'84 by RCA Records. Dist: RCA Distribution

HE'S MISSTRA KNOW IT ALL.
Single (7"): released on Motown, Oct'81 by RCA Records. Dist: RCA Distribution

Single (7"): released on Motown, Apr'85 by RCA Records. Dist: RCA Distribution

Single (12"): released on Motown, Apr'85 by RCA Records. Dist: RCA Distribution

HOTTER THAN JULY.
Album: released on Motown, Oct'81 by RCA Records. Dist: RCA Distribution

Cassette: released on Motown, Oct'81 by RCA Records. Dist: RCA Distribution

Compact disc: released on Motown, Dec'86 by Motown Records. Dist: BMG Distribution

I AIN'T GONNA STAND FOR IT.
Single (7"): released on Motown, Oct'81 by RCA Records. Dist: RCA Distribution

I DON'T KNOW WHY.
Single (7"): released on Motown, Oct'81 by RCA Records. Dist: RCA Distribution

I JUST CALLED TO SAY I LOVE YOU.
Single (7"): released on Motown, Aug'84 by RCA Records. Dist: RCA Distribution

Single (12"): released on Motown, Aug'84 by RCA Records. Dist: RCA Distribution

I'LL BE THINKING OF YOU (Wonder, Stevie & Andrae Crouch).
Single (7"): released on Light, Jun'81 by Light Records. Dist: Cord

INNERVISIONS.
Tracks: / Too high / Visions / Living for the city / Golden lady / Higher ground / Jesus children of America / All in love is fair / Don't you worry 'bout a thing / He's misstra know it all.
Compact disc: released on Motown, Mar'86 by Motown Records. Dist: BMG Distribution

Album: released on Motown, Oct'81 by RCA Records. Dist: RCA Distribution

Cassette: released on Motown, Oct'81 by RCA Records. Dist: RCA Distribution

IN SQUARE CIRCLE.
Tracks: / Part time lover / I love you too much / Whereabouts / Stranger on the shore of love / Never in your sun / Spiritual walkers / Land of la la / Go home / Overjoyed / It's wrong (la la).
Compact disc: released on Motown, Nov'85 by Motown Records. Dist: BMG Distribution

Album: released on Motown, Nov'85 by RCA Records. Dist: RCA Distribution

Cassette: released on Motown, Nov'85 by RCA Records. Dist: RCA Distribution

I WAS MADE TO LOVE HER.
Album: released on Motown, Feb'83 by RCA Records. Dist: RCA Distribution

Cassette: released on Motown, Feb'83 by RCA Records. Dist: RCA Distribution

Single (7"): released on Motown, Oct'81 by RCA Records. Dist: RCA Distribution

I WISH.
Single (7"): released on Motown, Oct'81 by RCA Records. Dist: RCA Distribution

Single (7"): released on Motown, Apr'85 by RCA Records. Dist: RCA Distribution

Single (12"): released on Motown, Apr'85 by RCA Records. Dist: RCA Distribution

JAZZ SOUL OF LITTLE STEVIE, (THE).
Album: released on Motown, Mar'82 by RCA Records. Dist: RCA Distribution

Cassette: released on Motown, Mar'82 by RCA Records. Dist: RCA Distribution

LAND OF LA LA.
Tracks: / Land of la la / Land of la la (instrumental).
Single (7"): released on Motown, Jun'86 by Motown Records. Dist: BMG Distribution

Single (12"): released on Motown, Jun'86 by Motown Records. Dist: BMG Distribution

LATELY.
Single (7"): released on Motown, Oct'81 by RCA Records. Dist: RCA Distribution

LIVE AT THE TALK OF THE TOWN.
Album: released on Motown, Mar'85 by RCA Records. Dist: RCA Distribution

Cassette: released on Motown, Mar'85 by RCA Records. Dist: RCA Distribution

LIVING FOR THE CITY.
Single (7"): released on Motown, Oct'81 by RCA Records. Dist: RCA Distribution

LOVELIGHT IN FLIGHT.
Single (7"): released on Motown, Nov'84 by RCA Records. Dist: RCA Distribution

Single (12"): released on Motown, Nov'84 by RCA Records. Dist: RCA Distribution

LOVE SONGS.
Tracks: / Contract on love / My cherie amour / Until you come back to me (that's what I'm gonna do) / Yester-me yester-you yesterday / Never had a dream come true / If you really love me / Heaven help us all / Never dreamed you'd leave in summer / Place in the sun, A / Alfie / Hey love / For once in my life / We can work it out / I was made to love her / Don't know why I love you / Blowin in the wind / Shoo be doo be doo da day / I'm wondering / nothing's to good for my baby / Signed, sealed, delivered I'm yours.
Compact disc: released on Telstar, Jul'86 by Telstar Records. Dist: RCA Distribution

Compact disc: released on Motown, Mar'86 by Motown Records. Dist: BMG Distribution

LOVE SONGS A.
Album: released on Telstar, Dec'84 by Telstar Records. Dist: RCA Distribution

Cassette: released on Telstar, Dec'84 by Telstar Records. Dist: RCA Distribution

MASTERBLASTER.
Single (7"): released on Motown, Oct'81 by RCA Records. Dist: RCA Distribution

MUSIC OF MY MIND.
Album: released on Motown, Oct'81 by RCA Records. Dist: RCA Distribution

Cassette: released on Motown, Oct'81 by RCA Records. Dist: RCA Distribution

MY CHERIE AMOUR.
Album: released on Motown, Apr'84 by RCA Records. Dist: RCA Distribution

Cassette: released on Motown, Apr'84 by RCA Records. Dist: RCA Distribution

MY CHERIE AMOUR/SIGNED, SEALED, DELIVERED 2 Classic albums.
Tracks: / My cherie amour / Hello young lovers / At last / Light my fire / Shadow of your smile, The / You and me / Pearl / Somebody knows, somebody cares / Yester-me, yester-you, yesterday / Angie girl / Give your love / I've got you / Never had a dream come true / We can work it out / Signed, sealed, delivered I'm yours / Heaven help us all / You can't judge a book by its cover / Sugar / Don't wonder why / Anything you want me to do / I can't let my heaven walk away / Joy (takes over me) / I gotta have a song / Something to say.
Compact disc: released on Motown, Jan'87 by Motown Records. Dist: BMG Distribution

ORIGINAL MUSIQUARIUM VOL 1.
Tracks: / Superstition / You haven't done nothin / Living for the city / Front line / Superwoman / Send on your love / You are the sunshine of my life / Ribbon in the sky.
Compact disc: released on Motown, Nov'84 by Motown Records. Dist: BMG Distribution

ORIGINAL MUSIQUARIUM VOL 2.
Tracks: / Higher ground / Sir Duke / Master blaster / Boogie on reggae woman / That girl / I wish / Isn't she lovely / Do I do.
Compact disc: released on Motown, Nov'84 by Motown Records. Dist: BMG Distribution

OUTSIDE MY WINDOWS.
Single (7"): released on Motown, Oct'81 by RCA Records. Dist: RCA Distribution

OVERJOYED.
Single (7"): released on Motown, Feb'86 by Motown Records. Dist: BMG Distribution

Single (12"): released on Motown, Feb'86 by Motown Records. Dist: BMG Distribution

PART-TIME LOVER.
Single (7"): released on Motown, Sep'85 by RCA Records. Dist: RCA Distribution

Single (12"): released on Motown, Sep'85 by RCA Records. Dist: RCA Distribution

PEOPLE MOVE HUMAN PLAY.
Album: released on Motown, Nov'83 by R Records. Dist: RCA Distribution

Cassette: released on Motown, Nov'83 by R Records. Dist: RCA Distribution

RIBBON IN THE SKY.
Single (7"): released on Motown, Sep'8 RCA Records. Dist: RCA Distribution

Single (12"): released on Motown, Sep'8 RCA Records. Dist: RCA Distribution

SECRET LIFE OF PLANTS.
Tracks: / Earth's creation / First garden, T Voyage to India / Same old story / Venus fly and the bug / Ai no sono / Seed's a star and medley, A / Power flower / Secret life of pla The / Tree / Finale; seasons / Send one for love / Race babbling (instrumental) / Send your love / Outside my window / Black orc Ecclesiates / Kesse ye lolo de ye / Come as a flower.
Double Album: released on Motown, Oct'8 Motown Records. Dist: BMG Distribution

Double cassette: released on Motown, O by Motown Records. Dist: BMG Distributio

Double compact disc: released on Mot Oct'81 by Motown Records. Dist: BMG Distribution

SEND ONE YOUR LOVE.
Single (7"): released on Motown, Oct'8 RCA Records. Dist: RCA Distribution

SIGNED, SEALED AND DELIVERE
Album: released on Motown, Oct'81 by Records. Dist: RCA Distribution

Cassette: released on Motown, Oct'81 by Records. Dist: RCA Distribution

Single (7"): released on Motown, Oct' RCA Records. Dist: RCA Distribution

SIR DUKE.
Single (7"): released on Motown, Oct' RCA Records. Dist: RCA Distribution

SOMEDAY AT CHRISTMAS.
Album: released on Motown, Nov'82 by Records. Dist: RCA Distribution

Cassette: released on Motown, Nov'82 b Records. Dist: RCA Distribution

SONGS IN THE KEY OF LIFE.
Tracks: / Love's in need of love today / I talk with god / Village ghetto land / Conf Sir Duke ngiculela-es una historia / I am / If it's magic / As / Another star / I wish / I me off my feet / Pastime paradise / Summ / Ordinary pain / Isn't she lovely / Joy ins tears / Black man.
Double Album: released on Motown, Oc Motown Records. Dist: BMG Distribution

Double cassette: released on Motown, by Motown Records. Dist: BMG Distribu

Double compact disc: released on M Oct'81 by Motown Records. Dist: BMG Distribution

STEVIE WONDER.
Cassette single: released on Motown, by RCA Records. Dist: RCA Distribution

STRANGER ON THE SHORE OF
Tracks: / Did I hear you say you love m

Single (7"): released on Motown, Ja Motown Records. Dist: BMG Distributio

Single (12"): released on Motown, Ja Motown Records. Dist: BMG Distributio

SUPERSTITION.
Single (7"): released on Motown, Ma RCA Records. Dist: RCA Distribution

TALKING BOOK.
Tracks: / You are the sunshine of r Maybe your baby / You and I / Tuesda break / you've got it bad girl / Superstit brother / Blame it on the sun / Lookin for true love / I believe (when I fall in love forever).
Compact disc: released on Motown, M Motown Records. Dist: BMG Distributi

Album: released on Motown, Oct'81 Records. Dist: RCA Distribution

Cassette: released on Motown, Oct'81 Records. Dist: RCA Distribution

THAT GIRL.
Single (7"): released on Motown, Ja RCA Records. Dist: RCA Distribution

TRIBUTE TO UNCLE RAY.
Album: released on Motown, Mar'82 Records. Dist: RCA Distribution

Cassette: released on Motown, Mar'8 Records. Dist: RCA Distribution

...IGHT.
...m: released on Motown, Oct'81 by RCA
...ords. Dist: RCA Distribution

...sette: released on Motown. Oct'81 by RCA
...ords. Dist: HCA Distribution

...m: released on Motown, '82 by RCA Rec-
...rd: RCA Distribution

...sette: released on Motown, '82 by RCA
...rds. Dist: RCA Distribution

...D TO BE (Wonder, Stevie & Charlene).
...le (7"): released on Motown, Nov'82 by
...Records. Dist: RCA Distribution

...ERE I'M COMING FROM.
...m: released on Motown, Jul'82 by RCA
...rds. Dist: RCA Distribution

...sette: released on Motown, Jul'82 by RCA
...rds. Dist: RCA Distribution

...H A SONG IN MY HEART.
...m: released on Motown, Mar'82 by RCA
...rds. Dist: RCA Distribution

...sette: released on Motown, Mar'82 by RCA
...rds. Dist: RCA Distribution

...MAN IN RED, (THE).
...m: released on Motown, Sep'84 by RCA
...rds. Dist: RCA Distribution

...sette: released on Motown, Sep'84 by RCA
...rds. Dist: RCA Distribution

...act disc: released on Motown, Sep'84 by
...rds. Dist: RCA Distribution

...ERME, YESTERYOU YESTER-
...e (7"): released on Motown, Oct'81 by
...Records. Dist: RCA Distribution

...ARE THE SUNSHINE OF MY LIFE.
...e (7"): released on Motown, Oct'81 by
...Records. Dist: RCA Distribution

...nder Stuff
...s: / Ten trenches deep / I am a monster /

...(7"): released on The Far Out Recording
...any, Aug'87 Dict: Nine Mile, Cartel

...(12"): released on The Far Out Recor-
...ompany, Aug'87 Dist: Nine Mile, Cartel

...DERFUL DAY, A.
...s: / Down here / It's not true... / Like a
...go round.
...(7"): released on Far Out Recording
...any, Feb'87 by Far Out Recording Com-
...Dist: Nine Mile, Cartel

...nder Woman...
**...DER WOMAN IN TORMENT IN
...DISE** Various artists (Various Artists).
...tte: released on MFP, Oct'85 by EMI
...s. Dist: EMI

...odbine Lizzie
...' OUT WITH WOODBINE LIZZIE,
...: released on Fellside (Cumbria), '83 by
... Records. Dist: Roots, Projection, CM,
...usic

**...DON'T WRITE 'EM LIKE THAT
...ORE.**
...: released on Fellside (Cumbria),
...by Fellside Records. Dist: Roots, Pro-
...CM, Jazz Music

...BINE LIZZIE BY NUMBERS.
...: released on Fellside (Cumbria), '83 by
... Records. Dist: Roots, Projection, CM,
...usic

...dcraft, Ray
...Y LADY SMILE.
...(7"): released on SRT, Jan'81 by SRT
... Dist: Pinnacle, Solomon & Peres Dis-
... SRT Distribution, H.R. Taylor Distribu-
...T Distribution

...d, David
...AN OF LOCHNAGAR.
...e: released on First Night, Nov'86 by
...cords. Dist: Pinnacle

...d, Douglas Group
...RACER.
...(7"): released on BBC, Apr'84 by BBC
... & Tapes. Dist: EMI, PRT

...den Horse
...EN HORSE Eric Williams (Han-
...lla).
...: released on Listen For Pleasure, '83
...Records. Dist: EMI

Woodentops
GIANT.
Compact disc: released on Rough Trade,
May'87 by Rough Trade Records. Dist: Rough
Trade Distribution

Album: released on Rough Trade, Jun'86 by
Rough Trade Records. Dist: Rough Trade Distribution, Cartel Distribution

Cassette: released on Rough Trade, Jun'86 by
Rough Trade Records. Dist: Rough Trade Distribution, Cartel Distribution

GOOD THING.
Tracks: / Good thing / Travelling man.
Single (7"): released on Rough Trade, May'86
by Rough Trade Records. Dist: Rough Trade
Distribution, Cartel Distribution

Single (12"): released on Rough Trade, May'86
by Rough Trade Records. Dist: Rough Trade
Distribution, Cartel Distribution

IT WILL COME.
Single (12"): released on Rough Trade, Nov'85
by Rough Trade Records. Dist: Rough Trade
Distribution, Cartel Distribution

Single (7"): released on Rough Trade, Nov'85
by Rough Trade Records. Dist: Rough Trade
Distribution, Cartel Distribution

LIVE HYPNOBEAT LIVE.
Compact disc: released on Rough Trade,
May'87 by Rough Trade Records. Dist: Rough
Trade Distribution, Cartel Distribution

Album: released on Rough Trade, May'87 by
Rough Trade Records. Dist: Rough Trade Distribution, Cartel Distribution

Cassette: released on Rough Trade, May'87 by
Rough Trade Records. Dist: Rough Trade Distribution, Cartel Distribution

**LOVE AFFAIR WITH EVERYDAY LIV-
ING.**
Tracks: / Love affair with everyday living / So
good today.
Single (7"): released on Rough Trade, Sep'86
by Rough Trade Records. Dist: Rough Trade
Distribution, Cartel Distribution

Single (12"): released on Rough Trade, Sep'86
by Rough Trade Records. Dist: Rough Trade
Distribution, Cartel Distribution

MOVE ME.
Single (7"): released on Rough Trade, Apr'85
by Rough Trade Records. Dist: Rough Trade
Distribution, Cartel Distribution

Single (12"): released on Rough Trade, Apr'85
by Rough Trade Records. Dist: Rough Trade
Distribution, Cartel Distribution

PLENTY.
Single (7"): released on Food, Jul'84 by Food
Records. Dist: Rough Trade, Cartel, WEA

Single (12"): released on Food, Jul'84 by Food
Records. Dist: Rough Trade, Cartel, WEA

WELL WELL WELL.
Single (7"): released on Rough Trade, Aug'85
by Rough Trade Records. Dist: Rough Trade
Distribution, Cartel Distribution

Single (12"): released on Rough Trade, Aug'85
by Rough Trade Records. Dist: Rough Trade
Distribution, Cartel Distribution

WHITE WHAT.
Single (7"): released on Button, Aug'83 by Musical Characters Records. Dist: Spartan

Woodham Ley Jun. Sch.
ENGLAND ARE ON THEIR WAY (Wood-
ham Ley Junior School).
Single (7"): released on Kick, Apr'82 by Joy
Records. Dist: Pinnacle

Woodhead Monroe
IDENTIFY.
Single (7"): released on Oval, Mar'82 by Oval
Records. Dist: Pinnacle

MUMBO JUMBO.
Single (7"): released on Oval, May'82 by Oval
Records. Dist: Pinnacle

VAMPIRE (SHE'S A).
Single (7"): released on Oval, Sep'80 by Oval
Records. Dist: Pinnacle

Woodhouse, Barbara
**TRAINING DOGS THE WOODHOUSE
WAY.**
Album: released on BBC, Sep'82 by BBC Rec-
ords & Tapes. Dist: EMI, PRT

Cassette: released on BBC, Sep'82 by BBC
Records & Tapes. Dist: EMI, PRT

Woodhouse, George
STAR.
Single (12"): released on Mile Stone, Mar'85

---

by Mile Stone Records. Dist: Jetstar Distribution

Woodland & Garden Birds
WOODLAND & GARDEN BIRDS.
Album: by BBC Records & Tapes. Dist: EMI,
PRT, Pye

WOODLAND & GARDEN BIRDS More
British wild birds (Various birds).
Album: released on BBC, Oct'76 by BBC Rec-
ords & Tapes. Dist: EMI, PRT,

Cassette: released on BBC, Oct'76 by BBC
Records & Tapes. Dist: EMI, PRT,

Woodleiff, Norman
**LONNIE AUSTIN & NORMAN WOOD-
LEIFF** (see also Lonnie Austin) (Woodleiff,
Norman & Lonnie Austin).
Album: released on Leader, '81 Dist: Jazz
Music, Projection

Woodman, Britt
IN L.A.
Album: released on Falcon, Apr'78 Dist: Jet-
star, M.I.S.

Wood, Orville
DON'T STAY AWAY.
Single (12"): released on Diamond C, May'85
by Diamond C Records. Dist: Jetstar

Wood, Robert
TAROT.
Album: released on In Jazz, Dec'77 Dist: JSU

Woodroffe, Jezz
PEACE IN OUR SPACE.
Single (7"): by Graduate Records. Dist: Nine
Mile, Cartel

Wood, Ronnie
1.2.3.4.
Album: released on CBS, Nov'81 by CBS Records. Dist: CBS

CANCEL EVERYTHING.
Album: released on Thunderbolt, Nov'85 by
Magnum Music Group Ltd. Dist: Magnum Music
Group Ltd, PRT Distribution, Spartan Distribu-
tion

Compact disc: released on Magnum, Jun'87
by Bulldog Records. Dist: Spartan

Cassette: released on Thunderbolt, Oct'85 by
Magnum Music Group Ltd. Dist: Magnum Music
Group Ltd, PRT Distribution, Spartan Distribu-
tion

MANCUNIAN WAY, THE (see Perry,
Roy/Ronnie Wood) (Wood, Roy).

Wood, Roy
1.2.3.
Tracks: / 1.2.3. / O what a shame.
Single (7"): released on Jet, Jul'87 by Jet Records. Dist: CBS

Single (12"): released on Jet, Jul'87 by Jet Records. Dist: CBS

BEST OF ROY WOOD (1970-1974).
Album: released on MFP, Apr'85 by EMI Records. Dist: EMI

Cassette: released on MFP, Apr'85 by EMI
Records. Dist: EMI

RAINING IN THE CITY.
Tracks: / Raining in the city / Raining in the city
(instrumental version).
Single (7"): released on Legacy, Oct'86 Dist:
PRT

SINGLES, THE.
Album: released on Speed, Jul'82

**SING OUT THE OLD..BRING IN THE
NEW.**
Single (7"): released on Legacy, Nov'85 Dist:
PRT

Single (12"): released on Legacy, Nov'85 Dist:
PRT

STARTING UP.
Tracks: / Red cars are after me / Raining in the
city / Under fire / Turn your body to the light /
Hot cars / Starting up / Keep it steady / On top
of the world / Ships in the night.
Album: released on Legacy, Feb'87 Dist: PRT

Cassette: released on Legacy, Feb'87 Dist:
PRT

UNDER FIRE.
Single (7"): released on Legacy, May'85 Dist:
PRT

Single (12"): released on Legacy, May'85 Dist:
PRT

Woodruff, Stanley
WHAT TOOK YOU SO LONG.
Single (7"): released on Grape-Vine, Dec'79
Dist: RCA, Swift

Woods
BATTLESHIP CHAINS.
Tracks: / Battleship chains / Sometimes.
Notes: Pic bag
Single (7"): released on Demon, Apr'87 by
Demon Records. Dist: Pinnacle

IT'S LIKE THIS.
Album: released on Demon, May'87 by Demon
Records. Dist: Pinnacle

Woods Band
WOODS BAND, THE.
Album: released on Mulligan, Sep'80 by Topic
Records. Dist: Roots Distribution, Jazz Music
Distribution, JSU Distribution, I & B Distribution,
Projection Distribution, Wynd-Up Distribution,
Celtic Distributions

Wood, Scott
SCOTT WOOD & HIS SIX SWINGERS
(1935-1936).
Album: released on World Records, Oct'77
Dist: Polygram

Woods, Gay
**SOMETHING'S GOTTEN HOLD OF MY
HEART.**
Single (7"): released on Rewind, Jun'84 by Re-
wind Records. Dist: Spartan

TENDER HOOKS (Woods, Gay & Terry).
Album: released on Mulligan, Sep'84 by Topic
Records. Dist: Roots Distribution, Jazz Music
Distribution, JSU Distribution, I & B Distribution,
Projection Distribution, Wynd-Up Distribution,
Celtic Distributions

Woods, Jimmy
CONFLICT (Woods, Jimmy Sextet).
Album: released on Boplicity, Jun'85 by Bo-
plicity Records. Dist: Ace Records, Pinnacle

Woods, Mick
TRIBUTE TO JOHN MCKENNA.
Album: released on Shanachie, '79

Woods, Pat
BUNCH OF THYME.
Single (7"): released on Homespun(Ireland),
Sep'81 by Outlet Records. Dist: Outlet

CONCERT REQUESTS.
Album: released on Homespun(Ireland),
Dec'83 by Outlet Records. Dist: Outlet

Cassette: released on Homespun(Ireland),
Dec'83 by Outlet Records. Dist: Outlet

CROCE-DI-ORO.
Tracks: / Croce-di-oro / In the corner of my old
prison cell.
Single (7"): released on Homespun(Ireland),
Apr'87 by Outlet Records. Dist: Outlet

GALWAY BAY.
Single (7"): released on Homespun(Ireland),
Feb'83 by Outlet Records. Dist: Outlet

GREEN FIELDS OF FRANCE.
Single (7"): released on Homespun(Ireland),
Sep'82 by Outlet Records. Dist: Outlet

IN THE CORNER OF MY PRISON CELL.
Tracks: / In the corner of my prison cell / When
it's moonlight in Mayo / May morning dew, The /
Moonshiner / Village of Astee, The / Donegal
Rose / Kitty Wells / Croca di oro (Cross of gold)
/ Rose of Clare / My Kathleen / Slievenamon /
Shamrock on mother's grave / Blarney Stone /
In a little pub in London.
Cassette: released on Homespun(Ireland),
Jun'87 by Outlet Records. Dist: Outlet

MY OWN NATIVE LAND.
Single (7"): released on Homespun(Ireland),
Nov'84 by Outlet Records. Dist: Outlet

RARE OUL TIMES, THE.
Album: released on Homespun(Ireland),
Oct'82 by Outlet Records. Dist: Outlet

Cassette: released on Homespun(Ireland),
Oct'82 by Outlet Records. Dist: Outlet

RATHLIN ISLAND.
Single (7"): released on Homespun(Ireland),
Mar'84 by Outlet Records. Dist: Outlet

WILD COLONIAL BOY, THE.
Album: released on Homespun(Ireland),
Aug'85 by Outlet Records. Dist: Outlet

Cassette: released on Homespun(Ireland),
Aug'85 by Outlet Records. Dist: Outlet

Woods, Phil

AT THE VILLAGE VANGUARD (Woods, Phil Quartet).
Compact disc: released on Polystar (Japan), '86 Dist: Target, Polygram

BIRDS OF A FEATHER (Woods, Phil Quartet).
Compact disc: released on Polystar (Japan), '86 Dist: Target, Polygram

CHROMATIC BANANA.
Album: released on Affinity, Mar'83 by Charly Dist: Charly, Cadillac

EUROPEAN TOUR, LIVE.
Album: released on Red Pepper, Sep'86 Dist: Jazz Music, Wellard, Chris

HEAVEN (Woods, Phil Quintet).
Tracks: / I'm getting sentimental over you / Heaven / Duke (The) / Azure / 222 / Occurrence.
Notes: Phil Woods - alto saxophone Tom Harrell - trumpet, flugelhorn Hal Galper - piano Steve Gilmore - bass Bill Goodwin - drums
Album: released on Blackhawk, Sep'86 by Blackhawk Records (USA). Dist: IMS-Polygram
Cat. no: BKH 50401
Cassette: released on Blackhawk, Sep'86 by Blackhawk Records (USA). Dist: IMS-Polygram

INTEGRITY (Woods, Phil Quintet).
Notes: Double album. The new Phil Woods Quintet live.
Double Album: released on Red, Jan'87 Dist: Projection, Jazz Horizons

MUSIQUE DU BOIS.
Album: released on Muse (Import), Apr'81

PAIRING OFF.
Album: released on Prestige (USA), Aug'84

PHIL & QUILL WITH PRESTIGE (Woods, Phil/Gene Quill quintet).
Album: released on Original Jazz Classics (USA), Apr'86 Dist: Fantasy (USA) Distribution, Chris Wellard Distribution, IMS-Polygram Distribution

RIGHTS OF SWING, (THE).
Album: released on Candid/Black Lion, Jun'86 Dist: Jazz Music, Swift

SONG FOR SISYPHUS (Woods, Phil Quintet).
Album: released on RCA, Feb'79 by RCA Records. Dist: RCA, Roots, Swift, Wellard, Chris, I & B, Solomon & Peres Distribution

THREE FOR ALL with Tommy Flanagan & Red Mitchell (Woods, Phil/Tommy Flanagan/Red Mitchell).
Album: released on Enja (Germany), Jan'82 by Enja Records (W.Germany). Dist: Cadillac Music

Woodstock

VARIOUS.
Compact disc: released on Atlantic, Mar'87 by WEA Records. Dist: WEA

WOODSTOCK Original soundtrack (Various Artists).
Compact disc: released on Mobile Fidelity, '86 by Mobile Fidelity Records.
Double compact disc: released on Atlantic, Jul'87 by WEA Records. Dist: WEA

WOODSTOCK MOUNTAINS various artists (Various original artists).
Album: released on Sonet, Aug'78 by Sonet Records. Dist: PRT

WOODSTOCK ONE various artists (Various Artists).
Triple album / cassette: released on Atlantic, '74 by WEA Records. Dist: WEA
Triple album / cassette: released on Atlantic, '74 by WEA Records. Dist: WEA

WOODSTOCK TWO various artists (Various Artists).
Double Album: released on Atlantic, '74 by WEA Records. Dist: WEA

Woodstock Mountains Revue

PRETTY LUCKY.
Album: released on Rounder, May'79 Dist: Roots Distribution

Woodstock Workshop Or-

NEW MOON.
Album: released on Palcoscenico (Italy), '81 Dist: Jazz Music

Wood, Tim

GETTING YOUR OWN BACK.
Album: released on Celtic Music, '82 by Celtic Music Distribution. Dist: Celtic Music, Jazz Music, Projection, Roots

---

Woodvale Quintet

GUIDE ME LORD.
Album: released by Pilgrim Records. Dist: Rough Trade, Cartel

Wood, Victoria

LUCKY BAG.
Album: released on Elecstar, Dec'85 by Elecstar Records. Dist: PRT
Cassette: released on Cherry Lane, Jul'85 by Cherry Lane Productions. Dist: PRT

RETURN TO OZ.
Single (7"): released on Cherry Lane, Jul'85 by Cherry Lane Productions. Dist: PRT

Woodvine, John

JOE LIVES.
Album: released on MWM, Jun'82 by Mawson & Wareham. Dist: Spartan Distribution, Jazz Music Distribution, JSU Distribution

Woodward Brothers, (The)

YOU SET ME UP.
Tracks: / You set me up / Physical attraction / You set me up (Dub version).
Single (12"): released on Debut, Oct'86 by Skratch Music. Dist: PRT

Woodward, Edward

AFRICAN QUEEN, THE C.S. Forester.
Cassette: released on Listen For Pleasure, Dec'80 by MFP Records. Dist: EMI

DON'T GET AROUND MUCH ANY-MORE.
Album: released on DJM, Nov'81 by DJM Records. Dist: CBS, Polygram
Cassette: released on DJM, Nov'81 by DJM Records. Dist: CBS, Polygram

EDWARDIAN WOODWARD.
Album: released on DJM, Nov'81 by DJM Records. Dist: CBS, Polygram
Cassette: released on DJM, Nov'81 by DJM Records. Dist: CBS, Polygram

LOVE IS THE KEY (Wood/weatherly).
Album: released on DJM, Nov'81 by DJM Records. Dist: CBS, Polygram
Cassette: released on DJM, Nov'81 by DJM Records. Dist: CBS, Polygram

ROMANTIC HOUR.
Cassette: released on DJM, May'81 by DJM Records. Dist: CBS, Polygram

THOUGHT OF YOU, THE.
Album: released on DJM, Nov'81 by DJM Records. Dist: CBS, Polygram
Cassette: released on DJM, Nov'81 by DJM Records. Dist: CBS, Polygram

WOODWARD AGAIN.
Album: released on DJM, Nov'81 by DJM Records. Dist: CBS, Polygram
Cassette: released on DJM, Nov'81 by DJM Records. Dist: CBS, Polygram

Wood, Windy

WEST TEXAS SWING.
Album: released on Sundown, Nov'86 by Magnum Music Group Ltd. Dist: Magnum Music Group Ltd, PRT Distribution, Spartan Distribution
Cassette: released on Sundown, Nov'86 by Magnum Music Group Ltd. Dist: Magnum Music Group Ltd, PRT Distribution, Spartan Distribution

Woody, Don

BARKING UP THE WRONG TREE.
Single (7"): released on MCA, '80 by MCA Records. Dist: Polygram, MCA

Woofe, Vicki

SHAPE UP FOR SEX.
Album: released on Lifestyle, May'84 by Zomba Records. Dist: BMG
Cassette: released on Lifestyle, May'84 by Zomba Records. Dist: BMG

Wooley, Sheb

BLUE GUITAR.
Album: released on Bear Family, Nov'85 by Bear Family Records. Dist: Rollercoaster Distribution, Swift

COUNTRY BOOGIE, WILD & WOOLEY (48-55).
Album: released on Bear Family, Jul'84 by Bear Family Records. Dist: Rollercoaster Distribution, Swift

---

Woolfe, Jai Dean

SWEET MISS AMERICA.
Single (7"): released on EMI, Aug'85 by EMI Records. Dist: EMI

Woolfe, Rita

BEAUTIFUL LAUNDERETTE.
Tracks: / Beautiful launderette / Beautiful launderette (dangerous mix) / / Take one look*.
Single (7"): released on Stiff, May'86 by Stiff Records. Dist: EMI, Record Services Distribution (Ireland)
Single (12"): released on Stiff, May'86 by Stiff Records. Dist: EMI, Record Services Distribution (Ireland)

Woolf, Jai Dean

SHANGRI-LA (Take me back to -).
Tracks: / Shangri-La (Take me back to -) / Shangri-La (Take me back to -)(Tropical instrumental mix).
Single (7"): released on EMI, May'86 by EMI Records. Dist: EMI
Single (12"): released on EMI, May'86 by EMI Records. Dist: EMI

SWEET MISS AMERICA.
Tracks: / Sweet miss america / Sweet miss america (Instrumental version) / Sweet thing*.
Single (7"): released on Parlophone, Aug'86 by EMI Records. Dist: EMI
Single (12"): released on Parlophone, Aug'86 by EMI Records. Dist: EMI

Woolley, Shep

GOODBYE SAILOR.
Double Album: released on Sweet Folk All, May'81 by Sweet Folk All Records. Dist: Sweet Folk All, Roots, Celtic Music, Dragon, Impetus, Projection, Chris Wellard, Festival Records

I WANT TO BE A SKINHEAD LIKE DAD.
Single (7"): released on Sweet Folk & Country, May'78 Dist: Chris Wellard Distribution

PIPE DOWN.
Album: released on Sweet Folk All, May'81 by Sweet Folk All Records. Dist: Sweet Folk All, Roots, Celtic Music, Dragon, Impetus, Projection, Chris Wellard, Festival Records

SONGS OF OARS AND SCRUBBERS & OTHER DIRTY HABITS.
Album: released on Sweet Folk All, May'81 by Sweet Folk All Records. Dist: Sweet Folk All, Roots, Celtic Music, Dragon, Impetus, Projection, Chris Wellard, Festival Records

Woolly, Rhino and Friends

WOOLLY RHINO AND FRIENDS.
Single (7"): released on Denmark, Nov'76

Woosh, Jah

DREADLOCKS AFFAIR.
Album: released on Trojan, Sep'81 by Trojan Records. Dist: PRT, Jetstar

IN LOVE WITH YOU.
Single (12"): released on Sweetcorn, Apr'85 by Sweetcorn Records. Dist: Jetstar

REBELLION (Woosh, Jah & Sis Bee).
Single (12"): released on Form, Oct'81 by Form Records. Dist: Pinnacle

RELIGIOUS DREAD.
Album: released on Trojan, Sep'81 by Trojan Records. Dist: PRT, Jetstar

Wootton, Brenda

BOY JAN.............CORNISHMAN.
Album: released on Burlington, Oct'86 by Plant Life Records. Dist: Jazz Music, Celtic Music, Clyde Factors Distributors, I.R.S., Projection, Wellard, Chris, Roots

FOUR LANES MALE CHOIR, (THE).
Album: released on Burlington, Oct'86 by Plant Life Records. Dist: Jazz Music, Celtic Music, Clyde Factors Distributors, I.R.S., Projection, Wellard, Chris, Roots

GRANDE CORNOUAILLAISE, (LA).
Album: released on Burlington, Oct'86 by Plant Life Records. Dist: Jazz Music, Celtic Music, Clyde Factors Distributors, I.R.S., Projection, Wellard, Chris, Roots

GWAVAS LAKE with the Four Lanes Male Choir.
Album: released on Burlington, Nov'81 by Plant Life Records. Dist: Jazz Music, Celtic Music, Clyde Factors Distributors, I.R.S., Projection, Wellard, Chris, Roots

LA GRANDS CORNOUALLAISE.
Album: released on Burlington, Nov'81 by Plant Life Records. Dist: Jazz Music, Celtic Music, Clyde Factors Distributors, I.R.S., Projection, Wellard, Chris, Roots

---

MY LAND.
Album: released on RCA (France), Mar'8[?] RCA Records. Dist: Discovery
Cassette: released on RCA (France), M[?] by RCA Records. Dist: Discovery

Worcester Cathedral

MUSIC FOR CHRISTMAS.
Album: released on Abbey, Nov'79 by Ab[?] Dist: PRT, Taylors, Gamut

WORCESTER CATHEDRAL CHO[?]TERS Various (Various Artists).
Album: released on Abbey, Jan'77 by A[?] Dist: PRT, Taylors, Gamut

Worcestershire

MARCH 'N' SWING & THE WOOF (Worcestershire & Sherwood Foresters ment).
Album: released on Music Masters, Apr[?] Music Masters Records. Dist: Taylors

WOOFERS IN CONCERT (Worcester[?] & Sherwood Foresters Regiment).
Album: released on Music Masters, Jan[?] Music Masters Records. Dist: Taylors

WOOFERS ON TOUR (Worcestershi[?] Sherwood Foresters Regiment).
Album: released on Music Masters, Jan[?] Music Masters Records. Dist: Taylors

Word

COLOUR IT.
Single (7"): released on Menace Music, N[?] by Menace Music Records. Dist: Cartel Di[?]tion

NEXT BIG THING, THE.
Single (12"): released on Menace [?] Nov'84 by Menace Music Records. Dist: [?] Distribution

SCHOOLBOY SAINT.
Tracks: / Schoolboy saint / World to the[?] Single (7"): released on Abstract, Jun[?] Abstract. Dist: Pinnacle

WIDE AWAKE.
Single (12"): released on Abstract, Jun[?] Abstract. Dist: Pinnacle

Word Family Christmas A[?]

WORD FAMILY CHRISTMAS A[?] Various (Various Artists).
Album: released on Word, May'82 by [?] Records. Dist: Word Distribution, CBS
Cassette: released on Word, May'82 b[?] Records. Dist: Word Distribution, CBS

Word of Mouth

COAST TO COAST (Word of mout[?] ing D.J.Cheese).
Tracks: / Coast to Coast / Coast to Coa[?] instrumental version) / Coast to Coast beats).
Single (7"): released on Champion, Au[?] Champion Records. Dist: RCA
Single (12"): released on Champion, Au[?] Champion Records. Dist: RCA

HEARTBEAT HEARTBREAK.
Single (7"): released on Challenge, Ja[?] Elite Records. Dist: Pinnacle
Single (12"): released on Challenge, J[?] Elite Records. Dist: Pinnacle

THAT'S THE WAY GOD PLANNE[?]
Single (7"): released on Columbia, Ma[?] EMI Records. Dist: EMI
Single (12"): released on Columbia, Ma[?] EMI Records. Dist: EMI

Words of Gandhi

WORDS OF GANDHI Attenbor[?] chard selection/Shankar, Ravi musi[?] sley, Ben).
Cassette: released on Caedmon(US[?] Caedmon (USA) Records. Dist: Cayl[?] lors, Discovery

Word Soun' 'ave Power

WORD SOUN' 'AVE POWER (Various Artists).
Album: released on Rounder (USA[?] Jan'84

Workforce

BACK IN THE GOOD BOOKS.
Tracks: / Back in the good books.
Single (7"): released on Rorschach Feb'86 by Rorschach Testing Reco[?] Rough Trade Distribution
Single (12"): released on Rorschach Feb'86 by Rorschach Testing Reco[?] Rough Trade Distribution

:N SCRAPED BACK.
gle (12"): released on Double Vision, '85 by Double Vision Records. Dist: Rough le, Cartel

/ork For The Future

RK FOR THE FUTURE (PART 1) ious Artists).
ım: released on Jah Lifetime, Jul'87

/orking Class

TTA GO GO.
ks: / Gotta go-go / Your love is mine.
le (7"): released on President, Mar'86 by ident Records. Dist: Taylors, Spartan

le (12"): released on President, Mar'86 by ident Records. Dist: Taylors, Spartan

GOING NOWHERE.
ks: / I'm going nowhere / Love everything t you.
le (7"): released on President, Oct'86 by ident Records. Dist: Taylors, Spartan

orking Week

IPANEROS.
ks: / Too much time / Dancing in motion / d (Touch pas a mon pote) / South Africa / in the dark / Soul train / King of the night / hing Heaven / Southern Cross.
m: released on Virgin, Sep'86 by Virgin rds. Dist: EMI, Virgin Distribution

ette: released on Virgin, Sep'86 by Virgin rds. Dist: EMI, Virgin Distribution

pact disc: released on Virgin, '86 by Virecords. Dist: EMI, Virgin Distribution

'T TOUCH MY FRIEND.
s: / Don't touch my friend / Walk the tight

(7"): released on Virgin, Oct'86 by Vircords. Dist: EMI, Virgin Distribution

(12"): released on Virgin, Oct'86 by Vircords. Dist: EMI, Virgin Distribution

OUGHT I'D NEVER SEE YOU N.
(12"): released on Virgin, Aug'85 by Vircords. Dist: EMI, Virgin Distribution

ERIGO BAY.
: / Roderigo Bay / Boogaloo.
(7"): by Virgin Records. Dist: EMI, Virtribution Deleted May'86.

(12"): released on Virgin, May'86 by Vircords. Dist: EMI, Virgin Distribution

ET NOTHING.
(7"): released on Virgin, May'85 by Vircords. Dist: EMI, Virgin Distribution

MUCH TIME.
: / Too much time / Soul train.
(7"): released on Virgin, Aug'86 by Vircords. Dist: EMI, Virgin Distribution

(12"): released on Virgin, Aug'86 by Vircords. Dist: EMI, Virgin Distribution

ERENOS.
(7"): released on Paladin, Feb'84 by Paecords. Dist: Rough Trade, Pinnacle

(12"): released on Paladin, Feb'84 by Records. Dist: Rough Trade, Pinnacle

KING NIGHTS.
: / Inner city blues / Sweet nothing / fooling who! / I thought I'd never see you Autumn boy / Solo / Venceremos / No pay.
: released on Virgin, Mar'85 by Virgin s. Dist: EMI, Virgin Distribution

tte: released on Virgin, Mar'85 by Virgin s. Dist: EMI, Virgin Distribution

act disc: released on Virgin, Mar'85 by Records. Dist: EMI, Virgin Distribution

k, Jimmy

IG BELIEVE.
/ That's the way it's gonna be / Rock Is- e / Puttin' on the dog / When she said Digging my own grave / Don't give me n to wonder why / Blind heart(1) / You've art like a merry-go-round / That cold, k in your eyes / Hands away from my That's the way the juke box plays / only one you / Making believe / Blind / Let 'em talk / Just like downtown / My ping ground / Don't knock just come on

released on Bear Family, Mar'86 by mily Records. Dist: Rollercoaster Dis- , Swift

kman, Reggie

JAZZ TRIO, THE (Workman, Reg- Tommy Flanagan and Joe Chambers).

S OF WORKMAN, THE.
released on Denon, Mar'82 by Denon . Dist: Harmonia Mundi

World

BREAK THE SILENCE.
Album: released on Elektra, Oct'83 by WEA Records. Dist: WEA

I'M SORRY.
Single (7"): released on WEA, Mar'84 by WEA Records. Dist: WEA

WORLD AT WAR (TV SOUNDTRACK) Various artists (Various Artists).
Album: released on Decca, Feb'84 by Decca Records. Dist: Polygram

WORLD CUP SOUVENIR ALBUM Various (Various Artists).
Album: released on Klub, May'82

Cassette: released on Klub, May'82

WORLD & MEN By Dr. Alexander King (World & men).
Cassette: released on Seminar Cassettes, Oct'81 by Seminar Cassettes. Dist: Davidson Distribution, Eastern Educational Products Distrib., Forlaget Systime Distribution, Laser Books Ltd Distribution, MacDougall Distribution, Talktapes Distribution, Watkins Books Ltd Distribution, Norton, Jeff Distribution

WORLD OF BALLET VOL 1 Various Orchestras (Various Orchestras).
Album: released on Decca, '70 by Decca Records. Dist: Polygram

WORLD OF BALLET VOL 2 Various Orchestras (Various Orchestras).
Album: released on Decca, '70 by Decca Records. Dist: Polygram

Album: released on Decca, '70 by Decca Records. Dist: Polygram

WORLD OF BLUES VOL 1 Various artists (Various Artists).
Album: released on Imperial(France), '83 by K-Tel Records. Dist: K-Tel, Taylors, Polygram

WORLD OF BRASS BANDS Various bands (Various bands).
Album: released on Decca, '69 by Decca Records. Dist: Polygram

Cassette: released on Decca, '69 by Decca Records. Dist: Polygram

WORLD OF BRASS BANDS VOL 2 Various bands (Various bands).
Album: released on Decca, '70 by Decca Records. Dist: Polygram

Cassette: released on Decca, '70 by Decca Records. Dist: Polygram

WORLD OF BRASS BANDS VOL 3 Various bands (Various bands).
Album: released on Decca, '74 by Decca Records. Dist: Polygram

Cassette: released on Decca, '74 by Decca Records. Dist: Polygram

WORLD OF BRASS BANDS VOL 4 Various bands (Various bands).
Album: released on Decca, Feb'76 by Decca Records. Dist: Polygram

Cassette: released on Decca, Feb'76 by Decca Records. Dist: Polygram

WORLD OF BRASS BANDS VOL 5 Various bands (Various bands).
Album: released on Decca, Jun'78 by Decca Records. Dist: Polygram

Cassette: released on Decca, Jun'78 by Decca Records. Dist: Polygram

WORLD OF CHRISTMAS (St. Johns College Choir).
Album: released on Decca, Nov'71 by Decca Records. Dist: Polygram

WORLD OF CHRISTMAS MUSIC (Kent College Choir).
Album: released on Decca, Oct'77 by Decca Records. Dist: Polygram

WORLD OF ENGLAND Various Artists (Various Artists).
Album: released on Decca, '72 by Decca Records. Dist: Polygram

Cassette: released on Decca, '72 by Decca Records. Dist: Polygram

WORLD OF FOLK VOL 2 Various (Various Artists).
Album: released on Argo, May'74 by Decca Records. Dist: Polygram

WORLD OF HITS VOL 5 Various artists (Various Artists).
Album: released on Decca, '71 by Decca Records. Dist: Polygram

WORLD OF HITS VOL 7 Various artists (Various Artists).
Album: released on Decca, Aug'74 by Decca Records. Dist: Polygram

WORLD OF IMMORTAL SERENADES (Chacksfield, Frank Orchestra).
Album: released on Decca, Jul'73 by Decca Records. Dist: Polygram

WORLD OF IRELAND Various artists (Various Artists).
Album: released on Decca, '70 by Decca Records. Dist: Polygram

Cassette: released on Decca, '70 by Decca Records. Dist: Polygram

WORLD OF MECHANICAL MUSIC (Automatic Instruments).
Cassette: released on Saydisc, Jun'78 by Saydisc Records. Dist: Essex, Harmonia Mundi, Roots, H.R. Taylor, Jazz Music, Swift, Projection, Gamut

WORLD OF MECHANICAL ORGANS Various artists (Various Artists).
Album: released on Decca, '71 by Decca Records. Dist: Polygram

Cassette: released on Decca, '71 by Decca Records. Dist: Polygram

WORLD OF, MEDIUM WAVE RADIO STATIONS Various artists (Various Artists).
Cassette: released on East Anglian Productions, Jan'78 by East Anglian Productions. Dist: Lightning

Double Album: released on East Anglian Productions, Jan'78 by East Anglian Productions. Dist: Lightning

WORLD OF MILITARY BAND Various artists (Various Artists).
Album: released on Decca, '69 by Decca Records. Dist: Polygram

Cassette: released on Decca, '69 by Decca Records. Dist: Polygram

WORLD OF MILITARY BANDS VOL 2 Various artists (Various Artists).
Album: released on Decca, '70 by Decca Records. Dist: Polygram

Cassette: released on Decca, '70 by Decca Records. Dist: Polygram

WORLD OF MUSIC HALL Various artists (Various Artists).
Album: released on Decca, '70 by Decca Records. Dist: Polygram

WORLD OF SCOTLAND Various artists (Various Artists).
Album: released on Decca, '70 by Decca Records. Dist: Polygram

Cassette: released on Decca, '70 by Decca Records. Dist: Polygram
Cat. no: **KCSP 41**

WORLD OF SCOTLAND VOL 2 Various artists (Various Artists).
Album: released on Decca, Jun'75 by Decca Records. Dist: Polygram

Cassette: released on Decca, Jun'75 by Decca Records. Dist: Polygram

WORLD OF THE COUNTRYSIDE Various artists (Narrator-John Arlott) (Various Artists).
Album: released on Decca, Jul'74 by Decca Records. Dist: Polygram

WORLD OF TV THEMES Various artists (Various Artists).
Album: released on Decca, '72 by Decca Records. Dist: Polygram

Cassette: released on Decca, '72 by Decca Records. Dist: Polygram

WORLD OF WALES Massed choirs (Massed Choirs).
Album: released on Decca, '72 by Decca Records. Dist: Polygram

Cassette: released on Decca, '72 by Decca Records. Dist: Polygram

WORLD OF WORLD WAR 1 Various artists (Various Artists).
Album: released on Decca, '69 by Decca Records. Dist: Polygram

WORLD OF YOUR 100 BEST TUNES VOL 1 various artists (Various Artists).
Album: released on Decca, '70 by Decca Records. Dist: Polygram

Cassette: released on Decca, '70 by Decca Records. Dist: Polygram

WORLD OF YOUR 100 BEST TUNES VOL 2 Various artists (Various Artists).
Album: released on Decca, '71 by Decca Records. Dist: Polygram

Cassette: released on Decca, '71 by Decca Records. Dist: Polygram

WORLD OF YOUR 100 BEST TUNES VOL 3 Various artists (Various Artists).
Album: released on Decca, '72 by Decca Records. Dist: Polygram

Cassette: released on Decca, '72 by Decca Records. Dist: Polygram

WORLD OF YOUR 100 BEST TUNES VOL 4 Various artists (Various Artists).
Album: released on Decca, '72 by Decca Records. Dist: Polygram

Cassette: released on Decca, '72 by Decca Records. Dist: Polygram

WORLD OF YOUR 100 BEST TUNES VOL 5 Various artists (Various Artists).
Album: released on Decca, '73 by Decca Records. Dist: Polygram

Cassette: released on Decca, '73 by Decca Records. Dist: Polygram

WORLD OF YOUR 100 BEST TUNES VOL 6 Various artists (Various Artists).
Cassette: released on Decca, '73 by Decca Records. Dist: Polygram

Album: released on Decca, '73 by Decca Records. Dist: Polygram

WORLD OF YOUR 100 BEST TUNES VOL 7 Various artists (Various Artists).
Album: released on Decca, Jun'74 by Decca Records. Dist: Polygram

Cassette: released on Decca, Jun'74 by Decca Records. Dist: Polygram

WORLD OF YOUR 100 BEST TUNES VOL 8 Various artists (Various Artists).
Cassette: released on Decca, Aug'74 by Decca Records. Dist: Polygram

Album: released on Decca, Aug'74 by Decca Records. Dist: Polygram

WORLD OF YOUR 100 BEST TUNES VOL 9 Various artists (Various Artists).
Album: released on Decca, Jun'75 by Decca Records. Dist: Polygram

Cassette: released on Decca, Jun'75 by Decca Records. Dist: Polygram

WORLD OF YOUR 100 BEST TUNES VOL 10 Various artists (Various Artists).
Cassette: released on Decca, Sep'75 by Decca Records. Dist: Polygram

Album: released on Decca, Sep'75 by Decca Records. Dist: Polygram

WORLD OF YOUR 100 BEST TUNES(NEW CHART) Various artists (Various Artists).
Album: released on Decca, Dec'76 by Decca Records. Dist: Polygram

Cassette: released on Decca, Dec'76 by Decca Records. Dist: Polygram

WORLD PIPE BAND CHAMPIONSHIPS 1983 Various artists (Various Artists).
Album: released on BBC, Nov'83 by BBC Records & Tapes. Dist: EMI, PRT,

Cassette: released on BBC, Nov'83 by BBC Records & Tapes. Dist: EMI, PRT

World Class Wrecking Cru

WORLD CLASS WRECKING FREAK.
Tracks: / World class wrecking freak / Mission possible.
Single (7"): released on Epic, Aug'86 by CBS Records. Dist: CBS

Single (12"): released on Epic, Aug'86 by CBS Records. Dist: CBS

World Damination Enterprises

ASBESTOS LEAD ASBESTOS.
Single (7"): released on Karbon, Oct'85 by Karbon Records. Dist: Pinnacle, Red Rhino, Cartel

World Domination

CATALOGUE CLOTHES (World Domination Enterprises).
Tracks: / Catalogue clothes / Saint Etienne.
Single (12"): released on Product, Oct'86

HOSTY GIRL.
Notes: Pic bag
Single (7"): released on Product Inc., Apr'87 Dist: Cartel

Single (12"): released on Product Inc., Apr'87 Dist: Cartel

World Famous...

HEY DJ (World famous supreme team).
Tracks: / Hey DJ.
Single (7"): released on Virgin, Apr'86 by Virgin Records. Dist: EMI, Virgin Distribution

Single (12"): released on Virgin, Apr'86 by Virgin Records. Dist: EMI, Virgin Distribution

World Famous Lobster..
WORKING FOR LOVE AGAIN.
Single (7"): released on Streetwave, Jan'84 by Streetwave Records. Dist: PRT Distribution

Single (12"): released on Streetwave, Jan'84 by Streetwave Records. Dist: PRT Distribution

World famous supreme team
HEY DJ.
Single (7"): released on Charisma, Jan'84 by Virgin Records. Dist: EMI

Single (12"): released on Charisma, Jan'84 by Virgin Records. Dist: EMI

RAPPIN'.
Album: released on Charisma, Jul'86 by Virgin Records. Dist: EMI

Cassette: released on Charisma, Jul'86 by Virgin Records. Dist: EMI

World party
PRIVATE REVOLUTION.
Tracks: / Private revolution / Holy water.
Single (7"): released on Ensign, Sep'86 by Ensign Records. Dist: CBS Distribution

Single (12"): released on Ensign, Sep'86 by Ensign Records. Dist: CBS Distribution

PRIVATE REVOLUTION.
Tracks: / Private revolution / Making love (to the world) / Ship of fools / All come true / Dance of the happy lads / It can be beautiful (sometimes) / Ballad of the little man / Hawaiian island world / All I really want to do / World Party / It's all mine.
Notes: World Party's debut album. Producer - Karl Wallinger
Album: released on Chrysalis, Aug'86 by Chrysalis Records. Dist: CBS

Cassette: released on Chrysalis, Aug'86 by Chrysalis Records. Dist: CBS

Compact disc: released on Ensign, Apr'87 by Ensign Records. Dist: CBS Distribution

SHIP OF FOOLS.
Tracks: / Private revolution / Trouble down here / World groove (do you mind guerrilla) / World groove - do the mind gorilla / Now here man*.
Single (7"): released on Ensign, Jan'87 by Ensign Records. Dist: CBS Distribution

Single (12"): released on Ensign, Jan'87 by Ensign Records. Dist: CBS Distribution

Compact disc single: released on Ensign, Feb'87 by Ensign Records. Dist: CBS Distribution

World Pipe Band...
WORLD PIPE BAND CHAMPIONSHIPS 1986 Various artists (Various Artists).
Album: released on Lismor, Dec'86 by Lismor Records. Dist: Lismor, Roots, Celtic Music

World Premiere
SHARE THE NIGHT.
Single (7"): released on Epic, Jan'84 by CBS Records. Dist: CBS

Single (12"): released on Epic, Jan'84 by CBS Records. Dist: CBS

World Saxophone Quartet
LIVE IN ZURICH.
Compact disc: released on Black Saint (Italy), '86 Dist: Target, Jazz Music, Harmonia Mundi

REVUE.
Compact disc: released on Black Saint (Italy), '86 Dist: Target, Jazz Music, Harmonia Mundi

STEPPIN'.
Compact disc: released on Black Saint (Italy), '86 Dist: Target, Jazz Music, Harmonia Mundi

STEPPIN' WITH.
Album: released on Black Saint, May'79 Dist: Projection, IMS, Polygram, Chris Wellard, Harmonia Mundi, Swift

W.S.Q..
Compact disc: released on Black Saint (Italy), '86 Dist: Target, Jazz Music, Harmonia Mundi

World Series
TRY IT OUT.
Single (7"): released on Baskerville, Oct'83 Dist: Pinnacle

World Service
CELEBRATION TOWN.
Single (12"): released on Rough Trade, Jun'83 by Rough Trade Records. Dist: Rough Trade Distribution, Cartel Distribution

World's Greatest Jazz Band
CENTURY PLAZA.
Album: released on World Jazz, Apr'79 by World Jazz Records. Dist: World Jazz, JSU.

Page 1118

Jazz Music

HARK THE HERALD....
Album: released on World Jazz, Apr'79 by World Jazz Records. Dist: World Jazz, Jazz Music

IN CONCERT AT CARNEGIE HALL, VOL 2
Album: released on World Jazz, Apr'81 by World Jazz Records. Dist: World Jazz, Jazz Music

IN CONCERT AT MASSEY HALL, VOL 1.
Album: released on World Jazz, Apr'81 by World Jazz Records. Dist: World Jazz, JSU, Jazz Music

ON TOUR
Double Album: released on World Jazz, Apr'81 by World Jazz Records. Dist: World Jazz, JSU, Jazz Music

WORLD'S GREATEST JAZZ BAND PLAYS COLE PORTER.
Album: released on World Jazz, Apr'81 by World Jazz Records. Dist: World Jazz, JSU, Jazz Music

WORLD'S GREATEST JAZZ BAND PLAYS DUKE ELLINGTON.
Album: released on World Jazz, Apr'81 by World Jazz Records. Dist: World Jazz, Jazz Music

WORLD'S GREATEST JAZZ BAND PLAYS GEORGE GERSHWIN.
Album: released on World Jazz, Apr'81 by World Jazz Records. Dist: World Jazz, JSU, Jazz Music

WORLD'S GREATEST JAZZ BAND PLAYS RODGERS & HART.
Album: released on World Jazz, Apr'81 by World Jazz Records. Dist: World Jazz, JSU, Jazz Music

World Sitizenz
LOCK IT UP.
Single (7"): released on Manhattan, Aug'85
Cat. no: MT 5
Single (12"): released on Manhattan, Aug'85 by EMI Records. Dist: EMI

World's Worst Records
WORLD'S WORST RECORDS VOL. 2, (THE) Various Artists (Various Artists).
Album: released on Rhino (USA), Jan'86 by Rhino Records (USA).

World war II
WORLD WAR II Various Artists (Various Artists).
Double Album: released on BBC, Nov'85 by BBC Records & Tapes. Dist: EMI, PRT,

Cassette: released on BBC, Nov'85 by BBC Records & Tapes. Dist: EMI, PRT,

Worlock, Monty
LIVE JAZZ FROM THE SOLENT AREA (Worlock, Monty and Ray D'Inverno Trios).
Cassette: released on All That's Jazz, Jun'86 Dist: Jazz Music

Worrell, Tony
EVERYTHING YOU DO (Worrell, Tony Box Office).
Tracks: / Everything you do / Don't turn away.
Single (7"): released on I Scream Music, Aug'86 by Red Rhino, Cartel

Single (12"): released on I Scream Music, Aug'86 by Red Rhino, Cartel

Worried All The Time
WORRIED ALL THE TIME Country blues 1929-36.
Album: released on Whoopee, Apr'78 by Whoopee Records. Dist: Whoopee Records, Waterfront Records, Jazz Music, JSU, Chris

Worries In The Dance
WORRIES IN THE DANCE Various artists (Various Artists).
Album: released on Empire (reggae), Oct'84 Dist: Jetstar

Worries & Problems..
WORRIES AND PROBLEMS DUB '86 Various Artists (Various Artists).
Album: released on Positive Music, Sep'86

Worse 'Em
TRIPLE M BASS.
Tracks: / Triple m bass (Dub mix).
Single (7"): released on Champion, Jan'87 by Champion Records. Dist: RCA

Single (12"): released on Champion, Jan'87 by Champion Records. Dist: RCA

Worth, Billie
CALL ME MADAM (Worth, Billie & Anton Walbrook).
Album: released on Monmouth, Jun'79

Worth, Irene
MADAME BOVARY (Flaubert, G.).
Cassette: released on Caedmon(USA), Oct'81 by Caedmon (USA) Records. Dist: Gower, Taylors, Discovery

Worzel Gummidge
FAIR OLD PULLOVER - A LITTLE LEARNING.
Cassette: released on Kidstuff, Nov'80

NEW FRIENDS FOR WORZEL - VILLAGE FETE.
Cassette: released on Kidstuff, Nov'80

SAUCY NANCY - WORZEL'S 'ANSOM 'EAD.
Cassette: released on Kidstuff, Nov'80

SCARECROW HOP - THE TEA PARTY.
Cassette: released on Kidstuff, Nov'80

WORZEL GIVES A LECTURE - WORZEL'S WEDDING.
Cassette: released on Kidstuff, Nov'80

WORZEL GUMMIDGE Various artists (Various Artists).
Cassette: released on Multi-Media, Jan'82 by Multi Media Tapes Records. Dist: Pinnacle, Conifer Distribution, H.R. Taylor Distribution, Stage One Distribution

WORZEL GUMMIDGE Waterhouse, Keith and Willis Hall (Pertwee, Jon).
Tracks: / New friends for Worzel / Village fete.
Cassette: released on Cover to Cover, Nov'86 by Cover to Cover Cassettes. Dist: Conifer

WORZEL GUMMIDGE - FIRE DRILL (Pertwee, Jon).
Cassette: released on Tempo, Aug'84 Dist: MSD Distribution

WORZEL GUMMIDGE & HIS NEPHEW (Pertwee, Jon).
Cassette: released on Tempo, Aug'84 Dist: MSD Distribution

WORZEL GUMMIDGE & MUVVERS DAY (Pertwee, Jon).
Cassette: released on Tempo, Aug'84 Dist: MSD Distribution

WORZEL GUMMIDGE - THE TRIAL... (Pertwee, Jon).
Cassette: released on Tempo, Aug'84 Dist: MSD Distribution

WORZEL'S NEPHEW - THE TRIAL OF WORZEL.
Cassette: released on Kidstuff, Nov'80

Wot Zat
READ BETWEEN THE LINES.
Single (7"): released on PVK, Oct'85

WOT ZAT.
Album: released on PVK, Oct'85

Wow Federation
YELLOW TELEPHONE.
Single (7"): released on Rococco, Mar'82 Dist: Pinnacle

Woyehyeh
GIVE THIS HEART.
Single (7"): released on Chrysalis, Oct'85 by Chrysalis Records. Dist: CBS

Single (12"): released on Chrysalis, Oct'85 by Chrysalis Records. Dist: CBS

W.Q.B.C.
LOVE ME ANYWAY.
Tracks: / Love me anyway / I'll be loving you.
Single (12"): released on Expansion, Apr'86 Dist: PRT

Wrabit
BACK HOME.
Single (7"): released on MCA, Jun'82 by MCA Records. Dist: CBS

TOO MANY YEARS.
Single (7"): released on MCA, Feb'82 by MCA Records. Dist: CBS

Wraith
WRAITH Original Soundtrack (Various Artists).
Tracks: / Where's the fire / Those were the days / Hearts vs heads / Hold on blue eyes / Young love, hot love / Secret loser / Never surrender / Bad mistake / Wake up call / Matter of the heart.

Album: released on Scotti Brothers (USA), Jan'86 by Scotti Brothers Records. Dist: Polydor

Cassette: released on Scotti Brothers (USA), Jan'86 by Scotti Brothers Records. Dist: Polydor

Wrath
FIT OF ANGER.
Album: released on Megaton, Jul'86 by Megaton Records. Dist: Rough Trade Distribution, Cartel Distribution

Wrathchild
ALRITE WITH THE BOYZ.
Single (7"): released on FM, Sep'84 by FM-volver Records. Dist: EMI

DO YOU WANT MY LOVE.
Single (7"): released on Bullet, Sep'83 Dist: Bullet Distribution

Single (12"): released on Bullet, Sep'83 Dist: Bullet Distribution

Picture disc single: released on Bullet, Sep Dist: Bullet Distribution

ROCK THE CITY DOWN.
Single (7"): released on Bullet, Mar'83 Dist: Bullet Distribution

STACKHEELED STRUT.
Single (12"): released on Bullet, Oct'83 Dist: Bullet Distribution

STAKK ATTAKK.
Album: released on Heavy Metal, Jun'84 FM-Revolver Records. Dist: EMI

Cassette: released on Heavy Metal, Jun'84 FM-Revolver Records. Dist: EMI

Album: released on Dojo, Mar'85 by Castle Communications Records. Dist: Cartel

TRASH QUEENS.
Tracks: / Do you want my love? / Rock the down / Lipstik killers / Trash queen / Teenage revolution / Twist of the knife / Rock, shock, a party.
Album: released on Dojo, Apr'86 by Castle Communications Records. Dist: Cartel

Wray, Link
AND THE RAYMEN (Wray, Link & Raymen).
Album: released on Edsel, Jun'85 by Demon Records. Dist: Pinnacle, Jazz Music, Projection

BATMAN (Wray, Link & His Raymen).
Single (7"): released on Ace, Mar'78 by Ace Records. Dist: Pinnacle, Swift, Hotshot, Cadillac

BULLSHOT.
Album: released on Charisma, May'79 by Virgin Records. Dist: EMI

EARLY RECORDINGS.
Album: released on Ace, Mar'79 by Ace Records. Dist: Pinnacle, Swift, Hotshot, Cadillac

GOOD ROCKIN' TONIGHT.
Album: released on Ace(Barnaby Ltd), May'83 by Ace Records. Dist: Pinnacle, Hotshot

LINK WRAY (Wray, Link & His Raymen).
Cassette: released on Ace, Feb'85 by Ace Records. Dist: Pinnacle, Swift, Hotshot, Cadillac

LIVE AT THE PARADISCO.
Album: released on Magnum Force, Jul'8 Magnum Music Group Ltd. Dist: Magnum Group Ltd, PRT, Spartan

LIVE IN 85.
Tracks: / Rumble / It's only words / Fire terry tram / I gotta woman / Baby let's play / Jack the ripper / Love me / King Creole / counting on you / Rawhide / Born to be wild.
Album: released on Big Beat, Jan'86 by Records. Dist: Projection, Pinnacle

ROCK'N'ROLL RUMBLE (Wray, Link & Raymen).
Album: by Charly Records. Dist: Charly, lac

RUMBLE.
Single (7"): released on Revival, Jul'8 Lightning, Swift

STUCK IN GEAR.
Album: released on Virgin, Mar'76 by Records. Dist: EMI, Virgin Distribution

THERE'S GOOD ROCKIN' TON (Wray, Link & His Raymen).
Album: released on Union Pacific, Sep'8 Swift, Jazz Music, Red Lightnin' Distribution

Wrecking Crew
YOU BROKE MY HEART.

ks: / Passion plays / You broke my heart /
sion plays.
gle (7"): released on ABR, Sep'87 by ABR
uctions. Dist: Spartan, Pinnacle

Reckless Eric

SMASH.
le Album: released on Stiff, Nov'80 by
Records. Dist: EMI, Record Services Dis-
ion (Ireland)

le cassette: released on Stiff, Feb'80 by
Records. Dist: EMI, Record Services Dis-
ion (Ireland)

KEN DOLL.
• (7"): released on Stiff, Mar'80 by Stiff
rds. Dist: EMI, Record Services Distribu-
reland)

NG WAITING HOPING.
• (7"): released on Stiff, '78 by Stiff Rec-
st: EMI, Record Services Distribution
d)

AND MISS JUDY.
• (7"): released on Stiff, Nov'79 by Stiff
s. Dist: EMI, Record Services Distribu-
eland)

SONG, A.
• (7"): released on Stiff, Jan'80 by Stiff
rds. Dist: EMI, Record Services Distribu-
eland)

ONNEZ CHERIE.
• (7"): released on Stiff, Feb'78 by Stiff
ds. Dist: EMI, Record Services Distribu-
eland)

E THE CASH.
• (7"): released on Stiff, '78 by Stiff Rec-
ist: EMI, Record Services Distribution
d)

DERFUL WORLD OF WRECK-
ERIC.
: released on Stiff, '78 by Stiff Records.
MI, Record Services Distribution (Ire-

LD WIDE WORLD.
(7"): released on Stiff, Aug'77 by Stiff
s. Dist: EMI, Record Services Distribu-
eland)

KLESS ERIC.
: released on Stiff, Mar'78 by Stiff Rec-
ist: EMI, Record Services Distribution

encher, John Big
OHN'S BOOGIE.
: released on Big Bear, '82 by Big Bear
. Dist: Big Bear, Swift

n, Jenny
RD AND MRS. SIMPSON.
(7"): released on RK, Dec'79

RD & MRS. SIMPSON.

tched
ORTE NON ASPETTA, LA!
released on Chaos Produzioni, Mar'87
s Produzioni Records. Dist: Revolver,

ht, Bernard
YOU (Remix).
/ After you (Remix) / After you (Remix)
ental) / Yo nard'.

"): released on Manhattan, May'86 by
. Dist: EMI

2"): released on Manhattan, May'86
. Dist: EMI

N' OUT.
"): released on Arista, Mar'81 by Aris-
cords. Dist: RCA

2"): released on Arista, Mar'81 by
cords. Dist: RCA

ELL.
Happy 2 be with u / Got to give it up /
er / I can tell / We'll keep striving / Don't
love from me, (Baby) / Tonight /
or the better / Crack.
d disc: released on Manhattan (USA),

IGHT.
After you / Who do you love / Love
Yo nard / Too damn hott / Killin' me /
n I thought you were mine / Brown

: Bernard Wright's third album.
- Marcus Miller.
eleased on Manhattan, Dec'85 by EMI
. Dist: EMI

NARD.
Album: released on GRP, Feb'81 by Ario-
la/Arista. Dist: Greyhound

Wright, Betty

PAIN.
Tracks: / Pain / Pain (The rap)
Single (7"): released on Cool Tempo, Jan'86
by Chrysalis Records. Dist: CBS

Single (12"): released on Cool Tempo, Jan'86
by Chrysalis Records. Dist: CBS

WRIGHT BACK AT YOU.
Album: released on Epic, Jun'83 by CBS Records. Dist: CBS

Cassette: released on Epic, Jun'83 by CBS
Records. Dist: CBS

Wright, Billy

HEY BABY DON'T YOU WANT A MAN
LIKE ME (Wright, Billy & Little Richard).
Album: released on Ace, Jan'87 by Ace Rec-
ords. Dist: Pinnacle, Swift, Hotshot, Cadillac

STACKED DECK.
Album: released on Route 66, Aug'87

Wright, Bob

ROCK AND ROLL M.C..
Single (7"): released on RPM, Mar'85 by RPM
Records. Dist: PRT Distribution

Wright Brothers

WRIGHT BROTHERS Biography - Spoken
word.
Cassette: released on Ice Berg, May'78 Dist:
Precision, Pye

Wright, Frank

ONE FOR JOHN.
Album: released on Affinity, Sep'79 by Charly
Records. Dist: Charly, Cadillac

Wright, Gary

DREAM WEAVER, THE.
Album: released on Warner Brothers, Nov'76
by Warner Bros Records. Dist: WEA

RIGHT PLACE, THE.
Album: released on Warner Brothers, Jun'81
by Warner Bros Records. Dist: WEA

Wright, George

ENCORES - VOL.2 Wurlitzer pipe organ.
Album: released on Doric, Sep'80 by Amberlee Records. Dist: H.R. Taylor

I'S ALL WRIGHT.
Album: released on Amberlee, '74 by Amberlee Records. Dist: Amberlee Records, H.R. Taylor

ROARING 20'S – WURLITZER
THEATRE ORGAN.
Album: released on Doric, Sep'80 by Amber-
lee Records. Dist: H.R. Taylor

SHOWTIME AT THE MIGHTY THEATRE
ORGAN.
Album: released on Doric, Sep'80 by Amber-
lee Records. Dist: H.R. Taylor

YOU ARE THE ONE I LOVE.
Single 10": released on Kingdom, Oct'82

Wright, Ginny

WHIRLWIND THE FABOR RECOR-
DINGS VOLUME 1.
Tracks: / Lonesome seagull / I'm in heaven /
Wonderful world / I love you / My chihuahua dog
/ Indian moon / Your eyes feasted upon her /
Where were you / I want you yes / I saw Esau
(kissing Mary Lou) / Whirlwind / I could still tell
you more / Turn around my darling / I've got
somebody new / Please leave my darlin' alone
/ How to get married.
Notes: Original Fabor Recordings
Tracks with Jerry Rowley, Tom Bearden, T.
Tommy Cutrer, Jim Reeves.
Album: released on Bear Family, Mar'86 by
Bear Family Records. Dist: Rollercoaster Dis-
tribution, Swift

Wright, Graeme

I HEAR MUSIC Farfisa Coronet organ.
Album: released on Grosvenor, Jan'78 by
Grosvenor Records. Dist: Taylors

SOMETHING SPECIAL.
Album: released on Grosvenor, Jun'83 by
Grosvenor Records. Dist: Taylors

Cassette: released on Grosvenor, Jun'83 by
Grosvenor Records. Dist: Taylors

Wright, Jim

SHANRON' ROSE.
Album: released on Praise, '75 Dist: Outlet

SHEPHERD OF LOVE.
Album: by Pilgrim Records. Dist: Rough
Trade, Cartel

Wright, John

LAUGHTER THROUGH TEARS.
Album: released on Neptune, Jun'79 by Lismor. Dist: Spartan

UNACCOMPANIED.
Album: released on Topic, '81 by Topic Records. Dist: JSU Distribution, Projection Distribution, Jazz Music Distribution

Wright, Katrina

SUSANNAH'S SECRET.
Cassette: released on Soundings, Mar'85 Dist:
Soundings

Wright, Oscar

OSCAR & EUGENE WRIGHT (Wright,
Oscar & Eugene).
Album: released on Rounder, Sep'79 Dist:
Roots Distribution

Wright, O.V.

GONE FOR GOOD.
Album: released on Charly, Jun'83 by Charly
Records. Dist: Charly, Cadillac

WRIGHT STUFF, THE.
Album: released on Hi, May'87 by Demon Records. Dist: Pinnacle

Wright, Peggy Sue

DYNAMITE COUNTRY.
Album: released on Metero, Jun'78

Wright, Peter

WHAT WOULD YOU SAY.
Single (12"): released on Jama, Apr'82 by
Jama Records.

Wright, Stephen

VALENTINE SONG.
Single (7"): released on Stephen Wright,
Jan'81

Wright, Steve

GAY CAVELIEROS.
Single (7"): released on MCA, Nov'84 by MCA
Records. Dist: CBS

Single (12"): released on MCA, Nov'84 by MCA
Records. Dist: CBS

Picture disc single: released on MCA, Nov'84
by MCA Records. Dist: CBS

GET SOME THERAPY.
Single (7"): released on RCA, Oct'83 by RCA
Records. Dist: RCA, Roots, Swift, Wellard,
Chris, I & B, Solomon & Peres Distribution

Single (12"):

I HAVE A PONY.
Album: released on Warner Bros., Jul'87 by
Warner Bros Records. Dist: WEA

Cassette: released on Warner Bros., Jul'87 by
Warner Bros Records. Dist: WEA

I'M SO ANGRY.
Single (7"): released on MCA, Aug'85 by MCA
Records. Dist: CBS

Single (12"): released on MCA, Aug'85 by MCA
Records. Dist: CBS

WILD WILD WOMAN.
Single (7"): released on Record Mart, Apr'78
by Record Mart Records. Dist: Tonal Distribution, Record Mart

Wright, Wayne

ACOUSTIC GUITAR DUETS (Wright,
Wayne and Marty Grosz).
Album: released on Aviva(USA), Apr'79 Dist:
Jazz Music, Swift

Wright, Winston

ARRIVAL OF COUNT SHELLEY.
Tracks: / Arrival of Count Shelley / Always re-
member (Dean Frazer).
Single (12"): released on World Enterprise,
Nov'86 Dist: Jetstar

Wrigley, Bernard

Biographical Details: see under - Roger Westbrook.

PHENOMENAL BERNARD WRIGLEY,
THE Folk songs, tunes & drolleries.
Album: released on Topic, '81 by Topic Records. Dist: JSU Distribution, Projection Distribution, Jazz Music Distribution

ROUGH AND WRIGLEY.
Album: released on Topic, '81 by Topic Rec-

---

ords. Dist: JSU Distribution, Projection Distribution, Jazz Music Distribution

SATURDAY COWBOYS.
Single (7"): released on DJM, May'80 by DJM
Records. Dist: CBS, Polygram

WESTBROOK/WRIGLEY (Wrigley, Ber-
nard/Roger Westbrook).
Notes: see under Westbrook, Roger.

Written In The Wind

WRITTEN IN THE WIND.
Album: released on Varese International,
Mar'79

Wunderlich, Fritz

GLORIOUS VOICE OF FRITZ WUNDER-
LICH, (THE).
Album: released on Memoir, '85 by Memoir
Records. Dist: PRT Distribution

Cassette: released on Memoir, '85 by Memoir
Records. Dist: PRT Distribution

GLORIOUS VOICE OF FRITZ WUNDER-
LICH, THE.
Album: released on Polydor, May'79 by Poly-
dor Records. Dist: Polygram, Polydor

GRANADA.
Album: released on Polydor, '74 by Polydor
Records. Dist: Polygram, Polydor

Album: released on Memoir, Nov'84 by Memoir Records. Dist: PRT Distribution

Cassette: released on Memoir, Nov'84 by
Memoir Records. Dist: PRT Distribution

Wunderlich, Klaus

16 GOLDEN CLASSICS.
Tracks: / Feelings / Wave / Portrait / From the
top / Air on a G string / Bach changes / Woodstock / If / Dance of the living / Lorelei / Duet for
guitar and koto / Lisa Larne / Dance of the emperor's clouds / Dance of the dead / A derrih dhu
/ Magic fly / I feel love / Derrin dhu, A / Night
fever / Disco / Take a chance on me / You're the
one that I want / Verde / Le reve / Grease /
Oxygene / More more b Get up and boogie
/ I'm a stain / Hustla-Puzzle / Amarillo - Sacramento - Don't go down to Reno / Power to
all our friends - Tie a yellow ribbon / Letter to Lu-
cifle - Yellow boomerang - Tipsy organ / Money
money money - Sunney - Tante Emma / A fair
l'amore - Standing in the rain - Love is in the air
/ Take me high / Free electric band.
Notes: All tracks licensed from Teldec Design:
Shoot that tiger(c) 1986/Castle Communica-
tions Place, Unit 7, 271 Merton Road, London
SW18 5JS. Bar code: 5013428/320176.
Album: released on Unforgettable, Dec'86 by
Castle Communications Records. Dist:
Counterpoint

Cassette: released on Unforgettable, Dec'86
by Castle Communications Records. Dist:
Counterpoint

Compact disc: released on Unforgettable, '86
by Castle Communications Records. Dist:
Counterpoint

28 TOP HITS.
Album: released on Ariola (Germany), Apr'84
Cat. no: 1205 674
Cassette: released on Ariola (Germany),
Apr'84

AROUND THE WORLD WITH KLAUS
WUNDERLICH.
Double Album: released on Telefunken, '74

Double cassette: released on Telefunken, '74

BRAZIL.
Album: released on Telefunken (Germany),
Nov'82 Dist: Decca Distribution, IMS, Polygram

Cassette: released on Telefunken (Germany),
Nov'82 Dist: Decca Distribution, IMS, Polygram

CLASSIC KLAUS.
Album: released on Decca, Nov'83 by Decca
Records. Dist: Polygram

Cassette: released on Decca, Nov'83 by Decca
Records. Dist: Polygram

CLUB DANCING.
Album: released on Telefunken Import, '74

Cassette: released on Telefunken Import, '74

COLLECTION: KLAUS WUNDERLICH.
Tracks: / Fly robin fly / Nights on Broadway /
Also sprach Zarathustra / Waterloo / Teenage
rampage / Devil gate drive / Chirpy chirpy cheep
cheep / Sunny / Rose garden / Cracklin' rose /
Never can say goodbye / Jenny gotta dance /
Shame shame shame / Let me be the one / Oh
boy / Only you can / Honey money / Kissin' in the
rain bow / Sugar baby love / This will be / Mississippi / There goes my first love / Guantanamera / Rhinestone cowboy / What am I going
to do with you / I write the songs / Concierto de
Aranjuez / Little love and understanding / A /
Nostalgia / Are you lonesome tonight / Look at
me / Delta Queen / Clair / Get down / Downtown
/ Sunshine lover / Amazing Grace / Mother of

mine / Sugar me / Standing in the road / Till I kissed you / Do you wanna dance / Kailaki Kailako / Una paloma blanca / Fox on the run / Only yesterday / Bye bye baby / Amore grande amore libero / Breaking up is hard to do / Mandy / Entertainer (The) / Si / I'm leaving it all up to you / Tweedle Dee Tweedle Dum / How do you do / Never ending song of love / Poppa Joe / You never listen to a reason / Let's twist again / Mamma mia / Jackson / Charly Brown / Love to love you baby / Last farewell (The) / My prayer.
Compact disc: released on Collector Series, '86 by Castle Communications Records. Dist: PRT, Pinnacle, RCA, Ariola

Double Album: released on Collectors, Apr'86 by Castle Communications Records. Dist: PRT, Pinnacle, Jazz Music

Double cassette: released on Collectors, Apr'86 by Castle Communications Records. Dist: PRT, Pinnacle, Jazz Music

DREAM CONCERTO.
Album: released on Telefunken Import, '77

Cassette: released on Telefunken Import, '77

EL CUMBANCHERO 16 South American Favourites.
Tracks: / El Cumbanchero / Rumba tambah / Amor, amor, amor / La felicidad / Ave Maria no morro / Besame mucho / Ole guapa / La Cumparsita / Maria Delores / Brazil / Cu-cu-rru-cu-cu, paloma.
Cassette: released on Teldec, Jun'87

Album: released on Teldec, Jun'87

EL CUMBANCHERO (CD) 21 South American Favourites.
Tracks: / El Cumbanchero / Rumba tambah / Amor, amor, amor / La felicidad / Ave Maria no morro / Besame mucho / Ole guapa / L Cumparsita / Maria Delores / Brazil / Cu-cu-rru-cu-cu, paloma.
Compact disc: released on Teldec, Jun'87

ENTERTAINER, (THE).
Double Album: released on Telefunken, Nov'80

Double cassette: released on Telefunken, Nov'80

FAVOURITES.
Album: released on Telefunken Import, Dec'75

Cassette: released on Telefunken Import, Dec'75

FROM NEW YORK TO YOKOHAMA.
Tracks: / New York, New York / Carnival in Rio / San Francisco / Das hab'ich in Paris gelernt / An einem Sonntag in Avignon / White rose of Athens, The / Nights are long in Hamburg, The / Londonderry air / Berliner luft / Foggy day in London town, A / Carnival of Venice, The / Heut' kommen d'Engerln auf Urlaub nach wien / Tulips from Amsterdam / Lisboa Antigua / Moscow / Yokohama melody.
Compact disc: released on Teldec, May'87

Cassette: released on Teldec, May'87

Album: released on Teldec, May'87

GOLDEN HAMMOND POPS.
Double Album: released on Telefunken Import, '74

Cassette: released on Telefunken Import, '74

GOLDEN SOUND OF HAMMOND, VOL 2.
Album: released on Telefunken Import, '77

Cassette: released on Telefunken Import, '77

GOLDEN SOUND OF KLAUS WUNDERLICH VOL.2.
Tracks: / Tico tico / Raindrops keep fallin' / La Paloma / La vie en rose / Anema e core / String of pearls / Delicado / Ambo polka / Pennies from heaven / Moskito killer / Clair / Wand'rin star.
Compact disc: released on Teldec, Jun'87

GOLDEN SOUND OF KLAUS WUNDERLICH.
Tracks: / Wonderland by night / Up, up and away / Bacarole / Brazil / Harlem nocturne / Hello dolly / Elizibethan serenede / Strangers in the night / Lara's theme / Love is blue / Red roses for a blue lady / Moon river / Tango bolero.
Compact disc: released on Teldec, Jun'87

HIT WORLD OF KLAUS WUNDERLICH, (THE).
Album: released on Telefunken, Aug'75

Cassette: released on Telefunken, Aug'75

ILLUSION.
Album: released on Ariola (Germany), Apr'84

Cassette: released on Ariola (Germany), Apr'84

IN A ROMANTIC MOOD.
Tracks: / Breeze and I (The) / More / I could have danced all night / Love story (Where do I begin) / Feelings / Don't cry for me / Un homme et un femme / I love Paris / Love is here to stay / La vie en rose / Over the rainbow / Lara's theme from Dr. Zhivago / Theme from Limelight / Twilight time / They can't take that away from me / C'est ci bon / Ich kusse ihre hand, Madame / If you could read my mind / Massachusetts / Somethin' stupid / Greensleeves / Parlez-moi d'amour / Song of the Indian guest / Killing me softly with his song / Ave Maria no morro / Dein spuren im sand / Strangers in the night / This guy's in love with you.
Notes: The first time on MFP for this ever popular artist. 28 tracks, many of which are blended together in medley form - typically Klaus Wunderlich. Recorded in 1982 by EMI Electrola and should achieve it's true potential sales volume of MFP. Many albums have been recorded by Klaus Wonderlich, but most are pop organ/partytype - this is a more relaxed and rich atmosphere.
Album: released on Music For Pleasure, Feb'87 by EMI Records. Dist: EMI

Cassette: released on Music For Pleasure, Feb'87 by EMI Records. Dist: EMI

IN THE GLENN MILLER MOOD.
Album: released on Teldec (Germany), Mar'84

Cassette: released on Teldec (Germany), Mar'84

IN THE MILLER MOOD.
Tracks: / In the mood / Moonlight serenade / Little brown jug / Tuxedo junction / Chattanooga choo choo / Pennsylvania 6-5000 / American patrol / String of pearls, A / St. Louis Blues March / I know why / Johnson rag / Flying home.
Compact disc: released on Teldec, Jun'87

IN THE WUNDERLICH MOOD.
Tracks: / In the mood / I just called to say I love you... / In Hamburg sind die nachte land / Londonderry air / Mit 66 jahren,eine hand is keine faust / I've grown accustomed toher face / Disco 'Beethoven', The... / Moonlight serenade / Live is life, Jenseits von eden, fur alle / Adagio cantabile / American patrol / Einsamer hirte, ballade pur Adeline / Oxygene IV / Magic fly / I feel love / Rivers of Babylon.
Compact disc: released on Teldec, Jul'87

Cassette: released on Teldec, Jul'87

KLAUS WUNDERLICH.
Album: released on Contour, Oct'82 by Pickwick Records. Dist: Pickwick Distribution, PRT

Cassette: released on Contour, Oct'82 by Pickwick Records. Dist: Pickwick Distribution, PRT

KLAUS WUNDERLICH PLAYS ROBERT STOLZ MELODIES.
Album: released on Telefunken Import, Dec'74

Cassette: released on Telefunken Import, Dec'74

LATIN COLLECTION.
Double Album: released on Telefunken, Sep'82

Cassette: released on Telefunken, Sep'82

MAGIC OF KLAUS WUNDERLICH, (THE).
Album: released on Contour, Nov'83 by Pickwick Records. Dist: Pickwick Distribution, PRT

Cassette: released on Contour, Nov'83 by Pickwick Records. Dist: Pickwick Distribution, PRT

MR HAMMOND.
Double Album: released on Teldec (Germany), Mar'84

MUSICAL.
Tracks: / There's no business like show business / Ol' man river / People will say we're in love / Aquarius / I've grown accustomed to her face / One / Maria / One (from "A chorus line") / Bali ha'i / Welcome / Maria / Hello, Dolly / If I were a rich man / Sound of music, The / I'll never fall in love again / Superstar.
Compact disc: released on Teldec, Jun'87

Cassette: released on Teldec, Jun'87

Album: released on Teldec (Germany), Apr'86 by Import Records. Dist: IMS Distribution, Polygram Distribution

MUSIC IS FOREVER.
Album: released on Contour, Feb'82 by Pickwick Records. Dist: Pickwick Distribution, PRT

Cassette: released on Contour, Feb'82 by Pickwick Records. Dist: Pickwick Distribution, PRT

NEW WUNDERLICH POPS.
Tracks: / Comment ca va / Biscaya / Jambo jambo / Wunderbar / Die sonne und du / Santa Lucia by night / Reach out / I just called to say I love you / Life is life / Jenseits von Eden / Fur alle / Angela / Also lebe ich / Am strand von Griechenland / Manner brauchen liebe / Lab es mich ganz leise sagen / Hurra, wir leben noch / Aufrecht geh'n / Goodbye my love / Frankreich, frankreich / Flieg mit mir zu den sternen / Blue night shadow / Mein tuut tuut / Katrin / I war am liabsten mit dir ganz alloa / Extension / Abends / Lieb ohne leiden.
Compact disc: released on Teldec, Jun'87

Cassette: released on Teldec, Jun'87

Album: released on Teldec, Jun'87

ON THE SUNNY SIDE OF THE STREET.
Tracks: / Honeysuckle rose / Exactly like you / Star wars / Flashdance / On the sunny side of the street / Falling in love again / When is your birthday Johnny / You came along / When day is done / Blue eyes / Song for Guy / Dallas/Dynasty / Puttin' on the Ritz / Blue skies / Alexander's ragtime band / When I take my sugar to tea / Ain't she sweet / Sirius/Eye in the sky/Lucifer / Too soon.
Album: released on Polydor, Aug'86 by Polydor Records. Dist: Polygram, Polydor

Cassette: released on Polydor, Aug'86 by Polydor Records. Dist: Polygram, Polydor

PHASE 4 WORLD OF KLAUS WUNDERLICH.
Album: released on Telefunken, '78

Cassette: released on Telefunken, '78

POLKA POPS.
Album: released on Telefunken (Germany), Nov'82 Dist: Decca Distribution, IMS, Polygram

POLKA POPS, VOL 2.
Album: released on Telefunken Import, '74

Cassette: released on Telefunken Import, '74

POP ORGAN PARTY.
Album: released on Pathe MarconiFrance), Jan'85

Cassette: released on Pathe MarconiFrance), Jan'85

POP PARTY, VOL 1.
Album: released on Teldec (Germany), Mar'84

Cassette: released on Teldec (Germany), Mar'84

PORTRAIT.
Album: released on Teldec (Germany), Mar'84

Cassette: released on Teldec (Germany), Mar'84

PORTRAIT IN GOLD.
Album: released on Telefunken, Feb'75

PROFILE.
Album: released on Telefunken Import, '74

Cassette: released on Telefunken Import, '74

RENDEZVOUS.
Album: released on EMI (Odeon), Jul'82 by EMI Records. Dist: Conifer

Cassette: released on EMI (Odeon), Jul'82 by EMI Records. Dist: Conifer

ROMANTIC MELODIES.
Tracks: / You make my world so beautiful / Memory / Swingin' safari, A / Laura / Dawn / Summer place, A (Theme from) / You taught my heart a song of love / Intermezzo of Notre Dame / Begin the beguine / Linger a while / Misty / Dreams are free / Premier rendezvous, Le / Good night.
Album: released on Polydor, Sep'84 by Polydor Records. Dist: Polygram, Polydor

Cassette: released on Polydor, Sep'84 by Polydor Records. Dist: Polygram, Polydor

Compact disc: released on Polydor, Sep'84 by Polydor Records. Dist: Polygram, Polydor

SENSATIONAL ORGAN SOUND OF KLAUS WUNDERLICH.
Cassette: released on Telefunken, Feb'79

SOUND VARIATION.
Album: released on Telefunken, Oct'74

Cassette: released on Telefunken, Oct'74

SOUTH AMERICAN HAMMOND ORGAN 1.
Album: released on Teldec (Germany), Mar'84

Cassette: released on Teldec (Germany), Mar'84

SOUTH AMERICAN HAMMOND ORGAN 2.
Album: released on Teldec (Germany), Mar'84

Cassette: released on Teldec (Germany), Mar'84

SOUTH AMERICAN HAMMOND ORGAN 3.
Album: released on Teldec (Germany), Mar'84

Cassette: released on Teldec (Germany), Mar'84

STRICKLY FOR DANCING.
Tracks: / Foxtrot- medley / Tango- medley / Samba- medley / Slow foxtrot- medley / Jive- medley / Waltz- medley / Paso doble- medley / Slow waltz- medley / Disco- medley / Rumba- medley / Quickstep- medley / Cha-cha- medley.
Compact disc: released on Polydor, Aug'85 by Polydor Records. Dist: Polygram, Polydo

STRICTLY FOR DANCING.
Album: released on Polydor, Aug'85 by dor Records. Dist: Polygram, Polydor

Cassette: released on Polydor, Aug'85 by dor Records. Dist: Polygram, Polydor

Compact disc: released on Polydor, Aug Polydor Records. Dist: Polygram, Polydo

SWING AND HAPPY (Wunderlich, Kl H. Deuringer).
Double Album: released on Telefunken

TIME FOR ROMANCE.
Album: released on Contour, Aug'83 by wick Records. Dist: Pickwick Distribution

Cassette: released on Contour, Aug' Pickwick Records. Dist: Pickwick Distri PRT

TRAVELLIN' ON.
Double Album: released on Telefu Aug'81 Deleted '87.

Double cassette: released on Telef Aug'81

TWENTY EIGHT POP ORGAN VOURITES.
Tracks: / Breeze and I / More / I coul danced all night / Love story (where do I / Feelings / Don't cry for me Argentin homme et une femme (a man & a wom love Paris / La vie en Rose / Over the ra Lara's theme from Dr Zhivago / Them limelight / Twilight time / They can't ta away from me / C'est si bon / Ich kus hand madame (I kiss your hand mada you could read my mind / Massachu Somethin' stupid / Greensleeves (trad) / moi d'amour / Song of the Indian guest me softly with his song / Ave Maria no Dein spuren im sand / Strangers in the This guy's in love with you.
Notes: All arrangements Klaus Wun Producer Klaus Wunderlich. Klaus Wu at the Wersi organ Helios, Wersi-Pi Synth-bass, drums & percussion.
Cassette: released on Music For Pl Feb'87 by EMI Records. Dist: EMI

UNIQUE KLAUS WUNDER SOUND, (THE).
Double Album: released on Tele Mar'78

Double cassette: released on Tele Mar'78

WONDERLAND BY NIGHT.
Album: released on Hallmark, Sep'85 wick Records. Dist: Pickwick Distributio Taylors

Cassette: released on Hallmark, Se Pickwick Records. Dist: Pickwick Dist PRT, Taylors

WUNDERLICH POPS 5.
Album: released on Teldec (Germany)

Cassette: released on Teldec (Ge Mar'84

WUNDERLICH POPS 6.
Album: released on Teldec (Germany

Cassette: released on Teldec (Ge Mar'84

WUNDERLICH POPS 7.
Album: released on Teldec (Germany

Cassette: released on Teldec (Ge Mar'84

Wurges, Paul

DEUTSCHE BILL HALEY MIT ROCKING ALL STARS, DER.
Album: released on Ariola (Germany

Wurzel

BESS.
Tracks: / Bess / People say I'm crazy / in London / ESP.
Notes: WIRE TRAIN IS A POP GRO
Single (7"): released on GWR, Mar'8 Records. Dist: RCA

Single (12"): released on GWR, M GWR Records. Dist: RCA

Wurzels

ALL FALL DOWN.
Tracks: / All fall down / Somerset crun
Single (7"): released on Dingles, Oct' gles Records. Dist: Projection

COUGHIN' SONG.
Single (7"): released on John Miles,

GIVE ME ENGLAND.
Album: released on EMI, '84 by EM Dist: EMI

ATEST HITS: WURZELS.
: released on Note, Nov'79 by EMI Rec-
ist: EMI

tte: released on Note, Nov'79 by EMI
s. Dist: EMI

EL RAP.
(7"): released on Goldliner, Jul'83 Dist:
, Stage One

ELS.
te: released on Ideal(Tapes), Jun'81
MI

hering Heights

ERING HEIGHTS (Bronte, Emily).
te: released on Listen For Pleasure,
by MFP Records. Dist: EMI

ERING HEIGHTS Emily Bronte
y, Daniel).
cassette: released on Listen For Plea-
ov'77 by MFP Records. Dist: EMI

Wendy

OUR LOVE.
7"): released on Epic, Mar'82 by CBS
. Dist: CBS

zles

ES, THE.
released on Cherry Lane, Nov'85 by
ane Productions. Dist: PRT

e: released on Cherry Lane, Nov'85 by
ane Productions. Dist: PRT

tt, Robert

984.
released on Rough Trade, Dec'84 by
rade Records. Dist: Rough Trade Dis-
Cartel Distribution

S.
released on Rough Trade, '84 by
rade Records. Dist: Rough Trade Dis-
Cartel Distribution

T I'M FREE.
"): released on Rough Trade, Nov'81
Trade Records. Dist: Rough Trade
on, Cartel Distribution

AN TO WOMAN (Wyatt, Robert &
Of Cast).
"): released on Virgin, Apr'82 by Vir-
s. Dist: EMI, Virgin Distribution

): released on Rough Trade, Aug'81
Trade Records. Dist: Rough Trade
on, Cartel Distribution

GHTINGALE, THE.
2"): released on Recommended,
Recommended Records. Dist: Rec-
d, Impetus, Rough Trade

G CAN STOP US.
disc: released on Rough Trade,
Rough Trade Records. Dist: Rough
tribution, Cartel Distribution

eleased on Rough Trade, '84 by
ade Records. Dist: Rough Trade Dis-
Cartel Distribution

released on Rough Trade, '84 by
ade Records. Dist: Rough Trade Dis-
Cartel Distribution

TTEN HAT.
leased on Rough Trade, Nov'85 by
de Records. Dist: Rough Trade Dis-
Cartel Distribution

released on Rough Trade, Nov'85 by
de Records. Dist: Rough Trade Dis-
artel Distribution

TTENHAT.
disc: released on Rough Trade,
Rough Trade Records. Dist: Rough
ibution, Cartel Distribution

SSION, THE.
oup song / Alifib / I'm a believer / Sea

"): released on Strange Fruit, Sep'87
lwood. Dist: Pinnacle

NAMERA.
: released on Rough Trade, Mar'80
Trade Records. Dist: Rough Trade
, Cartel Distribution

TTOM.
eased on Virgin, Jul'74 by Virgin
ist: EMI, Virgin Distribution

eleased on Virgin, Jul'74 by Virgin
st: EMI, Virgin Distribution

STRANGER THAN RICHARD.
eased on Virgin, May'75 by Virgin
Records. Dist: EMI, Virgin Distribution

Cassette: released on Virgin, May'75 by Virgin Records. Dist: EMI, Virgin Distribution

SHIPBUILDING.
Single (7"): released on Rough Trade, Aug'82 by Rough Trade Records. Dist: Rough Trade Distribution, Cartel Distribution

Single (12"): released on Rough Trade, Aug'82 by Rough Trade Records. Dist: Rough Trade Distribution, Cartel Distribution

STALIN' WASN'T STALLIN'.
Single (7"): released on Rough Trade, Feb'81 by Rough Trade Records. Dist: Rough Trade Distribution, Cartel Distribution

WIND OF CHANGE, THE.
Single (7"): released on Rough Trade, Oct'85 by Rough Trade Records. Dist: Rough Trade Distribution, Cartel Distribution

Single (12"): released on Rough Trade, Oct'85 by Rough Trade Records. Dist: Rough Trade Distribution, Cartel Distribution

WORK IN PROGRESS.
Single (12"): released on Rough Trade, Aug'84 by Rough Trade Records. Dist: Rough Trade Distribution, Cartel Distribution

Wycoff, Michael

DO YOU REALLY LOVE ME TELL ME LOVE.
Single (7"): released on RCA, Jul'83 by RCA Records. Dist: RCA, Roots, Swift, Wellard, Chris, I & B, Solomon & Peres Distribution

Single (12"): released on RCA, Jul'83 by RCA Records. Dist: RCA, Roots, Swift, Wellard, Chris, I & B, Solomon & Peres Distribution

ON THE LINE.
Album: released on RCA, Aug'83 by RCA Records. Dist: RCA, Roots, Swift, Wellard, Chris, I & B, Solomon & Peres Distribution

Cassette: released on RCA, Aug'83 by RCA Records. Dist: RCA, Roots, Swift, Wellard, Chris, I & B, Solomon & Peres Distribution

STILL GOT THE MAGIC (SWEET DELIGHT).
Single (7"): released on RCA, Apr'82 by RCA Records. Dist: RCA, Roots, Swift, Wellard, Chris, I & B, Solomon & Peres Distribution

Single (12"): released on RCA, Apr'82 by RCA Records. Dist: RCA, Roots, Swift, Wellard, Chris, I & B, Solomon & Peres Distribution

Wylie, Pete

DIAMOND GIRL.
Tracks: / Diamond girl / Spare a thought.
Single (7"): released on Siren, Aug'86 by Virgin Records. Dist: EMI

Single (12"): released on Siren, Aug'86 by Virgin Records. Dist: EMI

IF I LOVE YOU.
Tracks: / If I love you / Never fall for a whore.
Single (7"): released on Siren, Jul'87 by Virgin Records. Dist: EMI

Single (12"): released on Siren, Jul'87 by Virgin Records. Dist: EMI

SINFUL.
Tracks: / Sinful / I want the moon mother / Sophie's sinful / Sophie's sinful (for Maurice or Isabella) / Joy of beeing booed, The.
Double-pack single: released on MDM, Apr'86 Dist: Siren, Virgin, EMI

Single (12"): released on MDM, Apr'86 Dist: Siren, Virgin, EMI

Picture disc single: released on MDM, Apr'86 Dist: Siren, Virgin, EMI

Wyman, Bill

BILL WYMAN.
Album: released on A&M, Apr'82 by A&M Records. Dist: Polygram

Cassette: released on A&M, Apr'82 by A&M Records. Dist: Polygram

COME BACK SUZANNE.
Single (7"): released on A&M, Oct'81 by A&M Records. Dist: Polygram

DRINKIN' T.N.T 'N' SMOKIN' DYNAMITE (Wyman, Bill, Buddy Guy & Junior Wells).
Album: released on Red Lightnin', May'83 by Red Lightnin' Records. Dist: Roots, Swift, Jazz Music, JSU, Pinnacle, Cartel, Wynd-Up Distribution

NEW FASHION.
Single (7"): released on A&M, Mar'82 by A&M Records. Dist: Polygram

SI SI JE SUIS UN ROCKSTAR.
Single (7"): released on A&M, Jun'81 by A&M Records. Dist: Polygram

VISIONS.
Single (7"): released on A&M, May'82 by A&M Records. Dist: Polygram

WILLIE AND THE POOR BOYS (Wyman, Bill & Friends).
Tracks: / Baby please don't go / Can you hear me / These arms of mine / Revenue man / You never can tell / Slippin' and slidin' / Saturday night / Let's talk it over / All night long / Chicken-shack boogie / Sugar bee / Poor boy boogie.
Notes: Featuring Charlie Watts - drums/Bill Wyman - bass and vocals/Geraint Watkins - keyboards and vocals/Mickey Gee - guitar & vocals/Andy Fairweather Low - guitar and Vocals. Plus Ray Cooper - Jimmy Page - Willie Garnett - Chris Rea - Steve Gregory - Paul Rodgers - Kenny Jones - Henry Spinetti - Terry Williams. All nett proceeds from this album project will go directly ARMS (Action For Reseach Into Multiple Sclerosis).
Album: released on London, May'86 by London Records. Dist: Polygram

Cassette: released on London, May'86 by London Records. Dist: Polygram

Compact disc: released on London, May'86 by London Records. Dist: Polygram

Wymark, Patrick

WIND IN THE WILLOWS Spoken Word.
Double cassette: released on Argo (Spoken-word), Jul'82 by Decca Records. Dist: Polygram

Wynder, K.

FRENETIC.
Single (7"): released on Rockburgh, Jul'80

Wyndham-Read, Martin

ANDY'S GONE.
Tracks: / Bodmon town / Andy's gone with cattle / Grimsby lads / The soldier's dream of home / In the hills of Shilo / The plough boy / Lemony / The mower / Faithful Emma / Harry Dale the drover / The forlorn lover / Seasons of the year.
Notes: The distinctive and exciting voice Martin Wyndham-Read has been a feature of the British folk scene for a good many years and Martin is regarded with great respect by his many friends in the folk music world. This personal selection of English and Australian songs demonstrates the range and style of his singing very well indeed and the record will be a welcome addition to those who have obtained his previous recordings and a good starting point for those who have not. Instruments include:guitar, melodeon, tamborine, banjo, concertina, hammered dulcimer, descant recorder, zither harp, harmonium and fiddle. Featuring: Martin Wyndham-Read with Dave and Toni Arthur and Nic Jones.
Album: released on Broadside, Jun'81 by Broadside Records. Dist: Celtic Distributions, H.R. Taylor, Jazz Music, Projection, Jazz Services Unlimited Dist. (JSU)

Cassette: released on Broadside, Jun'81 by Broadside Records. Dist: Celtic Distributions, H.R. Taylor, Jazz Music, Projection, Jazz Services Unlimited Dist. (JSU)

EMU PLAINS.
Album: released on Fellside (Cumbria), '83 by Fellside Records. Dist: Roots, Projection, CM, Jazz Music

ENGLISH SPORTING BALLADS.
Album: released on Broadside, Jun'81 by Broadside Records. Dist: Celtic Distributions, H.R. Taylor, Jazz Music, Projection, Jazz Services Unlimited Dist. (JSU)

Cassette: released on Broadside, Jun'81 by Broadside Records. Dist: Celtic Distributions, H.R. Taylor, Jazz Music, Projection, Jazz Services Unlimited Dist. (JSU)

MARTIN WYNDHAM-READ.
Album: released on Leader, '81 Dist: Jazz Music, Projection

NED KELLY AND THAT GANG.
Album: released on Leader, '81 Dist: Jazz Music, Projection

OLD SONGS, THE.
Album: released on Greenwich Village, Nov'84 by Sweet Folk All Records. Dist: Roots, Projection, Lightning, Celtic Music, Wellard, Chris

ROSE.
Single (7"): released on Greenwich Village, Dec'84 by Sweet Folk All Records. Dist: Roots, Projection, Lightning, Celtic Music, Wellard, Chris

Wynette, Tammy

ALIVE AND WELL.
Tracks: / I'll be thinking of you.
Single (7"): released on Epic, Feb'87 by CBS Records. Dist: CBS

ANNIVERSARY: 20 YEARS OF HITS.
Tracks: / I don't wanna play house / D-I-V-O-R-C-E / Stand by your man / Singing my song / Run, woman, run / We sure can love each other / Good loving (makes it right) / Bedtime story / 'Til I get it right / Kids say the darndest things / Another lonely song / We're gonna hold on / Woman to woman / 'Til I can make it on my own / Golden ring / You and me / One of a kind / Two story house / Alive and well / Apartment No. 9 / Your good girl's gonna go bad.
Album: released on Epic, Apr'87 by CBS Records. Dist: CBS

Cassette: released on Epic, Apr'87 by CBS Records. Dist: CBS

Compact disc: released on Epic, Apr'87 by CBS Records. Dist: CBS

BEST OF TAMMY WYNETTE, (THE).
Album: released on Epic, Mar'81 by CBS Records. Dist: CBS

Cassette: released on Epic, Mar'81 by CBS Records. Dist: CBS

BIGGEST HITS.
Album: released on Epic, Mar'83 by CBS Records. Dist: CBS

CHRISTMAS WITH TAMMY WYNETTE.
Album: released on Epic, Nov'76 by CBS Records. Dist: CBS

Cassette: released on Epic, Nov'76 by CBS Records. Dist: CBS

CLASSIC COLLECTION.
Double Album: released on Epic, May'82 by CBS Records. Dist: CBS

Double cassette: released on Epic, May'82 by CBS Records. Dist: CBS

COUNTRY LIFE OF TAMMY WYNETTE.
Cassette: released on Ditto, Aug'84 by Pickwick Records. Dist: H.R. Taylor

COWBOYS DON'T SHOOT STRAIGHT.
Single (7"): released on Epic, May'81 by CBS Records. Dist: CBS

CRYING IN THE RAIN.
Single (7"): released on Epic, Nov'81 by CBS Records. Dist: CBS

D.I.V.O.R.C.E..
Single (7"): released on Epic, '80 by CBS Records. Dist: CBS

FIRST LADY OF COUNTRY.
Album: released on Spot, Feb'83 by Pickwick Records. Dist: H.R. Taylor, Lugtons

Cassette: released on Spot, Feb'83 by Pickwick Records. Dist: H.R. Taylor, Lugtons

Album: released on Hallmark, Sep'85 by Pickwick Records. Dist: Pickwick Distribution, PRT, Taylors

Cassette: released on Hallmark, Sep'85 by Pickwick Records. Dist: Pickwick Distribution, PRT, Taylors

HIGHER GROUND.
Tracks: / Your love / Tempted / Some things will never change / Beneath a painted sky / I wasn't meant to live my life alone / Higher ground / Talkin' to myself again / Slow burning fire, A / There's no heart so strong / All through throwing good love after bad.
Album: released on Epic, Sep'87 by CBS Records. Dist: CBS

Cassette: released on Epic, Sep'87 by CBS Records. Dist: CBS

I LOVE COUNTRY.
Album: released on CBS(France), Sep'86 by CBS Records. Dist: Conifer, Discovery, Swift

Cassette: released on CBS(France), Sep'86 by CBS Records. Dist: Conifer, Discovery, Swift

IN LOVE.
Album: released on Hallmark, Feb'80 by Pickwick Records. Dist: Pickwick Distribution, PRT, Taylors

Cassette: released on Hallmark, Feb'80 by Pickwick Records. Dist: Pickwick Distribution, PRT, Taylors

IT SURE IS GOOD (Wynette, Tammy and George Jones).
Album: released on Premier, Feb'87 by Premier Records. Dist: CBS

Cassette: released on Premier, Feb'87 by Premier Records. Dist: CBS

JUST TAMMY.
Album: released on Epic, Jul'79 by CBS Records. Dist: CBS

Cassette: released on Epic, Jul'79 by CBS Records. Dist: CBS Deleted '81.

KING & QUEEN OF COUNTRY MUSIC (Wynette, Tammy & George Jones).
Album: released on Pickwick, Feb'80 by Pickwick Records. Dist: Pickwick Distribution, Prism Leisure Distribution, Lugtons

ONLY LONELY SOMETIMES.
Cass: released on Spot, Apr'86 by Pickwick Records. Dist: PRT

QUEEN OF COUNTRY.
Cass. set: released on Pickwick(Ditto series), Jan'83 by Pickwick Records. Dist: PRT, Clyde Factors

LP: released on Pickwick, Sep'80 by Pickwick Records. Dist: PRT, Clyde Factors

Cass: released on Pickwick, Sep'80 by Pickwick Records. Dist: PRT, Clyde Factors

SOMETIMES WHEN WE TOUCH.
LP: released on Epic, May'85 by CBS Records. Dist: CBS

Cass: released on Epic, May'85 by CBS Records. Dist: CBS

STAND BY YOUR MAN.
Tracks: / You make me want to be a mother /

Another lonely song / Kids say the darndest things / Love's the answer / Woman to woman / Bedside story / Stand by your man / Good lovin' / Reach out your hand / Pleases come to Boston / 'Til I get it right / My man (understands) / There goes that old steel guitar / Help me make it through the night
LP: released on Epic, Mar'86 by CBS Records. Dist: CBS

Cass: released on Epic, Mar'86 by CBS Records. Dist: CBS

Single 7": released on Old Gold, Apr'83 by Old Gold Records. Dist: PRT, Counterpoint, Lightning, Jazz Music, Taylors

TAMMY WYNETTE I love country.
Tracks: / Womanhood / Two storey house / Cryin' in the rain / Bring my baby back to me / He was there when I needed you / Cheatin' is / Heaven's just a sin away / Cowboys don't shoot straight (like they used to) / Sometimes when we touch / Funny face / You need me / Sweet music man / Pair of old sneakers, A / Dear daughters / Easy come, easy go / I'd like to see

Jesus (on the midnight special)
LP: released on Epic, Mar'87 by CBS Records. Dist: CBS

Cass: released on Epic, Mar'87 by CBS Records. Dist: CBS

Cass. set: released on Pickwick, '83 by Pickwick Records. Dist: PRT, Clyde Factors

TAMMY WYNETTE IN CONCERT.
VHS: released on Vestron Music, '87 Dist: CBS

WOMAN TO WOMAN.
LP: released on Premier Records, Feb'87 Dist: CBS

Cass: released on Premier Records, Feb'87 Dist: CBS

Wynn, Big Jim
BLOW WYNN, BLOW.
LP: released on Whiskey, Women And Song, Apr'85 Dist: Swift, Celtic Music, Jazz Music

Wynne, Philippe
YOU AIN'T GOING ANYWHERE GONE.
Single 7": released on Sugarhill, Mar'8 MCA Records. Dist: Roots

Single 12": released on Sugarhill, Mar' MCA Records. Dist: Roots

Wyoming
OUTSIDE LOOKING IN.
Tracks: / Outside looking in / Luxury nocence
Single 7": released on CBS, Apr'87 by Records. Dist: CBS

Single 12": released on CBS, Apr'87 b Records. Dist: CBS

WYOMING.
LP: released on CBS, 30 May'87 by CBS ords. Dist: CBS

Cass: released on CBS, 30 May'87 b Records. Dist: CBS

X
AIN'T LOVE GRANDE.
LP: released on Elektra, Aug'85 by WEA Records. Dist: WEA

BURNING HOUSE OF LOVE.
Single 7": released on Elektra, Aug'85 by WEA Records. Dist: WEA

Single 12": released on Elektra, Aug'85 by WEA Records. Dist: WEA

MORE FUN IN THE NEW WORLD.
LP: released on Elektra Asylum, Sep'83 by Elektra/Asylum/Nonesuch Records. Dist: WEA Deleted '87.

Cass: released on Elektra Asylum, Sep'83 by Elektra/Asylum/Nonesuch Records. Dist: WEA

NEW WORLD / I MUST NOT THINK BAD THOUGHTS.
Single 7": released on Elektra, Jan'84 by WEA Records. Dist: WEA

SEE HOW WE ARE.
Tracks: / I'm lost / You / 4th of July / I the time it takes / Anyone can fill your shoes / See how we are / Left & right / When it rains / Holiday story / Surprise surprise / Cyrano de Berger's back
LP: released on Elektra(USA), Jul'87 by Elektra/Asylum/Nonesuch Records. Dist: WEA, Pinnacle

Cass: released on Elektra(USA), Jul'87 by Elektra/Asylum/Nonesuch Records. Dist: WEA, Pinnacle

WILD GIFT.
LP: released on Flash, Jul'81 by Relic. Dist: Swift Deleted '87.

X Collector
TELEVISION SET / CHRISTINE.
Single 7": released on Solar Sound, Oct'83 Dist: Wellard, Pinnacle

X, Francis
SOUL-INCEST (X, Francis And The Bushmen).
Tracks: / Mirror church / Come with me / Harlequin / Bits & pieces / Wicked love / Power of zero
LP: released on Revolver, Aug'86 by FM-Revolver Records. Dist: BMG

X, Malcolm
NO SELL OUT.
Single 7": released on Island, Mar'84 by Island Records. Dist: Polygram

Single 12": released on Island, Mar'84 by Island Records. Dist: Polygram

X, Rocky
IT'S GETTING ROUGH (X, Rocky & D.D. Dance).
Tracks: / It's getting rough / It's getting rough (version)
Single 12": released on Positive Beat, Jul'87 by Positive Beat Records. Dist: Jetstar

Xalam
APARTHEID.
CD: by EMI Records(UK). Dist: EMI

XALAM.
LP: released on Celluloid(France), Mar'85 by Island. Dist: Polygram, Celtic Music

Xanadu In Africa
XANADU IN AFRICA.
LP: released on Xanadu, Jul'82 Dist: Jazz Music, Jazz Horizons, Swift

Xarhakos, Stavros
DARK SIDE OF THE SUN, THE.
Single 7": released on BBC, Sep'83 by BBC Records & Tapes. Dist: EMI

LP: released on BBC, Sep'83 by BBC Records & Tapes. Dist: EMI

Cass: released on BBC, Sep'83 by BBC Records & Tapes. Dist: EMI

Xaviera
XAVIERA.
LP: released on Belmont, Feb'77 by Belmont Records.

X-Cells
SCHIZOID.
Single 7": released on Snotty Snail, Jul'81 Dist: Rough Trade

X-Certs
TOGETHER / UNTOGETHER.
Single 7": released on Recreational, Jan'81 by Revolver Records. Dist: Rough Trade

Xclusive
C'EST LA VIE.
Single 7": released on KA, Oct'82 by KA Records. Dist: CBS

FOOLS ARE FRIENDLY.
Single 7": released on Le Maitre, Jun'82 Dist: CBS

Xdreamysts
RIGHT WAY HOME.
Single 7": released on Good Vibration, '79 by Good Vibrations Records. Dist: Pinnacle, Rough Trade

X-Invaders
STORM BOYS.
Single 7": released on Pinner, Feb'85 by Pinner Records. Dist: Rough Trade, Cartel, Backs*

XL5's
FIREBALL / MISIRLOU.
Single 7": released on Fourplay, Sep'80 Dist: Pinnacle

X-Mal Deutschland
FETISCH.
CD: released on 4AD, Jun'87 by 4AD Records. Dist: Rough Trade

FETISCH.
LP: released on 4AD, '83 by 4AD Records. Dist: Rough Trade

INCABUS SUCCUBUS / VITO.
Single 7": released on 4AD, Sep'83 by 4AD Records. Dist: Rough Trade

Single 12": released on 4AD, Sep'83 by 4AD Records. Dist: Rough Trade

INCUBUS SUCCUBUS II.
Tracks: / Incubus succubus II / Vito
Single 12": released on 4AD, '86 by 4AD Records. Dist: Rough Trade

INCUBUS SUUCUBUS / BLUT 1ST LEIBE / ZU JUNG ZU ALT.
Single 12": released on Zick Zack(Germany), Aug'83 by Zick Zack Records. Dist: Rough Trade

MATADOR.
Tracks: / Matador / Paho
Single 7": released on X-Ile, '86 Dist: Phonogram

PEEL SESSION 13th May 1985.
Single 12": released on Strange Fruit, Nov'86 by Clive Selwood. Dist: Pinnacle

QUAL / ZEIT SEHNSUCHT.
Single 12": released on 4AD, May'83 by 4AD Records. Dist: Rough Trade

SEQUENZ.
Single 7": released on Red Rhino, Oct'85 by Red Rhino Records. Dist: Red Rhino, Cartel

Single 12": released on Red Rhino, Oct'85 by Red Rhino Records. Dist: Red Rhino, Cartel

SICKLE MOON.
Tracks: / Sickle moon / Illusion / In onyx
Single 7": released on X-Ile, Jan'87 Dist: Phonogram

Single 12": released on X-Ile, Jan'87 Dist: Phonogram

TOCSIN.
Tracks: / Mondicht / Elland / Reigen / tag / Augen blich / Begrab / Mein herz schatten / Xmas in Australia / Der wisch
CD: released on 4AD, Jun'87 by 4AD R Dist: Rough Trade

Cass: released on 4AD, Jun'84 by 4/ ords. Dist: Rough Trade

VIVA.
LP: released on Phonogram, Feb'87 by gram Records. Dist: Polygram

Cass: released on Phonogram, Feb'87/ nogram Records. Dist: Polygram

CD: released on Phonogram, Feb'87 nogram Records. Dist: Polygram

XDREAMYSTS.
LP: released on Polydor, Nov'80 by Records. Dist: Polygram

Xena
ON THE UP SIDE.
Single 12": released on Streetwave Dist: BMG

Xenon
WHEN YOU WEAR BLUE / H DREAMS.
Single 7": released on Zirron, Sep'83 Records.

Xero
OH BABY / HOLD ON / LONE W
Single 7": released on Brickyard, Jul'8 kyard Records. Dist: Pinnacle

Single 12": released on Brickyard, Brickyard Records. Dist: Pinnacle

X-Factor
CHEMICAL ROMANCE.
Single 7": released on Scorpio, Oct'8 pio Records. Dist: Jetstar

Single 12": released on Scorpio, Scorpio Records. Dist: Jetstar

Xmas Soul
XMAS SOUL Various artists (V tists).
LP: released on Rounder(USA), Ja Jazz Music, Projection, Swift, Celtic M dillac, Roos, Duncans, Impetus

X-Men
GHOSTS.
Single 7": released on Creation Jun'84 Dist: Rough Trade, Cartel

LILLIES FOR MY PUSSY.
LP: released on Media Burn, Nov'86 by Rocks Off Record Emporium. Dist: Rough Trade, Cartel

SPIRAL GIRL.
Single 7": released on Creation, Apr'85 Dist: Rough Trade, Cartel

Xoduz
NICE GIRL FROM THE CAKE SHOP.
Cass: released on Vision, '85 Dist: Vision

Xpertz
MY VALENTINE.
Single 7": released on Big One, Jun'85 Dist: Jetstar

Single 12": released on Big One, Jun'85 Dist: Jetstar

VALENTINE.
Single 7": released on B.B. Star, Mar'84 by B.B. Star Records. Deleted '87.

X-Posed
POINT OF NO RETURN.
Single 7": released on Pantera, Sep'84 by Pantera Records.

Xpozez
1000 MARCHING FEET / TERMINAL CASE.
Single 7": released on Red Rhino, Jul'82 by Red Rhino Records. Dist: Red Rhino, Cartel

FORCE FED THE TRUTH DRUG (EP).
Single 7": released on Children Of The Revolution, Jan'85 by Revolver Records. Dist: Revolver, Cartel

NEW YORK DOLL / IT'S BEEN DONE BEFORE.
Single 7": released on Sexual Phonograph, Mar'83 by Sexual Phonograph Records.

X-Ray Spex
DAY THE WORLD TURNED DAYGLO / I AM A POSEUR.
Single 7": released on EMI International, Apr'80 by EMI Records(UK). Dist: Conifer

GERM FREE ADOLESCENTS.
LP: released on EMI International, '78 by EMI Records(UK). Dist: Conifer

Cass: released on EMI International, '78 by EMI Records(UK). Dist: Conifer

OH BONDAGE UP YOURS.
Single 7": released on Virgin, Oct'77 by Virgin Records. Dist: Virgin, EMI

Single 12": released on Virgin, Oct'77 by Virgin Records. Dist: Virgin, EMI

XS
XS.
Tracks: / Love attack / Better late than never / Keep on believing / Rock'n'roll / Game, The / Just another lonely night / So lonely / Paint it black
LP: released on FM, Jul'87 by FM-Revolver Records. Dist: BMG

Cass: released on FM, Jul'87 by FM-Revolver Records. Dist: BMG

XS Energy
EIGHTEEN / JENNY'S ALRIGHT.
Single 7": released on Dead Good, '79 by Dead Good Records. Dist: Pinnacle, Rough Trade

USE YOU.
Single 7": released on Dead Good, '79 by Dead Good Records. Dist: Pinnacle, Rough Trade

XTC
3D EP - SCIENCE FRICTION / SHE'S SO SQUARE / DANCE BAND.
Single 12": released on Virgin, Apr'83 by Virgin Records. Dist: Virgin, EMI

ALL YOU PRETTY GIRLS.
Single 7": released on Virgin, Sep'84 by Virgin Records. Dist: Virgin, EMI

Single 12": released on Virgin, Sep'84 by Virgin Records. Dist: Virgin, EMI

BALL AND CHAIN / PUNCH AND JUDY MAN.
Single 7": released on Virgin, Mar'82 by Virgin Records. Dist: Virgin, EMI

Single 12": released on Virgin, Mar'82 by Virgin Records. Dist: Virgin, EMI

BEESWAX.
LP: released on Virgin, Nov'82 by Virgin Records. Dist: Virgin, EMI

BIG EXPRESS.
Tracks: / Wake up / All you pretty girls / Shake you donkey up / Seagulls / Screaming kiss her kiss her / This world over / Small town - The every day story of / I bought myself a liarbird / Reign of blows / You're the wish you are i had / I remember the sun / Train running low on soul coal
LP: released on Virgin, '84 by Virgin Records. Dist: Virgin, EMI

Cass: released on Virgin, '84 by Virgin Records. Dist: Virgin, EMI

CD: released on Virgin, '84 by Virgin Records. Dist: Virgin, EMI

BLACK SEA.
CD: released on Virgin, Mar'87 by Virgin Records. Dist: Virgin, EMI

COMPACT XTC.
CD: released on Virgin, '86 by Virgin Records. Dist: Virgin, EMI

DEAR GOD.
Tracks: / Dear God / Big day / Another satellite
Single 12": released on Virgin, 30 May'87 by Virgin Records. Dist: Virgin, EMI

DRUMS AND WIRES.
Tracks: / Making plans for Nigel / Helicopter / Day in day out / When you're near me I have difficulty / Ten feet tall / Roads girdle the globe / Reel by reel / Millions / That is the way / Outside world / Scissor man / Complicated game
CD: released on Virgin, '86 by Virgin Records. Dist: Virgin, EMI

ENGLISH SETTLEMENT.
Tracks: / Runaways / Ball and chain / Senses working overtime / No thugs in our house / Yacht dance / All of a sudden / Melt the guns / Leisure / It's nearly Africa / Knuckle down / Fly on the wall / Down in the cockpit / English roundabout / Snowman
LP: released on Virgin, '82 by Virgin Records. Dist: Virgin, EMI

Cass: released on Virgin, '82 by Virgin Records. Dist: Virgin, EMI

CD: released on Virgin, '82 by Virgin Records. Dist: Virgin, EMI

GO2.
Tracks: / Meccanik dancing / Crowded room / Battery bribes / Buzzcity talking / Rhythm / Beat-town / Life is good in the greenhouse / I am the audience / Ted / My weapon / Jumping in the Gomorrah / Supertuff
CD: released on Virgin, Jul'87 by Virgin Records. Dist: Virgin, EMI **Media Note:** Re-issue.

LP: released on Virgin, Mar'84 by Virgin Records. Dist: Virgin, EMI

Cass: released on Virgin, Mar'84 by Virgin Records. Dist: Virgin, EMI

GRASS.
Tracks: / Grass / Dear God / Extroverts
Single 7": released on Virgin, '86 by Virgin Records. Dist: Virgin, EMI

Single 12": released on Virgin, '86 by Virgin Records. Dist: Virgin, EMI

LOVE ON A FARM BOYS WAGES / BURNING WITH OPTIMISMS FLAME.
Single 12": released on Virgin, Sep'83 by Virgin Records. Dist: Virgin, EMI

MAKING PLANS FOR NIGEL.
Single 7": released on Virgin, Sep'79 by Virgin Records. Dist: Virgin, EMI

Cass: released on Virgin, Aug'83 by Virgin Records. Dist: Virgin, EMI

MEETING PLACE.
LP: released on Virgin, Jan'87 by Virgin Records. Dist: Virgin, EMI

Single 7": released on Virgin, Jan'87 by Virgin Records. Dist: Virgin, EMI

Single 12": released on Virgin, Jan'87 by Virgin Records. Dist: Virgin, EMI

MEETING PLACE (THE).
Tracks: / Meeting place, the / Man who sailed around his soul (The) / Terrorism / Let's make a den / Find the fox / Troubles, the / Man who sailed around his soul (The) [XTC home demos] / Terrorism / Let's make a den / Find the fox / Troubles (The)
Single 12": released on Virgin, Feb'87 by Virgin Records. Dist: Virgin, EMI

MUMMER.
Tracks: / Wonderland / Great fire / Elements / Love on a farm boy's wages / Ladybird / Me and the wind / Funk pup a roll / Deating of hearts / Human alchemy / In loving memory of a name
CD: released on Virgin, Mar'87 by Virgin Records. Dist: Virgin, EMI

NO THUGS IN OUR HOUSE / LIMELIGHT / OVER RUSTY WATER.
Single 7": released on Virgin, May'82 by Virgin Records. Dist: Virgin, EMI

SENSES WORKING OVERTIME / BLAME THE WEATHER.
Single 7": released on Virgin, Jan'82 by Virgin Records. Dist: Virgin, EMI

Single 12": released on Virgin, Jan'82 by Virgin Records. Dist: Virgin, EMI

CLAN OF XYMOX.
Tracks: / Day, A / Day, A / No words / Stumble and fall / Cry in the wind / Stranger / Equal ways / Seventh time / No human can drown / No human can drown
LP: released on 4AD, Nov'86 by 4AD Records. Dist: Rough Trade

CD: released on 4AD, Nov'86 by 4AD Records. Dist: Rough Trade

DAY, A.
Single 12": released on 4AD, Jul'85 by 4AD Records. Dist: Rough Trade

MEDUSA.
LP: released on 4AD, Nov'86 by 4AD Records. Dist: Rough Trade

CD: released on 4AD, Feb'87 by 4AD Records. Dist: Rough Trade

SKYLARKING.
Tracks: / Summers cauldron / Grass / Meeting place (The) / That's really super, supergirl / Ballet for a rainy day / 1000 umbrellas / Season cycle / Earn enough for us / Big day / Another / Mermaid smiled / Man who sailed around his soul (The) / Dying / Sacrificial bonfire
LP: released on Virgin, Oct'86 by Virgin Records. Dist: Virgin, EMI

Cass: released on Virgin, Oct'86 by Virgin Records. Dist: Virgin, EMI

CD: released on Virgin, Oct'86 by Virgin Records. Dist: Virgin, EMI

WAXWORKS.
LP: released on Virgin, Nov'82 by Virgin Records. Dist: Virgin, EMI

Cass: released on Virgin, Nov'82 by Virgin Records. Dist: Virgin, EMI

LP: released on Virgin, Mar'84 by Virgin Records. Dist: Virgin, EMI

Cass: released on Virgin, Mar'84 by Virgin Records. Dist: Virgin, EMI

WHITE MUSIC.
Tracks: / Radios in motion / Cross wires / This is pop? / Do what you do / Statue of Liberty / All along the watchtower / Into the atom age / I'll set myself on fire / I'm bugged / Spinning top / Neon shuffle / New town animal in a furnished cage
CD: released on Virgin, Mar'87 by Virgin Records. Dist: Virgin, EMI

WONDERLAND.
Single 7": released on Virgin, Jul'83 by Virgin Records. Dist: Virgin, EMI

Xtro
XTRO Original soundtrack.
LP: released on That's Entertainment, Apr'83 by That's Entertainment Records. Dist: Pinnacle

Y
LISTEN TO ME.
Single 7": released on War, Aug'85 by War Records.

Single 12": released on War, Aug'85 by War Records.

LONELY.
Tracks: / Many a time
Single 7": released on Polydor, Jan'87 by Polydor Records. Dist: Polygram

Single 12": released on Polydor, Jan'87 by Polydor Records. Dist: Polygram

Y Cyrff
PUM MUNUD.
Tracks: / Pum Mundu
Single 7": released on Sus-Recordiau Anhrefn, '86

Y & T
CONTAGIOUS.
Tracks: / Contagious / L.A. Rocks / Temptation / Kid goes crazy, The / Fight for your life / Armed and dangerous / Rhythm or not / Bodily harm / Eyes of a stranger / I'll cry for you
LP: released on Geffen, Jul'87 by Geffen Records. Dist: WEA

Cass: released on Geffen, Jul'87 by Geffen Records. Dist: WEA

Ya Ya
DON'T TALK.
Single 7": released on Scotti Bros(USA), Aug'84 by Scotti Brothers Records. Dist: Polydor

TRIBUTE TO MAL WALDRON, (A).
LP: released on Enja(Germany), Jan'82 by Enja Records (W.Germany). Dist: Cadillac, Jazz Music

Yamashta, Stomu
GO (Yamashta, Stomu & Steve Winwood).
LP: released on Island, Jun'76 by Island Records. Dist: Polygram

Cass: released on Island, Jun'76 by Island Records. Dist: Polygram

SEA AND SKY.
CD: released on Kuckuck, Jun'87 Dist: Celtic Music, TM Records

LP: released on Kuckuck(Germany), Aug'85 Dist: Conifer, TM Records

STOMU YAMASHTA.
LP: by Decca Records. Dist: Polygram

Yancey, Jimmy

IMMORTAL JIMMY YANCEY, THE.
LP: released on Oldie Blues, Feb'77 Dist: Projection, Celtic Music, Swift Deleted '83.

PIANO SOLOS 1939.
Tracks: / Jimmy's stuff / Rolling the stone / Steady rock blues / P.I.K. special / South side stuff / Yancey's gateway / La salle street breakdown / Two o'clock blues / Janie's joys / Lean bacon / Big bear train / Lucile's lament
LP: released on Joker, Apr'81 Dist: Counterpoint, Cadillac, Jazz Horizons, Jazz Music, Celtic Music

LP: released on Joker, '87 Dist: Counterpoint, Cadillac, Jazz Horizons, Jazz Music, Celtic Music

PITCHIN' BOOGIE.
LP: released on Swaggie(Australia), Jan'83 Dist: Jazz Music

yancey, Kym

DETERMINATION.
Single 12": released on Pinnacle, Apr'84 by Windsong. Dist: Pinnacle

Yancey-Loften

SESSIONS VOL.2.
Recording Notes: Mono.
LP: released on Storyville, '86 by Storyville Records. Dist: Swift, Wellard

Yang

POWER IS IN YOUR MIND.
Tracks: / Power is in your mind (Mix 1) / Power is in your mind (Mix 2) / Power is in your mind (Mix 4) / Power is in your mind (Radio Exit)
Single 12": released on Affair, '86 Dist: DMS, BMG

Yankee Brass Band

MUSIC FROM MID-NINETEENTH-VARIOUS ARTISTS.
Tracks: / Arizona quickstep / Bond's serenade / No one to love / Blondinette polka / Mabel waltz / Helene Schottisch / American hymn / Red stocking quickstep / Mockingbird quickstep / Memories of home-waltz / Schottische / Moon is above us / Brin d'amour polka / Goodnight my angel / Firemen's polka
Recording Notes: Full title: Yankee Brass Band, The music from mid-nineteenth century America. Featuring the American Brass Quintet Brass Band and the American Brass Quintett.
LP: released on New World(USA), Mar'87 by New World Records(USA). Dist: Conifer

Yankees

HALBSTARK.
LP: released on Bear Family, Jan'83 by Bear Family Records(Germany). Dist: Celtic Music, Swift, Rollercoaster

Yankovic, Frank

AMERICAS FAVOURITE.
LP: released on Smash (USA), Aug'87 Dist: IMS, Polygram

Cass: released on Smash (USA), Aug'87 Dist: IMS, Polygram

Yankovic, Frankie

40 GREATEST POLKAS & WALTZES.
LP: released on Accordion Record Club, '84 by Accordion Record Club. Dist: Accordion Record Club

Yankovic, Weird Al

LIKE A SURGEON.
Single 7": released on Epic, Jul'85 by CBS Records. Dist: CBS

Yarbrough & Peoples

BE A WINNER.
LP: released on Total Experience (USA), Apr'84

Cass: released on Total Experience, Apr'84 by Phonogram. Dist: Polygram

DON'T WASTE YOUR TIME.
Single 7": released on Total Experience, Apr'84 by Phonogram. Dist: Polygram

Single 12": released on Total Experience, Apr'84 by Phonogram. Dist: Polygram

GUILTY.
Tracks: / Wrapped around your finger / I'll give anything to have you back / Let the music play on / Anytime / Who is she / Everything / Closer love affair, A / Guilty / Guilty / Guilty (Inst.)
LP: released on Total Experience, '86 by Phonogram. Dist: Polygram

Cass: released on Total Experience, '86 by Phonogram. Dist: Polygram

Single 7": released on Total Experience, '86 by Phonogram. Dist: Polygram

Single 12": released on Total Experience, '86 by Phonogram. Dist: Polygram

HEARTBEATS.
LP: released on Total Experience, Mar'83 by Phonogram. Dist: Polygram

Cass: released on Total Experience, Mar'83 by Phonogram. Dist: Polygram

Single 7": released on Total Experience, Jan'83 by Phonogram. Dist: Polygram

Single 12": released on Total Experience, Jan'83 by Phonogram. Dist: Polygram

I WOULDN'T LIE.
Tracks: / I wouldn't lie / Ill be there / I wouldn't lie (Live)
Single 7": released on RCA, '86 by RCA Records. Dist: BMG

Single 12": released on RCA, '86 by RCA Records. Dist: BMG

Yacht Club Jazz Band

YACHT CLUB JAZZ BAND, THE.
LP: released on Swaggie(Australia), Jan'83 Dist: Jazz Music

Yachts

BOX 202.
Single 7": released on Radar, Jul'79 by WEA Music Ltd. Dist: WEA

FOOL LIKE YOU, A.
Single 7": released on Demon, Feb'81 by Demon Records. Dist: Celtic Music, Pinnacle, Jazz Music

IOU.
Single 7": released on Radar, Aug'80 by WEA Music Ltd. Dist: WEA

LOOK BACK IN LOVE.
Single 7": released on Radar, Sep'78 by WEA Music Ltd. Dist: WEA

LOVE YOU LOVE YOU.
Single 7": released on Radar, May'79 by WEA Music Ltd. Dist: WEA

NOW I'M SPOKEN FOR.
Single 7": released on Radar, Nov'79 by WEA Music Ltd. Dist: WEA

YACHTING TYPES.
Single 7": released on Radar, '78 by WEA Music Ltd. Dist: WEA

Yakity Yak

PLEASE DON'T ASK.
Single 7": released on Chick-A-Boom, Nov'80 by Chick-A-Boom Records. Dist: Tonal

RUN BABY RUN.
Single 7": released on Limp, '79 by Limp Records. Dist: Pinnacle, Rough Trade

YAKITY YAK.
LP: released on SRT, May'76 by SRT Records. Dist: Projection, Solomon & Peres, SRT, Pinnacle

Yakomettles

DANCE MUSIC, (THE).
Single 12": released on Zeds, May'85 Dist: Revolver, Red Rhino, Cartel

ONE AND ONLY (THE).
Tracks: / One and only (The) / No time to lose
Single 7": released on Zeds, '86 Dist: Revolver, Red Rhino, Cartel

Yamamoto, Tsuyoshi

ZEPHYR.
LP: released on Concord Jazz, Jun'83 by Concord Jazz Records (USA). Dist: IMS, Polygram

Yamashita, Yosuke

BANSLIKANA.
LP: released on Enja(Germany), Jan'82 by Enja Records (W.Germany). Dist: Cadillac, Jazz Music

CLAY (Yamashita, Yosuke trio).
LP:

INNER SPACE.
LP: released on Enja(Germany), Jan'82 by Enja Records (W.Germany). Dist: Cadillac, Jazz Music

Yard Band, The

MUM ITA COOKING.
Tracks: / Mum ita cooking
Single 12": released on Disco Tex, '86 by Disco Tex Records. Dist: Jetstar

Yard Style Christmas

YARD STYLE CHRISTMAS Various artists (Various artists).
LP: released on M.I.C., Dec'84 by M.I.C. Records. Dist: Jetstar

Yard Trauma

NO CONCLUSIONS.
LP: released on Eva-Lolita, '86 Dist: Pinnacle

Yardbirds

6 TRACK HITS.
Special: released on Scoop 33, Mar'84 by Pickwick Records. Dist: Pickwick, PRT

Special: released on Scoop 33, Mar'84 by Pickwick Records. Dist: Pickwick, PRT

20 GREATEST HITS: YARDBIRDS.
LP: released on Masters(Holland), Apr'87 Dist: Conifer

Cass: released on Masters(Holland), Apr'87 Dist: Conifer

CLASSIC CUTS.
Tracks: / Smokestack lightning / You can't judge a book / Let it rock / Boom boom / Who do you love / Too much monkey business / Got love if you want it / Here 'tis / What do you want / I ain't done wrong / Respectable / My girl Sloopy / You're a better man than I / New York City blues / Someone to love pt.1 / Someone to love pt.2
Recording Notes: Licensed from Charly International APS. This CD (P) 1987 Charly Holdings Inc. (C) 1987 Charly Records Ltd.
CD: released on Topline, Apr'87 by Charly Records.

EVIL HEARTED YOU.
Single 7": released on Import, '80

FIRST RECORDINGS-LONDON 1963.
CD: released on Bellaphon, '86 by Bellaphon Records. Dist: Celtic Music, IMS, Polygram, Target

FIVE LIVE YARDBIRDS.
LP: released on Charly, Aug'79 by Charly Records. Dist: Charly, Cadillac, Swift

Cass: released on Charly, Jan'82 by Charly Records. Dist: Charly, Cadillac, Swift

FOR YOUR LOVE.
LP: released on Topline, Nov'84 by Charly Records.

Cass: released on Topline, Nov'84 by Charly Records.

Single 7": released on Old Gold, Jul'82 by Old Gold Records. Dist: PRT, Counterpoint, Lightning, Jazz Music, Taylors

GREATEST HITS: YARDBIRDS VOL.1.
LP: released on Rhino (USA), '86 by Rhino Records(USA). Dist: Pinnacle

LEGEND OF THE YARDBIRDS VOL 1.
LP: released on Fontana Import, Sep'82 by Phonogram Records. Dist: Polygram

Cass: released on Fontana Import, Sep'82 by Phonogram Records. Dist: Polygram

LEGEND OF THE YARDBIRDS VOL 2.
LP: released on Fontana Import, Sep'82 by Phonogram Records. Dist: Polygram

Cass: released on Fontana Import, Sep'82 by Phonogram Records. Dist: Polygram

LEGEND OF THE YARDBIRDS VOL 3.
LP: released on Fontana Import, Oct'82 by Phonogram Records. Dist: Polygram

Cass: released on Fontana Import, Oct'82 by Phonogram Records. Dist: Polygram

LITTLE GAMES.
LP: released on Fame, May'85 by Music For Pleasure Records. Dist: EMI

Cass: released on Fame, May'85 by Music For Pleasure Records. Dist: EMI

OUR OWN SOUND.
LP: released on Charly, Jun'83 by Charly Records. Dist: Charly, Cadillac, Swift

OVER UNDER SIDEWAY DOWN.
Single 7": released on Edsel, Feb'83 by Demon Records. Dist: Celtic Music, Pinnacle, Jazz Music

PARTS 1 & 2.
Tracks: / I wish you would / Good morning little scoolgirl / I ain't got you / Boom boom / Good morning little schoolgirl (Instr) / Got to hurry / For your love / Too much monkey business / Got love if you want it / Here 'tis / Pontiac blues / 23 hours too long / Let it rock / Smokestack Lightning / Honey in your hips / Heart full of soul / Evil hearted you / Heart full of soul / Still I'm sad / I'm a man / Jeff's blues / You're a better man than I / Shapes of things / Stroll on
Recording Notes: All tracks licensed from Topline Records APS. Design: Shoot that tiger! Matrix number: 5 013428 131411. Double album and cassette.
LP: released on Castle Collectors, '86 by Castle Communications Records. Dist: Pinnacle

Cass: released on Castle Collectors, '86 by Castle Communications Records. Dist: Pinnacle

RACK MY MIND.
Single 7": released on Edsel, May'84 by Demon Records. Dist: Celtic Music, Pinnacle, Jazz Music

ROGER THE ENGINEER.
Tracks: / Happenings ten years time ago / Psycho daisies / Over,under,sideways,downs / Nazz are blue(The) / Rack my mind / Lost women / I can't make your way / Farewell / Jeff's boogie / Hot house of Omagarashid / He's always there / Turn into earth / What do you want / Ever since the world began
CD: released on Edsel, '86 by Demon Records. Dist: Celtic Music, Pinnacle, Jazz Music

LP: released on Edsel, Feb'83 by Demon Records. Dist: Celtic Music, Pinnacle, Jazz Music

LP: released on Edsel, Feb'83 by Demon Records. Dist: Celtic Music, Pinnacle, Jazz Music

Cass: released on Edsel, Feb'83 by Demon Records. Dist: Celtic Music, Pinnacle, Jazz Music

SHAPES OF THINGS A collection of classic Yardbirds recordings 1964-66.
Tracks: / Shapes of things / Too much monkey business / I wish you would / Good morning little schoolgirl / For your love / Certain girl, A / Got to hurry / Smokestack lightning / Evil hearted you / Still i'm sad / Steeled blues / Train kept a rolling / Here 'tis / What do you want / New York city blues / For R.S.G. / You're a better man than I / Jeff's blues / I ain't got you / I ain't done wrong / Someone to love (part 1) / Someone to love (part 2) / Boom Boom / My girl sloopy
Recording Notes: Produced by : Giorgio Gomelsky Licensed from Charly Records International APS This cassette published 1977 Charly Holdings Inc copyright 1986 Charly Records Ltd
LP: released on Charly, Nov'84 by Charly Records. Dist: Charly, Cadillac, Swift

Cass: released on Charly, Sep'87 by Charly Records. Dist: Charly, Cadillac, Swift **Media Note:** Doubleplay cassette

SHAPES OF THINGS/ I'M A MAN.
Single 7": released on Import, '80

STILL I'M SAD/ EVIL HEARTED YOU.
Single 7": released on Old Gold, Jul'82 by Old Gold Records. Dist: PRT, Counterpoint, Lightning, Jazz Music, Taylors

YARDBIRDS Greatest Hits.
Tracks: / For your love / Putty in your hands / Got to hurry / I wish you would / Good morning little schoolgirl / Evil hearted you / Still I'm sad / Heartful of soul / Jeff's blue / Shapes of things / Steeled blues / Stroll on / Certain girl, A / I ain't got you / Train kept rolling / I'm a man
CD: released on Charly, '86 by Charly Records. Dist: Charly, Cadillac, Swift

YARDBIRDS. Featuring Jeff Beck.
LP: released on Charly, Mar'83 by Charly Records. Dist: Charly, Cadillac, Swift

LP: released on Cambra, Feb'85 by Cambra Records. Dist: Celtic Music

Cass: released on Cambra, Feb'85 by Cambra Records. Dist: Celtic Music

YARDBIRDS, THE Featuring Eric Clapton (Yardbirds Music).
LP: released on Charly, Mar'83 by Charly Records. Dist: Charly, Cadillac, Swift

CARRYING MINE.
Single 7": released on Racket, Feb'87 Dist: Rough Trade

Single 12": released on Racket, Feb'87 Dist: Rough Trade

GET HIGH.
Tracks: / Get high
Single 12": released on Skysaw, '86 by Skysaw Records. Dist: Red Rhino, Cartel

Yarrow, Mick

TRISH TRASH.
Single 7": released on Baskerville, Jan'85 Dist: Pinnacle

Yasmin

I CAN'T FORGET.
Tracks: / I can't forget / Life surrounds me
Single 7": released on Total Control, '86

Single 12": released on Total Control, '86

Yates, Chris

DAY IN BED, A.
LP: released on Crepescule, Dec'86 by Island Records. Dist: Polygram, Pinnacle

FBI.
Tracks: / Wandering stranger
Single 7": released on Les Disques Du Crepuscule(Belgium), Dec'86 by Les Disques Du Crepuscule (Belgium). Dist: Rough Trade, Pinnacle, Island, Polygram

PARODY OF ME.
Tracks: / Parody of me / Parody of me (inst)
Single 7": released on Les Disques Du Crepus-

cule(Belgium), 13 Jun'87 by Les Disques Du Crepuscule (Belgium). Dist: Rough Trade, Pinnacle, Island, Polygram

Yates, Tom

SONG OF THE SHIMMERING WAY.
LP: released on Satril, Apr'77 by Satril Records. Dist: PRT

Yaz Kaz

EGG OF PURANA.
LP: released on Gravavision (USA), '85 by Gramavision Records (USA). Dist: Celtic Music, IMS, Polygram

Yazoo

DON'T GO.
Single 7": released on Mute, Jul'82 Dist: Spartan, Rough Trade, Cartel

Single 12": released on Mute, Jul'82 Dist: Spartan, Rough Trade, Cartel

EUROPE IN THE YEAR ZERO
(Yazoo/Various Artists).
Single 12": released on Sexual Phonograph, Aug'82 by Sexual Phonograph Records.

NOBODY'S DIARY.
Single 7": released on Mute, Apr'83 Dist: Spartan, Rough Trade, Cartel

Single 12": released on Mute, Apr'83 Dist: Spartan, Rough Trade, Cartel

ONLY YOU.
Single 7": released on Mute, May'82 Dist: Spartan, Rough Trade, Cartel

Single 12": released on Mute, May'82 Dist: Spartan, Rough Trade, Cartel

OTHER SIDE OF LOVE.
Single 7": released on Mute, Nov'82 Dist: Spartan, Rough Trade, Cartel

UPSTAIRS AT ERIC'S.
Recording Notes: Includes US remixes: Situation/The other side of midnight.
CD: released on Mute, Jan'87 Dist: Spartan, Rough Trade, Cartel

LP: released on Mute, '83 Dist: Spartan, Rough Trade, Cartel

Cass: released on Mute, '83 Dist: Spartan, Rough Trade, Cartel

YOU AND ME BOTH.
LP: released on Mute, Jul'83 Dist: Spartan, Rough Trade, Cartel

Cass: released on Mute, Jul'83 Dist: Spartan, Rough Trade, Cartel

CD: released on Vogue(France), '86 Dist: Discovery, Jazz Music, Swift

Yeah Jazz

JULIE & THE SEALIONS.
Special: released on Distinctive, Jun'84 by Distinctive Records. Dist: Distinctive Records
Media Note: Cassette single.

SHARON.
Tracks: / Sharon / Girl the years were kind to, The / This is not love
Single 7": released on Anagram, Nov'87 by Cherry Red Records. Dist: Pinnacle

Single 12": released on Anagram, Nov'87 by Cherry Red Records. Dist: Pinnacle

SHE SAID.
Tracks: / She said / Rain / Travel Scrabble
Single 7": released on Upright, '86 by Upright Records. Dist: Cartel, Rough Trade, Pinnacle

Single 12": released on Upright, '86 by Upright Records. Dist: Cartel, Rough Trade, Pinnacle

THIS IS NOT LOVE.
Tracks: / This is not love / This is not love / Any day / Childish games / Bob's song
Single 7": released on Upright, '86 by Upright Records. Dist: Cartel, Rough Trade, Pinnacle

Single 12": released on Upright, '86 by Upright Records. Dist: Cartel, Rough Trade, Pinnacle

Yeah yesh noh

BEWARE THE WEAKLING LINES.
Single 7": released on In Tape, Oct'84 by In Tape Records. Dist: Red Rhino, Cartel

COTTAGE INDUSTRY.
LP: released on In Tape, Jun'84 by In Tape Records. Dist: Red Rhino, Cartel

CUTTING THE HEAVENLY LAWN OF GREATNESS.
LP: released on In Tape, Sep'85 by In Tape Records. Dist: Red Rhino, Cartel

FUN ON THE LAWN LAWN LAWN.
LP: released on Buggum, '86 Dist: Red Rhino, Cartel

MRS. QUILL.
Single 7": released on In Tape, Aug'85 by In

Tape Records. Dist: Red Rhino, Cartel

Single 12": released on In Tape, Aug'85 by In Tape Records. Dist: Red Rhino, Cartel

PRICK UP YOUR EARS.
Single 7": released on In Tape, Feb'85 by In Tape Records. Dist: Red Rhino, Cartel

TEMPLE OF CONVENIENCE.
Single 7": released on In Tape, Nov'85 by In Tape Records. Dist: Red Rhino, Cartel

Single 12": released on In Tape, Nov'85 by In Tape Records. Dist: Red Rhino, Cartel

WHEN I AM A BIG GIRL.
Special: released on In Tape, Apr'85 by In Tape Records. Dist: Red Rhino, Cartel Media Note: 45rpm album.

Year Of Living Dangerously

YEAR OF LIVING DANGEROUSLY Original Soundtrack.
LP: released on That's Entertainment, Jul'83 by That's Entertainment Records. Dist: Pinnacle

Yello

1980-1985 THE NEW MIX IN ONE GO.
Tracks: / Daily disco / Swing / Evening's young (The) / Pinball cha cha / I love you / Sometimes(Dr. Hirsch) / Base for Alec / Oh Yeah / Lost again / Tub dub / Angel no / Desire / Bananas to the beat / Koladi-ola / Domingo / Bostich / Live at the roxy
Recording Notes: This superb album has already sold well as an import and now is available as a genuine British release. Previously only release in Germany. Features their most popular tracks and hits. All are specially remixed and sequenced to tell the Yello story 1980-1985. Double Album-Double Cassette.
LP: released on Mercury, '86 by Phonogram Records. Dist: Polygram

Cass: released on Mercury, '86 by Phonogram Records. Dist: Polygram

CD: released on Mercury, '86 by Phonogram Records. Dist: Polygram

BIMBO.
Single 7": released on Do-It, Apr'81 by Do-It Records. Dist: Virgin, EMI

BOSTICH.
Single 7": released on Do-It, Sep'81 by Do-It Records. Dist: Virgin, EMI

CALL IT LOVE.
Single 7": released on Mercury, May'87 by Phonogram Records. Dist: Polygram

Single 12": released on Mercury, May'87 by Phonogram Records. Dist: Polygram

CLARO QUE SI.
LP: released on Do-It, Oct'81 by Do-It Records. Dist: Virgin, EMI

DESIRE.
Single 7": released on Elektra, Aug'85 by WEA Records. Dist: WEA

Single 12": released on Elektra, Aug'85 by WEA Records. Dist: WEA

FISHERS GAME.
Tracks: / Love at the Roxy
Single 7": released on Mercury, Nov'86 by Phonogram Records. Dist: Polygram

Single 12": released on Mercury, Nov'86 by Phonogram Records. Dist: Polygram

GOLDRUSH.
Tracks: / Goldrush / She's got a gun / Pinball cha cha / Vicious games
Single 7": released on Mercury, '86 by Phonogram Records. Dist: Polygram

Single 12": released on Mercury, '86 by Phonogram Records. Dist: Polygram

Single set: released on Mercury, '86 by Phonogram Records. Dist: Polygram

I LOVE YOU.
Single 7": released on Stiff, May'83

Single 12": released on Stiff, May'83

Pic disc 7": released on Stiff, Jul'83

LOST AGAIN.
Single 7": released on Stiff, Oct'83

Single 12": released on Stiff, Oct'83

Single set: released on Stiff, Oct'83

ONE SECOND.
Tracks: / Habanera, Le / Moon on ice / Call it love / Secret farida, Le / Hawaiian chance / Rhythm divine, The / Santiago / Goldrush / Dr Van Steiner / Si senor and the hairy grill
Recording Notes: Supported on vocals by Billy Mackenzie and Shirley Bassey on various tracks. Yello is Dieter Meier and Boris Blank.
LP: released on Mercury, Jun'87 by Phonogram Records. Dist: Polygram

---

Cass: released on Mercury, Jun'87 by Phonogram Records. Dist: Polygram

CD: released on Mercury, Jun'87 by Phonogram Records. Dist: Polygram

PINBALL CHA CHA.
Single 7": released on Do-It, Jun'82 by Do-It Records. Dist: Virgin, EMI

Single 12": released on Do-It, Jun'82 by Do-It Records. Dist: Virgin, EMI

RHYTHM DIVINE, THE.
Single 12": released on Rise, Aug'87 Dist: Pinnacle

SHE'S GOT A GUN.
Single 7": released on Do-It, Jan'82 by Do-It Records. Dist: Virgin, EMI

Single 12": released on Do-It, Jan'82 by Do-It Records. Dist: Virgin, EMI

SOLID PLEASURE.
LP: released on Do-It, '80 by Do-It Records. Dist: Virgin, EMI

STELLA.
LP: released on Elektra, Apr'85 by WEA Records. Dist: WEA

Cass: released on Elektra, Apr'85 by WEA Records. Dist: WEA

YELLO.
LP: released on Mercury, '86 by Phonogram Records. Dist: Polygram

Cass: released on Mercury, '86 by Phonogram Records. Dist: Polygram

CD: released on Mercury, '86 by Phonogram Records. Dist: Polygram

YOU GOTTA SAY YES TO ANOTHER EXCESS.
LP: released on Stiff, Apr'83

Yellow....

YELLOW, THE PURPLE & THE NANCY Various Artists (Various artists).
LP: released on Greensleeves, Jan'83 by Greensleeves Records. Dist: BMG, Jetstar, Spartan

Yellow Chair

CHRISTMAS SONG.
Single 7": released on Mosa, Dec'82 by Pinnacle

Yellow Dog

ESCAPE.
Single 7": released on Escape, Jul'81

Yellow Jackets

FOUR CORNERS.
Tracks: / Out of town / Wildlife / Sightseeing / Open road / Mile high / Past ports / Postcards / Room with a view / Geneva
LP: released on MCA, Jun'87 by MCA Records. Dist: Polygram

Cass: released on MCA, Jun'87 by MCA Records. Dist: Polygram

CD: released on MCA, Jun'87 by MCA Records. Dist: Polygram

MIRAGE A TROIS.
LP: released on WEA(France), Jul'85 by WEA Records. Dist: Swift, Celtic Music

SHADES.
LP: released on MCA, Feb'87 by MCA Records. Dist: Polygram

Cass: released on MCA, Feb'87 by MCA Records. Dist: Polygram

Yellow, Joe

LOVER TO LOVER.
Single 12": released on Calibre, Sep'83 by Calibre Records. Dist: PRT

Yellow Magic Orchestra

AFTER SERVICE.
LP: released on Alpha, Nov'84 by Alpha Records. Dist: Taylors, Gamut

RYDEEN.
Single 7": released on Alfa, Mar'82 Dist: CBS

SOLID STATE SURVIVOR (ALFA/CBS VERSION).
LP: released on Alfa, Mar'82 Dist: CBS

Cass: released on Alfa, Mar'82 Dist: CBS

Yellowman

BAD BOY SKANKING (Yellowman & Fathead).
LP: released on Greensleeves, Oct'82 by Greensleeves Records. Dist: BMG, Jetstar, Spartan

BIMBAM.
Single 12": released on Ethnic, Jun'84 Dist: Kingdom

BLUEBERRY HILL.
Tracks: / Blueberry hill
Single 7": released on Greensleeves, Aug'87 by Greensleeves Records. Dist: BMG, Jetstar, Spartan

CD: released on Greensleeves, Sep'87 by Greensleeves Records. Dist: BMG, Jetstar, Spartan

DIVORCED (Yellowman & Fathead).
LP: released on Burning Sounds, Jun'83 by Burning Sounds Records. Dist: Burning Sounds Records

Single 7": released on Burning Sounds, Nov'84 by Burning Sounds Records. Dist: Burning Sounds Records

GALONG GALONG GALONG.
LP: released on Greensleeves, Sep'85 by Greensleeves Records. Dist: BMG, Jetstar, Spartan

GIRL IS MAN (Yellowman & Peter Metro).
Single 12": released on CSA, Mar'84 by CSA Records. Dist: PRT, Jetstar, CSA

GREGORY FREE.
Single 12": released on Hawkeye, Nov'83 by Hawkeye Records. Dist: Hawkeye, Lightning (WEA) Distribution, Jetstar

HOLD ON TO YOUR WOMAN (Yellowman & Fathead).
Single 12": released on Greensleeves, Nov'82 by Greensleeves Records. Dist: BMG, Jetstar, Spartan

HOW TO KEEP A DANCE.
Single 12": released on Gee Gee, Sep'82 Dist: Jetstar

KING Y. MEETS THE MIGHTY J.W. (Yellowman & Josey Wales).
LP: released on Arrival, Feb'84 by Arrival Records. Dist: Revolver, Cartel

KING YELLOWMAN (Yellowman & Charlie Chaplin).
LP: released on CBS, Mar'84 by CBS Records. Dist: CBS Deleted '86.

Cass: released on CBS, Mar'84 by CBS Records. Dist: CBS

LIVE AT REGGAE SUNSPLASH.
LP: released on Vista Sounds, Feb'84 by Vista Sounds Records. Dist: Jetstar

LOVERS CORNER.
Single 12": released on Grimmben, Jul'82 Dist: Jetstar

LOVERS TAKE OVER.
Single 12": released on Plantation, Mar'82 Dist: Jetstar

MISTER YELLOWMAN.
LP: released on Greensleeves, Mar'82 by Greensleeves Records. Dist: BMG, Jetstar, Spartan

NOBODY MOVE - NOBODY GET HURT.
LP: released on Greensleeves, Sep'84 by Greensleeves Records. Dist: BMG, Jetstar, Spartan

Single 12": released on Jah Guidance, Apr'84 by Jah Guidance Records. Dist: Jetstar

OPERATION RADICATION.
Single 10": released on Pama, Jun'82 by Pama Records. Dist: Pama, Enterprise, Jetstar

RAT (Yellowman & Fathead).
Single 12": released on Greensleeves, Sep'82 by Greensleeves Records. Dist: BMG, Jetstar, Spartan

RIB IT.
Single 7": released on Bebo, Mar'84 by Bebo Records. Dist: Jetstar

RUB-A-DUB PARTNER.
Single 12": released on Hawkeye, Jul'83 by Hawkeye Records. Dist: Hawkeye, Lightning (WEA) Distribution, Jetstar

SENSIMILLA.
Single 12": released on Hawkeye, May'83 by Hawkeye Records. Dist: Hawkeye, Lightning (WEA) Distribution, Jetstar

STAY WITH ME.
Single 10": released on Pama, Jun'82 by Pama Records. Dist: Pama, Enterprise, Jetstar

STRONG ME STRONG.
Single 7": released on CBS, Apr'84 by CBS Records. Dist: CBS

Single 12": released on CBS, Apr'84 by CBS Records. Dist: CBS

TWO GIANTS CLASH (Yellowman & Josey Wales).
LP: released on Greensleeves, Jan'84 by Greensleeves Records. Dist: BMG, Jetstar, Spartan

WALKING JEWEL STONE.
LP: released on Power House, Jun'85 by Power

House Records. Dist: Jetstar

WRECK-A-PUMPA.
Single 12": released on Greensleeves, Jun'84 by Greensleeves Records. Dist: BMG, Jetstar, Spartan

YELLOW LIKE CHEESE.
CD: released on RAS(Real Authentic Sound), Jun'87 by Greensleeves Records. Dist: Greensleeves, BMG, Jetstar

LP: released on RAS(Real Authentic Sound), Jun'87 by Greensleeves Records. Dist: Greensleeves, BMG, Jetstar

Cass: released on RAS(Real Authentic Sound), Jun'87 by Greensleeves Records. Dist: Greensleeves, BMG, Jetstar

YELLOWMAN GET'S MARRIED.
Single 7": released on Greensleeves, May'82 by Greensleeves Records. Dist: BMG, Jetstar, Spartan

YELLOWMAN GOING TO THE CHAPEL.
LP: released on Greensleeves, '86 by Greensleeves Records. Dist: BMG, Jetstar, Spartan

YELLOWMAN MEETS CHARLIE CHAPLIN (Yellowman & Charlie Chaplin).
LP: released on Power House, '85 by Power House Records. Dist: Jetstar

YOU WRONG TO SEND COME CALL ME.
Single 12": released on Hitbound, Sep'82 by Hitbound Records. Dist: Jetstar

ZUNGGUSUNGGUSUNGGUSUNGGUSUNG.
CD: released on Greensleeves, Apr'87 by Greensleeves Records. Dist: BMG, Jetstar, Spartan

LP: released on Greensleeves, Jul'83 by Greensleeves Records. Dist: BMG, Jetstar, Spartan

ZUNGGUZUNGGUGUZUNGGUZENE
(Yellowman & Charlie Chaplin).
Single 12": released on Greensleeves, Jun'83 by Greensleeves Records. Dist: BMG, Jetstar, Spartan

Yemen Arabia

MUSIC FROM YEMEN ARABIA.
LP: released on Lyrichord(USA), Oct'81 by Lyrichord Records(USA). Dist: Flexitron Ltd., Roots

LP: released on Lyrichord(USA), Oct'81 by Lyrichord Records(USA). Dist: Flexitron Ltd., Roots

Yemm, Bryn

BRYN YEMM CHRISTMAS COLLECTION.
LP: released on Bay, Nov'84 by Bay Enterprises. Dist: PRT, Spartan, Swift, Taylors

Cass: released on Bay, Nov'84 by Bay Enterprises. Dist: PRT, Spartan, Swift, Taylors

EVENSONG.
Single 7": released on Sierra, Nov'84 by Sierra Records. Dist: WEA

HOW DO I LOVE THEE.
LP: released on Lifestyle, Nov'83 Dist: BMG

Cass: released on Lifestyle, Nov'83 Dist: BMG

Single 7": released on Lifestyle, Nov'83 Dist: BMG

LET THERE BE PEACE.
Tracks: / Lord's prayer (The) / Nearer my God to Thee / Turn,turn,turn / Jesu joy of mans desiring
LP: released on Word(UK), '86 by Word Records(UK)Ltd.., CBS

Cass: released on Word(UK), '86 by Word Records(UK)Ltd.., CBS

WILL YOU STILL LOVE ME TOMORROW (Yemm, Bryn & Ann).
LP: released on Bay, Sep'80 by Bay Enterprises. Dist: PRT, Spartan, Swift, Taylors

Yeoman of the Guard

YEOMAN OF THE GUARD (D'Oyly Carte Opera Company).
Double Album: released on Decca, '64 by Decca Records. Dist: Polygram

Yeow Band

ANYONE SEEN DENNIS.
Single 12": released on Rumble Productions, Sep'82

GIVE MY HEART AWAY.
Single 7": released on Rumble Productions, Oct'83

Single 12": released on Rumble Productions, Oct'83

PREPARE YOURSELF.
Single 7": released on Yeow, Apr'82 by Yeow Records. Dist: Yeow

Single 12": released on Yeow, Apr'82 by Yeow Records. Dist: Yeow

Yepes, Narciso

GUITAR.
LP: released on DGG, Mar'85 by Polydor Records. Dist: Polygram

WORLD OF SPANISH GUITAR.
LP: released on Decca, '72 by Decca Records. Dist: Polygram

Cass: released on Decca, '72 by Decca Records. Dist: Polygram

Yes

9012 LIVE.
Recording Notes: Number of tracks: 9. Type of recording: Live. Total playing time: 67 minutes.
VHS: released on Polygram, '86 by Polygram Records. Dist: Polygram

VHS: released on Channel 5, '87 Dist: W.H. Smiths

9012 LIVE-THE SOLOS.
Tracks: / Hold on / Si / Solly's beard / Soon / Changes / Amazing grace / Whitefish
LP: released on Atco, '86 by Atlantic Records. Dist: WEA

Cass: released on Atco, '86 by Atlantic Records. Dist: WEA

90125.
Tracks: / Owner of a lonely heart / Hold on / It can happen / Changes / Cinema / Leave it / Our song / City of love / Hearts
CD: by WEA Records. Dist: WEA, Swift, Celtic Music

LP: released on Atlantic, Nov'83 by WEA Records. Dist: WEA, Swift,

LEAVE IT (RE-MIX).
Cass: released on Atco, May'84 by Atlantic Records. Dist: WEA

Cass: released on Atlantic, Nov'83 by WEA Records. Dist: WEA, Swift, Celtic Music

AMERICA.
Single 7": released on Atlantic(Import), '80 by WEA Records. Dist: Pinnacle

BIG GENERATOR.
Tracks: / Rhythm of love / Big generator / Shoot high aim low / Almost like love / Love will find a way / Final eyes / I'm running / Holy lamb
LP: released on Atlantic, Aug'87 by WEA Records. Dist: WEA, Swift, Celtic Music

Cass: released on Atlantic, Aug'87 by WEA Records. Dist: WEA, Swift, Celtic Music

CD: released on Atlantic, Aug'87 by WEA Records. Dist: WEA, Swift, Celtic Music

CLASSIC YES.
Tracks: / Heart of the sunrise / Wonderous stories / Yours is no disgrace / Starship trooper / Long distance runaround / Fish / And you and I
CD: released on Atlantic, Dec'86 by WEA Records. Dist: WEA, Swift, Celtic Music

LP: released on Atlantic, Nov'81 by WEA Records. Dist: WEA, Swift, Celtic Music

LP: released on Atlantic, Nov'81 by WEA Records. Dist: WEA, Swift, Celtic Music

CLOSE TO THE EDGE.
Tracks: / Solid time of change / Total mass retain / I get up I get down / Seasons of man / And you and I / Cord of life / Eclipse / Preacher / Teacher / Siberian Khatru
CD: released on Atlantic, Dec'86 by WEA Records. Dist: WEA, Swift, Celtic Music

LP: released on Atlantic, '72 by WEA Records. Dist: WEA, Swift, Celtic Music

Cass: released on Atlantic, '72 by WEA Records. Dist: WEA, Swift, Celtic Music

DON'T KILL THE WHALE.
Single 7": released on Atlantic, Aug'78 by WEA Records. Dist: WEA, Swift, Celtic Music

FRAGILE.
Tracks: / Roundabout / Cans and Brahms / We have heaven / South side of the sky / Five per cent for nothing / Long distance runaround / Fish / Mood for a day / Heart of the sunrise
CD: released on Atlantic, Dec'86 by WEA Records. Dist: WEA, Swift, Celtic Music

LP: released on Atlantic, '71 by WEA Records. Dist: WEA, Swift, Celtic Music

Cass: released on Atlantic, '71 by WEA Records. Dist: WEA, Swift, Celtic Music

FRAGILE / CLOSE TO THE EDGE.
Cass: released on Atlantic, Oct'82 by WEA Records. Dist: WEA, Swift, Celtic Music

GOING FOR THE ONE.
LP: released on Atlantic, Jul'77 by WEA Records. Dist: WEA, Swift, Celtic Music

Cass: released on Atlantic, Jul'77 by WEA Records. Dist: WEA, Swift, Celtic Music

LOVE WILL FIND A WAY.
Tracks: / Love will find a way / Holy lamb
Single 7": released on Atlantic, Sep'87 by WEA Records. Dist: WEA, Swift, Celtic Music

Single 12": released on Atlantic, Sep'87 by WEA Records. Dist: WEA, Swift, Celtic Music

OWNER OF A LONELY HEART.
Single 7": released on Atlantic, Nov'83 by WEA Records. Dist: WEA, Swift, Celtic Music

Single 12": released on Atlantic, Nov'83 by WEA Records. Dist: WEA, Swift, Celtic Music

RELAYERS.
LP: released on Atlantic, Nov'74 by WEA Records. Dist: WEA, Swift, Celtic Music

Cass: released on Atlantic, Nov'74 by WEA Records. Dist: WEA, Swift, Celtic Music Deleted '87.

ROUNDABOUT.
Single 7": released on Atlantic, '80 by WEA Records. Dist: WEA, Swift, Celtic Music

TALES FROM TOPOGRAPHIC OCEANS.
Double Album: released on Atlantic, '73 by WEA Records. Dist: WEA, Swift, Celtic Music
Cat. no: **K 80001**
Cass. set: released on Atlantic, '73 by WEA Records. Dist: WEA, Swift, Celtic Music

TIME AND A WORD.
LP: released on Atlantic, '70 by WEA Records. Dist: WEA, Swift, Celtic Music

Cass: released on Atlantic, '70 by WEA Records. Dist: WEA, Swift, Celtic Music Deleted '87.

YES.
LP: released on Atlantic, '70 by WEA Records. Dist: WEA, Swift, Celtic Music

Cass: released on Atlantic, '70 by WEA Records. Dist: WEA, Swift, Celtic Music

YES ALBUM, THE.
CD: released on Atlantic, Jul'87 by WEA Records. Dist: WEA, Swift, Celtic Music

LP: released on Atlantic, '71 by WEA Records. Dist: WEA, Swift, Celtic Music

Cass: released on Atlantic, '71 by WEA Records. Dist: WEA, Swift, Celtic Music

YESSONGS.
CD: released on Atlantic, Feb'87 by WEA Records. Dist: WEA, Swift, Celtic Music

Yes Let's

CARRIED AWAY.
Single 7": released on Irrepressable, Oct'84 by Irrepressable. Dist: CBS

Single 12": released on Irrepressable, Oct'84 by Irrepressable. Dist: CBS

Yes Minister

YES MINISTER 2 Episodes of this very popular BBC television series.
LP: released on BBC, Nov'81 by BBC Records & Tapes. Dist: EMI

Cass: released on BBC, Nov'81 by BBC Records & Tapes. Dist: EMI

Yes No People

MR. JOHNSON.
Tracks: / Mr. Johnson / Help yourself / Adventures of Mr. Johnson, The*
Recording Notes: * Extra track on 12" version only.
Single 12": released on London, Oct'87 by London Records. Dist: Polygram **Media Note:** Includes The adventures of Mr. Johnson.

Single 7": released on London, Oct'87 by London Records. Dist: Polygram

Yes sir, that's my baby

YES SIR, THAT'S MY BABY Various artists (Various artists).
Tracks: / Whispering / April showers / Collegiate / Dinah / Good man is hard to find, A / Gimme a little kiss,will ya huh? / Deed I do / There'll be some changes made / Sunday / Yes sir,that's my baby / Mississippi Mud / My blue heaven / Deep night / Ain't misbehavin
Recording Notes: Mono. The Golden Years of Pan Alley: 1920-1929
LP: released on New World(USA), '86 by New World Records(USA). Dist: Conifer

Yesterday

YESTERDAY Various artists (Various artists).
LP: released on Audio Fidelity(USA), Mar'83 by Audio Fidelity(USA). Dist: PRT

YESTERDAY WHEN WE WERE YOUNG
Various artists (Various artists).
LP: released on Warwick, Nov'85 by Warwick Records. Dist: CBS, MSD, Taylors, Solomon & Peres **Media Note:** 3 LP Box Set(2 Double Play Cassettes)

Cass: released on Warwick, Nov'85 by Warwick Records. Dist: CBS, MSD, Taylors, Solomon & Peres **Media Note:** 2 Double Play Cassettes(3 LP Box Set).

Yesterday & Today

EARTHSHAKER.
LP: released on A&M, Jul'82 by A&M Records. Dist: Polygram

Yetties

LITTLE BIT OF DORSET, A.
LP: released on ASV(Academy Sound & Vision), Mar'81 by Academy Sound & Vision Records. Dist: Pinnacle

Cass: released on ASV(Academy Sound & Vision), Mar'81 by Academy Sound & Vision Records. Dist: Pinnacle

NELLIE THE ELEPHANT.
Single 7": released on ASV(Academy Sound & Vision), Mar'81 by Academy Sound & Vision Records. Dist: Pinnacle

OUR FRIENDS THE YETTIES.
Cass: released on Argo, '71 by Argo Records. Dist: Polygram

PROPER JOB, A.
LP: released on ASV(Academy Sound & Vision), Sep'81 by Academy Sound & Vision Records. Dist: Pinnacle

Cass: released on ASV(Academy Sound & Vision), Sep'81 by Academy Sound & Vision Records. Dist: Pinnacle

UP MARKET.
LP: released on Decca, '84 by Decca Records. Dist: Polygram

WORLD OF THE YETTIES, THE.
LP: released on Decca, '84 by Decca Records. Dist: Polygram

Cass: released on Argo, '84 by Argo Records. Dist: Polygram

YETTIES IN CONCERT.
LP: released on Decca, '84 by Decca Records. Dist: Polygram

YETTIES, (THE).
Tracks: / Over the hills & far away / Rabbit winter / John Barleycorn / Polka medley / I live not where I love / We've got oil / Sally the salvage queen / Man at the nore,(The) / Carolina moon / Beautiful dreamer / Bread & cheese & Kisses / Wave over wave / Long pond / Praise o'Dorset
LP: released on ASV(Academy Sound & Vision), May'86 by Academy Sound & Vision Records. Dist: Pinnacle

Yglesia, Francisco

SHIMMERING HARP.
LP: released on MFP, Feb'82 by Music Fo[r] Pleasure Records. Dist: EMI

Cass: released on MFP, Feb'82 by Music Fo[r] Pleasure Records. Dist: EMI

Yiddish Tailla

YIDDISH SONGS - VOL.2.
LP: released on Arion, May'79 Dist: Discovery

Yig Yuze

FACE, THE.
Single 7": released on Nudge Nudge, Feb'8[4] by Backs Records. Dist: Cartel*

Yip Yip Coyote

YIP YIP COYOTE.
LP: released on Illegal, Jun'84 by Faulty Pro[d]ucts Records. Dist: Pinnacle, Lightning, Carte[l]

Yo La Tengo

NEWWAVE HOTDOGS.
LP: released on Goes On, Nov'87 by Goes O[n] Records. Dist: Rough Trade, Cartel

RIDE THE TIGER.
LP: released on Shigaku, Feb'87 Dist: Roug[h] Trade, Cartel

Yoakam, Dwight

GUITARS, CADILLACS.
Tracks: / Ring of fire
Single 7": released on Warner Bros., Nov'8[6] by WEA Records. Dist: WEA

GUITARS, CADILLACS.ETC.ETC..
Tracks: / Honky tonk man / It won't hurt / I'll b[e] gone / South of Cincinatti / Bury me / Guitars,ca[dillacs] / Twenty years / Ring of fire / Miner['s] prayer / Heartaches by the number
LP: released on Reprise(USA), Apr'86 by WE[A] Records. Dist: Pinnacle

Cass: released on Reprise(USA), Apr'86 b[y] WEA Records. Dist: Pinnacle

CD: released on Reprise(USA), Jan'87 by WE[A] Records. Dist: Pinnacle

HILLBILLY DELUXE.
Tracks: / Little ways / Smoke along the track / Johnson's love / Please, please baby / Readin['] rightin', RT.23 / Always late with your kisses

1,000 miles / Throughout all times / Little sister / This drinking will kill me
LP: released on Reprise(USA), Jun'87 by WEA Records. Dist: Pinnacle

Cass: released on Reprise(USA), Jun'87 by WEA Records. Dist: Pinnacle

CD: released on Reprise(USA), Jun'87 by WEA Records. Dist: Pinnacle

LP: released on Reprise(USA), Apr'87 by WEA Records. Dist: Pinnacle

Cass: released on Reprise(USA), Apr'87 by WEA Records. Dist: Pinnacle

HONKY TONK MAN.
Tracks: / Honky tonk man / Miner's prayer / I'll be gone*
Single 7": released on Warner Bros., Jul'86 by WEA Records. Dist: WEA

Single 12": released on Warner Bros., Jul'86 by WEA Records. Dist: WEA

LITTLE SISTER.
Tracks: / Little sister / This drinking will kill me / Hnky tonk man (live) / Cadillacs (live)
Single 7": released on Warner Bros., May'87 by WEA Records. Dist: WEA

Single 12": released on Warner Bros., May'87 by WEA Records. Dist: WEA

Yobs

YOBS CHRISTMAS ALBUM.
.P: released on Safari, '81 by Safari Records. Dist: Pinnacle

YOBS ON 45 Christmas medley.
Single 7": released on Fresh, Dec'81 Dist: Jetstar

Yodelling Hoovers

HAIRY THING IN PLASTIC BAG, A.
Single 7": released on Dubious, Oct'79 by Lobster Factory. Dist: Rough Trade

Yokels

'ER WE BE.
.P: released on Sweet Folk, May'81 Dist: Roots

Yonco, Frank

OLD GREYHOUND (Yonco, Frank And The Everglades).
.P: released on Sweet Folk, May'81 Dist: Roots

York

'S ON ME.
racks: / It's on me / Don't stop / You are everything*
ingle 7": released on Spartan, Mar'86 by Spartan Records. Dist: Spartan

ingle 7": released on Spartan, Mar'86 by Spartan Records. Dist: Spartan

IEW.
P: released on Spartan, Oct'85 by Spartan Records. Dist: Spartan

LAIN AS BLACK AND WHITE.
ingle 7": released on Spartan, Oct'85 by Spartan Records. Dist: Spartan

ingle 12": released on Spartan, Oct'85 by Spartan Records. Dist: Spartan

York, Barbara

LOSE TO YOU.
ingle 7": released on Banana, Mar'84 Dist: nnacle, Fresh

ingle 12": released on Banana, Mar'84 Dist: nnacle, Fresh

ork Minster Choir

HRISTMAS AT YORK MINSTER.
: released on Polydor, Nov'76 by Polydor ecords. Dist: Polygram

ass: released on Polydor, Nov'76 by Polydor ecords. Dist: Polygram

USIC FOR EASTER.
: released on Abbey, Jul'78 by Abbey Recs. Dist: PRT, Taylors, Gamut

ork, Nola

LES AWAY/ SWEET DESIRE.
igle 7": released on Aggro, Sep'82 by Chan-Records.

ork, Rusty

CK'N'ROLL MEMORIES.
: released on Jewel, Jul'79 Dist: Red Rhino, rtel

ork Waits

USIC FROM THE TIME OF RICHARD
cording Notes: Dance music from a variety medieval instruments from this spirited re-ssance town band.
: released on Saydisc, Oct'87 by Saydisc cords. Dist: Taylors, Jazz Music, Swift, Pro-tion, Essex, Gamut, Harmonia Mundi, Celtic sic

Cass: released on Saydisc, Oct'87 by Saydisc Records. Dist: Taylors, Jazz Music, Swift, Projection, Essex, Gamut, Harmonia Mundi, Celtic Music

Yorke, Janice

DISTANT SHORES/ THE WIND TALKING TO THE PINES/ JODIE.
Single 7": released on SRT, Jul'82 by SRT Records. Dist: Projection, Solomon & Peres, SRT, Pinnacle

Yorke, Peter

MOOD FOR LOVE.
LP: released on World, Feb'84 by EMI Records(UK). Dist: Conifer

Cass: released on Retrospect, Feb'84 by EMI Records(UK). Dist: EMI

Yorkshire Dialect Society

FIRST O'T SORT.
LP: released on Trailer, '81, Projection, Swift, Celtic Music, Cadillac, Ross, Duncans, Impetus

Yorkshire Garland

TROTTING TO LANE.
LP: released on Rubber, May'83 by Rubber Records. Dist: Projection, Roots, Jazz Music, Celtic Music, Spartan

Yorkshire Imperial Band

CONCERTO.
LP: released on Polyphonic, Oct'82 by Polyphonic Reproductions Ltd.. Dist: Taylors, Polyphonic

Cass: released on Polyphonic, Oct'82 by Polyphonic Reproductions Ltd.. Dist: Taylors, Polyphonic

MR SMITH'S PERENNIAL FAVOURITES.
LP: released on Polyphonic, Sep'80 by Polyphonic Reproductions Ltd.. Dist: Taylors, Polyphonic

Cass: released on Polyphonic, Sep'80 by Polyphonic Reproductions Ltd.. Dist: Taylors, Polyphonic

MUSIC OF NOEL GAY, THE.
LP: released on MFP, Sep'84 by Music For Pleasure Records. Dist: EMI

Cass: released on MFP, Sep'84 by Music For Pleasure Records. Dist: EMI

Yosser's Gang

GIS A JOB/ MAGGIE'S ECONOMIC POLICY.
Single 7": released on Rialto, Dec'82 by Rialto Records. Dist: Pinnacle

Single 12": released on Rialto, Dec'82 by Rialto Records. Dist: Pinnacle

You

SHE'S MINE/ HIGH WIRE.
Single 7": released on Allstars, Sep'83 Dist: Spartan

YOU FOUND THE VOCAL GROUP SOUND PART 1 Various artists (You Found The Vocal Group Sound).
LP: released on Solid Smoke(USA), Feb'85 Dist: Rhino

YOU FOUND THE VOCAL GROUP SOUND PART 3 Various artists (You Found The Vocal Group Sound).
YOU FOUND THE VOCAL GROUP SOUND PART 2 Various artists (You Found The Vocal Group Sound).
LP: released on Solid Smoke(USA), Feb'85 Dist: Rhino

LP: released on Solid Smoke(USA), Feb'85 Dist: Rhino

You Bet...

YOU BET WE'VE GOT SOMETHING AGAINST YOU Various artists (Various artists).
Recording Notes: Inc: Princess Tinymeat, Sonic Youth, Fini Tribe
LP: released on Cathexis, Jun'86 by Cathexis Records. Dist: Fast Forward, Cartel

You can't hurry love

YOU CAN'T HURRY LOVE All the greatest love songs of the last 25 years (Various artists).
Tracks: / Where did our love go / Baby love / Stop! In the name of love / You can't hurry love / Love is here and now you're gone / Love child / Stoned love / I was made to love her / I could never love another (after loving you) / Just my imagination (running away with me) / Ain't no mountain high enough / Love hangover / How sweet it is (to be loved by you) / Baby I need your loving / Sweet love / All this love / Endless love
CD: released on Motown, Mar'87 by Motown Records. Dist: BMG

You Heard It Here First

YOU HEARD IT HERE FIRST Various artists (Various artists).
LP: released on Capitol, Sep'85 by Capitol Records. Dist: EMI

Cass: released on Capitol, Sep'85 by Capitol Records. Dist: EMI

You & I

SHADY LADY/ I WANT TO BE WITH YOU.
Single 7": released on Steiner, Sep'81

You Must Be Joking

I'M A HOORAY HENRY.
Tracks: / I'm a hooray Henry
Single 12": released on Hooray, Jan'86 by Hooray Records. Dist: Spartan

You Only Live Twice

YOU ONLY LIVE TWICE Original film soundtrack.
LP: released on EMI(Germany), '83 by EMI Records(UK). Dist: Pinnacle

Youmans, Vincent

THROUGH THE YEARS WITH VINCENT YOUMANS.
Recording Notes: Double album with Millie Slavin, Nolan Van Way, Ellie & Bob Quint, Paul True blood, Rita Segree.
Double Album: released on Retrospect, Jan'87 by EMI Records(UK). Dist: EMI

Young at heart

YOUNG AT HEART Musical (Various artists).
Recording Notes: Stars Doris Day & Frank Sinatra
VHS: released on Video Collection, May'87 by Video Collection International Ltd.. Dist: Counterpoint **Media Note:** 115 minutes.

Young Bloods

POINT REYES STATION.
LP: released on Edsel, Oct'87 by Demon Records. Dist: Celtic Music, Pinnacle, Jazz Music

Young, Bob

IN QUO COUNTRY.
Tracks: / Down down / Caroline / Living on a island / Mean girl
LP: released on Making Waves, Jul'86 by Celtic Music. Dist: Celtic Music

Cass: released on Making Waves, Jul'86 by Celtic Music. Dist: Celtic Music

MEAN GIRL.
Tracks: / Mean girl / Living on an island
Single 7": released on Making Waves, Jun'86 by Celtic Music. Dist: Celtic Music

Young & Co

I LIKE (WHAT YOU'RE DOING TO ME).
Single 7": released on Excaliber, Oct'80 by Red Bus Records. Dist: PRT

Single 12": released on Excaliber, Oct'80 by Red Bus Records. Dist: PRT

Young & Company

STRUT YOUR SEXY STUFF LADY.
Single 7": released on Excaliber, Mar'81 by Red Bus Records. Dist: PRT

Single 12": released on Excaliber, Mar'81 by Red Bus Records. Dist: PRT

Young, Dennis De

DESERT MOON.
LP: released on A&M, Sep'84 by A&M Records. Dist: Polygram

Cass: released on A&M, Sep'84 by A&M Records. Dist: Polygram

Young, Devaney

SECOND CHANCE.
Single 7": released on Ryker, Aug'84 by Ryker Records. Dist: CBS

Young, Edwin

CHIEF CRAZY.
LP: released on Chief Crazy, Jul'87 Dist: Jetstar

Young, Eldridge, Edison

LAUGHIN'.
LP: released on Verve, Jan'82 by Phonogram Records. Dist: IMS, Polygram

Young, Faron

FOUR IN THE MORNING.
Tracks: / It's four in the morning / If you ain't lovin'(you ain't livin') / All right / Three days / Sweet dreams / Goin' steady / Hello walls / Backtrack / Wine me up / Your times comin' / I miss you already / This little girl of mine
LP: released on Topline, Sep'86 by Charly Records.

Cass: released on Topline, Sep'86 by Charly Records.

SHERIFF, THE.
LP: released on Allegience, Apr'84 by PRT Records.

Cass: released on Allegience, Apr'84 by PRT Records.

TALK ABOUT HITS.
Tracks: / Don't let the stars get in your eyes / I'll go on alone / Almost / Mom and Dad's waltz / I don't hurt anymore / Chattanooga shoeshine boy / Hey good looking / Bouquet of roses / Slowly / Tennessee waltz / Making believe / Bimbo

LP: released on Stetson, Sep'87 by Hasmick Promotions Ltd.. Dist: Counterpoint, Taylors, Swift, Wellard, Jazz Music

Cass: released on Stetson, Sep'87 by Hasmick Promotions Ltd.. Dist: Counterpoint, Taylors, Swift, Wellard, Jazz Music

TOP COUNTRY FRIEND.
LP: released on Bulldog Records, Jul'82 Dist: President, Jazz Music, Taylors, Spartan

SWEETHEARTS OR STRANGERS.
LP: released on Stetson, Oct'86 by Hasmick Promotions Ltd.. Dist: Counterpoint, Taylors, Swift, Wellard, Jazz Music

Cass: released on Stetson, Oct'86 by Hasmick Promotions Ltd.. Dist: Counterpoint, Taylors, Swift, Wellard, Jazz Music

Young Fresh Fellows

MEN WHO LOVED MUSIC.
LP: released on Walkthrufyre(USA), Aug'87 Dist: Pinnacle

Young, George

CHANT.
Tracks: / Chant / Reggie / Leetah / Chinos y criollas / Snake, (The) / Ode to a friend.(Sidney Bechet)
Recording Notes: Fusion jazz group led by New York Sax player George Young. Material is mainly Latin in flavour, interspersed with straight ahead Jazz. Personnel: George Young-tenor,alto, and soprano saxes, sopranino, flute, bass flute./Lewis Del Gatto- tenor & soprano saxes, flute./John Tropea- guitar./Pasquale Pratta-piano./Peter Philips-DX7./Tony marino-Bass./Grant Jarrett-Drums./Rbbena Bassini-percussion./Sue Evans-Mallets & percussion./Sammy Figuueroa-congas & percussion./Warren berhardt-electric piano.
LP: released on King (Japan), Jul'86 Dist: IMS, Polygram

Young Gods

DID YOU MISS ME.
Tracks: / Hello hello I'm back again / Did you miss me / Irrtum boys (The)
Single 12": released on Organik, Apr'87 Dist: Red Rhino, Cartel

Single 7": released on Product Inc., Apr'87 Dist: Rough Trade, Cartel

YOUNG GODS.
LP: released on Product Inc., Jul'87 Dist: Rough Trade, Cartel

Young, Gordon

ACCORDIAN TODAY.
LP: released on Lochshore, Jul'82 by Klub Records. Dist: Musac(Scotland)Ltd.

Cass: released on Lochshore, Jul'82 by Klub Records. Dist: Musac(Scotland)Ltd.

DANCING FINGERS.
LP: released on Lochshore, Apr'81 by Klub Records. Dist: Musac(Scotland)Ltd.

Cass: released on Lochshore, Apr'81 by Klub Records. Dist: Musac(Scotland)Ltd.

Young Holt unlimited

WACK WACK.
LP: released on Kent, Dec'86 by Kent Records. Dist: Pinnacle, Cadillac, Jazz Music

Young, James

BEHIND THE BARRICADES.
Tracks: / Behind the barricades / Latest news,The / I'm a Belfast beauty / Ireland in the sun / Ugliest woman in Ireland,The / Why some people go to church / Holidays in bangor / Belfast chambermaid,A / Glentoran supporter,The / Gas meter man,The / We emigrated / I eat all I can
LP: released on Emerald(Ireland), Oct'81 by Emerald Records. Dist: I & B, Ross, Solomon & Peres

Cass: released on Emerald(Ireland), Oct'81 by Emerald Records. Dist: I & B, Ross, Solomon & Peres

BEHIND THE BARRIERS.
LP: released on Emerald, Nov'84 by Emerald Records. Dist: PRT, Solomon & Peres, Ross

Cass: released on Emerald, Nov'84 by Emerald Records. Dist: PRT, Solomon & Peres, Ross

CITY SLICKER (Young,James(J.Y.)/Jan Hammer).
Tracks: / City slicker / Something to remember you by / Waiting / Still feel your love / Chain me down / No mistake / Prisoner of war / Wild dogs in the night / Empty promises
LP: released on FM, May'86 by FM-Revolver Records. Dist: BMG

Cass: released on FM, May'86 by FM-Revolver Records. Dist: BMG

JAMES YOUNG.
Tracks: / Meet James Young / Smithfield Market / Orange Lily / Behind the barricades / Presentation, The / Gerry's walls / Boy finds out the facts, A / Balleymena cowboy / TV commercial / I believe in Ulster / I married a Papist / Carpenter Crimmond / Stranger, The / Ould "black

man", The / Wee Davy / Slum clearance / Feud, The
Double Album: released on Emerald, Oct'81 by Emerald Records. Dist: PRT, Solomon & Peres, Ross

Cass. set: released on Emerald, Oct'81 by Emerald Records. Dist: PRT, Solomon & Peres, Ross

MEET JAMES YOUNG.
Double Album: released on Emerald, Nov'75 by Emerald Records. Dist: PRT, Solomon & Peres, Ross

YOUNG AT HEART.
Tracks: / Meets james young / T.V.commercial / Year 2001,(The) / I loved a parish / Boy finds out the facts,(A) / Slum clearance / On the hunt / Why am I here
LP: released on Emerald(Ireland), Jun'85 by Emerald Records. Dist: I & B, Ross, Solomon & Peres

Cass: released on Emerald, Nov'87 by Emerald Records. Dist: PRT, Solomon & Peres, Ross

YOUNG ULSTERMAN,THE.
Tracks: / Me mammy / Mr Thompson goes to Dublin / Young Ulsterman looks for a job,The / Saint Patrick / Orange Lily / History lesson,The / Romeo and Juliet / Man from Ballymena,The / We're here for such a little time
LP: released on Emerald(Ireland), Jun'86 by Emerald Records. Dist: I & B, Ross, Solomon & Peres

Cass: released on Emerald, Nov'87 by Emerald Records. Dist: PRT, Solomon & Peres, Ross

Young Jessie

HIT GIT & SPLIT.
LP: released on Ace, Sep'82 by Ace Records. Dist: PRT, Pinnacle, Celtic Music, Cadillac, Jazz Music, Wellard

SHUFFLE IN THE GRAVEL.
LP: released on Mr.R&B, Oct'86 Dist: Counterpoint, Celtic Music, Jazz Music, Swift

SHUFFLIN' AND JIVIN'.
LP: released on Ace, Sep'87 by Ace Records. Dist: PRT, Pinnacle, Celtic Music, Cadillac, Jazz Music, Wellard

Young, Jimmy

OUR JIMMY : THE BEST OF JIMMY YOUNG Video.
Recording Notes: Released on BBC/Screen Legends

TIMES ARE TIGHT.
Single 7": released on Nite Life, Apr'83

TOO YOUNG.
LP: released on PRT, Jan'81 by PRT Records. Dist: PRT

Cass: released on PRT, Jan'81 by PRT Records. Dist: PRT

TWO HEADS ARE BETTER THAN ONE/ BEER IS BEST (Young, Jimmy & Terry Wogan).
Single 7": released on Paramount, Nov'83 by Paramount Records.

UNCHAINED MELODIES Four stars of the 50's (Young, Jimmy/Lita Roza/Dickie Valentine/Joan Regan).
Tracks: / You make me feel so young / You're getting to be a habit with me / Eternally (limelight) / Hold me, thrill me, kiss me / Isle of Innisfree, The / Faith can move mountains / I'll never be the same / Unchained melody / Man from Laramie, The / I'm walking behind you / Secret love / P.S. I love you / Hey there / You've changed / Love is beautiful stranger / No one / Joey / Fools rush in / It could happen to you / Man in the raincoat, The / Kiss to build a dream on, A / Somebody loves me / It had to be you / I can't give you anything but love / Sunday / There'll be some changes made / Don't leave me now / One I love, The (belongs to somebody else) / Clown who cried, The / I see you again every night / I'll close my eyes / Two kinds of tears / I know why (and so do you) / That old feeling / For all we know / Blue bells of broadway, The / Till I waltz again with you / I know for sure / Someone else's roses / Tani
Recording Notes: See also under Lita Rosa or Dickie Valentine or Joan Regan.
Double Album: released on Decca(London), Mar'87 by Decca Records. Dist: Polygram, IMS

Cass: released on Decca(London), Mar'87 by Decca Records. Dist: Polygram, IMS **Media Note:** This is a double cassette.

WHAT A WONDERFUL WORLD.
LP: released on Flashback, Nov'85 by Flashback Records/PRT Records. Dist: Mainline

Cass: released on Flashback, Nov'85 by Flashback Records/PRT Records. Dist: Mainline

Young, John Paul

LOVE IS IN THE AIR/ LOVE YOU SO BAD IT HURTS.
Single 7": released on Old Gold, Jul'82 by Old Gold Records. Dist: PRT, Counterpoint, Lightning, Jazz Music, Taylors

Young, Jonathon

BOUND FOR MEXICO (Young,Jonathon & Supporters).
Single 7": released on Ritz-Homespun, Mar'86 Dist: Outlet, Spartan, Record Services(Ireland), Roots, Prism, Celtic Music, Solomon & Peres

Cassingle: released on Ritz-Homespun, Mar'86 Dist: Outlet, Spartan, Record Services(Ireland), Roots, Prism, Celtic Music, Solomon & Peres

Young, Karen

HOT SHOT.
Tracks: / Hot shot remixed
Single 12": released on Streetwave, Jan'87 Dist: BMG

LP: released on Atlantic, May'79 by WEA Records. Dist: WEA, Swift, Celtic Music

I'M HOT FOR YOU.
Single 7": released on Design Communications, Sep'83 by Design Sound & Vision. Dist: Design Sound & Vision

Single 12": released on Design Communications, Sep'83 by Design Sound & Vision. Dist: Design Sound & Vision

NOBODY'S CHILD.
Single 7": released on Old Gold, Sep'85 by Old Gold Records. Dist: PRT, Counterpoint, Lightning, Jazz Music, Taylors

THOUSAND STARS, A/ ANGEL BABY (Young, Karen & The Innocents).
Single 7": released on Revival, Jul'82 Dist: Lightning, Swift

YOU DON'T KNOW WHAT YOU'VE GOT.
Single 7": released on Firebird, Jun'83 by Pinnacle Records. Dist: Pinnacle

Single 12": released on Firebird, Jun'83 by Pinnacle Records. Dist: Pinnacle

Young, La Monte

THEATRE OF ETERNAL MUSIC.
LP: released on Shandar, Mar'78 Dist: Projection

Young, Larry

UNITY.
Tracks: / Zoltah / Monk's dream / If / Moontrane,The / Softly as a morning sunsrise / Beyond all limits
Recording Notes: Produced by Alfred Lion.(P) 1986 Manhattan Records,a division of Capitol RecordsInc.Larry Young was a superb organist who could play with the best of Jimmy Smith's disciples in the Blues and Funk groove.But he chose to go one step further and introduce to the organ the more progressive school of Modern Jazz.With a stunning cast of Trumpeter Peter Woody Shaw,Tenor Saxophonist Joe Henderson and Drummer Elvin Jones.Young hits his zenith with this album,which has become an underground classic among proffesional musicians who understand the influence that it had on the music of the day.Highlights include Woody Shaw's 'The Moontrane',Henderson's 'If' and a magnificent organ-drums duet on Thelonius Monk's 'Monk's Dream'.
LP: released on Blue Note, May'86 by EMI Records(UK). Dist: EMI

Young, Lester

1943 See also under Coleman Hawkins.
LP: released on Joker, '87 Dist: Counterpoint, Cadillac, Jazz Horizons, Jazz Music, Celtic Music

Cass: released on Joker, '87 Dist: Counterpoint, Cadillac, Jazz Horizons, Jazz Music, Celtic Music

COMPLETE SAVOY RECORDINGS.
Tracks: / Blue lester / Ghost of a chance / June bug / Indiana / Basie english / Jump lester jump / Crazy over J-Z / Ding dong / Blues 'n' belles / Circus in rhythm / Poor little plaything / Exercise in swing / Salute to fats / Tush / These foolish things
Recording Notes: Artists include:Joe Newman,Ted Donelly,Clyde Hart,Cozy Cole,Count Basie and Roy Haynes.These are really are 'the complete'Young Savoy recordings,incorporating various takes of classics like 'Ghost Of A Chance' and 'Poor Little Plaything',complete with matrix numbers of each title:a collectors dream,this one.Sessions recorded April and May 1944,June 1949.
Double Album: released on Savoy Jazz, Dec'85 by RCA Records (Germany). Dist: Conifer, Discovery

GENIUS OF LESTER YOUNG, THE.
Double Album: released on Verve, Jun'75 by Phonogram Records. Dist: IMS, Polygram

IN PARIS.
LP: released on Polydor, Aug'81 by Polydor Records. Dist: Polygram

IN WASHINGTON D.C. 1956.
LP: released on Pablo(USA), '82 by Ace Records. Dist: PRT

Cass: released on Pablo(USA), '82 by Ace Records. Dist: PRT

IN WASHINGTON D.C. - VOL.2.
LP: released on Pablo(USA), '82 by Ace Records. Dist: PRT

Cass: released on Pablo(USA), '82 by Ace Records. Dist: PRT

IN WASHINGTON D.C. - VOL.3.
LP: released on Pablo(USA), '82 by Ace Records. Dist: PRT

Cass: released on Pablo(USA), '82 by Ace Records. Dist: PRT

IN WASHINGTON D.C. - VOL.4.
LP: released on Pablo(USA), '82 by Ace Records. Dist: PRT

Cass: released on Pablo(USA), '82 by Ace Records. Dist: PRT

JAZZ GIANTS,THE.
CD: released on Polydor, Aug'86 by Polydor Records. Dist: Polygram

LESTER AMADEUS With Count Basie.
LP: released on Nostalgia(Sweden), Oct'82 Dist: Wellard, Jazz Music

LP: released on Chase Music, Nov'84 by Chase Records. Dist: Pinnacle

Cass: released on Chase Music, Nov'84 by Chase Records. Dist: Pinnacle

LESTER LEAPS.
Tracks: / Saxy blues / I cover the waterfront / These foolish things remind me of you / Lester leaps / Lovers leap / Leap frog
LP: released on Star Jazz(USA), Apr'86 by Charly Records. Dist: Charly

Cass: released on Star Jazz(USA), Apr'86 by Charly Records. Dist: Charly

LESTER LEAPS AGAIN.
Double Album: released on Affinity, Feb'82 by Charly Records. Dist: Charly, Cadillac, Swift

LESTER LEAPS IN.
LP: released on Jazz Live, Apr'81 Dist: Jazz Music, Jazz Horizons, Cadillac

LESTER MEETS MILES,M.J.O. & JACK TEAGARDEN ALL STARS.
LP: released on Unique Jazz, Apr'81 Dist: Swift, Jazz Music, Jazz Horizons, Cadillac

LESTER YOUNG.
LP: released on Giants of Jazz, Sep'87 by Hasmick Promotions Ltd.. Dist: Counterpoint, Taylors, Wellard, Swift, Crusader, Jazz Music

LESTER YOUNG & COLEMAN HAWKINS.
LP: released on Spotlite, '83 by Spotlite Records. Dist: Cadillac, Jazz Music, Spotlite

LESTER YOUNG STORY - VOL.5.
LP: released on CBS, Sep'80 by CBS Records. Dist: CBS

LESTER YOUNG - VOL.1.
LP: released on Jazz Reactivation, Jan'82

LESTER YOUNG - VOL.2.
LP: released on Jazz Reactivation, Jul'83

LESTER YOUNG - VOL.3.
LP: released on Jazz Reactivation, May'83

MASTERS OF JAZZ VOL.7.
LP: released on Storyville, May'86 by Storyville Records. Dist: Swift, Wellard

ON THE AIR.
LP: released on Queendisc(Italy), Apr'81 Dist: Celtic Music, Cadillac, Jazz Horizons

PRES AT HIS VERY BEST.
LP: released on Philips, Oct'83 Dist: IMS-Polygram

PRES LIVES.
LP: released on Savoy(France), Oct'85 Dist: Discovery

PRES & TEDDY (Young, Lester & Teddy Wilson).
CD: released on Polydor, Feb'87 by Polydor Records. Dist: Polygram

PRES - VOL.3.
LP: released on Pablo(USA), Sep'81 by Ace Records. Dist: PRT

Cass: released on Pablo(USA), Sep'81 by Ace Records. Dist: PRT

PRESS, THE.
LP: released on Audio Fidelity(USA), Sep'84 by Audio Fidelity(USA). Dist: PRT

PREZ AND FRIENDS (Young,Lester & The Kansas City Six).
LP: released on Commodore Class, May'87 by Teldec Records (Germany). Dist: Conifer, IMS, Polygram

PREZ & COMPLETE SAVOY RECORDS.
LP: released on Savoy, Sep'78 Dist: Swift, Jazz Music, Taylors

PREZ & FRIENDS.
LP: released on Commodore Class, Jul'82 by Teldec Records (Germany). Dist: Conifer, IMS, Polygram

PREZ - VOL.IV.
LP: released on Pablo(USA), Dec'81 by Ace Records. Dist: PRT

Cass: released on Pablo(USA), Dec'81 by Ace Records. Dist: PRT

LP: released on Verve(USA), Mar'83 by Polydor Records. Dist: Polygram

SAVOY RECORDINGS.
Tracks: / Circus in rhythm / Poor little plaything / These foolish things / Exercise in swing / Salute to Fats / Basie English / Blue Lester / I don't stand a ghost of a chance / Indianna / Crazy over J-Z / Jump Lester jump / Ding dong / Blues'n'bells / June bug
CD: released on RCA, Nov'86 by RCA Records. Dist: BMG

SWEET GEORGIA BROWN.
Tracks: / Up and at'em / Back home again in Indianna / Too marvellous for words / Mean to me / Sweet Georgia Brown / Im confessin' that I love you / Neenah / Neenah / I cover the water front
LP: released on MFP, Feb'87 by Music For Pleasure Records. Dist: EMI

SWINGIN' SAX.
LP: released on Manhattan, Jul'80 by President Records. Dist: Jazz Music, Swift, Wellard

LP: released on Star Jazz(USA), Oct'85 by Charly Records. Dist: Charly

TOO MARVELOUS FOR WORDS.
LP: released on Jazz Bird, '82

Cass: released on Jazz Bird, '82

Young Marble Giants

COLOSSAL YOUTH.
LP: released on Rough Trade, Feb'80 by Rough Trade Records. Dist: Rough Trade, Cartel

FINAL DAYS.
Single 7": released on Rough Trade, Oct'80 by Rough Trade Records. Dist: Rough Trade, Cartel

TESTCARD.
Single 7": released on Rough Trade, '81 by Rough Trade Records. Dist: Rough Trade, Cartel

Young messiah

NEW LONDON CHOIR.
LP: released on RCA, Oct'85 by RCA Records. Dist: BMG

Cass: released on RCA, Oct'85 by RCA Records. Dist: BMG

LP: released on Reprise(USA), '70 by WEA Records. Dist: Pinnacle

Cass: released on Reprise(USA), '70 by WEA Records. Dist: Pinnacle

YOUNG MESSIAH Original Cast Album (Various artists).
Recording Notes: Artists include:Madeline Bell,Vicki Brown,George Chandler and Steve Jerome.
CD: released on RCA, Jan'86 by RCA Records Dist: BMG

Young, Monalisa

DANCING MACHINE.
Single 7": released on Motown, Apr'83 by Motown Records. Dist: BMG

Single 12": released on Motown, Apr'83 by Motown Records. Dist: BMG

Young, Neil

AFTER THE GOLDRUSH.
CD: released on Reprise(USA), Jul'87 by WEA Records. Dist: Pinnacle

AFTER THE GOLDRUSH/ HARVEST.
Cass: released on Reprise(USA), Oct'82 by WEA Records. Dist: Pinnacle

AMERICAN STARS AND BARS.
LP: released on Reprise(USA), Jun'77 by WEA Records. Dist: Pinnacle

Cass: released on Reprise(USA), Jun'77 by WEA Records. Dist: Pinnacle

BEST OF NEIL YOUNG.
CD: released on Warner Bros., Feb'87 by WEA Records. Dist: WEA

COMES A TIME.
LP: released on Reprise(USA), Jul'78 by WEA Records. Dist: Pinnacle

Cass: released on Reprise(USA), Jul'78 by WEA Records. Dist: Pinnacle

DECADE.
Triple album/cass: DO NOT USE!?: released on Reprise(USA), Dec'77 by WEA Records Dist: Pinnacle

Triple album/cass: DO NOT USE!?: released on Reprise(USA), Dec'77 by WEA Records. Dist: Pinnacle

EVERYBODY KNOWS THIS IS NOWHERE.
LP: released on Reprise(USA), '69 by WEA Records. Dist: Pinnacle

EVERYBODY'S ROCKIN'.
Tracks: / Betty Lou's got a new pair of shoes / Rainin' in my heart / Payole blues / Wonderin' / Kinda fonda Wanda / Jolly roll men / Bright lights / Big city / Cry,Cry,Cry / Mystery train / Everybody's rockin'
LP: released on Geffen, Sep'86 by Geffen Records. Dist: WEA

Cass: released on Geffen, Sep'86 by Geffen Records. Dist: WEA

HARVEST.
Tracks: / Out on the weekend / Harvest / Man needs a maid / Heart of gold / Are you ready for the country? / Old man / There's a world / Alabama / Needle and the damage done / Words between the lines of age
CD: released on Reprise(USA), May'83 by WEA Records. Dist: Pinnacle

LP: released on Reprise(USA), '72 by WEA Records. Dist: Pinnacle

Cass: released on Reprise(USA), '72 by WEA Records. Dist: Pinnacle

HAWKS & DOVES.
LP: released on Reprise(USA), Aug'87 by WEA Records. Dist: Pinnacle

HAWKS & DOVES/ UNION MAN.
Single 7": released on Reprise(USA), Nov'80 by WEA Records. Dist: Pinnacle

HEART OF GOLD.
Single 7": released on Reprise(USA), '80 by WEA Records. Dist: Pinnacle

LANDING ON WATER.
Tracks: / Weight of the world / Violent side / Hippie dream / Bad news beat / Touch the night / People on the street / Hard luck stories / I got a problem / Pressure / Drifter
LP: released on Geffen, Aug'86 by Geffen Records. Dist: WEA

Cass: released on Geffen, Aug'86 by Geffen Records. Dist: WEA

CD: released on Geffen, Aug'86 by Geffen Records. Dist: WEA

LIFE (Young, Neil & Crazy Horse).
Tracks: / Mideast vacation / Long walk home / Around the world / Inca queen / Too lonely / Prisoners of rock'n'roll / Cryin' eyes / When your lonely heart breaks / We never danced
LP: released on Geffen, Jul'87 by Geffen Records. Dist: WEA

Cass: released on Geffen, Jul'87 by Geffen Records. Dist: WEA

CD: released on Geffen, Jul'87 by Geffen Records. Dist: WEA

LITTLE THING CALLED LOVE/ WE ARE IN CONTROL.
Single 7": released on Geffen, Jan'83 by Geffen Records. Dist: WEA

LIVE RUST (Young, Neil & Crazy Horse).
Double Album: released on Reprise(USA), Oct'81 by WEA Records. Dist: Pinnacle

Cass: released on Reprise(USA), Oct'81 by WEA Records. Dist: Pinnacle

LONG WALK HOME.
Single 7": released on Geffen, 30 May'87 by Geffen Records. Dist: WEA

NEIL YOUNG.
LP: released on Reprise(USA), '69 by WEA Records. Dist: Pinnacle

Cass. set: released on WEA, Nov'83 by WEA Records. Dist: WEA

OLD WAYS.
LP: released on Geffen, Sep'85 by Geffen Records. Dist: WEA

Cass: released on Geffen, Sep'85 by Geffen Records. Dist: WEA

ON THE BEACH.
LP: released on Reprise(USA), Jul'74 by WEA Records. Dist: Pinnacle

RUST NEVER SLEEPS (Young, Neil & Crazy Horse).
LP: released on Reprise(USA), Oct'81 by WEA Records. Dist: Pinnacle

Cass: released on Reprise(USA), Oct'81 by WEA Records. Dist: Pinnacle

TIME FADES AWAY.
LP: released on Reprise(USA), Jan'74 by WEA Records. Dist: Pinnacle

Cass: released on Reprise(USA), Jan'74 by WEA Records. Dist: Pinnacle

TONIGHT'S THE NIGHT.
LP: released on Reprise(USA), May'75 by WEA Records. Dist: Pinnacle

TRANS.
LP: released on Geffen, Sep'86 by Geffen Records. Dist: WEA

Cass: released on Geffen, Sep'86 by Geffen Records. Dist: WEA

WEIGHT OF THE WORLD.
Tracks: / Weight of the world / Pressure
Single 7": released on Geffen, Sep'86 by Geffen Records. Dist: WEA

Single 12": released on Geffen, Sep'86 by Geffen Records. Dist: WEA

ZUMA.
LP: released on Reprise(USA), '75 by WEA Records. Dist: Pinnacle

Young, Paul

12" TAPE: PAUL YOUNG.
Tracks: / Wherever I lay my hat (that's my home) / Come back and stay / Love of the common people / I'm gonna tear your playhouse down / Everytime you go away
Cass: released on CBS, Sep'86 by CBS Records. Dist: CBS

BETWEEN TWO FIRES.
Tracks: / Some people / Wonderland / War games / In the long run / Wasting my time / Prisoner of conscience / Why does a man have to be strong / Certain passion,A / Between two fires / Wedding day
LP: released on CBS, Oct'86 by CBS Records. Dist: CBS

CD: released on CBS, Nov'86 by CBS Records. Dist: CBS

Cass: released on CBS, Oct'86 by CBS Records. Dist: CBS

EVERY TIME YOU GO AWAY.
Single 7": released on CBS, Mar'85 by CBS Records. Dist: CBS

Single 12": released on CBS, Mar'85 by CBS Records. Dist: CBS

EVERYTHING MUST CHANGE.
Single 7": released on CBS, Dec'84 by CBS Records. Dist: CBS

I'M GONNA TEAR YOUR PLAYHOUSE DOWN.
Single 12": released on CBS, Nov'85 by CBS Records. Dist: CBS

LIVE AT LAST.
CD: released on CBS, '86 by CBS Records. Dist: CBS

LIVE: PAUL YOUNG & THE Q-TIPS (Young, Paul & The Q-Tips).
LP: released on Hallmark, Sep'85 by Pickwick Records.

Cass: released on Hallmark, Sep'85 by Pickwick Records.

NO PARLEZ.
Tracks: / Come back and stay / Love will tear us apart / Wherever I lay my hat (that's my home) / Ku-ku kurama / No parlez / Love of the common people / Oh women / Iron out the rough spots / Broken man / Tender trap / Sex
Recording Notes: Digital Stereo.
LP: released on CBS, Jul'83 by CBS Records. Dist: CBS

Cass: released on CBS, Jul'83 by CBS Records. Dist: CBS

CD: released on CBS, '83 by CBS Records. Dist: CBS

SECRET OF ASSOCIATION, (THE).
Tracks: / Bite the hand that feeds / Everytime you go away / I'm gonna tear your playhouse down / Standing on the edge / Soldier's things / Everything must change / Tomb of memories / One step forward / Hot fun / This means anything / I was in chains
LP: released on CBS, Mar'85 by CBS Records. Dist: CBS

Cass: released on CBS, Mar'85 by CBS Records. Dist: CBS

CD: released on CBS, Mar'85 by CBS Records. Dist: CBS

SOME PEOPLE.
Tracks: / Matter of fact, A / Matter of fact, A
Single 7": released on CBS, Nov'86 by CBS Records. Dist: CBS **Media Note:** a

Single 12": released on CBS, Nov'86 by CBS Records. Dist: CBS **Media Note:** Limited edition

Single 7": by CBS Records. Dist: CBS **Media Note:** Limited edition

VIDEO SINGLES, (THE).
Recording Notes: Total playing time 30 minutes 5 tracks
VHS: released on CBS-Fox, Jan'86 by CBS Records. Dist: CBS, Fox

WHEREVER I LAY MY HAT (Young, Paul & The Royal Family).
Single 7": released on CBS, May'83 by CBS Records. Dist: CBS Deleted '87.

Single 12": released on CBS, May'83 by CBS Records. Dist: CBS

WHY DOES A MAN HAVE TO BE STRONG.
Tracks: / Trying to guess the rest
Single 7": released on CBS, Jan'87 by CBS Records. Dist: CBS

Single 12": released on CBS, Jan'87 by CBS Records. Dist: CBS

WONDERLAND.
Tracks: / Wonderland / Between two fires
Single 7": released on CBS, Sep'86 by CBS Records. Dist: CBS

Single 12": released on CBS, Sep'86 by CBS Records. Dist: CBS

YOU ARE THE LIFE INSIDE OF ME (Young, Paul & The Q-Tips).
Single 12": released on Rewind, Jul'84 by Rewind Records. Dist: Spartan

Young Rascals

GROOVIN'.
Single 7": released on Atlantic, '80 by WEA Records. Dist: WEA, Swift, Celtic Music

Young Sherlock Holmes

YOUNG SHERLOCK HOLMES Original Soundtrack (Sinfonia of London).
Tracks: / Main title / Solving the crime / Library love - Waxflatter's first flight / Pastries & crypts / Waxing Elizabeth / Holmes and Elizabeth (love theme) / Ehtar's excape / Final duel, (The) / Final farewell / Riddles solved, (The) - End credits
Recording Notes: Composed, conducted and produced by Bruce Broughton.
LP: released on MCA, Mar'86 by MCA Records. Dist: Polygram

Cass: released on MCA, Mar'86 by MCA Records. Dist: Polygram

Young, Steve

LOOK HOMEWARD ANGEL.
LP: released on Mill(USA), Sep'86 Dist: Swift

NO PLACE TO FALL.
LP: released on RCA, May'78 by RCA Records. Dist: BMG

Cass: released on RCA, May'78 by RCA Records. Dist: BMG

OLD MEMORIES.
LP: released on Country Roads Records, Nov'81 by Country Roads Records. Deleted '87.

ROCK SALT AND NAILS.
LP: released on Edsel, Oct'86 by Demon Records. Dist: Celtic Music, Pinnacle, Jazz Music

SEVEN BRIDGES ROAD.
LP: released on Sonet, Oct'81 by Sonet Records. Dist: Jazz Music, Swift, Celtic Music, Roots, PRT, Sonet

Young, Tracie

CALL ME.
Tracks: / Call me / Italian girl / Find it in your nature*
Single 7": released on Polydor, Oct'86 by Polydor Records. Dist: Polygram

Single 12": released on Polydor, Oct'86 by Polydor Records. Dist: Polygram

I CAN'T LEAVE YOU ALONE.
Single 7": released on Respond, Jul'85 by A&M. Dist: CBS

Single 12": released on Respond, Jul'85 by A&M. Dist: CBS

INVITATION.
Single 7": released on Respond, Oct'85 by A&M. Dist: CBS

Single 12": released on Respond, Oct'85 by A&M. Dist: CBS

WE SHOULD BE TOGETHER.
Tracks: / We should be together / Find it in your nature
Single 7": released on Polydor, Jul'86 by Polydor Records. Dist: Polygram

Single 12": released on Polydor, Jul'86 by Polydor Records. Dist: Polygram

Young tuxedo brass band

NEW ORLEANS.
LP: released on 504, Sep'86 by 504 Records. Dist: Wellard

Cass: released on 504, Sep'86 by 504 Records. Dist: Wellard

Young 'Uns

PEACE ON EARTH.
Tracks: / Peace on Earth / Shout out so the world can hear
Single 7": released on MBS, Dec'86 Dist: PRT

Young, Val

IF YOU SHOULD EVER BE LONELY.
Tracks: / If you should ever be lonely / If you should ever be lonely (instrumental version)
Single 7": released on Gordy(USA), Feb'86 by Motown Records. Dist: BMG

Single 12": released on Gordy(USA), Feb'86 by Motown Records. Dist: BMG

SEDUCTION.
Tracks: / Mind games / If you should ever be lonely / Let's fall in love / Tellin' me lies / Come hang out / Seduction / Piece of my heart / Waiting for you / Make up your mind
LP: released on Motown, Apr'86 by Motown Records. Dist: BMG

Cass: released on Motown, Apr'86 by Motown Records. Dist: BMG

Single 12":

Young, Vic

BLIND DATE.
Single 7": released on Eagle(London), Aug'82 by Eagle Records(London).

Young, Victor

QUIET MAN, (THE).
LP: released on Varese International, Mar'79 by Varese Int.Records(USA). Dist: Silva Screen Records, Swift

Young, Webster

WEBSTER YOUNG PLAYS THE MILES DAVIS SONGBOOK, VOL 2.
LP: released on VGM(Import), '81 Dist: Jazz Horizons, Jazz Music

WEBSTER YOUNG PLAYS THE MILES DAVIS SONGBOOK, VOL 1.
LP: released on VGM(Import), '81 Dist: Jazz Horizons, Jazz Music

WEBSTER YOUNG PLAYS THE MILES DAVIS SONGBOOK, VOL 3.
LP: released on VGM(Import), '81 Dist: Jazz Horizons, Jazz Music

Young World

RED ROBIN ROCK.
Single 7": released on CJM, Dec'81 Dist: Jazz Music, Spartan

Young, Zora

STUMBLING BLOCKS & STEPPING STONES.
LP: released on Blue Sting, Aug'87 Dist: Cadillac, Projection, Swift, Celtic Music, Topic, Ross, Duncans, Impetus

Youngblood,Lonnie

BEST WAY TO BREAK A HABIT.
Single 7": released on WEA, Aug'81 by WEA Records. Dist: WEA

Single 12": released on WEA, Aug'81 by WEA Records. Dist: WEA

Younger, Cole

IT'LL BE ALRIGHT ON THE NIGHT (Younger, Cole & The Koolettes).
Single 7": released on Logo, Jul'81 by Logo Records. Dist: Celtic Music, BMG

Younger generation

YOUNGER GENERATION Various artists (Various artists).
LP: released on Black Link Int., Oct'85 Dist: Jetstar

Young,Johnny

CHICAGO BLUES BAND.
LP: released on Arhoolie(USA), May'81 by Arhoolie Records. Dist: Jazz Music, Projection, Roots, Celtic Music, Cadillac, Ross, Duncans, Impetus

Your 50 best loved Hymns

YOUR 50 BEST LOVED HYMNS (Various artists).
Tracks: / Let all the world in every corner sing / For all the Saints / How sweet the name of Jesus sounds / I am so glad / All in the April evening / O worship the King / Lord of the dance / Praise to the Lord / Onward Christian soldiers / All creatures of our God and King / How great thou art / To God be the glory / Lord Jesus Christ / O love that wilt not let me go / In heavenly love abiding / Jesus shall reign where'er the sun / All hail the power of Jesus' name / Love divine / There's a friend for little children / Soldiers of Christ arise / He hideth my soul / O for a thousand tongues to sing / Crown him with many crowns / Who is on the Lord's side / Now thank we all our God / Jesus wants me for a sunbeam / All people that on Earth do dwell / All glory laud and honour / Holy, holy, holy / And can it be / When I survey the wondrous cross / Lord is my shepherd, The / Rejoice the Lord is King / Praise my soul / Lead us heavenly father lead us / Rock of ages / O Jesus I have promised / Come ye thankful people come / Guide me O thou great Jehovah / Sun of my soul / Bless this house /

He lives / Fight the good fight / Just as I am / There is a green hill far away / Jesus keep me near the cross / Day thou gavest, The / Lord, is ended / O God our help in ages past / Now the day is over / God be with you 'till we meet again
Cass: released on Trio, Nov'86 by Music For Pleasure Records. Dist: EMI

Your Dinner
POWER OVER YOU.
Single 7": released on Foodgun, Jan'85 by Foodgun Records. Dist: Foodgun

Your Fantasies
ROLLER BOOGIE.
LP: released on Seville, Nov'80 by President Records, Jazz Music, Taylors, Spartan

Your Favourite Bird Songs
YOUR FAVOURITE BIRD SONGS.
LP: released on BBC, Apr'84 by BBC Records & Tapes. Dist: EMI

Cass: released on BBC, Apr'84 by BBC Records & Tapes. Dist: EMI

Your favourite hymns vol.3
YOUR HUNDRED FAVOURITE HYMNS VOL.3 Various artists (Various artists).
LP: released on MFP, Nov'83 by Music For Pleasure Records. Dist: EMI

Your favourite overtures
YOUR FAVOURITE OVERTURES Various artists (Various artists).
Cass. set: released on Pickwick(Ditto series), Mar'83 by Pickwick Records. Dist: PRT, Clyde Factors

Your favourite poems
YOUR FAVOURITE POEMS Various artists (Various artists).
Cass. set: released on Argo(Spokenword), Jul'82 by Decca Classics. Dist: Polygram

Your Hundred best tunes
YOUR HUNDRED BEST TUNES Various artists (Various artists).
LP set: released on Decca, Nov'75 by Decca Records. Dist: Polygram

Cass: released on Decca, Nov'75 by Decca Records. Dist: Polygram

Your hundred hymns......
YOUR HUNDRED FAVOURITE HYMNS VOL.1 Various artists (Various artists).
LP: released on MFP, Sep'82 by Music For Pleasure Records. Dist: EMI

Cass: released on MFP, Sep'82 by Music For Pleasure Records. Dist: EMI

YOUR 100 FAVOURITE HYMNS VOL.2 Various artists (Various artists).
LP: released on MFP, Sep'83 by Music For Pleasure Records. Dist: EMI

Cass: released on MFP, Sep'83 by Music For Pleasure Records. Dist: EMI

YOUR HUNDRED FAVOURITE HYMNS VOL.4 Various artists (Various artists).
LP: released on MFP, Jul'84 by Music For Pleasure Records. Dist: EMI

Cass: released on MFP, Jul'84 by Music For Pleasure Records. Dist: EMI

YOUR HUNDRED FAVOURITE HYMNS VOL.5 Various artists (Various artists).
LP: released on MFP, Sep'84 by Music For Pleasure Records. Dist: EMI

Cass: released on MFP, Sep'84 by Music For Pleasure Records. Dist: EMI

Your own.......
YOUR OWN YOUR VERY OWN (STARS OF THE MUSIC HALL) Various artists (Various artists).
LP: released on ASV-Living Era, Mar'81 by Academy Sound & Vision Records. Dist: Pinnacle

Cass: released on ASV-Living Era, Mar'83 by Academy Sound & Vision Records. Dist: Pinnacle

Your songs of praise..
YOUR SONGS OF PRAISE CHOICE Various choirs (Various artists).
LP: released on BBC, May'83 by BBC Records & Tapes. Dist: EMI

Cass: released on BBC, May'83 by BBC Records & Tapes. Dist: EMI

You're driving me crazy
YOU'RE DRIVING ME CRAZY Various artists (Various artists).
LP: released on Nostalgia(Sweden), May'82 by Wellard, Jazz Music

Cass: released on Nostalgia(Sweden), May'82 by Wellard, Jazz Music

Yours, Anne
YOURS, ANNE Original Off Broadway cast (Various artists).
Recording Notes: Musical drama adaptation of 'The Diary of Anne Frank', one of the most famous & moving stories to emerge from the 2nd world war. Recorded from the off Broadway production in 1985, this release ties in with the show's return to NY.
LP: released on TER, Apr'87 Dist: Pinnacle

Cass: released on TER, Apr'87 Dist: Pinnacle

Youth
EMPTY QUARTER, (THE).
LP: released on Illuminated, Mar'84 by IKF Records. Dist: Pinnacle, Cartel, Jetstar

Youth Brigade
WHAT PRICE HAPPINESS.
Single 7": released on Better Youth Orginisation, Oct'84 by Cartel, Red Rhino, Southern Record

Youth Of Today
BREAK DOWN THE WALLS.
LP: released on Wishing Well(USA), Aug'87 Dist: Pinnacle

SHAKE HANDS AND MAKE A FRIEND.
Single 7": released on Daylight, Aug'85 by Daylight Records. Dist: Daylight

Youth With A Mission
WINDOWS I I exalt thee.
Recording Notes: Celebrating its 25th year, Youth With A Mission is an interdenominational effort which trains and places 20,000 young missionaries in more than 200 countries throughout the world. As Gary Stevens, director of YWAM, Hong Kong, has said, "The foundation of our evangelism is set and laid in worship". People who visit the YWAM ministry often ask for recordings of the inspiring worship music they hear. In response to these requests, the young volunteers serving in Hong Kong have recorded some of their favourite praise songs.
LP: released on Word(UK), Jun'86 by Word Records(UK)Ltd.., CBS

Cass: released on Word(UK), Jun'86 by Word Records(UK)Ltd.., CBS

WINDOWS II Giving glory.
LP: released on Word(UK), Jun'86 by Word Records(UK)Ltd.., CBS

Cass: released on Word(UK), Jun'86 by Word Records(UK)Ltd.., CBS

You've got to laugh
YOU'VE GOT TO LAUGH Various artists (Various artists).
LP: released on Towerbell, Jul'86 by Towerbell Records. Dist: EMI

Cass: released on Towerbell, Jul'86 by Towerbell Records. Dist: EMI

YPY
ONE MORE HEARTACHE.
Single 7": released on Spartan, Jul'85 by Spartan Records. Dist: Spartan

Single 12": released on Spartan, Jul'85 by Spartan Records. Dist: Spartan

Yr Hwntws
YR HWNTWS.
LP: released on Loco, Jan'82 by Loco Records. Dist: Loco Records

Ysgol Morgan Llwyd
FFATRI BREUDDYDION.
LP: released on Loco, Jul'83 by Loco Records. Dist: Loco Records

Y&T
BLACK TIGER.
LP: released on A&M, Sep'82 by A&M Records. Dist: Polygram

DIRTY GIRL.
Single 12": released on A&M, Oct'81 by A&M Records. Dist: Polygram

DON'T WANNA LOSE.
Single 7": released on A&M, Sep'82 by A&M Records. Dist: Polygram

Single 12": released on A&M, Sep'82 by A&M Records. Dist: Polygram

DOWN FOR THE COUNT.
LP: released on A&M, Nov'85 by A&M Records. Dist: Polygram

Cass: released on A&M, Nov'85 by A&M Records. Dist: Polygram

IN ROCK WE TRUST.
LP: released on A&M, Aug'84 by A&M Records. Dist: Polygram

Cass: released on A&M, Aug'84 by A&M Records. Dist: Polygram

MEAN STREAK.
LP: released on A&M, Sep'83 by A&M Records. Dist: Polygram

Cass: released on A&M, Sep'83 by A&M Records. Dist: Polygram

OPEN FIRE.
LP: released on A&M, Jul'85 by A&M Records. Dist: Polygram

Cass: released on A&M, Jul'85 by A&M Records. Dist: Polygram

SUMMERTIME GIRLS.
Tracks: / Summertime girls / Lipstick and leather
Single 7": released on A&M, '86 by A&M Records. Dist: Polygram

Single 12": released on A&M, Aug'85 by A&M Records. Dist: Polygram

Yucca, Terence
FANTASY GAMES.
LP: released on Intersound, Jul'87 by Intersound Records. Dist: Jazz Music

Yugoslav Music
YUGLOSLAVIA: 3. CROATIA.
Cass: released on Folktracks, Nov'79 by Folktracks Cassettes. Dist: Folksound, Roots

YUGOSLAVIA:1.BOSNIA & HERCEGORINA.
Cass: released on Folktracks, Nov'79 by Folktracks Cassettes. Dist: Folksound, Roots

YUGOSLAV FOLK MUSIC.
LP: released on Lyrichord(USA), Oct'81 by Lyrichord Records(USA). Dist: Flexitron Ltd., Roots

YUGOSLAVIA: 2. MONTENEGRO & SLOVENIA.
Cass: released on Folktracks, Nov'79 by Folktracks Cassettes. Dist: Folksound, Roots

YUGOSLAVIA: 4. MACEDONIA.
Cass: released on Folktracks, Nov'79 by Folktracks Cassettes. Dist: Folksound, Roots

YUGOSLAVIA: 5. SERBIA.
Cass: released on Folktracks, Nov'79 by Folktracks Cassettes. Dist: Folksound, Roots

Yuka
ENDANGERED SPECIES.
Single 7": released on Speed, Nov'82 Dist: Spartan

WHO WOULD BELIEVE THE YOUNG MAN.
Single 7": released on Speed, Feb'83 Dist: Spartan

Yung Analysts
WISHING BALLOONS, (THE).
LP: released on Hamster, Sep'83 by Hamster Records And Tapes. Dist: Backs, Cartel

Yuro, Timi
ALL ALONE AM I.
Single 7": released on A.1, Jun'83 by A.1 Records. Dist: PRT

HURT.
Tracks: / Hurt / Make the world go away / What's the matter baby / Only love can break a heart / Little things mean a lot / Thank you for calling / It must be him / Smoke gets in your eyes / I'm sorry / Let me go lover / Its only make believe / All alone am I / It hurts to be in love / You've lost that loving feeling / Tears on my pillow / Cry / I can't stop loving you / Only you
LP: released on Charly, Aug'86 by Charly Records. Dist: Charly, Cadillac, Swift

Cass: released on Charly, Aug'86 by Charly Records. Dist: Charly, Cadillac, Swift

LP: released on EMI(Holland), May'83 by EMI Records(UK). Dist: Conifer

Single 7": released on EMI(Holland), Aug'84 by EMI Records(UK). Dist: Conifer

Single 7": released on Liberty(USA), May'80 by U.A.Records. Dist: Conifer

SENSATIONAL VOICE OF, (THE).
LP: released on Mercury(Italy), Jun'84 by Phonogram Records. Dist: IMS, Polygram

Cass: released on Mercury(Italy), Jun'84 by Phonogram Records. Dist: IMS, Polygram

VERY BEST OF TIMI YURO.
LP: released on Liberty-UA, Aug'80 by EMI Records(UK). Dist: EMI

Cass: released on Liberty-UA, Aug'80 by EMI Records(UK). Dist: EMI

VERY ORIGINAL AND GREATEST HITS.
LP: released on EMI(Holland), May'83 by EMI Records(UK). Dist: Conifer

Ywam
WINDOWS ON THE WORLD.
Tracks: / Victor's crown / Jesus we enthrone you / All that you are we want / We bow down When I survey / Let us adore / Crown him / We will glorify / Robed in majesty / Thou art my god / Glory that is due your name,The / Sin unto the lord / Great is the lord
LP: released on Star Song, May'87 by Word Records(UK)Ltd.. Dist: Word, CBS

Cass: released on Star Song, May'87 by Word Records(UK)Ltd.. Dist: Word, CBS

Z

Z

Forever now.
Single (12"): released on Young Blood in Nov'85 by Young Blood Records. Distributed by: Pinnacle

Z 6

You Eugene and me.
Single (7"): released on Aura in Feb'83 by Hollywood Nites Distribution. Distributed by: Pinnacle

Zabandis

Brothers & sisters (Zabandis/People Band, (The)).
Tracks: / Brothers and sisters.
Single (12"): released on People Unite in Apr'86 by People Unite Records. Distributed by: Jetstar, Rough Trade, Cartel, Pinnacle, Nine Mile

Zack, George

Barrelhouse   piano (Zack,George/George Wettling).

Zadig, Man Of Destiny

Zadig, Man of destiny (Various Artists).
Musicassette: released on Anvil in Apr'80. Distributed by: Anvil

Zedora, Pia

I am what I am.
Tracks: / Foggy day in London town, A / I am what I am / For once in my life / All of me / I've got it bad and that ain't good / Foggy day in London town, A / Day by day / I'm beginning to see the light / If he walked into my life / For once in my life / How about you / I had the craziest dream / One I love belongs to somebody else (The) / Time after time / Pennies from heaven / It's been a long, long time / Lady is a tramp, The.
Album: released on Epic in Nov'86 by CBS Records. Distributed by: CBS

Musicassette: released on Epic in Nov'86 by CBS Records. Distributed by: CBS

Single (7"): released on Epic in Nov'86 by CBS Records. Distributed by: CBS

I'm in love again.
Single (7"): released on Elektra in May'82 by WEA Records. Distributed by: WEA

Pia and Phil (Zadora, Pia & The London Philharmonic Orchestra).
Tracks: / Embraceable you / It had to be you / All my tomorrows / Smile(though your heart is breaking) / Come rain come shine / When the sun comes out / East of the sun(and west of the moon) / But not for me / I thought about you / Boy next door,The / Man that got away,The.
Album: released on Epic in Feb'86 by CBS Records. Distributed by: CBS

Musicassette: released on Epic in Feb'86 by CBS

Pia and Phil.
Album: released on Premier in May'85 by Premier Records. Distributed by: CBS

Musicassette: released on Premier in May'85 by Premier Records. Distributed by: CBS

When the rain begins to fall

Zagada

Island in the stream.
Single (12"): released on Face Int in Jun'84. Distributed by: Jetstar

We are not the first.
Single (12"): released on Vasko in Jan'85 by

Ray Edgar(Music). Distributed by: Indies

Zager/Evans

In the year 25-25.
Tracks: / In the year 2525 / American woman.
Single (7"): released on Old Gold in Oct'86 by Old Gold Records. Distributed by: Lightning, Jazz Music, Spartan, Counterpoint

Zager & Fasion

Hold on.
Single (7"): released on State in Dec'82 by State Records

Zager, Michael

Let's all chant (Zager, Michael Band).
Tracks: / Let's all chant / Traffic jam / Traffic jam (dub mix).
Single (12"): released on Domino in Jun'87 by Domino Records. Distributed by: Charly

Zager, Michael Band

Lets all chant.
Single (7"): released on EMI (France) in Apr'83 by EMI Records. Distributed by: Conifer

Zak

My world.
Single (7"): released on Insatiable in Sep'84 by Insatiable Records. Distributed by: Pinnacle

Single (12"): released on Insatiable in Sep'84 by Insatiable Records. Distributed by: Pinnacle

Zakrzewski, Paul

Let's all chant.
Single (12"): released on Domino in Jun'87 by Domino Records. Distributed by: Charly

Zambandis

When the party is over.
Single (12"): released on Zambandis in Dec'82

Zamfir

Harmony.

Zamfir, Georghe

Best of Georghe Zamfir.
Album: released on West Five in Oct'86. Distributed by: PRT

Musicassette: released on West Five in Oct'86. Distributed by: PRT

Greatest hits:Georghe Zamfir.
Compact disc: released on Delta in May'87 by Delta Records. Distributed by: Target

Harmony.
Tracks: / Cent mille chansons / I know him so well / Serenade / Another you, another me / Callvalleria rusticana / To my son Teo / Sleepy shores / Recuerdos / Concerto for clarinet & orchestra in A / Wild theme / Cavalleria rusticana / Rescuerdos / Only love / Elvira madigan / The manual.
Notes: Gheorghe Zamfir, the acknowledged master of the pan pipes with the beautiful orchestration of Harry Van Hoof, his collaborator on the Lonely shepherd and Classics by candlelight. A blend of MOR and popular classical material, including Mark Knopfler's Wild theme, Nana Mouskouri's Only love and the Rice/Lloyd-Webber standard I know him so well.
Compact disc: released on Polydor in Feb'87 by Polydor Records. Distributed by: Polygram, Polydor

Album: released on Philips in Feb'87. Distributed by: IMS-Polygram

Musicassette: released on Philips in Feb'87. Distributed by: IMS-Polygram

Master of the pan pipes, The.

Master of the Pan Pipes.
Notes: Greatest hits.
Compact disc: released on Delta in '86 by Delta Records. Distributed by: Target

Zamfir in Paris-live.
Notes: Pan pipes & orchestra.
Compact disc: released on Delta in '86 by Delta Records. Distributed by: Target

Zamfir, Gheorghe

Atlantis.
Tracks: / Andrew's theme(film theme from 'Misunderstood') / Wonderland / I'll give you the sun / Gymnopedie no.1 / Top of the world / Stranger on the shore / Message from atlantis / Seagulls / Elodie / Hi george / If you go away(Ne me quitte pas) / Ladie's waltz / Amapola.
Notes: New digital recording featuring Zamfir original compositions as well as well-known pieces by Eric Satie,Acker Bilk and Jacques Brel.
Album: released on Philips in Dec'85. Distributed by: IMS-Polygram

Musicassette: released on Philips in Dec'85. Distributed by: IMS-Polygram

Compact disc: released on Philips in Dec'85. Distributed by: IMS-Polygram

By candlelight.
Album: released on Arcade Music Gala in Apr'86. Distributed by: Stage One

Musicassette: released on Arcade Music Gala in Apr'86. Distributed by: Stage One

Christmas album, A.
Tracks: / O du froliche / Jingle bells / O tannenbaum / Six colours / Hark the herald angels sing / Noel roumaine(medley) / White christmas / Little drummer boy / Ava maria / Petit papa noel / Pour toi jesus / Silent night / Notre pere / Angels we have heard on high.
Notes: From Gheorghe Zamfir,the master of the Roumanian Pan Flute,a beautiful collection of Christmas melodies.Digitally recorded for maximum clarity,this is a lush,richly produced album that could only be made by the virtuoso Gheorghe Zamfir.
Album: released on Philips in Nov'84. Distributed by: IMS-Polygram

Musicassette: released on Philips in Nov'84. Distributed by: IMS-Polygram

Compact disc: released on Philips in Nov'84. Distributed by: IMS-Polygram

Classics by candlelight.
Compact disc: released on Philips in Jul' '6. Distributed by: IMS-Polygram

Extraordinary pan pipe of Gheorghe Zamfir Vol.2.
Video-cassette [Betamax]: released on CBS(France) in '81 by CBS Records. Distributed by: Conifer, Discovery, Swift

Extraordinary pan pipe of Gheorghe Zamfir Vol.3.
Album: released on CBS(France) in '81 by CBS Records. Distributed by: Conifer, Discovery, Swift

Extraordinary pan pipe of Gheorghe Zamfir Vol.1.
Album: released on CBS(France) in '81 by CBS Records. Distributed by: Conifer, Discovery, Swift

Great successes of....
Album: released on CBS(France) in '81 by CBS Records. Distributed by: Conifer, Dis-

covery, Swift

Hommage a Gheorghe Zamfir.
Album: released on Import in Mar'81. Distributed by: Stage One

Impressions.
Album: released on Epic in Jun'78 by CBS Records. Distributed by: CBS

Musicassette: released on Epic in Jun'78 by CBS Records. Distributed by: CBS

In Paris.
Double Album: released on CBS(France) in '81 by CBS Records. Distributed by: Conifer, Discovery, Swift

In Paris 1.
Album: released on CBS(France) in '81 by CBS Records. Distributed by: Conifer, Discovery, Swift

In Paris 2.
Album: released on CBS(France) in '81 by CBS Records. Distributed by: Conifer, Discovery, Swift

King of pan flute.
Musicassette: released on Timeless Treasures in Jul'86. Distributed by: Counterpoint Distribution

L'alouette.
Album: released on Phillips in Mar'78

Musicassette: released on Phillips in Mar'78

Lonely sheperd, The.
Album: released on Philips in May'84. Distributed by: IMS-Polygram

Musicassette: released on Philips in May'84. Distributed by: IMS-Polygram

Master of the pan-flute.
Album: released on Phillips Holland in Jul'84

Musicassette: released on Phillips Holland in Jul'84

Meister der panflote.
Notes: Starr Marketing Services Ltd,90 Queens Road,Twickenham,Middlesex.TW1 4ET.Tel:01 891 6487.
Compact disc: released on Delta in Oct'86 by Delta Records. Distributed by: Target

Motive series.
Album: released on Philips Import in Sep'81

Musicassette: released on Philips Import in Sep'81

Music by candlelight.
Tracks: / Adagio 8 / Bilitis / Black rose / Don't cry for me Argentina / Elisha / Floral dance / Laryssa / Limelight / She / Run to me / Summer of '42 / Meditation for 'Thias'.
Notes: Digital Stereo recording.
Compact disc:

Music for millions.
Album: released on Philips Import in Mar'83

Musicassette: released on Philips Import in Mar'83

Romance.
Tracks: / Blue navajo / Missing / Yesterday / Aranjuez mon armour / Just the way you are / Till / Chariots of fire / Midnight horses / Danny's night / Your song / Agata / Un amour de tchaikovsky.
Notes: Digital Stereo recording.

Compact disc: released on Philips in Sep'84. Distributed by: IMS-Polygram

Album: released on Philips Import in Mar'84
Cat.no 6313 438
Musicassette: released on Philips Import in Mar'84

Roumanian flutes Vol.1.
Album: released on Arion in Jun'79. Distributed by: Discovery

Musicassette: released on Arion in Jun'79. Distributed by: Discovery

Roumanian flutes Vol.2.
Album: released on Arion in Jun'79. Distributed by: Discovery

Musicassette: released on Arion in Jun'79. Distributed by: Discovery

Roumanian folklore instruments.
Album: released on CBS in '81 by CBS Records. Distributed by: CBS

Secret world of....
Album: released on CBS in '81 by CBS Records. Distributed by: CBS

Theme from 'Picnic at hanging rock', A.
Album: released on Epic in '79 by CBS Records. Distributed by: CBS

Musicassette: released on Epic in '79 by CBS Records. Distributed by: CBS

Theme light of experience.
Album: released on Epic in Oct'76 by CBS Records. Distributed by: CBS

Themes.
Album: released on Epic in Dec'76 by CBS Records. Distributed by: CBS

Musicassette: released on Epic in Dec'76 by CBS Records. Distributed by: CBS

Wereldsuccessen.
Double Album: released on Philips (Holland) in Aug'82

Double musicassette: released on Philips (Holland) in Aug'82

Zamfir.
Album: released on CBS in '81 by CBS Records. Distributed by: CBS

Zando

Sharing you.
Single (12"): released on Caribana in Oct'81. Distributed by: Pinnacle

Zandt, Townes Van

Delta momma blues.
Album: released on Tomato in Mar'79

High low and in between.
Album: released on Tomato in Mar'79

Late, great Townes Van Zandt, The.
Album: released on Tomato in Mar'79

Live at the old quarter.
Album: released on Tomato in Mar'79

Our mother the mountain.
Album: released on Tomato in Mar'79

Zang Tuum Tumb Sampled

Zang tuum tumb sampled Various artists (Various Artists).
Album: released on ZTT in Oct'85 by Island Records. Distributed by: Polygram

Musicassette: released on ZTT in Oct'85 by Island Records. Distributed by: Polygram

Zantees

Out for kicks.
Album: released on Charly in Nov'81 by Charly Records. Distributed by: Charly, Cadillac

Rhythm bound.
Album: released on Rockhouse in Mar'84 by Rockhouse Records. Distributed by: Swift Distribution, Charly Distribution

Zanti Misfitz

Heroes are go.
Single (12"): released on Clay in Feb'83 by Clay Records. Distributed by: Pinnacle

Kidz songs.
Single (7"): released on Clay in Apr'82 by Clay Records. Distributed by: Pinnacle

Love ends at 8.
Single (7"): released on Clay in Jul'82 by Clay Records. Distributed by: Pinnacle

Zant,Van

Midnight sensation.
Album: released on CBS(Import) in Jun'86 by CBS Records. Distributed by: Conifer, Discovery, Swift

Zapata,Zola

Don't turn me down.
Tracks: / Don't turn me down / Feel my love.
Single (7"): released on Juice in Apr'86 by IRS. Distributed by: A&M, CBS

Single (12"): released on Juice in Apr'86 by IRS. Distributed by: A&M, CBS

Zapp

Computer love(Part 1).
Tracks: / Computer love (Part 1) / Computer Love (Inst).
Single (7"): released on Warner Bros. in Apr'86 by Warner Bros Records. Distributed by: WEA

Single (12"): released on Warner Bros. in Apr'86 by Warner Bros Records. Distributed by: WEA

Dance floor.
Single (7"): released on Warner Brothers in Aug'82 by WEA Records. Distributed by: WEA

Single (12"): released on Warner Brothers in Aug'82 by WEA Records. Distributed by: WEA

It doesn't really matter.
Tracks: / It doesn't really matter / Make me feel good.
Single (7"): released on Warner Bros. in Jun'86 by Warner Bros Records. Distributed by: WEA

Single (12"): released on Warner Bros. in Jun'86 by Warner Bros Records. Distributed by: WEA

New Zapp 1V U, The.
Tracks: / It doesn't really matter / Computer love / Itchin' for your twitchin' / Radio people / I only have eyes for you / Rock 'n' Roll / Cas-ta-spellome / Make me feel good / Ja ready to rock.
Album: released on Warner Bros. in Dec'85 by Warner Bros Records. Distributed by: WEA

Radio people.
Tracks: / Radio people / Itchin' for your twitchin'.
Single (7"): released on Warner Bros. in Nov'86 by Warner Bros Records. Distributed by: WEA

Single (12"): released on Warner Bros. in Nov'86 by Warner Bros Records. Distributed by: WEA

Zappa, Dweezil

Havin' a bad day.
Album: released on Chrysalis in Aug'87 by Chrysalis Records. Distributed by: CBS

Zappa, Frank

200 motels.
Album: released on EMI (France) in '83 by EMI Records. Distributed by: Conifer

200 motels 1.
Musicassette: released on EMI (Italy) in Aug'86 by EMI Records. Distributed by: Conifer

Musicassette: released on EMI (Italy) in Aug'86 by EMI Records. Distributed by: Conifer

Apostrophe.
Album: released on Discreet in May'74

Chunga's revenge.
Album: released on Reprise in '78 by WEA Records. Distributed by: WEA

Does humor belong in music.
Tracks: / Zoot allures / Tinsel town rebellion / Trouble every day / Penguin in bondage / Hot-plate heaven at the green hotel / What's new baltimore? / Cock-Suckers' ball / WPIJ / Let's move to cleveland / Whippin' post.
Compact disc: released on EMI in Feb'86 by EMI Records. Distributed by: EMI

Frank Zappa meets the mothers of prevention.
Tracks: / We're turning again / Alien orifice / Yo cats / What's new in baltimore / I don't even care / One man-one vote / H.R. 2911 / Little beige sambo / Aerobics in bongdage.
Notes: European version.A brand new album from Frank Zappa it differs from the U.S release of the same album by the inclusion of the first 3 tracks on side 2 which areexclusive to this unique release.
Album: released on EMI in Feb'86 by EMI Records. Distributed by: EMI

Musicassette: released on EMI in Feb'86 by EMI Records. Distributed by: EMI

Hot rats.
Album: released on Reprise in '78 by WEA Records. Distributed by: WEA

Is there humor in music.
Video-cassette (VHS): released on PMI in Jun'86 by PMI Records. Distributed by: EMI

Video-cassette [Betamax]: released on PMI in Jun'86 by PMI Records. Distributed by: EMI

Jazz from hell.
Tracks: / Night school / Beltaway bandits / While you were art / Jazz from hell / G-spot tornado / Damp ankles / St Etienne / Massaggio galore.
Notes: A fine collection of 8 brand new jazz pieces written, produced and arranged by Frank Zappa. From the frantic up beat *Night school* to the guitar orientated *St Etienne, Jazz from hell* displays Zappa's hugely inventive, great talent for the instrumental.
Album: released on EMI in Dec'86 by EMI Records. Distributed by: EMI

Musicassette: released on EMI in Dec'86 by EMI Records. Distributed by: EMI

Joe's garage act 1.
Album: released on CBS in Sep'79 by CBS Records. Distributed by: CBS

Musicassette: released on CBS in Sep'79 by CBS Records. Distributed by: CBS

Joe's garage acts 2 & 3.
Double Album: released on CBS in Jan'80 by CBS Records. Distributed by: CBS

Double musicassette: released on CBS in Jan'80 by CBS Records. Distributed by: CBS

Man from Utopia.
Tracks: / Cocaine decisions / Dangerous kitchen,The / Tink walks amok / Radio is broken,The / Moggio / Man from utopia meets mary lou (medley) / Stick together / Sex / Jazz discharge party hats,The / We are not alone.
Album: released on EMI in Feb'86 by EMI Records. Distributed by: EMI

Musicassette: released on EMI in Feb'86 by EMI Records. Distributed by: EMI

Man from Utopia.
Musicassette: released on CBS in Jun'83 by CBS Records. Distributed by: CBS

Musicassette: released on CBS in Jun'83 by CBS Records. Distributed by: CBS

Old masters - box one, The.
Notes: Limited edition numbered box set of the following Zappa/Mothers of Invention LPs1-Freak Out (2 LP), 2-Absolutely Free, 3-We're Only In It For The Money, 4-LumpyGravy, 5-Cruising with Ruben & The Jets, plus previously un-released "Mystery Disc", containing rare material (live & studio outtakes) plus full colour lyrics book.
Boxed set: released on Barking Pumpkin (USA) in Jul'87. Distributed by: Capitol Records, CBS

Old masters - box two, The.
Notes: Numbered limited edition containing the following Zappa/Mothers albums (many with re-mixed tracks) 1-Uncle Meat (2LP), 2-Hot Rats, 3-Burnt Weeny Sandwich, 4-Weasels Ripped My Flesh, 5-Chungas Revenge, 6-Live At The Filmore East - June 1971, 7-Just Another Band From L.A., plus an unreleased "Mystery Disc" (side A live inLondon 1968, side B live in U.S.A.).
Boxed set: released on Barking Pumpkin (USA) in Jul'87. Distributed by: Capitol Records, CBS

Orchestral favourites.
Album: released on Discreet in Jun'79

Musicassette: released on Discreet in Jun'79

Roxy and elsewhere (Zappa, Frank & The Mothers).
Album: released on Discreet in '77

Sheik Yerbouti.
Double Album: released on CBS in Feb'79 by CBS Records. Distributed by: CBS

Double musicassette: released on CBS in Feb'79 by CBS Records. Distributed by: CBS

Sheik yerbouti.
Tracks: / Have been in you / Flakes / Broken hearts are for assholes / I'm so cute / Jones crusher / Whatever happened to all the fun in the world / Rat tomago / We gotta get into something real / Bobby brown / Rubber shirt / Sheik yerbouti tango,The / Baby snakes / Tryin' to grow a chin / City of tiny lites / Dancin' fool / Jewis princess / Wild mama / YO' mama.
Double Album: released on EMI in Feb'86 by EMI Records. Distributed by: EMI

Musicassette: released on EMI in Feb'86 by EMI Records. Distributed by: EMI

Ship arriving too late to save a drowning witch.
Tracks: / No not now / Valley girl / I come from nowhere / Drowning witch / Envelopes / Teenage prostitutes.
Notes: This album dates from 1982 and was digitally remastered last year when a number of Zappa albums were licensed to EMI. Conains his only sintle success "Valley Girl" which features his daughter Moon Unit Zappa.
Album: released on Fame in Jun'87 by Music For Pleasure Records. Distributed by: EMI

Musicassette: released on Fame in Jun'87 by Music For Pleasure Records. Distributed by: EMI

Album: released on EMI in Feb'86 by EMI Records. Distributed by: EMI

Musicassette: released on EMI in Feb'86 by EMI Records. Distributed by: EMI

Album: released on CBS in Jun'82 by CBS Records. Distributed by: CBS

Musicassette: released on CBS in Jun'82 by CBS Records. Distributed by: CBS

Shut up 'n' play your guitar.
Album: released on CBS in Aug'82 by CBS Records. Distributed by: CBS

Studio tan.
Album: released on Warner Brothers in '78 by WEA Records. Distributed by: WEA

Them or us.
Album: released on EMI in Oct'84 by EMI Records. Distributed by: EMI

Musicassette: released on EMI in Oct'84 by EMI Records. Distributed by: EMI

Thing fish.
Album: released on Capitol in Mar'85 by Capitol Records. Distributed by: EMI

Musicassette: released on Capitol in Mar'85 by Capitol Records. Distributed by: EMI

Tinsel town rebellion.
Tracks: / Fine girl / Easy meat / For the young sophisticate / Love of my life / I ain't got no heart / Party rap / Tell me you love me / Now you see it now you don't / Dance contest / Blue light,The / Tinsel town rebellion / Pick me,I'm clean / Bamboozled by love / Brown shoes don't make it / Peaches 111.
Double Album: released on EMI in Feb'86 by EMI Records. Distributed by: EMI

Musicassette: released on EMI in Feb'86 by EMI Records. Distributed by: EMI

Tinsel town rebellion.
Album: released on CBS in May'81 by CBS Records. Distributed by: CBS

Musicassette: released on CBS in May'81 by CBS Records. Distributed by: CBS

Waka/Jawaka hot rats.
Album: released on Reprise in '70 by WEA Records. Distributed by: WEA

You are what you are.
Single (7"): released on CBS in Feb'82 by CBS Records. Distributed by: CBS

Single (12"): released on CBS in Feb'82 by CBS Records. Distributed by: CBS

You are what you is.
Tracks: / Teenage wind / Harder than your husband / Doreen / Goblin girl / Theme from the 3rd movement of sinister footwear / Society pages / I'm a beautiful guy / Beauty knows no pain / Charlie's enormous mouth / Any downers? / Conehead / You are what you is / Mudd club

Meek shall inherit nothing,The / Dumb allover / Heavenly bank account / Suicide chump / Jumbo go away / If only she woulda / Drafter again.
Double Album: released on EMI in Feb'86 by EMI Records. Distributed by: EMI

Musicassette: released on EMI in Feb'86 by EMI Records. Distributed by: EMI

Zappa in New York.
Double Album: released on Discreet in Mar'78

Zoot allures.
Album: released on Warner Brothers in '76 by WEA Records. Distributed by: WEA

Musicassette: released on Warner Brothers in '76 by WEA Records. Distributed by: WEA

Zardis, Chester

Chester Zardis & his hot five/Michael White & his liberty... (Zardis,Chester & his hot five/Michael White & his liberty...).
Notes: No title given on card.
Album: released on 504 in Sep'86 by 504 Records. Distributed by: Chris Wellard, Jazz Music

Musicassette: released on 504 in Sep'86 by 504 Records. Distributed by: Chris Wellard, Jazz Music

Zarjaz

One charming night.
Single (7"): released on Creation in Apr'85. Distributed by: Rough Trade, Cartel

Zavaroni, Lena

Hold tight, its Lena.
Album: released on BBC in May'82 by BBC Records & Tapes. Distributed by: EMI, PRT

Musicassette: released on BBC in May'82 by BBC Records & Tapes. Distributed by: EMI, PRT

Lena Zavaroni & her music.
Album: released on Galaxy in May'81 by Galaxy Records. Distributed by: RCA, Red Lightnin' Distribution, Discovery, Swift

Musicassette: released on Galaxy in May'81 by Galaxy Records. Distributed by: RCA, Red Lightnin' Distribution, Discovery, Swift

Presenting Lena Zavaroni.
Album: released on Galaxy in May'81 by Galaxy Records. Distributed by: RCA, Red Lightnin' Distribution, Discovery, Swift

Musicassette: released on Galaxy in May'81 by Galaxy Records. Distributed by: RCA, Red Lightnin' Distribution, Discovery, Swift

Roses and rainbows.
Single (7"): released on President in Mar'81 by President Records. Distributed by: Taylors, Spartan

Somewhere south of Macon.
Single (7"): released on President in Sep'81 by President Records. Distributed by: Taylors, Spartan

Songs are such good things.
Album: released on Galaxy in Apr'78 by Galaxy Records. Distributed by: RCA, Red Lightnin' Distribution, Discovery, Swift

Zawinul

Ialects.
Tracks: / Harvest,The / Waiting for the rain / Aeebop / Great empire,The / Carnavalito / 6 A.M Walking on the Nile / Peace.
Album: released on CBS in Mar'86 by CBS Records. Distributed by: CBS

Musicassette: released on CBS in Mar'86 by CBS Records. Distributed by: CBS

Zawinul, Joe

Zawinul.
Album: released on Atlantic in '74 by WEA

Zawose, Hukwe

Tanzania yetu.
Album: released on Triple Earth in Mar'85 by Sterns Records. Distributed by: Sterns/Triple Earth Distribution

Zazou

Nu ya fuza (Zazou/Bikaye).
Single (12"): released on Illuminated in Jul'84

by IKF Records. Distributed by: Pinnacle, Cartel, Jetstar

Malimba (Zazou & Wemba).
Single (12"): released on Crammed Discs (Belgium) in May'83. Distributed by: Rough Trade, Nine Mile, Cartel

M'pasi ya m'pamba (Zazou/Bikaye/Cyl).
Single (12"): released on Illuminated in Apr'85 by IKF Records. Distributed by: Pinnacle, Cartel, Jetstar

Single (7"): released on Crammed in Oct'84. Distributed by: Rough Trade, Nine Mile, Cartel

Noir et blanc (Zazou/Bikaye).
Album: released on Crammed Discs (Belgium) in Nov'83. Distributed by: Rough Trade, Nine Mile, Cartel

Zazou,Hector

Geographies.
Album: released on Made To Measure in Feb'85 by Made To Measure Records. Distributed by: Pinnacle

Relvax au bongo.
Album: released on Crammed in Sep'84. Distributed by: Rough Trade, Nine Mile, Cartel

Revalx au bongo.
Album: released on Made To Measure in Mar'86 by Made To Measure Records. Distributed by: Pinnacle

Ze

Ze-A christmas record Various artists (Various Artists).
Album: released on ZE in Nov'81 by Island Records. Distributed by: Polygram

Musicassette: released on ZE in Nov'81 by Island Records. Distributed by: Polygram

Zebra

Repression.
Single (12"): released on Good Vibration in Jan'80 by Good Vibrations Records. Distributed by: Pinnacle, Rough Trade

Zebra 1

Banner of love(How I run to you).
Single (7"): released on Sound Vision in Nov'83 by Sound Vision Records. Distributed by: Pinnacle

Single (12"): released on Sound Vision in Nov'83 by Sound Vision Records. Distributed by: Pinnacle

Mountains and water.
Single (7"): released on Mercury in Jan'85 by Phonogram Records. Distributed by: Polygram Distribution

Single (12"): released on Mercury in Jan'85 by Phonogram Records. Distributed by: Polygram Distribution

Rain.
Single (7"): released on Mercury in Apr'85 by Phonogram Records. Distributed by: Polygram Distribution

Single (12"): released on Mercury in Apr'85 by Phonogram Records. Distributed by: Polygram Distribution

Rescue me.
Single (7"): released on Mercury in Oct'85 by Phonogram Records. Distributed by: Polygram Distribution

Double-pack single: released on Mercury in Oct'85 by Phonogram Records. Distributed by: Polygram Distribution

Single (12"): released on Mercury in Oct'85 by Phonogram Records. Distributed by: Polygram Distribution

Ten thousand voices message from the people.
Single (7"): released on Mercury in Apr'84 by Phonogram Records. Distributed by: Polygram Distribution

Single (12"): released on Mercury in Apr'84 by Phonogram Records. Distributed by: Polygram Distribution

West's awake.
Single (7"): released on Second Vision in May'83 by Second Vision Records. Distributed by: Pinnacle

Single (12"): released on Second Vision in May'83 by Second Vision Records. Distributed by: Pinnacle

Zebras

Now that I've met you.
Single (7"): released on Flamingo in Sep'80 by Carlin Music Corp

Single (12"): released on Flamingo in Sep'80 by Carlin Music Corp. Distributed by: RCA

Zebra, Tony

School girl (see under Melody, Delroy) (Zebra, Tony/Delroy Melody).

Zed

Visions of dune.
Album: released on Initial in Sep'79 by Initial Records. Distributed by: Pinnacle

Zed and Two Noughts

Zed and Two Noughts Original soundtrack.
Album: released on TER in Dec'85. Distributed by: Pinnacle

Musicassette: released on TER in Dec'85. Distributed by: Pinnacle

Zed, Mark

Energy.
Single (7"): released on Double Dancer in Apr'81 by Smile Records. Distributed by: Spartan

My calculator's right.
Single (7"): released on Gun in Jun'80 by B&C Records. Distributed by: Trojan, Pinnacle, Spartan

Situation normal.
Single (7"): released on B & C in Feb'81 by B&C Records. Distributed by: PRT

Zeitgeist

Ball of confusion.
Single (7"): released on Jamming in Nov'81

Freight train rain.
Tracks: / Freight train rain / Hill country theme.
Single (7"): released on DB in Jan'86 by DB Records. Distributed by: Pinnacle

Over again.
Single (7"): released on Jamming in Oct'82

Single (12"): released on Jamming in Oct'82

Shake rake.
Single (7"): released on Human in Mar'81. Distributed by: Roots, Stage One

Stop.
Single (7"): released on Jamming in Jun'82

Single (12"): released on Jamming in Jun'82

Touch.
Single (7"): released on Human in Apr'81. Distributed by: Roots, Stage One

Translate slowly.
Album: released on DB-Stiff in Nov'85 by Stiff Records. Distributed by: Stiff Records, EMI

Zeitlin, Denny

Tidal wave.
Album: released on Palo Alto (Italy) in Jan'85

Time remembers one time once (Zeitlin, Denny & Charlie Haden).
Album: released on ECM (Germany) in Mar'83 by ECM Records. Distributed by: IMS, Polygram, Virgin through EMI

Zen

Love can conquer all.
Single (7"): released on Zen in Nov'85 by Zen Records. Distributed by: MIS-EMI Distribution

Single (12"): released on Zen in Nov'85 by Zen Records. Distributed by: MIS-EMI Distribution

Zen Alligators

Invisible man, The.
Single (7"): released on Zodiac in Jul'82. Distributed by: Jazz Music

Zenana

Witches.
Tracks: / Time waits for no one.
Single (7"): released on Pinner in Feb'87 by Pinner Records. Distributed by: Rough Trade, Cartel, Backs

Zen Attack

Zen attack.
Album: released on Street Tunes in Sep'83 by Street Tunes Records. Distributed by: Pinnacle

Zeno

Little more love, A.
Tracks: / Little more love, A / Signs on the sky / Don't tell the wind"
Notes: "= Extra track on 12" only
Single (7"): released on Parlophone in Feb'86 by EMI Records. Distributed by: EMI

Single (12"): released on Parlophone in Feb'86 by EMI Records. Distributed by: EMI

Picture disc single: released on Parlophone in Mar'86 by EMI Records. Distributed by: EMI

Love will live.
Tracks: / Love will live / Far away.
Single (7"): released on EMI in Jul'86 by EMI Records. Distributed by: EMI

Single (12"): released on EMI in Jul'86 by EMI Records. Distributed by: EMI

Zeno.
Tracks: / Eastern sun / Little more love, A / Love will live / Signs on the sky / Far away / Don't tell the wind / Heart on the wing / Circles of dawn / Sent by heaven / Sunset.
Notes: Combining the force of the best hard rock with a pronounced classical influence,Zeno unleash their self-titled album during March.Recorded throughout the work during 1985,Zeno are:Zeno Roth(brother of Uli John),Ule Winsomie Ritgen,and also an outstanding vocalist Michael Flexig.Formed in Hanover,Germany they are joined on this album by such names as Stuart Elliot on drums(Alan Parsons,Kate Bush) and Don Airey on keyboards(Rainbow,Ozzy Osborne).The album was co-produced with Terry Manning(ZZ Top) and Ian Taylor(Cars,Psychodelic Furs).
Album: released on Parlophone in Mar'86 by EMI Records. Distributed by: EMI

Musicassette: released on Parlophone in Mar'86 by EMI Records. Distributed by: EMI

Compact disc: released on Parlophone in Jul'86 by EMI Records. Distributed by: EMI

Zenter, Si

Great band with great voices swing The great voices of the great bands (Zenter, Si & His Orchestra/Johnny Mann Singers).
Tracks: / Mississippi mud / Marie / Chattan-oga choo choo / At last / On the sunny side of 7e street / Undecided / Paper doll / If I didn't care / Hut sut song, The / It happened in Monterey / I'll never smile again / Rum & Coca Cola.
Notes: Full title: Si Zenter & His Orchestra with The Johnny Mann Singers."Great band with great voices swing.The great voices of the great bands".Quite a mouthful of title and quite an earful of swinging sound! This album, one of a pair released by time line up,has been re-issued due to public demand and radio interest-a substantial demand is anticipated.Contains lots of well known tunes from the swing era including"Chattanooga Choo Choo","On the Sunny Side of the Street","If I didn't care" & "It Happened in Monterey".
Album: released on Liberty in May'86 by Liberty-United. Distributed by: EMI

Musicassette: released on Liberty in May'86 by Liberty-United. Distributed by: EMI

Zephaniah, Benjamin

Big boys don't make girls cry.
Single (12"): released on Upright in Nov'84 by Upright Records. Distributed by: Cartel, Rough Trade

Dub ranting.
Album: released on Upright in Jun'83 by Upright Records. Distributed by: Cartel, Rough Trade

Single (12"): released on Radical Wallpaper in Dec'82. Distributed by: Cartel

Free South Afrika.
Tracks: / Free South Afrika / Stop de war.
Single (12"): released on Upright in Apr'86 by Upright Records. Distributed by: Cartel, Rough Trade

Rasta.
Album: released on Upright in Mar'87 by Upright Records. Distributed by: Cartel, Rough

Zernicke, Andrew

Organ player.
Single (12"): released on Carrere in Jun'85 by Carrere Records. Distributed by: PRT, Spartan

Zero 9

White lies.
Album: released on Heavy Metal in Dec'85 by FM-Revolver Records. Distributed by: EMI

Zero, Bernie Q

Numbers man.
Single (7"): released on Utopia in May'83

Single (12"): released on Utopia in May'83

Zeroheroes

Freedom fighters.
Musicassette: released on Jungle in Jun'83 by Jungle Records. Distributed by: Jungle.

Radio free Europe.
Album: released on Jungle in May'83 by Jungle Records. Distributed by: Jungle, Cartel

Zero Lacreche

Falling.
Single (7"): released on Cherry Red in May'85 by Cherry Red Records. Distributed by: Pinnacle

Single (12"): released on Cherry Red in May'85 by Cherry Red Records. Distributed by: Pinnacle

Last years wife.
Single (7"): released on Flicknife in May'84 by Flicknife Records. Distributed by: Spartan

Single (12"): released on Flicknife in May'84 by Flicknife Records. Distributed by: Spartan

Zero, Peter

Disposable tissues (Zero, Peter & The Options).
Single (7"): released on Someone Else's Music in May'83 by Someone Else's Music Records. Distributed by: Stage One

Zerra 1

Forever & ever.
Tracks: / Forever & ever / Golden.
Single (7"): released on Mercury in May'86 by Phonogram Records. Distributed by: Polygram Distribution

Single (12"): released on Mercury in May'86 by Phonogram Records. Distributed by: Polygram Distribution

Zerra 1.
Tracks: / Mountains & water / Tumblin' down / Diaries / I feel it / Other side, The / Rain / I know / Nothing / Young love / Children.
Notes: Digital stereo.
Compact disc: released on Mercury in Feb'85 by Phonogram Records. Distributed by: Polygram Distribution

Zerra One

Domino effect.
Tracks: / Domino effect / Stranger tonight / Emigrant.
Compact disc: released on Mercury in Jan'87 by Phonogram Records. Distributed by: Polygram Distribution

Single (7"): released on Mercury in Jan'87 by Phonogram Records. Distributed by: Polygram Distribution

Single (12"): released on Mercury in Jan'87 by Phonogram Records. Distributed by: Polygram Distribution

Zev

50 Gates.
Musicassette: released on Staal Tapes in Aug'86. Distributed by: Rough Trade Distribution

Wipeout.
Single (7"): released on Fetish in May'82 by Fetish Records. Distributed by: Cartel, Pinnacle

Zevon, Warren

Envoy, The.
Album: released on Asylum in Aug'82 by WEA Records. Distributed by: WEA

Musicassette: released on Asylum in Aug'82 by WEA Records. Distributed by: WEA

Excitable boy.
Album: released on Asylum in Mar'78 by WEA Records. Distributed by: WEA

Musicassette: released on Asylum in Mar'78 by WEA Records. Distributed by: WEA

Leave my monkey alone.
Tracks: / Leave my monkey alone / Nocturne.
Single (7"): released on Virgin in Jun'87 by Virgin Records. Distributed by: EMI, Virgin Distribution

Single (12"): released on Virgin in Jun'87 by Virgin Records. Distributed by: EMI, Virgin Distribution

Let nothing come between you.
Single (7"): released on Elektra in Aug'82 by WEA Records. Distributed by: WEA

Quiet normal life, A - the best of Warren Zevon.
Tracks: / Werewolves of London / Play it all night long / Roland the headless Thompson gunner / Envoy / Mohammed's radio / Desperados under the eaves / I'll sleep when I'm dead / Lawyers guns and money / Ain't that pretty at all / Poor poor pitiful me / Accidentally like a martyr / Looking for the next best thing.
Album: released on Asylum in Nov'86 by WEA Records. Distributed by: WEA

Musicassette: released on Asylum in Nov'86 by WEA Records. Distributed by: WEA

Compact disc: released on Asylum in Nov'86 by WEA Records. Distributed by: WEA

Sentimental hygiene (single).
Tracks: / Sentimental hygiene / Factory, The / Leave my monkey alone.
Single (12"): released on Virgin in Jul'87 by Virgin Records. Distributed by: EMI, Virgin Distribution

Sentimental hygiene.
Compact disc: released on Virgin in Jun'87 by Virgin Records. Distributed by: EMI, Virgin Distribution

Album: released on Virgin in Jun'87 by Virgin Records. Distributed by: EMI, Virgin Distribution

Musicassette: released on Virgin in Jun'87 by Virgin Records. Distributed by: EMI, Virgin Distribution

Stand in the fire.
Album: released on Elektra Asylum in Jan'81 by Elektra/Asylum/Nonesuch Records. Distributed by: WEA

Musicassette: released on Elektra Asylum in Jan'81 by Elektra/Asylum/Nonesuch Records. Distributed by: WEA

Werewolves of London.
Tracks: / Werewolves of London / Jesus mentioned / Poor man pitiful me.
Single (7"): released on Elektra (USA) in Mar'87 by Elektra/Asylum/Nonesuch Records. Distributed by: WEA

Single (12"): released on Elektra (USA) in Mar'87 by Elektra/Asylum/Nonesuch Records. Distributed by: WEA

Ziegler, Anne

Golden age of Anne Ziegler and Webster Booth (Ziegler, Anne & Webster Booth).
Album: released on Golden Age in Jul'83 by Music For Pleasure Records. Distributed by: EMI

Musicassette: released on Golden Age in Jul'83 by Music For Pleasure Records. Distributed by: EMI

Zimbabwe Dread

Earthman connection.
Album: released on Kingdom in Sep'83 by Kingdom Records. Distributed by: Kingdom

Zimbabwe Hits

Zimbabwe hits Various artists (Various Artists).
Album: released on Discafrique in Feb'86 by Discafrique Records. Distributed by: Sterns, Triple Earth

Zimmerman, Dick

My wife is dancing mad (Zimmerman, Dick & Ian Whitcomb).
Album: released on Stomp Off (USA) in Jan'84

My wife is dancing mad! (Zimmerman, Dick & Ian Whitcomb).
Album: released on Stomp Off (USA) in Jan'84

Zinc

I'm livin' a life of love.
Single (7"): released on Jive in Feb'83 by Zomba Records. Distributed by: RCA, PRT, CBS

Single (12"): released on Jive in Feb'83 by Zomba Records. Distributed by: RCA, PRT, CBS

Street level.
Single (7"): released on Jive in Aug'82 by Zomba Records. Distributed by: RCA, PRT, CBS

Single (12"): released on Jive in Aug'82 by Zomba Records. Distributed by: RCA, PRT, CBS

Zingari

Everybody's waiting.
Single (7"): released on Dakota in Oct'83 by Dakota Records. Distributed by: PRT

Single (12"): released on Dakota in Oct'83 by Dakota Records. Distributed by: PRT

Halcyon days.
Single (7"): released on PRT in Aug'85 by PRT Records. Distributed by: PRT

One more chance.
Single (7"): released on Dakota in May'84 by Dakota Records. Distributed by: PRT

Zinno

What's your name.
Single (12"): released on WEA International in Nov'85 by WEA Records. Distributed by: WEA

Single (12"): released on WEA International in Nov'85 by WEA Records. Distributed by: WEA

Zinova, Faina

Russian songs (Zinova, Faina and her Russian Gypsy Ensemble 'Tziganka').
Album: released on Sweet Folk All in May'81 by Sweet Folk All Records. Distributed by: Sweet Folk All, Roots, Celtic Music, Dragon, Impetus, Projection, Chris Wellard, Festival Records

Zion Band

Freedom city.
Single (12"): released on Freedom City in Dec'82 by Freedom City. Distributed by: Pinnacle

Zipz

Tonight.
Single (7"): released on Voyage International in Mar'80 by Code Records. Distributed by: PRT

Ziz

Albanian summer.
Album: released on Practical Music in Jul'85

Zodiac Mindwarp

High priest of love (Zodiac Mindwarp & The Love Reaction).
Album: released on Food in Jul'86 by Food Records. Distributed by: Rough Trade, Cartel, WEA

Love reaction, The.
Single (12"): released on Food in Aug'85 by Food Records. Distributed by: Rough Trade, Cartel, WEA

Prime mover.
Tracks: / Prime mover / Laughing in the face of death / Hangover from hell".
Notes: *Extra track on 12" only
Single (7"): released on Mercury in Apr'87 by Phonogram Records. Distributed by: Polygram

Single (12"): released on Mercury in Apr'87 by Phonogram Records. Distributed by: Polygram

Wild child (Zodiac Mindwarp & The Love Reaction).
Tracks: / Wild child.
Single (12"): released on Food in Jun'86 by Food Records. Distributed by: Rough Trade, Cartel,

Zodiac Motel

Sunshine miner.
Single (7"): released on Swordfish in Apr'87. Distributed by: Nine Mile Distribution, Cartel Distribution

Zodico

Louisiana cajun music.
Album: released on Rounder in Sep'79. Distributed by: Roots Distribution

Zoe

Fever.
Tracks: / Fever / Boy next door,The.
Single (7"): released on Amidisque in May'86 by Amidisque Records. Distributed by: RCA, Pinnacle

Single (12"): released on Amidisque in Jun'86 by Amidisque Records. Distributed by: RCA, Pinnacle

Foot happy.
Single (7"): released on Amidisque in Apr'84 by Amidisque Records. Distributed by: RCA, Pinnacle

La di de la di da.
Single (7"): released on Amidisque in Nov'83 by Amidisque Records. Distributed by: RCA, Pinnacle

love is all.
Single (7"): released on Amidisque in Dec'84 by Amidisque Records. Distributed by: RCA, Pinnacle

Rock me in your arms.
Tracks: / Rock me in your arms / Boy next door, The.
Single (7"): released on President in 20 Jun'87 by President Records. Distributed by: Taylors, Spartan

Zolar, Zak

Take me home.
Tracks: / Take me home.
Single (7"): released on Shanghai in Aug'86

Zoller, Attila

Common cause.
Album: released on Enja (Germany) in Jan'82 by Enja Records (W.Germany). Distributed by: Cadillac Music

Conjunction.
Album: released on Enja (Germany) in Jan'82 by Enja Records (W.Germany). Distributed by: Cadillac Music

Dream bells.
Album: released on Enja (Germany) in Jan'82 by Enja Records (W.Germany). Distributed by: Cadillac Music

Zombies

Begin here.
Album: released on Decca in Nov'84 by Decca Records. Distributed by: Polygram

Live on the BBC 1965-67.
Single (cassette): released on Rhino (USA) in Feb'86 by Rhino Records (USA)

Odessey & Oracle.
Notes: Personnel: Rod Argent - keyboards / Paul Atkinson - guitar / Colin Blunstone - vocals / Hugh Grundy - drums / Chris White - bass.
Compact disc: released on Transatlantic in Jul'87 by Transatlantic Records. Distributed by: IMS-Polygram

Odyssey & Oracle.
Album: released on Razor in Dec'86 by Razor. Distributed by: Pinnacle

She's not there.
Album: released on Decca (Rock Echoes) in Feb'82 by Decca Records. Distributed by: Polygram, IMS

Musicassette: released on Decca (Rock Echoes) in Feb'82 by Decca Records. Distributed by: Polygram, IMS

Single (7"): released on Decca-Originals in Mar'82 by Decca Records. Distributed by: Polygram, IMS

Single (7"): released on Old Gold (Reissue) in Oct'83

World of the Zombies.
Album: released on Decca in Sep'70 by Decca Records. Distributed by: Polygram

Zombies, The.
Tracks: / She's not there / Leave me be / Tell her no / She's coming home / I want her back / Whenever you're ready / Is this the dream / Remember you / Indication / Gotta get a hold of myself / Goin' out of my head / You make me feel good / Woman / What more can I do / I must move / I remember when I loved her / I love you / Don't go away / Just out of reach / How we were before / Way I feel inside, The / She does everything right for me.
Album: released on See For Miles in Jul'86 by See For Miles Records. Distributed by: Pinnacle

Zoo Boutique
Forgive and forget.
Single (7"): released on Lightbeat in Nov'82 by Lightbeat Records. Distributed by: Pinnacle

Zoom
Waiting.
Single (7"): released on Rex in Apr'84 by Eden Studios. Distributed by: Pinnacle

Single (12"): released on Rex in Apr'84 by Eden Studios. Distributed by: Pinnacle

Zoomitz
I'll be your spark.
Single (7"): released on RK in Feb'82

Zoom Lens & No Entry Band
Running in mazes.
Single (7"): released on Circle-In-The-Square in Feb'81 by Circle-In-The-Square Records. Distributed by: Circle-In-The-Square

Zoom Zoom
I want your body.
Single (12"): released on Carrere in Jun'84 by Carrere Records. Distributed by: PRT, Spartan

Zoo Q
Barry.
Single (7"): released on Abacus in Sep'85 by Abacus. Distributed by: Spartan

Single (12"): released on Abacus in Sep'85 by Abacus. Distributed by: Spartan

Zoot Alors
That feeling.
Single (7"): released on Zoot in Mar'84 by Creole Records. Distributed by: CBS, PRT

Single (12"): released on Zoot in Mar'84 by Creole Records. Distributed by: CBS, PRT

Zoot & The Roots
Bee jives out (EP), (The).
Single (12"): released on Indiscreet in Nov'84. Distributed by: Red Rhino, Cartel

Late little red rooster.
Single (7"): released on Red Rhino in May'83 by Red Rhino Records. Distributed by: Red Rhino, Cartel

Make me believe in you.
Single (12"): released on Indiscreet in Jul'85. Distributed by: Red Rhino, Cartel

Zorch Factor One
Zorch factor one Various artists (Various Artists).
Notes: Artists include:Frenzy/Torment/Outer Limits etc.
Album: released on Nervous in Oct'86 by Nervous Records. Distributed by: Nervous, Rough Trade

Zor Gabor
Nightrope.
Tracks: / Tightrope / Vigilante / Amber*.
Single (7"): released on In Tape in Jul'87 by In Tape Records. Distributed by: Red Rhino, Cartel

Single (12"): released on In Tape in Jul'87 by In Tape Records. Distributed by: Red Rhino, Cartel

Zorn, John
Big Gundown.
Notes: John Zorn plays the music of Ennio Morricone.
Album: released on Nonesuch in Jan'87

Musicassette: released on Nonesuch in Jan'87

Compact disc: released on Nonesuch in Jan'87

Zos Kia
Be like me.
Single (12"): released on Temple in Dec'85 by Temple Records. Distributed by: Rough Trade Distribution, Cartel Distribution

Rape.
Tracks: / Rape / Black action.
Single (12"): released on All The Madmen in Oct'86 by All The Madmen Records. Distributed by: Rough Trade, Cartel

Zoskla meets Sugar Gog
That's heavy baby.
Single (12"): released on Temple in Jul'87 by Temple Records. Distributed by: Rough Trade Distribution, Cartel Distribution

Zot
Zot.
Album: released on Elektra in Apr'85 by WEA Records. Distributed by: WEA

Zottola, Glenn
Christmas in jazztime.
Album: released on Dreamstreet in Dec'86. Distributed by: Swift

Zounds
Can't cheat karma.
Single (7"): released on Crass in Oct'81 by Exittstencil Music. Distributed by: Rough Trade, Cartel

Curse of Zounds, (The).
Album: released on Rough Trade in May'84 by Rough Trade Records. Distributed by: Rough Trade Distribution, Cartel Distribution

Dancing.
Single (7"): released on Rough Trade in Mar'82 by Rough Trade Records. Distributed by: Rough Trade Distribution, Cartel Distribution

Demystification.
Single (7"): released on R. Trade in Apr'81 by Rough Trade Records. Distributed by: Rough Trade Distribution

La vache qui rit (EP).
Single (7"): released on Not So Brave in Jun'82

More trouble coming everyday.
Single (7"): released on Rough Trade in Aug'82 by Rough Trade Records. Distributed by: Rough Trade Distribution, Cartel Distribution

Zuccarelli
Zuccarelli Holophonics.
Single (12"): released on CBS in Jul'83 by CBS Records. Distributed by: CBS

Single (cassette): released on CBS in Jul'83 by CBS Records. Distributed by: CBS

Zulce
Everyone's a winner.
Tracks: / Everyone's a winner / Sad to say goodbye / Everone's a winner(ext.)* / Everone's a winner(dub)* / Everone's a winner(LP mix)*.
Notes: *=Extra tracks on 12" only.
Single (7"): released on Club in Aug'86 by Phonogram Records. Distributed by: Polygram

Single (12"): released on Club in Aug'86 by Phonogram Records. Distributed by: Polygram

Zukie, Tappa
People are you ready.
Single (7"): released on Stars Recording in Sep'83

Single (12"): released on Stars Recording in Sep'83

Ragamuffin.
Album: released on World Enterprise in Nov'86. Distributed by: Jetstar

Reggae joey boy.
Single 10": released on Mobiliser in Oct'82 by Jetstar Records. Distributed by: Jetstar Distribution

Zukie, Tappa & U Roy
Understand the understanding.
Tracks: / Understand the understanding / Dance hall memory.
Single (12"): released on Tappa in Nov'86. Distributed by: Jetstar

Zukie, Tapper
Diplomatic killing.
Tracks: / Diplomatic killing / Three raggamuffin guys.
Single (12"): released on Tappa in Nov'86. Distributed by: Jetstar

Gong.
Single (12"): released on Stars in Nov'85

Human right.
Tracks: / Human right / Human right (Version) (big youth).
Single (12"): released on Tappa in Nov'86. Distributed by: Jetstar

I shot the cop.
Single (12"): released on Star in Jul'84 by Star Records. Distributed by: Jetstar Distribution

Visions of love.
Single (12"): released on Stars Recording in Aug'84

Zulu compilation
Zulu compilation Various artists (Various Artists).
Album: released on Zulu in Mar'84 by Zulu Records. Distributed by: Rough Trade

Zulu Jive
Zulu jive Various artists (Various Artists).
Album: released on Earthworks in Jan'86 by Earthworks Records. Distributed by: Earthworks Distributors, Rough Trade, Cartel, Projection

Zulu jive vol.1
Zulu jive vol.1 Various artists (Various Artists).
Musicassette: released on Earthworks in Aug'83 by Earthworks Records. Distributed by: Earthworks Distributors, Rough Trade, Cartel, Projection

Zulu Worker's Choir
Iscathamiya 1982-85.
Notes: Full lyrics transcriptions in Zulu and translations in English.
Album: released on Heritage in Sep'86 by Heritage Records. Distributed by: Chart

Zushii
Surprise surprise.
Tracks: / Surprise surprise / Let's stay home tonight.
Single (12"): released on Debut in Apr'86 by Skratch Music. Distributed by: PRT

Zu Zu
Calypso calypso

Zu Zu Sharks
Big Boys.
Single (7"): released on Polydor in Aug'82 by Polydor Records. Distributed by: Polygram, Polydor

Zwerin, Mike
Not much noise.
Album: released on Spotlite in May'83

Zwingerberger, Axel
Boogie woogie live.
Album: released on Calligraph in Dec'86 by Calligraph Records. Distributed by: PRT

Zwischenfall
Heute.
Single (12"): released on Mask (Germany) in Mar'84. Distributed by: Rough Trade

Sandy eyes.
Single (12"): released on Les Disques Du Crepuscule in Feb'85. Distributed by: Rough Trade, Pinnacle, Island, Polygram

Zydeco
Zydeco Various artists (Various Artists).
Album: released on Arhoolie in May'81 by Arhoolie Records. Distributed by: Projection, Topic, Jazz Music, Swift, Roots

Zydeco Blues Vol.2
Zydeco blues Vol.2 Various artists (Various Artists).
Tracks: / Snap beans aren't salty / Hey la la / It happened so fast / Goodbye baby / Worried life blues / Hey ma ma / You told me / Run here to my baby / Sweetest thing / You don't have to go / You got me running / Bald-headed woman.
Album: released on Flyright in Oct'86 by Flyright Records. Distributed by: Krazy Kat, Swift, Jazz Music

Album: released on Flyright (USA) in Aug'84 by Flyright Records. Distributed by: Swift, Jazz Music, Wellard, Chris, Cadillac

Zydeco, Buckwheat
100% Fortified Zydeco.
Album: released on Black Top (USA) in Feb'85

Waitin for my ya ya.
Album: released on Rounder Europa in Feb'87

Zyeyeye
Birds eye view part 1/2.
Single (7"): released on Le Rey in May'82

Album: released on Warner Brothers in Dec'83 by WEA Records. Distributed by: WEA

Musicassette: released on Warner Brothers in Dec'83 by WEA Records. Distributed by: WEA

Zygott
Trap door.
Tracks: / Trap door / Ghost chase(The ghost chasers).
Single (7"): released on Columbia in Sep'86 by EMI Records. Distributed by: EMI

Zykina, Ludmila
Folk songs.
Musicassette: released on Melodiya (USSR) in Feb'79. Distributed by: T.B.C Distribution

Popular folk songs.
Musicassette: released on Melodiya (USSR) in Feb'79. Distributed by: T.B.C Distribution

Zzero
Stereo.
Single (7"): released on Balaclava in Oct'83 by Balaclava Records

Single (12"): released on Balaclava in Oct'83 by Balaclava Records

ZZ Top
Afterburner.
Tracks: / Sleeping bag / Stages / Woke up with wood / Rough boy / Can't stop rockin' / Planet of women / I got the message / Velcro fly / Dipping low / Delirious.
Album: released on Warner Bros. in Nov'85 by Warner Bros Records. Distributed by: WEA

Musicassette: released on Warner Bros. in Nov'85 by Warner Bros Records. Distributed by: WEA

Compact disc: released on Warner Bros. in Nov'85 by Warner Bros Records. Distributed by: WEA

Best of ZZ Top.
Tracks: / Tush / Waitin' for the bus / Jesus just left Chicago / Francine / Just got paid / La grange / Blue jean blues / Backdoor love affair / Beer drinkers & hell raisers / Heard it on the X.
Compact disc: released on Warner Bros. in Jan'86 by Warner Bros Records. Distributed by: WEA

Deguello.
Tracks: / I thank you / She loves my automobile / I'm bad I'm nationwide / Fool for your stockings, A / Manic mechanic / Dust my broom / Lowdown in the street / Hi-fi mama / Cheap sunglasses / Esther be the one.
Compact disc: released on Warner Bros. in Apr'84 by Warner Bros Records. Distributed by: WEA

Album: released on Warner Brothers in Jan'85 by WEA Records. Distributed by: WEA

Musicassette: released on Warner Brothers in Jan'85 by WEA Records. Distributed by: WEA

Compact disc: released on Warner Brothers in Jan'85 by WEA Records. Distributed by: WEA

Eliminator.
Tracks: / Gimme all your lovin' / Got me under pressure / Sharp-dressed man / I need you to-night / I got the six / Legs / Thug / TV dinners / Dirty dog / If I could only flag her down.
Compact disc: released on Warner Bros. in '84 by Warner Bros Records. Distributed by: WEA

Picture disc album: released on Warner Brothers in Aug'85 by WEA Records. Distributed by: WEA

Album: released on Warner Brothers in Jun'83 by WEA Records. Distributed by: WEA

Musicassette: released on Warner Brothers in Jun'83 by WEA Records. Distributed by: WEA

Compact disc: released on Warner Brothers in Jun'83 by WEA Records. Distributed by: WEA

El loco.
Compact disc: released on Warner Bros. in Mar'87 by Warner Bros Records. Distributed by: WEA

Album: released on Warner Brothers in Sep'81 by WEA Records. Distributed by: WEA

Musicassette: released on Warner Brothers in Sep'81 by WEA Records. Distributed by: WEA

Fandango.
Compact disc: released on Warner Bros. in Jan'87 by Warner Bros Records. Distributed by: WEA

Album: released on Warner Brothers in Nov'83 bv WEA Records. Distributed by: WEA

Musicassette: released on Warner Brothers in Nov'83 by WEA Records. Distributed by: WEA

First album.
Compact disc: released on Warner Bros. in Jan'87 by Warner Bros Records. Distributed by: WEA

Gimme all you lovin' / If I could only flag her down.
Single (7"): released on Warner Brothers in Sep'83 by WEA Records. Distributed by: WEA

Single (12"): released on Warner Brothers in Sep'83 by WEA Records. Distributed by: WEA

Gimme all your lovin' / Jesus just left Chicago.
Single (12"): released on Warner Brothers in May'83 by WEA Records. Distributed by: WEA

Legs.
Single (7"): released on Warner Brothers in Feb'85 by WEA Records. Distributed by: WEA

Single (12"): released on Warner Brothers in Feb'85 by WEA Records. Distributed by: WEA

Rio Grande mud.
Compact disc: released on Warner Bros. in Jan'87 by Warner Bros Records. Distributed by: WEA

Album: released on Warner Brothers in Sep'84 by WEA Records. Distributed by: WEA

Musicassette: released on Warner Brothers in Sep'84 by WEA Records. Distributed by: WEA

Rough boy.

Tracks: / Rough boy / Delirious.
Single (7"): released on Warner Bros. in Mar'86 by Warner Bros Records. Distributed by: WEA

Single (12"): released on Warner Bros. in Mar'86 by Warner Bros Records. Distributed by: WEA

Sharp dressed man.
Single (7"): released on Warner Brothers in Dec'84 by WEA Records. Distributed by: WEA

Single (12"): released on Warner Brothers in Dec'84 by WEA Records. Distributed by: WEA

Sleeping bag.
Single (7"): released on Warner Brothers in Oct'85 by WEA Records. Distributed by: WEA

Single (12"): released on Warner Brothers in Oct'85 by WEA Records. Distributed by: WEA

Stages.
Tracks: / Stages / Hi-fi mama.
Single (7"): released on Warner Bros. in Jan'86 by Warner Bros Records. Distributed by: WEA

Single (12"): released on Warner Bros. in Jan'86 by Warner Bros Records. Distributed by: WEA

Tejas.
Compact disc: released on Warner Bros. in Mar'87 by Warner Bros Records. Distributed by: WEA

Album: released on Warner Brothers in Sep'84 by WEA Records. Distributed by: WEA

Musicassette: released on Warner Brothers in Sep'84 by WEA Records. Distributed by: WEA

Tres hombres.
Compact disc: released on Warner Bros. in Jan'87 by Warner Bros Records. Distributed by WEA

Album: released on Warner Brothers in Nov'8ı by WEA Records. Distributed by: WEA

Musicassette: released on Warner Brothers Nov'83 by WEA Records. Distributed by: WE.

Tres hombres / Fandango.
Double musicassette: released on Warner Brothers in Nov'83 by WEA Records. Distributed by: WEA

TV dinners.
Musicassette: released on Warner Brothers May'84 by WEA Records. Distributed by: WEı

Velcro fly.
Tracks: / Velcro fly(remix edit.) / Can't stc rockin'.
Single (7"): released on Warner Bros. Nov'86 by Warner Bros Records. Distributed bı WEA

Single (12"): released on Warner Bros. Nov'86 by Warner Bros Records. Distributed by WEA

ZZ Top's first album.
Album: released on Warner Brothers in Sep'8 by WEA Records. Distributed by: WEA

Musicassette: released on Warner Brothers Sep'84 by WEA Records. Distributed by: WE.

ZZ Top summer holiday EP, The.
Single (7"): released on Warner Brothers Jul'85 by WEA Records. Distributed by: WEA/I

Notes

Notes